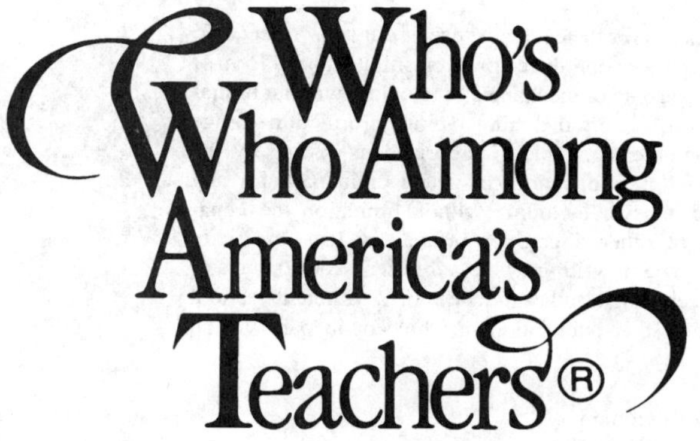

The Best Teachers in America
Selected by the Best Students®

4th Edition
1996
Volume I

Educational Communications, Inc.®

Teachers featured in this volume work in the states of:
Connecticut, Delaware, District of Columbia, Maine, Maryland, Massachusetts, New Hampshire, New Jersey, New York, Ohio, Pennsylvania, Rhode Island, Vermont, Foreign Countries

ISBN #1-56244-139-6 Volume I
ISBN #1-56244-140-X Volume II
ISBN #1-56244-141-8 Volume III
ISBN #1-56244-142-6 Volume IV
ISBN #1-56244-138-8 4 Volume Set
Library of Congress #90-662490

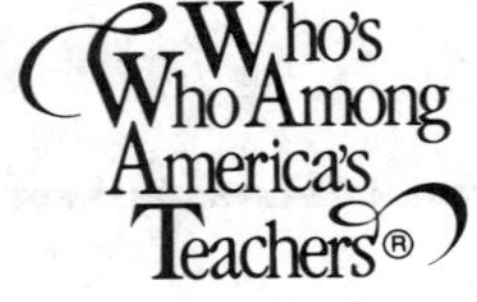

Manufactured in the United States of America

Table of Contents

Dedication v

Advisory Committee. vi

Selection Criteria and Process vii

Who's Who Teacher Profile viii

Publisher's Corner ix

Guest Editorials.. x

A Message to Teachers xii

Glossary of Abbreviations xiii

Sample Biography xv

Biographies 1

Geographic Occupation Index I-1

Summon The Heroes*

Summon the heroes. The community heroes. The 10,000 American heroes who were part of the 1996 Olympic Torch Relay. They started the 15,000 mile trek across the United States in Los Angeles and ended 84 days later in Atlanta at the opening ceremonies of the 26th Olympiad.

Heroes. Community heroes. Ten thousand American heroes nominated and selected to carry the flame symbolizing the continuity between the ancient and modern Games. They weren't star athletes. They weren't celebrities. They weren't connected to corporations that paid hefty fees to participate. No, they were regular people who, because of their goodwill, their spirit of volunteerism, and their contributions to their communities have added more light to the world than the Olympic flame itself.

It isn't surprising that many of the participants in the Olympic torch relay are students and teachers who are included in *Who's Who Among American High School Students* and *Who's Who Among America's Teachers* respectively. Educational Communications, Inc. salutes these heroes and is proud to honor them in our publications. Their lives exemplify the Olympic Creed:

> *The most important thing . . . is not to win but to take part, just as the most important thing in life is not the triumph but the struggle. The essential thing is not to have conquered but to have fought well.*

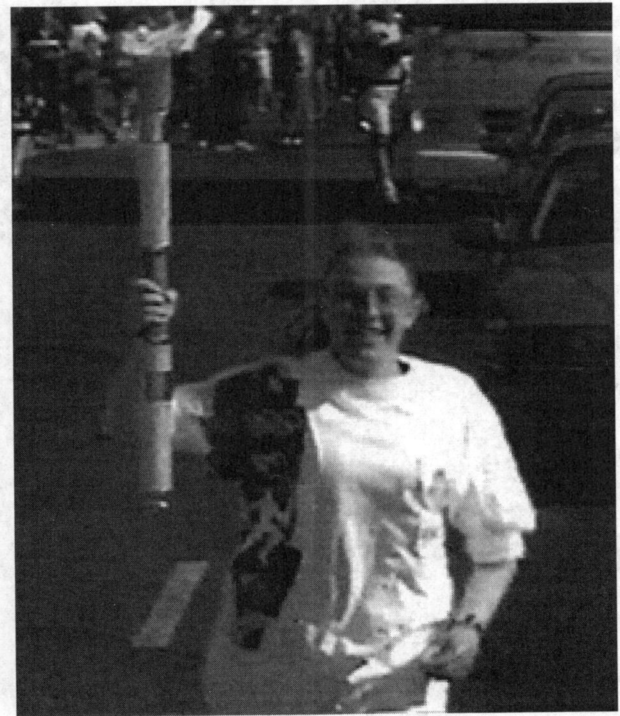

Jennifer Kurdy, a Junior at Bishop Kelly High School in Boise, Idaho is one of the students included in *Who's Who Among American High School Students* who was selected to be a participant in the 1996 Olympic Torch Relay. Featured on NBC's Coca-Cola Presents the Olympic Torch Relay, Jennifer is a Congressional Award Winner, a state tennis champion, plays the violin and counsels children. Her academic, personal and community accomplishments earned her this "opportunity of a lifetime". We salute Jennifer's achievements and all of the student and teacher participants who represented the educational community.

*"Summon the Heroes" is the title of John Williams' dramatic theme music featured in the television coverage of the 1996 Olympic Games.

Advisory Committee

Educational Communications, Inc. is dedicated to ensuring that the recognition of the teachers in *Who's Who Among America's Teachers* is one of the most meaningful honors a teacher can receive. We are also committed to helping to ensure that all students have excellent teachers.

Through the development and publication of *Who's Who Among America's Teachers* a unique and valuable database of exceptional educators has been developed and will continue to expand. We intend to use this resource to produce much-needed research and other information so vital to improving the quality of education in our country. In plain English, we know the teachers listed in this book are effective and we want to find out how and why from them and share this information with others.

Therefore, we have established an Advisory Committee of the following distinguished educators who will provide us with on-going advice and counsel to accomplish these objectives.

Members of the *Who's Who Among America's Teachers* Advisory Committee

Gloria Vickers Anderson
Teacher
Sontag School
Rocky Mount, VA

Lovely H. Billups
Director of Field Services
Educational Issues Department
American Federation of Teachers
Washington, DC

Roberta Felker
President
Seton Academy
South Holland, IL

Jeremiah Floyd
Associate Executive Director
National School Boards Association
Alexandria, VA

Susan Adler Kaplan
Former Member
National Board for Professional Teaching Standards
Providence, RI

Darlene Pierce
Former Director
National Teacher of the Year Program
Arlington, VA

Sylvia Seidel
Assistant Director
National Center for Innovation
National Education Association
Washington, DC

Selection Criteria and Process

The Best Teachers in America Selected by the Best Students®

The only way a teacher can be included in this publication is to be nominated by one or more of his or her former students. The only students who are invited to select their former teachers are students who are listed in *Who's Who Among American High School Students®* or *The National Dean's List®*. This universe of the top 5% high school and college students in America represents a unique group of consumers of education, well qualified to determine which teachers contributed most to their academic success.

Throughout the academic year all students who have been cited for academic excellence in the two student publications described above are invited to select one teacher from their entire academic experience who "made a difference" in their education.

There is no greater tribute a teacher can receive than to be recognized for teaching excellence by former students, particularly when the students themselves have been as successful as those included in this process. The selectivity demonstrated by the student nominators further validates the quality of the teachers listed in this book.

Who's Who Teacher Profile

(Statistics from 1996 Edition)

The fourth edition of *Who's Who Among America's Teachers* honors approximately 121,000 outstanding teachers in four separate regional volumes. Teachers are listed alphabetically in the volume of the state where they work. For maximum reference use, a comprehensive Geographic Occupation Index listing teachers from all volumes is included in each book.

Gender:

Female	62.3%
Male	37.7%

Marital Status:

Married	75.4%
Widowed	1.2%
Other	23.4%

Age Range:

30 & under	6.9%
31-35	9.9%
36-40	12.3%
41-45	18.6%
46-50	24.3%
51-55	15.5%
56-60	7.8%
61 & over	4.7%

Degrees Completed:

Average 1.8 degrees per teacher

Bachelors	99.3%
Masters	62.9%
Doctorate	6.5%

Area of Primary Involvement:

K-6 Grade	23.0%
7-8 Grade	19.3%
9-12 Grade	52.9%
College	11.7%
Graduate & Professional	2.2%

Type of School:

Public	86.4%
Private	7.7%
Parochial	5.9%

Current National Affiliation:

American Federation of Teachers	5.7%
National Education Association	41.3%
None	53.0%

Professional Expertise/Career Specialty:

Administration	6.7%
Adult Education	3.0%
Area Studies	0.7%
Athletics	8.3%
Business	1.6%
Bilingual Education	1.9%
Business Education	3.6%
Communications	3.0%
Computer Science	3.0%
Counseling	5.2%
Early Childhood Educ.	3.7%
Elementary Education	22.8%
Engineering	0.7%
English/Language Arts	20.9%
Fine/Applied Arts	4.1%
Gifted and Talented	5.7%
Health Sciences	3.4%
Home Arts	0.9%
Humanities	4.1%
Industrial Arts	0.9%
Language & Linguistics	5.9%
Library/Media Services	0.9%
Mathematics	13.5%
Music	5.1%
Occupational Education	1.3%
Performing Arts	3.9%
Physical Education	5.3%
Science	13.0%
Secondary Education	20.0%
Social Science	11.9%
Special Education	2.8%
Technology	2.8%
Other	12.9%

Other Activities:

Willing to Serve as a Mentor	31.6%
Willing to Serve as a "Spokesteacher"	23.3%
Willing to Write Education Articles	22.6%

PAUL C. KROUSE
Publisher

Publisher's Corner

Waving the Flag — Then & Now

As I was driving to my office on the morning of June 3, 1996, I saw a large crowd of people of all ages gathering around the railroad station and town square. Many of the little children were waving miniature American flags and lots of adults were toting cameras. Scattered throughout the throng were a number of American Legion members wearing their distinctive caps. I parked my car and walked across the street to find out what was going on. It seems that I was the only person in town who didn't know (or forgot) that the Olympic train carrying the torch was going to be passing through and making a short stop in Lake Forest.

As I was wandering through the crowd waiting for the train, it occurred to me that 30 years ago my wife and I created *Who's Who Among American High School Students.*[1] In 1966 most teenagers, particularly upperclassmen in high school and most college students were being characterized in a negative manner due to their demonstrations against the escalating war in Vietnam. *Who's Who* was created to balance the coverage. Flags were part of the scene 30 years ago too, except kids were burning them, not waving them.

As the train appeared in the distance, the chattering of the crowd diminished and we all stood quietly listening as the familiar train sounds approached closer and closer. When the train slowed to a stop at our depot, which was decorated with red, white and blue bunting, the crowd began clapping and cheering in unison, without any prompting whatsoever. The little children, some perched on their fathers' shoulders waved their flags proudly. It was such a warm and thrilling feeling. With all due respect to the political convictions of the young people who were burning flags 30 years ago, I must admit I enjoyed this demonstration much more.

Today as we debate the relevance of values education, whether they should be taught in the home or school or both, I can't help wonder where patriotism fits into the mix since it is so rarely discussed and even more rarely experienced. When I go to a ball game and the Star Spangled Banner is played, I notice that only a few people seem to know the words. I understand the controversy about school prayer, but I don't understand why our national anthem isn't taught or sung in all schools today.

In my youth, virtually all young men had to fulfill a military obligation and the cold war was a constant threat to world peace. Most of my peers had a parent or relative who served in World War II or Korea so patriotism was part and parcel of the "growing up" process. How do we instill a feeling of patriotism in our youth when there is no compulsory military training, no obligation to give something back to our country (not just taking what it has to offer), and a global economy where our business partners may work across an ocean, not just across the street? Is patriotism passé? If it is, what's next for the junk heap?

I never considered myself a super patriot or a left or right wing radical. In fact, I have often referred to myself as "a flaming moderate". Yet, the scene at the train station made me feel good and proud to be an American. Maybe I'm just a dinosaur, but I don't want anyone to miss the feelings I experienced and described. Let's all think about what we may miss and what we all stand to lose if patriotism becomes passé.

1. *The National Dean's List* was first published in 1978. *Who's Who Among America's Teachers* was first published in 1990.

Guest Editorials

We are pleased to present editorials written by prominent educators who represent teachers' partners and colleagues in the educational community.

The National Board for Professional Teaching Standards: Opportunities and Excellence

Susan Adler Kaplan
Former Member
National Board for Professional Teaching Standards
Providence, RI

Of all of the many reform initiatives that I have known in my long career, the most promising to me is one which will have the most powerful impact on our students and at the same time support and reward teachers. The National Board for Professional Teaching Standards is that initiative.

As I reflect on my experiences with the Board as a member of the Planning Group in 1985-1986, and then as a founding member beginning in 1987 and serving until my last term recently ended, I discover constantly the effects this experience has had on my professional and personal life. The increased awareness and practice of our art and craft and mission as teachers, through conversations about standards in specific disciplines, about student and teacher assessment, have brought many of us - colleagues on the Board - to even higher levels of teaching expertise, professionalism, dedication and knowledge.

What has caused the National Board to affect so many of us so profoundly? Why do I believe it is so important for you outstanding teachers to become Board-certified? My experience compels me to share some of these observations with you. A little history will pave the way for you to consider the journey that I hope all of you will take to become Board-certified teachers.

To begin, the National Board, in its Planning Group phase, summoned together thirty-three individuals, fourteen of whom had worked on the seminal document, *A Nation Prepared: Teachers for the 21st Century* released in May, 1986. We nineteen "new members" of that group were teachers, principals, teacher educators, policy makers; to a person, those of us engaged in teaching at the K-12 levels as well as administrators and teacher educators, considered ourselves teachers above all.

In that first planning year for the Board, we debated policy issues, by-laws, definitions of teaching excellence and academic areas for certification. We were a lively group, respectful and sincere, passionate and demanding. Our common ground was to prepare Board policies and procedures, that would, at every decision point, provide the best education for our students in an increasingly challenging world. We never once forgot our mission on behalf of students. We believed then and still do, almost ten years later, that teachers coming forward to demonstrate what they know and are able to do are critical to success for our students. As one of our members stated at our opening press conference in 1987 when we officially launched our sixty-four member Board: "I know that I am a good teacher. . . but without portfolio; the National Board gives me that portfolio." The word "portfolio," at that point, was figurative and implied public credibility and acknowledgment.

We worked hard in those nascent years of the Board to develop both our mission and those activities that would give teachers the best opportunity to demonstrate what they know and can do. We stated our mission clearly:

> The mission of the National Board for Professional Teaching Standards is to establish high and rigorous standards for what accomplished teachers should know and be able to do, to develop and operate a national voluntary system to assess and certify teachers who meet these standards, and to advance related education reforms for the purpose of improving student learning in American schools.

With development of standards in academic areas for teachers, with consultants working with us on issues of equity and access; on reliability and validity for our assessments, and on education reform issues, we all grew intellectually. We learned from each other, from and with researchers and legal advisers and from the experience itself of having deep intellectual conversations about the best teaching and learning. We sat next to one another: presidents and representatives of both major teacher organizations, school board members, superintendents, discipline area association representatives, governors, legislators, representatives from higher education, from business and state education agencies. All of us around the table communicated our concerns for our vital mission of improving student learning in our schools.

One of the most critical aspects of our development

then and now is that all of those stakeholders in our education continue to be at the same table; those discussions and challenges that led to major decisions were, for me, some of the most important experiences of my service on the Board. For whatever the issue, the necessity of all interest groups communicating on behalf of our students is still paramount.

For you, distinguished teachers, the opportunity to apply for National Board certification, to prepare a teaching portfolio and participate in an assessment that demonstrates what you know and can do is an opportunity that will benefit your students, yourself, your district, state and nation. As more and more organizations and states begin to support teachers undertaking this initiative, the chances for you to go forward and begin working for Board certification are growing. I invite you to join those teachers who have already become certified and who celebrated their accomplishment at the White House in October, 1996. For those of you, who may be the first Board-certified teachers represented in these volumes, heartiest congratulations. We need all of you to join those of us who began this twentieth century initiative to help us bring it successfully into the next century.

Keepers of the Flame

Gloria Vickers Anderson
Teacher
Sontag School, Rocky Mount, VA

This tribute to teachers in *Who's Who Among America's Teachers* again supports the fact that teachers can be the determining factor in the success or failure of most students. Statements written by students tell that teachers who showed concern, cared, and had patience really made the difference in their academic success. These exceptional teachers truly keep the flame in the lamp of learning burning.

One of the greatest challenges confronting our educational system now is in using advancing technology to the ultimate level of effectiveness, while not losing sight of how valuable interpersonal relationships are between students and teachers. Even when surrounded by computers, good teachers will take advantage of every moment to enrich the learning environment for all students. This means making learning come alive with their enthusiasm and energy to invite, motivate, encourage, evaluate, reteach, and reward the learners. Teachers who keep the flame bright and visible show students that they are not only interested in the student's academic growth, but in their personal, physical and social development as well.

A very pleasurable experience for me came this year when a former first grade student's mother walked into my classroom with an invitation to her son's graduation celebration. At the celebration, my former student came to me several times with a hug and asked me do you remember when you said . . . or do you remember when you did . . . I did remember that most of the things he remembered were not about school work or grades. They were about other things that were important to him at that particular time.

Teachers who radiate in the reflection of their flame seem to understand that every student will not become a great scientist, engineer, teacher, or physician. What they do realize is that if students are not challenged with high expectations, they will never know to what extent their potential talents can be developed. Helping students to believe in themselves and to realize that they are important and valued, is essential for productive achievement. Students who have confidence in doing something, and know that others also have confidence in them usually achieve far beyond their original goal.

A very dedicated and inspiring teacher was being honored by some of her former students. When she spoke to the group, she told them how proud she was of all of their accomplishments. One young man spoke up and said, "We just did what you told us to do." Without a doubt, that teacher had used a very positive approach in teaching her students. She knew what a critical role teachers play in determining which path students may choose to follow.

Teachers who keep the flame bright and visible know how to bring out the best in each student. Helping students develop positive self-esteem while utilizing their academic skills to notable achievement is certainly a primary challenge for good teachers. When students have low self-esteem they blame others for their failures regardless of their natural abilities.

Successful teachers refrain from taking credit for what they have done for students, but instead highlight what they have managed to get students to do for themselves. Students must be guided in overcoming the three fears: the fear of failure, the fear of criticism, and the fear of appearing stupid before their peers. When students reach this point, they emerge capable of making sound decisions and are proud of their accomplishments. These students are more willing to accept responsibility for their actions and more capable handling frustrations.

Teachers must take control of shaping their educational programs which should incorporate flexibility in instructional methods, teaching styles, learning opportunities, classroom environment, student assessment and interpersonal relationships. The teachers who do, without a doubt, will keep the flame in the lamp of learning burning eternally.

A Message to Teachers

Albert Shanker
President
American Federation of Teachers

On behalf of the American Federation of Teachers, I congratulate the outstanding teachers recognized in *Who's Who Among America's Teachers.* While the intrinsic rewards in teaching are great, external recognition is also important. So, I also congratulate Educational Communications, Inc. for their commitment to honoring great teachers.

Inclusion in *Who's Who* ranks among the most prestigious of professional honors, because you have been singled out by students as the mentors who strongly influenced their lives and contributed to their success. All of the students in the nominating process are high achievers. They reflect broad diversity in economic backgrounds, race, creed and gender. You found the strength and potential in each student and nurtured it. It is the student who learns, but the teacher who must open the doors to learning.

This book commemorates you as excellent teachers for what you have accomplished, but it does not say how you accomplished it. What you know about teaching and learning is inaccessible to most other teachers. Teachers remain isolated in classrooms, their experiences and discoveries are not available to their colleagues, nor are they published in journals or included as part of the formal preparation of prospective teachers. To the extent that successful teachers can pass on their expertise, it is only through the oral tradition. In fact, one of the ways we'll know that teaching has emerged as a full profession is when, in addition to finding outstanding teachers' names in *Who's Who*, their methodologies and school and classroom research are a part of education's professional literature and training.

The need for the full professionalization of teaching has become especially acute. For despite the successes of many teachers, many challenges remain. Some of the most serious challenges result from societal problems, such as drug abuse, inadequate health care or the crisis in the family. We cannot let these external problems be an excuse, no matter how heavily they weigh on the schools; serious deficiencies in our educational system are also implicated in America's shockingly poor record of student achievement, not only among our at-risk youngsters but among most students. Our job as a professional is to find the keys to helping the majority of youngsters achieve at the high levels demonstrated by the students who singled you out for excellence.

To teachers everywhere then, I offer the challenge to reflect upon your teaching and the ways in which students learn and to become leaders in the effort to reform public education. Consider the school system not as it is, but as it should be to foster a high level of achievement among diverse youngsters who learn in different ways and at different rates. How, for example, might we best involve students actively in their own learning, help them construct meaning from their own experience, encourage them to believe in themselves, and show them the paths to previously discovered knowledge, as well as the creation of new knowledge? Should we be using cross-age grouping, peer tutoring, cooperative small groups and coaching? Do we need to throw out the textbooks or use them in new ways? In what ways could education technology improve instruction? Might a group of teachers stay with a group of students over a period of years? Should teachers, rather than bells or arbitrary time limits, determine the time blocks into which the curriculum fits? What should be the role of the teacher and other personnel in a school in which each staff member's first priority is the success of all students? What assessment strategies will tell us what students know and are able to do?

These questions represent only a few of the important issues facing the professional today. If they are answered through the blinders of school tradition, we will lose a generation of youth and, very likely, public education in the bargain. This is a time of danger, but it is also a time of opportunity. More and more of the public realize that to invest in public education represents the social, political and economic hope of the future. They also realize that in this changing society, more of the same is no longer enough.

As teachers, you are leaders. We must learn together how to create schooling through which all children are equipped with the knowledge and skills necessary to contribute to and thrive in our increasingly complex society. As a profession, we must insist upon change and guide it to accomplish this goal. In the process, we must dare to think new thoughts and devise new strategies for fulfilling the traditional aspirations of public education in a democratic society.

Glossary of Abbreviations

To incorporate as much useful information as possible within the available space, abbreviations and acronyms are frequently used. Below is a list of the most frequently used abbreviations and acronyms.

AA Associate of Arts
AAPT American Association of Physics Teachers
AASA American Association of School Administrators
AATF American Association of Teachers of French
AATG American Association of Teachers of German
Acad Academic, Academy
ACEI Association for Childhood Education International
Achvmt Achievement
ACSI Association of Christian Schools International
Act Activities
Addl Additional
Addr Address
Admin Administration, Administrator, Administrative
Adv Advisor
AFB Air Force Base
AFSA American Federation of School Administration
AFT American Federation of Teachers
Ag Agriculture
ai: Additional Information
AIFS American Institute for Foreign Study
AK Alaska
AL Alabama
Amer American
AOJT Association of Orthodox Jewish Teachers
AR Arkansas
AS Associate of Science, American Samoa
ASCA American School Council Association
ASCD Association for Supervision & Curriculum Development
Assn Association
Assoc Associate
Asst Assistant
ATE Association of Teacher Educators
Ath Athlete, Athletics
Attnd Attended
AVA American Vocational Association
Ave Avenue
Awd(ed) Award(ed)
AZ Arizona
b: Place of Birth
BA Bachelor of Arts
BAE Bachelor of Art Education, Arts in Education, Agricultural Engineering
Bapt Baptist
BBA Bachelor of Business Administration
BCE Bachelor of Christian Education
Bd Board
BD Bachelor of Divinity
BE Bachelor of Education
BFA Bachelor of Fine Arts
Biling Bilingual
Bio Biology
Bldg Building
Blvd Boulevard
BS Bachelor of Science
BSA Bachelor of Science in Agriculture, Boy Scouts of America
Bsbl Baseball
Bsktbl Basketball
BSE Bachelor of Science in Education
BSEE Bachelor of Science in Elementary Education
BSME Bachelor of Science in Music Education
BSN Bachelor of Science in Nursing
BT Bachelor of Science in Theology, Teaching
Bus Business
BVA Bachelor of Science in Vocational Agriculture
c: Children
CA California
Cath Catholic
CEC Council for Exceptional Children
Cert Certificate, Certification
Chem Chemistry
Chldhd Childhood
Chm Chairman
Chprsn Chairperson
Chrldr Cheerleader
Chrstn Christian
Cmptr Computer
Cncl Council
Cnslr Counselor
Cntrl Central
Cntry Country
Co Company
CO Colorado
Coll College
Comm Committee, Communications, Community
Conf Conference
Coord Coordinator
Corp Corporation
Cr Circle
cr: Career Information
Ct Court
CT Connecticut
Ctr Center
Cty County
Curr Curriculum
DC District of Columbia
DE Delaware
dec Deceased
Del Delegate
Dept Department
Dev Develop(ed), Development
Dir Director
Dist District
Dr Doctor, Drive
E East
Ec Economic(s)
ed: Education
Ed Editor, Education
EDD Doctor of Education
EDS Education Specialist
Educl Educational
Elem Elementary
Eng English
Engr Engineer
Exch Exchange
Excl Excellence
Exec Executive
Fed Federation
FCA Fellowship of Christian Athletes
FFA National FFA Organization
FHA Future Homemakers of America
FL Florida
FM Federated States of Micronesia
Fnd Foundation
Fr French
Frosh Freshman
Ft Fort
Ftbl Football
GA Georgia
Ger German
Govt Government
Grad Graduate(d), Graduation
Grd Grade
GU Guam
Hghts Heights
HI Hawaii
His History
Hlth Health
Hrs Hours
HS High School
Hum Humanities
Hwy Highway
IA Iowa
ID Idaho
IL Illinois
IN Indiana

Inc Incorporated
Ind Independent
Inst Institute, Institution
Instr Instructor
Intnl International
IRA International Reading Association
ISD Independent School District
ITS International Thespian Society
Jr Junior
Jrnlsm Journalism
JTA Jewish Teachers Association
K/Kndgtn Kindergarten
KS Kansas
KY Kentucky
LA Louisiana
Lab Laboratory
Lang Language
Ldr Leader
Lib Library
Librn Librarian
Lit Literary, Literature
Ln Lane
Luth Lutheran
m: Married
MA Massachusetts, Master of Arts
MADD Mothers Against Drunk Driving
MAEd Master of Arts in Education
Math Mathematics
MBA Master of Business Administration
MD Maryland
ME Maine, Master of Education
Mem Member
Meml Memorial
Meth Methodist
MFA Master of Fine Arts
Mgmt Management
Mgr Manager
MI Michigan
Mid Middle
MN Minnesota
MO Missouri
MP Northern Mariana Islands
Mrktg Marketing
MS Master of Science, Middle School, Mississippi
MSW Master of Social Work
MT Montana
MTNA Music Teachers National Association
N North
NABE National Association for Bilingual Education
NABT National Association of Biology Teachers
NACST National Association of Catholic School Teachers
NAEA National Art Education Association
NAESP National Association of Elementary School Principals
NAEYS National Association for Education of Young Children
NASSP National Association of Secondary School Principals
Natl National
NBEA National Business Education Association
NC North Carolina
NCBE National Council for Better Education
NCEA National Catholic Education Association
NCSS National Council for Social Studies
NCTE National Council of Teachers of English
NCTM National Council of Teachers of Mathematics
ND North Dakota
NE Nebraska
NEA National Education Association
NH New Hampshire
NHS National Honor Society
NJ New Jersey
NM New Mexico
Nom Nominated, Nominee
NRTA National Retired Teachers Association
NSTA National Science Teachers Association
NV Nevada
NY New York
Ofcl Official
OH Ohio
OK Oklahoma
OR Oregon
Orch Orchestra
Org Organization
PA Pennsylvania
PE Physical Education
PHD Doctor of Philosophy
Phys Physical
Pkwy Parkway
Pl Place
Pol Political
PR Puerto Rico
Pres President
Presbyn Presbyterian
Presch Preschool
Prgm Program
Prin Principal
Prof Professional, Professor
Prsnl Personnel
Psych Psychology
PTA Parent Teacher Association
Pub Public, Published(ed)
Rd Road
Rdng Reading
Regnl Regional
Rel Religion, Religious
Rep Representative, Represented
Ret Retired
RI Rhode Island
RR Rural Route
Rt Route
S South
SADD Students Against Driving Drunk
SC South Carolina
Schl(s) School(s)
Schlsp Scholarship
Sci Science
Scndry Secondary
SD South Dakota
Sec Secretary
Sftbl Softball
Soc Social, Society
Soph Sophomore
Span Spanish
Spec Special
Spon Sponsor
Sq Square
Sr Senior
St State, Street
Stan Standard
Stdnts Students
Stu Student
Stud Study(ies)
Supt Superintendent
Supvr Supervisor
Tchng Teaching
Tchr Teacher
Tech Technical, Technology
Terr Terrace
TN Tennessee
Treas Treasurer
Trng Training
Twp Township
TX Texas
Univ University
US United States
USAF United States Air Force
UT Utah
VA Virginia
Var Varsity
VI Virgin Islands
Vlybl Volleyball
Voc Vocational
Vol Volume, Volunteer
VP Vice President
VT Vermont
w: Widowed
W West
WA Washington
WI Wisconsin
Wkshp Workshop
WV West Virginia
WY Wyoming
Yr Year
Yrbk Yearbook

Sample Biography

1 JOHNSON, ALISON BREWSTER; **2** Math Dept Chairperson; **3** *b:* Bailey's Harbor, WI; **4** *m:* George M. **5** *c:* Stephen F., Denise J., John J.; **6** *ed:* Univ of WI at Madison (BS) Scndry Ed 1975; **7** *cr:* Shawnee HS Math Tchr 1975-77, Grissom HS Math Tchr 1977-79; Philip Hansen HS Math Tchr 1979-82, Math Dept Chprsn 1982—; **8** *ai:* Math Marathon Adv; Jr Class Adv; WI Cncl of Tchrs of Math 1977—, Pres 1987-88, Outstanding Achvmt Awd 1989; NCTM 1981—; NEA; Bailey Twp Lib Bd; Rio Creek Chamber of Commerce Tchr of the Yr 1991; **9** *office:* Philip Hansen HS 543 Fairway Green Rio Creek WI 54231 **10** *

Key

1 Name
2 Current Position
3 Place of Birth
4 Spouse's Name
5 Children
6 Education
7 Career Information
8 Additional Information: Extracurricular Responsibilities; Professional Memberships; Civic, Service or Other Organization Memberships; Professional Achievements
9 Address (at biographee's discretion)
10 Denotes Willing to Serve as a Mentor

Each biography is presented in a uniform order as shown in the foregoing fictional listing. Biographees are listed in alphabetical order by surname. In those cases where surname is identical, biographees are arranged first by surname, then by first and middle name, and finally by age as denoted by Sr., Jr., or I, II, etc. For alphabetical arrangement, names having a space (Mc, Von, Des, etc.) or punctuation (O'Hara) are properly spelled but treated as though there was no space or punctuation. These surnames are listed under the first character of the surname (i.e., Mc under M). Surnames beginning with Saint (spelled either Saint or St.) will appear following Sains and be listed according to the first character of the second name. Abbreviations and acronyms most frequently used are shown in the glossary.

BIOGRAPHIES

A

:ON, KAREN M., Elementary Teacher; *b:* Far Rockaway, NY; *m:* Dr. k R.; *c:* Stacey Lynn, Lauren Jill; *ed:* Syracuse Univ (BS) Elem Ed, h 1972; LIU-CW Post Coll (MS) Elem Ed, Early Chldhd Ed 1974; Cert 1994; *cr:* Shelter Rock Schl Tchr 1972-; *ai:* AFT, NYSUT, MEA -; Sigma Delta Tau Schlsp Awd; Grad Honors; *office:* Shelter Rock Schl 27A Shelter Rock Rd Manhasset NY 11030

.ONSON, ANN SCHROEDER, 6th-8th Grade Art Teacher; *b:* Lima, *m:* Arthur; *c:* Jacob, Adam; *ed:* Siena Heights Coll (BA) Art Ed 1975; of Dayton (MS) Elem Ed 1995; Studied Art, Art His in Florence; *cr:* sic Migrant Schl K-8 Art Tchr Summers 1976-78; Shawnee Schls 1-5 Art Tchr 1976-85; Greeeview Cntrl Schl 6-8 Grd Art Tchr 1987-; *ai:* Adv; ONEA, NEA, OAEA 1987-; OH Artist & Crafters Guild 1990-; Kappa Gamma 1983-; St Francis Church 1988-, Craft Dir; BSA -, Advanced Chair; Maratha Holden Jennings Scholar 1993; Howard ost Excl in Ed Awd 1993; Illustrated: The Child in Children; *home:* Fowler Dr Bellbrook OH 45305*

TRUP, RONDI SUZANNE, English & Journalism Teacher; *b:* ham, MA; *ed:* Atlantic Union Coll (BA) Eng & His 1977; Andrews (MA) Lit 1983; Worcester St Work Towards Masters in Cnslng; Univ H Work Towards PHD in Lit; *cr:* Cedar Lake Acad Eng Tchr & Guid 1978-83; South Lancaster Acad Eng & Jrnlsm Tchr 1983-91; Atlantic n Coll Contract Tchr 1983-; Various Newspapers Free-Lance nalist 1991-; Pine Tree Acad His Tchr 1992-93; Greater Boston Acad His & Jrnlsm Tchr 1993-; *ai:* Jr Class Spon; Newspaper Adv; uiting Coord; Co-Organize Major Fund Raising Concert Series; MRA; NEA; NEPA; NESPA; New England Yth Ensemble 1991-; Pub erous Articles on Ed; Zapara Awd for Excl in Tchng 1995; *home:* 2 oall Ct Apt 306 Woburn MA 01801

TE, CHARLES JOSEPH, Electrical & Cmptr Tech Prof; *b:* Pittston, *m:* Christine Susan Baker; *ed:* Wilkes Univ (BA) Philosophy 1972; of IA (MA) Philosophy 1974; Suny Inst of Tech (BET) Electrical ng Tech 1982; Syracuse Univ (PHD) Philosophy 1986; *cr:* Syracuse Instr 1975-79; Onondaga Comm Coll Prof 1980-; Anaren Microwave est Engr 1985-; *ai:* Dept Chprsn; Tech Prep Trng Coord; ASEE 1990-, dng Edctr Awd 1995; NY St Sportfishing & Aquatic Resources Ed 1994-, Cert Instr; OCC Bd Trustess Recognition Awd 1989; Author erous Prof Articles; *office:* Onondaga Comm Coll Onondaga Hill Road cuse NY 13215

TO, BARBARA, Jr High Teacher; *b:* Brooklyn, NY; *ed:* St Josephs (BA) Child Stud, Math 1984; Working on MA in Ed, Math Brooklyn *cr:* St Therese of Lisieux Schl Tchr 1984-90; St Brendans Holy ly Schl Jr HS Tchr 1990-92, Jr HS Tchr, Math Coord 1992-; *ai:* Math ue, Math Bee Coord; Math Coord & Adv for Schl; Voc Dir; rmation Tchr; NCEA 1990-; Amer Med Assn Tchrs of Math 1989; : 2463 E 21st St Brooklyn NY 11235*

ARNO, JOHN MARK, Professor of Philosophy; *b:* Buffalo, NY; *m:* e Agati; *c:* Aaron; *ed:* Canisius Coll (BA) Philosophy 1970; Univ of on (MA) Philosophy 1972; Southern IL Univ at Carbondale (PHD) sophy 1977; *cr:* Canisius Coll Instr 1976-77; D'Youville Coll Prof -; *ai:* Undergraduate Curr, Lbrl Arts Prsnl Comm; Philosophy Club Lbrl Arts Division Chm 1985-89; Amer Soc for Value Inquiry 1983-, AAUP 1977-, Chptr Pres; Journal of Value Inquiry 1988-, Assoc Ed; alo Philharmonic Ath Club 1987-, Bd of Dirs; Friends of Night People Kitchen 1995-, Bd of Dirs; Natl Endowment for Hum Flwshp; Scholar r 1992; Pub 2 Books, Numerous Journal Articles; Conf of sophical Socs Archivist.

ATE-RYAN, LAURIE, HS Math Teacher; *b:* Bridgeport, CT; *m:* ard R. Ryan Jr.; *c:* Mikela; *ed:* Pace Univ (BS) Art 1985; hattanville (MS) Ed 1987; Fordham Univ Math Major Continuing Ed; chester Tchrs Inst 15 Credit Hrs; Attnd Westchester Comm Coll; *cr:* ander Hamilton Math Tchr 1989-; *ai:* Stu Govt; Yrbk; Sr Adv; Interact act; Scenery, Set Designer; Coach; NYSUT 1989-; *office:* Alexander lton Jr Sr HS 22 S Goodwin Ave Elmsford NY 10523

OT, MARIE PASSARO, Fourth Grade Teacher; *b:* Stamford, CT; *m:* ard L.; *c:* Richard Jr., Christy A. Bartnicki; *ed:* Western CT Univ (BS) Ed 1962; Univ of Bridgeport (MS) Elem Ed 1966; *cr:* Stamford Pub Grd 3-4 Tchr 1962-69; Holy Spirit Schl Grd 3 Tchr 1980-86; nwich Cath Schl Grd 4-5 Tchr 1986-; *ai:* Admissions, Scheduling egic Planning Comms; Soc Stud Chm; Mentor Prgm; NCEA 1980-; : Greenwich Catholic Schl 471 North St Greenwich CT 06830

OTT, ANITA HALFHILL, Secondary Spanish Teacher; *b:* ellsville, PA; *m:* Michael James; *c:* Michael Jr., Vashti, Josiah; *ed:* of Pgh (MED) Frgn Lang 1987; Rasias Methodology Cert; *ai:* Acad Team Coach; NHS Spon; NEA 1980-; *office:* Laurel Highland Sr HS Bailey Ave Uniontown PA 15401*

OTT, BRUCE R., Social Studies Teacher & Coord; *b:* Philadelphia, *m:* Reba J.; *c:* Lauren, Scott; *ed:* West Chester St Coll (BS) Scndry Ed, Stud 1968; Trenton St Coll (MA) His 1973; Supervisory Cert Soc Stud Bloomsberg Coll 1989; *cr:* Pennsbury HS Soc Stu Tchr 1968-; sbury Schl Dist Grds K-12 Curr Coord 1989-; *ai:* NEA, PA St Ed , Pennsbury Ed Assn 1968-; NCSS, PA Cncl for Soc Stud 1985-; Natl His Ed, Assn Supvr & Curr Dept 1990-; Commonwealth Tchng Fellow ; Co-Ed 1996; *office:* Pennsbury Sr HS 134 Yardley Ave Fairless Hills 9030

OTT, KAREN STITZLEIN, Mathematics Teacher; *b:* Millersburg, *m:* Ronald William; *c:* Steven, Michael; *ed:* Capital Univ (BA) Speech & Math 1973; Kent St Univ MEd 1995; Attnd Otterbein Coll & Kent St Univ; *cr:* Columbus Pub Math Tchr 1974-80; Northmor Local Math Tchr 1980-81; Cardington Local Math & cmptr Sci Univ 1984-87; Mathews Local Math & Speech Tchr 1988-; *ai:* Dir St Proficency Test; Tech Comm; Key Clb Adv; OH Cncl Tchrs of Math 1988-; Trumbull New Theater 1992-, Outstanding New Actress 1992-93 Season; *office:* Mathews HS 4429 Warren-Sharon Rd Vienna OH 44473*

ABBOTT, LORI ADAMS, Business Teacher; *b:* Orlando, FL; *m:* Michael Abbott; *c:* Nathan, Kelsey; *ed:* Southern Coll of SDA (BS) Bus 1983; Fairleigh Dickinson Univ (MA) Corp Comm 1995; *cr:* Cecil Jr Coll Bus Tchr 1986-87; Greater Dallas Acad Bus Tchr 1987-88; Jefferson Acad Bus Tchr 1988-92; Garden St Acad Bus Tchr 1992-; *ai:* Alumni Comm; Schl Newspaper; NBEA; *office:* Garden State Acad Rt 517 Tranquility NJ 07879

ABBOTT, MARK D., Sixth Grade Teacher & Coach; *b:* Norwich, NY; *m:* Robbin Rydzewski; *c:* Michael, Brooke; *ed:* SUNY at Brockport (BS) Eng 1981; SUC at Oneonta (MS) Elem Ed 1989; *cr:* Norwich City Schls Sixth Grd Tchr 1984-; *ai:* Bsbl 1984-, Boys Bsktbl 1986- Var Coaches; NEA 1984-; Sec IV Bsktbl Coach of Yr 1992-93, NYS Bsktbl Coach of Yr 1993-4; *office:* Perry Browne Intrmdt School Beebee Ave Norwich NY 13815

ABBOTT, MARY MILLIGAN, 9th-12th Grade English Tchr; *b:* Pittsburgh, PA; *m:* John Lawrence; *c:* Sean Lawrence, Stephen McLeod; *ed:* Otterbein Coll (BA) Eng 1960; MI St Univ (MA) Eng & Scndry Ed 1963; *cr:* East Lansing HS Eng Tchr 1960-64; Windham HS Eng Tchr 1977-; *ai:* Eng Class Poetry Coord; AFT & WFT 1977-, Soc Comm Chair; Amer Soc for 18th Century Stud 1989-; Pub in CT Eng Journal Volume 20 1992; *office:* Windham HS 355 High St Willimantic CT 06226

ABBOTT, PAOLA (ANTONELLI), Latin & Italian Teacher; *b:* Sassoferrato, Italy; *m:* Donald; *c:* Kathleen, Leslie; *ed:* Cath Univ of Amer (MA) Italian Lit 1988; Univ of Urbino Pharmaceutical Chem Dr of Pharmacy 1971; Ed Psych 15 Credit Hrs; *cr:* Berlitz Schl of Langs Programmer of Italian Courses & Instr 1984-90; Essex Comm Coll Italian Tchr 1987-90; Univ of MD Adjunct Prof of Italian 1986-87; Amer Univ Adjunct Prof of Italian 1988-; Suitland HS Latin & Italian Tchr 1990-; *ai:* Pride Adv; Prince George Cty Educators Assn, Modern Lang Assn of Amer 1990-; Amer Assn of Univ Profs 1991-; Amer Classical League 1994-; Amer Assn of Tchrs of Italian 1994-; Italian Ed for Italian Tape & Book Course; Prince George Cty Outstanding Educator by St of MD; Univ of Perugia Italy Schlsp Course from Italian St Ministry of Ed 1990; Rep MD at Pre-Conf for Italian Edctrs in New York City 1995; Italian Ed & Contributor for Grammar Portion of Book & Tape for Lang 30 Italian Course 1992; *home:* 3217 Birchmede Rd Ellicott City MD 21042

ABBOTT, PATRICIA LYNN, Instructor of Psychology; *b:* Framingham, MA; *ed:* Westfield St Coll (BA) Psych 1985; St Univ of NY at Buffalo (MA) Behavorial Neursci 1990; *cr:* St Univ of NY at Buffalo Tchng Asst 1987-90; D'Youville Coll Instr 1990-; *ai:* Adv Earth Wise Club; AAUP 1993-; Soc of Neurosci 1990-; *office:* D'Youville College 320 Porter Ave Buffalo NY 14201

ABBOTT, PHILIP KEENAN, High School Spanish Teacher; *b:* Miniola, NY; *m:* Maya Kuster; *ed:* Norwich Univ (BA) Span, Int'l Stud 1982; KS Univ (MA) Latin Amer Stud 1992; Defense Lang Inst Span Cert 1991; Proyecto Linguistico Francisco Marroquin, Antigua, Guatemala-Foreign Svc Inst Biling Cert; *cr:* US Army Military Attache-Latin Amer 1982-94; Oxon Hill HS Span Tchr 1994-; *ai:* Adv Span Hon Soc; NEA 1994-; *office:* Oxon Hill HS 6701 Leyte Dr Oxon Hill MD 20745

ABBOTT, RICHARD H., 6th Grade Science Instructor; *b:* Providence, RI; *m:* Dianne Elaine Fisher; *c:* Michael, Whitney, Dana; *ed:* VA Commonwealth Univ (BS) Mrktg 1969; Univ of Dayton (BS) Elem Ed 1974; Wright St Univ (MS) Sci Ed 1990; Winning In Sci & Ed, Project Discovery Post Grad; *cr:* Milton-Union MS Elem, MS Math, Sci Tchr 1974-; *ai:* Sci Olympiad Coach 1988-; Young Scientist Prgm Co-Founder 1990-93; Jr Teen Inst Co-Dir 1983-; OEA 1974-; SECO 1990-; Young Spirits 1988-, Steering Comm; West Milton Optimists 1984-, Pres; Outstdng Tchr 1985, 1991; Honorary NHS; OH Sci Olympiad Advy Comm; Project Discovery Staff; WOEA Outstdng Tchr Nom; Marth Holden Jennings Scholar; *office:* Milton-Union MS 146 S Spring St West Milton OH 45383

ABBOUD, BECHARA ELIAS, Associate Prof of Civil Engrng; *b:* Beirut, Lebanon; *m:* Roxanne T. Gregorio; *ed:* Roger Williams Coll (BSCE) Civil Engrng 1978; Drexel Univ (MSCE) Civil Engrng 1981, (PHD) Civil Engrng 1987; Post-Doctoral 1988; *cr:* Oliver & Becica Sr Structural Engr 1988-89; Temple Univ Asst Prof 1989-94; Furtaw & Abboud Consulting Prin, VP 1991-95; Temple Univ Assoc Prof 1994-; *ai:* Amer Soc of Civil Engrng Fac Adv Stu Chapter; TMS Codes, Standards Comm Mem; Masonry Standards Joint Comm Voting Mem; Amer Soc of Civil Engrs 1978-; Amer Concrete Inst, The Masonry Soc 1982-; Pub over 30 Papers, Reports; *office:* Temple Univ Coll of Engrng 12th & Norris St Philadelphia PA 19122*

ABDALLA, CECILIA GRUSZECKI, Bus Legal & Medical Instructor; *b:* East Liverpool, OH; *m:* Michael C.; *c:* Mike, Alicia; *ed:* Jefferson Tech Coll (AS) Exec Sec Sci 1973; Univ of Steubenville (BS) Bus Admin 1975; Kent St Univ (MS) Voc Ed 1991; OH St Univ 9 Hrs; Bowling Green St Univ 3 Hrs; Wright St Univ 3 Hrs; Youngstown St Univ 3 Hrs; *cr:* Toronto HS Bus, Voc Instr 1975-91; Jefferson Tech Coll Part-time Shorthand Instr 1975-78; Jefferson Cty JVS Bus Legal, Med Instr 1991-; *ai:* Bus Profs of Amer Club Adv; NEA, OEA, OBTA 1975-; DKG 1978-, 2nd VP; S & J Credit Union Advy Cncl 1995-, Cncl Mem; S Jr Hi Booster Club 1991-; EHS Booster Club 1994-; EHS Mothers Club 1995-; BPTA Dedicated Adv Awd; *office:* Jefferson Co Joint Voc Schl B-9 Ch # 22a R1 Bloomingdale OH 43910

ABDELLA, MARILYN TUFTS, 5th Grade Teacher; *b:* Batavia, NY; *c:* Timothy, Ann Marie, Carrie; *ed:* Buffalo St Tchrs (BS) Elem Ed 1968; 72 In-Svc Credit Hrs; *cr:* Alexander Cntrl Schl 4-5 Grd Tchr 1971-78; Pavilion Cntrl Schl K, 4-5 Grd Tchr 1985-; *ai:* NYSUT 1971-; *office:* Pavilion Central Schl 7014 Big Tree Rd Pavilion NY 14525

ABDOO, ANGELA DI LULLO, Math, Algebra & Geometry Tchr; *b:* Akron, OH; *c:* Lisa A. Liming, Joseph R., T. Michael; *ed:* Univ of Akron (BS) Elem Ed 1974; Martha Holden Jennings Scholar Math 1984, Lecture Series 1994; Madeline Hunter Trainer Essential Elements Instruction, Peer Coaching; Group Facilitator Trng 1992 Stow Yth Division Insight, CORE Group; Academically Talented Tchr Ed Prgm KSU Mentor ATTEP; Mentorship Prgm; *cr:* Innaculate Heart of Mary 7th, 8th Grd Math Tchr 1965-75; Kimpton MS 8th Grd Math Tchr 1975-; *ai:* Math Counts Competition Soc Prof Engrs Adv 1983-; Staff Evaluation Comm; Stow Tchr Assn, OH Educ Assn, NEA 1975-; NCTM; PTSA Tchr of Yr, Stow Jaycees Edctr of Yr 1986; *home:* 2267 11th St Cuyahoga Falls OH 44221*

ABDUL-GHAFUR, SHARON A., 6th Grade Teacher; *b:* Neptune, NJ; *c:* Aatif, Rafig; *ed:* Kean Coll of NJ (BA) Elem Ed 1974; Grad Stud 18 Credit Hrs; EC Cert Seton Hall Univ; *cr:* Chad Schl Preschl Tchr 1974-75; New Ark Schl Tchr 1975-80; Monmouth Cty Headstart Tchr 1981-84; Asbury Park MS Tchr 1985-; *ai:* NWEA 1984-; *office:* Asbury Park MS 1200 Bangs Ave Asbury Park NJ 07712*

ABDUL-TAWWAB, NAJWA, 1st-2nd Grd Tchr & Sci Coord; *b:* Princeton, NJ; *m:* Qasim; *c:* Fatimah, Faridah, Tariq, Maryann; *ed:* Northeastern Univ (BS) Elem Ed 1971; Wleelock Coll 9 Credit Hrs; *cr:* Clara Muhammad Schl Dean of Girls, Master Tchr 1971-85; Boston Pub Schls 1, 2 Grd Tchr 1986-; *ai:* Sci Coord; Mentor, Lead Tchr; Impact II Advy Bd Comm Svc Learning; NCTM; BEAM; Boston Museum of Sci Tchr, Advy Bd; MA Assn of Sci Tchrs 1995-; Boston Dawah Com 1995-, Sec; MA St Curr Frameworks, Advy Cncl; Grants Eisenhower, Impact II, Golden Apple; MA Tchr of Yr Finalists; *home:* 38 Sargent St Dorchester MA 02125*

ABDUR RAHIM, ZAIMAH, High School Mathematics Tchr; *b:* Newark, NJ; *m:* Abdul-Hakim Abdullah; *c:* Kuesi, Abdush-Shakur Cole II; *ed:* NJ Inst of Tech (BS) Civil Engrng 1982; *cr:* Morris Rospond Assoc Civil Engr 1984-86; RBA Assoc Civil Engr 1986-87; Islamic Schl of NJ Sixth-Eighth Grd Sci Tchr 2-8 1988-92; Islanic Day Schl Seventh-Twelfth Grad Math Tchr, Supervisory Tchr 1992-; *ai:* Stu Relationship Adv; Fundraising Comm; NCTM 1995-; AMTNJ 1994-.*

ABDUR-RAHMAN, LAURA, 6th-8th Grd Teacher; *b:* Jacksonville, FL; *m:* Howard; *c:* Ariel, Sahar, Amala, Ihsan, Muhsin; *ed:* Hampton Univ (BS) Elem Ed 1970; Philadelphia Coll of Tx at Sci (BS) Textile Design 1976; Addl 27 Hrs Towards Master in Ed; Presently Taking Last 6 Hrs Towars Masters Degree; *cr:* Harrington Elem Schl Tchr 1970-73; Islamic Comm Schl Tchr 1982-83, 1984-85; Sis Clara Muhammad Schl Tchr 1988-89; Al Madrasat W Islamiah Schl Tchr, Vice Prin 1990-; *ai:* Alphs Kappa Alpha 1968-.

ABEL, BONNIE LOU (ELLIS), 3rd Grade Teacher; *b:* Rochester, NY; *m:* Joseph Abel; *c:* Jaison, Justin; *ed:* SUNY at Brockport (BS) Elem Ed; Attnd SUNY at Albany, Syracuse Univ; *cr:* North Syracuse CSD 4th Grd Tchr; Greenville CSD 4th-6th Grd Tchr; Orchard Park CSD 3rd Grd Tchr; *ai:* Math, Whole Lang, Discipline, Shared Decision Making, Schl Spirit, Author Visit Comm; NYSUT; *office:* South Davis Elem S Davis St Orchard Park NY 14127

ABEL, THEODORE, English Teacher; *b:* Philadelphia, PA; *m:* Judith Diane Helveston; *c:* Rebecca; *ed:* Franklin & Marshall Coll (BA) Eng 1973; Temple Univ (MED) Scndry Eng Ed 1976; Rdng Specialist Cert Beaver Coll 1988; *cr:* William Tennent HS Eng Tchr, AP Comp & Lit Tchr 1973-; *ai:* Head Girls Cross Cntry Team, Girls Track & Field Team Coach; Key Club Co-Adv; Phi Delta Kappa 1988-; 5th Dist Civic Assn 1973-; Willow Grove United Meth Church 1974-, Trustees Pres; *office:* William Tennent HS 333 Centennial Rd Warminster PA 18974

ABELLO, JOANN PATRUNO, Language Arts Teacher; *b:* Jersey City, NJ; *m:* Anthony J.; *c:* Anthony Jr., Jason, Peter; *ed:* Jersey City St (BA) Elem Ed 1972; Rel Ed Cert; *cr:* Our Lady of Victories 7th Grd Tchr 1968-71; St Josephs Schl 7-8th Grd Sci Tchr 1978-82, 6-8th Grd Lang Arts Tchr 1983-; *ai:* Stu Cncl Adv; Mid St Assn Team Mem; Eng Chprsn; Tchr of Yr 1993; *office:* St Joseph Schl 865 Roosevelt Ave Carteret NJ 07008

ABELMANN, ARTHUR WALTER, Economics, Cmptr & Math Tchr; *b:* Boston, MA; *c:* Amanda; *ed:* Dartmouth Coll (BA) Environmental Stud, Ed 1984; Babson Coll (MBA) Operations Mngmt 1991; *cr:* Plymouth St Coll Prof of Operations Mngmt 1991-93; Tilton Schl Cmptr Ctr Dir, Ec, Cmptr, Math Tchr 1993-; *ai:* Head Alpine Ski, Bsbl Coach; Outing Club; Dorm Parent; Jr Adv; NH Soc for Tech in Ed 1993-; Town of Tilton Planning Bd 1993-95; Montessori House of Children 1995-, Parents Comm; *office:* Tilton Schl 30 School St Tilton NH 03276*

ABEND, ROBERT JAMES, Physical Education Teacher; *b:* New York, NY; *m:* Angela; *c:* Andrew; *ed:* Lehman Coll (BA) PE 1984; Coll of New Rochelle (MS) Admin & Supervision 1990; Hofstra Univ Working Toward 2nd MS in Hlth Ed; *cr:* Bronx HS of Sci Sub Tchr 1984; Briggs Acad of Arts & Sci PE Tchr & Coach 1985-; *ai:* Bronx HS of Sci Girls Var Soccer Coach; Ath Dir Deepdale Gardens Comm Ctr; Cert Bsktbl Referee Intnl Assn of Approved Bsktbl Officials Bd 119; United Fed of Tchrs 1987-; *home:* 24936 60th Ave Little Neck NY 11362*

ABERER, BILL JOHN, Chm Bus Dept & Ath Director; *b:* Jersey City, NJ; *m:* Susan E. Gates; *ed:* St Johns Univ (BS) Acctng 1971; *cr:* Regis HS Bsktbl Coach 1969-72; LaSalle Acad Tchr, Dept Chm, Bsktbl Coach & Ath Dir 1972-; *ai:* Hall of Fame Chm; Prin Advy Cncl; Acad Cncl; NEA 1978-; CHSAA Coaches Assn 1972-; Parish Advy Bd 1989-; St William the Abbot Memrl Comm 1995-, Chm; NYC Coach of the Yr 1995; Manhattan Eastern Bsktbl Coach of the Yr 1988; Newsday Man of the Yr; LaSalle Alumni Assn 1993; 30 Yr Achvmt Awd; 5 Star Bsktbl Camp; *office:* Lasalle Acad 44 E 2nd St New York NY 10003

ABERGAS, OLWEN GINES, Math & Science Teacher; *b:* Manila, Philippines; *ed:* Univ of Santo Tomas (BA) Comm Arts 1983; NY Univ

Filmmaking 1994; *cr:* Mid Sts Assn of Colls, Schls Evaluator, Comm Reader 1993-; *ai:* United Talmudical Acad 1987-, Level Head ESL Dept; NY St Effective Schl Outstdng Tchr Awd 1993; *office:* Blessed Sacrament Schl 183 Euclid Ave Brooklyn NY 11208*

ABERNATHY, DIANE WASHBON, 4th Grade Teacher; *b:* Buffalo, NY; *m:* Mark; *c:* Katelynn Ann, Shannon Elizabeth; *ed:* SUC at Geneseo (BS) Elem Ed, Rdng 1983; Univ of Buffalo (MS) Elem Ed, Rdng 1991; *cr:* Niagara Cty Schl Dists Elem Sub Tchr 1984-85; Niagara-Orleans BOCES Elem Sub Tchr 1984-85; Starpoint Cntrl Schl Kndgtn Tchr 1985-86, Second Grd Tchr 1986-87, Fourth Grd Tchr 1987-; *ai:* Starpoint Tchrs Assn, NY St United Tchrs, AFT 1985-; *home:* 4160 Mapleton Rd Lockport NY 14094

ABERNATHY, REGINA ANN, High School English Teacher; *b:* Cleveland, OH; *m:* Larry J.; *c:* Anthony, Aaron, Anise; *ed:* OH St Univ (BS) Eng 1972; John Carroll Univ (MS) Ed 1976; *cr:* Kirk Jr HS Eng Tchr 1972-76; NY Life Insurance Sale Rep 1976-78; Shaw HS Eng Tchr 1978-; Multicultural Ed Review Publisher 1986-94; *ai:* NEA 1972-; OEA 1972-; Phi Delta Kappa, Gamma RHO Chptr; Mt Hermon Bapt Church, Sunday Schl Tchr, Supt; Multicultural Ed Review Publisher; *office:* Shaw HS 15320 Euclid Ave Cleveland OH 44112*

ABLES, GLORIA JEAN, Business Education Teacher; *b:* Ft Campbell, KY; *m:* Thomas W.; *c:* Michael, Kimberly; *ed:* FAirmont St Coll (BA) Bus Ed 1975; WV Univ (MA) Ed Admin 1991; Robert Morris Coll Secretarial Sci 1970; *cr:* WV Career Coll Bus Ed Tchr 1985-87; Human Resource Dev Fnd Bus Ed Tchr 1987-90; Mapletown HS Bus Ed Tchr 1990-94; Laurel Highlands HS Bus Ed Tchr 1994-; *ai:* FBLA Adv; NEA 1990-; PA St Bus Advy Tech 1995-, Prep Bd; *office:* Laurel Highlands Sr HS 300 Bailey Ave Uniontown PA 15401

ABOOD, DIANE M., Human Biology Teacher; *b:* Akron, OH; *ed:* Univ of Akron (BA) Psych 1989, (BA) Ed 1991; Kent St Univ Ed Masters 1996; *cr:* Cntrl Hower HS Human Bio Tchr 1993-; *ai:* Ath Dir; Peer Mediation Adv; Staff Dev Comm; *office:* Central Hower HS 123 S Forge St Akron OH 44308

ABOSAMRA, CHARLES, Guidance Counselor; *b:* Pawtucket, RI; *m:* Angela Louise Scipone; *c:* Deborah Smith, Judith Pratt, Christie; *ed:* RI Coll (BED) Eng & Soc Stud 1964; Univ of MA (MED) Guid Specialist 1965; 30 Hrs Credit Masters; *cr:* Cranston Schl Dept Eng Tchr & Dept Chair 1965-92, Guid Cnslr 1992-; *ai:* NEA & AFT 1964-; Univ of MA Flwshp & Assistantship 1994-95; *office:* Cranston HS West 80 Metropolitan Ave Cranston RI 02920*

ABOUD, JUDITH HATEM, Language Arts & Math Teacher; *b:* Brooklyn, NY; *m:* Edward J.; *c:* Edward, Kathy, Christopher; *ed:* St Joseph's Coll (BA) Speech, Eng 1964; 15 Credit Hrs Group Facilitator Drug Prevention Prgm; *cr:* Ft Hamilton HS Eng, Typing Tchr 1965-66; Visitation Acad Lang Arts, Math Tchr 1966-67; Ft Hamilton HS Eng, Typing Tchr 1979-84; Kingsborough Comm Coll Rdng Tchr, GED Prgm 1980-82; Visitation Acad Lang Arts, Math Tchr 1985-; *ai:* Grd 7 Rap Group Facilitator; Cath Tchrs Assn 1964-; Brooklyn Friends of Thirteen PBS 1995-; *office:* Visitation Acad 8902 Ridge Blvd Brooklyn NY 11209

ABPLANALP, GEORGIANNA, Adj Tchr of Non-print Material; *b:* Dayton, KY; *ed:* Thomas More Coll (BA) Ed 1972; Xavier Univ (MA) Ed 1978; Univ of VT 6 Credits; LaMar Univ 3 Credits; Northern KY Univ 9 Credits; *cr:* St Agatha Acad 1st-6th Grd Tchr 1964-66; Our Lady of Sorrows Schl 5th-6th Grd Tchr 1966-69; St John the Bapt Schl 4th-8th Grd Tchr 1969-95; Coll of Mount St Joseph Adj Tchr 1996; *ai:* Yrbk Coord 1979-94; Singing Club Dir 1971-76; Be Wise Sci, Math Camp Instr 1990-95; NCEA 1969-; Gifted Ed Pilot Stud Univ of CT; Citizen Ambassador to Peoples Republic of China; *home:* 3732 Struble Rd Cincinnati OH 45251

ABRAHAM, EMILYANN, Math Teacher; *b:* New York, NY; *m:* David A.; *c:* Amanda Emily, John David; *ed:* Queens Coll (BS) Math 1963; Adelphi Univ (MA) Math & Ed 1968; 27 Credits Math & Ed Columbia Univ Tchrs Coll; *cr:* Island Trees HS Math Tchr 1965-; *ai:* Honor Soc Selection, Stu of Month Selection & Mid Sts & Steering Comms; AFT & NEA; N Sci F Summer Grant; *office:* Island Trees HS 59 Straight Ln Levittown NY 11756

ABRAHAM, JOSEPH ROBERT, Fourth Grade Teacher; *b:* Allentown, PA; *m:* Heidi A. Siegfried; *ed:* Penn St Univ (MS) Ed 1981; Kutztown Univ (BS) Ed 1976; *cr:* Catasauqua Area Schl Dist Elem Tchr 1976-; *ai:* Dist Sci Coord; HS Acad Stu of Month Adv & Coord; Safety Patrol Supvr; NEA & PSEA 1976-; Exchange Club 1976-, Past Pres, Exchangite of Yr, Medal of Hnr; St George Orthodox Church 1990-, Parish Cncl Pres, Distinction & Valor Awd; *office:* Sheckler Elem Schl 201 N 14th St Catasauqua PA 18032*

ABRAHAM, MICHAEL A., History Teacher; *b:* Danbury, CT; *ed:* St Michael's Coll (BA) Bus Admin 1981; Fairfield Univ (MA) Ed 1984; 30 Addl Hrs OH St Univ; *cr:* New Milford HS His Tchr 1986-; *ai:* Head Coach Cross Cntry, Tennis; NEA, CEA 1986-; Tchr of Yr 1993-94; 5 Natl Endowments, Hum Awds; *home:* 311 Sabbaday Ln Washington Depot CT 06794

ABRAHAM, PATRICIA ANN, English Teacher; *b:* New York City, NY; *m:* Charles Thomas; *c:* Susan Bogart, Jeanne Cabana, Michael Cabana, Julie Forrest, Robert Cabana; *ed:* Sacred Heart Univ (BA) Scndry Ed, Eng 1973; Fairfield Univ (MA) Prof Improvement Ed, Eng 1979; His Cert; 12 Credit Hrs; *cr:* Fairfield HS Eng Tchr 1973-; *ai:* Odyssey, HS Bowl Adv; Fac Laiason to PTA; NEA, CEA, FEA 1973-; NCTE; CT Cncl Tchrs of Eng; Yankee Pres Ed Network 1993-, Bd of Dirs; Lit Art Magazine Columbia Scholastic Press Assn 2 Time Medalist Winner, Received Highest Honor NCTE Prgm Excl Stu Lit Magazines, Yankee Pen Publications 1993 & 1995 Magazine of Yr; *office:* Fairfield HS Melville Ave Fairfield CT 06430

ABRAHAMSON, MICHAEL, Biology Teacher; *b:* New Britain, CT; *m:* Helen Goldband; *c:* Ilana, Sasha; *ed:* Cntrl CT St (BS) Bio 1966, (MS) Bio 1968; Wesleyan Univ (CAS) Earth Sci 1975; *cr:* Millikan Jr HS Sci Tchr 1967-71; Mt Lukens HS Bio Tchr 1972-75; R.C. Ketcham HS Bio Tchr 1975-; Dutchess Comm Coll Microbiology Adj Prof 1980-; *ai:* Sci Olympiad Team Adv; Schl Leadership Team; AFT 1967-; NYSUT, WCT 1975-, Building Rep 1985-; STANYS 1975-, Exec Bd 1991-, Outstanding Schl Tchr 1990; NSF 4 Yr Grant; HS Tchr of Excl; Summer Scholars; Cornell Inst for Bio Tchrs; *office:* Roy C Ketcham H S 99 Myers Corners Rd Wappingers Falls NY 12590*

ABRAM, GEORGE C., Sociology & Psych Teacher; *b:* Pittsburg, PA; *m:* Arlene N.; *c:* Michelle, Michael; *ed:* Duquesne Univ (BS) Soc Stud Ed 1964, (MS) Ed, Scndry Admin 1969; *cr:* Fifth Ave HS Tchr, Ath Dir 1964-76; Brashear HS Tchr, Ath Dir 1976-; *ai:* Ath Dir; Letterman Club; Pittsburgh Fed of Tchrs, Western PA Cncl for Soc Stud 1970-; PA Ath Dir Assn 1980-; *office:* Brashear HS 590 Crane Ave Pittsburgh PA 15216

ABRAMO, WREN MOOREFIELD, 8th Grade English Teacher; *b:* Pittsburgh, PA; *m:* Vincent J.; *c:* Joseph; *ed:* Univ of MD (MA) Ed 1974; *cr:* Whittier Woods Elem Schl Tchr 1965-85; Highland Elem Schl Tchr 1965-85; Sligo MS 8th Grd Tchr; Pyle MS 8th Grd Tchr; *ai:* NEA 1964-; WA Balalaika Orch 1995-; *office:* Pyle MS 6311 Wilson Ln Bethesda MD 20817

ABRAMS, DEBRA JOSEPHSON, Assistant Professor of English; *b:* Sea Isle City, NJ; *ed:* Amer Univ (BA) Interdisciplinary Stud, Comm 1981; George Mason Univ (MA) Eng 1987; Working on PHD Comm Col Ed; *cr:* George Mason Univ Adj Instr, Strand Lectures Coord 1987; Northern VA Comm Coll Adj, Temporary FT 1989-90; Montgomery Coll of Art & Design Adj Prof 1991; Montgomery Coll Adj Prof 1992, Asst Prof 1992-; *ai:* Coord Cherry Blossom Conf Critical Literacy, Writing Ctr; Co-Chair Mid Sts Tchng, Learning Work Team; Part-time Fac Dev, 50th Anniversary Comms; Northern VA Writing Project 1992-; AAUP 1992-, VP; ASCD 1996-; NCTE 1993; Essays, Poem Pub; Critical Literacy Seminar Series 1994-95; *office:* Montgomery Coll Germantown Campus 20200 Observation Dr Germantown MD 20876*

ABRAMS, DONNA SMITH, Art Teacher & Dept Chairperson; *b:* Plainfield, NJ; *m:* Jeffry M.; *c:* Dana, Aaron; *ed:* Douglass Coll (BA) Art Ed 1976; *cr:* J. C. Penny Art Owk Designer 1986-87; Taylor Bus Inst Fashion Illustration Tchr 1981-82; Mt St Mary Acad Art Tchr 1976-; *ai:* Art Club Adv; Discipline Bd; Art Dept Chrpsn; Frosh Class Adv; Faculty, Acad Cncl; NCEA, NJAIS & NAIS 1976-; Art Educators of NJ 1992-; NAEA; *office:* Mount Saint Mary Acad 1645 Rt 22 & Terrill Rd Watchung NJ 07060

ABRAMS, DOUGLAS J., Social Studies Teacher; *b:* Oceanside, NY; *m:* Joyce; *ed:* Univ of MI (BA) Chinese 1978, (MA) Chinese Lit 1980-; Univ of WA Tchr Cert 1982; Attnd St Johns Univ, Long Island Univ, SUNY at Stony Brook, Dowling coll, Naropa Inst; *cr:* William Floyd Pub Schls Tchr 1982-85; Suffolk Comm Coll Instr 1990-; Plainedge Pub Shls Tchr 1985-; Dru Assocs Inc Enviromental Consulting 1988-; *ai:* Amnesty Intnl Stu Group; Bari Brith a World of Difference Facilitator; LaCrosse Coach; Ninth Grd Team Ldr; AFT 1983-; NCSS 1985-; Josephson Inst 1989-; LI Poetry Coalition.

ABRAMS, ELAINE CHERAN, Fourth Grade Teacher; *b:* Westmoreland Cty, PA; *m:* John C.; *c:* Allison; *ed:* IN Univ of PA (BS) Ed 1967; CA St Coll (MS) Ed 1971; Several Post-Grad Courses Tchng; *cr:* Stewartsville Elem Schl 2nd Grd Tchr 1967-84; Hillcrest Elem Schl 4th Grd Tchr 1985-; *ai:* PSEA, NEA 1967-; PTA; PTA Awd Outstdng Edctr 1991-92; *office:* Hillcrest Elem Schl 11091 Mockingbird Dr North Huntingdon PA 15642

ABRAMSON, JANET, 1st Grd Tchr & Lang Art Coord; *b:* New Rochelle, NY; *m:* Martin; *c:* Jarett, Brooke; *ed:* St Univ of NY at Cortland (BS) Elem Ed 1964; Univ of PA (MS) Rdng 1967; SSI at Montclair St; *cr:* Thornwood Bd of Ed 5th Grd Tchr 1964-66; Philadelphia Bd of Ed Kndgtn Tchr 1966-67; White Plains Bd of Ed Rdng Specialist Tchr 1967-68; Wyckoff Bd of Ed Transitional 1st Grd Tchr 1968-70; Verona Bd of Ed Kndgtn, 1st & 4th Grd Tchr 1977-; *ai:* Lang Arts Comm Mentor; NEA; NJ St Tchr of Yr Awd 1986-87; EIRC-HAW Participant 1996; *office:* Forest Ave Elem Schl 118 Forest Ave Verona NJ 07044

ABRAVANEL, LYNN RAE, Teacher; *b:* Pittsburgh, PA; *ed:* Syracuse Univ (BA) Sociology 1970; Univ of Pittsburgh (MAT) Ed 1971; *cr:* Mc Keesport Pub Schls 4th Grd Tchr 1970-71; Fox Chapel Pub Schls 5th Grd Tchr 1971-72; Braintree Pub Schls 3-5 Grd Tchr 1972-; *ai:* NEA 1970-; Braintree Ed Assn, Norfolk Cty Tchr Assn, MA Tchr Assn 1972-.

ABREU, DIANA B., Spanish Teacher; *b:* Staten Island, NY; *m:* Alvaro E.; *c:* Peter, Aimee, Elizabeth; *ed:* Wagner Coll (BA) Span, Eng, Scndry Ed 1972; 15 Crest Hrs Rutgers Univ; *cr:* Jonathan Dayton Reg HS Span Tchr 1972-73; Mt Loretto Bi-Lingual Ed 1975-76; Staten Island Acad Span Tchr 1978-86; Mt Olive Adult Schl Span Tchr 1986-; The Pingry Schl Span Tchr 1991-93; *ai:* Spanish Club, Acad, Frgn Lang Magazine Adv; MS Soccer Coach; Fac Benefits Rep; Puerto Rican Writers Assn Awd; Norman Tomlinson Chair for Hum Pingry Awd; *office:* The Pingry Schl Martinsville Rd Martinsville NJ 08836

ABRUZZI, MARLENE C., Lang Arts Tchr; *b:* Warren, OH; *ed:* Youngstown St Univ (BS) Eng Ed 1990; *cr:* Lakeview HS Eng Tchr 1991-95; Upper Arlington HS 1995-; *ai:* Lit Magazine Adv; Asst Debate Coach; NEA, OEA, Lakeview Tchrs Assn 1991-; UAEA; *office:* Upper Arlington HS 1650 Ridgeview Rd Columbus OH 43221*

ABUKAMAIL, NASSEEF A., Computer Science Professor; *b:* Gaza, Palestine; *m:* Lisa Haupricht; *ed:* OH Univ (BSEE) Electrical Engrng 1986, (MS) Cmptr Sci 1988; *cr:* OH Univ Instr 1991-94; Univ of Rio Grande Asst Prof 1991-; *ai:* Assn for Computing Machinery 1990-; *office:* Univ Of Rio Grande 218 N College Rio Grande OH 45674

ABURTO, JOANNE ALLEN, Spanish Teacher; *b:* Marion, OH; *m:* Rolando Aburto Delfin; *c:* Rowena, Romayra, Joshua; *ed:* OH Univ (BSEd) Span 1986; Wright St Univ (MED) Supervision & Curr 1995; *cr:* Lima City Schls Span Tchr 1988-89; Ridgemont Local Schls Span Tchr 1989-; *ai:* Span Club; Prom, Class Adv; Prom Promise, Tour to Mexico Coord; OEA, NEA 1989-; Ridgemont Ed Assn 1989-, Pres 1992, 1994, VP 1991, 1992; First United Meth Church 1977-; Girl Scouts of Amer 1995-, Troop Ldr; *office:* Ridgemont Local Schls 162 E Hale St Box 87 Ridgeway OH 43345*

ACCAVALLO, ANTHONY F.,III, HS Guidance Counselor; *b:* Teaneck, NJ; *m:* Marianne J. Swanson; *c:* Alicia, Anthony IV; *ed:* Southwestern LA (BS) Hlth, PE 1973; William Paterson Coll (MA) Spec Ed 1980; Guid, Prin & Super Certs; *cr:* St Joseph HS PE Instr 1973-76; Passaic Co Voc & Tech HS Crises Cnslr 1976-88, Head Wrestling Coach 1973-88; Glen Meadow MS Guid Cnslr 1988-94; Vernon Twp HS Guid Cnslr 1994-; *ai:* Asst Wrestling Coach; Vernon Recreation Comm 1990-, Chprsn; Passaic Cty Coach of Yr 1984; Dist 13 Coach of Yr 1988; *office:* Vernon Township HS 1832 Cty Rt 565 Vernon NJ 07462

ACCIANI, LAWRENCE N., Art Teacher; *b:* Perth Amboy, NJ; *ed:* Kent St Univ (BFA) Art 1966; Rosary Coll (MA) Painting, Printmaking 1972; Supvrs Cert Kean Coll; *cr:* Herbert Hoover Jr HS Art Tchr 1966-70; Edison HS Art Tchr, Acting Dept Head 1970-; *ai:* Yrbk Adv 2 Yrs; Set Designer Schl Plays 17 Yrs; Art Club 12 Yrs; Natl Art Hnr Soc 8 Yrs; NEA, NJEA 1966-; NAEA 1990-; NJAEA 1985-; *office:* Edison HS Blvd Of The Eagles Edison NJ 08817

ACCUOSTI, SUE M., Social Studies Teacher; *b:* Waterbury, CT; *m:* William; *c:* Mary King, Therese Drake, Joan Ligon, Susan; *ed:* Central CT St Univ (BS) Soc Stud 1974, (MS) Guidance 1976; Southern CT St Univ Guidance 3 Credit Hrs; Central CT St Univ Asian Stud 6 Credit Hrs; *cr:* Sub Tchr 1976-78; Holy Cross HS Guidance Cnlsr, Tchr 1978-; *ai:* Moderator Fine Arts Club; CT Soc Stud; *office:* Holy Cross HS 587 Oronoke Rd Waterbury CT 06708

ACEBO, PHILIP STEVEN, 8th Grade History Teacher; *b:* Barre, VT; *m:* Cynthia Wark; *c:* Landen, Baleigh; *ed:* Castleton St (BS) His 1971; UVM Grad Stud Toward MAT; *cr:* Tumbarumba HS in Australia His Tchr 1971-74; Barre Town Elem His Tchr 1974-; *ai:* Amateur Radio; NEA 1974-, Pres; VT Soccer Ofcls 1976-; Natl Intercollegiate Soccer Ofcls Assn 1983-; Washington Cty Diversion 1994-; Barre Town Recreation Bd 1994-; Fire Dist #8 1995-, Chprsn; *office:* Barre Town Elem Schl RR 2 Box 4323 Barre VT 05641

ACERRA, DONNA SHIPMAN, Adj Prof of Comm & Theatre; *b:* Kingston, PA; *m:* Mario; *c:* Kali, Chloe, Carlo; *ed:* Temple Univ (BA) Radio, TV, Film 1979, (MA) Comm 1985; *cr:* Northampton Comm Coll Adj Prof 1989-; *ai:* Summer Yth Television Production Courses Coord, Tchr; Produce Weekly Radio Show; Oversee Operations Coll Radio Station; *office:* Northampton Comm Coll 3835 Green Pond Rd Bethlehem PA 18017*

ACEVEDO, AILEEN, Spanish Teacher; *b:* Brooklyn, NY; *ed:* Univ at Albany-SUNY (BA) Africana His & Span 1992; Working on Masters Scndry Ed & Span at Queens Coll-CUNY; Grad & Undergrad Courses in Spec Ed & Human Relations; *cr:* FDR HS Span Tchr 1993-94; South Shore HS Span Tchr 1994-; *ai:* 1995 Muevete Confernce Participant Consisted of Wrkshps from Media to Ed for City Youth; *office:* South Shore HS Flatlands Ave Brooklyn NY 11236*

ACEVEDO, GUS A., Spanish Teacher; *b:* Ponce, PR; *m:* Luane Olsc Gus III, Kristina; *ed:* Newark St Coll (BA) Eng, Ed 1971; Univ of Sou CA (MS) Span 1975; Rutgers Univ (ABD) Span 1978; Portuguese at of Lisbon 1975; Span Lit at Univ of So CA 1974; *cr:* Montclair St Span Instr 1978-81; Ocean Cty Coll Span Instr Adj 1983-85; Monsi Donovan HS Span Tchr 1986-; *ai:* Frgn Lang Club, Poetry Club, Frgn Abroad Adv; Frosh Bsbl Coach; Ath Comm Jackson Bd of Ed, Curr C Chm; Ocean Cty Schl Bds Assn Exec Comm; Cath Tchrs Assn 1 Ocean Cty, NJ Schl Bds Assn 1981-, VP, Treas; BSA, Scout Ldr; Ja Bd of Ed 1987-, Pres, VP; Ocean Cty Voc Schls Bd of El 1981-85, Schl Estimate; NJ Schl Bds Assn 1983-85, Bd of Dirs, Dist Svc Pl Jaycees 1982-, Top Ten Outstdng Young Citizens Awd, Most Distgn Awd; Latin Comm Org of NJ, Pres; Red Cross Bd; Mental Hlth Bd; Assn Bd; Ocean Ec Action Bd; Del Amo Fnd, Gulbenkian Fnd Sch Tchng Assistanships Univ of Southern CA, Rutgers Univ; Interview Frgn Lang Tchrs Honor Soc; Grgn Lang Stdnts Honor Soc.

ACHENBACH, CHARLES M., Anatomy & Physiology Professo Pottsville, PA; *m:* Julia; *c:* Kay; *ed:* Franklin & Marshall Coll (AB) Ger 1974; Univ of PA (DMD) Dentristry 1978; *cr:* Private Pra Dentistry 1978-81; Coll Prof, Bio 1981-; *office:* Northampton Comm 3835 Green Pond Rd Bethlehem PA 18017

ACHENBACH, KENNETH ROBERT, Social Studies Teacher; *b:* Sh PA; *m:* Tina Lynn Pheil; *c:* Kenneth M., Christopher J.; *ed:* Thiel Coll His 1978; Wilkes Coll Credits Toward Perm Cert; 24 Post Grad Cr *cr:* Laurel HS Soc Stud Tchr 1980; Meadville Jr HS Soc Stud 1980-88; Meadville Sr HS Soc Stud Tchr 1988-; *ai:* Head Ftbl, W Training & Conditioning Coach; NEA, PSEA & CCEA 1980-; Coaches Assoc 1984-; Meadville Little Grippers Assoc 1984-, Bd of 150th PVI Civil War Re-Enact Group 1992-; Northwest Ftbl Conf C of the Yr 1986 & 1990; Tchr of the Yr Meadville Jr High 1983; *o* Meadville HS RR 9 Box 462 Rt 102 Meadville PA 16335

ACHENBACH, LINDA GAY, First Grade Teacher; *b:* Wilson Boro *ed:* East Stroudsburg Univ (BS) Elem Ed 1967; His, Elem Post Courses; *cr:* Nazareth Area Schl Dist Elem Tchr 1967-; *ai:* Tchr Indu Prgm New Tchrs Mentor; Lang Arts, Behavior Stans Comms; Naz Educ Assn, NEA 1967-; St Luke's United Church of Christ 1945-, E Sec, Spec Events Chprsn, Schlsp Comm, Pianist; Nom Tchr of Yr *office:* Bushkill Elem Schl 960 Bushkill Center Rd Nazareth PA 180

ACHENBACH, RITA MARIA, English Teacher & Dept Chai Philadelphia, PA; *m:* Craig R.; *c:* Sara, Joseph; *ed:* Temple Univ Theater & Comm 1972; Athens Coll (BSEd) Eng & Bio 1975; Ma Equivalency 1995; *cr:* Holy Name HS Eng Tchr 1975-, Eng Dept 1980-81, 1985-; *ai:* Writing Contests Coord; Stu Adv; NHS Mode Stud Assistance Team; NCTE 1985-; NCEA 1975-; ASCD 1992-; NA 1995-; Natl Writing Project Fellow 1995; *office:* Holy Name HS 9 Wyomissing Blvd Reading PA 19611*

ACHENBACH, SARA SHARADIN, English Teacher; *b:* Washir DC; *w:* James A. (dec); *c:* Victoria; *ed:* Kutztown Univ (BS) Eng, Ru 1964; IN Univ (MA) Slabic Lang, Lit 1969; Dartmouth 8 Credit Kutztown Univ 3 Credit Hrs; Univ of PA 6 Credit Hrs; Albright Co Credit Hrs; *cr:* Northeast Jr HS Rdng Tchr 1964-65; Reading HS Russian Tchr 1965-; *ai:* NCTE 1993-; REA 1964-, IPD Comm Chm; Mawr Coll NEH Inst Russian 1989; Dartmouth Russian Inst NDEA 1966; IN Univ, USSR Travel NDEA Grant 1967; Plague Outstdng C of United Nations Club 1982; *office:* Reading HS 801 N 13th St Re PA 19604

ACHENBACH, TINA (PHEIL), French Teacher; *b:* Chambersburg *m:* Kenneth R.; *c:* Kenneth, Christopher; *ed:* Span Thiel Coll; Tchn Gifted Penn St Univ; *cr:* Sharon HS Fr Tchr 1976-83; Meadville A HS Fr Tchr for Sab Leave 1986; Maplewood HS Fr Tchr 1987-; *ai:* Fr Adv; Stu Assistance Prgm Mem; NEA 1976-; PA St Educ Assn 1 PSMLA 1980-95; Penncrest Area Ed Assn 1987-; ACTFL 1990-; 150t Civil War Era Reenactors 1992-; Tony Cook Meml Grant; *o* Maplewood Jr Sr HS RD 1 Guys Mills PA 16327

ACHUFF, ALBERT C., Asst Prin & Soc Studies Instr; *b:* Philadel PA; *ed:* LaSalle Univ (BA) Pol Sci 1966; Univ of Scranton (MA) U 1970; *cr:* Bishop Conwell HS Soc Stud Instr 1967-84; Bishop McL HS Asst Prin, Acad Affairs, Soc Stud Instr 1984-; Holy Family Lecturer, His Dept 1984-85; *ai:* NHS Adv; Stu Assistance Prgm; Acad Chprsn; Boys' Bsktbl Team Moderator; NCEA 1967-; Philadelphia C Textiles, Sci Outstdng Edctr Awd 1995; *office:* Bishop Mc Devitt H Royal Ave Wyncote PA 19095*

ACHUFF, ELIZABETH H., Fifth Grade Teacher; *b:* Cleveland, O E. Kenneth; *c:* Christian K., Gretchen E.; *ed:* West Chester Univ (BS) Ed 1972; 65 Credit Hrs; *cr:* Goodnoe Elem Schl 4th & 5th Grd 1972-75; Bellefonte Play Schl Tchr for 3 & 4 Yr Olds 1982-84; M Walker Elem Schl 5th Grd Tchr 1985; Benner Elem Schl 5th Grd 1986-; *ai:* NEA 1985; NCTM 1990; PSEA 1985; *office:* Benner Elem 490 Buffalo Run Rd Bellefonte PA 16823

ACKER, KENNETH L., Science Teacher; *b:* Parris Island, SC Patricia Kanavel; *c:* Kevin M.; *ed:* Temple Univ (BS) Scndry Univ Widner Univ Masters Prgm Scndry Ed; *cr:* Prospect Park Schl Sci 1989-; *ai:* Interboro HS Asst Var Ftbl Coach; NEA, TEA 1989-; *o* Prospect Park MS 9th & Penna Aves Prospect Park PA 19076

ACKER, LAWRENCE ARTHUR, Instrumental Music Instructo Pottsville, PA; *m:* Debra Ellen Armstrong; *c:* Jeremy Glendon; *ed:* Pe Univ (BS) Music Ed 1975; Post-Grad & Credit Hrs at E Stroudsburg & Millersville Univ; *cr:* Bellefonte Area MS Band Dir & Instrum Music Instr 1977-; *ai:* Bellefonte Area HS Band & Indoor Percu Ensemble Vol Instr; Concert, Marching & Stage Bands, Wind Ense Brass, Woodwind, Flute & Saxophone Choirs & Percussion Ensembl CCMEA 1977-; NEA 1977-; BAEA 1977-; PSEA 1977-; MENC 1 PMEA 1977-; Bellefonte Jaycees 1980-86, Various Offices & Awd Jaycees 1984-86, St Chm, Various Awds; BSA 1990-, Music Merit B Instr; Phi Mu Alpha Sinfonia 1973-; Bellefonte Jaycees Outstanding Educator 1989-90; *office:* Bellefonte Area HS 100 N School St Belle PA 16823

ACKERMAN, CHARLES LARUE, American History Teache Williamsport, PA; *m:* Joanne Otto; *c:* Cheryl Lynne Schonewolfe; *ed:* Haven Univ (BSEd) Comprehensive Soc Sci 1967; 44 Grad Hrs at Buc Univ; *cr:* South Williamsport Area Schls Tchr 1967-; *ai:* Ftbl Coa Yrs; Track Coach 26 Yrs; Key Club Adv 2 Yrs; Transition Outc Comm; Mentor Prgm; NEA, PSEA, SWAEA, NCFSS 1967-; *home* Brown St S Williamsprt PA 17701

ACKERMAN, LORETTA ANN, Amer Govt & World His Teache Ellwood City, PA; *m:* John Mc Kay; *c:* Michael, Melisa, Melana Indiana Univ of PA (BS) His, Govt 1959; Ashland Univ (MA) Ed 199 Addl Hrs; *cr:* Longfellow Jr HS Tchr 1959-60; Olean Jr HS Tchr 196 Fredericktown Jr HS Tchr 1964-; *ai:* Stu Cncl Adv; DC Trip C Intervention Team; Scheduling, Dist Conf Comms; NEA; OEA; N OCSS; NASAA; ASCD; Comm Concert Assn Bd; Local Lib Bldg C Fredericktown Lib Bd; OCLRE OH Bar Assn Lesson Plan Pub; Revie ford Univ Lesson Plan Review; *office:* Fredericktown HS 117 mbus Rd Fredericktown OH 43019*

:ERMAN, PATRICIA DRISCOLL, English & Speech Teacher; *b:* anapolis, IN; *m:* Franklin Kenneth Jr.; *c:* Franklin Kenneth III, Robert stian, Peter Jonathan; *ed:* OH St Univ (BS) Eng 1961; 18 Credit Hrs ne St Univ; 12 Credit Hrs Bloomsburg Univ; *cr:* Bellville HS 10 Grd Tchr 1961-62; Highland Park HS 10, 12 Grd Eng Tchr 1962-64; Milton 2 Grd Eng Tchr 1964-65; Danville HS 9-11 Grd Eng Tchr 1984-; *ai:* Adv; Forensic Coach; Acad Assistance Team; DEA, NEA, PSEA -, Fac Local Rep; NCTE 1984-; Bd of Children & Yth Svc 1985-86; copal Church Womens Guild 1965-88, Pres; Altar Guild Chm 1993-; inger Med Ctr Auxiliary 1964-; *office:* Danville Sr HS 600 Walnut St ville PA 17821

:ERSON, ANN HOGAN, 4th Grade Teacher; *b:* San Francisco, CA; ichard H.; *c:* Lynn Marie, Jeanine, Christine, Ricky; *ed:* Mt St Agnes Fr 1966; Iona (MS) Ed, Multiculturism 1995; 65 Addl Credit Hrs; *cr:* kstown CSD Fr Tchr 1966-69, 5 Grd Tchr 1971-72, 4 Grd Tchr -78, 6 Grd Tchr 1982-84, 2 Grd Tchr 1984-87, 4 Grd Tchr 1987-; *ai:* UT, AFT, Clarkstown Tchrs Assn 1966-; *office:* Bardonia Elem Schl ardonia Rd Bardonia NY 10954

:ERSON, ROBERT CHARLES, Social Studies Teacher; *b:* Suffern, *m:* Grace; *c:* Cynthia, Lynn, Susan; *ed:* Rockland Comm Coll (AA) Arts 1962; St Univ Coll at Oneonta (BS) Soc Stud 1964, (MS) Soc 1967; Grad Stud St Univ Coll at Albany; *cr:* Schenevus Cntrl Schl HS Stud 1964-; *ai:* Hnr Soc Comm; AFT, Schenevus United Tchrs 1990-; nevus Rotary Club 1984-, Sec; Arthur of Numerous Automotive His ks Including The Standard Catalog of Four-Wheel Drive Vehicles gnized as Antique Automobile Club of Amer's Outstdng Book of 1994; : 8 East St Schenevus NY 12155*

:ERSON, WALLACE, 4th Grade Teacher; *b:* Suffern, NY; *m:* Lucille aine; *c:* Wallace, Timothy, John; *ed:* Mercy Coll (BA) Sociology Elem 973; Fairfield Univ (MA) Ed 1977; Monmouth Coll 60 Credit Hrs; *cr:* ry Ln Elem Schl Tchr 1973-; *ai:* Schl Climate Comm; AFT 1973-; Boy ts 1982-91, Den Ldr, Asst Scout Master 1 Yr; *office:* Cherry Ln Elem 1 Heather Dr Suffern NY 10901

:LEY, JAMES RITTEW, Social Studies Teacher; *b:* Allentown, PA; East Stroudsburg Univ (BS) Soc Stud 1974; Masters Equivalant; *cr:* am Allen HS Soc Stud Tchr 1977-89, 1993-; Dieruff HS Soc Stud Tchr -90; Raub MS Soc Stud Tchr 1992; *ai:* YMCA Yth & Govt Adv; Sftbl Coach; AEA, PSEA, NEA 1977-; Police Ath League 1980-; Carole Schlsp Comm 1990-; Danforth Fndtn Rdng Schl Dist 1985-89; *office:* am Allen HS 126 N 17th St Allentown PA 18103

N, MARIAN R., English Teacher & Dept Chair; *b:* New Brighton, *n:* Herm; *c:* Brian, Karie; *ed:* Slippery Rock Univ (BA) Eng 1969,) Eng 1976; Attnd Robert Morris Coll for Mrktg & Ec 6 Hrs, IUP at sylvania for Interpersonal Skills 3 Hrs & Beaver Cty Comm Coll for rs & Ec 6 Hrs; *cr:* Rochester HS Eng Tchr 1969-, Dept Chprsn 1987-; ki & SOS Club; Induction Prgm, Long Range Plan & Act 178 Coord; Assistance Prgm Mem; RAEA, PSEA & NEA 1969-, Pres 2 Yrs; TE 1980-; 2 Tchr Excl Awds; Planning Commission Mem; *office:* ester Area Schl Dist 540 Reno St Rochester PA 15074*

R, ALLEN F., Substitute Teacher; *b:* Danville, PA; *m:* Shirley M. *c:* Allen II, Richard, Robert, Debra Kuntz, Kimberly, Merry; *ed:* mburg St (BA) Comprehensive Sci 1958; Union Coll (MS) Chem ; Wesley Seminary Parish Ministry 1982; Bucknell Univ 24 Credit Penn St Univ 3 Credit Hrs; *cr:* Ringtown HS Tchr 1958-59, Tchr & h 1961-64; Harlysville Insurance Co Claims Adjuster 1959-61; ville HS Tchr 1965-93; Minister 1972-; *ai:* Past Soccer Coach 4 Yrs; Bsktbl Coach 16 Yrs; Scorer & Timer for Soccer & Bsktbl Games; 1961-; NEA 1961-; MEA 1964-, Pres 1967-69; 4-H Ldr, Plaque; O Coach; Little League Coach; NSF 6 Times; Created Tech Sci ses for Sr Class; *home:* RR 1 Box 6 Bloomsburg PA 17815

STA, JOSEPH M., Spanish Teacher; *b:* Brooklyn, NY; *ed:* Dowling at Oakdale (BA) Romance Langs 1986; St Univ of NY at Stony Brook) Lbrl Stud, Ed 1992; Coll of New Rochelle (MS) Schl Admin, rvision 1996; *cr:* Bellport MS Span Tchr 1986-; *ai:* Stu Cncl Adv; WA Frost Vly Trip Coord; Extra Curr Fund Treas; Schl Musical Producer; hing Band Coord; ASDC 1994-; NYSUT, AFT, BTA 1986-; NYSAFLT -; South Cty Tchr Ctr 1985-, Policy Bd Co-Chprsn; Natl Eagle Scout 1982-; Shared Decision Making Comm 1994-; *office:* Bellport MS ner St Bellport NY 11713

UADRO, STEPHANIE NICHOLAS, English Teacher; *b:* Brooklyn, *n:* Allan; *c:* John; *ed:* Trenton St Coll (BA) Eng 1973; New York Univ) Hum 1982; *cr:* Watchung Hills Regnl HS Eng Tchr 1973-80; ford Trust Co Trader & Hum Resources Trainer 1980-82; Millburn Jr ng Tchr 1982-84; Summit Jr HS Eng Tchr 1985-86; Livingston HS Tchr 1986-87; Newark Acad Eng & Hum Tchr 1987-; *ai:* Honor Cncl ; Mentor; Adv; Fac Evaluation Comm; NEA 1973-; Tchrs & Writers borative 1993-; *office:* Newark Acad 91 S Orange Ave Livingston NJ 9*

UISTA, NICHOLAS RAYMOND, Social Studies Teacher; *b:* New , NY; *ed:* Long Island Univ (MBA) Finance 1980; *cr:* Moore Cath HS lis Tchr 1985-; Middlesex Coll Ec Prof 1991-; *office:* Moore Catholic 00 Merrill Ave Staten Island NY 10314*

ON, DANIEL D., Professor of Accountancy; *b:* Lancaster, OH; *m:* ; *c:* Amie; *ed:* Moskingon Coll (BA) Sociology 1967; Miami Univ) Finance 1970; Kent St Univ (PHD) Accounting 1985; NY St CPA; Alfred Univ; Marist Coll; Ulsten Comm Coll; *ai:* MBA Prgm, unting Prgm Dir; IMA TU Chapter Adv; AAA, AICPA, IMA; *office:* d Univ Coll of Bus Saxon Dr Alfred NY 14802

IR, JANINE MAHALEY, Theatre & English Teacher; *b:* Erie, PA; erry L.; *c:* Kristen; *ed:* Dickinson Coll (BA) Eng, Theatre 1977; ge Washington Univ (MA) Supervision, Human Relations 1987; *cr:* s Grove HS Eng Tchr 1978-79; St Marys Acad Eng Tchr 1980-81; Flower Schl Eng Tchr 1983-85; Chopticon HS Eng, Theatre Tchr -; *ai:* Dir, Tech Theatre Specialist; Drama Coach; Theatre Edctrs Assn, ter Mem; ASCD 1984-; Hollywood United Meth Church, Supt of ay Schl; Hollywood UM Presch, Bd Chprsn; Girl Scouts of Amer , Asst Ldr; *office:* Chopticon HS Rt 242 Morganza MD 20660*

IR, NANCY FARESE, Sixth Grade Teacher; *b:* East Orange, NJ; *m:* 1 Michael; *c:* Shane Michael; *ed:* Univ of Miami (BSEd) Elem Ed, Chldhd 1983; *cr:* Stafford Intermediate Schl 4th & 6th Grd Tchr -; *ai:* Sci & Techs Consortium; Stu Tchr Mentor; NJEA 1985-; STEA -, Sec; PTA; *office:* Stafford Intermediate Schl 1001 Mc Kinley Blvd ahawkin NJ 08050*

IR, NANCY VICTORIA, Asst Head & Dean of Academics; *b:* burgh, NY; *m:* James Patterson; *c:* Kathleen, Jennifer; *ed:* Marymount (BA) Ed, Psych 1971; Rider Univ (MED); Educl Fordham Univ -65; *cr:* Parochial Schls Grds 6-8 Eng Tchr 1967-70; Pub Schls Grd 6 1970-77; Mc Lean Schl Grds 7 & 8 Upper Schl Eng Tchr 1979-83; r Boychoir Schl Asst Head, Eng Tchr 1983-; *ai:* Scndry Schl ement Adv; Dir Dean of Fac Grad Coord; Parent Tchr Liason; editation Mid St Co-Dir; NCTE; NJAIS 1983-; NJMLEA 1990-; ch Org MA&S; Lectured Trenton St Coll Curr; Helped Script Documentary Film; Gave Wkshp; *office:* American Boychoir Schl 19 Lambert Dr Princeton NJ 08540*

ADAM, DEBORAH GLASGOW, Eighth Grade Lang Arts Teacher; *b:* Dover, OH; *m:* Martin; *c:* Zachariah; *ed:* Marietta Coll (BA) Interdisciplinary 1976, (MALL) Lbrl Arts 1983; OH Univ Credit Hrs; *cr:* New Lexington City Schls 7th-9th Grd Title I Rdng Tchr 1976-80, 8th Grd Lang Arts Tchr 1980-; Muskingum Area JVS ABE Instr 1977-80; *ai:* 6-12 Lang Arts Curr Chair; Eighth Grd Team Ldr; Power of the Pen Adv; AFT, OFT, NLEA, Bldg Rep; NCTE, OCTELA 1980-; SOCTE 1980-, Area Rep; NMSA 1991-; Southern OH Emmaus 1989-, Bd Mem; Tchr of Yr; Phi Delta Kappa Distinguished Edctr; Marth Holden Jennings Scholar, Grant; Articles Pub; *office:* New Lexington MS 2550 Panther Dr New Lexington OH 43764*

ADAM, DONALD G., Professor of English; *b:* Cleveland, OH; *c:* Andrew K. M., Elizabeth H. Smithers; *ed:* Harvard Coll (AB) Eng 1959; Univ of Rochester (PHD) Eng 1963; Attnd Bread Loaf Schl of Eng 1959; *cr:* Duchess Schl 3-8 Grd Master 1958-59; Univ of Rochester Instr 1962-63; Bowdoin Coll Instr, Asst Prof 1963-66; Chatham Coll Asst, Assoc Eng Prof; *ai:* Eng, Hum Div, Exec Comm, Masters of Lib Arts Chair; NCTE, CCCC; Amer Soc Eighteenth Century Stud; Ellis Schl Advy Cncl 1980-95, Past Trustee; Intnl Poetry Forum 1981-; Univ of Rochester Schlshp; Univ Flwshp; Buhl Professorship 1974, 1987; NEH Grant, PA Cncl Hum for Exhibition Shakespeare The Globe & The World Carnegie Inst; Nom Man of Yr in Arts 1981 Vectors Intnl; *office:* Chatham Coll Woodland Road Pittsburgh PA 15232

ADAMCEWICZ, GINA MARIE D'ALLESSIO, 8th Grade Homeroom Teacher; *b:* Newark, NJ; *m:* Peter; *c:* Nicholas; *ed:* Kean Coll (BA) Psych 1988; St Cert Spcl Ed 1990; *cr:* Woodbridge MS Resource Ctr & Homeroom Tchr 1991-95; *ai:* 8th Grd Farewell Dance Co-Chprsn; Mem of CORE; NEA 1991-; WTEA 1991-; *office:* Woodbridge MS Barron Ave Woodbridge NJ 07095

ADAMCHAK, LINDA A., Instructor; *b:* Jersey City, NJ; *ed:* Glassboro St Coll (BA) Bio 1977; Western States Chiropractic Coll (DC) Chiropractic 1988; 30 Credit Hrs Molecular Bio Univ of AL; *cr:* Hudson Vly Comm Coll Anatony, Physiology Instr 1992-; *ai:* Coll Acad Policy Comm 1994-95; Womens Golf League Pres 1993-94; Metropolitan Comm Church of Hudson Vly 1990-, Asst Dist Coord, Founder's Awd; Pres Awd for Excl in Tchng 1995.

ADAMI, CAROLYN JOHNSON, Resource Room Special Ed Tchr; *b:* Bel Air, MD; *m:* John Charkles; *c:* Jesse Christian; *ed:* Univ of MD (BA) Eng Ed 1965; Loyola Coll (MS) Spcl Ed 1981; *cr:* Hillcrest Hghts & Laurel Spcl Ctr Self Contained Spcl Ed 1965-70; Colmar Manor Elem Self Contained Resource 1971-74; Carroll Park HS Eng & Rdng Tchr 1975-81; Kenmoor MS Resource Room Spcl Ed 1981-86; Bladensburg HS Resource Room Spcl Ed 1986-; *ai:* Drama Resource Tchr; Soc Comm; Schl Mgmt Team; Savage Comm Assn 1982-, Treas; *office:* Bladensburg HS 5610 Tilden Rd Bladensburg MD 20710

ADAMO, KAREN L., 7th & 8th Grade Teacher; *b:* Atlantic City, NJ; *m:* Thomas R.; *c:* Jesse, Jason, Marissa; *ed:* Univ of NY (BA) Comparative His, Ideas, Cultures 1973; 33 Credit Hrs Towards MA Ed at Univ of ME; *cr:* Woodmere Jr HS Substance Abuse Cnslr 1973-76; Penobscot Elem Schl Long Term Sub Tchr 1986-88; Deer Isle, Stonington Schl GATE Tchr, Coord 1988-90; Orland Consolidated Schl Grd 7-8 Tchr 1990-; *ai:* Grd 8 Adv; Crisis Mngmt Team; Grd 6-8 Team Ldr; Staff Advy Comm; NEA, MEA 1988-; NELMS 1990-.*

ADAMOPOULOS, CHARLES ARTHUR, Business Education Teacher; *b:* Haverhill, MA; *m:* Beth; *c:* Catherine, Zachary, Molly, Brian; *ed:* Univ of RI (BS) Mrktg 1982; Bus Ed Tchng Cert Salem St 1984; *cr:* Cntrl Cath Tchr 1984-, Athletic Dir 1990-94; *ai:* Ftbl, Wrestling & Bsbl Coach; MA Bsbl Coaches Assn 1990-.

ADAMS, ANN MARIE (DEFAZIO), Fourth Grd Tchr & Psychologist; *b:* Erie, PA; *m:* Kenneth M.; *ed:* Mercyhurst Coll (BA) Elem Ed-Magna Cum Laude 1978; Gannon Coll (MS) Guid, Cnslng 1982; Edinboro Univ (MED) Schl Psych 1991; *cr:* Erie Schl Dist 1-3 Grd Elem Tchr 1978-83; 7 Grd Sci Tchr 1983-85, 4th Grd Tchr 1985-, Schl Psychologist 1996-; *ai:* Emerson Gridley Schl Store Coord; Discipline, Bldg Comms; Inclusion Team; Schl Newspaper; Schl Recycling Coord; NEA, PSEA, EEA 1978-; NASP 1990-; Dance Edctrs of Amer 1973-; PTA 1978-; Sam's Club Recycling Grant; Ec Grant; Emerson-Gridley Tchr of Yr 994-95; Nom Natl Math Tchr Awd; *office:* Erie Schl Dist 1511 Peach St Erie PA 16501

ADAMS, ANNA J., Physical Ed & Health Instr; *b:* Paterson, NJ; *m:* Richard J.; *c:* Richard, Robert; *ed:* William Paterson Coll (BA) PE & Hlth Ed 1977; Hlth Ed 14 Credits; Driver Ed 3 Cr; (MED) Currently Completing; Grad Study in Progress; *cr:* Paramus HS PE & Hlth Tchr 1976-77; Eastside HS PE, Hlth & Driver Ed Tchr 1977-86; Rosa Parks HS PE, Hlth & Driver Ed Tchr 1986-, 20 Yrs in Dist; *ai:* SADD Adv 1991-; Class of 1990 Adv; Mid Sts Visual Arts Comm 1993-94; Mid Sts Drivers Ed Comm Chprsn; Mid Sts Hlth Curriculum Comm; Eastside HS Head Sftbl Coach; Co-Dir Drama Productions 1990; Athletic Club Adv 1991; St Comprehensive Hlth Ed Comm 1994; Class Adv 1995; Midstate Comm Chr 1995-; Evaluation Proposal Review Comm, Rutgers Nwsltr; PAT Hlth Curr Comm Revision; Delta Psi Kappa; NE Chap Vlybl Assn 1976-, Sec 9 Yrs; NJSIAA & NFIOA, NEA, PEA & WPC Alumni Assn 1976-; WPC Movement Science Alumni Exec Bd, Natl Ed; NJEA, NEVB, Assn Exec Bd NJAHPERD; Little Falls PTA & Recreation; Triboro Little League; Hawthorne Recreation, Womens Softball & Volleyball; NNA, Notary Rep; Herald News Coach of Yr 1981; Record Coach of Yr 1981, Congressional Merit Awd 1993, William Paterson College; nominated for Governors Award 1991; nominated for Princeton Univ Distinguished Teacher Awd 1994; Recep WPC Schlsp Awd; NFIOA VB Outstdng Official Awd 1996.

ADAMS, ARMELIA M., Fourth Grade Teacher; *b:* Sanford, NC; *ed:* Jersey City St Coll (BA) Elem Ed 1971; Rutgers Univ at New Brunswick (MA) Ed 1978; 30 Addl Hrs Kean Coll of NJ Cnslng Ed 1992; Durham Bus Coll Diploma; *cr:* Newark Bd of Ed Clerk 1962-67, Tchr 1971-73; Hillside Bd of Ed Tchr 1973-; *ai:* NJEA, NEA 1973-; Tchr of Yr 1986; Commendation Geography Awareness Cert 1988; St of NJ Intergenerational Achvmt Awd 1990; Dr Martin L King Jr Awd of Excl 1992; *office:* A P Morris Schl 143 Coe Ave Hillside NJ 07205

ADAMS, BRUCE K., 6th-8th Grd Social Stud Tchr; *b:* Brooklyn, NY; *m:* Holly; *c:* Sam, Sarah; *ed:* Springfield Coll (BA) Scndry Ed 1971; Cntrl CT St Univ (MS) Counseling 1980; *cr:* Kent Ctr Elem Schl 6th-8th Grd Soc Stud Tchr 1972-; *ai:* Girls Var Soccer Coach-Housatonic Valley Reg HS; Kent Ctr Schl & Kent Babe Ruth Bsbl; NEA 1972-; *office:* Kent Ctr Elem Schl Judd Ave Kent CT 06757

ADAMS, CARRIE L., Social Studies Teacher; *b:* Lock Haven, PA; *ed:* Lock Haven Univ (BSEd) Ed, Scndry 1988; Bucknell Univ (MSEd) Ed, Scndry Cnslng 1995; *cr:* Bellefonte Area MS Long-Term Sub Tchr 1990-92; Keystone Cntrl Schl Dist Per-diem Sub 1992-93; Sugar Valley Schl Soc Stud Tchr 1993-; *ai:* Art Club Adv; NEA, PSEA 1993-; AAUW 1988-, Treas 1990-92; Lock Haven Univ Comm Orch 1983-; *home:* 230 S Water St Mill Hall PA 17751

ADAMS, CHERYL ANNE (KIRKNER), Parent & KDG Cmptr Teacher; *b:* Quakertown, PA; *m:* Robert E.; *c:* Joshua R., Michael S.; *ed:* Lock Haven Univ (BS) Elem, Early Childhood 1970; 24 Grad Credits PA St Univ, Marywood Coll, W Chester Univ; Cnslng Stud Shepherd of Hills; 8 Credit Hrs Caesar Rodney Schl Dist; Attnd Inst for Motivational Living; Chrstn Intnl Bible Coll 5 Audit Hrs; 9 Grad Hrs Cnslng Stud Elijah House; *cr:* Spring-Ford Schl Dist Elem Tchr, Mentor 1970-86; Caesar Rodney Schl Dist Elem Tchr, Mentor 1986-90; Jireh Chrstn Ctr Nursery Supt, Mentor Tchr 1990-92; First Bapt Church Schl Presch Tchr 1992-93; Home Schl Instruction Presch Tchr 1993-95; St John's Early Learning Ctr Vol KDG Cmptr Tchr 1995-; *ai:* Sign Lang Club Adv; Jireh Chrstn Ctr Ldr in Mentoring; JCC Dance, Fine Arts Ldrshp; JCC Creative Banners Design Dept Ldr; JCC Womens Cnslng, Tchng, Pub Speaking; US Senatorial Rep Campaign Assignment Del; PSEA 1970-80; Grace E C Church 1970-78, Asst Supt & Bible Tchr, Recognition Cert; Shepherd of the Hills UCC 1970-85, Elem Bible Tchr; Gospel Ctr Mission Summers 1984-86, Missionary Tchr; Southern de Young Life 1986-90, Comm Mem; Jireh Chrstn Ctr 1992-94, Ldrshp Womens Ministry; Comm Liason Svc Awd 1990; Ungoing Recognition Awds, Dedication to Svc & Tchng 1970-; *home:* 103 Todds Mill Rd Camden DE 19934*

ADAMS, CHERYL PALONIS, Pace Language Arts Teacher; *b:* Detroit, MI; *m:* John D.; *c:* Jessica, Cate; *ed:* Wayne St Univ (BA) Hum 1973; Univ of UT (MFA) Dance 1976; Pacific Luth Univ Cert Eng 1984; Hofstra Univ Theatre for HS Tchrs; Carnegie Mellon AP Instrs Coursework; Theatre Stud at Folger; *cr:* Univ of Toledo Dance Instr 1976-77; St Mary's Coll of MD Visiting Lecturer in Dance 1977-80; Leonardtown HS Eng, Forensics Tchr, Theatre 1986-94; Margaret Brent MS PACE Lang Arts Tchr 1994-; *ai:* Choreographer Schl Musicals; Forensics Coach; Schl Improvement Team; Cty Assessment Comm; NEA, MSTA 1986-; MASCAO 1994-; Appeal Elem PTA 1986-, Pub Chair; Ruth Circle UMC 1993-; Phi Eta Sigma; Frostburg St Univ Acad Excl, Ldrshp Awd; *office:* Margaret Brent MS Rt 5 Helen MD 20650*

ADAMS, CHRISTOPHER GERARD, Span Teacher & Dean of Stdnts; *b:* New Milford, CT; *m:* Christine Mary Jensen; *c:* Rachelle Maria, Thomas Christopher; *ed:* Bates Coll (BA) Span 1981; Middlebury Coll (MA) Span 1986; Post Grad Course Guernavaca Mexico; MacIntosh in Span Classroom Taft Educl Ctr; Grad Stud in Madrid Spain; *cr:* Canterbury Schl Span & Math Tchr & Coach 1981-85; Plainville HS Span Tchr & Stu Cncl Adv 1986-89; Cushing Acad Span & Math Tchr, Coach & Dean of Stdnts 1989-; *ai:* Boys & Girls Cross Country & Boys Track Head Coach; Attendance & Schl Evaluation Comm; Cushing Summer Schl Pgm Dean of Stdnts; Dormitory Dir; Mentor Tchr; MA for Lang Assn 1994; New England Champion Cross Country Teams Coach; *home:* 39 School St Ashburnham MA 01430

ADAMS, CHRYSTIE LARSON, General & Vocal Music Teacher; *b:* Kansas City, MO; *m:* Douglas M.; *c:* Rebecca; *ed:* Gettysburg Coll (BS) Music Ed 1971; Towson St Univ (MS) Music Ed 1976; OH St, Westminster Choir Coll 30 Addl Credit Hrs; *cr:* Lake Clifton HS General Music Tchr 1971-72; Francis Scott Key Jr HS General, Vocal Music Tchr 1972-79; Owen Brown Mid General, Vocal Music Tchr 1979-82; Ellicott Mills Mid General, Vocal Music Tchr 1982-95; Elkridge Landing MS General & Vocal Music Tchr 1995-; *ai:* After Schl Act Coord; Show & Handbell Choir Dir;Calendar Comm Chprsn; Schl Comm Action Team; Instrl Leadership Team; Discipline Comm; Related Arts Chprsn; MD Music Ed Assn 1971-, Excl Awd 1994; MD Scndry General Music Assn 1971-, Past Pres; MENC 1971-; HCEA, MSTA 1980-; Brown Meml Presbyn 1971-, Music for Sunday Schl, Choir 1971, Section Ldr, Asst Dir; Fine Arts Summer Bible Schl 1989-, Chprsn; Balto Bach Soc 1984-, Bus Mgr; Francis Scott Key Schl PTA Tchr of Yr 1975; Wrote Pilot Guitar Curr 1972-73; MENC Eastern Division Conf presenter; Organized MD 1st Jr All St Chorus 1986; Adjudicator, Clinician, Guest Conductor; *office:* Elkridge Landing MS 7085 Montgomery Rd Elkridge MD 21227

ADAMS, DAVID H., Math & Science Teacher; *b:* Pittsburgh, PA; *ed:* Cheyney St Coll (BS) Sci 1974; Univ of Pittsburgh Rdng Specialist; Beaver Coll Chem; Drexel Univ Sci; *cr:* West Mifflin Area Schls Tchr 1974-; Wallingford Swarthmore Tchr 1983-84; Philadelphia Schl Dist Tchr 1984-; *ai:* PFT 1984-; Path-Prisms Grants; *office:* Beeber MS 59th & Malvern Sts Philadelphia PA 19131

ADAMS, DAVID JOSEPH, Anatomy, Physiology & Bio Tchr; *b:* Altoona, PA; *ed:* Millersville Univ (BS) Bio, Safety Ed 1972; Slippery Rock Univ (MS) Ath Admin, PE 1991; Penn St Univ Continuing Ed Credits for Permanent Cert Tchng in PA; *cr:* Dongela HS Bio, Sci Tchr, Track Coach 1973; Bishop Guilfoyle HS Bio, Sci, Hlth Tchr, Bsbl, Bsktbl Coach 1974-81; Penn St Behrend Coll Residential Life Staff 1981-85; Slippery Rock Univ Residential Life Staff 1985-86; Northern Bedford HS Bio, Anatomy, Physiology Tchr 1986-; *ai:* Prom, Sr Class Trip Adv; Girls VAr Bsktbl Coach; Detention Supvr; Natl Fed of HS Bsbl Ofcls 1973-, Pres of Local Chptr; Autumn Estates Retirement Home 1990-, Vol Visitor; *office:* Northern Bedford Cty HS HC 1 Box 200 Loysburg PA 16659*

ADAMS, EDWARD THOMAS,JR., High School Math Teacher; *b:* Philadelphia, PA; *ed:* Cheyney St Univ (BS) General Sci 1967; *cr:* Cardinal O;Hara Math Tchr 30 Yrs; *ai:* Boys Cross Cntry Coach; Moderator of Chess Club; USCF 1988; NCEA; *office:* Cardinal O'Hara HS 1701 S Sproul Rd Springfield PA 19064

ADAMS, ELAINE MARIE, Computer Programming Teacher; *b:* Altoona, PA; *m:* Dean J.; *ed:* Indiana Univ of PA (BS) Math Ed 1981; *cr:* Bellwood Antis Jr Sr High Math Tchr 1981-85; Hollidayburg Area Sr High Cmptr Programming Tchr 1985-; *ai:* Newspaper Adv; Producer Schl Drama Productions; Trainer in Peer Mediation; NEA, PSEA, Local 1981-; *office:* Hollidaysburg Area Sr HS 1510 N Montgomery St Hollidaysburg PA 16648*

ADAMS, ELIZA JANE, Guidance Counselor; *b:* Bangor, ME; *c:* Mariah Adams Ernst; *ed:* Bishops Univ (BA) Psych, Sociology 1978; Univ of Southern ME (MED) Counseling 1982; Univ of New England (CAS) Marriage, Family Therapy 1996; *cr:* Schl Admin Dist 13 K-12th Grd Guidance Cnslr, Soc Worker 1982-86; ME Whitewater Inc ME Whitewater Guide, Licenses 1985-89; Windham MS 6th-8th Grd Guidance Cnslr 1989-; *ai:* Natl Jr Honor Soc Adv; NEA, ME Schl Cnslr Soc 1984-; Windham Tchrs Assn 1989-; Hlth Advy Comm 1992-; Adolescent Pregnancy Advy Comm 1991-; Cosco Bay Educl Alliance 1993-95; *office:* Windham MS 408 Gray Rd Windham ME 04062

ADAMS, HENRY MORRIS, Fifth Grade Teacher; *b:* Champaigne, IL; *m:* Cynthia Margarella; *c:* Justine Ling, Scott, Jennifer Eisenhower, Ryan; *ed:* Wagner Coll (BS) Ed 1966, (MS) Ed 1969; Coll of S I Prof Cert 1977; Educl Sabaticol 1993-94; *cr:* PS 31 4th, 5th, 6th Grd Tchr 1960-64; PS 20 Tchr, Trainer 1969-70; PS 31 5th Grd Tchr 1970-71; IS 61, Feeder Schls Drug Abuse Resouce Tchr 1971-72; Dist Office 31 Schl Comm Coord 1972-76; PS 69 1st, 2nd, 4th, 5th Grd Tchr, Adm Asst 1976-; *ai:* Cartooning, Latchkey Tchr; SI Rdng Assn 1980-; UFT; NEA; Cub Scout Comm Ldr 1992-; First Presby Church, Deacon; *office:* PS 69 Daniel Tompkins 144 Keating Pl Staten Island NY 10314

ADAMS, JAN EDWARD, Assoc Dean for Instrl Support; *b:* Tiffin, OH; *m:* Ann Augsburger; *c:* Benjamin, Rebecca; *ed:* OH St Univ (BS) Engrng Physics 1966, (PHD) Physics 1977; *cr:* OH St Univ Asst Prof 1972-79; Intnl Telephone & Telegraph Sr Engr 1979-81; Ridihalgh, Eggers & Assocs Sr Engr 1981-83; Firelands Coll BGSU Assoc Dean 1983-; *ai:* Fitness Club Adv; OH Section & Amer Phys Soc 1979-; BCS Schls Bd of Ed 1985-89, Bd Pres; OH St Univ Distngd Grad Tchng Awd; Numerous Publications & Contributed Presentations; *office:* Firelands College BGSU 901 Rye Beach Rd Huron OH 44839

ADAMS, JOANN CALVARIO, French & Spanish Teacher; *b:* Peckville, PA; *m:* Robert M.; *c:* Alyssa; *ed:* Marywood Coll (BA) Scndry Ed 1971; Addl Post Grad Stud Fr, Rdng Millersville; *cr:* North Scranton Jr HS Fr, Eng Tchr 1971-72; Mid Valley Schl Dist Fr, Span Tchr 1972-; *ai:* Fr Club Adv; Am Assn Tchrs Fr 1990-; *office:* Mid-Valley Secondary Ctr Underwood Rd Throop PA 18512

ADAMS, JOSEPH JOHN, Art Teacher; *b:* Baltimore, MD; *m:* Diane; *ed:* Balto Jr Coll (AA) Art Major 1970; Townson St Univ (BS) Art Ed 1972, (APC) Art Ed 1976; *cr:* Howard Comm Coll Ceramic Instr 1978-83; Oakland Mills MS Art Tchr 1972-78; Oakland Mills HS Art Dept Chm 1978-; *ai:* Coach Var Girls Sftbl 1981-91, JV Field Hockey 3 Yrs, JV Ftbl 1 Yr; Ski Club Spon 10 Yrs; NEA, MSTA, HCEA 1972-; Awds HS Talent Recognition 1981, Howard Cnty Pub Schl Tchng Excl 1988, Commnedation from Parents 1982; Howard Cty Coach of Yr 1988; *office:* Oakland Mills HS 9410 Kilimanjaro Rd Columbia MD 21045

ADAMS, JOYCE M., Sixth Grade Teacher; *b:* Gardner, MA; *ed:* Rivier Coll (BA) Elem Ed 1969; Post Grad Stud in Childrens Lit; Individualized Sci Instruction; Elem Stu Assistance Prgm; Facilitator Trng; *cr:* Broad Street Schl 6th Grd Tchr 1969-; *ai:* Stu Assistance Prgm Sec & Facilitator; 4th-6th Grd Sci Coord; Sci Club Adv; Dist Level Field Trip Comm; Nashua Tchrs Union 1969-, Bldg Rep; AFT, AFL-CIO 1969-; NH Sci Tchrs Assn 1996; Kids Kare Awd Scholastic Magazine 1990; Fleet Youth Leaders Fleet Banks of NH 1994; *office:* Broad Street Elem Schl 390 Broad St Nashua NH 03063*

ADAMS, JUDITH WHITFORD, Retired 7th Grd English Tchr; *b:* Wakefield, RI; *ed:* RI Coll (BED) Soc Stud 1962; 36 Addl URI; *cr:* High St Schl 6th Grd Tchr 1962-63; Chariho Regnl Schl Dist 7th Grd Eng Tchr 1964-94; *ai:* NEA 1964-; NEA-Charaho 1964-, VP, Treas; *home:* PO Box 364 Wakefield RI 02880

ADAMS, JULIUS GREGG, Assoc Professor of Education; *b:* Buffalo, NY; *m:* Carmon Grigsby; *ed:* SUNY at Buffalo (BA) Psych 1978, (MA) Ed & Psych 1985, (PHD) Ed & Psych 1988; *cr:* Buffalo Pub Schls Psych 1982-87; WNY Childrens Psychiatric Ctr Psych II 1987-88; SUNY Coll at Fredonia Assoc Prof 1988-; WNY Inst for the Psychotherapies Asst Psych 1992-; *ai:* Hlth Core Ad Hoc Comm Chprsn; Fac Senator; UUP 1988-; AERA 1994-; Amer Diabetes Assn 1994-, Bd of Dirs; First Shiloh Bapt Church; SUNY Chancellors Awd for Excl in Tchng 1993; Reviewer for West Pub Co; Numerous Articles Pub; *office:* S U N Y Coll At Fredonia E236 Thompson Hall Fredonia NY 14063*

ADAMS, KAREN M., First Grade Teacher; *b:* Johnstown, PA; *m:* Lawrence W.; *c:* Erin, Kristin, Beth, Meredith; *ed:* IN Univ of PA (BS) Elem Ed 1967; Masters Equivalency; *ai:* NEA 1984-; PSEA 1984-; DAEA 1984-; *office:* Leaders Hghts Elem Schl 49 Indian Rock Dam Rd York PA 17403

ADAMS, LINDA C., 5th Grade Teacher; *b:* Canton, OH; *m:* Kim H.; *c:* Donna, Kimberly; *ed:* Mount Union Coll (BA) Elem Ed 1976; Youngstown St Univ (MSEd) GATE 1992; *cr:* Southern Local Schls Tchr Grds 5-8 1976-; *ai:* Odyssey of Mind Regnl Judge; NEA, OEA 1976-; SLTA 1976-, Treas; Salineville Comm Choir 1987-, Pianist; *office:* Southern Local Int Schl 54 W Main st Salineville OH 43945

ADAMS, LINDA MORAN, Math & Comp Teacher; *b:* Willimantic, CT; *m:* Spencer E. Jr.; *c:* Matthew B., Spencer E. III; *ed:* Eastern CT St Univ (BS) Intermediate & HS Math & Ed 1970; Southern CT St Univ (MS) Intermediate Ed 1990; *cr:* Helen St Schl 6th Grd Tchr 1970-73; Ezra Acad 5th-8th Grd Math & Comp Tchr & Coord 1985-; *ai:* Mathcounts Coach; NCTM; St of CT Mathcounts Coach Natl Competition 1993; *office:* Ezra Acad 75 Rimmon Rd Woodbridge CT 06525

ADAMS, LYNDAA HUEBSCH, Science Department Head; *b:* Mineola, NY; *m:* Richard T. Jr.; *ed:* SUNY at Stonybrook (BS) Biological Scis 1989, (MA) Sci Tchng 1993; Coll of New Rochelle (SAS) Staff Dev 1996; 60 Grad, Insvc Hrs Educl Practices Coll of St Rose, Long Island Inst for Prof Stud; *cr:* Play Groups Schl Summer Presch Dir 1984-; Vly Stream Cntrl HS 10-12 Grd Sci Tchr 1989-, Sci Dept Head 1995-; *ai:* 7th-8th Grd Girls Soccer Coach; VSTA 1989-, Action Comm Head; VSPTSA 1989-, Tchr Liaison, Lifetime Mbrshp; NYSASCD 1991-; NYSBTA; Tchr of Yr; Nom NYS Tchr of Yr; 2 Articles Pub; Authentic Tchng Confs; *office:* Vly Stream Cntrl HS 135 Fletcher Ave Valley Stream NY 11580*

ADAMS, M. DIANE, French & Spanish Teacher; *b:* Grove City, PA; *c:* Veronica; *ed:* Westminster Coll (BA) Fr, Span 1969; Duquesne Univ (MA) Span 1983; Undergraduate Stud Sorbonne Univ of Paris; Grad Stud Universidad Nacional Autonoma de Mexico; *cr:* North Allegheny Fr, Span Tchr 1969-72; Colegio Westminster Eng Tchr 1972-76; Mrs Longs Eng Schl Eng Tchr 1978-81; Hampton Schls Fr, Span Tchr 1981-; *ai:* Intnl Interest Group; Bowling Club; NEA, PSEA 1981-, Membership Chprsn; AAUW 1995-; Hampton MS Tchr of Yr; Thanks for Tchrs Nom; *office:* Hampton MS 4589 School Rd Allison Park PA 15101

ADAMS, MARCIA LOUISE WILLIAMSON, Science Teacher; *b:* Philadelphia, PA; *m:* Merrill Jerome; *c:* Merrill, Jerome, Kwame, Violet; *ed:* Fisk Univ (BS) Sci & Bio 1980; 30 Credits at Trenton St in Educl Courses 1983-84; *ai:* Black His Club Adv; Black Coll Tour Spon; NJSTA, NEA, NJEA, NJBTA, PTEA 1985-.

ADAMS, MAXINE ANN (KOWALCHIK), Second Grade Teacher; *b:* Scranton, PA; *m:* James William; *c:* Melissa, Nicholas, Andrew; *ed:* Marywood Coll (BA) Elem Ed 1969; Instrl Theory into Practice Madeline Hunter's Course; *cr:* Mid Vly Schl Dist Second. Thrid Grd Tchr 1969-71, Part-time HS Latin Tchr 1969; Rockaway Twp Schls Second Grd Tchr 1971-; *ai:* Math Curr, Report Card, Lang Arts Comms; Assn Negotiating Team; NEA 1969-; NJEA, MCCEA 1971-; RTEA 1971-, Treas; Sacred Heart Church 1993-, Choir; *office:* Birchwood Elem Schl 1 Art St Dover NJ 07801

ADAMS, PATRICIA E., High School Teacher; *b:* Pittsburgh, PA; *ed:* Univ of Pgh (BS) PE 1975; Masters Equiv; *ai:* Girls Sftbl Coach; PFT 1975-; AFT 1975-; City of Pittsburgh Coach of Yr.

ADAMS, PAUL EDWIN, Science Teacher; *b:* Salamanca, NY; *m:* Barbara Ann Jones; *c:* Lucas, Casey; *ed:* Houghton Coll (BS) Gen Sci 1974; SUC at Buffalo (MS) Gen Sci Ed 1979; *cr:* Grand Island MS 6th Grd Sci Tchr 1974-76; Houghton Coll Admission Cnslr 1976-78; Chrstn Heritage Schl 6th-8th Grd Sci Tchr 1978-81 Chrstn Schl of York 6th-9th Grd Sci Tchr 1981-; *ai:* MS Pgm & Sci Fair Coord; Outdoor Ed Dir; Bsbl Coach; ACSI 1978-; York Cty Sci & Engineering Fair 1988-, Coord; *office:* Christian Schl Of York 907 Greenbriar Rd York PA 17404*

ADAMS, PETER A., Social Studies Teacher; *b:* Key West, FL; *m:* Linda Gerster; *c:* Kristina, Alicia, Benjamin; *ed:* Univ of MD (BA) Ed 1971, (MA) His 1976, (PHD) Amer Stud 1996; *cr:* Univ of MD Grad Tchng Asst 1971-73; Laurel HS Soc Stud Tchr 1973-93, Major Area Coord 1993-95, Soc Stud Tchr 1995-; *ai:* Track Coach; Natl Endowment MD Cncl for the Hum Grant 1984, 1986, 1987; MD Cross Cntry Coach of Yr 1985; Cty Coach of Yr, Cross Cntry 1984-85, Winter Track 1993; Article Pub 1993; *office:* Laurel HS 8000 Cherry Ln Laurel MD 20707

ADAMS, RALPH EDWARD, Social Studies Teacher; *b:* Cincinnati, OH; *m:* Angela Hull; *c:* Walker, Briana; *ed:* Emporia St Univ (BA) His & Govt 1986; Grad Work at Pittsburg St Univ of KS; *cr:* El Dorado Springs HS Soc Stud Tchr 1988-90; Felicity-Franklin HS Soc Stud Tchr 1990-; *ai:* Acad Team Spon; Var Tennis Coach; Articles Pub in Ohio Southland; Cons for OH Div of Wildlife; *office:* Felicity-Franklin Schl 415 W Washington St Felicity OH 45120

ADAMS, RICHELE BROOKS, 5th Grade Math & Reading Tchr; *b:* New York City, NY; *m:* Theodis L.; *c:* Javid; *ed:* Hofstra Univ (BA) Ed 1972; Queens Coll (MS) Ed 1977; *cr:* Hempstead Pub Schls 4th, 5th Grd Tchr 1972-; *ai:* 5th Grd Coord; South Hempstead Congretational Church Sunday Schl Tchr; AFT, NYSUT 1872-; Salvation Army; Nature of A Sister; *office:* Jackson Main Elem Sch 451 Jackson St Hempstead NY 11550

ADAMS, ROBIN BROOKS, Chemistry Teacher; *b:* Camden, NJ; *ed:* Howard Univ (BS) Chem 1982; Nazareth Coll of Rochester (MS) Scndry Ed 1989; Attnd Univ of Rochester; *cr:* Eastman Kodak Co Analytical Chemist 1982-86; Amer Red Cross Product Mngmt Clerk 1987-89; Rochester City Schl Dist Chem Tchr 1989-; *ai:* Schl of Arts Yrbk Adv; AFT, NY St United Tchrs, Amer Chem Soc Assn 1989-; Urban League of Rochester; Zeta Phi Beta 1980-; Most Admired African Amer Tchr 1994; Sci Tchr Awd 1993; *office:* Schl Of The Arts 45 Prince St Rochester NY 14607

ADAMS, SPENCER E.,JR., Science Teacher; *b:* Stamford, CT; *m:* Linda M.; *c:* Matthew, Spencer III; *ed:* Southern CT State Univ (BS) Bio 1971; 60 Addl Credits; *cr:* Lyman Hall HS Sci Tchr 1971; Norwalk HS Sci Tchr 1971-; *ai:* NHS Fac Mem; AFT 1972-; CT Earth Sci Tchrs 1987-, Former VP; NSTA, CSTA, NESTA; NSTA Excl Sci Ed; Distngd Tchr; White House Commission on Presidential Scholars; *office:* Norwalk HS 23 Calvin Murphy Dr Norwalk CT 06851

ADAMS, SUETTE C., HS English Teacher; *b:* Columbus, OH; *ed:* OH Univ (BA) Eng 1970, (MS) Scndry Ed 1971; Post Grad Stud; *cr:* Tri-Cty Voc Schl Eng Tchr 1971-72; Athens HS Eng Tchr 1972-; *ai:* Yrbk Adv; Eng Dept Chair; NEA 1971-; OEA 1971-; SEOEA 1971-; AEA 1972-, VP 1989-91 & Pres 1991-95; Martha Holden Jennings Scholar; *office:* Athens HS 1 High School Rd The Plains OH 45780

ADAMS, VELMA JONES, Vocal, Choral & Music Teacher; *b:* Baltimore, MD; *m:* Kenneth G.; *c:* Mark; *ed:* Howard Univ (BME) 1968; Morgan St Univ (MA) Music 1978; Admin Prof Diploma 1996; *cr:* Baltimore City Pub Schls General Music Tchr 1968-80; Uniondale Pub Schls Chorus & General Music Tchr 1980-; *ai:* Drama & Musical Theater Productions Dir; Stu at Risk Tchr Mentor; Peer Mediation Coord; Nassau Music Educators Assn 1980-, Exec Brd Mem 1994-; Choral Chair 1993-94; Long Island Theater Educators Assn, New York Theater Educators Assn 1989-; Nassau All-Cty Music Festival Coord; Choral Dirs Assn 1993; *home:* 7124 Sutton Pl # 2 Fresh Meadows NY 11365*

ADAMSKI, GARY MATTHEW, French & Spanish Teacher; *b:* Niagara Falls, NY; *m:* Blanche Viavada; *ed:* Niagara Comm Coll (AA) Lbrl Arts 1967; SUNY at Buffalo (BS) Psych, Lang 1969; St Michael's Coll (MSEd) Admin 1975; Univ de Montreal 15 Hrs; Univ de Grenoble 9 Hrs; Univ of VT 24 Hrs; Univ de Salamanca 9 Hrs; *cr:* PS 54 5th Grd Span, Soc Stud Tchr 1969; Main St MS 6-8 Grd Fr, Eng Tchr 1969-81; Montpelier HS 9-12 Grd Fr, Span, Eng Tchr 1979-90; Whitcomb HS 7-12 Grd Fr, span, Eng, TESL Tchr 1990-93; Spaulding HS 9-12 Grd Fr, Span tchr 1993-; *ai:* Adv Mexico, Swiss Exchange, Quebec Trips; Drama Group; Fr Club; Newspaper; Barie City Relicensur Bd, Schlsp, Exam Review Comms; Bowling, JV Ftbl Coach; MEA 1969-90, VP 1971-73, Pub Rel Chari 1976-80; NEA, VTNEA, BEA 1990-, Pres 1992, Negotiator 1993; VT for Lang Assoc 1969-, Brd 1980-81, Pres 1981-84, Svc Awd 1984; AATF 1969-, VT Treas, Soc d'Hannear 1986; Cntrl VT Tchrs Credit Union 1974-, Chm Bd Dir 1990-; Barie Ethnic Heritage Com 1988-; Barie Area Fr Heritage Group 1994-; Montpelier Fr Group 1987-; *office:* Spaulding HS 155 Ayers St Barre VT 05641*

ADAMSKY, GRACE FIORENZA, Spanish Teacher; *b:* Scranton, PA; *m:* John W.; *c:* Matthew; *ed:* Marywood Coll (BA) Scndry Ed Span 1972; Univ of Scranton Eng Cert; Attnd Proficiency Inst; *cr:* Montrose Schl Dist Span Tchr 1972-74; Scranton Schls Span Tchr 1980-; *ai:* Span Club Monitor; AFT 1989-; NEH Grant Wkshp 1993.

ADAMSKY, RICHARD ALLEN, 7th Grade Teacher; *b:* Morristown, NJ; *ed:* Temple Univ (BA) Commnctns 1982, (MA) Elem Ed 1991; *cr:* WBUX Radio Newsman 1983-86; Nativity of Our Lord 7th Grd Instr 1987-; *ai:* Sftbl Pgm; Warrington Ath Assn Ftbl Pgm; CYO Bd; Warrington Ath Assn Sftbl Pgm; NCTM 1994-.

ADAMSON, CHARLES RALPH, Bio, Anatomy & Zoology Tchr; *b:* Waynesburg, PA; *m:* Carol Mooney; *c:* Charles Scott, Stephen Shawn; *ed:* Waynesburg Coll (BS) Bio 1968; CA St Coll (MS) Bio 1972; *cr:* Cntrl Greene Schl Dist Bio, Anat, Zoo Instr 1969-; *ai:* GOM-BOM Comm; NEA, PSEA, CGPA 1969-; Greene Co Sheep & Wool Growers Assn 1964-.

ADASIAK, KATHY TADIO, French Teacher; *b:* Rochester, NY; *m:* David; *c:* Lauren; *ed:* SUNY at Potsdam & Brockport (BS) Ed, Fr 1970; Nazareth Coll (MSEd) 1976; *cr:* Iroquois MS Core Tchr 1971-79; Iroquois Rogers Schl Fr, Span Tchr Part-Time 1981-84; Dake Schl Fr Tchr 1984-; West Irondequoit HS Fr Tchr 1984-; *ai:* Fr Club Adv; Wellness Comm Mem; Tchrs Assn Mem; AATF 1990-; NYSAFCT 1986-; Alliance Francaise 1994-; Sorbonne at Paris 1 Month Scholarship 1984; Fulbright Tchr Exch in ALsace 1991-92.*

ADCOCK, SUE ELLEN, Home Instructor; *c:* Laura, Alice Bucy; *ed:* Mount Union Coll (BA) Eng Ed 1966; *cr:* Sandusky Pub Schls Jr High Tchr 1966-67; South-Western City Schls Mid Schl Tchr 1967-71, Home Instr 1980-; *ai:* Key Club Adv 1990-93; Kiwanis Club 1992-, Newpaper Ed, Past Publicity Dir; *office:* Westland HS 146 Galloway Rd Galloway OH 43119

ADDICOTT, ALEXIS ANN (WHITE), Algebra Teacher; *b:* Sharon, PA; *m:* Jeffery Paul Sr.; *c:* Jeffery Paul Jr., Jennifer Ann, Adrienne M.; *ed:* Youngstown St Univ (BS) Math 1985, (MS) Ed 1995; *cr:* Lakeview HS Math Tchr 1986-; *ai:* Stu Cncl, Jr Beta Club Adv; NEA, NEOTA 1986-; NCMT 1987-; Masury-Brookfield Women's Club 1991-; *home:* 7138 Sunnydell Dr Brookfield OH 44403

ADDY, SANDRA PARKS, Soc Stud, His & Geography Tchr; *b:* Newcomerstown, OH; *c:* Jerry Allan, Vicki Sue Davis; *ed:* Muskingum Coll (BS) Psych, Ed 1979; Working on Masters; *cr:* Newcomerstown Exempted Village Tchr 24 Yrs; *ai:* Acad Challenge Team Coach; Planning Comm; Tchrs Assn Bldg Rep, Bd of Dirs; NEA 1980-; N Tchrs Assn 1980-, Bd of Dirs; United Meth Church 1957-; Booster Club 1965-; *office:* Newcomerstown MS 325 W State St Newcomerstown OH 43832

ADELSON, ELLEN DEE, Third Grade Teacher; *b:* New York, NY; *m:* Allan; *c:* Lisa Krauze, Debra; *ed:* Hunter Coll (BA) Eng 1967; Lehman Coll (MS) Ed 1970; *cr:* PS 46 4th-5th Grd Tchr 1967-71; MCESC K-8 Grd Basic Skills Tchr; Bangs Ave Schl 3rd Grd Tchr 1985-; *ai:* After Schl Basic Skills Instr; NEA 1985-; *office:* Bangs Ave Primary Schl 1300 Bangs Ave Asbury Park NJ 07712

ADELSON, LOUIS DAVID, Asst Prof of Computer Science; *b:* Kittanning, PA; *ed:* Washington & Jefferson (BA) Psych 1964; Control Data Inst (AS) Programming & Syst Dev 1971; Clarion Univ of PA (BS) Cmptr Sci 1986; Univ of Pittsburgh (MS) Information Sci 1990; 20 Credit Hrs Post Grad Stud Univ of Cntrl OK; *cr:* Clarion Univ of PA Instr, CIS Dept 1986-90, Asst Prof, CIS Dept 1990-; *ai:* Adult Learners Org Adv; Mem Parking, Cmptr, Fnd Fac Fund Raising Comms; Campus Fac Forum; APSCUF 1986-, Exec Comm; ACM, PACISE 1986-; Rotary 1974-, Pres Twice, Outstdng Newsletter; Church Bd 1980-, Pres, Sec; Jaycees 1972-79, Regnl Dir; Oil Creek Railway Historical Soc 1985-, Pres, VP, Sec, Treas; *office:* Clarion Univ Of PA Venango 1801 W 1st St Oil City PA 16301

ADKINS, ANGELA LYNN, Band & Choir Director; *b:* Columbus, *ed:* Capital Univ (BM) Music Ed 1993; *cr:* Carroll HS Band, Choi 1993-; *ai:* Musical Dir; Stdnts Against Dangerous Decisions; Pi K Lambda, Alpha Chi, OH Music Ed Assn, Music Ed Natl Conf 1993 Chapter of Phi Beta 1990-, Pres, Treas; *office:* Carroll HS 4524 Linder Dayton OH 45432*

ADKINS, ANITA E. SCHAAB, English Teacher; *b:* Philadelphia, PA Harold D.; *c:* Denise Hearn, Donna Blackburn; *ed:* Univ of DE (AS) Ed 1974; Salisbury St Univ (BA) Eng 1978, (MA) Eng 1988; 61 Addl *cr:* Worcester Cntry Schl Eng Tchr 1979-82; Indian River Schl Dis Tchr 1983-; *ai:* HS Task Force, Eng Lang Arts, Literacy Connection, Writing Comms; NCTE 1976-; IREA, DSEA, NEA 1983-; Selbyvill Tchr of Yr 1987; *office:* Indian River HS Clayton Ave Frankford DE

ADKINS, ANZORA, Sixth Grade Teacher; *b:* Bessemer, AL; *c:* Ar Reginald, Arnetta, Deidre Simpson; *ed:* Univ of Cinti (BSW) Soc 1978, (MED) Cnslr Ed 1984; Xavier Univ Elem Ed Cert 1986; Lice Soc Worker 1987; *cr:* Cinti Pub Schls Sub Tchr 1982-86, 6th Grd 1986-; *ai:* Future Edctrs of Amer Co-Adv; Teen Inst Adv; Soc Stud & UNCF Coll Fund Chprsn; AFT Assn 1986-; Golden Leaf Bapt Cl 1964-; Alpha Kappa Alpha Inc 1993-; Univ of Cinti Mentoring Pgm; *h* 3436 Fernside Pl Cincinnati OH 45207

ADKINS, HAROLD DALE, Business Teacher; *b:* East Liverpool, O Margo Owen; *c:* Todd, Tim; *ed:* Kent St Univ (BS) Bus Ed 1969; 15 Semester Hrs; 30 Grad Semester Hrs Univ of Akron; 37 Undergraduat Hrs Baldwin-Wallace Coll; *cr:* Mobil Oil Corp Mrktg Rep 1969-70; HS Bus Tchr 1971-; *ai:* Bus Dept Chprsn; Bus Prof of Amer Advy; Comm; Stow Tchrs Assn 1970-, Pres; NEOEA, NEA, PTA, OH Ed 1970-; *office:* Stow HS 3227 Graham Rd Stow OH 44224

ADKINS, NANCY G., Kindergarten Teacher & Dir; *b:* Licking Cty, *m:* David M.; *c:* Crystal; *ed:* OH Univ (BS) Elem Ed 1995; Early Ch *cr:* Playmate Schl Kndgtn Tchr, Dir 1969-92; Fun Time Schl Kndgtn Dir 1994-; *ai:* Advy Comm Licking Co Joint Voc Schl; OH Univ Sc *office:* Fun Time Schl 149 N High St Hebron OH 43025*

ADKINS, SALLY S., English Teacher; *b:* Defiance, OH; *m:* David V Kathy Kistler, Karen, Tom, Nathan Payne; *ed:* Univ of Toledo (Registered Nrsng 1983, (MED) Scndry Ed 1990; *cr:* Vairous Pub Agencies Pub Hlth Nurse 1973-87; Clay HS AP Eng Tchr 1990-; NCTE, Toledo Area Writing Project 1990-; NW OH Writers Forum Grad Asst Position at Univ of Toledo 1989-90 Coll of Ed; *office:* Cla 5665 Seaman Rd Oregon OH 43616

ADKINS, SANDRA KAY, Vocal Music Director; *b:* Mechanicsburg *m:* James; *c:* Christopher, Jennifer; *ed:* Lebanon Valley Coll (BS) Ed 1972; Towson St Univ (MED) Music Ed 1979; Loyola Coll in (MED) Guidance, Counseling 1991; *cr:* Fullerton Elem Schl Vocal Tchr 1972-75; Howard HS Vocal Music Tchr 1975-86; Glenelg HS Music Tchr 1987-88; Wilde Lake HS Vocal Music Tchr 1989-; *ai:* Co Choir; Madrigal Singers; Barbershop, Beautyshop Quartet; Mu Theater; NEA, MSTA, HCTA, MENC, MMEA 1972-; Delta Kappa Ga 1982-, Pres 1994-; Howard Cty Summer Theater Bd Mem; Howard C Coll Excl in Tchng Awd; Howard Cty Tchr of Yr Nom 1989; *home:* Furrow Ave Ellicott City MD 21042

ADLER, GAIL ROSEN, Third Grade Teacher; *b:* Brooklyn, N Robyn, Lauren; *ed:* Long Island Univ (BS) Bus Mngmt 1969, (MBA Mngmnt 1971, (MS) Guid, Cnslng 1973; 2 Credit Hrs GATE, Cmp Credit Hrs Writing, Art, Speech, Hearing, Psychological Disorde Chldhd, Hlth Ed; 3 Credit Hrs Consumer Ed, Methods Courses Music Stud, Math, Lang Arts, Sci, Diagnosis & Remediation Rdng Disabilit Credit Hrs Books Ldrshp; *cr:* Gen Electric Co Rsrch Asst 1969-70; P Brooklyn Schl 2-4th Grd Tchr 1970-73; Duval Cty Bd of Ed Schl Cnslr 1974-77; Francis Lewis Elem Schl PS 79 1-4th Grd Tchr 1977- UFT, AFT 1970-; Article Pub 1990; *home:* 1865 211th St Apt 4A Ba NY 11360*

ADLER, LINDA BLUM, 7th Grade Lang Arts Teacher; *b:* Brooklyn *m:* Martin N.; *c:* Eric, Jeff, Leslie, Maxwell; *ed:* Brooklyn Coll (BA) Eng 1962; Adelphi Univ (MS) Rdng & Spcl Ed 1980; *cr:* PS 2 at Bro 2nd Grd Tchr 1962-64; IS 53 at Queens Lang Arts & Soc Stud Tchr *ai:* Mentoring New Tchrs; Planner & Presenter of Wkshps Rdng Co Cooperative Learning, Interdisciplinary Curr; AFT 1962-; NY St T Eng Award 1985 & 1995; *office:* IS 53 Brian Piccolo I S 53 Far Rock NY 11691*

ADLER, LORI ROBIN (PRAGUE), Business Educator; *b:* Hartford *m:* Lawrence; *c:* Steven, Jeffrey, Marc; *ed:* Bryant Coll (BS) Ed 1983; CT St Univ (MS) Orgnl Mngmt 1990; *cr:* Windsor HS Bus Edctr 13 *ai:* FBLA Adv; NEA, CEA, CT Bus Ed Assn 1983-; *office:* Windsor H Sage Park Rd Windsor CT 06095*

ADLER, MORTON, Criminal Justice Teacher; *b:* New York, N Sandra Korenthal; *c:* Frederic, Scott, Andrea Smigielski; *ed:* John Ja Crim Justice (BS) Police Sci 1985; SUNY at New Paltz (MS) Gen Ed; 54 Post Grad Credit Hrs; *cr:* NYC Police Dept Detective, Instr 196 Monroe-Woodbury Schl Retired 1987-89, Permanent Sub 198 Newburgh Schl Dist Tchr 1990-; *ai:* Swimming, Track, Soccer, Sports Officiater; NTA 1990-; DEA 1973-, Del; *office:* Newburgh Acad 201 Fullerton Ave Newburgh NY 12550

ADMAN, MARLYNE, Art & Architecture Teacher; *b:* Boston, M Heather Lee Marun; *ed:* Queens Coll (BA) Fine Art, Art His 1974; CW Univ (MS) Spec Ed 1995; *cr:* Van Wyck JHS 217Q Art, Architecture 1988-; *ai:* UFT 1988-; Pub Original Architecture Curr; Prof Hand W & Jewelry Designer; *office:* Van Wyck Jr HS 85-05 144th St Briarwo 11435

ADOLPH, HOLLY GAUMNITZ, Mathematics Teacher; *b:* Balti MD; *m:* Thomas Miller; *c:* Tommy Jr., Elizabeth; *ed:* Lynchburg Coll Hlth, PE 1974; Towson Univ (MS) Scndry Ed 1982; Coll of Notre Math Cert 1986; Sexuality, Drug Ed, Nutrition, Learning Math Th Hands On Experiences Grad Courses; *cr:* Notre Dame Prep Schl PE, Tchr, Dept Chprsn, Ath Dir, Coach 1975-88, Math Tchr 1989, Maryvale Prep Schl Math, Algebra I, II Tchr 1994-; *ai:* Badminton, B Lacrosse, Soccer, Chrldng Coach; Ath Assn, Gym Meet, Schl Play Sc Moderator; NCEA 1975-; NCTM 1994-; Merrion Ct II Homeo 1987-89, Bd Mem, Pres 1989; Cath Schls Girls Ath Assn Pres 198 *home:* 11700 Mayfair Field Dr Timonium MD 21093*

ADOLPHSON, THOMAS JOSEPH, History & Humanities Teach Mankato, MN; *m:* Ute Hedy Nicklas; *ed:* Gustavus Adolphus Coll (BA 1980; Univ of MN (MA) His 1983; *cr:* Univ of MN Tchng Asst 198 Lake Forest Acad His Tchr 1984-86; The Gunnery Schl His, Hum 1986-; *ai:* Arts Option Adv; Metropolitan Opera Ed Prgm 1993-; W Society of NY 1989-; *office:* Gunnery Schl 99 Green Hill Rd Washi Depot CT 06793*

ADONIZIO, SARA G., First & Second Grade Teacher; *b:* Danville *m:* Robert J.; *ed:* Bloomsburg Univ (BS) Elem Ed 1971; Marywood (MS) Rdng; 45 Credits Beyond Masters; *cr:* Roslund Elem 1st & 2n Tchr 1971-; *ai:* NEA 1971; PSEA 1971; TAEA 1971-, Sec; NCTM; Sec, Young Careerest; *home:* 1651 Falls Rd Clarks Summit PA 1841

ADREON, NANCY C., Math Teacher; *b:* Pittsburgh, PA; *m:* Charle Duquesne Univ (BS) Math 1990, (MSEd) Scndry Ed 1991; *cr:* Osway

/ath Tchr 1991-93; Bethlehem Ctr MS Math Tchr 1993-; *ai:* Schl /val Team; NEA, PSEA, NCTM, PCTM 1991-; Gift of Time Awd.

/AN, GEORGE M., 4th Grade Teacher; *b:* Buffalo, NY; *m:* Frances do; *c:* Michelle, Christa Murrison; *ed:* SUNY at Buffalo (BA) His (EDM) Ed 1973; *cr:* Alexander Cntrl Schl Instr 1968-; *ai:* Grd, Elem /hprsn; NEA, NYSUT 1968-; Alexander United Tchrs 1968-, Pres, *office:* Alexander Central Schl 3314 Buffalo St Alexander NY 14005

/AN, SCOTT STEVEN, Spanish Teacher; *b:* Bristol, PA; *ed:* /field Univ (BA) Span 1986; Post Grad Courses at Widener Univ & /sville Univ; *cr:* Millersburg Area HS Span Tchr 1990-; *ai:* Frgn Lang Adv; JV Soccer Coach; PSEA 1990-; NEA 1990-; *office:* Millersburg HS 799 Center St Millersburg PA 17061

/ON, SUZANNE NAPIER, Assistant Professor of History; *b:* /ester, NY; *m:* Charlie; *c:* Amy; *ed:* Ramapo Coll of NJ (BA) /umma Cum Laude 1983; Rutgers (MA) His-Magna Cum Laude 1990; /amapo Coll of NJ Asst Prof of His 1991-; *ai:* AFT 1992-; Hillsdale /ns Club 1986-, Pres 1993-94; Hillsdale Democratic Club 1983-, /cratic Comm Person; Hillsdale Sftbl 1985-, Pres; Phi Alpha Theta

/BATO, GERARD MICHAEL, 6th Grade Teacher; *b:* Newark, NJ; /eton Hall Univ (BS) Ed & Spcl Ed 1977; Seton Hall Law Schl (JD) /990; Cert K-8 NJ Elem Ed; NJ Cert of Spcl Ed; *cr:* Ringwood MS /rd Tchr 1977-79; Spring Garden Schl 6th Grd Tchr 1979-; *ai:* Chess Extended Day Care, Stock Market Game & Safety Patrol Coord; /1977-; Nutley Referral & Information Group 1995-, Founding Mem; /Disneys Golden Apple Awd.

/, IMOGENE MC DONOUGH, Business Teacher; *b:* Washington, /: Charles; *c:* Ruth Mc Kinzie, Joy West, Mark, Mary Daughety; *ed:* /esburg Coll (BS) Bus Admin 1955; W VA Univ (MA) Comm 1980; /esburg Coll Ed Cert; Post Grad Stud OH Univ; *cr:* Bentleyville HS /955-56; Mc Kees Rocks HS Bus Ed Tchr 1957-60; Warren HS Bus /hr 1968-72; OH Valle Coll Prof of Bus, Secretarial Sci 1972-86; /ngton Co Career Ctr Computerized Bus Tech Tchr 1987-; *ai:* Bus /of Amer Adv; NEA, OEA 1968-; NBEA 1980-; Stepping Stones of /ly Coll 1961-, Pres 1975-77; OH Univ Jennings Scholar 1989; OH Conservation League Various Chptrs Speaker 1980-; OH Vly Coll /e Outstdng Svc Awd 1981; *office:* Washinton Cty Career Ctr Rt 2 /own Rd Marietta OH 45750

/S, K. JAMES, Asst Prin, Ath Dir & Sci Tchr; *b:* Central Lake, MI; /sie (Mc Connell); *c:* Heidi Tripp, Stephen; *ed:* Bob Jones Univ (BS) /73; Auto Cad Univ of Cincinnati; *cr:* Easley Chrstn Schl Tchr, Coach, /73-76; Milford Chrstn Acad Asst Prin, Ad, Tchr 1976-; *ai:* Var Boys / Coach; First Baptist Church 1976-, Sunday Schl Supt; Tchry of Yr *office:* Milford Christian Acad 1365 Woodville Pike Milford OH

/, ROXANNE REINIGER, Kindergarten Teacher; *b:* Rochester, NY; /enn Robert; *c:* Carl, Sean, Jonathan, Andrew; *ed:* SUNY at Brockport /Sociology 1971; SUNY at Albany (MS) Rdng 1973; 9 Credit Hrs at /nan Univ & Russell Sage; *cr:* Scotia Glenville 1st & 4th Grd Tchr 6 /aratoga Springs Sub Tchr 9 Yrs; Broadalbin Perth 3rd Grd Tchr 4 /ndgtn Tchr 4 Yrs; *ai:* Math Curr Coord; Former Odyssey of the Mind & Yrbk Adv & Mentor; 2nd Grd Rel Ed Tchr; AFT 1988-; Cath /nters 1992-; Broadalbin Perth Classroom Grant; *office:* /albin-Perth Elem Schl School St Broadalbin NY 12025

/ECK, SILVIA, Latin Teacher; *b:* Derbyshire, England; *m:* Robert; /n, Elisabeth; *ed:* Univ of Sheffield (BA) Fr & Latin 1966; Univ of /Dip Ed) Frgn Lang 1967; 15 Credit Hrs Span Univ of Pittsburgh; 15 Hrs Ed Univ of Pittsburgh; *cr:* Abbeydale Scndry Schl Fr Tchr /71; Lesmahagow HS Fr Tchr 1978-81; North Allegheny HS Fr & /Tchr 1985-88; North Hills HS Latin Tchr 1989-; *ai:* Latin Club Spon; /of Local Chptr of PAJCL; NEA 1989-; PSEA 1989-; Intnl Camp of 1988-, Dean of Fr Camp; St Brendans Episcopal Church 1989-, Mem & Coord of Meals for Miryams; PA Classical Assn 1992-; North Hills Sr HS 53 Rochester Rd Pittsburgh PA 15229

/E, CAROL WHITNEY, French Teacher; *b:* Rockville Centre, NY; /ith D.; *c:* Sean Keith, Donald Whitney; *ed:* St univ of NY at Cortland Early Scndry Fr 1972, (MS) Fr 1975; Cours de /tionnement-Universite de Neuchatel 1973; *cr:* Cincinnatus Cntrl 7th Grd & Fr Tchr 1973-81; Cortland HS Fr Tchr 1981-87; /ateles HS Fr Tchr 1987-88; Homer HS Fr Tchr 1988-; *ai:* Intnl & / Tchr Club Adv; Fr Exch Coord; AFT; AATF; NY Foreign Lang Assn; Cntrl NY Foreign Lang Assn; Nason Schlsp Comm; *office:* / HS West Rd Box 500 Homer NY 13077*

/, GERALD L., Human Svcs Instr; *b:* Brush Creek, TN; *m:* Buenae /e; *c:* Mark, Michelle Beyer, Pamela, Aimee; *ed:* Phillips Univ at /BA) Bible & Soc Work 1959; *cr:* St of CO Juvenile Probation, Parole /ency Supv 1960-70, Dir Yth Svcs 1971-75, Dir Adult Corrections /78; St of OH Buckeye Yth Ctr Supt 1988-89, Dept of Yth Svcs /are Dir 1989-90; Hocking Coll Human Svc & Corrections Inst; *ai:* /tern Supvr; Juvenile Parole Agent of the Yr 1965; CO Yth Worker of 1967; Outstndg Svc to Yth of Cty Awd 1968; Blue Ribbon Ed Comm /89; Policy Advy 1988-89; Article Pub 1990; *office:* Hocking Coll Hocking Pkwy Nelsonville OH 45764

/SE, GLORIA, High School Math Teacher; *b:* New York, NY; *ed:* /lyn Coll (MS) Ed 1977; *cr:* Holy Child Jesus Schl 3rd & 4th Grd Tchr /54; St Ann's Schl 2nd-7th Grd Tchr 1964-70; St Agnes Schl 6th-8th /chr 1970-88; Our Lady of Perpetual Hslp HS 9th-12 Grd Math Tchr /; *ai:* Chrldrs, Parent's Assn Moderator; Prgm for Dev Human /ial Facilitator; NCEA; Math, Sci Grants Potsdam Univ & Brooklyn Lions-Quest Skills for Adolescence Wkshp 1991-94; Trng in /fication & Reporting of Child Abuse & Maltreatment Luth Med Ctr *home:* 636 59th St Brooklyn NY 11220

/EW, MAUREEN BRENNAN, English Teacher; *b:* Providence, RI; /nes E.; *c:* Dawn Dunn, Wendy Maynard, Scott Maynard; *ed:* RI Coll /) Eng 1965, (MA) Eng 1973; 30 Addl Hrs Soc Stud; *cr:* Warwick Long-term, Daily Sub Tchr 1965-85; St Raphael Acad Eng Chair, /985-88; Gorton Jr HS Eng Tchr 1988-89; Pilgrim HS Eng, Hum Tchr /; *ai:* Acad Decathlon Team Coach; Mem Eng Steering Comm; AFT / Auditor; RI Cncl Tchrs of Eng 1989-; St Peter's Schl Bd 1995-; / Pilgrim HS 111 Pilgrim Pky Warwick RI 02888*

/OLI, JEFFREY MICHAEL, English Teacher; *b:* Paterson, NJ; *m:* /ne; *c:* Jona, Alicia, Micah; *ed:* Wm Paterson St Coll (BA) Eng 1971; /clair St Coll (MA) Rdng 1973; 15 Credit Hrs; *cr:* Eastside HS Eng 1973-79; Kingston HS Rdng Tchr 1979-85; Geo Washington Elem Tchr 1985-87; Zena Elem 4th Grd Tchr 1987-88; MV Regnl HS Eng /1988-; *ai:* Stu Mediation Project & Seabreezes Lit Magazine Adv; /973-79, Local VP 3 Yrs; NEA 1980-; Marthas Vineyard Literacy Pgm , Tutor & Coord; Marthas Vineyard Mediation Project 1989-, /ator; *office:* Marthas Vineyard Reg HS Edgartown Rd Oak Bluffs MA

/OSTAK, LAURA MUNSIE, First Grade Teacher; *b:* Elizabeth, NJ; /nn Kenneth; *ed:* Trenton St Coll (BA) Kndgtn-Primary 1963; Attnd /rs Univ, Kean Coll, Northeastern Univ, Fairleigh Dickinson Univ, /hi Univ; *cr:* Clinton Schl 1st Grd Tchr 1963-66; Schl #5 1st & 2nd /Tchr 1966-70; Evergreen Schl 1st Grd Tchr 1970-; *ai:* First Grd Assessment & Planning Comm; Mentor for First-Yr Tchr; NEA 1970-; NJEA 1970-; Scotch Plains Ed Assn 1970-, Schl Rep; Suburban Rdng Cncl 1980-; St Peters Church: Lector 1986-; Respect Life Comm 1990-, Treas; Childrens Liturgist 1995-; NJ St Systemic Initiative Math, Sci & Tech Grant; Scotch Plains Mini-Grant; *office:* Evergreen Elem Schl 2280 Evergreen Ave Scotch Plains NJ 07076

AGOGLIA, PAUL, Technology Education Teacher; *b:* Bronx, NY; *ed:* St Univ of NY at Oswego (BS) Indstrl Arts, Tech 1974, (MS) Indstrl Arts, Tech 1982; Tech Tchng Trng Network-CAD TRng 1992-94; *cr:* Unatego Cntrl Jr Sr HS Tech Ed Tchr 1974-94; Cobleskill-Richmondville MS Tech Ed Tchr 1994-; *ai:* Shared Decision Making, Mid Level Ed, MS Curr Dev Teams CRCS; Project Coord Implementation of Modular Delivery System for MS Tech CRCS 1995-; ITEA 1990-; NYSTEA 1984-; NYSUT 1974-; Amer Radio Relay League 1987-; Northeast Sustainable Energy Assn 1991-; Southern Poverty Law Ctr 1992-; Schoharie Cty Gender Equity Task Force 1994-; Unatego Employee of Yr 1991; Sigma XI Cert of Achvmt 1992; Pub Articles 1991; Tech Edctr 1992-93; ARRL Ed Proceedings 1993; HS Stu Constructed Solar Car Entered in Amer Tour De Sol 1992-94; Radio Link W-Space Shuttle 1993; Implemented Legislative Grant for Model Tech Ed Classroom UHS 1990-92.

AGONITO, JOSEPH, History Professor; *b:* Port Chester, NY; *m:* Rosemary Giambattista; *c:* Giancarlo, Mae Lee; *ed:* Westchester Comm Coll (AAS) Bus 1956; Pace Coll (BA) His 1959; Niagara Univ (MA) His 1961; Syracuse Univ (PHD) Amer His 1972; Addl Post Grad Work African-Amer His; *cr:* Syracuse Univ Asst Instr 1963-64; Onondaga Comm Coll His Prof 1964-; NYS Schl Indstrl, Labor Rel Adj Instr Labor His 1983-; *ai:* Native Amer Stud Comm; AFT 1968-, Pres, Local 1845 1968-69; NEH Rsrch, Travel Grant; Book: The Making of The American Catholic Church; 11 Scholarly Articles; Documentary Video, Silver Apple Awds; Nat Edu Film & Video Festival; Chris Plaque, Columbus Internat Film Festival; Finalist Amer Film, Video Festival Woman Priest; *office:* Onondaga Comm Coll Onondaga Hill Road Syracuse NY 13215

AGOSTINACCHIO, NICHOLAS, Guidance Counselor; *b:* New York, NY; *m:* Linda; *c:* Danielle, Stephen; *ed:* Queens Coll CUNY (BA) Foreign Lang 1971; Hunter Coll CUNY (MA) Tchng Eng as Foreign Lang 1974; LIU, CW Post (MS) Counseling Schl 1982; *cr:* Freeport HS Foreign Lang Tchr 1971-84; New School for Soc Research Foreign Lang Tchr 1974-84; Freeport HS Guidance Cnslr 1981-; *ai:* Past Pres Nassau Cnslrs Assn; Test Supvr for ETS Freeport Ctr; AFT 1971-; NCA 1985-, Pres; NY Cnslrs Assn 1992-; *office:* Freeport HS 50 S Brookside Ave Freeport NY 11520

AGOSTINI, HECTOR P., Prof of Bus Admin; *b:* New York, NY; *ed:* Hunter Coll (BA) His 1970; Baruch Coll (MBA) Bus Admin 1977; Working Towards JD in Law MA Schl of Law; 24 Addl Credits Post Grad Work Acctng; 12 Credits in Ed; *cr:* Commonwealth of PR Economist 1971-74; Girard Trust Bank Intnl Credit Analyst 1974-76; Yes Prgm Fin Ofcr 11976-77; Chamberlayne Jr Coll Chm, Prof 1977-81; Middlesex Comm Coll Prof 1981-; *ai:* Acctng Tutoring Lab Adv; Lowell Campus Various Comms; Former Treas of Union Local 8 Yrs; NEA, MTA, MCCC 1981-Treas; Hunter Coll Alumni 1970-; Baruch Coll Alumni 1977-; Cardinal Hayes HS Alumni 1966-; Ctr for Span Spkg 1977-84, VP; South End Fed Credit Union 1981-84, Pres, Vp; IBA of Boston 1982-83; Bus Tchr of Yr 1987-89; *office:* Middlesex Comm Coll 33 Kearney Sq Lowell MA 01852*

AGOSTINI, JOHN CHARLES, Special Education Teacher; *b:* Kingston, PA; *m:* Carole Pettingill; *c:* Christopher, Michael, Nicholas; *ed:* Luzerne Cty Comm Coll (ASE) Ed 1977; Mansfield Univ (BSE) Spec Ed 1979; Penn St Univ (MED) Hlth Ed 1985; *cr:* Elkland HS Spec Ed Tchr 1979-81; Williamsport HS Spec Ed Tchr 1981-82; Lock Haven HS Spec Ed Tchr 1985-89; Bald Eagle Nittany HS Spec Ed Tchr 1989-; *ai:* NEA, PSEA 1977-; West Branch Drug & Alcohol Commission 1995-, Bd Mem; Nittany Hockey League 1986-, Bd of Governors; *office:* Bald Eagle Nittany HS Ben Ave Mill Hall PA 17751

AGOSTINI, JOYCE, History & Humanities Teacher; *b:* Vineland, NJ; *ed:* Temple Univ (BS) His & Eng 1962; Fairleigh Dickinson (MA) Human Dev 1986; Addl 30 Credits in His 1965-67; Attnd St Univ of NY at Albany Adult Ed Courses 1968; *cr:* Memorial Jr HS His Tchr 1962-69; Adult Ed Eng Tchr 1964-75; Vineland Sr HS His Tchr 1970-; *ai:* NEA, NJEA, VEA 1962-; Grad Comm & Ski Club in Past Yrs; *office:* Vineland Sr HS South 2880 E Chestnut Ave Vineland NJ 08360

AGRESTI, ARLENE CAPPELLE, 7th-8th Grade Math Teacher; *b:* Passaic, NJ; *m:* Joseph J.; *c:* Maria; *ed:* Montclair Univ (BA) Math 1971; *cr:* Christopher Columbus Jr HS 8th-9th Grd Math Tchr 1971-81; Elmwood Park HS 10th-11th Grd Math Tchr 1984-86; Clifton HS 9th-11th Grd Math Tchr 1986-90; Woodrow Wilson Schl 7th-8th Grd Math Tchr 1990-; *ai:* Math League Adv; NEA, NJEA, NCTM 1971-; *office:* Woodrow Wilson MS 1400 Van Houten Ave Clifton NJ 07013*

AGSTER, KATHLEEN MARY (MC CARTHY), Theology Teacher; *b:* Norristown, PA; *m:* Ronald Edward; *ed:* Gwynedd Mercy Coll (BS) 1980; St Charles Seminary (MA) Theology; *cr:* St Patricks 2nd Grd Tchr 1965-70; St Matthews 4th Grd Tchr 1970-72; St Christopher 4th Grd Tchr 1973-78; Immaculate Conception 4th Grd Tchr 1978-82; Little Flower HS 12th Grd Tchr 1982-83; Bishop Mc Devitt HS 10th & 12th Grd Tchr 1983-; *ai:* Moderator of the School Yearbook "The Realm" & the Soph Hop; NCEA 1982-; NHS Brd 1990-91; *home:* 608 Overbrook Ln Oreland PA 19075*

AGUAYO-GIELATA, EMELINA, Spanish Teacher; *b:* Concepcion, Chile; *m:* Richard P.; *c:* Joesph, Natalie; *ed:* Univ of Concepcion (BS) & (MA) Eng 1973; Univ of Pittsburgh (MA) Span Linguistics 1992; Geneva Coll 12 Post Grad Credits for PA Eng Cert 1986; *cr:* Pub & Private Chile Schls Eng Tchr 1972-77; Comm Coll Beaver Cty Span Tchr 5 Yrs; Geneva Coll Span Instr 3 Yrs; South Fayette Jr Sr HS Span Tchr 1993-; *ai:* NEA 1993-; PSEA 1993-; Union Cultural Latinoa Mericana; Chilean-Amer Fdntn; *office:* South Fayette Twp Jr Sr HS 2254 Old Oakdale Rd Mc Donald PA 15057

AGUILAR, MARY PEDROZA, English Teacher; *b:* Hondo, TX; *m:* Ismael; *c:* Michael, Laura, James; *ed:* Our Lady of the Lake Univ (BA) Bus Ed, Eng 1971; Grad Credit Hrs Boston Univ, Univ of MD; *cr:* Edison HS Eng Tchr 1971-72; Kubasaki Nine Schl Bus, Eng Tchr 1972-74; AFCENT Intnl Sch Eng Tchr 1986-; *ai:* Stu Cncl, NHS Spon; OEA Tchrs Assn 1986-; NASSP 1990-; Phi Delta Kappa 1990-94; PTSA, Booster Club 1986-; Tchr of Yr 1994; Sustain Superior Performance Awds 1991-94; Spec Act, On the Spot Cash Awds 1991; *office:* AFCENT International HS Unit 21606 APO AE 09703

AGUILAR, SHARON MARIE (RUDD), Seventh Grade Teacher; *b:* Hackensack, NJ; *m:* Samuel; *c:* Dawn Marie Black, Amy Marie, Samuel John; *ed:* William Paterson Univ (BA) Elem Ed 1970; Jersey City St Coll 15 Grad Credits Cmptr Literacy; *cr:* Little Ferry Wilson Schl 5th Grd Tchr 1970-72; Little Ferry Meml Schl Rd, LA Tchr, SS Tchr 1987-92; Little Ferry Meml MS 7th Grd Tchr 1992-; *ai:* Centennial Town Comm Schl Rep 1994; Comms: Discipline Code, Parent Involvement, Curr 1987-89, Pupil Assistance 1995-; Little Ferry Ed Assn 1970-72, Sec 1987-; NJEA, NEA 1970, 1987-; NJ Governor's Tchr Recognition Awd 1994; *office:* Memorial MS 130 Liberty St Little Ferry NJ 07643

AGUIRRE, MARIA SOPHIA, Economics Professor; *b:* San Antonio, TX; *ed:* Cath univ at Argentina (MBA\CPA) Banking Fin 1985; Univ of Notre Dame (MA) Dev 1988, (PHD) Pub Fin 1991; CPA US 1986; Univ of Chicago Ec Dept 1991-93; *cr:* Univ of Chicago Visiting Scholar 1991-93; Cath Univ of Amer Asst Prof 1993-; *ai:* Bd Pres Prgm for Acad & Ldrshp Skills; Hnrs Prgm; AEA 1989-,Status of Women Commission; Intnl Ec Assn 1991-; Pi Gamma Mu 1994-; Undergrad Bd 1993-, CUA; CUA 1993-, Hnrs Prgm; Natl Inst of Womenhood 1994-, Ec Dir; Intnl Population & Family Assn 1994-, Bd Mem; Dorothy Danforth Compton Flwshp 1989-91; Zaham Travel Rsrch Grant 1990; CUA Rsrch Grant 1994; *office:* The Catholic Univ Of America Dept of Economics 620 Michigan Ave NE Washington DC 20064

AGUSTINI, MARY ANNE C. SHABELSKI, Kindergarten Teacher; *b:* Kingston, PA; *m:* Ronald E.; *ed:* Coll Misercordia (BA) Elem Ed, Eng 1967; Attnd Penn St, IU 18, IU 19 In-Svc, Wilkes Coll Grad Courses; *cr:* Cecil Cty Schl Dist Third Grd Tchr 1967-68; Lake Lehman Schl Dist Elem Tchr 1968-; *ai:* NEA 1967-; PSEA, LLEA 1968-.

AGUZZI, ROBERT THOMAS, Physical Ed Teacher & Coach; *b:* New Haven, CT; *m:* Teri Kennedy; *c:* Robert K., Carrie L.; *ed:* Mc Kendree Coll (BA) PE 1968; Southern CT St Univ (MS) PE 1974; *cr:* East St Louis Jr HS Sci Tchr 1968-69; Jared Eliot MS PE Tchr 1969-; *ai:* Var Bsbl Coach 1990-; CT Dist III Sr All Star Bsbl Coach 1995-; Morgan Booster Club All St Rsrch Comm 1996; CAHPERD 1980-, Outstdng Prgm Awd 1987; CEA, NEA 1970-; CHSCA 1980-; NHSBCA 1990-; Morgan Boosters 1980-; Clinton Pub Info Comm 1993-; Clint Pub Schls 25 Yrs Svc Awd 1994; Clinton Dist Coord of PE 1978-83; Project Adventure Presenter at Inservice Wkshps 1986-88; Pres Phys Fitness St Champion Awd 1980; *office:* Jared Eliot MS Fairy Dell Rd Clinton CT 06413

AHALT, SUSAN JAMES, Foreign Language Dept Chair; *b:* Leominster, MA; *m:* Christopher R.; *c:* Samantha, John; *ed:* Dickinson Coll (BA) Fr 1974; Middlebury Coll Grad Stud; Attending Western Coll Towards MS; *cr:* Holicong Jr HS Fr Tchr 1974-77; Inst of Modern Lang Inc Customer Relations Rep 1877-78; Gaithersburg MS Fr Tchr 1990-; *ai:* Taylor Learning Ctr PTA Sec 1989-90; Montgomery Cty Ed Assn, NEA 1990-; Mid Village Homes Corp 1990-, Bd of Dir; *office:* Gaithersburg MS 2 Teachers Way Gaithersburg MD 20877

AHEARN, REBECCA BIRT, Spanish Teacher; *b:* Muncie, IN; *m:* Vincent P. III; *c:* Vincent P. IV, Alec Clayton, Natalie Brooke; *ed:* Ball St Univ (BA) Span 1981; Univ of Houston (MA) Admin & Supervision 1985; Summer Stud Univ of AZ at Guadalajara 1980; *cr:* Thomas Edison Jr HS Tchr 1981-85; Doerre Intermediate Schl Tchr 1985-86; Highland HS Tchr 1986-87; Good Counsel HS Tchr 1988-89; Magruder HS Tchr 1989-; *ai:* Fac Wellness Dir; Yth for Christ; Renaissance Schl Coord; Exxon Awd; Edison Jr HS Outstdng Young Edctr Nom 1982; IN Pam Amer Games Interpreter 1987; *office:* Colonel Zadok Magruder H S 5939 Muncaster Mill Rd Rockville MD 20855*

AHERN, BARBARA FORAND, Coordinator of Health Programs; *b:* Worcester, MA; *m:* Ronald Joseph; *c:* Stephen Patrick, Deborah Ahern Evans; *ed:* Saint Vincent Hospital Schl of Nursing (RN) Nursing 1961; Emmanuel Coll (BS) Rehabilitation Counseling 1977; Boston St-Univ of MA at Boston (MED) Counseling 1982; Anna Maria Coll (MSN) Nursing Admin 1987; Inst of Aitical & Creative Thinking in the Scis Cert; Univ of MA at Amherst Donohue Inst of Govt Stud Leadership Inst Cert; *cr:* Tufts NE Medical Ctr Surgical & Operating Room Nurse 1962-64; Harvard Medical Open-Heart Research Nurse 1964-66; Boston Hospitals Spec Care Nurse 1967-77; Billerica HS Crisis Cnslr 1977-78; Shawsheen Tech HS Instr 1978-87, Lead Tchr & Cluster Ldr 1983-93; Shawsheen Tech HS & Schl of Practical Nursing Coord & Dir 1993-; *ai:* 9th-12th Grd Adv; Drama Adv 4 Yrs; Cheerleading Coach 2 Yrs; Voc Industrial Clubs of Amer Local, St & Natl Coach; Shawsheen Tchrs Assn 1980-, Sec, Exec Bd Mem; MA Tchrs Assn, NEA, MA-RI Nurses Assn; Burlington Childrens Theatre, Originator, Dir; Exemplary Tchr of Yr Awd 1985; Wrote Competency Based Curr in Medical Asst Area for St of MA; Psi Chi Natl Honor Soc for Psych; *office:* Shawsheen Tech HS 100 Cook St Billerica MA 01821

AHERN, DANIEL P., 6th Grade Teacher; *b:* Plattsburgh, NY; *m:* Marilyn M.; *ed:* Castleton St Coll (BS) Ed 1968; Grad Credit Hrs SUNY at Oneonta, SUNY at Plattsburgh, Univ of AZ, Univ Northern Co; *cr:* Corinth Cntrl Schl Elem Tchr 1968-; *ai:* AFT; NYSUT 1973-; Corinth Tchrs Assn 1973-, Exec Comm.

AHERN, RONALD JOSEPH, Social Studies Teacher; *b:* Boston, MA; *m:* Barbara Forand; *c:* Stephen Patrick, Deborah Ahern Evans; *ed:* Northeastern Univ (BS) Ed & His 1960; Boston St & Univ of MA at Boston (MED) 1965; Attnd Salem St Coll Amer His & Ec Stud; *cr:* Onteona Cntrl Schl System His Tchr 1960-62; Saugus Jr HS His Tchr 1963-65; Saugus HS Advanced Placement His Tchr 1965-95; Middlesex Comm Coll Evening European His Tchr 1977-78; Saugus HS Advanced Placement His & Psych Tchr 1995-; *ai:* Boys & Girls Tennis Head Coach; Track Asst & Head Coach; Ftbl Asst Coach; MS Cross Cntry Team Coach; Natl Assn of Soc Stud Tchrs; Saugus Tchrs Assn 1962-, Past Pres 1975-77, Negotiation Comm, Former Chprsn, Selection Comm for NHS; MA Tchrs Assn, Williams Coll Del; NEA; World Affairs Cncl 1972-74; St Stu Govt Day, Adv 1985-92; Framingham St Coll His Conf, Adv 1986-; Salem St Coll His Conf, Adv 1993-; Ed of Stud Guide on Imperialism; Fellowships-Univ of NY at New Paltz Asian Stud, RI Coll Ec Developing Nation, Tufts Coll World Affairs Inst, Boston Univ European Stud; Designed US His Advanced Placement Prgm & Curr; *office:* Saugus HS Pierce Dr Saugus MA 01906

AHERN, SKAIDRITE VARKALIS, English Teacher; *b:* Rezekne, Latvia; *m:* Richard; *c:* Marina Picciotto, Adrianna; *ed:* IN Univ (BA) Eng-Magna Cum Laude 1961, (MA) Eng 1972; *cr:* BMCC Adj Lecturer 1971-; Coll of New Rochell Adj Lecturer 1975-; *ai:* Tutor Stdnts; PSC Union 1986-; Phi Beta Kappa; Marble Collegiate Church, Vol Feed Elderly, Homeless; Woodrow Wilson Scholar; *office:* Borough Of Manhattan Comm Coll 199 Chambers St New York NY 10007

AHLBORN, PATRICIA L. (HORN), Math Teacher & Department Head; *b:* Norristown, PA; *m:* Thomas J.; *c:* Karen Ahlborn Crocker, Janet, James; *ed:* West Chester Univ (BSEd) Scndry Ed, Math 1969; Univ of DE (MS) Math 1972; *cr:* West Chester Univ Instr 1971; Univ of DE Instr 1988-91, 1993; Wilmington Chrstn Schl Tchr, Dept Head 1977-; *ai:* NHS; Math Team; Cmptr Coord; Acad Advy Comm; SAT Prep Course; Dept Heads Comm; NCTM 1978-; DE Cncl Tchrs of Math 1978-, 1978-, Pvt Schl Rep; Cncl of Presidential Awardees in Math 1991-; Evangelical Presbyn Church 1987-; Presidential Awd Excl in Math Tchng 1991; Webber Awd Univ of DE 1993; Tandy Tech Schlsp 1993; DuPont Mini Grant 1993; Hercules Mini Grant 1993; *office:* Wilmington Christian Schl 825 Loveville Rd Hockessin DE 19707

AHLBRAND, NIKKI ROSKY, Jr HS Math & Science Teacher; *b:* Greensburg, PA; *m:* Stephen D.; *c:* Stephanie, John; *ed:* St Mary of the Woods Coll (BA) Elem Ed 1968; Attnd Drake Univ, Western MD Coll, Shenandoah Univ; *cr:* Howard Cty Pub Schls Tchr 1968-69; Our Lady of Perpetual Help Schl Tchr 1984-; *ai:* Jr HS Yrbk, Class Ofcr Adv; Sci Coord; ESTA, NCEA 1984-; NCTM 1991-; *office:* Our Lady Perpetual Help Schl 4801 Ilchester Rd Ellicott City MD 21043

AHLHOLM, BETH ANN, Literature & Writing Teacher; *b:* Doylestown, PA; *m:* Vincent; *c:* Ashley, Audrey, Alden; *ed:* Univ of ME at Farmington (BS) Elem Ed 1982; Univ of Southern ME (MS) Rdng Ed 1987; *cr:* Whitefield Schl 6th-8th Grd Lit, Writing Tchr 1982-; *ai:* Yrbk Adv 1986-; Stu Cncl Adv 1995-; Fun Fair Comm Chair 1993-; Eng Dept Chair 1987-; ME Tchrs Assn 1990-; ME Rdng Assn 1992-, Sec 1994-; IRA 1988-; NCTE 1993-; New England League of MS 1994-; *office:* Whitefield Schl RR 1 Box 2 Whitefield ME 04353

AHLM, CARL EDWARD, Senior English Teacher; *b:* Hamilton, OH; *m:* Damona E. Oler; *c:* Holly Mc Henry, Stacey M.; *ed:* Wittenberg Univ (BA) Eng 1969; Wright St Univ (MED) Bus Ed 1984; Addl Research & Statistics; *cr:* Century Housewaves Mgr 1973-82; Clark St Comm Coll Adjunct Bus Instr 1982-85; Wright St Univ Adjunct Fac of Ed 1983-87; Kenton Ridge HS Eng Tchr 1985-; *ai:* Hyperbole Team Coach; NEA 1985-; Grad Stu of Yr Wright St Univ 1984-85; Martha Holden Jennings Fnd Scholar 1989-90; Distinguished Tchr Awd 1993-95; *office:* Kenton Ridge HS 4444 Middle-Urbana Rd Springfield OH 45503

AHLSTROM, EDWIN ARTHUR, Professor of Art; *ed:* Schl of the Art Inst of Chicago (BFA) Drawing, Painting & Printmaking 1966, (MFA) Drawing, Painting & Printmaking 1968; *cr:* Montgomery Coll Art Prof 1971-; *ai:* Art Dept Chair 1992-95; AAUP 1978-; Fulbright Hayes Grant 1976; Numerous Painting Awds; *office:* Montgomery Coll Takoma Park 51 Mannakee St Rockville MD 20850

AHLUWALIA, USHA, French Teacher; *b:* Nagpur, India; *ed:* LaSorbonne Univ(BA) French Stud 1978, (MA) French Stud 1980, (PHD) Frencn Stud 1990; Addl Grad Level Stud Curr Dev, Educl Methodology, Tcng of French to Non Native Speakers; *cr:* Lycee Lambert Fr Prof 1978-79; Cours Pascal Fr, Eng Prof 1980-81; Inst of Tech Stud Fr Instr 1981-83; Colle Gio Santa Maria Fr Instr 1983-85; Zama Amer Schl Fr Tchr 1985-86; MSML Fr Instr 1986-89; Largo HS Fr Tchr 1989-; *ai:* Largo Debating Soc; Its Acad Team Co-Spon; Modern Lang Assn; NEA; MO St Tchrs Assn; Greater WA Area Tchrs of Frgn Lang; Intnl Red Cross Vol; Global Nomads Spec Events Comm; Fr Govt Schlsp for Higher Stud; UNESCO Internship; Articles Pub; *office:* Largo HS 505 Largo Rd Upper Marlboro MD 20774*

AHMADIZADEH, EBRAHIM, Math Professor; *b:* Tehran, Iran; *m:* Sicilia; *c:* Brenda, Kiyan, Victoria; *ed:* NJ Inst of Tech (BS) Electrical Engrng 1975; MS St Univ (MS) Electrical Engrng 1978; *cr:* Essex Cty Coll Adj Prof 1982-84; Lyons Inst Sr Instr 1983-84; Northampton Comm Coll Prof 1984-; *ai:* Interface Cmptr Club Adv; Acad Discipline, Appeals Comms; AFT, IEEE 1984-; PSMATYC, AMATYC 1991-; Title 3 Grant 1984, 1986; Microprocessor Lab Manual 1987, 1993; Electronics Trng Manual; *office:* Northampton Comm Coll 3835 Green Pond Rd Bethlehem PA 18017

AHMED, GAIL HORNER, General Music Teacher; *b:* Martins Ferry, OH; *m:* Bashir Gakhru; *c:* Aisha; *ed:* West Liberty St Coll (BA) Music Ed 1975; Univ of Dayton (MS) Ed 1991; 6 Credit Hrs Admin; *cr:* Edison Local Schls Asst Band Dir 1975-77; Tippecanoe HS Band Dir 1977-80; Tipp City Schls Gen Music, Band Dir 1982-89, Gen Music Dir 1990-; *ai:* Orchestra Dir; Musical Variety Show Dir; OMEA 1975-, Gen Music Comm; Tipp Comm Band 1979-, Dir; Friends of Lib 1995-; OMEA Convention Presenter 1995; Pub Lesson Plan; *office:* Nevin Coppock Elem Schl 525 N Hyatt St Tipp City OH 45371*

AHNEMANN, GAIL BEATTY, Second Grade Teacher; *b:* Jamaica, NY; *m:* James C.; *ed:* SUNY Coll at Oswego (BSEd) Ed 1963; Critical Thinking Inst at Montclair Univ, Appt Clinical Adj Fac Mem 1993, Courses Taken Summers Since 1993-; *cr:* Secatogue Schl 2nd Grd Tchr 1963-64; Longfellow Schl 1st Grd Primary Tchr 1964-67, Non-graded Primary Tchr 1967-71; Intervale Schl 1st Grd Tchr 1971-76, 2nd Grd Tchr 1985-86; Northvail Schl Kndgtn Tchr 1976-77; 2nd Grd Tchr 1977-; *ai:* PTA Liason; Math Club Spon; NEA, NJEA 1964-; MCEA 1970-; NJ Alpha Delta Kappa 1972-, Corr Sec 1978-80, Pres 1980-82, St Corr Sec 1982-84, St Pres of Pres Cncl 1980-82, St Parliamentarian; NJ Schoolwomen"s Club 1980-, Trustee 1982; Co-Chprsn Prepare Math Kits 1972; Chprsn Tchr Admin Conf Team 1969; Nom Outstdng Elem Tchrs of Amer 1974; *office:* Northvail Elem Schl 10 Eileen Ct Parsippany NJ 07054*

AHRENS, SARA ANN, French Teacher; *b:* York, PA; *m:* Christian Voss; *c:* Seth, Megan; *ed:* Shippensburg Univ (BS) Fr 1970; Attnd PA St Univ, Temple Univ; *cr:* East Pennsboro HS Fr Tchr 1971-73; Camp Hill HS Fr & Stud Skills Tchr 1988-; *ai:* NHS Adv; Quiz Bowl Coach; AATF 1990-95; PSEA 1990-; NEA 1990-; *office:* Camp Hill Jr Sr HS 100 S 24th St Camp Hill PA 17011

AICHELE, WENDY ANDERSON, Science Teacher; *b:* Pittsburgh, PA; *m:* Gary Jan; *c:* Anne Elizabeth, Molly Anderson; *ed:* Univ of VA (BA) Music 1974, (MA) Music 1977; Norwich Univ (AS) Medical Lab Tech 1987; Juniata Coll Bio Tchrs Cert 1991; *cr:* St Annes Belfield Schl Glee Club Dir, Music Tchr 1973-76; United Church Northfield Organist Choir Dir 1984-87; Gifted Hospital Lab Technician 1986-87; Grace United Church of Christ Organist Choir Dir 1994-96; Linden Hall Schl Bio & Physics Tchr 1991-; *ai:* Vlybl Coach; Natl Honor Soc Adv; *office:* Linden Hall Schl For Girls 212 E Main St Lititz PA 17543

AIELLO, CYNTHIA KATHRYN, English Teacher; *b:* Pittsburgh, PA; *m:* Gennaro Carmen; *c:* Erin, Kathryn; *ed:* Gannon Univ (BA) Eng 1976; 15 Addl Hrs Masters Equivalency; *cr:* Ridgway Mid HS Eng Tchr 1978-; *ai:* Schl Lit Magazine Adv; Ridgway Tchrs Assn, PSEA 1978-; Church Eucharistic Minister 1994-; Numerous Stu Publications; *home:* 220 Montmorenci Ave Ridgway PA 15853*

AIELLO, JOHN FRANCES, Receptionist; *b:* Johnsonburg, PA; *cr:* St Peter Schl 2nd-6th Grd Tchr 1954-57; St Patrick Schl 2nd-6th Grd Tchr 1954-57; St Andrew Schl 2nd-6th Grd Tchr 1954-57; St Joseph Home for Children Group Mother 1957-69; Blessed Sacrament Schl 5th Grd Tchr 1969-92; Villa Maria Elem Schl Part-time Receptionist 1992-.

AIKEN, KATHRYN CAULEY, English Teacher; *b:* Pittsburgh, PA; *m:* James; *c:* James, Todd, Sean, Matthew, Joshua Peter; *ed:* Carlow Coll (AS) Psych Ed.

AIKEY, PATRICIA ANN (BOBACK), Math Teacher & Dept Chprsn; *b:* Ehrenfeld, PA; *m:* David Lee; *c:* Christine Marie Compton, Leigh Ann Hopkins, Laura Jean, Karen Lynn; *ed:* IUP (BS) Scndry Math 1962; Masters Equivalent at Commonwealth of PA; Grad Stud at St Francis of Loretta, WV Univ Coll of Grad Stud; *cr:* Richland Jr HS Math Tchr 1962-66; North Star HS Math Tchr & Dept Chprsn 1978-; *ai:* Counted Cross-Stitch & 9th Grd Class Adv; Strategic Planning Task Force; NHS Selection Comm; NEA 1978-; PSEA 1978-; NSEA 1978-; NCTM 1993-; Church Choir Mem 1972-; Church Admin Bd 1995-; Nom for the Presidential Awd for Excl in Sci & Math Tchng 1991; *office:* North Star HS 400 Ohio St Boswell PA 15531

AIKMAN, MARIE OSTERMAN, Literature Teacher; *b:* Brooklyn, NY; *c:* Bradley; *ed:* St Johns (BA) Eng 1969; CW Post (MS) Rdng 1989; 30 Hrs Post Grad Eng; *cr:* St Martin of Tours 7th & 8th Grd Tchr 1975-82; St Peter of Alcantara Lit Tchr 1982-; *ai:* Spirit of Life Group Ldr; Center in Planning; Cath Charismatic Prayer Group; *office:* St Peter Of Alcantara Schl 1321 Port Washington Blvd Port Washington NY 11050

AILI, ROBERT STEVEN, Math Teacher; *b:* Minneapolis, MN; *m:* Marcy Lynne Keith; *ed:* NY St Univ (BA) Math 1977; Boston Univ (MAT) Math Ed 1990; *cr:* Somerville HS Stu Tchr 1/2 Yr; New England Hebrew Acad Math, Cmptr Tchr 1 Yr; St Clement HS Math, Cmptr Tchr 9 Yrs; *ai:* Chess Club Adv; NCTM 1989-; *office:* St Clement HS 579 Boston Ave Somerville MA 02144*

AIMERS, JOHN L., English Master; *b:* Dublin, Ireland; *ed:* Concordia Univ (BA) Eng & Pol Sci 1972; Diploma in Eng Ed from McGill Univ 1974; *cr:* Selwyn House Schl Eng Master 1974-78; Saint Johns-Ravenscourt Schl Housemaster & Dir of Dev 1980-83; Appleby Coll Housemaster 1983-91; Toronto Fr Schl Asst to Headmaster 1991-92; Yeshiva Gedolah & Yesodei Eng Master 1995-; *ai:* Monarchist League of Canada 1970-, Chm; Canada Royal Heritage Trust 1995-, Trustee; Founder of Intnl Ind Schls Speaking Competition & Awd Designated in Name 1992; Ontario Govt Good Citizenship Awd 1991; *office:* Yeshiva Godolah Schl 367 Lawrence Ave W N York Toronto ON M5M 1B8 Canada CN

AIRES, AL, Health & Physical Ed Teacher; *m:* Phyllis Angellella; *c:* Ashley; *ed:* Temple Univ (BS) Hlth, PE 1985; *cr:* Jackson Memorial HS Hlth, PE Tchr 1985-; *ai:* Head Wrestling, Head Sftbl Coach; Sportsmanship Comm; NEA, NJEA, JEA Region Coaches Assn 1985-; USLA 1983-; NJWCOA 1985-; Dist 25 Coach of Yr 3 Times; *office:* Jackson Memorial HS Don Conner Blvd Jackson NJ 08527*

AKER, JEFFREY CHARLES, Social Studies Teacher; *b:* Cleveland, OH; *m:* Karen Sue Workman; *c:* Jessica, Jennifer, Kelly; *ed:* Bowling Green St Univ (BS) Ed-Cum Laude, Jrnlsm-Cum Laude 1978; Kent St Univ (MA) Educl Admin 1986; Legal Update Coursework; *cr:* Mayfield City Schls Soc Stud Tchr 1978-79; Solon City Schls Soc Stud Dept Chm 1990-93, Soc Stud Tchr 1979-; *ai:* Mentor Tchr 1994-; Golf Coach 1994-95; Asst Bsktbl Coach 1980-93; Solon Ed Assn 1980-, Bldg Rep, Welfare Fin Comm; Past Ed Comm Newsletter, US House of Reps Intern to Rep John Breckinridge of KY 1976; *office:* Solon HS 33600 Inwood Dr Solon OH 44139

AKERS, CATHY JO (CRUM), 6th Grade Teacher; *b:* Marion, OH; *m:* Richard Shane; *c:* Jason, Arika; *ed:* OH St Univ (BA) Elem Ed Math 1991; Enrolled Ashland Univ Masters Prgm; *cr:* Pleasant MS 7th-8th Grd Math, His Tchr 1991-95, 6th Grd Tchr 1995-; *ai:* JV Vlybl Coach; NEA, OEA 1987-; Pleasant Assn Tchrs 1991-, Sec 1995; *office:* Pleasant MS 3507 Smeltzer Rd Marion OH 43302

AKERS, HAROLD WILLIAM,JR., English Instructor; *b:* Mt Pleasant, PA; *m:* Karen Lee Barnes; *c:* Sean Alexandrew, Dawn Alysandrea; *ed:* Slippery Rock Univ (BA) Eng 1971; *cr:* Penn MS Instr of Gifted; Seton Hill Coll Comp Instr 1992-; Penn-Trafford HS Lang Arts, AP Eng & Jrnlsm Tchr 1993-.

AKERS, PAULA JEAN (WNUK), Teacher of Gifted; *b:* Providence, RI; *m:* Kirby Alan; *c:* Jameson, Jessica; *ed:* RI Coll (BS) Elem Ed 1971; Addl 48 Grad Hrs Elem Ed URI, RIC; *cr:* Cntrl Falls Schl Dist Tchr 1971-; *ai:* Calcutt After Schl Act; Prof Dev Acad Founding Mem; Math, Sci Tech Schl Ldrsp Team; Schl Improvement Team 1994-; Facilitator Classrrom Alternatives Prgm Spec Needs Pre-Referral System; Cntrl Falls Tchrs Union 1971-, Sec 1994-; RIFT-AFT #1567; RI Math Tchrs Assn 1990-92; Cub Scouts, Den Ldr; RI Math Tchr Assn Awd for Math Excl; Outstdng Edctr on RI's Child; Project REAP Grant 1986-; Gifted-ESL Grant 1990-92; Co-Author Ride Mentoring Grant; *office:* Dr Earl F. Calcutt Schl 112 Washington St Central Falls RI 02863*

AKEY, WAYNE JAMES, Math Teacher; *b:* Gloversville, NY; *m:* Shelly Howland; *c:* Coleman; *ed:* SUNY at Plattsburgh (BA) Math Ed 1986; SUNY at Albany (MA) Math Ed 1991; *cr:* Ballston Spa Cntrl Schl Math Tchr 1987-; *ai:* Var Boys Soccer, Tennis Coach; AFT 1987-; Challenger Flwshp; Article Pub.

AKIN, DENNIS PETER, Prof of Fine Arts Emeritus; *b:* Ames, IA; *m:* Marjorie Pennington; *c:* Christopher, Lilian; *ed:* Univ of KS (BFA) Painting, Drawing 1956; Univ of CO (MFA) Fine Arts, Esthetics 1958; Rijksakademie Van Beelden Kunsten-Amsterdam Holland; Pilchuck Schl WA; *cr:* Southwestern Coll Instr, Asst Prof 1958-67; Motive Magazine Art Ed 1967-69; Dickinson Coll Assoc, Full Prof 1969-92, Prof Emeritus 1992-; *ai:* Stu Cncl Awd Tchng Excl 1969; Lindback Awd Distngd Tchng 1978; Ganoe Awd Inspirational Tchng 1992.

AKINS, JAMES E., Gifted Support Teacher; *b:* Springfield, MO; *m:* Claire J. Burnside; *c:* Jodi, Janice, Tanya; *ed:* West Chester St (BS) Hlth, PE, Rec 1968; Eastern Bapt Seminary (MA) Rel Ed 1970; Slippery Rock Univ (MED) PE 1985; 60 Addl Credits Grad Work, In Svc Courses Penn St, Pitt, Youngstown St, Clarion; *cr:* Eastern Bapt Coll PE Tchr, Coach 1968-70; Sharon Jr HS PE Tchr 1970-86; Sharon HS Gifted Support, TV Production Tchr 1986-; Kent St Univ Dir of Governor's Schl for GATE 1991-; *ai:* Acquatics Dir; Sharon Tchrs Assn, Penn St Ed Assn 1970-; NEA 1970-, Pres, Interpreter; PIAA 1970-, Swimming Ofcls Local Chapter; YMCA 1976-, Bd of Dirs, Past VP; BSA 1978-, Merit Badge Comm; Amer Red Cross 1972-, Past Water Safety Chm; PA Tchr of Yr Nom 1991; Acad Boosters Friend of Ed Awd 1994; Amer Legion Citizenship Awd 1991; *home:* 123 White Ave Sharon PA 16146

AKINS, JULIE (BRALLIER), Language Arts Teacher; *b:* Roarings Spring, PA; *m:* George M. Akins, Jr.; *c:* Taylor Lenore; *ed:* Shippensburg Univ (BSEd) Elem Ed 1982; Millersville Univ (MS) Ed 1988; Addl 30 Degrees; *cr:* Alexander B. Goode Elem Schl 4th Grd Tchr 1983; Hannah Penn MS 6th, 7th Grd Rdng, Lang Arts Tchr 1983-; *ai:* Activity Coord 1985-86; Co-Dir Spring Show 1986; Fac Advy Comm 1988-89, 1994-; Rdng Dept Chprsn 1990-94; Organizer Acad Fair 1990; Gymnastics, Vlybl, Sftbl, Bsktbl, Soccer IMS 1988-95; YCEA 1984-, Negotiator; PSEA, NEA 1984-; H. P. Peace Club 1994-; *office:* Hannah Penn MS 329 S Lindbergh Ave York PA 17403

AKLONIS, RAYMOND JOHN, High School History Teacher; *b:* Elizabeth, NJ; *ed:* Upsala Coll (BA) His 1971; Seton Hall Univ (MA) His 1978; Seton Hall Univ Cert Supervision & Prin; NY Univ 20 Grad Credits His; Ball St Univ 8 Grad Credits Amer Stud; NY Univ Schl Continuing Ed 3 Non Credit Courses Art, Lit; *cr:* Grover Cleveland Jr HS His Tchr 1971-75; Thomas Jefferson HS His Tchr 1975-77; Elizabeth HS His Tchr 1977-; *ai:* Curr Comm; Artist; NEA, NJEA, EEA 1971-; AFT, ASCD 1990-92; Elizabeth Ed Assn Edward Kappy Awd Outstanding Educl Leadership 1983; Elizabeth HS Outstanding Educator Awd 1993; *office:* Elizabeth HS 600 Pearl St Elizabeth NJ 07202*

AKOS, DENNIS J., Mathematics Teacher; *b:* Cleveland, OH; *m:* Nona Ann; *c:* Dennis, Michael, Patrick; *ed:* OH Univ (BSEd) Math 1965; Boston Coll (MA) Math 1971; Colgate Univ Summer NSF Math 1968; Attnd Cleveland St & Kent St; Mini Courses; *cr:* Hillside Jr HS Math Tchr 1965-71; Parma Sr HS Math Tchr 1971-; Cuyahoga Comm Coll Math Instr 1975-; *ai:* Drivers Ed; Ftbl & Wrestling Coach; Cmptr Sci Instr; PEA, OEA, NEA, NCTM, OCTM 1965-; AARP 1990-; Holy Family PSR 1978-; Natl Sci Fnd Grants Summer 1968, 1970-71; *office:* Parma Sr H S 6285 W 54th St Parma OH 44129

AKSAMIT, SCOTT F., Martial Artist; *b:* New Britian, CT; *m:* Nancy Scheely; *ed:* Cert from Black Belt Schls of Amer; *cr:* East West Karate Asst Instr 1987-89; Action Karate Head Instr 1989-90; Martial Art Inst Owner 1991-; *ai:* Attnd Seminars from Tom Hopkins, Zig Ziglar, Omar Peru & Tony Robbins; Winner of Intnl Karate Championships 1988; Black Belt Schls of Amer Gold Club Mem; Winner of Ice Burg Awd 1992 & Personal Dev Awd; *office:* Martial Arts Institute 140 Albany Tpke PO Box 732 Canton CT 06019*

ALAGIA, MARGARET ROSE, Secondary English Teacher; *b:* Union City, NJ; *ed:* Douglas Coll (BA) Eng 1965; NY Univ, Montclair St NJ, Jersey City St Coll 52 Credits; *cr:* Teaneck Pub Schls Elem, Scndry Eng Tchr 1954-1991; Fairleigh Dickinson Univ Supvr MAT, Alternate Route Tchrs 1991-93; Immaculate Conception HS Eng Tchr 1993-; *ai:* Bergen Cty Ed Assn, NJEA, NEA 1954-; Teaneck Tchrs Assn 1954-, Fac Rep; *home:* 517 Saint Pauls Ave Cliffside Park NJ 07010*

ALAICA, JOANNE BUFALINI, 9th-10th Grade English Teacher; *b:* Pittsburgh, PA; *m:* John Paul; *c:* Rebecca Anne; *ed:* PA St Univ (BA) Scndry Ed Comprehensive Eng 1969; Grad Work Univ of Pittsburgh; *cr:* Aliquippa Jr HS 7-9 Grd Eng Tchr 1969-76; Aliquippa Sr HS 9-12 Grd Eng, Yrbk Production Tchr 1976-; *ai:* Yrbk Spon; NHS Adv; Prof Dev C Co-Chprsn; NEA 1969-; PSEA 1969-, Collective Bargaining St C Aliquippa Ed Assn 1969-, Pres, Sec, Treas; *office:* Aliquppa HS Ha Ave Aliquippa PA 15001*

ALAIMO, ESTHER, Professor of Accounting; *b:* Springfield, M Lisa Oneto, Dawn Oneto, Jennifer Oneto, Michele Oneto; *ed:* Univ c (BS) Acctng 1962; Univ of Hartford (MS) Acctng 1988; Credit Hrs C Stud; 18 Continuing Ed Credits Acctng; *cr:* Asnuntuck Comm-Tech A Instr 1980-86, Acctng Dept Chprsn 1986-89, Acting Dean of Instru 1989-90, Prof 1990-; *ai:* St Wide Wkshp Coord; Instrl Excl C Fredrick Bartlett Schlsp Fund Trustee; Steering Comm for Accredi Co-Chair; Ctr for Tchng 1992-, Coord; AAUP 1985-; Enfield Town 1990-92, Cncl Person; Enfield Bd of Ed 1979-89; Womens Pol C 1980-; *office:* Asnuntuck Comm-Tech College 170 Elm St Enfiel 06082

ALAMIA, CAROL MADELINE, Lang Arts & Soc Stud Teach Passaic, NJ; *m:* Vincent J.; *c:* James; *ed:* William Paterson Coll (BA) Ed 1966; 27 Credit Hrs Montclair St Univ Rdng Specialist; 32 Addl Grad Credits; *cr:* HACKENSACK Elem Schl 1-3 Grd Tchr 196 Hackensack MS 4-6 Grd Tchr, 6-8 Grd Rdng Appreciation & Writing S Tchr 1966-, 6 Grd Lang Arts & Soc Stud Tchr 1992-; *ai:* Stu Cncl Co- Mentoring Prgm; NEA, NJEA, BCEA 1966-; HEA, IRA 1995-; Phi K Phi 1993-; Governors Tchrs Recognition Awd; NJ Governors Awd for 1992-93; Distngd Svc Awd 1994-95; *office:* Hackensack MS Uni Hackensack NJ 07601*

ALBANESE, BETH KULLMAN, Social Studies Teacher; *b:* Zanes OH; *m:* Paul Joseph; *c:* Brittany Ann, Daulton Joseph; *ed:* OH St Univ Soc Stud 1986; 150 Hrs; Marietta Coll Ath Trng; *cr:* New Lexingto Soc Stud Tchr 1987-; *ai:* JV Vllybl Coach Granville HS; NLEA 1 *office:* New Lexington HS 2549 Panthers Dr New Lexington OH 437

ALBANESE, JAY S., Professor; *b:* Mineola, NY; *m:* Leslie E. Kir Thomas, Kelsey; *ed:* Niagara Univ (BA) Sociology, Natural Sci Rutgers Univ (MA) Criminal Justice 1976, (PHD) Criminal Justice *cr:* Niagara Univ Dept Political Sci, Crim Justice Prof 1981-, Political Sci, Crim Justice Chm 1988-94, Criminal Justice Admin Prgm Dir 1994-; *ai:* Natl Crim Justice Honor Soc Alpha Phi Sigma Fa 1982-; Justice, Peace Cncl 1984-95; Pre-Law Adv 1982-92; Acad Cri Justice Scis 1979-, Pres 1995-96; Northeastern Assoc of Crim Justice 1983-, Pres 1988-89; Amer Soc of Criminology 1977-; Niagara Fr Transportation Authority Bd of Ethics, 1991-; Niagara Frontier Rdng Sci 1990-91; Who's Who in: Amer; American Ed, Amer Law; Tchng Excl 1990, Excl Research 1988 Awds; Books: White Collar C in Amer 1995, Dealing with Delinquency 1993, Crime in Amer Organized Crime in Amer 1996; *office:* Niagara Univ Crininolo Criminal Justice Niagara Univ NY 14109

ALBANESE, JUDIE MARIE, Pre School Teacher; *b:* Warren, O Stephen A.; *c:* Jeffrey; *ed:* Youngstown St (BS) Ed 1967; Early Chldho 1972; 27 Quarter Hrs Guid, Cnslng 1976-80; 3 Grad Hrs Preve Intervention Kent St Univ 1994; 3 Grad Hrs Rdng, Writing Whole 1995; *cr:* St Nicholas Schl 2nd Grd Tchr 1966-67; St Rose Schl 1s Tchr 1967-70; Sacred Heart Schl 1st Grd Tchr 1970-71; Warren City Emerson 2nd Grd Tchr 1971-80; Warren City Schl Garfield 3-4th Grd 1980-94; Ursuline Presch Tchr 1994-; *ai:* Taught Charm, Sewi Counseled Unwed Mothers Florence Crittenden Home; Chrldr C CYO Spon; CCD Dir & Summer Day Care; Taught Adult Basic Youngstown Inner City; Dev Curr for Rights, Responsibilities Handb Helped Inst Drug, Alcohol Prevention Prgms Warren City Schls; H Create Model At Risk Ed; Graded Rdng, Math Courses of Stud; Supt Advy Cncl; Literacy Learning, Instruction Westminster Coll; Lead Drug Prevention Prgm; IAT Team Chprsn; OEA, NEA 1971-94; 1971-94, Negotiation Team 1990; NEOTA; Assn For Ed Young Chi 1994-96; Delta Kappa Gamma Soc 1993-; Blessed Sacrament Ch Bereavement Comm, Mercy Meal Chprsn 1993-94; Tchrs Applying W Lang 1988-92; A+ Tchr Awd 1991; Outstdng Tchr Awd 1992; Class Act Mini Grants; Prof Svc Awd Longitudinal Stud Compensatory Prgms 1992-94; *office:* Ursuline Preschool 4300 Shields Rd Canfiel 44406

ALBANESE, LINDA BORELLA, Spanish Teacher; *b:* Jersey City, N Donald R.; *c:* Michael, Mark; *ed:* Montclair St Coll (BA) Span & 1964, (MA) Span Lit 1992; 45 Credits in Foreign Langs Beyond Ma *cr:* Belleville Jr HS Span & Eng Tchr 1964-70, Eng Tchr 197 Belleville HS Span Tchr 1985-; *ai:* NEA, NJEA, Belleville Ed Assn US Fencing Assn 1961-; Numerous Foreign Lang Grants from 196 *home:* 56 Renner Ave Bloomfield NJ 07003

ALBANO, LEONARD D., Civil Engineering Professor; *b:* Somer MA; *m:* Kathleen M. Baskin; *c:* Christopher, Julianne, Mark; *ed:* Univ (BS) Civil Engrng 1982; Northwestern Univ (MS) Civil Engrng MIT (PHD) Structural Engrng 1992; *cr:* Stone & Webster Eng Corp 1983-88; MIT Lecturer 1992-95; Worc Polytechnic Inst Asst Prof 1 *ai:* Fac Adv ASCE Stu Chptr; ASCE, Tau Beta Pi 1981-; Sigma Xi 1 5 Articles Pub; *office:* Worcester Poly Inst 100 Institute Rd Worceste 01609

ALBANO, MICHAEL A., English & Theater Arts Tchr; *b:* Brooklyn *m:* Marie A.; *c:* Nicholas, Michael Paul; *ed:* Saint Johns Univ (BA 1968, (MA) 17th Century Poetry & Prose 1972; 36 Credit Hrs Toward in Eng; *cr:* Lindenhurst HS Eng Tchr 1973-; *ai:* Stu Musical Dir; NY NEA, AFT, TAL 1973-; Vietnam Veterans of Amer 1986-; NDEA Tit Fellowship for Grad Stud 1972-73; Tchr of Yr 1987; NHS Life Honorary Mem 1990; *office:* Lindenhurst Sr HS 300 Charle Lindenhurst NY 11757

ALBAUGH, F. DARLENE, Business Education Teacher; *b:* Grove PA; *m:* Daniel K.; *c:* Amanda L., Daniel M.; *ed:* Grove City Coll (BA Ed 1976; Attnd Slippery Rock Univ, Wilkes Coll, Penn St, Gar Clarion; *cr:* Warren Area HS Bus Ed Tchr 1976-; *ai:* Dragon Bus Bd PBEA 1985-; WCEA, NEA 1976-; Girl Scouts Troop Ldr; *office:* W Area HS 345 E 5th Ave Warren PA 16365

ALBECK, RAE BELLE, Third Grade Teacher; *b:* Binghamton, N Gerald Porter; *ed:* Cedarville Coll (BA) Elem Ed 1973; Marywood Co Equiv Elem Ed 1986; NEIU Credits; Cmptr Credits; *cr:* Mt View Ele Grd Tchr 1973-90, 3rd Grd Tchr 1990-; *ai:* Chorus, Plays, Musicals, Piano Accompanist; GED Tchr, Test Admin; NEA; SNMB Ch Organist; Harford Fair 1978-, Supt, Organist; Private Piano Lessons *office:* Mountain View Elem Schl RR 1 Box 339 Kingsley PA 18826

ALBEE, MARY JO ZEMEK, English Teacher & Chair; *b:* Johnson NY; *m:* Jeremy M.; *c:* Christopher, Heather; *ed:* Broome Comm Coll (Liberal Arts 1966; SUNY Coll at Cortland (BA) Eng 1968; 40 Addl C Hrs SUNY Binghamton & SUNY Cortland; *cr:* Vestal Sr HS Eng 1968-, Eng II Dept Chprsn 1983-; *ai:* Honor Soc Selection Comm Future Tchrs of Ameria Adv 1974-80; Discipline Comm 1988-90; T Show Judge 1973-83 & 1992; NEA, NYEA & VTA 1968-; Czechos Moravian Club 1975-, VP 2 Yrs, Correspondence Sec 2 Yrs, Sec 1 Yr, 2 Yrs, Cultural Awd 1986; Hillcrest Comm Assn 1975-82, Cultural C 1 Yr, Sec 2 Yrs; Czechoslovak-Moravian Club Dancers Choreographer & Instr 1984-, St Catherines PTO 1975-82; Seton Cntrl HS PTO 1980-89; Univ of Chicago Outstanding Tchr Awd Vestal HS 20 Yr Service Awd 1990; Cornell Univ Outstanding Tc

ill Presidential Awd; SUNY Fredonia Outstdng Tchr Awd; Svc Awd 25 1995; *office:* Vestal Sr H S Woodlawn Dr Vestal NY 13850

ERGHINI, HELEN, Religion & Social Studies Tchr; *b:* Lynn, MA; ouis P.; *c:* Anthony L., C. Scott, Eric A.; *ed:* Salem St Coll (BSEd) Soc Stud 1963; Attnd Worcester St, Fitchburg St; *cr:* Saugus Jr HS 3rd Eng, Rdng Tchr 1963-64; Marian Hill Jr Sr HS Eng, Rdng Tchr -86; Oxford HS 8-9 Grd Eng Lit, Writing Tchr 1986-88; St Mary 5-8 All Subject Tchr 1988-92; Millbury HS 9-12 Grd Eng, Lit Summer Tchr 1991; St Stephen 6-8 Grd Eng, Rdng, Rel, Soc Stud Tchr 1992-; rama Club Tchr; Jr HS Coord; NCEA 1985-; *office:* St Stephen Schl Grafton St Worcester MA 01604*

ERT, CINDY LEE, Early Multiage Teacher; *b:* Ft Kent, ME; *ed:* on Coll (BA) Early Chldhd, Elem Ed 1992; *cr:* Ft Fairfield Elem Schl Grd Tchr 1992-94, Early Multiage Experience Tchr 1994-; *ai:* Family ; Northern Educl Partnership's; Reflective Groups; Svc Learning ect Elem Tutoring Prgm; OM Judge; ME Educl Assessment Scorer; Alliance of Multiage Edctrs 1995-; NEA, ME Ed Assn, Ft Fairfield s Assn 1992-; Cty Alliance of Math & Sci 1994-; Presenter ME Schl nt Assn; Blaine House Scholar; *home:* RR 3 Box 13-9 Caribou ME 6*

ERT, EUGENE N., HS Instructional Team Teacher; *b:* Pittsburgh, *m:* Donna Marie Burns; *c:* Gene, Tara, Alayna; *ed:* CA St Univ (BS) Ed 1971; Duquesne Univ 27 Grad Credits; *cr:* South HS Tchr 1971; gheny HS Tchr 1971-81; Carrick HS Chprsn, Team Ldr, Coach, Tchr Ed 1981-; *ai:* Girls Soccer, Boys Vlybl Coach; Governance Bd; an Resource Dev, PFT Spec Ed, Strategic Planning Comm; AFT, PAFT -; CEC; USCYSA 1989-; News Media All Star Tchr; *office:* Carrick 25 Parkfield St Pittsburgh PA 15210

ERT, JAMES G., High School Biology Teacher; *b:* Johnstown, PA; ebbie Callihan; *c:* Cory, Chris; *ed:* Concord Coll (BA) Biological Sci ; SUNY at Stony Brok (MALS) Lbrl Stud 1975; 75 Addl Credit Hrs; Vest Islip HS Bio Tchr 1972-; *ai:* Var Track, Cross Cntry, Soccer; West Tchrs Assn 1972; St & Natl Org 1972-; Sachem Soccer Club 1984-; *:* West Islip HS Hibgie Ln West Islip NY 11795

ERT, LARRY JOHN, Music Department Chairman; *b:* Buffalo, NY; onna Horner; *c:* Rick, Tracy; *ed:* Berklee Coll (BA) Music Ed 1971; Y at Buffalo (MED) Music Ed 1975; *cr:* Frontier Cntrl Schls Music 1971-, Music Dept Chm 1993-; *ai:* Music Club Adv; Musical Dir; a Asst Dir; NYSUT, AFL CIO #92 & MENC 1971-; Reserve Fire Co -, Pres Sec Chief; *office:* Frontier Central Sr HS S-4432 Bay View Rd burg NY 14075

ERT, PAULINE L., PE & Health Teacher & Coach; *b:* Nashua, NH; lymouth St Coll (BS) PE 1972; Springfield Coll (MED) Tchng, Admin ; *cr:* YWCA Asst Program Dir PE, Rec 1972-73; Fairgrounds Jr High chr 1973-85; Springfield Coll Scndry PE Tchng Fellow 1985-86; ua HS PE, Hlth Tchr 1982-83, 1986-; *ai:* Girls Track, Field Coach or 1978-, Outdoor 1973-; AFT 1973-; NHPHERD 1980-; Nashua Park ecreation Comm 1991-95; HS Hall of Fame Comm 1989-; NH athlon Championships 1978-, Founder, Dir, Meet Dir; Springfield Coll wship 1985-86, Tchng; HS Ath Hall of Fame Inductee 1993; Pub le; Outstanding Young Woman of Amer Cited for Excel in Coaching & Field 1983; NH Coach of Yr 1982, 1985, 1990, 1993, 1996; Natl oaches Assn Region I Coach of Yr 1985; *office:* Nashua High School side Dr Nashua NH 03062

ERT, RONALD RUSSELL, Choral Director; *b:* Sandusky, OH; *m:* Steinert; *ed:* Heidelberg Coll (BME) Music Ed 1980; Grad Hrs ing Green St Univ, Ashland Coll, Walsch Univ; *cr:* Sandusky City 1-6 Grd Music Tchr 1980-81, 8 Grd Music Tchr 1981-93, 9-12 Grd Tchr 1993-; *ai:* OH Music Ed Assn, Amer Choral Dir Assn 1980-; usky Concert Assn 1985-; Mildred Mc Crystal Schlsp Bd 1990-; n Chorus Dir; Zion Luth Church Choir, Bell Choir Dir; us-Keynote, Bell Choir Dir; *office:* Sandusky HS 2130 Hayes Ave usky OH 44870

ERTELLI, JOSEPH LOUIS, Science Teacher; *b:* Corona, NY; *m:* n Pierro; *c:* Ann Marie, Andrea, Aimee; *ed:* St John's Univ (BS) Bio, , Math 1963; Adelphi Univ (MA) Sci Ed 1969; Attnd Notre Dame San Diego St Coll, Boston Coll, Brooklyn Polytechnic Inst, Hofstra Stony Brook Univ; *cr:* Elmont HS Sci Tchr 1963-64; Bishop Reilly Sci Tchr, Chm 1964-73; Plainview Jr HS Sci Tchr 1973-74; ogue-Medford Schl Dist Sci, Lead Tchr 1974-; *ai:* AFT 1973-; nts of Columbus 1958-; NSF Grants: Univ of Notre Dame, San Diego Coll, Boston Coll, Brooklyn Polytechnic Inst; *office:* ogue-Medford HS Buffalo Ave Medford NY 11763*

ERTSON, HAROLD JOSEPH, Math Teacher & Athletic Dir; *b:* nsburg, PA; *m:* Doris May Dendler; *c:* Brian, Brent; *ed:* Bloomsburg (BS) Math 1968; 38 Post Grad Credits; *cr:* Danville Schl Dist Ath Dir, Tchr 28 Yrs; *ai:* Head Bsbl, Legion Bsbl Coach; NEA 1968-; PSADA , Dist Rep; Dist IV Comm 2 Yrs; Elks 1970-, Montour Cty Recreation 1994-; Danville Stadium Cncl 1992-; Legion Bsbl St Hall of Fame *office:* Danville Sr HS 600 Walnut St Danville PA 17821*

ERTY, MIGUEL ANTONIO, Fifth Grade Teacher; *b:* Santo ngo, Dominican Repub; *ed:* Bronx Comm Coll (AAS) Bus Acctng Fordham Univ (BA) Ec-Cum Laude Laude 1994; Herbert H. Lehman City Univ of NY Elem Ed Eighteen Credit Hrs; *cr:* US Navy keeper 1973-79; St Lukes Elem Schl 5th-8th Grd Tchr 1983-94; n Elem Schl 58X Fifth Grd Tchr 1994-; *ai:* Bsktbl Coach; Yth Adv; f Cath Tchrs 1983-94, Delegate, Flwshp to Fordham Univ; United Fed hrs 1994-; Assn of Black Edctrs of NY 1994-, Exec Bd Mem; Phi a Phi 1991-; Amer Legion Post 620 1992-; Alpha Sigma Nu 1993-; *:* Comm Elem Schl 58 X 459 E 176th St Bronx NY 10457

NDER, ERIC R., Band Director; *b:* Kew Gardens, NY; *m:* Moris B.; haca Coll (BM) Music Ed 1986; Queens Coll (MS) Music Ed 1989; ma Schl Adm, Supervision 1993; *cr:* Kings Park Cntrl Schls Band nstrumental Music Tchr 1986-; *ai:* Marching, Concert, Symphonic s; Pit Orch; Natl Eagle Scout Assn 1980-; Phi Mu Alpha Sinfonia -; MENC 1985-; Suffolk Cty Music Edctrs Assn 1986-, Exec Bd; NY hl Music Assn 1986-, Adjudicator; North Shore Pops Bands 1986-, uctor; *office:* Kings Park Cntrl Schl Dist 101 Church St Kings Park 1754

NO, LORI ANN, High School English Teacher; *b:* New Haven, CT; homas A.; *c:* Nicole, Lindsay; *ed:* Trinity Coll (BA) Eng & Psych Southern Ct St Univ (MS) Eng Ed 1986; *cr:* Holy Cross HS Eng Tchr ; Southern Ct St Univ Adj Fac Eng Dept 1989-92; Teikyo Post Univ Fac Eng Dept 1989-; *ai:* NCEA 1983-; AAUP 1989-; *office:* Holy HS 587 Oronoke Rd Waterbury CT 06708*

RECHT, MARJORIE GREEN, Spanish Teacher; *b:* Brooklyn, NY; hn Joseph; *c:* Joshua, Zachary; *ed:* Montclair St Coll (BA) Span, 1978; Stud Abroad Spain 1977; Elem Ed K-8 Cert 1994; *cr:* South field HS Span Tchr 1978-79; Freehold Regnl HS Dist Span Tchr 83; Toms River HS North Span Tchr 1994-95; Toms River HS East Tchr 1993-; *ai:* Coadvisor Span NHS; Foreign Lang Edctrs of NJ, NJ ssn, NEA 1993-; *office:* Toms River HS East Raider Way Toms River 753

RECHT, THEODORE JOHN, Music Professor; *b:* Jamestown, NY; arol Padgham; *ed:* St Marys Univ (BME) Music Ed 1967; North TX St Univ (MM) Musicology 1969, (MLS) Library Sci 1973, (PHD) Musicology 1975; *cr:* Appalachian St U Visiting Asst Prof 1975-76; Case Western Reserve U Lecturer 1976-80; Park Coll Assoc, Full Prof 1980-92; Philharmonia of KS City Music Dir 1980-92; Kent St Univ Assoc Prof 1992-; *ai:* Amer Musicalogical Soc 1966-; Coll Music Soc 1979-, Edtr Symposium 1983-85; Amer Beethoven Soc 1986-; Sonneck Soc 1976-; Outstdng Fac Awd Park Coll 1985; Excl in Ed Awd Northland Chamber of Commerce 1985; Rsrch Grants NEH, KSU; Numerous Articles Pub; Books: Salieri Rival of Mozart 1989, Transl Weingartner On Conducting Symphonies of Schubert Schumann & Mozart 1986, Leters to Beethoven 3 Vols 1996; *office:* Kent St Univ Kent OH 44242*

ALBRIGHT, ELEANOR ZARINSKY, 7th & 8th Grade Math Teacher; *b:* Bethlehem, PA; *m:* Charles; *c:* Robin; *ed:* Avernia Coll (BA) Elem Ed, Math 1972; Attnd Kutztown Univ, PA St Univ; *cr:* St Francis of Assisi Schl 7th-8th Grd Math Tchr 1972-74; St Catharine fo Siena Schl 7th-8th Grd Math Tchr 1974-; *ai:* K-8th Grd Math, AV Coords; K-8 Instructional Support Team; 8th Grd Act Co-Chm; Cath Schls Week Chm; Stu Cncl Moderator; Strategic Planning Comm for Schl Bd; NCEA 1972-; ADLTA 1989-; NCTM 1994-; St Benedict's Church 1975-, Lector, Greeter, Women's Club 1976-, Past Sec; St Catharine's Home & Schl Org 1974-, Past Fac Rep; Nom 1994 Presidential Awd Excl Math Tchng; *home:* RR 2 Box 236 Morgantown PA 19543*

ALBRIGHT, LARRY RICHARD, 12th Grd Culinary Arts Chef; *b:* Lebanon, PA; *m:* Carmen Day; *c:* Karen, Gregg; *ed:* Culinary Inst of Amer (AOS) Culinary Arts 1966; Penn St Univ Permanent Tchng Cert 1975; Continuing Ed Courses 1985; Addl 9 Credits 1993-94; *cr:* Lebanon Career & Tech Ctr Chef & Instr 1968-; Lebanon Valley Coll Food & Beverage Mgmt Instr 1986-89; Penn St Univ Voc Field Resources Rep 1993-94; *ai:* VICA Club Adv; Tchr Mentor; Curr Comm; LCATC Ed Assn 1968-, Comm Chm; PSEA, NEA 1994-; Central PA Chapter ACF 1985-; Lebanon Cty Educl Honor Soc; Delaware Valley Chefs Culinary Arts Saloon Honors 1982-87; *office:* Lebanon Co Career Tech Ctr 833 Metro Dr Lebanon PA 17042

ALBRIGHT, LESTER E., Math Teacher; *b:* York, PA; *m:* Virginia F.; *c:* Kim; *ed:* Shippensburg Univ (BS) Math 1970; Attnd Univ of DE, Penn St, DE Tech, Comm Coll; *cr:* Hanby Jr High Math Tchr 1970-81; Glasgow HS Math Tchr 1982-; *ai:* NEA 1970-; *office:* Glasgow HS 1901 S College Ave Newark DE 19702

ALBRIGHT, MARJORY HELFREY, Fourth Grade Teacher; *b:* Woodbury, NJ; *m:* James; *c:* Christina Albright Smith, Jaime, James; *ed:* Rider Coll (BA) Elem Ed 1973; Mercer Cty Comm Coll Acctng 1980-81; *cr:* Monument Elem Schl 4th Grd Tchr 1974-; *ai:* 4th Grd Unit Ldr; Citizenship Comm, Blue & White Sports Chprsns; Cmptr Comm; NEA, NJEA 1974-; TEA 1974-, Chief De 1980-84; Order of Eastern Star 1991-, Ways & Means; N Trenton Little Legue Spon 1990-; Masonic Muscular Dystrophy Fund Raiser 1985-; No Trenton Little League Appreciation Awd 1990; Outstdng Tchr Governors Recognition Prgm 1991; Cert of Recognition Outstdng Accomplishmens & Exceptional Performance at Tchr 1995; *home:* 1209 Silver Ct Trenton NJ 08690

ALBRIGHT, RICHARD C., Math Department Chairman; *b:* Greensburg, PA; *m:* Betty Lee Snyder; *c:* Rebecca, Sandra; *ed:* Indiana Univ of PA (BS) Math 1968; California Univ of PA (MED) Math 1975; 6 Grad Hrs Lehigh Univ; 9 Grad Hrs Penn St Univ; *cr:* Hempfield Area HS Math Tchr 1968-74, Math Tchr, Dept Chair 1974-; *ai:* Spon, Coach Math Team; Statistician Ftbl Prgm; Scorekeeper Bsktbl Team; NEA, PSEA, Hempfield Area Ed Assn 1968-; Lions Club 1994-, VP; *office:* Hempfield Area Sr HS Rd 6 Box 77 Greensburg PA 15601

ALBRITTON, NADA LITTLE, Second Grade Teacher; *b:* Robersonville, NC; *m:* William; *ed:* Fayetteville St Univ (BA) Elem Ed 1966; Western CT St Coll 1974-84; *cr:* East End Elem Schl Grd 3 Tchr 1966-69; Morris St Schl Grd 2 Tchr 1969-; *ai:* Accelerated Schls Climate Comm 1995; Dist Lang Arts Assessment Comm 1994; NEA, CT Ed Assn 1969-; CT Tchr Applying Whole Lang 1991-; New Hope Bapt Church 1974-; Gospel Chorus Choir 1975-, Sec 1975-88, Sunday Schl Tchr 1989-93, Fin Bd 1992, Tutoring l081-85; Evaluation Team for Schl Accreditation; New England Assn Awd for Visiting Comm 1988; Featured in Local Newspaper 1994; *home:* 15 Vale Rd Brookfield CT 06804

ALDERDICE, DOUGLAS A., Microcomputer Coordinator; *b:* Buffalo, NY; *ed:* Susquehanna Univ (BA) Computer Sci 1986; Canisius Coll (MS) Ed 1993; *cr:* Lafayette HS Microcomputer Coord 1986-; *ai:* Amateur Radio Club Adv; NEA 1986-; Buffalo Amateur Radio Repeater Assn 1986-, VP, Pres & Journal Ed; *office:* Lafayette HS 370 Lafayette Ave Buffalo NY 14213

ALDERFER, MARK RICHARD, Science Teacher; *b:* Lancaster, PA; *m:* Karen Jean Sweeney; *c:* Kevin, Jillian, Jeffrey; *ed:* Daemen Coll (BS) Bio 1981; 29 Credit Hrs Tchr Certs at Rutgers Univ & Univ of Scranton; *cr:* Edgewood Regnl HS Chem Tchr 1982-84, Bio Tchr 1984-86; Delaware Valley MS 8th Grd Sci Tchr 1990-; *ai:* NEA, NSTA 1990-; MS & HS Sftbl Coach; MS Girls Bsktbl Coach; Odyssey of Mind Judge; *office:* Delaware Valley MS Star Rt 1 Box 379A Milford PA 18337

ALDRICH, SHIRLEY M. (SMITH), Second & Third Grade Teacher; *b:* New Britain, CT; *m:* Raymond A.; *c:* Betsy Aldrich Horton, Timothy A., William A. (dec); *ed:* Central CT St Univ (BS) Elem Ed 1961; 21 Credit Hrs Remedial Rdng; *cr:* Broad St Schl 1st Grd Tchr 1961-62; Dudley Elem Title I Rem Rdng Tchr 1977-80; Dudley Webster Sub Tchng 1974-77; Faith Bapt Acad K-4th Grd Tchr 1981-87; *ai:* ACSI 1993-; Bible Bapt Church 1988-; *office:* Cortland Christian Acad West St Cortland NY 13045

ALDRIDGE, ELAINE GAWLIK, 6th Grade Teacher; *b:* Cuero, TX; *m:* David Edward; *c:* Jason E., John P., Sarah C., Jacob D.; *ed:* TX Womans Univ (BS) Elem Ed 1969; Attnd Univ of Dayton, Univ of Seattle, Temple Univ, Wright St Univ, Miami Univ; *cr:* St Michael's 5th Grd Tchr 1969-70; J. C. Mc Dade Elem Schl 5th Grd Tchr 1970-71; St Michael's 6th Grd Tchr 1971-72; St Brigid 6-8 Grd Lang Arts & Soc St Tchr 1989-94; Precious Blood Schl 6th Grd Rdng, Eng, Soc Stud Tchr 1994-; *ai:* Schl Advy Bd Spon; Cath Schls Week Comm; NCEA 1989-; OH Writing Project Fellow Miami Univ; *office:* Precious Blood Schl 4870 Denlinger Rd Dayton OH 45426

ALEKSIEWICZ, WILLIAM, Geog, Psych & Sociology Tchr; *b:* Erie, PA; *m:* Susan M.; *c:* Christopher, Julie; *ed:* Gannon Univ (BA) Comprehensive Soc St 1971; Edinboro Univ (MA) Guid & Cnslng 1977; *cr:* Meadville HS Soc Stud Tchr 1972; Cochranton Jr Sr HS Soc Stud Tchr 1972-, Guid Cnslr 1975-76; *ai:* Girls Asst Sftbl Coach; NEA 1972-; PSEA 1972-; CCEA 1972-; *office:* Cochranton Jr Sr H S 2nd St Cochranton PA 16314

ALEMAN, FRANK, Business Professor; *b:* Dunban, South Africa; *c:* Alyson, Alexander, Eric; *ed:* Univ of Natal (BS) Quantity Survey 1962; NY Univ (MBA) Mngmt, Mrktng 1966; Columbia Univ (MA) Admin Ofcrs 1973, (EDD) Higher, Adult Ed 1976; *cr:* Walters & Simpson Quantity Surveyor 1958-64; Union Cabide Corp Mgr, Long Range Planning 1966-72; CT Commission Higher Ed Intern 1973; Quinebaug Vly CTC Prof, Prgm Coord 1974-; *ai:* Hnr Soc Adv; Various Coll Comms; Brooklyn Lib Bd; Univ of Hatal 5 Awds Outstdng Achvmt; Ford Intnl, Kellogg Comm Coll Ctr Flwshps; Yale Univ Visiting Fac Summer Prgm; *office:* Quinebaug Vly Comm-Tech Coll 742 Upper Maple St Danielson CT 06239

ALEONG, CHANDRA, Business Professor; *b:* San Trinidad, West Indies; *m:* John; *c:* Ryan, Steven; *ed:* Univ of West Indies (BA) Ec, Span 1967; Univ of Toronto (MBA) Fin, Acctng 1971; Univ of Pa PHD in Progress; Attnd Univ of VT; *cr:* Univ of VT Asst Dir of Budgeting, Inst Stud 1977-78; IBM Staff Fin Analyst 1982-94; Univ of VT Lecturer 1995; Lincoln Univ Lecturer 1995-; *ai:* Bus Club Fac Adv; *office:* Lincoln Univ Dept of Business & Economics Lincoln University PA 19352

ALESTOCK, KAREN (LEBER), Math Tchr & Asst Principal; *b:* Euclid, OH; *m:* Joe; *c:* Ryan, Emily; *ed:* Kent St Univ (BA) Elem Ed 1986; Masters Prgm Ed Admin 1994-; *cr:* St Hilary Schl Tchr 1986-, Tchr, Asst Prin 1994-; *ai:* Stu Cncl, Newspaper Adv; Math Team Coach; Stud Skills Elective Tchr; Comm Svc Coord; DARE Liason; Chi Omega 1993-, Housing Corp, Sec; Holy Family Cath Church 1991-; *office:* St Hilary Schl 645 Moorfield Rd Fairlawn OH 44333*

ALEVAS, RENEE K., Ret Compensatory Writing Tchr; *b:* Berlin, Germany; *c:* Deborah Zampariello, Donald Alevas; *ed:* Adelphi Suffolk Coll (BA) Ed 1967; Adelphi Univ (MA) Ed 1969; 70 Post Grad Hrs Mostly from Southampton Coll; *cr:* Ctr Moriches SD 6th Grd Tchr 1967-69; Bayport-Blue Point SD 6th Grd Tchr 1969-77, 5th Grd Tchr 1977-85, Compensatory Writin Tchr Dist Wide 1985-90; *ai:* NYSUT 1967-, Del; AFT 1967-, Del; BBPEA 1969-VP; Tchr of Yr; Village of Patchogue Bd of Trustees 1983-95, Elected Trustee, 3 Four Yr Terms; Patchogue Jeffersonian Club 19830, Recording Sec; Woman's Club of Pakh 1984-; Br ookhaven Bus, Profess Women, Woman of Yr; Chair Patchogue Centennial Comm 1992-93; *home:* 38 Pine Blvd Patchogue NY 11772

ALEX, STANLEY EARL, 4th Grade Teacher; *b:* Steubenville, OH; *m:* Pamela Anne Graham; *c:* Todd, Kim; *ed:* West Liberty St (BA) Ed 1972; Attnd Kent St Univ, WV Univ, Univ of Steubenville, Univ of Dayton, Mount St Joseph; *cr:* Steubenville City Schls Tchr 1975-; *ai:* Safety Patrol Adv; Steub Ed Assn, East OH Educ Assn, OH Educ Assn, Natl Ed Assn 1975-; T-Ball Coach, 5 Yrs; Sftbl Coach, 10 Yrs; Toronto Band Parents 6 Yrs, Various Comm; Toronto United Meth Church, Various Comm; *home:* 932 Logan St Toronto OH 43964

ALEXA, MICHAEL KURTY, Math Teacher; *b:* Erie, PA; *ed:* St Francis Coll (BA) Math 1974; Gannon Univ Ed Credits; *cr:* J S Wilson Jr High Math Tchr 1977-78; Tech HS Math Tchr 1978; Cathedral Ctr Schl Math Tchr 1978-81; Cathedral Prep Schl Math Tchr 1981-; *ai:* IM Dir; Asst Tennis Coach; Ski Club & Soph Class Adv; Discipline Review Bd; NCEA 1981-; PCTM 1994-; 1st Night Erie 1995-, HS & Coll Art Contest Co-Chprsn; *office:* Cathedral Prep Schl 225 W 9th St Erie PA 16501*

ALEXANDER, BARBARA, Primary Resource Room Teacher; *b:* Morrisville, VT; *m:* William Everett; *c:* Heather Tia; *ed:* Bridgewater St Coll (BS) Spec Ed 1978; *cr:* Bay Path Regnl Voc HS Generic Specialist 1979-82; Dudley Elem Schl Learning Specialist 1982-84; West Brookfield Elem Schl Primary Resource Room Tchr 1983-; *ai:* FHA Stu Adv; Schl Cncl; Stu Asst Team; Prof Dev, Prof Rights & Responsibilities Comms; Cncl of Exceptional Children 1978-; NEA, MTA 1979-; QEA 1983-; Stowe VT Comm Svc Awd; Greater Worcester Jaycees Outstdng Young Ldr Awd; *office:* West Brookfield Elem Sch 89 N Main St West Brookfield MA 01585

ALEXANDER, BETSY L., Coord of GATE & Career Prgms; *b:* Fremont, OH; *m:* William A.; *c:* Jason L., Joshua M.; *ed:* Heidelberg Coll (BA) Elem Ed 1977; Wright St Univ (MED) Supervision, Gifted Ed 1988; 15 Hrs Ed Admin Ashland Univ, OH St Univ; *cr:* Mohawk Local Schls 1st Grd Tchr 1976-78; Cornell Area Schls 1-2, 6 Grd Tchr, HS Coach 1979-84; Gibsonburg Exempted Village Schl Gifted Ed Tchr, Home Tutor 1984-85; Median Cty Schl Adult Ed, Sub Tchr 1985-86; Ft Recover Local Schls Gifted Edctr 1986-90; Mansfield City Schls Coord Gifted, Career Ed 1990-; *ai:* Future Problem Solving Coach; Odyssey of Mind Consultant, Dir; Curr, Instruction Comm; Phi Delta Kappa 1992-, VP, Mbrshp Prgm Presenter; OH Assn for Gifted Children 1986-; Consortium Coord for Gifted 1988-; Career Ed Assn 1990-, Historian, Conf Comm; Children's Theatre Fnd 1990-, Sec; Bus Advy 1995-, Partners for Profgress Coord; YMCA Achievers Prgm 1995-, Advy Bd; Grants.*

ALEXANDER, CHRISTOPHER SCOTT, Asst Prof of Mrktg; *b:* wilkes-Barre, PA; *m:* Melissa Church; *ed:* King's Coll (BS) Govt & Politics 1979; the Amer Univ (MBA) Mngmt 1982; Doctoral Candidate SUNY at Albany; *cr:* Coll Misericordia Instr of Fin 1983-84; Keuka Coll Chair, Div of Bus & Pub Affairs, Assoc Prof of Mngmt 1984-89; King's Coll Asst Prof of Mrktg 1989-; *ai:* Stu Govt, Mrktng & Mngmt Assn Fac Advs; Acad of Mngmt, IACS 1994-; South Wilkes-Barre Rotary 1996; Friendly Sons of St Patrick 1993-; Articles Pub; All Coll Awd Fac 1995; Cooperative Ed Grant 1983; *office:* Kings Coll 133 N River St Wilkes-Barre PA 18711*

ALEXANDER, DAVID JOHN, Physical Ed Tchr & Asst Prin; *b:* Columbia, SC; *m:* Nancy Ann Rogers; *c:* Shannon, David Jr., Kevin; *ed:* Ashland Univ (BS) Ed 1975; 2 Credits Games that Work Malone Coll; *cr:* St Columbkille Schl PE Tchr, Asst Prin 1976-; *ai:* Trinity HS Girls JV Bsktbl Coach; TV News Show Producer; OAHPERD, Cleveland Bsktbl Coaches Assn 1980-; NCEA 1976-; *office:* St Columbkille Schl 6740 Broadview Rd Parma OH 44134

ALEXANDER, DONNA M., Business Teacher & Dept Head; *b:* Amsterdam, NY; *m:* Joseph P.; *c:* Christine; *ed:* Marywood Coll (BA) Bus 1963; SUNY at Albany (MS) Bus 1969; 30 Addl Hrs; *cr:* Saratoga Springs HS Bus Tchr 1963-95; Burnt Hills HS Summer Schl Bus Tchr 1965-69; Saratoga Springs HS Bus Dept Head, Bus Tchr 1995-; *ai:* Cmptr Tech, Shared Decision Making Comms; Project InVest Coord, Instr; Saratoga Springs Figure Skating Club Pres; Saratoga Springs Tchrs Assn 1963-, Corresponding Sec, Bus Dept Head; NYSUT; AFT; BTA 1963-; *home:* 5 Meadow Ln Saratoga Springs NY 12866

ALEXANDER, DOROTHY JEAN, Child Studies Instructor; *b:* Norwood, MA; *m:* William Joseph; *c:* Mark, Nicola; *ed:* Bridgewater St Coll (BS) Early Chldhd Ed 1983, (MED) Early Chldhd Ed 1991; *cr:* Mansfield Childrens Ctr Tchr 1983-86; Boston Schl for the Deaf Childrens Ctr Dir & Tchr 1986-89; Dean Coll Child Stud Instr 1991-; *ai:* NAEYC & BAEYC 1991-; *office:* Dean Coll 99 Main St Franklin MA 02038

ALEXANDER, JOSEPH P., Third Grade Teacher; *b:* North Creek, NY; *m:* Donna M.; *c:* Christine; *ed:* Potsdam St Coll (BS) Elem Ed 1962; Plattsburgh St Coll (MS) Elem Admin 1971; Post Grad Stud Curr Albany St Univ, Oneonta St Coll; *cr:* Chestertown Cntrl Schl 6th Grd Tchr 1962-64; Saratoga City Schl Dist 5th Grd Tchr 1964-66; Schuylerville Cntrl Schl 6th Grd Tchr 1966-70; Saratoga City Schl Dist 6th Grd Tchr 1970-72, Asst Prin 1972-74, 3rd Grd Tchr 1974-; *ai:* Saratoga Schl Dist Bsktbl Coach 1964-66, Comms Curr Stud 1974-75, Math Curr 1975-76, Rdng Curr 1970-72; Schuylerville Tchrs Assn 1966-70, Negotiations Team; Saratoga Tchrs Assn 1970-, Pres, 1st VP, 2nd VP, Sec; NY United Tchrs 1962-, Dist #10 Rep; Elks Club #161 1964-, Schlsp Chm 1965, Stu Bowling Chm 1966; Opalescent Club 1970-; *home:* 5 Meadow Ln Saratoga Springs NY 12866

ALEXANDER, MICHELE MCCLURE, Spanish Teacher; *b:* Warren, OH; *m:* Bruce E.; *c:* Matthew, Alison; *ed:* Univ of Toledo (BE) Span & His 1971; Post Grad Credit Hrs at Univ of Salamanca Spain & Bowling Green St Univ; *cr:* Washington Local Schls Span Tchr 1971-76; Toledo Museum of Art Docent & Art His Educator 1978-92; Saint Francis de Sales HS Span Tchr 1991-; *ai:* Discipline Bd Mem; Prins Advy Bd Chprsn; Toledo Museum of Art Docents 1978-, VP 1987, Pres 1988; Episcopal Church Women 1976-, Pres 1985-88; Vestry Saint Pauls Church 1986-89; Selected as a Speaker at 2 Natl Docent Symposiums Natl Gallery in Washington DC

& Toledo Museum of Art; *office:* St Francis Desales HS 2323 W Bancroft St Toledo OH 43607

ALEXANDER, NORMAN FREDERICK, Instrumental Music Teacher; *b:* N Tonawanda, NY; *m:* Lynn Christman; *c:* Sarah L., Katherine D.; *ed:* SUNY at Buffalo (BA) Music Ed 1976, (MMed) Music Ed 1991; Post Grad Stud in Wind Lit, Conducting; *cr:* North Tonawanda HS Music Tchr, Coord 1978-; *ai:* Orch, Wind Ensemble, Telecommunications Club Adv; Alternative Scheduling, Facility, Music Prgm Review Comms; Mentor Tchr; North Tonawanda United Tchrs 1978-, Bldg Rep, Tchr Ctr Rep; NYSSMA, MENC 1976-, Registered Music Ed; Niagara Co Music Edctrs 1976-, VP; Tonawanda Musicians Assn 1972-, Exec Bd; Pi Kappa Lambda; First United Meth Church; North Tonawanda Centennial Comm 1996; Univ at Buffalo Pep Band Dir 1986-; All-Cty Music Festivals Guest Conductor; Trumpet Prof Musician; *office:* North Tonawanda HS 405 Meadow Dr North Tonawanda NY 14120*

ALEXANDER, PATRICIA BOURGOINE, Business Education Teacher; *b:* Peterborough, NH; *m:* R. Gregg; *c:* Kristin, Thomas; *ed:* Plymouth St Coll (BS) Bus Ed 1978; Travel Ed Ctr Cert Travel & Tourism 1995; *cr:* Milford Area HS Tchr 1978-80; Jaffrey-Rindge HS Tchr 1980-81; Self-Employed Computerized Acctng 1985-94; Contoocook Vly Regnl HS Tchr 1994-; *ai:* Sr Class Adv; Information Svcs, Region 14 Applied Tech Advy Comm; *office:* Contoocook Valley Regional HS Rt 202 N Peterborough NH 03458

ALEXANDER, ROBERT PAUL, Fourth Grade Teacher; *b:* Bronx, NY; *ed:* St Univ of NY at Brockport (BS) Elem Ed 1970; Fairfield Univ (MA) Elem Ed 1975; *cr:* Oakwood Schl 6th Grd Tchr 1971; Midland Schl 5th Grd Tchr 1971-92; Milton Schl 5th Grd, 4th Grd Tchr 1992-; *ai:* Produced, Directed, Accompanied Sr Musicals 1976, 1980-82; Dist Elem Report Card Comm; Rye Tchrs Assn 1971-, Milton Schl Fac Club Pres 1993-95; NYSUT, AFT 1971-; Profuced Sing Alongs at Area Sr Citizen Ctrs, Nrsng Homes 1983-87; *office:* Milton Schl Hewlett Ave Rye NY 10580

ALEXANDER, ROBERT WM., 6th Grade Teacher; *b:* Darby, PA; *m:* Robbi Kelly; *c:* Jacqueline, Jordan; *ed:* St Josephs Univ (BA) Pol Sci 1973; Trenton St Coll Soc Stud, Elem Ed Cert 1986; *cr:* Timberland Jr HS 7th-8th Grd His, Soc Stud Tchr 1986-87; Hopewell Elem Schl 6th Grd Tchr 1987-; *ai:* Hopewell Vly Ed Assn VP; Safety Patrol Adv; NEA; Viet Nam Veterans of Amer 1991-; 1st Marine Aircraft Wing Assn 1993-; *office:* Hopewell Elem Schl 425 S Main St Pennington NJ 08534

ALEXANDER, SANDRA ANDERSON, 5th Grade Teacher; *b:* Dayton, OH; *m:* Charles; *c:* Kimani Anderson, Jemele, Lakisha; *ed:* Univ Dayton (MS) Tchr Ed 1994; Central St Univ (BS) Elem Ed 1975; *cr:* Scioto Vlg Math Tchr 1979-80; Innis Elem 2nd Grd Tchr 1981-87, 5th Grd Tchr 1988-; *ai:* NEA 1979-; CEA 1979-; *office:* Innis Elem Schl 3399 Kohr Blvd Columbus OH 43224*

ALEXANDER, SARAH A., Vice Principal; *b:* Adale, GA; *m:* Richard Martin; *c:* Tristan, Keely; *ed:* CA St at Dominguez Hills (BA) 1973; Johns Hopkins Univ (MS) Admin, Supervision 1990; CA St at Dominguez Hills Tchr Cert 1974; *cr:* markham Jr HS Eng, Soc Stud Tchr 1974-78; Hartman Jr HS Eng Tchr 1978-85; Bucklodge MS Eng Tchr 1985-91; High Point HS Vice Prin 1991-; *ai:* Multi-Cultural, Mid States, Stu Intervention Comm Chprsns; NASSP 1996; Assn Supervisory & Admin Schl Prsnl 1990-; Howard Cty Parent Advy 1995-; Alpha Wives 1993-; *office:* High Point HS 3601 Powdermill Rd Beltsville MD 20705*

ALEXANDER, SHERAN JONES, Secondary English Instructor; *b:* Erie, PA; *m:* Wesley E.; *c:* Miles; *ed:* Clarion Univ of PA (BA) Comm Arts 1982; *cr:* Gannon Univ Upward Bound Prgm Cnslr 1982-86; East HS Eng Tchr 1986-; *ai:* African Amer Interest Club, Stdnts Interested in Tchng Adv; NEA, PSEA, EEA 1986-; NAACP, Primary Hlth Care, Penn St Advy Bds; Strategic Planning Comm Chprsn, Schl Dist of Erie.

ALEXANDER, TODD ELWOOD, HS Mathematics Teacher; *b:* Richmond, IN; *m:* Diane Lynn Smith; *c:* Denver Herman; *ed:* Univ of Indianapolis (BS) Math Ed 1981; Univ of Dayton (MS) Math Ed 1993; *cr:* Southport MS Math Tchr 1981-82; Union HS Math Tchr 1982-83; Natl Trail HS Math Tchr, Chprsn 1983-, Started Advanced Coll Project Classes Through IN Univ; North Central Riverview Board; Earned Adj Prof Status by Teaching Night Classes at IN Univ East; *ai:* Prins Advy Comm; NEA, OEA 1985-, Uniserv Rep; Coblenta Classroom Tchrs Assn 1986-, Pres; OH Classroom Tchrs of Math 1986-; Natl Rifle Assn 1988-; Introduced Team Tchng Interdisciplinaries to Preble Cty; Nom for Presidential Excl in Tchng Math Awd; *home:* 615 Lakengren Dr Eaton OH 45320

ALEXION, JOHN C., Social Studies Teacher; *b:* Providence, RI; *ed:* Rhode Island Coll (BA) His, Pol Sci 1979; Providence Coll (MA) His 1985; Addl 60 Credit Hrs Beyond Master of Arts ESL Content Endorsement; *cr:* Nathan Bishop MS Soc Stud Chair 1990-; Providence Schl Dept Soc Stud Curr Facilitator 1993-; *ai:* Mock Trial, Nathan Bishop MS Soc Stud Olympiad Adv; AFT 1986-; Soc Stud Curr 7-12 Grd Wkshp Facilitator, Writer, Ed; *office:* Nathan Bishop MS 101 Sessions St Providence RI 02906

ALFANO, FRANK JOHN, Mathematics Teacher; *b:* Providence, RI; *m:* Joan Elizabeth Connolly; *c:* Frank Jr., David, Julie, Stephanie; *ed:* Univ of RI (BA) Ed & Math 1975; Doctorate in Sports Psychology; MS Equivalent From PC, RIC, Salve Regma 1981; *ai:* Ftbl, Girls Sftbl & Bsktbl Coach; Class of 1994 & Ski Club Adv; NEA, Del RI Assembly 1993, RI Rep 1994; Income Tax Preparer Assn; Warren Town Cncl 1986-, VP 6 Yrs; Bristol YMCA 1989-, Bd of Dirs; Cable Advisory Comm 1989-; Bd of Dir Briston Cnty Water Auth; Warren Tax Revn Comm Mem; St RepDist 89; Warren Town Tax Assessor 1976-84; Coach of Yr RI 1995; *office:* Portsmouth H S Education Ln Portsmouth RI 02871*

ALFANO, RAYMOND LOUIS, English Teacher; *b:* Providence, RI; *m:* Carol; *c:* Bethany, Allyson, Scott; *ed:* Univ of RI (BA) Eng, Sec Ed 1969; 30 Addl Credits; *cr:* East Greenwich HS Eng Tchr 27 Yrs; *ai:* Adv Yrbk 26 Yrs, Class 1976, 1980, 1984, 1990, 1996, Newspaper 10 Yrs, Quill & Scroll, Interact, Lit Mag; Feinstein Comm Svc Prgm Coord; E. Greenwich Ed Assn 1969-, Treas; NEA RI; NCTE; West Bay Jewish Comm Ctr, Pres; Yankee PEN 1989-, Sec; Presidential Scholar's Distinguished Tchr Awd 1984, 1993; Amer Assoc of Univ Women Influential Ed Awrd 1991, 1996; *office:* East Greenwich HS 300 Avenger Dr East Greenwich RI 02818

ALFARE, CARLO, Chemistry Professor & Coord; *b:* New York, NY; *m:* Mary Healy; *c:* Kathleen; *ed:* Stevens Inst of Tech (BS) Chem 1964, (MS) Chem 1966; 60 Addl Credits; *cr:* Stevens Inst of Tech Instr of Chem 1967-71; Fairleigh Dickenson Adjunct Fac 1971-73; Passaic Co Comm Coll Tchng Asst 1972-73; Mercer Co Comm Coll Prof of Chem 1973-; *ai:* Coll Senate 1975-; ACS 1967-, Dir; SIGMA XI 1968-; NSTA 1980-; Trenton Sect ACS 1983-, Schlsp Comm; Flwshp Stevens Inst of Tech 1964-67; Pub Gen Chem Course, Lab Manuals; Pub Phys Sci Course, Lab Manuals; Distngd Tchr Awd 1995; *office:* Mercer County Community Coll 1200 Old Trenton Rd Trenton NJ 08690

ALFIERI, NANCY J., Math Teacher; *b:* Plainfield, NJ; *m:* Anthony; *c:* Sharon, Toniann; *ed:* Glassboro ST (BA) Ed 1969; Georgian Court (MA) Supervision, Admin 1982; *cr:* Carpenter Schl 4th, 6th Grd Tchr 1969-82; Salk Schl 7th Grd Math, Rdng, Sci Tchr 1987-; *ai:* NJEA, MCEA, OBEA 1964-, Rep; Pt Pleasant Soccer Assn 1986-, VP: Pt Pleasant Recreation Commission 1990-, Vice Chair, Chprns; Republican Comm Woman 1990-; Republicans for Pt Pleasant 1995-, Sec; *office:* Jonas Salk MS W Greystone Rd Old Bridge NJ 08857

ALFIERI, RALPH,JR., Science Teacher; *b:* Brooklyn, NY; *m:* Rosemary; *c:* Michael, Donna; *ed:* St Univ of NY at Plattsburg (BS) Ed 1977; St Univ of NY at Stony brook (MA) Liberal Stud 1980; 30 Hrs Post Grad at Various Insts; 30 Hrs of Inservice Ed on Various Ed Issues & Topics; *cr:* Longwood Jr HS Sci Tchr 1977-; *ai:* AFT 1977-; NYSUT 1977-; Middle Island TA 1977-, Sec-treas; Prin Golden Apple Awd Twice; *office:* Longwood Jr HS 198 Longwood Rd Middle Island NY 11953

ALFIERI, ROSALIE (SCAGLIONE), Art Teacher; *b:* Brooklyn, NY; *m:* Philip; *c:* Craig; *ed:* Brooklyn Coll (BA) Ed 1967, (MS) Ed, Rdng 1971; Addl 30 Credit Hrs Post Masters Stud Educl Areas; *cr:* PS 73 Brooklyn Schl 1st Grd Rdng Tchr 1967-74; Per Diem Sub Various Grd Tchr 1975-79; PS 73 Brooklyn Schl 3rd Grd Tchr 1979-80; PS 212 Brooklyn Schl 1st, 5th-6th Grd Tchr 1980-91, Art Tchr 1991-; *ai:* Art Club 1991-; Dist 21 Annual Soc Stud, Multicultural Expostion Coord; UFT, AFT 1967-; NYC Admin Women in Ed Recognition Awd 1992; Dist 21 Excl in Tchng Awd 1994; Outstdng Achvmt in Multicultural Ed Awd 1994; Dist 21 Baca Spec Recognition Awd 1995; *office:* PS 212 Lady Deborah Moody 87 Bay 49th St Brooklyn NY 11214

ALFIERI, THERESA MESKIS, Early Training Program Teacher; *b:* Passaic, NJ; *m:* John C. Jr.; *c:* Christopher, Carlea; *ed:* William Paterson Coll (BA) Elem Ed 1970; Nursery Schl Cert 1981; Trained in Format Tchng Method; *cr:* Lodi Pub Schl Tchr 1970-83; Private Schl Tchr 1984-90; Saddle Brook Pub Schl Tchr 1990-; *ai:* Saddle Brook HS Band Trustee, Soccer Parents Assn Sec; Boys Bsktbl Parents Assn; Tchr Parent Stu Assn; Presch Handicapped, Project Grad Commss; Saddle Brook Ed Assn, Bergen Cty Ed Assn, NJ Ed Assn, NEA 1995-; Assn of Kndgtn Edctrs 1984-91; Boy Scout Troop 213 1989-, Comm; Friends of Saddle Brook Lib 1991-; Saddle Brook Main Lions Club 1995-; *office:* Salome H. Long Meml Schl 260 Floral Ln Saddle Brook NJ 07663*

ALFONSE, ROBERT H., High School Science Teacher; *b:* Jersey City, NJ; *m:* Kathleen; *ed:* RI Coll (BS) Sci, Hlth 1978; Rutgers Univ (EDM) Sci Ed 1987; *cr:* Our Lady of Victories Schl 7-8th Grd Earth Sci Tchr 1/2 Yr; Columbia Schl 7th Grd Life Sci Tchr 1/2 Yr; Keyport HS 9-12th Grd Phys Sci Tchr 2 Yrs; Point Pleasant HS 9-12th Grd Bio, Earth Sci Tchr 15 Yrs; *ai:* Girls Cross Cntry, Winter, Spring Track Coach; Class Adv; NJEA, NEA 1978-; Tchr of Yr 1995; Dist Tchr of Yr 1994; Nom Distngd Tchr Awd 1994; Eisenhower Grant Costa Rica Tropical Ecology Rsrch 1993; Adult HS Tchr of Yr 1991; *office:* Point Pleasant Borough HS Laura Herbert Dr Point Pleasant NJ 08742

ALFONSO, REGINA MARIE,SND, Education Dept Assoc Prof; *b:* Memphis, TN; *ed:* St John Coll (BSE) Elem Ed 1953; St Louis Univ (EdM) Supervision, Admin 1967; Attnd Ball St Univ, John Carroll Univ, Cleveland St Univ; *cr:* 14 Elem Schls in OH, VA, Washington DC 3rd-6th Grd Tchr 1950-78; Notre Dame Coll of OH Assoc Prof Ed Dept 1978-; *ai:* Frosh Seminar Re-Entry Prgm Acad Adv; In-Svc Wkshps for Tchrs; NCTM, NCTE, IRA, NSTA 1978-; OCSS 1996; Phi Delta Kappan 1992-; Distngd Fac Awd 1985; NEH Grant 1985; Univ of CT Inst of Children's Lit Sears, Roebuck Fnd for Tchng Excl & Campus Ldrshp 1991; Authored: How Jesus Taught Methods and Techniques of the Master; Articles Pub; *office:* Notre Dame Coll of OH 4545 College Rd Cleveland OH 44121*

ALFORD, JOYCE DEANS, Guidance Counselor; *b:* Washington, DC; *m:* Ken R.; *c:* Yolanda, Kenny; *ed:* Univ of DC (MA) Guid, Cnslng 1994; Conflict Mediation, Resolution Trng; *cr:* Nichols Ave Primary Schl K-1st Grd Tchr 1970-82; Birney Elem Schl 1 Grd Tchr 1982-86; J. G. Whittier Elem Schl 2nd-3rd Grd Tchr 1987-94; Scott Montgomery Elem Schl Guid Cnslr 1994-; *ai:* Handbell Choir Directress; Substance Abuse Ed SAY Yes Prgm; Girls Only 6th Grd Girls Group; Schl Attendance Comm; WA Tchrs Union, AFT 1970-; DC Schl Cnslng Assn 1994-; Sigma Gamma Rho 1968-.

ALGEE, JOHN R.,III, Religion Teacher; *b:* Toledo, OH; *m:* Earma G. Latson; *c:* Juanita, Valquita, John IV, Joshua; *ed:* Univ of Toledo (BA) Soc Work 1991; *cr:* St Patrick Historic Cath Church Pastoral Assoc 1981-87; Cath Diocese of Toledo Dir 1987-92; Cntrl Cath HS Rel Stud Tchr 1992-; *ai:* Club Adv; Pastoral Cncl & Team; NEA 1992-; Alpha Phi Alpha 1971-; Prince Hall Free & Accepted Masons 1981-; Natl Black Cath Clergy Caucus 1987-; Natl Assn African Amer Deacons 1994-; Toledo Chptr Negro Woman Bus & Prof Org Man of Yr; *office:* Central Catholic HS 2550 Cherry St Toledo OH 43608

ALGEO, ANN M., Assistant Professor of English; *b:* Philadelphia, PA; *m:* Randy Jones; *ed:* Lebanon Valley Coll (BA) Eng 1974; Temple Univ Schl of Law (JD) 1982; Lehigh Univ (PHD) Eng 1992; *cr:* Bucks Cty Court of Common Pleas Law Clerk 1982-85; Lehigh Univ Tchng Asst 1985-90, Asst Learning Ct Dir 1991; DE Valley Coll Asst Eng Prof 1992-; *ai:* Modern Lang Assn 1990-; E. W. Fairchild Fellowship Amer Lit; Article Pub 1993; Co-Authored Article Pub 1987; Book Pub 1996 The Courtroom as Forum: Homicide Trials by Dreiser, Wright, Capote, & Mailer; *office:* Delaware Valley Coll 700 E Butler Ave Doylestown PA 18901

ALGER, ANN MARIE, Third Grade Teacher; *b:* Lowville, NY; *ed:* Jefferson Comm Coll (AAS) Liberal Arts 1967; St Univ of NY at Albany (BS) Ed 1969, (MS) Ed 1971; Attnd Cultural Stud Acad at Salzburg Austria; *cr:* St Univ of NY Instr 1971-76; Baldwinsville Cntrl Schls Tchr 1976-; *ai:* NEA 1971-; Baldwinsville Tchrs Assn & Pi Omega Pi 1976-; Big Brothers Big Sisters; Cultural Resources Cncl; Scott, Foresman Publishing, Tchr Consultant & Critic Reader; *office:* L Pearl Palmer Elem Schl Hicks Rd Baldwinsville NY 13027

ALI, GAIL LOUISE (MACK), Fifth Grade Teacher; *b:* Cleveland, OH; *m:* Syed Irshad; *c:* Shahnaz, Syed Ehitisham; *ed:* OH Univ (BS) Elem Ed 1971; Cleveland St Univ (MED) Admin 1984; Cert Curr & Instruction 1982; *cr:* Cleveland Pub Schls Tchr 24 Yrs; *ai:* Schl Safety Cncl, Parent Involvement, Parent Advy, Curr & Instruction & Staff Lead Team Chprsn; Co-Chprsn Union Conf Comm; Lead Tchr; Liaison Adopt A Schl Comm; Liaison TEAMS Transportation Comm; John Hay-West Tech Rep; Schl Based Mgmt Comm; AFT 1971-; Cleveland Tchrs Union 1972-; Supts Prof Team 1993-95; Safetytown Safety Patrol 1995-, Supervising Tchr; Beachwood PTA 1988-, Coord 1994, Appreciation Luncheon & Cert; Schl Comm for Bell Ctr, Agency Rep, Univ Credits Cert; Martha Holden Jennings Scholar 1984-85; Schl Coord Fatima Comm Ctr; *home:* 2355 S Green Rd Beachwood OH 44122*

ALICEA, GLORIA, Biology Teacher; *b:* San German, PR; *ed:* Inter Amer Univ (BA) Bio 1980; Post Grad Stud Ashland Univ 1993-95; *cr:* Lincoln West HS Bio Tchr 1980-; SYETP Coord 1985-89; *ai:* Sr Adv; AFT 1980-; CRAB 1995-; Cryst; St Test 1993-, Stdnts Tutor; B P Amer Grants; *office:* Lincoln-West HS 3202 W 30th St Cleveland OH 44109

ALIGNAY, JAMES NEIL, Chemistry Teacher; *b:* Bethesda, MD; *ed:* Columbia Union Coll (BS) Bio, Chem 1994; Attnd Johns Hopkins Univ; *cr:* Columbia Union Coll Tchng Asst 1992-94; Takoma Acad Chem Tchr 1994-; *ai:* Network Adv; Internet Admin; NSTA 1994-; Bio Achvmt Awd 1994; Biochem Achvmt, Comm Svc Awds 1993; *office:* Takoma Acad 8120 Carroll Ave Takoma Park MD 20912*

ALIOTTA, PHILLIP VINCENT, Spanish Teacher; *b:* Bronx, NY; *m:* Jo-Ann Aliotta; *c:* Christine Cavazza, Dina Cavazza, Vincent; *ed:* Iona Coll (BA) Span 1963; Hunter Coll (MA) Span 1968; *cr:* PS 30 5th Grd Tchr 1963-64; JHS 44 Span Tchr 1964-73; IS 200 Span Tchr, Schedule Programmer 1973-; *ai:* Asst Adv Sr Act; UFT 1963-; Knights of Columbus 1974-; Washingtonville Little League 1986-; IS 200 Tchr of Yr 1990-92,; *home:* 11 Finley Dr Salisbury Mills NY 12577

ALJANCIC, ANDREW A., English & Speech Teacher; *b:* Cleveland *m:* Joanie; *c:* Andy, Andrea, Jon, Mike; *ed:* Kent St Univ (BS) En 1964, (MED) Ed, Eng 1968; *cr:* Louisville HS Eng, PE Tchr, 1964-68; Lake HS Eng, PE Tchr, Coach 1968-72; St Thomas Aquin Eng, Speech Tchr, Coach 1972-; *ai:* Chess Club Adv; Debate C Origins Comm Chm; Christ United Meth, Boys Choir, Sunday Schl Louisville City Cncl 1992-95, Councilman; Louisville Schl Bd 199 Mem; Citizen of Yr 1983; *home:* 940 Church St Louisville OH 4464

ALJUWANI, KHALEDAH, Secondary English Teacher; *b:* Buffalo *m:* Ali Ibn; *c:* Ali R., Yusef J., Maryam F.; *ed:* Villa Maria Coll (AA Sci 1974; Univ of Buffalo (BA) Ed 1976, (MS) Ed 1981; 30 Addl Hr Grad Stud Tchr Ctr Military St Buffalo; *cr:* Kensington Magnet H Tchr 1976-; *ai:* Bennett HS Tchr of Month 1979; Pub Speaking 1982-85; Eng Dept Chair 1986-87; NEA 1976-; PTA 1995-; *o* Kensington Magnet Schl 245 Stanton Buffalo NY 14212*

ALKIRE, CAROL COURTNEY, Fourth Grade Teacher; *b:* Parkers WV; *m:* Clair Wayne; *c:* Clair Jr., Jennifer C.; *ed:* WV Univ (ASSO 1972; OH Univ (BS) Elem Ed 1974; Addl 153 Hrs Post Grad 197 Cutler Elem Schl First, Second Grd Tchr 1974-78; Barlow Vincent Schl Third, Fourth Grd Tchr 1979-80, Fourth Grd Tchr 1980-; *ai:* OEA, SEOEA, Warren Local Ed Assn 1974-; Heritage Rdng Cncl Nom Ashland Tchr of Yr; *office:* Barlow Vincent Elem Schl Rt 1 V OH 45784

ALKIRE, CYNTHIA BAYNE, Science Teacher; *b:* New London, C Gary D.; *c:* Kathryn Lynn, Christopher Dean; *ed:* St Univ of NY C Fredonia (BS) Medical Tech 1980; Eastern CT St Univ Post-Baccala Tchr Cert 1993; *cr:* Bolton HS Long-Term Sci Sub Tchr 1991-94; Co HS Sci Tchr 1994-; *ai:* Trust Schlsp Comm Mem; Ind Stud Adv; Dances, Coffeehouses & Proms Chaperone; NSTA, Bio Tchrs Assn Girl Scouts of Amer 1989-, Ldr, Trainer, Outstanding Ldr Awd; Coventry HS 78 Ripley Hill Rd Coventry CT 06238*

ALLAIRE, BOBBIE CAROL, HS Art Teacher; *b:* New Brunswick *m:* Sean; *c:* Jamie, Kaitlyn; *ed:* Georgian Court Coll (BA) Art Ed 19 Jackson Meml HS Art Tchr 1984; Sylvia Rosenauer Elem Schl Art 1985-86; St Mary's Acad K-8 Grd Art Tchr 1986-88; Sylvia Rose Elem Schl Art Tchr 1988-89; Jackson Meml HS Art Tchr 1989-; *ai* Sts Art Chprsn; Drama, Musical Productions Set Designer, Stage Conflict Mngmt Instr; Saturday Schl Tchr; JTA 1989-; NEA 1988-; NAEA 1990-; *office:* Jackson Memorial HS 101 Don Connor Blvd Ja NJ 08527*

ALLAIRE, BRITTA ELISABET (BROMAN), Sixth Grade Teach Worcester, MA; *m:* Arnold Victor; *ed:* Univ of MA (BA) Eng Continuing Grad Courses at Anna Maria Coll at Paxton & Worces Coll; *cr:* Oxford HS 8-9th Grd Tchr Eng & Math 1973-74; Oxford M Grd Tchr Eng, Spelling, Rdng & Soc Stud 1974-; *ai:* Support St Month Act; Participation in Ethnic Fair; Pioneered Inclusion Co- Prgm; NEA, OEA 1973-; *office:* Oxford MS Main St Oxford MA 01

ALLAIRE, ELLEN FOX, Social Studies Teacher; *b:* Manchester, N Donald; *ed:* Keene St Coll (BED) Soc Stud 1973; Suffolk Univ (ME 1977; *cr:* Varney Schl Rdng, Elem Tchr 1973-76; Parkside Jr HS Soc Eng Tchr 1977-86; Meml HS Soc Stud Tchr 1987-; *ai:* NEA, NHEA, 1973-, Sr Rep; *office:* Memorial HS South Porter St Mancheste 03103*

ALLAIRE, NANCY H., Sixth Grade Teacher; *b:* Ithaca, NY; *ed:* Univ (BA) Soc Sci 1972; SUNY Coll of Env Scis, Forestry Environmental Sci 1979; Eastern MI Univ Elem Cert 1973; Russell Evening Division NYS Cert 1974; *cr:* Owego Cntrl Schls 1, 2, 4 Grd Tchr 1974-78; Newfield Cntrl Schl 6 Grd Elem Tchr 19 Union-Endicott Schls 4-6 Grd Elem Tchr 1979-84; Norwich City GATE Tchr 1984-88, 6 GRd Tchr 1988-; *ai:* Co-Adv Stu Cncl; Dist-Wide Site Based, Intermediate Authentic Assessment Teams; No Edctrs Org 1984-, 2nd VP; St Paul's Church, Parish Cncl Mem Chenango Co Habitat for Humanity, Family Selection Comm Mem; Perry Browne Intermediate Schl Beebe Ave Norwich NY 13815

ALLAMAN, PAUL W., 9th Grd Social Studies Teacher; *b:* Oil Cit *m:* Peggy A Wimer; *c:* Chris, Heather, Lea; *ed:* Clarion Univ (BS) So 1975, (MS) Rdng Specialist 1977; Westminster Coll (MS) Scndry Admin 1980; *cr:* Cranberry HS Rdng Tchr 1976-79, Asst Prin 1980-9 Stud Tchr 1990-; *ai:* Jr Class Adv; Strategic PLanning Assessment C PSEA, NEA 1976-; Church Admin Cncl 1992-, Chm; *office:* Cranbe Sr HS 1 Education Dr Seneca PA 16346*

ALLAN, TIMOTHY RICHARD, Assoc Professor of History; *ed:* Carroll Univ (BS) His 1967; Christ the King Seminary (MATh) The 1988; SUNY at Buffalo (MA) His 1990, (PHD) His 1992; *cr* Enterprise Corporate Mgmt 1968-88; SUNY Coll at Fredonia Adj As His 1989-; Trocaire Coll Soc Scis Chair 1994-.

ALLARD, DONNA MARIE, Music Teacher & Choral Dir; *b:* Leom MA; *m:* Randall D. Buzzell; *ed:* Univ of Lowell (BM) Music Ed Fitchburg St Coll (MA) Elem Ed 1991; Attnd Univ of ME at Bangor, of NH at Durham, Wheaton Coll, Queens Univ at Kingston; *cr:* B.F. MS Music Tchr, Choral Dir 1978-90; Crocker Elem Schl Music Choral Dir 1990-; *ai:* Suzuki Piano Tchr; Tchng Ballroom Dancing; S Festival; NEA, MTA 1978-; Suzuki Assn of Amer 1984-; Childrens Network; *home:* 10 Lincoln St Leominster MA 01453

ALLARD, PAULA MINNUCCI, Art Teacher; *b:* Quincy, MA; *m:* G.; *c:* Stephanie; *ed:* Univ of WI at Superior (BFA) Studio Art & 1968; RI Coll (mAT) Art 1977; Univ of RI 14 Addl Hrs; RI Schl of D 3 Addl Courses; *cr:* Cranston W 7th-9th Art Tchr 1968-69; East Gree HS K-12th Art & Jr High 9th-12th Grd Tchr 1969-; *ai:* Schlastics Art NEA 1968-; RI Art Tchrs Assn 1970-; Exceptional Art Tchrs RISD *office:* East Greenwich HS 300 Avenger Dr East Greenwich RI 0281

ALLARD, TIMOTHY R., Secondary Mathematics Teacher; *b:* U NY; *ed:* St Univ Coll at Cortland (BS) Sec Ed, Physics, Math 1984; of MN (MS) Statistics 1988; *cr:* Bradford Cntrl Schl Sci Tchr 1984, Tchr 1984-86; Univ of MN Statistics Dept Tchng Asst 1986-88; Br Cntrl Schl Math Tchr 1988-; *ai:* Fac Aths Mgr; Acad All Stars Co-Ad Cncl Adv; Lamoka Lodge F&AM 1984-, Past Master, Sec; Univ o Outstanding Tchng Asst Awd Nom 1988; Cty Cross Cntry Cham Coach 1986; *office:* Bradford Central Schl 2820 Rte 226 Bradfor 14815

ALLEGRETTO, JUDITH CARIBARDI, Secondary Mathem Teacher; *b:* Ridgway, PA; *m:* David J.; *c:* John Paul; *ed:* Univ of Pitts (BS) Applied Math 1988; St Bonaventure Univ (MSE) Comm Cnslng Scndry Ed Cert 1988; *cr:* Johnsonburg Area HS Scndry Math Tchr *ai:* NHS Adv; NEA 1988-; Johnsonburg Area Ed Assn 1988-, Bldg *office:* Johnsonburg Area Jr Sr HS Elk Ave Ext Johnsonburg PA 158

ALLEN, ARLENE CLAIR (CRESCENZI), English Teache Brooklyn, NW; *m:* Craig E.; *ed:* Montclair St Coll (BA) Eng & His Kean Coll (MA) Ed & Hum 1973; *cr:* Union Cty Regnl HS Eng T Yrs; *ai:* Prin Advy Cncl; Schlsp Comm; AFT; NCTE 1964-; *office:* Cty Regnl HS 365 Westfield Ave Clark NJ 07066

ALLEN, CHRISTOPHER W., Chemistry Professor; *b:* Waterbury, C Elizabeth Fleming; *c:* Stephen, Mark; *ed:* Univ of CT (BA) Chem Univ of IL (MS) Chem 1966, (PHD) Inorganic Chem 1967; *cr:* Univ Asst Prof 1967-72, Assoc Prof 1972-76, Prof 1976-, Dir VT EP

-; *ai:* Amer Chemical Soc; Royal Soc Chem UK; Kidder Outstdng Fac ; Univ Scholar Phys Scis; 93 Scientific Journal Articles, Chptrs; *e:* Univ Of VT & St Agri Coll Dept of Chemistry Burlington VT 05405

EN, DARLENE TRUSSELL, Business Teacher; *b:* Zanesville, OH; ohn Reed; *c:* Jan Allen Baughman, Jennifer, Joseph; *ed:* OH Univ (BS) prehensive Bus Ed 1981; OH St Univ (MA) Ed 1987; Addl Stud operative Learning, Tchrs Human Relations Skills; Desktop Pub; MS ks; Tech Prep Conf; Focus on Tech; Future Classroom; *cr:* OH Univ k Steno II 1962-65; P. L. Thornbury Legal Sec 1965-68; Perry Cty iff Private Sec; West Muskingum HS Bus Tchr 1981-; *ai:* Delta Pi lon Recording Sec; Delta Kappa Gamma Chm; OCCL VP; WMHS A Adv; FBLA OH St Chm; NBEA 1983-; OBTA; WMEA 1981-; DPE, i Sec, Mem Chair; OCCL 1971-; Effective Schls Grant; *office:* W kingum HS 200 Kimes Rd Zanesville OH 43701*

EN, DAVID C., Mathematics Teacher; *b:* Boston, MA; *m:* Meredith wles; *c:* Suzana, Natasha, Robert, Gregory; *ed:* Stonehill Coll (AB) Ed ath 1961; Bridgewater St Coll (MED) Ed & Guidance 1978; Addl rses in Psych; *cr:* Holbrook Jr HS Math Tchr 1961-65; Dept of Defense rseas Dependents Schls System Math Tchr 1965-69; Braintree Pub s Math Tchr 1971-; *ai:* NEA, MTA, BEA 1961-; *office:* South Jr HS Peach St Braintree MA 02184

EN, DENISE DISABATINO, Elementary School Librarian; *b:* nington, DE; *m:* Ronald R.; *c:* Tanner D., Chelsea R.; *ed:* Univ of DE Ed) Elem Ed 1982; DE St Univ (MA) Curr, Instr; Currently Persuing Sci Degree; 30 Addl Hrs; *cr:* Colegio Jorge Washington Third Grd Tchr ; South Dover Elem Schl Third Grd Tchr 1982-83, Fourth Grd Tchr -84, First Grd Tchr 1984-94; Hartley Elem Schl Librn 1994-; East er Elem Schl Librn 1994-; *ai:* Summer Rdng Camp Coord; Instrl Advy m; Diamond St Rdng Assn; Kent Cncl of Rdng; DE Lib Assn; rvision, Curr Assn; Read Aloud; Tchr of Yr 1987; Superstars to Ed 1990; *home:* 17 Scioto Ct Dover DE 19904*

EN, DOLORES ROTHBARD, Kindergarten Teacher; *b:* New York NY; *m:* Martin; *c:* Robyn Hennigan, Michael B.; *ed:* Brooklyn Coll Psych-Summa Cum Laude, PBK 1956; 18 Credit Hrs Ed Kean Coll -70; *cr:* So Plainfield Pub Schls Kndgtn Tchr 1965-; *ai:* Curr Revision m; Co-Dev Manipulative Math Prgm; SPEA, MCEA 1965-, Sec; A, NJAKE, NEA 1965-; Deborah Hosp Fnd 1960-, Pres, Trustee; Mini t NJEA; Tchr of Yr Governors Recognition Prgm 1992; *home:* 9 ra Cir Westfield NJ 07090*

EN, DONALD E., Agricultural Science Teacher; *b:* Mt Kisco, NY; *m:* ela Simmons; *c:* Donald Jr., Dawn, Daniel, Danette; *ed:* St Univ NY S) Ag Engrng 1965; Cedarville Coll (BA) Bus Admin 1972; Attnd OH niv, Central St Univ; *cr:* Xenia HS Ag Satellite Tchr 1972-; Greene Co er Ctr Ag Satellite Tchr 1972-; *ai:* FFA Adv; Co-Chprsn Ag Dept a HS; OEA; NEA; Greene Co EA; Old Timers Club 1994-; Grace Bapt ch 1972-, Deacon; FFA Mbrshp Highest Increase Awd 1994-95.

EN, DOUGLAS TYLER, Mathematics Teacher; *b:* Akron, OH; *ed:* e City Coll (MA) His & Math 1990; Kent St Univ (MA) His 1992,) Ed 1993; *cr:* North Hagarstown HS Math Tchr 1993-; *ai:* Adv NHS, Mediation; Coach var Asst Ftbl, Jr Var Head Bsktbl, Jr Var Asst Bsbl; 1993-; Phi Alpha Theta, Omicron Delta Kappa 1990-; *office:* North rstown HS 1200 Pennsylvania Ave Hagerstown MD 21742*

EN, ERLENE (HAGAN), Business Ed Teacher; *b:* Portland, ME; *m:* ory R.; *c:* Jason, Eric, Erin, Jenny; *ed:* Thomas Coll (BS) Bus Ed 1970; Coll (MBE) Bus Ed 1992; *cr:* Rumford HS Bus Ed Tchr 1970-73; oscoggin Cty Trng Bus Ed Tchr 1978-81; Lewiston Adult Ed Word essing Instr 1976-92; Oak Hill HS Bus Ed Tchr 1981-; *ai:* FBLA Adv; Comm; Class Adv; Schl Union K-12 Cmptr Curr Comm; Oak Hill Alliance 1981-, Treas; ME Ed Assn, NEA 1981-; Bus Ed of ME 1981-, on Dir; Delta Pi Epsilon 1991-; FBLA Adv of Yr; *office:* Oak Hill HS ox 400 Sabattus ME 04280

EN, FRANK, Social Studies Teacher; *b:* Greenwood, MS; *m:* Eloise; i, Keith; *ed:* MS Valley St Univ (BS) Comprehensive Soc Stud 1970; eland St Univ (MA) Ed 1984; *ai:* Key Club, Close-Up Adv; Ftbl, Track h; Career Beginner Mentor; AFT 1971-; *office:* South HS 7415 dway Ave Cleveland OH 44105

EN, GERALDEAN, Sixth Grade Teacher; *b:* Altro, KY; *ed:* Lees Jr (AA) Ed 1967; Morehead St Univ (BA) Ed 1969; Miami Univ (MA) & Supervision 1974; Attnd Xavier Univ, Wright St, Univ of Dayton, of Cincinnati; *cr:* Franklin City Schl Tchr 1969-; *ai:* Subject Comms; NEA, OEA, FEA 1969-, Exec Comm Chprsn; Eastern Star 1972-, Star s; Grace Bible Church Sunday Schl Treas 1992-; Tchr of Yr 1994.

EN, GRETCHEN MARIE, Biology Teacher; *b:* Watertown, NY; *ed:* wick Coll (BA) Bio, Scndry Ed 1991; Adirondack HS Regents Sci, 1987; 9 Grad Credit Hrs Drake Univ; *cr:* Newark MS Sci Tchr -93; Walton HS Regents, Gen Bio Tchr 1993-; *ai:* 10th Grd Class, Sci Adv; WTA, NEA, ASD, discipline Comm; AVP; WTA 1993-; NEA -; Lib 1994-; *office:* Walton Cntrl Schl Stockton Ave Walton NY 5*

EN, JAYMA SUE (SMITH), 7th-8th Grd Lang Arts Teacher; *b:* nce City, OH; *m:* Gregg; *c:* Abby, Alex; *ed:* West Liberty St Coll (BA) Ed, Early Chldhd 1981; Univ of Dayton (MA) Rdng 1988; *cr:* ellsville Area Cath Schl Elem Tchr 1981-83; Edison Local Schl Dist Grds Tchr 1983-; *ai:* Media Club Adv; NEA 1983-; Ldrshp Awd Given u Cnsl; Tchr of Yr; *office:* Springfield Jr HS RD #2 B Bergholz OH 8

EN, JENNIFER LYNN, Tchr of Devlpmntly Handicapped; *b:* leston, WV; *ed:* Wright St Univ (BA) LD & DH K-12 1992; OH St Working on Masters; *cr:* Brookpark MS CD Tutor 1992-93; Ashville DH Tchr 1993-; *ai:* Girls HS Soccer Coach 3 Yrs Teays Vly HS; NEA -; *office:* Ashville Elem Schl 190 Plum St Ashville OH 43103

EN, JOHN MICHAEL, Army JROTC Instructor; *b:* Ann Arbor, MI; yce Ann; *ed:* Pikes Peak Comm Coll (BA) Bus 1982; Austin Peay St (BA) His 1994; *cr:* US Army Pvt, SGM 1969-94; Preston HS JROTC 1994-95; Kenton HS JROTC Instr 1995-; *ai:* JROTC Drill Team, Color d, Rifle Team, Club Act Asst; Assn of US Army 1981-; AM Vets, Lions Intl 1995-; *office:* Kenton HS 200 Harding Ave Kenton OH 43326

EN, JOHN ROBERT, Chemistry Teacher; *b:* Wilkes Barre, PA; *m:* stine Chasse; *c:* John, Ben, Sarah; *ed:* Univ of Scranton (BS) Bio 1986; of CO 12 Grad Credits; *cr:* Wallenpaupack HS Chem Tchr 1988-89; ick HS Chem Tchr 1989-; *ai:* Sci Olympiad Coach; Sci Fair nizer; *office:* Berwick Area HS 1100 Fowler Ave Berwick PA 18603

EN, JOSEPH CARR, Science Teacher; *b:* Durham, NC; *ed:* NC St (BS) Earth Sci 1972; Univ of WY (MS) Natural Sci 1979; *cr:* Yarapai Geology & Zoology Instr 1983-84; Laramie Jr HS Phys & Earth Sci 1986-89; Amer Intl Schl Israel Sci Dept Chair 1989-90; Kenmore W S Earth & Bio Instr 1990-93; St Univ of NY at Buffalo Environmental Adjunct Prof 1991-; D'Youville Coll Human Anatomy & Physiology unct Prof 1991-; Kenmore East HS 1993-, Enviromental Sci, Anatomy ysiology Instr; *ai:* Dist Cmptr Comm; Environmental Club-GAIA Soc; onmental Stud Group; Wilderness Club; AFT, NYSUT, KTA 1990-; 1983-87; AAUP 1991-; Phi Delta Kappa 1985-; Wildlife Soc 1990-; zoic Soc 1991-; GAIA Soc 1990-, Spon & Fac Coord; NY St rnors Environmental Awd, Tchr Ctr Grant; St of WY Educl Grant nic Study; Marine Bio Educl Grant Jamaica; Environmental Stud Grp Univ at Buffalo Gues Speak; Adjunct Fac Coord; Outdoor Ed Grant Field Stud; Natl Tchng Fellow Prescott AZ; *office:* Kenmore East HS 350 Fries Rd Tonawanda NY 14150*

ALLEN, JUDITH MANN, Spanish Teacher; *b:* Lancaster, PA; *m:* William H.; *c:* Mark L., J. Thomas; *ed:* Bloomsburg Univ (BS) Span 1966; Universidad Ibero-Americana at Mexico City 6 Post Grad Hrs; Millersville Univ 15 Post Grad Hrs; Temple Univ 3 Post Grad Hrs; *cr:* Danville HS Span & Eng Tchr 1966-67; Lancaster City Schl Dist Span Tchr 1967-70; Penn Manor HS Span & Eng Tchr 1970-, Frgn Lang Dept Coord 1985-90; *ai:* Natl Right to Work Comm 1979-; PA Right to Work 1981-, Bd Mem; *office:* Penn Manor HS E Cottage Ave Millersville PA 17551

ALLEN, LINDA A., Program Coordinator; *b:* Beverly, MA; *m:* Jere K.; *ed:* Salem St Coll (BA) Fr 1971, (MED) Cnslng 1980; 50 Addl Hrs Curr Dev, Supervision, Evaluation; *cr:* Triton Regnl Jr Sr HS Fr Tchr 1971-, Lang Dept Prgm Coord 1990-; *ai:* Dist Subj Area Comm World Lang in Elem Schl Chair; Dist Staff Dev Comm; Teach Fr 3-6 Grd Elem Schl Stdnts; MA Frgn Lang Assn, MA Tchrs Assn, NEA 1971-, Northeast Cnslrs Assn 1985-; Triton Tchrs Assn 1971-, Pres, Bargaining Package Comm, VP, Negotiating Team, Soc Comm, Prof Rights & Responsibilities Comm; Essex Cty Lang Tchrs 1994-; Museum of Fine Arts 1991-; *office:* Triton Reg Jr Sr HS 112 Elm St Byfield MA 01922

ALLEN, LINDA KOEHLER, 7th Grade Language Arts Tchr; *b:* Upper Sandusky, OH; *m:* Daniel Lee; *c:* Timothy, Matthew, Nathaniel, Darcianne; *ed:* Muskingum Coll (BA) Ed & Eng 1982; Wright St Univ (MS) Ed 1988; Addl Credit Hrs at Ashland Univ; *cr:* Marysville Schl Dist 7th Grd Lang Arts Tchr 1982-; *ai:* Spelling Bee & Sr Citizens Comms; Activity Period Participating Instr; Delta Kappa Gamma 1993-; NEA; 1st Congregational United Church of Christ 1986-, Sec of Bd of Chrstn Ed, Bd of Homeland Ministries, Worship Comm, Bibles Schl Tchr, Summer Camp Cnslr & Choir Mem; OH Chrstn Conservation Leage Mothers Stud Group; Harold Lewis Schl for Developmental Disabilities, Vol; *office:* Marysville MS 833 N Maple St Marysville OH 43040

ALLEN, MARCIA, Lang Dept Chair & French Tchr; *b:* Troy, NY; *ed:* Coll of St Rose (BA) Fr, Latin 1956, (MA) Fr 1960; Rivier Coll at Nashua Grant, 8 Credit Hrs; *cr:* St Mary's Acad 7th-8th Grd Tchr 1939-47; St Brigid's Schl 7th-8th Grd Tchr 1947-49; St Mary's Home 7th-8th Grd Tchr 1949-53; St Mary's Schl 7th-8th Grd Tchr 1953-56; St Patrick's HS Latin Tchr 1956-58; St John the Bapt HS Fr, Latin Tchr 1958-66; St Mary's HS Fr I-IV Tchr 1966-70; Cath Cntrl HS Fr II-IV Tchr 1970-73; Cardinal Mc Closky HS Fr I-IV Tchr 1973-82; Bishop Maginn Fr I-IV Tchr 1973-82; Cath Cntrl HS Fr II-V Tchr 1982-; *ai:* Fr Club Moderator; NYSAFLT 1966-; Outstdng Fr Curr & Prgm Commendation.*

ALLEN, MARGARET ELIZABETH, 4th-5th Grade Teacher; *b:* Auburn, ME; *c:* Gardner Seekins, Elizabeth Seekins; *ed:* Univ of ME (BS) Elem Ed 1974; Univ of S ME (MS) Admin 1989; Working on Cert AP, Ed Ldrshp; *cr:* Kaler Schl 4th Grd Tchr 1974-75; Lincoln Schl 5, 5-6, 6 Grd Tchr 1976-81; Henley Schl 5 Grd Tchr 1981-82; Sawyer Schl 4th Grd Tchr 1982-93; Skillin Schl Tchr 1993-; *ai:* Yrbk Adv, Co-Chair Schl Improvement Team; GATE Selection Comm; Wkshp Presenter Foxfire Conf; Quality Review Team for Dist; Summit Writer, Assisted in Drafting St Stans Task force on Learning Results; Foxfire Bd of Dirs 1994-; Fire Prevention Edctr of Yr 1991; Wkshp Presenter; Many Rivers Schl Strengthening Group Process Colsultant 1990; BEST Awd; *office:* Waldo Skillin Elem Schl 180 Wescott Rd South Portland ME 04106*

ALLEN, MARY ANN, Language Arts Teacher; *b:* Van Wert, OH; *ed:* Bowling Green St Univ (BS) Elem Ed 1988; OH Arts Cncl Experience in Writing at Wright State Univ 1994-95; Post Grad Credit BGSU, WSU, & Walsh Univ; *cr:* Van Wert City Schls Sub Tchr 1988-92; Wayne Trace Jr HS Lang Arts Tchr 1992-; *ai:* Drama Club Adv; Flag Corps Instr; NEA 1992-; OEA 1992-;, WTEA 1992-; OCTELA 1992-; Van Wert Civic Theatre 1989-, Coord for Prgms, Childrens Theatre, Newsletter & Lights, Honorable Mention in Acting & Lighting; Kappa Ph; i 1986-; *office:* Wayne Trace Jr High 4915 US Route 127 Haviland OH 45851

ALLEN, MICHAEL DUFFY, Band Director; *b:* Canton, OH; *ed:* Univ of Akron (BA) Music Ed 1993; *cr:* Leetonia HS Band Dir 1993-; *ai:* Soph Class Adv; Jazz Band Instr; NHS 1989-; Music Edctrs Natl Conf 1991-; OH Music Edctrs Assn 1991-; LEA 1993-; *office:* Leetonia HS 181 Walnut St Leetonia OH 44431

ALLEN, MICHAEL GARY, Social Studies Teacher; *b:* Los Angeles, CA; *m:* Marcella Mae Comstock; *c:* Lamont; *ed:* CA Plytechnic at Pomona (BS) Soc Sci;1961; Claremotn Grad Schl (MA) US His 1970; *cr:* Colton Elem Schl 4-5 Grd Classroom Tchr 1962-64; Fontana Jr HS World His Tchr 1965-67; Hanau Elem Schl 4-5 Grd Classroom Tchr 1967-71; Mannheim HS Soc Stud Tchr 1971-; *ai:* SS Chprsn 1994-95; Cross Cntry Coach 1972-80, 1986-93; NEA 1963-, Fac Rep; Medal of Excl 1996; Olympic Torch Bearer 1996; Articles Pub; *home:* RR 1 Box 515 Willcox AZ 85643

ALLEN, NANCY LEE, Secondary Soc Studies Teacher; *b:* Rome, NY; *ed:* St Univ of NY Coll at Cortland (BA) His & Scndry Soc Stud Ed 1983, (MS) Scndry Soc Stud Ed 1987; *cr:* Auburn HS Tchr 1983-85; Palmyra-Macedon HS Tchr 1985; Fayetteville-Manlius HS Tchr 1986-87; Oswego HS Tchr 1987-; *ai:* Jr Class Adv Auburn HS 1984-85; Ski Club Adv Auburn HS 1983-85; Stu Cncl Adv 1991-; SADD Club Adv 1988-92; NY St United Tchrs 1987-; AFT 1987-; Summer Seminar on the Renaissance 1992; Union Seminary; *office:* Oswego HS 2 Buccaneer Blvd Oswego NY 13126

ALLEN, NANCY NIEHOFF, English Teacher; *b:* Saint Louis, MO; *m:* Abe T.; *c:* Nicole Brooks, David Neuergall, Gabrielle Pile; *ed:* Southern CT St Univ (MS) Eng 1991; Educl Fnds Prgm; *cr:* Marshfield HS Eng & Span Tchr 1965-68; Clinton Pub Schls Eng as Second Lang Consultant 1979-84; The Oxford Acad Eng & Lang Arts 1984-87; Naugatuck HS Eng Tchr 1987-; *ai:* Lit Club Spon; New Tchrs in Dept Mentor; NEA 1987-; IRA 1995-; NCTE 1994-; Persephone Revisited-Janis Angstrom in Updikes Rabbit Trilogy; Newspaper Spon 1993-94; *office:* Naugatuck HS 543 Rubber Ave Naugatuck CT 06770*

ALLEN, PAMELA J., 7th Grade Math Teacher; *b:* Presque Isle, ME; *ed:* Potsdam St (BA) Math 1983, (MS) Ed, Scndry Math 1988; *cr:* Clifton Fine Cntrl Schl Math, Cmptr Tchr 1983-84; Owego HS Math Tchr 1984-85; Copenhagen Cntrl Schl Chptr I Math Tchr 1985-86; Lowville Cntrl Schl Math Tchr 1996-; *ai:* Currently Coadvising Soph Class; AMTNYS 1983-; NYSMSA 1994-; Beta Sigma Phi 1986-, Treas; Ducks Unlimited 1993-; *office:* Lowville Acad & Cntrl Schl 7668 State St Lowville NY 13367

ALLEN, PATRICIA A., Sixth Grade Teacher; *b:* Newark, NJ; *c:* Mark Mattox; *ed:* Jersey City St Coll (BA) Elem Ed 1975; 12 Addl Credit Hrs; *cr:* Newark Bd of Ed Permanent Sub Tchr K-8 1970-72; East Orange Bd of Ed Kndgtn, 5th Grd Tchr 1972-74; Irvington Bd of Ed 6th Grd Tchr 1975-; *ai:* Educl Improvement Plan; Grd Coord; Math Curr Comm; NJEA 1975-; IEA 1975-, Bldg Rep; Leaguers Inc 1984-, Prgm Coord; Delta Sigma Theta 1967-; Mentor; *home:* 42 Linden Ave Irvington NJ 07111*

ALLEN, PATRICK, Assoc Professor of English; *b:* Long Beach, CA; *m:* Marie Costa; *ed:* Univ of CA at Berkeley (BA) Eng 1963; IN Univ (MA) Eng 1967, (PHD) Eng & Amer Stud 1974; *cr:* Union Coll Asst Prof 1969-75, Assoc Prof & Dir Educl Stud 1992-; Shenendehowa HS Tchr 1975-91; *ai:* Union Coll Tchng & Learning Ctr Dir; NCTE 1992-, Commission on Curr; NYACTE 1992-; AERA 1992-; Ed Washington Irving Hearthside Tales; NY Stock Exchange 1st Prize for Ec; Numerous Grants 1996; *office:* Union College Lamont Grad Ctr Schenectady NY 12308

ALLEN, RAYMOND JOHN, Band Director; *b:* Clarksburg, WV; *ed:* OH Univ (BA) Music Ed 1990; *cr:* Ft Frye Local Schls 5th-12th Grd Band Dir 1990-92; OH Univ Grad Asst 1992-94; Little Miami Jr Sr HS 7th-12th Grd Band Dir 1994-; *ai:* Marching, Pep Bands; Asst Schl Dramas, Musicals; MENC, OH Music Edctrs Assn 1986-; Phi Mu Alpha Sinfonia 1994-; Amer Legion Red White, Blue Awd; Marching Band QualifiedSt Competition 2 Yrs Receiving Excellent, Superior Ratings; Awded Grad Associateship with Stipend, Grad Schlsp; *office:* Little Miami HS 605 Welch Rd Morrow OH 45152

ALLEN, RHONDA K., School Counselor; *b:* Penn Yan, NY; *m:* Thomas R.; *c:* Timothy, Casey, Morgan; *ed:* SUNY at Bockport (BS) PE 1971; SUNY at Cortland (MS) PE 1977; Alfred Univ (MS) Schl Cnslng 1989; *cr:* Hammondsport Cntrl Schl PE Tchr, Ath Dir 1972-93; Dundee Cntrl Schl Schl Cnslr 1993-; *ai:* Sr Class Adv; Schl Comm Action Team; NYSUT 1993-; ACA 1989-; *office:* Dundee Central Schl 55 Water St Dundee NY 14837

ALLEN, RONALD SIBIE, Mngmt & Mrktg Dept Chprsn; *b:* Williamsport, PA; *ed:* Westchester Bus Inst (AA) Bus Adm 1987; Iona Coll (BS) Gen Bus Adm 1989; 20 Credits MBA Intnl Bus; Insurance License NY Registered; Natl Assn of Security Dealers; *cr:* Westchester Bus Inst Instr, Chprsn 1989-; *ai:* Insurance, Investment Allmerica Fin; Life Underwriters Trng Cncl 1995-, Field Assoc; Numerous Articles Pub; *office:* Westchester Bus Inst 325 Central Ave White Plains NY 10606

ALLEN, ROSALIE KAY, Music & Drama Director; *b:* Upper Sandusky, OH; *ed:* Cedarville Coll (BME) Vocal, General Music, Scndry 1978; *cr:* Donnell Jr HS 7-9 Grd Vocal & General Music 1979-80; Victory Chrstn Acad K-12 Vocal & General Music 1981-84; Maranatha Chrstn Schl 5-12 Grd Vocal, General, Handbells 1985-; *ai:* Dir of HS Vocal, Handbell Touring Ensemble & HS Drama Productions; Class of 1995 Adv; MENC 1978-; ACSI 1985-; *office:* Maranatha Chrstn Schl 4663 Trabue Rd Columbus OH 43228

ALLEN, SALLY J., Art Teacher; *b:* Littleton, MA; *c:* Mark Power, Beth Power, Christopher Power, Gregory Power, Leo Mc Donough; *ed:* UNH (BS) Art Ed 1971; Lesley Coll (MS) Ed, Arts 1994; Many Credits & Post Grad Stud in Expressive Arts & Arts in Curr Design; *cr:* Dover HS Art Tchr 1971-81, Dept Chm 4 Yrs; Horne St Schl Art Tchr 1981-; *ai:* Arts Club Adv; Poster Club; Curr Bd for Arts Dover; Cooperating Tchr for Stdnt Tchrs; Enrichment Team; NEA 1976-; Arts 1000 1990-; NAEA 1972-; NHAEA 1972-, Pres, Rep, Art Tchr of Yr 1980; *office:* Horne Street Elem Schl 78 Horne St Dover NH 03820

ALLEN, SANDRA ALEX DENISE (MILLS), Mathematics Teacher; *b:* Saint Kitts, West Indies; *m:* Carl Ernest; *c:* Kyle Andrae, Sasha Mae Caresse, Xylia Janel; *ed:* Univ of West Indies (BA) Math 1979; Howard Univ (MAT) Curr & Tchng 1988; Working on PHD at Univ of MD at College Park Math Ed; *cr:* Sandy Point HS Math Tchr 1979-85; Convent HS Math Tchr 1985-86; Hamilton Jr HS Math Tchr 1988-89; Banneker HS Math Tchr 1990-; *ai:* Class of 1995 Spon; NCTM 1987-; MAA 1991-; DCCTM 1988-; Phi Delta Kappa 1988-; Cafritz Fellowship 1991; *office:* Benjamin Banneker HS 800 Euclid St NW Washington DC 20001

ALLEN, SHARON L., Third Grade Teacher; *b:* Fresno, CA; *m:* Donald B.; *c:* Todd, Kelly Allen Cooney, Jody Allen Haber, Corrie, Kathryn; *ed:* Fresno St Coll (BA) Ed 1963; *cr:* Washington Schl 5th-6th Grd Tchr 1963-67; Tapley Schl 5th Grd Tchr 1967-68; Atwood-Tapley Schl 3rd-4th Grd Tchr 1981-; *office:* Atwood-Tapley Schl 6 Heath St Oakland ME 04963

ALLEN, SHEILA M., Social Studies Teacher; *b:* Newark, NJ; *ed:* VA St Univ (BA) Sociology 1970; Montclair St Univ (MA) Urban Ed 1974; 4 Credit Hrs Cooperative Learning Kean Coll; 3 Credit Hrs Eagleton Inst Rutgers Univ; *cr:* Newark Bd of Ed Tchr 1970-72; Orange Bd of Ed Intern, Lang Arts-Rdng 1972-73; Montclair Bd of Ed Soc Stud Tchr 1973; *ai:* Affirmative Action Prgm; Block Assn; Montclair Bd of Ed 1973-; NJEA; NEA; NCSS 1992-; St James AME Church Mentorship 1950-; Judy & Josh Weston Awd Tchng Excl; Globe Fearon Critic Reader.

ALLEN, STEPHEN JACKSON, Fourth Grade Teacher; *b:* Burlington, VT; *m:* Janet Messier; *c:* Amy Allen Burkey, Timothy Wallace; *ed:* Johnson St Coll (BS) Elem Ed 1967; Credit Hrs Cmptrs, Prof Comm, Math Instr; *cr:* Chester Elem Schl Math, Sci Lab Tchr 1967-68; Barretown Elem Schl 4th Grd Tchr 1969-; *ai:* Staf Dev Comms; BArretown Ed Assn 1969-, Pres; Vermont NEA, NEA 1967-; Mystic Star Phoenix Lodge FCAM 1967-; Intnl Farm Youth Exch Del India 1968-69; East Brookfield Congregational Church 1963-; 4-H 1955-86; Bd Resolution Awd Portfolio Work 1992, Awd for Exemplary Recognition 1994; *office:* Barre Town Elem Schl RR 2 Box 4323 Barre VT 05641

ALLEN, STEPHEN RICHARD, Business Education Teacher; *b:* Patterson, NJ; *m:* Lucinda Louise; *c:* Carrie Ann, Cassie Louise; *ed:* Hawthorne Coll (BS) Bus Admin 1970; Potsdam St Coll (MS) Ed-Rdng 1980; St Lawrence Univ Admin Cert 1995; *cr:* Gouverneur Cntrl Schl Elem Tchr 1971-79; Ogdensburg Free Acad Bus Tchr & Acting Asst Prin 1980-; *ai:* Soph Class Adv; NEA 1970-; AFT 1970-; Ogdensburg Ed Assoc 1980-; Org of Bus Math & Schl Store Pgm Recognized by Mid St Accreditation Dev of Alternative Ed Pgm, Piloted Introduction to Occupations Course for NY St Ed Dept; *office:* Ogdensburg Free Acad 1100 State St Ogdensburg NY 13669*

ALLEN, SUE FAY, Music Teacher & Coordinator; *b:* Buffalo, NY; *m:* Carl Klingenschmitt; *c:* Elizabeth Ann, Paula Louise; *ed:* SUNY Potsdam (BS) Music Ed 1961, (MS) Music 1965; Attnd Fredonia SUNY, Univ of Buffalo, Westminster Choir Coll; *cr:* St Lawrence Cntrl Schls Music Tchr & Coord 1961-65; Norwood Norfolk Schls Music Tchr & Music Coord 1965-66; Amherst Cntrl Schls Music Tchr & Coord 1966-; *ai:* Musical Dir; Pop Chorus; Madrigals; Barbershop; Beauty Shoppe; NY St Schl Music Assn 1961-, Voice Chm; Amer Choral Dir Assn 1965-, Pres NY Chptr; Erie Cty Music Assn 1967-, Choral Chair; Clarence Concert Assn 1989-, Bd of Dirs; Founder of Amherst Bel Canto Childrens Choir & Dir; Co-founder of Erie Cty Music Coord Assn; NY St Distinguished Svc in Music Awd; Amherst Excel in Tchng Awd; Guest Conductor of 50 Different Cty & St Choirs; Numerous Articles Pub; *office:* Amherst MS 55 Kings Hwy Amherst NY 14226*

ALLEN, SUSAN M., Spanish Teacher; *b:* Peekskill, NY; *c:* Chelsea; *ed:* Hartwick Coll (BA) Span 1976; Middlebury Coll (MA) Span 1977; Undergrad Ger Summer 1982-83; Rowan Coll Grad Curr, Supervisory Courses 1986-87; *cr:* Cumberland Reg HS Span Tchr 1977-80; Abington Friends Schl Span Tchr 1980-81; Eastern Sr HS Span Tchr 1981-; *ai:* Interact Club Adv; Span Honor Soc Co-Adv; NJEA, AATSP 1977-; Tchr of Yr 1988-89; Camden Co Tchr of Yr 1989; *office:* Eastern Sr HS PO Box 2500 Voorhees NJ 08043

ALLEN, TIMOTHY THORPE, Assistant Professor of Geology; *b:* New London, NH; *m:* Wendy Thorpe; *ed:* Harvard Univ (BA) Geological Scis 1984; Dartmouth Coll (MS) Geology 1990, (PHD) Geology 1992; *cr:* Kearsarge Regnl HS Math Tchr 1985-86; Keene St Coll Ski Coach 1986-87; Dartmouth Coll Tchng & Research Asst 1987-92; Keene St Coll Asst Prof Geology & Environmental Stud 1992-; *ai:* Environmental Stud Steering Comm Chair; Coll Information Tech Comm; NH Geological Soc 1989-, Dir; Geological Soc of Amer 1992-; Amer Geophys Union 1992-; Research in Petrology, Tectonics, Geochem & Hydrogeology; *office:* Keene St Coll 229 Main St Keene NH 03435

ALLEN, VERA MAREN TAYLOR, Hlth, Fam Life, Cnsmr Sci Tchr; *b:* Hartford, CT; *m:* William C.; *c:* Vera Maren Christy; *ed:* Univ of CT (BS) Home Ec Ed 1957; 12 Grad Credits in Hlth at Wes Conn; 16 Grad Credits in Ed at UCONN; 6 CEU from Inst of Child Abuse; 6 CEU Spec Inst on Aids; *cr:* RHam HS Home Ec Tchr 1957-60; New Milford HS Home Ec Tchr 1960-65; Washing HS Home Ec Tchr 1965-69; Shepaus HS Home Ec Tchr 1979-83; Lewis Mills HS Home Ec Tchr 1983-84; Shepaus HS Home Ec, Hlth Tchr 1984-90; Thomaston HS Home Ec Tchr 1990-92; Danbury HS Family Life, Consumer Sci, Hlth Tchr 1993-; *ai:* CEA, NEA 1957-; Comm Vol Work; Tchr of Month 1993-94; *office:* Danbury HS 49 Clapboard Ridge Danbury CT 06810

ALLEN, VIRGINIA, Third Grade Teacher; *b:* Far Rockaway, NY; *ed:* St Johns Univ (BS) Elem Ed 1969, (MLS) Lib Sci 1973; *cr:* St Raymond Schl Tchr 1969-; *ai:* Stu Cncl Moderator; Primary Coord; NCEA; St Raymond Schl Outstanding Tchr Awd; *office:* St Raymond Schl 263 Atlantic Ave East Rockaway NY 11518

ALLEN, WILLIAM ARTHUR, Eng Teacher & Dir of Dramatics; *b:* Cortland, NY; *m:* Katrina Allen; *ed:* U of Nortnern CO (BA) Eng 1972; SUNY at Cortland 58 Grad Hrs Eng, Theater; *cr:* Homer Cntrl HS Eng, Tchr, Dir of Dramatics 1975-; *ai:* Dramatics Dir; Awds Comm; AFT; NYSUT; Amer Prof Captains Assn; Articles in NY Outdoors, Threads Magazines; US Coast Guard Captain's License; *office:* Homer Cntrl HS West Rd Box 500 Homer NY 13077

ALLEN, WILLIAM C., Fifth Grade Teacher; *b:* Waterbury, CT; *m:* Vera Maren Taylor; *c:* Vera Maren Christy; *ed:* Quinnipiac Coll (BS) Bus 1960; Western Ct St Coll (MS) Elem Ed 1972; 30 Addl Credit Hrs; *cr:* Regnl Dist #6 HS Math Tchr 1 Yr, 4th-5th Grd Tchr 28 Yrs; *ai:* NEA, CEA 1967-; Involved in Yale Univ Psych Dept Tchng Curr 1991-93; *office:* James Morris Elem Schl 10 East St Morris CT 06763

ALLEN, WILLIAM J., English Instructor; *b:* Cleveland, OH; *m:* Kathryn Racz; *c:* Meghan Turon, Rachel; *ed:* St Stephens Coll (BA) Philosophy 1965; Kent St Univ (MED) Ed 1973; Attnd Univ of HI, Cleveland St; *cr:* Cathedral Latin Schl Instr, Vice Prin 1966-72; Kenston HS Instr 1973-; *ai:* Acad Decathlon, Quiz Bowl; KEA 1973-, Pres; *office:* Kenston HS 17425 Snyder Rd Chagrin Falls OH 44023*

ALLEN, YVONNE HOBBS, English Teacher; *b:* Jacksonville, FL; *m:* John W.; *c:* Julia Nicholle, Andre Ramone; *ed:* Allegheny Coll (BA) Eng 1972, (MA) Ed 1973; North East OH Writing Project Cleveland St Univ; Evergreen Educl Symposium John Carroll Univ; Element of Effective Instruction Cleveland St Univ; *cr:* South HS Eng Tchr 1972-77; Jane Addams Career Ctr Eng Dept Chprsn 1978-79; Mentor Ridge Jr HS Eng Dept Chprsn 1983-93; Mentor HS Eng Tchr 1993-; *ai:* Amer Experience Team Taught Model Course Co-Tchr; Mentor Incoming Tchrs; Action Research Comm for Schl Improvement; Project HAL, Looking Toward the 21st Century; ASCD 1990-; North East OH Ed Assn 1984-; Delta Kappa Gamma 1995-; Alpha Kappa Alpha 1972-, Various Comm Chairpersonships; PTSA 1983-; Beaumont Schl Bd of Trustees 1993-, Svc Recognition; Fairmount Presbyn 1995-, Comm Chair; Mt Zion Joint Task Force; Facilitator of Ventura Capital 4 Yr Educl Grant; Excl in Tchng Awd 1988; Tchr of Yr Finalist OH 1989, Mentor; Project Upward Bound Case Western Reserve Univ O utstdng Instr; Martha Jennings Fellow; *office:* Mentor HS 6477 Center St Mentor OH 44060*

ALLENBAUGH, RICHARD E., Math Teacher; *b:* Punxsutawney, PA; *m:* Jeannie B. Rishel; *c:* Michael, Natalie, Christine; *ed:* IN Univ of PA (BS) Math 1967; Attnd IN Univ at Bloomington, Penn St Univ, Clarion Univ, Gannon, East Stroudsburg Univ; Masters Equ + 36 Credits; *cr:* Ridgway HS 9-12th Grd Math Tchr 1967-; *ai:* Building Rep Ridgway Area Tchrs Assn; New Tchr Mentor; NEA, PSEA, RATA 1967-; Comm Chm Boy Scout Troop 1982-; Trinity United Meth Church Bd of Trustees 1967-; Ridgway Rifle Club 1985-; St Marys Sportsman Club 1982-; *home:* PO Box 362 Ridgway PA 15853

ALLENCHEY, JOAN M., Biology Teacher; *b:* Amherst, MA; *m:* Kenneth C. Watson; *c:* Zachary A. Watson; *ed:* Univ of MA at Amherst (BS) Zoology 1973; Lesley Coll (MS) Cmptr; 30 Plus Grad Credit Hrs in Various Sci & Educl Courses; *cr:* Taunton HS Bio Tchr 1973-; *ai:* Yrbk Adv 1987-90; Jr Red Cross Adv 1977-83; Sr Class Video Co-Producer 1985; Photography Club Adv; NHS Selection Comm 1983-; Faculty & Comm Schlsp Comm 1981-; Sci Fair Comm 1994-; NEA, MA Tchrs Assn & Taunton Ed Assn 1973-; NSTA; NABT; Red Cross Spon of Bloodmobile 1977-83; Taunton Yrbk Dedication 1980; *office:* Taunton H S Williams St Taunton MA 02780

ALLERA, LYNDA GRACE, French & Spanish Teacher; *b:* Lewisburg, PA; *m:* Michael P.; *c:* Jean-Pierre, Nicolas, Maria; *ed:* Loyola of Baltimore (MA) Admin 1989; *cr:* Chiwquapin MS Fr Tchr 1983-85; Harpers Choice MS Fr & Span Tchr 1985-; *ai:* NEA 1985-; *office:* Harper's Choice MS 5450 Beaverkill Rd Columbia MD 21044

ALLISON, EDNA, Mathematics Teacher; *b:* Tarentum, PA; *m:* Stanley P. Weissman; *ed:* PA St Univ (BS) Scndry Ed 1973; Johns Hopkins Univ (MS) Guid, Cnslng 1979; *cr:* Havre de Grace MS Math Tchr 1973-76; Cecil Comm Coll Math Tchr 1977-84; Cherry Hill MS Math Tchr 1984-85; North East HS Math Tchr 1985-; *ai:* NHS, Math Club Spon; Schl Improvement Team; NCTM 1984-; *office:* North East HS 300 Irishtown Rd North East MD 21901

ALLISON, JAMES MICHAEL,JR., Science Teacher; *b:* Cincinnati, OH; *m:* Michelle Lynn Hendricks; *c:* James M. III; *ed:* Univ of Evansville (BA) Scndry Ed & Bio 1985; Attnd Univ of Cincinnati; *cr:* McArthur HS Sci Tchr 1985-91; Fairfield HS Sci Tchr 1992-; *ai:* Head Track Coach; NEA 1992-; NSTA 1992-; Howard Hughes Initiatives in Bio Rschr Grant 1993 & 1995; *office:* Fairfield HS 1111 Nilles Rd Fairfield OH 45014*

ALLISON, MICHAEL EDWARD, Seventh Grade Science Teacher; *b:* Williamsport, PA; *m:* Kelly Marie Stetts; *ed:* Shippensburg Unv (BSEd) Earth & Space Sci 1987; *cr:* South Williamsport Jr-Sr HS 7th Grd Sci Tchr 1988-; *ai:* Var Girls Bsktbl Head Coach; Class of 1992 & 1995 Adv; *office:* South Williamsport Jr/Sr HS 700 Percy St South Williamsport PA 17701

ALLOCCA, DONNA BARBAROTTO, Librn, Clerical & Sub Teacher; *b:* Brooklyn, NY; *m:* James; *c:* Michele; *ed:* Attnd Brooklyn Coll; *cr:* US Corp Co Ex Sec, Biller, Office Mgr 1972-80; St Elizabeth Schl Clerical, Librn 1988-; *ai:* Helped Coach Girls Sftbl Team to 1st Diocesan Championship; Started Boys, Girls Club; St Albans Hosp Cath War Veterans Vol; *office:* Saint Elizabeth Schl 94-01 85th St Ozone Park NY 11416

ALLWINE, CONSTANCE MARSH, Calculus Teacher; *b:* Jamestown, NY; *m:* Kenneth B.; *c:* Kenneth R., Brett M.; *ed:* IN Univ of PA (BS) Math-Scndry Ed 1969; Penn St & Shippensburg 24 Credits; *cr:* Lower Dauphin Schl Dist Math Tchr Jr HS 1969-76, 1983-93, Algebra I II Sr HS 1993-94; AP Calculus, Algebra II 1994-; *ai:* Math Tutor Dept; Knowledge Master Open Coach; *office:* Lower Dauphin Sr HS 201 S Hanover St Hummelstown PA 17036*

ALMEIDA, JOHN M., Science Teacher; *b:* Fall River, MA; *m:* Debra D.; *c:* Matthew A., Joshua L.; *ed:* URI (BA) Sec Ed, Bio, Chem 1972, (MA) Ed, Sci 1983, (MA) Ed, Sci 1990; Addl 30 Hrs; *cr:* S. Kingstown HS Chem, Sci Tchr 1972-; *ai:* Yrbk Adv 7 Yrs; Class Adv 8 Yrs; SADD Adv 2 Yrs; Fac Comms; UZA 1972-, Bldg Rep 2 Yrs, Union Pres 1 Yr; Cert Nursing Asst 1984-; PTA 1984-, Pres 2 Yrs; Church Groups; *office:* South Kingstown HS 215 Columbia St Wakefield RI 02879

ALMEIDA, SANDRA S. (ALESSANDRO), Second Grade Teacher; *b:* Fall River, MA; *c:* Jean; *ed:* RI Coll (BS) Ed 1968; Addl 36 Hrs at Roger Williams Univ; *cr:* Blessed Sacrament 2nd Grd Tchr 1970-71; East Providence Schl Dept 2nd Grd Tchr 1971-; *ai:* Tchrs Credit Union Bd of Dirs; Bldg Bridges Prgm; NEA 1971-; PTA 1971-, Sec 1994; Tchrs Credit Union 1971-, Bd of Dirs; Tchr of Month 1991.

ALMONTE, NEREIDA RAMOS, Spanish Teacher; *b:* Jayuya, Puerto Rico; *m:* Bruno D.; *c:* Jose A., Angela M., Nancy B.; *ed:* Douglas Coll (BA) Span 1985; *cr:* Woodbridge HS Span Tchr 1985-; *ai:* NEA 1985-; FLENJ 1990-; *home:* 260 Barclay St Perth Amboy NJ 08861

ALMY, KATHLEEN FURNAS, HS Resource Teacher; *b:* Fall River, MA; *m:* Frederic A. III; *c:* Frederic IV; *ed:* Salve Regina Coll (BA) Psych, Spec Ed 1977; 3 Grad Credit Hrs; *cr:* Tiverton MS Resource Tchr 1989-90; Tiverton HS Resource Tchr 1991-; *ai:* Sr Class Adv; 4-H Club Ldr 1989-, Ldr of Yr; *office:* Tiverton H S 100 N Brayton Rd Tiverton RI 02878

ALOISE, CONSTANCE P., English Teacher; *b:* Summit, NJ; *m:* Peter Alexander; *ed:* Univ of CT (BS) Clothing, Textiles, Related Arts 1967; Trinity Coll (MA) Eng Lit 1981; 30 Hrs Writing Northeastern Univ 1988; 56 Hrs Rhetoric & Composition SUNY at Albany; Eng Cert Cntrl CT St Univ 1975; *cr:* Bloomfield Jr HS Eng Tchr 1968-86; Farmington HS Eng Tchr 1986-; *ai:* Prins Advy Cncl; NEA, CEA, FEA 1968-; NCTE, CCTE 1978-; CCCC; Marthas Vineyard Writing Prgm Advy Bd 1989-; CT Writing Project Planning Bd 1990-; NEH Seminar Yale 1985; CT Writing Project Flwshp 1983; CT Writing Project Tchr Rsrch Grant; CT Cncl Hum Speaker Grant; CT Cooperating Tchr & Mentor Awd; *office:* Farmington HS 10 Montieth Dr Farmington CT 06032

ALOISI, HENRY ANTHONY, Band & Chorus Teacher; *b:* Monessen, PA; *m:* Lucille Musial; *c:* Dino, Janine; *ed:* St Vincent Coll (BSME) Clarinet 1960; Duquesne Univ (MA) Music 1966; *cr:* West Jefferson Hills Elem, Jr High Vocal Instr 1960-65; Mon-Valley Cath HS Instrumental, Marching, Concert Bands Tchr 1965-72; Charleroi HS Bands, Chorus Tchr 1972-90; Belle Vernon HS Bands, Chorus Tchr 1990-; *ai:* Broadway Musicals Dir; MARS Comm Band Conductor 25 Yrs; PMPA, MENC, PSEA 1960-; Monessen Elks, K of C, Planning Commission.

ALONSO, LILY, Fourth Grade Teacher; *b:* Habana, Cuba; *m:* Frank; *c:* Jason A., Jenielle A.; *ed:* St Peter's Coll (BA) Elem Ed 1980; *cr:* Roosevelt Schl 7th-8th Grd Biling Tchr 1980-81; St John Nepomucene Schl 6th-8th Grd Soc Stud Tchr 1981-90, Fourth Grd Tchr 1990-; *ai:* Soc Stud Coord; NCEA 1981-; *office:* St John Nepomucene Schl 7111 Polk St North Bergen NJ 07047

ALPERT, ANDREA L., Specific Lrng Dis Tchr & Tutor; *b:* New York ; *m:* Arnold; *c:* Samuel (dec), Michael; *ed:* OH St Univ (BA) Elem Ed 1967, (MA) Elem Ed 1981; Certfd Specific Learning, Behavioral Disorders Rdng; *cr:* Lakewood Local Schls Tchr 1968-69; Columbus Pub Schls Tchr 1974-; *ai:* CASA Vol; Columbus Tutor Assn, Pres; CO Ed Assn Bd Governors 1988-91; Stock Club, Pres; Usher, Theatre; Ingram Grant; *home:* 689 Stag Pl Gahanna OH 43230

ALPETER, JANICE SKROMME, French Teacher; *b:* Akron, OH; *m:* John F.; *ed:* Univ of Akron (BA) Fr 1970; OH St Univ (MA) Fr & Foreign Lang Ed 1976; Attnd Univ de Chambery; 15 Grad Hrs Kent St Univ Post Masters Curr; *cr:* Stow City Schls Fr Tchr 1970-, Foreign Lang Dept Chair 1978-; *ai:* Fr Club Adv, Staff Dev; NEA, OEA, ACTFL, AATF 1970-; delta Gamma Alumni, Pledge Adv 1978-79; Jr League of Akron 1993-; Akron Childrens Hospital, Stan Hywet Hall Womens Guild Vol; Oustanding Educator Awd 1984; Essential Elements of Instruction Trainer; Pi Lambda Theta; Pi Delta Phi; Phi Sigma Alpha Honoraries; *office:* Stow-Munroe Falls HS 3227 E Graham Rd Stow OH 44224*

ALPTEKIN, OMER KEMAL, Social Studies Teacher; *b:* Brooklyn, NY; *ed:* Vassar Coll (BA) Pol Sci 1986; Fordham Univ (MA) Pol Sci 1993; Semester Abroad Prgm at Tel Aviv Univ Dayan Cntr for Middle Eastern & African Stud 1989; amer Research Inst in Turkey Summer Lang Prgm at Bosporus Univ 1987; *cr:* Jewish Child Care Assn Milieu Cnslr 1990-93; Mt Pleasant Cottage Schl Dist Tchr Aide 1990-93; Arlington Hs Global Stud Tchr 1993-; *ai:* Fac Rep to Arlington HS Shared Decision Making Team; Mem of Adolescent Care Team for At Risk Stdnts; Chaperone for Arlington Ski Club; Natl Endowment for the Hum Summer Grant 1994; Fordham Univ Presidential Schlsp 1987-89; NATO Youth Exch Fellowship 1989; Vassar Coll Thesis Distinction and Cum Laude General & Pol Sci; *office:* Arlington Cntrl Schls 120 Dutchess Turnpike Poughkeepsie NY 12603*

ALSTON, WANDA LYANE TAYLOR, Second Grade Teacher; *b:* Ethel, WV; *m:* James Otis Jr.; *c:* Ebony M., James Otis III; *ed:* Glassboro St at Rowan (BA) K-8th Grd Ed 1973; Minor in Black Stud; *ai:* Drill Team Steppers Adv; Black His, Grd Level Comms; NJEA, NEA 1973-; MTA 1973-, Bldg Rep; Clayton Bd of Ed 1994-, Mem; Mt Zion Bapt Church 1990-, Mem, Schlsp Comm; Black His Ministry 1990-, Mem.*

ALTAVENA, ROBERT LEWIS, Sixth Grade Teacher; *b:* Rochester, NY; *ed:* Univ of Saint Thomas at Houston (BA) Ec 1969; St Univ of NY at Brockport (MA) Elem Ed 1972; *cr:* Schl #10 6th Grd Tchr 1972-74; Schl #12 6th Grd Tchr 1974-76; Schl #37 6th Grd Tchr 1976-79; Kodak Park Schl #41 6th Grd Tchr 1979-; *ai:* Soc & Comm Svc Comms; AFT, NEA, Rochester Tchrs Assn 1972-; Omicron Delta Epsilon 1968; *office:* Kodak Park Schl #41 279 Ridge Rd W Rochester NY 14615*

ALTENBURGER, MARY LOU, Science Teacher; *b:* Lima, OH; *m:* Robert; *c:* Dana, Benjamin, Adam; *ed:* St Josephs Coll (BS) Bio & Chem 1975; Wright St Univ (MS) Tchr Ed 1993; Attnd Bowling Green St Univ, OH Northern Univ & OH St Univ; *cr:* Fort Jennings HS Sci Tchr 1978-; *ai:* Sci Day Coord; Class Adv; Fort Jennings Ed Assn 1978-, Treasurer & Rep; OH Ed Assn & NEA 1978-; OH Governors Awd for Excl in Youth Sci Opportunities 1993; *office:* Fort Jennings HS PO Box 98 Water St Fort Jennings OH 45844*

ALTENDERFER, STEPHEN H., Science Tchr & Dept Coord; *b:* Rochester, NY; *m:* Carolyn M. Rowe; *c:* Karen M. Baier, Kristin K.; *ed:* Lafayette Coll (AB) Chem 1962; Cornell Univ (MST) Chem 1966; 61 Addl Credits; *cr:* Hanover Park HS Sci Tchr 1962-65; Whippany Park HS Sci Tchr, Sci Dept Coord 1966-; *ai:* Negotiator Tchrs Assn 23 Yrs; NEA; NJEA; MCCEA; HPREA, Negotiator; AAPT; NJSTA; NJSSA; Sigma Xi; Tandy Tech Scholars Outstanding Tchr Awd; Rutgers Univ Citation for Distinguished High Schl Tchng; Scientific Excl Awd Twice; Publications Physics of the Cmptr, Television & Video Imaging; *office:* Whippany Park HS 165 Whippany Rd Whippany NJ 07981

ALTER, DEBORAH, Art Teacher; *b:* New York, NY; *m:* Ramon K. McMillan; *c:* Virgil, Bruce; *ed:* CT Coll (BA) Studio Art 1977; Manhattanville Coll (MAT) 1990; *cr:* United Media Enterprises Staff Designer; Doubleday & Co Promotion Mgr; Freelance Designer; Nyack HS Art Tchr 1990-; *ai:* The Nyack Spectrum Co-Adv; AFT; NY St Art Tchrs Assoc; NAEA; The Dewey Network; *office:* Nyack HS 360 Christian Herald Rd Nyack NY 10960*

ALTER, E. JANE, Business Teacher; *b:* Sewickley, PA; *m:* Robert B.; *c:* Bruce, Debra Wildriek, Sherry Healey; *ed:* Westminster Coll (BBA) Bus 1960; Univ of Dayton, Wright St Univ, Miami Univ 45 Credits in Bus Ed; *cr:* Radnor HS Bus Tchr 1960-61; Baldwin HS Bus & Eng Tchr 1984-85; Centerville HS Bus Tchr 1985-; *ai:* Muse Machine Adv, Drug Awareness Team; OH Bus Tchrs Assn 1985-; Philharmonic Womens Assn 1989; Church Yth Group Adv; Awds: Bus Week Ed, Golden Apple State, Montgomery Cty Excl in Ed, Centerville Schl Dist Tchr of the Yr, OH Insurance Inst Tchr of the Yr; *office:* Centerville HS 500 E Frank Centerville OH 45459

ALTHOFF, RONALD JAMES, Agriculture Teacher; *b:* Gettysburg *m:* Deborah Elaine Smith; *c:* Rodney, Christopher; *ed:* Penn St Univ Ag Ed 1973, (MED) Ag Ed 1977; *cr:* St Coll HS Ag Tchr 1973; So HS Ag Tchr 1973-; *ai:* Solanco Young Farmer Assn Adv; Solanco Ed 1973-, Treas; PSEA & NEA 1973-; Solanco Fair Assn 1974-; *o* Solanco HS 585 Solanco Rd Quarryville PA 17566

ALTHOUSE, LINDA HAAG, Amer History & Civic Teacher; *b:* Rea GA; *m:* Robert; *c:* Michael; *ed:* Kutztown St Univ (MS) Soc Stud (MED) Soc Stud 1974; 18 Grd Hrs Univ of AK, Lehigh Univ, Carlow IN Univ of PA; *cr:* Tulpehocker Tchr 24 Yrs; *ai:* Stu Cncl, Yth in Govt NEA, PSEA 1971-; *office:* Tulpehocken HS 430 New Schaefferstow Bernville PA 19506

ALTHOUSE, ROBERT L., Social Studies Dept Chair; *b:* Reading, P Linda Haag; *c:* Michael; *ed:* Kutztown St Coll (BSEd) Comprehensiv Stud 1970, (MED) Soc Stud 1974; Grad Stud Penn St Univ, Wilkes Millersville St Univ, Carlow Coll, Univ of AK; *cr:* Hamburg Area Sch HS Soc Stud Tchr 1970-, Soc Stud Dept Chair, Tchr 1989-; *ai:* Fac Comm; Perm Mem of Curr, Instruction Comm; NEA, PSEA, HAEA 1 NCSS, PCSS 1980-; Police Civil Svc Commission 1986-90, Sec; Scout Master 1990-93; Scoutmaster 1993-; Mentor Tchr for Soc *office:* Hamburg Area Schl Dist Windsor St Hamburg PA 19526*

ALTINGER, JOSEPH, Mathematics Professor; *b:* Passaic, NJ; *m:* Siciliano; *ed:* Univ of Pitt (MS) Math 1960; Case Western Reserve (Math 1970; *ai:* Undetermined Major Adv; Church Lector, Distri Albegra Coord; NCTM 1957-; OEA, NEOA 1970-; Orion Awd Nontraditional Stdnts; Articles in FOCUS on MATH; NCHC Jo *office:* Youngstown St Univ 410 Wick Ave Youngstown OH 44555

ALTIZIO, MAURO, Social Studies Teacher; *b:* Hoboken, NJ; *m:* M. Trumble; *c:* Scott M, Jenny M., Bonnie A.; *ed:* Univ of NE (B 1965; Fairleigh Dickinson Univ (MED) Human Growth & Dev 197 Ft Crook Schl Elem Tchr 1965-67; Emma Havens Young Schl Elem 1967-68; Brick Twp HS Soc Stud Tchr 1968-69; Tosms River HS Eas Stud Tchr 1969-; *ai:* NJEA, OCEA 1969-; NEA; Forked River Pr Church 1994-, Elder & Session.

ALTLAND, WILLIAM G., English Teacher; *b:* New Cumberland, P Susan E. Leonhard; *c:* Christopher, Michael, James; *ed:* Lebanon Vly (BA) Eng 1965; Millersville Univ (MED) Eng 1995; *cr:* Northern Leb HS Eng Tchr 1965-66; Milton Hershey Schl Eng Tchr 1966-; *ai:* Coach; PSEA 1993-, Pres; NCTE 1981-; Conf on Eng Ldrshp 1986-; *o* Milton Hershey Schl Senior Hall PO Box 830 Hershey PA 17033

ALTMAN, CAROLE RONNIE, French Teacher; *b:* New York, N Ross C.; *c:* Seth L., Keith D.; *ed:* Brooklyn Coll (BA) Fr 1970; Queen (MSEd) Fr Ed 1992; Attnd LIU, Coll of St Rose; *cr:* Walt Whitman Fr, Span Tchr 1970-75; Port Washington Pub Schls Sub Tchr 19 Roslyn Pub Schls ESL, Adult Ed Tchr 1988-92; Louis Pasteur MS Span Tchr 1992-; *ai:* Schl Trip, Tchrs Choice Coord; Tchr-Self-Sust Prgm Fr Help; Saturday Acad Passport to World; UFT 1970-; *offic* 67 Louis Pasteur 51-60 Marathon Pkwy Little Neck NY 11362*

ALTMAN, JAN, Third Grade Teacher; *b:* Newark, NJ; *m:* Harv Debbie, Laurie; *ed:* William Paterson Coll (BA) Elem Ed 1977; Montclair St Univ, Monmouth Cty Coll, St Peter's Coll, Univ of MA, Coll; *cr:* Parsippany Schls Permanent Sub 1970-77; William Paterso Tutor 1976; St Claire's-Riverside Adolescent Psychiatric Hospital Morris Cty Learning Resource Ctr Consultant 1978-79; Wharton Bo Schls Tchr 1977-; Private Tutor; NJ Symphony; Consultant Biosph *ai:* Teach Recorders & Eng Sign Lang; Soc Problem Solving, Sci C NJ Ed Assn 1976-; NEA, Wharton Ed Assn 1977-; World Wil Greenpeace; Arbor Day Assoc; Trees for Life; Geraldine R. D Fellowship Opportunity Awd & Grant; Rudolph Excl in Sci Awd; Inst & Good Apple Magazines; Who's Who in Amer Ed; Who's Who in the Sozio Music Awd; *office:* Marie V. Duffy Schl 137 E Central Ave W NJ 07885*

ALTMAN, MICHAEL E., English Teacher & Drama Instr; *b:* Titus PA; *ed:* St Bonaventure Univ (BA) Eng 1985; CA Univ of PA Scndr Cert 1990; *cr:* Steel Vly HS Eng & Drama Instr 1991-; *ai:* Head of D Club; Fall Play & Musical & Stage Crew Dir; Boys & Girls Tennis C Travel Spon; *office:* Steel Valley HS 3113 Main St Munhall PA 1512

ALTMAN, THOMAS C., Physics Teacher; *b:* Nurenburg, German Mary J. Larkin; *c:* Virginia, Benjamin, Jonathan; *ed:* St Univ of Os (BS) Sci Ed 1981, (MS) Physics Ed 1985; 8 Credit Hrs Univ of NM Medium Energy Particle Physics; 6 Hrs Penn St MS Atomic Energ USAF Radio Repairman 1972-78; Oswego City Schl Dist Sci Tchr *ai:* Sci Club Adv; Publicity for Schl Musical; AFT & NYSTA 1985 Tchr of Yr; STANYS 1986-, Presidential Awd; NSTA 1987-, Star 19 1992 1st Runner Up; Gideons Intnl 1987-; Amer Legion 1993-; The A Holography Method & Altman Laser Optics Kit Inventor; Videos: Las & Altman Holography Method; Book: The Holography Primer; *o* Oswego HS 2 Buccaneer Blvd Oswego NY 13126*

ALTOMARI, CYNTHIA F., Science Teacher; *b:* Philadelphia, PA Temple Univ (MED) Sci Ed; East Stroudsburg Univ (BA) Environ Sci; Portland-Falmouth Tchrs Acad; *cr:* Spring Ford MS Sci Tchr 2 Gorham HS Sci Tchr 2 Yrs; Westbrook HS Sci Tchr 5 Yrs; *ai:* N Helper Adv; *office:* Westbrook HS 125 Stroudwater St Westbroo 04092

ALTOMARINO, GABRIELA FERSCHTMAN, Spanish Teach Montevideo, Uruguay; *m:* Enrique Sergio; *c:* Sebastian; *ed:* Tchrs Uruguay (BA) Scndry Ed 1985; Adelphi Univ Working on Maste Credits; Hum & Scis Univ at Uruguay MS Linguistics 15 Courses; *cr:* Richman HS Tchr 1992-93; Grover Cleveland HS Tchr 1993-; *ai:* 1992-; *office:* Grover Cleveland HS 2127 Himrod St Ridgewood NY

ALTONIAN, CHARLES VINCENT, Assistant Principal; *b:* C Falls, RI; *m:* Elaine F.; *c:* Scott Charles, Eric Christopher; *ed:* Provi Coll (BA) Scndry Ed 1965, (MA) Amer His 1966; RI Coll (CAGS) Admin 1983; 30 Additional Credits; *cr:* Jenks Jr HS Tchr, Houselea Coach 1967-92; Shea Sr HS Var Swimming Coach 1974-78; Tolman H Sftbl Coach 1985-91; Jenks Jr HS Asst Prin 1992-; *ai:* Oversee Disci Curr & Attendance; Pawtucket Tchrs Alliance 1967-, Asst VP; RI F Tchrs, AFT & AFL-CIO 1967-92; NAS SP 1992-; RIASSP 1 Pawtucket Admin Assn; Alliance Credit Union 1967, Exec Bd 1992-; Mixed Bowling League 1986-, Pres; Pawtucket Mens Sftbl League 1984-89; Blackstone Vly Comm Action Pgm; Comp Camp Co-Dir Designed & Wrote Stu & Tchrs Handbook & Sub Survival Kit; Grants; Equiped Comp Lab; *office:* Pawtucket Schl Dept 350 Divis Pawtucket RI 02860*

ALU, ROBERT, 10th Grade Teacher; *b:* Astoria, NY; *ed:* Long Univ (BA) His 1976; Pratt Inst (MLS) Lib, Information Sci 1978; Ad Univ Lawyers Asst Prgm; *cr:* NY Law Schl Law Librn, Tech Svcs Friesner & Salzman Law Firm Managing Clerk, Litigation Dept 197 Mineola HS His Tchr 1986; East Meadow HS His Tchr 1986-; *ai:* NH Adv; Natl Cncl for His Edu 1989-; Long Island Cncl for Soc Stud 1 Stu Cert of Appreciation 1990; *office:* East Meadow Sr HS 101 Carma East Meadow NY 11554*

BAIDI, MUTHAR RADIF, Energy Professor; *b:* Wasit, Iraq; *m:* Pia asotta; *ed:* Univ of Baghdad (BS) Mechanical Engrng 1967; Univ of on (MS) Nuclear Engrng 1974; Univ of Cincinnati (PHD) Nuclear ig 1984; *cr:* Iraqi Natl Oil Co Field Engr 1968-70; Nuclear Rsrch Inst or Engr 1970-72; Coll of Applied Sci Univ of Cincinnati Lecturer 85, Visiting Asst Prof 1985-86, Asst Prof 1986-91, Assoc Prof 1991-; oc Comm, Stud Tribunal, Scepter Soc & OCAS Tech Expo Advs; nencement, Acad Affairs, Stu Life & Svcs Comms; Intnl Planning Amer Soc of Mech Engrs 1985; Amer Soc for Engr Ed 1986-, Chair Div, Outstdng Svc 1995; Interamerican Cncl for Engrng & Tech Ed , Chair of Bd; Soc of Manufacturing Engrs; Intnl Festival 1985-, Vice , Svc Awd; Cincinnati Theatrical Assoc 1988-; Cincinnati Art um 1989-; Cincinnati Zoo 1989-; Cincinnati Historical Soc 1989-; of Cincinnati George B Barbour Awd; Whos Who in Midwest ing Fac of Yr Awd; Tau Alpha Pi Acad Achvmt Awd; Stu Tribunal of Yr; The Globalization of Engrng Ed an Intnl Manufacturing Stud *office:* Univ of Cincinnati Coll of Applied Sci 2220 Victory Pky nnati OH 45206

EN, GINA SUZANNE, English & Drama Teacher; *b:* Jersey City, NJ; ofstra Univ (BA) Theatre Arts 1975; Rutgers Univ (EDM) Ed 1978 '; g Advanced Placement Stdnts Eng Roan Coll of NJ 1992; AP Eng Lit mp Smnr Bates Coll 1989; *cr:* Ft Dix Ed Ctr ESL Instr 1978-82; a Rgnl HS Eng, Drama Tchr 1983-; *ai:* Adv to Drama Club; Dir Schl NEA, NJEA 1983-; Kappa Delta Pi; NJRHPT Writing List Comm COre Course Proficiency Comm Eng 1009-92, Performing Arts *office:* Delsea Regional HS Blackwoodtown Rd Franklinville NJ

ES, BENNIE RUTH, Kindergarten Teacher; *b:* Jacksonville, FL; *m:* *c:* Glen, Andrea; *ed:* St Univ at Farmingdale (AA) Early Chldhd St Univ at Old Westbury (BS) Elem Ed 1984; Alantic Union Coll e Work Towards Sci, Ed MS; *ai:* Early Chldhd Ed Cncl Nassau Cty; Chldhd Ed Intnl; Assn of Adventist; Regnl Conf Edctrs; Amer Legion iary, Oakwood Coll Alumni Assn 1992-; Appreciation Cert Suffolk xec Robert J. Gaffney 1996; Thomas & Violet Zapara Tchng Excl 1991; Ministry of Tchng Credential 1991; SUNY at Farmingdale gd Academic Achv Awd 1983, Diane Inge Stu Tchng Excl Awd 1982; aul S. Riley Outstdng Early Chldhd Ed Grad Awd 1982; *home:* 181 son Ave Amityville NY 11701

S, CARLOS SERRA, Mathematics Professor; *b:* Lisboa, Portugal; nna Jean Salvucci; *ed:* Univ Porto-Portugal (BA) Math 1975, (MS) ed Math 1978; PA St Univ (MA) Math 1980, (PHD) Math 1985; *cr:* NC at Wilmington Asst Prof 1985-89; Trenton St Coll Asst Prof 95, Assoc Prof 1995-; *ai:* Amer Math Soc, Assn Symb Logic 1978-; appa Phi 1983-; Pi Mu Epsilon 1987-, Chapter Adv 1993-95; Math Tchr of Yr 1995; Fulbright Grant; Articles Pub; *office:* Trenton St Cn 4700 Trenton NJ 08650

ES, LISA CYNTHIA, Music Teacher; *b:* Fall River, MA; *ed:* RI Coll Music Ed 1991; 18 Credit Hrs Elem Ed Cert; 6 Credit Hrs Towards rs; *cr:* Mc Govern's Family Restaurant Waitress, Cook 1985-92; is Churches Vocal Soloist 1988-; Private Voice, Piano Lessons 1992-; socket Ed Dept Music Edctr 1992-; *ai:* All-City Elem Chorus Dir; 1992-; MENC, RI Music Edctrs Assn 1988-; NATS Singing etition 1st Place; Melody Stappas Meml Schlsp; Cantor Jacob nemser Awd.

ARD, WANDA SANDY, Chemistry Teacher; *b:* Morning Sun, IA; *m:* D.; *c:* Alicia Shirk, Melinda; *ed:* Clarion Univ of PA (BA) Chem 24 Post Grad Stud Hrs Edinboro Univ of PA; *cr:* Butler MS Tchr 66; Fort Le Bo HS Tchr 1966-68; Gen Mc Lane HS Tchr 1968-69, ; *ai:* Jets Team Adv; NEA, PSEA 1965-; AMEA 1976-; CMA 1975-, y Schl Tchr; Regnl Chem Tchr of Yr Local Amer Chem Soc; Selected end TIE Wkshp in Harrisburg 1996; *office:* General Mc Lane HS Edinboro Rd Edinboro PA 16412

INE, JUDITH S. WEIGLE, Third Grade Teacher; *b:* Johnstown, PA; obert Allen; *c:* Camille S., Robert W.; *ed:* Indiana Univ of PA (BS) Ed; *cr:* St Benedict Schl 3-5 Grd Tchr 1983-; *ai:* 4-H Club Tchr; PJAS ; *home:* 320 Boise St Johnstown PA 15904

HASSAN Y., Assoc Prof of Economics; *b:* Alexandria, Egypt; *m:* L.; *c:* Rasha, Reem, Pharis; *ed:* Alexandria Univ (BA) Ec 1977; ern IL Univ (MS) Ec 1982, (PHD) Ec 1986; Qualifying Masters e 1978; *cr:* Alexandria Univ Lecturer Ec 1986-87; Southern IL Univ ig Asst Prof 1987-89; OH St Univ Asst Prof 1989-, Assoc Prof 1996; dv Bus, Ec Stu Club; Budget, Cmptr, Evaluation Fac Comms; Amer sn 1982-; Midwest Ec Assn 1986-; Eastern Ec Assn 1992-; Omicron Epsilon 1986-; 15 Articles Pub; 8 Grants, 2 Svc Awds Kuwait Univ 94; *office:* OH St Univ at Marion 1465 Mount Vernon Ave Marion 3302*

DEI, LILLIAN LLOYD, 6th-8th Grade English Teacher; *b:* Chester, ; Jerry; *c:* Seth, Adam; *ed:* Widener Univ (BA) Eng 1972, (BA) e Arts 1972; *cr:* St Mary's Regnl Schl Eng Tchr 1986-; *ai:* Yrbk, Patrol Adv; Lang Arts Curr Coord; NCEA 1986-; Lang Arts Curr Co-Author; *office:* St Mary's Regnl Schl 8 S Union Rd Vineland NJ

IO, CAROLE B., High School English Teacher; *b:* Bridgeport, CT; iv of CT (BA) Eng 1968; Univ of Hartford (MA) Ed 1973; 40 Credits ; Hum Scholar 1995; Attnd Hartford Coll of Women; *cr:* Hartford Pub g Tchr 1968-; *ai:* New England Assn of Schls & Colls Accreditation Admin Chprsn; AFT 1968-; *office:* Hartford Public HS 55 Forest St ord CT 06105

RA, VINCENT H., Science Teacher; *b:* Augusta, Italy; *m:* Anna -Amara; *c:* Luca, Angela; *ed:* Northeastern Univ (BS) Ed 1970; n St Coll (MS) Biling & Bicultural Ed 1977; Fitchburg St Univ rs Pgm Media & Commnctn; *cr:* Boston Pub Schl Tchr 1973-; *ai:* HS r Coach; Schl Site Cncl 1995-; BTU 1973-; MFT 1973-; AFT 1973-; Alighieri Soc 1978-, Bd of Dir; Pirandello Lyceum 1990-, Media 990; Sons of Italy Lodge 2057, VP 1995-; Il Mondo in Cui Viviamo & TV; Book: Manvale D'Impieghi; Plan For Excl 1986 & 1988; for the Stars 1993; Numerous Articles Pub; Programming for Italian ers in Greater Boston Area; *office:* Umana-Barnes MS 312 Border St oston MA 02128

RAKOON, VASANTHA R., Prof of Ceramic Eng; *b:* kotapola, nka; *m:* Savithri W. Panditaratne; *c:* Shanika, Shaminda; *ed:* Univ of n (BS) Phys Sci 1967; Univ of Leeds (BS) Ceramic Sci 1972; Univ (MS) Cermaic Eng 1980, (PHD) Cermaic Eng 1984; *cr:* Ceylon ics Corp Asst Mgr-Tech 1967-75; Natl Cncl for Scientific Research f Ofcr 1975-78; Alfred Univ Asst Prof 1984-89, Assoc Prof 1989-95, 995-; *ai:* Grad Prgm Dir; Grad Research, Fac Adv; Engrng Cncl Tchng, Curr Comms; Amer Ceramic Soc 1977-; IEEE 1989-; Natl Ceramic Engr, Educl Cncl 1980-; Tchng Awds Alfred Univ 1986-89, 1993, Mc Mahon Excl 1986, 1995, SUNY Chancellor's 1988; Assoc ner Ceramic Soc Journal 1988-; *office:* Alfred Univ NYS Coll of ics 26 N Main St Alfred NY 14802*

TO, ANTHONY MICHAEL, Chemistry Teacher; *b:* Pittsburgh, PA; A Univ of PA (BA) Chem, Bio 1964; Univ of Notre Dame (MS) ic Chem 1972; Post-Grad Stud Univ of WV, Vanderbilt Univ; *cr:* ster City Schls Chem Tchr 1965-66; Ringgold HS Chem Tchr 1966-; STA 1969-; NEA, PA St Ed Assn 1966-; Notre Dame Alumni Assn 1972-; Excl in Tchng Awd Duquesne Univ; *office:* Ringgold HS 3645 Dry Run Rd Monongahela PA 15063

AMATO, BARBARA JONES BROUGH, Senior English Teacher; *b:* Detroit, MI; *m:* Philip; *ed:* Miami Univ (BSEd) Eng 1975; Grad Hrs at Univ of Cincinnati, Xavier Univ, Northern KY Univ, OH Univ, Coll of Mt St Joseph, Wright St Univ; *cr:* Anderson HS Eng Tchr 1975-; *ai:* OH Tests of Scholastic Achvmt Sr Eng Coach 1986-; NEA & OEA 1975-; Delta Kappa Gamma 1984-, Pres 1992-94; MENSA 1991-; Cum Laude 1991-; Anderson HS Tchr of Yr 1991; Delta Kappa Gamma Schlsp Winner 1995; MENSA Schlsp Contest 2nd Pl 1995; Numerous Articles Pub; *office:* Anderson HS 7560 Forest Rd Cincinnati OH 45255

AMATO, DEBRA DEFILIPPO, School Psychologist; *b:* Paterson, NJ; *m:* Patrick; *c:* Matthew, Patrick, Amanda; *ed:* Northern IL Univ (BS) Sp Ed, Elem Ed 1973; Montclair St Univ (MA) Psych 1980; Montclair St Univ, Prof Diploma, Schl Psych 1982; *cr:* Paramus Pub Schls Tchr Spec Ed 1973-89, Child Stud Team, Psychologist 1989-; *ai:* Peer Relations, Buddy Club; Spec Ed PTA VP; NJEA 1973-; NJASP 1990-; St Paul's Church, Soc Concerns 1992-; Psi Chi 1980-; *office:* Paramus Pub Schls Spring Valley Rd Paramus NJ 07652*

AMATO, JOHN MARK, Social Studies Teacher; *b:* Meadville, PA; *m:* Terri Lee Russell; *c:* Kayleigh, Joseph, Teresa, Elizabeth; *ed:* Mansfield St Univ of PA (BA) Criminal Justice Admin 1981; Soc Stud Cert 1989; US Army Infantry Officers Advanced Course 1986; US Army Ranger Schl 1982; US Army Air Defense Officers Course 1982; *cr:* US Army Platoon Ldr 1982-86, Staff Officer 1986-88, Company Commander 1988-89; Crawford Cntrl Schl Dist Sub Tchr 1989-91; Meadville Area Sr HS Soc Stud Tchr199 1-; *ai:* Asst Ftbl, Head JV Wrestling Coach; NEA, PSEA 1991-; Crawford Cntrl Ed Assn 1991-; Amer Legion 1992-; US Army Reserves 1989-, Captain; Italian Civic Club 1989-; PA Gun Collectors Assn 1992-; Crawford Cty Historical Soc 1993, Historic Preservation Soc 1995; *office:* Meadville Area Sr HS North Street Ext Meadville PA 16335

AMATO, LEAH ASHENDORF, Fifth Grade Teacher; *b:* New York City, NY; *c:* Michael A.; *ed:* Fairleigh Dickinson Univ (BS) Elem Ed 1966; Johns Hopkins Univ (MS) Elem Schl Cnslng 1990; MSDE Credit; *cr:* Paterson Schl Dist First Grd Tchr 1966-70; Morris Schl Dist 1-6 Grd Remedial Math Tchr 1974-75, 1-3 Grd Tchr 1975-80; Howard Cty Schl System Fifth Grd Tchr 1985-; *ai:* Instrl Consultation, Mngmt Teams; Lang Arts Comm; Hlth Ed Schl Rep; NEA 1966-; HCEA, MSEA 1985-; Phi Delta Kappa 1991-; Children of Separation & Divorce Inc 1993-, Peer Cnslr; Inclusion, Spec & Regular Ed Mini Grant.

AMATO, MARIANNE, English Teacher; *b:* Yonkers, NY; *m:* Lawrence; *c:* Jonathan; *ed:* St Leo Coll (BA) Ed 1973; Fordham Univ (MA) Eng; Iona Coll (MA) Ed & Eng 1988; *cr:* Gorton HS Eng Tchr 1973-76; Amity Regnl HS Eng Tchr 1978-84; New Rochelle Pub Schls Eng Tchr 1986-88; Tuckahoe HS Eng Tchr 1989-; *ai:* Sr Class Adv; Coord for the WISE Pgm; AFT 1988-; NEA 1988-; *office:* Tuckahoe Union Free Schl Dist 65 Siwanoy Blvd Eastchester NY 10707*

AMAZALORSO, PATRICIA PENDLETON, Eng, French & Homeroom Tchr; *b:* Winona, MN; *m:* Roy; *c:* Hilary Lea; *ed:* City Coll of City Univ of NY (BA) Lit, Lang 1970; St Univ of NY At New Paltz 6 Credit Hrs Rdng, Scndry Ed; *cr:* Restaurant Assoc Inc Corp Rsrch Librn 1963-70; Dynamic Bus Svcs Inc Co-Owner, VP 1978-91; St James the Apostle Schl Eng, Fr, 8th Grd Homeroom Tchr 1987-; *ai:* Yrbk Adv; Lib Dev Comm; FCT 1996-; ASCD 1994-; Sierra Club 1991-; Nature Conservancy 1990-; Wildlife Defense Fund 1994-; Natl Wildlife Fed 1989-.*

AMBERT, ANITA, 6th Grade Teacher; *b:* New York City, NY; *c:* Jesse, Keith Barbalato; *ed:* Mercy Coll (BS) Psych, Ed 1979; Lehman Coll (MA) PE 1987; *cr:* Columbus Schl 1st Grd Tchr 1983; Longfellow Schl 6th Grd Tchr 1984-; *ai:* Yrbk Adv 10 Yrs; Mt Vernon Rec Dept After Schl Homework Rec Prgm 4 Yrs; Schl Talent Show Organier.*

AMBLER, CHARLES HENRY, English Teacher; *b:* Philadelphia, PA; *m:* Maria Patricia Bense; *c:* Gregory, Matthew; *ed:* PA St Univ (BA) Comprehensive Eng 1969; Beaver Coll (MA) Ed 1977; *cr:* Elkins Park Jr HS Eng Tchr 1969077; Cheltenham HS Eng Tchr 1977-; *ai:* PSEA, NEA 1969-; CEA 1969-, VP; Pub Articles; *office:* Cheltenham HS Rices Mill Rd & Carlton Ave Wyncote PA 19095

AMBRAZIEJUS, RIMAS MARIUS, 9th-12th Grade History Teacher; *b:* Dorchester, MA; *m:* Nancy Podoski; *c:* Annalea; *ed:* Univ of MA (BS) Bus Mngmt 1984, (MED) Ed 1993; Cert His 1991; Attnd JFK Lib Summer Inst, Military Trng Schls; Contiuating Ed Courses; *cr:* Torah Acad His Tchr 1993-94; North Quincy HS His Tchr 1994-; *ai:* Acad Decathlon Tutor; Stu Union Head; Curr Review, Revision Comm; NEA, MTA, QEA 1994-; US Army Reserve, Noncommissioned Ofcr 1981-; Phi Alpha Theta 1991-, Local Chptr Organizer; *office:* North Quincy HS 316 Hancock St North Quincy MA 02171*

AMBROSE, ALAN A., Bible Teacher; *b:* Wilmington, DE; *m:* Penny L.; *c:* Abby, Chad; *ed:* Bapt Bible Coll (BA) Youth, Bible 1990; *cr:* Ambassador Bapt Church Youth Pastor 1990-93; Meadowwood Adolescent Hospital Mental Hlth Assoc 1991-93; New Castle Bapt Acad 1993-; *ai:* Taekwondo Instr; *office:* New Castle Baptist Acad 901 E Basin Rd New Castle DE 19720

AMBROSE, CATTIE, English Teacher; *b:* Rowland, NC; *m:* John L.; *c:* Jenette Ambrose Young, Juan, Sherri Ambrose Holt, Byron, Johnathan, Carissa; *ed:* Morgan St Univ (BA) Eng 1980, (MA) Eng 1984; *cr:* Morgan St Univ Asst Eng Prof 1980-84; Mergenthaler Voc Tech Sr HS Eng Tchr 1984-87; Greenspring MS Eng Tchr 1987-88; Hamilton Elem, MS Eng Tchr 1988-; *ai:* Writers' Club, Shakespeare Plays, Schl Newspaper Adv; AFT; Girl Scouts 1981-, Ldr, Vol Awd; Pepsi Achiever Awd; *office:* Hamilton Elem, MS 2500 E Northern Pky Baltimore MD 21214

AMBROSIA, MICHELE (LEPAGE), Sixth Grade Teacher; *b:* Reading, PA; *m:* Ronald; *c:* Mario, Damian; *ed:* Kutztown Univ (BS) Elem Ed 1972; Received Master Equivalency 36 Grad Credits 1989; *cr:* Lebanon Schl Dist Chapter I Remedial Rdng Tchr 1972-74; S S Cyril & Methodius Schl 5th & 6th Grd Tchr 1974-79; St Catherine Laboure Schl 6th Grd Tchr 1979-80; Annville-Cleona Schl Dist Chapter I Remedial Rdng Tchr 1981-82; Our Lady of the Valley Schl 6th Grd Tchr 1982-; *ai:* Our Lady of Valley Schl Math & Math Olympiad Coord; Diocesan Human Sexuality Comm Mem; Thinking Cap Quiz Bowl Team Moderator; Safety Patrol Moderator; Kids Banking Moderator; Extraordinary Minister; Mem of Schl Finance Comm; Coord for John Hopkings Talent Search Applicants 5th & 6th Grd Our Lady of the Valley; Coord For Schl Level 24 Math Challenge Contest, Proctor for Dist Level Comp; NCEA 1982-; St Paul the Apostle Church 1977-; Northeast Swim Club Parent Assn 1990-; St Paul's Church Parish Cncl 1993-94; Article & Photo on Use of Learning Stations Pub in Cath Tchr Magazine 1975; *office:* Our Lady Of The Valley Schl 740 Willow St Lebanon PA 17046

AMBROSI-LEPORE, ERSILIA, Retired Teacher; *b:* Rochester, NY; *c:* Peter, Philip, Martine; *ed:* St Univ of NY at Brockport (BA) Early Chldhd Ed 1953; 40 Grad Hrs Child Dev, Assessment in Early Yrs, Early Chldhd Ed; *cr:* 39 Schl Kndgtn Tchr 1953-59; Wm. C. Munn Schl Kndgtn Tchr 1969-95; *ai:* Child Dev Speaker to Nursery Schl Parents; Parent's Assn Tchr Liaison; Videotaped, Assisted with Music Prgms; Spencerport Tchrs Assn 1969-; NYSUT, AFT 1970-; NAEYC 1975-; Trinity Emmanuel Luth Church, Help Us Grow; Meals on Wheels; Strong Hosp, Story Time Prgm Dir; *home:* 660 Elmgrove Rd Rochester NY 14606

AMBROSINI, CATHERINE, Life Science Teacher; *b:* Manhattan, NY; *m:* Robert William; *c:* Robert, Anthony, Dominick; *ed:* Hunter Coll CCNY (BA) Bio 1972; SUNY at Stonybrook (MALS) Gen Acad 1977; Post-Grad Credit Hrs Spec Techniques; *cr:* Orentrech Dermatology Aging Stud Rsrch Scientist 1972; Wading River Schls Pre K-4th Grd Tchr Asst, Sub, Nursery Schl 1972-73; Connetquot HS 10th-12th Grd Environmental Sci Tchr 1975-78; Ronkonkoma Jr HS 9th Grd Non Regent's Earth Sci Tchr 1978-88, 7th Grd Life Sci Team Tchr 1988-; *ai:* Adv Conservation Clubs; Coach JV Chrldng, Jr HS Soccer; Connetquot Bsbl Boosters 1995-, Pres; *office:* Ronkonkoma Jr HS 501 Peconic St Ronkonkoma NY 11779

AMBROSINO, JOAN, Counselor; *b:* New York, NY; *ed:* Queens Coll City Univ of NY (BA) Ed, (MS) Ed; St John's Univ (PD) Schl Psych; NY St Permanent Cert Schl Cnslr; *cr:* Roslyn Pub Schls Tchr, Cnslr; *ai:* Human Relations, Prgm Evaluation, Interview Comms; AFT; Roslyn Tchrs Assn; NY St Tchrs Assn; Honorary Life Mem NY St Congress of Parents & Tchrs; *office:* Roslyn MS Locust Ln Roslyn Heights NY 11577*

AMBROSIO, JOSEPH MICHAEL, Music Teacher; *b:* Brooklyn, NY; *m:* Constance Anne Rast; *c:* Joseph, John, Jean; *ed:* Manhattan Schl of Music (BM) Music 1976; *cr:* Free-Lance Composer, Arranger for Music Publishing Cos 1978-92; Islip HS Music Chours & Theory Instr 1992-; *ai:* HS Swing Choir, Musical Dir; Amer Fed of Musicians 1960-; Amer Soc of Composers Authors & Publishers 1978-, Recipient of Spec Awd; Concert Band Compositions Published by Carl Fisher, Boosey & Hawkes, Columbia Picures, Lorenz Music Publishers; *office:* Islip HS 2508 Union Blvd Islip NY 11751

AMBROZA, NELSON LARRY, HS Math Teacher; *b:* Lima, OH; *m:* Anita Kay Shaw; *c:* Eric, Sally Jo Shafer; *ed:* OH St (BS) Math Ed 1965; Bowling Green (MS) Math Ed 1974; *cr:* Elida Jr HS Math Tchr 1965-66; Lima Sr HS Math Tchr 1966-69; Spencerville Local Schl Math Tchr, Coach 1969-; *ai:* Bsbl Asst; Dist Coach of Yr, Tchr of Yr; *home:* 120 S Dale Dr Lima OH 45805

AMBRULAVAGE, JANICE ANN, Seventh Grade Teacher; *b:* Shenandoah, PA; *ed:* Cedar Crest Coll (BS) Bio & Scndry Ed 1986; Kutztown Univ (MED) Ed & Rdng Specialist-Summa Cum Laude 1990; *cr:* Shenandoah Vly Schl Dist K-12th Grd Sub Tchr 1986-87, Dist Sci Tutor 1986-87, Permanent Sub, 7th-8th Grd Dev & Remedial Rdng Tchr 1987; Mahanoy City Cath Schl 7th Grd & Sci Tchr 1987-; *ai:* Diocesan & Cty Spelling Bee Coach; Co-Moderator for Astronomy Club; Asst Coach Diocesan Acad Bowl; Sci Curr Guidelines Comm; Sci Curr Coord; Schl SOLO Pgm Coord; NCEA 1987-; ADLTA 1988-; IRA 1989-; ASCD 1991-95; Cedar Crest Alumnae Assn 1986-; Presenter Sci Coord Meeting & Diocesan Educl Convention; Whos Who in Amer Ed; Nom Whos Who in the World; Delta Kappa Gamma Outstdng Work in Ed; *office:* Mohanoy City Cath Schl 29 S Catawissa St Mahanoy City PA 17948*

AMBUSKE, GREGORY CHARLES, Chemistry Teacher; *b:* Salamanca, NY; *m:* Helen Frances Carroll; *c:* Amy, Gregory, Carly; *ed:* Gannon Univ (BS) Sci, Bio 1968; Syracuse Univ (BS) Sci, Forestry 1971; 75 Post-Grad Hrs St Univ of NY, Coll of Environmental Sci & Forestry at Syracuse 1971-73; *cr:* Lord Corp Hughson Chemical Sr Lab Tech 1965-67; Worthington Corp Application Engr 1967-69; Schl St Jr HS 7-9 Grd Sci Tchr 1973-75; Bradford Area HS Scndry Sci Tchr 1975-; *ai:* Girls Track & Field Coach; NEA, PSEA, BAEA 1973-; *home:* 614 Interstate Pkwy Bradford PA 16701

AMEND, KENNETH C., Chemistry Teacher; *b:* Englewood, NJ; *m:* Lee Ann; *c:* Mei Lee, Kathleen; *ed:* Ursinus Coll (BS) Chem 1967; Worchester Polytechnic Inst (MS) Chem 1969; Worchester St Coll Tchr Cert 1986; *cr:* St Peter Marian HS Chem Tchr 1978-85; Auburn HS Chem Tchr 1985-; *ai:* Schl Evaluation Subcommittee Chm; Odyssey of Mind Teams Coach; NEA, MTA & NSTA 1985-; Church Choir 1975-, Past Pres; *office:* Auburn HS 99 Auburn St Auburn MA 01501

AMENDT, SUSAN PURDY, Junior English Teacher; *b:* Fort Wayne, IN; *m:* Donald Lee; *c:* Matthew Edward, Megan Rye; *ed:* Indiana Univ of PA (BS) Comm, Ed 1976, (MS) Lit 1991; *cr:* Indiana Area Schl Dist Eng Tchr 1976-; Chautauqua Summer Schl Instr; *ai:* Creative Writing Club, Shakespeare Club Advs; Drama Dir; Inservice Instr for Area Schl Dists; NCTE 1988-; ASCD 1993-; Arts Cncl 1989-; New Growth Arts Festival; Invitational Comm Chprsn 1984-, Comm Chair; South Central PA Wrtng Project Fellow; Tchr Consultant; Tchr Asst; *office:* Indiana Area HS 450 N Fifth St Indiana PA 15701*

AMENTO, JANET, Mathematics Teacher; *b:* New Haven, CT; *ed:* Southern CT St Univ (BS) Inter-Upper Ed 1977; Fairfield Univ (MA) Ed 1982; 6th Yr Admin & Supervision 1986; *cr:* Amity Regnl Jr HS Tchr 1977-; *ai:* Homework Hot-Line Coord; Cooperating & Mentor Tchr Comm; NELMS 1995-, Schl Rep, Presenter 3 Times; NEA, CEA 1977-; AEA 1977-, Corresponding Sec; ATOMIC, NCTM 1980-; CCSM 1992-, Mid Level Adv; CBIA Math Fellow; Gold Pen Awd; *office:* Amity Jr HS 190 Luke Hill Rd Bethany CT 06524*

AMERO, RICHARD A.,JR., Business Teacher; *b:* Lewiston, ME; *m:* Wendy K. Howe; *ed:* Husson Coll (BA) Bus Ed 1989; *cr:* Monmouth Acad Bus Tchr & Schl to Work Coord 1989-; *ai:* Girls Var Bsktbl Coach; Var Cross Cntry Coach; Jr Var Sftbl Coach; FBLA & Bus Team Adv; Soph Awareness Tech & Schl to Work Comms; NEA, ME Educators Assn 1989-; NBEA 1988-; Bus Ed Assn of ME 1989-, VP, Dir, Pres; New England Bus Ed Assn 1989-, Dir; Womens Bsktbl Coaches Assn 1993-; FRIENDS Comm Drug Awareness 1995-; Monmouth Youth Bsktbl 1992-, Dir; ME Career Advanteage 15000 Dollar Grant 1995; *office:* Monmouth Acad 96 Academy Rd Monmouth ME 04259*

AMES, CHARLES G., Mathematics Teacher; *b:* Evansville, IN; *m:* Janice D. Walker; *c:* Stephanie, Jeffrey; *ed:* Suny Coll Brockport (MEd) Math 1969, (BS) Math 1966; LaSalle Univ (Ph.D.) 1994; 80 Post Grad Hrs at Various Insts; *cr:* Newfane Cntrl Schl Math Tchr 1966-, Driver Ed Instr 1978-89; Niagara Cty Comm Coll Math Instr 1969-; DeSales HS Summer Math Tchr 1973-76; Wilson Cntrl Schl Driver Ed Instr 1990-; *ai:* Bible Club Adv; Building Liason Comm; Assn of Math Tchrs NYS 1967-, Pres 1982-83; NYS Assn of Math Supvrs 1972-, Pres 1977-78; NYSOT 1966-; Assn of Math Tchrs NYS Cty Chm 1979-, Pres 1986, VP 1981-82; Ideas for Math Club Act AMTNYS Journal 1977-80; Stu Run Geometry Contest NCTM Math Tchr 1982; Tchr of Yr Newfane HS 1978; NYS Assn Math Supvrs VP 1976-77, Pres 1982; *office:* Newfane Sr H S 1 Panther Dr Newfane NY 14108*

AMES, JOHN JOSEPH, Theology Dept Teacher & Chair; *b:* Philadelphia, PA; *ed:* St Charles (BA) Philosophy 1978, (MA) Theology 1982; Cath Univ of Amer (STD) Theology 1995; *ai:* Guid Cnslng; Var Ftbl, Bsktbl Moderator; CTSA 1994-; *office:* Cardinal O'Hara HS 1701 S Sproul Rd Springfield PA 19064

AMES, KELLY ANN, Health & Physical Ed Teacher; *b:* Norristown, PA; *ed:* Ursinus Coll (BS) Hlth, PE 1989; 25 Credit Hrs; *cr:* Arcola Intermediate Schl Hlth, PE Tchr 1989-90; Methacton HS Hlth, PE Tchr 1990-91; Arcola Intermediate Schl Hlth, PE Tchr 1991-; *ai:* Coach of 8th Grd Field Hockey, LaCrosse, 7th Grd Bsktbl, HS Swim Team, Asst HS Field Hockey; PSAHPERD 1989-; US Field Hockey Assn 1990-; Achvmt in Coaching Aths M Awds; *office:* Arcola Intermediate Schl Eagleville Rd Norristown PA 19403

AMESBURY, NORINE MARY, English Teacher; *b:* Wilkes-Barre, PA; *ed:* Coll Misericordia (BA) Eng 1972; Univ of Scranton (MA) Eng 1977;

36 Credit Hrs; *cr:* Dallas Jr HS, MS Eng Tchr 1972-; *ai:* Stu Cncl Adv; Initiated Schl, Comm Svc Projects, Awds Day Prgm; DEA, PSEA, NEA, Lambda Iota Tau 1972-; Phi Delta Kappa; The Peace Ctr; Northeast PA Genealogical Soc Inc; PA Tchr of YR Nom; *office:* Dallas Schl Dist PO Box 2000 Dallas PA 18612

AMICUCCI, FRANK VINCENT, Social Studies Dept Chair; *b:* Erie, PA; *c:* Theresa, Sean; *ed:* Gannon Univ (BA) Soc Sci 1974; Edinboro Univ (MS) Rdng 1978; *cr:* Blessed Sacrement 7th-8th Soccer Coach 1974-79; Holy Rosary Prin 1979-81; Mercyhurst Prep Tchr, Soccer Coach 1981-; *ai:* Boys Var Soccer Coach; *office:* Mercyhurst Prep Schl 538 E Grandview Blvd Erie PA 16504

AMIDEO, ANN M., Health Teacher; *b:* Manhasset, NY; *ed:* SUNY at Cortland (BS) Hlth Ed 1982; SUNY Stony Brook (MA) Hlth Sci 1988; MA Theology Now Stud; *cr:* Atufts Hlth Plan at Boston, MA Hlth Promotion Mgr 1984-87; Amer Heart Assoc Corporate Hlth Promotion Tchr 1987-88; Islip HS Hlth Tchr 1988-92; *ai:* Mentoring Prgm; Fellowship, Prayer Club Adv; Schl Improvement Team, SADD; NYSFPHE; AFT; Cath Church, in Prayer, Bible Stud; *office:* Brentwood HS 3rd 5th Ave Brentwood NY 11717

AMIN, JULIUS A., Associate Professor; *b:* Kumba, Caeroon; *c:* Lori Ann; *ed:* Univ of Cameroon (BA) His 1979; West TX St Univ (MA) His 1983; TX Tech Univ (PHD) His 1988; *cr:* TX Tech Univ Part-time Instr 1985-88; Handbook of TX Research Asst 1986-89; Univ of Dayton Asst Prof 1989-93, Assoc Prof 1993-; *ai:* Advising Stdnt on Campus Act; Advy Cncl Omicron Delta Kappa; African Stud Assn 1989-; Org of Amer Historians, Amer Historical Assn 1988-; Book: The Peace Corps in Cameroon 1992; Articles & Reviews in Referred Journals; John F. Kennedy Fnd Majorie Kovler Fellow 1992; *office:* Univ Of Dayton Dept of History 300 College Park Ave Dayton OH 45469*

AMIOT, ROXANNE MONTARRO, Automotive Instructor; *b:* Bridgeport, CT; *m:* Christopher H.; *c:* Luke Arthur; *ed:* Housatonic Comm Coll (AS) General Stud 1990; Voc Tech Ed Major 120 Credits Cntrl CT St Univ; General Motors Trng Courses Gateway Comm Tech Coll; *cr:* Bullard-Havens Regnl Voc-Tech Schl Automotive Instr 1988-; *ai:* Sr Class Adv, Non-Traditional Shops Group Adv; Stu Assistance Team; Staff Club Sec; Security Comm; St Voc Tchr Fed 1988-; AFT, CSFT, CPEF, AFL-CIO; Automotive Service Excl 1988-, Certified ASE Tech; Who's Who Among Amer HS Stdnts 1982; *home:* 1460 Elm St Unit 220 Stratford CT 06497

AMIRAN, MINDA RAE, English Prof & Dept Chprsn; *b:* Gary, IN; *m:* Nahum; *c:* Edoh, Eyal; *ed:* Univ of Chicago (AB) 1951; Swarthmore Coll (BA) Psych 1953; Radcliffe Coll (MA) Eng 1954; Hebrew Univ in Jerusalem (PHD) Eng 1968; *cr:* Hebrew Univ Eng Tchr 1956-66; Tel Aviv Univ Eng Tchr 1966-76; Bd Ed City of Chicago Consultant 1978-81; SUNY Coll Dean 1981-90, Eng Prof 1981-; *ai:* AAUW Schlsp Chair; Numerous Fac Comms; MLA 1976-; UUP 1990-; AERA 1979-; AAHE 1990-; Phi Beta Kappa; AAOW 1981-, Chair, Schlsp Comm; Textbooks, Numerous Articles Pub; *office:* State Univ Of NY At Fredonia Dept Of English Fredonia NY 14063

AMISS, CHRISTINE ELIZABETH, Intnl Baccalaureate Coord; *b:* London, England; *m:* Amiss; *ed:* London Univ (BED) Ed 1982; Johns Hopkins Elem (MLA) Lbrl Arts 1991; Cert of Ed 1975; *cr:* Inner London Ed Authority Eng & Drama Tchr 1975-81, Eng Dept Chair 1982-83; Lansdowne Sr Eng Tchr 1983-84; Millford Mill High Eng & Theatre Arts Tchr 1984-91; Overlea High Eng & Theatre Arts Tchr 1991-93; Kenwood High Intnl Baccalaureate Coord 1993-; *ai:* Intnl Baccalaureate Pgm Spon; Pub Relations Comm Chprsn; Baltimore Cty Magnet Pgm Rep; NEA 1987-; MSTA 1987-; Phi Delta Kappa 1989-; Magnet Schls of Amer 1994-; Fullbright Exch Pgm Participant 1983-84; CAST 1986; Stud Mission to Ukraine & Russia NASSP 1995; *office:* Kenwood HS 501 Stemmers Run Rd Baltimore MD 21221*

AMITRANO, ROBERT JOHN, Professor of Biology; *b:* Teaneck, NJ; *m:* Suzanne L. Jacobsen; *c:* Robert H.; *ed:* Seton Hall Univ (BS) Bio 1980; NY Chiropractic Coll (DC) Chiropractic 1984; Post Grad Stud in Nutritional Medicine, Clinical Nutrition, Neurology, MRI Diagnosis, Phys Rehabilitation, Myofascial Pain Treatment, Homeopathy, X-ray Diagnosis, Sports Medicine, Dale Carnegie Effective Speaking & Human Relations 1985; *cr:* Bergen Comm Coll Adjunct Tchr 1988-92, Lecturer 1992-93, Instr 1993-95, Asst Prof 1995-; *ai:* Fac Senate Mem; Univ Of Medicine & Dentistry Liason; NJEA 1992-; HAPS 1993-; MACUB 1994-, Conf Chair 1996; AHC 1982-; NRA 1992-, Life Mem; ANJRPC 1991-; Bergen Cty Emergency Medical Techician Prgm Guest Lecturer; 2 Books Pub by Harper Collins & Kendall Hunt 1996; *office:* Bergen Comm Coll 400 Paramus Rd Paramus NJ 07652*

AMODEO, DAVID PATRICK, French Teacher; *b:* Albany, NY; *m:* Margaret Kelly; *c:* Zachary, Benjamin; *ed:* Siena Coll (BS) Fin 1986; St Univ of NY at Albany (MS) Ed Admin 1994; *cr:* Philip Livingston MS Fr Tchr 1989-92; Albany HS Fr Tchr 1992-; *ai:* Stu Cncl Adv; Test Ctr Supvr SAT Exams; European Stu Trip Coord; AFT, NY St United Tchrs 1989-; *home:* 19 Fleetwood Ave Albany NY 12208

AMON, CHERYL ANN, 6th Grade Teacher; *b:* Wellsville, NY; *c:* Amanda Cheryl; *ed:* Slippery Rock Univ of PA (BS) Eng 1969, (MED) Rdng 1982, (MA) Cnslng Psych 1981; *cr:* Slippery Rock Area Schls HS Eng Tchr 1969; Franklin Area Schls MS Eng, Rdng Tchr 1969-80, 6th Grd Tchr 1980-; Southern Internet Svcs Forum Coord, Online Transformations Forum 1995-; *ai:* NEA, PSEA, Franklin Area EA 1969-; Order of Eastern Star 1968-; *office:* Victory Elem Schl RD 1 Box 154 Harrisville PA 16038*

AMOROSO, GAETANO NICHOLS, Meat Science Teacher; *b:* Philadelphia, PA; *m:* Linda DiGiavonni; *c:* Gina, Lisa, Lindsay; *ed:* Temple Univ Voc II in Ed 1995; *cr:* Meat Mgr for Major Super Market 20 Yrs; Neshimary HS Adult Ed Tchr 5 Yrs; *ai:* Jr Class Spon; Meat Sci Club; Talent Show Coord; FFA 1992-, Adv; *office:* Walter Biddle Saul HS 7100 Henry Ave Philadelphia PA 19128

AMOS, ARTHUR WILLIAM, Social Studies Teacher; *b:* Mercer, PA; *m:* Linda Sue Votino; *c:* Arthur Anthony, Sarah Lynn; *ed:* Thiel Coll (BA) His 1976; Post-Grad Stud Slippery Rock Univ of PA, Clarion Univ of PA; *cr:* Mercer HS Soc Stud Tchr 1976-83; Slippery Rock HS Soc Stud Tchr 1983-95; Mercer HS Soc Stud Tchr 1995-; *ai:* Bsbl, Bsktbl & Ftbl Coach; PSEA, NEA 1976-; SRAE 1983-95; MEA 1995-; Mercer Area Little League 1987-, Coach, Mgr, Player Agent; Tchr of Yr 1986 & 1993; Act Tchr of Yr 1993.*

AMOS, BEVERLY JEAN, Fifth Grade Teacher; *b:* Fredericton NB, Canada; *ed:* Bethany Bible Coll (BSC) Chrstn Ed 1983; Pensacola Christian Coll (MS) Elem Ed 1994; Pensacola Chrstn Coll Elem Ed Working Toward MS; *cr:* Meadowbrook Chrstn Schl 1, 4, & 5 Grd Tchr 1983-93; *office:* Meadowbrook Christian Schl R D #2 Box 2000 Milton PA 17847

AMOS, RUTH NORANN MUELLER, Grad Instructor; *b:* Cincinnati, OH; *m:* Richard; *c:* Christine Noelle Rinehart, Karen Michelle; *ed:* Ball St Univ (Assoc) Arts 1974; Univ of Akron (BA) Voc Home Ec 1980; Mt St Joseph (MS) Ed 1991; *cr:* Stark Co Voc Schl Therapeutic Recreation Instr 1981-91; Eastland Career Ctr GRADS Instr 1991-92; Walnut Ridge HS GRADS Instr 1992-; Columbus St Coll Adj Instr Early Chldhd 1992-; *ai:* FHA; HERO; Perfect Attendance Co-Chair; Canton Assn for the Ed of Young Children 1980-; NEA 1980-; OVA 1980-; NAEYC 1980-; Kappa Omicron Nu 1979-; *office:* Walnut Ridge HS 4841 E Livingston Ave Columbus OH 43227

AMPADU, ALEX B., Accounting & Law Asst Prof; *b:* Oso, Ghana; *c:* Alex Jr., Kofi; *ed:* Roch Inst of Tech (MBA) Acctng; Univ of Ghana (BS) Admin; CPA; CMA; CIA; *cr:* Columbia Banking Operations Analyst 3 Yrs; Touche Ross, Co Audit Mgr 6 1/2 Yrs; Univ at Buffalo Asst Prof 1996; *ai:* Fac Liaison Career Placement Office; Fac Adv Zeta Theta Chptr of Beta Alpha Psi; AICPA 1983-; NYSSCPA 1981-, Comm; IMA 1986-; IIA 1991-; AIESEC 1994-, BOD; Beta Alpha Psi Outstdng Fac Awd; Schl of Mngmt Tchng Effectiveness Grant; Price Waterhouse Fac Flwshp Awd 1994-95; *office:* Univ at Buffalo 340 Jacobs Ctr Buffalo NY 14260*

AMROD, CLAUDIA MARIE, Mathematics Teacher; *b:* Albany, NY; *ed:* Coll of St Rose (BA) Mth 1970; Colgate Univ (MAT) Math 1982; *cr:* Cath Cntrl HS Math Tchr 1972-78; Keveny Meml Acad Math Tchr 1978-86; Franciscan Acad Math, Rel Tchr 1986-88; Arlington Cath Math Tchr 1988-; *ai:* NHS Adv, Moderator; *office:* Arlington Catholic HS 16 Medford St Arlington MA 02174

AMSPACHER, DALE PAUL, Spanish Teacher; *b:* Lancaster, PA; *ed:* Millersville Univ of PA (BSE) Span 1991; 6 Credits; *cr:* Cocalico HS Span Tchr, In Schl Suspension Monitor 1992-93; Pequea Vly HS Span Tchr 1993-; *ai:* HNS Adv; Co-Coach Mock Trial Competition; Self-Esteem Comm Meetings; Restructuring, Rescheduling Comm; NEA, PSEA, NASSP 1992-; PVEA 1993-; Trinity United Meth Choir 1995-, Singer; Trinity's Living in Faith Everyday Comm & Rsrch Team 1992-, Church Ldr; Poem Pub; Rsrch Team to Explore Restructuring Hatboro HS; Chosen by EMC Publishing Co to Represent Book; *office:* Pequea Valley HS 4033 E Newport Rd Kinzers PA 17535*

AMSTER, PATRICIA GATTI, Social Studies Teacher; *b:* Nyack, NY; *m:* Dr. Arnold; *c:* Hollie, Joseph, Ann; *ed:* Coll of St Rose (BA) His-Cum Laude 1967; SUNY at New Paltz (MS) Soc Sci-Asia 1970; His, Ed & Counseling Courses; *cr:* Rensselaer HS Tchr 1967-69; Clarkstown HS Tchr 1970-; St Thomas Aquinas Coll Adjunct Instr 1980, 1982 & 1986; *ai:* NHS Fac Comm; Renaissance Prgm Comm; Pilot Group Mem Mainstreaming Stdnts From Lower Tracks; AFT 1967-; Rockland Cty Cncl of Soc Stud Tchrs; Democratic Comm 1984-; Rockland Cty Holocaust Museum Mem; Rockland Ctr for the Arts; Rockland Cty Assn for Children with Learning Disabilities; Grant for Sci, Tech & Soc Trng; Developer of Curr for Dist; Treas for Charles Holbrook, Town Supvr & Legislator; *office:* Clarkstown Sr HS South Demarest Mill Rd West Nyack NY 10994*

AMUSO, JOSEPH GERARD, Religious Education Teacher; *b:* New Hartford, NY; *ed:* St Univ of NY at Cortland (BA) Pol Sci 1989; Fordham Univ (MA) Philosophy 1993; *ai:* Soc of Jesus 1989-; *office:* Xavier HS 30 W 16th St New York NY 10011

AMY, BARBARA BLAIR, Business Teacher & Dept Chprsn; *b:* Pittsburgh, PA; *m:* Ralph E.; *c:* Amy Lynn Farster, Renee Farster, Brandon Farster; *ed:* IN Univ of PA (BS) Accounting & Bus Ed 1969; Univ of Pittsburgh (MED) Bus Ed 1972; Compled Cert in Elem Ed 1994, Working on Masters in Elem Ed; Obtained Cmptr Prgm Specialist Cert; *cr:* Burrell Sr HS Bus Tchr 1969-72; Westmoreland Cty Comm Coll Bus Instr Part-time 1975-80; IN Univ of PA at Armstrong Campus Bus Instr 1982-84; Freeport Area Sr HS Bus Tchr 1984-; *ai:* Co-Adv of FBLA; Graduation Requirements Action Team Leader; Tech Task Force; Bus& Tech Chprsn, Attnd Comm; Career Day Team; NEA, PSEA 1969-; FEA 1984-, Chprsn of Outcome Bd Ed Comm, Schlsp Comm; Coll Club 1974-94; Past Pres; Buffalo Elem PTO 1977-78, Past Treas, Sec; Phi Kappa Phi, Delta Phi Epsilon; *office:* Freeport Sr HS 625 S Pike Rd Sarver PA 16055*

ANANIA, KENNETH JOSEPH, Professor of English; *b:* Brockton, MA; *ed:* Massasoit Comm Coll (AA) Lbrl Arts 1968; Stonehill Coll (AB) Eng 1970; Fairleigh Dickinson Univ (MAT) Eng 1971; *cr:* Massasoit Comm Coll Eng Prof 1971-; *ai:* Massasoit Theatre Co Adv; Acting Coord of Coll Dev Prgm; Stu Appeals Comm; Self Stud Comm for Coll Re-accreditation; NEA, MTA 1971-; LAANE 1988-; NCTE 1972-; *office:* Massasoit Comm Coll 1 Massasoit Blvd Brockton MA 02402*

ANASTAS, GEORGE MICHAEL, Social Studies Tchr & Coach; *b:* Framingham, MA; *m:* Annabelle Marie Green; *c:* Kerri, Karen; *ed:* Univ of MA at Boston (BA) Ed 1971, (MS) Ed & Spec Ed 1981; Leslie Coll Spec Ed Cert 1980; Fitchburg St Coll Voc Cert 1972; *cr:* Assabet Valley Regnl Voc HS Soc Stud, Spec Ed Tchr, Drug Adv, Summer Schl Prgm Prin; *ai:* Var Track, Hockey, Field Hockey & Bsbl Coach; Class Adv; Jr Olympic Girls Sftbl Coach; AFT 1972-; NHS Tchr of Yr.

ANATER, PAUL F., Science & Technology Dept Chm; *b:* Pittsburgh, PA; *ed:* Duquesne Univ (BS) Chem 1964; Univ of Pittsburgh (MED) Scndry Ed 1966, (PHD) Sci 1978; Cert Admin 1972; Univ of AARHUS Cert ICMS 1971; Attnd Natl Defense Univ 1984, Armed Svcs Staff Coll 1985; Baylor Univ Hlth Care Admin 1987; *cr:* Steel Vly Schl Dist Earth Bio Tchr 1965; Bethel Park Area HS Chem Tchr 1966; Med Field Svc Preventive Med Fac 1966-69; Univ Pittsburgh Spec Ed Tchr 1975; West Mifflin Area Sch Dist Chem Tchr 1976-; *ai:* Scndry Sci Curr; Revision Comm; Chem Chm; Mid St Evaluation; Bldg & Facilities Chm; Ski Team Coach; Chess Club Spon; Coach PA St Champs 1979; Chemical Safety in Workplace Spokesman 1984-88; PA Accr of Coll Sci Std 1992-93, Evaluator; NEA, Nat Sci T Assn 1969-, Presenter; AFT, Reg Sci-Math Collab 1981-, Reviewer; Spectroscopy Soc Pgh 1986-, 1988-91, HS Equip Grant; US Army Reserve 1970-, Col, Commendation Medal; Exp Fld Med Badge; NSD Medal ARCAM; PGH Min, Lap Soc 1970-, Pres 1985-86, Dir 1988-90; World of Poetry Assn 1989-, Golden Poet Awd 1990-91; 4th Army Pistol Team 1966-, Capt, TX St Pistol Champion 1968; Article Pub 1973; Journal of Teach Ldrshp 1995; Rsrch Journal of Visual Impaired 1980; PA Comp Class Awd 1983; PA Finalists NASA Tchr in Space 1985; Ed Consort Grant 1989, 1991; Presenter PA Nat Sci Tchr Assn St Convention 1994, NSTA Natl Convention 1995; *home:* 414 N Monongahela Ave Glassport PA 15045

ANAYA, JESSICA, Bilingual Teacher; *b:* New York, NY; *ed:* Saint Francis Coll (BA) Soc Stud 1993; Saint Johns Univ (MSEd) Scndry Ed 1996; *cr:* Queen of All Saints 8th Grd Tchr 1993-94; Sarah J Hale HS Biling SS Tchr 1994-; *ai:* AFT 1994-; *office:* Sarah J Hale HS 345 Dean St Brooklyn NY 11217

ANCONA, FRANCESCO ARISTIDE, Prof of English & Mythology; *b:* Manhattan, NY; *m:* Janet Lee Simons; *ed:* Ramapo Coll (BA) Amer Stud-Hnrs 1974; Montclair St Univ (MA) Eng 1977; St John's niv (DArts) Eng, Psychoanalysis 1983; 15 Credits Ed Admin, Tchr Supvr Cert; 9 Credits Comp Sci, Acct, Econ; *cr:* Middlesex Cty Coll Instr 1980-84; Pvt Industry Prsnl Agency Cnslr 1984-86; Cty Coll of Morris Asst Prof 1986-90; Upsala Coll Adj Prof 1991-92; Sussex Cty Comm Coll Asst Prof, Hnrs Prgm Coord 1992-; *ai:* Coll Senate; Promotions Comm Chair; Tenure Comm Lib Arts; Stu Group, Lit Magazine Adv; Stu Disciplinary, Acad Stans Comms; AFT 1992-, Treas; NJ Coll Eng Assn 1992-, Trustee; Inst for Evol Psych 1992-, Journal Asst Ed; Joseph Campbell Archives, Lib 1993-, Charter Mem; Inst for Psych Stud of Arts; MENSA; NE NCHC; Assn Lit Scholars, Critics; Modern Lang Assn; Skylands Artists, Writers Assn 1994-; Sussex Cty Arts, Heritage Cncl 1993; Montclair St Univ Assistantship; St John's Univ Flwshp; Articles Pub; 2 Books: Writing the Absence of the Father, Myth: Matter of Mind? Pub; *office:* Sussex County Comm Coll College Hill Newton NJ 07860

ANCONE, KENNETH JOSEPH, Math Teacher; *b:* Philadelphia, PA; *ed:* St Joseph's (BS) Math 1970; Villanova (MA) Sec Admin 1974; *cr:* West Cath Boys Math Tchr 1970-79; Archbishop Carroll Math Tchr 1979-88; Bishop Shanahan Math Tchr 1988-89; Cardinal O'Hara Math Tchr [illegible] *ai:* NHS Advy Bd; NCTM, ATMOPAV, Past Mem; Math Chm [illegible] 1972-81, Pres 1975; *home:* 14 S Woodland Ave Glenolden PA 19036

ANDERS, LARRY ALAN, Sixth Grade Teacher; *b:* Lancaster, O[illegible] Cynthia Ann Armstrong; *ed:* OH Univ (BS) Elem Ed 1983; *cr:* Berne [illegible] Elem 6th Grd Tchr 1984-88; Berne Union Jr HS Soc Stud Tchr 198[illegible] 6th Grd Tchr 1994-; *ai:* Berne Union Ed Assn, OH Ed Assn, NEA [illegible] *office:* Berne Union Schl Dist 506 N Main St Sugar Grove OH 4315[illegible]

ANDERSEN, ROY STUART, Emeritus Professor of Physic[illegible] Springfield, MA; *m:* Barbara Anne Norris; *c:* Karen J. Andersen-V[illegible] Loring D., Scott W.; *ed:* Clark Univ (BA) Chem 1943; Dartmouth [illegible] (AM) Physics 1948; Duke Univ (PHD) Physics 1951; *cr:* Univ o[illegible] Assoc Prof Physics 1952-60; Clark Univ Physics Prof 1960-; *ai:* [illegible] Phys Soc 1949-, Fellow 1968; AAPT 1947-; His of Sci Soc; NA[illegible] Fellow 1973.

ANDERSON, ALBERT F., Legal Asst Pgm of Studies Dir; *b:* Broo[illegible] NY; *ed:* Univ of Bridgeport (BS) Accounting 1954, (MS) Soc Sci [illegible] Univ of CT (JD) Law 1965; Univ of CT Ec Schlsp Ec 1960, 1962; U[illegible] Syracuse Ec Schlsp GE Co Ec 1964; *cr:* St Joseph Coll Prof Legal [illegible] 1986-87; Mt Aloysius Coll Legal Asst Prgm Dir 1987-; Attorney a[illegible] 1965-86; Pub Acct 1959-65; US Army; *ai:* Legal Advy Comm Chair [illegible] Continuing Legal Ed CT 1971, 1974; ABA 1965-; CBA 1966-; Amer [illegible] Para Legal Ed 1988-; *office:* Mount Aloysius Coll One College Pl Cr[illegible] PA 16630

ANDERSON, ALICIA VEREMEL, Music Teacher; *b:* Youngstown[illegible] *c:* Simeon F.; *ed:* OH St Univ (BME) Music 1973; Attnd Univ o[illegible] George Mason, Kent St Univ; *cr:* Columbus Pub Schls Choral Music [illegible] 1973-76; Lynchburg Pub Schls Elem Music Tchr 1976-77; Manassa[illegible] Schls Elem, Jr HS Music Tchr 1978-86; Youngstown City Schls C[illegible] Music Tchr 1986-; *ai:* Summer Arts Day Camp Physically Chall[illegible] Children Dir; Jr Connection, Royal Rangers Parent Booster; C[illegible] Soloist; YEA, OEA, NEA 1986-; Kent St Univ Martha Holden Jer[illegible] Scholar 1993; Awded Prin Recognition 1992; Sylvan Learnin[illegible] Outstdng Tchr Awd 1992; Iota Phi Lambda Apple for the Tchr Awd [illegible] Comm Svc Awd 1991; Outstdng Comm Svc Awd 1980.*

ANDERSON, ANGIE MARIE, 7th Grade Math Teacher; *b:* Sidney[illegible] *m:* Howard Michael; *c:* Shelbie; *ed:* Bowling Green (BA) Elem Ed [illegible] Univ of Dayton (MS) Elem Ed 1992; Project Discovery 15 Quarter H[illegible] Holy Rosary Schl Self-Contained 6th Grd Tchr 1987-89; Bridgevie[illegible] 7th Grd Math Tchr 1989-; *ai:* Math Counts Coach; Staff Dev Comm; [illegible] 1989-, Local Treas; OMSA 1994-; NCTM 1989-; Women of Moose [illegible] Copeland Educl & Act Grants; Article Pub; *home:* 11701 St Rt 29W [illegible] OH 45302*

ANDERSON, ANNA PRYCHODCZENKO, Music Teacher; *b:* S[illegible] OH; *m:* David Ammon; *c:* Nicholas, Peter; *ed:* YSU (BA) Voice, Ed [illegible] Youngstown St U MM Vocal Performance 1996; *cr:* Brown Local [illegible] Music Tchr 1982-; *ai:* MENC, NEA, Malvern Tchrs Assn 1982-; Na[illegible] of Music CLubs, Ohio Fed of Music Club 1983-; Salem Music Stud[illegible] 1983-, 1st VP, Opal Taylor Awd; MENC, NEA, Malvern Tchrs Assn [illegible] *office:* Malvern Brown Local Schls 401 W Main St Malvern OH 446[illegible]

ANDERSON, ANTON S., English Teacher; *b:* New York City, N[illegible] Sherryl Wolff; *c:* Christian, Emily; *ed:* Cornell Univ (BA) Eng 1965 [illegible] Coll (MSEd) Eng 1971; Attnd Columbia Univ; Univ of SC, Harvard [illegible] NEH Seminar Grant; *cr:* New Rochelle Acad Eng Tchr 1967-69; Gra[illegible] HS Eng Tchr 1969-; *ai:* Poetry Soc; NEA 1967-; 2 NEH Seminar G[illegible] Pub Poetry Local Newspapers, Small Magazines; *office:* Greenwich [illegible] Hillside Rd Greenwich CT 06830

ANDERSON, AUDREY HALM, Soc Studies Teacher; *b:* [illegible] Sandusky, OH; *c:* Michael, Susan, Steven, Kelley, Glen; *ed:* Tiffin[illegible] (AA) Bus 1950; Bluffton Coll (BA) Ed 1973; Bowling Green Uni[illegible] Stud Undergrad; Findlay Univ Ed Undergrad; *cr:* Angeline Schl Tchr [illegible] St Peter Schl Tchr 26 Yrs; *ai:* Church Cncl; Sub St Peter & O L C [illegible] CLC; Vol Thrift Shop; Church Hostess, Distributor; NCEA 1969-; [illegible] 1990-; *home:* 433 Circular St Upper Sandusky OH 43351

ANDERSON, BARBARA JEANNE, Second Grade Teache[illegible] Bronxville, NY; *m:* David; *c:* David Barrett; *ed:* Molloy C Coll (B[illegible] Ed, Eng 1973; Nassau C Coll (AAS) El Ed; 28 Grad Hrs UNH, U[illegible] Mc Donough Schl 2nd Grd Tchr 8 Yrs; West Side Cath Schl 2nd Gr[illegible] 7 Yrs; *ai:* Wellness Comm; MEA 1988-, Rep; Sigma Beti Xi 1984-, Treas, VP, Woman of Yr; ADK ETA Chptr 1990-, VP; Elliot Hosp A[illegible] 1976-; *home:* 300 N River Rd Manchester NH 03104

ANDERSON, BART G., Asst Prin & Activities Dir; *b:* Toledo, O[illegible] Miami Univ (BS) Math Ed 1991, (MS) Ed Admin 1993; Univ of D[illegible] (EDS) Ed Admin 1994; *cr:* Tri-City North HS Tchr 1992-95; Bethel [illegible] Asst Prin & Act Dir 1995-; *ai:* Bsktbl, Ftbl & Track Coach; Ath Di[illegible] Cncl & Yrbk Adv; OEA 1991-, Pres of Local; Trinity Church [illegible] Lewisburg Emergency Unit 1992-, EMT; *office:* Bethel Jr Sr HS 7490 Route 201 Tipp City OH 45371*

ANDERSON, BETH STONE, English Teacher; *b:* S Weymouth, M[illegible] Christopher; *ed:* Univ of MA at Amherst (BA) Eng & Fr 1963; (M[illegible] 1994; Theater Arts Mngmt; *cr:* Meier & Assocs Office Mgr [illegible] Whitman Hanson Regnl Eng Tchr 1965-; *ai:* Spellman Essay C[illegible] Coach; SADD Adv; MTA, NEA 1965-; NCTE 1989-; Drama [illegible] 1966-86; Presidential Citation 1989; Quincy Patriot Ledger Golden [illegible] Awd 1991; Noven Dedication 1990; Tchr of the Year 1992; [illegible] Whitman-Hanson H S Franklin St Whitman MA 02382

ANDERSON, BRYANT THOMAS, Arch & Structural Drftng Tc[illegible] Medford, MA; *m:* Karen Johnson; *c:* Bryant T., Janice M. Barry, Dav[illegible] Danny E., James, Kristin E. Kalweit; *ed:* Fitchburg St Coll (TC); E[illegible] Nazerene Coll; *cr:* Congdon Gurney & Towle Engr, Draftsman 19[illegible] Weymouth Voc Tech HS Math, Drafting Instr 1964-67; Eastern Assoc [illegible] Project Engr 1967-77; Weymouth HS Archt, Struct Drafting Tchr [illegible] Voc HS Archt, Struct Drafting Tchr 1977-; *ai:* Southeast MA Tech[illegible] Consortium Coll & HS; MTA, WTA, Wey Voc Tchrs Assn 1977-[illegible] Fellows 1964-77; Lions 1972-84; Nazerene Church 1946-84, Trea[illegible] Mem; Soc Amer Military Engrs 1967-77; Weymouth Korean War [illegible] Design; Bd of Selectmen Commendation Awd; *home:* PO B[illegible] Centerville MA 02632

ANDERSON, CANDACE L., Senior English Teacher; *b:* Portland [illegible] *ed:* Wheaton Coll Coll (BA) Eng Lit, Women's Stud 1987; Univ [illegible] Alcohol Ed Cnslr Cert 1988; Univ of S ME Adult Literacy, [illegible] Acquisitio; Taking Ocassional Theology Courses for MS; *cr:* [illegible] William Coll Residence Hall Coord 1987-88; Univ of S ME Residenc[illegible] Dir, Coord 1988-91; Catherine Mc Auley HS Sr Eng Tchr 1991-; J[illegible] Comm Ctr Day Camp Dir 1989-; *ai:* Sr Class Moderator; Natural H[illegible] Adult Facilitator; Key Club Adv; NCTE 1991-; Jane Austin Soc [illegible] Amer Camping Soc 1989-; DOCC St Alban's Parish 1992-; H[illegible] Pruszinsky Leadership Awd; Banning-Ford Prize Ed; *office:* Catherir[illegible] Auley HS 631 Stevens Ave Portland ME 04103

ANDERSON, CAROL FUCCI, Fifth Grade Teacher; *b:* New Have[illegible] *m:* Gil; *c:* Erica; *ed:* Southern CT Univ (BS) Elem 1964, (MS) El[illegible] 1968; 90 Addl Credit Hrs Math, Sci, Arts, Cmptr, BEST Pgm; *cr:* [illegible] Brook Schl 4th-5th Grd Tchr 1964-80; Turkey Hill Schl 3-5th Grd [illegible] 1981-; *ai:* 5th Grd Level Chm; Sci, Strategic Planning, Report [illegible] Testing, Values, Soc Stud, Long Range Planning, Lang Arts, Fac

s Comm, BOWA Sci; NEA, OTL 1964-; PTA, Pres 4 Yrs; New Haven wd; *office:* Turkey Hill Schl 441 Turkey Hill Rd Orange CT 06477

:RSON, CAROL MONGILLO, Spanish Teacher; *b:* Meadville, PA; nothy F.; *c:* Laura M., Sarah C.; *ed:* St Bonaventure Univ (BA) Span (MSEd) Scndry Ed, Span 1977; Attnd Universidad de Salamanca SUNY at Buffalo; *cr:* Salamanca HS Span Tchr 1972-; Empire State Tutor 1993-; *ai:* Span Honor Society Adv; Exchange Stu Coord; ive Schls Building Leadership Team; AATSP 1975-; NYSFLT 1973-; FLEC 1990-; ACTFL 1993-; Delta Kappa Gama 1993; Zonta of anca 1990-; Outstanding Proficiency in Span Lang & Lit St venture Univ 1972; Articles Pub NYSFLT Assn Bulletin 1982; na de Honor Instituto de Cultura Hispanica 1972; NEH Awd, Spain Inst at Madrid 1992; Carnegie-Mellon Grant, Fordham Univ 1993; ac Consultant, Rdr 1995-; *office:* Salamanca HS 50 Iroquois Dr anca NY 14779

:RSON, CATHY L., Asst Prin & Math Dept Chprsn; *b:* Titusville, Lisa Ann Mangel; *ed:* Edinboro Univ (BS) 1973, (MED) 1987; y Supervision Math, Scndry Schl Admin 1988; Post Grad Stud Penn Forest Area Schl Dist Math Tchr 1975-80; Photo Magic Owner, tor 1980-84; Cytemp Quality Control Auditor1984-86; Titusville HS Tchr, Dept Chprsn, Vice -Prin 1986-; *ai:* NCTM 1986-; Order of n Star 1983-, Past Matron; *office:* Titusville H S 302 E Walnut St ille PA 16354

:RSON, CATHY S., Fifth Grade Teacher; *b:* Kansas City, KS; *m:* t L.; *c:* Demille L.; *ed:* KS St Univ (BSE) Elem Ed, Soc Stud 1972; edits Loyola Coll; *cr:* Chelsea Elem Schl 3rd Grd Tchr 1972-76; Van len Elem Schl 3rd, 5th Grd Tchr 1978-; *ai:* Anti-Tobacco Use Prgm Schl Improvement Team; Family Lit; Grd Group Chm; TAAAC ; *office:* Van Bokkelen Elem Schl 1140 Reece Rd Severn MD 21144

:RSON, CYNTHIA SILVIS, Physical Education Teacher; *b:* e, PA; *m:* Dennis L.; *c:* Lynnette L.; *ed:* Slippery Rock Univ (BS) PE, Recreation 1968; Attnd Univ of Pittsburgh, Western MD, Azusa c, Bowie St, Towson; *cr:* Francis Mc Clure Jr HS PE, Hlth Tchr 69; Suitland Elem Schl PE Tchr 1969-74; William Beans Elem Schl hr 1969-74; Fort Foote Elem Schl PE Tchr 1969-74; Lord Baltimore PE, Hlth Tchr 1974-77; Oxon Hill Jr HS PE, Hlth Tchr 1977-78; B. r Jr HS PE, Hlth Tchr 1978-79; James Madison MS PE, Hlth Tchr ; *ai:* Vlybl, Hockey, Sftbl Coach; Dept Chprsn; AFT 1974-; CCVA ; *office:* James Madison MS 7300 Woodyard Rd Upper Marlboro MD

:RSON, DANIEL NORRIS, Biology Instructor; *b:* Jamestown, NY; auna E. Brown; *c:* Bradley, Melanie; *ed:* Fredonia St Coll (BS) Bio (MS) Bio 1969; Addl 33 Hrs Post Grad Hrs; Attnd Jamestown Comm Buffalo St Coll Bio; *cr:* Fredonia St Coll Tchng Asst 1967-68; rk HS Bio Instr 1968-70; Jamestown Comm Coll Bio Instr 1969-84; ield HS Bio Instr 1970-; *ai:* Environmental Club Adv; NEA 1968-; 1970-; Impact Wellness Prgm 1987-; Natl Arbor Day Assn 1990-; Forest Owners Assn 1992-; Roger Tory Peterson Assn 1994-; Boy s of Amer 1993-; St Lukes Episcopal Church 1993-, Usher, Youth Ldr; kes Episcopal Chrch; Vestry 1995-; Summer Honorarium 1967; Lake Plankton-Albany Benchmark Stud 1972-74; Jamestown Comm Coll mark Stud 1972; Fredonia St Coll Gammarus Metal Uptake & rey Survey; Oaxaca, Mex Indian culture Wrk Prgm; Pub Laboratory ntures Bio 1990; SIP Wildlife Mngmt Prgm 1993-; *home:* PO Box 55 NY 14785

ERSON, DAVID WILLIAM, Math Teacher & Dept Chair; *b:* hester, NH; *m:* Linda Goldsmith; *c:* Kristin, Brittany; *ed:* Plymouth ll (BE) Math Ed 1967; Post Grad Stud Plymouth St Coll, NH Tech Notre Dame Coll; *cr:* Merrimack Vly HS Math Tchr, Dept Chair, 1967-; *ai:* Math Team, SADD, Class Adv; Bsktbl, Bsbl, Cross Cntry ; NHEA, NEA, ATMNE 1970-; NH Coaches Assn 1970-, Sec, Treas, VP, Natl Coaches Assn Distinguished Svc Awd 1989; United Church nacook 1970-, Fin Comm; penacook Yth Ctr, Bd of Dirs; Local Yth 3d of Dirs, Coach; Amer Legion; VFW; VVA; Articles Pub; NH HS 1 of Yr 1978; *home:* 85 Abbott Rd Penacook NH 03303*

ERSON, DENISSA (WHITTINGTON), English Instructor; *b:* nbus, OH; *m:* Ronald Keith; *c:* Eric, Leigh; *ed:* OH Univ (BA) Eng OH St Univ Masters Degree Hrs; *cr:* OH Univ Eng Instr & Tutoring Coord 1978-; *ai:* Literacy Cncl Vol; Test Preparation Classes for vantaged Stdnts; NADE 1981-; NCTE 1990-; AAUP 1995-; *office:* niv Lancaster Branch 1570 Granville Pike Lancaster OH 43130*

ERSON, ELIZABETH A., Retired Elementary Teacher; *b:* Medina, *d:* SUNY Geneseo (BS) Elem Ed 1958, (MS) Elem Supervision 1965; us Colls, In-Svc Courses; *cr:* Oakfield-AL CS Tchr 1958-62; Penfield Schls Tchr, SS Coord 1962-95; *ai:* Policy Bd Penfield Staff Dev Ctr; eld Instrl Cncl; NYSUT 1958-; Penfield Ed Assn; *home:* 55 Flower y Cir Penfield NY 14526

ERSON, GUY EDWARD, Chemistry Teacher; *b:* Kane, PA; *m:* y Lloyd; *c:* John L., Eric M.; *ed:* Clarion St Coll (BS) Scndry Ed 1972; of Pittsburgh Grad Stud Chem; PA St Univ Grad Stud Sc Sci Ed; *cr:* Eagle Area HS Chem Tchr 1973-; *ai:* Sci Fair Adv; NEA & PSEA , Local Pres 1979; PA Sci Tchrs Assn 1986-, Bd Mem 1990-92; Cntrl ssn Chem Tchrs 1985-, Pres 1991; AM NUC Sci Tchrs 1992-; Cntral ection ACS 1990-, Sec Ed Liaison; SSP Equip Grant 1991; Nom nt Awd 1991, Catalyst Awd 1992 & Pres Awd 1994; Sci & Math g; *office:* Bald Eagle Area HS 751 S Eagle Valley Rd Wingate PA 3

ERSON, JAMES ARTHUR, Assistant Dean; *b:* Providence, RI; *m:* cia Braza; *c:* Erik, Nicholas; *ed:* RI Coll (BA) Eng 1977, (MA) Eng Univ of RI (PHD) Eng & Amer Lit 1992; *cr:* Johnson & Wales Univ nstr 1984-87, Dir of Grants & Adj Prof 1987-93, Asst Prof 1993-95, Dean & Assoc Prof 1995-; *ai:* Fantasy League Adv; Arts & Sci Curr n Chair; Cultural Events & Outcomes Assessment Comms; NE Assn chrs of Eng 1993-; Horror Writers Assn 1985-; Intnl Soc for the stic in the Arts 1989-; Books: Illustrated Bradbury 1990; Out Of The ows Pub; Finders Keepers Pub 1996; Articles Pub; *office:* Johnson Wales Univ 8 Abbott Park Pl Providence RI 02903*

ERSON, JAMES ELGIN, Mathematics Teacher; *b:* Twin Falls, ID; onnie Jean Hendrix; *c:* Adriane; *ed:* Boise St Univ (BA) Math 1978; t Univ (MS) Admin 1984; Cmptr & Tech Ed 15 Hrs; Assertive pline & TST Trng 7 Hrs; Math Ed 8 Hrs; *cr:* Payette jr HS Math Instr -80; Murtaugh SHS Math Instr 1980-83; Incirlik HS Math Instr -85; DGF HS Math Instr 1985-; *ai:* Mathcounts Spon; Tennis Coach; M 1993-; ID Coach of Yr Ftbl 1983; PDK Innovative Tchr Awd 1994; *e:* David Glasglow Farrugut HS PSC Box 819 Box 63 FPO AE 09645*

ERSON, JANET THOMPSON, Third Grade Teacher; *b:* Lawrence, *m:* Arthur Peter Jr.; *c:* Bruce Paul, Kristen Anderson Huber; *ed:* Mt oke Coll (AB) Zoology 1956; Southern CT St Coll (MS) Ed 1973; Childrens Lit 3 Coll Credit Hrs; CONFRATUTE 3 Coll Credit Hrs; eep River Elem Schl 3rd Grd Tchr 1966-70 & 1993-, 4th Grd Tchr -76 & 1991-93, 6th Grd Tchr 1976-78, Gifted Pgm Tchr & Coord -91; *ai:* Schoolwide Enrichment Comm Chprsn; Quest for Tech; Schl ovement Team; NEA8, CEA 1966-; Reg Dist #4 Ed Assn 1966-; Alpha a Kappa (Tchrs, Tau Chptr) 1990-; Episcopal Church 1950-; dwide Marriage Encounter 1974-, Admin Presenter 50+ Weekends, NE USA & Canada Exec, Intnl Expansion Exec; *office:* Deep River Elem Schl 12 River St Deep River CT 06417

ANDERSON, JANICE LYN, Biology Teacher; *b:* Flemington, NJ; *ed:* Case Western Reserve Univ (BA) Bio 1986; Univ of Dayton (MS) Ed 1992; AP Bio Inst NC St Univ; Univ of Dayton; *cr:* Chaminade-Julienne Cath HS Bio Tchr 1992-; *ai:* Sr Class Moderator; Sci Fair; Statistician Vllybl; Womens Bsktbl Statistician & Acad Coord; NCEA 1992-; Alpha Phi Intnl 1989-94, Advy Bd 2W Chptr; Governors Awd for Excl in Sci Tchng 1995; MECA Grant for Tech Improvement in Sci Dept; Alliance for Ed-Wright Connection Flwshp; *office:* Chaminade-Julienne HS 505 S Ludlow St Dayton OH 45402

ANDERSON, JANICE PEARSON, Retired Elementary Teacher; *b:* Springfield, MA; *m:* Charles R.; *c:* Scott, Kirk, Loryn A. Hamilton, Timothy; *ed:* Colby Coll (BA) Sociology 1952; Univ of Bridgeport (MS) Ed 1971; 12 Credit Hrs Fairfield Univ in Ed; *cr:* Fairfield Pub Schls 3-5 Grds Tchr 1972-87; *ai:* Harwich Elem Schl Vol 1990-93; NEA 1972-; CEA, FEA 1972-87; Garden Club 1990-; Chatham Drama Guild 1991-; *home:* 23 Fernwood Cir Harwich MA 02645

ANDERSON, JOANNE MARIE (GRAZIANO), Second Grade Teacher; *b:* Warren, PA; *m:* Paul E. Jr.; *c:* Jennifer Shernard, Cheryl; *ed:* Clarion Univ (BA) Elem Ed 1964; 24 Credit Hrs & Post Grad Stud at Edinboro Univ, Villa Maria Coll, Penn St; *cr:* Irvinedale Elem Schl Second-Third Grd Tchr 1964-68; St Joseph Schl Second Grd Tchr 1977-; *ai:* Liturgical Tchr for Reconciliation & Communion Classes; Mentor for Other Tchr; NCEA 1977-; PSEA 1964-68; Beta Sigma Phi 1968-, Pres, Treas; Coll Women 1986-; Dedicated Yrs of Svc to St Joseph 1987; Outstdng Tchr of Warren Cty 1995; *office:* St Joseph Schl 608 Pennsylvania Ave W Warren PA 16365*

ANDERSON, KAREN BRETT, 2nd Grade Teacher; *b:* Brooklyn, NY; *m:* Kristian M.; *ed:* Johnson St Coll (BA) Elem Ed 1982; UVM Problem Solving Math, Reshaping Curr & AIMS Dev; *cr:* Hyde Park Elem 2nd & 3rd Grd Tchr 1985-; *ai:* NEA 1985-, Negotiating Team 1992-93, Mini Grant Comm; IST Mem; *office:* Hyde Park Elem Schl RR 1 Box 3989 Hyde Park VT 05655

ANDERSON, KATHLEEN G., English Teacher; *b:* Jamestown, NY; *m:* Charles A.; *c:* Clark; *ed:* St Univ of NY at Brockport (BA) Eng 1973; Nazareth Coll (MST) Rdng 1977; Post Grad SUNY at Fredonia; *cr:* Lyons HS Rdng Tchr 1974-77; Frewsburg HS Eng, Rdng Tchr 1977-; *ai:* Sr Class, NHS Adv; NY St Rdng Assn 1985-; Natl Assn Compensatory Ed 1995-; NASAA 1993-; NYSUT 1979-; Chautauqua Lake Yacht Club 1979-; *office:* Frewsburg HS 26 Institute St Frewsburg NY 14738

ANDERSON, KEITH, Social Studies Teacher; *b:* Marion, OH; *m:* Mary Ann Lightfoot; *c:* Kevin J., Lesley E., Megan L.; *ed:* Univ of Toledo (BED) His & Pol Sci 1964, (MS) Ed Admin 1984; Eastern MI Univ (MS) Ed Admin 1971; 25 Post Grad Credit Hrs; *cr:* Berkeley HS Soc Stud Tchr 1964-67; Yale HS Soc Stud Tchr 1967-69; Brighton HS Soc Stud Tchr 1969-72; Coshocton HS Soc Stud Tchr 1972-76; Delta HS Soc Stud Tchr 1976-; *ai:* Mock Trial Adv; Girls JV Bsktbl & Asst Var Ftbl Coach; NEA 1964-; OEA 1972-; OCCS 1974-; OCLRE 1984-; ASCD 1994-; Christ Meth Church, Admin Bd; 9th Congressional Dist OH Ed Advy Comm; *office:* Pike-Delta-York HS 605 Taylor St Delta OH 43515*

ANDERSON, LARRY, English Teacher; *b:* Washington, DC; *m:* Gail Graham; *c:* Katie, Michael; *ed:* Allegheny Coll (MA) Ed 1977; *cr:* East Tech HS Eng Tchr 1974-; *ai:* CTU, AFT 1974-, Del, Conf Comm; Trinity Cathedral 1990-, Vestryman; OH Nordic Cross Cntry Ski Club 1985-, Pres; Book Review; Article Pub; Martha Holden Jennings Scholar; *office:* East Technical HS 2439 E 55th St Cleveland OH 44104*

ANDERSON, LAWRENCE ARTHUR, Science Teacher; *b:* Mineoloa, NY; *m:* Joan Metzler; *c:* Eric T.; *ed:* SUNY at Oswego (BS) Ed 1972; SUNY at Stony Brook (MA) Ed 1977; Nassau Comm Coll (AS) Comp Sci 1981; 45 Post Grad Credits; *cr:* York Prep Schl Sci & Math Tchr 1975-85; Jericho HS Chem & AP Tchr 1985-; *ai:* Stu Cncl Adv; Girls Var Bowling & Girls JV Sftbl Coach; Prins Advy Cncl; NYSUT 1985-; JTA 1985-; *office:* Jericho Sr HS 99 Cedar Swamp Rd Jericho NY 11753

ANDERSON, LAWRENCE GEORGE, Social Studies Teacher; *b:* Staten Island, NY; *m:* Beverly Lynn Pietracatella; *c:* Lawrence W., Mark, Peter Garcia, Andrew Garcia, Mark Garcia; *ed:* NY Univ (BA) His 1964; Wagner Coll (MS) Ed 1966; 38 Grad Hrs Coll of Staten Island; *cr:* Bernsterin Intermediate Schl Soc Stud Tchr 1965-66; Curtis HS Soc & Legal Stud Tchr 1966-; Wagner Coll Var Bsbl Coach 1980-83; Sport Newspaper Reporter, St Island Advance; *ai:* Legal Stud Coord 9 Yrs; Mock Trial & Moot Ct Coach 9 Yrs; Curtis Bsbl Coach 3 Yrs, Bsktbl 9 Yrs; UFT 1965-; SI Bsbl Oldtimers 1980-; Hall of Fame Nom Comm; NYC Tchr Recognition Awd; NY Daily News Coach of Yr 1972; Dist Nomination for Reliance Awd for Excl in Ed 1992; *home:* 314 Lighthouse Ave Staten Island NY 10306

ANDERSON, LESLIE CATHERINE, Science Teacher; *b:* Indiana, PA; *ed:* Rutgers Univ (BA) Chem 1993; *cr:* Arthur L. Johnson Regnl HS Sci Tchr 1993-; *ai:* Class of 1998, Sci Club Adv; Clark Sci Fair; Amer Chemical Soc 1994-; NSTA, NJ Sci Tchrs Assn 1993-; Sallie Mae Awd Nom; Selected to Participate in Assessments for Sci Tchng; Sci Alliance Presenter, Module Writer; *office:* Arthur L Johnson Regnl HS 365 Westfield Ave Clark NJ 07066*

ANDERSON, LINDA BROWN, 3rd Grade Teacher; *b:* Kenton, OH; *c:* Shawn, Darin; *ed:* ONU (BS) 1965; Ashland Univ (MA) Elem Ed 1989; Attnd BGSU ELem Ed 1986, OSU ELem Ed 1987; *cr:* Fairbanks Schl Tchr 1965-68; Beaufort Schl Tchr 1968-69; Findley Schl Tchr 1975-76; Wynford South Schl Tchr 1979-93; *ai:* Fairbanks Schls Tchr 1965-68; Beaufort Schl Tchr 1968-69; Findlay Schls Tchr 1975-76; Wynford South Schl Tchr 1979-93; Chrldr Adv; Librn; NDOP 1993-, Co-Dir; *office:* Wynford South Primary Schl 200 South St Nevada OH 44849*

ANDERSON, LYNDA GREESON, Materials Sci & Math Instr; *b:* Binghamton, NY; *m:* Roy H.; *ed:* Rensselaer Polytechnic Inst (BS) Materials Engrng 1983, (MS) Materials Engrng 1985; *cr:* Intnl Bus Machines Assoc Engr 1985-87, Sr Assoc Engr 1987-91, Staff Engr 1991-93; Schenectady Cty Comm Coll Asst Prof 1994-; *ai:* Fac Adv for Tech Club; Fac, Stu Assn Bd of Dir; Institutional Equity Comm; ASNT 1994-, Sec; ASM Intnl 1987-; Sunday Schl 1991-, Tchr, Supt; Die Bergvaga Sanden Schenectady 1980-, Sec, Treas; *office:* Schenectady County Comm Coll 78 Washington Ave Schenectady NY 12305

ANDERSON, MARCIA ELAINE, 10th Grade Biology Teacher; *b:* Cleveland, OH; *c:* Armand Dehaney; *ed:* Cleveland St Univ (BS) Bio 1983; Attnd John Carroll Grad Classes 1989-90, Kent St Masters in Bio 1993-95; *cr:* Villa Sancta Anna Phys Therapist Asst 1979-81; Warrensville Jr HS 7th Grd Sci Tchr 1985-89; Warrensville Sr HS Bio Tchr 1989-; *ai:* Girls Vlybl, Track Coach; Formal Dance Comm for DST; Venture; Capital Grant Comm; WEA, OEA, NEA 1985-; SECO 1991-; CRABS 1994-; NSTA 1993-; Delta Sigma Theta 1980-, Treas; *office:* Warrensville Hts Sr HS 4270 Northfield Rd Cleveland OH 44128

ANDERSON, MIGNON HOLLAND, Eng & Modern Lit Lecturer; *b:* Nassawadox, VA; *c:* Averill V., Nora C.; *ed:* Fisk Univ (BA) Eng 1966; Columbia Univ (MFA) Long & Short Fiction Writing 1970; *cr:* Black Communicator Asst Ed & Ed 1972-73; Resources Inc Staff Writer 1973: Northern VA Schl Systems Fiction Writing & Racial Sensitivity Consultant 1975-92; AARP Cross-Cultural Consultant 1990-91; *ai:* Adv Honors Conf Team; Dir Eng Dept Lecture Series; Coord Eng Dept Honors Curr; DE & Salisbury Lib Lecturer; Mem Telecommunications Advy Comm; Ford Grad Fellowship Arts & Columbia Univ; Fellow VA Ctr Creative Arts Sweet Briar: Book Pub-Mostly Women Folk & Man or Two; Short Stores: Short Story Intl, MD Review, Black World, Galliman Fry Press; Assoc Ed, Lit Journ; UMES Pres Tchr of Yr 1995-; *office:* Univ of Maryland Eastern Shore Wilson Hall Princess Anne MD 21853

ANDERSON, NANCY BARTHEL, English Teacher; *b:* Kyushu, Japan; *m:* John; *c:* Scott, Kevin; *ed:* St Univ of NY at Stony Brook (BA) Eng 1969, (MA) Eng 1982; *cr:* Smithtown East HS Eng Tchr 1969-73; Smithtown West HS Eng Tchr 1973-74; Holy Family Diocesan HS Eng Tchr 1980-81; Holy Trinity Diocesan HS Eng Tchr 1981-; *ai:* Vol Club Adv; Tech, Learning Comm; Fac Advy Cncl; LFA 1982-; *office:* Holy Trinity Diocesan HS 98 Cherry Ln Hicksville NY 11801*

ANDERSON, NORMA LAUREL, Elementary School Teacher; *b:* Brooklyn, NY; *m:* Norma Price; *c:* Laurel Rene Anderson Cowell; *ed:* City Coll of NY (BS) Elem Ed 1952; Queens Coll (MS) Ed 1973; St Johns Univ Cert Supvr of Elem Ed, Schl Admin Supvr 1972; *cr:* Hofstra Univ Team Ldr 1980-82; SUNY Learning Lab Specialist 1981-82, Comm Instr 1982-83, ESL Instr 1984-, Adj Prof; Powell's Lane Elem Schl Tchr 1952-; *ai:* Television Instr; Curr Designer; Script, Manual Writer; Consultant, Evaluator 1958-62; Television Math Tchr 1972; Natl Assn of Educl Broadcasters 1964-66; Dev Curr for Children in Amer Samoa; Elem Schl Curr Coord 1968-71; Woman of Excl Awd 1995; *office:* Powell's Lane Schl 603 Powell's Ln Westbury NY 11590*

ANDERSON, OTTAWANA SAUNDERS, Second Grade Teacher; *b:* Washington, DC; *c:* Jacquita; *ed:* Winston-Salem Univ (BA) Elem Ed 1966; George Washington Univ 12 Credit Hrs Guid; Comp Ed 40 Sessions; *cr:* Stevens Schl Tchr 1966-70; Limestone Pub Schls 1970-71; Springfield Pub Schl Tchr 1972-, Mgr Evening Comp Lab 1986-; *ai:* Seton Hall Univ & Kean Coll Supversion for Stu Tchrs; Comp Ed Wkshps for Parents; Soc Stud Comm Mem; Chprsn Bicentennial Comm 1975-76; T & E 1976; NJ Rdng Assn 1972-77; Springfield Tchrs Assn 1972-, 1st VP, Treas & Mbrshp Chair; NJEA 1972-; NJ Assn for Supervision & Curr Dev 1975-76; AKA 1965-; Union Bapt Church 1972-, Womans Day; NAACP 1972-, Yth Adv, Natl Yth Adv Awd; Comm Helpers Teenage Support 1973-, Pres, VP & Dance Chair; Tchr of the Yr NJ 1988; Presenter for Newspapers in Ed NJ; Union Cty USOE Fulbright Hayes Trng Grant; Head Tchr for Project Head Start; Merit Awd Springfield Bd of Ed; Tchr for Upward Bound at St Elizabeth Coll; *office:* Thelma L Sandmeier Elem Schl 666 S Springfield Ave Springfield NJ 07081*

ANDERSON, PATRICK DONALD, Humanities Prof, Dept Chairman; *b:* Lansing, MI; *m:* Elizabeth Beal; *c:* Jason P., Christian M., Katharine B.; *ed:* Univ of Notre Dame (AB) Amer Stud 1972; Univ of MI Amer Culture (MA) 1974, (PHD) 1976; 30 Addl Credit Hrs Univ of Innsbruck Austria 1969-70; *cr:* Philipps-Univ at Marburg W Germany Lektor 1976-77; Colby-Sawyer Coll Prof, Dept Chair 1977-; Univ of Notre Dame Visiting Prof 1985-86; *ai:* Lecturer New Hampshire Hum Cncl; Dep of Hum Chm; Lecturer New England Fnd Hum; Colby-Sawyer Coll Elderhostel Prgm Coord; Soc Cinema Stud 1980-; Amer Stud Assn 1977-; Book In Its Own Image 1978; Numerous Articles & Lectures in Film, Lit & Amer Cultural Stud; Phi Beta Kappa & Summa Cum Laude Grad at Notre Dame; *office:* Colby Sawyer Coll 100 Main St New London NH 03257*

ANDERSON, PAUL MARK, Communications Teacher; *b:* Port Clinton, OH; *m:* Tamara Ann Fritz; *c:* Phillip; *cr:* Evergreen HS Comm Tchr 1980-83; Clay HS Comm Tchr 1983-85; Port Clinton HS Comm Tchr 1985-; *ai:* Drama Club Adv; Schl Plays, Musicals Dir; Seventh Grd Ftbl Coach; Jr High Athletic Director; PCFT 1985-; OCTELA 1992-; AFT, OFT 1985-; Intnl Thespian Soc 1993-; Presenter OCTELA Conf 1993-94; Tchr of Month 1985; Jennings Scholar; Intern Tchr; *home:* 5676 W Harbor Rd Port Clinton OH 43452*

ANDERSON, RACHEL LYNN (SPRACKLEN), English Teacher; *b:* Springfield, OH; *m:* Douglas; *ed:* Wright St Univ (BS) Scndry Eng Ed 1993; Working on Masters in Ed at Bluffton Coll; *cr:* Arlington Local Schl Eng Tchr & Dept Chair 1993-; *ai:* JV Vlybl Coach 1994-95; Soph Class Adv; Intervention, Renaissance Prgm, AP Comms; AFT 1994-; PR Rep Local Co; Pub Several Articles; *office:* Arlington Local Schl 336 S Main St Arlington OH 45814

ANDERSON, RAINY, Creative Thinking Teacher; *b:* Washington, DC; *ed:* US Peace Corps Vol, Tchr Trainer 1970-72; Willingboro Bd of Ed Gifted Prgm, Creative Thinking Tchr 1974-; *cr:* US Peace Corp Tchr Trainer, Vol 1970-72: Willingboro Bd of Ed Tchr, Gifted Prgm, Creative Thinking Tchr 1974-; *ai:* PTO VP 2 Yrs; PANORAMA Lit Mag Fac Ed 10 Yrs; PTO Pres 2 Yrs; Gifted Prgm Curr; Report Card, Spelling Book Comm; Lang Arts Curr; NJ & Willingboro Ed Assn 1974-; Romance Writers of Amer 1983-, Bd of Dir, Natl Svc Awd; NJ Romance Writers 1984-, VP, Conf Coord; Embroidery Guild of Amer 1978-; Costume Soc of Amer 1994-; Historical Soc of Burlington 1990-; Pub 3 Novels of Historical Fiction; Won 2nd pl Natl Rdrs Choice Awd for Book; Ecstasy's Flame; Won KISS Awd for Book: Bewitching Kisses; Natl Writers Svc Awd; *office:* Willingboro Bd of Ed Levitt Bldg 50 Salem Rd Willingboro NJ 08046*

ANDERSON, RENNIE LOUDON, Art Teacher & Dept Head; *b:* New York City, NY; *ed:* Macalester Coll (BA) Pol Sci, Intnl Relations 1960; Attnd Idyllwild Schl of Music & Arts, Providence Coll, RI Schl of Design; *cr:* Cntrl Falls Jr Sr HS Art Tchr 1967-, Art, Tech Chprsn 1994-; *ai:* AFT 1967-; RIATA 1972-; South Cntry Art Assn 1965-; *office:* Central Falls Jr Sr HS 24 Summer St Central Falls RI 02863*

ANDERSON, SARA MATHEWS, English Teacher; *b:* Princeton, NJ; *m:* Lorne R.; *ed:* IN Univ (BA) Fr, Theatre Arts 1975; Trenton St Coll (MAT) Eng 1978; Jersey City St Coll, Wilkes Coll, St Peter's Coll, Western IL Univ, Allentown Coll, Goddard Coll, Rutgers Univ Cmptr Sci, His, Writing, Learning Strategies, Classroom Mngmt 60 Grad Credit Hrs; *cr:* Lawrence HS Eng Tchr 1978; Montgomery HS Fr, Drama Tchr 1978-79, Eng, Jrnlsm, AP Lit, Composition Tchr 1979-; *ai:* Yrbk Adv 1981-; Sftbl Coach 1980; Play Dir 1979; Montgomery Ed Assn 1978-, Negotiations & Mbrshp Chair, Vice Pres; IN Univ Alumni Assn 1975-; Pennington Players 1975-78, Costume Designer.*

ANDERSON, SHEILA JEFFERSON, Business Data Processing Tchr; *b:* Cincinnati, OH; *m:* Stephen Foster; *c:* Shawn Jefferson, Stephanie, Leah, Steveland; *ed:* Union Inst at Cincinnati (BA) Bus Information Mngmt 1992; Wright St Univ 36 Hrs Voc Tchng Cert; *cr:* Cmptr Dynamics Inc Data Processing Consultant 1985-86; Cmptr Horizons Inc Data Processing Consultant 1986-87; OH Natl Life Insurance Co Sr Analyst, Programmer 1988-90; Cincinnati Pub Schls Tchr 1990-; *ai:* Cincinnati Fed Tchrs 1990-; Centre ACT 1994-, Tech Adv, Appreciation Cert; *office:* Hughes Ctr 2515 Clifton Ave Cincinnati OH 45219

ANDERSON, SIDNEY EDWARD, Special Education Teacher; *b:* Cleveland, OH; *ed:* Bowling Green St (BA) Spec Ed; Cleveland St; *cr:* Collinwood HS Tchr 1975-; *ai:* Union Bldg Rep; JV Ftbl Coach; Spec Ed Work-Stud Coord; AFT 1975-, Union Bldg Rep; CEC 1975-; *home:* 250 E 284th St Willowick OH 44095

ANDERSON, STEPHEN JAMES, 8th Grade Geography Teacher; *b:* Providence, RI; *m:* Rita Burnham; *c:* Christopher, Jeremy, Jill; *ed:* Roger Williams Coll (AA) His 1969; RI Coll (BA) His, Ed 1971; *cr:* Exeter-West Greenwich Schl Dept 4th-6th, 8th-12th Grd Tchr 1972-; *ai:* Cross-Cntry

Coach; RI Soc Stud Assoc 1991-; RI House of Rep 1989-, Rep; *office:* Exeter-West Greenwick Jr Sr HS 930 Nooseneck Hill Rd West Greenwich RI 02817

ANDERSON, STEPHEN S., Biology & Chemistry Instructor; *b:* Manchester, CT; *m:* Lisa Salo; *c:* Trevor, Cody; *ed:* Susquehanna Univ (BA) Chem 1985; Bucknell Univ (MS) Bio 1987; Cornell Univ (MAT) Sci Ed 1991; *cr:* Phillips Acad Bio & Chem Instr 1991-; *ai:* Girls Cross Cntry Head Coach; Track & Field Asst Coach; MAST 1993-; *office:* Phillips Acad 180 Main St Andover MA 01810

ANDERSON, TERRANCE WILLIAM, 6th Grade Teacher; *b:* Buffalo, NY; *m:* Jane Lee Wieland; *c:* Jared, Katelyn; *ed:* St Univ Coll At Oswego (BS) ELem Ed 1969; St Univ Coll at Brockport (MS) Cnslng 1974; *cr:* Eng Village Schl 4th, 5th Grd Tchr 1969-74; Millville Elem Schl 5th, 6th Grd Tchr 1974-75; Millville Schl Elem Guid Cnslr 1975-78; Dewey Schl Elem Guid Cnslr 1975-78; Conant Schl Elem Guid Cnslr 1975-78; Castle Products Self-Employed 1978-80; Conant Elem Schl 6th Grd Tchr 1980-92; Conant Elem Schl Interim Prin 1992-93, 6th Grd Tchr 1993-; *ai:* Pres Bd of Dirs Pats Peak Ski Race Club; Schl Math Comm; Yth Soccer, Girls Lacrosse Coach; NEA 1969-; US Ski Assn; Meth Church; Server for Soup Kitchen; BSA; *home:* 27 Carter St Concord NH 03301

ANDERSON, TIM WILBUR, Dir Training & Development; *b:* New Castle, PA; *ed:* Clarion Univ of Pa (BA) Psych 1980, (BS) Speech Com 1980; Youngstown St UNiv (MSEd) Cnslng 1984; Kent St Univ 24 Hrs Toward PHD Comm Stud; *cr:* Kent St Univ Instr 1985-92; Clairon Univ of PA Instr 1992-95; Comm Alternative Inc Dir Training, Dev 1996; *ai:* Hospice Vol in Cnslng; SEA 1985-; *home:* 309 E Falls St New Castle PA 16101*

ANDERSON, VICTORIA GLEDHILL, Title I Reading Teacher; *b:* Bath, NY; *c:* Laurie Anderson-Hahn, Daniel J.; *ed:* Ithaca Coll at New York (BS) PE 1968, (MS) Rdng 1986; *cr:* Cohoes City Schl Dist PE, Elem, MS Tchr 1968-71; Avoca Cntrl Schl PE K-12 Grd Tchr 1985-91, Title I Rdng 6-12 Grd Tchr 1991-; *ai:* Ath Club Adv; Shared Decision Making Team Dist Level; Shared Decision Making Team Parent Rep, S/A BOCES; Disciplinary Comm; NYSUT 1984-; Howard Lib Bd 1975-, Treas; Avoca Yth Commission 1995-; *office:* Avoca Cntrl Schl Oliver St Avoca NY 14809

ANDERSON, WANDA S., Business & Computer Teacher; *b:* Toledo, OH; *m:* John A. Jr.; *c:* John A. III; *ed:* Univ of Toledo (BE) Bus Ed 1974; 69 Quarter Hrs in Ed Tech & Media; *cr:* Cardinal Stritch HS Bus Tchr 1974-75; Stautzenberg Bus Coll Acctng Tchr 1975-78; Pike-Delta York HS Bus Tchr 1978-87; Toledo Pub Schls Sub Tchr 1987-92; Springfield HS Bus, Cmptr Tchr 1992-; *ai:* Bus, Cmptr Club Co Adv; NEA 1992-; NWOBTA 1987-, Mbrshp Chair; SEA 1992-, Bldg Rep 1995-; Alpha Omicron Pi 1971-, Numerous Offices, Horor Cert 1985; St Catherine Church 1990-; *office:* Springfield HS 1470 S Mccord Rd Holland OH 43528

ANDES, BARBARA MARIE,SNJM Math Teacher; *b:* Chicago, IL; *ed:* Barry Univ (BS) Ed 1960; Univ of MD (MS)Ed 1973; NY St Cert; *cr:* Mary Immaculate HS Tchr 1966-68; Holy Names HS Tchr 1968-81, Headmistress 1982-85; Acad of the Holy Names Tchr 1986-; *ai:* Textbook Coord; Tandy Tech Scholar 1993-94; *office:* Acad of the Holy Names HS 1075 New Scotland Ave Albany NY 12208

ANDRADE, CHARLES PIRES,JR., Business Law Professor; *b:* Wareham, MA; *m:* Carol Ann Backus; *c:* Daron F., Derek A., Brian C.; *ed:* Cape Cod Comm Coll (AA) Lbrl Arts 1972; Boston Univ (BA) His 1974; Univ of Santa Clara Law Schls (JD) Law 1977; *cr:* Cape Cod Comm Coll Bus Law Prof 1978-84; Law Offices of Charles Andrade Private Law Practice 1985-88; Barnstable Dist Ct Asst Cler, Magistrate 1988-94; Barnstable Cty Juvenile Ct Clerk, Magistrate 1994-; Cape Cod Comm Coll Bus Law Prof 1988-; Fisher Coll Para Legal Stud Prof 1992-; *ai:* MA Bar Assn, MA Tchrs Assn 1978-; Comm for Pub Cncl Svcs 1995-, Bd of Dir; *office:* Cape Cod Comm Coll 2240 Rt 132 West Barnstable MA 02668

ANDRADE, SUZETTE M., French & Portuguese Teacher; *b:* Azores, Portugal; *c:* Keith; *ed:* UMA at Dartmouth (BA) Fr 1977, (BA) Portuguese 1977; Attnd Northeastern Univ, Bridgewater St Coll, Johnson & Wales Univ; Sorbonne, Paris; Brown Univ; *ai:* MAFLA 1992-; ASTSP 1993-; Fr Evening Lioness, Bd Mem, Comm Chair; Portuguese Bus Assn Sec; *home:* 185 Underwood St Fall River MA 02720

ANDRAKE, NANCY C., Latin & Greek Teacher; *b:* Elmira, NY; *c:* Jennifer, Carolyn, Edward III, Patrick Joziorski; *ed:* Coll Misericordia (BA) Latim-Cum Laude 1965; FL St Univ (MA) Classics 1967; Elmira Coll 36 Credits; Univ of DE NEH Flwshp 6 Credits; Amer Schl Classical Stud Athens Rockefeller Flwshp; *cr:* FL St Univ Tchng Asst 1965-67; Hammondsport Schl Dist Latin, Eng Tchr 1966-70; Horsehead Sch Dist Latin, Eng, Greek, Stud Skills Tchr 1970-; Elmira Schl Dist Eng Tchr 1987-89, 1995-; *ai:* SUNY at Stoneybrook, Pace Univ Wkshp; Latin Club Adv; Chaperone Stu Trips; Horseheads Tchr Assn 1970-, Rep; NYS Jr Classical League 1966-, Co-Chair; Amer Classical League 1965-; Natl Jr Classical League 1966-; St Casimirs Church 1944-, Yth Group Spon; Girl Scouts 1956-, Past Cadette, Sr Ldr; *office:* Horseheads MS & HS 401 Fletcher St Horseheads NY 14845*

ANDREAS, CAROLINE STRUNK, Retired Teacher; *b:* Nanticoke, PA; *m:* Carl; *c:* Susan Posey, Thomas, Kay Long; *ed:* Coll Miscricordia (BA) Eng 1968; 22 Hrs PA St Univ; 6 Hrs Bloomsburg Univ; 6 Hrs Wilkes Univ; 18 Hrs Others; Masters Equivalency 1985; *cr:* Greater Nanticoke Area Schl Dist Eng Tchr 1968-93; *ai:* Drama Club 1975-85; NEA; 4-H Club Ldr.

ANDREN, RICHARD JOHNSON, Prof of Biological Sciences; *b:* Providence, RI; *m:* Joan Spruill; *c:* Joel David, Nora; *ed:* Bates Coll (BS) Bio 1964; Lehigh Univ (MS) Bio 1966; Columbia Univ (EDD) Sci Ed 1979; *cr:* US Army Medical Research 1996-68; Montgomery Cty Comm Coll Prof Biological Scis 1968-; *ai:* Adv Environmental Club; AFT 1980-, VP, exec Comm; Wissahickon Valley Watershed Assn 1975- VP, Pres, Bd of Dirs; Clean Air Cncl of Phil 1970- VP, Pres, Bd of Dirs; Amer Lung Assn of Phil & Montgomery Cty 1972- Bd of Dirs; Amer Lung Assn of PA; Mem of Open Space Planning Comm Montgomery Cty; *office:* Montgomery County Comm Coll 340 Dekalb Pike Blue Bell PA 19422

ANDREONE, KAREN MARIA, PE Teacher & Athletic Director; *b:* Bronx, NY; *ed:* Nassau Comm Coll (AS) PE 1970; SUNY at Cortland (BS) PE 1972; Adelphi Univ (MA) PE 1974; *cr:* Hofstra Univ Coach 1978-80; Nassau Comm Coll Coach 1972-78; St Agnes CHS Tchr, Coach, Adv 1973-87; Our Lady of Mercy Acad Tchr, Coach, Adv 1987-; *ai:* Vlybl, Sftbl Coach; Ldrs Club, Sports Night Moderator; Musical Play Producer; Ath Dir; AAPHER; Womens Sports Fdn; NIAAA; NFICA; NYSAAA; NY St Coaches Assn; NY St Section Admin of Yr; Coach of Yr in Vlybl, Sftbl; Ocean Spray Wave Grant; *office:* Our Lady Of Mercy Acad 815 Convent Rd Syosset NY 11791

ANDREONI, DAVID N., Social Studies Teacher; *b:* Woonsocket, RI; *m:* Debra L. Lewis; *c:* Michael, Jennifer; *ed:* RI Coll (BA) Soc Stud, Scndry Ed 1976; *cr:* Bellingham HS Soc Stud Tchr 1978-93; Medway HS Soc Stud Tchr 1993-; *ai:* AFT 1993-; NEA 1978-; Woonsocket Little League 1992-; *office:* Medway HS 45 Holliston St Medway MA 02053

ANDRES, LINDA, Advanced Composition Teacher; *b:* New Kensington, PA; *m:* Gary P.; *c:* Alexis, Zabina, Lauren, Marisa; *ed:* Univ of Pgh (BA) Sociology 1972, (MED) Socially & Emotionally Maladjusted 1973; Addl 30 Inservice Credits; *cr:* Capital Schl Dist Spec Ed Tchr 1973-77; Kent Co Orthopedic Schl Spec Ed Tchr 1977-80; Capital Schl Dist Gifted Ed Tchr 1980-; *ai:* NEA 1973-; *office:* William Henry MS Carver Rd Dover DE 19901

ANDRES, RICHARD J., Mathematics Teacher; *b:* New York, NY; *m:* Margaret G. Gerety; *c:* Kathleen; *ed:* Coll of the Holy Cross (AB) Math 1960; Fordham Univ (MA) Eng 1962, (PHD) Eng 1977; *cr:* Archbishop Stepinac HS Math & Eng Tchr 1962-65; Iona Prep Schl Math & Eng Tchr 1965-66; Golf Magazine Writer & Tech Ed 1966-67; Pius X HS Math & Eng Tchr 1967-68; Jericho Schl Dist Math & Eng Tchr 1968-; *ai:* Educl Rsrch & Dev for the Dist; NLMT; NYSUT; Pub Book: Preparing For SAT Mathematics 1996; *office:* Jericho Sr HS 99 Cedar Swamp Rd Jericho NY 11753*

ANDRESKI, RICHARD W., Mathematics Teacher; *b:* Rahway, NJ; *m:* Claudia Coates; *c:* Richard W., John E. Adam D.; *ed:* Kean Coll (BA) Math 1968 & (MA) Math Ed 1974; Kean Coll Post Grad; Rutgers Univ Post Grad; *cr:* Rahway HS Tchr 1968-70; John F Kennedy HS Tchr 1970-; *ai:* Adv Cntrl Jersey Math League; NJEA 1980-; NCTM 1990-; AMTNJ 1990-; *office:* John F Kennedy Memorial H S Washington Ave Iselin NJ 08830

ANDREWS, BARBARA JACOB, German & English Teacher; *b:* Easton, PA; *m:* William N.; *c:* W. Christopher, Robert J.; *ed:* Univ of Pittsburgh (BA) Ger & Eng 1963; 32 Grad Hrs; *cr:* Upper St Clair HS Ger & Eng Tchr 1985-; *ai:* Vol Coord; AATG; NCTE; Jr League.

ANDREWS, BARBARA WHITSON, Fourth Grade Teacher; *b:* Elmira, NY; *m:* Merwin; *c:* Chad, Casey; *ed:* Elmira Coll (BS) Elem Ed 1966; Addl 9.6 Credit Hrs; *cr:* Horseheads Cntrl Schl Dist Elem Ed Tchr 1966-; *ai:* CORE Team, Numerous Comms; NYSUT; AFT; HTA; *office:* Horseheads Ctrl Schl Dist One Rider Ln Horseheads NY 14845

ANDREWS, BRENDA J., School Counselor; *b:* Lebanon, PA; *m:* Gregory; *ed:* IN Univ of PA (BS) Child Dev, Family Rel 1986; Shippensburg Univ of PA (MED) Schl Cnslng 1992; *cr:* Carefree Learning Ctr Preschl Tchr 1986-87; PA Farmworkers Assn Food & Nutrition Coord 1987-90; Mechanicsburg Schl Dist Scndry Schl Cnslr 1992-; *ai:* Strategic Planning, Portfolio Dev Comm; Ski Club; PA Schl Cnslr 1992-; Keystone Cnslng Assn 1995-; NEA 1992-; *office:* Mechanicsburg Sr HS 500 S Broad St Mechanicsburg PA 17055

ANDREWS, CHARLES EVERETT, Earth Science Teacher; *b:* Waterville, ME; *m:* Ann Mary Turbyne; *c:* Elizabeth Ann, Amanda Jayne; *ed:* Springfield Coll (BS) Arts, Scis 1980; 30 Addl Credits Various Geologic, Astronomy, Other Coursework; *cr:* Lawrence Jr HS 8th Grd Earth Sci Tchr 1980-; *ai:* Girls Jr HS Soccer Coach; ME Ed Assn, NEA, SAD #49 TA 1980-; Saint Andrews Soc of ME 1992-; Enviromental Clubs Orgs; MSCA, Sentinel Girls Soccer Coach of Yr 1983; Waterville Girls Soccer Boosters Outstdng Achvmt Awd 1989; Ath Journal Cover Story Pub 1983; *office:* Lawrence Jr HS School St Fairfield ME 04937*

ANDREWS, DAVID JOHN, Health & Physical Ed Teacher; *b:* Erie, PA; *m:* Rebecca Sue Write; *c:* Cristen, Candice, Courtney; *ed:* Edinboro Univ (BA) Hlth, PE 1980; 24 Hrs Post Grad; *cr:* Mercyhurst Prep HS HPE Tchr 1980-81; Fort LeBoeuf HS HPE Tchr 1981-; *ai:* Head Track, Field Coach; SAP Coord; Pep Club Adv; NEA, FLEA 1981-; *office:* Fort LeBoeuf HS 931 High St Waterford PA 16441

ANDREWS, DENNIS, Physics & Mathematics Teacher; *b:* Phoenixville, PA; *ed:* Penn St Univ (BS) Scndry Ed 1985; 25 Post Baccalaureate Credits; *cr:* Paxon Hollow MS Math Tchr 1986-92; Marple Newtown Sr HS Physics & Math Tchr 1992-; *ai:* Class Adv; Vllybl Coach; Physics Curr Writing Comm; NEA, PSEA & MNEA 1986-; NCTM 1986-; NSTA 1992-; Amnesty Intl USA Group #431 1987-, Treas; Woodrow Wilson Natl Flwshp in Math 1992; *office:* Marple Newtown Sr HS 120 Media Line Rd Newtown Square PA 19073

ANDREWS, EDWARD J., Health & Physical Ed Tchr; *b:* Millville, NJ; *m:* Bonnie Griner; *c:* Kimberley Andrews Dacy, Amy, Melissa; *ed:* Salem Coll (BA) His 1970; Glassboro St 15 Credit Hrs; *cr:* Millville HS Tchr 1966-; *ai:* Ftbl & Bsbl Asst Coach; Core Team Mem; Natural Helpers Mem & Instr; MTA, NEA & NJEA 1966-; *home:* 400 W Main St Millville NJ 08332*

ANDREWS, JACQUELYN GAULT, 8th Grd American History Tchr; *b:* McKeesport, PA; *m:* Martin F.; *c:* Mysty S., Martin F. II, Jade L.; *ed:* Penn St Univ (BS) Comprehensive Soc Stud 1972; Westminister Coll Intnl Stud 1977; Conflict Resolution & Mediation Cert; *ai:* After Schl Tutorial Pgm Supvr; Acad Bowl Games & Mr Pres Acad Games Coach; Strategic Plan for Prof Dev; Safe Schls Comm; MAEA 1972-; PSEA 1972-; NEA 1972-; Coll Club 1992-; Educl Comm for Womens Place-Shelter for Abused Women 1995-; Apple for the Tchr Awd 1995; *office:* Cornell MS 1600 Cornell St Mc Keesport PA 15132*

ANDREWS, LINDA J., Fourth Grade Teacher; *b:* Cowanesque, PA; *ed:* Houghton Coll (BA) Fr 1969; Mansfield Univ (MED) Elem Ed 1973; *cr:* Northern Tioga Schl Dist 4th Grd Tchr 1969-; *ai:* NEA 1969-; PSEA 1969-; Church Musician.

ANDREWS, LINDA KAYE, Fourth Grade Teacher; *b:* Bellefonte, PA; *ed:* Penn St (BS) Elem Ed 1985; *cr:* St Coll Classroom Tchr 1986-; *ai:* Prof Dev, Math Curr & Revision Sci Comm; Mentor Prgm; NEA 1986-; PSEA 1986-; PA Cncl Tchrs of Math 1987-; Mid St Rdng 1994-; United Way 1994-; *office:* State Coll Schl Dist Nittany Ave State College PA 16801

ANDREWS, MICHAEL ROGER, Junior High Science Teacher; *b:* Dayton, OH; *m:* Lillion Barnes; *ed:* Cntrl St Univ (BS) Elem Ed 1975; Bio Field Geology Alpine Bio; Attnd Miami Univ at Oxford OH, Univ of Dayton, OH St Univ at Columbus; *cr:* Jefferson Twp Schls Sci, Soc Stud, Hlth, Math Tchr Grd 5-8 1975-79; IN Univ Upward Bound Asst Dir, Curr Dir 1979-81; Townview Elem Math, Sci, Soc Stud Tchr 1981-; Trotwood Madison Jr HS Sci Tchr Grd 7-8; *ai:* Jr HS Girls Bsktbl, Sr HS Girls Track Coach; Team Ldr; Dist Sci Curr Comm; TMEA, NEA, OEA 1978-, TMJHS Tchr of Yr 1992-95; Trotwood City Schls Tchr of Yr 1994; Project Discovery St of OH; *office:* Trotwood-Madison Jr HS 3594 N Snyder Rd Trotwood OH 45426

ANDREWS, PATRICIA A., English & Mythology Teacher; *c:* Stephanie; *ed:* James Madison Univ (BA) Eng; Working Toward MA in Lbrl Arts Johns Hopkins Univ; *cr:* Owen Brown MS Eng Tchr, GATE Prgm 1980-83; Federal Bureau of Investigation Spec Agent 1983-92; Gateway Schl MS Tchr 1992-94; Stephen Decatur HS Eng Tchr 1994-; *ai:* Var Bsktbl Chrldng Squad & Frosh Competition Squad Chrldng Coach; Jr Class Comm Co-Adv; NEA 1980-; HCEA, WCEA 1980-, Fac Rep; CHILDHELP 1985-; Outstdng Sr Scholastic Achvmt Awd James Madison Univ 1977; *office:* Stephen Decatur HS 9913 Seahawk Rd Berlin MD 21811

ANDREWS, PATRICIA S., Professor of Biology; *b:* Frostburg, MD; *m:* Robert W.; *c:* Bryan, Todd; *ed:* Frostburg St Univ (BS) Bio 1968, (MED) Bio 1973; 14 Addl Credit Hrs Plus CEU's; *ai:* Fac Status, MSA Steering Comms; Fac Mentor; Drumfest 1989-, Sec; Miriam Sanner Outstdng Tchr Awd 1991-92; *office:* Allegany Coll of MD Willow Brook Road Cumberland MD 21502

ANDREWS, VALERIE WARNER, Fr Tchr & Frgn Lang Dpt Chprsn; *b:* Hamden, CT; *m:* Howard K.; *ed:* SCSU (BS) Fr, Eng 1962, (MS) Fr 1968; *cr:* Cheshire HS Fr Tchr 1962-95, Frgn Lang Dept Chair 1989-; *ai:* Lang Cadet Tchrs Adv; Former Yrbk Adv 25 Yrs; AATF 1975-, VP, Bd of Dirs; COFLIC 1989-, Co-Chair 1996; COLT 1975-; Alliance Francaise of New Haven 1980-, Bd of Dirs; Who's Who Nom 1991; *office:* Cheshire H S Main St Cheshire CT 06410

ANDREWSON, ROSEMARIE BETH, Biology & Chemistry Teach Greensburgh, PA; *ed:* Juniata Coll (BS) Bio 1986; Duquesne Univ Scndry Ed 1992; Addl 35 Credits; *cr:* Leonardtown HS Bio, Chem 1987-; *ai:* Girls Bsktbl Asst Coach 1992-94; Class of 1990 Spon 198 Class of 1995 Spon 1991-95; Evening HS Tchr in Charge 1994-; MAST 1987-; Tchr of Yr 1993; Tchr of Yr St Mary's Cty 1993; Ambas MD St Governor's Acad; *office:* Leonardtown HS Rt 1 Box Leonardtown MD 20650

ANDROKITES, ALLEN DAVID, Technology Education Coor Philadelphia, PA; *m:* Virginia Ann Sines; *c:* Alayna, Andrew, Ale. Millersville Univ (BS) Tech Ed 1979, (MED) Tech Ed 1981; *cr:* Penr Schl Dist Tech Ed Tchr, Dept Coord 1981-; *ai:* NEA, PEA, Tech Ed of PA 1981-; Intnl Tech Ed Assn 1980-; PA Guild of Craftsmen Juried Mem; Wood Turning Ctr 1990-; Author Book Measured Dra of Woodwork; *office:* Pennridge Schl Dist 1228 N 5th St Perkasie PA

ANDRUCHOW, ELAINE, Third Grade Teacher; *b:* Lynn, MA; *c:* Michael; *ed:* Univ of MA at Amherst (BA) Ed 1968; Cambridge (MED) Ed 1994; *cr:* Lakeside Unified Schl Dist Second Grd Tchr 196 Reading Pub Schls Third Grd Tchr 1974-; *ai:* Sci Curr Comm 198 Math Curr Comm 1994-; NEA 1974-; Rdng Tchrs Assn 1974-, Exe 1992-94.

ANDRULONIS, RICHARD GEORGE, Social Studies Teache Ellsworth, PA; *ed:* IN Tchrs Univ (BA) World Geog 1963; Post Grad Tchng Asst at Univ of MD 1963-65; *cr:* DuVal HS World Geog Tchr, Cntry, Track Coach 1966; Bowie HS 9-12 Grd Soc Stud Tchr, Cross Track Head Coach 1967-; *ai:* Cross Cntry, Indoor & Outdoor Track Coach; Girls & Boys Club Head Track Coach; Tracksters Track Team Coach; Olympics City Recreation Track Meet Dir 25 Yrs; NEA, M 1966-; MPSSAA Indoor Track Comm of St of MD 1985-; Natl Geogr Soc 1971-; Natl Scholastic Sports Fnd 1991-; Nation HS Sports Co of Amer 1985-; Track & Field Org 1995-; MD Track Ofcls Certfd 1994-; East Coach Track Meet Coach & Ofcl of MD 1975-, Coach, Plaque, Watch, Jacket Awds for 5, 10, 15 & 20 Yrs of Officiat Coaching; Jaycees 1970-75, Plaque for Outstdng Phys Fitness Ldr i 1973; Recreation Coach of Track & Field 1967-, Coach, Plaqu Outstdng Contribution to Yth of MD; Washington DC Roadrunners of 1995-; *office:* Bowie HS 15200 Annapolis Rd Bowie MD 20715*

ANDRUS, FAITH I., Arabic, French & Spanish Tchr; *b:* Grand Ra MI; *ed:* Western MI Univ (BA) Fr, Span 1976; Univ of MI (MA) Ed OH St Univ Arabic Degree 1994; *cr:* Newaygo HS Fr, Span, Worl Tchr 1976-77; Cntrl Montcalm Schl Fr, Span Tchr 1977-79; Green H Span Tchr 1979-, Arabic Tchr 1991-; *ai:* Acad Challenge Adv 198 OFLA 1979-, VP Publications, Outstdng Prof Svc; AATA, AATF, A ACTFL 1979-; Natl Endowment for Hum 1977; Rockefeller Fellow Master Tchr 1989; Tchr of Yr 1984, 1989; Marth Holden Jennings T Yr 1984; *office:* Green HS PO Box 218 Green OH 44232*

ANDY, EMIL J.,JR., Asst Headmaster & Math Teacher; *b:* Augusta *m:* Eleanor York; *c:* Mark; *ed:* Gorham St Coll (BS) Math 1965; Attnd of Me, Syracuse Univ; *cr:* Limeville Jr HS 6-8 Grd Math, Sci 1965-66; Putter Acad Math Tchr 1966-67; Marchward Jr HS Math 1967-69; George Stevens Acad Math Tchr 1970-; *ai:* Curr Comm; NEA 1965-; MPA, NASSP 1974-; Blue Hill Fire Dept 1973-; NSF Syracuse Univ; *office:* George Stevens Acad Union St Blue Hill ME

ANGELETTI, JOSEPH JOHN, Retired Principal; *b:* New Haven, C Cally Barbara; *c:* Joseph Jr., Betsy Angeletti-Friedah, Maribeth Southern CT St Coll (BS) Ed 1956; Univ of CT (MA) Ed Admin 196 Yr Prof Cert Ed Admin 1964; Attnd New England-Japan Inst, Hamp Coll at Amherst; Project Create Conf Eugene O'Neill Theater Hamilton St Elem Schl Grd VI Tchr 1956-57; US Army Intellig 1957-58; Dwight Schl Grd 4-6 Tchr 1958-65; New Haven Bd of Ed Svc Tchr 1965-66; S. E. Baldwin Schl Prin 1967-68; Woodward Schl 1968-69; Helene Grant Schl Prin 1969-82; Worthington Hooker Schl 1982-94, Retired Ed Consultant 1994-; *ai:* New Haven Schl Admins 1967-, Head Negotiations; Amity Club 1973-, Historian; Japan Roun World Women Awd Trip to Japan Guest Speaker 1995; New Haven Schls Admins Svc Awd 1994; *home:* 1108 Hartford Tpke North Have 06473

ANGELINE, FRAN, Retired Latin & German Teacher; *b:* Endicott *m:* Patricia Hanley; *c:* Chris, Larry, Vaun; *ed:* Colgate Univ (BA) Lati 1956-, (MA) Latin, PE 1957; *cr:* Johnson City HS Latin, Hlth Tchr, Ftbl Coach 1957-60; Union-Endicott HS Latin, Ger Tchr, Head Tennis Coach 1960-95; *ai:* Tennis Coach; NY St Coach of Yr Ftbl Natl Ftbl Coach of Yr Natl Ftbl Coachs Assn 1979; Region I Tennis C of Yr, Natl HS Ath Coaches Assn 1990.*

ANGELINI, DIANE BERGERON, High School Math Teache Lowell, MA; *m:* David Paul; *c:* Lauren; *ed:* Univ of NY (BS) Math Tchr Cert Prgm Franklin Pierce Coll 1991; *cr:* LIfe Cycle Engrng Inc 1986-92; Oyster River HS Math Tchr 1992-93; Salem HS Math Tchr 1 *ai:* NEA 1993-; Salem Ath Club 1992-, Aerobics Instr; *office:* Saler 44 Geremonty Dr Salem NH 03079

ANGELIS, GENIA MARIE, English Teacher; *b:* Bronx, NY; *m:* Nic Glinias; *c:* Marcina, Steven; *ed:* Manhattan Coll (BA) Eng, Ed Lehman Coll Working Towards MA in Eng, World Lit; *cr:* St Cath Acad Eng Tchr 1991-; *ai:* NCTE 1994-; *office:* St Catharine Acad Williamsbridge Rd Bronx NY 10469

ANGELITA, MARIA, Sixth Grade Teacher; *b:* Manila, Philippines Univ of Santo Tomas (BSN) 1983; De La Salle Univ Ed, Credit Units Admin MA; *cr:* Immaculate Conception Schl 4th Grd Tchr 1984-88 Grd Tchr 1988-90, Prin 1992-94, Part-time 6th Grd Tchr 1995-; *o* Immaculate Conception Schl Babbitt & Heller Aves Pen Argyl PA 18

ANGELO, ALAN LEE, Social Studies Teacher; *b:* Brockton, MA Susan Geer; *c:* Gabrielle Wynne, Ryan; *ed:* 72 Post Grad Credits USMC Base Ed Officer, Lieutenant 1970-71; Westerly Jr HS Soc Stud 1971-74; Westerly HS Soc Stud Tchr 1974-; *ai:* Stu Cncl Litter-a-Thon, Blood Dr Coord; Talent Show Spon; NEA, RIEA 1 WTA 1971-, Bldg Rep; Law-Related Ed 1988-; Natl Assn of Stu Act Charlestown Parks & Recreation Commission 1986-, Commissioner; Scouts 1987-92, Den Ldr; NEA Tchr to Remember 1992, 1995; Wes RI Tchr of the Yr 1995-96; RI Constitution Bicentennial Speaker; *h* 35 Hemlock Rd Wakefield RI 02879

ANGELO, CARMEN, Guidance Counselor; *b:* McKees Rocks, PA Ann Krasinski; *c:* Richard, Denise; *ed:* DuQuesne Univ (BS) Bus A 1968, (MA) Scndry Ed & Cnslng 1980; *cr:* Sto-Rox HS Math 1968-89, Cnslr 1990-; *ai:* NHS Spon; Allegheny Cty Cnslrs Assoc 1 *office:* Sto-Rox HS 1105 Valley St Mc Kees Rocks PA 15136

ANGELO, CHRISTINE HENDRICKSON, 5th Grade Teacher Youngstown, OH; *m:* Henry J.; *c:* Nicole, Christopher; *ed:* Hiram (BA) Early Chldhd & Elem 1972; Rdng Cert 1982; 19 Grad Hrs Beyo Certs; *cr:* Maple Ave Schl Headstart Tchr 1972-73; Elm Rd Schl 1st Tchr 1973-77; Emerson Schl 1st Grd Tchr 1977-80; St Pias Rdng & Tchr 1980-81; McKinley Schl Kndgtn Tchr 1981-82, Kndgtn 1985-92, 5th Grd Tchr 1992-; Secrest Schl Kndgtn Tchr 1982-85; *ai:* 1972-; WEA 1972-; *home:* 195 Oak Knoll Ave NE Warren OH 44483

ELO, GREGORY PHILLIP, English Teacher; *b:* Naples, Italy; *m:* Eileen Gehron; *c:* Melissa Ann Rouse, Jon Gregory; *ed:* California of PA (BS) Ed, Eng 1985; 24 Addl Credit Hrs Eng; *cr:* US Army Sp lass Electronic Technician 1963-66; PA Job Svc Employment Cnslr -77; Natl Mines Corp 1st Class Mechanic Welder 1977-85; nsville Area HS Eng Tchr; *ai:* After Schl Alternative Ed Prgm Tchr; hed Amer Legion Bsbl; Owns & Operates PA LURES, Dev US ted Lures; NEA 1990-; Fairbanks Rod & Gun Club 1990-; AMVETS -; *home:* 368 3rd Isabella PA 15447

ELO, JOSEPH SAMUEL, Mathematics Professor; *b:* Pittsburgh, *n:* Shirley Ann Malek; *c:* Joseph, Thomas, Mary O'Toole, James, n Zilinskas, David, John; *ed:* IN Univ of PA (BSEd) Math 1956,)) Math 1963; Univ of Pittsburgh (PHD) Higher Ed, Math 1970; 20 Stud Credit Hrs OH St Univ; *cr:* US Steel Corp Metallurgical nician 1956-59; Baldwin-Whitehall Schls Jr HS Math Tchr 1959-62; esne Univ Math Prof 1962-64; IN Univ of PA Math Prof 1964-; *ai:* nan Stu Assn Adv; Master of Ed Prgm Coord; Scndry Math Ed Comm, of Chrstn Initiation for Adults Team Mem; MAA 1970-; NCTM, PA c of Math Tchrs 1965-; Arc of IN Cty 1973-, Pres, Treas; Arc of PA -, Pres, VP, Treas, Humanitarian Awd; Mental Hlth, Ret 1984-, Pres, em; PA Protection & Advocacy 1992-, Treas, Bd Mem; Humanitarian Montgomery Cty Arc, Allegheny Cty Arc; Outstdng prof Awd Stu a; Natl Security Seminar Participant; IN Cty Group Homes Founder; : Indiana Univ Of PA 213 Stright Hall Indiana PA 15705*

ELO, SUSAN G., Science Teacher & Dept Chair; *b:* Wallingford, CT; an L.; *c:* Gabrielle Angelo Wynne, Ryan; *ed:* Univ of RI (BA) Sci Bio 1977; 70 Hrs beyond BA; *cr:* Westerly HS Sci Tchr & Field Hockey h 1977-78; South Kingston HS Sci Tchr 1978-96, Sci Chair 1995-; *ai:* ns Tech, Portfolio, Scheduling; Mentor New Tchr, Stu & Tchr Prgm; Adv; Founding Mem Coalition to Support Ed in South Kingstown; NEASC Co-Chair; NEARI, NEA 1977-; RI Sci Tchrs Assn, NSTA & A; Lib Vol, Cub Scout Ldr; *office:* South Kingstown HS 215 Columbia akefield RI 02879*

ELOS, JUNE DRUIAN, Business Education Teacher; *b:* Bronx, NY; chel; *ed:* St Univ of NY at Albany (BS) Bus Ed 1963, (MS) Bus Ed 64 Credits Beyond Master Degree; *cr:* West Islip HS Bus Ed Tchr -; *ai:* Yrbk, Photography Adv; Wall of Fame Comm; Pubications Copy Adv; Scorekeeper Var Vlybl, Bsktbl; WITA 1964-, Del, 30 Yr Tchng AFT, NYSUT 1964-; *office:* West Islip HS 1 Lions Path West Islip 1795

ER, TIMOTHY ALAN, Math, Sci Tchr & Asst Prin; *b:* Brainerd, *m:* Donna Coulton; *c:* Sarah, Amanda, Ben, Thomas; *ed:* Maranatha Coll (BS) Scndry Ed, Math, Sci 1984; Bob Jones Univ (MS) Schl n 1994; *cr:* Koolau Bapt Acad Math, Sci Tchr 1984-89; Emmaus Bapt Math, Sci Tchr 1989-; *ai:* Yrbk Adv; Cmptr Coord; *office:* Emmaus st Acad 4702 Colebrook Ave Emmaus PA 18049

ERT, MARY C., Mathematics Teacher; *b:* New Castle, PA; *ed:* ery Rock Univ (BSEd) Math & Ed 1973; Univ of Pittsburgh (MSEd) & Ed 1976; Post Grad Stud; *cr:* Butler Area Schl Dist Math Tchr -; *ai:* Tutoring; Schl Paper, Schl Art & Lit Magazine Proofreader; , PSEA, BEA 1973-; NCTM, PCTM; *office:* Butler Area Schl Dist 167 Castle Rd Butler PA 16001

ERVILLE, EDWIN DUYANEL, Accounting Professor; *b:* St Marc, ; *ed:* York Coll (BS) Acctng 1984; Certfd Pub Accountant NY; *cr:* rick Todman & Co Staff Accountant 1987; Zucker & Shernicoff CPAs ccountant 1988-89; York Coll Adj Prof 1986-; Edwin D. Angerville Founder, Owner 1990-; *ai:* Comm Eliminate Media Offensive to can People; Medgar Evers Coll Citation for Small Bus Ctr; epreneurial Bus Classes; *office:* City Univ Of NY York Coll 135-02 rty Ave Richmond Hill NY 11419*

EVINE, MICHAEL E., 6th Grade Teacher; *b:* Toledo, OH; *m:* en A. Crane; *c:* Christine, Erin; *ed:* Univ of Toledo (BED) Elem Ed , (MED) Admin 1974; 15 Post Grad Hrs Admin; *cr:* Jerusealm Elem 6th Grd Tchr 1971-88; Eisenhower MS 6th Grd Tchr 1988-; *ai:* AFT -, Bldg Rep; Kappa Delta Phi 1980-; Recognized as Tchr Who Made fference in A Stdnts Life 1993; *home:* 2435 Eastvale Ave Oregon OH 6*

IONE, DALE ANN, Chemistry Teacher; *b:* New York City, NY; *m:* ph Vincent; *c:* Tracy, Scott, Christopher; *ed:* Hunter Coll (BA) Chem ; SUNY at Stony Brook (MS) Ed 1970; 100 Plus Grad & Post Grad it Hrs Sci & Math; *cr:* Army Ed Ctr Germany GED Tchr 1964-66; orn Cntrl Jr HS Sub Tchr 1966-67; Kings Park MS Sub Tchr 1967-70; Glenn HS Sci & Chem Tchr 1970-; *ai:* Schl Photographer; NHS & Adv; NEACT 1976-; NY St Sci Tchr Nom; Nicolls Fellow Nom; Yrbk op 10 Percent Nationwide; *office:* John H Glenn HS 478 Elwood Rd E hport NY 11731

OVE, DOUGLAS L., Physics Tchr & Sci Dept Chair; *b:* Warren, PA; ancy I.; *c:* Scott, Toby; *ed:* Clarion Univ of PA (BS) Physics 1969; boro Univ of PA (MED) Phys Sci 1973; *cr:* Warren Area HS Physics 1969-, Sci Dept Chair 1987-; *ai:* PSEA, NEA 1969-; BSA 1981-, Cncl Mem, Pres Awd; Soc for Preservation & Encouragement of Barbershop tet Singing in Amer 1991-, Chapter Pres; *office:* Warren Area HS 345 n Ave Warren PA 16365

RAND, GUY, History Teacher; *b:* Cap Haitien, Haiti; *c:* Dalia, ey, Guy Raoul; *ed:* Brooklyn Coll (BA) Sociology 1976; Long Island (MA) Urban Stud 1981; 21 Credits above Master Degree; *cr:* stdale Soc Worker 1979-86; Erasmus Hall Tchr 1986-; *ai:* Haitian Club ; Tutoring Act Supv; UFT 1986-; Haitian Educl Fndtn Inc 1983-, Pres hprsn; *office:* Erasmus Hall HS Math & Sci Campus 911 Flatbush Ave oklyn NY 11226

STADT, GINGER, Language Arts & Drama Teacher; *b:* Dover, DE; DE St Univ (BA) Eng Ed Scndry 1976; Cath Univ of Amer (MFA) atre, Directing 1981; Addl 56 Hrs in Theatre, Ed Units, Spec Ed, atre Mngmt, Tech Theatre, Basic Ed Drama Prgm; *cr:* DE St Coll Eng Fac 1985-88; Lake Forest HS 9-12 Grd Eng Tchr 1982-87; Dover HS , 12 Grd Eng, His Tchr 1987, 1989; Cntrl MS 8 Grd Eng Tchr, Drama boratory 1989-; *ai:* Co-Spon Theatre Prgm Lighting Designer, Music ; Multicultural, Black His Comms; NCTE, DATE, WILLA 1993-; atre Comm Group 1992-; AAVP 1992-; NEA, DSEA, CEA 1982-, CEA 1987; Governors Visual, Performing Arts Commission 1994-, Ldrshp n; Dover Arts cncl 1989-93, Sec, Comm Svc Plaque; Dover Art League -, Second Street Players 1993-, Lighting Design Chair; Kent Cty atre Guild 1996; DE St Arts Cncl 1990-91, Ecarte Lighting Assign nt; DE Division of Arts; Grant coord 1981-93; Co-Founder Ecarte ce Theatre; Inclusion in Legacy From DE Women 1987; *office:* Central l Delaware Ave Dover DE 19901*

GU, EMELDA SIRI-NTINGLET, Computer Professor; *b:* Cameron, Africa; *m:* Richard; *c:* Michelle, Stacy; *ed:* Univ of Dist of Columbia Cmptr Info Syst Sc 1990; Bowe St Univ (MS) MIS 1992; *cr:* TESST Instr Supvr 1993-94; Strayer Coll Assoc Prof 1992-; Pacific Inst for ch Database Systems Admin 1992-; GE Information Svcs EDI sulting Specialist 1994-; *ai:* NAFE 1992-; Amer Montessori Soc -; Certfd Systems Analyst; World Who's Who of Women; *office:* yer Coll 1025 15th St NW Washington DC 20005*

ANIBAL, GALIANA S., Mathematics Professor; *b:* Burgos, Spain; *m:* Sonia Cajina; *c:* Sonia M., Anibal A., Valerie; *ed:* Nicaragua Univ (BA) Physics, Math 1963; City Coll (MS) Math 1983; Columbia Univ 76 Credits Towards PHD Math; *cr:* Pedagogico Schl Math Prof 1963-73; Hostos Comm Coll Math Prof 1973-; *ai:* Math Club Adv; Admissions Curr Comm; Sanders Calculus Textbooks Consultant; AAUP 1980-; AFT 1985-; Algebra, Trigonometry Textbook; Analysis, Analytic Geometry; The Best Among Coll Math Profs Awd; Outstdng Achvmt Awd; *office:* Hostos Comm Coll 475 Grand Concourse Bronx NY 10451

ANIBARRO, JUSTINE SANTIAGO, ESL Teacher; *b:* Denville, NJ; *m:* Marcelo; *c:* Gennaro; *ed:* Hamilton Coll (BA) Span 1990; SUNY at Albany (MS) Tchrs of Eng as 2nd Lang 1994; *cr:* Kernan Elem Schl ESL Tchr 1990-92; Donovan MS ESL Tchr 1992-; *ai:* AFT & NYSUT 1990-; Utica City Schl Dist Awd for Excl in Ed 1992; *office:* James H Donovan MS 1701 Noyes St Utica NY 13502

ANINAO, KELLY LYNN (MC WILLIAMS), High School English Teacher; *b:* Canton, OH; *m:* Mark W.; *ed:* OH St Univ (BS) Eng Ed, Rdng Cert 1987; Curr, Instruction Univ of Cincinnati; *cr:* Felicity-Franklin HS Eng Tchr 1987-95; *ai:* Jr Class Spon; *office:* Felicity-Franklin HS 415 Washington St Felicity OH 45120

ANKROM, MERRI LU, Middle School Guidance Cnslr; *b:* Warren, PA; *m:* John; *c:* Nicholas, Nathan; *ed:* Edinboro Univ (BA) Elem Ed 1974; CA Univ of PA (MA) Cnslng 1985; 26 Credits Beyond Masters; *cr:* West Green Schl Dist Grds 1-4 Elem Tchr 1974-93, MS Cnslr 1993-; *ai:* Peer Helper, PULSE Retreat Facilitator; NEA 1974-; PSEA, WGEA 1974-, Bldg Rep; PSCA 1993-; Greene Cty Soccer 1990-, Summer Camp Coord; *office:* West Greene MS HS RD 5 Box 36-A Waynesburg PA 15370

ANNABLE, RICHARD LEE, Retired MS Guidance Counselor; *b:* Alliance, NE; *m:* Doris Ruth Leister; *c:* Judith Webb, James; *ed:* Kearney St Coll (BS) Math, Phys Sci 1977, (MS) Ed Guid, Cnslng 1979; *cr:* US Navy Master Chief Petty Ofcr 1952-74; Kearney Jr HS Math, Alternative Ed Tchr 1977-79; Southwestern Intermediate Schl Guid Cnslr 1986; Cntrl York MS Alternative Ed Tchr, Guid Cnslr 1987-95; *ai:* Aviatoin Club Adv; NEA, PSEA, CYEA 19987-; *home:* RR 7 Box 7526 Spring Grove PA 17362

ANNAND, CARL F., Instrumental Music Teacher; *b:* Roslyn, NY; *m:* Nancy E. Clements; *c:* James E.; *ed:* Eastman Schl of Music (BM) Applied Music 1969; Trenton St Coll (MA) Applied Music 1973; Post Baccalaurate Credits Wagner Coll; *cr:* US Army UN Hnr Guard Trumpet Player 1969-71; Edison Pub Schls Instrumental Music Tchr 1979-; *ai:* Peer Mediation, Mad About Music Club, Earth Day Assembly, Talent Shw Adv; MENC 1980-; ASCAD 1994-; NJEA, NEA, ETEA 1979-; NJ Governor's Tchr Awd Recipient 1989; *office:* Woodrow Wilson MS 50 Woodrow Wilson Dr Edison NJ 08820

ANNE, CATHLEEN SUTHERLAND, Regents Earth Science Teacher; *b:* Rochester, NY; *m:* Thomas G.; *ed:* SUNY at Cortland (BA) Elem Ed, Sci 1987; Nazareth Coll (MS) Scndry Ed 1995; *cr:* Bishop Kearney HS Sci Tchr 1989-91; Webster Cntrl Schl Dist Sci Tchr 1991-; *ai:* Sci Olympiads Jr HS Team Co-Adv; Frosh Chrldng Coach; *office:* Thomas MS 800 5 Mile Line Rd Webster NY 14580*

ANNESS, CANDANCE R. (STRATTON), Fifth Grade Teacher; *b:* North Vernon, IN; *m:* Fred; *c:* Brandon; *ed:* Eastern KY Univ (BS) Elem Ed 1970; Wright St Univ (ME) Ed 1983; *cr:* Guilford Elem Schl Third Grd Tchr 1970-71; Morrow Elem Schl Fifth Grd Tchr 1971-; *ai:* Stu Cncl Adv; Operetta Dir; Grandparents Day, Spec Prgms, Hnrs, Warren Cty Soc Stud Curr Comms; Citizenship Bee, DC Trip Coord; Southwestern OH Regnl Prof Dev Ctr Soc Stud; NEA, OEA 1971-; Kappa Delta Pi 1969-72; Warren Cty Area Progress Cabinet 1988-91; Hope Free Evangelical Church 1995-; Whitacre Ladies Golf League, Hamilton Elks 1990-; OH Dept of Ed Incentive Grant 1990; Consumer Ed Grant 1990; WArren Cty Project Excl Awd 1988; *office:* Morrow Elem Schl 10 Miranda St Morrow OH 45152*

ANSELMINO, LORI ARNOLD, Biology Teacher; *b:* McKeesport, PA; *m:* Randy S.; *ed:* Penn St Univ (BS) Bio 1989; Univ of Pittsburgh (MAT) Ed 1991; *cr:* South Fayette Twp Jr-Sr HS Bio Tchr 1990-92; Norwin HS Bio Tchr 1993-; *ai:* Fac Advy Comm; Educl Support Team; NEA & SPEA 1991-; *office:* Norwin Sr HS 251 Mcmahon Dr North Huntingdon PA 15642

ANSMAN, MARJORIE ELLEN (BARE), Retired Teacher; *b:* Altoona, PA; *w:* James E. (dec); *c:* Gail Martynuska, Deborah J., James H., Jon E., Wendy Dee; *ed:* Penn St (BA) Elem Ed 1974; 3 Addl Credit Hrs Remedial Rdng; 9 Credit Hrs; *cr:* Altoona Area Schl Dist Elem Tchr 1979-84; Our Lady of Mt Carmel Schl Elem Tchr 1984-92, Art Tchr 1992-94; *home:* 1209 Walton Ave Altoona PA 16602

ANSON, BRENDA, Biology Teacher; *b:* Elizabethtown, NY; *c:* Gretchen, Jennifer; *ed:* SUNY at Plattsburgh (BS) Sci Ed Tchr 1974, (MS) Bio 1979; *cr:* Moriah Schl Jr HS Tchr 1974-87; Westport Schl Bio & Earth Sci Tchr 1987-; *ai:* Class Adv; WEA 1987-, Pres; AAUW 1990-; *office:* Westport Central Schl PO Box 408 Westport NY 12993

ANSTEY, ALAN DAVID COLLINWOOD, Mathematics Dept Chairman; *b:* Falmouth Cornwall, United Kingdom; *m:* Elizabeth A. Wilson; *c:* Cedric, Heather, Edmund; *ed:* Univ of London (BA) Fr 1974; Open Univ (BA) Math 1981; Advanced Cert Rel Ed; Avery Hill Coll Post Grad Cert Ed 1976; *cr:* British Govt Svc Exec Ofcr 1967075; St John's Schl London Math, Cmptr Sci Tchr 1976-84; Anglo Amer Intnl Schl Math Tchr 1985-92; Dwight Schl Math Dept Chm 1992-; *ai:* Head of 9th Grd; NCTM 1990-; Astella Dev Corp 1988-, Bd Mem; *office:* Dwight Intnl Schl 291 Cntrl Park W New York NY 10024

ANTAL, LINDA M., Teaching Assistant; *b:* Charleroi, PA; *m:* Thomas S.; *c:* Laurie, Jeffrey; *ed:* Fairmont St Coll (BA) Eng 1970; *cr:* Father James B Hay Schl Eng Tchr 1970-73; St Sebastian Schl Audio Visual Coord 1973-79; St John the Bapt Schl Eng & Math Tchr 1983-94.*

ANTALEK, DIANE CAROL, Reading Teacher & Consultant; *b:* Beacon, NY; *m:* Michael P; *c:* Allison, Michael II, David; *ed:* Mt St Mary Coll (BA) Elem Ed 1971; SUNY at New Paltz (MA) Elem Ed 1975; *cr:* Marlboro Cntrl Schl Dist Elem Tchr 1971-73, 6-8 Grds Rdng Tchr 1975-91, Rdng Tchr, Consultant 1991-; *ai:* Drama Club, 8th Grd Adv; Prins Cncl; MEA 1971-, VP 1992-; NYSUT, AFT 1971-; NY St MS Assn 1992-; *office:* Marlboro MS 1375 Rt 9 W Marlboro NY 12542

ANTELL, JAMES ANDREW, HS Vocal Music Teacher & Coord; *b:* Youngstown, OH; *m:* Carol Lynn Theisler; *c:* April Kaye, Daniel James; *ed:* Youngstown St Univ (BME) Music Ed 1965, (MME) Music Ed 1975; Addl 30 Credit Hrs Eastman Schl of Music, Carnegie-Mellon Univ, Kent St Univ, Whitenberg Univ, Cleveland St Univ, NY St Univ at Fredonia, Ashland Coll; *cr:* George Washington Jr HS Vocal Music Tchr 1965-68; Austintown MS Vocal Music Tchr 1969-86; Aus Fitch HS Voc Mus Tchr, Coord 1987-; *ai:* Music Dept Chm; Annual Comm Performances; St Soc General Music Comm Mem; Annual Choir Tour, Competition; NEA, OEA, NEOTA, AEA, MENC, OMEA, ACDA 1968-; Phi Delta Kappa 1990-; Saxon Club 1973-; Phi Mu Alpha 1964-; Austintown Choral Parents 1992-, Ofcl; East OH Meth Church Conf 1987-; Marth H. Jennings Scholar; 28 Yrs Austintown Local Schls, 32 Yr Dir of Music Awds; Article for TRIAD; *office:* Austintown Fitch HS 4560 Falcon Dr Austintown OH 44515*

ANTENUCCI, JOSEPH WILLIAM, Assoc Professor of Accounting; *b:* Niles, OH; *m:* Margaret J. Blasse; *c:* Joey, Patrick; *ed:* Harvard (BA) Arch 1975; Univ of NM (MBA) Human Resources 1977; VA Tech (PHD) Acctng 1993; *cr:* Antenucci Plumbing Office Mgr 1977-87; VA Tech Grad Tchng Asst 1988-91; Mid TN St Univ Asst Prof of Acctng 1991-93; Youngstown St Univ Assoc Prof of Acctng 1993-; *ai:* Fac Dev Comm Chair; Intellectual Contributions, Tchng Enhancement, Schlsp Awds Comms; Amer Acctng Assn 1991-; Amer Taxation Assn 1989-; Univ Rsrch Prof 1994-; Local, St, Regnl, Natl, Intnl Scholary Tax Journal Articles Pub 1991-; *office:* Youngstown St Univ Williamson Coll of Bus Admin 410 Wick Ave Youngstown OH 44555*

ANTES, CAROL LYNN (MICKEL), Third Grade Teacher; *b:* Altoona, PA; *m:* Victor C.; *ed:* Shippensburg Univ (BS) Elem Ed 1969; Univ of DE (MED) Elem Ed 1974; 60 Addl Credit Hrs; *cr:* John R. Downes Elem Schl Third Grd Tchr 1969-; *ai:* Grd Level Chm; Liaison, Soc Comms Rep; Math Chm; St Tchr Ctr, Dist Math Rep; NEA 1969-; St Mark's Luth Church; 9 DuPont Co, Hercules Co, Title II Eisenhower Grants; Nom Presidential Excl Sci, Math Tchng Awd; *office:* John R Downes Elem Schl 200 Casho Mill Rd Newark DE 19711*

ANTHONY, ANNE C., Retired Teacher; *b:* Norristown, PA; *m:* Theodore Nicholas; *c:* Charles N., Peter C., M. Lorraine Verity, Katharine E. Harvick; *ed:* Queens Coll (BA) His, Ed 1975; St John's Univ (MS) Rdng Diagnostics K-12 Tchr 1977; *cr:* Jamaica Day Schl Tchr Gen Subject Area 1975, His, Soc Stud Tutorials 1991; ArchBishop Iakovos HS Tchr Push, Prod, Encouraged All Ages, All Levels.*

ANTHONY, EDWARD E., 6th Grade Teacher; *b:* Lorain, OH; *ed:* Kent St (BA) Elem Ed 1972; Attnd Ashland Coll, Geneva Coll; *cr:* Amherst Bd of Ed Tchr 29 Yrs; *ai:* Comp Lab Head; 6th Grd Trip to DC; NEA & OEA 1969-; ATA 1969-, Pres; *office:* Shupe MS 600 Shupe Ave Amherst OH 44001*

ANTHONY, SHARON KAY, Former 6th Grade Teacher; *b:* Greenville, OH; *ed:* Otterbein Coll (BS) Elem Ed 1968; Ashland Coll (MS) Cirriculum, Instruction 1989; Addl 15 Credit Hrs; *cr:* Newton Elem Schl 4th Grd Tchr 1968-81, 6th Grd Tchr 1981-95; Chrstn Endeavor United Meth Church Minister of Ed 1995-; *ai:* IM Instr; Stu Cncl Co-Adv; Tchr in Charge in Absense of Prin; Prins Advy Comm; NFEA, OEA, NEA 1968-; North Fork Feature Tchr 1988; Dow Exchange in Ed Awd 1989; Mentor 3 Yrs; *home:* 746 Garfield Ave Newark OH 43055

ANTI, PETER N., Level Six Teacher; *b:* Plymouth, MA; *m:* Barbara L. Beall; *c:* Stacia L., Thomas N., Jessica L.; *ed:* Cape Cod Comm Coll (AA) Ed 1967; Bridgewater St Coll (BS) Elem Ed 1969, (ME) Elem Admin 1973; 36 Credit Hrs Post Grad; *cr:* North Pembroke Elem Schl Level 5 & 6 Tchr 1969-80; Hobomock Elem Schl Level 6 Tchr 1980-; *ai:* Audio Visual Coord; Acad Comm; MTA 1969-; NEA 1982-; United Church of Christ 1983-, Chm of Diaconate 3 Yrs; Camp Ashmere, Dir; Horace Mann Grant 1987, 1988; Presenter of Numerous Wkshps, Cmpter Consultant; Adult Ed Tchr; *office:* Hobomock Elem Schl 81 Learning Ln Pembroke MA 02359

ANTIGNANI, GLORIA RISELEY, Fifth Grade Teacher; *b:* Kingston, NY; *m:* Serafin; *c:* Laura Hoydick, Mark, Lisa, Paul, Stephen; *ed:* New Haven St Tchrs Coll (BS) Elem Ed 1956; Fairfield Univ (MA) Ed 1960; 30 Addl Credit Hrs St Joseph's Coll; *cr:* Jane Ryan Schl Second Grd Tchr 1956-60; Wilcoxson Elem Fifth Grd Tchr 1977-; *ai:* Challenge Club Adv; SEA, CEA, NEA 1977-; Sterling House Comm Ctr 1967-, Cncl Mem; Who's Who in Amer Ed; The World Who's Who of Women; *office:* Wilcoxson Elem Schl 600 Wilcoxson Ave Stratford CT 06497

ANTINORE, DAVID, Mathematics Teacher; *b:* New York, NY; *m:* Rosalia Polizzi; *c:* Christopher, John; *ed:* Pace Univ (BA) Math, Ed 1970; Adelphi Univ (MA) Ed, Math 1975; *cr:* Mother Butler Meml MS Math Tchr 1970-78; St Catharine Acad Math Tchr 1978-; *ai:* Jr Yr, Jr Prom, Ring Day Coord.

ANTINORE, DONNA L., Special Ed & Resource Teacher; *b:* Dansville, NY; *c:* Salar; *ed:* Genesee Comm Coll (AS) Psych 1979; Buffalo St Coll (BS) Spcl Ed & Mental Retardation 1981; Genesee St Coll (MS) Spcl Ed & Learning Disabilities 1988; *cr:* Dansville Jr HS Spcl Ed Resource Tchr 1983-86; N Rose Wolcott Schls 3rd Grd Spcl Ed Self-Contained Tchr 1986-93, 9th-12th Grd Resource Tchr 1993-; NYS Dept of Corrections Adult Basic Ed, Pre GED, Tchr & Pre Release Coord Part Time 1992-95; *ai:* NEA 1981-; *home:* 8130 Caywood Rd Red Creek NY 13143

ANTINOZZI, ANTHONY JAMES, Teacher & Coach; *b:* Hazleton, PA; *m:* Alice Marie Brogam; *c:* Cynthia Marie Somers, Lori Ann Kringer; *ed:* King's Coll (BA) Ec 1961; Bloomsburg Univ (MA) Scndry Ed 1975; *cr:* US Gvot Treasury Agent 1961-65; St Gabriel's Acad Tchr, Coach 1965-72;Weatherly HS Tchr, Coach 1972-; *ai:* Ftbl Coach 1972-76; Head Bsktbl Coach 1972-; PSEA, NEA, WEA 1972-; Recreation Dir 20 Yrs; Coaching & Recreation Awds; *office:* Weatherly Area HS 6th Street Weatherly PA 18255

ANTISDEL, MARYELLEN O'TOOLE, Retired Teacher; *b:* New York, NY; *m:* James C.; *c:* James M., Mary Ann Zaruba, Tom C.; *ed:* St John's Univ Coll of Bus Admin (BBA) Mrktg 1952; Univ of Pittsburgh Coll of Bus Ed (BS) Bus Ed 1970; 50 Addl Credits Rutgers Ed 1959-62, Seton Hall Acctng 1963, Fairleigh Dickinson Acctng, Mngmt 1965-68; *cr:* G. C. Haas & Co Securities, Cage Asst 1952-54; St Francis Hosp Office Mgr 1955-57; Pyne Pt Jr HS Bus Tchr 1959-61; Pennsauken HS Bus Tchr 1961-62; Hammersgold MS Math Tchr 1962-63; Boguta HS Bus Tchr 1963-64; Leonia HS Bus Tchr 1964-69; Comm Coll Bus Tchr 1969-72; Washington Ed Ctr Bus Tchr 1972-74; Brashear HS Bus Tchr 1974-82; Langley HS Bus Tchr 1982-84; Greenway MS Bus Tchr 1985-91; Oliver HS Bus Tchr 1991-95; *ai:* PA St, Pgh Ret Ed Assns 1995-; Friends of Lib 1990-; Ben Avon Heights Comm Club 1969-, Prgm, Soc, Holiday Offices, Svc Plaque; Crime Watch 1985-, Captain; Pittsburgh Bd of Ed Grant Used to Write Office Jobs Trng Book Connelly Skill Ctr; Wrote Trng Handicapped Stdnts in Bus Skills Manual for Pittsburgh Bd of Ed Grant; *home:* 11 Banbury Ln Pittsburgh PA 15202*

ANTOINETTE, PATRICIA NAPOLI, English Teacher; *b:* Brooklyn, NY; *m:* Richard Hill; *c:* Marissa Leigh, Vanessa Lynne; *ed:* SUNY at Albany (BA) Eng 1973; Hofstra Univ (MA) Scndry Ed 1976; MA +60 Credit Hrs; *cr:* Oceanside Pub Schls Eng Tchr 1973-; *ai:* LILAC 1985-; *office:* Oceanside HS Skillman & Brower Aves Oceanside NY 11572

ANTOLA, ANDREA MARIA, Science Teacher; *b:* Montclair, NJ; *ed:* Rutgers Univ at Newark (BA) Geology 1990; Attnd Coll of Arts & Scis, Montclair St Univ, 16 Grad Credits in Ed, 6 Credits in Geology; *cr:* Immaculate Conception HS Sci, Math educator 1990-; *ai:* Prom Coord, Sci Week, Vlybl Club Adv; Walk-A-Thon Co-Chprsn; Girls Track, Bsktbl Asst Coach; NSTA, Earth Sci Tchrs Assn 1990-; ASCD 1995-; Natl Cath Tchrs Assn 1990-; Whos Who Among Amer Young Prof 1988; Phi Beta Kappa 1990; Sigma Gamma Episilon 1987; *office:* Immaculate Conception HS 33 Cottage Pl Montclair NJ 07042

ANTONELLI, RONALD PATRICK, Sixth Grade Math Teacher; *b:* Youngstown, OH; *m:* Bridget Italiano; *c:* Ronald J., Sherri L. Mc Keown; *ed:* Youngstown St Univ (BS) Elem Ed 1965; Westminster Coll (MED) Elem Schl Admin 1968; 30 Addl Hrs Mount St Josephs of Cincinnati; *cr:* Levitt Elem Schl 6th Grd Tchr 1962-63; Freedom Elem Schl 6th Grd Tchr 1963-64; Science Hill Elem Schl 6th Grd Tchr 1964-65; Davis Elem Schl 6th Grd Tchr 1965-67; Austintown MS 6th Grd Tchr 1967-; *ai:* Adult Basic, Literacy Ed Prgm Dir 1972-; Negotiating Team; NEA, OEA, NEDEA, Austintown Ed Assn 1962-; Italian Schlsp League 1992-; Youngstown Area Bd, Natl Assn Realtors 1974-; Tippecanoe Cntry Club 1980-; Tech Grant Comms; *home:* 5687 Lamplighter Dr Girard OH 44420*

ANTONIETTI, LOUIS, Lead English Teacher; *b:* New York, NY; *m:* Laura Greaney; *c:* Julia; *ed:* Manhattan Coll (BA) Eng 1970; Lehman Coll

(MA) Eng Ed; *cr:* Saint Martin of Tours Schl 7th-8th Grd Eng Tchr 1971-74; Nyack Jr HS 7th-8th Grd Eng Tchr 1974-80; Nyack HS Eng Tchr 1980-; *ai:* Nyack Tchrs Union; *office:* Nyack HS 360 Christian Herald Rd Nyack NY 10960

ANTONISWAMI, ANTHONY, Mathematics Teacher; *b:* Mugaiyur, India; *ed:* Govt of Madras (BTC) Tchng Math 1959; Univ of Madras (BSC) Math 1964, (BT) Tchng Math 1968; Federal City Coll (MA) Educl Admin 1977; Cath Univ of Amer (EDD) Educl Admin 1983; *cr:* R. C. Basic Tchr Trng Schl Model Tchr 1959-60; St Ann's HS Head Math Tchr 1964-71; St Benedict the Moor Schl Head Math, Sci Tchr 1973-78; St John's Coll HS Math Tchr 1978-88; Jefferson Jr HS Math Tchr, Chair 1988-; *ai:* Mathcounts Team Coach; Curr Dev Comm; DC Commission on Asian Pacific Islander Affairs Chm; NCTM, DCTM, Mathematical Assn of Amer, Washington Tchrs Union 1988-; Tamil Sangam of Metropolitan Washington & Baltimore Inc 1983-, Pres; Cncl of Asian Indian Assns 1983-, Pres, Distngd Comm Svc; Nom Pres Awd for Excl in Tchng; PASS Inc Tutorial Svcs Pres; Spirit of India Radio Prgm Host, Dir, Producer; *home:* 4901 13th St NW Washington DC 20011*

ANTOSZYK, CHARLES D., Earth & Space Sci Teacher; *b:* Greensburg, PA; *c:* Jamie, Tamilyn; *ed:* Clarion Univ of PA (BS) Earth & Space Sci 1966; California Univ of PA (MED) Geography & Earth Sci 1977, (MS) Earth Sci 1983; *cr:* South Allegheny Jr-Sr HS Earth Sci Tchr 1970-; *ai:* NHS, Soph Class, Sr HS Newspaper & Photography Club Spon; PSEA, NEA & SAEA 1970-, Grievance Chm; Westmd Co His Soc 1980-; West Newton Comm Singers 1980-, Bd of Control; Amer Legion Life Mem 1970-, Adjutant; PIAA Off Bsbl, Sftbl 1970-; Amer Legue Umpire 1970-; Natl Geog Soc Mem; Amvets Life Mem; TV Commercial WTAE 4 Pittsburgh Joe Said It Would; *office:* South Allegheny Jr-Sr HS 2743 Washington Blvd Mc Keesport PA 15133

ANTOVEL, DONNA MARIE, Spanish Teacher; *b:* Brooklyn, NY; *m:* Cary S.; *c:* Ryan; *ed:* SUNY at Stony Brook (BA) Span 1987, (MA) Linguistics 1991; Long Island Univ 8 Credits; Adelphi Univ 12 Credits; Univ de Salamanca 100 Credit Hrs; *cr:* Centereach HS 9th-12th Grd Stu Tchr 1986; St Patricks Schl 6th-8th Grd Span Tchr 1986; Riverhead HS 8th Grd Span Tchr 1987-; Mestract Span Tchr 1989; Long Island Univ Gifted & Talented Inst 4th-6th Grd Span Tchr 1989; *ai:* Moving Up Comm; Peer Coach Prof Growth Option; NYSAFLT 1987-; LILT 1987-; NYSUT 1987-, Bldg Rep; AFT 1987-; Spon, Organized & Chaperoned Educl Trip to Spain 1987; Awded Multinational & Comparative Educl Schlsp Univ of Salamanca; *office:* Riverhead MS 600 Harrison Ave Riverhead NY 11901

ANTWINE, STELLA LOUISE, Fifth Grade Teacher; *b:* Cleveland, OH; *c:* Yusef, Yasin; *ed:* OH St Univ (BS) Ed 1970; Cleveland St Univ (MS) Ed 1986; Post-Grad Stud John Carroll Univ; *cr:* Tremont Schl Tchr 1970-75; O. H. Perry Elem Schl Tchr 1970-75; Stephen Howe Schl Tchr 1985-; Cuyahoga Comm Coll Part-time Eng Tchr 1988-90; *ai:* Safety Patrol Adv; Girl Scout Ldr; Drug Liason; Union Conf Comm; SLT; ON Tasc Chm; Prgm Comm; PTA Ofcr; Delta Sigma Theta 1968-; Shiloh Bapt Church, Life Time Mem; Jennings Scholar Tchr of Yr 1990; *office:* Stephen E Howe Schl 1000 Lakeview Rd Cleveland OH 44108*

ANUSAVICE, BERNARD, Drafting Teacher; *b:* Worcester, MA; *m:* Mary Carroll; *c:* Mary, Kevin, Paul; *ed:* Worc Jr Coll (AS) Mechanical Engr 1961; Northeastern Univ (BS) Indstrl Tech 1969; *cr:* Morgan Construction, Parker & Harper Mfg, Avco Corp Drafting & Design 1959-1973; *ai:* Worcester Homing Pigeon Club Pres; AFT, MVA 1974-; NHS Stdnts Voc Tchr of Yr 1992; *home:* 156 Brigham Hill Rd North Grafton MA 01536

ANZALDI, SALVATORE PAUL, Principal; *b:* Passaic, NJ; *m:* Barbara Edore; *c:* Lorrie, Sal, Kimberly, Jamie; *ed:* Fairleigh Dickenson Univ (BS) Soc Stud Sec Ed 1969; William Paterson Coll (MA) Spec Ed 1975; Montclair Univ 6th Yr Adm-Supvr 1978; Elem Ed Courses; *cr:* Clifton Pub Schls Grd Four Tchr 1969-72, Spec Ed Tchr 1972-88, Elem Schl Prin 1980-; *ai:* After Schl Prgms; Extracurricular Acts; Pub Schl Admin 1980-; Clifton Admin Assoc 1980-; Clifton Tchrs Assoc 1968-80, VP; Clifton Adult Opportunity Ctr 1980-84, VP; Clifton Yth Assn 1980-86; Charmers Sftbl 1988-, Coach, Mgr; School Nine Outstdng Citizen Awd; Presented Drug, Alchohol Abuse Prgm 1984; Recreation Bd Mem 1981-84; NJ St Championships, Regnl Championships ASA Sftbl; *home:* 30 Fairmount Ave Clifton NJ 07011

APANA, JAMES LESLIE, English Department Chairman; *b:* Cleveland, OH; *m:* Sandra Drobet; *c:* Jeffrey, Christy, Scott; *ed:* Western Reserve Univ (BA) Eng 1967; John Carroll Univ (MA) Ed 1975; Rdng K-12 Cert; *cr:* Baldwin-Wallace Coll Instr Upward Bound 1977-81; Cleveland Pub Schls Tchr, Dept Head 1967-; *ai:* Spon Flight Club, Annual City-Wide Spelling Contest; Comms Lib Power, Fin; NCTE 1966-, Cert Lifetime Achvmt; IRA 1967-; Cub Scouts 1978-, Den Ldr; Who's Who in the World, Amer, Amer Ed; Intnl Who's Who of Intellectuals; 2000 Notable Amer Men; Dictionary of Intnl Biography; Intnl Book of Honor, Ldrs in Achvmt, Men of Achvmt; *home:* 6822 Renwood Dr Parma OH 44129

APARO, DIANE MARIE, First Grade Teacher; *b:* Rochester, NY; *m:* James B.; *c:* Brian J., Annmarie L., Robin L.; *ed:* SUNY at Potsdam (BS) Elem Ed 1970; 76 Credit Hrs; *cr:* Fairport Cntrl Schls 2nd Grd Tchr 4 Yrs, First Grd Tchr 1970-; *ai:* Schlsp Comm; NEA, AFT 1970-; *home:* 290 Whispering Hls Victor NY 14564

APGAR, ANDREW RUSSELL, Vocal & Choral Music Teacher; *b:* Plainfield, NJ; *m:* Teresa Hollinger; *ed:* Millersville Univ (BSME) Music Ed 1991; Permanent Cert Credits Univ of Arts at Villanova, Millersville, West Chester Univ; *cr:* Dover Intermediate Schl Vocal, Choral, Gen Music Tchr 6-8 Grds 1991-; *ai:* Marching Band Perc Instr; Musical Vocal Coach; Mrktg Comm; Pvt Piano, Vocal Instruction; MENC, PSEA 1988-; NEA 1991-; Dover UCC 1995-; *office:* Dover Intermediate Schl 4500 Intermediate Ave Dover PA 17315

APITO, PAMELA NORMAN, Teacher of Gifted & Talented; *b:* Orange, NJ; *m:* Frank V.; *ed:* Coll of William & Mary (MA) Elem Ed 1975; Attnd Rutgers Univ, Seton Hall Univ, Georgian Court Coll; *cr:* Brielle Schl 3rd-5th Grd Tchr 1969-74, 7th-8th Grd Tchr 1974-78, Gifted, Talented Prgm Tchr 1974-; *ai:* NEA, NJEA 1969-; PTO 1969-, Treas, Tchr Rep; Amer Assn of Univ Women 1969-72; First Presbyn Church 1994-95, Ed Comm; NJ Dept of Ed Various Grants; NJ Historical Comm; *office:* Brielle Elem Schl 605 Union Ln Brielle NJ 08730

APOL, JOEL H., History & English Teacher; *b:* Lansing, MI; *m:* Mary; *c:* Matthew; *ed:* Calvin Coll (BA) His 1977, (MAT) Eng, Ed 1989; *cr:* Dakota Chrstn HS Tchr, Coach 1979-84; Eastern Chrstn HS Tchr, Coach 1986-; *ai:* Track Coach; Class Sponsorships; *office:* Eastern Chrstn HS 50 Oakwood Ave North Haledon NJ 07508

APOLD, DORIS C., Math Teacher; *b:* Panama, Panama; *m:* Robert N.; *c:* Andrew, Susanna; *ed:* Southwestern St Univ (BS) Bio, Math 1963; Mercy Hosp Schl of Med Tech (MT) Lab Tech 1964; Univ of Miami (MS) biling Ed 1980; *cr:* Mercy Hosp MT 1964-68; Central TX Coll Math Tchr 1976-80; Panama Canal Coll Math, Sci Tchr 1978-82; St Mary's Schl Math Tchr 1980-84; Curundu MS Math Tchr 1984-; *ai:* Math Dept Chprsn; NCTM, Phi Delta Kappa 1980-; Ancon Ecological Org 1984-.

APONICK, LYNN J., Science Teacher; *b:* Ashland, PA; *m:* Peter J.; *c:* Taylor, Mitchell; *ed:* Bloomsburg Univ (BS) Sec Ed, Bio 1979; 51 Addl Credit Hrs; Penn St, Wilkes, Shippensburg MA Equiv Ed 1987; *cr:* Upper Dauphin MS Sci Tchr 1980-81; Eastern Lebanon Co HS Sci Tchr 1981-; *ai:* Envirothon Team, Stream Stud Advs; PSEA, NEA 1979-; ELCEA 1980-; NSTA 1995-; PSTA 1988-; Lebanon Co Ed Hnr Soc 1993-; *office:* Eastern Lebanon Co HS 180 Elco Dr Myerstown PA 17067

APOSTLE, NANCY MARY, Theology Teacher; *b:* Cleveland, OH; *m:* Paul; *c:* P.J., Amy; *ed:* Cleveland St Univ (BA) Rel Stud 1973; Grad Work at John Carroll & Boston Coll; *cr:* Saint Edward HS Theology Tchr 1973-74; Nazareth Acad Theology Tchr 1974-78; Villa Angela HS Theology Tchr 1978-81; Padua Franciscan HS Theology Tchr 1990-; *ai:* Theology Dept Chair; *office:* Padua Franciscan H S 6740 State Rd Parma OH 44134

APOSTOLOU, ARGYRI, HS ESL & Greek Teacher; *b:* Karditsa, Greece; *m:* Konstantinos; *c:* Vasilios John, Irene Noel; *ed:* Athens Univ (BA) Philology Classics 1971; NY Univ (MA) Soc Stud 1976; St John's Univ (PD) Supervision & Admin 1995; *cr:* Ministry of Ed Asst 1966-71; St Demetrios HS of Astoria Head of Greek Dept, Teached 1978-84, Head of Greek Dep 1984-91; St Demetrios HS Jamaica Head of Greek Dep 1991-94; Ft Hamilton HS Tchr 1994-; *ai:* Greek Club Adv; Daughters of Penelope Former Pres; Teach Greek Language St John's Univ; AFT 1994-; St John's Univ Flwshp; *office:* Fort Hamilton H S 8301 Shore Rd Brooklyn NY 11209

APP, THELMA E., Kndgtn Tchr & Preschool Dir; *b:* Philadelphia, PA; *ed:* Northeastern Bible Coll (BA) Biblical Lit 1970; Rowan St Coll (MA) Elem Ed 1976; *cr:* Amer Chrstn Schl Tchr 1970-73; Gloucester Cty Chrstn Schl Tchr & Admin 1973-78; Cedar Grove Chrstn Acad Tchr & Preschool Dir 1978-; *ai:* Foster Parent; Assoc of Chrstn Schls 1985-; Bensalem Bapt Church, Ladies Sunday Schl Tchr; *office:* Cedar Grove Christian Acad Bingham & Helleman Sts Philadelphia PA 19124

APPEL, MARGARET DENISE (LEFEBORE), Secondary Education Teacher; *b:* New York City, NY; *m:* Marvin; *ed:* Farleigh Dickinson (BA) Eng 1978; *cr:* Fiarlawn Schls Dramatic Coach 7 Yrs, Curr Adv 2 Yrs, SAT Coord 4 Yrs; *ai:* Newspaper Adv; Mentor; NEA 1969-; NJEA 1969-, Tchr of Yr; Lib Bd 1975-, Sec; Hackensack Hospital Vol, Svc Awd; CP Ctr Vol; SAT Bus Tchr & Assoc; *office:* Memorial Schl 12-00 1st St Fair Lawn NJ 07410*

APPEL, SHEILA COOPERSTEIN, 7th-8th Grade Science Teacher; *b:* Philadelphia, PA; *m:* Murray; *c:* Matthew, Allison; *ed:* Temple Univ (BS) Medical Tech 1968; Beaver Coll (MS) Ed 1986; 30 Hrs Above Masters; Cert for Bio & General Sci; *cr:* Temple Univ Hospital & Medical Schl Research & Clinical Medical Technologist 1969-76; Saint Christophers Hospital Supvr Hematology Lab 1976-80; Philadelphia Schls Sci Sub Tchr 1984-86; Morrison Elem Sci Tchr 1986-; *ai:* Sci Sizzlers Club; Sci & Sci Resource Ldr; Project 2061 AAAS 1991-, Team Mem; PAESTA 1987-; NSTA 1995-; PSST 1994-; Beth Torah Synagogue PTA 1988-, VP; Several Dwight D Eisenhower Grants; Southeastern Leadership Grant from West Chester Coll; Natl Inst of Hlth SEPA Awd; PATHS-PRISM Grants & Stipends; Goals 2000 Standards Team 1994; *office:* Andrew J Morrison Elem Schl 5100 N 3rd St Philadelphia PA 19120

APPEL, SUSAN LEONORE (GRANEK), Assistant Principal & Sci Tchr; *b:* New York City, NY; *m:* Lloyd; *c:* Ilene Levy, Karen Devernoe; *ed:* Brooklyn Coll (BA) Bio 1961, (MS) Bio 1968; LIU Prof Diploma Ed Supv 1986; *cr:* Jamaica HS Bio Tchr 1965-84; Townsend Harris HS Bio Tchr 1984-89, AP Sci Tchr 1989-; *ai:* Westinghouse Adv & Coord; Sci Dept Adv; Schl Comms; NY Bio Tchrs Assn 1975-, Membership Coord; NABT 1979-; NY Sci Chms Assn 1985-; NSTA 1991-; AWIS 1992-; NSTA 1993-; *office:* Townsend Harris HS 149-11 Melbourne Ave Queens College Flushing NY 11367

APPELFELLER, SHERRIL KAY (CONVERSE), Health & Phys Ed Teacher; *b:* Kenton, OH; *m:* Paul Andrew; *c:* Benjamin A., Jennifer L., Jonathan C.; *ed:* Bowling Green St Univ (BS) Hlth, PE 1972; *cr:* West Liberty-Salem HS Hlth, PE Tchr 1972-73; Elgin HS Hlth, PE Tchr 1973-; *ai:* HS Var Vlybl Coach; OH Cntrl Dist Vlybl Assn 1992-; OH HS Vlybl Assn 1986-; United Meth Church 1959-; *office:* Elgin HS 1239 Keener Rd S Marion OH 43302

APPLE, THOMAS TURLEY, Asst Eng Prof & Theatre Dir; *b:* Abington, PA; *m:* Nancy Lee Bates; *c:* Benjamin; *ed:* USNY at Albany (BA) Eng 1986; NY Univ (MA) Medieval Stud 1987; Bryn Mawr Coll (PHD) Renaissance Drama 1991; Attnd Dartmouth Schl of Criticism & Theory 1989, Folger NEH Inst 1991; *cr:* Ursinus Coll Instr 1988-91, 1993-95; Bryn Mawr Coll Instr 1990; Univ of Canterbury Lecturer 1992; Haverford Coll Asst Prof 1993-95; Widener Univ Asst Prof & Theatre Dir 1995-; *ai:* Actors Equity Assn 1980-; Screen Actors Guild 1983-; Bryne Rubel Traveling Flwshp 1989-90; NEH Flwshp 1991; *office:* Widener Univ 1 University Pl Chester PA 19013

APPLEBY, GLORIA J. (HOLT), French & English Teacher; *b:* Cincinnati, OH; *c:* Carmen; *ed:* Wright St Univ (MS) Ed 1989; Univ of Paris Fr 1981; Univ of Cinti (BA) Ed 1984; *cr:* Blanchester HS Eng & Fr Tchr 1984-; *ai:* HS Newspaper; BEA 1984-, Co-Pres; *office:* Blanchester HS 3482 State Route 28 Blanchester OH 45107*

APPLEBY, LINDA ROSE LOMBARDO, 5th-8th Grade Music Teacher; *b:* Jamestown, NY; *m:* Rodney; *c:* Venezia Monique, Zuri Elise; *ed:* Damaen Coll (BS) Music Ed 1974; Buffalo St Coll (MS) Stu Prsnl Admin 1980; *cr:* Olmsted Schl 56 5th-8th Grd Vocal & General Music Tchr 15 Yrs; Saint Mary of Sorrows Church Choir Directress 6 Yrs; Private Studio at Home Piano Tchr 22 Yrs; Buffalo Pub Schls k-8th Grd Vocal & General Music Tchr 22 Yrs; *ai:* Compact for Learning Rep for Home Schl; Turn Key Rep for Music Educators; All Cty Chorus Participation; Music in Our Schls for March; Exam Wrting Comm; Cncrts at Various Comm Organ; Prison Music Ministry; Mscl Dir; NEA & MENC 1974-; ECMEA 1980-; Agate 1990-; Saint Mary of Sorrow Church 1986-, Music Minister, Litugary Comm, Parish Cncl Mem; Rcpnt of WWA Amer Tchrs 1994; Grant Received From Tchr Ctr for Work in Computerized Music Composition; Pub Svc Recognition for Performances at Buffalo Psychiatric Ctr, Broadway MKT, Nursing Homes, NFTA & Other Schls; Pub Svc Recognition for Performances at Annual Tchr Conf at Kleinhans Music Hall; *office:* Olmsted Schl 56 716 W Develan Ave Buffalo NY 14222

APPLEBY, PENNY LIGLER, Literacy Speclst & Drama Coach; *b:* Chicago, IL; *m:* Donald T.; *c:* Paul A Harrison, Stephen A. Harrison, Jennifer, Kristin R. Harrison; *ed:* Stetson Univ (BME) Voice, Music Ed 1973, (MED) Rdng 1983; 15 Credit Hrs SUNY Univ of NY Rdng Diagnosis, Prescription; *cr:* Wooward Ave Elem Schl K-6th Grd Music Specialist 1973-83; Golden Hill Elem Schl K-6th Grd Music Tchr; SS Seward HS 7th, 12th Grd Rdng Tchr 1983-85; Woodward Ave Elem Schl K-6th Grd Music Specialist 1985-86; Edward Little HS Literacy Specialist 1986-; *ai:* Drama Club Adv, Dir; Fac Senate, Color Guard Instr; NEA 1973-; ASCD 1993-; Delta Kappa Gamma 1978-, Music Chair; High St Cong Choir 1987-; Girl Scouts 1956-, Adult Ldr Sr Gold; Comm Little Theatre 1988-; Innovative Grant 1988; Maine Comm Grant 1995; *office:* Edward Little HS Auburn Hts Auburn ME 04210*

APPLEGATE, EDITH (METZGER), Professor of Science & Math; *b:* Battle Creek, MI; *m:* Stanley J.; *c:* David, Douglas; *ed:* Andrews Univ (BA) Bio 1958; Univ of MI (MS) Zoology 1959; OR St Univ 12 Quarter Hrs; Syracuse Univ 6 Sem Hrs; Univ of AR 13 Sem Hrs Cont Ed; *cr:* Andrews Univ Bio Instr 1959-62; Spring Valley Acad Chem & Math Instr 1972-76; Kettering Coll of Medical Arts Instr, Asst Prof, Assoc Prof & Prof 1976-; Anatomy Tchr 1996; *ai:* Pre Med, Pre Dent, Pre PT Stdnts Adv; Conduct Sectional Anatomy Seminars for AERS; AAAS, NABT, AERS, HAPS 1990-; Kettering SDA Church 1971-; Zapara Awd Excl in Tchng; KCMA Honorary Alumnus; AERS Honor for Outstanding Contributions; 2 Pub; 2 Articles Written; *office:* Kettering Coll Of Med Arts 3737 Sou Blvd Kettering OH 45429*

APPLEMAN, MARY LOU (TOMLINSON), German Teache Altoona, PA; *m:* Lee S.; *ed:* PA St Univ (BA) Ger 1976, (ME) Eng 1981; *cr:* Roosevelt Jr HS Ger, Eng Tchr 1976-84; Altoona Area HS Eng Tchr 1984-, Frgn Lang Dept Chair 1986-; *ai:* Delta Epsilon Phi AATG 1978-; APPLES 1992-; PSMLA 1994-; AATG Stu Achvmt o Ger Schlsp Test Achvmt Awd, Cert 1993; *office:* Altoona Area HS 14 Ave Altoona PA 16602*

APPLER, STEVEN ANDREW, Art Teacher; *b:* Buffalo, NY; *m:* Ogorek; *ed:* Suny Coll at Buffalo (BS) Art Ed 1988, (MS) Art Ed 199 Olean Hs Art Tchr 1989-94; Amherst MS Art Tchr 1994-; Daemen Co Ed Instr 1995-; *ai:* Odyssey of the Mind Coach; Yrbk Adv; NAEA AFT 1994-; *office:* Amherst Mid Schl 55 Kings Hwy Amherst NY 1

APPLESTEIN, ELIOT JOSEF, Psychology Teacher; *b:* Baltimore, *m:* Martha A. Vogel; *c:* Cara V., Johna R.; *ed:* Univ of MD at Coll (BA) Eng 1975, Eng Ed 1980; George WA Univ (MA) Compar Religion 1982; Univ of MD at Baltimore (MSW) Master of Soc Work *cr:* Francis Scott Key Jr High Eng Tchr 1980-83; Sligo Intermediat Eng Tchr 1983-85; Montgomery Blair Sr High Psych, Compa Religion, US His Tchr 1985-; *ai:* Natl Assn of Soc Workers 1994- for Play Therapy 1995-; Excel in Tchng Awd 1991; *home:* Breezewood Ter Rockville MD 20852*

APPLESTONE, CELIA GOLDMAN, Retired Elementary School *b:* Bronx, NY; *m:* Robert N.; *c:* Jessica; *ed:* Brooklyn Coll (BA) Ed St Univ at Stony Brook (MA) Ed 1981; Attend Long Island Univ In-Svc Credits; NYSUT Courses; 75 Addl Hrs; *cr:* PS 89 3rd-4th Grd 1954-60; Northside Schl 1st, 3rd, 4th, 6th Grd Tchr 1960-95; *ai:* Stu Mentor; Dist GATE, Tchr, Prin Selection, Effective Schls, S Decision-Making, Whole Lang Comms; AFT; NEA; NYSUT; FFT Girl Scout Ldr; Synagogue Soc Action Comm; Schl Dist Nom Tchr 1980, Soc Stud Tchr of Yr 1990; Book: Story of Harlem 1958; *home* Bay Dr Massapequa NY 11758*

APPLETON, SHARON GOODALE, Second Grade Teacher; *b:* Syra NY; *m:* David A.; *c:* Jeremy; *ed:* Auburn Comm Coll (AA) Lbrl Arts SUNY at Geneseo (BS) Elem Ed 1967; 30 Grad Hrs SUNY at Broc Oswego; *cr:* Greece Cntrl Schls 3rd Grd Tchr 1967-68; Sodus Cntrl 3rd Grd Tchr 1968-73; Cntrl Square Cntrl 2nd, 4th-6th Grd Tchr 197 NYSUT, AFT 1976-; Cntrl Square Tchrs Assn 1976-, First VP; Legion Aux Post 915 1983-; BSA, Merit Body Instr; Cub Scouts, Comm; Fire Dept, Kiddie Parade Chprsn; *home:* 1487 State Rou Constantia NY 13044

APPLING, INEZ GAMBLE, Science Teacher; *b:* Mobile, AL; *m:* Tullis Sr.; *c:* Henry Jr.; *ed:* AL St Univ (BS) Bio 1966; Montclair St (MA) Ed 1982; Cert Admin & Supervision Jersey City St 1988; *cr:* M Califf Schl Bio, Chem Tchr 1966-68; Nwk Bd of Ed Curr Dev, W 1994-95; Barringer Prep Schl Gen Sci & Phys Sci Tchr 1968-; *ai:* J Cross Adv; Soc & Welfare Ctr Co-Chair; PTSA Co-Chair; AFT 1975-; Tchr Union NTU 1969-; NJ Sci Tchr Assn Urban Exec Bd; Eisenh Grant 1994-95; Bergen Record 1981; Urban Classroom Portraits Tchr Make a Difference, Bredemeier; Governor's Awd Outstndng Tchr Nom PAESMT Sci Awd 1990; *office:* Barringer Prep Schl 63 Webs Newark NJ 07104

APRILE, HENRIETTA V.,MPF, Eighth Grade Teacher; *b:* Jersey NJ; *ed:* Villa Walsh Coll (AA) Elem Ed 1961; Cath Univ of Am Washington DC (BA) Elem Ed 1965; Marywood Coll Scranton PA Bus Ed 1972; *cr:* St Bartholomew Elem Schl 6th Grd Tchr 1956-5 Anthony Elem Schl 6th Grd Tchr 1958-59; St Joseph Elem Schl 6th Tchr 1959-60; Cath Univ of America Stu, Apostolic Delegation 1960-65; St Joseph HS Bus Ed Chprsn, Bus Subjects Tchr 1965-73; Rosary Elem Schl 8th Grd Tchr 1973-82; St Anthony of Padua Elem 8th Grd Tchr 1982-; *ai:* 8th Grd Forensics Coach; NCEA 1989-; *offic* Anthony of Padua Schl 700 Central Ave Union City NJ 07087

AQUALINA, GRACE A., Sixth Grade Teacher; *b:* Hackensack, N Tchr's Coll Columbia Univ (MA) Curr & Tchng 1974; 83 Add Columbia Univ Writing, Univ of CT Confratute, Middlebury Ita Montclair St Coll Philosophy for Children; *cr:* Amer Intnl Schl of T 4 Grd Tchr 1970-71; Hackensack Schls 3-6, 8 Grd Tchr 1964-70, 1 *ai:* Coach Odyssey of Mind, Hum Enrichment; NEA, NJEA, HEA, B 1964-; NJIGT 1986-; NEA Tchr Exchange Omiya City Japan; Co-Aut Better Than Our Best Branden Press; Contributed Womens Pr Scarecrow Press.*

AQUAVIA, JAMES MICHAEL, English Teacher; *b:* Red Bank, N Brookdale Coll (AA) Hum 1990; Montclair St Univ (BA) Eng 199 Lincoln HS Eng Tchr 1993-93; Montclair HS Eng Tchr 1994-; *ai:* Lit Magazine Adv; HS Performance Assessment Design Team; Se Educl Equity & Diversity; NEA, NJEA, NCTE, Kappa Delta Pi NJCTE 1994-, Publications Ed; Book Review Pub; *office:* Montcla 100 Chestnut St Montclair NJ 07042

AQUILA, NAVY V., Math Teacher; *b:* Columbus, OH; *m:* Toni Benthuysen; *c:* Kelli Michelle; *ed:* OH St Univ (BS) Math Ed 197 Columbus Schls Math Tchr 1972-86; Worthington Schls Math Tchr 1 *ai:* OEA, NEA, WEA, OCTM, COTA 1986-; *office:* Worthin Kilbourne HS 1499 Hard Rd Columbus OH 43235

AQUILA, TONI VAN BENTHUYSEN, Mathematics Teacher; *b:* Ca OH; *m:* Navy Victor; *c:* Kelli Michelle; *ed:* Otterbein Coll (BA) Home Ec 1980; Post Grad Stu OH St Univ; *cr:* Reynoldsburg MS Hom Tchr 1980-82; Dublin HS Math Tchr 1983-95; Dublin Scioto HS Math 1995-; *ai:* Soph Class Adv; OEA, NEA 1980-; OCTM; Girl Scouts 1 Asst Ldr.

AQUINO, CHRISTINE ALOI, Sixth Grade Teacher; *b:* Ambridge, P Thomas Anthony; *c:* Tara Marie, Tory Lynnette; *ed:* Edinboro (BA) Ed 1970; Slippery Rock (MS) Early Chldhd 1973; *cr:* Hopewell Area Dist Kndgtn Tchr 1970-74, 4th Grd Tchr 1974-82, 2nd Grd Tchr 198 1st Grd Tchr 1990-92, 6th Grd Tchr 1993-; *ai:* HEA 1970-, Bldg PSEA, NEA 1970-; PTA 1970-, Parent, Tchr Liason, Corresponding Talent Show Co-Chm; PTA Honorary Lifetime Mbrshp; *office:* Hope Area Schl Dist 2121 Brodhead Rd Aliquippa PA 15001

ARAGAO, VICTOR JOHN, Retired Band Director; *b:* Cumberland *m:* Theresa Monteiro; *c:* Deborah Draper, Dr. David, Laura; *ed:* Bo Univ (BM) Music 1960; 50 Addl Hrs in Guidance at Providence Masters Equivalency; *cr:* Cumberland Schls Music Tchr 1960-63; Norton Schl Music Tchr & Band Dir 1963-69; Cumberland MS Band 1969-95; *ai:* Cumberland Arts Festival Co-Chm; 25th Anniversary Co Inclusion Steering Comm; Bus Mgr; NEA, RINEA & MENC 1 Cumberland Youth Bsbl 1991-, Coach; Club Lusitana 1956-; Knigh Columbus 1964-; St Josephs Church 1986-, Adult Ed; CCD Coord at Lady Fatima Church 15 Yrs; Plaque for Svc to Children at Fatima Ch 1982; Grant From Champlin Fnd for Cmptrs in Music Classes 1994.

ARAGONA, JOHN JOSEPH,SR., Chemistry Teacher; *b:* Newark, N Rosalie A. Sinscera; *c:* Christine Joan, John Joseph Jr.; *ed:* Seton Hall (BS) Sci Ed 1969, (MA) Scndry Ed 1974; 30 Credits Towards EDD Ru Univ; *cr:* Arthur L. Johnson RHS Sci Tchr 1969-; *ai:* Prin Adviso Cultural Arts Comm; AFT 1982-; Outstanding Tchr Governors gnition Prgm 1988; Co-Authored Laboratory Manual for HS Chem Co-Recipient of NJ BISEC Mini Grant 1987 & PSE & G Mini Grant *office:* Arthur L Johnson Regional H S 365 Westfield Ave Clark NJ *

NCIBIA, SANDRA L. S., Spanish Teacher; *b:* Akron, OH; *m:* Jose Bryana, Marisa; *ed:* Cleveland St Univ (BA) Span & Comm 1985,) Curr & Instr 1994; Tchr Cert 1989; *cr:* Parma Sr HS Span Tchr ; *ai:* AFS Intercultural Exch Prgms Adv 1993-; Parma Ed Assn, NEA ; *office:* Parma Sr HS 6285 W 54th St Parma OH 44129

NGER, RICHARD K., Mathematics Teacher; *b:* Toledo, OH; *m:* e Ann Rybak; *c:* Jason, Michael, Kristen; *ed:* Bowling Green St Univ Ed 1973; *cr:* Start HS Math Tchr 1975-; *ai:* Head Bsbl Coach 21 Yrs; Bsbl Coach of Amer; *office:* Start HS 2100 Tremainsville Rd Toledo 3613

OR, ELAINE FRANCES, Family & Consumer Sci Tchr; *b:* dence, RI; *m:* Neil C.; *c:* Mitchell, Eric; *ed:* URI (BS) Family, mer Sci 1973, (MS) Ed 1977; Working on Degree Early Chldhd Ed; anston Schl Dept Family, Consumer Sci Tchr 1973-92; Cranston Area r & Tech Ctr Child Dev Tchr 1993-; *ai:* 4-H Prgm; AAFCS 1973-, VICA 1993-, Adv; NEA 1973-; Spec Ed Advy Comm 1988-, Sec; CS Grant; Carl Perkins Voc Ed Act Grant; Article Pub; *office:* ton Area Career & Tech Ct 100 Metropolitan Ave Cranston RI 02920*

OUR, SANDY D., Physical Education Teacher; *b:* Augusta, ME; *ed:* of ME (BS) PE 1965; Univ of Southern CA (MS) Ed 1975; Attnd Univ D, City Colls of Chicago, Mc Pherson Coll; *cr:* Gould Acad Tchr 67; Bitburg HS Tchr 1967-69; Kubasaki HS Tchr 1969-71; Incirlik chr 1971-72; Hanau HS Tchr 1972-; *ai:* Dept of Defense Dependent ; Var Vlybl, Track & Field Coach; Schl Improvement Team; Ed Assn Mem; FEA Fac Rep Spokesperson; NEA, FEA 1967-; AAHPERD ; *office:* Hanau HS Cmr 470 Box 7401 APO AE 09165

E, LUIS G., ESOL Teacher; *b:* Danli, Honduras; *c:* Marcelo Antonio; Coastal Carolina Univ (BS) PE 1984; MD Univ (MS) Exercise ology 1988; 30 Hrs ESOL Cert Trinity Coll; *cr:* Socastee Elem PE 1984-86; Coastal Carolina Univ Asst Soccer Coach 1984-86; Sports cine Ctr Phys Therapist Tech 1989-91; Quince Orchard HS ESOL Soccer Coach 1991-; *ai:* Cultural Liason Between Hispanic Stdnts, ts, Schl; Minority Stdnts Mentor; NEA 1991-; Natl Soccer Assn ; *office:* Quince Orchard HS 15800 Quince Orchard Rd Gaithersburg 20878

H, STEPHEN PAUL, English Instructor; *b:* Pittsburgh, PA; *m:* Mary ; Antonia, Stefan; *ed:* Edinboro Univ (BS) Eng Ed 1979-; Univ of burgh (MS) Educl Admin 1983; Working on PHD Amer Lit Duquesne *cr:* Pittsburgh Pub Schls Eng Instr 1979-81; South Park HS Eng Instr -83, Asst Supt 1983-85; Montour HS Eng Instr 1985-; *ai:* Yrbk, Curr, egic Planning, Assessment Comms; Mentor Tchr; NCTE; Fac ultant AP Prgm; SAT, SAT II Prgm Readers; Pa St Writing Assessment Chief Reader.*

HAMBAULT, LEO ZAK, Retail Merch & Bus Prof; *b:* Stoneham, *m:* Mary Zak; *c:* Elizabeth, Leocadia; *ed:* Suffolk Univ (BS) Lbrl Arts Salem St Coll (MBA) Mgmt 1987; Higher Ed Admin Courses at n Coll; *cr:* Almy Stores Inc Mgr 1979-83; Child World Inc Mgr -86; Chamberlayne Jr Coll Asst Prof 1986-88; Mt Ida Coll Assoc Prof -; *ai:* SIFE Club Adv; Curr Comm Chprsn; Centennial Comm Pgm Amer Mrktg Assoc 1989-; Assoc of Collegiate Retail Edctrs 1993-; Soc of Experimental Ed 1993-; Lynn Classical HS Improvement Cncl ; Phi Theta Kappa 1996-, Honorary Inductee; SIFE-Sam Walton w; Designed Retail Simulation for MA Migrant Ed Pgm; *office:* t Ida Coll 777 Dedham St Newton MA 02159

HEY, LAUREL MOWERY, Health Occupations Instructor; *b:* stown, PA; *m:* Jeffrey; *c:* Nathan, Matthew; *ed:* Bloomsburg St Coll Nrsng 1982; Level I, Level II Voc Tchng Cert; *cr:* Geisinger Med Ctr Nurse, Orthopedics Nurse 3 Yrs, CCU 2 Yrs 1983-87; Geisinger ms Svcs Clinic Nurse 1987-88; Columbia-Montour AVTS Hlth pations Instr 1988-; *ai:* Hlth Occupations Stdnts of Amer Adv; Cub t Ldr, Danville Area Schl Dist Practicla Nrsng Prgm, Strategic ning, Curr Dev Northeastern Tech Prep Consortium Comms; Church stry Team; Church Camp Cnslr; Sigma Theta Tau 1983-; NEA, PSEA ; HOSA 1988-, North Cntrl PA Regnl Adv 1995-, HAP Bd; Columbia Tobacco Free Yth Coalition 1994-; Buckhorn Comm Vol Fire Co 1985-; dng Voc Edctr Awd 1994; Cert First Responder; *office:* Columbia our AVTS Schl 5050 Sweppenheiser Dr Bloomsburg PA 17815

CHIBALD, ROBERT A., English & French Teacher; *b:* Orange, CA; ne Martyn; *c:* Elizabeth; *ed:* Univ of OR (BA) Rom Lang, Eng 1959,) Rom Lang 1970; Attnd Princeton Univ 1961-62, Amer Intnl Coll -63, Worcester St Coll 1986; *cr:* Suffield Pub Schls Eng Tchr 1962-66; of OR Tchng Asst 1966-68; Miss Porter's Schl Tchr, Dean 1968-86; bury HS Eng, Fr Tchr 1987-; *ai:* As Schls Match Wits Adv; CEA, ; Fulbright Scholar 1960-61; Klingenstein Fellow Columbia Univ -78; NEH Seminar Brown Univ 1989.

CHIE, ELEANOR ALICE (BLAKE), Guidance Counselor; *b:* Canal , Panama; *m:* Williard Nelson Sr.; *c:* Williard Jr., Lachelle, stopher; *ed:* Brooklyn Coll (BA) Math 1967, (MS) Guid & Cnslng ; Adv Cert in Guid & Cnslng 1991, Schl Admin & Supervision 1994; Boys HS Math Tchr 1967-92; Stuyvesant HS Guid Cnslr 1992-; *ai:* k Stu League Adv; United Fed of Tchrs, AFT 1967-; Kappa Delta Pi ; Jack & Jill of Amer Inc 1992-, Prgm Chprsn, Ed Chprsn; Grad Stu of Brooklyn Coll Awd for Outstdng Dedication & Outstdng Svc; ect Attendance Awd at Boys & Girls HS 1988-89, 1991-92; Staff toring Awd Boys & Girls HS 1990; *office:* Stuyvesant HS 345 mbers St New York NY 10282

CIDIACONO, PATRICIA KELLY, Nursing Professor; *b:* Kearny, NJ; eter; *ed:* Fairleigh Dickinson Univ (BS) Nrsng 1981; NY Univ (MA) g Ed 1985; Clara Maass Schl of Nrsng Diploma 1974; *cr:* Clara Maass RN 1974-78; Clara Maass Schl of Nrsing Tchr 1981-88, Interim Dir -89, Curr Coord 1989-90; Cty Coll of Morris Asst Prof 1990-; *ai:* ducts Wkshps & Assists Comm Orgs with Focus Groups; Amer Nurses 1981-; NJ League for Nrsng 1985-; Sigma Theta Tau Intnl Hnr Soc of ses; ANA Med & Surgical Nurse Cert; *office:* County Coll Of Morris 0 & Center Grove Road Randolph NJ 07869

CIDIACONO, STEVEN JOHN, Director of Drama Program; *b:* adelphia, PA; *m:* Karen Larsen; *c:* Joseph, Katherine, Julia; *ed:* Temple (BBA) Acctng 1979; *cr:* Haverford HS Drama Dir 1989-; *ai:* Sr ect Mentor; Act Comm; Sr Project Guides; Screen Actors Guild 1994; r Fed TV, Radio 1983; Theatre Awds.

COUETTE, GERALD PAUL, Social Studies Teacher; *b:* Fall River, ; *ed:* Univ of RI (BA) Pol Sci 1975; Addl 60 Credits in Soc Stud, Bus rses, Ed Courses; *cr:* Tiverton MS Soc Stud Tchr 1978-85; Tiverton HS Stud Tchr 1986-; *ai:* Head Bsktbl Coach; Class Adv 1986, 1989; tegic Planning Comm; NEA 1978-, VP.

DINI, ROXANN, Sixth Grade Teacher; *b:* Johnstown, PA; *ed:* Univ of burgh (BS) Elem Ed, Sci 1974; Penn St Univ (MEQ) Elem Ed 1988; v of AK Southeast 12 Addl Credits Environmental Stud; *cr:* Blacklick Elem Ctr Schl Grd 4 Tchr 1974-78, Grd 6 Tchr 1978-; *ai:* ironmental Ed Specialist Coord 4th-6th Grd Stdnts; 5th-6th Grd Rdng mpetition Coach; NEA, PSEA 1974-; BVEA 1974-, Exec Bd, Pub Relations; BPW 1978-, Dist Dir, PA St Young Careerist 1981; St Mary's Roman Cath Church 1970-, Yth Choir Dir; Cambria Cty Conservation Dist 1978 Tchr of Yr, Outstdng Environmental Conservation Ed Awd 1987; Soil Conservation Svc 1984, Edctr Awd; 1984 NACD Tchr of Yr Nom; 1993 Nom KDKA'S Thanks to Tchr Campaign; 1994 Nom PA Tchr of Yr; Presented Trng Wkshps; *office:* Blacklick Valley Elem Ctr 1000 W Railroad St Nanty Glo PA 15943

ARDITO, DONNA M., Second Grade Teacher; *b:* Steubenville, OH; *ed:* Univ of Steubenville (BS) Elem Ed 1973; Univ of Dayton (MA) Admin, Supervision 1976; Lang Arts Courses; *cr:* Wintersville Elem Schl 3 Grd Tchr 1973-78, 2 Grd Tchr 1978-; *ai:* Odyssey of Mind Coach, State Champ 1995, 10th in World Comp 1995; HS Musicals Asst Dir; Second Grd Musical Dir; OEA, NEA 1973-; ICEA 1973-, Bldg Rep; Martha Jennings Scholar Awd; Ashland Oil Tchr Nom; *office:* Wintersville Elem Schl 125 Fernwood Rd Wintersville OH 43952

ARDITO, JOHN ANTHONY, Graphic Arts Teacher; *b:* Newark, NJ; *m:* Anne L. Andiorio; *c:* Crista, Gina; *ed:* Montclair St Coll (BA) Indstrl Arts 1977; *cr:* East Side HS Indstrl Arts Tchr 1972-; *ai:* Graphic Arts, Sportsmans Club Adv; Schl Improvement Comm; AFT, Newark Indstrl Arts Assn 1972-; Benedetto Croce Ed Soc 1995-; Newark Tchrs Union 1972-; St Peter's Nursery Schl 1978-, Bd Dirs; Rainbow Child Care Ctr 1985-, Consultant; Meritorious Svc Cert 1983; NJ Tchr of Yr Candidate 1992; Princeton Univ Prize Nom 1993; *office:* East Side HS 238 Van Buren St Newark NJ 07105

ARDOLINE, MARY ANN ELISABETH, Asst Prof of Writing & Reading; *ed:* Kutztown Univ (BA) Sociology 1979; Lehigh Univ (MED) Rdng Spec Cert 1983; Kutztown Univ (MA) Eng 1991; Scndry Ed Cert Soc Stud 1981; Cambridge Univ Hum Inst 1989; *cr:* Allentown Coll Rdng, Stud Skills, Supvr, Instr 1982-89; Northampton Comm Coll Asst Prof of Writing, Rdng 1983-; *ai:* Adv Stu Senate, Dev Ed Task Force; Acad Appeal CCCP; Transition Team; AFT 1984-; NCTE 1991-; CCH; Tchng Assistantship Lehigh Univ; NEH Seminar Flwshp; *office:* Northampton Comm Coll 3835 Green Pond Rd Bethlehem PA 18017*

ARDUINI, KATHLEEN MOORE, 5th Grade Teacher; *b:* Springfield, MA; *c:* Vincent, Roger; *ed:* Westfield St Coll (MA) Admin 1989; *cr:* J. F. K. Jr HS Grd 5 Tchr 1969-70; Prudence Crandull Schl 4-5 Grd Tchr 1970-73; Consolidated Schl Grd 4 Tchr 1977-80; Woodland Schl Kndgtn Tchr 1980-81; Powder Mill MS 4-5, 8 Grd Tchr 1981-; *office:* Powder Mill MS 94 Powder Mill Rd Southwick MA 01077*

AREES, GEORGE A., English Teacher; *b:* Woonsocket, RI; *ed:* Ricker Coll (BA) His 1971; NY Univ (MA) Asian Stud 1975; Various Eng & His Courses at RI Coll, Providence Coll & Univ of RI; *cr:* Woonsocket Sr HS Soc Stud Tchr 1971-82; Woonsocket Jr HS Eng Tchr 1982-87; Johnson & Wales Univ Part-Time CEE Instr 1983-90; Woonsocket Sr HS Eng Tchr 1987-; *ai:* NHS Adv; AFT, Woonsocket Tchrs Guild 1971-; Cncl of Scndry Eng Tchrs 1982-; Names Project 1995-; Fulbright Fellowship to India; *office:* Woonsocket Sr HS 777 Cass Ave Woonsocket RI 02895

ARENDAS, DAVID WILLIAM, Math & Cmptr Programming Tchr; *b:* Mc Keesport, PA; *ed:* Clarion Univ (BS) Math 1969, (MA) Math 1971; Post-Grad Math, 18 Credits Math, 6 Credits Cmptr Programming 1971-80; *cr:* Clarion Area Jr-Sr HS Math, Cmptr Programming Tchr 1969-; *ai:* Act 178 Continuing Prof Dev, Clarion Univ Curr Re-Evaluation Comm; Kappa Delta Pi, CAEA, PSEA, NEA, MAA 1969-; Duquesne Univ Excl in Tchng Awd 1992; *office:* Clarion Area Jr-Sr HS 219 Liberty St Clarion PA 16214

ARENDT, DONALD M., Social Studies Chair; *b:* York, PA; *m:* Elizabeth A. Repman; *c:* Heather E., Paul A., Emily J.; *ed:* Shippensburg St Coll (BS) Ed 1967, (MED) Ed 1970; Supervision of Soc Stud Cert Millersville Univ 1987; *cr:* Dover Area HS Soc Stud Tchr 1968-, Soc Stud Dept Chair 1983-; York Coll of PA Adjunct His Prof 1987-88; Dover Area HS Supvr of Soc Stud 1988-93; *ai:* Acad Coach for Advanced Placement Stdnts; Acad Quiz Bowl Coach; NEA, PSEA 1969-, Local Pres 1973-75; ASCD 1987-; NCSS 1983-; Mason-Dixon Cncl for Soc Stud 1988-, Sec 1988-92; Dover Schl Employees Credit Union 1976-, Pres 1976-83; Habitat for Humanity; NEH Fellow 1985, 1988 & 1993; Am Family Inst Gift of Time Tribute 1990; *office:* Dover Area HS W Canal St Dover PA 17315

ARENDT, EILEEN D., Mathematics Teacher; *b:* Newark, NJ; *ed:* Trenton St Coll (BA) Math Ed 1991; 6 Credits Math Georgian Ct Coll; 9 Credits Math Trenton St Coll; 4 Credits Math Ed Mt Holyoke Coll; 6 Credits Ed Saint Peter's Coll; *cr:* Long Branch HS Math Tchr 1991-; *ai:* Math Club Adv; Four Block Comm; NCTM 1990-; NJEA, AMTNJ 1991-; Ldrshp Day Assembly Awd 1994; Tchr of Yr 1994; Calculus Network Grant 1993.

ARENO, JAMES LESLIE, HS Mathematics Teacher; *b:* Poughkeepsie, NY; *m:* Rhonda Lettieri; *ed:* Univ of Rochester (BA) Fr 1975; SUNY at New Paltz (MS) Math & Ed 1982; 44 Credit Hrs; *cr:* FD Roosvelt HS Math Tchr 1978-; *ai:* 7th-8th Grd Girls Vllybl Coach 8 Yrs; Jr Var Girls Bsktbl Coach 7 Yrs; AFT 1978-; NYSUT 1978-; HPTA 1978-, Pres 1983-86; Mid-Hudson Vly Approved Bsbl Umpires Assoc 1983-; Hudson Vly Umpires Assoc 1983-; *office:* F D Roosevelt HS S Cross Rd Hyde Park NY 12538

ARENSTEIN, LORI, Biology Teacher; *ed:* SUNY at Stony Brook (BS) Bio 1980; CUNY Brooklyn Coll (MA) Tchr Scndry Sci Ed 1987; Advanced Cert in Admin, Supervision; *cr:* Midwood HS Gen Sci Tchr 1981-82; Solomon Schechter HS Bio, Chem Tchr 1982-85; Bialik Day Schl 3-8 Grd Sci Tchr 1985-87; Brooklyn Coll Acad HS Bio, Chem Tchr 1987-; *ai:* Sr, Coll Adv; Transcript Coord; Mentor for Stu Tchr; Attendance Comm; *office:* Brooklyn Coll Acad HS 2900 Bedford Ave Brooklyn NY 11210

ARENT, CYNTHIA THAXTON, First Grade Teacher; *b:* Cambridge, OH; *m:* J. Michael; *ed:* OH St Univ (BSEd) Elem 1-8 1977; Credit Hrs OH Univ, IN-Purdue Univ, Muskingum Coll, Ashland Coll; *cr:* Lore City Senecaville Elem Schl Remedial Rdng Tchr 1978-82; Beech Grove Elem Schl First Grd Tchr 1982-90; Brook Elem Schl First Grd Tchr 1990-; *ai:* Discipline, Budget, Grd Level Comms; NEA, OEA, Rolling Hills Ed Assn 1978-; Natl Cambridge Collectors Inc 1984-, VP, Bd Mem; Martha Holden Jennings Scholar 1989; *office:* Brook Elem Schl 58601 Marietta Rd Byesville OH 43723

ARESTO, HELEN JEAN HUTCHISON, Science Teacher; *b:* New Kensington, PA; *m:* Patrick C.; *c:* Brian Lovett; *ed:* Univ of DE (BSEd) Earth Sci 1975; Minors in Chem, Physics & Math; Masters Equivalence in Sec Sci Emphasis on Environmental Ed; *cr:* Cleveland Clinic Spcl Hematology Tech 1968-70; Ames Dept Store Asst Mgr 1971-74; Highlands Schl Dist 9th Grd Sci Tchr 1975-81; N Allegheny Schl Dist 8th-12th Grd Sci Tchr 1984-; *ai:* Discipline Comm & Stu Assistance Core Team Mems; Environmental Club & Bold Chrstn Flwshp Club Spons; AFT & NAFT 1984-; PAFT; WPA Dressage Assn 1991-, Treas; Gift of Time Tchr Awd; *office:* North Allegheny H S 10375 Perry Hwy Wexford PA 15090

ARGAZZI, PAUL D., Math Tchr & Team Adv; *b:* Hartford, CT; *m:* Judith Merli; *c:* Amanda; *ed:* Bates Coll (BS) Math 1967; Cntrl CT St (MS) Math 1972; Attnd Cntrl St, Sacred Heart Univ, Univ CT, Fairfield, Univ of LaVerne; *cr:* Palaski New Britain HS Math, Cmptr Sci Tchr, Bsbl, Track 1967-82; Tunxis Comm Coll Cmptr, Math Tchr 1982-94; New Britain HS Math, Cmptr Sci Tchr 1982-; *ai:* Math Team Adv; AFT, NBFT 1967-; Lewis S. Mills Schlsp Fund 1983-, Pres; *office:* New Britain HS 110 Mill St New Britain CT 06051

ARGEMIL, VIVIAN, Bilingual & ESL Resource Tchr; *b:* Habana, Cuba; *c:* William, Brian, Argemil; *ed:* Kean Coll of NJ (BA) Tchr, Librn K-12 1973; Biling Cert 30 Credit Hrs 1977; Assoc Educl Media Specialist 1986; Bellcore Tchr Inst 1991; *cr:* Perth Amboy Bd of Ed Ed Media Specialist 1973-86, GATE Math Tchr 1978-82, 3rd Grd Tchr 1986-87, Kndgtn Tchr 1987-94, Biling, ESL Resource Tchr 1994-; *ai:* Assertive Discipline Trainee; Middlesex CT Coll, PA Tchr Mentor; Minority Access to Profession Scholars; Cooperating Tchr; Saturday Family Schl Instr; Drama Coach; Lang Arts Pilot Tchr; Home Schl Relation Comm; EPIC Trainer; Soc Problem Solving; PTA, Pres; AFT 1973-; NJTESOL-Be Inc 1994-; Jackson Citizen Advy Comm 1995-; Jackson Meml HS, Exec Cncl 1992-95; IKE Sci Grant 1993; Schl #5 Tchr of Yr 1993; Prins Awd 1992; TV Show Panel Mem 1992; NJTESOL Conf Presentor 1991; Governor's Tchr Recognition Prgm 1992-93; *office:* Edward J. Patten Schl 500 Charles St Perth Amboy NJ 08861*

ARGENTATI, DAVID MARK, Business Education Teacher; *b:* Easton, PA; *m:* Christina Gillman; *ed:* Wilkes Univ (BS) Acctng 1990; Bloomsburg Univ (MED) Ed 1993; *cr:* Governor Mifflin HS Bus Ed Tchr 1993-; *ai:* JV Bsktbl Coach; FBLA Co-Adv; Project 2000; Tech Comm; Stu Asst Prgm; PSEA, GMEA 1993-; *office:* Governor Mifflin HS 10 S Waverly St Shillington PA 19607*

ARGENZIANO, MICHAEL R., MS Social Studies Teacher; *b:* West Islip, NY; *ed:* SUNY at Plattsburgh (BS) Scndry Ed, Soc Stud 1992; Working Towards Masters Lbrl Stud SUNY at Stonybrook; *cr:* Islip Schl Dist Psych Tchr 1993-94, Global Stud Tchr 1994-95, 8th Grd Amer His Tchr 1995-; *ai:* JV Soccer, MS Bsktbl & Bsbl Coach; ITA 1993-; NYSUT 1995-; JV Soccer Coach of Yr 1995; *office:* Islip Schl Dist 2508 Main St Islip NY 11751

ARGESKI, BERNARD GERALD, Earth Science Teacher; *b:* Passaic, NJ; *m:* Carol Jean Glinka; *c:* Andrew; *ed:* Montclair St Coll (BA) Bio 1972; Fairleigh Dickinson Univ (MA) Sci 1978; 45 Addl Credit Hrs Geology, Meteorology, Cmptr Usage; *cr:* Pascack Hills HS Bio, Earth Sci Tchr 1972-; *ai:* Sci League Adv; NEA, NJEA, BCEA 1972-; NJ Earth Sci Tchr Assn 1985-; Town Bsbl Helper 1994-; PDF Grant for Meteorological Instruments; Nom 4 Times Govenors Tchr Awd.*

ARGUS, MARYANN, Math Teacher; *b:* Syracuse, NY; *ed:* Maria Regina Coll (AA) Lbrl Arts 1969; Cath Univ of Am (BA) Math 1978; St Univ of NY at Oswego (MS) Scndry Math 1985; *cr:* Bishop Ludden HS Math Tchr 1980-82; Oswego Cath HS Math, Cmptr Sci Tchr 1982-85; Notre Dame Utica Math, Cmptr Sci Tchr 1985-90; Chrstn Brothers Acad Math Tchr, Dept Chrprsn 1990-; *ai:* Math Dept Chprsn; Acad of Math Edctrs-SU 1995-; OCTMA 1990-; NCTM 1991; Tandy Tech Outstdng Tchr Math, Cmptr Sci 1993-94; CYO-Outstdng Svc to Yth of Utica 1985; *office:* Christian Brothers Acad 6245 Randall Rd Syracuse NY 13214*

ARIAS, NANCY COONS, Spanish Teacher; *b:* Canton, PA; *m:* Ermel; *c:* Jolene Smyth, Cynthia Delgadillo, James J.; *ed:* Grove City Coll (BA) Span, Fr 1954; Millersville Univ (MA) Span 1976; 25 Grd Hrs Columbia Univ; 6 Grd Hrs Inter-American Univ; *cr:* Canton Jr Sr HS Eng, Span Tchr 1954-58; Colegio Americano De Quito Eng Tchr, Elem Prin 1958-68; Canton Jr Sr HS Span, Eng Composition 1968-; *ai:* Frgn Lang Club; Adv; Delta Kapap Gamma 1974-, Phi Delta Kappa; PSEA, NEA 1968-; Church of Christ Disciples of Christ 1945-, Elder, Chm; Lit Club 1958-, Past Pres; Woman of Yr 1995 Church of Christ Disciples; *home:* 4 W Union St Canton PA 17724

ARIEH, TOBY SAMUELS, Judaic Studies Teacher; *b:* New York ; *m:* Raphael; *c:* Ronit, Yoel, Michal; *ed:* Yeshiva Univ Tchrs Inst (BRE) Bible & Ed 1965; City Coll (BA) Bio & Hum 1967; Attnd Hebrew Univ; *cr:* ETZ Chaim Tchr 1968-70; Yeshiva HS Tchr 1978-90; Yeshiva Univ HS Tchr & Grd Adv 1990-; *ai:* Gruss Awd for Excl in Tchng; *office:* Yeshiva Univ HS 8686 Palo Alto St Holliswood NY 11423

ARIOLA, KELLY MARIE, Business Education Teacher; *b:* Syracuse, NY; *ed:* LeMoyne Coll (BS) Bus Admin 1992; Bowie St Univ Grad Schl Guid & Cnslng Pgm; *cr:* Broadneck Sr HS Bus Ed Tchr 1993-; *ai:* Club Adv: DECA & FBLA; Acad of Fin Coord; NEA 1993-; TAAC 1993-; *office:* Broadneck Sr HS 1265 Green Holly Dr Annapolis MD 21401*

ARK, PAMELA BUTLER, Language Arts Teacher; *b:* Cleveland, OH; *m:* Stephen; *c:* Alyson, Darcy, Jacob; *ed:* Denison Univ (BA) Eng 1972; 30 Grad Hrs Antioch Univ; *cr:* Northeastern HS Eng Tchr 1973-84; Greenon HS Eng Tchr 1992-93; South Vienna Mid Lang Arts Tchr 1993-; *ai:* Power of the Pen; Rubric Comm; Writing Source Book & Competency Based Ed Writing Comms; NEA 1974-; OCTELA 1994-; WOCTELA 1994-; *office:* South Vienna MS 140 W Main St South Vienna OH 45369

ARKILANDER, PATRICIA MC DOUGALL, Social Studies Teacher; *b:* Greenville, PA; *m:* John E.; *c:* Bruce; *ed:* Thiel Coll (BA) His, Biological Scis 1947; Post Grad Stud Geog, His at Slippery Rock Univ; *cr:* East Fallowfield HS 9-12 Grd Soc Stud Tchr 1947-48; West Salem Elem Schl Self-Contained 7th Grd Tchr 1959-60; Reynolds HS 7-9, 11 Grds Soc Stud Tchr 1960-; *ai:* Citizens Bee Club Adv 1993-, Local Winner to St 1995; Reynolds Model Legislators Organizer, Adv 1986-95; Reynolds Horse, Pony Club 1972-95 Organizer, Adv; PA St Ed Assn, NEA, Reynolds Ed Assn 1959-; 4-H Horse Club Founder, Adv 1955-58; YMCA St Adv of Yr 1988; *office:* Reynolds HS 531 Reynolds Rd Greenville PA 16125

ARLEN, BARBARA GOLDSMITH, HS Mathematics Teacher; *b:* New York City, NY; *m:* STeven Richard; *c:* Stacy, Gregory; *ed:* C. W. Post Coll (BA) Math, Ed 1970; Adelphi Univ (MS) Math 1975; 27 Addl Credits; *cr:* East Meadow HS Math Tchr 1970-79; Half Hollow Hills HS Math Tchr 1979-85; Seneca Vly HS Math Tchr 1985-; *ai:* Asst Ath Dir; NEA, MCPS 1986-; *home:* 12 Scottish Autumn Ct Darnestown MD 20878

ARLT, INGRID, Math & Computer Sci Tchr; *b:* New York, NY; *ed:* SUNY at Binghamton (BS) Comp Sci, (BA) Ger 1986; CUNY Queens Coll (MS) Math Ed 1991; CUNY Brooklyn Coll Advanced Cert Admin & Supvn 1993; *cr:* NY City Bd of Ed Math Tchr 1988-93; Monroe-Woodbury Cntrl Schls Math & Comp Sci Tchr 1993-; *ai:* Orange Cty Acad League Adv; NYSUT 1988-; AFT 1988-; UFT 1988-; *office:* Monroe Woodbury Sr HS 265 Dunderberg Rd Central Valley NY 10917

ARLUNA, VIRGINIA, Language Arts Teacher; *b:* Newark, NJ; *m:* John; *c:* Michael, David, Kristin, Lauren; *ed:* Seton Hall (BS) Eng & His 1972, (MA) Elem Ed 1974; K-12 Cert; Caldwell Coll Pursuing Credits; Post Grad 30 Credits in Curr; Montclair St Univ Adj Prof; *cr:* Cedar Grove Pub Schls Tchr 1973-; *ai:* Stu Cncl & Lit Magazine Adv; Eng Curr; Holistic Scoring Comm; Performance Assessment Coord; 7th Grd Outdoor Ed Pgm Supervising Vol; NJEA 1973-; NEA 1973-; CGEA 1973-; Tchr of Yr 1992; Chm of Grant From Montclair St on Handicapped Awareness; Kappa Delta Phi; *office:* Memorial MS Rugby Rd Cedar Grove NJ 07009

ARMENI, TONY, Art Instructor; *b:* Youngstown, OH; *ed:* Youngstown St Univ (BFA) Ceramics, Sculputre 1982; Univ of Cincinnatti (MFA) Ceramics 1987; *cr:* Yountstown St Univ Instr, Art Dept 1989-; *home:* 3579 Bee St Mineral Ridge OH 44440

ARMENTANO, JANET RASCOE, Art Teacher; *b:* Worcester, MA; *m:* George Francis; *c:* Michelle, Robert; *ed:* Univ of CT (BFA) Graphic Design 1977; Art Ed Cert Univ of Hartford; CCSU; Anna Maria Coll; *cr:* Conard HS 1977-85; Hall HS 1977-85; Holliston HS Art Tchr 1987-; *ai:* Art Club Adv; *office:* Holliston HS 370 Hollis St Holliston MA 01746

ARMER, DONNA LEE, Sixth Grade Teacher; *b:* Oneonta, NY; *m:* R. Thomas; *c:* Lorilee Anthony, Juliane; *ed:* St Univ of NY at Cobleskill (AAS) Nursery Ed-Cum Laude 1964; St Univ of NY at Oneonta (BS) Elem Ed 1967; Coll of St Rose 30 Hrs in Rdng 1973; *cr:* City Schl Dist of

Saratoga Springs Elem 1, 2, 4, 6 Grd Tchr 1967-; *ai:* NY Tchrs Assn 1967-; 4-H, Ldr; 25 Yrs of Svc Awd Saratoga City Schl Dist; *office:* Maple Avenue MS 515 Maple Ave Saratoga Springs NY 12866

ARMFIELD, CAROLYN DEVONNE STINSON, Director; *b:* Cornelius, NC; *m:* David Sr.; *c:* David Samuel Jr., Christy D.; *ed:* Livingstone Coll (BA) Sociology 1957; City Coll of NY (MSED) Ed 1986; *cr:* Irvington House Cnslr for Children 1957; Yth House for Girls Recreational Worker 1963; Barrett House Cnslr 1964; Jacob Riis Settlement House Group WOrker Promotectto Prgm Dir 1964; Elizabeth Mayfield Nursery Schl Dir 1992-; *ai:* Amer Cancer Soc; Comm Hlth Ctrs; Summer Tutoring; Livingstone Coll Alumni 1957-; Svc Awds Jacob Riis Ctr 1972, Parent Assn, Black His, Article Promoted 1991; *home:* 640 Riverside Dr Apt 9H New York NY 10031

ARMILLEI, PATRICIA CARVER, Physics Teacher; *b:* Philadelphia, PA; *m:* Robert L.; *c:* Amanda; *ed:* West Chester Univ (BS) Chem 1973, (MS) Physics 1975; 20 Grad Credits Geology, Earth Space Sci, Astronomy; 10 Grad Credits Chem NSF; *cr:* Abington Schl Dist Chem, Physics Tchr 1973-82; Council Rock HS Physics Tchr 1982-; *ai:* Curr Dev; Engrng Competition Adv; New Tchrs Mentor; Amer Assn Physics Tchr 1990-; Council Rock Ed Assn 1982-, Bldg Rep; Northeast Optimist 1986-91, Sftbl Coach; Fox Chase Rec 1992-95, Sftbl Coach; Philadelphia Sci Cncl Awd 1991; DE Vly Sci Cncl Awd 1994; *office:* Council Rock HS 62 Swamp Rd Newtown PA 18940

ARMINIO, DAVID A., English Teacher; *b:* Newark, NJ; *m:* Kathy Armstrong; *c:* Gloria, Thomas; *ed:* Seton Hall Univ (BS) Eng 1972; *cr:* Union HS Eng Tchr 1971-72; Kawameeh MS Eng Tchr 1972-; *ai:* Girls Var Soccer & Asst Var Wrestling Coach; Natl Jr Honor Soc Adv; NEA & NJEA 1972-; UTEA 1972-, Negotiator 9 Yrs; Elks Club 1991-; Knights of Columbus 1985-; Friends of Union Pub Lib; Union Twp Historical & The Planetary Soc; Governors Tchr Recognition Awd 1987.

ARMOCIDA, ROBERT CARL, Vice Principal & Athletic Dir; *b:* New York City, NY; *m:* Nancy McLaughlin; *c:* Zachary, Amanda; *ed:* Univ of Buffalo (BS) Bus & Mrktng Ed 1976; Nazareth Coll at Rochester (MS) Bus Ed 1982; SUNY at Brockport (CAS) Admin 1993; *cr:* Greece Olympia HS Bus Tchr 1977-93, Vice Prin 1993-95, Vice Prin & Ath Dir 1995-; *ai:* Ath Dir for 44 Male & Female Teams; SAANYS 1993-; Scndry Curr Supvrs 1995-; Yth Ftbl Coach 1994-; Yth Bskbtl Asst Coach 1996; Univ of Rochester Scndry Tchr of the Yr 1988; Adv for Clarkson Univ Mgmt Challenge; 1st Pl Teams 1989, 1991 & 1992; DECA Adv NY St Chptr; *office:* Greece Olympia HS 1139 Maiden Ln Rochester NY 14615*

ARMS, BEVERLY JILL, Social Studies Teacher; *b:* Wellston, OH; *m:* Darren A.; *c:* Tesa G., Leah R.; *ed:* Rio Grande Coll (BA) Soc Sci Comp 1984; *cr:* Miller HS Soc Stud Tchr 1985-; *ai:* Stu Cncl, COSA Adv; Soc Stu Curr Comm; SLEA 1985-; Wellston Mothers Club 1994-; Mentor Tchr 3 Yrs; Lead Tchr Cmptrs; 2 Culture Grants from Univ of OH; *office:* Miller HS 10397 SR 155 SE Hemlock OH 43743

ARMSTRONG, CAROL ELAINE, High School Art Teacher; *b:* Syracuse, NY; *ed:* St Univ of NY at Buffalo (BS) Art Ed 1971; 40 Addl Credit Hrs Including 30 Hrs for NYS Permanent Cert; *cr:* Warner Elem Schl Art Tchr 1971-79; West Genesee Sr HS Art Tchr 1979-83; Camillus Jr HS Art Tchr 1983-87; West Genesee Sr HS Art Tchr 1987-; *ai:* NEA 1971-; NY St Art Tchrs 1990-; Natl Art Tchrs Assn 1985-; Friends of Burnet Park Zoo 1991-; Burnet Park Zoo 1993-, Ed Vol; *office:* West Genesee Sr HS 5201 W Genesee St Camillus NY 13031

ARMSTRONG, DAVID W., Technology Teacher; *b:* Syracuse, NY; *c:* Adam; *ed:* St Univ at Oswego (BS) Tech Ed 1990, (MS) Tech Ed 1995; *cr:* Watertown City Schl Dist Tech Tchr 1990-; *ai:* Schl Newspaper Adv; Article Pub; *office:* Watertown HS 1335 Washington St Watertown NY 13601

ARMSTRONG, DENISE LYNN PERKINS, Spanish & English Teacher; *b:* Gallipolis, OH; *m:* Dean Lance; *c:* Carrie, Lara; *ed:* OH Univ (BSEd) Span & Eng 1974; Univ of Dayton (MSEd) Guidance & Counseling 1987; *cr:* Jackson HS Span & Eng Tchr 1974-; *ai:* NEA, OEA, JCEA, OFLA & SOCTE 1974-; JCS Employees Federal Credit Union, Bd of Dir Secy; Wesley United Meth Church, Admin Bd Secy, Comms; *office:* Jackson HS Tropic St Jackson OH 45640

ARMSTRONG, DOUGLAS C., Fifth Grade Teacher; *b:* Syracuse, NY; *m:* Eudora D.; *c:* Douglas Jr., Daniel, Amanda; *ed:* Southern IL Univ (BS) Elem Ed 1969, (MS) Instructional Materials 1972; 3 Credit Post Grad Hrs at St Univ of NY at Oswego; *cr:* Comm Unit Dist 186 5th Grd Tchr 1969-72; Skaneateles Cntrl Schls 3rd-5th Grd Tchr 1972-; *ai:* Schl Fair Comm; Schl Improvement Team; NEA 1969-72; NYSUT, AFT 1972-; Skaneateles Tchrs Assn 1972-, Bldg Rep; West Genesee Jaycees; Jackson Cty Conservation Tchr of Yr 1970; *office:* Skaneateles Cntrl Schls 49 E Elizabeth St Skaneateles NY 13152

ARMSTRONG, DOUGLAS L., Computer Applications Teacher; *b:* Columbus, IN; *m:* Jeanne I.; *ed:* Western MI Univ (BS) Bus Ed 1971; Bowling Green St Univ (MEd) Bus Ed 1980; 30 Hrs Past Masters Cmptr; *cr:* Port Clinton HS Bus Tchr 1971-, Bus Dept Chair 1988-, Network Admin 1990-; *ai:* Dist Tech Comm; Girls Bsktbl, Track Coach; PCFT 1975-, Treas; OBTA 1972-; OHSBCA 1985-; Dist Coach Of Yr 1989; *office:* Port Clinton HS 821 Jefferson St Port Clinton OH 43452

ARMSTRONG, JAMES DAVID, Fourth Grade Teacher; *b:* Rochester, NY; *m:* Nancy J. Effinger; *c:* Allison, Andy; *ed:* St Univ of NY at Geneseo (BS) Elem Ed 1969; Attnd St Univ of NY at Brockport, Univ of Rochester & Penn St Univ; *cr:* West Webster Elem 3rd Grd Tchr 1969-71; Klem Rd South Elem 6th Grd Tchr 1972-86; Klem Rd North Elem 3rd & 6th Grd Tchr 1987-92; Schlegel Rd Elem 4th Grd Tchr 1993-; *ai:* Project Adept; NYSU Tchrs, W T Assn 1969-; Monroe Cty Conservation Cncl Awd; *office:* Schlegel Rd Elem Schl 1548 Schlegel Rd Webster NY 14580

ARMSTRONG, JAMES J., 7th-8th Grade English Teacher; *b:* Pittsfield, MA; *ed:* St Michael's Coll (BA) Eng 1970; North Adams St Coll (MED) Ed 1993; Addl Hrs; *cr:* St Mark's Schl 3rd Grd, 5th Grd Tchr 1970-72; St Mary's Schl 5-8th Grd Sci Tchr 1972-73; St Mark's MS 5, 6, 8th Grd Eng, Soc Stud Tchr 1973-78; Notre Dame MS 8th Grd Soc Stud Tchr 1978-79; Searles MS 7-8th Grd Eng Tchr 1979-; *ai:* Curr Coordinating Cncl Mem, Sec; Newspaper Adv; Berkshire Hills Ed Assn 1979-, VP 1991-95; NCTE 1979-; MA Tchrs Assn 1979-, Convention Del; Dev Rdng Prgm; NELMS, WAMS, Schl Bd Presenter; Co-Authored Handbooks; *office:* Searles MS 79 Bridge St Great Barrington MA 01230

ARMSTRONG, MARY LOU, Language Arts Teacher; *b:* Niagara Falls, NY; *c:* Adrienne Bradley, Jamie; *ed:* SUC at Potsdam (BA) Scndry Eng 1971; SUC at Brockport (MA) Ed 1975; *cr:* Caledonia-Mumford Eng Tchr 1971-73; Lewiston-Porter Eng Tchr 1974-; *ai:* Supervising Tchr; LPUT Rep; Staff Dev Chprsn; Dist-Wide Soc Chprsn; Tchr Ldr; Tchr Facilitator; Bldg Planning Team; Natl Jr Hnr Soc Fac Cncl; Supt Quality Cr; NYSUT 1971-; LPUT 1975-, Rep; NCTE 1980-; NYSMSA 1990-; *office:* Lewiston Porter MS 4061 Creek Rd Youngstown NY 14174

ARMSTRONG, PATRICIA COLELLA, English Teacher; *b:* Anniston, AL; *m:* Andrew O.; *c:* Katherine, Allison; *ed:* Boston Coll (BA) Eng, Ed 1975; RI Coll (MS) Urban Ed, Admin 1980; *cr:* Danvers HS Eng Tchr 1976-77; East Providence Schls 7th-12th Grd Eng Tchr 1977-; *ai:* Adv NHS; Texts, Tchrs Prgm Brown Univ; NEA, East Providence Ed Assn 1976-; Bd Kendbrin Swim, Tennis 1994-, Corresponding Sec; Tchr St Luke's CCD 1990-; RI Girl Scouting 1985-, Ldr; MS Schl PTO 1990-, Pres 2 Yrs; HS Parent Assn 1994-, Hospitality; Schl Improvement Team 1996; *office:* East Providence Sr HS 2000 Pawtucket Ave East Providence RI 02914*

ARMSTRONG, RICHARD W., Fifth Grade Teacher; *b:* Abington, PA; *m:* Lauren S. Mogree; *c:* Bradley A.; *ed:* Bucks Cty Comm Coll (AA) Ed 1970; Lock Haven St Coll (BS) Ed 1973; 31 Addl Post Grad Credit Hrs Alternate Educl Programming; *cr:* Gwyn-Nor Elem Schl 5th Grd Tchr 1973-76; North Wales Elem Schl 5th Grd Tchr 1976-; *ai:* Soccer Coach Harkysville Travel Team 1990-; NEA, NPEA, PSEA 1973-; Lock Haven Univ Mentor 1992-; Gwynedd Mercy Coll Appreciation Awd 1991; Temple Univ Mentor 1985; N PA Schl Dist Educl Fnd Stu Enrichment Grant 1995-; *office:* North Wales Elem Schl 201 Summit St North Wales PA 19454

ARMSTRONG, SALLY SMITH, Music Teacher; *b:* Lancaster, PA; *m:* Danieal Dean; *c:* Sarah, Rachel; *ed:* Millersville Univ (BA) Music Ed 1988; *cr:* Dayspring Chrstn Acad Classroom, Choir, Band Music Tchr, Dir of Musical Productions 1988-94; Private Piano, Voice, Instrumental Instr 1989-; *ai:* Worship Team; Sunday Schl Tchr; *home:* 217 Meadia Ave Lancaster PA 17602

ARMSTRONG, VIRGINIA BARTOL, English Teacher; *b:* Hartford, CT; *m:* Robert; *c:* Matthew, Kyle; *ed:* SUNY at Stony Brook (MALS) Liberal Stud 1985; Ithaca Coll (BA) Eng & Philosophy 1970; 80 Hrs Post Grad in Eng, Ed & AP Eng Ed; *cr:* Bellport HS Eng Tchr 1972-74; Mount Sinai HS Eng Tchr 1980-; Columbia Univ Literary Judge & Evaluator 1993-; AP Reader in Eng Lit for Coll Bd 1996; *ai:* NHS, Lit Magazine & Chess Club Adv; NEA & MSTA 1980-; 1st Pl Awds Annually for Schl Lit & Art Pub from Columbia Univ & All Columbian Awds for Lit Creativity & Design; *office:* Mount Sinai HS Gertrude Goodman Dr Mount Sinai NY 11766*

ARMSTRONG, WILLIAM ALLEN, Mathematics Professor; *b:* St Marys, OH; *m:* Lisa Marie Riblet; *ed:* The OH St Univ (BS) Math 1988, (MA) Math 1991; Romanian; *cr:* The OH St Univ Undergraduate TA 1986-88, Grad TA 1988-91; Phoenix Coll Math Prof 1991-1994; Lakeland Comm Coll Math Prof 1994-; *ai:* Content Comm Maricopa Math Consortium Co-Chair; NCA Assessment Comm Mem; Intermediate Algebra, Coll Algebra, Trigonometry Textbook Selection Comms; MAA 1988-; AMATYC 1991-; 5 Grants from NSF; NISOD Natl Tchr Excl Awd 1994; Presented AZ MATYC, AMATYC SW Regnl, AMATYC Natl Conventions; *office:* Lakeland Comm College 7700 Clocktower Kirtland OH 44094*

ARNDT, KAREN SUSAN, English Teacher; *b:* Pittsburgh, PA; *m:* John H.; *c:* Krista, Jeffrey; *ed:* Bloomsburg Univ (BS) Eng Scndry Ed 1970; Widener Univ (MS) Eng Scndry Ed 1990; 45 Grad Stud Credit Hrs; *cr:* Pennsbury Schl Dist Eng Tchr 1971-; *ai:* Drill Team Spon; NEA, PSEA, PEA 1971-; *office:* Medill Bair HS 608 S Olds Blvd Fairless Hills PA 19030

ARNEY, BARBARA ANN, Fifth Grade Teacher; *b:* Coshocton, OH; *ed:* Mt Univ Coll (BA) Elem Ed 1986; Acad Challenge Prgm OH St Univ 1990-91; *cr:* Keene Elem Schl LD Tutor 1 Yr, 3rd Grd Tchr 1 Yr, 5th Grd Tchr 8 Yrs; *ai:* Natl Geographic Geog Bee Chprsn; NEA, OH Ed Assoc, River View Ed Assoc 1986-; Canal Lewisville United Meth Church Life Mem; *office:* Keene Elem Schl 27052 CR 1 Box 651 Keene OH 43828

ARNHEITER, PRISCILLA ROSE ALABURDA, AP Biology I & II Instructor; *b:* Passaic, NJ; *m:* Lyle; *c:* Lyle Scott; *ed:* Montclair St Univ (BS) 7-12 Grds Sci 1964; East Stroudsburg Univ (MS) Molecular Genetics 1978; 24 Credits Var Bio Courses William Paterson Coll, Univ of ME; 12 Credits Scndry Schl Ed Seton Hall Univ; *cr:* W Caldwell Jr HS Sci Tchr 1964-65; Rockaway Twp DBO Schl Math, Sci Tchr 1965-67; Morris Knolls HS Bio I II, AP Tchr 1971-; John Hopkins Univ Fast Paced Bio Instr Summers 1992-94; *ai:* Sr Class Adv; Alternate Block Schedule Task Force; NEA, NJEA. MCCEA 1991-; Morris Hills Regnl Dist Assn 1971-, Treas; *office:* Morris Knolls HS 50 Knoll Dr Rockaway NJ 07866

ARNHOLS, MARILYN A., Mathematics Teacher; *b:* Jersey City, NJ; *ed:* Jersey City St (BA) Math 1973, (MA) Math Ed 1976; Post Grad Work in Supervision, Curr Dev & Cmptr Sci at Saint Peters Coll; *cr:* Lincoln Jr HS Math Tchr 1973-76; Secaucus Mid-Scndry Schl Math Tchr 1976-88; Secaucus MS Math Tchr 1988-; *ai:* Natl Jr Honor Soc Co-Adv; NEA, NJEA, SEA 1973-; NCTM 1991-; NASAA 1988-; Saint Joseph Church 1976-; Tchr of Yr Hudson Cty NJ 1995; Saint Peters Coll Tchr Recognition Awd 1990; *office:* Secaucus MS Mill Ridge Rd Secaucus NJ 07094*

ARNOLD, BARBARA STUDEBAKER, 8th Grd Reading & Comm Teacher; *b:* Troy, OH; *m:* Herbert B. Jr.; *c:* Mark Allen, Micque Ann Arnold Brickson, Matt Aaron; *ed:* Antioch Univ (BA) Elem Ed 1979; Univ of Dayton (MS) Rdng & Rdng Supervision 1986; Wittenberg Univ Cadette Cert Elem Ed 1959; Univ of KS Ed Problems Stud; *cr:* Bethel Local Schls 7th Grd Eng Tchr 1960-61; New Carlisle Bethel Schl 4th Grd Tchr 1961-62; Clark Cty Schls Sub Tchr 1965-79; Mad River Green Rdng & Comm Tchr 1979-; *ai:* Stu Cncl & Jrnlsm Club Adv; Career Ed Coord; HS & MS Drama Club & Washington DC Trip Adv; OFT & AFT 1985-, Corresponding Sec; Phi Delta Kappa 1989-; NCTE & OTELA 1986-; Girl Scouts 1969-, Ldr, Neighborhood Chm, Thanks Badge; Sundail Garden Club 1965-, Pres, Tour Dir; Excl in Tchng Springfield Rotary; Noon Optimist Speech Coord; Whos Who in Amer Ed 1989-92; *home:* 162 Green Vista Dr Enon OH 45323*

ARNOLD, BILL, Chemistry & Physical Sci Tchr; *b:* Bucyrus, OH; *m:* Judith E. Pope; *c:* Tracey, Robert; *ed:* Miami Univ (BA) Chem 1961; Luth Theo Seminary in Philadelphia (MD) Theology & Ed 1966; 33 Semester Hr at Temple Univ & 23 Semester Hrs at Bowling Green St Univ; *cr:* Central Bucks Schl Dist Chem & Bio Tchr 1970-78; Buckeye Cntrl Chem & Phys Sci Tchr 1978-; *ai:* Track & Field Coach 1970-; Swimming Coach 1990-; *office:* Buckeye Central HS 306 S Kibler New Washington OH 44854*

ARNOLD, C. WILLIAM, Humanities & Anthropology Tchr; *b:* Fulton, NY; *m:* Margaret; *c:* William, Holly, Shavana; *ed:* Syracuse Univ (AB) His 1964; SUNY at Oswego (MA) His 1967; Pending PHD Anthropology; Hypnotherapy Trng; *cr:* St Johns Acad Tchr 1963-64; Altmar Parish Schl Dist Tchr 1965-70; Oswego City Schls Tchr 1970-; SUNY at Albany Anthropology Inst 1965; Syracuse Univ Anthropology Instr 1966; Cayuga Comm Coll His Instr 1994-; *ai:* NEA, AFT 1970-; Amer Anthropology Assn 1990-; Anthropology of Consciousness 1989-; SUNY at Albany Fellowship Research; Fulbright-Hayes Fellowship Brazil; *office:* Oswego HS 2 Buccaneer Blvd Oswego NY 13126

ARNOLD, CAROL FOSTER, English Teacher; *b:* Staten Island, NY; *w:* Edward Lawrence (dec); *c:* Chad Hastings, Scott Lawrence; *ed:* Beaver Coll (BS) Ed 1956; Middlebury Coll (MA) Eng 1983; *cr:* Summit Pub Schls 4th Grd Tchr 1956-59; Ann Arbor Pub Schls 4th Grd Tchr 1959-60; The Bentley Schl 7th Grd Tchr 1960-61; The Chapin Schl 3rd Grd Tchr 1962; Flemington-Raritan Pub Schls 4th-6th, 7th Grd Tchr 1962-79; The Hun Schl of Princeton Dean of Stdnts 1979-92, 12th Grd, Post-Grad Eng Tchr 1992-; *ai:* After Schl Tutorials; NJEA 1962-; NEA, NAIS, NCTE 1979-; St Barnabas Episcopal Church 1968-, Vestry Mem, Sr & Jr Warden, Altar Guild Dir; St Barnabas Awd Svc to God & Comm; *office:* Hun Schl Of Princeton 176 Edgerstoune Rd Princeton NJ 08540*

ARNOLD, FELICIA ATRIA, Third Grade Teacher; *b:* New York City, NY; *c:* Eugene III, Nicole; *ed:* Richmond Coll (BS) Behavioral Sci 1969, (MS) Elem Ed 1971; Supervisors Cert William Paterson Coll 1989; *cr:* PS 40 SINY Above Quota Tchr 1969-70; PS 42 SINY 2nd Grd Tchr 1970-71; Rolling Hills Primary Schl 3rd Grd Tchr 1981-, Intermediate Coord [illegible]; *ai:* After Schl Math Brainteasers Club Tchr 1992-; Family Math 1994-; NEA, NCTM 1991-; ASCD 1990-; Phi Delta Kappa 1992-; A[illegible] Awd 1989; Tchr of Yr 1985; Pub Twice NJEA Review 1993-; Summer Grant 1984; Pub Learning, Instr Mag 1996; *office:* Rolling[illegible] Primary Schl PO Box 769 Sammis Rd Vernon NJ 07428*

ARNOLD, FREDERICK ALBERT, Art Teacher; *b:* Abington, P[illegible] Carol DuBois; *c:* Charles E., Nathaniel F., Theodore D.; *ed:* U[illegible] Cincinnati (BFA) (BS) Art Ed 1965; Temple Univ (MFA) Crafts 1970[illegible] Chester Univ (MS) Ed 1975; Ind Art Courses Taken at Various Local [illegible] & Museums; *cr:* Upper Dublin Schl Art Tchr 1966-; *ai:* Drama; Hon[illegible] Advy; Stu Assn St Assessment Comm; Class Spon; NEA, UDEA, [illegible] 1966-; Calvary United Meth Church 1948-, Many Offices Held; A[illegible] Cub & Boy Scouts; *office:* Upper Dublin Schl Dist 800 Loch Alsh Av[illegible] Washington PA 19034

ARNOLD, GAIL ANNE, School Counselor; *b:* Ithaca, NY; *m:* R[illegible] Lee; *ed:* SUNY at Cortland (BSE) Ed 1979; SUNY at Oswego [illegible] Cnslng 1989; Colgate Univ Cnslr Cert 1982; *cr:* Clinton Cntrl Sc[illegible] Tchr 1979-81; Lyons Cntrl Schl Cnslr 1981-83; Mynderse Acad Schl [illegible] 1983-85; Marth Brown Jr HS Schl Cnslr 1985-87; Finger Lakes Are[illegible] Ctr Schl Cnslr 1987-91; Midlakes HS Schl Cnslr 1991-93; M[illegible] Whitman MS & HS Cnslr 1993-; *ai:* Peer Mediation, Commnctn Ski[illegible] Stdnts & People Skills Inst Trainer; Ice Skating & SAT Instr; Penn S[illegible] Adj Instr; Article Pub; *office:* Marcus Whitman Jr Sr H S Baldw[illegible] Rushville NY 14544*

ARNOLD, JEANNE CAROL, Second Grade Teacher; *b:* Pittsburg[illegible] *ed:* Penn St Univ (BS) Elem Ed 1964; Villanova, Penn St Extension, [illegible] Univ 36 Credit Hrs Masters Equivalency, 30 Credits In-service MCI[illegible] N. Allegheny Schl Dist 3rd Grd Tchr 1964-65; Bensalem Twp Schl Di[illegible] Grd Tchr 1965-67; Gloucester Twp Schl Kndgtn Tchr 1967; [illegible] Georges Co Schl Dist Kndgtn Tchr 1967-68; Fairfax Co Schl Dist K[illegible] Tchr 1968-69; Dade Co Schls Kndgtn Tchr 1969-70; Lower Merion[illegible] Dist K,1,2 Grd Tchr 1970-; *ai:* NEA, PSEA, LMEA 1970-.

ARNOLD, JOHN CHARLES, 5th-6th Grd Science Teacher; *b:* Eri[illegible] *m:* Carole Ann Goss; *c:* Jennifer, Christine; *ed:* Edinboro Univ (MA) Ed 1970; *cr:* Clark Ele Schl 5th-6th Grd Sci Instr 1966-; *ai:* Harb C[illegible] Assn, PA St Edu Assn, NEA 1966-; PA Sci Tchrs Assn 1985-; NSTA [illegible] NASA Tchr in Space Prgm; Tchr of Yr 1994; Awds Keystone Enery PA Salute to Tchng Awd 1990; *office:* Clark Elem Schl 3650 Depot R[illegible] PA 16510

ARNOLD, JOHN J., 6th Grade Teacher; *b:* Truxton, NV; *ed:* Su[illegible] Cortland (BS) EE 1962; (MS) Ed; *cr:* Sodus Cntrl Schl 4th, 5th Grd [illegible] 1962-64; Homer Cntrl Schl 4th-6th Grd Tchr 1964-; *ai:* NEA [illegible] Negotiator; AFT 1980-; Hunter Safety Instr 1977-; Town Counc[illegible] 1996; NRA 1970-; Worked With Boy Scouts; Mentor for Several Tchrs; Pub a Book on Local His; *home:* 3141 State Route 13 Truxto[illegible] 13158*

ARNOLD, LOIS JEAN, American Government Teacher; *b:* Cleve[illegible] OH; *m:* David C.; *c:* Donna Garlinger, Beth Harb; *ed:* Cleveland St (BA) His 1971, (MED) Curr, Instruction 1978; Admin, Guid, Adole[illegible] Issues Courses; *cr:* Cuyahoga Comm Coll Remedial Rdng, Writing 1970-71; John F. Kennedy Jr HS Eng, His, Rdng Tchr, Librn 197[illegible] Eastlake North HS Civics, Global Geog, Global His, Amer Govt 1984-; *ai:* Care Team Chprsn Fac & Adv Stu; Curr Dev; Stu Mento[illegible] Review Team; Willoughby Eastlake Tchrs Assn 1971-, VP, Outs[illegible] Ldrshp Awd; OH Ed Assn 1971-, Del; NEA 1971-; OCSS 1985-; [illegible] 1986-; IFAW 1978-; Supt Advy Comm 1984-93; Various Grants Class Project Dev; *office:* Eastlake North HS 34041 Stevens Blvd Eastlak[illegible] 44095*

ARNOLD, MATTHEW DEAN, Social Studies Teacher; *b:* Dayton, *ed:* Otterbein Coll (BS) Scndry Soc Stud 1976; Univ of Dayton Supervision 1994; 30 Addl Hrs; 10 Hrs Antioch Coll; 12 Hr[illegible] Beavercreek Schls Tchr 1979-84; Woodmans Lanes Mgr 198[illegible] Tecumseh Schls Tchr 1987; Bevercreek Schls Tchr 1987-; *ai:* Cross C[illegible] Bsktbl, Track Coach; Stu Cncl Adv; Dist Staff Dev Comm Ch[illegible] Beavercreek Ed Assn 1979-, VP; NCSS 1983-; Frateral Order of E[illegible] 1994-; Grant for Gifted Stdnts 1994-95; Dist Tchr of Yr 1979; Cross [illegible] Coaching Awd for 10 Yrs of Coaching; Martha Holden Jennings Sc[illegible] 1981; *office:* Ankeney Jr HS 4085 Shakertown Rd Dayton OH 45430

ARNOLD, MILAGROS BARROZO, 6th Grd Math & Lang Arts Tc[illegible] Pangasinan, Philippines; *m:* James L.; *c:* Elizabeth, James; *ed:* Un[illegible] Pangasinan (BA) Math 1968; The Citadel (MED) Elem Schl Adm[illegible] Supervision 1977; Credit Hrs St Joseph Coll, Coll of Charleston; Post Stud Boston Univ, Univ of MD; *cr:* San Fabian HS Math, Eng 1968-69; Charleston Cty Schl Dist 3 math, Lang Arts Tchr 197[illegible] Roosevelt Elem Schl GATE Tchr 1982-83; New Hampshire Coll, Angels, Metropolitan Coll, US Naval Base PR Coll Algebra Prof 198[illegible] Roosevelt Roads HS Math, Soc Stud Tchr 1983-85; Naples Elem Math, Lang Arts Tchr 1988-; *ai:* Math Extravaganza Dir, Produ[illegible] Multi-Ethnic Comm Chprsn; SC Ed Assn, Natl Assn of Math Tchrs, [illegible] 1972-; AFT, OFT 1989-; Fil-Am Club 1971-, Adv; Roosevelt Raods [illegible] Comm Station 1981-, VP; USS Independence Ofcrs Wives Club 1[illegible] Sec; US Naval Station Cath Comm 1987-, CCD Tchr; *office:* Naples [illegible] Schl PSC Box 810 Box 39 FPO AE 09619*

ARNOLD, NORMA JOYCE (NEWELL), High School Math Teach[illegible] Nieut, WV; *m:* Herbert Neal; *c:* Mark Alan, Tamala Whitnable, Mat[illegible] Eric, Jonathan Luke; *ed:* Glenville St Coll (AB) Math, Eng 1960; 17 C[illegible] Hrs OH Univ Math 1989-94; *cr:* S Charleston Jr HS Math Tchr 196[illegible] Parkersburg HS Bus Math Tchr 1961-62; Belpre HS Math Tchr 1976[illegible] NEA 1976-; OCTM; NCTM; Torch Bapt Church 1968-, Clerk; Tc[illegible] Month 1990; Martha Holden Fnd Grant; *office:* Belpre HS Stone Rd B[illegible] OH 45714

ARNOLD, RICHARD D., Physics Teacher; *b:* Albany, NY; *m:* Deb[illegible] A. Kulbako; *c:* Amanda B.; *ed:* SUNY at Albany (BS) Physics 1972, of St Rose (MSEd) Educl Psucy 1977; 30 Hrs Grad Stud Scis Union [illegible] *cr:* Rensselaer Jr, Sr HS Sci Tchr 1972-74; Guilderland Cntrl HS Ph[illegible] Tchr 1974-; *ai:* Adv HS Musical; Piano Accompanist Choral Gr[illegible] Soloists; AFT, NYSUT 1972-; Guilderland Tchrs Assn 1974-; Saratoga Historical Soc 1980-; Dutch Settlers Soc of Albany 1991-, Life M[illegible] Schenectady Cty Historical Soc 1992-; Grants Natl Sci Fnd; Ge[illegible] Electric Corporate Research, Dev Ctr; Amer Soc Biochem, Molecular Tchr of Yr 1993; Master Tchr Citation 1984; Author; *office:* Guilder[illegible] Central HS School Rd Guilderland Ctr NY 12085

ARNOLD, RICHARD LEROY, Mathematics Teacher; *b:* Dayton, *ed:* DE St Coll (BS) Math 1963; Univ of DC (MST) Math 1985[illegible] Coolidge Sr HS Math Tchr 1976-; *ai:* Taking Grd Level Course Reinforce; Tutoring Lunch, After Schl Days; Learning to Play Clas[illegible] Double Bass; WA Tchrs Union 1977-; NCTM 1994-; *home:* 905 6th St # 308B Washington DC 20024

ARNOLD, ROBERT WAYNE, Chem Tchr & Sci Dept Chm; *b:* Fu[illegible] NY; *m:* Irene Nevling; *c:* Robert L., Michael W., Dawn, Wendy Renee; Defiance Coll (BS) Chem 1961; St Univ of NY at Buffalo (MST) Sci T[illegible] 1969; Colby Coll (MS) Chem 1971; 8 Hrs Radiation Bio from Wayn[illegible] Univ; 18 Hrs Ed from St Univ of NY at Oswego; 3 Hrs from Syracuse [illegible] Utica Coll; *cr:* Morrisville-Eaton Cntrl Schl 7th-10th Grd Sci [illegible] 1961-63; Royalton Hartland Cntrl Schl Chem Tchr 1963-; Niagara

Coll Chem Instr 1979-80; Royalton Hartland Cntrl Schl Sci Dept 1982-; *ai:* Shared Decision Making Steering & Discipline Comms; ton Hartland Tchrs Assn 1963-, Pres, Grievance Chm 1967-; NY St Tchrs Assn 1963-; NSTA 1969-; ASCD 1989-; Cncl of St Sci Supvrs ; Orangeport Cementary Commission 1996; NY United Tchrs rship & Commendation Awds; *office:* Royalton Hartland Central Schl ate St Middleport NY 14105

OLD, SIMONE G., ESL Teacher; *b:* Bucharest, Romania; *m:* David Mark; *ed:* Youngstown St (BS) Elem Ed; *cr:* Youngstown City Schls 1981-91; Akiva Acad ESL Tchr 1991-93; Boardman Bd of Ed ESL 993-; *ai:* NEA 1993-; *office:* Boardman Bd of Ed 777 Glenwood Ave man OH 44512

OLD, WILLIAM JAMES, Fifth Grade Teacher; *b:* Dennison, OH; sbury Coll (BA) Ed 1965; Attnd Kent St Univ & Univ of NE; *cr:* East Local Schl Music Tchr 1965-68; Coshocton City Schls Music Tchr 69; Indian Valley Local Schls 5th & 6th Grd Tchr 1969-; *ai:* Young rs Adv; Right to Read Comm; Local IVTA 1969-; OEA 1965-; NEA ; *home:* 207 Clubside Dr NW New Philadelphia OH 44663

ONE, MARY ANN, 6th Grade Teacher; *b:* Utica, NY; *c:* Steven, sa; *ed:* SUNY at Cortland (BS) Ed 1962, (MS) Ed 1969; SUNY at go (CAS) Educl Admin 1993; *cr:* Lakeshore Schl 4th Grd Tchr 1962; ant St Schl 6th Grd Tchr 1963-67; East Syracuse MS 6th Grd Tchr 71; Fremont Schl 6th Grd Tchr; *ai:* Dist Cmptr Comm 1985-90; Svcs ion 1988-; ESM Tchr of Excl 1990; Cntrl NY Tchng Ctr Grant 1991; : Fremont Elem Schl Richmond Rd W East Syracuse NY 13057

ONE, SAMUEL FRANK, Band Director & Music Chrprsn; *b:* nsburg, PA; *m:* Jayne Garman; *c:* Philip A., Samuel N.; *ed:* Clarion (BA) Music Ed 1973; 30 Grad Hrs Towards MED, Supervisory Cert St; *cr:* Lock Haven HS Band Dir 1973-81; Hughesville HS Chm, Dir 1984-; *ai:* Tri M Music Honor Soc; Lock Haven Indoor Color Dir, Adv; Stu Assistance Team At-Risk Stdnts; Phi Beta Mu 1975-, Sec-Treas; PMEA, MENC, NEA 1973-; ASCD 1982-; Lock Haven 1982-; Lock Haven Rotary 1981-84, Bd of Dir; Lock Haven Sons of 1981-; SPCA 1975-; Article BDG; Guest Conductor Hnrs Band vals; Presenter St Music Conf; Who's Who In Amer Ed 1987-88; Hughesville HS 349 Cemetery St Hughesville PA 17737*

STEIN, JOE, Latin & Spanish Teacher; *b:* Chicago, IL; *c:* Valeri ce; Andrea; *ed:* Holy Cross (AB) Eng 1966; Univ of NH (MST) Eng *cr:* Portsmouth HS Latin, Span, Eng Tchr 1969-; *ai:* Latin Club Adv; 1969-; King Juan Carlos Schlsp 1991; Natl Endowment for the Hum ap Univ of KY 1993; *office:* Portsmouth HS Alumni Cr Portsmouth 3801

NE, KATHRYN ANN, Retired Italian & French Tchr; *b:* Bronx, NY; ouglass Coll (BA) Italian, Fr 1964; Middlebury Coll Grad Schl (MA) n 1965; Middlebury Coll (MA) Fr 1983; Stu Ger 2 Yrs; *cr:* Broadway S Italian Tchr 1965-67; Teaneck HS Italian, Fr Tchr 1967-; *ai:* mer Italian Prgms Elem Schls Puppet Shows; NEA, NJEA, Italian of Amer 1965-; Drawing Cartoons for Children in Hosp 1995-, Vol; r Citizens 1995-, Play Piano; Schlsp Stud Italian Middlebury Coll Schl of Italian.*

NICA, MICHELE TERESA,RSM, Associate Prof of Sociology; *b:* attan, NY; *ed:* St Joseph's Coll (BA) Sociology 1974; Long Island (MA) Sociology 1976; Boston Coll (PHD) Sociology 1985; *cr:* St h's Coll Fac Mem 1978-81, Acting Chair 1981-82, 1984-85, Dept of ology Chair 1985-95; Univ of Detroit Mercy Admin Intern 1995-; *ai:* ology Club Adv; Fac Adv, Chair Soc Justice & Peace Comm; Chrstn lachian Work Fest Projects Adv; Mercy Higher Ed Colloquium 1982, 94, Treas, Chair 1994-; Amer Sociological Assn; Mercy Hosp 1993-, ee, Fin Comm; ME Off of Subst Abuse 1993-, Ad Hoc Comm to ate Proposals; Mc Auley Residence Inc 1986-93, Trustee, Bd Sec; Fnd Excl in Tchng Awd 1990; NSF Grant for Dev of Instrl Cmptr s Quantitative Analysis of Amer Soc 1991; Book: Beyond Charismatic ership The New York Catholic Worker Movement; Numerous Articles, ntations, Wkshps; *office:* Saint Josephs Coll Standish ME 04084*

NOW, STUART L., English & Humanities Teacher; *b:* New York NY; *m:* Vivian; *c:* Elliot; *ed:* Brooklyn Coll (BA) Eng, Ed 1969, (MA) 1974; *cr:* JHS 228 Eng Tchr 1969-74; South Shore HS Eng Tchr -75; John Dewey HS ENg Tchr 1975-; *ai:* HS Broadway Play Dir; AFT -; UFT 1969-; *office:* John Dewey HS 50 Avenue X Brooklyn NY 3

NOWITZ, BARBARA L., High School English Teacher; *b:* Far away, NY; *m:* Gerald; *c:* Mark Lagon, Amy Lauren; *ed:* Syracuse Univ Eng 1965; NYU (MA) Eng 1966; 45 Hrs Inservice Courses; *cr:* ence HS Eng Tchr 1966-67; Lawrence MS Eng Tchr 1967-68; ence HS Eng Tchr 1982-; *ai:* Dist Writing Comm; LI Writing Project; 1966-; Sisterhood of Cntrl Syn 1982-, Bd Mem, Various Comms; : Lawrence HS Reilly Rd Cedarhurst NY 11516

NSON, MARILYN RUTH (RUBCICH), English Teacher; *b:* Staten d, NY; *m:* Donald; *ed:* St John's Univ (PHD) Eng Lit 1989; Wagner (MS) Amer Lit 1969; Hunter (BA) Eng 1964; Hum 94; Lit Critics ; Lives Worth Knowing Biographies 1993; Univ of Guelph Canine ning 1993; *cr:* Wagner Coll Assoc Prof 1975-90; Tottenville HS Eng 1970-90; Staten Island Tech Eng Tchr 1990-; *ai:* Lincoln-Douglas ate Team Coach; NHS Adv; Schlsp Comm; Amer Legion Roatorical e; Theatre Club Adv; English-Speaking Union Shakespeare petition Coach; Irish Soc Oratorical Coach; Natl Cncl Tchrs of Eng -94; Delta Kappa Gamma 1992-; Tchr Honor Soc; NY St Eng Cncl -94, Regnl Dir 1986-92; NY City Assn of Tchrs of Eng 1965-94, VP -94; Borough Pres Awd 1987-, Comm Svc; Lighthouse Hill Civic Assn -, Advy Bd; Greenbelt Stewardship Cncl 1980-, Exec Bd; Oxford Univ w 1990; Natl Head Consultant 1992; NYS Tchr of Excl; AP, NTE ler; Contributor; Who's Who in East; NYC Hum Inst Fellowship 1993; *e:* Staten Island Tech HS 485 Clawson St Staten Island NY 10306*

S, ANDREW S., Social Studies Teacher; *b:* Paterson, NJ; *m:* Mary os; *c:* Andreas; *ed:* Seton Hall Univ (BS) His 1961; Univ of Hartford Scndry Admin 1976, (CAGS) Ed 1982; Addl 30 Credits in His & Soc *cr:* Paterson Tech & Voc HS Eng & His Tchr 1962-63; Hawthorne HS Stud Tchr 1963-68; Newington HS Soc Stud Tchr 1968-; May aurant Equipment & Supply Purchasing Agent 1974-91; *ai:* NEA, , NTA 1968-, PPC Contract Negotiation 1981-; Order of AHEPA -, Sec, Newspaper, Current Schlsp Comm; Church, Parish Cncl -94, Sunday Schl Dir 1983-88; Best Mentor Tchr Prgm Stu Tchr; *e:* Newington HS 605 Willard Ave Newington CT 06111

A, CATHERINE MARY, Eng & Creative Writing Teacher; *b:* ton, NY; *ed:* Suny New Paltz (BA) Eng, Scndry Ed 1978, (MS) Eng, ry Ed 1982; Attnd Columbia Univ, Wesleyan Univ; *cr:* Kingston HS 1977-78; M.C. Clifford Jr HS Tchr, Writing Coord 1978-88; Rondout Cntrl HS Tchr 1988-; *ai:* Yrbk; Lit Adv; Rondout Vly Fed of Tchrs -; Byrdcliffe Writers of NY 1990; Ulster Cty Comm Coll Poetry m 1994-; Pub Short Fiction, Poetry; *office:* Rondout Valley Cntrl Schl ox 9 Accord NY 12404

RANTE, MICHELLE DENISE, Secondary Math Teacher; *b:* burgh, PA; *m:* Joe; *c:* Joelle Briana; *ed:* Edinboro Univ (BS) Scndry Math 1989; Enrolled MS Prgn Admin, Supervision Loyola Coll; *cr:* Rising Sun HS Math Tchr 1989-; *ai:* Class 1992-95, Chrldng 1989-91 Adv; Fac Advy Comm; *office:* Rising Sun HS 100 Tiger Dr North East MD 21901

ARRIETA, CELINA M., Spanish Teacher; *b:* Medellin Colomb, Columbia; *m:* Raul E.; *c:* Andres F., Juan C., Jesse A.; *ed:* Pontifical Bolivarian Univ (BA) Eng & Span 1981; *cr:* Los Cedros Schl Eng & Fr Tchr 1982-87; Night Schl Span & Fr Tchr 1987-88; Zarephath Chrstn Schls Span Tchr 1989-; *ai:* Yrbk Adv; *office:* Zarephath Chrstn Schls Weston Canal Rd Zarephath NJ 08890

ARRIGONIE, JEAN MARIE, 4th Grade Teacher; *b:* Wilkes-Barre, PA; *m:* John Daniel; *c:* John Michael, Amy; *ed:* Lock Haven Univ (BS) Elem Ed 1981; 24+ Credits at Penn St Univ, Mansfield Univ & Indiana Univ of PA; Permanent Cert; *cr:* Lock Haven Cath Schl Tchr 1982-; *ai:* Phi Delta Kappa 1988-, Pres, Past Pres, Prgms VP; NCEA 1982-; Immaculate Conception Church, Lector, Liturgy Planning; Bsbl Youth League, Team Mother; YMCA Vlybl League, Team Captain; PA Dairy Cncl Outstanding Tchr Awd; *home:* PO Box 55 Castanea PA 17726

ARRISON, JERRY L., 7th Grade Life Science Teacher; *b:* Chambersburg, PA; *m:* Daisy V. Shipley; *c:* Jerry II, Daniel; *ed:* PA St Univ (BS) Ed 1973; Masters Equivalence Awded by PA Dept of Ed; *cr:* Gettysburg Jr HS Sci Tchr 1973-; *ai:* Cmptr Resource Mgr; *office:* Gettysburg Jr HS Lefever St Gettysburg PA 17325

ARROYO, FLORENCE D., Chemistry Teacher; *b:* Brooklyn, NY; *m:* Eugene R.; *c:* Jeanine Arroyo Martin, Robert F.; *ed:* St Johns Univ (BS) Chem 1958, (MS) Chem 1958; 18 Credits Grad Ed at C. W. Post; 6 Credits Grad Ed at St Rose Albany; 3 Credits Grad Ed at SUNY Purchase; 6 Credits Grad Ed at Micellaneous Credits; *cr:* United St Testing Co Chemist 3 Yrs; Office of Chief Examiner Sr Chemist 3 Yrs; L I Schl for Gifted Sci Tchr 3 Yrs; Francis Lewis HS Chem Tchr 4 yrs; *ai:* Sci Club Adv; Chem Regents Review Tutoring; UFT; NYSUT; AFT; Muncey Park Womens Org 1994-; Brooklyn Cat Franciers Assn 1979-; Animal Protutim Inst 1980-; Humane Soc of US 1994-; Journal of Ag; Flwshp to St Johns Univ; *office:* Francis Lewis HS 5820 Utopia Pky Fresh Meadows NY 11365

ARRUDA, JOAO PEREIRA, Portuguese & Spanish Teacher; *b:* S Jorge Azores, Portugal; *m:* Deborah May; *c:* Ariana, Mikaela; *ed:* Southeastern MA Univ (BA) Portuguese, Span 1980; Finishing Masters Ed with a Scndry Prin Cert; *cr:* Taunton HS Span Tchr 1980-81; Bristol Comm Coll Portuguese Instr 1981-82; Salve Regina Univ Part-time Portuguese Instr 1993-94; Portsmouth HS Portuguese, Span Tchr 1982-; *ai:* Campus Shop Adv; Wall-of Fame Coord; Intnl Vlybl Coord; NEA, RI 1982-, Del; AATSP 1986-; TOPAC 1985-, Sec; LASA 1982-, VP; Pro Cultura Portuguesa 1996, Exec Bd; Pres Clintons Awd for Outstdng Comm Svc; Parents Helping Stdnts Org Tchr Recognition; *home:* 20 Maria Ln Taunton MA 02780

ARSENAULT, DANIEL MARK, ESL & English Teacher; *b:* Skowhegan, ME; *ed:* 21 Hrs Post-Grad at Univ of CA at Northridge, Univ of TX at Pan Amer; *cr:* PSJA North HS Eng as Second Lang 1992-94; Montpelier HS ESL, Eng Tchr 1994-; *ai:* Jrnlsm; Amnesty Intnl, Girls JV Soccer Coach; Sierra Club 1995-; *office:* Montpelier HS Memorial Dr Montpelier VT 05602

ARSENAULT, JOSEPH ERNEST, Sixth Grade Teacher; *b:* Boston, MA; *ed:* Boston St Coll (BSEd) Elem Ed 1970, (MED) Schl Admin 1975; Bridgewater St (CAGS) Schl Admin 1983; Univ of MA (EDD) Educl Leadership 1991; *cr:* Pembroke Schl Dist Tchr 1970-; *ai:* Head Tchr; Audio Visual Coord; MTA, NEA, PTA 1970-, Pres, VP; ASCD 1975-; Phi Delta Kappa 1981-; IRA 1992-; BSA 1970-84, Scoutmaster, Silver Beaver Awd; Supts Svc Awd 1992; Plymouth Cty Distinguished Svc Awd 1993; Marshfield Jaycees Man of Yr 1975; *office:* Bryantville Elem Schl 29 Gurney Dr Pembroke MA 02359

ARSENIS, AGNES LEMONIOTIS, Chemistry Teacher; *b:* Avgerinos Kozanis, Greece; *m:* Peter; *ed:* Rutgers Univ (BA) Chem 1985; Barry Univ (MBS) Biomedical Sci 1988; *cr:* ACHS Chem I, AP Chem Tchr 1991-; *ai:* Amer Chem Soc, NJSTA, Natl Mole Day Fnd 1993-; Notary Pub 1988-; *office:* Atlantic City HS 1400 N Albany Ave Atlantic City NJ 08401

ARTERBRIDGE, DENISE BELINDA, 8th Grade Teacher; *b:* Wilmington, DE; *m:* LeRoy; *c:* Belinda, Brooke; *ed:* Wesley Coll (AA) Elem Ed 1985; Salisbury St Coll (BA) Elem Ed 1987; *cr:* Various Schl Dists Sub Tchr 1988-90; Red Lion Chrstn Acad 8th Grd Tchr 1990-; *office:* Red Lion Christian Acad 1400 Red Lion Rd Bear DE 19701

ARTH, ALEX J.,JR., Biology Tchr & Sci Dept Chair; *b:* Braddock, PA; *m:* Mary Kay Lauerman; *c:* Douglas, Brian; *ed:* Clarion Univ of PA (BS) Bio 1966; Indiana Univ of PA (MED) Bio 1974; *cr:* Clarion Area HS Bio Tchr 1966-; *ai:* Ftbl Asst Head Coach; Girls Track Asst Coach; Wrestling & Bsktbl Clock Operator; NEA & PSEA 1966-; Clarion Area Ed Assn 1966-, Pres 3 Yrs.

ARTHUR, WENDY JACQUELINE, English Teacher; *b:* Philadelphia, PA; *ed:* Hampton Univ (BS) Elem Ed 1976; Scndry Eng Cert TX Southern Univ 1984; African Amer Stud Stockton St Coll; Attnd Rowan Coll; *cr:* E.H. Slaybaugh MS Eng Tchr 1976-83; Egg Harbor Twp HS Eng Tchr 1984-; *ai:* African Amer Soc Adv; NEA, EHTEA, ACCEA 1976-; *home:* 42 E Pacific Ave Pleasantville NJ 08232

ARTHURS, JEFFREY ALAN, World History & Geography Tchr; *b:* Dennison, OH; *m:* Diane Frances Ford; *c:* Keith, Jennifer; *ed:* West Liberty St Coll (BA) Soc Sci 1971; Addl 28 Grad Hrs; *cr:* Claymont HS World His & Geogrpahy Tchr 1971-; *ai:* Cross Cntry, Track Coach; NEA, OEA, ECOEA, CEA 1971-; Clyamont Booster Club; EDT, CCCA 1972-, Pres; OAT, CCCA 1972-; Eastern Dist Track Officials Assn 1977-; Eastern Dist Cross Cntry, Track Coach of Yr; *office:* Claymont HS 215 E 6th St Uhrichsville OH 44683*

ARTIS, ARTHUR, Retired Mathematics Teacher; *b:* Speers, PA; *m:* Mary Catherine Gladys; *c:* Shelly Cardinale, Scott, Kristi; *ed:* CA St Coll (BSEd) Math 1963; 12 Addl Credits 1967; *cr:* Golden Glades Elem Schl 5th Grd Tchr 1963; Allapattah Jr HS 7th Grd Math Tchr 1963-64; Elizabeth Forward Jr HS Math & Algebra Tchr 1964-; *ai:* 7th-9th Grd Bsktbl & HS Bsbl Head Coach; HS Bsktbl & Bsbl Asst Coach; Jr Var Bsktbl Coach; NEA 1967-; PSEA & EFEA 1964-.

ARTZ, DAVID S., German & Social Studies Tchr; *b:* West Reading, PA; *m:* Karen Young; *c:* Christopher, Rebecca, Jason; *ed:* Kutztown St Coll (BS) Ger 1970, (MA) Russian Lang & Lit 1982; Defense Lang Inst Diploma Basic 47 Week Russian Course 1971; *cr:* US Army Security Agency Voice Intercept Operator 1970-73; N Hunterdon-Voorhees Regnl HS Dist Ger, Soc Stud & Russian Tchr 1974-; *ai:* Ger Club Adv; NEA, AATG 1974-; BSA 1988-91, Asst Den Ldr; Summer 1978 Selected by IREX for 9 Week Exch Prgm at Moscow St Univ; *office:* North Hunterdon HS 1445 State Route 31 Annandale NJ 08801*

ARTZ, REBECCA SUE SHANK, Third Grade Teacher; *b:* Ashland, OH; *m:* Gary Robert; *c:* Candace; *ed:* Kent St Univ (BS) Elem 1970; Attnd Akron Univ, Ashland Univ 45 Hrs; *cr:* Indian Trl Elem 3rd Grd Tchr 1970-80; Echo Hills Elem 2nd & 3rd Grd Tchr 1981-; *ai:* FAC; Tech & Various Grd Level Comms; NEA 1970-; OEA 1970-; STA 1970-; Stow Schl Bd Awd 1986: Exemplary Ability in Organizing Parent Vols to Assit Stdnts in Comp Work; Friend of Children PTA Awd 1993.*

ARVANITIS, JAMES G., Computer Education Chairperson; *b:* Fall River, MA; *m:* Chrystine M. Gardner; *c:* Brandon, Bryson; *ed:* Plymouth St Coll (BS) Math 1974; Boston Univ (MS) Cmptr Sci 1984; *cr:* Amherst MS Cmptr Coord 1978-80; Digital Equipment Corp DP Corporate Ed Support 1980-81; Wang Laboratories Telecommunication Analyst 1981-85; Alvirne HS Cmptr Tchr 1985-; *ai:* Cmptr Club Adv; NEA, HFT 1985-; Author 2 Books & 15 Magazine Articles; Martial Artist of the Yr Awd 1989, 1993; *office:* Alvirne HS 200 Derry Rd Hudson NH 03051

ARVAY, CAMIE MARIE, Elementary School Principal; *b:* Coatsville, PA; *ed:* West Chester Univ (BS) Elem Ed 1972; Villanova Univ (MA) Educl Admin 1977; Elem Prins Cert; Superintendency Cert; *cr:* Coastvulle Area Schl Dist Elem Tchr 1972-81, Title 2 Supvr 1981-82, MS Asst Prin 1982-84, Elem Prin 1984-; *ai:* NAESP 1982-; Dist Admin Assn 1982-, Treas & Co-Pres; ASCD 1985-; Church Womens Club 1972-; Hosp Nrsng Cncl 1988-; West Chester Univs Field Advy Bd 1994-; Dist Outstdng Svc Awd (3 Times); *office:* Reeceville Elem Schl 248 Reeceville Rd Coatesville PA 19320

ARVAY, LISA B., High School Math Teacher; *b:* Cleveland, OH; *ed:* Univ of Akron (BS) Math 1988, (MS) Educl Admin 1993; Scndry Ed Cert 1988; *cr:* Univ of Akron Painter 1985-87; N Royalton HS Math Tchr 1988-; *ai:* Var Vlybl Coach; NEA 1988-; *office:* North Royalton HS 14713 Ridge Rd North Royalton OH 44133

ASAITHAMBI, N. S., Associate Professor; *b:* Madras Tamilnadu, India; *m:* Sasikala Sivaprakasam; *c:* Ganesh; *ed:* Indian Inst of Tech (MS) Comp Sci 1980; Univ of WI at Madison (PHD) Comp Sci 1985; B Tech Electrical Engrng 1977; *cr:* MS St Univ Asst Prof 1985-, Assoc Prof 1990-92; Lincoln Univ Assoc Prof 1992-; *ai:* Stu Chptr of ACM Fac Adv; AAUP 1995-, VP; AMS; SIAM; Book: Numerical Analysis: Theory & Practice; *office:* Lincoln Univ Lincoln University PA 19352

ASAPH, PHILIP, Creative Writing Teacher; *b:* Huntington, NY; *ed:* Eckerd Coll (BA) Creative Writing 1990; Finishing MA at NY Univ; *ai:* The Ludwig Vogelstein Fndtn Grant for Poetry; Flwshp to NY Univ for Poetry; Spcl Talent Schlsp to Echerd Coll For Poetry; *home:* 19 Juniper Pl Huntington NY 11743

ASARE, KAREN GILLIAM, 5th-6th Grade Teacher; *b:* Brooklyn, NY; *m:* William; *c:* Anton; *ed:* Hunter Coll (BS) Speech, Eng 1976, (MS) Spec Ed 1978; *cr:* St Augustine Schl Tchr 1978-; Educl Opportunity Ctr Tchr 1990-; *ai:* NCEA, FCT 1978-; PSC, UFT 1990-; Sigma Gamma Rho 1993-; Article Pub; Who's Who in Amer Ed; 100 Notable Women Entry; *office:* St Augustines School 1176 Franklin Ave Bronx NY 10456*

ASARO, IGNATIUS, History Teacher; *b:* Brooklyn, NY; *m:* Valerie Ann Piaseczny; *c:* Constance; *ed:* Suffolk Comm Coll (AA) Lbrl Arts 1969; CW Post (BA) His, Ed 1971; SUNY at Stonybrook (MA) His, Ed 1974; 30 Addl Credit Hrs; *cr:* HUDSD #3 His Tchr, Bsbl Coach 1971-; *ai:* Jr Var Girls Sftbl 1976-90; Frosh Ftbl Head Coach 1982-90; Var Bsbl 1991-; Assn Tchrs of Huntington 1971-; *home:* 34 Acorn Dr East Northport NY 11731

ASCHER, JOEL RAYMOND, Teacher; *b:* New York, NY; *ed:* CCNY (BA) His 1959; Yeshiva Univ 30 Grad Credits His; 15 Addl Credits Ed; NYU 40 Grad Credits PE; *cr:* Bureau of Attendance Tchr 1 Yr; PS243K Tchr 7 Yrs; PS273K Tchr 3 Yrs; IS238Q Tchr 17 Yrs; P4Q Tchr 6 Yrs; *ai:* August Martin HS Girls Bsktbl Coach 17 Yrs; UFT, AFT 1958-; Coaches Assn 1980-; NYC, NYJ Girls Bsktbl Coach of Yr.

ASCIENZO, NICHOLAS JOSEPH, Mathematics Teacher; *b:* Sacramento, CA; *ed:* St Univ of NY at Albany (BA) Math Ed 1973; 36 Credit Hrs; *cr:* Red Hook Jr High 7th-8th Grd Math Tchr 1974-80; Red Hook HS 9th-12th Grd Math Tchr 1980-; *ai:* Var Sftbl Co-Coach; Sr Class Co-Adv; Bldg Level Team in Shared Decision Making Process Mem; Red Hook Fac Assn 1974-, Treas; NY St Math Tchrs 1974-; Watermill Bd of Mgrs 1993-, Treas; *office:* Red Hook HS W Market St Red Hook NY 12571

ASERMELY, THOMAS A., Biology Teacher; *b:* Pawtucket, RI; *m:* Maria C. Biondi; *c:* Alex, Lauren; *ed:* Univ of RI (BA) Ed & Bio 1977; RI Coll (MED) Hlth Ed 1979; *cr:* Slater Jr High Sci Tchr 1977-86; Shea High Bio Tchr 1986-91; Tolman High Bio Tchr 1991-; *ai:* Var Bsbl Coach; AFT 1977-; N Providence Little League 1990-; *office:* William E Tolman HS 150 Exchange St Pawtucket RI 02860

ASH, BETH LYNN, Spanish Teacher; *ed:* Indiana Univ of PA (BA) Span 1982; Frostburg St Univ (MS) Rdng 1988; *cr:* FBI Clerk 1 Yr; North Star Schl Dist Span Tchr 3 Yrs; Tussey Mountain Schl Dist Span Tchr 7 Yrs; *office:* Tussey Mountain Jr Sr HS Rd 1 Box 178a Saxton PA 16678

ASH, GERALD ERNEST, HS Band Director & Hum Tchr; *b:* Cambridge, MA; *c:* Stella M. Mc Mahon; *ed:* Univ of North TX (BA) Music Ed 1972; Attnd Univ of MA at Lowell, New England Conservatory, Berklee Coll of Music; *cr:* Watertown Schl Band Dir 1973-74; Natick Pub Schls Band Dir 1974-76; Las Vegas Pub Schls Band Dir 1976-77; Natick Pub Schls Band Dir, Hum Tchr 1977-; *ai:* Amateur Radio, Weather Club; MetroWest Comm Band Founder, Conductor; NEA, MENC, MS Tchrs Assn 1974-; Boston Musicians' Assn 1967-; *office:* Natick HS 15 West St Natick MA 01760

ASH, MARJORIE BROWN, English Teacher; *b:* E Liverpool, OH; *m:* Robert L.; *c:* Lindsay; *ed:* Westminster Coll (BA) Eng 1965; Post Grad Stud Univ of Dayton, Kent St, Youngstown St; *cr:* Mc Dowell HS Eng Tchr 1965-70; Jefferson Union HS Eng Tchr 1971-88; Edison South HS Eng Tchr 1988-93; Edison HS Eng Tchr 1993-; *ai:* North Cntrl Steering, Tech Prep Curr Comms; OH Ed Assn, NEA 1971-; East Liverpool Women's Club 1984-, VP, Pres Elect; Jefferson Cty Mini-Grant 1992; *home:* 316 Imperial Dr East Liverpool OH 43920*

ASH, STANLEY, Administrative Assistant; *b:* New York, NY; *m:* Aneita Mitchell-Ash; *c:* Dara Saran, Aisha Ayana, Canara Kamal; *ed:* Doane Coll (BA) Ec 1972; Temple Univ (MED) Ed 1976; *ai:* AFL-CIO Admin Cncl 1988-; Woodrow Wilson Alumni Assn; Lifetime Achvmt Awd 1973-; *office:* Woodrow Wilson HS 3100 Federal St Camden NJ 08105*

ASHBY, MARY CURRY, Spanish Teacher; *b:* Monterey, CA; *m:* Michael Frederick; *ed:* West Chester Univ (BA) Span, Linguistics 1984, (MA) Eng as Second Lang 1986; *cr:* Greenwood Schl ESL Tchr 1987-92; Columbia Schl ESL Tchr 1987-92; Lincoln Schl Span Tchr 1992-; *ai:* Soph Class, Amnesty Intnl Club Adv; AATSP, MAFLA, RIFLA 1992-; Literacy Vol of Amer 1992-; *home:* 69 Kay St Newport RI 02840

ASHCRAFT, RICHARD WAITMAN, Mathematics Teacher; *b:* Idamay, WV; *m:* Renae Kniceley; *c:* Angela R. Plitanoff, Denise E. Jacoby; *ed:* Chapman Coll in CA (BA) Bus Admin 1972; Albright Coll in PA Ed, Cert Math 1986; Grad Credit Penn St 6 Diagnostic Prescriptive Math, Liberty Univ 6 MA, Bus Admin; *cr:* Rdng HS Math Tchr 1986; Southwest Mid Math Tchr 1987-; *ai:* Superintendents Advy Cncl; Principals Advy Cabinet; Act 978 Staff Development Comm; Stu Act Club Spon; NEA, PSEA 1986-; Rdng Ed Assn 1986-, Pub, MS VP; VFW 1989-; Fleet Reserve Assn, Marine Corp C I Assn 1990-; USMC Ret Assn 1986-; *office:* Southwest MS 3rd, Chestnut St Reading PA 19602

ASHCRAFT, WILLIAM L., Mathematics Teacher; *b:* Philadelphia, PA; *m:* Phyllis Ervais; *c:* Christopher, Jonathan; *ed:* Trenton St Coll (BA) Math Ed 1979; Rider Coll (MA) Curr, Instruction & Supervision 1993; *cr:* Hopewell Valley Cntrl HS Math Tchr 1979-; *ai:* Formed Fly Fishing, Tying Clb; NEA, NJEA & MCEA 1979-; Hopewell Valley EA 1979-, Bldg Rep; Phi Kappa Phi & Kappa Delta Pi 1978-; NCTM 1979-, Inconsecutively; BSA 1993-, Ldr; *office:* Hopewell Valley Central HS Pennington Titusville Rd Pennington NJ 08534

ASHENDORF, ROBERT SCOTT, Art Teacher; *b:* Montreal, Canada; *m:* Marlene Halpern; *c:* Kim Ashendorf Bouma, Jodi; *ed:* Philadelphia Coll of Art (BFA) Fine Arts & Art Ed 1968; Univ of MD (MFA) Sculpture 1971; *cr:* Beltsville Jr HS Tchr 1968-80; Parkdale HS Tchr 1980-; *ai:* Schl

Improvement & Crisis Intervention teams; Attendance Task Force & Dept Chprsn; Fac Advy Cncl; Sculptures Exhibited at Baltimore Museum of Art & Inner Harbor Baltimore MD; *home:* 7041 Loganberry Ln Fulton MD 20759*

ASHER, ANN TENBOSCH, Art Teacher; *b:* Banbury, England; *m:* Merrill; *c:* Benjamin; *ed:* Univ of Cincinnati (BA) Graphic Design 1968; Univ of Dayton (MS) Ed 1979; Univ of Dayton Specialist Ed 1994; Admin, Supervision Certs 1979; Permanent Tchng Cert 1986; *cr:* Sidney City Schls 1-5 Grd Art Tchr 1968-71, Learning Disabilities Tchr 1973-75, 1-6 Grd Art Tchr 1975-81; Sidney HS 9-12 Grd Art Tchr; *ai:* Art Club; Frosh Class Adv; Dept Co-Chair; OAEA 1986-; Sidney Women's League 1975-, Sec, Pres; Charity League 1976-86; Hit of Ms Investment Club; Grants: Copeland Stu Support 1991-93, Ed Enrichment 1991, Chapter II Tchr 1985; OH Gov Youth Art Excel 1991; *office:* Sidney HS 1215 Campbell Rd Sidney OH 45365*

ASHER, DONALD FRANCIS,JR., Biology Teacher; *b:* Annapolis, MD; *m:* Victoria McLaughlin; *c:* Tim, Kevin, Shawn; *ed:* U MD (BS) Zoology 1979, (BS) Sci Ed 1981; Loyola 15 Credit Hrs; Bowie St 15 Credit Hrs; *cr:* Chopticon HS Bio Tchr 1981-, Sci Dept Chair 1991-; *ai:* Sci Dept Chair 1991-; MSTA 1981-; NEA 1981-; EASMC 1981-, Bd of Dirs; MD Assoc of Bio Tchrs 1995-; BSA 1993-, Asst Scoutmaster; Pres Awd Excl; Sweco Awd; 2 Governors Commendations; Patent 1986; AFCEA Awd 1994-95; 7 Species of Fossils Named in Hnr; *office:* Chopticon HS Rt 242 Morganza MD 20660

ASHEROFF, JOAN SCHULER, Principal & Gen Stud Teacher; *b:* Newark, NJ; *m:* Michael; *c:* Ellen Asheroff Trichon, Tracey; *ed:* Hofstra Univ (BSEd) 1964; Queens Coll 9 Grad Credits 1966; C W Post Coll LIU 18 Credits Toward Supervisory Cert Completed 1996; *cr:* Massapequa Pub Schls 6th Grd Tchr 1964-66; North & South Colonie Schls Sub Tchr 1973-76; North Babylon Schls 2nd & 5th Grd Tchr 1980-83; Hebrew Acad of Wassau Cty 4th & 6th Grd Tchr 1983-94; *ai:* ASCD 1995-; City of Hope 1980-; Womens Amers ORT 1980-; Wiskayuna Pub Schls Former PTA Pres; Schl Bd Liaison Person; *office:* Hebrew Acad Of Nassau Co 609 Hempstead Ave West Hempstead NY 11552

ASHETTINO, ELAINE (GORDON), Asst Prof of Communication Art; *b:* Providence, RI; *m:* Stephen N.; *c:* Stephen N. Jr., Jessica Marie; *ed:* Univ of RI (BA) Eng Ed 1971; Boston Univ (MS) Jrnlsm 1980; Cape Cod Comm Coll Desktop Publishing 3 Credits; *cr:* Dean Coll Asst Prof, Comm Arts 1991-; *ai:* Lib, Admissions, Hnrs & Awds, Fac Prsnl & Policy Comms; Stu Newspaper Adv; Natl Search Comm for Acad Affrs VP; Org & Governance Accreditation Comm Co-Chair; Coll Media Advs 1991-; Jrnlsm Ed Assn, Certfd Jrnlsm Edctr; MA Fac Dev Consortium 1992-, NCTE, MA Cncl of Tchrs of Eng 1994-; West Dennis Yacht Club, Bd of Dirs; St Anselms Church, Ed 25th Anniversary Newsletter; Sudbury Town Report Preparation Comm; Article Pub 1993; Natl Scholastic Press Assn Associated Collegiate Press Annual Coll Newspaper Contest Natl Judge 1993, 1996; *office:* Dean Coll 99 Main St Franklin MA 02038

ASHFORD, JUDI ANNE, English & Latin Teacher; *b:* Danville, PA; *m:* Robert J.; *c:* Meghan I., Zachary R.; *ed:* Bloomsburg Univ (BS) Scndry Ed 1988; Eng Cert 1988; Susquehanna Univ Latin Cert 1995; *cr:* Shenandoah Vly HS Eng, Latin Tchr, Drama Coach 1990-; *ai:* 11 Grd Class Adv; 7-12 Grd Drama Coach; NEA, PSEA 1990-; *home:* 887 Rupert Dr Bloomsburg PA 17815

ASHFORD, STEPHANIE GRAIR, English Teacher; *b:* Cleveland, OH; *c:* Shannon K.; *ed:* OH Univ (BSEd) Eng 1975; Cleveland St Univ (MS) Curr, Instruction 1978; *cr:* Cleveland Hts HS Eng Tchr 1975-; *ai:* Image Makers Adv 1993-; Schlsp Comm; AFT 1975-; NCTE; Phi Delta Kappa 1995-; Race Relations Facilitator; Free-Lance, Staff Writer; *home:* 3668 Riedham Rd Shaker Heights OH 44120

ASHLEY, DAVID LEE, Math Teacher; *b:* Canton, OH; *m:* Lucinda Leigh Blackstone; *ed:* Mount Union Coll (BS) Math 1963; Univ of ME (ME) Math 1972; 17 Credit Hrs Post Grad Stud Kent St Univ; 14 Credit Hrs Post Grad Stud Univ at Akron; *cr:* North Nimishillen Elem Schl Math Tchr 1962-67; Louisville Jr HS Math Tchr 1967-91, Math Dept Head 1968-87; Louisville HS Math Tchr 1991-; *ai:* Girls Bsktbl Asst Coach; OEA 1962-, NEA, ECOEA, LEA; OCTM 1986-; GCTM; NCTM; Jennings Scholar Awd 1975-76; Nom for Ashland Oil Tchr Achvmt Awds 1993; *home:* 814 44th St NW Canton OH 44709

ASHLEY, MURIEL TANNENBAUM, Social Studies Teacher; *b:* New York City, NY; *m:* Alvin; *c:* Sharon Ashley Lewis, Mitchell; *ed:* Hunter Coll (BA) Psych 1957; Addl 30 Credits; MA Equivalent 36 Credits; *cr:* PS 109 Schl 4th Grd Tchr 1957-61; PS 24 Schl 1st, 4th Grd Tchr 1972-90, 6th Grd Tchr 1990-92, 5th Grd Soc Stud Tchr 1992-; *ai:* Debate, Drama Coach; Class Newspaper Ed; Parent, Tchr Liason, Selection Comm; Stock Market Club Adv; AFT; NEA; B'na B'rith, Pres 1958; Cancer Care; Love, Appreciation of Fine Art Grant.*

ASHLEY, RONALD L., Principal; *b:* Cleveland, OH; *m:* Nela Litweiler; *ed:* Hiram Coll (BA) His 1967; Univ of Akron (MA) Elem Admin 1979; Post Grad Stud Elem Ed; *cr:* Crestwood HS His Tchr 1967-68; Aurora MS Grd 5 Tchr 1968-73; Northfield Elem Schl Grds 5 & 6 Tchr 1976-85; Rushwood Elem Schl Grds 4, 5, 6 Tchr 1985-90, Prin 1990-; *ai:* K-12 Soc Stud, Elem Report Card Comm Chairs; NAESP, BAESA, SCESAA 1990-; Martha Holden Jennings Scholar 1970-80; Outstdng Edctr; *office:* Rushwood Elem Schl 8200 Rushwood Ln Northfield OH 44067

ASHLEY, SHEILA STARR, Spanish Teacher; *b:* Wichita, KS; *ed:* Wilson Coll (BA) Span 1964; Univ of PA (MSED) Scndry Ed 1967; Univ of Madrid 63 Credit Hrs Span, Eng; *cr:* Westinghouse Elec Co Accounts Payable 1965-66; Radnor HS Span Tchr 1967-; *ai:* Frgn Lang Dept Head; Frgn Lang Dist Curr Comm; Frgn Exch Spon Sr Project; 18 Day Stud Homestay Stu Asst Team; ACTFL, Radnor TEA, PSEA, NEA 1967-; AATSP 1975-; Coopertown Civic Assn 1983-; ACTFL Grant for Oral Proficiency Wkshp 1983; Rockefeller Tchng of Frgn Lang Grant 1988-89; Wrote Text for Ancient Civilizations for Sp IV Hnrs Classes 1994; *office:* Radnor HS 130 King Of Prussia Rd Wayne PA 19087

ASHLEY, THOMAS T., 5th Grd Teacher & Program Ldr; *b:* Brooklyn, NY; *m:* Kathleen Dunlap; *c:* Elizabeth, Christopher; *ed:* Univ of RI (BA) His, (BA) Elem Ed 1976; Attnd RI Coll; *cr:* Narragansett Elem Schl 5th Grd Tchr 1976-90; Narragansett Pier Schl 5th Grd Tchr 1990-; *ai:* Var Coach Boys HS Soccer; NEA, Narragansett 1976-; RI Soccer Coaches Assn 1980-, Past Pres, Hall of Fame; Natl Soccer Coaches Assn Amer 1984-, St Rep; Narragansett Housing Authority 1992-, Commissioner; South Cty Yth Soccer Club 1991-, League Dir; *office:* Narragansett Pier Schl 235 S Pier Rd Narragansett RI 02882

ASHMAN, STANLEY VIRGIL, History & Philosophy Teacher; *b:* Baltimore, MD; *c:* Gabriel Q., Jessica R.; *ed:* Johns Hopkins Univ (BA) Philosophy 1974; *cr:* Park Schl His, Philosophy Tchr 1972-; *ai:* Asst Var Soccer Coach; Dalsheiner Grants to Dev Course on Latin Amer His, 9th Grd His.

ASHPES, APRIL ALLEN, 7th Grade Intnl Studies Tchr; *b:* Hyannis, MA; *m:* Kermit Harold; *c:* Alison, Deborah F.; *ed:* Drew Univ (BA) Pol Sci 1965; Univ of MD Educl Psych 3 Credits; Western MD Coll Proj TEPCH Coop Lerning, PRIDE 9 Credits; Trinity Coll Exceptional Children Dysfunctional Families, Tchng Emotionally Impaired 9 Credits; *cr:* Internal Revenue Svc US, Overseas Tax Auditor 1965-75; Attorney MC Dowell Accountant 1984-89; P. G. Cty Schls Sub Tchr 1982-90; Andrew Jackson MS 7th Grd Intl Stud Tchr 1990-; *ai:* Hum, Intl Stud 7th Grd Team Ldr; Geog Club Adv; Schl Based Mngmt Comm; Comer Facilitator; P. G. Cncl Soc Stud, MD Cncl for Soc Stud 1995-; Natl Geographic Soc 1988-; NSTA, NEA 1990-; *home:* 6918 100th Ave Lanham MD 20706

ASHWORTH, BONNIE L., Science Teacher; *b:* Bangor, ME; *ed:* Amer Intnl Coll (BA) Interdepartmental Sci 1981; MIT's HS Tchrs Sci, Tech Prgm; Keene St Coll Tech Ed Strategies Summer Inst; *cr:* Wethersfield HS Sci Tchr 1981-82; East Windsor HS Sci Tchr 1982-84; Mexico HS Sci Tchr 1984-86; Ashland HS Sci Tchr 1987-89; Laconia HS Sci Tchr 1989-; *ai:* Birls Var Vlybl Coach; Tchr Adv US First Team; Frosh Class Tchr, Helper; New England Sci Tchrs 1990-; *office:* Laconia HS 345 Union Ave Laconia NH 03246*

ASKEW, THOMAS A., Professor & Chair of History; *b:* Lorain, OH; *m:* Jean M. Somerville; *c:* Thomas Randall, Robyn G. Jackson, Timothy Christopher; *ed:* Wheaton Coll (BA) His, (MA) New Testament Stud 1958; Northwestern Univ (MA) His 1962, (PHD) His 1969; *cr:* Wheaton Coll His Asst Prof 1960-68; National Coll of Ed Prof & Assoc Dean 1968-72; Univ of IL at Chicago His Dept Visiting Fac 1969-72; Gordon Coll Prof & Chair of His 1972-, Asst Acad Dean 1975-76, 1993-94; *ai:* East-West Inst of Intnl Stud Assoc Dir; Fac Senate 1975-; Amer His Assn 1965-; NCSS 1968-75; New England His Assn 1990-; Conf on Faith & His 1967-; Essex Inst 1977-87, Bd of Trustees; HS of Seven Gables 1990-92, Planning Comm; Beverly MA Amer Revolution 1974-76, Bicentennial Comm; Beverly Hospital Capital 1980-83, Campaign Comm; New England Higher Ed Commission Accreditation Examiner 1977-85; Danforth Fdn Research Grantee for Outstanding Young Profs 1963-66; Gordon Coll Sr Excl in Tchng Awd 1988; Author & Ed of 5 Books, Numerous Articles & Reviews; Publisher of Chrstn Scholars Review Scholarly Journal 1979-87; *office:* Gordon Coll 255 Grapevine Rd Wenham MA 01984

ASREGADOO, VERNON EDWARD, Social Studies & English Tchr; *b:* Wakenaam, Guyana; *m:* Kaisree Narine; *c:* Samantha, Neota, Shellita; *ed:* Univ of Guyana (BA) Geog 1973; Brooklyn Coll (MA) Soc Stud 1988; Tchrs Trng Coll TTC Geog 1966; Univ of Guyana Diploma in Ed 1974; Caribbean Examinations Cncl Trained Examiner in Geog; 60 Credit Hrs Curr Dev Comm; *cr:* Rose Hall HS Deputy Prin 1959-62; Novar HS Prin 1962-69; Campbell Educ Trust coll Prin 1969-74; Lilian Dewar Tchrs Trng Coll Geog & Soc Stud Lecturer 1975-78; Pierson HS Dep Prin 1978-81; St Mark's Day Schl Deputy Prin 1983-90; IS 126 Soc Stud Tchr 1990-; *ai:* Crown Business Schl, Universal Bus & Media Schl Office Procedures, Evening Coord; AFT, NEA, Bus Tchrs Assn, Amer Bus Assn 1990-; St George's Episcopal Church, Chalice Bearer & Lay Reader 1983-; Guyana Geographical Assn 1962-, Exec Ofcr, Geog Awd; PTA 1990-; Wrote 3 Eng Workbooks, 1 Basic Math Workbook, 65 Poems & Short Stories; *office:* IS 126 Astoria 3151 21st St Long Island City NY 11106*

ASSELTA, NELLY, Spanish Teacher; *b:* Gurabo, PR; *m:* Richard M.; *c:* Victor Manuel, Shirley Ann; *ed:* Univ of PR (BS) Psych-Magna Cum Laude 1971; Western CT St Coll (MS) Elem Ed 1975; Scndry Ed Span Cert 1986; *cr:* Univ of PR Librn Spcl Ed 1970-72; Span Learning Ctr Danbury Summer Pgm Tchr 1972; Danbury Schl System Sub Tchr 1974-76; Span Summer Pgm Dir 1980; Frank Repole Adult Ed Tchr 1979-81; Western CT St Coll Sub Tchr 1978, Lecturer 1984; New Milford HS Math Tchr 1985-87; Brookfield HS Span Lang & Culture Tchr 1985-, Sub Tchr 1986; Berol Co Report Translator; Westchester Visiting Nurses Document Translator; Danbury Hilton Hotel Translator & Consultant; *ai:* Span Learning Ctr 1972-81; Danbury Cultural Commission Ethnic Pgms; Hispanic Group Caucus Mem 1978-80; Hill & Plain Schls Cultural Comm 1981; Alternative Ctr Ed Outdoor Pgms; CT St Educl Conf Biling Ed; CT Elem Cert Test Bias Comm Mem 1991; Parents Advy Cncl Danbury HS 1990-95; News Times Advy Cncl 1993-95; Field Trips with Stdnts to Europe; Exch Pgm to PR; CEA 1988-; NEA 1988-; Colt 1988-; Phi Delta Kappa 1990-; Danbury Affirmative Action Advy Comm 1982-; Univ of CT, Rsrch Asst; Women Ctr, Battered Women & Rape Cnslr 1982-90; Amer Red Cross Vol, Swim Marathon; Danbury Coalition Minority Stdnts; Danbury Regnl Symposium, Panelist 1986; Tchr of Yr 1993; Numerous Wkshps & Spcl Trng; *office:* Brookfield HS 45 Long Meadow Hill Rd Brookfield CT 06804*

ASSENHEIMER, CARL FREDERICK,III, 9th-12th Grade English Teacher; *b:* Tiffin, OH; *m:* Suzanne Elizabeth Donovan; *c:* Christopher; *ed:* Bowling Green St Univ (BSE) Eng, HPE 1968, (MED) Admin 1980; *cr:* Gibsonburg Ex Village 9-12 Grd Eng Tchr 1968-70; Bay HS 9-12 Grd Eng Tchr 1971-; *ai:* Coached Ftbl 25 Yrs, Bsktbl 15 Yrs; NEA, OEA 1968-; BTA 1971-, Pres, Bldg Rep, Chprsn; NCTE 1968-69; Booster Club 1992-93; Lions Club 1970-71; Supts Best Recipient 4 Yrs; Pub Poet; *home:* 151 Fay Ave Avon Lake OH 44012*

ASSUMPTE ROSSI, ROSE, 7th & 8th Grd Science Teacher; *b:* Poughkeepsie, NY; *ed:* Fordham Univ (BS) Ed 1955, (MS) Ed 1972; In-Service Courses Rel, Math, Sci, Soc Stud; *cr:* Immaculate Conception Schl 5th Grd Tchr 1954-57; St Catherine Schl 5th Grd Tchr 1957-63; Immaculate Conception Schl 7th-8th Grd Tchr 1963-81; Annunciation Schl 7th-8th Grd Tchr 1981-; *ai:* Natl Sci Fnd Astronomy, Analytical Chem; Math Jr HS Tchrs.

AST, MARLENE MARTY, Spcl Ed Inclusion Tchng Asst; *b:* Syracuse, NY; *c:* Heidi Finch Adam, Erika, Ahnika Hansen, Liesl, Gretchen; *ed:* SUNY Cortland (BS) PE 1965, (MS) Hlth, PE 1989; 23 Addl Grad Hrs; *cr:* Central Squore Jr HS PE Tchr 1965-71; YMCA Gymnastics Coach 1975; Town of Lysander Swimming Instr, Gymnastics Soccer Coach 1979-; Baldwinsville Cntrl Schls Adopted PE Asst Tchr 1991-95, 3rd Grd Asst Tchr 1995-; *ai:* Var Girls Gymnastics, Modified Girls Gymnastics Coach; Elem Gymnastics Instr; NEA 1965-; Baldwinsville ESP 1991-; *home:* 9320 Dinglehole Rd Phoenix NY 13135

ASTARE, EDWARD J., Math Teacher; *b:* Philipsburg, PA; *m:* Janet Isbell; *c:* Jodi, Johnston, Jeffrey; *ed:* Lock Haven Univ (BS) Math, Scndry Ed 1973; Masters Equivalency plus 36; *cr:* Wyalusing Schl Dist Math Tchr 1973-; *ai:* Ath Dir; Former Bsktbl, Bsbl Coach; Math Dept Head; NEA, PSEA 1973-; Wyalusing Tchrs Assn 1973-, Treas; *office:* Wyalusing Valley HS RR 2 Box 7 Wyalusing PA 18853*

ASTE, MARIO, Professor of Languages & Hum; *b:* Carloforte, Italy; *m:* Dorothy E. Balbirer; *c:* Stephen R., Marie F., Kristina E.; *ed:* Istituto Tecnico Industriale at Cagliari Italy (PI) Engrng 1962; Cath Univ of Amer (MA) Italian 1969, (PHD) Italian Philology, Romance 1971, (MA) Span 1981; *cr:* Lowell St Coll Prof 1971-75; Univ of Lowell Lang Dept Prof, Chair 1975-89; Univ of MA at Lowell Lang Dept Prof, Chair 1989-; *ai:* MSP-MYA Pres; Italian Club, Italian Hnr Soc Adv; Yth Soccer Coach; Rank & Tenure, Dean Search Comms; Higher Ed Ldrshp Cncl; MTA-NEA 1971-, Chptr Pres; Amer Assn Tchrs of Italian 1971-; Amer Assn for Italian Stud 1981-, Ed Italian Culture; MLA 1969-; Intnl INst 1974-, Bd Pres; Knights of Columbus; Centralville Neighborhood 1981-, Vice Chair Exec Comm; Historical Soc 1977-; NEH Summer Grants 1979, 1983, 1988; Cultural Grants 1985, 1995; Outstdng Young Man of Yr 1977; Sp Hnr Soc 1976; It Hnr Soc 1979; Distngd Comm Svc 1990; Bronze Pellican Emblem on Scouting 1993; Outstdng Tchr Awd Nom Stu Givern Assn 1995; Articles, Books Pub; *office:* Univ Of MA At Lowell 1 University Ave Lowell MA 01854

ASTEMBORSKI, YVONNE MARIE (HAYES), Third Grade Teacher; *b:* Erie, PA; *m:* Thomas J.; *c:* Ashley, Ryan; *ed:* Villa Maria Coll (BA) Elem Ed 1979; Edinboro Univ (ME) Elem Ed 1987; *cr:* St James Schl Tchr 1979-; *ai:* St James Yth Group Coord; St James After Schl Care Pgm Co-Dir; STARLAB Coord; NCEA 1979-; WIBC 1979-; Natl 600 B Club 1994-; Introduction to Windows & Hyperstudio; US Brig Niag Educl Resource; Mini-Soc; ITEC; The Zoo Educl Experience; WILD; Lake Erie, The Great Lakes Project; STARLAB; *home:* 400 Dr Erie PA 16510

ASTON, CAROLYN ANN, Fourth Grade Teacher; *b:* Mt Joy, Donald L.; *c:* Jamie David; *ed:* Millersville Univ (BS) Elem 19 Credit Hrs Penn St Univ; *cr:* Farmdale Elem Schl First Grd Tchr Columbia Boro Schl First Grd Tchr 1964-65; Farmdale Elem Schl 1965-66, Third Grd Tchr 1966-73, Fourth Grd Tchr 1974-; *ai:* Sci Bldg Level Team; Instrl Support Team; NEA, PSEA 1963-; HEA Fac Rep; *office:* Farmdale Elem Schl 814 Prospect Rd Mount Joy PA

ASTOR, DIANE, Business & English Teacher; *b:* Wintrop, M Edward; *c:* Lisa, Justin; *ed:* Salem St Coll (BS) Bus 1973; Suffol (MS) Bus 1979; PDPS Bus Ed; Involved Implementation Tech Pr Shadowing; *cr:* Gardner HS Bus Tchr 23 Yrs; *ai:* Tech Prep Clu Accreditation, Statement of Purpose Dev Comms, Chprsn, Bus De Shadowing Coord; NEA, GEA, MBEA 1973-; *office:* Gardner H Catherine St Gardner MA 01440

ASTOR, MARK JOHN, Special Education Teacher; *b:* Bronx, N Lucinda Jean; *c:* Kristen, Steven, Jonathan, Joshua; *ed:* Nyack Co Pastoral Ministries 1982; Herbert H Lehman Coll (MS) Spcl Ed 19 Greer-Woodycrest Temp Rehab Specialist Asst & Asst Guid Worker Eugene T Maleska Intermediate Schl 174 Chptr I Read Asst & 7th G Ed Tchr 1984-86; DE Vly Cntrl Schl 7th-12th Grd Spcl Ed Tchr 19 Downsville Cntlr Schl 7th-12th Grd Spcl Ed Tchr 1987-; *ai:* 9th-12t & SADD Adv; 4-H & Church Yth Group Co-Ldr; Sr High Sunda Tchr; Bible Quiz Team Co-Coach; Home Schl Prin; 4-H 1996, C Chprsn Comm of Spcl Ed 1990-91; *office:* Downsville Central Schl P J Downsville NY 13755

ASTRI, ROBERT, Physics & Chemistry Teacher; *b:* Baltimore, M Sen Ho; *c:* Julian, Jeremy; *ed:* Towson St Univ (BS) Chem 1980; A Post Grad Credits in Physics, Accounting & Ed; *cr:* Yorkridge Sav Loan Commercial Loan Underwriter 1987-89; West Springfield H 1989-91; Centennial HS Physics, Chem & Advanced Placement Che 1992-; *ai:* Chematon Teams; Soc Comm; NEA 1994-; *office:* Cen HS 4300 Centennial Ln Ellicott City MD 21042*

ASTUDILLO, JOHN ARTURO, Spanish Teacher; *b:* Cuenca, Ec *m:* Marleen Ackerman; *c:* Ahren, Alicya; *ed:* Buffalo St Coll (B 1968; Univ of Buffalo (MS) Instruction, Psych 1975; Natl Co Accreditation 50 Hrs; In Svc Credit 20 Hrs; Cmptr Tech 20 H Williamsville Schls 9-12th Grd Span Tchr 1970-; Univ at Buffalo Soccer Coach 1987-; *ai:* Amer Field Svc; Var Club; NHS; Span, Ski Boys & Girls Var Soccer Coach; Earth Day; Variety Show; Intnl AFT, NEA, NYSUT, AAUP 1987-; US Army Reserves 1968-; Amer 1989-; *office:* Williamsville North HS 1595 Hopkins Rd Williamsvi 14221*

ASWELL, JANE FURCA, Professor of Biology; *b:* Hammond, L James E.; *c:* Michael, Sarah, Rebecca; *ed:* Southeastern LA Univ Microbiology 1972; Univ of MS Med Ctr (PHD) Microbiology 1976 Doctoral Research VA Tech; *cr:* MS Bay Comm Coll Adjunc 1992-94; Mt Ida Coll Adjunct Prof 1992-95; Framingham St Coll A Prof 1993; Roxbury Comm Coll Asst Prof 1994-; *ai:* Schlsp, Core Comms; Nursing Advy Bd; NEA, MTA 1992-; *home:* 19 Haven St MA 02030

ATCHESON, KENNETH W.,II, Social Studies Teacher; *b:* Caribou *m:* Judith L. Kierstead; *c:* Amanda, Abigail; *ed:* Univ of ME (MED) S Ed 1993; Univ of ME at PI (BS) His 1979; *cr:* Caribou HS Soc Stu 1980-; Lubec HS Soc Stud Tchr 1979-86; *ai:* Grad Coord; Sr Class Chair Curr & Instruction; NEA, MTA, NCS 1979-; HHRC Holocaust & Human Right Cncl Tchr of Yr St of ME 1995; *office:* C HS 410 Sweden St Caribou ME 04736*

ATCHLEY, STEVEN WAYNE, Criminal Justice Instructor; *b:* Flin *m:* Janice M.; *c:* David; *ed:* DE Tech (AA) Criminal Justice Wilmington Coll (BS) Criminal Justice 1977; 41 Grad Credits Chester Univ; *cr:* Dept of Corrections Correctional Supvr 1977; Prob Parole Ofcr 1978; DE Tech Criminal Justice Instr; *ai:* Dept Coord; Adv; Bowling Coach; *office:* DE Tech & Comm Coll 400 St Christiana Rd Newark DE 19703

ATER, TERRY D., Language Arts Teacher; *b:* Clarksburg, OH; *m:* ellen; *c:* Bret, Brad, Amy, Brian; *ed:* Otterbein Coll (BA) Eng, Ed OH Univ (MA) Ec Ed 1978; *cr:* Circleville City Schls Lang Arts 1964-67; Chillicothe City Schls Lang Arts Tchr 1967-; *ai:* Lang Arts Coord; Chillicothe Ed Assn 1967-, Bldg Rep; OH Ed Assn 1974-; 1970-; Pickaway Cty Farm Bureau 1994-; US Trotting Assn 1965- Horsemen's Assn 1975-; Several Poems Pub; WBNS-TV Tchr of 1994; *office:* Smith MS 345 Arch St Chillicothe OH 45601

ATES, KENNETH HOGAN, Social Science Teacher; *b:* Passaic, N. Morris Brown Coll (BA) His 1978; Columbia Univ (MA) Soc Sci Post Grad 32 Credits; *cr:* Summit Pub Schl Sub Tchr 1978-79; Dw Brathwaite Schl Tchr, Admin Disciplinary Affairs 1980-82; Archdioc Newark Tchr Soc Stud 1982-84; Bloomfield Pub Schls Tchr Soc Sci 1 *ai:* Stage Crew, Stu Govt Assn, Yth Week Adv; Dir Multicultur Celebrations; Prin Schl Improvement, Renaissance Prgm Comms; 1984-; NCSS 1985-; ASCD 1989-; Kappa Alpha Psi 1974-; Gove Tchr Recognition Prgm Awd 1993; Who's Who Among Young Amer 1988-89; Who's Who in Amer Ed 1989-90, 1991-92; Who's Who in the 1990, 1993; Prin Renaissance Awd 1995.*

ATHANASIOU, ROBERT, Medical Director; *b:* Danbury, CT; *m:* Ba Bardeen; *c:* William, Kenneth; *ed:* Resselaer (BEE) Elec Eng 1962, Psych 1964; Univ of MI (PHD) Psych 1969; Albany Med Coll (MD) 1977; *cr:* Johns Hopkins Univ Asst Prof 1969-71; Johns Hopkins S Med Asst Prof 1971-73; St Univ of NY at Albany Visiting Asst Prof Rensselaer Polytech Inst Adj Prof 1986-; *ai:* Adv Amateur R Ball-Room Dance Clubs; AMA 1977-; ACEP 1979-, Fellow; Numerous Scientific Articles Pub; *office:* Rensselaer Polytechnic Ins Eighth St Troy NY 12180

ATHERTON, RAE SMITH, Retired Teacher; *b:* Bloomsburg, PA James Edward; *c:* Kathleen Bauman, James Scott, Stephen Edward Mansfield St Tchrs Coll (BS) Home Ec 1947; Bloomsburg Univ Elem 1970; *cr:* Catawissa HS Jr & Sr HS Home Ec Tchr 1947-50; Gato Colmbia Elem Schl Kndgtn Tchr 1967-70, 1970-76; G. C. Hartman Schl Kndgtn Tchr 1976-82; *ai:* Southern Columbia Area Schl Bd 1 Chm Retired; Columbia-Montour Vo-Tech Operating Comm, Oper Comm 10 Yrs Pres, Prsnl, Facility, Activity, Curr, Policy Comms; 1970-82; PSEA, Southern Col Area Assn 1967-82; Amer Cancer Soc 1 Bd Mem, Ray Calabrese Awd; Order of the Eastern Star 1942-, W. M. & St Comm; Past Matrons & Patrons Assn of Dist 1959-, Pres; Cata Garden Club 1976-, Pres; Red Cross 1982-, Vol; Heart Assn 1982-, *home:* 500 Shuman St Catawissa PA 17820

ATHERTON-ELY, H. DALE, English Teacher; *b:* Batavia, NY; *m:* K Patricia Brozyna; *c:* Brenda, Zachary; *ed:* Monroe Comm Coll (AA) Arts 1971; St Univ of NY at Albany (BA) His, Eng 1973, (MA) En 1975; *cr:* Saratoga Springs Sr HS Eng Tchr 1976-; *ai:* Eng 12 Re Coord; AFT, NY St Tchrs 1976-; BSA 1993-, Asst Scoutmaster;

lle Vol Fire Dept 1985-, Med First Responder; *office:* Saratoga Spgs 186 West Ave Saratoga Springs NY 12866

RTON-ELY, KAREN P., English Teacher; *b:* Schenectady, NY; *m:* : Zachary; *ed:* St Univ Coll at Oswego (BS) Eng Ed 1975; St Univ at Albany (MS) Rdng Ed 1980; *cr:* Williamson Cntrl Schls Eng Tchr 6; Saratoga Springs City Schls Eng Tchr 1976-; *ai:* IRA, NYST 975-; 4-H 1994-, Asst Ldr; *office:* Saratoga Spgs Sr HS 186 West aratoga Springs NY 12866

I, BARBARA ANN, English Teacher; *b:* Passaic, NJ; *m:* Gary L.; *c:* el; *ed:* Glassboro College at Rowan (BA) Jr HS Ed 1968; 30 Hrs ta St; *cr:* Vernon Valley Schl 7-8 Grd Eng Tchr 1968-69; retville Cntrl Schl 7-9 Grd Eng Tchr 1969-; *ai:* Class of 1989, 1994 r HS Hon Soc Selection 1990, Shared Decision Making Comms; 1968-69; NEA, NYSTA 1969-; Margaretville Tchrs Assn 1969-, ponding Sec, Gifts & Condolences Comm; Yrbk Dedicated 1989, *office:* Margaretville Central Schl PO Box 319 Main St retville NY 12455

NS, KENNETH W., Fourth Grade Teacher; *b:* Winooski, VT; *m:* Miller; *c:* Randi Kay Atkins Metivier, Jessica Wells; *ed:* Univ of VT ng 1964, (MEd) Rdng 1985; 60 Credit Hrs Cmptrs; *cr:* Winooski ist Elem Tchr 1969-; *ai:* Tech, Math Curr Comm; St Stephen's 1967-, Parish Cncl; *home:* 138 Dion St Winooski VT 05404

NS, MARJORIE ANN, Mathematics Dept Chairperson; *b:* East ool, OH; *ed:* Clarion Univ (BS) Math 1968; Edinboro Univ 12 Credit enn St 3 Credit Hrs; *cr:* Midland HS Math Tchr & Chprsn 1968-86; od City HS Math Tchr 1986-93, Chprsn 1993-; *ai:* NEA 1986-; & PCTM 1993-; *office:* Lincoln HS 501 Crescent Ave Ellwood City 17*

NS, PATRICIA A., Phys, Sci, Chem & Bio Teacher; *b:* Meriden, CT; omas A.; *c:* Matthew, Kevin, Margaret, Brendan; *ed:* Annhurst Coll Bio & Chem 1978; Penn St Univ Grad Courses; Wesleyan Univ at Masters Pgm Sci & Art; *cr:* New London HS Tchr 1978-83; Project Sub Tchr 1992-93; Griswold Jr & Sr HS Tchr 1994-; *ai:* CEA 1995-; hrs Chem Org 1996-; CSEA 1996-; Vol Park & Rec Bsktbl & Farm e Bsbl; Wesleyan Univ NSF Grant Schlrshp; *office:* Griswold Jr-Sr 7 Slater Ave Jewett City CT 06351

NS, RICHARD J., English Teacher; *b:* Brooklyn, NY; *ed:* St Johns BA) Eng & Ed 1991, (MS) Eng & Ed 1993; EED Instrl Ldrshp in ss; *cr:* Richmond Hill HS Eng Tchr 1991-92; Benjamin N Cardozo ng Tchr 1992-; *ai:* Yrbk Adv; AFT; UFT; TDF; MMA; EIEIO; St s Hosp Svc; *office:* Benjamin N Cardozo HS 57-00 Bayside NY

NSON, DANIEL WILLIAM, Math Teacher; *b:* Elmira, NY; *m:* J. Cirricone; *c:* Lisa Zino, Jennifer; *ed:* Corning Comm Coll (AS) 1968; SUNY at Stony Brook (BS) Math 1970, (MALS) Lbrl Arts 18 Grad Credits; 27 Credit Hrs In-Service; *cr:* Lindenhurst Jr HS Tchr 1970-84; Lindenhurst Sr HS Math Tchr 1985-; *ai:* Asst Var Boys Coach; NYSUT 1970-; *home:* 19 Pershing Ave Babylon NY 11702

NSON, EDITH FROLA, English Teacher; *b:* Smithdale, PA; *m:* s L.; *c:* Jennifer, Adrian; *ed:* Clarion St Coll (BS) Eng 1968; IN Univ 26 Addl Credit Hrs in Eng; *cr:* Thomas Jefferson HS Eng Tchr 69; Pine Jr High Eng Tchr 1969-76; Knoch Jr-Sr High Eng Tchr ; *ai:* Frosh Class Spon; Discipline Comm Chprsn; South Butler Cty NEA 1989-; PA St Ed Assn 1968-76; Trinity Lutheran Church 1970-, ry Coord; *office:* Knoch Jr-Sr HS Knoch Rd Saxonburg PA 16056

NSON, JAY MICHAEL, Adjunct Professor of English; *b:* Methuen, : Liam; *ed:* Acadia Univ at Nova Scotia (BA) Philosphy-Hnrs 1979; of FL (MA) Creative Writing & Lit 1982; *cr:* Univ of MA at Lowell ng Prof 1992-; *ai:* Frosh Writing & Summer Writing Pgm Comms; keag Rugby Ftbl Club 1985-, Player, Capt 1988 & 1995; ACE Winner Boston Magazine Fiction Contest Winner 1995; Natl Video Script Numerous Articles Pub; *office:* Univ Of MA At Lowell 1 University owell MA 01854*

NSON, MEREDITH O., English Teacher; *b:* Charlotte, NC; *m:* ge R.; *c:* Rebecca, Geoffrey; *ed:* Hood Coll (BA) Eng 1969; ebury Coll (MA) Eng 1974; *cr:* Dedham HS Eng Tchr 1969-71; outh HS Eng Tchr 1971-77; Northeastern Univ Eng Instr 1981-; outh HS Eng Tchr 1987-89; Ursuline Acad Eng Tchr 1990-; *ai:* Schl paper & Independent Stud Adv; NCTE, MCTE; Norwell Pub Lib , Trustee, Vice Chair; Articles Pub; *office:* Ursuline Acad 65 Lowder dham MA 02026*

AS, ROBERTA TEAL, Art Teacher & Yearbook Advisor; *b:* nbus, OH; *ed:* OH St Univ (BAEd) Art Ed 1984; Columbus Coll of nd Design 18 Semester Hrs Fine Arts; Univ of Santa Cruz-CA graphy; Currently Working on Masters in Art Ed; *cr:* n-Franklin HS Art Instr Yrbk Adv 9 Yrs; *ai:* Yrbk adv, Nom to Train eer Mediation Adv; Coord for Multicultural Mural Painting on Schl ors; Mem of Bus Consortium Group; OEA 1987-; NEA 1987-; CEA ; OAA NAA; OH St Fac Photographer; OH Governors Youth Art oition, Installation Dir 1988; Worked with Cole Weston, son Of rd Weston Prominent Photographer in Early Amer Photography; Tchr onth 1995; *office:* Marion-Franklin HS 1265 Koebel Rd Columbus OH 7*

CE, BENJAMIN CHAMPNEYS, English Instructor; *b:* Lancaster, : Ana, Laura, Lawton; *ed:* Franklin & Marshall Coll (BA) Eng 1967; rsville Univ (MA) Eng 1980; Eng Claremont Mc Kenna Coll 1962-64; Univ Eng 1970-72; Trenton St Univ Ed 1969; *cr:* The Peddie Schl Instr 1967-69; Lawrenceville Schl Eng Instr, Chm 1969-; *ai:* Coach Bsbl 1977-, Asst Var Soccer; Adv Mock Trial Team 1983-; NCTE, rn Lang Assn 1987-; Lawrenceville Village Civic Assn, Pres 1990, VP ; Pub Poetry; Prep Coach or Yr 1992, 1993; Area Coach of Yr 1987; AA Coach of Yr 1988, 1990, 1991, 1993.*

UNYO, MATTSON KUDJO, Asst Prof of Mngmt & Intnl Bus; *b:* anyo, Ghana; *m:* Esther Akua Asempah; *c:* Roland, Joyce, Antoinette, om; *ed:* Univ of Cape Coast at Ghana (BBA) Bus Admin 1981; Univ ew Haven (MBA) Intnl Bus 1986; Univ of MA (PHD) Mngmnt, Org 1992; *cr:* Univ of Cape Coast Assoc Tchng 1981-84; Univ of MA Asst g 1987-90; Mt Saint Mary Coll Asst Prof 1991-; *ai:* MBA Prgm Dir; Nrsng Curr Comms; Eastern Acad of Mngmt, Acad of Mngmt 1987-; P 1991-; MSMC Black Stdnts Union 1991-, Adv; Rotary Club of ourgy New Windsor 1993-, Assoc; Eastern Acad of Mngmt 1987, 1994, ; Wrote Journal; *office:* Mount Saint Mary Coll 330 Powell Ave ourgh NY 12550*

AR, MICHELE ACHTSAM, Second Grade Teacher; *b:* Bronx, NY; ack; *c:* Adam; *ed:* Queens Coll (BA) Ed 1974, (MS) Early Chldhd Ed ; Working Toward Addl 30 Credits; *cr:* Rodeph Shalom First Grd Tchr -76, Kndgtn Tchr 1976-78; The Bialik Schl Nursery Tchr 1979-80; PS Q Schl First Grd Tchr 1984-89; *office:* PS 133 24805 86th Ave rose NY 11426

ILI, MARY L., Instr of Eng Composition Lit; *b:* Reading, PA; *m:* d Schwartz; *c:* Robert K. Steinmetz, Gretchen L. Keith, Matthew M. metz; *ed:* Kutztown Univ (BA) Eng 1964, (MS) Ed 1976, (MA) Lit ; *cr:* Muhlenberg HS Eng Tchr 1966-86; PA St Univ Adjunct Prof of 1987-89; Reading Area Comm Coll Adjunct Prof of Eng 1987-89; ight Coll Adjunct in Eng 1986-; *ai:* Stu Assistance Prgm, Consultant in Drugs Alcohol Field; *office:* Albright Coll PO Box 15234 Reading PA 19612*

ATTLESON, ERIC EDSON, 7th-12th Grd Technology Tchr; *b:* Cortland, NY; *m:* Anastasia Spence; *ed:* SUNY at Oswego (BS) Tech Ed 1991; SUNY at Cortland (MS) Rdng Tchr 1995; *cr:* Binghamton HS Tech Ed Tchr 1991-; *ai:* Graphic Arts Club Adv; Tech Prep Curr, Schl-To-Work Transition, Prins of Tech Curr & Applied Tech Curr Dev Teams; Comp Tech Comm Chair; VATEA; Tech Prep; Broome Cty Tech Prep; Mentor Pgm; Apprenticeship; Chase Manhattan Bank Partnership; Broome Cty Apprenticeship; NYSTEA 1987-; STTEA 1991-; BTA 1991-; NEA 1991-; Southern Tier Concert Band of NY St 1994-, Percussionist; EDCORE Grant Non-Traditional Careers for Women Elem & MS Girls; *office:* Binghamton HS 31 Main St Binghamton NY 13905*

ATTURIO, ANDREA JEAN (VIELE), Social Studies Teacher; *b:* Providence, RI; *m:* Gary A.; *c:* Gary J.; *ed:* Rhode Island Coll (BA) His 1973; Providence Coll (MED) Spec Ed 1993; *cr:* Gorton Jr HS Soc Stud Tchr 1990-; *ai:* AFT 1990-; *office:* Gorton Jr H S 69 Draper Ave Warwick RI 02889

ATWELL, CAROLE ANN (TERCHILA), Fifth Grade Teacher; *b:* Sharon, PA; *c:* Ross C., Matthew C.; *ed:* Edinboro Univ (BS) Elem 1970; Masters Equivalency in Elem Ed Plus 18 Credit Hrs Beyond Towards Continuing Ed; *cr:* Sharon Schl Dist PE Tchr 1970-74, SED Prgm Aide 1983-87, Chapter 1 Tchr 1987, Elem Ed Tchr 1988-; *ai:* Dist Wide Comms; DARE; Kids Around Town PA Govt Prgm Speaker; Sharon City Recreation Bd Art Dir; NEA, PSEA, Sharon Tchrs Assn 1988-; Awd from The Herald Local Newspaper; *home:* 185 Lyle Dr Hermitage PA 16148

ATWOOD, JOANNE LAWRENCE, Media Specialist & Eng Tchr; *b:* Walla Walla, WA; *c:* Marcelyn Atwood-Adkins, Kent B.; *ed:* Portland St Univ (BS) Elem Ed 1970, (MS) Ed Media, Eng 1979; Pub Schl Admin Cert 1983; Advanced Placement Training from Coll Bd 1995; *cr:* Reedville Dist Elem Tchr 1970-75; Central Howell Tchr, Curr Dir 1975-80; Yamhill-Carlton Media Specialist, Jr HS Eng 1980-85; Dept of Defense Dependents Schl s Media Specialist, Eng 1985-87; George Dewey HS Media Specialist 1987-92; Seoul Amer HS Media Specialist, Sr HS Eng, AP Eng 1992-; *ai:* Sr Class, Yrbk Spon; Phi Delta Kappa 1990-, 2nd VP; Local Tchr Unions, Trained Negotiator; Order of Eastern Star 1953-; Amers for Philippines Scholars 1987-92; Bataan Regugee Ctr Philippines 1987-92, Distinguished Svc; Articles Pub; Woman of Yr Subic Bay Philippines 1991; Spec Arts Awd George Dewey HS 1988-92; Spec Arts Awd 1995; *office:* Seoul American HS DODDS SAHS Box 1 Unit 15549 APO AP 96205

AUBREY, ALISON ADAMS, Rdng, Lang Arts & Civics Tchr; *b:* Freehold, NJ; *ed:* Univ of DE (BA) Anthropology 1983; Univ of DE Cert Elem Ed 1990; Psych, Black Amer Stud; *cr:* Sanford Schl MS Staff Tutor 1990-91; Tower Hill Schl After Care 5, 6 Grd Tchr 1990-91; Caravel Acad Rdng, Lang Arts, Civics Tchr 1991-; *ai:* MS Coord Asst; Mid Sts Stu Svcs Comm; Literacy Vols of Amer 1996; FFA Alumni Org 1976-, Svc Awd; 1 Article Pub; Odyssey of Mind Awd of Appreciation for Judging; *office:* Caravel Acad 2801 Del Laws Rd Bear DE 19701*

AUCAR, HILDA-JUDITH A., Span Tchr & Lang Dept Chprsn; *b:* Cuba; *ed:* Pace Univ at White Plains (BA) Span, Italian, Fr, Eng, Bus 1975; NY Univ (MA) Span & Hispanic Culture & Lit 1976; St Johns Univ at Jamaica (MS) Urban Ed, Biling Lang 1977; Prof Diploma Supervision, Admin Iona Coll 1986; Attnd Bryn Mawr Coll; Centro de Estudios Hispanicos en Madrid Spain 1972; NY Univ Madrid 1976-77; Fulbright Schlsp Mexico 1993; *cr:* Ponus Ridge MS ESOL & Biling Tchr 1978-81; Pace Univ Span Adj Prof 1979-89; White Plains Span Adj Prof 1979-89; Pleasantville Campus Span Adj Prof 1979-89; Brien Mc Mahon HS Span Tchr, Adj Instr 1981-; *ai:* CT Cncl of Lang Tchrs 1981-90; Westchester Prof Advy Comm 1987-89; Phi Delta Kappa 1986-92; White Plains Commission Human Rights 1987-88; Steering Comm for Supts Restructuring Comm 1992-; Amer Cancer Soc, Ed Comm 1985-; Schlsp Comm Centro Hispano 1980-, Co-Chair; Excl Awd in Span Pace Univ 1975; Title VII Flwshp St John's Univ 1977; Governor's Awd Outstdng Hispanics 1993; *office:* Brien McMahon HS 300 Highland Ave Norwalk CT 06854

AUCLAIR, FERNAND C.,JR., Social Studies, Lang Arts Tchr; *b:* Fall River, MA; *m:* Barbara Winterton; *c:* Megan, Daniel; *ed:* Westfield St Coll (BS) Elem, Spec Ed 1973; Bridgewater St Coll (MEd) Rdng 1982; His Credit Hrs; Certfd to Give WAIS, WISC-r, WPPSI Intelligence Tests; *cr:* Somerset North MS 6th Grd Soc Stud Tchr 1973-84; Somerst South MS Adult Spec Ed Tchr 1984-88; Somerset Jr HS 7th-8th Grd Rdng, Soc Stud Tchr 1988-90; Somerset HS Rdng Clinic Instr 1990-91; Somerset Jr HS 7th Grd Lang Arts, Soc Stud Tchr 1991-; *ai:* Somerset Tchrs Assn, Pres 1975-77, Negotiations Mem 1990-, Bldg Rep 1975-; MA Tchrs Assn, NEA 1973-; Southeastern MA Bsbl Assn 1973-; Southeaster MA Ftbl Assn 1974-; Intnl Assn Bsktbl Ofcls 1975-; Jr HS Level Christopher Baldwin Awd Chm; *office:* Somerset Jr HS 1141 Brayton Ave Somerset MA 02726

AUDET, FRANCES MOLLICA, Early Chldhd Occupations Tchr; *b:* Gardiner, ME; *m:* Michael Joseph; *ed:* Univ of ME at Farmington (BS) Home Ec 1967; Mass Media & Human Interaction; Topics in Human SexualityProject Teach; Infant Mental Hlth Conf; Game Free Tchng; Responding to Child Care Crisis; Governors Co nf on Child Care; Voc Curr Dev; *cr:* Key West HS Child Care Tchr 1968-70; Sanford HS Childcare Tchr 1970-71; Key West HS Child Care Tchr 1971-72; Westbrook Regnl Voc Ctr Early Chldhd Occupations Ed Tchr 1980-; WRVC Teen Parenting Ctr Tchr, Supvr 1989-; *ai:* ECOE Voc Adv; Mentor for ECOE Tchr; ECOE of ME 1993-, Treas; Westbrook Ed Assn, ME Tchrs Assn, NEA 1980-; ME Voc Assn 1990-; St Pius X Roman Cath Church 1985-, Ecclesiastical, Floral Designer; New England Assn of Schls & Colls Commission on Voc, Tech, Career Insts Visiting Comm Waterville Reg Voc Ctr 1991, West Bay Voc Tech Schl 1990, 1995; *office:* Westbrook Regional Voc Schl 125 Shoudwater Sr Westbrook ME 04092*

AUDETTE, WILLIAM EVERETT,JR., Math Teacher; *b:* Portland, ME; *m:* Heather Creamer; *c:* William III, Colin; *ed:* Univ of Southern ME (BS) Math 1973; *cr:* Brunswick Jr HS Math Tchr 1974-94; Brunswick HS Math Tchr 1994-; *ai:* Math Team Coach; ME Ed Assn, NEA, NCTM 1974-; 2 St Titles for Math Team Competitions 1989, 1991; 6th Place Natl Math Counts Competition 1991; *office:* Brunswick HS 116 Maquoit Rd Brunswick ME 04011

AUERBACH, CURT, Social Studies Teacher; *b:* New York, NY; *m:* Marilyn Mintz; *c:* Diane C.; *ed:* Pace Univ (BBA) Bus Admin 1969; Coll of Staten Island (MSE) Soc Stud 1994; *cr:* Paul Robeson HS Bus Ed Tchr 1990-91; Franklin D Roosevelt HS Soc Stud Tchr 1991-; *office:* Franklin D Roosevelt HS 5800 20th Ave Brooklyn NY 11204*

AUFIERI, STANLEY VINCENT, Health & Physical Ed Chairman; *b:* Bronx, NY; *m:* Roxanne Dorfman; *c:* Leslie; *ed:* Fordham Cool at Bronx (BA) Pol Sci 1972; Herbert H. Lehman Coll at Bronx (MS) PE 1983; *cr:* Cardinal Hayes HS Head Jr Var Ftbl Coach 1972-73; Holy Cross HS Chm, Hlth, PE Dept 1975-, Head JV Ftbl Coach 1975-93; Edenwald Schl Asst Summer Recreation Supvr1981-82; Holy Cross HS Asst Var Ftbl Coach Defensive Coord 1994-95; *ai:* Holy Cross HS Asst Var Ftbl Coach Defensive Coord; Dir of IMs; AAHPERD 1977-, Mem; John Dunbar Amer Legion 1974-, Mem; Elected to Cath HS Ftbl League Bd of Governors 1982; *office:* Holy Cross HS 26-20 Francis Lewis Blvd Flushing NY 11358

AUFIERO, HARRY, Science Teacher; *b:* Jersey City, NJ; *m:* Debra Cordes; *c:* Ben, Clifford; *ed:* Rutger Univ at New Brunswick (BA) Biological Scis 1974; *cr:* Palisades Park Jr Sr HS Sci Tchr 1974-79, 1992-; Self-Owned Construction Builder 1979-92; *ai:* Girls Var & JV Tennis Coach; 7th & 8th Grd Tennis Club; NEA & NJEA 1974-79, 1992-; BCSL Tennis Coach of Yr 1994-95; Authored Golf Instrl Book: Completing the Visual Circuit; *office:* Palisades Pk Jr Sr HS 1 Veterans Plz Palisades Park NJ 07650

AUGENSTEIN, RUTH PRITCHARD, First Grade Teacher; *b:* Westmoreland, NY; *m:* James R.; *c:* Marianne R.; *ed:* St Univ of NY at Cortland (BS) Elem Ed 1966, (MS) Elem Ed 1972; *cr:* Columbus Elem Schl First Grd Tchr 1966-79, 1985-, Second Grd Tchr 1974-75, Pre-First Grd Tchr 1983-85; *ai:* Rome Tchrs Assn, NY St United Tchrs, AFT 1966-; 4-H Club 1961-, Ldr; First United Meth Church 1966-, Sr Choir; *office:* Columbus Elem Schl 112 Columbus Ave Rome NY 13440

AUGSBURGER, JANE ELIZABETH, Art Teacher; *b:* Bluffton, OH; *ed:* Bluffton Coll (BA) Art Ed K-12 1991; Working Towards MA Ed; *cr:* Arlington Local Schl Art Tchr Grds 1-12 1992-; *ai:* Art Club Adv; *office:* Arlington Local Schl 336 S Main Arlington OH 45814

AUGUST, ARLENE BRAND, Prof Emerita of Office Info; *b:* Brooklyn, NY; *m:* John Howard; *c:* James, Carole Lanzarone, Charles, Deborah, David; *ed:* Hunter Coll (BA) Bus, Ec 1945, (MA) Bus Ed 1953; Addl 42 Credits Toward EDD NY Univ; *cr:* NYC Schls HS Tchr 1950-53; Manpower Dev Trng Prgm Instr 1963-66; Pace Univ Prof 1966-; *ai:* Dept Curr Comm; NBEA; OSRA; WCBEA; Phi Delta Kappa; Pi Lambda Theta; Acad Fed Credit Union Bd Mem; Articles Pub; *office:* Pace Univ At White Plains One Martine Ave White Plains NY 10606*

AUGUST, KATY ANDERSON, Third Grade & Chemistry Tchr; *b:* Sidney, OH; *m:* Darryll; *ed:* Pensacola Chrstn Coll (BS) Math Ed 1993; *cr:* Heritage Chrstn Schl Third Grd Tchr, Chem, Physics, Geometry Tchr 1993-; *ai:* Vlybl Coach; *office:* Heritage Christian Schl 2000 Broad Ave Findlay OH 45840

AUGUST, MARILYN BURKE, Third Grade Teacher; *b:* Rochester, PA; *c:* Kathleen Bares, Edward J., Marjorie; *ed:* Indiana Univ of PA (BS) K-8th Grd Ed 1957; Cleveland St Univ (MS) Curr, Instruction Ed 1984; 6 Credit Hrs for Permanent PA Cert at Univ of Pittsburgh; 15 Addl Semester Hrs in Rdng, Writing; *cr:* North Alleghany Schls 1st Grd Tchr 1957-60; North Hills Schls 2nd Grd Tchr 1961-64; Lakewood Schls Kndgtn Tchr 1966-67; Cleveland Pub Schls 3rd Grd Tchr 1971-; *ai:* Tchrs Enhancing Elem Math Mem to Train Tchrs in Math Act; Girl Scouting in Schls Ldr; AFT 1971-, Math Site Coord; NCTM, OCTM 1991-; Delta Kappa Gamma 1985-, Pres, Rho Golden Gift Fund 1995-; Girls Scouts Lake Erie Cncl 1983-, Del; 2 Grants from Cleveland Ed Fund; 1 Impact Grant from OH Dept of Ed; 1 Grant Centerior Energ Inc; One of 3 Tchrs to Attend IMPACT Conf at Snowbird UT 1992; *office:* William Rainey Harper Schl 5515 Ira Ave Cleveland OH 44144*

AUGUSTE, GABRIEL J., Mathematics Teacher; *b:* Cap Haitien, Haiti; *m:* Evelyne A.; *c:* Joanne, Stephan, Tania; *ed:* Poitiers Univ France (BAMS) Ec 1970; 23 Credits Cmptr Sci, 12 Credits Ed Brooklyn Coll; 24 Credits Math, 15 Credits Ed Long Island Univ; MS Mth Ed Long Island Univ 1994; *cr:* Prospect Heights HS Math Tchr 1984-; *ai:* ATMNYC 1988-94; KME Lambda NY 1992-; ACE 1990-; *office:* Prospect Heights HS 883 Classon Ave Brooklyn NY 11225

AUGUSTIN, YVONNE WILLIAMS, Vocal Music Teacher; *b:* New York City, NY; *m:* Lys J.; *c:* Lynn, Lysaine; *ed:* Hampton Inst (BS) Music 1972; C. W. Post Coll 33 Credits Spec Ed; Nassau Comm Coll 27 Credits; *cr:* IS 320 Jackie Robinson Vocal Music Tchr 1972-86; Brooklyn Borough Wide Chorus Tchr 1974-76; Virgil I. Grissom Jr HS #226 Vocal Music Tchr 1986-; *ai:* AFT, UFT 1974-; L. I. Writing Conf 1994-; *office:* Virgil I. Grissom Jr HS #226 121-10 Rockaway Blvd S Ozone Park NY 11420

AUGUSTYNIAK, DONNA, 6th Grade Language Arts Tchr; *b:* Toledo, OH; *m:* John Ronald; *c:* Jeffrey, Gregory, Mark, Kathryn Wawrzyniak, Jay, Jennifer Morrissey, Michael, Laura; *ed:* Madonna Coll (BA) Eng 1959; Univ of Detroit & Univ of Toledo Grad Credit Hrs; *cr:* Archdiocese of Detroit Tchr 1959-62; Diocese of Toledo Tchr 1962-; *home:* 1520 Parkside Blvd Toledo OH 43607

AUKERMAN, MARIE TERLIZZI, Second Grade Teacher; *b:* Cleveland, OH; *m:* Ronald; *c:* Lynnette, Ronald, Cynthia; *ed:* Cleveland St Univ (BS) Elem Ed 1966; 15 Post Grad Hrs; *cr:* Transfiguration Schl Tchr Grd 2 1978-85; Marion C. Seltzer Elem Schl Tchr Grd 2 1986-; *ai:* Cleveland Tchrs Union 1986-, Chptr Chprsn; *office:* Marion C. Seltzer Elem Schl 1468 W 98th St Cleveland OH 44102

AULT, BRENDA GIFFIN, Business Teacher; *b:* Bedford, PA; *c:* Andrea, Daniel; *ed:* Indiana Univ of PA (BS) Bus Ed 1979; Shippensburg Univ (MED) Bus Ed 1985; *cr:* Allegany Comm Coll Part-time Tchr 1989-; Everett Area HS Tchr 1979-; *ai:* FBLA; NEA, PSEA, EAEA, NBEA, PBEA 1979-; Order of Eastern Star 1981-, Past Matron; *office:* Everett Area HS 12 N River Ln Everett PA 15537*

AULT, DIANE LYNN ANDERSON, Mathematics Dept Chm & Teacher; *b:* Bowling Green, OH; *m:* Steven Robert; *c:* Jessica Lynn, Zachariah Matthew; *ed:* Bowling Green St Univ (BS) Math 1973, (MA) Scndry Ed 1984; Wright St Univ Leadership Math, Tchrs Math Camp, & Tchrs Math Retreat 1990-91; Courses in Time Stress Management, Stress Management, Using Humor Effectively, Improving Stud Test Scores; Careers in NW OH Univ of Toledo 1991; Addl wkshp Drake Univ 1992-1993; Addl courses BGSU 1992-1993, Wkshps 1994-95; *cr:* Penta Cty Voc HS Math Coord 1974; Elmwood HS Math Tchr 1974-; *ai:* Math Dept Chprsn; Future Tchrs of Amer Adv; Co Adv Peer Tutoring Prgm; Wood Cty Mentor Tchr Prgm Mem; Acad Boosters; Intervention Assistance Team Mem; Head of Math Curr Revision; Proficiency Math Tutor; Youth Group Adv; NEA 1974-; OCTM 1982-; NCTM 1991-; Wood Co Heart Assn Special Gifts Comm 1989-1992, Area Chprsn 1989-1992; Delta Kappa Gamma 1991-; Fnd for Royal Pride Mem 1991-; BSA Comm Chm; Math Tchr Advisory Panel Mem; Wood Cty Office of Ed Wkshps for Area Tchrs; Wright St Univ Assist with Math Camps for Tchrs; Selected for Marth Holden Jennings Math Wkshp 1991; Mem of Content Review Comm for Math Proficiency Test; Prof Dev Battelle Aw 1991-92; *office:* Elmwood HS 7650 Jerry City Rd Bloomdale OH 44817

AURAND, DALE K., Retired Teacher; *b:* Lewistown, PA; *c:* Roderick, Douglas, Dwight, Marc, LaVonda; *ed:* Shippensburg St Univ (BS) Elem Ed 1955; Penn St Univ (MED) Educl Admin 1962; Cert Elem, Sec Admin; *cr:* South Middleton Schls 5th Grd Tchr 1955-56; Newton Wayne Schls 6th Grd Tchr, Bldg Prin 1956-65; Mt Unoin Area Schls 5th-6th Grd Tchr, Bldg Prin 1965-93; *ai:* HS Coach; Conducted Plays; AFT 1958-; NEA PSEA 1982-; 4-H, Ldr; Grange 1958-; *home:* RR 1 Box 198B Mc Veytown PA 17051

AUSMANN, STEPHEN WADE, Asst Prof & Music Ed; *b:* Columbus, OH; *m:* Diane Williams; *c:* Katie, Matthew, Andra; *ed:* Capital Univ Conservatory of Music (BM) Voice, Music Ed 1975; OH St Univ (MA) Music Ed 1984, (PHD) Music Ed 1991; *cr:* J. F. Kennedy Jr HS Choral, Gen Music Tchr 1975-77; Marion Harding HS Choral, Gen Music Tchr 1977-87; OH St Univ Grad Tchng Assoc 1987-90; Youngstown St Univ Asst Prof 1990-; *ai:* Choral Dir Natl Hnrs Chorus European Tour 1995-; MENC, OMEA 1975-; ACDA 1980-; Phi Mu Alpha 1972-, Ep Phi Chptr Pres 1974-; Dissertation Characteristics of In-Service, Urban Music Tchrs, Pre-Service Music Tchrs in OH, Attitudes Toward Tchng Music in Urban

Schls; *office:* Youngstown St Univ Bliss Hall Wick Ave Youngstown OH 44555*

AUSTIN, BETSY JEAN, French Teacher; *b:* Paris, France; *m:* Larry Snow Damon; *c:* Lee M., Cassandra; *ed:* Univ of VT (BA) Fr 1973, (MA) Ger 1978, (MA) Fr 1995; 5th Yr Tchng Cert 1978; *cr:* Intnl Bus Machines Ger Instr 1978-80; Bellows Free Acad Fr Tchr 1978-80; Stowe Mid HS Fr Tchr 1980-; *ai:* Organize 10 Day Bi-Annual Trip to France; Comm Svc Comm; VEA, NEA 1980-; Stowe Tchrs Assn 1980-, Pres 1990-91; VT Foreign Lang Assn 1978-; *office:* Stowe HS 413 Barrows Rd Stowe VT 05672*

AUSTIN, CAROL APPELT, Scndry Learning Support Tchr; *b:* Pittsburgh, PA; *c:* Johnny; *ed:* Slippery Rock Univ (BS) Spec Ed 1980, (MED) Learning Disabilities 1982; *cr:* Karns City Area Schl Dist Learning Support Tchr 1981-; *ai:* NEA, PSEA, KCEA 1981-; *office:* Karns City Area Schl Dist 1446 Kittanning Pike Karns City PA 16041

AUSTIN, DEBORAH S., Associate Professor of Chem; *b:* Stuttgart, Germany; *ed:* Clarion St Coll (BS) Chem 1980; IA St Univ (PHD) Analytical Chem 1984; Visiting Scientist 1986, 1988, 1992; Post-Doctoral Appointment 1987; *cr:* Penn St Mont Alto Instr 1987; Wilson Coll Instr 1985-89, Asst Prof 1989-95, Assoc Prof 1995-, Head of Sci Div, Asst Dean for Acad Advng; *ai:* Frosh, Soph Acad Adv; Comms, Acad Prodecures, Admissions, Curr, Assessment Task Force; Lilly Endowment Wkshp on the Liberal Arts 1994; Amer Chem Soc;1976-; Amer Assn Advancement Sci 1985-; Assn Women in Sci, Natl Acad Advising Assn 1994-; Awds Christian R., Mary F. Lindaback Fnd Distinguished Tchng 1991, Outstanding Tchng in Analytical Chem 1982; Ben Franklin Grant 1988; Publications in Analytical Chem 1983, Journal of Electrochemical Soc 1984-85, Electroanalysis 1989, Langmuir 1991; Quality Control Consultant Pine Instrument Co 1981-84, 1989-; Excl in Tchng Awd 1995; Spectroscopy Soc of Coll Grant 1995; *office:* Wilson College 1015 Philadelphia Ave Chambersburg PA 17201

AUSTIN, DOUGLAS SCOTT, English, Comm & Drama Teacher; *b:* Port Jervis, NY; *m:* Carol Ann Rolland; *c:* Bryan Douglas; *ed:* SUNY Geneseo (BA) Speech Ed 1968; Montclair St (MS) Eng, Drama 1975; Addl 60 Hrs; *cr:* US Army Sgt 1969-71; Suffern HS Speech Tchr 1968-69, Eng, Comm, Drama Tchr 1971-; *ai:* Musical Dir, Adv Video Yrbk; NEA, AFT 1968-; Outstdng Tchr Awd Univ of Chicago 1991; Yrbk Dedication 1975, 1993; NYS Cncl of Eng Tchng Excl Awd 1995; Winner Poetry Writing NYS Dpt of Ed 1985; Outstdng Tchr Awd Univ of Rochester 1982; Co-Creator, Adv Lit Magazine 1974-82; Dir, Creator Cabaret Theatre 1975-84; Creater, Adv Video Yrbk 1987-; *office:* Suffern HS Viola Rd Suffern NY 10901

AUSTIN, EILEEN C., Third Grade Teacher; *b:* Springfield, MA; *ed:* (BS) Elem Ed 1975; (MED) Ed 1984; (CAGS) Admin 1987; *cr:* Ware Pub Schls Title I Tchr 1975-78; Belchertown Pub Schls Title I Tchr 1977-78, 2-4 Grd Tchr 1978-80, 2-3 Grd Head Tchr 1980-; *ai:* Stu Savings Prgm Albank Co-Chair; Stu Store Adv; NEA, MTA, Hampton Cty Tchrs Assn 1978-, BTA, Pres; Lib Coord; Grant Writer; Prof Dev Courses Instr Bay Path Jr Coll; *home:* 348 West St Belchertown MA 01007*

AUSTIN, FELICIA WILLIAMSON, Vocational Teacher; *b:* Cleveland, OH; *m:* Nathan E.; *ed:* Ashland Univ (BS) Bus Nutrition 1986; Univ of Akron Post Grad Hrs Completion Scndry Home Ec, Voc Home Ec Certs; *cr:* Westview Manor Nursing Home Asst Food Svc Dir 1987-88; Sky-Chefs Inc Food Supvr 1988-89; Cleveland City Schls Voc Tchr 1989-; *ai:* Military Drill Team 1991- Adv, City Champs 3 Yrs, Natl Competition 3rd Place; Greater Cleveland Home Ec Assn 1992, 1995-; Cleveland Alliance Black Edctrs 1993-94; *home:* 1650 E 243rd St Euclid OH 44117

AUSTIN, JANE CORSON, Administrative Asst to Supt; *b:* Bridgeton, NJ; *m:* Frank; *c:* Frank, Steven; *ed:* Rider Univ (BS) Bus 1967, (MA) Bus 1988; Cert Admin 1988; *cr:* Maecom Schl Contracted Trng Tchr 1976-78; Brookdale Comm Coll Adj Prof Bus Part-Time 1978-91; Midtown HS South Bus, Eng Tchr 1979-95; Middletown Twp Bd of Ed Admin Asst to Supt 1995-; *ai:* FBLA Adv 1989-95; NJBEA 1988-95, Treas, Exec Bd Ofcr 1988-92, Outstdng Contributions; NJEA 1979-95; Juvenile Conf Comm 1979-90; Historical Soc Atlantic Highlands 1980-92; Brower Awd Bus Grad Stu of Yr 1988; Middletown HS South's Tchr of Yr 1991; *office:* Middletown Twp Bd of Ed 59 Tindall Rd Middletown NJ 07748

AUSTIN, JUDY DANFORTH, Kindergarten Teacher; *b:* Syracuse, NY; *m:* Patrick; *c:* Adam, Emily; *ed:* Canton Ag & Tech Coll (AS) Nursery Schl Ed 1969; St Univ of Potsdam (BS) N-6 1972; MA Equivalent Permanent Cert 1977; 3 Credit Hrs Handicapped Stdnts at Risk; 3 Credit Hrs Possitive Environment; 1 Credit Hr Mastery Learning; 2 Credit Hrs Cmptrs; *cr:* St Lawrence Cntrl Elem Second Grd Tchr 1972-90, Kndgtn, Pre-K Tchr 1990-; *ai:* Grd Level Chprsn; Swing Team Statistician; Bldg Planning & Alpha Teams; NYSUT, AFT 1973-; Delta Kappa Gamma 1987-, Sec; Amer Legion Aux 1974-; Eagles Awd for Excl, Excl in Tchng Awd 1984; *office:* St Lawrence Cntrl Schl PO Box 307 George St Brasher Falls NY 13613

AUSTIN, KAREN F., Mathematics Teacher; *b:* Oxford, OH; *m:* Steven; *c:* Allysn; *ed:* Miami Univ (BS) Math Ed 1986; *cr:* Fairfield HS Math Tchr 1986-, Dept Chr 1995; *ai:* Acad Team Adv; Jr Class Spon; NHS Adv; FCTA, NEA, OEA, OCTM 1986-; Phi Delta Kappa 1994-; Ashland Tchr, Presidential Awd Noms; CGE Tchr of Month 1993, 1994; *office:* Fairfield City Schls 1111 Niles Rd Fairfield OH 45014

AUSTIN, LYLE P., Business Teacher; *b:* Southampton, NY; *m:* Sandra Hunter; *c:* Troy, Jason, Jaime, Jonathan; *ed:* Murray St Univ (BS) Bus Ed 1968, (MA) Bus Ed 1969; 120 Credit Hrs in Ed, Bus Courses; *cr:* Newfield HS Bus Tchr 1969-70; Centereach HS Bus Tchr 1970-; *ai:* Bus Svc Club; FBLA; NBEA; Suffolk Cty Bus Tchrs Assn; Mid Cntry Tchrs Assn; Centereach HS PTSA; NY St United Tchrs; AFT.

AUSTIN, MARILYN ELIZABETH (MARANO), Third Grade Teacher; *b:* Waterbury, CT; *m:* Gerald Raymond; *c:* Alison Leigh; *ed:* Western CT St Univ (BS) Ed 1975; Southern CT St Univ (MS) Early Ed 1980; *cr:* Griffin Elem Schl Third Grd Tchr 1975-; *ai:* Watertown Spelling Curr Comm; Advy Comm; WIST Team Watertown Stu Assistance Team; CEA, NEA, Watertown Ed Assn 1976-; PTO, Tchr Rep; *home:* 33 Country Club Wood Cir Waterbury CT 06708

AUSTIN, MYRNA BOGNER, First Grade Teacher; *b:* Brooklyn, NY; *m:* Fred; *c:* Martin, Howard; *ed:* Stony Brook Univ (MALS) Lbrl Art 1975; 18 Credits Post Grad; *cr:* Bethpage UFSD 4 Grd Tchr 1959-60; HASC 3-5 Grd Art Tchr 1969-79; Burr Jr HS TA Remedial Eng Tchr 1979-81; Indian Hollow Schl TA Cmptr Tech Tchr 1981-87; Rolling Hills Schl 5th, 1st Grd Tchr 1987-89; Indian Hollow Primary Schl 1st Grd Tchr 1989-; *ai:* Art Club Adv; Cmptr Lab Innovator; Craft Corps Ldr; Originator of TAWL; NEA, NYSUT 1979-; PTA 1966-, VP, Honory Life Mbrshp; Commack JC Bd 1970-; *office:* Indian Hollow Schl Kings Park Rd Commack NY 11725*

AUSTIN, NEVILLE P., Assistant Principal; *b:* Flemington, NJ; *m:* Cynthia T.; *c:* Neville II, Noah Joshua; *ed:* Eastern Coll (BA) His, Scndry Ed 1977; West Chester Univ (MA) His 1983; Admin Cert at PA St Univ; Intro to IBM, MAC; St Cert SAT; Project Teach; Tchng Through Learning Channels Assertive Discipline 1, 2; Using Achvmt to Build Self-Esteem; *cr:* Downingtown Sr HS Classroom Tchr 1977-81; Lionville Jr HS Team Ldr, Admin Asst 1981-93; Conestoga Vly MS Asst Prin 1993-; *ai:* Soccer, Indoor-Outdoor Track & Field, Curr Coach; PSEA, NEA 1977-, Union Rep; BSA 1989-, Exec, OA Adv, Outstdng Svc 1994, Asst Scoutmaster 1990-, Troop Advancement Ofcr 1990-, Webelos Ldr; NASSP, PASSP, ASCD, PASCD 1993-; Disruptive Stu Project 1994; Lionville Jr HS Bldg Rep 1993-94; Order of Arrow 1993-; Blue Ribbon Task Force, Soc Stud, Natl Schls Recognition 1992-93; Supts Comm 1991-93; PA Tchr of Yr Nominee 1989-90; Coatesville City Zoning Hearing Bd 1989-90; Whos Who in Amer Coll; Phi Alpha Theta Charter Mem; *office:* Conestoga Vly Schl Dist 2110 Horseshoe Rd Lancaster PA 17601

AUTEN, CARLA OVERHISER, Instructional Support Teacher; *b:* Williamsport, PA; *m:* Harold E.; *c:* Garth, Brian; *ed:* Bloomsburg Univ (BS) Spec Ed 1967, (MS) Spec Ed 1971; Addl Credits in Early Chldhd; *cr:* Williamsport Area Schl Dist Spec Ed Tchr 1967-68; Armed Forces Schl in Germany Spec Ed Tchr 1698-70; Muncy Schl Dist Itinerant Spec Ed Learning Disabled, Instructional Support Tchr 1970-; *ai:* Assessment, Lang Arts Comm Person; Early Chldhd Parent, Child Night at Schl Organizer; PSEA, NEA 1967-; Womens Org 1970-, Pres, VP, Sec; Youth Commission 1990-; Muncy Boro Cncl Elected Mem; PA Tchr of Yr Awd Candidate; Parent Conf, Tchr In-Svc Speaker; PA Speakers Bureau; *office:* Ward L Myers Elem Schl 125 New St Muncy PA 17756*

AUTH, WILLIAM F., Fifth Grade Teacher; *b:* Floral Park, NY; *m:* Paula LaCommare; *c:* William M. Kerin; *ed:* Southeast MO St (BA) Soc Stud 1971; Adelphi (MS) Elem Ed 1988; 75 Grad Credits; *cr:* US Army Scout Dog Handler 1968-70; Grundy Ave Schl Tchr 1971-; *ai:* Jr Wrestling Pgm 5-12 Yr Olds Coach; Bldg Ldrshp Team Mem; SCTA 1971-, Bldg Rep; *home:* 2 Locust Ct Miller Place NY 11764*

AUTUORI, MICHAEL J., Professor of Biology; *b:* New York City, NY; *ed:* St Johns Univ (BS) Bio 1962, (MS) Zoology 1966, (PHD) Physiology 1969; *cr:* St Johns Univ Bio Instr 1968-69; Univ of Bridgeport Bio Asst Prof 1969-75, Bio Assoc Prof 1975-91, Bio Prof 1991-; *ai:* Pre Med Adv; Class Rank, Weighting; Advy Comm Ridgefield Bd of Ed; Var Prsnl Comms; AAAS, AIBA 1970-; Nature Conservancy 1985-; Wilderness Soc 1990-; Audubon Soc 1991-; CT Fund for Environment 1992-; Ridgefield Consevation Commission 1976-79; Adv, Open Space Ranger 1980-; Ridgefield Planning & Zoning Cmmsn 1993-; Inland Wetland Branch 1993-; Aquifer Protection Agency 1993-; Articles Pub; Various Grants Supporting Stud Rsrch; Emphasis to Environmental Activisor, Ldrshp Greenway Movement, Open Space & Habitat Preservation, Etc; *office:* Univ Of Bridgeport Bridgeport CT 06601*

AVAKAME, EDEM FRANK, Criminal Justice Professor; *b:* Ghana; *ed:* Univ of Cape East (BA) Sociology 1985; Univ of Alberta (MA) Criminology 1990, (PHD) Criminology 1993; *cr:* Temple Univ Asst Prof 1993-; *ai:* AFT 1995-; Amer Soc of Criminology 1990-; Univ of Alberta Grad Stu Awd for Tchng Excl 1993; 1993 Amer Soc of Criminology Gene Garte Stu Paper Competition Gold Medal; *office:* Temple Univ Gladfelter Hall 5th Floor Philadelphia PA 19122*

AVALLE, LINDA RAPKOWICZ, School Psychologist; *b:* Pittsfield, MA; *m:* Bernard J.; *ed:* North Adams St Coll (BSEd) Elem Ed 1973; Amer Intnl Coll (MED) Schl Psych 1989, (CAGS) Schl Psych 1990; *cr:* Pittsfield Pub Schls 4 Grd Tchr 1992, Schl Psychologist 1992-; *ai:* Berkshire Initiative; Natl Assn Schl Psychologists 1990-; MA Tchrs Assn 1973-; Rel Ed Bd; CCD Tchr; Tchr of Yr 1988; *office:* Pittsfield Pub Schls 269 1st St Pittsfield MA 01201

AVALLONE, PATRICIA LIBERATORE, Elem Admin; *b:* Norwalk, CT; *m:* Neil Anthony; *c:* Tara Maturo, Scott Maturo, Melissa, Donna; *ed:* Masters in Special Ed 1993; Southern CT St Univ 6th Yr Adm, Supervision, Addl 60 Hrs Interdisciplinary Stud 1992; CT St Assessor 1987-; Mentor-Cooperating Tchr 1989-; *cr:* St Lawrence Schl Grds 1, 5, 6 1970-73; Forest Elem Grds 5, 6 1984-90; Carrigan MS Tchr 7th Grd Eng 1990-92; Bailey MS Math Tchr 1992-; Helen St Schl Prin; 6 Yrs In Educl Ldrshp; *ai:* Producer, Dir Good Morning Bailey Closed-Circuit News Show; Dir, Choreographer MS Production; Career Incentive, Staff Dev Comm; Mentor Tchr; Tchr of Yr Dinner Chm 1990-91; Connecticut St Assessor; Comprehensive Advy Comm for the St of CT 1996; AFT 1985-; Phi Delta Kappa; CT St Fed of Tchrs 1985-, Ex Bd 2 Yrs; West Haven Fed of Tchrs 1985-, Soc Chm 7 Yrs; Delta Kappa Gamma; Muscular Dystrophy Assn 1991-, West Haven; Master of Ceremonies Jerry Lewis Labor Day Telethon West Haven 1991; Univ of New Haven Alumni Cncl; We Are the World Chm, Staff Developer; Pub Service Awd CT St Fed of Tchrs 1990; CT Tchr of Yr 1995; West Haven Women of Yr; Univ of New Haven Distinguished Alumni Awd 1995; *home:* 99 Honey Pot Rd West Haven CT 06516*

AVALLONE, WENDY LEE, 9th-12th Grd Mathematics Tchr; *b:* Torrington, CT; *m:* Robert Anthony; *c:* Robert J., Dawn K.; *ed:* Cntrl CT St Univ (BS) Math 1981, (MS) Scndry Ed 1991; *cr:* Oliver Wolcott RVTS Adult CETA Instr 1979-81, 9th-12th Grd Chapter I Instr 1981-90, 9th-12th Grd Math Instr 1990-; *ai:* Total Quality Ed (O.K. Team); End of Yr Activity Comms; Jr Math Competition Coord; Schl Evaluation Comm; ATOMIC 1990-; NCTM 1992-; Girl Scouts, Asst 1988-91; Band Parents Torrington Mid Schl 1992-; Cntrl CT St Univ Scndry Ed Grad Stu of Yr 1990; Tchr of Yr 1992-93; *office:* Oliver Wolcott RVT Schl 75 Oliver St Torrington CT 06790*

AVALLYNN, SHERILEE, Vcl Music & Theatre Arts Tchr; *b:* Sewickley, PA; *m:* Michael Todd Messer; *c:* Krista S. Shallcross, Robert G. Shallcross; *ed:* Glenville St Coll (BA) Music Ed 1986; Addl Credit Hrs in Musical Stud at WV Univ; Working towards Speech & Commnctn BA Degree at Kent St Univ; *cr:* Wood Cty Schls Sub Tchr 1986; Gilmer Cty Schls K-8th Grd Voc Cal, Instrumental & Gen Music Tchr 1986-87; Wellsville Schl Dist Sub Tchr 1987-88; Beaver Local Schls Theatre Arts & Vocal, Instrumental & Gen Music Tchr 1989-; *ai:* Masquers Club Thespian Adv; Showstoppers Showchair Dir; HS Theatre Dir; HS & Jr HS Chair Dir; Asst Band Dir; Guard Line Adv; Chrldng Adv; Band Dir; NEA 1989-; BLEA 1989-; Moonlight Players 1988-, Sec, Actress & Choreographer, Various Awds; Salem Comm Theatres 1993-, Dir, Production Bd Mem, Actress & Choreographer, Standing O Awd; Stageleft Players 1995-, Actress & Choreographer; Poetry Pub; Ashland Oil Outstdng Tchr Awd Nom 1993; Beaver Local HS 1st Tchr of the Month in Renaissance Pgm; *office:* Beaver Local HS 13187 State Route 7 Lisbon OH 44432

AVANT, SUSAN MC CALLUM, Biology & Science Teacher; *b:* Washington, DC; *m:* Michael E.; *c:* Mischelle; *ed:* NC A&T St Univ (BS) Home Ec, Gen Sc Ed 1973; Ed; Bio; *cr:* Banneker Jr HS Sci Tchr 1973-80; Hine Jr HS Rdng Tchr 1981-82; P. C. Pub Schls Sci Tchr 1988-; *ai:* Sci Dept Chprsn; 1995 Class Spon; City Wide Elem Sci Fair Judge 1990-; Lead Tchr BRASS Prgm NIH; *office:* Duke Ellington Schl of Arts 3500 R St NW Washington DC 20007

AVARD, RALPH EDWARD, Social Studies & History Tchr; *b:* Frankfurt Main, Germany; *m:* Polly Sue Newbold; *c:* Karl, Kurt, Karoline; *ed:* Valparaiso Univ (BA) His, Geog 1973; Southern CT St Univ (MS) Ed, Soc Stud 1975; Attnd Concordia Coll, Univ of Cntrl FL; *cr:* St Louis Cntry Day Soc Stud, His Tchr 1980-82, Saddle River Day Schl Soc Stud, His 1982-84; Our Redeemer Luth Schl Head Tchr 1984-87; Madison Borough HS Soc Stud, His Tchr 1987-89; South Brunswick HS Soc Stud, His Tchr 1989-; *ai:* Coach Girls Bsktbl; OAH, NJCSS, NCSS 1980-; Greenwich Twp Bd of Ed 1995-; *office:* S Brunswick HS Major Rd Monmouth Junction NJ 08852*

AVELLA, ARISTIDE A., Guidance Counselor; *b:* Newarkk, NJ; *m:* Andrea S.; *c:* Nicole, Scott; *ed:* Kean Coll (BA) Gen Ed 1971, (MA) Cnslng 1978; 21 Post Grad Hrs in Admin, Cnslng; *cr:* Kean Coll Cnslr 1971-72; M. L. Vetter Schl Tchr 1971-91; Grade Chm Tchr 1976-91; M. L. Vetter Schl Cnslr 1991-; *ai:* Tenured Tchr Comm 1978; Tchrs Assn 1971-, Bldg Rep 3 Yrs; NJCA, ACA 1991-; Eatontown Municipal Drug Alliance 1989-, Dir 4 Yrs; Grants: Safe Schls, Chemical Hlth Through Ed; Started Cnslng Prgm in Eastontown; Tchr of Yr 1991; *home:* PO Box 1501 River NJ 08754*

AVELLINO, GRENARDO L., Vice Principal; *b:* Brooklyn, N Theresa R.; *c:* Rose Elizabeth, Louis Henry; *ed:* SUNY at Cob (AAS) Early Chlhd Ed 1983; SUNY at Cortland (BS) Elem Ed Syracuse Univ (MS) Instructional Design, Dev, Evaluation 1987; SU Oswego (CAS) Admin 1993; *cr:* Meachem Elem Schl 6th Grd 1985-91; Lincoln MS Admin Intern, Tchr 1991-93; Corcoran HS Vi 1993-; *ai:* St Admin of NY St Bd of Dirs; Syracuse Assn of Admin Cncl; Jr Class Adv; General Ed Dev Test Chief Examiner; NSSSP Phi Delta Kappa, ASCD 1986-, Recruiting New Mems Assoc; Comm Church 1994-, Youth Group Adv; Syracuse Admin Assn Lead Incentive Awd; *office:* Corcoran HS 919 Glenwood Ave Syracus 13207*

AVENA, LINDA LEOTTA, Library Teacher; *b:* Staten Island, N Joseph; *c:* Amanda, Gregory, Brittany; *ed:* Univ of Tampa (BS) Ed Richmond Coll (MA) Ed 1973; Coll of Sci 30 Post-Grad Credits; Cty Coll 16 Post-Grad Credits; *cr:* PS 23 3rd Grd Tchr 1968-78, 2n Tchr 1984-85, 3rd Grd Tchr 1985-91, 4th Grd Tchr 1992-95, Librn *ai:* AFT 1968-; UFT 1968-; *office:* PS 23 30 Natick St Staten Islan 10306

AVENA, LUCILLE MARY, Junior High School Teacher; *b:* Bridg CT; *ed:* Sacred Heart Univ (BA) Elem Ed, Eng 1970; 30 Credit Hrs A Supervision; *cr:* Holy Rosary Schl 4th, 6th Grd Tchr 1971-76; St A Schl 5th-8th Grd Tchr 1976-94; Our Lady of The Assumption Jr HS 1994-; *ai:* Stu Cncl, Yrbk Moderator; Stu Asst Team; Crisis Team; 1971-; *home:* 36 Winslow Rd Trumbull CT 06611

AVERY, CHARLENE CORNELL, Office Systems Program Ins Bryan, OH; *m:* Harold E.; *c:* Michael, Steven; *ed:* Bowling Green St (BS) Bus Ed 1962; MS Degree Equivalent 30 Grad Hrs; *cr:* Birmir Groves HS Bus Tchr 1962; Davis Coll Bus Instr 1962-66; North Balt HS Eng Tchr 1966-67; Woodville-Woodmore HS Eng Tchr 1967-69; Cty Pub Lib Reference Librn, Sec 1970-75; Vanguard Joint Voc Schl 1975-; *ai:* Bus Profs of Amer Adv; Continuous Improvement, In-Svc, Support Svcs Comms: AVA, Mem of Office Systems Advy Comm; O Assn; OH Cncl on Voc Ed, Awd of Spec Commendation; Trinity U Meth Church 1966-, Co-Dev of Jr Church; Pi Omega Pi; Jennings Sc *office:* Vanguard Joint Voc Schl 1306 Cedar St Fremont OH 43420

AVERY, JEAN (CARMELL), Chemistry & Physics Teacher; *b:* Pitts MA; *m:* Gordon C. Jr.; *ed:* Univ of MA (BS) Chem 1969; Worcester Tech (MNS) Chem 1984; Attnd Univ of IA, Anna Maria, Bridgewat *cr:* Solon Jr HS Sci Tchr 1969-70; West Liberty HS Chem & Physics 1970-72; U of MA Med Schl Rsrch 1972; Quabbin Regnl HS Ch Physics Tchr 1973-85; Wachuseh Regnl Chem Tchr 1985-86; Chath Sr HS Chem & Physics Tchr 1990-; *ai:* Jr Sci & Hum Symposium Sci Curr Comm Co-Chprsn; Sci Safety Adv; NSTA; MTA; MME & M NSTA Funded Sci Grant for Grad Work; Bell System Outstdng Tch 1979; Friends of Pleasant Bay Grant; AT&T Grant; *office:* Chatham HS 425 Crowell Rd Chatham MA 02633*

AVERY, JOHN HERBERT, Agribusiness Dept Chair; *b:* Sunfield, M Marsha Elena Hancock; *c:* Deborah Ann Serradilla, John Paul, James; *ed:* MI St Univ (BS) Ag 1952; Univ of WI at Platteville (MS) Ag 1976; Univ of IL (DR) Ed 1984; *cr:* Dairyland Seed Dist Sales 1965-78; Southwest WI Tech Coll FArm Oper Instr 1974-78; Ric Comm Coll Ag Coord 1978-85; DE Vly Coll Agribusiness Chm 1985 Natl Ag Mrktg Assn, Stu Chptr Adv; Intnl, Hnrs Comms; Natl Ag M Assn 1987-, Stu Adv, Most Improved Chptr; Penn Ag Industries 1976-; Roth Living Museum 1995-, Curator; Bucks Co Intnl Trade 1994-; Tech Adv, Participant 3 Object Lession Videos; E Publications, Articles 1977-; *office:* Delaware Valley Coll 700 E Butle Doylestown PA 18901*

AVERY, MARIA ROSE, 8th Grade Teacher; *b:* Hartford, CT; *c:* Ur CT (BS) Ed 1988; *ed:* Addl 40 Hrs Central St Univ; Summer A Jagiellonian Univ, Poland 1995; St Lucy Schl 3rd Grd Tchr 1988-9 Grd Tchr 1990-95; Portland MS Long Term Sub 1995-; *cr:* St Lucy 3rd Grd Tchr 1988-90, 6th Grd Tchr 1990-95; Portland MS Long Term 1995-; *ai:* Martin & Sophie Grzyb Prize for Excl in Polish Stud 199

AVERY, ROBERT A., Guidance Counselor; *b:* Portsmouth, NH Virginia Potosek; *c:* Todd, Susan, Catherine; *ed:* Univ of MA (BA) Admin 1963; Westfield St Coll (MED) Cnslng 1969; Univ of MA (C Ed 1974; *cr:* Turners Falls HS Bus Tchr 1964-69, Guid Cnslr 1969-78, Prin 1978-80, Guid Cnslr 1980-; *ai:* Cross Cty, Track Coach; Peer C Adv; St Awd Winning Stu Cncl Adv; NEA, MA Tchrs Assn, Gill-Mon Tchrs Assn 1963-; Town of Montague Assessor 1970-82, Ch Moutague Zoning, Bd of Appeals 1968-70; Lib Trustee 1970-; Polish Sport & Cultural Org Pres, Founder; Tchr of Eng Poland 1992-93, *office:* Turners Falls HS Turnpike Rd Turners Falls MA 01376

AVIDON, RICHARD S., History & English Teacher; *b:* New York, *ed:* Yale Univ (BA) His 1980; Univ of VA (JD) Law 1984; *cr:* Arent, Kinter, Plotkin & Kahn Attorney 1985-86; Self Employed Carp 1986-88; Georgetown Day HS Tchr 1989-; *ai:* MD Bar 1986-; *o* Georgetown Day Schl 4200 Davenport St NW Washington DC 20016

AVINGTON, CARLA MICHELLE, Biology Teacher; *b:* Parkers WV; *ed:* Xavier Univ (BS) Tchng Bio 1991, (MED) Scndry Ed 1995 Parkersburg City Pk Tennis Instr 1990-92; Norwood HS Bio, Phys Sci 1991-92; St Bernard-Elmwood HS Sub Tchr 1992; Roger Bacon HS C Bio Tchr 1992-; *ai:* Boys, Girls Var Tennis 4 Yrs; Chaperone Right to Group; Stu Spiritual Life Team Head; Jaycees 1996-; Nom Ashland Tchr Recognition 1996; *office:* Roger Bacon HS 4320 Vine St Cinci OH 45217*

AVINO BARRACATO, KATHLEEN, Dean of Academic Affair Brooklyn, NY; *m:* Joseph L. Jr.; *c:* Katrina; *ed:* Pratt Inst (BA) Archite 1978; NY Univ Cert; U of TX at Austin Grad Stud; *cr:* Michael H Sp Archit Draftsperson 1974-78; Brodsey & Adler Arch & Eng Draftsp & Designer 1978-79; Emery Roth & Son Arch Designer 1979; NYC of Parks & Recreation Borough Design Mgr 1979-81; *ai:* Stu Cnslng; Prep Pgm Dir; Employment Cnslr; Prof Women in Construction 1 Marquis, 2000 Notable Women, Whos Who in American Women & W Who in Bus & Industry; *office:* Inst Of Design & Construction Willoughby St Brooklyn NY 11201*

AVOSSO, LOUIS JOHN, Professor of Biology; *b:* Brooklyn, NY Marion Corin; *c:* Michele, Danny; *ed:* CO St Univ (BS) Zoology 1 (MAT) Bio 1965; Sarasota Univ (PHD) Ed 1972; *cr:* Nassau Comm Prof 1967-; *ai:* Nea 1969-; BSA 1983-85, Ldr.*

AXEL, NATHAN STEVEN, Band Director & Music Teacher Brooklyn, NY; *m:* Judith Brickman; *c:* David, Daniel; *ed:* NY Univ Music Ed 1969; 30 Credits Above BS in Different Courses Brooklyn Jersey City St Coll; *cr:* Tottenville HS Band & Music Apprecia Beginner Band, 1969-; All City Concert Band Assoc Dir 1992-; *ai:* Band Dir; Concert Band Dir; Marching Band Asst Dir; United Fed of T 1969-; MEAN YC 1994-; Chancellors Awd; Partners in Ed Awd; Ex Tchng Awd; Very Spec Arts Awd; Dixie Classic Grand Champion I *office:* Tottenville HS 100 Luten Ave Staten Island NY 10312

AN, DOUGLAS N., Director; *b:* New Hyde Park, NY; *ed:* SUNY at ıgdale (AAS) Recreation Supervision 1971; SUNY at Brockport Hlth Ed 1973; Adelphi Univ (MA) Hlth Ed 1977; Admin Cert SAS, NY St; *cr:* Bethpage Schls Hlth, PE Tchr 1973-74; Locust Vly Schls Ed Tchr 1974-85, Admin Asst 1985-87, Dir Alternative Schl 1987-; r Wrestling, Asst Var Ftbl Coach; NYSAHPERD, NYSFPHE 1973-; u Cty Wrestling Coaches Assn 1973-, Pres 1992-; *office:* Locust Vly Schl Dist Horse Hollow Rd Locust Valley NY 11560

LL, ROBERT STOCKTON, Prof of Exercise Sci Dept; *b:* Salem, *m:* Roberta Walker McColl; *ed:* Springfield Coll (BS) PE 1975; IN (MS) PE 1976; OH St Univ (PHD) PE & Exercise Physiology; on Acad Post Grad General Stud 1971; *cr:* IN Univ Grad Tchng Asst 76; Berkshire Comm Coll PE Instr 1976-81; OH St Univ Grad rch Asst 1982-84; Southern CT St Univ Prof of Dept of Exercise Sci siology of Exercise Tchr 1984; *ai:* Var Soccer Prgm Conditioning Amer Coll of Sports Medicine 1982-; New England Chapter Amer f Sports Medicine 1984-, Pres 1995-; Natl Strength & Conditioning 1994-; CT St Univ Grant 29000 Dollars 1995; *office:* Southern CT St 501 Crescent St Human Performance Lab New Haven CT 06515

A, HERMINZUL,JR., Biling Math & Science Teacher; *b:* Cali ıbia, South America; *m:* Damaris Rodriguez; *c:* Rachael, Victoria, nzul III; *ed:* Universidad del Valle (BA) Bio, Chem 1981; Brooklyn MA) Gen Sci 1992; 15 Semester Hrs Biling Ed; *cr:* Edward R. w HS Tchr 1989-; *ai:* Hispanic, Soccer Adv; After Schl Tutoring; Group Brooklyn Schls; Translation Span Bio Lab NYS Schls, Bio ts Test Brooklyn Schls; *office:* Edward R. Murrow HS 1600 Avenue oklyn NY 11230

A, HOMERETTA M., Library Media Specialist; *b:* Taylorville, IL; seph; *c:* Jared; *ed:* FL St (BME) Music Ed 1973; Western MD (MS) Media 1995; West Chester Univ Post-Grad Stud Westminster Choir; n St Masters Equivalency in Music Ed 1983; *cr:* Leon HS Assn Dir 1973-77; Antilles Schl Music Tchr 1977-79; Sparrows Point Mid sic Chair 1980-89; Chesapeake High Music Chair 1989-94; Fullerton Lib Music Specialist 1995-; *ai:* Fullerton Players; NEA 1980-; Music 1980-; Amer Choral Dirs Assn 1980-; MEMO 1995-; Music Dir Hiss Stdnts Have Received Top Ratings at Choral Festivals; Performed acys Day Parade; Conducted more than 50 Musicals for Summer Dinner Theaters; *home:* 9015 Gardenia Rd Baltimore MD 21236*

R, KAREN E., High School Soc Studies Tchr; *b:* Manchester, NH; *m:* rd A.; *c:* Stephanie; *ed:* Notre Dame Coll (BA) 1973; *cr:* Manchester HS Soc Stud Tchr 1974-; *ai:* MEA, NHEA, NEA 1974-; NH Cncl Soc Studies; *office:* Manchester Meml HS Porter St Manchester NH

R, WILLIAM LLOYD, Math, Social Stud & Rdng Tchr; *b:* nantic, CT; *m:* Mara Vimba; *c:* Kyle, Thomas, Jack; *ed:* Willimantic hrs Coll (BA) Ed 1961; Univ of CT (MA) Elem Admin 1965; *cr:* ntry Grammer Schl 5th Grd Tchr 1961-66; Coventry HS 8th Grd Tchr 70; Kramer Schl 8th Grd Tchr 1971-73; Captain Nathan Hale Schl rd Tchr 1974-; *ai:* HS & MS Bsbl, Bsktbl & Soccer Coach in ntry & Willimantic 28 Yrs; CEA, NEA 1961-; CIAC 1967-85; ntry Jr Soccer 1970-, Pres, Founder; Coventry Little League 1970-85; & Coach; Coventry Recreation Comm 1973-79, Pgrm Dir Willimantic oved Bsbl Umpires, Pres & Tres, 20 Yrs Svc Awd; Math Curr Comm Coventry 25 Yr Svc Awd; CT Umpiring Awd 20 Yrs; United Way Rep Coventry Tchr of Yr 1987-88; *home:* 44 Plains Rd Windham CT

RS, ANN MERRIGAN, Professor; *b:* Springfield, MA; *w:* Paul L. Jr. *c:* Cathy Keohane, Paul III, Peter, Richard, William, Jennifer; *ed:* of MA (BS) Foods, Nutrition 1953; Nutrition, Ed Credits Plymouth amingham St; *cr:* Deerfield HS Home Ec Tchr 1953-55; Duxbury HS Ec Tchr 1970-79; Massasoit Comm Coll Culinary Arts Dept Chm ; *ai:* Culinary Art Club Adv; Dietary Nutrition, Acad Adv to Stdnts; 1953-; Amer Assn of Univ Woman 1956-68; Amer Fed of Chefs -95; Wolfeboro Chamber of Commerce 1990-91; Village Players ; *home:* 19 Pointe Sewall Rd Wolfeboro NH 03894

RS, CAROL PEERY, Foreign Language Dept Chair; *b:* Columbus, *m:* Randall D.; *c:* Ryan V., Cameron A.; *ed:* Miami Univ (AB) Span (BSEd) Span 1977; Univ of CO (MA) Span Linguistics 1980; Attnd Urbino Italy, Univ de Costa Rica; *cr:* Univ of CO Tchng Asst -80; Miami Univ Asst to Dir of Admissions 1980-81; Columbus Schl irls Chair Frgn Lang Dept 1981-; *ai:* Former Asst Vllybl Coach; Span Black Awareness Club & Stu Cncl Adv; Sigma Delta Pi 1977-; SP 1981-; AATFL 1981-; Cum Laude 1981-; Bd Directions for Yth ; Ballet Met 1994-, Comm Mem; Article Pub 1981; *office:* Columbus For Girls 56 S Columbia Ave Columbus OH 43209

RS, DEBORAH, Art Teacher; *b:* Houston, TX; *ed:* CO Coll (BA) Cum Laude 1971; Univ of NH (MAT) Art Ed 1973; Attnd Southern MA Univ of NH, Univ of VA; *cr:* Kennett Jr HS Art Tchr 1973-75; SAU al Dists Elem, Jr HS Art Tchr 1975-88, Chprsn Art Dept 1978-89; John r Schl K-6 Grd Art Tchr 1988-; *ai:* Art Clubs Adv; Art Curr Comm; A, NEA 1973-; Lake Winnipesaukee Assn 1985-; MT Washington Vly Assn; Taoist Tai Chi 1995-; Outstdng Young Woman Amer 1984; NH dng Elem Art Tchr 1985; Finalist NH Christa Mc Auliffe Sabbatical 1987; US Art Delegation Japan People to Peopl e 1992; Author The of The White Mountains 1989; Illustrator for Field Guide; *home:* PO 701 North Conway NH 03860*

RS, DEBORAH A., Economics Instructor; *ed:* Robert Morris Coll (BA) Ec 1990; 9 Credit Hrs Penn St Univ; *cr:* Butler Cty Comm Coll nstr 1990-; *ai:* Write a Bi-Weekly Ec Column for N Hills News rd; Numerous Articles Pub; *office:* Butler Cty Comm Coll PO Box Butler PA 16001

RS, JAMES RAY, Assoc Prof in Pastoral Studies; *b:* Hanover, PA; *m:* Ann Sterner; *c:* Jared Ray, Joel James, Jeremiah James; *ed:* Lancaster Coll (BS) Bible, Pastoral Stud 1980; Rider Coll (MA) Cnslng 1985; rd Grad Schl (PHD) Rel, Soc 1992; *cr:* Philadelphia Coll of Bible Dir nrstn Svs 1980-86; Easton Union Church Sr Pastor 1986-93; Lancaster Coll Chair, Pastoral Stud Dept 1993-; *ai:* Shepherds Staff Adv; angelical Theological Soc 1993-; Oxford Soc of Scholars; Oxford ice Awd; Articles Pub 1995; *office:* Lancaster Bible Coll 901 Rd Lancaster PA 17601

RS, MARIANNE KOZAK, Sixth Grade Teacher; *b:* Toms River, NJ; onald; *c:* Joseph A.; *ed:* East Stroudsburg Univ (BS) Elem Ed 1988; er's Equivalency 1993; Rdng Specialist Cert; *cr:* Pocono Elem Ctr Grd Tchr 1988-93; Pocono Intermediate Schl Sixth Grd Tchr 1993-; PMEA, PSEA, NEA 1988-; *office:* Pocono Mountn Intrmdt Schl ono Mountain Schl Rd Swiftwater PA 18370*

RS, PHILLIP DENNIS, Technology Education Instr; *b:* Washington, *m:* Charlotte Dunson; *c:* Allen Phillip; *ed:* Cntrl St Univ (BS) Elem 972, (BA) Industrial Arts Ed 1973; Bowie St Univ (MED) Scndry Ed ; 15 Hrs Tech Ed Trng; 6 Hrs Adult Ed Classes at Washington-Tech 3 Hrs Drafting-Design Classesat PG Comm Coll; *cr:* DC Pub Schls strial Arts Tchr 1973-81, Adult Ed Inst 1979; Charles Cty Pub Schls Ed Instr 1981-, Dept Chr; *ai:* Anacostia HS 7 Yr Stud Govt Spon; key HS Girls Track Team 2 Yr Head Coach; Adv of 12 Good Men Elite ; 7 Yr Asst Supt of Sunday Schl; AFT 1973-; NEA 1973-, Charles E. ng Awd; NAIA 1975-; Alpha Phi Alpha 1970-, VP, Chapter MVP; Pershing Rifles 1969-, Corp Sec, Charles E. Young Awd; Anacostia HS Class of 1968 Inc 1989-, 1st Pres, Co-Founder, Bd Chm; Cntrl St Univ Alumni Assn 1975-, Bd of Dir Alumni Assn, Chapter VP; HS Stdnts 1968, Stdnts Amer Univ & Colls 1971 Who's Who; Stdnts Voted Most Influential Educator 1988; *home:* 8712 Jeremy Ct Clinton MD 20735

AYLESWORTH, CHRIS ROBERT, HS Science Teacher & Chprsn; *b:* Johnson City, NY; *m:* Gayle G.; *c:* Jennifer, Brendan, Jillian, Ryan; *ed:* Cornell Univ (BS) Animal Sci 1971; NY St Coll of Veterinary Medicine (DVM) Veterinary 1974; 21 Hrs for Tchr Cert 1989-95; *cr:* Self-Employed Veterinarian Equine Sports Medicine 1974-88; Rangeley Region Sport Shop Owner & Operator 1988-; Rangeley Lakes Regnl Schl HS Sci Tchr & Chprsn 1989-; *ai:* Envirothon Coach 1991-; Jr HS Boys Bsktbl Coach 1994-; AVMA 1974-; NEA, MEA, MSTA, NSTA 1989-; RTA 1989-, Negotiator; Chamber of Commerce 1988-, Advertising Comm; Rangeley Region Fishing Assn, Comm Mem, Consultant; Franklin Cty Environmental Tchr of Yr 1993-94; Commencement Speaker 1994; *home:* PO Box 1118 Rangeley ME 04970

AYLWARD, CHRISTOPHER MICHAEL, Sixth Grade Teacher; *b:* Boston, MA; *m:* Mary A. Wiley; *c:* Jamie Lynn; *ed:* Boston Coll (BA) Elem Ed 1973; *cr:* Mastricola Elem Schl 4th Grd Tchr 1973-75, 5th Grd Tchr 1975-79; Thornton's Ferry Elem Schl 5th Grd Tchr 1979-84; Gove MS 6th Grd Tchr 1989-; *ai:* NEA 1989-, Bldg Rep; Awded Cert of Achvmt Dedication to Ed & Children Merrimack Tchrs Assn 1980; *home:* 418 Merrimack St Manchester NH 03103

AYOTTE, MARILYNN OLDS, Sixth Grade Teacher; *b:* Scranton, PA; *m:* Dennis J.; *c:* Eileen L. Ball; *ed:* PA St Univ (BS) Elem Ed 1967; West Chester Univ (MS) Soc Sci 1972; Attnd Washburn Univ Law Schl, Villanova Univ; *cr:* USD No 437 6th Grd Tchr 1967-69; Haverford Twp schl Dist 6th Grd Tchr 1969-74; Downingtown Area Schl Dist 5th-6th Grd Tchr 1974-; *ai:* Future Problem Solvers; NEA, PSEA, DAEA; PA St Alumni; Fulbright Exchange Tchr 1986-87; *office:* Pickering Valley Elem Schl 121 Byers Rd Chester Springs PA 19425*

AYTON, ROBERT WARD, History Teacher & Coach; *b:* Wuwei, China; *m:* Claire Louise McCall; *c:* Charlynne, Kimberly, Robert; *ed:* Taylor Univ (BS) Ed & His 1965; Lehigh Univ (MA) Guidance & Counseling; *cr:* Kendallville IN Jr HS Tchr & Coach 1965-68; Hatboro Horsham HS Tchr 1968-; *ai:* Boys Cross Cntry & Spring Track & Field Coach; NEA 1965-; Suburban Bucks Jaycees Outstanding Young Educator Awd 1985; Hatboro Horsham HS Champions of Learning Awd 1991-92; Hatboro-Horsham Yrbk Dedication; *office:* Hatboro Horsham Sr HS 899 Horsham Rd Horsham PA 19044

AYUB, JAMSHED, Chemistry Professor; *b:* Agra, India; *m:* Bushra Seema; *c:* Suniah, Rimsha; *ed:* Aligarh Muslim Univ (BS) Chem 1975, (MS) Biochemistry 1977; Old Dominion Univ (MS) Clinical Chem, (PHD) Biomedical Sci; *cr:* Pan Data Systems Inc Chemist 1985-86; Natl Heart, Lung & Blood Inst Chemist 1986-89; Natl Cancer Inst Chemist 1989-93; Montgomery Coll Assoc Prof 1993-; *ai:* Curr & Stu Review Comms; ASCP 1985-; NRCC 1985-; AAUP 1993-; Aligarh Alumni Assn 1986-, Sec; Clinics in Lab Medicine 1993; Journal of Virology 1987 & 1988; Infect Control Hosp Epidemiol 1992; *office:* Montgomery Coll Takoma Park 7600 Takoma Ave Takoma Park MD 20912

AZZARELLI, LISA MARIE, Former English Teacher; *b:* Cincinnati, OH; *ed:* St Univ of NY at Buffalo (BA) Eng, Comparative Lit 1994, (MA) Eng Lit 1996; Tchr Cert Prgm; Natl Hum Summer Tchr Inst; *cr:* Mt St Mary Acad Eng Tchr 1993-95, Sub, Eng, His Tchr 1995-; *ai:* Lit Magazine Moderator; Fine Arts Week Comm; Sr Career Adv; Buffalo Americanist Digest 1995-; Golden Key 1994-, Natl Acad Hnr; Natl Hum Inst Fellow 1995.

AZZARTO, ANTHONY JOSEPH,SJ, Chaplain & Teacher of Religion; *b:* Brooklyn, NY; *ed:* Fordham Univ (AB) Eng 1962, (MA) Eng 1964; Woodstock (MDIV) Theology 1970; Seminars in Eng, Theology, Spirituality; *cr:* St Peter's Prep Eng, Theology Tchr 1963-66, 1972-80, 1985-; *ai:* Schl Chaplain; Retreat, Liturgy Coord; JSEA 1985-; Pastor in Nigeria 5 Yrs.

B

BAACKE, NANCY L., English Teacher; *b:* Johnstown, PA; *m:* Timothy A.; *c:* George J. Burns, Christopher M. Burns, Patrick R.; *ed:* Univ of Pittsburgh at Johnstown (BA) Scndry Ed, Comm 1988; Indiana Univ of PA (MS) Eng Lit 1996; *cr:* Univ of Pittsburgh Frosh Wrtg Instr 1987-88; Portage Area HS Eng Tchr 1988; Penn Cambria Schl Dist Eng Tchr 1989-; *ai:* Authentic Assessment, OBE Comms; PA Wrtg Assessment; Tchr Excl, Stu Achvmt Educated; NEA, PSEA 1989-; Presidential Scholar; Univ Scholar; *office:* Penn Cambria Schl Dist 401 Linden Ave Cresson PA 16630

BAACKE, TIMOTHY A., Director of Bands; *b:* Pittsburgh, PA; *m:* Nancy L.; *c:* George Burns, Chris Burns, Patrick Burns; *ed:* Edinboro Univ (BS) Music Ed 1982; Grad Stud Indiana Univ of PA, Vandercook Coll of Music at Chicago, West Chester Univ; *cr:* Conemaugh Twp Area HS Bands Dir 1982-88; Bald Eagle Nittany HS Bands Dir 1988-89; Penn Cambria HS Bands Dir 1989-; *ai:* Marching, Jazz, Symphonic Bands; NEA, MENC, PMEA, PSEA 1982-; Outstdng Young Man of Amer 1985; *office:* Penn Cambria HS 401 Linden Ave Cresson PA 16630

BABB, CATHLYN BORGGAARD, Teacher of the Deaf; *b:* Worcester, MA; *m:* Robert A.; *c:* Megan, Ryan; *ed:* Boston Univ (BS) Spcl Ed & Elem Ed 1981; Gallaudet Univ (MA) Ed of the Deaf 1985; Western MD Coll 30 Credit Hrs; *cr:* MD Schl for the Deaf HS Lang Arts Tchr 1985-92; Frederick Cty Pub Schls Elem Tchr of the Deaf 1992-; *ai:* Parent Vol; Daisy Girl Scout Troop Parent Asst; Screening Comm Interpreter; CED 1985-, Prof Cert; Frederick Interpreters Group 1986-; PCRID 1986-; RID 1988-, Transliteration Cert; Frederick Rdng Cncl 1992-; SMD IRA Chptr 1992-; FCTA 1992-; MSTA 1992-; NEA 1992-; IRA 1994-; Girl Scouts of USA 1968-, Adult Mem; Deaf Access Svcs Inc 1986-; *office:* Parkway Elem Schl 300 Carroll Pky Frederick MD 21701*

BABB, FREDA CRISSINGER, Business Education Teacher; *b:* Sunbury, PA; *m:* David D.; *c:* Matthew, Michele; *ed:* Elizabethtown Coll (BS) Bus Ed 1965; Tech, Cmptr Trng; *cr:* Tri-Valley HS Bus Educ Tchr 1965-67; Allentown Schl Dist Bus Educ Tchr 1972-77; Emmaus HS Bus Educ Tchr 1982-88; Northwestern Lehigh HS Bus Educ Tchr 1988-; *ai:* Local Occupational Advy Cncl Mem; Cmptr Wkshp Instr; NEA, PSEA, NWLEA, PBEA 1988-; John Robert Gregg Meml Awd; *office:* Northwestern Lehigh HS 6493 Route 309 New Tripoli PA 18066

BABBIT, BARBARA A., 6th Grade Teacher; *b:* Bronx, NY; *ed:* Lesley Coll (MA) Spcl Ed 1974; 60 In-Svc Credits Beyond Masters; *cr:* Maimonides Sch 2nd & 3rd Grd Tchr 1974-78; Herricks Pub Schl 4th-6th Grd Tchr 1978-; *ai:* Maimonides Schl Poetry Club; Report Card & Portfolio Assessment Comms; Curr Dev in Math & Soc Stud; Collegial Circles in SS Rsrch & LA Writing; AFT 1974-; NEA 1974-; NYSUT 1978-; *office:* Herricks MS 7 Hilldale Rd Albertson NY 11507

BABBITT, LUCIENNE CARTER, Social Studies Teacher; *b:* Baltimore, MD; *m:* Mark G.; *c:* Timothy, Andrew, Melissa; *ed:* Wesley Coll (BS) Soc Stud 1993; Post Grad Univ of DE; *cr:* Poly Tech HS Soc Stud Tchr 3 Yrs; *ai:* Soph Class Adv; Sr Project Comm; Comm Svc Outreach; NEA; Natl Soc Stud Assn; Psych Assn; DE Stock Market Winner HS Division 1994-95; Univ of DE Ec Ldr Prgm; *office:* Polytech HS PO Box 97 Woodside DE 19980

BABCOCK, JOHN WINFORD, Mathematics Teacher; *b:* Cornwall, NY; *m:* Schrene Mattingly; *ed:* SUNY at Geneseo (BA) Math, Ed 1987; SUNY at Potsdam (MA) Math, Ed 1993; *cr:* South Jefferson Cntrl Schl Math Instr 1988-; *ai:* Coach JV Wrestling 1990-, Girls Soccer 1988-91; Class Adv1988-92; NYSUT 1988-.

BABCOCK, MAXINE KATHRYN (BUTTON), Social Studies Teacher; *b:* Syracuse, NY; *m:* Craig Eugene; *c:* Grace Alicia; *ed:* Alma Coll (BA) His & Eng 1983; Syracuse Univ (MS) Soc Stud Ed 1985; *cr:* Thousand Islands HS Soc Stud Tchr & Soccer & Bsktbl Coach 1985-; *ai:* SADD Adv; Jr Var Soccer Coach 1985-94; Jr Var Bsktbl Coach 1982-88; Var Bsktbl Coach 1988-89; *office:* Thousand Islands HS Sand Bay Rd PO Box 1000 Clayton NY 13624

BABCOCK, MICHAEL CARTER, Biology & Chemistry Teacher; *b:* Albion, NY; *m:* Dianna Zientarski; *ed:* SUNY Coll at Plattsburgh (BS) Bio & Chem 1974, (MS) Rdng 1983; 30 Grad Hrs Spcl Ed; *cr:* Liverpool HS Sci, Bio & Chem Tchr 1975-; *ai:* AFT, NYSUT & ULFA 1975-; NSTA & STANYS 1977-; NYSATE 1992-, Tchr of the Yr 1992-93; *office:* Liverpool HS 4338 Wetzel Rd Liverpool NY 13090*

BABEL, GERRI ARBUTINA, 1st Grade Teacher; *b:* New York City, NY; *m:* Dale; *c:* Denise Koehler, Greg; *ed:* Geneva Coll (BA) Elem Ed 1974; Penn St Beaver Campus 18 credit Hrs for Cert; *cr:* Chippewa Elem 1st Grd Tchr 1975-80; Northwestern Elem 1st Grd Tchr 1980-; *ai:* BEA, NEA 1975-; Western PA Conservancy 1990-; *home:* 106 Morgans Ln Darlington PA 16115

BABERADT, STEPHEN JAY,JR., High School Music Director; *b:* Brooklin, MA; *m:* Jeanine Marie Larsen; *c:* Samantha June; *ed:* Univ of Lowell (BM) Music Ed 1983, (BM) Theory, Composition 1984; Attnd New England Conservatory of Music; Ed, Supervisory, Wind Ensemble Conducting, Orff Cert Levels I-III 1985-87; Jazz Improv Stud Berklee Coll of Music 1995; *cr:* Stoneham Pub Schls Instrumental, Classroom Instr HS, MS 1984-86; Peabody Veterans Meml HS Instrumental, Choral, Classroom Music Tchr 1986-; *ai:* Composer; Adjudicator; Clinician; Dir Jazz Ensemble; Show Choir; Marching Band; Color Guard; Comm Musicals; Drill Writer, Instr; Bus Entrepreneur; MMEA, MENC 1984-; AFT, MTA 1984-; Natl Eagle Scout Assn 1977-; SPEBSQSA 1985-; AOPA 1989-; Eagle Scout 1977; Golden Apple Awd 1989-90; *office:* Peabody Veterans Memorial HS 485 Lowell St Peabody MA 01960*

BABIAK, ROBERT JOSEPH, 8th Grd Social Studies Teacher; *b:* Pittsburgh, PA; *m:* Renee Michelle; *ed:* Univ of Pittsburgh (BA) Scndry Ed 1987; 12 Credit Hrs Bowie St Univ, Schl Admin, Supervision; *cr:* Benjamin Stoddert MS Soc Stud Tchr 1987-; *ai:* Stu Cncl Spon, Yrbk Adv; 8th Grd Team Ldr; Schl Improvement, Crisis Team Mem; Ed Assn Bldg Rep; NEA 1987-, Bldg Rep; *office:* Mattawoman MS 10145 Berry Rd Waldorf MD 20603

BABICH, KATHLEEN SIMKO, Family & Consumer Sci Tchr; *b:* Staten Island, NY; *m:* Charles Joseph; *c:* Timothy, Daniel; *ed:* Marywood Coll at Scranton (BS) Home Ec & Dietetics 1969; NY Univ (MA) Specialist in Nutrition & Dietetics 1972; Cert in Supervision from Kean Coll at Union; Home Ec Ed Cert; *cr:* Raritan Bay Medical Ctr Clinical Nutritionist & Educator 1970-76; Johnson & Johnson Nutrition Consultant 1979-86; Muhlenberg Medical Ctr-Schl of Nursing Nutrition Instr 1981-86; Edison Twp Bd of Ed Family & Consumer Scis Tchr 1986-; *ai:* FHA Adv; Curr Comm; NEA, NJEA, Amer Assn of Family & Consumer Scis 1986-; Amer Dietetic Assn 1970-; NJ Dietetic Assn 1970-, Sec, Pub Relations, Nominating Comm Chair, NJ Recognized Young Dietician Of Yr; Publications in Topics in Clinical Nutrition, Nutrition Support in Home Hlth; Allied Hlth Traineeship for Grad Stud; Whos Who Among Stdnts in Amer Colls & Univs; Omicron Mu; Pi Lambda Theta; US Pub Hlth Svc Dietetic Internship & Registration; Future Tchrs Club Past Adv; *office:* John P Stevens HS 855 Grove Ave Edison NJ 08820

BABIEC, EDWINA M. (GUGEL), 4th Grade Teacher; *b:* Brooklyn, NY; *m:* Peter F.; *c:* Dianne M. Dalton, Susan C. Goodwin; *ed:* RI Coll (EdB) Elem Ed 1957; 15 Hrs Post Grad Stud; *cr:* North Schl 5th Grd Tchr 1957-60; Heartwood Schl 5th Grd Tchr 1960-61; North Schl 4-5th Grd Tchr 1961-; *ai:* Seekonk Tchrs Assn, MTA, NEA 1957-; Pawt Comm Players 1970-, Recording Sec 4 Yrs, Bd of Governors 16 Yrs, Membership Chm 10 Yr, Presidents Awd 1983, 1989; *office:* North Schl North St Seekonk MA 02771

BABINSKI, KAREN V., First Grade Teacher; *b:* Kearny, NJ; *c:* Carl Jr.; *ed:* Nework St Tchrs Coll (BA) Elem Ed 1969; Kean Coll of NJ (MA) Curr Dev 1992; 40 Addl Credits; *cr:* Schuyler Schl First Grd Tchr 1969-; *ai:* Var Chrldng Coach; HS Musical Choreographer; NEA 1975-, Del Assem; NJEA, HCEA 1969-; Kearney Educ Assn 1969-, Treas; Schuyler Schl PTA 1969-; KHS Band Parent Assn 1972-; Kardinal Booster Club 1987-, Dir; Presbyn Boys, Girls Club 1980-, Prgm Dir; Natl PTA Life Mem; Kappa Delta Pi; Polish Amer Citizens Club Citizen of Yr 1995; *office:* Schuyler Schl 644 Forest St Kearny NJ 07032*

BABISH, DOROTHY OLIVA, 6th Grade Reading Teacher; *b:* Brooklyn, NY; *m:* Don; *c:* Paul V. Oliva Jr., James Scott Oliva; *ed:* Queens Coll (BA) Ed 1957; Temple Univ (MED) Ed 1978; 20 Addl Credits; *cr:* Toby Farms Elem Schl 1st Grd Tchr 1966-70; Nether Providence Elem Schl 1st, 3rd, 5th Grd Tchr, Chprsn 1970-94; Strath Haven MS 6th Grd Rdng Tchr 1994-; *ai:* Site Base Team Lang Arts Represent; Stu Life Chprsn; WSEA Exec Cncl Mem; Drama Club Dir; Chester Twp EA 1966-, VP; WSEA 1970-, Head Fac Rep, Fac Rep, Exec Cncl; PSEA, NEA 1966-; Cert Merit for Outstdng Contributions to Educl Prgm Wallingford, Swarthmore Schl Dist 1988 1990, 1992-93; WSEA Edctrs Awd 1993; *office:* Strath Haven MS 200 S Providence Rd Wallingford PA 19086*

BABUSH, SYDNEY MARIS, Social Studies Teacher; *b:* Brooklyn, NY; *ed:* Univ of Rochester (BA) His 1967; C W Post Coll (MA) His 1977; NY Univ (MBA) Mrktg 1981; Univ of Sheffield England Exch Stu; Hebrew Univ 8 Credits; 12 Credits Terrorism, Israeli Politics & Culture; St Univ at Oneonta Pgm in Israel; *cr:* Jericho HS Soc Stud Tchr 1971-72; JFK HS Soc Stud Tchr 1972-73; Great Neck South HS Soc Stud Tchr 1973-74; G W Hewlett HS Soc Stud Tchr 1974-; *ai:* Hewlett Model Congress, Russian Exch Pgm & NEH Adv; HWFA & NYSUT 1974-, Union Rep 1987-93; NY St Cncl Soc Stud 1980-; USIA Grant; NEH Younger Scholars Mentor; *office:* G W Hewlett HS 60 Everit Ave Hewlett NY 11557

BACA, FRED A., Spanish Teacher & Dept Head; *b:* Johnstown, PA; *ed:* Univ of Pittsburgh (BA) Ed 1976; 15 Credits Post Grad Univ of Pitt, Penn St; *cr:* Everett Area HS Span, Eng Tchr 1976-; Appalachia I U 08 Schl

In-Svc Instr 1980-; *ai:* Renaissance Fnd Chm; Sr HS Stu Cncl Adv 19 Yrs; NHS Comm; Lang & Culture Club Adv; Scndry Advy Comm; NEA, PSEA, Everett Area Educ Assn 1976-; Everett Rotary 1991-; Renaissance Trustee 1992-, Chm; Numerous Articles Pub; *office:* Everett Area HS 12 N River Ln Everett PA 15537

BACA, MARY GARCIA, Retired Teacher; *b:* Albuquerque, NM; *m:* George H.; *c:* Paula M., Gerald M.; *ed:* Univ of Albuquerque (BS) Sci Composite 1959; NM Highlands U (MS) Natural Sci 1971; Addl 60 Grad Hrs from FL Inst of Tech, Trenton St Coll, Goddard Coll, Nova Univ, Fresno Pacific Colls, Univ of SAn Diego, Penn St,; *cr:* Las Lunas HS Sc Tchr 1959-63; John F. Kennedy HS Sc Tchr 1964-66; Curundu Jr HS Math, Sc Tchr 1967-78; Balboa HS Math, Sc Tchr 1979-82; Panama Canal Coll Math, Sci Tchr, Soc Sci Dept Chprsn 1982-; *ai:* Panama Canal Coll Fac Senate, Curr Comm; Chprsn Math, Sci, Soc Sci Depts; NABT 1992-; NCSM 1992-; NSF Grants Marine Bio-Adelphi Univ, Natural Sci-NM Highlands Univ, Geology-NM Schl of Mines, Tech. Physics-NM St Univ.

BACCARI, ALBERT A.,JR., Assistant Prof of Biol Sci; *b:* Niskayuna, NY; *m:* L. Francine Heitman; *c:* Kimberly, Kira, Kristopher; *ed:* SUNY Fredonia (MS) Biochemistry 1973, (BS) Bio 1971; MCCC Blue Bell PA (AAS) Registered Nursing 1986; *cr:* Jamestown Comm Coll Adjunt Prof of Bio 1971-73; Mont Cty Comm Coll Asst Prof of Bio 1973-; *ai:* MCCC, AAUP 1981-82, Pres; MCCC, AFT 1982-; HAPS 1993-; St Marks Evang Luth Church 1976-, Pres 2 Terms Upper Perkiomen Rec Cncl 1980-87, Sec; Upper Hanover Open Space Comm 1994-95, Co Chair; Upper Hanover Env Adv Comm 1995-, Co Chair; Zoology of Mont Cty Chapter for Mont Cty 2nd Hundred Yrs 1984; Cert of Recognition Mont Cty Bicentennial Comm 1984; MCCC Chapter of Phi Theta Kappa.

BACCHIA, JACK A., 9th Grade Earth Science Tchr; *b:* Queens, NY; *m:* Lori Oshetski-Bacchia; *c:* Jack Anthony Jr.; *ed:* SUNY Coll at Buffalo (BS) Geoscience 1986, (MS) Sci 1995; *cr:* South Park HS Grd 10-12 Bio Tchr 1986-91; FFCS Grd 9 Earth Sci Tchr 1991-; *ai:* Save Earth, Ski Club; AFT 1991-; South Park HS Selected Natl Schl of Excl 1989-90; *office:* Fonda Fultonville HS Cemetary St Fonda NY 12068*

BACHA, CONNIE A., Business Ed Instructor; *b:* Pittsburgh, PA; *m:* John; *c:* John, Jason; *ed:* Duquesne Univ (BED) Bus Ed 1963, (MED) Scndry Ed 1966; Courses Taken in Bus Ed, Cmptrs for Word Processing, Software Applications; *cr:* US Steel Corp Sec 1963-64; Chartiers Vly Schl Dist Bus Ed Tchr 1964-; *ai:* Dept Chprsn; Various Comms; Tri St Bus Ed Founded; PBEA, NBEA 1995-; CVFT; AFT; Coll Club of Carnegie 1995-; Eucharistic Minister at Church 1989-; Outstdng Young Women of Amer 1974; *office:* Chartiers Valley HS 50 Thoms Run Rd Bridgeville PA 15106*

BACHER, GERALD JAMES, Mathematics Teacher; *b:* Elyria, OH; *m:* Janice Baratta; *c:* Brian R., Jeffrey J., Steven M.; *ed:* Lorain Cty Comm Coll (AA) Coll Parallel Math 1967; Bowling Green ST Univ (BSEd) Math Ed 1969; Cleveland St Univ (MA) Math 1979; 30 Sem Hrs Coll Stu Prsnl John Carroll Univ; 20 Quarter Hrs Cmptr, Calculus Cuyahoga Comm Coll; 2 Sem Hrs AP Inst for Calculus Tchrs St Mary's Coll; *cr:* Elyria Northwood Jr HS Math Tchr, Bsktbl, Track Coach 1969-70; Berea HS Math Tchr 1970-71; Strongsville Albion Jr HS Math Tchr, Bsktbl, Sftbl Coach 1972-80; Cuyahoga Comm Coll Part-Time Math Instr 1980-; North Royalton HS Bsktbl Coach 1980-81, Math Tchr 1980-; *ai:* Bus, Parking Lot Duty; Ofcl Scorer Boys Var & JV Bsktbl; Coach Jr Engineering Tech Soc Competitions; Acad Concerns Comm; Supts Comm Comm; NEA, OEA, NEOTA 1972-; NREA 1980-, Building Rep 1986-; OCTM 1984-; Consortium for Math & Its Application 1989-; Kappa Delta Pi 1969-; Holy Name Soc 1989-, Tres 1990-92 & 1994-, VP 1992-94; BSA 1987-, Webelos Ldr 1987-88, Cubmaster 1988-89, Comm 1989-; *office:* North Royalton H S 14713 Ridge Rd North Royalton OH 44133*

BACHERT, VINCE MICHAEL, 7th-8th Grade Teacher; *b:* Pittsburgh, PA; *c:* Vinny R. W., Amy C.; *ed:* Northern AZ Univ (BS) Elem Ed 1973, (MA) Elem Ed 1980; Outdoor Ed; *cr:* Prescott Pub Schls 4th-6th Grd Tchr 1973-80; DODDS Stuttgar 5th-6th Grd Tchr 1980-84; DODDS HBL Berchtesgaden K-Adult Outdoor Ed Instr 1984-89; DODDS Garmisch Amer Schl 7th-8th Grd Tchr 1989-; *ai:* Outdoor Ed Club; Stu Cncl; NEA 1973-, Bldg Rep 1978-80; Ger Alpine Club 1984-; DPDDS Sustained Superior Work Performance Cert 1986-87; Hinterbrand Lodge Summer Instr 1984-; *office:* Garmisch American Schl Unit 24511 APO AE 09053

BACHMAN, BETTY ANNE, Asst Professor of Psychology; *b:* Philadelphia, PA; *ed:* Univ of VA (BA) Psych 1986; Villanova Univ (MS) Psych 1988; Univ of DE (PHD) Psych 1993; *cr:* Siena Coll Asst Prof 1993-; *ai:* Women & Minorities Steering Comm; Tchng Comm; Grants Subcommittee Chair; Human Rights Comm; Amer Psychological Assn, Acad of Mngmt 1993-; Amer Psychological Soc 1994-; Univ of DE Women of Promise Awd for Distngd Dissertation Rsrch; Numerous Articles Pub; *office:* Siena Coll 515 Loudon Rd Loudonville NY 12211

BACHMAN, SANDRA J., 2nd Grade Teacher; *b:* Allentown, PA; *ed:* PA St Univ (BS) Elem, Kndgtn Ed 1962; Temple Univ (MS) Ed 1966; Attnd Carbon Lehigh Intermediate Unit, PA Dept of Ed, Allentown Schl Dist 23 Credits In Computers, Sign Lang, Power Tchng, ADAPT, Writing Process, Environmental Ed; *cr:* Lincoln Elem Schl 2nd-5th Grd Tchr 1962-84; Union Terrace Elem 2nd-3rd Grd Tchr 1984-; *ai:* AEA 1962-, Outstanding Tchr 1993; PSEA, NEA 1962-; Alpha Delta Kappa 1966-, Chm, Intnl Exec Bd 1993-95, St Pres 1976-78, Intnl Offices 1977-83, 1989-95, Cncl Pres, Regnl VP, Historian, Ex Bd Mem; *office:* Union Terrace Elem Schl 1939 W Union St Allentown PA 18104

BACHMAN, SUSAN MARIE (MOORE), Choral Director; *b:* Binghamton, NY; *m:* Jerry; *c:* Matthew; *ed:* Crane Schl of Music at Potsdam Coll (BM) Music Ed 1980; Binghamton Univ (MS) Rdng 1983; *cr:* Tioga Cntrl Schls Classroom Music Tchr & Chorus 1980-87; Binghamton City Schl Choral Dir 1987-; *ai:* Sing With Univ Chorus BU, Madrigal Choir of Binghamton; Partcptng Tchr in southern Tier INst; Vol at Cider Mill Plyhs; Genealogy; Rdng; NYSSMA, MENC & Kappa Delta Pi 1980-; ACDA 1990-; BCMEA 1987-; Registered Music Educator MENC; Guest Conductor at Various Cty Music Festivals; *office:* Binghamton HS 31 Main St Binghamton NY 13905*

BACHTELL, DAVID LARRY, Music Coordinator; *b:* Hagerstown, MD; *m:* Virginia Hunsicker; *c:* Jenny Dora; *ed:* Lebanon Valley Coll (BA) Music 1967; UNC (MA) Musicology; Attnd West Chester Univ, Villanova; *cr:* Baltimore Cty Schls 7-9th Grd Vocal Tchr 1968-72; Pennridge Schl Dist Scndry Vocal Tchr 1972-; *ai:* Concert, Chamber Choir; Music, Summer Theatre; PSEA 1972-; PMEA, MENC 1970-, 25 Yr Awd; Perkasie Planning Commission 1978-92, Chm; Articles for PMEA News; Music Tech Seminars; Outstanding Contribution to Arts Awd; *office:* Pennridge HS 1228 N 5th St Perkasie PA 18944*

BACK, KIM L., English Teacher; *b:* Rutland, VT; *m:* Jeffrey; *c:* Ashley, Megan; *ed:* St Univ of NY at Oneonta (BS) Elem Ed N-6 & Eng 7-9 1989, Ed & Rdng 1993; *cr:* Laurens Cntrl Schl Eng Tchr 1989-; *ai:* Class of 1998 Adv; Scheduling & Soc Comms; NCTE, NYSEC 1994-; NYSUT 1989-; CARC 1991-; CATE 1992-; *office:* Laurens Central Schl Main St Laurens NY 13796

BACK, YVONNE DARST, Volleyball & Basketball Coach; *b:* Columbus, OH; *m:* Dwight; *cr:* World Harvest Chrstn Acad Girld Var Bsktbl Coach 1988-, Girls Var Vlybl Coach 1994-; *office:* World Harvest Christian Acad 4595 Gender rd Canal Winchestr OH 43110

BACKENSTOSS, STANLEY, Bio & Environmental Sci Tchr; *b:* Harrisburg, PA; *m:* Jane L.; *c:* Sean, Tessa; *ed:* Millersville St Coll (BS) Bio 1969; Trenton St Coll (MA) Bio 1972; Attnd Penn St Univ & East Stroudsburg Univ; *cr:* Delhaas HS Sci Chair 1969-81; Exeter HS Tchr 1985-; *ai:* NEA & PSEA 1969-; Berks Cty Enivronmental Ed Consortium; PA Alliance for Env Ed; PA Sci Tchrs Assn; PIAA Ofcl 1989-, Interpreter; Environmental Ed Grant from PA DER 1994; *office:* Exeter Twp Sr HS 201 E 37th St Reading PA 19606

BACKFISH, CHARLES G., Social Studies Instructor; *b:* New York City, NY; *m:* Valerie Jane Yates; *c:* Emma Marie; *ed:* SUNY at Stony Brook (BA) His 1966; NY Univ (AM) His 1968; Grad Work in Admin Hofstra Univ; *cr:* Suffolk Cty Comm Coll Adjunct His 1975-78; Adelphi Univ Adjunt Hist 1978-; Smithtown HS E Soc Stud Instr 1969-; Smithtown HS Soc Stud Instr 1994-; *ai:* Adv NHS; Org of Amer Historians; Port Jefferson Village Cultural Center Comm 1990-; WUSB-FM Radio SUNY at Stony Brook 1978-; SUNY at Stony Brook Alumni Assn, Bd of Dirs Mem 1991-, VP 1995; NY Univ McKenzie Fellow 1967-68, Grad Fac Fellowship 1968-69; Adult Achvmt Awd Smithtown Youth Bd 1991; Presenter of Paper at Conf the Modern Condition Adelphi Univ 1991; Acad Conf on The Vietnam War 1993, The Road to The White House 1992, The Nixon Presidency 1991, The Kennedy Presidency 1990, The COld War 1994, The Modern Presidency 1995, Confs on The Sixties 1996, Co-Dir; *office:* Smithtown H S 100 Central Rd Smithtown NY 11787

BACKHAUS, GEORGE R., Science Dept Chair; *b:* Troy, NY; *m:* Nancy Pollock; *c:* Michelle, Brian; *ed:* SUNY at Albany (BS) Bio Ed-Cum Laude 1969, (MS) Advanced Classroom Tchng-Magna Cum Laude 1973; 24 Credit Hrs Above Masters; *cr:* Tamarac HS Bio Tchr & Sci Dept Chair 1969-; *ai:* Bio Club Adv; Yrbk Staff Adv; Class of 96 Co-Adv; British Amer Club Co-Spon; NYSUT 1969-; AFT 1969-; Brittonhill Tchrs Assn 1969-, Treas, VP, Previous Pres; Howard Hughes Flwshp Molecular Bio Inst 1991; *home:* 9307 Ny Highway 66 Averill Park NY 12018

BACKHERMS, KATHRYN ANNE, Music Director; *b:* Cincinnati, OH; *ed:* Coll of Mt St Joseph (BA) Music 1977; Conservatory of Music at Univ of Cincinnati (MM) Music Ed 1981; Addl Post Grad Credits in Orff-Schulwerk Ed Level I, Electronic Music, Organ, Voice, Percussion & Classical Guitar; *cr:* St Ursula Villa 1st-8th Grd Music Specialist 1977-79; McAuley HS 9th-12th Grd Choral Music Dir 1980-86; Coll of Mt St Joseph Music Dept Chprsn 1986-89; St Ursula Acad Music Dir 1989-; *ai:* Dir of Vocal & Instrumental Ensembles, Ministry Tm; Music Dir for Spring Musical; OH Music Educators Assn 1979-; Mu Phi Epsilon Alumnae Chapter 1989-, Acting VP 1993-95; Kappa Gamma Pi; Greater Cincinnati Fnd Tchr Awd for Production of Original Musical for Jr & Sr HS Stdnts 1984; Composer of 7 Original Musicals & Assorted Choral Works; *office:* St Ursula Acad 1339 E Mc Millan St Cincinnati OH 45206

BACKSTON, ROBERT PHILLIP, Art Teacher; *b:* Cleveland, OH; *m:* Nancy; *c:* James, Scott; *ed:* Baldwin Wallace Coll (BA) Art 1959; Kent St Univ (MA) Art 1965; *cr:* Parma City Schls Art Tchr 1959-; *ai:* PEA, OEA, NEA 1959-; *office:* Hillside Jr HS 1320 Educational Park Dr Seven Hills OH 44131

BACON, BRUCE CROCKER, Biology Teacher; *b:* Littleton, NH; *c:* David, Christopher; *ed:* Univ of NH (BA) Zoology 1965, (MED) Ed 1989; 20 Credit Hrs Beyond Masters; *cr:* Barrington MS Sci & Math Tchr 1983-86; Nute HS Bio Tchr 1986-; *ai:* Ski Club Adv; NEA 1986-; USNR 1983-; Amer Legion 1990-; NATM Convention Speaker 1986; *home:* 671 Post Rd Greenland NH 03840

BACON, ERNEST ALLEN, Earth Science Teacher; *b:* Sodus, NY; *m:* Sally; *c:* Eric, Rebecca; *ed:* Syracuse Univ (BA) Sci Ed 1968; Attnd SUNY at Oswego; *cr:* North Syracuse Cent Schls 8th-9th Grd Sci Tchr 1968-; *ai:* Sci Olympiad Coach; Tchr Ctr Rep; Hlth,Safety Comm; Dept Chprsn; NYSUT 1987-, Subject Area Rep; NESTA, NSTA 1988-; Village Bd 1991-, Trustee; Lions Club 1986-, Zone Chm; Author Sci Prgm; NY St Earth Sci Mentor; Outstanding Tchr Awd, Tech Club Syracuse; *office:* North Syracuse Jr HS 5353 W Taft Rd Syracuse NY 13212

BACOTE, DENISE WHITEHEAD, English Teacher; *b:* Brooklyn, NY; *w:* Ralph (dec); *ed:* Northeastern Univ (BS) Ed 1974; Boston St Coll 6 Hrs; Inst for Thinking, Writing Bard Coll 1987; Tech, Prep Prgm Univ of MA at Boston 1994-95; *cr:* Brooklin Summer Schl Eng Tchr 1977-84; Brookline Adult, Comm Ed SAT Review 1984-86; Brookline HS Eng Tchr 1974-; *ai:* Yrbk Fac, Frosh Homeroom Adv; Tchr Classroom Comm; BEA; MTA; NCTE; Union Bapt Church; *office:* Brookline HS 115 Greenough St Brookline MA 02146*

BACZ, RICHARD ALAN, Bands & Instrmntl Music Dir; *b:* Bethlehem, PA; *ed:* Bucknell Univ (BSME) Music Ed 1988; Attnd Villanova Univ, Univ of South FL, MI St Univ; *cr:* Blue Mountain HS 1988-; *ai:* Ski Club Adv; Jazz Ensemble Dir; Private Music Tchr; Music Edctrs Natl Conf 1987-; Natl Band Assn 1988-; Sigma Alpha Epsilon 1985-; Schuylkill Cty Band Assn 1988-, Treas; *office:* Blue Mountain HS RR 1 Box 1215 Schuylkill Haven PA 17972

BACZEK, LINDA ANTINOZZI, Sixth Grade Teacher; *b:* Derby, CT; *m:* Francis; *c:* Brett; *ed:* Souther CT St Univ (BS) Elem Ed 1972; Univ of Bridgeport (MS) Instrl Media 1976; *cr:* Irving Schl Fourth, Sixth Grd Tchr 1972-84; Lincoln Schl Sixth Grd Tchr 1984-95; Irving Schl Sixth Grd Tchr 1995-; *ai:* Sci Curr, Report Card, Prof Dev Comms; Newspaper, Chrldr, Safety Patrol Stud Yrbk Adv; Stu Ldr, Earth Day Project Coord; Girls Bsktbl Coach; Spring Show Dir; NEA, CEA, DEA 1972-75; AFT, CSFT, DFT 1975-; Phi Delta Kappa 1993-; *office:* Irving Schl 9 Garden Pl Derby CT 06418

BADER, CONRAD F., Retired Soc Stud & Math Tchr; *b:* Rockville Center, NY; *m:* Carol Ann Fedyk; *c:* Julie Brizzee, Janice, Lynette; *ed:* Union Coll of NY (BA) Ec 1959; SUNY at Albany (MA) Ed 1963; *cr:* Henderson Settlement Schl Jr HS Tchr 1960-61; Sharon Springs Cntrl Schl Soc Stud, Math Tchr 1961-95; *ai:* NEA 1961-; *home:* RR 2 Box 189 Sharon Springs NY 13459

BADER, DAVID EDWARD, World History Teacher; *b:* Cincinnati, OH; *m:* Patti Zinser; *c:* Beth, Rachel, Chris, Adam; *ed:* Pikevilel Coll (BS) Hlth, PE 1973l St Xavier (MS) Ed, PE 1988; *cr:* Harrison HS Tchr, Coach 1974-; *ai:* Var Bsbl, Frosh Ftbl Coach; SW Local Tchrs Assn, OEA, NEA 1974-; *office:* William Henry Harrison HS 9860 West Rd Harrison OH 45030

BADER, NANCY SQUIRE, English Teacher; *b:* Syracuse, NY; *c:* Mark, Ruth Beasley, Daniel; *ed:* St Univ of NY at Oswego (BA) Scndry Ed & Eng 1972; Syracuse Univ (MS) Rdng Ed 1975; St Univ of NY at Oswego (CAS), (SAS Ed) Admin 1981; *cr:* Cntrl Square Schls Scndry Eng Tchr 1972-77, Rdng & Writing Lab Supvr 1977-81, Eng Supvr 1981-85; Luth Jr Seminary Tanzania Eng Tchr 1985-86; Baldwinsville Schls Scndry Eng Tchr 1986-; *ai:* Yrbk Adv; Stu Support Team; NEA, BTA 1986-; Hospice of CNY 1984-, Vol of Yr Awd; Vanderkamp Bd 1990-; Grant to Attend Hum Tchr Inst Sponsored by NY Cncl for Hum 1995; *office:* Baker HS 29 E Oneida St Baldwinsville NY 13027

BAER, JAMES WILSON, Retired Teacher; *b:* Buffalo, NY; *m:* Joan F. Bamberg; *c:* Thomas H., Elizabeth A. Swafford, Patricia J. White, Douglas W.; *ed:* SUNY Coll at Buffalo (BS) Elem Ed 1956; MI St Univ (MA) Ed 1957; *cr:* Mason Consolidated Schl 3rd-4th Grd Tchr 1957-60; Southwestern Cntrl Schl 6th Grd Tchr 1960-90; *ai:* Helped Institute 6th Grd Camping Prgm 1969; Vol Svcs; NEA 1956-; NYSOEA; Hazeltine Lib Bd, Bd Mem; Busti Federated Church 1960-, Various Capacities; Roger Tory Peterson Inst 1990-; BSA Troop 38 & 138, Scoutmaster, C[...] *home:* 371 Busti Sugar Grove Rd Jamestown NY 14701

BAER, MARGARET ANN, Spanish Teacher; *b:* Greencastle, P[...] Lawrence Bennett; *ed:* Eastern Mennonite Coll (BA) Span Ed 1976; [...] Univ (MA) Frgn Lang 1991; Univ of Barcelona 18 Hrs; *cr:* Sandy S[...] Schl Span & ESOL Tchr 1978-81; Berkeley Springs HS Span[...] 1984-89; West VA Univ Grad Asst of Span 1989-91; Williamsport HS[...] Tchr 1991-; *ai:* Span Club Adv; Co-Chair Schl Improvement Team; S[...] on Re-Structuring Comm; Grad Asst Flwshp; Awd Excellence in T[...] Article Pub; *office:* Williamsport HS 5 S Clifton Dr Williamspo[...] 21795

BAER, ROGER ALAN, 7th Grade Geography Teacher; *b:* Harrisbur[...] *m:* Melissa Rose; *c:* Matthew Scott; *ed:* Millersville Univ (BS) Scnd[...] Soc Stud 1987; PA St Univ (MED) Tchng, Curr 1996; *cr:* Middletow[...] Schl Dist 7th Grd Geog Tchr 1988-; *ai:* Ftbl, Track, Field Asst Var C[...] PA Geographic Alliance 1992-, Tchr, Consultant; NEA 1988-; Cen[...] United Meth Church 1976-; PA Geographic Alliance Awd Geog Awa[...] Week Act; Facilitator PA Geog Bee Championship 1993; *office:* Geo[...] Feaser MS 214 N Race St Middletown PA 17057

BAER, ROY K., Biology Teacher; *b:* Clinton, MA; *m:* Norma L. Bov[...] *c:* Cherrie Lee Sweeney, Kenneth; *ed:* Atlantic Union Coll (BA) Bio [...] Worcester Polytechnic Inst (MS) Natural Sci 1968; Attnd Worces[...] Coll, Univ of CO, Univ of MA, Simmons Coll, Ball St Univ; *cr:* Wac[...] Regnl HS Bio Tchr 1964-; *ai:* Acadia Natl Park Field Trip; Ski [...] NABT 1968-, Textbook Reviewer; WRTA; MTA; NEA; MASS; M[...] Nim Rod League 1975-; Textbook Writer BSCS 1974-78; *office:* Wac[...] Regional H S 1401 Main St Holden MA 01520

BAFARO, JOANNE L., Reading Teacher; *b:* Huntington, NY; *m:* Jo[...] *ed:* Georgetown Univ (BA) 1976; *cr:* St Agnes Schl Kndgtn Tchr 197[...] St Thomas More Schl 3rd Grd Tchr 1980-88; St Ursula Schl Rdng[...] 1989-; *ai:* Liturgy Comm; Cath Schl Tchrs Assn; MD Assn of Dy[...] Adults, Yth; Baltimore Diocesan Affiliate of Natl Cath Office for P[...] with Disabilities; *office:* St Ursula Schl 8900 Harford Rd Baltimor[...] 21234

BAGAN, BETTY ANN BOULDEN, First Grade Teacher; *b:* Trento[...] *m:* Frank N.; *c:* Nicholas; *ed:* Glassboro St (BA) General Elem 196[...] Woodland Schl Second Grd Tchr 1968-72, First Grd Tchr 1972-80; [...] Schl First Grd Tchr 1980-91; A. L. Tomaso First Grd Tchr 1991[...] Mentor to Kndgtn Tchr 1995-; NJEA, NEA 1968-; WTEA 1968-, Bu[...] Rep 5 Yrs; Scotch Plains First United Meth Church 1962-, Asst [...] Church Schl 1991-93; Govs Tchr Recognition Awd 1994; *office:* Ang[...] Tomaso Schl 46 Washington Valley Rd Warren NJ 07059

BAGGS, BERNARD THOMAS, PE, Hlth & Fine Arts Supvr; *b:* [...] City, NJ; *m:* Patricia Luongo; *ed:* Seton Hall Univ (MA) Supervis[...] Admin 1981; Montclair St Coll (BA) Music Ed 1975; *cr:* Butler Schls[...] 1975-83; Watchung Regnl Schl Tchr 1983-84; Hackettstown Schl [...] 1989-93, Admin 1993-; *ai:* Coach Girls Bsktbl; Hackettstown High[...] Marching & Jazz Concert Bands Hackettstown High; NJPSA 1[...] AAHPERD 1994-; NSDC 1994-; ASED Mem 1993-; NMSA 1993-, [...] NAEA 1993-, Mem; MENC 1975-, Mem; NASSP 1995-; ASCD 199[...] Morris Comm Band 1985-87, Dir & Conductor; Summer Music P[...] 1975-92, Dir & Tchr; *office:* Hackettstown HS Warren St Hackettstow[...] 07840

BAGIONI, JOHN JOSEPH, HS Science Teacher; *b:* New Britain, C[...] Patricia Cugno; *c:* Jessica, Rachel; *ed:* Cntrl CT St Univ (BA) Eart[...] 1973; 36 Post Grad Credit Hrs in Ed & Sci; *cr:* Walcott HS Sci T[...] Team Ldr 1973-; *ai:* Adv to Walcott HS Weather Club; Sci Dept Team[...] Sci Ldrshp Team; NEA 1973-; Walcott Ed Assoc 1973-; CT Ed [...] 1973-; Amer Meteorological Soc 1990-; Recipient of CT Celebrati[...] Excl Awd for Innovative Curr Project; *home:* 31 Woodhaven Dr Burlin[...] CT 06013

BAGLEY, LINDA SUE KIRCHENBAUER, Pre-First Grade Teach[...] Van Wert, OH; *m:* Ronald Ray; *c:* Jeff, Jon, Julie White, Mark; *ed:* Bo[...] Green St Univ (BS) Ed 1962; Math Their Way; Aims; Sci Math; *cr:* H[...] Mann Schl Kndgtn Tchr 1956-58; Anthony Wayne Schl Kndgtn [...] Horace Mann Schl Kndgtn, Pre-First Grd Tchr; *ai:* AFT; Trinity U[...] Meth Church, Sunday Schl Tchr; *office:* Horace Mann HS 501 E 3rd S[...] Wert OH 45891

BAGLIERI, ANTHONY M., High School Math Teacher; *b:* Hoboken[...] *m:* Edith Rotondi; *c:* Susan E., Jill M.; *ed:* Jersey City St Coll (BA) [...] 1970, (MA) Math 1974; William Paterson Coll Supvrs Cert 1979[...] Thomas Jefferson HS Math Tchr 1970-71; Hackensack HS Math [...] 1971-; *ai:* Messiah Luth Church 1981-, Treas 1985-90; Distngd Svc [...] 1989; Nom MIT's; Distngd HS Tchr; *office:* Hackensack HS 1st & B[...] Sts Hackensack NJ 07601

BAGLIO, ROSE ANNE BRINKLEY, Business Education Teach[...] New Bern, NC; *m:* Anthony M.; *ed:* Salem St Coll (BS) Bus Ed [...] Suffolk Univ (MS) Bus Ed 1979; Advanced Grad Stud at Va[...] Locations; Cmptr Classes in IBM Windows, Desktop Publishing, [...] Perfect, Microsoft Word, Power Point & Microsoft Excel; *cr:* George[...] Mid-Sr HS Bus Ed Tchr 1969-; *ai:* MTA, NEA 1969-; GEA 1969-, [...] 1972-73; MA Bus Ed Assn, NBEA 1990-; Guest Speaker at George[...] HS Grad 1978; Sr Class Adv 1978 & 1993; Jr Class Adv 1992; Soph C[...] Adv 1986 & 1991; *office:* Georgetown Middle Sr HS 11 Winte[...] Georgetown MA 01833

BAGWELL, BILL L., Mathematics Teacher; *b:* Aurora, IL; *c:* Ma[...] Nicola, Grady; *ed:* Sinclair Comm Coll (AA & AS) 1974; Souther[...] Coll (BA) Math 1975; Univ of Dayton (MS) Tchng 1979; US N[...] Explosive Ordnance Disposal Schl, 1970; *cr:* Sinclair Comm Coll [...] 1975-91; Hillel Acad Tchr 1977-78; Beavercreek HS Tchr 1980-; *ai:* [...] Math Club & Whitewater Rafting Adv; Math Club Spon; KAVONiA [...] OCTM 1995-; The Edyth May Slitte Awd; Rose Hulman Outstdng HS T[...] Green Cnty Tchr of the Yr; *office:* Beavercreek HS 2660 Dayton Xeni[...] Beavercreek OH 45434

BAGWELL, BILLIE R. JOHNSON, Second Grade Teacher[...] Cleveland, TN; *m:* James W.; *c:* Sally Ann Bagwell Heck, Mark W.[...] Univ of Akron (BS) Elem Ed 1978; Attnd Kent St Univ; *cr:* Akron [...] Schls Sub Rdng Tchr 1979-82; Barberton Pub Schls Second Grd Rdng [...] 1983-; *ai:* New Teachers Mentor; Grade Card, Handwriting, Spelling, [...] Venture Capital Grant Comms; Phi Delta Kappa 1985-; Phi St K[...] Kappa Iota, Pres, Sec 1984; BTA, OEA, NEA 1983-; Akron Bapt Te[...] 1980-, 2nd Grd S S Tchr; *office:* Oakdale Elem Schl 165 3rd St [...] Barberton OH 44203

BAHANTKA, SCOTT, Physical Education Instructor; *b:* Elmira, NY[...] Catherine; *c:* Bryan, Megan; *ed:* Elmira Coll (MS) Ed 1990; Purs[...] Admin Degree at Cortland St Coll; *cr:* Addison Cntrl Schl Dist PE [...] 1985-; *ai:* Class of 1998 Adv; Girls Track Coach, Cty Track Coord; N[...] Asst Sect IV Girls Track Coord; Corning-Painted Post Little League 19[...] bSA 1994-, Cubmaster; *office:* Addison Central Schl Colwell St Add[...] NY 14801*

BAHDE, STEPHEN JAMES, English Dept Chairman; *b:* Fitchburg, [...] *m:* Marta Piermarini; *c:* Juliane, Stephen; *ed:* Fitchburg St Coll (B[...] Scndry Ed Eng 1970, (MED) Scndry Ed 1978; *cr:* Fitchburg HS Eng [...] Chm 1970-; *ai:* Assessment Learning Ctr; Lang Arts Frameworks C[...]

Fitchburg Tchrs & MA Tchrs Assn; NEA; NCTE; *office:* Fitchburg Academy St Fitchburg MA 01420

A, DAVID ANDREW, Chemistry Teacher; *b:* Toledo, OH; *ed:* OH iv (BS) Chem Ed 1993; 24 Hrs Toward MA in Research & rement; *cr:* Sylvania Northview HS Chem Tchr 1993-; *ai:* Asst Bsbl , NEA 1993-; *office:* Sylvania Northview HS 5403 Silica Dr Sylvania 560

SEN, CAROLYN GOOD, Specific LD Teacher; *b:* Seneca Cty, OH; nald F.; *c:* Douglas, Diana Anderson, Donna Wagner; *ed:* Heidelberg BA) Ed & Home Ec 1956; Attnd OH St Univ, Bowling Green St Univ; ng Disabilities, EMR & SBH Certs; *cr:* OH St Univ Home Ec Instr 61; Ottawa Co Extension Agent; Benton-Carroll-Salem Schls ic Learning Disabilities Instr 1975-; *ai:* Treas Schl Store Operated Spcl Ed Stdnts; Kids Helping Kids Adv; NEA & OHEA 1980-; CEC DKG 1987-, Cor Sec & Historian; PC Mothers of Twins 1967-, All s, Mother of the Yr Awd, St Chaplain, St Schlsp Chm; Home mists in Homemaking 1961-, All Offices; Farm Bureau Cncl 1986-, utstdng Career Ed Ctr of the Yr 1987-88; Jennings Scholar 1994-95; Oak Harbor MS 315 N Church St Oak Harbor OH 43449

, WILLIAM ROGER, Science Teacher; *b:* Chester, OH; *m:* Kay ee; *c:* Cara, Brandy; *ed:* Rio Grande Coll (BS) Scndry Ed, Chem, Bio Univ of Dayton (MS) Ed Admin, Supervision 1985; St Univ of NY ny Brook 4 Sem Hrs DNA Tech; Miami Univ 4 Sem Hrs Chem; OH iv 4 Qtr Hrs Cmptr Sci; Marshall Univ 11 Sem Hrs Bio; Univ of nnati 4 Sem Hrs Solid St Chem; *cr:* Rio Grande Coll Part-time gical Rsrch 1963-67; Gallia Acad HS Sci Instr, Dept Head 1965-71; rande Coll Part-time Instr, Bio Rsrch 1971-73; River Vly HS Sci Tchr , *ai:* Sr Class, Sci Club Adv; NEA, OEA, SEOEA, GCLEA 1973-, Yrs, Outstdng Ldrshp; OH Acad of Sci 1965-, Acker Outstdng Sci OH Jr Acad of Sci 1985-, Dist 12 Councilperson; Gallia Co rvation Club 1990-; Co-Author 3 Sci Papers; Author 1 Sci Ed Paper; 206 Greer Rd Bidwell OH 45614

R, BARBARA, High School Mathematics Tchr; *b:* Bronx, NY; *ed:* a St Univ (BA) Math 1972; Binghamton Ed 1974; *cr:* African Rd JHS Tchr 1972-79; Mepham HS Math Tchr 1979-80; Kennedy HS Math 980-88; Calhoun HS Math Tchr 1988-; *ai:* Math Stu Mentor; NEA , Bellmore Merrick Tchrs Union 1979-; *office:* S H Calhoun HS 1786 St Merrick NY 11566

R, JOYCE F., Sci & Math Tchr & Math Chair; *b:* Cleveland, OH; *ed:* ne Coll (BA) Bio 1967; CT Wesleyan Univ (MALS) Multiple Fields 1973; Various Coursework in Physics Ed & General Educl Issues at and St Univ, Case-Western Reserve Univ, Akron Univ; *cr:* Saint John ath & Sci Tchr 1967-70; Villa Maria HS Math & Sci Tchr 1970-74; ficat HS Sci Tchr 1974-83; Central Cath HS Sci Tchr 1983-87; Saint nt-Saint Mary HS Sci Tchr 1987-89; John Adams HS Math Tchr 91; Brooklyn HS Sci & Math Tchr 1991-; *ai:* Math Dept Chair; North Assn Local Self-Stud Steering Comm Co-Chair; Dimensions of ing Dist Trainer; Math & Sci Curr Revision Comms; NEA, OEA ; AAPT, Local Section 1979-; NCTM, OCTM, Local 1989-; ASCD ; Natl Sci Fnd Grants for Summer Stud at Wake Forest Univ 1968, yan Univ 1970-72, Coll of Staten Island 1985, Univ of Akron 1987; Brooklyn HS 9200 Biddulph Rd Brooklyn OH 44144

R, THOMAS C., AP Eng Lit & Comp Teacher; *b:* Pittsburgh, PA; *m:* Gardella; *ed:* Duquesne Univ (BS) Eng, Scndry Ed 1969, (MS) Hum Post Grad Hrs Eng Lit & AP Eng Carnegie Mellon Univ; Grad Hrs y Ed Villanova, Penn St; *cr:* North Hills Sr HS 9-10 Grd Tchr 1970-, Composition 1980-91, Eng Lit & Comp Tchr 1983-, 12th Grd AP Eng Composition Tchr 1989-; *ai:* Boys & Girls Var Track & Field Head n; Womens Cross Cntry Coach; NCTE; NEA; PSEA; NHEA; Amer y Inst Gift of Time 1990-91; *office:* North Hills Sr HS 53 Rochester ttsburgh PA 15229

AR, ALAN LEE, Biology Teacher; *b:* Sidney, OH; *m:* Pamela Ann ; *c:* Joshua, Nathan, Mary Beth; *ed:* Urbana Coll (BS) Bio 1972; Univ yton (MS) Ed 1990; 1 Qtr Hrs Wright St Univ 1974-; 3 Qtr Hrs Miami 1993; 1 Qtr Hr Univ of Cincinnati 1996; *cr:* Fort Loramie HS Bio, Scis Tchr 1974-; *ai:* 9 Grd Class Adv; Head Tchr; Favirothon Adv; 1974-; SECO 1993-; 2 Grants Awded Major Industry; Participate, pleted Project Discovery, DNA Tech Summer Wkshp Miami Univ; : 11126 Shanley Rd Quincy OH 43343

E, CAROLE RICHARDSON, Mathematics Teacher; *b:* Havrede , MD; *m:* John E.; *c:* Julie E. Brown, Jeffrey P.; *ed:* Western MD Coll Math 1964; APC 36 Grad Credits in Math, Ed; Inservice Credits St 3, Loyola Coll 3; *cr:* Westminster Jr HS Tchr 1964-68; Westminster Tchr 1975-; *ai:* NHS Adv; NEA, MSTA, CCEA 1975-; *office:* minster HS 1225 Washington Rd Westminster MD 21157

ER, THOMAS WILLIAM, 8th Grade English Teacher; *b:* Syracuse, *ed:* Suny Coll (BA) Scndry Ed 1991, (MS) Affective Ed 1996; *cr:* n Jr HS 8th Grd Eng Tchr 1991-; *ai:* Drama Club Adv; Bsktbl Coach; n Jr Bsbl 1993-95, Coach, Bd of Dirs; NYSTEA 1996-; Prince of Luth 1993-, Youth Ldr; *office:* Fulton Jr HS 129 Curtis St Fulton NY

EY, DARLENE CANNATA, Middle School Teacher; *b:* New Haven, *m:* Robert B.; *c:* Michele, Michael, Matthew; *ed:* Southern CT St Coll Elem Ed 1974; Southern CT St Univ (MS) Ed 1984; 15 Credit Hrs; rbk & Vol Svcs Adv; NCEA 1986-.

EY, DINITA A., Mathematics Teacher; *b:* Atlantic City, NJ; *c:* a Michelle; *ed:* Cntrl St Univ (BA) Math 1973; *cr:* Atlantic City Bd K-12th Grd & Adult Ed Math Tchr 1973-80; Saint Andrews HS Math 1980-81; Atlantic City Bd of Ed K-12th Grd & Adult Ed Math Tchr -93; Egg Harbor Twp HS Math Tchr 1983-; Atlantic City Housing ority Supvr 1993-95; *ai:* Tchr Mentor; Natural Helpers Adv; NJEA, 1973-; EHTEA 1983-; AMTNJ 1984-; Alpha Kappa Alpha 1970-; ed Meth Women 1996; *office:* Egg Harbor Twp HS 24 High School Dr Harbor Tp NJ 08234

EY, DOROTHY POWER, First Grade Teacher; *b:* Tarentum, PA; *m:* L. Jr.; *c:* Jessica, Hannah; *ed:* Edinboro Univ (BS) Elem Ed 1978; boro Univ Early Chldhd Ed Cert 1990; *cr:* Central Elem Schl 3rd Grd 1979; Utica Elem Schl 1st & 2nd Grd Tchr 1979-82, 1st Grd Tchr -; *ai:* Cmptr Comm; Early Chldhd Taskforce; NEA & PSEA 1980-; *e:* Utica Elem Schl PO Box 128 Utica PA 16362

EY, GARY DEAN, 8th Grade English & LA Tchr; *b:* Morristown, *n:* Janet E. Smith; *c:* Adam, Josh, Zach; *ed:* Moravian Coll (BA) Eng ; Millersvill Univ Master Equivalency Eng 1982; 6 Credit Hrs Ed; Stu Trng Intervention & Referral at Risk Stdnts; *cr:* Dover Area Schl Dist 3rd Eng Tchr 1974-; *ai:* Stu Asst Team; NEA, PSEA 1974-; DAEA -, Local Rep, Negotiations, PR & R Chair; Lititz Moravian Church -, Church Bd, Vice Chair 10 Yrs Svc.

EY, JACKLYN EVANS, 2nd Grade Teacher; *b:* Scranton, PA; *ed:* msburg Univ (BS) Elem Ed 1987; Abington Hghts Schl Dist K-12 ; Keystone Jr Coll 1 Yr Transfer; Masters Equivalency Instrl II BS Plus redit Hrs; *cr:* Our Lady of Peace 1st Grd Tchr 1988; Abington Hghts 5th Grd Tchr 1988-89; Abington Hghts Elem 2nd Grd Tchr 1989-; *ai:* Children Tutor; Womens Field Hockey Head Coach; Womens Soccer rack Asst Coach; PSEA 1988-; First Presbyn Church 1977-, Deacon, day Schl Tchr & Bible Schl Tchr.

BAILEY, JANE MOENING, Third Grade Teacher; *b:* Lima, OH; *m:* Michael; *c:* Jenette Jeffries, Alison J.; *ed:* OH St Univ (BS) Elem Ed 1979; Bowling Green St Univ (MED) Elem Ed 1989; Addl Class Work & Grad Credits OSU, Wright St Univ; Arts, Math, Spec Ed; *cr:* Bath Elem Schl 3rd Grd Tchr 1981-82, 2nd Grd Tchr 1982-83, 3rd Grd Tchr 1983-84, 4th Grd Tchr 1984-85, 3rd Grd Tchr 1985-; *ai:* Inclussion, Collaborative Tchng Teams; Cty Math Curr Dev Core; 4-H Club Adv; Asst Prgm Tutoring Prgm; Bath Ed Assn 1981-, Bldg Rep, Schlsp Chprsn; OH Ed Assn, NEA 1981-; Natl Fed Small Businesses 1987-; Chamber of Commerce 1988-; Tchr Effectiveness Trng; OH Dept of Ed Prof Svc Awd; OSU Cert Appreciation Cooperating Tchr; Mentor Tchr; ONU Outstdng Ldrshp Ed Awd; *home:* 2418 N Dixie Hwy Lima OH 45801*

BAILEY, JOAN WEISENFELD, Associate Professor; *b:* Brooklyn, NY; *m:* Lawrence H.; *ed:* Hunter Coll (BA) Honors Curr 1980; Grad Schl, Univ Ctr of City Univ of NY (PHD) Soc Personality Psych 1988; *cr:* Queens Coll Adjunct Lecturer 1982-84; Grad Schl, Univ Ctr of CUNY Research Asst 1983-87; Jersey City St Coll Assoc Prof 1988-; *ai:* Amer psychological Assn 1989-; AFT 1988-; Amer Psychological Assn, CUNY Grad Ctr Fellowships; 1 Book Article; 4 Journal Articles; Merit Awd; *office:* Jersey City State Coll Psych Dept 2039 Kennedy Blvd Jersey City NJ 07305

BAILEY, JOHN H., English Teacher & Dept Chm; *b:* Butler, PA; *m:* Zetta Yost; *c:* Toni Snyder, John Jr.; *ed:* Lock Haven Univ (BA) Eng 1961; Penn St Univ 21 Hrs; *cr:* Lock Haven HS Tchr 1961-; *ai:* Summer Recreation Dir; PSEA, NEA, NCTE 1961-; Lock Haven Rec & Parks Bd 1964-; *office:* Lock Haven HS W Church St Lock Haven PA 17745*

BAILEY, LUGENE, Librarian; *b:* Macon, MS; *ed:* Rust Coll (BA) Eng 1966; Atlanta Univ (MS) Lib Sci 1970; Miami Univ (MA) Eng 1989; *cr:* Hayti Pub Schls Scndry Eng Tchr 1966-69; Rust Coll Librn 1969-77; Cntrl St Univ Librn, Eng Instr 1977-; *ai:* Steering Comm North Cntrl Accreditation; St Wide Fac Senate Chairs Comm; AAUP 1972-, Local Chptr Pres, Comms; Amer Lib Assn 1974-; Alpha Kappa Alpha 1974-, VP, Pres of Local Chptr, Ed Chm, Outstdng Chptr Pres 1989; Holy Trinity African Meth Church, Yth Dir; *home:* PO Box 98 Wilberforce OH 45384

BAILEY, MERRILL-JEAN TERRY, Asst Professor of English; *b:* Mt Pleasant, PA; *m:* Joseph B. Jr.; *c:* Tatia Leonne; *ed:* Cheyney St Univ (BA) Eng 1968; Univ of PA (MA) Eng 1975; Grad Stud Columbia Univ, Tchrs Coll; *cr:* NJ Dept of Higher Ed Prgm Analyst 1974-76; US Dept Ed Regnl Grants Rep 1976-91; Atlantic Comm Coll Asst Prof 1991-; *ai:* Chm Tech Comm; Curr, Minority Affairs, Basic Skills Comms; Coord Dev Rdng, Writing; NJEA; Delta Sigma Theta 1966-, Comm Svc; Natl Bapt Congress 1989-, Bd Dir, Excl Chrstn Ed Sunday Schl Publishing Bd; Full Flwshp Univ of PA; Who's Who Amer Colls, Univs; BA With Hnrs; Outstdng Young Woman Amer; Excl Govt Awd Youghiogheny Western Bapt Assn; Pub Svc Awd Afro One Dance Drama, Drum Theater; *office:* Atlantic Comm Coll 5100 Black Horse Pike Mays Landing NJ 08330

BAILEY, RAYMOND E., English Teacher; *b:* Concord, NH; *m:* Amanda S.; *c:* Brett, Benjamin; *ed:* Univ of CT (BA) Eng, Ed 1980; Grad Hrs FL Atlantic Univ; *cr:* Merrimack Vly HS Tchr, Coach 1980-82; St Andrews Schl Tchr, Coach 1982-83; Pope John Paul HS Tchr, Coach 1983-84; Derryfield Schl Ath Dir 1984-86; Merrimack Vly HS Tchr, Coach 1986-; *ai:* Var Bsbl Coach 1987-94; Head Bsbl Coach; Asst Coach Post 21 Amer Legion Bsbl; NH Tchrs of Eng; NCTE 1981-; NEA 1984-; Dept of Recreation Salisbury 1990-, Chm; *office:* Merrimack Valley HS 163 S Main St Penacook NH 03303

BAILEY, ROBERT PENDLETON,JR., 8th Grd Social Studies Teacher; *b:* Frederick, MD; *m:* Margaret Helene Hodges; *c:* Mary Denise Simpson, Robert P. II; *ed:* Antioch U (MA) Mgmt 1977, (BA) Lang Arts 1976; St Marys Coll of MD (AA) Lang Arts 1962; Attnd George Washington; *cr:* Mechanicsville Elem Tchr 1964-65; Margaret Brent Tchr 1965-; *ai:* PTSA; EASMC 1964; MSTA 1964; NEA 1964; Awded Lifetime Mbrshp PTSA; Awded Special Plaque from PTSA for 36 Yrs Svc.

BAILEY, ROSE MARIE BERNIER, 2nd Grade Teacher; *b:* Amesbury, MA; *m:* Jackson D.; *c:* Craig, Kristen, Cara; *ed:* Salem St Coll (BS) Elem Ed 1969; 42 Grad Credits & Inservice; *cr:* Horace Mann & Amesbury Elem 2nd Grd Tchr 1966-; *ai:* Soc Comm; STAR Team; Coordinate Intergenerational Prgm; MTA & NEA; AFT 1970-; Kiwanis 1987-, Bd of Dirs; Church Choir 1970-, Pres; Amer Cancer Soc 1992-, Pub Ed Comm; Rotarys Edctr of the Yr 1987; Awded Partial TIP Grant; *office:* Amesbury Elem Schl S Hampton Rd Amesbury MA 01913

BAILEY, THOMAS JOHN, History & Drama Teacher; *b:* Buffalo, NY; *m:* Kathleen Rose David; *c:* Justin, Libbie, Michael; *ed:* St Univ Coll at Buffalo (BS) His 1964; Addl Grad Hrs in Ed; *cr:* Lake Shore Cntrl Schls Tchr 1968-72; Park Schl Tchr & MS Head 1973-; *ai:* Drama Dir; Bd of Trustees Fac Rep; YMCA Youth Leadership Awd 1980; John Pontius Leadership Awd 1983; First Novel Waterman Farm in Process of Being Pub.*

BAILEY, WILLIAM A., Professor of Law Enforcement; *b:* Philadelphia, PA; *c:* Christopher, Jennifer Griffith; *ed:* Westchester Univ (BS) Ed 1960; Temple Univ (MED) Ed 1965; Columbia Coll (JD) Criminal Justice 1994; USAF Schl of Aviation Med; FBI Training Acad; *cr:* Cherry Hill Schl PE Tchr, Coach 1960-65; Fed Bureau of Investiagion spec Agent 1966-71; Gloucester Cty Coll Prof, Law Enforcement 1971-; *ai:* NJ St Certified Instr Gloucester Cty Police Acad; Congressional Selection Comm for Military Acad Applicants; AFT 1975-; Intnl Asso Chiefs of Police 1980-; Soc of Former FBI Agents 1971-; Nationally Recognized Expert on Robert F. Kennedy Assassination, Contributed to Numerous Books, Articles, Appeared Several Nationally Televised Documentaries on Assassination.

BAILIN, KAREN LEE, English Teacher; *b:* Newark, NJ; *ed:* Douglass Coll (BA) Eng, His 1976; *cr:* Union HS Eng Tchr 1976-84; Cranford HS Eng Tchr 1987-; *ai:* NHS Adv; Acad Team Adv; NEA, NJ Ed Assn 1976-; Union Cty Ed Assn 1976-, Dist Rep; Cranford Ed Assn 1987-; Union Cty Heart Assn 1976-82; Natl Westminster Bank Customer Liaison 1992-; Cranford Prof Dev Cncl; Grant for Research on Aging, Death & Dying; Seminars on Higher Order Thinking Skills, Cmptr Programming & Dealing with Death & Dying; Douglass Coll Tchr Appr Day Aw; *office:* Cranford HS West End Place Cranford NJ 07016

BAILLIE, ADAM J., Mathematics Teacher; *b:* Canton, OH; *m:* Virginia Kloots; *c:* Shari Lynn VanBuren, Cindi Sue Downer, Staci Janele; *ed:* Muskingum Coll (BS) Math 1961; Kent St Univ (MEd) Math 1967; *cr:* Lorain Cty Comm Coll Math Tchr 1980-91; North Ridgeville HS Math Tchr 1961-; *ai:* Var Golf Coach 1965-80; Prom Class Adv 1964-79; Math Curr Comm 1984; Var Girls & Boys Tennis Coach 1992-; NEA, OEA, NEOEA 1961-; NREA 1964-, Treas 2 Yrs, Negotiator 6 Yrs; Comm United Meth 1966-; NSF Summer Inst KSU 1964; Outstanding Young Educator NR Jaycees 1972; Nom Ashland Oil Tchr Achvmt Awd 1989; Nom Presidential Awd for Math Tchng NSF 1984; Erie Shore Conf Girls Tennis Coach of the Yr 1993; *home:* 242 Huntington Cir Elyria OH 44035

BAILO, LYNDA MORRIS, Honors English II Teacher; *b:* Delaware, OH; *m:* Michael George; *c:* Adrian Michael, Brady Christian; *ed:* OH St Univ (BS) Eng Ed 1969; SUNY at New Paltz (MS) K-12 Rdng 1985; Addl In-Svc Credits Cmptr Tech, Curr Mapping, GATE, Peer Coaching, Madelain Hunter Trng, Drug & Alcohol Awareness; *cr:* Richwood Schl Kndgtn Tchr 1968-69; Upper Arlington HS 10 Grd Eng Tchr 1969-71; Miami Trace HS 12 Grd Eng Tchr 1971-75; Washingonville HS 10 Grd Eng Tchr 1981-82; Minisink HS Eng, Rem Rdng Tchr 1982-; *ai:* SAT I Prep Course; Alternative Evening HS; NYSUT 1980-; NCTE 1995-; *office:* Minisink Valley HS PO Box 217 Rt 6 Slate Hill NY 10973*

BAIN, BRUCE, Social Stud Instr & Dept Head; *b:* Zanesville, OH; *c:* Nicholas, Brian; *ed:* OH St Univ (BS) Comprehensive Soc Stud 1972, (MA) Hum 1977; *cr:* Johnstown-Monroe HS Amer Govt Tchr, Asst Var Ftbl Coach 1973-78; Westerville Blendon Schl Soc Stud Tchr, Dept Head 1978-; *ai:* Curr Dev, Course of Study Writer; Soc Stud Textbook, Tech Dev Comm; Summer Schl Advanced Amer Govt Instr; IQT Comm; NEA 1978-; OH Ed Asso 1978-, Recognition Awd; Westerville Ed Asso 1978-, Bldg Rep; OH St Alumni Asso 1975-; Newark City Govt 1980-, City at Large Councilman, Majority Ldr; Second Presbyn Church 1975-; Licking Cty Democratic Club 1979-, Former Pres; The Planetary Soc 1993-; Ashland Oil Corp Regnl Tchr Achvmt Awd 1993; Natl Patriotism Awd 1994; Golden Apple Awds 1988, 1991-92; Bd of Ed A+ Awd 1985; Mc Donald's Outstdng Tchr Awd 1984; Outstdng Young Man of Amer 1980-82, 1984; Yrbk Dedication 1977; Tchr of Yr 1975-77; Natl Recognition Awd Tchng of Amer Govt 1977; Outstdng Ftbl Coaching Awd; *office:* Westerville Blendon Schl 223 S Otterbein Ave Westerville OH 43081

BAINBRIDGE, LISA DONNA, Cheerleading Coach; *b:* Wilmington, DE; *ed:* Golden Beacon Coll (AS) Exec Secretarial Sci 1983; Univ of DE (BA) Interdisciplinary Stud Human Resources, Bus 1994; Certfd Bus Ed; NAEOP III Cert Prof Standards; DPI Standard Cert Admin Support Prsnl, Sr Sec; Chrldng AACCA Certfd, NCA Certfd; *cr:* Ticor Title Basil Bahaglia & Bayard Handleman & MurdochTitle Searcher, Asst Mgr Searching Dept 1983-88; NCCVTSD Sec, Pupil Svcs, Asst Prin, Stu Act 1989-; *ai:* Chrldng Head Coach; NAEOP 1993-; DCCA 1993-, Pres; Article Pub; *office:* Delcastle Tech HS 1417 Newport Rd Wilmington DE 19804

BAINO, WILLIAM A., Fifth Grade Teacher; *b:* Boston, MA; *ed:* Stonehill Coll (BA) Elem Ed 1978; Bridgewater St Coll (MED) Schl Admin 1991; *cr:* Weymouth Pub Schls 3rd-6th Grd Tchr 1978-81; Houston Ind Schl Dist 5th Grd Tchr 1982; Milton Pub Schls 3rd, 5th & 6th Grd Tchr 1985-, Asst Prin 1994-95; *ai:* Transition, Diversity Comm; Fac Rep, Bldg Improvement; 5th Grd Grad Comm; NEA, MA Tchrs Assn, Milton Educators Assn 1985-; MAAIP 1995-; Homestead Civic Assn 1981-; Elected Schl Comm 1985-88, Sec 1987-88; 2 Golden Apple Awds Recipient 1989 & 1991; Boston Coll HS Excl in Tchng Awd Recipient 1995; *office:* Cunningham Elem Schl 44 Edge Hill Rd Milton MA 02186*

BAIOCCO, MAUREEN ELIZABETH, English Teacher; *b:* Buffalo, NY; *m:* John F.; *c:* Patrick; *ed:* SUNY at Buffalo (BA) Eng 1969, (MA) Eng Ed 1973; Elem Ed Cert; *cr:* Cleveland Hill Schl Dist 7-12 Scndry Eng Tchr 1969-; *ai:* Stu Cncl, Future Tchrs Club Co-Moderator; Acad Achvmt Assemblies Coord; K-12 Grd Eng Curr Team Chprsn; NEA, AFT, CHEA 1969-; Bishop's Comm Christ the King 1993-; WNED-TV Awd; *office:* Cleveland Hill MS 105 Mapleview Rd Cheektowaga NY 14225

BAIR, JAMES F., English Dept Chair; *b:* Pittsburgh, PA; *m:* Janet Machalowski; *c:* Joanna L., Emily F.; *ed:* Harvard (AB) Eng 1972; Southern CT St Univ (MS) Eng Ed 1987; *cr:* Grace Heritage Chrstn Schl HS Tchr 1980-83; Chrstn Heritage Schl Eng Dept Chair 1984-; *ai:* Acad Quiz Team Coach; Conf Christianity, Lit 1981-; Harvest Chrstn Cntr 1985-, Treas, The Gideons 1991-, Sec; CT Orhithological assn 1981-; NCTE Dept Awd 1987; G. E. Stu Tchr Recognition Tchr 1990; Pub Numerous Articles; *office:* Christian Heritage Schl 575 White Plains Rd Trumbull CT 06611

BAIR, JAY C., Earth Sci Tchr & Dept Chprsn; *b:* Newport News, VA; *m:* Jan E. Towson; *c:* Heath C., Megan E., Cathryn J.; *ed:* Miami Univ (BS) Earth Sci & Comprehensive Soc Stud 1967; OH St Univ (MA) Sci Ed 1981; 3 Post-Grad Semester Hrs; 8 Post-Grad Quarters; *cr:* Richland Cty Schl Bd Cty Curr Comm 1972-86, 1994-; Madison Local Schls Earth Sci Tchr 1967-; Sci Dept Chprsn 1975-; *ai:* Sci Dept Chprsn; Madison Field Stud Coord 1972-84; NEA 1967-; OEA 1967-; SECO 1976-; OESTA; BSA 1972-89, Asst Scoutmaster; Fredericktown Meth Church 1984-, Fin & Pastor Parish Comms, Vision 2000; Fredericktown Lions Club 1987-, Bd of Dirs; Co-Author OH Achvmt Test in Earth Sci 1970-71; Mentor Tchr 1992-93; Chosen for Miami Univ Eisenhower Pgm 1992; NHS Outstdng Tchr 1994; *home:* 102 W Sandusky St Fredericktown OH 43019*

BAIRD, DEANNA MORRISON, German Tchr & Foreign Lang Ldr; *b:* Altoona, PA; *m:* Richard L. Jr.; *c:* Jessie, Margot; *ed:* IN Univ of PA (BS) German, Sec Ed 1972; Middlebury Coll in Germany (MA), German 1973; Duquesne Uniok, Addl 15 Credits; *cr:* Upper St Clair Schl Dist Ger Tchr 1973-, For Lang Curr Ldr 1992-; *ai:* Ger Amer Partnership Prgm; Ger Club; AATG, ACTFL 1972-; Fulbright Assn 1985-; Fulbright Schlsp; Cert for Oral Proficiency Interview; *office:* Upper Saint Clair HS 1825 Mc Laughlin Run Rd Pittsburgh PA 15241*

BAIRD, JOSEPH L., Emeritus Professor; *b:* Gastonia, NC; *c:* Eve; *ed:* Appalachian St Univ (BA) Eng, Soc Stud 1957, (MA) Eng 1960; Univ of KY (PHD) Medieval Stud 1966; *cr:* Pine Forest HS Eng, Soc Stud Tchr 1957-58; Appalacian Demonstration Schl Rdng Tchr 1958-59; Kent St Univ Prof, Medieval Stud 1964-; *ai:* Medieval Acad of Amer 1964-; Distngd Tchr Awd KSU 1989; Books The Chronicle of Salimbere de Adam, Rossignol, Roman de La Rose Letters, The Letters of Hildegard of Binger, Toward Solomon's Mountain; 100 Articles Pub; *home:* 1369 Greenwood Ave Kent OH 44240

BAIRD, MARY JACQUELINE, Gifted Ed & 7th Grd Eng Tchr; *b:* Sandusky, MI; *ed:* Western MI Univ (BA) Eng, Speech Scndry 1972; Univ of MI 16 Hrs; Univ of Toledo 8 Hrs; Univ of Tours France Studied Fr; *cr:* Sylvania Schls 7th Grd Eng Tchr 10 Yrs, Grd 7 Eng, 7-8 Grd Gifted Ed Tchr 12 Yrs; *ai:* Power of Pen Competition Coach; Newspaper Adv; Eng Dept Head; Optimist Club Speech, Essay Competition Coach; Sylvania Ed Assn, OH Ed Assn 1974-; Sylvania Schls Tchr of Yr 1995; *home:* 2524 Melva Ct Toledo OH 43611

BAIRD, VAN, Deputy Principal & 8th Grd Tch; *b:* Guyana, So America; *m:* June Lucienne King; *c:* Brian, June, Roystan, Heather Lepraund, Lindsay, Richard; *ed:* 57 Credit Hrs Towards BA Eng Hunters Coll; Guyana Tchrs Coll Cert Eng & Ecs 1966; *cr:* Vryheids Lust Montrose Govt Schl Class Tchr & Sr Master Act 1971-79; Borno Tchrs Coll Dept Head & Eng Lecturer 1979-86; United Bus Inst Eng as 2nd Lang Lecturer 1986-88; Arista Prep Schl Homeroom, Comp Sci Tchr & Deputy Prin 1988-; *ai:* Tchr of Yr 1989-92; *office:* Arista Prep Schl 755 Eastern Pky Brooklyn NY 11213*

BAJDEK, ANTHONY JOSEPH, Assoc Dean & Sr His Lecturer; *b:* Lynn, MA; *m:* Cynthia J. Warden; *c:* Christopher J., Peter A.; *ed:* Northeastern Univ (BA) His 1964, (MA) His 1966; *cr:* Northeastern Univ His Tchng Fellow 1964-65, His Lecturer 1966-76, Asst Dean of Stdnts 1969-79, Sr His Lecturer 1976-, Assoc Dean Adm, Svcs Ops 1979-; *ai:* Univ Comm on Honors, Schlsps; Univ Centennial Comm; Polish Studnts Club Adv; Amer Assn for Advancement of Slavic Stud 1986-; Polish Amer Historical Assn 1983-; Polish Amer Congress of Eastern MA Inc 1991-, VP; MA Army Natl Guard, Army Reserve 1956-, Sgt; Phi Alpha Theta Natl Honor Soc His 1962; Pi Sigma Alpha Natl Honor Soc Pol Sci 1963; Northeastern Univ Tchng Fellowship Awd 1964; Boston Coll Grad Assistantship Awd 1964; Woodrow Wilson Natl Fellwoship Nom 1964; *office:* Northeastern Univ 360 Hungington Ave Boston MA 02115

BAKALAR, RONALD A., English & Speech Teacher; *b:* Cleveland, OH; *m:* Marilyn Kay Stelmack; *c:* Scott, Tracy Dorko; *ed:* Kent St Univ (BS) Speech, Eng Ed 1961; Bowling Green St Univ (MED) Scndry Ed 1981; 30 Addl Grad Hrs; *cr:* Admiral King HS Speech, Eng Tchr 1961-70; Radio

Station WWWE Newscaster 1970-77; Admiral King HS Speech, Eng Tchr 1977-; *ai:* Lorain Ed Assn 1961-, Pres 1968-70.

BAKER, ALLEN DALE, Biology Teacher; *b:* Meyersdale, PA; *m:* Karen Ludy; *c:* Mark, Melissa; *ed:* IN Univ of PA (BA) Ed, Bio 1973; Shippensburg Univ (MS) Ed, Bio 1980; Various Educl Insts Addl 39 Credit Hrs; *cr:* Anne Arundel Sr HS Bio Tchr 1973-74; James Buchanan Sr HS Bio Tchr 1974-; Mont Alto Campus of Penn St Bio lab Instr 1995-; *ai:* Core Team of Strategic Planning Comm; Bd of Dir for Tuscarora Wildlife Ed Project; Stu Asst Prgm; Fac Advy Cncl for NHS; NABT 1980-; PA Sci Tchrs Assn 1985-; NEA, PSEA 1974-; TEA 1974-, Past Pres 1993-94; PA Wildlife Fed 1995-; Jaycees 1978-1991, Past Pres 1982-83; First United Meth Church 1976-, Bd of Trustee's; *home:* 121 Beech Ln Mercersburg PA 17236

BAKER, BARBARA JEAN (STAPLES), Art Teacher; *b:* Boston, MA; *m:* Dederick Arnold; *c:* Aletra, Kirstyn; *ed:* Bowling Green St Univ (BS) Art Ed 1979; Cleveland St Univ (MA) Curr, Instruction 1985; Kent St Doctoral Prgm; *cr:* Cuyahoga Hills Boys Home Math Tchr 1979; Warrensville Heights HS Math Tchr 1979-80; East Cleveland Bd of Ed Art Tchr 1980-85; Cleveland Heights HS Art Tchr 1985-; *ai:* Chrldng, Dance & Drill Team Adv; Model Schl, Curr Advy Comms; Class Adv 8 Yrs; AFT 1980-; AEA 1981-; Delta Sigma Theta 1985-, Cotillion Dance Coord; Tots & Teens 1993-, Teen Coord; *office:* Cleveland Heights HS 13263 Cedar Rd Cleveland Heights OH 44118

BAKER, BRENDA KAY, Seventh-Eighth Grd Eng Tchr; *b:* Corning, NY; *m:* Matthew E.; *ed:* Corning Comm (AAS) Paralegal 1987; Elmira Coll (BA) Eng 1989; Scndry Eng Ed; *cr:* Elmira City Schl Dist 7th-8th Grd Eng Tchr 1989-; *ai:* Quiz Club Adv; Bldg Planning Team Mem; Futures Comm Rep; AFT 1989-; Excl in Writing Schlsp Corning Comm Coll 1986; Prize in Eng Elmira Coll 1989; Thomas Derham Schlsp Elmira Coll 1988-89; *home:* 129 Main St Wellsboro PA 16901

BAKER, CINDY PRESTON, High School Mathematics Tchr; *b:* Hornell, NY; *m:* Robert J.; *c:* Jay, Andrea, Joshua; *ed:* William Smith Coll (BA) Math 1974; Alfred Univ (MS) Ed 1981; *cr:* Andover Cntrl Schl HS Math Tchr 1975-; *ai:* HS Choir Accompanist; NHS, Class of 96 Adv; NEA, NEA NY 1981-; Andover Tchrs Assn 1981-, Treas 1985-; Delta Kappa Gamma 1989-; Phi Kappa Phi 1981-; MAA; AMTNYS; NCTM; Anna W. Mac Arthur Chapter Order of Eastern Star 1981-; *home:* 3798 Baker Street Ext Andover NY 14806

BAKER, DANA LOUISE, Student Development Professor; *b:* Washington, DC; *c:* Jessica, Danielle; *ed:* Coll of Wooster (BA) Psych 1981; Trinity Coll (MA) Cnslng 1992; 6 Credits Toward PHD in Ed; *cr:* Cath Univ Assoc Dir of Admission 1989-92; Montgomery Coll Asst Prof 1992-; *ai:* Mentor, Martial Arts Club Adv; Campus Advising Comm; AAUP 1993-; Amer Cnslng Assn 1994-; *office:* Montgomery Coll At Rockville 51 Mannakee St Rockville MD 20850*

BAKER, DAVID W., Science Teacher; *b:* West Point, NY; *m:* Sharon Hogan; *c:* Brian, Christine; *ed:* Lafayette Coll (BA) Geology 1968; Columbia Univ (MS), (MED) Tchng, Curr 1987, (EDD) Tchng, Curr 1989; SUNY at New Paltz 39 Hrs Geology; *cr:* Highland Falls MS Sci Tchr 1971-93; James I O'Neill HS Sci Tchr 1993-; *ai:* Enrichment Act, Cmptr Ed Dist Coord; Sci Tchrs Assn of NY St 1973-, Earth Sci SAR; NYS Marine Ed Assn 1990-; NYS United Tchrs 1971-, Pres, VP; Rotary Club 1995-; NYS Excl & Accountability Prgm 1990-, Chprsn; Pi Lambda Theta Innovation in TchngAwd 1993; Sci Tchrs Assn of NYS Outstdng Sci Tchr Awd in Earth Sci 1996; *office:* James I. O'Neill Jr. Sr HS Route 9 W Highland Falls NY 10928*

BAKER, DIANE MAWHINNEY, Vocal Music Teacher; *b:* New York, NY; *m:* Steven Alfred; *c:* David Riley; *ed:* Ithaca Coll (BM); NYS Permanent Cert Elmira Coll, Coll of St Rose; *cr:* Marcus Whitman Schl Dist Vocal Music Tchr 1975-76; Dryden Cntrl Schl Dist Vocal Music Tchr 1976-78; Homer Cntrl Schl Dist Vocal Music Tchr 1978-82; Cortland City Schl Dist Vocal Music Tchr 1983-87; Fayetteville Manlius Schl Dist Vocal Music Tchr 1987-; *ai:* Personal, Pupil Svc, Bldg Comms; Backstage Backers, All Sports Booster; NYSUT, MENC, NYSSMA 1975-; OCMEA, FMTA 1987-; BMPOA Bd 1989-, Dir; Pub Kendor Music Co; *office:* Fayetteville Elem Schl 704 S Manlius St Fayetteville NY 13066

BAKER, DON FORREST, 12th Grade Government Teacher; *b:* Warren, OH; *m:* Carol Crosby; *c:* Sarah M., Rachel L.; *ed:* OH Univ (BSEd) Soc Stud 1969; Youngstown St Univ (MSEd) Gui, Cnslng 1976; 15 Addl Hrs US His, Govt; *cr:* Newton Falls Exempted Vly Schl Dist Tchr 1969-, Soc Stud Dept Head 1980-; *ai:* AFT 1992-; OH Fed of Tchrs 1992-, Del; Newton Falls Classroom Tchrs Assn 1969-, Pres; Gideons Intnl 1993-; Taft Inst 1978; ITT Inst for Soc Stud, Ec Tchrs 1982-84; Amer His Tchr Wkshp Youngstown St Univ 1988; *office:* Newton Falls HS 907 Milton Blvd Newton Falls OH 44444*

BAKER, DON PAUL, Social Studies Tchr; *b:* Plattsmouth, NE; *ed:* Wesleyan (BA) His 1958; *cr:* Cass Country Schl Tchr 1 Yr; Plattsmouth Elem Schl 1 Yr; Clark AB Schl Tchr 3 Yrs; Itazuke AS Schl 2 Yrs; Kunto Mura & Yokota Schls Tchr 3 Yrs; *ai:* NEA 1952; OEA, NEATA 1959; Outstdng Tchr Awd 1964-65.

BAKER, DONALD WILLIAM, Spanish Teacher; *b:* Reading, PA; *ed:* Howard Univ (BA) Span 1970; Kutztown Univ (MA) Span 1975; 15 Credit Hrs of Post Grad Stud; *cr:* Pottstown Jr HS Span Tchr 1972-76; Pottstown HS Span Tchr 1976-; *ai:* Span Club Adv; Class Adv; Restructuring Comm; Tchr Evaluation Comm; Diversity Comm; TESA Coord; AATSAP 1976-; AFT 1984-; PFT 1984-, Pres; *office:* Pottstown Sr HS N Washington St Pottstown PA 19464*

BAKER, DONNA M., English Teacher; *b:* Pittsburgh, PA; *m:* Gary L.; *ed:* Edinboro Univ (BS) Ed 1971; Allegheny Coll (MA) Ed 1974; Media Specialist Cert 1981; *cr:* Conneaut Valley HS Eng Tchr 1973-; *ai:* Schl Newspaper Spon; NCTE, NWCPTE, NEA, PSEA, CEA; Awded Keystone Integrated Framework Grant 1995; *office:* Conneaut Valley HS Box 330A Conneautville PA 16406

BAKER, ELIZABETH LEE, German Teacher & Club Advisor; *b:* Canton, OH; *m:* Mark A.; *ed:* Kent St Univ (BA) Ger 1985, (BS) Ed 8-12 1987; *cr:* Louisville City Schls Substitute Tchr 1988; Louisville Sr HS Ger Tchr 1988-; *ai:* Ger Club Adv; Louisville Ed Assn 1988-, Building Rep 3 Yrs; OEA, NEA, AATG, OH Foreign Lang Assn 1988-; Congress-Bundestag Youth Exch Prgm Mem 1985-86; Worked in Bank at Frankfort & Anna Schmidt Schl; *office:* Louisville H S 1201 S Nickelplate Louisville OH 44641

BAKER, FREDERICK LESLIE, Legal Studies Dept Chprsn; *b:* Columbus, OH; *m:* Nancy Nestor; *c:* Adam N., Caley S., Harold F.; *ed:* Otterbein Coll (BAEd) His 1978; Capital Univ Law Schl (JD) 1982; *cr:* Nationwide Life Ins Co Attorney 1982-83; Columbus St Comm Coll Bus Law Instr 1983-89, Legal Assisting Prof, Coord 1989-95, Legal Stud Chprsn 1995-; *ai:* Westerville South HS Ath Boosters Bd Mem; Westerville City Cncl Old Westerville Task Force Exec Bd Mem; Old Westerville Neighborhood Alliance; OH St Supreme Court Bar 1982-; Amer Assn of Paralegal Edctrs 1989-; Amer bus Law Assn 1982-; Cntrl Coll Presbyn Church Bd of Trustees; Amer Bar Assn; Natl Fed of Paralegal Assoc; Natl Assn of Legal Assistants; Presenter OH St Bar Assn Annual Convention Del US to Japan 1994; People to People Conf 1988; *office:* Columbus St Comm Coll 550 E Spring St Columbus OH 43215

BAKER, GINA CIAMBOTTI, Biology Teacher; *b:* Altoona, PA; *m:* John Scott; *c:* Matthew A., Catherine J., David J.; *ed:* Penn St (BS) Ed 1987; 26 Credit Hrs for Permanent Cert; *cr:* Bedford HS Bio Tchr 1989-; *ai:* Class Adv; NEA 1989-; Southern Alleg Tech Prep Integration Awd 1994-95; *home:* 1431 Polk Ave Altoona PA 16602

BAKER, HELEN (WAGNER), First Grade Teacher; *b:* Port Clinton, OH; *m:* Patrick L.; *c:* Patrick, Stephen, Nicholas, Joseph; *ed:* Bowling Green St Univ (BSEd) Elem Ed 1969; 24 Grad Hrs; *cr:* Fremont St Ann's Schl First Grd Tchr 1967-68; Fremont City Schls Sub Tchr 1968-71; Clyde Green Springs Schls Sub Tchr 1972-76; Green Spring Elem Schl First Grd Tchr 1976-; *ai:* Staff Advy, Boosters Comms; Cooperating Tchr Heidelberg Coll Stu Tchr 1995; NEA, OH Ed Assn 1980-; Clyde-Green Springs Ed Assn 1980-, Bldg Rep 1990-96; St Mary's CCD Prgm 1984-; Clyde St Marys Parish 1971-; *office:* Green Springs Elem Schl 420 N Broadway St Green Springs OH 44836

BAKER, JANICE HERMAN, English Teacher; *b:* Vancouver, WA; *m:* Frank; *c:* Molly Emma Aitkena; *ed:* Pomona Coll (BA) Eng Lit 1961; Harvard Grad Schl of Ed (MAT) Tchng of Eng 1962; John Hopkins Evening Coll 27 Grad Credits Eng Lit, Film, Rdng; *cr:* Wycombe Court Schl for Girls Eng Tchr 1963; Doshisha Women's Coll Eng as Frgn Lang Tchr 1966-67; Patterson HS Eng Tchr 1974-79; Baltimore Schl for the Arts Eng Tchr 1979-; *ai:* Natl Endowment for Hum Flwshp Harvard Univ 1983; Cncl for Basic Ed Mellon Fnd Ind Stud Flwshp 1985; Panel Mem NEH Dir Lynne Chaney's Amer Memory Report 1987; NEH Review Panelist 1984-85; US Dept of Ed Review Panelist 1988-90; Reader, AP Exams Educl Testing Svc 1988-90, 1992-93; *office:* Baltimore Schl For The Arts 712 Cathedral St Baltimore MD 21201

BAKER, JEAN HARVEY, History Professor; *b:* Baltimore, MD; *m:* Robinson; *c:* Susan Bauman, R. Scott, Robert W., Jenny; *ed:* Goucher Coll (AB) His 1962; John Hopkins Univ (MA) 1965, (PHD) 1971; *cr:* Notre Dame Coll Lecturer 1971-73; Goucher Coll Asst Prof, Assoc Prof, Prof 1975-; *ai:* His Club Advy; AAUP; AHA; OAH; Who's Who; NEH Flwshp; 5 Books: Ambivalent Americans, Affairs of Party, Mary Todd Lincoln, The Stevenons Biography of an American Family 1996, Politics of Cahnurty; *office:* Goucher Coll Dulaney Valley Rd Towson MD 21204

BAKER, JOHNNIE W., Professor of Computer Science; *b:* El Paso, TX; *m:* Oberta Ann Slotterbeck; *c:* Jonobie Dale; *ed:* Hardin-Simmons Univ (BA) Math Ed 1958; Univ of TX at Austin (MA) Math 1965, (PHD) Math 1968; NSF Acad Yr Awd Prgm for HS Math & Sci Tchrs 1962-63; *cr:* Cuero TX Pub Schls Ninth Grd Sci Tchr 1960-62; FL St Univ Math Asst Prof 1968-72; Kent St Univ Math Asst Prof 1973-75, Math Assoc Prof 1975-95, Cmptr Sci Full Prof 1995-; *ai:* Assn of Computing Machinery Stu Chptr Spon 1978-; Assn of Computing Machinery 1978-; IEEE Cmptr Soc 1982-; AAUP; Math Rsrch Papers; Cmptr Sci Publications; Invited Address at ACS on Computational Chem; Parallel Processing Letters Journal Ed 1991-; CS Coord 1990-; *office:* Kent St Univ Dept of Math & Cmptr Sci Kent OH 44242*

BAKER, JONELL HARRISON, Fifth Grd Inclusion Class Tchr; *b:* Elyria, OH; *m:* Carl S. II; *c:* Darby, Michael; *ed:* Kent St (BS) Elem Ed 1970; Many at Variety of Colls, Univs; *cr:* Brush Elem Schl Third, Fifth Grd Tchr 1970-; *ai:* NEOEA 1970-, Del; MEA 1970-, Treas, Various Comms, Offices; OEA 1970-, Inculsion Task Force; NEA; Univ of Dayton Research Inst 1995-, Bd Mem; *office:* Brush Elem Schl 11600 Durkee Rd Grafton OH 44044*

BAKER, JOSEPHINE C. (JOHNSON), Sixth Grade Teacher; *b:* Washington, DC; *m:* Isham O.; *c:* Melanie Baker-Della Rocca, Vicki Baker Simmons, Todd P.; *ed:* Howard Univ (BA) Sociology, Psych 1952, (MA) Ed Psych, Gifted Ed 1981; Trinity Coll, Univ of CT, Howard Univ Prof Update & Advancement; *cr:* DC Pub Schls Tchr & Gifted Talented Coord 1970-95; Goerge Wash Univ Visiting Prof 1995-96; *ai:* Art, Essays, Oratory City-Wide Contest; Media Festival Competition; Odyssey of Mind; Folger Shakespeare Stu Festival; Natl History Day; Phi Delta Kappa 1981-; Amer Classical League 1989-, Natl Mythology Exam Comm; Alpha Kappa Alpha 1949-; Palisades Civic Assn; Christa Mc Auliffe Fellow; Cafritz Fellow Prof Dev Awd; Washington Post Outstanding Tchr; George Washington Univ Natl Sci Fnd Grant Hypermedia Prgm; US Dept of Ed Presenter; Natl Endowment for Hum Odssey Project Fellow; *office:* Shepherd Elem Schl 14th & Kalmia Rd NW Washington DC 20012

BAKER, JUNE WITMER, Health & Physical Ed Teacher; *b:* PA; *m:* Thomas; *c:* Kari, Katie; *ed:* Lock Haven Univ (BS) Phys Ed, Hlth 1973; 24 Credits Post-Grad Penn State Univ, M Equiv; *cr:* Millersburg Area HS Hlth & Phy Ed 15 Yrs; *ai:* Dept Curr Planner; SADD Adv; NEA, PSEA 1980-.

BAKER, KENNETH CARROLL, Principal; *b:* Upper Sandusky, OH; *m:* Deborah Ann Moser; *c:* Sarah, Eric, Brett; *ed:* Miami Univ (BS) Eng 1978; Bowling Green St Univ (ME) Admin, (EDS) Admin 1987; *cr:* Arlington HS Prin 1983-88; Wynford HS Prin 1988-91; Greenville HS Prin 1991-94; Pickerington HS Prin 1994-; *ai:* OH Assn of Admin 1983-, Bd of Dirs; Phi Delta Kappa 1984-; Kiwanis 1991-, Pres; YMCA 1991-, Bd of Trustees; *office:* Pickerington HS 300 Opportunity Way Pickerington OH 43147

BAKER, LAVERNE H., Math Teacher; *b:* Wharton, TX; *m:* George M.; *c:* KaDeana, GeoRon, Garrett; *ed:* TX A&M Univ at Kingsville (BS) Scndry Ed 1974; 30 Addl Hrs Trinity Univ; *cr:* Galveston ISD Math Tchr 1974-76; Suitland HS Math Tchr 1977-79; Potomac HS Math Tchr 1979-; *ai:* Acad Coach, Tutoring, Guid Advy Comm; Preparing Stu Academically For Coll, Careers Lead Team; MSTA, NEA, Prince Georges Cty Ed Assn 1981-; Alpha Kappa Alpha 1973-; Pilgrim's Rest Bapt Church 1994-; Deans List; Grad Magnum Cum Laude TX A&M Univ 1974; Acad Coach Awd; *home:* 7272 Joplin St Capitol Heights MD 20743

BAKER, LINDA LAWSON, English & Language Arts Tchr; *b:* Wilmington, DE; *m:* Claytin I. Jr.; *c:* Christopher, Courtney, Cody; *ed:* Univ of ME at Gorham (BS) Ed, Eng 1969; Univ of Southern ME (MS) Exceptionality, Gifted Chldhd Ed 1992; 18 Addl Credit Hrs; *cr:* Bath Jr HS 9th Grd Eng Tchr 1980-85; Mt Ararat Schl 3ng, Lang Arts Tchr 1985-, Acad Coord 1993-; *ai:* NEA, NCTE, ME Tchrs Assn 1980-; ME Cncl Eng Lang Arts 1985-; ME Educators Gifted, Talented 1990-; MSAD #75 Gifted, Talented Comm 1987-; Topsham Finance Comm 1978-86, Sec, Vice Chair, Chair; Topsham Bd of Selectmen 1986-89, Vice Chair 1989; Blaine Schlsp Selection Comm 1992-; Blaine House Schlsp Grad Stud; Pub Unit on Novel 1990; *office:* Mount Ararat Schl Main St Topsham ME 04086*

BAKER, LISA, High School English Teacher; *b:* Gainsville, FL; *ed:* Amer Univ (BA) Eng 1988; Johns Hopkins Univ MS Counseling; *cr:* Montgomery Village MS Team Ldr, Tchr 1989-93; Damascus HS Eng Tchr, Coach 1993-; *ai:* Girls Bsktbl, Vlybl; Class Adv; Mentor; Intermural Spon; NEA, MSTA 1989-; Re-Write Eng Curr Mem; *office:* Damascus HS 25921 Ridge Rd Damascus MD 20872*

BAKER, LISA S., Spanish Teacher; *b:* Hammond, IN; *m:* Kevin; *ed:* IN Univ (BS) Span, Eng 1990; John Carroll Univ Working Towards Masters of Ed; *cr:* West Noble MS, HS At-Risk, Rdng, Eng, Span Tchr 1990-93; *ai:* NEA 1990-; *office:* Parma Sr HS 6285 W 54th St Parma OH 44129

BAKER, MARGARET CUNNINGHAM, English Teacher; *b:* Wilberforce, OH; *m:* Lawerence; *ed:* Central St Univ (BS) Eng 1971; Wright St Univ (MS) Prsnl Counseling 1978; Bowling Green St Univ Tutoring 1990; *cr:* Lorain Admiral King Schl Eng Tchr 1987-; *ai:* Lorain Ed Assn, NEA 1980-; Cum Laude Undergraduate; Pres Schlsp 1977; *home:* 4709 Edgewood Dr Lorain OH 44053

BAKER, MARSHALYN ELAINE (WING), Mathematics Teac Lewiston, ME; *m:* Richard Paul; *c:* Ryan, Randen; *ed:* Univ of M Elem Ed 1973, (MS) Rdng Ed 1977; Attnd OK St Univ, Univ England; *cr:* Belgrade Cntrl Schl 4th Grd Tchr 1973-74; Herbert G 4-5th Grd Tchr 1974-75; Belgrade Cntrl Schl 5th Grd Tchr 1 1981-93, 6th Grd Tchr 1975-76, 1980-81; Williams Jr HS 7-8th G Tchr 1993-; *ai:* Mentor Tchr; Math Specialist; Math Team Coac Counts Team Coach, Tech, Math Comm; NEA, ME Ed Assn, Messa Tchrs Assn 1973-, NCTM 1989-; Assn of Tchr of Math ME 1989 Comm; Math Assn of Amer 1995-; DC Stevens Trust Fund, Mem; Sigma Sigma 1972-; Presidential Awd in Math, Sci Tchng; Artic NEWMAST NASA Participant; *office:* Williams Jr HS 19 Plea Oakland ME 04963

BAKER, NANCY BUZZELL, High School Science Teac Northampton, MA; *c:* David S.; *ed:* Johnson St Coll (BS) Bio 197 30 Grad Credits; *cr:* Browns River MS Tchr 1972-77; Richford HS S 1980-; *ai:* CARE Team; Instrl Support Team; Schlsp, Attendance C Sci Dept Head; NEA, VEA, RTA 1980-; VT Sci Tchrs Assn 198 Edctrs Assn 1989-, Pres; VT Inst of Natural Sci; Friends of Music; V & Wildlife Conservation Group; Outstdng Tchr Awd.

BAKER, ROBERT K., Coord of Gifted & Tech Coord; *b:* New Cas *c:* Alyssa, Andrew; *ed:* Slippery Rock Coll (BS) Elem Ed Westminster Coll (MS) Ed 1972; *cr:* Neshannock Meml Schl 4, 6 G 1969-83, Tchr Cmptr, Gifted 1984-95; Neshannock Jr Sr HS Co Gifted, Tech 1995-; *ai:* Acad Games Coord; Forensics Coach; NEA, NTEA 1969-; *home:* 600 Hickory Dr New Castle PA 16101

BAKER, RONALD L., Science Teacher; *b:* Mt Vernon, OH; *m:* Ka Michin; *c:* Dawn M. Nelson; *ed:* OH St Univ (BS) Sci Ed 1971, (M Ed 1982; 10 Hrs Geology; 5 Hrs Meterology; 10 Hrs Astronomy; *cr:* Elm HS Sci Tchr 1972; Uticia HS Sci Tchr 1972-; *ai:* NEA, OHEA North Fork EA 1972-, Pres, Treas, Innovative Tchr Awd; Dow Outstdng Tchr Awd; *office:* Utica Sr HS Jefferson St Utica OH 430

BAKER, ROSEMARY L., Assistant Professor of Eng; *b:* Syracus *c:* James Jr., Margarte Formica; *ed:* SUNY at Oswego (BA) Eng Syracuse Univ (MA) Eng 1986; Tchng Cert Eng Lemoyne Coll 19 Syracuse Rsrch Corp Tech Ed 1982-90; Syracuse Univ Part-tim 1985-91; O'Brien & Gere Engrs Inc Tech Writer 1990-91; SU Morrisville Asst Prof 1991-; *ai:* Fac Congress, Rep; Stu Affairs, Pro Comms; United Univ Prof 1991-; Outstdng Tchr Univ Coll of Sy Univ 1990; Phi Theta Kappa 1995; *office:* S U N Y Coll Of A & T M Morrisville NY 13408*

BAKER, RUTHANN KING, Fifth Grade Teacher; *b:* Portland, M Dan M.; *c:* Siobhan; *ed:* Univ of Southern ME (BS) Elem Ed 19 South Portland Schl Dept Sub Tchr 1976-80; Brown Hamin Schls Tc 1980-84; Brown Schl 5th Grd Tchr 1984-; *ai:* Math Team Coac Support Team; *office:* Frank I. Brown Schl 37 Highland Ave South P ME 04106

BAKER, SANDRA ACKER, Library Media Specialist; *b:* Utica, John; *c:* Joshua Kirnie; *ed:* St Univ of NY at Oswego (BA) Scnd 1971, (MS) Ed 1985; Syracuse Univ (MLS) Information Stud 19 North Syracuse HS Eng Tchr 1971-83; Cicero-No Syracuse HS En 1983-90, Lib Media Specialist 1991-; *ai:* Stu Planning Team Adv Planning Team Chair; Tech Comm; AFT, NYSUT 1971-; ASCD *office:* Cicero-North Syracuse HS Rt 31 Cicero NY 13039

BAKER, SANDRA KAY, Ohio Studies & Amer His Tchr; *b:* Akro *c:* Andrew; *ed:* Univ of Akron (BS) Ed Scndry 1972; 18 Addl Cred *cr:* Norton MS 7th Grd Soc Stu, Sci Tchr 1972-73, 8th Grd US his, S 1973-76, 8th Grd World Geography Tchr 1976-78, 6th-8th Grd Mat 1978-92, 7th Grd OH Stud, 8th Grd US His Tchr 1992-; *ai:* Kalman Chapter of Natl Jr Honor Soc Former Adv 10 Yrs; NEA, OEA, N NCTA 1972-; *office:* Norton MS 3390 S Clevelan Massillon Rd Nort 44203

BAKER, SCOTT MARTIN, Social Studies Teacher; *b:* Lock Have *m:* Kelly Jo Smith; *ed:* Lock Haven Univ (BS) Soc Sci 1991; 12 Credits Toward Permanent Cert; *cr:* Lock Haven HS 9th Grd Amer H Grd Civics Tchr 1993-; *ai:* 8th Grd Ftbl, JV Bsktbl Coach; YMC Bsktbl Dir, Coach; NEA, PSEA 1993-; *office:* Lock Haven HS W C St Lock Haven PA 17745*

BAKER, STEVEN J., High School Mathematics Tchr; *b:* Oneida, N Alfred Univ (BS) Mrktg, Mngmt 1985; Clarkson Univ (MBA) Mrktg Utica Coll NYS Cert Math 7-12, Bus Ed 1989; *cr:* Mohawk Valley Coll Adjunct Bus Instr 1988-90; Camden Cntrl Schl Dist 9-12 Grd Tchr 1990-; *ai:* Frosh Advisor; Boys, Girls Tennis, Boys Bowling C NYSUT 1990-; AMTOC 1990-; Camden Pub Lib Bd 1994-, H Comm; *office:* Camden Central HS Oswego St Camden NY 13316*

BAKER, SUSAN BRANDON, First Grade Teacher; *b:* Tampa, F James Houston; *c:* James Whitney, Kimberly Grace; *ed:* Univ of GA Ed 1962; Westminster Coll (MA) Rdng 1995; Attnd Youngstown St Kent St Univ, OH St Univ; *cr:* Austintown Local Schls First Grd 1962-63, Bedford Local Schls First Grd Tchr 1963-64; United A Flight Attendant 1964-65; Austintown Local Schls Second Grd 1965-66; South Range Local Schls Sixth Grd Tchr 1969-70; West Local Schls First Grd Tchr 1970-72; South Range Local Schls Firs Tchr 1975-82, Fifth Grd Tchr 1982-90, First Grd Tchr 1990-; *ai:* Improvement Team; SREA, OEA, NEA 1965-; Delta Kappa Gamma Upcoming Yr 1st VP; Alpha Chi Omega 1960-; Collectors Soc Western Reserve 1975-; Canfield Presbyn 1965-, Deacon, Trustee; J Henderson Schlsp from Phi Delta Kappa of Westminster Coll; Clas Tchr WFMJ-TV; *office:* South Range Elem 11836 South Ave North OH 44452

BAKER, SUZANNE EAMES, Mathematics Teacher; *b:* Attleboro, *m:* Kendall; *c:* Scott, Stacey; *ed:* Keene St Coll (BED) Elem Ed Lehigh Univ (MED) Scndry Ed 1986; 4 Credit Hrs Univ of NH 19 Credit Hrs St Univ of NY at Oneonta 1972-76; *cr:* Honeoye Cntrl Sc Grd Tchr 1969-70; Walton Elem Schl Sub Tchr 1972-76; Perkiome Math Tchr, Coll Adv 1981-; *ai:* NCTM, PASSCAC 1990-; *o* Perkiomen Schl PO Box 130 Pennsburg PA 18073

BAKER, WILLIAM E., Math Teacher & Department Head; *b:* St A VT; *m:* Maylo Baker; *c:* Matthew, Sara, Jill; *ed:* Eastern Nazarene C Math 1969; Johnson St C (MA) Math Ed 1985; 48 Grad Hrs; *cr:* Jo St Coll Adjunct Math Tchr 15 Yrs; Lamoille Union HS Math Dept He Yrs; *ai:* NHS Comm; Babe Ruth Bsbl, Elem Schl All-Star Bsktbl C NCTM, VCTM 1987-; NEA 1989-; Former Vol Fireman, Pres; Air Sergeants Assn; Presidential Awd Excl Math Tchng 1987; Tchr of Yr HS Grad Address 1984; *home:* RR 1 Box 170 Waterville VT 05492

BAKER, WILLIAM R., English Teacher; *b:* High Point, NC; *m:* Nelson; *c:* Caitlin, Joshua, Lisa Gerhan, Andy Gerhan; *ed:* Syracuse (BA) Eng 1965; SUNY at Albany (MA) Eng, Tchng 1972; Duke Univ Credits in Eng Lit; Univ of PA PHD Credits in Amer Lit; *cr:* Schal HS Eng Tchr 1968-; *ai:* AFT, Bldg Rep; Tchr of Yr.

BAKEY, ANN T., 6th Grade Teacher; *b:* Philadelphia, PA; *m:* Denr *c:* Dennis, Peter, Kathryn; *ed:* East Stroudsburg Univ (BS) Hlth, PE *cr:* St Francis of Assisi Schl 4th, 6th Grd Tchr 1986-; *ai:* NCEA *office:* Saint Francis Of Assisi Schl 112 Saxer Ave Springfield PA 1

US, KARLET J., Third Grade Teacher; *b:* Corpus Christie, TX; oh M. E.; *c:* Tara, Bethany, Aaron; *ed:* St Coll at Buffalo (BS) Elem ; Addl Work Toward Masters at Bonaventure Univ; *cr:* Olean Schl Elem Tchr 1966-69; Vicenza Amer Elem Schl Elem Tchr 1969-70; chl System Elem Tchr 1970-75, 1987-; *ai:* Natl Geography Bee; e Comm; Lang Arts Comm; Math, Sci & Tech Comm; Math Nights; OTA 1987-; PTA 1966-, Pres, VP & Sec, Schlsp Awd; Boy Scouts , Ldr; Church Bishops Conm 1975-82, Ldr; *home:* 103 Highland lean NY 14760*

ER, ALICE J., Business Teacher; *b:* Passaic, NJ; *ed:* Montclair St BA) Bus 1970, (MA) Bus 1980, (MA) Supervisory Cert 1981; us In-Service Courses; *cr:* Parsippany Hills HS Bus Tchr 1970-; *ai:* o-Adv; NEA, NJEA 1970-; NJBEA 1970-, Conf Coord; Delta Pi 1974-, Sec & Pres; *office:* Parsippany Hills H S 20 Rita Dr any NJ 07054*

, DARLENE MARIE, Home Economics Teacher; *b:* Batavia, NY; k; *c:* Aaron, Adam, Laura; *ed:* SUNY at Morrisville (AAS) Food 1970; SUC at Oneonta (BS) Home Ed Ed 1972; SUC at Buffalo ome Ec Ed 1975; SUC at Brockport (CAS) Educl Admin 1992; *cr:* d-Alabama Cntrl Schl Home Ec Tchr 1975-; *ai:* Reach Out Kids re Vol; NYSUT 1975-; Delta Kappa Gamma 1990-, Pres, VP.

AN, EDWARD ELLIOT, Assistant Principal; *b:* Brooklyn, NY; *m:* axelrod; *c:* Howard Ross, Marc Ian; *ed:* Hofstra Univ (CAS) Educl 1978; Syracuse Univ (MS) Jrnlsm, Pub Relations 1974; Attnd C.W. ll, LIU, US Navy; Accepted Doctoral Stud SUNY at Albany, Nova astern Univ; *cr:* Turtle Hook Jr HS Ind Arts Tchr 1974-81; ale HS Ind Arts Tchr, Work Coop Coord 1981-82; US Navy Surface Officer 1982-93; Olean HS Asst Prin 1993-; *ai:* Sports Boosters; ine, Wellness Comms; Bldg Level Team; Schl Store Project; ation Team; NASSP, SAANYS 1993-, Phi Delta Kappa 1994-; Lion 94-, Pres; Amer Legion 1992, Temple B'Nai Israel 1993-, Publicity DT Seal Assn 1991-; Numerous Articles Pub; Ed Awd Vol 1992; Mem Awd 1980; Tchr of Yr 1980; NYS Conspicuous Svc Cross; ommendation, Achvmt Medal; *office:* Olean HS 410 W Sullivan St NY 14760*

GUER, BARBARA WALKER, 1st Grade Teacher; *b:* Boston, MA; E.; *c:* Scott, Jayne Balaguer Salvucci, Amy Beth; *ed:* Univ of MA ociology & Ed 1956; Katherine Gibbs Secretarial Schl at Boston 0 Credit Hrs; *cr:* Oakdale Elem Schl 2nd Grd Tchr 1966-67; -Center Schl 3rd Grd Tchr 1967-68; Barron Elem Schl 4th Grd Tchr 8, Readiness Tchr 1988-89, 1st Grd Tchr 1989-; *ai:* Strategic Pub Relations Comm; Write Connection Process Writing Coach; alem Ed Assn, NHEA 1973-; Contemporary Woman's Club 1974-, Yrs; Valley Singers 1982-; Church Schl Coord 1980-; Youth Choir 8-; Tchr of Yr Salem HS 1982; Selected for Participation in Grant overnor's Cncl for Excl in Ed 1987; *office:* Barron Elem Schl Butler m NH 03079*

VITCH, CAROLYN KUDLA, 5th Grade Teacher; *b:* Lawrence, John M.; *c:* Lauren, Stacy; *ed:* Attnd Boston Coll, Leslie Coll Post tud; *cr:* West Schl 3rd-4th Grd Tchr 1975-77; Tenney MS Resource Tchr 1977-87, 5th Grd Tchr 1987-; *ai:* Invent Amer Schl Coord; y of Mind Judge; Staff Support Team; MA Tchrs Assn 1975-; NEA Barron Schl PTO 1992-; *home:* 16 Poplar Rd Salem NH 03079

EWICZ, SUSAN A., Math Teacher; *b:* Flushing, NY; *ed:* Cortland (BS) Math Ed 1970, (MS) Ed 1975; 90 Addl Grad Hrs in Admin swego St Univ; *cr:* Morgan Rd MS Math Tchr 1970-74; Soule Rd ath Tchr 1974-; *ai:* Curr Dev Comm; Develop Curr for Math Stdnts ; Track Coach 1975-80; Participant in "PBS Mathline- a MS Math ." 1995-96; OCMTA & NCTM 1980-.

KAREN LYNNE, English Teacher; *b:* Bryn Mawr, PA; *ed:* West r Univ (BS) Eng & Ed 1977, (MEQ) Ed 1989; 60 Grad Credit Hrs l Masters; *cr:* Downingtown Sr HS Eng Tchr 19 Yrs; *ai:* Yrbk Bus, g Club & Career Experience Adv; Christmas Food Dr Co-Chprsn; Official; Downingtown Area Educators Assn 1977-, Recording Sec ; PSEA, NCTE & NEA 1977-; General Electric STAR Tchr Awd Downingtown Tchr of Yr Awd 1991-92; *office:* Downingtown Sr H S anor Ave Downingtown PA 19335

ASARE, ANTHONY, Pupil Affairs Dept Chprsn; *b:* Aliquippa, PA; ston Coll (BS) Psych, Ed 1979; Univ of Pittsburgh (MS) Cnslng 1983; Post Grd Work Admin; *cr:* Aliquippa Schl Dist Tchr, Cnslr 7; Pittsburgh Pub Schls Tchr, Cnslr 1987-; *ai:* Core Team in Human rces Dev; Schl to Work Core Team for Re-Structuring Schls; rgh Hlth Careers Initiative; Co-Spon Western PA Hosp Asst; Prep Core Team; AFT, PA Assn of Tchrs 1987-; Natl Cnslrs Assn, eny Cty Cnslrs Assn 1980-; Supts Comm on Re-Structuring Schls; Schls that Work in Amer; *office:* Schenley HS 4101 Bigelow Blvd rgh PA 15213*

ISSERO, KATHLEEN S., Art Teacher; *b:* Vineland, NJ; *m:* d; *c:* Brian, Amy; *ed:* Rowan Coll of NJ (BA) Art 1970; *cr:* Vineland Schls Art Tchr 1970-80; D'Ippolito Interm Schl Art Tchr 1981-; *ai:* Art Club Adv; Citizen of Month Comm Chprsn; NEA, NJEA, A 1970-; ADK, Phi 1994-, Corresponding Sec; Governors Tchr nition Awd 1990; *office:* Solve E D'Iprolito Interm Sch 1578 N Ave Vineland NJ 08360

WIN, ANNETTE M., Chemistry Teacher; *b:* Buffalo, NY; *m:* Peter; edonia St Coll (BS) Sci & Bio Chem 1990; (MS) 1994; Post Grad at us Coll & SUNY at Buffalo; *cr:* Frontier HS Chem Tchr 1990-; *ai:* Adv; Tech Comm; AFT 1990-; NYSUT 1990-; *office:* Frontier Sr 4432 Bayview Rd Hamburg NY 14075

WIN, CHARLES WILLIAM, Assoc Naval Science Instructor; *b:* eld, IL; *m:* Salvatorica Nieddu; *c:* Antonella, William; *ed:* Univ of egents Coll (BS) Sociology 1995; Wilmington Coll 9 Addl Credit Hrs y Admin; *cr:* US Navy Command Master Chief 1968-92; Seaford HS Naval Sci Instr 1992-93; Christiana HS Assoc Naval Sci Instr 1993-; ecision Drill Team, Color Guard, Marksmanship Coach; Surface Assn 1993-, Advy Bd; Navy League 1993-; Veterans of Foreign Wars ; Fleet Reserve Assn 1986-; Amer Legion 1993-; Selected Finalist for s Top Enlisted Position 1992; Awded Two Presidential Medals for orious Svc; Command Master Chief Nuclear Aircraft Carrier USS ht D. Eisenhower; *office:* Christiana HS 190 Salem Church Rd rk DE 19713*

OWIN, STEPHEN JAMES, Upper School Spanish Teacher; *b:* on, NY; *ed:* Syracuse Univ (BA) Span Lang, Lit, Culture 1989; Univ A Ibero-Amer Lit 3 Semesters Towards MA; La Universidad De nanca Spain Summer Inst 1995; Syracuse Univ Prgm Abroad Division d 1988; *cr:* Univ of KS Grad Tchng Asst 1990-91; Packer Collegiate pper Schl Span Tchr 1991-, Frgn Lang Dept Head 1994-95; *ai:* 10th AIDS Awareness Fac Adv; Dance Concert Fac; ACTFL 1994-; assy of Spain Schlsp 1995; *home:* 327 W 35th St Apt 4F New York NY

ENT, SCOTT ANDREW, Social Studies Teacher; *b:* Dayton, OH; *m:* ner; *ed:* Benedictine Coll (BA) Soc Stud & Sendry Ed 1989; Working rds Masters; *cr:* Archbishop Alter HS Soc Stud Tchr 1991-; *ai:* Asst Coach 1991-; Asst Ath Dir 1992-; Head Bsbl Coach 1993-; *office:* bishop Alter H S 940 E David Rd Kettering OH 45429

BALEST, RICARD JAMES, Science Teacher; *b:* Johnstown, PA; *m:* Cathy Lyons; *c:* Michele, Eric, Kristen; *ed:* Gannon Univ (BS) Sci 1970, (MS) Sci 1980; *cr:* Westlake MS Sci Tchr 1972-93; Walnut Creek MS Sci Tchr 1993-; *ai:* PSTA 1993-; PSEA, NEA 1972-; *office:* Walnut Creek MS 5901 Sterrettania Rd Fairview PA 16415

BALESTRIERI, GAYTANA PINO, Science Teacher; *b:* Philadelphia, PA; *m:* John J.; *c:* Jean Anne Madden, Beth Ann Schumacher, John Jr., Francis Paul, Ann D. Balestrieri; *ed:* immaculate College (BA) Biology 1964; LaSalle Univ MA in Process Theology, 24 Credits Glassboro St; *cr:* Willingboro Scndry Schls Sci Tchr 2 Yrs Full Time, 18 Yrs Part Time; McCorristin Cath HS Sci Tchr 3 Yrs; *ai:* Environment Club; SADD; NSTA 1991-; NEA, NJEA 1991- NCTA 1993; Immaculate Coll Alumnai 1968, Class Rep; Marian Chptr 1965 Treas, VP, Womens Club of Amer 1980; Garfield East Civic Assn 1970-, Pres & Treas; *office:* Mc Corristin HS 175 Leonard Ave Trenton NJ 08610

BALL, ALISON COLES, Choreographer, Dancer & Tchr; *b:* Baltimore, MD; *m:* Todd C. Rothenhaus; *ed:* Amer Univ (BA) Dance 1986; George Washington Univ (MFA) Theatre, Dance 1991; Yr Round Tech Trng in Ballet, Modern, Improvisation; *cr:* George Washington Univ Dance Instr 1988-90; Schl Withouth Walls Dance, Video, PE, Art Tchr 1991-95; Dance Complex Freelance Choreographer, Dancer 1995-; *ai:* Chrldng Coach; Schl Video Yrbk Ed, Co-Ed; Recycling Club; Intnl Arts Day Coord; Natl Endowment for Arts Internship; 2 Full Dance Schlsps George Washington Univ; Full Schlsp Jacobs Pillows Dance Festival.

BALL, CATHERINE BUDA, Sixth Grade English Teacher; *b:* Jersey City, NJ; *m:* Christopher; *c:* Christopher J.; *ed:* William Paterson Coll at Wayne (BA) Elem Ed 1972, (MA) Urban Ed, Comm Affairs 1977; Learning Diabilities Tchr Consultant Cert 1983; *cr:* Preakness Elem Schl 2-3 Grd Tchr 1971-77; John F. Kennedy Elem Schl 1-2 Grd Tchr 1997-79; Schuler-Colfax MS 6-8 Grd Tchr 1979-89, 6 Grd Tchr 1989-; *ai:* Schl Production Co-Dir 1980-; Design Comm 1996; Stu Cncl Adv 1980-86; Fac Cncl Liasion Sec 1995-; PTO Tchr Liasion 1995-; NJEA, NEA, WEA 1971-; IHM Church 1992-, 2nd Grd CCD Tchr; 5th Place TV Fox 5 Kids Club Earth Contest 1989-90; Pride of NJ Contest Governor's Awd 1989-90; *office:* Schuyler Colfax MS 1500 Hamburg Tpke Wayne NJ 07470

BALL, DONNA D., Pom Squad Coach & Sponsor; *b:* Washington, DC; *ed:* Prince Georges Comm Coll (AA) Dental Assisting 1974; Univ of MD 60 Addl Hrs Hlth Ed; *cr:* Children's Hosp NMC Dental Off Coord 10 Yrs; Vitro Corp Sec 10 Yrs; *ai:* Poms Spon 13 Yrs; Coached Univ of MD Poms 1 Yr; US Twirling Assn 1970-, Pub Relations Commission Chair; USTA Baton Co of MD 1970-, Pres 5 Yrs, VP 5 Yrs; MD St Pom Assn 1976-, Judges Chair; MD St Pom Judges Assn, Competitions Judges Assigner; Pom Squad Awds & Hnrs: MD St Champions 1983, Disney World, Busch Gardens, Epcot US Naval Acad Performances, Cty Championship Title; *office:* Eleanor Roosevelt HS 7601 Hanover Pky Greenbelt MD 20770*

BALL, MARCHAN RAWLINS, 8th Grd World History Teacher; *b:* Federalsburg, MD; *m:* Debra B. Daugherty; *ed:* Salisbury St Univ (BA) Ed & His 1972; Advanced Prof Cert 1980; *cr:* Wicomico MS 8th Grd His Tchr 1973-; *ai:* Soc Stud Dept Chm; Admin Advy Comm; MD Stu Assistance Prgm; Schl Improvement Team; NEA, MD St Tchrs Tssn, Wicomico Cty Tchrs Assn 1973-; Wicomico Cty MS Tchr of Yr 1993; *office:* Wicomico MS 635 E Main St Salisbury MD 21804

BALL, MARGARET ANN, Business Teacher & Dept Chprsn; *b:* Toledo, OH; *m:* Ronald S.; *c:* Daniel S.; *ed:* Defiance Coll (BA) Bus Ed Comprehensive 1966; Grad Stud Univ of Toledo; *cr:* Adams Cntrl Schls bus Tchr 1966-68; Washington LOcal Schls Bus Tchr 1968-73; Owens Tech Coll Bus Tchr 1973-79; Anthony Wayne Local Schls Bus Tchr 1980-, Dept Chprsn 1990-; *ai:* Cmptr Tech Comm; Anthony Wayne Ed Assn Treas; Acad Honesty Comm; OEA, NEA 1966-; NBEA 1990-; AWEA 1980-, Treas; Handbook For Voc Block Tchng with BGSU; Ashland Oil Golden Apple Awd Nom; *office:* Anthony Wayne HS 5967 Finzel Rd Whitehouse OH 43571

BALL, RAYMOND BERNARD, Lang Arts & Soc Stud Tchr; *b:* Buffalo, NY; *m:* Julie Ann Miller; *c:* Raymond Lloyd, Ellen Catherine; *ed:* St Univ of NY Coll at Buffalo (BS) Elem Ed, Eng Minor 1989; Working on MS Ed, Rdng; *cr:* East Elem Schl 3rd Grd Tchr 1990-91, 5th Grd Lang Arts Tchr 1991-92; 5th Grd Lang Arts, Soc Stud Tchr 1992-; *ai:* Budget, Tech Comms; Young Writer's Club; Pvt Tutoring; AFT, West Seneca Tchrs Assn 1990-; Golden Apple Awd 1993; *office:* East Elem Schl 1415 Center Rd West Seneca NY 14224*

BALL, WILLIAM DAVID, Jr High English Teacher; *b:* Melrose, MA; *m:* Laurie Colt; *c:* William, Patricia; *ed:* Norwich Univ (BS) Elem Ed 1978; Post Grad Work Salem St Coll, Notre Dame Coll; *cr:* Exeter Jr HS Eng Tchr 1978-; *ai:* Head Ftbl, Asst Bsktbl Coach; Supvr of Ofcls; NEA 1978-; Amer Ftbl Coaches Assn 1984-; NILOA Lacrosse Offcls 1979-; NH Ftbl Fnd 1993-, Bd of Dirs; CHAD Awd; Asst Bsktbl Coach of Yr 1986; Asst Coach Ftbl Shrine Game 1989; *office:* Exeter Area Jr HS 38 Linden St Exeter NH 03833

BALLA, GREGORY JOSEPH, Secondary Social Studies Tchr; *b:* New Kensington, PA; *m:* Carol Jane Fedorek; *ed:* IN Univ of PA (BS) Scndry Soc Stud 1974; Univ of Pittsburgh (MED) Admin & Supervision 1979; Admin Scndry Prin Cert 1982; Attnd IN Univ of PA; Attndng Univ of Pittsburgh; *cr:* Washington Twp Jr HS Soc Stud Tchr 1976-85; Amer Heritage Schl Soc Stud Tchr 1985-86; Kiski Area HS Soc Stud Tchr 1986-; *ai:* Cooperative Tchr Pre Stu Tchrs; Tchr of Gifted Soc Stud Forum; Announcer & Scorekeeper Var & Jr Var Boys Bsktbl Team; Bldg Comm; NEA, PSEA 1976-; KAEA 1976-, Legislative Chprsn 1981-83; Dist Mini Grants 1988-91; Tchr of Yr Sr Class 1990-91; Tchr of Yr Admin Awd Kiski Area Schl Dist 1992-93; *office:* Kiski Area Schl Dist 200 Poplar St Vandergrift PA 15690*

BALLANTINE, JAMES ARTHUR, Social Studies Teacher; *b:* Oneonta, NY; *m:* Kathleen Emily Bouboulis; *c:* Erin M., Katie Beth; *ed:* Clarkson Univ (BS) Soc Sci 1972; 36 Addl Hrs Grad Scndry Ed Stud; 14 Addl Post Grad Hrs Bus Ed; 9 Addl Hrs; *cr:* Cherry Valley-Springfield Bus Tchr 1979-82, Soc Stud Tchr 1982-93; Milford Central Schl Soc Stud Tchr 1993-; *ai:* AFT, NYSUT 1979-93, Local Pres 1982, 1990-91; NSCAA 1982-92; NEA 1993; AYSO 1985-92; USSF 1993-; NYSANG 1972-77; *office:* Milford Central Schl W Main St Milford NY 13807

BALLANTYNE, ELIZABETH KNORR, Third Grade Teacher; *b:* Hewburgh, NY; *m:* William D.; *c:* William, Robert, Beth; *ed:* Syracuse Univ (BS) Home Ec 1953; Skidmore Coll; Glassboro Coll Elem Ed Cert 1974; *cr:* Countryside Schl 3rd-4th Grd Tchr 22 Yrs; *ai:* Delta Kappa Gamma 1990-; NEA, NJEA 1974-; *office:* Countryside Elem Schl 115 Schoolhouse Ln Mount Laurel NJ 08054*

BALLANTYNE, ROBERT L., Adj Instr of Environmental Sci; *b:* Philadelphia, PA; *m:* Nancy A. Devore; *c:* Robert Jr., Scott D., Todd A., Keith W., Denise A. Yergey, Davelle A. Lautrup; *ed:* West Chester St Coll (BS) Scndry Ed, Bio 1961; Univ of DE (MED) Natural Sci 1969; 34 Addl Grad Hrs Bio, Cmptr Sci; *cr:* US Marine Corps; Helicopter Pilot 1961-64; Boyertown Area HS Bio, Hum Physiology 1964-94; Rdng Area Comm Coll Part-Time Adj Instr Environmental Sci 1993-; *ai:* Coached Soccer 1975-83; Coord Prgms Academically Gifted 1986-93; Adv Graduating Classes 1974, 1978; NEA 1964-1994; PA Outdoor Writers Assn 1980-; Ret Officers Assn 1989-, Dist Awd of Merit; BSA 1950-, Troup Comm, Dist Awd of Merit; Boyertown Jaycees Outstdng Edctr 1994; Tchr In-Service Trng; Prof Free-Lance Outdoor Writer; *home:* 1684 Swamp Pike Gilbertsville PA 19525

BALLARD, CONNIE SPENCER, Fourth Grade Teacher; *b:* Sumner, OH; *c:* Brian, Chad, Jason; *ed:* OH Univ (BS) K-8th Grd Ed 1965; 20 Post Grad Hrs Elem Ed; *cr:* Highland North 5th-7th Grd Sci & Math & 5th-8th Grd PE Tchr 1966-69, 6th Grd Tchr 1972-91, 4th Grd Tchr 1991-; *ai:* NEA, OH Ed Assn 1965-; Highland Ed Assn 1965-, Bldg Rep; Selover Pub Lib Bd 1986-87; Chesterville Village Cncl 1987-94; Morrow Cty Regnl Planning Comm 1988-94; *office:* Highland North Elem Schl Star Rt 314 N Chesterville OH 43317

BALLAUER, ANDREW, Chemistry Teacher; *b:* Cincinnati, OH; *m:* Susan; *c:* Sarah, Thomas; *ed:* Miami Univ (BS) Soc Stud 1975; Wright St Univ (MS) Ed 1981; *cr:* Huber Hgts City Schls Tchr 1975-; *ai:* Dist Sci Coord for 7 Elem & 2 MS; NEA 1976-; OEA 1976-; Christa McAuliffe Fellow 1995; Finalist for OH Tchr of Yr 1994; *office:* Wayne HS 5400 Chambersburg Rd Huber Heights OH 45424*

BALLENAS, CARL E., Sixth Grade Teacher; *b:* Brooklyn, NY; *ed:* York Coll (BA) Art His 1976; Post Grad Stud in Theology Seminaryof Immaculate Conception; *cr:* St Marys Schl 5th-8th Grd Soc Stud Tchr 1980-81; St Catherine of Sienna Schl 6th Grd Tchr 1982-; *ai:* Cntrl Queens Historical Soc Bd of Dir; Richmond Hall Historian; Comm Bd #9 1983-85; Newspaper Articles Pub; Queens Forum; *office:* St Catherine Of Sienna Schl 118-34 Riverton St Saint Albans NY 11412

BALLETTO, THERESA, Mathematics Teacher; *b:* Bridgeport, CT; *ed:* Cntrl CT St Univ (BS) Math 1975, (MS) Scndry Ed 1980; *cr:* Coginchaug Regnl HS Math Tchr 21 Yrs; *ai:* Jr Var Girls Bsktbl Coach 18 Yrs; REA, CEA, NEA 1975-; NCTM 1993-; *office:* Coginchaug Regnl HS 135 Pickett Ln Durham CT 06422

BALLIN, KATHRYN BLIZZARD, Math Teacher; *b:* Charleston, WV; *m:* Jeffrey S.; *ed:* Morris Harvey Coll (BS) Math, Eng 1973; 24 Credit Hrs WV Grad Coll Curr Dev; Cert Prgm WV St Coll Acctng; *cr:* Kanawha Cty Schls Math Tchr 1973-89; Newark Schl Dist Math Tchr 1989-; *ai:* Barringer Schl Improvement Team Chprsn; AFT 1986-, Bldg Rep 1987-88; NCTM 1990-; Presidental Awd for Excl in Tchng of Math 1988; *office:* Barringer HS 90 Parker St Newark NJ 07104

BALLING, FRANK B., Elementary Principal; *b:* Brockport, NY; *m:* Jane; *c:* Betsy, Cristy, Amy; *ed:* SUNY at Brockport (BS) Elem Ed 1961, (MS) Schl Admin 1966; *cr:* Greece Cntrl Schl 5th & 6th Grd Tchr 1961-68; Brockport Cntrl Schl MS Coordng Tchr 1968-72, MS Asst Prin 1972-88, Elem Prin 1988-; *ai:* Schl Admins of NY St 1973-; *office:* Fred W Hill Schl 40 Allen St Brockport NY 14420

BALLINGER, KAY H., Physical Education Teacher; *b:* Bridgeton, NJ; *ed:* Salem Coll of WV (BS) HE & PE 1969; *cr:* Bridgeton HS PE Tchr 1969-; Athletic Dir 1987-; Var Field Hockey Coach 1973-86; Var Sftbl Coach 1974-86; *ai:* Girls Tennis Coach; Girls Athletic Dir; NEA, NJEA, CCEA, BEA 1969-; DAANJ 1987-; Induction Into NJSCA Hall of Fame 1995; Kay H Ballinger Merit Awd; *office:* Bridgeton HS 111 N West Ave Bridgeton NJ 08302

BALLOU, DENNIS RAWSON, Fifth Grade Teacher; *b:* Providence, RI; *m:* Joan Waterman; *c:* Dennis; *ed:* RI Coll (BA) Soc Sci 1967; Providence Coll (MED) Elem Admin 1976; *cr:* W L Callahan Schl Tchr 1969-; *ai:* NEA 1969-; Universalist Church 1943-, Moderator; Recreation Dept 1976-80; *home:* 1244 Sherman Farm Rd Harrisville RI 02830*

BALM, DEBRA F., Mathematics Teacher; *b:* Grinnell, IA; *m:* Timothy K.; *c:* Cheryl L.; *ed:* Univ of Cincinnati (BBA) Accounting 1977, (MBA) Accounting & Mgmt 1979; Univ of Dayton (MS) Tchng 1991; *cr:* Mason City Schls Math Tchr 1986-; *ai:* NCTM, OCTM 1987-; Girl Scouts, Neighborhood Registrar 1985-; *home:* 5580 Senour Dr West Chester OH 45069

BALMERT, MICHAEL E., Assoc Prof of Commnctn Stud; *b:* Baltimore, MD; *ed:* Harford Comm Coll (AA) Gen Stud 1976; Towson St Univ (BS) Mass Commnctn & Pub Address 1978; Univ of Pittsburgh (MA) Rhetoric & Commnctn 1980; Univ of KS (PHD) Commnctn Stud 1987; *cr:* Univ of KS Basic Commnctn Pgm Asst Dir & Asst Instr 1980-84; IN Univ at Indianapolis Orgnl Commnctn Dir 1984-92, Asst Prof 1987-92; Carlow Coll Commnctn Stud Assoc Prof 1992-, Prof Ldrshp 1995-; *ai:* Distance Ed, Fac Senate, Fac Dev & Grad Pgms in Prof Ldrshp Comms; Fac Mentor for New Fac; Delta Epsilon Sigma & Natl Cath Hnr Soc Fac Adv; Cntrl Sts Commnctn Assoc 1980-92, Top Competitive Paper in Comm Theory; Speech Commnctn Assoc 1980-; Amer Soc for Trng & Dev 1989-92; Seneca Vly Dist PTA 1993-; Intnl Commnctn Assoc Awd for Tchng Excl 1984; IN Univ Distngd Fac Mem of Yr for Excl in Tchng, Rsrch & Svc 1988-89; Cntrl Sts Commnctn Assoc Outstdng Young Edctrs Awd 1989-90; IN Univ Pres FACET Awd For Excl in Tchng 1990; Articles Pub; *office:* Carlow Coll 3333 5th Ave Pittsburgh PA 15213

BALOG, JACQUELINE, Art Teacher; *b:* Perth Amboy, NJ; *ed:* Philadelphia Museum Coll of Art (BS) Art Ed 1964; *cr:* Edison Twp Schls Elem Art Tchr 1965; Hanamen Hosp Asst Med Illustrator Half Yr; Camden City Schls Jr HS Art Tchr Half Yr; Northern Burlington Co Reg Schl Art Tchr 23 Yrs; *ai:* Lit Magazine Art Adv; Art Hnr Soc; NEA, NJEA 1965-; NJAE 1975-; NAEA 1988-; South Jersey Ctr for Arts 1994-; Water Color, 1st, South Jersey Center for Arts; Purchase Awd W. C. Show Camden Cty Historical; Meml Awd W. C. Basto Art Show; *office:* N Burlington Co Reg Jr/Sr HS 160 Mansfield Rd E Columbus NJ 08022

BALOUSKUS, RICHARD A., Science Teacher; *b:* Derby, CT; *m:* Laura; *c:* Richard, Anna Tess; *ed:* Windham Coll (BA) Geology 1974; Southern CT St Univ (MS) Environmental Stud 1986; Ed Cert 1975; Attnd Univ of Bridgeport; *cr:* Ansonia HS Sci, Bio, Earth Sci, Microbiology Tchr 1977-; *ai:* Vlybl Coach 1980-92; Sci Club, Ecology Club Adv; AFT, Second VP, Bus Agent; Yth Ldrshp Cncl 1987-92; CT Coach of Yr Recognition for Vol Spec Ed Spec Olympics; *office:* Ansonia HS 115 Howard Ave Ansonia CT 06401

BALSLEY, CHRISTOPHER BARRY, Earth Science & Biology Tchr; *b:* Boston, MA; *m:* Jean Campbell Peterson; *c:* Elaine Balsley Orr, David Barry; *ed:* Colby Coll (BA) Sociology 1968; Wesleyan Univ (MAT) Tchng 1972, (MS) Geology 1972, (DAS) Geology 1972; *cr:* Waterville HS Sci Tchr 1968-69; Killingworth Elem Sci Tchr 1971-72; Woodward HS Sci Tchr 1972-74; New Fairfield HS Sci Tchr 1974-; *ai:* Track Coach; Staff Dev, Restructuring, Rescheduling Comm; Fac Senate; Sci, Environmental Club; NEA, CEA 1974-; NFEA 1974-, Pres, VP, PR & R; NABT CABT, NESTA, CESTA 1980-; CT Bio Tchr of Yr 1993-94; US Dept of Energy & Univ of OK Energy Ed Grant; USA-Russia Conf on Ed at Moscow; *office:* New Fairfield MS 54 Gillotti Rd New Fairfield CT 06812*

BALTREN, PETER JAMES, Social Studies Dept Chairman; *b:* Montague, MA; *m:* Mary J. Wallace; *c:* Katherine, Michael, Anne; *ed:* Boston Coll (BA) Ed, His 1971, (MED) Admin 1974; Attnd Westfield St Coll, Worcester St Coll, Amer Intnl Coll; *cr:* Ware HS Soc Stud Tchr 24 Yrs; *ai:* Stu Cncl Adv 24 Yrs; Soc Stud Dept Chm; Schl Steering Comm for Coalition of Essential Schls; Ware Tchrs Assn 1972-, Sec 1985, Pariamentarian 1985-92; MA Tchrs Assn, NEA 1972-; Ware Rotary Club 1974-, Pres 3 Times, Citizen of Yr 1984, Paul Harris Fellow 1992; MA Assn of Stu Cncls Warren Schull Awd Nom 1991; Natl Assn Stu Cncls Region 1 Adv of Yr 1991; Stu Ldrshp Prgm Hall of Fame Inductee 1995; *office:* Ware HS 237 West St Ware MA 01082*

BALTZER, CINDY EISENHAUER, Vocal Music Teacher; *b:* Pittsburgh, PA; *c:* Shannon Evangeline; *ed:* IN Univ of PA (BS) Music Ed 1977; Pvt Voice, Carnegie Mellon Univ; *cr:* Derry Area Schl Dist Fourth, Sixth, Eighth Grd Vocal Music Instr 1978-, Vocal Music Supvr 1984-93; *ai:* Dir 7th, 8th Grd Muscial Drama, Choruses, Drama Sr High Musical; MENC, PA Music Edctrs, Westmoreland Cnty Music Edctrs 1978-; Ligonier Vly Players 1979-, Mem at Large; Greensburg Civic Theatre 1982-, Preformer; Won Partnerships in Ed Western PA; *office:* Derry Area MS RR #1 Box 169 Derry PA 15627*

BALUH, MARILYN YOUNG, Fourth Grade Teacher; *b:* Wilkes-Barre, PA; *m:* Edward Thomas; *c:* Joni Beall, Maureen OBoyle, Steven; *ed:* Cedar Crest Coll (BA) His & Elem Ed 1984; 28 Post Grd Credits in His & Elem Ed; *cr:* Wyoming Valley West 2D Learning Disab Tchng Assoc 1971-78; East Penn 2D Mixed Categories Tchng Assoc 1978-83; Allentown Diocese 4th Grd Tchr 1984-; *ai:* Sports Comm Rep; Tchr Rep Allentown Diocese Schl Bd; Tutor Stdnts with Spec Learning Problems; Phi Alpha Theta 1983-; Eastern PA Cncl of Tchrs of Math & Natl Cath Ed Assn 1984-; Chosen to Stud 1st Amendment to Constitution at George Mason Univ; *office:* St Ann Elem Schl 6th & Fairview Sts Emmaus PA 18049

BALUKAS, JANET V., Lang Arts & Soc Stud Teacher; *b:* Teaneck, NJ; *m:* Albert; *ed:* Alderson Broaddus Coll (BA) His 1970; Wilkes Univ (MA) Elem Ed 1976; Widener Univ (EDD) Educl Admin 1992; *cr:* Upper Merion Schl Dist 4-6 Grd Tchr 1973-; *ai:* Co-Teach Tchr Wkshps; PSEA 1973-; Women in Ed 1994-; *office:* Upper Merion Area Schl Dist 435 Crossfield Rd King Of Prussia PA 19406

BALZANO, JOHN G., Math Teacher & Consultant; *b:* Gloversville, NY; *m:* Barbara Anne Gilman; *c:* Kristine, Joseph, Julie; *ed:* LeMoyne Coll (BA) Math 1971; Univ of VT (MAT) Math 1973; St Univ of NY at Brockport (SAS) Ed Admin 1977; *cr:* Fairport Cntrl Schls Tchr & Math Dept Chm 1973-; *ai:* Math Counts Coach; PTSA Rep; Johns Hopkins CTY Coord; Prof Mentor Support Team 1995; AFT & AFL-CIO 1973-; NCTM 1973-; AMTNYS 1978-, VP 1987; AMTRA 1980-; Phi Delta Kappa 1991-; Fairport Soccer Club & Fairport Boosters 1989-; Fairport Tchr of Yr 1987 & 1990; Houghton-Mufflin Co "Unified Math" & "Integrated Math" Author & Consultant; Fairport PASE Tchr of the Yr 1991, 1995; *home:* 10 Chipping Rdg Fairport NY 14450*

BAMBERGER, MARNETTE, 5th & 6th Grade Teacher; *b:* New York, NY; *ed:* St John's Univ (BS) Ed; Manhattan Coll (MS) Theology; Attnd Valparaiso Univ, Howard Inst, Vanderbilt Univ, Pace Coll, OH Univ, Wilkes-Barre Univ; *cr:* Good Shepherd Schl 1-3-5-6 Grds Tchr 1949-60; Queen of Rosary Acad Bio, Rel, Algebra Tchr 1960-76; Holy Family Regnl Schl 5-6 Grds Tchr 1976-; *ai:* NEA 1976-; Grants Valparaiso Univ, Pace Coll, Howard Inst, OH Univ, Vanderbilt Univ, Wilkes Barre Univ; *home:* PO Box 284 Commack NY 11725

BAMBINO, JACQUELINE MARIE, Retired Spanish Teacher; *b:* Queens, NY; *m:* Dennis C.; *c:* Annemarie, Mary Elaine Dennie, Jackie; *ed:* St John's Univ (BSEd) Elem Ed, Span 1967; 33 Hrs Spec Ed C. W. Post; *cr:* Burns Ave Elem Schl 1st Grd Tchr 1 Yr; South Shore Chrstn Schl 4th Grd Tchr 6 Yrs, Span Tchr 3 Yrs; *ai:* Spiritual Cnslr.

BAMBRICK, CATHERINE E., English Teacher; *b:* New York, NY; *ed:* Fordham Univ (BA) Eng 1968; Grad Eng 60 Addl Credits; *cr:* JHS 22X Tchr 1969-72; CIS 166X Tchr 1972-86; DeWitt Clinton Tchr 1986-; *ai:* New Tchr Mentor; UFT & AFT 1969-; NCTE 1972-; NYC Writing Project 1980; Fellowship NYC Writing Project 1980; Field Test Participant- Natl Bd for Prof Tchng Standards; *office:* De Witt Clinton HS 100 W Mosholu Pkwy Bronx NY 10468

BAMDAD, CAROL, English Teacher; *b:* Hoboken, NJ; *m:* Rasoul; *c:* Aubrey, Darien; *ed:* Trenton St Coll (BA) Eng 1969; Rutgers Univ (MA) Eng 1975; Kean Coll 24 Credit Hrs Towards Lbrl Stud MA; *cr:* Amer HS Tchr 1975-77; Middlesex Cty Coll Instr 1980-83; Union Cty Coll Coord of Learning Lab 1983-86; Edison HS Tchr 1986-; *ai:* Intnl Women's Day Coord; ETEA, NCTE 1986-; *office:* Edison HS Blvd Of The Eagles Edison NJ 08817*

BAMFORD, REBECCA (SHEFTMAN), MS Home Economics Teacher; *b:* Alameda, CA; *m:* Robert; *c:* David, Deborah Formica, Michelle Kwiatkowski; *ed:* Drexel Univ (BS) Home Ec Ed 1958; Masters Equivalency Plus 20 Grad Credist Penn St UNiv, Temple Univ, Westchester Univ, Univ of Arts; *cr:* Veterans Meml Jr HS Home Ec Tchr 1958-62; Upper Merion Area MS Home Ec Tchr 1975-; *ai:* After Schl Act Spon; Home Ec Dept Chair; Hebrew Tutor; PSEA, NEA, UMAEA 1981-; Hadassah 1970-, Treas; *office:* Upper Merion Area MS 435 Crossfield Rd King Of Prussia PA 19406

BANACH, CORINNE L., Principal; *b:* Denver, CO; *m:* Denis; *c:* Nicholas Scudero; *ed:* Adelphi Univ (BS) Elem Ed 1974, (MS) Rdng 1978; Queens Coll Prof Diploma in Educl Admin 1992; *cr:* Elmont UFSD Tchr 1974-88, Core Skills Coord 1988-91; Garden City UFSD Asst Prin 1992-94; Shore Road Intermediate Ctr Prin 1994-; *ai:* Phi Delta Kappa; Nassau Cty Elem Prins Assn; Assn for Supervision & Curr Dev; Nassau Rdng Cncl; Recipient of Jenkins Meml Awd, Lifetime Membership; *office:* Shore Road Intermediate Ctr 2801 Shore Rd Bellmore NY 11710

BANCROFT, EDWARD PALMER, Social Studies Teacher; *b:* Plattsburg, NY; *c:* Mikel A., Peter J., Naomi E., Liam B.; *ed:* St Univ of NY at Albany (BA) Anthropology 1978, (MA) Ed 1987; Post-Grad Stud Anthropology; *cr:* Schenectady City Summer Schl Tchr 1987-95; Greater Amsterdam Schl Dist Tchr 1987-; *ai:* Var Soccer Coach; Amnesty Intnl Fac Adv; NY St United Tchrs 1987-; Select Seminar on Holocaust; *office:* Amsterdam HS Saratoga Ave Amsterdam NY 12010*

BANER, MARY ANN (WALTER), Retired Chemistry Teacher; *b:* Harrisburg, PA; *m:* A. Lawrence; *c:* Virginia, Lawrence, Carl, Mary Alley; *ed:* Dickinson Coll (BS) Chem 1956; Syracuse Univ (MS) Bio Chem 1963; 80 Grad Hrs in Chem, Bio-chem, Ed; *cr:* Pennsburg HS Chem & Bio Tchr 1956-57; St Andrews HS Bio Tchr 1957-58; Westhall Cntrl Schls Gen Sci Chem Tchr 1961-64; Marcellus Sr HS Chem Tchr 1964-95; Suprv for Sci Stu Tchrs for St Univ of NY at Cortland 1995-; *ai:* Sr Class Adv 1980-95; Sci Olympiad Coach 1990-95; NY Sci Honor Soc Adv 1993-95; NY St Chem Mentor; Sci Tchrs Assn NY St 1964-, Chem Subject Area Rep, HS Sci Tchr of Yr 1994; Amer Chem Soc Ed Div 1982-95, Natl Chem Wk Syracuse Area Co-Chair, Phoenix Awd 1993; NSTA 1982-95; Jordan-Elbridge Recreation Commission 1988-, Chprsn; Jordan Elbridge Pool Comm Chprsn 1975-82; Learn to Swim Prgm Vol Water Safety Instr 1952-, 25 Yr Pin Arc; Jordan Meth Educ Comm; Syr Univ Excl in Tchng Awd 1987; Cntrl STANYS Section Svc Awd 1990; Comm Civic Awd 1986; PTA Life Mem 1980; Title II Dev Awd Microscale Chem 1990; Ceiba-Beigy NY St Outstanding HS Tchr 1994.*

BANERJEE, MARIA NEMCOVA, Professor of Russian; *b:* Prague, Czechoslovakia; *m:* Dibyendu Kumar; *ed:* Universite De Montreal (MA) Etudes Stud 1957; Harvard Univ (PHD) Slavic Lang & Lit 1962; Coll Marie De France Baccalauriat & Philosafhie 1955; *cr:* Brown Univ Asst Prof 1962-64; Smith Coll Asst Prof 1966-72, Assoc Prof 1972-81, Prof 1981-; *ai:* Major Russian Lit & Comparative Lit Adv; AAASS 1966-; AAT SEEL 1966-; SVU 1966-; Book: Terminal Paradox The Novels of Milan Kunde; *office:* Smith Coll Wright Hall 211 Northampton MA 01063

BANFILL, CARMEN BROWN, Fourth Grade Teacher; *b:* Lake Placid, NY; *m:* Terry L.; *c:* Sean Michael; *ed:* Lock Haven Univ (BS) Ed 1971; PA St Univ (MED) Ed 1977; 48 Credit Hrs Beyond Masters; *cr:* Dickey Schl 2nd Grd Tchr 1971-74, 4th Grd Tchr 1974-; *ai:* Homework Club Adv; Act 178 Co-Chair; Insvc; Curr Cncl; Union Rep; Fac Cncl Mem; Lock Haven Univ Bd of Dir; Dist Wellness Comm; NEA 1971-; IRA 1973-, Treas, Literacy Awd; Phi Delta Kappa 1970-, Pres; Beta Sigma Phi 1971-, Pres, Rec Sec, Queen; Sentimental Journey 1988-; *home:* 1328 S Hillview St Lock Haven PA 17745*

BANFILL, MAYNARD, Fourth Grade Teacher; *b:* Lock Haven, PA; *c:* Gerard L., Stephanie A.; *ed:* Lock Haven Univ (BS) Elem Ed 1965; 30 Credits Beyond Bachelors at Penn St Univ; *cr:* Woodward Elem 3rd-6th Grd Tchr 1965-; *ai:* Lang Arts Comm & Math Comm Adv; Discipline Comm Chprsn; Report Card Awds Comm Co-Chprsn; PSEA 1965-, Bldg Rep 2 Yrs; *home:* 31 Woodland Dr Lock Haven PA 17745

BANGS, LAWRENCE BAILEY, Headmaster; *b:* Brattleboro, VT; *m:* Joan Eileen Larwood; *c:* Douglas, Rebecca Amos, Nathan, Sarah, Benjamin; *ed:* Univ of MA (BS) Chem Engrng 1956; Univ of Akron (MS) Nuclear Physics 1960; Rensselaer Polytechnic Inst (MS) Astro Physics 1969; *cr:* Goodyear Tire & Rubber Rsrch Physicist 1956-60; Univ of MA Physics Instr 1960-63; Williams Coll Physics Instr 1963-69; Wildridge Acad Headmaster, Founder 1969-; *home:* RR 1 West Burke VT 05871

BANIECKI, PATRICIA KRAJNAK, 8th Grd Lang Arts Teacher; *b:* Masontown, PA; *c:* John, Laura, Mary Lynn; *ed:* Indiana Univ of PA (BS) Home Ec 1962; WV Univ (MA) Rdng Specialist 1975; CA Univ of PA St Cert Elem 1977; Post Grad Stud 18 Credit Hrs; *cr:* Ctr Twp HS Home Ec Tchr 1962-62; Kawam Hee Jr HS Home Ec TChr 1963-65; Tucson Cath Schls Elem Tchr 1965-68; Cntrl Greene Schl Dist Rdng Specialist 1975-77, Lang Arts Tchr 1978-; Waynesburg Coll Upward Bound Tchr 1980-; *ai:* PSEA 1980-; Phi Delta Kappa 1975-; Presentations: PA Assn for Supervision & Curr Dev, PA Cncl Tchrs of Eng, PA MS Conf, Curr Art Resources & Ed Svcs, Upward Bound Parent; *office:* Margaret Bell Miller MS 126 E Lincoln St Waynesburg PA 15370

BANIK, ALEXIS R., 8th Grade Language Arts Tchr; *b:* Pittsburgh, PA; *m:* Paul; *c:* Melissa, Amy; *ed:* Trenton St Coll (BA) Elem Ed 1984; *cr:* Wall Intermediate Stud Skills 1990-92, 8th Grd Lang Arts Tchr 1992-; *ai:* NJEA 1984-; *home:* 17 Butternut Rd Sea Girt NJ 08750

BANIK, DAVID RICHARD, Social Studies Teacher; *b:* Wilkes-Barre, PA; *m:* Louise Klukoske; *ed:* King's Coll (BA) His, Ed 1975; *ai:* Weightlifting Adv, Coach; *office:* Elmer L Meyers Jr Sr HS 341 Carey Ave Wilkes Barre PA 18702

BANKER, LINDA C., Kindergarten Teacher; *b:* Latrobe, PA; *m:* Barron E.; *c:* Bethany, Becki; *ed:* IN Univ of PA (BS) Elem Ed, Elem Math 1970, (MS) Elem Math 1974; Courses Carlow Coll; *cr:* Baggaley Elem Schl 1st Grd Tchr 4 Yrs, Kndgtn Tchr 22 Yrs; *ai:* Act 178 Comm; NEA, PSEA 1970-; Nom Tchr of Yr Awd 1994; *office:* Baggaley Elem Schl RD 6 Box 495 Latrobe PA 15650

BANKS, BRENDA CAROL, 2nd Grade Teacher; *b:* Thomasville, NC; *ed:* Livingstone Coll (BA) Elem Ed 1968; Univ of Bridgeport (MA) Elem Ed 1978; 6th Yr Elem Ed 1990; *cr:* Stevens Schl Tchr 1969-72; Stillmeadow Schl Tchr 1972-; *ai:* Stamford Bd of Ed Diversity Comm; Lead Tchr for Differentiated Instr; Stamford Tchrs Assn 1972-; Grad Chptr of Delta Sigma Theta 1966-, Sec; *office:* Stillmeadow Schl 800 Stillwater Rd Stamford CT 06902

BANKS, JANET FITZROY, English Teacher; *b:* Bareilly, India; *m:* Reginald; *c:* Jeremy, Priya; *ed:* Delhi Univ at India (BA) Eng Lit 1974, (MA) Eng Lit 1976, (BED) Eng Ed 1977; Rdng Specialist Millersville Univ 1989; *cr:* Lancaster Mennonite HS Eng Tchr 1978-; *ai:* Soc Comm Chprsn; Judicial & Homework Comms Fac Rep; Worship Team & Bible Schl Supt; AP Coord; MADD 1990-94; Svc Awd for 15 Yrs of Tchng at LMH.

BANKS, JOHN DAVID, Math & Computer Science Tchr; *b:* Pittsburgh, PA; *m:* Trudy Marie Easler; *ed:* Univ of Pittsburgh (BS) Math 1970, (MAT) Scndry Ed 1972; Addl 20 Credits, Math & Cmptr Sci; *cr:* St Francis DeSales Grd Schl 6-8th Grd Math & Sci 1967-79; Shaler Area Sr HS Math & Cmptr Sci 1970-; *ai:* NCTM 1970-; Gift of Time Awd 1990 & 1991; Univ of Pittsburgh, Pittsburgh Press Excl Tchng Awd 1992; Univ of Pittsburgh, Pittsburgh Post Gazette Excl in Tchng Awd 1994; *home:* PO Box 35 Connoquenessing PA 16027*

BANKS, LINDA DIANE, English Teacher; *b:* Mc Keesport, PA; *c:* Nadine, Christine; *ed:* Bucknell Univ (BA) Eng Lit 1968; Widener Univ (MED) Ed, Rdng 1984; *cr:* Laurfal Schl Tchr 1977-84; B Reed Henderson HS Eng Tchr 1984-; *ai:* Newspaper Adv; Lit Magazine Adv; Coach Girls & Boys Speaking Contests.*

BANKS, MARY TEPAS, English Teacher; *b:* Buffalo, NY; *m:* Neal E.; *c:* Gregory, Michael; *ed:* St Bonaventure Univ (BA) Modern Lang 1973; SUNY at Buffalo (MA) Eng 1977; *cr:* Kenmore Schls Eng, Foreign Lang Tchr 1974-76; Annunciation Acad Eng, Fr Tchr 1976-77; Buffalo Pub Schls Eng, Fr Tchr 1978-79; Williamsville Cntrl Schls Eng Tchr 1979-; *ai:* Scholastic Bowl Adv; Team Ldr Eng Dept; BRIET Cooperating Tchr; NYSUT, AFT 1978-; Williamsville Tchr Assn 1979-; Halocaust Resource Ctr of Buffalo 1995-, Bd of Dirs, At-Large; Farmington Woods Comm 1991-, Bd of Dirs, Newsletter; PTSA 1978-, Tchr Rep Membership; *office:* Williamsville North HS 1595 Hopkins Rd Williamsville NY 14221

BANKS, PATRICIA ANN, Language Arts Teacher; *b:* Brooklyn, NY; *ed:* Saint Peter Coll (BS) Eng 1971; William Paterson Coll (MED) Rdng 1987; *cr:* Morris Hills Regnl HS Eng Tchr 1971-72; Bayley-Ellard HS Eng Tchr 1972-73; Saint Anthony Schl 5th-8th Grd Tchr 1973-; *ai:* 8th Grd Adv; Eng Dept, Steering Comm Mid Sts Assn Self-Stud Chairs; NCEA 1973-; NCTE 1971-; Masters Thesis Pub Research Text; *office:* Saint Anthony Schl 270 Diamond Bridge Ave Hawthorne NJ 07506

BANKS, PETER EDWIN, Physics Teacher; *b:* Bridgeport, CT; *m:* Nancy E. Wallace; *ed:* Univ of Bridgeport (BSME) Mechanical Engrng 1972, (MS) Ed 1977; *cr:* Holy Cross HS Physics Tchr 1978-85; Amer Comm Schl England Sci Tchr 1985-86; Amer Schl London Physics Tchr 1986-87; Frank Scott Bunnell HS Physics Tchr 1991-; *ai:* NHS & Youth Against Drugs Adv; JETS Team Coach; AAPT, CT Assn of Physics Tchrs 1991-; *office:* Frank Scott Bunnell HS 1 Bulldog Blvd Stratford CT 06497

BANKS, ROBERT, Latin Teacher; *b:* E Liverpool, OH; *m:* Margaret A. Jones; *c:* Christine M. Day, Colleen A., Robert D.; *ed:* Youngstown St (BSEd) Latin 1964; Attnd St Mary's Coll, Athenaeum of OH; *cr:* Cardinal Mooney HS Latin Tchr 1963-; *ai:* Golf Coach 1967-; Yrbk Adv 1988-; Latin Club Moderator 1964-; Yrbk Photographer 1989-; Frgn Lang Dept Head 1980-; *office:* Cardinal Mooney HS 2545 Erie St Youngstown OH 44507*

BANKS, TRUDY GROSE, 9th-12th Grade French Teacher; *b:* Huntingdon, PA; *m:* William Ridley III; *c:* Patricia Banks Nolan, Jennifer Banks Vamos; *ed:* Juniata Coll (BA) Fr 1967; PA St Drivers Ed 1973; IN Univ of PA Guid Cnslr; Nice Univ Summer Prgm; *cr:* Tyrone HS Fr Tchr 1967-68; Meyer Jonasson Clothing buyer 1969-70; Cambria Cty Lib Cataloguer, Ref Dept 1970-72; Portage Area HS Fr Tchr 1972-; Yale Univ Dept Head, Life in Amer, ESL Tchr 1989-; *ai:* Ski Club, Chrldng Adv; Fr Club; Guided Tours to France; NEA, PSEA, MLA 1972-; Sunday Schl Tchr 25 Yrs; Church Sec 5 Yrs; Regnl Coord EF Fnd 10 Yrs, Supvr; Outstdng Regnl Coord 1994-95; Several Orientations Given for Exch Stdnts; *office:* Portage Area HS 800 High St Portage PA 15946

BANKS-BURKE, BETTY A., Business Ed, Computer Sci Tchr; *b:* Niagara Falls, NY; *m:* David R.; *c:* David J.; *ed:* Kent St Univ (BS) Comp Voc Bus, Of Ed 1973, (MED) Bus 1976; Ashland Coll Cmptr Cre[illegible] *cr:* Hudson HS Bus Ed, Cmptr Sci Tchr 1973-; Kent St Univ S[illegible] Continuing Ed Wkshp Tchr 1985-87; *ai:* Open Forum Co-Adv; Huc[illegible] 1973-, Past Sec, Legislation, Welfare Comm Ofcr; OEA; NEA; N[illegible] Delta Kappa Gamma Gamma Lambda Chptr 1987-, Past Schlsp[illegible] Chair; Hudson African-Amer Families Assn 1993-, Publicity, [illegible] Chair; Hudson Local Schls Distngd Tchr 1987; First Recipient [illegible] Univ's Elizabeth M. Lewis Distngd Stu Tchr Awd 1973; *office:* Hud[illegible] 2500 Hudson Aurora Rd Hudson OH 44236

BANKS CAMPBELL, L. DIANE, Asst Prof of Psychology; [illegible] Wilkesboro, NC; *c:* Monifa Banks, Keisha Banks, Ayanna; *ed:* Mo[illegible] Univ (BS) Elem Ed 1969; Trenton St Coll (MED) Stu Prsnl Svc[illegible] Rutgers St Univ (EDD) Soc & Philosophical Fndtn of Ed 1990; [illegible] Conflict Resolution; Kellogg Flwshp 1993-94; 3 Credits Interr[illegible] Baltimore Pub Schls Tchr 1969-72; Trenton St Coll Grad Asst 1[illegible] Mercer Cnty Comm Coll Dir of Placement 1978-79, Dir of Coopera[illegible] 1979-80; Dir of Career Svcs 1980-88, Asst Dean of Stu Dev Svcs [illegible] *ai:* Curr & Strategic Planning Comms; Stu Mentor; NJ Comm Coll [illegible] Assn 1990-; NJ Collegiate Consortune for Intnl Intercultural Ed 199[illegible] Cadwalader Place Civic Assn 1989-, Sec; Henry J Austin Hlth [illegible] Chprsn; Ctr Bd Trenton Area 1993-; Campus Ministry Bd; Comm S[illegible] Urban League; Numerous Articles Pub; Kellogg Flwshp 1993-94.

BANNER, ELIZABETH SCHLUGETER, HS Music Teach[illegible] Rochester, NY; *m:* Craig Scott; *c:* William Arthur; *ed:* Ithaca Co[illegible] Music Ed 1984; SUC Brockport (MA) Liberal Stud 1989; *cr:* Br[illegible] Cntrl Elem Music 1984-89, HS Music 1989-; *ai:* Drama Club Vocal [illegible] NYSSMA & MENC 1984-; *office:* Brockport HS 40 Allen St Brockp[illegible] 14420

BANNISTER, LOIS CAMERON, Eighth Grade Reading Teac[illegible] Elkton, MD; *w:* Ralph (dec); *c:* Jennifer Bannister Clark, Kathleen [illegible] *ed:* Towson St Coll (BS) Elem 1968; Masters Equivalency 1978; [illegible] View Elem Schl 4th Grd Tchr 1968-69; Rising Sun Elem Schl 2-[illegible] Tchr 1969-91; Rising Sun MS 8 Grd Rdng Tchr 1991-; *ai:* Boo[illegible] Discussion Ldr Cecil Cty Pub Lib 1995; Yrbk Comm; NEA, [illegible] CCCTA 1968-; PTA 1968-, Life Mem; Mt Pleasant United Meth [illegible] Nom Cecil Cty Tchr of Yr 1988; *home:* PO Box 473 Aberdeen MD [illegible]

BANNON, SARA MANION, Science Chprsn & Chem Tchr; *b:* C[illegible] IL; *m:* Michael; *c:* Patrick, Carolyn; *ed:* St Procopius Coll (BS) [illegible] Univ of Notre Dame (MS) Chem; St Univ of NY at Stony Brook [illegible] Math; *cr:* Acad of St Joseph Chem Tchr; Suffolk Coll Math [illegible] Brentwood HS Chem Tchr; *ai:* NHS; Sci Olympiad; Suffolk Cty Sci [illegible] NSTA; Natl Presidential Scholars Prgm Distinguished Tchr 1994.

BANSBACH, DIANE CORMANY, Mathematics Teacher; *b:* Westc[illegible] PA; *m:* James J.; *ed:* PA St Univ (BS) Scndry Ed math 1989; Villanov[illegible] (MS) Math 1994; *cr:* Dover HS Math Tchr 1989-90; Conestoga H[illegible] Tchr 1990-92; Strath Haven HS Math Tchr 1992-; *ai:* SADD, Go[illegible] Math Clubs Advs; NCTM 1989-; NEA 1990-; *office:* Strath Haven [illegible] N Providence Rd Wallingford PA 19086

BANTLY, BARBARA LYNN, English Teacher; *b:* Johnstown, [illegible] Robert Milton; *c:* Tricia Deneen, Alissa Jane; *ed:* IN Univ of PA[illegible] Scndry Eng 1969; *cr:* Westmont Hilltop Schls 7-9 Grd Eng Tchr 19[illegible] Johnstown Chrstn 7-12 Grd Eng Tchr 1979-81, 1983-85, 1989-, MS[illegible] Tchr 1994-.

BAPST, JACOB LAMAR, Dir of Instrl Media Center; *b:* Chillicoth[illegible] *m:* Joann Snyder; *c:* Suzanna; *ed:* Rio Grande Coll (BS) His, Speech[illegible] Marshall Univ (MA) Comm Arts 1989; *cr:* Scioto Vly Schls Tchr 19[illegible] Rio Grande Coll Tchr 1976-77; Gallia Cty Local Schls Tchr 1980-85[illegible] of Rio Grande Instrl Media Ctr Project CHAMP Dir 1990-; *ai:* C[illegible] AmeriCorps Coord; AIDS Task Force; Interactive Television Dir; Ph[illegible] Gamma 1991-, Past Pres; Grace Meth Church 1989-; Gallia Cty St[illegible] Planning 1992-; NSSA Article Awd 1990; Photographer & Writer; [illegible] Univ Of Rio Grande Wood Hall 127-URG Rio Grande OH 45674*

BAPTISTE, KATHRYN RUSSO, Math Teacher; *b:* Providence, [illegible] Brian; *c:* Jeana, Alaina, Erica, Rachael; *ed:* RI Coll (BS) Math 19[illegible] Addl Hrs Post Grad Courses; *cr:* Lincoln HS Math Tchr 1978-79; [illegible] Stang HS Math Tchr 1980-91; Pvt Tutor 1978-; New Bedford HS [illegible] Tchr 1992-; *ai:* Curr Comm Math Dept; Sec, Treas NE All-Star [illegible] Camp; NCTM 1980-; New Bedford Edctrs Assn 1992-; NEA 1992[illegible] Tchrs Assn 1992-; *home:* 5 Gentle Valley Dr North Dartmouth MA [illegible]

BARAILLOUX, CAROL ANN (WILLIAMS), Sixth Grade Teac[illegible] Toledo, OH; *m:* Jesse D.; *c:* Christopher Calhoun, Gregory Ca[illegible] Melissa Calhoun; *ed:* Univ of Toledo (BED) Elem Ed, Spec Ed [illegible] (MED) Admin, Supervision 1985; *cr:* Lake Local Schls Tchr 19[illegible] Toledo Pub Schls Tchr 1974-; *ai:* Stu Assistance Team; Hlth Resourc[illegible] AFT, TFT 1974-; OH PTA 1974-94; Longfellow PTO 1994-.

BARAN, VIRGINIA MCCABE, First Grade Teacher; *b:* Ravenna, O[illegible] William Albert; *c:* Scott A., Todd A., Gregg A.; *ed:* Kent St Univ (BS)[illegible] Ed 1955; Westminster Coll (MS) Admin & Supervision 1963; [illegible] Youngstown St Univ, NY St Univ, Ashland Univ, Wickcliff Inst; *cr:* L[illegible] Schl Dist 3rd Grd Tchr 1955-58; Newton Falls Exempted Village 2n[illegible] Tchr 1958-63; Warren City Schls 1st Grd Tchr 1963-65; Howland [illegible] Schls 1st & 3rd Grd Tchr 1976-; *ai:* PTA Rep; Sunshine Comm; Prin [illegible] Bd; Mentor Tchr; NEA 1955-; OEA & NEOEA 1955-; Warren Ed A[illegible] LaBrae Tchrs Assn 1955-65; Howland Classroom Tchr 1976-; Delta [illegible] Gamma 1980-, VP & Legistative Chair; Trumbull Area Rdng Cncl [illegible] Literacy Chair; Martha Holden Jennings Scholar; Howland Bd Ed F[illegible] Tchr Awd; Warren Tribune Chronicles A+ Tchr Awd; *home:* 3541 S[illegible] Dr Warren OH 44484*

BARANELLO, CHARLAINE, English Teacher; *b:* New York, N[illegible] Theodore Levy; *cr:* Erasmus Hall HS Eng Tchr 1966-; *ai:* Prgm C[illegible] *office:* Erasmus Hall HS 911 Flatbush Ave Brooklyn NY 11226

BARANOSKI, KAREN METZGER, Life Science & Biology Teach[illegible] Wilkes-Barre, PA; *m:* Joseph T.; *c:* Amy, Kristin, Joseph; *ed:* Wilkes [illegible] (BS) Bio 1973, (MS) Bio Ed 1977; Post Grad Stud Molecular Bio, Cr[illegible] Cooperative Learning; *cr:* Hanover Area Schl Dist 2nd, 5th-6th Grd [illegible] Life Sci Tchr 1973-; *ai:* PA Jr Acad of Sci Spon, Judge; Jr Hnr Soc [illegible] Project LEARN Presenter; NEA, PSEA, Luzerne Co Sci Tchrs Assn [illegible] HAEA 1973-, VP: PJAS 1977-; St Aloysius Church 1984-, Bible Schl [illegible] Howard Hughes Grant Univ of Scranton; Excl in Tchng 1986; *o*[illegible] Hanover Area Jr Sr HS 1600 Sans Souci Pky Wilkes Barre PA 18702[illegible]

BARANOWSKI, NANCE L., Retired Social Studies Teacher; *b:* Bu[illegible] NY; *c:* Steve; *ed:* SUNY at Brockport (BS) Elem Ed, Scndry Ed, Soc [illegible] 1961; SUNY at Buffalo (MS) Elem Supervision, Admin 1968; *cr:* R[illegible] Kelley 4 Grd Tchr 1961-62; Iroquois Cntrl Schl 6 Grd Soc Stud [illegible] 1962-95; *ai:* Iroquois Cntrl 6 Grd Team Ldr; Iroquois Fac Assn [illegible] Chm; NYNEA, NEA 1962-; Girl Scouts of Am 1954-; Exch Tchr R[illegible] 1992; Iroquois Cntrl Outstdng Alumna Awd 1993; Outstdng Young W[illegible] of Amer 1969.

BARATTO, MICHAEL ANTHONY, 6th Grade Teacher; *b:* Arund[illegible] Sussx, England; *m:* Margaret Rimkunas; *c:* Michele, Bridgett [illegible] Gretchen Scott, Suzanne Scott; *ed:* SUC at Plattsburgh (BA) Ed [illegible] (MS) Supervision 1970; *cr:* Stillwater Cntrl 5th Grd Tchr 196[illegible] Hoosick Falls Cntrl 4th-6th Grd Tchr 1968-; *ai:* Natl Spelling Bee Ch[illegible] Var & IM Golf Coach; Strategic Planning, Policy Review & HFTA [illegible] Comms; Past Jr High Bsktbl & Past Girls JV Bsktbl Coach; AFT 1[illegible]

1968-, Grievance Chair, VP & Pres; *home:* 416 Bovie Hill Rd k Falls NY 12090

, CYNTHIA M., Mathematics Professor; *b:* Akron, OH; *ed:* Univ of 'BS) Math 1985, (BS) Statistics 1985, (MS) Math 1990; Cert Scndry 6; Doctoral Candidate PHD Math Ed Kent St Univ; *cr:* Univ of Grad Tchng Asst 1985-86; Tallmadge City Schls Sub Math Tchr 3; Stow City Schls Sub Tchr 1988-89; Univ of Akron Visiting Prof 989-90; Kent St Univ Math Instr 1990-; *ai:* Schlsp, Lib, Fac Search Comm; Vol Fac Tutor, Adv; Mentor HS Stdnts, Math Ed; Amer Ed Assn 1995-; Mathematical Assn of Amer 1990-; NCTM 1994-; OH Tchrs of Math 1994-; Phi Sigma Alpha Natl Acad Honorary Grad wd Univ of Akron 1985-86; Distngd Tchng Awd 1992; Marquis Who Midwest 1994-95; Who's Who Amer Women 1995-96; Who's of Engrng 1996-; Who's Who in World 1995-; Articles Pub; Referee Journals; *office:* Kent St Univ 7000 Frank Ave NW Canton OH

A, SUZANNE, Ath Trainer, Health & PE Tchr; *b:* Kearney, NJ; *ed:* roudsburg St Coll (BS) Hlth, PE 1983; East Stroudsburg Univ (MS) ci, Ed 1991; Emergency Med Technician Defibrillator; CPR, First str Amer Red Cross; Extensive Continuing Ed Credits Ath Trng, Pre Care; *cr:* West Morris Cntrl HS First Aid Attendant 1983-85; West Regnl Chester Schl Sub Tchr 1983-84; WA Twp Schl Dists Sub Tchr 4; St Vincent De Paul Schl K-8 PE Tchr 1984-85; St Bernards Schl Tchr 1984-85; West Morris Cntrl HS Ath Trainer, Hlth PE Tchr *ai:* Ath Trainer Boys, Girls Teams; Adv Stu Ath Trainer Club; Lead PR Marathon Jrs, Srs; Natl Ath Trainers Assn 1982-, Certfd Trainer; NJEA 1991-; Ath Trainers Soc of NJ 1984-; Long Vly First Aid 1983-, Capt, Lieutenant, Rookie of Yr; Squad Mem of Yr, Life Mem; r First Aid Squad 1995-; Pre Hosp Excl Morristown Meml Hosp Resolution WA Twp Mayor First CPR Marathon; Selected Ath 1996 Olympic Games; *office:* West Morris Central HS Bartley Rd r NJ 07930

AGALLO, PHYLLIS MANZI, Counselor; *b:* Boston, MA; *m:* ; *c:* Derek, Joseph; *ed:* Salem St Coll (BS) Ed 1968; Suffolk Univ Ed 1973; *cr:* Oliver Schl Tchr 1970-87; Kane Schl Cnslr 1987-95; Lawrence East Schl Cnslr 1995-; *ai:* NECA 1994-, MS, Cnslng Awd; 1995-.

ER, CAROLE J., Second Grade Teacher; *b:* New Brunswick, NJ; *c:* L.; *ed:* Monmouth Univ (BS) Elem Ed 1965; *cr:* Robert Morris Schl Grd Tchr 1965-71; Voorhees Schl 3rd Grd Tchr 1978-81; N K ton Schl 5th-6th Grd Rdng, Lang Arts Tchr 1981-84; Voorhees Schl Grd Tchr 1985-; *ai:* Educl Cncl; Schl Planning Comm; Chrldr Adv 1, 1978-86; NJEA, NEA 1965-; RMEA 1965- VP, Sec; SCEA 1965-, ep; Tchr Recognition Awd 1988; *home:* 110 Stratford Pl Bound NJ 08805*

ER, CONSTANCE ANN, Social Studies Teacher; *b:* Providence, Univ of ME (BA) Pol Sci 1969; RI Coll (MA) Guidance 1975; *cr:* rovidence Schl Dept Soc Stud Tchr 1971-; *ai:* Senate Youth Prgm; People Competition on the Constitution & Bill of Rights; NEA EPEA VP; Tchr of Yr 1992; Ocean St Ctr for Law & Ciizen Ed Tchr 991; RI Comm to Review the Natl Standards for Civic Ed 1993-94; East Providence Sr HS 2000 Pawtucket Ave East Providence RI

ER, DEANNA MARIE, Spanish & Reading Teacher; *b:* St Marys, *l:* Oh Northern Univ (BA) Span Ed 1991; 53 Addl Credit Hrs in MS t Univ of Dayton Coll Stu Per Csnlng; *cr:* Houston HS Span & Rdng 991-; *ai:* Span Club, Jr Class & Prom Adv; Hardin Houston Ed Assn 3, Treas 1992, Pres Elect 1994, Pres 1995, Superior Treas; Oh n Lang Assn 1991-; Minster Jaycees 1994, Sec 1994-95, VP 1995-, 1st Mem of Yr 1995, Top 1st Yr Mem of OH 1995; Veterans Of n Wars Aux 1987-; Alumni Admissions Rep for OH Northern Univ Shelby Cty Chamber of Commerce Schlrsp; *home:* 188 N Frankfort ster OH 45865

ER, EILEEN MILLER, Second Grade Teacher; *b:* Teaneck, NJ; *m:* ; *c:* Sean, Ryan; *ed:* William Paterson Coll (BA) Elem Ed 1971; island Univ (MS) Elem Ed & Comp 1991; *cr:* Ridgefield Park Pub Elem Ed Tchr 23 Yrs; *ai:* Grd K-3rd Unit Ldr; NEA 1972-; NJEA Lincoln Schl PTA 1972-, 2nd VP & Corres Sec, Lifetime Mbrshgp; velt Schl PTA 1989-, 2nd VP; *office:* Roosevelt Elem Schl 508 k Rd Ridgefield Park NJ 07660

ER, FRANCES (COX), Family & Consumer Sci Edctr; *b:* New n, CT; *m:* Joseph Charles; *c:* Joseph, Timothy; *ed:* WV Wesleyan BS) Home Ec 1964; Cntrl CT St Univ (MS) Early Chldhd Ed 1983; tly Working on Masters Prgm Schl Cnslng; *cr:* Irving Robbins Jr HS Ec Tchr 1964-70; Farmington HS Home Ec Tchr 1970-71; Gilbert amily, Comsumer Sci Edctr 1980-; *ai:* Tech-Prep Coord; NEA; CEA; Kappa Gamma, Schlsp Chrpsn; Amer Assn of Family, Consumer 'th Svcs Bd 1991-93; *office:* Gilbert Schl 200 Williams Ave Winsted 098

ER, FRANCES NOEL, English Dept Chprsn & Tchr; *b:* Waverly, *i:* John K.; *c:* Matthew, Luke; *ed:* Miami Univ (BS) Eng Ed 1974; of Dayton (MS) Ed Admin 1988; 17 Post Grad Semesters Hrs for s Cert; *cr:* Pike Cty Head Start Schl Tchr 1974; Valley View Schls Dept Head 1974-79; Cedar Cliff Local Schls Eng Tchr & Dept Head *ai:* Stdnts in Action for Ed & NHS Adv; Competency Prgm Design n; Valley View Schl Future Tchrs of America Adv; Phi Delta Kappa ASCD; NCTE; Twigs; St Brigid Parish; Heart Fund Dr; Miami Univ iter; Cedar Cliff Tchr of Yr Awd 1982 & 1987; Top 10 OH Tchrs of 82; Honorary Tchr Awds, Validectorian 1987 & 1991, Salutatorian 1991; 2 Articles Pub in Educl Journals; *office:* Cedar Cliff Local Box 45 Cedarville OH 45314

ER, JAMES ALLEN, PE Tchr & Bsktbl Coach; *b:* Washington, DC; mmy McPhee; *c:* Tyler; *ed:* United Wesleyan Coll (BS) Ed 1989; *cr:* ose Chrstn Schl PE Tchr 1992-; *ai:* Girls Bsktbl Coach; Montrose Bsktbl Dir; PE Dept Chprsn; WBCA 1993-; CSAA League pionships in Bsktbl 3 Consecutive Times; *office:* Montrose Christian 100 Randolph Rd Rockville MD 20852

ER, JUANITA ELAINE, First Grade Teacher; *b:* Youngstown, OH; lliam Andrew; *c:* Amanda Sue Cairns, Marcia Ellen Marsteller; *ed:* stown St Univ (BS) ELem, K-Pri Specialist 1966, (MS) Elem Ed, Specialist 1979; 18 Addl Credit Hrs Kent St Univ, Ashland Univ; *cr:* r Goose Nursery Schl Day Camp Aide, Cnslr 1956-65; Ellsworth Schl Kndgtn Tchr 1965; E. J. Blott Elem Schl First Grd Tchr 1966-70, er Schl Math, Rdng Tchr 1967, 1972-74; Guy Schl Summer Schl Rdng Tchr 1967, 1972-74; E. J. Blott Elem Schl Second Grd Tchr 76, First Grd Tchr 1976-; *ai:* Cmptr Comm; Resource Person Tech n; Sci COS, Report Card, Math CBE Test Comms Trumbull Cty; oord Blott 100 Day Celebration; NEA, OEA 1966-; Liberty Tchrs 1966-, Bdlg Rep; Phi Delta Kappa 1980-, Fnds Rep, 20-20 Club; bull Area Rdng Cncl 1986-, Pres, VP, Corres Sec; IRA; OCIRA; ; DKG; WROTE; Girard Jr Women 1975-, Pres, VP, Treas; Red Cross , Vol; CISV 1981-, Bd of Dir; Trumball Area Rdng Cncl Literacy Awd Jennings Scholar; Presenter Math Inservice Trumbull Cty; Cmptr vice Presenter Tchrs & Parents; Schlsp Selection Comm PDK Intl; Trumball Cty Literacy Conf Presenter; *office:* E. J. Blott Elem Schl Shady Rd Youngstown OH 44505*

BARBER, LAURA L., Guidance Counselor; *b:* South Bend, IN; *m:* Kenneth L.; *c:* Kristen, Shannon; *ed:* Marshall Univ (BA) Sociology 1969, (MA) Counseling 1972; Southern CT (CAS) Schl Admin 1990; Univ of Bridgeport 21 Hrs Guidance & Counseling; Fairfield Univ 6 Hrs Guidance; SUNY at Albany 6 Hrs Career Equity; SUNY at New Paltz 3 Hrs NY St Schl Law; *cr:* St Joseph's Schl 4th Grd Tchr 1969-70; Marshall Univ Womens Dorm Resident Dir 1970-72; Westlake HS 9-12 Grd Guidance Cnslr 1973-77; Westlake MS 6-8 Grd Guidance Cnslr 1977-81; Westlake HS 9-12 Grd Guidance Cnslr 1981-, 6-12 Grd Guidance Dept Chair 1989-93, Westlake MS 6-12 Grd Guidance Dept Chair 1989-93; Guid Cnsl 8-12 194-; *ai:* Schlsp Chprsn; NHS Adv; Scheduling, Schl Activities Mid States, Stu Advocacy, Career Expo Comms; Spec Ed Cnslr; Westchester Putnam Transitional Plan Consortium; Coll Articulation Prgm; Middle Schl Stu Cncl Adv Coll Clinic; Travel & Tourism Bd; WPRACD 1976-, Pres, Org Svc Awds 1991-93; NYSACD 1976-; NYSSCA 1985-; NYSUT, MPTA 1973-; Westchester Putnam Cosortium for LD, Westchester Self-Advocacy Comm, Boces Career Expo Comm 1993-; NY Spec Olympics Vol 1989, 1990, 1994, CT World Olympics Vol; Gwen Chimneys Youth Svc Awd 1993; Article Pub 1993; *office:* Westlake HS Westlake Dr Thornwood NY 10594

BARBER, SHARYN L., 6th-8th Grade Teacher; *b:* Newark, NJ; *m:* David; *c:* Kelly, Keith; *ed:* Seton Hall Univ (BS) Ed 1968; 30 Grad Credits in Admin & Supervision; *cr:* Newark Bd of Ed Tchr 1968-70; Immaculate Heart of Mary Tchr 1980-; Maplewood & South Orange Bd Ed ESL Tchr 1990-93; *ai:* Standardized Testing Coord; NCEA 1980-; Kappa Delta Pi-Intl Honor Soc; Revised Rdng Prgm 6th-8th Grd at Immacualte Heart of Mary; *home:* 3 Woodland Rd Short Hills NJ 07078

BARBER, TOM ALDEN, Fourth Grade Teacher; *b:* South Bend, IN; *m:* Ling Hong Yu; *c:* Kyna Ling; *ed:* CA St Coll (BS) Elem Ed 1973; Wright St Univ (MS) Elem Admin 1980; *cr:* US Army S-4 1970-72; Cambridge City Schls Elem Tchr 1973-; *ai:* US Swimming Coach; YMCA; Cambridge City Schls Ed coord 1986-; NEA 1973-; Cambridge Ed Assn 1973-, Sec; North Amer Bluebird Assn 1983-; OH Bluebird Assn 1986-, Dist Rep; Save the Manatee Club 1986-; 9 Articles Pub; *office:* Liberty Elem Schl 9259 Liberty School Rd Cambridge OH 43725

BARBERIO, CYNTHIA MALYNN, English Teacher; *b:* Haverhill, MA; *m:* Frank J. Jr.; *c:* Patrick, Elizabeth; *ed:* Fitchburg St (BS) Eng Tchr 1974, (MS) Eng Tchr 1984; Addl 60 Hrs Post Grad Stud Tchng Writing, Cooperative Learning; *cr:* Haverhill HS Eng Tchr 1974-; *ai:* Co-Supvr HS Lit Magazine; NCTE; St Rita's Church, CCD Tchr; *office:* Haverhill HS 137 Monument St Haverhill MA 01830

BARBERIO, DEBORAH LYNN, Math Teacher; *b:* Newark, NJ; *m:* Stephen Louis; *c:* Jennifer, Andrea; *ed:* Merrimack Coll (BS) Math 1974; Worcester Poly Tech (MS) Math 1982; *cr:* Marlboro HS Math Tchr 1974-77; Rutgers Coll Adj Math Prof 1983-87; Eastern Sr HS Math Tchr 1987-; *ai:* NHS Adv; IAC & PDT Comm; NEA 1986-; NJEA 1986-; NCTM 1986-; *office:* Eastern Sr HS 1306 Laurel Oak Rd Voorhees NJ 08043*

BARBIER, ROBERT A., English Teacher; *b:* Hackensack, NJ; *m:* Susan A. Jackovitz; *ed:* Rutgers Coll (BA) Eng 1989; William Paterson Coll Tchng Cert Prgm 1991; *cr:* Garfield HS Eng Tchr 1992-94 & 1995-; *ai:* Fishing & Drama Clubs; Eng Tutoring Ctr; *office:* Garfield HS 500 Palisade Ave Garfield NJ 07026

BARBIERI, JOSEPH GENE,JR., Science Teacher; *b:* Lawrence, MA; *ed:* Merrimack Coll (BA) Bio 1969; Attnd Northeastern Univ, Salem St Coll, Notre Dame Coll & Rivier Coll; *cr:* St Michael's Schl Sci Tchr 1969-70; Woodbury Schl Sci Tchr 1970-; *ai:* Sci Fair Coord; Pub Relations Contact Person; Advanced Anatomy Club Adv; Jr Teenof Month Selection Comm 1993-; NEA, NH NEA, Salem Ed Assn 1970-; Democratic City Comm 1974-75; Plan Intnl-USA Foster Parent, Child Spon 1987-; Marconi Credit Union Bd of Dir 1983-91; Church of Latter Day Saints Cert of Appreciation 1990-91; NSTA & NASA Space Sci Stu Involvement Prgm Tchr Adv Stu Submitted Experiement 1987; *office:* Woodbury Schl 206 Main St Salem NH 03079

BARBONE, PATRICIA R., 6th Grade Teacher; *b:* Queens Cty, NY; *ed:* Queens Coll (BA) Ed 1962; Univ of CT (MA) Span 1964; Adelphi Univ (MSW) Clinical Soc Worker 1988; Univ of Valencia Spain 15 Credits Span; Pamma CA 9 Credits Span; Ithica Coll 9 Credits Shakespeare; Hofstra 12 Credits Shakespeare; St Johns 3 Credits Bible; *cr:* UFSD #30 Tchr 1961-62; Univ CT Tchng Asst 1962-64; Dever Schl 6th Grd Tchr 1964-; West Nassau Mental Hlth Clinic Psycho Therapist 1988-95; *ai:* Guest Lecturer Alcoholism Cnslng Prgm Long Island Univ 1991-92, Winthrop Univ Hosp 1990-91, Long Island Cncl on Alcoholism; AIT, NEA 1964-; Natl Assn of Soc Workers, Nassau Cty Mental Hlth Assn 1989-; Sigma Delta Pi; Phi Beta Kappa; Comm Cnslng Svcs of West Nassau 1993-, Bd of Dir VP; Natl Defense Ed Act Schlsp; *office:* James A Dever Elem Schl 585 N Corona Ave Valley Stream NY 11580

BARBOUR, HENRY J., Social Studies Educator; *b:* Wicomico, MD; *m:* Annie K. Kennedy; *c:* Michael, Jeffrey (dec); *ed:* Bowie St Univ (BS) Jr HS Ed 1952; Attnd Cath Univ, G. W. Univ, Univ of MD; *cr:* Bel Alton HS Jr HS Tchr 11 Yrs; St Mary Star of Sea Edctr 1969-; *ai:* Soc Stud, Rel Chprsn; Bus Monitor; AARP 10 Yrs; Tri Cty Bowie St Alumni Assn, Chaplain; Knights of Columbus 1968-, Outstdng Tchr Awd; Archdiocese of DC 1995-, 24 Yrs Svc Awd; Outstdng Cath Ed Awd; Archdiocese of DC Outstdng Tchr.*

BARBOUR, NANCY C. (MENEELY), Art Teacher; *b:* Boston, MA; *m:* Richard K.; *ed:* Univ of MA at Amherst (BA) Art Ed 1972; Attnd MA Coll of Art, Schl of Calligraphy; *cr:* Wm H. Galvin MS Art Tchr 1973-; *ai:* Girl's Bsktbl, Sftbl Coach; Taught Adult Ed Pottery Class; Stu Cncl Adv; Alternative Ed Planning Bd 1996; Tchr of Yr Awd; Yrbk Dedications; Golden Apple Awd; *office:* William H. Galvin MS 55 Pecunit St Canton MA 02021

BARBOUR-PANICO, BETSY, English Teacher; *b:* Bronx, NY; *m:* Anthony L. Panico; *c:* Amanda Barbour, Marisa Barbour; *ed:* Elmira Coll (BA) Eng Lit 1964; Attnd Columbia Univ, Hunter Coll, Romapo Coll; *cr:* Spring Valley Jr HS Eng Tchr 1964-70; Palisades Park HS Eng Tchr 1983-85; Northern Valley Eng Tchr 1985-; *ai:* Honor Soc Adv; Multicultural Comm; Speech Coach; Acad Decathlon Tutor; NEA 1983-; NYEA 1985-; Article Pub in Grand Journal of Liberal Stud; *office:* Northern Valley Regnl HS Central Ave Old Tappan NJ 07675

BARBOZA, TOBIAS JOSEPH, Adj Instr & Head Ath Trainer; *b:* Catskill, NY; *m:* Martha E. Pedhoretzky; *c:* Meghan; *ed:* Springfield Coll (BS) PE 1968; Univ of VA (MED) Sports Medicine 1979; Attnd Univ at Albany; *cr:* William Paterson Coll Head Ath Trainer 1974-, Adj Instr 1976-; *ai:* Natl Ath Trainers Assn 1974-; NY Times Op & Ed Article; Scholastic Coach.

BARBUS, ARLENE M., Mathematics Teacher; *b:* Spangler, PA; *m:* Steven A.; *ed:* IN Univ of PA (BS) Scndry Math 1989; 24 Credit Hrs Elem Ed Slippery Rock Univ of PA; *cr:* North Allegheny Sr HS 11-12 Grd Math Tchr 1989-90; Carson MS 8th Grd Math Tchr 1990-; *ai:* NCTM, North Allegheny Fed Tch, AFT 1989-; *office:* Carson MS 200 Hillvue Ln Pittsburgh PA 15237

BARBUS, GEORGIA ANN (KINLEY), French Teacher; *b:* Lock Haven, PA; *ed:* Lock Haven St Coll (BS) Fr 1965; 6 Credits in Fr Laval Univ 1964; 24 Credits in Fr Millersburg Univ 1967-70; *cr:* Shreveport Schl Dist Sub Tchr 1965-66; Corning Schl Dist Fr Tchr 1966-67; Montgomery Area Schl Dist Fr Tchr 1967-; *ai:* Fr Club Adv; Girls Tennis Coach; MAEA 1967-, Pres 1992-95; PSEA, NEA, MLA 1967-.

BARBUSH, THOMAS DONALD, 6th Grade Teacher; *b:* Harrisburg, PA; *m:* Tami Massenkiel; *ed:* Bloomsburg Univ (BS) Elem Ed 1989; Working Toward MS in Admin East Stroudsburg Univ; Certfd in Elem & Scndry Instrl Support; *cr:* Pocono Elem Schl 6th Grd Tchr 1989-93; Pocono Intermediate Schl 6th Grd Tchr 1993-; *ai:* 7th-8th Grd Ftbl Coach; Weightlifting Adv; 6-7th Grd Ski Coord; Instrl Support Team; SAP Mem; NEA, PMEA 1989-, Sigma Iota Omega 1986-; Sally Mae Awd Nom 1989; *home:* RR 1 Box 252 Tannersville PA 18372

BARCHIK, RAYMOND HENRY, History Teacher; *b:* Cambra, PA; *m:* Corrine Angeli; *c:* Benjamin, Ashley Elizabeth; *ed:* Millersville Univ (BS) Soc Stud 1972; 36 Grad Credit Hrs for Masters Equivalent from PA Dept of Ed; *cr:* NW Area Schl Dist Soc Stud Tchr & Head of Dept 1974-75; *ai:* NEA, PSEA 1972-; *office:* Northwest Area Jr Sr HS RR 2 Box 2271 Shickshinny PA 18655*

BARCLAY, NANCY BURDGE, Third Grade Teacher; *b:* Long Branch, NJ; *ed:* Glassboro St Coll (BA) Elem Ed 1974; Farleigh Dickinson (MA) Human Dev 1978; 12 Substance Abuse Georgian Ct; *cr:* Leonardo Schl Third Grd Tchr 1974-; *ai:* Bldg Rep MTEA; NJ, EA, NEA 1974-; MTEA; Eastern Star of NJ 1972-; Tchr of Yr 1988; Middletown Twp Withycombe Grant 1988; *office:* Leonardo Grade Schl 14 Hosford Ave Leonardo NJ 07737

BARDAGLIO, PETER WINTHROP, Associate Professor of History; *b:* Hartford, CT; *m:* Wrexie Lainson; *c:* Sarah Agan, Jesse Agan, Anne; *ed:* Brown Univ (BA) His, Eng 1975; Stanford Univ (MA) His 1978, (PHD) His 1987; *cr:* Univ of MD Visiting Lecturer 1981-83; Goucher Coll Instr 1983-87, Asst Prof 1987-93, Assoc Prof 1993-95, Todd Assoc Prof 1995-; *ai:* Gen Hnrs Prgm Dir; Fac Comm Reappointment, Promotion Chair; Chief Fac Marshall; Task Force on Fac, Curr Bd of Trustees; Amer Historical Assn; Org Amer Historians; Southern Historical Assn; Amer Soc for Legal His; Catonsville Presbyn Church 1989-, Elder; James Rawley Prize Best Book His Race Relations in US 1995; Book: Reconstructing the Household, Families, Sex and the Law in the Nineteenth Century South; Caroline Doebler Brucker Awd Outstdng Tchng 1994; Natl Endowment for Hum Summer Stipend 1992; *office:* Goucher Coll 1021 Dulaney Vly Rd Baltimore MD 21204

BARDOL, JOYCE SASTER, 6th Grade Teacher; *b:* Franklin, MA; *m:* William H.; *c:* Rebecca, William Jr., Mark; *ed:* Farmingham St Coll (BS) Elem Ed 1968; 18 Post Grad Credits; *cr:* Horace Mann Schl Grd 3 Tchr 1968-69, K-8 Grd Sub Tchr 3 Long Term 1979-86; Horace MS 6 Grade Tchr 1987-; *ai:* Co-Adv Proud to be Substance Free Club 3 Yrs; NEA, FEA, MTA 1968-; Frances Eddy King Schlsp Comm 1980-, Bd; Delta Kappa Gamma 1995-; *office:* Horace Mann MS 224 Oak St Franklin MA 02038

BARDUA, WAYNE J., 5th Grade Science Teacher; *b:* Danburg, CT; *ed:* Dutchess Comm (AA) Gen 1972; SUNY at Oswego (BS) Elem Ed 1974; SUNY at New Paltz (MS) Elem Ed 1978; *cr:* Highland Falls MS Grd 5 Tchr 1974-; *ai:* Hydroponic Club Adv; Earth Shuttle Adv, Coord; NY St Unified Tchrs 1974-; AFT; Nom Outstdng Sci Tchrs Awd; *office:* Highland Falls MS 40 Mountain Ave Highland Falls NY 10928

BARE, ROBERT TODD, Elementary Hlth & PE Teacher; *b:* Lebanon, PA; *ed:* Messiah Coll (BA) Hlth & PE 1991; Penn St Univ at Harrisburg for Masters in Hlth Ed; *cr:* Ebenezer Elem Schl Hlth & PE Tchr 1993-; *ai:* HS Cross Cntry, Jr HS Wrestling & HS Track & Field Coach; AHPERD 1990-.

BAREN, ROBERT, Mechanical Engineering Prof; *b:* Philadelphia, PA; *ed:* Univ of Pennsylvania (BSC) Metallurgical Engr 1958, (PHD) Metallurgical Engr 1966; Cmptr Programming; Acctng; Ec; Failure Analysis; Strain Gage Tech; Microscopy; *cr:* Budd Co Project Engr 1962-82; Temple Univ Prof 1982-; *ai:* Coll Dir of Comm; Head of Coll Tutoring Prgm; Univ Writing Comm; Grad, Undergrad Curr Comms; ASEE 1982-; ASM, AIME 1960-; ASTM 1970-; Lindback Awd for Tchng; Fac Alumni Awd for Tchng; *office:* Temple Univ 12th & Norris Sts Philadelphia PA 19122

BARESSI, TERRI MOORE, Second Grade Teacher; *b:* Corry, PA; *m:* Frank Baressi; *c:* Heather, Amy, Frank, Adrian; *ed:* Edinboro Univ (BS) Elem Ed, Early Chldhd 1979; Masters Equivalency Plus 6 Credit Hrs; *cr:* Spartansburg Elem Schl First Grd Tchr 1979-80, Second Grd Tchr 1980-92; Wright Elem Schl Fifth Grd Tchr 1992-93, Third Grd Tchr 1993-94; Columbus Elem Schl Second Grd Tchr 1994-; *ai:* PSEA, NEA, CEA 1979-; *office:* Columbus Elem Schl 100 W Main St Corry PA 16407

BARGE, ALBERT, English Teacher; *b:* Berea, OH; *m:* Brenda Kay Jacobs; *c:* Tracy, Scott; *ed:* OH St Univ (BS) Eng 1970; 17 Hrs Post Grad; *cr:* US Army Specialist 4 1970-72; Buckeye HS Eng Tchr 1972-; *ai:* Drama Set Designer; AFT; *office:* Buckeye HS 3084 Columbia Rd Medina OH 44256

BARGER, KATHY HALL, Art Instr & Computer Liasion; *b:* Dayton, OH; *m:* Brian; *ed:* Xavier Univ (BA) Art 1971; Wright St Univ (MED) Ed Ldrshp 1993; Post Grad Work Univ of Cincinnati, Mt St Joseph, Miami Univ; *cr:* Fairborn City Schls 1-5 Grd Art Instr 1971-72; St Thomas 1-8 Grd Art Instr 1972-73; Winston Salem Art Cncl Dir Children's Art 1973-74; Northwest Schl Dist 1-5 Grd Art Instr 1974-75; *ai:* Just Say No Adv; PTA Bldg Rep; Bldg Cmptr Liasion; Schl Newspaper Co-Chprsn; NAE, OAEA, SWOABA 1974-; Westwood Civic Assn 1985-; Cinti Art Museum 1980-; Hospice of Cinti; Vol Cnslr Bethesda; Outpatient, Drug Rehab Unit; Tchr of Yr; Scripps Howard Grant; Artist in Residence OH Arts Cncl; Getty Fnd Improvement Visual Arts; *office:* Welch Elem Schl 12084 Deerhorn Dr Cincinnati OH 45240*

BARICKMAN, JOAN ESTES, English Teacher & Director; *b:* St Louis, MO; *m:* Richard; *c:* Christopher, Julia; *ed:* Columbia Tchrs Coll (MA) Eng Ed 1976; Addl 30 Hrs; *cr:* Gateway Schl Eng, Math Tchr 1964-68; Hopkins-Day Prospect Schl Creative Writing, Eng Tchr 1968-69; Fox Lane HS Eng, Soc Stud Tchr 1977-; *ai:* IMS, Camping Canoing, Skiing, Hiking, Sftbl; Stu Travel-To Learn, Adventure-Based Cnslng Prgm, Elem-Scndry Mentorship Prgm Coords; NYSAEA 1977-, Pres, Founding Mem, VP, Bd, Alt Edctr of Yr 1986; AFT, NCSS, NYCSS, NCTE 1977-; NY Cncl Ed Assoc 1984-; Bed Comm Resource Cen 1980-, Bd; Bedford Comm Ed Fnd 1992-, Bd; Danforth Fnd Flwshp; Outstdng Tchr of Writing Awd; NEH Yth At Risk Grant; NY Arts Coun Grant; Articles Pub; Book: Schoolwise, 1992; *office:* Acad Comm for Educl Success 200 Railroad Ave Bedford Hills NY 10507

BARIE, ELIZABETH J., Social Studies Teacher; *b:* Webster, NY; *ed:* St Univ of NY Coll at Geneseo (BA) His 1993, (MS) Scndry Soc Stud Ed; *cr:* York HS 10th Grd Global Stud Tchr 1993-; *ai:* JV Girls Soccer Coach; Indoor Soccer Coach; Scndry Stu Support Team; AFT 1993-; NYSUT 1993-; *office:* York Cntrl Schl Dist 2578 Genesee St Retsof NY 14539

BARILE, FRANK PATRICK, Sixth Grade Teacher; *b:* Warren, OH; *m:* Andrea Minchoff; *c:* Katherine, Allyson; *ed:* Bowling Green St Univ (BS) Elem Ed 1971; Youngstown St Univ (MS) Elem Prin 1980; Attnd Kent St Univ; *cr:* Warren Cty Schls Tchr 1971-; *ai:* Safety Patrol Adv; PTO Treas; NEO, OEA 1971-; NEOEA 1971-, Positive Image Awd; WEA 1971-, Grievance Comm; Trumbull Co Umpires 1975-, VP Natl Umpire Awd; Martha Holden Jennings Scholar 1984-85; *home:* 629 Fairmount Ave NE Warren OH 44483

BARILLA, JACK GEORGE, Retired Teacher; *b:* Monessen, PA; *m:* Beverly; *c:* Robyn; *ed:* Penn St Masters Equivalency 1978; *cr:*

Shenandoah Elem Schl 6th Grd Tchr 1965-88, 5th Grd Tchr 1989-94; William Penn Elem Schl 5th Grd Tchr 1995; *ai:* PSEA Ret 1995; Alcoma Cntry Club 1994-; Plum Boro Jaycees 1971-77, VP, Jaycee of Yr 1976; *home:* 1791 McClure Rd Monroeville PA 15146

BARILLA, JAMES S., English Teacher; *b:* Allentown, PA; *m:* Anne; *ed:* St Josephs Univ (BA) Psych 1970; Chestnut Hill Coll (MS) Counseling Psych 1992; Eng, Latin & Greek Permanent Cert 1982; *cr:* West Cath HS Eng Tchr 1970-; Montgomery Cty Comm Coll Psych Tchr; *ai:* Stu Asst Prgm Mem & Past Coord; West Cath Newspaper Moderator 1987-91; NACST & NEA 1970-; Amer Psychological Asn 1989-; Bryn Mawr Hospital Drug & Alcohol Cnslr; *home:* 500 Gordon Ave Narberth PA 19072

BARIMANI, ALI, Computer Science Instructor; *b:* Sari, Iran; *m:* Rushaan; *ed:* W Chester Univ (BA) Math 1983, (MS) Cmptr Sci 1985; *cr:* Lincoln Univ Cmptr Instr 1985-; *ai:* Serve on Curr, Stu Hlth & Wlfr, Comp, Nmntns Comm; USTA; Lilly Grant; S African Stu Orientation Tchr Awd; Mgmt Trng Pgm Apprctn Awrds.

BARINGER, DEBORAH ANN, Middle School Science Educator; *b:* Defiance, OH; *m:* Bill M.; *c:* Anissa; *ed:* Defiance Coll (BS) PE, Hlth 1973; Post Grad Work IPFW, Bowling Green St Univ, Toledo Univ; *cr:* Hicksville Schls K-12 Grd Hlth, PE Tchr 1973-74, 1976-87, LD, Hlth Tchr 1988-90, 7-8 Grd Sci Tchr 1991-; *ai:* Chrldr Adv; Track 1973-87, Vlybl 1973-85 Coach; NEA, OEA, HEA 1976-, Sec, Treas; *office:* Hicksville Exempted Vlg Schl 105 E Smith St Hicksville OH 43526

BARKER, BARBARA U., Retired Teacher; *b:* Needham, MA; *w:* H. Stuart (dec); *c:* Jeffrey, Alison, Holly Beneville, Elizabeth Ritchie; *ed:* Univ of MA (BA) His, Ed 1954; Eastern Nazarene Coll (MA) Family Cnslng 1985; *cr:* Hickville NY 3rd Grd Tchr 1954-55; Riverhead NY 3rd Grd Tchr 1955-56; Needham MA 3-45h Grd Tchr 1958-61; Hanover MA 4-5th Grd Tchr 1966-94; *ai:* Stress Mngmt Prgm Bicentennial Chm; Math Club; Curr Comms; Hanover Tchrs 1967-94; Plymouth Cty Tchrs 1967-94, Comm Svc Hnr Awd 1985; Hanover Historical 1964-, Bd Mem, Prgm Chm; Friends of Stetson House 1980-, Pres 10 Yrs; Hanover Garden Club 1970-, Bd of Dirs; Book: Houses of the Revolutuion; Articles Pub.

BARKER, GUY KENNETH,JR., Chemistry Teacher; *b:* Kittanning, PA; *ed:* Indiana Univ of PA (BSE) Chem, Bio 1977; 23 Grad Credit Hrs; *cr:* Butler Area Jr HS Sci Tchr 1977-78; Lenape AVTS Chem Tchr 1978-; Butler Cty Comm Coll Part-time Chem, Bio, Cmptr Sci Instr 1981-; *ai:* Former Stu Govt, Voc Industrial Clubs of Amer Adv; NEA 1977-; VICA 1984-; Adv of Yr; Past-Gazette All-Star Educator; Adv of Yr Nom; Outstanding Fac Mem Nom; *office:* Lenape Area Voc Tech Schl 2215 Chaplin Ave Ford City PA 16226*

BARKER, HELLEN ELIZABETH, Social Studies Teacher; *b:* Durham, NC; *m:* Robert A. Anderson; *ed:* Duke Univ (BA) His 1983; Univ of CT (MA) Ed 1989; *cr:* Hilton Head HS 9th-12th Grd Soc Stud Tchr 1983-85; Fitch HS 9th-12th Grd Soc Stud Tchr 1985-86; Edwin O. Smith HS 9th-12th Grd Soc Stud Tchr 1986-89; Carl Sandburg MS 8th Grd Soc Stud Tchr 1990-; *ai:* Curr, Prof Dev Comms; Chrldng, Stu Cncl, Newspaper Adv; Current Events Team; Acad Olympics Coach; MS Team Ldr; Soc Stud Dept Chprsn; AFT 1990-; Phi Delta Kappa 1987-; NCSS 1983-; *office:* Carl Sandburg MS 30 Harmony Ln Levittown PA 19056

BARKER, JOEL C., Sixth Grade Teacher; *b:* Governeur, NY; *m:* Nancy Gruber; *c:* Lisa, Lauren; *ed:* St Univ of NY at New Paltz (MS) Elem Ed 1982; 60 Credits Hrs Above Masters from Long Island Univ; Inservice Courses from Newburgh Schl System; *cr:* Meadow Hill Schl Third Grd Tchr 1973-76, Second Grd Tchr 1976-77; Third Grd Tchr 1977-79, Fifth Grd Tchr 1979-84, Sixth Grd Tchr 1984-; *ai:* Administer Fourth Grd Sci Manipulative Test; Scanning Electron Microscope Tchr; Order All Sci & Audio-Visual Equipment for Schl; Sci Liaison; NEA & AFT 1973-; Nom for 1994 Presidential Awds for Excl in Sci Tchng; *home:* 187 Windsor Hwy New Windsor NY 12553*

BARKER, JOYCE ELIZABETH, Fifth Grade Teacher; *b:* Chicago, IL; *m:* William H.; *c:* Sharon Barker Whitman, Laura, William D., Stephen; *ed:* St Mary of the WOods Coll (BS) Elem Ed 1961; Loyola Univ Cnslng Master Equiv 1980-83; *cr:* Dept of Defense Schls First Grd Tchr 1966-68; Dept of Defense Schls Fifth Grd Tchr 1974-78; Van Bokkelen Elem Schl Second, Third, Fifth Grd Tchr 1979-86; Waugh Chapel Elem Schl Third, Fourth, Sixth, Fifth Grd Tchr 1986-; *ai:* Conducted Dimensions of Learning Insvcs 1983-84; Sci Comm Chprsn; Materials of Instruction Comm; Safety Patrol Spon; Stu Govt Spon 1986-92; Spon of Stu Variety Show 1987-92; NEA, TAAC 1979-; PTA 1990-, Fac Rep, VP 1992-; Excl in Ed Awd 1994; Tesa Awd; *office:* Waugh Chapel Elem Schl 840 Sunflower Dr Odenton MD 21113

BARKER, LAURA BOND, Former Math Teacher; *b:* Toul Rosieres AFB, France; *m:* John Dailey; *c:* Kathleen Tulloh, Martha Massee; *ed:* Duke Univ (BSME) Mech Engrng 1984; Attnd GA St Univ, MI St Univ; *cr:* Gupton Engrng Assocs Inc Project Mgr, Design Engr 1985-89; North Springs HS Math, Magnet Tchr 1989-93; *ai:* Engrng Team Class Spon, Coach; Won NEDC in GA 1992; Jr League of Atlanta 1988-, Treas; Cathedral of St Philip 1978-; Igreja Crista Unida 1995-, Cncl Comm; *home:* Rua Joaquim Jose Esteves 60 Edificio Santa Esmeralda Sao P Brazil XX 00000

BARKER, MARY L., Social Studies Teacher; *b:* Utica, NY; *m:* Laurence J.; *c:* Lauren Alaina; *ed:* SUNY Coll at Buffalo (BA) His, Ed 1970, (MA) His, Ed 1971; 30 Post Hrs; *cr:* T. R. Proctor HS Soc Stud Tchr 25 Yrs; *ai:* AFT, NEA 1971-; *office:* T. R. Proctor Sr HS Hilton Ave Utica NY 13501

BARKER, MELANIE GRAHAM, French Teacher; *b:* Cobleskill, NY; *m:* James Howard; *c:* Michelle M., Christopehr M., Kenneth J., Jennifer L. Trieschman, Laura L. Trieschman; *ed:* Geneva Coll (BA) Fr Ed 1981; Eng Cert 1993; Gannon 15 Grad Credits; Penn St 6 Grad Credits; *cr:* Conemaugh Vly Jr, Sr HS Fr Tchr 1986-87; Seton Schl 7-8 Grd Lbrl Arts Tchr 1988-93; Beaver Area Jr, Sr HS Fr Tchr 1993-; *ai:* Fr Club 1993-; Schl Cncl 1994-95; Eighth Grd Class Adv 1980-93; PSMLA 1995-; First Presbyn Church 1993-, Sixth Grd Sunday Schl Tchr 1994-95; Ed Fnd Grant 1995-; *home:* 250 Neville Rd Beaver PA 15009*

BARKER, NANCY GREENE, English Teacher & Dept Chair; *b:* Schenectady, NY; *m:* Gary L.; *ed:* Asbury Coll (BA) Eng, Scndry Ed 1967; Univ of KY (MA) Ed, Eng 1970; 19 Post Grad Hrs OH Writing Project Miami Univ of OH; *cr:* Robinson Schl Eng Tchr 1967-69; Norwood Jr HS Eng Tchr 1970-84; Norwood HS Eng Tchr 1984-, Eng Dept Chair 1994-; *ai:* 6-12 Grd Eng Dept Coord; Inservice Presenter for OH Writing Project; Mem Acad Achvmt Comm; Co-Chair Local Comm for North Cntrl Evaluation; OEA; NEA; NCTE; ASCD; OCTELA; Greater Cincinnati Fnd Learning Links Grant 1991; Article & Poetry Pub; Inservice Presenter on Portfolio Assessment, Writing Across the Curr, Intervention Strategies for Proficiency Testing; *office:* Norwood HS 2020 Sherman Ave Norwood OH 45212

BARKLEY, KAREN H., 6th Grd Social Studies Tchr; *b:* West Chester, PA; *ed:* West Chester Univ (BS) Scndry, His 1965; Elem Ed Cert; *cr:* Lincoln Elem Schl 6th Grd Tchr 1966-69; Pottstown Intermediate Schl 6th Grd World Cultures Tchr 1969-72; Lincoln Elem Schl 5th Grd Tchr 1972-92; Pottstown MS 6th Grd Soc Stud Tchr 1992-; *ai:* AFT 1980-; PA PTA 1965-; Sr Pals Alumni Assn 1990-; NAACP 1965-; Tchr of Yr Lincoln Elem Schl; PA PTA Life Time Mbrshp; *office:* Pottstown MS Franklin & Evans Sts Pottstown PA 19464*

BARKOVITZ, JEAN LAVELLE, AP English Teacher; *b:* Ashland, PA; *m:* Robert W.; *c:* Robert L., Brian L.; *ed:* Coll of St Elizabeth (BA) Eng 1972; Montclair St Univ (MA) Eng 1980; Addl 9 Credits Writing as Process, Poetry, Autobiographical Writing William Paterson Coll; *cr:* St. Alozsius HS Eng Tchr 1972-76; Morris Cath HS Eng Tchr 1976-80; Passaic Cty Comm Coll Eng Adj Prof 1980-84; Pompton Lakes HS Eng Tchr 1980-82; William Paterson Coll Eng Adj Prof 1983-92; Paramus HS AP Eng Tchr 1993-; *ai:* Co-Chaperone of Lit Trip to London 1996; Co-operating Tchr 1994; NJEA, NCTE 1993-; Northern NJ Writing Consortium 1984-; St Mary's Marriage Preparation Team 1984-; Monthly Book Club Discussion Group 1984-; *office:* Paramus HS E99 Century Rd Paramus NJ 07652

BARKOVITZ, ROBERT WALTER, Physics Teacher; *b:* Jersey City, NJ; *m:* Jean Lavelle; *c:* Robert, Brian; *ed:* St Peters Coll at Jersey City (BS) Physics 1973; Fordham Univ at New York City (MS) Religion 1979; Post Grad Work in Cnslng Montclair St, Nuclear Sci Penn St, Energy Stevens Inst of Tech & NJ Inst of Tech, & Chem, other NJIT & Univ of AL; *cr:* St Aloysius HS Physics & Math Tchr 1972-75; Secaucus HS Physics & General Sci Tchr 1975-84; Millburn HS Physics Tchr 1984-; *ai:* Sci Project Adv & Mentor; Former Bsktbl Coach; Club Adv; AAPT 1976-; NJ Assn of Physics Tchrs 1988-; Contact Telephone Crisis Hotline 1972-, Dir & Natl Bd Mem, Numerous Achvmt Awds; Pub Svc Electric & Gas Co 1982-, Educl Adv; Manhattan Coll Schl of Engrng Centennial Awd for Outstanding HS Tchr Achvmt; *office:* Millburn HS 462 Millburn Ave Millburn NJ 07041*

BARLETT, ELIZABETH HABECKER, Fifth Grade Teacher; *b:* Philadelphia, PA; *m:* A. Curtis; *c:* J. Scott, Melissa B. Ames; *ed:* DE St Univ (BS) Elem Ed 1979; *cr:* W R Brown Elem Classroom Tchr 1979-; *ai:* CREA 1979-, Bldg Rep; Kent Cty Rdng Assn 1980-; 30 Inservice Hrs; *office:* W. Reily Brown Elem 360 Webbs Ln Dover DE 19904

BARLETT, JOHN REXFORD, Industrial Education Teacher; *b:* Philipsburg, PA; *m:* Peggy Wolford; *c:* John R. II, Rebecca A., Gretchen L., Matthew W.; *ed:* Millersville Univ (BS) Indstrl Arts Ed 1962; PA St Univ 16 Credits; *cr:* Triton Regnl HS IA Tchr 1962-63; E. I. duPont de Nemours Inc Production Planner 1963-68; NJ St Dept of Ed Unit Coord 1969-71; Tyrone Area HS I Ed Tchr 1971-; *ai:* Sr Adv; Sr Exhibition Adv, Evaluator; Tyrone Area Ed Assn 1971, Pops Awd 1985; PA Ed Assn, NEA 1971-; F&AM Lodge 494 1987-; Tyrone Shrine Club 1994-, 2nd VP; *office:* Tyrone Area HS Clay Ave Ext Tyrone PA 16686

BARLETTA, FREDERICK A.,JR., Social Studies Teacher; *b:* Hazleton, PA; *m:* Paula Nemeth; *c:* Shawn, Angela, Matthew; *ed:* East Stroudsburg St Coll (BS) soc Sci 1978; Masters Equiv Cert PA Dept of Ed 1992; 30 Addl Credits; *cr:* West Hazleton Jr Sr HS Soc Stud Tchr, Ath Dir1978-92, Girls Track Coach 1983-92; Hazleton Area HS Soc Stud Tchr, Girls Track 1992-; *ai:* NEA, PSEA 1978-, Bldg Rep; Amer Cancer Br 1994; Men of Malvern Laymans Retreats 1970-, Co-Capt, 25 Yr Awd; Greater Hazleton Historical Soc 1980-86; Wet Hazleton Booster Club 1982-; Sports Columnist, Writer 1982-93; Sports Broadcaster 1985-; Sports Dir, Broadcaster 1995-; *office:* Hazleton Area HS 1601 W 23rd St Hazleton PA 18201

BARLEY, CHARLES F., Teacher; *b:* Pittsburgh, PA; *m:* Nancy Vaslowski; *c:* Eric, Dana, Nicole, Benjamin; *ed:* CA St Coll (BS) Eng Ed 1966; Penn St Univ (MED) 1974; *cr:* West Mifflin Area Schls Tchr 1966-; *ai:* WMFT 1972-, Pres; AFT 1972-; PAFT 1972-, Exec Comm Rep; *office:* West Mifflin Area HS 91 Commonwealth Ave West Mifflin PA 15122*

BARLOWSKI, NANCY MACKIEWICZ, High School Math Teacher; *b:* Bristol, CT; *m:* Thomas P.; *c:* Katrina Lynn, Michael Paul; *ed:* Rivier Coll (BA) Math & Elem Ed 1973; CCSU (MS) Ed 1978, (6th Yr) Ed 1982; *cr:* Memrl Blvd Schl Math & Soc Stud Tchr 1973-80; Bristol Eastern HS Math Tchr 1980-81; Bristol Cntrl HS Math Tchr 1981-; *ai:* BFT 1975-; Prof Ski Instrs of Amer 1983-94; *office:* Bristol Central HS 480 Wolcott St Bristol CT 06786

BARNADA, KURT, Assoc Prof of Modern Languages; *b:* Upper Darby, PA; *ed:* West Chester Univ (BA) Span, Ger 1979; West VA Univ (MA) Frgn Langs 1982; Georgetown Univ (PHD) Linguistics 1986; Phillips Univ at Marburg Germany Diploma; Universidad de Valladolid at Valladolid Spain Diploma; *cr:* West Chester Univ Span, Ger Instr 1986-87; Salisbury St Univ Asst Prof Span 1987-88; Elizabethtown Coll Asst Prof of Modern Lang 1988-95, Assoc Prof of Modern Lang 1995-; *ai:* Intnl Club, Soph Class, Intnl Stu Coord Adv; Fac Rep to Friends of the Coll Lib, Coll Presidential Bd on Diversity; Popular Culture Assn 1990-; HISPANIA 1979-; ACTFL 1986-; Coll Lib Bd 1989-; Kappa Delta Pi 1995-; Sigma Delta Pi, Alpha Mu Gamma 1980-; *office:* Elizabethtown Coll 1 Alpha Dr Elizabethtown PA 17022

BARNEA, ANNE M., English Teacher; *b:* Manchester, NH; *c:* Colin; *ed:* Univ of NH (BA) Eng Tchng 1985; *cr:* Pembroke Acad Eng Tchr 1986-; *ai:* Class of 1997 Adv; NEA, NHATE, NCATE 1986-; *office:* Pembroke Acad 209 Academy Rd Pembroke NH 03275*

BARNEA, RAVID (ORON), Hebrew Teacher; *b:* Ramat Gan, Israel; *m:* Amir; *c:* Liad, Shir-el, Ro-ee; *ed:* 30 Addl Credits; *cr:* Amal Schl at Tel-Aviv 7th-9th Grd Math Tchr 1985-90; Private HS at Tel-Aviv 11th-12th Grd Math Tchr 1986-91; JEI at Pittsburgh Hebrew 6th-12th Grd & Adults 1991-; Yeshiua at Pittsburgh 9th-12th Grd Hebrew Tchr 1992-; *ai:* Kibbuzim Seminar on Math & Physics 1986; Jewish Educl Inst, Hebrew Tchng Seminar; Levinski Seminar for Math Coll Prep for Adults 1991-; *office:* Yeshiua Schls 2100 Wightman St Pittsburgh PA 15217*

BARNES, DAWN COOPER, Asst Prof of Performing Arts; *b:* Nashville, TN; *m:* M. Nathaniel; *c:* Nyema, Julien, Henry, Zwannah; *ed:* Univ of MI at Ann Arbor (BA) Speech & Fr 1978; Hunter Coll (MA) Theater 1979; Univ of MD at Coll Park (PHD) Cinema 1992; *cr:* Fisk Univ Speech Instr 1980-83; Montclair St Coll Adjunct Speech Instr 1984-86; Cty Coll of Morris Adjunct Communication Prof 1984-86; Howard Comm Coll Performing Arts Asst Prof 1988-; *ai:* Aurora Dance Co Artistic Dir; Howard Cable 8 On Location Monthly Prgm Host; Soc for Cinema Stud 1990-, Mem; MD Cncl for Dance 1994-, Bd Mem; MD St Arts Cncl 1994-, Dance Panelist; Howard Cty Arts Cncl 1995-, Advy Cncl; Origin of Afro-Amer Dance Original Video 1983; Notable Black Women Book II Pub Three Entries 1996; *office:* Howard Comm Coll 10901 Little Patuxent Pkwy Columbia MD 21044*

BARNES, DONNA SHALLCROSS, Third Grade Teacher; *b:* Elizabeth, NJ; *m:* Herbert M.; *c:* Stephanie Morecraft, Lawrence, Matthew; *ed:* Newark St Coll (BA) Elem Ed 1961; *cr:* Harding Schl 2nd Grd Tchr 1961-64, 4th Grd Tchr 12 Yrs, 6th Grd Tchr 2 Yrs, 3rd Grd Tchr; *ai:* Suburban Rdng Cncl Bd of Dirs Treas; Math Curr Comm; NEA, NJEA 1980-; IRA 1991-; Suburban Rdng Cncl 1986-, Treas; Kent Place Bd of Trustees; Kent Place Pres Parents Assn; Colony Club of Cranford, Amer Home Chm; Lafayette Parents Assn Bd; Math Articulation Comm; Strategic Planning Comm; TAB Comm; *office:* Harding Schl 426 Boulevard Kenilworth NJ 07033

BARNES, DORIS L., OH His & World Geography Tchr; *b:* Bellaire, OH; *m:* Dale R.; *c:* Gary, Gina, Sharon; *ed:* OH Univ (BS) Elem Ed 1970; 171 Credit Hrs, 12 Credit Hrs Cmptr Sci; *cr:* Fairpoint Schl 4th-5th Grd Elem Tchr 5 Yrs; St Clairsville Schl Dist 4th-6th Grd Elem Tchr 2 Yrs, 7th Grd MS Soc Stud Tchr 15 Yrs; *ai:* NEA, OEA 22 Yrs; SEA 22 Yrs, Sec; Sacred Heart Church Neffs 1950-; *office:* St Clairsville Ave Schls 108 Woodrow Ave Saint Clairsville OH 43950

BARNES, ELCENA O., Coordinator of Gifted Programs; *b:* Sain OH; *m:* Burl E.; *c:* Lesta Barnes Searles, Laurie, Scott, Amy; *ed:* De Coll (BA) Bio Ed 1972; Bowling Green St Univ (MS) Ed & Gifted Addl 6 Hrs Post Grad; *cr:* Paulding Exempted Village Schls Jr HS Life Sci Tchr 1972-90, K-12th Grd Coord of Gifted Prgms 1990-; *ai* Quiz Bowl Adv; Tech Comm Mem; OAGC, COCG, NAG Wassenberg Art Ctr 1990-; Optimist Club 1996-, Charter Outstanding Sci Tchr Dist I 1985; OAGC Conf Presenter Outstanding Tchr Awd Denison Univ 1991; *office:* Paulding Exe Village HS 405 N Water St Paulding OH 45879

BARNES, JENNIFER ANN (IRVING), Mathematics Teach Portland, ME; *m:* Gary M.; *c:* Jessica Rose, Thomas Michael, Whitney; *ed:* Univ of ME at Farmington (BS) Ed 1981; *cr:* Limest Math Tchr 1982-86; Presque Isle HS Math Tchr 1986-; *ai:* Math Tea NCTM 1988-; ATMIM, ATMNE 1995-; Presque Isle Snowmobil 1986-; *office:* Presque Isle HS 16 Fort St Presque Isle ME 04769

BARNES, KATHY HARRIS, English Teacher; *b:* New York, N Ronald M.; *ed:* Tufts Univ (BA) Eng 1967; 27 Credits Eng Boston U Credits Ed Natl Coll of Ed; *cr:* Newton HS Eng Tchr 1968-1973; Ne East HS Eng Tchr 1973-1979; Greenwich HS Eng Tchr 1979-; *ai:* En Learning Facilitator; Adv to Assn for Black Culture; CEA 1979- 1968-; Distinguished Tchr Awd Greenwich Pub Schls; Outstandin Awd Univ of Chicago 2 Yrs; Distinguished Tchr Awd Presidential Sc Comm; *office:* Greenwich HS 10 Hillside Rd Greenwich CT 06830

BARNES, LARRY DANA, Psychology Professor; *b:* Dansville, N Jerianne Louise Miller; *c:* Diana Fox; *ed:* Jamestown Comm Coll Math, Sci 1961; Harpur Coll (BA) Psych 1963; Univ of IA (MA) 1965; Genesee Comm Coll (AAS) Model Making 1992; *cr:* Mohaw Comm Coll Instr 1966-68; Genesee Comm Coll Prof 1968-; *ai:* EPA NEA; Planned Parenthood Rochester & Genesee Vly, Dir; Town of Planning Bd, Chair; 1st Universalist Church of Rochester, Trustee Distngd Svc Awd; *office:* Genesee Comm Coll 1 College Rd Batav 14020

BARNES, LAURA ANN (GLAWE), 4th Grade Teacher; *b:* Lake OH; *m:* Tyrone L.; *ed:* Bowling Green SU (BS) Elem Ed, Spec Ed Baldwin Wallace Coll 6 Credit Hrs; Ashland Univ 11 Credit Hrs; Bo Green SU 3 Credit Hrs; *cr:* Homewood Schl LD Tchr 1974-84, 6 Tchr 1984-85, 4Th Grd Tchr 1985-; *ai:* Toll Collector OH Tu Commission 1981-; NEA, LEA, OEA 1974; *office:* Homewood Eler Goble & Charleston Lorain OH 44055

BARNES, PATRICIA QUINN, Foreign Lang Dept Chair; *b:* Hartfor *m:* Brian A.; *c:* J. Bradford, J. Stoddard; *ed:* Coll of New Rochelle (1965; Boston Coll (MAT) Fr Ed 1967; Univ Laval Cert 1963; Univ d Cert 1964; Univ d'Auignon Cert 1987; *cr:* Glastonbury HS F 1966-67; Naugatuck HS Fr Tchr 1967-71; Holy Cross HS Fr, Spar 1981-; Teikyo Post Univ Asst Prof Fr 1992-; *ai:* Adv La Societe Hon de Francais; Honors Convocation Comm; AATF, COLT, NCEA Women's League of Wtby Symphony 1967-, Pres 1971; Gilbert & Su Troupe of Wtby 1978-, Choreographer; Jr League of Greater Wtby Pres 1981; Distinguished Svc Awd Jaycees 1978; AATF Fellowshi at Avignon 1987; Univ of CT Cooperative Tchr 1988-; *office:* Holy HS 587 Oronoke Rd Waterbury CT 06708

BARNES, SANDRA KNIPES, Mathematics Teacher; *b:* Granville *m:* Richard; *c:* Eric, Kathryn, Ethan; *ed:* SUC at Geneseo (BA) Math 1971; SUNY at Albany (MA) Math & Ed 1972; Attnd Castleton Col of Saint Joseph, Univ of AK Southeast & George Washington Uni Granville Cntrl HS Math Tchr 1972-; *ai:* Math Team Coach; A NYSUT 1972-; GTA 1972-, Bldg Rep, Pres, VP; United Bapt C 1975-, Clerk; *office:* Granville Central HS Quaker St Granville NY

BARNES, SCOTT D., Professor of Bus & Soc Science; *b:* Ric Center, WI; *m:* Saerie Kirshner; *c:* William, Carol; *ed:* Ripon Coll (B 1966; Univ of TN (MACT) Ec 1969; Attnd St Univ of NY, Bradley Univ of OR, Univ of UT; *cr:* Glenville St Coll Instr 1968-70; C Comm Coll Prof 1970-; *ai:* Fac Assn Pres 1977-82, 1986-89, 1992-; H Prgm Co-Dir 1983-87; Outdoor Club Adv 1979-85; NEA, NYNEA St Dir; Industrial Relations Research Assn 1974-; Cay Cty Demo 1988-, Vice Chair; Stu Senate; Excl in Tchng Awd 1994; Excl Awd N 1993; NYS Chancellors Awd Excl in Tchng 1992; Excl in Tchng 1988-89; Auburn Correctional Facility Grad Class Tchng Awd Veterans Club Tchr of Yr 1974; *office:* Cayuga County Comm Coll Fr Street Auburn NY 13021

BARNES, THEODORE A., History Department Chairman; *b:* Wa OH; *m:* Diane Linda Tanner; *c:* Nicholas, Stephanie; *ed:* Bowling Gr Univ (BS) Soc Stud 1968; *cr:* Perrysburg Jr HS 8th Grd Amer His 1968-; *ai:* His Dept Chm; Bsktbl Coach 25 Yrs; Fac Awd & Freedom Cont Coord; PEA Schlsp Comm; NEA, OEA, PEA 1968-; Perrysburg Fnd Outstanding Educator Awd; Martha Holden Jennings Fnd Tchr; O Coaches Hall of Fame; *office:* Perrysburg Jr HS 140 E Indiana Perrysburg OH 43551

BARNES, WILLIAM WARREN, Supervise Academy '98 Coor Roanoke, VA; *c:* William W. Jr., Lisa Summerville; *ed:* Oakwood SDA (BA) Bus Ed 1961; NY Univ (MA) Educl Psych 1972; Barauch Hunter Coll Credit Hrs; Walden Univ Post Grad Stud; *cr:* Farmingdal Bus Ed Tchr 1963-67; IS 136 Career Dev Prgm Coord 1970-78; G Washington HS Stu Opportunity for Advancement & Retention Coord 1985-91, Project Welcome Coord 1991-93, Acad '98 Coord *ai:* Performing Arts Club Dir; Stu, Parents Advy Staff Coord; St Ed GED Prgm Chief Examiner; AFT 1972-; ASCD 1990-, Cert; Tabernacle Church Bd 1984-, Yth Dir, Noteworthy Svc Awd; Out Scndry Edctrs of Amer, Office HS Support Svcs Awds; NYC Bd Outstdng Tchr Awd Nom; *home:* 78 Manhattan Ave #2A New Yor 10025*

BARNETT, GEORGE R.,III, History Teacher & Dept Chm; *b:* Lew PA; *m:* Barbara Alice Perlman; *ed:* Univ of PA (BA) His 1968, (MA 1987, (PHD) His 1991; *cr:* Charles Ellis Schl His Tchr 1969-70; Irwin Schl His Tchr 1970-; *ai:* Debate Club Adv; Amer Historical 1990-.

BARNETT, JERRY LYNN, Fifth Grade Teacher; *b:* Zanesville, O Deborah Kay Bailey; *c:* Brice Christopher, Blaine Edmund; *ed:* Rio G Coll (BS) Elem Ed 1985; Post Grad Work OH Univ; *cr:* Galia Acad HS Sci Tchr 1975-78; Beverly Elem Schl Fifth-Sixth Grd Tchr 197 Waterford Elem Schl Fifth Grd Tchr 1987-; *ai:* Local Spelling Bee C OEA, NEA 1975-; *home:* PO Box 102 Waterford OH 45786*

BARNETT, M. JANE DAVIS, Fourth Grade Teacher; *b:* Cambridge *m:* Jack Lee; *c:* Jacie, Janae, Jacalyn; *ed:* OH Univ (BS) Elem Ed Muskingum Coll (MS) Elem Ed 1994; *cr:* Senecaville Elem Schl 3r Tchr 1969-71; Summerfield Schl 3rd Grd Title I Tchr 197 Shenandoah Elem Schl 4th Grd Tchr 1985-; *ai:* OEA, NEA, CTA 1 *home:* 25936 Molbar Acres Summerfield OH 43788*

BARNETT, ROBERT JAMES, Instrumental Music Director; *b:* Erie *m:* Arlene Farmer; *c:* Ryan James, Alexander Earl; *ed:* Youngstown St (BM) Music, Percussion 1977; Attnd Ashland Univ; *cr:* West Branc Band Dir 1977-; Mt Union Coll Percussion Stud Prof 1985-86; Branch Local Schls Instrumental Music Dept Chm 1989-; Youngst Univ Adjunct Prof of Percussion 1990-91; *ai:* Warrior Marching

›nic Wind Ensemble, Jazz Ensemble, Percussion Ensemble, Pep ›ir; Phi Mu Alpha Sinfonia 1973-, Pres Delta Etz 1976, Del to Nat; Educators Natl Conf 1977-, Dist Honors Band Chm; NEA 1977-; ive Arts Soc 1984-; Youngstown Symphony Orchestra 1980-, le Timpanist; W.D. Packard Concert Band 1985-, Principle ist; Calvary Bapt Church 1992-, Assoc Choir Dir; Freedom Fnd ho's Who Among Stdnts in Amer Univs & Colls 1976-77; Composer signer; *office:* West Branch HS 14277 Main St Beloit OH 44609

EY, DIANE BARTIMOCCIA, Spanish & French Teacher; *b:* town, WV; *m:* William E.; *c:* Amanda, Benjamin, Brooke; *ed:* c St Coll (BA) Arts & Scis 1967; West VA Univ (BA) Span 1969; n Fr 1969, Masters Equivalency in Ed 1994; *cr:* Centerburg Local th Grd Eng, Span, Fr Tchr 1969-75; Knox Cty Voc Ed Eng to Frgn chr 1974-75; Union City Area HS Eng, Span, Fr Tchr 1975-76; Cty Schl Dist Span, Fr Tchr 1988-; *ai:* PA St Ed Assn, NEA, Schl Dist Assn 1988-; PA Modern Lang Assn 1993-; St Elizabeth Guild 1976-, Pres, VP, Sec; *office:* Warren Area HS 345 E 5th Ave PA 16365*

EY, JANICE G., Science Teacher; *b:* Taunton, MA; *m:* Michael G.; theastern MA Univ (BS) Bio 1979; Bridgewater St Coll (MAT) Bio *r:* Morton Hospital Microbiologist 1979-82; Intnl Clinical Labs iology Supvr 1983-85; St Bernards HS Sci Tchr 1985-91, Sci Dept 1991-93; *ai:* Ski Club Adv; Acad Advisory Cncl; Class Adv; Math ampaign Comm; MA Assn of Sci Supvrs & MA Area Sci Tchrs Assn Amer Soc of Clinical Pathologists 1980-; AFT 1986-; Eisenhower ev Comm; Tandy Tech Scholars Outstanding Tchr & Presidential r Excl in Sci Tchng Nom 1991-92; Univ of MA Fellowship 1989; 183 Massachusetts Ave Lunenburg MA 01462*

EY, PAMELA ULERY, English & AP US History Tchr; *b:* Goshen, Daniel G.; *c:* Scott M., Elizabeth O.; *ed:* Butler Univ (BA) Eng & 1964; 45 Post Grad Credit Hrs in Phys, Cultural, Pol, Geog, His & of Writing; *cr:* Seoul Intnl Schl ELS, Eng & His Tchr 1977-79; HS Eng & Soc Stud Tchr 1980-81; Dalevill HS TAG & Eng Tchr 3; Heidelberg HS Eng & Soc Stud Tchr 1984-; *ai:* Womens JV Coach; Lit Magazine Spon; Writing Across the Curr Comm; NEA NCTE 1983-; Episcopal Church 1964-; German-Amer Womens 984-; German-Amer Chorale 1989-; Dept of Defense Dependent chr of the Yr 1990; *office:* Heidelberg American HS Cmr 419 Box PO AE 09102

EY, PAUL EDWARD,JR., Assistant Professor of Biology; *b:* Erie, : Gannon Univ (BS) Biology 1975; Univ of KY (MS) Plant ogy, (PHD) Plant Physiology 1984; Post Doc Kent St Univ 1985-86, Univ 1986-87; *cr:* Pinkerton Tobacco Co Rsrch Scientist 1988; Penn Instr 1989-94; Gannon Univ Asst Prof 1993-; *ai:* Amer Assn for ement of Sci 1995-; Amer Soc of Plant Physiology 1980-; Pi Kappa Fac Adv; *office:* Gannon Univ Dept of Biology University Square 16541

HART, CHERYL KOHLI, Fifth Grade Teacher & Chprsn; *b:* ›re, MD; *m:* Robert E.; *c:* Brooke E.; *ed:* Shippensburg Univ (MS) d 1976; 45 Hrs Beyond Masters at Penn St, Univ of HI & Wilson : Shippensburg Area Schl Dist 4th & 5th Grd Tchr 1970-, Grd Level 1980-, Head Tchr 1983-87; *ai:* Curr Comm; NEA 1970-; NCTM IRA 1993-; *home:* 21 Carla Dr Shippensburg PA 17257

HART, DEBRA L., Third Grade Teacher; *b:* Johnstown, PA; *ed:* Pittsburgh (BS) Elem Ed Sociology 1972; *cr:* Ferndale Area Sch d Grd Tchr 1972-; *ai:* PSEA, NEA 1972-; *office:* Ferndale Area chl 100 Dartmouth Ave Johnstown PA 15905

HART, FRANK H., Mathematics Department Head; *b:* Paterson, Patricia C.; *ed:* Rutgers Coll (BA) Math & Romance Lang 1970; air St Coll (MA) Scndry Schl Admin 1974; Doctoral Prgm in ; *cr:* Garfield HS Math Tchr 1970-80; NJ Dept of Ed Schl Prgm 1980-85; Garfield HS Math Dept Head 1986-; *ai:* Sr Class & Math Soc Adv; Math Team Coach; AFT 1980-, Local VP; NCTM 1970-; ors Tchr Recognition Awd 1986; Garfield Pub Schl Distinguished r 1988; *office:* Garfield HS 500 Palisade Ave Garfield NJ 07026

HART, PATRICIA COLLONS, Spanish Teacher; *b:* New York, ; Frank H.; *ed:* Douglass Coll (BA) Span & Ed 1970; Fairleigh son Univ (MA) Multi-Lingual Tchng 1975; Attnd Montclair St Univ, e Franchise, Bergen Comm Coll; *cr:* East Brook & West Brook Jr n Tchr 1970-71; Park Ridge HS Span Tchr 1991-, Gifted & Talented oord 1980-; *ai:* Future Problem Solving Team Adv; Acad Bowl Adv; NJEA, BCEA, PREA 1970-, Pres, VP, Soc Comm Chair; AATSP Mem Chair; FLENJ 1970-; NJ Governors Tchr Recognition Awd Mid St Steering Comm Chprsn 1991-93; *office:* Park Ridge HS 2 ve Park Ridge NJ 07656

HART, PATRICIA READ, Fourth Grade Teacher; *b:* Baltimore, : Kenneth M.; *c:* Scott Read; *ed:* Towson St Univ (BA) Elem Ed Western MD Coll (MLA) Liberal Arts 1981; Johns Hopkins Univ Counseling, Sign Lang Grad Stud; *cr:* William Winchester Tchr 0; Robert Moton Tchr, Team Ldr 1975-92; Gifted & Talented Prgm , Dir 1981-; Western MD Coll Lecturer, Adjunct Instr 1984-; ship Valley Tchr, Team Ldr 1992-; *ai:* Co-Chair Schl Improvement Lit, Rdng Coord; Soc Stud Curr Comm; Spon: Tchr 1978-, Stamp NEA, MD St, Carroll Co Tchrs Assns 1978-; Delta Kappa Gamma VP; Literacy Cncl 1988-; West United Meth 7 Yrs, Supt Sunday Beta Sigma Phi 1963-72, VP, Who's Who Young Women 1973; Mem Shipley Fnd 1970-, 1st VP, Geneaological Publisher Honor; nding Spon Tchr of Yr St Winner 1990; Nom Co Outstanding Tchr; 3rd Grds Gifted Prgm Author 1981-82; *office:* Friendship Valley Schl 1100 Gist Rd Westminster MD 21157

HART, THOMAS H., Mathematics Dept Chairman; *b:* Tiffin, OH; e Reinman; *c:* Michael, Daniel, Andrea, Matthew; *ed:* Purdue Univ Math 1968, (MAT) Math 1973; NSF Cmptr Sci Inst Bowling Green St 975; *cr:* Calvert HS Math Tchr & Asst Band Dir 1968-69; Nordonia ath Tchr & Asst Band Dir 1969-70; Lima Cntrl Cath HS Math Tchr t Head 1970-; *ai:* Curr Coord; Math Contest Adv; AP Coord; NCTM NCEA 1970-; OH Cncl of Tchr of Math 1980-; Findlay Racing Club 1988-, Race Sec; Natl Pigeon Assn 1985-; BPOE 1984-; nding Young Men of Amer as Aviculturist 1980; Lima Area nding Young Educator 1981; Educator of Month 1990; OH St Univ Campus Lecturer in Math 1981-; Several Articles Pub in Natl Homing Magazines.

ING, BETH MAGOOLAGHAN, Jr High Math & Science Teacher; oklyn, NY; *m:* Steven L.; *c:* Eric; *ed:* SUC at Potsdam (BA) Math SUNY at Stony Brook (MA & LS) Math & Sci Ed 1995; *cr:* Catholic east 6th-8th Grd Math Tchr 1976-77; St Peter & Paul 7th-8th Grd & Sci Tchr 1977-80; St Patricks 6th-8th Grd Math Thcr 1980-83; Jesus 6th-8th Grd Math & Sci Tchr 1985-93; Our Lady of Wisdom h Grd Math & Sci Tchr 1993-; *ai:* Child Stud Comm; NCEA 1986-; Dyslexia Soc 1987-; STANYY 1992-; ASCD 1995-; NCTM 1995-; -St Gerard Majella 1984-; SEPTA 1994-, 2nd VP; *office:* Our Lady sdom Schl 114-116th Myrtle Ave Port Jefferson NY 11777

ISHAW, ROBERT GARY, History Teacher; *b:* Philadelphia, PA; *m:* M. Luck; *c:* Emily; *ed:* Glassboro St Coll (BA) His 1979; Villanova (MA) US His 1988; *cr:* Black H Pike Schls Sub Tchr 1980-81; ngton Twp Schls Tchr 1981-; Gloucester Cty Coll Adjunct Instr 1990-; *ai:* Dist Affirmative Action Comm; Multicultural Club Adv; NEA 1981-; Civil War Soc 1990-; Phi Alpha Theta 1979-; Chews Meth Church 1976-, Sunday Schl Tchr; NJ Governors Tchr Recognition Awd 1988-89; *office:* Washington Township HS 529 Hurtville Crosskeys Rd Sewell NJ 08080*

BARNSHAW, THOMAS J., Algebra Teacher; *b:* Norristown, PA; *m:* Margaret L. DiGiovanni; *c:* Erik, Lisa; *ed:* Villanova U (BS) Soc Stud 1965, (MA) Cnslng 1971; *cr:* Kenned Kenrick Cath HS Tchr, Cnslr & Guid Dir 1965-; *ai:* Girls Tennis Coach; ACT 1970-; Boy Scouts, Vol; Soup Kitchen, Vol; Helped Sr Citizen to Earn HS Diploma; *office:* Kennedy Kenrick Cath HS 250 E Johnson Hwy Norristown PA 19401

BARNUM, KIRK THOMAS, Mathematics Teacher; *b:* Medina, NY; *m:* Cynthia Hilger; *c:* Peter, Karie, Jennifer, Heather; *ed:* SUC at Fredonia (BS) Math 1982; St Univ of NY at Brockport (MS) Scndry Ed 1988; *cr:* Medina HS 9th-12th Grd Math Tchr 1984-94; Victory Chrstn Acad Math Tchr & Asst Admin 1994-; *ai:* Cross Cntry Coach; *office:* Victory Christian Acad PO Box 484 Lockport NY 14095

BARON, BETH, Associate Professor of History; *b:* White Plains, NY; *ed:* Dartmouth Coll (BA) His 1980; Univ of London SOAS (MA) Mid Eastern Stud 1982; UCLA (PHD) His 1988; Ctr for Arabic Stud Abroad Amer Univ in Cairo 1985; *cr:* Franklin & Marshall Coll Visiting Asst Prof 1988-89; City Coll Asst Prof 1989-93, 1994-; Grad Schl & Univ Ctr Doctoral Fac 1995-; *ai:* Intl Fed for Rsrch in Women's His 1990-; Amer Historical Assn 1988-; Mid East Stud Assn 1983-; ACLS Flwshp 1995-; NEH Stipend 1993; Woodrow Wilson Women's Stud Rsrch Grant 1988; *office:* City Univ Of NY City Coll Convent Ave At 138th St New York NY 10031

BARON, CHRISTOPHER JOHN, Seventh Grade Soc Studies Tchr; *b:* New Hartford, NY; *m:* Christine Kowalski; *ed:* SUNY at Cortland (BA) 7-12 Soc STud Grd Tchr 1988; SUNT at Oneonta (MS) Ed 1993; *cr:* Cobleskill-Richmondville CSD Tchr, Coach 1988-; *ai:* Modified Ftbl Coach; HS Track Coach; AFT 1993-; NEA 1988-92; CRTA 1988-; BPO Elks Lodge 2040 1990-, Past Exalted Ruler, Robert M. Bender Mem Awd; *office:* Cobleskill-Richmond Central SD Washington Hts Cobleskill NY 12043

BARON, EDWARD S., English Teacher; *b:* Webster, MA; *m:* Victoria; *c:* Kristen, Adam; *ed:* Eastern CT St Univ (BA) Eng 1971, (MS) Eng 1978; *cr:* Woy Woy HS Eng, His Tchr 1974-76; Killingly HS Eng Tchr 1977-; Norwich Free Acad Performing Arts Dir 1994-; Eastern CT St Univ Part-time Adj Prof Eng 1987-; *ai:* Performing Arts Dir; NEA 1977-; AAUP 1988-; *home:* 359 Wyassup Rd North Stonington CT 06359

BARON, JOHN DAVID, 6th Grade Sci & Soc Stud Tchr; *b:* Willimantic, CT; *m:* Donna Keith; *c:* Jonathon Williams, Benjamin Elhardt; *ed:* Univ of CT (BA) His-Degree with Distinction 1975; Eastern CT St Uni (MS) Elem Ed 1990; Attnd Univ of ME, Dominion of Canada, Inst of Irish Stud at Dublin, Worcester St Coll, Anna Maria & U MA; *cr:* Old Sturbridge Village Lead Tchr 1975-82; Noah Webster Fndtn Dir of Ed 1982-85; Burgess Elem Schl 6th Grd Sci & SS Tchr 1988-; *ai:* SS Textbook & Sci Curr Comms; NEA 1988-; Hebron Historic Properties Comm 1990-, Researcher; *office:* Burgess Elem Schl Burgess Elem Schl Rd Sturbridge MA 01566

BARON, STEVEN HOWARD, Social Science Instructor; *b:* Norristown, PA; *m:* Cynthia Stoner; *c:* Steven, Michael; *ed:* Univ of DE (BA) Psych, Soc 1984; Univ of Southern CA (MA) Sport Psych 1987; Temple Univ (PHD) Psych-Soc Int Grad 1987; Univ of DE (MC) Cnslng Psych 1989; *cr:* Montgomery Co Comm Coll Adj Fac 1992-; The Horsham Clinic Res, Ed Dir 1992-; Dr. David Baron Therapist 1993-; Journal of the Amer Coll of Neuro Psych Assoc Ed 1993-; Gwynedd Mercy Coll Adj Fac 1994-; *ai:* Lenape Vly Soccer Club Head Coach; Psych NHS, Soc NHS 1984-; AAASP 1994-; Lenape Vly Soccer Club 1993-, Exec Bd Mem; Author of 6 Articles; 14 Presentations; Co-Author NIMH RO-3 Grant Rural Hlth Outreach 1994; *office:* Montgomery County Comm Coll 340 Dekalb Pike Blue Bell PA 19422*

BARONE, BARBARA MAGNANE, Vice Principal & 8th Grd Tchr; *b:* Jersey City, NJ; *ed:* Jersey City St Coll (BA) Elem Ed 1974; 30 Credit Hrs Post Grad Courses; *cr:* Saint Paul of the Cross 7th & 8th Grd Tchr 1974-; *ai:* Stu Cncl Moderator; NJ Cath Educator 1974-; Newark Archdeacon Tchr of Yr;Dare Officer Hudson Cty Tchr of Yr; *office:* St Paul Of The Cross Schl 211 Sherman Ave Jersey City NJ 07307

BARONE, GIOSAFATTO ANTONIO, Italian Teacher; *b:* Colledimacine, Italy; *m:* Aileen P.; *c:* Jennifer, Jordan; *ed:* St Univ of NY at New Paltz (BA) Fr 1971, (MS) Ed 1989; *cr:* Orange Cty Govt Soc Caseworker 1975-86; Roy C. Ketcham HS Italian Tchr 1986-; St Univ Italian Instr 1990-; Dutchess Cty Boces ESL Instr 1986-; *ai:* Assessor NHS Applications & Admissions; AFT, Wappingers Tchrs Congress, NYSAFLT 1986-; Circolo Italiano 1970-; Tchr of Yr 1993-94; *office:* Roy C. Ketcham HS 99 Myers Corners Rd Wappingers Falls NY 12590

BARONE, JOANNE FRANK, Secondary Science Teacher; *b:* Buffalo, NY; *ed:* SUNY at Brockport (BS) Hlth, PE 1963, (MS) Hlth, PE 1973; Permanent Cert Bio, Gen Sci 1975; RIT NSF Courses; Paralegal Prgm Genesee Comm Coll; Cornell Univ Indstrl, Labor Relations, OSHA Hazard Trng; *cr:* Pavilion Cntrl Schls PE Tchr 1968-71; East Irondequdit Schls PE Tchr 1965-67; Lancaster Cntrl Schls PE Tchr 1963-65; Pavilion Cntrl Schls PE Tchr, Dept Chair 1974-86, Tchr 1973-; Genesee Comm Coll Adj Prof Bio 1993-; *ai:* Effective Schls Comm; MUSVT 1963-, Local Exec Comm, Chptr Pavilion 1963-; STANYS 1973-; NYSAHPER Cntrl Western Sec 1966-67; Kappa Delta PI 1963-80; Past 4H Asst Achvmt Awd, Cert; Tri-Cty Coaches Assn 1967-69, Pres 1969-70; Local Tchr of Yr 1971; Univ of Rochester Tchng Awd 1987; *home:* 6608 Main Rd Stafford NY 14143*

BARONE, MARGUERITE CURRERI, Spanish & Latin Teacher; *b:* Brooklyn, NY; *m:* John; *c:* Erica; *ed:* C. W. Post Coll of LIU (BA) Span, Scndry Ed 1969; Long Island Univ (MA) Span 1970; Prof Diploma Educl Admin 1986; *cr:* Long Island Univ Tchng Fellow 1969-70; Roslyn HS Span, Latin Tchr 1970-; Roslyn Summer Scndry Schl Prin 1989-90; *ai:* Shared Decision Making Comm; Prins Advy Cncl; Tchr Ctr Policy Bd; NY St Assn of Frgn Lang Tchr 1969-; Nassau Classical Soc 1985-, Sec; Sigma Delta Pi; Holtsville Civic Assn 1978-, Pres; Sachem Schl Dist Comm Ed Advy Cncl 1989-, Vice-Chair; C. W. Post Coll Oral Span Schaewitz Awd; *office:* Roslyn HS Round Hill Rd Roslyn Heights NY 11577

BARONE, MARIAN, Eighth Grade Teacher; *b:* Buffalo, NY; *ed:* St Bonaventure Univ (BA) Jrnlsm 1976; Univ of SC at Columbia (MED) Stu Prsnl Svc & Higher Ed Tchr 1978; *cr:* Mankato St Univ Asst Dir of Stu Act 1977-79; Time Share & Travel Freelance Writer 1980-83; Mount St Joseph Sub Tchr 1984-85; St Joseph Schl 8th Grd Tchr 1985-; *ai:* Yrbk Adv; Safety Patrol; Math Tutoring; NCEA 1985-; Kolbe Cath 1995-, Schl Bd Ed Comm; Numerous Articles Pub; *office:* St Joseph Schl 3275 Main St Buffalo NY 14214

BARONE, ROBERT G., Eng & Creative Writing Tchr; *b:* Batavia, NY; *m:* Linda Mary Trabert; *c:* Kathrin Trabert; *ed:* SUNY at Geneseo (BS) Speech, Drama Ed 1964; Syracuse Univ (MA) Drama 1968; Attnd NY Univ, Northwestern Univ; *cr:* Oswego HS Speech, Drama Tchr 1964-65; Onardago Cntrl Sch Eng Tchr 1967-68; Utica Free Acad Speech, Drama Tchr 1968-90; T. R. Proctor Sr HS Eng, Drama, Writing Tchr 1990-; *ai:* Speech, Debate Adv; Drama Mentor; ACTSO Competition; AFT, NY St Tchr, Utica Tchrs Assn 1968-; Cntrl NY Comm Arts Cncl 1975-, Bd of Dir 1975-78; Utica Players Theatre 1970-, Pres 1994-; 1976 Summer Flwshp Theatre Northwestern Univ; Outstndng Tchr of Drama 1976 Awded by NY St Cncl of Tchrs of Eng 1978; Pub Plays; *home:* 67 Prospect St Utica NY 13501

BARONE, SAMUEL M., Biology Teacher; *b:* Batavia, NY; *m:* Anne Louise Loeffler; *c:* Michael H., Jeffrey S., Daniel J.; *ed:* Gannon Univ (BS) Bio & General Sci 1966; *cr:* Byron-Bergen Cntrl Life Sci & Bio Tchr 1966-; *ai:* AFT 1972-; NYSUT 1972-, Negotiations Chair, Leadership Awd 1989; Bucknell Univ NSF Awd Post Grad 1969; Syracuse Univ NSF Awd Regents Bio 1993; *office:* Byron-Bergen Cntrl Schl 6917 W Bergen Rd Bergen NY 14416

BARONE, STEPHEN NICHOLAS, Health Teacher; *b:* Waterbury, CT; *m:* Hope M. Burgio; *c:* Shaelynn; *ed:* Southern CT St Univ (BS) Scndry Ed & His 1991, (MS) Schl Hlth 1996; *cr:* Watertown HS Hlth Tchr & Substance Abuse Coord 1993-; *ai:* Stdnts Against Doing Drugs, Stu Cncl, Peer Advocate & Mediation Adv; Morale & Curr Comms; Watertown Against Substance Abuse Mem; Project Grad Coord; Watertown Intervention Team; NEA & Watertown Ed Assn 1993-; Amer Red Cross 1991-, Instr; Waterbury Elks Club 1992-; WASA & Drugs Dont Work 1993-; *home:* 21 Deering Ln Waterbury CT 06706*

BAROODY, FRANCES DEGRANDPRE, Mathematics Teacher; *b:* Plattsburgh, NY; *m:* John M.; *c:* David John, Michael George; *ed:* Coll of New Rochelle (BA) Math 1972; SUNY at Plattsburgh 57 Grad Hrs Cnslng, Math; *cr:* Plattsburgh Sr HS 9-12 Grd Math Tchr 1972-; *ai:* Delta Kappa Gamma 1993; NYSUT, AFT 1972-; *office:* Plattsburgh Sr HS Ste 102 1 Clifford Dr Plattsburgh NY 12901

BAROVERO, LYDIA MARIE, Spanish Teacher; *b:* Livingston, NJ; *ed:* Dickinson Coll (BA) Span 1994; *cr:* Mercersburg Acad Span Tchr 1994-; *ai:* Asst Sftbl Coach; Dorm Supv; NAIS 1994-; Hispanic Amer Org 1990-; Penn St Assistantship 1996; *office:* Mercersburg Acad 300 E Seminary St Mercersburg PA 17236

BAROWSKI, RENEE ISABEL, Spanish Teacher; *b:* Lima, Peru; *m:* J. A. Barowski Scruggs; *c:* Erika, Monica, Miguel, Daniel; *ed:* Attnd Montemar at Lima Peru, Escuela Nacional; *cr:* Drafting 1975-78; Chesapeake Chrstn Schl Span Tchr 1990-; *office:* Chesapeake Christian Schools 900 Trimble Rd Joppa MD 21085

BARR, DAVE, 7th Grade Science Teacher; *b:* Gallipolis, OH; *c:* Kaitlynn; *ed:* Urbana Univ (BS) Scndry Ed 1989; *cr:* Mechanicsburg Jr HS Sci Tchr 1989-91; Little Miami HS General Sci Tchr 1991-92; Eastern HS Coll Prep Bio Tchr 1992-95; Wellston Jr HS 7th Grd Sci Tchr 1995-; *ai:* Head Ftbl Coach 1992-; Track Coach 1989-95; Soph Class Adv 1992-93; Curr Comm 1990-95; Wrestling Coach 1992, 1994; NEA, OEA, NSTA 1989-; *home:* 29420 Sanford Davis Rd Langsville OH 45741

BARR, MONA JOYCE, Mathematics Teacher; *b:* New York, NY; *m:* Bruce; *c:* Ryan, Michael; *ed:* Univ of PIttsburgh (BS) Sec Ed, Math 1971; 24 Grad Credits; Loyola Coll 3 Grad Credits; *cr:* Mt Lebanon HS Math Tchr 1971-73; Arlington HS Math Tchr 1975-76; Mc Donough Schl Math Tchr 1980-; *ai:* Comm Svc, Amnesty Intnl Group Adv; MD Cncl Tchrs of Math 1988-; *office:* Mc Donogh Schl Box 380 Owings Mills MD 21117

BARR, MONICA GRAZAN, Music Teacher & Chorus Dir; *b:* Greensburg, PA; *m:* Paul M. Jr.; *c:* Gregory; *ed:* Seton Hill Coll (BM) Piano, Ed 1978; 72 Addl Hrs Ed; *cr:* Sixth St Jr HS Music Tchr, Chorus Dir 1978-87; Norwin MS West Music Tchr, Chorus Dir 1987-; *ai:* 6th, 7th, 8th Grd Chorus Dir; PSEA, NEA, MENC, Westmoreland Cty Music Edctrs Assn 1978-; St Paul's Church 1981-, Liturgical Ministry, Organist; *office:* Norwin MS West 10870 Mockingbird Dr Irwin PA 15642

BARRA, JAMES RICHARD, English Teacher; *b:* Brooklyn, NY; *m:* Alma Arnone; *c:* Jamie, James; *ed:* St Francis Coll (BA) Eng 1967; Stony Brook Univ (MA) Lbrl Arts 1972; Addl 45 Credits; *cr:* Massapequa HS Eng Tchr 30 Yrs; *ai:* NYSUT, AFT 1967-; *office:* Massapequa HS 4925 Merrick Rd Massapequa NY 11758

BARRAN, THOMAS PAUL, Russian Professor; *b:* Warren, OH; *m:* Barbara Caplan; *ed:* Columbia Coll (AB) Eng, Russian 1968; Columbia Univ (MA) Slavic Lang 1975, (PHD) Slavic Lang 1984; *cr:* Inst for Intnl Educ Sr Placement Admin 1984-86; WA Univ Asst Prof 1986-88; Brooklyn Coll Assoc Prof 1988-; *ai:* Fac Adv Russian Amer Cultural Ctr; Curr & Appts, Tech for Modern Langs Comms; AAUP 1995-; MLA, AAASS, AATSEEL 1978-; Mg Ed Soviet & Post Soviet Review; IREX Rsrch Grant 1976-77 USSR; *office:* Brooklyn Coll CUNY Boylan Hall Brooklyn NY 11210

BARRATT, SUSANNAH PATT, History & Social Studies Tchr; *b:* New York, NY; *m:* Gregg Thomas; *c:* Jake, Grant; *ed:* Miami Univ (BA) Pol Sci 1985; Sacred Heart Univ (MAT) Tchng 1990; *cr:* Danbury HS His, Soc Stud Tchr 1990-; *ai:* Former Class Adv 3 Yrs; NEA 1985-; Literacy Vols 1987-; CT Writing Project Mentor; Critical Incident Stress Family Factor Trng; Comm Involvement; Multicultural Mural Recognized by Local Medias, Mayor's Office; *office:* Danbury HS Clapboard Ridge Rd Danbury CT 06811*

BARRECA, MARIA JIMENEZ, 6th Grade Teacher; *b:* Queens, NY; *m:* Roy Vincent; *c:* Gloria Gabrielle; *ed:* Queensborough Comm Coll (AA) Lbrl Arts 1973; Queens Coll (BA) Eng Lit 1976; Adelphi Univ (MA) Elem Ed 1985; *cr:* St Catherine of Sienna 4th Grd Tchr 1977-85; PS 44 6th Grd Tchr 1985-86; PS 27 Agnes Y. Humphrey Schl 4th-6th Grd Tchr 1986-; *ai:* Magic Tchr Arts Connection; Curr Dev Schoolwide Project; UFT 1985-, Chptr Chrpsn; *office:* PS 27 Agnes Y Humphrey 27 Huntington St Brooklyn NY 11231*

BARRELL, TRINA YVETTE (SPARKS), 8th Grd Rdng & Lang Arts Tchr; *b:* Nelsonville, OH; *m:* Michael A.; *c:* Andrew, Nickolas; *ed:* OH Univ (BS) Elem Ed 1990; Cert of K-12 Rdng & Working towards Masters in Schl Cnslng at Univ of Dayton; *cr:* Union Furnace Elem Sch 3rd & 4th Grd Tchr 1991-92; Logan HS 9th-12th Grd Rdng Tchr 1992-95; Logan Hocking MS 8th Grd Rdng Tchr 1992-; *ai:* Adv of MS Newspaper; Head of Lang Arts Team Lhms; Mem of Venture Capitol Grant Comm; Delta Kappa Gamma 1995-; Non-Traditional Stndts at OU Honorary 1988-; NEA; *office:* Logan-Hocking MS 1 Middle Schl Dr Logan OH 43138*

BARRETT, EDWARD JAMES, Science Teacher; *b:* Scranton, PA; *m:* Maria Gonkavich; *c:* Michael, Matthew, Daniel; *ed:* PA St Univ (BS) Ed 1972; Univ of Scranton (MS) Ed & Gen Sci 1976; *cr:* Lakeland Jr-Sr High Sci Tchr 1972-; *ai:* Head Golf & Asst Bsbl Coach; Class & Environmental Sci Club Adv; Stu Tchr Co-Op; SC Modrtr; NEA, PSEA & LEA 1972-; Univ of Scranton Purple Club 1988-; *office:* Lakeland Jr-Sr High RD 1 Jermyn PA 18433

BARRETT, ELIZABETH NANCY ALLEN, Graphic Arts Instructor; *b:* Springfield, VT; *m:* Kim David; *c:* Tamara Starr Matulonis; *ed:* Green Mountain Coll (AS) Graphic Commercial Design 1977; Johnson St Coll Behavioral Sci, Anthropology, Sociology; *cr:* Hurds Offset Printing Commercial Artist 1977-85; VT Graphics Inc Prepress Supvr 1985-92; The Tech Ctr at Springfield Graphic Arts Instr 1992-; *ai:* VICA; Summer Yth, Instr; Tech Comm; Quota Intnl 1992-, VP; GATE 1995-, Mem; Springfield Historical Soc 1994-, Mem; *office:* The Technical Ctr Springfield 303 South St Springfield VT 05156

BARRETT, ESTHER MAE (SCOTT), Special Education Teacher; *b:* Cuba, NY; *m:* Paul R. Desnoyers; *c:* Patrick L. Jr., Paul L., Phillip L., Peter L., Jackline M., Michael R. Desnoyers; *ed:* Brockport Univ (AS) Hum 1969-70; Jamestown Comm Coll (AS) Hum; Alfred Univ (BS) Elem & Spcl Ed; St Bonaventure Univ (MSED) Ed 1993; Portville Cntrl Schl HS

Diploma Math & Sci 1969; *cr:* The Rehabilitation Ctr Direct Child Care Worker 1985-87, Habilitation Specialist 1987-90; Cattaraugus-Allegany Cty BOCES Spcl Ed Tchr Opt 2B 1990-93, Spcl Ed Tchr Opt 4 1993-; *ai:* Spcl Olympics Coach; Bldg Team Level Comm; NYSUT, UBTA 1995-, Treas; Compact for Learning 1993-95, Bldg Team Level; Alcoholics Anonymous 1990-; Interdisciplinary Team Mem Rehab Ctr 1987-89; NYS Cert in 1st-6th Grd, Nursery & Kndgtn 1993 & K-12th Grd Spcl Ed Tchr 1994; Tenure on BOCES Bd 1973; *office:* Cattaraugus-Allegany BOCES 1825 Windfall Rd Olean NY 14760*

BARRETT, ETHLYN, Social Studies Teacher; *b:* Alexandria Jamaica, West India; *c:* Nicole, Shane; *ed:* Mico Tchrs Coll (TT2) Ed, Elem 1070; Western Carolina Univ (BSEd) Ed 1983, (MAEd) Scndry Ed 1984; NYC Bd of Ed In-svc Courses; Grad Ctr Courses; Lehman Coll; *cr:* Morris HS Soc Stud Tchr 1985; DeWitt Clinton HS Soc Stud Tchr 1986-89; W.H. Taft HS Soc Stud Tchr 1990-; *ai:* UFT, AFT, K 1985-; *office:* William Howard Taft HS 240 E 172nd St Bronx NY 10457*

BARRETT, JOANNE L., Middle Grades Teacher; *b:* Castine, ME; *m:* Dennis R. King; *c:* John Beardsley, Christina Beardsley; *ed:* Univ of ME (BS) Ed 1979; Post Grad Coursework in Gifted & Talented Ed; Ind Stud & Coursework on MS Issues & Ed; *cr:* Lamoine Consolidated Schl Kndgtn & 8th Grd Tchr 1979-83; Blue Hill Consolidated Schl 8th Grd Math Tchr 1986-87; Surry Elem Schl 6th-8th Grd Tchr 1987-; *ai:* Coord of Gifted & Talented; Drama Coach; NCTE; Penobscot Historical Soc 1974-, Sec, Pres; Gilbert & Sullivan Soc 1980-, Treas; Blue Hill Soc for Aid to Children 1984-; Maine Album Features in Farmstead Magazine; *home:* HC 80 Box 31 Penobscot ME 04476*

BARRETT, JOHN W., Social Science Professor; *b:* Pittston, PA; *m:* Emily Gargano; *c:* John G. III, Christopher, Erik; *ed:* King's Coll (AB) His, Eng, Scndry Ed 1957; Univ of Detroit (MA) His, Pol Sci 1959; Georgetown Univ (PHD) Intnl Diplomacy 1970; Attnd Syracuse Univ Maxwell Schl of Citizenship & Pub Affairs, Lehigh Univ, Harvard Univ, Univ of PA; *cr:* Marywood Coll Soc Sci Dept Chm 1968-72, 1982-; *ai:* Books, Articles Author; Poems in Several Anthologies; Directory of Amer Scholars; Outstanding Educators of Amer; *office:* Marywood Coll 3200 Adams Ave Scranton PA 18509

BARRETT, JOSEPH CHARLES,JR., English Teacher; *b:* Newark, NJ; *m:* S. Ellen; *c:* Joseph III, Alicia C.; *ed:* Glassboro St Coll (BA) Soc Stud & Eng 1970; *cr:* Lenape HS Eng Tchr 1971-; *ai:* Ftbl & Track Coach; NJEA, NEA 1971-; *office:* Lenape HS Church & Hartford Rds Medford NJ 08055

BARRETT, JUDY TOPETCHER, English Department Chairperson; *b:* Pittsburgh, PA; *m:* Edward; *c:* Matthew, Joel; *ed:* Allegheny Coll (BA) Eng, His 1966; Univ of Pittsburgh (MA) Anthropology 1988; *cr:* Hempfield Schl Dist 7-9 Grd Eng & Soc Stud 1961-67; Neshaminy Schl Dist 9th Grd Eng 1967-68; Ringgold Schl Dist 11th Grd AP Eng II, Anthropology 1978-; *ai:* NEA, PSEA, REA, NCTE, PCTC, WPCTC1978-; Amer Anthropological Assn 1988-; Peter's Creek & Monongahela Historical Society; Classroom Text The Mound Builders; *office:* Ringgold H S RD 4 Box 604 Monongahela PA 15063

BARRETT, KATHLEEN THERESA, Fourth Grade Teacher; *b:* Philadelphia, PA; *ed:* West Chester Univ (BS) Ed 1987; 6 Addl Hrs; 6 Continuing Ed Hrs Immaculata Coll; *cr:* St Philomena Schl Fourth Grd Tchr 1987-; *ai:* Sci Coord; Sacred Heart Church 1995-, Parish Cncl; *home:* 18 Glenwood Cir Clifton Heights PA 19018*

BARRETT, KENNETH BRANDON, Guidance Counselor & Teacher; *b:* Chicago, IL; *m:* LaTonya Musgrove; *ed:* Lincoln Univ (BS) Pub Pol 1989; Loyola Coll (MED) Cnslng 1994; Baltimore City Police Acad 1989-90; *cr:* Regnl Mgmt Inc Rental Agent 1986-88; Baltimore Police Dept Police Ofcr 1989-92; Loyola HS Guid Cnslr & Tchr 1992-; *ai:* Adult Ldr for Peer Ed Pgm; Fraternal Order of Police 1989-; Natl Schl Cnslng Assn 1992-; Amer Cnslng Assn 1992-; Vanguard Justice Soc 1989-; Midtown Baltimore Optimist Club 1993-, Bd of Dir, VP, Pres & Chm of Yth Act; Exemplary Police Officer Awd.*

BARRETT, KENNETH P., Social Studies Teacher; *b:* Jamaica, NY; *m:* Margaret Mary O'Kelly; *c:* Patrick, Mary Banschback, Kathleen Barrett-Snyder, Gabrielle, Timothy; *ed:* St Johns Univ (BS) Scndry Ed 1960, (MS) Amer His 1965; Hofstra Non Western Stud; Lincoln Ctr Inst; *cr:* Lynbrook HS Soc Stud Tchr 1961-; *ai:* Coaching: Jr HS Bsbl & Bsktbl, JV Sftbl & Bsktbl, Var Asst Soccer & Var Sftbl; Lynbrook Tchrs Assn 1961-; NYSTA; AFT; L I Cncl for Soc Stud; Wantagh Little League, Coach; Wantagh Police Ath League, Coach; BSA, Scoutmaster; CYO, Coach; *office:* Lynbrook H S 9 Union Ave Lynbrook NY 11563

BARRETT, NORA M., Assistant Professor; *b:* Paterson, NJ; *m:* Art Baumgarten; *c:* Timothy Baumgarten; *ed:* Syracuse Univ (BS) Psych 1978; NY Univ (MSW) Clinical Soc Work 1984; *cr:* El Centro CMHC Cnslr 1980-82; Mount Carmel Guild CMHC Supvr, Clinical Soc Worker 1984-87, Day Treatment Svcs Coord 1987-92; Montclair St Univ Instr 1990-92; UMDNJ Schl of Hlth Related Professions Psychological Rehabilitation Prgm Asst Prof 1992-; *ai:* Stu Assn of Mental Illness Ed Club Adv; Project Live Bd; Acad Affairs Comm Chprsn; NJPRA 1985-; NASW 1984-; SAHP 1994-; Albrook Parents Assn 1995-, Sec; Outstdng & Dedicated Svc Awd Project Live 1988; Natl Distngd Svc Registry for Med & Voc Rehabilitation 1987; Natl Rehabilitation Assn Achvmt Awd 1986; *office:* Univ of Medicine & Denistry NJ MCC-LH-203 155 Mill Rd Edison NJ 08818

BARRETT, PAUL F., English Instructor; *b:* Lynn, MA; *m:* Priscilla Ann Burt; *c:* Stephen Kevin, Brian Jeffrey, Matthew; *ed:* Salem St Coll (BSE) Eng 1960; Boston Coll (MA) Poly Sci 1970; Civic, Basic Adult Ed Boston St Tchrs Coll; *cr:* Chatham Cntrl Schl System 9th Grd Eng Tchr 1960-61; Lynn Cabbet Jr High 8th-9th Grd Eng, Soc Stud Tchr 1962-82; Adult Basic, Civic Ed Instr 1966-76; Lynn Classical HS 10th-12th Grd Eng Tchr 1983; *ai:* Frosh Class Adv; Peabody MA City Cncl, Councillor 1976-90; *office:* Classical HS 33 N Common St Lynn MA 01902

BARRETT, RICHARD JOSEPH, Automotive Tech Instructor; *b:* New Bedford, MA; *m:* Patricia Nicholson; *ed:* Fitchburg Cert Voc Ed 1969; Natl Inst Automotive Svc Excl (ASE) Cert; *cr:* Chevrolet Dealer Technician 1966-68; Ford Technician 1968-69; New Bedford Voc Instr 1969-77; Gr NB Reg Voc Tech HS Instr 1977-; *ai:* Chprsn; NATEF Cert; Auto Tech Pgm; MVA 1988-; *home:* 15 Hereford Hill Rd Mattapoisett MA 02739

BARRETT, ROBERT T., Assistant Principal; *b:* Scranton, PA; *c:* Laurie, Robert; *ed:* Penn St Univ (BS) Elem Ed 1968; Univ of Scranton (MS) Admin 1973; (MS) Elem Admin; Marywood Coll 51 Addl Credits Beyond Masters; *cr:* North Pocono SD Math Tchr 1969-95, Asst Prin 1995-; *ai:* Stu Cncl, Ski Club Adv; PSEA, NEA 1969-, Pres; Phi Delta Kappa 1973-; Knights of Columbus 1990-, Grand Knight.

BARRETT, ROBERT THOMAS, Health Teacher; *b:* Brigham City, UT; *m:* Patricia A.; *c:* Thomas, Danielle, William, Mark; *ed:* St Univ of NY at Buffalo (BED) 1965, (MED) Hlth 1970; Niagara Univ (SEA) Educl Admin 1976; 60 Grad Credit Hrs Ed; *cr:* Greece Cntrl Schl Dist PE Tchr 1965-66; Cloverbank Elem Schl PE Tchr 1966-70; Frontier Cntrl Sr HS Hlth Tchr 1970-; *ai:* Tchrs Assn Grievance Chm; AFT 1965-; NYEUT 1966-; Frontier Cntrl Tchrs Assn 1966-, Bldg Rep, 25 Yr Awd; Niagara Frontier Tchr to Tchr 1975-, Guest Lecturer; Hamburg Citizens Advy Comm 1981-, Chm; NYS Tchrs Retirement 1985-, Del; St Mary's Home Schl Assn 1981-, Treas; BSA 1980-, Merit Badge Cnslr; Voluntary Drug Ed Prgm; Hamburg Chrstn Bd of Ed; Drug Ed Guest Lecturer; *office:* Frontier Cntrl Sr HS S-4432 Bayview Rd Hamburg NY 14075*

BARRETT, ROSEMARY THERESE, Retired Teacher; *b:* Flushing, NY; *ed:* St Johns (BA) Lang Sp 1948, (MA) Lang Sp 1958; 30 Credits Univ of Puerto Rico 1960; 30 Credits Cath Univ of Puerto Rico 1962; *cr:* Elem Schls Tchr 1935-65; Academia Santa Maria Schl Prin 6 Yrs; Stella Maris HS H D & Sp Tchr 1966-82; Sacred Heart Acad Span Tchr 1982-94.

BARRETT, TIMOTHY R., Instrumental Music Tchr; *b:* Rocky River, OH; *m:* Patricia Anne Mocarski; *c:* Devin Patrick; *ed:* Kent St Univ (BM) Music Ed 1983; Ashland Univ 21 Credit Hrs Towards Educl Admin Degree; *cr:* Akron Pub Schls Orch Dir 1983-88, Orch Dir 1988-; *ai:* Dir for Aurora Youth Orch; OH Music Ed Assn 1983-; Amer String Tchrs 1993-; Above & Beyond Awd; Tchr of Yr Awd Akron PTA.*

BARRETT, YVONNE ATIYEH, Fourth Grade Teacher; *b:* Amar, Syria; *m:* Thomas A.; *c:* Thomas Jr., Tammi Roggeri, Kelly, Michael; *ed:* LCCC (AS) Elem Ed 1984; Kutztown Univ (BS) Elem Ed 1988; 24 Credits; *cr:* Sheridan Elem SED, Paraprof 1973-74, Bi-Lingual Paraprof 1974-79, ESOL Paraprof 1979-87, 4th Prof Tchr 1987-; *ai:* 4th Grd Team Ldr; Sci, Prof Dev, PA New Stans Portfolio Writing Comms; NEA 1987-, Outstdng Tchr Awd 1988; PSEA; AACA 1980-85, Vol, Allentown Human Relations Awd; Pub Booklet, Book: The Arabic-Speaking Student's Culture; *home:* 2323 W Stanley St Allentown PA 18104*

BARRETTS, H. DANIEL, Secondary Business Teacher; *b:* Berwick, PA; *m:* Barbara L. Kishbaugh; *c:* Todd, Tricia, Erica; *ed:* Bloomsburg Univ (BS) Bus Ed 1970; Masters Equivalent Plus 48 Credits; *cr:* Muncy HS Bus Tchr 1970-71; Crestwood HS Bus Tchr 1971-; *ai:* Bus Dept Chprsn 10 Yrs; NEA, PSEA 1970-; CEA 1971-; Ftbl, Cross Cntry & Track-Field Coach 1970-93; *office:* Crestwood HS 281 S Mountain Blvd Mountain Top PA 18707

BARRICELLI, JANE ELLEN LYNCH, English Teacher; *b:* Flushing, NY; *m:* Anthony Louis; *c:* Thomas Charles, Daniel Anthony; *ed:* St Peter's Coll (BA) Eng Lit 1977; Queens Coll (MA) Eng Lit 1987; Doctoral Candidate in Eng Prgm at Grad Center of CUNY; *cr:* Liberty Mutual Insurance Co Claims Adjustor 1977-78; St Francis Prep Eng Tchr 1978-81; URS Engineering Firm Proofreader 1981-82; St Francis Prep Eng Tchr 1982-; *ai:* Asian Club & Stdnts for Soc Awareness Moderator; NEA, NCEA 1983-; 1 of 50 Tchrs Chosen to Attend Month Long Seminar on World Lit at Sarah Lawrence 1984; Received Grant to Attend Seminar at Oxford on Britain Today 1985; *office:* Saint Francis Prep 6100 Francis Lewis Blvd Fresh Meadows NY 11365

BARRICK, MARGARET, English Teacher; *b:* St Peter, MN; *m:* Joseph A.; *c:* Michael, Matthew, Miriam; *ed:* Bemidji St Univ (BS) Eng 1970; Roosevelt Univ (MA) Educl Supervision, Admin 1984; *cr:* Grand Rapids HS Long Term Sub 1970-73; Wetherfield HS Lang Arts Tchr 1975-77; Glenbard North HS Eng Tchr 1978-86; Mechanicsburg HS Eng Tchr 1987-; *ai:* Natl Honor Soc Adv; NEA; PSEA; AAUW; PEO 1988-, Chaplain, Church Cncl 1988-92, VP, Chrstn Ed 1988-91, Chprsn; Svc to Stdnts Awd.*

BARRICK, MICHAEL PATRICK, Physics Tchr & Sci Dept Head; *b:* Waltersburg, PA; *m:* Barbara Hubany; *ed:* CA St Univ of PA (BS) Physics & Math 1963; Ohio St Univ (MA) Sci Ed 1968; Addl Hrs at Cuyahoga Comm Coll in Aviation & Cmptr Sci; *cr:* Valley Forge HS Physics Tchr & Sci Dept Head 1963-; Cuyahoga Comm Coll Instr Eng Tech 1968-78, Instr Aviation Tech 1978-83; *ai:* Astronomy Club; Educl TV, Cmptr Curr & Hardware & to Review Methods of Establishing Class Rank Comms; Ohio Acad of Sci 1963-, VP Ed Sect, Fellow; Amer Assn Physic Tchrs 1963-; Intnl Planetarium Soc 1980-; City of Willoughby Aviation Comm; Jennings Scholar Master Tchr Awd; Articles on Physics Tchrs & Private Pilot; Unpublished Cmptr Software; *office:* Valley Forge HS 9999 Independence Blvd Cleveland OH 44130

BARRINGER, JOHN H., English Teacher; *b:* Brooklyn, NY; *m:* Linda R. Frigard; *c:* Janis, Sara, Evan; *ed:* Assumption Coll (BA) Ec 1965, (MAT) Eng 1967; *cr:* Auburn HS Eng Tchr 1967-; *ai:* Amnesty Intnl & Floor Hockey IM Adv; NEA 1967-; Quabbin Regnl Schl Comm 1974-92, Chm 1985-92; Auburn High Tchr of Yr 1993-94; *office:* Auburn HS 99 Auburn St Auburn MA 01501*

BARRON, CAROL N., 5th Grade Teacher; *b:* Charleroi, PA; *c:* Corey J.; *ed:* CA Univ (BS) Elem Ed 1967; 24 Credits Post Grad at Penn St Univ 1967-69; *cr:* Sunrise Elem Schl 2nd Grd Tchr 1967-74, 4th Grd Tchr 1975-80; McCullough Elem Schl 5th Grd Tchr 1981-; *ai:* NEA 1967-; PSEA 1967-; *home:* 252 Mount Vernon Dr Export PA 15632

BARRON, CAROL TALBOT, Assoc Prof of English; *b:* New Rochelle, NY; *ed:* Univ of MA (BA) Eng 1968, (MED) Eng Ed 1983, (DED) Eng Ed 1987; *cr:* Mohawk Trl Regnl HS Eng Tchr 1971-87; Western New England Coll Eng Prof 1987-89; Northern Essex Comm Coll Eng Prof 1989-; *ai:* NEA, MTA 1970-; Nisod Excl Awd 1995; Pride in Performance, Nom, Cert 1995; NEH Grant Yale 1994; Yrbk Dedication Mohawk Trl 1980; Grad Speaker Mohawk Trl 1987; *office:* Northern Essex Comm Coll 100 Elliott Way Haverhill MA 01830

BARRON, CAROLE JANE, English Dept Chprsn & Tchr; *b:* Worcester, MA; *c:* Mary O'Rordan, James, Kevin, Kerry Desz, Patricia O'Sullivan; *ed:* Coll of Mt St Vicent (BA) Eng 1957; Adelphi Univ (MS) Ed 1979; Attnd NY Inst of Tech, St John's Univ; *cr:* Warwick HS Eng Tchr 1957-72; Sewonhoka HS Dist Eng, Rdng Tchr 1975-82; Maria Regina HS Rdng Supvr 1982-84; Queensborough CC Eng Instr 1985-; St Mary's HS Eng Tchr 1986-; *ai:* Moderator Schl Lit Magazine; NATE 1984-; Pub Several Short Stories; *office:* St Mary's HS 51 Clapham Ave Manhasset NY 11030

BARRON, GARY EDWARD, Science Teacher; *b:* Phoenixville, PA; *m:* Susan Doebling; *ed:* West Chester St Coll (BS) Scndry Ed, Gen Sci, Earth & Space Sci 1976; West Chester Univ (MA) Scndry Ed, Sci Geology & Astronomy 1990; Philadelphia Coll of Textiles Sci (MS) Instrl Tech 1994; *cr:* Devereux Schl Sci Tchr 1976-78; St Gabriels Hall Sci Tchr 1980-83; Phoenixville Area HS Marine Sci & Ecology Tchr, Sci, Math & Comp Lab Coord 1983-; *ai:* Head Wrestling Coach 9 Yrs; Envirothon Adv; Dist Tech & Sci Curr Comms; NSTA 1977-; NEA & PSTA 1980-; Natl Wrestling Coaches 1982-; Presenter at PA Sci Tchr Assoc Convention 1994, NY Sci Tchr Convention 1995, Natl Sci Tchr Convention 1996.*

BARRON, ROBERT REID,JR., Band Director; *b:* Elkins Park, PA; *m:* Donna Lee Coleman; *c:* Lindsay Marie; *ed:* West Chester Univ (BS) Music Ed 1977, (MM) Music 1987; *cr:* Upper Moreland Schl Dist Elem Instrumental Music Tchr 1977-88, HS Instrumental Music Tchr 1988-; *ai:* Concert, Marching, Jazz Bands; Brass Choir; Small Group Ensembles; Pit Orch for All Schl Musicals; Indoor Guard; Scheduling Comm; NEA, PMEA, MENC 1977-; *office:* Upper Moreland HS 3000 Terwood Rd Willow Grove PA 19090

BARROWS, DORIS JEAN, Middle School Teacher; *b:* Kingston, NY; *m:* Gerald Leland; *c:* Kenneth, Dennis; *ed:* Cortland St Tchrs Coll (BS) Elem Ed 1960; Bachelors Plus 20 Hrs; *cr:* Niagara Wheatfield Dist 2nd Grd Tchr 1960-63; Newfane MS Tchr 1975-; *ai:* Lib, Bldg Liaison & Master Scheduling Comms; Schl Store Coord; *home:* 5128 Ridge Rd Lockport NY 14094

BARROWS, MARY E. (KLEMETTI), Physics & Math Professor; *b:* Gardner, MA; *c:* Michael W. Mc Carthy, Kathleen Gale, Thomas J.; *ed:* Fitchburg St Coll (BS) Scndry Ed, Physics 1972, (MS) Sci Ed 1978; 3 Credit Hrs Digital Circuits Mt Wachusett Comm Coll 1979; *cr:* Holy Family HS Sci, Math Tchr 1972-78; Quinsigamond Comm Coll Phyics, Math Prof 1980-; *ai:* Womens Ctr Advy, Writing Across the Curr AAPT 1981-; NSTA 1982-; NEA, MTA, MCCC, QCC 1980-, Lo VP 6 Yrs; Fitchburg BPW 1980-85; Amer Legion Auxiliary 1975- Quinsigamond Comm Coll 670 W Boylston St Worcester MA 016

BARROWS, ROBERT THOMAS, Amer His & Govt Tchr & C Lackawanna, NY; *m:* Theresa Marie Coughlin; *c:* Susan, Patrick, T Teresa, Mary Kathleen; *ed:* Canisius Coll (BS) Eng, His 1955, (M His 1962; 90 Addl Hrs Canisius, Univ of Buffalo; *cr:* Timon H Coach 1955-60; Orchars Park Cntrl Schl Tchr, Var Bsbl Coach 19 Var Bsbl Coach 35 Yrs; Var Club Adv; Timer for Ftbl, Boys, Girls Wrestling, Soccer; Wellness Comm; AFT, NEA, OPTA 1960-; Coach of Yr 1984, 1988; NY St coach of Yr 1992; Natl Coach of Yr 1993; Bishop Timon HS Comm Svc Awd 1990; ECIC Dirs Awd 1 Boys, Girls Club Man of Yr 1995; Post of Fame Recipient 199 Offenhamer Awd 1993.

BARRY, ANN MARIE SEWARD, Communication Professor; *b:* MA; *m:* David F.; *ed:* Salem St Coll (BS) Ed, Eng, (MA) Eng 1979; Univ (MS) Mass Comm 1983, (PHD) Perceptual Aesthetics Comparative Rel Harvard Univ; Alternative Dispute Resolution M Courts; Natl Cncl of Better Bus Bureaus; *cr:* Marblehead Pub Schls Tchr 1978-82; Boston Coll Asst Prof 1984-89, Assoc Prof with 1989; *ai:* IVLA; AEJMC; CAM; MAMP; BAESP; Phi Kappa Phi MA Assn of Mediation Prgms, Bd of Dirs 1992-93; Salem & Mediation Prgm, Bd of Dirs 1990-93; Intnl Visual Literacy Assn Dirs 1988-94, 1995-, VP 1994-95; Golden Key NHS Hnr Fac Mem Natl Broadcasting Co & Carnegie Fdn for Advancement of Tchr Natl Tchrs Awd 1989; Salem St Coll Gold Key Awd for Excl in Who's Who Among Stdnts in Amer Univs & Colls; Books: The Adv Portfolio 1992, The Mediation Reference Manual 1991, Visual Inte 1996; *office:* Boston Coll Dept of Communication Lyons Hall 215 C Hill MA 02167

BARRY, DEBORAH J., 5th Grade Classroom Teacher; *b:* Hutc KS; *m:* Timothy Mark; *c:* Heidi Sharp, Heather Sharp, Rebecca; *e* of IL (BA) Elem Ed 1977; Portland St Univ 30 Credits; Westfield 6 Credits; Fitchburg St Univ 3 Credits; *cr:* Danville IL Pub Schls Tchr 1977-82; Tigard OR Pub Schls TAG & 4th Grd Tchr 1983- Longmeadow Pub Schls 5th Grd Tchr & Prof Dev Coord 1989-; *ai:* Cncl Mem; Jr Great Books Afterschool Pgm Ldr; MTA & NEA Happy Hilltop Preschool 1986-88, Sec; Christa MacAuliffe Recipient Invention Convention in Washington DC 1986; Byrom El Schl of Excl 1987; Tigard Pub Schls Appreciation Awd 1988; St Gifted & Talented Grant 1996; *office:* East Longmeadow Pub Sc Mapleshade Ave East Longmeadow MA 01028*

BARRY, ELAINE SULLIVAN, Third Grade Teacher; *b:* Boston, Joseph Jr.; *c:* Joseph III, Richard S.; *ed:* Boston St Coll (BS) Elem E *cr:* Myles Standish Schl Kndgtn Tchr 1960-64; St Gregory Schl Tchr 1981-; *ai:* Primary Level, Schl Show Coord; AFT 1981-; Pari 1992-94; *office:* St Gregory Grammar Schl 2214 Dorchest Dorchester MA 02124

BARRY, RONALD, Assistant Principal; *b:* Brooklyn, NY; *m:* Glennan; *c:* Christopher, Anne Millard, Katherine, Susan; *ed:* Hol Coll (BS) Ed 1956; T C Columbia Univ (MA) Eng 1957; 60 Cre Attnd Adelphi, C W Post, Hofstra, NYU, Syracuse; *cr:* Syosset HS Jrnlsm Tchr 1957-68, Admin Asst 1969-70, Asst Prin 197 Extra-Curricular Act Admin Supvr; AFT & NASSP 1970-; CAS 1970-; ASCD 1985-; Newspaper Fund Flwshp Grant; Former Empire Scholastic Press Assn; Articles Pub; *office:* Syosset Cntrl S 70 S Woods Rd Syosset NY 11791

BARRY, SHARON (SCHLOSSER), English Teacher; *b:* Mott, Richard O. Jr.; *c:* Richard III, Kevin, Caitlin; *ed:* Coll of St Benedi Eng, Scndry Ed 1969; Bridgewater St Coll (MAT) Tchng, Eng 19 Wareham Intermediate Schl Rdng & Lang Arts Tchr 1969-71; Pad Presch Tchr & Admin 1973-83; Dartmouth HS Eng Tchr 1983-; *a* Class Adv; Lit Mag Adv; NEA, MA Tchrs Assn, Dartmouth Ed Assn, MCTE 1984-; *office:* Dartmouth H S 366 Slocum Rd Dartmouth MA 02747

BARRY-SUTHERLAND, JEAN, 4th Grd Tchr & Asst Prin; *b:* Sto MA; *m:* Thomas Sutherland; *ed:* Boston St Coll (BS) Elem Ed (MED) Ed Admin 1978; Course Work Centered in Areas of Spec Apply to Inclusion Prgm & Supervision; *cr:* Gleason Elem Schl Classroom Tchr 1969-70; W C Wait Elem Schl 2nd-5th Grd Cla Tchr 1970-81; L L Dame Elem Schl 4th- 6th Grd Tchr & Asst Prin *ai:* Schl Improvement Cncl; NEA 1974-; MTA 1969-, Sec; Assn fo & Curr Dev 1992-; Selected to Participate in Inclusion Model for M Pub Schl 1993; Recipient of Travel Grant to Japan Awded by Ja Lang Schl Parents, Konwakai & Consul Gen of Japan 1989; Safety with Med P D on Local Cable Station Lt Dichiara 1988; *office:* Lori Elem Schl 80 George St Medford MA 02155

BARSZCZ, EDWARD L., Mathematics Teacher; *b:* Niagara Falls, Christine; *c:* Aleta, Jennifer, Jennessa; *ed:* Buffalo St (BS) Math Ed WV Univ (MA) Math Ed 1969; 60 Grad Hrs in Math Ed Univ of B *cr:* Iroquois Cntrl Tchr 1968-72; Ed Research Inst Evaluation Sp 1973-74; Iroquois Cntrl Tchr 1974-; *ai:* Team Ldr; Math Counts Co Magic Ring Adv; NYSUT 1994-; Intl Brotherhood of Magicians 19 of Dirs; *office:* Iroquois MS Girdle Rd Elma NY 14059

BARTA, DANIEL STEPHEN, Music Professor; *b:* Cleveland, C Peggy Marcouiller; *c:* Jessica, Jonathan; *ed:* Temple Univ (BM) Composition 1984, (MM) Music, Composition 1988; Moody Bib Diploma Music, Piano 1975; *cr:* Temple Univ Adj Fac 1987-91; Phi of Bible Adj Fac 1991-94, Asst Prof 1994-; *ai:* Soph Class Adv; Coll Soc 1996; Phila Chrstn Flwshp 1981-, Elder; Commissions; Pub *office:* Philadelphia Coll Of Bible 200 Manor Ave Langhorne PA 1

BARTA, MARGARET BENDER, Occupational Child Care In Coranado, CA; *m:* George E.; *c:* Lorrie Sue, Travis Blair; *ed:* Poto Coll Assoc Home Ec 1971; West VA Univ Bachelor Home Ec, Resources 1973; Penn St Working on MS Voc Ed Admin; *cr:* Somer Vo Tech Culinary Arts Tchr 1975-91, Occupational Child Care Instr *ai:* Vica Club Adv; SAP Team; PSEA 1974-; VICA 1985-; Home Ec Head Start, Policy cncl; Honary Chptr Farmer; *office:* Somerset C Voc-Tech Sch Rd 5 VO Tech Rd Somerset PA 15501

BARTA, NANCY LAUB, First Grade Teacher; *b:* Newark, NJ; *m:* S.; *c:* Jodie, Jennifer; *ed:* Trenton St Coll (BA) Kndgtn, Primary 19 St Cloud Elem Schl Transitional 1st, 1st Grd Tchr 1969-73; Pleasa Elem Schl 1st-2nd Grd Tchr 1973-; *ai:* Career Day Comm; Amer Ed NJEA, NEA, WOE Assn 1969-; Natl Cncl Jewish Women 19860 Essex OTA 1993-; Pleasantdale PTA 1973-; *office:* Pleasantdale Ele 555 Pleasant Valley Way West Orange NJ 07052

BARTEK, TIMOTHY ALLEN, Industrial Electricity Instr; *b:* Al PA; *m:* Dorothy Marie Wirfel; *c:* Kaitlyn, Kelsey; *ed:* PA St Univ Voc Ed 1995; Attnd IN Univ of PA; *cr:* Greater Johnstown Area Vo Schl Sub Tchr 1989-92; IN Cty Area Voc Tech Schl Sub Tchr 19 Altoona Area Voc Tech Schl Indstrl Electricity Instr 1993-; *ai:* Voc Clubs of Amer Adv; NEA, PA St Ed Assn 1993-; Altoona Voc Tech Rep Cncl; Alpha Delta Lambda 1989-; Amer Familyn Insts Gift of Tribute Awd 1994; *office:* Altoona Area Voc Tech Schl 1500 4t Altoona PA 16601*

ELS, MICHAEL STANLEY, Seventh & Eighth Grade Teacher; *b:* ville, OH; *m:* Janet Kennedy; *c:* Michael, Jacqueline; *ed:* OH Univ em Ed 1978; Univ of Dayton (MS) Admin & Supervision 1983; *cr:* Local Schl Dist 1st, & 3rd-7th Grd Tchr 1978-; *ai:* OH Ed Assn & 978-; *office:* Belmont Schl Union Local Schl Dist 3rd St Belmont '18

ER, DEBORAH ANNE (LYTTLE), Fourth Grade Teacher; *b:* , MA; *c:* Robert, John; *ed:* Framingham St Coll (BS) Elem Ed 1963; dge Coll (MS) Integrated Stud 1994; *cr:* Sudbury Pub Schls Tchr 5; Marlborough Pub Schls Chptr I Parent Schl Facilitator 1980-82, 982-; *ai:* NEA 1982-; MA Tchrs Assn 1982-; Marlborough Tchrs 982-; *office:* Bigelow Schl 57 Orchard St Marlborough MA 01752

H, DENNIS, Baseball & Basketball Coach; *b:* Camden, NJ; *ed:* VA (BA) Ec, Acctng 1985; *cr:* Joseph W. Barth & Co Accountant *ai:* Head Bsbl Coach 1994-95; Head Bsktbl Coach 1995-; Tri Cty hamps; Enrolled Agent 1992-; Natl HS Bsbl Coaches Assn 1994-, Coaching; *office:* Gloucester Catholic HS 333 Ridgeway St ster City NJ 08030

HEL, RICHARD LAWRENCE, Mathematics Teacher; *b:* on, NY; *c:* Richard Jr., Kim Serfis, Michael; *ed:* SUNY at New Paltz Math Ed 1965, (MS) Math Ed 1969; *cr:* Saugerties Jr Sr HS Math 965-67; Onteora HS Math Tchr 1967-; SUNY at New Paltz Part-time g Math Tchr 1978; Ulster Cty Comm Coll Part-time Evening Math 996-; *ai:* Golf, Ski Coach; AFT, NYSUT 1965-; AMTNYS 1970-; 967- Dist Cncl; SUNY at New Paltz Alumnae Assn 1987-; Outstdng wd Univ of Chicago; SUNY at New Paltz Ath Hall of Fame; Math nm 1973-75; *office:* Onteora HS Rt 28 Boiceville NY 12412

HELMES, RONALD ALAN, Math & Hnrs Geometry Tchr; *b:* Erie, Bonnie; *c:* Tim; *ed:* Edinboro Univ (BS) Math 1971; 27 Post Grad *r:* Gridley Jr HS Tchr 1971-72; McDowell HS Tchr 1972-73; vell Intermediate HS Tchr 1974-; *ai:* Bowling Coach; Millcreek Ed 971-, Bldg Rep; PSAT 1971-; NEA 1971-; *office:* Mc Dowell ediate HS 3320 Caughey Rd Erie PA 16506

HLOW, CHERYL WORTHINGTON, Director of Curriculum; *b:* , OH; *m:* Thomas E.; *ed:* Univ of Dayton (MS) Elem, Rdng 1988; f Dayton Supvr Cert 1994, Prin Cert 1996; The OH St Univ ABD ate Candiate, Tchr Ed, Stat & Rsrch 1991-; *cr:* Ada Exempted Schls Spec Ed DH 1978-80, Grd 2 1981-92; The OH St Univ Ed 1992-93; Ada Exempted Village Schls Grd 3 1993-94; Hardin Co Svc Ctr Dir of Curr 1994-; *ai:* Chrldng Adv; Var Textbook Selection s; Grd Level Chprsn; NEA, AEA 1978-94, Bldg Rep; Phi Delta 1993-; Octela 1990-; Order of Eastern Star 1989-; Tchng Asst OH r; 1st Mentor Tchr; *office:* Hardin Co Educl Svc Ctr One Courthouse 50 Kenton OH 43326*

HLOW, ROBERT LEE, Adj Professor of Psych & Ed; *b:* Reading, Doris June Guske; *c:* Thomas Evan, Deanna Lynn; *ed:* Kutztown St Coll (BS) SOc Stud 1958; Ball St Univ (MA) Cnslng 1962; IN Univ Higher Ed 1965; *cr:* IN Univ Admissions Ofcr, Ed Instr 1966-68; d Comm Coll Dean Gen Stud, Psych Instr 1968-69; Frostburg St rad Stud Dir 1969-71; Lehigh Carbon Comm Coll VP 1971-82, Pres 2, Adj Prof 1992-; *ai:* Phi Delta Kappa 1962-; PA Commission for Colls, Pres 1987-88; PA Assn Colls, Univs, Exec Comm 1987-92; Vly Comm Action Comm, Bd of Dirs 1987-90; PA Ben Franklin ship, Advy Comm 1989-92; Lehigh Cty Cooperative Extension Pres 1994-; Kutztown Univ Distngd Alumni 1991; *office:* Lehigh Comm Coll 4525 Education Park Dr Schnecksville PA 18078

HOLD, JENNY R., English Dept Chair; *b:* Toledo, OH; *c:* Stephen, , Lydia Hankins; *ed:* Vassar Coll (BA) Eng 1961; *cr:* Maumee Vly ng Tchr 1966-; *ai:* Winterim; SCAP; Lit Magazine; *office:* Maumee ountry Day Schl 1715 S Reynolds Rd Toledo OH 43614

HOLOMEW, DEBORA KLOCK, Elem Music Tchr & Choir Dir; acuse, NY; *m:* Donald; *c:* Nicholas, Kristen, Gina; *ed:* Onon Comm AAS) Music 1975; Syracuse Univ (BA) Music Ed 1977; Ithaca Coll rs of Music) Music Ed 1983; Orff-Schulwork Level 3 Cert from a Univ; *cr:* Minetto Elem Schl Gen Music Tchr & Chorus Dir 1977-; FT 1977-; NYSUT 1977-; NYSSMA 1977-; *office:* Minetto Elem ranby Rd Oswego NY 13126

HOLOMEW, JAMES CRAIG, Mathematics Teacher; *b:* Warren, Brenda Lucile Graves; *c:* Michael J., Emily M., Sarah N.; *ed:* AZ v (BA) Scndry Ed-Math 1985; 3 Semester Hrs Cooperative Learning, ester Hrs NCTM Standards; *cr:* Taylor Jr HS Math Tchr 1987; ZAMA HS Math Tchr 1987-; *ai:* NCTM 1992-; Fed Ed Assn 1987-; *home:* sg Cm Box 2301 APO AP 96338

LUCCI, ROBERT, Physical Education Teacher; *b:* New York, NY; herine Ghioni; *c:* Michelle, Lauren; *ed:* Queens Coll (BA) Hlth & 76, (MS) Hlth & PE 1979; *cr:* United Nations Intnl Schl PE Tchr 5 & 1991-; *ai:* MS Girls Vlybl, MS Boys Track & Var Boys Track , *office:* United Nations Intl Schl 24-50 E River Dr New York NY

IMOLE, CARMELLA COLANGELO, Bereavement Coordinator; by, CT; *m:* John Ernest; *c:* Jennifer M., Christine A., Francesca T.; acred Heart Univ (AS) Secretarial Sci 1975, (BS) Eng 1978; St enture Univ (MSEd) Comm Cnslng 1987; *cr:* Parent Ed Prgm Parent 1986-87; Jamestown Comm Coll Cnslr, Tchr 1987-90, 1993; St enture Univ Adj Tchr 1987-94; Comstock Hospice Care Network vement Coord 1993-; *ai:* The Rehabilitation Ctr Human Rights, s Appeal Comms; Western NY Aids Prgm Vol; Amer Cnslng Assn Natl Hospice Org 1995-; PTA 1995-; Outstdng Young Women of 1978; Who's Who Among Amer Coll & Univ Stdnts 1978; Outstdng nt Awd St Bonaventure Univ 1987; Pub Books: Preventing Missing en, Teenage Alcoholism and Substance Abuse, Protect Your Child, Miracles.

IMUS, JO ANN, Teacher of Talented & Gifted; *b:* Wheeling, WV; chael J.; *c:* Michele, Janelle; *ed:* OH Univ (BS) Ed 1969; Attnd WV Rio Grande Univ, Ashland Univ; Grad Work at OH Univ; *cr:* sville Cty Schls Tchr Grd 5, 6 1968-70; Wood Co Schls Music, Soc Tchr Grd 5, 6 1970-72; Belpre Cty Schls Tchr Grd 6, TAG Grd 3-8, holars 1973-; *ai:* OH Univ Governor's Scholars Soc, MS Newspaper HS Drama Play Troupe Dir; Bldg Ldrshp Team Mem; Chrprsn Budget Venture Capital Fund; NEA, OEA 1968-; SEoEA, Bepre Educ Assn Sec; Delta Kappa Gamma 1989-, Sec; OAGC; Belpre Band Boosters Sec, Treas; Belpre Choir Boosters 1992-, Sec; Belpre Bicentennial e 1988-90; Acad Excl Recognition Org 1987-, Treas; Parents-Friends G 1977-, Pres; Martha Holden Jennings Scholar, Grant; World Who's of Women 12th Ed; Intnl Woman of Yr 1992; OH Univ Governor's rs Recruiter Awd; OH Historical Soc Awd Bicentennial Musical; 802 Boulevard Dr Belpre OH 45714

KO, PAUL A., Business Education Teacher; *b:* Shamokin, PA; *m:* Ann Breck; *c:* Heather Ann; *ed:* Bloomsburg Univ (BS) Bus Ed & nting 1970, (MED) Bus Ed 1976; Penn St Univ Cmptr Sci Credits; S Army Specialist & Military Intelligence 1970-72; Mount Carmel HS Tchr 1972-; *ai:* Bus Club Co-Adv; Former Var Bsktbl Coach; & NEA 1972-; NBEA; Army Commendation Medal; Shamokin News n the Spotlight; *office:* Mount Carmel Area Jr-Sr HS W 5th St Mount l PA 17851

BARTLETT, H. THOMAS, Biology Teacher; *b:* Washington, DC; *m:* Paula M.; *c:* Laura; *ed:* Heidelberg Coll (BA) Interdepartmental Stud 1974; Univ of Toledo (BS) Bio, Ed 1991; Bowling Green St Univ Scndry Ed Cert; *cr:* Clyde Jr HS Life Sci, Cmptr Tchr 1976-92; Tiffin Columbian HS bio Tchr, Sci Dept Chair 1992-; *ai:* Planetarium Dir; Environmental Club Adv; Sci Course of Stud, Stu Motivation Comms; NEA, OEA 1976-; CGSEA 1976-, Pres 1985-86; TEA 1992-; Expanded Horizons in Learning 1989-, Bd 1990-92; Black Swamp Bird Observatory 1994-, Bd 1994-; Nature Conservancy 1978-, Bd 1979-91, Oak Leaf Awd 1985; Inland Bird Banding Assn 1973-, Bd 1988-91, Treas 1991-; OH Biological Survey 1994-, Advy Bd; Daisy Sticksel Conservation Awd 1995; Presidential Excl Sci, Math Tchng Awd 1983, 1994; OH Tchr Forum 1986; Meritorious Svc Awd 1985; Eagle Scout Awd 1966; 24 Articles Pub; Co-Author Book: Birds of Seneca County 1989; *home:* 1833 S Winfield Dr Tiffin OH 44883*

BARTLETTA, FRANK X.,JR., Guidance Counselor; *b:* Hoboken, NJ; *m:* Geraldine; *c:* Lance, Frank III, Jamie Lynn; *ed:* Jersey City St Coll (BA) Eng 1970, (MA) Guidance 1975; Cert Prin, Supvr 1986; 9 Credit Hrs Univ of Bridgeport; *cr:* Secaucus HS Eng Tchr 1970-74, Guidance Cnslr 1975-; Hudson Cty Adult HS Asst Prin 1986-; *ai:* Schlsp Chm, Selection Comms; Var Sftbl Coach 19 Yrs; Var Ftbl Coach 5 Yrs; NEA, NJEA 1970-; SEA 1970-, Treas 1988; Hudson Cty Personnel 1970-; *office:* Secaucus HS Mill Ridge Rd Secaucus NJ 07094

BARTLEY, EUGENE ANTHONY, Instrumental Music Director; *b:* Westfield, MA; *m:* Susan Shaffer; *c:* Anthony J., Lisa M., Carrie G. Dirats; *ed:* Lowell St Coll (BMED) Music Ed 1968; *cr:* Westfield Pub Schls 5th-12th Grd Instrumental, Choral Music Tchr 1968-; *ai:* Dir Extra-curricular Jazz Prgm; Mem, Chair Curr, Scheduling, DisciplineComms; NEA, MTA, MENC, MMEA 1968-; Amer Fed Musicians 1963-; Citizens Schlsp Fund 1969-71; Church Comms; Guest Conductor MA Dist Music Festivals; Founder Westfield All-City Jazz Festival; Conductor Westfield MS Schl Gold Medal Winning Jazz Band; Guest Clinician; Westfield St Coll Stu Tchr Practioner; *home:* 90 Valley View Dr Suffield CT 06078

BARTLEY, RUSTY, Sixth Grade Teacher; *b:* Springfield, OH; *m:* Robin; *c:* Greg, Meghan; *ed:* Heidelberg Coll (BA) Elem Ed 1976; Univ of Dayton (MS) Interdisciplinary Stud 1980; Math Pentathlon Inst; Windown 1995 Trng; *cr:* Bethel Local Schls 6-8 Grd Tchr 1976-78; Troy City Schls 5th-6th Grd Tchr 1978-; *ai:* Washington DC, Gettysburg PA 6th Grd Field Trips Schl, Dist Coord; Troy Tech Team; NEA, OEA, WOEA 1978-; TCEA 1978-, Bldg Rep; Troy Jr Bsbl Inc 1991-, League Rep, Sec; Troy Chamber of Commerce Ec Ed Awd; *office:* Concord Elem Schl 3145 State Route 718 Troy OH 45373

BARTO, DAVID MONROE, English Teacher; *b:* Reading, PA; *ed:* Grove City Coll (BA) Eng 1972; Trenton St Coll (MED) Eng Ed, (MA) Eng 1988; *cr:* Pennsbury Schl Dist Eng Tchr 1972-; *ai:* Soccer Coach; Living Lit, His Performances; PEA, PSEA, NEA 1975-; His of Myself at Walden, Henry DAvid Thoreau Educl Videotape Producer; Natl Endowment for Hum Fellow 1984; Roland Robbins Merit Achvmt Awd 1992; *office:* Medill Bair HS 608 S Olds Blvd Fairless Hills PA 19030

BARTOE, JAMES FRANKLIN, Electronics Teacher; *b:* Newark, OH; *m:* Sharon K. Donaghue; *c:* Malanie Perry, James Jr., Elaine Bruck; *ed:* OH St Univ (BA) Ed 1983; *cr:* US Navy Chief Warrant Ofcr 1954-76; Licking Cty Joint Voc Schl Tchr 1978-; *ai:* IM Sports Boys Coord; NRA 1995-; Vlg of Buckeye Lake Mayor; Vlg of St Louisville Police Ofcr; *home:* 236 Union Ave Buckeye Lake OH 43008

BARTOLET, CHARLES ELSWORTH,JR., 8th Grade History Teacher; *b:* Harrisburg, PA; *m:* Rita M. Roseman; *ed:* Moravian Coll (BA) His 1960; Lehigh Univ (MA) Ed 1966; 24 Credits Scndry Schl Prin Cert; *cr:* Saucon Vly MS-Sr HS 10-12 Grd His Tchr 1960-79, Asst Prin Jr HS 1979-90, MS His Tchr 1990-; *ai:* Former Head Wrestling, Asst Ftbl Coach; NEA, PSEA 1960-; Int Lions Club 1974-, Pres; *home:* 2515 Black River Rd Bethlehem PA 18015*

BARTOLOTTA, ARDELL MATHEWS, Third Grade Teacher; *b:* Rutland, VT; *m:* Joseph; *c:* Bret, Brian; *ed:* Southern CT St Coll (BS) Elem Ed 1965; 5th Yr Elem Ed 1974; *cr:* Mathewson Schl Fourth Grd Tchr 1965-70; St Michael's Schl Third Grd Tchr 1984-86; Our Lady of Victory Schl Third Grd Tchr 1986-; *ai:* Rainbows for All God's Children Coord; Yrbk, Stu Lectors Adv; *home:* 159 Hilltop Ln West Haven CT 06516

BARTOLOTTA, BRUCE BENJAMIN, Social Studies Teacher; *b:* Hudson, NY; *m:* Hilary Jaeger; *c:* Lucy; *ed:* Columbia-Greene CC (AA) Criminal Justice 1977; Marist Coll (BS) Criminal Justice 1979; Coll of St Rose (MA) His, Pol Sci 1988; 36 Grad Credits; *cr:* Germantown HS Soc Stud Tchr 1982-; Russell Sage Coll Adj His Lecturer 1992-93; Jr Coll of Albany Adj His Lecturer 1992-93; *ai:* Stu Cncl Adv; Heterogeneous Grouping, Grievance Comms; Union Rep; Pub Relations Chair; NY St United Tchrs 1988-, Local Pres 2 Terms; Fulbright Alumnus Assn 1994-; Jaycees 1977-85, Local Pres 3 Terms; Lions Club 1983-93, Local Pres 1 Term, Treas 2 Terms; Fulbright Schlsp Svendborg Denmark Gymnasium Lecturer 1993-94; Articles Pub; *office:* Germantown Central Schl 123 Main St Germantown NY 12526*

BARTOLOTTI, MARGARET BEUERLEIN, Social Studies Teacher; *b:* Dansville, NY; *m:* Frank A.; *ed:* D'Youville Coll (BA) His 1967; SUNY at Brockport (MS) Soc Stud Ed 1972; 60 Addl Grad Hrs; *cr:* Our Lady of Good Counsel 7th-8th Grd Tchr 1967-69; St Stanislaw Schls- Diocese of Rochester 7th-8th Grd Tchr 1967-69; Spry MS SS Tchr 1969-; *ai:* Stu Govt Adv; NY St United Tchr, AFT 1969-; Phi Delta Kappa 1983-; Roch Area Cncl for Soc Stud 1994-, Bd Mem; NYSCSS, NCSS 1969-; Webster Tchrs Assn 1969-, 2nd VP, Pol Action Chair; PAC Dir for 53rd, NY Senate Dist NYSUT-1; Kappa Gamma Phi 1967-; TAFT Fellow 1976; *office:* Spry MS 119 South Ave Webster NY 14580

BARTOLOTTI, MICHAEL JOSEPH, MS Physical Education Tchr; *b:* Buffalo, NY; *m:* Kim Marie Schwarzmueller; *ed:* Frostburg St Univ (BS) Hlth & PE 1989; St Univ of NY at Fredonia Working on Masters in Ed; *cr:* Northampton MS Hlth & PE Tchr 1 Yr; Lake Shore MS Hlth & PE Tchr 5 Yrs; *ai:* JV Ftbl & Var Bsbl Coach 5 Yrs; NYSUT 1991-; *office:* Lake Shore MS 8855 Erie Rd Angola NY 14006

BARTOLUCCI, JEAN SOPPELSA, Social Studies Teacher; *b:* Cleveland, OH; *c:* Anthony, Michael, Walter; *ed:* OH St Univ (BS) Ed 1976; Attend Baldwin Wallace Coll Grad Schl; *cr:* Polaris Career Ctr Soc Stud Tchr 1976-82; Parma HS Soc Stud Tchr 1991-95; Valley Forge HS Soc Stud Tchr 1995-; *ai:* Acad Team Adv; PEA, NEA, OEA 1991-.

BARTON, JAY S., Instrumental Music Instructor; *b:* Milford, CT; *m:* Katrina Stahl; *c:* Nicole, Krista, Joseph; *ed:* IN Univ of PA (BS) Music Ed 1983; Mansfield Univ of PA 30 Credits Masters Music Ed; *cr:* Mingo Cty K-6th Gen Music Tchr 1983-86; North Penn Jr Sr HS Instrumental Music Tchr & Band Dir 1986-; *ai:* Marching Band; MENC 1983-; PSEA 1986-.

BARTON, JOHN CHARLES, English Teacher; *b:* Allentown, PA; *m:* Mary Kay Eversberg; *c:* Chad, Matt; *ed:* WV Univ (BS) Ed 1987; CA Univ of PA Ed Admin; *cr:* Northern Bedford Cty HS Eng Tchr 1988-90; Waynesburg Cntrl HS Eng Tchr 1990-; *ai:* NEA 1988-; NCTE 1986-; PSFCA 1988-; *office:* Waynesburg Central HS Central Greene Schl Dist Waynesburg PA 15370

BARTON, KELLY J., English Teacher; *b:* East Stroudsburg, PA; *m:* Thomas E.; *ed:* PA St Univ (BSEd) Scndry Ed 1990; Cabrini Coll (MS) Ed 1994; *cr:* Lionville Jr HS Eng Tchr 1990-; *ai:* Spelling Bee, Intensive Scheduling, strategic Planning Comms; Fac Forum; Track coach 5 Yrs; Stu Assistance Prgm; NEA 1990-, Bldg Rep; St Agnes Roman Cath Church 1993-; *office:* Lionville Jr HS 50 Devon Dr Downingtown PA 19335*

BARTON, MARCELLA BIRO, History Professor; *b:* Cleveland, OH; *c:* Louis, Patricia; *ed:* Univ of CA (BA) His 1970; Univ of Akron (MA) His 1973; Univ of Chicago (PHD) His 1981; Harvard Univ His of Sci; *cr:* Univ of Rio Grande Prof 1980-; *ai:* Grad Ed Cncl; OH Acad of His 1980-, Pres 1996; Phi Alpha Theta 1973-, Fac Adv; Gallipolis Dev Ctr Bd 1985-, Pres; Rotary Intnl 1993-, Bd of Dirs, Outstdng Performance; Edwin A. Jones Excl in Tchng Awd 1986; Hnrs Excl in Tchng Awd 1992-93; *office:* Univ Of Rio Grande Coll of Liberal Arts Rio Grande OH 45674

BARTON, ROGER E., United States History Instr; *b:* Newark, NJ; *m:* Taia Felder; *ed:* Hampton Univ (BS) His Soc Sci Ed 1992; Grad Stud MA Seeking Curr Specialist Bowie St Univ; *cr:* Hampton Univ Tchrs Asst, C-UPS 1990-92; NJ Inst of Tech Tchng Asst, Cnslr 1991-92; Prince George's Cty Pub Schls US His Instr 1992-; P G Cty Schls Adult Basic Ed Pre-GED Instr 1994-95; *ai:* Stu Govt Adv; Asst Umoja Coord; Homework Club Tutor; Equity Assurance Comm; NEA 1992-, Bldg Rep; PGCEA 1992-; Phi Beta Sigma 1990-, VP, Sec, DP; Brothers of 1-5-1 Inc 1989-, Historian, DP; *home:* 12975 Claxton Dr Laurel MD 20708*

BARTON, SCOTT A., Business Education Teacher; *b:* York, PA; *m:* Peggy Yearsley; *c:* Nate, Chris, Jessica, Jackie, Julie; *ed:* Grove City Coll (BA) Bus Ed 1977; Clarion Univ 18 Credits; Indiana Univ of PA 6 Credits; Millersville Univ 8 Credits; *cr:* North Clarion HS Tchr 1979-84; Santa Fe HS Tchr 1984-85; Leganon HS Tchr 1986-88; Lower Dauphin HS Tchr 1988-; *ai:* Boys Bsktbl, Boys & Girls Track Head Coach; Fellowship of Chrstn Aths Adv; NEA 1994-; High on Kids 1992-, Event Coord; *office:* Lower Dauphin Sr HS 291 E Main St Hummelstown PA 17036*

BARTON, WALTER,JR., Mathematics Teacher; *b:* Jersey City, NJ; *ed:* NY Univ (BS) Math 1964, (MA) 1966; Addl 49 Credits; Sups Cert; Span & ESL Cert; *cr:* Union Hill HS Math Tchr 1964-94; Bergen Comm Coll Adjunct Prof of Math 1984-; *ai:* NJEA, NEA 1964-; Union City Ed Assn 1964-, Former VP, Recording Sec; *office:* Bergen Community College 400 Paramus Rd Dept of Natural Sci & Math Paramus NJ 07087

BARTON, WILLIAM THOMAS,III, English Teacher; *b:* Philadelphia, PA; *m:* Alice Hinton; *c:* William, Virginia Anne Eccles, Brian John; *ed:* West Chester Univ (BS) Eng 1962; Temple Univ (MS) Instrl Design 1981; Univ of MD (PHD) Policy, Planning, Admin 1991; 49 Credit Hrs Eng Rutgers St Univ; *cr:* Passaic Vly Regnl HS Eng, Drama Tchr 1962-64; John F. Kennedy Meml HS Eng, Speech, Drama Tchr 1964-66; Old Bridge Twp Pub Schls Eng, Speech, Drama Tchr 1966-72; Middlesex Comm Coll Adj Fac 1966-72; Pvt Industry Curr Writer, Trainer 1972-80; Prince George Pub Schls Eng, Drama, Tv Tchr 1980-; *ai:* Drama; Photography; Researching Via Internet; AFT 1982-; *office:* Friendly HS 10000 Allentown Rd Fort Washington MD 20744*

BARTON-WILLIS, PAULA ANN, Biology & Chemistry Teacher; *b:* Montgomery, AL; *m:* Joe W.; *c:* Barton; *ed:* LA St Univ (BS) Horticultural Sci, Botany 1979; Univ of CA at Riverside (PHD) Plant Pathology 1984; *cr:* Univ of CA Rsrch Asst 1979-84; KS St Univ Post Doctoral Rsrch Assoc 1984-86; Life Ctr Acad Bio, Chem Tchr 1992-; *ai:* Sci Fair Coord; Sci Bowl Team, Asst Girl's Sftbl Coach; Abundant Life Chrstn Flwshp 1987-, Co-Head Evangelism Dept; Co-Recipient of USDA Rsrch Grant; Articles Pub; *office:* Life Ctr Acad 2045 Burlington Columbus Burlington NJ 08016

BARTOS, JOANNA H., Russian Teacher; *b:* Binghamton, NY; *m:* Lewis J.; *c:* Carrie, Stephen; *ed:* Harpur Coll (BA) Russian Lang, Lit 1967; SUNY Binghamton (MA) Comparative Lit, Russian, Eng 1974; Attnd Middlebury Coll 1969; 30 Addl Hrs; *cr:* Vestal Sr HS Russian, Eng Tchr 1967-69, Eng Tchr 1969-83, Eng II Chm 1974-85, Russian, Eng Tchr 1983-85, Russian Tchr 1985-; *ai:* Russian Club Adv; Presidential Exch Coord; NEA, NEA-NY, Vestal TA 1967-; ACTR, AATSEEL 1983-; Binghamton Borovichi Sister City 1988-, Bd of Dirs 1988-92; Broome-Tioga Tchrs Ctr Bd 1987-91; NCTE Outstdng Tchr 1982; *office:* Vestal Sr HS 205 Woodlawn Dr Vestal NY 13850

BARTOS, LARRY MARK, Speech & English Teacher; *b:* Youngstown, OH; *m:* Barbara J.; *c:* William, Andrew; *ed:* OH St Univ (BS) Eng, Speech 1972; Kent St Univ (MA) Speech, Ed 1977; *cr:* Poland Seminary HS Speech, Eng Tchr 1972-; Youngstown St Univ Speech Limited Svc Tchr 1991-; *ai:* Natl Forensic 1973-84, Diamond Coach; OH HS Speech League 1973-84, St Comm; Sallie Mae Tchr Tribute Awd Newsweek; Poland Ed Assn Outstdng Edctr Awd 1994; *office:* Poland Seminary HS 3199 Dobbins Rd Youngstown OH 44514*

BARTOSZ, JOHN, Teacher; *b:* Stevens Point, WI; *ed:* Stanford (BA) Classics 1967; Harvard (MA) Ed 1969; Quinnipiac (JD) Law 1980; US Power Squadron; *cr:* New Canaan HS Tchr 1968-69; US Army SFC 1969-70; West Haven HS Tchr 1971-; *ai:* Hnrs Comm; Hockey, Adv Ski Club Coach; Amer Bar Assn, CT Bar Assn 1980-; AFT; CSFT; AARP 1990-; AWSA 1962-; AAA 1960-; Cherokee Archives of Amer; *office:* West Haven HS Circle St West Haven CT 06516*

BARTRAM, LINDA CLARK, Third Grade Teacher; *b:* Huntington, WV; *m:* Ronald Eugene; *c:* Bianca Ann; *ed:* Morehead St Univ (BA) Elem Ed 1983; Working Towards Master's Degree; *cr:* Symmes Vly Multi-Level Schl Third Grd Tchr 13 Yrs; *ai:* NEA 1983-; Pace Gifted Prgm 1995-; Wal-Mart Children Miracle Network on TV 1991-; PE Book Pub; 2 Specs on Local TV; *office:* Symmes Vly Multi-Level Schl 14860 St Rt 141 Willow Wood OH 45696

BARTSCH, NANCY J., Mathematics, Computer Sci Tchr; *b:* Ossining, NY; *c:* R. J., Heather, Jamie; *ed:* SUNY at New Paltz (BS) Math Ed 1967; Union Coll (MS) Math Ed 1972; Working Towards MS Cmptr Sci SUNY at Albany 1988-; *cr:* Greater Amsterdam Schl Dist HS Math Tchr 1967-85, Cmptr Sci Tchr, Dist Cmptr Specialist 1985-90, Math, Cmptr Sci Tchr 1990-; *ai:* Teach Cmptr Related Inservice Courses; AFT 1967-; NY Assn for Cmptrs, Techs in Ed 1985-; CYO Girls Bsktbl 1985-, Asst Coach; Town of Florida Yth League 1985-, Sftbl Coach; Greater Capital Region Tchr Ctr, Cmptr Courses Tchr; *office:* Amsterdam HS Saratoga Ave Amsterdam NY 12010*

BARTSCH, STEPHEN LEONARD, Science Teacher; *b:* Fall River, MA; *m:* Darcy Braatz; *ed:* Plymouth St Coll (BA) Bio 1986; De Paul Univ (MED) Curr Dev 1992; 45 Credits Podiatric Med Dr. William Scholl Coll of Podiatric Med; *cr:* Univ of IL Rrsch Specialist 1987-91; Hanna Sacks HS Sci Tchr 1992; Conval HS Sci Tchr 1992-; *ai:* Asst Var Ftbl Coach; Hlth Occupations Comm Chair; NSTA 1990-; NEA 1992-; Sci Assn for Persons with Disabilities 1995-; Access Excl Fellow 1995; Marine Awarness Rsrch Expedition 1993; Robert L. Boyd Bio Awd Plymouth St Coll 1986; *office:* South Meadow Schl Rt 202 N Peterborough NH 03458

BARTZ, MARY ALICE, Kindergarten Teacher; *b:* Scranton, PA; *m:* David F.; *c:* Kenley Bartz Stewart, Courtenay; *ed:* Marywood Coll (BA) Elem Ed 1976; 36 Addl Hrs; Masters Equil +57 Grad Credits; *cr:* Our Lady of Peace Schl First Grd Tchr 1979; Local Day Care Ctr 1976-79; St Gregtorys' Kndgtn Tchr 1979-83; Abington Heights Schl Dist Kndgtn Tchr 1983-; *ai:* Sci Curr, Report Card Comms; NEA, PSEA, AHEA 1983-; Waverly Comm House 1984-; Sant' Andrea Soc 1979-; *home:* PO Box 191 Waverly PA 18471

BARUGEL, ALBERTO, Professor of Modern Languages; *b:* Tangier, Morocco; *m:* Marla Joy Rosenfeld; *c:* Avidor, Michael; *ed:* Queens Coll CUNY (BA) Span, Fr 1974, (MA) Span 1976; City Univ of NY (PHD) Span

1987; Coll of New Rochelle Scndry Ed 1981; *cr:* Queens Coll CUNY Adj Span Lecturer 1975-76; Rye Cty Day Schl Span, Fr Instr 1977-85; Rutgers Univ Span Lecturer 1986-92; Jersey City St Coll Chprsn, Asst Prof 1992-; *ai:* Sigma Delta Pi Adv; Gen Stud Comm; AFT 1992-; MLA 1988-; AAVP 1987-; Amer Sephardi Fed 1987-; Best Cmptr Software of Yr Awd 1983; Book: The Sacrafice of Isaac in Spanish and Sephardic Balladry 1990; Articles Pub; *office:* Jersey City St Coll 2039 Kennedy Boulevard Jersey City NJ 07305

BARVINCHACK, M. A. ROMAN, Business Education Teacher; *b:* Binghamton, NY; *m:* Mary Ann Barges; *c:* Shane, Shawn, Shannon, Shelly; *ed:* Shippensburg Univ (BS) Bus Ed 1968, (MS) Ed 1972; *cr:* Williamsport HS Bus Tchr 1968-69; Clear Spring HS Bus Tchr & Diversified Occupations 1969-; *ai:* Instructional Tech Advy Comm; Schl Improvement Team; SADD, Prom Promise, Bible Club Advs; NEA, MSXEA 1968-; Delta Pi Epsilon 1968-, 7th Mem Beta Lambda Chptr Shippensburg Univ; Wa Cty Tchrs Assn 1968-; Natl Speleological Soc 1988-; Appalachain Trail Conf 20 Yrs; BSA 30 Yrs; *office:* Clear Spring HS 12630 Broadfording Rd Clear Spring MD 21722

BARZAK, JOYCE E., Fifth Grade Teacher; *b:* Warren, OH; *m:* Donald L. II; *c:* Doanld J., Stephen, Christopher; *ed:* Kent St Univ (BA) Ed 1973; Attnd Coll of Mt St Joseph; *cr:* Maplewood East 2nd Grd Tchr 1978-80, 5th Grd Tchr 1980-; *ai:* Stu Cncl Adv; Girls IM Coach; NEOTA 1978-; MEA 1978-; OEA 1978-; TARC 1980-; Johnston UM Church 1975-; Johnston Civic Club 1985-, Treas; Johnston Homecoming 1986-, Queen Chm; Martha Jennings Holden Scholar; Ashland Golden Apple Achiever Awd 1991 & 1993; WFMJ-TV Class Act Awd 1993; Trumbull Cty Career Dev Grant; *office:* Maplewood East Elem Schl 4174 Greenville Rd Cortland OH 44410*

BASALIK, SUSAN ESPOSITO, Elementary Music Teacher; *b:* Philadelphia, PA; *m:* Kenneth J.; *c:* Benjamin K.; *ed:* Temple Univ (BM) Music Ed 1981, (MM) Music Ed 1987; 10 Addl Credits Post Grad Stud Music & Cmptr Ed, Musical Performance Practices, Suzuki Cello Tchr Trng Levels 1A-5; *cr:* Methacton Schl Dist Elem Music Tchr 1981-; *ai:* Elem Schl Orchs, Hnrs Orch Dir; AFT 1988-; MENC, Natl Schl Orch Assn 1978-; Amer String Tchrs Assn, Suzuki Assn of the Amers 1989-; North Penn Symphony Orch 1986-, Advanced Cello Stud Schlsps 1991-94; Numerous Articles Pub; Philadelphai Orch Educl Advy Cncl 1991-93; Presentation for Grad Class Philadelphia Orch, Univ of the Arts 1993; *home:* 324 Colonial Ave Collegeville PA 19426

BASANAVAGE, SANDRA STARR, Elementary Math Teacher; *b:* Lewistown, PA; *m:* Vincent; *ed:* Muhlenberg Coll (AB) Psych 1970; 68 Post Grad Hrs with an Emphasis on Elem Math; *cr:* Fallsington Elem 3rd Grd Tchr 1970-71; Fairless View Elem 2nd Grd Tchr 1971-77; Quarry Hill Elem 2nd Grd Tchr 1977-84; Village Park Elem 2nd Grd Math Tchr 1984-91; Eleanor Roosevelt Elem Math Tchr 1991-95; *ai:* Comm: Math, Grouping Rsrch & Demonstration Renew; NEA 1970-; NCTM 1994-; Nom for the Presidential Awd for Excl in Math Tchng 1992; Math Ed Trust Awd 1993; *home:* 977 Weber Dr Yardley PA 19067*

BASCIANO, ANTHONY NORMAN, HS Guidance Counselor; *b:* Latrobe, PA; *m:* Sherry Ann Neese; *c:* Matthew, Kristin, Luke; *ed:* IN Univ of PA (BS) Ed 1966, (MED) Cnslng 1971; 60 Credits Post Grad Stud; *cr:* US Military Lieutenant Platton Ldr 1967-69; Derry Area Schl Dist Soc Stud Tchr 1969-90, HS Guid Cnslr 1990-; *ai:* HS Var Bsbl Coach; NEA, PSEA, DAEA 1969-; PA Schl Coun Assn, Westmoreland Schl Coun Assn 1990-; Westmoreland Cty Coaches Assn 1980-; BPO Elks 1985-; *office:* Derry Area HS Rd 1 Box 169 Derry PA 15627

BASDEN, LOIS R., Social Studies & History Tchr; *b:* Orchard Park, NY; *w:* Harold O. (dec); *ed:* Univ of Buffalo (BA) Sociology, Anthropology, Ed 1955; NY Univ Retailing; Columbia Univ Tchrs Coll Ed; *cr:* Erie Cty Dept of Welfare Caseworker; Studio Boutique Self-employed Designer, Fashion Coord, Dressmaker; Bloomingdale's Exec Trng Asst Buyer; Vogue-Butterick Patterns Ed Counter Catalog; Harlem USA Museum Curator; PS 123 Manhattan Soc Stud, Afro-Amer His Tchr 1966-; *ai:* UFT 1966-; *home:* 70 W 95th St Apt 27D New York NY 10025

BASH, DEBORAH FISCHER, High School Mathematics Tchr; *b:* New York City, NY; *m:* Jeffrey P.; *c:* Katherine M., Mary E.; *ed:* Fordham Univ (BA) Math 1970; New York Univ (MS) Math 1972; CUNY at Staten Island (MS) Cmptr Sci 1986; *cr:* JHS 65 Math Tchr 1970-72; Hillcrest HS Math Tchr 1972-74; Jamaica HS Math Tchr 1974-81; Tottenville HS Math Tchr 1981-; *office:* Tottenville HS 100 Luten Ave Staten Island NY 10312

BASHAAR, PATRICIA LEIGHTON, Mathematics Teacher; *b:* Philadelphia, PA; *m:* Matthew Robert; *c:* Christopher Rosser, Rebecca Jordan; *ed:* Shippensburg Univ (BSEd) Math Ed 1989; *cr:* Plymouth Whitemarsh HS Math Tchr 1991-; *ai:* Class of 1996 Co-Spon; NEA, PSEA 1992-; *office:* Plymouth-Whitemarsh HS Germantown Pike Plymouth Meet PA 19462*

BASHER, KATHLEEN, Retired French Teacher; *b:* Lancaster, NY; *ed:* Nazareth Coll (BA) Fr 1961; Middlebury Coll (MA) Fr 1969; Attnd Sorbonne Paris, Univ of Dijon France, Anger France, Avignon France, Bordogne & ALSACE; *cr:* West Seneca Schls Fr Tchr 1961-, Dept Chair 1988-; *ai:* Fr Club Adv 1961-93; AFT, NYSATFL, WSTA 1961-; AATF 1961-, Summer Schlsp; AAUW 1988-; Tchr of Yr 1986; Natl Defense Grant 1965; AATF Schlsp to France 1983.

BASHER, MAUREEN ELLEN, Chemistry & Earth Science Tchr; *b:* Flushing, NY; *m:* James W.; *c:* James William; *ed:* SUNY at Geneseo (BS) Bio 1983; Long Island Univ (MS) Ed 1990; Coll of Saint Rose 3 Credit Hrs; CUNY Lehman Coll 4 Credit Hrs; SUNY at Purchase 17 Credit Hrs; 6 Credit Hrs; *cr:* Saint Catharine Acad HS Sci Tchr 1987-93; Yorktown HS Sci Tchr 1993-; *ai:* NSTA; Sci Tchr Assn NY; *office:* Yorktown HS 2727 Crompond Rd Yorktown Heights NY 10598*

BASHOOR, JANETTA TAYLOR, HS Math Teacher & Guid Cnslr; *b:* Somerset, KY; *m:* Michael; *c:* John, Marc, Scott; *ed:* Univ of KY (BA) Psych 1960; Bowie St Univ (MA) Cnslng Psych 1980; Educl Testing 3 Hrs; *cr:* Captiol Chrstn Acad Guid Cnslr & HS Math Tchr 14 Yrs; *ai:* Jrnlsm & Yrbk Adv; Calvary Bapt Church 1962-, Sec, Treas, SS Tchr; *office:* Capitol Christian Acad 610 Largo Rd Upper Marlboro MD 20774

BASHOOR, SUSAN FOSSELMAN, Math Teacher & Dept Head; *b:* Des Moines, IA; *m:* John; *c:* Kurt, Sarah; *ed:* Kent St Univ (BSEd) Math 1970; Ashland Univ (MED) Cmptr Ed 1990; *cr:* Timken Voc HS Tchr 1971-76; Mc Kinley Sr HS Tchr 1976-77, 1983-94, Tchr, Dept Head 1994-; *ai:* Y-Teens, Stu Cncl Adv; Supts Advy Bd; Sftbl Scorekeeper & Stats Mgr; CPEA, OEA, NEA 1971-, Bldg Rep; NCTM 1990-; Phi Delta Kappa 1994-; Lady Lions 1971-; *office:* Mc Kinley Sr HS 2323 17th St NW Canton OH 44708*

BASIAK, GERALD JOSEPH, 5th Grade Teacher; *b:* Bayonne, NJ; *ed:* JCSC (BA) Ec 1971; *cr:* The Old Mill Schl 3rd, 5th-6th Grd Tchr 1992-; *ai:* Head Girls Gymnastic Coach 1978-; Master Adv NJSMG; NEA; USGF; NFICA; NJGGC; 200 Club Monmouth Cty; *office:* Old Mill Schl 2119 Old Mill Rd Wall NJ 08750

BASILE, JOSEPH JOHN, English Department Chairman; *b:* Jamestown, NY; *m:* Carol Dispenza; *c:* James, Michael; *ed:* Murray St Univ (BA) Eng, His 1969; SUNY at Fredonia Eng; *cr:* Frewsburg Cntrl Schl HS Eng Tchr 1969-; *ai:* Eng Dept Chm; Local Newspaper Stu Publications Writing Staff; Ftbl, Wrestling Supvr; HS Ftbl Games Play by Play Announcer; Jr HS Bskbl Coach; NY St United Tchrs 1970-; AFT 1969-; *office:* Frewsburg Central Schl 26 Institute St Frewsburg NY 14738

BASINGER, AMY MILLIKEN, Biology & Life Science Teacher; *b:* Wheeling, WV; *m:* Chris; *c:* Madison; *ed:* West Liberty St Coll (BA) Bio & Gen Sci 1990; Comm Masters Pgm 20 Credit Hrs Completed; *cr:* Buckeye Local HS Bio, Life Sci & Anatomy Tchr 1990-; *ai:* Class Adv; NCA Steering & Bio Course of Stud Comms; NEA 1990-; OEA 1990-; *office:* Buckeye Local HS Rd 2 Box 475 Rayland OH 43943

BASINGER, KAREN S., Psychology Professor; *b:* Lima, OH; *ed:* OH St Univ (BS) Elem Ed 1981, (MA) Dev Psych 1985, (PHD) Dev Psych 1990; *cr:* OH St Univ Grad Tchng Assoc 1986-89; Marshall Univ Asst Prof 1990-91; Urbana Univ Asst Prof 1991-; *ai:* Fac Dev Comm Chair; APA 1990-; APS 1994-; 1 Book, 4 Articles Pub; *office:* Urbana Univ 579 College Way Urbana OH 43078*

BASKINGER, MARYANN S., Art Teacher; *b:* Passaic, NJ; *m:* John M.; *c:* Mark, Kim; *ed:* William Paterson Coll (BA) Art Ed 1966, (MA) Visual Arts 1972; Attnd Jersey City St Coll, Montclair St Univ; *cr:* Clifton HS Art Tchr 1966-73; Clifton Elem Schls Art Tchr 1986-89; Manchester Regnl HS Art Tchr 1989-90; Clifton HS Art Tchr 1990-; *ai:* HS Art, Lit Magazine Art Adv; NEA, NJEA, Clifton Tchrs Assn 1990-; NJEA Review; Schl Arts; *office:* Clifton HS 333 Colfax Ave Clifton NJ 07013

BASLER, PATRICIA BRUNING, Social Studies Teacher; *b:* Urbana, IL; *m:* Gary W.; *c:* Christopher; *ed:* (BSEd) Soc Stud Comprehensive 1975; (MSEd) Soc Stud Concentration 1981; 11 Credit Hrs; *cr:* St Bernard-Elmwood Pl HS Tchr 1977-85; McAuley HS Tchr 1985-; *ai:* Club Adv; Amnesty Intnl Adv & Coach; Mock Trial Team; NEA 1977-85; NCSS 1985-, Mem of SS Dept; Mt Auburn Presbyn Church 1991-, Deacon.

BASS, CAROL PALEVSKY, Library Teacher; *b:* Brooklyn, NY; *m:* David; *c:* Adam, Wayne; *ed:* Brooklyn Coll (BA) Early Childhood 1969; NY Univ (MA) Ed, Psych & Remedial Rdng 1971; 30 Credit Hrs Elem Ed; *cr:* PS 115K Tchr 1969-71; PS 16R Tchr 1983-92; 1993-; NY City Tchr Ctr Consortium Tchr Trainer 1992-93; Fordham Univ Adj Prof 1992-; *ai:* Story-Telling Contest Coach; AFT & UFT 1969-; *office:* Public Schl 16 80 Monroe Ave Staten Island NY 10301*

BASS, CHRISTINE C., Director of Choral Activities; *b:* Manhatten, KS; *m:* Martin V. Jr.; *c:* Martin V. III, Trina Christine; *ed:* Westminster Choir Coll (BA) Music Ed K-12 1975; Work on Masters; *cr:* Long Branch Jr HS Choral, Gen Music Tchr 1975-79; Long Branch Sr HS Choral Dir 1980-82; Cherry Hill HS West Dir of Choral Act 1989-; *ai:* Budget, Multicultural Task Force Comms; MENC 1989-, NJ Master Music Tchr 1996; ACDA 1990-; SJCDA 1989-, Sec; Top Choirs in Heritage Natl Choral Festival of Gold, NJ St ACDA Festivals, Various St & Interstate Festivals; Stu Placed All South Jersey, All St & All Eastern Choruses Goverors Schl; *office:* Cherry Hill West HS 2101 Chapel Ave Cherry Hill NJ 08002

BASS, MARY LEE ATTARIAN, Director of the Reading Center; *b:* Philadelphia, PA; *m:* Harris Merill; *c:* Mandy Michelle; *ed:* Millersville Univ of PA (BS) Elem Ed 1969; Monmouth Univ (MSEd) Rdng 1992; Rutgers Univ Literacy Doctoral Stu; *cr:* Benchmark Schl Lang Arts Tchr 1987-90; Brookdale Comm Coll Rdng Lab Instr 1990-92; Monmouth Univ Adj Instr 1992-, Dir of Rdng Ctr 1992-; *ai:* Steering Comm NJ Consortium for Placement Testing; IRA 1984-; Phi Delta Kappa 1993-; Coll Rdng Assn 1994-; Headstart 1969-, Tchrs Asst Vol; Neighborhood Model Cities 1971-, Pgm Coord Vol; Adult Ed 1987-, Exec Bd Mem; Cognitive Rsrch Conf Presenter Univ of MD 1990; Book Awd 1992; Article Pub 1995; *office:* Monmouth Univ Coll Skills Ctr Cedar Ave West Long Branch NJ 07764*

BASS, PAUL DENNIS, Social Studies Teacher; *b:* New York City, NY; *m:* Kim; *c:* Zachary, Conner; *ed:* Bloomsburg Univ (BS) 1982; Stony Brook Univ (MALS) 1986; *cr:* William Floyd Schl Dist 7th Grd His Tchr 1982-84; Westhampton Beach Schl Dist HS Soc Stud Tchr, Advanced Placement Amer His 1984-; *ai:* Head Wrestling Coach; Weight Lifting Club Spon; NYSJT 1982-; Elem Age Children Wrestling 1982-, Vol Tchr; League Var Wrestling Coach of Yr 1990-91; *office:* Westhampton Beach HS Lilac Rd Westhampton Beach NY 11978

BASSANI, DEBORAH GRAY, English Teacher; *b:* Suffern, NY; *m:* John; *ed:* St Thomas Aquinas (BA) Eng, Ed 1986; Iona Coll (MA) Eng, Ed 1989; 45 Credit Hrs; *cr:* Tuxedo HS Eng Tchr 1986-87; North Rockland HS Eng Tchr 1989-; *ai:* Stu Govt, Yth Against Cancer Adv; Active Comm Mem; NYSUT 1986-; PTA 1989-; *office:* North Rockland HS 106 Hammond Rd Thiells NY 10984

BASSARO, ROSE R., Math & Computer Teacher; *b:* Spangler, PA; *m:* Rudy G.; *c:* Matthew, Lauren; *ed:* Penn St (BS) Scndry Ed 1985; Post Grad Stud Cmptrs, Parent Comm, Learning Styles; *cr:* St Bernard Schl Math Tchr 1985-87; Lancaster Cty Schls Sub Math Tchr 1987-88; St Bernard Schl Math, Cmptr Tchr 1988-; *ai:* Yrbl, Chrldng, Stu Govt Adv; NCTM 1985-; *office:* St Bernard Schl 1375 Spangler St Hastings PA 16646

BASSETT, BELVA ANN (ZEEOLYK), Retired 2nd Grade Teacher; *b:* Kankakee, IL; *m:* Rex D.; *c:* Janie, Rex Jr., Kathy, Karen; *ed:* BGSU (BA) Elem Ed 1974; Grad Hrs Toledo Univ, Dayton, IU Purdue 1979-85; *cr:* Farmer-Sherwood Elem Schl 2nd Grd Tchr 1974-95; *ai:* TALCS 1974-, Bldg Rep; NWOEA, OEA 1974-; *home:* 08867 Breinger Rd Mark Center OH 43536

BASSETT, DAVID E., Business Education Instructor; *b:* Danville, PA; *m:* Marie Kline; *c:* Mark; *ed:* Bloomsburg St Coll (BS) Bus Ed 1966; Temple Univ (MED) Voc Ed Ec 1972; 28 Hrs Beyond MED in Ec; *cr:* Pequea Valley Schl Dist Tchr 1966-; *ai:* Sr Class Adv; PSEA; NEA; PVEA 1966-, Pres; *office:* Pequea Valley HS 4033 E Newport Rd Kinzers PA 17535

BASSETT, R. DIANE (PERRY), Mathematics Teacher; *b:* Lynn, MA; *m:* Merrill E. Jr.; *c:* Michael S., Jennifer L.; *ed:* Boston Coll (BA) Math 1969; Grad Prgm U Mass at Lowell; *cr:* Pickering Jr HS Math Tchr 1969-74; North Andover HS Math Tchr 1981-; *ai:* Stu Cncl Adv; Chair of Math Frameworks Curr Comm; MTA, NEA 1981-; Amer Math soc 1994-; NASAA 1990-; N Andover Yth Svcs Vol Awd 1993; *office:* North Andover HS 675 Chickering Rd North Andover MA 01845

BASSETT, SHARON BURDETTE, 7th-8th Language Arts Teacher; *b:* Mercer, PA; *m:* Bruce A.; *c:* Carrie; *ed:* Mt Union Coll (BA) Elem Ed 1972; Attnd John Carroll Univ, Lakeland Comm Coll; *cr:* Cricket Lane Elem 5th Grd Tchr 1972-75; Thomas Jefferson Elem 6th Grd Tchr 1975-76; St Mary of the Assumption 5th-8th Grd Tchr 1979-; *ai:* Yrbk, Newspaper, Literacy Magazine & Grad Adv; Drama Coach; Cath Schl Week & Right to Read Week Comm; LA Coord; ASCD; NCET; IRA; NCEA; Eastern Reg of Diocese Tchr of Yr 1989; Nom NCEA Distngd Tchr Awd 1993; Recipient of Martha Holdings Jennings Fndtn Grant; Recognized by St of OH for Contribution to Writing Through Power of Pen; *office:* Saint Mary of The Assumption 8540 Mentor Ave Mentor OH 44060

BASSETTE, LORRAINE PRATT, Prof of Business Management; *b:* Washington, DC; *m:* Paul D. Jr.; *c:* Paul III, Darryl, Pauraine; *ed:* Cntrl St Univ (BS) Bus Admin 1970; Cath Univ (MA) Admin & Supervision 1972; VA Tech Doctoral Prgm; *cr:* Prince George's Comm Coll Accountant 1976-77, Prof 1977-; Pratt-Bassette & Assoc Pres 1982-; Univ of MD Univ Coll Adj Prof 1989-; *ai:* Fac Salary & Benefits, Collegewide Nominating Comms; Fac Adv to Studnts; Mentor Prgm; Phi Beta Kappa 1979-, Svc Awd; Jack & Jill of Amer 1994-, Grp Chm, Exec Bd, Svc Awd; Tchng Excl Nom at Univ of MD; Yrs Outstdng Svc Awd; Shepherd Park Elem Schl Svc Awd; *office:* Prince Georges Comm Coll 301 Largo Rd Uppr Marlboro MD 20774

BASSLER, LIDA MAC AULAY, English Teacher & Dept C Antigonish, NS Canada; *m:* Richard Langford; *c:* Elizabe Maldonado, Susan Laurel Belt; *ed:* Russell Sage Coll (BFA) Art Univ of NY at Albany (MA) Scndry Eng, Ed 1971; 59 Addl Grad Binghamton North HS Eng 10-11, R, NR Tchr 1966-69; Harpursvil Eng 10-12, R, NR, Dept Chr 1969-; *ai:* Town Poet; AFT, NYSU TA 1966-, Pres, VP, Grievance, Rep, Newsletter Ed, EDII Del, Chair; Town Historians Comm 1989-, Poet, Comm Mem, T Recognition; Numerous Items Pub; Poem Entered in Towns Pe Records; *office:* Harpursville Cntrl Schl Main St Harpursville NY

BAST, JAMES RICHARD, Music Teacher; *b:* Reading, PA; *m:* Ann Trimmer; *c:* Andrew J., Steven J., Michael S.; *ed:* Gettysbu (BMEd) Music Ed 1970; Temple Univ (MMEd) Music Ed 1979; Sup Cert St of NJ; *cr:* US Army Bandsman 1970-73; Wall Twp Bd of E Ed Tchr 1973-; Unit Chm Spec Areas, PE 1987-; *ai:* Soccer Coach; Helpers Prgm Spon; Phi Mu Alpha Sinfonia 1967-, Pres, Brothe NEA, NJEA, WTEA 1973-, Pres Wall Twp Ed Assn; MENC, 1973-; All Shore Band Assn 1973-, Pres; Greater Shore Conce 1975-, Dir; Atonement Luth Church 1980-, Pres; *office:* Wall Inter Schl Allaire Rd & Baileys Corner Rd Wall NJ 07719*

BASTEDO, SANDRA FANCHER, Fine Arts Chprsn & Vocal Albion, NY; *m:* Richard D.; *c:* Kevin, Katherine; *ed:* SUNY Potsda Music Ed 1983; SUNY Buffalo (MM) Music Ed 1990; *cr:* Attic High Vocal Tchr 1984-85; Perry HS Vocal Music Tchr 1985-; East Presbyn Church Organist 1987-95; *ai:* Chorus Club Adv; Fine Arts Sigma Alpha Iota 1981-; NYSUT AFL-CIO 1984-; NYSSMA, 1985-; *office:* Perry Central HS 33 Watkins Ave Perry NY 14530

BASTIAN, DOUGLAS PORTER, Retired 8th Grade Science Williamsport, PA; *m:* Shirley Jean Pelleschi; *c:* Lorraine Lehman Kurt, Rachelle Mc Connell; *ed:* Penn St Univ (BS) Orna Horticulture 1955; Lycoming Coll (BA) Ed 1963; *ai:* WEA, PSE 1972-; Sergeant, US Marine Corp, Korean War; *home:* 341 E 2n Williamsprt PA 17701

BASTIEN, GERARD EMILE, Music Edctr, Band & Chorus Lowell, MA; *m:* Denise C. Martel; *c:* Daniel, Jeffrey; *ed:* Univ of (BA) Music 1976; Notre Dame Coll (MED) Admin, Supervision 1 Self Employed Musician Prof Performer; Chester Elem Schl Musi 1986-88; South Londonderry Elem Schl Music Edctr 198 Londonderry Tech Task Force Curr, Instruction; Assessment Com Crisis Response Team; NEA NH 1986-, Pres, Sec of Local Chptr; 1986-; ASCD 1993-; Amoskeag Lions Club 1988-, Historian; Tak Karate Club 1988-, 2nd Degree Blk Belt Instr, 1st Pl Keta Champio PTA Tech Grant; Outstdng Ed Stud 1993; Hum Rep Prgm Steering *home:* 465 Cartier St Manchester NH 03102

BASTIN, DAN EDMUND, Visiting Tchr & Social Worker; *b:* Vernon, OH; *m:* Diane M.; *c:* Julie, Jaime, Nate, Rebekah; *ed:* Green St U (BA) Psych, Eng 1958; Pittsburgh Seminary (MDIV) T 1961; U of Pittsburgh (MSW) Group Work, CO 1977; Continuing of Ed, Soc Work License, Schl Soc Work Specialist; *cr:* Urban Ministry Dir 1967-77; Hlth Care Systems CEO, VP 1977-83; Yth System Dir 1984-86; Pickaway-Ross JVS Visiting Tchr, Schl Soc 1986-; *ai:* OEA, St Task Force on Violence in Schls; OEA, NEA 1986-; NASW 1978-; Beaver Area Schl Bd; Domestic Violence MADD, Pres; Gt Seal Family Care Ctr, Pres; *office:* Pickaway-Ros Voc Schl 895 Crouse Chapel Rd Chillicothe OH 45601*

BATCHELOR, IRENE RUMPF, Math Dept Coord & Teac Dumont, NJ; *m:* Richard Harris; *c:* William, Karen Batchelor Pet Finch Coll (BS) Chem 1964; Columbia Univ (MA) Math Ed 19 Northern Vly Regnl HS Math Tchr 1965; Roy W Brown MS Ma 1965-67; Vernon Twp HS Math Tchr 1976-, Math Dept Coord 19 NCTM 1964-; NEA 1976-; NJEA 1976-; AMTNJ Glenwood-Pochuck Vol Ambulance Corp 1987-, Past Pres, Co Recording Sec & Current Trustee; Pi Lambda Theta; *office:* Township HS PO Box 800 Vernon NJ 07462*

BATCHELOR, JON DAVID, Math Teacher; *b:* Camden, NJ; Nelson; *c:* Judi Bayer, John, Janet DePersia; *ed:* US Naval Ac Engrng 1959; George Washington Univ (MA) Scndry Ed 1967 Glassboro St Coll, Lafayette Coll, Burlington Cty Coll, Camden C *cr:* Woodrow Wilson HS Math Tchr 1967-69; Eastern HS Math Tchr *ai:* NEA, NJEA 1967-; NSF Grant; *office:* Eastern HS Laurel Voorhees NJ 08043

BATE, GEORGE DONALD, 5th Grd Math & Science Teac Paterson, NJ; *m:* Patricia Mary Skelly; *c:* LInda Dinndorf, Susan Nancy; *ed:* Montclair St Coll (BA) Bus Ed, Acctng 1957; William P Coll (MA) Schl Admin, Supervision 1964; *cr:* Franklin Jr HS 7th- Tchr 18 Yrs; Has Hgt Adult Schl Asst Dir, Dir 1966-69; Has Hgt S Schl Prin 1968-75, 1978-94; Washington Schl Prin 1975-78; Eucl 4th-6th Grd Tchr 1978-; *ai:* Head Coach Cross Cntry 1964-; NJ S Ofcl Assn 1970-; NEA, NJEA, BCEA 1957-; Has Hgts E A 195 1970; Jaycees 1956-72, Pres 1966-67, Man of Yr 1962, JCI Senato Fairlawn Drug Abuse Cncl 1970-72, Pres 1970-72; Fairlawn P Maintenance Comm 1995-, Chm 1995-; Fairlawn March of Dime 1970-72; US Army 1958-60; Bergen Cty Young Tchr Awd 1961; Class 1st Place in Nation Org Environmental Awd 1971-72; Who Amer Colls, Univs 1956; *home:* 3-23 17th St Fair Lawn NJ 07410*

BATEMAN, CARL J., Mathematics Supervisor; *b:* Easton, PA; *m:* (Bryksa); *c:* Heather Palm, Jennifer; *ed:* Montclair Univ (BA) Mat Scranton Univ (MS) Scndry Schl Admin 1985; *ai:* ASCD 1987-; 1987-; NJPSA 1987-; *office:* Kittatinny Regional HS 77 Halsey Rd NJ 07860

BATEMAN, CYNTHIA LEE, Fourth Grade Science Teach Harrisburg, PA; *m:* Hugh Daniel; *c:* Kelly Hill; *ed:* OH St Univ 1975; Univ of Dayton (MS) Ed 1986; Mount St Joseph Coll at Cin Univ of Rio Grande, Ashland Univ, OH Univ Ed Courses; *cr:* Cnt Title I 5th, 6th Grd Tchr 1975-76; Coalton Elem Schl 1st, 4th Grd S 1976-; *ai:* Sci Club Adv; Discipline, Venture Capital Comms; NE 1975-; Wellston Tchrs Assn 1975-, VP; Sci Ed Cncl of OH 1995- Kappa Gamma 1991-; Comm Choir 1982-; OH Genealogical Soc First Families of OH 1996; Martha Holden Jennings Scholar; Coalton Elem Schl PO Box 8 Coalton OH 45621

BATEMAN, DAVID F., Sponsored Research Director; *b:* Lynchbu *m:* Lisa Dorrill; *ed:* Univ of VA (BA) Govt 1985; William & Mary Spec Ed 1986; Univ of KS (PHD) Spec Ed 1992; *cr:* Waynesbor Tchr 1985-87; Charlottesville Schls Spec Ed Tchr 1987-88; North Univ Spec Ed Tchr 1988-89; Univ of KS Grant Project Dir 1 Emporia St Univ Asst Prof 1992-; *ai:* CEC Spon; The Aths Congres CEC 1984-, St VP; AAMR 1985-; Flint Hills Hospice 1993-, Bd; Nu Grants; *office:* Shippensburg Univ Dept of Teacher Ed Shippensburg PA 17257

BATEMAN, JOAN KUSHNIR, Business Education Teach Duquesne, PA; *m:* Robert N.; *c:* Sandra, William; *ed:* Indiana Univ (BA) Bus 1962, (MA) Bus 1967; 3 Credit Hrs Westmoreland Comm 3 Credit Hrs Penn St Univ; *cr:* West Mifflin Schl Dist Bus Tchr 1 Norwin Schl Dist Bus Tchr 1967-70; Yough Schl Dist Bus Tchr 19 NEA, PSEA 1962-; Yough Ed Assn 1984-; *office:* Yough Senior Lowber Rd Herminie PA 15637

IAN, TONI CHICHESTER, Physical Education Teacher; *b:* gton, DC; *m:* John R.; *c:* Alison, Michael; *ed:* Charles Cty Comm A) 1974; Frostburg St Univ (BS) Hlth & PE 1976, (MA) PE 1979; MD Post Grad Stud; *cr:* Charles Cty Parks & Recreation Tumbling nastics Instr 1975-85; Dr Gustavus Brown Elem Schl PE Tchr , 1989-; *ai:* Girls Sftbl Coach; Aerobics Club Ldr; Safety Patrol & Comm Coord; Adaptive & Spcl PE Tchr; Wellness Conf & Comm 'eam Ldr; EACC 1977-; MSTA 1977-; NEA 1977-; MAHPERD Pinefield Civic Assn 1984-, Block Capt; St Peters Cath Church Eucharist Minister; Simon A McNeely Merit Awd 1993; *office:* Dr is Brown Elem Schl University Dr Waldorf MD 20602

, ALTHEA THOMPSON, Media Specialist; *b:* Hartsville, SC; *m:* ; *c:* John H. Jr.; *ed:* Allen Univ (BA) Eng 1964; Univ of MD (MLS) 1979; Attnd IN Univ, Salisbury St Coll, Coppin St Coll, George gton Univ; *cr:* Gallman HS Eng Tchr 1964-65; Somerset HS Soc hr 1965-66; Woodson HS Eng Tchr 1967-69; Somerset HS Eng Tchr 4; Lansdowne MS Eng Tchr 1974-78; Wilde Lake HS Media ist 1979-; *ai:* Club Adv; Awds Comm; NEA, MSTA 1965-; HCEA, C 1979-; Dela Sigma Theta 1961-, Sec, Treas, Fin Sec, Flwshp Awd; MD Flwshp; Instrl Materials Criteria Review Comm; *office:* Wilde S 5460 Trumpeter Rd Columbia MD 21044*

, CYNTHIA A., Spanish Teacher; *b:* Chelsea, MA; *c:* Richard, pher; *ed:* Salve Regina Coll (AB) Span, Fr 1970; Middlebury Coll pan 1971; Attnd Univ de Madrid 1968-69, Middlebury Coll Madrid ; *cr:* Methuen Jr HS Span Tchr 1971-75; Methuen HS Span Tchr *ai:* Soph Class, Intnl Club, Sociedad Honoraria Hispanica Adv; 'Brien Yth Fnd Coord; AATSP, NEA, MTA, MEA 1971-; ECLAT Grant Coord; BSA 1985-, Various Merit Badge Councilor; St s Church 1980-, Confirmation Tchr; Salem Heritage Days 1991-, prsn; *office:* Methuen HS 1 Ranger Rd Methuen MA 01844

, JENNIFER DAMMER, English Teacher; *b:* Syosset, NY; *m:* e J.; *ed:* Bloomsburg Univ (BA) Scndry Ed Eng 1992; *cr:* Benton Tchr 1994-; *ai:* Drama Coach; Susquehanna Univ Holocaust Stud NEA 1992-; PSEA 1992-; *office:* Benton Area HS RR 2 Park St PA 17814

, RICK ALAN, 8th Grd Language Arts Teacher; *b:* Zanesville, OH; ley Diane Surratt; *ed:* OH St Univ (BA) Eng Ed 1985; Dayton Univ cndry Cnslng 1995; *cr:* Buckeye Trail HS Scndry Eng 1985-86; on Coll Ftbl & Sftbl Coach 1986-87; Lancaster City Schls Scndry 88-; *ai:* Ftbl & Grls Bsktbl Coach; NEA & OEA 1985-; OH MS 94-; Fiction Writers Circle 1995-, Pres; Ashland Tchr Awds Nom; Assn Conf Presenter; *office:* Thomas Ewing Jr HS 825 E Fair Ave er OH 43130

, SUZANNE, Voc Consumer Homemaking Tchr; *b:* Elyria, OH; *ed:* t Univ (BS) Ed 1978; John Carroll Univ Post Grad Hrs, Cert al; *cr:* Oberlin HS Sub Tchr 1979; John Hay HS Tchr 1980-81; ood HS Tchr 1982-; *ai:* FHA Spon; AFT 1979-; Rdng Enrichment lt Dev 1993-; Cleveland Educ Fund Grants; *office:* Collinwood HS Saint Clair Ave Cleveland OH 44110

, TONY, 7th Grade Teacher; *b:* Lebanon, NH; *m:* Bamby Pierpont; cer, Tyler; *ed:* Univ of VT (BA) Eng 1981; Castleton St Col (MED) ; *cr:* Union 36 Elem Schl 7th Grd Tchr 1985-86; MT Abraham UHS l Tchr 1986-88; Middlebury UHS 7th Grd Tchr 1988-; *ai:* NEA Taught Grad Level Courses Rdng, Writing, Heterogeneous Grouping; Middlebury Union HS Charles Ave Middlebury VT 05753

RICHARD JOHN, Mathematics Teacher; *b:* Easton, PA; *m:* Elaine Witt; *c:* Kristie L., Jonathan R.; *ed:* Moravian Coll (BS) Math 1969; te Coll 18 Credit Hrs; East Stroudsburg Univ 6 Credit Hrs; Penn St Credit Hrs; *cr:* Easton Jr HS Math Tchr 1969-76; Shawnee ediate Schl Math Tchr 1976-; *ai:* NEA, PSEA, Easton Area EA *office:* Shawnee Intermediate Schl 1010 Echo Trl Easton PA 18040

ERSON, JOANNA PARK, Second Grade Teacher; *b:* Boston, MA; Richard; *c:* Stephen W., Timi Ann Hedger; *ed:* Univ of ME at gton (BS) K-8th Grd Ed 1963; Univ of Southern ME (MS) Rdng r: Mexico Schls Kndgtn Tchr 1963-66; Rumford Schl Dept Kndgtn 966-; SAD #43 2nd Grd Tchr; *ai:* Support Team Mentor & Chprsn; TAT Team; MVTA Bldg Rep; MTA, MVTA, NEA 1963-; NERA Tchr of Month; *office:* SAD #43 Schl Parker St Mexico ME 04224

, DEBORAH S., Biology & Adv Biology Teacher; *b:* Ft Bragg, NC; id A.; *c:* Mikee, Markee, Maddie; *ed:* CA Univ (BA) Bio 1977; Addl Cert; *cr:* Carmichaels Schl Bio Tchr 1983-; *ai:* Spon Jr HS Stu Cncl; n Jr Standing Comm; Adv Envirothon Team; *office:* Carmichaels Sr HS 300 W Greene St Carmichaels PA 15320*

N, NANCY OSBORNE, Spanish Teacher; *b:* Plainfield, NJ; *m:* n C.; *c:* Kim Dickey Meusel, Michael James Dickey; *ed:* St Francis A) Span 1970; Kean Coll (MA) Admin 1988; Post Grad at St Peters ersey City St Coll; *cr:* David Brearley HS Span Tchr 1976-92, VP 3; Arthur L. Johnson HS Span Tchr 1993-; *ai:* Peer Ldrshp, Peer ion Adv; Prins Advy Comm; Schl Issues Comm; Intnl Dinner air; AFT 1980-; NJFLTA 1976-; St Helens Church 1984-, Pastoral res; Phi Kappa Phi; Kappa Delta Pi; Governor Kean Awd for g Tchng; Whos Who in Amer Univs, Colls; *office:* Arthur L n Regnl HS 365 Westfield Ave Clark NJ 07066

A, PREM P., Biochem & Molecular Bio Prof; *b:* Jhang Maghiana, *m:* Rosemarie Lewandowski; *c:* Joni, Renee; *ed:* Punjab Univ (BS) 1955, (MS) Chem 1958; Univ of AZ (PHD) Ag Chem 1961; octoral at Univ of UT & Johns Hopkins Univ; *cr:* VA Hospital at ore Biochem 1964-65; Okayama Univ of Sci in Japan Visiting Prof 1988; Wright St Univ Asst Prof 1964-67, Assoc Prof 1967-72, Prof *ai:* Sci Apprenticeship Prgm for HS Stdnts & K-12th Grd Tchrs Dir; oc of Biochem & Molecular Bio 1970-; 3 Postdoctoral Fellowships; & 2 NSF Grants; 4 Tchng Awds; *office:* Wright St Univ Schl of Med & Maths Colonel Glenn Hwy Dayton OH 45435*

ON, CAROL BARBER, Fourth Grade Teacher; *b:* Youngstown, OH; ert C.; *c:* Robert T., David T., Brian K., Scott B.; *ed:* Kent St Univ lem Ed 1963; Attnd Youngstown Univ, Univ of Dayton, Ashland r: Niles City Schls Elem Tchr 1957-60, 1969-; *ai:* NEA, OEA, 1957-; Niles Historical Assn 1980-90, Treas 3 Yrs; Art Tchr Awd office: Washington Elem Schl 805 Hartzell Ave Niles OH 44446

ON, SUSAN KURTZ, Chem Teacher & Planetarium Dir; *b:* Mc Kees PA; *m:* Wesley Brayton; *c:* Francis, Edward, Brayton; *ed:* Clarion (BS) Chem 1979; Masters Equivalency St of PA; 47 Grad Credits eny Intermediate Unit Inservice, Penn St, Clarion St, Univ of rgh, West Chester Univ; *cr:* North Hills Schl Dist Sci Tchr, arium Dir 1980-; *ai:* Environmental Club Spon; Ind Guided Stud in arium Mngmt Mentor; PSEA, NEA 1980-; Great Lakes Planet Assn PA Alliance for Env Ed 1995-; Amer Chem Soc 1975-; Church of sumption 1983-, St George Medal; BSA 1990-, Dist Awd of Merit; nentation Grant Spectroscopy Soc of Pgh 1989; NHSD Mini-Grant Monthly Evening Planetarium Shows Produced by Stu; Day Camp os Prgm Dir 1993-; *office:* North Hills HS 53 Rochester Rd rgh PA 15229

AGLIA, DEBRA GARRY, Mathematics Teacher; *b:* Jersey City, NJ; eph A.; *ed:* Fairleigh Dickinson Univ (BA) Sec Ed Math 1973; lair St Coll (MA) Math Ed 1977; Prin, Supvr Cert 1980; *cr:* Ridgefield Park Jr-Sr HS Math Tchr 1973-; *ai:* Advy Cncl; NEA, RPEA 1973-; NJ St Math Test Dev Comm 1989-; NJ Algebra Project Trainer 1989-91; *office:* Ridgefield Park Jr Sr HS 1 Ozzie Nelson Dr Ridgefield Park NJ 07660

BATTAGLIA, FRANK LOUIS, Social Studies Teacher; *b:* Buffalo, NY; *ed:* St Univ of NY at Buffalo (BS) Scndry Soc Stud 1964, (MS) Scndry Soc Stud 1969; 24 Hrs Beyond Masters; *cr:* Troy HS Soc Stud Tchr 1964-65; Starpoint HS Soc Stud Tchr 1965-; *ai:* Sr High Stu Cncl Adv; Stu of Month, New Tchr; Schls Motivation Comms; NYSUT 1964-; Starpoint Tchr Assn 1965-; Natl Assn of Stu cncl Adv 1965-; Grant to Study in India 1969-70; Robert Taft Awd to Study Politics in NYC; Lifetime Awd PTA; *office:* Starpoint Cntrl HS 4363 Mapleton Rd Lockport NY 14094

BATTAGLIA, JUDITH FOSTER, Elementary Art Teacher; *b:* Philadelphia, PA; *m:* Joseph Michael; *c:* Scott, Kristin, Elizabeth; *ed:* Unif of Arts (BA) Art Ed 1968; Tyler Schl of Art 19 Grad Credist Fine Arts; Penn St Univ 6 Grad Credits Spec Ed; Trenton St Coll 3 Grad Credits Spec Ed; *cr:* Baldwin Schl for Girls HS Fine Arts, Craft Tchr 1968-69; Neshaminy Schl Dist Elem Art Tchr 1970-76; Bloomfield Schl Dist Elem Art Tchr 1981-83; East Windsor Schl Dist Elem Art Tchr 1983-84; Edgewater Pk Schl Dist Elem Art, Gifted Tchr 1984-; *ai:* Organized, Ran Several Artistic Happenings, Art Exhibits, Learning Fairs; NAEA 1969-; Philadelphia Art Museum 1992-; Franklin Inst 1985-; Owned, Ran Educl Concepts, Art Schl for Elem Stdnts; Tyler Schl of Art Alumni Shows, Nutkey Symphony Orch Show, Faleen Gallery Exhibits; Written, Illustrated Educl Materials; *home:* 3 Elm Ave Yardley PA 19067

BATTAGLIA, ROSEMARY NYE, Second Grade Teacher; *b:* Ithaca, NY; *m:* Thomas; *c:* Troy T., Dale A.; *ed:* St Univ of NY at Cortland (BS) PE 1976; Western CT St Univ (MS) Rdng 1989; *cr:* Kent Primary Schl 4th Grd Tchr 1987-88; Kent Elem Schl 2nd Grd Tchr 1988-; *office:* Kent Elem Schl Rt 52 Carmel NY 10512

BATTEN, ANDREA LYNN, Language Arts Teacher; *b:* Woodbury, NJ; *m:* Kenneth Jennett; *c:* Kendall, Camille; *ed:* Montclair St (BA) Eng 1973; Glassboro St (MA) Rdng Ed 1976; Supversion; Rdng Specialist; *cr:* Clayton HS MS Lang Arts Tchr 1973-; *ai:* Stu Cncl Adv; NJEA 1974-; Haddon Grange 1956-; DAR 1984-; Gloucester Cty Outstdng Tchr 1993; *office:* Clayton HS MS 350 E Clinton St Clayton NJ 08312

BATTERSHALL, WILLIAM H.,JR., Hlth, Physical Education Tchr; *b:* Newark, NJ; *m:* Deborah D. Durant; *c:* Kenneth; *ed:* Seton Hall Univ (BS) Hlth, PE 1964; St Peter's Coll 16 Credit Hrs; *cr:* Essex Cath HS Tchr, Ath Trainer 1962-69; St Peter's Coll Tchr, Ath Trainer 1969-87; West Essex Reg Schls Tchr, Ath Trainer 1987-; *ai:* Soph Class Grad Comm Adv; Stdnts Against Driving Drunk Adv; All Aths Trainer; Sr Class Act Comm; NJEA, NEA, West Essex Ed Assn 1987-; Natl Ath Trainers Assn 1960-; Svc Awd; NJ Ath Trainers Soc 1964-, Pres, Distngd Mem; Knights of Columbus 1980-; *office:* West Essex Sr HS W Greenbrook Rd North Caldwell NJ 07006

BATTERSON, DOLORES KUPRES, 6th Grade Teacher; *b:* Manhattan, NY; *m:* Greg; *c:* Patrick, Karyn; *ed:* Ithaca Coll (BA) Math 1973; Elmira Coll (MS) Ed 1976; *cr:* Thomas A. Edison HS Math Tchr 1973-80; H & R Block Income Tax Preparer 1982-84; Elmira Coll Math Instr 1983-84; Cohen Elem Schl 6th Grd Tchr 1984-; *ai:* Natl Intercollegiate Soccer Ofcls Assn USSF Soccer Referee; Southern Tier HS Soccer Ofcl; NEA 1973-; St Charles Borromeo Parish, Lecture, Eucharistic Minister; CCSD Bd of Dir 1992-, Nominations Chair; Soaring Capital Soccer Bd of Dirs 1989-, Registrar; *office:* Cohen Elem Schl 100 Robinwood Ave Elmira Heights NY 14903*

BATTIATO, JOSEPH ANTHONY, English Tchr & AP Coord; *b:* Newark, NJ; *m:* Dorthee; *c:* Jennifer; *ed:* St Peter's Coll (BA) Eng 1967; Seton Hall Univ (MA) Eng 1972; Rider Univ (MA) Educ Admin 1991; Prins Cert; 18 Credits Admin & Supervision Seton Hall Univ; *cr:* Cedar Ridge HS Eng Tchr 1967-69; So Plainfield HS Eng Tchr 1969-72; Watchung Hills Regnl HS Eng Tchr, AP Coord 1972-; *ai:* Acad Affairs Adv Coll Bd; AP Consultant; Ed & Bus Partnership Prgm; NEA, NJEA, NJ Cncl Eng Tchrs 24 Yrs; ASCD 5 Yrs; Hillsborough Soccer Club 8 Yrs; Church Yth Prgm 10 Yrs; Outstdng Tchr of Rdng Awd; Coll Bd Excl in Tchng Awd; Governor's Awd 1995; Tchr of Yr.*

BATTISTA, CARMINE P., History Teacher; *b:* Paterson, NJ; *m:* Patricia Atkinson-Battista; *ed:* William Paterson Coll of NJ (BA) His 1985; *cr:* Dismus MS Tchr 1985-87; Morristown HS Tchr 1987-89; Boonton HS Tchr 1989-90; Dwight Morrow HS Tchr 1992-; *ai:* Schl Newspaper Adv; Jr Var Bsbl Coach; *office:* Dwight Morrow HS 274 Knickerbocker Rd Englewood NJ 07631*

BATTISTA, JOSEPH L.,JR., HS Music Teacher; *b:* Newark, NJ; *m:* Michele; *c:* Caitlin; *ed:* Jersey City St Coll (MA) Urban Ed 1991; Cert Tchr of Handicapped; Cert Substance Awareness Co; *cr:* East Hanover Cntrl Schl Elem Music Tchr 1989-91; Keansburg HS Music Tchr 1991-; *ai:* Marching Band, Musical Adv, Chorus; NEA 1989-; All Shore Band Dir Assn 1991-; Alliance for Arts Ed Mini Grant 1993; AT&T Tech in Classroom Grant 1995; *office:* Keansburg HS 140 Port Monmouth Rd Keansburg NJ 07734

BATTLES, JAMIE HIMES, Math Teacher; *b:* Oswego, NY; *m:* Thomas Battles; *c:* Matthew, Margaret; *ed:* SUNY at Oswego (BS) Scndry Ed Math 1986, (MS) Curr Scndry Ed 1970; *cr:* Mexico HS 9-12 Grd Math Tchr 1986-; *ai:* AFT 1986-; *office:* Mexico H S Main St Mexico NY 13114*

BATTS, SHARON DENISE, 6th-8th Grade Reading Instr; *b:* Brooklyn, NY; *ed:* Herbert H. Lehman (BA) Psych 1986; Attending Brooklyn Coll Grad Schl; *cr:* Saint Anselm Schl Instr 1987-; *ai:* Childrens Tutor; Check Homework; Organize Art Act; Fed of Cath Tchrs 1987-; *office:* St Anselm Schl 685 Tinton Ave Bronx NY 10455

BATZEL, CHARLES WILLIAM, High School Math Teacher; *b:* Montrose, PA; *m:* Jane Umberger; *ed:* East Stroudsburg Univ (BS) Math 1965; Mary Wood Coll (MS) Math 1968; 60 Hrs Beyond MS; *cr:* Elk Lake HS Math Tchr 1965-70; Halifax Area Schls Math Tchr 1971-; *ai:* PSEA 1971-; HEA 1971-; NCTM 1971-; NSF Grant for Syracuse Univ; *home:* 254 Baddorf Rd Halifax PA 17032*

BATZER, DEBORAH MOXEY, Science Teacher; *b:* Baltimore, MD; *m:* John T.; *c:* Kyle Alexander, James Randall; *ed:* Salisbury St Univ (BS) Phys Sci 1984; 30 Post Grad Hrs Towson St Univ, Loyola Coll of Baltimore, Univ of MD; *cr:* Fairfax Cty Pub Schls Chem, Physics Tchr 1989-93; Howard Cty Pub Schls Chem, Physics, 8th Grd Sci Tchr 1993-; *ai:* Stu Support Guid Team 1989-; Drug Awareness Comm 1993-95; Swim & Dive Team Coach 1984-; NEA 1984-; *office:* Elkridge Landing MS 7085 Montgomery Rd Elkridge MD 21227*

BAU, PETER JOHN, Assoc Professor of Business; *b:* Detroit, MI; *m:* Ann Griffith; *c:* Karl Bonar, Paul Bonar; *ed:* Kent St Univ (BSBA) Transportation 1966, (BSBE) Bus Ed Acct 1969; Duquesne Univ (MED) Assoc Prof 1970-; *cr:* Alsco Inc Acctng 1963-64; Dixie OH Express Interline Traffic Mgr 1964-66; Hocking Tech Coll Asst Prof 1969-70; Comm Coll of Beavor City Assoc Prof 1970-; *ai:* Stu Chptr of Inst of Mgmt Accountants Spon; Mid Sts Accreditation; NEA 1970-, Pres, VP & Treas; Inst of Mgmt Accts 1972-, Treas; Muscular Dystrophy 1970-78; Cty Mental Hlth 1979-; *office:* Comm Coll Of Beaver County College Drive Road Monaca PA 15061

BAU, RONALD DAVID, Fifth Grade Teacher; *b:* Nanticoke, PA; *m:* Margaret Reese; *c:* Jeannifer, Jessica, Jeanna; *ed:* Kings Coll (BA) His Ed 1969; Wilkes Univ (MS) Elem Ed 1972; 60 Credit Hrs Past Masters; *cr:* Kosciuszko Elem 5th Grd Tchr 1969-85; Nanticoke MS 6th-8th Grd SS Tchr 1985-90; Lincoln Elem 5th Grd Tchr 1990-; *ai:* Vol Bsktbl Coach; PSEA 1969-; NEA 1969-; *office:* Lincoln Elem Schl 615 Kosciuszko St Nanticoke PA 18634

BAUDER, NANCY PANGBURN, English Teacher; *b:* Geneva, NY; *m:* Charles C. W.; *ed:* CCFL at Canandaigua (AA) Hum 1973; SUC at Geneseo (BA) Eng Lit 1974; Syracuse Univ Grad Stud Permanent NY St Tchr Cert 1975-79; *cr:* De Sales HS Eng Tchr 1974-77; Newark HS Eng Tchr 1978-79; Romulus Cntrl Schl Eng Tchr 1979-; *ai:* NHS, Stu Cncl Adv; Romulus 2000 Long-Range Planning Comm Co-Facilitator; Shared Decision Making Comm; Mem Romulus Team Ldrshp Comm; NCTE 1975-; Delta Kappa 1982-, Chapter Pres 1992-94; Trinity Church Geneva 1974-; Geneva Free Lib, Friends of Lib Chair 1984-90, Bd of Trustees 1987-; PEO Sisterhood 1989-, Chair Budget & Finance Comm; Geneva Free Library, Bd of Trustees Pres 1990-; NEH Fellowship 1988; Univ of Rochester Excl in Scndry Tchng Awd 1990; Tchr of Yr 1993; Wye Fac Seminar Aspen Inst Fellowship 1993; Filene Flwshp, Harvard Grad Schl of Ed 1994; NEH Flwshp 1995; *home:* 138 Oak St Geneva NY 14456

BAUER, BARBARA ANN (COLUZZI), Fifth Grade Teacher; *b:* Lancaster, PA; *m:* Tony; *c:* Jeffrey, Kirsten; *ed:* Rowan Coll (BA) Elem Ed 1981; West Chester Univ Elem Ed 1960-62; Addl 24 Grad Stud Credit Hrs Several Colls; *cr:* E. T. Hamilton Schl 3rd Grd Tchr 1981, 2nd Grd Tchr 1981-82; Kresson Schl 3rd Grd Tchr 1982-89, 5th Grd Tchr 1989-; *ai:* Supts Round Table Comm Schl Rep; Dist Math, 5th Grd Rep Laison Comms; Voorhees Twp Ed Assn 1981-, Bldg Rep; NJ Ed Assn, NEA 1981-; Parent Fac Assn 1988-; *office:* Kresson Elem Schl School Ln Voorhees NJ 08043*

BAUER, EDWARD WILLIAM, Chemistry & Physics Teacher; *b:* Philadelphia, PA; *m:* Carol Collins; *c:* Andrew, Deborah Howard; *ed:* Temple Univ (BS) Scndry Sci Ed 1956, (EDM) Sci Curr Dev 1961; 30 Addl Credit Hrs; *cr:* Riverside HS Phys Sci Tchr 1956-57; US Army Specialist 4th Class 1958-60; Conestoga HS Tchr, Dept Chm Phys 1960-93, Summer Schl Dir 1970-92; Plumbstead Chrstn Schl Phys Sci Tchr, Sci Dept Chm 1993-; *ai:* Sr Class Adv; Ind Stud Stu Rsrch; Audio-Visual Repair & Maintenance Club; AAPT 1968-, Innovative Tchr of Yr 1972; Davisville Bapt Church 1985-, Deacon; 7 NSF Stud Grants; Boy Scout Merit Badge Cnslng; Part of Childrens Book; Sci & Math Tutor Vol; *office:* Plumbstead Chrstn Schl 5765 Old Easton Rd Plumsteadville PA 18949*

BAUER, ELAINE A. WATSON, Teacher & Director; *b:* Kingston, PA; *m:* William Barrett; *c:* Kenneth B.; *ed:* Wilkes Coll (BA) End Ed 1971, (MS) Eng Ed 1974; Univ of Scranton (MS) Scndry Schl Admin 1984; *cr:* WY Vly West HS Tchr 1971-; *ai:* Fall Dramatics Production Musical Dir; Ctr Stage Dramatics Adv; Schl, Comm Advy Cncl; Textbook Adoption Comm Chair; NEA 1971-; *office:* Wyoming Valley West HS 150 Wadham St Plymouth PA 18651

BAUER, HELEN P., Band Director; *b:* New York City, NY; *c:* Erin Ashley; *ed:* Ithaca Coll (BM) Music Ed 1968; Hofstra Univ (MA) Scndry Ed 1976; Hofstra Univ (CAS) Educl Admin 1994; Stud at Hofstra Univ for EDD Educl Admin; *cr:* Baldwin Elem Schl Instrumental Tchr 1968-71; Baldwin Jr HS Band Dir 1971-81; Baldwin Sr HS Music Theory Band Dir 1981-, Prin Summer Schl 1996; *ai:* Shared Decision Making Team; Prin Advy Bd; AIDS Advy Cncl; ACDA 1994-, Treas Eastern Division; MENC, NYSSMA, NMEA, NYSBDA 1968-; Doctoral Fellow 1996; Honorary Lifetime Mbrshp PTA 1972; Deans List 1991.

BAUER, HOWARD DANIEL, High School Business Teacher; *b:* Lancaster, OH; *m:* Clarice Alta Oberholzer; *c:* Ellen Mae; *ed:* OH Univ (BS) Bus Ed 1963; Marshall Univ (MA) Bus Ed 1968; 3 Hrs Wright St Univ; 3 Hrs Oh St Univ; 6 Hrs Ashland Univ; 3 Hrs Walsh Univ; *cr:* Licking Heights HS Bus Instr 1963-94; Whitehall Yearling Adult Ed Bus Instr 1969-86; *ai:* NHS Adv; Mngmt Team Chm; Dist Morale, County In-Service Comms; LHEA 1963-, Treas & Negotiator; COTA, OEA, NEA 1963-; Tri Village Church of Christ 1977-, Deacon & Elder; OH Tchr of Yr Nom 1985; LHEA Tchr of Yr Awd 1985; Ctr of Alternative Resources Bd of Dirs Awd 1989; North Cntrl Assn Awd 1989; Leadership for Learning Awd 1993; Golden Apple Achiever Award 1995 Ashland Oil; *home:* 287 Summit Glen Dr SW Pataskala OH 43062*

BAUER, ILENE, Language Arts English Teacher; *b:* Brooklyn, NY; *m:* Mel; *c:* Geoffrey, Briana; *ed:* Richmond Coll (MS) Ed; Brooklyn Coll (BA) Eng; 30 Credit Hrs Above Masters Degree; *cr:* IS 72 Lang Arts Tchr; I S 51 Lang Arts Tchr; *ai:* Poetry Pub; *office:* Rollo Laurie IS 72 Schl 33 Ferndale Ave Staten Island NY 10314

BAUER, LAURA A., Mathematics Teacher; *b:* Worecester, MA; *m:* William J.; *c:* George, Vincent, Amanda; *ed:* Siena Heights Coll (BS) Chem 1965; Attnd UCLA, Aquinas Coll, Univ of PA; Immaculate Coll Tchr Cert; *cr:* Menelik II HS Math, Sci Tchr 1965-67; Wyandotte Roosevelt HS Sci Tchr 1967-68; Army Ed Ctr Math, Sci Tchr 1968-71; Saisen Intnl Schl Math Tchr 1981-84; Villa Maria Acad Math Tchr 1987-; *ai:* JV Aths Coach, Moderator; NHS Advy Cncl; NCTM, PCTM, ATMAPOV 1986-; *office:* Villa Maria Acad Green Tree Malvern PA 19355

BAUER, LINDA LOU, Assoc Prof of Professional Ed; *b:* Oak Hill, OH; *ed:* Univ of Rio Grande (BS) Elem Ed 1960; OH Univ (MED) Supervision, K-12 Curr 1963; Addl Stud Elem Prin, Supervision & Curr, Learning Disabilities, Dev Handicapped, Individualized Instruction; *cr:* Oak Hill Union Schls Elem, Elem Art Tchr 1958-64; Jackson Cty Schls K-12 Supvr 1964-66; Athens Hocking & Perry Cty Ed Ctr K-12 Lang Arts Consultant 1968-70; Southeastern OH Special Ed Ctr Coord of Instructions Resources 1970-74; Univ of Rio Grande Prof 1974-; *ai:* Bd Mem Jackson Gallia Meigs Bd of Mental Hlth Alcohol, Drug Addiction; Mem Jungian Assn of Cntrl OH; Tenure Comm; Amer Assn of Colls for Tchr Ed 1974-; *office:* Univ Of Rio Grande Rio Grande Campus Rio Grande OH 45674*

BAUER, PAUL FRANKLIN, Philosophy Professor; *b:* Logansport, IN; *m:* Karen Webber; *c:* Mary Rebecca, Sarah Elizabeth; *ed:* Miami Univ at OH (MA) Psych 1967; Johns Hopkins Univ (MED) Ed 1970; Iliff Schl of Theology (MDiv) Divinity 1973, (ThD) Theology 1975; *cr:* Harford Comm Coll Psych Instr 1967-70; North Shore Comm Coll Psych Instr 1970-71; Cecil Comm Coll Philosophy Prof 1976-; *ai:* Tchr of Yr 1978-79; Pub Book Chapter, Numerous Articles; *office:* Cecil Comm Coll 1000 N East Rd North East MD 21901

BAUER, ROBERT T.,JR., Physical Education Teacher; *b:* Suffern, NY; *m:* Charice A.; *c:* Angela Marie; *ed:* Saint Leo Coll of FL (BA) PE K-12 1982; New Paltz St Coll (MS) K-6 Elem Ed 1989, (SDA) Admin-CAS 1994; 39 Post Grad Credit Hrs Beyond Masters; *cr:* Washingtonville HS Sub Tchr, Ftbl, Bsktbl & Bsbl Coach 1982-88; Clarkstown North HS 9th-12th Grd PE Tchr 1989-; *ai:* Var Ftbl & Bsbl Head Coach; Var Athletes Against Substance Abuse Coord; Rockland Cty PE Steering Comm; Rickland Cty Coaches Assn 1991-, Exec Bd; Section One Bsbl Coaches Assn 1989-; Amer Alliance for Hlth, PE, Recreation & Dance 1989-; Jr Coll & Coll Bsktbl Ofcl Assns 1986-, Referee; IABO #180, HS Referee; Natl Rifle Assn of Amer; *office:* Clarkstown HS North Congers Rd New City NY 10956*

BAUER, SUSAN ECKART, Vocal Music Director; *b:* Middletown, OH; *m:* Mark; *c:* Alison, Danny; *ed:* Defiance Coll (BA) Music Ed 1985; Wright St Univ 20 Hrs Music Ed; *cr:* Fairborn City Schls Long Term Sub Tchr 1985-86; Triad Local Schls Vocal Music Dir K-12 Grd 1986-90; North Coll HIll City Schls 6-12 Grd Vocal Music Dir 1990-; *ai:* Choral, Musical Dir;

Show Choir; MENC 1987-; Outstdng Tchr of Yr 1993-1994; *office:* North College Hill HS 1620 W Galbraith Rd Cincinnati OH 45239

BAUER, SUZANNE P., Library & Media Specialist; *b:* Brooklyn, NY; *m:* Robert; *c:* Allison F., Adam Scott; *ed:* Univ of Rochester (BS) Elem Ed 1961; C. W. Post (MS) Gifted Ed 1983; Palmer Schl of Lib Sci (MLS) Schl Lib Media Specialist 1991; *cr:* Long Beach Schl Dist Tchr 1962-64; Shallow Jr HS Sub Tchr 1964-66; Long Beach City Schl Dist Created, Dir Sat Enrichment 1974-77; Carle Place Schl Dist Tchr of Gifted 1977-90; Rushmore Schl Lib, Media Specialist 1990-; *ai:* LISMA 1990-; NYSUT, CPTA 1977-; ALA, NYSC, TE 1994-; Delta Kappa Gamma 1987-, Sec; Hadassah L. B. Chptr 1970-, VP FundRaising; Cancer Care Long Beach 1969-, Pres 1974-75; Distngd Performance in Ed 1984; Jewish War Veterans Brotherhood Awd 1977; Director of Gifted Programs in Nassau County 1983; *office:* Rushmore Avenue Elem Schl 251 Rushmore Ave Carle Place NY 11514*

BAUER, THOMAS WALTER, Span Tchr & Frgn Langs Supvr; *b:* Brooklyn, NY; *c:* Jacqueline Grady, Timothy; *ed:* Marist Coll (BA) Span 1968; Fairleigh Dickinson Univ (MA) Span 1970; William Paterson Coll Supervisory Cert 1979; *cr:* Park Ridge HS Span Tchr 1968-, Frgn Lang Dept Chprsn 1979-84, Frgn Lang Supvr 1984-, Fine Arts Supvr 1985-90; *ai:* Asst Var Ftbl Coach; Weight Trng Coach, Supvr; NEA, NJEA, BCEA, NJAATSP, BCSSPSA 1968-; PREA 1968-, Former VP, Pres 1978-81; PEP Players 1978-, Actor; P. R. Municipal Pool 1990-, Mgr; *office:* Park Ridge HS 2 Park Ave Park Ridge NJ 07656

BAUER-BLAZER, KAREN A., Social Studies Dept Chair; *b:* Cleveland, OH; *m:* Allen Joseph Blazer; *c:* Lauren; *ed:* Baldwin-Wallace (BA) His 1972; Cleveland St Univ (MA) His 1981; Assertive Discipline Course 5 Cr Hrs BW 1993; *cr:* Villa Angela Acad Tchr, Team Chair 1976-91; Villa Angela-St Joseph Schl Tchr, Soc Stud Dept Chair 1991-; *ai:* Soc Stud Dept, North Cntrl Steering Comm Chair; Close Up Coord; Natl Assn of Scndry Cath Tchrs 1980-; CHALTA 1976-; Tchr of Yr Sr Poll 1992-95; *office:* Villa Angela St Joseph HS 18491 Lake Shore Blvd Cleveland OH 44119

BAUGH, VERNEDA HAMM, Asst Prof of Psychology; *b:* Philadelphia, PA; *m:* Allen; *c:* Allen Jr.; *ed:* Fisk Univ (BA) Psych 1983; Temple Univ (PHD) Experimental Psych 1989; *cr:* PA St Univ NIA Post-Doctoral Fellow 1988-90; Xavier Univ of LA AsstPharmacy Prof 1990-92; Kean Coll of NJ Asst Psych Prof 1992-; *ai:* Fac Co-Adv; ACE-NIP; APA 1992-; Psi Chi, Co-Coord; Numerous Articles Pub; *office:* Kean Coll Of NJ 1000 Morris Ave Union NJ 07083

BAUGHMAN, JOHN LESTER, Fourth Grade Teacher; *b:* Cleveland, OH; *m:* Susana Cristina Gianotti; *ed:* Miami Univ (BS) Elem Ed 1977; Wright St Univ (MA) Ed 1989; *cr:* Morrow Elem Schl 4th Grd Tchr 1967-; *ai:* Musical Dir; Curr Person; Mentor Tchr; Schl Comms; Little Miami Tchrs Assn, OEA, NEA 1967-; Lions Club 1980-, Treas; Lebanon Presbyn Church 1996; Excl Tchng Awd 1993; *home:* 218 Saddleback Dr Loveland OH 45140

BAUGHMAN, SANDRA ELBEL, Elementary Teacher; *b:* Punxsutawney, PA; *m:* Bruce B.; *c:* Alyssa, Bryan, Colton; *ed:* Clarion St Coll (BS) Elem, Music 1974; Masters Equival IUP; *cr:* Purchase Line Schl Dist 4-6th Grd Tchr 1976-; *ai:* PSEA, PLEA 1976-; *office:* Purchase Line North Elem RD 1 Box 135 Mahaffey PA 15757

BAUGHN, KYLE SHANE, Mathematics Teacher; *b:* Findlay, OH; *m:* Elizabeth Burris; *ed:* The Defiance Coll (BS) Math & Music 1993; *cr:* The Defiance Coll Tutor 1992-93; Northwest OH Substitute Tchr 1993-94; Ridgemont HS Math Tchr 1994-; *ai:* Ftbl Asst Head Coach; Odyssey of the Mind Coach; Var Track Head Coach; Wrestling Asst; Weight Room Coord; BSA 1980-, Asst Scoutmaster, Eagle Scout; Tech-Prep Rep; *office:* Ridgemont Jr Sr HS 162 E Hale St Ridgeway OH 43345*

BAUKMAN, CHRISTABELL V. BATES, Intensity IV Teacher; *b:* Washington, DC; *m:* David Alan; *ed:* Prince George's Comm Coll (AA) Elem Ed 1983; Univ of VA (BS) Spec Ed 1985; George Washington Univ (MS) Seriously Emotionally Disturbed Adolescents 1988; *cr:* Stephen Decatur MS Math, Sci Tchr 1982-88, Self Contained Tchr of Emotionally Impaired 1988-89; Guide Shelter Home Cnslr Summer 1988-; Stephen Decatur MS Soc Stud, Life Skills Tchr 1989-93, Soc Stud, Math Tchr 1993-; *ai:* Team Ldr; PGCEA 1987-; Unity Ctr of Light 1991-, Team Captain Usher, Book Clerk; Federal Govt Schlsp Awd to Attnd George WAshington Univ for Participation in Seriously Emotionally Disturbed Adolescents Prgm; *home:* 5903 Hil Mar Dr Forestville MD 20747

BAUM, JOSEPH JOHN, Spanish & English Teacher; *b:* Canton, OH; *m:* Kathleen Hinton; *c:* Laura-Jeanne Morgan, Joseph III, Anne Melissa; *ed:* Walsh Univ (BA) Ed 1967; 10 Sem Hrs Cnslng Univ of Akron; 9 Sem Hrs Jrnlsm, Discipline Kent St Univ; *cr:* Lake HS Tchr, Coach 1967-68; Glenwood HS Tchr, Coach 1968-71; Cntrl Cath HS Tchr, Coach 1971-77; Alliance HS Tchr, Coach 1977-78; Windham HS Tchr, Coach 1978-; *ai:* Head Vary Ftbl Coach; Variety Show Adv; NEA 1977-, Rep; OH Ed Assn 1977-, Assemblyman; Windham Tchrs Assn 1978-, Pres 1982, 1984, 1988, 1990, 1992, 1994, 1996; Portage Co Coaches Assn 1996; OH HS Ftbl Coaches Assn 1978-; Founding Mem Portage Co Eng Festival Comm; Articles Pub.

BAUM, KATHERINE SEITZ, Geometry Teacher; *b:* Upper Darby, PA; *m:* Eric D.; *c:* Meghan A.; *ed:* Edinboro Univ (BS) Math Ed 1984; Millersville Penn St Masters Equivalency; *cr:* Palmyra Area Schl Dist Math Tchr 12 Yrs; *ai:* Lebanon Cty Educl Hnr Soc 1994-; Tchr of Month Palmyra HS 1995; Presidential Awd of Excl Math Tchng Nom 1996; *office:* Palmyra HS 1125 Park Dr Palmyra PA 17078

BAUM, LYNDA SPRAGUE, Second Grade Teacher; *b:* Bar Harbor, ME; *m:* Joseph; *c:* Keely, Tucker; *ed:* Univ of Southern ME (BA) Elem Ed 1977; *cr:* SAD #5 5th Grd Tchr 1977-82, 2nd Grd Tchr 1982-; *ai:* Staff Dev Comm; Japanese Intern Spon; NEA, MEA 1977-; Whos Who in Amer Colls; *office:* Gilford Butler Primary Schl PO Box 146 South Thomaston ME 04858*

BAUM, TERRY GALVIN, 6th Grade Social Stud Tchr; *b:* Oswego, NY; *m:* Jeffrey S.,; *c:* Justin, Kristopher; *ed:* SUNY at Oswego (BS) Elem Ed 1978, (MS) Elem Ed 1984; 12 Post Grad Credits; *cr:* Fulton Cath Elem 3rd Grd Tchr 1979-80; Mexico MS 6th Grd Soc Stud Tchr 1980-; *ai:* NYSUT 1980-; AFT 1980-; Alpha Delta Kappa 1994-; *office:* Mexico MS Rt 104 East Mexico NY 13114

BAUMAN, B. LEE, Implementation Specialist; *b:* Flushing, NY; *m:* Edward C.; *ed:* PA St Univ (BA) Ed 1963; 12 Credit Hrs; *cr:* Penn Hills Schl Dist Elem Tchr 1963-66, Implementation Specialist for Mid-Atlantic Lab; *ai:* NEA, PSEA, PHEA 1963-; *office:* Penn Hills Schl Dist 309 Collins Dr Penn Hills PA 15235

BAUMAN, CLARE L., English Teacher; *b:* Queens, NY; *m:* Larry Woodbridge; *ed:* Univ of WI at Madison (BA) Eng 1977; Hunter Coll (MA) Eng, Ed 1987; *cr:* CCNY Writing Tutor 1986-87; Hunter Coll Writing Tchr 1987-88; Telecommunications HS Eng, Drama Tchr 1989-; *ai:* Drama Dir 1990-; Writing Tchr 1994 Woman Coll Participant; Creative Arts Team at NYU 1993-; Licoln Ctr Theatre Pgm 1993-; UFT 1988-; Arts In Ed Roundtable 1993-; Hunter Coll Amer Soc His Project 1993-; Brooklyn Acad of Music Ed Advy Bd 1993-; Lincoln Ctr Inst 1990-; NY St Cncl of Arts; Womens Stud, Womens Lives; *office:* Telecomm Arts & Tech HS 394 First St #3R Brooklyn NY 11215

BAUMAN, DEBORAH JANE, Health & PE Teacher; *b:* Natrona Hghts, PA; *ed:* Slippery Rock Univ (BS) Hlth, PE, Recreation 1973; PA St Univ (MED) Hlth 1991; Jean Houston's Mystery Schl Extraordinary Human Capacities 1993; Pathways to the Future 1994; *cr:* South Butler Cty Schls Jr, Sr HS Tchr 1975-, Var Coach 1975-82, Jr HS Coach 1980-93; *ai:* Coord Stu Assistance Prgm; Assisted With the Dev of REACH Prgm; NEA; Gift of Time 1992; *home:* 1031 Ekastown Rd Saxonburg PA 16056

BAUMAN, JOAN LOU CLYMER, Third Grade Teacher; *b:* Bluffton, OH; *c:* Michael, Maureen K. Noe, Calvin; *ed:* Bluffton Coll (BS) Ed 1954; Dayton Univ (MA) Ed 1990; Attnd Univ of Findlay; *cr:* Cleveland Pub Schl Tchr 1954-58; Niceria Schl Tchr 1962; Streetsboro Schl Tchr 1966; Cory-Rawson Schl Tchr 1973-; *ai:* AFT 1980-; AFS 1981-, Pres, Hosting; Church; *office:* Cory-Rawson Schl 220 S Main St Rawson OH 45881

BAUMAN, M. GARRETT, Professor of English; *b:* Paterson, NJ; *m:* Carol Nobles; *c:* Cynthia, Amy, Diana, Jeremy; *ed:* Upsala Coll (BA) Eng 1969; SUNY At Binhamton Eng 1971; *cr:* Monroe Comm Coll Prof 1971-; *ai:* Leavy Awd for Ed; NYS Fnd for Arts Fellowship in Creative Nonfiction; Chancellors Awd for Tchng; Author Ideas & Details, Shape of Ideas; 100 Articles Pub; *office:* Monroe Comm Coll 1000 E Henrietta Rd Rochester NY 14623

BAUMAN, MARY JOHNSON, High School Math Teacher; *b:* Cincinnati, OH; *m:* Louis Henry; *c:* Barbara Potting, Michael, Denise; *ed:* Univ of Akron (BS) Elem Ed 1985, (MS) Cnslng Classroom Tchr 1990; Addl 18 Semester Hrs Scndry Ed, Math, Gen Sci; *cr:* St Matthews Schl 7, 8 Grd Math Tchr 1986; St Francis Xavier 5, 6 Grd Math Tchr 1986-87; Padua Franciscan HS Math Tchr; *ai:* Tri C Metro Campus Tchr; Veterans Upward Bound; *office:* Padua Franciscan HS 6740 State Rd Parma OH 44134*

BAUMANN, CANDICE JEANNE, 6th Grade Literature Teacher; *b:* Phoenix, AZ; *m:* Michael J.; *c:* Michael, Molly, Patrick; *ed:* Marymount Coll (BA) Drama & Eng 1973; Slippery Rock Univ 18 Hrs Post Grad; *cr:* Kirby Jr High 8th Grd Eng Tchr 1973-75; Vincentian HS 9th-11th Grd Regular & Hnrs Eng Tchr 1991-94; Sewickley Acad 6th Grd Lit Tchr 1994-; *ai:* Lit Magazine Co-Chprsn; Compensation Comm; TAP Mem; *office:* Sewickley Acad 315 Academy Ave Sewickley PA 15143

BAUMANN, MICHAEL J., School Counselor; *b:* Rochester, NY; *m:* Angela M. Patti; *ed:* Canisius Coll (BA) Psych 1986, (MS) Schl Counseling 1989, (MS) Educl Admin 1995; *cr:* West Seneca West Sr HS Schl Cnslr 1989-; *ai:* Wrestling, Track Head Coach; Ftbl Asst Coach; Var Club Adv; ACA 1989-; ASCD 1994-; Phi Delta Kappa 1996-; *office:* West Seneca West Sr HS 3330 Seneca St West Seneca NY 14224

BAUMBACH, WALTER DAVID, School Counselor; *b:* Lancaster, PA; *m:* M. Michele Stackhouse; *ed:* York Coll (AS) Sci 1968; Millersville Univ (BS) Ed & Physics 1971, (MS) Cnslr Ed 1983; Franklin & Marshall 6 Hrs; *cr:* Dauphw Cty Tech Schl 10th 11th & 12th Grd Tchr 1 Yr; Solanco Schl Dist 8th Grd Phys Sci Tchr 13 Yrs; Penn Manor Schl Dist MS Counselor 11 Yrs; *ai:* Peer Helper & Peer Mediation Adv, Parent Ed Instr; Natl Peer Helpers Assn 4 Yrs; Penn Peer Helpers Assn 1985-, Treas, Bd of Dir, Svc Awd; Willow St UCC 1985-, Deacon; Samaritan Cnslng Ctr Willow St Advy Bd 1990-, Chm; Penn Manor Edctrs of the Yr Avd 1991-; Article Pub in Natl Peer Helper's Assn Quarterly; *office:* Penn Manor Schl Dist 356 Frogtown Rd Pequea PA 17565

BAUMGARDNER, LOIS KAY BOHAM, Fourth Grade Teacher; *b:* Lima, OH; *m:* James Clinton; *c:* Scott, Michelle; *ed:* OH St Univ (BA) K-8th Grd Elem Ed 1986, (MS) Elem & Rdng Specialty 1991; Drake Univ High Performing Tchr 3 Hrs, Parents on Your Side 3 Hrs, Motivating Stdnts 3 Hrs; Univ of Dayton Succeeding with Difficult Stdnts 3 Hrs; *cr:* Waynesfield-Goshen 3rd-6th Grd Chapter I & Jr HS Rdng Tchr 1986-91, 4th Grd Tchr 1991-; *ai:* IAT Comm; Bldg Leadership Comm; NEA 1986-, Local Pres; Class Prepares Items for Sr Citizens Meeting Monthly; *office:* Waynesfield-Goshen Sch Westminster St PO Box 370 Waynesfield OH 45896

BAUMGARTNER, SHERILL, Biology Teacher; *b:* Philadelphia, PA; *m:* Wayne R. Acker; *c:* Sarah Krista Acker, Travis Acker; *ed:* Syracuse Univ (AB) Art His 1972; Penn St Univ (MS) Animal Nutrition 1978; Cabrini Coll (MED) Ed 1990; *cr:* Harcum Jr Coll Lab Animal Sci, Animal Ctr Mngmt Prgms Dir 1983-87; Thomas Jefferson Univ Lab Animal Facility Mgr, Admin of Ed Prgm 1987-89; Montgomery Cty Comm Coll Bio Instruction 1989-90; Norristown Area HS Bio Tchr 1990-; *ai:* Sci Olympiad Team Coach; Eagles of Nature Spon; NEA, PSEA 1990-; Church 1983-, Trustee; Audubon Soc; Appalachian Mountain Club; *office:* Norristown Area HS 1900 Eagle Dr Norristown PA 19403

BAUN, WILLIAM ROBERT, 4th-6th Grade Citizenship Tchr; *b:* Youngstown, OH; *m:* Cindy Oyster; *c:* Katherine, Hollie, Michael; *ed:* Younstown St Univ (BS) Ed 1983, (MS) Rdng Specialist 1988; 15 Credit Hrs Beyond MS; *cr:* Youngstown Pub Schls Tchr 1983-; *ai:* Odyssey of the Mind Coach; NEA 1985-; Impact II Grant 1990, 1992-93; Venture Capital Grant Writer & Recipient 1995; *office:* John White Elem Schl 1061 Lyden Ave Youngstown OH 44505

BAUR, CHERYL ANN, Secondary Mathematics Teacher; *b:* Pittsburgh, PA; *ed:* Clarion Univ (BS) Math 1977; 24 Post Grad Credits; *cr:* Amherst Jr HS Math Tchr 1977-84; Dorseyville Jr HS Math Tchr 1984; Springdale Sr HS Math Tchr 1985-86; Avella Jr HS Math Tchr 1988-; *ai:* Frosh Class, Soph Class Spon; OBE Steering Comm; NCTM, NEA, PSEA, AEA 1988-; *office:* Avella Area Jr Sr HS 1000 Avella Rd Avella PA 15312

BAUR, LORETTA MUMAW, Second Grade Teacher; *b:* Orrville, OH; *m:* Roger Lee; *ed:* Goshen Coll (BA) Elem Ed 1975; 20 El Ed Grad Credit Hrs at Akron Univ, Ashland Univ; *cr:* Chestnut Ridge Elem Schl Title I Rdng Tchr 1975-78; Berlin Elem Schl Grd Two Tchr 1978-; *ai:* Intervention Assistance Team Pilot Project 1993-; NEA, OEA 1975-; East Holmes Tchrs Assn 1975-, Sec, Treas; Delta Kappa Gamma 1984-; Our Holmes Cty Office of Ed Sci Enrichment Grant 1989, Soc Stud Enrichment Grant 1990; *office:* Berlin Elem Schl PO Box 310 4978 SR 39 Berlin OH 44610

BAUSHER, RICHARD SCOTT, 7th Grade Geography Teacher; *b:* Reading, PA; *ed:* IN Univ of PA (BA) Elem Ed 1976; Lehigh Univ (MS) Educl Admin 1980; *cr:* Governor Mifflin Schl Dist 6 Grd Elem Tchr 1976-95, 7 Grd Geog Tchr 1995-; *ai:* Girls Var Bsktbl Head Coach 1983-; PSEA, NEA 1976-; GOTA Berks Cty Girls Bsktbl Coaches 1983-, Pres; *office:* Gov Mifflin Middle School 10 S Waverly St Shillington PA 19607*

BAUTISTA, JUSTO BAUTISTA, Math Dept Chprsn & Teacher; *b:* Altavas Aklan, Philippines; *m:* Dolores Alonzo; *c:* Jeffrey, Jayhdeeh, Jerrimie, Jennifer; *ed:* Feati Univ (BA) Math 1968; Manuel L. Quezon Univ (MS) Math; 15 Addl Credits; *cr:* Tagaytay City Inst Tchr 1968-69; Sacred Heart Acad Tchr, Asst Prin 1969-76; Garki Tchrs Coll Tchr, Dept Head 1976-86; Acad of St Aloysius Tchr, Dept Chprsn 1987-; *ai:* Moderator Math League; *office:* Acad Of Saint Aloyius 2495 Kennedy Blvd Jersey City NJ 07304

BAUTZ, WILLIAM F., Science Teacher; *b:* Buffalo, NY; *m:* Judy Rush; *ed:* SUNY at Stony Brook (MA) Lbrl Stud 1974; *cr:* Mt Sinai Schl Tchr 1972-; *ai:* Sci Club; GATE; AFT, NYSUT 1972-; MSTA 1972-, Grievance Chm; Parent Wkshp, St Ed Dept Presenter; *office:* Mt Sinai MS Rt 25A Box 397 Mount Sinai NY 11766

BAVARO, DEBORAH ANN, Second Grade Teacher; *b:* Buffalo, NY; *ed:* Trocaire Coll (AAS) Early Chldhd Ed 1976; Buffalo St Coll (BS) Elem Ed & Early Chldhd 1978, (MS) Elem Ed & Early Chldhd 1980; *cr:* Gardenville Elem Title I Math Tchr 1978-79; Saint Columba 1st Grd Tchr 1979-82; Saint Ambrose Schl 2nd-3rd Grd Tchr 1982-; *ai:* Travel Extensively in US, Europe & South Amer; *office:* St Ambrose Schl 260 Okell St Buf[illegible] 14220

BAXENDELL, ROBIN JEAN BURGER, Art Teacher; *b:* Queens, Andrew; *c:* Mark Andrew, Scott Alan, Kenneth Steven; *ed:* Nazar[illegible] (BS) Art Ed 1974, (MS) Art Ed 1981; Attnd SUNY at Buffalo; *cr:* [illegible] Cntrl Schls 4th-6th Grd Art Tchr 1974-80, HS Art Tchr 1980-84, Grd Art Tchr 1984-86, HS Art Tchr 1986-; *ai:* Prins Cncl; Rsrc[illegible] Scheduling Comm; Artist-in-Residence Pgm Coord; Fairport Ed 1974-; NYSUT 1974-; Penfield Schl Bd 1976-79; USABDA Flow Chpter 1985-, Newsletter Ed 1991-, Pres 1993-95; Art Gallery Ceramics 1981; St of the Art Exhibit 1995; Regnl Advy Bd Schola[illegible] 4 Yrs; *office:* Fairport HS 1358 Ayrault Rd Fairport NY 14450

BAXTER, BRENDA S., 5th Grade Teacher; *b:* Monroeville, [illegible] Calvin; *c:* Candice, Calvin II; *ed:* WV St Coll (BA) Elem Ed 1969; St Coll (MS) Eng 1973; Masters Plus 10 Addl Hrs; *cr:* St Boniface [illegible] Tchr 1969; BUILD Acad 5th Grd Tchr 1970-76, 1978-; Schl #57 [illegible] Tchr 1977-78; *ai:* Pleasant Bapt Church Yth Adv; Chrstn Bd of Mem; Private Tutor; NEA 1969-; Delta Sigma Theta 1967-, 25 Yr S[illegible] Pleasant Grove Bapt Church; *home:* 144 Huntley Rd Buffalo NY 1[illegible]

BAXTER, CYNTHIA LYNN, 8th Grade English Teacher; *b:* Ba[illegible] MD; *ed:* Messiah Coll (BA) Eng 1989; Univ of MD (MA) Eng 1[illegible] Perry Hall MS 7th-8th Eng Tchr 1991-; *ai:* 8th Grd Team New[illegible] *office:* Perry Hall MS 4300 Ebenezer Rd Baltimore MD 21236

BAXTER, RICHARD K., Science Department Chairman; *b:* K[illegible] Falls, OR; *c:* Michele, Michael; *ed:* OR St Univ (BS) PE 1965, (M[illegible] Ed 1969; Post Grad Hrs at Univ of MD, Boston Univ, San Diego S[illegible] of CA at Hayward, Troy St, West MI; *cr:* Warm Springs Elem Schl [illegible] Tchr 1969-70; Centerville Jr HS 7-8 Grd Tchr 1970-71; Heilbronn [illegible] HS 7-8 Grd Sci Tchr 1971-73; Heidelberg Amer HS 9-12 Grd S[illegible] 1973-; *ai:* Sci Dept, Schl Profile Chm; Schl Improvement Pla[illegible] Comms; NEA; NSTA; US Pro Tennis Assn; Overseas Ed Assn; *hom[illegible]* 419 Box 1361 APO AE 09102

BAXTER, SAUNDRA MARIE, 6th Grade Teacher; *b:* Butler, Robert R.; *c:* Carly M., Cole M., Caitlin M.; *ed:* Slippery Rock Un[illegible] Elem Ed 1988; Youngstown St Univ (AAS) Med Tech 1982; *cr:* Butl[illegible] Schl Dist 6th Grd Tchr 1989-; *ai:* Comp Facilitator; BASD; BEA PSEA 1989-; NEA 1989-; Unionville Presbyn Church 1992-; Clearfield Elem Schl 621 Clearfield Rd Fenelton PA 16034

BAXTER, SHIRLEY NELSON, Former Teacher; *b:* Columbus, [illegible] Ronald D.; *c:* Brenda, Anne, Christine; *cr:* Tremont Elem Schl 1st G[illegible] 1956-60; Upper Arlington Schls Spec Ed 1969-73; Faith Chrstn S[illegible] Grd Tchr 1980-89.

BAY, JANET G., Fifth Grade Teacher; *b:* Albany, NY; *m:* Lawrenc[illegible] Katherine J. Hincher, Brian G.; *ed:* SUNY Oneonta (BS) K-6 1[illegible] Univ (MED) Curr, Supervision 1963; *cr:* Lincoln Elem Schl Grd Tchr 1959-63; Westminster Elem Schl Grd 5 Tchr 1963-64; North[illegible] Univ Schl Tchr 1969-71; Minoa Elem Schl Resource Room Asst Grd 1982-; *ai:* Tchr Retirement Incentive Comm; Tchrs Union 1982-; Excl 1990-.*

BAYAT, CAROLYN ANNE SMITH, French Teacher; *b:* Jersey C[illegible] *m:* Ted; *c:* Mary Anne, Todd, Michael; *ed:* OH Univ (BA) Fr 1973, Elem Ed 1987; Rdng Recovery Cert 1991-92; *cr:* Athens MS F[illegible] 1973-91; Anna HS Fr Tchr 1991-; Anna Elem Schl Rdng Recove[illegible] 1991-; *ai:* Fr Club, Fr Schlsp Team Adv; NEA, OEA, AEA 1973-; Ph[illegible] Kappa; Jennings Scholar 1988-89; *office:* Anna HS 1 Mc Rill Wa[illegible] OH 45302

BAYEWITZ, HOWARD S., Social Studies Teacher; *b:* Brooklyn, Ellen Sandman; *c:* Andrea Neusner, Michael; *ed:* Long Island Uni[illegible] His 1964; St Univ of NY at New Paltz (MS) Asian Stud 1979; A[illegible] Credits Beyond Masters at Various Insts; *cr:* La Salle Jr HS Soc St[illegible] 1965-69; M C Miller MS Soc Stud Tchr 1970-86; Kingston HS S[illegible] Tchr 1986-; *ai:* AFT, NY St Cncl of Soc Stud 1970-; Kingston Tc[illegible] 1970-, Grievance Chm, Exec Comm; NCSS 1990-; Sino-Judaic Inst Fulbright to India 1991; Woodrow Wilson Fellowship World His NEH Insts Fordham Univ 1990, CA St at Long Beach 1994, Smi[illegible] 1995; NEH Seminar at Univ of MA 1993; *office:* Kingston H[illegible] Broadway Kingston NY 12401

BAYLIES, SUSAN MICHEL, 5th Grade Classroom Teacher; *b:* [illegible] OH; *m:* Peter W.; *c:* John, David; *ed:* Kent St Univ (BGS) Eng, Phil 1985, (BS) Elem Ed 1986; *cr:* Immaculate Conception Schl 5-8 Classroom Tchr 1986-89; Atkinson Elem Schl 5th Grd Tchr 1989-; [illegible] Dev Comm Chprsn; MTA; ASCD 1995-, Basic Mem; Tchng Ex[illegible] 1989; North Andover Fnd Grant 1996; *office:* Atkinson Elem S[illegible] Phillips Brooks Rd North Andover MA 01845

BAYLISS, JAMES LEROY, Social Studies Teacher; *b:* Ney, OH; [illegible] *ed:* Defiance Coll (BA) Soc Stud 1963; Xavier Univ (MS) Scndry 1984; *cr:* Continental HS Tchr 1963-64; Mt Healthy HS Tchr 1964- Healthy South Jr HS Tchr 1972-; *ai:* NEA, OEA 1963-; Mt Healthy Assn 1970-, Pres, Tchrs Hnr Awd; *home:* 8004 Mildway Ct Cincinn[illegible] 45239

BAYLOR, BARBARA ANNELIESE, German & Speech Teac[illegible] Braunschweig, Germany; *m:* Terry William; *c:* Heidi Barbara H[illegible] Christine Lena, Kelly Ann, Michael; *ed:* Millersville Univ (MA) Ge[illegible] *cr:* Waynesboro HS Ger & Eng Tchr 1966-67; Cntrl Dauphin HS E[illegible] 1967-68, Ger Tchr 1982-83; Milton Hershey Schl Ger & Eng Tchr [illegible] *ai:* Drama Dir; Yrbk Adv; Frgn Lang Dept Chair; March of Dimes Yth Walk Fac Adv; AATG 1993-; ACTFL 1994-; United Meth 1966-; *office:* Milton Hershey Schl 300 Hotel Rd Hershey PA 1703[illegible]

BAYLOR, SCOTT A., Chemistry Teacher; *b:* Danville, PA; *m:* Jan Reichenbach; *ed:* Bloomsburg Univ (BS) Scndry Ed 1987; 18 Grad [illegible] Millersville Univ; 12 Grad Credits Carlow Coll; 6 Grad Credits P[illegible] *cr:* Lancaster Cath HS Chem Tchr 1987-95; Elizabethtown Area HS Tchr 1995-; *ai:* Grad Project Ldr; NEA 1995-; PSEA, ASCO 19[illegible] Vincent Coll Great Tchr, Scholars in Ed Awds; *office:* Elizabethtow[illegible] HS 600 E High St Elizabethtown PA 17022*

BAYNE, LOIS MERCHANT, Social Studies Dept Chairm[illegible] Baltimore, MD; *m:* Dale J.; *c:* Dale J. Jr., Gerald, Donald, Rodg[illegible] Towson St Univ (BA) Soc Stud 1972; Addl 15 Credits; AP Cert (M[illegible] Stud 1980; AA Essex Comm Coll Credits for Fun Learning 19[illegible] Northern HS Tchr 1972-82; Childrens Emporium Shop Owner 1[illegible] Cath HS Tchr & Dept Head 1986-; *ai:* Stu Cncl Moderator; Fgn Coord; Cultural Moderator 1992-95; NCSS; MCSS; NEA 1974- Flwshp; *office:* The Catholic HS Of Baltimore 2800 Edison Hwy Bal[illegible] MD 21213*

BAYUK, JO-ANN LORRAINE, Business Education Teacher; *b:* NY; *m:* Kevin M.; *c:* Tony, Rebecca, Jason; *ed:* Long Island Uni[illegible] Accounting 1978; Lehman Coll (MS) Bus Ed 1986; Manhattan Col[illegible] Spec Ed 1991; Fordham Univ (PD) Supervision, Admin 1994; *cr:* [illegible] Hospitals Corp Fiscal Records Analyst 1978-79; Brooklyn DA's Accountant 1979-80; Jane Addams Voc HS Tchr 1981-82; Harry S. T[illegible] HS Tchr & Co-op Coord 1982-; *ai:* Work-Experience Coord; Liaiso[illegible] Guardia Comm Coll Co-op Now Prgm; Mainstream Comm; Annu[illegible] Bus Yth Educl Svcs Embrkmnt Liason; AFT, UFT 1981-; BEA *office:* White Plains HS 550 North St White Plains NY 10605*

, KAREN A., Social Studies Teacher; *b:* Auburn, NY; *ed:* Auburn (AS) Lbrl Arts 1973; SUNY at Cortland (BA) Ed 1975, (MS) Ed 36 Hrs Syracuse Univ; *cr:* West Genesee Jr & MS Soc Stud Tchr 3; W Genesee Schl Tchr of GATE 1989-90; Camillus MS Tchr of 1989-90; W Genesee HS Soc Stud Tchr 1991-; *ai:* Prof Dev; Educl amillus Optimist Oratorical Contest Adv; Coordinate Natl Geog & ıd Olympiad Contests; W Genesee Tchrs Assn 1975; CNYCSS; S; NYSUT; W Genesee, SU Tchng Ctr Policy Bd Directing Cncl; West Genesee Sr HS 5201 W Genesee St Camillus NY 13031

A, MICHELLE MONAHAN, French Teacher; *b:* Clarksburg, Robert A.; *c:* Alyssa Rae, Abby; *ed:* Indiana Univ of PA (BA) Fr, ade 1985; Univ of Pittsburgh (MAT) Ed 1988; 12 Addl Credits; *cr:* ntnl Stud Acad Fr Tchr Intern 1987-88; John A. Brashear HS Fr Tchr, Advanced Stud Prgm Co-Facilitator 1988-; *ai:* Fr Club Spon; s Club; AATF 1990-; AFT, PFT 1988-; *office:* John A. Brashear HS ane Ave Pittsburgh PA 15216

A, MARY THERESA ANN, Fourth Grade Teacher; *b:* own, PA; *ed:* Gwynedd Mercy Coll (BS) Elem Ed 1978; Certs Cmptr Tech, Math Challenges, Integrated Lang; Provisional Rel *r:* Sts Cosmas & Damian Fourth Grd Tchr 1973-80; Sacred Heart Fifth Grd Tchr 1980-82; St Matthew Fourth Grd Tchr 1985-; *ai:* Beverage Prgm 6 Yrs, Summer Math Prgm Coord; AIDS Seminars; Asst Sftbl Coach.

, JOANNE, Fourth Grade Teacher; *b:* Brooklyn, NY; *ed:* Hunter A) Elem Ed 1990; Working on MS Elem Ed; *cr:* St Cecilia Schl Grd Tchr 1990-91, 4th Grd Tchr 1991-, Enrichment Prgm Coord *ai:* Rel Ed Instr, Children's Liturgy Catechist; Environment, Lang dng Comm; Latin Tchr; NCTE 1990-; *office:* St Cecilia Schl 1-15 r St Brooklyn NY 11222*

ET, JAMES RICHARD, Fifth Grade Teacher; *b:* Lewiston, ME; esa Anna Caron; *c:* Steven; *ed:* Univ of ME at Farmington (BS) Soc 72; Univ Southern ME 18 Credit Hrs; *cr:* Lewiston Schl Dept Tchr *ai:* Store Adv; Montello Staff Dev Comm; NEA, MEEA, Lewiston 2-; Phi Delta Kappa 1996-; Lewiston Jaycees 1982-84, Outstanding Man 1982; ME Jaycees 1982-84, Outstanding Young Man 1983; books Search for Great Amer Tchr Awd 1988; *office:* Montello chl East Ave Lewiston ME 04240

CO, JOHN A., Social Science Dept Chm; *b:* New York, NY; *m:* Ann Holian; *c:* John III, Christopher; *ed:* Amherst Coll (BA) His North Adams St Coll (MEd) Scndry Admin 1968; Univ of AZ (MA) Ed 1972; *cr:* Cornwall Acad Tchr & Coach 1964-65; Berkshire egnl Tchr & Coach 1965-; *ai:* Bd of Selection 1972-, Chm 1977-.

H, ALAN ROBERT, High School Counselor; *b:* Dayton, OH; *m:* ufderheide; *c:* Michael A., Lauren S.; *ed:* Univ of Dayton (BS) Ed, 1970; Wright St Univ (MS) Cnslng 1974; Post Grad Work Univ of , Wright St Univ, Univ of Cincinnati, Cleveland St Univ; *cr:* nade HS Eng Tchr 1970-71; Montgomery Cty JVS Eng, Soc Stud 71-76; Miami Vly CTC Voc, HS Cnslr 1976-; *ai:* Natl Voc Tech Hnr m; Hnr Awds Assembly Coord; AFT, OFT Exec Comm Schl; Bsbl, Ftbl, Sftbl Coach 10 Yrs; AFT, OFT 1988-, VP; OSCA 1985-; Christi Ath Assn 1988-; North Riverdale Bsbl, Sftbl 1986-, Coach, rpus Christi Church Fund Raising 1989-, Chm; Licensed Prof Cnslr St Certfd GED Examiner 1988; *office:* Miami Valley Career Tech 0 Hoke Rd Clayton OH 45315

H, BRENDA L., First Grade Teacher; *b:* Wauseon, OH; *ed:* Capital BS) Elem Ed 1964; IN Univ (MS) Elem Ed 1969; Univ of HI 5 Hrs; Kent St Univ, Akron Univ; *cr:* West Unity Local Schls First & Fourth chr 1964-69; Wooster City Schls Tchr of Learning Disabilities 7, First Grd Tchr 1977-; *ai:* Lib Comm Fundraisers, Book Selection PSTA Bd Tchr Rep; Martha Holden Jennings 1975-76; Alpha Delta 1969-; *office:* Parkview Elem Schl 144 N Market Wooster OH 44691

H, DEBRA WRIGHT, Physical Education Teacher; *b:* Keene, NH; rles W.; *ed:* Keene St Coll (BS) PE 1977; 15 Hrs PE & Coaching; anon HS PE Tchr 1977-; *ai:* Sr Class & Var Letter Club Adv; Var Hockey & Var Sftbl Coach; NEA & LEA 1978-; AAH PERD & PERD 1979-; NHCA 1990-; NFHCA 1985-; NHIAA Sftbl Comm ; *office:* Lebanon HS 195 Hanover St Lebanon NH 03766

H, DONALD L., Fifth Grade Teacher; *b:* Montour Falls, NY; *m:* Pridmore; *c:* Jennifer, Lisa; *ed:* St Univ Coll at Geneseo (BS) Ed Permanent Cert 30 Hrs; *cr:* Geneva Pub Schls Sixth Grd Tchr 2; Penn Yan Cntrl Schls Fifth Grd Tchr 1972-; *ai:* Schl Mngmt 5th Grd Staff Rep; Just Say No Prgm, Rdng Incentives Comms; Penn hrs Assn 1972-; NEA; BPO Elks USA 1988-; *office:* Penn Yan Elem School Dr Penn Yan NY 14527

H, JENNIFER ANNE, English Teacher; *b:* Baltimore, MD; *ed:* PA (BA) Eng, Womens Stud 1990; Johns Hopkins Univ (MAT) Eng dry Ed 1993; Working Toward (PHD) Eng Ed Univ of MD; 6 Credits Stud Johns hopkins; *cr:* Cmptr Law Reporters Inc Publishing tion Mgr 1991-92; Bishop Mc Namara HS Eng Tchr 1993-; EsseX Coll Part-time Eng Instr 1994; Anne Arundel Comm Coll Part-time tr 1994-; *ai:* Newspaper Adv; NCTE 1993-; Phi Delta Kappa 1996-; ant Course Tchng Shakespeare Funded Grant Natl Endowment *office:* Bishop Mc Namara HS 6800 Marlboro Pike Forestville MD

H, KATHLEEN SEGALE, Mathematics Teacher; *b:* Summit, NJ; vard L. III; *c:* Gregory, Jessica; *ed:* Montclair St Coll (BA) Math, 974; *cr:* Union HS Math Tchr 1979-; *ai:* Twirling Coach; NCTM; ms Presbyn Church 1982-, Elder, Deacon.

HUM, JANICE L., Eighth Grade English Teacher; *b:* Youngstown, Lock P. Sr.; *c:* Jenise D. Beachum Phillips, Lock P. Jr.; *ed:* town St Univ (BA) Eng 1966; Coll of Mt St Joseph (MA) Eng 1982; l Credit Hrs; *cr:* Youngstown City Schls Eng Tchr 1966-75; Warren chls Eng Tchr 1975-; *ai:* Acad Prep Bowl Coach; Schl Improvement Young Scholars Prgm OH St Univ Tutor; Warren Ed Assn 1975-, nding Tchr; NEA, NEOTA 1966-; Youngstown Black Womens ship 1983-, Pres; Black Educators Minority Assn 1977-, Sec; Hand in Hand 1986-, Sec, Schlsp Chair; Youngstown Urban League *home:* 915 Colby Ave Youngstown OH 44505

LE, SUSAN SINGER, Global Studies Teacher; *b:* Binghamton, NY; nary, Emily; *ed:* SUNY at Oswego (BS) Soc Stud 1975; SUNY at (MA) His 1982; *cr:* Union Endicott HS Tchr 1975-77; Lake George chr 1977-86; Queensbury HS Tchr 1986-; *office:* Queensbury HS 88 n Rd Queensbury NY 12804

AN, JOSEPH SHERIDAN, English Teacher; *b:* Clearfield, PA; *m:* Test; *c:* Amber, Erin Mc Gary; *ed:* Lock Haven Univ (BS) Eng 1965; dit Hrs PA St Univ; *cr:* Big Spring Schl Dist Eng Tchr 1965; West Area Schls Eng Tchr 1965-; *ai:* Ski Club Adv; PSEA, NEA 1965-; lub 1981-; *office:* West Branch HS Rd 2 Box 194 Morrisdale PA

AN, JUDITH ARKELL, Business Teacher; *b:* Chicago, IL; *m:* John : Lynn Marie, John J. III; *ed:* Albany St Univ (BS) Bus Ed 1970; 0 Hrs Grad Courses & In-svc Trng in Field; *cr:* Arlington HS Bus 971-; *ai:* Club 17 Adv; Bi-Annual Blood Drive; *office:* Arlington chl Dist 263 State Route 55 Lagrangeville NY 12540

BEALER, RICHARD H., Eighth Grade Geography Teacher; *b:* Pottstown, PA; *m:* Virginia Werstler; *c:* Karen, Jennifer; *ed:* West Chester St Univ (BS) Soc Sci 1972, (MS) Soc Sci 1976; Univ of PA Rdng Cert 1986; *cr:* Pottsgrove Schl Dist Tchr 1972-; *ai:* Sftbl Coach; Pine Forge Panthers 18 & Under Head Coach; NEA 1992-; AFT 1972-92, Local Sec; Pine Forge Ath Assn 1988-, VP; Douglas Twp Rec Bd 1990-; Tri-Cnty Sftbl Assn 1988-, Pres; *home:* RR 2 Box 552 Boyertown PA 19512

BEALL-BRANDES, TAMARA, Music Educator; *m:* Russell W.; *c:* Rowan W.; *ed:* Baldwin-Wallace Conservatory (BME) Voice 1981; Attnd Music Courses at Kent St, Heidleberg, Ashland; *cr:* Strongsville Schls Vocal Music 1981-85; Triway HS Vocal Music 1985-89; Buckeye HS Vocal Music 1989-; *ai:* Chamber Ensembles, Dramatic Productions; OMEA 1981-; OCDA 1995-; AFT 1989-; NEA 1981-; NATS 1981-; Delta Kappa Phi 1981-.

BEAM, JANET A., Third Grade Teacher; *b:* Hazleton, PA; *m:* Harry W.; *c:* John, Dennis; *ed:* Bloomsburg Univ (BS) Elem Ed 1981; Wilkes Univ (MS) Elem Ed 1991; 60 Addl Credits in Ed Penn St Univ 1993; *cr:* Hazelton Area Schl Dist Tchr 1981-; *ai:* ACT 178 Staff Dev Comm Prof Bd Mem 1993-95; PSEA, NEA 1981-, Tchr Rep to 1995 Rep Cncl Bd; Parent Tchr Exec Bd 1990-92; League Women Voters, Easter Seals Org 1994-; Helping Hands Soc 1995-; YMCA, YWCA, Vol Svc Awd, Yth of Comm Awd 1993; Wilkes Univ Spec Achvmt in Ed Awd 1995; League Women Voters St Recognition Kids Around Town Prgm.

BEAMS, CYNTHIA RUPRECHT, Adj Prof of Social Science; *b:* Englewood, NJ; *m:* Frederick B.; *c:* Susannah, Martha; *ed:* Univ of CO (BA) Latin Amer St 1972; Lesley Coll (MA) Cnslng Psych 1990; Addl 21 Credit Hrs Continuing Ed in Art His & Music, 9 Credit Hrs Ed, 3 Credit Hrs Orgnl Behavior; *cr:* Groton Schl Admissions Ofcr 1985-90; Univ of MA Adj Prof 1990-92; Middlesex Comm Coll Adj Prof 1992-95; Ind Consultant Exec Dev & Coach 1992-; *home:* PO Box 991 Groton MA 01450

BEAN, JUDITH WITTMAN, Fifth Grade Teacher; *b:* Utica, NY; *m:* Frederick Warren; *ed:* Keuka Coll (BA) Eng, Ed 1972; SUNY at Corland (MS) Elem N-6 1976; Addl 30 Hrs; NYSUT Courses; Whole Lang; *cr:* Adirondack Cntrl Schl 7-8th Grd Eng Tchr 1972-73; Chadwicks Union Free Dis 4th Grd Tchr 1975-80, 6th Grd Bus, Eng Tchr 1980-85; Sanquoit Vly Cntrl Schl 5th Grd Tchr 1990-; *ai:* Fac, Detention, Discipline Comm; NYSUT, AFT 1972-; Chadwicks Tchrs Assn 1975-, Pres; Sauquoit Tchrs Assn 1985-, Sec; Lib Bd NY 1975-80, Trustee; Friends of Lib 1985-88, Pres; Deacons Pres Church 1990-93, Moderator; Girl Scout Ldr; *office:* Sauquoit Vly Cntrl Schl 2601 Oneida St Sauquoit NY 13456

BEAN, KAREN GULBRANDSEN, 7th Grd Language Arts Teacher; *b:* Boston, MA; *m:* Donald Arthur; *c:* Nathan R., Matthew A.; *ed:* Bates Coll (BA) Psych 1967; Coll of William & Mary (ME) Guidance & Counseling 1971; Practicum CCSC 6 Credits; Boston Univ 6 Credits; Univ of ME at Farmington 9 Credits; Univ of VA 3 Credits; Univ of Glasgow Scotland 30 Credits; Univ of NH 3 Credits; Univ of ME at Augusta 6 Credits; *cr:* Stonington Elem 4th Grade Tchr 1967-68; Dartmouth Elem 4th Grade Tchr 1968-69; York Cty Schls 2nd & 4th Grade Tchr 1969-71; Crescent Park Schl 4th Grade Tchr 1978-85; Telstar MS Lang Arts Tchr 1985-; *ai:* Scheduling & Rdng Curr Review Comm; Peer Coach; DKG 1991-; NCTE, MCELA 1985-; NEA, MEA, TEA 1967-; Lib Book Comm at Bethel 1990-; Crisis Intervention Team 1988-; Comm Awarness 1984-86; AAUW 1971-77; ME Master Tchr 1992; Bd Cert EA, ELA; Natl Bd for Prof Tchng Standards; Pub Voices from Mid NCTE; Tableleader MEA Writing Prompt 1985-; *office:* ME Schl Admin Dist #44 284 Walkers Mill Rd Bethel ME 04217*

BEANE, JANICE M., Teacher; *b:* Memphis, TN; *m:* Michael; *c:* Marshall Strickland; *ed:* TN St Univ (BS) Eng 1971; OH St Univ (MA) Eng Ed 1995; *cr:* Memphis City Schls Tchr 1971-73; Columbus Pub Schls Tchr 1973-75; Pulaski Cty Spec Schls Tchr 1976-79; Columbus Pub Schls Tchr 1987-; *ai:* NEA, OH Ed Assn, Cntrl OH Tchrs Assn 1989-; NCTE 1981-; NAACP 1994-; *office:* Columbus South HS 1162 Ann St Columbus OH 43206

BEANE, PATRICIA JEAN JOHNSON, Second Grade Teacher; *b:* Massillon, OH; *m:* Frank Llewellyn; *c:* Frank Clarence II, Adam Tyler; *ed:* Ashland Univ (BS) Ed 1966; 3 Credit Hrs; *cr:* Akron City Schls First Grd Tchr 1966-67; Massillon City Schls First Grd Tchr 1967-68, Second Grd Tchr 1968-; *ai:* PTO Exec Bd; Schl Wide Educl Planning Comm; NEA, OEA 1966-; Massillon Ed Assn 1967-, Bldg Rep; Akron Ed Assn 1966-67; Nat'l DACWC; OH Assn Colored Women's Club; NACWC, DACWC 1980-; NE Dist DACWC 1980-, Sec, Chaplain; Nannie Burrough Fed Club, Sec, VP; Akron Symphony Chorus 1966-67; Canton Civic Opera Chorus 1969-80; Grace Chrstn Flwshp Music Dir; Outstdng Comm Svc Awd; *home:* 1134 3rd St SE Massillon OH 44646

BEAR, ROSELLA MAE (WALTON), Retired Elementary Teacher; *b:* Upper Sandusky, OH; *m:* Robert Frederick; *c:* Craig Allen, Sharon Elaine Sattler, Duane Edwin; *ed:* Bluffton Coll (BS) Elem Ed 1959; 1 Hr Bowling Green Univ, 3 Hrs Ashland Coll, 1 Hr OH St Univ, 3 Hrs Drake Univ; *cr:* Marseilles Elem Schl 4th, 5th Grd Tchr 1958-62, Title I or Chptr Rdng Tchr 1969-85, 1st Grd Tchr 1985-; Retired after 30 Yrs 1995; *ai:* Upper Sandusky Ed Assn 1985-, Bldg Rep; OH Ed Assn, NEA 1985-; Marseilles Mothers 1963-, Pres, VP, Recording, Corresponding Sec, Treas, Reporter; Marseilles United Meth Church 1948-, SS Tchr, Ch Treas, SS Supt, Children's Music Dir, Historian, United Meth Women Pres; *home:* 13267 County Hwy La Rue OH 43332

BEARD, DAVID C., Civics Teacher; *b:* Mt Savage, MD; *m:* Beverly Jean Cuffley; *c:* Michael B., Kelly Gayle Beard Smith; *ed:* Frostburg St Univ (BS) His & Soc Stud 1965; MD St Dept of Ed APC 1973; *cr:* Southern Garrett HS Tchr 30 Yrs; *ai:* GCFT, AFT 1973-, Pres; Oakland Mt Lake Pk Lions 1980-, Lion of Yr 1993; Democrat St Cntrl Comm Chm; Garr Co Bd Election Supvrs, Pres; Oakland Optimist Club, Pres, Friend of Boy; So Garr Ath Assn, Citizen of Yr 1990; *home:* 53 Kuskie Ln Swanton MD 21561

BEARD, GARY W., Academic Advisor & Eng Tchr; *b:* Martinsburg, WV; *m:* Darlene; *c:* Cheryl, Jodi; *ed:* Washington Bible Coll (BA) Bible & Music 1971; *cr:* Emmanuel Chrstn Schl 4th Grd Tchr 1971-73; Clinton Chrstn Schl 6th Grd Tchr & Prin 1973-78; Independent Baptist Acad Eng Tchr & Prin 1978-83; Carroll Chrstn Schls Prin, Eng Tchr & Acad Adv 1983-; *ai:* Sr Class Spon; City of Westminster 1993-, Bd of Zoning Appeals; *office:* Carroll Christian Schl 550 Baltimore Blvd Westminster MD 21157

BEARD, JACK, English & Reading Teacher; *b:* Dayton, OH; *m:* Margaret Louise Stiver; *c:* John Charles, Jeffrey Thomas, Joshua Allan; *ed:* Wright St Univ (BS) Elem Ed 1979; 150 Hrs; 11 Hrs Grad Work Principalship & Local Superintendent; *cr:* Kitty Hawk Elem 4th Grd Tchr 1979-80; L T Ball MS 7th Grd Phys Sci & Math 1980-83; Upper Sandusky Elem 5th Grd Tchr 1983-87; Upper Sandusky HS Gen Math & Algebra 1987-88; Urbana Jr HS 7th-8th Grd Eng & Rdng Tchr 1988-; *ai:* Ftbl, Wrestling, Womens Sftbl, & Tennis Head Coach; Jr HS Wrestling, Track & Bsbl Asst Coach, Jr HS Stu Cncl Adv; NFIOA 1983-; GMVWCA 1987-; NGTM 1988 & 1996; Mental Retardation & Developmental Disabilities 1989-, Bd Chm; OHSFCA 1990-; OAT & CCC 1995-; Urbana City Bd Ed Grant; Urbana City Schls Outstndg Tchr Awd; Coach of Yr; *office:* Urbana Jr HS 500 Washington Ave Urbana OH 43078*

BEARDSLEE, DONNA MARIE, English Teacher; *b:* Troy, PA; *c:* Bret Alan, Joel Aaron; *ed:* Lock Haven St Coll (BS) Comm & Lit 1976; Mansfield St Coll Grad Stud in Lit; *cr:* Towanda Area HS Eng Tchr 1976-; *ai:* Stu Assistance Team Chprsn; Tchng Strategies of Hanson, Silver & Strong to Educators in Schl Dist; NEA, PSEA & TAEA 1976-; *office:* Towanda Area H S Towanda High Schl Dr Towanda PA 18848*

BEARDSLEY, COBY L., English Teacher; *b:* Buffalo, NY; *m:* Robert C.; *c:* Coby J. Troidl, Lorelei Cruz, Amanda; *ed:* SUNY at Fredonia (BA) Eng 1980, (MA) Eng 1986; 39 Hrs Grad EN 500, 600 Level Courses; *ai:* DTA 1980-, VP; Grad BA, MA Summa Cum Laude; *office:* Dunkirk MS 525 Eagle St Dunkirk NY 14048

BEARDSLEY, DIANE COPPOLA, French & Language Arts Teacher; *b:* New York, NY; *m:* Wayne R.; *c:* Eric, Peter; *ed:* Potsdam Coll (BA) Fr Ed 1969; Iona Coll (MS) Ed 1991; Queens Coll 27 Credits Fr Ed 1970-72; CCNY Coll of New Rochelle Fordham 30 Addl Credits Ed 1976-; Attnd Univ St Thomas Aquinos; *cr:* Haverstraw MS Fr, Lang Arts Tchr 1969-; *ai:* Schl Improvement Planning Team; Adv to Schl Nwsp; NYSUT, NYSAFLT 1969-; ASCD; Kappa Delta Pi 1968-; Phi Delta Kappa 1990-; After Schl Elem Prgm Davis Schl 1986-87, Founding, Bd of Dirs Mem; *office:* Haverstraw MS Grant St Haverstraw NY 10927

BEARDSLEY, MICHELEANN (DRAVEC), Math Teacher; *b:* Elmira, NY; *m:* Harold R.; *c:* Teresa, Timothy; *ed:* SUNY AG&T at Alfred (AAS) Cmptr Sci 1972; SUNY at Brockport (BS) Math 1989; Nazareth Coll (MS) Scndry Cmptr Sci Ed 1994; *cr:* Churchville-Chili HS 9-12th Grd Math Tchr 1990-; *ai:* Class of 1996 Adv; Peer Mediation Coord; NCTM 1993-; NEA 1990-; NYSMTA 1995-; Co-Writer of Grant for Peer Mediation; Peer Mediation-Conflict Resolution Trainer; *office:* Churchville-Chili Sr HS 5786 Buffalo Rd Churchville NY 14428*

BEASLEY, JUANITA DUNCAN, 6th Grade Teacher; *b:* Winston-Salem, NC; *c:* Natasha Smith, Damon, Julian; *ed:* Winston-Salem St Univ (BS) Elem Ed 1970; Univ of Hartford 30 Addl Hrs; Hartford Tchrs Curr Extentino Courses from MIT, Yale 60 Credit Hrs; *cr:* Martin Luther King Jr. Elem Schl 6th Grd Tchr 1970-; *ai:* Schl Governance Team; Hnr Roll Comm; Yrbk Adv; Cooperating Mentor Tchr St of CT; AFT, HFT 1970-; Delta Sigma Theta 1965-; The N Innovation 1991-, Corresponding Sec; CT Coral Artists 1993-, Bd of Dirs; CT Historical Soc; Wadsworth Atheneum, Covenant to Care 1995-; Blue Hill Civic Assn; Bethel AME Church 1978-; Comm Newspaper; *office:* Martin Luther King Jr Elem Sch 25 Ridgefield St Hartford CT 06112

BEATI, MARK ANTHONY, PE & Health Teacher; *b:* Lowell, MA; *m:* Karen Condaris; *ed:* Springfield Coll (BS) PE 1980; 6 Grad Credits; *cr:* Lowell Pub Schls Jr High Sci Tchr 1980-83; Greater Lowell Regnl Sci Tchr 1984 & PE, Hlth Tchr 1985-; *ai:* Lowell HS Asst Ftbl Coach 1980-88 & Head Coach 1989-92, Notre Dame Acad Asst Spring Track Coach 1993; JV Bsbl Coach 1994-; NEA 1980-; *office:* Greater Lowell Reg Voc Tech HS Pawtucket Blvd Tynsboro MA 01879

BEATO, CAROL FIELDS, Mathematics Teacher; *b:* Niagara Falls, NY; *m:* Alfred M.; *c:* Mary Nicole, Christopher, Gregory; *ed:* D'Youville Coll (BA) Math 1962; Hunter Coll (MA) Math 1966; Attnd Canisius Coll, SUNY at Brockport & Univ of Rochester; *cr:* Gates-Chili HS Math Tchr 1962-63; Greece Arcadia HS Math Tchr 1963-65 & 1966-70; Greece Athena HS Math Tchr 1970-74 & 1981-95; Greece Arcadia HS Math Tchr 1995-; *ai:* Math Team Adv; NEA; NYEA; Greece Tchrs Assn; Natl Sci Fnd Acad Yr Inst; *office:* Greece Arcadia HS 120 Island Cottage Rd Rochester NY 14612

BEATON, DELORIS JORDAN, Third Grade Teacher; *b:* Savannah, GA; *m:* Charles; *c:* Renee Grunfelder, Chris Sims, Jeff Sims; *ed:* Armstrong St Coll (AA) General Stud 1982, (BS) Early Chldhd Ed 1983; Queens Coll (MS) Rdng 1988; Addl 50 Credit Hrs at Columbia, St. John's, and Long Island Univ; *cr:* Whitebluff Rd Schl Second Grd Tchr 1983-85; James A. Dever Schl Third Grd Tchr 1985-; *ai:* Report Card, Rdng Anthology Selection & Nutrition Comms; PTA Fac Rep; AFT 1985-; Assn for Curr Dev; Hospice of Long Island 1992-, Vol; PTA Lifetime Membership Awd 1993; Trained 5 Stu Tchrs; Led Grd Level in Incorporating Rdrs and Wrtrs Wrkshps into Daily Routine; *office:* James A. Dever Schl 585 N Corona Ave Valley Stream NY 11580*

BEATON, NANCY GUERCIA, Science Teacher; *b:* Philadelphia, PA; *c:* Joel, Jessica; *ed:* West Chester St Coll (BA) Elem Ed 1971, (MA) Phys Scis 1976; *cr:* Parkesburg Elem Schl 2nd Grd Tchr 1971-79; Octorara Elem Schl 2nd-3rd Grd Tchr 1979-87, Sci Coord 1987-92; Octorara ISD 5th Grd Tchr 1981-82; Octorara Area HS Sci Tchr 1987-; *ai:* Audio-Visual Coord; Sci Curr Comm; Octorara Area Educl Assn 1971-; PSEA; NEA; Birdsboro Legion Bsbl Assn 1995-; Philadelphia Electric Co Energy Ed Grant 4 Yrs; Dev Sci Discovery Area; *office:* Octorara Area HS RD 1 Box 501 Atglen PA 19310

BEATRICE, JONELLE COHEN, Instr of Rdng & Study Skills; *b:* Salem, OH; *m:* Mark A.; *c:* Jared, Blythe; *ed:* Mount Union Coll (BA) Elem Ed 1973; Miami Univ (MED) Remedial & Diagnostic Ed 1974; *cr:* New Carlisle Bethel Local Schls 6th Grd Tchr 1974-75; East Palestine MS 7th & 8th Grd Rdng Tchr 1975-79; Durham Cty Schls Basic Skills Rdng Coord 1979-81; Youngstown St Univ Adjunct Faculty 1986-, Rdng Lab Coord 1994-95; *ai:* Run Private Learning Svc Learning Enhancement; Consult Local Pub Schls & Hospitals; Present Seminars Teaching for Thinking, Learning Styles, Memory, Learning Systems, Standardized Test Preparation; IRA 1974-; Natl Assn of Dev Ed, OH Assn of Dev Ed 1990-; PTA 1986-; Swim Club 1982-; MADD; Stellar Awd for Outstanding Support of Non-traditional Stdnts; Pub Textbook Learning to Study Through Critical Thinking 1995Richard D Irwin; Presented Session on Adult Learners at NACADA Natl Convention; Univ Grant to Dev Orientation, Stud Skills Course. Ranked Top 20% All Univ Instrs Stdnt Evaluations; Dev 3 Rdng Fundamental Prgms in Two Sts; Right to Read Dir E Palestine City Schls 1978; *home:* 1857 Alverne Dr Poland OH 44514*

BEATRICE, ROBERT JOHN, Teacher & Coach; *b:* Hackensack, NJ; *m:* Elizabeth Ann; *c:* Megan, Ryan; *ed:* Marist Coll (BA) Soc Stud 1976; William Paterson Coll Tchrs Cert 1977, Spec Ed Cert 1984; *cr:* EADS HS Tchr, Ftbl Wrestling Head Coach 1977-79; William Paterson Coll Ftbl Coach 1979-81; Wayne Hills HS Tchr 1979-81; Bloomfield HS Tchr, Coach 1981-; *ai:* Track Coach; Spec Olympics Spon; Children Theater Performer; NEA, BEA 1981-; Greystone Pk Psychiatric Hosp 1986-, Tchr Adv; Spec Olympics 1986-, Coord; Spec Olympics 1992-, Vol.

BEATTIE, JEAN THURBER, Fifth Grade Teacher; *b:* Providence, RI; *m:* Franklin R.; *c:* Kim Beattie Wild, Pam; *ed:* RI Coll (BS) Elem Ed 1973; 46 Post Grad Credit Hrs Univ of RI 1973-; *cr:* North Scituate Elem 3rd, 4th & 6th Grd Tchr 1973-74 & 1978-80; Clayville Elem Schl Kndgtn, 2nd-6th Grd Tchr 1974-78; Hope Elem 5th Grd Tchr 1985-; *ai:* Tchr Coll Level Inst of Rel Classes BYU; NEA 1973-, Bldg Rep, VP, A Tchr to Remember Awd 1991; Active Parenting of Teens Tchr 1993-; *office:* Hope Elem Schl 391 North Rd Hope RI 02831

BEATTY, JAMES S., Fourth Grade Teacher; *b:* Buffalo, NY; *m:* Cheryl Hansen; *c:* Rachel, Joshua, Margaret; *ed:* William Penn Coll (BA) Elem Ed 1969; St Univ Coll at Buffalo (MA) Elem Ed 1972; Post Grad Hrs St Univ Coll at Fredonia, St Univ NY at Buffalo, St Univ Coll at Buffalo; *cr:* Hamburg Cntrl Schls 6th Grd Tchr 1969-71, 4th Grd Tchr 1971-; *ai:* Shared Decision Making Comm Bldg & Dist, IM Coach, Redisign Comm; Hamburg Tchrs Assn 1969-, Pres 1990-94, Chief Negotiator 1975-90, NY St United Tchrs 1972-, Delegate, Ldrshp Awd 1994; AFT 1972-, DGate; Hamburg Presbyn Church 1958-, Elder Clerk of Session 1985-92; Prospect

Lawn Cemetery Assn 1980-, Pres 1993; Unified Sci & Math in the Elem Schl Grant NSF 1976; *office:* Armor Schl Hamburg Cntrl Schls 5301 Abbott Rd Hamburg NY 14075*

BEATTY, JOHN R., Social Studies Teacher; *b:* Buffalo, NY; *m:* Sandra e.; *c:* Allison, Jillian; *ed:* Niagara Co Comm Coll (AA) Liberal Arts 1973; Buffalo St Coll (BS) Soc Stud 1975; Niagara Univ (MS) Ed 1980; 60 Addl Hrs His, Ed, Coaching, Admin; *cr:* Pioneer Cntrl Schl Soc Stud Tchr 1975-77; North Park Jr HS Soc Stud Tchr 1977-90; Lockport HS Soc Stud Tchr 1990-; *ai:* Girls Var Tennis Coach; Summer Schl Dir; AFT, NYSUT 1975-; LEA 1979-, Bldg Rep; Living His Assn 1994-, Civil War Re-Enactor; First Bapt Church 1984-, Trustee; *office:* Lockport HS 250 Lincoln Ave Lockport NY 14094*

BEAUCHAMP, MALCOLM E., Band Dir & Department Chrmn; *b:* Baton Rouge, LA; *m:* Suzanne; *c:* Malcolm C.; *ed:* Vanderbilt (BM) Applied Music 1966, (MM) Applied Music 1968; LSU (PHD) Music 1980; *cr:* Simpson Jr HS Band Dir 1970-88; Harrison HS Band Dir 1988-90; W. T. Clarke HS Band Dir, Dept Chm 1990-; *ai:* Marching Band; Jazz, Woodwind Ensembles; EMSEAA 1990-, Intnl Trumpet Guild 1975-; Article Pub; *office:* W. T. Clarke HS 740 Edgewood Dr Westbury NY 11590

BEAUCHEMIN, PHILIP ERNEST, Social Studies Teacher; *b:* Boston, MA; *m:* Phyllis Friel; *c:* Michael, Helen, Lucas; *ed:* Univ of NC (BA) His & Ed 1970; Temple Univ (MED) Ed 1972, (MA) His 1973; Juris Doctor in Law at Temple Schl of Law 1983; *cr:* Wilson Jr HS Soc Stud Tchr 1970-73; Lamberton HS Soc Stud Tchr 1974-82; Washington HS Soc Stud Tchr 1982-83; Sayre Jr HS Soc Stud Tchr 1983-85; Overbrook HS Soc Stud Tchr 1985-; *ai:* Var Bsbl Head Coach; Mock Trial Team Coach; PFT 1971-, Bldg Comm; Amer Bar Assn, PA Bar Assn, Philadelphia Bar Assn 1984-; Lyndon B Johnson Fellowship 1974; *home:* 349 Wayne Ave Lansdowne PA 19050*

BEAUDIN, DORIS PINTAL, Third Grade Teacher; *b:* Lewiston, ME; *m:* Robert; *c:* Scott, Nicole; *ed:* Gorham St Coll (BS) Elem Ed 1965; *cr:* Minot Consolidated Schl 2nd & 3rd Grd Tchr 1965-68; St Patricks Schl 4th Grd Tchr 1968-72; Jordan Schl 3rd Grd Tchr 1973-83; Montello Schl 3rd Grd Tchr 1983-; *ai:* Montello Staff Dev Sec; NEA 1965-; MEA 1973-; LEA 1973-; *office:* Montello Schl East Ave Lewiston ME 04240

BEAUDOIN, PAMELA ANNE, High School History Teacher; *b:* Woonsocket, RI; *ed:* Simmons Coll (BA) Pol Sci 1991, (MA) MAT 1992; *cr:* Lebanon HS His Tchr 1992-93; Holbrook HS His Tchr 1993-94; Ipswich HS His Tchr 1994-; *ai:* Coll Bown, Stu Govt Adv; *office:* Ipswich HS 130 High St Ipswich MA 01938

BEAULIEU, CONRAD, French & Portuguese Teacher; *b:* New Bedford, MA; *m:* Dianne M. DaLimonte; *c:* Michele L., Joel A.; *ed:* Univ of MA at Dartmouth (BA) Fr 1970, (BA) Portuguese 1974; RIC (MED 1978; 36 Grad Credits Univ of Lisbon, Portugal; *cr:* Tiverton HS Fr, Portuguese Tchr 1970-76; Tiverton MS Fr, Portuguese Tchr 1976-; *ai:* Adv 8th Grd Class, Schl Bookstore; NEA, RI, TEA 1970-; RIFLA 1976-; *office:* Tiverton MS 10 Quintal Dr Tiverton RI 02878*

BEAULIEU, RONALD C., Assistant Professor; *b:* Rochester, NH; *m:* Jeanne Grondin; *c:* Lea, Matthew; *ed:* NH Coll (BS) Accounting 1973; Univ of NH Grad Work; *cr:* City Concrete Co Inc Comptroller 1984-90; NH Tech Coll Asst Prof 1990-; Self Employed Pub Practice 1990-; *ai:* Natl Soc PA 1991-; Share Fund 1993-95; Club Richelieu 1985-90, Treas; Advy Bd, Rochester Cath Schl 1995-; *home:* 5 Fortier Dr Rochester NH 03867

BEAUMONT, RICHARD ALAN, Human Physiology & Chem Tchr; *b:* Winchester, MA; *m:* Wendy S.; *c:* Jared Alan; *ed:* Salem St Coll (BA) Bio 1972; Northeastern Univ (MED) Schl Admin 1984; Salem St Coll Marine Bio, Northeastern Univ Organic Chem, Southwest LA Marine Research 45 Addl Credits; *cr:* Burlington HS Human Physiology, Bio Tchr 1973-74; Marshall Simands MS Life Sci Tchr 1974-76; Burlington HS Human Physiology, Bio, Chem Tchr 1976-; bunker Hill Comm Coll 1994-; *ai:* Var Golf Coach 10 Yrs; Dir Operation Environment 17 Yrs; NEA, MTA 1973-; Natl Sci Fnd, Earthwatch Research Marine Stud Grants; Var Coach of Yr 1989; Recognition Excl Tchng 3 Times Tufts Univ; *office:* Burlington HS 123 Cambridge St Burlington MA 01803*

BEAUREGARD, DAVID FRANCIS, Bio & Environmental Sci Tchr; *b:* Gardner, MA; *m:* Laura LeBlanc; *c:* Megan, Nicholas; *ed:* Univ of MA (BA) Bio 1973; Fitchburg St Coll (MS) Bio, Ed 1978; Univ of MA Medical Ctr 18 Credits Exercise Physiology, Sports Medicine, 30 Credits Sci Ed, BioTech Research; *cr:* Gardner Jr High Sci Tchr 1973-78; Gardner HS Bio-Environmental Sci Tchr 1978-; Mount Waschusett Comm Coll Part-Time Bio Tchr 1994-; *ai:* NEA, MTA, GEA 1973-; NSTA, MSTA 1985-; *home:* 24 Mayfield Rd Gardner MA 01440

BEAUREGARD, KENNETH G., Eighth Grade Teacher; *b:* Hartford, CT; *m:* Carol Ann Chenail; *c:* Andrew; *ed:* Champlain Coll (ABA) Bus Mgmt 1966; Univ of Hartford (BS) Elem Ed 1972; Cntrl CT St Univ Planned Prgm Elem Ed 1977; *cr:* Carmen Arace Schl 6th Grd Tchr 1972-79; CT Army Natl Guard Trng & Ed Tchr 1983-87; Saint Martha Schl 8th Grd Tchr 1988-; *ai:* Ski Club Adv; NCEA 1989-; Farmington River Watershed Assn 1982-; Silver Lake Land Trust 1994-; *office:* St Martha Schl 214 Brainard Rd Enfield CT 06082

BEAUREGARD, LINDA MASLYN, Biology Teacher; *b:* Clifton Springs, NY; *c:* Eric Carruth, Amy Carruth; *ed:* Cornell Univ (BS) Bio 1971; Ball St Univ, Rutgers Univ, Rowan Coll Grad Work; *cr:* Muncie Southside HS Bio Tchr 1971-73; Scotch-Plains Fanwood HS Bio Tchr 1975-76; Maple Shade HS Bio Tchr 1976-; *ai:* Human Relations Club Adv; PAC, CORE Team; Bio Club; NABT, NJABT 1976-; NEA, NJEA, MSEA 1974-, Bldg Rep; NSTA; Natl Sci Fnd Grant; Rutgers Univ Citation for Distngd HS Tchng 1991; Tchr of Yr Governor's Tchr Recognition 1988; Litter Abatement Grant 1995; *office:* Maple Shade HS Frederick & Clinton Sts Maple Shade NJ 08052

BEAUVAIS, SANDRA E., Seventh Grade Mathematics Tchr; *b:* Springfield, MA; *m:* Mark E.; *c:* Audra, Kristen; *ed:* Elms Coll (BA) Ed 1963; Antioch Univ (MS) Ed 1986; *cr:* Westover AFB Sixth Grd Tchr 1963-67; Winnisquam MS Fifth Grd Tchr 1977-80; Bow Meml Schl Seventh Grd Math Tchr 1980-; *ai:* Math Team Coach 1980-95; Math Counts Coach 1990-95; Schl Store Adv 1990-; NH NEA, NH ATMNE, NCTM 1977-; Bow Ed Assn 1977-, Former Pres; Cntrl NH Ed Collaborative Cert of Recognition 1994; Math Counts Coaching Awds; *office:* Bow Memorial Schl 20 Bow Center Rd Bow NH 03304

BEAVAN, ROBERT ALLAN, HS Agriculture Teacher; *b:* Leonardtown, MD; *m:* Eva Varie Putman; *c:* Laurel E.; *ed:* Univ of MD (BS) Ag Ed 1981, (MS) Ag Ed 1986; Western MD Coll (MS) Ed Admin 1993; Frederich Comm Coll 9 Credits; *cr:* Catoctin HS Ag Tchr 1981-; *ai:* FFA Adv; NVATA 1981-; MATA 1981-, Mbrshp Chm; FCTA 1981-, Pres Elect Schl Rep; FFA Alumni 1981-; Optimist Club 1984-, Publicity Chm & VP; Farm Bureau 1985-; Honorary Amer Farmer Degree; Honorary Chapter Farmer Degree; Cougar Pin of Excl; Frederick Cty Bd of Ed Recognition Pin; *office:* Catoctin H S 14745 Sabillasville Rd Thurmont MD 21788

BEAVER, BARBARA LAIS, Jr HS Math & Science Teacher; *b:* Paterson, NJ; *m:* Barrie C.; *c:* Susan G., John D.; *ed:* Montclair St Coll (BA) Math 1963; 33 Credit Hrs Cert, Masters Prgm Wm Paterson Coll; 3 Credit Hrs Monmouth Coll; 12 Credit Hrs Natl Sci Fnd Univ of Chicago; *cr:* Lincoln Schl Jr HS Tchr 1963-68; Sussex Christian Schl Jr HS Tchr 1977-; *ai:* 7-8th Grd Class Adv; Former Cmptr, Aerobics Club Adv; Phi Lambda Theta 1988-, NHS in Ed; Kappa Delta Pi 1989-, NHS in Ed; CSI 1977-; Work Shop Ldr Chrstn Schl Convention 1987; *home:* 16 Up A Way Dr Sussex NJ 07461

BEAVER, BARRIE C., Teacher; *b:* Long Branch, NJ; *m:* Barbara E. Lais; *c:* Susan G., John D.; *ed:* Montclair Univ (BA) Math 1961, (MA) Ed Admin & Super 1972, (MA) Comp Sci 1978; 12 Credits at Natl Sci Fndtn Summer Inst; Attnd Univ of Chicago 1967; *cr:* Nutley HS Math Tchr & Wrestling Coach 1961-73; Vernon Twp HS Wrestling Coach 1973-74, Adv 1976-81, VP 1981-85, Math Tchr & Stu Cncl Tchr 1973-; *ai:* Wrestling Coach 1961-73; Stu Cncl Adv 1973-78, 1994-; NJEA 1961-; Sussex Cty Mental Hlth Bd 1980-83; Math Articles Pub; *home:* 16 Up A Way Dr Sussex NJ 07461

BEAVER, C. WAYNE, Bible, Greek & Drama Teacher; *b:* Bartlesville, OK; *m:* Jacqueline Parker; *ed:* 40 Addl Hrs Wheaton Grad Schl; 3 Yrs Private Greek, Latin; *cr:* Cincinnati Chrstn Schls Tchr 1980-; *ai:* Drama Dir; Class Spon; Biblical Stud Dept Chm; *home:* 10358 Menominee Dr Cincinnati OH 45251

BEBOUT, LORI LATTURE, Math Teacher; *b:* Akron, OH; *m:* Randall L.; *c:* Kayla; *ed:* OH Univ (BS) Elem Ed 1981; Credit Hrs; *cr:* Homer Union Elem 5-8 Grd Soc Stud, Lang Arts Tchr 1982-85; Mc Connelsville Elem Schl 2nd Grd Tchr 1985-87; Windsor Elem 5th Grd Tchr 1987-89, 7-8 Grd Math, Pre-Algebra, Algebra Tchr 1989-; *ai:* 2nd-3rd Grd Soccer, 8-10 Yr Olds Sftbl Coach; 8th Grd Class, 7th-8th Grd Acad Challenge Co-Adv; NEA 1982-; Morgan Local Ed Assn 1982-, Treas 1985; OH Cncl Tchrs of Math 1989-; *office:* Windsor Elem Schl Broadway St Box 288 Stockport OH 43787

BECCIA, NANCY LAMOTTE, Eighth Grade English Teacher; *b:* Gadsden, AL; *m:* Anthony; *c:* Steven; *ed:* Marietta Coll (BA) Eng 1966; Southern CT St Univ 30 Credit Hrs British Lit; Wesleyan Univ 30 Credit Hrs Lbrl Stud, Hum; *cr:* Francis Walsh Intermediate Schl Eng Tchr 1966-; *ai:* ARISTA Comm Chair; BEST, Lang Arts Curr Comms; NEA; NCTE; NEATE; CEA; BEA; First Congregational Church, Sr Deacon, Chrstn Ed Comm Chair; *office:* Francis Walsh Intermediate Sch 185 Damascus Rd Branford CT 06405

BECHAN, BARBARA BUCINSKAS, Rdng Specialist & Eng Instr; *b:* Worcester, MA; *m:* Richard; *c:* Ann, Elizabeth Stern, Cathleen; *ed:* Worcester St Coll (BS) Elem Ed 1963, (MED) Rdng 1991; *cr:* Auburn Pub Schls 2nd Grd Tchr 1963-64; Oakham Pub Schls 1st Grd Tchr 1964-65; Quinsigamond Comm Coll Eng Instr Voc Ed 1990-, Rdng Specialist 1992-; *ai:* Cntrl MA Rdng Assn, MA Rdng Assn 1990-; IRA 1989-; Friends of the Oakham Lib 1982-, Treas; Parish Cncl 1986-; *office:* Quinsigamond Comm Coll 670 W Boylston St Worcester MA 01606

BECHARD, DENNIS P., Biology Teacher; *b:* Lancaster, PA; *m:* Mary Jean Fisher; *c:* Scott F., Ginger E.; *ed:* Grove City Coll (BS) Bio 1973; Millersville Univ (MED) Bio 1980; 9 Hrs; *cr:* PA Der Bureau of Forestry Forest Patrolman 1974-75; PA Der Bureau of Parks Env Interp Tech 1975-77; WASD Bio Tchr 1977-; *ai:* Sci Task Force; Planning Comm; Wrestling Booster Club Treas; NSTA; Top 1% Soc 1994-; Cert Substance Abuse Crisis Intervention; *office:* Waynesboro Area Sr HS 550 E 2nd St Waynesboro PA 17268

BECHTEL, DONALD EUGENE, Music Department Chairman; *b:* Canton, OH; *m:* Donna Botteicher; *c:* Hope, Aaron, Timothy; *ed:* Grace Coll at Winona Lake (BME) Ed 1971; Kent St (MM) Trumpet Performance 1979; Kent St Univ in Ed, Conducting; *cr:* Crestview HS Band Dir, Dept Chm 1971-72; Brethren Chrstn Schls Band & Choir Dir 1973-78; Cuyahoga Valley Chrstn Acad Music Dept Chm, Vocal & Instrumental Music Tchr 1978-; *ai:* Church Orch Dir; Recording Staff Musician Heat Recording & Kopperhead Studios; Csehy Summer Schl Music Fac; Sectional Rehearsal Dir Akron Youth Symphony; OMEA 1978-, Dist VI Bd Mem 1989-91; MENC, IMEA 1973-; CIDA 1988-; Optimist Intnl 1975-78; Children's Hospital Vol, Band Provides Valet Parking for Charity Events; NEC World Series of Golf, Band Provides Valet Svc for Tournament; Articles Pub by CIDA Journal; St Tchr's Convention Seminars; *office:* Cuyahoga Valley Christian Acad 4687 Wyoga Lake Rd Cuyahoga Falls OH 44224*

BECK, AILEEN KAHRAR, 6th Grade Social Studies Tchr; *b:* Norfolk, VA; *m:* Thomas Andrew; *ed:* Rider Univ (BA) Ed & Comm 1990; *cr:* Holy Family Acad Kndgtn, 6th-8th Grd Tchr 1990-93; Hammarskjold MS 6th Grade Tchr 1993-; *ai:* East Brunswick HS Boys & Girls Swim Team Coach; Stu Cncl Adv; Tchr Stu Mentor Prgm; 6th Grd Outdoor Ed Trip Adv; NEA 1990-; EBEA 1993-; *office:* Hammarskjold MS 200 Rues Ln East Brunswick NJ 08816

BECK, AUDREY MARIE, Sixth Grade Teacher; *b:* Chicago, IL; *m:* Bryan M.; *ed:* Univ of Akron (BS) Elem Ed 1988; *cr:* Lakeview Elem 6th Grd Tchr 1988-; *ai:* PTA & Kids Vote Reps; Young Authors & Soc Stud Advs; NEA, OEA 1988-; *office:* Lakeview Elem Schl 1819 Graham Rd Stow OH 44224*

BECK, CATHY LYNN, 8th Grade Science Teacher; *b:* Marion, OH; *m:* Michael A.; *c:* Kyle Christopher, Chad Thomas; *ed:* OH St Univ (BA) Ed 1985; Ashland Univ (MS) Educl Admin 1994; 15 Credit Hrs; *cr:* Olentangy Local Schl 8th Grd Sci Tchr 9 1\2 Yrs; *ai:* Asst Var Sftbl Coach; Mentor Tchr; NEA, OEA 1986-; *office:* Olentangy MS 814 Shanahan Rd Lewis Center OH 43035*

BECK, CHARLES O., Instr of Dev Math & Tech Wrtng; *b:* Mt Gilead, OH; *m:* Barbara Jo Brotherwood; *c:* Elizabeth, Heather; *ed:* OH Wesleyan Univ (BA) Elem Ed 1977; Bowling Green St Univ (MM) Music Composition 1991; Scientific, Tech Comm; *cr:* St Mary Grd Schl 6th Grd Tchr 1978-80; Dept of Defense Dependents Schls 4th Grd Tchr 1988-90; Eastwood Local Schl Dist Choral, Gen Music Tchr 1992-95; Owens Comm Coll Part-time Fac, Dev Ed 1995-; *ai:* Local Stu Chptr STC; NEA, OEA, EEA, OMEA 1992-; STC 1995-; Grad Assistantship; Numerous Hnrs, Awds USAF; Natl Merit Schlsp Recipient; *home:* 470 E Main St Portage OH 43451*

BECK, DAVID SCOTT, Technology Chairperson; *b:* Topeka, KS; *m:* Catherine T.; *c:* Cassandra; *ed:* CA Univ (BS) Indstrl Arts 1976; Attnd Millersville Univ, Allentown Coll; *cr:* East Penn Schl Dist Tchr 1976-83; Palisades Schl Dist Tchr 1983-; *ai:* Tech Club; Natl Engrng Design Challenge Sci Olympiad; Boston Univ Peak Performance Musical Sets; Dist Tech Comm Chair; Strategic Plan Sr Project Benchmarking Comm; PEA 1976-,VP, Sec; Tech Assoc of PA 1980-; Nom for Tandy Outstdng Tchr Awd; Nom Lehigh Vly Bus, Ed Partnership; Participation in PA Stu Tech Showcase 1994, 1996; *office:* Palisades HS 35 Church Hill Rd Kintnersville PA 18930

BECK, DOUGLAS ALAN, English Teacher; *b:* Bethlehem, PA; *ed:* PA St Univ (BS) Scndry Ed, Eng, Bus & Liberal Arts 1991; Addl 24 Credits of Jrnlsm Undergraduate Level; *cr:* Phillipsburg Chrstn Acad 6th-8th Grd Eng Tchr 1992-95; *ai:* Bsktbl Head Coach; Newspaper Adv; Book Fair Spon; NCTE 1995-; *home:* 217 Georgia Ave Bethlehem PA 18017

BECK, JAMES HERBERT, Career Graphics Teacher; *b:* Columbus, OH; *m:* Cindy Rust; *c:* Alesia, Jessica, Jason; *ed:* Morehead St Univ (BS) Voc Ed, Indstrl Ed 1983, (MS) Indstrl Ed, Voc Ed 1984; Post Grad Work Ed, Scndry, Voc Univ of Toledo, Kent St Univ, OH St Univ; *cr:* DE JVS Career Graphics Tchr 1984-; *ai:* VICA Club Adv; NEA, OEA, DJVSEA 1987-, Pres, VP; Phi Delta Kappa 1984-; OVA 1989-; OWECA 1992-; Cntrl OH Diabeties Assn 1978-; Tchr of Yr 1994; Honorary Chptr FFA Degree 1994; FFA Appreciation Awd 1995; First Place Decorations Exhibit 1995; *office:* Delaware Joint Voc Schl 1610 State Route 521 Delaware OH 43015

BECK, KAREN A., Retired Teacher; *b:* New York, NY; *m:* Jame[s] *c:* Scott E. Swan, Todd A. Swan, Carrie B. Hoover; *ed:* Kent St Un[iv] K-8th Grd Elem Ed 1965, (MS) Spec Ed 1973; Attnd Univ of Ashland Univ; *cr:* Streetsboro Schls 2nd-4th, 6th Grd Elem Tchr 1[...] Field Local Schls 5th Grd Elem Tchr 1968-69; Ravenna Schls 3[...] Learning Disabilities Tchr 1969-85; Brown MS 7th Grd Sci Tchr 1[...] Ravenna Schls Stu Assistance, Prevention Coord 1990-95; Kent [...] Temporary Instr 1995; *ai:* Raven Action Team of Stdnts; NEA; PEA[...] Alcohol Drug Abuse Prevention of OH 1988-, Awarness 1989; Ke[...] Hlth Bd 1986-, Pres; Kent Soc Svcs Bd of Trustees 1996; KSU [...] Assn 1975-; Governors Awd Red Ribbon Campaign OH 1990; *hor[...]* Valleyview Dr Kent OH 44240

BECK, MAUREEN DENISE (MOCK), English Teacher; *b:* Nels[...] OH; *m:* Michael W.; *c:* Drew, Justin; *ed:* OH Dominican Coll (B[...] 1984; Pursuing Masters Ed at Univ of Dayton; *cr:* Lancaster HS E[...] 1984-; *ai:* Soc Comm Chair; Restructuring Comm Mem; Discip[...] Attendance Comm Mem; Var Asst Vlybl Coach at William V Fish[...] HS; OEA, NEA, NCTE 1984-; St Bernadette Church Lectors; Ashl[...] Golden Apple Recipient 1992; *home:* 1660 Valley Forge Dr Lancas[...] 43130

BECK, MAXINE SHEELEY, English Teacher; *b:* Waynesboro, [...] Stephen E.; *c:* Stephen Jr., Katherine, Brian; *ed:* WV Univ (BA) Ed [...] Arts 1972; Shippensburg Univ (MA) Eng 1990; *ai:* Frosh Class Ad[...] Lib Friends; United Way; *home:* 12413 Wedgewood Dr Waynesb[...] 17268

BECK, PATRICIA, Science Teacher; *b:* Watertown, NY; *m:* Alber[...] Peter C., Patrick M., Susan Beck Bryan; *ed:* Cornell Univ (BA) Bi[...] Univ of MI (MS) Bio 1952; 75 Addl Credit Hrs; *cr:* Allen Park H[...] 1952-55; Ithaca HS Tchr 1955-59; Clarkstown Schl Dist Su[...] 1976-80; Nyack Schl Dist Tchr 1980-; *ai:* Sci Olympic Coach; [...] Tchrs Assn; Sci Tchrs Assn Outstdng Sci Tchr; *office:* Nyack M[...] Highland Ave Nyack NY 10956

BECK, PHYLLIS ELAINE, Aquatics Instructor & Coach; *b:* Lar[...] PA; *ed:* Univ of DE (BA) Biological Scis 1977; Gettysburg Coll [...] Cert 1978; *cr:* Redland HS Bio & Gen Stud Tchr 1978-86, Swim [...] 1978-; Westshore Natatorium Aquatics Instr 1986-; *ai:* WSEA [...] PSEA 1979-; NEA 1979-; NISCA 1980-; PHSSCA 1980-, Dist AA[...] Cayman Natl Trust 1994-; Coached 1991 State Champion & Nu[...] Qualifiers; *office:* Red Land HS 560 Fishing Creek Rd Lewisbe[...] 17339

BECK, RICHARD W., Associate Prof of Psychology; *b:* Portsmou[...] *m:* Sharan L. Laessle; *c:* James H., Pamela Bork; *ed:* The OH St Un[...] Scndry Ed 1960, (MA) Counseling 1962, (PHD) Counseling, A[...] 1971; Attnd Univ of Toledo, Univ of CO; *cr:* Columbus Pub Schl[...] Cnslr 1960-67; Child Stud Dept Columbus Pub Schls Admin, [...] Psychologists 1967-72; Dir Assessment Testina Columbus Schls 1[...] Urbana Univ Assoc Prof Psych 1988-; *ai:* Spon Alpha Chi; Pres Adv[...] Admissions Selection for Stdnts, Presch Search, Awds Comms, D[...] Chm; Honors Night Chprsn; Fac Ath Rep; NEA, OEA, CEA, ASCI[...] Alumni Assoc 1960-; AMUETS; Amer Legion 35 Yrs; NEOACACIA[...] 595; Champaign Cty Teen Ctr 2 Yrs, Bd of Dirs; Nom SEADS Outs[...] Tchr Awd 1990-91; ACT, NACADA Cert of Merit 1992; Pub Educl [...] 1960; Five Yr Awd; *office:* Urbana Univ North Hall-4 Urbana OH [...]

BECK, RICK L., Law Enforcement Instructor; *b:* Bellefontaine, [...] Terry R.; *c:* Brittany; *ed:* Attn OH St Univ, Urbana Univ; *cr:* OH H[...] Law Enforcement Instr 8 Yrs; *ai:* VICA Adv; Soc Comm Chprsn; [...] Comm; WA Twp Trustee 5 Yrs; Indian Joint Fire Dist, Chm; Logan C[...] Assn, VP; Logan Cty Master Plan, Planning Comm; Logan Cty 9[...] Force; OH Voc Ed Law Enforcement Tchr of Yr; *office:* OH H[...] Career Ctr 2280 State Route 540 Bellefontaine OH 43311

BECK, TIMOTHY C., Middle School Reading Teacher; *b:* Pitt[...] PA; *m:* Brenda Kermes; *c:* Ryan, Jason, Kristen; *ed:* CA Univ (MA[...] Specialist 1975; CA Univ Elem 1971; *cr:* Marion Elem Schl 6th G[...] 1973-76; North Belle Vernon Elem 6th Grd Tchr 1976-85; Bellm[...] Rdng Tchr 1986-; *ai:* AFT 1989-; NEA 1972-; *office:* Bellmar M[...] Perry Ave Belle Vernon PA 15012

BECK, WENDELL DALE, Mathematics Teacher; *b:* Pettisville, [...] Bonnie King; *c:* Douglas, Debra Zimmerman, Kathy Sauder, La[...] Goshen Coll (BA) Math 1966; 8 Hrs Grad Stud Bowling Green St U[...] Hrs Grad Stud Univ of Toledo; *cr:* Ridgeville HS Math Tchr 1[...] Archbold HS Math Tchr 1968-; *ai:* Head Girls Bsktbl, Asst Girl[...] Coach; Math Dept Chprsn; OCTM 1966-; AEA 1968-, Pres; NCTM [...] *office:* Archbold HS 600 Lafayette St Archbold OH 43502

BECKELMAN, MARLENE ANN, Pre-Kindergarten Teach[er] Brooklyn, NY; *m:* Richard; *c:* Michael; *ed:* Brooklyn Coll (BA) E[...] (MS) Early Chldhd Ed 1973; 30 Credit Hrs in Addition to Masters [...] *cr:* PS 233 Classroom Tchr 1969-70, Classroom Tchr 1977-; *ai:* [...] 1977-.*

BECKER, CARMEN PRINCE, Professor; *b:* New York, NY; *c:* M[...] Bean, Bernard Mc Bean; *ed:* Forham Univ (BS) Arts, Scis 1986, [...] Soc Work 1987; Hunter Coll Post Grad Course Psych; *cr:* Katari[...] Home Soc Worker 1987-90; Rockaway Mental Hlth Group Facilato[r] Alzheimers Assn Group Ldr 1992-; Touro Coll Prof 1991-; *ai:* S[...] Group Ldr Alzheimers Families; Camp St Edward Staten Island [...] Head Cnslr; *home:* 3546 74th St Jackson Heights NY 11372*

BECKER, CHRISTINE ANNE, Spanish Teacher; *b:* Lima, Peru; [...] ST Univ (BA) Span 1965; CA St Univ At Sacra (MA) Span 1989, [...] Univ Ecuador, Univ of Harford, Univ Vac De Mexico, Middlebur[y] Brigham Young Univ, Cal St at Sac in Spain, Peru, Mexico, Columbi[a] Univ of KS Cntrl Univ of Venezuela, Cath Univ of Venezuela; *cr:* [...] Latin Amer Stud Rsrch 1968-69; Mainland Reg HS Span Tchr 197[...] ATSP; NEA; MEA; Diplomate Advanced Span Mastery Exam C[...] Spain 1994; Natl Endowment for Hum Fellow 1990; Rockefeller Fe[...] Outstdng Frgn Lang Tchr 1988; Natl Frgn Lang Defense Scholar 1[...] Fulbright Scholar Venezuela 1965-66; Articles Pub; *office:* Ma[...] Regional HS 1301 Oak Ave Linwood NJ 08221

BECKER, DONNA ROTHERMEL, Second Grade Teacher; *b.* [...] Reading, PA; *m:* David E.; *c:* Michael, Erin; *ed:* Millersville Uni[v] Elem Ed 1973; PA St Grad Work Masters Equivalency; *cr:* ELCO Sc[...] Grd 2, 4-5 Grd Tchr 1973-; *ai:* PSEA, Lebanon Cty Educl Hnr Soc [...] *office:* Eastern Lebanon Cty Schl Dist 101 S Railroad St Myerst[own] 17067

BECKER, FRANCIS DAVID, Math Teacher & Dept Chairm[an] Baltimore, MD; *ed:* St Joseph's Univ (BS) Math 1971; St Charles Se[...] (MA) Theology 1989; Liberal Arts, Ed 60 Grad Credits; *cr:* West C[...] for Boys Math Tchr 1971-81; Malvern Prep Schl Math Tchr & Dep[...] 1981-; *ai:* 7-8th Grd Soccer Coach; Math Counts & MS Mathlet[...] Chess Club Moderator; 7th Grd Bsbl Coach; NCTM 1975-; NCEA [...] MAA 1988-; Constructed Pre-Test Used in Pilot Testing Prgm [...] Edition of Cmptr Sci with Pascal for West Publishing Co; *office:* M[...] Prep Schl 418 S Warren Ave Malvern PA 19355

BECKER, JEAN SALERNO, Biology Teacher; *b:* New York City, [...] Kenneth; *c:* Janelle, Kyle, Kevin; *ed:* C. W. Post Coll (BA) Scndry [...] 1970, (MS) Bio 1971; 45 Addl Credits Cmptrs, Mid-East Culture, [...] Methods; *cr:* Private Tutoring & Per-diem Sub Tchr 1977-88; Herri[...]

hr 1971-77, 1988-; *ai:* Regents Bio Laboratory Comm Write riate Lab Procedures; Rewrote Recommendation Forms for AP Sci ; Attnd Exp AP Bios Tchrs Conf; NYSUT, Herricks Tchrs Assn Full Tchng Asst Fellowship to C. W. Post Grad Schl 1970-71; Full chlsp to C. W. Post Coll; *office:* Herricks HS 100 Shelter Rock Rd de Park NY 11040

ER, KAREN M., Social Studies Teacher; *b:* Riverhead, NY; *m:* ; *ed:* St Univ of NY at Stony Brook (BA) His, Scndry Ed 1990; C.W. Long Island Univ (MA) Amer His 1995; *cr:* Riverhead HS Soc chr 1990-; *ai:* Attendance Schl Improvement Comm; Phi Beta

ER, KATHLEEN A., Secondary Biology Teacher; *b:* Shamokin, Timothy J.; *c:* Rebekah, Hannah; *ed:* Penn St Univ (BS) Animal 1982; Elizabethtown Coll Tchr Cert 1985; *cr:* Zoo Amer Zoo ist 1980-83; Hershey Medical Ctr Animal- Artificial Heart h 1982-83; Susquenita HS Bio Tchr 1986-; *ai:* Sci Fair Dir; Stu nce Team; Capital Area Sci Ctr 1989-, 2nd VP; NEA & PSEA; PTA VP; Hershey Symphony Orchestra 1983-90; *office:* Susquenita HS hoolhouse Rd Duncannon PA 17020

ER, LORRAINE BEEBE, Mathematics Teacher; *b:* Brooklyn, NY; an L.; *c:* Darrin, Jeffrey; *ed:* St Johns Univ (BA) Math 1968; g Coll (MS) Ed 1985; *cr:* Vly Steam CSD Math Tchr 1968-70; Half Hills CSD Math Tchr 1970-73; St Anthonys HS Math Tchr 1985-; Concerns Comm; Moderator; Girls Var Soccer, Bsktbl, JV e; NCTM 1985-; Tufts Univ Spec Recognition Outstdng Tchr; St Anthony's HS 275 Wolf Hill Rd S Huntington NY 11757

ERMAN, ANNETTE S., Cooper Bus Ed Teacher & Coord; *b:* New Y; *m:* Howard; *c:* Jeff, Natalie; *ed:* Trenton St Coll (BS) Bus Ed ddl 21 Post Grad Credits, 9 Credit Hrs Continuing Ed Camden Cty : Port Authority of NY Legal Sec 6 Yrs; Slimm, Dash & Goldberg ec 3 Yrs; Stark & Stark Legal Sec 3 Summers; Gloucester City Jr, BE Tchr, Coord 1975-; *ai:* FBLA Adv; Exec Bd Mem of NJBEA: n VP of NJCBECA; Core Values Comm Mem; Schl Bd Curr Comm; ed Cncl Rep to NJEA; GCEA Sec; Dev Articulation Agreemtn with n Cty Coll; NJBEA 1980-, Affiliated Cncl Rep, Cert of ation; NJCBECA 1990-, Southern VP, Cert of Appreciation; GCEA Sec; Eastampton Ec Dev Cncl 1990-, Sec; Grad Magna Cum Laude enton St Coll; FBLA Fall Ldrshp Conf Speaker; Montclair St Coll Conf Speaker; Round Table Presenter; *office:* Gloucester City Jr Sr 30 & Market St Gloucester City NJ 08030*

EY, JANE ELLEN (ASPACHER), Elementary Teacher; *b:* , OH; *w:* Thomas Henry (dec); *c:* Matthew Thomas; *ed:* Bowling t Univ (BS) Elem Ed & Learning Behavior Disorders 1972; 30 Addl Lakota Schl 3rd Grd Elem Tchr 1966-67; Gibsonbury Exempted Schl Elem Learning Disabilities Tchr 1967-69; Clyde Exempted Schl Elem Tchr 1970-71; Gibsonbury Exempted Village Schl Elem g Disabilities Tchr 1972-74; Fremont Schl Elem Spec Ed Tchr *ai:* Lutz PTO Tchr Rep To Exec Bd; NEA, OH Edctrs Assn 1967-; t Edctrs Assn 1975-; Shiloh United Meth Church 1974-, Organist, Veracious Voices of Victory Choir 1992-, Accompanist; OH Tchr om 1980; OH Spec Ed Regnl Resource Ctr Excl in Ed 1986; *home:* cker Rd Fremont OH 43420

NELL, MARY BALL, Kindergarten Teacher; *b:* Spring Vly, NY; *w:* . (Dec); *c:* Dr. Gail Jope, Craig Willard; *ed:* Elmira Coll (BA) Pol ecretarial Stud 1952; Univ of St of NY at New Paltz Elem Ed 1976; Hrs Orange Cty Comm Coll; *cr:* Ellenville Cntrl Schl Kndgtn Tchr ; Cumberland Chrstn 1st Grd Tchr 1978-81; Park Bible Acad & 1st-2nd Grd Tchr 1981-; *ai:* NYSTA 1969-; MACSA 1978-; 978-; Ellenville Garden Club; Ellenville Citizens Advy Comm.

WITH, CLYFE, Instructor of Physics; *b:* The Hague, Netherlands; y Boulger; *ed:* Dartmouth Coll (BA) Physics, Math 1987; Boston A) Physics 1989, (PHD) Physics 1992; *cr:* Phillips Acad Physics 92-; *ai:* Soccer, Ski, Vlybl Coach; Dormitory House Cnslr; APS, 991-; *office:* Phillips Acad S Main St Andover MA 01810

WITH, E. KENNETH, Regents Chemistry Teacher; *b:* sville, NY; *m:* Carole Redmond; *c:* Justin, Geoffrey, Andrew; *ed:* n Coll (BA) Chem 1966, (MS) Chem 1967; Attnd Colgate Univ, Rsrch; *cr:* Whitesboro HS Chem Tchr 1967-; Mohawk Valley Coll Instr 1970-; *ai:* Mid Sts Assn of Colls & Schls Visitation Niagara Mohawk Tchr Advy Panel; Chem Visualization Team Natl Supercomputing Application; AFT; NSTA; Kayahoora Yacht Club Commodore; Rotary Intnl 1980-, Pres; Order of Founders & Patriots 976-, Assoc; Flagon, Trencher Soc; Rsrch Corp Partners Sci Awd *home:* 8365 Sand Rd Barneveld NY 13304

WITH, SANDRA K., MS Computer & English Tchr; *b:* Sewickley, Terry F.; *c:* Heather, Emily; *ed:* Grove City Coll (BA) Bus Admin niv of Pgh Tchr Cert Bus Ed 1974; Attnd Comm Coll of Alleghney Hampton HS Bus Ed Tchr 1974-78; CCAC Non Credit Bus Ed Tchr ; Hampton HS Permanent Sub Bus Ed Tchr 1989-90; Eden Chrstn Cmptr, 8 Grd Eng Tchr 1990-; *office:* Eden Christian Acad 206 Rd Pittsburgh PA 15237

WITH, SUSANNE EVELYN, Second Grade Teacher; *b:* gh, PA; *m:* Clair R.; *c:* Christine, Daniel; *ed:* Slippery Rock St (BS) d 1973; *cr:* Shaler Area Schls Elem Tchr 1974-; *ai:* NEA, PSEA CAPBAP 1996-; *office:* Burchfield Schl 1500 Burchfield Rd Allison 15101*

RD, KATHLEEN DUNNINGTON, HS Chemistry & Biology ; *b:* Newport News, VA; *m:* Gary S.; *c:* Jonathan; *ed:* Coll of & Mary (BS) Chem 1987; George Mason Univ (MED) Scndry Sci ; Penn St 10 Hrs; Seattle Pacific Univ 6 Hrs; *cr:* Auburn HS Chem, Tchr 1989-91; Dallastown HS Chem, Bio Sci Tchr 1991; Summer enn St Organic Chem Rsrch 1992-93; Cntrl York HS Chem, Bio Sci 91-; *ai:* Phi Delta Kappa 1993-, Awds Comm Chair; Amer Chem 89-; Penn Sci Tchrs Assn 1993-; Cath Yth Group 1992-, Dir; Penn hrs Convention Presentor 1993; Mentor, Mentee Prgm Mentor ; *office:* Central York HS 300 E 7th Ave York PA 17404*

RD, MARY MC LAUGHLIN, Facilitating Teacher; *b:* Chester, PA; ph A. (dec); *c:* Joseph A., Edward D., John R., Michael F., Mary Pat Longo; *ed:* Trinity Coll (AB) Chem, Bio 1954; Trenton St Coll Elem Ed 1972; Cert in Scndry Ed at West Chester Univ 1954; *cr:* Schl Tchr 1955; Junior Two Schl Tchr 1955; Fisher Elem Schl Tchr 0; William Antheil Elem Schl Tchr 1980-95, Facilitating Tchr *ai:* Human Relations, Spec Ed Review, Elem Schls Strategic g Comms; Prof Partner for First Yr Tchr; Kappa Delta Pi 1980-; JEA, MCEA, ETEA 1972-; Incarnation Church 1955-, Altar Rosary s, Census Comm Chprsn, RCIA Parish Team Dir; Governors Tchr ition Prgm 1988-89; Tchr of Yr 1988-89; *office:* William Antheil chl 339 Ewingville Rd Ewing NJ 08638

RD, PATRICIA L. (MARTIN), 10th-11th Grd Eng Teacher; *b:* urgh, NY; *m:* Kenneth J.; *c:* Kristopher, Kelly; *ed:* SUNY at urgh (BS) Elem Ed 1977, (MS) Scndry Eng 1985; 60 Credit Hrs Post tud; *cr:* AuSable Valley Cntrl Schl Sub Tchr 1978-86, Eng Tchr *ai:* Jr Class Adv; Writing Skills Scoring Team; Dept Chair; Dist Comm; PEE for SUNY at Plattsburgh; Yth Commission Coach 1988-, Bsbl & Sftbl Coach; *office:* Ausable Valley Cntrl Schl 1490 Rt 9N Clintonville NY 12924

BEDARD, TODD BRENT, Automotive Technology Instr; *b:* Newport, VT; *m:* Julie Ann Thompson; *c:* Corey, Ryan, Chantal; *ed:* UVM Trades & Industry 1993; Addl 40 Credit Hrs; *cr:* Midas Muffler Shop Mgr, Trainer, Front End Svc 1984-91; Bennys Auto Clinic Techician 1979-84; Lamoille Area Voc Ctr Automotive Instr 1991-; *ai:* Ford AAA Trouble Shooting Contest, VICA Skills Contest, Voc Ctr Weight Room Adv; VVA, AVA 1991-; Middlesex Vol Fire Dept 1985-, Chief; Middlesex Boy Scout Troop 1989-, Adv; *office:* Lamoille Area Voc Ctr PO Box 304 Hyde Park VT 05655*

BEDDOW, LINDA SUE, Language Arts Teacher; *b:* Akron, OH; *m:* Ralph; *ed:* Univ of Akron (BA) Eng & Rdng Ed 1970; Addl Credit Hrs in Rdng; *cr:* Norton City Schls HS Eng Tchr 1972-75, MS Lang Arts Tchr 1975-; *ai:* MS Yrbk Adv; NEA & OEA 1972-; Jr Achvmt Tchr of the Yr 1995; Mem of Summit Cty Tech Acad.

BEDIENT, KIM LORI, Kindergarten Teacher; *b:* Geneva, NY; *m:* James; *c:* Amy, Holly; *ed:* Cortland St (BS) PE 1980; Geneseo St (MS) Elem Ed 1982; *cr:* Prattsburgh Cntrl Schl Kndgtn Tchr 1987-; *ai:* Tech Comm; Sftbl Coach; NEA 1983-; *office:* Prattsburgh Central Schl Academy St Prattsburgh NY 14873

BEDNAR, KATHYANN (ZANELLI), Guidance Counselor; *b:* Dover, NJ; *m:* Robert William; *c:* Andrea; *ed:* Moravian Coll (BA) His 1964; Seton Hall Univ (MA) Scndry Ed 1968; 45 Post Grad Credits Ed & Psych Courses; *cr:* Dover Schl Dist Eng Tchr & Guid Cnlsr 1964-68; Ramsey Schl Dist Soc Stud Tchr 1968-70, Guid Cnslr 1970-; *ai:* Stu Congress Adv; Pupil Assistance Comm; Stu Ldrshp Group Tchr Consultant; NEA 1964-; NJEA 1964-; BCEA 1968-; RTA 1968-; Wyckoff Reformed Church 1977-, Consistory Deacon; *office:* Ramsey HS Main St Ramsey NJ 07446

BEDNARCIK, KERRI A., PTA Program Co-Director; *b:* PA; *m:* Scott; *ed:* Thos Jefferson Univ (BS) Phys Therapy 1985; *cr:* Moss Rehab Hosp Staff Therapist 1985-88; Rehab Care Corp PT Supvr 1988-90; Elkins Park Hosp Asst Dir PT 1990-93; Prime Profs Contract, Home Therapist 1993-; Harcum Coll Co-Dir PTA Prgm 1993-; *ai:* Amer Phys Therapy Assn, PA Phys Therapy Assn 1993-; *office:* Harcum College 750 Montgomery Ave Bryn Mawr PA 19010

BEDNARIK, ANDREW F., Science Teacher; *b:* Derby, CT; *m:* Emma Partenheimer; *c:* Amanda, Emily; *ed:* Southern CT St Univ (BS) Scndry Ed, Bio 1970; (MS) Bio 1975; Purdue Univ (PHD) Systematics, Entomoloy 1978; Addl Work Univ of UT; *cr:* Andrew Warde HS Sci Tchr 1970-76; Purdue Univ Tchr Entomology 1977;Univ of UT Entomology Tchr 1978; Fairfield HS Alt Ed & Sci 1979-; *ai:* Fairfield Ed Assn, CT Ed Assn, NEA 1972-; Sigma Xi Scientific Research Soc; Book; 5 Schlsp on Entomology; David Ross Fellowship; Purdue Followship 2 Yrs; UT Post-Toc Tchng Fellowship; Tchr Of Yr Andrew Warde HS; *office:* Fairfield HS Melville Ave Fairfield CT 06430

BEDNARIK, ANTOINETTE SOSPIRATO, Business Teacher; *b:* Cleveland, OH; *m:* Edward J.; *c:* Marie, Frank; *ed:* Univ of Akron (BS) Comprehensive Bus Ed 1975; Ashland Univ (MA) Curr & Instruction 1994; *cr:* Nordonia HS Bus Tchr 1975-78; Maple Hghts HS CBE Coord & Bus Chprsn 1979-; *ai:* Bus Profs of Amer Adv; Class of 1996 Adv; Maple Hghts Tchrs Assn 1979-, Tres; OEA 1979-; OBTA 1979-; NEOTA 1979-; Chi Omega Alumni 1972-, Tres & Pledge Trainer; *office:* Maple Heights HS 5500 Clement Ave Maple Heights OH 44137*

BEDNARZ, DENNIS JOHN,CSC, US History Teacher; *b:* Chicago, IL; *ed:* Univ of Notre Dame (BA) His 1979; IN Univ (MAT) Soc Stud 1985; Attnd Spaulding Univ, John Carroll Univ, Kent St Univ; *cr:* Bishop David Meml HS Tchr 1979-84; Le Mans Acad Tchr, Ath Dir 1984-86; Saint Edward HS Tchr, Ath Dir 1986-91; Archbishop Hoban HS Tchr 1992-; *ai:* Pub Relations Dir; Frosh Bsbl Coach; NCEA 1987-; Amer Bsbl Coaches Assn 1987-, Century Awd 1989; Akron Press Club 1992-; Phi Beta Kappa Univ of Notre Dame 1979; Cath Yth Org Cleveland Western Region Recognition Awd 1991; *office:* Archbishop Hoban HS 400 Elbon Ave Akron OH 44306

BEDNORCHIK, SONIA, First Grade Teacher; *b:* Olyphant, PA; *ed:* Marywood Coll (BA) Ed 1963; *cr:* VA Beach Schl Dist Third Grd Tchr 1963-64; Windsor Schl Dist First Grd Tchr 1964-; *ai:* Yearly Musical Dir; Windsor Tchrs Assn 1964-, Treas; NY St United Tchrs 1972-; NEA 1963-72; AFT 1972-; *office:* C R Weeks Elem Schl 440 Foley Rd Windsor NY 13865

BEDY, LORRAINE ANNE, High School English Teacher; *b:* Yonkers, NY; *m:* Zoltan Joseph; *c:* Julia, Dylan; *ed:* Fordham Univ (BS) Eng Ed 1970; Syracuse Univ (MS) Eng Ed 1977; *cr:* W Genesee Cntrl Schls Tchr 1971-; *ai:* Writing Pgm Dev; NYSUT 1971-; NEA 1971-; NCTE 1993-; AERA 1994-; Spencer Mentor Flwshp; Articles Pub; *office:* West Genesee HS 5201 W Genesee St Camillus NY 13031*

BEEBE, JAYE HOWARD, Assistant Headmaster; *b:* Jamestown, NY; *ed:* Penn St at Behrend (BA) Amer Stud 1975; *cr:* Macaleoter Coll Asst Dir Admissions 1977-83; WY Seminary Dir, Coll Cnslng 1984-85; Prairie Schl Dir, Coll Cnslng 1986-88; Eastern MT Coll Enrollment Mgr 1989; South Kent Schl 1991-; *ai:* Bsktbl, Ftbl Coach.

BEEBE, KEITH A., Asst Prof of Business Admin; *b:* Hudson, NY; *m:* Marjan Lankhof; *ed:* St Univ of NY at Delhi (AAS) Mrktg 1969; St Univ of NY at Albany (BS) Bus Admin 1971; Babson Coll (MBA) Bus Admin 1972; St Univ of NY at Albany (MS) Bus Ed 1975; *cr:* Guilderland HS Bus Tchr 1975-83; Burnt Hills HS Bus Tchr 1983-84; St Univ of NY at Cobleskill Prof of Bus Admin 1984-92; Columbia-Greene Comm Coll Prof of Bus Admin, Bus Division Chair 1992-; *ai:* Class Adv 4 Yrs; HS Track Team Coach; Outdoor Club, Orange Key Club Adv; Acad Stans Comm Chair; NEA; Assn of NYS Two-Yr Colls; Stockport Vol Fire Co 1972-, Admin Sec; Outstdng Dedication to Stdnts Spec Recognition Medal SUNY at Cobleskill Inter-Dorm Cncl 1991; *office:* Columbia Greene Comm Coll 4400 Rt 23 Hudson NY 12534

BEEBE, LARRY FRANCIS, Math Teacher; *b:* Gloversville, NY; *m:* Sarah Gibbs; *c:* Edward D., Joel A., Seth A.; *ed:* Hudson Vly Comm Coll (AA) Lbrl Arts 1965; Castleton St Coll (BA) His 1967; Norwich Univ (MAT) His 1974; Post Grad St Michaels Coll, Univ of VT, Univ of CA at Berkley, Ithaca Coll; *cr:* Williamstown Jr, Sr HS Jr HS Sci, His Tchr 1968-77; Spaulding Graded Schl 8th Grd Soc Stud Tchr 1977-82; U-32 Jr, Sr HS Math Tchr 1982-; *ai:* Drama Club; Tchr Advy, Stu Achvmt Comm; NEA VT 1968-; U-32 Tchrs Assn 1982-, Grievance Comm; NCTM, VCTM, ATMINE 1982-; Barretown Schl Math Comm 1992-; Bara Congregational Church 1976-, Deacon; Tech, Eisenhower Grant; *office:* Union 32 HS RR 2 Montpelier VT 05602

BEEBE, ROBERT D., English & Spanish Teacher; *b:* Milford, DE; *m:* Wanda Baker; *c:* Sarah, Michael; *ed:* Bob Jones Univ (BA) Hum 1983; *cr:* Dover Chrstn Schl Span Tchr 1983-84; Seaford Chrstn Acad Span & 5th Grd Tchr 1984-86; Chrstn Tabernacle Acad Eng & Span Tchr 1986-; *office:* Christian Tabernacle Acad PO Box 148 Lincoln DE 19960

BEECROFT, THOMAS KENNETH, Professor of Psychology; *b:* Philadelphia, PA; *m:* Rebecca Strickland; *c:* Jeremy Tooley, Alison Tooley; *ed:* Millersville St Univ (BS) Comp Soc Sci & Psch 1970, (MS) Clinical Psych 1975; Univ of MD (PHD) Human Dev 1982; Attnd: Penn State Univ, Univ of DE, Grad Stud; Harvard Univ Post Doctoral Stud; *cr:* Penn Manor Schl Dist, Psychology Tchr 1970-75; Supv of Soc Sci 1975-80; Univ MD Tchng Asst & Rsrch 1982-84; Hagerstown Jr Coll Prof of Psychology 1984-; *ai:* Wkshp Dev Trainer, Consultant; Fac Prof Dev Comm; Human Svcs Internship Coord; Amer Psychological Assn 1984-; Amer Psychological Sco 1994-; PA Psychological Assn; Turning Point of WA Cty, Past Bd Mem; Pub Svc Lectures; Licensed Psychologist in Private Practice; Outstndg Young Man in Amer; Prof of the Yr Awd; *office:* Hagerstown Jr Coll 11400 Robinwood Dr Hagerstown MD 21742*

BEEDON, JOHN W., 6th Grade Teacher; *b:* Medina, NY; *m:* Janice H.; *c:* John Hobart, Kent, Bethany, Jason, Rebecca; *ed:* Northern IL Univ (BSEd) Amer His & Pol Sci 1966; Univ of Buffalo (MS) Elem Ed 1973; *cr:* Memence IL Schls 6th-8th Grd Soc Stud Tchr 1966-67; Lockport City Schls 9th Grd Soc Stud Tchr 1967-68; Royalton-Hartland 6th Grd Tchr 1968-; *ai:* Orleans Cnty Legislator; Past Mem Medina NY Bd of Ed; Pres of Medina Lions Club; Pres of Medina Mini League Bsbl Pgm; NEA 1967-, Life Mem; AFT & NYSUT 1973-; Royalton-Hartland Tchrs Assn 1968-; *office:* Gasport Elem Schl 4500 Orchard Pl Gasport NY 14067

BEEDY, LOIS MAHON, Sixth Grade Teacher; *b:* New Bedford, MA; *m:* Adelbert P.; *c:* Florence Baiocchi, Ann Marie Milazzo, Michael Milazzo; *ed:* Univ of VT (BS) Ed 1976; Attnd New England Conservatory of Music 1960-62; Univ of ME Continuing Ed Grad Level; *cr:* Orleans Elem Schl Kndgtn, Second Grd Tchr 1968-76; Wayne Elem Schl Kndgtn Tchr 1976-78; Maranacook Comm Schl Migrant Ed Tchr 1980-83; Mt Vernon Elem Schl Sixth Grd Tchr 1983-; *ai:* Cert of Tchrs Support System; MS Dev Comm; ME Tchrs Assn, NEA 1980-; *office:* Mt Vernon Elem Schl Box 3520 North Rd Mount Vernon ME 04352

BEEDY, RONALD BRADFORD, History Teacher; *b:* Lewiston, ME; *m:* Barbara Etta Varney; *c:* Ronald B. Jr., Jonathan, Thomas; *ed:* Univ of ME at Farmington (BA) His 1971; *cr:* Livermore Falls MS His Tchr 1971-85; Livermore Falls HS His Tchr 1985-; *ai:* Soph Class Adv; Ftbl & Track Coach; NEA 1975-; ME Coaches Assn 1972-; Amer Legion 1971-; *home:* PO Box 705 Livermore ME 04253

BEEGLE, JUDITH FREY, Business Teacher; *b:* Aiken, SC; *m:* Richard Gerald; *c:* Jean Osterkamp, John, Ann, Warren Brindle, Buckley Brindle; *ed:* Shippensburg Univ (BA) Bus Ed 1966; Grad Credits in Bus & Ed; Grad Credits in Ed at Penn St Univ & Wilkes Univ; *cr:* Letterkenny Army Depot Cmptr Programmer 1966-67; Chambersburg Area Schl Dist Sub Tchr 1979-80; Greencastle-Antrim Schl Dist Bus Ed Tchr 1981-; *ai:* Bus Dept Chprsn; Prof Dev Comm; Stu Tchr Mentor; NEA 1981-; First United Meth Church 1991-; Piney Mountain Retirement Home 1988-, Weekly Visitation; *office:* Greencastle-Antrim HS 300 S Ridge Ave Greencastle PA 17225*

BEELER, BRIDGETTE MICHELLE (WHITAKER), 6th Grade Teacher; *b:* Toledo, OH; *m:* Jon Edwin; *c:* Michael; *ed:* Univ of Toledo (BA) Elem Ed 1983; 16 Addl Hrs; *cr:* Sylvania Schls 6th Grd Tchr 1984-; *ai:* Stu Cncl Adv; Bldg Advy Comm Chair; Labor Mngmt, Jr High Restaffing Comm; Sylvania Ed Assn 1984-, VP Elections, Ed 1993-; OH Ed Assn, NEA 1984-; *office:* Hill View Elem Schl 5424 Whiteford Rd Sylvania OH 43560*

BEELER, CURTIS H., Art Instructor; *b:* Washington, DC; *ed:* Howard Univ (BFA) Art Ed 1980; *ai:* Sr, Jr Class Spon; Art, Drama, Modeling Clubs; Rites of Passages; Yrbk Adv; Hum Prgm; Alpha Phi Alpha 1985-; Duke Ellington Yth Project 1994-95; Theodore Roosevelt HS Outstdng Svc 1988-90, 1993-95; Lifetime Svc Alumni, Excl Awds 1989; Appreciation Awds 1988-90, 1993-95; Sr Spon Awds 1989, 1994; *office:* Calvin Coolidge HS 5th & Tuckerman Sts NW Washington DC 20012*

BEER, SALLY RUTH, ESL Teacher; *b:* Monticello, NY; *m:* Leon; *c:* Naomi, Ira; *ed:* Brooklyn Coll (BA) Fr 1964, (MA) Fr 1968; NYU, Kingsboro Comm Coll 30 Credit Hrs; *cr:* Shallow Jr HS Eng Tchr 1965-67; Walt Whitman Sr HS Fr Tchr 1967-68; Midwood HS Fr Tchr 1968-70; Maholia Jackson Jr HS Fr Tchr 1977-78; Midwood HS Esl Tchr 1978-; *ai:* NYS TESOL 1978-; Recognition Day Awd; Excl in Tchng Sidney Millman Awd; *office:* Midwood HS Bedford Ave & Glenwood Rd Brooklyn NY 11230

BEERBOWER, SUSAN HNAT, English Teacher; *b:* Sharon, PA; *m:* James N.; *c:* Anne S., Robert B.; *ed:* Allegheny Coll (BA) Eng 1973, (MA) Ed 1974; *cr:* Newbury HS Eng Tchr 1973-76; Fairborn HS Eng Tchr 1993-; *ai:* NCTE 1985-; NEA 1993-; *home:* 600 Redwood Sq Tipp City OH 45371

BEERS, MARSHA J., 7th-12th Grd Span & Ger Tchr; *b:* Bethlehem, PA; *m:* Howard Allen Jr.; *c:* Lauri, Alissa; *ed:* West Chester Univ (BA) Ger 1974; East Stroudsburg Univ (MED) Curr & Admin 1989; Working for MA Counseling Psych Kutztown Univ; *cr:* Rexroth Corp Sec, Translator 1977-79; Growing Place Part-time Tchrs Helper 1986-88; Pleasant Valley Schls Spa, Ger Tchr 1988-; *ai:* Choir Dir, Organist St Matthews UCC; Frosh Cls Adv; Travel Coord For Stu Summer Excursions; AATG, AATSP, NEA, PSEA 1988-; PDK 1993-; *office:* Pleasant Valley Schl Dist Rt 209 Brodheadsville PA 18322

BEERS, SUSAN MARIE, English Teacher; *b:* Manhasset, NY; *m:* Charles R.; *ed:* Geneva Coll (BA) Eng, Ed 1990; Long Island Univ (MS) Eng Ed 1995; *ai:* Jr High, Newspaper, Natl Jr Hnr Soc Adv; Girls Var Tennis Coach; *office:* Long Island Lutheran Jr/Sr HS 131 Brookville Rd Brookville NY 11545

BEERY, CHRISTIAN EUGENE, High School English Teacher; *b:* Wadsworth, OH; *m:* Dawn Michelle Brice; *c:* Allison Nicole; *ed:* Univ of Akron (BA) Scndry Ed 1992; *cr:* Mogadore Jr HS 8th Grd Lang Arts Tchr 1992-93; Mogadore HS Lang Arts Tchr 1993-; *ai:* Asst Ftbl, Frosh Bsktbl, Head Var Track Coach; Jrnlsm, Newspaper Adv; MEA 1992-, Bldg Rep; NEOEA, OEA, OCTELA 1992-; Seville United Meth Church 1982-; *office:* Mogadore HS 130 S Cleveland Ave Mogadore OH 44260*

BEERY, LEAFEE J., 1st Grade Teacher; *b:* Hillsboro, OH; *ed:* Morehead St Univ (BA); *cr:* CO Pub Schls; *ai:* Mange & Own Old Hotel Built in 1823; NEA; OEA; CEA; Wrote Grant to Get Money Total Schl Rdng Prgm; Edctr of Yr 1987-88; *office:* Sullivant Elem Schl 791 Griggs Ave Columbus OH 43223

BEFUMO, DEBRA JOY, English Teacher; *b:* New York City, NY; *ed:* Saint Johns Preparatory (BA) Eng 1982, (MA) Eng 1985; *cr:* Saint Catharine Acad Eng Tchr 1982-83; Saint Johns Preparatory Eng Tchr 1985-; *office:* Saint Johns Preparatory HS 2121 Crescent St Astoria NY 11105*

BEGENY, NANCY ZAHN, First Grade Teacher; *b:* Beaver Falls, PA; *w:* Donald Joseph (dec); *c:* Mark S., Lynda B. Manning, John P.; *ed:* Westminster Coll (BSEd) Elem Ed 1957; John Hopkins (MS) Communicative Disorders 1985; *cr:* Mercer Elem Schl Second Grd Tchr 1957-59, Lone Oak Elem First Grd Tchr 1966-67; Northfield Elem Schl Math Specialist 1977-81, First Grd Tchr 1981-; *ai:* Team Ldr Team I; Coaching; Math Comm Chprsn; Delta Kappa Gamma 1990-; NEA, MSTA, HCEA 1977-; St John's Schl 19890, Bd Mem; *office:* Northfield Elem Schl 9125 Northfield Rd Ellicott City MD 21042*

BEGIN, DAVID G., Music Teacher; *b:* Hartford, CT; *m:* Catherine; *c:* John, Anne, Ellen; *ed:* Univ of Hartford (BA) Music 1977; *cr:* East Hartford Schls Music Tchr 1977-79; John Wallace MS Music Tchr 1979-.

BEGIN, PAULETTE MARIE (MAZIE), Former Jr High Teacher; *b:* Lorain, OH; *m:* Jerome P.; *c:* Jerome P. Jr., Karen S.; *ed:* Coll of St Francis (BA) Ed 1969; 17 Grad Credits OH St, Ursuline, Baldwin-Wallace; *cr:* Mt Pleasant Cath Schl Jr High Eng, Rdng Tchr 1969-73; Notre Dame Elem

Schl Jr High Eng, Rdng Tchr 1982-95; *ai:* Moderator Young Author's Conf; Yrbk Supvr; Dev Jr High Career Unit; Stu Cncl Adv; Strategic Planning Comm; NCEA; HS Music Boosters, Pres, VP, Project Coord; Couple Ministry; Staff Dev Inservices Presentor; Dev of Inner City Jr High Eng Prgm; *home:* 6643 N Palmerston Dr Mentor OH 44060

BEGLEY, CHARLES F., Latin & Greek Teacher; *b:* New York City, NY; *m:* Lois A.; *c:* Stephen A., Andrew W.; *ed:* SUNY at Albany (BA) Latin 1967; Canisius Coll (MS) Ed 1973; Tufts Univ 1984, 1990, 1991, Bowdoin Coll 1986, 1987; Amer Schl of Classical Stud in Athens Greece 1992; Amer Acad in Rome Italy 1994; *cr:* Lockport HS Tchr Latin, Eng & Greek 1967-; *ai:* Latin Club; AFT; NYSUT; CAWNY; CAES; CANE & CAAS; Dante Summer Seminar in Italy 1988; NEA Summer Seminar on Thucydides at St Peter MN 1993; Flwshps: NEH Frgn Lang 1994; Cncl For Basic Ed for Ind Stud in Hum 1995; *office:* Lockport HS 250 Lincoln Ave Lockport NY 14094

BEGLEY, URSULA C., 6th Grade Teacher; *b:* Boston, MA; *ed:* Newton Coll of the Sacred Heart (BA) Eng 1969; Fordham Univ at Bronx 18 Addl Credits Rel Ed 1979-81; Attnd Fordham Univ Schl of Ed at Lincoln Ctr 1978-79; *cr:* Regina Pacis Schl 8 Grd Lang Arts Tchr 1972-81; Epiphany of Our Lord 8 Grd Lang Arts Tchr 1981-86; St Cecilia Schl 6 Grd Lang Arts Tchr 1988-; *ai:* Integrated Lang Arts Coord; *office:* St Cecilia Schl 525 Rhawn St Philadelphia PA 19111

BEGRES, SHERRILL JEAN, Associate Professor; *b:* Stambaugh, MI; *c:* Phillip Grammatico, Shauna Hines; *ed:* Univ of MI at Flint (BA) Eng & Philosophy 1978; Wayne St Univ (MA) Philosophy 1982, (PHD) Philosophy 1986; *cr:* Wayne St Univ Lecturer 1982-83; Univ of MI at Flint Lecturer & Visiting Prof 1980-89; Mott Comm Coll Lecturer 1985-87; Indiana Univ of PA Assist & Assoc Prof 1989-; *ai:* Philosophy Majors & Minors Adv; HIV Ed & Intervention Team; Institutional Review Bd for Protection of Human Subjects; Natl Collegiate Honors Cncl 1995-; Amer Philosophical Assn 1986-; Amer Assn of Univ Women 1994-; IN Hospital Ethics Comm 1994-; Univ of Pittsburgh Ctr for Medical Ethics, Ethics Consortium Prgm 1993-; IUP Tchng Excl Awd 1993; Thomas Rumble Fellowship Wayne St Univ; Beta Sigma Phi 1st Lady for AIDS Work; Publications on Metaphor & AIDS; *office:* Indiana Univ Of PA 446 Sutton Hall Indiana PA 15701

BEGUN, ALAN H., Computer Coordinator; *b:* Brooklyn, NY; *m:* Rhonda Hellman; *c:* Jason, Jayme; *ed:* Long Island Univ (BS) Ed 1966; Brooklyn Coll (MS) Ed 1969; St Johns Univ Educl Admin Cert 1973; *cr:* P.S. 67 Tchr 1966-73; P.S. 214 Tchr 1973-89, Cmptr Coord Tchr 1990-; *ai:* Schl Treas; UFT 1966-; Cmptr Learning Fnd Cert Schl Level I 1994; *office:* P.S. 214 Schl 2944 Pitkin Ave Brooklyn NY 11208

BEHAN, LINDA HEUVEL, Spanish & English Teacher; *b:* Big Spring, TX; *m:* Robert; *c:* Erin, Rebecca; *ed:* Southwest TX St Univ (BA) Eng, Span 1969; Attnd Abilene Chrstn Coll; *cr:* Sequin HS Eng Tchr 1969-70; College Heights Elem 1st Grd Biling Tchr 1970-73; Chaads Ford Elem Span, Supplemental Prgm Tchr 1985; West Chester Chrstn Schl Span, Eng Tchr 1985-; *ai:* Vlybl Coach 1991-; Bible Quiz Coach 1992-93, 1995-; Keystone Chrstn Ed Assn 1985-; Bible Bapt Church 1979-, Sunday Schl Class Sec, Ladies Missionary Fellowship Sec, VP, Wednesday Night Prayer Ldr; *office:* West Chester Christian Schl 1237 Paoli Pike West Chester PA 19380

BEHM, MARGARET VANDRIEL, English Teacher; *b:* Reading, PA; *c:* John R., Susan A.; *ed:* Albright Coll (AB) Eng 1969; Kutztown Univ (MA) Eng 1976; Addl 15 Hrs; *cr:* Beaufort Cty Schls Eng Tchr 1969-72; Wilson HS Eng Tchr 1972-77; Hamburg Area HS Eng Tchr 1985-; *ai:* Stu Cncl Adv 8 Yrs; HAEA, PSEA, NEA 1985-; Strausstown Woman's Club 1978-, Pres 1984-86, Sec 1994-; Region G Stu Cncl Adv of Yr 1995; Sr Class Tchr of Yr; *office:* Hamburg Area Jr Sr HS Windsor St Hamburg PA 19526

BEHM, MICHAEL JOSEPH, Physical Education Teacher; *b:* Bath, NY; *m:* Carol Ann Grosso; *c:* Michael, Andrew, Daniel; *ed:* St Univ of NY at Buffalo (BS) PE 1976, (MS) PE 1978; 19 Credit Hrs Admin Canisius Coll; *cr:* Holland Cntrl Schls 5-8 Grd PE Instr 1977-78; NYS Assn for Retarded Chil Adapted PE Instr 1978-80; Orchard Park Cntrl Schls PE, Adapted PE Instr 1980-; *ai:* JV Girls Soccer, JV Girls Bsktbl, Modified Girls Sftbl Coach; Orchard Park Tchrs Assn, NYSUT, AAHPERD 1980-; Orchard Park Little League 1980-, Mgr; *office:* Orchard Park HS 4040 Baker Rd Orchard Park NY 14127

BEHNKEN, DIANE EATON, English, Jrnlsm & Typing Tchr; *b:* Three Rivers, MI; *m:* Mark A.; *ed:* Midwestern Bapt Coll (BRE) Ed 1970; Univ of Detroit Guidance & Cnslng 21 Credit Hrs; *cr:* Midwestern Bapt Coll Registrar 1980-84; Landmark Chrstn Schl Tchr 1986-; *ai:* Yrbk Adv; *home:* 40 Applewood Dr Fairfield OH 45014

BEHR, LAURA HOMAN, Special Education Teacher; *b:* Celina, OH; *m:* Thomas Edward; *ed:* OH St Univ (BA) Ed 1977; Wright St Univ (MS) Ed 1984; Attnd Elkhart Medical & Dental Technique; *cr:* Philburn Medical Ct Medical Asst 1966-72; Norworth Convalescent Ct Nurses Aide 1973-76; OSU Hospital Ward Clerk 1976-77; Centerburg Schls Spec Ed Tchr 1977-80; Sidney City Schls Spec Ed Tchr 1980-; *ai:* Sacred Heart Church Rel Ed of Presch Coord; NEA 1977-, Bldg Rep; IRA, OCRA 1994-; Shelby Cty Cncl IRA 1990-; *office:* Longfellow Elem Schl 1250 Park St Sidney OH 45365

BEHREND, CARL W., Guidance Counselor; *b:* New Rochelle, NY; *m:* Judith Heiman; *c:* Scott, Christofer; *ed:* Wittenberg Univ (BS) Ed & His 1968; Fordham Univ (MS) Cnslng Ed 1970; Niagara Univ CAS Educl Admin 1980; 20 Credit Hrs Buffalo St Coll Spcl Ed 1982-85; *cr:* New Rochelle Acad Tchr 1968-70; Ben Franklin Jr High Tchr 1970-74; Orchard Park Jr High & MS Cnslr 1974-77; Orchard Park MS Asst Prin 1983; Orchard Park HS Cnslr 1977-; *ai:* Club Adv; Fair Coord; NYSUT 1970-; NYSACAC 1989-, Chair, Schl Coll Rel & HS Del, Distngd Svc Awd 1993; NACAC 1994-; *office:* Orchard Park HS 4040 Baker Rd Orchard Park NY 14127

BEHRENSMEYER, MARY JO EUVINO, Latin Instructor; *b:* Gary, IN; *m:* Robert; *c:* Robert, Matthew, Sarah; *ed:* IN Univ (BS) Classical Stud 1973,(MSEd) Classical Stud 1975; Addl 24 Grad Hrs; Attnd CA St Univ at Northridge, Tufts Univ & Ashland Univ; *cr:* Indianapolis Pub Schls 1975-85, 6th Grd Latin Prgm Dir; Mt Vernon HS Latin Instr 1985-; *ai:* Latin Club Adv; NEA, Amer Classical League, Pompeiiana Inc 1980-; OH Classical Conf, Greater Columbus Latin Club 1985-; St Vincent de Paul Church 1985-, Lector & Eucharistic Minister; Gerrit Roelofs Meml Fellowship 1988, 1993, 1996; Martha Holden Jennings Grant Mosaic Project 1993; Arthur Patch Mc Kinlay Fellowship 1988, Archaeological Dig Israel 1993; Book Pub; Charles T. Murphy Fellowship 1993; Hildesheim Vase Awd, OH Latin Tchr-Prgm of Yr 1993; Natl Endowment for the Hum For Fwlshp 1995; *office:* Mount Vernon HS 300 Martinsburg Rd Mount Vernon OH 43050

BEHRINGER, MARY ALICE A., First Grade Teacher; *b:* Brooklyn, NY; *m:* George; *c:* George, Patricia DellaVecchia, Sally Ann Finkelstein; *ed:* Coll of New Rochelle (BA) Art, Ed 1959; 6 Hrs Fordham; 3 Hrs Brooklyn Coll; *cr:* St Gregory the Great Schl 3rd Grd Tchr 1959-61; St Pancras Schl 6th Grd Tchr 1961-63; St Francis of Assisi Schl Art Tchr 1965-66, 1st-2nd Grd Tchr 1970-; *ai:* Asst Prin; Mid Sts Comm; Mentor Tchr; Rap Group Facilitator; Yrbk Modreator; Rel, Math Coord; Drama Dir; ASCD 1995-; St Francis Parish, Eucharistic Minister; 25 Yr Rel Tchr; *home:* 2230 76th St Flushing NY 11370*

BEHRMAN, LYNN GROVER, Business Education Teacher; *b:* New York, NY; *m:* Arnold Richard; *c:* Gavin J., Matthew E.; *ed:* Long Island Univ (BS) Bus, Ed 1965; 9 Post Grad Credits; 9 Post Grad Credits Monmouth Univ; 6 Post Grad Credits Rider Coll; Software Cert Brookdale Comm Coll; *cr:* Morris HS Bus Ed Tchr 1964-68; Manpower Prgm Trng Welfare Recipients 1964-66; Thorne Jr HS Bus Tchr 1970-71; Franklin Jr HS Bus Tchr 1979-82; Keyport HS Bus Ed Tchr 1982-; *ai:* New Tchrs Mentor; Class Adv; MCEA, NJEA, NJBEA, NEA 1982-; *home:* 301 Pleasant Valley Rd Morganville NJ 07751

BEHRMANN, LINDA DIANE, Fourth Grade Teacher; *b:* Jersey City, NJ; *ed:* Newark St Coll (BA) Elem Ed 1969; Fairleigh Dickinson Univ (MA) Human Dev 1986; 32 Addl Credit Hrs at Monmouth Coll; *cr:* Indiana Avenue Schl #18 Tchr 1969-; *ai:* Stu Cncl Adv; Family Math Instr; Self-Esteem Support Group for Children Facilitator; NJ Ed Assn, NEA, Woodbridge Twp Ed Assn 1980-; NJ Governors Tchr Recognition Awd 1986; *office:* Indiana Avenue Schl #18 256 Indiana Ave Iselin NJ 08830

BEHRNS, GARY M., French Teacher; *b:* North Tonawanda, NY; *m:* Nancy L. Lombardi; *c:* Eric, Maria, Steven; *ed:* SUNY at Albany (BA) Fr 1969; Univ of WI (MA) Fr 1972; Grad Courses at SUNY at Buffalo, Univ of Auignon France; *cr:* Niagara Falls HS Fr Tchr 1969-70; Amherst Cntrl HS Fr, Span Tchr 1970-74; Maryvale HS Fr Tchr 1974-76; West Seneca Cntrl Schl Fr, Span Tchr 1976-; *ai:* Fr Club, NHS Adv; Bible Club Chaperone; Comprehensive Schl Improvement Comm Mem; AFT, NYSUT 1969-; WNYFLEC, NYSAFLT 1969-, Comm Mem; AAFT 1967-, Comm Mem, Contest Chm, Travel Stud Schlsp; Wheatfield Neighborhood Church 1969-, Choir Dir, SS Supt, Tchr, Governing Bd; Articles Pub NEH Schlsp, AAFT Schlsp; Take Stdnts on Educl Trips Abroad; *office:* West Seneca Sr HS 3330 Seneca St West Seneca NY 14224*

BEHUNIAK, MARIE DONOFRIO, 5th Grade Teacher; *b:* Auburn, NY; *m:* Gregory; *ed:* Cayuga Comm Coll (AA) Ed 1967; Empire St Coll (BS) Ed 1978; SUNY at Oswego Grad Courses; *cr:* St Francis Schl Grd 6 Tchr 1964-69; St Aloysius Schl Grd 5 Tchr 1969-70; St Patrick Schl Grd 5 Tchr 1970-; *ai:* Aurburn Schl Bd 1989-92; Yth for Understanding Intnl Exchange Prgm 1989-93; Tchr of Yr 1989; Tchr of Yr 1991; *home:* 82 Wall St Auburn NY 13021

BEIDELMAN, REBECCA ELLEN, Social Studies Teacher; *b:* Allentown, PA; *m:* James H.; *c:* Rachel Kolb, Elias; *ed:* Kutztown Univ (BS) Scndry Ed, Soc Stud 1993; 18 Credit Hrs Scndry Ed, Soc Stud; *cr:* Emmaus HS Soc Stud Tchr 1993-; *ai:* Organize Annual Model UN at Lehigh Univ for Area Schls; Kappa Delta Pi 1992-; NEA, PSEA 1993-; DAR 1996; *office:* Emaus H S 851 North St Emmaus PA 18049

BEIERLE, JEAN STEINBACH, Spanish Teacher; *b:* Perth Amboy, NJ; *m:* Brill; *c:* Sharon, Kara; *ed:* Georgian Ct Coll (BA) Span 1974; Univ of MD (MED) Foreign Lang, Curr & Dev 1989; Univ of Salamanca Spain Schlsp to Stud Span 1993; *cr:* Saint Marys HS Span Tchr 1974-76; Thomas Stone HS Span Tchr 1981-; For Lang Dept Chprsn; *office:* Thomas Stone HS Hwy Rt 5 Waldorf MD 20601

BEIGEL, ANDREW RICHARD, Asst Professor of Education; *b:* Syracuse, NY; *m:* Marianna Clark De Long; *c:* Virginia, Peter, Marianna; *ed:* SUNY at Potsdam (BA) Amer His 1975, (MS) Rdng 1986; PA St (PHD) Ed 1991; *cr:* Sunmount Dev Ctr Comm Residence Dir 1984-86; PA St Grad Asst 1986-90; D'Youville Coll Asst Prof 1990-; *ai:* Tchrs Assn Adv; Acad Policies Comm Chprsn; Cmptr Comm; IRB Comm, Grad Curr & Prgms Chprsn; Fac Cncl Sec; Pgm Comm Gloria Parks Commnty Center; RESNA 1992-; IRA 1986-; AAUP 1990-; Fac Dev Grant; Research Grant; Articles Pub; Textbook; *office:* D'Youville Coll 320 Porter Ave Buffalo NY 14201*

BEIRNE, BERNARD JOSEPH, English Teacher; *b:* Brooklyn, NY; *m:* Laura Dickinson; *c:* Amanda, Laura, Elizabeth; *ed:* Fairfield Univ (BA) Eng 1969; Adelphi Univ (MA) Eng 1977; 36 Credits Soc Stud Cert; 38 Credits Bus Cert; *cr:* St Joseph Schl 7th Grd Tchr 1969-74; Centereach HS Eng Tchr 1974-; *ai:* Acad Mentathlon Team Coach; Fac Advy Comm; Mid Cntry Tchrs Assn 1974-, Labor Negotiator; NCTE 1977-; MCTA 1974-, Bldg Rep; US Life Saving Assn 1984-; *office:* Centereach HS 14 43rd St Centereach NY 11720

BEISEL, PATRICIA ANN, Third Grade Teacher; *b:* Erie, PA; *ed:* Mercyhurst Coll (BS) Elem Ed 1969; Edinboro St (MS) Rdng; 26 Addl Credit Hrs; *cr:* Prince George's MD Schls 1, 3 Grd Elem Tchr 1969-73; Japan's Dept of Defense Schls 3 Grd Elem Tchr 1973-74; Germany's Dept of Defense Schls 1 Grd Elem Tchr 1976-78; Girard Schl Dist 3-4 Grd Elem Tchr 1978-; *ai:* AFT 1978-; Outstdng Performance Awd Germany 1977-78.

BEITEL, DONICE CHERYL, Chemistry Tchr & Asst Band Dir; *b:* Charleroi, PA; *m:* Bruce E.; *c:* Donice, Bruce; *ed:* CA Univ (BS) Chem 1965; Univ of Pittsburgh (MLIS) Admin Sci Lib 1971; *cr:* Hempfield HS Chem Tchr 1965-; *ai:* Asst Band Dir; Asst Stage Band, Jazz Ensemble Dir; PMEA 1990-; *office:* Hempfield Area HS Rd 6 Box 77 Greensburg PA 15601

BEITZEL, REBECCA MASTEN, Math Dept Head & Teacher; *b:* Akron, OH; *m:* Paul E.; *ed:* Malone Coll (BA) Math 1974; OH Univ 16 Quarter Hrs; Akron Univ 6 Sem Hrs; Muskingon 4 Sem Hrs; *cr:* New Philadelphia HS Math Tchr & Dept Head 1974-; *ai:* Labor-Mgmt Comm; OEA 1974-; NEA 1974-; New Phila Ed Assn 1974-, Treas & VP; OCTM 1993-; Little Theatre Tusc Cty 1977-, Treas; Tusc Philharmonic Chorus 1980-; *office:* New Philadelphia HS 343 Ray Ave NW New Philadelphia OH 44663

BEKIC, LEILA ESPER, Math Teacher; *b:* Braddock, PA; *c:* George Paul, Ronald Michael; *ed:* Indiana Univ of PA (BS) Scndry Ed, Math 1967; Math, Psych, Cmptr, Ed Classes Edinboro Univ, Gannon Univ, IU #5; *cr:* Park Terrace Jr HS 7th-8th Grd Math Tchr 1967-70; J. S. Wilson Jr HS 8th-9th Grd Math Tchr 1970-71; Community Country Day Schl 7th-12th Grd Math Tchr 1981-84; Tech Memorial HS 10th-12th Grd Math Tchr 1984-86; Gridley MS 6th-7th Grd Math Tchr 1986-92; Strong Vincent HS 7th-8th Math Tchr 1992-94; East HS 9th-12th Grd Math Tchr 1994-; *ai:* Pep Club Adv; Hnrs Banquet Chprsn; SAP Team; Curr, Chptr V In-Service Comm; NEA, PSEA, Erie Ed Assn, PACE 1984-; Greek Ladies Org 1990-, Bd Sec; Greek Orthodox Yth 1992-, Adv; *home:* 4413 Holiday Dr Erie PA 16506

BELANGER, DONALD JOSEPH, Biology Teacher; *b:* Washington, DC; *m:* Linda Munson; *c:* Joey, Michael; *ed:* Univ of MD (BS) Zoology 1975, (MS) Scndry Ed, Sci 1977; 45 Addl Hrs; *cr:* Robert Goddard MS Sci Tchr 1977-82; Oxon HS Bio Tchr 1982-; *ai:* Head Var Swim Team Coach 1986-; Turtle Rescue Project Spon; NEA, PGCEA 1977-; US Swimming 1987-, Coach; Waldorf Hockey League 1995-, Head, Asst Coach, Spring Championship, Stanley Cup; Scorpions Martial Arts Club 1990-, Green Belt; Point Ridge Swim & Racquet 1991-, Head Coach, Division Champs; South Bowie Blues 1993-, Head Coach; PEPCO Outstdng Sci Edctr of Yr; Phi Sigma 1977 Inductee; *office:* Oxon Hill HS 6701 Leyte Dr Oxon Hill MD 20745*

BELANGER, SHARON LAWSON, English & Jrnlsm Tchr of GATE; *b:* Bar Harbor, ME; *m:* Clayton D.; *c:* Michelle, Danielle; *ed:* Univ of ME at Portland (BS) Elem Ed K-8 1971; Univ of ME (MS) Rdng, Lang Arts K-12 1987, (CAS) Rdng, Lang Arts K-12 1991; 15 Credit Hrs Scndry Eng; *cr:* St John Elem Schl 1st Grd Tchr 1971-72; Champlain Elem Schl 4th Grd Tchr 1972-76; Gateway Elem Schl Fourth Grd Tchr 1976-88; Van Buren Dist Sec Schl Tchr, GATE Coord 1988-; *ai:* Drama Coach; Class, Project Grad, NHS, Band Advs; Miss Van Buren Pageant Coord; Stu Asst Team; Adult Ed Instr & Tutor NMTC; Delta Kappa Gamma 1984-, Pres, VP; Van Buren Ed Assn 1971-; Aroostook Regnl Dir of GATE 1989-; Legion Auxillary 1989-; HOPE Team Drug Free 1980-; Wellness Team; I Club Inductee for Work with Stdnts, Schls; Cath Yth Group St Recc Work with Stdnts; Golden Attitude Awd Adult Ed Dir Dana Greer Adult Ed Classes; Worked on & Received Many Schl Based Gra Tech, Classroom, Integration; *office:* Van Buren Dist Secondary S Main St Van Buren ME 04785*

BELBIN, EDWARD L.,JR., HS Social Studies Teacher; *b:* Prov RI; *m:* Julie A.; *c:* David R.; *ed:* Saint Anselm Coll (BA) His 1 Credit Hrs Post Bachelors; *cr:* Londonderry HS Soc Stud Tchr 19 Bsbl & Hockey Coach; Londonderry Ed Assn 1988-, Contract Neg NEA 1988-; Manchester Historic Assn 1995-, Vol; Saint Jean t Parish 1991-, Marriage Prep Cnslr; *office:* Londonderry HS 295 Ma Rd Londonderry NH 03053*

BELCHER, CATHERINE LEE, Social Studies Teacher; *b:* C. CA; *ed:* Stanford Univ (BA) His 1990, (MA) Tchr Ed 1991; *cr:* Eden HS His Tchr 1991-92; Ochoa Intermediate Schl His & Lang A 1992-93; Haverford Sr HS Soc Stud Tchr 1994-; *ai:* Sr Class & Asi Adv; Dance Group Dir; NCSS, NEA, PSEA 1994-; Mellon Fnd 1991; Natl Endowment for the Hum Fellow 1992; *office:* Haverford Mill Rd Havertown PA 19083*

BELCHER, CHERRIE FULLER, First Grade Teacher; *b:* Roper, Charlie F. Sr.; *c:* Charlena B. Martin, Charlenzo, Charlie Jr.; *ed:* C Univ (MED) Elem Ed; Elizabeth City St (BS) Elem Ed; Prin Cert; Schl Dist Elem Schl Tchr; *ai:* Safety Patrol Spon, New Tchr Me Peters Choir Directress; Sunday Schl Tchr.*

BELCHER, JOHN JOSEPH, Science Teacher; *b:* St Louis, Justine; *ed:* Queens Coll (MA) Sci Ed 1986; 30 Addl Hrs Undergra Tutorial Coursework Biological Scis; *cr:* Belcher Woodworking Designer, Craftsman 1972-84; JHS 189 Q Sci Tchr 1984-; *ai:* Presentations Sci Tchrs; *office:* JHS 189 Q Daniel Carter Beard Barclay Ave Flushing NY 11355

BELCHIKOFF, TERESA EMMA, Mathematics Teach Philadelphia, PA; *m:* Frederick; *ed:* Glassboro St Coll (BA) Math E (MA) Math Ed 1971; 30 Credit Hrs Post Grad; *cr:* Cherry Hill HS E 1968-; *ai:* Ed Assn Fac Rep; CHEA Liason; Affirmative Action C Assn Negotiating Team; NJEA, NEA 1968-; NCTM; *office:* Che East HS Kresson Rd Cherry Hill NJ 08003

BELDEN, DAVID, Seventh Grade Lang Arts Tchr; *b:* Ravenna, Barbara Wagner; *c:* Ray, Grant; *ed:* Bowling Green St Univ (BS) 1975, (MED) Spec Ed 1979; Post Grad Work; Univ of Toledo, Col St Joseph, Drake Univ Grad Work; *cr:* Four Cty JVS Adult 1978-83; Hope Schl Tchr 1975-76; Montpelier Schls Tchr, De 1976-; *ai:* Lang Arts Dept Chm; Jr High Play Dir; Schl Newspap Creative Writing Journal Editor; NEA, OEA 1976-; MEA 1976- Terms; Jennings Scholar; Golden Apple Awd; NW OH Adult Edct Employed Managing Editor Local Newspaper; *office:* Montpelier S MS State Rt 576 Montpelier OH 43543

BELDEN, PATRICIA ANNE, Sixth Grade Teacher; *b:* Westerly, Tamas Michel; *c:* Bomira; *ed:* RI Coll (BS) Elem Ed, Lang Art Attnd Providence Coll, Univ of RI; *cr:* Hope Vly Elem Schl 4th G 1986-88; Chariho MS 6th Grd Tchr 1989-; *ai:* Sci Club, Washing Trip Adv; RINEA, NEA, RIPACE 1987-, Elections Comm; NSTA RI League of Mid Schls 1990-; RI Soc Stud Tchr Assn 1991-; St Church 1992-; St Vincent's Church 1963-; Senate Citation for Tch 1989; Town of Hopkinton Proclamation for Tchng Excl; *office:* MS 455 B Switch Rd Wood River Junctio RI 02894*

BELFIORE, ARTHUR FRANCIS, Band Director; *b:* Mahanoy C *m:* April Dawn Strong; *ed:* Penn St Univ (BS) Music Ed 1981, Music Ed 1990; *cr:* Lock Haven HS Band Dir 1981-83; Clearview H Dir 1983-85; Concord-Carlisle HS Asst Band Dir 1985-86; George Band Dir 1986-88; Union HS Band Dir 1990-91; Lewistown Area of Bands 1991-; *ai:* Marching Band; Symphonic Wind Ensemb Band; Brass Choir; Flute Ensemble; Clarinet Choir; Saxophone Percussion Ensemble; Indoor Guard; Indoor Percussion; PA Educators Assn 1981-; Coll Band Dirs Natl Assn 1988-; NEA; Lev Comm Elks Band 1991-, Dir; Mifflin Cty 2000 1995-, Awd-Composer in Residence Proposal 1995; *office:* Lewistown HS Dr Lewistown PA 17044*

BELGIOVENE, JOANN PENZA, Kindergarten Teacher; *b:* Vi NJ; *m:* Thomas Belgiovene; *c:* Michael, Steven; *ed:* Trenton St Co Elem Ed 1970; Coll of New Rochelle (MA) Gifted Ed 1989; *cr:* M Schl 3rd Grd Tchr 1970-71; Lincoln Schl Remedial Rdng Tchr 1 Windsor Schl Remedial Math Tchr 1975; GL Cooke Schl Kndg 1986-; *ai:* Schl Improvement Bldg Level Team; Sullivan Cty Whol Sullivan Cty Comm Coll Field Supv Early Chldhd Ed; AFT & 1986-; GL Cooke PTA 1986-, Tchr Rep; Amer Cancer Soc, Annual D Sale Rep; Brownie Scouts Ldr; Cub Scouts Ldr, Citizens Comm Wurtsboro Pub Lib Charter Mem; Chase Schl PTO 1983-90, Pres Wurtsboro Fire Co Ladies Auxiliary; *office:* George L Cooke Prima 1 Franklin Ave Monticello NY 12701

BELGRAVE, MARIO GERARDO, Educl Consultant; *b:* Panam Republica de Pa; *ed:* Rutgers Univ (BA) Elem Ed 1977; *cr:* Newco 8th Grd Tchr 9 Yrs; Pemberton Twp HS ABE-GED Tchr 9 Yrs; Ho Elem Schl 3-8 Grd Tchr 4 Yrs; Charles Schwab & Co Stockbroke Houghton-Mifflin Pub Co Educl Consultant 8 Months; *ai:* NEA, PTEA, BCEA 1977-; Natl Cncl of Panamanians Inc 1969-, Mem Schlsp Comm; Tchr of Yr 1981-82; Superior Performance Fi Compensation 1987-89.*

BELHUMEUR, CATHERINE HARKINS, English Teach Springfield, MA; *m:* George; *ed:* Coll of Our Lady of the Elms (B 1970; *cr:* Kiley MS Eng Tchr 1970-; *ai:* NEA; *office:* Kiley M Cooley St Springfield MA 01128

BELIKIS, PATRICIA, English Teacher; *b:* New York City, NY; *m:* *c:* Eleanor, Peter; *ed:* St Johns Univ (BA) Eng 1971; New Schl Rsrch (MA) Lib Arts 1976; Grad Ctr City univ of NY Eng Lit; 20 Hrs; *cr:* Queenborough Comm Coll Adj Tchr 1980-81; Baldwin Sr Tchr 1971-; *ai:* Curr & Film Club Adv; Mentor for New Tchrs; 1975-; Modern Lang Assn 1980-; LI Eng Cncl 1985-; Yth Affairs 1985-, Chair; *office:* Baldwin HS 841 High School Dr Baldwin NY

BELISLE, KATHLEEN KANE, First Grade Teacher; *b:* Putnam, James H.; *c:* Eric, Daniel; *ed:* Eastern CT St UNiv (BA) Elem E (MA) Rdng 1983; 15 Credit Hrs Sacred Heart Univ; *cr:* Liston Cn First-Second Grd Tchr 1982-; *ai:* Lang Arts, Soc Stud, Prof Dev PTO; CT Cooperating Tchr Prgm; NEA, CEA 1982-.

BELISLE, SALLY FRANK, Retired Teacher; *b:* Lewiston, ME; *m* *c:* Dennis Mac Donald, Scott Mac Donald; *ed:* Univ of Portland,Gorham (BS) Elem Ed 1968; Univ of Southern ME (MS Sci 1976; Math A Way of Thinking 1988; Math Solutions I 1993, *cr:* Lake St Schl 4th Grd Tchr 1968-79; City of Auburn K-12th Coord 1979-82; Washburn Schl 2nd-3rd Grd Multi-Age Tchr 1 Webster Schl 4th Grd, Multi 4th-5th Grd Tchr 1986-95; *ai:* Ma 1977-95; Drama; Creative Comm; Readers', Roadside Theaters Cntry Skiing; NEA, AEA 1968-; Habitat for Humanity 1989-, Habitat for Humanity ME 1993-, Treas; *home:* 11 Laase Ave Lewis 04240*

:AU, ROBERT, Second Grade Teacher; *b:* Worcester, MA; *m:* Bourisk-Beliveau; *c:* Courtney, Alexander; *ed:* Worcester St Coll Elem Ed 1971; Assumption Coll (MA) Spec Ed 1977; 30 Credit Hrs Math Courses at Worcester St Coll; *cr:* Mc Elvie Schl 4th Grd Tchr , F. G. Houghton Schl 3rd Grd Tchr 1973-80; Chocksett Schl 3rd r 1980-90, Second Grd Tchr 1990-; *ai:* MA Tchrs Assn, NEA, Tchrs Assn 1973-; Wachusett Reg Tchr Assn 1993-.

ASLEAN POOLE, Seventh Grade Math Teacher; *b:* Bessemer, AL; t; *c:* Albert, Antonio; *ed:* Cleveland St Univ (BS) Elem Ed 1970; stern Reserve Univ (MS) Ed 1973; Attnd Kent St Univ, John Univ; *cr:* St Agnes Cath Schl Tchr 1966-69; East Cleveland City hr, Admin 1970-; *ai:* Unit Ldr; NEA, OEA, ECEA 1970-, VP, Sec, Relation Awd; Assn for Supervision 1978-; Kappa Delta Pi; Phi appa; Toastmasters, Pres; Edctr of Yr Awd 1986-87; Martha Jennings Scholar; Bowling Green St Univ Project Teach Adj Prof; Rdng Book for Bldg Level Usage; Natl Cncl for Accreditation of Team Mem; *office:* East Cleveland City Schls 14410 Terrace Rd veland OH 44112*

BARBARA J. BARRY, Fourth Grade Teacher; *b:* Indiana, PA; *m:* F. III; *c:* Jamie Marie, Katie Renee, Andrew Thomas; *ed:* IN Univ BA) Elem Ed 1979; *cr:* East Pike Elem Schl Tchr 1979-; *ai:* s Comm & Participant in Annual Corporate Cup Ath Competition; : Planning Dist Citizenship Team; Literary Bd Mem; Vlybl Coach tr League; NEA, PSEA 1979-; Womens Club of Homer City 1987-, ped Write Several Grants for IN Schl Dist; *office:* East Pike Elem E Pike Indiana PA 15701

BARBARA T., US History AP & Honors Tchr; *b:* Peekskill, NY; sell Sage Coll (BA) His & Govt 1960; Maxwell Grad Schl at e Univ (MA) US His 1966; Attnd North Adams St Coll; *cr:* Crosby l Sci Tchr 1966-81; Taconic HS Pol Sci & US His Tchr 1981-84; l HS US His Tchr 1984-; *ai:* Grad Org Comm; MA Cncl for Soc estern MA Cncl for Soc Stud; Jaycees Young Tchr of Yr 1971; l Schl System Golden Apple Awd; DAR Monument Restoration *ice:* Pittsfield HS 300 East St Pittsfield MA 01201

CAROL KELLNER, Fifth Grade Teacher; *b:* Hazleton, PA; *m:* James; *c:* Jennifer Bell Wanner, Kathleen Suzanne Bell Haines; ers Univ (BA) Frgn Lang 1966; 30 Credit Hrs Rowan Coll; *cr:* Miller Schl Fifth Grd Tchr 1966-67; Crescent Park Schl Second r, Rdng Specialist 1967-69; Osage & Kresson Schls Kndgtn, Fifth Grd Tchr 1979-; *ai:* NEA, NJEA 1966-; CCEA 1967-; VTEA J Governors Tchr Recognition Awd for Excl Pub Schl 1984; *office:* Elem Schl 1 School Ln Voorhees NJ 08043*

CATHIE L., Middle School Teacher; *b:* New York City, NY; *c:* Morelli, Heather Morelli; *ed:* NY Inst Tech (BS) Bus 1972; NY A) Ed 1990; Attnd CUNY Tchrs Coll; *cr:* Crossroads Magnet Schl rs; PS 84 Magnet Schl Tchr 2 Yrs; *ai:* Pub Sr Yrbk; Create & Direct und Raising Play; AFT 1989-; Coallition of Essential Schls 1991-, Coallition of Collaborative Ed, Mentor; Numerous Article Pub; 44 W 16th St New York NY 10011

CHARLES J., Soc Studies Dept Chair & Instr; *b:* Reno, NV; *m:* , *c:* Jeremy; *ed:* SUNY at Oswego (BA) Soc Stud, Ed 1972; SUNY burgh (MA) US His 1978; *cr:* Saranac Lake HS Tchr, Coach, Dept 72-; *ai:* Var Ftbl Coach; Stu Accounts Treas; Sr Class Adv; SL ssn 1972-, Pres Two Terms; NYSUT, AFT 1972-; *office:* Saranac 99 LaPan Hwy Saranac Lake NY 12983*

DAVID M., Head Choral Director; *b:* Waukesha, WI; *m:* Lois Jean Lauren Elizabeth, Amanda Leigh; *ed:* Northern IL Univ (bA) erformance 1975; Univ of Cincinnati (MM) Choral Conducting Credit Hrs at Univ of Dayton; 12 Credit Hrs at Univ of WA; *cr:* rts Ensemble of Cincinnati Asst to Conductor 1979-82; Dayton anz-Turner Soc Music Dir 1979-87; Dayton Belmont HS Choir Dir , Winton Woods HS Head Choral Dir 1982-; *ai:* Music Dir for Musical; No Cntrl Evaltn Steering Comm; Leadership Team; Amer Dir Assn 1977-, Sw OH Regnl Chair; Music Ed Natl Conf 1979-, Chair 1993, St Convention; NEA 1979-, Building Rep; PI Kappa 1979-, Natl Music Honor Soc; Articles in Music Edcators Journal, ic Ed Assn Triad, OH Choral Dirs Assn OCDA News; Outstanding Prgms by Kent Univ; Cited for Excl in Performing Arts by OH Bd Model Tchr for Univ of Cincinnati Coll Conservatory of unding Artstc Dir Choir Music Fest 1995; *office:* Winton Woods W Kenper Rd Cincinnati OH 45240*

EDWARD F., Gymnastics Director; *b:* Connelsville, PA; *ed:* ir St Coll (BS) PE 1983; YMCA Core Understandings; *cr:* USMC Yrs; Morris Ctr YMCA Phys Dir 10 Yrs; South Mountain YMCA tics Dir 4 Half Yrs; *ai:* Teen Ldrs Club Dir, Adv; Girls Gymnastics Head Coach; South Orange Comm Coordinating Cncl; Girls tic Leage Dir; USA Gymnastics 1991-; Boonton Recreation Comm Mem; Hosted Several St Championship, Regnl Meets; *office:* South n YMCA Child Care 13 Jefferson Ave Maplewood NJ 07040

HARRIS MITCHELL, US & Global History Teacher; *b:* New y, NY; *m:* Janeth Wynter-Bell; *ed:* Westchester Comm Coll (AA) 5; Lehman Coll (BA) His 1980; City Univ of NY (MA) Ed 1993; 1 sework NY Writing Consortium Human relations, Spec Ed; *cr:* Print Photo Labs Color Printer 1981-84; Syska & Henessy ctural Firm Proof Reader & Ed 1984-85; Theodore Roosevelt HS Photography Tchr; *ai:* Started Photography Club 1986; ltural Events Coord; Monthly Multicultural Schl Bulletin for Tchrs r; Schl Newspaper Photo Arranger, Contributor; United Fed of 85-; Fieldstone Pond Townhouse Comm 1996, Bd Mem; Buddy Creater; Multicultural Music Lib Developer; *office:* Theodore lt HS 500 E Fordham Rd Bronx NY 10458*

JAMES EDWARD, Professor of Psychology; *b:* Chicago, IL; *m:* ilder; *c:* Carl Douglas, Sara Wilder; *ed:* Univ of MN (BA) ogy 1963, (PHD)-Summa Cum Laude Psychology 1967; *cr:* Coll Asst Prof 1966-68; Elmira Coll Asst Prof 1968-71; Howard Coll Asst Prof 1971-74, Assoc Prof 1974-82, Prof 1982-; *ai:* Cty PTA Ed Comm Chprsn 1975-77, Area Coord 1974-75; low PTA Ed Com Chprsn 1975-77; Early Chldhd Ed Bd of Howard 3-74; Cty Bd of Mental Retardation 1967-68; Amer Psych Assn; Tchrs of Undergrad Psych; Assn for Advancement of Comm Coll Amer Psych Assn Tchng Awd 1982; Outstndg Youn Men of Amer Pub 4 Books; *home:* 5411 Storm Drift Columbia MD 21045*

JAMES M., Eighth Grade English Teacher; *b:* Miami, FL; *m:* Martino; *c:* Christopher, Andrea, Laura, Jamie; *ed:* C.W. Post Coll Island Univ (BA) Eng, Ed 1967; Ft Lee Accounting Instr Army ing Procedures 1968; 45 Hrs Grad Stud in Eng, Ed C.W. Post Coll; Army Instr Trng Ctr Army Accounting Instr, Specialist 1968; lle Jr HS 7th-9th Grd Eng Tchr 1970-87; Hicksville Sr HS 9th-10th g Tchr 1987-88; Hicksville HS 8th Grd Eng Tchr 1988-; *ai:* Wide Steering Comm; Improvement Comm Past Chm, Mem; NEA Hicksville Congress of Tchr 1970-, Del, Negotiator; Woodside Civic Assn 1976-80, Officer, Founder, Exec Bd Mem; Semi-finalist Tchr of Yr Awd 1991-92; *office:* Hicksville MS Jerusalem Ave lle NY 11801*

JANET COOPERMAN, K-8th Grade Teacher; *b:* Newark, NJ; *c:* , Furgang; *ed:* Boston Univ (BA) His, Ed 1967; Monmouth Coll (MS) Stu Prsnl Svcs, Guid 1973; 24 Credit Hrs Elem Ed, Scndry Ed, Lang Arts; *cr:* D. A. Smith Schl 7th Grd Tchr 1967-68; Keyport Cntrl Schls 3, 5, 7 Grds Tchr 1968-75, Title 1, K-8 Grd Tchr 1975-; *ai:* Mentoring Prgm Mentor; NEA, Mon Cty Ed Assn, Keyport Tchrs Assn 1968-; NJ Assn Math Tchrs 1995-; *office:* Keyport Central Schl Union & Division Sts Keyport NJ 07735*

BELL, JONATHAN, 6th Grade Science Teacher; *b:* Rochester, NY; *m:* Nancy Stiegler; *c:* Erin, Kevin; *ed:* SUNY at Brockport (BS) Ed 1967, (MS) Ed 1969; *cr:* Dake Schl 5th Grd Core, Learning Improvement, 7th Grd Soc Stud Tchr 1967-79; Rogers Schl 5th Grd Core, 6th Grd Sci Tchr 1979-; *ai:* Yrbk, Recycling Club Adv; Contact Tchr; St Luke's Church 1966-, Warden; Amnesty Intnl 1993-; Lifetime Mem of PTSA; Tchr of Yr; Coaches Hall of Fame; *office:* West Irondequoit Schl Dist 370 Cooper Rd Rochester NY 14617

BELL, JOSEPH,JR., Algebra & Mathematics Tchr; *b:* South Fork, PA; *m:* Mary Anne Elders; *c:* Joseph John; *ed:* IN St Coll (BS) Math 1964; IN Univ of Penna (MED) Ed 1969; *cr:* Cochran Jr HS Algebra, Math Tchr 1964-80; Johnstown MS Algebra, Math Tchr 1980-; *ai:* Coin Club, Mathcounts 1989-92 Adv; GJEA, PSEA, NEA 1964-; *office:* Johnstown MS 280 Decker Ave Johnstown PA 15906

BELL, KENNETH WAYNE, Social Studies & AVID Teacher; *b:* Tonasket, WA; *m:* Teddie Speier; *ed:* Ft Hays St Univ (BS) Psych 1974; Humboldt St Univ at Arcata (MA) PE 1988; Eastern WA St Univ at Cheney His Tchng Cert 1975; *cr:* London Cntrl HS Dept of Defense 7th-12th Grd PE Tchr, Head Women's Bkstbl, Cross-Cntry, Track Coach 1977-82; Croughton Amer HS Dept of Defense 9th-12th Grd PE Tchr, Track, Cross Cntry, Women's Bsktbl Head Coach 1982-87; Humboldt St Univ Asst Track, Cross-Cntry Coach 1987-88; Croughton Amer HS Dept of Defense 7th-12th Grd PE, Soc Stud Tchr, Ath Dir, Track Coach 1988-; *ai:* Jr Class Spon; Ath Dir; X-Cntry Coach; Soc Stud Dept Chm; AZ St Univ at Tempe 1991-, DODDS PE Fitness for Life Implementation Wkshp; DODDS Atlantic Region PE Conf 1989, Speaker, Instr; Humboldt St Univ at Arcata 1987, Speaker, Cnslr Jim Hunt's Distance Running & Steeplechase Camp; Amer Running & Fitness Assn; Southern Counties Veterans Ath Assn; Overseas Ed Assn; British Lawn Tennis Assn; Inland Empire TAC; Oxford City Ath Clb; Brackley Tennis Clb; Superior Awd Tchng 1995, 1987; Outstdng Coll Ath of Amer 1974; WA St 2 Mile Champion 1969-70; *home:* PSC Box 50 Box 217 APO AE 09494

BELL, MARLENE L., Computer & Business Teacher; *b:* Shaker Heights, OH; *m:* Milo J.; *c:* Lisa, Julie, Erik; *ed:* Bowling Green St Univ (BS) Comprehensive Bus 1966; Otterbein coll 4 Credit Hrs; Ashland Coll 3.9 Credit Hrs; Coll of St Joseph 3.9 Credit Hrs; *cr:* Bd of Revisions Typist; C & S Lighting Girl-Friday; Barons Scrap Metal Part-Time Girl-Friday; Lakewood HS COE Coord 1966-69; E Knox HS Cmptr & Bus 1980-; *ai:* Cmptr Club Adv; Bus Dept Chm; NEA 1967-; E Knox Tchrs Assn 1980-, Treas; Lioness Club 1978-94, Bd Mem, Sec, Treas, 1st 2nd & 3rd VP, Pres; Welcome Neighbors 1978-93, Prgm Chm, VP; Meet the Expert Panel; *office:* East Knox HS PO Box 128 Howard OH 43028

BELL, MARLIN NORMAN,JR., 4th Grade Teacher; *b:* Harrisburg, PA; *m:* Vicki L.; *c:* Christopher; *ed:* Harrisburg Area Comm Coll (AS) Elem Ed 1968; PA St Univ (BS) Elem Ed 1970; *cr:* Middletown Area Schls 4th Grd Tchr 1970-; *ai:* Math Curr Comm; Report Card Update Comm; Tech Update Comm; NEA 1970-; Swatara Church God, Elder, Cncl Pres, Sunday Schl Tchr; *home:* 1521 Woodridge Dr Middletown PA 17057

BELL, MARY FRANCES, Fifth Grade Teacher; *b:* Alfordsville, IN; *m:* Charles J.; *c:* Todd A., Julianne H., Jeremy C. F.; *ed:* Cincinnati Bible Coll (BA) Eng, Bible 1961; Univ of Cincinnati (MED) Ed 1964; 30 Hrs Past Masters; *cr:* Northwest Schl Dist Tchr 1961-63; Lusaka Girls Schl Tchr 1969-71; Christ-Centered Schl Tchr 1984-85; Oak Hills Local Schl Dist Tchr 1986-; *ai:* Vol Tutoring; Assn of Amer Edctrs 1994-; Church Mbrshp, Act-Missionary to Africa, Taught Sunday Schl 7 Yrs, Life Skills Series in Sewing; Outstdng Young Women of Amer 1968.

BELL, MARY KATHARINE, Lang Arts & Social Stud Tchr; *b:* Washington, DC; *ed:* OH St Univ (BS) Elem Ed 1988; Various Classes OH Univ, Univ of Athens; *cr:* Riverview Schl Systems 6th Grd Tchr 1991-; *ai:* Lifetime Mem Supreme Cncl of House of Jacob; Children's Band Directress; Sunday Schl Tchr & Supvr; Police Ath League; Arts & Crafts Coord; 4-H Adv; TLC Tutoring Prgm Site Supvr; NEA, RVEA, OEA 1991-; YWCA Bd of Dirs 1991-, Pres, VP; 4-H Advy Panel 1992-; Safety City, Amer Red Cross 1995-; *office:* Keene Elem Schl 27052 CR 1 Box 651 Keene OH 43828*

BELL, MELINDA DONOVAN, ILEX Alternative Teacher; *b:* Waco, TX; *m:* Ronald; *c:* Nicholas, Susannah, Ronald; *ed:* St Lawrence Univ (BA) Eng 1975; Univ of Denver (MA) Mass Comm 1978; Syracuse Univ Project Advance 1991; *cr:* Various Media Jobs Movie, Cable TV Mrktg 1978-84; Eastern Dist HS Eng Tchr 1985-89; Corcoran HS Tchr 1989; Fayetteville Manlius HS Eng, ILEX Tchr 1990-; *ai:* STING Adv; Brownie Asst Troop Ldr; Characler Ed Comm; Fac Choir; Internet Ethics Comm; Elizabeth Roberts Rdng Cir 1994-; Tchr of Excl 1995; *office:* Fayetteville-Manlius HS E Seneca Turnpike Manlius NY 13104*

BELL, MICHAEL SHANE, 8th Grade Reading Teacher; *b:* Houston, TX; *m:* Carol Lynn; *c:* Megan Lynn, Michael Chad; *ed:* Mount Union Coll (BA) Ed 1989; Kent St Univ (MED) 1995; *cr:* Belfaire Schl Tutor 1989; Arlington Elem 6th Grd Tchr 1989-90; Greenbriar Jr High 8th Grd Rndg Tchr 1990-; *ai:* Fresh Ftbl Parma Sr High Asst Coach; Greenbriar Wrestling Head Coach; Greenbriar Weightlifting Club Adv; NEA 1989-; NCTE 1991-; Presentation at Natl Cncl of Tchrs of Eng 1992; *office:* Greenbriar Jr HS 11810 Huffman Rd Cleveland OH 44130

BELL, RICHARDS S., Social Studies Teacher; *b:* Pittsburgh, PA; *m:* Mary Palmer; *ed:* Univ of Pittsburgh (BA) Scndry Ed, Soc Stud 1988; Addl 21 Credit Hrs; *cr:* St Raphaels Soc Stud, Eng, Religion Tchr 1989-90; Peters Twp HS Soc Stud Tchr 1990-; *ai:* Jr Class Spon; Coord Ineligibility Prgm; Head Boys Bsktbl Coach; AFT 1990-; Outstanding Tchr Awd St Vincent's Coll 1994; *office:* Peters Township HS 264 E Mc Murray Rd Mc Murray PA 15317*

BELL, RUSSELL A., Physics Teacher; *b:* Brighton, MI; *m:* Alice Chapman; *c:* Linda Pizarro, Mark, Jeff, Dorene, Mike; *ed:* Purdue Univ (BS) EE 1965; Univ of Akron (BS) Ed 1983; 41 Post Grad Hrs Physics & Math; *cr:* US Navy Various 1958-81; Archbishop Hoban HS Tchr 1983-; *ai:* Amer Assn of Physics Tchrs 1983-; Amer Legion 1984-, Commander, Adjutant Treas; VFW 1984-; Mayor of Village of Lodi OH 1988-; *office:* Archbishop Hoban HS 400 Elbon Ave Akron OH 44306

BELL, SYLVIA MITCHELL, Mathematics Teacher; *b:* Bridgeton, NJ; *c:* Thomas, Mark, Cybill, Christopher; *ed:* Rowan Coll (BA) Math 1966; Cmptr Awareness; Span I, II; *cr:* Penn Treaty Jr HS Tchr 1967-69; Mulville Sr HS Tchr 1987-; *ai:* Mr Millville Contest; NJEA, NEA 1987-; NCTM 1988-; *office:* Millville Sr HS 200 Wade Blvd Millville NJ 08332

BELL, VIRGINIA RUSSELL, Elementary Physical Ed Teacher; *b:* Annapolis, MD; *m:* Everett Douglas; *c:* Lyn; *ed:* St Marys Jr Coll (AA) PE, Recreation 1963; Univ of MD (BS) Recreation 1965; Bowie St Univ (MED) Ed 1969; *cr:* Annapolis Elem PE Tchr 1965-67; Hillsmere Elem PE Tchr 1967-71; Tyler Heights Elem PE Tchr 1972-73; Germantown Elem PE Tchr 1973-; *ai:* NEA, MSTA, TAAAC 30 Yrs; Chase Creek Swim Club 1975-85, Sec; SPY Swim Parents Club 1980-, Sec; Nom for WA Post Agnes Meyer Tchr Awd; *office:* Germantown Elem Schl 1411 Cedar Park Rd Annapolis MD 21401*

BELLA, NORENE JUNE, Fourth Grade Teacher; *b:* Indiana, PA; *ed:* Kent St Univ (BS) Ed-Cum Laude 1974; Grad Work Akron Univ, Kent St Univ; *cr:* Rootstown Elem Schl Fourth Grd Tchr 1974-75; Woodland Elem Schl Fourth Grd Tchr 1975-77, Second Grd Tchr 1977-87, Fifth Grd Tchr 1987-88, Fourth Grd Tchr 1988-; *ai:* Advy Comm; Educl Hlth Promotion Comm; NEA, OH Ed Assn, Kappa Delta Pi, Kent St Univ Alumni Assn 1974-; Kent United Meth Church 1968-; Akron Beacon Journal Classroom of Month 1993; PTA Outstdng Edctr of Yr 1995-; *office:* Woodland Elem Schl 2908 Graham Rd Stow OH 44224

BELLACE, ANITA D., English Teacher; *b:* Hoboken, NJ; *m:* Victor J.; *c:* John V., Caroline; *ed:* Immaculata Coll (AB) His & Eng 1961; Nazareth Coll at Rochester (MS) Rdng Specialist 1980; Villanova Univ 12 Credit Hrs His; Univ of VA 12 Credit Hrs Ed; *cr:* Cherry Hill Pub Schl His Tchr 1971-72; Thoreau MS His & Eng Tchr 1972-76; Rochester City Sch Dist Rdng Specialist 1980-81; Washington Twp HS Eng Tchr 1985-; *ai:* NHS Fac Comm; Conceived & Organized Symposium on Hum; WTED Assn 1985-, Bldg Rep; NEA & NJEA 1985-; Planned Parenthood, Crisis Cnslr & on Air Spokesperson 1978-79; Penfield Pub Lib, Bd Mem 1979-84; Jr League of Rochester, Bd Mem 1980; Attnd VAST 1994-95; Belfer Schlsp for Holocaust Stud at Holocaust Memrl Washington DC 1995; *office:* Washington Township HS 529 Hurffville Crosskeys Rd Sewell NJ 08080

BELLAMY, CHARLOTTE, Adjunct Lecturer; *b:* Youngstown, OH; *c:* Laurie Tatarsky, Andrew Tatarsky, Miles; *ed:* Goddard Coll (BA) Ed 1971; City Coll of NY (MS) Ed, Supervision 1973; *cr:* Everett Schl Tchr, Supvr 1965-72; BCC Child Dev Ctr Dir 1972-; Bx Comm Coll Adj Lecturer Dept of Ed 1984-; *ai:* Direct Campus Child Care Svcs, Day Care After Schl Prgm; Child Care Cncl at CUNY 1984-, Chprsn; NAEYC 1972-; Child Care Inc 1986-, Bd Mem; MOSAIC 1990-, Bd Mem; Ed Opportunity Ctr Ch Care 1993-, Bd Mem; Mayor's Outstdng Pub Svc Awd 1993; *home:* 890 W End Ave New York NY 10025*

BELLAVIA, ELIZABETH ANN (REICHARD), Choral Director; *b:* Kettering, OH; *m:* Daniel W.; *ed:* Bowling Green St Univ (BMEd) Voice, Choral 1992; *cr:* Lemon-Monroe HS Choral Dir 1992-; George M. Verity MS Choral Dir, Gen Music 1996; *ai:* Show Choir; Musical Dir; OMEA 1987-; NEA 1992-; Local Theater Productions, Dayton Area Bapt Musicals, HS Musicals Dir; *office:* Lemon Monroe HS 101 W Elm St Monroe OH 45050

BELLES, SUZANNE LEE, Latin Teacher; *b:* Upland, PA; *ed:* Hamilton Coll (BA) Classics 1984; Coll Yr in Athens 1982-83; Tufts Univ New England Classical Inst 1985; Monterey Penninsula Coll Personal Enrichment 1986-90; St Andrews Univ Summer Schl for Classicists 1990; Kent St Univ Summer Stud in Italy 1992; Univ of GA Summer 1994; *cr:* Santa Catalina Schl for Girls Latin Tchr 1984-90; Shady Side Acad Latin Tchr 1990-; *ai:* Shady Side News Adv; Judicial Comm; Womens Issues Adv; ACL 1985-; CAAS 1990-; Vergilian Soc of Amer 1990-; Natl Org of Women; Planned Parenthood of Amer; Natl Endowment of Hum Summer Seminar Participant 1993; Benedum Tchng Flwshp 1992; New England Classical Inst 1985; *office:* Shady Side Acad 423 Fox Chapel Rd Pittsburgh PA 15238

BELLETTIERE, MARC PHILIP, Social Studies Teacher; *b:* Somerville, NJ; *m:* Shannon N. Perate; *ed:* Kutztown Univ (BSEd) Soc Stud 1993; Elem Ed; *cr:* Kutztown Univ Tutor 1990-93; Bridgewater Sports Arena Ice Skating, Hockey Instr 1993-94; Exeter Sr HS Sub, Long Term Sub Tchr 1994-95, Soc Stud Tchr 1995-; *ai:* Exeter Jr HS Boys Bsktbl Head Coach; Jr Amer Legion Coach; Im Roller Hockey League Adv; Kappa Delta Pi 1992-; Phi Alpha Theta 1992-, VP 1992, Outstdng Achvmt; NEA, PSEA, ETA 1995-; Spec Olympics 1984-, Coord; *office:* Exeter Twp Sr HS 201 E 37th St Reading PA 19606*

BELLEZZA, NINA H., Life Science Teacher; *b:* Bronxville, NY; *ed:* Univ of DE (BS) Entomology 1989; *cr:* Gunning Bedford MS Life Sci Tchr 1989-90; Talley MS Life Sci Tchr 1990-; *ai:* Coach Sci OLympiad 4 Yrs, Girls Bsktbl 1990; DE Acad, Talented Yth Summer Prgm Instr 1994-95; NSTA, BEA, DTS 1990-; Nom Presidential Awd Sci 1995-; Pub Newspaper Articles 1992, 1995; *office:* Talley MS 1110 Cypress Rd Wilmington DE 19810*

BELLIN, ALLAN, Counselor; *b:* Cleveland, OH; *m:* Evelyn Richman; *c:* Jodie Belin Weiss, Barbara Bellin Janouitz, Sandy; *ed:* Adelbert Coll (BA) Chem 1949; Ohio Univ (MED) Guid 1951; 60 Addl Hrs; *cr:* Cleveland Heights Tchr, Cnslr, Dir Career Dev Prgm 1953-89; Univ Heights Tchr, Cnslr, Dir Career Dev Prgm 1953-89; Shaker Heights Tchr, Cnslr, Dir Career Dev Prgm 1953-89; Warrensville Hts Tchr, Cnslr, Dir Career Dev Prgm 1953-89; Beachwood Schl Cnslr 1989-; *ai:* Sr Search Prgm, Mentorship Prgm, Bus Ed Cncl Dir; AFT 1955-; OSCA 1963-; Beachwood Art Cncl 1990-, Stu Art Juried Show; Bnai Brith; Dr. George E. Hill Grad Asst; Meyer Sarkin Outstdng Guid Person; People for Amer Way; *office:* Beachwood HS 25100 Fairmount Blvd Beachwood OH 44122*

BELLINGER, LAURA JEAN, High School Business Ed Tchr; *b:* Amsterdam, NY; *ed:* St Univ of NY at Cobleskill (AAS) Secretarial Sci 1984; St Univ of NY at Albany (BS) Bus Ed 1986, (MS) Bus Ed 1987; *cr:* FMCC Bus Ed Tchr 1987-91; FFCS Bus Ed Tchr 1987-; Johnstown Cont & Adult Ed Bus Ed Tchr 1992-94; *ai:* Peer Leadership Adv; NOICC Equity, Bus Ownership Curr, Shared Decision Making & Youth Leadership Day Planning Comms; Tchrs Assn 1987-, Sec 1992-; Capital Dist Bus & Mrktg Ed Assn 1990-; Montgomery Co Cooperative Extension 1989-, Sec & Treas; Montgomery Co Youth Cncl 1992-94, Co-Adv; NYS Youth Cncl Gus Potter Meml Awd 1993; *office:* Fonda-Fultonville CHS 112 Old Johnstown Rd Box 1501 Fonda NY 12068

BELLINO, FORTUNATO JOSEPH, Global Studies II Teacher; *b:* Brooklyn, NY; *ed:* St Francis Coll (BA) His 1974; 15 Post Grad Credits Ec Fordham Univ, Coll of Staten Island; *cr:* St Francis of Assisi Grammar Schl 8th Grd Soc Stud, Rel Tchr 1974-79; Bishop Ford Cntrl Cath HS Global Stud, Ec 1980-; *ai:* Head Girls JV, Asst Boys Var Bsktbl Coach; Lay Fac Assn 1995-; Coach of Yr CHSAA Frosh Boys Bsktbl 1981-82, 1984; Coach Boys Frosh City Champions Bsktbl 1984; *office:* Bishop Ford Cntrl Cath HS 500 19th St Brooklyn NY 11215

BELLIOTTI, RAYMOND ANGELO, Professor of Philosophy; *b:* Dansville, NY; *m:* Marcia Dalby; *c:* Angelo, Vittoria; *ed:* Union Coll (BA) cum laude 1970; Univ of Miami (MA) 4.00 GPA 1976, (PHD) 4.00 GPA 1977; Harvard Law Schl (JD) cum laude 1982; *cr:* Phillips, Nizer, Benjamin, Krim & Ballon Summer Assoc 1981; Barrett Smith Schapiro Simon & Armstrong Attorney 1982-84; Brooklyn Law Schl Adjunct Assoc Prof 1983-84; St Univ of NY Coll at Fredonia Asst Prof 1984-86, Assoc Prof 1986-91, Prof 1991-; *ai:* Fac Adv Il Circolo Italiano; Chautauqua Italian Amer Ort 1985-, Bd of Dirs 1995-96; Books: Justifying Law: The Debate Over Foundations, Goals & Methods 1992; Good Sex: Perspectives on Sexual Ethics 1993; Seeking Identity: Individualism versus Comm in an Ethnic Context 1995; Pub 40 Articles; Kasling Lecture Awd for Excl in Research, Schlsp 1995; William T. Hagen Awd Excl in Research, Schlsp 1991; St Univ of NY Chancellor's Awd for Tchng Excl 1991; *office:* S U N Y Coll At Fredonia Fenton 2109 Fredonia NY 14063*

BELLIS, RICHARD J., Teacher; *b:* Rillton, PA; *m:* Jean A.; *c:* Beverly Stout, Sharon Williams; *ed:* Slippery Rock (BS) Comprehensive Soc Sci 1967; IN Univ (MA) European His 1971; *cr:* Mercer HS Tchr 1967-68; John Dickinson HS Tchr 1968-70; Marple Newtown HS Tchr 1971-78;

Downingtown HS Tchr 1978-; *ai:* Ftbl Coach 1975-80; Indoor Track Coach 1978-; Outdoor Track Coach 1984-; *office:* Downingtown Sr HS 445 Manor Ave Downingtown PA 19335*

BELLIS, WILLIAM W., Phys Ed Teacher; *b:* Jamaica, NY; *m:* Virginia; *c:* William, Kerin; *ed:* Cent CT St Univ (BA) Elem Ed 1970; Adelphi Univ (MS) PE 1974; 45 Credit Hrs; *cr:* Deer Park HS PE 1970-; *ai:* Head Ftbl, Head Girls Vlybl Coach; Weight Room Coord; NEA, NYSUT 1970-; Ftbl Coach of Yr 1983, 1986, 1993; Vlybl Coach of Yr 1995, 1993, 1992; *office:* Deer Park Sr HS 30 Rockaway Ave Deer Park NY 11729*

BELLIVEAU, GREGORY KENNETH, English Dept Chair & Teacher; *b:* Tampa, FL; *m:* Patricia Anne; *ed:* Kent St Univ (BA) Eng 1991, (MA) Eng 1995; *cr:* Orange Chrstn Acad Eng Tchr 1992-; *ai:* Yrbk; Readers Theatre; Play; Pub, Performed WCRF 1996; *office:* Orange Christian Acad 27200 Emery Rd Cleveland OH 44128*

BELLMAN, ALLAN EDWARD, Math & Computer Science Tchr; *b:* Washington, DC; *m:* Donna H. Niewiaroski; *ed:* Duke Univ (BA) Math 1969; Univ of MD (MED) Math Ed 1975; Attnd Lehigh Univ, Amer Univ, Princeton Univ; *cr:* John F. Kennedy HS Math Tchr 1969-89; Watkins Mill HS Math Tchr, Cmptr Coord 1989-; *ai:* Coach Track, Cross Cntry; Montgomery Cty Assessment Comm; NEA, MCEA 1969-; NCTM 1988-; Woodrow Wilson Fellow 1987; Tandy Tech Winner 1992; Author CoMap Arise Project, Prentice Hall Algebra II; Articles Pub; *office:* Watkins Mill HS 10301 Apple Ridge Rd Gaithersburg MD 20879

BELLMORE, PATRICIA THOMSON, English as a Second Lang Tchr; *b:* New Haven, CT; *m:* Bruce R.; *c:* Thomas, Micheline; *ed:* Albertus Magnus Coll (BA) Fr-Cum Laude 1980; 21 Credits TESOL Southern CT St Univ; *cr:* Southern New England Telecommunications Repair Svc Clerk, Supvr, Cmptr Programmer 1984-94; Bailey, Carrigan Schls ESL Tchr 1994-; *ai:* Conn TESOL 1994-; Alliance Francaise 1980-; *office:* West Haven HS 1 Circle St West Haven CT 06516

BELLOR, SUSAN J. (SPADAFORE), Spanish Teacher; *b:* Massena, NY; *m:* Kenneth P.; *c:* Jennifer, Katherine; *ed:* SUNY at Potsdam (BA) Scndry Span 1973, (MS) Rdng 1978; Attnd Univ of Madrid Spain 1971-72; *cr:* H. W. Smith Jr HS Span Tchr, Chprsn 1973-77; Cntrl Tech Night Schl Adult Span Tchr 1974-75; T. J. Corcoran HS Span Tchr, Chprsn 1977-80; Sacred Heart Jr HS Eng, Span Tchr 1980-81; St Lawrence Univ Span Instr 1981-83; massena HS Span Tchr 1986-; *ai:* Span Club Adv; Span NHS Spon; Massena Dist Family Involvement, Bldg Mngmt Teams; Parent Resource Lib, Span Immersion Day Coords; Yrbk Adv; Massena Women's Coll Club 1986-87, Pres; Bus & Prof Women 1976-, 1st VP 1978-79; AATSP 1989-; Sacred Heart Church 1990-, Usher, Church Schl Tchr; Parish Cncl Trustee Massena Twn Lbry; Translated Election Ballot Comm Pub Svc 1974; Pub & Private Inst Rdng Grant 1976-77; Wrote Curr Schl Credit Span 1988; New Span Tchrs Mentor 1990-92; Wrote Massena Dist Grant, Coord Parent Involvement Wkshp 1992; Coord Parent Resource Lib, Family Involvement Team 1993; *home:* 19 Churchill Ave Massena NY 13662*

BELLOTTI PUPPO, JANET MARIE, French & Religion Teacher; *b:* Washington, PA; *m:* Giovanni; *c:* Joseph, Anna Maria, Gina; *ed:* Carlow Coll (BA) Fr, Sec Ed 1972; Duquesne Univ (MSED) Rel Ed 1996; 24 Post Baccalaureate Credit Hrs Italian, Ed Univ of Pittsburgh; *cr:* Our Lady of Mercy Acad Fr, Rel Tchr 1972-73; Canevin Cath HS Fr, Italian, Rel Tchr 1973-78, Holy Trinity Cath Elem Schl Fr, Span Tchr 1988-90, St Joseph's Cath Elem Schl Fr, Span Tchr 1990-91, Our Lady of The Sacred Heart HS Fr, Rel Tchr 1990-; *ai:* Asst Moderator, Moderator Liturgical Affairs; Modern Lang Assn, ACTFL 1994-; Holy Trinity Parish Cncl 1983-, Mem 1988-92; Carlow Coll Jeanne D'Arc Awd Outstdng Achvmt Fr 1972; *home:* 69 Fawnvue Dr Mc Kees Rocks PA 15136

BELLSEY, JANET LYNN, Social Worker; *b:* New York, NY; *ed:* Boston Univ (BS) Ed 1979; NY Univ (MSW) Soc Work 1986; Post Masters Cert Clinical Soc Work 1994; 24 Credits Post Masters; *cr:* Altro Hlth & Rehabilitation Svcs Intake Worker, Case Mgr 1986-91; Federation Employment & Guid Svcs Soc Worker, Supvr 1991-92; Mt Sinai Hosp Adolescent Hlth Ctr Acting Coord Schl Based Hlth Ctr 1992-; *ai:* NASW.

BELLUCCI, MEG, Accounting & Finance Professor; *b:* Leicester, England; *m:* Albert; *c:* Debbie Bellucci-Martin, Donna Bellucci-Pratt, Gina Bellucci-Delizia; *ed:* Springfield Tech Comm Coll (AS), (BS) Acctng 1976; Western New England (BS) Acctng 1978; Univ of Hartford (MS) Acctng 1981; *cr:* Burd Mfg Accountant 1976-80; Bank of New England Fin Analyst 1980-84; Springfield Tech Comm Coll Prof 1984-; *ai:* Stdnts Acad Advs; Alumni of Yr Selection, Earth Week Comm; VITA Income Tax Asst Vol; NEA, MTA 1984-; MCCC 1984-, Election Comm; MA Acctg Profs 1985-; Springfield Schl 1991-, Vol, 5 Yr Cert, Tutoring Homeless Children; Make-A-Wish Fnd Svc Awd 1988; Distngd Alumni Awd STCC 1993; *office:* Springfield Tech Comm Coll 1 Armory Square Springfield MA 01105

BELMONTE, GRACE MANTONE, Former Teacher; *b:* Brooklyn, NY; *m:* Peter; *c:* Andrea Scelfo, Stephanie, John; *ed:* St John's Univ (BS) Ed, N-9 Soc Stud Concentration 1988; *cr:* Diocese of Brooklyn Schl Asst Spec Ed Tchr 1980-85; St Helen Schl 7-8 Grd Jr High Soc Stud Tchr 1988-94; *ai:* Stu Cncl Moderator; Coord Grd Level Class Trips; NEA 1988-; Republican Club 1980-.

BELT, LEESA CAROLE, Sr HS Speech & English Tchr; *b:* Baltimore, MD; *ed:* Rodford Univ (BS) Eng, Speech 1992; Johns Hopkins Univ; *cr:* Hammond HS Eng, Speech Tchr 1992-; Marylands Tomorrow Facilitator 1993-94; *ai:* Chrldng, Speech & Debate Coaches; Class of 98 Spon; 9th Grd, Crisis Intervention Teams; NEA, MSTA, HCEA 1992-; *office:* Hammond HS 8800 Guilford Rd Columbia MD 21046*

BELTEMPO, JERRY ALAN, K-4th Grade PE Teacher; *b:* Salem City, OH; *m:* Connie Sue Hanna; *ed:* Kent St Univ (BS) PE 1978, (MA) Sports Admin 1994; *cr:* Springfield Local Schls Tchr, Coach 1978-79; Beaver Local Schls Tchr, Coach 1979-81; Austintown Local Schls Tchr, Coach 1987-; *ai:* Girls Sftbl Head Coach; OEA, NEA, AEA 1987-; *home:* 1973 Pearce Cir Salem OH 44460

BELTZ, JOEL L., Geometry & Trigonometry Tchr; *b:* Johnstown, PA; *m:* Carole E. Fox; *c:* Derek B., Julie G., Lindsey C.; *ed:* IN Univ of PA (BS) Math 1969, (MED) Cnslr Ed 1976; *cr:* North MS Math Tchr 1972-76; Independence MS Math Tchr 1976-85; Bethel Park HS Math Tchr 1985-; *ai:* After Schl Math Tutor; AFT 1969-, Bldg Rep; Nom PA Tchr of Yr 1992; *home:* 110 Thomas Rd Mc Murray PA 15317

BELTZ, JULIE DUNN, Business Teacher; *b:* Akron, OH; *m:* James; *c:* Ryan; *ed:* Univ of Akron (AS) Secretarial Sci 1975, (BS) Ed 1975; *cr:* Marlington HS Bus Tchr 20 Yrs; *ai:* Marlington Chptr of Bus Profs of Amer Adv; NEA 1975-; *office:* Marlington HS 10450 Moulin Ave NE Alliance OH 44601

BELZER, BARBARA BLOOM, Third Grade Teacher; *b:* Hartford, CT; *m:* Leonard; *c:* Lisa, Jennifer; *ed:* Cntrl CT St Univ (MS) Spec Ed 1976; Southern CT St Univ (BS) Elem Ed 1972; *cr:* John F. Kennedy Schl 3-4th Grd Tchr 1972-; *ai:* Math, Cmptr, Cmptr Tech, Main Textbook Selection Comms; Rep Cncl; NEA, CT Ed Assn 1972-; *office:* John F. Kennedy Schl 530 Park Ave Windsor CT 06095

BELZNER, CHARLES JOSEPH, Guidance Counselor; *b:* Baltimore, MD; *ed:* St Marys Seminary, Univ (BA) Theology 1980, (MA) Theology 1982; 30 Credits Toward MED Guid, Cnslng at Loyola Coll 1997; *cr:* Mt St Joseph Schl Guid Cnslr 1994-; *ai:* Stu Assistance Prgm Chprsn; SAT Testing Coord; Spiritual Life Comm; Alternative Sports Club Adv; *office:* Mount Saint Joseph HS 4403 Frederick Ave Baltimore MD 21229*

BEM, JOHN EUGENE, Physics & AP Chem Teacher; *b:* Spangler, PA; *ed:* St Francis at Loretto (BS) Chem 1969; Indiana Univ of PA (MED) Chem 1973; 30 Addl Hrs Indiana Univ of PA, Univ of Pittsburgh; *cr:* Cambria Hghts Physics & AP Chem Tchr 1969-; *ai:* Prof Dev Comm; NHS Fac Review Comm; PIAA Ftbl Ofcl; Amer Chemical Soc, Cambria Hghts Ed Assn, PSEA, NEA 1969-; NSTA 1973-, Chem Natl Cert; Hasting Vol Fire Co #1 1972-, Sec, Treas, Outstanding Svc 1989; Cambria Cty Fireman Assn 1973-, Treas, Sec 1976, Honorary Past Pres 1989; Cntrl Dist Vol Fireman Assn 1973-, Pres 1989, Outstanding Svc 1980; Hastings Civic Assn 1973-, Sec, Treas; PIAA Ftbl Ofcl 1968-, Sec, Treas; NSF Fellowship in HPP Physics 1973; NSTA 1st 100 Nationally Certified Tchr; Outstanding Young Men Awd 1972; Penn St Univ Honors Tchr Awd 1992; St Vincent Coll at Latrobe Grant Tchr Awd 1990 & 1992; *office:* Cambria Hghts Sr HS PO Box 6 426 Glendale Lake Rd Patton PA 16668*

BEMAN, JAMES A., Science Teacher; *b:* Mt Vernon, NY; *m:* Dorothy L.; *c:* Kathy Benincasa, James Jr.; *ed:* Hartwick Coll (BA) Bio 1964; SUNY at New Paltz (MS) Scndry Sci 1982; 75 Grad Credits; *cr:* Milford Schl Tchr 1964-66; Carmel Schl Tchr 1966-; *home:* RR 12 Carmel NY 10512

BEMONT, PATRICIA HAINES, 5th Grade Teacher; *b:* Albion, NY; *m:* Don; *c:* Sean, Andy; *ed:* Wittenberg Univ (BSME) Music Ed 1971; IN Univ (MSEd) Music Ed 1973; SUNY Brockport Elem Ed Cert; Nazareth Coll Specl Ed; *cr:* St Marys Schl 3-4th Grd Tchr 1985-90; Pavlion Elem Schl Enrichment Tchr 1990-95; Pavilion MS 5th Grd Tchr 1995-; *office:* Pavilion MS Big Tree Rd Pavilion NY 14525

BEMONT, THOMAS DAVID, History Teacher; *b:* Binghamton, NY; *ed:* St Univ of NY at Albany (BA) His Ed 1983; St Univ of NY at New Paltz (MA) Ed 1991; *cr:* Adelphi Inst Tchr 1984-86; Pine Bush HS His Tchr 1986-; *ai:* Sr Class Adv; NYSUT, AFT 1986-; Pine Bush PTA 1986-; *office:* Pine Bush HS Rt 302 Pine Bush NY 12566

BENANDER, VINCE A., Math Instructor; *b:* Cleveland, OH; *m:* Nancy Opaskar; *c:* Besty, Christy, Kathy, Vince, John, Megan, Mandy, Brian; *ed:* John Carroll Univ (BA) Math 1967, (MS) Math 1969; Attnd Kent St, Cleveland St; *cr:* St Ignatius HS Math Instr 1968-; John Carroll Univ Math Instr 1970-; *ai:* Bsbl Coach 15 Yrs; Math Club, Mu Alpha Theta, Ignatius For Life, Zenn Club Moderator; OH Cncl Tchrs Math, Math Assn of Amer 1968-; St Paschal PTO 1980-83, Pres, VP; Sports Data 1981-, Pres; Richmond Heights Recreation Bd 1982-84; Rossing Awd Winner; Outstanding Tchr of Yr 1988.

BENANTI, FRED WILLIAM, Retired Teacher; *b:* New York, NY; *m:* Eleanor Sharpe; *ed:* New York Univ (BS) Ed 1948; Boston Coll (MS) Intnl Relations 1978; Addl 50 Hrs of Ed Courses; *cr:* New York City Schl Tchr 1951-57; Dept of Defense Schls Tchr, Admin 1957-94; *ai:* NEA 1957-64; AFT 1986-; Outstdng Tchr Awd; Superior Awd 3 Times; Spec Awd of Recognition for Spec Performance; *home:* 74 Overhill Rd Wading River NY 11792

BENBURY, KAREN ZAK, Assoc Professor of Mathematics; *b:* Northampton, MA; *m:* Peter J.; *ed:* U-Mass at Amherst (BS) Math 1969, (MA) Math 1971, (PHD) Math 1979; Various Courses; *cr:* US Naval Acad Asst Prof 1979-87; Washington Coll Asst Prof 1987-90; Bowie St Univ Assoc Prof 1990-; *ai:* Stu Chapter NSBE adv; Actuarial Exams Coach; Quality Control Comm; Policy & Stans Comm; General Ed Review Comm; AMS, MAA 1977-; AWM 1982-; COMAP 1994-; Nature Conservancy; CO-PI on Model Insts for Excl; NSF & NASA Grant; 1 Book Pub, 2 to Appear; *office:* Bowie St Univ Jericho Park Road Bowie MD 20715

BENCE, PATRICIA JEAN SCHULAK, Professor; *b:* Ft Lauderdale, FL; *m:* Richard M.; *c:* Jennifer (Bence) Holleran, Kendra K.; *ed:* SUNY at Oswego (BS) Ed 1967; SUNY at Cortland (MS) Ed 1977; Cornell Univ (PHD) Developmental Psych 1989; 15 Credits SUNY at New Paltz; 9 Credits SUNY at Oswego; 3 Credits Alfred Univ; *cr:* Liverpool Schl Dist MS Tchr 1967-68; Tompkins Cortland Comm Coll Instr & Prof 1976-; Cornell Univ Visiting Prof 1995-; *ai:* Chair Mid Sts Review Comm; Chair Liberal Arts Soc Sci Dept; Mem Pres Cabinet; Amer Psych Assn 1988-; Amer Psych Soc 1990-; Soc for Research in Child Dev; Soc for Research Adol; NEA; AAUW; SUNY Chancellors Awd for Excl in Tchng 1991; Featured in a Comm of Excl 1995; NISOD Excl in Tchng Awd; *office:* Tompkins Cortland Comm Coll 170 North St Box 139 Dryden NY 13053

BENCIVENGA, DOMINIC MICHAEL, Technology Teacher; *b:* Erie, PA; *m:* Marcyann; *c:* Michael, Christopher; *ed:* PA St Univ (BS) Indstrl Arts 1971; 36 Credit Hrs-Master's Equivalency from Edinboro Univ of PA, Rochester Inst of Tech, St Univ Coll at Buffalo, Clarion Univ of PA; *cr:* Fairview HS Tech Tchr 1972-; *ai:* Yrbk Adv; NEA, PA St Educ Assn 1972-; Fairview Ed Assn 1972-, Sec; Tech Educ Assn of Northwest Pa, Newsletter Ed, Man of Yr 1994; MA Inst of Techs Sci, Engrng Prgm for Mid, HS Tchrs 1992; *home:* 5249 Countryside Dr Mc Kean PA 16426

BENDER, CARYN R., Mathematics Teacher; *b:* Buffalo, NY; *m:* Rudolph H. III; *ed:* Geneva Coll (BS) Math 1972; Westminster Coll (MA) Cnslng 1976; *cr:* Wilmington Area Schl Math Tchr, Dept Chprsn 1972-; Westminster Coll Instr 1995; *ai:* Math Team Adv; Curr Comm; CORE Team; NCTM, PCTM 1988-; MCWP 1985-; *office:* Wilmington Area HS 350 Wood St New Wilmington PA 16142*

BENDER, CHRISTINE KRISTICH, Chemistry Teacher; *b:* Vandergrift, PA; *m:* George; *c:* Leigh Ann, Michael; *ed:* Indiana Univ of PA (BS) Chem Ed 1973; Post-Grad Credits Penn St, Villanova, Indiana Univ of PA; *cr:* Plum Sr HS Chem Tchr 1973-; *ai:* NHS Adv; NEA, PSTA, PBEA 1973-; Amer Chem Soc, Past Mem; *office:* Plum Sr HS 900 Elicker Rd Pittsburgh PA 15239*

BENDER, DAVID W., Chemistry Teacher; *b:* West Seneca, NY; *m:* Suzanne Reardon; *c:* Gregory (dec), Rebecca, Andrew; *ed:* Colgate Univ (BS) Chem, Bio 1959; 30 Addl Hrs Colgate Univ; 6 Addl Hrs SUNY at Buffalo; *cr:* Albion Cntrl Schl Chem Tchr 1959-60; Army Finance Office 1960-62; Baldwinsville Cntrl Schls Chem Tchr 1962-; *ai:* NEA, NEA NY 1968-; Baldwinsville Tchrs 1962-, Treas 1974; *office:* Baldwinsville Cntrl Schls Oneida St Baldwinsville NY 13027

BENDER, HILDEGARDE, English Teacher; *b:* New York City, NY; *m:* C. Earl; *c:* William, Clifford, Jennifer, Amy B. Vincent; *ed:* Univ of Akron (BS) Eng 1973, (MA) Eng 1984; Addl 30 Hrs; *cr:* Highland HS Eng Tchr 1973-; *ai:* Initiated Several Prgms, All Schl Musicals, AP Courses; North Cntrl Accreditation Steering Comms; NCTE, HEA, OEA, NEA 1973-; *office:* Highland HS 3880 Ridge Rd Medina OH 44256*

BENDER, JANE HOOSE, First Grade Teacher; *b:* Cleveland, OH; *m:* John C.; *c:* Laura Herron, Megan Jane Busch, Heather Marie, John Garth; *ed:* Kent St Univ (BA) Early Chlhd 1980; Ashland Univ 12 Grad Hrs; *cr:* Holy Family Elem Schl First Grd Tchr 1980-85; Woodridge Elem Schl First Grd Tchr 1985-; *ai:* OEA, WEA 1995-; Prof Wkshps Tchng, Rdng Through Poetry; Mentoring Prog Summit Cty; *office:* Woodridge Elem Schl 3313 Northampton Rd Cuyahoga Falls OH 44223*

BENDER, JUDITH ANNE, Asst Prof & Dir Med Asst Prgm; *b:* Jersey City, NJ; *c:* Jennifer R. Gangemi; *ed:* Jersey City St Coll (BA) Ed 1970, (MA) Cnslng 1975; 400 Hrs CME, CEU Ed; Certfd Med Asst; *cr:* Jersey City St Coll Adj Asst Prof; Hudson Cty Comm Coll Asst Prof 1980-; *ai:* Meds Asst Pgrms; Middle Sts Self Stud Steering Comm; Med Asst Club Adv; Acad Affairs Cncl; Tenure Review, Staff Dev Comms; Hlth Professions Magnet Curr with Univ of Medicine, Dentistry; AAMA, AMA, CAAHEP, Site Surveyor; Amer Assn of Medical Assts 1980-, Disti Medical Asst Edctr 1988; NJ Soc of Medical Assts 1980 Parliamentarian Prof Achvmt, Continuing Ed Awds; NJFA, HC(Assn 1991-, VP; YWCA Hudson Cty 1988-, Recording Sec; Intn NJ Intercollegiate Ath Cncl for Jersey City St Coll 1993-; Jers Lincoln Assn 1996-, Trustee; Medical Soc of NJ 1993-, Consultan Relations Cncl; Jersey City St Coll Merit Awd; Outstdng Young W Amer; *office:* Hudson County Comm Coll 25 Pathside Jersey 07306*

BENDER, MATTHEW PATRICK, Science Teacher; *b:* Malone, Katherine Edrington; *ed:* Potsdam Coll (BA) Arts Chem 1993, (Tchng 1994; *cr:* Middleburgh Cntrl Sci Tchr 1994-; *ai:* Sci O Coach; Sci Club Adv; Phi Delta Kappa Outstndng Stu Tchr Aw *office:* Middleburgh Central Schl PO Box 400 Middleburgh NY 1

BENDER, NORMA JEAN, 6th-8th Grade Music Teacher; *b:* Lev PA; *ed:* Westminster Coll (BM) Music 1978; Attnd Millersville Un St Univ, Temple Univ & West Chester Univ; *cr:* Oxford Area S General & Vocal Music Tchr 1978-; *ai:* Schl Play; Choral En Chorus; MENC & PMEA 1976-; NEA & PSEA 1978-, Bldg Rep Me Chr; St Christophers Episcopal Church 1978-; Vestr, Vicars Warde Pres, Chair & Various Comms; Choir; Choir Dir; Substitute Orgnst; Pub; *office:* Penns Grove Intermediate Schl 602 Garfield St Ox 19363

BENDER, PAULA GAIL, English Teacher; *b:* Marietta, OH; *m:* *c:* Paul, Valerie; *ed:* Lincoln Meml Univ (BA) Eng Educl 1988; *cr:* Meml Univ Adj Writing Instr 1988-90; *ai:* NEA 1993-; *hom* Dragoo Rd Nashport OH 43830

BENDER, ROSE MARIE, 7th-12th Grade History Teac Washington, IA; *ed:* Messiah Coll (BA) Behavioral Sci 1991; S Cert; *cr:* Greenwood Mennonite Schl Scndry His 1991-95; Merce Acad Scndry His 1995-; *ai:* Drama Coach; *office:* Mercer Chrstn A Box 7299 West Trenton NJ 08628

BENDIXEN-NOE, MARY K., Child Development Professor; *b.* IA; *m:* William Joseph Noe; *c:* Jeremy; *ed:* Morehead St Univ (Home Ec 1980, (MS) Voc Ed 1981; OH St Univ (PHD) Child Dev, 1992; *cr:* Gallipolis City Schls Scndry Tchr 1981-89; OH St Univ 1989-91; OH Dept of Ed Supvr 1992-93; OH St Univ Asst Prof 1 Advising PHD Stdnts; Grant Writing; Conducting Rsrch; ATE NAEYC 1992-; ACEI 1993-; 2 Articles, 1 Chptr in Yrbk Pub; OH Ed, OSU Grants Awded; *office:* OH St Univ At Newark 1179 Unive Newark OH 43055

BENEDICT, JAMES A., Social Studies Teacher; *b:* Cleveland, Patricia Ann Fisher; *c:* Jonathan; *ed:* Hillsdale Coll (BA) His & 1964; Case-Western Reserve Univ (MA) Scndry Ed 1968; Constitutional Origins Ashland Univ; Grad Hrs MI St Univ His & Grad Hrs Kent St Univ in Ed; *cr:* Glenville HS Soc Sci Tchr 1 Athletic Directory; Spon of St & Regnl Bicentennial Competition Trial Teams; Stu Council Adv; Tennis Coach; NCSS, OCSS 1988-; 1990-; AFT, OFT, CTU 1966-; Co-Author of AP Govt Less Inspiritional Tchr of Yr 1991 & 1995; *office:* Glenville HS 650 E Cleveland OH 44108

BENEDICT, JOSEPH PARK, 8th Grade Science Teac Philadelphia, PA; *m:* Suzanne L. Devoe; *c:* Christopher, Kevin; *ed:* Univ (BA) Bio 1979; 12 Credit Hrs Grad Courses; *cr:* Marlton MS Sci Tchr 1979-93; Cherry Hill Assn for Gifted Tchr 1983-87; G Alternative HS Sci Tchr 1984-91; De Masi MS 8th Grd Sci Tchr 1 A. V. Club; NEA 1980-; Tchr of Yr Marlton MS 1989; *office:* DeM 199 Evesboro Medford Rd Marlton NJ 08053*

BENEDICT, JOYCE ARENDOSH, Retired Third Grade Tea Uniontown, PA; *m:* John A.; *c:* Matthew, Leah; *ed:* PA St Univ (B & Kndgtn Ed 1974; *cr:* Laurel Highlands Schl Dist K-8th Grd Pe Tchr 1974-75; Napoleon City Schls 3rd Grd Tchr 1975-90; *ai:* Ste Math Curr Comms; Grd Level Chprsn; OEA 1975-; Delta Kappa 1985-, Sec 1994-; Acad Boosters Clb, Sec 1995-; *home:* 1095 W Ave Napoleon OH 43545

BENEDICT, JUDITH WEAVER, Spanish Teacher; *b:* Sewickley, John R.; *c:* Keith, Brad; *ed:* IN U of PA (BS) Span 1965; Duqu (MED) Scndry Ed 1969; *cr:* Upper St Clair HS Span Tchr 1 Westlake Jr HS Span Tchr 1968-71; Mc Dowell Intermediate HS Sp 1986-; *ai:* Stu Cncl Adv; Spon Stu Trip Mexico - Spain; MEA, NEA AAUW 1968-, Named Gift Educl Fnd; *office:* Mc Dowell Intermed 3320 Caughey Rd Erie PA 16506

BENEDICT, MARGIE PRESTON, Retired Second Grade Tea Salina, KS; *m:* Claude B.; *c:* Jeffrey, Claudia; *ed:* Cleveland St Ur Ed-Cum Laude 1973; 8 Credit Hrs Kent St Univ Post Grad in Ed; Hrs Baldwin Wallace Post Grad in Ed; *cr:* Dentzler Elem Schl Sec Tchr 1977-78; Thoreau Park Elem Schl First Grd Tchr 1978-7 Hammarskjold Schl Second-Third Grd Tchr 1979-82; Thoreau Pa Schl Second Grd Tchr 1982-95; *ai:* NEA, OEA 1977-; OH PTA Honorary Life Mem Awd; Meals on Wheels 1990-, Client Intervie Hr Winner; Brecksville Art Mart 1968-, Check-Out Chm, Charte Amer Red Cross 1960-, Gray Lady Vol; Nom Parma Tchr of Yr; Class Act Tchr; Cox Cable TV Spotlight Tchr; *home:* 9391 High Brecksville OH 44141

BENEDICT, MARY GERBIG, Kindergarten Teacher; *b:* Canast *m:* Jon H.; *c:* Craig; *ed:* Western MI Univ (MS) Elem Ed 1968; Gra Coll of St Rose; *cr:* Willard Prior Elem Kndgtn Tchr 1975-82, 1st C 1982-84, 3rd Grd Tchr 1984-88; Pre-1st Grd Tchr 1988-95; Kndg 1995-; *ai:* AFT 1975-; *office:* Willard Prior Elem Schl 205 E Oneida NY 13421*

BENEDICT, SUZANNA ENGMAN, Instructor of English; *b:* Ro NY; *m:* Lawrence; *c:* Augustin; *ed:* Nazareth Coll (BS) Psych 198 of NM (MA) Rhetoric & Lang 1989; 1 Yr toward PHD Univ 1989-90; *cr:* Univ of NM Upward Spcl Svcs Eng Instr & Tutor 1 Univ of NM Tchng Asst 1987-90; Monroe Comm Coll Adj Prof 1 Rochester Inst of Tech Adj Prof 1991-93; Finger Lakes Comm C Instr 1993-; *ai:* Tchng & Instrl Assessment & Constitutional (Classroom Assessment Techniques Project & African Amer Read In Yates Cty Yth Bureau Bd Mem; NCTE 1990-; CCCC 1990-; TYCA St Rep; *office:* Finger Lakes Comm Coll 4355 Lake Shore Dr Cana NY 14424

BENEKOS, PETER J., Professor of Admin of Justice; *b:* Potsda *ed:* Clarion Univ of PA (BA) Soc Sci 1971; Univ of Cincinna Sociology 1975; Univ of Akron (PHD) Sociology, Criminology 1 Mercyhurst Coll Prof 1979-; *ai:* Admin Justice Grad Prgm Dir; Ctr & Mental Hlth Issues Assoc Dir; Acad Criminal Justice Sci, Ar Criminology 1980-; Citizens Advy Comm PA Bd of Parole 1979 Citizens' Advy Com Dept of Corr 1993-; Corrections Dilem Directions Co-Edited; Articles: Women as Victims & Perpetra Murder, Shock Incarceration Military Model in Corrections, Pub F Sentencing Reform; *office:* Mercyhurst Coll 501 E 31st Erie PA 1

BENETT, SHARON, Instructor of Voice; *b:* West Jefferson, Eastman Schl of Music (BM) Vocal Performance 1960, (MM) Perf & Pedagogy 1962; Performance Cert 1961; OH Univ 1 Grad C 1995; IL St 2 Grad Credit Hrs 1995; *cr:* Univ of IA Asst Prof 1 in Coll Adj Lecturer 1986-86; Capital Univ Instr 1985-; *ai:* Acad Comm; NATS 1980-; Coll Music Soc 1995-, Comm on Music, & Gender; Sigma Alpha Iota 1957-; AAVP 1991-; Red Cross 1994-; n Singers Bd Mem; YWCA Women of Achvmnt Awd; Books Pub; eller Grants; Corbett Fnd Grants; Old Gold Flwshp; Fac Dev Grant; Capital Univ 2199 E Main St Bexley OH 43209*

TTI, MARSHA BURNS, Second Grade Teacher; *b:* Ellwood City, Joseph N.; *c:* Tracy Scott, Jason Eric; *ed:* Slippery Rock Univ (BS) d 1965; Masters Equiv Penna Dept of Ed 1994; *cr:* Blackhawk Schl t Grd Tchr 15 Yrs, 2nd Grd Tchr 15 Yrs; *ai:* NEA, PSEA, BEA *office:* Blackhawk Schl Dist 256 Elmwood Blvd # Sr 168 Darlington 15

VENTO, EVA SCHUCK, Fifth Grade Teacher; *b:* Stoberdorf, ; *m:* Anthony P.; *c:* Joshua, Hannah; *ed:* William Paterson Coll (BA) 9, (MA) Comm Arts 1970; 9 Credit Hrs Fairleigh Dickenson Univ; lit Hrs Long Island Univ; *cr:* William Paterson Coll Speech, Theater 970-72; Teaneck Pub Schl Elem Tchr 1972-; *ai:* Imagine Magazine ech 2000 Comm; NEA, NJEA, BCEA 1970-; ITEA 1972-; LeSea Harvest 1994-; Tchng Flwshp Wm Paterson Coll; Pub Articles; Essential Tchng Styles & Strategies; *home:* 25 Biscayne Dr Ramsey 46*

ER, BONNIE HALL, Health & Physical Ed Teacher; *b:* Ft Knox, Amanda; *ed:* Lock Haven Univ of PA (BS) Hlth, PE, Ath Coaching hippensburg Univ of PA 24 Grad Credits; Penn St Univ at Univ Park l Credits; Wilkes Univ of PA 9 Grad Credits; *cr:* Eastern York Schl em PE Tchr, Coach 1979-80; Penn ST Univ Tchng Asst, Intern to Coord 1987-88; Penns Vly Jr Sr HS Hlth, PE Tchr, Coach 1980-; *ai:* irls Track, Cross Cntry Coach; Assoc Var Club Adv; PVEA, PSEA, 979-; PA Track & Field Coaches Assoc, PA W Cntrl Coaches Assoc Phi Delta Kappa 1996; Jaycees Outstdng Young Edctrs 1987-88, 4; Jacyees Outsdtng Young Fitness Ldr 1985-86, 1988-89; Vol Coord Heart Assoc Jump for Heart 1985-93; Amer Cancer Soc Daffodil 989-95; *office:* Penns Valley Jr Sr HS RR 2 Box 116 Spring Mills 75

E, MARY E. DOWNEY, Kindergarten Teacher; *b:* Bellefontaine, David R.; *c:* Sara E., Rachel A.; *ed:* Bowling Green St Univ (BS) d K-8 1971; Post Grad Hrs in Math Their Way, Whole Lang, Child kshp Way, Learning Channels; Wright St Tchr-Ldr Pgm; *cr:* Triad h Grd Tchr 1971, 3rd Grd Tchr 1971-72, 1st-2nd Grd Tchr 1972-74, Grd Chapter I Rdng Tchr 1974-77 & 1979-89, 4th Grd Tchr), Kndgtn Tchr 1989-; *ai:* Play Dir; Safety Patrol Adv; LA Curr; urr; Competency Comm; Right to Read Coord; Mem Right to Read Book Fair Chprsn; Inclusion Team-K; NEA 1974-; Triad Ed 1974-, Pres; OEA 1974-, Pacesetter; COTA 1974-, PR Grant; IRA, OCIRA nber of Rdng Cncl 1990-, 1st & 2nd VP; Delta Kappa Gamma 1990-, riad Band Boosters 1988-, Publicity Chair; N Lewisburg Friends of 93-; NL United Meth Church 1985-; Ashland Oil Tchr Achievement om 1993; *home:* 106 S Sycamore St North Lewisburg OH 43060*

AM, DARIA SETZCO, First Grade Teacher; *b:* Concord, MA; *m:* k Charles; *ed:* Northeastern Univ (BS) Elem Ed 1970; Lesley Coll arly Chldhd 1979; Attnd Tufts Univ, Simmons Coll; *cr:* Roosevelt rst Grd Tchr 26 Yrs; Green Meadow Schl First Grd Tchr 26 Yrs; *ai:* Tchr; Many Comm, Wkshps; NEA, MTA, MEA 1970-80; *office:* Meadow Elem Schl 143 Great Rd Maynard MA 01754

EWICZ, JOSEPH, Assistant Principal; *b:* Baltimore, MD; *ed:* St th Coll Seminary (BA) Philosophy 1983; St Anthony on Hudson ry (MDiv) Theology 1988; 12 Grad Credits St Univ of NY at ; *cr:* St Francis HS Dept Chair & Instr 1988-89 & 1991-95, Asst 95-; *ai:* Textbook Coord; JV Bsbl Coach; Mid Sts Reaccredidation s Adv; Parents Guild Co-Moderator; NCEA 1988-; NASSP 1995-; s of Columbus 1994-; *office:* St Francis HS 4129 Lakeshore Rd prings NY 14010

AR, TONY, Physical Education & Hlth Tchr; *b:* Cleveland, OH; *m:* *c:* Andrew, Adam; *ed:* Kent St Univ (BA) PE, Hlth 1970; Grad Environmental Stud; *cr:* Lincoln Elem Schl PE K-6th Grd Tchr 3; Wickliffe Elem Schl PE K_4th Grd Tchr 1983-86; Wickliffe MS 8th Grd Tchr 1986-; *ai:* Ath Dir; Ftbl, Tennis Coach; NEA, OH Ed Northeast OH Ed Assn, Wickliffe Ed Assn 1970-; *office:* Wickliffe 240 Euclid Ave Wickliffe OH 44092

AS, JOHN R., 4th Grade Reading Specialist; *b:* Farrell, PA; *m:* J. Hyde; *c:* Jeanette E., John B.; *ed:* Edinboro St Tchrs Coll (BS) Ed, Eng, Comp Soc Stud 1974; Westminster Coll (MS) Ed, Rdng list 1986; Attending Northwestern Univ Garrett Evangelical gical Seminary; *cr:* Sharon Kennedy Chrstn HS Tchr, Coach 7; Cortland Lakeview HS Tchr, Coach 1977-79, 1981-83; Niles HS oach 1979-81; Hubbard HS Tchr, Coach 1983-; Hubbard Elem Tchr, 1983-; *ai:* Math Textbook Comm 1995-; Former Soc Stud Dept Coach Ftbl 20 Yrs, Track 15 Yrs, Bsktbl 3 Yrs, Wrestling 1 Yr; Sr, Class Adv; Adult Ed Tchr 2 Yrs; NEA 1977-; Hubbard Chrstns in Tchr of Yr 1990; Track Coach of Yr: Trumbull Cty 3 Yrs, Mahoning Yrs, NE OH; Trumbull Cty Asst Ftbl Coach of Yr 2 Yrs; *office:* d Roosevelt Elem Schl 110 Orchard Ave Hubbard OH 44425

ATI, MARGARET ANN, Business Teacher; *b:* Millville, NJ; *m:* y; *c:* Kathleen, Mary Ann; *ed:* Rider Univ (BS) Bus Ed 1972, (MA) 1976; *cr:* Oakcrest HS Bus Tchr 1974-83; Egg Harbor Twp HS Bus 983-; *ai:* Key Club, FBLA Adv; Delta Pi Epsilon 1976-, Pres; Phi Kappa 1989-; NJBEA 1974-, St Pres 1992-93; Millville Jaycee-ettes 6, Jaycee-ette of Yr; EHT Mini-Grant 1996; Prentice Hall ant 1994; *office:* Egg Harbor Township HS 24 High School Dr Egg Townshi NJ 08234

ATI, RINO, Seventh Grade Science Teacher; *b:* Chelsea, MA; *m:* eisbach; *c:* Laura, Kevin, Kara; *ed:* Salem St Coll (BA) Bio 1979; dge Coll (MA) Ed 1990; 15 Credits in Cmptr Ed from Fitchburgh l; *cr:* Eunice Kennedy Shriver Medical Center Asst Lab Tech 9; Woodbury School 7th Grd Sci Tchr 1979-; *ai:* HS Soccer, MS Bsktbl Coach; NEA 1979-; NSTA 1980-; *office:* Woodbury Schl 206 t Salem NH 03079

ATO, PAUL PHILLIP, Music & Choir Director; *b:* Lawrence, MA; y Sue Linder; *c:* Sara Marie, John Paul; *ed:* Univ of MA at Lowell Music 1980, (MM) Music 1982; Tchr Cert K-12 Music 1985; Boston ost-Grad Credit 1990-; *cr:* Lawrence HS Choir Dir 1985-; Lawrence hls Music Dir; *ai:* Accrediation Steering Comm; Curr Cncl Pres Curr Team; Amer Choral Dir 1989-, R&S Chm Mass; Music Edctrs onf 1986-; AFT 1985-; Mass Music Edctrs 1986-; Horance Mann Accreditation Visiting Team NEASC; Handel, Haydn Soc Educl 3d All St Choir Mgr 1995; *office:* Lawrence HS 233 Haverhill St nce MA 01841

H, LINDA SENDER, Eng, His & Jewish Studies Tchr; *b:* Chicago, Allan; *c:* David, Jeffrey, Marci; *ed:* Roosevelt Univ (BA) Ed 1968; cago Pub Schl 3rd Grd Tchr 1968-70; Solomon Schechter Day Schl 1-8th Grd Tchr 1984-; *ai:* Bible Cantillation Tchng; Jewish Fed of sex Cty 1992-, Bd Mem, Klein-Belikove Ldrshp; Jewish Family Svc Bd Mem; Monroe Township HS Parents Assn 1991-, Bd Mem, Past Mbrshp; Cong Beta Ohr 1983-, Chair, Ed & Ritual Comms; Curr Dev seph Fnd Grant; *office:* Solomon Schechter Day Sch 511 Ryders Ln runswick NJ 08816*

BENJAMIN, DEBORAH ANN, English Teacher; *b:* New Britain, CT; *ed:* Univ of CT (BA) Scndry Ed, Eng 1975; Cntrl CT St Coll (MS) Cnslng 1981; 30 Hrs Post Grad; *cr:* Southington HS Tchr 1976-; *ai:* Writer's Club-Lit Magazine Adv; Quality Plus Prgm; Curr Comm; NCTE 1980-; CCTE 1986-; NEA 1976-; New Britain Museum of Amer Art 1982-; CT Poetry Soc 1990-; Church of Jesus Christ of Latterday Saints 1975-, Pres Stake Primary; *office:* Southington HS 720 Pleasant St Southington CT 06489*

BENJAMIN, GERALDINE L., Home Economics Teacher; *b:* Chicago, IL; *m:* Michael H.; *c:* Blake, M. L.; *ed:* Univ of MA (BS) Home Ec Ed 1977; Certified Hlth Educator; *cr:* Bay Path Voc Tech HS Foods & Nutrition Instr 1977-83; Tantasqua Regnl HS Home Ec Instr 1985-87; Tantasqua Regnl Jr HS Home Ec Instr 1989-90; Thornton Burgess MS Home Ec Tchr 1991-93; David Prouty HS Home Ec Instr 1993-; *ai:* Peer Educator Adv; NEA, MTA 1977-; MA Peer Ed Assn 1994-; Recipient of Numerous Comm Svc Learning Mini-Grants; Pub Unit on Intergenerational Learning & Awareness.

BENJAMIN, KATHRYN, Asst Professor of Mathematics; *b:* Newport News, VA; *m:* Ross; *c:* William Holden, Laura; *ed:* SCC Selden (AA) Math 1982; Hofstra Univ (BA) Math 1984, (MA) Applied Math 1989; 12 Credit Hrs Stony Brook Univ; *cr:* Nassau Comm Coll Math Tech Asst 1984-89; Hofstra Univ Adjunct Instr 1984-89; Suffolk Comm Coll Math Asst Prof 1989-; *ai:* Western Stu Press Adv; SCC Acad Standards Comm; SCC Western Campus Acad Assembly Sec; Underrepresented Minority Stu Pgrm Mentor; AAUW 1992-; MAA 1993-; NYSMATYC 1993-; Excl in Tchng SUNY Chancellor's Awd 1995; *office:* Suffolk Community Coll Crooked Hill Rd Brentwood NY 11717*

BENJAMIN, KEITH WARD, Accel Biology Teacher; *b:* Cleveland, OH; *m:* Wendy E. Sims; *c:* Brian, Beth, Katie, Kristen; *ed:* Kent St Univ (BSEd) Biological Scis 1971, (MA) Bio 1976; *cr:* Kent St Univ Schl MS Sci Tchr 1971-72; Kent Pub Schls Bio Tchr 1972-; *ai:* Class Adv; KEA 1971-, Pres 1982-84; Neoucom Iacue Bd 1993-; Franklin Twp Trustee 1993-, Chm 1995; Frosh Tchr of Yr 1993-94; *office:* Kent Theodore Roosevelt HS 1400 N Mantua St Kent OH 44240

BENJAMIN, LEAH RAYE, Gifted & Reading Teacher; *b:* Lawshe, OH; *c:* Julie, Donnie R. Hall, Katie Hall; *ed:* Xavier Univ (BA Elem Ed 1981; Northern KY Univ (MA) Rdng 1986; Rdng Specialist K-12; Gifted Cert; *cr:* Felicity Franklin Kndgtn Tchr 1981-88, 7th Grd Rdng, Gifted L A 1988-; *ai:* Gifted Coord; Yrbk, 10th Grd Adv; Clermont Coll 1991-, Advy Bd; Mensa; *office:* Felicity Franklin HS 415 Washington St Felicity OH 45120

BENJAMIN, LENI KRUGER, Career Awareness Teacher; *b:* Durham, NC; *m:* Wellington L.; *c:* Dana Kyle Dychtwald, Scott Eric Dychtwald, Rachel Ann Dychtwald, Khadisha Leandra; *ed:* Newark St Coll (BA) Elem Ed 1967; NY Univ (MA) Ed Psych 1969; Drake Univ 16 Credit Hrs Ed Admin 1980-81; Kean Coll 6 Credit Hrs Curr Dev, Family Life Curr 1984; *cr:* Benjamin Franklin Schl #13 5-6 Grd Tchr 1967-69; St Joseph Schl 1-2 Grd Tchr 1977-79; St Pius X Schl 6-8 Grd Tchr 1979-81; St Helena's Schl 7-8 Grd Tchr 1982; Edison Job Corps Tchr 1983-84; Roosevelt Jr HS 6-8 Grd Tchr 1984-85; Maxson &Hubbard Jr HS 6-8 Grd Tchr 1985-87; North Main Street Schl K-8 Grd Tchr 1987-; Sout h Main Street Schl K-8 Grd Tchr 1987-; *ai:* NJEA, NEA 1985-; NCTM 1987-; Tchr of Month 1992; Tchr of Yr 1995-; Elizabeth Ed Assn Schlsp 1963; *office:* Pleasantville Schls W Decatur Ave Pleasantville NJ 08232*

BENJAMIN, LINDA STOLL, First Grade Teacher; *b:* Sayre, PA; *m:* Russell J.; *c:* Eric, Clay, Ryan; *ed:* Kutztown Univ (BA) Elem Ed 1969; *cr:* Northeast Bradford 1st Grd Tchr 1969-70; Sayre Area 4th Grd Tchr 1970-72; Northside Chrstn K-1st Grd Tchr 1977-; *office:* Northside Christian Schl 2655 Schrock Rd Westerville OH 43081

BENJAMIN, MARSHA KAY, Social Studies Teacher; *b:* Binghamton, NY; *m:* Leonard M.; *c:* Kevin, Keith; *ed:* SUNY at Oneonta (BA) Elem Ed, Eng 1968; SUNY at Cortland (MS) Elem Ed 1973; 10 Credits at SUNY at Binghamton; *cr:* Maine-Endwell Schl Dist Grd 4-7 Tchr 1968-; *ai:* Oratorical Contest Coach; Outdoor Ed Camp Dir; NEA, NYEA 1968-, Various Comms; PTA 1990-, Schl Rep; AAUW 1 Yr; Vestal United Meth Church 1975-, Crmn Ed Comm; *office:* Maine Endwell MS 1119 Farm To Market Rd Endicott NY 13760

BENJAMIN, MURIEL, Fourth Grade Teacher; *b:* Brooklyn, NY; *m:* David I.; *c:* Jonathan, Richard; *ed:* Brooklyn Coll (BA) Ed 1966, (MA) Ed 1970; 30 Addl Credits; *cr:* PS 75 Tchr 1966-67, 1972; Temple Shaari Emeth Nursery Schl Dir 1972-78; Jefferson Schl Tchr 1978-; *ai:* NEA 1978-; Kappa Delta Pi; SOMAC Awd Dr. Martin Luther King Jr. Play; Harper Collins 1995 Video; *office:* Jefferson Elem Schl 518 Ridgewood Rd Maplewood NJ 07040

BENJAMIN, PENELOPE SMITH, Third Grade Teacher; *b:* Glens Falls, NY; *w:* Elmer (dec); *ed:* Lesley Coll (BS) Elem Ed 1962, Wheelock Coll (MS) Elem Ed 1974; 30 Credits Elem Ed Boston Coll; *cr:* Newton Schl Dept Cabot Schl Third, 4th Grd Tchr 1962-; *ai:* Classrooms of 21st Century Comm; Assessnient; Advy Bd Field Placement of Stu Tchrs Boston Coll; NEA, MA Tchrs Assn, Newton Tchrs Assn 1962-; Delta Kappa Gamma 1987-; Natl Bd for Prof Tchng Stndrds Early Chldhd Gen Cert Co-Founder; Environmental Educator Awd 1990; Outstanding Tchr of Yr 1990; Spon Grand Winner of Young Pub A Book Contest; Awded $8000 Tech Grant for Classroom Use With Indusion Child 1994; Sally Lenhardt Prof Ldrshp Awd 1995; *office:* Cabot Schl 229 Cabot St Newtonville MA 02160

BENJAMIN, SUSAN NORDSTROM, Home & Careers Teacher; *b:* Port Allegany, PA; *m:* Barry B.; *c:* Robert, Debra Daniels; *ed:* Mansfield Univ (BS) Home Ec 1968; Fredonia St UNY (MS) Early Chldh 1994; Attnd PA St Univ; *cr:* Maple Grove HS Home Ec Tchr 1968-70; Austin Area Schl Home Ec Tchr 1972-85; Triple C Schl Home Ec, Hlth Tchr 1987-92; Clymer Cntrl Schl Home Ec Tchr 1992-; *ai:* 7th Grd Adv; NEA, NYSTA 1992-; *home:* 3083 Strunk Rd Jamestown NY 14701*

BENKEN, CHERYL M., French Teacher; *b:* Cincinnati, OH; *c:* Nicole, Blair; *ed:* Univ Cincinnati (BS) Fr 1969, (MED) Scndry Ed 1972; Xavier Univ Elem Ed 1978; Unniversite de Paris Diplome 1968; CAREL-Royan Cert 1989; *cr:* Cincinnati Pub Schls Fr Tchr 1978-83; Webutuck HS Fr Tchr 1983-; *ai:* NY St Multi-Cultural Schlsp 1989; Rockefeller Flwshp 1991; Fulbright Finalist 1993; *office:* Webutuck HS Amenia-Haight Rd Amenia NY 12501

BENN, GALE MAURIELLO, French Teacher; *b:* Newark, NJ; *m:* Jerome; *c:* Kyle, Courtney; *ed:* Montclair St Univ (BA) Fr & Span 1974; CUNY Summer Inst 4 Grad Credits; *cr:* Aurora Gardens Acad Fr & Span Tchr 1978-79; Union HS Fr & Span Tchr 1979-89; Watchung Hills Regnl HS Fr Tchr 1990-; *ai:* NJEA 1979-; AATF 1990-; SCEA 1990-; CUNY Summer Inst Grant From Natl Endowment for the Hum; Union HS Tchr of Yr Nom; *office:* Watching Hills Regional HS 108 Stirling Rd Warren NJ 07059

BENNARDO, DAVID P., Social Studies Teacher; *b:* Plainview, NY; *m:* Jill Reichardt; *c:* Tiana; *ed:* SUNY at Stonybrook (BA) Soc Stud Ed 1988; C. W. Post Univ (MS) Ed Ldrshp 1995; *cr:* Bethpage HS Soc Stud Tchr 1990-91; New Hyde Park HS Soc Stud Tchr 1991-; *ai:* Var Ftbl, Lacrosse Coach; NCSS; ASCD; NASSP; *office:* New Hyde Park Memorial JSHS 500 Leonard Blvd New Hyde Park NY 11040*

BENNARDO, JILL C., Science Teacher; *b:* Syosset, NY; *m:* David P.; *c:* Tiana; *ed:* St Johns Univ (BS) Sci & Ed 1988; Adelphi Univ (MS) Rdng Specialist 1994; *cr:* JFK MS 9th Grd Sci Tchr 1 Yr, 6th Grd Sci Tchr 3 Yrs, 7th & 8th Grd Sci Tchr 2 Yrs; *ai:* Sci Olympiad Coach; Chrldng Coach; NYSUT 1989-; NSTA; *office:* John F Kennedy MS 500 Broadway Bethpage NY 11714

BENNATI, GENE ANTHONY, Business Dept Chairperson; *b:* Syracuse, NY; *m:* Rosamond Elizabeth; *ed:* Murray St Univ (BS) Bus 1967; Syracuse Univ (MS) Educl Admin 1981; Cortland Univ (CAS) Educl Admin 1984; *cr:* Vernon Verona Sherrill Cntrl Schls Bus Tchr, Dept Chair 1967-; Madison Oneida BOCES Vice Prin, Summer Prgm 1989-; *ai:* Ftbl, Golf, Little League Bsbl Coach; NYSUT 1967-; NYSSSPA 1989-; NBEA 1975-; Comm Chest, Bd of Dir; Vernon Town Bd 1985-, Councilman; *office:* VVS Cntrl HS Rt 31 Verona NY 13478

BENNATTI, ROGER JOEL, Teacher & Sci Dept Chprsn; *b:* New Haven, CT; *m:* Carolyn Reid; *ed:* Bates Coll (BS) Geology 1973; 42 Post Grad Hrs; *cr:* Stevens Acad Chem & Physics Tchr & Sci Dept Chprsn 1973-; *ai:* GSAEA 1973-, Pres; ACS 1995-; AAPT 1981-; NSTA 1974-; NAGT 1976-; NEA 1973-; AAVSO 1994-; *office:* George Stevens Acad Union St Blue Hill ME 04614

BENNET, KENNETH F., Clinical Psychologist; *b:* Jackson, MI; *m:* RosAnne Thompson; *c:* Aaron; *ed:* Northern MI (BA) Eng Scndry Ed 1980; Bread Loaf Schl of Eng (MA) Eng 1985; Union Inst (PhD) Clinical Phychology 1995; *cr:* De Soto Mid, HS 7-12th Grd Eng Tchr 1980-90; Viterbo Coll at LaCrosse Eng, Psychology 1991-93; Neurobehavioral Assoc Intern 1994-95, Clinical Psychologist 1995-; *ai:* Bsktbl Coach 1980-90; Amer Psychological Assoc 1991-; NEE, WEA 1980-90; Domestic Violence; Doctoral Dissertation; Stud Shakespeare, Dante in Italy; Pub Poetry.

BENNETT, BERNARD GEORGE, Teacher & Dept Chairman; *b:* Boston, MA; *m:* Marie; *c:* Devaney, Heather; *ed:* Wentworth Inst (AA) Mechanical Design 1962; Fitchburg St Coll (BSEd) Indstrl Tech 1966; Univ of AZ (MED) Cnslng Guid 1968; Attnd Univ of CA at San Diego, Northern AZ Univ, Boston St Coll; *cr:* Calexico Schl Dist Tchr, Guid Cnslr 1968-72; Linden Park Const Draftsman, Proj Mgr 1972-74; Georgetown MHS Tchr, Dept Chm 1974-; Rubin Glass, Alumin Draftsman, Estimator 1978-92, Draftsman, Estimator, Proj Mgr 1992-; *ai:* Instruction, Curr Comm Chm; NEA, MEA, GEA 1974-.

BENNETT, BETSY KRAUS, Mathematics Teacher; *b:* Lakewood, OH; *m:* David A.; *c:* Gregory, Rebecca; *ed:* Denison Univ (BS) Math 1964; Northwestern Univ (MAT) Math Ed 1965; Amer Univ (PHD) Math Ed 1981; Woodrow Wilson Summer Inst Math 1992; *cr:* Ithaca HS Math Tchr 1967-71; Middlebury Coll Math Tchr 1975-79; The Maret Schl Math Tchr 1981-94; St Albans Schl Math Tchr 1994-; *ai:* Upper & Lower Schl Math Teams; JETS Engrng Team; NCTM 1980-; MAA 1972-; Woodrow Wilson Flwshp 1992; Numerous Articles Pub; *office:* St Alban's Schl For Boys Mount St Alban Washington DC 20016

BENNETT, BILL, English Professor; *b:* Pittsburgh, PA; *m:* Claudia; *c:* Ian, Mark, Alexandra, Katherine, Victoria, Gavin; *ed:* Univ of Pittsburg (BA) Eng 1961, (MA) Eng, Medieval Stud 1964; 18 Doctoral Hrs; *cr:* WV Univ Eng Instr 1964-67; CA Univ of PA Asst Prof Eng 1967-; *ai:* Dir Stu Publications 1978-94; APSCUF 1970-; Alpha Psi Omega 1988-; Articles Pub; Ed; *office:* California Univ Of PA Third Street California PA 15419

BENNETT, CHERYL LOUISE, Fourth Grade Teacher; *b:* Sayre, PA; *ed:* Corning Comm Coll (AS) Lbrl Arts 1970; St Univ of Oswego (BS) Elem Ed 1972; Elmira Coll (MS) Elem Ed 1976; 40 Credits Inservice Courses; *cr:* Coldbrook Schl 6th Grd Tchr 1973-76; Broadway Elem Schl 4th Grd Tchr 1976-77; Pine City Elem Schl 4th Grd Tchr 1977-80, 5th-6th Grd Tchr 1980-81, 6th Grd Tchr 1981-93, 4th Grd Tchr 1993-; *ai:* Math Action Team Chm; Crisis Mngmt Team; Elmira Tchrs Assn 1973-, Bldg Rep, Negotiating Team, Retirement Bd Rep; Southside Bapt Church 1963-; Yth Group Adv; *office:* Pine City Elem Schl 1551 Pennsylvania Ave Pine City NY 14871

BENNETT, CYNTHIA CORIELL, 6th Grd Lang Arts & Sci Tchr; *b:* Berea, OH; *m:* P. Russell; *c:* Adam, Matt; *ed:* Miami Univ (BS) Elem Ed 1974; Baldwin-Wallace Coll (MS) Rdng; *cr:* Miamisburg City Schls Tchr 1974-77; Olmsted Falls City Schls Tchr 1985-; *ai:* Curr Comm Olmsted Falls City Schls; Intervention Team; Olmsted Falls Tchr Assn 1985-, Pres 2 Yrs, Negotiating Team; Dover Congregational Church 1993-, Curr Comm; Martha Holden Jennings Awd; *office:* Olmsted Falls MS 26184 Bagley Rd Olmsted Falls OH 44138

BENNETT, DEBORAH J., Assistant Professor of Math; *b:* Tuscaloosa, AL; *m:* Michael Hirsch; *ed:* Univ of AL (BS) Math 1972; George WA Univ (MS) Operations Research 1980; NY Univ (PHD) Math Ed 1993; *cr:* Inst of Defense Analysis Prof Staff 1973-75; Gen Acctg Office Operations Research Analyst 1975-80; US Peace Corps Math Tchr 1980-81; Monar Mrktg Consultant 1981-82; NY City Dept Fin Consultant 1982-84; SUNY at Farmingdale Asst Prof 1984-93; Jersey City St Coll Asst Prof 1993-; *ai:* Math Club Adv; Coll Senator; Senate; Honorary Awds Comm; AFT, UUP 1984-, Dr Nvala Brewscher Sabbatical 1989; NCTM 1984-; Kappa Delta Pi 1988-; NYS-UUP New Fac Dev Awd 1985; GAO Systems Analysis Schlsp 1978; Certs of Appreciations 1978, SUNY-Farmingdale Univ Club 1992, GAO Cert of Merit 1981; *office:* Jersey City St Coll 2039 Kennedy Boulevard Jersey City NJ 07305

BENNETT, DONNA WEST, Business Education Teacher; *b:* Johnstown, PA; *m:* Thomas A.; *c:* Jason T., Craig T., Megan D.; *ed:* IN Univ of PA (BS) Bus Ed 1978; 42 Post Grad Credits Cmptrs, Bus; Voc Stud; *cr:* Ligonier Vly Schl Dist Bus Ed Tchr 1979-84; Laurel Vly MS, HS Bus Ed Tchr 1983-; *ai:* Yrbk Bus Adv 14 Yrs; Yrbk Lit Adv 11 Yrs; Girls JV Vlybl Coach 3 Yrs, Jr HS 4 Yrs; Fac Mgr 4 Yrs; Girls Var Club Adv 4 Yrs; Ath Equipment Mgr 1 Yr; Prin Advy Comm; NEA, PSEA, LVEA 1979-, PR Chm, Pub Chm; NBEA, PBEA, Tri St BEA 1979-; Ft Ligonier Fed Credit Union 1979-, Asst Treas, Supervisory Comm Chprsn, Bd of Dir; Ligonier Vly Ed Assn 1979-, Bldg Rep; Girls Var Vlybl, Var Sftbl, Jr Var Bsktbl Coach; Dist Strategic Planning Comm; *home:* 212 Ligonier St New Florence PA 15944

BENNETT, DOROTHY M. HOVORKA, History Teacher; *b:* Cleveland, OH; *m:* Don A.; *c:* Andrew C.; *ed:* Univ of Dayton (BA) His 1966; Cleveland St (MA) Voc Ed 1987; Pilots Licenses: Private Commercial, Instrument Rating Flight Instr; *cr:* Cuyahoga Comm Coll Instr 1976-79; Cleveland Bd of Ed Tchr 1966-; *ai:* Proficient Test Coord; Union Conf Comm; AFT, OFT 1966-; *office:* Max S. Hayes HS 4600 Detroit Ave Cleveland OH 44102

BENNETT, ELIZABETH FAYE, Mathematics Teacher; *b:* Wilsons Mills, NC; *m:* Jesse Carl; *c:* William Heath; *ed:* East Carolina Univ (BS) Math 1964, (MAEd) Math 1967; 60 Addl Credits Univ of UT, Fairfield, Manhattan Coll, St Peters; *cr:* Winterville HS Math Tchr 1964-66; East Carolina Univ Math Tchng Asst 1966-67, Math Instr 1967-69; Skyline HS Math Tchr 1969-71; Clarkstown HS South Math Tchr 1971-; *ai:* AFT, NYSUT, CTA, Assn of Math Tchrs of NY St 1971-; NCTM 1964-; New Hempstead Presbyn Church 1984-, Deacon, Sunday Schl Tchr; *office:* Clarkstown South HS 31 Demarest Mill Rd West Nyack NY 10994

BENNETT, GLEN HOWARD, Associate Professor of Biology; *b:* Takoma Park, MD; *ed:* Univ of MD (MA) Schl Cnslng 1988; Univ of MD at Coll Park (PHD) Sci Ed 1993; *cr:* Takoma Acad Sci Tchr 1972-89; LaSierra Acad Sci Tchr 1989-90; Colubia Union Coll Assoc Prof of Bio, Dept Chair 1972-; *ai:* Campus Quality Cncl; Fac Prof Dev Comm; Phi Delta Kappa 1992-; Natl Assn for Rsrch in Sci Tchng 1991-; AAAS; Zapara

Awd of Excl in Tchng 1989, 1995; *office:* Columbia Union Coll 7600 Flower Ave Takoma Park MD 20912

BENNETT, JAMES EDWARD, Science & Health Teacher; *b:* Cleveland, OH; *ed:* OH St Univ (BS) Hlth Ed 1986; Ithaca Coll (MS) PE 1992; *cr:* Padua Franciscan HS Bio, Hlth Tchr 1986-88; Carl F. Shuler Intermediate Schl Sci Tchr 1988-91; Berry MS Sci, Hlth Tchr 1992-; *ai:* Ecology Club Coord; Track Coach; Lebanon Ed Assn 1992-; OH Ed Assn, NEA 1988-; *office:* Berry MS 23 Oakwood Ave Lebanon OH 45036

BENNETT, JOAN WALTERS, Sixth Grade Teacher; *b:* Milwaukee, WI; *m:* Roger V.; *c:* Mary Kate; *ed:* Univ of WI at Milwaukee (BS) Elem Ed, Deaf Ed, Soc Scis; Univ of WI at Milwaukee 12 Hrs; Madison Coll 6 Hrs; Bowling Green St Univ 13 Hrs; *cr:* City of Glendale, Village of Riverhills 2nd-3rd, 6th Grd Tchr 7 Yrs; Charlottesville 1st-2nd Grd Tchr 4 Yrs; Fairfax Cty 1st-4th Grd Tchr, Multiaged 2nd-7th Grd Tchr 5 Yrs; Wild Rose 2nd-3rd Grd Tchr 3 Yrs; Bowling Green 5th-6th Grd Tchr 9 Yrs; *ai:* NEA; Episcopal Church; ASCD, AERA Presentations on Death in Schls; *office:* Kenwood Elem Schl 710 Kenwood Ave Bowling Green OH 43402

BENNETT, JOHN D., Art, American Stud & Hum Tchr; *b:* Newport, NH; *m:* Carol A. Mooney; *c:* David, Sarah; *ed:* Keene St Coll (BED) Art Ed 1967; CANE Inst Dartmouth Coll; Hay Flwshp Williams Coll; *cr:* Fall Mtn Regnl Sch Dist Art Coord 1967-68; Claremont Sch Dist Art Coord 1968-72; Stevens HS Art, Hum Tchr 1972-; *ai:* NHAEA 1967-, Pres 1970-72; Claremont City Cncl 1981-93, Cnclr Ward I; Claremont Opera House Inc 1972-, Pres 1972-86; Conservation Commission 1978-, Chr 1978-86; Hist Dist Commission 1981-, Chair 1990-; Kiwanis Citizen of Yr; NHAEA Art Tchr of Yr; Articles Pub; *office:* Stevens HS 175 Broad St Claremont NH 03743

BENNETT, KATHLEEN JOYCE, English Teacher; *b:* Columbus, OH; *ed:* PA St Univ (BA) Eng, Sec Ed 1968; Johns Hopkins Univ (MLA) His of Ideas 1979; Attnd Bowie St Univ, Cath Univ, Anne Arundel Comm Coll; *cr:* Punxsutawney HS Eng Tchr 1968-69; Bowie HS Eng Tchr 1969-; *ai:* Awds Comm; NEA, MSTA, PGCEA 1969-; NCTE; MD Exch Tchr to Japan 1991.

BENNETT, KAY K., English Teacher; *b:* Belfast, NY; *m:* George E.; *ed:* Houghton Coll (BA) Eng 1959; Bread Loaf Schl of Eng Middlebury Coll (MA) Eng 1966; *cr:* Royalton-Hartland CS Eng Tchr 1960-62; Oakfield-AL CS HS Eng Tchr 1963-67; Fayetteville Manlivs CS HS Eng Tchr 1968-69; Sewanee Military Acad HS Eng Tchr 1970-71; Oakfield-AL CS HS Eng Tchr 1972-; *ai:* Former Drama Dir, Class, Scholastic Bowl Adv; NYSEC; NCTE; Jr Miss Schlsp Prgm 1982-; Genesee Cty 3 Yrs; Meth Church; *office:* Oakfield-Alabama Central Schl 7001 Lewiston Rd Oakfield NY 14125

BENNETT, LINDA ANN, Home Economics Teacher; *b:* Shelby, OH; *w:* Joe Thomas (dec); *ed:* OH St Univ (BS) Home Ec 1972, (MS) Home Ec 1976; *cr:* Xenia City Schls Home Ec Tchr 1972-74; Morehead St Univ Instr 1976-79; Eastern Local Schls Home Ec Tchr 1984-; *ai:* FHA; NEA.

BENNETT, MARY MORRISON, Professor of Biology; *b:* Holyoke, MA; *m:* William J.; *c:* Stephen, Joanne Jennison, Timothy (dec), Thomas; *ed:* Mount Holyoke Coll (AB) Zoology 1951; Women in Sci Prgm 1984; Westfield St Coll 6 Credits Methods, Materials 1972-73; Amer Intnl Coll 3 Credits Philosophy of Ed 1975-76; Chatauqua Courses Hampshire Coll, MIT, MHC 1985-; *cr:* Mt Holyoke Coll His Research Asst 1951-52, 1955-57; Albert Einstein Med Ctr Pathology Lab Tech 1952-54; Holyoke Jr Coll Zoology A&P Lab Instr 1957-63; Agawam Pub Schls Sub Tchr 1973-79; Asnuntuck Comm Coll Part-time Instr 1976-77; Springfield Comm Coll Bio Prof 1978-; *ai:* Fac Rdng Group; Honors Prgm Stu Advising; Curr Comm Bio Dept; Mentor for Pt Time Fac; MA Tchrs Assn, NEA 1983-; HAPS 1993-; Wrote Specialized Lab Manual Human Bio; Produced Video DNA; Commonwealth Citation Outstanding Performance; Enrollment Mngmt Task Force.

BENNETT, MARY ANN E., Computer & Science Teacher; *b:* Rhinebeck, NY; *m:* Wayne T. Blanchard; *c:* Zachary Bennett Blanchard; *ed:* Windham Coll (BA) Eng 1972; Keene St Coll (AS) Cmptr Sci 1984; Antioch NE Grad Schl (MED) Ed 1991; Credit Hrs Univ of VT, Plymouth St Coll, Keene St Coll; *cr:* St of VT Dept of Soc Welfare Income Maintenance Specialist 1973-81; C & S Wholesale Grocers Cmptr Programmer & Operator 1984-86; VT Natl Bank Cmptr Programmer 1986-87; Leland & Gray Eng, Cmptr Tchr 1991-92, Cmptr Sci Tchr 1987-; *ai:* Yrbk Adv; Fac Cncl Rep; WCSU Dist Tech, Tech Comms; VT NEA, Windham Cntrl Tchrs Assn 1987-; VT St Tech Cncl 1989-; So VT Tech Consortium 1995-; Parlar Hill Assn 1986-, Dir; Saxtons River Rec Assn 1992-, Past Bd Mem; *office:* Leland & Gray Union H S Rt 35 The Common Townshend VT 05353*

BENNETT, MICHAEL STEPHEN, Assoc Prof of Social Science; *b:* Madison, WI; *m:* Susan J. Cawan; *c:* Meghan; *ed:* OH St Univ (BS) Soc Admin 1967, (MSW) Soc Work 1969, (PhD) Human Dev 1976; Univ of Akron Post Doctoral Credit Courses; *cr:* Brunswick Bd of Ed Cnslr 1971-74; Univ of Akron Prof 1976-; *ai:* Friends of Univ Lib, Pres; Merit Raise, Prof Dev, Div Acad Affairs, TAC, ABET Evaluation Comms; AAUP 1976-; Advanced Clinical Practice & Amer Bd of Examiners Diplomate; *office:* Univ Of Akron Polsky 131 222 N Main St Akron OH 44235

BENNETT, PAUL I., Biology Instructor; *b:* Kingston Jamaica, West Indies; *ed:* Syracuse Univ (BS) Bio 1983; NY Univ (MA) Scndry Sci Ed 1994; Our Lady of Mercy Med Ctr Clinical Lab Technologist; *cr:* Our Lady of Mercy Med Cntr Lab Technologist 1985-87; Wake-Eden Chrstn Acad Early Chldhd Tchr 1987-89; Mabel Dean Bacon Voc HS Sci, Bio Tchr 1989-92; Truman HS Bio, Sci Tchr 1992-; *ai:* Seekers Chrstn Club Adv; Regents Marathon, Sci Ind Stud Coord; Manhattan Mabel Dean Bacon Tchr of Yr 1990; Bronx Tchr of Yr 1995; *office:* Harry S. Truman HS 750 Baychester Ave Bronx NY 10475*

BENNETT, PAULA GALAT, Fourth Grade Teacher; *b:* Barberton, OH; *m:* Jake; *c:* Jay, Jayne Joyce, Shelley Ference, Ginger Mitchell; *ed:* Akron Univ (BS) Ed 1967, (MS) Math 1979; *ai:* NEA 1967-; CTA 1967-; Martha Jennings Awd; *office:* Ft Island Primary Schl 496 Trunko Rd Fairlawn OH 44333

BENNETT, RAY, 4th Grade Teacher; *b:* Erie, PA; *ed:* Edinboro St Coll (BSEd) Ed 1971, (MSEd) Ed 1975; *cr:* Iroquois Schl Dist Tchr 1972-81; Self Employed Mr B's Italian Baking Co Owner 1981-85; Wattsburg Schl Dist Tchr 1985-; *ai:* Rocket, Bd Games Club; Coach JV Bsktbl, Var Girls Sftbl; Lead Tchr, Presenter; NEA, PSEA 1971-; Eastside YMCA 1968-, Asst Yth Dir; Messiah Luth Coll 1954-, Yth Adv; Golden Apple Awd 1995; *office:* Greene Elem Schl 9333 Tate Rd Erie PA 16509*

BENNETT, RHODA G., English Teacher; *b:* Baltimore, MD; *m:* Arthur M.; *c:* Cheryl, Jeffrey, Laurie B. Augustino; *ed:* Towson Univ (BAEd) Elem Ed & Scndry Ed 1957; Mtg Cty Schls MA Equivalent Scndry Ed 1993; Peabody Conservatory Music Piano; *cr:* Baltimore City Dept of Ed Elem Tchr 1957-61; Hungerford Park Elem Schl Early Problem Identification Spcl Ed 1973-79; Montgomery Village JHS Scndry Eng Tchr 1979-90; Tilden MS Scndry Eng Tchr 1990-; *ai:* Yrbk Spon; Odyssey of the Mind; NHS; MCEA 1980-; MSTA 1980-; NEA 1980-; NCTE 1980-; IRT Montgomery Village JHS; Pub Elem Fantasy Skit; Curr Dev Gifted & Talented 7th-8th Grd Eng; U of MD, Hood Coll, Johns Hopkins Univ Stu Tchr Trainer; *office:* Tilden MS 11211 Old Georgetown Rd Rockville MD 20852*

BENNETT, RICHARD P., Social Studies Teacher; *b:* Ludlow, MA; *c:* Rebecca, Michael, Eric; *ed:* Univ of MA (BA) His 1969, (MA) His 1971; *cr:* Springfield Pub Schls Tchr 1970-; *ai:* AFT 1970-, Bldg Rep; NEA 1980-; MA Audobon Soc, Arcadia Wildlife Sanctuary 1990-; Sartrean Soc of North Amer 1993-; *office:* HS Of Commerce 495 State St Springfield MA 01105*

BENNETT, RICHARD ROBERT,JR., Mathematics Teacher; *b:* Coaldale, PA; *m:* Debra Lee Murphy; *c:* Murphy, Spencer; *ed:* Bloomsburg Univ (BS) Scndry Ed Math 1988; Level I & II Permanent Cert; *cr:* Lehighton Area HS Math 1988-; *ai:* Head Ftbl, JV Bsbl Coach; Sr Class Adv; LAEA 1988-, VP; PSEA, NEA 1988-; Amer Legion 1980-; Amer Hose Fire Co 1975-; *home:* 239 Mauch Chunk St Tamaqua PA 18252

BENNETT, ROBERT CLAY, Sci Dept Chm & Physics Tchr; *b:* Lawrence, MA; *m:* Janice Moran; *c:* Rob, Chris, Elisabeth Nicholson; *ed:* Keene St Coll (BED) Sci 1966; Boston St Coll (MED) Sci Ed 1971; Masters Plus 50 Credits; *cr:* North Andover HS Physics, Chem Tchr 1966-73, Sci Dept Chm 1973-; *ai:* Connecting Teens to Elderly; Schl Reacreditation Comm; Frame Work Comm; NEA 1966-, MAST, NSSSA 1973-; Grange, 1992, Var Chairs; Big Brother Big Sister 1991-; Historic Soc 1993-; NSF Grants; Ipswitch Savings Bank Grant; *office:* North Andover HS 675 Chickering Rd North Andover MA 01845*

BENNETT, RUTH ELIZABETH, British & World Lit Teacher; *b:* New Haven, CT; *ed:* Drew Univ (BA) Classics, Eng LIt 1964; Yale Univ (MA) Rel, Eng, Ed 1966; Attnd Cambridge, Oxford, Exeter, St Andrews, Univ of London; *cr:* Chatham Twp HS Eng, Latin Tchr 1966-67; Belleville Jr HS Eng, Latin Tchr 1967; Millburn HS Eng Tchr 1968-; *ai:* NEA, NJEA 1966-; MEA 1968-; Amer Inst Foreign Stu 1969-75, 1983-88, Cnslr Overseas Mostly Britain; Sabbatical Stu U of London 1982-83 Thomas Hardy Early 20th Century British Lit; Exchange Tchr St John's Church of England Schl, Leatherhead, Surrey, England 1988; *office:* Millburn Sr HS 462 Millburn Ave Millburn NJ 07041*

BENNETT, TIMOTHY JOSEPH, Fifth Grade Teacher; *b:* Fall River, MA; *m:* Annette Bibeau; *c:* Amy, Katie, Scott; *ed:* Univ of MA at Dartmouth (BA) Eng 1971; Cambridge Coll (MED) Integrated Stud 1995; Fitchburg Coll CAGS Pgm Educl Ldrshp & Mgmt; *cr:* Morton Jr HS 8th Grd Eng Tchr 1971-72; Spring Street Schl 5th Grd Tchr 1972-73; F M Silvia Schl 5th Grd Tchr 1973-; *ai:* Sci Peer Coach; PTO Chair; FREA 1971-, Bd of Dir; MTA 1971-; NEA 1971-, Life Mem; Tansey PTO 1980-, Pres; Bristol Cty League 1986-, Rep; Amer Little League 1993-, Coach, Vol of Yr; Green Futures 1994-, Pres; Fall River Pony & Colt 1995-, VP; F R Herald News Apple Awd 1994-95; *office:* Frank M Silvia Elem Sch 128 Hartwell St Fall River MA 02720*

BENNETT-HAYES, JOAN ST CLAIR, Mathematics Teacher; *b:* Springfield, MA; *m:* Thomas F.; *c:* Marcia Bennett Williams, Jeffrey Bennett, Scott Bennett, Stacey Bennett; *ed:* Our Lady of Elms (BA) Math 1963; Univ of Bridgeport (MS) Math 1974; Post Grad Stud in Comp Sci; *cr:* Chicopee Comprehensive HS Math Tchr 1963-64; Wilbur Cross HS Math Tchr 1965-71; Polly McCabe Ctr 1972-78; North Haven HS Math Tchr 1978-79; Guilford HS Math & Comp Sci Tchr 1979-; *ai:* Atomic; NCTM; NEA; *office:* Guilford HS New England Rd Guilford CT 06437*

BENNING, KAREN ANN, Fifth Grade Teacher; *b:* Buffalo, NY; *ed:* Genesee Comm Coll (AA) Lbrl Arts, Ed 1974; SUC at Geneseo (BA) Elem Ed, His 1976, (MS) Early Chldhd Ed 1981; *cr:* Alexander Cntrl Schl Dist Kndgtn, 4th, Pre-First Tchr 1977-81; Springville Griffith Inst 2-5th Grd Gifted, Talented Tchr 1984-90, Fifth Grd Tchr 1990-; *ai:* Fifth Grd Adv; Back to Schl Night Plays; Shared Decision Making Site Comm Mem 1993-95; Griffith Inst Fac Assn 1981-, Negotiation Team; E Aurora Historical Soc 1995-; Natl Trust for Historic Preservation 1994-; *office:* Springville Griffith Inst CSD 307 Newman St Springville NY 14141

BENNINGTON, DOUGLAS R., Social Studies Supvr & Teacher; *b:* Scranton, PA; *m:* Sandra Egen; *c:* Neal D., Ned W.; *ed:* Wilkes Univ (BS) His 1964; Tchrs Coll, Columbia Univ (MA) Soc Stud 1969; 12 Credit Hrs Rutgers Univ; 12 Credit Hrs Jersey City St Coll; *cr:* Bergenfield HS Soc Stud Tchr 1964-, Soc Stud Supvr 1968-; *ai:* NEA, NJEA, BEA 1964-; NJCSS, NCSS 1980-; GBCSS 1980-, Pres 1985; Natl Railway Historical Soc 1975-, VP, Berger Rockland Chapter 1992-95; ACLU Berger Cty 1968-74, Chr, Bergen Cty Chapter 1970-72; William Paterson Coll Scholars Recognition Awd 1992; *office:* Bergenfield HS 80 S Prospect Bergenfield NJ 07621

BENNS, CHARLES E., Technology Education Teacher; *b:* North Olmsted, OH; *m:* Mary Hartman-Benns; *ed:* John Carroll (MED) Admin 1996; *cr:* Mentor Meml Jr HS Tech Tchr 1989-; *ai:* 7th-8th Grd Wrestling, Ftbl Coach; MBC Video Club Adv; NEA, NEOEA, OTEA 1989-; WKYC Channel News Class Act Recipient; *office:* Mentor Meml Jr HS 8979 Mentor Ave Mentor OH 44060

BENNS, EDDIE L., Aerospace Science Commandant; *b:* Chattanooga, TN; *m:* Grace Elizabeth Atkinson; *ed:* TN St Univ (BS) Math, Music 1962; Southern IL Univ (MS) Educl Admin 1976; Cath Univ of Amer (PHD) Educl Admin 1978; *cr:* Potomac HS Aerospace Sci Commandant 14 Yrs; *ai:* AFJROTC Drill Team Supvr; Alpha Phi Alpha 1960-; NAACP 1960-; Math Schlsp to Tuskegee Inst.*

BENOIT, NANCY LOUISE, High School Spanish Teacher; *b:* New Haven, CT; *m:* Raymond; *c:* Michael, Patrick; *ed:* Albertus Magnus Coll (BA) Classics & Span 1965; Wayne St Univ (MED) Scndry Ed 1969; 30 Credits Providence Coll & RI Coll; *cr:* St Vincent de Paul Acad Span Tchr 1965-69; Day Care Ctr Dir & Kndgtn Tchr 1971-73; Northwest Head Start Ed Coord 1978-84; St Teresa Schl 6th Grd Tchr 1986-88; St Raphael Acad HS Span Tchr 1989-; *ai:* Jr Class & Model Legislature Moderator; RI Frgn Lang Tchrs Assn 1992-; Thundermist Hlth Assocs 1975-, Past Pres; Woon Headstart 1985-; Woon Neighborhood Dev Corp 1986-; Tri Hab Substance Abuse Pgm 1992; Blackstone River Vly Natl Heritage Corridor Comm 1992-, Sec; Elected RI House of Rep Serve as Chair of the Hlth, Ed & Welfare Comm 1984-; *office:* St Raphael Acad 123 Walcott St Pawtucket RI 02860

BENOWITZ, CORINNE JOAN, Mathematics Teacher; *b:* Brooklyn, NY; *m:* Gordon; *c:* Cory, Lance; *ed:* Hunter Coll (BA) Math 1960; Post Coll (MS) Math 1966; Attnd Hostra Univ, Vermilion Coll; *cr:* Bellmore Kennedy Cntrl HS Math Tchr 1961-68; SUNY at Farmingdale Adj Math Tchr 1979-83; Sewanhaka Cntrl HS Math Tchr, GATE Mentor 1985-; *ai:* Math Team; Tech Mentor; Math Fair Mentor, Judge; RAVE Comm; Math Magazine; NCTM 1963-; AMTNYS 1986-; NEA 1985-; NCJML 1965-, Pres; United Cerebral Plasy of Nassau 1960-, Treas; Plainedge Aux; PTSA 1980-, Pres; Tchr of Yr 1995-; Tandy Schlr; Outstdng Tchr; Amer Legion; Citation of Appreciation for Outstndg Svs; Supts Grant Educl Innovation; *office:* Elmont Memorial HS 555 Ridge Rd Elmont NY 11003*

BENOY, ROBERT FRANK, Fifth Grade Teacher; *b:* Lynxville, WI; *w:* Margaret Irene Blanchard (dec); *c:* Thomas; *ed:* OH Univ (BSEd) Elem Ed 1973, (MED) Elem Ed 1978; Educl Admin Elem Principalship 1979; *cr:* Southern Local Schl 6th-7th Grd Tchr 1973-75; Logan Hocking Schl 5th-6th Grd Tchr 1975-; *ai:* Safety Patrol Supvr; Peer Mediation Trainer, Supvr; Southern Local Ed Assn 1973-75, Pres Elect; Logan Ed Assn 1975-, Bldg Rep; OH Ed Assn, NEA 1973-; Comm Mediation Svc Comm 1995-; *home:* 860 E Front St Logan OH 43138

BENSE, ROGER STEVEN, Assistant Principal; *b:* Oceanside, NY; *m:* Marie; *c:* Danielle, Jaclyn; *ed:* Adelphi Univ (BA) Liberal Arts 1969; Stony Brook Univ (MA) Liberal Arts 1973; Long Island Univ (SAS) & (SDA) Ed Admin 1992; 15 Hrs of In Svc Courses Various Subjects; 6 Hrs Methods of Maintaing Discipline; 3 Hrs Project ZEST at Bronx Zoo S Effectiveness of Zoo Curricula in Classroom; *cr:* Deer Park Schl S 1969-90, Tchr & Dean 1990-91, Sci Chm 1991, Admin Asst 1991-9 Prin 1992-; *ai:* STEP Prgm Coord; Stu Leadership Confs Coord; De Tchrs Assn 1969-91 Bldg Rep; Natl Sci Fnd Grant; Tchr Rep Ba Lomb Sci Awd; Natl Sci Fnd ZEST Report; Recognized for 99.8 Rate on Bio Regents 11 Yrs; Sci Club Dir 1978-90.*

BENSING, CLAIRE MCCALL, History Teacher; *b:* Mahanoy C *ed:* East Stroudsburg Univ (BS) Eng; Millersville Univ (MED Supvr; ATTND Temple Univ; *cr:* Cedar Crest Mid 8th Grd T Knowledge Master Coach; Dir of Drama Club; NEA; CLEA; Hi Preservation Soc; Lebanon Historical Soc & Comm Theatre; Jr W Club; *office:* Cedar Crest MS 101 E Evergreen Rd Lebanon PA 17

BENSON, BARBARA J., Art Chairperson & Teacher; *b:* Chester, Robert; *c:* Jason, Erin, Joshua; *ed:* Philadelphia Coll of Art Advertising 1965; *cr:* Hallmark Greeting Cards Artist 1965-6 Brothers Layout Artist 1967-70; Archdiocese of Philadelphia Schl Art Tchr & Chprsn 1979-; *ai:* Fine Arts Curr Comm; Mid Sts Curr Comm Svc Corp Moderator; AFFIRM Stu Assistance Pgm; Stage NCEA 1995-; *office:* Archbishop Carroll HS 211 Matson Ford Rd PA 19087

BENSON, DEE ANN (DAGWELL), Physical Education & Art T Kokomo, IN; *m:* David L.; *c:* Bethany, Tiffany; *ed:* Grace Coll (BS Ed 1987; 2 Hrs Grad Credit Ashland Univ; *cr:* Chapel Hill Chrstn S Grd Tchr 1987-90, PE, Art Tchr 1990-; *ai:* Young Author's Day Chm Bsktbl Coach 1987-91; ACSI 1987-; Grace Coll Outstdng Prospecti Awd 1987; Who's Who Among Amers Colls & Univs 1987; *office:* Hill Chrn School-North 1090 Howe Ave Cuyahoga Falls OH 4422

BENSON, DIANE L., 9th & 11th Grd English Tchr; *b:* Jamestow *ed:* Jamestown Comm Coll (AA) Eng 1964; SUNY at Fredonia (B 1966, (MA) Eng 1972; 36 Credit Hrs Beyond MA; *cr:* Ben Franklin Eng Tchr 1966-67; Southwestern MS Eng Tchr 1967-70; Frewsbur Schl Eng Tchr 1970-; *ai:* Oratorical Coach; NY St United Tchrs Frewsburg Fac Assn 1970-; Amer Assn of Univ Women 1971-; Historical Soc 1984-; Amer Legion Oratorical Coaching Awds; Frewsburg Cntrl HS Institute St Frewsburg NY 14738

BENSON, ERIC WILLIAM, Earth Science Teacher; *b:* Yonkers, Doreen K. Reilly; *ed:* SUNY at Buffalo (BA) Geology 1990; 12 Cre Curr & Instruction Pace Univ; *cr:* St Nicholas of Tolentire S 1990-91; Mt St Michael Acad Earth Sci Tchr 1991-; *ai:* Chess Club Team Moderator; Frosh Ftbl Coach Archbishop Stepinac HS; NCEA *office:* Mount St Michael Acad 4300 Murdock Ave Bronx NY 1046

BENSON, GARY RICHARD, Fourth Grade Teacher; *b:* Buffalo, Mary Wehrum; *c:* Scott, Mark; *ed:* SUNY Coll at Buffalo (BS) E 1967, (MS) Elem Ed 1971; Rdng, Children's Lit Post Degree Stud *cr:* Buffalo Pub Schl Tchr 1967-69; Orchard Park Cntrl Schls Tchr *ai:* Sci, Lang Arts Instrl Ldr; Stu Cncl Adv; Textbook Comms; N AFT.*

BENSON, GORDON C., 7th-8th Grade Science Teacher; *b:* Ma PA; *m:* Brenda Ensor; *c:* Bradley, Chad, Amie; *ed:* Mansfield St C Scndry Ed 1963; Birmingham Southern Coll (MAT) Scndry Ed 196 Hrs Univ of KS 1965, Johns Hopkins Univ 1967-69, Univ of MD 1 Catonsville Jr HS 7th-9th Grd Gen Sci Tchr 1963-68; Pikesville 7th-9th Gen Sci Tchr 1968-84; Hereford Jr-Sr HS 8th Grd Gen S 1984; Hereford MS 7th-8th Grd Gen Sci Tchr 1984-; *ai:* Girls Soccer 1990-93, 1995, Track 1996; NSF Grant 1965-68; *office:* H MS 712 Corbett Rd Monkton MD 21111

BENSON, HOPE M. (LAJEUNESSE), Chemistry Teach Springfield, MA; *m:* Thomas J.; *c:* Karyn, Lauren, Thomas R.; *ed:* St Coll (MA) Ed 1982; Math Tchng Cert; *cr:* Notre Dame HS S 1981-82; Allentown HS Sci Tchr 1982-86; Hamilton High East S 1992-; *ai:* NJ Sci League Adv; New Tchr Mentor; NJEA, NEA; Hamilton High School East 2900 Klockner Rd Trenton NJ 08690

BENSON, JAMES PATRICK,JR., English Teacher; *b:* Woodsid *ed:* New Paltz St Coll (BA) Eng 1992; Attending St John's Univ John's Prep HS Eng Tchr 1992-; *ai:* Var Bsbl Coach; Co-Moderator Home Bsktbl Games Announcer; NCTE 1995-; *office:* Saint Preparatory HS 21-21 Crescent St Astoria NY 11105*

BENSON, JEAN GARTNER, Retired Elementary Teacher; *b:* MA; *m:* Kirk L.; *c:* Judy Harrold, Kirk Jr., Douglas, Glen; *ed:* Univ (BA) Sociology 1946; Case-Western Reserve (MA) Ed 1969; Attn of Akron; *cr:* Claridon Local Schl 7th-8th Grd Tchr 1965-67; Be Schl Elem Tchr 1967-87; *home:* 12164 Bardwell Dr Chesterland OH

BENSON, JOHN W., 5th Grade Teacher; *b:* Abington, PA; *m:* K L.; *c:* Mc Kenna, Devon; *ed:* Lock Haven Univ (BSEd) Elem Ed Masters Equivalency; *cr:* Council Rock Schl Dist Tchr 1977-; *ai:* St Drama Clubs; After Schl Sports; Grd Level Chm; Conflict Res CREA, NEA, PSEA 1977-.

BENSON, KATHLEEN J., Biology Teacher; *b:* Long Branch, George J.; *c:* William, Evan, Julie; *ed:* Drew Univ (BA) Botany 196 Stroudsburg Univ (MED) Microbiology 1992; Courses in Bioche Cell Pscyh, Cytology, Limnology; Summer Ins Dept Molecu Princeton Univ 1994; *cr:* Sandoz Pharmaceuticals Agro chem 1 Celaneze Phys Testing 1987-88; Warren Hills MS Sci Tchr 1988 Hunterdon HS Sci Tchr 1988-; *ai:* NJ Sci League Acad Coach; NEA Rep; NJSTA 1988-; North Jersey Orchid Soc 1993-; Somerset A 1994-; NJSBA 6 Yrs, Pres, VP, Mem; *office:* North Hunterdon H State Route 31 Annandale NJ 08801

BENSON, THOMAS WILLIAM, HS Social Studies Instruc Camdon, NJ; *m:* Terri; *c:* Kelli, Brian, Katie; *ed:* Stockton St Co Pol Sci 1976; *cr:* Trenton HS Tchr 1977-; *ai:* Class Adv 1982, 1984 1994, 1999; Ladies Var Tennis, Track Coach; NEA, NJEA 1977-, As CCEA; BHPEA; Renaissane Comm 1995-; Gloucester Twp Girls At Ath Booster Club; Soc Stud Mid Sts Chprsn; Liason to VFW V Democracy Contest; *office:* Triton Regional HS 250 Schube Runnemede NJ 08078

BENT, MARY ARTHUR, French Teacher; *b:* New York City, NY John's Univ (BA) Span, Fr 1936, (MA) Fr 1941; NY St Permanent A Oral Work 1935; Post Grad Laval Univ, Quebec Fr 6 Credits 1945; Coll Scndry Schl Coll Articulation 3 Credits 1964; Univ de Paris 1 St Brendans Diocesan HS Fr Tchr 1935; St Joseph's Jr HS Fr Tchr 1 1944-47; St Agnes Seminary HS Fr Tchr 1939-43; St Angela Hal Tchr 1943-44, 1947-49; St Mary Louis Acad HS Fr Tcrh 1948 Cecilia's Elem Schl 1-8 Grd Princ 1964-70; Sacred Heart HS Fr, Sp 1970-; Manhattan Coll; Brentwood Coll Summers, Saturdays; *ai:* I Yrs; AATF 25 Yrs.

BENT, SANDRA DIANE, Science Department Head; *b:* Swam MA; *ed:* Atlantic Union Coll (BA) Chem 1962; Walla Walla Coll (M 1972; Ed-Admin 6 Hrs; Med Schl 2 Yrs; *cr:* So Mecklenburg HS B 1972-77; Northfield Jr Acad Tchr 1977-80; Greater Boston Acad Librn 1966-71, 1980-; *ai:* Church Treas; Yrbk Spon; K-12 Curr NSTA 1984-; NABT; MAST; Zappora Awd for Excl in Tchng; Greater Boston Acad 20 Woodland Rd Stoneham MA 02180*

EY, DIANE MARIE, History Teacher; *b:* Buffalo, NY; *c:* Brian eld, Deborah Langenfeld; *ed:* SUNY at Buffalo (BA) His 1976, s 1989; 90 Credit Hrs PHD Prgm; *cr:* Heritage Spec Ed Tchr 1 Yrs; , Coll Level Sub Tchr 2 Yrs; SUNY Tchng Asst 2 Yrs; Mt Mercy s Tchr 6 Yrs, Archival Rsrch Asst, Ind Contract, Prof of His y; *ai:* Acad Bd of Trustees; Fac Rep Curr Framework Comm; HS 1994-, Home Schl Assn Mem; Infant of Pregue Schl 1986-; Mount Mercy Acad 88 Red Jacket Pky Buffalo NY 14220*

EY, JOHN, Science Teacher; *b:* Upland, PA; *m:* Susan Koster; *ed:* Univ (BS) Chem, Bio 1967; Temple Univ (MS) Sci Ed 1976; 30 edits; *cr:* Barrett Jr HS Sci Tchr 1967-68; Lea Jr HS Sci Tchr ; Overbrook HS Sci Tchr 1969-; *ai:* Asst Ftbl Coach; Grd Chprsn r Office; AFT 1967-; *office:* Overbrook HS 59th & Lancaster Ave phia PA 19131

EY, PAUL, English Teacher; *b:* Torrington, CT; *m:* Karen Anne; yle; *ed:* Univ of CT (BA) Eng 1973; Cntrl CT St Univ (MA) Eng n Yr Ed 1980; *cr:* Har Bur MS Eng Tchr, Lewis Mills HS Eng Tchr *ai:* Mentor, Cooperating Tchr; NEA, CEA 1976-; Elks; Torrington al Soc, Ed Comm; Army Reserve 10 Yrs; Free Lance Writer, is Pieces Pub; *office:* Lewis Mills HS RR 4 Burlington CT 06013

N, GLORIA LEGGETT, Art Teacher; *b:* Philadelphia, PA; *m:* d Gregory; *c:* Anthony; *ed:* Winston-Salem Univ (BA) Art Ed *r:* J. H. Moore Elem Schl Art Tchr 22 Yrs; *ai:* Immaculate ion Dance Ensemble Dir; Dance Coord; Pub Schl Dance Comm of phia; BSA, Comm Chm; Germantown Settlement Day Camp ir, Outstdng Achvmt; *office:* J Hampton Moore Elem Schl Tyson Aves Philadelphia PA 19111

N, ROBERT HUGH,JR., Criminal Justice Instructor; *b:* , NY; *m:* Penny Lynn Suda; *c:* Robert III; *ed:* Onondaga Comm AS) Criminal Justice; St Univ at Onconta (BS) Bio & Physics; Sci; Federal Emergency Mgmt; *cr:* TASIS Criminalist 1979-; Forensic Lab Forensic Scientist 1986-; Corning Comm Coll Sci Instr 1986-; DCMO BOCES Criminal Justice Instr 1986-; *ai:* NEANY 1986-; Amer Soc Law Enforcement Trainers 1992-; Natl ssn 1960-; Rotary Intnl 1975-, Pres, Bd Trustees; United Meth 1986-, Bd Trustees; Amer Legion 1987-; BOCES Tchr of Yr; Book: ok for Document Examinations; *home:* RR 1 Box 199B Sherburne 50*

, CHRISTOPHER T., Social Studies Teacher; *b:* Lebanon, PA; *m:* nn Beattie; *ed:* LaSalle Univ (BA) Scndry Ed in Soc Stud 1989; t Cert Granted by St of PA; 24 Grad Credit Hrs; *cr:* Lancaster Cath Stud Tchr 1989-; *ai:* HS Var Ftbl Equipment Mgr; Boys Bsktbl oach; Natl Cath Tchrs Assn 1989-; City of Lebanon FD 1984-, Vol; Week 1992; Newspaper Intelligencer Journal Teenage & Weekend Section; *office:* Lancaster Catholic HS 650 Juliette Ave Lancaster 1

, WESLEY EARL, Professor of Chemistry; *b:* Spokane, WA; *m:* Moyer; *c:* Daniel W., Caroline Gardiner, Chaunee Francis, Cheryl ght, Cindy Martin; *ed:* Whitman Coll (BA) Chem 1965; Univ of er (PHD) Organic Chem 1971; *cr:* Alfred Univ Instr 1970-71, Asst 71-75, Assoc Prof 1975-83, Prof 1983-; *ai:* Alpha Phi Omega Svc ty Adv; Lbrl Arts Fac Cncl 1994- Chair; Acad Advising & ic Standards Comms; Amer Chemical Soc 1967-, Local Section lfred Fire Dept 1971-, Captain & VP; Alfred Comm Chest 1980-, Vice Chair; Union Univ Church 1981-, Elder; Excl in Tchng Awds ; *office:* Alfred Univ Saxon Dr Alfred NY 14802*

D, ANTHONY D.,JR., Math & Computer Sci Professor; *b:* Lynn, Louise Mc Nertney; *ed:* The Citadel (BS) Math 1964; Western Univ (MA) Math 1967; Case Western Reserve Univ (PHD) Math : Air Force Inst of Tech Asst Math Prof 1968-72; King's Coll Assoc Math 1972-76, Math Dept Chair 1983-86, Math & CS Prof 1976-; Cmptr Sci Club, MAA Stu Chptr Adv; Cmptr Graphics Lab, Math ab Dir; Planning & Budget, Tech Comms; Mathematical Assn of 964; Amer Mathematical Soc 1968-; Amer Computing Machinery Brockhill Assn 1972-; EPADEL 1972-, Newsletter Ed; O'Hara Prof of Sci; Articles Pub; *office:* Kings Coll N River St Barre PA 18711*

DELLI, WILLIAM RANDAL, Social Studies Teacher; *b:* wn, PA; *m:* Janet Tenpas; *c:* Laura Ann, William Jay; *ed:* WV Univ ndry Ed 1979; Wilkes Univ (MS) Ed 1989; *cr:* Upper Perkiomen Stud Tchr 1981-87; North Penn HS Soc Stud Tchr 1987-; *ai:* Cultural Club Adv; NEA 1981-; *office:* North Penn Sr HS 1340 S orge Rd Lansdale PA 19446

DINELLI, BARBARA KEPNER, Chemistry Teacher; *b:* , PA; *m:* John L.; *c:* James, David, Beth; *ed:* Juniata COll (BS) 962; IN Univ Chem; Saint Francis Coll Tchng Cert Ed 1988; *cr:* NJ Medicine Rsrch Chemist 1964-66; Jefferson Med Coll Rsrch 1966-68; Bishop Guilfoyle HS Chem Tchr 1988-89; Altoona Area m Tchr 1989-; *ai:* Stu Assistence Intervention Team Mentor; PSEA, NEA 1989-; Blair Cty Med Aux 1974-, Safety Chm; Articles *ice:* Altoona Area HS 1415 6th Ave Altoona PA 16602*

NI, MARYANN LEDONNE, Teacher & Asst Administrator; *b:* gh, PA; *m:* Gerald R.; *c:* Dana, Drew, Dawn; *ed:* Seton Hill y, Ed; Saint Vincent Ed; Carlow Ed; Dev Classes; SAP Trng; *cr:* id, Greensburgh Pittsburgh Dioceses Tchr 1965-, Asst Admin *ai:* Dev SAP Chprsn; PA Jr Acad of Sci Staff Mem; Core Team NCEA 1970-, Chprsn; Eng Tchrs of Amer Chprsn; Outstdng Tchr 74.*

NIER, DORIS ANNE, Family & Consumer Science Tchr; *b:* OH; *m:* F. Nace; *c:* Barry, Bruce, Brian, Sherri Stewart; *ed:* OH St A) Home Ec Ed 1954; Ashland Univ (MS) Curr 1982; Rdng Skills : Butler Local Schls Home Ec Voc Tchr 1954-55; Shelby Schsl Sub ator 1959-69; Lexington Local Schls Voc Home Ec Tchr 1969-90, Consumer Sci, Rdng Tchr 1990-; *ai:* NEA 1969-; OHEA, AHEA)AFCS, AFS 1995-; Dir Logos Church 1992-, Yth Dir; *home:* 3660 Rd Shelby OH 44875

NE, JANICE, English Teacher & Dept Chprsn; *b:* New York City, St John's Univ (BA) Eng 1982, (MA) Eng 1984; *cr:* The Mary cad Eng Tchr & Head Dept 1984-; *ai:* Fac Ed "Spring Magazine"; & Cath Tchrs Assn 1984-; *office:* The Mary Louis Acad 176-21 d Terr Jamaica Estates NY 11432

IDES, M. BENEDICTA,IHM, College Professor; *b:* New York, Marywood Coll (BM) Music Ed 1955; Univ of Notre Dame (MM) ogy 1962; Univ of Pittsburgh (PHD) Musicology 1973; Ch M Amer Organists; Post Grad Stud The Cath Univ of Amer; Our Lady of niv at San Antonio; Univ of TX at Austin; *cr:* Various Elem & Sec Music Specialist 1948-70; Marywood Coll Prof 1973-; *ai:* t-Marian Convent, Regina Hall; Acad Adv to Stdnts; AAUP 1974-; sicologicals Soc 1970-; Am Guild of Organists; Natl Pastoral ns 1976-; Diocesan Liturgical Comm 1985-, Sec; NEH Grant 1982; abbatical 1992-93; Review for Modern Liturgy; *office:* Marywood 00 Adams Ave Scranton PA 18509

CIK, SUSAN J. (KNECHTEL), English & Journalism Teacher; *b:* , IL; *m:* Andrew G.; *c:* Andrew G. IV, Tara Lynn; *ed:* Miami Univ ng, Scndry Ed 1969; Sacred Heart Univ (MED) Scndry Ed, His 1989; *cr:* Trumbull HS Eng, Jrnlsm Tchr 1969-74, 1992-;; Trumbull Continuing Ed SAT Verbal Prep Tchr 1979-95; Hometown Publications Freelance Writer 1989-; Intnl Editing Wkshps Ed, Presenter 1993-; *ai:* Yrbk Adv; Constitutional Knowledge Competition Eng Tchr Coach 1992-; Publicity Liaison Local Newspaper; Sunshine Club Tchr Rep; NEA, CEA, TEA 1969-74, 1991-; NCTE 1993-; CT Press Assn 1994-; Fox TV Channel 61 Kids' News Tchr 1994-; Tri Sigma 1967-, CT Alumna Chptr Founder 1994; Trumbull Arts Festival 1991-, Lit Competition Chm 1991-93, Lit Judge 1994-, Penworks Ed 1991-93; Amer Scholastic Press Assn 1st Pl Yrbk 1994-95; Journal Pub 1989; Yale Sci, Hum Awd 1973; 1600 Newspaper Stories, Photographs Pub; Show! Don't Tell! How to Personalize College Applications 1993 Ed; *office:* Trumbull HS 72 Strobel Rd Trumbull CT 06611

BERG, HARVEY ALLEN, Technology Professor; *b:* Brooklyn, NY; *m:* Marja-Terttu Heinonen; *ed:* Rensselaer Polytechnic Inst (BA) Architecture 1955; Fulbright Schlsp Helsinki Finland; *cr:* Newark Coll of Engrng Rutgers Univ Instr 1968-70; Orange Cty Comm Coll Asst Prof 1985-; *ai:* OCCC Tech Awd Pgm Dir & Spon; Soc of Amer Magicians 1988-; Hudson Vly Builders Assn 1990-; Orange Cty Chamber of Commerce 1995-; Prin in Architectural Practice 35 Yrs; Licensed Registered Architect & Prof Civil Engr; Natl Architectural Design Awd; Numerous St, Regnl & Cty Design Awds; Endorsement of Design by Pres of US; Patent for Fndtn Design; *office:* Orange County Comm Coll 115 South St Middletown NY 10940

BERG, JILL, Assoc Prof Nursing & Health; *b:* Brooklyn, NY; *m:* Bruce; *c:* Cate, Alex; *ed:* Brooklyn Coll (BA) Eng 1978; Syracuse Univ (BSN) Nrsng 1980; Univ of Plonda (MSN) Nrsng 1986; Univ of Pittsburgh (PHD) Nrsng 1995; *cr:* IUP Instr 1988-89, Asst Prof 1989-93, Assoc Prof 1993-; *ai:* Class Adv of 1991, 1993 & 1997; Sigma Theta Tau; Soc Behavior of Med; ENRS & ATS; NINR Predoctoral Trng Awd Grant; Numberous Articles Pub; *office:* Indiana Univ Of PA 228 Johnson Hall Indiana PA 15701

BERG, LENNIE HOWARD, Social Studies Teacher; *b:* Bronx, NY; *ed:* Adelphi Univ (BA) His 1986; Queens Coll (MS) Scndry Ed Soc Stud 1995; *cr:* August Mertin HS Soc Stud Tchr 1986-; *ai:* AFT 1986-; Phi Alpha Theta; *office:* August Martin HS 156-10 Baisley Blvd Jamaica NY 11434

BERG, LESLIE RENEA, Mathematics Teacher; *b:* Warren, PA; *m:* Timothy Craig; *ed:* Gannon Univ (BS) Math 1991; Addl 15 Grad Credits Med Guid, Cnslng Bowie Univ, 3 Credits in Math Ed Univ of MD; *cr:* Frewsburg Cntrl Schl Math Tchr 1992; Univ of MD Math Camp Cnslr 1993; Great Mills HS Math Tchr 1992-; *ai:* Chrldng Coach; Class of 1995 Spon; NEA 1988-; MD St Tchrs Assn 1991-; Ed Assn of St Mary's Cty 1991-; *office:* Great Mills HS Great Mills Rd Great Mills MD 20634*

BERG, SHEILA BLUMENTHAL, Earth Science Teacher; *b:* Brooklyn, NY; *m:* Jerome David; *c:* Eileen, Allison; *ed:* SUNY at Stony Brook (MSLA) Ed 1976; CUNY at Queens Coll (MS) Ed 1969; SUNY at Cortland (BS) Elem Ed 1964; Recertification Courses Earth Sci Suffolk Comm, Stony Brook; *cr:* San Remo Elem Schl Tchr 1964-71; Our Lady of Mercy Acad Earth Sci Tchr 1986-; *ai:* Sci Ecology Club Moderator, Founder; Photography Club, Stu Cncl Moderator; NYSTA 1986-; SCSTA 1990-; *home:* 4 Veronica Ct Smithtown NY 11787

BERGAN, LOIS DASCOMB, Fourth Grade Teacher; *b:* Olean, NY; *m:* Timothy J.; *c:* Bonnie, Janeen; *ed:* Cazenovia Coll (AA) Lbrl Arts 1970; St Bonaventure Univ (BS) Elem Ed 1973, (MS) Advanced Tchr Ed 1978; *cr:* Allegany-Limestone Cntrl Schl Elem Tchr 1974-; *ai:* NEA 1973-; Humphrey Town Bd 1989-; Tchr of Yr Awd Alcas Cutlery; *office:* Allegany-Limestone Cntrl Schl N 4th St Allegany NY 14706

BERGASSI, PAULINE ELIZABETH, English Teacher; *b:* Providence, RI; *m:* Henry; *c:* Cheryl, David, Michael; *ed:* RI Coll (BA) Eng & Scndry 1972; Anna Maria Coll (MED) Eng & Scndry 1991; Curr Planning & Multicultural Ed Prof Dev Seminars; *cr:* North Smithfield Jr-Sr HS Eng Tchr 1972-75; Shrewsbury HS Eng Tchr 1985-87; St Marys HS Hum Dept Chair 1987-; *ai:* Jrnlsm Adv; Trips Abroad Adv & Chaperone; Delta Kappa Gamma 1990-, Schlsp Comm; Natl Tchr of Yr 1990; Carnegie Inst Grant; *office:* St Mary's Catholic Schl 50 Richland St Worcester MA 01610*

BERGBOM, JOANNE PICCARELLA, English Tchr & Stu Act Dir; *b:* Brooklyn, NY; *m:* Bruce; *c:* Kristin, Nancy Bergbom Nelson, Bart, Brad; *ed:* Hofstra Univ (BA) 1965, (MS) Scndry Ed 1985; 33 Credits at Cornell Univ 1961-63; Lincoln Ctr Summer Inst for Aesthetic Ed; *cr:* Floral Park Memorial HS Eng Tchr 1983; H. Frank Carey HS Eng Tchr & Dir of Stu Act 1983-; *ai:* Stu Act Dir & Fac Schlsp Comm; STAR Adv; Drug Free Schl Comm; NEA, NCTE & Sewanhaka Fed of Tchrs 1983-; PTSA GCP Schl 1969-, Pres, Honorary Life Mem, NHP HS 1974-, Pres, Disting Svc, Sewanhaka Cncl 1970-, Pres, Natl Life Mem, H.F. Carey 1983-, Tchr Rep, Nassau Ldrshp; Nassau Cncl Girl Scouts 1969-, Ldr & Trainer; STAR Mini Grant; HFC Tchr of the Yr 1992, George M Estabrook Distngd Svc Awd, Edctr of The Month Awd; Acad Tchr of the Yr 1993 NY St Tchr Cert Exams Grdr; Howard Nordahl Comm Svc Awd; *office:* H Frank Carey HS 230 Poppy Ave Franklin Square NY 11010*

BERGEL, STEVEN P., Science Teacher; *b:* New York City, NY; *m:* Patricia A.; *c:* Afton P.; *ed:* PA St Univ (BS) Sec Ed 1967, (MED) Earth Sci 1970, (PHD) Acad Curr & Instruction 1976; *cr:* St Joseph's Coll Geology Instr 1991-; South Country Schl Dist Sci Tchr 1967-; *ai:* Natl Jr Honor Soc Adv; NYSUT 1973-; Bellport TA 1968-; *office:* Bellport Sr HS 205 Beaver Dam Rd Brookhaven NY 11719

BERGEN, JAMES LYMAN, High Schl Mathematics Teacher; *b:* St Georges, Bermuda; *m:* Nancy Brewster Griffin; *c:* Jeffrey, Kevin, Katherine; *ed:* Susquehanna Univ (BA) Math 1973; PA St U 24 Credit Hrs; *cr:* Montoursville Area Math Tchr 23 Yrs; *ai:* Head Ftbl Coach; Stu Assistance Team Head; Weight Lifting Club Supvr; Org of Montoursville Edctrs 1985-, Bd Mem; Coach of Yr 5 Times; *home:* 795 Weaver St Montoursville PA 17754*

BERGEN, MICHAEL L., Math Teacher; *b:* Brooklyn, NY; *m:* Elaine Waksman; *c:* Robin Michelle; Marc Kenneth; *ed:* Brooklyn Coll (BA) Math 1965; Yeshiva Univ (MS) Math, Ed 1970; 60 Post Masters Credits in Math, Ed, Admin at Various Colls, Univs; *cr:* Peace Corps Colombia SA Math Tchr 1965-67; Boys HS Math Tchr 1967-68; John Jay HS Math Tchr 1969-71; Sheepshead Boys HS Math Tchr 1971; West Babylon Sr HS Math Tchr 1971-; *ai:* West Babylon Tchrs Assn 1971-, Past Treas, HS Bldg Exec; NYSUT 1967-; Peace Corps Vol Colombia 1965-67; *office:* West Babylon Sr HS 500 Great East Neck Rd West Babylon NY 11704

BERGEN, SUSAN E., 11th Grd Amer History Teacher; *b:* Pittsburgh, PA; *c:* Bill, Ann, Ned; *ed:* Miami Univ (BA) Scndry Ed 1960; Attnd Kent St Univ, Univ of CO & John Carroll Univ; *cr:* Euclid HS Eng Tchr 1960-65; Solon HS Amer His Tchr 1982-; *ai:* CORE Group for At-Risk Stdnts; Amer His DC Trip Coord & Chaperone; Soc Stud Curr Comm; Solon Ed Assn 1982-, Bldg Rep 1 Yr; Cooperative Learning Trng Wkshps; Coalition for Amer Schls Comm; Inter-Disciplinary Wkshp; Chem Dependency Trng Wkshp; Advanced Placement Wkshp; Comm Wkshp; Diad Tchng; *office:* Solon HS 33600 Inwood Dr Solon OH 44139*

BERGER, CLAIRE NACHLIS, Assistant Professor of English; *m:* Joseph; *c:* Jonathan, Steven, Ellen, Neil, Linda, Loretta; *ed:* Penn St Univ (BA); Rowen Coll (MA); *cr:* Camden HS Eng Tchr; Xerox Cmptr Svcs Tech Writer; Camden Cty Coll Eng Asst Prof; *ai:* Honors Prgm; Curr Comm; Mid Sts Task Force; Lit Live; NEA; General Ed Grant; Pub Poet; *office:* Camden County Coll PO Box 200 College Dr Blackwood NJ 08021

BERGER, DIANE THOMAS, Chemistry Director; *b:* Brooklyn, NY; *m:* Mitchel V.; *c:* Alphonse F. Vota, David A. Vota; *ed:* St John's Univ (BS) Chem 1964; Coll of Staten Island (MS) Sci Ed 1982; Prof Cert Admin, Sup 1990; *cr:* Tottenville HS Tchr 1980-85; New Dorp HS Tchr 1985-89; Staten Island Tech HS Tchr, Research 1989-; *ai:* Sci Club; UFT 1980-; PDK 1993-; Urban League 1993-; *office:* Staten Island Tech HS 486 Clawson St Staten Island NY 10306*

BERGER, LORRAINE MARTIN, Spanish Teacher; *b:* Brooklyn, NY; *m:* Clyde L.; *c:* Brain, Madeline; *ed:* Nassau Comm Coll (AA) Lbrl Arts 1971; SUC NY at New Paltz (BA) Elem Ed & Span 1973; SUNY at Stonybrook (MA) Lbrl Stud 1976; 9 Post Grad Credits; *cr:* Smithtown Elem Schl 5th & 3rd Grd, Kndgtn & Jr HS Span Tchr 1973-77; Noahs Ark Nursery Schl Tchr for 4 Yr Olds 1983-84; Plainedge Pub Schls MS & HS Span Tchr 1986-; *ai:* Span Hnr Soc; Site Based Mgmt Team Chprsn; NYSAFLT 1988-; LILT 1988-; AATSP 1988-; Huntington Choral Soc 1980-; Named by Stdnts as a Positive Influence 1992-95; *home:* 25 Lewis Ct Huntingtn Sta NY 11746

BERGER, MARK, Spanish & French Teacher; *b:* Winthrop, MA; *ed:* Boston St Tchrs (BSEd) Fr His 1960; Boston Univ (MED) Ed 1967; Berlitz Lang Schl; *cr:* Boston Eng HS Fr & Span Tchr 1960-69; Boston Latin Schl Fr & Span Tchr 1969-.

BERGER, MARTIN, History Professor; *b:* Columbus, OH; *m:* Louisa Rae Lipari; *c:* Daniel, Emily, Barbara; *ed:* Columbia (BA) His 1964; Pittsburgh (MA) His 1965, (PHD) His 1969; *ai:* Adv His Club; Phi Alpha Theta; Phio Ed Assn, OH Acad of His 1970-; Amer Historical 1967-; First Unitarian Church 1972-, Sec; Engels Armies & Revolution 1977; *office:* Youngstown St Univ 410 Wick Ave Youngstown OH 44555

BERGER, MARY BUTLER, Soc Stud Tchr & Dept Chair; *b:* Dayton, OH; *m:* Roy J.; *c:* Michael, Laura, Nicholas; *ed:* Wright St Univ (BSED) Soc Stud Comp 1972; 30 Hrs; *cr:* Mad River Jr HS 7th-9th Grd Soc Stud Tchr 1972-78; Chaminade-Julienne Schl 9th-12th Grd Soc Stud Tchr 1986-; *ai:* Dept Chair; Acad Cncl; Pastoral Team; Band Parents 1990-, Sec; Grant to Attend U. N. Wkshp NY; Grant to Bring Sim City 2000 to Classroom; *office:* Chaminade-Julienne HS 505 S Ludlow St Dayton OH 45402

BERGER, MIRIAM G., Social Studies & Reading Tchr; *b:* New York City, NY; *m:* Stanley L.; *c:* Scott, Eric, Dawn Fairbanks, Kurt; *ed:* Trenton St Coll (BA) Hlth, PE 1960; 30 Grad Credits Elem Ed, Soc Stud William Paterson Coll; *cr:* Hackettstown Elem Schl PE Tchr 1960-61; Long Valley MS Soc Stud, Rdng Tchr 1978-; *ai:* Washington Twp Ed Assn 1978-, Record Sec, Head Rep, Corres Sec; Morris Cty Ed Assn 1978-, Legislative Chair, MCCEA Rep; NJEA, NEA 1978-; *office:* Long Valley MS 51 W Mill Rd Long Valley NJ 07853

BERGER, MYRA SUE, Third Grade Teacher; *b:* Kenton, OH; *ed:* OH Northern Univ (BSEd) Elem Ed 1972; Univ of Dayton (MSEd) Schl Counseling 1992; 6 Hrs in Admin; *cr:* Allen East Local Schls 6th Grd Tchr 1972-73; Ada Exempted Village Schls Primary LD Tchr 1975-78, 1st Grd Tchr 1978-81, Transitional 1st Grd Tchr 1981-83, 2nd Grd Tchr 1983-92, Model IV Intermediate Spec Ed Tchr 1992-95; *ai:* Stu Dev Comm Staff; NEA, OEA, AEA 1972-, Treas, Pres Elect, Pres; United Meth Church 1962-, Sunday Schl Tchr, Pastor & Parrish Com Communion Steward.

BERGER, SELMAN A., Prof of Chem & Sci Dept Chair; *b:* Brooklyn, NY; *w:* Frances Balinsky (dec); *c:* Mark M., Erik J.; *ed:* Brooklyn Coll CUNY (BS) Chem 1964; Univ CT (PHD) Chem 1969; Dalhousie Univ Post Doctoral Fellow; *cr:* John Jay Coll of Criminal Justice CUNY Asst Prof to Prof 1971-, Dept of Sci Chair 1982-; *ai:* ACS 1970-; Numerous Articles Pub; *office:* J Jay Coll Criminal Justice 445 W 59th St Ofc New York NY 10019

BERGER, TERI LYNN, Sixth Grade Teacher; *b:* Watertown, NY; *m:* Russell K.; *c:* Patrick, Thomas; *ed:* SUNY at Oswego (BS) Elem Ed 1976; 12 Grad Credits SUNY at Stony Brook; 3 Grad Credits; 15 Grad Credits SUNY at Potsdam; *cr:* South Cntry Schl Dist Sub Tchr 1977-79; Sackets Harbor Cntrl Schl 2nd Grd Tchr 1979-85, 6th Grd Tchr 1985-; *ai:* Staff Selection, Textbook Selection, Curr Dev Comms; NEA 1979-, Treas, Co-Pres, VP, Exec Comm; Sackets Harbor Tchrs Assn, Exec Comm, Past Treas, VP, Co-Pres; Jeff-Lewis Tchr Ctr 1988-; Guest Speaker Legislative Meetings; Childrens Lit Grad Courses; Inservice Rdng Trainer; Wkshps on Whole Lang, Lit-Based Rdng Prgms; *office:* Sackets Harbor Central Schl Broad St Sackets Harbor NY 13685*

BERGERON, DEAN JOSEPH, Professor of History; *b:* Coventry, VT; *ed:* St Michaels Coll (BA) Ed 1961; Villanova Univ (MA) His 1963; Brown Univ 30 Credit Hrs; *cr:* Villanova Univ Tchng Asst 1961-63; Windsor HS Tchr 1963-64; Univ of MA at Lowell Prof 1965-; *ai:* Intnl Relations Club Adv; Cncl on Tchng & Learning; Task Force on Campus Life; NEA 1980-; Mid East Stud Assn 1986-; Org of Amer Historians 1967-; Common Cause 1979-, Acting Dir; Democratic Town Comm 1984-, Natl Convention Del; Parish Cncl 1982-; Secular Franciscan 1986-; NEH Summer Seminar 1982, 1985; Summer Fulbright 1988; *office:* Univ Of MA At Lowell 1 University Ave Lowell MA 01854*

BERGERON, NORMAND A., English Teacher & Hum Coord; *b:* Woonsocket, RI; *m:* Susan; *c:* Marc, Beth; *ed:* Worcester St Coll (BS) Eng 1970; *cr:* North Attleboro Jr HS 6th Grd Eng, Soc Stud, 7th Grd Eng, Hum Coord 26 Yrs; *ai:* AFT; NCTE; MCTE; ASCD; Blackstone Fin Comm 1986-, Chm; *office:* North Attleboro Jr HS 45 S Washington St North Attleboro MA 02760

BERGERON, ROLAND J., French & Spanish Teacher; *b:* Winooski, VT; *m:* Carolyn Morin; *c:* Michelle Miles, Sue Barber, Denise; *ed:* Assumption Coll (BA) Fr, Span 1965, (MAT) Fr 1967; *cr:* Harwood Union HS Frgn Lang Tchr 1966-69; St Michael's Coll ESL Instr 1967-95; Winooski HS Frgn Lang Tchr 1969-88; US Immigration Adjudicator 1989; Williamstown HS Frgn Lang Tchr 1990-; *ai:* Frgn Lang Club; VFLTA 1967-; VEA, NEA 1966-; *office:* Williamstown HS Brush Hill Rd Williamstown VT 05679

BERGERT, JOHN CALVIN, 5th Grade Teacher; *b:* Canton, OH; *m:* Margaret Ann Williams; *c:* Christopher, Megan; *ed:* Malone Coll (BS) Elem Ed 1968; Univ of Akron (MS) Ed 1985; *cr:* Waco Elem 4th-6th Grd Spec Ed Tchr 1968-71, 6th Grd Tchr 1971-77, 3rd Grd Tchr 1977-86; Walker Elem 5th Grd Tchr 1986-; *ai:* After Schl Advanced Math Wkshp; Celebrate Me Comm; NEA, OEA 1968-; CLEA 1968-, Pres 1980-81; Martha Holden Jennings Fnd Jennings Scholar 1981-82; *office:* Walker Elem Schl 3525 Sandy Ave SE Canton OH 44707

BERGFELD MILLS, DR., Professor of Psychology; *b:* St Charles, MO; *c:* Ridgway Mills; *ed:* Univ of MO at Columbia (BA) Psych 1970; Univ of MD at College Park (MA) Psych 1973, (PHD) Cognitive Psych 1976; *cr:* Univ of MD Instr 1983-89; Army Rsrch Inst Rsrch Psychologist 1984-85; Amer Inst for Rsrch Sr Rsrch Scientist 1985-91; Goucher Coll Psych Prof 1986-; *ai:* Psych Club; Psi Chi; Amer Psychological Assoc; Psyc Info Advy, Numerous Coll Comms; Amer Psychological Assn 1990-; Psychonomic Soc 1985-; Numerous Articles Pub; *office:* Goucher Coll 1021 Dulaney Rd Towson MD 21204

BERGGREN, JOHN WILSON, Third Grade Teacher; *b:* Brooklyn, NY; *m:* Carol; *c:* John A., Peter C.; *ed:* St Univ of NY at Oswego (BS) Ed 1963; St Univ of NY at Albany (MS) Ed 1971; *cr:* Forts Ferry Elem Schl Sixth Grd Tchr 1963-80, Third Grd Tchr 1980-; *ai:* Schlsp Comm; Crisis

Response Team; NY St United Tchrs 1963-; AFT 1970-; North Colonie Tchrs Assn 1963-, Past Bldg Rep; Town of Malta Planning Bd 1973-, Vice-Chm, Chm 1986; Malta Ridge Vol Fire Co 1968-, Past Sec, Past Asst Chief; *office:* Forts Ferry Elem Schl 95 Forts Ferry Rd Latham NY 12110

BERGMAN, BRUCE CHARLES, High School Business Teacher; *b:* Morristown, NJ; *m:* Ellen Simpson; *c:* Kim Bergman Barrineau, Dennis, Marc; *ed:* Wake Forest Univ (BBA) Mrktg, Mngmt 1971; Montclair St Coll (MA) Bus Ed 1979; *cr:* The Meridian Group Mrktg Field Specialist 1971-72; Hopatcong HS Bus Tchr 1972-73; West Morris Mendham HS Bus Tchr 1973-95; *ai:* Var Bsbl 2 Yrs; JV Bsbl 5 Yrs; Frosh Bsbl 8 Yrs; Ftbl Coach 12 Yrs; Future Bus Ldrs of Amer 11 Yrs; Mock Trial Coach 3 Yrs; Schl Store Adv 8 Yrs; Understanding Amer Bus Adv 13 Yrs; *office:* West Morris Mendham HS E Main St Mendham NJ 07945

BERGMAN, JANET MANUEL, Third Grade Teacher; *b:* Champaign, IL; *m:* John; *c:* Derek, Kyle, Andrea, Trenton; *ed:* OH St Univ (BA) Elem Ed 1985; Univ of Dayton 9 Credit Hrs; *cr:* Anna Schls 2-6th Grd Tchr 1986-; *ai:* OEA, NEA 1986-; St Lauerence Cath Church 1995-; Awded 2 Grants Soc Stud, Math, Sci Stud; *office:* Anna Elem Schl 607 N Pike St Anna OH 45302

BERGMAN, MARY ELIZABETH, Guidance Counselor & Fr Tchr; *b:* Hartford, CT; *ed:* Univ of CO at Boulder (BA) Sociology 1967; Villanova Univ (MA) Scndry Ed, Cnslng 1976; Univ De Caen France 1970; Chestnut Hill Coll Intermediate Fr Immersion Prgm 1993; Univ De Toulon, VAR France 1995; *cr:* Acad of the New Church Cnslr, Fr Tchr 1968-80, 1992-; *ai:* Delta Mu Adv; Frgn Lang, Rel, Educl Support Dept Mem; *office:* Acad Of The New Church PO Box 707 2815 Benade Cr Bryn Athyn PA 19009

BERGMAN, RONALD CLAIR, Mathematics Teacher; *b:* Johnstown, PA; *c:* Greg A., Joy Bergman; *ed:* Indiana Univ of PA (BS) Ed 1962; Atlanta Univ (MS) Math 1967; Univ of Pittsburgh Educ Admin 30 Credit Hrs; *cr:* Richland HS Math Tchr 1962-66; Atlanta Univ Math Instr 1967; PA Fed of Tchrs Staff Rep 1972-74; North Allegheny HS Math Tchr 1967-; *ai:* AFT, PAFT 1970-; NAFT 1970-, Pres, Chief Negotiator; NCTM; PCTM; *office:* North Allegheny Schl Dist 10375 Perry Hwy Wexford PA 15090*

BERGQUIST, JANE BREWER, Third Grade Teacher; *b:* Ashland, ME; *m:* Clinton T.; *ed:* Aroostook St Tchrs Coll (BS) Elem Ed 1958; Univ of Bridgeport (MS) Elem Ed 1965; Prof Diploma of Advanced Stud in Admin from Southern CT St Univ 1990; Certified Lang Arts Consultant; Certified in Admin; Addl 30 Plus Grad Credits Beyond Masters Degree; *cr:* Trng Schl 2nd Grd Tchr 1958-60; Hightstown Elem 2nd Grd Tchr 1960-61; Norwalk Pub Schls 3rd Grd Tchr 1961-; *ai:* Summer Rdng Prgm Dir; Lib & Prsnl Selection Comms; St of CT Beginning Educator Prgm Support Tchr & Mentor 1987-; NFT, CEA, AFT, NEA 1961-; Delta Kappa Gamma 1985-, Pres; Sweet Adelines Intnl 1992-; Priority Schl Improvement Team Chair 1967-75; *office:* Silvermine Elem Schl 157 Perry Ave Norwalk CT 06850

BERGSTROM, KENNETH IVER, Lecturer in English; *b:* Chicago, IL; *m:* John Carol Hawley; *c:* Rowena, Eric, Olin, Michael, Marianna; *ed:* US Naval Post Grad Schl (BA) Pol Sic 1963, (MS) Mgmt 1963; Plymouth St Coll (BA) His 1980; Univ of CT MA & PHD Pgms 40 Credit Hrs; St Olaf Coll Premed 64 Credit Hrs; *cr:* MIT NROTC Instr 1972-76; Plymouth St Coll Lecturer 1985-; *office:* Univ Of NH Plymouth St Coll Plymouth NH 03264

BERIDON, JUDITH DUCOTE, Third Grade Teacher; *b:* Bunkie, LA; *m:* O. P. Jr.; *c:* Thomas; *ed:* LA St (BA) Ed 1968, (MED) Ed 1973; 18 Addl Hrs; *cr:* East Baton Rouge Schls Tchr 1968-82; Norwood City Schls Tchr 1983-; *ai:* Dist Internet, Dist Writing, Bldg Rdng Comms; Quarterly Dist Idea Exchange Chm; Bldg Acvmt Team; Bldg Mentor; NEA 1968-; Alpha Delta Kappa 1970-, Pres; OCTELA 1988-; Outstdng Young Edctrs; Who's Who in Amer Women; *office:* Norwood City Schools 2132 Williams Ave Norwood OH 45212

BERIE, JENNIFER L., Spanish Teacher; *b:* Salamanca, NY; *m:* Ronald; *ed:* SUNY at Cortland (BA) Span 1992; SUNY at Potsdam 27 Credit Hrs; *cr:* Jeff Lewis BOCES Span Tchr 1992-95; Sackets Harbor Schl Span Tchr 1995-; *ai:* Sr Class, SADD & Span Club Adv; Modified Girls Soccer & Sftbl Coach; NYSAFLT 1991-; *office:* Sackets Harbor Central Schl PO Box 290 Sackets Harbor NY 13685*

BERISSO, GEORGE EUGENE, Science Curriculum Specialist; *b:* Jersey City, NJ; *m:* Jane Rohair; *c:* Kevin, Janice; *ed:* William Patterson Coll (BA) Bio Ed 1963, (MA) Sci Ed 1966; Univ of OR (MS) Bio 1969; Attnd Montclair St Univ, Long Beach St & Pacific Luth Coll; *cr:* Essx Cty Coll Adj Fac 1985-91; Montclair St Univ Clinical Adj Fac 1993-; James Caldwell HS Sci Tchr 1963-, Sci Coord 1988-95, Sci Curr Specialist 1995-; *ai:* NJTFOA Track Ofcl; Sci Revision Chprsn; EWCEA 1963-, Chm; NJEA 1963-; NEA 1963-; NABT 1965-; West Caldwell Pub Lib 1986-, Trustee & Treas; Essex Cncl BSA, Exec Bd, Cncl Trng Chm 1992-; NSF Summer Grant 1967; NSF Acad Yr Grant 1969; NJ Ed Grant Environmental Sci 1971; *office:* James Caldwell HS 265 Westville Ave West Caldwell NJ 07006

BERK, PATRICIA A., Art & Mechanical Engineer Tchr; *b:* Phila, PA; *c:* Colleen, George; *ed:* Tyler Art Schl at Temple Univ (BS) Art Ed 1978; Temple Univ (MA) Cartography & Geog 1985; Mosaic Apprenticship Wales 1993; Ind Stud Church Architecture France 1995; Ceramic Apprenticship Mattaponi Indian Reservation 1996; *cr:* West Cath Boys HS Art & Soc Stud Tchr 1985-90; West Cath Co-Ed HS Art, Soc Stud & Mechanical Drawing Tchr 1990-; *ai:* Yrbk; Art & Comp Clubs; SAP; PAL Soccer & Sftbl Coach 1979-85; NCEAA 1985-; PAL 1979-85, League Coach; Home & Schl Assn 1980-85, Pres; Flwshp Murals PEW Fndtn 1993-95; Grant To Stud in Whales Mural & Mosaic Apprenticship 1993; Amer Medical Jouranl 1990; PA Atlas 1993; Atlas of Armenia 1995; *office:* West Catholic H S 4501 Chestnut St Philadelphia PA 19139

BERKELEY, MURIEL V., Director; *b:* New York City, NY; *m:* Alfred Rives; *c:* Cary Brooke, Helen Elisabeth, Leila Muriel; *ed:* Radcliffe Coll (BA) Soc Relations 1968; Johns Hopkins Univ (PHD) Soc Relations 1978; *cr:* Greater Baltimore Comm Ed Dir 1978-84; Comm Coll of Baltimore Interim Dean, Continuing Ed Tchr 1984-85; Roland Park Schl Tchr, Curr Coord 1985-95; Baltimore Curr Project Dir 1996; *ai:* Drama Club; NFT; AAUW; Church Vestry Schl Improvement Team; *home:* 301 Northfield Pl Baltimore MD 21210*

BERKEY, CHARLES C., Art Teacher & GED Instructor; *b:* Huntingdon, PA; *m:* Mary Ann Roseborough; *c:* Timothy, Christopher, Jonathon, Andrew, Amy Jo; *ed:* Kutztown Univ (BS) Art Ed 1962; PA St U (MS) Art Ed 1972; *cr:* Danville Area Sr HS Art Tchr 1962-95; *ai:* Club Adv; NEA, PSEA 1962-; *office:* Danville Area Sr HS 600 Walnut St Danville PA 17821

BERKEY, JOHN CHARLES,JR., English Teacher; *b:* Philadelphia, PA; *m:* Margaret Hughes; *ed:* Rutgers Univ (BA) Eng Lit 1985; Scndry Eng Tchng Cert 1989; 9 Credits Toward MA in Brit Lit; *cr:* PA Energy Ctr Comm Coord 1985-88; Natl Fed of Abstract & Index Svcs comm Coord 1988-89; Delsea Regnl HS Eng Tchr 1989-; *ai:* Ed, Negotiations, Pride in Ed, SRA, Tech, Schlsp Awd Comms; NEA, NJEA 1989-; DEA 1989-, Negotiations Comm; Nancy Higginson Dow Scndry Ed Excl Awd 1988-89; Baccalaureate Speaker 4 Yrs; *office:* Delsea Regional HS PO Box 405 Franklinville NJ 08322*

BERKHOFER, GEORGE H.,IV, Latin Govt & Economics Teacher; *b:* New York, NY; *m:* Karen Marie Ipsen; *c:* Elizabeth M., Julia A., George V; *ed:* Univ of MI (BA) Fine Arts 1961; Univ of IL (MA) Classical Phisiology 1964; Post Grad Stud 1962-66; *cr:* Wittenburg Univ Asst Classics Prof 1966-73; Clark Cty Historical Soc Exec Dir 1970-82; Heritage Commissions Corp Exec Dir & Pres 1979-; Urbana Univ Adj Instr 1989-; Cath Cntrl HS Tchr 1991-; *ai:* Heritage Commission Corp Pres; South Charleston Town Hall Bd of Control Mem; Jr Achvmnt Tchr of the Yr 1994 & 1995; *office:* Catholic Central HS 1200 E High St Springfield OH 45505*

BERKHOFER, KAREN IPSEN, Language Art Teacher; *b:* Denver, CO; *m:* George Henry IV; *c:* Elizabeth, Julia, George V; *ed:* Mt St Joseph (BME) Piano, Music 1960; Univ of Dayton (MED) Supervision, Prin 1978; Grd Schl Ed Addl Credits; *cr:* Archdiocese of Cincinnati Grds 5-6, Music Tchr 1960-68; Mt Heathy Schls Grd 2 Tchr 1968-69; Donnelsville Grd 5 Tchr 1969; Southeastern Schls Grds K-1, 5-8 Tchr 1970-; *ai:* Stu Cncl Supvr; NEA 1970-, Pres, Rep; OEA 1970-; St Charles Church 1970-, Organist, CCD Dir; Cath Ladies of Columbia 1970-, Pres, Sec; S Charleston Heritage Commission 1981-, Accompianist; Jennings Scholar; Wittenberg Univ Piano Tchr; Title I Prgm Dir; *office:* Miami View Elem Schl 230 Clifton Rd South Charleston OH 45368

BERKHOUSE, SALLY LIPHART, English & Composition Teacher; *b:* Johnstown, PA; *m:* Terrence A.; *c:* Brian, Molly, Douglas; *ed:* Bowling Green St Univ (BS) Eng 1968; Youngstown St Univ (MS) 1993; Attnd Youngstown St Univ & Ashland Coll Post Grad Stud; *cr:* Champion HS Eng & Latin Tchr 1968-75; Youngstown St Univ Composition Instr 1989-90; Champion HS Eng & Composition Tchr 1984-; *ai:* Youngstown St Univ Eng Festival Adv; OEA & NEA 1984-; OCTELA & NCTE 1990-; Youngstown St Univ Grant; OCTELA & NCTE Conf Presenter; Pub OCTELA Journal; Written Tchr Lang Arts Newsletter; *office:* Champion H S 5976 Mahoning Ave NW Warren OH 44483

BERKLEY, MIRA TETKOWSKI, Asst Prof of Early Chldhd Ed; *b:* Buffalo, NY; *m:* John L.; *c:* Jory W., Alexander D.; *ed:* Cornell Univ (BS) Early Chldhd Dev 1974; SUC at Buffalo (MS) Early Chldhd Ed 1976; Working Toward PHD Early Chldhd Ed at SUNY at Buffalo; *cr:* Kenmore Pub Schls Early Chldhd Tchr 1974-76; Manzanita Daycare Univ of NM Head Tchr, Supvr 1976-78; Grants Pub Schls Kndgtn Tchr 1978-79; LaFrontera Clinic Child, Family Specialist 1979-82; BOCES Head Start Tchr 1982-86; Silver Creek Elem Schl Kndgtn Tchr 1987-90; Jamestown Comm Coll Asst Prof 1991-; *ai:* Early Chldhd Educators Club Adv; Children's Ctr Advy Bd; Natl Assn for Ed of Young Children 1974-, NY St Pres-Elect, Chaut Co Pres, Newsletter Ed, Prof Achvmt Awd 1994; Article Pub 1991; *office:* Jamestown Comm Coll 525 Falconer St Jamestown NY 14701

BERKMAN, DUANE MAC LEAY, Retired Fourth Grade Teacher; *b:* Buffalo, NY; *m:* Gerald D.; *c:* Kevin, David, Nancy, Freeman; *ed:* D'Youville Coll (BS) Ed 1960; 18 Credit Hrs at UNIY of Buffalo; *cr:* PS #33 in Buffalo 5th Grd Tchr 1950-65; St John Vianney Schl 3rd-4th Grd Tchr 1977-90; *ai:* Lothlorien Therapeu Tic Riding Ctr 1991-, Vol Ldr.

BERKOWITZ, HOWARD CRAIG, English Teacher & Theatre Dir; *ed:* Dickinson Coll (BA) Eng, Psych 1975; IN Univ (MA) Rel Stud 1979; *cr:* Cranbrook Schl Rel Tchr 1979-85; Glenelg Cntry Schl Eng, His Tchr 1985-89; Park Schl Eng, Drama Tchr 1989-; *ai:* Outdoor Hiking Club; Class of 1997 Adv; Glenelg Cntry Schl Tchr of Yr; Howard Cntry Bd of Ed 1985; *office:* Park Schl Of Baltimore 2425 Old Court Rd Brooklandville MD 21022*

BERKOWITZ, STUART M., Social Studies Teacher; *b:* Boston, MA; *m:* Denise H. Albert; *c:* Tamar; *ed:* Northeastern Univ (BA) Liberal Arts, His 1971, (MA) His 1972; Bridgewater St (CAGS) Educl Admin 1988; Addl Courses Norfolk Cty Tchrs Assn; *cr:* Sharon MS Soc Stud Tchr 1972-; *ai:* Stu Cncl Adv 1972-; Schl Musical Dir 1989-; Past Yrbk Adv 1972-94; MA Tchr Assn, nEA 1972-, Mem; Norfolk Cty 1972-, Mem, Tchr of Yr; Sharon Tchr Assn 1972-, Mem, Pres 1987; Jaycees 1980-89, Pres, VP, Jaycee of Yr 1984; louis Feinstein Comm Svc Grant 1994; Horace Mann MA Ed Grant 1989; Eric Reference Catalog Article on Aging; *office:* Sharon MS 75 Mountain St Sharon MA 02067*

BERKSON, RHODA FRANK, Health Teacher; *b:* Brooklyn, NY; *m:* Mark Barry; *c:* Scott, Paul; *ed:* Jewish Hosp of Brooklyn Schl of Nrsng (RN) Nrsng 1967; St Josephs Coll (BS) Comm Hlth 1990; Adelphi Univ (MA) Hlth Ed 1992; Continuing Ed Courses with Substance Abuse, Stress, Cnslng, Nrsng & Child Abuse; *cr:* Deepdale Hosp Emergency Rm Supvr 1971-87; E Rockaway Jr & Sr HS Schl Nurse 1987-90; Nassau Boces Part-Time Classroom & Clinical Instr for Nrsng Pgm 1990-; Herricks HS Nurse & Hlth Tchr 1990-; *ai:* SADD Adv; Sexual Harrassment, Bias Crime, Inclusion & Substance Abuse Comms; PTSA Fac Rep; Parents PTA Meeting Edctr; Emergency Nurses Assoc 1980-; NYSPHED 1990-; NYST 1990-; Pres Temple Sisterhood 1976-, Pres, VP & Sec, Svc Awd; Jewish Temple Bd 1986-, Bd Mem; Harassah 1970-, Rec Sec; Womens Amer Ort 1967-, VP & Pres; Cert in Emergency Nrsng; *home:* 607 Knollwood Dr West Hempstead NY 11552*

BERLEAN, JACQUELYN PIGAN, High School Teacher; *b:* Steubenville, OH; *m:* Bradley; *c:* Beau, Heidi; *ed:* W Liberty St Coll (BA) Diversified Specialization 1969; Credit Hrs in Comm Relations, Involvement in Ed; *cr:* Indian Valley Schls Elem Tchr 1969-70; Ridgewood Local Schl Elem Tchr 1970-74, MS Tchr 1978-79; Ridgeville Chrstn Schl Jr-Sr High Algebra, Govt, Bible, Rdng & Study Skills Tchr 1980-86; *ai:* Sr Adv; Homecoming Coord; Fund Raising Chm; Co-Chair Math Dept; Mission Trip Coord; ACSI 1980-; Republican Party 1994-, Comm Chm; *office:* Ridgeville Christian HS 946 E Lower Springboro Rd Springboro OH 45066

BERLIN, BARBARA Z., Advanced Plcmnt Art His Tchr; *b:* New York, NY; *m:* Donald L.; *c:* Geoffry R., Eric P.; *ed:* Smith Coll (BA) Art His 1956; Grad Courses at Tchrs Coll, Columbia Univ, Rutgers Univ; *cr:* Inst of Intnl Ed Assoc Ed 1956-61; The Pingry Schl Art His Tchr 1975-; *ai:* AP Hnrs Comm; Smith College 1956- Class Ofcr, Fund Raiser; *office:* The Pingry Schl Martinsville Rd Martinsville NJ 08836

BERLIN, MARY WOBBEKING, Math Teacher; *b:* Baltimore, MD; *m:* Thomas Clark; *c:* Thomas David, Daniel Clark; *ed:* Catonsville Comm Coll (AA) Gen 1967; Towson St (BS) His 1969; Masters Equivalancy at Western MD Coll; *cr:* Rock Glen Jr HS Math Tchr 1969-77; Glenelg HS Math Tchr 1983-; *ai:* Chess Club; Sr Boys Bsktbl Coach 3 Yrs; Commissioner Boys Bsbl 1988-93; MSTA, NEA 1985-; MCTM 1990-; *home:* 6231 Old Washington Rd Sykesville MD 21784

BERLIN, NANCY, Guidance Counselor; *b:* Brooklyn, NY; *ed:* Brooklyn Coll (BS) PE 1973; Coll of Staten Island (MS) Cnslng 1988; *cr:* Mabel Dean Bacon HS PE Tchr 1979-83; Susan Wagner HS PE Tchr 1983-86; Sarah J Hale HS Guid Cnslr 1986-; *ai:* Chair Alateen Meeting; Track, Gymnastics, Bowling, Handball Coach; Brooklyn & Staten Island Schls Guid Cnslr of Yr 1992-93; 3rd Place Girls Gymnastics 1988; *home:* 11 Riverside Dr New York NY 10023

BERLIN, RENE MICHELE, History & Economics Teacher; *b:* New York, NY; *m:* Mark Kaufman; *ed:* Queens Coll (BA) Pol Sci, His 1986; Working on MA His, Sec Ed; *cr:* PS 155 1st Grd Tchr 1988-89; PS 156 Music Tchr 1989-90; Richmond Hill HS Soc Stud Tchr 1990-; *ai:* Jr Achvmt Bus, Ec; MESE Competition; UFT, AFT 1988-; Jr Achvmt Ec Flwshp; Taft Flwshp; *office:* Richmond Hill HS 89-30 114th St Richmond Hill NY 11418*

BERLINGER, GARY LEE, 6th Grd World History Teacher; *b:* Cincinnati, OH; *m:* Leslie Bobenmoyer; *c:* Chanda, Veronica, Trent; *ed:* Morehead St Univ (BA) Elem Ed 1970; Xavier Univ (MA) Elem 1980; *cr:* Ripley Union Lewis Schls Scndry Spec Ed Tchr Georgetown Exempted Village MS His, PE Tchr 1971-73; Mt Orab Grd His, Math Tchr 1973-; *ai:* Mission Statement, Classroom Comms; Childrens Clothing Fund Admin; NEA 1970-; WBEA Hopewell Spec Ed Exceptional Achvmt Awd; Mt Orab MS Tchr 1995; *home:* 108 E Plum St Georgetown OH 45121

BERLINGHIERI, MARY, Eighth Grade Teacher; *b:* Teaneck, Univ of Scranton (BS) Scndry Ed, Math 1990; *cr:* River Vale Schl Tchr 1990; Dwight Morrow HS Math Tchr 1990-91; Northern V HS Math Tchr 1991-3, 1995; Saint Lucy's Schl Eighth Grd Tchr 1 Math Comm Chprsn; Eighth Grd Class Moderator; Yrbk, Math Adv; Mid Sts Accreditation Comm; NCTM 1991-; Mid Sts As Schls 1992-, Visiting Evaluation Team; Camp Fatima NJ Handicapped, Spec Needs Children Cnslr; Church of the Ass 1994-, Spec Needs Rel Ed Tchr; *office:* Saint Lucy's Schl 12 A Newark NJ 07104

BERLUCCHI, BARBARA L., Biology Teacher; *b:* Boston, Stephen F.; *c:* Jonathan, Justen; *ed:* Univ of MA (BS) Bi Bridgewater St Coll (MS) Phys Sci 1987; Addl 30 Credits Ed; *cr:* Hingham Sci Tchr 1982-; *ai:* IM Tennis Coach; Bio Club Adv; NE NABT, HTA 1982-; PTO, Sec; NSF Grant; Hingham Ed Fnd Hingham Sr HS 14 Main St Hingham MA 02043*

BERMAN, CHRISTINE MORIN, English & Social Studies Haverhill, MA; *m:* Joel R.; *c:* Adam R.; *ed:* Amer Intnl (BA) Pol S Univ of MA (MS) Eng 1989; 45 Post Grad Credits; *cr:* Scituate Soc Stud Tchr 1974-; *ai:* Frosh Class, Schl Newspaper Adv; Coo Tchr for UMASS Stu Tchr; NCTE, PCEA; MTA, STA 1974-; Sha'aray Shalom 1980-; Tchr of Month; Tchr Who Most Inspir Tufts Univ Tchr Recognition for Outstdng Tchr 1996; *home:* 3102 Dr Hingham MA 02043

BERMAN, CONSTANCE HARTOFIL-MILLIKEN, English F & Dept Coord; *b:* Astoria, NY; *m:* Steven Paul; *c:* Robert John John's Univ (BA) Eng, (MA) Eng; *cr:* Valley Stream No HS E Elective Chair 1965-81; Placentia Unified Schls Jrnlsm, E 1982-86; Southern VT Coll Grant Trng Prgm Admin 1989-91, E Dept Coord 1986-; *ai:* Oxford Prgm SVC Coord, Life Exp P Manchester Journal VT St Writer Awd 1987; Roxbury Publications Comm Advy Bd; Finalist Dow Jrnlsm Fellowship Search; Nom W Higher Ed Awd 1990; *office:* Southern Vermont College Monum Bennington VT 05201

BERMAN, JAY D., Principal; *b:* Brooklyn, NY; *m:* Shelley Eite Gary, Matthew; *ed:* Brooklyn Coll (BA) Bio 1968, (MA) Bio 19 Univ (MA) Ed Admin 1973; *cr:* Abraham Lincoln HS Bio Tchr Grover Cleveland HS Sci Tchr, Asst Prin 1985-86; Midwood HS S Asst Prin 1986-95; John Dewey HS Prin 1995-; *ai:* Westinghouse S Mentor; Sci Cncl of NYC 1985-, Treas; NYC Sci Chm Assn 19 NYC Bd of Ed Tchr of Yr 1983, Supvr of Yr 1987; *office:* John De 50 Avenue X Brooklyn NY 11223

BERMAN, MARLENE RACHEL, Eng Teacher & Coord of Stu New York, NY; *m:* Stephen; *c:* Jason, Paul; *ed:* CCNY (BA) E (MA) Eng 1973; Hofstra (EDD) Lang & Cognition 1990; *cr:* Win Eng Tchr 1970-75; Five Towns Coll Eng Tchr 1983-86; Hewlett Tchr & Coord of Stu Act 1987-; *ai:* Coord of Stu Act; Fac Ad Magazine; Hofstra Univ Flwshp; Pub The Patterned Learning System; Hewlett HS Tchr of Yr 1995; *office:* George W Hewle Everit Ave Hewlett NY 11557*

BERNABE, JOSEPH MICHAEL, Band Director; *b:* Raritan, Alice; *c:* Nicole, Michael; *ed:* Fairleigh Dickinson Univ (BS) M 1977; Post Grad Stud Montclair St Univ, Jersey City St; *cr:* Parsip Band Dir 1978-; *ai:* Golf Coach; Regnl, St Music Act; Music Te NEA, North Jersey Area Band Assn, NJ Music Edctrs Assn 1977-; Assn 1980-; Rockaway Recreation Comm 1992-; Grls Soccer Coac Girls Sftbl Coach 1991-; *office:* Parsippany HS 309 Bald Parsippany NJ 07054

BERNAL, MARIA BOVA, School Counselor; *b:* Buffalo, NY; *m:* D.; *c:* Leah Christine, Valerie Amanda, Diana Terese; *ed:* SUNY Buffalo (BS) Soc Work 1979, (MED) Schl Counseling 1983; Pe Cert 1986; *cr:* Chektowaga Youth Bureau Admin Asst 1978-80; Fillmore Hospital Soc Worker 1978-84; John F. Kennedy Jr-Sr Cnslr 1984-; *ai:* Stud of Month Comm Chprsn; Sloan Cheektowag Action Network; WNY Suburban Cnslr Assn & WNY MS Cns 1983-; *office:* John F. Kennedy Jr-Sr HS 305 Cayuga C Cheektowaga NY 14227

BERNAL, MERCEDES, ESL Head Teacher; *b:* Habana, C Arienne, Rueda; *ed:* Rutgers Univ (BA) Fr, Span & Ed 1972, (ED & Biling Ed 1979-80; 30 Post-Grad Credit Hrs St Peters Coll, Jer St Coll & Columbia Univ; *cr:* Weehauken Schls ESL Tchr Ramapo Coll ESL Tchr Summer Pgms 1976-77; Memrl HS 1976-78, Fr & Span Tchr 1978-80, ESL Tchr 1980-95, Head of E 1995-; HCC Coll ESL Tchr 1981-95; *ai:* Intnl Club Adv 1990-; E Revision Comm Mem 1991; Dist Wide Testing Pgm Comm Me ESL Curr Revision 1995-; Co-Chprsn; NJEA 1972-; Weehau 1972-75; WNYEA 1976-; NJ Bd of Realtors 1985-; Hudson C Realtors 1985-; Bergen Cty Bd of Realtors 1991-; Albio TX Wome 1995-; *office:* Memorial HS 5501 Park Ave West New York NJ 07

BERNAL-CARLO, AMANDA, Assistant Professor; *b:* Colombia; *m:* Janis A. Roze; *c:* Jano E. Roze, David A. Roze; *ed:* U of Colombia (BA) Bio 1981; City Univ NY (MS) Bio 1987, (PHD Ecology 1991; *cr:* Univ Nacional of Colombia Prof 1977-81; City Prof 1991-93; Hostos Comm Coll Asst Prof 1993-; *ai:* Several C Hostos Comm; Co-Dir Ecological Inst Bazios Brazil; Intnl Integrative Stud 1991-; Rsrch Grant Earthwatch 1994-; *home:* 1270 Apt 12R New York NY 10029*

BERNARD, DAVID F., Computer Graphics Teacher; *b:* Boston, Mary C. Dower; *c:* Kimberly, Michael; *ed:* Boston St Univ (BSE 1969, (MSEd) Admin 1975; Attnd MA Schl of Pharmacy, Bridge Coll, Univ MA at Boston; *cr:* Abraham Lincoln Schl Math Tchr William Barton Rogers Schl Math, Cmptr Tchr 1974-91; West Rox Cmptr Tchr 1991-; *ai:* Tchrs in Tech Instr; Bridgewater St Coll, at Boston Guest Lecturer; AFT, MEA 1969-; Stoughton Yth 1981-94, Bd of Dirs; *office:* West Roxbury HS 1205 Vfw Pky W MA 02072

BERNARD, KATHLEEN LOUISE, Third Grade Teacher; *b:* War *ed:* Kent St (BSEd) Elem Ed 1972; Westminster (ME) Rdng Champion Elem Schls 3rd Grd Tchr 1972-; *ai:* NEOTA, NEA *office:* Champion Central Elem Schl 5759 Mahoning Ave NW Wa 44483

BERNARD, KENNETH JAMES, Assoc Prof & Math Dept C Batavia, NY; *m:* Sandra Catino; *c:* Jennifer, Rebecca; *ed:* Niaga (BS) Math 1971; Univ of Rochester (MA) Math 1973, (EDD) 1979; *cr:* Genesee Comm Coll Adj Math Tchr 1975-77; Consortiu Niagara Frontier Adj Math Tchr 1977-; Niagara Univ Prof of Mat *ai:* Kappa Mu Epsilon, NY ETA Chptr, Math Club Moderator; 1977-; MAA 1983-; AAUP 1981-; Lew-Port Super Advy 1990-; Mu ara 1993-, Bd of Dirs; Excl in Tchng Awd 1994; Book: Foundations ematics 1996; Dir Math & Sci Summer Camp; *office:* Niagara Univ Mathematics Niagara University NY 14109

RD, PAMELA JANE, Tchr of Prmry Lrng Dsblts; *b:* Canton, OH; ling Green St Univ (BS) Elem Ed, Spec Ed 1981; Attnd Akron : Canal Fulton Elem Schl Tutor of LD 1981-82; Stinson Elem Schl LD 1982-83; Canal Fulton Elem Schl Tchr of LD 1983-; *ai:* SST Schl Newspaper Adv; NEA, OEA 1981-; *office:* Canal Fulton Elem 5 Market St E Canal Fulton OH 44614

RD, SYLVIA PARKER, Reading Teacher; *b:* Washington, DC; *c:* D.; *ed:* Hampton Inst (BS) Scndry E, His 1964; AZ St Univ (MA) Ed, Rdng 1970; Attnd Kean Coll, Rutgers Univ, OK St Univ, Coll, Inst de Guadaljara; *cr:* Sousa Jr HS His Tchr 1965-67; S n HS Rdng Tchr 1969-72; Rutgers Univ Asst Prof of Rdng ; Plainfield HS Rdng, His Tchr 1985-; *ai:* Stu Cncl; Interact, Civil ol; Class of 1997 Adv; NJ SEED; Stu SEED, Div Team; African ture Club; Assembly Coord; Div Stu Activities; NASSP; NEA NJEA 1985-; Jaycettes at Somerset Outstdng Woman of 1971-; gma Theta 1995-; Outstdng Woman in NJ Jaycees; Outstdng Edctr smen Plainfield; Outstdng Tchr Appreciation Day Douglas Coll, *office:* Plainfield HS 950 Park Ave Plainfield NJ 07060*

RDI, GRACE C., Prevention Specialist; *b:* Brooklyn, NY; *m:* B.; *c:* Elizabeth B. Seaden, R. Bruce, Sarah; *ed:* Good Counsel A) Soc Stud Ed 1966; Villanova Univ (MS) Counseling, Human 84; West Chester Univ Guidance Cert; *ai:* SADD; Peer Counselors; ounseling Assn, PA Counseling Assn 1984-; PSEA 1995-; PA SAP *ffice:* Henderson HS Lincoln & Montgomery Aves West Chester 0

RDINI, BRETT ANDREW, Performing Arts Director; *b:* olis, MN; *ed:* Shenandoah Univ (BMe) Music Ed 1984; Working Liberal Stud; *cr:* Southington HS Music Tchr 1986-87; Retgion Dist Music Tchr 1987-89; Norwich Free Acad Dir of Performing 89-; Artstc Dir Encore! Prod Plus Inc; CT Music Assmnt Advsy *ai:* Carnivale Intnl Acclaimed Performance Ensemble Creator, Dir; erforming Arts Ctr Design Team; Producer, Dir for Schl ons; Ed Theater Assn 1990-, St Dir; CT Drama Assn 1990-93; Comm Group 1992-94; New England Theater Conf 1990-94; Music Conf 1990-; CT Music Educators Assn 1990-; Newtwork Schls of ng, Visual Arts 1991-94; Norwich Arts Cncl 1991-, Assessment Comm; Amer Choral Dir Assn; CT General Assembly; Offcial for Excl; Norwich Bulletin's Reader's Poll Outstanding Tchr CT 1993; CT Interdistrict Grant for Summer Theater Pgrm; acket Tribal Grant Prgm Funding; *office:* Norwich Free Acad 305 ay Norwich CT 06360

TH, DONN L., Retired Mathematics Teacher; *b:* Defiance, OH; *m:* idarsic; *c:* Amy; *ed:* OH Univ (BA) Math & Physics 1960; BGSU Schl Admin 1962; 60 Hrs Beyond MED; *cr:* North Fork Local Schl 1960-61; Delta Local Schl Math Tchr 1962-64; Maple Hghts City th Tchr 1964-94, Asst Prin 1972-73; *ai:* Fac Mgr for Ath; Credit P; MHTA 1964-; OEA & NEA 1960-; Jennings Scholar; Phi Kappa

T, LILLIAN JEAN, HS English Teacher; *b:* Hollis, NY; *m:* R.; *c:* Christine, Kimberly; *ed:* SUNY at Stony Brook (BA) Fr owie St Univ (MED) Rdng 1977; 24 Post Grad Credit Hrs; *cr:* La Generale Translator & Teletyper 1967; Andrew Jackson Jr HS ecialist 1976-83; Nicholas Orem MS Eng Tchr 1983-85; Parkdale ng Tchr 1985-88; Largo Sr HS Eng Tchr 1988-92; High Point Sr Tchr 1992-; *ai:* Asst Tennis Coach; Mid Sts Staff & Admin on Comm; PGCEA 1988-; AFT 1992-; USTA 1996-; Sr Regnl hampionship USTA 1995; *office:* High Point HS 3601 Powder Mill ville MD 20705*

R, KELLY ANN, English Teacher & Coach; *b:* Chatham, NJ; *ed:* William & Mary at Williamsburg (BA) Eng & Govt 1992; *cr:* Chubb e Co Operations Supvr 1992-93; Cushing Acad Tchr & Field & Lacrosse Head Coach 1993-; *ai:* Stu Govt Adv; Stdnts Adv; Lacrosse Coach; HOBY Seminar Chm; New England Prep Schl crosse Assoc; HOBY 1994-, Cnslr & Chm; NEPSWLA 1995-, Pres er; *office:* Cushing Acad 39 School St Ashburnham MA 01430*

R, NANCY KRATZER, Third Grade Teacher; *b:* Allentown, PA; arke; *ed:* Kutztown St Univ (BS) Elem Ed 1968; Lehigh Univ Ed 1972; *cr:* Whitehall-Coplay MS 5th-7th Grd Tchr 1968-88; Elem Schl 3rd Grd Tchr 1988-; *ai:* IRA; NCTE; Outstdng Tchr high Univ 1995; *home:* 3756 Lehigh Dr Northampton PA 18067

ARD, DEBRA LEVAN, Secondary Mathematics Teacher; *b:* e, PA; *c:* Nicole; *ed:* Shippensburg Univ (BS) Math Scndry Ed asters Equivalency Ed 1993; *cr:* Palmyra MS Math Tchr 1974-83; HS Math Tchr 1984-; *ai:* Stu Assistance Prgm; Sr Class Dean; uring Comm; Tchr Mentor; PA Cncl Tchrs Math, Cntrl PA Math 85-; NEA, PSEA 1974-; Delta Kappa Gamma 1995-; AAUW 1979-; en's Club 1986-; Annville-Cleona Acad Boosters 1995-; *office:* Sr HS 1000 S 8th St Lebanon PA 17042

EIM, JEANNE MARIE, Retired Teacher of GATE; *b:* Cincinnati, ohn; *c:* John R., Sue, Robert; *ed:* Miami Univ (BA) ELem Ed Tchr avier Univ (MS) Rdng Specialist 1975; Gifted Ed Cert; *cr:* Rdng Schl Classroom Tchr 1967-79, Remedial Rdng Tchr 1979-86, d Tchr 1986-95; *home:* 796 Kenray Ct Reading OH 45215

EISEL, MARILYN HENRY, Fifth Grade Teacher; *b:* Abington, ohn M.; *c:* Steven, Michael; *ed:* Millersville Univ (BS) Elem Ed MED) Elem Ed 1971; Beaver Coll (MA) Cnslng Psych 1990; 15 edits Penn St 1973-74; *cr:* State St Schl 4th Grd Tchr 1971-72; Dale Elem Schl 6th Grd Tchr 1972-76; Shelmire Elem SChl 6th Grd 77-78; Johnsville Elem Schl 5th Grd Tchr 1978-79; Mc Donald hl Grds 4-6 Tchr 1983-; *ai:* Instrl Support Team Mem 1990-; Class 3-; NEA, PSEA 1972-; ASCA, APA, ACA 1989-; ASCD 1990-; Phi appa 1991-; Natl Dean's List 1991; *office:* Everett A Mcdonald hl 666 Reeves Ln Warminster PA 18974

ER, ROBERT RAYMOND, Latin & English Teacher; *b:* ce, RI; *m:* Jean M. Chamberlain; *ed:* Coll of Holy Cross (BA) Langs 1985; Fairfield Univ (MA) Ed 1989; Attnd OH St Univ MA Classics 1985; *cr:* Fairfield Coll Preparatory Schl Latin, Greek & r 1986-; *ai:* Bsbl Coach 1986-92; Hockey Coach 1991-; Frosh Ftbl 993-; Sr Class Adv 1990-92; Stu Govt Moderator 1992-; Intramural -; Latin Club Moderator 1994-; Amer Classical League 1991-; CT g Tchrs 1988-; Saint Pius X Church 1992-; Holy Cross Almuni 85-, Alumni Interviewer 1990-; Led 2 Stu tours of Rome 1991 & *fice:* Fairfield College Prep Schl N Benson Rd Fairfield CT 06430

ER, STEPHANIE, Social Studies Teacher; *b:* Bangor, ME; *ed:* ME (BS) Ed 1995; *cr:* Dr Lewis S. Libby Schl Girls Bsktbl Coach , Orono HS Girls JV Bsktbl Coach 1994-; *ai:* AAU Girsl Bsktbl; Rich Waterman Awd.

, CATHERINE A., Elementary Montessori Teacher; *b:* ton, DC; *m:* John P.; *c:* Sarah E.; *ed:* Univ of WI (BA) ology 1966; 30 Hrs Elem Tchr Cert; Washington Montessori Inst & Elem Montessori Certs; 30 Plus Hrs Univ of Cincinnati, d St Univ, Mount St Joseph Coll, Xavier Univ, Miami Univ of OH & Loyolla Coll; *cr:* Day Care Svcs for Children Tchr of 4 Yrs Olds 1969-70; Belleair Montessori Schl Tchr of 3-5 Yr Olds 1972-73; Villa Madonna Early Learning Ctr Tchr of 3-5 Yr Olds 1974-76; Montessori Schl of Huntsville Tchr of 3-5 Yr Olds 1977-78; Mercy Montessori Ctr Tchr of 3-5 Yr Olds 1979-83; Cincinnati Pub Schls 1st-3rd Grd Tchr 1983-; *ai:* Outdoor Ed, Sci Fair, Cultural Fair Staff Comms; 4-H Asst Ldr; Suzuki Violin Parent; Assn Montessori Intnl 1974-; N Amer Montessori Tchrs Assn 1974-; Cincinnati Fed of Tchrs 1983-; OH Valley Assn Montessori Intnl Wkshp Ldr 1978-84; N Amer Montessori Tchrs Assn Wkshp Ldr 1985-86, 1988, 1994-95; Cincinnati Gas & Electric Co Awd of Inspiration for Tchng 1993; Cincinnati Pub Svc Awd 1994; Clean Cincinnati Competition for Cleaner Schls 1st Pl Awds 1986-88, 1990, 1992-94; *office:* North Avondale Montessori 615 Clinton Springs Ave Cincinnati OH 45229

BERNO, JOHN P., Elementary Montessori Teacher; *b:* Brooklyn, NY; *m:* Catherine Abel; *c:* Sarah E.; *ed:* Univ of South FL (BA) Soc Stud, Ed 1967; Univ of WI at Milwaukee (MA) Specific Learning Disabilities Ed 1971; 20 Hrs Univ of Cincinnati; 10 Hrs Univ of Coll of Mt Joseph Elem Tchr Cert; 60 Hrs Washington Montessori Inst Presch, Elem Certs; *cr:* Pinellas Cty Schls Learning Disabilities Specialists 1971-73; Mercy Montessori Schl Monterrori Elem, Presch Tchr 1974-77; Monterrori Schl of Huntsville Dir, Tchr 1977-78; Mercy Monterrori Schl Elem Montessori Tchr 1978-82; Cincinnati Pub Schls Grds 4-6 Montessori Tchr 1982-; *ai:* Sci Fair; Staff Comm; Cultural Fair, Outdoor Ed Staff Comms; Schl Theater Dir; Suzuki Violin Parent; Cub-Scout Ldr; Soccer Coach; Grad Chprsn; Assn Montessori Intnl, North Amer Montessori Tchrs Assn 1974-; Cincinnati Fed of Tchrs 1983-; North Avondale Montessori Tchrs Assn, Wkshp Ldr 1978-84; Vista Vol 1968-70, Comm Librn; Cincinnati Montessori Soc, Wkshp Ldr 1983-86, 1989; Univ of WI Flwshp; Clean Cincinnati Competition First Place Awd 1989-90; *office:* North Avondale Montessori Schl 615 Clinton Springs Ave Cincinnati OH 45229

BERNON, JONATHAN ROBERT, Math Teacher; *b:* Boston, MA; *ed:* Lafayette Coll (BS) Math 1984; Harvard Univ (AM) Sociology 1986; *cr:* The Taft Schl Math Tchr 1986-; Tech Coord 1995-; *ai:* Western CT Soccer Ofcl Assn 1987-; Northern CT Lacrosse Ofcl Asnn 1992-; *office:* The Taft Schl 110 Woodbury Rd Watertown CT 06795

BERNOSKI, DANIEL M., Spanish Teacher; *b:* Kingston, PA; *m:* Pamela Ann Myers; *c:* Daniel, Brenda; *ed:* Bloomsburg St Univ (BS) Span 1971; Trenton St Coll (MS) Ed 1978; *cr:* Fisher Jr HS Span Tchr 1971-95; Ewing Twp HS Span Tchr 1995-; *ai:* Asst Ftbl & Head Sftbl Coach; NEA 1971-; NJEA 1971-; Coach of Yr 1985 & 1990.

BERNOSKY, DAVID JOSEPH, Social Studies Teacher; *b:* Luzerne, PA; *m:* Nancy L. Ehrhardt; *c:* Christine, David Jr.; *ed:* Seton Hall Univ (BS) Elem & Scndry Ed 1964, (MA) Elem & Scndry Ed 1974; 3 Post Grad Credits; *cr:* Lincoln-Franklin Elem Sch 5th-8th Grd Soc Stud Tchr 1966-; *ai:* Head Tchr; 8th Grd Class Adv; Class Registers; Local Tchrs Assoc 1966-, Pres, VP & Treas; NIEA 1966-; NEA 1966-; Governors Tchr Recognition Awd 1981-82; *office:* Lincoln-Franklin Elem Schl 2nd Ave Garwood NJ 07027

BERNREUTHER, JANET M., French Teacher; *b:* Oswego, NY; *m:* Scott D.; *c:* David, Michelle; *ed:* State Univ of NY Coll Oswego (BA) Scndry Ed, Liberal Arts, Fr 1971; NY Univ in France (MA) Fr Lit 1974; Syrcause Univ (MLS) Lib Sci, Schl Media 1993; 24 Hrs Span Grad Stu; 9 Hrs Basic, Intermediate Accounting; *cr:* Waterloo Jr High 6th-8th Grd Fr, Span Tchr 1975; Lyons HS 9th-12th Grd Fr Tchr 1975-77; N. Rose Wolcott HS 9th-12th Grd Fr Tchr 1977-79; SUNY Coll at Oswego Temporary Adjunct Fr Tchr 1983; Oswego HS 9th-12th Grd Fr, Span Tchr 1986-; *ai:* Fac Liaison Comm Mem; AFT 1986-; Amer Lib Assn 1993-; *office:* Oswego HS 2 Buccaneer Blvd Oswego NY 13126

BERNS, BRIAN KEITH,SR., PE & Health Teacher; *b:* Reading, PA; *m:* Megan Elizabeth; *c:* Brian Jr., Patrick, Kylee; *ed:* Slippery Rock St (BA) PE, Hlth 1981; DE St (MS) Ed 1989; *cr:* Dover Air Jr HS PE, Hlth Tchr 1981-82; Nellie Hughes Stokes Elem Schl Behavior Mgr 1982-85; Dover Air MS PE, Hlth Tchr 1985-; *ai:* Coach Asst Var Ftbl, Head Girls Track; Yrbk Adv; NEA, CREA 1983-; AAHPERD 1995-; Tchr of Yr 1987; Girl's St Track Coach of Yr 1993; *office:* Dover AFB MS Hawthorne Dr Dover DE 19901

BERNSTEIN, ALAN, 8th Grade Social Studies Tchr; *b:* Brooklyn, NY; *m:* Eileen Hack; *c:* Howard, Scott; *ed:* Brooklyn Coll (BA) Ec 1962; Grad Work NY Univ, Rutgers Univ, Union Coll; *cr:* NYC Bd of Ed Tchr 1962-; *ai:* Dean; Cafeteria Coord; Team Ldr; AFT, UFT 1962-; *office:* Bernstein IS 7 1270 Huguenot Ave Staten Island NY 10312

BERNSTEIN, ALAN LLOYD, Music Teacher & Orchestra Dir; *b:* Providence, RI; *m:* Karen O'Brien; *c:* Chelsea; *ed:* Univ of RI (BM) Music Ed 1984, (MOM) music Ed 1986; Jazz Stud RI Schl of Music; Gen Stud Southeastern MA Univ; *cr:* URI Tchng Asst 1984-86; Fall River Pub Schls Music Tchr 1986-88; Newport Schl Dept Music Tchr 1988-; *ai:* Jazz & Spcl Ensemble Dir; Amer Fed of Musicians 1980-; MENC 1980-; ASTA 1980-; IAJE 1986-; NEA 1988-; Grants: Champlin, Newport Pub Ed Fndtn & Benefactors of the Arts; *office:* Thompson MS 39 Broadway Newport RI 02840

BERNSTEIN, GAIL EISEMAN, Resource Teacher; *b:* Brooklyn, NY; *m:* Karl E.; *c:* Amy Jane Bernstein-Feldman, Jan Rosenblum; *ed:* Pratt Inst (BS) Art Ed 1962; Adelphi Univ (MED) Spec Ed & Common Br 1980; *cr:* Meyer Levin Jr HS Art Ed Tchr 1962-65; Pub Schl 279 5th & 6th Grd Tchr 1977-85; Samuel J Tilden HS Resource Room Tchr 1986-; *ai:* AFT; Brooklyn High Schls Tchr of Yr 1995; *office:* Samuel J Tilden HS 5800 Tilden Ave Brooklyn NY 11203*

BERNSTEIN, JULES, PE Teacher & Dept Head; *b:* Baltimore, MD; *m:* Alberta Bland; *c:* Alex, Grant; *ed:* Catonville Comm Coll (AA) PE 1967; Westchest St Univ (BS) PE 1970; Towsen St Univ (ME) Scndry Ed 1974; Loyola Coll +33 Hrs Admin; *cr:* Aberdeen Mid Tchr 1976-87; Bel Air Mid 1987-92; Harford Tech HS 1992-; *ai:* Var Bsktbl Coach; MSTA 1976-; HCEA 1976-; Harford Jewish Ct 1984-, Trustee & VP; *office:* Harford Technical HS 200 Thomas Run Rd Bel Air MD 21015

BERNSTEIN, LAURA, Athletic Trainer; *b:* New Brunswick, NJ; *ed:* West Chester Univ of PA (BS) Ath Trng 1991; Emergency Med Tech 1988; *cr:* Scotch Plains-Fanwood Bd of Ed Ath Trainer, Equipment Mgr 1991-; *ai:* Supervise Stu Trainers; Speak at Seminars; Natl Ath Trainers Assoc 1987-, Cert Mem; Ath Trainers Soc of NJ 1991-; 5 of 9 Stu Trainers Follow Trainer Career & 1 in Sports Psych; *office:* Scotch Plains Fanwood HS Westfield Rd Scotch Plains NJ 07076

BERNSTEIN, PATRICIA LANGE, Health & Physical Ed Teacher; *b:* Darby, PA; *m:* Michael; *c:* Michael C.; *ed:* West Chester Univ (BS) Tchng, Hlth & PE 1988; Post Grad Stud Penn St Univ; *cr:* Archdiocese of Philadelphia PE Tchr 1988-89; Sandy Run MS Hlth & PE Tchr 1989-; *ai:* Boys Track Team Coach; PSAHPERD 1988-; NEA 1989-; PSEA 1989-; Amer Heart Assn 1992-, Jump Rope for Heart Coord; Presented at St AAPHRD; *office:* Sandy Run MS 520 Twining Rd Dresher PA 19025*

BERNSTEIN, ROBERT J., Admin & Soc Science Teacher; *b:* Brooklyn, NY; *c:* Eric, Alison, Lily; *ed:* Hofstra Univ (BA) His 1955; Columbia Univ (MA) His 1963; *cr:* Amer Schl of Paris Chm, K-12 Soc Stud Tchr 1961-63; Mineola HS Soc Stud Tchr; Wheatley Schl Admin Schl-Within-Schl, Soc Sci Tchr 1968-; *ai:* Mock Trial Invitational Tournament Coord; Mock Trial Team Coach; Key Club Adv; Long Islnd Cncl for Soc Stud 1968-; Sierra Club; Amer for Democratic Action; Amer Civil Liberties Union, Bd Mem, Nass Chptr 1960-; Outstdng Tchng Pres Awd Cornell Univ; Co-Author Philosophy, His of Ed; *office:* The Wheatley Schl 11 Bacon Rd Old Westbury NY 11568*

BERNSTEIN, STUART, Social Studies Tchr & Dept Ldr; *b:* Brooklyn, NY; *m:* Frances Schneck; *c:* Lisa C., Lauren J., Allison S.; *ed:* Brooklyn Coll (BA) His 1967; Queens Coll (MS) Soc Stud Ed 1970; Hofstra Univ (CAS) Educl Admin 1975; C. W. Post-Long Island Univ (MLS) Acad Libs 1995; *cr:* William Alexander Jr HS #51 Soc Stud Tchr 1967-71; Dawnwood Jr HS Soc Stud Tchr 1971-79; SUNY Adj Prof Soc Sci 1970-81; C. W. Post Coll Adj Prof Sociology 1995-, Newfield HS Soc Stud Tchr, Dept Ldr 1979-; *ai:* Acad Teams Coach 1987-94; AFT 1967-; NYSCSS 1988-; North Shore Jewish Center, Bd of Trustees, Bulletin Ed; *office:* Newfield HS 145 Marshall Dr Selden NY 11784

BERNSTOCK, MAUREEN ANN SCAGNELLI, Reading Specialist; *b:* New York, NY; *m:* Joel David; *c:* Christine, Jennifer; *ed:* Hunter Coll (BA) Psych, Elem Ed 1970; St Univ of NY at Albany (MS) Rdng 1976; Wm. Paterson Coll (MA) Educl Ldrshp, Admin 1995; *cr:* NY City Pub Schls Tchr 1970-74; Shenendehowa Cntrl Schls Sub Tchr 1974-76; Lenox Schl Classroom Tchr 1983-94, Rdng Specialist 1994-; *ai:* NJEA, NEA 1983-; PLEA 1983-, 1st VP 2 Terms, Bldg Rep; Pompton Lakes Women's Club 1985-; Tchr of Yr 1991-92; Mentored 2 Fellow Tchrs 1994-; *office:* Lenox Elem Schl 35 Lenox Ave Pompton Lakes NJ 07442

BERNSTORF, PAUL S., Middle School Math Teacher; *b:* Hackensack, NJ; *m:* Linda S. Brown; *c:* Bryan, Stephan; *ed:* Univ of Richmond (BA) Math, Hlth, PE 1980; OH St Univ (MA) Ath Admin 1884; Discovering Geometry Inst; *cr:* Haverford HS Math Tchr 1980-81; Columbus Acad MS Math, Upper Schl PE Tchr 1981-88; Haverford Schl Upper Schl Math, PE Tchr, Asst Ath Dir 1988-95; St Paul's MS Math Tchr 1995-; *ai:* Stu Adv; Admissions Comm; Var Ftbl, Bsbl; NCTM 1990-; AFCA 1985-; AAHPERD 1980-; Manoa Presbyn Church 1988-, Deacon; *office:* St Paul's Schl Falls Rd Brooklandville MD 21022

BERO, STEPHEN JAMES, Environmental Studies Teacher; *b:* Oneida, NY; *m:* Gayle A. Trushaw; *c:* Maria, Angela, Lara, Michael; *ed:* LeMoyne Coll (BS) Multiple Sci 1968; St Univ of NY (MS) Scndry Ed 1974; Grad Work Environmental Stud, Scndry Ed Admin 69 Hrs; *cr:* Liverpool HS Environmental Stud 1968-; Ithaca Coll Adjunct Prof 1994-; *ai:* Yth Environmental Action Club Spon 1990-95; AFT, NYSUT 1968-; STANYS 1988-; Izaak Walton League of Cntrl NY 1990-, 1st VP; NSF Summer Inst for Tchrs 1990, 1994-; Tech Club of Syracuse Outstdng Tchr Awd 1992-93; Sci Tchr of Yr 1991; Cntrl NY Waterfowlers Conservationist of Yr 1993; *office:* Liverpool HS 4338 Wetzel Rd Liverpool NY 13090

BERQUIST, STEPHEN BARRETT, Stud Skill & Career Exp Tchr; *b:* Baltimore, MD; *ed:* Salisbury St Univ (BS) PE 1988, (MS) Ed 1995; *cr:* Worcester Cty Schl Jr Var Lacrosse Coach 1988-89; Stephen Decatur HS Var Soccer Coach 1988-, Tchr 1989-; *ai:* Sr Class Adv; Var Soccer, Tennis Coach; Schl Improvement Team; Dir of Saturday Schl; Worcester Cty Tchrs Assn, NEA 1988-; MD St Soccer Coaches Assn 1989-; Conf Soccer Coach of Yr 1988; Regnl Soccer Champions 1994; Worcester Cty Tchr of yr Candidate 1995; *home:* PO Box 574 Berlin MD 21811

BERREND, PATRICIA ANN, Ballet Mistress, Tchr & Coach; *b:* Wisconsin Rapids, WI; *ed:* WA Schl of Ballet for Trng; Natl Ballet of Canada Tchng Trng; *cr:* kiel Ballet Co Ballet Dancer 1967-68; Bremen Ballet Co Ballet Dancer 1970-71; Hamburg Ballet Co Ballet Dancer 1971-76; WA Ballet Dancer, Tchr, Coach, Ballet Mistress 1976-; *ai:* Ballet Mistress; Regisseur Nutcracker Production; Coach Dancers for Natl, Intnl Ballet Competitions; Distinguished Tchr Awd for Presidential Scholar in the Arts 2 Times; Arts Recognition, Talent Search Tchr Awd 6 Times; *office:* Washington Schl Of Ballet 3515 Wisconsin Ave NW Washington DC 20016

BERRIER, MONICA GOGUL, Spanish Teacher; *b:* Steubenville, OH; *m:* Dennis; *c:* Kristan, Meghann; *ed:* Seton Hill Coll (BA) Span 1971; Attnd Univ of Madrid, Spain; Otterbein Coll; Wright State Univ Masters Program; *cr:* Brooke HS Span Tchr 1971-72; St John HS Span Tchr 1974-75; Braden & Edgewood HS Span Tchr 1979-84; Westerville North HS Span Tchr 1988-; *ai:* NEA, WEA 4 Yrs; LINC 1989-; St Ann Hosp Vol 5 Yrs; *office:* Westerville North H S 950 County Line Rd Westerville OH 43081

BERRY, BARBARA A., Coord & Cmptr Sci Lead Instr; *b:* Lynn, IN; *ed:* Hocking Coll (AAB) Cmptr Sci, Acctng; Earlham Coll (BA) Ed; Ball St Univ (MA) Ed; *cr:* Hockins Coll Cmptr Sci 1983-; *office:* Hockins Coll 3301 Hocking Coll Nelsonville OH 45764

BERRY, CATHERINE CLAGETT, English & Reading Teacher; *b:* Baltimore, MD; *m:* Michael Kenneth; *ed:* Salisbury St Univ (BA) Eng, Scndry Ed 1977; Western MD Coll (MED) Rdng 1985; Cmptr Literacy Courses Mac Intosh, Desk-Top Publishing; Adult Ed Courses, Flower Design, Photogrphy, Conversational Fr; *cr:* North Carroll MS 7th Grd Dev Rdng Tchr, Team Ldr 1977-83; Westminster HS Eng, Rdng Tchr 1983-; *ai:* Western MD Coll Stu Tchr Cooperating Tchr; Co-Class Adv; Awds, Grad Comms; Chaperoned Sr Class Act; Schl Newspaper Adv 1983-93; Schl Pub Relations Comm Chair; NEA, MD St Tchrs Assn, Carroll Cty Ed Assn 1977-; Zeta Tau Alpha 1974-, Sec, Judicial Bd; Omicron Delta Kappa 1977-; Sacred Heart Roman Cath Church 1993-; Meals on Wheels 1990-, Summer Sub; Received Recognition from Carroll Cty of Ed for 1st Place Ratings for Owl Newspaper from Quill, Scroll, Columbia, MD Scholastic Press Assn 1934-93; Nom MD Tchr of Yr 1992; Young Careerist Contest Spon by MD Bus, Prof Women 2nd Place 1990; *home:* 3144 Coon Club Rd Hampstead MD 21074*

BERRY, CRAIG STEVEN, High School Counselor; *b:* Dayton, OH; *m:* Christine; *c:* Alison, Steven, Robert; *ed:* Miami Univ (BS) Ed, Bus 1974, (ME) Cnslng 1978; 30 Hrs in Continuing Ed at Wright St Univ & Univ of Dayton; *cr:* Sheridan HS Bus Tchr 1974-77; Wayne HS Guid Cnslr 1978-87;Miamisburg HS Prof Schl Cnslr 1987-; *ai:* Hnr Soc Adv; Dist Career Rep for Tech Prep; New Cnslr Mentor Through OSCA; NEA, OEA, Dist Assn 1974-; OH Schl Cnslr Assn 1978-, Dist Rep Pub Relations; ASCA, OCA 1990-; BSA, Cub Scouts 1990-, Asst Scout Master, Webelo Ldr, Started New Troop; *office:* Miamisburg Sr HS 1860 Belvo Rd Miamisburg OH 45342

BERRY, EDGAR ALLEN, Instrumental Director; *b:* Columbus, OH; *m:* Michelle W.; *ed:* OH St Univ (BME) Music Ed 1992; *cr:* Huron HS Instrumental Dir 1992-; *ai:* Var Girls Asst Bsktbl Coach; Jr Class Trip Adv; Musical Dir; OMEA 1990-; MENC 1992-; OEA 1992-; BSA 1976-, Eagle Scout; Order of the Arrow 1986-, Chief, Vigil Hnr; Huron Chamber of Commerce Comm Awd for Dedication to Band Pgm; *office:* Huron HS 710 Cleveland Rd W Huron OH 44839*

BERRY, JAMES EDWARD, 8th Grade English Teacher; *b:* Cumberland, MD; *m:* Nancy Jane; *c:* Nathan, Meredith; *ed:* Mount St Marys Coll (BS) Ed 1972; Frostburg St Univ (MS) Counseling Psych 1980; *cr:* Washington MS 8th Grd Eng Tchr 1972-88; Allegany HS Guidance Cnslr 1988-91; Braddock MS 8th Grd Eng Tchr 1991-; *ai:* Team Ldr; Spelling Bee Coord; NEA, Allegany Cty Tchrs Assn, MD St Tchrs Assn 1972-; St Patricks Cath Church 1981-; Allegany Cty Bd of Ed Cert of Recognition; *home:* 716 White Ave Cumberland MD 21502

BERRY, JOHN WALTER, Instrumental Music Teacher; *b:* Whitesboro, NY; *m:* Paula Ann Mills; *ed:* SUCE at Potsdam (BS) Music Ed 1952; NC Univ (MA) Educl Media 1969; Addl Hrs at: Univ of MI at Ann Arbor Music

28, Owoudaga Comm Coll Cmptr Sci 15; *cr:* Ououdaga Cntrl Schls HS Music 1955-58; Syracuse City Schls General Music 1958-59; East Syracuse Winoa HS Music, Jr High Elem 1959-; *ai:* Dist Instrument Repair Person; Stage Band Dir; Pres ESM Federal Credit Union 7 Yrs & Tchrs Assn 1967-68; AFT; MENC; NYSSMA; NY St Bd Dirs Assn; CNY Flute Assn; Syracuse Power Squadron 1985-, Ed Officer 1990-93, Navigation Instr 1985-90; NC Fellowship for Educl Media for Disadvantaged 1969; Cert Metware Admin; *office:* Fremont Elem Schl Richmond Rd W East Syracuse NY 13057

BERRY, LA RUE, Art Teacher; *b:* Lancaster, PA; *m:* Charles A.; *c:* Chuck, Shane; *ed:* Kutztown Univ (BS) Art Ed 1959; Fairleigh Dickinson Univ (MA) Human Dev; Addl 47 Credits; Prin & Supvr Cert; *cr:* Livingston Schl Dist Art Tchr 1959-61; Mt Olive Schl Dist Art Tchr 1976-; *ai:* Natl Art Honor Soc; NAEA, NJEA, EAMO; Tchr of Yr 1990.

BERRY, LLEWELLYN L.,III, Radio Production Instructor; *b:* Washington, DC; *c:* Jenifer; *ed:* Parsons Coll (BA) Eng, Comparative Lit 1969; Univ of DC (MS) Media, Information Learn Systems 1975; *cr:* Lit Arts Prgm Photo Jrnlsm Tchr 1971-84; Urban Jrnlsm Wkshp Photo Jrnlsm Tchr 1971-84; Lemuel Penn Career Ctr Photo Jrnlsm Tchr 1971-86; Duke Ellington Schl of Arts Radio Production, Broadcast Tchr 1986-; *ai:* Arts Chairs; Lit Arts, Media Co-Chair; Pan Africa Org Chair; WDUK Radio Gen Mgr; Natl Assn Black Journalists 1996; Numerous Pvt Fnd Grants; Grant to Establish Stu Broadcast News Network; Outstdng Tchr Awd 1977, 1978, 1979; *office:* Duke Ellington Schl Of Arts 3500 R St NW Washington DC 20007

BERRY, MARGARET ELAINE, English Teacher & Dept Chair; *b:* Durham, NC; *ed:* E Carolina Univ (BS) Eng 1976; Johns Hopkins Univ (MLA) 1984; Univ of MD at College Park 27 Grad Credits in Eng; *cr:* Chesapeake HS Eng Tchr 1978-92; Sparrows Point HS Eng Tchr & Dept Chair 1992-; *ai:* Forensics Coach; Class Spon; TABCO, MSTA & NEA 1978-; ASCD; MCTELA & NCTE; Johns Hopkins Univ Alumni Assn 1984-; Exec Womens Golf 1992-; USGA; PTA; 1993 Participant in Natl Endowment for the Hum Summer Seminar for Schl Tchrs; 1995 Cncl for Basic Ed Ind Stud in the Hum Fellow; *office:* Sparrows Point HS 7400 N Point Rd Baltimore MD 21219

BERRY, NANCY W., Accounting Professor; *b:* Indiana, PA; *m:* Charles E. Galgoci; *c:* Stephen; *ed:* Bucknell Univ (BA) His 1968; IN Univ (MA) Russian His 1974; PA St Univ (MBA) Accounting 1978; Grad Level Work Accounting, Intnl Bus Statistics 1985-87; *cr:* Piper Aircraft Corp Mgr, Taxes 1978-84; Lock Haven Univ Asst Prof 1984-89, Assoc Prof 1989-; *ai:* Convisor Duffy CPA Review Course Local Instr; Alpha Kappa Psi Prof Bus Fraternity for Stdnts Adv; Dept of Cmptr Sci, Mgmt, Accounting Chprsn; Inst of Mgmt Accts 1978-, Cntrl PA Chapter Dir of Yr 1981-82, 1984-85; Amer Acct Assn 1988-; Amer Inst of CPAs, PA Inst of CPAs 1991-; *office:* Lock Haven Univ 224 Akeley Bldg Lock Haven PA 17745

BERRY, ROBERT H., Global Studies I Teacher; *b:* Carbondale, PA; *m:* Cecilia Anne; *c:* Jeff, Jason, Lynn, Ann Tella, Yasmin Samahon, Tuan Samahon, Rohan Samahon; *ed:* St Univ of NY (BS) Ed, His, Geo & Lit 1966; Brockport NY (MS) Ed, His, Geo & Culture 1971; U of Scranton Bus Admin; U of Rochester Bus Admin; Post Grad 18 Credits Hrs; *cr:* West Ironde Quoit Schl Dist 6th Grd Tchr 1966; Webster Cntrl Schls 7th-9th Grd Tchr 1966-; *ai:* After Schl Skill Dev; Magic Club Adv; NYSUT 1966-; AFT 1966-; Webster Tchrs Assn 1966-, Politician Office Chair, Exec Cncl, Sr Bldg Rep & Rep Cncl; Natl Cncl of Geog Ed; NYASA; Roch Area Cncl for SS; NY St Cncl for Soc Stud; Phi Delta Kappa; ASCD; St Lukes Episcopal Church 1976-, Ed Comm Chair 2 Yrs, Property Comm 20 Yrs; PTA; Taft Seminar GWU 1976; US Fulbright Summer Pgm Korea 1984; US Fulbright Summer Pgm China 1994; *office:* Webster Central Schls 800 Five Mile Line Rd Webster NY 14580

BERRY, THOMAS, Mathematics Teacher; *b:* Williamsport, PA; *m:* Cynthia M. Childs; *c:* Joel, Janine, Thomas; *ed:* Lock Haven Univ (BS) Math 1969; Villanova Univ (MA) Educl Admin; Addl Credits from Montclair St Coll, William Patterson Coll, Rutgers Univ & Seton Hall Univ; *cr:* The Chrisitan Acad 7th-12th Grd Math Tchr 4 Yrs; Wharton Bd of Ed Dir of NJ Title IV-C Math Project 4 Yrs; Scoth Plain-Fanwood Bd of Ed 9th-12th Grd Math Tchr 2 Yrs; Midland Park Bd of Ed Schl Bus Admin & Bd Sec 2 Yrs; Bloomfield Bd of Ed 7th & 8th Grd Math Tchr 7 Yrs; *office:* Bloomfield MS 60 Huck Rd Bloomfield NJ 07003*

BERRYMAN-SINGLETON, TRACEY LYNNE, 5th Grade Math Teacher; *b:* Richmond, VA; *m:* William H. Singleton; *c:* Alonzo, Sade, Marcel; *ed:* Morgan St Univ (BS) Ed 1989; *cr:* Green Valley Elem 4th-5th Grd Tchr 1989-; *ai:* Friendly HS Asst Track Coach; NEA, PGCEA 1989-.

BERSANO, JUDY ELIZABETH, Biology Teacher; *b:* Paterson, NJ; *ed:* William Paterson Coll (BA) Bio 1972, (MA) Bio 1977; 60 Credit Hrs Post Grad Guid, Cnslng, Admin, Supervision, Bio; *cr:* Ramsey HS Bio Tchr 1972-; *ai:* Jr Class Adv; NHS Cncl; HS Renewal, Schlsp Comms; NEA, NJEA, Bergen Cty Ed Assn 1972-; Ramsey Teacher Assn 1972-, Exec 1995-97; NJ Audubon Soc, Natl Audobon Soc, NJ Sci Tchr, NSTA, Natl Inter Wildlife Assn 1972-; 1st Clinical Inst Tchrs; 1st NJ Govenors Awd Excl Tchng; *office:* Ramsey HS 266 E Main St Ramsey NJ 07446

BERSCHE, JAMES H., Social Studies Teacher; *b:* Fairmont, WV; *m:* Linda F. Lombardo Adelman; *ed:* Wheaton Coll (BA) Pol Sci 1955; Eastern MI Univ (MA) Sec Admin 1962; Bowling Green St Univ (EDS) Admin 1977; Lawrence Inst of Tech Bldg Construction 1960-62; Oakland Univ 1963; Nyack Coll 1950-51; Ashland Coll 1979; Drake Univ 1991; *cr:* Crary Jr HS Tchr, Track, Ftbl Coach 1955-62; Bersche Construction co Office Mgr, Bookkeeper 1962-64; Brasscraft Mfr Purchasing Dir 1964-70; Norwalk HS Tchr, Track, C Cntry Coach 1970-; *ai:* NEA 1990-; OH HS Ath Assn 1982-, Track Ofcl, Local Assn Pres; Abigail Pregnancy Ctr 1988-, Treas; Taught Adult Sunday Classes Various Yrs; Norwalk City Charter Review Commission Chair 1985; Jennings Scholar 1985; *office:* Norwalk HS 80 E Main St Norwalk OH 44857

BERSON, JAMES HENRY, Professor of Management; *b:* New York, NY; *m:* Gail F.; *c:* Richard, Lesley; *ed:* U of MI (BS) Chem Engrng 1961, (MBA) Mrktg 1963; Columbia Univ (PHD) Pub Policy 1973; *cr:* M&T Chemicals Inc Supvr of Spec Ventures 1963-68; Polytechnic Inst of Brooklyn Instr 1970-72; BMCC Prof 1972-; *ai:* Deputy Chm Dept of Bus Mgmt; AAHE 1994-; Castle Village Owners Corp 1985-, Chm, Fin Comm; Freedoms Fnd at Vly Forge 1983-, Leavy Awd for Excl in Pvt Enterprise Ed; Annotated Chronological Bibliography of Selected Bus Novels in Eng; Decision-Making in Bus Kendall-Hunt 1988, 1992; *office:* Borough Of Manhattan Comm Coll 199 Chambers St #S661 New York NY 10007

BERST, FRANK J., HS Soc Studies & Soc Sci Tchr; *b:* Buffalo, NY; *m:* Felicia Louise Scaccia; *c:* Leah Patricia; *ed:* Buffalo St Coll (BA) Anthropology & Philosophy 1986; Univ of Buffalo (MA) His 1990; 16 Credit Hrs Toward Doctoral; *cr:* St Thomas Aquinas Schl Jr HS Amer His Tchr 1988-91; Erie Comm Coll Sociology Instr 1990-93; Mount Mercy Acad HS Soc Stud Tchr 1991-; *ai:* Mock Trial & Model United Nations Moderator, Coach; NEA 1988-, Contributing; Buffalo & Erie Cty Civil War Round Table 1987-, Contributor; Natl Trust for Historic Preservation 1991-, Contributor; *office:* Mount Mercy Acad 88 Red Jacket Pky Buffalo NY 14220*

BERTELLO, ANDREW ANGELO, Alumni Coordinator; *b:* Canale D'Alba, Italy; *ed:* Conti Rebaudengo Inst (AA) Pattern Design 1945; RCA Inst NY (AE) Electronics 1961; NYU Eng 1964; *cr:* Bernardi Semeria Tchr 1943-46; Oficinas S. Jose Portugal Dept Head 1946-58; RCA NY Schl Stu 1958-61; Don Bosco Tech Electronics, Cmptr Head 1961-94; *ai:* Drama, Glee Club; Stu Civil Svc.

BERTISCH, CAROLEE ACKERSON, Retired English Teacher; *b:* New York City, NY; *m:* Gerald A.; *c:* Andrew, Michael; *ed:* Sycracuse Univ (BA) Eng-Cum Laude 1956; Manhattan Coll (MAH) Hum-Hnrs 1974; Lehman Coll Post Grad Flwshp, Rsrch & Tchng of Writing; Tchrs Coll Columbia 90 Hrs Posd Grad Work Writing, Supervising Stu Tchrs; *cr:* Massapequa HS Eng Tchr 1956-57; Rye Neck HS Eng, Soc Stud Tchr 1973-78; Rye Neck HS MS Writing Coord, Eng Facilitator 1979-95; *ai:* Panther St Schl Newspaper, Lit Magazine Writers of Month; Prof Dev Comm; Westchester Yourn Writers Contest Coord; AFT, UFT, NCTW 1973-; NY St Tchrs of Eng 1984-, NY St Tchr of Excl; Westchester Cncl of Eng Edcts, VP; Lehman Coll Matsushita Flwshp; Pub Articles; Westchester Outstdng Tchr Gannett Publications; Grant SUNY Purchase Tchrs Ctr; *home:* 56 Rock Ridge Dr Rye Brook NY 10573*

BERTOCCI, ROSEMARY JUEL, Associate Professor; *b:* Pittsburgh, PA; *m:* Francis H. Rohlf; *ed:* Carnegie Mellon Union (BA) Eng 1983; St Vincent Seminary (MA) Theology 1986; Duquesne Univ (PHD) Systematic Theology 1995; *cr:* St Francis Coll Assoc Prof; *ai:* Delta Epsilon Sigma Adv Head; Svc Learning Admin; NHS Tchr of Yr; *office:* Saint Francis Coll PO Box 600 Loretto PA 15940

BERTOLAMI, LORRAINE MAIER, High School Mathematics Tchr; *b:* Jersey City, NJ; *m:* Renald; *c:* John; *ed:* Fairleigh Dickinson Univ (BA) Elem Ed 1971; 25 Post-Grad Credits Trenton St Coll 1989; *cr:* St Matthew Schl Grds 6-8 Math Tchr 1972-77; St Peter Schl Grd 5 Math Tchr 1982-84; Barnegat Schl Grd 8 Math Tchr 1984-89; Point Pleasant Beach Schl HS Math Tchr 1989-; *ai:* Math League Adv; NCTM 1989-; NEA 1986-; Tchr of Yr 1993-94; *office:* Pt Pleasant Beach HS 700 Trenton Ave Point Pleasant Bea NJ 08742

BERTOLINI, EDWARD ALBERT, Social Studies Teacher; *b:* Englewood, NJ; *ed:* Manhattan Coll (BA) Pol Sci 1980; Grad Work Montclair St Univ Admin & Supervision; *cr:* Paramus Cath Soc Stud Tchr 1980-, Soc Stud Chair 1984-95, Dir of Ath 1987-95; *ai:* Model Congress Moderator; Jr Class Moderator; Advy Cncl to Admin; *office:* Paramus Cath Girls HS 425 Paramus Rd Paramus NJ 07652

BERTOLINO, LINDA WINGARD, Cheerleading Coach; *b:* Winthrop, MA; *m:* Leonard Peter; *c:* J. Christopher, William O.; *ed:* Attnd Northeast LA St Univ; *cr:* Dental Asst; Hertz Corp Sales Rep; Home Interiors Sales Distributor; Spring Fnd Sales Distributor; *ai:* Weymouth Pop Warner Ftbl Chrldrs Coord, Coach; So Shore Midget Ftbl Chrldng Asst Dir; Chrldrs Assn Summer Camp Dir Nat; Weymouth HS Homecoming Comm Adv; So Shore Parochial Schl Bsktbl League Comm; Amer Assn for Chrldr Coaches & Advs; Our Savior's Luth Church Rel Ed Tchr, Choir, Teen Yth Group Adv; Ralph Talbot Elem Schl Parent Cncl Pres; So Shore Viking Assn Stenkil Lodge #92; Weymouth Pop Warner Steve Ondrick Awd; Bd of Dirs & dedication; Presenter of Linda Bertolino Awd to Deserving Ath; *home:* 81 May Ter South Weymouth MA 02190

BERTONE, JOHN ANTHONY, Asst Prof of New Testament; *b:* Niagara Falls, Canada; *m:* Beth Joy Hoban; *c:* Jonathan Christian; *ed:* Southeastern Coll of the Assemblies of God)BA) Biblical Stud 1989; Mc Master Univ (MDiv) New Testment 1992; Princeton theological Sminary (THM) New Testment 1993; Grad Rdng Course in Ger; Attnd Ursinus Coll, West Chester Univ; *cr:* Amer Motors Corp Production Scheduler1981-82; Slater Steels Corp Production Scheduler 1983-90; Vly Force Chrstn Coll Asst Prof of New Testment 1993-; *ai:* Soc of Biblical Lit 1993-; Soc of Pentecostal Stud 1996; Sisters of Charity Hosp 1991-, Stu Chaplian; Hotel Dieu Hosp 1991-92, Vol Chaplain; High Hnrs Southeastern Coll, Mc Master U, Princeton; *office:* Valley Forge Christian Coll 1401 Charlestown Rd Phoenixville PA 19460*

BERTONI, SHEILA SCANLON, Specialist & Recovery Teacher; *b:* Scranton, PA; *m:* Louis F. Jr.; *c:* Ryan, Briana; *ed:* Mansfield Univ (BS) Elem Ed 1975; Elmira Coll (MS) Rdng 1982; 6 Grad Hrs NYU Certfd Rdng Recovery Tchr; *cr:* Washington Gladden Schl First Grd Tchr 1976-82; Owego Elem Schl First Grd Tchr 1982-93, Rdng Specialist & Rdng Recovery Tchr 1993-; *ai:* Lang Arts Comm; Dir Childrens Programming Tioga Cty Cncl on the Arts; Co-Chair Acad Design Model Comm; Scorer NY St Tchr Examinations; IRA 1990-; BARC 1982-; NYSRA 1991-; ACE 1993-; Tchrs as Readers Founder; Writers Wkshp Centers, Early Literacy, Rdng Strategies; Literacy Act & Parents Success Grant 1995-; *office:* Owego Elem Schl George St Owego NY 13827

BERTRAND, LINDA J., High School English Teacher; *b:* Syracuse, NY; *ed:* St Univ of NY at Potsdam (BA) Eng Ed 1973; Post Grad Stud 30 Credit Hrs NY St Tchr Cert; Post Grad 6 Credit Hrs Towards Masters Ed; *cr:* Morristown Cntrl Schl Scndry Eng Tchr 1973-74; Heuvelton Cntrl Schl Scndry Eng Tchr 1975-; Mater Dei Coll Adjunct Eng Prof 1992-; *ai:* Lit Club Adv; New Restructuring of Schls Dist Rep; Shared Decision Team HS Grd Level Comm; AFT 1980-; HCS Tchrs Assn 1975-, Treas; NCTE 1993-; Mater Dei Coll 1995-, Continuing Ed Advy Bd; Participate in Poetry Presentations for Ogdensburg Pub Lib; *office:* Heuvelton Central Schl Washington St Heuvelton NY 13654

BERTRAND, WAYNE CHARLES, Health Educator; *b:* Cohoes, NY; *m:* Sylvia Arnold; *c:* Sara, Dana; *ed:* St Univ of NY at Brockport (BS) PE 1979; Russell Sage Coll (MS) Hlth Ed 1991; *cr:* Ballston Spa HS Hlth Educator 1985-, Stu Conduct Coord 1994-; *ai:* Var Ftbl Asst Coach 1981-; Var Bsbl Coach 1996; Ftbl Booster Club; NYSTU 1981-; Jr Var Bsbl Coach 1984-95; Frosh Bsktbl Coach 1981-83; Russell Sage Coll Cooperating Tchr for Stu Tchr Trng; Recognized by Russell Sage Grad Schl Hlth Ed Dept for Acting as a Consultant for Grad Thesis & Project Seminar; *office:* Ballston Spa HS 480 Garrett Rd Ballston Spa NY 12020*

BERTSCH, HAL F., Accounting Teacher; *b:* Pottsville, PA; *m:* Karen Kovel; *c:* Ryan; *ed:* Bloomsburg St Coll (BS) Bus Ed 1977, (MEd) Bus 1980; 15 Credit Hrs Past MS; *cr:* Pine Grove Area HS Accounting Tchr 1977; Pottsville Area HS; *ai:* PBEA, PSEA; Dr. Alex Ahy Awd Outstanding Tchr 1984; *office:* Pottsville Area HS 16th & Elk Ave Pottsville PA 17901

BERUBE, JUDITH KANE, Applied Arts Teacher; *b:* Lowell, MA; *m:* Richard O.; *c:* Richard Jr., Elizabeth, Alison Sullivan, Joanne, Monica; *ed:* Boston Univ (BS) Bus Ed 1986; Rivier Coll (MA) Clinical Mental Hlth Cnslng 1994; *cr:* Tewksbury Meml HS Tchr 20 Yrs; *ai:* DECA Adv; Tewksbury Tchrs Assn, NEA, MBEA 1976-; *office:* Tewksbury Memorial HS 320 Pleasant St Tewksbury MA 01876*

BESANTE, JULIA DONNELLY, Home Economics Teacher; *b:* Elizabeth, NJ; *m:* Michael J.; *c:* Mary E., Jamie; *ed:* Coll of St Elizabeth (BS) Home Ec, Ed 1976; Jersey City St Coll Nursery Schl Cert Pre-K Ed 1981; Spec Ed; *cr:* Cntrl Regnl HS Home Ec Tchr 1976-80; Lacey Twp HS Home Ec Tchr 1980-; *ai:* Family Life Curr Comm; NEA, NJEA, Local Affiliates 1976-; Amer Assn Family, Consumer Scientist 1972-; St Joseph's R C Church 1976-, First Communion Coord, Rel Ed Prgm; *office:* Lacey Township HS PO Box 206 Lanoka Harbor NJ 08734*

BESCHER, ARTHUR F.,JR., Social Studies Teacher; *b:* Brooklyn, NY; *ed:* SUNY at Albany (BA) His 1982; MontgomeryCo Pub Schls MEQ Ed 1989; *cr:* John F. Kennedy HS Soc Stud Tchr 1982-88; Quinc Orchard HS Soc Stud Tchr 1988-; *ai:* It's Acad Team Coach; NEA 1983-; *office:* Quince Orcard HS 15800 Quince Orchard Rd Gaithersburg MD 20878*

BESECKER, JAY ALLEN, Science Teacher; *b:* Dayton, OH; *m* Nye; *c:* Todd, Tyler; *ed:* Bowling Green St Univ (BA) Ed 1971; Toward MA Educl Admin, Prin Cert; *cr:* Bluffton HS Bio Tchr Lima South Jr HS Bio, Sci Tchr 1976-90; Lima South MS S 1990-92; Lima South Accelerated MS Sci Tchr 1992-; *ai:* Ath Di Ftbl, Bsktbl, Bsbl, Golf, Wrestling Coach.*

BESECKER, SCOTT JOE, Math & Science Teacher; *b:* Piqua, Patricia J.; *c:* Nikole, Anthony; *ed:* Edison St Comm coll (AS) 1977; Wright St Univ (BSEd) Sci, Ed 1979, (MED) Principalship Hrs Beyond MED in Ed, Admin, Math, Physics & Cmptr Sci; *cr:* T Schls 7th Grd Sci Tchr 1979-84; Bradford Ex Vill Schls 7-8 M Chem, Phys Tchr 1986-; *ai:* HS Bsktbl 8 Yrs; Var Girls Bsktbl Coac Vllybl 3 Yrs; Jr Hs Ath Dir 2 1/2 Yrs; OH Cncl Tchrs in Math 19 HS Bsbl Coaches Assn 1986-95; OH HS Vlybl Coaches Assn Wright St Univ Camp Discovery Math Mem 1995-; Co-Appli Mini-Grant for Purchasing Laser Equipment for HS Sci Demons Labs; *office:* Bradford Ex Vill Schls 712 N Miami Ave Bradf 45308*

BESHORE, SHARON FITZ, Instructional Support Teacher; *b:* Y *m:* Richard E.; *c:* Rebecca, Julia, R. J.; *ed:* Millersville Univ (BS Spec Ed 1976; 30 Credits; *cr:* Red Lion Schl Dist Spec Ed Tchr Instrl Support-Drop-Out Prevention 1988-; *ai:* Successful Stu Part Co-Adv NHS; Stu Assistance Team; NEA, RLAEA 1976-; Jr Le York 1984-; Exemplary Prgm Awd Shippensburg Univ Schl S *office:* Red Lion Area Sr HS 200 Horace Mann Ave Red Lion PA

BESOLD, STEPHEN GERARD, Social Studies Teacher; *b:* Bro *m:* Nancy Palie; *ed:* Westfield St Coll (BA) Sec Ed 1976; Harva (MA) His 1993; Addl 12 Credit Hrs; *cr:* Bubbling Brook Schl Tch 1977-78; North Jr HS Spec Needs, Resource Room Tchr Broomfield Schl Soc Stud Tchr 1984-; *ai:* Sr Class Adv; Bsktbl Prof Dev Points Comm; NEA, HTA 1984-; BFOE 1981-; Featured *office:* The Bromfield Schl 14 Massachusetts Ave Harvard MA 01

BESS, JOYCE, Second Grade Teacher; *b:* Jamestown, NY; *ed.* Fredonia (MS) Dev Rdng 1977; *cr:* Persell Elem Schl Second G 1974-88; Lincoln Elem Schl Second Grd Tchr 1988-96; *ai:* Nego Comm; NFA, J Tchrs Assn 1974-; Jamestown Human Rights Com 1986-; *office:* Lincoln Elem Schl 301 Front St Jamestown NY 147

BESSE, GERALD A., Soc Studies Teacher & Director; *b:* Coving *m:* Judith Marchetti; *c:* Anthony, Annemarie; *ed:* Thomas More C His 1971; Northern KY Univ (MED) 1976; Univ of KY K-12 F 1978; *cr:* Blessed Sacrament Schl 7th-8th Grd Tchr 1972-82; St A Schl 7th Grd Tchr 1982-; *ai:* Acad Team, Speech Team Coach NCEA 1972-; N KY Jaycees 1976-; OH Vly Inst Grant 1983; *o* Antoninus Schl 5425 Julmar Dr Cincinnati OH 45238

BESSETTE, NORMAND H., Spanish Teacher; *b:* pawtucket, Noella B.; *c:* Nicole; *ed:* Cath Univ of Amer (BA) Fr Lit 1965; Riv (MA) Fr 1972; 30 Credits Span; *cr:* St Augustine HS Fr Tchr Bishop Bradley HS Fr Tchr 1968-72; East Greenwich HS Fr, Sp 1972-; *ai:* Natl Span Contest; NEA 1972-; *office:* East Greenwich Avenger Dr East Greenwich RI 02861

BESSLER, CATHERINE LYNN, French & English Teac Cincinnati, OH; *ed:* Univ of Cincinnati (BS) Scndry Ed 1971; 27 Hrs Grad Schl; *cr:* Delhi Jr HS Fr & Eng Tchr 1971-; *ai:* Fr Clu Dept Head; Past Dir & Choreographer of Jr HS Eaglettes; *office:* HS 5280 Foley Rd Cincinnati OH 45238

BESSLER, TIMOTHY JOSPEH, English Teacher; *b:* Cincinnati, Univ of Cincinnati (BS) Ed 1975; 24 Semester Hrs in Admin; *cr:* O Local Schl Dist Eng Tchr 1975-; *ai:* Shakespeare Troupe Dir; *offic* Jr HS 5280 Foley Rd Cincinnati OH 45238

BEST, ALLAN WILLIAM, Psych, Ec & Soc Stud Teacher; *b:* B NY; *ed:* Edinboro St Univ (BS) Soc Stud 1962; Univ of SD (MA) E His 1967; *cr:* Westfield HS Tchr, Coach 1962-64; Cassadaga H Coach 1964-65; Elk Point HS Tchr, Coach 1966-67; Amer Embas Contract 1968-71; Greece Cntrl Schls Tchr, Coach 1971-; *ai:* Bsktbl, Track Coach; NEA 1971-; WBCA 1990-; Monroe Cty Bsktbl League 1985-, Chair; Asian Schlsp Stud Univ of SD 1966 of Yr Section 5 1978, 1981; Coach of Yr Eastman Kodak Class 1986, 1991, 1993-94; Coach of Yr Monroe Cty 1981, 1986, 1991, Team Sportsmanship Awd 1985, 1991, 1993-95; NY St Empire Coach Region 6 1978-82, 1993-; Recognized 'The Spcl Tchr' by S Fredonia 1995; *office:* Greece Athena HS 800 Long Pond Rd Roche 14612

BEST, CHARLES E.,JR., 8th Grade Teacher; *b:* Wilson, Bridgette Lowe; *c:* Charles E. III, Tomica Layfay, Kalissa Quastawn Anthony; *ed:* Fordham Univ Law Schl (PHD) Criminal Kean Coll (BA) Early Chldhd, Elem Ed 1983, (MA) Spec Ed 1 Orange Child Dev Group Tchr 1983-85; Mt Vernon Elem Schl 8th 1985-; *ai:* Sophisticated Gents Boys Club Adv; AFT 1986-; Phi Be 1985-, Dir of Ed, Outstdng Comm Svc; Epsilon Phi Epsilon 199 Outstdng Comm Ldr; NAACP 1981-; Elizabeth Gen Hosp Sic Anemia Fnd, Vol 1983-85; Vol Fashion Designer; Orange Child Outstdng Tchr Achvmt 1984; Kean Coll of NJ Outstdng Achv 1983-84; Epsilon Omega 1983-84; Black Stu Union Outstdng 1983; 1st Place March of Dimes Dance Marathon 1989; 1s Runner-Up Best Male Ldr of Comm NC Tech; Outstdng Achvmt Aw Outstdng Achvmt Awd 1989, 1991, 1992; Outstdng Young Man Awd 1988-90; *home:* 1171 Main St Apt 7H Rahway NJ 07065

BEST, DOROTHY DILUZIO, 3rd-5th Grd Basic Skills Tchr; May, NJ; *m:* Paul; *c:* Megan, Danielle; *ed:* Waynesburg Coll (BA) 1975; 30 Addl Hrs; Attnd St Joseph's Univ; *cr:* Upper Twp Elem Grd Tchr 1976-95, 3-5 Grd Basic Skills Tchr 1995-; *ai:* Trouble Mentor; NEA 1976-; NCTM 1994-; St John's Luth Church, Sub Schl Tchr; Presidential Awd Excl in Math Tchng 1994-95; Tch 1988-89; *office:* Upper Twp Elem Schl 50 Old Tuckahoe Rd Marr 08223

BEST, HARRY M.,III, Technology Education Teacher; *b:* West PA; *m:* Karen Joyce; *c:* David Jose, Zachary David; *ed:* Millersvi (BS) Indstrl Arts Ed 1971; *cr:* Stebon MS Tchr 1972-82; Eat 1982-84; Fugett MS Tchr 1982-84; Peru MS Tchr 1984-88; Hend HS Tech Ed Tchr 1988-; *ai:* MS Track, Gymnastics, Head St Cham HS Advanced Girls Gymnastics 1992-94, PA St Gymnastics Team Coach; PSEA 1971-, Bldg Rep; Brian's Run, Comm Head 16 Yr Schl Night, Pres; *office:* Henderson Sr HS Lincoln & Montgome West Chester PA 19380

BESTEN, JOHN JOSEPH, Instrumental Music Teacher; *b:* Spri MA; *m:* Susan O'Connor; *c:* Richard, Karen; *ed:* Onondaga Con (AAS) Music 1973; Syracuse Univ (BM) Music Ed 1975; 30 Ad Hrs; 3 Grad Hrs at Potsdam Crane Schl of Music; *cr:* LaFayette Cn Instrumental Music Tchr 1975-76; Syracuse Parochial Schls Instr Music Tchr 1976-78; LaFayette Jr & Sr HS Instrumental Music Tch *ai:* Drama Productions Musical Dir; Dixieland Combo & Marchin Dir; Schl Improvement Team 1988-92; NEA & LaFayette Tch 1975-; Onondaga Cty Music Educators 1978-, VP 1987-89; NY Dir Assoc; Onondaga Cty Music Ed Wind Ensemble 1986-, Tubis

NY Brass Quintet 1982-94 Tubist 12 Yrs; *office:* LaFayette Jr & Sr 11 N La Fayette NY 13084

PROCTOR, YVONNE DENISE, Business Education Teacher; *b:* A; *m:* Edward Daniel Proctor; *c:* Lance Edward Proctor; *ed:* Robert Coll (AS) Secretarial Sci 1985, (BS) Bus Admin 1987, (MS) Bus 3; 30 Addl Hrs; *cr:* Bradford Area Schl Dist Bus Ed Tchr 1987-89; us Ctr Bus Ed Tchr 1989-93; Strong Vincent HS 1989-; *ai:* Future Irs of Amer, Region, Sr, Jr Class, Prom Adv; NBEA, EBEA, PSEA DPE 1993-; Erie Ed Assn 1989-; Erie Bus Ctr 1990-, Adv Bd; Strong t HS 1994-95 Tchr of Yr; John Hinman Tchr Flwshp Applicant 1996; Strong Vincent HS 1330 W 8th St Erie PA 16502*

GH, MARYFLOR SANDRA, Spanish Teacher; *b:* Caracas, ela; *m:* Nicolas Martin; *c:* Nicole M., Kristie S.; *ed:* Villanova Univ cndry Ed, Span 1973, (MS) Guid, Cnslng in Sec Ed 1976; *cr:* Garnet S Span Tchr 1973; Lower Merion HS Span Tchr 1974-; *ai:* Spon of 1986; Two Exch Prgms 1991, 1995; Fac Senate Treas 1995-; FL, PASE 1995-; AATSP 1991-; PLEA, NEA, LMEA 1978-; ng Contribution to Schl & Comm John Fritz Brennan Awd 1985-86; Lower Merion HS 301 Montgomery Ave Ardmore PA 19003*

ULAUD, YVETTE, HS Spanish & French Teacher; *b:* Vinh, m; *c:* Fabienne Hordern, Francois, Sophie; *ed:* Univ of Akron (BS) 0; Fr Univ of Kent; *cr:* Fr Radio, TV 1964-; Brunswick HS Fr, Span 990-; *ai:* Fr Club, Span Club Adv; Akron Shelter for Homeless Vol; NEA, OFLA 1990-; Intnl Inst 1983-, Vol Tchr; Frgn Lang Wkshp for Stdnts; Discipline Comm; *office:* Brunswick HS 3581 Center Rd vick OH 44212*

HER, RONALD E., Advanced Placement Eng Teacher; *b:* Eureka, Dorian Kim; *ed:* Coll of Emporia (BA) Eng, Fr, Ger, Ed 1971; Attnd ches Lehrergangsheim, Dept of Defense Dependents Schls Hum sium in Bejing, UC at Berkley, Univ of Boston, La Verne Univ, ad St Univ, MI St Univ, San Diego St, Univ of HI at Hilo, KS St *cr:* SOS Kinderdorf Fr, Eng, Math Tchr 1971; Scott City KS Comm il Prep, Eng, Ger, Jrnlsm Tchr 1971-74; Dept of Defense Dependent Eng, Ger, Fr Tchr 1974-77; DODDS Taegu Korea Amer Schl Eng, Fr, hr 1977-90; Kaeym Young Univ Eng Tchr, Re-Cert Prgm 1985-88; g-bok Natl Med Univ Eng Conversation Tchr 1988-90; DODDS a Japan Edgren HS AP Eng, Fr, Ger Tchr 1990-; AVID Coord; *ai:* ac Cncl; Schl Improvement Comm Chair; Guidance Advy Cncl; Authors Soc; DODDS Pacific Region Writing Task Force, World Writing Assessment Comm; Tchng Stud Bldg Based Facilitator; a Japan Educators' Day Comm Chair; Sr Class Authentic ment; Overseas Ed, Northeast Asis Tchrs Assns 1990-; NEA 1990-, p 1991-92; Phi Delta Kappa 1992-, Misawa Club Exec Bd 1993; PTA 1992-, Rug Bazaar Comm; Royal Asiastic Soc 1978-; Scottish Free Masonry, Fidelity Lodge 1971-; Midian Temple 1971-, Nobel; oosters Club 1990-; Auction Comm 1993-; officers' Spouse Club Bazaar 1992-; DODDS Spec Act Merit Awds 1990, 1992, 1994; Warrior Korean Poetry 1st, 2nd Place Entries; DODDS Okinawa Publication; Yrbk Dedications 1973, 1989; Sustained Superior Mrt 995; *office:* Edgren HS PSC 76 Gen Del Misawa AB Japan APO AP

ENCOURT, HELEN GUTHRIE, 3rd Grade Teacher; *b:* Taunton, : Clifford W.; *c:* Wayne, Susan Williamson, Maureen, Mark, Linda; amingham St Coll (BSEd) Elem Ed 1958; *cr:* Martin Schl 1st Grd 3 Yrs, 3rd Grd Tchr 11 Yrs; *ai:* TEA 1972-; NEA; MTA; *home:* 100 d St Raynham MA 02767

ENCOURT, JOSEPH SOUSA,JR., Professor of Biology; *b:* idge, MA; *m:* Martha Gerroir; *c:* Theresa, Joseph, James; *ed:* Univ (AB) Bio 1962; Univ of New Hempshire (MS) Zoology 1965, Zoology 1976; *cr:* Marist CAoll Instr 1965-67, Asst Prof 1968-77, Prof 1978-; *ai:* Sigma Zeta Sci, Math Hnr Soc Adv; Fac Exec, Ath Chm Dept Bio; Hlth prof Adv; Amer Assn for Adv Sci, Amer Soc rasitology 1965-; Sigma Xi Hn Soc 1964-; Mid-Hudson Med Ed tium 1993-; Physical Handicapped Sci Grant NSF; Tchr of Yr Awd office: Marist Coll 82 North Dr Poughkeepsie NY 12603

ERLY, JOHN ANDREW, His Independence Fndtn Chair; *b:* on, PA; *m:* Nancy Cushman; *c:* John, Margaret Robinson, Jessica, Barkley; *ed:* Yale Univ (BA) His 1955; Harvard Univ (MA) His Attnd Univ of NC at Asheville, Russell Sage Coll; *cr:* WY Seminary 958-62; St Marys Hall His Dept Head 1962-66; Emma Willard Schl 966-; *ai:* Black & Hispanic Awareness Adv; Employee Benefits Fulbright India, Japan Soc & NY St Regents Grants; *office:* Emma 1 Schl 285 Pawling Ave Troy NY 12180*

I, MARIE BENOVITCH, Mathematics Teacher; *b:* Peckville, PA; othy M.; *c:* Natasha, Santina, Francesca; *ed:* Marywood Coll (BS) Ed & Math 1990; Working Towards Masters; Certfd Stu Assistance r: LaSalle Acad Comp Tchr 1992; St Pauls Comp Tchr 1992; Sacred r-Sr High Math & Comp Tchr 1992-; *ai:* Newspaper Club; Hnr Soc; cl; Math Counts Coach; NPCTM 1993-; *office:* Sacred Heart HS 44 ch St Carbondale PA 18407*

IS, GAIL MEREDITH, Biology Teacher; *b:* Brooklyn, NY; *m:* Chisholm; *c:* Chane Chisholm; *ed:* Queens Coll (BA) Bio 1983; gh Dickinson Jr Coll of Dental Medicine (DMD) Dentistry 1987; *cr:* lls Ctr Inc Bio Tchr 1993-94; Sci Skills Ctr HS Bio Tchr 1994-; *ai:* yn Regents Bio Exam Comm 1995-; Bio Turnkey Meetings sion, Implementation Bio Curr 1994-; UFT 1994-; Natl Fnd try for Handicapped Svc Awd 1989; Meritorious Svc Awd Queens 983; *office:* Science Skills Ctr HS 49 Flatbush Avenue Ext Brooklyn 201

S, CYNTHIA TUCKER, English Teacher; *b:* Washington, DC; *m:* s Anderson; *ed:* Indiana Univ of PA (BA) Eng 1983, (BS) Eng 1985, Eng, Lit 1991; *cr:* Marion Center Area HS Eng, Latin Yrbk 1983-; k Duties; Sr Class Adv; Mock Trial Adv; Musical Asst; NEA 1983-; 1992; *office:* Marion Center Area HS PO Box 127 Marion Center PA

S, PATRICIA TALIAFERRO, Guidance Counselor; *b:* Pittsburgh, Benjamin Sherman; *c:* Blair, Elizabeth; *ed:* Univ of Pittsburgh (BA) Ed 1973; Duquesne Univ (MS) Ed 1975; Post Grad Stud; *cr:* en Yth Svcs Admin Asst 1975-76; Womens Hlth Svcs Cnslr 1976-77; Coll of Allegheny Co Instr; Project Succeed Cnslr 1991-92; Penn Sr HS Guid Cnslr 1996; *ai:* Asian Stud Conf, African Amer ness Play, Carnegie Mellon, Slippery Rock Univ Stu Advocate Spon; Univ Advy Comm; NEA, Penn Hills Ed Assn 1973-; Allegheny Co Assn, Natl Cnslrs Assn 1985-; Delta Sigma Theta 1975-; Penn Hills ight of Inspiration Awd; All Star Edctr Awd Univ of Pittsburgh, rgh Post Gazette 1995; WAMO Comm Svc Awd; USAF Recruiting Awd; *office:* Penn Hills Sr HS 12200 Garland Dr Pittsburgh PA

S, STEPHEN CHRISTOPHER, Former Instructor; *b:* Paterson, NJ; Inst of Tech (MS) Mngmt Engrng; NJ Inst Tech (BS) Indstrl Engrng; dit Hrs PHD Mngmt Prgm Rutgers Univ Org Mngmt Dept; *cr:* NJ Tech Spec Lecturer 1983-89; Essex Cty Comm Coll Adj Instr 8; William Paterson Coll Adj Instr 1991-95; Passaic Cty Comm Coll st 1991-95; *home:* 22 Howe Ave Nutley NJ 07110*

BETZ, ANNE LOUISE, Mathematics Teacher; *b:* Brooklyn, NY; *m:* John H.; *c:* John, Carolyn, Steven; *ed:* Concordia Coll (AA) Lbrl Arts 1968; Concordia Tchrs Coll (BS) Math Ed 1970; St Johns Univ (MS) Scndry Math Ed 1986; 15 Credits Comp; 9 Credits Math Ed; 9 Credits In Svc Courses; 3 Credits Acctng; 3 Credits Math Supervision; 3 Credits Real World Math; *cr:* Our Savior Luth Sch K-2nd Grd Tchr 1970-72; Redeemer Luth Schl 7th Grd Math & Sci Tchr 1980-81; Jean Nuzzi Jr HS Math Tchr 1983-85 Linden MS Math Tchr 1985-; *ai:* Project Prize After Schl Pgm Math Enrichment Tchr for CUNY Rsrch Fndtn; Dist 29 Math Comm; UFT 1983-; Republican Party Queens Cty Comm Person 1995; NYS Excl Grant for Math Tchr 1986-86; *office:* Linden MS 10989 204th St Jamaica NY 11412*

BETZ, ANTOINETTE CONTE, Eighth Grade Teacher; *b:* Philadelphia, PA; *m:* Joseph M.; *c:* Michael, Elise, Elizabeth Coutts, Margaret Hull; *ed:* Villanova Univ (BA) Amer His 1975, (MA) Amer His 1981; *cr:* Ss Colman-John Neumann Schl Grd 7 Tchr 1977-86, Grd 8 Tchr 1986-; *ai:* Elem Soc Stud Curr Comm; Archdiocese of Phila; Interfaith Hospitaly Network of Main Line; Chair, Soc Justice Comm, SCJN Schl; NCEA 1977-; *office:* SS Colman-John Neumann Schl 372 Highland Ln Bryn Mawr PA 19010

BETZ, MARYANN, Vocational Business Ed Instr; *b:* Akron, OH; *m:* James G.; *c:* Eric G.; *ed:* Univ of Akron (BS) Comp Bus Ed 1973, (MS) Tech Ed 1985; *cr:* Ashtabula Cty JVS Voc Bus Instr 1973-75; Medina Cty Career Ctr Voc Bus Instr 1975-; Univ of Akron Part-Time Lecturer Office Admin 1994-; *ai:* MCVCEA 1975-, Treas (3 Yrs); OH Bus Tchrs 1975-; OH Ed Assn 1978-; NEA 1978-; OH Bus Tchrs Fndtn, Trustee, Sec; Ridgewood Lake Assn, Past Sec; Copley All-Sports Booster Club, Past Trustee; TWIGS; Bus Prof of Amer Adv; Insurance Ed of the Yr; *office:* Medina County Career Ctr 1101 W Liberty St Medina OH 44256

BETZA, BARBARA CARLUCCI, Science Teacher; *b:* Philadelphia, PA; *m:* Steven; *ed:* St Josephs Univ (BS) Bio 1983; Univ of Penn (MS) Cell Bio 1985; Binghamton Univ (MAT) Sci Tchng 1991; *cr:* Maine-Endwell HS Sci Tchr 1993-; *ai:* Sci Olympiad Coach; Future Tchrs Club Adv; NSTA 1993-; NABT 1992-; Alph Sigma Nu 1982-; STANYS, NSTA Wkshp Presenter; *office:* Maine Endwell Sr HS 750 Farm To Market Rd Endicott NY 13760

BETZIG, JAMES WALTER, 8th Grd Math & Algebra Teacher; *b:* Bronx, NY; *m:* Andrea P. Piccirrllo; *c:* James Andrea, Melissa Louise, Thomas Christopher; *ed:* Southern CT Coll (MA) Ed 1973; 6th Yr Admin 1976; Univ of New Haven His 1969; *cr:* St Gabriels Schl 5th Grd Tchr 1969-73; Milford Bd of Ed 8th Grd Math, Algebra Tchr 1973-; *ai:* Jonathan Law HS Head Bsktbl Coach; Coll, HS Sftbl Umpire; HS Vlybl Ofcl; CEA, MEA, NEA 1972-; Milford Umpires Assn 1974-, VP; *office:* Harbroside MS High St Milford CT 06460*

BEUCLER, ROB G., 7th & 8th Grade Math Teacher; *b:* West Union, OH; *m:* Veronica Koehler; *c:* Rob Jr., Brett, Cody; *ed:* Wilmington Coll (BA) Ed 1982; Dayton Univ (MS) Admin 1986; 15 Addl Hrs; *cr:* Eastern Local Schl Dist Elem Tchr 1982-; *ai:* Boys, Girls Var Cross Cntry, Track, Boys Var Bsktbl Coach; Math Curr Comm; OH Bsktbl Coaches Assn 1995-; OH Educl Assn 1982-; OH Track n Field, Cross Cntry Assn 1988-; Dist Cross Cntry Coach of Yr 1992, Track Coach of Yr 1993; *office:* Russellville Elem Schl Box 128 St Rt 125 Russellville OH 45168*

BEUKELMAN, ANN S., Mathematics Teacher; *b:* Grand Rapids, MI; *m:* James; *c:* Jedd, Alison, Braden; *ed:* Hope Coll (BS) Math 1968; Iona Coll (MS) Comp Ed 1988; *cr:* Upper Morelan JHS 1970-73; East Chester Schls Math Tchr 1983-84; Port Chester Schls Math Tchr 1984-87; Tri-Valley Cntrl Schls Math Tchr & Math Curr Coord 1987-93; Ellenville Cntrl Schls Math Tchr 1993-; *ai:* Class 1999 Adv; AFT 1968-; AMTNYS 1985-; NCTM 1990-; Ellenville Reformed Church 1987-; *office:* Ellenville HS 28 Maple Ave Ellenville NY 12428*

BEUKEMA, STEPHEN GRANT, 11th & 12th Grd Soc Stud Tchr; *b:* Binghamton, NY; *m:* Kimberly Swartz; *c:* Johanna, Jackson; *ed:* Binghamton Univ (BS) Soc Sci 1983, (MAT) Ed & His 1993; *cr:* Binghamton City Schl Dist Long Term Sub 1989-93; Whitney Point Schl Dist 11th & 12th Grd Soc Stud Tchr 1994-; *ai:* Resistance Weight Trng Coach; Soc Stud Outcomes, Assessment & Multi Cultural Ed Comms; AFT & NYSUT 1989-; MCROA 1985-, Marine Corps Reserve Ofcrs Assn; NY St Militia 1989-; NCSS 1992-; Broome Cty Historical Soc 1992-; US Marine Corps Reserve 1984-, Armor Ofcr, Rank of Major; *home:* 17 Old Nanticoke Rd Maine NY 13802

BEURSKEN, MICHAEL ROBERT, Chemistry & Physics Teacher; *b:* Amherst, OH; *m:* Sandra K.; *c:* John, Alexandra, Erika, Diana; *ed:* Bowling Green St Univ (BS) Ed 1985; Environmental Physics; Sci Curr Stud Ashland Univ; *cr:* Lorain City Schls Sub Bio Tchr 1985; S Amherst Local Schls HS Sci Tchr 1985-88; Firelands Local Schls Chem, Physics Tchr 1988-; *ai:* Sci Fair Dir; NEA 1985-; Amer Humanist Assn 1995-; *office:* Firelands HS 10643 Vermilion Rd Oberlin OH 44074

BEVAN, CYNTHIA SUSAN, First Grade Teacher; *b:* Mc Kees Rocks, PA; *m:* Richard William; *c:* Steven; *ed:* Clarion Univ (BS) Elem, Early Chldhd 1978; Penn St Master Equivalency Elem; *cr:* Crafton Elem Schl 4th Grd Permanent Sub Tchr 1980-84; Carnegie Elem Schl 1st Grd Tchr 1985-; *ai:* AFT 1980-; *office:* Carnegie Elem Schl Franklin Ave Carnegie PA 15106

BEVAN, RONALD VERLE, Choral Dir & Music Dept Chm; *b:* New Kensington, PA; *ed:* Indiana Univ of PA (BS) Musec Ed 1967, (MED) Music Ed 1974; Columbia Univ (EDM) Arts in Ed 1987, (EDD) Arts in Ed 1989; Attnd Kent St Univ 1978-79, Cincinnati Conservatory of Music 1979; *cr:* Mars Area Schl Dist Edctr 1967-72; Gateway Schl Dist Edctr, Chm 1972-; *ai:* Frosh Class Adv; Music Dept Chair; NEA, MENC, Phi Mu Alpha 1967-; Kappa Delta Pi 1989; Belting & Chest Voice; *home:* 1001 Parkview Dr New Kensington PA 15068*

BEVARD, LARRY RUSSELL, 9th-12th Grd Math Teacher; *b:* Newark, OH; *m:* Karen Rambo; *c:* Kayley; *ed:* Ashland Univ (M) Ed Admin 1993; Muskingua Coll (BS); *cr:* Marion-Elgin HS Math Tchr 1989-90; Zanesville HS Math Tchr 1990-; *ai:* Sr Class Adv; NEA, OEA 1989-; ZEA 1990-; *office:* Zanesville HS 1701 Blue Ave Zanesville OH 43701*

BEVELACQUA, DONNA RAE CACCIATORE, Biology Teacher & Sci Coord; *b:* Johnson City, NY; *m:* Jerome P.; *c:* Kevin, Keith, Denise; *ed:* SUNY Binghamton 30 Hrs Bio; Mercyhurst Coll Bio, Chem 1965; Cornell Univ 6 Credit Hrs 1991-92; Ithaca Coll 9 Credit Hrs 1974; *cr:* Binghamton HS Chem, Bio Tchr 1960-69; Binghamton Psy Ctr Sci Tchr 1971-74; Seton MS 7-8th Grd Math Tchr; Windsor HS Bio Tchr, Sci Coord 1985-; *ai:* Soph Adv; Bio, NY St Tech Ed Mentor; Tech-Prep, Schlsp, Curr Dev Comms; 6-12th Grd Sci Coord; Marine Bio Instr Montauk LI 1985-; STANYS 1985-; NSTA 1993-; NABT 1994-; Grants: Howard Hughes Molecular Bio 1991, Natl Sci Fnd Evolution, Ecology, Behavior 1992, NSF Bio Elmira Coll 1993, NSF Hofstra Univ 1994-, St Tech Ed; *office:* Windsor HS Rt 79 Windsor NY 13865

BEVERLY, ANNE VERONICA,CSJ, Mathematics Teacher; *b:* Brooklyn, NY; *ed:* St Francis Coll (BA) Fr 1965; Brooklyn Coll (MS) Ed 1975; 18 Credits in Admin & Supervision at Fordham Univ; *cr:* Our Lady of Perpetual Help Tchr 1955-57; Marys Nativity Schl Tchr 1957-59; St Patrick Schl Tchr 1959-62; Transfiguration Schl Tchr 1962-66; Colegio Schl Tchr 1966-70; St Charles Borromeu Schl Tchr 1970-77; St Mary Mother of Jesus Schl Tchr 1977-81; St Angela Hall Acad Prin 1981-85; Holy Child Jesus Schl Tchr 1985-89; Holy Spirit Schl Math Tchr 1989-; *ai:* Natl Jr Hnr Soc Moderator; Math, Schl Testing Coord; NATM 1993-; Brooklyn Diocese Elem Math Cncl 1981-, Pres, Outstdng Jr HS Tchr; NSF Grant in Math Univ of Western IL at Moline 1967; *home:* 250 Newkirk Ave Brooklyn NY 11230*

BEVILACQUA, MIQUEL MARIE, Spanish Teacher; *b:* Lewiston, NY; *ed:* Canisius Coll (BA) His, Span 1992; Working Toward MS in Ed; *cr:* St Mary's HS Span Tchr 1994-95; Niagara Falls HS Span Tchr 1995-; *ai:* Lang Club Organizer, Adv; Attendance, Discipline, Peer Mediation Advy Comms; WNYFLEC, NYSAFLT 1994-; St Francis Guild 1993-; *office:* Niagara Falls HS 1201 Pine Ave Niagara Falls NY 14305

BEVINO, JEFFREY F., Head Coach & Dir of Athletics; *b:* Stamford, CT; *m:* Deborah Urbanowicz; *c:* KatieLynne; *ed:* Southern CT St Univ (BS) PE, Driver Ed 1977; MS Sacred Heart Univ (MS) Ed; *cr:* Stamford Bd Ed PE, Driver Ed Tchr 1977-88; St Thomas More Schl Bio Instr 1989-90; Milford Acad Dir Ath, Bio Instr 1990-; *ai:* Head Coach Ftbl, Rated 1 Prep Schl Cntry; Amer Ftbl Coaches Assn 1990-; Elks Club; Article Pub 1988.*

BEWICK, DOROTHY VANVOORHIS, Teacher of Gifted Students; *b:* New Eagle, PA; *m:* Ronald W.; *c:* Ronald Jr.; *ed:* IN St Coll (BS) Elem Ed 1965; Univ of Pittsburgh (MED) Elem Ed 1970; Gifted Ed Credits CA Intermediate Unit; *cr:* Pitcairn Elem Schl Second Grd Tchr 1965-66; Ginger Hill Elem Schl Second Grd Tchr 1967-77; Ringgold Elem Schls Elem Gifted Tchr 1977-; *ai:* PSEA, NEA 1968-; Bus & Prof Women 1970-, Past Sec; Chrstn Mothers Guild 1970-, Past Pres; Monofiga Trust Fund 1977-, Sec; Piloted Open Classroom Prgm 1973; Planned, Implemented Ringgold's Elem Schl Gifted Prgm 1978-; Awded Great Ideas Grant Mon Vly Consortium 1991; Nom PA Tchr of Yr; *office:* Monongahela Elem Ctr 1200 Chess St Monongahela PA 15063

BEWICK, GERI RISPOLI, Drama Director; *b:* Amityville, NY; *m:* Patrick Joseph Jr.; *c:* Patrick, Hannah; *ed:* Marywood Coll (BA) Theater & Ed 1984; *cr:* North Pocono HS Drama Dir of Musicals 1990-; *ai:* AATE 1995-; Cultural Dev Awd PTSA 1993; Lackawanna Cty Yth Pgm Grant 1994, 1996; *home:* 107 Terrace Dr Moscow PA 18444*

BEY, PATRICIA A., English, Lang Arts & Math Tchr; *b:* Camden, NJ; *m:* Thomas Dukes; *c:* Johnika L., LaVaughna; *ed:* Rowand Col of NJ 71 Credit Hrs 1975-78; *cr:* Monroe Twp Pub Schls Sub Tchr 1980-82; REAP Preschl Asst Prgm Coord 1982-84; A. S. Bey Prep Schl Head Classroom Tchr 1984-; *ai:* MST of A Inc 1958-, Comm Chprsn, Sisters Aux, Fin Sec; *office:* Alqueena S. Bey Prep Schl 2725 Winslow Rd Williamstown NJ 08094

BEYER, SARA LASETTA (SCHUTZ), Teaching Assistant; *b:* Elgin, ND; *m:* Dennis Ray; *c:* Amy Renee DeLaHunt, Andrea Gail, Corey Dennis; *ed:* Dickinson St Univ (BA, BS) Eng 1964, (BA, BS) Span 1988; Miami Univ at Oxford (MA) Span 1996; Stud Abroad UNAM at Mexico City, Cuernavaca, Puebla, Granada Spain; Grad Work Univ of ND, ND St Univ, Univ of Mary; *cr:* Bowman HS 1-12 Grd Librn, 9-12 Grd Span Tchr 1964-68; Rhame HS 9-12 Grd Eng Tchr 1969-70; Bowman HS 9-12 Grd Span, Eng Tchr 1981-94; Miami Univ Tchng Asst 1994-; *ai:* Span Club; Jr Class Prom Adv; Bowman Ed Assn RIF Policy, Newman Lounge Comms; Frgn Lang Assn ND 1982-, Sec, Treas 1987-91, Nom Tchr of Yr 1994; AATsP 1982-, St Pres 1986-87; Cntrl Sts Conf on FL 1988-, Advy Cncl; Miami Vly Frgn Lang Alliance 1996; Bowman Luth Church Women 1968-, Pres 1975; Faith Luth Church 1994-; Sigma Delta Pi 1995-; Continuing Ed Schlsp 1995; Ctr for Adolscent Dev Grant 1992; 2 Articles Pub 1988-89; Recognition from Experiemtn in Intnl Living as Coord 1990-91; ND Bd of Higher Ed Grants 1987-88; *office:* Miami Univ Dept of Spanish Oxford OH 45056

BEYERLE, SUSAN D., Supplemental Services Teacher; *b:* Cleveland, OH; *c:* Richard II, Theresa S., Sandee E.; *ed:* Lakeland Comm Coll (AA) Lbrl Arts 1973; Lake Erie Coll (BS) Elem Ed 1976; John Carroll Univ (MED) Learning Disabilities Behavorial Disorders 1983; Cleveland St Univ K-12 Rdng, Supervision Certs; 30 Misc Grad Credits; *cr:* Mayfield City Schls Title I Tutor 1976-79; Painesville City Local Schls Specific Learning Disabilities Grd 9-12 Tchr 1979-94, Supplemental Svcs Tchr 1994-; *ai:* IB-MFE Team Consultant; Inservice Presentations; Bldg Level Planning Comm; NEA, ASCD, LOA, CEC 1979-; Cleveland Museum Natl His 1988-, Docent; OEA 1992 Holloways Human Relations Awd; NCCJ Annual Grants HS Human, Relations Prgm Dev, Maintenance; OH Spec Ed RFP Inclusive Prgms; *office:* Painesville City Local Schls 58 Jefferson St Painesville OH 44077

BEZDEK, JAMES THOMAS, 5th Grade Teacher; *b:* Cleveland, OH; *m:* Cynthia Shadwick; *c:* Mark, Laura; *ed:* Bowling Green St Univ (BSEd) Elem Ed Hpe 1968; Kent St Univ (MSEd) Elem Admin 1972; 28+ Hrs in Gen Course Work; *cr:* Mayfield City Schls Elem PE Tchr 1968-74, 5th Grd Tchr 1974-; *ai:* Jr Ldrshp Cncl & Family Leaders Advs; 7th & 8th Grd Girls Track Coach; Elem Core Team Founder & Mem; Dist CAT Team; Mayfield Ad Assoc' 1968-, VP; NEA 1968-; Mayfield Hts Jaycees 1970-82 VP; Highland Hts Park & Rec Comm 1990-; Martha Holden Jennings Awd & Schlsp 1982; Mayfield Schls Excl Fndtn Awd 1987; Mayfield Schls Excl Awd 9 Times; *office:* Mayfield Ctr Elem Schl 6625 Wilson Mills Rd Richmond Heights OH 44143

BHAGOJI, SHAMTANU A., Computer Teacher; *b:* Narayanpet, Andhre Pradesh; *ed:* Osmanis Univ in India (BS) Biological Sci 1972; RIT at Rochester NY (MS) Cmptr Sci 1986; *cr:* MCI Bunners Inst Cmptr Instr Instr; PACE Bus Inst Cmptr Instr 1989-92; Westchester Bus Inst Cmptr Instr 1993-; *office:* Westchester Bus Inst PO Box 710 White Plains NY 10602

BHALLA, HAPPY, Adj Instructor of Philosophy; *b:* London, England; *m:* Margareta Amman Sallstrom; *c:* Karolina, Frederik; *ed:* CA Inst of Integral Stud (MA) Philosophy, Rel 1991; Queens Coll (BA) His 1977; *cr:* Sullivan Cty Com Coll Tennis, Soccer Coach 1980-82; Lew Hoad's Campo De Tenis Asst Mgr 1984-86; Hampton Ath Club Tennis Dir 1990-94; Westhampton Beach HS Tennis Coach 1992-94; Suffolk CCC Adj Instr 1995-; *ai:* Reebok Urban Yth League, Advanced Tennis Coach; *home:* 28 N Quarter Rd Westhampton NY 11977*

BHAME, J. MICHELE, 4th Grade Teacher; *b:* Bayport, NY; *m:* Thomas H.; *c:* Pamela N. Cura, Matthew A.; *ed:* Philadelphia Coll of Bible (BS) Bible 1965; West Chester Coll (MS) Elem Ed 1983; 45 Addl Credits; *cr:* East Ward Elem Schl 2nd Grd Tchr 1985-89, 4th Grd Tchr 1990-; *ai:* IST; Mentor; DAEA, NEA 1985-; *office:* East Ward Elem Schl 435 Washington Ave Downingtown PA 19335

BHAROSAY, BOADNARINE, Assistant Professor; *b:* Berbice Guyana, South America; *m:* Meena K.; *c:* Davina, Kavina, Avinash; *ed:* York Coll-City Univ of NY (BS) Accounting 1985; Brooklyn Coll-City Univ of NY (MA) Accounting 1991; Post Masters Cert in Taxation at Baruch Coll 1996; Prof Cert as Certified Pub Accountant 1989; *cr:* F S Todman & Co Certified Pub Accountants Sr Accountant 1985-89; CMI Bus Furniture Svc Controller & CFO 1989-92; York Coll- City Univ of NY Asst Prof 1992-; *ai:* AICPA 1989-; NY Soc of Certified Pub Accountants 1989-, SEC Comm, Accounting & Review Svcs Comm; NSTP 1992-; Hillside Cricket Club 1982-, Treas, MVP Awd 1993; Seminar Entitled SEC Update NY Soc of Certified Pub Accounts 1995; Seminar Entitled Current Dev in SEC Practice 1995; Cmptr & Industry Show Hilton Hotel NY 1995; Article Entitled SAB 93 & Discontinued Operations Certified Pub Accountants Journal 1995; *office:* City Univ Of NY York Coll 94-20 Guy Brewer Blvd Jamaica NY 11451

BIAGIOTTI, DEBORAH A., High School Mathematics Tchr; *b:* Lowell, MA; *ed:* U of Lowell (BA) Math Scndry Ed 1979, (MS) Math & Comp Option 1987; *cr:* Billerica Memrl HS Math Tchr 1979-; *ai:* AFT 1985-; NCTM 1989-; Generation Gap Bowling League 1978-, Sec & Treas; *office:* Billerica Memorial HS 35 River St Billerica MA 01821

BIAGIOTTI, SANDY, Fourth Grade Teacher; *b:* Queens, NY; *m:* Joseph; *c:* Emilio, Maria Flynn, Marguerite Sperrazza, Joann Bellacicco; *ed:* Queens Coll (BA) Elem Ed 1957; C. W. Post (MS) Elem Ed; *cr:* Parkway Oaks Schl Fifth Grd Tchr 1957-62; St Frances de Chental Schl Fourth Grd Tchr 1980-.

BIALICKI, CORNELL J., 5th Grade Teacher; *b:* New Haven, CT; *ed:* Southern CT St U (BS) Ed 1969, (MS) Guid & Psych 1972; 6th Yr Cert Admin & Supvr 1980; *cr:* Bethany Comm Schl Tchr 1970-; Amity HS Var Ski Coach 1985-88; *ai:* Stu Cncl; Ski Club; Tech & Soc Stud Comms; Best Tchr Assessment Mentor Pgm; NEA 1969-; CEA 1969-; BEA 1969-, VP; NCSS 1980-; PSEA 1984-; St Vincent Ferrer Church 1985-, Parish Cncl; Map Skills in the Soc Stud, Ed & Tech Presenter; Tchr of Yr; *office:* Bethany Comm Schl 44 Peck Rd Bethany CT 06524

BIAMONTE, LYNNE ADRIENNE, Fifth Grade Teacher; *b:* Paterson, NJ; *m:* Robert T.; *c:* Robert Jr., Stephanie; *ed:* Wm Paterson Coll (BA) Elem Ed 1970, (MED) Arts Concentration 1992; 21 Credits Post Grad; *cr:* Carlstadt Pub Schls 5th Grd Tchr 1983-84, 2nd Grd Tchr 1984-87, 5th Grd Tchr 1987-; *ai:* Just Say No Adv; Schl Magazine Editor; Pub Relations Chprsn CEA; NEA, BCEA, CEA 1983-; Kappa Delta Pi 1992-; Carlstadt Mother's Club 1980-, Treas, VP, Pres; Girl Scouts 1980-86, Svc Unit Chair; Woman's Club 1990-, Recording Sec; Centennial Comm 1994-, Cent Ball Chprsn; Governor's Tchr Recognition 1989; *office:* Lindbergh Elem Schl 550 Washington St Carlstadt NJ 07072

BIANCHI, ANTHONY ALAN, Social Studies Teacher; *b:* Rochester, NY; *m:* Theresa Feroce; *c:* Anthony; *ed:* Univ of Rochester (BS) Soc Sci, His 1986; Brockport St Univ (MA) Liberal Stud, Ed 1992; Rochester City Schl DIst Stu Tchr Sub 1987-88; Webster Cntrl Schls Soc Stud Tchr 1988-; *cr:* Rochester City Schl Dist Stu Tchr Sub 1987-88; Webster Central Schls Soc Stud Tchr 1988-; *ai:* St John Fisher Coll Offensive Line Ftbl Coach 1993-95; Head Ftbl Coach 1996; Webster Tchrs Assn 1988-; Rochester Area Cncl for Soc Stud 1990-.

BIANCHI, LUCIA V., French Teacher; *ed:* Russell Sage Coll (BA) Fr Scndry Ed; Boston Univ (MA) Modern Frgn Lang & Lit; Cert Schl Dist Admin Coll of St Rose; Attnd La Sorbonne; *ai:* AATF; NYSAFLT; Fullbright Hays Schlsp Univ of Perugia Italy; AATF Grant Univ of Avignon France; *office:* Saratoga Springs HS West Ave Saratoga Springs NY 12866

BIANCHI, TINA, Spanish & French Teacher; *b:* Goshen, NY; *m:* Vincent; *c:* Lisa; *ed:* Russell Sage Coll (BA) Fr, Sec Ed 1970; St Univ at Albany (MS) Advanced Classroom Tchng 1974; Cert Span 30 Addl Hrs; In-Svc Effective Tchng Model, Cooperative Learning, Classroom Mngmt; *cr:* Valley Cntrl Schls Foreign Lang Tchr 1971-72; Niskayuna Pub Schls Foreign Lang Tchr 1972-73; Shenendehowa Cntrl Schls Foreign Lang Tchr 1973-; *ai:* Reorganization Dist Admin Roles Comm; Schl Envrnmt Comm; NYSUT 1971-; Shenendehowa TA 1973-; NYSAFLT 1970-; Niskayuna HS PTA; Niskayuna Booster Club; Nom Johns Hopkins Awd; Mentor; Excl Tchng Awd; *office:* Koda Jr HS Rt 146 Clifton Park NY 12065

BIANCHI, VINCENT, Spanish Teacher; *b:* Schenectady, NY; *m:* Elvira Micieli; *c:* Lisa Marie; *ed:* St Lawrence Univ (BA) Span 1969; St Univ at Albany (MA) Ed 1973; Coll of St Rose SDA Admin 1987; *cr:* Niskayuna HS Span Tchr 1969-,Bsktbl Coach 1970-94, Asst Prin 1986-87; *ai:* Span Club Adv; Awds Comm; Bsktbl Coach; Founder of Yth Bsktbl Prgm; AFT, Niskayuna Tchrs Assn, NYSAFLT 1969-; NYS Bsktbl Coaches Assn 1985-; Niskayuna Jr Warriors Inc 1989-, Pres; *home:* 2485 Angelina Dr Schenectady NY 12309

BIANCO, DONALD ROBERT, Guidance Counselor; *b:* Providence, RI; *m:* Cheryl Lanni; *c:* Nicholas, Marissa, Bianco; *ed:* Providence Coll (BA) Ed 1972, (MED) Guidance, Counseling 1978; *cr:* North Providence HS 1972-78, Work Stud Coord 1979-89, Classroom Tchr 1990-91, Guidance Cnslr 1992-; *ai:* Bsktbl Coach 1974-80; North Providence Girls Sftbl Recreation; AFT 1972-; New England Assn of Coll Admissions Cnslrs 1992-; North Providence Vol Fire Dept 1967-75, Treas; North Providence Lib Assn; Greystone PTO; *office:* North Providence HS 1828 Mineral Spring Ave North Providence RI 02904

BIANCO, JOSEPH ANTHONY, High School Math Teacher; *b:* Utica, NY; *m:* Camille Scala; *c:* Joseph, Michelle; *ed:* Syracuse (MS) Ed 1971; *cr:* Westmoreland Cntrl Schl Math Tchr 1965-; *ai:* Bowling Club Adv; Var Sftbl Coach; NEA 1975-; *office:* Westmoreland Cntrl Schl Rt 233 Westmoreland NY 13490

BIAS, BONNIE (FULWIDER), 6th Grade Teacher; *b:* Ronceverte, WV; *m:* Willie J.; *c:* Benjamin J., Jeremy B., Joshua B.; *ed:* Univ of Toledo (BS) Ed Elem 1970, (ME) Ed Elem 1981; *cr:* Hawthorne Elem 5th Grd Tchr 1970-72; Spencer Sharples 4th-6th Grd Tchr 1972-80; Hawkins Elem 2nd Grd Tchr 1980-83, 6th Grd Tchr 1983-; *ai:* Bldg, Soc Comms; Tutoring; Delta Kappa Gamma 1989-; Phi Delta Kappa 1992-; Ridgewood Church of Christ 1982-, Ed Dir; Impact Grant 1992, 1994; Career Ladder 1989-; Intern Consultant 1994-95; Cable Grant 1996; *office:* Hawkins Elem Schl 5550 W Bancroft St Toledo OH 43615*

BIASI, JOSEPH ANTHONY, Social Studies Teacher; *b:* Indianapolis, IN; *m:* Julie Lynn Cicene; *c:* Carmela; *ed:* Muskingum Coll (BA) Soc Stud 1990; *cr:* East OH Correction Ctr Tchr 1990-93; Steubenville HS Tchr, Coach 1991-; *ai:* Girls Var Bsktbl, Frosh Ftbl Coach; NEA 1993-; *office:* Steubenville HS 420 N 4th St Steubenville OH 43952

BIBBEY, VAUGHN DAVID, Cmptr Sci Tchr & Tech Coord; *b:* Portsmouth, OH; *m:* Melissa Comer; *c:* Sean, Joshua; *ed:* OH Univ (BA) Bus Ed 1975; Marshall Univ (MS) Schl Admin 1978; *cr:* Valley HS Tchr, Coach 1975-; *ai:* Head Girls Track Coach; Dist Tech Coord; OH Ed Assn 1975-; Valley Tchrs Assn 1975-, Past Pres; OH Assn of Track Coaches 1987-; Southeastern OH Track Coaches Assn 1990-, Dist Coach of Yr 1991, 1994; Scioto Soccer League 1988-, Trustee, Treas, Pres; Ath Parks Boosters 1993-, Chprsn; Southern OH Conf Track Coach of Yr 1990-95; US Track & Field Level I Cert; *office:* Valley HS PO Box 888 Lucasville OH 45648

BIBBINS, DONNA BARNEY, Third Grade Teacher; *b:* Watertown, NY; *m:* Richard K.; *c:* Karla Palmer, Kenneth; *ed:* SUNY at Plattsburgh (BS) Schl Nurse Tchr 1966; 30 Hrs SUNY at Oswego, SUNY at Potsdam, St Lawrence Univ; *cr:* Watertown City Schl Dist Schl Nurse, Tchr 1966-68 & 1970-76, Elem Tchr 1976-; *ai:* Spon Tchr SUNY Potsdam Stu Tchrs; Dist Math Comm; NYSUT, AFT 1971-; Watn Ed Assn 1966-; OES 1970-, Matron; Delta Kappa Gamma 1976-, Sec; Reviewer & Contributor Addison Wesley Math Series; *office:* Watertown City Schl Dist 376 Butterfield Ave Watertown NY 13601*

BIBLE, RONALD LEE, 8th Grade History Teacher; *b:* Lima, OH; *m:* Karen Kowalczyk; *c:* Jodi Mooreman, Eric, Megan, Derek; *ed:* OH Northern (BS) Hist & Govt 1967; Wright St (MS) Ed 1973; Inst of Amer Studies OH Northern; Jennings Scholar at Bowling Green; *cr:* Robin Rogers Tchr 1966-67; Perry Local 6th Grd Tchr 1967; Bath Local Schls 7th Grd, 8th Grd & His Tchr 1968-; *ai:* Bath Ed Assn 1968-, Bldg Rep St Del; OEA 1968-; NEA 1968-; *office:* Bath Middle Schl 2700 Bible Rd Lima OH 45801

BICE, MICHAEL R., Physics Teacher; *b:* Altoona, PA; *m:* Margaret C. Ticho; *c:* Michael, William, Mary Claire; *ed:* Penn St Univ (BS) Physics & Ed 1960; Unif of PA (MSEd) Sci Ed 1964; Franklin & Marshall Coll 8 Addl Credits Physics; Univ of DE 6 Addl Credits Physics; Polytech Univ of NY 18 Addl Credits; Hofstra Univ 12 Addl Credits Admin, Cmptrs & Physics; *cr:* Charlotte High Physics Tchr 1960-63; Herricks High cmptr Coord 1969-91, Physics Tchr 1964-; *ai:* Honors Research & Westing House Sci Adv; Ed Use of Cmptrs Comm; Dist Curr Cncl; AFT, VFT & HTA 1960-; Long Island Physics 1985-; AAPT 1965-; *office:* Herricks HS 100 Shelter Rock Rd New Hyde Park NY 11040

BICK, JON ERIC, 8th Grd Social Studies Tchr; *b:* Syracuse, NY; *m:* Theresa Parry; *c:* Jon Tyler, Alyssa Catherine; *ed:* St Univ of NY at Cortland (BA) Scndry Soc Stud 1985, (MS) Ed 1992; *cr:* Hillbrook Detention Fac Soc Stud & Math Tchr 1985-86; North Syracuse Cntrl Schls Alternative Ed Prgm Tchr 1986-88; Baldwinsville Cntrl Schls 8th Grd Soc Stud Tchr 1988-; *ai:* Baldwinsville Tchrs Assn 1989-; NEA of NY 1988; *office:* Baldwinsville Cntrl Schl Dist E Oneida St Baldwinsville NY 13027

BICKART, MARY F., Fifth Grade Teacher; *b:* Hazleton, PA; *m:* Charles J.; *c:* Matthew, Daniel; *ed:* East Stroudsburg Univ (BS) Elem Ed 1974; Attnd Kutztown Univ; *cr:* Stroudsburg MS 8th Grd Lang Arts Tchr 1976-89, 5th Grd Tchr 1990-; *ai:* Lit Comm; NEA 1976-; *office:* Stroudsburg MS Chipperfield Dr Stroudsburg PA 18360

BICKEL, CAROLE PARIS, Mathematics Dept Chair & Tchr; *b:* Massillon, OH; *m:* Blair Myron; *c:* Bradley, Barbara, Bethany; *ed:* OH St Univ (BS) Ed, Math 1970, (MA) Math 1989; Grad Tech Courses Beyond Masters OSU, BG; *cr:* Columbus Pub Schl Math Tchr 1970-74; Franklin Univ Adj Math Instr 1980-89; OH St UNiv Grad Tchng Assoc 1987-89; Gahanna Lincoln HS Math Tchr, Dept Chair; *ai:* Schl Net, Acad Policy, Tech Prep Comm; NCTM, OCTM, COCTM 1987-; ASH Advy Bd OSU 1985-, Vice-Chair; Windrush Homeowners Assn 1978-, Treas; Flwshp OSU 1987; NSF Stu 1995; NCTM Mini-Grant Venture Capitol 1995; *office:* Gahanna Lincoln HS 140 Hamilton Rd Gahanna OH 43230

BICKELMAN, JOHN CARL, Secondary American His Tchr; *b:* Pottsville, PA; *m:* Diane Glincosky; *c:* Ryan, Jillian, Kirsten; *ed:* PA St Univ (BA) Soc Sci 1984; Wilkes Univ (MED) Ed 1991; *cr:* Hamburg Area HS Soc Stud Tchr 1984-; *ai:* Ftbl & Bsbl Coach; Soc Stud Club, Mock United Nations Team, Mock Trial Team & Jr Statesman of America Adv; NEA & PSEA 1984-; S Cass Fire Co 1975-; Hamburg Stu Assistance Team 1989-; Nom for PA Tchr of Yr 1992; Nom for Thanks To Tchrs Awd 1990; Hamburg Area Schl Dist Outstanding Vol Recognition; *office:* Hamburg Area H S Windsor St Hamburg PA 19526

BIDDLE, KAREN NORTON, Mathematics Teacher; *b:* Lewistown, PA; *m:* Eric D.; *c:* Justin Alexander; *ed:* Juniata Coll (BS) Math Ed 1982; Wilkes Coll, Saint Francis Coll Grad Courses; *cr:* East Windsor Regnl Schl Dist Math Tchr 1982-83; Parkland Schl Dist Math Tchr 1984-88; Spring Cove Schl Dist Math Tchr 1988-; *ai:* Stu Cncl Adv; Cooperting Tchr for Coll Stu; NEA 1982-; PSEA 1984-; Local SCEA 1988-; Juniata Coll, Class Fund Agent; *office:* Central HS Rd #1 Box 420 Martinsburg PA 16662*

BIDDLE, KEVIN LEE, Social Studies & Reading Tchr; *b:* Salem, NJ; *m:* Paula Jean Young; *ed:* Indian Wesleyan (MSQ) Elem Ed 1995; *cr:* Salem City Pub Schls Seventh Grd Tchr 1987-89; Elizabethtown Area Schls Seventh Grd Soc Stud, Rdng Tchr 1989-; *ai:* Drama Club Adv; Schl Plays, Musicals Dir; ALPHA Team Ldr; NEA, PSEA 1989-; NEA, NJEA 1987-89; Annville Comm Theatre 1989-, Pres, Artistic Dir; Encore Musical Productions 1987-, Pres, Dir; Christ Church UCC 1990-, Music Dir; *office:* Elizabethwon Area MS 600 E High St Elizabethtown PA 17022*

BIDINGER, KAY LAZIO, Social Studies Teacher; *b:* Chicago, IL; *m:* George H.; *c:* G. Michael, Stephen, David, Anne Soule, Mark Christopher, Chuck, Traci Elizabeth, Thomas Edward; *ed:* Notre Dame Coll (BA) His, Eng Ed 1958; 30 Credit Hrs Masters Equivalency Montgomery Co Pub Schls; *cr:* St Francis de Sales HS 10th-11th Grd Eng Tchr 1958-59; Sub Tchng All Grds 1970-72; Farquhar MS 6th Grd Soc Stud, Interdisciplinary Resource Tchr 1978-; *ai:* Stu Tchr Trng Prgm Univ of MD; Outdoor Ed Prgm Coord; Admin Ldrshp Team; Awds Prgm Chm; NEA 1979-; NCSS 1980-; Amer Legion, Vol Svc; St Patrick's Cath Church 1972-, Couple to Couple Cnslng; Jr Scholastic Magazine Advy Bd Mem; Handbook for Tchrs Co-Author MCPS Vol Prgm; Mini Grant Project Ross Bobby Ctr Summer Skills Prgm; *office:* Farquhar MS 16915 Batchellors Forest Rd Olney MD 20832*

BIEBERBACH, YVONNE LATHOM, Retired Educator; *b:* Beaver Falls, PA; *m:* Max W.; *c:* Roger, Jill; *ed:* Geneva Coll (BSED) Elem Ed 1954; 12 Hrs Art Ed PA St Univ; 30 Hrs Art Ed, 12 Hrs Supervision Rowan; *cr:* Northeastern Beaner Co Art Ed 1954-56; Richland Co Dist #2 5th Grd, Art Tchr 1956-58; Cherry Hill Pub Schls 3rd Grd, Art Coord, Sr HS Art Dept 1958-94; *ai:* NEA, CHEA; NJEA, Treas; AENJ, Treas; NJ Teen Arts; Cherry Hill Mall Merchant Exhibit Consultant; PTA Art Goes to Schl; NJ St Guides #1 Insights into Elem Art Ed 1970, #2 Spec Ed 1970-95; May Commendation Ed Excl 6 Editions; Dist Grant Creativity in Time, Space Arts; 1994 Governor's Awd Outstdng Tchr.

BIEBUYCK, LIZABETH HOGSETT, Math Tutor; *b:* New Brighton, PA; *c:* Christopher H.; *ed:* Geneva Coll (BA) Scndry Ed 1972; PA St Univ Credit Hrs Math & Psych; 24 Credit Hrs Toward Masters in Psych; *cr:* Big Beaver Falls Area Schls Jr HS Fr Tchr 1972-73; Utica Chrstn Schl Elem Tchr 1975-78; Self Employed Tutor Math & Statistics Tutor 1982-; PA St Univ Math Tutor & LC Coord 1985-; *ai:* Inter Var Chrstn Flwshp Adv; Church 1972-, Single Parents Act Comm; Womens Ctr 1996, Cnslr; *office:* PA St Univ Beaver Cmps Brodhead Road Monaca PA 15061

BIEDER, JEFF, Asst Prin, Hlth & PE Dept; *b:* Brooklyn, NY; *m:* Georgia; *c:* Rachel, Stacy, Jaclyn; *ed:* Univ of Bridgeport (BS) Hlth & PE 1968; Brooklyn Coll (MS) Hlth & PE 1972; Hunter Coll 6th Yr Prof Degree in Admin & Supervision 1991; *cr:* Hunter Coll Mens Bsktbl Head Coach 1984-88; Long Island City HS Hlth & PE Tchr 1968-76; Murry Bergtraum HS Dean & Bsktbl & Bsbl Coach 1976-86; Long Island City HS Dean & Bsktbl & Bsbl Coach 1986-92; South Shore HS Asst Prin & Hlth & PE Tchr 1992-; *ai:* Girls Bsktbl & Boys Soccer Coach; Hillel Cntry Day Camp Asst Dir; Cncl of Supervision & Admin 1991-; Brooklyn A-P of Hlth & PE 1992-, Pres; Gatorade Coaches Care Awd; Pub Article The Value of PE in UFT Newspaper; *office:* South Shore HS 6565 Flatlands Ave Brooklyn NY 11236

BIEDERMAN, MARIANNE MILLER, Fifth Grade Teacher; *b:* Toronto, OH; *m:* Earl D.; *c:* Scott A.; *ed:* Kent St Univ (BA) Elem Ed 1969, (MED) Rdng Specialization 1980; Post Grad Ashland Coll, Cleveland St, Mount St Marys; *cr:* Wintersville Bd of Ed Elem Tchr 1958-59; Toronto Bd of Ed Elem Tchr 1959-60; Willoughby-Eastlake Bd of Ed Elem Tchr 1956-58, 1963-65; Akron Bd of Ed Elem Tchr 1966-68; Kenston Bd of Ed 5th Grd Tchr, Gifted Ed 1968-; *ai:* OH Quiz Bowl Tchr Adv; Math Team, Lang Arts Olympiad Adv; Sci Ed Cncl of OH 1989-; OH Cncl of Tchrs of Math 1988-; NEA, OEA 1956-; KEA 1968-; OH Quiz Bowl Team Placed 5th in St; Natl DAR Essay Contest 1 of 4 Finalist; *office:* Timmons Elem Schl 9595 E Washington St Chagrin Falls OH 44023*

BIEGLER, CHAD ALAN, US History Teacher; *b:* Berea, OH; *m:* Ellen Jeanne Smith; *c:* Craig T.; *ed:* Muskingum Coll (BA) His 1976; OH St Univ (MA) His 1978; 18 Hrs Continuing Ed; 33 Hrs Educl Policy & Leadership; 20 Hrs Post Grad His; *cr:* OH St Univ Tchng Asst 1976-78; Muskingum Coll Track Head Coach 1978; Jonathan Alder Local Schls Jr HS Soc Stud Tchr 1978-80; Dublin City Schls HS Soc Stud Tchr 1980-; *ai:* Boys Cross Cntry Head Coach; NEA, OEA, DEA 1982-; OH Historical Soc Cntrl OH Track & Cross Cntry Coaches 1980-; Cntrl OH Cross Coach of Yr Div I Boys 1992 & 1994; *office:* Dublin Coffman H Coffman Rd Dublin OH 43017

BIELEFELD, IRMA, German Teacher; *b:* Breslau, East Germa Jeremias Kurzi; *c:* Hans; *ed:* MI St Univ (BA) Lbrl Arts 1962, (M 1963; Rutgers Univ NJ (PHD) Ger 1984; Cert Swiss Med Asst 19 Mid East Tech Univ Eng Tchr 1963-66; Pvt Translator 1963-70; Swi of Modern Lang Eng Tchr 1971-81; Kearny HS Ger Tchr 1985-; Club; Ger Hnrs Soc; Delta Epsilon Phi; Intrnl Folk Music Co-Dir; NJEA 1985-; HS Folk Dancers 1985-, Dance Tchr; Seven Short Stor in Das Fenster; *home:* 248 Beech St Kearny NJ 07032*

BIELER, EDWARD K., United States History Teacher; *b:* Pennsbu *m:* Kathleen W.; *ed:* West Chester Univ (MED) Scndry Ed 1973; Univ Prins Cert 1988; Penn St; Wilkes Coll; *cr:* Plymouth-Whitema Soc Stud Tchr 1967-72; Upper Perkiomen HS Soc Stud Tchr 197 Comm Svc Coord; UPEA, PSEA, NEA 1967-; Red Hill Band 1963-; Schwenkfelder Choir 1982-, Dir; E Greenville Boro Cncl 1988-; *office:* Upper Perkiomen HS 2 Walt Rd Pennsburg PA 18073

BIELER, JACK F., Asst Principal & Lead Teacher; *b:* New York, Joan Glick; *c:* Dani, Miriam, Sara, Avi; *ed:* Yeshiva Univ (AA) Juda 1969; Yeshiva Coll (BA) Eng Lit 1969; Ferkauf Grad Schl (MA) Jew 1974; Yeshiva Univ Riets Ordination 1974; Attn Fischel Grad Schl, Univ at Jerusalem, Kerem B'Yavne; *cr:* Ramaz Schl Head of Talmu 1974-88; Kehilath Jeshurun Permanent Scholar-in-Residence 19 Hebrew Acad of Greater Washington Asst Prin, Lead Tchr 1988-; Mill Synagogue Rabbi 1993-; *ai:* Judaic Stud Curr, Post-Grad Isra Coord; Editorial Bd Ten Daat; 9th Grd Class Spon; ASCD, Jer Fellows 1985-; Rabbinical Cncl of Amer 1993-; Union of Orthodox Congregations 1979-; Yeshiva Coll Alumni Assn, Rabbinic Alumni Gruss Excellent Tchr Awd; Jerusalem Flwshp; Yeshiva Univ Ha Torah Awd; Numerous Publications; *office:* Hebrew Acad Of Wash 2010 Linden Ln Silver Spring MD 20910

BIEN, PEGGY CHERRINGTON, Third Grade Teacher; *b:* Alle PA; *c:* Scott Snyder, Michael, Jessica; *ed:* Kutztown Univ (BSEd) S & Elem Ed 1974, (MED) Elem Ed 1979; *cr:* Overbrook Schl for th Math Tchr 1975; Weisenberg Elem Schl 3rd Grd Tchr 1975-; *ai:* Coord; NEA, PSEA & NWLEA 1975-; Comm Theatre 1991-, A *office:* Weisenberg Elem Schl 2665 Golden Key Rd Kutztown PA 1

BIENVENUE, JANET C., Economics Teacher; *b:* Santa Ana, Gary; *ed:* Bridgewater St Coll (BA) Soc Stud 1991; Post Grad St Stud; *cr:* Somerset HS Soc Stud Tchr 1991-92; Apponequet Regnl Stud Tchr 1992-; *ai:* Asst Field Hockey Coach; Sr Class, Jr Achvm Stu of Month Comm; Natl His Day; Voice of Democracy Judge; MTA, SSCSS 1991-; Jr Achvmt 1991-, Adv; Commendation Unite Commendation for Pub Scv to Amer Cancer Soc; Comm Visiting Agency of Attleboro Comm Involvement Awd; *office:* Appo Regional HS 100 Howland Rd Lakeville MA 02347*

BIER, JANE KLEIN, HS Social Studies Teacher; *b:* Ft Wayne, Ron; *ed:* OH St Univ (BS) Edctr 1987; Cleveland St Univ (MA) Eu His 1995; *cr:* Oberlin City Schls Sub 1987-88; Cleveland Pub Sch Coord 1988-89; Elyria City Schls Tchr 1989-; *ai:* Peer Mediatio Ldr; OH Cncl for the Soc Stud 1989-; *office:* Elyria HS 6th St Ely 44035*

BIEREMA, RONALD WILLIAM, Mathematics Teacher; *b:* Holla *m:* Linda Marie Schwarz; *c:* Christine, Jeremy; *ed:* Calvin Col Scndry Ed 1982; Beaver Coll (MA) Cmptr Ed 1987; *cr:* Phil-Mont Acad Math Tchr 1983-; *ai:* Boys, Girls Var Tennis Coach; Math Dep NCTM 1983-; Tchr of Month 1996; *office:* Phil-Montgomery Ch Acad 35 Hillcrest Ave Glenside PA 19038

BIERNOT, JAMES JOSEPH, 6th-7th Grade Science Teac Wheeling, WV; *ed:* OH Univ (BA) Elem Ed 1984; *cr:* Lord Baltimor Shipping Clerk 1969-70; US Army Military Police 1970-73; Industries Inspector 1973-84; St Clairsville MS 6th-7th Grd Sc 1987-; *ai:* Jr HS Ftbl Coach 8 Yrs; Outdoor Ed Coord 7 Yrs; 5-8 Fair Coord 7 Yrs; NEA 1984-; OH Univ Stu Svcs 1986-, Stu Svc A MP Battalion Soldier of Month 1971-72; South Vietnamese Bronz Army Accommadation Medal; 1984-85 Natl Deans List; Belmont C Ribbon Commission 1991; *office:* St Clairsville MS 102 Woodro Saint Clairsville OH 43950

BIESECKER, CHARLES CALVIN, 7th Grade Life Science Teac Hanover, PA; *c:* Christopher, Jessica; *ed:* St Francis Coll (BS) Bio Shippensburg Univ (MED) Rdng 1972; *cr:* Hanover Pub Schl Dist S 1965-; *ai:* NEA 1965-; PSEA 1965-; Hanover Ed Assn 1965-, Pr Chief Negotiator; *office:* Hanover MS 300 Keagy Ave Hanover PA

BIFANO, ANTHONY J., HS Mathematics Teacher; *b:* Niagara Fal *m:* Marguerite; *c:* Jennifer, Anthony, Stephanie; *ed:* St Univ at (BA) Math 1964; St Univ Coll at Buffalo (MS) Scndry Ed 1969; *cr:* Cntrl Schl Math Tchr, Cmptr Sci Tchr 1964-; *ai:* Math Curr Coo Girls Bsktbl, Sftbl Coach; AFT, Cheek Cntrl Tchrs Assn, NYSUT, AMTNYS 1964-; NY St United Tchr; Natl Cncl Teach of Math; Ass Tchrs of NY St; Cheektowaga Chamber Commerce Tchr of Yr 1968; Cheektowaga Cntrl HS 3600 Union Rd Cheektowaga NY 14225

BIFANO, THOMAS GARY, Professor; *b:* Hackensack, NJ; *m:* Ma Weaver; *c:* Eliza; *ed:* Duke Univ (BS) Mech Eng & Materials Sc (MS) Mechanical Engrng 1983; NC St Univ (PHD) Mechanical 1988; *cr:* Boston Univ Prof of Engrng 1988-; *ai:* Amer Soc for Pr Engg 1986-, Bd; ASME 1995-; *office:* Boston Univ 110 Cumming Boston MA 02215

BIGA, VICTORIA PHYLLIS, Teacher of Gifted; *b:* Taylor, PA; *e* Misericordia (BS) Ed 1964; Seton Hall Univ (MA) Ed 1968; *cr:* Je Twp Schl Tchr 1964-72; Pittston Area Schl Tchr 1972-; *ai:* AFT; Gamma Pi 1964-; Holy Rosary Choir 1975-; *office:* Pittston Area Sc New St Pittston PA 18640

BIGALL, EDMOND JOHN, 2nd Grade Teacher; *b:* Westbury, N Cheryl Hendrix; *c:* Evan, Leah, Alexa, Dale; *ed:* Hofstra Univ (B Sci 1969; Long Island Univ (MS) Early Chldhd Ed 1972; 75 Addl Hrs at Coll of New Rochelle, Coll of St Rose; *cr:* St Raymond Schl 7 Soc Stud Tchr 1970-71; Southold Pub Schls 2nd Grd Tchr 1971-; *a* Conf, Spirit Comms; AFT, NEA, NYSUT 1971-; Southold PTA 1971 Newsletter; Marriage Crisis Ctr 1982-, Sec; Southold Fac Assn Sayville Splashers Booster Club 1982-; *office:* Southold Pub Oaklawn Ave Southold NY 11971*

BIGATEL, CHRISTINA, 5th Grade Teacher; *b:* Allentown, P Immaculata Coll (BA) Eng, Theology 1989; St Charles Semina Ministry Cert Prgm; Currently in MA Prgm Boston Coll; *cr:* St A Schl 4 Grd TChr 1983-86; St Katharine of Siena Schl 4, 6 Gr 1986-88; St Jane Schl 8 Grd Tchr 1988-92; St Maria Goretti Schl Tchr 1992-94; St Michael Schl 5 Grd Tchr 1995-; *ai:* Rel Coor Helper Moderator; NCEA 1983-; Connelly Fnd Schlsp Boston Coll Yth Ministry Columnist 1994-95.*

BIGELOW, ELIZABETH XAROS, Computer & Economics Teac Lowell, MA; *m:* John S.; *c:* Elizabeth Steeves, John Elias; *ed:* Univ Beach (BS) Bus Ed 1970; New Hampshire Coll (MBA) Bus Admin Boston Univ (EDD) Bus Ed 1981; *cr:* Timberlane Regnl HS Di gator Cmptr-Based Career Information Project 1979-82, Tchr 1970-; shp Cncl Comm; Frosh Class Adv; New England Schl Accreditation AFT 1991-; Eastern Bus Ed Assn, NE Bus Ed Assn, NH Bus Ed Assn Philoptuchos Philantropic Soc 1995-; Merrimack Vly Chamber of erce 1994-; Career Ed Grant 1979-82; USOE Grant; Phi Delta Kappa Outstdng Young Women Amer 1981; Meritorious Tchr Awd 1984; ous Articles Pub; *home:* 10 Wabanaki Way Andover MA 01810

OW, SALLY TETLOW, 8th Grade English Teacher; *b:* Adams, James P.; *c:* Christopher, Jenna; *ed:* North Adams St Coll (BA) Eng MEd) 1973; 54 Credit Hrs Beyond Masters; *cr:* Renfrew Schl 2nd hr 1967-69; Plunkett Schl 6th Grd Lang Arts Tchr 1969-83; Hoosac 8th Grd Eng & 9th-12th Jrnlsm Tchr 1983-94; Adams Memorial MS Tchr 1994-; *ai:* Schl Newspaper, Schl Lit Magazine Adv; Jr Prize ng Coach; MTA, NEA 1967-; JEA, NSPA 1995-; 2 Horace Mann Awded by St of MA 1988 & 1989; Natl Standards Portfolio Prjct Portfolio Assessment St Grant; Great Bks Trnd Presenter, Instr; Art ng Well Trnd Tchr; *office:* Adams Memorial MS 30 Columbia St MA 01220

, EDMUND LOGAN, Business Professor; *b:* Mattoon, IL; *c:* *ed:* KS St Univ (BS) Accounting 1965; Univ New Haven (MBA) 83; SUNY at Buffalo (PHD) Ed Admin 1991; 15 Credit Hrs MSEd Univ; 45 Credit Hrs Cmptrs Military Schls; 30 Credit Hrs Contract Military; *cr:* Bank Night Cmptr Specialist 1963-65; Union Natl Mngmt Trainee 1965-66; Air Force Officers Trng Schl 1966-67; d AFB Supply Logistics Officer 1967-68, Cmptr Programming 1968-69; Asst Data Automation Officer Vietnam 1969-70; Cmptr s Analyst, Programmer Germany 1970-72; US Naval Supply Corps 72; Supply Officer USS Sellers 1973-74; Defense General Supply ocurement Officer 1974-76; Antarctica Asst Supply, Material , Support Force 1976-78; Naval Weapons Center Planning, Admin , Aviation Supply Offier 1978-79; New England Region roller, SUBASE, Commanding Officer, Regnl Accounting & sing; Liaison Officer Defense Logistics Agency NY; Erie Comm ssoc Prof 1983-; Banking, Insurance, Real Estate Coord 1986-; *ai:* Beta Gamma Adv; NEA 1983-; VFW 1988-, Adjutant; Amer Legion Mem; Optimist Intnl 1984-86, VP; Who's Who in the East; Who's the World; *office:* Erie Community Coll 121 Ellicott St Buffalo NY

, HARRY LEE,JR., Social Studies Teacher; *b:* Keyser, WV; *m:* Jo DiSimone; *c:* Shelly Crotts, Marci Danielle; *ed:* Frostburg St BS) Pol Sci 1975; Grad Stud; Garrett Coll Comm; Amer Mgmt Assn; lem Co, Hall Fin Group, Union Pacific Corp, Browning Foodlands nl Mgr 1976-88; Garrett Cty Hlth Dept Mental Hlth Assoc 1988-90; Cty Bd of Ed Tchr 1989-; *ai:* Chrstn Club Spon; AFT 1989-; Crellin Brethen in Christ Church 1977-, Lay Del, Deacon Bd, Yth Ldr, Schl Tchr, Admin Bd & Prsnl Relations Bd; *office:* Southern HS 345 Oakland Dr Oakland MD 21550

, SUSAN J., HS Chem & 8th Grd Sci Tchr; *b:* Newton, MA; *ed:* ross Coll (BA) Chem 1981; St Joseph Coll (MS) Chem 1989; Univ tford Working on (MA) in Ed; *cr:* Loomis Chaffee Schl Chem 4; Watkinson Schl 8th Grd Chem Tchr 1995-; *ai:* Field Hockey CSTA 1991-; *home:* 471 Hazard Ave Enfield CT 06082*

AM, SUSAN HUGHES, 8th Grd Phys Science Teacher; *b:* Denver, John A. Jr.; *c:* John III; *ed:* Tufts Univ (BS) 1970; Adelphi Univ Earth Sci, Ed 1974; Addl 6 Grad Credits Sci Tchng Methods Newton Grad Credits Sci Tchng Methods Univ of PA, 33 Grad Credits Ed Temple Univ; *cr:* Haddonfield Memorl HS Bio Tchr 1970-71; Stream South HS Earth Sci, Phys Sci Tchr 1971-74; TredYffrin vn Jr HS Phys Sci Tchr 1974-75; Great Valley HS Phys Sci Tchr, in 1975-81; Arcola Int Schl Phy ASci Tchr 1989-; *ai:* NEA 1970-; 1974-; Soc of Prof Engrs Outstanding Sci Tchr; *office:* Arcola ediate Schl Eagleville Rd Arcola PA 19426

Y, LYNN M., 8th Grade Teacher; *b:* Johnsonburg, PA; *m:* Michael Michelle, Shari; *ed:* Gannon Univ of PA (ME) Ed 1989; *cr:* Holy Schl 8th Grd Tchr 1980-; *office:* Holy Rosary Schl 605 Market St nburg PA 15845

LL, MARK STEPHENUS, Humanities & Music Teacher; *b:* San CA; *m:* Jean Carmella; *c:* Joel T., Hana R.; *ed:* San Diego St Univ axophone Performance 1983; Univ of North CO (MM) Saxophone mance 1985; Prof Ed Univ of MD, Boston Univ; *cr:* Inarajan HS Sci, Tchr 1987-88; George C. Marshall k-12 Music Tchr 1988-93; David w Farragut HS Music, Hum Tchr 1993-; *ai:* Music Club Spon; OFT Schl Advy Comm 1995-, Vice Chair; NEH Fellow 1988, 1992; Host rkey Musical Festival 1993; Soloist Ankara New Music Festival Tchr Merit Awds 1993-94; *office:* David Glasgow Farragut HS PSC 9 Box 63 FPO AE 09645*

SHIRLEY ANN, Language Arts & Religion Tchr; *b:* Hamilton, : Miami Univ (BS) Span & Typing 1975, (BS) Elem Ed 1987; Rel rt) Archdiocese of Cincinnati Whole Lang Trng; *cr:* Southwest Schls Sub Tchr 1975-77; Northwest Local Schls Sub Tchr 1975-77; the Bapt Schl Jr HS Tchr 1977-; *ai:* Grad Coord 19 Yrs; 8th Grd Yrs; PAL Adv Mentoring Prgm 3 Yrs; Confirmation Coord 5 Yrs; Chprsn 4 Yrs; Co-Dir of Jr HS Plays 6 Yrs; Kappa Delta Pi Ed ry 1974-79; Sigma Delta Pi Span Honorary 1974-79; NCEA 1977-; d Oil Tchr Achvmt Awd Nom 1990; McAuley HS Awd of Inspiration 1996; *office:* St John Baptist Schl 508 Park Ave Harrison OH 45030

, THOMAS MICHAEL, Electrical & Electronics Instr; *b:* Buffalo, Karen Lee; *c:* Thomas C., Kristin Ann; *ed:* ERie Comm Coll (AAS) cal Engineering Tech 1970; Buffalo St Coll (BS) Voc, Tech Ed 1981; ch Tech HS Electrical, Electronics Instr 1981-; Erie Comm Coll t Electrical Prof 1988-; *ai:* Audio-Visual Aid Coord; Dept Head; Crew Supvr; Articulations Coord; Electrical Soc Fac Adv; Amer Soc ngineering Technicians 1987-; Natl Inst Cert in Engineering Techs NEA 1981-; Rochester Inst of Tech Distinguished Tchr Recognition 993; *office:* Hutchinson Cntrl Tech HS 256 S Elmwood Ave Buffalo 201*

, P. RAITA, 5th Grade Teacher; *b:* Cleveland, OH; *c:* Adrienne, Leon, Lindsay; *ed:* Bluffton Coll (BA) Elem Ed 1976; Certfd Reiki seology; Ashland Coll Credit Hrs; *cr:* Shawnee Local Schls Tchr 7; Akron Pub Schls Tchr 1977-; *ai:* Bldg Ldrshp Team; Sci, Sci Fair Enhancement Comm; Rites of Passage Ldr After Schl; Akron Ed 977-; African Natl Rites of Passage United Kollective 1991-, air; OH Rites of Passage United Kollective 1991-, Co-Scribe; 2 Ed Grants; Wrote 2 Aprroved, Implamented Buchtel Urban Grants; ed 2 Rites of Passage Manuals; Co-Authored 2 ROP Manual; KOOL ers Nom; *home:* 990 Peckham St Akron OH 44320*

, JAMES M., English Teacher; *b:* Lackawanna, NY; *ed:* D'Youville S) Eng Ed 1974; SUNY Coll at Buffalo (MA) Eng 1978; *cr:* Silver Cntrl Eng Tchr 1974-; *ai:* Bowling Coach; Stu Cncl; AFT, NYSUT *office:* Silver Creek Cntrl HS 1 Dickinson St Silver Creek NY 14136

H, BORISLAW NICHOLAS,II, Chem, Physics & Phys Sci Tchr; nipegManitoba, Canada; *m:* Natalia K. Voronka; *c:* Oleksandra Ulana Roma; *ed:* Univ of Manitoba (BS) Gen Sci Phys, Zoology Rutgers Univ (EDM) Sci Ed 1993; Inst for Chem Ed; Woodrow nsts for Chem, PE 1990-92; AT&T Tchrs, Tch Inst 1993; *cr:* Queen ce HS NJ Chem, Phys Sci Tchr 1986-93; INROADS Rutgers Univ Chem Tchr 1990-92; Essex Cty Coll Tchr of Physics 1992-93; Silver Burdett Freelance Sci Ed 1992; Summit HS Chem, Physics, Phys Sci Tchr 1993-; Summit HS Supvr 6-12 Sci Ed; *ai:* NJ Sci Convention Demo Den Coord; NJ Chem Olympics Team, Sci Olympiad, Chem Olympics; NJ Chem Tchrs Alliance Group 1991-, Demo Den Coord; Amer Chemical Soc TA 1988-, Bd Mem; NJSTA, NEA, NJEA 1993-; AAPT 1991-; NJ Sci Suprv Assn 1986-, Bd Mem; PLAST Ukrainian Youth Assn SCOUTING 1971-, Scoutmaster;, Dir of Scout Training, Cert of Recognition 1984; Middle States Assn 1991-, Visiting Comm; Inst for Chem Ed Fellowship 1989; Prin QPHS Creative Tchng Awd 1991-93; Archdiocese of Newark Tchr Recognition Awd Nom, Recognized by NJ Sci Tchrs ssn 1992-93; Nom for Regnl Catalyst Awd, Chemical Manufacturers Assn 1992; Nom for Pres Awd for Excl Sci Tchng, Named NJ Governor Fellow of Sciences, 2 Yr Research Grant Awded Research Corp 1993; Co-author of A Demo a Day 180 Chemical Demonstrations 1994; *home:* 31 Rosedale Ave Millburn NJ 07041*

BILBREY, ROBERT E.,JR., Director of Bands; *b:* Maryville, TN; *ed:* TN Tech Univ (BS) Music Ed 1983; Wright St Univ Grad Stud; *cr:* Alcoa City Schls Band Intern 1979-80; Wayne Local Schls Band Dir 1984-; *ai:* Band Act; MENC 1982-, Registered Music Educator; OMEA 1982-, Pres Dist XIII; Lions Club 1995-; AAYHM Prgm Assoc Conductor; *office:* Waynesville HS 735 Dayton Rd Waynesville OH 45068*

BILBY, PAMELA RENCHER, Social Studies Teacher; *b:* East Point, GA; *m:* Donald L.; *ed:* Messiah Coll (BA) Soc Stud 1988; Liberty Univ 21 Credit Hrs Masters Cnslng; *cr:* Dawn Treader Schl 3rd Grd Tchr 1989; Passaic Votech HS Soc Stud Tchr 1989-90; Kittatinny HS Soc Stud Tchr 1990-; *ai:* Peer Ldrshp; Mentor Tchr; Discipline Comm; CORE Comm; Block Scheduling Comm; NEA 1990-; NJ Peer Helping Assn 1994-; *office:* Kittatinny HS 77 Halsey Rd Newton NJ 07866

BILDERBACK, KRISTINE ARRIVIELLO, Mathematics Teacher; *b:* Woodbury, NJ; *m:* Jason; *ed:* Glassboro St Coll (BA) Math 1993; Rowan Coll of NJ Cert Scndry Ed 1993; *cr:* Bridgeton HS Math Tchr 1993-; *ai:* Var Girls Soccer, JV Girls Sftbl Coach; Class Adv 10th Grd; NJEA, NEA, BEA 1993-; *office:* Bridgeton HS West Ave Bridgeton NJ 08302*

BILELLO, JACK, Soc Stud Teacher & Dept Chm; *b:* Brooklyn, NY; *m:* Medina Mercuri; *c:* Tracy Caspary, Melissa, Christopher; *ed:* City Coll of NY (BA) His 1959; Brooklyn Coll (MA) Soc Scis 1964; Attnd Hofstra Univ, Amer Univ at Beirut; *cr:* Lindenhurst HS Tchr, Chm 1959-; Long Island Univ Adj Prof 1981-; *ai:* LASA 1970-, VP; AFT 1970-; NCSS, LICSS 1960-; Phi Beta Kappa; Fulbright Scholar; Author of Three Novels, Short Stories, Newspaper Articles, Book Reviews; *home:* 387 1st Ave Massapequa Park NY 11762

BILHEIMER, MARGARET I., Span Tchr & Rdng Specialist; *b:* Bethlehem, PA; *c:* Willard, Christina; *ed:* Univ of Pittsburgh (BA) Span & Russian 1969; Lehigh Univ (MEd) Scndry Ed 1973, (EdD) Rdng 1992; Univ of Moscow, USSR 9 Credits Grad; Univ of Seville, Spain Cert; *cr:* Bethlehem Schl Dist Tchr 3 Yrs; Lehigh Univ Tchr of Eng as 2nd Lang 5 Yrs; Allentown Coll Prgm Dir & Lecturer 13 Yrs; Northampton Span & Rdng Tchr 7 Yrs; *ai:* Instructional Support Team; IRA 1985-; Colonial Assn of Rdng Educators 1988-, Promoting Lit Awd; Univ Grant to Carry Out Doctoral Stud; Recognized Natl & St for Directing Equal Opportunity Prgm for Disadvantaged Stdnts in Higher Ed 1985; *office:* Northampton Area Sr HS 1619 Laubach Ave Northampton PA 18067

BILINSKI, KATHLEEN MILLER, French & Latin Teacher; *b:* Springfield, IL; *m:* Joseph Robert; *c:* John, David; *ed:* Univ of IL (BA) Fr, Latin 1967; Amer Univ (MA) Western European Area Stud 1970; Ed, Amer & Fr Lit, Art His, Span, His Courses; *cr:* Douglass HS Frgn Lang Dept Chair 1970-86; Friendly HS Frgn Lang Dept Chair 1987-; *ai:* Class, Ponpom, Fr, Latin Hnr Socs Spon; Fr Club; Awds Comm Chair; Curr Wkshps; AATF 1980-; GWATFL 1985-; NEA, PGCEA 1970-; Church Choir 1980-; Prince George's Cty Writing Task Forces; Numerous Publications; *office:* Friendly HS 10000 Allentown Rd Fort Washington MD 20744

BILLE, DONNA L., Science & Math Teacher; *b:* Gallipolis, OH; *m:* Timothy D.; *c:* Matthew, Elizabeth; *ed:* Union Coll (BS) Math, Physics 1970; Univ of Akron (MS) Math Ed 1985; 12 Hrs Towards Doctorate Math Ed; *cr:* Brown Local Schls Tchr 18 Yrs; *ai:* Tech Prep Ed Liaison; MEA 1984-, Sec Treas; OEA, NEA 1984-; Alpha Pi Omega 1990-; Church Women's Club 1971-; Am Red Cross Vol 1995-; *office:* Malvern HS 401 W Main St Malvern OH 44644*

BILLESIMO, JO-ANNE, 7th-8th Grade Spanish Teacher; *b:* Newburgh, NY; *ed:* Mt St Mary Coll (BA) Sociology & Biling, Bicultural Elem Ed 1981; SUNY at New Paltz (MS) Cmptrs in Ed & Instrl Tech, 7-12 Grd Span 1990; *cr:* Marlboro Cntrl MS Span Tchr 1985-; *ai:* Yrbk Adv 1994-; 7th Grd Class, Photo Club Adv; Adv/Advisee Prgm; Marlboro Fac Assn, AFT, NYSAFLT, NYSMSA, AASCD 1985-; NYSASSP 1985-, Adv Mbrshp; PTA; Wkshp Presenter, Coord of Immigration 1994-; Empire St Press Assn Bronze Yrbk Pub Awd 1995; *office:* Marlboro Cntrl MS 1375 Rt 9-W Marlboro NY 12542

BILLINGS, KATHLEEN DIANE, Business Education Head Tchr; *b:* Long Branch, NJ; *m:* Raymond D.; *ed:* Montclair St Univ (BA) Bus Ed 1973; Monmouth Univ (MS) Admin 1996; Paralegal Cert Monmouth Univ 1991; *cr:* Long Branch Jr HS Bus Ed Tchr 1973-79; Long Branch HS Bus Ed Tchr, Cooperative Ed Coord 1979-; *ai:* Organize Var Scholars Prgm; NJEA, NEA 1973-; NJBEA 1992-; Dist Tchr of Month 1994; *office:* Long Branch HS 391 Westwood Ave Long Branch NJ 07740

BILLINGTON, DARRYL MANLEY, High School Art Teacher; *b:* Buffalo, NY; *m:* Garry F.; *c:* Julie B. Kuhlmann, B. Tate; *ed:* Univ of HI (BED) Art Ed 1964; SUNY Coll at Buffalo (MS) Art Ed 1969; SUNY at Cortland Prsnl Admin 1989; *cr:* USAR HI Spcl Svcs Arts & Crafts Dir 1963-67; East Aurora Schl Dist Scndry Art Tchr 1967-79; Ithaca City Schl Dist Scndry Art Tchr 1980-89; Massena Cntrl Schl Dist Scndry Art Tchr 1989-, Liberty Partnership Coord 1989-; *ai:* Friends of Gibson Art Gallery of SUNY at Potsdam 1992-, Bd Mem; Numerous Juried Art Shows & Awds.

BILLIONS, KARIN FERGUSON, Assoc Professor of Mass Media; *b:* Kansas City, MO; *c:* Diana Gwyneth; *ed:* OK Bapt Univ (BA) Eng 1965; Univ of Akron (MA) Rhetoric 1983; Kent St Univ (PHD) Rhetoric 1992; *cr:* Univ of Akron Wayne Coll Assoc Prof of Comms 1988-; *ai:* Acad Affairs, Mrktg, Pub Relations, Promotion Guidelines Review, Search Comms; Speech Comm Assn 1988-; Assn Univ Regnl Campuses of OH 1993-, VP, Pres; Ldrshp Ashtabula Cty, Lorain Cty 1990-, Honoray Mbrshp; Friends of Libs of OH 1988-; Book Chptr, Article, Natl, Intnl Confs Papers Pub; Master's, PHD Flwshps; Mass Media-Comm Area Coord; *office:* Univ Of Akron-Wayne Coll 1901 Smucker Rd Orrville OH 44667

BILLMAN, MATTHEW LEWIS, 10th Grade Biology Teacher; *b:* Harrisburg, PA; *m:* Jennifer Avis Helms; *ed:* Messiah Coll (BS) Bio 1992; Shippensburg Univ 4 Grad Credits; *cr:* Cumberland Vly MS Bio Tchr 1993-; *ai:* Mens Var Soccer Asst Coach 1993-; Angler Club Adv 1995-; NEA 1993-; Mechanicsburg CMA Church 1986-, Usher; *office:* Cumberland Vly Schl Dist 6746 Carlisle Pike Mechanicsburg PA 17055

BILLS, BEVERLY SOKOSKY, Instructional Support Teacher; *b:* Greensburg, PA; *m:* Kenneth William; *c:* Brian; *ed:* California Univ of PA (BS) Elem Ed 1968, (MED) 1970; Commonwealth of PA Dept of Ed Instructional Support Trng, Life Skills Trng; *cr:* Greensburg Salem Schl Dist Second Grd Tchr 1968-73; Hempfield Area Schl Dist 2, 4-6 Grd Tchr 1973-93, GATE Tchr 1975-77, Instructional Support Tchr 1993-; *ai:* PSEA, NEA 1968-; HAEA 1973-; Greensburg Coll Club 1970-; Amer Family Inst Positive Tchng Awd 1986; *home:* 201 Margaret Ave Jeannette PA 15644*

BILLUPS, HARRIET GURLEY, French Teacher; *b:* Warrior, AL; *m:* Leonard H.; *c:* Christopher, Courtney; *ed:* Heidelberg Coll (BA) Fr & Latin 1962; Western Reserve Univ (MA) Fr 1965; Univ of MD (PHD) Fr 1981; *cr:* Cleveland Pub Schl System Fr Tchr 1963-65; Tuskegee Inst Fr Instr 1965-66; Univ of MD Fr Instr, Grad Tchng Asst 1968-72; Prince George's Co Schl System Fr, Latin Tchr 1973-; *ai:* Intnl Club Spon; Foreign Lang Dept Chprsn; NHS Comm; NEA, Prince Georges Co Ed Assn 1973-; Amer Cncl on Tchng of Frgn Langs; Fr Fellowship Case Western Reserve 1962; Doctoral Stud Fellowship Natl Fellowships Fund; Outstanding Tchr Rotary Club of Bladensburg 1988; Phi Sigma Iota; Eta Sigma Phi; *office:* Bladensburg HS 5610 Tilden Rd Bladensburg MD 20710*

BILLUS, JOHN E., French Teacher; *b:* Waterbury, CT; *ed:* Rutgers Univ (BA) Romance Lang 1969, (MA) Fr 1971; Yale Summer Schl 6 Credit Hrs Russian 1975; Norwich Univ 6 Credit Hrs Russian 1977; *cr:* Westport Bd of Ed Jr HS Fr Tchr 1974; Weaton Bd of Ed MS, HS Fr Tchr 1974-; Northfield Mt Hermon Group Ldr in France, Tchr 1980-95; *ai:* Coord Annual Fr Exch Prgm; NEA, CEA 1974-; AATF 1990-; Phi Beta Kappa 1969-; *office:* Weston HS 115 School Rd Weston CT 06883

BILMANIS, ANDRIS,JR., High School Track Coach; *b:* Washington, DC; *m:* Mary Kathryn Coltrane; *c:* Andris John, Timothy Micheal, Amy Kathryn; *ed:* Univ of MDat College Park (BS) Mechanical Eng 1974; *cr:* Bechtel Power Corp Engr 1974-76; Potomac Electric Power Co Engr, Mgr 1976-; *ai:* Yth Summer Teen Club Ldr; St Pauls Episcopal Church, Yth Group Ldr, Sunday Schl Tchr, Vestry Mem, Renovation Comm; Thunderbolt Ath CLub, Pres, Head Coach Track; Ldr Bus, Schl Partnership Prgm; NSPE 1978-, Natl Eng Week Chair, MD Eng of Yr 1991; Amer Soc Mech Eng 1974-.*

BILODEAU, IDA BARTO, Sixth Grade Teacher; *b:* Greenwich, CT; *m:* Denis E.; *c:* Mark, Nadine Gustafson, Rene, Camille Nemanic, Monique; *ed:* Cntrl CT Univ (BS) Ed 1954; Attnd PA St, Univ of Phoenix, St Joseph Masters Equivalency Ed; *cr:* Greenwich Pub Schls 2nd Grd Tchr 1954-55; Ft Wayne Ind Pub Schl 4th-5th Grd Tchr 1955-56; Phoenixville Area Sch Dist 4th Grd, 6th Grd Tchr 1975-; *ai:* Builders Club Spon; NEA, PAEA 1975-; Sweet Adelines Intern 1965-, Judge, Intnl Fac.*

BILOTTI, HELEN ROFRANO, 2nd Grade Teacher; *b:* Brooklyn, NY; *m:* John C.; *ed:* St Johns Univ (BS) Ed 1968; Richmond Coll (MS) Ed 1971; 6th Yr Cert Admin & Supervision Coll of SI 1979; *cr:* PS 41 R Tchr 1968-80; PS 39 R Tchr 1980-82; PS 41 R Tchr 1982-; *ai:* UFT, AFT 1968-; Amer Comm for Italian Migration 1990-, Recording Sec; New Dorp Fnd 1992-, Bd of Dirs; Fund for NYC Ed, CLASP Grants; *office:* PS 41 R Clawson & Locust Ave Staten Island NY 10306

BILOVESKY, SANDRA CIMINERO, Third Grade Teacher; *b:* Youngstown, OH; *w:* Robert E. (dec); *c:* Stephen J.; *ed:* Youngstown St (BS) Ed 1968, (MS) Rdng Ed; 32 Post Grad Hrs; *cr:* Niles City Schls 1st, 2nd, 3rd, 5th Grd Tchr 1968-; *ai:* Prep Team Adv; Effective Schls Rep; Mentor Tchr; Cty Math Comm; Rdng Dept Head, Ld Tchr; Schl Cncl 1992-94; NEA, NCTA 1968-, Local Sec; PDK 1991-; TARC Rdng Cncl 1978-; Niles Historical Soc 1993-; Parish Cncl 1991-, VP; Cath Women's Guild 1975-, Pres; PTA 1960-, Sec.

BILY, MARGARET M. (KING), English Teacher; *b:* New York City, NY; *m:* William F. Jr.; *c:* William F. III, Allison T.; *ed:* Western CT St (BS) Ed, Eng 1973; 40 Addl Hrs; *cr:* St Lawrence O'Toole 5-8th Grd Tchr 1976-79; Tot Time Nursery Div Dir 1981-88; Summer Camp 3-4 Yr Olds Dir 1981-; St Marys Schl 4, 7, 8th Grd Tchr 1989-92; St Patricks Schl 6, 7, 8th Grd Tchr 1992-; *ai:* Chrldng 1989-92; Svc Club 1989-92; Svc Moderator; Valentines for Shut-ins; Pi Lambda Theta 1976-; FCT 1992-; Somers PTA 1984-, Pres, VP, Liason with Comm; Lake Purdys Owners Assn 1977-, Pres, Sec; Outdoor Classroom Grant.*

BINAGHI, GIULIO PAUL, Spanish Teacher; *b:* Stoneham, MA; *ed:* Eastern Nazarene Coll (BA) Span, Ed 1982; Boston Univ (Ed M) 1995; Grad Work Univ of MA Salamanca Spain; *cr:* Timberlane Regnl HS Span Tchr 1982-; *ai:* Founder Soc Hon Hispanica Garcilaso de la Vega Chapter; AFT 1991-; AATSP 1980-; MFLA 1988-; Cert Excl Lang Stud NE Conf Tchng For Lang Recipient; Pi Lambda Theta Excl Ed Awd; *home:* 708 Washington Ave Revere MA 02151

BINDER, ALAN STEPHEN, Music Teacher; *b:* Far Rockaway, NY; *m:* Cheryl Gizang; *c:* Hayley Aja, Kathy Alyssa; *ed:* Long Island Univ (BA) Music Ed 1973; 30 Grad Credits NYS Permanent Cert; *cr:* Carmel HS Music Tchr 1973-; George Fischer MS Music Tchr 1973-; *ai:* Guitar Lessons 23 Yrs; Carmel Rock Ensemble; NYSUT 1973-; NYSSBA 1994-, Schl Bd Mem Millbrook Schl Dist; *office:* Carmel HS 30 Fair St Carmel NY 10512

BINDERNAGEL, JAMES WILLIAM, 6th Grade Teacher; *b:* Cleveland, OH; *m:* Julianne; *c:* Steven, Andrew; *ed:* Hiram Coll (BA) Elem Ed 1975; Attnd Cleveland St Univ, Notre Dame Coll, Kent St Univ; *cr:* Cleveland Pub Schl Tchr 1975-76; Bedford Pub Schl Tchr 1976-; *ai:* Schl Newspaper & Yrbk Co-Adv; Conflict Mngmt Team Mem; Food Drive Coord; New Tchr Mentor; NEA, OEA 1975-; Bedford Ed Assn 1976-, Election Chm; PTA 1975-, Tchr Rep; CYO Ftbl Coach; Tchr of Yr 1994-95; *office:* Aurora Upper Intermediate Sch 24200 Aurora Rd Bedford OH 44146*

BINEK, JOANN, Ret Elem & Intermediate Tchr; *b:* Castle Shannon, PA; *ed:* Duquesne Univ (BED) Elem Ed 1959, (MED) Elem Ed 1965; 20 Credits Pitt; *cr:* Beechwood Schl Tchr 33 Yrs; *ai:* PSEA 1959-, Life Mem; PA Assn of Schl Retirees 1992-, Life Mem; Pittsburgh Assn of Schl Retirees 1992-, Life Mem; Delta Kalla Gamma 1968-, Pres 1990-92, Co-Pres 1996-, Ldrshp Roles; Saint Anne's Church Parish Cncl 1990-, Ed Chm; ACEI Convention 1989-90, Hospitality Chm, Steering Comm; Article Pub 1966-67; Who's Who in Amer Ed 1987-88; All-Star Edctr Awd 1990; AFI Gift of Time Awd 1990; Unsung Hero Awd Pittsburgh Amer Red Cross 1990-91.

BINGGELI, SANDRA SCHLEGEL, Algebra Teacher; *b:* Fremont, OH; *m:* Jeffrey C.; *ed:* Bowling Green St (BA) Elem Ed, Scndry Math 1978, (MS) Educl Supervision 1982; *cr:* Jefferson Jr HS 7th, 8th, 9th Grd Math Tchr 1978-79; Midview MS 8th Grd Algebra, Math Tchr 1979-85; Lorain Cty Joint Voc Schl Math Specialist 1985-89; Fielands HS Algebra Tchr 1989-; *ai:* Scholastic Challenge Team Coach; OH Cncl of Math Tchrs 1990-; *office:* Firelands HS 10643 Vermilion Rd Wakeman OH 44889

BINGHAM, DAWN LORRAINE, 7th & 8th Grd Lang Arts Tchr; *b:* Springfield, OH; *m:* Roger Brentley; *c:* Seth; *cr:* Rockway Schl Lang Arts, Soc Stud & Math Tchr 1991-; *ai:* Gifted & Talented Comm; Rockaway Talent Show Coord; Power of Pen Coach; SLEA & OEA 1991-; Historic Osborn Preservation Soc 1991-; Fairborn 1st Bapt Church 1993-; *office:* Rockway MS 3500 W National Rd Springfield OH 45504

BINGMAN, DAVID BERNARD, Mathematics Teacher & Dept Chm; *b:* Marion, OH; *m:* Bonita Guy; *c:* Christopher, Andrew; *ed:* OH Wesleyan Univ (BA) Math, Eng 1973; Bowling Green St Univ (MEd) Educl Admin, Supervision 1981; *cr:* Marion City Schls Math Tchr 1973-84; Mud River Green Local Schls Tchr, Dept Chm 1984-; *ai:* Math Competitions Club Adv; OH Cncl Tchrs of Math, NCTM 1974-; MRGTA; OFT; AFT; Richwood Pub Affairs Bd 1991-92; Richwood Village Cncl 1994-, Pres; AP

Calculus Seminar IN Univ 1994; *office:* Greenon HS 3950 S Tecumseh Rd Springfield OH 45502*

BINIEK, MATTHEW JAMES, Chemistry Teacher; *b:* Wilkes Barre, PA; *ed:* Univ of Scranton (BS) Scndry Ed, Bio 1989; Chem Cert 1993; *cr:* Plains Jr HS 7th-8th Grd Sci Tchr 1990-91; GAR Meml Jr Sr HS Chem I-II Tchr 1992-; *ai:* Sr HS Sci Olympiad, Drama Club Adv; PSEA, NEA, Luzerne Cty Sci Tchrs Assn 1990-; 1992 Wilkes Barre Cmptr Aided Lab Grant; *home:* 9 Chamberlain St Wilkes Barre PA 18705*

BINKO, NAOMI K., Third Grade Teacher; *b:* Baltimore, MD; *c:* Bruce, Steven, Paul; *ed:* Towson St Univ (BS) Early Chldhd Ed 1976; 60 Addl Hrs; *cr:* Dundalk Meth Church Organist 1954-59; Rowe, Rowe & Vick Law Firm Oegal Sec 1956-59; United Evangelical Church Choir Dir, Organist 1959-64; Northside Bapt Church Choir Dir, Organist 1965-69; Ascension Luth Church Asst Nursery Schl Tchr 1968-72; Baltimore Cty Pub Schls Tchr 1976-; *ai:* Tchrs Assn of Balimore Co, MD St Tchrs Assn, NEA 1976-, Rep for Local Assns, Attend St & Natl Conventions; Soc for Nutrition Ed 1990-; Amer Guild of Organists 1980-, Exec Bd; Ascension Luth Church, Sub Organist, Choir, Worship & Music Comm; Who's Who Among Stdnts in Amer Univ 1975-76; Towson St Univ Hon Ment Most Promising Elem Tchr 1976; MD Dept of Ed Nutrition Tchr of Yr 1990; NASA Tchr in Space Project Participant 1985; USDA Mid-Atlantic Sts Nutrition Task Force 1992-94; *home:* 617 Wilton Rd Baltimore MD 21286

BINKOSKI, JOHN PHILIP, Latin & Greek Teacher; *b:* Norwalk, CT; *m:* Mary Ann Jasper; *c:* Peter, Jacqueline, Michael; *ed:* Univ of MA at Amherst (BA) Classics 1975, (MAT) Classics 1977; NEA Classical Inst Tufts Univ 1993-94; *cr:* Univ of MA at Amherst Grad Tchng Asst 1975-77; Framingham South HS Latin Tchr 1977-86; Boston Latin Schl Classical Lang Tchr 1986-; *ai:* Cntrl MA Bsbl Umpires Assn; New England Coll Bsbl Umpire Assn; AFT 1986-; CANE 1977-.

BINKUNSKI, DENISE O'LEARY, Fourth Grade Teacher; *b:* New York, NY; *m:* Robert C.; *c:* Sean (dec); *ed:* Penn Hall Jr Coll (AS) Merchandising 1965; Dominican Coll (BA) Eng 1982; Long Island Univ (MS) Elem Ed 1991; *cr:* Continental Can Co Sr Prsnl Clerk 1967-71; Grace Episcopal Church Sec 1972-73; Allstate Ins Co Sec 1974-77; St Margaret's Schl Tchr 1982-; *ai:* FCT 1988-; *office:* St Margaret's Parochial Schl 33 N Magnolia St Pearl River NY 10965

BINNING, WILLIAM C., Political Science Professor; *b:* Boston, MA; *m:* Maureen Fanon; *c:* Patrick, Catherine; *ed:* St Anselm Coll (BA) Politics 1966; Univ Notre Dame (PHD) Govt 1970; *cr:* Youngstown St Univ Asst Prof 1970-77, Assoc Prof 1977-85, Prof 1985-; *ai:* Coll Republicans Adv; Amer Pol Sci Assn 1970-; Urban League 1980-, Vice Chair; Article Pub; *office:* Youngstown St Univ Dept Of Pol Sci Youngstown OH 44555*

BINNS, MARY ELLEN STRAUB, Home Economics Teacher; *b:* Camp Polk, LA; *m:* John Douglas; *c:* Carl; *ed:* OH St Univ (BS) Scndry & Voc Home Ec 1972, (MS) Textiles & Clothing 1977; 18 Hrs Scndry Admin; Voc Home Ec Supervision License; *cr:* Columbus Pub Schls Tchr 1972-; *ai:* Girls & Boys Var Vlybl Head Coach, Girls Var Track Head Coach; ski Club Adv; Home Ec Club; Columbus Home Ec Tchrs Assn 1972-, Pres; Franklin Cty Home Ec Tchrs Assn 1974-; HUB of OH Vlybl Ofcls 1986-, Pres; Motor Maids Inc 1988-, Publicity Dir; McGraw Hill Classroom Ideas; *office:* Independence HS 5175 Refugee Rd Columbus OH 43232*

BIO, ANNA MARIA ROSANO, Italian Teacher; *b:* Patermiti, Italy; *m:* Ernest; *c:* Ernest A., Angela A.; *ed:* Monmouth Univ (BA) Span, Ed 1969; Middlebury Coll (MA) Span 1972; Fairleigh Dickinson at Madisn NDEA Italian Lang, Cult 1968; Amer Cuniv 15 Credits 1975; Fulbright Prgm in Italy 15 Credits1984; *cr:* Long Branch Adult Prgm Italian Tchr 1969-72; Oceantownship Adult Prgm Italian Tchr 1972-76; Brookdale Comm Coll Summer Italian Tchr 1981-83; Oceantown HS Italian, Span Tchr 1971-; *ai:* Italian Club Adv; Schl Dist Instrl Counsel; PTO; Chaperone Stdnts Traveling in Italy; NJEA, NEA 1971-; Fulbright Alumni Asso 1984-; Frgn Lang Ed of NJ 1971-; Voice of Italian Tchr 1994-; St Michael's Church 1970-, Bible Instrustion; IAATO 1985-, Prgm for Children Dir, 3 Spec Hnrs; Mentor, Spon Italian Stdnts 1980-; NDEA Prgm Schlsp 1968; AIFS Travel Prgm Awd; Arm Chair Travel Prgm Presenter; Fulbright Flwshp for Stud in Italy; *office:* Ocean Township HS 550 W Park Ave Oakhurst NJ 07755*

BIRCHLER, ROBERT SAMUEL, HS Mathematics Teacher; *b:* Sparta, IL; *m:* Roberta Jean Kennedy; *c:* Deborah Raja, Barbara, Robert N., Peter; *ed:* Covenant Coll (NBA) Math 1967; NELA St Univ (MS) Math 1969; *cr:* Cono Chrstn Schl Math Tchr 1969-72; Beaver Cty Chrstn Schl Math Tchr 1972-; *ai:* Christ Presbyn Church 1972-, Session Mem.*

BIRDI, ASHWI, Biology Teacher; *b:* Jalandhar, India; *m:* Amarjeet Singh; *c:* Shiva, Kanu; *ed:* Govt Coll for Women (BSC) Bio 1974; Punjab Agricultural Univ (MSC) Zoology 1977; Banaras Hindu Univ (PHD) Zoology 1983; Maharishi Dayanano Univ (BED) Ed 1989; *cr:* Delhi Pub Schl Bio Tchr 1986-90; Wolmer Girls HS Bio Tchr 1990-92; Univ of West Indies Lecturer in Histology 1990-93; Preston HS Sci Tchr 1994-; *ai:* After Schl Help; Trng an Intern; Help Stndts Interested in Rsrch; Curr Comm 1994-95; NYBTA 1995-; NY Acad of Sci 1995-; ASCD 1995-; Univ Flwshp for Rsrch; Jr Rsrch Flwshp Cncl of Scientific & Industrial Rsrch; Papers Pub; *office:* Preston HS 2780 Schurz Ave Bronx NY 10465

BIRDSALL, CINDY ANN, HS Phys & Health Ed Teacher; *b:* Germany; *ed:* Cntrl CT St Univ (BS) PE 1985; Southern CT St Univ (MS) Hlth Ed 1994; Working Towards Second Masters Degree Schl Cnslng; *cr:* Plainville HS PE, Hlth Edctr 1987-; *ai:* Girls Vlybl Coach; Frosh Class, SADD, Comm Awareness Adv; NEA, CIAC 1987-; Natl SADD 1992-, Adv; CIAC 1987-, Coach; *home:* 18 Bokum Rd Chester CT 06412

BIRDSALL, ROBERT PERRY, 4th Grade Teacher; *b:* Sidney, NY; *m:* Susan E.; *c:* Sabra, Seth, Sonya Dean, Stacey Dean, Robert C. P.; *ed:* St Univ at Oneonta (BA) Sci, Eng 1971; 30 Addl Credit Hrs Grad Courses 1971-75; *cr:* Valleyview Elem 6th Grd Tchr 20 Yrs; Greater Plains Elem 4th Grd Tchr 4 Yrs; *ai:* Proprietor of Birdsall Painting, Adirondeck Wild Guide Svcs; NEA 1971-; NYS Outdoor Guides Assn 1981-, Charter; *office:* Greater Plains Elem west End Ave 40 Valleyview St Oneonta NY 13820

BIRKBECK, CHERYL MORRIS, 5th Grade Teacher; *b:* Trenton, NJ; *m:* Roger; *c:* Jessica, Nicole; *ed:* PA St Univ (BS) Elem Ed, Math 1985; 27 Credit Hrs Whole Lang, Cooperative Learning; *cr:* Manor Elem Schl 5th Grd Tchr 1986-; Dmnstrtn Tchr; *ai:* NEA; *office:* Manor Elem Schl 401 Penn Valley Rd Levittown PA 19054*

BIRKEMEIER, JUDY SCHROEDER, Fifth Grade Teacher; *b:* Lima, OH; *m:* Larry C.; *c:* Keith, Amy, David, Diana; *ed:* Univ of Dayton (BS) Ed 1970; Wright St Univ (MS) Ed 1988; Bowling Green St Univ 18 Hrs Grad Credits; *cr:* Kalida Elem 4th Grd Tchr 1970-83, 5th Grd Tchr 1984-; *ai:* Book Adoption & Curr Comms; NEA 1970-; IRA 1970-; Cath Ladies of Columbia 1975-; Rosary Altar Sodality St Michaels Parish 1975-; Jennings Scholar Lecture Pgm Rep 1985-86; Modern Woodmen of Amer Svc Recognition 1991; *office:* Kalida Elem Schl PO Box 358 208 N 4th St Kalida OH 45853

BIRNBACK, SIDNEY R., Prof of Psych & Behavrl Sci; *b:* New York City, NY; *c:* Nicholas; *ed:* City Coll of NY (BA) Psych 1968; Long Island Univ (MS) Clinical Psych 1970; NY Univ (PHD) Psych 1974; Clinical Sexology Diplomate; Bd Cert Amer Bd of Clinical Sexology; *cr:* City of NY Psychologist 1971-73; NY Univ Grad Instr of Psych 1973-76; Bergen Comm Coll Prof of Psych 1976-; *ai:* Psych Advisement; Psychological Cnslng; Curr Dev; Envinonmental Impact Stud; Environmental Psych Courses Taught FL Everglades 1980-; Amer Psych Assn 1974-; NEA 1973-; NJPA 1976-; Philpharmonic Orch 1982-, VP; Palisades Nature Assn 1978-, VP; Numerous Environmental Orgs 1970-; Distngd Prof Awd 1995; Natl Environmental, NJ Environmental Awd DAR 1994.

BIRO, MICHAEL LEROY, Bus Tchr & Head Bsktbl Coach; *b:* Tiffin, OH; *m:* Laura Wagner; *c:* Casey, Michael; *ed:* Bowling Green St Univ (BSEd) Bus Ed 1982, (MED) Bus Ed 1984; Ashland Univ Scndry Prin, Asst Supt Certs; *cr:* Bowling Green St Univ Grad Asst in Bus Ed 1983-84; Greenville City Schls Voc Bus, Bus Tchr 1984-86; Northern Local Schls Bus Tchr 1986-90; Upper Sandusky Exempted Village Schls Bus Tchr, Head Bsktbl Coach 1990-; *ai:* Bus Club Adv; OH HS Bsktbl Coaches Assn 1992-; NBEA, Delta Pi Epsilon 1984-; Pheasants Forever 1994-; *home:* 406 Center Dr Upper Sandusky OH 43351

BISBANO, JULIE A., English Teacher; *b:* Providence, RI; *ed:* Roger Williams Univ (BFA) Creative Writ-Lit 1983; RI Coll (MAT) Eng 1990; Univ of RI 30 Addl Credits Eng; *cr:* Arts Gallery, Wkshps Art Instr 1986-87; Ports HS Eng Tchr 1990-; Roger Williams Univ Part-time Prof 1993-; *ai:* Adv Lit Mag, Film Club; NEA 1990-; NCTE 1989-; 3 Tapes Original Music Pub Siren 1988, Lifers 1990, Not in a Box 1992; Pub Poetry; Presentations at Major Confs IRA, CCC, NCTE; *office:* Portsmouth HS 120 Education In Portsmouth RI 02871

BISBING, RICHARD G., Anatomy & Physiology Teacher; *b:* Leighton, PA; *m:* E. Rebekah Fetterolf; *c:* Richard, Pamela Mertz; *ed:* Kutztown Univ (BS) Bio 1960; Colby Coll (MS) Sci Ed 1972; *cr:* Leighton Area HS Sci Tchr 1960-; *ai:* Former Asst Boy's Bsktbl Coach; Head Girl's Bsktbl, Head Track Coach; Soph Class Adv; PSEA, NEA 1960-; NSF Grant 1969-72; *office:* Lehighton Area Sr HS 1275 Mahoning St Lehighton PA 18235

BISCARDI-MENSCH, LINDA, English Teacher; *ed:* Univ of Miami (BA) Eng 1973; FL Atlantic Univ (MFA) Eng 1974; Southampton Coll (MS) Media Specialist 1978; Seton Hall Regents 1969; Post Grad Work Portfolio Assessment, Film Stud; *cr:* Marymount Coll Eng Instr 1973-74; East Hampton HS Eng Tchr 1974-81; East Hampton MS Eng Tchr 1981-; *ai:* Lit Arts, Yrbk, Class Adv; Beachplums, Waves Magazine; Chrldng, Drama Coach; Mediator Project Adventure Ldr; Educl Comms; NCTE, AFT, NEA, NYSUT 1974-; Hamptons Intnl Film Festival, Bd of Dirs, Chprsn Educ Comm; Nom Long Island Univ Tchr of Yr 1995; NY St Tchr Rep Christa Mc Auliffe Meml Svcs; *office:* East Hampton MS 76 Newtown Ln East Hampton NY 11937

BISCHAK, KATHLEEN (HUFF), Art Teacher; *b:* Pittsburgh, PA; *m:* Ralph E.; *c:* Jennifer, Daniel; *ed:* Univ of PA at Edinboro (BS) Art Ed 1973; Permanent PA Cert; 30 Hrs Credit Via Intermediate Units IV & XXVII; 3 Grad Art Credits at Univ of Pa at Kutztown; *cr:* Freedom Area HS Art Tchr 1973-75; Private & Merrick Art Galleries Art Tchr 1978-80; Allegheny Cty Comm Coll Art Tchr 1981-82; Seneca Valley Schls Art Tchr 1980-; *ai:* Jr & Sr HS Art Clubs; Evans City Elem 6th Grd Art Club; NEA 1981-; NAEA, PA Art Ed Assn 1985-; Pittsburgh Soc of Artists 1993-, Mem; Merrick Art Gallery 1980-93, Mem; Assn of Valley Artists 1978-, Mem; Our Lady of Peace Church 1973-; Exhibited Art Work at Three Rivers Arts Festival; Exhibited & Received Awds at North Hills Art Ctr; Best of Show & Many Awds at Assn of Valley Artists; Best of Show Wearable Art at Beaver Art Festival; One Person Exhibit at Hoyt Inst of Fine Arts; *office:* Evans City Elem Schl 345 W Main St Evans City PA 16033*

BISCHOFF, BEVERLY ANN (FURNARI), 4th Grade Teacher; *b:* Poughkeepsie, NY; *m:* Ronald E.; *c:* Anthony Roberts, Wendy Ann Roberts Pruss, Craig M. Roberts; *ed:* St Univ of New Paltz (BS) Elem Ed 1966; *cr:* Wappingers Cntrl Schl 1st Grd Tchr 1966-67; Boston Schl Dists K-6th Grd Tchr 1967-71; Wappingers Cntrl Schl K-6th Grd Sub Tchr 1971-77; Poughkeepsie MS 6th Grd Math Tchr 1987; Wappingers Cntrl Schl 5th, 3rd, 4th Grd Tchr 1987-; *ai:* AFT, WCT, NYSUT 1987-; *office:* Sheafe Road Elem Schl 145 Sheafe Rd Wappingers Falls NY 12590

BISCHOFF, BONNIE PHILO, Adjunct Instructor of English; *b:* New York City, NY; *m:* Peter; *c:* Heidi, Katy, Dan; *ed:* Moravian Coll (BA) Eng 1968; Trenton St Coll (MED) Eng 1976; Tchr of Handicapped Cert Georgian Court Coll 1992; *cr:* Colonia HS Eng Tchr 1970-72; Lakewood Comm Schl Eng Tchr, HS Equivalency 1973-76; Ocean Cty Coll Eng Adj Instr 1977-87; Lakewood Prep Schl Eng, Soc Stud Tchr 1987-94; Ocean Cty Coll Eng Adj Instr 1995-; *ai:* Ocean Cty Girls Scouts 1980-88, Troop Ldr, Ldr of Yr; *office:* Ocean Cty Coll College Dr PO Box 2001 Toms River NJ 08754*

BISCHOFF, DOUGLAS, Choral Music & Theatre Teacher; *b:* Cliffside Park, NJ; *m:* Linda Elsasser; *c:* Christopher, Susanne, Cynthia; *ed:* West Chester Univ (BS) Music Ed 1967; NY Univ (MA) Choral Conducting 1979; Theatre at St Univ of NY at Purchase; Choral Conducting at Mansfield Univ, Akron Univ, Saint Johns Univ & St Univ of NY at Stony Brook; *cr:* Pub Schl 18 General & Choral Music Tchr 1967-74; Yonkers HS Choral & Theatre Tchr 1974-86; Gorton HS Instrumental Band Tchr 1982-83; Cambridge Cntrl Schl Choral & Theatre Tchr 1986-; *ai:* Schl Play; Vocal Festivals; Choral Festivals; MENC 1967-; ACDA 1982-; NY Choral Dirs Guild 1992-; Jaycees 1974-80; Whos Who Young Men of Amer; Yonkers Tchr of Month; Citizenship Awd From WFAS Radio; *office:* Cambridge Central Schl 24 S Park St Cambridge NY 12816

BISCOTTI, SHARON LOIS, Third Grade Teacher; *b:* Baltimore, MD; *ed:* Towson St Univ Elem Ed (BS) 1986, (ME) 1994; *cr:* Riverside Elem Schl 2nd-3rd Grd Tchr 1986-.

BISGROVE, DONNA WOOD, First Grade Teacher; *b:* Neptune, NJ; *m:* Donald E.; *c:* Dean W., David L., Dale John; *ed:* Univ of DE (BS) Elem Ed 1956; Fairleigh Dickinson Univ (MA) Human Dev 1977; 43 Post Grad Stud; *cr:* Middletown Bd of Ed First-Third Grd Tchr 1956-; *ai:* Alpha Delta Kappa 1987-, Chaplain Cor Sec; Phi Delta Kappa 1985-; New Mon Bapt Church, Bd of Chrstn Ed 2 Terms; Sunday Schl Tchr 1960, 1970, 1980; Tchr of Yr; *office:* New Monmouth Elem Schl 121 New Monmouth Rd New Monmouth NJ 07748

BISHARA, ANN DIANA, English Teacher & Co-Curr Dir; *b:* Philadelphia, PA; *m:* William; *c:* William J., David M., Michael D.; *ed:* Niagara Comm Coll (AAS) Lbrl Arts 1971; SUCB (BS) Elem N-6, Scndry 7-12 Eng 1972, (MS) Rdng, Elem 1975; Canisius Medeille (MS) Rdng Specialist 1982; Canisius (MS) Admin 1985; Niagara Univ 6 Hrs Span, Cmptrs, Acctng; SUNY 3 Hrs Arts in Ed; Coll of St Rose 3 Hrs Assertive Discipline; *cr:* Family Bus Mgr Restaurant, Delicatessen 1 Yr; Marine Midland Bookkeeping, Machine Operator 1 Yr; Cedars of Lebanon Hosp Traffic, Controll Clerk 8 Yrs; Ed Town MS, Sr HS Rdng Tchr 3 Yrs; Niagara Wheatfield Benior HS Eng Tchr 25 Yrs; *ai:* NW Comm Booster's Stu of Month Awds Chprsn; NFLSAC Sportsmanship Adv, Coord of All Advs; PAVAS Asst Dir of Childrens Theatre, NYC Field Trip; Chprsn Pep Club, Coord Homecoming Activities; Tchr Retirement Dinner Chprsn 2 Yrs; Taste of Wheatfield 40th Anniversary Comm; NWTA; NYSUT; NCTE, Convention Flwshp, 1st Yr Tchng, Philadelphia Convention; NW Comm Boosters 1978-, VP, Booster Mem of Yr; Police Ath League, Cornerstone Awd; NW Ftbl Parents 1976-; MO Musc Parents 1975-; Grad Western NY Arts Ed 7 Yrs, MS Started Coord; Grant Stratford Antaso Shakespeare Theatre.

BISHARD, LOIS BURD, Fifth Grade Teacher; *b:* Doylestown, PA; *m:* Bradford; *c:* Elizabeth, Suzanne, Brett; *ed:* Elizabethtown Coll (BS) Elem Ed 1972; *cr:* Dover Schl Dist Second Grd Tchr 1972-76, Third Grd Tchr 1977-81, Fifth Grd Tchr 1982-; *ai:* Dist Curr Advy, Schl Site Base, IST Co-Chair Comms; DAFA, NEA, PSEA 1972-; ASCO 1986-; Tchr Ldr Mini-Grant South Cntrl PA Tchr Ldrshp Ctr 1994-; *home:* RR 10 B York PA 17404

BISHOP, CATHRYN BROWN, 2nd Grade Teacher; *b:* Watertow *m:* William E.; *c:* Rebecca, Colleen; *ed:* Jefferson Comm Coll (A Arts 1967; SUNY at Potsdam (BA) Elem Ed 1969; SUNY at Oswe Arts; 30 Addl Hrs SUNY at Geneseo & Nazareth Coll at Rocheste Trng Cert Affiliate Trainer Lions Quest Intnl; *cr:* Copenhagen Cn 3rd Grd Tchr 1969-70; Manchester Shortsville Cntrl Schl Kndg 1970-85, 2nd Grd Tchr 1985-; *ai:* Affiliate Trainer Lions Quest In Assoc Pres; Numerous Comms; NYSUT 1969-, Local Pres; Delta Gamma 1993-; *home:* 22 Kathlyn Ave Phelps NY 14532

BISHOP, EDWARD F., High School Principal; *b:* Seneca Falls, Laurie O'Connell; *c:* Brian, Jeffrey, Kaley, Meghan; *ed:* SU Brockport (BS) Soc Sci 1969, (MS) Ed Admin 1984; *cr:* Waterlo Tchr 1969-84; Waterloo Sr HS Asst Prin 1984-88; Byron-Bergen 1988-; *ai:* ASCD 1984-; SAANYS 1988-; Kiwanis 1989-; *hom* Hessenthaler Rd Byron NY 14422

BISHOP, JEANNE COTTER, Business Teacher; *b:* Newton, Thomas A.; *c:* Allan, Jillian; *ed:* NHVTC at Laconia (AAS) Secreta 1973; Plymouth St Coll (BS) Comprehensive Bus Ed 1976; 2 Grad NH Coll, 3 Grad Credits Castleton St Coll, 6 Grad Credits Univ of Mt Abraham Union HS Bus Tchr 1975-78; Pittsfield HS Bus Tchr 1 Laconia HS Bus Tchr 1986-; *ai:* Swim Team Coach 2 Yrs; Chrldng 6 Yrs; Class Adv 15 Yrs; NHBEA 1978-; *office:* Laconia HS 345 Un Laconia NH 03246

BISHOP, JEANNE EMMONS, Science Tchr & Planetarium Dir; Angeles, CA; *m:* Allan R.; *c:* Eric P.; *ed:* Kent St Univ (BS) Scn Sci, Math 1963; Univ of Pittsburgh (MS) Scndry Ed 1968; Univ o (PHD) Scndry Ed, Sci 1980; *cr:* Hoover-Price Planetarium Dir 1 Penn Hills Schl Dist Planetarium Dir, Math, Astronomy, Geolog 1965-68; Berea Schl Dist Sci Tchr 1969; Westlake Pub Schls Plan Dir, Astronomy, Geology, Chem, Phys Sci Tchr 1969-; *ai:* Adv, I Women in Sci Seminars; Elem Sci Olympiad Planetarium Helper; Observing Sessions; Strategic Planning, Sci Curr Writing Planetarium Soc 1974-, Pres, Exec Sec, Svc Awd, Fellow; Grea Planetarium Soc 1964-; Ed Chair, Newsletter Ed, Armand Spitz Me Fellow; NSTA 1974-; NEA; Cleveland Astronomical Soc, Pr Cleveland Geological Soc; Thomas Brennan HS Astronomy Tchr 1995; Presidential Sci, Math Tchng Awd St Nom 1994; Basic Ed S Stud Cncl 1990; Martha Holden Jennings Master Tchr 1976; NS Tchng Ohaus Awd 1976, STAR Awd 1977; *office:* Westlake HS Hilliard Blvd Westlake OH 44145

BISHOP, J. ERIC ERIC, English Instr & Dept Chair; *b:* Doylestov *m:* Linda Hostetler; *c:* J. Wendell, Angela K.; *ed:* Eastern Mennoni (BA) Eng Ed 1978; Beaver Coll (MAEd) Eng 1984; Kent St Univ D Stud; James Madison Univ Post Masters Stud; *cr:* Christopher D Tchr 1978-; Eastern Mennonite Coll Writing Tchr 1988-89; Chri Dock HS Master Tchr & Mentor 1989-, Instructional Support 1990 Curr Comm Sec; Spring Drama Production Mgr; NCTE 1994-; So Mennonite Church 1989-, Adult Sunday Schl Tchr, Church Cncl Franconia News Conf 1994-, Editorial Consultant; *office:* Chri Dock Mennonite HS 1000 Forty Foot Rd Lansdale PA 19446

BISHOP, LINDA GOON, Math Teacher; *b:* Baltimore, MD; *m:* Wayne; *ed:* Univ of MD at College Park (BS) Ed 1988; Johns H (MS) Ed 1993; *ai:* Stdnts Helping Other People Spon; NCTM MSTA, MCTM 1988-; *office:* Glenelg HS 14025 Burntwoods Rd MD 21737

BISHOP, LORI KOONS, Family & Consumer Sci Teacher; *b:* Wy MI; *m:* Robert J.; *c:* Robby, Alexander; *ed:* Keystone Coll (AA) Res Mngmt 1986; Marywood Coll (BA) Home Ec Ed 1992; *cr:* Blue Rid Dist Family, Consumer Sci, Home Ec Tchr 1992-; *ai:* Stu Cncl C Blue Ridge Ed Assn 1993-; *office:* Blue Ridge Schl Dist RR 2 Box 2 Milford PA 18834

BISHOP, RICHARD ALLEN, Science Teacher; *b:* Spangler, PA; Marie Merriman; *c:* Ryan, Brandon, Seth; *ed:* Univ of Pittsb Johnstown (BS) Bio & General Sci 1978; St Francis Coll (MED) E Acceptance to the Prin Prgm at Indiana Univ of PA; *cr:* Blacklick Jr Sr HS Sci Tchr 1978-84; Cambria Heights HS Sci Tchr 1984-; *a* 8th Grd Ftbl Head Coach; Var Wrestlng Head Coach; NEA & PSEA CHEA 1984-; *office:* Cambria Heights HS RD 1 Box 6 Patton PA

BISHOP, SUSAN MASON, First Grade Teacher; *b:* Philadelphia, George C.; *ed:* Cedar Crest Coll (BA) Elem Ed 1968; Univ of OK Music, Organ Performance 1970; 30 Addl Credits; *cr:* Jarrettow Schl First Grd Tchr 1970-; *ai:* Primary Curr Review Comm; NEA, UDEA 1970-; *office:* Jarrettown Elem Schl 1520 Limekiln Pike Dre 19025

BISHOP-LONG, BETH E., English Teacher; *b:* Findlay, OH; *m:* Long; *ed:* BGSU (BS) Eng 1974; Mt St Joseph (MA) Ed 1987; *cr:* F City Schl Tchr 1974-76; Riagedale Local Schl Tchr 1976-86; Elgi Schl Tchr 1981-; *ai:* OEA 1974-; Delta Kappa Gamma, Phi Delta 1980-; *office:* Elgin Local Schl 1239 Keener Rd Marion OH 43302

BISKO, ROSLYN JEAN (FORMECK), 7th Grade Pre-Algebra T *b:* Spangler, PA; *c:* Kimberly (dec), Nicole; *ed:* Univ of Pittsburg Sociology & Psych 1969; St Francis Coll (BS) Elem Ed 1978; Degree 30 Hrs; *cr:* Northern Cambria Cath Rdng, PE & Eng Tchr 1 Northern Cambria Mid 7th Grd Math, Pre Algebra & 6th Grd S 1980-; *ai:* Senate, Reconstruction & Math Comm; Staff Dev; Mento 1980-; PA St Ed Assn 1980-; Northern Cambria Ed Assn 1980-; PTA Dir Pius Rdng Club; Tchr of the Month; *home:* 308 Susqueha Barnesboro PA 15714

BISKUP, SUSAN LYNN, Chemistry & Physical Sci Tchr; *b:* Beave PA; *m:* Rodney G. Sr.; *c:* Rodney G. Jr., Michael; *ed:* Univ of Pit (BS) Chem 1983; Geneva Coll Cert Ed 1984; *cr:* Quigley Cath HS Tchr 1985-, Sci Dept Head 1994-; *ai:* NHS Moderator; Stu Tut NCEA, FPDT 1986-; NASAA 1994-; *office:* Quigley Cath HS 200 Dr Baden PA 15005

BISON-ROSSI, ANNETTE, First Grade Teacher; *b:* Barre, Vittorio; *c:* Maria, Marco, gemma; *ed:* VT Coll & Norwich Uni Human Svcs 1978; Johnson St Coll (BS) Elem Ed 1986; Grad Cour Barretown Elem Spcl Ed Para Edctr 1978, 1979-85, 1st-2nd Gr 1986-; Brandon Trng Inst Spcl Ed Para Edctr 1978-79; *ai:* Tchr Team; Understanding Epilepsy MS Presentations; NEA 1986-; Mountain Teen Inst Family Dialogue Night; Aldrich Lib 1993-, Granile Presentation; Barretown Elem & MS 1996, Facilitator; Barre Town Elem Schl RR 2 Box 4323 Barre VT 05641*

BISSELL, BETTY ANN, Retired Elementary Teacher; *b:* Ma Springs, AR; *ed:* Evangel Coll (BA) Eng 1972, (BS) Elem Ed 1977 Univ of Newfoundland (MAEd) Early Chldhd Ed 1981; *cr:* Spr Pentecostal Schl Kndgtn, Grd I Tchr 1960-62; Windros Pentecost Kndgtn, Grd I Tchr 1962-67; Garden Grove Chrstn Schl 2 Gr 1965-66; Garrigus Acad Kndgtn, Grd I Tchr 1967-70; A. C. Palme Kndgtn, Grd I Tchr 1970-79; Southbrook Pentecostal Schl 1 & 2 G 1980-81; Vaters Acad Kndgtn, Grd Tchr 1981-93; *ai:* NTA 196 1964-; RNLTA 1993-; Grad Flwshp Meml Univ of NF; *hom* Cumberland Cres St John's NF A1B 3M5 Canada CN

.LE, ANDREW PHILIP, History Teacher; *b:* Utica, NY; *m:* Mary ; *ed:* Colgate Univ (BA) Pol Sci 1988; CT Coll (MAT) His 1992; is Schl His Tchr 1990-91; The Taft Schl His Fellow 1989-90, His 92-; *ai:* Coach Soccer, Ice-Hockey, LaCrosse; Day Stu Adv; Ath *office:* Taft Schl 110 Woodbury Rd Watertown CT 06795

'T, SUSAN, Secondary Librarian; *b:* Mercer, PA; *ed:* Clarion Univ .ib Sci 1977; Univ of Pittsburgh (MLS) Lib Sci 1981; *cr:* Northn Scndry Librn 1977-; *ai:* Speech Team Head Coach; PSLA 1990-; NEA 1977-; *office:* North Star HS 400 Ohio St Boswell PA 15531

NETTE, THOMAS E., Science Teacher; *b:* Buffalo, NY; *m:* Smith; *c:* Michele; *ed:* St John fisher Coll (BS) Chem 1968; aer Polytechnic Inst (MS) Chem 1971; 110 Grad hrs RIT, Univ of er, NSF Grant Berkley; *cr:* Ciba-Geigy Corp Rsrch Chemist ; Waterloo HS Chem Tchr; *ai:* Var Boys, Girls Tennis Coach; NEA ISF Grant Berkley; NY St Physics Mentor Tchr; Numerous Articles *ice:* Waterloo HS Center St Waterloo NY 13165*

NNETTE, ANNE EVELINE, Collections Manager; *b:* Montreal, *ed:* LaSalle Coll (DEC) Fashion Design 1988; Univ de Montreal rt His 1991; Fashion Inst of Tech (MA) Museum Stud, Costume, 1993; *cr:* The Museum at Fashion Inst of Tech Asst Conservator aSalle Coll Intnl Fashion Prgm Coord 1994; Stephens Coll Instr ; Kent St Univ Museum Collections Mgr 1995-; *ai:* Costume Soc 1993-; *office:* Kent St Univ Museum PO Box 5190 Rockwell Hall I 44242

R, RUTH LOUISE, Chemistry Teacher; *b:* Portland, ME; *ed:* Univ t Orono (BS) Chemical Engrng 1982; Univ of Southern ME (MS) 1in 1990; Univ of Southern ME Tchrs for Scndry Schls Prgm , Tchr Cert Prgm for People with Bachelors Degrees; *cr:* Morse HS chr 1984-85; Yarmouth HS Chem Tchr 1985-86; South Portland HS chr 1986-89; Gardiner Area HS Asst Prin 1989-90; Windham HS chr 1990-; *ai:* Envirothon Team, Pi-cone Math League Adv; Staff mm Chair; Recognition Awd for Programming Excl From Univ of) & Paper Fnd, Nom By Stdnts 1993; *office:* Windham HS 406 Gray dham ME 04062

Y, CHARLES WARREN, 8th Grade Mathematics Teacher; *b:* iet, NY; *m:* Maureen Houck; *c:* Matthew, Sarah; *ed:* SUNY at (BA) Math, Sociology 1974, (MA) Math Ed 1976; *cr:* W.K. Doyle h Instr 1977-; *ai:* AFT, NYSUT 1977-.*

R, RITA C., Retired 6th Grade Teacher; *b:* Philadelphia, PA; *m:* *ed:* Immaculata Coll (BA) Elem Ed 1969; Miami Univ Edt, Math elf-Concept, Mus, PE Elem Schl 1972; PA St Classroom Tchng on 1974; Goddard Coll Supervision World Travel, 1 Grad Credit rof Comp Cert in Relgn, Archdiocese of Phila; *cr:* Most Blessed ent 1-3 Grd Tchr 1956-59; St Charles Grd 4 Tchr 1959-61; St James Tchr 1961067; St Monica 6-8 Grd Math, Read Tchr 1967-73; St rd 7 Tchr 1973-76; Various Pub Elem Schl Sub Tchr 1976-77; St angelist Grd 4 Math, Eng, Sci Read, Mus, SS Tchr 1977-81; Holy 5-8 Grd Tchr 1981-95; *ai:* Schl Bd, Religion Coord, Mentor Tchr; 90-96; Grant 1970 Miami Univ; Distinguished Cath Edctrs Awd chdiocese of Phila.

N, HENRY, Economics & Writing Teacher; *b:* Paterson, NJ; *m:* *c:* Brian, Kylene; *ed:* Concordia Univ (BA) His 1968, (MED) Eng Y Univ (PD) Soc Stud Ed 1982; 3 Credit Hrs Johns Hopkins Univ; Hrs Fairfield Univ; 6 Credit Hrs Columbia Univ; 12 Credit Hrs Patterson Coll; *cr:* Martin Luther HS Soc Stud Tchr 1969-80; ood HS Soc Stud Tchr 1980-90; Ramapo Indian Hills HS Soc Stud Tchr 1990-; *ai:* Rotary Interact & Amnesty Intnl Clubs; NJCSS GBCSS 1981-, Pres; NJCHE 1993-, Treas; Natl Forensic League Outstdng Distinction; Debate Coach of Yr Bridgewater Invitational atl Water Alliance Debate Coach Finalist 1986; Debate Coach of of MA 1989; NJ Forensics Leage Debate Coach Awd 1990; NJCSS Yr Awd 1994; *office:* Ramapo HS 331 George St Franklin Lakes NJ

IG, GRETA FRANTZ, Mathematics Teacher; *b:* Jersey Shore, PA; F.; *c:* Kent A., Julie C., Lori A.; *ed:* Bucknell Univ (BS) Math *:* Shippensburg MS Math Tchr 1971-72; Littletown HS Math Tchr *ai:* Class Adv 1986-90; NHS Adv 1991-95; LEA, PSEA, NEA Tchr Rep; *office:* Littlestown HS 200 E Myrtle St Littlestown PA

ER, BRAN ALAN, Vocational Agriculture Teacher; *b:* St Marys, Nancy London; *c:* Kayla; *ed:* Delaware Vly Coll (BS) Horticulture ert Vo-Ag, Gen Sci PA St Univ; *cr:* Houghton Wine Co Pty Ltd 1990-91; Vir Terra Svcs Landscape Construction Co 1990-; Penn Grad Asst 1992-93; Brockway Area HS Vo-Ag Instr 1995-; *ai:* FFA ar Bsbl Vol; PA St Ed Assn 1995-; PA Vo-Ag Tchrs Assn 1994-; Brockway Area Jr Sr HS 100 Alexander St Brockway PA 15824

ER, ROSEMARY CHERBAN, Assistant Professor of Nursing; *c:* *ed:* Penn St Univ (BSN) Nrsng 1977; IN Univ of PA (MSN) Nrsng niontown Hosp Schl of Nrsng Diploma in Nrsng 1971; *cr:* Mount s Coll Asst Prof of Nrsng 1980-; *ai:* Sigma Theta Tau 1984-, Past *ie:* 1364 Ben Avon St Indiana PA 15701

S, PENELOPE ELAINE, Assistant Professor of Voice; *b:* I, ME; *ed:* Ithaca Coll (BM) Vocal Perf, Mus Ed 1976; New England Music (MM) Vocal Perf 1978; *cr:* Gustavus Adolphus Coll PT nstr 1981; Ithaca Coll Asst Prof of Voice 1985-90; Wagner Coll PT nstr 1991-93; Boston Univ Asst Prof of Voice 1993-; *ai:* Bd Mem Musical Adv Metropolitan Greek Chorale NYC; Chprsn ons & Recruitment; Stu Life, Hnrs Comms; AGMA 1981-; NATS Nat'l Semi-Finalist Metropolitan Opera Auditions; Outstdng Young of Amer; Performed Tanglewood Music Festival, MN Opera Bauff New Music Ensemble.

NO, J. MARTIN, Instrumental Music Director; *b:* Cortland, NY; na L.; *c:* John, Maria, Tony; *ed:* Lincoln Coll (AA) Music Ed 1969; Univ (BM) Music Ed 1971; Univ of Akron (MA) Scndry Schl 1979; Post Grad Work at Ashland Univ Cmptr Ed; *cr:* Chippewa chl Dist HS Band Dir 1972-74; Canton Local Schl Dist Band Dir *ai:* Stu Instrumental Performances Ldr; NEA, OEA, MENC 1972-; Local Band Booster 1992-; Outstanding Musicians Awd & Arts Awd Lincoln Coll 1969; *office:* Faircrest Memorial MS 616 st St SW Canton OH 44706

S, BARBARA PERRY, Teacher & Coordinator; *b:* Durham, NC; *m:* W.; *c:* Robert Jr.; *ed:* Temple Univ (MED) Bus Ed 1972; Attnd Univ Drexel Univ & St Josephs Univ; *cr:* Overbrook HS Tchr 1966-; *ai:* t Coord; Phila Fed of Tchrs 1966-; AFT; Delta Pi Epsilon; Phi Delta; Awds: Schl Dist of Phila Excl in Tchng, Rose Lindenbaum g Tchr, Ruth W Hayre Svc, Arco Chemical Excl in Tchng & Bus hila; Phila Writing Project Flwshp; Schl Dist of Phila Mini Grant; Overbrook HS 59th St & Lancaster Ave Philadelphia PA 19131

S-HUDSON, PHYLLIS, Language Arts Teacher; *b:* Suffolk, VA; tis Lee Hudson; *c:* Tawana Latrice Bivins, Zammeah Monique Eric Lee Hudson; *ed:* Jersey City St Coll (BA) Elem Ed 1979; oaf Schl of Eng (MA) Eng Lit 1993; *cr:* Dept of Pub Works Admin 74-77; John L. Costley MS 7th-8th Grd Lang Arts Tchr 1979-94; Orange MS 7th Grd Lang Arts Tchr 1994-; Ramapo Coll Adjunct ev Writ, Eng I 1995-; *ai:* Saturday Enrichment Prgm Tchr; Delta Sigma Theta 1986-, Recording Sec, Membership Comm Chprsn; NJ St Governor TPrgm for Excl, Tchr of Yr Awd 1990; Oxford Univ Fellowship Grant 1992; Pub Poetry; *office:* South Orange MS 70 N Ridgewood Rd South Orange NJ 07079*

BIXEL, ALLEN P., Music Director; *b:* Johnstown, PA; *m:* Kimberlie Elms; *c:* Shauna Marie; *ed:* IN Univ of PA (BS) Music Ed 1985; Clarion Univ of PA (BM) Music Performance 1983; *cr:* Harmony Area Schl Dist K-12 Music Dir 1985-90; Blacklick Valley Schl Dist Instrumental Music Dir 1990-92; Holy Name Elem Instrumental Music Dir 1993-; Bish op Carroll HS Music Dir 1990-; *ai:* Bowling Coach; Staff Photographer; Lit Comm; Marching, Concert Bands Dir; Jazz, Brass Ensembles; Show Choir; Cath Band Assn 1993-; NCEA 1990-; PMEA, MENC, Local 41 AFM 1985-; Intnl Freelance Phtgrphrs Org 1995-; Childrens Choir Asst Music Dir Trinity Luth Church; Johnstown Reed, Band Princ Percussionist; Richland Lanes Automotive League Sec; St Vincent Coll Great Tchr Recognition Awd; Prize Winning Freelance Photographer; *office:* Bishop Carroll HS RT 422 W Ebensburg PA 15931

BIXLER, DARYL ELIZABETH, Secondary English Teacher; *b:* Hershey, PA; *ed:* Lock Haven Univ (BA) Liberal Arts 1980, (BS) Eng 1984; Wilkes Univ (MS) Ed 1990; *cr:* VISTA Vol Project Dev Literacy 1982-84; Williamsport Comm Coll Part-Time Instr 1983-84; Lycoming Cty Literacy Project Coord 1983-85; Muncy Schl Dist Scndry Eng Tchr 1985-; *ai:* Sr Class Spon; Staff Dev; Phi Kappa Phi 1980-; Literacy Bd Mem 1983-, Exec Dir 1983-85; Founder Lycoming Cty Literacy Project Inc; *office:* Muncy Schl Dist Penn St Muncy PA 17756

BIXLER, THOMAS LORIN, Band Director; *b:* Wadsworth, OH; *m:* Kay Lynn Nicholson; *c:* Gregory Robert; *ed:* OH St Univ (BME) Instrumental Music Ed 1981; Attnd Bowling Green St Univ, FL St Univ, Univ of Akron, Ashland Coll; *cr:* Ottoville Local Schls Music Dir 1981-84; Port Clinton City Schls Band Dir 1985-; *ai:* Jazz, Pep Bands; Natl Band Assn, Music Edctrs Natl Conf, Ohio Music Ed Assn 1981-; AFT 1985-, Bldg Rep; Ohio St Marching Band Alumni Assn, Ohio St Alumni Assn 1981-; *office:* Port Clinton HS 821 Jefferson St Port Clinton OH 43452

BIZINKAUSKAS, CHARLENE CASSIANI, Special Needs Teacher; *b:* Brockton, MA; *m:* Peter Mark; *c:* Peter Charles, Jeffrey Mark; *ed:* Lesley Coll at Cambridge (BSEd) Moderate Spec Needs, Elem Ed 1978; Anna Maria Coll 3 Grad Credit Hrs 1994; Bridgewater St Coll 3 Grad Credit Hrs 1994; Cmptrs in the Classroom, Percentiles-Assessement Evaluations, ADD-Dr. Marwil, I.E.P. Trng, Tech in Classroom, What is Dsylexia Brown Univ, Learning Disabilities Network Conf, Inclusive Curr HS Setting, Middleboro HS Inclusion Prgm, Co-Tchng Morton Hosp ADD Lectures 1995; Modifying Curr Inclusive Classrooms, Educl Tech, Video Tech Classrooms, Dr. Ed Hallowell 1994; *cr:* Avon Pub Schls Tchr 1978-81; Stafford Cty Pub Schls Tchr 1981-83; Middleborough Pub Schls Spec Needs Tchr 1984-85, 1993-; *ai:* MHS Key Club Cert of Recognition 1995; MA Rdng Assn 1995-; MA Tchrs Assn 1994-; Cncl for Exceptional Children 1976-77; Middleboro Town Republican Comm 1994-, Nom Comm Mem; *office:* Middleborough HS 72 E Grove St Middleboro MA 02346*

BIZJAK, FRANK A., 7th-12th Grd Ag Ed Teacher; *b:* Montique, NJ; *m:* Shannon Newman; *ed:* PA St Univ (BS) Ag Ed 1992; 13 Hrs Post Grad Work; *cr:* Conneaut Vly HS AG Ed Tchr 1992-; *ai:* FFA Club Adv; Ag Ball Coach; Crawford Cty Fair Bd; Livestock Comm; NEA, PSEA 1991-; Conneaut ED Assn 1992-; Received 2 Ag Rural Ed Grants; *office:* Conneaut Vly HS 12154 State Hwy 18 Conneautville PA 16406

BIZZARRI, ELLEN BARRETT, English Teacher; *b:* Rochester, PA; *m:* John; *ed:* Geneva Coll (BA) Eng 1993; *cr:* Ambridge Jr HS Lang Arts Permanent Sub Tchr 1993-94; Western Beaver Jr Sr HS Eng Tchr 1994-; *ai:* Color Guard Adv; All Schl Musical Dir & Choreographer; Choreography Club Adv; NEA, PSEA, WBEA 1994-; First UP Church of Monaca 1982-, Deacon; *office:* Western Beaver Co Jr Sr HS 216 Engle Rd Industry PA 15052

BIZZIGOTTI, EDNA BECKER, Retired Second Grade Teacher; *b:* Flushing, NY; *m:* Raymond A.; *c:* George, Susan Rickmeyer; *ed:* SUNY at New Paltz (BS) Ed 1952; *cr:* Carle Place Pub Schls First & Second Grd Tchr 1952-57; Freehold Twp Pub Schls Second Grd Tchr 1966-92; *ai:* NJEA, NEA 1966-; Molly Pitcher Womans Club 1992-.

BJERKE, MAUREEN ELAINA, English Teacher; *b:* Amityville, NY; *m:* Harold W.; *ed:* SUNY at Stony Brook (BA) Eng 1970, (MA) Eng 1974; Magna Cum Laude; 85 Credit Hrs; *cr:* Lindenhurst HS Eng, Writing Tchr 1970-; *ai:* Peg Confrey Schlsp, Regents Action Plan, HS Attendance Policy Comms; NYSUT, AFT, Tchrs Assn of Lindenhurst 1970-; O Co-Nee Assn 1983-90, Sec; Hospice of the South Shore 1991-95, Chairlady, Black Tie Gala; Vol Breast Cancer Coalition, Fundraising/Charity Work; Articles Pub NY Sunday Times; *office:* Lindenhurst HS 300 Charles St Lindenhurst NY 11757*

BJORHOVDE, REIDAR, Prof of Civil & Envrnmntl Engr; *b:* Harstad, Norway; *m:* Patricia Ellery Ordonez; *c:* Ian Douglas, Heather Leah; *ed:* Norwegian Inst of Tech (MS) Civil Engrng 1964, (DrIng) Civil Engrng 1968; Lehigh Univ (PHD) Civil Engrng 1972; *cr:* Norwegian Inst of Tech Asst Prof 1964-68; Lehigh Univ Rsrch Asst, Assoc 1968-72; Amer Inst of Steel Constr Regnl, Rsrch Engr 1972-76; Univ of Alberta Assoc, Full Prof 1976-81; Univ of AZ Prof 1981-87; Univ of Pittsburgh Prof, Chm 1987-; *ai:* Intern Assn of Bridge, Struct Engg; Amer Soc Civil Engrs 1969-, Multiple Offs, Croes Medal 1992; Amer Inst Steel Const 1981-, Multiple Offs, Higgins Awd 1987; Struct Stab Res Cncl 1973-, Exec Comm, Vice Chm; Canad Soc for Civil Eng 1976-, Multiple Offs, Duggan Medal 1979; Amer Iron, Steel Inst 1981-, Multiple Offs Svc Awd 1995; BSA 1952-, Multiple Offs, Svc in 3 Countries; Numerous Publications; Numerous Presentations Worldwide; Numerous Rsrch Grants; Rsrch Flwshp of Japan Soc Promotion of Sci 1992; NATO Sr Guest Scientist 1987; NATO Sci Flwshp 1969; South African Steel Inst Awd 1989; Numerous Visiting Prof Awds; *office:* Univ Of Pittsburgh Dept of Civil & Env Engrng 949 Benedum Hall Pittsburgh PA 15261*

BLACK, BARBARA H., Social Studies Dept Chair; *b:* Brooklyn, NY; *c:* Samantha Chadwick; *ed:* St Josephs Coll (BA) His 1966; Coll of Staten Island (MS) Soc St Ed 1988; *ai:* Former Stu Cncl Adv; NCEA 27 Yrs; Natl Endowment for the Hum Grants 1987, 1988 & 1990; NY St Cncl for the Hum Grant 1992 & 1994; Outstdng Tchr in Queens 1995; *office:* Stella Maris HS 140 Beach 112th St Far Rockaway NY 11694

BLACK, BARRY DIEHL, Math & Computer Science Tchr; *b:* York, PA; *m:* Jane Diane Amspacher; *c:* Barry David; *ed:* Millersville Univ (BA) Math 1966; Shippensburg Univ (MED) Math 1970; 3 Credit Hrs Assembler, Cobol, Pascal, Basic, Advanced Placement Math, Fortran; *cr:* York City Schls Math Tchr 1966-67; Spring Grove Schls Math Tchr 1967-; *ai:* Cmptr Help Session; SAT Prep Clss; NEA, PSEA 1966-; SGEA 1967-; York Cty Golf Assn 1976-, Pres, Slope Chm, Man of Yr, Life Mem; Bon Air Cntry Clb, Bd Dir; *home:* 28 Campus Ct Spring Grove PA 17362*

BLACK, CLYNTELL Y., His, Eng Lit & Bio Teacher; *b:* Dallas, TX; *ed:* Univ of Montevallo (BA) His & Anthropology 1973; Penn St Univ 20 Hrs Grad Work; Carnegie Mellon Univ 9 Hrs Grad Work; *cr:* Minor Schl 3rd & 6th Grd Tchr 1969-71; Connellsville Area HS Scndry Long Term Sub 1973-78; Metro Acad Scndry Tchr 1981-85; Youngwood Schl Scndry Tchr 1986-; *ai:* Girls Vllybl Coach; S Connellsville PA Bicentennial Chm; First Chrstn Church Teenage Class Sunday Schl Tchr; *home:* 755 W Main St # 3 Mount Pleasant PA 15666*

BLACK, DARLENE ANN, 5th-12th Grade Music Teacher; *b:* Meadville, PA; *m:* Gerald David; *c:* Kyle Robertson, Tyler James; *ed:* Indiana Univ of PA (BS) Music Ed 1983; Attnd Vandercook Coll of Music, Bowling Green Univ & Duquesne Univ; *cr:* Ft LeBoeuf MS Instrumental Music Tchr 1985-90; Ft LeBoeuf HS Choral, Instrumental & Jazz Instr 1991-; *ai:* Flute Choir; Pep Band; PMEA 1985-; PSEA & NEA 1993-; C&MA Church, Choir Dir 1987-, Music Dir; *home:* 5158 Route 97 Waterford PA 16441*

BLACK, GAIL PATRICIA, Soc Stud, Sci, Lang Arts Instr; *b:* Northampton, MA; *c:* Kelley Jeannette, Taunya Michelle; *ed:* Fayetteville St Coll (BS) Soc Stud 1966; Univ of MA (ME) 1973; Natl Standards for US His; Conversations in His; Writing to Learn 6-12 Grd Soc Stud; Rescuers of the Holocaust; Natl Geography Awareness Week; Issues in Childrens Lit; Robert Cormier Symposium; Literacy Learning in the Classroom; Working Toward Recertification; *cr:* Town of Easthampton Instr 1966-; *ai:* Success for All Stdnts; The Learning Network; Make a Difference Day; Annual Food Dr; Natl Cncl for His Ed 1994-; Southern Proverty Law Ctr 1994-; MA Cultural Cncl Grant; Local Cultural Cncl Grant; Community Svc Learning Grant; Outstdng Make a Difference Day Project Congratulatory Cert; Presentation First Annual Learning Network Conf; *office:* White Brook MS 200 Park St Easthampton MA 01027*

BLACK, JANET MARIE (HONROTH), English Teacher; *b:* Cleveland, OH; *m:* Jeffrey J.; *c:* Jennifer, Jason; *ed:* OH Univ (BFA) Theatre & Eng 1969; Kent St (MA) Theatre 1978; Ashland Univ Additional Grad Hrs; *cr:* Strongsville HS Eng & Drama Tchr 1969-74; Bellevue Jr HS Eng 1974-77; North Royalton HS Eng 1977-; *ai:* Yrbk Publications Adv; NEA 1969-; OEA & NEOEA 1969-; North Royalton Ed Assn 1977-, Exec Bd & Bldg Rep; *office:* North Royalton HS 14713 Ridge Rd North Royalton OH 44133

BLACK, JEFFREY, Social Studies Dept Chair; *b:* Cleveland, OH; *m:* Janet Marie Honroth; *c:* Jennifer, Jason; *ed:* Ashland Coll (BSED) His, Eng 1970; Bowling Green St Univ ME Supervision, Adm; Attnd Ket St Univ; *cr:* Willard HS Tchr, Coach 1970-72; Strongsville HS Tchr, Coach; Bellevue HS Tchr, Coach 1973-77; Aurora HS Dept Chair, Head Ftbl Coach 1977-88; *ai:* Ftbl Coach; Stock Market Club; Lift-A-Thon; Mentorship; Model United Nations Intrshp; NEA, OEA, OCS Stud 1970-; YMCA Brd 1987-; Mason 1970-; *office:* Aurora HS W Pioneer Trail Aurora OH 44202*

BLACK, JOHN THOMAS,JR., Social Studies Teacher & Coach; *b:* Cumberland, MD; *m:* Jane L. Moorehead; *c:* John, Jeffrey, Joseph; *ed:* Shippensburg St Coll (BS) Soc Sci 1973; *cr:* Chestnut Ridge HS Soc Stud Tchr, Bsktbl Coach 1973-88; Bedford HS, MS Soc Stud Tchr, Bsktbl Coach 1988-; *ai:* Var Boys Bsktbl Coach; NEA 1973-; *office:* Bedford HS 330 E John St Bedford PA 15522

BLACK, KEITH DONALD, 5th Grade Teacher; *b:* Waynesboro, PA; *c:* Andrew K.; *ed:* Shippensburg St (BA) Elem Ed 1970; Attnd Penn St Mont Alto; *cr:* Greencastle Antrim Schl Dist 4-5 Grd Elem Tchr 1970-; *ai:* PSEA, NEA, GAEA 1970-; BSA 1984-, Asst Scoutmaster, Scoutmaster, Prgm Dir Sinsquipe Scout Reservation, Dist Awd of Merit.

BLACK, LEEANA DAWN, Spanish Teacher; *b:* Denville, NJ; *ed:* Clemson Univ (BA) Lang & Intnl Trade 1990; Montclair St Univ (MS) Span & Ed 1995; *cr:* Planned Parenthood of Greater Northern NJ Span Speaking Hlth Care Specialist 1989-; Hopatcong HS Span Tchr 1991-93; Hackettstown HS Span Tchr 1993-; *ai:* Peer Support; ERASE & Frgn Lang Club Adv; NJEA 1991-; NEA 1991-; FLENJ 1994-; AATSP 1994-; NEH Flwshp Pgm Frgn Lang Tchrs Finalist 1995; Tony Cook Memrl Grant Amer Inst for Learning; Natl Awd to Promote Frng Langs 1993; *office:* Hackettstown HS Warren St Hackettstown NJ 07840*

BLACK, LISA DORNER, Spanish Teacher; *b:* St Louis, MO; *m:* Robert M.; *c:* Amy, Rebecca; *ed:* Univ of MO (BA) Span 1970; Cnslng Peer, Adolescence, Cmptrs; *cr:* Shrewsbury HS Span Tchr 13 Yrs; *ai:* Class Adv 1995; World Lang Club; MaFla 1982-; *office:* Shrewbury HS 45 Oak St Shrewsbury MA 01545

BLACK, NADINE S. (KOUBA), Gftd & Tlntd Pgms Tchr & Coord; *b:* San Francisco, CA; *m:* Robert L.; *c:* Richard H. Bellars; *ed:* Douglas C (BA) Eng 1968; Rutgers U (MED) Eng & Writing 1974; Nova Southeastern U Doctoral Stu EdD Candidate; *cr:* St Johns Schl Tchr 1970-71; Bergen AM HS Tchr & Admin 1977-78; West Windsor-Plainsboro HS Tchr & Coord 1974-; *ai:* Comm Mbrshps: Prof Growth, Insvc, Site-Based Cncl & Gifted & Talented; Gifted & Talented Stu Dev, Spon, Mentor & Facilitator; NJEA 1980-; NEA 1980-; ASCD 1994-; Pop Warner Parents 1977-85, Pres Mothers Club 1 Yr; Little League Parents 1977-86, Pres Mothers Club 1 Yr; Jackson HS Mothers Club Pres 1987-88; Elks 1994-; Reader, Writer & Trainer for Various Local & St Spon Writing Initiatives, Core Curricula & Tchr Exams; NEH Flwshp Recipient.*

BLACK, STEPHANIE EILEEN, Business Teacher; *b:* Sharon, PA; *ed:* Robert Morris Coll (BS) Bus Ed & Admin 1990; Working Toward Masters in Bus Ed at Youngstown St Univ; *cr:* Sharon HS Bus Tchr 1993-; *ai:* NEA, STA, PSEA 1993-.

BLACK, WILLIAM JEFFREY, High School Vocal Instructor; *b:* Onzonta, NY; *m:* Kathleen Carey; *c:* Eric; *ed:* Syracuse Univ (BME) Music Ed 1966, (MSM) Vocal Performance 1972; *cr:* Westhill HS Choir, Vocal Stud Dir 1966-; *ai:* Select Group Singers Dir, Adv; NYSSMA, OCMEA, NYSUT 1966-; Syracuse Opera Reach-Out 1994-; Civic Morning Musicals 1980-, Prin Soloist; Oswego Opera Theater 1979-, Prin Lead; Syracuse Opera Co 1967-, Prin Lead; Outstanding Conductor Awd at Fiestval Choral Competition 1992; *office:* Westhill Sr HS 4501 Onondaga Blvd Syracuse NY 13219

BLACKBURN, BRIAN KEITH, Media Technician; *b:* Saint Louis, MO; *m:* Mariann; *c:* Ashley, B. Kyle; *ed:* Widener Univ (BA) Media Stud 1992; *cr:* Widener Univ Production Asst 1991-92; Interboro HS Media Technician 1992-; *ai:* SADD & Video Club Spon; Yrbk Asst Spon; *office:* Interboro HS 16th Ave & Amosland Rd Prospect Park PA 19076

BLACKBURN, MARGARET ELLEN, French Teacher; *b:* Alpena, MI; *ed:* MI St Univ (BA) Fr 1980; Univ of MI (MA) Fr Lit 1982; *cr:* Maumee Vly Cntry Day Schl Fr Tchr 1982-; *ai:* Track & Cross Cntry Coach; Frgn Lang Dept Chair; AATF; ACTFL; U of MI Alumnae; NW OH Track & Field Ofcls Assn; Columbia Univ Tchrs Coll Klingenstein Flwshp 1986; Rotary Stud Grant to Nigeria 1987.

BLACKETOR, JEAN FITCH, Social Studies Teacher; *b:* Bennington, VT; *ed:* Keene St Coll (BED) Soc Stud 1969, (MED) Schl Admin 1970; Vanderbilt Univ (DED) Schl Admin 1983; Law Related Ed; *cr:* Bellows Falls Union HS Tchr 1971-; Comm Coll of VT Instr 1986-; Keene St Coll Adj Fac 1988-95; *ai:* Sr Class Adv; NHS Adv 1972-; Wellness Pgm; VT Yth for Justice Summit Coord; NEA 1971-; VTNEA 1971-; WNEA 1971-, Past Pres, Schlsp Comm & Newsletter Writer; Grange 1960-; Delta Kappa Gamma 1973-; VT Mothers Inc 1974-, VP, Sec & Treas; UVM Outstdng Tchr; NY Bar Assn Article Pub; Write & Edit Articles Promoting Schl & Stdnts; VT Dept Ed Grant; *office:* Bellows Falls Union HS Rt 5 S Bellows Falls VT 05101*

BLACK-GREGG, MARY JANE, 7th Grd Rdng & Math Team Ldr; *b:* Dennison, OH; *m:* Gary Richard Gregg; *c:* Stephanie Black, Stacy Black; *ed:* Miami Univ Oxford (BS) Elem Ed 1977; Wright St Univ (MS) Tchr & Ldr 1983; 30 Hrs Beyond Masters; Ashland Univ at Walsh; *cr:* Clearcreek Elem 5th Grd Tchr 1969-71; Carlisle Primary 2nd Grd Tchr 1977-78; Jonathan Wright Elem 3rd Grd Tchr 1979-89; Springboro Jr HS 7th & 8th Grd Rdng, Math & Eng Tchr 1989-; *ai:* 7th Grd Team Ldr; Jr HS Study

Comm; Jr HS Recognition Pgm Developer & Coord; OH MS Assn 1990-; NEA & OEA; SEA, Rep, Sec, & Pres, Negotiational Team; Kappa Delta Pi Hnr Soc; OH Eastern Star; Church Choir; Vol Nike Tour; Booster Club; After Prom Decorating Chprsn; Martha Holden Jennings & Springboro Comm Schls Grant Recipient; Outstdng Grad Stu WSU; OH MS Conf Presenter; *office:* Springboro Jr HS 705 S Main St Springboro OH 45066*

BLACKMAN, BARBARA (LEE), Counselor; *b:* Pittsburgh, PA; *m:* Warren C.; *c:* Sean, Hilary; *ed:* Howard Univ at Washington (BS) Psych 1965; City Univ of NY Herbert Lehman Coll (MSEd) Guid & Cnslng 1984; 18 Credits Post Grad Stud in Cnslng & Schl Psych; *cr:* NY St Div for Yth Aftercare Soc Worker 1965-67; Office of Probation for Courts Probation Ofcr 1967; Cleveland Bd of Ed Testing Dir, Cnslr 1968-70; Lee Harvard Yth Ctr Evenings Dir 1968-70; City Univ of NY Brooklyn Coll Cnslr 1970-74; City Univ of NY Hunter Coll SEEK Fin Aid Dir 1970-74; Dept of Psychiatry Veterans Adm Med Ctr Cnslr 1977-82; Mt Vernon Pub Schls Chprsn Comm on Spec Ed, Cnslr 1984-; *ai:* Schl Bd Mngmt Team; Prsnl Screening Comm; Cnslr Trainer for Coll of New Rochelle; Long Island Univ Dobbs Ferry Supvr, Cnslr Interns on Site Practicener; Natl Bd for Certfd Cnslr 1984-; Natl Bd for Certfd Schl Cnslr 1993-; AFT 1984-; Westchester, Rockland, Putnam Cnslng Assn 1995-; Alpha Kappa Alpha 1963-, Parlimentarian; My Sisters Place 1995-, Recognition; Jessie Smith Noyes Scholar Howard Univ; Kappa Delta Phi; Psi Chi; My Sisters Place AwdCert of Appreciation; *office:* Mt Vernon HS 100 California Rd Mount Vernon NY 10552

BLACKMAN, ELISE BERNADETTE, 5th Grade Teacher; *b:* New York, NY; *ed:* Our Lady of Good Counsel Coll (BA) His 1957; Hunter Coll (MS) Ed 1977; *cr:* Grimes Magnet Schl for Creative Ed 6th Grd Tchr 1966-84; Traphagen Schl 5th Grd Tchr 1988-; *ai:* Mt Vernon Music Theater Mem; Schl Twirlers Unit Dir; Peer Mediation Tchr Mentor; AFT, NEA, Cath Tchrs Assn 1966-; Mt Vernon Tchrs Fed 1966-, Bldg Rep; Mt Vernon Tchrs Credit Union 1966-, Bldg Rep; UJA Fed; Sacred Heart Church Lector; Building Tchrs Union Rep; Mt Vernon Tchrs Bldng Rep 10 Yrs; Sacred Heart Mt Carmel Mgnt Schl Ed Comm; *home:* 348 S 9th Ave Mount Vernon NY 10550

BLACKMER, SALLY V., Global Studies Teacher; *b:* Canandaigua, NY; *c:* Cynthia, Mark; *ed:* SUNY at Geneseo (BS) Ed 1964; Univ of Rochester (MED) Ed 1970; Addl 48 Credit Hrs; *cr:* Honeoye Cntrl Schl Tchr 1964-66; Canandaigua City Schl Tchr 1966-67; Honeoye Cntrl Schl Tchr 1967-; *ai:* Class Adv 1969-80; His Club Adv 1975-94; Cross Cntry Ski IMs Instr 1992-94, 1996; NY St United Tchrs 1964-, VP, Sec, Treas; NCSS 1995-; Honeoye Historical Soc 1985-, NYS 129th Assembly Dist Leg Advy Cncl; United Neighborhoods Involvement for Families & Yth Co-Founder 1990-; Allens Hill Pub Lib 1960-, Pres 1995-; Natl Org of Women 15 Yrs; Natl Women's Hall of Fame Mem, Summer Vol; Joint Cncl on Ec Ed Natl & St Awd 1978; NY Utilization of Television in Ed Awd 1986, Regnl & St Awd 1988; Excl in Scndry Tchng Awd 1988; Women's Natl Historical Park Tchr Comm; TA Tchr of Yr 1976; *home:* 4718 Allens Hill Rd Honeoye NY 14471*

BLACKSTONE, CARLEN L., HS Math & Comp Sci Teacher; *b:* Pittsburgh, PA; *ed:* Bucknell Univ (BS) Math 1979; Villanova Univ (MS) Comp Sci 1985; Supvrs Cert in Math Lehigh Univ; Ed, Math, Comp Sci Courses Master +36; *cr:* PA Power & Light Co Systems Analyst & Programmer 1979-81; EPA Schl Dist HS Math & Comp Sci Tchr 1981-; *ai:* Comp Club; Pgm Dev Chair for HS Transition Team; Planning Subcommittee; Tchr Trng in Claris Works; Adult Ed; Amer Comp Sci League; NEA 1981-; NCTM 1981-; EPCTM 1988-; YWCA 1986-, Teach Swimming; Asbury V Meth 1992-, Singles Group, Vllybl Team, Lay Readers & SS Tchr; All-Star Contest of Amer Comp Sci League 2nd Place; *office:* Emaus H S 851 North St Emmaus PA 18049*

BLACKWELL, SCOTT C., Math Department Chairperson; *b:* Pottsville, PA; *m:* Karen; *c:* Donald, Keith; *ed:* Mansfield Univ (BS) Earth, Space Sci, Geology, General Sci 1977; Albright Coll (BS) Math 1980; Attnd PA St, Wilkes, Carlow Coll Grad Stud; *cr:* Tamaqua Area Jr Sr HS General Math, Sci Tchr 1978-80; Williams Valley Math Tchr 1980-; *ai:* Math Dept Chprsn; Mentor, Lead Tchr; NEA, PSEA 1977-; Adult Basic Ed Prgm 1988-, Instr; Hometown Fire Co 1991-; *home:* RR 4 Box 413A Tamaqua PA 18252*

BLACK-WILLISON, KAY, Acctng & Computer Ed Teacher; *b:* Springfield, KY; *m:* Max J.; *ed:* Campbellsville Coll (BS) Bus 1971; Union Coll (MA) Ed 1976; 30 Addl Hrs Univ of KY, Wright St, OH Univ, Hocking Coll; *cr:* New Lexington Jr HS PE, Bus Ed Tchr 1972-78; New Lexington HS Acctng, Cmptr Ed Tchr 1979-; *ai:* Dist Tech, 21st Century Instrl Improvement, Regnl Tech Comms; AFT 1972-, Treas, Sec, VP; Eastern Star 1986-; Eagles 1988-; KY Colonial 1985-; Tchr of Yr 1986; Ashland Oil's Tchr of Yr Finalist 1990; *office:* New Lexington HS 2549 Panther Dr New Lexington OH 43764

BLADEL, RITA DONALDSON, High School Mathematics Tchr; *b:* Bronx, NY; *m:* John Thomas; *c:* John F., Elizabeth K., Kristen N.; *ed:* St Thomas Aquinas Coll (BS) Math, Elem, Scndry Ed 1971; Fordham Univ (MS) Ed 1973; Ed, Cmptr Sci Post Grad Stud 12 Credits; *cr:* Felix V. Festa Jr HS East Math Tchr 1971-85; Clarkstown HS South Math Tchr 1985-; *ai:* Renaissance Comm; Advs Class of 1998; NCTM, NYSUT, Clarkstown Tchrs Assn 1971-; NSF Cmptr Sci Grant CCNY 1982; PTA Lftme Mem Awd 1983.

BLADON, MARILUCI T., Assoc Prof of Biotechnology; *b:* Santos Sao Paulo, Brazil; *c:* Christina Maria, Denise Maria; *ed:* Cath Univ (BS) Bio 1967; Univ of Pittsburgh (MS) Bio 1971; MI Univ (PHD) Human Genetics 1976; Eunice Kennedy Schriver, Ctr for Mental Retardation, Harvard Med Schl, Genetics Div, Post Doctoral Fellow 1976-79; *cr:* Northeaster Univ Human Genetics Instr 1979-90; DuPont Staff Sciestist 1982-85; Baxter Hlth Care 1985-88; Middlesex Comm Coll Assoc Prof, Biotechology Coord 1990-; *ai:* Coord Biotechnology Prgm; Teach 3 Biotechnology Courses; Amer Soc Human Genetics 1976-; Amer Assn Bio Tchrs 1994-; Amer Assn for Sci Advancement 1976-95; ASPCA 1990, Donor; Boston Ballet 1984, Donor; Pasteur Gold Medal; Intnl Fullbright Flwshp Recipient 1967; Exxon Ed Awd 1996; *office:* Middlesex Comm Coll Springs Rd Bldg #3 Bedford MA 01730*

BLAIN, MARY PERRON, Physics Instr & Sci Dept Head; *b:* Chicopee, MA; *m:* Stephen E.; *ed:* Trinity Coll (BS) Chem 1975; Wesleyan Univ (MALS) Sci 1979; Attnd Univ of CT; *cr:* Parish Hill HS Chem & Physics Tchr 1975, 7th-9th Grd Sci Instr 1979; Glastonbury HS Sci Dept Head & Physics Instr 1979-; *ai:* NEA, CEA, NSTA & CSTA 1975-; ASCD & PDK 1985-; Tchr & Adv to NASA & NSTASSIP Natl & Regnl Winners; CT & Intnl Sci Fair Finalists; Westinghouse Talent Search Winner; Sigma Xi CT Sci Tchr of the Yr 1987; NASA & NSTA Coord; St of CT Celebration of Excl Winner 1993 & 1988; *office:* Glastonbury HS 320 Hubbard St Glastonbury CT 06033

BLAINE, JOHN M., Culinary Foods Instructor; *b:* Cornwall, NY; *m:* Gail E. Morabito; *c:* Victoria; *ed:* Culinary Inst of AMer (AOS) Culinary Arts 1978; SUNY at Oswego VTE; Orange Cty Boces Food Svc Degree; *cr:* Cornwall Hosp Food Svc 1973-78; Bluebeards Castle Hotel Pastry Chef 1978-85; Lakevilla Inn Chef 1986-92; Culinary Connections Owner 1994-; Orange Ulster Vo-Tech Instr 1985-; *ai:* Mem NY St Bsbl Umpires Anns Inc Certfd Ofcl Class I; Amer Culinary Fed 1994-, Sec, Westpoint NY Branch; Highland Eng Co #1 1976-, Bd of Trustees; NYSUT; Silver Medal Carribean Hotel Assn 1984; Gold Medal NY St VICA Baking & Cake Decorating 1976; *home:* 33 Holloran Rd RD 8 New Windsor NY 12553*

BLAINE, JUDITH M., Business Teacher; *b:* Cambridge, MA; *m:* William H.; *c:* Bethany; *ed:* NCW Hampshire Coll (BA) Bus 1969; *ai:* FBLA; DECA; NE Bus Edctrs 1971-; *office:* Manchester HS W 9 Notre Dame Ave Manchester NH 03102

BLAIR, AVA L. CORNETT, Sixth Grade Teacher; *b:* Blackey, KY; *m:* Donald; *c:* Don Jr., Curtis, Lisa; *ed:* Univ of Cincinnati (BA) Elem Ed 1972; Miami Univ (MS) Elem Ed Rdng Spec 1974, (MS) Rdng Spec 1976; Addl 30 Hrs; *cr:* Letcher Co Schls Tchr 1 Room Schl 1955-56; Ledford Kndgtn Tchr 1966-68; Clermont Cty ABE Instr 1978-; Williamsburg Elem Tchr 1969-; *ai:* Elem Mentor; Yrbk Adv; NEA, OEA, WEA 1974-, Negotiator; ASCD 1992-; OCIRA & Little Miami Rdng Cncl 1984-, Past Pres; OH Cncl IRA 1984-; Little Miami Rdng Cncl 1984-, Pres; *office:* Williamsburg Elem Schl 839 Spring St Williamsburg OH 45176

BLAIR, BONNY J., 1st Grade Teacher; *b:* Warsaw, NY; *m:* Thomas C.; *c:* Korynne, Ryan; *ed:* SUNY at Cortland (BS) Elem Ed 1974, (MS) Remedial Rdng 1979; *cr:* Oakfield-AL Cntrl 4th Grd Tchr 1974-76; Southern Cayuga Cntrl K-1st & 3rd Grd Tchr 1976-; *ai:* Rdng Curr & Staff Dev Comms; Schl Improvement Team; Spcl Ed Task Force; AFT 1974-; NYSUT 1974-; SCC Tchrs Assn 1976-; Cayuga Cty Childrens Comm 1992-; Southern Cayuga Mini-Grant Winner 1993, 1994 & 1996; Cayuga-Onondaga Tchr Ctr Mini-Grant Winner 1993; *office:* Emily Howland Elem Schl 2892 State Route 34b Aurora NY 13026*

BLAIR, CHARLES E., Teacher; *b:* Natrona, PA; *m:* Keene Smith; *c:* Joren, Brooke, Gage; *ed:* Univ of Pittsburgh (MED) Ed 1991; *cr:* Pittsburgh City Schls Tchr 1989-90; Fox Chapel Schl Dist LaCrosse Coach 1989-90; Pocono Mtn Schl Dist Tchr 1990-, Swim Team Coach 1991-; *ai:* NEPA, NEA 1989-; Gen Church of New Jerusalem 1986-; *office:* Pocono Mountain Sr HS PO Box 200 Swiftwater PA 18370*

BLAIR, FARNHAM, English Teacher; *b:* Washington, DC; *m:* Lynne K. Kolarsey; *c:* Sarah Blair Reeves, Emily Farnham; *ed:* Yale Univ (BA) Eng 1965; Georgetown Univ (MA) Eng 1969; *cr:* The Millbrook Schl Eng Tchr 1968-73; Dutchess Comm Coll Eng Tchr 1973-74; George Stevens Acad Eng Tchr 1974-80; Orono HS Eng Tchr 1980-; *ai:* NEA 1974-; Yale Alumni Schls Comm 1980-, Chm; Kneisel Hall Chamber Music Schl 1978-, Trustee; Books: The Blue Line Essays on Landscape & Narrative 1989, Immenent Green 1991, The Movie Queen & Other Poems 1996; *office:* Orono HS 14 Goodridge Dr Orono ME 04473

BLAIR, HELENE ROCHE, English Teacher & Dept Head; *b:* Nantucket, MA; *m:* William V.; *ed:* Emmanuel Coll (BA) His 1961; Amer Intl Coll (MED) Ed 1980; *cr:* Fitchburg HS Eng Tchr 1961-64; Peter Lassen Schl Eng Tchr 1964-65; Feltham Schl for Girls Eng Tchr 1965-67; NYC Dept of Welfare Soc Worker 1967-68; Nantucket HS Eng Tchr 1968-; *ai:* NHS Adv; Eng Dept Head; NCTE 1968-; New England Cncl Tchr of Eng 1970-; Democratic Town Comm 1968-; Terrific Tchrs Making a Difference Awd 1993; *office:* Nantucket HS 10 Surfside Rd Nantucket MA 02554*

BLAIR, KATHLEEN M., Seventh Grade Science Teacher; *b:* Philadelphia, PA; *ed:* Univ of DE (BSEd) Elem Ed 1988; Widener Univ (MSEd) Cmptr Sci Ed 1993; *cr:* Beverly Hills MS Sci, Math Tchr 1989-; *ai:* 7th Grd Girls Bsktbl Coach; Sci Book, Supply Coord; NEA 1989-; NSTA 1985-; *office:* Beverly Hills MS 1400 Garrett Rd Upper Darby PA 19082

BLAIR, MARGARET S., English Teacher; *b:* Nashua, NH; *m:* Lawrence C.; *ed:* New England Coll (BA) Scdnry Ed, Eng 1972; Potsdam St Coll (MS) Rdng 1984; *cr:* Alvirne HS 9-10th Grd Eng Tchr 1972-73; Pembroke Acad 10-11th Grd Eng Tchr 1973-80; Madrid-Waddington Cntrl Schl 8-12th Grd Eng Tchr 1981-83; Goffstown HS 10-12th Grd Eng Tchr 1984-; *ai:* Newspaper Adv; NHEA, NEA 1984-; NCTE; *office:* Goffstown HS 27 Wallace Rd Goffstown NH 03045

BLAIR, THOMAS C., 8th Grd Health Teacher; *b:* Auburn, NY; *m:* Bonny J. Williams; *c:* Korynne, Ryan; *ed:* SUNY Cortland (BS) PE 1974, (MS) PE & Hlth 1981; *cr:* Auburn Enlarged City Schl Dist Hlth Ed Tchr 1975-; *ai:* Asst Var Ftbl Coach; *office:* West MS 108 N Genesee St Auburn NY 13021

BLAIR, WILLIAM, English Teacher; *b:* Waterbury, CT; *c:* Courtney; *ed:* Cntrl CT St Univ (BS) Eng 1969, (MS) Eng 1974; 30 Addl Credit Hrs; *cr:* Wolcott HS Eng Tchr 1970-; *ai:* NEA, CEA 1970-; WEA 1970-, Chief Negotiator; Articles 1 Hawthorne, 2 Orwell; Free Lance Newspaper Editorials Separate Articles on Cuba, Vietnam, Cambodia, Kenya & Lebanon; *home:* 57-5 Sharon Rd Waterbury CT 06705

BLAIS, LYNN ANN (CAMERON), English Teacher; *b:* Massena, NY; *ed:* Potsdam St Coll (BA) Eng Ed 1982, (MS) Eng Ed 1988; *cr:* St Lawrence Cntrl Schl 8 Grd Eng Tchr 1983-87; St Regis Falls Cntrl Schl 8, 10-11 Grd Eng Tchr 1992-; *ai:* Shared Decision Making Comm; Adirondack Tchr Ctr Policy Bd; Franklin Cty Insurance Consortium; NYSUF 1983-, Sec; *office:* St Regis Falls Central Schl PO Box 306 St Regis Falls NY 12901

BLAKE, CAROLE I., Instrumental Music Teacher; *b:* Hanover, NH; *ed:* New England Conservatory of Music (BMus) Music Ed 1964; Boston St Coll (MED) Supervision 1972; *cr:* Medway Pub Schls 7-12 Grd Gen Mus Tchr 1964-66; Woonsocket Pub Schls K-6 Grd Gen Mus Tchr, 7-8 Grd Inst Tchr 1966-69; Malden Publ Schls 4-12 Grd Instrumental Mus Tchr 1969-88; Mascoma Vly Regnl Schls 5-12 Grd Instrumental Tchr, HS Gen Mus Tchr 1988-; *ai:* Yankee Brass Band 9 Yrs; Lakes Region Music Festival HS Pres, Jr HS Sec; MENC, NEA 1964-; Mascoma TA 1988-; Upper Vly Comm Band 1984-, Assoc Cond 1985-90, Dir 1991-; Friends of Yankee Brass Inc 1995-, Treas; Newmont Military Band 1995-, Dir; Upper Vly Comm Band Assoc of Concert Band Natl Convention 1994, Boston Festival of Bands 1995-; *office:* Mascoma Valley Regnl Schl Dist RR 1 Box 168a Canaan NH 03741

BLAKE, CLIFFORD JOSEPH,JR., English Dept Chairman; *b:* Westfield, MA; *m:* JoAnn H.; *c:* Lisa, Caryn, Justin, Jodie, Zachary; *ed:* Westfield St Coll (BED) Ed 1965, (MA(Eng 1969; Psych, Eng, Spec Ed, GAT; *cr:* Granby Jr, Sr HS Eng Chm 1965-; *ai:* Debate Coach 1966-69; Lit Magazine Adv 1970-76; Drama Adv, Coach 1977-; Class Adv 1991-; Educl Philosophy Chm 1972-; MTA, NEA, GEA 1965-; NAET 1972-; Green Peace Mem 1983-; Natl Org for Hum 1979-, Outstdng Mem, Prgm Dev; World Wildlife Org 1979-; Nature Conservancy 1973-; Natl Audoban Soc 1974- cles Pub; Numerous Articles Pub; *office:* Granby Jr Sr HS 202 E State St Granby MA 01033*

BLAKE, DOLORES A., Math & Computer Teacher; *b:* New York City, NY; *c:* Arlene, Keith; *ed:* New Rochelle (BA) Math 1979; Hofstra Univ (MS) Ed 1992; *cr:* Richard Grosseley Acad Math, Cmptr Tchr 13 Yrs; *ai:* Chess Coach; NCTM 1990-; Rockdale Village Exec Bd, Treas; *office:* Richard Grossely Acad 108th & 167th Sts Jamaica NY 11433*

BLAKE, DOROTHY LIPKA, 8th Grade Home Economics Tchr; *b:* Youngstown, OH; *m:* Thomas M.; *ed:* Youngstown St Univ (BSEd) Home Ec 1969; Univ of TN at Knoxville (MS) Textiles & Clothing 1977; *cr:* Liberty HS 9th-12th Grd Home Ec Tchr 1969-83; W. S. Guy Schl 8th Grd Home Ec Tchr 1983-; *ai:* NEA, OEA, North East OEA 1969-; Liberty Ed Assn 1969-, Sec; *office:* W S Guy MS Liberty Local Schls 4115 Shady Rd Youngstown OH 44505

BLAKE, ED, Social Studies Teacher; *b:* Rome, NY; *m:* Kathleen Leonard; *c:* Devin Patrick, Cara Elizabeth; *ed:* SUC at Oswego (BS) Ed, Soc Stud 1970; SUC at Cortland (MS) Ed, Soc Stud 1976; 90 Addl Grad Hrs SUNY at Albany, Univ of Exeter, U of AZ at Guadalajara; *cr:* Whitesboro MS Tchr 1970-; *ai:* Living Schoolbook Comm; Vote-Cope Regnl Coord; WTA 1970-, Pres; NYSUT 1976-; AFT; Rotary Intnl Stud England Grad Leve Whitesboro MS 75 Oriskany Blvd Whitesboro NY 13492

BLAKE, GAYLE ELAINE LARKIN, Fifth Grade Teacher; *b:* Jer NJ; *m:* Frederick Jr.; *c:* William; *ed:* Jersey St Coll (BA) Elem E *cr:* Clifton Bd of Ed Kndgtn Tchr 1969-70, Second Grd Tchr 1970- Grd Tchr 1972-74, Kndgtn Tchr 1974-82, Second Grd Tchr 1982- Grd Tchr 1989-; *ai:* Bd Advy Cncl 1995-96; Soc Stud Comm 1989- 1969-85; Home & Schl Tchr Rep 1986-96; PTA Class Parent Chldhd Inst of Higher Learning Parent Rep 1980; Pompton Lak Schl Historian 1981, PTA Pres 1982-85; Clifton Tchr Assn 19 Negotiator; Passaic Cty Tchrs Assn 1969-, Rep to NEA Conventi 1969-; St Paul of the Cross Rel Instr 1965-69; St Paul of the Cros Soc Guest Speaker 1990-92; Acad of the Sacred Heart Alum Ass Clifton Safety Patrol Spon 1985-, Clifton Mustangs Ftbl 1989-9 Governors Awd Excl 1995; *office:* Clifton Pub Schl #11 147 Mers Clifton NJ 07011

BLAKE, JEAN (GRAFE), 3rd Grade Teacher; *b:* New Britain, Wheelock Coll (BS) Early Chldhd Ed 1968; Cntrl CT St Univ (M Rdng 1974; Cert Advanced Grad Stud 1984; 30 Addl Credit Hrs Brophy Elem Schl Grd 2 Tchr 1968-70; Elizabeth Green Elem S 1-3 Tchr 1970-; *ai:* CT Mentor, Cooperating Tchr; Delta Kappa 1982-84; Newington Tchrs Assn 1970-, Schl Rep; NEA 1970-; N Bd, CT St Dept of Ed Certs of Appreciation, Accomplishme William P. Ward Humanitarian Project Awd 1996; *office:* Elizabe Elem Schl 30 Thomas St Newington CT 06111

BLAKE, JOSEPH DANIEL, Fourth Grade Teacher; *b:* Findlay, Margaret Mary Roerig; *c:* Kelly Marie; *ed:* Miami Un Comprehensive Soc Stud 1985; Univ of Findlay, Bowling Green Elem Cert 1989; City of David Archaeology Project Hebrew Un *cr:* Carey HS Soc Stud Tchr 1986-87; Univ of Findlay Psych Tchng Asst 1988-89; Superior MS 4th Grd Tchr 1989-; *ai:* Jr Bsktbl, HS, Jr HS Cross Cntry Coach; NEA 1994-; Marcelle Self 1992-, Sr Ofcr, C. Huffman Awd; *home:* 307 S East Ave Montp 43543

BLAKE, LYDIA SMYTH, 6th Grade Teacher; *b:* Mt Vernon, Ronald F.; *ed:* St Univ at Cortland (BS) Elem Ed 1964; *cr:* Colum Schl 3rd, 4th & 6th Grd Tchr 27 Yrs; Valhalla MS 6th Grd Tch Valhalla MS 6th Grd Math Tchr; *ai:* 6th Grd Adv; Gifted & Talente Selection Comm; Jr Natl Honor Soc Fac; Dist Test Selctn Comm, Midd Schl PTSA; AFT, NYSUT 1964-; Delta Kappa Gamma 197 Valhalla Curr Revision Comm; Jr League of Cntrl Westcheste White Plains Hospital Auxiliary; Scarsdale Women's Exch; *office:* MS 300 Columbus Ave Valhalla NY 10595

BLAKE, MANDY SHRECKENGOST, Earth & Space Science *b:* Clarion, PA; *m:* Kenneth C.; *c:* Steven, Kenndra; *ed:* Clarion U Ed, Earth & Space Sci 1986, (MS) Sci Ed 1992; *cr:* Kittanning S Tchr 1988-90; Shannock Vly HS Earth & Space Sci Tchr 19 Conservation Club, SADD Spon; Eco Team Coach; PSEA 198 1994-; Redbank Vly Park Authority 1993-, Vice Chm; Seminole B 1995-, Co-Chm; *office:* Shannock Valley Jr, Sr HS PO Box 32 Valley PA 16249

BLAKE, MARCIA SAYWARD, 4th Grade Teacher; *b:* Guilford Susan; *ed:* Univ of ME (BSEd) Ed & Soc Stud 1961; 60 Credit Buker Schl 7th Grd Tchr 1961-63; East Boothbay 2nd Grd Tchr Boothbay Harbor Elem 3rd-6th Grd Tchr 1969-78; Boothbay Regi 4th Grd Tchr 1978-; *ai:* 6th-8th Grd Sftbl Coach 16 Yrs; Numer Comms 1991-; NEA 1961-; MTA 1961-; BRTA 1964-, Sec; NCTE WMSGA 1963-, Prize chprsn; AFS 1984-, Pres 5 Yrs; SMWGA 1 Chptr Pub; *home:* HC 65 Box 23 Boothbay Harbor ME 04538*

BLAKE, MARIE, Fifth Grade Teacher; *b:* Anniston, AL; *c:* K Tuskegee Univ (BS) Elem Ed 1965; Univ of DC (MAT) Elem Chldhd Ed 1975; Numerous Courses in Writing, Sci, math, Rdng & *cr:* Carver Elem Schl 3rd Grd Tchr 1965-66; Woodridge Elem 5th 1966-74; Noyes Elem Schl 4th Grd Tchr 1975-79; Shepherd Ele 4th-6th Grd Tchr 1979-; *ai:* Odyessy of Mind Spon; SCAC; G Chair; Curr Comm Mem; Writing Wkshp Enrichment Clust TEAMS Distance Learning Pgm Co-Chair; AFT 1970-; NSTA Paul AME Church 1967-, Chancel Choir Pres; Wash Tuskegee 1970-, Sec, Pres & Reporter; Shepherd PTA 1979-, Nominatin Chair; Hardy PTA 1991-95, Mbrshp Comm Chair; Coolidge PT Two Tchr to Tchr Awds for Exemplary Classroom Pgms; Boo Pioneers in the Westward Movement; Articles pub; *office:* Shephe Schl 14th & Kalmia Rd NW Washington DC 20012

BLAKE, RACHEL NORTON, Language Arts & French Tea Skowhegan, ME; *m:* Richard E.; *c:* Laurie A. Gordon; *ed:* Univ Orono (BA) Fr, Eng 1970; Numerous Credit Hrs Lang Arts, Ca Learning Styles, Motivating the Unmotivated, Tchng Strate Exceptional Children, Others; *cr:* Oxford Hill Jr HS 7-8th Grd Fr, 1970-73; Madison Jr HS 7-8th Grd Lang Arts, Fr Tchr 1978-; Involved Doing Svc Planners Adv; Staff Dev Comm Mem; 8th G Ldr; Chrstn Pub Schl, Tchr, Mem of Local Church Body; Artic *office:* Madison Jr HS 199 Main St Madison ME 04950

BLAKE, SCOTT JAMES, Science Teacher; *b:* Pompton Plains, Janel W.; *ed:* Cornell Univ (BS) Psych 1990; Columbia Univ Tc (MA) Scndry Sci Ed 1994; Harvard Univ Post-Baccalaureate Wor & Medicine; *cr:* Glen Rock HS Sci Tchr 1994-; *ai:* Ftbl & Track Stdnts for Environmental Action Adv; Curr Forum; NEA 1994- 1994-; AAPT 1994-; *office:* Glen Rock HS 400 Hamilton Ave Gl NJ 07452

BLAKELY, KAY LACEY, Kindergarten Teacher; *b:* Charleston, Andrew J.; *ed:* WV St Coll (BS) Elem Ed 1968; Xavier Univ (MS Admin 1972; 30 Hrs Post Grad Work Rdng Specialist Cert; Trng in Multi-Aged Classrooms, Developmentally Appropriate Practice Chldhd Ed, Expeditionary Learning Outward Bound, Cincinnat Systematic Initiative; *cr:* Heberle Elem Schl Math Facilitator, I 1968-75; Highland Elem Schl Rdng Specialist 1975-77; St Jose Rdng Specialist 1977-82; Midway Elem Schl Kndgtn Tchr 19 Opportunity to Learn Correlate Comm; AFT; Cincinnati Fed o Sheldon Gardens Housing Complex 1994-, Bd of Dirs; Zion Bapt 1969-, Announcement Clerk; Ashland Oil Tchr Achvmt Awd Pr Recognition for Exlc in Tchng; *office:* Midway Elem Schl 3200 Ave Cincinnati OH 45238

BLAKEMAN, ALAN E., Social Studies Teacher; *b:* East Orange Joanne Murray; *c:* Jennifer Barlow, Patricia Torley, Judith, Derek; of Wooster (BA) US His 1956; Plymouth St Coll NH (MEd) Soc Stu *cr:* Chippewa HS Soc Stud Tchr 1956-57; Montpelier HS Soc St 1959-; Amer Inst of Banking Instr 1974-; *ai:* Schlrs Bowl; Boys Team Timekeeper; Javelin Track Coach; Soc Stud Curr Coord; Boy Team Scorebook; NEA, VT NEA 1959-; Montpelier Ed Assn 19 1964-65; Montpelier Tchrs Prof Standards Comm 1991-95, Chair 1 Montpelier Kiwanis 1986-, Sec 1995-; Montpelier Planning Com 1981-91, Chair 1983-91, Cith Cncl Commendation; Bethany Chur 1961-; Montpelier Boosters Club 1992-; Montpelier Jaycees Young Man of Yr Awd 1968; Record Yrbk Dedication 1980, 19 Japan Stud Group Fellowship 1983; Video Yrbk Dedication 1995 Your Life Dedication 1995; Northern VT Coaches Assn Golden

es Pass 1995; Natl Sci Fnd Tsongas Ctr Fellowship Univ of Lowell office: Montpelier HS 5 High School Dr Montpelier VT 05602*

ENEY, JUDITH E., Spanish Teacher; b: Amityville, NY; m: Brian; dy Cliff Coll (BA) Span, Scndry Ed 1969; SUNY at Stony Brook Liberal Stud 1974; cr: Newfield HS Span Tchr 1969-; ai: Span Honor oreign Lang Club Adv; AFT, NYSUT, MCTA 1969-; AATSP 1988-; Newfield HS 145 Marshall Dr Selden NY 11784

ER, LOUISE A., Professor of Biology; b: Garards Fort, PA; c: Churchill; ed: Waynesburg Coll (BS) Bio 1961; WV Univ (MA) Ed Univ of HI NSF; Credits Univ of Pittsburgh; cr: Wilkinsburgh HS hr 1961-67; Penn St Univ Adj Fac Hlth Tchr 1975-83; Comm Coll egheny Co Prof of Bio 1967-; ai: Womens Initiative; AFT 1969-; Bio Lab Manual with 2 Others; office: Comm Coll Algny Co Boyce 595 Beatty Rd Monroeville PA 15146

ESLEE, CLARE EUGENE, English Teacher; b: Union City, PA; en M.; c: Brenda, Clare II, Shawn; ed: Edinboro St Coll (BS) Eng (MED) Eng 1973; cr: US Army Corps of Engineers E-5 1962-65; urg Area HS Eng Tchr 1971-; ai: Bsktbl Coach; Cribbage Club Adv; PSEA & WEA 1971-; Amer Legion 1964-, Commander Svc officer, ne Mem; F & AM of PA Lodge 366 1990-; VFW Life Mem; Voiture -8 Life Mem; Natl Amer Legion Gold Brigade Awd 19878, 1989-91; mer Legion Ed Cert of Appreciation Awd 1995; PA Commendation 1995; home: 18222 Wilson Rd Union City PA 16438

E-WILCOX, KIM RENEE, Secondary English Teacher; b: Detroit, Nicole Yolanda; ed: St Univ of NY (BS) Eng 1978; Nazareth Coll Scndry Ed 1996; MI St Univ Liberal Arts Stud; cr: Phoenix Job Corps str 1978-81; Rio Salado Comm Coll Adult Basic Ed Instr 1988-89; tte MS Eng Tchr 1990-91; Churchville-Chili HS Eng Tchr 1991-; ai: ultural Club, Class & Step Team Adv; Ctr for Alternative Dispute tion Newsletter Ed; Black Educators Assn of Rochester 1991-; NEA Amer Assn of Univ Women 1991-; Urban League 1989-; NAACP of ster 1993-; Tchr of Yr 1980; office: Churchville-Chili Sr HS 5786 Rd Churchville NY 14428*

NEY, STEVEN DWIGHT, Principal & HS Teacher; b: Kittanning, : Bapt Bible Coll of PA (BS) Bible, Elem Ed 1989; St Cert Elem Ed iv of PA 1991-92; Grad Level Courses; Assn Chrstn Schls Intnl Cert 1989-; cr: Cntrl Bapt Chrstn Acad Lang Arts 5-7th Grd Tchr 1; Worthington Bapt Acad HS Head Supvr, Prin 1992-; ai: Yrbk Alpha Gamma Epsilon Baptist Bible Coll of PA 1987-; Worthington hurch 1978-, Yth Dir 1991-, Asst Pianist 1995-, Vacation Bible Schl Yrs; Senator Rick Santorum Steering Comm 1994-, Grassroots ign Co-Chm Armstrong Cty PA; Charles Ingram Schlsp Chrstn Ed Paul Douglas Tchrs Schlsp 1988; Who's Who Among Stdnts Amer Univs 1989; 5 Articles Pub; home: RR 3 Box 330 Kittanning PA

C, THELMA ROSENBLUM, Sixth Grade Teacher; b: New York, : Robert; c: Lisa Lonschein, Donna; ed: Queens Coll of City Univ (BA) Elem Ed-Summa Cum Laude 1971, (MS) Elem Ed 1975; 30 Credit Hrs; cr: PS 116 Elem Schl Tchr 1971-77; PS 173Q Elem Schl 977; PS 116 Elem Schl Tchr 1978; PS 173Q Elem Schl Tchr 1979-; s Coll Adj Childrens Lit Ed Tchr 1980; ai: Lincoln Ctr Inst; Dir, r Storytelling Club; UFT, Kappa Delta Pi 1971-; home: 4265 Kissena pt 631 Flushing NY 11355*

CHARD, ANDREW SCOTT, Physical Education Teacher; b: ster, MA; m: Ellen M. Georas; c: Kara Smith, Christopher Smith; ed: field Coll (BS) PE 1976; cr: Eagle Hill Schl Tchr, Tutor 1976-77; St Home PE Tchr 1977-79; Conway Elem Schl PE Tchr 1979-; ai: PE Comm Chm; Jump Rope Demonstration Team Coach; AAHPERD Jump Rope for Heart Natl Recognition Awd 1991, Eastern Dist ential Awd 1990, EDA-AAPHERD Merit Awd 1988; NHAHPERD JFH St Coord, Merit Awd 1987, 1990; Amer Heart Assn, Bd of Dirs 5; Outstdng Edctr Awd 1993; office: Conway Elem Schl 160 Main way NH 03818

CHARD, DANIEL FRANK, Social Studies Lead Teacher; b: , MA; ed: Tufts Univ (BA) His 1957, (MED) Ed 1966; Addl Credits; well Jr HS Soc Stud Tchr 1957-60; Wakefield HS Soc Stud Tchr 7, Tchr, Dept Chm 1977-; ai: Stu Cncl Fac Adv; Announce Ftbl 5, Bsktbl 1972-; Wakefield Tchrs Assn 1957-, Past Pres; NCSS North of Boston Soc Stud 1977-, Co-Pres, Dept Chm; Wakefield ical Soc 1977-, Pres 1983-85; Citizens Schlsp Fnd 1987-, Pres 3; Freedoms Fnd Medal 1988; DAR His Tchr of Yr 1988; office: ield HS 60 Farm St Wakefield MA 01880

CHARD, MARY ELLEN L., English Teacher; b: Warsaw, NY; m: n; c: Meggan, Carly; ed: SUNY at Fredonia (BA) Theatre Arts 1977; at Brockport (MS) Eng Ed 1988; cr: Port Chester HS Eng Tchr 4; Rochester Inst Tech Adjunct Eng Tchr 1989-91; Nazareth Coll t Eng Instr 1989-91; Brighton HS Eng Tchr 1986-88, 1991-; ai: 982-; AIDS Awareness Task Force 1989-, Co-Chair; Tchr of Yr 3; office: Brighton HS 1150 Winton Rd Rochester NY 14618*

CHETTE, BRADLEY N., English & Social Studies Tchr; b: ski, VT; ed: Univ of VT (BA) Eng 1972, (MED) Eng 1980; burg Coll (MA) Eng 1985; cr: Colchester HS Eng, Soc Stud Tchr ai: Tchr Evaluation Comm; Classroom Tchr; NEA, NCTE 1980-; 993-, Vice Chair; VT Tchr of Yr 1986; Christa Mc Auliffe Awd 1986; Kirk Jr. Awd 1983; office: Colchester HS PO Box 31 Colchester VT

CHETTE, CHERYL PRENDERGAST, French Tchr & Frgn Lang b: Kew Gardens, NY; m: Ralph; ed: New Paltz St Univ (BA) Fr Lit (MS) Fr Scndry 1973; Cert 7-12 Grd Span 1978, Schl Dist Admin nent Cert 1990; Middlebury Coll 1978, Univ of Paris 1978-79 al Stud Fr Lit; cr: Monticello HS Fr, Span Tchr 1967-69; Arlington Span Tchr 1970-, Coord Frgn Lang, 1988-; Arlington Summer Schl n Level I, II Tchr 1972-76; Arlington HS North Campus Fr VI Tchr Distance Learning Fr AP Tchr 1993-; ai: New Bldg Comm; ntship Natl Minister of Ed Lycee Decour Paris 1972; Methodloly r Lang Tchng Cert Awd; Ossego St Univ 1982; Peer Coach Tchr, Adv 1993; office: Arlington HS-N Campus 263 State Route 55 geville NY 12540

CO, AMERICA SAINZ, HS Spanish Teacher; b: Miami, FL; m: o; c: Jazmin, David; ed: Marymount Manhattan Coll (BA) Span Iona Coll (MA) Span 6 Credits; cr: Cathedral HS Span Tchr 4; St Catharine Acad Span Tchr 1985-; ai: Span Club Adv; Prom Chprsn; Span Natl Honor Soc Chprsn; AATSP 1990-; office: St ine Acad 2250 Williamsbridge Rd Bronx NY 10469

D, AMY LOUISE (HANDO), HS English Teacher; b: Somerville, Daniel E.; ed: Trenton St Coll (BA) Eng 1992; Working Towards Eng; cr: Kepner-Tregoe Inc Admin 1988-92; East Brunswick Schl chr 1992-; ai: Schl Newspaper Adv; NCTE, NEA 1992-; HS Jrnlsm ones Grant 1994-95; office: East Brunswick HS 380 Cranbury Rd runswick NJ 08816*

D, STEPHANIE YANCEY, Third Grade Teacher; b: Akron, OH; m: Robert; c: Preston, Aja; ed: Univ of Akron (BS) Elem Ed 1985; cr: bright Classroom Tchr 1985-; ai: Staff Dev Chprsn; Leadership nent, Dev; Career Ed Comm; Bldg Leadership Team 1993; Lang Arts Buildg Person; Key Communicator 1993; Akron Tchr Assn 1985-; Alph Kappa Alpha 1981-; home: 2030 Ayers Ave Akron OH 44313*

BLANDING, JADE MARIE, 7th-9th Grade English Teacher; b: Binghamton, NY; ed: St Univ of NY at Oswego (BA) Scndry Ed 1990; Univ of Phoenix (MAEd) Counseling 1994; St Univ of NY at Brockport (CAS) Admin 1996; cr: Mesa Pub Schls Rdng & Eng Tchr 1991-93; South Jefferson Schl Dist Eng Tchr 1993-; ai: Model Schls Eng Rep; Compact Comm; NYSUT 1993-; ASCD 1995-; home: PO Box 574 Sackets Harbor NY 13685*

BLANDING, VERMELL, Instructor of Writing & Rdng; b: Brooklyn, NY; ed: City Univ of NY (BA) Eng, Scndry Ed; Columbia Univ (EDM) Educl Psych, (MA) Tchr of Eng; 14 Credits Fr, 14 Credits Span City Coll of NY; cr: Hostos Comm Coll Lecturer Writing, Rdng Coord of Libra Prgm 1970-; ai: Eng Dept Personnel, Budget; Writing Aud Eng Dept Curr, Hnr, Grad, Women's His Month, Alex Halety Lecture Series Comm; Eng Dept Senator to Coll Wide Senate; Rdng Coord Engl Dept; CUNY Assn of Rdng Edctrs; IRA; office: Hostos Comm Coll 500 Grand Concourse Bronx NY 10451

BLANEY, VIRGINIA LOU (BRIGGS), Mathematics Teacher; b: Warren, OH; m: Clifford Dean; c: Lynnette, Bridget; ed: Kent St Univ (BSEd) Math 1966; Youngstown St Univ (MSEd) Tchr Math 1982; 2 Post Grad Hrs Mentor Tchng Trng; cr: Mineral Ridge HS Math Tchr 1966-72 & 1976-; ai: Mentor Tchr; SAD Advsr, OH Math League Advsr; Bldg Ldrshp Team; Weathersfield Tchrs Assn 1966-, Pres 1 Yr, Treas 1 Yr; BEA, NEOTA & NEA 1966-; EOCTM 1970-; Braceville United Meth Church, Treas, Many Comms; Labrae Bd of Ed 1984-, Past Pres, Past VP; Curr VP Peer Ct Advisory Cncl 1992; home: 5406 Nelson Mosier Rd Southington OH 44470

BLANK, JOHN K., 8th Grd Physical Sci Teacher; b: Ellwood City, PA; m: Susan Wolfe; c: James, Katherine, Laura; ed: IN Univ of PA (BS) Chem Ed 1971, (MED) Chem Ed 1976; cr: Franklin Regnl Jr HS Sci Tchr 1971-; ai: Sci Olympics Team, PA Jr Acad of Sci, Pittsburgh Regnl Schl Sci & Engrng Fair & Robertshaw Arts & Sci Fair Spon; PSEA & NEA 1971-; NSTA 1971-; NMSA 1994-; BSA 1985-, Den ldr, Asst Scoutmaster, Dist Commissioner Dist Merit Awd & Silver Beaver; Franklin Regnl Schls Credit Union Treas, Mgr 1981-; office: Franklin Regional Jr HS 4660 Old William Penn Hwy Murrysville PA 15668*

BLANK, NANCY CROSSLEY, Art Department Head; b: Hagerstown, MD; m: Charles S.; c: Martin, Nicholas, Rebecca; ed: RI Schl of Design (BFA) Painting & Art Ed 1965; MD Inst Coll of Art (MFA) Painting 1973; Cmptr Graphic Classes; cr: Vernon MS Art Tchr 1967-71; St Maria Goretti Art Dept Head 1973-; Hagerstown Jr Coll Art Instr 1980-; ai: Art Club; Natl Art Honor Soc, Artist Proff Adv; NAEA 1980-; MD Printmakers 1990-; Goretti Bd 1990-, Fac Rep 1990-; MD Symphony Orch Guild; Wash Co Arts Cncl, Pres; Art Matters Gallery, Bd & founding Mem; Marthas Vineyard; Museum Comm, Chm; Marthas Vineyard; Camp Meeting Assn; One Man Shows; Paintings in Wash Co Museum; Awds for Work; office: St Maria Goretti HS 1535 Oak Hill Ave Hagerstown MD 21740*

BLANK, PATRICIA NEIDRAUER, Sixth Grade Teacher; b: Buffalo, NY; m: Jeff; c: Aaron, Adam, Jessica; ed: SUNY at Plattsburgh (BS) Ed 1967; Sacred Heart Univ (MS) Ed 1990; 30 Hrs at Univ of Rochester; 9 Hrs at Weslyan Univ; 3 Hrs at SUNY at Geneseo; cr: Center Reach Elem Ed Tchr 1967-68; Brighton 4th Grd Tchr 1968-73; N Syracuse Elem Ed Tchr 1973-78; Trumbull 1983-; Ex Curr- Trck Coach; ai: Model Rocket Club; Field Hockey, Odessey of Mind & Explorations Coach; NEA 1967-; CEA & NSTA 1983-; Trumbull Arts & Challenger Space Ctr; PIMMS Fellow; Greater Bridgeport Area Grant from GE; Grant from United Illuminating; Tchr of the Year, Trumbull 1992; office: Madison MS 4630 Madison Ave Trumbull CT 06611*

BLANK, WALTER MAXAMILIAN, High School Math Teacher; b: LaCrosse, WI; m: Debra Lynn Wyman; c: Christian; ed: Univ of WI at Eau Claire (BS) Math Ed 1974; Boston Univ (MED) Cmptrs 1989; cr: Brookwood HS Tchr 1974-80; Math Tchr 1980-83; Mannheim MS Cmptr Tchr 1983-84; Mannheim HS Math Tchr 1984-; ai: Ftbl Coach; Ath Dir; Spon Spirit Club; Bison Booster Club; Renaissance Comm; FEA, NEA 1981-, HS Rep 1993-95; WEA, NEA 1974-80, Negotiator 1977-79; Innovative Tchr of Yr 1991 Phi Delta Kappa; Tchr of Yr Excl Ed HS Colleagues 1991-92; Coach of Yr 1995; office: Mannheim American HS Unit 29239 APO AE 09086

BLANKENSHIP, M. DIANE, Business Education Teacher; b: Fairbanks, AK; m: Paul D.; c: Beth, Jay, Molly; ed: Marshall Univ (BA) Bus Ed Comp 1975, (MS) Voc Ed 1980; cr: OIC Tchr 1975-76; South Point HS Tchr 1976-78; Lawrence Co JVS Tchr 1978-79; Buckeye Hills Career Ctr Tchr 1979-80; Wellston HS Tchr 1980-; ai: Chrldng Adv 1987-95; Vlybl Coach 1985-86; Future Tchrs of Amer 1976-77; NEA, OEA 1980-; WTA 1980-, Treas; Mothers Club 1980-, Pres; Jackson Ftbl Mothers Club 1995-, Pres 1996; Sts Peter & Paul Schl Bd, Sec; office: Wellston HS 600 S Penn Ave Wellston OH 45692

BLASI, DONNA MARIE, Science Teacher; b: Wilmington, DE; m: Raymond; ed: Instructional II Cert; Tchr Enhancement Inst St Vincent Coll; cr: Most Holy Name Tchr 1975-78; St Edward Schl Sci Tchr 1981-; ai: Space Club Adv-Young Astronaut Club 4th-8th Grd; Stdnts for PA Coach; Jr Acad of Sci; PJAS; Sci Fair 4th-8th Grd Coord; Pub Tchng Beyond Classroom NCEA; Hills Educl Grant for Sci; office: St Edwards Schl 89th 6th St Extension Herminie PA 15637

BLASKO, STEVEN JOSEPH, English Teacher; b: Monongahela, PA; m: Nancy Howard; c: William Auth, kerin Auth; ed: Cal Univ of PA (BS) Ed 1970; C. W. Post (MS) Ed 1981; 90 Hrs Post Grad Masters Stud; cr: Newfield HS Eng Tchr 1970-; ai: Var Golf Coach; AFT 1970-; Suffolk Golf Coaches 1982-, League Chm; office: Newfield HS 145 Marshall Dr Selden NY 11784

BLATHERWICK, CHARLES A., Science Teacher; b: Pratt, KS; m: Carol Meline; c: Chad, Adam, Luke, Joy; ed: Monmouth Coll (BA) Bio 1967; Westeyan Univ (MA) Population Genetics 1969; Rutgers Univ 45 Credits Towards PHD; cr: Edgewood Reg Jr HS Sci Tchr 1972-94; Edgewood Reg Sr HS Sci Tchr 1994; ai: Jr Hi Wreslting Coach 2 Yrs; Wood Carving Club 4 Yrs; Environmental Club Adv 2 Yrs; NJEA, NEA 1972-; NRA 1980-; Winslow Twsp Parks Commission 1989-92; home: 120 Pine Rd Hammonton NJ 08037*

BLATNICA, DOROTHY ANN,VSC, Religious Studies Professor; b: Cleveland, OH; ed: Marillac Coll (BA) Theology 1971; Univ of Notre Dame (MA) Theology 1977; John Carroll Univ (MED) Schl Admin 1979; Case Western Reserve Univ (PHD) Amer Stud 1992; cr: Lumen Cordium HS Theology Tchr 1971-83, Asst Prin 1978-81; Ursuline Coll Rel Stud Instr 1983-90, Rel Stud Prof 1991-; ai: Amer Stud Assn, Amer Cath Historical Assn 1993-; Amer Acad of Rel, US Cath Historical Soc 1992-; Coll Theology Soc 1994-; Article Pub; Book At The Altar of Their God 1995; office: Ursuline Coll 2550 Lander Rd Pepper Pike OH 44124

BLATNIK, MICHAEL W., High School Science Teacher; b: Martins Ferry, OH; ed: West Liberty St Coll (BA) Scndry Ed, Sci 1974; Wheeling Jesuit Coll (MA) Ed, Schl Admin 1978; cr: Union Local Schl Dist 8th Grd Sci 1974-75; Union Local Schl Dist HS Bio Tchr 1975-77; St Clairsville City Schls HS Bio, Anatomy Tchr 1977-; ai: Coach Ftbl, Bsktbl, Track; Adv Various Acad Comms; NEA: OEA 1974-; OH Vly Ath Conf 1978-; St Clairsville Saints Club 1977-78; St Clairsville Red Devil Moms; St Marys Church 1980-, Usher; Boosters Club Awd Most Outstdng Ath Sr Yr Coll; Commendations from OH Univ for Excl of Anatomy Classes; home: 203 Greentree Dr Saint Clairsville OH 43950*

BLATTSTEIN, DEBORAH ANN ROTHWELL, First Grade Teacher; b: Riverside, NJ; m: Marc; ed: Univ of ME (BA) ELem Ed 1986; Univ of Southern ME (MS) Instrl Ldrshp; cr: Jack Elem Schl Tchr 1987-; ai: Family Literacy; Bsktbl Coach; Nea 1987-; NE Rdng Assn 1990-; office: W B Jack Elem Schl 414 Eastern Promenade Portland ME 04101

BLAU, RIVKAH TEITZ, Principal; b: Elizabeth, NJ; m: Rabbi Yosef; c: Rabbi Binyamin, Rabbi Yitzchak, Rabbi Yaakov; ed: Barnard (BA) Eng 1962; Columbia (MA) Eng & Comp Lit 1963, (PhD) Eng & Comp Lit 1983; cr: Ulpana Ohr-Torah Prin 1976-81;Shevach HS Prin 1983-; ai: Tradition, Mem Editorial Bd; UOJCA, Mem Bd of Governors; The Future of Jewish Womens Ed; office: Shevach HS 7509 Main St Flushing NY 11367

BLAUFUSS, RENEE PRILOP, Basic Skills Mathematics Tchr; b: Bayonne, NJ; m: Gary C.; ed: Jersey City St Coll (BA) Math, Ed 1968; Fairleigh Dickinson Univ (MA) Human Dev 1981; 45 Grad Credits Beyond MA; cr: Ross Intermediate Schl Math Tchr 1969-70; Long Vly MS Math Tchr, Basic Skills Instr Math 1970-; ai: NEA, NJEA, WTEA 1970-; NCTM.

BLAUM, JOSEPH PAUL, 12th Grade US Government Tchr; b: Wilkes Barre, PA; m: Patricia Louise Mc Andrew; c: Jennifer Ashley, Brian Joseph; ed: Kings Coll (BA) Govt, Politics 1972; Soc Stud Scndry Ed Cert 1974, Post Grad Stud; PA St Univ Post Grad Stud; cr: Sharon Hill HS Problems of Democracy Tchr, Ftbl, Wrestling Coach 1975-76; Abington Hghts HS JV Wrestling Coach 1976-77; Bishop Hafey HS Soc Stud Tchr, Wrestling Coach 1977-79; Western Wayne HS Soc Stud Tchr, Ftbl, Wrestling, Track Coach 1979-87, Ath Dir, Tchr, Ftbl, Wrestling Coach 1987-90, Tchr, Ftbl Coach 1990-; ai: Sharon Hill HS Asst Track, Ftbl Coach, Head Wrestling Coach; Abington Hghts HS Asst Wrestling Coach; Video His Club Adv; Bishop Hafey HS Head Wrestling Coach, Asst Ftbl Coach; Asst Bsbl Coach; NCSS 1994-; Tri-Cty CC Bd of Dirs 1993-, Dir; office: Western Wayne HS RD 2 Lake Ariel PA 18436*

BLAUSS, WESLEY, 6th Grade Teacher; b: Plymouth, MA; m: Joanne Marie Mosesso; c: Nathaniel; ed: Marietta Coll (BA) Eng 1972; Bridgewater St (MED) Elem Ed 1977; Attnd Simmons Coll Elem Sci, Bridgewater St; cr: Indian Head Schl 6 Grd Tchr 1973-95; Marriage 6 Grd Team Tchr 1980-95; ai: Co-Dir of Theater Club; Club Adv; Stu Television News Prgm; Prof Rights & Responsibilities Comm; NEA, MA TA, Hanson TA 1973-; Hanson Recreation Commission 1972-, Chm, Sec, Treas; Kiwanis 1990-; Continental Cable Comm Vol 1988-; Co-Sabbatical with Wife 1993-94 for Medieval Stud; Citizen of Yr; Comm Television Excl Awd; office: Indian Head MS 750 Indian Head St Hanson MA 02341*

BLAUVELT, EILEEN C., English Teacher; b: Brooklyn, NY; m: John A.; c: Mary, Karen; ed: Montclair (MS) Non-Western 1977; cr: Thomas Jefferson Schl Soc Stud, Eng Tchr 1964-68; Ramapo Ridge Lang Arts, Soc Stud, Rdng Tchr 1978-84; Mahwah HS Eng Tchr 1984-; ai: Lit Magazine Adv; NEA 1960-; office: Mahwah HS 50 Ridge Rd Mahwah NJ 07430

BLAUVELT, MARY E., Science Teacher; b: Patterson, NJ; ed: Univ of Scranton (BS) Bio & Philosophy 1991, (MS) Sci Scndry Ed 1993; 7 Credit Hrs; cr: Waldwick HS HS Bio, Chem & Anatomy Tchr 1994-; ai: JV Girls Soccer Coach, Environmental Club Adv; Vol for the Courtyard Garden Project Vol; NHS Selection Comm; NSTA 1993-; NJEA 1993-; NJSCA 1995-; office: Waldwick Jr Sr HS 155 Wyckoff Ave Waldwick NJ 07463

BLAZER, LISA NEWKIRK, Fourth Grade Teacher; b: Ramey AFB, PR; m: Frank J.; c: Stephen F., Jessica A.; ed: Wright St Univ (MA) Math Ed 1982; 30 Hrs Sci, Cmptr; 12 Hrs Data Processing 1984; cr: Southeastern Local Schl Tchr 1977-; ai: Tech Comm; Lounge Fund Chprsn; Southeastern Local Ed Assn 1977-, Pres, Grievance Chair; OEA, NEA 1977-; Clark Cty Rec, Soccer Coach; Northridge Girls Sftbl 1994-, VP; Land Lab Grant 1992; office: Miami View Elem Schl 230 Clifton Rd South Charleston OH 45368

BLEACHER, DARTHI ANN, Special Education Teacher; b: Ridley Park, PA; m: Edward Benjamin II; ed: La Salle Univ (BA) Spec & Elem Ed 1990; Widener Univ 27 Credits Working on Masters in Scndry Ed; cr: Ridley MS Spec Ed Tchr 6 Yrs; ai: Ridley Park Chrldrs Coach, Dir; Ridley Park Ath Club, Dir, Bd Mem; Ridley Schl Dist Impact Grant 1994; Citations: Borough of Ridley Park 1995, PA St Sen Bell, PA Gov Casey, PA Rep Gannon, Mayor T. Kennedy; Coached Chrldng Team to 11 Championships & NCA Natl Championships; office: Ridley MS Free & Dumont Streets Ridley Park PA 19078*

BLEAM, CHRISTOPHER ALLEN, Health & PE Teacher; b: Allentown, PA; ed: Penn St Univ (BS) Hlth, PE 1987; Grad Work East Stroudsburg Univ; cr: Ironton Elem Schl PE Tchr 1987-93; Parkland HS Boys, Girls Soccer Coach 1989-, Hlth, PE Tchr 1993-; ai: Asst Swimming Coach; NEA 1987-; Lehigh Valley Youth Soccer League 1990-, Bd of Dirs; office: Parkland HS 2675 PA Rt #309 Orefield PA 18069*

BLECK, CAROL CARLSON, HS Social Studies Teacher; b: Dunkirk, NY; m: David John Jr.; c: David John III, Megan Elizabeth; ed: Fredonia St Univ (BA) Scndry Ed, Soc Stud 1980, (MS) Rdng 1983; Post Grad Work Math for Tchng, Mid Eastern Stud; cr: Dunkirk HS Scndry Ed, Soc Stud Tchr 1983-; ai: Stu Cncl, Class, NHS Adv; AFT; NYSUT; DTA; office: Dunkirk Sr HS W 6th St Dunkirk NY 14048

BLEDSOE, RALPH CORNELIUS, Physics Teacher; b: Los Angeles, CA; m: Diane; c: Naomi; ed: Univ of Southern CA (BS) Chem 1983; Univ of MA at Amherst 6 Credit Hrs; Educl Admin MS & Doctorate; cr: Northfield Mount Hermon Schl Sci Fac 1990-; ai: Track & Field Coach; Japanese Club Adv; Local Alumni Assn & African Amer Alumni Assn Pres; Mahar Regnl HS 1991-, Annual Sci Fair Judge; Columbia Univ T C Klingenstein Summer Inst 1993; NMH Parents Fund Fac Chair Ath 1994; office: Northfield Mt Hermon Schl 28 Mount Hermon Rd Box F Mount Hermon MA 01354

BLESEDELL, PATRICIA ROSS, First Grade Teacher; b: Wayne, WV; m: John P. Jr.; c: John P. III, Jason Ross; ed: OH Univ (BA) K-Eighth 1981; Mount St Joseph Coll (MS) Rdng K-Twelth 1986; cr: Huntington HS Seventh-Eighth Grd Math, Rdng Tchr 1982-83; Huntington Elem Schl First Grd Tchr 1983-; ai: Dist Sci, Improvement Comms; NEA, RCEA 1982-; Delta Kappa Gamma 1993-, Mbrshp Chprsn; Phi Delta Kappa 1991-; Huntington's Edctr of Yr 1991-92; office: Huntington Elem Schl 188 Huntsman Rd Chillicothe OH 45601

BLEVINS, ISABEL ROSENDALE, MS Teacher; b: Bradshaw, MD; c: Julie Lynn, Charlotte Michelle, Stephanie Anne; ed: Towson St Univ (BS) Elem Ed 1975; Loyola Coll (MA) Guid, Cnslng 1990; Notre Dame, Loyola Coll (MS) Admin; MD Writing Project 6 Credits; MSDE MVA Driving Edctrs Courses 80 Hrs; Natl Acad of Drama 3 Credits 1969-71; cr: Jarrettesville Elem Schl 4 Grd Tchr 1976-77; St Stephens Elem Schl K-8 Grd Tchr, Cnslr 1982-93; The Cath HS of Balto 9-12 Grd Theology Tchr 1993-95; St Joseph Schl 6-8 Grd Tchr 1995-; ai: Liturgy Comm; Confirmation Ldr; Write, Direct Plays, Skits, Meditations; NCEA 1982-; Chi Sigma Iota 1990-, NHS Cnslrs; St Stephen Church 1982-, Choir, Lector, Eucharistic Minister, Cantor; MD Save Our Streams 1989-, Svc Vol; Educl, Notre Dam Educl, Loyola Edcl Grants; Ran Stud Skills, Peer Tutoring; Grief Cnslng; Self Esteem Groups; office: St Joseph Schl 101 Church Ln Cockeysville MD 21030*

BLIGEN, EDITH J., English Link Teacher; b: Scottsville, VA; c: John, David; ed: Upsala (BA) Eng K-12 1975; cr: East Orange HS Eng Tchr

1978-; *ai:* NEA 1978-; NJEA 1975-; NAACP; PTA; *home:* 70 Lincoln St East Orange NJ 07017

BLINKE, JOHN DAVID, US History Tchr & Dept Chm; *b:* Baltimore, MD; *m:* Linda L. Lynch; *c:* Jacqueline, Jennifer; *ed:* Towson St Univ (BS) Tchr Ed 1972; Loyola Coll (MMS) Modern Stud 1992; *cr:* Boys Latin Schl Chm His Dept 1973-; *ai:* Var Bsbl, Ftbl; NHS; OAS 1980-; Knights of Columbus 1993-, Chancellor; Historic Towson 1990-, Bd; Towson Jaycees 1980-, Bd; Williams Coll Tchrs Awd 1990; McDonalds Regnl Tchr of Yr Awd 1992; *office:* Boys' Latin Sch Of Maryland 822 W Lake Ave Baltimore MD 21210

BLINN, LOIS ANN, Second Grade Teacher; *b:* Centerburg, OH; *ed:* Bowling Green St Univ (BSEd) Elem Ed 1962, (MED) Admin 1968; Addl Credits; *cr:* Walbridge Elem Schl First-Third Grd Tchr 1962-; *ai:* NEA, OEA 1962-; Toledo E A 1962-78, Bldg Rep; TFT 1978-; Libbey Schlsps; Holden-Jennings Tchr Scholar 1977; *office:* Walbridge Elem Schl 1245 Walbridge Ave Toledo OH 43609

BLINZLER, KAY KINGSTON, Second Grade Teacher; *b:* Erie, PA; *m:* David; *ed:* Edinboro Univ (BS) Elem Ed 1963; Gannon Univ (MS) Guid 1970; Addl Grad Credit hrs; *cr:* Millcreek Schl Dist 1st-2nd Grd Tchr 1963-; *ai:* Prof Action, Long Range Planning, Curr Comms; NEA, PSEA, MEA 1963-, Dist Liaison Chm, negotiation Team; Northwest Lead Tchr Assn, Bd Mem; MEA Tchr of Yr 1981; *home:* 551 W 6th St Erie PA 16507

BLISS, BRIAN ANDREW, HS English Teacher; *b:* Philadelphia, PA; *ed:* Penn St Univ (BSEd) Scndry & Eng 1994; *cr:* Manheim Twp High Eng Tchr 1994-; *ai:* Asst Ftbl Coach; Quiz Bowl Coach; Tech Pioneer; INTASC PA Dept of Ed New Tchr Vol; Scheduling Comm; Grad Req Comm; NCTC 1993-; NEA 1995-; Natl Coalition of Ed Actvists 1993-; Golden Key Natl Honor Soc; Phi Eta Sigma Theta Natl Honor Soc; Penn St Deans List; *office:* Manheim Twp HS 5134 School Rd Lancaster PA 17601*

BLISS, HARRY F., Teacher; *b:* Rochester, NY; *c:* Alexander Harrison; *ed:* Univ of the Arts (BFA) Illustration 1990; Syracuse Univ (MA) Illustration 1994; PA Acad of Fine Arts in Life Painting; *cr:* Parsons Schl of Design Instr of Life Drawing, Drawing 1991-93; The Univ of The Arts Instr Illustration 1991-93; Moore Coll of Art & Design, The Univ of The Arts Lectures 1991-; *ai:* Selected Exhibitions: Bliss Group Show 1990-, Soc of Illustrators 1991, Family Bliss 1993, Mothers, Fathers, Sons & Daughters 1995, Fac Exhibition 1995; PUblications 1994; Illustration First Prize Awds 1990-; Gold & Silver Awds 1991, 1994; *home:* 900 Fitzwater St Philadelphia PA 19147*

BLISS, SARA GADSBY, Third Grade Teacher; *b:* Grove City, PA; *m:* Paul William; *c:* Bill; *ed:* Clarion Univ (BAE) Elem Ed 1968, (MED) Ed 1973; *cr:* Valley Grove Schl Dist 6th Grd Tchr 1968-69; Venango Cty Head Start Preschl Tchr 1969-71; Valley Grove Schl Dist 6th Grd Tchr 1971-80, 3rd Grd Tchr 1980-; *ai:* Mentor Tchr; Geography Comm; VGEA 1971-, Negotiating Team; *home:* RR 2 Box 2217 Stoneboro PA 16153*

BLIVEN, JUDYL (WINTERHALTER), Physical Education Teacher; *b:* Wellsville, NY; *m:* James C.; *c:* Tracie Lee Preston, Danyelle; *ed:* S.U.C. at Brockport (BA) Hlth & PE 1966; Univ of Alfred 30 Hrs Post Grad PE Permanent Cert 1975; *cr:* B.O.C.E.S. Hlth & PE Tchr 5 Yrs; Belmont Cntrl PE Tchr 25 Yrs; *ai:* Ath Dir; Var Girls Soccer Coach; Sftbl, Vlybl, Bsktbl Coach; Ath Assn Adv; NEA 1966-; Exec Comm Section V 1994-, PE Girls Rep; NYSPHSAA Section V Rep 1994-, PE Girls Rep; Coach of Yr Alleg Co 1984; NY St Coaches Awd 1995 for Class D Girls Soccer.

BLIZMAN, JOSEPH J., Eighth Grade Teacher; *b:* Wilkes-Barre, PA; *m:* Edith Conley; *c:* Angela M., Allyson J.; *ed:* Wilkes Coll (BA) Philosophy, Psych 1980, (BA) Elem Ed 1981; *cr:* Wilkes-Barre Area Schl Dist Sub Tchr 1981-83; Sacred Heart Schl Eighth Grd Tchr 1983-; *ai:* Cmptr Programming Team Adv; Mid St Steering Comm; NCEA 1983-; Slovak Citizens Club 1993-; *office:* Sacred Heart Schl 421 Madison St Wilkes Barre PA 18705

BLIZZARD, NANCY SNYDER, Language Arts Teacher; *b:* Philadelphia, PA; *m:* Michael R.; *c:* Robert, Jessica; *ed:* St Marys Coll of MD (BA) Eng 1974; Univ of MD (MED) Rdng 1980; *cr:* John Hanson MS Lang Arts Tchr 1974-77; Benjamin Stodderr MS Lang Arts Dept Chair & Gifted Ed Resource Tchr 1977-95; Mattawoman MS Lang Arts Tchr, Enrichment & Acclerated Faciltator 1995-; *ai:* Odyssey of the Mind Spon; Coach; A & E Pgm Facilitator; Johns Hopkins Talent Search Adv; NCTE 1978-; MGATE 1990-; AAUW 1995-; Good Shepard Choir 1986-; BSA 1992-, Comm Mem; MYF 1992-, Spon; Charles Cty Pub Schls Outstdng Tchr; Eng & Scholars Pgm OM Svc Awd.

BLOCHOWSKI, MICHAEL J., Computer Science Teacher; *b:* Toledo, OH; *m:* Kristin Romaine-Blochowski; *c:* Luke; *ed:* Bowling Green St Univ (BS) Mngmt Information Systems 1987; Cmptr Sci Cert; *cr:* Phillips Coll Bus Instr 1990-91; Sylvania Southview Tchr, Coach 1991-93; Sylvania Northview Tchr, Coach 1991-93; St Francis De Sales Cmptr Sci Tchr, Coach 1993-; *ai:* Bsbl, Ftbl, IM Bsktbl Coach; Spec Olympics1994-, Asst Coach; *office:* St Francis DeSales HS 2323 W Bancroft St Toledo OH 43607

BLOCK, JOEL WARREN, Science Teacher; *b:* New Haven, CT; *m:* Deborah A. Cutuli; *c:* Ivan, Eric; *ed:* The Citadel (BS) Ed 1961; Southern CT St Univ (MS) General Sci 1970; Wesleyan Univ (CAS) Earth Sci 1975; *cr:* Brien McMahon HS Sci Tchr 25 Yrs; Southern CT St Univ Earth Sci Lecturer 12 Yrs; Univ of CT at Stamford Geology Lecturer 9 Yrs; Sacred Heart Univ Astronomy Adj Asst Prof 9 Yrs; *ai:* Geological Field Investigators Inc, Pres; Project Advance in Europe; Tchr In-Service Courses; Norwalk Fed of Tchrs; CT Sci Tchrs Assn; Presidential Awd for Excl in Sci Tchng 1984; Sci Mat Fellowship 1993; CT Acad for Ed in Math, Sci & Tech Fellow 1993; *office:* Brien McMahon HS 300 Highland Ave Norwalk CT 06854*

BLOCK, LAURENCE ERWIN, Teacher & Dept Chairman; *b:* Washington, DC; *m:* Shirley Little; *c:* Melissa, Megan; *ed:* Princeton (AB) His 1965; Johns Hopkins (MAT) His 1967, (PHD) His of Ed 1972; *cr:* Annapolis Jr Tchr 1972-77; Bates Mid Tchr & Dept Chair 1977-; *ai:* 9th Grd NY Trip Tour Dir; Fac Cncl Chm; NEA 1972-; MD St Tchrs 1972-; Tchrs Assoc of Anna Arundel Cty 1972-; NDEA Flwshp; Anne Arundel Cty Pub Schls Human Relations Awd; *home:* 3109 Catrina Ln Annapolis MD 21403*

BLOCK, STAN A., Biology Teacher; *b:* Waynesburg, PA; *m:* Sandra Kay DuKate; *c:* Emily, Shelby; *ed:* CA Univ PA (BS) Environmental Sci 1986; PA Tchng Cert Scndry Bio & Environmental Ed 1989, Working on MS Earth Sci; *cr:* Essex Intermediate Schl 7th Grd Life Sci Tchr 1989-92; Chartiers-Houston HS Bio Tchr 1992-; *ai:* Envirothon Team, Field & Stream & Fly-Fishers Clubs Adv; PJAS Spon; AFT, PFT, NSTA, PSTA 1992-; Safari Club Intnl-Northwoods Publications Grant 1993; PA Water Environment Assn-PA St Envirothon Grant 1995; Jackson WY Amer Wilderness Leadership Schl Grad 1993; *office:* Chartiers-houston Schl Dist 2050 W Pike St Houston PA 15342

BLOM, KENNETH G., K-12th Grd Science Director; *b:* Batavia, NY; *m:* Carol Barnes; *c:* Amy V., Rebecca C.; *ed:* St Univ of NY at Oneonta (BS) Bio 1968; St Univ of NY at Albany (CAS) Curr & Instruction 1983, (EDD) Sci Ed 1988; *cr:* Catskill Cntrl Schl Sci Tchr 1968-71; Ballston Spa Cntrl Schl Sci Tchr & HS Sci Chair 1971-88; Niskayuna Cntrl Schl HS Sci Chair 1988-95; Niskayuna Schl Dist K-12th Grd Sci Dir 1995-; *ai:* Sci Olympiad Co-Adv; Sci Bowl Competition Coach; Sci Tchrs Assn of NY St 1975-; NY St Sci Supvrs Assn 1988-; Phi Delta Kappa 1983-; NYS United Tchrs 1968-; Capital Area Sci Supvrs Assn 1988-, Treas; Schl Admin Assn of NY St 1996; Niskayuna Tchrs Assn 1988-; Amer Bio Tchr Article 1983; NY St Music Assn Journal Article 1993; Sci Tchrs Assn of NY St Teleconference 1993; Adjunct Prof of Ed at Union Coll 1991-, St Univ of NY at Albany 1983-91; *office:* Niskayuna Schl Dist Van Antwerp Rd Niskayuna NY 12309*

BLOMGREN, GUSTAVE ERIC,JR., Fourth Grade Teacher; *b:* Lawrence, MA; *m:* Rosalind Ramirez-Blomgren; *ed:* Univ of Lowell (BA) Span 1976; Univ of MA at Lowell (MEd) Admin, Planning, Policy 1993; Salem St Coll Tchr Cert 1977; P-6 Grd Prin Cert 1993; Coll Credit Estudio Internacional Sampere Spain 1974; Working on Prin Cert 5-9 Grd; *cr:* Central Schl Tchr 1977-90; Oakland Schl Tchr 1977-90; Corliss Schl Tchr 1977-90, Head Tchr 1979-80, 1988-90, 1994-; Howe Schl Tchr 1977-90, Head Tchr 1979-80, 1988-90, Acting Prin 1989, Head Tchr 1994-; Comprehensive Grammar Schl Head Tchr 1979-80, 1988-90, 1994-, Tchr 1990-, Supervising Tchr of Apprentice Tchr 1996-; *ai:* Assertive Discipline Comm; Tchr Resource Team Chprsn 1990-; Methuen Schl System Sci Action Comm; After Schl Prgm Tchr; Schl Cncl 1994-; ASCD; Methuen Ed Assn, MA Tchrs Assn, Natl Tchrs Assn 1977-; Methuen Historical Soc, Benevolent Order of Elks 1986-; St Mary's Church Restoration Comm; Organized, Implemented Kndgtn-4th Grd Buddy Prgm; Methuen Unit Curr Dev Participant; Planned, Organized Schl Store Through Grant Written; Greater Lawrence Educl Collaborative Pen Pal Prgm Schl Coord; 4th Grd Stdnts, Elem Staff Carnegie Self-Stud Survey Prgm Coord; *home:* 125 Ashland Ave Methuen MA 01844

BLOOM, DAVID S., Special Education Teacher; *b:* New York, NY; *m:* Beverly Kaufman; *c:* Adrienne, Abbie; *ed:* SUNY at New Paltz (BA) Scndry Ed, Soc Stud 1970, (MS) Spec Ed 1975; Instrmental Enrichment Cert Trainer; *cr:* Greenwood Schl Spec Ed Tchr 1970-73; Astor Day Treatment Ctr Spec Ed Tchr 1973-75; Wappingers Cntrl Schls Spec Ed Tchr 1976-; Marist Coll Adj Instr Spec Ed 1989-91; *ai:* Peer Mediation, Drama, Schl Sci Fair, Schl Talent Show Adv; Schl Ldrshp Team Chprsn; Spec Ed Tchr in Charge; AFT, NYSUT 1976-; Mill St Loft 1982-, Dir; Cert Schl of Theatre 1983-, Dir; Childrens Radio Broadcasting Area Fund Grant, Arts Cncl Grant Awd; *office:* James S. Evans Elem Schl 26 Old Rt 9 Wappingers Fls NY 12590*

BLOOM, FRANCIS A., Math Teacher & Dept Chairman; *b:* Clearfield, PA; *m:* Paulette R. Irwin; *c:* Jamie Francis; *ed:* Clarion St Coll (BS) Math 1971; *cr:* Tyrone Area HS Math Tchr 1972-; *ai:* Math Competition Coord; NEA, PSEA 1972-; NCTM 1990-; *office:* Tyrone Area Jr Sr HS Clay Avenue Ext Tyrone PA 16686

BLOOM, GARY L., English & Drama Teacher; *b:* Bloomsburg, PA; *m:* Maxine Gerstein; *c:* Myrna Jo Hetter; *ed:* Bloomsburg Univ (BS) Eng, His, Govt, Speech & Theatre-Philo 1968, (MED) Comp Eng 1975; Temple & PSU in Gifted; IM Pgm Specialist for Soc Gifted 1981; *cr:* Lewisburg Federal Prison Lit & Stud Skills Tchr; Line Mountain HS 11th-12th Grd Tchr of Coll Prep Eng, Dept Chair & Drama Coach 1968-78; CSIU #16 Facilitator for Gifted 1978-82; Restaurant Owner & Operator 1986-89; Our Lady of Lourdes Regnl HS Tchr & Drama & Forensic Coach 1989-90; Eastern York SHS Tchr of Eng AP 12th & Drama, Facilitator of Gifted 1990-; *ai:* Forensics Coach; NHS Adv; PAGE, Ofcr 1978-; PCTE, Ofcr 1968-; Masons; Amer Legion; VFW; *home:* 120 Greystone Rd York PA 17402

BLOOM, MICHAEL ALAN, Special Education Teacher; *b:* Greenville, SC; *m:* Helen; *c:* Noah, Erica; *ed:* Boston Univ (BA) Bio 1969; Brooklyn Coll (MA) Bio, Ed 1978; C. W. Post Coll Spec Ed Cert 1980; *cr:* Glen Cove MS Sci Tchr 1971-78; Glen Cove HS Spec Ed Tchr 1978-; *ai:* Camp Chen-A-Wanda Boys Head Cnslr; NEA, AFT 1971-; *office:* Glen Cove HS 150 Dosoris Ln Glen Cove NY 11542*

BLOOM, NANCY STAWICKI, Business & Technology Teacher; *b:* Boston, MA; *m:* John; *c:* Jeffrey; *ed:* Husson Coll (BA) Bus Educ 1971; Suffolk Univ (MS) Bus Educ 1979; Fitchburg St Univ Post Grad Courses; *cr:* Franklin HS Bus, Tech Tchr 1971-; Dean Coll Bus, Tech Tchr 1978-88; *ai:* Prof Bus Orgs Desktop Publishing & Multimedia Spokesperson; MA Bus Educator's Assn 1971-, Dir; RI Bus Educator's Assn 1986-; Delta Pi Epsilon 1987-, Ed; NEA, MA Tchrs Assn 1971-; Norfolk Cty Tchrs Assn 1986-; Natl Desktop Publishing Assn 1989-; Boston Cmptr Soc 1988-; MA Cmptr Using Educators 1985-; NBEA 1975-; Co-Author Word Processing Textbook; Husson Coll Tchr Excl Awd 1987; *home:* 371 Village St Medway MA 02053*

BLOOM, SARAH COWAN, Mathematics Teacher; *b:* Cumberland, MD; *m:* Martin; *c:* Peter, Jane; *ed:* WV Univ (BS) Math 1973; Coll of William & Mary (MED) Diagnostic Prescriptive Tchng 1977; Mount St Marys 9 Credit Hrs; *cr:* Bishopville HS Math Tchr 1973-74; Tabb Intermediate Math Tchr 1974-76; Psychiatric Inst Math & Sci Tchr 1977-79; Anne Arundel Cty Math Tchr 1979-81, Math Tchr 1986-; Las Vegas Math Tchr 1981-85; *ai:* Yrbk Adv; Class of 1997 Spon; Acad Adv for Ath Dept; MCTM 1986-; NCTM; St Martins Comm Theatre Bd of Dirs 1993-, Publicity; HEW Flwshp Coll of William & Mary 1975; Articles Pub 1977; *office:* Southern Sr HS 4400 Solomons Island Rd Harwood MD 20776*

BLOOM, SHARON DAIGLE, Family, Consumer Tchr & Admin; *b:* Lynn, MA; *m:* Robert A.; *c:* Amy, Seth; *ed:* Framingham St Coll (BS) Family, Consumer Scis 1968, (MED) Family, Consumer Scis 1973; 8 Credit Hrs Parenting, Nutrition; 4 Credit Hrs Child Dev; *cr:* Clinton HS Tchr, Admin 1968-; *ai:* Evaluation, Curr Comms; MTA, NEA 1968-; MFACS, AAFACS 1968-, Pres; AAUW 1979-, Pres, Vice Prgm Ch; Delta Kappa Gamma 1988-; Perkins Grant Awd; *office:* Clinton HS 80 Church St Clinton MA 01510

BLOOMBERG, LINDA WHITELY, Math Teacher; *b:* Willard, OH; *m:* Robert Kurt; *c:* Brianna, Brennan; *ed:* OH St Univ (BS) Elem Ed 1983; Heidelberg Coll (MS) Cnslng 1992; *cr:* St James Schl 7th Grd Tchr 1984-86; Seneca East Schl Jr High Math Tchr 1986-; *ai:* NEA, OEA 1986-; *home:* 11812 Knauss Rd Bellevue OH 44811

BLOOMFIELD, DAVID ROSS, 6th Grade Teacher; *b:* Lorain, OH; *m:* Carmen Santiago; *ed:* OH Univ (BSC) Comm 1984; Ashland Univ (MED) Curr, Instruction 1991; *cr:* Ely Elem Schl Tchr 1989-; *ai:* 6th Grd IM Bsktbl Instr; *office:* Ely Elem Schl 312 Gulf Rd Elyria OH 44035*

BLOOMFIELD, DEREK IVAN, Professor of Mathematics; *b:* Utica, NY; *m:* Marcella Baca; *c:* Jennifer, Max, Derek Jr., David; *ed:* AZ St Univ (PhD) Math 1971; Purdue Univ (MS) Math 1967; SUNY at New Paltz (BS) Math 1965; *cr:* Orange Cty Comm Coll Math Prof 1971-, Dept Chair 1989-92; *ai:* Fac Adv Masters Elements Club; NYS Math Assn, NEA 1971-; Amer Math Assn 1978-; Occupations Inc 1978-87, Trustee, Bd Pres; Museum Village 1988-91, Bd Mem, VP; Neversink Valley Area Museum 1990-, Bd Mem; 8 Math, Algebra Textbooks Prentice Hall & West Pub Co; Journal Articles; *office:* Orange County Comm Coll 115 South St Middletown NY 10940*

BLOOR, RUTH PEARL (DAVISON), Math Teacher; *b:* Tekemah, NE; *m:* Sidney R.; *c:* Beth Edminster, Lynn Dobi, Dan; *ed:* Geneva Coll (BS) Math 1955; Univ of Pittsburgh 3 Hrs; Earlham Coll 2 Yrs; *cr:* Westinghouse Atomic Power Mathematician 1955-57; Toronto HS Math Tchr 1957-58; Deshler HS Math Tchr 1966-68; Patrick Henry HS Math Tchr 1971-; *ai:* Quiz Team Judge; NEA, OEA, PHEA 1966-, Building Rep; Phi Delta Kappa 1986-93; 1st Presbyn Ch 1963-, Mant, Ed Trustee, Choir, Sunday Schl Tchr; CCL 1963-73, VP 1963; Outstanding Scndry Educators of America 1975; Patrick Henry Ed Assn Exec Comm 1972-74, 1989-8 Comm 1974; *home:* 217 W Main St Deshler OH 43516

BLOSE, RUTH ELAYNE, Spanish & French Teacher; *b:* Wayne PA; *m:* Phillip R.; *c:* Scott, Phillip, Amanda; *ed:* IN Univ of PA Span 1974; Millersville Univ 6 Credits; Washington & Jefferson Credits, Fr Cert 1993; CA Univ of PA 18 Credits; Carlow Coll 3 C *cr:* Various Schl Dists Sub Tchr 1977-88; Uniontown HS Permane 1986-87; Avella Area HS Tchr 1988-; *ai:* Jr Class, NHS Spon; Coord; Strategic Planning Curr Comm; Avella Ed Assn 1988-, S Rep; PSEA, NEA 1988-; PSMLA 1989-; ACTFL 1995-; Richeyville Church 1976-, Sunday Schl Sec; *office:* Avella Area Jr Sr HS 1000 Rd Avella PA 15312*

BLOT, DAVID ROBERT, Associate Professor of ESL; *b:* White NY; *ed:* Cath Univ (BA) Eng 1965; Tchrs Coll (MA) TESOL Fordham Univ (PHD) Curr & Tchng 1991; *cr:* Hostos Comm Coll Second Lang Tchr 1984-89; Bronx Comm Coll Asst Prof of Eng as S Lang 1989-; *ai:* Prof Staff Congress, City Univ of NY Eng as Secon Cncl 1984-; Put It in Writing Newbury House 1980; Write From th Newbury House 1984; Starting Lines Heinle & Heinle 1995; *offic* Univ Of NY Bronx Comm Col University Ave Bronx NY 10453*

BLOUIN, BONNIE BLANCHET, 4th Grade Teacher; *b:* Barre, Ronald Roger; *c:* Tyson James; *ed:* Johnson St Coll (BA) Elem Ed 30 Addl Hrs Ed Courses; *cr:* Barre Town Elem Schl Spec Ed Paraed 1973-74, 3rd Grd Tchr 1974-88, 6th Grd Tchr 1988-95, 4th Grd Tchr *ai:* Past Mem Tripod; Tchng Sign Lang to Stdnts; Advocating fo Hard-of-Hearing; NEA, Barretown Tchrs Assn 1973-; VAMLE Nelms Conf Participation 1992; *home:* 158 Church Hill Rd Barre VT

BLOUIN, GEORGE ROBERT, English Teacher; *b:* Lewiston, M Univ of ME (BS) Eng 1961; Stony Brook Univ (MA) Hum 19 Bangor HS Eng Tchr 1963; Lowville Acad Eng Tchr 1963-66; Kenn Eng Tchr 1966-; *ai:* NEA 1963-; PCT; PTA 1980-90, Union Rep Lifetime Mem 1980; NY PTA Distinguished Service Awd 1983; Plainview Old-Bethpage HS John F Kennedy HS Plainview NY 11

BLOZZON, SUSAN CORTINA, Chemistry Teacher; *b:* Bridgepo *m:* Robert Jr.; *c:* Meaghan, Brody; *ed:* Univ of New Haven (AS) 1987, (BS) Bio 1987; Chapman Univ (MS) Ed, Curr, Instr 1991; *cr:* Schl Sci, Math Tchr 1987-89; Sahuarita HS Chem, Physics Tchr 1 Amity HS Chem Tchr 1992-; *ai:* JV Sftbl Coach; Co-Coach Jets NEA 1990-; Flwshp CT Audobon Soc to Dev Sci Curr that Encom all Disciplines; Project Search, Mem, St of CT DEP; *office:* Regional Sr HS 25 Newton Rd Woodbridge CT 06525*

BLUBAUGH, ROBERT LOUIS, Senior Social Studies Teacher; *b:* Vernon, OH; *ed:* Kent St Univ (BA) Liberal Arts 1967; Mt Nazarene Coll (BA) Ed 1978; Univ of Steubenville (BA) Eng Ashland Univ Certs Prin & Asst Supt; *cr:* Mt Vernon MS Soc Stu 1978; Jefferson Cty JVS Soc Stud Tchr 1978-; *ai:* Citizenship, Registration, Close-Up Comms; Adv Vocational Honor Soc, Citiz Bee Contest; ASCD 1980-; Bldg Tchrs Assn 1981-, Pres; OCSS Danville Lions Club 1977-, Treas, Attendance Awd; Vietnam Vete Amer 1980-; Knox Cty Humane Soc 1993-; Families of MIA, 1984-; Voc Acad Tchrs Consortiums Organizer; *home:* PO B Danville OH 43014*

BLUCHER, ROLAND EDWARD, Fourth Grade Teacher; *b:* Brighton, PA; *m:* M. Darlene Bolinger; *c:* Kirsten D. Blucher Si Daniel William; *ed:* Geneva Coll (BS) Ed 1964; Slippery Rock Univ Ed 1967; Regent Univ (MAEd) Chrstn Schl Admin 1982; *cr:* Blac Schl Dist Tchr 1964-; *ai:* Prof Enrichment Comm; Curr Cncl; Dist Team; TESA Tchng Model; PSEA 1964-, Nominating Comm Chm 1964-; First Assembly of God 1991-, Deacon; Gift of Time Rec *home:* 2904 6th Ave Beaver Falls PA 15010

BLUE, DAVID ALLEN, Social Studies Teacher; *b:* Rock Springs, Julie; *ed:* Muskingum Coll (BA) His 1984; IN Purdue at For Wayne Admin 1996; *cr:* Monticello HS Soc Stud Tchr 1984-85; Hicksville Stud Tchr 1985-; *ai:* Head Boys Bsktbl Coach 1985-94; Asst Ftbl 1985-92; Head Ftbl Coach 1993; Ath Dir 1988-92; Jr High Coach Frosh Class Adv 1995-; Colloburnive Action Team 1994-95; NEA *office:* Hicksville HS Smith & Main Hicksville OH 43526

BLUE, FREDERICK JUDD, Professor of History Dept; *b:* Staten NY; *m:* Judith Hertwig; *c:* Karen Evenson, Eric; *ed:* Yale Univ (B 1958; Univ of WI (MS) His 1962, (PHD) His 1966; *cr:* Youngstown S Prof His 1964-; *ai:* Master Prgm His Dir; Org of Amer Historian Books: The Free Soilers: Third-Party Politics, 1848-54 1973, Sal Chase: A Life in Politics 1987, Charles Sumner and the Conscience North 1994; *office:* Youngstown St Univ Dept of History Youngsto 44555

BLUE, RONALD CALVIN, Asst Professor of Psychology; *b:* C NC; *m:* Wanda Eileen Hatcher; *c:* Leanne, Allison; *ed:* Appalach Univ (BS) Pol Sci 1968, (MA) Psych 1970; 6 Semester Hrs Univ o Semester Hrs Temple Univ; 8 Semester Hrs Lehigh Carbon Comm C North Surry HS Soc Sci Tchr 1968-69; Veterans Admin Ctr Psych 1970; Brunson-Dargan Jr HS Guid Cnslr 1970-71; Lehigh Carbon Coll Psych Prof 1971-; *ai:* TIPS for Psych Tchrs, Neurosci, Sociob Epilepsy, Tramatic Brain Injury, Stroke, Psych, Brain, N Psychoneuroimmunology, Chaos Internet Discussion Groups; NEA PA Ed Assn 1971-; Lehigh Mental Hlth Assn 1977-82, Bd of Dirs; Hlth Assn of PA 1979-82, Bd of Dirs; Band Parents of Northwest 1986-, VP; Mental Hlth Assn Outstdng Vol of Yr, Wkshps Keynote S Coord 1979; Articles Pub 1976, 1983, 1995; *office:* Lehigh Carbon Coll 2549 Education Park Ave Schnecksville PA 18078*

BLUEM, CHARLES ROBERT, World Regions & Psych Teac Detroit, MI; *m:* Dagmar S.; *c:* Gregory L.; *ed:* MI St Univ (BA) Hi 1966; *cr:* Mona Shores HS Soc Stud Tchr 1966-69; Berlin Amer Stud Tchr 1969-94; Lakenheath Amer HS Soc Stud, US Governmer 1994-; *ai:* Fed Educl Assn 1969-, Fac Rep Spokesperson 12 Yrs; Tchr Awd via Dept of Ed Presidential Schlars Pgm 1989; Commencement Speaker for Berlin Amer HS; Named by Presi Scholar Tiffany A. Madden; *office:* Lakenheath HS DODDS CCSH Box 811 APO AE 09464

BLUHM, JOHN M., Chemistry Teacher; *b:* South Bend, IN; *m:* A Nichols; *ed:* WV Univ (BS) Sec Ed 1966; Colby Coll (MST) Sec Sc *cr:* Norwin Sr HS Tchr 1966-; *ai:* NEA, PSEA 1966-; Woodrow Master Tchr Inst 1988; Judge Awd PA Jr Acad of Sci 1975; *office:* HS 251 McMahon Rd North Huntingdon PA 15642

BLUM, CAROL KRAMER, Eng Teacher & Lit Magazine A Brooklyn, NY; *m:* Bernard M.; *c:* Gary, Cindy Rampp, Jeff; *ed:* U MD (BA) Eng 1978; St of MD (MA) Equiv Scndry Ed 1984; 30 H Grad; *cr:* W. Churchill HS Eng Tchr 1979-, Lit Mag Adv 1990-; *ai* Drug & Alcohol Policy Comms; Schl Brochure Ed; NEA 1979-; 1990-; MD Schl Press Assn 1990-, Bd Mem; Article Pub; Distng White House Commission on Presidential Scholars 1995; Ray Kr Donald's Tchr Achvmt Awd 1995; Kent Esprit D Corps Awd 1995; Winston Churchill HS 11300 Gainsborough Rd Potomac MD 2085

BLUM, JUDITH OPPER, Tchr of Learning Disabilities; *b:* Cle OH; *m:* Neil; *c:* Karen Bialosky, Sandra, Richard; *ed:* OH Univ Elem Ed 1959; John Carroll Univ (MED) Learning Disabilites 1988

t Univ, Ashland Univ, Multicultural Ed Inst; *cr:* South Stickney Schl d Tchr Gen Ed 1959-61; Fairmount Elem Schl 3 Grd Tchr Gen Ed 5; Northwood Elem Schl Learning Disabilites Tutor 1975-79; Elem Schl 2-3 Grd Tchr Gen Ed 1979; Northwood Elem Schl ng Disabilities Tchr 1979-83; Boulevard Elem Schl Learning ites Tchr 1983-; *ai:* Educating Multiculturally Team; Site-Based Accelerated Schls Model Coach, Trainer; Planned, Implemented s; Schl Improvement Comm; Learning Disabilites Assn of Greater and1988-, Advy Bd, Learning Disabilites Tchr of Yr 1989, LDA St AFT 1975-; CEC 1988-; PVA 1980-; *office:* Boulevard Elem Schl ee Rd Cleveland OH 44118

, LINDA STEINER, Third Grade Teacher; *b:* Summit, NJ; *m:* D.; *ed:* Gordon Inst (BS) Elem Ed 1970; 23 Grad Credits Kean Coll; Credits Ithaca Coll; 3 Grad Credits Inst of Children's Lit; *cr:* Union d of Ed Elem Tchr 1971-; *ai:* NEA 1971-; *office:* Battle Hill Elem 00 Killian Pl Union NJ 07083

E, WENDY MALKOFF, Assoc Prof in Med Lab Tech; *b:* town, OH; *m:* Charles; *c:* Jonathan, Jeffrey, Seth; *ed:* Case Western e Univ (BS) Medical Tech 1973; Thomas Jefferson Univ (MS) al Microbiology 1977; Temple Univ (EDD) Hlth Ed 1994; *cr:* s Jefferson Univ Instr 5 Yrs; Comm Coll of Philadelphia Assoc Prof *ai:* MLT Prgm Dir; Tech Prep Curr comm; Curr Facilitating Team; Soc Clinical Lab Sci 1982-; *office:* Community Coll Of Philadelphia pring Garden St Philadelphia PA 19130

ENTHAL, TATIANA S., Russian & Spanish Teacher; *b:* Moscow, *m:* Mark Indursky; *c:* Leonid Indursky; *ed:* Moscow St Univ (BA) BA) 1972; Towson St Univ Span 16 Cred Hrs; *cr:* Schl #15 Moscow 964-89; Roland Park Cntry Schl Tchr 1990-; *ai:* Model UN Club Educ Issues & Hum Relations Day Comms; ACTR 1991-; Slavic Soc; HATSP; MD Intl Div Summerjob Interpretour; Articles Pub.*

I, THOMAS DANIEL, Science Teacher; *b:* Brooklyn, NY; *m:* ; *c:* Scott, Sean, Thomas, Kristen; *ed:* St Francis Coll (BS) Bio 1963; 0 Credits SUNY Oswebo, 15 Credits Adelphi Univ, 15 Credits a Univ, 18 Credits Brooklyn Coll; *cr:* Bishop Ford HS Sci Tchr 5; John F. Kennedy HS Sci Tchr 1965-; *ai:* Sci Rsrch Club Adv, ; Sr Awds, NHS Comms; NYSSTA 1965-; BMUST 1965-, Prof of rch Assoc Brookhaven Labs; NSF Grant Rsrch Brookhaven Labs; NYS Bio Regents Exam; Articles Pub; *office:* John F Kennedy HS ellmore Ave Bellmore NY 11710*

KOSKY, JAMES A., Chem Tchr & Sci Dept Chprsn; *b:* Carnegie, Sally Miller; *c:* Derek, Robert, Leigh Anne Tropek; *ed:* Slippery t Univ (BSEd) Chem 1965; Antioch Coll (MST) Sci Tchng 1971; f Pittsburg, Penn St Univ, IN Univ of PA, Hope Coll 3 Credit Hrs *r:* South Fayette Twp Schl Dist Sci Chem & Physics Tchr 1965-70; ers Valley Schl Dist Chem Tchr, Dept Chm 1970-; *ai:* Sci orative; Amer Chemical Soc; Sci Bowl Coach; NEA 1965-; AFT Free & Accepted Manson of PA 1972-, WM 1995; Amer Chemical 76-; *office:* Chartiers Valley H S 50 Thoms Run Rd Bridgeville PA

T, BESS, Eighth Grade English Teacher; *b:* Presque Isle, ME; *ed:* astern Univ (BS) Educl Eng 1973; Boston Univ (MEd) Admin s Dev & Analysis 1981; *cr:* Leominster HS Eng Tchr 1973-81; Dame Prepatory Schl Eng Tchr 1982-83; Hawthorne Brook MS Eng 983-; *ai:* Stu Cncl, Yrbk, Drama Club Adv; Tchr Advisory Comm; v; Schl Based Mngmt; Curr Coord Comm; Prof Dev; Portfolio; Prof eering Comm; Inner Odyssey Wrtng Wrkshp Tchr; Mem of Writers Tchr Poets; Phi Delta Kappa 1988-, Past Montachusett Chapter *office:* N Middlesex Regnl Schl Dist 23 Main St Townsend MA

TZER, OTTO,JR., Continuing Education Teacher; *b:* Goliad, TX; h Ann Koenders; *c:* Anne Marie Bennett, Daniel James, Thomas el, Matthew Clemens, Eric Anthony; *ed:* TX A&M Univ (BS) ial Arts 1959, (MS) Scndry Ed Admin 1963; 6 Addl Hrs at Univ of ddl 60 Plus Hrs Beyond Masters; *cr:* Killeen ISD HS Industrial Arts 959-64; Gates-Chili Cntrl Schl Dist MS Tech Tchr 1964-94, ning Ed Tchr & Small Engine Repair Tchr 1966-; *ai:* NY St Tchrs 964-; Intnl Tech Educators Assn 1980-; Rochester Amateur Radio 965-, Pres, Life Membership Awd; Amer Radio Relay League 1970-, em Awd; Rochester Theater Organ Soc 1980-, Restoration Crew; llog Fnd for Prospective Admins Stud Grant Prgm Entitled Fnds in Admin; *home:* 95 Mariposa Dr Rochester NY 14624*

TONE, JANE MARIE, English Teacher; *b:* Corry, PA; *m:* Rodney *ed:* Edinboro Univ (MED) Rdng Specialist 1980; Cedarville Coll Comms 1973; Working Toward PHD Rhetoric, Linguistics Indiana f PA; Fellow Northwestern PA Writing Project 1986; *cr:* Baptist HS hr 1973-75; Bethel Chrstn Schl Eng Tchr 1975-78; North East HS hr 1979-; *ai:* Quill & Scroll, Newspaper, Yrbk, Lit Magazine Adv; Coach; PA Schl Press Assn 1979-, St Pres, Outstdng Ldrshp; estern PA Cncl Tchrs of Eng 1980-, Cncl VP; PA Cncl Tchrs of Eng St Convention Chair; Exch Club of North East 1985-, Pres Elect; East Comm Fair 1979-, Fair Photographer; Erie Civic Music Assn Bd of Dirs; Northwestern PA Writing Project; Numerous Articles; te Place Newsletter; *office:* North East HS 1901 Freeport Rd North A 16428*

D, NATHAN SAMUEL, English Teacher; *b:* Detroit, MI; *m:* Susan sky; *c:* Jamie, Michael, Joshua; *ed:* St Univ of NY at Stony Brook Eng 1969; NY Univ (MA) Eng Ed 1974; St Univ of NY at Stony (MA) Applied Sociology 1980; 30 Addl Grad Credit Hrs Eng, Ed, , etc; *cr:* Cook Cty Schl Dist 218 Eng Tchr 1969-71; Syosset HS hr 1971-80; H. B. Thompson JHS Eng Tchr 1980-81; Syosset HS hr 1981-; *ai:* Faculty Adv-Martin Luther King Club; Former Faculty t/Art Magazine; AFT 1971-; NCTE 1991-; A.S.C.D.(Assoc for Supv Dev) 1994; Wrote Tchr's Guides for CBS Television Rdng Prgm; lly Invited Speaker (to Present Wkshps) at CSPA Natl Conf; ed in "Writing to Win"; *office:* Syosset H S Southwoods Rd Syosset 791

DMAN, KENNETH P., Social Studies Teacher & Supvr; *b:* New ity, NY; *ed:* Rutgers Coll (AB) His 1972; Rutgers Univ (EdM) Ed 1976; 38 Credits toward Doctorate; *cr:* Sayreville HS Tchr 4; Highstown HS Soc Stud Supvr 1984-; *ai:* NJ Cncl for Soc Stud Amer Soc Curric Dev 1984-; NASSP 1984-; Prin & Supvr Assn Natl Cncl for His Ed; Recreation Coach 1985-; Recreation ssion 1994-, Commissioner; Phi Beta Kappa; Douglas Coll Tchr ition; *office:* Hightstown HS Leshin Ln Hightstown NJ 08520

DMAN, LINDA S., Mathematics Teacher; *b:* Watertown, NY; *m:* III; *c:* Brycelyn Marie; *ed:* SUNY at Potsdam (BA) Math 1971; Upper Division at Utica Marcy Cmptr Sci Masters Prgm; *cr:* rd MS Math Tchr 1971-72; Holland Patent MS Math Tchr 1972-84; Free Acad Math Tchr 1984-; *ai:* Girl's Bsktbl, Field Hockey, Vlybl, Parents Support Group; Gifted, Talented, Ed Excl, Policy Comms; Holland Patent Girls Swim Team, Pittsford Syncronized Swimming; YSUT 1971-; Rome Tchrs Assn 1971-, Treas, Negotiations Chprsn; Theatre Parents Support Group 1987-; *office:* Rome Free Acad 500 t Rome NY 13440*

DMAN, NANCY (SAYWARD), Fourth Grade Teacher; *b:* Newport, James S.; *c:* Matthew, Christopher; *ed:* Bridgewater St Coll (BS) Elem Ed 1970; 18 Addl Hrs; Attending Cambridge Coll; *cr:* Belisle Elem Schl 4th Grd Tchr 1970-78; Fowler Elem Schl 4th Grd Tchr 1978-; *ai:* Fall River Ed Assn, MA Tchrs Assn, NEA 1970-; Elem Tchr of Yr 1990-91; *home:* 658 New Boston Rd Fall River MA 02720

BOARDWAY, MARION FOX, Mathematics Teacher; *b:* Gloversville, NY; *m:* Paul; *c:* Kristine, Scott; *ed:* SUNY at Oneonta (BS) Elem Ed with Early Scndry 1968; SUNY at Albany (MS) 7th-12th Grd Math Ed 1973; *cr:* Estee Jr HS Math Tchr 1968-72; Gloversville HS Math Tchr 1972-; *ai:* AFT & NEA 1968-; NYSUT 1968-; AMTNYS 1968-, Cty Chair; *office:* Gloversville HS Ext Lincoln St Gloversville NY 12078

BOATMAN, DWIGHT, Peer Mediation Teacher; *b:* Chicago, IL; *m:* Sandra C. Coleman; *c:* Bianka, Esther Lorrie Clayton; *ed:* Northern VA Comm Coll (AAS) Bus Mngmt 1980; Marymount Univ (BBA) Bus Admin 1982; Bowie Univ Guid, Cnslng 9 Credit Hrs; *cr:* Forte Foote Elem Schl Sub Tchr 1993-94; Potomac HS Conflict Resolution, Peer Mediation Tchr 1994-; *ai:* Akido; Asst Bsbl coach 1995; NEA 1994-; NFBPA 1989-; Big Brothers Natl 1996; US Marine Corps 20 Yrs Active Duty; Numerous Unit, Personal Awds & Commendations; *office:* Potomac HS 5211 Boydell Ave Oxon Hill MD 20745

BOBALA, CHESTER PETER,JR., Guidance Counselor; *b:* Springfield, MA; *m:* Kathryn Jagadowski; *c:* Robert, Doreen; *ed:* Morehead St Univ (BA) Soc Sci 1970; Westfield St Coll (MA) Ed 1980; 30 Addl Hrs; *cr:* Barry Elem 5-6 Grd Classroom Tchr 1970-78; Szetela Elem 5-6 Grd Classroom 1970-78; Fairview Mem Elem 5-6 Grd Classroom Tchr 1970-78; Chicopee Comp HS Spec Ed Voc Skills Tchr 1978-82; Bellamy MS Sci Tchr 1982-94, Guid Cnslr 2 Yrs; *ai:* Steering Comm St MS Systemic Change; West MA Pers, Guid Assn 1994-; NEA, MA Tchrs Assn 1970-; Chic Ed Assn, VP 4 Yrs; Chicopee Bd of Lib Trustees 1976-92; Boys, Girls Soccer, Ice Hockey, Girls Bsktbl Past HS Coach; *office:* Bellamy MS 314 Pendleton Ave Chicopee MA 01020

BOBEL, JOSEPH,JR., Seventh & Eighth Grade Teacher; *b:* Elizabeth, NJ; *m:* Jane Williams; *c:* Marisa, Jaclyn; *ed:* Kean Coll of NJ (BA) Elem Ed 1976, (MA) Rdng Specialization 1981; *cr:* Nathan Hale Schl 4th Grd Tchr 1976-80; Columbus Schl Supplemental Instr 1980-84; Cleveland Schl Supplemental Instr 1980-84; Columbus Schl 5th-6th Grd Tchr 1984-91, 7th-8th Grd Tchr 1991-; *ai:* Stu Cncl Adv; Food Drive Coord; 7th-8th Grd Bsktbl Coach; NEA, NJEA 1976-; Iselin Ath Assn 1986-; Woodbridge Bd of Ed 1994-, Civilian Vol; NJ Govenors Tchr Recogition Awd 1992; Eisenhower Grant 1992; Tchr of Yr 1995; *office:* Columbus Schl 149 Roosevelt Ave Carteret NJ 07008

BOBISH, DEBRA MCDONALD, Reading & English Teacher; *b:* Sharon, PA; *m:* Gregory Michael; *ed:* Edinboro Univ (BS) Elem Ed 1974; Slippery Rock Univ (MED) Ed 1981; Rdng Specialist Cert 1981; Working on Cert in Religion Through Diocese of Erie as Youth Catechist 18 Hrs; *cr:* James W Parker MS Rdng Tchr 1974-77; Reynolds HS Stud Skills Tchr 1977-78; Reynolds, Hermitage & Farrell Schl Dists Long & Short Term Sub Tchr 1978-86; Monsignor Geno J Monti Schl Rdng & Eng Tchr 1986-; *ai:* Drug Task Force; Newspaper Adv; Veterans Day Jump Rope for Heart Chm; Pub Relations Dir; NCEA 1986-; IRA 1978-; Smithsonian Assoc 1990-; Supervision & Curr Dev Assoc 1980-; Saint Ann Parish Cncl 1994-; Pro-life 1995-; Whos Who in Amer Ed; Outstanding Young Women of Amer; *home:* 56 Shenango Blvd Farrell PA 16121*

BOBNAK, MARSHA CORE, Choral Music Teacher; *b:* Martins Ferry, OH; *m:* George S.; *ed:* Bethany Coll (BA) Music 1981; Westminster Choir Coll (MM) Choral Conducting 1992; *cr:* Drexel Hill MS General & Choral Music Tchr 1983-88; Haverford HS Choral Music Tchr 1987-; *ai:* Concert Chorale; HS Chamber Singers; Conductor 4th-5th Grd All Dist Chorus & Vocal Coaching for PMEA Dist; Regnl, St Choral Festvials; MENC & PMEA 1987-; ACDA 1994-; Elsie Hillman Fellowship Westminster Choir Coll; Selected for PiKappa Lamda Music Acad Soc by Westminster Fac; Grad from Westminster with Distinction; *office:* Haverford HS 200 Mill Rd Havertown PA 19083*

BOBROFF, SANDRA RAHL, English Teacher & Dean; *b:* Greensburg, PA; *ed:* Temple Univ (MS) Cnslng Therapy 1980, (BS) Eng, Comm; Addl 60 Credit Hrs Sec Ed; *cr:* West Phila HS Tchr 1980-; West Phila HS Dean of Discipline 1990-; *ai:* NHS Adv; Phila Fed of Tchrs 1980-, Women in Ed 1985; ASCD 1995-.*

BOBST, CYNTHIA WOJCIK, Third Grade Teacher; *b:* Bristol, PA; *m:* Gerald Dennis Jr.; *ed:* Shippensburg Univ (BS) Ed 1981; Permanent Cert in Rel Archdiocese of Philadelphia; *cr:* St Thomas Aquinas Tchr 1981-, Dir of Rel Ed 1992-; *ai:* Tch CCD; Church Usher; Tutor Children with Educl Difficulties; Parish Cncl 1994- Cncl Mem; *office:* St Thomas Aquinas Schl Walnut Ave Bristol Pike Croydon Manor PA 19021

BOBWICK, SUSAN B. LIBER, Teacher; *b:* Toledo, OH; *m:* Morton; *c:* Marla, Michelle; *ed:* Univ of WI (BS) Elem Ed 1963; Boston Univ (MED) Elem Ed 1964; Post Grad 22 Credit Hrs; *cr:* Burlington Schls 4th Grd Tchr 1965; Montgomery Cty Schls 6th Grd Tchr 1966; Ottawa Hills Schls LDBD Tutor 1978-85; Sylvania Schls 7th, 8th Grd Eng Tchr 1985-; *ai:* Power of the Pen Coach; NEA; SEA 1985-; Jewish Fed of Toledo 1995-, ESL Tutor; *office:* Sylvana Schools 5334 Whiteford Rd Sylvania OH 43560*

BOBY, CHARLES ANTHONY, 8th Grd Earth Science Teacher; *b:* Ft Bragg, NC; *m:* Barbara Ann Gasper; *c:* Dylan, Corey; *ed:* CA univ of PA (BS) Earth Sci 1968, Penn St (MS) Earth Sci 1974; 12 Credits Comp Sci; *cr:* Norwin Schl Dist Tchr 1969-; *ai:* Comp Club; NEA 1969-; *home:* 100 Evanstown Rd Irwin PA 15642

BOCCARDY, STEVEN JOHN, HS Civics Teacher; *b:* Athol, MA; *ed:* Univ of MA (BA) Psych & Eng 1975, (MED) Instructional Ldrshp 1992; *cr:* LS Starren Co Salesman 1978-85; Athol HS Tchr 1987; Murdock MS HS Tchr 1989-; *ai:* Future Tchrs of Amer Club, Model Congress, Model UN & Class Adv; Stu Tchr Mentor; NEA 1987-; Winchendon Tchrs Assn 1989-; Athol Bird & Nature Club 1994-; Winchendon Rod & Gun Club 1989 -; *office:* Murdock Mid Sr HS 3 Memorial Dr Winchendon MA 01475*

BOCCHINO, ALAN JOHN, 6th Grade Science Teacher; *b:* Morristown, NJ; *m:* Joan Winnicki; *c:* Lauren M., Andrew A.; *ed:* Trenton St Coll (BS) Elem Ed 1972; William Paterson Coll (MED) Educl Media 1983; *cr:* Black River MS 6th Grd Sci Tchr 1972-73; Marie V. Duffy Elem Schl 5th Grd Tchr 1974-94; Alfred MacKinnon MS 6th Grd Sci Tchr 1994-; *ai:* 6th Grd Class, Media Club Adv; Schl Curr Cncl; Tech Comm; NEA, NJ Educl Assn 1972-; NSTA, NJ Sci Tchrs Assn 1995-; Dover Renaissance 1985-; Vols Bsktbl 1995-; CYO Bsktbl 1990-; Governor's Tchr Recognition Prgm 1990; Sci Excl Rudolph Awd 1991, 1994; Merck Summer Sci Inst 1992; *office:* Alfred MacKinnon MS 137 E Central Ave Wharton NJ 07885

BOCHENEK, PAUL BARTON, Teacher; *b:* Newark, NJ; *c:* Jason, Randy; *cr:* Alexander Hamilton Jr HS Tchr 1969-78; Elizabeth HS Tchr 1978-; *office:* Elizabeth HS 600 Pearl St Elizabeth NJ 07202*

BOCHETTE, DAVID E., Health, First Aid & PE Teacher; *b:* Troy, NY; *m:* Bernardine Ann Gully; *c:* Anthony, Nicholas; *ed:* Brockport St Coll (BS) PE, Hlth 1973; Attnd Russell Sage Coll Hlth; *cr:* Ctr of Disabled Dir PE 1973-76; St Anthonys Schl PE, Sci Tchr 1976-77; Lansingburgh Cntrl Schl Hlth, PE Tchr 1977-; Hudson Vly CC Schl Hlth, PE Tchr 1992-; *ai:* Head Ftbl Hudson Vly CC, Ftbl, Bsbl, Bsktbl, Wrestling Coach; Class, Ski Club Adv; AFT, NYSUT 1977-; Natl Ftbl Coaches 1988-; Amer Ftbl Coaches 1990-; *home:* 15 E Schaghticoke Rd Schaghticoke NY 12154

BOCKSTEIN, SHERRY MAE, Second Grade Teacher; *b:* New York, NY; *m:* Richard; *c:* Staci, Joy; *ed:* Hunter Coll (BA) Sociology 1966; Queens Coll (MS) Ed 1970; *cr:* PS 198M 3rd Grd Tchr 1966-68; IS 231 8th Grd Sci & Music Tchr 1978; PS 134Q 2nd & 3rd Grd Tchr 1978-80; PS 131Q 2nd Grd Tchr 1980-; *ai:* UFT 1966-; *office:* PS 131 Queens 172nd St & 84th Ave Jamaica NY 11432

BODAMER, TIMOTHY BAUN, Band Director; *b:* Erie, PA; *m:* Jill Marie Warner; *ed:* Edinboro Univ (BA) Music Ed 1991; *cr:* LaPlata HS Band Dir 1991-; *ai:* Asst Girls Var Bsktbl Coach; Southern MD Concert Band 1995-, Conductor; Charles Cty Arts Alliance Grant; *office:* La Plata HS PO Box 790 Radio Station Rd La Plata MD 20646

BODDERY, SARA COLEMAN, Science Teacher; *b:* Waco, TX; *m:* Simon Jr.; *c:* Sherry Aglietti, Scott; *ed:* OH St Univ (BS) Bio, Ed 1967; SUNY at Brockport (MS) Bio; 4 Credit Hrs Univ of Rochester; *cr:* Greece Olympia HS Bio, IPS Tchr 1967-73; Holy Cross Schl Sci Tchr 1983-87; Greece Athena MS Life Sci Tchr 1987-88; Greece Athena HS Regents Bio, Gen bio, Horticulture Tchr 1988-; *ai:* Class, Bio Club Adv; Peer Mediation Coach, Trainer; Staff Dev, Classroom Mngmt Trainer; NEA, Greece Tchrs Assn 1987-; NYSTA 1990-; *office:* Greece Athena HS 800 Long Pond Rd Rochester NY 14612*

BODENBERG, LYNN ALAN, English Teacher; *b:* Greensburg, IN; *m:* Judith Ann Davis; *c:* Jennifer, Rachel, Scott; *ed:* Harrisburg Area Comm Coll (AA) Scndry Ed, Comm 1972; Mansfield Univ (BS) Scndry Ed, Comm 1974; Kutztown Univ (MA) Eng Lit 1987; Attnd Temple Univ, Kutztown Univ; *cr:* Blue Mountain HS Eng Tchr 1977-78; Metropolitan Life Insurance Instr 1978-81; Pottsville Area HS Eng Tchr 1981-; *ai:* PSEA, NEA 1981-, Rep; NCTE 1987-; Grace E. C. Church Bd 1989-, Supt; Alpha Psi Omega 1973-; PA Theaterworks 1988-, Dir; *office:* Pottsville Area HS 16th St & Elk Ave Pottsville PA 17901*

BODENLOS, GAIL PATRICIA, Social Studies Teacher; *b:* Rockaway Beach, NY; *ed:* St Johns Univ (BS) 7-12 Soc Stud Ed 1963, (MS) Scndry Ed 1968; Addl 30 Credits; *cr:* H. Frank Carey HS Soc Stud Tchr 1963-; *ai:* Sunshine Comm; NEA 1975-; Tchr of Yr NHS, PTSA Founder's Day Awd; Yrbk Dedication; *office:* H Frank Carey HS 230 Poppy Ave Franklin Square NY 11010

BODNAR, LINDA, 3rd Grade Teacher; *b:* Rahway, NJ; *ed:* Kean Coll of NJ (BA) Elem Ed, Rdng 1975; *cr:* Cleveland Schl Tchrs Aide 1977; Columbus Schl Tchr 1977-; *ai:* NEA, MCEA, CEA 1977-; St Demetrius Church; Governor's Tchr Recognition Awd; *office:* Columbus Schl 149 Roosevelt Ave Carteret NJ 07008

BODNOVICH, THOMAS A., Information Systems Professor; *b:* Youngstown, OH; *ed:* Youngstown St Univ (BS) Cmptr Sci 1979; OH St Univ (MS) Cmptr, Info Sci 1981; Youngstown St Univ (MBA) Mngmt 1995; Working Toward PhD in Mngmt Information Systems at Kent St Univ; *cr:* IBM Systems Programmer 1979-81; Republic Steel Co Lead Appliations Programmer 1981-82; Youngstown St Univ Cmptr Systems Analyst 1982-88; Youngstown St Univ Information Systems Prof 1988-; *ai:* Assn for Systems Mngmt, Trumbull Cty Information Systems Prgm Adv; ASM, OASI 1988-, ACM 1986-; OH St Univ Flwshp; Rsrch Grant; Soc for Advancement of IS Distngd Paper Awd 1996; Articles Pub; *office:* Youngstown St Univ 410 Wick Ave Youngstown OH 44555

BOEDICKER, LAURIE BELLEW, Former Physics & Math Teacher; *ed:* Wittenberg Univ (BA) Physics 1987; Post Grad Stud Akron Univ, Kent St Univ; *cr:* Springfield HS Physics, Math Tchr 1988-94; *ai:* Math Dept Chprsn; SECO; AAPT; NASTS; Jennings Scholar; Inst for Math & Cmptr Sci Ed Participant.

BOEHLER, CYNTHIA LOU, Chem & Applied Science Instr; *b:* Lebanon, PA; *ed:* Lebanon Vly Coll (BS) Chem 1976, (BA) Ger 1976; Cmptrs in Chem, Numerous Cmptr Courses; Criminal Law, Investigation; Criminalistics; Cooperative Learning; Project Teach; Writing Process; Beginning, Int, Adv Sign Lang; *cr:* Cumberland Vly HS Chem Instr 1978-79; Eastern Lebanon Co HS Chem, App Sci Instr 1979-, Home Bound Instr 1979-; Eastern Lebanon Co MS 7th Grd Sci Tchr 1995-; *ai:* Sci of Kids Club; Intensive Scheduling Comm; Tennis IM; Field Hockey oach 1988-95; PSEA, NEA 1979-; NSTA 1985-; PIAA 1991-; Amer Red Cross 1983-, Instr; US Field Hockey 1972-, Assn Pres, Regnl Treas; Leb Co Humane Soc 1990-, Bd Mem; Sexual Assault Resource 1985-, Cnslr; Leb-Lanc Hockey, Leb0Lanc Track, Field 1990-; Xerox Schlsp Acad Excl; Svc Awd Amer Red Cross 10 Yr; *office:* Eastern Lebanon Co Sr HS 180 Elco Dr Myerstown PA 17067*

BOEHM, CHRISTOPHER SCOTT, Social Studies Teacher; *b:* Cleveland, OH; *m:* Sandra; *c:* Bradley, Eric, Kerry; *ed:* Kent St Univ (BS) Comp Soc Stud 1977; Cleveland St (MA) Curr, Instruction 1984; *cr:* North Royalton HS Tchr 1978-; *ai:* NEA, OEA, NREA 1978-; Medina Yth Bsbl Assn 1994-, Dir of Coaches; *office:* North Royalton HS 14713 Ridge Rd North Royalton OH 44133

BOEHMER, LINDA M., Teacher of the Hearing Imprd; *b:* Shamokin, PA; *m:* Robert C.; *c:* Christopher; *ed:* Bloomsburg Univ (BA) Elem Ed 1977, (MS) Ed of the Hearing Impaired 1978; Kutztown Univ 12 Credit Hrs in Rdng; Lehigh Univ Elem Prin Cert; *cr:* Carbon-Lehigh IU 21 Tchr of the Hearing Impaired 1978-; *ai:* NEA, PSEA & CLEA 1978-; Ag Bell Assn for the Deaf; PESDHH 1994-; *office:* Carbon Lehigh Intrmdt Unit 21 200 Orchard Rd Schnecksville PA 18078

BOEHMLER, GEORGE CHARLES, Chemistry Teacher; *b:* Philadelphia, PA; *w:* Carol Anne (dec); *c:* Erick, Joel; *ed:* West Chester Univ (BS) Chem, Math 1960; Villanova Univ (MS) Chem 1963; *cr:* Current Position 34 Yrs; *ai:* Yrbk; MEA, NJEA, NEA 1962-; *office:* Moorestown HS 350 Bridgeboro Rd Moorestown NJ 08057

BOEHNE, GREGG W., Gifted & English Teacher; *b:* Nyack, NY; *m:* Ruth Munch; *c:* Kara, Katie; *ed:* Dickinson Coll (BA) Eng 1970; Shippensburg Unvi (MED) Eng 1972; Attnd Cath Univ, Draexel Univ, Shippenburg Univ; *cr:* Hanover Pub Schl Dist Gifted, Eng Tchr 1970-; *ai:* NEA, PA St Ed Assn, Hanover Ed Assn 1970-; PA Assn for Gifted Ed 1983-; Adams-Hanover Cnslng Svcs Bd 1988-, Sec; Girl Scouts of Amer 1985-; EIP&P Investment Group 1988-, Pres; *office:* Hanover HS 401 Moul Ave Hanover PA 17331

BOEHNER, ELEANOR A., Mathematics Dept Chprsn & Tchr; *b:* Philadelphia, PA; *ed:* Ursinus Coll (BS) Math 1963; Temple Univ (MED) Educl Admin 1985; Addl 30 Credits Beyond Masters Ed Admin, 21 Post Grad Credits Math Univ of NC; *cr:* Methacton HS Math Tchr 1963-, Math Dept Chprsn 1978-79, 1995-; *ai:* Environmental, Red Cross Clubs; Inservice Curr Comm; NEA, PSEA 1963-; NCTM 1973-; PA Cncl of Tchrs of Math 1980-; ATMOPAV 1975-; Red Cross Bd of Dir 1970-78; Red Cross Vol 1965-; Woodrow Wilson Natl Flwshp Inst; NSF Hewlett-Packard Graphing Calculator Grant; NSF Grant for Lead Tchrs in Calculus & Pre-Calculus Sic, Math; Outstdng Math Tchr of Montgomery Cty 1996; *office:* Methacton HS 1001 Kriebel Mill Rd Norristown PA 19408

BOEHNKE, CHARLES R., Math Teacher; *b:* Grand Island, NE; *m:* Cynthia; *c:* Chad, Mark, Jill; *ed:* Doawe Coll at Crete (BA) Psych 1969; SUNY Brockport 30 Credit Hrs; *cr:* Waterloo Jr HS Math Tchr 1971-92; Waterloo HS Math Tchr 1992-; *ai:* Waterloo Ed Assn 1971-; NY Ed Assn, NEA 1985-; Waterloo Zoning Bd of Appeals 1986-, Chm; US Army Reserve 1969-, Command Sergent Major; *office:* Waterloo HS Center St Waterloo NY 13165

BOEHNLEIN, CAROLYN JOYCE (BOLEK), Jr High Math Teacher; *b:* Cleveland, OH; *m:* Richard John; *c:* Lance; *ed:* St John Coll of Cleveland (BSE) Ed 1965; Kent St UNiv 3 Hrs Ed; *cr:* St Charles Borremeo 6th Grd Tchr 1965-67; Pleasantvie Elem Schl 5th Grd Tchr 1967-77; St Thomas More Jr HS Math Tchr 1986-; *ai:* Lit, Transforation, Social Comms; NEA 1967-77; NCEA 1986-; Kappa Gamma Pi 1965-; St Honorary, Life Mbrshp; *office:* Saint Thomas More Schl 4180 N Amber Dr Brooklyn OH 44144*

BOEHR, JUDITH HERRING, Fourth Grade Teacher; *b:* Brookline, MA; *m:* Gary; *c:* Jonathan, Rachel; *ed:* Boston Univ (BA) His, Ed 1967; Columbia Univ (MA) Elem Ed 1968; *cr:* PS 125 6th Grd Tchr 1968-73; Bardonia Schl 3rd, 6th Grd Tchr 1973-80; Woodglen Schl 5th Grd Tchr 1981-82; Congers Schl 3rd, 4th Grd Tchr 1985-; *ai:* Curr Redesign, Writing Curr, Advy Comms; Schoolwide Interdisciplinary Project Theme of Harmony; Mentor New Tchrs; AFT; NYSUT; Clarkstown TA; Congregation Sons of Israel 1985-, Bd Trustees, Chair Soc Action Comm, Co-Chair Caring Comm; Woodlands Comm Temple 1976-85, Bd Trustees, Ritual Comm; Selected to be Part of Grant Awded for Purpose Mentoring New Tchrs, Supervising Stu Tchrs; *office:* Congers Elem Schl 9 Lake Rd W Congers NY 10920*

BOEPPLE, GALE KLEBOSIS, Math Teacher & Dept Chairman; *b:* Irvington, NJ; *m:* Todd; *ed:* Montclair St Coll (BA) Math 1971, (MA) Math Ed 1972; 30 Addl Post Grad Hrs; *cr:* Coll HS OF Montclair Grad Asst, Math Tchr 1971-72; Scotch Plains-Fanwood HS Math Tchr 1972-76; Madison HS Math Tchr 1976-, Dept Chair 1985-; *ai:* Fall Drama, Spring Musical Productions Dirs; Dist Math Curr Comm; NEA, NJEA 1972-; NCTM; AMTNJ; Morris Cty Comm Theatre 1972-, Actress, Best Supporting Actress 1982-83; Tchr Recognition Prgm; Tchr of Yr 1986; Barrett-Caprip Tchng Award 1994, Madison HS Stud Cncl; *office:* Madison HS 170 Ridgedale Ave Madison NJ 07940*

BOERNER, TINA MARIE (CHRISTIE), Math Teacher; *b:* Massillon, OH; *m:* Richard; *ed:* The Univ of Akron (BA) Scndry Ed 1987; Working on Masters at Ashland Univ; *cr:* Massillon City Schls Sub Math Tchr 1987; Plain Local Schls Math Tchr 1987-; *ai:* NEA 1987-; OEA 1987-; *office:* Glen Oak Career Ctr 2300 Schneider St NE Canton OH 44721

BOESEL, L. JAN, English Teacher; *b:* Brady, TX; *m:* Donald E.; *c:* Amber, Ashley; *ed:* Southern Nazarene Univ (BA) Eng 1968; *cr:* Buhler HS Eng Grd 10 Tchr 1968-1969; Crown Point HS Eng Grd 11 Tchr 1969-72; Dayton Chrstn HS Eng Grd Tchr 1992-; *ai:* NCTE 1994-; *office:* Dayton Christian HS 325 Homewood Ave Dayton OH 45405

BOESL, LINDA LEE, 9th-12th Grade English Tchr; *b:* Newark, OH; *m:* Jerome Louis; *c:* Christopher Cook, Amanda Sauter, Jennifer Cook; *ed:* Nazareth Coll (BA) Eng 1980, (MS) Ed 1982; Univ of Rochester (MA) Eng 1992; *cr:* St Stephens Elem Schl Second Grd Tchr 1967-68; Dir of Rel Ed Rochester Area Churches 1971-1978; BOCES of Rochester Jr High Tchr 1977-80; Our Lady of Mercy HS 1980-; *ai:* Bluestockings, Parent Group Bluestockins for Moms, Mercedes Staff Adv; NCTE 1985-; NYSEC 1995-; First Bapt of Penfield Chr Ed; AAUW 1995-; Ceirls, Inc 1995-; Inspirational Tchr Awd by Nazareth Coll; Harvard-Radcliff Awd for Innovative Tchng; Educator of Excl NYSEC 1995; Tchr of the Yr at Merry HS; Tchr Spon for NY St 1st Place Winner of NYS Cncl for Hum; *home:* 7 Vixen Run Rochester NY 14625*

BOGACZYK, JAMES JOSEPH, Math Tchr & Dean of Students; *b:* Covington, PA; *m:* Glenda Mae Bell; *c:* Carol Young, Debra Everett, Dennis, Philip, James II; *ed:* Mansfield St Tchrs Coll (BS) Math, Sci 1961; 6 Addl Credits; Elmira Coll 15 Credits; Millersville St 3 Credits; *cr:* USAF Navagator, Radar Intercept Ofcr 1954-58; Elmira Schl Dist Math Tchr 1961-65; Self Employed Beverage Distributor 1959-76; Real Estate Dev, Salesman 1977-80; North Penn HS Math Tchr 1980-; *ai:* Stu Cncl Adv; Stu Act Dir; Jr High Bsktbl Coach; PSEA, NEA 1980-; Phi Delta Kappa 1987-; Kiwanis 1974-75, Pres 1985-86; Blossburg Borough Cncl 1978-, Pres 14 Yrs; Blossburg Recreation Bd 1978-, Pres 4 Yrs; Blossburg Improvement Comm 1976-, Pres 16 Yrs; Southern Tioga Schl Dist Tchr of Yr 1993-94; *office:* North Penn HS 300 Morris St Blossburg PA 16912

BOGAN, CLAUD E., Air Force JROTC Teacher; *b:* Acworth, TX; *m:* Maisley M. Minors; *c:* Jean A. Fowler; *ed:* Univ of West FL (BA) Psych-Magna Cum Laude 1975, (MA) Psych 1982; 23 Post-Grad Credit Hrs; *cr:* US Air Force Supervisory 1955-86; Air Force Ldrshp Acad Human Relations in Mngmt Instr 1972-79; City Colls of Chicago Part-time Instr 1981-83; Potomac HS AFJROTC Instr 1986-; *ai:* Golf Coach; AFJROTC Drill Team & Color Guard Spon; Clinton View Homeowners Assn 1986-, Pres; Parents, Stdnts, Tchrs Assn 1986-; NW FL Mental Hlth Ctr 1976-79, Bd of Dirs; *office:* Potomac HS 5211 Boydell Ave Oxon Hill MD 20745

BOGAN, LEONARD, English Teacher; *b:* Teaneck, NJ; *m:* Linda Schwarzbach; *c:* Rachel, Daniel; *ed:* Univ of PA (BS) Acctng 1961; Columbia Tchrs Coll (MA) Eng 1963; *cr:* Ben Franklin MS Eng Tchr 1963-; *ai:* NJEA, NEA, TTEA 1963-; *office:* Benjamin Franklin MS 1315 Taft Rd Teaneck NJ 07666

BOGART, MAYNARD WILLIAM, Secondary Mathematics Teacher; *b:* Williamsport, PA; *m:* Glenna McEwen; *c:* Crystal, Alison; *ed:* Lock Haven Univ (BS) Math 1968; PA St (ME) Math 1983; Post Grad Stud at Marywood; *cr:* Montoursville HS Algebra II & Pre-Calculus Tchr 28 Yrs; *ai:* Mentor for Tchrs; Ftbl Coach; Key Club Adv; Negotiating Team; OME-Local Tchrs Org 1985-, Treas; Lions Club 1975-; Faith UM Church 1970-, Pres, Trustees Finance Comm; Class Adv for Classes of 1975, 1981, 1988 & 1992; *office:* Montoursville Area Sr HS 100 N Arch St Montoursville PA 17754

BOGATZ, WILLIAM R., Teacher & Coach; *ed:* Oneonta St Coll (BS) Scndry Ed & Soc Stud 1974; CW Post Coll (MA) Pol Sci 1981; Grumman Data Systems Inst Prof Cert Comp Programming & Systems Analysis 1983; *cr:* Amtrak; Mepham HS Tchr; Levittown Memrl Jr HS Tchr & Coach; Wantagh Jr & Sr HS Edctr, Tutor & Coach; *ai:* Wantagh Little League Umpire; Fac Supvr of Spcl Events; Tutor Homebound Stdnts; Var Girls Track & Field Team Coach; Mepham Parent, Fac & Stu Club Mem; Founder Levittown Memrl Jr High Hlth & Fitness Club; Frost Vly Environment & Expedition Camp Fac Ldr; HS Drama & Musicals Bus Mgr; Stu Suggestion, Complaint Bd & Spcl Events Fac Supvr; Ombudsman & Outreach Pgm Coord; Spcl Tutor; Wantagh Yth Cncl; Acad of Pol Sci; Outstdng Young Men of Amer; Great Neck League of Women Voters; Oneonta St Coll Alumni Assn, Bd of Dirs; Mepham HS Alumni Assn; Book Review Writer for Social Education 1978.

BOGDAN, FRANK JOHN, Social Studies Teacher; *b:* Middletown, CT; *c:* Brett; *ed:* Cntrl Ct St Univ (BS) Soc Scis 1971, (MA) Counseling 1975; Trinity Coll VT (MA) Ed 1996; Addl 30 Plus in Ed; *cr:* Keigwin MS Soc Stud Tchr 1973-83; Aetna Life & Casualty Research Analyst & Trainer 1983-89; MS of Plainville Soc Stud Tchr 1989-; *ai:* Yrbk Adv; NEA, CEA 1989-; *office:* MS of Plainville 150 Northwest Dr Plainville CT 06062

BOGERT, JAMES R., Mathematics Teacher; *b:* Endicott, NY; *m:* Kathie F. Fischer; *c:* Keith J.; *ed:* SUNY at New Paltz (BS) Math 1964, (MS) Math Ed 1967, (CAS) Admin 1982; Colgate Univ Post Grad Math 1967-69; *cr:* John Jay HS Math Tchr 1964-72, Math Tchr in Charge 1972-83, Asst Prin 1983-85; Wappingers Schl Dist Math Tchr in Charge 1985-; *ai:* Adjunct Prof Marist Coll 1968-72; AFT, NYSUT. Wapp Conf of Tchrs; Pub Math Tchr; Colgate Fellowship; *office:* John Jay HS Rt 52 Hopewell Junction NY 12533

BOGGAN, CHERYL ANN, Fifth Grade Teacher; *b:* Syracuse, NY; *m:* Tracy Andrew Dybowski; *ed:* SUNY at Fredonia (BS) Elem Ed 1980, (MS) Elem Ed 1984; *cr:* St Francis of Assissi 2, 7 Grd Tchr 1981-82; SUNY at Fredonia Residence Hall Dir 1982-84; WV Inst of Tech Housing Admin 1984-88; West Seneca 6 Grd Tchr 1989-90; Central Schls 5 Grd Tchr 1990-97; *ai:* Shared Decision Making Team; West Seneca Tchrs Assn Bldg Rep; NYSUT, WSTA 1989-; NCTM 1996; Smithsonian Assn 1990-; Amer Museum Natural His 1994-; *office:* East Elem Schl 1415 Center Rd West Seneca NY 14224*

BOGGESS, JOSETTE TRENT, 7th & 8th Grd English Tchr; *b:* Clearfork, WV; *m:* Bryson; *c:* Vanessa; *ed:* Marietta Coll (BA) Eng-Cum Laude 1981; WV Univ (MA) Speech Comm 1989; OH Univ Addl Credits; *cr:* Belpre HS Eng Tchr 1981-82; Barlow-Vincent Elem Eng Tchr 1983-; *ai:* Drug Awareness Bldg Coord; WLEA 1983-; CEA 1992-; OCTELA 1994-; Telesis 1991-; Lifetouch Grant Awd 1993; Ashland Golden Apple Achvr Awd 1994 & 1995; OH CEA Tchr Awd 1995; US ARmy Plng for Life Awd 1995; *office:* Barlow-Vincent Elem Schl Rt 1 Vincent OH 45784*

BOGGIS, DONALD EARL,JR., Physical Education Teacher; *b:* Nashua, NH; *m:* Susan Anita Deshaies; *c:* Spencer Paul; *ed:* Plymouth St Coll (BS) Hlth, PE 1982; 200 Credit Hrs Trng Ropes Course, Experiential Ed, Project Adventure, Drug, Alcohol Ed; *cr:* Hollis HS Asst Track Coach 1982-83, 1985-86; Weare HS PE Tchr, Hlth, Head Track, Bsktbl, Soccer Coach 1984; Con Val Schl PE Tchr, Head Track, Field Coach 1986-, MS Bsktbl Coach 1987-94; *ai:* Ropes Course Coord; Chess Club Adv; Mens Track, Field Coach Con Val HS; NEA 1986-; NH Coaches Assn 1983-, Pres 1987, 15 Yr Coaches Awd; NH Coaches Assn 1993-, Exec Comm; Trng Cntr Granite St Track, Field Ofcls Assn 1995-; Spec Olympics, Vol; Articles Pub; New England Masters Javelin, Discus Champion 1994; Eastern Masters Javelin Champion 1994; USA Track, Field Level I Coach Top 20 Natl Rank in Masters Track, Field; ACEP Cert Ldr Level Coach; *office:* South Meadow Schl Rt 202 N Peterborough NH 03458*

BOGGS, BRENDA LEE (KAISER), His, Bio & Accounting Teacher; *b:* Pittsburgh, PA; *w:* James (dec); *c:* Sandra Thomas, Donald Gene, Danel Hugh; *ed:* Bapt Chrstn Coll (BA) Ed 1974; Andrew Bapt Coll (MA) Chrstn Ed 1977; Intnl Seminary DRelEd Chrstn Ed 1988; Univ of Pittsburgh, Univ of CA Undergraduate 1952-83; *cr:* Jim Boggs Real Estate Sec 1952-74; Bear Rock Construction Bookkeeper 1972-76; Mt Zion Chrstn Acad His, Bio, Accounting, Hlth Tchr 1974-; *ai:* Keystone Chrstn Ed Assn Prof Recognition Cert; Mt Zion Comm Church Doctoral Recognition 1988.

BOGGS, CHARMAINE M., 5th-6th Grade Science Teacher; *b:* Niagara Falls, NY; *m:* Bruce; *c:* Tara; *ed:* Wright St Univ (BSEd) Elem Ed 1973, (MEd) Visual Arts Ed 1986; *cr:* St Luke Schl Tchr 1973-77; Incarnation Schl Tchr 1977-78, 1980-84; Suicide Prevention Ctr Inc Educl Consultant 1985-87; Incarnation Schl Tchr 1987-; *ai:* Intermediate Dept, Substance Abuse Prevention Coord; NSTA 1994-; Safe, Drug Free Schls & Comm Advy Bd 1993-; Terrific Partners in Sci 1989-90; Top 10 Tchr 1993; Innovative Tchng Grant 1995-; Pub Project Lifesaver 1986, Natl Forum of Applied Educl Research Journal 1988-89; *office:* Incarnation Schl 45 Williamsburg Ln Centerville OH 45459*

BOGGS, LUCY MESSING, 5th & 6th Grade Teacher; *b:* Ruth, MI; *m:* David L.; *c:* John, Jason; *ed:* Siena Heights Coll (BA) Sociology, Ed 1964; 40 Credit Hrs Undergrad; 10 Addl Credit Hrs; MI St Univ 3 Grad Hrs; Loyola Univ at Chicago 6 Grad Hrs; OH St Univ & Xavier Univ 9 Grad Hrs Ed Admin; *cr:* St John 5th-8th Grd Tchr 1965-67; St Joseph Cath Schl 7th-8th Grd Tchr 1967-69; Cumberland Schl 5th-6th Grd Tchr 1969-72; St Paul Schl 5th-8th Grd Tchr 1981-; *ai:* Cath Schls Week Chair; CDEA 1981-; Jr Achvmt 1983-94, Consultant, Cooperating Tchr; *office:* St Paul Schl 61 Moss Rd Westerville OH 43082*

BOGGS, RONALD BRUCE, Health & First Aid Teacher; *b:* Carlisle, PA; *m:* Gayle Carolyn Smith; *c:* Scott C. Nicole M.; *ed:* West Chester St Coll (BS) Hlth & PE 1969; Western MA (MS) PE 1977; Certfied PA Emergency Technician; Certified PA Emergency Technician Instr; *cr:* Boiling Springs HS Hlth & PE Tchr 1969-82, Hlth & First Air Tchr 1982-; *ai:* Adv Class of 1997; NEA, PSEA & SMEA 1980-; New Bloomfield Ambulance Club 1982-, Past Pres; Commonwealth of PA 1978-; Emergency Medical Techincian; Hlth & PE Dept Chm 1970-82; *office:* South Middleton Schl Dist 4 Forge Rd Boiling Springs PA 17007

BOGGS, THEODORE ARTHUR,JR., Health & PE Teacher; *b:* Youngstown, OH; *m:* Marie Helen Ianazone; *c:* Michele Marie Wolfson; *ed:* Kent St Univ (BS) Ed 1969; Westminster Coll (MED) Admin 1972; Post Grad Stud Youngstown St Univ; *cr:* Frank Ohl MS Hlth & PE Tchr 1969-; *ai:* Frank Ohl MS Drug Coord; CPR Instr; NEA, OEA, AEA 1969-; Masonic Org 1993-, Sr Deacon; Scottish Rites Org 1993-; Frank Ohl Edctr of Yr 1989; *home:* 3226 Eldora Ave Youngstown OH 44511

BOGORAD, JOEL, Spanish & ESL Teacher; *b:* NYC, NY; *m:* Elaine Faye Stern; *c:* Lyle Andrew; *ed:* Washington Square Coll at NYU (BA) Span 1963; Brooklyn Coll (MA) Scndry Schl Span 1971; *cr:* Midwood Annex Schl Permanent Sub Span Tchr 1964; Brandeis HS Permanent Sub Span Tchr 1965; John D. Wells Jr HS Span, ESL Tchr 1965-67; Cararsie HS Span, ESL Tchr 1968-; *ai:* Peer Tutoring Prgm Master Tchr, Pvt Tutoring; YFT, AFT 1967-; Jewish Tchrs Comm Chest 1970-, Fund Raiser for Philathropic Orgs; *office:* Canarsie HS 1600 Rockaway Pky Brooklyn NY 11236

BOGOSIAN, NANCY DOBIES, 7th-8th Grd Soc Stud Teacher; *b:* Massena, NY; *m:* John M.; *c:* David, John, Stephen; *ed:* Marymount Coll (BA) His & Ed 1976; St Univ of NY at Potsdam (MS) Ed & His 1980; Addl 15 Hrs Ec; *cr:* Massena-Saint Lawrence Cntrl Sub Tchr 1976-80; Massena HS 9th-12th Grd Tchr 1985-88; Massena Jr HS 7th-8th Grd Tchr 1988-; *ai:* 85 Plus Club Adv; Nursing Home Vol Supvr; Career Day & Schl Day Planner; NYS Soc Stud Assn 1996; Massena Fed of Tchrs 1976-; Massena Womens Coll Club 1980-, All Offices Including Pres 1985; 2 Tchr Learning Ctr Grants to Build Up Historical Novel Lib & Clean Up & Repair Local Cemetery; *office:* J W Leary Jr HS 290 S Main St Massena NY 13662*

BOGOSIAN, ROBERT G., Science Teacher & Dept Head; *b:* New Britain, CT; *m:* Crystal Peterson; *c:* Alexis R., Daniel L.; *ed:* Univ of CT (BS) Bio 1977; Cntrl CT St Univ (MS) Sci Ed 1992; *cr:* Wamogo Regnl HS Sci Tchr 1984-, Sci Dept Head 1995-; *office:* Wamogo HS 98 Wamogo Rd Litchfield CT 06759

BOGUS, JOSEPH P.,JR., Director of Guid & Psych Tchr; *b:* Phoenixville, PA; *m:* Karen Marie Vaile; *c:* Matthew, Stacey; *ed:* Kutztown Univ (BS) Sec Ed Soc Stud 1972; Villanova Univ (MA) Sec Ed Guid 1976; Post Grad East Stroudsburg, Penn St; *cr:* Phoenixville Area Jr HS Soc Stud 1972-76; Phoenixville Area HS Guid, Soc Stud 1977-; *ai:* Asst HS Ftbl Coach; Scndry Space Comm; NEA, PSEA 1972-, Bldg Rep; PA Scholastic Ftbl Coaches Assn 1987-; Chris Minor Schlsp 1992-, VP, Bd of Trustees; Danny Gnias Schlsp 1993-, Mem, Bd of Trustees; *office:* Phoenixville Area HS Gay & City Line Ave Phoenixville PA 19460

BOGUSKY, JOYCE LIVINGSTON, English & Drama Teacher; *b:* New York City, NY; *m:* Joseph H.; *c:* Karen Berkenstock, William Berkenstock; *ed:* Hofstra Univ (BA) Comm 1971; East Stroudsburg Univ (MS) Rdng 1988; PA Writing Project 3 Grad Credits; *cr:* Bethlehem ASD, Liberty HS Tchr 1982-; *ai:* Lit Magazine Adv; Drama Coach; NCTE 1983-; RTA 1984-86; *office:* Liberty HS 1115 Linden St Bethlehem PA 18018

BOHAN, JAMES F., K-12th Grd Math Program Coord; *b:* Chicago, IL; *m:* Jane M. Dicke; *c:* John, Jane Ellen, Julie, Jamie; *ed:* Loyola Univ Chicago (BS) Math 1968, (MA) Math 1972; Supvr Cert 1986; *cr:* Loyola Ac 1969-80; Elein Acad Tchr, Sec, Dept Head 1980-85; Manheim Grade Math Coord 1986-; *ai:* Adj Instr of Math at Numerous Coll & IL; NCTM & PCTM 1970-; NCSM & PCSM 1986-, Outstnd 1993; ASCD & PASCD 1988-; Lions Club 1989-; Parks & Rec Bc Vice-Chair; Articles Pub in NCTM & PCTM Journals; *office:* M Twp HS Box 5134 School Rd Lancaster PA 17601*

BOHART, EDYTHE PAULINE, Quantity Foods Voc In Williamsport, PA; *c:* Amy Schmohl, Edward Jr.; *ed:* Williamspo Comm Coll (AAS) Food, Hospitality Mngmt 1986; Temple Univ Quantity Foods Instr 1993; Lock Haven Univ 109 Credit Hrs Tow Schl, Clinical Psych; *cr:* Bradford Co AVTS Long Term Sub Instr 1 Cntrl Chester Co AVTS Instr 1987-89; DE CO Tech Schl Instr 1 Keystone Cntrl AVTS Instr 1990-; *ai:* Safety Comm; NEA, PSEA Phi Kappa Phi 1995-; Smithsonian Inst 1990-; Williamsport Area Coll Outstdng Stu Awd 1986; Lock Haven Univ Outstdng Stu Aw PA Coll of Tech Scholars Recognition Awd 1994; *home:* 43 1/2 Was Blvd Williamsport PA 17701*

BOHBOT, JOAN ELLEN, English Teacher; *b:* Manhattan, Jacqueline, Jennifer; *ed:* Long Island Univ at C W Post (BA) Scn 1967, (MS) Scndry Eng 1974; *cr:* North Shore Schls Eng Tchr 1 Maria Regina Diocesan HS Eng Tchr 1980-84; Baldwin Pub Schls Tchr 1986-; *ai:* Site Based Mngmt Team; Baldwin Tchrs Assn Intern Pgm Co-Dir; NCTE 1967-; ASCD; *office:* Baldwin HS 84 School Dr Baldwin NY 11510

BOHEN, MARION RITA, Sixth Grade Teacher; *b:* New York C *ed:* Mt St Vincent (BA) Latin, Ed 1963; Hunter Coll (MA) Latin Credit Hrs Theology at Manhattan Coll; 40 Hrs Eng at Georgian C Credit Hrs Ed at Jersey City St; *cr:* Archdiocese of NY Tchr 4 1962-73; Howell Twp Schl Tchr 7-8 Grds 1973-79, Tchr Gifted 1979-94; Howell MS Latin I Tchr 1994-95; Howell Twp Schl Tch 1995-; *ai:* NEA, NJEA 1973-; Natl Jr Class ICAL League 1979-; Yr Monmouth Cty 1992; Natl Endowment of Arts Flwshp 1991.

BOHI, CHARLES WESLEY, Social Studies Teacher; *b:* Estherv *m:* Lynnette Leverette; *ed:* Simpson Coll (BA) His 1963; Case- Reserve (MA) His 1969; Summer Seminar on Canadian Stud, Manitoba 1982, Univ of VT 1987; *cr:* Oskaloosa HS Soc St 1963-64; Cleveland Pub Schls Soc Stud Tchr 1964-69; Lansing Pu Soc Stud Tchr 1969-71; Hanover HS Soc Stud Tchr 1971-; *ai:* NHNEA 1975-; Hanover Ed Assn 1975-, Pres 1985-87, 1993- 1987-89; Upper Valley Youth Ser 1989-92, Bd 3 Yrs; Fulbright Ex Edmonton, Alberta 1980-81; Visiting Scholar NEH Summer Semin of MN; Author Canadian Natls Western Depots; Co-Author The Railroad Station in America; Author, Co-Author of 50+ Arti Railroad Subjects, Co-Author of Canadian Pacific's Western *office:* Hanover H S Lebanon St Hanover NH 03755

BOHLAND, EUGENE RAYMOND,JR., Band Director; *b:* Tole *m:* Carol Ann Christoph; *c:* Kathryn Lee, Lindsey Marie; *ed:* Toledo (BE) Music 1978, (ME) Admin 1986; *cr:* Napoleon City Sc Band Dir 1978-86; Sylvania Northview HS Band Dir 1986-; *ai:* Ma Pep, Jazz, Symphonic, 8th Grd & Elem Band Dir; NEA & OEA, M OMEA 1978-; *office:* Northview HS 5403 Silica Dr Sylvania OH

BOHN, BRENDA WILLIAMS, Sixth Grade Lang Arts T Winchester, VI; *m:* William Howard; *c:* Chad William, Craig Mich Madison Coll (BS) Elem Ed 1973; Frostburg St (MS) Elem Ed 1 Urbana Elem 3rd Grd Tchr 1973-75; North Frederick Elem 4th G 1975-76; South Frederick Elem 4th Grd Tchr 1976-80; Myersvil 3rd Grd Tchr 1980-81; Wolfsville Elem 5th Grd Tchr 1981-91; Mid MS 6th Grd Lang Arts Tchr 1991-; *ai:* Sixth Grd Team Ldr; Frede Tchrs Assn, NEA 1973-; Ldr for Fifth Grd Tchrs 1988-91; Conduct Arts Feeder Meetings Frederick Co; Suburban Kiwanis Club Achv for Outstanding Tchr 1993; Essential Curr Comm for Frederick C Sub-Comm Stu Achvmt, Thinking Assessment for St of MD; MIddletown MS 100 High St Middletown MD 21769*

BOHN, VIDA GOODMAN, Retired Teacher; *b:* Altoona, PA; *m:* Kenneth; *c:* Jeff, Erik; *ed:* Penn St (BS) Elem, His, Eng 1941; Lock St Coll Elem Ed Cert 1933; *home:* 203 S 22nd St Altoona PA 166

BOHNER, HARVEY CLIFFORD, 8th Grade Science Teac Chester, PA; *m:* Katherine Elizabeth Potts; *c:* Steven, Susan Esheln Widener Univ (BS) Sci Ed 1965, (MS) Sci Ed 1975; *cr:* Pulaski Grd Sci Tchr 1965-67; E. T. Richardson MS 8th Grd Sci Tchr 19 Team Ldr; Stage Crew Mgr; NEA, PSEA 1965-; NSTA 1985-; Spr Ed Assn 1969-, Tchr Rep; Boy Scouts Troop 355 1981-, Sec, Forme Chm; Holmes Prebyn Church 1981-, Elder, Sundy Schl Tdch Springhill Townwatch 1975-, Crew Chief; *office:* E T Richardson W Woodland Ave Springfield PA 19064

BOHNETT, SALLY MARIE, Rel Tchr & Campus Minister; *b:* OH; *ed:* Univ of Dayton (BS) Bio 1974; Creighton Univ (MA) Spirituality 1994; Cert Spiritual Direction; *cr:* Medical Coll of O Tech 1974-77; Elem Ed Jr HS Tchr 1980-88; Notre Dame Aca Campus Minister 1988-; *ai:* Pastoral Svcs Spiritual Acts; Retreat Chprsn; NDEA 1994-; NCEA 1980-; *home:* 3535 W Sylvania Ave OH 43623

BOHRER, MARY JONES, 4th Grade Teacher; *b:* Ary, KY; *m:* D.; *c:* Anthony, Jordan; *ed:* Morehead St Univ (BA) Elem Ed 197 of Dayton (MA) Admin 1980; 30 Hrs Above Masters from Coll o Joseph & Univ of Cincinnati; *cr:* Mt Orab Elem Schl 7th Grd E 1972-73, 4th Grd Tchr 1973-; *ai:* Lang Arts Comm; OEA, WBEA We Have Received Several Grants as a Joint Effort of 4th Grd Through Cty Bd of Ed, 2 Through Fine Arts Comm.

BOHRER, ROBERT LEE, Math Teacher; *b:* Berkeley Springs, Shepherd Coll (BA) Math & Eng 1965; Trinity Coll 12 Credit Hrs Admin; *cr:* Morgan Cty Ed MS Math Tchr 1965-66; Archbishop High Math Tchr 1966-69; Lareine High Sr High Math Tchr 1 Bishop McNamara High Sr High Math Tchr 1992-; *ai:* Sr Class Mo Discipline Bd; Pastoral Cncl; NCTM 1984-; MCTM 1994-; Loyal Moose 1973-; Heritage Preserve 1978-, Pres, Treas; Rotary Intn Treas, Service Above Self; *office:* Bishop Mc Namara HS 6800 M Pike Forestville MD 20747

BOHRMAN, KRISTINE, Biology Teacher; *b:* Pottsville, Kutztown Univ (BS) Sec Ed & Bio 1989; Penn St, Wilkes, Allento Masters Equivalent 1994; *cr:* D A Harman Jr High Bio Tchr 1 Hazleton Jr High Bio Tchr 1992-; *ai:* Jr Acad of Sci Consultant & ECO-Tigers Adv; NEA 1989-; *office:* Hazleton Jr HS 700 N Wyo Hazleton PA 18201

BOICE, WENDY JANE, Nursing Instructor; *b:* Watertown, Christian, Joshua Durant, Jorden Durant, Danielle Durant; *ed:* Je Comm Coll (AS) Nrsng 1987; Regents Coll (BA) Nrsng 1996; Oswe Cert Tchng 1991; *cr:* E. J. Noble Hosp Registered Nurse 1982-94; Hosp Nursing Supvr 1990-91; Howard G. Sackett Tech Ctr Nrsr 1989-; *ai:* Lead Adv 1990-94; NHS Comm; VICA 1990-, Adv; Pub 1987; Distngd Edctrs Awd 1993; *office:* Howard G Sackett Techn Rt 12 Glenfield NY 13343

BOICH, PEGGY ANN, Guidance Counselor; *b:* Fredrickstown, John J.; *ed:* OH St Univ (BS) Home Ecs Ed 1964; Dayton Uni e Cnslr 1987; *cr:* Loudonville-Perrysville HS S Voc Home Ec Tchr ; Union Local HS Voc Home Ecs Tchr 1971-73; Newcomerstown ıe Ecs Tchr 1974-78; Union Local HS Voc Home Ecs Tchr 1970-90, e Cnslr 1991-; *ai:* OH Sch Cnslng Assn, OH Assn Coll Admission 1991-; OEA, NEA 1965-; Kappa Delta Gamma 1984-, Friendship Master Adv Voc Home Ecs 1988; *office:* Union Local HS 66859 r Rd Belmont OH 43718*

', PAUL EDWARD, Total Quality Mngmt Consultant; *b:* New CT; *m:* Suellen Bunting; *c:* Paul E. Jr., Tracy K.; *ed:* Univ of AK Eng & Ed 1971; Univ of OK (MA) Human Relations 1981; *cr:* e Schl Head Tchr 1971-75; Dept of Defense Race Relations & pportunity Inst Master Lecturer, Trainer 1980-85; Dept of Defense ent Schls Guid Cnslr, Eng Tchr 1990-92; 104th Area Support Group onsultant, Lecturer, Trainer 1993-; *ai:* Vol Tutor; Dept of Defense Lecturer & Master Trainer.

S, GINA RICCIARDELLI, Fourth Grade Teacher; *b:* Jersey City, Christian Joseph Sr.; *c:* Sherri Lynn, Christian Jr., Lisa Marie; *ed:* n Dickinson Univ (BS) Elem Ed 1967; William Paterson Coll Elem Ed 1993; Jersey City St Coll 9 Credits Microcomputers in Ed; Univ 3 Credits Gender in Lit; St Peters Coll 3 Credits Assertive ne; *cr:* Washington Schl 3rd Grd Tchr 1967-72; Meml Schl 3rd Grd 88-93, 4th Grd Tchr 1993-; *ai:* Family Sci Instr; Liaison, Math Tech Learning Activity Chprsn; EAP Assn Rep; NEA, NJEA d Assn of Paramus 1988-, Assn Rep; Meml Schl PTA 1988-; Stony A 1978-90, Pres 2 Yrs, VP 2 Yrs; NJ Governor's Tchr Recognition 993-94; Univ Family Sci Instr Awded by Rutgers Univ; Charge; *home:* 188 Morningside Rd Paramus NJ 07652

LY, CLAUDETTE ELAINE (HOULE), French Teacher; *b:* MA; *m:* Ronald; *c:* Carol Donohue O'Neil, Nancy Donohue; *ed:* el Coll (BA) Fr, Ed 1963; River Coll (MA) Fr, Ed 1978; 30 Addl nington St Coll; *cr:* Dracut Jr HS Fr Tchr 1963-64; Lowell HS Fr 54-; *ai:* Intnl Language Club Adv; MAFL 1995-; Schlsp COmm of Club 1981-; *office:* Lowell HS 50 Fr Morrissette Blvd Lowell MA

LY, RONALD FRANCIS, French Teacher; *b:* Lowell, MA; *m:* e Houle; *c:* Carol O'Neil, Nancy; *ed:* Merrimack Coll (BA) Hum, ; River Coll (MA) Fr 1979; Univ Cath de l'Quest Angers France; ell HS Fr Tchr 1968-; *ai:* AATF 1970-; MAFLA 1994-; Focus or St Frameworks of MA 1996; *office:* Lowell HS 50 Fr Morrissette well MA 01852

ERT, RONALD SHERIDAN,JR., Sixth Grade Teacher; *b:* , NH; *m:* Maureen Anita Fitzpatrick; *c:* Lea C., Eleanor H.; *ed:* h St Coll (BA) Soc Stud 1972; 30 Credits Ed Univ of NH at ster; *cr:* Main Dunstable Elem Schl Sixth Grd Tchr 20 Yrs; *ai:* Year th Curr Audit Comm; Bldg Math Coord; AFT 1975-; Nashua Girls Assn 1990-, Coaching Coord; *home:* 178 Proctor Hill Rd Hollis NH

SEK, FRANK ROBERT, Spanish & US History Teacher; *b:* nd, OH; *m:* Marion Faye Moro; *c:* Michael; *ed:* Kent St Univ (BS) n 1965, (MED) His 1975; *cr:* Holy Redeemer Elem Schl 6th-7th r 1965-67; St Joseph HS His, Span Tchr 1967-90; Villa Angela-St Schl His, Span Tchr 1990-; *ai:* Var Bowling Coach; IM Bowling or; CHALTA 1970-; OCEA 1968-; Svc Awds 1978, 1988, 1996; Villa Angela St Joseph HS 18491 Lake Shore Blvd Cleveland OH

A, GRACE ELIZABETH, Social Studies & English Tchr; *b:* em, PA; *ed:* Houghton Coll (BA) Eng & Soc Stud 1964; Asbury ical Seminary (MRE) Chrstn & Rel Ed 1968; St Univ of NY at New Grad Credits Eng 1964-66; *cr:* Wartick Vly HS 7th Grd Eng Tchr ; Hightstown MS 8th Grd Eng Tchr 1969-71; Manasquan Elem & 8th Grd Eng Tchr 1971-77; St Catherine Laboure Schl 6th-8th & Soc Stud Tchr 1988-; *ai:* Soc Stud Dept Chprsn; NCEA 1988-; t Catherine Laboure Schl 4020 Derry St Harrisburg PA 17111

D, JOSEPH THOMAS, 10th-12th Grd Math Teacher; *b:* Orange, Eileen Barbara Kelly; *c:* Katie, Annie, Megan; *ed:* Seton Hall Univ th 1970, (MAT) Math Ed 1981; Addl 36 Credits; *cr:* Oratory Prep th Tchr 1970-89; Seton Hall Prep Schl Math Tchr 1989-; *ai:* Quiz am Coach; Homeroom Act Dir; Excl Tchng Comm; Holy Name Soc 'Hara Assoc 1978-; Univ Adj Prof Math Dept; *office:* Seton Hall) Northfield Ave West Orange NJ 07052

D, LAWRENCE J., Mathematics Teacher; *b:* Bridgeport, CT; *m:* redrickson; *ed:* Western CT St Coll (BS) Math 1964; Fairfield Univ omp Sci 1975; *cr:* Avco Lycoming Scientific Comp Programmer ; Norwalk HS Math Tchr 1970-75; Fairfield HS Math Tchr 1975-; Coach; FEA; CEA; NEA; *office:* Fairfield HS 755 Melville Ave l CT 06432

D, M. PATRICIA ROHAN, Kindergarten Teacher; *b:* Hyde Park, St Marys ND (BA) Early Ed 1947; Attnd Mt Holyoke Coll; *cr:* W n Diocese Tchr 41 Yrs; *ai:* SMC Alumni; NEA; ND Alumni, Pres; uxiliary; Religious Educator of Yr 1986; *office:* Saints Peter & Paul E Main St Hamburg NY 14075

DER, FAY SCHWAMBERGER, Retired Jr HS & Elem Tchr; *b:* , OH; *m:* Henry L.; *c:* Ted, Samuel; *ed:* Bowling Green St (BE) l, (MED) Elem Ed; *cr:* Genoa Area Schls Jr Hi, Elem Grd Tchr *ai:* OEA 1958-; NEA; GAEA, Treas, Pres; ORTA; Trinity United of Christ 1945-, Bd of Chrstn Ed, Sunday Schl Tchr, Ret Treas; 7230 W Toussaint North Rd Graytown OH 43432

N, EVELYN MATTHEWS, Business & Technology Supvr; *b:* ville, VA; *m:* Arthur H.; *c:* Sydne, Arthur II, Troy; *ed:* Hampton S) Bus Admin 1963; Montclair St Univ (MA) Educl Admin 1990; ia Univ (EDS) Educl Admin 1996; *cr:* Dover Bd of Ed Bus Ed, Tech 2 Yrs; *ai:* Tech K-12 Curr Dev; Safe Schls K-12; NJPSA; Jack & 1982-, Ed Chair; Links Inc 1982-, Pres, Arts Awd; AT&T Tech Article Pub; *home:* 24 Runnymede Ct Whippany NJ 07981

N, KRISTIN SPINDLER, Spanish Teacher; *b:* Marietta, OH; *m:* William; *c:* James W. Jr., Bruce, Cindy Linton; *ed:* OH Northern SE) Dual Ed, Span 1961; Marietta Coll (MA) 1989; Attnd Univ of Ashland Coll, OH Univ; *cr:* OH Northern Univ Span Tchr 1961; m Fourth Grd Tchr 1961-62; Warren HS Span, Eng Tchr 1962-; *ai:* lub; Span Honor Soc; OEA, NEA, AATSP 1961-; WLTA 1962-; appa Gamma 1978-, Pres; First Presbyn Church 1968-, Elder, Chm Ed; Sanctuary & Handbell Choir; Jennings Scholar 1977; *office:* HS Rt 1 Vincent OH 45784

N, PAMELA L., Vice Principal; *b:* Philadelphia, PA; *ed:* Penn St S) Elem, Spec Ed 1977; Rutgers Univ (MS) Educl Theory 1981; Credits Contemporary Issues in Ed; *cr:* Washington & Forest Hill -4 Grd Tchr, GATE 1977-91; Edgewood Jr HS Asst Prin, Supvr ; Eastern Regnl HS Vice Prin, Supvr 1994-; *ai:* Supvr Stu Acts; Stu ; Dist Affirmative Action Ofcr; NASSP 1991-; NABSE 1992-; gma Theta 1976-; NJ Exemplary Prgm Grant; Multi-Cultural Ed ATE Elem Stdnts; *office:* Eastern Regnl HS PO Box 2500 Voorhees 3*

N, STEPHANIE TERESA, Business Education Teacher; *b:* gton, DE; *ed:* DE St Univ (BS) Bus Ed 1965; Boston Coll (MS) d; *cr:* Northlands Scndry Schl Bus Tchr 1977-81; Lincoln Univ Dir of Stu Act 1981-86; Eastside Substance Abuse Prgm Dir 1989-91; Howard HS of Tech Acctng Tchr 1991-92; Christiana HS Acctng Tchr 1992-; *ai:* Natl Tchrs of Amer; Prof Bus Women's Org; Afro-Amer Historical Soc; Natl Black Womens Hlth Project of DE; Police Advy Cncl; Bd SoJourner's Place; Howard Alumni, VP; DE Bus Ed Assn; Delta Sigma Theta; Eastside Citizen Inc, Bd Mem; NAACP; St Joseph's Cath Church; New Direction; Wilmington City Cncl; *office:* Christiana HS 190 Salem Church Rd Newark DE 19713

BOLDUC, KAREN A., Earth & Environmental Sci Tchr; *b:* Portland, ME; *ed:* Bates Coll (BS) Sci 1983; 52 Post Grad Credits; *cr:* Kennebec Girl Scout Co Jr ME Guide Instr 1977-94; Camp Runoia Jr ME Guide Instr 1984, 1995-; Mahoney Jr HS 8th Grd Sci Tchr 1988; Lake Region HS Sci Tchr 1990-; *ai:* 9th Grd Team Ldr 1993-96; Class Adv 1992-96; Stu Asst Team; Rise Team; Aids Awareness & Aids Curr Coord; Interactive Theater Adv; Intl Exchange Organizer 1993, 1995; NEA, MTA 1990-; Amer Counseling Assn, Amer Camping Assn 1995-; Girl Scouts USA 1967-; *office:* Lake Region HS RR 2 Box 1545a Naples ME 04055*

BOLESKY, STEPHEN ANTHONY, Social Studies Teacher; *b:* Evansville, IN; *m:* Constance L. Oxley; *ed:* IN St Univ (BS) Soc Sci 1966, (MS) Soc Sci Ed 1971; Addl 60 Hrs Ed, Soc Sci; *cr:* Tuttle Jr HS Soc Stud Tchr 1966-77; Mt Anthony Union HS Soc Stud Tchr 1977-; *ai:* Spon Chess, Outing Clubs; NEA 1966-; VT Tchrs Assn 1977-; Amnesty Intnl 1990-; *home:* Myers Rd Box 360 Shaftsbury VT 05262*

BOLIANITES, CHARLES, Mathematics Teacher; *b:* Lowell, MA; *ed:* Univ of Lowell (BS) Bus & Comp 1983, (MED) Math Curr & Instruction 1988; *cr:* Lowell Pub Schls Long Term & Temporary Sub Tchr 1983-88; Lowell HS Math Tchr 1988-; *ai:* Ticket Mgr; Math Frameworks Comm Curr; United Tchrs Of Lowell 1988-; Friends of Lowell HS 1993-, Bd of Dirs; *office:* Lowell HS 50 Fr Morrissette Blvd Lowell MA 01852

BOLIN, DOUGLAS S., Math Teacher; *b:* Lock Haven, PA; *ed:* Lock Haven Univ (BS) Math 1975; 50 Addl Credits; Drivers Ed 1977; *cr:* Bellefonte Area HS Math Tchr 1975-; *ai:* Golf Coach 1984-89; NEA, PSEA, BAEA 1975-; Undefeated Golf Teams Schl His 1984, 1987; Golf Dist Title 1987; *office:* Bellefonte Area H S 301 N Allegheny St Bellefonte PA 16823

BOLINSKY, JOSEPH JOHN,JR., Carpentry Instructor; *b:* Hazleton, PA; *m:* Marie Elaine Lesnefsky; *c:* Joseph III; *ed:* Penn St Univ Assoc Mechanical Eng 1968, Voc Cert Carpentry 1985; *cr:* Kennedy Van Saun Draftsman 1967-68; US Army Transportation 1968-69; Cornell Iron Works Drafting & Design 1969-70; Residental Construction Foreman & Supvr 1971-84; Columbia-Montour AVTS Instr 1985-; *ai:* CMAUTS Home Bldg Project Coord; NEA & PSEA 1985-; Natl St & Local Susquehanna Home Builders Assoc 1988-; Beaver Twp 1980-, Chm & Bd of Supvrs; *office:* Columbia Montour Voc Tech Sch 5050 Sweppenheiser Dr Bloomsburg PA 17815

BOLL, PAUL ANTHONY, Biology Teacher; *b:* Portsmouth, OH; *m:* Barbara Elane Stephen Boll; *c:* Shawn, Brenda, Sarah, Jessica; *ed:* OH Dominican (AS) Chem 1976, (BS) Bio 1977; Miami Univ of OH (MA) Bio 1992; 30 Grad Hrs Ed OH Univ; *cr:* St Charles Preparatory Bio Tchr, Coach 1977-78; St Paul's HS Bio Tchr, Coach 1978-82; Wheelersburg HS Bio Tchr, Coach 1982-; *ai:* Head Soccer Coach 1986-; Asst Ftbl Coach 1977-85; Head Track Coach 1977-85; Asst Wrestling Coach 1977-82; OH Soccer Coaches 1988-, St Rep; St Peters Mens Club 1989-; Soccer Coaching Record; SOC Coach of Yr 1989, 1992, 1995; Coach of Southeast Dist All St Team 1990-91, 1993-1995; SE Coach of Yr 1994-1995; *home:* 1227 Sprouce Ln Wheelersburg OH 45694*

BOLLELLA, DOMINICK, Biology Teacher; *b:* Bronx, NY; *m:* Ruth Murray; *c:* Brian; *ed:* Marist Coll (BA) Bio 1968; SUNY at New Paltz 40 Credit Hrs; Herbert H. Lehman Coll 3 Credit Hrs; Page Univ at Manhattan 5 Credit Hrs; *cr:* Bedford Park Acad Sci Tchr, Dept Chair 1968-70; Red Hook HS Sci Tchr 1970-; *ai:* NHS Adv; Scholatic Match-UP Team Quiz Bowl Coach; Bldg Team for Shared Decision Making; Curr Comm Schl Dist; NYSUT 1970-; Red Hook Fac Assn 1970-, Bldg Rep, Chief Bldg Rep; STANYS 1976-; Marist Coll Alumni Assn 1968-, REp 1968-72; Lion 1991-, Sec; Awded NSF Grant Urban Ecology 1971; Co-Ed First Marist Coll Alumni Magazine, Co-Author Red Hook HS Bio Lab Manual; Certified Instr Non-Violent Crisis Intervention CPI; Cooperating Tchr 5 Stud Tchrs 1974-; *office:* Red Hook Central HS W Market St Red Hook NY 12571*

BOLLENBACHER, DUANE R., Mathematics Teacher; *b:* Celina, OH; *m:* Deborah Basinger; *c:* Duanna Rae, Spring Rene Potts; *ed:* Miami Univ (BS) Math 1964; Northwestern Univ (MA) Math 1969; Attn OH St Univ, Univ of Dayton, Wright St Univ, Findlay Coll, Baldwin-Wallace Coll, Earlham Coll; *cr:* Miamisburg HS Math Tchr 1964-67; Covington HS Math Tchr 1967-72; Wapakoneta HS Math Tchr 1973-86; Bluffton HS Math Tchr 1986-94; Bluffton Coll 1995-; *ai:* Math Team Coach; Math Club Adv; NEA, OEA, NCTM 1964-, OCTM 1970-, St Contest Dir, St Bd of Dir, OH Math Tchr of Yr 1991; Presidential Awd Finalist 1989; Organize, Conduct Own Summer Math Camp for Tchrs; Numerous Articles on Math Pub in Journals; *office:* Bluffton Coll 280 W College Ave Bluffton OH 45817

BOLLENBACK, DIRK F., Soc Studies Tchr & Dept Chm; *b:* Evanston, IL; *m:* Beverly Colvin; *c:* Ann Elizabeth Jamison, Sarah Jane; *ed:* Wesleyan Univ (BA) Govt 1953; Schl of Advanced Intnl Stu John Hopkins (MA) Intnl Stu 1955; Wesleyan Univ MAT Prgm Spec Stu 1957-58; Univ of Chicago 1963-64; Western CT St Univ; *cr:* US Army Psychological Warfare Schl Ft Bragg NC Instr 1955-57; *ai:* Various Comms; NEA, CEA 1958-; Many; John F Kennedy Lib Award 1992; John Hay Fellows Scholar 1963-64; Excl in Tchng Awards from Univ of Chicago & Tufts Univ; *office:* Ridgefield HS 700 N Salem Rd Ridgefield CT 06877

BOLLER, BRUCE RAYMOND, Professor of Physics; *b:* New York City, NY; *m:* Susan Schoelch Saunders; *c:* Janet, John; *ed:* Iona Coll (BS) Physics 1961; Univ of Pittsburgh (MS) Experimental Nuclear Physics 1964; The City Univ of NY (PHD) Physics 1970; Univ of Buffalo 4 Credit Hrs in Engineering Mechanics, Cmptrs 1991; *cr:* City Coll of NY Instr of Physics 1970-73; SUNY Martime Coll Prof of Physics 1975-89; Bergen Comm Coll Asst Prof of Physics 1990-95, Assoc Prof of Physics 1995-; *ai:* Physics Club Adv; Fac Dev, Nom, Elections Comms; Partners in Learning; Tchng and Learning Study Group Chair, Middle States Self Study 1994-95; AAPT 1961-; AGU 1966-; ANS 1979-; AAPT NJ 1990-; NYAS, NEA 1990-; APS 1995-; Univ Awd St Univ of NY 1979; Journal of Geophysical Research Pub 1970, 1973-74; *office:* Bergen Comm Coll 400 Paramus Rd Paramus NJ 07652*

BOLLING, SUZANNE SCHRYVER, Dean of Students; *b:* North Adams, MA; *m:* David M.; *ed:* Skidmore Coll (BA) Eng 1987; U of NY at Albany (MS) Dev Rdng 1991; Post Grad Work in Creative Writing at Bennington Coll; Courses in Fiction Writing Rivier Coll 1995-96; *cr:* Emma Willard Schl Eng Intern, Admissions 1987-91; Cascade Schl Eng Instr 1991-92; Tilton Schl Lang Specialist 1992-95; Acad of Notre Dame Dean of Stdnts, Eng Tchr 1995-; *ai:* Coach Cross Cntry Running; Adv Stu Cncl; *office:* Acad of Notre Dame 180 Middlesex Rd Tyngsboro MA 01879*

BOLLINGER, ELLEN RUSHNOK, 5th Grade Teacher; *b:* Arcadia, PA; *c:* Candace, Glenn; *ed:* SUNY at Buffalo (BS) Elem Ed 1962; 18 Credit Hrs; 12 Inservice Hrs; *cr:* Hamburg Cntrl 5th Grd Tchr 1962-64; Hamburg & Frontier Sub Tchr; Frontier Cntrl Pre-1st-K, 4th-5th Grd Tchr 1984-; *ai:* Math Portfolio Assessment Comm; AFT, NYSUT 1994-; PDK 1995-; FCTA 1984-; *office:* Cloverbank Elem Schl 2761 Cloverbank Rd Hamburg NY 14075*

BOLLINGER, MICHAEL S., 8th Grade Social Studies Tchr; *b:* N Tonawanda, NY; *ed:* St Univ Coll at Buffalo (BS) Soc Stud Ed 1990; 24 Addl Credit Hrs Soc Stud Ed; *cr:* Niagara Falls City Schl Dist Scndry Sub Tchr 1990-92; Tonawanda Jr Sr HS Scndry Soc Stud Tchr 1991-95; North Tonawanda Alternative HS Scndry Soc Stud Tchr 1992-93; Lewiston-Porter MS 8th Grd Soc Stud Tchr 1993-; *ai:* Youth-to-Youth, Banana Splits, Chess Club Adv; Girls Var Sftbl Asst Coach; AFT 1991-; NY St MS Assn 1994-; Tonawanda Boys & Girls Club Alumni Assn 1992-; *office:* Lewiston-Porter MS 4061 Creek Rd Youngstown NY 14174*

BOLLINGER, RONALD R., Fourth Grade Teacher; *b:* Sunbury, PA; *m:* Tammy Bennett; *c:* Meghan, Micah, Mallery, Marc; *ed:* Bloomsburg Univ (BS) Elem Ed 1983; 36 Credit Hrs Chem; *cr:* Mifflinburg MS 7-8 Grd Sci Tchr 1983-93; Mifflinburg Elem Schl Fourth Grd Tchr 1993-; *ai:* IM Supvr; Var Game Mgr; *office:* Mifflinburg Elem E Shipton St Mifflinburg PA 17844

BOLTON, MARION GRANT, Fourth Grade Teacher; *b:* Eatonton, GA; *m:* Lenora; *c:* David Len; *ed:* Bennett Coll (MS) Elem Ed 1959; Post Grad Stud Temple Univ; *cr:* Dr. Ethel D. Allen Elem Schl Tchr 1961-; *ai:* Fourth Grd, Assembly Comm Chprsn; Black His Oratorical Contest Coord; After-Schl Geog Club Spon; Phila Fed of Tchrs, AFT 1963-; NAACP 1980-; St Matthew AME Church 1959-, Steward, Lay Person of Yr; *office:* Dr Ethel Allen Elem Sch 3200 W Lehigh Ave Philadelphia PA 19132

BOLTON, MARY CATHERINE, Mathematics Teacher; *b:* Whiteford, MD; *m:* David; *ed:* Lebanon Valley Coll (BS) Math 1990; Temple Math Ed Masters Prgm 21 Credits Completed; *cr:* Havre de Grace HS Math Tchr 1990-92; Holicong MS Math Tchr 1992-93; Central Bucks HS W Math Tchr 1993-94; Bucks HS E Math Tchr 1994; *ai:* Bible Club Supvr; Pioneer Girls 1995-, Pal for Gal; Childrens Choir 1993-, Tchr; *office:* Central Bucks-East HS PO Box 405 Buckingham PA 18912

BOLTON, MARY FERREIRA, Teacher of GATE & Coordinator; *b:* Fall River, MA; *m:* Dennis A.; *c:* Tracey A., Dennis A. II; *ed:* Salve Regina Univ (BA) Eng 1972, (MA) Human Dev 1976; Providence Coll (MED) Admin 1992; 27 Addl Hrs in GATE; *cr:* Pocasset Schl 5th Grd Tchr 1973-76; Tiverton MS 5th Grd Tchr 1976-83, Tchr & Grds Coord 1983-85, 5th & 6th Grd GATE Prgm Tchr & 7th & 8th Grd GATE Prgm Coord 1985-; *ai:* Mock Trial Tournament Team Coach; Curr Stud & Discipline Review Comms Mem; GATE cncl Chprsn; NEA & NEARI 1973-; Tiverton Ed Assn 1973-, Past Sec 1975-76; NCTE & RICTM 1987-; NMSA 1990-, Bd of Dirs, Nom Awd 1992-93; RIMLEA, RIASCD & NASCD 1990-; Sakonnet Cncl of IRA 1982-, Past Pres 1986-87, Past Sec 1982-83; RIASP, Pres 1991; NASSP 1993; Wake Forest Univ Ctr for Research & Dev Schlsp 1987-88, 1993; Pub Lesson Plans Available in Natl Respository Catalog of Tchr Dev; MS Law Related Ed Tchr of Yr 1995; *office:* Tiverton M S 10 Quintal Dr Tiverton RI 02878*

BOLTZ, ELAINE LESLIE, Health Teacher; *b:* Columbus, OH; *ed:* OH St Univ (BS) Hlth & PE 1970; 30 Hrs in Hlth Ed Post Grd Work; Wkshp Clinics involving COA Alcoholic Families; *cr:* Northland HS Tchr & Coach 1970-; *ai:* Girls Vylbl & Bsktbl Head Coach; CoFacilitator of COAS; Crsis Cnslng; Soph Float Adv; CEA 1970-; OEA 1970-; NEA 1970-; *office:* Northland HS 1919 Northcliff Dr Columbus OH 43229*

BOLTZ, FRANCES SPELL, 6th Grd Language Arts Teacher; *b:* Hazlehurst, GA; *m:* Daniel R.; *c:* Matthew, Adam, Jason; *ed:* FSU (BS) Elem Ed 1960; GA St Univ (MS) Rdng, Corrections 1966; GATE Ed Rutgers, Fairleigh, Univ of CT; *cr:* Palm Springs Elem Schl 1st Grd Tchr 1960-61; Cntry Day Pvt Schls 4-6th Grd Tchr 1961-64; Mt Brook Elem Schl 3rd Grd Tchr 1964-65; *ai:* Variety Show; Environmental Ed Outdoor Camp; Historical Soc; DE ra-ptor Ctr; NEA 1960-; NJEA 1972-; Democratic Club 1980-, Sec; Teen Arts 1981-, Bd of Dir, Treas; Peace Messenger Awd Sec Gen UN 1990; Warren Cummings Awd Svc Sussex Cty 1989; WWOR TV Grant 1989; Tchr of Yr 1981; *office:* Lounsberry Hollow MS Box 219 Sammis Rd Vernon NJ 07462

BOLTZ, JEAN BEAUMONT, Secondary Mathematics Teacher; *b:* Warsaw, NY; *m:* Dale C.; *c:* Ann; *ed:* SUC at Brockport (BS) Ed & mAth 1965; SUC at Buffalo (MS) Ed 1969; Attnd SUNY at Buffalo Comp Courses; *cr:* Depew MS 7th & 8th Grd Math Tchr 1969-93; Depew HS Math Tchr 1991-; *ai:* Math Club Adv; Comp Resource; AMTNYS; NYSUT & AFT 1969-; NCTM 1989-; Lancaster Presbyn Church 1972-, Sunday Schl Supt & Elder; *office:* Depew HS 5201 Transit Rd Depew NY 14043

BOLTZ, MICHAEL GENE, Sixth Grade Teacher; *b:* Lebanon, PA; *ed:* Penn St Univ (AA) Hotel, Restaurant Mngmt 1986; Kutztown Univ (BS) Elem Ed 1989; Regent Univ (MS) Educl Ldrshp 1996; *cr:* Tulpehocken Schl Dist 6th Grd Tchr 1991-; *ai:* Asst Coach Girl's & Boy's Tennis; Instrl Support Team; NEA 1992-, Bldg Rep, Tchr of the Quarter; Lebanon Church of God 1995-, Yth Ldr; Puppet Praise Yth Minn 1992-, Music Dir; *home:* 611 1/2 S Railroad St Myerstown PA 17067*

BOMBA, CAROL ANN, Third Grade Teacher; *b:* Derby, CT; *ed:* Southern CT St Univ (BS) Intermediate-Upper Ed 1961; Attnd Southern CT St Univ; *cr:* Bungay Elem Schl 3-4 Grd Tchr 1961-; *ai:* Staff Advy Comm; Tchr of Yr Comm; Seymour Ed Assn 1961-, Exec Bd; CT Ed Assn, NEA 1961-; *office:* Bungay Elem Schl 35 Bungay Rd Seymour CT 06483

BOMBARA, BRUCE JOHN, Social Studies Teacher; *b:* Brooklyn, NY; *c:* Jessica, John, Bruce; *ed:* St Francis Coll (BA) Soc Stud 1972; St John's Univ (MS) Ed 1975; Post-Grad Adelphi Univ; *cr:* St Agatha's Schl Soc Stud Tchr 1972-74; Chaminade HS Soc Stud Tchr 1974-; *ai:* Swim Coach 1979-90; Water Polo coach 1988-; *office:* Chaminade HS Jackson Ave Mineola NY 11501

BOMBARD, MICHELE, Fifth Grade Teacher; *b:* Massena, NY; *ed:* Potsdam St Univ (BA) His, Ed 1986; *cr:* Trinity Cath Schl Fifth Grd Tchr 1986-; *ai:* Liturgy Team; Schoolwide Enrichment Comm Chprsn; Fifth Grd Choir Dir; Lyricist Pub Songs; 5th Grd Class Poem Pub; *office:* Trinity Catholic Schl 188 Main St Massena NY 13662

BOMBERGER, DONALD C., Health & PE Teacher; *b:* Lititz, PA; *m:* Judith Marie Miller; *c:* Elisha, Tiffany, Tara, Isaiah, Toshalea, Joel; *ed:* West Chester Univ (BS) Hlth, PE 1991; Millersville Univ; Christ of Nations; *cr:* Living Word Acad PE Dir 1983-; *ai:* Head Var Soccer, Track Coach; Jr Class Adv; PE, Ath Comm; PSAHERD, PIAA Ofcl 1989-; *office:* Living Word Acad 2384 New Holland Pike Lancaster PA 17601

BOMS, MICHAEL, Bio, Chem & Biochemistry Tchr; *b:* Boras, Sweden; *m:* Beth Besterman; *c:* Erica; *ed:* Brooklyn Coll (BA) Bio, Ed 1972; SUNY at New Paltz (MS) Bio 1980; *cr:* Intermediate Schl 210 Sci Tchr 1972-77; Ellenville HS Sci Tchr 1977-79; Onteora HS Sci Tchr 1979-; *ai:* Yrbk, Sr Class, Stu Affairs Cncl, Stu Govt Adv; Var Track Head Coach; Onteora Tchrs Assn, STANYS 1979-; *office:* Onteora Jr Sr HS Rt 28 Boiceville NY 12412*

BOMZER, JO ANN WEINER, English Associate Professor; *b:* Philadelphia, PA; *c:* Elisabeth; *ed:* Mount Holyoke Coll (AB) Eng 1977; Univ of PA (MA) Eng 1975, (PHD) Eng 1981; *cr:* Beaver Coll Eng Assoc Prof 1977-; *ai:* Writing Prgm Dir; AAUP, NCTE, MLA; Article Pub 1990; *office:* Beaver Coll Glenside PA 19038

BONACCI, MARK A., Asst Prof of Human Services; *b:* New York City, NY; *ed:* Manhattanville (BA) Psych 1980; NY Univ (MSW) Soc Work 1982; SUNY at Buffalo (PHD) Psych 1987; Oxford Univ Psychoanalysis

1978-79; *cr:* SUNY at Buffalo Full-time Lecturer 1985-87; West Seneca Dev Ctr Clinical Psychologist 1986-89; Niagara Cty Comm Coll Asst Prof 1989-; *ai:* Intnl Voluntary Svcs Hlth Projects Dir; Intnl Ed Comm, NCCC; Psi Chi 1978-, Pres; Books: The Legacy of Colonialism, Health Care in Southeast Asia, Senseless Casualties the Aids Epidemic in Asia, Sharing the Challenge HIV AIDS Counseling, Caregiving for Persons with AIDS an Integrated Approach; *office:* Niagara County Comm Coll 3111 Saunders Settlement Rd Sanborn NY 14132

BONACIC-MARKER, MELISSA, 10th Grade English Teacher; *b:* Ridgewood, NJ; *m:* Henry William Marker; *ed:* Univ of Scranton (BA) Eng 1989; SUNY at New Paltz Provisional 7-12 Grd Scndry Ed Cert 1993, Working on Eng Ed MA; *cr:* Vly Cntrl HS Eng Tchr 1993-; *ai:* Sr Class Adv; NYSUT, Vly Cntrl Tchrs' Assn 1993-; Bd of Ed Prof, Courteous Image Commendations; *office:* Valley Central HS 1175 Rt 17k Montgomery NY 12549

BONACORSI, SHARON BOND, 7th Grade Life Science Teacher; *b:* Oswego, NY; *m:* Anthony; *c:* Nikole, Nick Anthony; *ed:* SUNY Oswego (BS) Ed, Bio 1984, (MS) Ed 1987; *cr:* Oswego HS 9-10 Grd Sci, Phys Bio Tchr 4 Yrs; Oswego MS 7 Grd Life Sci Tchr 6 Yrs.

BONAGURA, JOHN L., 5th Grade Teacher; *b:* Kingston, NY; *ed:* Dutchess Comm Coll (AA) Liberal Arts 1968; SUNY at Oswego (BA) Elem Ed 1970; SUNY at New Paltz (MS) Elem Ed 1975; *cr:* East Coldenham Elem 2nd Grd Tchr 1970-72, 3rd Grd Tchr 1972-77, 5th Grd Tchr 1977-; *ai:* Drama Dir 25 Yrs; Schl Store Adv 5 Yrs; Dist Shared Decision Making Team; Bldg Level Team; Effective Schls Project; Compact for Learning Project; NYSUT, AFT, NEA 1970-; Valley Cntrl Tchrs Assn 1970-, Treas; BSA Cubs 1971-, Ldr Webelos, Pack Chm 1990-; Valley Cntrl Schlsp Cncl 1981-, Treas; Valley Cntrl Tchrs Assn Benefit Fund 1986-, Treas; St Marys & Saint Charles CCD Tchr 1966-91; *office:* East Coldenham Elem Schl 286-290 Rt 17k Newburgh NY 12550

BONAMICO, ROSEANNE, Comm Arts & Religion Teacher; *b:* Dennison, OH; *ed:* Kent St Univ (BS) His, Soc Psych 1974; Advanced Cert in Rel; *cr:* St Joseph Elem Schl Eighth Grd Tchr 1974-; *ai:* Yrbk, Washington DC Trip Adv; Rel Comm Chprsn; Coord 7th-8th Grd Soc Act, Rel Act, Prayer Svcs; Mission Coord; Co-Dir Christmas Prayer Pageant; Coord 8th Grd Awds Night & Grad; OCEA 1974-; Trumpet in the Land Vol; Providence Partner; Short Script Pub; *office:* St Joseph Elem Schl 600 N Tuscarawas Ave Dover OH 44622

BONASERA, LINDA J., Assistant Principal; *b:* Bronx, NY; *ed:* St Thomas Aquinas Coll (BS) Ed Sci 1967; Villanova Univ (MA) Ed Math 1973; Manhattan Coll 24 Credits Admin 1979-83; Iona Coll 3 Credits Educl Cmptr 1983; *cr:* St Brendan's Schl 1st Grd Tchr 1966-67; St Anthony's Schl 7th-8th Grd Math Tchr 1967-68; St Catherines Schl 2nd Grd Tchr 1968-69; Msgr. Scanlan HS Math, Sci Tchr, Math Dept Chprsn 1969-79, Asst Prin, Math Tchr 1979-; *ai:* ASCD, CSAANYS, CNEA 1980-; *office:* Monsignor Scanlan HS 915 Hutchinson River Pky Bronx NY 10465

BONASIA, JOSEPH, High School English Teacher; *b:* Queens, NY; *ed:* Nassau Comm (AA) Lbrl Arts 1976; SUNY at Binghamton (BA) Eng, Gen Lit 1978; CUNY at Queens (MS) Scndry Ed 1989; 30 Credit Hrs; *cr:* West Hampstead HS Eng Tchr; *ai:* Environmental Club Adv; NYSUT, AFT 1984-; Articles Pub; *office:* West Hempstead Sr HS 400 Nassau Blvd West Hempstead NY 11552

BONAVENTURA, LOUIS J.,III, School Counselor; *b:* Bridgeport, CT; *ed:* Eastern CT St Univ (BA) Sociology 1990; Univ of Bridgeport (MS) School Counseling 1993; Univ of Delaware Sociology; *cr:* St Joseph HS Schl Cnslr 1994-; Bunnell HS Schl Cnslr 1996; *ai:* Asst Girls Vlybl, Boys Bsktbl, Bsbl Coach; ACA, ASCA 1992-; CCA, CSCA 1994-; ASCD 1995-; *office:* St Joseph HS 2320 Huntington Tpke Trumbull CT 06611

BONAVITA, JOHN F., Social Studies Teacher; *b:* Warren, PA; *m:* Cheryl Davidson; *c:* Saleena, Christopher, Nicholas; *ed:* Univ of Pittsburgh (BA) Pol Sci & Criminology 1975; PA St Police Acad Cert Law Enforcement 1976; Saint Bonaventure Univ Cert Scndry Ed 1991, Pursuing Masters in Counseling Degree; *cr:* Tidioute Area HS Industrial Arts Tchr 1992-93; Warren Area HS Soc Stud Tchr 1993-95; Warren-Beaty MS Soc Stud Tchr 1995-; *ai:* Ftbl Asst Coach 1982-94; Asst Wrestling Coach; NEA, WCEA 1992-; FOP 1975-92; Outstanding Felony Arrest, Protection of Comm in & Deadly force Situation & Peaceful Resolution of Deadly Force Situation Citations; Outstanding Cadet PSP Acad 1976; NW trng Ctr; *office:* Warren-Beatty MS 3rd & Conewango Sts Warren PA 16365

BONCZEWSKI, ROBERT OWEN, Biology & General Science Tchr; *b:* Wilkes Barre, PA; *ed:* Lycoming Coll (BA) Bio 1992; Univ of Scranton (MS) Schl Cnslng 1993-; Masters Equivilent 1996; *cr:* Jackson Schl Dist Tchr 1992-93; WY Vly West HS Tchr, Coach, Class Adv 1993-; *ai:* Jr Class Adv; Bsktbl Coach; Stu Svcs Exec Comm; PSEA, NEA 1993-; Kappa Delta RHO 1990-; Beta Beta Beta 1989-; *office:* Wyoming Valley West HS 150 Wadham St Plymouth PA 18651

BOND, E. DENTON, Stu Asst Coord & Math Instr; *b:* Tarentum, PA; *m:* Marilyn Barger; *c:* Angela, Trina, Erika; *ed:* Clarion Univ (BEd) Elem Ed 1965; Indiana Univ of PA (MEd) 1967; Attnd Univ of Pittsburgh; *cr:* East Brady Schl Dist 5th Grd Tchr 1966; Kaneohe Schl Tchr 1968; North Allegheny Schls Math Instr, Stu Assistance Coord 1969-; *ai:* Alcohol & Other Drugs Comm; AFT 1970-, Bldg Rep; Presbyn Church 1971-, Elder; Racquetball Club 1980-, Pres, Club Pro.

BOND, HOLLY CHAPPELL, English & Journalism Teacher; *b:* Newark, NY; *m:* Matthew; *ed:* SUNY Coll at Geneseo (BA) Eng 1991; 30 Hrs Grad Stud in Plymouth Coll; *cr:* William Smith Coll; Eng Tchr 1992; Canajoharie MS Eng Tchr & Comp Coord 1992-95; Holland Patent HS Eng & Jrnlsm Tchr 1995-; *ai:* Schl Newspaper Adv; Schl Tech Comm Mem; NYSUT 1992-; AFT 1992-; *office:* Holland Patent HS HPCS 9601 Main St Holland Patent NY 13354

BOND, JEANNE CARLSON, Sixth Grade English Teacher; *b:* Cincinnati, OH; *m:* Lee; *c:* Mark Rogers, Christy Rogers; *ed:* Hardin-Simmons Univ (MED) Spec Ed 1989; Eastern KY Univ (BS) Elem Ed 1968; Attnd Univ of Cincinnati, Miami Univ, Drake Univ, McMurry Coll, Abilene Chrstn, Walsh Univ; *cr:* Princeton City Schl Dist Grd Level Chair 1968-74, 2nd & 5th Grd Tchr 1970-74; Abilene Ind Schl Dist Eng Tchr Grds 6, 7 & 8 1985-89; Hardin-Simmons Univ Multicultural Course for Tchrs 1988; Lakota Local Schl Dist 6th Grd Engl Tchr 1989-; *ai:* Grd Level Chprsn; Vertical Team Chprsn; Dist Wide Lang Arts Rep; Annual Schl Spelling Bee; Mentor for New Tchrs; NEA, OEA, LEA 1989-; Kappa Delta Pi 1988-; DAR 1995-; PTA Bd 1986-89; Sunday Schl 1986-89, Pres; Author of Present Lang Arts Document for Dist Wide Use; Author of Benefits of Oral Rdng; *home:* 3478 Cornell Rd Cincinnati OH 45241

BOND, JEFFREY MILLER, Classics Teacher; *b:* Cincinnati, OH; *m:* Donna Camloh; *c:* Isak B., Leo F., Ivanna M., Joseph A., Luke D.; *ed:* Kenyon Coll (BA) Pol Sci 1978; Univ of Chicago (MA) Pol Sci 1981, (PHD) Pol Sci 1992; *cr:* Princeton Day Schl His, Rel Tchr 1986-88; The Delbarton Schl Chm Dept of His 1988-89; Thomas Aquinal Coll Prof Great Books Prgm 1989-92; Mountain Lakes HS Classics, His Tchr 1992-; *ai:* Head Coach Var Bsbl Team; Phi Beta Kappa 1977; Earhart Fnd Fellow 1979-83; Dodge Flwshp Awd 1992; Outstdng Tchr Awd Univ of Chicago 1993; Natl Endowment of Hum Grant 1995; *office:* Mountain Lakes HS Powerville Rd Mountain Lake NJ 07046

BOND, JENNIFER ANN, National Figure Skating Coach; *b:* Southampton, England; *m:* Craig Harrison; *c:* Geoffrey James, Christopher John Pete; *cr:* Gold Medalist Figure Freestyle Natl, Sectional Competitors Coach 14 Yrs; British Intnl Team British Jr Champion; Genesee Figure Skating Club Gold Medalists Figure Skating Coach; *ai:* Prof Skating Assoc 1985-; NCIFA; Southern Regnl Champion; British Jr Champion; Choreographer TV Skating Shows.

BOND, PATRICIA LOUISE TURNER, 4th Grade Teacher; *b:* New Boston, OH; *m:* Charles A.; *c:* Karen Bond Coriell, Dianne Bond Volz, Charles A. II; *ed:* OH Univ (BS) El Ed 1975; Miami Univ Grad Stud Eng, TAG Prgm, Tchng Lit & Critical, Writing Using Films, El Schl Sci; Edctrs Industry, TAG Prgm, Career Ed; *cr:* Portsmouth City Schls Federal Rdng Prgm 1975; Minford MS 6th Grd Tchr 1975-77, 4th Grd Tchr 1978-; *ai:* Schlsp Comm; Fac Cncl, MEA Bldg Rep; NEA; OEA; MEA 1975-, Sec; PTA, VP, Sec; Bigelow Church 1985-, Trustee, Sec, Ed Newsletter; *home:* 2842 State Route 335 Portsmouth OH 45662

BOND, RAYMOND C., Social Studies Teacher; *b:* Brooklyn, NY; *m:* Patricia A.; *c:* Patricia C.; *ed:* NY City Tech Coll (AAS) Mechanical Tech 1964; Long Island Univ (BA) Pol Sci & Ed 1983; Adelphi Univ (MS) Spcl Ed 1988; Attnd Yale Univ; *cr:* Bd of Ed of NY City Tchr 1983-; *ai:* FBLA Club Adv; FBLA 1993-; NY Citys Vol Svc Honoree; *home:* 195 Willoughby Ave Brooklyn NY 11205

BONEBRAKE, ROBERT C.,JR., Sixth Grade Teacher; *b:* Waynesboro, PA; *ed:* Shippensburg Univ (BS) Elem Ed 1970, (MED) Elem Ed 1974; 30 Post Grad Credit Hrs Temple Univ Eng; *cr:* Gettysburg Schl Dist Fourth Grd Tchr 2 Yrs, Second Grd Tchr 1 Yr, Sixth Grd Tchr 24 Yrs; *ai:* Grd Six Head Tchr; NEA, PSEA 1970-; Gettysburg Area Ed Assn 1970-, Past Pres; Church, Treas; Natl Audubon Soc 1980-; Antietam Humane Soc; *home:* 154 Mount Union Rd Fayetteville PA 17222

BONELL, FRANCES FORAN, 4th Grade Teacher; *b:* Williston Park, NY; *c:* Erin Kate; *ed:* Univ of Tampa (BS) Elem Ed 1968; Adelphi Univ (MA) Elem Ed 1973; 60 Credit Hrs in Post Grad Stud; *cr:* Kings Pk Ft Salonga Elem 4th Grd Tchr 1968-71, 1991-, 2nd Grd Tchr 1982-91; Kings Pk Ralph J Osgood Elem 5th Grd Tchr 1971-76, 4th Grd Tchr 1978-82; *ai:* Parent Org Tchr Rep 1992-93, 1993-94; NYSUT 1968-; Kings Park CTA 1968-; Bread of Life Inn 1989-, Nutritional Network; Cert of Recognition 1992; Outstdng Tchr Awd 1993; Tchr Ctr Grant Winner 1994; *office:* Fort Salonga Elem Schl 39 Sunken Meadow Rd Northport NY 11768

BONEZZI, NINA ALICE, Social Studies Teacher; *b:* Cleveland, OH; *ed:* Bowling Green St Univ (BSEd) His, Pol Sci 1972; 60 Qtr Hrs Ed, Soc Stud, Eng; *cr:* Cedar Point Arts & Crafts Mgr 1981-85; Richmond Gallery Crafts Painter, Framer 1986-88; Parma City Schls Sub Tchr 1988-91, Soc Stud Tchr 1991-; *ai:* Model United Nations Club, Bible Club Adv; Co-Coord Geography Fair; NEA, OEA, PEA, Cleveland Cncl World Affairs 1991-; OH Geographic Alliance 1992-; Grace Chrstn & Missionary Alliance 1989-; PTA Grant Geography Fair; *office:* Parma Sr HS 6285 W 54th St Parma OH 44129

BONHAGE, LAUREL ROWLETTE, Prof of Communication Design; *b:* Nassau Cty, NY; *m:* William J. Jr.; *ed:* Moore Coll of Art (BFA) Design, Illustration 1975; Tyler Schl of Art of Temple Univ (MFA) Graphic Design 1985; Post Grad Stud 16 Credits; Kutztown Univ Post Grad Stud 6 Credits; *cr:* Tyler Schl of Art of Temple Univ Grad Asst, Instr 1983-85; Kutztown Univ Comm Design Prof 1986-; *ai:* Consultant, Designer for PA Sinfonia Orch; Univ Hlth & Safety, Gallery, Coll Safety, Orientation Advy, Sabbatical Comms; Coll Art Assn 1984-; Dir of Summer Prgm for Disadvantaged Jr HS Stdnts Titled Career Awareness, Acad Enrichment with Specialization in Visual & Performing Arts; *office:* Kutztown Univ Of PA Kutztown PA 19530*

BONHAM, MICHAEL E., 6th Grade Science Teacher; *b:* Dayton, OH; *m:* Ruby A. Kuhns; *c:* Bob, Ben, Jennifer, Julie; *ed:* Grace Coll (BA) His, Soc Stud 1970; Wright St Univ (MA), (MED) Classroom, Elem 1974; *cr:* New Carlisle-Bethel Schl 6th Grd Tchr 1970-71; Huber Heights Schls 6th Grd Tchr 1974-; *ai:* OEA, NEA 1985-; *office:* Weisenborn MS 6061 Old Troy Pike Huber Heights OH 45424

BONI, JIMMY JULIAN, 6th Grade Social Studies Tchr; *b:* Sewickley, PA; *m:* Karen Ann; *c:* James, Michael, Matthew; *ed:* Tarkio Coll (BA) Hlth & PE 1971; Univ of Pittsburgh (BA) Soc Stud 1989; 30 Credit Hrs 1989-90; *cr:* Moon Area Schl Dist Soc Stud, Hlth & PE Tchr 1971-; *ai:* Var Ftbl Coach; NEA 1971-; *office:* Moon Area MS 1407 Beers School Rd Moon Township PA 15108*

BONI, LORENZINA SAGNELLA, First Grade Teacher; *b:* Benevento, Italy; *m:* Clemente; *c:* Guerrino, Claudio; *ed:* Southern CT St Univ (BS) Italian, Span 1973, (MS) Italian 1978; Early Chldhd 1980-81; *cr:* Westhill HS Span, Italian Tchr 1973-74; Hamden New Haven Co-op Kndgtn-6th Grd Multilingual Prgm Tchr 1974-81; Bear Path Elem Schl 2nd Grd Tchr 1982-89, 1st Grd Tchr 1989-; *ai:* Staff Dev, Scheduling Comm; HEA 1982-, Bldg Rep; CEA, NEA 1982-; *home:* 885 Hartford Tpke Hamden CT 06517*

BONICH, MARIA A., Sixth Grade Teacher; *b:* Queens, NY; *ed:* Molloy Coll (BA) Sociology, Math, Ed 1974; Gordham Univ (MS) Theology, Cnslng 1978; 75 Addl Post Grad Credits Math, Sci, Arts; *cr:* Saint Boniface Parochial Schl 3rd-4th Grd Tchr 1974-76, 7th-8th Grd Math, His Tchr 1976-84; Gotham Ave Elem Schl 6th Grd Tchr 1985-; *ai:* Yrbk, Math Olympiad Coach, Chess Club Adv; Dist Math Assessment, 5th-6th Grd Dist Sci Comms; Shared Decision Team for Bldg; AFT, NEA 1985-; Long Island Cncl of Math Tchrs 1975-; St Boniface Parish 1977-85, Folk Group Music Dir; Queen of The Most Holy Rosary Parish 1989-90, 1992-95, Music Dir; Fed Grant for Expanding, Restructuring of Math Prgm in St Boniface; *office:* Gotham Avenue Elem Schl 181 Gotham Ave Elmont NY 11003

BONIFAS, JOSEPH ARTHUR, AP Art His & Sculpture Tchr; *b:* Delphos, OH; *m:* Mary Partch; *c:* Patrick; *ed:* OH Bowling Green St Univ (BS) Art Ed 1975, (MA) Sculpture, Jewelry 1981; Attnd Carleton Coll, Northfield MN, AP Art His Inst; *cr:* Shawnee Schl System Art Tchr 1975-; *ai:* Spirit Club, Art Exhibition Adv; OH Designer Craftsman 1980-, Bd Mem; OH Art Ed Assn 1975-; Artist Blacksmith Assn of North Amer 1976-; Martha Holden Jennings Scholar 1982-83; Numerous Articles Pub; *office:* Shawnee HS 3333 Zurmehly Rd Lima OH 45806

BONILLA, AIDA L., 7th & 8th Grade Teacher; *b:* PR; *m:* Robert Stram; *ed:* City Coll (BA) Span, Ed 1971; 30 Grad Credits Lehman Coll, NY Univ; *cr:* IS 193 Tchr 1975-88; CS 211 Tchr 1988-; *ai:* AFT 1975-; *office:* C S 211 Twin Parks Upper Schl 2055 Mapes Ave Bronx NY 10460

BONILLA, FELIX CARLOS, Bilingual Social Studies Tchr; *b:* Santurce, PR; *m:* Evelyn Murphy; *c:* Roselyn, Caroline, Jean, Amy, Jane; *ed:* Univ of PR (BA) Philosophy, Soc Sci 1975; New Schl for Soc Research (MA) Philosophy 1978; Columbia Univ (MA) Philsophy 1981, (PHD) Comparative, Intnl Ed & His 1983; *cr:* Newtown HS Soc Stud Tchr 1975-; Boricua Coll Philosophy Adjunt-Lecturer 1980 & 1988; Fomaica Learning Ctr GED Preparation Tchr Adult Ed 1984-; *ai:* UFT 1976-; *office:* Newtown HS 48-01 90th St Elmhurst NY 11373

BONN, KATHY KADISH, Spanish Teacher; *b:* Tarrytown, CT; *m:* Leonard J.; *c:* Aimee, Brendan, Kelianna; *ed:* So CT St Coll (BS) Span & Sec Ed 1976; So CT St Coll 5th Yr Fr 1984, Masters with St Cert Schl Cnslng 1995; Universidad de Salamanca Summer Study 3 Credits 1975; Culture Stud of Mexico City CEU 1990; *cr:* Sleeping Giant Jr HS Permanent Sub 1976-77; Notre Dame HS Permanent Sub 1977-78, Bus Tchr 1978-79, Span Tchr 1979-, Fgn Lang Dept Head 1982-89; *ai:* NHS Moderator; Natl Span Exam Schl Organizer; AATSP 1979-; COL NCEA; SCSU Alumni Assn 1976-; *office:* Notre Dame HS 24 Ri West Haven CT 06516

BONNAVIAT, BONNIE, French & Social Studies Tchr; *b:* Jers NJ; *ed:* Middlebury Coll (BA) Fr 1962; The Sorbonne (MA) Ongoing Post Grad Credits Since 1970 at Columbia Univ, Univ Overseas Branches; *cr:* Roosevelt Jr HS Fr Tchr 1962-64; Dept of Overseas Fr & Soc Stud Tch 1965-78; Cranford HS Fr Tchr 1982; HS Fr Tchr 1983-85; Schls in Ireland, Bahrain, Japan, Germany, T France Lang Arts Tchr 1985-; Menwith Hill Schl Fr & Soc St 1989-; *ai:* Natl Jr Honor Soc Adv; Holocaust Meml Week Com Advy Cncl; NEA 1989-; Natl Network for Early Lang Learning Comm Alliance 1989-; *office:* Menwith Hill Elem MS PSC Box 45 APO AE 09468

BONNELL, KENNETH LEE, Band Director; *b:* Wheeling, Judith Elaine Gazzola; *c:* Kristin Lynn, Jennifer Erin; *ed:* Mor Univ (BME) Music Ed 1975; Univ of Dayton (MS) Ed Admin 198 OH Univ, Akron Univ; *cr:* Beallsville HS Band Dir 1975-77; Sc Southwest HS, Buckeye Local HS Band Dir 1977-; *ai:* OH Vly A All Star Band Coord 14 Yrs; St Clairsville-Richland Schl Dist o Community Comm; OMEA 1975-, Certfd Judge; OEA 1975-, St A Rep; NEA 1975-; Buckeye Local Classroom Tchrs Assn Negotiations Comm, OEA Del; Elks 1977-; Kiwanis; St Clairs Alumni Assn 1991-, Bd of Dir, VP, Chm Schlsp Comm; *home:* 109 Ln Saint Clairsville OH 43950

BONNER, JANE A., 8th Grade Teacher; *b:* Philadelphia, PA; *ed:* C Hill Coll (BS) Elem Ed 1971; Millersville Univ (MED) Elem E Attending St Joseph's Univ; PA for Cert in Rdng; *cr:* St Matthias S 1983-89; St Athanasius Immaculate Conception Tchr 1989-; *ai:* L Coord; *office:* St Athanasius Immaculate Schl 7105 Limek Philadelphia PA 19138

BONNER, THOMAS PATRICK, 3rd Grade Teacher; *b:* Coaldale Susan Swartz; *c:* Tommy, Michael; *ed:* Kutztown Univ (BS) Elem I *cr:* Tamaqua Area Tchr 1978-; *ai:* Ftbl Coach 20 Yrs & 9 Yrs Head Asst Ftbl Coach Blue Mt HS; PSEA & NEA 1978-; Coach of Y Newspapers & Coaching Orgs.

BONNET, GORDON PAUL, Biology Teacher; *b:* Quantico, VA; Marie Wahler; *c:* Lucas Daniel, Nathan Christopher; *ed:* Southwestern LA (BS) Physics 1982; Empire St Coll (MA) Lin 1995; Tchng Cert, Grad Work Oceanography at Univ of WA; *cr:* F Jr HS 8th-9th Grd Sci Tchr 1987-88; Lake Washington HS Bio, Math Tchr 1988-92; Charles O. Dickerson Bio, Math Tchr 1992- Drama Prgm; NEA 1987-; *office:* Charles O Dickerson HS 100 Trumansburg NY 14886*

BONNET, ROBERT LOCKWOOD, Eighth Grade Life Science NJ; *m:* Amber Shannon Rafferty; *c:* Robert M., Marjorie L.; *ed* Coll (AA) Lib Arts 1967; Kean Coll (BA) Elem Ed 1971; Glass Coll (MA) Environmental Ed; Spec Course in Sci-Sci Tchng Fel Dennis Twp Elem Schl 6th Grd Tchr 1972-80, 8th Grd Life Sci Tch *ai:* Coaching Chess Club; Writing Sci Books; NEA, NJEA, CMC DTEA 1971-, Bldg Rep; DEP St of NJ, Naturalist, YCC Ca Belleplain St Forest 1978-90; Grants Curr Writing, Tech for C Career Ed; Pub 9 Sci Books.

BONNETTE, DENNIS, Prof of Philosophy & Dept Chm; *b:* Gardn *m:* Lois Ann Packard; *c:* Timothy, Christina, Denise, Nichola Gregory, Elizabeth; *ed:* Univ of Detroit (AB) Philosophy 1960; Un Dame (MA) Philosophy 1962, (PHD) Philosophy 1972; *cr:* Univ Diego Instr Philosophy 1963-64; Loyola Univ at New Orleans A Philosophy 1964-65; Univ of Dayton Asst Prof Philosophy 1 Niagara Univ Assoc Prof Philosophy 1970-90, Prof Philosophy 19 ACPA 1967-; Scholars for Soc Justice 1996-; Aquinas Proofs f Existence, Martinus-Nijhoff, the Hague, 1972; Nine Scholarly Ar Philosophy; *home:* 518 Northfield Dr Youngstown NY 14174

BONOMI, MARILYN ALKUS, American Literature T Philadelphia, PA; *m:* Don Joseph; *c:* Erica Beth; *ed:* Temple Univ Eng with Honors 1965; Southern CT St Univ (MS) Rdng 1968; 6th of Advanced Stud in Admin & Supervision 1983; *cr:* Marple-N Schls Rdng Tchr 1965-66; Amity RSD Schls Eng Tchr 1966-; *ai:* Tchr; Co-Operating Tchr-CT Stu Tchng PSM; The Trident News People Learning About Homophobia & Discrimination; Research Mem Staff Dev Planning Comm; Attendence Policy Planning Evaluation Comm; NCTE; Amity Ed Assoc 1966-, Pres, VP, Sec, D 1965-; ASCD 1981-; PDK 1982-; Parents Familys of Lesbians 1994-; Uniterian Soc of New Haven, Bd of Trustees 1981-83; PT of Yr; Co-Author or Author- 4 Eng Curricula; Adjunct SCSU; Reg Dev Trnr-Curr, think Skills, Assessment; *office:* Amity RSD #5 Newton Rd Woodbridge CT 06525*

BONOMO, DANIEL, Music Educator & Dir of Bands; *b:* Scran *m:* Phoebe Bonfardine; *ed:* West Chester Univ (BS) Music Ed 1 Dept of ED M Equiv 1992; 15 Credit Hrs Vandercook Coll of M Chicago; 3 Credit Hrs Villanova Univ; *cr:* Granada Schl Elem, J Choral, Instrumental Music Tchr 1984-85; Hazleton Area Schl Di Jr, Sr HS Instrumental Music Tchr 1985-88; Pope John Paul II C Schl K-8 Music, PE Tchr 1988-89; DuBois Area Schl Dist 9- Instrumental Music 1989-; *ai:* Marching Band; Pit Orch; Ski Clu Judges Assn 1985-, Music Judge; PMEA, MENC, Tournament o Assn 1985-; DAEA, PSEA 1989-; *office:* Dubois Area Sr HS 40 Ave Du Bois PA 15801*

BONSALL, RUSSELL P., Mathematics Tchr & Pgm Ldr; *b:* Phil PA; *m:* Dorothy Seibert; *c:* Christine Britton, Mark, Todd; *ed:* Valley Coll (BA) Math 1964; OH St Univ (MA) Math 1970; *cr:* HS Tchr 1964-; *ai:* Head Var Bsbl 1970-; Wrestling 1965-80; Cl 1969; NCTM, NEA, PSEA 1964-; Hershey Ed 1964-, Treas com Grant OH St U 4 Summmer; Hewlett-Packard 48G Grant 1995; Hershey HS PO Box 898 Homestead Rd Hershey PA 17033*

BONSKY, KATHLEEN ANN (BECKER), 1st Grade Teacher; *b:* OH; *m:* Bradley D.; *c:* Christopher, Kyle; *ed:* Univ of Akron (B Elem Ed 1976; Addl 22 Hrs for Prof Cert; *cr:* Uniontown Elem S Grd Tchr 1977-82, 4th Grd Tchr 1982-87; 3rd Grd Tchr 1987-88, Tchr 1988-89, 3rd Grd Tchr 1989-95, 1st Grd Tchr 1995-; *ai:* Read, Grading & Report Card, Soc, Levy Campaign, PTO, Fa Comms; Martha Holden Jennings Fnd 1987-, Jennings Scholar Uniontown Elem Schl 13244 Cleveland Ave NW Uniontown OH 4

BONTEMPO, CATHERINE MARY (LOCKER), Mathematics T *b:* Cleveland, OH; *m:* James; *c:* Dan, Jim; *ed:* John Carroll Un Math, PE 1973; Ashland Univ (MED); *cr:* Richmond Hts MS Ma Tchr 1973-80; Mentor HS Math Tchr 1988-; *ai:* Richmond Hts MS Adv, Bsktbl Coach, Vlybl Coach 1973-80; NEA, OEA 1973-; NE Mentor Tchrs Assn 1988-; *office:* Mentor HS 6477 Center St Me 44060

BONTEMPO, MARY JONES, Learning Support Teacher; *b:* Can *m:* Vic; *c:* Dawn Bontempo Sudmeyer, Dori; *ed:* Mansfield Univ (B & Spcl Ed 1968; Masters Equivalency; *cr:* Clark Wood Elem 1st 4th Grd Tchr 1968-73, Learning Support Tchr 1980-87; Elkland 7th-12th Grd Emotional Support Tchr 1987-92, Learning Supp *i:* Future Tchrs Assoc Adv; Prof Dev Comm; Tchr Rep for Strategic ange Planning; PSEA 1968-, St Comm for Stu Org; NEA 1968-; 968-, Fin Sec; Delta Kappa Gamma 1990-; Eastern Star 1986-; e Dodge Fndtn Recipient; *office:* Elkland Area HS Ellison Rd PA 16920

MPO, MICHAEL THOMAS, Technology Education Tchr; *b:* p, MA; *m:* Karen Ann Wasileski; *ed:* Univ MA at Boston (BA) Pol ; Cambridge Coll (MED) Ed 1995; Fitchburg St Coll Indstrl Arts Saugus HS Tchr 1974-; *ai:* Ftbl Coach Chelsen HS; NEA, MTA, 4-; St Ftbl Championship 1996; Northeast Conf Coach of Yr 1988; augus HS Pearce Dr Saugus MA 01906

, CHERYL MILNE, Fourth Grade Teacher; *b:* Lakewood, OH; *c:* nus Gribbel, Brady Alan, Casey Milne; *ed:* Kent St Univ (BSED) 1967; *cr:* Pleasant Lake Elem Schl 3rd Grd Tchr 1964; Wilkins chl 3rd-4th Grd Tchr 1985-; *ai:* NEA 1985-; Jr League Omaha r League Cherry Hill 1968-; Jr Amherst 1980-85, Sec; *office:* Elem Schl PO Box 420 Amherst NH 03031

LLE, JOSEPH R., Music Teacher; *b:* Albany, NY; *m:* Eileen ell; *c:* Brian Joseph; *ed:* Coll of St Rose (BS) Music Ed 1980; Coll (MA) Music 1983; Coll of St Rose (MS) Educl Admin 1991; olic Cntrl HS Band Dir 1980-83; Watervliet Elem Schl Band Dir ; Watervliet Jr-Sr High Band Dir 1985-; *ai:* Class of 1999 Adv; semble Dir; Curr Comm; Dist Music Coord; NYSUT 1983-; Union l in Tchng Awd 1995; Remo, Pro-Mark Excl in Percussion Ed Awd l Amer Music Festival Awd 1995; Scholar Recognition Prgm Tchr 90, 1993; *office:* Watervliet Jr Sr HS Wiswall Ave Watervliet NY

, SUSAN MONICA, Assoc Prof & Dir Undgrd Pgrm; *b:* Rockford, Northern IL U (BSE) Eng 1967, (MA) Lib Sci 1978; Rockford Coll Eng 1974; Univ of IL (PHD) Information Sci 1983; Syracuse Univ it Hrs Toward MA; *cr:* Byron Jr HS Tchr 1967-76; Northern IL U sst 1976-79; Univ of IL Asst Dir Lib Resource Ctr 1979-83; e Uni Asst & Assoc Prof 1983-; *ai:* Dir Undergrad Pgm in tion Mgmt Tech; SU Outstdng Female Edctr 1991; 1st Tchr of the ; Numerous Articles Pub; *office:* Syracuse Univ 4-116 Ctr for Sci Syracuse NY 13244

'N, DONALD S., Retired 4th-8th Grade Teacher; *b:* Springfield, Mary Bronson; *c:* Bonnie, Barbara Rutalis, James; *ed:* SUNY at ort (BSEd) Ed 1955; Addl 18 Grad Hrs; *ai:* Coached Swimming , HS Var 1967-87; Swimming Ofcl Local, St, Natl; Chess Club ; Natl Interscholastic Swimming Coaches Assn 1967-87; Amer Coaches Assn 1955-81; NY St Tchrs Assn 1956-; NY St United AFT; *home:* 25 Cullens Run Pittsford NY 14534

ER, REBECCA REA, English Teacher; *b:* Washington, PA; *m:* William Jr.; *c:* Donald William III, Brian Matthew; *ed:* WA & n Coll (BA) Eng 1979; Attnd CA Univ of PA; *cr:* Trinity HS Sub Yrs, Eng Tchr 11 Yrs; McGoffey HS Perm Sub 1 Yr; Grove City HS r 1 Yr; *ai:* PA Yth Ed Assn; Future Tchrs Club Adv 3 Yrs; NEA EA 1985-; PEA 1985-; *office:* Trinity HS 231 Park Ave Washington 01*

DAVID G., Social Studies Teacher; *b:* New Castle, PA; *m:* Shirley afuse; *c:* Bonnie; *ed:* Clarion Univ (BS) Soc Stud 1968; Slippery niv (MED) 1974; *cr:* George Washington Jr HS Tchr 1969; New IS Tchr 1970-; *ai:* Dist Discipline, Intermediate Unit Advy Comms; 80-; NEA 1969-80; NCEA 1969-80, Pres; *office:* New Castle Sr HS incoln Ave New Castle PA 16101

MAUREEN HUTCHINSON, 4th Grade Teacher; *b:* Long Beach, Albert Charles; *c:* Doug, Brad; *ed:* CA St Univ at Long Beach (BA) 1957, (MA) Admin, Supervision 1964; 30 Addl Hrss Lehigh Univ, oh's, Gratz; *cr:* Long Beach USD Tchr 1957-69; Cntrl Buck Schl hr 1976-; *ai:* Tech Coord; CBEA 1969-, Sec; PSEA 1969-; NEA Scouting 1980-, Comm Chprsn; *office:* Cntrl Bucks Schl Dist Rt 413 Buckingham PA 18912

BINDER, LINDA OLMSTEAD, Mathematics Teacher; *b:* a, OH; *m:* Dave G.; *c:* Kelly; *ed:* Kent Univ (BSEd) Math 1974; Univ (MED) Curr, Instruction Aug 1996; Grad hrs Kent St Univ, Wallace, Mt St Joseph Coll; *cr:* Berkshire HS Math Tchr 1974-78; HS Math Tchr 1985; Ledgemont HS Math Tchr, Dept Chair 1985-; Rep; Stu Cncl Adv 1985-95; NEA, OEA, LEA, OH Cncl of Tchrs 1985-; Colebrook United Meth Church; *home:* 2283 Hague Rd OH 44076

E, KEVIN EARL, Physics, Bio & Earth Sci Tchr; *b:* Newburgh, Deborah Denise; *c:* Tearra Margaret; *ed:* Morgan St Univ (BS) Planetary Sci 1982; Cedit Hrs in Spec Ed, Space Sci, Weather e Tech, Cmptrs in Ed at Johns Hopkins Univ, Loyola Coll & r Coll; *cr:* Eastern HS Earth Sci Tchr 1983-86; Lake Clifton Eastern ci Tchr 1986-87; Southern HS Earth Sci, Bio & Physics Tchr 1987-; s Var Bsktbl Head Coach 1987-; Earth Observations from Space dv 1993-; GLOBE Project Lead Tchr 1995-; NSTA 1993-; 1140 Grant for Earth Observations Club Funded by the Fund for Educl ffice: Southern HS 1100 Covington St Baltimore MD 21230

E, MARIE TAYLOR, 8th Grade Social Studies Tchr; *b:* Point t, NJ; *m:* John C.; *c:* Brittany; *ed:* Montclair St (BA) His, Ed 1978; milton HS West His Tchr 1978-79; Penns Grove HS His Tchr); Abseqani HS His Tchr 1980-81; Atlantic City Casinos Supvr, ainer 1981-85; Pinelands Regnl Schls Soc Stud Tchr 1988-; *ai:* Asst rs Soc Stud Close Up; NEA, PTA 1988-; Phi Alpha Theta 1977-; Assn 1978-; *home:* 18 Club Pl Absecon NJ 08201*

E, TRACY KOSHKO, Secondary Math Teacher; *b:* Bellefonte, PA; id; *ed:* Lock Haven Univ (BS) Sec Math Ed 1992; Penn St Univ 12 Hrs Toward MS; *cr:* Bedford HS Algebra Tchr 3 Yrs; Learn Right chr 1 Yr; Penn St Univ Part-Time Math Prof 1 Yr; *ai:* Girls Track NHS Adv; Ski Club Adv & Chaperone; NCTM 1991-; PCTM 1991-; PSEA 1993-; Southern Alleghanies Tech-Prep Consortium Chptrs fice: Bedford HS 330 E John St Bedford PA 15522

E, TERRY LEE, Electronics Instructor; *b:* Lewistown, PA; *ed:* PA Tech (AS) Electronics Tech 1989; Attnd PA St Univ Voc Ed; PA Voc 994; *cr:* Wilhold Corp Electronics Tech 1989-92; SUN Area Tech ectronics Instr 1992-; *ai:* Stu Adv for Voc Indstrl Clubs of Amer; NEA 1992-, VP 1995-; VICA 1993-; Prof Dev Comm 1994-; er of Commerce 1996, Tech Adv; *office:* Sun Area Tech Schl 815 E St New Berlin PA 17855

D, JAMES EDWARD, Music Teacher; *b:* Charleroi, PA; *m:* h Israel; *c:* Jimmy, Kaitlyn; *ed:* Frostburg St Coll (BS) Music Ed Frostburg St Univ (MEd) Admin, Supervision 1987; *cr:* Northern Sr High Music Tchr 1981-94; Westmar HS Music Tchr, Band Dir Barton & Georges Creek Elem Music Tchr Band Dir 1995-; *ai:* Jazz Band, Guard, Indoor Percussion, Indoor Guard; St Pauls Luth Mem 1980-; Music Credit Count Comm; Learning Objectives for rts Music.*

T, DAVID ALLAN, Fifth Grade Teacher; *b:* Toledo, OH; *m:* Sandra *c:* Ashley, Brian; *ed:* Univ of Toledo (BED) Soc Stud & Bus 1968, Elem Ed 1976; *cr:* Mason HS 9th Grd Soc Stud Tchr 1968-70; ulate Conception Schl 5th-8th Grd Tchr 1970-73; Fallen Timbers h Grd Tchr 1973-; *ai:* 7th Grd Vlybl Coach 10 Yrs; MS Yrbk Photographer 9 Yrs; Soc Stud Textbook & Course of Stud Comms; Anthony Wayne Ed Assn 1973-, Bldg Rep, Treas, Negotiations, Del; OH Ed Assn, NEA 1973-; Phi Delta Kappa, Newsletter Ed; Article Instr Magazine 1976; *office:* Fallen Timbers MS 6119 Finzel Rd Whitehouse OH 43558

BOOTH, FRANK S.,JR., English & Journalism Teacher; *b:* Spokane, WA; *ed:* Kent St Univ (BS) Eng, Ed Media 1987; Grad Work for Masters in Prof Writing; Courses at Towson St Univ; *cr:* Stambaugh-Thompson Co 1st Asst Mgr 1972-87; Brunswick HS Eng Tchr 1987-; *ai:* Future Tchrs of Amer Adv; The Schl Newspaper Jrnlsm Adv; NCTE 1987-; Most Inspirational Tchr in Ed; Distngd Svc Awd as Outstdng Instr of Frosh Orientation Kent St Univ; Poetry Pub; *office:* Brunswick HS 101 Cummings Dr Brunswick MD 21716

BOOTH, JEFFREY L., Health Teacher; *b:* Steubenville, OH; *m:* Deborah A. Admonius; *c:* Alexis, Alan; *ed:* OH St Univ (BA) PE 1975, (MA) Sports Admin 1976; Attnd Univ of Akron, Baldwin-Wallace Coll, Kent St Univ, Mt St Joseph Univ; *cr:* Mayfield HS Hlth & PE Tchr 1976-; *ai:* HS Staff Senate & Dist Hlth Curr Comm Mems; OH St Univ Schl of Hlth, PE & Recreation Alumni Assn 1975-; Mayfield Ed Assoc 1976-; OH Ed Assoc 1976-; NEA 1976-; Amer Red Cross CPR Instr 1977-; Amer Red Cross Outstdng Tchr Awd & Outstdng Svc Awd; Mayfield City Schls Avis Awd Winner & Top 40 Awd Winner; Schl Spokesperson on Comm Related Hlth Issues; Basic-Life Support Instr for Coaches Clinics; *office:* Mayfield HS 6116 Wilson Mills Rd Mayfield OH 44143*

BOOTH, JOHN A., Learning Support Teacher; *b:* Pittsburgh, PA; *m:* Constance M. Allen; *c:* Ryan A., Shannon M., Brendan A.; *ed:* Duquesne Univ (BSEd) Spec Ed & Soc Stud 1970, (MSEd) Spec Ed 1973; *cr:* Peters Twp HS Spec Ed Tchr 1970-; *ai:* Stu Assistance Prgm Team Mem; Stage Crew Spon; Audio Visual Coord; Peters Twp Fed of Tchrs & AFT 1978-; Sec; BSA 1992-, Cubmaster; *office:* Peters Twp HS 264 E Mc Murray Rd Mc Murray PA 15317*

BOOTH, MICHAEL DENNIS, Academy Dean & English Teacher; *b:* Pittston, PA; *ed:* King's Coll (BA) Eng 1972; Wilkes Univ (MS) Ed 1978; Cert Schl Admin Marywood Coll 1995; Post Grad Stud PA St Univ Cnslng; *cr:* St Jude Schl Rdng, Soc Stud Tchr 1972-73; Bishop Hoban HS Sr Eng Tchr 1973-; Luzerne Cty Comm Coll Project Rise Eng Tchr 1981; Wilkes Univ Upward Bound Eng Tchr 1982-83; Bishop Hoban HS Acad Dean 1995-; *ai:* NCEA, NCTE 1972-; Northeast Writing Cncl 1988-; Natl Assn for Supervision & Curr 1994-; Knights of Columbus 1972-; Friendly Sons of St Patrick 1969-; St Marys Assumption Schl Advy Bd 1995-; Articles Pub; Wilkes Univ Upward Bound Tchr Svc Awd 1991, Outstdng HS Tchr Nominations 1989, 1993; *office:* Bishop Hoban HS 159 S Pennsylvania Blvd Wilkes Barre PA 18701

BOOTH, WILLIAM P., Math Teacher; *b:* Darby, PA; *m:* Janice Penrose; *c:* Bill, Megan; *ed:* West Chester St (BS) Sec Ed Math 1967, (ME) Tchng of Math 1977; *cr:* Interboro Schl Dist Math Tchr 1967-68; Upper Darby Schl Dist Math Tchr 1968-77; Self-Employed Sales 1977-82; Haverford Schl Dist Math Tchr 1982-; *ai:* Asst Ath & IM Dir; Math Counts Contest Team Spon; NEA 1967-77; NCTM 1982-; ATMOPAV 1982-; PSEA 1987-; *office:* Haverford MS 1701 Darby Rd Havertown PA 19083*

BORAH, KEN ROY, Biology, Chem & Physics Tchr; *b:* Macon, GA; *m:* Nancy Ellis Strickler; *c:* Katherine, Robby; *ed:* Univ of GA (BS) Chem 1973; Johns Hopkins (MAT) Ed 1989; Grad Stud in Food Chem at Univ of GA 34 Hrs, Biochemistry at GA Tech 60 Hrs; 9 Hrs Grad Stud in Ed Tech; *cr:* GA Tech Tchng Asst 1976-80; Brandon Hall Physics & Sci Tchr 1980-81; Marist Schl Chem, Physics & Sci Tchr 1983-88; Baltimore Polytechnic Inst Bio, Chem & Physics Tchr 1991-; *ai:* Chess & SADD Clubs Adv; Badminton Coach; NEA, MD Tchrs Assn 1992-; Glendale Comm Assn 1994-; 2 Articles in Biochemistry, Biophysics & Actu 1980; Nom for MD Tchrs Assn Tchr of Yr Awd; *office:* Baltimore Polytechnic Inst 1400 W Cold Spring Ln Baltimore MD 21209

BORATENSKI, MATTHEW JOHN, English Teacher; *b:* Washington, DC; *m:* Estelene Williamson; *c:* Christopher, Dana, Ashley; *ed:* Univ of MD (BA) Eng 1972; 21 Post Grad Credit Hrs Western MD Coll; M Eq Montgomery Cty Pub Schls; *cr:* Thomas Wootton HS Eng, Soc Stud, Cmptr Application Tchr 1972-; *ai:* Var Sftbl, Soccer; Staff Dev, Tech Comm; MD Stu Assistance Prgm; NEA, MCEA, MD St Tchrs Assn 1972-; Natl Soccer Coaches Assn 1975-; *office:* Thomas S Wootton HS 2100 Wootton Pky Rockville MD 20850*

BORAWSKI, SUZANNE MARY (DRUMSTA), 8th Grade Social Studies Tchr; *b:* Bufflo, NY; *m:* David Fabian; *ed:* Daemen Coill (BA) His, Govt 1971; Canisius Coll (MS) Ed 1976; 20 Hrs Learning Disabled; *cr:* Holy Angels Acad 11th-12th Grd AP Soc Stud Tchr 1971-81; Batavia Schl Dist 8th Grd Soc Stud Tchr 1983-; *ai:* Union Rep 1985-; Union Schlsp Chprsn 1988-; Dist Calendar Co-Chair; Cultural Diversity Comm 1995-; Instrl Forum 1989-; Jr NHS Moderator 1988-95; Stu Cncl Moderator 1984-93; 8th Grd Co-Moderator 1987-; Union Environmental Safety Chair 1994-; Dist Stud Skills Review Chair 1992-94; NYSUT, AFT 1983-; Parish Cncl 1994-; Jaycees 1985-87; MS Tchr of Yr 1992.*

BORBI, LOUIS, Fifth Grade Teacher; *b:* Roebling, NJ; *ed:* Univ of MD (BS) His 1967; 50 Post Grad Credits; *cr:* Clara Barton Elem Schl 6th Grd Tchr 1966-67; Roebling Pub Schl 6th Grd Tchr 1967-94, 5th Grd Tchr 1994-; *ai:* Artronomy Club; AVA Coord; NEA 1966-; Fire Dept 1956-; Historical Soc 1980-; *office:* Roebling Pub Schl Hornberger Ave Roebling NJ 08554

BORCHERS, DAVID WHITNEY, Science & Mathematics Teacher; *b:* Berlin, NH; *m:* Catherine Jean Cuchetti; *c:* Matthew, Kristen; *ed:* Tufts Univ (BS) Experimental Psych 1971; Plymouth St Coll (MED) Educl Supervision 1989; Simmons Coll Grad Stud; *cr:* Franklin Pub Schls Tchr 1974-80; Laconia Chrstn Schl Tchr & Admin 1980-; *ai:* Cross-Cntry Coach; Chorus Dir; NHSTA 1974-; TMNE 1987-; Phi Kappa Phi 1989-; NH Chrstn Coalition 1995-, Cty Chair; *office:* Laconia Christian Schl 1386 Meredith Ctr Rd Laconia NH 03246

BORDELL, PATRICIA A., Chemistry Teacher; *b:* Springdale, PA; *m:* George R.; *c:* Joseph; *ed:* IN Univ of PA (BS) Chem & Math 1966; Temple Univ (MED) Sci Ed 1971; Univ of Pittsburgh (PHD) Admin & Schl Law 1980; *cr:* Lower Merion HS Algebra & Geometry Tchr 1966-68; Corning-Painted Post Schl Dist 8th Grd Sci Tchr 1968-69; Penn Hills HS Chem & Advanced Placement Chem Tchr & Sci Dept Chair 1969-; *ai:* Western PA Regnl Sci & Math Collaborative Comm; Advanced Placement Chem Reader & Wkshp Ldr; Advanced Placement Chem Summer Instr at Manhattan Coll & LaSalle Univ; Chem Lab Assts Spon; Chem Tutoring Club; Amer Chem Soc Ed Gr 1981-, Chm, Vice Chair Twice; Soc for Analytical Chem of Pittsburgh 1990-, Keivin Burns Awd 1995; Spectroscopy Soc of Pittsburgh 1991-, HS Equipment Grants; NSTA 1987-; BSA Troop 205 1989-, Asst Scoutmaster; Performing Arts for Children 1983-, Pres, VP; Pittsburgh Childrens Festival 1983-; FAST Swim Team Parents Assn 1987-, Awds Chprsn; SSP Keivin Burns Outstanding Sci Tchr Awd 1995; Penn Hills Tchr of Yr Awd 1991; Pittsburgh Section of ACS Tchr Awds in Curr & Lab 1993; 4 Articles Pub in ACS Newsletter, The Crucible; Recipient of SSP HS Equipment Grants in 1983, 1991 & 1995; *office:* Penn Hills Sr HS 12200 Garland Dr Pittsburgh PA 15235

BORDEN, FRANCES E., English Teacher; *b:* Wasco, CA; *ed:* Lubbock Chrstn Coll (AA) Speech & Eng 1964; TX Tech Univ (BSEd) Ed, Speech & Eng 1967, (MSEd) Ed & Speech 1973; *cr:* Gruver Ind Schl Eng & Speech Tchr 1969-71; Sublette Unified Schl Eng & Speech Tchr 1971-75; Midland Chrstn Schl Eng & Jrnlsm Tchr 1975-76; Milford Cntrl Eng Tchr 1982-84; South New Berlin Cntrl Eng Tchr 1984-; *ai:* Stu Cncl Adv; Acad Challenge Coach; DMCO BOCES Acad Challenge Coord; Spirit & Stu Recognition Comms; South New Berlin Fac Assn 1984-; NEA 1967-75, 1982-; Thirteen-Contributor & Co-Editor; Canadian Poetry Magazine Contributor; *home:* RR 3 Box 81-070 Oneonta NY 13820*

BORDEN, MARK STEPHEN, HS Instrumental Music Director; *b:* Honeoye Falls, NY; *m:* Lindsey Jane Simmonds; *c:* Kelsey Anne; *ed:* Ithaca Coll (BM) Music Ed 1983, (MM) Music Ed 1986; *cr:* Cincinnatus Cntrl Schl Instrumental Music Dir 1983-85; Honeoye Falls-Lima HS Instrumental Music Dir 1986-; *ai:* Var Vllybl Coach; Jazz Ensemble & Musical Pit Orch Dir; NYSSMA & MENC 1994-; Honeoye Falls Comm Concert Band 1989-, Asst Dir; *office:* Honeoye Falls Lima HS 83 East St Honeoye Falls NY 14472

BORDEN, ROBERT F., English & Journalism Teacher; *b:* Philadelphia, PA; *m:* Arashay; *ed:* Millersville St (BS) Eng 1973; +33 Credit Hrs; *cr:* Conestoga Valley HS Eng Tchr 1977-; *ai:* Boys Bsktbl Head Coach 1982-; Asst Ftbl Coach 1977-; NEA & PSEA 1977-.

BORDER, CONSTANCE CORSSAR, French Teacher; *b:* Cleveland, OH; *m:* Randy Jay; *c:* Donald, Michael; *ed:* Baldwin-Wallace Coll (BA) Fr 1972, (MA) Scndry Admin 1980; Attnd Middlebury Coll, OH St Univ, Univ of Aix-en Provence France; *cr:* Normandy HS Fr Tchr 1974-81; Pleasant Valley Fay Jr HS Fr Tchr 1981-82, Valley Forge HS Fr Tchr 1982-84, 1989-91, 1991-; *ai:* Mentor First Yr Tchr; Tutor for Proficiency Test; Remedial Work for Stu for Math Portion OH Proficiency; NEA, OEA, NEOEA, PEA 1974-; Jennings Scholar 1982-83; 2 Wkshps Pub by Natl Textbook Vocabulary Bingo Games Verb Bingo Games; *home:* 18172 Winchester Ct Strongsville OH 44136

BORDER, RICHARD ALLEN, Head Teacher; *b:* Everett, PA; *ed:* Grace Coll (BS) Elem Ed 1974; PA St Univ Post Grad Work; *cr:* Everett Area Schl Dist Head Tchr 1974-; *ai:* Site Base Mgmt Co-Chair 1989-; PSEA 1974-; NEA 1974-; Everett Area Ed Assn 1974-, Pres; Comm Grace Brethren Church 1984-, Moderator, Vice Moderator, Worship Ldr, Sunday Schl Supt, Recording Sec.

BORDICK, JOHN DANIEL, Science Teacher; *b:* Kittanning, PA; *c:* Nathan; *ed:* Clarion St Univ (BS) Bio 1973, (MS) Sci Ed 1976; 3 Hrs Sci Ed; *cr:* St Marys HS Earth Sci, Bio Tchr 1973-77; St Marys MS Gen Sci Tchr 1977-86; St Marys HS Earth Sci Tchr 1986-; *ai:* Asst Soccer Coach; SAP; NEA 1977-; PSEA 1973-; St Marys Rec Soccer 1984-, Dir; *office:* St Marys Area HS 977 S Saint Marys Rd Saint Marys PA 15857

BORDNER, DEBRA CLIFFORD, Family & Child Specialist; *b:* Sunbury, PA; *m:* William Andrew; *c:* Shelbi Ann, Carli Joelle, Lindsey Brooke; *ed:* Susquehanna Univ (BA) Sociology, Scndry Soc Stud 1978; Bloomsburg Univ Cert Elem Ed 1979; *cr:* Selinsgrove Yth Svc Bureau Dir 1979-81; Selinsgrove Area Schl Dist Sub Tchr 1986-90; Snyder Union Office of Human Resources Employment, Trng Coord 1987-90; Midd-West Schl Dist Tchr 1990-95; *ai:* Career Assn Adv; Summer Girls Sftbl 8-12 Yrs Coach 7 Yrs; Selinsgrove Area Recreation 1989-; *home:* RR 1 Box 171B Selinsgrove PA 17870

BORECKY, CATHERINE MARY, Science Teacher; *b:* Sewickley, PA; *m:* Stephen R.; *c:* Michael Hennessy, David Hennessy; *ed:* Carlow coll (BS) Bio 1987; Scndry Ed Cert Bio & Gen Sci; *cr:* St Thomas More Schl Sci Tchr 1988-; *ai:* PA Jr Acad of Sci Prgm Moderator; Pittsburgh Regnl Schl Sci & Engrng Fair Spon; 7th-8th Grd Sci Fair Coord; PA Sci Tchrs Assn; PA Jr Acad of Sci 1993-, Judging Comm Mem; Soc of Analytical Chemists Tchr Awd 1994; Pittsburgh Regnl Schl Sci & Engrng Fair Tchr Awd 1996.

BORECKY, STEPHEN R., Associate Professor of Biology; *b:* Johnstown, PA; *m:* Catherine; *c:* Michael Hennessy, David Hennessy; *ed:* Univ of Pittsburgh (PHD) Anatomy 1977; *cr:* Univ of PA Tchng Fellow 1971-77; Penn St Univ Instr 1975-81; Carlow Coll Assoc Prof 1979-; *ai:* PA Sci Tchrs Assoc; PA Acad of Sci; Carlow Coll Pres Awd for Excl in Tchng; Carnegie Museum Awd for Sci Achvmt; Wilson Awd.

BORELLI, VINCENT J., Head Teacher; *b:* Jersey City, NJ; *m:* Angela Mangione; *c:* Annamaria, Antonia; *ed:* Montclair St U (BA) Speech, Theatre 1972; Hunter Coll (MA) Theatre 1996; Monmouth Univ Cert 1994; *cr:* Long Branch JHS Tchr 1972-79, Comm, Dance, Theatre Head Tchr 1979-; *ai:* Drama, Speech & Forensic, Announcement Club; Sr Class; NJEA, STANJ 1971-, Tchr of Yr 1988; NJFF 1972-; Church Men's Club, IAMA 1990-; 16 Best Dir; Flwshp Pub Issues Seminar; Article Forensic Team; Outstdng Svc 1990; *office:* Long Branch HS 391 Westwood Ave Long Branch NJ 07740*

BORESTA, COLLEEN BERRY, Social Studies Teacher; *b:* Chicago, IL; *m:* John; *ed:* Berry Univ (BA) His 1976; Marquette Univ (MA) European His 1978; *cr:* Moore Cath HS Soc Stud Tchr 1979-.*

BORGEN, THOMAS JOHN, 7th & 8th Grd Science Teacher; *b:* Catskill, NY; *w:* Lorraine (dec); *c:* Alesia, Robert, Ashley; *ed:* Delhi Ag & Tech (AA) Lbrl Arts 1974; Oswego St (BA) Sec Ed, Bio 1976; 30 Addl Grad Hrs; *cr:* Red Creek Cntrl Schls Sci Tchr 1977-80; Govt of Guam Sci Tchr 1980-81; Kuwait Amer Schl Tchr 1981-83; Chatham MS Sci Tchr 1983-; *ai:* NEA 1977-; STANYS 1989-; Comm Little League, Soccer, Coach; *office:* Chatham MS Woodbridge Ave Chatham NY 12037

BORING, ELIZABETH CREA, Sixth Grade Teacher; *b:* Sharon, PA; *m:* Arthur H.; *ed:* KY Chrstn Coll (BA) Chrstn Ed 1964; Milligan Coll (BA) Elem Ed 1969; Kent St Univ (MA) Elem Ed 1984; Univ of AL 6 Post Grad Hrs Air & Space Ed; 15 Post Grad Hrs Elem Ed; Ashland Coll 2 Post Grad Hrs Tech; *cr:* Fowler-Vienna Dist 6th Grd Tchr 1966-68; Badger Dist 2nd & 4th-6th Grd Tchr 1969-87; Badger MS 6th & 8th Grd Tchr 1987-; *ai:* Lang Arts Comm; Parent-Tchr Involvement; Scheduling & Sci Comms; 6th Grd Bldg Level Assessment Team; Optimist Oratorical Contest & Acad Challenge Team Coach; Badger Ed Assn 1966-, Pres, Bldg Rep, Membership Awd; NEA, OEA 1966-, St Rep; Delta Kappa Gamma 1992-; Eastern Star 1965-; Certified Lay Speaker 1983-; Church, Womens Soc 1981-, Pres; Martha Holden Jennings Grant; *office:* Badger MS 6144 Youngstown-Conneaut Rd Kinsman OH 44428

BORISON, MARIA VEJAR, Spanish Teacher; *b:* Ecuador; *ed:* Univ of MA at Boston (BA) Sociology 1981; New Hampshire Coll (MS) Psych 1987; Rivier Coll at Nashuo; *cr:* Private Lang Consultant Tchr 1980-; Dept of Soc Svc Soc Worker, Cnslr 1981-92; Alpha Lang Inst Span Tchr, Translator 1988-93; Bishop Guertin HS Span Tchr 1993-; *ai:* Soph Class Adv, Moderator; Span Club Coord; Neighbor to Neighbor Clinic, Vol; Children, Family Svc Awd; *office:* Bishop Guertin HS 194 Lund Rd Nashua NH 03060

BORJA, MARIANNE E., Assoc Professor; *b:* Allentown, PA; *m:* Francisco E.; *ed:* Coll Misericordia (BS) Food & Nurition 1968; Cornell Univ (MS) Human Nutrition & Food 1971; Temple Univ (EDD) Sci Ed 1985; Syracuse Univ 3 Credits 1973; NY Univ 16 Credits 1973-79; PA St Univ 1 Credit 1994; *cr:* VA Medical Ctr Ed Coord & Clinical Instr 1976-85; Marywood Coll Asst Prof 1971-76 & 1985-; *ai:* Coll Rank & Tenure, Curr & Hlth Promotion Comms; Amer Dietetic Assn 1973-, Natl Delegate & Dist Pres, PA Keystone Awd, Fellow of the Amer Dietetic Assn; Inst of Food Techs 1995-; March of Dimes 1990-, Hlth Promotion Comm; Meals on Wheels 1974-; Articles Pub; Registered Dietician; *office:* Marywood Coll Grad Schl Of Arts & Sciences 2300 Adams Ave Scranton PA 18509*

BORKHUIS, CHARLES, Creative Writing & Eng Prof; *b:* Jamaica, NY; *ed:* TX Chrstn Univ (BA) Eng, Philosophy 1968; San Francisco St Univ (MA) Eng 1973; *ai:* Coord of Frosh Fnd Dept; Former Ed; Books Pub: Hypnogogic Sonnets, Proximity; Numerous Plays Produced, Poems, Essays Pub in Lit Journals; *office:* Touro Coll 25-27 W 23rd St New York NY 10010

BORKON, JEFFREY ALAN, Illustration & Cartooning Tchr; *b:* New York, NY; *m:* Betty Ann; *ed:* Lehman Coll (BA) Art, Ed 1973, (MA) Art 1974; City Coll 30 Addl Credit Hrs Voc Ed; *cr:* Borough of Manhattan Comm Coll Production, Graphic Asst 1973-74; Westlake MS Art Tchr 1976-78; HS of Art & Design Art Tchr 1980-; *ai:* Tchr Adv for Ind Stud in Art; UFT, NEA 1980-; Designed & Illustrated Tech Manuals for NY City Bd of Ed; *office:* The HS of Art & Design 1075 2nd Ave New York NY 10022*

BORLAND, STEPHEN ARTHUR, Naval Science Teacher; *b:* Rapid City, SD; *m:* Judith; *c:* Michele, Jason; *ed:* MD USMC (BA) Naval Sci 1985; *cr:* US Marine Corps MSGT E-8 1969-91; *ai:* Rifle Team, Drill Team, Color Guard Adv Coach; AFT 1991-; Amer Legion 1985-; *office:* William Allen HS 17th & Turner St Allentown PA 18104

BORLESKE, BARBARA LESH, Chemistry Teacher; *b:* Jackson, TN; *m:* Stephen G.; *c:* Julie, Andrew, Holly; *ed:* Rhodes Coll (BS) Chem 1968; Duke Univ (MA) Chem 1970; Post Grad Study Univ of DE, Univ of Richmond & VA Commonwealth Univ; *cr:* Northern HS Chem Tchr 1970-72; New Castle Cty Learning Ctr Adult Ed Instr 1983-84 & 1988-92; VA Union Univ Instr 1985-86; Clover Hill HS Chem & Earth Sci Tchr 1986-87; John Dickinson HS Chem Tchr 1992-; *ai:* Environmental Club Spon; Sci Olympiad Team Spon & Coach; DSEA & NEA 1992-; NSTA 1994-; Amer Soc for Biochemistry & Molecular Bio Flwshp 1993; *home:* 29 Slashpine Cir Hockessin DE 19707*

BORMAN, BARRY J., Biology Teacher & Athletic Dir; *b:* Cincinnati, OH; *m:* Patricia Ann; *c:* Jon, Matt, David, Jill, Tracy, Christopher; *ed:* Univ of Cincinnati (BS) Microbio 1968, (MED) Scndry Admin 1972; Xavier Univ Post Grad Schl Admin; *cr:* Cinti Pub Schls Sci Tchr 1968-69; Moeller HS Sci Tchr, Sci Dept Chm, Alumni Dir & Ath Dir 1969-; *ai:* Ath Dir of Operations 4 Yrs; Alumni Dir 16 Yrs; Coach: Track 6 Yrs, Bsbl 8 Yrs & Cross Cntry 2 Yrs; NSTA 1969-; NCEA 1969-; Smithsonian Soc 1978-; Natl Geographic Soc 1980-; All Saints Parish 1969-, Pres & Ed Commission, Bsktbl & Bsbl Coach, 5 City Championships; Moeller HS Distngd Alumni & Hall of Fame Alumni Awds; *office:* Moeller HS 9001 Montgomery Rd Cincinnati OH 45242

BORN, ATHENA THEODOREU, Spanish Teacher; *b:* New York, NY; *m:* Donald; *c:* Alyson, Christopher; *ed:* Adelphi Univ (MA) Span 1980, (BA) Span 1973; 75 Addl Credits MA; *cr:* Babylon Jr Sr HS Span Tchr 1974-75, 1976-77; Holy Trinity HS Span Tchr 1976; West Islip HS Span Tchr 1979-; *ai:* WI Tchrs Assn 1979-; NYSAFLT, AATSP; *office:* West Islip H S 1 Lion's Path West Islip NY 11795*

BORN, JEFFERY ALLEN, Associate Professor of Finance; *b:* Elyria, OH; *m:* Mary Ann Dalessio; *c:* Sarah, Jeffery, Megan; *ed:* Bowling Green St univ (BS) Bus Admin, (MA) Ec 1978; U of NC at Chapel Hill (PHD) Bus Admin, Fin 1986; *cr:* Univ of KY Asst Prof Fin 1983-87; Northeastern Univ Assoc Prof Fin 1988-; *ai:* Yth Soccer Coach; Chair Jr HS Bldg Comm; Eastern Fin Assoc 1983-, VP 1991-94; Fin Mngmt Assoc 1982-; Amer Fin Assoc 1980-; Assoc Ed Fin Review; Co-Authored Articles; 30 Plus Presentations at Prof Assn Meetings; *office:* Northeastern Univ 412 Hayden Hall Boston MA 02115

BORNHORST, TONY JOE, Health & Physical Teacher; *b:* Troy, OH; *m:* Dina Arias-Bornhorst; *c:* Kylee, Becca; *ed:* OH Wesleyan Univ (BA) Hlth, PE 1980; Miami Univ (MA) PE 1981; 30 Post Grad Hrs in Ed Admin; *cr:* Riverside HS Hlth Edctr 1981-88; Brookfield HS Hlth Edctr 1981-88; Jackson HS Hlth Ed, PE Tchr 1988-93; Dublin Coffman HS Hlth Ed, PE Tchr 1993-; *ai:* Head Coach Boys Var Bsktbl; Asst Ath Dir; OHSBCA 1988-; NEA, OEA 1981-95; SEOAL Coach of Yr Jackson HS 1990-91; Sectional Champs Dist 10 All Star Coach 1993-94; Dist Champs 1994-95; *home:* 7250 Hopewell Ct Dublin OH 43017

BORNSTEIN, DAVID STUART, English Teacher; *b:* Hartford, CT; *ed:* Emerson Coll (BA) Ed 1969; Cntrl CT St Univ (MA) Guid 1979; *cr:* King Philip Jr High Eng Tchr 1969-79; Hall High Eng Tchr 1979-; *ai:* Frosh Bsktbl Coach 1979-82; Acad Adv 1979-82; Schl Evaluation Comm 1993-94; CEA 1969-; NEA 1969-; Newington Little League 1990-, Coach & Mgr; *office:* Hall HS 975 N Main St W Hartford CT 06117

BORON, BETH WALKER, Kindergarten Teacher; *b:* Buffalo, NY; *m:* Eric T.; *c:* Andrew T., Caroline E., Allison M.; *ed:* St Univ Coll at Buffalo (BS) Elem Ed 1978, (MS) Early Chldhd Ed 1986; *cr:* Buffalo Parochial Schls Kndgtn, Pre-Kndgtn Tchr 1978-81; Sidway Elem Schl Kndgtn Tchr 1981-83; Kaegebein Elem Schl 3 Grd Tchr 1984-86; Huth Rd Elem Schl Kndgtn, 4 Grd Tchr 1987-93; Charlotte Sidway Schl Kndgtn Tchr 1993-; *ai:* Sidway Shared Decision Making Team, Tech Comm; Sidway & Huth Rd Schl PTA's; GI Comm Ed Tchr; NYSUT, AFL-CIO 1978-; GITA 1981-; Cub Scout Pack 510 1993-, Web Den Ldr; Celebration of Inspiration Awd; NY St PTA Life Mbrshp Awd; *office:* Charlotte Sidway Schl 2451 Baseline Rd Grand Island NY 14072

BOROVAC, DANIEL MICHAEL, Math & Soc Stud Teacher; *b:* Cleveland, OH; *m:* Mary Harrington; *c:* Daniel, Mary Kay, Meg Reese, Amy Beno, Tracy; *ed:* Kent St Univ (BS) Elem Ed 1974; Univ of Akron (MS) Elem Admin 1992; Elem Prin Cert 15 Post Grad Hrs; *cr:* Caledonia Elem Schl 4th & 6th Grd Tchr 1974-; *ai:* Dist Focus Stud Group; Venture Capital Comm; ECEA 1974-, OEA 1974-; NEA 1974-; Phi Delta Kappa 1992-; Holy Cross Church PSR 1993-, Soc Justice Comm 1995-; Martha Holden Jennings Outstdng Edctr Awd 1987; *home:* 90 E 200th St Euclid OH 44119*

BOROWICZ, ROBERT JOSEPH, Economics Teacher; *b:* Buffalo, NY; *ed:* Ithaca Coll (BA) Soc Stud 1971; 34 Grad Credit Hrs Scndry Ed at Hofstra Univ; 6 Grad Credit Hrs Spec Ed at Adelphi Univ; *cr:* Walt Whitman HS Ec Tchr 1972-83; Half Hollow Hills West HS Amer His Tchr 1983-84; Walt Whitman HS Ec Tchr 1984-; *ai:* Former HS, Hofstra Univ Bsbl Coach; AAFT, NYSUT 1972-; South Huntington Tchrs Assn 1972-, Bldg Rep; Amer Bsbl Coach Assn 1975-; Articles PUb 1992-93; *office:* Walt Whitman HS 301 W Hills Rd Huntington Sta NY 11746

BOROWSKI, KELLY SIMON, Psychology & Sociology Teacher; *b:* Baltimore, MD; *m:* Richard A.; *ed:* Frostburg St Univ (BA) Soc Sci 1986; The Johns Hopkins Univ (MS) Ed; MD St Cert Admin & Supervision; *cr:* Mt Hebron HS Tchr 1986-; *ai:* Stdnt Govt Assn Spon; Schl Improvement Team, Mid St Evaluation Chprsn; Commencement Act Coord; NEA, MSTA, HCEA 1987-; MAACIE 1993-, MSAP 1988-; NASSP 1993-, TOPSS 1996; Tchr Support Team 1990-, Chprsn; Stdnts Support Team 1988-, Chprsn; HCC Evening of Excl; *office:* Mt Hebron HS 9440 State Route 99 Ellicott City MD 21042*

BORRUSO, ANNETTE, English Chairperson & Teacher; *b:* Brooklyn, NY; *ed:* Molloy Coll (BA) Eng 1969; St John's Univ (MA) Eng 1973; *cr:* Presentation Schl 4th Grd Tchr 1960-62; St Patrick's Schl 5th Grd Tchr 1962-65; All Saints Elem Schl 5th Grd Tchr 1965-66; St Catherine of Genoa 5th, 7th-8th Grd Tchr 1966-70; Dominican Commercial HS 11th-12th Grd Chprsn, Eng Tchr 1970-; *ai:* Spring Musical, Drama Club, Spirit Days Dir; Motivation Comm; Chprsn of Philosophy Comm for Mid St Accreditation; NCTE 1968-; BQCTE 1967-69, VP; NCEA 1965-; Adj Prof Molloy Coll 1978, St John's Univ 1974-; *office:* Dominican Commercial HS 161-06 89th Ave Jamaica NY 11432

BORSETTI, ELIZABETH M., Physical Ed Teacher & Coach; *b:* New York, NY; *m:* Charles V.; *c:* Kathryn, Danielle; *ed:* St Josephs Coll at Patchogue (BS) Recreation 1982; *cr:* Miller Place HS Head Coach 1983-; Our Lady Queen of the Apostles Schl Elem PE Tchr 1983-; Our Lady of Mercy Schl Elem PE Tchr 1985-; *ai:* Var Sftbl, Var Bsktbl & JV Field Hockey Head Coach; Suffolk Cty Sftbl Coach 1983-; Field Hockey Coach 1983-; Suffolk Cty Womens Bsktbl Coach 1988-; Bsktbl Coach of the Yr 1990; *office:* Miller Place HS 15 Memorial Dr Miller Place NY 11764

BORST, JAMES ROBERT, US History Teacher; *b:* Lowell, MA; *m:* Virginia A. Wasik; *c:* Jamie, Kerry, Christopher; *ed:* St Francis Xavier Univ (BA) Psych 1964; Salem St Coll (MED) Guid 1969; Attnd Boston Univ, Rivier Coll; *cr:* Middlesex Acad Tchr 1991-95; Lowell HS Tchr 1965-; *ai:* Pelham Little League; Pelham Boy Scouts; Minister of Communion St Pat's; VP Local Tchrs Union; UTH 1972-, VP; Outstdng Tchr by Seminar Class 1995; Tchr of Yr Middlesex Acad 1995; *home:* 14 Saw Mill Rd Pelham NH 03076

BORSTORFF, ROBIN LYNN, Physical Education Teacher; *b:* Union City, PA; *ed:* Slippery Rock Univ (BS) Hlth & PE 1985; Edinboro Univ (MA) Cnslng 1995; *cr:* Meadville YMCA Sports & Fitness Dir 1986-87; Robeson Cty Schls Elem PE Tchr 1987-89; St Luke Cath Schl Elem PE Tchr 1989-90; Southwestern Cntrl Schls HS PE Tchr 1990-; *ai:* Girls Var Vllybl & Bsktbl Coach; Stu Support Team; SADD Adv; Inservice Comm; Timbercrest Cnslr; NEA 1990-; *office:* Southwestern HS 600 Hunt Rd Jamestown NY 14701

BORSUK, EDWARD JOSEPH, Sci, Physics & Geology Instr; *b:* Cleveland, OH; *m:* Rose Marie Vecchio; *c:* Michael; *ed:* Edinboro Univ of PA (BS) Scndry Ed, Earth Sci 1975, (MS) Elem Ed, Microcomputers 1986; Case Western Reserve Univ Nuclear Physics; Kent St Univ Voc Ed Cert; *cr:* St Edward HS 9th Grd Earth Sci Tchr 1976-77; Erie Mc Dowell HS 9th Grd Earth Sci Tchr 1978-84; Mentor Mem Jr HS 9th Grd Earth Sci Tchr 1984-87; Stow-Munroe Falls HS Sci, Physics, Geology, Polymer Sci Instr 1987-; Univ of Akron Polymer Testing Instr 1994-; *ai:* VICA Adv; Swim Team Coach; Tech Comm; Tech Prep Dev Comm; Stow Tchrs Assn 1987-; OH Ed Assn, NEA 1984-; United Way Summit Co 1993-, Chm 1993-95; Diabetes Assn of Greater Cleveland 1994-, Vol 1994-; OH Sports Festival 200 Meter Swimming Champion 1992; OH Dept of Dev Schl to Work Grant; OH Tech Prep Matching Funds Grant; *office:* Stow-Munroe Falls HS 3227 E Graham Rd Stow OH 44224*

BORTLE, BARBARA COON, Third Grade Teacher; *b:* Williamsport, PA; *m:* Collin Lee; *c:* Christy; *ed:* St Univ of NY at Oswego (BS) Elem Ed N-6 1969; 30 Grad Credit Hrs at Western CT St Univ at Danbury; *cr:* Pawling Cntrl Schl 3rd Grd Tchr 1969-; *ai:* NEA, NEA-NY 1969-; Pawling Tchrs Assn 1969-, Prof Practices Comm; 150 Plus Hrs of Inservice Work; *home:* RR 2 Box 93 Poughquag NY 12570

BORTON, LINDA BOYERS, 7th & 8th Grade English Tchr; *b:* Wauseon, OH; *m:* Jerry Allen; *c:* Andrea, Stephanie, Emily; *ed:* Adrian Coll (BS) Hlth, PE 1970; Elem Cert Bowling Green St Univ 1985; Grad Courses Univ of Toledo; *cr:* Madison Plains HS PE, Speech Tchr 1971-73; Napoleon MS Eng Tchr 1986-; *ai:* Power of the Pen Coach; Search Comms; Mentor Tchr; NEA, OEA, Napoleon Fac Assn 1986-; Hospice Vol 1996; Church Choir 1993; Fulton Cty Family Issues Task Force 1995-; Venture Capital Grant Writer; *office:* Napoleon MS 303 W Main St Napoleon OH 43545

BORUCKI, CATHERINE FLAMM, Fourth Grade Teacher; *b:* Reading, PA; *m:* Thomas; *c:* Alex, Brigitte; *ed:* Xavier Univ (BS) Elem Ed-Magna Cum Laude 1978; Miami Univ (MED) Elem Ed, Cert GATE Ed 1990; 4 Semester Credits Sherlock Math 1993-94; *cr:* St Francis de Sales Elem Schl 2nd & 3rd Grd Tchr 1978-87; Bruce Elem Schl GATE Tchr 1987-88, 4th Grd Tchr 1988-; *ai:* NEA 1987-; Martha Holden Jennings Fnd Grant 1991-92; Various Cty Grants; *office:* Bruce Elem Schl 201 E Saint Clair St Eaton OH 45320

BORUSIEWICZ, TERRI BURKE, Language Arts Teacher; *b:* Ambler, PA; *m:* Stephen; *c:* Colin; *ed:* LaSalle Univ (BA) Eng Lit 1989; *cr:* St Agnes-Sacred Heart Schl Lang Arts Tchr 1991-; *home:* 472 Cheswyck Dr Harleysville PA 19438

BORZELLO, KATHLEEN MACK, Special Education Teacher; *b:* Bay Shore, NY; *m:* Ralph; *ed:* SUNY at Farmingdale (AAS) Early Chldhd 1977; St Josephs Coll (BA) K-6th Grd Ed & Spec Ed 1980; St Johns Univ (MS) Ed & Elem 1983; Prof Diploma Admin & Supervision 1991; *cr:* St Francis of Assisi 5th-6th Grd Tchr 1980-82; St Boniface 7th-8th Grd Tchr 1982-85; Cntrl Islip HS Spec Ed Tchr 1985-86; Copiague Schl Dist Spec Ed & HS Resource Room Tchr 1986-; *ai:* Colorguard & Key Club Adv; Copiague Tchrs Assn 1986-, Bldg Rep, Co-Grievance Chprsn 1995; *office:* Copiague HS 1100 Dixon Ave Copiague NY 11726*

BOSAK, JAN K., Social Stud & Driver Ed Tchr; *b:* New Kensington, PA; *ed:* Slippery Rock Univ (BS) Soc Stud 1968; Edinboro Univ (MED) Soc Stud 1973; *cr:* Ft LeBoeuf HS Tchr 1968-, Dept Chm 1992-; *ai:* Acad Challenge Team Adv; NEA 1968-; *office:* Fort Le Boeuf HS 931 N High St Waterford PA 16441

BOSCH, ANNE DOLORES, 5th-9th Grade French Teacher; *b:* Brooklyn, NY; *c:* Julia, Gary; *ed:* City Coll of NY (BA) Fr & Ed 1960, (MA) Fr & Ed 1964; La Sorbonne Paris France Degre Superieur; *cr:* Ardsley Schls Fr Tchr 1960-61; JHS 135 Fr & Span Tchr 1961-68; Rutgers Preparatory Fr Tchr 1979-; *ai:* 7th Grd Level Coord; Fr Annual TEA Foreign Lang Week Coord; New Tchrs Mentor; AATF, SOFT 1989-; FLENJ 1988-; Rutgers Univ Zimmerli Museum 1991-, Vol Worker Friends; *office:* Rutgers Preparatory Schl 1345 Easton Ave Somerset NJ 08873*

BOSCH, FRANCINE AUNGIER, Home & Careers Teacher; *b:* Syracuse, NY; *m:* William C.; *c:* Stephen, Kelly; *ed:* SUNY at Oneonta (BS) Home Ec Ed 1973; Grad Work at SUNY Oswego; *cr:* Hannibal Jr-Sr HS 7-12 Grd Home Ec Tchr 1973-; *ai:* Shared Decision-Making Dist Comm; NYSUT 1973-; Minetto Home, Schl Assn 1989-, Co-VP 1994-.

BOSCH, JENIFER ROSE, Art & Theology Teacher; *b:* Toledo, OH; *ed:* Lourdes Coll (AA) Fine Art 1982; Bowling Green St Univ (BFA) Fine Art & Art Ed 1985; 3 Credit Hrs; *cr:* Toledo Pub Schls Sub Tchr 1985-87; Cardinal Stritch HS Art & Theology Tchr 1987-; *ai:* Art & Photo Club Moderator; Artist-In-Residence; Intervention & Prevention Team Co-Capt; Schl Steering Comm for OH Accreditation; NAEA 1988-; NCEA 1990-; YES 1992-; *office:* Cardinal Stritch HS 3225 Pickle Rd Oregon OH 43616

BOSCH, KARIN PATRICIA, Health & Physical Ed Teacher; *b:* Drexel Hill, PA; *ed:* East Stroudsburg St Coll (BS) Hlth, PE 1973; 28 Post Grad Credits HPE West Chester St Coll; 60 Post Grad Credits Ed Various Intermediate Units, Univs; *cr:* Drexel Hill Jr HS HPE Tchr 1976-78; Beverly Hills Jr HS HPE Tchr 1978-81; Upper Darby HS HPE Tchr 1981-; *ai:* Var Sftbl Coach; UDEA Fac Rep; NEA 1976-; UDEA 1976-, Fac Rep; PSEA 1976-; Amateur Sftbl Assn 1974-; Scholastic Coach Magazine Bronze Medal Awd Achvmt Sftbl, Bsktbl Coaching 1987; *office:* Upper Darby HS 601 N Lansdowne Ave Upper Darby PA 19082

BOSCO, MARJORIE ABRAMS, French & Italian Teacher; *b:* Newark, NJ; *m:* Filippo; *c:* Paolo, Alessan Dro Alex; *ed:* Boston Univ (BA) Fr Lit 1967; Seton Hall Univ (MA) Fr Lit 1974; Rutgers Univ 9 Grad Credits Ital Lit; Montclair St Univ 6 Grad Credits 1995; *cr:* NY Univ Frgn Stu Coord 1967-68; Wilson Ave Schl ESL Tchr 1968-1970; Amer Schl of Milan Italian, Fr Tchr 1970-73; Irvington HS Tchr of Italian 1973-74; Evening Course Division Tchr of Italian 1974-78; Union Cty Regnl Dist # Italian, Fr 1974-78; Governor Livingston HS Tchr of Itali Westfield HS Tchr of Italian 1981-82; Gaudineer MS Tchr of F 1982-85; Millburn HS Tchr of Hnrs Fr, Italian Bridgewater-Raritan HS AP Fr, Italian Tchr, Ldr, Organizer F Exch 1988-; *ai:* Frgn Exchs 1985-; NEA, FLENJ, Modern La 1985-; Voice of Italian Tchr in Amer 1989-, Lectures; *home:* 35 B Lebanon NJ 08833*

BOSCO, SIMON MICHAEL, English Teacher; *b:* Camden, NJ; *r* Severin; *c:* Anthony, Mark, Greg; *ed:* King's Coll (BA) Eng 1971 Univ (MED) Admin & Super 1976, (EDD) Labor Stud 1986; Sandburg Eng Tchr 1971-78; Old Bridge HS Eng Tchr 1978-; Bridge Ed Assn 1971-, Pres; NJEA 1971-; NEA 1971-, Natl Del; N Newspaper Articles; Doctoral Dissertation; *office:* Old Bridge H Old Bridge NJ 08857

BOSEVICH, ANTOINETTE CORONITI, 6th Grade Tea Ashland, PA; *m:* Frank M.; *c:* Elizabeth, Frank, Angela; *ed:* Blo St Coll (BS) Elem Ed 1970, (MS) Elem Ed 1972; *cr:* Washington Grd Tchr 1970-74; Saint Judes Schl 7th Grd Tchr 1985-90, 6th 1990-91, 8th Grd Tchr 1991-92 & 6th Grd Tchr 1992-; *ai:* Coord League Contest; Faith Formation Comm; Cath Schls Week Comm Saint Judes Schl 422 S Mountain Blvd Mountain Top PA 18707

BOSLEY, CHERYL LYNN (MARKUTEN), Assistant Professor Brighton, PA; *m:* Bradley R.; *c:* Bethaney, Brennan; *ed:* Kent (BSN) Nrsng 1979, (MSN) Nrsng & Clinical Specialist 1984; You St Univ Doctoral Courses; *cr:* Western Reserve Care System Sta & Critical Care 1984, Clinical Specialist & Cardiovascular 198 Elizabeth Hosp Med Ctr Clinical Specialist & Critical Care Youngstown St Univ Instructor 1988-94, Asst Prof 1994-; *ai:* Nrsr Comm Mem; Dept of Nrsng Curr Comm & Coll of Hlth & Hum Curr & Pgm Comm Chprsn; AACN 1979-; NEOACCN 1979-; OE Northwestern OH OEA 1988-; Critical Care Nurse Cert 1985; Ce BLS Instr; Numerous Articles Pub; *office:* Youngstown St Univ Nrsng 410 Wick Ave Youngstown OH 44555

BOSLEY, JOSEPH WILLIAM,III, Social Studies Teacher; *b:* Ba MD; *m:* Catherine Manger; *c:* Erik Tyler, Mary Catherine; *ed:* Tc Univ (BS) His & Scndry Ed 1983; 45 Post Grad Credits; *cr:* Rand High Soc Stud Tchr 1984-88, 1992-94; Johnnycake Mid Soc St 1988-92; Pikesville High Soc Stud Tchr 1994-; *ai:* Var Ftbl & JV W Head Coach; Weight Room Coord; Schl Safety & Security Team; P Theta 1983-; NEA 1985-; MD Scholastic Ftbl Coaches Assn 19 Scholastic Ftbl Coaches Assn 1995-; Reisterstown Area Rec Cnc *office:* Pikesville HS 7621 Labyrinth Rd Baltimore MD 21208*

BOSSARD, CRYSTAL CALBERT, Professor of Humanities Cincinnati, OH; *c:* Camille K., Nicole; *ed:* Coll of Mt St Jose Mental Hlth, Gerontology-Cum Laude 1986; Univ of Cincinnati Mental Hlth 1988; Licensed Soc Worker St of OH; Cert Stress Mng Cert Chem Dependency Cnslr III; *cr:* Ford Mtr Co Hlth Prog Co 1967-91; Univ of Cincinnati Clinical Soc Worker 1988-91; Linc Hlth Ctr Clinical Soc Worker 1991-92; Cincinnati St Tech Coll Pro *ai:* Chm of Bd of Dir Family of God Childcare Ctr; Day Camp & La Prog Adv; Girl Scout Ldr; AAUP 1992-; Acad Family Mediator *office:* Cincinnati St Tech & Comm Coll 3520 Central Pky Cincin 45223

BOSSARD, HERBERT PAUL, Mathematics Teacher; *m:* Georgia *c:* Trevor, Ty; *ed:* Penn St (BS) Math 1984; Edinboro U Tchng Ce *cr:* Union City HS Math Tchr 1987-89; Linesville HS Math Tchr 19 Ftbl Coach; Pep Club & JETS Team Adv; SAP Team Mem; NE PSEA 1986-; Elks Club 1991-; PSFCA 1993-; *office:* Linesville H St Linesville PA 16424

BOSSELER, KATHRYN AMEY, Social Studies Teacher; *b:* Corn *c:* Amey C, Matthew G., Carolyn A.; *ed:* St Bonaventure Univ (Sci 1969; Elmira Coll (MS) Ed 1985; *cr:* Corning Painted Post Soc Stu Tchr 4 Yrs; Corning Free Acad MS Eng, Latin, Soc Stud Yrs; Brockport Cen Schl Soc Stud Tchr 1 Yr; *ai:* NHS Adv; Acad A Adv; Discipline & Attendance Comms; NY St Tchrs Union 1982 Kappa Gamma 1994-; Corning Free Acad 1990-, Excl in Svc; Corning-Painted Post West HS Victory Hwy Painted Post NY 148

BOSSERT, NORMAN, 7th Grade Teacher; *b:* Kew Gardens, Shelley Kuhner; *c:* Aaron, Seth; *ed:* Old Dominion Univ (BS) E Spec Ed, Theatre 1973; 48 Addl Hrs Rem Rdng, Mid Ed, Theatre, *cr:* Tidewater Comm Schl Tchr 1973-75; VA Learning Ctr Asst D 1975-78; Mexico Acad Tchr 1978-81; Shape Amer Elem Schl Sp 6 Tchr 1981-88; Shape Amer HS Spec Ed, Grd 7 Tchr 1988-; *ai:* Spon; Drama Dir; Women's Bsktbl, Speech Coach; Mid Level Com 1981-; SEA Pres 1985; Jewish Comm 1981-, Lay Ldr; Tchr of Yr Dist 1993; Exceptional Rating Sustained Superior 5 Yrs; Nom by & Kelly; *office:* Shape American HS CMR 451 Box 283 APO AE

BOSSLER, BRYAN KENT, Social Studies Teacher; *b:* Reading, Jill Ruth; *ed:* Alvernia Coll (BA) Ed 1985; Kutztown Univ (MED) Laude 1989; West Chester Univ Sports Admin; *cr:* Daniel Boone A Dist Soc Stud Instr 10 Yrs; *ai:* Daniel Boone Boys Bsktbl Coach; Information Club Adv; NEA, PSEA, DBYEA 1985-; *office:* Daniel Area Schl Dist P O Box 450 Birdsboro PA 19508

BOSSONG, ELIZABETH MORELAND, Spanish Teacher & Dep *b:* Buffalo, NY; *m:* James E.; *c:* Meagan; *ed:* Juniata Coll (BA) S 1977; Elmira Coll (MED) Foreign Lang Ed 1983; Art His, Latin Fr Lit Post Grad Stud; *cr:* Horseheads HS Span, Fr Tchr 1977-86 HS Span, Fr Tchr, Dept Chm 1986-; *ai:* Span Club Adv; Sports Aerobic Trng Coach; Advisors Consortium; Building Planning Tea Articulation, MS Exploratory Steering, Discipline Comms; Hum Chair; AATSP 1975-, Chapter Pres 5 Yrs; NYSAFLT 1977-, Bd AAAI 1989-; ACTFL; NEA; NYSAFLT VP, Pres 1996; Pub 2 Art Curr Guide; Lecture Nationally on FL Issues; *office:* Vestal Woodlawn Dr Vestal NY 13850*

BOST, DIANN ECKLEY, 9th-12th Grd Art Teacher; *b:* Greenvil *m:* Thomas L.; *c:* Andre W.; *ed:* PA St Univ (BS) Art Ed 19 Greenville HS 9-12 Grd Art Tchr 1973-; *ai:* PSEA, NEA 1973-; Hnr from St Vincent Coll Great Tchr Recognition Prgm 1995; Greenville HS 9 Donation Rd Greenville PA 16125

BOSTIC, JOHN E., Social Studies Educator; *b:* Gallipolis, OH; Murphy; *ed:* Rio Grande Coll (BS) Soc Sci, Ed 1988; Attnd Ashlan WA St Comm Coll, Marietta Coll; *cr:* Fort Frye HS Soc Stud Edctr *ai:* Ftbl, Bsktbl Coach; Prom, Class Adv; OEA, NEA 1988-; OH C Assn 1990-; Alpha Sigma Phi, Rio Grande Coll Alumni Assn1988-; Fort Frye HS Rt 60 Box 68 Beverly OH 45715

BOSTOCK, PAUL TIMOTHY, Latin Teacher; *b:* Mansfield, Engla Jennifer Eldred; *c:* Tristan C., Ashly R.; *ed:* Leeds Univ (BA) Archa Latin 1979, (PGCE) Ed 1981; Post-Grad Ed Cert; *cr:* Grace Churc Latin Tchr 1982-85; Lancaster Cntry Day Schl Latin Tchr 1985-; *ai* Prof Dev, Schl Objectives Comms; MS Adv & Dance Coord; CA AREA CLASSICS ASSN 1986-, VP, PRES; CLASSICAL AS ATLANTIC STS, AMER CLASSICAL LEAGUE 1986-; PA CLAS ASSN 1986-, PANEL MODERATOR; Lancaster Symphony Chorus inger; *office:* Lancaster Country Day Schl 725 Hamilton Rd er PA 17603

CK, WILLIAM FRANCIS, Data Processing Teacher; *b:* ter, MA; *c:* Diana Frances LeBlanc, Kathleen Patricia; *ed:* 30 Hrs Russian Lang Syracuse Univ; 60 Credit Hrs Bus Admin; *cr:* Bay g Voc Tech HS Data Processing Tchr 1978-; *ai:* NEA, MTA, BPTA *office:* Bay Path Reg Voc Tech HS 57 Old Muggett Hill Rd Charlton 507

N, MARTHA BIBEE, Psychologist & Adjunct Prof; *b:* Los s, CA; *m:* Christopher Mc Kenney; *c:* Amy Jo Mc Kenney, Seth Coston; *ed:* Harding Univ (BS) Home Ed 1970; Univ of DE (MS) pan Dev 1982, (PHD) Psych 1984; Allentown Coll Clinical hip; *cr:* Univ of DE Rsrch Asst 1980-84; Allentown Coll Asst Prof 7; Neumann Coll Assoc Prof 1987-93, Adj Prof 1993-; Pub Svc & Gas Staff Psychologist 1993-; *ai:* Amer Psychological Assn Amer Psychological Soc, Charter Mem; Eastern Psychological Natl Org for Women 1979-, Bucks Cty Pres 1986-87; United Meth 1971-, Adult Ed Coord 1988-91, Counsel on Ministries 1974-79, Bd 1975-79, 1981-84, Peninsula, DE Conf Response Team 1986; s Pub; Pres, Woodrow Wilson Awds 1984; *home:* 2601 Kimbrough mington DE 19810

ELL, CAROL LYNN, English Teacher; *b:* Philadelphia, PA; *m:* Kelly, Kristy, John; *ed:* Monmouth Coll (BA) Speech, Drama Ed Fairleigh Dickinson Univ (MA) Human Dev 1980; *cr:* Cherry Hill st Eng Tchr 1973-; *ai:* Peer Meditation Adv; Forensics Club; g Team; Adv Class Competition Plays; Dir Children's Play, Fall tion Reasers Theatre; Chaperoned Plays, Dances, Class Trips; on Many Comms; NEA, NJEA 1973-; *office:* Cherry Hill West HS Ave Cherry Hill NJ 08002*

ELL, JAMES AURTHUR,JR., Eng Prof & Writing Tutor Coord; burgh, PA; *ed:* Slippery Rock Univ (BA) Eng 1975, (MA) Eng 1980; nm Coll of Allegheny Cty Instr 1981; Harrisburg Area Comm Coll 981-; *ai:* Melrose Elem Schl Rdng Project; Black Stu Union Adv; 's Rdng Group; Church Choir, Deacon, Comms; NCTE 1983-; PA ctrs 1982-; PCTE 1981-; Articles Pub; Comm Coll Grant; Edited s; Who's Who in the East 1995-; Sec of Fac Cncl 1987-89; Chair Task Force on Stu Affairs; *office:* Harrisburg Area Comm Coll One Dr Harrisburg PA 17110*

ELL, JEFFREY D., Fifth Grade Teacher; *b:* Hammonton, NJ; *ed:* on St coll (BS) Cmptr Sci 1980; Glassboro St Coll (MA) Elem Ed *cr:* Warren E. Sooy Jr. Elem Schl Fifth Grd Tchr 1984-; *ai:* Stu Cncl, dv; NJEA, HEA, NEA 1984-; *office:* Warren E. Sooy Jr Elem Schl 4th St Hammonton NJ 08037

ORTH, FRANK MALING,III, Pgm Dir & Assoc Prof of Arch; *b:* ngton, DC; *m:* Leslie Hope Lightbourne; *c:* Christopher; *ed:* laer Polytechnic Inst (BS) Bldg Sci 1971, (BARCH) Architecture VA Polytechnic Inst (PHD) Environmental Design, Planning 1995; ng Melody Assoc Arch & Eng VP 1972-76; Frank M. Bosworth ecture Inc Pres 1976-83; C. E. Maguire VP 1983-86; VA Tech Rsrch 1986-89; Bowling Green St Univ Assoc Prof, Prgm Dir 1989-; *ai:* Inst Architecture Stdnts, Grad Stdnts of Tech Adv; Registered ect 1972-; Soc of Arch Historians 1990-; William Everett Warner Awd Epsilon Pi Tau; Natl Edctr of Yr Sigma Lamba Chi; Fac Excl psilon Pi Tau; 2 Aurora Awds; Norman Waxman Awd; *office:* g Green St Univ Coll of Technology Bowling Green OH 43403*

ORTH, KIRK, English Teacher; *b:* Bristol, VT; *m:* Jean land; *c:* Terry, Kevin, Martha; *ed:* Miami Univ (BA) Eng 1955; Univ (MA) Eng 1970; 100 Plus Hrs Beyond MA; *cr:* USN Pilot 1955-64; ct HS Eng Tchr 1964-94; St Michaels Coll Eng Tchr 1994-; Univ of g Tchr 1995-; *ai:* Natl Ski Patrol; *home:* 196 Brigham Hill Rd Essex on VT 05452

ORTH, RICHARD, 6th Grade Teacher; *b:* Cleveland, OH; *m:* Terri cken; *c:* Jason, Gary, Erin, Cortney, Joe; *ed:* Mansfield St Univ (BA) Ed 1971; Elem Cert Plus 10 Credits; *cr:* Richland Schl Dist 6th Grd 971-; *ai:* Asst Wrestling, Head Bsbl Coach; MS Discipline Comm; ewspaper Adv; NEA, PSEA, REA 1991-; Adam Twp Lions Club Svc Awd 1994-95; *office:* Richland MS 280 Theatre Dr Johnstown 904

NA, CLARA MARIA (ANCA), Spanish & Social Studies Tchr; *b:* a, Cuba; *c:* Joseph Daniel, Xavier E., James Francis; *ed:* Univ of a (PHD) His, Span 1958; Roosevelt Univ (MA) Tchng Span 1967; de cer vantes Inst Univ of Malgon Advanced Span Philology 1970; emitism & Tchng Holcaust Cert; Acheology & Archeological ration Copperatie Learning; Skilful Tchr Intnl Relations; Critical ng; *cr:* Bloom Twp HS Span Tchr 1965-67; Comm Coll Span Scndry 67; Ingal Twp HS Span, Eng Tchr 1967-71; Univ of MD European on Lecturer 1971-; Dept of DefenseDependent Schls Tchr, Scndry *ai:* NJHS Spon; Span Club; Intercultural Coord; OFT, AFT 1983-; P; NCSS; NCTFL; PDK 1989-; Cert of Distngd Svc Univ of MD; s of Commendation; Cert of Achvmt; *office:* David Glasglow ut HS PSC Box 819 Box 63 FPO AE 09645*

LER, MARY ELIZABETH, Social Studies Teacher; *b:* New York, : Robert Eugene; *ed:* Boston Coll (BA) His 1970; Hood Coll (MA) n Sci 1984; Drake Univ 3 Credits in Ed; Univ of MD 12 Credits in nthropology at George Washington Univ; *cr:* Manida Juvenile Ctr 970-71; Sherwood HS Soc Stud Tchr 1971-; *ai:* Curr & Dev for New His; Curr Controlled Comm for New Schl Enrollment Policies; AFT Amer Psych Assn 1980-; NCSS 1980-; Phi Kappa Phi 1980-; Mid valuation Chprsn; Schl Nom for Agnes Meyer Awd; NSF Grant opology for Tchrs; *office:* Sherwood HS 300 Olney Sandy Spring Rd Spring MD 20860*

OS, NAGY HEMAYA, Mathematics Teacher; *b:* Cairo, Egypt; *m:* M. H.; *c:* Markos N., Christina N.; *ed:* Ain Shams Univ (BA) Pure & Physics 1970, (MS) Theory of Complex Variables 1973; 6 Credits Pgmng & Problem Solving; *cr:* St Aloysious Acad Math & Physics 976-78; Union HS Math Tchr 1979-83; East Brunswick HS Math 1983-; *ai:* NEA 1979-; 1964-, Preacher & Ldr of Yth Meetings; reous Articles Pub; 2 Books: Geometry & Algebra for Eng Mission Cairo, Egypt; Won Summer Internship Pgm at Union Carbide icals & Plastics; *office:* East Brunswick HS 380 Cranbury Rd East wick NJ 08816*

, JEFFREY THOMAS, Health & PE Teacher; *b:* Philadelphia, PA; est Chester Univ (BS) Hlth, PE 1994; *cr:* Sleighton Schl Recreation 994-95; Henderson HS Hlth, PE Tchr 1995-; *ai:* Head Boys, Girls ning 1993-, Asst Track Coach; *office:* West Chester Henderson HS n & Montgomery Ave West Chester PA 19380

, KATHRYN MORRELLY, Biology Teacher; *b:* Jericho, NY; *m:* c: Kendall; *ed:* Long Island Univ (BS) Bio 1975, (MS) Microbiology 75 Addl Credit Hrs in Ed, Bio; *cr:* Long Island Univ Adjunct Prof 78; Friends Acad Sci Tchr 1978-82; Jericho HS Sci Tchr 1987; *ai:* Sr Adv; AFT 1987-; STANYS 1988-; NABT 1994-; *office:* Jericho Sr Cedar Swamp Rd Jericho NY 11753

, KATHY HICKLIN, Art Teacher; *b:* Evansville, IN; *m:* John Crist; on; *ed:* Univ of Evansville (BA) Art Ed 1977; Elaine DeKooning rs Class 1977; *cr:* Towle Richards Elem Art Tchr 1980-81; Newport Mid HS Art Tchr 1981-; *ai:* Natl Art Hnr Soc Spon; NEA 1980-; NAEA 1980-; NH Art Ed Assoc 1980-; Colby-Sawyer Coll Ed Pgms Advy Bd; NH St Bd of Ed Bd of Examiners Alternative III; Sabbatic System Leave Travels in Europe Exhibits of Prsnl Art Work Cross Cntry 1987; Interactive Comp & Laser Disc Grant Recipient 1988; NH Dept of Ed, NH St Cncl on the Arts & NH Art Ed Assn Excl in Ed The Visual Arts Awd 1993 & 1995; *office:* Newport Mid HS Rt 10 N Newport NH 03773

BOTTA, GREGORY JOHN, Health & Physical Ed Teacher; *b:* Pittsburgh, PA; *m:* Patricia Thibault; *c:* Gregory, Nicholas; *ed:* IN Univ of PA (BS) Hlth & PE 1975-, (MS) 1995; *cr:* Penn Hills Schl Dist Hlth & PE Tchr 1975-, Defensive Coord 1986-91; Swissvale Schl Dist Defensive Coord 1982-85; Franklin Reg Schl Dist Defensive Coord 1992-93, Head Ftbl Coach 1994-95; *ai:* NEA 1975-; PSEA 1975-; Penn Hills Ed Assn 1975-; Manordale Civic Assn, VP 1991, Pres 1992; Penn Hills Elem Tchr of the Yr 1981; Greensburgh Tribune Review Coach of the Yr 1995; *home:* 5764 Evans Rd Export PA 15632

BOTTGER, MARILLYN BIZJAK, Spanish Teacher; *b:* Cleveland, OH; *m:* James Stephen; *c:* Laura, Thomas, Mara, Melanie; *ed:* Hiram Coll (BA) Span 1966; Kent St Univ (MED) Scndry Ed 1993; *cr:* Newbury HS Span Tchr 1969-75; West Geauga HS Span Tchr 1980-83; Berkshire HS Span Tchr 1983-; *ai:* AFS Stu Club, Span Hnr Soc & Soph Class Adv; Levy Comm; NEA, OEA 1969-; Berkshire Ed Assn 1983-, Pres; St Helen Church 1954-, Stewardship; New Celebration Singers 1994-; Jennings Scholar; King Juan Carlos Flwshp; *office:* Berkshire HS 14510 Main St Burton OH 44021*

BOTTI, ARLENE CWIEKALO, High School Spanish Teacher; *b:* Rahway, NJ; *m:* Thomas D.; *c:* Gregory, Amanda, Jeffrey; *ed:* Montclair St Coll (BA) Span 1974; *cr:* Woodbridge Twp Schl Span Tchr 1975-79, 1993-; *ai:* Sales & Publicity Sr Class Play Adv; NEA 1993-; NJFLE 1994-; PTO 1990-, Co-Pres; *office:* John F Kennedy Memorial HS Washington St Iselin NJ 08830

BOTTI, CARL JOHN, Math Teacher & Department Head; *b:* Brooklyn, NY; *c:* John, William; *ed:* Queens Coll (BA) Math 1965, (MS) Math-Ed 1970; C W Post Coll (PD) Admin 1980; *cr:* Vly Stream North HS Math Tchr 1965-, Math Dept Head 1986-; Vly Stream HS Dist Coord of Educl Tech 1986-; Vly Stream Tchr Ctr Dir 1986-93; *ai:* Math Cncl, Comp-Tech Planning & Curr Writing Comm; NYSUT, AFT 1965-; PTSA 1965-; NCAMS 1986-; Grants: Local Boces Tech, Tchr Ctr St 8 Yrs Consecutivly; Software Reviews in Magazines; PTA Tchr of Yr Nom; *office:* Valley Stream North HS 750 Herman Ave Franklin Square NY 11010

BOTTINI, ROBIN MARCHESE, Science & Computer Teacher; *b:* Norfolk, VA; *m:* Benard A.; *c:* Brian, Michelle; *ed:* SUNY at Cortland (BS) Ed N-9 Sci 1985, (MS) Curr, Instruction 1990; 6 Credit Hrs Admin; *cr:* Westmoreland Cntrl Schl 7-10 Grds Sci Tchr, Cmptr 7 Tchr 1985-; *ai:* MS Concerns, Schl Quality Review Team, MS Advy Comms; Jr Class Adv; Yrbk Fin Mgr; Sci, Curr Fair, Portable Planetarium Coord; PTA; NYS MS Assn 1994-; NYS MS Conf Presenter; Various MS Presentations for Area BOCES: BD Presentations for Integrated Sci, Laser Disk Tech; Master Tchr; Armed Forces Grant for Sci Consummable Products; *office:* Westmoreland Cntrl Schl Rt 233 Westmoreland NY 13490*

BOTTONE-RANDAZZO, PATRICIA A. M., Foreign Lang & ESL Teacher; *b:* Newark, NJ; *m:* Patrick A.; *ed:* Villanova Univ (BA) Modern Lang 1980; Seton Hall Univ (MA) Scndry Ed, Eng Second Lang 1990; *cr:* Randolph HS Fr, Span tchr 1981-84; Hopatcong Adult Schl ESL Tchr 1986-87; Corfinio Coll Italian Instr 1988; Dover Adult Schl ESL Tchr 1988-92; Dover HS Fr, Italian, Span, ESL Tchr 1984-; montclair St Univ Adjunct 1989-92; Sussex Cnty Comm Coll Adjunct; *ai:* Fr, Italian Club Advs; Staff Chorale; Schl Play Comm; NEA, NJEA 1981-; Kappa Delta Pi 1983-; DEA 1984-; Morris Cty Tchrs of ESL 1986-; VITA 1994-; ASCD 1995-; Morris Cty Juvenile Conf Comm 1987-92, Appointed by Juvenile Court; Made Dover Fnd 1992, Prgm Cnslr, Spec Appointment; *office:* Dover HS 100 Grace St Dover NJ 07801*

BOTTORFF, MERRILY S., Secondary Art Teacher; *b:* Warren, OH; *m:* Alan Douglas; *c:* Luke, Thomas; *ed:* Thiel Coll (BA) Art Ed 1976; 24 Post Grad Credits Youngstown St Univ; 6 Art His Credits Kent St Univ; 6 IU Continuing Ed Credits; IU 4 Credit Hrs; *cr:* Greenville HS Art Tchr 1976-; *ai:* NEA, PSEA 1976-; NAEA; Univ Women 1986-; *office:* Greenville HS 9 Donation Rd Greenville PA 16125

BOUCHARD, EUGENE U., Bio Genetics Microbiology Tchr; *b:* Ware, MA; *m:* Claire Jane Guerin; *c:* Hugh, Christopher, Andrea; *ed:* Amer Intnl Coll (BA) His & Bio 1968; OK Univ (MNS) Microbial Genetics 1971; Post Grad Stud Holy Cross Coll & Worcester St Coll; *cr:* Quinsigamond Comm Coll Microbiology Lab Instr 1975-77; David Prouty HS Bio, Genetics & Microbiology Tchr 1968-; *ai:* MTA 1968-; NEA 1968-; New England Fly Tyers 1967-82, Pres; Town of Leicester 1982-85, Fin Comm & V-Chm; Town of Leicester 1985-88, Chm & Selectman; Grants: 4 NSF Acad & 1 NSF Acad Yr; 3 Pub Articles; *office:* David Prouty Regnl HS Rt 9 Spencer MA 01562

BOUCHARD, MARTIN ALONZO, Communications Technology Tchr; *b:* Hammonton, NJ; *m:* Renee Elizabeth Trautz; *c:* Madison, Lacey; *ed:* Glassboro St Coll (BA) Elem Ed 1977, Tech Ed 1983; Certified in Cooperative Industrial Ed in TV Production; *cr:* YALE Schl Tchr 1983-84; WA Twp HS Tchr 1984, TV Studio Mgr 1990-; *ai:* Sr Trip Videographer; Morning Announcement Crew; Tech Meet Adv; NEA 1984-; NJEA 1984-, Pub Relations Comm; WTEA 1984-, Pride Comm Chm; ITEA 1990-; *office:* Washington Township HS 529 Hurffville Crosskeys Rd Sewell NJ 08080

BOUCHER, CHARLES LOUIS, Technology Ed Dept Chair; *b:* Providence, RI; *m:* Mary Jean Hall; *c:* Christina, Craig, Steven; *ed:* RI Coll (BS) Industrial Arts Ed 1981; Cntrl CT St (MS) Industrial Arts Ed 1984; Addl 10 Plus Credits in a Variety of Areas; *cr:* LADD Ctr 3rd Shift Supvr 1979-81; Bethel HS Industrial Arts Tchr 1981-83; Howe Furniture Corp Materials Mgr & Design Engr 1983-85; Burrillville HS Industrial Arts Tchr & Dept Chair 1990-; *ai:* Tech Stu Assn St Rep; Tech Club; NEA, RI Tech Educators 1985-; Natl Tech Ed Assn 1992-; 18 St & Natl Champions Since 1985; Outstanding Tech Educator 1993; Outstanding Tech Prgm 1993; *home:* 55 Hemlock Farm Trl Harrisville RI 02830*

BOUCHER, PATRICIA NARDONE, Law, Psych & History Teacher; *b:* Somerville, MA; *m:* Larry; *c:* Jill; *ed:* Boston Coll (BA) Soc Sci Ed 1973; *cr:* Limestone HS Soc Stud Tchr 1974-76; PAALC Adult Ed Tchr 1980-; Raymond HS Soc Stud Tchr 1985-; *ai:* RAP Advocate & Steering Comm Chprsn; Stu Court Mem; AFT; NH Cncl of Soc Stud Tchrs 1985-; Tchr of Yr 1995; Santa Claos 1975; *office:* Raymond HS 45 Harriman Hill Rd Raymond NH 03077

BOUCHER, YVONNE RUTH, ESL & German Teacher; *b:* Gleiwitz, Germany; *m:* Robert; *c:* Nancy Perman, Patricia Rathay, Wayne, Andrew; *ed:* Smith Coll (BA) Fr 1972; Univ of MA at Amherst (PHD) Fr 1983; Learning Span 3 Yrs; Courses for ESL Cert; *cr:* Amherst Coll Fr Tchr 1978-79; City of Northampton Fr Tchr 1979-81, ESL Tchr 1983-; *ai:* MS Transitional Comm; Comm at HS to Review World Langs Ed Reform of 1993; NEA 1989-; MAFLA 1993-; MARE 1985-; LWV 1957-, VP & Book Sale Chair; Schlsp to Smith Coll; Tchng Asst & Later Assoc at Univ of MA; Grants to Obtain ESL Cert; Phi Beta kappa & Phi Kappa Phi Mem; *office:* Northampton HS 380 Elm St Northampton MA 01060

BOUDREAU, ANNMARIE M., Social Studies Teacher; *b:* Brighton, MA; *ed:* Univ of NH (BS) Bus Admin 1983; Northeastern Univ (MED) Curr & Instruction 1991; NEH Fellowship World His, Civilizations 1994-97; Attnd Harvard Univ; *cr:* Northeastern Univ Ed Dept Lecturer 1989-94; Snowden Intnl HS Tchr 1990-93; Amer Intnl Schl of Malaysia Tchr 1990; Marian Coll in Johannesberg South Africa Tchr 1992; Charlestown HS Tchr 1993-; *ai:* Stu Govt, Prom Comm Adv; Law Prgms, Comm Outreach Coord; Close-Up Adv Washington Prgm; Mentor Tchr Harvard Univ, Simmons Coll, Boston Univ; MFT 1993-; *office:* Charlestown HS 240 Medford St Charlestown MA 02129*

BOUDREAU, FRANCES KAZALSKI, Business Education Teacher; *b:* Lowell, MA; *m:* Richard; *ed:* Salem St Coll (BS) Bus Ed 1964; Post Grad Studies Bus Ed, Cmptr Tech, Applications; *cr:* Wilmington HS Bus Ed Tchr 1964-; *ai:* Mentor Stu Schl to Work Prgm; NHS Advy, Schlsp, Project Rose Comms; Wilmington Chamber of Commerce Tchr Coord; NBEA 1994-; NEA, Wilmington Tchrs Assn 1964-; *office:* Wilmington HS 159 Church St Wilmington MA 01887

BOUDREAU, KENNETH R., Science Teacher; *b:* Buffalo, NY; *ed:* Purdue Univ (BS) Chem 1971; Cornell Univ (MS) Chem 1973; Post-Masters Stud Sci Ed at SUNY Buffalo; Working on MS in Ed Admin at Canisius Coll; *cr:* North Arlington HS 7-8th Grd Sci Tchr 1974-75; Bennett HS Chem Tchr 1977-78; Hutch Tech HS Physics Tchr 1978-; *ai:* Buffalo Tchrs Fed Bldg Del Chprsn; Site Based Mgmt Team & Schl Acad Cncl; NEA 1978-, NSTA 1980-; STANYS & AAPT 1986-; ASCD 1994-; Sci Dept Chair 1986-89; Former Jr Class Adv & Math Team Coach; Research Assoc Physics 1986-88; Mentor Tchr Physics 1989-90; *office:* Hutchinson Tec HS 256 S Elmwood Ave Buffalo NY 14201

BOUDREAU, RICHARD M., Electrical Instructor; *b:* Boston, MA; *m:* Janet Morrill; *c:* Catherine, Colette, Karen; *cr:* Quincy Voc Tech Electrical Instr 1979-81; Quinobin Voc Tech Electrical Instr 1981-86; Attleboro HS Electrical Instr 1986-; *ai:* NEA 1986-; MTA 1986-; MVA 1986-; Intnl Assn of Electrical Inspectors 1990-; Natl Fire Prevention Assn 1990-; AARP 1993-; MA Electrical Contractors Assn 1993-; *office:* Attleboro HS Rathbun Willard Dr Attleboro MA 02703

BOUDREAU, SUSAN MARIE, Fifth Grade Teacher; *b:* Floral Park, NY; *m:* Henry; *c:* Matthew; *ed:* Lasell Jr Coll (AS) Retailing 1962; Dowling Coll (BE) Ed 1967, (ME) Ed 1989; 75 Credits Beyond Masters; Working on Cmptr Cert; *cr:* Bay Avenue Schls 4th & 5th Grd Tchr 1967-69; Gardiner Manor Sc 4th & 5th Grd Tchr 1973-; *ai:* Stu Cncl Adv; Sci Curr & Enrichment Comms; NYSUT; BSCTA; Dollars & Sense Investment Club 1994-, Founder, Pres 1994; O-Co'Nee Comm Assn, Pres 1986-88; Bay Shore Beautification Comm, Vol; Working on Prgm to Involve Elem Stdnts in Volunteering for Neighborhood Beautification; Succeeded in Making with Class a 1995 Governors Quilt Which Has Signed Cloths from all 50 Governors & Pres Clinton, Been Displayed at Natl Educators Convention & Various Local Meetings; *office:* Gardiner Manor Schl 125 Wohseepee Dr Bay Shore NY 11706

BOUEIL, COLLEEN ANN, Latin Teacher; *b:* Neptune, NJ; *c:* Laurence; *ed:* Heidelberg Coll (BA) Latin 1970; OH St Univ (MA) Latin 1972; L'Alliance Francaise Cert Lang Parle 1983; *cr:* Laurel Schl Latin Tchr 1972-73; Home Insurance Co Insurance Underwriter 1973-76; Fed Insurance Co Insurance Underwriter 1976-82; Berlitz-Paris Schl ESL Tchr 1983-85; Holmdel HS Latin Tchr 1989-; *ai:* Latin Honor Soc Adv; World Langs Curr Comm; Amer Classical League, NJ Classical Assn, Shore Latin Cncl 1989-; NEH Grant 1992; Alternative Assessment Grant; Honored Tchr NHS Induction; *office:* Holmdel HS 36 Crawfords Corner Rd Holmdel NJ 07733

BOUFFARD, JANE DENISE, Band Director; *b:* Newport, VT; *ed:* SUNY at Potsdam (BM) Music Ed 1983; Univ of IL (MS) Music Ed 1987; Addl 23 Credits Ed, Music; *cr:* Canaan Pub Schls K-12 Grd Music Tchr 1983-85; Burr & Burton Seminary 9-12 Grd Music Tchr 1985-86; Univ of IL Grad Asst 1986-87; Stowe Pub Schls 4-12 Grd Instrumental Dir 1987-; *ai:* Tchr Adv Jr Class; Accompanist HS Musicals; HS Restructuring, Elem Arts & Cultural Comms; NEA, VT NEA 1983-; Natl Band Assoc 1994-; Music Edctrs Natl Conf 1983-, Sec Exec Bd 1989-95; VMEA, MENC 1983-, Secr Exec Bd 1989-95; Lamoille Cty Players 1990-, Exec Bd 1995-; Stowe Performing Arts 1991-95, Exec Bd, Prgm Comm; Hill Crest Homeowners Assoc 1995-, Sec; Grad Assistantship Univ of IL at Champaign-Urbana; Guest Conductor Jr High Music Festivals; *office:* Stowe Pub Schls 413 Barrows Rd Stowe VT 05672

BOUGERE-HARRIS, GALE, Home Economics Teacher; *b:* Napoleonville, LA; *m:* Eddie Jr.; *c:* Brian C., Cordell A.; *ed:* Nicholls St Univ (BS) Home Ec, Soc Svcs 1972; 12 Hrs Early Chldhd Ed, Richmond Coll, 18 Hrs Comm Hlth, Brockport St Coll; *cr:* Flwshp Comm Day Care Lead Tchr 1972-74; Rochester City Schl Dist Early Chldhd Tchr 1975-81, Home Ec, Careers Tchr 1981-; *ai:* NHS Adv 1990-; Class Adv 1988, Fundraisers, Proms, Balls, Dances; Class Adv 1994, 1997; Chprsn, Coord Oletian Cncl, Provide Guest Speakers 9th Grd Career Awareness; AFT, NYSUT, RTA 1975-; BEAR 1988-; *office:* Edison Tech & Occupational Ctr 655 Colfax St Rochester NY 14606

BOUGHNER, MARTHA REED, Elementary Band Teacher & Supv; *b:* New Brunswick, NJ; *ed:* Douglass Coll (BA) Music Performance 1971; Syracuse Univ (MM) Clarinet 1973; Rutgers Univ (MED) Supervision, Admin 1986; Attending Drew Univ Seminary MTS; *cr:* J. W. Pepper & Sons Music Co Customer Svc 1973-76; Music for Amer Tchr, Area Coord 1977-79; Future Musicians Inc Tchr, Supv 1979-85; Jersey City St Coll Co-Operative Ed 1985-86; Roxbury Pub Schls HS Orch, Theory Tchr 1986-87; Future Musicians Inc Tchr, Supv 1987-; *ai:* All-St Concert Chprsn, Jazz Band; NJMEA, MENC, NCEA 1977-; AF of M Local 16 1983-; Douglass Coll Alumnae 1971-, Class Pres, Bd Mem, Comms; St James Episcopal Church 1978-, Vestry 2 Terms, Lay Asst; Garden St Concert Band 1985-, Clarinet; Music Edctrs Natl Conf Registered Music Edctr; Guest Conductor Future Musicians of CT All-Star Band; *home:* 149A E Bradford Ave Cedar Grove NJ 07009

BOUGHTON, KATHLEEN ANN, PE Teacher & Coach; *b:* Rochester, NY; *ed:* Genesee C C (PE) 1981; Eastern Ky (BS) PE & Hlth 1983; Brockport Coll; *cr:* Mercy HS PE Instr & Coach 1984-; Mercy HS Ath Dir 1988-; *ai:* Var Bsktbl & Soccer Coach; 7 Sectional Championships; Rochester Coach of Yr in Soccer 1995; Numerous Coaches of Yr Hnrs in Bsktbl; *office:* Our Lady of Mercy HS 1437 Blossom Rd Rochester NY 14610

BOUGILL, JAMES WINTHROP, Assoc Professor of Business; *b:* Middletown, NY; *m:* Eileen Thoet; *c:* William, Trevor; *ed:* SUNY at Albany (BS) Bus 1967, (MS) Bus 1969; *cr:* Valley Cntrl HS Bus Tchr 1967-69; Orange Cty Comm Coll Bus Instr 1969-72; Clinton Comm Coll Assoc Prof Bus 1973-; *ai:* Schl Newspaper; Cultural Affairs, Acad Stans Comms; NEA 1973-93; NYS Bus Tchrs 1975-85; Elks Club 1971-, Trustee; *office:* Clinton Comm Coll 136 Clinton Point Dr Plattsburgh NY 12901*

BOUILLON, STEPHEN CARL, History Teacher; *b:* Tiffin, OH; *m:* Rebecca L.; *c:* Jackie, Betsy; *ed:* Eastern MI Univ (BS) His 1974; 30 Credit Hrs Bowling Green St Univ; *cr:* St Wendlin Schls Tchr, Coach 1974-79; New Riegel Schls Tchr, Ath Dir 1979-; *ai:* Ath Dir; Cross Cntry Coach, Sr Clas, Quiz Bowl Adv; NEA 1979-; OH Assn of Cross Cntry Coaches 1985-; OH Assn of Ath Admins 1984-; 10 Yr Awd; Schls Advy Commission; St Wendelin Schls; *office:* New Riegel HS 44 N Perry St New Riegel OH 44853

BOULANGER, MICHELE JEANNE, Music Director; *b:* Rolulus, NY; *c:* Benjamin, Julia; *ed:* Univ of NH (BM) Music Ed 1976, (MS) Music Ed 1991; *cr:* Rochester Schls JH Band, Elem Music Tchr 1976-83; Dover Schls HS Band, Chorus, Music Tchr 1983-; *ai:* Elem Band; Music Cncl, Variety Show Adv; NHMEA 1976-, Treas; NEA, NBA 1983-; Who's Who in Amer Ed 1990; Nationally Registered Music Edctr 1991; *office:* Dover HS 25 Alumni Dr Dover NH 03820*

BOULAY, BARBARA J. LEBLANC, 5th Grade Teacher; *b:* Worcester, MA; *m:* Robert; *c:* Katie, Kerrie; *cr:* MA 6th-7th Grd Chptr I Rem Rdng Tchr 1977-90; Oxford MS 7th Grd Tchr 1990-91; A M Chaffee 1st Grd Tchr 1991-93, 3rd Grd Tchr 1993-94; A L Joslin 4th Grd Tchr 1994-95, 5th Grd Tchr 1995-; *ai:* Schl Advy Cncl; *office:* A L Joslin Schl Maple Rd Oxford MA 01540

BOULES, THEODORE LOUIS,III, Math Teacher; *b:* Uniontown, PA; *m:* Barbara Tracy; *c:* Jeffrey, Gregory, David; *ed:* Slippery Rock Univ (BS) Math 1969; Rutgers Univ (MST) Math 1974; *cr:* Pittsburgh Pub Schls Math Tchr 1969-; *ai:* AFT 1969-; *office:* Perry Traditional Acad 3875 Perrysville Ave Pittsburgh PA 15214

BOULRISSE, MONA BOUCHARD, Business Education Teacher; *b:* Van Buren, ME; *m:* Richard; *c:* Chelsea; *ed:* Univ of ME at Machias (BS) Bus Ed 1988; *cr:* Mt Abram Regnl HS Bus Ed Tchr 1988-90; Sumner Meml HS Bus Ed Tchr 1990-; *ai:* Schlsp, Tech-Prep, Jobs for ME's Grads Advy Comm; Crisis Mngmt Team; NEA, MTA 1988-; Bus Ed Assn of ME 1988-, Regnl Dir; Amer Legion Aux 1970-, Schlsp; *office:* Sumner Memorial HS RFD 1 Box 42 Gouldsboro ME 04607*

BOULTON, WILLIAM L., Social Studies Teacher; *b:* Watertown, NY; *c:* Deborah Jackson, Jennifer, Julie; *ed:* Jefferson Comm Coll (BA) Lbrl Arts 1966; Potsdam St Univ of NY (BA) His 1968; Addl 45 Post Grad Credit Hrs; *cr:* Case Jr HS Soc Stud Tchr 1968-; *ai:* Learning Comm Compact; Peer Tutoring Dir; GATE Teach; Watertown Ed Assn 1968-, Dir; NYS Cncl for Soc Stud 1968-; Dexter Village Bd 1970-, Trustee; Amer Legion 1970, Commander; Dexter Fire Dept 1968-, Pres, Firefighter of Yr 1981; Dexter Planning Bd 1989-, Chm; Dexter Citizen of Yr 1989; Watertown Schl Dist Lifesaving Awd 1983; SUNY at Potsdam Tchr Awd Spon; *home:* 103 E Church St Adams NY 13605

BOUNDS, SHIRLEY WATSON, Associate Principal; *b:* Rockville Centre, NY; *m:* Ron; *c:* laura; *ed:* Ursinus Coll (BA) Fr 1972; Wilmington Coll (MEd) Educl Leadership 1993; 18 Credit Hrs Univ of DE; 3 Credit Hrs Millersville Univ; *cr:* St Elizabeth HS Fr, Span Tchr 1973-94, Asst Prin, Fr & Span Tchr 1978-94, Assoc Prin 1994-; *ai:* Lang Club; European Trip Dir; NCEA 1973-; NASSP, ASCO 1993-; AATF, AATSP, ACTFL, DECTFL 1980-; St of DE Foreign Lang Frameworks Commission; DE Assn Ind Schls VP; *office:* St Elizabeth HS 1500 Cedar St Wilmington DE 19805

BOURASSA, GUY JEAN, Technology Instructor; *b:* Hartford, CT; *m:* Jill Mary; *ed:* Cntrl CT St (BS) Soc Sci 1977; Westfield St (ME) Cmptr Tech 1985; Dept Chair Cert Univ of Hartford; *cr:* JFK Jr HS Soc Stud Tchr 1977-81; Kosciuszko Jr HS Soc Stud Tchr 1981-82; JFK MS Math Tchr 1982-93; Hazard Meml Schl 6th Grd Tchr 1993-94; JFK MS Tech Instr 1994-; *ai:* Tech Comm Chair; Best Prgm Beginning Edctr; Mentor Prgm; NEA, CEA 1977-; ETA 1977-, VP, Tchr of Yr; NCTM 1982-; Holy Family Men's 1987-; Enfield Tchr of Yr 1993; Univ of CT Flwshp Awd 1987; Outstdng Svc Awd 1990; *office:* John F Kennedy MS 155 Raffia Rd Enfield CT 06082*

BOURDEAU, MARK WILLIAM, English Assistant Professor; *b:* Cleveland, OH; *m:* Wendy Lynn Tigchelaar; *c:* Althea Isabella; *ed:* Miami Univ in OH (BA) Eng 1981; Purdue Univ (MA) Eng Lit 1984, (PhD) Eng Lit 20th centi 1990; *cr:* Purdue Univ Eng Visiting Instr 1990-92; Suffolk Comm Coll Eng Eng Asst Prog; *ai:* Founding Editor of Newsletter; AFT, NYSVT, NCTE 1992-; MLA 1990-; *office:* Suffolk Cty Comm Coll 533 College Rd Selden NY 11784

BOURDELAIS, JILL DENISE, Third Grade Teacher; *b:* Amesbury, MA; *m:* Arthur; *c:* Dorean; *ed:* Plymouth St Coll (BS) Elem Ed 1971; 50 Addl Grad Credits; *cr:* Memorial Schl 3rd-4th Grd Tchr 25 Yrs; *ai:* Strategic Planning, Essential Skill Dev, Math Facilitator, Planning Bd Bldg Comms; Dist Accreditation Steering Comm 1986; NEA, NHEA 1971-; *office:* Memorial Elem Schl 31 W Main St Newton NH 03858

BOURGEOIS, ERNEST JOSEPH,JR., Professor of Business Admin; *b:* Burlington, VT; *ed:* Champlain Coll (ABA) Mngmt 1968; Castleton St Coll (BS) Bus Admin 1970; St Michael's Coll (MED) Ed Admin 1974; Clarkson Univ (MBA) Mngmt, Mrktg 1991; *cr:* Winooski HS Bus Tchr 1971-74; Burlington HS Bus Tchr 1974-77; Castleton St Coll Bus Admin Prof 1977-; *ai:* VP Fac; Chair Educl Resources Comm; NCAA Fac Rep; Chair Campus-Wide Fiber Optic Comm; AFT, NBEA 1977-; VBTA 1971-; Seven Book Reviews; Sabbatical; Seven Journal Articles; Outstdng Fac Awd; Exemplary Fac Awd; *office:* Castleton St Coll Seminary St Castleton VT 05735*

BOURKE, LAETITIA C., Secondary Social Studies Tchr; *b:* Buffalo, NY; *m:* William B.; *c:* Celine Bourke Kuhn, Elizabeth L.; *ed:* D'Youville Coll (BA) His 1966; Canisius Coll (MS) Ed 1969; 30 Hrs in Ed Admin SUNAB; *cr:* Schl 43 Tchr 1966-72; Schl 4 Tchr 1977; Schl 9 Tchr 1979; City Hnrs Schl Tchr 1987-; *ai:* Mock Trial; Citizen Bee; NEA 1966-; Women Tchrs 1977-; Rho Delta Kappa 1982-; Natl Endowment for Hum Grant Participant 3 yr Prgm; *office:* City Honors Schl Masten & North Sts Buffalo NY 14204*

BOURKE, MARY E., Art Teacher; *b:* Rockville Centre, NY; *m:* Michael Margolis; *c:* Sam Brosnan, Molly Brosnan; *ed:* Boston Coll (BA) Eng & Art 1976; *cr:* Prof Artist Painter 1979-; Riley Schl K-9th Grd Art Tchr 1991-; *office:* Riley Schl Warrenton Rd PO Box 91 Glen Cove ME 04846

BOURLAND, DAVID E., Science Teacher; *b:* Detroit, MI; *m:* Cheryl Renard; *c:* Nicole, David; *ed:* Bowling Green St Univ (BS) Paleontology 1978; Univ of Toledo Tchng Cert 1979; *cr:* Toledo Pub Schl Tchr 1979-; *ai:* Environmental Sci Club; Toledo Fed of Tchrs 1979-; Waterville Historical Soc 1990-; *office:* Bowsher HS 3548 S Detroit Ave Toledo OH 43614

BOURN, MAUREEN EDDY, Third Grade Teacher; *b:* Thompson, CT; *m:* James D.; *c:* Jennifer, Kevin; *ed:* Cntrl CT St Univ (BS) Elem Ed 1968, (MS) Spec Ed 1974; 12 Credit Hrs Rdng, Speech; CT Continuing Ed Units; *cr:* Pleasant Vly Elem Schl 3rd-4th Grd Tchr 1968-81; Philip R. Smith Schl 6th, 3rd Grd Tchr 1982-84; Pleasant Vly Elem Schl 3rd Grd Tchr 1984-; *ai:* System Tchr Evaluation, Lit Magazine, Read-at-Home, Report Card, Schl Dev Cncl Scheduling Comms; PTO Tchr Rep; Schl Planner Comm Chprsn; South Windsor Ed Assn 1968-, Past Sec, Comm Chprsn; CEA, NEA 1968-; Wood Meml Lib 1990-, Bd Mem, Ed Comm Chprsn; South Windsor Tchr of Yr 1988-89; *office:* Pleasant Valley Elem Schl 591 Ellington Rd South Windsor CT 06074*

BOURQUE, MARY H. (CARREIRO), Kindergarten & Preschl Teacher; *b:* Charleston, SC; *m:* Happy J.; *c:* Candi A., Brian K., April L. Bourque Hultman; *ed:* Bridgewater St Coll (BSEd) SPED & ECE 1990; Lesley Coll (MED) Creative Arts & Learning 1992; *cr:* Berkley Schl System Tchr Aide, Tchr 1984-90; Early Chldhd Learning Ctr K & Presch Tchr 1990-92; Britol Cty Agricultural Schl Sped Eng & Math Tchr 1992-94; Taunton Boys & Girls Club Presch K & Presch Lead Tchr 1994-; *ai:* Early Chldhd Cncl Rep; *office:* Taunton Boys, Girls Clb Prschl 31 Court St Taunton MA 02780

BOUSTEAD, DIANE BEHNKE, Chemistry Teacher; *b:* Sewickley, PA; *m:* Charles Oren; *c:* Jared, Amanda, Kristen; *ed:* Westminster Coll (BS) Chem 1976; 14 Credit Hrs at Univ of Pittsburgh Schl of Pub hlth, Industrial Hygiene; 12 Credit Hrs at Univ of Pittsburgh schl of Ed, Sci Ed; *cr:* Bayer Corp Chemist & Industrial Hygiene 1976-79; NUS Corp Industrial Hygiene 1984-90; West Allegheny Schl Dist Chem Tchr 1990-; *ai:* Sci Olympiad Coach; WAEA, NEA 1990-; Montour Trail 1994-, Vol; Findlay Twp Fair Bd 1986-, Treas; West Allegheny Schl Dist Band Parents Publicity Chprsn; Findlay Twp Fair Bd 1986-, Treas; Articles On Thin Layer Chromatography Separation of Isocyanates & Protection Provided by Disposible Respirators Against Isocyanates 1978; *office:* West Allegheny HS 205 W Allegheny Rd Imperial PA 15126*

BOUTHILLIER, PHILIPPE HENRI, Chemistry Tchr & Sci Dept Head; *b:* Nashua, NH; *m:* Mona Bechard; *c:* Paul, David, Gary; *ed:* St Michael's Coll (BA) Chem 1966; NSF Chemical Instrumentation Univ of CA at Berkley 1987; NSF Chem Supplements Univ of AZ 1986; NSTA Dhatauqua Short Courses 1984-85; NSF & NSTA Energy VT Yankee 1986; Dow Chemical 1988; MIT Sci & Engineering Prgm 1989; VTC VT Inst for Sci, Math, Tech 1993; *cr:* Sprague Electric Co Resistor Coatings Technician 1964-66; IBM Chemical Engr & Quality Control 1966; Hartford HS Chem Tchr 1966-; *ai:* Ice Hockey Ofcl Jr Var & Youth Prgms 1978-92; Jr Class Adv 1966-; High Schl Hockey Coach 1966-77; Schl Prom Coord 1966-89; VEA, NEA, HTA 1966-; NSTA 1980-; Riverwatch 6 Yrs; Friends of Hartford Hockey & Skating Inc 1978-91; Amer Chemical Soc Outstanding High Schl Chem Tchr 1989; Hartford Parks & Rec Vol Awd 1971; Hartford Grange Comm Citizenship Awd 1989; Begian HS Ice Hockey Prgm 1966; *home:* 22 Meadow Ln White Riv Jct VT 05001

BOUTIN, PAULINE PEREIRA, Fifth Grade Teacher; *b:* Fall River, MA; *w:* Ronald H. (dec); *c:* David; *ed:* Bridgewater St Univ (BS) Elem 1966, (MED) Elem 1971; SCIS Classes 1969; Salem St Coll Sci Collaboration 1970; *cr:* Jerome Dwelly Schl Sixth Grd Tchr 1966-70; Fall River MS Sixth Grd Sci, Hlth Tchr 1970-71; Mc Kay Schl Fourth-Sixth Grd Tchr 1971-; *ai:* Safety Patrol Adv; Inventions Coord; Bd Dirs Danvers Amer Legion Bsbl; Innovator Arithmetic Dynamics Report Card 1975-83; Creator, Coord Schl Sci Fair 1971-90; Core Tchr, Planning Comm; Co-Creator, Coord Display Gallery 1987-88; BTA, MTA, NEA 1966-; Danvers Amer Legion Bsbl 1994-, Bd Dirs, Plaque Continued Support 1995; Safety Patrol Ldr, Disciplinarian 1971-86, 1988-; Presenter Numerous Wkshps; Co-Author Curr Guide; Interdisciplinary Prgm Inventors, Invention.*

BOUTSIKARIS, BARBARA, Psychology Instructor; *b:* Summit, NJ; *m:* Timothy Brookes; *c:* Maddy Brookes; *ed:* Boston Univ (BM) Music Performance 1982; Univ of VT (MS) Cnslng 1992; Attnd Boston Conservatory of Music; *cr:* Middlebury Coll Flute Instr 1991-92; Johnston St Coll Flute Instr 1992-93; CCV Intro to Psych & Adolescent Dev Instr 1993-; Spectrum Yth & Family Svcs Adolescent & Family Cnslr 1993-; *ai:* Play Flute with VT Symphony Orch; Ensembles Coach; Facilitate Parenting Groups; Teach Wkshps; Adolescents & Adults Flute Tchr.*

BOUTWELL, ELENOR MILLER, Music Teacher; *b:* Rockwood, PA; *m:* Daniel L.; *ed:* IN Univ of PA (BSEd) Music 1973; Elmira Coll (MSEd) Psych 1976; Addl Grad Courses at Ithaca Coll & Alfred Univ; *cr:* Hammondsport Cntrl Schl Music Tchr 1973-; *ai:* NEA, NEANY, HTA, MENC & NYSSMA 1973-; SCMTA 1973-, Sec & Pres; Delta Kappa Gamma 1983-; Corning Philharmonic Chorus 1990-; St James Episcopal Church 1976-, Organist & Choir Dir; *office:* Hammondsport Central Schl Main St Hammondsport NY 14840

BOVINE, KATHI TURTURRO, Art Teacher; *b:* Stamford, CT; *m:* J. Peter; *c:* Megan, Christian; *ed:* Coll Misericordia (BA) Art Ed; *cr:* Tunkhannock Area HS Art Tchr 1984-85; Wyalusing Area Elem Schl Art Tchr 1985-93; Wyalusing Area HS Art Tchr 1993-; *ai:* Sr Prom Spon; Mentor; Jr Class Adv; NEA, PA St Ed Assn 1984-; Jr Women's Club 1973-82; Tyler Hosp Auxiliary 1973-; *office:* Wyalusing Area HS 115 Main St Wyalusing PA 18853

BOWDEN, ALAN, Electricity Teacher; *b:* Brownsville, PA; *m:* Patricia Gliebe; *c:* Brad, DarNel; *ed:* Univ of Pittsburgh (BS) Psych 1973; Voc-Ed Cert Masters Euivalency; *cr:* Cntrl Westmoreland Careerr & Tech Ctr Tchr 27 Yrs; *ai:* VICA Club Adv; PSEA 1969-, Local Treas; NEA 1969-; Youth Ath Assn 1989-, Pres; *office:* Cntrl Westmoreland Career Cntr Arona Rd New Stanton PA 15672

BOWDEN, JOHN, English Teacher; *b:* Erie, PA; *m:* Cynthia Scariato; *c:* Patrick, Valerie; *ed:* Rider Univ (BA) Sec Ed, Eng 1980; Rutgers Univ (EDM) Ed Admin, Supvr 1992; *cr:* Burl Co Inst Tech Eng Tchr 1980-84; Wall HS Eng Tchr 1984-85; Lenape HS Eng Tchr 1985-; *ai:* Peer Mediation Coord; Play Dir; NCTE 1984-; ASCD 1992-; NEA, NJEA 1980-; Tchr of Yr 1995-96; *office:* Lenape HS 235 Hartford Rd Medford NJ 08055*

BOWDEN, MANDA LEE, Tchr of the Gifted & Talented; *b:* Bridgeton, NJ; *ed:* Glassboro St Coll (BA) Elem Ed-Cum Laude 1979; Peer Mediation Ldrshp Trng; Addl Courses Cmptr Tech, Photography; Math Ed Minor; *cr:* Woodstown Day Care Ctr Asst Head Tchr 1974-78; Bridgeton Chrstn Schl 2 & 4 Grd Tchr 1979-88; Lower Alloways Creek Schl Tchr of GATE 1988-; *ai:* GATE Consortium 1990-; Odyssey of Mind Coach 1988-91; Curr, Liason, Negotiations Comms 1988-; NEA, NJEA, LAC Tchrs Assn 1988-; Bridgeton Chrstn Schl Bd of Dirs 1993-, Bd, Ed Comm; Deerfield Presbyn Church 1988-; GS Coll Deans LIst; Nom 1990 Thanks to Tchrs Excl Awd; CPR Cert Amer Heart Assn; *office:* Lower Alloways Creek Schl 967 Main St Canton Salem NJ 08079*

BOWEN, ALFRED RICHARD, CIE Coordinator; *b:* East Liverpool, OH; *m:* Margaret S.; *c:* Patricia Lynn Bowen Quelch, Barbar Ann Bowen Finney; *ed:* WV Univ (BA) Ed 1960; Trenton St Univ (MS) Scndry Ed 1976; *cr:* Westgate Jr HS Indstrl Arts Tchr 1959-66; New Cumberland Jr HS IA, Sci Tchr 1966-67; Warren Hills Regnl HS IA Tchr 1967-, Dept Chm, CIE Coord 1972-; *ai:* Jr HS Ftbl Coach 1960-65; Ftbl Coach 1967-71; Sr Class Adv 1972-84; NJEA, NEA 1967-80; NJ CIA 1972-, Coords; *office:* Warren Hills Regional HS Jackson Valley Rd Washington NJ 07882*

BOWEN, CHARLES P.,JR., English Teacher; *b:* Cleveland, OH; *m:* Margaret Hart; *c:* Sarah; *ed:* Comm Coll of Allegheny Cty (AA) Liberal Arts 1978; Univ of Pittsburgh (BA) Creative Writing 1981; Post-Baccalaureate Cert Scndry Eng 1987; *cr:* Steel Vly Schl Dist Sub Tchr 1987-88; All Saints Schl Eng Tchr 1988-; *ai:* Pub Quarterly, Anthology of Stu Writing; NCTE 1996; Magna Cum Laude Grad; Univ Scholar; Nom Thanks to Tchrs Awd; Wrote Theme Music for PBS Spec; Pub, Released 2 Audio Cassettes of Orginal Music; *home:* 3007 Short St Munhall PA 15120

BOWEN, JONATHAN, Band Director; *b:* Niagara Falls, NY; *m:* Katherine; *c:* Heather, Melanie; *ed:* SUNY at Fredonia (BM) Music Ed 1970; SUNY at Cortland (CAS) Admin; Ithaca Coll (MM) Music Ed 1972; *cr:* Margaretville CS Band Dir 1971-73; Port Byron HS Band Dir 1974-79; Homer HS Band Dir 1979-88; C. W. Baker HS Band Dir 1988-; *ai:* Marching Band; Jazz Ensemble; MENC, NYSSMA 1970-; NYSBDA 1975-, Bd of Dirs; NYSSMA 1970-; NBA 1985-; *office:* Charles W Baker HS 29 E Oneida St Baldwinsville NY 13027*

BOWEN, RICHARD ALLEN, Chemistry Teacher; *b:* Allentown, PA; *m:* Betty Jean Strock; *c:* John C.; *ed:* Albright Coll a9bs0 Bio 1972; Beaver Coll (MAEd) Chem 1989; Attnd Temple Univ, Bloomsburg Univ, Trenton St Coll; *cr:* William Penn MS 8th Grd Sci Tchr 1972-85; Pennsbury HS Chem Tchr 1986-; *ai:* Schl Store Mgr; Adult Schl Tchr Cmptrs; Asst Band Dir; Site Base Mngmt Team; Chem Hygiene Ofcr; Pennsbury Ed Assn 1972-, Mbrshp Chm; PA St Ed Assn, NEA 1972-; BSA 1985-, Cub Scout Ldr, Asst Boy Scout Ldr, Dist Awd of Merit; St John's Luth Church 1981-, Sunday Schl Supt, Church Cncl Sec, Pres.

BOWEN, WARREN JOHN, Retired Social Studies Teacher; *b:* N MA; *m:* Mary Anderson; *c:* Margaret Hayes, Anne Ogden, John, Kathleen Bishop, Patrick; *ed:* Merrimack Coll (BA) (BS) Ec 1959 St (MED Ed 1964; Addl 21 Credit Hrs; *cr:* Tewksbury HS Tchr Tchr, Dept Head 1967-94; *ai:* Tewksbury Tchrs Assn 1959-94, P Tchrs Assn 1959-94; NEA 1962-94; Natl Inst of Mental Hlth Drug Ed Amer His Inst 1967-94; Article on Grade Point Average.

BOWENS, ELVA MARIE, Former MSPAP; *b:* Cambridge, M Salisbury St Coll (BS) Elem Ed 1978, (MED) Elem Ed 1982; Early Math, Elem, MS Certs; Amer Sign Lang Level I, II; *cr:* Preston S I Math Specialist 1978-79, Primary-ECE Classroom Tchr 1 Western MD Coll Grad Fac Adj Instr 1987-89; Caroline Cty Pub S Math Specialist 1991-93, MD Schl Performance Asst Prgm Tchr S 1993-95; *ai:* ASCD; NEA; MSTA; CCTA; MASCD; NCTM; MCT SMIRAC; MSRC; NCTE; MCTELA; Eisenhower Math-SCi Con ODK 1977-; PDK 1993-; PTA; 4-H All Stars; Awds MCTM Smal CCPS Mini-Grant; Baltimore Sun Featured Edctr Foucs; Amer Leg Essay Winner; Candidate Local Tchr of Yr 1987; Outstdng Dorchester Countian; St Math Ed of Yr Finalist; Articles Pub; *hom* Preston Rd Hurlock MD 21643

BOWENS, JOYCE A., HS Social Studies Teacher; *b:* Memphis, Pratt Inst (BS) Sociology 1972; Long Island Univ (MS) Guid Cnslr *cr:* Boys & Girls HS Soc Stud Tchr 1988-; *office:* Boys & Girls Fulton St Brooklyn NY 11213*

BOWENS, KEITH KARNELL, Guidance Counselor; *b:* Newpor VA; *c:* Brian, Essence, Kendra; *ed:* Hampton Univ (BA) Crim Sociology 1980; Cambridge Coll (MED) Cnslng Psych 1991; St License Mental Hlth Cnslr; Wayne Comm Coll at Detroit Art, Bus I Centerville Comm Coll Elem Ed 1971-72; *cr:* Hines MS Adm 1980-86; Cath Charities Dir Yth Intervention 1987-93; Brid Raynham HS Guid Cnslr 1993-; *ai:* Peer Ldrshp Stdnts Agains Driving, Culture, Diversity, Art Club Adult Adv; Numerous Awds, Merit, Appreciation; *office:* Bridgewater Raynham Reg HS 166 Prospect St Bridgewater MA 02324

BOWER, CAROL LANGLEY, Lead Teacher; *b:* Biloxi, MS; *m:* K.; *c:* Lawrence Harrison, Geoffrey Copeland; *ed:* Univ of FL (BS 1963; Univ of WI (MS) Organic Chem 1964; *cr:* US Forest Prod Rsrch Asst 1964-67; DE Tech & Comm Coll Chem Tchr 1 Dayspring Chrstn Acad First Grd Tchr, His, Sci Lead Tchr 1987-; Senate, Yrbk, Outreach Comm Adv; Coll Guid Cnslr; *office:* Da Christian Acad 139 E Vine St Lancaster PA 17602

BOWER, CHRISTOPHER MICHAEL, English Teach Williamsport, PA; *m:* Gloria Fenderson; *c:* Jennifer, Tami; *ed:* Lock Univ (BSEd) Scndry Eng Ed 1970; Bloomsburg Univ (MS) Commu 1990; *cr:* Montoursville Area HS Eng Tchr 1970-; PA Coll Tech E 1990-; *ai:* Eng Dept Chprsn; Boys Track & Field Coach; Fac Advy NCTE 1985-; Mentor PA Governors Schl for Tchrs 1993; Fello Seminars 1985 & 1995; *office:* Montoursville Area HS 100 N Montoursville PA 17754*

BOWER, EDWIN CHARLES, English & Communications T Kittanning, PA; *m:* Susan King; *c:* Benjamin, Maggie; *ed:* Slippe Univ (BS) Commnctn 1974; *cr:* Kittanning Jr HS Eng Tchr 1 Kittanning Sr HS Eng & Commnctn Skills Tchr 1979-; *ai:* Fro Bsktbl, 8th Grd Boys Bsktbl & Head Boys Bsktbl Coach; Play Crew for Musicals Dir; Asst Tech, Ski Club, Morning Announce Video Yrbk Adv; Var Ftbl Announcer; Armstrong Ed Assn 1974- 1974-; Applewold Borough Cncl 1991-, VP; Armstrong Cty YM BPOE Lodge 203; *office:* Kittanning Sr HS 1200 Orr Ave Kittanr 16201

BOWER, JACK R., Band Director; *b:* Berwick, PA; *m:* Pamela C Jon, Scott; *ed:* Wilkes Univ (BS) Music Ed 1974; 24 Post Grad Ithaca Coll; *cr:* Northwest Schl Dist Elem Band Tchr 1974-76; D Area Schl Dist Jr Hs Band Tchr 1976-95, HS Bnd Tchr 1995-; *ai:* PSEA 1974-; Natl Band Assn 1992-; PMEA 1995-; *office:* Danvil Jr HS 600 Walnut St Danville PA 17821*

BOWER, JENNIFER SEYMOUR, Fourth Grade Teacher; *b:* Wat NY; *m:* Kyle Chapman; *ed:* Jefferson Comm (AS) Lbrl Arts 1990 Coll (BS) Elem Ed N-6 1992; Working Towards MS SUNY C Advanced Tchng; *ai:* Girls Var Soccer Coach; *office:* Dundee Cent 55 Water St Dundee NY 14837

BOWER, KATHLEEN YINGER, Fourth Grade Teach Mechanicsburg, PA; *m:* William A.; *c:* Douglas, Phillip; *ed:* Albrig (BA) Sociology 1968; Millersville Univ (MED) Elem Ed 1973; Ac Grad Credits Penn St Univ; *cr:* School Dist of Lancaster Second G 1969-74; Salem PREP Nursey Schl Presch Tchr 1981-86; Manhei Schl Dist Fourth Grd Tchr 1988-; *ai:* Sci, Act 178 Comms; Cur MCEA 1988-; PSEA, NEA 1970-; IRA 1988-; St Mark's Unite Church 1972-, Chprsn of Staff Parish Relations Comm; BSA 1981- Comm; 3 Tchr Grants; Participant in Lebanon Vly coll Sci Partn Tchr of Yr 1995; *office:* Doe Run Elem Schl 281 Doe Run Rd Manh 17545

BOWER, KELLY ANN, English Teacher; *b:* Allentown, P Bloomsburg Univ of PA (BS) Scndry Ed Eng 1986; Kutztown Univ (MA) Eng 1991; *cr:* Whitehall HS Eng Tchr 1986-; *ai:* Class Adv; NEA 1986-; Allentown Coll PA Shakespeare Festival, Guild Mem; Whitehall HS 3800 Mechanicsville Rd Whitehall PA 18052

BOWER, STEVEN ALLEN, Art Teacher; *b:* Williamsport, PA; C.; *c:* Nicholas, Ariana, Marcus; *ed:* Mansfield Univ (BS) Art Ec (MED) Art, Ed 1986; *cr:* Elmira City Schls Art Tchr 1970-73; Pro 1973-88; Southern Tioga Schl Dist Art Tchr 1988-; *ai:* NEA 1988- Pres; *home:* 638 S Market St S Williamsprt PA 17701

BOWERS, BEGE, Prof of English & Editor; *b:* Nashville, Tn; *ed:* E cume laude, Vanderbilt U 1971;MACT Univ TN 1973; PhD 1984; for Fin Aid Baylor Univ 1975-76; Wassily Leontief NYU E 1976-78;Florence Darlington Tech Col Instr of Bus 1979-80; St Jol Tchr Frgn Lang 1980-82; Univ TN Eng Dept Tchng Asst 19 Youngstown St Univ asst Prof of Eng 1984-88; Assoc Prof 1988-9 1992-; Comp Coord Eng Dept 1984-95; Actg Dept Chrmn 1989, Dean Arts & Scis 1992-93; Freelance Ed MLA, NYC 1978-80; *ai:* Arete, Youngstown Pub Schls, 1986-91; Cnty Pub Schls 19 Macmillan Pub Co 1986; Trumbuss Cnty Schls 1988; Akron Bea 1994-95; Co Ed CEA Critic, CEA Forum 1988-; " A Study of the N Manners", 1991; Intrnshp in Tech Commn 1991; Ed Brd South A Review; Editor of various pamphlets, children's books videoscript Execu Brd; NCT; New Chaucer Soc; Ass Tchrs Tech Writng So Commn; No Ohio Tech Tech Commn; NEH Awd 1991; Gould Soc F Pres 1991-93; Phi Beta Kappa; Phi Kappa Phi pres 1991-92, Sec Recp John C. Hodges Awd 1973; Alumni Fnd Rsch flwshp Univ TN Dissertation flwshp 1984; Grad Rsch Coun grantee Youngstown S Distng Grad Fac 1988-; Distng Prof Awd 1987; Centurian Otsdr Award 1987; *office:* Youngstown St Univ 410 Wick Ave Youngstow 44555

BOWERS, DOUGLAS ARTHUR, Science Chairperson; *b:* Buffal *m:* Elaine M. Homka; *c:* Thomas A., Ryan P., Kevin D., Amanda E.; Univ Coll of NY at Buffalo (BS) Sci Ed-Suma Cum Laude 1 rad Credits Ed; *cr:* North Tonawanda HS Physics, Chem ı91-92; Cardinal O'Hara HS Bio Tchr 1992-93; Bishop Timon, St S Bio, Chem, Physics Tchr, Sci Chair 1993-; *ai:* Coach HS Hockey, Team; Textbook Comm; Sci Tchrs Western NY 1993-; WNY Physic Assn 1995-; Erie Cty Child Abuse Cncl 1988-90; *office:* Bishop Schl 601 Mc Kinley Pkwy Buffalo NY 14220

RS, GLORIA MILLS, Art Teacher; *b:* Brookville, PA; *m:* Ralph ; *c:* Amy Lynn; *ed:* PA St Univ (BS) Art Ed 1973; *cr:* Jersey Shore ırt Tchr 1973-76; Lock Haven HS Scndry Art Tchr 1982-95; Sugar Elem Art Tchr 1995-; Sugar Valley HS Art Tchr; Woolrich Elem Art Lamar Twp Elem Art Tchr; *ai:* Giving Assn Progress & Svc Sr ıst Adv; Assn of Clinton Co Educators, PSEA 1982-; Amer Assn of Women 1991-; Pi Lambda Theta, NHS Women in Ed 1973; Beta Phi 1980-, Pres 1983, VP 1982, Woman of Yr 1984 & 1985; *home:* Water St Lock Haven PA 17745*

RS, JAMES, Assoc Prof of Pol Science; *b:* Danville, IL; *m:* Janice Dale John Kyoo-Sung; *ed:* Sangamon St Univ (BA) Pol Stud 1979, Pol Stud 1981; Northern IL Univ (PHD) Pol Sci 1988; *cr:* St John Coll Asst Prof of Pol Sci 1988-94, Assoc Prof of Pol Sci 1994-; *ai:* v Pre-Law Stu Assn; AM Pol Sci Assn, Midwest Pol Sci Assn 1982-; rn Pol Sci Assn 1988-; Urban Affairs Assn 1995-; Mayor's dship 1995-; Books: Regulating the Regulators 1990, American 1993, Pro-Choice And Anti-Abortion 1994, Hypotheticals; *office:* ohn Fisher Coll 3690 East Ave Rochester NY 14618

RS, KENNETH R., English Teacher; *b:* Ellwood City, PA; *ed:* Univ llay (AB) Speech & Eng 1963; Masters of Ed Equivalency in Amer m Slippery Rock Univ 1968; *ai:* NEA 1963-, Bldg Rep; PSEA, A 1963-; Civic Chorale 1980-, Dir & Producer Centennial Musical; ed Bowling for 25 Yrs; Coached Tennis; *home:* RR 2 Box 2740 d City PA 16117

RS, MARK THOMAS, Assoc Prof of Civil Engrng; *b:* nville, OH; *m:* Rita Grobins; *c:* Corrie Scheidegger, Jennifer, v, Eric, Emma, Spencer; *ed:* Brigham Young (BS) Civil Engrng 1977, Civil Engrng 1980; AZ St (PHD) Civil Engrng 1986; *cr:* Univ of nati Asst Prof 1985-95, Assoc Prof 1995-, Asst Dept Head 1995-; *ai:* of 1996 Civil Engrng Coord Adv; Coll Acad Standards, Grad Tchng kshp Planning Comms; ASCE 1977-, Section Treas; ASEE 1985, ngineering Edctr Excl; Church of Jesus Christ of Latter Day Saints Bishop, St Presidency; $2.8 Million Funded Rsrch; 16 Tchng Awds ept Coll of Engrng; chi Epsilon Great Lakes Dist; Natl Chi Epsilon xcl Tchng; *office:* Univ Of Cincinnati PO Box 210071 Cincinnati 221*

RS, MICHAEL EVERETT, Soc Stud Dept Chprsn & Instr; *b:* ter, PA; *m:* Gail Marie Hoxworth; *c:* Christopher; *ed:* Millersville BSEd) Soc Stud 1972, (MA) His 1977; Univ of DE 30 Post Grad ; Univ of VA 6 Post Grad Credits; *cr:* Seaford HS Soc Stud Tchr, rin 1993-1995; US Senate Pg Schl Soc Stud, Instr; *ai:* Amer Legion Amer Historical Soc 1972-; US Capitol Historical Soc & Colonial nsburg Fnd 1989-; Taft Fellow 1992; Monticello-Stratford Hall er Inst 1991; *office:* US Senate Pg Schl United States Senate ıgton DC 20510*

RS, NANCY MARSHALL, Chorus & General Music Teacher; *b:* ley, PA; *c:* Dawn Marie, Aaron Tad; *ed:* Indiana Univ of PA (BS) Ed 1970; Attnd Edinboro Univ of PA, St Univ NY at Fredonia; *cr:* sburg Schl Dist Music Tchr 1970; North East Schl Dist Music Tchr 4; Park United Meth Church Music Dir, Organist 1970-, Music Tchr *ai:* NEA, PSEA, PMEA, MENC 1970-; Jaycee Wives; North East nans Club, Pres, Outstdng Young Woman 1976; North East Choral North East Home Hlth Agency, Pres; *office:* North East HS 1901 rt Rd North East PA 16428*

RS, WILLIAM E., Chemistry Teacher; *b:* Lancaster, PA; *m:* Julia ker; *c:* Michelle J. Harada, Shaaron R., Mandy L.; *ed:* Millersville BS) Bio, Comprehensive Sci 1969, (MS) Bio 1974; Univ of PA al Sci Prgm 1971; *cr:* Lower Dauphin Jr High Sci Tchr, Cross Cntry , Asst Track Coach 1969-71; Hempfield HS Bio, Chem Tchr, Cross Coach, Girls Track Coach 1971-; *ai:* Boys & Girls Cross Cntry Head , Track & Field Asst Coach; NEA, PSEA 1969-; NSTA 1980-; *office:* ield HS 200 Stanley Ave Landisville PA 17538

ERSOX, MARK ALAN, World Geography Teacher; *b:* Findlay, OH; enda; *c:* Erik, Hanna; *ed:* York Coll of PA (BS) Soc Stud Ed 1979; t Univ (MS) Ed 1993; *cr:* Manassas Park HS Soc Stud Tchr 1979-85; Western Schls World Geog Tchr 1985-; *ai:* Wrestling Coach 12 Yrs; Dist IM Dir; Multicultural Ed Comm; Spring Grove Little League Coach; NEA 1979-; PSEA 1985-; Grant at William & Mary Coll to S-Soviet Cold War 1984; *home:* RR 3 Box 332 Hanover PA 17331*

ERSOX, ROBERT E., World Cultures & Soc Stud Tchr; *b:* New hem, PA; *m:* Paula Boyd; *ed:* Westminster (BA) Bus Admin 1966; n Univ (MED) Supervision 1980, (MBA) Mngmt 1982; Doctoral s Univ of Pittsburgh 1983; *cr:* Clarion Area HS Soc Stud Tchr 81; Clarion Univ Mngmt Asst Prof 1981-85; Clarion Area HS Soc Tchr 1985-; *ai:* Track, Cross Cntry, Gofl Coach; Curr Comm; Class Soc Stud Dept Acting Chprsn; Track, Field Ofcl; Clarion Area Ed 1969-, Chief Negotiator; NEA 1969-, Natl Convention Del 1974; west Mountain Coaches Assn 1970-, Past Pres; Clarion Cty Track 1980-, Pres, Rules Interpreter; Jaycees 1966-69, VP; Nom PA Tchr 1980; Amer Assn for Higher Ed Awd 1992; Educl Partner & Co-Dir rion Capstone Project 1995; *office:* Clarion Area H S 219 Liberty St n PA 16214*

ES, CHARLES THOMAS, Integrated Language Arts Tchr; *b:* , OH; *m:* Ann Wilbur; *c:* John W., Thimothy A., George E.; *ed:* Univ edo (BA) Elem Ed 1973; 40 Hrs Post Grad Class; *cr:* Toledo Bd of ır 1974-; *ai:* Sci Chprsn; Toledo Fed of Tchrs 1974-; Kappa Delta Pi Pres, VP; *office:* Mc Kinley Elem Schl 1901 W Central Ave Toledo 3606

ES, JANE LOUISE, Special Education Professor; *b:* Williamsport, Jim F.; *c:* Christopher J., Erich R.; *ed:* Lock Haven Univ (BS) Elem c Ed 1985; West Chester Univ (MA) Psych 1988; PHD Candidate PA v Curr & Supervision; *cr:* PA Delco Schl Dist Spec Ed Tchr 1985-86; Grove Schl Dist Spec Ed Tchr 1986-88; Williamsport Area Schl Dist Ed Tchr 1988-93; Lock Haven Univ Spec Ed Prof 1993-; *ai:* Adv LHU er of Cncl for Exceptional Children; Kappa Delta Pi 1984-; Cncl for tional Children 1983-, Adv; Assn for Curr & Supervision 1995-; 1991-; *office:* Lock Haven Univ Robinson Hall Lock Haven PA

IE, CAMILLE FINNEY, Business Education Teacher; *b:* esboro, PA; *m:* David Allen; *c:* April Louise, Jared David, Kevin n, Karen Nicole; *ed:* Shippensburg Univ (BS) Bus Ed 1977, (MED) d 1985; *cr:* Waynesboro Area Sr HS Bus Ed Tchr 7 Yrs; Waynesboro r HS Bus Ed Tchr 5 Yrs; Greencastle-Antrim HS Bus Ed Tchr 3 Yrs; Class Adv; Class Trip Planning & Indoor Guard Parent Comms; Soc LDS Church 1975-, Pres; *office:* Waynesboro Area Sr HS 550 E Waynesboro PA 17268

KER, ROBERT D., English Department Chair; *b:* Delhi, NY; *m:* ne L. Edwards; *c:* Jennifer, Elizabeth, Jeremy; *ed:* St Lawrence Univ Govt 1980; SUNY at Binghamton (MS) Tchng 1988; *cr:* First Bapt Acad Tchr 1980-84; Hallstead Chrstn Acad Tchr & Admin 1984-89; Cntrl Bapt Chrstn Acad Eng Tchr & Dept Chm 1989-; *ai:* Chrstn Writer's Fellowship; Cited in Tchng Soc Stud in Mid & Sr HS Decisions Decisions 1991; Article Pub in Journal for Chrstn Educators 1992 & 1994; *home:* RR 1 Box 12C Hallstead PA 18822

BOWLBY, JUDY ANN, Family & Consumer Sci Teacher; *b:* Lancaster, PA; *m:* David H.; *c:* Jennifer, John David, Jeffrey, Jeremy; *ed:* Albright Coll (BS) Home Ec 1971; Post Grad Stud 36 Credit Hrs; *cr:* Manheim Twp HS Family & Consumer Sci 1971-73, Tchr 1986-; *ai:* Stu Asst Pgm Mem; Lancaster Cty Home Ec Assoc 1986- Recording Sec; *office:* Manheim Twp HS 5134 School Rd Lancaster PA 17601

BOWLER, MARGARET, Co-Director of Guidance; *b:* New York City, NY; *ed:* St Thomas Aquinas (BS) Ed 1962; Manhattan Coll (MS) Psych Cnslng 1973; *cr:* St Ann's Schl 4-5th Grd Tchr 1959-62; St Christopher's Schl 4-6th Grd Tchr 1962-67; ST Jerome Schl 7th-8th Grd Tchr 1967-73; St Rita's Schl 7th-8th Grd Tchr 1967-73; St Pius V HS Sr Guid Cnslr 1973-88; Monsignor Scanlan HS Co-Dir Guid 1988-; *ai:* Coord Stu Spon Prgm; Moderator Scanlan Schlsp Achievers; NCEA 1976-; St Frances de Chantal Parish 1987-, Eurastic Minister; *office:* Monsignor Scanlan H S 915 Hutchinson River Pky Bronx NY 10465

BOWLER, SHEILA MARY (HARRINGTON), Health & Human Services Prof; *b:* Springfield, MA; *m:* Edmund Dunbar; *c:* Julianne M., James E., Ellen R. Mongeau; *ed:* Amer Intnl Coll (BS) Human Svcs 1981; Univ of MA (MA) Higher Ed 1986; Boston Coll Schl of Nrsng Successful Completing 96 Hrs for BSN; Mercy Hosp Schl Nrsng Diploma Prgm for Licensure RN; *cr:* Boston Health Dept Staff Nurse Schl Communicable 1961-63; Mercy Hosp Staff Nurse OR, ER, & W Therapy 1971-83; Spfld Tech Comm Coll Prof Div Hlth, Human Svcs 1983-; *ai:* Holyoke MA St Parick's Day Parade Comm West Spfld Contingent; NEA, MTA, MNA 1983-; Am Red Cross 1995-, Hlth & Safety Svc Comm; *office:* Springfield Tech Comm Coll 1 Armory Sq Springfield MA 01101

BOWLES, JOY E., High School Business Teacher; *b:* Flushing, NY; *m:* Jack J.; *c:* Scott Santagata, Brett Santagata (dec), Wayne Santagata; *ed:* Pace Univ (AAS) Secretarial Stud 1962, (BBA) Bus Admin 1964; SUNY at Potsdam (MS) Ed 1985; *cr:* Seaway Tech Ctr Adult Ed Tchr 1973-78; Salmon River Cntrl Schl HS Bus Tchr 1978-79; Parishville-Hopkinton Cntrl Schl HS Bus Tchr 1979-; *ai:* Sr Class Adv; HS Stans, Tech Comms; Grace United Meth Church 1992-, Treas; United Meth Women 1988-, VP; Joint Cncl on Ec Awd; *office:* Parishville Hopkinton Ctl Sch School St Parishville NY 13672

BOWLING, SHANNON MAUREEN, PE Teacher & Athletic Trainer; *b:* Wyoming, NY; *m:* Todd Douglas; *c:* Cody Douglas, Tyler Patrick; *ed:* Univ of Dayton (BS) PE 1987; Univ of NC (MA) Sports Medicine 1989; Allegheny Coll 2 Yrs; *cr:* Univ of NC Grad Asst 1987-89; Cincinnati Sports Med Ath Trainer 1989-91; Northwest HS PE Tchr, Ath Trainer 1991-; *ai:* Ath Trainer; Future Tchrs of Amer Spon; Soph Class Adv; Attendance Intervention Team; Stu of Month Comm; Natl Ath Trainers Assn 1985-; NEA 1991-; OEA; *office:* Northwest HS 10761 Pippin Rd Cincinnati OH 45231

BOWMAN, CAROL LEE, Latin, French & English Tchr; *b:* Roaring Spring, PA; *m:* Bill E.; *c:* Marina Link, Mark G. Bollman, Andrea Mathias, Cynthia E. Lee; *ed:* PA St Univ (BA) Eng 1965, (MED) Scndry Guid Cnslr 1970; *cr:* Bedford Area HS Frgn Lang, Eng Tchr 1965-; *ai:* NHS Advy Cncl Chprsn; ASCD, PSMLA 1994-; Bedford Area Ed Assn, PSEA, NEA 1965-; Bedford Springs Chap OES 1960-; Bedford City Soroptimist Cl 1988-, VP, Corr Sec; Bedford Cty BPW 1986-; *home:* RR 1 Box 40 Bedford PA 15522

BOWMAN, CAROL MARKER, Chemistry & Physics Teacher; *b:* Marion, OH; *m:* Thomas A.; *c:* Adam, Aaron, Hollie, Benjamin, Joshua, Sarah; *ed:* OH St Univ (BS) Comprehensive Sci 1993; 150 Addl Hrs; *cr:* Northridge HS Chem, Physics Tchr 1993-; *ai:* Environmental, Sci Club; Cty Sci Curr Comm; Sci Edctrs Cncl of OH 1991-; NEA 1993-; PTA 1981-, VP, Many Comms; LDS Church Yth Groups 1979-, Pres; BSA 1983-, Dist Roundtable Comm Pres, Den Ldr; *office:* Northridge HS 6066 Johnstown Utica Rd Johnstown OH 43031*

BOWMAN, CONNIE SUE SIMPSON, Secondary English Teacher; *b:* Robinson, IL; *m:* Thomas; *c:* Andrew, Lisa; *ed:* The Coll of Wooster (BA) Eng 1968; MI St (MA) Eng Ed 1973; Numerous Addl Hrs; *cr:* Portland HS Eng & Soc Stud Tchr 1968-72; DSU & ATI Eng & Soc Stud Tchr 1973-81; Wooster HS Eng Tchr 1981-; *ai:* Frosh Class Adv; NEA, NCTE 1968-; OEA, OCJELA 1973-; Wooster Enrichment Fund Awd; Humanities Inst Study Florence Italy.

BOWMAN, DEBORAH LEE, 7th & 8th Grd Pre-Algebra Tchr; *b:* Harrisburg, PA; *m:* Thomas Calvin; *c:* Brandt, Bryan; *ed:* Shippensburg St Coll (BS) Elem Ed 1980; MS Equivalency plus 30; *cr:* Millersburg MS Sixth Grd Math Tchr 1983-90, Seventh & Eighth Grd Math; *ai:* MS Stu Cncl Adv; Math Curr Planner; Dist 8 PASC Bd Mem; NEA, PSEA 1983-; MAEA Sec; NCTM; Civic Club 1987-; YMCA Brd Mem 1992; YMCA Soccer Coach 1995; Fundraiser Chr Cub Scouts, Little League; *office:* Millersburg M S 799 CenterSt Millersburg PA 17061

BOWMAN, DEBRA (BETTS), 5th Grade Teacher; *b:* Bluffton, OH; *m:* Gary L.; *c:* Megan, Cari, Lindsey; *ed:* OH Northern Univ (BA) Elem Ed 1991; *cr:* Mc Comb Local Schls 6th Grd Tchr 1991-92; Forest Bldg, Riverdale Schl 2nd Grd Tchr1992-93; Mt Blanchard Bldg, Riverdale Schl 5th Grd Tchr 1993-; *ai:* NEA, OEA, REA 1991-, Exec Comm, Bldg Rep; SOAP 1994-, Funding Chprsn; SERRC Awd; *office:* Mt Blanchard Elem Schl S Main St Mt Blanchard OH 45867

BOWMAN, DONNA RAE, Science Teacher; *b:* Cumberland, MD; *ed:* Frostburg Univ (BS) Bio 1970; Attnd Towson Univ, Univ of MD, Loyola; *cr:* North Point Jr HS Sci Tchr 1970-80; General Stricker MS Sci Tchr 1981-; *ai:* Publicity, Photography Chprsn; Fac Cncl; Yrbk; Soc Comm; NEA, MSTA 1970-; TABCO 1970-, Recognition Awd 1991; Discovery Channel Tchr Advisory Bd 1990-; Rdng Sci Presentations to Baltimore Co; *office:* General John Stricker M S 7855 Trappe Rd Baltimore MD 21222

BOWMAN, JAN ALBRIGHT, English Teacher; *b:* Lancaster, PA; *m:* Timothy L.; *c:* Erin, Wesley; *ed:* Lock Haven St Coll (BS) Comm 1976; 24 Addl Credit Hrs at Indiana Univ of PA; In-Service Credits at Univ of Pittsburgh at Johnstown; *cr:* Marticville MS Jr HS Eng Tchr 1976-77; Shade HS Jr & Sr HS Eng Tchr 1977-84; Conemaugh Twp Area HS Sr HS Eng Tchr 1985-; *ai:* Sr HS Scholastic Quiz Adv; Instrl Ldr Eng, Lang, Libr Team; Fellow, Sthcentral PA Wrtng Proj Summ 1995; Tchr, Cnsltnt PA Wrtng Proj; Currently in MA, TE Prog, IUP; PSEA, NEA & NCTE 1976-; Geraldine R Dodge Fnd "Celebration of Tchng" Grants 1990, 1991 & 1992; *office:* Conemaugh Township Area HS W Campus Ave Davidsville PA 15928*

BOWMAN, JILL ANASTASI, 5th Grade Teacher; *b:* Port Jefferson, NY; *m:* Ronald; *c:* Tracey Lynn, Amy Marie; *ed:* SUNY at Cortland (BA) Elem Ed 1971; Dowling Coll (MS) Elem Ed 1992; 50 Post Grad Credits; *cr:* Boyle Rd Schl 3rd Grd Tchr 1971-75, 1977-79; Ridge Schl 3rd Grd Tchr 1982-86, 4th Grd Tchr 1987-92, 5th Grd Tchr 1993-; *ai:* NEA 1971-; AFT 1971-; MITA 1982-; *office:* Ridge Elem Schl 105 Ridge Rd Ridge NY 11961

BOWMAN, KAREN BARKHYMER, Secondary Soc Studies Teacher; *b:* Johnstown, PA; *m:* Ronald L.; *c:* David D., Kristin L., Daniel W.; *ed:* IN Univ of PA (BSE) Scndry Soc Sci Ed 1977, (MED) Scndry Soc Sci Ed 1983; Post Grad Credits Millersville Univ, Carlow Coll, Intermediate Univ 8, PA Dept of Ed; *cr:* Northern Cambria Schl Dist Scndry Soc Stud Tchr 1977-; *ai:* Earth Week Act Co-Spon; NEA, PSEA 1977-; Northern Cambria Ed Assn 1977-, Schlsp Comm; Delta Kappa Gamma 1992-; Church Missions Comm 1993-; Cambria Elem PTO 1988-; Schl Dist Grant; Outstdng Tchr; NEH Stud Participant 1995; *office:* Northern Cambria HS 807 N 11th St Barnesboro PA 15714

BOWMAN, LEE JAMES, Band Director; *b:* Massillon, OH; *m:* Mary Lou Antonille; *c:* Lee II, Mark, Carrie; *ed:* Bowling Green St Univ (BM) Music 1966; Univ of Dayton (MED) Admin, Supervision 1985; Kent St Univ Post Grad Stud; *cr:* Buckeye HS Band Dir 1966-67; Canton South HS Band Dir 1967-; *ai:* Band Boosters Supvr; NEA, OEA, CLEA, MENC 1966-; NBA; BSA 1979-; Rotary Intnl Guest Speaker; *office:* Canton South HS 600 Faircrest St SE Canton OH 44707

BOWMAN, RICHARD EDWARD, History Teacher; *b:* York, PA; *m:* Rita Brueggeman; *c:* Stephen, Elizabeth, Matthew; *ed:* Millersville Univ (BS) His, Soc Stud 1962; Western Maryland (MED) Admin of Ed 1972; York Coll Acctng; Penn St York Cmptr; *cr:* York City Tchr 1963-64; York Cath HS 12th Grd Amer Frgn Policy, Contemporary Issues, 10th Grd European His, 8th Grd Ancient His Tchr 1964-; *ai:* Dept, Stu Enrichment Chprsn; Coord York Cath Blood Donors, Grad Baccalaureate; Knights of Columbus 1960-; Cath War Veterans 1962-, Med Ofcr; *office:* York Catholic HS 601 E Springettsbury Ave York PA 17403

BOWMAN, TAMMY LYNN, Business Teacher; *b:* Williamsburg, KY; *ed:* Cumberland Coll (BS) Bus Admin 1984; Univ of Dayton (MS) Ed 1987; *cr:* Dayton Chrstn HS Bus Tchr 1984-; *ai:* Discipleship Ldr; Stu Senate Adv; *office:* Dayton Christian HS 325 Homewood Ave Dayton OH 45405

BOWSER, ANITA QUINLISK, Substitute Teacher; *b:* Punxsutawney, PA; *m:* James D.; *c:* Timothy, Stephen, DeeAnne Anderson, Julie; *ed:* Chapman Coll at Orange (BS) Sci & Soc Stud 1969; Univ of NE (MS) Cnslng 1975; *cr:* Soonyong Univ Instr 1979; Franciscan Schl Prin 1979-81; SS Cosmas & Damian 7th Grd Sci Tchr 1981-95; *home:* 105 Sycamore St Punxsutawney PA 15767

BOWSER, HARRY PAUL, Scndry World Cultures Teacher; *b:* Connellsville, PA; *m:* Karon J. Hester; *c:* Ryan, Adam; *ed:* Univ of Pgh (BA) His 1972; *cr:* Southermoreland Schl Dist Soc Stud Tchr 1972-; *ai:* Ftbl Coach 10 Yrs; Bsbl Coach 18 Yrs; Bsktbl Coach 19 Yrs; Jr Class Spon; PSEA & NEA 1972-; *office:* Southmoreland Sr HS PO Box A Alverton PA 15612*

BOWSER, MARILYN HARTMAN, Fourth Grade Teacher; *b:* Meadville, PA; *m:* Ira David Jr.; *c:* Jeff, Mark, Jennifer Mc Tiernan; *ed:* Edinboro Univ (BS) Elem Ed 1960; Masters in Elem Ed; *ai:* NEA, PSEA 1966-; League of Women Voters 1985-, Bd Mem; Thurston Hot Air Balloon Event 1990-, Hospitality Chair; Stone United Meth Church 1950-, Trustee.

BOWSER, MELANIE DODSON, Health & Physical Ed Teacher; *b:* Bedford, PA; *m:* Brent A.; *c:* Brandon, Brittany, Bronson; *ed:* Lock Haven St Coll (BS) Hlth & PE 1981; 31 Credit Hrs; *cr:* Northern Bedford Schl Dist Hlth, PE 1981-; *ai:* Var Club Adv; Track Coach; United Church of Christ, Sunday Schl Tchr, Sunday Schl Piano Player; Red Cross 1980-, CPR & First Aid Instr; *office:* Northern Bedford HS HCR 1 Box 200 Loysburg PA 16659

BOX, ANITA, Fifth Grade Teacher; *b:* Scranton, PA; *c:* Jennifer, Jodi; *ed:* E Stroudsburg Univ (BS) Elem Ed 1970; Masters Equivalency 36 Grad Credits ESU, Marywood Coll; *cr:* Ft Bragg Army Schls Learning Disabilities Tchr 1972-74; Wallenpaupack MS 5th, 7th-8th Grd Tchr 1979-81; Wallenpaupack Hawley Elem Schl 4th Grd Tchr 1981-87; Wallenpaupack South Elem Schl 3rd Grd Tchr 1987-95, 5th Grd Tchr 1995-; *ai:* Stu Assistance Prgm; FAME Team Mem; Staff Induction Cncl; New Tchrs Mentor; Curr, Soc Stud, Communications Comms; Mid St Co-Chr; IST; PSEA, NEA 1976-; Delta Kappa Gamma 1992-; Kappa Delta Pi 1970-; Queen of Peace Roman Cath Church 1980-; Drug Free Schls Comm Cncl 1993-; Featured on Touch of Class Prgm; *home:* RR 1 Box 396E Greentown PA 18426*

BOYAH, PAUL B., Mathematics Teacher; *b:* Monrovia, Liberia; *m:* Sharon Zonn; *c:* Elsyn, Ama E. Brown, Mosio; *ed:* Univ of Vienna (MS) Meteorology 1981; Univ of Karlstuhe West Germany VOR Diploma Meteorology 1974; Meteorology, Hurricane Forecasting Cert Univ of Miami; *cr:* Montclair St Coll Adj Math Instr 1984-86; Immaculate Conception HS Math, Physics Tchr 1984-88; Seton Hall Univ Adj Math Instr 1987; Essex Co Voc Schls Math Tchr 1988-89; Newark Pub Schls Math Tchr 1989-; *ai:* Weather Club Adv; NEA, NJEA 1984-; NCTM, Newark Assn of Math Edctrs 1991-; World Meteorological Org Flwshp 1979-83; *office:* Weequahic HS 279 Chancellor Ave Newark NJ 07112

BOYAN, KITTY STEIN, 5th Grade Teacher; *b:* Baltimore, MD; *m:* A. Stephen Jr.; *c:* Justin A.; *ed:* Univ of Chicago (BA) Ed 1966; PA St Univ (MED) Ed 1971; Attnd Lehigh Univ 1976; *cr:* Alfarata Elem Schl Tchr 1966-69; Clarksville Elem Schl Tchr 1973-; *ai:* Coord, Schl Comm Wide Effort to Build Environmental Stud Area; Trainer of Tchrs in Use of Project Wild Prgm; Fifth Grd Gardening Club Ldr; NEA; NSTA; NCTM; MD Assn of Sci Tchrs; MD St Tchrs Assn; Howard Co Edctrs Assn; MD Assn for Environmental & Outdoor Ed; Audubon Soc; Sierra Club; Wilderness Soc; Nature Conservancy; Conservation Tchr of Yr MD Assn of Soil Conservation 1991; Howard Cty Tchr of Yr Howard Chamber of Commerce 1992; MD Sci Tchrs Assn Tchr of Yr 1993; Presidential Awd for Excl in Sci & Math Finalist 1994; *office:* Clarksville Elem Schl 12041 State Route 108 Clarksville MD 21029*

BOYAR, GAIL TUCKER, History Teacher; *b:* Cleveland, OH; *m:* Jay H.; *c:* Seth M.; *ed:* Smith Coll (BA) His 1961; Yale Univ (MAT) His 1962; Georgetown Univ, The Amer Univ, Univ of MD 30 Addl Credit Hrs Beyond Masters; *cr:* Hanover Park Regnl High His Tchr 1962-63; Northwestern Sr High His Tchr 1963-74; Prince George Comm Coll His Instr 1974-78; Eleanor Roosevelt HS His Tchr 1978-83; Charles E Smith Jewish Day Schl His Tchr 1983-; *ai:* Stu Govt Adv; Various Comms; AFT 1983-; *office:* Charles E Smith Jewish Dy Schl 1901 E Jefferson St Rockville MD 20852

BOYCE, CORY BRITTON, Mathematics Teacher; *b:* Louisville, KY; *m:* Pauline Rhodes; *c:* Deryn, Tyler, Jency; *ed:* VA Tech (BS) Mechanical Engrng 1987; Lehigh Univ (MA) Scndry Ed 1992; *cr:* E. I. duPont deNemours & Co Field Engr 1987-90; Acad of New Church Math Tchr 1991-; *ai:* Frosh Class Adv; Var Soccer Coach; Summer Camp Dir; NCTM 1990-; NSCAA 1992-; ATMOPAV 1991-; Pastor's Cncl 1994-; Alpha Iota Omega 1985-; Dorothea Homiller Glenn Excl in Tchng Awd; *office:* Acad Of The New Church PO Box 707 Bryn Athyn PA 19009

BOYCE, DOLORES WILSON, English Teacher; *b:* Jersey City, NJ; *c:* Lonie MC Gowan, Melody Mc Gowan-Parker; *ed:* Jersey City St Coll (BA) Ed, Comparative Lit 1978, (MA) Urban Ed, Supervision 1992; 6 Addl Credit Hrs Multicultural Stud 1994-; St Peters Coll Durant Schlr 3 Credit Hrs 1992, Multicultural Stud 9 Credit Hrs 1994-95; *cr:* Meadowview Mental Disease Hosp Staff Nurse 6 Yrs; Model Cities of Jersey City Hlth Specialist Coord 3 Yrs; Jersey City Job Corp Principles of Nrsng Tchr 3 Yrs; Jersey City Bd of Ed Eng Tchr 18 Yrs; *ai:* Strutters Coach 1983-92; Jr Class Adv 1991-93; Models 1994-; JCEA, NEA, NJEA 1980-; Natl Phi Delta Kappa 1983-; Phi Delta Kappa 1993-; Order of Eastern Star 1966-, Conductress; Democratic Women of Jersey City 1965-; *office:* James J Ferris HS 35 Colgate St Jersey City NJ 07302

BOYCE, JACQUELINE ELIZABETH, Elementary Physical Ed Tchr; *b:* Niagara Falls, NY; *ed:* Univ of Buffalo (BA), Health, PE, & Recreation

1966; Buffalo St Tchrs Coll (MS) Mental Retardation 1973; Buffalo St Tchrs Course Work Tchng, Rdng & dance; *cr:* Niagara Falls Schls Elem PE 30 Yrs; *ai:* IM Soccer; AFT; NYSUT; Intl Twins Assn; Amer Red Cross; Champion Staff Mem 1993; *home:* 6836 Walmore Rd Niagara Falls NY 14304

BOYCE, SUSAN MC CLELLAND, Third Grade Teacher; *b:* Newburgh, NY; *ed:* Mt St Mary Coll (BA) Lbrl Arts, Eng Lit 1971; SUNY at New Paltz (MS) Elem Ed 1982; 15 Addl Hrs; *cr:* St John the Evangelist Schl 3rd Grd Tchr 1971-74; Regina Coll 1st, 3rd Grd Tchr 1976-80; Netherwood Schl 1st, 5th Grd Tchr 1980-83; Hyde Park Elem Schl 2nd-3rd Grd Tchr 1983-, GATE Tchr 1986-; *ai:* Bldg Level Team Fac Rep; Adv Discipline Comm; Primary Options Comm; Advanced Gesell Examiner; AFT 1980-; Nortern Dutchess; Bus, Prof WOmen 1980-, Sec, VP, Pres 1984-86; Rhinebeck TheatreSoc 1986-, Sec, VP, Pres 1988-90; Area Fund Dutchess Cty Grant 1994; *office:* Hyde Park Elem Schl 599 Albany Post Rd Hyde Park NY 12538*

BOYD, ANN LEWIS, Dean of Graduate School; *b:* Shreveport, LA; *m:* James Pierce; *c:* Kathryn; *ed:* Northwestern St Univ (BS) Chem 1965, (MS) Microbiology 1969; LA St Univ (PLD) Microbiology 1971; Post-Doctoral Fellow in Virology Baylor Coll Med 1971-73; *cr:* Natl Cancer Insts Frederick Cancer Reserach Ctr Research Scientist 1973-82; Hood Coll Assoc Prof Biol 1982-88, Prof, Chair Biol 1988-93, Assoc VP Acad Affairs 1993-; *ai:* Acting Dean Grad Schl; Sr Staff; Strategic Planning; Grad Cncl; Acad Affaris; Hlth Professions Advy Cncl; Biosafety Comm NCI-GCRDC; Amer Assn Univ Women 1988-, Chair, Am Fellowship Panel; AAUP, Sigma Xi 1982-; Am Assn Ad Sci, Amer Soc Micro 1973-; Phi Kappa Phi 1971-, Pres; People to People Int'l 1983-, Ambassador to Europe, China, Japan, Russia; Girls Scouts 1975-, Bd Mem, United Way 1988-, Allocations Comm; Advocates Homeless 1988-, Bd Mem; NCI Grant EBU Mapping 1984-87; NSF Equipment Grant 1986, 1988; Whitaker Fnd Grant 1989-92; Glano Sponsored Reserach 1992-; *office:* Hood College 401 Rosemont Ave Frederick MD 21701

BOYD, CHARLES A., Asst Prof of Eng Intermdt Stud; *b:* Elyria, OH; *m:* Connie Parsons; *c:* Sasha; *ed:* OH St Univ (BA) Hum 1974; Emporia St Univ (MA) Eng 1978; 18 Credit Hrs Univ of OR; *cr:* Univ of MN Eng Instr 1978-80; Pioneer Comm Coll Eng Intervention Instr 1981-84; Univ of OR Eng Instr 1985-88; Genesee Comm Coll Asst Prof of Eng & Intermediate Stud 1988-; *ai:* Acad Senate; Inst Rsrch & Dev, Internet, GCC Homepage, Chancellors Awd, GEA Schlsp Chair Intermediate Stud Comm; NEH Summer Inst Coord 1995; NCTE 1987-; GEA, NEA 1988-; NYCSLA 1988-; NISOD Awd for Tchng Excl 1992; NEH Summer Inst Participant 1992; Chancellors Awd for Tchng Excl 1993; *office:* Genesee Comm Coll 1 College Rd Batavia NY 14020*

BOYD, CHRISTOPHER WILLIAM, English Teacher; *b:* Harrisburg, PA; *m:* Maria Nagel; *c:* Kyle Christopher; *ed:* Shippensburg Univ (BS) Commnctn Arts 1987; Presently in Masters Pgm for Educl Admin; *cr:* James Buchanan MS 8th Grd Eng Tchr 1987-; *ai:* 8th Grd Class, Juggling Club, Weight & Speed Club Adv; Stu Assistance Pgm Team Mem; NEA 1987-; PSEA 1987-; Tuscarora Ed Assn 1987-, Former Treas; *office:* James Buchanan M S 5191 Ft Loudon Middle School Rd Mercersburg PA 17236*

BOYD, CRAIG EARL, Music Department Head; *b:* Riverhead, NY; *ed:* Suffolk Cty Comm Coll (AA) Arts 1976; Berklee Coll of Music (BM) Music Composition 1980, (BM) Music Ed 1981; Long Island Univ (MA) Music Composition 1987; 21 Credits Lbrl Ars, Sci; *cr:* Southampton Town Police Dept Traffic Control Ofcr 1981-82; Riverhead MS6th Grd Choral Dir, 6th, 7th & 8th Grd Gen Music Tchr 1985-90; Music Box Schl of Music D ir 1985-89; Suffolk Cty Comm Coll Music Dept Head 1990-; *ai:* Jazz Club Adv; Fac Senate; Stu Liaison; ASCAP 1982-; SCMEA, NYSSMA, MENC l(()_; *office:* Suffolk Cty Comm Coll 533 College Rd Selden NY 11784

BOYD, DANIEL S., Physical Education Teacher; *b:* Troy, NY; *m:* Cathy J. Henley; *c:* Timothy, Gregory, Carissa Lafica; *ed:* Russell Sage Coll (MS) Hlth 1982; *cr:* Waterford Halfmoon Schl PE Tchr 1979-; *office:* Waterford-Halfmoon Schl 125 Middletown Rd Waterford NY 12188

BOYD, EDITH J. MAJOR, 8th Grade Social Studies Tchr; *b:* Newark, NJ; *m:* Jeffrey E.; *ed:* Hofstra Univ (BA) His, Scndry Ed 1972; *cr:* Mc Manus MS 7-9 Grd Soc Stud Tchr 23 Yrs; *ai:* Project Bus Adv 1984-; Bookfair Coord 1978-; Peer Ldrshp Adv 1984-85; Amer Ed Coord 1979, 1981, 1985-86; NJEA 1972-; Linden Educl Fnd 1988-, Charter Mem; Continental Socs Inc 1989-, Recording Sec; NJ Governors Tchr Recognition Awd 1987; Tchr of Yr 1987; Jr Achvmt Distngd Svc Awd 1988-90, 1992; *home:* 60 Fleetwood Dr Hazlet NJ 07730

BOYD, GINA MARY, PE & Health Instructor; *b:* Geneva, NY; *ed:* Cayuga Comm Coll (AAS) Liberal Arts & Hum 1988; Cortland St (BSE) PE 1990; Brockport St (MSE) PE; *cr:* Alfred St Coll Tchr, Coach & Dir of Fitness Ctr 1990-; *ai:* Womens Bsktbl & Sftbl Coach; Search Comm for Ath Dir, Sports Infomation Dir & Womens Soccer Position; Learn to Swim Dir; WBCA; NSCAA Bsktbl 1990-; Coach of Yr 1993-94; Penn York Coach of Yr 1994-95; Won Regnl Sftbl Tournament First Time Ever at Alfred St 1994.

BOYD, JOAN WEBSTER, Allied Health Associate Prof; *b:* Youngstown, OH; *m:* Willard; *c:* Keith, Mark, Jaison, Brent; *ed:* Youngstown St Univ (BS) Chem & Medical Tech 1975; Cntrl MI Univ (MA) Hlth Ed 1980; The Union Inst (PHD) Pub Hlth 1993; Saint Elizabeths Hospital Internship in Medical Tech 1960; 10 Credit Hrs at Kent St Univ in Immunology, Epidemiology & Hlth Mgmt; *cr:* Saint Elizabeths Hosptial Medical Ctr Radioisotopes Supvr 1961-77; Youngstown St Univ Staff Asst 1977-78, Allied Hlth & Clinical Lab Scis Assoc Prof 1978-; *ai:* Mentor for Disadvantaged Stdnts; UNCF Fund Raising Act; Hlth Ministries Coord; Hlth Screening Comm Act Stu Supvr; City Schl Adolescents Art Act Asst & Dir; Amer Soc Clinical Pathologist 1961-; Amer Soc Clinical Lab Sci, OH Soc Of Clinical Lab Sci 1961-, Nominating Pres; Amer Assn of Pub Hlth 1993-; Alpha Kappa Alpha 1957-, Treas, Adv; The Links Inc-Youngstown Chapter 1976-, Pres, Sec, Svcs to Youth Awd; Lambda Tau 1978-, Adv, Honorary Mem; WYSU 1989-, Advy Bd Adv; Edna McDonald Awd Cultural Diversity Tchng at Youngstown St Univ; YWCA Hlth Ed Women of Yr; 2 Articles Pub in Journals-Research Act; Nom as Outstanding Prof by Black Stu Union; Assoc Ed of Journal of Multicultural Nursing & Hlth; *office:* Youngstown St Univ 410 Wick Ave Youngstown OH 44555

BOYD, KAREN ANGEL, Instrumental Music Teacher; *b:* Newburg, NY; *m:* Kevin Dean; *c:* Katharine, Kristy; *ed:* St Univ Coll at Fredonia (BM) Music Ed 1976; 30 Grad Hrs; *cr:* Brocton Cntrl Schl 5th-12th Grd Instrumental Music & Band Tchr 1976-; *ai:* Pep Band; Music Asst Dir; Compact Bldg Level Team Co-Facilitator; SADD Adv; Music Edctrs Natl Conf 1976-; NY St Schl Music Assn 1976-, Past Cty Pres; Chautauqua Cty Music Tchrs Assn 1976-, Past Pres; NY St Band Dir Assn; Girl Scouts of Amer 1964-, Ldr 3 Yrs; *office:* Brocton Central Schl 138 W Main St Brocton NY 14716*

BOYD, KIM STURGEON, Music Department Chair; *b:* Washington, IN; *c:* Matthew, Ann; *ed:* IN St Univ (BS) Music Ed 1966; OH St Univ (MA) Vocal Pedagogy 1974, (MM) Conducting 1975; *cr:* Frankfort City Schls Elem Music Supvr 1966-67; Rochester City Schls HS Vocal Tchr 1967-68; OH St Univ Grad Tchng Assoc 1973-75; DE Hayes HS Music Dept Chair 1975-; *ai:* Choirs, Orch, Showchoir & Musical Dir; OMEA 1973-, Region Chair; MENC 1966-; ACDA 1975-; Ashland Gldn Apple Achvmnt Awd; Kiwanis Svc Awd; Distinguished Tchng Awd; *office:* Delaware Hayes HS 289 Euclid Ave Delaware OH 43015

BOYD, MARTHA ELLEN, 10th-12th Grade English Tchr; *b:* Johnstown, PA; *ed:* Univ of Pittsburgh (BA) Soc Scis 1983; Univ of Pittsburgh at Johnstown (BA) Ed 1985; Southern IL Univ 8 Credit Hrs; Univ of MD 8 Credit Hrs; *cr:* Duval Cty Pub Schls Tchr 1985-86; Frederick Cty Pub Schls Tchr 1986-88; Forest Hills Schl Dist Tchr 1988-; *ai:* Co-Chair Strategic Planning Comm; PSEA & NEA 1988-, Sec & Grievance Chair; Forest Hills Comm Band 1994-; Ed The Story of Johnstown; *office:* Forest Hills Sr HS 489 Locust St PO Box 325 Sidman PA 15955*

BOYD, M. EUNICE, Chm & Prof of Nat Science Dept; *b:* Portland, ME; *ed:* St Josephs Coll (BA) Natural Sci 1964; Univ of PA (MS) Sci Ed 1967, (EDD) Sci Ed 1970; *cr:* Diocese of Portland Elem Schl Tchr 1953-62; Cathedral HS Bio & Chem Tchr 1964-66; St Josephs Coll Nat Sci Dept Chair 1970-; *ai:* Superior Gen Dioceson Sisters of Mercy of Portland; Delta Epsilon Sigma 1964-; Pi Lambda Theta 1970-; Amer Teilhard Assn 1975-; ESEA Title III Advy Bd 1971-74; Mercy Hosp, Trustee 1972-88; Advy Cncl for Coordinated Home Hlth Care 1973-74; St Josephs Coll, Overseer 1976-78; Grants: NSF 1965-67, Office of Ed, Dept Hlth, Ed & Welfare 1969-70; Kent St U 1973 & 1977, Chautauqua Schlsp & Natl Radio Astronomy Observatory 1983; *office:* Saint Josephs Coll 278 Whites Bridge Rd Standish ME 04062

BOYD, MICHAEL D., Associate Professor; *b:* Cincinnati, OH; *m:* Aileen Hurd; *c:* David, Jennifer Mc Callister; *ed:* Univ of MD (BA) His 1970; Hood Coll (MA) Human Scis 1981; Post Grad Work Loyola Coll in MD; *cr:* Division of Parole & Probation Regnl Trng Ofcr, Substance Abuse Coord, Agent 1973-83; Division of Corrections Institutional Trng Dir 1983-87; Frederivck Comm Coll Assoc Prof 1987-; *ai:* Stu Discipline, Fac Evaluation, Addictions Advy Comm; Frederick Cnty Drug & Alcohol Advy comm 1994-; Prof Advy Bd 1993-; Fac Focus Excl Awd 1991; Tchr Excl Higher Ed Awd 1992.

BOYD, MICHAEL P., English Teacher; *b:* Rochester, PA; *m:* Martha Elizabeth Hadaway; *ed:* Penn St Univ (BS); Attnd Univ of DE; *cr:* W.T. Chipman MS Eng Tchr 1987; Lake Forest HS 1987-; *ai:* Future Edctrs of Amer Adv; Acad Bowl; Lit Magazine, NHS Co-Adv; NEA, Lake Forest EA 1987-; Christ Church Milford 1994-; 2 Who's Who Nominations; *office:* Lake Forest HS 5407 Killens Pond Rd Felton DE 19943*

BOYD, NANCY BOSHER, Home Economics Teacher; *b:* Honolulu, HI; *m:* James; *c:* Jason; *ed:* Mansfield Univ (BS) Clothing & Textiles 1978; Tchr Cert Home Ec & Family & Consumer Sci 1982; *cr:* Littlestown Schl Dist Home Ed & Family & Consumer Sci Tchr 1983-84; Gettysburg Schl Dist Home Ec & Family & Consumer Sci Tchr 1985-; *ai:* SADD Adv; MADD 1993-; Parent Advy Cncl 1992-, Pres; PA Governors Awd for SADD; *office:* Gettysburg Sr HS Lefever St Gettysburg PA 17325*

BOYD, PEGGY-ANN BASTIAANS, German Teacher; *b:* Djakarta, Indonesia; *m:* Thomas M.; *c:* Darren, Shaun L.; *ed:* IN Univ of PA (MS) Ger Ed 1970; Univ of Pittsburgh (MED) Ger Ed 1972; Rowan Coll (MA) Supvr & Rdng 1983; 30 Credit Hrs Bonn Univ Cert, Goethe Inst; *cr:* Burrell Sr HS Ger Tchr & Supvr 1970-72; Oakcrest HS Ger Tchr 1972-78; Liebfrauen Gymnasium Eng & Swim Tchr 1978-79; Oakcrest HS Ger Tchr 1979-82; Egg Harbor Twp HS Ger & Rdng Tchr 1983-; *ai:* Ger Club, Intnl Club Adv; Ger Hnr Soc; AATG 1970-; PEA 1970-72; NEA 1970-; NJEA 1972-; Contact-Atlantic 1983-, Mem & Vol; Lib Assn 1992-, Pres; Mini-Grants EHT HS; St of NJ Grant in Hum; Outstdng Ger Tchr Awd NJ.*

BOYD, ROBERTA DANA, Eng Tchr & Dept Chprsn; *b:* Brooklyn, NY; *m:* Richard B. Sr.; *c:* Kathleen Goodwin Boyd, Susan, Richard, Elizabeth, Therese; *ed:* Univ of MD (BA) Psych 1982; 4 Credit Hrs Grad Stud; *cr:* Our Lady of Czestochowa 3rd Grd Tchr 1960-62; St Andrew Apostle Jr HS Rdng & Eng Tchr 1984-94; Eng Tchr 1995-; *ai:* 6-8 Grd Safety Patrol Moderator 11 Yrs; Jr HS Dept Chr 1994-; NCEA 1984-; ASCD 1988-; NCTE 1989-; St Andrews Schl Bd 1989-, Tchr Rep 6 Yrs; *office:* St Andrew Apostle Schl 11602 Kemp Mill Rd Silver Spring MD 20902

BOYD, ROSA MARBERIO, High School Resource Teacher; *b:* Middleton, NY; *m:* Gilbert Fisk; *c:* Diana Lee Pignatelli, Linda Lee De Stefano, Michael Clark, Maria Lee Clark; *ed:* Mt St Mary Coll (BA) Spec Ed, Elem Ed 1978; Spec Ed SUNY at New Paltz 1985; *cr:* Valley Cntrl HS Resource Tchr 1979-; *ai:* AFT, NEA 1979-; Middletown Democrats 1993-, Comm Person; Thrall Lib 1990-; *office:* Valley Central HS 1175 Rt 17k Montgomery NY 12549*

BOYEA, MARGARET PERRY, First Grade Teacher; *b:* Bellmont, NY; *m:* John H.; *c:* JoAnn Boyea Rivers, Stephen, John P.; *ed:* SUNY Plattsburgh (BS) Elem Ed 1973; Addl 50+ Post Grad Hrs; *cr:* Malone Central Schl Kindergarden & 1st Grd 1973-95; *ai:* Playground Comm; Bookfair Chair; Stu Interest Day; NYSUT 1973-; AFT 1973-; PTO 1989-; Lib Bd 1991-; Hospice Bd 1989-; Pastoral Cncl 1990-; Hospice Vol 1985-; *home:* PO Box 31 Chateaugay NY 12920

BOYER, ANGIE DIGIORGIO, Fourth Grade Teacher; *b:* Trenton, NJ; *m:* Leon; *c:* David, Donna, Janet; *ed:* T 4 C Stud; *cr:* Hamilton Twp Schl Dist Tchr 26 Yrs; Mc Galliard Tchr 4 Yrs; Kusthard Tchr 1 Yr; Mercerville 1 Yr, Sub Tchr 3 Yrs; *ai:* Tech for Children, Schl Spon; Class Trip Coord; NEA; HTEA 26 Yrs; St Mark's Church, Sunday Schl Tchr 23 Yrs, Women's Group 33 Yrs; Tchr of Yr 1993; *office:* Sunnybrae Elem Schl 166 Elton Ave Hamilton NJ 08620

BOYER, ANNE E., Varsity Head Softball Coach; *b:* Johnstown, PA; *ed:* Messiah Coll (BA) His 1992; *cr:* Berlin Brothers Vly High Jr High Vllybl Asst Coach 1 Yr, Head Var Sftbl Coach 2 Yrs; *ai:* Little League Pres & Mgr; *office:* Berlin Brothers Valley Schl 1025 E Main St Berlin PA 15530

BOYER, CANDYCE L. (AGNEW), Reading, Math & Computer Tchr; *b:* Lima, OH; *m:* Robert W.; *c:* Terri, Roberta; *ed:* Bluffton Coll (BA) Math & Comp Sci Tchr 1978; OH St Rdng Endorsement 1996; *cr:* Telephone Svc Co Comp Tech 1979-91; Botkins Local Schl Tchr 1991-; *ai:* 8th Grd Class Adv; 7th Grd Vllybl Coach; Tech Planning Comm; AFT 1991-, Sec & Treas; NCTM 1992-; VFW Auxilary 1992-; Copeland Grant to Tch Early OH Hist; *office:* Botkins Local Schl PO Box 550 Botkins OH 45306*

BOYER, CARY R., AP Biology Tchr, Sci Dept Chm; *b:* West Reading, PA; *m:* Jane E. Dickey; *c:* Jeffrey, Michael; *ed:* Kutztown St Coll (BA) Bio 1970; Lehigh Univ (MA) Scndry Ed 1972; Temple Univ (EDD) Scndry Sci Ed 1992; *cr:* Parkland HS Sci Dept Chm, Bio Tchr 1970-; *ai:* Sci Club Adv; NEA; PSSA; PEA; NABT; Sanctuary Ctr for Marine Conservation; Sierra Club; NSTA; Schnecksville Playground Assn 1980-, Yth Sports; Lehigh Cty Conservation Tchr of the Yr 1992; 1994 Envirothan Natl Championship Team Coach; Mentor Tchr; Jason VII; Lehigh Univ PINS Site; *office:* Parkland HS 2675 Pa Route 309 Orefield PA 18069*

BOYER, DAVID MICHAEL, Physics & Chemistry Teacher; *b:* Warwick, RI; *ed:* RI Coll (BA) Physics, Chem 1974, (MAT) Physics, Chem 1978; 25 Post Grad Hrs Prof Dev, Lab Safety, Cooperative Learning, Cmptr & Laser Disc Tech; Internet Trng; Mod Physics; *cr:* Johnston HS Physics, Chem Tchr 1974-81; South Kingston HS Physics, Chem Tchr 1981-84; Home, Hospital Math, Sci Tchr 1984-87; Warwick Veterans Meml HS Physics, Chem Tchr 1987-; *ai:* Adv Explora Vision Teams 1993-, NYNEX Teams; Warwick Veterans Governance Org Senator 1993-; Adv RI St Sci Olympiad 1992; AFT 1974-, RI Sci Tchrs Assn 1977-; NSTA 1993-; RI Math & Sci Coalition 1993; Tchrs Industrial Fellowship Recipient; Cooperating Industry RAYTHEON Co; *office:* Warwich Veterans Memorial HS 2401 W Shore Rd Warwick RI 02886*

BOYER, GAY KAREN, 7th & 8th Grd Reading Teacher; *b:* Har PA; *m:* Bradley; *c:* Branden, Bennett; *ed:* Bloomsburg Univ (BS) E 1982; *cr:* Halifax Elem Schl 1st Grd Tchr 1984-85; Halifax MS 7t Grd Rdng Tchr 1985-; *ai:* Yrbk & Stu Cncl Adv; Var Vllybl Coac Arts Task Force; Character First & Assessment Comms; NEA & 1986-; *office:* Halifax HS 3940 Peters Mountain Rd Halifax PA 17

BOYER, GUY H., Amer Political Behavior Tchr; *b:* York, PA; *m:* J Faye Strom; *c:* Julia, Trevor; *ed:* Millersburg Univ (BA) Sociolog Franklin & Marshall Coll Cert Pol Sci 1981; 30 Grad Credits In Boys Club of Lancaster Cnslr 1977-78; Lanc Cty Court of Comme Probation Ofcr 1975-82; Penn Manor Sr HS Tchr 1982-84; Warwic Tchr 1984-; *ai:* Stu Percussion Org Adv; WEA 1984-; PSEA, NEA Unity Coalition of Lanc 1995-; *office:* Warwick Sr HS 301 W Or Lititz PA 17543

BOYER, HARRY STARR, Industrial Arts & Tech Ed T Williamsport, PA; *m:* Karen Smith; *c:* Heather Garton, Mark, Aa PA St Univ (BS) Indstrl Arts K-12 1972; 18 Credit Hrs; *cr:* Monto Area Schl Dist Tchr 1972-; *ai:* Stdnt Asst Team Chprsn; NEA, MAEA 1972-; PASAP 1991-; TEAP, IAAP 1972-; Comm Bapt 1972-, Elder, Deacon, Treas; Who's Who in Amer Churches L *office:* C E Mccall MS 600 Willow St Montoursville PA 17754*

BOYER, JEAN GROVES, Kindergarten Teacher; *b:* Leechburg, Dale E.; *c:* Alyson J., Megan E., Jasin; *ed:* Indiana Univ of PA (BS Ed 1953; Univ of Pgh Credits for Cert; *cr:* Penn Hills Schl Dst 2 Tchr 1953-57; Mt Lebanon Schl Dist Kndgtn Tchr 1969-; *ai:* Schl C PSEA; NEA; MLEA; Coll Club 1970-; Literate Group 1986-, Chm 509 Hillcrest Pl Pittsburgh PA 15216

BOYER, JEFFREY A., Educational Lab Director; *b:* Granville, Rachelle Elaine Cochran; *c:* Joshua, Brooke; *ed:* Rio Grande Co Elem Ed 1979; 30 Credit Hrs Toward Masters in Sports Admin at A Univ; *cr:* Licking Heights Schls Tchr 1979-; *ai:* Bsbl Head Coac Asst Coach; NEA, OEA, LHEA 1979-; Cntrl Dist Bsbl Coaches First Comm Church 1975-, Bd of Trustees, Bd of Deacons; Tchr of Y Coach of Yr 1989.

BOYER, KENNETH CARL, Math Department Chairman; *b:* Lew PA; *m:* Jean Ann; *ed:* Bloomsburg Univ (BS) Math 1970; Wilkes Un Educl Tchng Strategies 1994; Master Equivalency Math Buckne 1971-75; Mt St Marys Coll NSF Grant 1995-; *cr:* Camp Hill HS Ma 1970-, Math Dept Chm 1985-; Harrisburg Area Comm Coll Adjunc Instr 1975-; Novell Network Mgr 1995-; *ai:* Tech Comm; CHEA PSEA 1970-; NEA 1970-; Natl Sci Fnd Grant Environmental Chincoteague Natl Wildlife Refuge; Curr to Retrain Employees Hydno Inc Bethlehem Steel; *office:* Camp Hill Jr Sr HS 100 S 24th S Hill PA 17011*

BOYER, LINDA JEAN, Spanish Teacher & Dept Chprsn; *b:* So PA; *m:* Clyde William; *c:* Heather, Eric; *ed:* Univ of Pittsburgh (BA Scndry Ed 1977; 30 Credits; *cr:* Carrick HS Span Tchr 1977; Peabo Span Tchr 1978; Allegheny HS Span Tchr 1979-83; Allegheny M Tchr 1983-84; Oliver HS Span Tchr 1984-; *ai:* Trained Clinica Pittsburgh Pub Schls Univ Collaborative Frgn Lang Dept Head Cabinet; Fac Assn Coord; Frgn Lang Resource Team; Coord Frg Festival Chprsn; Instruction, Assessment, Schl Work Comms; Modern Lang Assn; Pittsburgh FEd of Tchrs 1977-; PTO 1984-; PTA Twp Schl 1990-; Parent Rep Frgn Lang Comm 1995- Peters Twp *office:* Oliver HS 2323 Brighton Rd Pittsburgh PA 15212

BOYER, MARIKAYE S., Business Education Teacher; *b:* Lewisbu *ed:* Cntrl PA Bus Schl (Assoc) Admin Asst 1987; Bloomsburg Uni Bus Ed 1989; Working Towards MS Rdng Specialist 1996; *cr:* Com Instr 1990; Milton HS Bus Ed Tchr 1990-91; Middleburg HS Bus E 1991-; *ai:* FBLA Adv; Drama Dir; Adult Ed Instr; Stu Assistance Mentor Pgm & Strategic Planning Comm Mem; PA Bus Ed Assn NBEA 1989-; Teen Pregnancy Prevention Task Force 1995-.

BOYER, PAULA JEANNE, Third Grade Teacher; *b:* Pomeroy, Joshua; *ed:* Cleveland St Univ (BS) Ed 1977, (MS) Educl Cnslng Cuyahoga Comm Coll (AA); *cr:* Brookridge Elem Schl Fifth Gr 1979-82, Third Grd Tchr 1982-; *ai:* NEA 1979-; Jennings Scholar; Brookridge Elem Schl 4500 Ridge Rd Brooklyn OH 44144*

BOYER, TED, Business Teacher; *b:* West Chester, PA; *ed:* Clario of PA (BS) Bus Admin 1990; Masters Prgm at DE St Univ; *cr:* Sojo Place Resident Supvr 1990-93; Appoquinimink SD Bus Tchr 199 Boys Bsktbl, Girls Tennis Head Coach; *office:* Middletown HS Broad St Middletown DE 19709

BOYER, TERRY N., Physics & Chemistry Teacher; *b:* Joliet, F Kathryn Henry; *ed:* Kutztown St (BS) Chem 1964; PA Dept of Ed (1990; Susquehana Univ Physics Cert 1986; Attnd Worcester Polyt Inst, Penn St Univ, Univ of ME Coll of Atlantic, Millersville Univ, V Univ; *cr:* Millersburg Area Schl Physic, Chem Tchr 1964-95; Olympic Team Coach; Sr Class Adv; Prin Advisory Cncl; NEA, PS Yrs; Millersburg Ed Assn 1964-95, Treas, Building Rep 30 Yrs; Collectors Assn 11 Yrs; *office:* Millersburg Area Schl Dist 799 Cer Millersburg PA 17061

BOYER, WAYNE M., Business Teacher; *b:* Union County, PA; *m:* R.; *c:* Tamara Ciampoli, Teri Westbrook, Michele Ingersol Bloomsburg Univ (BA) Bus Ed 1957; Elmira Coll (MS) Ed 1968; *cr:* Central HS Bus Ed Tchr 35 Yrs; *ai:* Adv Yrbk 20 Yrs, Class 35 Yrs; Bus Tchrs Assn 30 Yrs; Cady Lib Bd 10 Yrs, Treas; Nichols Village Yrs; Twice Booster Club Tchr of Yr.

BOYKAS, LINDA, HS Social Studies Teacher; *b:* Allentown, P Univ of FL (BA) Ger & Fr His 1971; Lehigh Univ (MED) Scndry Ed Pursuing Doctorate; *cr:* Nitschmann Jr HS Soc Stud Tchr 19 Broughal Jr HS Soc Stud Tchr 1973-78; Freedom HS Soc Stud Tchr Staff Dev Chprsn 1995-; Moravian Coll Adjunct Prof of Ed 1990-; *ai* & Amnesty Intnl Fac Adv; NEA, PSEA & BEA 1971-; Natl Cncl f Stud & Lehigh Valley Cncl for Soc Stud 1975-; Delta Kappa Gamma *office:* Freedom HS 3149 Chester Ave Bethlehem PA 18017*

BOYKO, DEBORAH M., History & Geography Teacher; *b:* Johns PA; *m:* Joseph R.; *ed:* Univ of Pittsburgh at Johnstown (BS) Elem Ed 28 Credits Lang Comm, 7 Credits ITEC Cmptr Prgm; *cr:* Windbe Schl His, Geography Tchr 1977-79; Windber Area Schl Permanent Sub Tchr 1980-81; St Joseph Schl His, Geography Tchr 1982-; *ai:* 8t Adv; Geography Bee, NIE Design-An-Ad Coach, Spon; IST, ESA C Spring Musical Co-Dir; NCEA 1982-; Parish, Liturgy Cncls Inter-Parish Planning Comm 1995-, Chprsn; Master Catechist 1996; Mid Sts Evaluation Comm Chprsn; *office:* St Joseph Schl 511 Caldwe Portage PA 15946

BOYLAN, DORETTE ELAINE, English Teacher; *b:* Steubenville *ed:* Lake Erie Coll for Women (BA) Eng 1960; Univ of Dayton MST Addl Post Grad Hrs; *cr:* Indian Creek Sr HS Eng Tchr 36 Yrs; *ai:* A Club, Hi Times, Soph & Jr Class; Prom Spon; Chrldr Chaperone; Comm; European Schl Trip Chaperone; JCTA, OEA, EOTA, SEOTA, 1960-; ICEA, Former Bldg Rep; NCTE; Hemlock Twig OH Valley Ho 1962-, Pres; OVH Vol, 50 Hr Patch 1991, 100 Hr Pin 1992; Jr Womens 1960-61; *office:* Indian Creek HS 200 Park Dr Wintersville OH 43

BOYLAN, ELIZABETH A., Pre-First Grade Teacher; *b:* Philade PA; *m:* Owen P.; *c:* Sean, Meghan; *ed:* St Joseph Univ (BS) Elem Ed artin of Tours 3rd & 6th Grd Tchr 1970-78; Spring Garden Kndgtn 9-82; Holy Angels 6th-8th Grd Tchr 1983-86; St Timothy Kndgtn, 4th Grd Tchr 1986-; *ai:* Rel Comm; Spirit Day; NCEA 1970-; Timothy Schl 3033 Levick St Philadelphia PA 19149

N, SHEILA, PE & Health Teacher; *b:* Newark, NJ; *c:* Shawn Sabo; tclair St (BA) PE & Hlth 1970, (MA) Hlth 1972, (MA) PE 1975; efield Pk HS Tchr PE & Hlth 1970-; *ai:* NEA, NJEA & BCEA akland Tennis Club 1980-, Treas; *office:* Ridgefield Park Jr-Sr HS Nelson Dr Ridgefield Park NJ 07660

ALICE T.,SSJ, English Teacher; *b:* Bayonne, NJ; *ed:* Chestnut) Eng 1970; Seton Hall Univ (MA) Eng 1976; Villanova Univ 6 d Hrs; Patterson St 6 Post Grad Hrs; Rutgers Univ Dow-Jones J. Writing; *cr:* St Kevin Schl Primary Grd Tchr 1965-70; Pius X mary Grd Tchr 1965-70; Holy Rosary Schl Primary Grd Tchr Our Lady of The Valley Schl Eng Tchr 1970-75; Archbishop HS Eng Tchr 1975-79; St John's Schl Prin 1979-83; Queen of S Eng Tchr 1983-91; Holy Family Acad Eng Tchr 1991-; *ai:* Schl per, Lit Magazine Moderator; Sr Class Adv; NCTE; Dow Jones Newark Intensive Journalistic Writing; *office:* Holy Family Acad nue A Bayonne NJ 07002

BARBARA EILEEN, History Teacher; *b:* Cleveland, OH; *ed:* Coll (BA) His 1971; Cleveland St Univ (MA) His 1993; Pol Sci ron Univ Hrs Towards Eng Cert; *cr:* St Josephs Acad His Tchr Rocky River HS His Tchr 1978-; *ai:* Asst Drama Dir; FACE NEA, OEA 1979-; NCSS, GCCSS 1985-; NCHE 1994-; Westside er Club 1991-; Southern Poverty Law Ctr 1994-; Rocky River Tchr 998-93; Articles Pub; *office:* Rocky River HS 20951 Detroit Rd d OH 44116*

CONNELL J., Mathematics Professor; *b:* Brooklyn, NY; *m:* affney; *c:* Kevin, Kenneth, Noreen, Michael; *ed:* St Francis Coll th 1958; IA Univ (MS) Math 1960; 60 Credit Hrs Adelphi Univ; hampton Coll Asst Prof 1970-74; Suffolk Comm Coll Full Time 74-; *ai:* Math Dept Chair; AMA 1960-; AMS 1962-; NY St ors Awd for Excl in Tchng 1977; *office:* Suffolk Comm Coll Cmps Crooked Hill Road Brentwood NY 11717

DENNIS FRANCIS, Choral Director; *b:* New York, NY; *m:* rbeck; *ed:* Montclair St Coll (BA) Music 1970; Trenton St Coll usic Ed 1971; Supvs Cert Music 1976; Robert Shaw Wkshps 42 Irs 1975-82, 1985-87; Choral, Orch Conducting, Performance 8 Hrs; *cr:* Burnet Jr HS Vocal Tchr, Asst Band Dir 1971-75; on Elem Schl Vocal Tchr 1975-76; Highland Park MS Vocal Tchr ; Highland Park HS Choral Dir 1979-89; East Brunswick HS Dir 1989-; *ai:* Afterschool Choral Groups; NEA, NJ Ed Assn, NJ Music Edctrs Assn 1971-; Amer Choral Dirs Assn; Conductors horus Amer, Amer Fed of Musicians; Phi Mu Alpha Natl Music Highland Park Comm Chorus 1986-, Fnd, Dir; Kappa Delta Pi Natl y Ed 1970-; Philomusica Chamber Choir 1982-, Music Dir, or; Knights of Columbus; Concert Choir Performance at NJ St 993; Highland Park HS Capella Choir Performance at NJ Assn of min Fall Conf, Govenor's Awds in Arts Ed Ceremony; Philomusica r Choir Invited to Perform Vatican Rome, Duomo in Florence, St n Venice 1994; Chosen Nationwide 1 of 15 for Chorus America's Conducting Wkshp 1995; Philomusica Chamber Choir Accepted ant in Prestigious Bela Bartok 15th Intnl Choir Competition n Hungary 1992.

FRANK J., Accounting Teacher; *b:* Philadelphia, PA; *m:* Eileen Connell, Brigid, Kiera; *ed:* Temple Univ (MBA) Bus 1974; Coll Planning 9 Credits; *cr:* Archbishop Wood HS Acctng Tchr 1970-; Univ Part-Time Adj Instr 1976-; *ai:* Assn of Cath Tchrs 1970-, Sr EA 1970-; PA Inst of Cert Pub Acctng 1992-; Upper Dublin Jr Ath 90-, Coach; *office:* Archbishop Wood HS 655 York Rd Warminster 4

FREDERICK JOHN, Religious Studies Teacher; *b:* Cleveland, Marie D.; *c:* Tara, Stephen; *ed:* St Pius X Seminary (BA) phy 1983; 30 Credit Hrs St Vincent Seminary; 26 Credit Hrs Univ s; *cr:* Bishop McCort HS Rel Stud Tchr 1984-85; Ursuline Acad d Tchr 1986-88; Bishop Guilfayle HS Rel Stud Tchr 1992-93; McCort HS Tel Stud Tchr 1993-; *ai:* Chrstn Svc Club Adv; Amer ccer Or, Coach; *office:* Bishop Mc Cort HS 25 Osborne St wn PA 15905

JOHN RICHARD, Global Studies Teacher; *b:* Nassau Cty, NY; a Sessions; *c:* Fallon; *ed:* C. W. Post Coll (BS) Criminal Justice MS) Schl Cnslr 1992; Ed Cert; Attnd Capital Law Schl 1985; *cr:* St Schl Sci Tchr 1981; W. T. Clarke HS Soc Stud Tchr 1987-; *ai:* bl Coach 1987-; Asst Lacrosse Coach 1994-; Eligibility Comm; elping Aths; Nassau Co Ftbl Coaches Assn 1987-, Sec, 2nd VP; ssn, VP, Pres; Acad Schlsp C. W. Post Coll; *office:* W. T. Clarke HS gewood Dr Westbury NY 11590

, SHARON DENISE, Assistant Professor of English; *b:* Brooklyn, OH Univ (BA) Eng Lang & Lit 1988, (MA) Eng Lang & Lit 1990; Univ Tchng Assoc 1988-90; OH Univ at Lancaster Part-Time Instr); Mohawk Vly Comm Coll Asst Prof 1990-; *ai:* Acad Complaint, ppeals, Topics in Hum, Eng I On-Line Comms; Summer Inst Adv, sbian, Bisexual Alliance; NCTE 1989-; Articles Pub in OH Journal Lang Arts, KS Eng; Tchng Eng in Two-Yr Coll; Contemporary Writers of US-A Bio-Bibliographic Source Book; *office:* Mohawk Comm Coll 1101 Sherman Dr Utica NY 13501

EN, CHARLES WILLIAM, Professor of Biology; *b:* Baltimore, Kathryn Lane Anastasio; *c:* Charles Brent, Mark Edward; *ed:* IN Bloomington (BA) Biological Scis 1964; Univ of WI at Madison Microbiology 1966, (PHD) Microbiology 1969; Attnd Ames Rsrch 59-71, Univ of WI; *cr:* Rensselaer Polytechnic Inst Asst Prof 7, Assoc Prof 1978-89, Prof 1989-, Darrin Fresh Water Inst Dir 3 & Analytic Facilities Assoc Dir 1993-, Life Scis Electron copy Lab Dir 1990-; Woods Hole Oceanographic Inst Visiting Prof 3; *ai:* Journal of Applied & Environmental Microbiology 1976-82 & Lib Journal 1976-85 Editorial Bds; NSF 1990-93 & Natl Rsrch Cncl Advy Review Bds; Amer Soc for Microbiology 1966-, Eastern NY Pres & Environmental Microbiology Natl Comm Mem; Hudson nvironmental Soc 1990-, Exec Bd Mem; Univ of WI Alumni Rsrch 1964-66; Natl Aeronautics & Space Admin Fellow 1967-69; Natl Cncl Post-Doctoral Fellow 1969-71; Hrachan Atcharian Univ ic of Armenia Honorary Professorship 1993; *office:* Rensselaer hnic Inst Dept of Bio 110 8th St Troy NY 12181*

AR, SHIRLEY CHERVENAK, Family & Consumer Sci Teacher; eveland, OH; *m:* Dennis; *c:* Jennifer, Ronald, Bryan; *ed:* n-Wallace Coll (BA) Eng, Family & Consumer Sci 1967; Cuyahoga Coll Family & Consumer Sci 1992; *cr:* Schaaf Jr HS Tchr 1967-69; Franciscan HS Tchr 1985-; *ai:* Sr Moderator.

TON, NANCY J., Assistant Professor of Math; *b:* Battle Creek, MI; ion Coll (BA) Math, Ger 1973; Western MI Univ (PHD) Math 1979; Technological Univ Instr, Asst Prof 1978-82; SUNY Coll Asst Prof *ai:* Math Club Adv; Math Curr Comm Chair; Fac Cncl; natical Assn of Amer 1978-; Sigma Xi 1982-; Amer Statistical Assn Assn for Women in Math 1985-; Articles Pub; Charles H. Butler Excl in Tchng Awd 1977; *office:* S U N Y Coll At Fredonia Math & Computer Science Dept Fredonia NY 14063

BOZIGAR, VIRGINIA QUILLEN, Sixth Grade Teacher; *b:* Vandergrift, PA; *m:* Gary W.; *c:* Gary M., Lesley; *ed:* Edinboro St Coll (BA) Elem Ed 1970; *cr:* Lancaster City Schls Primary I Spec Ed, Sub Tchr & Tutor 1970-73; Northern Local Schls Sub Tchr 1979-84, 4th & 6th Grd Tchr 1985-; *ai:* NEA 1985-; PTA; OCCL Local Premiere Mothers Club 1976-, Pres, VP, Treas; AMVETS 1995-.

BOZOYAN, MARY VICTORIA, Mathematics Teacher; *b:* Astoria, NY; *ed:* Hunter Coll (BA) Math 1985; *cr:* William Cullen Bryant HS Math Tchr 1985-; *ai:* Grd Adv 1989-91; Dropout Verification Roster Coord 1991-; Frosh & Soph Math Team Coach 1986-87; AFT, UFT 1985-; NCTM 1987-; Parents Assn Sponsored Stdnts Choice Tchr of Yr Awd 1993; *office:* William Cullen Bryant HS 48-10 31st Ave Long Is City NY 11103*

BOZZONE, DONNA M., Associate Professor of Biology; *b:* New York, NY; *m:* Douglas S. Green; *c:* Samantha, Allison; *ed:* Manhattan Coll (BS) Bio 1978; Princeton Univ Bio (MA) 1980, (PHD) 1983; *cr:* Worcester Fnd for Experimental Bio Post Doctoral Research Asst 1983-86; Holy Cross Coll Visiting Instr of Bio 1987; St Michaels Coll Asst Prof of Bio 1987-94, Assoc Prof of Bio 1994-; *ai:* Math, Sci & Tech Strategic Planning Comm; Stu Research Adv; Amer Fern Soc 1994-; NABT 1995-; ABLE 1991-; AAUW 1983-, Dissertation Fellowship; Soc for Developmental Bio 1980-; NSF Predoctoral, NIH Postdoctoral Fellowships; NSF, NSF VT EpScor, Prof Dev Grants; Class of 1990 Appreciation Awd; Articles Pub; Manuscript Reviewer for NSTA; *office:* Saint Michaels Coll Winooski Park Colchester VT 05439

BRACEBRIDGE, EDWARD LEE, Culinary Arts Instructor; *b:* Holden, MA; *m:* Sharon K. Krikorian; *c:* Shelley Glockner, Shawn Edward; *ed:* Culinary Inst Culinary Arts Hnr Grad 1963; Tchng Cert Culinary Arts 1976; Master Mngmt Cert 1974; Working on Cert CEVS Fitchburg St; Johnson & Wales Univ Various Tasks; *cr:* Holiday Inns of Amer Corp Chef 1964-68; Wilbur Food Svc Chef, Mgr 1968-70; Astra Pharmaceutical Products Chef, Mgr 1970-74; Blackstone Vly Tech Schl Chef, Instr 1974-; *ai:* Dept Headl Culinary Arts; Amer Culinary Fdn Jr Mem Chair; Founder Rutland Pop Warner Ftbl Team; MA Tchr Assn 1974-; Amer Culinary Fdn 1988-; Various Ldrshp Roles; Johnson & Wales Advy Bd Mem; Rutland Fire Dept 1958-, Dept Chief; Rutland Fire Brigade 1965-, Treas 20 Yrs; Spencer Congregational Church Choir 1988-; American Culinary Fdn Mbrshp Chair; Tchr of Yr 1986; New Egland Culinary Inst Bd of Dirs; Advy Bd, Food Edctr Adv Johnson & Wales Univ; *office:* Blackstone Vly Reg Voc Tec HS Pleasant St Upton MA 01568*

BRACH, KATHIE R., Mathematics Teacher; *b:* Passaic, NJ; *m:* Stan; *c:* Melissa, Rachel, Jessica; *ed:* Cntrl CT St Univ (BS) Math 1974; Montclair St Univ (MA) Math Ed 1980; *cr:* Clifton HS Tchr 1974-80, 1991-; Coll of St Elizabeth Instr 1983-90; *ai:* Knights of Pythagoras, Continental Math League Calculus Adv; NEA, NJEA 1991-; NCTM, AMTNJ 1993-; Schls Parent Org 1985-, Pres HSA; *office:* Clifton H S 333 Colfax Ave Clifton NJ 07013

BRACKER, CHRISTINE FLORENCE, Fourth Grade Teacher; *b:* Syracuse, NY; *ed:* St Univ Coll at Plattsburgh (BS) Elem Ed 1966; Syracuse Univ Cert Spec Ed Mental Retardation 1972; Attnd UT St Coll, Coll of St Rose, Salem Univ, Elmira Coll, Long Island Univ, Univ of CA, Northeastern Univ; *cr:* Canastota Cntrl Schl 4th Grd Tchr 1966-67; Fayetteville-Manlius Cntrl Schl 3rd, 4th Grd Tchr 1967-71; Bd of Cooperative Ed Learning Disability Tchr 1971-72; Bayetteville-Manlius Cntrl Schl 1st, 2nd, Multigrage 1-4 Tchr 1972-; *ai:* Prof Advancement Chair; Sci, Metric Comm; Soc Stud Curr Writer; Elem, Dist Curr Cncl; Whole Lang Steering Comm; Math Curr Writer; Dist Insvc Comm; Fayetteville-Manlius Tchr Assn 1967-, Sec, Negotiator; Fay-Man Tchrs 1968-, Credit Comm, Bd; Schl Empl of CNY Fed Credit Union 1995-, Credit Comm; Coauthur Dist Writing Wkshp Guide; Who's Who in Amer ED; *home:* 4702 Enders Rd Manlius NY 13104

BRACKETT, KRISTINE KOSENSKI, Health, Phys Educator & Coach; *b:* Newark, NJ; *m:* John Thomas; *c:* Justin; *ed:* West Chester Univ (BS) Hlth, PE 1981; *cr:* Toms River HS North Hlth Tchr, Phys Educator 1983-; *ai:* Spring Track Coach; IM Dir; NEA, Toms River Ed Assn, AAHPERD 1983-; *home:* 901 Stonehedge Ln Pt Pleas Bch NJ 08742

BRACKETT, MARILYN JANICE, Nursing Instructor; *b:* Auburn, ME; *m:* Norman; *c:* James, David; *ed:* St Josephs Coll (BSPA) Sociology 1975; Univ of ME, Portland (MEd) Adult Ed 1979; Central ME General Hospital Schl of Nursing Diploma Registered Nurse 1958; 90 Credits in BSN Prgm; *cr:* Central ME General Hospital Surgical Unit Staff Nurse, Med Surg Asst Head Nurse, Recovery, Med Unit, Coronary Care Unit Head Nurse; Central ME Medical Center Schl of Nursing Instr 23 Yrs; *ai:* Admissions, Recruitment Comm, Stu Affairs Chprsn; Stu Adv; ME Assn for Continuing Ed 1985-; ME Cncl of Assoc Degree Nursing Prgms 1996-; ME Assn for Counseling & Dev 1985-; Lewiston Auburn Comm Ed Coalition 1991-; CMG, CMMC Schl of Nursing Alumni Assn 1988-; St Josephs Coll Aslumni Assn 1975-; Pub Coronary Care Unit; Amer Nurses Assn Medical Surgical Nursing Cert; *office:* Central ME Medical Center 300 Main St Lewiston ME 04240

BRACY, MARYSUE, Math & Earth Science Teacher; *b:* Syracuse, NY; *m:* Wayne A.; *c:* Megan, Matthew, Nathan; *ed:* St Univ Coll at Cortland (BA) Sec Math Ed 1970; 24 Addl Credit Hrs; *cr:* Newark Valley Cntrl Schl Math Tchr 1970-72; Southern Cayuga Cntrl Schl Math Tchr 1972-74; Dept of Defense Schl Math Tchr 1974-76; Mountain View MS Math & Earth Sci Tchr 1976-; *ai:* NEA 1970-, Treas 1992-; *office:* Mountain View MS 41 Lauren Ln Goffstown NH 03045

BRADBURY, CONNIE STIDHAM, Home Economics Teacher; *b:* Gallipolis, OH; *m:* Charles L.; *ed:* Morehead St Univ (BA) Home Ec 1974; Univ of Dayton (MA) Schl Counseling 1990; *cr:* Kyger Creek HS Home Ec Tchr 1974-92; River Valley HS Home Ec Tchr 1992-; *ai:* FHA/HERO Adv; OEA; Bossard Lib Advy Bd; Cheshire Bapt Church Mem; Gallia Cty Tchr of Yr 1980, 1993; Ashland Oil Tchr Achvmt nom 1990, 1992; Jennings Schlsp 1992; *office:* River Valley HS 1482 Little Kyger Rd Cheshire OH 45620

BRADBURY, ELIZABETH ADAMS, Librarian & French Teacher; *b:* Eagle Lake, ME; *m:* Eugene M.; *ed:* Univ of ME at PI (BS) Eng 1974; 15 Addl Credit Hrs Lib, Information Sci; *cr:* MSAD #45 Tchr 1984-, Tchr, Dist Librn 1995-; *ai:* Fr Club Adv; Stdnts Against Substance Abuse Comm; *office:* MSAD #45 Washburn HS 40 N Main St Washburn ME 04786

BRADEMEYER, KATHRYN HUELSMAN, Third Grade Teacher; *b:* Dayton, OH; *m:* Donald L.; *c:* Caroline A. Schneider, Stephanie L.; *ed:* Univ of Dayton (BS) Elem Ed 1966; Remedial Rdng Miami Univ at Oxford OH; *cr:* Northmoor Elem Schl Fourth Grd Tchr4 1966-68, Learning Disability Tchr 1970-72; OR Edgington Elem Schl Third Grd Tchr 1969-70; Northwood Elem Schl Third Grd Tchr 1974-; *ai:* Northmont Dist Ed Assn 1966-, 25 Yrs; NEA, OH Ed Assn 1966-; Educator of Yr 1989; *office:* Northwood Elem Schl 6200 Noranda Dr Dayton OH 45415

BRADEN, JOHN B., School Counselor; *b:* Pittsburgh, PA; *m:* Judy; *ed:* Edinboro St U (BS) Bio Ed 1968; Slippery Rock U (MED) Cnslng Ed 1975; Univ of Pittsburgh; *cr:* Ingomar MS Life Sci Tchr 1968-74; Carson MS Life Sci Tchr 1974-80, Schl Cnslr 1980-; *ai:* Stu Cncl Adv 26 Yrs; NAFT Schlsp Comm Chprsn; AFT 1970-, Bldg Rep; Penna Schl Cnslr Assn 1980-; Alleg Co Stu Cncl Assn 1975-, Bd Mem; North Allegheny Achvmt Awd 1985; Educator of Yr AAUW 1989; Stu Cncl Adv of Yr 1995; Gift of Time Tribute; *office:* Carson MS 200 Hillvue Ln Pittsburgh PA 15237

BRADFORD, BONNIE J., Third Grade Teacher; *b:* Framingham, MA; *ed:* Bridgewater St Coll (BS) Elem Ed 1968; *cr:* Clyde Brown Schl Third Grd Tchr 1968-; *ai:* Tchr Assistance Team; Millis Tchrs Assn, Exec Bd; MA Tchrs Assn; Norfolk Cty Tchrs Assn; NEA; *office:* Clyde Brown Elem Schl 5 Park Rd Millis MA 02054

BRADFORD, JOHN RICHARD, Geography Teacher; *b:* Baltimore, MD; *m:* Diane Marie Kuhn; *c:* Julie E., John C.; *ed:* Frostburg St Coll (BS) Soc Sci, Sec Ed 1977; Wilkes Coll (MS) Educl Strategies & Dev 1988; *cr:* Joppatowne HS Soc Stud Tchr 1979-82; Shippensburg Area Jr HS Geography Tchr 1982-; *ai:* NEA 1982-; PMI 1996; Release Time Bd 1991-; Best Ed Grant Chambersburg Area Ed & Bus Partnership 1991-92; Shippensburg Univ Schl Stud Cncls Outstdng Tchr Awd 1992-93; *office:* Shippensburg Area Jr HS 317 N Morris St Shippensburg PA 17257*

BRADISH, MICHAEL JAMES, Fifth Grade Teacher; *b:* Lowville, NY; *m:* Barbara Kornmeyer; *c:* Benjamin, Rebecca, Laura; *ed:* SUNY at Canton (AA) Lbrl Arts 1973; SUNY at Plattsburg (BA) Elem Ed 1975; 30 Credit Hrs Post-Grad at SUNY at Potsdam; *cr:* South Lewis Cntrl Glenfield 6th Grd Tchr 1976-95; South Lewis Cntrl Port Leyden 5th Grd Tchr 1995-; *ai:* Safety Patrol Coord; Negotiations Comm; AFT, NYSUT 1976-; Greig Town Bd 1994-, Town Councilman; ELKS Club 1988-; *home:* North Shore Rd Brantingham NY 13312

BRADLEY, BEVERLY DONCHEZ, Business Educator; *b:* Bethlehem, PA; *m:* Daniel L.; *ed:* Bloomsburg St Coll (BS) Bus Ed 1971; Bloomsburg Univ (MS) Bus Ed 1986; *cr:* Southern Lehigh Schl Dist Bus Edctr 1971-; *ai:* Lehigh Carson Comm Coll Legal Svcs Working Group Crim Justice, Paralegal Curr; Supts Comm Cncl Rep; Southern Lehigh Ed Assn 1971-, Sec, Bldg Rep; PA Bus Ed Assn Scndry Tchr of Yr 1988; *office:* Southern Lehigh Schl Dist 5800 Main St Center Valley PA 18034*

BRADLEY, CAROLYN VEENOY, Third Grade Teacher; *b:* Troy, OH; *ed:* Warren Wilson Coll (AA) Liberal Arts 1965; OH St Univ (BS) Ed 1971; Ashland Univ (MS) Ed 1988; *cr:* S. W. Licking Local Schls Kndgtn, 2nd, 5th, 3rd Grds 1967-; *ai:* Olympics Odyssey of Mind Coach; Right to Read Building Comm, Dist Coord; Young Author's Coord; NEA, OEA 1967-; Southwest Licking Ed Assn 1967-, Pres 1985, 1993, VP 1990-93, Pres 1990-93; NCTE 1985-; Pataskala Lib Friends 1990-; Rockwell Grant 1991; Cntrl OH Tchrs Assn Grant 1992; Dow Grant 1992; Rockwell Grant 1992; Ashland Oil Golden Apple Awd 1993; *office:* Etna Elem Schl 927 South St Etna OH 43018

BRADLEY, DOLORES DAVIDSON, Guidance Counselor; *b:* Garysburg, NC; *m:* Paul; *c:* Pamela Davidson Ferguson; *ed:* NC Cntrl Univ (BA) PE, Soc Stud 1954; Upsala Coll (MA) Stu Personnel Svcs 1978; Columbia Univ 6 Credit Hrs; Kean Coll 12 Credit Hrs; Continuing Ed Credits, Certs; *cr:* Clinton Farms Women's Reformatory Cottage Supvr, Tchr 1955-57; Newark Bd of Ed PE Tchr, Guid Cnslr 1957-; Bloomsburg St Coll Admissions Cnslr 1979; Passaic Cty Coll Recruitment Cnslr 1981; Ramapo Coll Tchr, Cnslr EOF Summer Prgm 1991-93; *ai:* Peer Mediation, Conflict Resolution Spon; Mentor Girlfriends; Life Skills Vol Lighthouse Homeless Shelter; NEA, NJEA 1958-; AFT, Amer Cnslng Assn, Essex Co Cnslng Assn 10 Yrs; Hospice Inc 1995-, Vol Bereavement Cnslr; Chrstn Advocates Pub Ed 1982-, Pres; Ramapo Coll Comm Advy Bd 1992-95; CHUMS Intnl Svc Org, VP Local; Co-Chprsn Essex Cty UNCF Telethon Spec Vol Svc Awd; Tchr Orientation, Insvc Classes New Tchrs 1970-80; Article Pub; *office:* West Side HS 403 S Orange Ave Newark NJ 07103*

BRADLEY, GEORGE E.,II, Biology Teacher; *b:* Pittsburgh, PA; *m:* Joy Ann Taylor; *c:* Molly A., David G., James P.; *ed:* Edinboro Univ (BS) Scndry Ed, Bio 1969; Slippery Rock Univ (MS) Bio 1973, (MS) Scndry Guid 1989; Bucknell Univ Grad Courses Molecular, Cellular Bio; IN Univ Grad Courses Microbiology; Univ of CO Tchng BSCS; Ball St Univ Grad Courses Human Genetics, Statistics, Occupation Cnslng; *cr:* Penn Hills HS Bio Tchr 1969-72; Shaler Area Sr HS Bio Tchr 1972-; *ai:* Stu Assistance Team Guid Dept; Intensive Scheduling Comm; SAEA, PSEA, NEA 1972-; Mars Area Bsbl Assn 1988-; Mars Wrestling Assn 1994-; *office:* Shaler Area HS 381 Wible Run Rd Pittsburgh PA 15209

BRADLEY, JAMES EUGENE, Geological Science Professor; *b:* Morgantown, WV; *m:* Nancy Ann Brown; *c:* Elizabeth, James; *ed:* Muskingum Coll (BS) Geology 1954; Oh St Univ (MS) Geology 1963, (PHD) Mineralogy 1972; *cr:* Oh St Univ Prof 1960-; *ai:* Cty Planning Comm 1980-, Chair; Cty Historical Soc 1982-, Pres; Cty Park Dist 1987-, Chair; Edward Orton Fellow; Sigma Xi; Article Pub; *office:* OH St Univ At Newark University Drive Newark OH 43055

BRADLEY, JANET L., Earth Science Teacher; *b:* Glastonbury, CT; *m:* Douglas Mc Nally; *ed:* Russell Sage Coll (BA) Bio 1974; Coll of St Rose (MA) Bio 1978; Tchr Cert Smith Coll; Cert Sci Univ of MA, Westfield St Coll; *cr:* Sterling Winthrop Pharmaceutical Research Biologist in Virology 1975-80; Berlin Cntrl Schls Earth Sci Tchr 1981-; *ai:* Yrbk Adv 1985-89, 1994-; Jr, Sr, Frosh Class Adv; Environment Club, Recycling Adv; STANYS; MA Trustee of Reservations Notchview 1992-; *office:* Berlin Central Jr Sr HS PO Box 259 Berlin NY 12022

BRADLEY, JEFFREY R., 8th Grade Mathematics Teacher; *b:* Lancaster, PA; *c:* Elizabeth, Lori; *ed:* Millersville U (BS) Math Ed 1974, (MS) Math Ed 1983; *cr:* Lampeter Strasburg HS 9th Grd Math Tchr 1974-75; Conrad Weiser HS 9-11 Grd Math Tchr 1975-77; Hempfield Schl Dist 7th & 8th Grd Math Tchr 1977-; *ai:* Head Track Coach 1981-; Math Counts Coach 1986-; Dir Millersville U Marauder Cross Cntry Camp 1981-; Dir Track & Field Camp 1991-; NEA, PSEA 1974-; *home:* 142 Pinnacle Point Dr Lancaster PA 17601*

BRADLEY, JUDITH S., Seventh Grade Science Teacher; *b:* Weymarth, MA; *m:* Robert R. Jr.; *ed:* Boston Univ (BS) Elem Ed 1974; Bridgewater St Coll (MAT) Phys Sci 1987; 30 Addl Hrs Lesley Coll, Fitchburg St Coll, Bridgewater St Coll; *cr:* Cambridge Pub Schls Sci Tchr K-8th 1 Yr; Plymouth Pub Schls 7th Grd Sci Tchr 18 yrs; *ai:* Pub Schls Tech Comm; Schl Bowling CLub Adv; NSTA, MA Tchrs Assn, NEA 1977-; MA Assn of Sci Tchrs 1985-; Natl Middle Level Sci Tchr Assn 1989-; Drop Out Prevention Grant; Reach for the Stars Grant; CESAME Grant; Manuscrip Writing for DC Hlth Pub Co; Curr Writing Based on MS Curr Frameworks F; *office:* Plymouth Cmty Intermediate Sch 117 Long Pond Rd Plymouth MA 02360

BRADLEY, KITTY LEA, Drama Dir & Newspaper Advisor; *b:* Tulsa, OK; *ed:* Mary Washington Coll (BA) Theatre 1971; Univ of MD at College Park (MA) Theatre 1976; Tchr Cert 21 Hrs at Hood Coll; *cr:* Damascus HS Drama & Jrnlsm Tchr 1979-89; Seneca Valley HS Drama & Jrnlsm Tchr 1989-; *ai:* Drama Dir; Newspaper Adv; TV Club; Thespians Spon; MCEA, NEA & MD Scholastic Press Assn 1986-; Theatre Ed Assn 1990-; ITS 1981-; *office:* Seneca Valley H S 12700 Middlebrook Rd Germantown MD 20874

BRADLEY, LYNNE SWEETLAND, Mathematics Teacher; *b:* Horseheads, NY; *m:* Michael; *c:* Katy, Ryan; *ed:* St Univ of NY at Albany (BA) Math 1974; St Univ of NY at Binghamton Post Grad Stud; *cr:* Union-Endicott HS Math Tchr 1974-80, 1988-; *office:* Union Endicott HS 1200 E Main St Endicott NY 13760

BRADLEY, MARCIA DALEY, Associate Professor of Science; *b:* New York, NY; *m:* David Alan; *c:* Dylan Daley; *ed:* Caldwell Coll (BA) Bio 1962; NM St Univ (MS) Bio, Entomology 1971, (PHD) Bio, Entomology

1977; Seton Hall Univ 26 Credits in Ed; Monmouth Coll 4 Credits in Ed; NJ Tchrs Cert Sci 1988; *cr:* Monmouth Coll Asst Prof Bio 1980-87; Jackson HS Bio, General Sci Tchr 1987-88; Ocean Cty Coll Assoc Prof Sci 1988-; *ai:* Chm Comm on Instruction; President Citizens Advy Bd Ed Opportunity Fund Steering Comm; Middle Sts Institutional Self Study Gender Subcomm; Mentoring Prgm Mentor; Entomological Soc of Amer; NEA; NJ Educl Assn; Bd of Trustees; First Unitarian Church of Mounmouth Cty VP for Finance; Natl Acad of Sci Fellow 1982-83 with the Czechoslovakia Acad of SciPrague, Czech; Who's Who in West 16th Edition; Outstanding Grad Stu 1975 Entomological Soc of Amer; NJ Sci Adv 1981; 10 Peer Reviewed Papers; 2 Chapters in Books; 1 Report to Governor of NJ; 1 EPA Report; Veritas Awd 1990 Awarded Caldwell Coll to Alumni in Recognition to Committment to Excl; Who's Who in Amer 46th Edition; *office:* Ocean County College College Dr Toms River NJ 08753*

BRADLEY, MICHAEL JOHN, Assoc Prof of Math & Cmptr Sci; *b:* Lawrence, MA; *m:* Arleen Potvin; *c:* Kelly, Brian; *ed:* Merrimack Coll (BA) Math 1978; Univ of Notre dame (MS) Math 1980, (PHD) Math 1983; *cr:* Merrimack Coll Asst Prof 1983-88, Assoc Prof 1988-, Dept Chair 1989-93; *ai:* Rank, Tenura Comm; Fac Adv Math Club; Accept Challenge Prgm Biling HS Stdnts; Sci Camp Elem Schl Tchrs, Stdnts; Acad Olympics Cmptr Competition HS Stdnts; Math Assn of Amer 1985-; Little League 1994-, Coach; Sacred Heart Parish Pastoral Cncl 1993-; Author Textbook Calculus for Business; Articles Pub; Author Textbook Supplements; *office:* Merrimack Coll 315 Turnpike St North Andover MA 01845

BRADLEY, MIMI F., Health & Physical Ed Teacher; *b:* Carrolltown, PA; *m:* Daniel A.; *ed:* Slippery Rock (BS) Hlth, PE 1976; Penn St Univ & Indiana Univ of PA 58 Post Grad Credits; *cr:* Summit Ath Club Aquatic Dir 5 Yrs; Cambria Heights Schl Dist Tchr 13 Yrs; *ai:* Boys & Girls Swim Team Coach; CPR, Lifeguard Trng, 1st Aid Instr; NEA, PSEA, AEA; Amer Red Cross 1971-, Vol Instr; *office:* Cambria Heights HS PO Box 6 Glendale Lake Rd Patton PA 16668

BRADLEY, PETER JAMES, Division Head & Math Teacher; *b:* Portsmouth, RI; *m:* Nancy Doherty; *c:* Erin P., Michael P.; *ed:* Shippensburg St Coll (BS) Acctng 1980; *cr:* New Canaan Cntry Schl 5th Grd Apprentice 1981; Fessenden Schl Math Tchr, Coach, Dorm Parent 1981-90; The Fenn Schl Division Head, Tchr, Coach 1990-; *ai:* Var Bsktbl, MS Soccer Coach; *office:* Fenn Schl 516 Monument St Concord MA 01742

BRADLEY, RONALD JOHN, Chemistry Tchr & Sci Dept Chm; *b:* Philadelphia, PA; *m:* Carol Ann Wigton; *c:* Michael, Nicole, Timothy, Kevin; *ed:* CA St (BS) Chem 1967; West Chester Univ (MS) Chem 1972; Univ of PA Post Grad Stud; *cr:* Rehoboth Beach Schls Tchr 1965-66; Harriton HS Tchr 1967-68; Lower Merion HS Tchr 1968-91; Harriton HS Tchr 1992-; *ai:* Acad Decathlon Head Coach; Sci Olympiad Co-Coach; NEA 1970-; PSEA 1970-; LMEA 1970-; Lower Merion Comm Awd 1982; Montgomery Cty Outstdng Sci Tchr 1991; *office:* Harriton HS 600 N Ithan Ave Rosemont PA 19010*

BRADLEY, SALLIE PEACE, Basic Skills Teacher; *b:* Oxford, NC; *m:* Allen Martin; *ed:* NC Cntrl Univ (BA) Elem Ed 1972; Rdng Specialists3 Credit Hrs Kean Coll, 6 Credit Hrs Seton Coll, 6 Credit Hrs Rutgers Univ, 3 Credit Hrs Johnston Coll, 3 Credit Hrs Montclair St 1996; *cr:* Summit Elem Schls Tchr 1972-92; Summit's Jefferson Schl Rdng Recovery Tchr 1992-94; Summit's Elem Schls Basic Skills Tchr 1995-; *ai:* HS Track & Field Events Asst; Tutor; NJEA, NEA, SEA 1972-; Summit Ed Fnd Two Grants; *office:* Jefferson Elem Schl 110 Ashwood Ave Summit NJ 07083

BRADLEY, WILLIAM H., English Teacher; *b:* Fulton, NY; *m:* Suzanne Linda; *c:* Kellie Ann, Kristin Andrea; *ed:* SUNY at Oswego (BA) Eng Ed 1969, (MS) Eng Ed 1973; *cr:* Cicero HS Eng Tchr 1969-81; Cicero-North Syracuse HS Eng Tchr 1987-; *ai:* JV Sftbl Coach; Jr Class Adv; Ski Club Adv, Founder; Yrbk Co-Adv; MIRAGE Fac Adv; AFT 1969-; NYSUT; Town of Cicero 1980-92, Councilman; Optimists 1990-; *office:* Cicero-North Syracuse HS Rt 31 Cicero NY 13039

BRADMAN, ROBERT R., High School Math Teacher; *b:* Bangor, ME; *m:* Holly Hoppough; *c:* Marc, Courtney; *ed:* Univ of ME at Orono (BS) Math 1969; 30 Hrs Stud in Math; Prof Growth; *cr:* Chelmsford HS Math Tchr 1970-; *ai:* Various Comms; Sports; AFT; *office:* Chelmsford H S 200 Richardson Rd Chelmsford MA 01863

BRADOC, SONYA K., Reading Specialist; *b:* New Haven, CT; *m:* Keith A.; *c:* Tracey, Keith, Melanie; *ed:* Southern CT (BA) Rdng, His 1949; Coll of New Rochelle (MA) 1965; Rdng Cert Iona 1959; 14 Summers Post Grad Stud Lincoln Ctr Stud of the Arts; 6 Yrs H B Studio Playwriting & Drama; *cr:* Point Beach Schl Elem Tchr 2 Yrs; Calf Pen Meadow Schl 1-3 Grd & Art Tchr 4 Yrs; Southern CT Trng Supvr 2 Yrs; Mayflower Schl Rdng Specialist 5 Yrs; Coll of New Rochelle Instr 2 Yrs; Jefferson Schl Rdng Specialist 20 Yrs; *ai:* Westchester Rdng Cncl 6 Yrs; NY St Rdng Assn 10 Yrs; Westchester Comm of Players 8 Yrs; Plays Produced Off Broadway, Quaigh Theatre, H B Studio; Writing Grant; Scholastic Magazines Creative Ideas Ed; *office:* Jefferson Schl 131 Weyman Ave New Rochelle NY 10805

BRADSHAW, AILEEN O'BRIEN, Mathematics Teacher; *b:* Troy, NY; *m:* Frederick L.; *ed:* St Francis Coll (BA) Math 1988; SUNY at Albany (MA) Math Ed 1989; *cr:* Hoosic Vly Cntrl HS Math Tchr 1989-90; Bethlehem Cntrl HS Math Tchr 1990-92; Shaker HS Math Tchr 1992-; *ai:* Math Club Adv; NCTM 1989-; *office:* Shaker HS 445 Watervliet Shaker Rd Latham NY 12121

BRADSHAW, ANNETTE M., Art Teacher; *b:* Clearfield, PA; *m:* Jeffrey D.; *c:* Katie, Patrick; *ed:* Edinboro Univ PA (BS) Art Ed 1979, (MA) Fine Arts 1991; *cr:* Cochranton Elem Art Tchr 1983-85; Art Tchr 1987-; *ai:* Art Club Spon; Act 178 Curr Dev Comm; Yrbk Adv; NAEA 1990-; NEA, Crawford Cntrl Ed Assn 1982-; *home:* RR 3 Saegertown PA 16433

BRADSHAW, BARBARA ANN, 7th Grade Literature Teacher; *b:* Camden, NJ; *m:* Frank; *c:* Michael, Eileen, Brian, Kevin; *ed:* Springhill Coll (BS) His 1964; Drug-Alcohol Course 3 Post Grad Credit Hrs; *cr:* St Leonard 3rd & 6th Grd Elem Tchr 1964-66; Elem Schl 1st Grd Tchr 1967-68; Wilcox Elem 1st Grd Tchr 1969-70; St Jude 7th Grd Tchr 1984-; *ai:* Var Forensic Coach; NEA 1984-; SADAT 1992-; PTG &Welcome Wagon 1974-, Treas & Pres 2 Yrs; Church Ministry 1988-, Lector & Dev Comm; Parents Club 1982-; *office:* Saint Judes Schl 422 S Mountain Blvd Mountain Top PA 18707

BRADSHAW, BUNNY PETERSON, Third Grade Teacher; *b:* Wilmington, OH; *m:* Ed; *c:* Heath, Curt; *ed:* Wilmington Coll (BA) Elem Ed 1978; Miami Univ (MA) Elem Ed 1981; *cr:* Belfast Elem 7th Grd & Kndgtn Tchr 1978-79; Sugar Tree Ridge Elem 3rd Grd & Remedial Math Tchr 1979-80; Clinton Massie Elem 3rd Grd Tchr 1980-; *ai:* Curr Comm; NEA; OEA & Local Assoc 1978-; 4-H Clubs 1976-, Advs.

BRADY, ARTHUR D., French & Spanish Teacher; *b:* Brooklyn, NY; *m:* Lynn Ann Strassburger; *c:* Arthur; *ed:* U TX (BA) Fr, Span 1962; U CO (MA) Fr, Span 1965; Middlebury Coll (DML) Fr, Span 1976; *cr:* Nyack HS Fr, Sp Tchr 1964-; Westchester Comm Coll Adj Prof 1993-; *ai:* Fr Club Hnr Soc; Acad League; AATF 1964-; Dobbs Ferry Schl Bd 1983-89, Pres; Article Pub 1980; *office:* Nyack HS 360 Christian Herald Rd Upper Nyack NY 10960

BRADY, BARBARA, Remedial Reading Teacher; *b:* Brooklyn, NY; *c:* Cyrus Townsend, Susan, Terence, Jonathan; *ed:* OH Univ (BA) Eng 1971, (MS) Ed 1975, (MS) Eng 1975; *cr:* Huntington Remedial Rdng 1972-82; Pickaway Ross JVS Remedial Rdng 1982-; *ai:* NEA 1972-; AAUW 1981-, Pres; League of Women Voters 1981-; *office:* Pickaway Ross Co Jt Voc Schl 895 Crouse Chapel Rd Chillicothe OH 45601

BRADY, BRIGETTE, Science Teacher; *b:* Schwetzingen, West Germany; *c:* Lauren, Peter; *ed:* Queens Coll (BA) Bio 1971, (MS) Scndry Ed, Bio 1995; Specialized Courses Histopathology; *cr:* Meml-Sloan Kettering Inst Clinical, Rsrch Lab Tech 1971-74; Hosp Spec Surgery Clinical, Rsrch Lab Tech 1974-87; St Margaret's Parochial Schl Sci Tchr 1987-90; IS 93 Queens Schl Sci Tchr 1990-; *ai:* Stuyvesant HS Part-time Tchr Spec Prgm Sponsored Inst of Math & Sci; AFT, UFT 1990-; ASCP 1973-; Sunday Schl Tchr 1966-; *office:* I S 93 Q 66-56 Forest Ave Ridgewood NY 11385

BRADY, ELSIE ILENE (BURRELL), Retired Elementary Teacher; *b:* Kitzmiller, MD; *m:* George E.; *c:* Deborah Ann, George Michael, Melissa E., A. Leigh; *ed:* Piedmont Coll at Demorest (BS) Elem Ed 1952; 30 Hrs Early, Elem Ed Frostburg St Univ; 6 Hrs Early Chldhd Ed WV Univ; 12 Hrs Methods, Resources Garret Comm Coll; *cr:* Tchr 1969-71; Oak Street Kndgtn Schl Tchr 1971-76; Broadford Elem Schl Kndgtn Tchr 1976-80; Kitzmiller Elem Schl Kndgtn Tchr 1980-93; *home:* 1504 Park St Kitzmiller MD 21538

BRADY, HEATHER SHAW, High School Biology Teacher; *b:* Bridgeport, CT; *m:* Mark; *ed:* Mt Holyoke Coll (BA) Biological Sci 1991; Boston Univ (MAT) Scndry Sci Ed 1994; *cr:* John Stark Regnl HS Tchr 1994-; *ai:* Biotechnology Club 1994-95; Odyssey of Mind Coach 1995-; NSTA 1994-; NABT 1994-; NHSTA 1994-; Pi Lamda Theta 1994-; NEA 1995-; *office:* John Stark Regional HS 618 N Stark Hwy Weare NH 03281

BRADY, JOHN C., AP & Chemistry Teacher; *b:* Utica, NY; *m:* Diane Hickel; *c:* John Jr.; *ed:* Utica Coll of Syracuse Univ (BS) Bio 1974; 30 Grad Hrs; *cr:* New Hartford Cntrl HS Chem Tchr 1974-; *ai:* New Hartford Tchrs Assn 1974-, Building Rep 1982; Twice Received Outstanding Educator Rotary Club; MIT Commendation; Tuft Commendation; *office:* New Hartford Central Sr H S 33 Oxford Rd New Hartford NY 13413

BRADY, KATHLEEN PATRICIA, Art Teacher; *b:* Boston, MA; *c:* Carrie Anne Sumner; *ed:* Bridgewater St (BA) Art Ed 1991; Fitchburg St 15 Addl Hrs; *cr:* Brockton HS Related Math Tchr 1991-92; Whitman Hanson HS Art Tchr 1992; Indian Head MS Art Tchr 1992-; *ai:* After Schl Art Club; Tchr Advy Cncl; Brockton System Home Tchr; Brockton System Summer Schl 7-8 Grd Math Tchr; Onset Creative Arts Ceramic Tchr; HS Stdnts Career Mentor; NTA 1991-; NEA 1995-; *office:* Indian Head MS 750 Indian Head St Hanson MA 02341*

BRADY, MARTIN A., Accounting Professor; *b:* Sikeston, MO; *m:* Laura Lea Hart; *ed:* Westminster Coll (BA) Acctng & Ec 1980; Univ of MO at Columbia (MA) Acctng 1983; Certfd Pub Accountant 1983; Certfd Mgmt Accountant 1984; *cr:* Ernst & Whinney Staff Accountant 1980-81; Univ of MO Tchng Asst 1982-83; Southeast MO St Univ Acctng Instr 1983-85; Muskingun Coll Assoc Acctng Prof 1985-; *ai:* Ec, Acctng & Bus Dept Chair 1987-90; Acad Computing Planning & Tech Advy Comms; Amer Acctng Assn 1983-; Inst of Mgmt Accountants 1984-, Cert of Distngd Performance CMA Exam 1984; Muskingun Area Tech Coll 1990-, Acctng Advy Bd; Fin Acctng Textbook 1996; OH Soc of CPAs Educl Fndtn Grant; *office:* Muskingum Coll 136 Cambridge Hall New Concord OH 43762

BRADY, PATRICK MARTIN, General Music Teacher; *b:* Bethlehem, PA; *m:* Trina Johnson-Reiner; *ed:* Moravian Coll (BMus) Music 1987; Kutztown Univ (MED) Elem Ed 1995; *cr:* South Mountain MS Vocal, Gen Music Tchr 1987-; *ai:* Chorus; Show Choir; Homework Club; Wrestling; NEA 1987-; MENC, PMEA 1995-; *office:* South Mountain MS Emmaus Ave & Church St Allentown PA 18103

BRADY, SHARON A., Former Earth Artist & Teacher; *b:* Stugartt, AR; *ed:* Caldwell Coll (BA); NY Univ (MA) Painting; Art Stdnts League NYC; *ai:* Environmental Club Founder; NEA; Tepari Burrito Soc 1986-, Dir Eastern Division; Earth Angels 1993-, Co-Founder; Last Straw Newsletter 1993-, Staff Writer; Rsrch Pub; Artist-in-Residence; Two Geraldine R. Dodge Grants 1985, 1993; Earth Pathway Installations; Earth Art Installations; MOAB; *home:* 531 Herrick Dr Dover NJ 07801*

BRADY, SHELAGH ANN, Language Arts Teacher; *b:* Lowell, MA; *ed:* Emmanuel Coll (BA) Tchr Ed, Soc Stud 1966; Fitchburg St Coll (MED) Ed 1983; *cr:* St Joseph Schl 3, 6 Grd Tchr 1965-70; St Bridget Schl 5 Grd Tchr 1970-73; Norman E. Day Schl 5 Grd Rdng, Math, LA Sc, 6 Gr LA Tchr 1973-90; Abbott MS 6 Grd Lang Arts Tchr 1990-92; Blanchard MS 6 Grd Lang Arts Tchr 1992-; *ai:* Adv Environmental Club 1991-95; NEA, MA Tchrs Assn, Westford Ed Assn 1973-; NCTE; New England Assn of Tchrs of Eng; *office:* Blanchard MS 20 West St Westford MA 01886

BRADY, THOMAS J., Assistant Professor of Biology; *b:* Buffalo, NY; *ed:* Univ of Buffalo (MS) Bio 1988, (PHD) Ecology 1993; *cr:* Univ of Buffalo Zebra Mussel Researcher 1990-94; Siena Coll Prof 1994-; *ai:* Aquatic Ecology Rsrch; 5 Publications; *office:* Siena Coll 515 Loudonville Rd Loudonville NY 12211

BRAFMAN, KENNETH ABRAHAM, Assistant Principal; *b:* Monticello, NY; *m:* Carol Marie Woodward; *c:* Chelsea; *ed:* Orange Cty CC (AS) Liberal Arts 1985; SUNY at Cortland (BS) Hlth Ed 1987, (MS) Hlth Ed 1991; St Lawrence Univ Cert Educl Admin 1994, 6 Hrs Towards Supts Cert; *cr:* Potsdam Cntrl Schl 8-12 Grd Hlth Ed, Coach 1987-95; Canton Cntrl Schl Summer Schl Hlth Ed Tchr, Coach 1992-94; Union-Endicott MS Asst Prin 1995-; *ai:* First Aid-CPR Instr 1994-; Audio-Visual Coord 1989-95; Frosh Adv 1988-95; Coach Out Door Track 1989-95, Wrestling 1990-95; Drug Curr, Aids Advy, Spec Ed Couns; Crises Comm; Weight Lifting Trainer; NYSUT 1987-; SAANYS 1995-; Nom Eta Sigma Gamma; *home:* 1673 White Bridge Cir Homer NY 13077*

BRAGG, GILES G., Retired Teacher; *b:* Greensboro, NC; *m:* Diane Wilson; *c:* Deirdre Parker, Ellicia Gamblin, Giles G. Jr.; *ed:* NC A&T Univ (BS) Instrumental Music 1956; Univ of MD (MS) Cnslng 1969; *cr:* Washington Tech Inst Cnslr 2 Yrs; Bowie St Univ Dean of Men, Coll Admin 13 Yrs; Coppin St Univ Coll Admin 8 Yrs; Suitland HS Sub Tchr 2 Yrs; *ai:* Vol in the Support Prgm; Local 161-710 Musicians Union 1960; Omega Psi Phi 1956-; Metro-Vatter Corvette Club; Bulldog Club Pres; *home:* 8812 Monmouth Dr Upper Marlboro MD 20772*

BRAGG, KIM D., Computer Business Skills Instr; *b:* Zanesville, OH; *m:* Timothy A.; *c:* Derek, Cody; *ed:* Muskingum Area Tech (AA) Secretarial Sci 1981; OH Univ (BA) Comprehensive Bus Ed 1983; Kent St Univ Vo Ed Cert 1983; Working on Masters Higher Ed Coll Tchng OH Univ at Zanesville; *cr:* Morgan HS Bus Instr 1983-; *ai:* Bus Prof of Amer; Class, Club 1983-, Regnl 1994 Adv; Girl's JV Bsktbl 1983-86; Little League Bsbl, Bsktbl; NEA, Office Ed Assn 1983-; Morgan Local Ed Assn 1983-, Sec, Bldg Rep; MHS Advy Comm 1995-; *office:* Morgan HS 800 S Raider Dr Mc Connelsville OH 43756

BRAGG, ROBIN BRASIER, 1st & 2nd Grade Teacher; *b:* Skowhegan, ME; *m:* Richard Earle; *c:* Erika, Amy L. Wright; *ed:* Univ of ME at Farmington (BS) Ed 1970; Univ of Southern ME (MS) Prof Tchr 1985; Master Tchr Awded by St of ME; *cr:* SAD #9 1st-2nd Grd Tchr 1970-93, 1st-2nd Grd Team Tchr 1995-; Univ of ME Ed Practicum Supvr, Stu Tchr 1993-95; *ai:* Stu Assistance Team; Multiage Comms; Univ of ME Advy Comm; UMF Stu Tchrs, Practicum Stdnts Supervision; MTA, NEA, SAD #9 EA 1970-; Wilton Schlsp Comm 1995-; Farmington Emblem Club 1970-; Wilton Playground Comm; Tchrs, Parents Multiage, Multiple Intelligences, Process Writing Seminars.

BRAGOLI, PATRICIA CARNICELLI, Third Grade Teacher; *b:* Brooklyn, NY; *m:* John Joseph Jr.; *c:* John III, Cindy, Erica; *ed:* Molloy Coll (BA) Chem & Ed 1972; SUNY at Stony Brook (MALS) Lib S *cr:* St Vincent de Paul Elem 6th Grd Tchr 1972-74; St Isidores 6th 1974-76; Brookhaven Elem 2nd-3rd Grd Tchr 1982-; *ai:* NYSU *office:* Brookhaven Elem Schl Fireplace Neck Rd Brookhaven N

BRAHM, WALTER RICHARD, High School Counselor; *b:* NJ; *m:* Catherine Herman; *c:* James, Creghton, Catherine; *ed:* Coll (BA) Elem Ed 1967; NY Univ (MA) Cnslng 1973; Seton (EDS) Admin 1979; *cr:* Knollwood Schl Elem Tchr 1967-68; Vietnam Infantry Sgt 1968-70; Conackamack MS 6th & 8th 1970-80; HS Eng Tchr 1980-83; MS & HS Cnslr 1983-; *ai* Potential Civic Comm; NJEA; NEA; Middlesex Cty Assoc; Rut Livingston Coll Advy Comm.

BRAHOSKY, ADAM C., HS Social Studies Teacher; *b:* Portsm *m:* Anita Gmuer; *ed:* Washington & Jefferson Coll (BA) His 199 Accreditation St Vincent Coll; *cr:* Mardell MS & HS Soc Stud Tc *ai:* Intramural Ftbl Coach; Detention Hall Monitor; NEA, NCSS 1994-; Mardela Youth Bsbl League 1995-, VP; Amer Kenpo Kara 1995-; Phi Kappa Sigma 1989-, VP; *office:* Mardela Middle & HS A Mardela Springs MD 21837

BRAIA, THOMAS JOSEPH, Business Education Teacher; *b:* NY; *m:* Catherine Mazzei; *c:* Joseph, Jaime; *ed:* Iona Coll (MS) Stud 1976; 45 Addl Credits in Ed, Bus & Admin; *cr:* Clarkstown Bus Ed Instr 1974-82; Clarkstown HS South Bus Ed Instr 1982-; S Aquinas Coll Adj Prof 1982-; Full-time Employer Tom-Cat Dry *ai:* AFT, NYSUT, FBLA 1974-; Colts Boys Club 1988-; Cub Scou Den Ldr; Yrbk Dedication 1988; *home:* 77 Homecrest Oval Yor 10703

BRAINARD, SUSAN L., Assistant Principal; *b:* Schenectady, Univ of MI (BS) PE 1967; Boston Univ (MED) Ed 1973; Bridge COll (CAGS) Admin 1987; *cr:* Walpole HS PE Tchr, Var Girl Coach 1967-75, Var Girls Bksbtl Coach 1967-95, Var Field Hock 1967-84, Hlth, PE Chprsn 1975-85, Asst Prin 1985-; *ai:* Rest Comm Chair; Walpole Tchrs Assn, NEA 1967-; MA Scndry P 1985-; Walpole Cntry Club 1972-, 3 Times Chprsn, Bd of Govern Bsktbl Coachs Assn Coach of Yr 1987, 1989, 1993, 1995; Bost Bsktbl Coach of Yr 1984, 1989, 1994, 1995; New Agenda N Women Hall of Fame 1989; Boston Globe Field Hockey Coach of Boston Honorary Achvmt Awd 1985; Niskayuna HS Hall of Far Univ of MI branstrom Scholar 1964; *office:* Walpole HS 257 Co Walpole MA 02081

BRAITHWAITE, ANTONY XAVIER, Theology Teacher; *b:* Me *ed:* Georgetown Univ (BA) Theology 1993; *cr:* Saint Josep Theology Tchr 1994-; *ai:* Speech Coach; Dramatics Moderator; Assembly Adv; Crew Asst Coach; Kairos Retreat Ldr; Stu Cn Admissions Assoc; *office:* Saint Josephs Prep Schl 1733 W Gi Philadelphia PA 19130

BRAITHWAITE, BRENDA EVELYN, Fifth Grade Teacher; *b:* City, NJ; *ed:* Cheyney Univ (BSEd) Elem Ed 1969; Beaver Coll (1984; Attnd Penn St at Great Vly, Temple Univ, St Josephs, Gr Marywood Coll; 60 Addl Hrs; *cr:* Hackett Schl Tchr 1969-73; Pri Schl Tchr 1973-; Hosp Workers Union 1199C Instr 1995-; *ai:* Safet 24 Challenge Spon; AFT, PFT 1969-; NCTM; Delta Sigma The Custodian.

BRAJKOVIC, HENRY, History Teacher; *b:* New York City, Rosanna; *c:* John; *ed:* City Coll of NY (BA) Eng 1953; Tchrs Columbia Univ (MA) His 1956; Attnd Yale Ed Improvement Ctr, Y Haven Tchrs Inst; *cr:* Nathan Hale Jr HS Eng, Soc Stud Tchr 1956- Haven Jr HS Eng, His Tchr 1958-66; Wilbur Cross HS His Tchr 1 AFT 1963-; *office:* Wilbur Cross HS 181 Mitchell Dr New Ha 06511

BRAMBLE, GLORIA MAXINE, Secondary Math Resource Tch Rainier, MD; *m:* William; *c:* Brian; *ed:* Univ of MD (BA) Ed 1966 Human Dev 1975; *cr:* Benjamin Stoddert MS Eng Tchr 7 Yrs; F Douglas HS Eng Tchr 1/2 Yr; Southern MS Math, Eng Tchr Northern MS Math Tchr 8 Yrs; Calvert Co Bd of Ed Scndry Math Tchr 3 Yrs; *ai:* Calvert Ed Assn, MD Ed Assn, NEA 6 Yrs; NCTM Outstdng Adult Ed Tchr of Yr 1976; Outstdng Tchr of Yr Nom 1991 Calvert Cty Pub Schl System Dares Beach Rd Prince Frederic MD

BRAMHALL, ROBERTA, English Teacher; *b:* West Orange, Montclair St Coll (BA) Eng 1958, (MA) Eng 1968; 24 Credits; HS Eng Tchr 1958-60; Maplewood Jr HS Eng Tchr 1960-63; Li HS Eng Tchr 1963-; *ai:* Friends of High Point, Sec, Vol Awd; Pa Vly Trl Comm, Trustee; Foster Fields The Willows, Docent, V Montclair Historical Soc, Docent.

BRAMLEY, DOREEN ANN LAMBERT, Professor & Director of *b:* Providence, RI; *m:* Russell; *c:* Jennifer, Douglas, Jessica; *ed.* Coll of RI (AFA) Drama & Directing 1988; Emerson Coll (BA) 1990, (MA) Drama & Directing 1992; 6 Credits in Childrens Course; *cr:* St Xavier HS Drama & Dance Dir 1988; Emerson Coll TA 1989-91; Comm Coll of RI Prof of Drama & Directing; England Theatre Conf; Drama Club Adv; NETC 1985-; Acad 1978-, Bd Mem, Dir & Best Regnl Play Awd 1984; Warwick Con of The Arts 1983-, Bd Mem; Acad Players Best Producer Awd 1984 Comm Coll Of RI Flanagan Camps East Ave Warwick RI 02886

BRAMLEY, GEORGIE MEGAS, Third Grade Teacher; *b:* Bet PA; *m:* David M.; *c:* Christopher, Timothy; *ed:* St Univ of NY at (BS) Elem Ed 1970; Nazareth Coll of Rochester (MS) Elem Ed 1 Baltimore Cty Schl Dist 6th Grd Tchr 1970-71; Intnl Schl of Belg Grd Tchr 1973-75; Pittsford Cntrl Schl Dist Kndgtn, 2nd-3rd G 1972-; *ai:* Odyssey of Mind Vol Judge; Instrl Ldrshp Team; AFT NYSTU 1971-; Jr League of Rochester 1985-, Cookbook Chm; Wh Among Univ Stdnts 1970; *office:* Mendon Ctr Elem Schl 42 W J Rd Pittsford NY 14534*

BRANCACCIO, VINCENT CHRISTIAN,JR., Fifth Grade Tea Brooklyn, NY; *m:* Denise Martello; *c:* Dawn, Deborah; *ed:* Betha (BA) ELem Ed 1974; Suny at Stony Brook 30 Hrs of Grad Ed; *cr:* Cntrl Schl Dist Tchr 1974-; *ai:* NY St 1974- Bldg Rep; United *home:* 845 Broadway Ave Holbrook NY 11741*

BRANCHAUD, C. ANDRE, Foreign Lang Dept Chairpers Woonsocket, RI; *m:* Suzanne Vanasse; *c:* Elise Shatraw, Nicole Jacques; *ed:* Providence Coll (BA) Ed 1966, (MAT) Ed 19 Woonsocket Sr HS Fr Tchr, Chm 1966-, Var Hockey Coach 1966- Curr Comm; AFT, AATF, RIFLA 1966-; *office:* Woonsocket Sr Cass Ave Woonsocket RI 02895

BRANCO, DANIELLE RIVARD, Mathematics & SAT Prep Teac Waterbury, CT; *m:* Artur Carlos; *ed:* Providence Coll (BA) Mat Southern CT St Univ Working Towards MS Math Ed; *cr:* Cheshi Summer Schl Math Tchr 1992-94; New Haven Adult Ed Intermedia Instr 1993; Cheshire HS Math Lab Instr 1994; Seymour HS Math, S Instr 1994-; *ai:* Math Tutor; Seymour Ed Assn, CT Ed Assn, NCTM ATOMIC 1992-; *home:* 78 Melissa Ln Prospect CT 06712

BRANCO, MARIA CLOTILDE, Spanish Teacher; *b:* Horta-Portugal; *ed:* U-Mass at Dartmouth (BA) Portuguese 1976, (MA) B 1979, (BA) Eng 1982; Minor in Span, Ed 1976; 18 Hrs R Supervision; *cr:* Lawrence Schl, FHS Part-Time Biling Tchr 1

et Elem Ed Biling Tchr 1980-83; Morse Pond Schl Rdng, Biling)83-86; Falmouth HS Span, Portuguese Tchr 1986-; *ai:* Portuguese)under; Portuguese Newspaper Creative Works; NEA, MTA, FL Ed 976-; Portuguese Amer Assn 1987-; Mt Carmel Church 1969-; Best .u Horta Azores 1968; Best Stu Eng as 2nd Lang 1971; Honors New d High 1973; *office:* Falmouth HS 874 Gifford St Falmouth MA

)ER, DIANE GREEN, Fourth Grade Inclusion Teacher; *b:* ury, NJ; *m:* Fred; *c:* Jason, Heather, Zachary; *ed:* Elizabethtown 3S) Elem & Early Chldhd Ed 1985; Attnd Rowan Coll; *cr:* Saint Elem Schl 6th-8th Grd Tchr 1985; Woodbury Schl Dist 5th Grd Tchr 8; Penns Grove-Carneys Point Schl Dist Tchr 1988-; *ai:* Yrbk NEA, NJEA 1985-; *office:* Paul W Carleton Elem Schl 251 E Maple nns Grove NJ 08069

)LER, JACOB ALFRED, Mathematics Teacher; *b:* Bronx, NY; *m:* Rosenblatt; *c:* Ethan, Simon, Benjamin; *ed:* City Coll of CUNY Math 1964; Univ of AZ (MS) Math 1965, (PHD) Math 1971; *cr:* ell Univ Asst Prof 1969-71; Brooklyn Coll Asst Prof 1971-76; g Coll Asst Prof 1978-81; York Coll Asst Prof 1981-86; Brooklyn IS Math Tchr 1986-; *ai:* Westinghouse Sci Rsrch Stdnts Mentor; Search Competition; Math Assn of Amer 1968-; 3 Articles Pub; Brooklyn Technical HS 29 Fort Greene Pl Brooklyn NY 11217

DLEY, JOSEPH S., English Teacher; *b:* Philadelphia, PA; *m:* J. Summerall; *c:* Veronica; *ed:* La Salle Univ (BA) Ed 1970; Temple MA) Ed 1976; Beaver Coll (MA) Ed Admin 1994; *cr:* Bishop Mc HS Eng Tchr 1972-; *ai:* Stu Cncl Moderator; Homecoming Coord; oss Bloodmobile Coord; Spirit Comm Moderator; Montgomery Cty rum Moderator Adv; Assn of Cath Tchr 1972-; NACST 1975-; 1984-; NASSA 1984-; NTE 1972-; *office:* Bishop Mc Devitt HS yal Ave Wyncote PA 19095*

)DON, L. FRAN (SHIPLEY), Health Teacher; *b:* Madison Cty, NC; vid T.; *c:* Richard M., Teri J.; *ed:* Milligan Coll (BS) Hlth, PE 1962; Akron Univ, Kent St, Ashland Univ; *cr:* Ross N. Robinson Jr HS PE 962-63; Stow HS Hlth, PE Tchr 1963-; *ai:* STA 1975-, Exec Comm; NEA 1975-; *home:* 1967 Hawthorne Ave Stow OH 44224

DT, BARBARA PASQUALONE, Third Grade Teacher; *b:* Geneva, : Neil J.; *c:* Anney, Jacob; *ed:* Lakeland Comm Coll 9AA) 1971; OH BS) Elem Ed 1973; John Carroll Univ (MS) PRof Tchng 1982; ng Toward PHD Curr, Instruction Kent St Univ; *cr:* Worden Elem rd Grd Tchr 1973-78; Mapledale Elem Schl 2-3, 5 Grd Tchr 1978-82; ffe Elem Schl 2-3 Grd Tchr 1982-; *ai:* PTA; Curr Cncl; Intervention ance Team; Venture Capital Grant Writing Comm; Make A ence Day Co-Chprsn; NCTE, IRA 1994-; OH Cncl Tchrs Eng Lang 994-, Outstdng Eng Edctr Awd 1996; Phi Delta Kappa 1995-; OH Ed 1973-; St Noel Church 1982-, Liturgical Minister, Vacation Bible raft Dir, Rel Instr; Presenter OCTELA Spring Conf, NCTE Spring, Confs, Mahoning Cty Tchr Insvc 1995, Schl Tchr Insvc, IRA 41st l Convention 1996; Who's Who in Amer Ed 1996; *office:* Wickliffe Schl 1821 Lincoln Rd Wickliffe OH 44092*

IDT, IRENE H., HS Mathematics Teacher; *b:* Meriden, CT; *ed:* CT St Univ (BS) Math 1964, (MS) Math 1969; 6th Yr Admin & vision 1989; *cr:* Jefferson Jr HS Math Tchr 1964-67; Platt HS Math 967-; *ai:* Chief Adv Summit Club; Class of 1971 Chief Class Adv; 1964-; ASCD 1990-; New England Math Tchrs, CT Math Tchrs 964-; AFT, CSFT 1967-; MFT 1967-, Sec; Atomic Conventions Pres Mem of ATOMIC 1964-; Named Infulential Tchr by Srs 1988, 1989, Yrbk Dedication 1971; Who's Who of Amer Women 1995; *office:* HS 220 Coe Ave Meriden CT 06451

IDT, JEFFREY EARL, 8th Grade Math Teacher; *b:* Hershey, PA; elissa Harris; *c:* Marie Daniela, Christopher; *ed:* Bloomsburg Univ Math 1978; *cr:* Danville Area Schl Dist Math Tchr 1978-; *ai:* Boys, Cross Cntry, Winter Track & Field, Girls Track & Field Coach; Peer tion Adv; NEA 1978-; *office:* Danville MS Rt 11 Danville PA 17821

IDT, KAREN WOLFE, 9th & 11th Grd English Tchr; *b:* Bedford, : James R.; *ed:* PA St at Harrisburg (BA) Hum 1987; Tchng Cert Working Toward Masters of Amer Stud 30 Grad Credits; *cr:* ethtown Area HS 9th & 11th Grd Eng & Speech Tchr 1988-; *ai:* er Debate Team, Sprint Car Club & Radio Club Adv; Lower Dauphin l Asst to Track Team 1988-, Cross Cntry Track Team; Stu Asst Prgm; the Month Comm; Grad Prjct Comm; NEA & PSEA 1988-; *office:* ethtown Area H S 600 E High St Elizabethtown PA 17022

NDT, MARIE PINELLO, 4th Grade Teacher; *b:* Rockville Center, : James F.; *ed:* St Johns Univ (BS) Ed 1968; Queens Coll (MS) Ed 30 Grad & In-Svc Credits; *cr:* Floral Park Bellerose Schl 2, 4-6 Grd 5th Grd Chprsn 1968-; *ai:* Math, Metric System, Spelling Comms; NYSUT; Floral Park Bellerose Dist Tchr Assn; *office:* Floral ellerose Schl Larch Ave Floral Park NY 11001

NDT, ROSALIE B., Adjunct Professor; *b:* Lebanon, PA; *m:* Richard; sie Marie Green; *ed:* Millersville St Univ (BS) Scndry Ed, Eng 1970, Psych 1974; Schl Psych Cert 1974; Assoc Trainers Clinical otherapy Cert 1982; Attending Harrisburg Area Comm Coll; *cr:* al Area I V #15 SED, LD Tchr 1969-74, Schl Psychologist 1974-85; iated Psychologists Licensed Psychologist 1981-; Harrisburg Area n Coll Adjunct Prof 1992-; *ai:* Golden Lake Pet Loss Grief Group tator; Harrisburg Area Speaker's Bureau Mental Hlth Assn; St James Church, WELCA Pres, Youth Group Adv, Youth Church Schl Tchr, Guild Coord; *office:* Harrisburg Area Comm Coll Lebanon Campus umberland St Lebanon PA 17042

NDTONIES, WILLIAM H., Secondary Guidance Counselor; *b:* nsville, PA; *m:* Carol R. Yuhas; *c:* Jennifer, Michael, Jill; *ed:* CA Univ (BA) Psych, Soc Stud 1969; IN Univ of PA (MED) Scndry Guid, ng 1972; Natl Board Certfd Cnslrs Extensive Trng Chemical ndency, Stu Assistance Trng; *cr:* Waynesburg HS 9-12 Grd Psych, ology Tchr 1969-70; Mt Lebanon Jr HS 7 Grd Soc Stud Tchr 1970-72; r St Clair HS 9-12 Grd Guid Cnslr 1972-; *ai:* Conducted D&A care Groups; Started Newcomers Club; Jr HS Track, Ftbl Coach 72; AFT 1969-; PA Schl Cnslr Assn, Allegheny Cty Cnslr Assn 1972-; Ctr Schl Bd 1984-92, Pres, VP; Church Fin Cncl 1990-93, Chprsn; ch Lector 1980-92; *office:* Upper Saint Clair HS 1825 Mclaughlin Run ttsburgh PA 15241

NGMAN, DOROTHY SPEIGHT, House Director & Teacher; *b:* delphia, PA; *m:* Clarence; *c:* Deborah, Stephen; *ed:* Cheney Univ (BS) pec Ed 1975; Beaver Coll (MS) Ed, Spec Ed 1978; Goddard Coll Lbrl Westchester Univ Ldrshp Course 1995-; *cr:* Morris E. Leeds MS 7th House Dir; *ai:* Ldrshp Comm; AFT 1975-; *office:* Morris Leeds MS Mt ant Ave & Woolston St Philadelphia PA 19150

NHAM, ANNE KINNEY, Eng & Creative Writing Tchr; *b:* sville, KY; *m:* Leslie B. Jr.; *c:* Erin Lynn Jacobsen, Kristin aughlin, Bronwyn Kaye, Ryan L., Megan Leigh; *ed:* Southern IL Univ Writing & Eng 1973; Shippensburg Univ (MED) Eng 1980; *cr:* nbersburg Area Sr HS Eng & Creative Writing Tchr 1986-; *ai:* Cashs ction Lit Magazine & SAP Team Adv; NCTE 1993-; Art Alliance & ppreciation; Poetry Pub April 1994 on "To Kill a Mockingbird", le Pub By Eng Journal 1996; *home:* 1546 Fairview Ave Chambersburg 7201

BRANHAM, PAMELA FOLEY, Fourth Grade Teacher; *b:* Knox Cty, KY; *c:* Donnie, Thomas, Rob; *ed:* Union Coll (BS) Ed 1971; Northern KY Univ (MA) Ed 1987; Addl 30 Hrs Miami Univ, Drake Univ, Ashland Univ, Univ of Dayton, Loyola Mary Mount, Xavier Univ; *cr:* West End Elem Schl Tchr 1971-73; Willowville Elem Schl Tchr 1973-; *ai:* Intervention Assistance Team; Re-Districting Comm; NEA 1971-; Clough Pike Bapt Church 1974-, Childrens Sunday Schl Dir; Martha Holden Jennings Scholar; *office:* Willowville Elem Schl 4529 Schoolhouse Rd Batavia OH 45103*

BRANIGAN, MARY GRACE, Resource Room Teacher; *b:* Philadelphia, PA; *c:* Eryn Naomi; *ed:* Wilkes Univ (BA) Fr 1973, (BA) Eng 1973; Beaver Coll (MED) Spec Ed 1981; Attnd Temple Univ, Millersville Univ, Philadelphia Coll of Textiles Sci, Univ of the Arts, Gratz Coll; *cr:* Philadelphia Schl Dist Long Term Sub-Tchr 1974-80; Rsrch for Better Schls Curr Writer 1979; Philadelphia Schl Dist Var Swim Team Coach 1985-; George Washington HS Scndry Ed Tchr 1980-; *ai:* Var Swimming, Diving Coach 1985-; Israel Stud Tours Spon 1995-; Bermuda Tour, Tournament Girls Field Hockey Acad Mentor 1987; Philadelphia Fed of Tchrs Assn 1974-, Bldg Rep 1989-; Emerald Ed Comm 1980-, Exec Bd; AFT 1974-; Deborah Hosp Fnd 1974-, Exec Bd, Woman of Yr 1981; Amer Red Cross 1985-; City of Philadelphia Dept pof Commerce 1982-, Airport Advy Cncl, Distngd Svc Awd 1995; City of Philadelphia Spec Prgms, Ofcl Hostess 1982-; City of Philadelphia Distngd Humanitarian Awd 1993; Natl Endowment for Hum Flwshps 1980, 1983; Pew Charitable Trust Flwshp 1985; White House Advance Team Motorcade Driver, Secret Svc 1992, Reception Hostess 1992; *office:* George Washington HS Bustleton Ave & Verree Rd Philadelphia PA 19116

BRANNAN, SHIRLEY BISTLINE, Teacher; *b:* Bryan, OH; *m:* William; *c:* Jennifer; *ed:* Adrian Coll (BA) Eng & His 1969; Univ of Toledo (MA) Scndry Ed 1983; Bowling Green 15 Credit Hrs; *cr:* Montpelier Exempted Village Tchr 1969-70; North Cntrl HS Tchr 1971-79; Anthony Wayne HS Tchr 1981-; *ai:* Evaluation Co-Chair & Visiting Team; Trip Supvr 1996; Class Adv; NEA & OEA 1969-, Pres, Sec & Bldg Rep; NCTE 1969-; IRA 1985-; Bowling Green Presbyn Church; Amer Red Cross; Amer Cancer Soc; Phi Delta Kappa 1982-; Jennings Scholar 1983-84; *office:* Anthony Wayne HS 5967 Finzel Rd Whitehouse OH 43571

BRANSFIELD, ROSEMARY, Child Development Teacher; *b:* Malden, MA; *c:* Meaghan Lynn; *ed:* Salem St Coll (MS) Early Chldhd; Framingham St Coll (MS) Ed; *cr:* Burlington HS Home Ec Tchr, Child Dev 1977-; *ai:* NAEYC; ACEI; MTA; *office:* Burlington HS 123 Cambridge St Burlington MA 01803

BRANSON, PATRICIA MCEWAN, English Teacher; *b:* Panama Canal Zo, Panama; *m:* Robert James; *c:* Hilary, Christine, Austin; *ed:* Tchr Cert Ed Cath Univ; *cr:* Acad of Holy Names Eng Tchr 1973-78; Georgetown Visitation Eng Tchr 1988-; *ai:* Jr Class Moderator; Jr Sr Chair; Visi Network; *office:* Georgetown Visitation Prep Sch 1524 35th St NW Washington DC 20007

BRANT, JOANNE C., Law Professor; *b:* Grand Island, NY; *m:* Kevin D. Hill; *c:* Geoffrey; *ed:* Cornell Univ (AB) Philosophy, Govt 1983; Case Western Reserve Univ (JD) Law 1986; *cr:* US Ct Appeals 6th Cir Law Clerk Hon Pierce Lively 1986-87; Thompson, Hine & Flory Assoc 1987-89; Squire, Sanders & Dempsey Assoc 1989-90; OH Atty Gnel Campaign Issues Dir 1990-91; OH Northern Univ Law Prof 1991-; *ai:* Spring Natl Moot Ct Team Coach; Univ Cncl; Admissions, Chair Fac Dev Comms; AALS 1991-, Exec Bd, Sect on Empl Discr; OSBA 1986-; ABA 1983-; OH Atty Gens Cncl on Ethics & Prof Resp 1991-; Hardin Cty Herb Soc 1995-; Articles Pub; Phi Delta Phi Legal Ethics & Professionalism Awd; *office:* OH Northern Univ 525 S Main St Ada OH 45810

BRANT, JOYCE ARBUTHNOT, Fifth Grade Teacher; *b:* Akron, OH; *m:* Walter Edwin; *c:* Robert, Michael, James; *ed:* Akron Univ (BS) Elem Ed 1964; Ashland Univ 4 Credit Hrs; *cr:* Dunbar Schl 3rd Grd Tchr 1959-61; Middletown Schl 3rd Grd Tchr 1961-62; Dunbar Schl 3rd Grd Tchr 1962-65; David Bacon Schl 4th Grd Tchr 1966-71, 6th Grd Tchr 1972-85; Munroe Schl 5th Grd Tchr 1986-; *ai:* NEA, OEA, NEOEA, Uniser, Tallmadge 1959-; *home:* 2059 Tallmadge Rd Kent OH 44240

BRANT, MICHAEL L., Social Studies Dept & Teacher; *b:* Parkersburg, WV; *m:* Christina A.; *ed:* OH Univ (BS) Ed 1970, (MA) His 1980; *cr:* US Army Infantry 1970-72; Warren Local Schls Soc Stud Tchr 1972-; *ai:* Soc Stud Dept Chm; Jr High Wrestling Coach; Warren Ed Assn 1972-, Bldg Rep; OH Ed Assn 1972-; NEA 1972 -; *office:* Warren HS Rt 1 Vincent OH 45784

BRANTLEY, WANDA L., Assoc Prof, Guid & Cnslng Dept; *b:* Gibson, GA; *m:* William E.; *c:* Robin, Brian; *ed:* Temple Univ (BS) Bus Ed 1961, (MED) Distributive Ed 1966; West Chester St Coll (MED) Cnslr Ed 1979, (MED) Rdng 1995; *cr:* South Phila HS Bus Ed Tchr 1961-68; York HS Bus Ed Tchr 1968-69; York Coll of PA Bus Ed Dept 1973-76; Cheyney Univ Cooperative Ed Tchr 1976-, Guid, Cnslng Dept 1981-; *ai:* Curr, Fac Prof Dev, Judicial Comm; Acad Cncl; APSCUF 1976-, Mbrshp Chair, Svc; IRA 1990-; OIC Bd 1983-, Secty 1987-94, Svc 1992; Delta Sigma Theta; The Links Inc 1993-; Key Awd for Svc; *office:* Cheyney Univ Box 95 Cheyney PA 19319

BRANZEL, DONALD ALLAN, Third Grade Teacher; *b:* Cleveland, OH; *m:* Jean Harris; *c:* Kelly, Kyle, Evan; *ed:* Kent St Univ (BS) Elem Ed 1978; Ashland Univ (MA) Curr & Instr 1995; Attnd Cleveland St Univ, Mt Saint Joseph; *cr:* Clearview Local Schls 5th & 6th Grd Tchr 1978-81; Elyria City Schls 3rd, 4th & 6th Grd Tchr 1981-; *ai:* Peer Mediation Adv; Ftbl Coach 17 Yrs; OEA 1978-; NEA 1978-; EEA 1981-; *home:* 10318 Aspen Ct Elyria OH 44035*

BRASCH, PETER, Band Director; *b:* NY City, NY; *m:* Nickie; *c:* Julie, Christine; *ed:* Ithaca Coll (BS) Music Ed; CW Post LI Univ (MS) Music Ed; *cr:* Brentwood Schls Band Dir; Commack Schls Band Dir; *ai:* Jazz Ensemble; Tri-M Music Honor Soc; Commack Tchrs; NYSSMA Pres; Amer Fed of Musicians; *home:* 260 Fire Island Ave Babylon NY 11702

BRAS-DANGES, MARIA, Social Studies Teacher; *b:* Portugal; *m:* Robert F.; *c:* Kyle; *ed:* Western CT St Univ (BS) His & Scndry Ed 1985, (MA) Intnl Relations 1990; Dijon Univ France Intermediate Fr Diploma 1989; 4 Credits Beyond Masters AP European Seminar at Taft Inst; *cr:* Pocono Mountain HS Soc Stud Tchr 1991-; *ai:* Mock Trial Coach; NEA, PSEA, PMEA 1991-; *office:* Pocono Mountain HS PO Box 200 Swiftwater PA 18370

BRASHER, DEBORAH E., History Teacher; *b:* Essex, NJ; *ed:* Elmira Coll (BA) Classics Latin, Greek, Fr 1957; Grad Courses Grad Faculties; 24 Credits His Columbia Univ; *cr:* Rye Cntry Day Schl Tchr Latin & His 1959-64; Renbrook Schl Tchr His, US His, AncientClassical His, 29th Century, Latin1964-; *ai:* His Dept Chprsn Upper Schl Grds 6-9; Pioneer Vly Classical Assn1990-; Natl Endowment for Humanities Grant Summer 1991 Gustavus Adolphus Coll; Seminar The Tragic Voice of Thucydided Completed With Distinction; *office:* Renbrook Schl 2865 Albany Ave W Hartford CT 06117

BRASKO, ROBERT JAMES, Social Studies Teacher; *b:* Sewickly, PA; *m:* Twyla Ann Eggers; *c:* R. J., Jennifer; *ed:* Univ of MD (BS) Bus 1979; Univ of Pittsburgh (BS) Ed 1991; Attnd Comm Coll of Allegheny Cty & Bethany Coll; *cr:* St Louise de Marillac Soc Stud Tchr 1991-94; Our Lady of the Sacred Heart Soc Stud Tchr 1994-; *ai:* Frosh Boys Bsktbl, Boys & Girls Var Bowling Coach; Sr Class Adv; Pep Club Adv & Spon; Hard Rock Cafe Spon; Stu Assistance Team; *office:* Our Lady of The Sacred Heart 1504 Woodcrest Ave Coraopolis PA 15108*

BRASOVEANU, ALEXANDRA, Mathematics & Physics Teacher; *b:* Bucharest, Romania; *ed:* Univ of Bucharest Fac of Math (BS) Math 1981; Currently Grad Stu Univ of MD at Coll Park; *cr:* Schls #280 #122 & #34 Bucharest Math Tchr 1981-88; Schl #150 Bucharest Math Tchr 1988-92; Odenton Chrstn Schl Math & Physics Tchr 1993-; *ai:* NCTM 1994-; Municipal Prof Broad Mem; Romanian Natl Math Team Org & Trainer; Pub Articles 1988 & 1991; Participated at Summer Inst for Math Tchrs 1994; *office:* Odenton Christian Schl 8410 Piney Orchard Pky Odenton MD 21113*

BRASSARD, DEBORAH ELLEN, English Professor; *b:* Laconia, NH; *ed:* Boston Univ (BA) Eng Lit 1975; Boston Coll (MA) Eng Lit 1977; Purdue Univ (PHD) Eng Lit 1984; *cr:* Purdue Univ Tchng Fellow 1977-84; Penn St Asst Prof of Eng 1984-90; Marywood COll Asst Prof of Eng 1990-94; *ai:* Hnrs Advy Bd; Women's Task Force; Fac Senate; MLA 1983-; NCTE 1984-; NEPA Writing Cncl 1984-; Lit Tutor 1993-; NESCH 1985-; Purdue Univ Excl in Tchng Awd 1982, 1984; Penn St Clyde Birth Mem Awd 1985, Hayfield Awd For Outstanding Fac 1987-88, Fac Marshall 1991; *office:* Marywood Coll 2300 Adams Ave Scranton PA 18509*

BRATIS, DEAN C. T., Professor of Biology; *b:* Trenton, NJ; *m:* Elaine Muni; *c:* Adam, Livia, Erica; *ed:* Trenton St Coll (BA) Chem 1964; Univ of PA (MS) Bio 1966; Attnd St Louis Univ; Addl 30 Credits; *cr:* Lawrence Sr HS Sci Tchr 1965-66; Mercer Cty Comm Coll Bio Instr 1966-68; Delaware Cty Comm Coll Prof of Bio 1970-; *ai:* Chm Bio Dept 1990-95; Pre-med Adv 20 Yrs; Commencement Speaker 1995; Nurses & Elder Confs Speaker; Fac Del; Chair of Prof Standards; Educl Affairs; Early Matriculation, Instrl Governance Comm; Phila Zoological, Animal Behavior Soc; NEA; Mother Goose Nursery Schl 1988-90, Bd of Trustees; YMCA 1978-83, Bktbl Coach; Chapel of Four Chaplains Awd 1985; Rel Soc of Friends 1988-92, Clerk of Bus Meeting; Friends Journal 1983-84, Editorial Bd; Selected NSF Short Courses 1975, 1980, 1990, 1996; Philadelphia Area Writers Honoree 1987, 1988; Nom Tchr of Yr 1988, 1995; Outstanding Svc Awd from Stu Govt; Numerous Articles; *office:* Delaware Cnty Comm Coll 901 S Media Line Rd Media PA 19063*

BRATOWICZ, JOHN WILLIAM, Social Studies Teacher; *b:* Jersey City, NJ; *m:* Ellen; *c:* William, John Jr.; *ed:* Jersey City St Coll (BA) Ed & Soc Stud 1967, (MA) Modern European His 1970; Cert in Prin & Supvr Admin & Scndry Schl; 45 Credits Beyond MA Degree; *cr:* Edison Jr HS His Tchr 1968-69; Lyndhurst HS His Tchr 1969-71; Henry P Becton Regnl HS Supvr & Tchr 1971-; *ai:* Supvr Soc Stud, Bus & Spec Ed Depts; NEA, NJEA 1968-; Phi Delta Kappa 1969-, Charter Mem; Becton Ed Assn 1971-, Negotiations Comm; N Arlington Lib Bd of Trustees 1975-, Pres & VP; Bergen Cty Parks Commission 1980-, Pres & VP; Bergen Cty Housing Comm 1979-; Jersey City St Coll Tchng Assistanship; *office:* Henry P Becton Reg HS Cornelia St & Paterson Ave East Rutherford NJ 07072

BRATT, ANNE C., Mathematics Teacher; *b:* Poughkeepsie, NY; *m:* David; *ed:* SUNY at Albany (MS) & (BS) Math; Dutchess Comm Coll (AAS) Math; *cr:* Wappingers Cntrl Schl Dist Math Tchr 1986-; *ai:* Math Club Adv; EDC Mem; WCT 1986-; *office:* John Jay HS PO Box 38 Hopewell Jct NY 12582

BRAUCHER, ELAINE CULTON, Third Grade Teacher; *b:* Williamstown, PA; *m:* Jack E. Jr.; *ed:* West Chester Univ (BS) Elem Ed 1969; PA St (MED) Elem Ed 1972; *cr:* North Side Elem Schl Tchr 27 Yrs; *ai:* Tchr Mentor; Soc Stud Comm; MacMillan, Mc Graw Hill Schl Div Tchr Reviewer; NEA 1969-; AAUW; Immanual Presbyn Church Bd of Deacons Elder, Progress Moderator; Class Act Tchr; Inst of Museum Svc PA Fed of Museums, Historical Orgs Grant 1995; Cntrl Dauphin Schl Dist Distngd Svc Awd 1995.

BRAUER, MARY ELIZABETH, Fifth Grade Teacher; *b:* Stoneham, MA; *m:* G. Robert; *c:* Corinne; *ed:* Boston St Coll (BS) Elem Ed 1970, (MED) Elem Ed 1978; Various Courses; *cr:* Maplewood Schl 4th Grd Tchr 1970-72; Salemwood Schl 4th & 5th Grd Tchr 1973-80; Beebe Schl 6th Grd Tchr 1980-81; Forestdale Schl 6th Grd Tchr 1982-85; Glenwood Schl 5th Grd Tchr 1985-; *ai:* Malden Tchrs Assn, MA Tchrs Assn, NEA 1970-; Horace Mann Grant; Boston Gas Co Sci Grant; Wkshps in Cooperative Learning, Learning Styles, Great Books Ldr Prgm & Hands-On Sci; *office:* Glenwood Elem Schl 145 Glenwood St Malden MA 02148

BRAUER, SHELLY MAFFEY, Art Department Chair; *b:* San Diego, CA; *m:* Ben; *c:* Tobias, Noah; *ed:* Edgecliff Coll (BA) Art Ed 1974; *cr:* Mt Notre Dame HS Art Dept Chair 1986-; *ai:* Core Team Yrbk Adv 5 Yrs; Kairos Retreat Adult Team Mem; Scholastics Judge; NAEA 1988-; AAAE, Amer Craft Cncl 1995-; Parish Cncl Resurrection Parish 1982-; *office:* Mount Notre Dame H S 711 E Columbia Ave Cincinnati OH 45215*

BRAUN, AARON, Film Appreciation Teacher; *b:* Kefar Saba, Israel; *c:* Ilana, Jonathan; *ed:* Brooklyn Coll (BA) Cinema Stud 1978; Coll of Staten Island (MA) Cinema Stud 1994; Univ of CA at Los Angeles Amer Studios & Animation Courses 1991; *cr:* Museum of Modern Art Film Traffic Mgr 1977-82; Worldvision Enterprises Foreign Home Video Mgr 1983-89; South Shore HS Film & Eng Tchr 1989-; Coll of Staten Island Adjunct Film Prof 1992-94; Hofstra Univ Adjunct Film Prof 1995-; *ai:* Coll of Staten Island Fellowship 1992; Natl Endowment for the Hum Grant & Seminar Japanese Culture & Four Texts 1993; Ecological Seminar & Field Trip Fulbright Schlsp 1994; *office:* South Shore HS 6565 Flatlands Ave Brooklyn NY 11236*

BRAUN, AUDREY HAUSTVEIT, Business Ed Dept Chairperson; *b:* Stanley, ND; *m:* Carl J.; *ed:* Cocordia Coll (BA) Bus Ed, Psych Ed 1958; 9 Credits Bus Ed Montclair St Coll; 2 Credits Bus Ed Ridge Coll; 6 Credits Bus Ed OR St Coll; 3 Credits Bus Ed Western St Coll; *cr:* Washington HS Bus Ed Tchr 1964-67; Bridgewater-Rawten HS Bus Ed Tchr 1967-68; New Providence HS Bus Ed Tchr 1968-69, 1971-77; Millville HS Bus Ed Tchr 1977-78; Bogota HS Bus Ed Tchr, Bus Ed Chprsn 1978-; *ai:* Bus Ed Dept Chprsn; Prepare All Concert Prgms for Music Dept Plus Prgm, Brochures for Other HS Clubs & Acts; NJ Bus Ed Assn 1964-; NJ Prin & Supvrs Assn 1989-; *office:* Bogota HS 2 Henry C Luthin Pl Bogota NJ 07603*

BRAUN, DANA CANDACE OSTHOLTHOFF, 5th & 6th Grade Math Teacher; *b:* Cincinnati, OH; *m:* Richard William; *c:* Deron Keith, Datosha Courtney-Ann; *ed:* Univ of Cincinnati (BS) Elem Ed 1967; Coll of Mount Saint Joseph (MS) Elem Ed 1980; *cr:* Covedale Elem Schl 4-5 Grd Arts, Soc Stud Tchr 1967-72, 5-6 Grd Math, Sci Tchr 1972-87, 5-6 Grd Math Tchr 1987-; *ai:* Scrabble Club 1995, Newspaper 1993, Stu Cncl 1991 Adv; Math Dept Chm 1972-; AFT; CFT; Tchrs Aid & Annuity 1978-, Bd of Dirs; Cincinnati Cncl Edctrs; Alpha Chi Omega 1967-, Chptr Schlsp Adv; Pilgrim United Church of Christ, Pres; CG&E's Awd of Inspiration Excl in Tchng 1994; Cincinnati Distngd Tchr 1984; *home:* 6065 Countryhills Dr Cincinnati OH 45233

BRAUN, NORMAN F., 8th Grade Algebra Teacher; *b:* Pittsburgh, PA; *m:* Linda G. Hamley; *ed:* Indiana Univ of PA (BS) Math 1970; 70 Post Grad Credits; *cr:* Interboro Jr HS Math Tchr 1970-80; Interboro MS Algebra I Tchr 1981-; *ai:* NEA 1970-; PSEA 1970-, Region, PACE Comm; Interboro Ed Assn 1970-, Pres, Treas; NCTM; Phi Sigma Kappa 1967-; Math Dept Chm; Impact Grant.

BRAUNE, MABEL BROWN, Retired Elementary Teacher; *b:* Westminster, MD; *m:* David Norman; *c:* Mark T. Walters, Donna M. Gault, Matthew W. Walters; *ed:* Towson St Univ (BA) Elem Ed 1972; Western MD

Coll (MED) Rdng Specialist 1978; 30 Addl Hrs; *cr:* Sandymount Elem Schl 4th-5th Grd Tchr 1961-93; *ai:* CCEA 1961-, Rep 3 Yrs; MSTA; NEA; AAUW 1985-, VP Branch Mbrshp; Western MD Coll Undergraduate Relations Comm 1988-, Pres; Carroll Cty Historical Soc 1990-; Carroll Cty Outstdng Tchr 1993; *home:* 5 Pine Hill Dr Westminster MD 21157

BRAUNSCHEIDEL, DANIEL WILLIAM, Physical Science Teacher; *b:* Buffalo, NY; *m:* Karen Marie Rice; *c:* Zachariah P., Jacob D.; *ed:* St Univ of NY Coll at Buffalo (BS) Information Systems Mngmt 1986; Tchng Cert for Scndry Sci, Chem, Earth Sci 1993; Working Towards MS 18 Credit Hrs Ed Cmptng; *cr:* Orchard Park MS Phys Sci Tchr 1993-; *ai:* Earth Week Bldg Coord; IM Sports Supvr; Cmptr Comm Mem; STANYS, OPTA, NSTA, NYSUT 1993-; Natl Arbor Day 1990-; *office:* Orchard Park MS 60 S Lincoln Ave Orchard Park NY 14127*

BRAUNSCHEIDEL, PATRICK PHILLIP, Social Studies Teacher; *b:* Lackawanna, NY; *c:* Patrick; *ed:* Canisius Coll (BA) Soc Stud Ed 1991, (MS) Rdng Ed 1995; Driver Ed Cert; *cr:* West Seneca Cntrl Schls Tchr 1991-; *ai:* Stu Cncl Adv; Jr Var Ftbl Head Coach; Modified Wrestling & Bsbl Coach; Mentor for Non-Tenured Tchrs; WSTA 1991-, Bldg Rep; NYSUT 1991-; West Seneca Cntrl Federal Credit Union 1991-, Trustee, Bd of Dirs; Tchr of Month February 1993; *office:* West Seneca Cntrl Schls 1397 Orchard Park Rd West Seneca NY 14224

BRAVACO, JOSEPH, English Teacher; *b:* Newark, NJ; *ed:* Seton Hall Univ (BA) Eng 1973; Montclair St Coll (MA) Speech & Comm 1977; Rutgers Univ 9 Credits Eng; Univ of Bridgeport 15 Credits Guidance; Montclair Univ 6 Credits Eng; *cr:* Bayley Ellard HS Eng Tchr, Drama Coach 1973-76; Pompton Lakes HS Eng Tchr, Drama Coach 1977-81; Data Processing 1981-89; Clifton HS Eng Tchr, Newspaper Adv 1990-; *ai:* NJEA 1990-; Awd Winning, Produced Playwright; *office:* Clifton HS 333 Colfax Ave Clifton NJ 07013*

BRAVANTE, LORRAINE PFIZENMAYER, Sixth Grade Teacher; *b:* Paterson, NJ; *m:* George Robert; *c:* George, Beth Bravante Loftus, Thomas, Stephen; *ed:* William Paterson Coll (BA) Ed 1974, (MED) Cnslng Schl 1987; Addl 60 Credits Ed; *cr:* West Milford Bd of Ed 6 Grd Tchr 1974-; *ai:* NEA, NJEA 1974-; W. M. Ed Assn 1974-, Schl Rep 1960-66; Kinnelon Pub Lib Bd of Trustees 1994-, Sec; St of NJ Governors Awd 1989-90; *office:* Maple Rd Schl 36 Maple Rd West Milford NJ 07480

BRAVERMAN, MICHAEL ALAN, Sixth Grade Teacher; *b:* Manhattan, NY; *m:* Adrianne; *ed:* Oberlin Coll (BA) Math 1987; Tchrs Coll (MA) Math Ed 1988; *cr:* Davies MS 6th-8th Grd Math Tchr 1988-92; Hess Ed Complex 6th Grd Tchr 1992-; *ai:* Drama Club; NCTM, AMTNJ 1988-; South Jersey Joint Mens Club Cncl 1993-; Numerous Articles Pub; *home:* 418 Northfield Ave Northfield NJ 08225*

BRAVERMAN, WILLIAM PAUL, Social Studies Teacher; *b:* St Albans, NY; *m:* Barbara Dale Kushner; *c:* Peter; *ed:* Kingsborough Comm Coll (AA) Liberal Arts 1974; Hunter Coll (BA) His 1975; Long Island Univ (MSE) Scndry Ed 1994; *cr:* Keid Acad of NY ESL Tchr 1992-94; Gorton HS Soc Stud Tchr 1994-; *ai:* Peer Tutoring Prgm; Museum Research Club; AFT 1994-; *office:* Gorton HS 100 Shonnard Pl Yonkers NY 10701

BRAVMAN, JEFFREY H., Third Grade Teacher; *b:* Brooklyn, NY; *m:* Sylvia Marie Gobeil; *c:* Justin; *ed:* Lebanon Vly Coll (BS) Elem Ed 1985; *cr:* Warnsdorfer Schl 4th Grd Tchr 1985-86; Robert Frost Elem Schl 3-5th Grd Tchr 1986-; *ai:* 5th Grd IM Prgm; NEA, NJEA, EBEA 1985-; *office:* Robert Frost Elem Schl 65 Frost Ave East Brunswick NJ 08816

BRAXTON, MARSHALL SANDRA, Social Studies Teacher; *b:* Washington, DC; *ed:* Morgan St Univ (BA) His, Soc Stud 1969; Bowie St Univ (MED) Scndry Ed 1975; Attnd Univ of MD; *cr:* Maryland Park Jr HS Math, Soc Stud Tchr 1969-73; Benjamin Di Foulois MS 7th-8th Grd Soc Stud Tchr 1973-86; Thurgood Marshall MS 7th Grd Soc Stud Tchr 1986-; *ai:* Schl Planning, Mngmt Team; PECCS, MCSS, MSCSS, PGCEA, NEA 1969-; Alpha Delta Kappa 1982-, Historian, Chaplain; GESPHA 1983-; Golden Cr 1985-; Amer Red Cross 1993-, Vol; Cty Outstdng Edctr Nom Twice; *office:* Thurgood Marshall MS 4909 Brinkley Rd Temple Hills MD 20748

BRAXTON, SHEILA MELINDA, English Teacher & Dept Chprsn; *b:* Washington, DC; *ed:* Amer Univ (BA) Eng 1972, (MA) Eng 1977; Univ of MD Eng Classes, Tchng Stdnts with Spec Needs Course, Multiculutral Ed, Cmptr, PG Cty Adult Ed, ATLAS Leadership Wrksp; *cr:* Prince George's Comm Coll Prof 1989-91; High Point HS Eng Instr 1972-, Instr, Dept Chprsn-Tchr Coord 1992-; *ai:* ATLAS Restructuring, Instruction Assessment, Multiculutral Awds, Schlsp, Black His 1987-91, Contest 1989-91, Black Male 1989-90 Comms; Site Based Mngmt Team; Competitive Writing Awds Prgm; Future Tchrs of MD Club 1989-91; Curr Assesment and Instruction Comm; Middle States Curr Comm, Steering Comm; Schl Climate Comm; SAT Comm; Christa McAuliffe Awards Comm; NEA, MSTA 1972-; PGCEA 1972-, Rep 1990; NCTE 1989-; MADD 1980-90; Humane Soc 1990-; Smithsonian Assocs 1990-92; NAACP 1989-91; Democratic Natl Comm; Tchr of Yr Baltimore Chamber of Commerce 1990; Ray A. Kroc Tchr Achvmt Awd 1990, 1992; Tchng Excl Awd Univ of MD 1992; Narrator & Script Consultant for Coll Bd Video Series; Featured in Coll Bd Film; Narrator of Film Focusing on Various Learning Methods; Wrote Cty Honors' Curr, Cty 11th Grd Eng Curr; Receipient of Letter of Commendation Outstanding Tchng of Writing NCTE Featured in PG Journal Article on FTM Club; *office:* High Point HS 3601 Powder Mill Rd Beltsville MD 20705

BRAY, JOHN N., Secondary Science Teacher; *b:* Rahway, NJ; *m:* Lynetta R.; *c:* Daniel, Nathaniel; *ed:* Roberts Wesleyan Coll (BA) Bio 1966; Syracuse Univ (MS) Bacteriology 1970; Potsdam Coll SUNY (MS) Bio Ed 1976; Columbia Univ (MA) Adult Ed 1993; Columbia Univ (EdD) Adult Ed 1995; *cr:* Syracuse Univ Tchng Asst 1966-70; Hermon DeKalb Cntrl Schl Scndry Sci Tchrs 1970-; *ai:* ASCD 1980-; AFT 1973-; NABT 1975-; HDTA 1970-; Adlt Ed Rsrch Assn 1993-; Clarkson Univ Outstanding Tchr Awd 1984; Articles Pub; Tandy Tech Schlr Awd 1994; Nom NY State Tchr of Yr 1995; *office:* Hurmon De Kalb Central Schl Rt 1 Box 13 De Kalb Junction NY 13630

BRAY, LISA MARIE, Sixth Grade Teacher; *b:* Smithtown, NY; *m:* Robert; *c:* Robert; *ed:* Suffolk Comm (ASS) Early Chldhd Ed 1986; St Josephs Coll (BA) Elem Ed 1989; Dowling Coll (MS) Rdng Diagnosis & Treatment 1993; *cr:* Miller Place Sound Beach Schl 6th Grd Tchr 7 Yrs; *home:* 2 Regis Pl Shoreham NY 11786

BRAYMAN, GLENDA K., Adj Prof Criminal Justice Dept; *b:* Buffalo, NY; *m:* Howard C.; *c:* Adrienne, Courtney, Terry; *ed:* Syracuse Univ Coll of Law (LB) Law 1979; *cr:* Monroe Cty Dist Attorney Asst Dist Attorney 1979-82; NYS Supreme Court Attorney 1983-; Monroe Comm Coll Adj Prof Criminal Justice Dept; *ai:* Monroe Co Bar Assn 1990-, Chprsn of Crminal Justice Section 1995-; Greater Rochester Assn of Women Attorneys, Womens Bar Assn of NYS 1990-; *office:* Monroe Comm Coll 1000 E Henrietta Rd Rochester NY 14623

BRAZIER, WILLIAM B. J., Band Director; *b:* Woodbury, NJ; *m:* Jana Allaman; *c:* Julie, Melissa; *ed:* WV Wesleyan Coll (BME) Music Ed 1979; Post Grad at Clarion Univ; Grad at Troy St Univ; Vander Cook Coll of Music; *cr:* Sunshine Bible Acad Music Dir 1979-80; Oelrichs Schl Dist Music Dir 1980-81; Hot Spring Schl Dist Dir of Bands 1981-82; Rehobeth HS Music Dir 1986-88; Alleghany-Clarion Vly HS Band Dir 1988-93; Punxsutawney Area Sr HS Band Dir 1993-; *ai:* Marching, Pep, Stage Bands; MENC 1979-; PSEA, NEA 1988-; US Army 1983-; PA Army Natl Guard 1989-, Commander, Bandmaster 28th Div Band; US Army Commendation, 2 Achvmt & Good Conduct Medals; *office:* Punxsutawney Area Sr HS 450 N Findley St Punxsutawney PA 15767

BRAZIL, ERA BUCHANAN, English Language Dev Teacher; *b:* Fayetteville, TN; *c:* Jeanera Brazil Lowry, Paula B., Leslie T. III; *ed:* Tuskegee Univ (BS) Scndry Ed, Eng 1955; Studies Akron Univ for MS; 20 Credit Hrs OH St Univ; 35 Credit Hrs Cleveland Bd of Ed; 10 Credit Hrs Yongstown St Univ; *cr:* C. J. Johnson HS Tchr 1955-56; Tuskegee Inst HS Tchr 1956-59; Cleveland Pub Schls Tchr 1962-; *ai:* Young Scholars Club Adv; TASC Comm Mem; Enrichment Fund; Schl Climate Comm; Grantwriter; NCTE 1980-; AFT 1962-; Tchng Eng to Speakers of Foreign Lang 1978-; Phi Delta Kappa 1985-; Alpha Kappa Alpha 1987-; Oxford Elem Schl Neighbors 1972-; Glad Learning Ctr 1982-, Adult Tchr; YWCA Hillcrest Bd 1982-; HS Prin Awd 1990, 1994-95; Bp Amer Partnership Svc Awd 1991; Inspirational Tchr of Yr Awd 1992; Svc Awd to Biling Stdnts 1985; Cleveland Fdn Educl Fund Grant Awd 1989; Appreciation Career Fair Expo Cert 1994-95; *office:* Lincoln West HS 3202 w 30th St Cleveland OH 44109*

BRAZILL, JAMES EDWARD, Physical Education Teacher; *b:* Trenton, NJ; *m:* Deborah M.; *c:* James, Michael; *ed:* West Chester Univ (BS) Hlth, PE 1975, (MS) PE 1983; 18 Addl Credit Hrs Ed Courses; *cr:* Salesianum Schl PE Tchr 1975-; *ai:* Head Ftbl Coach; Yth Phys Fitness Adv; Counciling Team; DIFCA 1985-, Ofcr; Cath Schls Assn 1990-; Touch Love Awd 1994-95.

BREAULT, MARY ANN, Math Teacher; *b:* Clinton, MA; *ed:* Emmanuel Coll (AB) Chem 1971; Lowell Technological Inst (MMT) Math 1974; Anna Maria Coll (MA) Cnslng Psych 1976, (CAGS) Cnslng Psych 1978; Univ of CT (PHD) Ed Psy, Math 1981; *cr:* St Josephs Schl Grd 2 Tchr 1968-69; Northboro MS Grds 7-8 Tchr 1969-; Anna Maria Coll Assoc Prof Psych 1982-; Pvt Practice Psychologist 1971-; *ai:* NMS Mutual Respect Comm Guide; Crisis Team; Stdnts Helping Stdnts Prgm 1980-; NEA, MTA 1969-; ACS 1968-75; Psych Advy Bd 1985-; Northborough Yth Commission 2 Yrs; People Partnership 1995-; MA St Portfolio Assessment Group 1993-; MA St Portfolio Grant for NMS 1995-; *office:* Northborough MS 145 Lincoln St Northborough MA 01532

BRECHT, LINDA JEAN, Fourth Grade Teacher; *b:* Greensburg, PA; *ed:* Univ of Pittsburgh-Johnstown (BS) Elem Ed 1986; Duquesne Univ (MED) Spec Ed 1991; Univ of Pittsburgh (MED) Elem Math Ed 1995; *cr:* St Paul Elem Schl Fourth Grd Tchr 1986-88; Franklin Regnl Schl Dist Fourth Grd Tchr 1988-; *ai:* Instrl Software, Math Curr Comms; Dist Chprsn United Way Campaign Drive; NEA 1988-; United Way Franklin Area 1993-, Bd of Dir, Sec; *office:* Sloan Elem Schl 4121 Sardis Rd Murrysville PA 15668

BRECKEL, JILL, US History & Government Tchr; *b:* Utica, NY; *ed:* Elmira coll (BA) Liberal Arts 1969; Colgate Univ (MAT) Soc Stud 1974; Utica Coll of Syracuse Univ; *cr:* Whitesbor Cntrl Schl Soc Stud Tchr 1969-; *ai:* Chm Whitesboro Tchrs Assn Schlsp Comm, Fac Cncl; AFt, NY St Unified Tchrs 1970-; Moravian Church, Life, Altar Chair, Women's Fellowship Outreach, Tchng; Rotary Intnl Outstanding Educator 1985, 1992-93; 1993 Observer-Dispatch, All Star Tchr of Yr, Fellowships Freedom Fnd, Natl Sci Fnd, NY St Cncl Hum; *office:* Whitesboro HS Rt 291 Marcy NY 13403

BRECKHEIMER, CHARLES THOMAS, Chemistry Teacher; *b:* Syracuse, NY; *m:* Carol A. Williams; *c:* Katherine, Elizabeth; *ed:* MIT (BS) Chem 1966; Cornell Univ (MS) Chem 1969, (MAT) Tchng, Bio 1969; *cr:* Peace Corps Comm Dev, Tchng 1969-71; Ithaca HS Tchng 1971-; *ai:* Environmental Awareness Club Adv; NEA 1971-; Dryden United Way 1980-, Pres; Dryden Footlighters 1975-, Pres, Phoebe Awd; Tompkins Cty Trust Co Awd for Excl 1991; *office:* Ithaca HS 1401 N Cayuga St Ithaca NY 14850

BREDICE, RICHARD FRANK, Mathematics Teacher; *b:* Torrington, CT; *m:* Susan Leffingwell; *ed:* Cntrl CT St Univ (BA) Math 1968, (MA) Ed 1973; *cr:* Torrington HS Math Tchr 1969-; *ai:* NEA, NCTM, ATOMIC; *office:* Torrington HS Major Besse Dr Torrington CT 06790

BREDL, DAVID M., Jr High Science Teacher; *b:* Pittsburgh, PA; *m:* Ginny Whippo; *c:* Christopher, Colon, Madison; *ed:* Slippery Rock Univ (BS) Ed 1976; Westminster Coll (BS) Bio 1981; Youngstown St Univ (AS) Electrical Engrng 1986; *cr:* Mohawk HS Jr HS Sci Tchr 1976-; *ai:* Girls' Cross Cntry, Track Coach; PSEA, NEA 1976-; *office:* Mohawk Area Schl Dist Mohawk School Rd Bessemer PA 16112

BREEGER, CHRIS ANN A., Adv Chemistry Teacher; *b:* Jeannette, PA; *ed:* Clarion Univ of PA (BS) Chem, General Sci & Ed 1989; Univ of Pittsburg (MS) Environmental Chem 1998; Univ of VA 3 Grad Credit Hrs Ed; Wilkes Univ 3 Grad Credit Hrs Comp; *cr:* Stonewall Jackson MS Phys Sci, Life Sci & Earth Sci Tchr 1990-93; Norwin HS Advanced Chem Tchr 1993-; *ai:* Interact Spon; PA Jr Acad of Sci Spon & Judge; Norwin Fac Advy Bd Comm Mem; Earth Day Coord; Norwin Ed Assn & PSEA 1990-; NSTA 1993-; Amer Chem Soc 1993-; Norwin Rotary 1995-, Appreciation Awd for Svc Above Self; KDKA Thanks to Tchrs Nom 1995; *office:* Norwin Sr HS 251 Mcmahon Dr North Huntingdon PA 15642

BREEN, DAVID CHRISTOPHER, Third Grade Teacher; *b:* Hartford, CT; *m:* Irene Rubbins; *c:* Sarah I., Callie H., Julianna W., Emma R.; *ed:* Boston Univ (BS) Commnctn 1970; Tchng Cert; *cr:* Tisbury Schl 2nd Grd Tchr 1974-79; Neshobe Schl 2nd-3rd & 6th Grd Tchr 1980-; *ai:* 5th-6th Grd Girls Bsktbl Coach; Family Fun Night Coord; Bd of Dirs of Childrens Growth Co; NEA 1984-; Big Brother Big Sister Org 1977-79, Founder; Town Civil Servant 1985-, Justice of Peace; *office:* Neshobe Elem Schl RR 3 Box 3215 Brandon VT 05733

BREEN, KATHLEEN HOLLAND, English & Amer History Teacher; *b:* Lowell, MA; *m:* Philip John; *c:* Philip, Joseph, John; *ed:* U MA at Lowell (BA) Eng 1966; Fitchburg St (MED) Ed 1990; 60+ Credit Hrs Post Grad Stud; *cr:* Billerica HS Tchr 1966-; *ai:* Lit Magazine Adv; NCTE 1966-; MCE 1994-; *home:* 28 Wellesley Ave Lowell MA 01851

BREESE, MARLISSA MARIE, Social Studies Teacher; *b:* Dayton, OH; *m:* Bradley D.; *c:* Alexis; *ed:* Wright St Univ (BS) Sec Ed Soc Stud & Comps 1986; Univ of Dayton (MS) Supervision 1992; *cr:* Bellbrook HS Soc Stud Tchr 1986-; *ai:* Chrldng & Class Adv; SEA, OEA & NEA 1987-; *office:* Bellbrook HS 3491 Upper Bellbrook Rd Bellbrook OH 45305

BREFFITT, STEVEN WAYNE, Bands Director; *b:* Abington, PA; *m:* Brenda; *c:* Amanda, Molly; *ed:* Millersville Univ (BS) Elem Ed 1971; Univ of DE (MED) 1987; Coursework Needed Music Cert St of DE; *cr:* George Read MS 5th Grd Tchr 1971-72; Wilmington Manor Elem Schl 5th Grd Tchr 1972-73; Gunning Bedford MS Band Dir 1973-; *ai:* Dept Chm; Former Ftbl, Bsktbl Coach; Host Colonial Band Festival; Asst Site Coord Summer Schl; DSEA; NEA; NCCEA; MENC; DMEA; Oaklands Pool Assn, Suburban Swim League, Newark HS Band Boosters, Newark HS Swimming Booster, Pres; US Swimming, Ofcl; Colonial Schl Dist Tchr of Yr 1985.

BREHM, KRISTEN MARIE, English & ESL Teacher; *b:* Brooklyn, NY; *ed:* Coll of Staten Island (BA) Eng 1991; NY Univ (MA) TESOL 1994; *cr:* Ft Hamilton HS Eng, ESL Tchr 1991-.

BREHMER, CARL R., Science Teacher; *b:* Gary, IN; *ed:* Ball St Univ (BA) Bio & Chem 1960; AZ St Univ (MA) Bio & Ed 1962; Attnd San Jose St Coll, Fullerton St Coll, Immaculate Heart Coll, Pasadena City Coll, Univ of Southern CA, UCLA, Sweet Briar Coll, Beaver Coll, Philadelphia Coll of Textiles, Sci & Villanova Univ; *cr:* AZ St Univ Grad Asst & Life Scis Tchr 1960-62; New Schl Dist Jr High Sci Tchr 1962-63; Te Schl Dist HS Sci Tchr & Sci Dept Chm 1963-67; Polytechnic Sci Stu Chem & Phys Sci Tchr 1967-71; Abington Friends Schl 6th- Sci Dept Chair & Sci Tchr 1971-82; Philadlephia Pub Schls Jr & S Tchr, Sci Facilitator & Parkway Pgm 1982-; *ai:* Camp Wassoke Abington Friends Schl Summer Enrichment Pgm 1972, 1973 & Penn Ctr Acad 1982; Meadowlane Day Camp 1983; Cntr for Acad Talented Yth 1986-93; Coll of Fast Paced Scis Acad Chm 1988-92 Coll of Phiadlephia Adj Fac Mem 1990 & 1992; Hughes Fndtn Pgm 1991; Manor Jr Coll Adj Fac Mem 1993; Org & Executed Trips Tchrs Through PECO Energy 1988-94; Philadelphia Scndry Sc Assn, Conf Org 1984-, Treas, VP & Pres (Twice); Philadelphia Ar Sci Tchrs Assn; Energy Ed Advy Cncl, Policy Task Force 1985-, Sc Task Force Vice Chm 1983-85, Continuing Ed Task Force Vi 1985-86; Continuing Ed Task Force Chm 1986-93, Exec Comm 199 Chemical Soc; NSTA, Mem of Local Arangements Comm 19 Debates on Energy 1980-, Judge; PA Jr Acad of Sci 1982-, Judg 1982-93, Org & Presenter, Electricity & Nuclear Merit Badges; Conf for Sci, Math & Soc Sci Tchrs 1986-93, Chm & Org; LaS Environmental Day 1990-95, Presenter; Sci & Educl Group, Conventions & Inservice Days, Presenter; Sci Explorer, Adv; Frank Tchr Advy Bd; Philadelphia Zoo Tchr Advy Group; Nu Publications; Regular Contributor to Curr Materials & Period Energy Ed Advy Cncl & the Philadelphia Scndry Sci Tchrs Instrumental in Bringing Bernard Harris the First Africa Amer A to Walk in Space to Philadelphia Pub Schls Stdnts 1995; *hom* Cinnaminson St Philadelphia PA 19128*

BREIMAN, ROBYN HOPE, Director; *b:* Brooklyn, NY; *m:* Wi Scannella; *c:* Jordan Scannella; *ed:* SUNY at Binghamton (BA) Er Xavier Univ (MED) Montessori Ed 1975; Montessori Cer Montessori Soc Pre-Primary 3-6 1975, Elem 6-9 1981, Elem 6-12 1 The New Schl 6-9 Grd Tchr 1979-82, (-12 Grd Head Tchr 1982- 1986-; Center for Montessori Tchr Ed Fac 1986-; *ai:* Co Montessori Schls, Tchrs, Tchr in Trng; Amer Montessori Soc Presenter at Natl Conf; *office:* New Schl 3 Burton Woods Ln Ci OH 45229

BREINDEL, RENEE POLLACK, Spanish Teacher; *b:* Bronx, Mark; *c:* Matthew, Eric; *ed:* St Univ of NY at Albany (BA) Span & Ed 1973; 30 Credit Hrs Grad Work at St Univ of NY at Oswego & S Univ; *cr:* Central Square Schls Span Tchr 1973-79; West Genese Span Tchr 1982-85; North Syracuse Schls Span Tchr 1986-; *a* Planning Team 2 Yrs; Respect Comm Mem; Dist Character Ed Ethic Comm; NSUT 1973-; North Syracuse Ed Assn; AFT; *office* Syracuse Jr HS 5353 W Taft Rd North Syracuse NY 13212

BREITENBACH, DEBORAH JONES, English Teacher; *b:* Sin Malaysia; *m:* John C. Jr.; *c:* Katie, John III; *ed:* Bucknell Univ (Ed 1976; St Rose Univ (MA) Eng Lit 1983; *cr:* Voorhees HS E 1977-79; Ticonderoga HS Eng Tchr 1979-; *ai:* Natl Honor Societ Bowl & HS Effective Schl Work Building Leadership Teams Helping Stdnts Adv; Amer Legion Oratorical Contest Coord; Tico Tchrs Assn 1979-; NY St Tchr of Excl 1987; Amer Legion Cert 1986, 1988, 1990-91; Eng Dept Chrprsn 1988-90; AP Reader 1994 Ticonderoga H S Calkins Pl Ticonderoga NY 12883

BREITIGAM, JULIE ANN, Health & Physical Ed Tchr; *b:* Blufft *ed:* Ohio St Univ (BA) PE & Hlth 1988; *cr:* Lakota HS Hlth & PE 1 Allen East HS Hlth & PE Tchr 1990-; *ai:* Var Vlybl Coach; NEA Var Bsktbl Coach 1994-95 St Tournaments Division 4; *office:* All HS 105 N Washington St Lafayette OH 45854

BREMER, KAREN MAOLA, 8th Grd Language Arts Teacher; Liverpool, OH; *m:* William F. Jr.; *ed:* Kent St Univ (BSEd) Eng 1968, (MED) His 1972; Attnd Coll of Mt St Joseph, Akron Univ, A Univ; *cr:* Canton City Schls Horace Mann Elem Lang & Arts Tchr 1 Canton City Schls Crenshaw Jr High Rdng Tchr 1972-76; Cant Schls Jr High Lang Arts Tchr 1976-; *ai:* Lang Arts Dept Chprsn Sou NEA 1968-; OH Ed Assn 1968-; Canton Prof Edctrs Assn 1968-; Assn 1994-; Canton City Schl Lang Arts Grant 1969; Canton Ci Mentor Tchr Pgm 1989-91; Ameritech Impact II Grant 1991; *office* Souers MS 2800 13th St SW Canton OH 44710

BRENDEL, JANE ANNE, Social Studies & Lit Tchr; *b:* Queens, Suffolk Cty Comm Coll (AA) Lbrl Arts 1975; C. W. Post Ctr (B 1977; Southampton Coll (MS) Rdng 1983-; Paralegal Cert Adelph *cr:* Our Lady of Mercy Schl Soc Stud, Lit Tchr 1981-; *office:* Our L Mercy Schl 520 S Oyster Bay Rd Hicksville NY 11801

BRENER, ELLEN HOCK, Guidance Counselor; *b:* New York, Bruce J.; *c:* Robert, Deborah, Richard; *ed:* UCLA (BA) Ed, Psych Seton Hall Univ (MA) Counseling 1984; *cr:* Westwood Pub Sch 1962-66; Columbia HS Cnslr 1987-; Millburn HS Cnslr 1988 NACAC, NJACAC, ECGA, MASA 1988-; NJ Ctr for Family Stud Bd, Sec 1995-; Multiple Sclerosis Fnd 1990-93, Bd; *office:* Millburn 462 Millburn Ave Millburn NJ 07041

BRENKUS, MARILYN RUNO, Music Teacher; *b:* Cleveland, Michael Brenkus (dec); *c:* Martha Lulovics, Mary Ellen, Micha Ursuline Coll (BS) Music Ed 1961; 15 Hrs Post Grad at Case W Reserve; *cr:* Transfiguration Music Tchr 1961-62; Nazareth Acad Tchr 1962-65; Nathan Hale Music Tchr 1965-66; Collinwood Mus 1966-69; Saint Stanislaus Music Tchr 1987-; *office:* St Stanislaus Schl 6615 Forman Ave Cleveland OH 44105

BRENNA, JUDY HAEFNER, English Teacher; *b:* Williamsville, Robert L. Jr.; *c:* Elizabeth, Robert III; *ed:* SUNY Coll at Buffalo (1973, (MS) Ed 1981; *cr:* Cheektowaga Cntrl HS Tutorial Wksh 1977-82; Thomas MS Eng Tchr 1983-; *ai:* Standards & Assessment AFT, NEA, NYSUT 1977-; Webster Tchrs Assn 1983-; *office:* Thom 800 Five Mile Line Webster NY 14580

BRENNAN, CAROL J., MS English Teacher & Team Ldr; *b:* Sidne *ed:* Trenton St Coll (BA) Elem Ed 1964; Fairfield Univ (MA) Ed 19 Yr Rdng & Writing 1986; *cr:* Oradell Schl Kndgtn Tchr 1964-65; Egg Harbor Schl Tchr 1968; Trumbull Schl Kndgtn Tchr 1968-71, Tchr 1971-77, 5th Grd Tchr 1977-87, 6th-8th Grd Lang Arts Tchr *ai:* 6th Grd Team Ldr & Lit Magazine 1987-; Newspaper Adv 1988 Arts Week Coord 1987-91; NEA, CEA & TEA 1968-; NCTE 1986-; 1988-; Condominium Assn, Pres 1985-86; Sweet Adelines, Pres 19 Trumbull Lit Arts Competitian, Coord & Judge 1988-91; Various A Pub; Numerous Wkshps in Rdng & Writing; *office:* Madison M S Madison Ave Trumbull CT 06611*

BRENNAN, CHARLES, Sixth Grade Teacher; *b:* Bryn Mawr, P Georgetown U (BA) Eng 1964; Immaculata Coll El Ed Permaner 1978; Villanova Univ 30 Grad Credits Eng; *cr:* St Monica Schl Grd 1965-70, Grd 4 Tchr 1970-72, Grd 6, Grd 7-8 Soc Stud, Cmptr Tchr *ai:* Cmptr, Soc Stud Coord; Write, Produce, Direct Christmas NCEA; Distngd Cath Edctr Philadelphia Archdiocese 1990; *offi* Monica Schl 601 1st Ave Berwyn PA 19312*

BRENNAN, CORINNE A. (BUECHS), 6th Grade Teacher; *b:* B MA; *m:* George Patrick; *ed:* Bridgewater St Coll (BS) Elem Ed 198 Morse Pond Schl 6th Grd Tchr 1988-; *ai:* Team Ldr Responsi Organizing After School Pgm & Representing 6th Grd Tchr & Fac MTA 1988-; NEA 1988-; His Cncl on Ed 1991-; WHSTEP 1992-; P

Work with Area Bus on Safety Film & Tchng Materials; *office:* h Pub Schls Teaticket Hwy Falmouth MA 02540

IAN, CORINNE LUCIER, English Teacher & Supervisor; *b:* , NJ; *m:* Thomas F.; *c:* Thomas, Sarah; *ed:* Coll Misericordia (BA) 1969; Georgian Ct Coll (MA) Curr, Supervision 1988; 8 Credits n St; *cr:* Pt Pleasant Borough HS Fr, Eng Tchr 1969-89, Eng Tchr, 989-; *ai:* Acad Team, Yrbk Adv; NEA, NJEA 1969-; OCEA, ASCD, 1985-; St Gregory's Food Pantry 1990-; St Martha's 1988-, CCD Governors Tchr Recognition Awd 1988; *office:* Point Pleasant n HS Laura Herbert Dr Point Pleasant NJ 08742

IAN, ERIN MARIE, Math Teacher; *b:* Portsmouth, VA; *ed:* Boston A) Math 1992; *cr:* Passaic Vly HS Math Tchr 1992-93; New nce HS Math Tchr 1993-; *ai:* Frosh Girls Bsktbl & Asst Track Soph Class Stu Cncl Adv; NCTM 1991-; NJEA & NEA 1992-; 1993-; *office:* New Providence HS 35 Pioneer Dr New Providence 74

IAN, JAMES JOSEPH, Theology Teacher; *b:* Norristown, PA; *ed:* les Seminary (BA) Philosophy 1985, (MDiv) Theology 1988, (MA) gy 1989; *cr:* Cardinal O'Hara HS Guid Cnslr 1992-93, Tchr 4, Dir Campus Ministry 1994-; *ai:* Band, Sr Prom Moderator; Dept Asst Dir; Peer Ministry Dir; Adult Ed Instr; *office:* Cardinal HS 1701 S Sproul Rd Springfield PA 19064

IAN, KATHRYN KEEPING, High Schl Mathematics Teacher; *b:* eepsie, NY; *m:* Timothy; *c:* Erin, Courtney; *ed:* SUNY at Cortland Ed N-9 1974; 30 Grad Hrs SUNY at New Paltz; Attnd ia-Greene Comm Coll; *cr:* New Paltz Cntrl Schl HS Math Tchr 5; Coxsackie-Athens Cntrl Schl HS Math Tchr 1987-; *ai:* Class, Stu AFS & NHS Adv; Curr & Prof Growth Cncl; AFT & NEA 1974-, kie Athens Tchrs Assn 1987-; Alpha Nu 1992-93; Greenville s Park Comm 1992-; SUNY at New Paltz Ulster Cty Excl in Tchng Awd 1986; *office:* Coxsackie Athens HS 24 Sunset Blvd Coxsackie 051

IAN, LINDA J., Physical Education Teacher; *b:* Bridgehampton, Ithaca Coll (BS) PE 1967; Univ of WI (MS) PE 1968; *cr:* Wallkill Tchr & Coach 1968-; *ai:* Modified Soccer & Sftbl Coach; Winter urals; NYSTA 1968-; AAPHER 1968-; WMBA 1970-; *office:* l MS Rt 208 Wallkill NY 12589*

IAN, MARGARET M., English Teacher; *b:* Up Montclair, NJ; *ed:* otion Coll (BA) Eng & His 1993; Courses in Environmental Ed; *cr:* orris Cntrl HS Eng Tchr 1985-; *ai:* Girls Track & Field Asst & Head 4 Yrs; Cross Cntry Head Coach 6 Yrs; Soccer Coach 1 Yr; mental Club & NHS Adv 3 Yrs; Asst Drama Dir 2 Yrs; NEA 1989-; 1989-; NCTE; Geraldine Dodge Fndtn Grant 1995.*

IAN, MARK ETIENNE, Dean of Special Education; *b:* ence, RI; *m:* Blanca Pena; *ed:* Columbia Univ (BA) Art Hist 1982; oll of NY (MS) Elem Ed 1991; 30 Addtl Credit Hrs; *cr:* Macomb Jr th Tchr 1987-91, Art Tchr 1991-94, Dean Spec Ed 1994-; *ai:* Schl Mngmt Comm Chm; AFT 1987-; Bronx Rookie Tchr of Yr Awd Most Influential Tchr Aws 1993; IMB Rewarding Success Grant *office:* Alexander Macombs Jr HS 82 1700 Macombs Rd Bronx NY

IAN, MARYELLEN FEELEY, 5th Grd Teacher & Asst Prin; *b:* ore, MD; *m:* Edward Robert; *c:* Deirdre Lawrence, Corinne an, T. Conor; *ed:* Coll of Notre Dame (BA) Elem Ed 1970; Loyola MED); 18 Post Grad Credits Towson St Univ; *cr:* Blessed Sacrament chr 1965-68; C&P Telephone Co Educl Rep 1968-73; Hereford HS 979-89; Immaculate Conception Schl Tchr 1989-; *ai:* Balto Co Assn 1979-89, Schl Rep 1989-91; *office:* Immaculate Conception 2 Ware Ave Baltimore MD 21204*

IAN, ROBERT TIMOTHY, Elem PE Coord & Tchr; *b:* New York Y; *m:* Julie; *c:* Robert Jr., Scott, Sandra, Amy; *ed:* High Point Univ lth & PE 1965; Cortland St PE 1966; Oswego St PE 1967; Syracuse 68-69; Keene St PE 1986; *cr:* Canastota Jr Sr HS Sci Tchr 1965-69; Jr HS Sci Tchr 1969-71; Monadnock Regl Schls Elem PE Tchr *ai:* Cross Cntry Coach; Weight & Fitness Instr; Track & Field NH Interscholastic Athletic Assn St Bd Mem; Swanzey Recreation Fitness Adv; NEA; Natl Fed Interscholastic Coaches Assn, NH s Assn 1990-; NH Coach of Yr Track 1991; Cheshire Cty Sportsman 995 & 1996; Outstanding Coaching 6 Consecutive St Titles 1995; Bldg 1st Place in NE All Natural Championship age 52 1996; *office:* nock Regnl Schls Swanzey Ctr Keene NH 03431*

NEISEN, CLAUDIA (GROGAN), High School English Teacher; *b:* kley, PA; *m:* William C.; *c:* Carol, Mary, William J.; *ed:* Chatham BA) Eng 1964; Post Grad Stud Univ of Pittsburgh, Penn St Univ, Robt s Coll; *cr:* Moon Area Schl Dist Eng Tchr 1964-65; Univ of rgh Asst Dir of Admissions 1965-68; The Allegheny Times Ofc Mgr, 1985-88; Moon Area Schl Dist Information Specialist 1988-91, Eng 991-; *ai:* Class of 1997, Creative Writing Club Spons; Prof Staff ; NCTE, NEA, Western PA Conf Tchrs, Eng 1991-; BSA 1992-95, Comm Mem.

NEMAN, JOSEPHINE HARTMANN, Biology Tchr & Sci Dept *b:* Los Angeles, CA; *m:* David William; *c:* Karin Elise, Mari Dawn nter; *ed:* Coll of Wooster (BA) Bio 1965; 8 Credit Hrs Univ of MD er Bio Inst 1993; 3 Credit Hrs Ecology of the Chesapeake 1995; 25 Hrs Western MD Coll; Attnd Webster Coll St Louis MO, CO St *cr:* Shaw Jr HS 7th Grd Sci Tchr 1965-67; Lexington Jr HS 8th Grd hr 1967-68; Kubasaki Jr HS 9th Grd Sci, Math Tchr 1970; Marycrest , 2nd Yr Bio Tchr 1979; Extended Credit HS Sci, Hlth, Consumer Ed 1980-82; Bishop Mc Namara HS Anatomy, Environmental Sci, Bio Dept Chair 1987-; *ai:* Moderator Environmental Action Comm; Sci o-Coord; Sex Ed Curr Comm; NABT, NSTA, NCEA, MABT, MAST ; Girl Scouts 1950-, Troop Ldr, Svc Unit Rep; Red Cross 1981-87, Aid Instr; Chesapeake Bay Trust for Stream Monitoring, Restoration Grant; *office:* Bishop Mc Namara HS 6800 Marlboro Pike Forestville 0747

NNER, MARY JO (ROTILI), Family & Consumer Science Tchr; *b:* esport, PA; *m:* Robert M.; *ed:* PA St Univ (BS) Individual Family 1974; Univ of MD (ME) Ed & Arts 1986; Working Towards Hlth Cert ssage Therapy Cert; *cr:* Baltimore Cty Schls Tchr 1974-78; Linkletter Stud Lead Tchr 1978-80; Baltimore & Wash DC Theaters Performer oreographer 1977-86; Montgomery Cty Schls Tchr 1978-; *ai:* NEA; A; Phi Upsilon Omicron Honorary 1974; *office:* Paint Branch HS Old Columbia Pike Burtonsville MD 20866

NNER, SCOTT A., 7th Grade English Teacher; *b:* Willkes-Barre, PA; rry Perillo; *c:* Jared, Lindsay; *ed:* East Stroudsburg St (BA) Eng 1973; of MD (BS) Ed 1977; George Washington Univ (MS) Supervision *cr:* Kettering MS Eng Tchr 1977-85; Walker Mill MS 7th Grade E, Eng Tchr 1985-; *ai:* St Peter's Schl Bd; Bannister Swim Team Bd; n Svcs Bsktbl Coach; WSC Soccer Coach; NEA 1978-.

NTIN, LINDA KRISTINE, Fifth Grade Teacher; *b:* Pittsburgh, PA; egis R.; *c:* Brad, Scott; *ed:* California Univ of PA (BS) Elem Ed 1974; St Satellite Prgm; Intermediate Unit Credits; *cr:* Dade Cty Schl Dist Grd Tchr 1974-75; South Fayette Schl Dist Third-Sixth Grds Tchr ; *ai:* NEA 1978-93, Treas; AFT 1993-95; PTG, PTA 1988-; Beverly nts UP Church, Vacation Bible Schl Dir, Deacon, Asst Supt Sunday Schls; Thanks to Tchrs Nom; *office:* South Fayette Elem Schl 2256 Old Oakdale Rd Mc Donald PA 15057

BRESANI, JANE MARIE, Biology Tchr & Science Chprsn; *b:* Merrick, NY; *m:* Fred; *c:* Nicholas, Paul, Aimie; *ed:* Rutgers Univ (BA) Bio 1978; 8 Grad Hrs Bio; *cr:* Edgewood Sr HS Bio Tchr 1978-; *ai:* JV Sftbl Coach 1979-81; NEA 1980-; NJEA 1981-; NJSSIA 1986-; Woodbury Little League 1991-, Fundraiser, Coach; Woodbury Soccer Club 1991-, Fundraiser, Coach; *home:* 22 S Jackson St Woodbury NJ 08096

BRESLIN, DEBORAH KAY, Mathematics Teacher; *b:* Lubbock, TX; *ed:* TX Chrstn Univ (BS) Math 1988; Addl 30 Hrs Masters Equivalency in Ed, Math & Tech at Grad Level; *cr:* Yeshiva HS Anatomy Tchr 1990-91; Richard Montgomery HS Math Tchr 1991-; *ai:* Class of 1999 Spon; Peer Mediation Comm; NEA, MCEA 1991-; *office:* Richard Montgomery HS 250 Richard Montgomery Dr Rockville MD 20852

BRESNAHAN, DAVID CHARLES, Band Director; *b:* Manchester, NH; *m:* Lorraine M.; *ed:* Plymouth St Coll (BS) Music Ed 1974; *cr:* Manchester Pub Schls Elem Music Tchr 1974-76; Crownpoint HS 7-12 Grds Instrumental Music Tchr 1976-77; Sanborn Reg HS Grds 7-12 Instrumental Music Tchr 9177-78; Manchester Pub Schls Grds 7-12 Instrumental Music Tchr 1978-; *ai:* MENC, NEA 1974-; NHBDA 1993-, Pres; NH Arts Cncl, Governor's Awd for Ed; *office:* Manchester Central HS 207 Lowell St Manchester NH 03104

BRESNAHAN, MAUREEN WALSH, Student Assistance Counselor; *b:* New York, NY; *m:* Jeremiah P.; *c:* Tom, Laura Liminski, Kevin, Courtney, Maureen; *ed:* SUNY of New Paltz (BB) Speech, Hearing 1976; Rutgers Univ (MS) Comm Disorders 1983; Certified Alcohol & Drug Cnslr 1986; Certified Psychosynthesis Therapist 1987; *cr:* Phillipsburg Schl System Speech, Lang Specialist 1976-80; Parsippany Schl System Speech, Lang Specialist 1980-88; Montville Schl System Stu Assistance Cnslr 1988-; *ai:* Peer Leadership, Cultural Diversity Prgm Adv; NEA 1977-; NJAAODC 1986-; NJASAP 1987-; HS & MS Core Team Trng Grant; *office:* Montville HS 100 Horseneck Rd Montville NJ 07045

BRESSI, EUGENE RICHARD, 8th Grade Mathematics Teacher; *b:* Canton, OH; *m:* Joanne Baum; *c:* Eugene, Daniel; *ed:* Walsh Univ (BA) Liberal Arts 1967; Malone Coll Grad Ed Classes; *cr:* Sandy Valley 5th Grd Tchr 1967-68, 8th Grd Lang Arts, Math Tchr 1968-; *ai:* SVEA, OEA, NEA 1967-; Prof Ftbl Hall of Fame, Vol; *office:* Sandy Valley Jr Sr HS 5362 St Rt 183 NE Magnolia OH 44643

BRETHAUER, ALMA STOELTING, 10th Grade Health Educator; *b:* Sheboygan, WI; *m:* David H.; *c:* Peter Lincoln, James Fredrick; *ed:* Univ of WI at Madison (BS) Hlth & PE 1958; Wester Chester Univ (MED) PE 1969; 45 Addl Hrs in Health, Drug Ed; *cr:* West Milwaukee HS PE Edctr 1958-60; Wester Chester Univ Dance Edctr 1968-70; Phoenixville Area Schl Dist Hlth, PE Edctr 1970-; *ai:* SADD; NEA 1970-, Women's Ldrshp Trng Prgm Trainer, Orgnl Analysis Skills Cadre 1993; PSEA 1970-, Region Sec 1983-88, Women's Ldrshp Trng Prgm Trainer 1983-; PAEA 1970-, Pres 1981-86; Amer Schl Hlth Assn 1987-; PA Schl Hlth Assn 1987-, Historian 1993-; AAHPERD 1987-; Chester Cty Schl Hlth Ed Coalition 1983-; Delta Kappa Gamma1990-, Pres 1996; Chester Cty Cncl of Addictive Diseases 1991-, Pres 1996; Chester Cty Consultation & Ed Comm of Mental Hlth, Retardation Bd 1986-; AAUW 1993-; PA Horticulture Soc Philadelphia Flower Show 1982-, Vol; Mc Donald's LPGA Championship 1981-, Vol; Mid Sts Evaluation Comm 1987-; Phoenixville Acad Boosters Club 1988-; Who's Who in Prof & Exec Woman 1987; 10,000 Notable Amer Women; Who's Who in Amer Ed 1992-93; *office:* Phoenixville Area HS Gay St & City Line Ave Phoenixville PA 19460*

BRETHERICK, SHARON, Third Grade Teacher; *b:* Shamokin, PA; *c:* Jennifer, Robyn; *ed:* West Chester Univ (BS) Elem Ed 1972; Masters Equiv Grad Credits Widner Univ, Temple Univ; *cr:* Rose Tree Elem Schl Third Grd Tchr 24 Yrs; *ai:* Elem Schl Sci Coord 20 Yrs; PSEA 1972-; NEA 1992-; *office:* Rose Tree Elem Schl 1101 First Ave Media PA 19063

BRETON, ELEANOR VIRGINIA, Office Assistant & Tutor; *b:* Putnam, CT; *ed:* Dincesan Tchrs Coll (BA) Ed 1954; Fairfield Univ (MA) Ed 1963; Catechist Training Inservice; *cr:* St Anthony Schl Grd 1 Tchr 1954-56; Assumption Schl Grd 1 Tchr 1956-62; St Mary Schl 2-3 Grd Tchr 1965-85; All Hallows Schl K-4 Tutor, Office Asst 1985-, Summer Rdng Clinics 8 Yrs; *ai:* Parish Catechetical Ministry Rel Ed Tutoring; 20 Yrs Svc Recognition 1995; NCEA 1986-; *office:* Plainfield Catholic Schl 120 Prospect St Moosup CT 06354

BRETSCH, SUSAN C., Fourth Grade Teacher; *b:* Buffalo, NY; *ed:* St Univ Coll at Potsdam (BA) Elem Ed 1969; St Univ Coll at New Paltz (MS) Elem Ed 1973; 27 Addl Grad Credits; *cr:* Brinckerhoff Elem Schl 2nd Grd Tchr 1969-76, 3rd Grd Tchr 1977-81, 4th Grd Tchr 1982-; *ai:* Mentor Prgm; Cooperating Tchr for Stu Tchrs SUNY New Paltz, Mt Saint Mary's Coll; ESPET Rep; AFT, WCT 1990-; NYSUT 1969-; Fishkill United Meth Church 1992-, Admin Bd Mem; Fishkill Historical Soc 1995-, Trustee; Brinckerhoff PTA 1969-; Lunch Box Soup Kitchen 1992-, Part-time Vol; *office:* Brinckerhoff Elem Schl 10 Wedgewood Rd Fishkill NY 12524

BRETT, JOCELYN (MASLO), German & English Teacher; *b:* Johnstown, PA; *m:* David; *c:* Benjamin, Jonathan; *ed:* Univ of Pittsburgh at Johnstown (BA) Scndry Ed 1974; *cr:* BMHS Tchr 1983-; *ai:* Ger Club Adv; NCTA 1986-; Tchr Recognition Awd 1991; St Vincent Coll Tchr Recognition Awd 1995-; *office:* Bishop Mc Cort High School 25 Osborne St Johnstown PA 15905

BRETZIUS, DAVID CHARLES, Music Specialist; *b:* Pottsville, PA; *m:* Karen Sebastian; *c:* Krista, Matthew; *ed:* West Chester Univ (BS) Music Ed 1976, (MM) Music Ed 1981; 18 Addl Grad Credits; *cr:* Phoenixville Area Schl Dist Vocal Music K-5 Grd Tchr 1976-; *ai:* Dist Music Coord; Mentor Tchr; Elem Choral Dir; MENC, PMEA, PSEA 1976-; Phi Mu Alpha Sinfonia 1975-; First United Meth Church 1980-, Organist, Music Minister; Hymn Tune Pub; *office:* Barkley Elem Schl 320 2nd Ave Phoenixville PA 19460*

BREUER, STEPHEN, Mathematics Instructor; *b:* Geneva, NY; *m:* Gretchen Galliher; *c:* Brian, Kevin; *ed:* Saint Bonaventure Univ (BS) Math 1964; Attnd Colgate Univ & SUNY at Brockport; *cr:* Penn Yan MS Jr HS Math Tchr 1964-66; Hamilton HS Math Tchr 1966-67; Penn Yan MS Jr HS Math Tchr 1967-91; Penn Yan Acad Sr HS Math Tchr 1991-; *ai:* Ftbl & Bsktbl Coach; Math Dept Chm; Bldng Mgmt Team; Kueka Coll Tchr; NYSTA; NEA; ACME; Fire Dept 22 Yrs; Little League Coach 25 Yrs; Elks Club 18 Yrs, Youth Act Chm; AMTNYS; NCTM; Brockport Course I, II, III Integration; Brockport Real Wolrd Math 2 Yrs.

BREUKER, JOHN,JR., Latin Teacher; *b:* Muskegon, MI; *m:* Christine L. Garveline; *c:* John Patrick, Jamieson David; *ed:* Calvin Coll (BA) Latin, Math 1960; Univ of MI (MA) Scndry Ed 1964; Univ of IA (MA) Latin 1967; OH St Univ PHD Classics Coursework Completed; *cr:* Christian HS Latin Tchr 1960-65; Ashland Coll Asst Prof of Classics 1967-72; Western Reserve Acad Latin Tchr 1972-; *ai:* Acad Affairs, Admissions, Coll Guidance Comms; OH Classical Conf 1967-, Treas, VP, Pres; Classical Assn of Mid West, South 1960-, St VP, Regnl VP; Vergilian Soc 1967-, Trustee 1996-; Calvin Coll, Seminary, Trustee 1982-88; Fulbright Hays Summer Fellow 1969; Rdr ETS Advanced Placement Latin Exams 1983, 1987, 1994; Fac NEH 1986; Basic Ed Summer Fellow 1987; Sabbatical Awd 1987-88; *office:* Western Reserve Acad 115 College St Hudson OH 44236

BREW, STACIE JOY, Secondary English Teacher; *b:* Patchogue, NY; *ed:* Averett Coll (BA) Ed, NK-12 Art, 7-12 Eng 1985; *cr:* Sachem Central Schls K-12 Sub Tchr 1988-90; Smithtown Chrstn Schl Scndry Eng Tchr 1990-; *ai:* NHS Fac Adv Bd; Dramatic, Pub Speaking Coach; ACSI 1990-; *office:* Smithtown Chrstn Schl Higbie Dr Smithtown NY 11787*

BREWER, BEVERLY LYNN, 6th Grade Teacher; *b:* Middletown, OH; *ed:* Miami Univ (BA) Elem Ed 1978; 30 Grad Hrs Miami Univ; *cr:* Jefferson Elem & Middletown City Schls 1st Grd Tchr 1978-80, 6th Grd Tchr 1980-95; Creekview Elem & Middletown Schls 6th Grd Tchr 1995-; *ai:* Safety Patrol Adv; Bus Duty Contract; Creative Writing Class; Bldg & Dist Level, Curr & Awds Comm; NEA 1978-; OEA & MTA 1978-; ASCD 1987-; PDK 1986-; Middletown Monroe Youth Bsktbl League 1981-85, Sec & Treas; Instrumental in Writing Several Grants; Jennings Schlr; Crystal Apple Awd & Ashland Oil Tchr Nom; *office:* Creekview Elem Schl 301 Loretta Dr Middletown OH 45044

BREWER, EDWARD ALLAN, 7th Grade Soc Studies Teacher; *b:* Johnson City, NY; *c:* Michelle, Jennifer Brewer Mangino; *ed:* SUC at Cortland (MS) Scndry Soc Stud 1974; *cr:* Union-Endicott HS SS Tchr 1969-70; Hancock Cntrl Schl Spec Ed Tchr 1970-71; Town of Union Dept of Soc Svcs Examiner 1971-72; Union-Endicott Pub Schls SS Tchr 1972-; *ai:* Endicott Tchrs Assn Bldg Rep; Broome Cty Cncl for Soc Stud, NY St for Soc Stud 1992-; First Tchr Awded Lifetime Mbrshp PTSA; *office:* Jennie F Snapp MS 101 S Loder Ave Endicott NY 13760

BREWER, JANICE NICKENS, French Teacher; *b:* Newark, NJ; *m:* Ralph J.; *c:* Rhett K., Monique; *ed:* Montclair St Coll (BA) Fr 1962; Kean Coll (MA) Admin, Supervision 1980; Addl 9 Credit Hrs Guid; *cr:* Elizabeth HS Levels I-IV Fr Tchr 1962-; *ai:* Stu Cncl, Fr Hnr Soc Adv; Frgn Lang Curr Revision Comm; AFT 1963-; NEA, NJEA 1988-; NASAA 1980-; NDEA Grant Fr Lang Stud Univ of Pittsburgh 1963, Fr Inst for Tchrs of Fr 1964; *office:* Elizabeth HS 600 Pearl St Elizabeth NJ 07202

BREWER, MARILYN SUE, Spanish Teacher; *b:* Beaver Falls, PA; *ed:* OH St Univ (BS) Ed 1970; San Jose St Univ (MA) Admin & Supervision Ed 1985; *cr:* Heinold Jr High Span & Eng Tchr 1970-72; Delhi Jr High Span & Fr Tchr 1972-73; Oak Hills HS Span & Fr Tchr 1973-; *ai:* Past Span Club Adv; Past Span Lang Dist Dept Head; Amer Cancer Soc Vol 1975-; Hamilton Co Textbook Selection Comm Several Times During Tchng Career; Steering Comm for North Central Evaluation.*

BREWER, MARK RICHARD, 7th-8th Grd Soc Stud Teacher; *b:* Worcester, MA; *m:* Laurie Facciarossa; *c:* Nicholas, Madeline; *ed:* Gloucester Cty Coll (AA) Lbrl Arts 1981; Glassboro St Rowan Coll (BA) Scndry Ed 1984; Temple Univ (MA) US His 1991; *cr:* Oak Knoll Soc Stud Tchr 1984-; *ai:* Drama Dir; AFT 1984-; NEA 1984-; Numerous Articles Pub; *office:* Oak Knoll Schl Bodine Ave Williamstown NJ 08094*

BREWER, MARTIN JOHN, English Teacher; *b:* Rustington, England; *ed:* Univ of Ulster (BA) Eng 1984; W Sussex Inst (PACE) Eng, Drama; W. Sussex Inst of Higher Ed PACE Eng, Drama 1985; London Acad of Music, Dramatic Arts Gold Awd Honor 1989; *cr:* The Littlehampton Comm Schl Eng Tchr, Head of Drama 1986-91; St Thomas Aquinas Eng Tchr, Coach 1991-; *ai:* Var Girls Soccer, Tennis Coach; NHIAA Soccer Coach of Yr 1993; Foster Daily Democrat Soccer Coach of Yr 1993, 1995; *office:* St Thomas Aquinas HS 197 Dover Point Rd Dover NH 03820

BREWER, MARY LOU, History Teacher; *b:* Amarillo, TX; *ed:* North Adams St Coll (BA) His 1967; Westfield St Coll (MA) His 1976; Attnd Springfield, Amer Intnl Colls; Univ of NH Inservice Credit; Univ of San Diego; *cr:* Minnechaug Regnl HS His Tchr 1967-; *ai:* Model Congress, Mock Law Team, MA Stu Govt Day Delegation, Presidential Classroom Adv; Cmptr, 3 Schl MELM Partnership Comms; NEA, MA, Minnechaug Tchrs Assns, Western MA Soc Stud Cncl 1967-; NCTE; Monson Historical Commission 1976-; Keep Museum Educl Commission 1990-; Monson Arts Cncl 1976-, Bd of Dirs 1985-88; MA Tchr of Yr Finalist 1987; Woodrow Wilson HS Fnd Fellowship; John Hancock Fellow; His from the Bottom Up Contributor; Woodrow Wilson Fnd Master Tchr; NEH Grant to Attend Sturbridge Village Wkshps; Clark Univ Scndry Educator of the Yr 1992; MA Tchr of the Yr Nom 1993; NCTE Presentor 1996; *office:* Minnechaug Regional H S 621 Main St Wilbraham MA 01095*

BREWER, RONALD E., Industrial Technology Teacher; *b:* Lebanon, PA; *m:* Susan Elizabeth Feeman; *c:* Ronald Vincent, Elaine Marie, John Douglas, David Michael; *ed:* Millersville Univ (BS) Ed & Industrial Arts 1970; Educl Admin Grad Work Temple Univ; *cr:* Elco HS Tchr 1970-74; Northern Lebanon HS Tchr & Head Ftbl Coach 1974-79; Plain N Fancy Kitchens Plant Production Mgr 1979-83; Northern Lebanon HS Tchr & Dept Chair 1983-; *ai:* Asst Ftbl, Strength & Trng Coach; 9th Grd Class & Flwshp of Chrstn Ath Adv; NEA 1970-; PSEA 1970-; Northern Lebanon EA 1974-, Pres; PA St Ftbl Coaches Assn 1978-, 20 Yr Svc Awd; Masonic Lodge 226 1978-; *office:* Northern Lebanon HS PO Box 100 Fredericksburg PA 17026

BREWER, TAMARA JOAN (WOOTTEN), Former Mathematics Teacher; *b:* Milford, DE; *m:* Steven E.; *c:* Joshua; *ed:* Salisbury St Univ (BS) Math 1973; Masters Equivalency 30 Hrs Ed; *cr:* Bennett MS Math Tchr 1973-74; J. M. Bennett Sr HS Math Tchr 1974-82; Wicomico MS Math Tchr 1985; Beaver Run Elem Math Tchr 1988-89; Parkside Sr HS Math Tchr 1989-94; Home Schl Tchr, Tutor 1994-; *ai:* JV Math Team Co-Coach; Admin Advy & Discipline Comms; Stu Assistance Prgm; NCTM 1989-95; *home:* 30507 Danwood Dr Delmar MD 21875

BREWER, WM. TERRY, Fifth Grade Teacher; *b:* Scranton, PA; *m:* Kathryn Rayne; *c:* Blake, Emily; *ed:* East Stroudsburg Univ (BS) Elem Ed 1972; *cr:* Upper Dublin Schl Dist 5th Grd Tchr 1972-; *ai:* Soccer, Hockey, Sftbl Coach; UDEA; Upper Dublin Outstdng Edctr Medal 1986; *office:* Thomas Fitzwater Elem Schl School Ln Willow Grove PA 19090

BREWINGTON, LOUISE TAYLOR, Guidance Counselor; *b:* Tunstall, VA; *m:* John D. Sr.; *c:* Tracye, J. David; *ed:* VA Union Univ (BA) Eng 1955; Montclair St Univ (MA) Stu Prsnl Svcs 1963; Cnslng 6 Hrs; Admin, Supervision 6 Hrs; *cr:* G. W. Carver Regnl HS Tchr 1955-58; Clinton Place Jr HS Tchr, Cnslr 1958-62; East Orange HS Tchr 1964-68, Guid Cnslr 1970-; *ai:* Strategic Planning Comm; Seton Hall Univ Upward Bound Project Liaison; Essex Cty Ed Assn 1964-, EOEA Ed Pride Plaque; Essex Cty Schl Cnslr Assn 1982-, Mbrshp Chprsn, Cnslr of Cty Plaque; NEA 1964-; Delta Sigma Theta 1954-, Arts & Letters Chprsn, Miss Courtesy Awd; Friends of Montclair Free Pub Lib 1991-, Life Mem; Visiting Nurse Assn of Montclair Inc 1990-, Trustee; Union Bapt Church Schlsp Comm 1973-; Dramadora Group 1960-, VP; YWCA 1975-, Nominating Comm; Thesis Pub 1963; William Paterson Coll Scholars' Recognition Awd 1990; Seton Hall Univ Upward Bound Project In Appreciation Awd; *office:* East Orange HS 34 N Walnut St East Orange NJ 07017

BREWINGTON, WILLIAM A., Science Teacher; *b:* Terre Haute, IN; *m:* Charlotte Kerkman; *c:* Lukas, Elisabeth, Gabriel; *ed:* Sonoma St Univ (BA) Bio 1990; Univ of Southern ME (MS) Ed 1994; Applied Immunology Summer Inst; BioTech Summer Inst; *cr:* Cape Elizabeth HS Sci Tchr 1991-; *ai:* Cultural Exch Club Adv; ME Sci Tchrs Assn 1995-; *office:* Cape Elizabeth HS 345 Ocean House Rd Cape Elizabeth ME 04107

BREWITT, LEEANN ADELE, Second Grade Teacher; *b:* Holdredge, NE; *m:* Fred Baxter; *c:* Jeff Michael, Scott Edward; *ed:* Framingham St Coll (BS) Elem Ed 1976, (MED) Elem Ed 1986; *cr:* Josiah Haynes Schl Kndgtn Tchr 1976-77; Fay Schl Fifth Grd Tchr 1977-78, Second Grd Tchr 1978-;

ai: Acad Affairs Comm; Marlboroughft Symphony Bd 1995-, Sec; *office:* Fay Schl 48 Main St Southborough MA 01772

BREWSTER, CHARLOTTE BURNS, First Grade Teacher; *b:* Logan, OH; *m:* Charles; *c:* Jennifer Brewster-Bailey; Jeffrey; *ed:* Univ of Rio Grande (BS) Elem Ed 1965; *cr:* S Bloomingville Elem Schl 2nd-3rd Grd Tchr 1961-66; East Elem Schl 1st Grd Tchr 1966-68; West Elem Schl Spec Ed Tchr 1968-69; S Bloomingville Elem Schl 1st-2nd Grd Tchr 1969-70; Marion Elem Schl 1st-2nd Grd Tchr 1970-72; East Elem Schl 1st Grd Tchr 1973-75; Rockbridge Elem Schl 1st & 3rd Grd Tchr 1975-78; East Elem Schl 1st Grd Tchr 1978-; *ai:* NEA, OEA 1961-; LEA 1966-; Venture Capital Grant; *home:* 606 Wyandotte Ave Logan OH 43138*

BREWSTER, GAIL LEILA, HS Social Studies Teacher; *b:* Cleveland, OH; *ed:* Kent St Univ (BSEd) Soc Stud, His 1961, (MED) His, Ed 1968; Attnd Univ of HI, Sophia Univ at Japan, Stanford Univ, Pepperdine Coll, John Carroll Univ; Freedoms Fnd Scholar; Univ Stoneybrook 62 Hrs; *cr:* Cleveland Hts Bd of Ed Canterbury & Northwood Daycamp Dir 1961-69; North Royalton City Schls His, Jrnlsm Tchr 1961-65; Beachwood HS Soc Stud Tchr 1965-; Cuyahoga Comm Coll West His Instr 1976-79; Beachwood HS Exec Tchr 1994-; *ai:* Soc Stud Exec Tchr; Jr Cncl World Affairs, Intnl Debate Club Adv; Ath Dept Scorekeeper; Beachwood Fed of Tchrs 1966-, Sec, Pres 22 Yrs, Mbrshp Increase Awd; AFT, AFL-CIO, Del; Delta Kappa Gamma 1979-, Corresponding Sec, Recording Sec; South Euclid Women's Club 1989-; Delta Gamma Kamma 1979-, Corresponding Sec, Recording Sec, Comm Chr; COE Fellow Three Times; St Dept Schlsp Summer Inst Asian Stud; Presidential Classroom Scholar; *office:* Beachwood HS 25100 Fairmount Blvd Beachwood OH 44122

BREWSTER, RON, US History Teacher; *b:* Tazewell Cty, VA; *m:* Brooke Wright; *c:* Heather, Jennifer, Melissa; *ed:* OH Univ (BS) Ed, Soc St 1964; Ball St Univ (MA) Guid, Cnslng 1973; 40 Addl Credit Hrs; *cr:* Kenton Pub Schls Dean of Boys, Tchr 1964-68; Upper Arlington City Schls Psych, AP Ec, Tchr 1968-; *ai:* Aviation Club Adv; NEA, OEA 1964-; *office:* Upper Arlington HS 1650 Ridgeview Rd Upper Arlington OH 43221

BREZINSKI, RICHARD ANTHONY, Psychology Teacher; *b:* Taunton, MA; *m:* Alyce Mullen; *c:* Elisabeth, Catherine; *ed:* Franklin Pierce Coll (BA) Psych 1967; *cr:* Somerset HS Psych Tchr 1968-; *ai:* Select Text Books Comm; NEA, MTA, Somerset Tchrs Assn 1968-; Helped Start Two Yr Psych Prgm; *office:* Somerset HS Grandview Ave Ext Somerset MA 02726

BRIA, AMY, Guidance Counselor; *b:* Passaic, NJ; *ed:* William Paterson Coll (BA) 1975; Fairleigh Dickinson Univ (MA) 1983; 30 Addl Credits; *cr:* Bishop Navagh Regnl 6-7th Grd Tchr 1975-77; Schl #16 Kndgtn & 4th Grd Tchr 1977-86; John F. Kennedy HS Math Tchr 1986-91, Guidance Cnslr 1991-; *ai:* NEA, NJEA, PCEA, Paterson Ed Assn 1977-, Recording Sec; Governor's Tchr Recognition Awd 1986; *office:* John F Kennedy HS 61-127 Preakness Ave Paterson NJ 07522

BRIAN, MARILYN S., Mathematics Teacher; *b:* Amsterdam, NY; *m:* James W.; *c:* Jaclyn; *ed:* Hartwick Coll (BA) Math 1972; SUNY at Albany (MA) Math Ed 1976; *cr:* Batavin Jr HS Math Tchr 1972-81; Batavia HS Math Tchr, Dept Co-Chm 1981-; *ai:* NYSUT, AFT 1972-; AMTNYS 1981-; Batavia Tchrs Assn 1972-, Rep; First Presbyn Church 1985-, Deacon; Honor Fac 1983; Extramile Awd 1988; Letters Commendation Batavia City Schls 1984, 1988, 1990; Univ of Rochester Excl Tchng 1989; *office:* Batavia HS 260 State St Batavia NY 14020

BRIAND, ELLA E., 8th & 10th Grade English Tchr; *b:* Colorado Springs, CO; *ed:* St Univ of NY at Oswego (BA) Pol Sci 1984, (MA) Ed 1989; 12 Post Grad Hrs in Eng from UNH; *cr:* Oswego MS 7th Grd Eng Tchr 1989-90; Poland Cntrl Schl 8th & 10th Grd Eng Tchr 1990-; *ai:* Tennis Coach 1990-; Bldg Level Team Mem 1995-; Discipline Team 1995-; NYSUT 1990-; Class Adv 1991-95; *office:* Poland Central Schl Rt 8 Box 8 Poland NY 13431*

BRICK, ARLINE ROTH, Biology & Psychology Teacher; *b:* New York, NY; *m:* Lawrence Samuel; *c:* Jason, Sheri, Adam; *ed:* Univ of Hartford (BA) Bio 1969, (MED) Urban Ed 1972; 45 Addl Credit Hrs Schl Psych, Schl Admin; *cr:* Univ of Hartford Rsrch Assoc 1968-69; Bulkeley HS Bio, Psych Tchr 1969-; *ai:* Cooperating Tchr to Stu Tchr; AFT, HFT 1970-; NSTA; Tchrs of Psych in Scndry Schls; West Hartford Bd of Ed 1981-89, 1991-95, Chprsn 1986-89, 1993-95; West Hartford Ed Assns Citizen of Yr 1989-90; *office:* Bulkeley HS 300 Wethersfield Ave Hartford CT 06114*

BRICK, FRANCINE ARTIN, 5th Grade Teacher; *b:* Syracuse, NY; *m:* Kenneth; *c:* Alison; *ed:* SUNY at Brockport (BS) Elem Ed 1970; SUNY at Cortland (MS) Elem Ed, Rdng 1975; Several Cmptr Programming Courses; *cr:* Lakeland Elem Schl 4th Grd Tchr 1970-71, 5th Grd Tchr 1971-89; Solvay Elem Schl 5th Grd Tchr 1989-; *ai:* Solvay Tchrs Assn 1970-, Bldg Rep, Pres; NYSUT, AFT 1970-; Awarded 3 Impact Mini Grants by CNYTC, 4 Mini-Grants; *office:* Solvay Elem Schl 701 Woods Rd Syracuse NY 13209

BRICKER, ALAN KEITH, MS Band & French Teacher; *b:* Mc Keesport, PA; *ed:* Edinboro Univ (BA) Music 1974; Pittsburgh Univ (MED) Admin 1990; Working on PHD Admin; Cert Elem Ed, Fr Lang & Cultures CA Univ; Cert Elem Prin, Schl Supt; *cr:* Elizabeth Forward Schl Dist Band Dir 1976-; *ai:* Mentor Tchr; Peer Mediation; Conflict Resolution; Outcome Based Ed Assessment & Benchmarks; NEA 1976-; Amer Red Cross 1974-; Round Hill Presbyn 1995-, Choir Dir; *home:* 213 Narragansett Dr Mc Keesport PA 15135

BRICKER, LILLIAN (FAZI), 7th & 8th Grade Math Teacher; *b:* Stuebenville, OH; *m:* J. Douglas; *c:* Brian, Kevin; *ed:* Univ of Steubenville (BA) Math 1973; 24 Post Grad Hrs Ed Duquesne Univ; 12 Hrs Acctg OH Northern Univ; *cr:* Findlay Coll Algebra Instr 1983-86; Sts Simon & Jude Math Tchr 1987-88; St Louise De Marillac Math Tchr 1988-; *ai:* Mathcounts Coach; NCTM 1988-; Nom Golden Apple Awd 1994, 1996; *office:* St Louise De Marillac Schl 310 Mcmurray Rd Pittsburgh PA 15241

BRICKLEY, LYNDELL TROY, Science Teacher; *b:* Perryton, TX; *m:* Ruth Griffin; *c:* Troy, Todd; *ed:* Univ of CO (BA) Bio & Chem 1965; St Univ of NY at Potsdam (MS) Chem 1972; 23 Credit Hrs Above Masters; *cr:* Harrison Schl Dist Jr HS Tchr 1967-75; Stuttgart Amer HS Sci Tchr 1975-87; Kinnick HS Sci Tchr 1987-89; Seoul Amer HS Sci Tchr 1989-; *ai:* Pacific Wide Model United Nations Host Dir; Schl Chem Hygiene Ofcr; NEA 1967-, Fac Rep, CO Ed Assn Bd Mem & Pol Action Comm; Pacific Sci Tchrs Assn 1990-, Korean Area Dir; NSF Grant 1970-72; *office:* Seoul American HS Dodds Sahs 24 Unit 15549 APO AP 96205

BRICKLIN, LOIS, English Teacher; *b:* Philadelphia, PA; *m:* James M. Walsh; *ed:* Univ of Pittsburgh (BA) Eng, Scndry Ed 1971; Jersey City St Coll (MA) Eng, Media Tech 1982; *cr:* Hillside HS Eng Tchr 1971-86; Vernon Twp HS Eng Tchr 1986-; *ai:* HS Newspaper Adv; NJEA, NEA 1971-; CBE Flwshp; NEH Seminar Fellow; *office:* Vernon Township HS PO Box 800 Vernon NJ 07462

BRICKMAN, BARBARA FELSENSTEIN, Speech & Fine Arts Teacher; *b:* Brooklyn, NY; *m:* Steven M.; *c:* Elizabeth, David; *ed:* York Coll of PA (BA) Comm 1977; Univ of MD at College Park (MA) Theatre 1981; *cr:* Penn St Schl Fine Arts Tchr; York Coll Speech Tchr; Howard Comm Coll Speech, Fine Arts Tchr; *ai:* Acting, Directing Regnl Theatre; Howard Arts United, Bd; Volantary Action Ctr, Bd; Howard Cty Heritage Comm, Bd; Magic Minstrel Players Inc Childrens Theatre, JB Co Productions Inc Dinner Theatre, New Stage Inc Perspective Theatre Group, Brickman Productions Inc Co-Founder.*

BRICKNER, MICHAEL JOHN, Mathematics Teacher; *b:* Tiffin, OH; *m:* Tricia Marvel; *c:* Trevor; *ed:* Heidelberg Coll (BS) Math 1982; Attnd Bowling Green St Univ, Univ of Toledo; *cr:* Tiffin Calvert HS Math Tchr 1983-87; Tiffin Univ Adjunct Instr 1985-86; Maumee HS Math Tchr 1989-93, 1995; Delta HS Math Tchr 1987-; *ai:* Boys Var Bsktbl Coach; Girls Sftbl Aide; Asst Ath Dir; OCTM 1983-; NCTM 1987-; Coach of Yr 1994-95; Nom Educator of Yr 1996; *office:* Delta HS 605 Taylor St Delta OH 43515

BRICKNER, PATRICK DAVID, Remedial, Enrichment Math Tchr; *b:* Homestead, PA; *m:* Dorinda Young; *c:* Carlin, Colleen, Cristin; *ed:* Edinboro St Coll (BS) Elem Ed 1974, (MED) Math Ed 1982; *cr:* Erie Schl Dist 3rd Grd Per Sub Tchr 1974-75; St Boniface Schl 7th-8th Grd Sci, Math Tchr 1976-78; NW Tri-Cty Inter Unit Remedial, Enrichment Math Tchr 1978-; *ai:* Math Counts Coach for 2 Schls; Erie Diocese Math Curr Comm; ACT Planning Comm 1989; NCTM 1990-; Knights of Columbus 1980-, Little League, Soccer Coach; Elks 1990-; Coached Stdnts Who Advanced to St Level of Math Counts; *office:* NW Tri-Cty Intermediate Unit 252 Waterford St Edinboro PA 16412

BRIDGES, DALE EUGENE, Fourth Grade Teacher; *b:* Claysburg, PA; *m:* Marion Kaye Dodson; *c:* James S., Jason S.; *ed:* Penn St Univ (MS) Elem Ed 1990; *cr:* Blair Elem Schl 4th-5th Grd Tchr 1971-93; Frankstown Elem Schl 4th Grd Tchr 1993-; *ai:* Elem Sports Coach; Elem Sci Comm Chm Dev New Curr; Order, Distribute Needed Sci Equipment; NEA, PACE, PA St Ed Assn, Hollidaysburg Area Ed Assn 1971-; *office:* Frankstown Elem Schl RR 3 Box 592 Hollidaysburg PA 16648

BRIDGES, K. ROBERT, Asst Professor of Psychology; *b:* Greensburg, PA; *m:* Michele; *c:* Robert; *ed:* Indiana Univ of PA (BA) Psych; Temple Univ (MA) Psych; Univ Pittsburgh (PHD) Child Dev 1980; *cr:* Penn St Univ Whole Career Psych Dept Asst Prof; *ai:* Amer Psych Assn; Eastern Psych Assn 1983-; Intnl Cncl of Psychologists; *office:* Penn State Univ New Kensington Campus New Kensington PA 15068

BRIDGES, PATRICIA ROSS, Mathematics Teacher; *b:* Easton, MD; *m:* George Thomas; *c:* Cadie Michelle; *ed:* Towson ST Coll (BS) Scndry Ed, Math 1973; Attnd Loyola, Salisbury St Coll; *cr:* St Michael HS 8-12 Grd Math Tchr 1973-79, 1981-; *ai:* Sr Class Adv; HS Work Team; Schl Improvement Team; MSPP Chrprsn; Scheduling, Tech, Curr Dev Comms; MSTA, TCEA, NEA, NCTM, MCTM 1973-; Shore Gymnastics Parents Assn 1983-, Treas; Dedication of HS Yrbk 1994; *office:* Saint Michaels H S 200 Seymour Ave Saint Michael MD 21663

BRIDGES, ROBERT ARTHUR, History Teacher; *b:* Attleboro, MA; *m:* Barbara Elizabeth Eayrs; *c:* Steven, Eric, & John; *ed:* Drury Coll (BA) His & Pol Sci 1959; Bridgewater St Coll (MED) Ed 1964; 96 Grad Credit Hrs; *cr:* Foxborough HS Soc Stud Tchr 1962-; *ai:* Foxborough HS Fac Cncl; NHS Fac Comm; Boys Var Tennis Coach; Foxborough Ed Assn 1962-, Pres 1964; MA Tchrs Assn 1962-; NEA 1962-; MCSS 1962-; US Prof Tennis Assn 1972-; Sigma Phi Epsilon 1956-, Pledge Trainer; Omicron Delta Kappa 1959-; New England & US Tennis Assn 1963-; Troop 68 BSA 1980-, Advancement Comm Chprsn; Assn for Supervision & Curr Dev 1993-; Foxborough Exeplary Tchr; South Shore Cncl for Soc Stud, Bill Spratt MVP Awd, 1992; Natl HS Coaching Gold Awd 1989; *home:* 12 Pheasant Ln North Easton MA 02356*

BRIDGETTS, MARY LUCILLE, French Teacher; *b:* Brooklyn, NY; *ed:* Good Counsel Coll (BA) Fr 1945; Villanova Univ (MA) Fr 1960; 6 Credit Hrs at Saint Anselms Coll 1961; *cr:* Saint Frances de Chantal Grammer Schl 4th & 6th Grd Tchr 1949-54; Good Counsel Acad 3rd Grd Tchr 1954-57; Preston HS Fr Tchr 1957-; *ai:* Fr Club Moderator; NY St Foreign Lang Assn 1958-; Preston HS Distinguished Tchr Awd 1994.

BRIDGFORD, KIM SUZANNE, Associate Professor of English; *b:* Moline, IL; *m:* Peter Arsene Duval; *ed:* Univ of IA (BA) Eng 1981, (MFA) Creative Writing 1983; Univ of IL A(AM) Eng 1985, (PHD) Eng 1988; *cr:* Hamilton Coll Asst Prof Eng 1988-89; Fairfield Univ Asst Prof Eng 1989-94, Assoc Prof Eng 1994-; *ai:* Lit Magazine, Eng Club, Eng Hnr Soc Fac Adv; Writing Prgm Dir; Acad of Amer Poets 1993-, Assoc Mem; Amer Assn of Univ Women 1993-; Danforth Assocs of New England 1995-; Numerous Poems, Stories, Reviews Pub; Tchr of Yr 1993; CT Prof of Yr 1994; *office:* Fairfield Univ Fairfield CT 06430

BRIGATI, MARILYN DRAKE, Lang Arts Tchr & Dept Chair; *b:* Dayton, OH; *m:* Robert J.; *c:* Nicholas, Erin; *ed:* Miami Univ (BS) Speech & Eng Ed 1973; Univ of Dayton (MA) Commnctn 1980; Attnd Wright St Univ; *cr:* Miamisburg HS Tchr 1973-, Dept Chair 1977-; *ai:* Steering Comm; Dept Chair; Alumni Hnr Roll; AP; OEA, NEA & MCTA 1973-; ASCD 1988-; Centerville Org for Gifted 1992-, Liaison Coord; Lang Arts Tchr Ldr Network-WRPDC; Local Grants; Dist Exemplary Tchr; Mead Internship; Curr Dev; Selected as Mentor Tchr; *office:* Miamisburg Sr HS 1860 Belvo Rd Miamisburg OH 45342*

BRIGGS, GEORGE E., High School Soc Stud Teacher; *b:* Central Falls, RI; *m:* Marlyn Hart; *c:* Heather, Heidi, Holly, Brian, Stacey; *ed:* RI Coll (BA) Soc Stud 1972, (MED) Scndry Ed 1974; 33 Post Grad Credits; *cr:* Woonsocket JHS Eng & Soc Stud Tchr 1972-90; Woonsocket High Soc Stud Tchr 1990-; *ai:* Girls Cross Cntry Coach 1980-; Boys Indoor & Outdoor Track Coach 1972-; Woonsocket Tchrs Guild 1972-; AFT #951, Steward; Slatesville Congregational Church 1975-, Deacon; Coach of the Yr 6 Times; *office:* Woonsocket Sr HS 777 Cass Ave Woonsocket RI 02895

BRIGGS, JANIS STEINMETZ, Music Teacher; *b:* Upper Sandusky, OH; *m:* Craig E.; *c:* Amy Briggs Dissanayake, Jennifer Briggs Latham, John, Sarah; *ed:* OH Wesleyan Univ (BMUS) Mus Ed 1961; *cr:* Lake George Cntrl Schl Music Tchr 1961-65; Canterbury Elem Schl Music Tchr Part-time 1987-; Gilford Elem Schl Music Tchr Part-time 1989-90; Belmont Elem Schl Music Tchr Part-time 1990-; *ai:* Childrens After Schl, Select Music Ensembles; Music Edctrs Natl Conf 1989-; Appalachian Mountain Club, Audubon Soc 1990-; Pub Book & Tape O Little Children Shaker Songs; *home:* 22 Old Gilmanton Rd Canterbury NH 03224*

BRIGGS, JOAN STRATTON, French & Gifted Support Tchr; *b:* Blossburg, PA; *m:* Larry S.; *c:* Rebecca; *ed:* Albright Coll (BA) Fr, Eng 1963; Middlebury Coll (MA) Fr 1968; Univ of Southwestern LA Cajun Stud 1986; Mc Gill Univ Fr Stud Cert 1962; U of NM Francophone Smmr Schl 1995; *cr:* Troy Area HS Fr Tchr 1963-67; Thomas A. Edison HS Fr Tchr 1967-71; Wellsboro Area HS Fr, Gifted Support Tchr 1975-; *ai:* Schlsp Challenge Team, Intnl Club Adv; Lead French-Speaking Countries Stu Tours, Odyssey of the Mind; AATF, NEA, PSEA 1963-; WAEA 1975-; *office:* Wellsboro Area HS 67 Nichols St Wellsboro PA 16901

BRIGGS, JOHN A., Retired Social Studies Teacher; *b:* Utica, NY; *m:* Katherine Hanly; *c:* Megan Briggs Gibeau, Andrew J.; *ed:* Cath Univ (BA) His 1958; Univ of CT (MA) Ed 1967; Tufts Univ Addl 30 Credits; *cr:* St John's Prep Fr Tchr 1958-63; St Thomas More Prep Eng, Soc Stud Tchr 1963-65; Montville HS Soc Stud Tchr 1965-68; Lynnfield HS Soc Stud Tchr 1968-86; Lynnfield MS Soc Stud Tchr 1986-94; *ai:* Soc Stud Dept Head; Var Bsbl St Thomas More, JV Bsbl St John's Prep-Lynnfield, Frosh Bsbl Lynnfield, Frosh Girls Bsktbl Coach; MTA, Lynnfield Tchrs 1968-; Wyoma Little League 1977-, Coach; St Pius Bsktbl 1980-, Coach; St Pius CCD 1986-, Confirmation Tchr; *home:* 127 Commonwealth Rd Lynn MA 01904*

BRIGGS, SUSAN DARLENE (KING), 4th Grade Teacher; *b:* Marietta, OH; *m:* Don Frederick; *c:* Kristen Leigh, Mark Frederick; *ed:* Marietta Coll (BA) Elem Ed & Psych 1974-; OH Univ (MA) Elem Ed 1982; *cr:* Caldwell Elem Schl 4th-6th Grd Tchr 1974-; *ai:* Schl Post Office, Book-It McDonalds Perfect Attendance Coord; Just Say No Club; Recyc Coord; Marietta Times Edctnl Cnsltnt; Marietta Area Arts & League; Caldwell Tchrs Assn 1974-, Sec; NEA & OEA; First Bapt Sunday Schl Tchr; Cntrl OH Coal Co Grant for a Books & Beyond *office:* Caldwell Elem Schl 44350 Fairground Rd Caldwell OH 4

BRIGGS, SUSAN JUNE, Health Occupations Teacher; *b:* Port Je *m:* Lance W.; *ed:* Orange Cty Comm (AAS) Nursing 1975; Mercy C Behavior Sci 1981; Univ of Scranton (MS) Schl Counseling 1986 Univ Masters Equivalent Voc Ed; Bloomsburg Univ Post Grad Doctors Sunnyside Hospital Registered Nurse 1975-78; Delawar High Hlth Occupations Tchr 1978-; *ai:* HOSA Adv; Fac Adv Cncl PSEA 1978-; Matamoras Fire Dept 1992-, Vol Fireman & EMT Delaware Valley HS HC 77 Box 379C Milford PA 18337

BRIGHAM, GLENN, 4th Grade Teacher; *b:* Binghamton, NY; *m:* Megan, Ryan; *ed:* SUNY Coll at Old Westbury (BS) Elem Ed 1982 Cortland Coll (MS) Ed 1990; *cr:* Head Start Tchr 1982-84; J C S Tchr 1984-; *ai:* Olympics of Mind Coach; NEA 1984-; *office:* John Schl Dist 666 Reynolds Rd Johnson City NY 13790

BRIGHAM, WALTER COLE,III, Computer & Math Teacher; *b* NY; *m:* Sonya King; *ed:* SUNY at Albany (BS) Math 1992; *cr:* Island Schl Cmptr, Math Tchr 1992-; *ai:* 12 Grd, Comp Club Adv HS Cross Cntry, JV Bsktbl, Var Track Coach; Project EXCEL Presbyn Church, SI Yth Group 1992-; Pioneering Partners in Te 1995; Golden Apple Awd 1994; *office:* Shelter Island Schl 33 N F Shelter Island NY 11964*

BRIGHT, CAROL, Third Grade Teacher; *b:* Lancaster, PA; *c:* S Sheila; *ed:* Millersville Univ (BS) Elem Ed, Early Chldhd 1988; Grad Credits in Masters Prgm; *cr:* H. C. Burgard Elem Schl Sixth C 1989-90, Fifth Grd Tchr 1990-92, Third Grd Tchr 1992-; *ai:* Safet Supvr 1993-; Stu Store Mgr 1994-; Comm Task Force 1994; NEA MCEA 1988-; CPBY's Foster Parent Agency 1995-, Foster Pare Grant 1994; *office:* H C Burgard Elem Schl 111 S Penn St Manh 17545

BRIGHT, DANIEL A., Guidance Counselor; *b:* Drexel Hill, Geraldine; *c:* Rebecca June, Travis David; *ed:* Bob Jones Univ (1979, (MA) His 1981; Attnd Trenton St Coll, Univ of CA at Los A *cr:* Cedar Grove Acad Soc Stud Instr 1981-83, HS Prin 1 Headmaster 1987-95; Cedar Grove HS Guid Cnslr 1995-; *ai:* JR C Cncl Adv; Stu Recruitment Dir; Educl Ldrshp, NASSP 1983-; ISM Article Pub 1992; *office:* Cedar Grove Chrstn HS 413 E Ta Philadelphia PA 19120

BRIGHT, KAREN B., 4th Grade Language Arts Tchr; *b:* Des Moi *m:* Robert I.; *c:* Robby, Tiffanie, Chante; *ed:* Xavier Univ (MS Specialist 1978; Learning Disabilities; Madeleine Hunter Discipli Dignity; *cr:* Princeton City Schls Tchr 1971-; *ai:* After Schl Stud Crises Team; Band Chaperone, Concessions; Team Ldr; ASCD NEA, Princeton Assn of Classroom Edctrs 1971-; Princeton Boosters 1994-, Pres Nom; Quinn Chapel AME Celestrial Choir Ashland Oil Golden Apple Tchr Achvmt Awd; *office:* R E Intermediate Schl 3900 Cottingham Dr Cincinnati OH 45241

BRIGHT, MARCY, High School Resource Teacher; *b:* Brooklyn, Jerry L.; *c:* Scott; *ed:* Western St Coll (BA) Elem Ed 1974, (MA) L Disabilities 1978; Misercordia Coll Educl Admin 1995; 63 Grad *cr:* Baltimore City Schls 5th Grd Tchr 2 Yrs; St Stephens Indian S Ed Tchr 3 Yrs; Brushton-Moira Cntrl Schl Spcl Ed Tchr 14 Yrs; *ai:* Adv; Comm Schlsp Fund Trustee; Brushton-Moira Tchrs Assn 198 St United Tchrs 1982-; AFT 1982-; PTSO Bd of Dirs; *office:* B Moira Central Schl Gale Rd Brushton NY 12916

BRIGHT, NEIL H., District Curriculum Coord; *b:* Flushing, Pamela Johnstone; *c:* Zachary James; *ed:* SUNY Oneonta (BA) E NY Univ (MS) His 1983; SUNY New Paltz (CAS) Ed Admin Doctoral Stud His SUNY Binghamton 1991; *cr:* Tri Valley Schl Si Tchr 1971, MS Soc Stud Tchr 1972-76, HS Soc Stud Tchr 1 Sullivan Cntry Coll Adjunct Prof 1988; Tri Valley Schl Soc Stu Chair 1990-91, Dist Curr Coord 1993; *ai:* Mid Hudson P Assessment Project 1993-; Tri Valley Tchrs Assn 1971-, VP, Twic Contract Negotiator; ASCD, NYSASCD 1993-; AFT, NYSUT Mem Finalist NY St Tchr of Yr Competition 1992; Winner of Dist Wi Scully Awd Outstanding Tchr 1992; *office:* Trivalley Jr Grahamsville NY 12740*

BRIGHT, PATRICIA DOWELL, Coordinator of Student S Gallatin, TN; *m:* Christopher B.; *ed:* Univ of PA (BA) His 1986; Univ (MED) Cnslng Psych 1992; Temple Univ Educl Psych; Univ Wharton Schl Post-Baccalaureate Prgm; *cr:* Univ of PA Admission Life 1986-90; Temple Univ Acad, Pre-Law Adv 1992-93; Peirc Cnslng Coord, Stu Support 1993-95; PA Coll of Podiatric Med C Stu Svcs 1995-; *ai:* Stu Natl Podiatric Med Assn Adv; Peirce Coll Club, Gospel Chair; NAWE 1991-; PA Educl Opportunity Prgm 1993-95; *home:* 250 S 44th St # 3 Philadelphia PA 19104*

BRIGHTBILL, JUDY K., Math Teacher; *b:* Reading, PA; *ed:* Bloo Univ (BS) Math 1973; Attnd Kutztown Univ; *cr:* Tulpehocken Are HS Math Tchr 1973-; *ai:* Cross Stitch Club Adv; Stu Assistance Prins Adv Comm; Mentor Tchr; NEA, PSEA 1974-; TEA 1974-, Berks Cty Performance Assessment Consortium 1995-; *office:* Be HS 8390 Lancaster Ave Bethel PA 19507

BRIGHTLY, CHARLES M., Biology Tchr & Sci Dept Chair; *b:* NY; *m:* Joan Brady; *c:* Christopher, David; *ed:* Danbury St Tchrs Co Sci Ed 1965; Western CT St Univ (MS) Sci Ed 1976; Southern CT S 6th Yr Admin & Supervision 1992; *cr:* Danbury Jr HS 7th-8th Grd S 1965-69; Brookfield Jr HS 7th Grd Sci Tchr 1969-73; Brookfield H & 12th Grd Bio Tchr 1979-; WCSU Adjunct Fac & Bio Dept 199 NHS; Supt Advy Comm; Curr Advy Cncl; BEA, CEA, NEA, PDK Furman Univ Outstanding Tchr Awd; Univ of Chicago Outstandin Awd; Alumni Assn of Univ CT Excl in Tchng Awd; New England Assn Awd for Excl in Tchng; *office:* Brookfield HS 45 Long Meado Rd Brookfield CT 06804

BRIGHTON, KENNETH LYLE, Assistant Prof of Educati Bloomington, IN; *m:* Maryanne Newsom-Brighton; *c:* Casey; *ed:* IN (BA) Zoology 1971; East TN St Univ (MAT) Ed 1973; IN St Univ Ed 1993; Endorsement in Gifted & Talented Ed; *cr:* Cntrl Elem Sch 1971-73; Owen Valley MS Tchr & Coach 1973-89; IN St Univ T Residence 1990-91; Johnson St Coll Asst Prof 1993-; *ai:* VT Assn f Level Ed Bd Mem; VT Mid Level Prof Dev Collaborative Mem; Na Assn 1990-; New England League of MSs 1993-, Tchr Ed Comm; Phi Kappa 1991-; *office:* Johnson St Coll Clayhill Rd Johnson VT 0565

BRILHART, CHRISTINE M., Fourth Grade Teacher; *b:* Hanover, Dirk A.; *c:* Elizabeth; *ed:* Shippensburg Univ (BS) Elem Ed 1988; W on MED Curr, Instruction Western MD Coll; *cr:* Hanover Pub Schl D Grd Tchr 1988-89, 5th Grd Tchr 1989-90; 4th Grd Tchr 1990-; *ai:* Va Hockey, Elem IM Coach; NEA, PSEA 1988-; *office:* Hanover Street Sch 101 E Hanover St Hanover PA 17331

BRILLINGER, RUTH W., Academic Chair; *b:* Butler, PA; *c:* Bri Brett H., Beth E.; *ed:* PA St Univ (BS) Bus Admin & Hlth Care 1982; *cr:* Capital Hlth System Healthgain Ctr Mgr 1982-94; Cntrl

Acad Chair, Allied Hlth Division 1994-; *ai:* Soc, Curr Review & Comms; Ind Contractor-Stress Mgmt Trainer; PA Fed of Womens 62-84, Pres; *office:* Central Penn Bus Schl College Hill Rd ale PA 17093

A, MATTHEW P., Chemistry Teacher; *b:* Pittsburgh, PA; *m:* A. Nied; *c:* Matthew Jr., Marissa; *ed:* Grove City Coll (BS) Bio NY at Brockport (MS) Scndry Sci Ed, Ed 1993; *cr:* Webster hl Sci Tchr 1987-88; Eastridge HS Chem Tchr 1988-94; Webster Tchr 1994-; *ai:* Sci Olympiad Coach; Elem Sci Show Presenter; SUT 1988-; Excl in Scndry Ed Awd 1990; *office:* Webster HS 875 Webster NY 14580

E, KAREN BARBARA, Kindergarten Teacher; *b:* Beverly, MA; n St Coll (BS) Early Chldhd Ed 1971, (MED) Elem Schl Guid idgewater St Coll (CAGS) Early Chldhd 1990; *cr:* Cntrl Schl rd Tchr 1971-73, Kndgtn Tchr 1974-76, Second Grd Tchr 1977, Tchr 1979-80, Kndgtn Tchr 1981-86, Fourth Grd Tchr 1987-93, Tchr 1994-; *ai:* Schl Improvement Cncl; Hlth Ed Comm; East ater Tchrs Assn 1971-, Bldg Rep, Staff Cncl; MTA, NEA, Cty Tchrs Assn 1971-; Beverly Lib Comm; Ocean Park Assn; dhd Achvmt Testing Grant; Curr Dev; Sabbatical 1978-79; *office:* gewater Central Schl 107 Central St East Bridgewater MA 02333

EY, GRACE JULIA, Admin for Curr & Personnel; *b:* Brooklyn, eter; *c:* Barbara Ann, Theresa Marie, Gilbert Samuel, Samantha eter; *ed:* SUNY at Stony Brook (BA) Fine Arts 1972; Adelphi E) 1973; LI Univ (SDA) Admin 1983; Staff Dev Coll of New , *cr:* Miller Place Schl Dist Tchr 1973-83, Dir of GATE 1983-88, 1987-88, Prin 1988-93, Admin for Curr & Persnl 1993-; *ai:* 83-; ASAA 1988-; Phi Delta Kappa 1983-; PTO 1969-, Sec 1970; 94-; *office:* Miller Place Schl Dist 191 N Country Rd Miller Place 4

IAN, DEBRA ANN, Vocal Music Teacher; *b:* Fostoria, OH; *ed:* Green St Univ (BM) Music Ed 1981; Wright St Univ (MED) Educl 996; Show Choir Camps of Amer; *cr:* Tipp City Ex Vlg Schls Vocal hr 1981-; *ai:* OMEA 1981-, Dist XI Festival Co-Cordinator; Gem et Adelines 1984-, Asst Dir, Choreography Comm; OMEA St, Dist Superior Ratings; *office:* Tippecanoe HS 555 N Hyatt St Tipp City 1

K, RAYMOND, Earth & Space Science Teacher; *b:* Pittsburgh, Denise Bowling; *c:* John, Jena; *ed:* Edinboro Univ (BS) Earth, i, Phys Sci & Scndry Ed 1973; George Washington Univ (MA) Ed 1977; 30+ Credit Hrs; *cr:* Bel Alton MS Sci Tchr 1973-77; ugh HS Earth, Space Sci & Physics Tchr 1977-, Evening HS Instr : Sci Dept Chair 1975-; Var Girls Bsktbl Head Coach 1978-85; 3-; MD St Tchrs Assoc 1973-; Charles Co Tchrs Assoc 1973-; Natl Hlth Flwshp 1992; Co-Pub Article 1994; *office:* Maurice Mc HS 7165 Marshall Corner Rd Pomfret MD 20675

DAVID M., English Teacher; *b:* Pittsburgh, PA; *m:* Rita sky; *c:* Sean; *ed:* Duquesne Univ (BSEd) Eng 1969, (MED) Rdng hl Admin 1972; Continuing Ed Real Estate License; *cr:* Pgh Pub ng, Eng Tchr 1969-; *ai:* Stu, Fac Discipline Comm Mem; Stu Cncl T, PAFT, PFT 1969-; WPCTE, NCTE 1990-; 5th Northumberland -Scion of BSI 1977-, Ed, Publisher; Stud Guide Co-Ed; *office:* HS 2940 Sheraden Blvd Pittsburgh PA 15204

SYLVIA CORLEY, 3rd-4th Grade Teacher; *b:* Bristol, CT; *m:* L.; *c:* Scott C.; *ed:* Keene St Coll (BS) Elem, Spec Ed 1978; CT St Univ (MS) Elem Ed 1989; Boston Coll Peripatology; *cr:* Schl for Blind Tchr 1978-81; Damascus Schl 2nd Grd Tchr ; John B. Sliney Schl 3rd-4th Grd Tchr 1984-; *ai:* Head Diving Cooperating, Mentor Tchr; NEA, BEA, CEA 1983-; Stratford ers 1989-93, Exec VP; *office:* John B. Sliney Schl 23 Eades St CT 06405

ON, COLIN MEAGHER, Social Studies Teacher; *b:* Buffalo, NY; ssa Ann Masters; *c:* Joel; *ed:* Amherst Coll (BA) His 1989; Buffalo (MSED) Social Stud 1992-; *cr:* Nichols Schl Sos Stud Tchr ; John F. Kennedy Jr-Sr HS Soc Stud Tchr 1992-; *ai:* Head Vars ch; JFK Bldg Goals Comm Chm; *office:* John F. Kennedy Jr-Sr HS uga Creek Rd Cheektowaga NY 14227

MICHAEL E., Assoc Prof & Humane Stud Dir; *b:* Albuquerque, Camille Collett; *c:* Casey Tyler; *ed:* Univ of CA (BA) Politics niv of Oxford (PHD) Politics 1983; *cr:* Stanford Univ Instr ; Univ of VA Asst Prof 1985-93; Kenyon Coll Assoc Prof 1993-; ed Program In Humane Studies Dir; *ai:* APSA 1983-; Head Start c Awd for Outstdng Fac Mem; Tchr of Yr; Tragedy & Denial; sm in Law & Soc; Genealogy of Pol Culture; Intnl Culture Wars; Kenyon Coll Timberlake House Gambier OH 43022*

A, RICHARD D., English Teacher; *b:* Sewickley, PA; *m:* Catherine uarella; *ed:* California Univ of PA (BS) Eng 1964; Univ of gh (MAT) Eng 1967; Temple Univ 27 Grad Hrs Eng; Millersville PA 18 Credits, Grad Level; *cr:* Havre de Grace HS Eng Tchr ; Nyack HS Eng Tchr 1967-68; Ambridge Area HS Eng Tchr ; Penn Manor HS Eng Tchr 1969-; *ai:* Organize Group Tours; NEA, Ed Assn, Penn Manor Ed Assn 1969-; *office:* Penn Manor HS E Ave Millersville PA 17551*

, KAREN SMITH, Biology Teacher; *b:* Elmira, NY; *m:* Gordon R.; ; *ed:* SUNY At Fredonia (BS) Bio 1989; SUNY At Binghamton Bio 1995; *cr:* Horseheads MS 7th Grd Life Sci Tchr 1991-92; Victor Tchr 1992-; *ai:* Victor HS Bldg Cncl; Frosh Class Adv; Dollars For s Selection Comm; Victor Tchrs Assoc 1992-; STANYS 1990-; 1991-; *office:* Victor HS 953 High St Victor NY 14564*

ES, MA. PURIFICACION MENDOZA, 5th-8th Grade English ; *b:* Manila, Philippines; *m:* Amador Custodio Briones Sr; *c:* Ma. ion, Jose Jr., Jose Amando II; *ed:* Roosevelt Coll (BA) His 1966; Manila (BSE) Eng, Span 1968, (MA) Soc Scis 1970; Secretarial Basic Programming 1987; ESL, Biling 30 Credits; *cr:* Col San , Phi SBA Tchr, Eng & Span Dept Head 1966-81; Women Tchrs ng Instr, Coord 1981-85; Uceda Eng Inst SCS Bus Schl Eng Instr ; St Anthony of Padua Schl Coord, Lang Arts Eng Tchr 1985-; Cty Comm Coll Adj Prof Eng 1995-; *ai:* Paterson Diocese Fac ncl Rep; Diocese Lang Arts Curr Comm; Our Ladyof Penafrancia e Assn Vice Chm; St Anthony Filipino Amer CommSec; NCEA NMBEA 1987-; NMSA 1994-; NCTE 1995-; FACSA 1994-, Sec; 1991-; Amer Filipino Tchrs Assn 1989-; Title VII Grant; Most ng Tchr of Month; Seminar, Wkshp Presentor; ESL Using rimiento Methodology Demo Tchr; *office:* St Anthony Of Padua Tulip St Passaic NJ 07055*

ANE, GENE DENNIS, Soc Stud, Math & Eng Teacher; *b:* burg, PA; *m:* Carol L. Backus; *c:* Kelli, Mindy, Shawn; *ed:* Univ of rgh (BS) Elem Ed 1974, (MED) Elem Ed 1979; *cr:* Maxwell Elem d Tchr 1974-75, 6th Grd Tchr 1975-85, 5th Grd Tchr 1985-86, 6th hr 1986-90, 5th Grd Head Tchr 1990-93; Harrold MS 7th Grd Tchr *ai:* Hempfield HS Head Women's Bsktbl Coach; Girls Bsktbl Club; ys & Girls Bsktbl Coach 1974-; NEA, PSEA, HAEA, Westm Cty s Assn 1974-; Lions Club 1995-; Amer Family Inst Positive Tchng HS Girls Bsktbl Coach of Yr; *office:* Harold MS W Newton Rd burg PA 15601

BRISCESE, BARBARA BAUER, English Teacher; *b:* Butler, NY; *m:* Rocco; *ed:* Harper Coll (BA) Ger 1963; Cornell Univ (MED) His 1965; Stud in Gender Theory Syracuse Univ; Islam; Neo Historicism in Textual Stud Syracuse Univ; Peace & the Comm Empire Coll; *cr:* Binghamton North HS Soc Stud Tchr 1965-67; Greece Arcadia HS Soc Stud Tchr 1967-68; Pine Ridge Indian Schl Soc Stud, Eng, Ger Tchr 1969-71; Gordon Alternative HS Soc Stud, Eng Tchr 1971-73; North Rose Wolcott HS Soc Stud, Eng Tchr 1973-; Syracuse Univ Adj Eng Instr 1985-; *ai:* Yrbk Adv; Soph Class Adv; Mem Bldg Team; NEA, NYS Tchrs Org, Wayne Cty Tchrs 1973-; NCTE 1983-; Historical Soc 1990-, Butler Town Historian; Nature Conservancy 1989-; Wayne Cty Historical Soc 1995-, Bd Mem; Environmental Defense League 1989-; Southern Law Poverty Ctr 1989-; Tchr of Yr; NY St Humanities Grant; Univ of Rochester Tchr of Yr for North Rose Wolcott; *home:* 4455 Spring Lake Rd Wolcott NY 14590

BRISCOE, FRANK WILLIAM, Physical Education Teacher; *b:* Washington, DC; *m:* Patricia Burchette; *c:* Jerome Kelly Burchette; *ed:* Midland Luth Coll (BS) PE 1974; *cr:* Cardozo Sr HS PE Tchr 1979; Anacostia sr HS PE Tchr 1979-81; DC Pub Schls Adaptive PE Tchr 1986-88; Anacostia Sr HS PE Tchr 1988-; *ai:* Boys, Girls Cross Cntry, Girls Bsktbl Head Coach; Boys, Girls Outdoor Track; DCTU, AFT 1986-; DC Coaches Assn 1980-; V Street Block Club 1984-, Pres; Union Temple Bapt Church Man of Yr 1990; DC Coaches Assns Track Coach of Yr; *office:* Anacostia Sr HS 16th & R Sts SE Washington DC 20020

BRISCOE, PATRICK MORRIS, Conflict Resolution Counselor; *b:* Ridgely, MD; *m:* Brenda Sue White; *c:* Michelle Shreeves, Juanita Lynn, Darrell; *ed:* Glenville St Coll (BA) PE, Soc Stud 1965; Salisbury St Univ (MED) Admin 1983; 47 Addl Hrs; *cr:* James M. Bennett Sr HS Coach, His, Driver Ed Tchr 1965-74; Parkside HS Coach, Driver Ed Tchr 1975-94, Conflict Resolution Cnslr 1994-; *ai:* Wrestling, Ftbl Coach; Var Club Adv; Discipline Comm; MD Wrestling Comm Dist Rep; NEA, MSTA, WCTA 1965-; MD, Dists 7-8 Wrestling Halls of Fame; *office:* Parkside HS 1015 Beaglin Park Dr Salisbury MD 21801

BRISCOE, ROSSLYN MICHELLE, Business Teacher; *b:* Leonardtown, MD; *ed:* Univ of MD (BS) Indstrl, Technological Ed 1991; *cr:* Calvert Cty Pub Schls Bus Tchr 1992-; *ai:* Sigma Iota Sigma Girls Club Spon; Calvert Ed Assn, MD St Tchrs Assn 1992-; Alpha Kappa Alpha 1991-; Zion United Meth Church, Vacation Bible Schl Instr; *office:* Calvert HS 600 Dares Beach Rd Prince Frederick MD 20678

BRISSON, DONALD PAUL, English Teacher; *b:* New York, NY; *m:* Margaret Fody; *c:* Christine, Michael, Daniel, Nancy; *ed:* SUNY Stony Brook (MA) Lbrl Stud 1971; 90 Credit Hrs of Combined Grad, In-Svc Work in Ed, Eng, Comm, Area Stud, Mass Media; *cr:* Dawnwood Jr HS Eng Tchr 1966-70; Centereach HS Eng Tchr 1971-; *ai:* MCTA AFT NYSUT 1970-, Negotiator Local, St, Natl Rep; PAL 1981-82, Soccer Coach; *office:* Centereach HS 14 43rd St Centereach NY 11720

BRISSON, MATTHEW BERNARD, Health Teacher; *b:* East Patchogue, NY; *m:* Kathryn A.; *c:* Tara, Amanda, Reilly; *ed:* Oneonta St Coll (BA) Gen Stud 1983; Stony Brook Univ (MS) Arts, Lbrl Stud 1989; C. W. Post Univ Cert 1984; *cr:* Sachem Cntrl Schls Jr HS Hlth Tchr 1984-; *ai:* Var Girls Bsktbl Head Coach; IM Bsktbl Dir; SYAG Girls Summer Camp Bsktbl Co-Dir; Amer Heart Assn, First Aid CPR Instr; US Coast Guard, 100 Ton Inland Operator Capt; Suffolk Cty League I Coach of Yr 1993-94; *office:* Seneca Jr HS 850 Main St Holbrook NY 11741

BRITEZ, HELEN FERRANTE, HS Choral Director; *b:* Plainfield, NJ; *m:* Crispin; *c:* Ida; *ed:* Hartt Schl of Music (BMEd) Vocal Music Ed 1990, (MMEd) Choral Conducting 1992; *cr:* Hanover Park HS Choral & Spring Musical Dir 1992-; *ai:* Chamber Singers, Mens, Womens & Jazz Choir Dir; MENC 1986-; ACDA 1986-; *office:* Hanover Park HS 63 Mount Pleasant Ave East Hanover NJ 07936*

BRITO, ELIZABETH, English Dept Chair; *b:* Washington, DC; *m:* Joseph M. Jr.; *c:* Joseph M. III, Christopher; *ed:* Wittenberg Univ (BA) Eng 1970; Cambridge Coll (MED) Ed 1995; *cr:* Bristol HS Eng Tchr 1970-78, Eng Dept Chair 1978-94; Mt Hope HS Eng Dept Chair 1994-; *ai:* Curr Steering Comm; Steering Comm for Ten Yr Evaluation; Lang Arts Comm; ASCD, RIASCD, IRA 1989-; RI ASCD 1992-, Treas; NEA 1970-; Lib Bd; Amer Heart Assn 1990-; Christa Mc Auliffe Fellow; A Plus Awd from NEA; *office:* Mount Hope HS 199 Chestnut St Bristol RI 02809*

BRITT, DENISE EIZZO, Former Eighth Grade Teacher; *b:* Philadelphia, PA; *m:* Stephen J.; *c:* Benjamin Therman III; *ed:* Rutgers Univ (BA) His 1986; Chestnut Hill Coll (MED) Elem Ed 1989; *cr:* St Helena Schl Fifth Grd Tchr 1987-91, Eighth Grd Tchr 1991-94; *ai:* Safety, Yrbk Coord; Rel Comms.

BRITTAIN, JANET ANN WILMA BENKENDORF, Chemistry Teacher; *b:* Paterson, NJ; *m:* Russell James; *c:* Dorothy, Beverly; *ed:* Montclair St Coll (BA) Phys Sci 1960; Princeton Theological Seminary (MA) Chrstn Ed 1994; 10 Credits Phys Chem Fairleigh Dickinson Univ; 6 Credits Accounting Rider Coll; 4 Credits Cmptr Sci Mercer Cty Comm; Attnd Princeton Adult Schl; *cr:* Westfield Sr HS Chem Tchr 1960-63; Union Cath HS Sci Tchr 1976-82; Princeton HS Chem Tchr 1982-; Princeton Univ Visiting Lecturer Tchr Rep 1984-87; Somerset Presbyn Church Consultant Chrstn Ed 1988-90; *ai:* Sci Team Coach; Prin Advy, Grading, Use of Wednesday Comms; NEA, NJEA, NJSTA 1960-; PREA 1982-, Treas 1987-89; NSTA 1982-; ASCD; Somerset Presbyn Church 1967-71, Tchr, Church Schl Supt, Elder 1990-, Nursery Schl Bd Mem, Sec 1993-; Girl Scouts 1970-73, Lder; Young Life Comm 1986-92; Wrote Questions for HS Chem Achvmt Test, New Natl Tchrs Exam 1990-92; Steven's Inst Awd Excl Tchng 1989-90; Who's Who in Amer Ed; *home:* 35 Knoll Dr Princeton NJ 08540*

BRITTEN, RICHARD LANE, Business Education Chairperson; *b:* Anderson, IN; *m:* Deanna Lynn Smith; *c:* Megan Lane, Hannah Noel; *ed:* IN Univ of PA (BA) Bus Ed 1987; Liberty Univ Masters in Counseling 9 Hrs; *cr:* Johnsonburg Area HS Bus Ed Tchr 1988-; *ai:* Asst Ftbl, HS Head Wrestling Coach; Vars Club Adv; Newspaper Editdor; Curr Comm; Chrprsn of Cmptr Comm; Detention Co-Ordinator; NEA 1988-, Bldg Rep 1 Yr; Sunday Schl Tchr 1 Yr; Wrote Curr for SPOC Grant; *office:* Johnsonburg Area HS Elk Ave Ext Johnsonburg PA 15845

BRITTIN, BETH ANN, Middle School History Teacher; *b:* Ankara, Turkey; *ed:* Pensacola Chrstn Coll (BS) Elem Ed 1992; 23 Credits; *cr:* New Castle Bapt Acad MS His Tchr 1992-; *ai:* YELL Adv 1994-95; JV Field Hockey Coach 1992-93; JV Bsktlb Coach 1992-; Var Sftbl Coach 1993-; Jr Achvmt 1992-.

BRITTINGHAM, CINDY DENNIS, Business Education Teacher; *b:* Logan, OH; *m:* David; *c:* Emma, Polly; *ed:* Rio Grande Coll (BS) Bus Ed 1985; Northern KY Univ (M) Bus Ed 1995; *cr:* Fayetteville-Perry HS Bus Tchr 1986-88; New Richmond HS Bus Tchr 1988-; *ai:* Jr Class Adv 1989-92; JV Girls Bsktbl Coach 1988-91; JV Girls Fastpitch Sftbl Coach 1989-93; NEA, OEA 1986-; *office:* New Richmond HS 1131 Bethel New Richmond Rd New Richmond OH 45157

BRITTNER, STEWART E., Biology Teacher; *b:* Brooklyn, NY; *ed:* Elmira Coll (BS) Bio 1992; *ai:* Frosh Class, Future Physicians & Nurses Club Adv; Acad Quiz Bowl Team Asst Coach; NJEA 1994-; *office:* Millburn HS 462 Millburn Ave Millburn NJ 07041

BRITTON, RAYMOND GEORGE, Hlth & Physical Education Tchr; *b:* Trenton, NJ; *m:* Janice Lynn Meyer; *c:* Rhiannon; *ed:* Trenton St Coll (BS) Hlth & PE 1972; *cr:* Holmdel HS Drivers Ed Tchr 1972-73; East Windsor Regnl Schl Dist Hlth & PE Tchr 1973-74; M H Kreps Schl Hlth & PE Tchr 1974-81; Hightstown HS Hlth & PE Tchr 1981-94, Content Specialist, Hlth & PE Tchr 1994-; *ai:* Cross Cntry & Track Teams Coach; Outward Bound Adv; Leadership Team, Stu Achvmt Awds & Block Scheduling Comms; NEA 1972-; EWEA 1973-; NJAHPERD 1995-; Governors Tchr Recognition Awd; Bd of Ed Recognition Awd; Coach of Yr Awd In Cross Cntry Twice; Article Pub in The Reporter for NJAHPERD; 3 Dist Action Grand Awds for Outdoor Ed & Leadership Dev; *office:* Hightstown HS 25 Leshin Ln Hightstown NJ 08520*

BRITTON, TRICIA SARAPPO, 7th Grade Life Science Teacher; *b:* Wilmington, DE; *m:* Terry B.; *c:* Stephanie, Jacqueline, James; *ed:* Indiana U of PA (BS) Bio 1979; OH St Univ (BS) Sci Ed 1988; Shippensburg U of PA (MS) Bio 1994; *cr:* Cntrl Dauphin Schl Dist Sub Tchr 1988-89; Cntrl Dauphin East Jr HS 8th Grd Phys Sci Tchr 1989-93, 7th Grd Life Sci Tchr 1993-; *ai:* Silver Spring Presbyn Church Sanctuary Choir; Sci Olympiod Coach, Judge; Capital Area Sci, Engrng Fair Coach; Ski Club Adv; NEA, PSEA 1989-; CDEA 1989-, Meet, Discuss Comm 1995-; Indian Creek Rec Club 1989-, Bd Mem 2 Yrs, Treas 3 Yrs; Distngd Svc Awd 1995; *office:* Central Dauphin East Jr HS 628 Rutherford Rd Harrisburg PA 17109*

BRITVICH, JOETTA L., Chemistry Teacher; *b:* Brownsville, PA; *m:* Charles A.; *c:* Bradley Ryan; *ed:* The PA St Univ (BS) Bio 1977; CA Univ of PA (MS) Schl Psych 1985; Working on Scndry Prin Cert; *cr:* Gateway HS Chem Tchr 1979-83; Frazier HS Chem Tchr 1983-; *ai:* Spon Stu Trips to Europe 1994; PSTA 1995-; NSTA 1995-; Spectroscopy Soc of Pittsburg 1995-; PSTA Convention Presenter 1994; NSTA Convention Presenter 1995; *office:* Frazier HS 403 W Constitution St Perryopolis PA 15473*

BRIZZIE, MARGARET TRAUDT, Sixth Grade Teacher; *b:* Poughkeepsie, NY; *ed:* SUNY at Plattsburgh (BS) Elem Ed 1975; SUNY at New Paltz (MS) Elem Ed 1978; Hudson Vly Portfolio Assessment Project Fac 1993-; *cr:* Webutuck Schl Dist Fourth Grd Tchr 1985-89, Sixth Grd Tchr 1991-; *ai:* Dutchess Cty Area Fund Grants 1989, 1994; *office:* Webutuck Schl Dist Haight Rd Amenia NY 12501

BROADBENT, PEGGY MC CREEVY, First & Second Grade Teacher; *b:* Brockton, MA; *m:* Frank William; *c:* F. William, Susan Ann; *ed:* Wheelock Coll (BS) Early Chldhd Ed 1956; Syracuse Univ (MS) Elem Ed 1975; *cr:* Broadbent Primary Schl Owner, Dir, Tchr 1973-75; Fayetteville Elem Schl Combined First, Second Grd Tchr 1978-; *ai:* Gifted Ed Comm; AFT 1970-; Piagetian Article Pub NY St Cncl Children; *office:* Fayetteville Elem Schl 704 S Manlius St Fayetteville NY 13066

BROADHURST, SANDRA A. THORNTON-SHISL, Fifth Grade Teacher; *b:* Nashua, NH; *m:* Robert; *c:* Timothy Daniel Thornton, Kathleen Kelly Thornton Raymond; *ed:* Plymouth St Coll (BED) Elem 1964; 30 Credits Univ of NH at Notre Dame; *cr:* Salem NH Schl Dist 2nd-6th Grd Tchr 1964-; *ai:* Hlth Comm; Sci & Math Curr Revision Comm; Summer Schl Prgm; SEA 1964-; NEA 1964-; *office:* Haigh Elem Schl 24 School St Salem NH 03079

BROADMAN, SANDRA KAPLAN, Mathematics Teacher; *b:* Providence, RI; *m:* Ira; *c:* Jeprey, Stephen; *ed:* Brown Univ (BA) Sociology 1960; NY St Univ (MS) Ed 1963; 20 Credits Beyond MS in Ed, Math; *cr:* Myron J. Michael Jr HS Math Tchr, 1960-62; Arlington Jr HS Math Tchr 1962-65; Argyle Jr HS Math Tchr 1974-79; Wootton HS Math Tchr 1979-; *ai:* Peer Mediator Spon; NEA, MSMT 1974-; Beth Tikua Synagogue 1968-, Bd, VP; Women's Amer ORT 1965, Bd, Sec, Treas; *office:* Thomas S Wootton HS 2100 Wootton Pky Rockville MD 20850*

BROADWATER, MICHAEL ROBERT, Mathematics Teacher; *b:* Canton, OH; *m:* Amy Lynn Spencer; *c:* Ashley, Meredith; *ed:* OH St Univ (BS) Math Ed 1987; Kent St Univ (MA) Admin 1994; *cr:* North Royalton Math Tchr 1987-; *ai:* Bsktbl & Ftbl Coach; Articulation Comm Mem; North Royalton Educl Fnd Grant; *office:* North Royalton City Schls 14713 Ridge Rd North Royalton OH 44133

BROBST, DUANE JAMES, Economics Professor; *b:* Sellersville, PA; *m:* Maryann K.; *c:* Daniel Emerson, Rachel Emily; *ed:* Temple Univ (BBA) Ec 1986, (BBA) Finance 1986, (MBA) Finance 1987; *cr:* Bucks Cty CC Accounting Tchr 1990-91; Montgomery Cty CC Ec & Mrktg Prof 1987-; *ai:* Var of Church Functions; BSA; Robert Morris Assoc 1987-, Sr Mem; Harleysville Rotary 1993-, Charter Mem; *office:* Montgomery County Comm College 340 De Kalb Pike Blue Bell PA 19422

BROCCI, ANN SPENCER, Fourth Grade Teacher; *b:* Holland, MI; *c:* Michael A., Christopher A., Andrew T.; *ed:* North TX Univ (BS) Elem Ed 1961; Alfred Univ (MS) Ed 1980; *cr:* Lansing Cntrl Schls Third Grd Tchr 1961-63; Grubb Advertising Copy Writer 1968-70; Wellsville Cntrl Schls Adult Ed Tchr 1978-80, Third Grd Tchr 1980-89, Fourth Grd Tchr 1989-; *ai:* Grd Level Chm 1994-; HS Mentorship Prgm; Governors Environmental Ed Task Force; Odyssey of Mind Coach; NEA; Elem Tchr of Yr 1989; Excl Tchr Awd 1993; *office:* Wellsville Cntrl Schls 98 School St Wellsville NY 14895

BROCHU, DENIS O., Dean Acad Affairs & Fr Instr; *b:* Quebec, Canada; *m:* Linda L. Camp; *c:* Renee Alexandra; *ed:* Plymouth St Coll (BS) Fr & Span Lang Ed-Magna Cum Laude 1970; Rivier Coll (MA) Fr Lit 1978; Attnd Universite de Dijm; *cr:* Franklin HS Fr Instr & Chair of Lang & Art Dept 1970-83; Phillips Exeter Acad Fr Inst 1983-93, Dean of Acads & Fr Instr 1993-; *ai:* Head of Browning House; Acad Advising Comm Chair; Schl Yr Abroad Coord; Off-Campus Pgms Comm Chair; Past Comms: Curr, Dept Heads & Admissions; Dorm Head & AP Comms; AATF 1973-, Pres NH, Past Pres Awd & Runner Up Tchr of The Yr Awd & Philllips Exeter Brown Awd for Tchng; ACTFL 1993-; Spcl St Recognition Awd for Tchr of the Yr Project; *office:* Phillips Exeter Acad 20 Main St Exeter NH 03833*

BROCK, KEVIN L., Mathematics Teacher; *b:* Springfield, MA; *m:* Suzanne C.; *c:* Jennifer, Richard; *ed:* Westfield St Coll (BS) Gen Sci 1974, (MS) Sec Sch Admin 1981; Holyoke Comm Coll 18 Hrs; Westfield St & Worcester St 15 Hrs; Springfield Tech Coll 12 Hrs; *cr:* Kosciuszko Jr HS Sci Tchr 1974-76; Kiley Jr High Sci & Math Tchr 1976-; *ai:* Asst Wrestling Coach; Boys Soccer & Girls Sftbl Coach; Spfld Ed Assn 1981-; MA Tchrs Assn 1981-; W Spfld Soccer Assn Soccer Coach Yth; WS Park & rec Bsktbl & Bsbl Asst Coach; *office:* Kiley MS 180 Cooley St Springfield MA 01128

BROCKHOFF, TRACIE BLASKOVICH, Biology Laboratory Instructor; *b:* Pittsburgh, PA; *m:* Dale Eric; *ed:* PA St Univ (ASD) Sci, Med Lab Tech 1984; *cr:* PA St Univ Bio Lab Instr 1986-, Demonstration & Equipment Specialist 1995-; *ai:* Females Involved Regnl Schls in Tech, Eng Co-Dir 1993-; Engrng Exposition; Amer Soc of Clinical Pathologist, Bd of Registry 1984-; BSA 1988-, Dist Registrar, Merit Badge Cnslr, 1996 Scouting for Food Co-Coord; Begolly J. T. Brookhoff 1995 PA Assn 2 Yrs Coll; Ziegenfus, T. T. Brockhoff 1992, PA Acad of Sci; Ziegenfus, T. K. Neal, T. Brockhoff 1995, PA Acad of Sci; Begolly J. T. Brockhoff 1995 Amer Soc for Engrng Ed.

BROCKMAN, FRANK, Science Teacher; *b:* Philadelphia, PA; *m:* Francine Samson; *c:* Marla, Brianna, Beth (dec); *ed:* West Chester Univ (BSc) Hlth, PE 1961, (MED) Bio 1969; 75 Post Grad Credits from Drexel Univ, Gratz Coll, Haverford Coll, PA Environmental Ed Ctr, Rutgers Univ, St Josephs Coll, Temple Univ, West Chester Univ, Univ of WI at Lasalle; *cr:* Olney HS Hlth, PE Tchr 1961-62; Haverford Jr HS Sci Tchr 1963-87; Haverford HS Sci Tchr 1987-; *ai:* Tchr, Stu Mentor; HEART Comm; PSEA, NEA, HTEA 1963-; NSTA 1965-; Presented Paper 1977 NSTA Convention, 1978 PSTA Convention; Sci, Tech & Soc 1990, Natl Inst for

Tchrs of Bio 1991, Biotech Update Wkshp 1993 Grants; Alumni Awd Innovative Tchng Technique 1995; *home:* 74 Knollwood Dr Cherry Hill NJ 08002*

BROCKMAN, WILLIAM LEE, High School Mathematics Tchr; *b:* Columbus, OH; *m:* Eloise W. Wright; *c:* Leah M.; *ed:* OH St Univ (BED) Math 1970; Xavier Univ (MEd) Scndry Admin 1974; Ashland Univ 10 Hrs; Univ AL at Huntsville 3 Hrs; Univ Cntrl FL 3 Hrs; *cr:* Blendon MS Math Tchr 1970-75; Westerville North HS Math Tchr 1975-; *ai:* NEA, OEA, OTA & WEA 1970-; Acad Boosters 1975-; PTSA, PTA & PTO 1975-; All Star Brass Bands 1990-, Pres; Columbus & Suburban Cncl of Tchrs of Math; Tchr of Yr 1987; *office:* Westerville North HS 950 County Line Rd Westerville OH 43081

BROCKWAY, JOHN A., Fifth Grade Teacher; *b:* Bridgeport, CT; *m:* Betsy Holderle; *c:* Brian, Amie; *ed:* Wagner Coll (BA) Pol Sci 1965; Western CT St Coll (MS) Elem Ed 1975; *cr:* Carpenter Technologies Quality Inspector 1965-66; US Navy USS Saratoga VA176 Air Crewman 1966-68; Carmel Schls 5th Grd Tchr 1968-; *ai:* Wrestling Coach; Rocket Club; NYSUT 1968-; Carmel Tchrs Assn 1968-, Bldg Rep; Christ Church 1975-, Deacons Chm; Chamber of Commerce 1978-, Adopt-A-Hwy Chm; BSA 1951-, Cubmaster, Merit Badge Coach; UNICEF-Youth Ending Hunger, Rep; Exch Tchr to Great Britain 1974; Outstanding Elem Tchr of Yr 1979; DeWitt Clinton Awd-Masons 1990; *office:* George Fischer MS 275 Fair St Carmel NY 10512

BROCKWAY, SUSAN PALMER, Fourth Grade Teacher; *b:* New Haven, CT; *m:* Clifford E.; *c:* Eric W., Elizabeth B. Anderson, Linda B. Smith, Aaron D.; *ed:* New Haven St Tchrs Coll (BS) Elem Ed 1956; *cr:* North Haven Pub Schls Second Grd Tchr 1956-63; West Woods Chrstn Acad Third, Fourth Grd Tchr 1983-90, Fourth Grd Tchr 1992-; *office:* West Woods Christian Acad 165 Hillfield Rd Hamden CT 06518

BRODBECK, BARBARA, HS Math Teacher; *b:* Cincinnati, OH; *ed:* Univ of Cincinnati (BSEd) 1970; Xavier Univ (MS) Math in Ed 1986; 12 Hrs Summer Cmptr Kent St; Cmptr Assisted Instruction Inst for Math Ed; *cr:* Sawyer Jr HS Sci Tchr 1971-72; St Vivians Jr HS Sci, Math Tchr 1972-77; Mt Notre Dame HS Algebra Tchr 1972-78; Roger Bacon HS Math, Algebra Tchr 1978-; *ai:* Stdnts Against Substance Moderator; NEA 1988-; Articles Pub; Grant Summer Inst Kent St; *office:* Roger Bacon HS 4320 Vine St Cincinnati OH 45217

BRODBECK, CARL AXEL, Instrumental Music Teacher; *b:* Perth Amboy, NJ; *m:* Frednia Lois Johnson; *c:* Lisa, Max, Jonathan; *ed:* Alma White Coll (BS) Music & S Ed 1970; *cr:* Hubbard MS Instrumental Music Tchr 1973-75; W C McGinnis MS Instrumental Music Tchr 1975-; *ai:* Marching Band, Stage Band & Jazz Ensemble Dir; AFT 1975-; Ocean Cty String Band 1983-, Musical Dir; NJ Governors Tchr Recognition Awd 1994; Founded & Direct the Island Heights Instrumental Prgm at Island Heights Grd Schl Part-Time; *office:* William C McGinnis MS 271 State St Perth Amboy NJ 08861*

BRODER, LINDA H., Librarian; *b:* Philadelphia, PA; *m:* Robert M.; *c:* Melissa L., Hayley S.; *ed:* Temple Univ (BS) Elem Ed 1971, (MS) Elem Ed 1974; Villanova Univ Lib Sci Lib Cert 1990; *cr:* Smedley Elem Schl Classroom Tchr 1971-79; Kenderton Elem Schl Lang Arts Specialist 1983-86; Hanna Elem Schl Lib Sci Tchr 1986-90; Olrey Elem Schl Librn 1990-; *ai:* PFT 1971-; Women's Amer ORT 1976-, Region Ofcr; *office:* Olney Elem Schl 5301 N Water St Philadelphia PA 19120*

BRODERICK, CLARICE MILLER, Fourth Grade Teacher; *b:* New York City, NY; *m:* Robert; *c:* John (dec), Eileen; *ed:* SUNY at Plattsburgh (BS) Ed 1962; St John's Univ (MS) Ed 1967; Post-Grad Guid, Admin, Supervision; *cr:* Fulton Schl Tchr 1962-; *ai:* Math, Newspaper Clubs; Stu Cncl; Hempstead Tchrs Assn 1962-, Recording & Corresponding Sec; Excl in Tchng Awd 1985; NYSUT Awd for Exemplary Svc 1995; *office:* Fulton Elem Schl 40 Fulton Ave Hempstead NY 11550

BRODERICK, PATRICIA BEGLEY, HS Health Education Teacher; *b:* Flushing, NY; *m:* Kevin M.; *c:* Shannon, Erin, Meghan; *ed:* Suny Cortland (BSE) Hlth 1981; Adelphi Univ (MS) Spec Ed 1986; Post Grad 15 Credit Hrs; *cr:* Ithaca HS Stu, Sub Tchr 1980-81; Half Hollow Hills Schl DIst Sub, Leave Replacement Tchr 1981-82; Sachem Cntrl Schl Dist Hlth Ed Tchr 1982-; *ai:* Club Adv Random Acts of Kindness CLub; Aids Garden; Aids Quilt; AFT; NYSUT; Sachem Cntrl Tchrs Assn; Girl Scouts on & off Leader; Rel Ed Tchr St James Church; PTA 1983-; Tchr of the Week; *office:* Sachem HS South 51 School St Ronkonkoma NY 11779

BRODEUR, VIRGINIA CHAMBERS, Lead Teacher of Science Dept; *b:* Brighton, MA; *m:* Gerard R.; *c:* Todd; *ed:* Farmington St Coll (BA) Bio 1969; Rivier Coll (MS) Bio 1980; 30 Credit Hrs Boston Univ Sci Fellow 1984-85; *cr:* Wakefield HS Bio Tchr 1969-95, Lead Tchr 1995-; *ai:* Schl Cncl; Interdiscipline, Study Skills Comms; NABT, MTA, NEA, WTA 1969-; MASS, MAST 1986-.

BRODMERKEL, BETTY JANE MADUCA, Spanish Teacher; *b:* Bronx, NY; *m:* William; *c:* Douglas, Jon-Paul, Audra, Adam, Stephanie; *ed:* SUNY at Oswego (BA) Scndry Span 1968; SUNY at Stony Brook (MA) Lbrl Stud 1978; 75 Hrs Post Grad Stud; *cr:* West Islip HS Span Tchr 1968-70; Lindenhurst HS Eng & Span Tchr 1971-; *ai:* Schl Newspaper Adv; Tchrs Assn of Lindenhurst 1971; Long Island Lang Tchrs 1982; *office:* Lindenhurst Sr HS 300 Charles St Lindenhurst NY 11757

BRODSKY, CARYN GOTTLIEB, HS Spanish Teacher; *b:* Philadelphia, PA; *m:* Jeffrey M.; *c:* Wendy, Lisa; *ed:* Douglass Coll (BA) Span Ed 1972; 30 Hrs Grad Work Loyola Coll, Goucher Coll; *cr:* Chantilly Scndry Schl Span Tchr 1973-76; Howard Comm Coll ESL Instr 1980-88; Atholton HS Span Tchr 1988-; *ai:* Fac Advy Comm; Chair United Way Campaign; MSTA, NEA, MFLA 1988-; B'nai Brith Women 1978-, Past Pres; Stu Tchr Mentor 1994.*

BRODSKY, RICHARD, Retired English Teacher; *b:* New York City, NY; *m:* Tema Placer; *c:* Douglas, Allyson; *ed:* CCNY (BBA) Acctg 1963; St Johns Univ (MS) Eng 1967; NYU EDD Ed 15 Credit Hrs; *cr:* Parsons Jr HS Eng Tchr 1963-68; BN Cardozo HS Eng Tchr 1968-; *ai:* AFT, UFT 1963-; Eng Tchr of Yr 1973; SAT PSAT & Educl Tapes Appeared on Learning Channel.*

BRODY, ROSEMARIE (WOLFEL), English Teacher; *b:* Saint Marys, PA; *m:* Aaron W.; *c:* Zachary; *ed:* Thiel Coll (BA) Eng 1989; 25 Grad Credits; Northwestern St Univ of LA Writing Project; *cr:* Vernon Parish Schl Dist Eng Tchr 1989-91; Cameron Cty Schl Dist Eng Tchr 1991-; *ai:* Jr Class Adv; Tchr Writing Consultant; Prof Dev Comm; Stu Assistance Pgm; Creative Arts Cncl Spon; PSEA & NEA 1989-; Elk Cty Cncl on Arts 1985-; St Marys Book Club 1991-; Article Pub; *home:* 133 Averyville Rd Saint Marys PA 15857

BRODY, THOMAS COBB, Ninth Grade English Teacher; *b:* New York, NY; *m:* Helen Owens; *c:* Joshua, Liza, Kelly; *ed:* Univ of VA (BA) Eng 1960; *cr:* White Plains Reporter Dispatch Reporter 1958-59; Rome Daily Amer Reporter, Sports Ed 1959-61; Sports Illustrated Staff Writer 1962-70; Greenwich Cntry Day Schl Eng Tchr 1970-; *ai:* Fac Adv; Lit Publication; Bsktbl, Bsbl Coach; Shakespeare Stud Guide Julius Caesar; Critical Writing Format; 200 Articles Pub; *office:* Greenwich Country Day Schl PO BOX 623 Old Church Rd Greenwich CT 06836*

BROENIMAN, CLIFFORD SCOTT, Assistant Prof of Classics; *b:* Oconomowoc, WI; *m:* Elizabeth Broeniman; *ed:* Univ of WI (BA) Classics Greek & Latin 1983; Univ of IL (MA) Classics Greek & Latin 1986, (PhD) Classical Philology 1989; Amer Schl of Classical Stud at Athens Greece 1982; *cr:* Westminster Coll Instr of Classics 1988-89; St John Fisher Coll Asst Prof of Classics 1989-; *ai:* Dir of Lang Lab; Curr & Instruction, Lib Comm; Undergrad Adv; Great Beginnings Prgm; Strategic Planning Comm; Amer Philological Assn 1987-; Amer Schl of Classical Stud at Athens 1982-; NY Coll Eng Assn 1990-; Classical Assn of The Atlantic States 1990; Summer Research Grant, Author of Prof Articles Greek & Latin Lit His, Prof Reviews on Classical Antiquity & pub Lectures on Greek & Roman Lit & Early Church His; *office:* Saint John Fisher Coll 3690 East Ave Rochester NY 14618*

BROERMAN, DAVID W., Physics & Biology Teacher; *b:* Cincinnati, OH; *m:* Ralenda Hotze; *c:* Bradley, Gregory; *ed:* John Carroll Univ (BS) Physics 1965; Univ of Notre Dame (MS) Physics 1969; Tchng Xavier Univ; Bio Univ of Cincinnati; *cr:* Clermont Northeastern HS Physics, Math Tchr 1970-72; Finneytown HS Sci, Math Tchr 1972-75; Roger Bacon HS Physics Tchr 1975-78; Batavia HS Sci Tchr 1978-80; Walnut Hills HS Math, Sci Tchr 1981-; Raymond Walters Coll Lecturer, Math Tchr 1990-; *ai:* Amer Phys Soc 1965-; *home:* 3936 Brown Rd Hamersville OH 45130

BROGAN, FRANCES CROWLEY, Third Grade Teacher; *b:* Chester, PA; *m:* John J.; *c:* Jonathan; *ed:* West Chester Univ (BS) Elem Ed 1973; Univ of Scranton (MS) Ed 1976; 48 Grad Credit Hrs; *cr:* Mehoopany Elem Schl 2nd Grd Tchr 1973-74; Roslund Elem Schl 4th Grd Tchr 1974-78, 1st Grd Tchr 1978-90, 3rd Grd Tchr 1994-; *ai:* Portfolio Assessment Comm; NEA 1973-; Tunkhannock Area Ed Assn 1973-; *office:* Roslund Elem Schl 99 Digger Dr Tunkhannock PA 18657

BROGAN, MICHAEL SPENCER, Asst Prof of Phys Therapy Dept; *b:* Buffalo, NY; *m:* Victoria Ann Murphy; *c:* Kelly, Michael; *ed:* Erie Comm Coll (AS) Lbrl Arts Sci 1978; Daemen Coll (BS) Phys Therapy 1984; SUNY at Buffalo (MS) Hlth Behavioral Sci 1989; Yrs of Prof Continuing Ed Courses; *cr:* Sistes Hospital Phys Thrapist 1984-85; Daemen Coll Tenured Asst Prof 1985-; Geneva B Scruggs Dir of Phys Therapy 1985-; Manor Oak SNF Dir of Phys Therapy 1986-; *ai:* Amer Phys Therapy Assn 1984-; NY Phys Therapy Assn 1984-; Sports Phys Therapy Section 1995-; *office:* Daemen Coll 4380 Main St Amherst NY 14226

BROGA-NORTON, SANDRA, Professor & Pgm Coordinator; *b:* New Britain, CT; *c:* Jenifer Broga, Timothy Broga; *ed:* So Cntrl Comm Coll (AS) Bus Mgt, Admin 1983; Tieko Post Univ (BS) Bus Mgt, Admin 1985; Univ of New Haven (MA) Comm, Clinical Psych 1987; Attnd New England Schl of Alcohol Stud Bentley Coll 1986, Rutgers Summer Schl Alcohol Stud 1985; *cr:* So Cntrl Comm Coll Adj Fac 1987-92; Human Resource Ed Inst Dir 1988-91; Gateway Comm Coll F-T Fac Drug & Alcohol Rehabilation Prgm Coord 1992-; *ai:* CT Cert Bd 1991-, Chair Clinical Supv Comm, Intervention Cert; CT Fed Alcohol, Drug Abuse Cnslrs 1987-, VP, Ed Chair; CT Pvt Practioners 1991-; West Haven Task Force 1990-, Treatment Comm; Robert Johnson Wood Fnd 1991-, Treatment Comm; Shubert Theatre 1995-, Vol Performing Arts; Cnslrs Publication; Visiting Fac at Yale 1996-97; *office:* Gateway Comm Tech Coll 88 Bassett Rd North Haven CT 06473

BROK, STEPHANIE SUE, English & Writing Process Tchr; *b:* Reading, PA; *m:* Philip A. Yoder; *ed:* Kutztown St (BA) Comm 1976, (ME) Comm 1990; *cr:* Baltimore Schl Dist Jr HS Eng, Drama Tchr 1976-78; Wilson Schl Dist Jr HS Eng, Writing Process Tchr 1978-; *ai:* Jr HS Wrestling Timer; Stu Assistance Team; AFT 1986-; WEA 1978-86; Showman's Assn 1985-; Rdng Comm Players 1986-; Genesius Theater 1991-; APT Schlsp Comm 1984-; *office:* Wilson Schl Dist 2601 Grandview Blvd West Lawn PA 19609

BROKAMP, LISA MARIE, Science Teacher; *b:* Cincinnati, OH; *m:* Marc R. Gilioli; *c:* Kaitlyn R. Gilioli; *ed:* Univ of Cincinnati (BBA) Mrktg, Mngmt 1988; Xavier Univ (MED) Scndry Ed 1994; Bio, Gen Sci Cert 1991; *cr:* MCR Mrktg Sales, Tech Writer 1989; Zino's Inc Mgr, Trainer 1986-90; Withrow HS Bio Tchr 1991; St Ursula Acad Bio, Gen Sci Tchr 1992-; *ai:* Sci Olympics Team Co-Moderator; Yth Soccer Coach; NBTA, NSTA 1994-; *office:* Saint Ursula Acad 1339 E Mcmillan St Cincinnati OH 45206

BROKER, JAMES FRED, Electronic Tech Instructor; *b:* Greensburg, PA; *m:* Diane M. Matiasic; *c:* Michael, Christopher; *ed:* IN Univ of PA (Vocl) Voc Ed 1994; *cr:* US Navy Cryptologic Maintenance Tech 1977-90; Forbes Rd East Auts Electronic Instr 1990-91; Cntrl Westm Ctc Electronics Instr 1991-; *ai:* Voc Industrial Clubs of Amer Adv; HS Hockey Assoc Treas; Jeannette & PT Flames Roller Hockey Coach; PSEA Local 1990-, Sec 1994-; Penn Rod & Gun Club 1975-; *office:* Ctl Westmoreland Vo Tech Schl 240 Arona Rd New Stanton PA 15672

BROMLEY, KATHLEEN KAYSON, Economics Professor; *b:* Rochester, NY; *c:* Mark K., Nicole K.; *ed:* SUNY at Buffalo (BA) His, Ec 1966, (MED) Ed, Russion Stud 1968, (MA) Ec 1985; *cr:* Gates-Chili HS Sub Tchr, Summer Schl Tutor 1966-78; Monroe Comm Coll Ec Prof 1979-; *ai:* Mid St Steering Comm; AFT 1979-; Gates-Chili Hall of Fame, Treas 1993-; Ford Fnd Grant; 2 Supplement Workbooks Pub; *office:* Monroe Community Coll 1000 E Henrietta Rd Rochester NY 14623

BROMMER, WANDA MARSHALL, French Teacher; *b:* Easton, PA; *m:* George Kenneth Jr.; *c:* George III, Lucas; *ed:* Montclair St (BA) Fr 1970; Penn St, St Joseph at Kutztown & Allentown (MED) Ed 1994; *cr:* Salisbury Twp Schl Dist Fr Tchr 1970-, Dept Chair 1985-; *ai:* NEA; PSEA; PMLA; PTA, Pres; *office:* Salisbury Sr HS 500 E Montgomery St Allentown PA 18103*

BRONCHETTI, ROSEMARY ISABEL, Physical Education Teacher; *b:* Massena, NY; *ed:* Hudson Vly Comm (AA) PE 1977; Brockport St (BS) PE 1979; Potsdam St (MS) Elem Ed 1985; *cr:* St Lawrence Cntrl Schl PE Tchr 1988-; *ai:* Var Girls Soccer, Sftbl Coach; NYPEA 1990-; *office:* St Lawrence Cntrl Schl Rt 11 C PO Box 307 Brasher Falls NY 13613

BRONDER, JOSEPH, Department of Music Chair; *b:* Pittsburgh, PA; *ed:* Saint Vincent Coll (BA) Philosophy 1965; Saint Vincent Seminary (MDIV) Theology 1968; Yale Univ Schl of Music (MM) Music, Piano 1972; *cr:* Saint Vincent Coll Dept of Music Chair 1972-; Carnegie Mellon Univ Music Prep Division Tchr 1980-83; Duquesne Univ City Music Ctr Tchr 1991-94; *ai:* Concert Series Dir 1972-; Music Dept Concert Series Dir; BURDA Music Schlsp Selection Comm Chair; Coll Music Soc 1976-; MTNA 1995-; 80 Piano Recitals Performed 1972-88; Directed Camerata 1972-82, Prep Schl Choir 1968, Play of Daniel 1974; Pvt Post Grad Stud with Harry Franklin, William Masselos, Yoheved Kaplinsky; *office:* Saint Vincent Coll 300 Fraser Purchase Rd Latrobe PA 15650

BRONFMAN, EBEN MICHAEL, Adj Professor of Govt Dept; *b:* New York, NY; *c:* Allysa Currie; *ed:* John Jay Coll (BA) Govt & Pub Admin 1982, (MA) Crim Just 1989; *cr:* NYS Assembly Chief of Staff 1977-86; NY Cty Dist Atty Spcl Asst to the DA 1986-; John Jay Coll Adj Govt Dept 1989-; *ai:* John Jay Democratic Club Adv; NYS Demo Comm 1982-86, Elected Mem; NYS Dist Attys Assn 1986-; *office:* John Jay Coll 1 Hogan Pl 827C New York NY 10013

BRONNER, STEPHEN ERIC, Professor of Political Science; *b:* New York, NY; *m:* Anne Burns; *ed:* City Coll of NY (BA) Pol Sci 1971; Univ of CA at Berkeley (MA) Pol Sci 1972, (PHD) Pol Sci 1975; Univ of Tubinger Philosophy 1973; *cr:* Rutgers Univ Pol Sci 1976-; *ai:* AAUP 1976-; Caucus for a New Pol Sci 1975-, Preside 5 1995-; Fulbright AAYS Flwshp 1973-74, 1989; DAAP Flwshp 1990; *office:* Rutgers St Univ At New Brnswck Hickman Hall New Brunswick NJ 08903*

BRONSON, MARTHA B., Assoc Prof of Early Chldhd Ed; *b:* Cincinnati, OH; *m:* David Bennet; *ed:* Boston Univ (BA) Psych 1968; Harvard Univ (EDM) Human Dev 1970, (EDD) Human Dev 1978; *ai:* NAEY[illegible] APA; AERA; Numerous Books & Articles Pub; *office:* Bo[illegible] Campion Hall Chestnut Hill MA 02167

BRONSON, VINSON, Physics & Chemistry Teacher; *b:* Dallas[illegible] Margarete Friedrich; *c:* Lisa, Vanessa; *ed:* MIT (SB) Civil E[illegible] Ripon Coll (BA) Physics, Math 1953; Harvard (MED) Adm[illegible] Harvard Law Schl 1955-57; *cr:* Thayer Acad Physics & M[illegible] 1957-62, Summer Prgm for Advanced Sci Stdnts Univ & Lab E[illegible] 1959-61; Newton S HS Physics & Chem Tchr 1962-, Sci D[illegible] 1970-72; *ai:* Schl Cncl Tchr, Parent, Stu Bd; Mentor for Ne[illegible] Alternative Assessment Group; Past Adv Schl Newspaper; NE[illegible] NTA 1962-, House Rep; AFT, MFT, NFT 1975-77 VP; AAPT[illegible] Physics Tchr Awd; APPE 1985-; Presenter 1991 APPE Cornell [illegible] Process, Event Cosmology of Whitehead A Framework for In[illegible] Epistemology Into Sci Tchng; *office:* Newton South HS 140 Bra[illegible] Newton Center MA 02159*

BROOKER, MARK WILLIAM, Instrumental Music Tea[illegible] Syracuse, NY; *ed:* Onondaga Comm Coll (AAS) Music 1983; Potsdam (BM) Music Ed 1985; Syracuse Univ (MM) Music Ed 19[illegible] Crane Schl of Music; *cr:* Charlotte Valley CS Instrumental Music [illegible] Tchr 1985-87; General Brown CSVocal Music K-6 Grd Tchr [illegible] Lowville Acad Instrumental Music 7-12 Grd Tchr 1989-; [illegible] Ensemble; Marching Band; Colorguard; Pit Orch Dir; Effecti[illegible] Comm; NYSSMA, MENC 1985-; Catskill & Utica Symph[illegible] 1985-87; NY St Schl Music Assn Certified Woodwind Adjudicat[illegible] Lowville Acad & Central Schl 7668 State St Lowville NY 13367

BROOKER, WALTER RONALD,JR., Orchestra Dir & Strings [illegible] Springfield, OH; *m:* Cynthia Lynn Clark; *c:* Elizabeth K., R[illegible] Carolyn R.; *ed:* Bowling Green St Univ (BME) Music Ed 1985 [illegible] Music Ed 1989; *cr:* Findlay City Schls Strings Instr, Orch Dir [illegible] Sandusky City Schls Orch Dir, Strings Instr 1991-; *ai:* STRADS[illegible] Orch Conductor; NEA; SEA; MENC, OMEA, NSOA 1985-; Phi M[illegible] Sinfonia; *office:* Sandusky HS 2130 Hayes Ave Sandusky OH 44[illegible]

BROOKHOUSE, PHIL, 8th Grade Science Teacher; *b:* Lynn, [illegible] Patricia B.; *c:* John R., Kathy Karlsson; *ed:* Univ of ME Fa[illegible] (BSEd) Elem Ed 1974; Univ of Southern ME (MS) Prof Ed S[illegible] Summer Inst Tchrs of Gifted, Talented 6 Credits; Wastewater Te[illegible] Credit; Integrating Sci, Math Bates Coll 3 Credits; *cr:* US Army P[illegible] Spec 1969-72; Lewiston Schl Dist Tchr 1974-80, Asst Tchr [illegible] Commodom Cmptrs NE Region Educl Consultant 1980-81; Bates [illegible] Process Coord 1993-; Lewiston Schl Dist Tchr 1981-; *ai:* Educl [illegible] Team; Recertification, K-12 Sci Curr, Insurance Stud, Gifted, [illegible] Beacon Schl Grand Writing, Common Ground Tchng Steering [illegible] NEA, ME Ed Assn 1981-, Spec Svcs Comm, Rep Assembly Del; [illegible] Ed Assn VP 1990-91, Pres 1992-93, Pub Relations Chair, Geneva [illegible] Pub Svc 1993; MEA Benefits Trust 1993-, Vice Chair; Comm Littl[illegible] 1972-87, VP; Ust Unitarian Universalist Church 1972-, Trust[illegible] Rabboni Lodge Mason 1984-; ASCD 1984, 1 Yr; Lewiston As[illegible] Partnership 1994-; Steering Comm; ME Math & Sci Alliance Bd [illegible] *office:* Lewiston Jr HS Central Ave Lewiston ME 04240*

BROOKINS, GILBERT M., Prof of Mgmt & Org Stu[illegible] Gloversville, NY; *m:* Marlene E.; *c:* Jonathan, Elizabeth; *ed:* St [illegible] NY at Albany (BS) Bus 1966, (MS) Ed 1972, (CAS) Evaluatio[illegible] Harvard Univ Mgmt Inst; *cr:* Coll of Saint Rose Fin Aid Dir [illegible] Southern VT Coll Treas 1975-76; Albany Bus Coll Dean 1976-8[illegible] Coll Mgmt & OB Prof 1985-; *ai:* Stdnts in Free Enterprise Chptr A[illegible] Sftbl Coach & Mgr; Delta Pi Epsilon Grad Bus Honorary Soc 1975[illegible] Pres 3 Yrs; Eastern Acad of Mgmt 1990-; Eastern Casewriters Ass[illegible] Admin Mgmt Soc Chptr Pres; Bethlehem Republican Comm 19[illegible] Walton Fellow in Free Enterprise 1996; *office:* Siena Coll 515 Lou[illegible] Rd Loudonville NY 12211

BROOKINS, SHARON MARIE, Math & English Teacher; *b:* Jers[illegible] NJ; *ed:* Jersey City St Coll (BA) Elem Ed, Biol 1979; Working Tow[illegible] Admin, Supervision; St Peters Coll 3 SH; Fairleigh Dickenson 3 [illegible] St Patricks Schl Grd 1 Tchr 1979-84; St Peters Comm Prgm Kndg[illegible] Tchr 1984-87; St Patrick Schl Grd 2 Tchr 1987-87, Grd 3 Tchr [illegible] Grd 8 Math, Eng Tchr 1991-; *ai:* Adult Ed Tchr 1990-94; S[illegible] Moderator; Math Coord; ASCD 1994-; NCEA 1979-; NAACP [illegible] League; Cath Tchr of Yr 1993; Eisenhower Math Sci, St Pet[illegible] Challenge, Bell Atlantic Inennet Grants; Cath 10 Yr Svc Awd 1990 [illegible] St Patrick Schl 509 Bramhall Ave Jersey City NJ 07304*

BROOKS, AMY L., Physical Education Teacher; *b:* Dayton, [illegible] Murray St Univ (BS) PE & Hlth 1976; Univ of Dayton; *cr:* [illegible] Tilghman HS PE Tchr 1976-77; New Carlisle Jr High PE Tchr 1[illegible] Tecumseh HS PE Tchr 1980-; *ai:* Jr Var Sftbl Coach; NEA 199[illegible] Tchrs Assn 1993-; OHSAA Vllybl Ofcl 1994-; *office:* Tecumseh H[illegible] W National Rd New Carlisle OH 45344

BROOKS, ANDREW WAYNE, Fifth Grade Teacher; *b:* Parkersbu[illegible] *m:* Carla Sue Criss; *c:* Jacob Andrew, Adam Christopher; *ed:* Gle[illegible] Coll (BA) Elem Ed (Math Specialization 4th-8th Grd) 1983; WV [illegible] Hrs Admin; WA St Comm Coll 3 Quarter Hrs Cmptr Course; OH [illegible] Quarter Hrs Cooperative Learning & Dimensions of Learning; *cr:* [illegible] Elem Schl 7th-8th Grd Math Tchr 1984-94; WA St Comm Coll Ma[illegible] Algebra 1989-93; Barlow-Vincent Elem Schl 5th Grd Tchr 199[illegible] WLEA 1984-, Bldg Rep; *office:* Barlow-Vincent Elem School Rt 1 [illegible] OH 45784*

BROOKS, ANGELA CAMARDO, Mathematics Teacher & Team [illegible] Utica, NY; *m:* James A.; *ed:* Utica Coll of Syracuse Univ (BA) Mat[illegible] 30 Post Grad Hrs; *cr:* Utica City Schl Dist Tchr 1965-; *ai:* Natl Jr H[illegible] Adv; AFT; NEA; NYSUT; UTA; *office:* James H Donovan Schl 170[illegible] St Utica NY 13502

BROOKS, CARMI M., Accounting & Business Teacher; *b:* Vinela[illegible] *m:* Gregory; *c:* Ann Marie, Carolyn; *ed:* Rowan Coll (BA) Acctn[illegible] Monmouth Univ (MBA) Bus 1986; *cr:* Security Savings Bank F[illegible] 1987-92; Cumberland Cty Coll Part-time Instr 1991-95; Meridian B[illegible] Ofcr 1993-94; Sacred Heart HS Acctng Tchr 1994-; *ai:* Soph Clas[illegible] Beta Sigma Phi; NJBEA 1994-; *office:* Sacred Heart HS North E[illegible] Vineland NJ 08360

BROOKS, CAROLYN BRANCH, Dean & Associate Profes[illegible] Richmond, VA; *m:* Henry M.; *c:* Charles, Marcellus, Alexis, To[illegible] Tuskegee Univ (BS) Bio 1968, (MS) Bio 1971; OH St Univ [illegible] Microbiology 1977; Attnd Univ of MD, Univ of MN, IN Univ, Univ[illegible] at LaCrosse for Molecular Bio Trng; *cr:* Univ of MD Eastern Sho[illegible] Prof 1984-88, Assoc Prof 1988-, Ag Dept Chair 1992-95, Dean Sch[illegible] & Natural Scis 1995-; *ai:* Ag Club Adv; HS Stu & Undergraduates [illegible] Amer Soc for Microbiology 1980-; Natl Assn of Univ Women 198[illegible] Woman of Yr; MD Assn of Higher Ed Outstanding Ed Awd 1990; Sa[illegible] Army Youth Club Advy Cncl 1988-, VP; MD Multiple Schlerosis Li[illegible] 1994-; Acquired Several Federal Grants for Schlsps; Fac Awd for [illegible] Achvmt; 1st Annual White House Awd for HBCU Fac Excl in Scis &[illegible] Chancellors Research Scholar Awd 1988; Outstanding Fac A[illegible] Research; Dissertation Yr & OH St Fellowship 1972-74; *office:* U[illegible] MD Eastern Shore Research & Grants Bldg Princess Anne MD 21[illegible]

BROOKS, CAROLYN ELIZABETH, Social Studies Teach[illegible] Charlottesville, VA; *ed:* Norfolk St Univ (BA) His, Soc Stud 1971; M[illegible] Work Completed in His, Soc Sci Southern CT St Univ; *cr:* John Jr [illegible] ır 1971-89; Bunnell HS Soc Stud Tchr 1989-; *ai:* Stan Comm; nt Comm; Beginning Edctrs Support Team Mentor, Cooperating gm; NEA; NCSS; *office:* Bunnell HS 2 Bulldog Blvd Stratford CT

S, DIANE ROSE (HICKS), 4th Grade Teacher; *b:* Washington, William E.; *c:* A. Nicole Foreman; *ed:* James Madison Univ (BA) 65; Akron Univ (MS) Elem 1982; *cr:* Arlington Pub Schls Tchr ; Cincinnati Pub Schls Tchr 1966-67; Akron Pub Schls Tchr 1974-; *ai:* AEA; *office:* Hotchkiss Elem Schl 33 Dorcas Ave H 44305

S, GLENN MICHAEL, Business Education Teacher; *b:* n, NY; *m:* Yolanda Marie Breen; *ed:* Westchester Comm Coll s Admin 1983; Boston Univ (BA) Mngmt, Fin 1985; Pace Univ ndry Ed; *cr:* Carmel HS Tchr 1992-; *ai:* FBLA Adv; Child Stud HS Selection Comm; NYSUT 1992-; *office:* Carmel HS 30 Fair St NY 10512

S, JANET PFOHL, Social Studies Teacher; *b:* Oswego, NY; *m:* P. Jr.; *c:* Charles, Elaine, Stephen; *ed:* Agnes Scott Coll (BA) His, 1970; SUNY at Oswego (MS) Scndry Ed, Soc Stud 1976; *cr:* Ft Jr HS Math Tchr 1970-71; Sandalwood Sr HS Soc Stud Tchr, Stu 1971-74; Liverpool HS Soc Stud Tchr 1975-; *ai:* Adv Stu Cabinet; 1975-; CNYCSS 1978-; NYSCSS 1980-; Baldwinville Schls arent Advy Cncl; Girl Scouts of Amer 1993-, Troop Ldr; House III Yr; *office:* Liverpool HS 4338 Wetzel Rd Liverpool NY 13090

S, JAY STEVENS, Art Teacher; *b:* Batavia, NY; *ed:* -Mellon Univ (BFA) Painting, Drawing 1988; Columbia Univ Painting, Drawing 1990; Lehman Coll 12 Credit Hrs; SUNY at rt 3 Credit Hrs; *cr:* MS 180 art Tchr 3 Yrs; Monticello HS Art Tchr *i:* Art Club Adv; High Schl Musical; Cashetunk Sharpshooters ed Fox Game Preserve 1995-; Works Exhibited at Oxford Gallery; Monticello HS Port Jervis Rd Monticello NY 12701*

S, JEANNE NADEAU, French Teacher; *b:* Auburn, ME; *m:* ruce Sterling; *ed:* Univ of NH (BA) Fr 1971; Middlebury Coll 1990; 15 Credit Hrs Various Insts; *cr:* CES Jules Ferry Maitresse aire d'Anglais 1971-72; S A Sovoda Schl Biling Adm Asst ; Mt Blue HS Fr Tchr 1977-79; Mt Ararat HS Fr Tchr 1979-; *ai:* ng Dept Head 1980-; NEASC Schl Comm; Flame Conf Presenter AATF 1978-; ACTFL 1980-; FLAME 1979-, Pres 1990-91; NEA Articulation, Achvmt Project FIPSE, Coll Bd, ACTFL Spon 1996-; Mt Ararat HS 117 Main St Topsham ME 04086*

KS, JOAN BELTZ, Mathematics Teacher & Chprsn; *b:* Norwich, Leonard; *c:* Jennifer Lynn; *ed:* Cedarville Coll (BA) Math 1988; Heights Chrstn Acad Jr-Sr HS Math Tchr 1989-; *ai:* Sr, Jr Class *fice:* Valley Heights Christian Acad 75 Calvary Dr Norwich NY

KS, LISA DIANE, High School Band Director; *b:* Newark, DE; *m:* Dennis Crain; *ed:* West Chester Univ (BS) Music Ed 1987; Boston nglewood Inst, Univ of De Post Grad Credits; Univ of MD at Coll orking Towards MM in Music Ed; *cr:* Crisfield HS Band Dir ; Parkdale HS Band Dir, Inst Music Tchr 1994-; *ai:* Jazz, Pep, g Bands Pvt Instruction; MD St Tchrs Assn 1989-; Prince George's Assn 1994-; MD Band Dirs Assn 1989-; Univ MD Comm Band *office:* Parkdale HS 6001 Good Luck Rd Riverdale MD 20737

KS, MARY ANN A., Bus Dept Chair, Tchr & Adv; *b:* Ashland, OH; s Arthur; *c:* Mary-Jane Brooks Perkins, James Paul, Jason Andrew; mi Univ (BS) Bus Ed 1959; 5th Yr Grad Work IN Univ, Ball St Univ, Indianapolis, Univ of Dayton, IN Weslyn Univ, Purdue Univ 1992; ns Fork Schl First Grd Tchr 1959-60, Eng, Bus PE Tchr 1960-61; oblentz Schl Dist Bus Tchr 1961-66; Eaton City Schls Bus Dept Tchr 1967-; *ai:* Jr Class Adv; Prom Act 10 Yrs; Prom Act 3 Yrs z Schl; Chair North Cntrl Evaluation Comm; ECTA 1961-, Bldg eas, Sec; OEA, NEA 1961-; Preble Cty Ed Assoc Treas; Eta Pi 960-85, Pres, Sec, Treas; Petal & Stem Garden Club; Cntrl United hurch.

KS, MICHAEL M., Science Teacher; *b:* Glen Cove, NY; *m:* Judith; Kenzie; *ed:* St Univ of NY at Oswego (BS) Elem & Sci Ed 1989; St NY at New Paltz (MS) Sci Ed 1992; *cr:* Washingtonville MS Sci 989-; *ai:* AFT, NYSUT, STANYS 1989-; Washingtonville Tchrs 989-, Pres; *home:* 19 Farmstead Rd New Windsor NY 12553*

KS, RAECHELLE LYNNE, History & Typing Teacher; *b:* ctady, NY; *ed:* Cedarville Coll (BA) Bible 1994; Working Towards SL St Michaels Coll; *cr:* Perth Bible Chrstn Acad His, Typing Tchr 5; *ai:* Curr Revision Comm; Frosh Class Adv; Bapt Church of lle 1982-, Youth Coral Dir, Sunday Schl Tchr; *home:* PO Box 245 lle NY 12134

KS, REGINALD D., Athletic Director; *b:* Baltimore, MD; *m:* Renee Polson; *c:* Reginald Jr., Erika; *ed:* Morgan St Univ (BS) PE 4 Post Grad Hrs PE Bowie St Coll; 15 Post Grad Hrs Schl Admin Coll; *cr:* Catonsville HS PE, Hlth Tchr 1986-87; Owings Mill HS h Tchr 1987-88; Randallstown HS PE, Hlth Tchr 1988-94; Milford ad Ath Dir 1994-; *ai:* Head Ftbl, Asst Boys Lacrosse Coach; Var dv; MD Tchrs Assn 1990-; MD Ath Dr Assn 1994-; Baltimore Cty s Assn 1986-; *office:* Milford Mill Academy 3800 Washington Ave re MD 21244

KS, ROBERT, Comp Sci, His, Govt Lecturer; *b:* Savannah, GA; *m:* gers; *ed:* Univ of MD (BA & BS) His & Military Sci 1960 & 1965; bilt (MA) His 1962; Boston Univ (MA & MED) Intl Rel & Ed 1965 ; Nova Univ (EDD) Higher Ed 1992; Attnd Industrial Coll of Armed *cr:* US Army Ofcr 1950-74; Univ of MO Lecturer 1967-68, 1973-75 -; Brevard Comm Coll Adj; *ai:* Am Hist Assn 1973-; Ret Ofcrs Assn Laubach Literacy 1992-, Tutor; *office:* Univ of MD APO AE

KS, RONALD R., Asst Prof & Dept Coord; *b:* Beaver Falls, PA; *m:* . Hicks; *c:* Ronald R. Jr., JOhn H., Heather M. Cleary, Amy Hicks; egheny Coll (BS) Math, Ed 1962; SUNY at Plattsburgh (MA) Lbrl 994; *cr:* NY St Police Major, Retired 1964-90; Town of Plattsburgh Justice 1994-; Clinton Comm Coll Instr 1990-91, Instr, Coord 5, Asst Prof, Coord 1995-; *ai:* Curr, Safety Comms; Criminal Justice o-Adv; Criminal Justice Edctrs Assn of NY 1991-; Kiwanis Club *home:* 14 Westland Ave Morrisonville NY 12962

KS, STEPHEN MICHAEL, Scndry Soc Studies & Dept Chm; *b:* ille, OH; *m:* Kendra Paynter; *c:* Lukas; Abigail; *ed:* 35 Hrs Towards Soc Stud OH Univ; *cr:* Caldwell Exempted Village Schls Scndry ud 1986-; *ai:* Head Var Bsbl Coach 1987-; Asst Var Ftbl Coach Soc Stud Curr Dev Comm; *home:* 10300 Traci Ln Norwich OH

KS, WARREN HOLLAND, Retired Physical Sci Tchr; *b:* ws, VA; *m:* Victorine Fisher; *c:* Jauan Marissa; *ed:* VA St Univ (BS) Scndry 1955; 31 Addl Credit Hrs at Glassboro St Coll, Trenton St Monmouth Coll; *cr:* A. T. Wright HS Math Tchr 1956-57; Swift Jr ci Tchr 1957-70; Slaybaugh Mid Phys Sci Tchr 1970-92; Egg Harbor Mid 1992-94; *ai:* Sci Club, Banking Club & Stu Cncl Adv; Sci Curr r Evaluation Comms; NEA, NJEA & Atlantic Cty Ed Assn 1957-; arbor Twp Ed Assn 1957-, VP, Sec & Treas 13 Yrs; McKee Cty is 1976-, Pres 1 Yr, Sec 12 Yrs; Outstanding Sec 1979-81; Egg Harbor Twp Ed Fnd 1989-, Bd; Alpha Phi Alpha Grad Chapter; NJ Governor's Tchr of Yr 1987.

BROOMHALL, CHARLES H.,II, Phys Ed & Adventure Teacher; *b:* Lewiston, ME; *m:* Mary Altenbern; *c:* Jennifer, Pete, Jackie; *ed:* Keene St Coll (BSEd) PE 1977; Project Adventure Inc; *cr:* Kennett HS Tchr, Coach 1980-; *ai:* Ski Coach 1980-; NH Nordic Coaches Assn Pres 1989-90, 1992-94, VP 1995-; NH Team Ldr, Cross Cntry 1985-; Jr Class Adv; AAPHER 1984-; NEA 1983-; US Ski Assn 1980-; NH Coaches Assn 1986-, Pres 1991; Eastern Slope Ski Club 1970-, Bd of Dirs; White Mt Milers 1990-; NH Ski Coach of Yr 1989-90; Marathon Runner; *home:* Box 1651 Conway NH 03818

BROPHY, JAMES A., Third & Sixth Grade Teacher; *b:* Oneida, NY; *c:* Jane Martinez, Blakeman, Rhoda; *ed:* SUNY at Potsdam (BS) Music 1959; Hofstra Univ (MS) Admin 1974; Attnd Southampton Coll, Adelphi-Suffolk, Syracuse Univ, SUNY at Oswego; *cr:* Westhampton Beach Schls Music Tchr 1959-61; Oneida Consolidated Schl Elem Tchr 1961-62; Canastota Cntrl Schls Elem Tchr 1962-64; East Quogue UFSD Elem Tchr 1964-, Acting Prin, Supt 1968-71; BOCES I Summer Inst GATE Tchr 1978-; *ai:* Soc Stud Coord; Shared Decision Making, Schl Improvement Teams; Enrichment Team, Comm; East Quogue Tchr Assn 1965-, Pres 1966-69, Treas, Sec; NYSUT 1965-; NYSSMA 1959-61, 1994-; Hampton Cncl of Churchs Ecumenical Choir 1967-; Jaycees 1961-64; NY St Grant Inst in Clinical Team Supervision of Beginning Tchrs; Drafted & Received NYS Grant; Guest Speaker, Lecturer at Conferences; *office:* East Quogue Elem Schl 6 Central Ave East Quogue NY 11942*

BROSIUS, JANICE DEJESUS, French & Latin Teacher; *b:* New Bedford, MA; *m:* Donald L.; *c:* Michael, Christopher; *ed:* Regis Coll (AB) Fr 1968; Boston Coll (MA) Fr 1971; *cr:* Brockton HS Fr, Latin Tchr 1968-; *ai:* World Langs Frameworks Comm; MAFLA 1969-; CAM, CANE 1991-.

BROSKY, JEFFREY J., Health & PE Teacher; *b:* Allentown, PA; *m:* Colleen Sweeny; *c:* Emily, Olivia; *ed:* East Stroudsburg Univ (BS) Hlth, PE 1983; 24 Credit Hrs Penn St Univ 1986-93; *cr:* Allentown Diocese Elem PE Tchr 1984-88; Whitehall HS Scndry Hlth, PE Tchr 1989-; *ai:* Ftbl, Vlybl IM Coach; Schlsp Comm; NEA, PSEA 1989-.

BROSNAN, MARGARET CESLACK, Kindergarten Teacher; *b:* Bay Shore, NY; *m:* Edward J.; *c:* Susan L.; *ed:* Long Island Univ (BA) Elem Ed 1967, (MS) Rdng 1995; 20 In-Svc Credits; *cr:* Hampton Bays Elem Schl Kndgtn Grd Tchr 1967-; *office:* Hampton Bays Elem Schl 72 Ponquogue Ave Hampton Bays NY 11946

BROSSART, PATRICIA LOUISE, Lang Arts & Soc Studies Tchr; *b:* Hammond, IN; *ed:* Ball St Univ (MS) Elem Ed 1970, (BA) Elem Ed 1968; *cr:* Munster Pub Schls 5th Grd Tchr 1968-69; Newington Pub Schls MS Team Tchr 1970-; *ai:* NEA, Pi Lambda Theta 1968-; Music Series 1995-, Bd of Dirs; Dev Comm Svc Prgm; Article Pub; *office:* John Wallace MS 71 Halleran Dr Newington CT 06111

BROTSCHUL, DIANA, Computer Teacher; *b:* Passaic, NJ; *ed:* William Paterson Coll (BA) Elem Ed 1972; Fairleigh Dickinson Univ (MA) Human Dev 1977; 30 Addl Credits; *cr:* Hillside Schl 3rd Grd Tchr 1972-75; Brookside Schl 4th Grd Tchr 1975-79, 6th Grd Tchr 1979-89, Cmptr Tchr 1989-; *ai:* Cmptr Club Adv; NEA, NJEA Allendale Ed Assn 1972-; SS Peter & Paul's 1970-, Pres, Choir Dir 1989-, Gramota Awd; RO Choir; *office:* Brookside Elem Schl 100 Brookside Ave Allendale NJ 07401

BROTZMAN, JAMES W., Biology Tchr & Sci Dept Chm; *b:* Phillipsburg, NJ; *ed:* Lafayette Coll (BA) Bio 1968; West Chester Univ (MED) Bio 1974; 36 Grad Hrs; *cr:* Spring-Ford HS Bio Tchr 1968-, Sci Chm 1985-; *ai:* NEA, PSEA, SFEA, Montgomery Co Sci Tchrs Assn 1968-; NABT, PSTA 1988-; Greater Norristown Art League 1977-, Bd of Dirs, Mbrshp Chm; Univ of Chicago Outstdng Tchr Awd 1990; PA St Univ Outstdng Tchr of Hnrs Stdnts 1990-91; *office:* Spring-Ford High School 413 Lower Lewis Rd Royersford PA 19468

BROUGH, CYNTHIA L., Veterinary Medical Tech Prof; *b:* Carlisle, PA; *ed:* Edinboro Univ (BS) Ed 1977; IA St Univ (DVM) Vet Med 1988; *cr:* Private Practice Vet 1988-; Wilson Coll Vet Med Tech Prof 1991-; *ai:* Private Tutoring Math, Chem & Vet Med; AVMA 1984-; AABP 1988-; NAVTE 1991-; Newburg First Church of God 1995-, Sunday Schl Tchr; *office:* Wilson Coll Philadelphia Avenue Chambersburg PA 17201*

BROUGH, KATHLEEN WELTER, Third Grade Teacher; *b:* Elyria, OH; *m:* Jonathon Paul; *c:* Michael, Marc; *cr:* Otis Schl Spec Ed Tchr 1974-76; Washington Schl Second Grd Tchr 1976-79; Otis Schl Third Grade Tchr 1981-; *ai:* OEA, NEA 1974-; FEA 1974-, Rep; Friendship Circle 1980-, Pres, VP; Univ Women 1974-78; Jr Civic League 1980-1990, Treas, Pres; BGSU Falcon Club 1987-; *office:* Otis Schl 718 Brush St Fremont OH 43420

BROUGH, LINDA ANN, Eight Grade Science Teacher; *b:* Bronx, NY; *m:* Gary; *c:* Stephen, Christine Glockenmeier, Lenore Convery, Daniel; *ed:* St John's Univ (BS) Ed 1965; *cr:* Pope Pius X 5th Grd Tchr 1965-66; Our Lady of the Snows Schl Jr HS Sci Tchr 1981-93; Immaculate Conception Schl Jr HS Sci 1993-; *ai:* Yrbk Adv; BSA 1973-, Mothers Club Pres; Jr League of Queens Village 1969-79, Pres; *home:* 988 Maple Dr Franklin Square NY 11010

BROUGHAM, MARY THOMPSON, Fifth Grade Teacher; *b:* Sayre, PA; *m:* William K.; *c:* Natalie; *ed:* Alderson-Broaddus (BA) Elem Ed 1973; Elmira Coll (MED); *cr:* Retail Bus Co-Owner 1990-; Tioga Cntrl MS 5th Grd Tchr 22 Yrs; *ai:* Sunday Schl Tchr 9 Yrs; Exec Cncl Rep; Grd Level Bldg Comm; NEA 1989-; NEA-NY; Church of The Redeemer Musical Comm 1993-; *office:* Tioga MS 5th Ave Tioga Center NY 13845

BROUGHTON, JOHNNIE LEE, Seventh & Eighth Grade Teacher; *b:* Manhattan, NY; *m:* Roberta Glover; *c:* Christina, Leah, Celestine, Lisa; *ed:* Wilmington Coll (BA) Elem Ed 1979; *cr:* Gospel Mission Church Sunday Schl Tchr, Minister 1983-93; Melrose Comm Schl Tchr, Coach, Dean 1980-, Gospel Temple Chrstn Church Pastor; *ai:* Girls & Boys Bsktbl Coach; Tchr of Yr Awd; *home:* 1212 Olmstead Ave Apt 2B Bronx NY 10462

BROUILLARD, DIANE TRYBULSKI, First Grade Teacher; *b:* Ludlow, MA; *ed:* Elms Coll (BA) Math 1974; Univ of Hartford (MED) Admin 1990; Rsrch Better Tchng Course; *cr:* Liberty Schl Tchr 1975-81; Indian Orchard Elem Schl Tchr 1981-88; Mary A. Dryden Veterans Meml Schl Tchr 1988-; *ai:* Tchr in Charge Head Tchr; Grade Level Chprsn; Schl Centered Decision Making Team; NEA, SEA 1975-; Alumnae Assn Elms Coll 1974-; Alumnae Assn Univ of Htfd 1990-; Goodspeed Opera House 1995-; Math Grant Project 1987; Multi Cultural Grant Project 1989; *office:* Dryden Veterans Memorial Sch 190 Surrey Rd Springfield MA 01118*

BROWELL, MARILYN JEAN, First Grade Teacher; *b:* Roaring Spring, PA; *m:* George; *c:* Megan, Jeff; *ed:* Kutztown Univ (BS) Elem Ed 1973; Shippensburg Univ (MED) Elem, Early Chldhd 1975; *cr:* Northern Bedford Elem Schls Kndgtn Tchr 1973-77, First Grd Tchr 1977-; *ai:* Tech Comm; NBCEA 1973-; PSEA; NEA; PTO, Pres 1993-94; *home:* PO Box 2 New Enterprise PA 16664

BROWN, AIMEE J., Latin Teacher; *b:* Cleveland, OH; *m:* Christopher; *c:* Stephanie, Allison, Sharon, Stephen; *ed:* Cleveland St Univ (MA) Eng 1973; 6 Credits Post Grad Stud; *cr:* Oberlin HS Eng & Latin Tchr 1971-72; Cleveland St Univ Tchng Asst 1972-73; Berea HS Eng & Latin Tchr 1973-83; North Royalton HS Latin Tchr 1983-; *ai:* Latin Club Adv; ACL 1971-, Schlsp Summer Inst 1987; OCL 1993-; St FX PTU 1987-; MSA 1991-95; NRHS PTA 1995-; Schlsp to ACL Summer Inst 1987; Columnist for Pompeianna Newsletter 1995-; *office:* North Royalton HS 14713 Ridge Rd North Royalton OH 44133

BROWN, ALAN D., Third Grade Teacher; *b:* Altoona, PA; *m:* Diane M. Bryson; *c:* Kyle R.; *ed:* PA St Univ (BS) Elem Ed 1981; Master Equivalence ME Ed 1990; *ai:* PSEA, NEA 1981-; *office:* Altoona Area School District 910 Poland Ave Altoona PA 16601

BROWN, ALBERT BRIAN, Fourth Grade Teacher; *b:* Petoskey, MI; *m:* Cathleen Sue; *c:* Stephanie, Michelle; *ed:* Bowling Green St Univ (BSEd) Elem Ed 1976, (MS) Educl Adm & Supvr 1982; *cr:* Kenwood Elem Schl 5th Grd Tchr 1976-77; Bowling Green City Schls Elem Tchr 1976-; South Main Elem Schl 4th Grd Tchr 1977-; *ai:* CADETS Fac Adv; Woodco Federal Credit Union Bd of Dir; BGSU Make A Bright Choice Pgm; BGSU HPER Hlth Practicum Stu & Intern Field Site; BGSU I CAN DO Pgm; OAESA 1994-; NEA; BGEA; Med Coll of OH 2 Yrs, Staff; South Main PTO 19 Yrs, Advocate & Supporter; South Main PTO Ice Cream Soc, Master of Ceremony; Stu Cncl Fac Adv 16 Yrs; Stu Cncl Talent Show Dir & Producer 16 Yrs; CADETS Founder; Presenter at SECO Sci Conf 1991; Career Day Coord 17 Yrs; Finalist BGCSD Tchr of Yr 1986; *office:* South Main Elem Schl 437 S Main St Bowling Green OH 43402*

BROWN, ANDREW JACKSON,JR., Counselor; *b:* Washington, DC; *m:* Barbara Stowell Battison; *c:* Andrew J. III, Rebecca I. Petricoin; *ed:* Bowie St Univ (BS) Elem Ed 1974, (MED) Guid, Counseling 1985; 30 Addl Hrs; *cr:* Queen Anne Schl PE Tchr 1971-72, 1977-82; Calvert Co Pub Schls PE Tchr 1974-77, 1982-92, Cnslr 1992-; *ai:* VICA Adv; MS Girls Bsktbl, Sftbl Coach; Optimist 1995-; CEA 1974-; VICA 1992-; Chamber Commerce 1993-; AVA 1994-; Coach of Yr 1987; Tchr of Month 1994; *office:* Calvert Career Ctr 330 Dorsey Rd Prince Frederick MD 20678

BROWN, ANTHONY L., Program Coordinator of Tutors; *b:* Boston, MA; *m:* Annette J. Adams-Brown; *c:* Anthony L. II; *ed:* SUNY Coll at Cortland (BA) Theatre Arts 1989; Syracuse Univ (MFA) Drama 1996; *cr:* Urban League of Onondaga Cty Field Placement Coord 1989-90; Syracuse Univ Adj Dance Instr 1993-95; Onondaga Comm Coll Prgm Coord of Tutors 1990-; *ai:* IM Bsktbl; Syracuse Univ Minority Mentorship Prgm Adv; Minority Access Consortium 1992-; Omega Psi Phi 1993-, Editor; *office:* Corcoran HS 919 Glenwood Ave Syracuse NY 13207

BROWN, ARLENE BARBARA, Mathematics Dept Chairperson; *b:* Pawtucket, RI; *m:* George F.; *c:* Mike Cram, Donna L. Pereira; *ed:* Clarkson Univ (MS) Math 1969; Bridgewater St Coll (BSED) Math 1962; Attnd Northeastern Univ, Portland Univ, Boston Univ, Harvard Univ; *cr:* Seekonk Jr HS Math, Sci Tchr 3 Yrs; Medway Pub Schls Jr High Math Tchr 3 Yrs, HS Math Tchr 20 Yrs, Dept Chair, Tchr 11 Yrs; *ai:* Math Coord; AFT; Medway Tchrs Assn; NCTM; ATMIM; OCTM; ATMNE; Tchr of Yr Jaycees; Exemplary Prgm Grant Ed for Ec Seurity Act; Article Pub; Recognition for Contribution & Achvmt Awd New England Region Coll Bd; *office:* Medway Pub Schls 45 Holliston St Medway MA 02053

BROWN, BARBARA ANN, PE & Special Ed Teacher; *b:* Oceanside, NY; *ed:* Suffolk Comm Coll (AAS) Liberal Arts 1977; Cortland St Coll (BSEd) PE 1979; Hofstra Univ (MS) Spec Ed 1981; 60 Addl Credits in Eng; *cr:* North Babylon Pub Schl PE Tchr 1982-; *ai:* Var & MS Vlybl Coach; Girls Ldrs Club Adv; AFT 1981-; NBTO 1982-; *office:* North Babylon HS 1 Phelps Ln North Babylon NY 11703

BROWN, BETH LEE, Spanish Teacher; *b:* Cumberland, MD; *ed:* Frostburg St Univ (BA) Span 1989; *cr:* Biospherics Inc Information Specialist, Translator 1989-90; Berkeley Springs HS Span Tchr 1990-92; Allegany HS Span Tchr 1992-; *ai:* Tchr of Yr Selection Chprsn; ACTA Bldg Rep; Tri-Hi-Yi Org Adv Berkeley Springs HS 1991-92; NEA, 1992-, Bldg Rep 1994-; Ladies Auxi of Moose 1994-; *office:* Allegany HS 616 Sedgwick St Cumberland MD 21502*

BROWN, BETTINA BELEFONTE, Literature Teacher; *b:* Philadelphia, PA; *m:* Francis X. Jr.; *c:* Arlene Baratz, Melanie Fukui, Francis X. III; *ed:* West Chester St (BS) Elem Ed 1955; Univ of PA (MS) Elem Ed, Rdng Specialist 1958; 30 Addl Credits Univ of Pittsburgh; *cr:* Hillcrest Elem Schl 5 Grd Tchr 1956-58; Marple Elem Schl 5-6 Grd Tchr 1967-69; Peters Twp MS 6-8 Grd Rdng, Lit Tchr 1976-; *ai:* Co-Dir Variety Show 1978-; Co-Spon Stu Cncl 1978-; Spon Eng Lit Festival 1992-; NEA 1956-58, 1976-80; AFT 1980-; Keystone Rdg Assoc 1976-; Phi Delta Kappa 1991-; NCTE 1988-; League Women Voters 1975-78; Pinellas Cty League to Aid Retared Children Forever 1969-75, Treas, Tchr Liaison; PTA; Vly Forge Family Inst Gift of Time 1989-90; Most Influential Person in My Acad Life from Stu at PA Governor's Schl 1990; *office:* Peters Township MS 625 E Mcmurray Rd Mc Murray PA 15317

BROWN, CAMILLE LEWIS, Principal; *b:* Philadelphia, PA; *c:* Joshua K.; *ed:* Franklin & Marshall Coll (BA) His 1981; St Charles Borremo Seminary (MA) Theology 1994; Ctr Improvement Child Care Effective Parenting Trng; *cr:* Phila Bd of Ed Tchr 1980-81; A. L. Williams Sales Mrktg Assoc 1983-90; Our Lady of Victory Schl Tchr 1990-94; St Therese of Child Jesus Schl Prin 1994-; *ai:* Effective Black Parenting Skills Instr; Master Rel Tchr Archdiocese of Philadelphia; Elem Schl Admin Assn 1994-; Cath Yth Org 1990-, Coord; St Carthage Cath Church, Catechist; *office:* St Therese of Child Jesus Schl Anderson & Upsal Sts Philadelphia PA 19119

BROWN, CANDICE ANN, Assistant Professor; *b:* Tucumcari, NM; *ed:* NM St Univ (BA) Theatre Arts 1987; Univ of Pittsburgh (MFA) Acting 1993; *cr:* SUNY Coll at Fredonia Asst Prof 3 Yrs; *ai:* Dir, Voice Coach Theatre Arts; Affirmative Action, Women's His Moth Comms; Presidential Appointee Cncl for Women's Concerns; Fac Cncl Arts & Hum Rep; URTA Coaching; Excl in Directing Awd 1994 Theatre Assn of NY St; *office:* S U N Y Coll At Fredonia 212 Rockefeller Arts C Fredonia NY 14063

BROWN, CAROLE THAYER, World Studies Teacher; *b:* Washington, DC; *c:* Gregory, Andrew, Daniel; *ed:* Univ of MD (BA) Geog & Ed 1969; Masters Equivalency Through Course Work U of MD; In Svc in Montgomery Cty; *cr:* North Bethesda Jr HS Classroom & 8th Grd Soc Stud Tchr 1969-77; Several Schl Part-Time Classroom & 7th & 8th Grd Tchr 1977-83; Hoover MS Classroom & 7th Grd Soc Stud Tchr 1984-89; EB Wood MS Classroom & 8th Grd Soc Stud Tchr 1989-; *ai:* MSAP Chprsn; Awds Comm Co Chair; MCEA, MSTA & NEA 1989-; Mid Sts Soc Stud Assn 1994-, Annual Convention of Mid Sts Region Presenter; Manor Lake Civic Assn 1992-, Ed Chprsn; Excl in Tchng Awd LORAL Corp 1994; *office:* Earle B Wood MS 14615 Bauer Dr Rockville MD 20853

BROWN, CAROLYN COSBY, 6th Grade Teacher; *b:* Richmond, VA; *m:* Warren Stuart; *c:* Tamara Lynette; *ed:* VA Union Univ (BA) Ed 1968; Bowie St Univ (MED) Elem Ed 1979; *cr:* Garfield Elem Schl Classroom Tchr 1968-; *ai:* Local Schl Restructuring Team, Grd Chprsn; AFT, WA Tchrs Union 1968-; *home:* 11815 Fairgreen Ln Upper Marlboro MD 20772

BROWN, CATHERINE ALICE, Vocal Music Teacher; *b:* Cleveland, OH; *m:* J. Douglas; *c:* Christine, Nathan; *ed:* OH Univ (BM) Music 1975; Cleve St Univ Off Cert Level I 1977; Memphis St Univ Off Cert Level II 1978; Univ of OK Kodaly Cert 1990; *cr:* Fairbanks Local Schls Vocal Music Tchr 1975-76; Bucyrus City Schls Vocal Music Tchr 1976-77; Norman City Schls Vocal Music Tchr 1977-80; Moore City Schls Vocal Music Tchr 1982-90; Lancaster City Schls Vocal Music Tchr 1990-; *ai:* Spcl Olympia Auron Coach; Vocal Coach for Dist 15 Solo & Ensemble Contest; MENC & OMEA 1975-; ACDA 1980-; OEA 1990-; Lancaster-Fairfield Yth Choir 1992-, Select Cty Wide Choir, Founder; Whos Who Among Young Women

1978; Kelley Elem Moore Tchr of Yr 1989; *office:* General Sherman Jr HS 701 Union St Lancaster OH 43130*

BROWN, CATHERINE MARGARET (EDENFIELD), Physical Education Teacher; *b:* Staten Island, NY; *m:* Dwayne Allen; *c:* Timothy, Thomas; *ed:* Glassboro St Coll (BS) Hlth & PE 1983; NDIETA Aerobic Cert; *cr:* Ceril S. Collins Elem Schl Hlth & PE Tchr 1983-91; Russell O. Brackman MS PE Tchr 1991-; Step Aerobic Instr; *ai:* Girls Sftbl Coach 1987-94; Boys & Girls Cross Cntry Coach 1986-94; Mentor Prgm; Conflict Mediation & Peer Leadership Adv; Site Based Mngt; Liaison Comm; Jump Rope for Heart Coord; AFT 1983-; NJAHPERD 1981-, Stu Div, VP, Eastern Dist Rep Actus VP; AAHPERD 1984-; Amer Red Cross 1983-, Instr, 5 & 10 Yr Awds; Boy Scouts of Amer Summer Camp First Aid Dir; *office:* Russell O Brackman MS 23 Birdsal St Barnegat NJ 08005

BROWN, CELIA D., Seventh Grade English Teacher; *b:* Wakefield, RI; *m:* Donald M.; *c:* Whitney A.; *ed:* Univ of RI (BA) Eng 1966; 36 Addl Hrs Eng 1971; 27 Credits Diversified Course Work; *cr:* Ex-West Greenwich Regnl Dist 4 Grd Tchr 1966-70, 5 Grd Tchr 1970-90. 7 Grd Tchr 1990-; *ai:* Curr Advy Comm; NEA 1967-; EWGTA 1967-, Pres, Currently Bldg Rep; RICTE 1990-; *office:* Exeter-West Greenwich Jr HS 930 Nooseneck Hill Rd West Greenwich RI 02817

BROWN, CHRISTOPHER ROBIN, Science Teacher; *b:* Cincinnati, OH; *m:* Margaret Pletikapich; *c:* Morgan; *ed:* Univ of Cincinnati (BS) Ed 1986, (MA) Educl Admin 1991; Post Grad Toward Supt Cert; *cr:* Harrison Jr Schl Sci Tchr 1986-; *ai:* Var Vlybl Coach 1986-; Chprsn Levy Steering Comm; Strategic Planning Comm, Dist; ASCD 1992-; Natl Mid Schl 1993-; Vlybl Coach of Yr 5 Times; Hamilton Cty Friends of Ed Awd 1993; Tchr of Yr 1991-92; Admin Dev Acad Univ of Cincinnati 1990; *home:* 3968 Buckridge Dr Okeana OH 45053

BROWN, CLAIRE TOBISON, English Teacher; *b:* New York City, NY; *m:* Robert M.; *c:* Keith, Adam, Tyler; *ed:* Skidmore Coll (BA) Eng 1969; St Univ of NY at Albany (MA) Eng 1974; *cr:* Shenendehowa Cntrl Schls Eng Tchr 1974-; *ai:* AFT, NYSUT, STA; NCTE; Phi Delta Kappa; NY St Cncl for the Hum Inst Summer 1995; NYSUT Trainer & Facilitator; Adjunct-Saint Rose Coll Long Island Univ; *office:* Shenandehowa Schl 970 Rt 146 Clifton Park NY 12065

BROWN, CLARICE NOLDEN, HS Physical Ed & Health Tchr; *b:* San Antonio, TX; *m:* Ronald; *c:* Darius Ryan; *ed:* TX Southern Univ (BS) All-Level PE 1985; 9 Credit Hrs Grad Class; *cr:* Woodrow Wilson Elem PE Tchr 1985-88; Yokota HS Hlth Ed Tchr 1988-92; David Glasgow Farragut HS PE & Hlth Ed Tchr 1992-; *ai:* Coached 6 Yrs Girls Vlybl, 3 Yrs Boys Vlybl, 3 Yrs JV Girls Bsktbl, 1 Yr Girls Soccer, 1 Yr Chrldng; 8th-10th Grd Class Spon; OEA 1988-; *office:* David Glasgow Farragut HS Psc 819 Box 63 FPO AE 09645*

BROWN, CLINTON HARVEY, Chemistry Teacher; *b:* Elkton, MD; *m:* Virginia Sieber; *c:* Christy, Jeremey, Jim, Michael, Robby, Trevor; *ed:* Towson St Univ (BS) Bio & Chem 1970; Univ of MD at College Park (MA) Sci Ed 1973; *cr:* Thomas S Wootton HS Bio Tchr 1970-77, Chem Tchr 1995-; Richard Montgomery HS Resource Tchr 1977-95; Hebrew Acad Chem Tchr 1995-; *ai:* Editorial Review Team Newtons Apple 1994-; Outstdng Scndry Schl Tchr Gifted & Talented Assn of Montgomery Cty 1993-94; Article Pub 1980; *home:* 8010 Seneca View Dr Gaithersburg MD 20882*

BROWN, DARLA JEAN WILLIAMS, 8th Grade Math & Algebra Tchr; *b:* Gallipolis, OH; *m:* R. Duane; *c:* Julie, Lisa; *ed:* Hiram Coll (BA) Ed 1965; Kent St Univ (MED) Master Tchr 1986; 15 Credit Hrs from Kent St, Ohio St, Ashland Univ; *cr:* Parma Ridgebrook Elem Schl 6th Grd Tchr 1965-67; KSU Grad Asst 1967-68; Weymouth Schl 6th Grd Tchr 1968-70; Wadsworth MS 7th Grd Tchr 1970-75; Wadsworth City Schls 3rd, 4th, 8th Grd Tchr 1986-; *ai:* Adv to MS Drama Club; Asst Dir of Musical Godspell, Joseph; First Chrstn Church, Soc Chprsn of Women's Network; Girl Scout & Scout Ldr 30 Yrs; *office:* Wadsworth Cntrl MS 151 Main St Wadsworth OH 44281

BROWN, DARLENE TEN EYCK, Biology Teacher; *b:* Poughkeepsie, NY; *m:* Paul J.; *c:* Michael, Kristen; *ed:* Rochester Inst of Tech (BS) Bio 1971; St Univ Coll at New Paltz (MA) Bio 1981; Courses in Ed; *cr:* St Francis Histology, Med Lab Technologist 1971-72; Dutchess Comm Coll Instr, PT, FT 1981-85; *ai:* Districtwide Inservice, Schlsp Comms; Bldg Advy; NYS Flwshp Sci Tchr Trng; Regents Schlsp; *office:* Beacon HS 72 Fishkill Ave Beacon NY 12508*

BROWN, DAVID LAUREN, Instrumental Music Teacher; *b:* Fremont, NE; *m:* Judby Hendriksen; *c:* Jason, Scott; *ed:* Univ of NE (BS) Music Ed 1975; 10 Addl Hrs Music; *cr:* Teaneck Pub Schls Brass Specialist, Elem Instumental Music Tchr 1977-89; Thomas Jefferson MS Instrumental Music Tchr 1990-; *ai:* Jazz Band; MENC, IAJE 1979-; NJEA 1977-; *office:* Thomas Jefferson MS 655 Teaneck Rd Teaneck NJ 07666

BROWN, DEBRA MAHONEY, Kindergarten Teacher; *b:* Cleveland, OH; *m:* Kenneth Lee; *c:* Lisa M., Lori A.; *ed:* Walsh Univ (BA) Elem Ed 1975; *cr:* St Barbara Schl Kndgtn Tchr 1976-77; St Mary Schl Kndgtn Tchr 1979-; *ai:* Cath Schls Week Comm Chm; Mission Comm; NCEA 1979-; Ashland Oil Tchr Achvmt Awd; OCEA St Convention Wkshp Presenter; *office:* St Mary Schl 726 1st St NE Massillon OH 44646

BROWN, DEBRA URSULA, English Teacher; *b:* Trinidad, West Indies; *c:* Jamal; *ed:* Brooklyn Coll (BS) TV, Radio Comm 1984; Queens Coll (MS) Sec Educ, Eng 1991; *cr:* NYC Bd of Ed Tchr 1995-; *ai:* Lead Tchr of Anderson Acad; Conflict Resolution Specialist, Mediator; Poetry Adv; AFT, UFT 1985-; Curr Writer; Publish Acad Newsletter; *office:* George W Wingate HS 600 Kingston Ave Brooklyn NY 11203

BROWN, DENNIS MICHAEL, 7th Grade Teacher; *b:* Jersey City, NJ; *m:* Suzanne ODonnell; *c:* Heather, Keri; *ed:* Jersey City St Coll (BA) Gen Elem Ed 1970; Seton Hall Univ (MA) Admin & Ed Supervision 1977; Glassboro St Coll Credits; *cr:* Harry L. Bain Schl 7th & 8th Grd Tchr 1970-87; West NY Dist Asst Prin & Substance Awareness Coord 1987-89; West NY PS #3 7th & 8th Grd Tchr 1989-; *ai:* Schl Improvement Team Mem; After Schl Math Enrichment Tchr; Girls Bsktbl Coach; Breakfast & Lunch Pgm Monitor; Chess Tournament Spon; West NY Ed Assn 1970-; NJ Ed Assn 1970-; NEA 1970-; Holy Name Soc of ICC 1972-, Pres; Parish Cncl of ICC 1987-, Trustee; WNY Vision 2000 1995-, Charter Mem; Penn St Parent Alumni Assn 1995-; Pub in Book of Poetry 1993; Glassboro St Coll Schlsp; Secaucus Bd of Ed Trustee Awd; Secaucus New Democratic Org Pres; *office:* PS #3 5401 Polk St West New York NJ 07093*

BROWN, DIANN ELLEN (GEISER), Jr HS Soc Stud & Eng Teacher; *b:* Napoleon, OH; *m:* William Dana; *c:* William Geiser, Jayson Geiser, Stacy Geiser; *ed:* OH Northern Univ (BS) Music Ed 1970; Bowling Green St Univ (MS) Elem Ed 1975; 21 Addl Hrs Motivation, Gifted, Geography & His Bowling Green St Univ; Cmptr Univ of Toledo; Political Sci Xavier Univ; Skills for Adolescence Western MI; Immigration Georgetown Univ; OH Geographic Summer Inst OH St Univ; *cr:* Patrick Henry Local Schls 2nd Grd Tchr 1969-70, Vocal Music 5-12 1970-74, 3-6 Grd Tchr 1974-82, Jr HS Soc Stud & Eng Tchr 1982-; *ai:* 7th Grd Vlybl Coach; Musical Asst Dir; Citizenship; Rdng & Eng Proficiency Test Tutor; Writing Competency Test Evaluator; Curr Comm for Soc Stud; Chrldr Adv; NEA, OEA, NWOEA 1970-, Outstanding Service 1985-86; PHEA 1970-, Pres, Sec, Building Rep & Bd Liasion; OCTELA 1991-; ASCD; OH Geographic Alliance 1992-; OCSS 1992-; St Stephens Luth Church & WELCA 1948-; Amer Legion Auxiliary 1966-, Sargeant at Arms, Americanism & Music Chprsn; Child Conservation League, Pres; OCSS Pgm of Excel Aw 1995; OCSS Middle Schl Tchr of the Yr Aw 1994; NWOEA & OEA Rep Assembly; Taft Inst Two Party Govt 1988; Freedoms Fnd Seminar at Valley Forge 1991; Ec Ed Mini Grant Careers; Outstanding Young Women of America 1984; Ashland Oil Golden Apple Outstanding Achvmt Awd 1988; Co-Presenter OCTELA Convention 1991, 1993; Natl Geographic Soc Instructional Ldrshp Inst; Lang Arts & Geography Wkshp Presenter; *home:* E-015 Rd 8 Hamler OH 43524*

BROWN, DONALD O., Industrial Technology Teacher; *b:* Goffstown, NH; *c:* Scott, Eric; *ed:* Keene St Coll (BS) Indstrl Arts 1974; Summer Inst Keene St 1991; Concord Tech Schl Math, Electronics, Photography; Manchester Tech Schl Aut Codd Courses I,II,III; *cr:* Kearsarge Regnl HS Indstrl Arts Tchr 1974-78; Aerotronics Electrial Control Circuit Designer 1979-85; Free Lance Drafter, Designer 1985-87; Hillsboro-Deering HS Indstrl Tech Tchr 1987-; *ai:* Printing of Schl Forms, Newspaper, Raffle Tickets, Prom Invitation, Grad Prgms, Stu Handbooks; AFT 1987-; Police Ofcr Part-Time 1982-, Chief 1982-89; Fire Dept 1980-, Duty Chief; Comm Ctr 1974-; *office:* Hillsboro-Deering HS 12 Hillcat Dr Hillsboro NH 03244

BROWN, DONNA TERESA, Sixth Grade Teacher; *b:* Dayton, OH; *ed:* Mount Union Coll (BA) Ed 1977; Wright St Univ (MA) Eng 1988; Rdng Recovery Trained; *cr:* Casstown Elem Third Grd Tchr 1977-78, Second Grd Tchr 1978-82; Fletcher Elem First Grd Tchr 1982-85; Miami E Inter Sixth Grd Tchr 1985-92; Miami E North Rdng Recovery Tchr 1992-95 Maimi E Inter Sixth Grd Tchr 1995-; *ai:* Odyssey of Mind; Troy Tennis Assn; USTA; Bldg, Facilities Comm; MEEA 1978-, Pres, Pres Elect, Sec, Treas, Negotiations Chprsn; IRA; Batty Binders Quilt Guild 1995-, Sec; Diogenes Project & Presenter; *office:* Miami East Intermediate Schl 4308 E St Rt 55 Casstown OH 45312*

BROWN, DUDLEY COWAN, 4th Grade Teacher; *b:* Philadelphia, PA; *m:* Ardie Stuart; *c:* Heather, Heath, Hayva; *ed:* Penn St Univ (BA) His 1966; Antioch Univ (MA) Admin 1988; Univ of PA SOAR Prgm for Veterinary Med; Philadelphia Coll of Textiles & Sci Post Grad Sci Cred; Lasale Univ Sci, Math Post Grad Cred; *cr:* H. R. Edmunds Elem Schl 5th Grd Tchr, Chair, Drama, Track 1966-72; Amy MS His Dept Head 1980-81; A. D. Bach MS Sci Dept Head 1981-84; Samuel Gompers Elem Schl 4th Grd Sci, Drama Tchr, Art Head 1984-; *ai:* Pvt Tutoral Scholars Prgm Spon; Art & Crafts Projects & Displays Club Spon & Dir; Children's Art Theater Drama Dir; Tutoral Comm; AFT 1967-; NEA 1973-; NAACP 1965-; Omega Psi Phi 1964-, VP Nu Chptr; Spring Schl of Arts 980-, Bd Mem; Mantua Comm Bd 1974-; Univ of PA SOAR Grant; Ruth W. Hayre Honored Tchrs Awd; Cornelius Awd; Joint Pub-Parochial Planning Cncl; Poems Pub; *home:* 1008 S 49th St Philadelphia PA 19143*

BROWN, E. SCOTT, Math & Computer Science Tchr; *b:* Sellersville, PA; *m:* Sandra E.; *ed:* Bluffton Coll (BS) Math 1961; Univ of OK (MS) Math 1966; Over 90 Credit Hrs Post Grad Temple Univ, San Diego St Univ, Univ of Hartford, Hope Coll & Villanova Univ; *cr:* North Penn HS Math Tchr 1961-95; Plymouth Whitemarsh HS Math & Comp Tchr 1966-; *ai:* NEA 1961-, Bd of Dirs 1987-93; PA St Ed Assn 1961-, Bd of Dirs 1987-93; NCTM 1961-; Whitemarsh Jr Womens Club Tchr of the Yr.*

BROWN, EARLENE LOUISE (BESMEHN), Dept of Defense 4th Grade Tchr; *b:* Walla Walla, WA; *ed:* Augsburg Coll (BA) Elem Ed 1963; MI St Univ (MA) Curr, Tchng 1981; *cr:* Richfield Elem Schl Grd 1 Tchr 1963-64; Elmendorf Air Force Base Schl Grd 1 Tchr 1964-65; Chambley Air Force Base Schl Grd 1 Tchr 1965-66; Weisbaden-Lindsey Air Station 3-4 Grd Tchr 1967; Rosemont Pub Schls Grd 6 Tchr 1969-72; Naha MS Grd 6 Tchr 1972-73; Clark Air Force Base Grd 2, 5, 6 Tchr 1973-89; Ambera Elem Schl 2nd Grd Tchr 1989-91; Mannheim Elem Schl 3rd-4th Grd Tchr 1991-; *ai:* FAST Families, Schls Together; Fed Ed Assn 1987-; NEA 1966-, Rep for Schl; *office:* Mannheim Elem Schl Unit 29938 APO AE 09086*

BROWN, ETHEL LUCIEL, Sixth Grade Teacher; *b:* Bethel, NC; *ed:* Fayetteville St Univ (BS) Elem Ed, Eng 1968; Grad Courses Bowie St, Univ of MD, West Chester St; Trinity Advanced Professional Cert Credentials 1980; *cr:* Green Valley Elem Schl 2 Grd, 5-6 Grd Tchr 1968-86; Berkshire Elem Schl 4&6 Grd Tchr 1986-; *ai:* Grade Level, FAC Chprsn; 6 Grd New Tchr Lead Mentor; PGCEA 1968-; Minority Affairs 1990-, Chprsn; MSTA; NEA Delegate; Phi Delta Kappa 1995-, Recording Sec; MCPT PTA 1983-, Life Mem, Pin, Plaque Cert; Kettering Bapt Church Nursery Duties; Green Vly Elem Outstdng Edctr 1977; Outstdng Edctr 1991; *home:* 3243 Mass Ave SE Washington DC 20019*

BROWN, GARY ALLEN, Professor of Biology; *b:* New York, NY; *m:* Jean Moir Torrance; *c:* Thomas, Michael, Scott, Emily; *ed:* SUNY at Farmingdale (AAS) Bio Tech 1964; Univ of GA (BSA) Entomology 1966, (MS) Entomology 1968, (PHD) Entomology & Radiation Ecology 1970; *cr:* USDA Spir & DL Entomologist 1969-70; SUNY at Farmingdale Prof of Bio 1970-; *ai:* Past BSA Cub Master, Scout Master, Comm Mem & Merit Badge Adv 12 Yrs; Horticulture Club Adv 5 Yrs; UUP 1970-; LI Arboricultural Assoc 1994-; Bulletin Pub; Co-Author of Lab Manual Blueprint of the Plant; *office:* S U N Y Coll Of Tech At Frmgdl Rt 110 Farmingdale NY 11735

BROWN, GEORGE GIBSON, Teacher, Coach & Meteorologist; *b:* Staten Island, NY; *m:* Catherine; *c:* Jeremy, Kamie; *ed:* St Univ at Plattsburgh (BS) Earth Sci, Geology 1971, (MS) Earth Sci, Meteorology 1986; 60 Addl Hrs Sci, Ed; *cr:* Camflo Mines Ltd Geologist 1971-72; Peru HS Tchr 1972-85; WPTZ TV Weekend Meteorologist 1985-; Ausable Valley CS Tchr 1986-, Gymnastic Coach Var 1986-; *ai:* Var Gym Coach; Sci Fair; Project Dir; Mentor Tchr Trng Inst; AFT 1985-; Stancys 1972-, SAR Earth Sci; Amer Meteorological Soc 1985-, TV Broadcasting Seal of Approval; Natl Assn Earth Sci Tchrs 1989-; Amer Red Cross 1988-, Pub Relations; Tchr of Yr 1996; AMS Seal of Approval 500; Great Performance Awd 1991; Sci Area Rep STA; *office:* Ausable Valley HS Rt 9N Box 1490 Clintonville NY 12924*

BROWN, GEORGE WILLIAM,JR., Retired 6th Grd Soc Stud Tchr; *b:* New Freedom, PA; *ed:* Shippensburg Univ (BS) Elem Ed 1964; Towson Univ (MED) Elem Ed 1970; 30 Addl Hrs Scndry Ed Western MD Coll, Goucher Coll 1985; *cr:* Nancy Grayson Elem Schl 6th Grd Tchr 1964; Ore Valley Elem Schl 6th Grd Tchr 1964-65; Eastwood Elem 5th-6th Grd Tchr 1965-71; Cockeysville Elem 5th-6th Grd Tchr 1971-73; Churchville Elem 6th Grd Tchr 1973-80; Southampton MS 6th Grd Eng, Rdng, Soc Stud Tchr 1980-95; Antiques Shop Owner; *ai:* Schl Newsletter Comm; NEA 1964-, Convention Del; MSTA 1965-, Convention Del, 1993 MVP Awd for Harford Cty; HCEA 1973-, Exec Bd, Assn Rep, Membership Comm.

BROWN, GINA GAYLE BAIR, 6th Grade Teacher; *b:* Urbana, OH; *c:* Kyle B. Neer; *ed:* Urbana Coll (BA) Elem Ed 1973; OH St Univ (MA) Early & Mid Chldhd Dev 1987; Wilmington Coll Elem Ed; MA & 30 Addl Sem Hrs; *cr:* Mechanisburg Schls 4th-5th Grd Tchr 1973-75 & 1980-83; Delaware City Schls 6th Grd Tchr 1983-; *ai:* 6th Grd Team Ldr; Var & Jr Var HS Bsktbl Chrldrs; Jr High Ftbl Chrldng Adv; OH MS Assn 1983-; *office:* Willis Intermediate Schl 74 W William St Delaware OH 43015

BROWN, GLORIA MURPH, Multiculture Ed Tchr; *b:* New York City, NY; *c:* Jabari; *ed:* CCNY (BS) ELem Ed 1971, (MS) Elem Ed 1976; 12 Addl Credit Hrs Brooklyn Coll Admin, Supervision; *cr:* P.S. 123 Tchr 1971-75; P.S. 269 Tchr 1975-; *ai:* AFT, UFT 1971-; Brooklyn Skyhawks 1992-94, Parent Vol; Flatlands Yth Cncl 1987-89, Vol; Outstdng Tchr Awd 1995; *office:* PS 269 Nostrand 1957 Nostrand Ave Brooklyn NY 11210

BROWN, HARTSON W., Applied Tech Dept Chair & Prof; *b:* Farmington, ME; *m:* Gwendolyn A. Labrecque; *c:* Timothy W., Bruce A., Kenneth O.; *ed:* Univ of Southern ME (BS) Voc Ed 1987; *cr:* US Navy Shipfit[...] Southworth Machine Co Machinist Apprentice 1957-, Tooling & Engr 1968-; NHTC at Berlin Dept Chair, CAD & CAM Prof 1982-[...] Cabinet Comm; Applied Tech Dept Dept Chair; Fr, Sr Stu Adv; SN[...] Sen; SEIU 1982-; NAIT 1993-, Cert Sen Indstrl Tech; VFV[...] Quartermaster; Yrbk Dedication 1994-95; *home:* RR 2 Box 2336 B[...] 03570

BROWN, HILARY M., Humanities Teacher; *b:* Brooklyn, NY; *m*[...] *c:* Kieran, Blair, Gordon; *ed:* OH Univ (BA) Eng & Creative Writ[...] Princeton Univ Post Grad Coursework in Mid-East Stud & Wr[...] Mobil Oil Corp Ed 1968-71; Princeton Univ, Woodrow Wilson [...] Intnl Stud Dissertation Ed 1971-74; Linn Hill Schl for the Gifted [...] 1982-93; Saint Joseph HS Eng & Hum Tchr & Cnslr of Gifted E[...] *ai:* NJLTA 1995-; NCTE 1986-; ASCD 1985-; HSUS 1979-; [...] 1986-; Founder of Internationally Recognized Linn HS for G[...] Author of Articles, Media Presentations & Pub Ed Prgms on [...] Alternative Ed; Creator, Ed of Soundings Youth Lit Magazine [...] Advocate Gifted Young Writers.

BROWN, IFETEO J., Honors English I & II Teacher; *b:* Pittsbu[...] *c:* Kyatawna R. Coger, Rasheid O., Malaika R. Hall; *ed:* Uni[...] Scndry Ed 1968-72; Univ of Ile Ife Nigeria Youruba 1971-72; G[...] BSAP Crisis Intervention, Mac-Tech Prep, Jr Great Books; *cr:* [...] Supplement Ctr 1980-84; CEO Yo Area Urban League 1986-198[...] High Tchr 1988-93; Rayen High Tchr 1993-; *ai:* Jr Class A[...] Laureate Luncheon Co-Spon; NEA; Southside Comm Coalition 19[...] W Princeton Block Club 1988-, Pres; *office:* Rayen HS 250 Be[...] Youngstown OH 44504

BROWN, IRA HUGO, Guidance Counselor; *b:* South Hill, VA; *m*[...] Macklin; *c:* Tyira Anita Brown-McElhaney, Terrance Anthony; *ed.*[...] Univ (BS) Bio 1965; Bowie St Univ (MED) Cnslng & Psych 1[...] Union Inst (PHD) Cnslng & Psych 1993; 45 Credits Sci Inst NSF; [...] Cty Bd of Ed Bio Tchr 8 Yrs; Prince Georges Cty Bd of Ed Bio T[...] Guid Cnslr 20 Yrs; *ai:* Guid Dept Chm; NEA 1960-; MSTA 1967-[...] 1967-; ACA & Affiliates 1980-; Omega Psi Phi 1953-; Prince Hall [...] 1959-, Past Master, Outstdng PM; Holy Royal Arch Masons 19[...] High Priest, Outstdng HP; Knights Templar 1971-, Past E Cmdr, [...] E Cmdr; Amer Legion 1993-; NSF.*

BROWN, JACQUELINE KIENZLE, Sophomore English Tea[...] Canton, OH; *m:* Matthew T.; *ed:* Kent St Univ (BS) Eng & Scndry [...] (MS) Schl Counseling 1994; *cr:* Tallmadge HS Eng Tchr 1990-; [...] Class Adv; *office:* Tallmadge HS 484 East Ave Tallmadge OH 442[...]

BROWN, JACQUELYN C., 9th Grade English Teacher; *b:* Vi[...] MS; *m:* David G.; *c:* Melissa B. Lynn; *ed:* Newcomb Coll & Tula[...] (BA) Theatre 1964; Lehigh Univ (MAEd) Eng/Ed 1967; *cr:* East[...] 7th & 9th Grd Eng Tchr 1967-76; Shawnee Intermediate Schl 9th [...] Tchr 1976-; *ai:* Shawnee Intermediate Schl Little Theatre Dra[...] Co-Adv Shawnee Lit Mag; NEA, PSEA, EAEA 1967-; *office:* S[...] Intrmediate Schl 1010 Echo Trl Easton PA 18040

BROWN, JAMES ELBA, Amer Lit, Speech & Drama T[...] Chillicothe, OH; *m:* Laura Swonger; *c:* Molly; *ed:* Rio Grande C[...] Comm 1984; *cr:* Southeastern HS Rdng, Speech, Drama Tchr [...] Amer Lit, Speech Drama Tchr 1991-; *ai:* OH Holstein Assn; AS[...] Bd; NRA 1992-; Farmers Club 1984-, VP, Pres; Soil, Water Cons[...] Dist 1994-, Fiscal Agent, Sec, Farm Family Awd 1991; First Bapt[...] of Coalition 1985-; Numerous Articles Pub; *office:* Southeastern [...] Box 108 Richmond Dale OH 45673

BROWN, JAMES M., HS English Teacher; *b:* Troy, NY; *m:* Chri[...] *c:* Jamie, Jeremy, Julie; *ed:* Adirondack Comm Coll (AA) His, E[...] SUNY at Oneonta (BA) Scndry Ed, Eng 1973; Addl 30 Hrs NY Ed[...] *cr:* Warrensburg HS Eng Tchr 1973-; *ai:* NCTE 1973-; Warrensbu[...] Assn 1973-, Chair, Pol Action Comm; Chptr 79 Vietnam Veterans [...] 1981-, Pres; *office:* Warrensburg HS 1 James St Warrensburg NY [...]

BROWN, JAMES MARK, Mathematics Teacher; *b:* Mercer, [...] LaVerne Alderson; *c:* Margaret Ellen; *ed:* Grove City Coll (BS) Ma[...] *cr:* Sharpsville MS Math Tchr 1970-; *ai:* PSEA, NEA, SAEA [...] Mercer Cty Historical Soc 1970-, Pres, Sec; *office:* Sharpsville [...] Quarry Way Sharpsville PA 16150

BROWN, JANADEAN WRIGHT, Proficiency Intervention T[...] Dover, OH; *m:* Joe; *c:* Rebecca Smith, Matt; *ed:* Mt Union Coll (B[...] 1971; Malone Coll 20 Credit Hrs Towards MA in Cnslng; *cr:* Tus[...] Cty Schls Sub Tchr 1971-93; Indian Vly HS Tchr 1993-; *ai:* NEA, [...] NTA 1993-; *office:* Indian Valley HS PO Box 130 Gnadenhutten O[...]

BROWN, JEANNE CRIST, Third Grade Teacher; *b:* Jersey Shore, [...] Larry E.; *c:* Abby L.; *ed:* Lycoming Coll (BA) Ed 1965; Penn St [...] Credit Hrs, Mansfield Univ 6 Credit Hrs Post Grad; *cr:* Jersey Sh[...] Schl Third Grd Tchr 1967-; *ai:* PTO Exec Bd, Tchr Rep; NEA, PSE[...] 1967-; Jersey Shore BPW 1970-, Past Pres; *office:* Jersey Shore A[...] Schl 601 Locust St Jersey Shore PA 17740

BROWN, JEFFREY SEAN, Mathematics Teacher; *b:* Camden, [...] LaSalle Univ (BA) Scndry Ed, Math 1991; *cr:* Holy Cross HS Ma[...] Discipline Comm 1991-95; Palmyra Adult HS Math Tchr, Curr Adv[...] Pemberton Twp HS Math Tchr, Hspt Instr 1995-; *ai:* Camden Ca[...] Var Soccer, Corpus Christi Girls Soccer V-15 Head Coach, Unite[...] Amateur Soccer Coach; NJEA 1995-; SJ Coaches Assn 199[...] Championship 1995-1996; Amer Math Tchrs NJ 1991-; Maple Sha[...] Soccer 1991-94, Rep; Corpus Christi Girls Soccer 1994-, Rep; Ca[...] Soccer Olympic Conf Natl Div Championship 1995; *office:* Per[...] Twp HS 125 Arney's Mt Rd Pemberton NJ 08068

BROWN, JERRY R., 5th Grade Teacher; *b:* Montrose, PA; *m:* C[...] Groover; *c:* Jay Alan, Adam Todd; *ed:* Union Coll (BA) Elem[...] Sociology 1968; Masters Equivalency +45 Hrs; *cr:* Montrose Ar[...] Tchr 1968-; *ai:* Bsktbl & Wrestling Game Mgr, Intramurals, Bowlin[...] & PSEA & MEA 1972-; Montrose Recreation Comm 1988-; Montrose Area Elem Schl 14 Lathrop St Montrose PA 18801*

BROWN, JODI WADE, 5th Grade Teacher; *b:* Jamestown, NY; *m*[...] Clayton; *c:* Eric, Ashley; *ed:* Jamestown Comm Coll (AAS) Co[...] 1977; Fredonia St (BA) Elem Ed 1985, (MS) Curr 1990; *cr:* Pine V[...] Elem Grds Tchr 1985-; *ai:* NYSUT 1985-; Randolph Amer Legio[...] PTA Randolph & Pine Vly; Grace Episcopal Church; *office:* Pine [...] Elem Schl 7755 Rt 83 South Dayton NY 14138

BROWN, KAREN LYNN (ZIMMER), Coordinator for The Gi[...] Coshocton, OH; *m:* Daniel P.; *c:* Craig Stephen, Kyle Matthew; *e*[...] St Univ (BS) Elem Ed 1968; OH St Univ (MA) Ed 1973; Ashlan[...] Univ VA, OH St Univ Grad Work; *cr:* Coshocton City Schls Seco[...] Tchr 1968-70; Fairfax Cty Pub Schls Third Grd Tchr 1970-71; Wort[...] City Schls First Grd Tchr 1971-76; Montessori Pre-Schl Admin 1[...] Coshocton Cty Schls Coord, Tchr for Gifted 1986-; *ai:* Odyssey [...] Governing Bd; Model United Nations Adv; Citizens Advy [...] Ridgewood Local Schls Bsktbl, golf Boosters; Phi Delta Kappa [...] Delta Kappa Gamma 1987-; Amer Assn of Univ Women 1968-; Ridg[...] Local Schl Bd 1986-, Pres; Jaunsian Club 1980-, Pres, Treas; Co[...] Toastmasters 1995-; Layleader 1994; Sunday Schl Tchr 1980; USA[...] Parents' Club 1995; West Lafayette United Meth Church, Admin B[...] Day Care Bd 1995; *home:* 54180 Township Road 158 W Lafaye[...] 43845*

, KATHERINE DREMANN, School Counselor; *b:* Mt Vernon, Daniel; *c:* Dane, Luke; *ed:* BGSU (BS) Ed 1980; OSU (MA) Guid g 1987; *cr:* Graveport Schls Tchr 1980-82; St Peters Schls Tchr Mt Vernon Schls Tchr 1984-85; Kenyon Coll Cnslr 1988-92; uilders Guid Cnslr 1992-93; Fredericktown Schls Cnslr 1993-; *ai:* st & Homeroowm Cncl Adv; NEA 1980-; OSCA 1993-; Meth 1983-; Farm Bureau 1983-.

, KATHRYN MAKOWSKI, English & Journalism Teacher; *b:* d, OH; *c:* Sarah; *ed:* Cuyahoga Comm Coll (AA) Bus 1970; Univ 1 (BA) Ed, Eng 1989; Post Grad Stud Ashland Univ; *cr:* Medina s Eng, Jrnlsm Tchr 1989-; *ai:* Jrnlsm Adv; Var & JV Cheer Coach; 1995-; *office:* Medina HS 777 E Union St Medina OH 44256

, KATHY SHIFFER, English Teacher; *b:* Harrisburg, PA; *m:* .; *c:* Traci, D. Timothy; *ed:* Gettysburg Coll (BA) Eng 1969; Univ MA) Eng 1976; 60 Credit Hrs Beyond MA; *cr:* St of PA Dept of Ed Consultant 1976-85; Elizabethtown Area MS Lang Arts Tchr ; Cedar Crest HS Eng Tchr 1986-; *ai:* Drama Club Adv; Musical graphy; Acad Quiz Bowl Coach; NEA, PSEA, CLEA 1970-, Comm Chair; NCTE 1976-; Christ Luth Church 1947-, Cncl unday Schl Tchr; BSA 1986-, Troop Comm, Advamcement Chair; Pub in NCTE; PA Writing Assessment Advy Cncl, Charter Mem; Area Writing Project Mem; *office:* Cedar Crest HS 115 E Evergreen non PA 17042*

, KATRINA SEIDEL, English Teacher; *b:* Altoona, PA; *m:* T.; *c:* Emily, Christopher; *ed:* IN St Univ (BA) Art Ed 1980; Penn (MEG) Ed 1992; Penn St Univ 4 Cred; St Francis Coll Eng Cert; lichaels Schl 7th & 8th Grd Eng & 4th-8th Grd Art Tchr 1981-82; Guilfoyle HS Eng II, 9th Grd Art His, & 9th-12th Grd Studio Art ; Voc Tech Altoona 10th Grd Eng & Drop Out Prevention Coord ; Altoona Area HS 12th Crd Acad, Applied Comm-IV & 10th-12th nsition Pgm 1988-; *ai:* Comms: Alt Ed, Collaboration, Applied School-to-Work; Stu Tchr Mentor; SAIT; NEA 1987-; Parish Lector 1995-; CARE Awd 1993; St Tchr of the Yr Nom 1992; Grant At Risk 1994-96; *office:* Altoona Area HS 1415 6th Ave Altoona PA

N, KEN DAVID, Special Education Teacher; *b:* Dingess, WV; *m:* aner; *c:* Chad, Travis; *ed:* OH Univ (BS) Ed Spec 1974; *cr:* oth City Schls Spec Ed Tchr 1972-78; Chesapeake Schls Spec Ed 978-; *ai:* Ftbl, Wrestling, Track Coach; Schl TV News, Math ncy Coord; POPS Good Stu Club Organizer; NEA, OEA, CLTA riev Rep; LL Hite Saunders 1980-, Pres; Bev Hills Youth Bsktbl Pres; Huntington Track Club 1988-, Pres; *office:* Chesapeake d Village Sch PO Box 10 Chesapeake OH 45619*

N, KENNETH LEE, Orchestra Dir & Music Teacher; *b:* Carlisle, Anne Little; *c:* Rachel, Amanda, Nathanael; *ed:* Ithaca Coll (BS) d 1969; Eastman Schl of Music Univ of Roch (MS) Music Ed 1975; ce Schl Dist Music Tchr 1969-71; Fairport Cntrl Schls Orchestra sic Tchr 1971-; *ai:* NYSSUT 1969-; MENC 1969-, Nationally ed 1991; NYSSMA 1969-, Tchr.

N, KERRY MICHAEL, HS English Teacher; *b:* Providence, RI; mary Rolinger; *c:* Andrew, Emily; *ed:* MA Coll of Art (BSEd) Art ; Salem St Coll (MAT) Amer Lit 1979; Addl 60 Credits; *cr:* B. F. Schl Art Tchr 1965-67; Holten Richmond Art Tchr 1970-71; HS Eng Tchr 1972-; *ai:* Fac Cncl; Danvers Tchr Assn, MA Tchrs IEA 1970-; Horace Mann Grant; Articles Pub Journal of Rdng, head Magazine, Living BLues, Poolwip Retrorock Review & rg Sentinel; Paintings Exhibitied at Copley Soc; *office:* Danvers HS st Rd Danvers MA 01923

N, LEISA SOKOL, Third Grade Teacher; *b:* Cambridge, OH; *m:* ; *c:* Aarica DuBeck; *ed:* OH Univ (BS) Elem Ed, Minor Eng 1982; ling Hills Schls 3rd, 5-6th Grd Tchr 1982-; *ai:* IAT, Mem; NEA, olling Hills Ed Assn 1982-; Jennings Scholar; *home:* 120 Sunrise sville OH 43723

N, LINDA DAUM, Family & Consumer Science Tchr; *b:* Neptune, Frederick W.; *c:* Lexi, Sarah; *ed:* Univ of RI (BS) Home Ec Ed 1972; Credits; *cr:* Tiverton HS Family & Consumer Sci Tchr 1972-; *ai:* S 1976-; *office:* Tiverton H S 100 N Brayton Rd Tiverton RI 02878

N, LINDA SUE, Sixth Grade English Teacher; *b:* Washington, DC; ale; *ed:* Univ of MD at College Park (BS) Ed 1973, (MS) Ed 1979; Coll (MS) Guid, Cnslng 1992; Attnd Caryl Maxwell Schl of Ballet, Seivert Schl of Dance, Carroll Cty Schl for Performing Arts; *cr:* n Elem Schl Fourth, Fifth Grds Tchr 1974-79; Clemens Crossing chl Grd 3-5 Tchr, Team Ldr 1979-89; Glenwood MS Grd 7 Eng, chr 1989-93; Harper's Choice MS grd 6 Eng Tchr, Team Ldr 1993-; Improvement Team; Human Relations Comm; NEA, MSTA, HCTA NCTE 1990-; ACA 1992-95; ASERVIC 1993-95; *office:* Harpers MS 5450 Beaverkill Rd Columbia MD 21044

N, LISABETH J., Education Professor; *b:* Oil City, PA; *m:* Dr n R.; *c:* Seth J., Courtney L.; *ed:* Merryhurst Coll (BA) Elem Ed Edinoro St Coll MED) Elem Ed & Early Chldhd 1972; IN Univ of J) Elem & Early Chldhd Ed 1989; *cr:* Millcreek Schl Dist Elem Tchr 3; Becker Schl Clarion Univ Instr 1973-80; Ed Dept Clarion Univ 980-; *ai:* Lambda Eta Chptr of Kappa Delta Pi Cnslr; Dept, Coll & omms; Fac Senate; Phi Delta Kappa 1976-, VP; ACEI 1980-, St VP; C 1980-; Kappa Delta Pi 1984-, Cnslr; Rsrch Grants to Stu Childrens m Solving; Parent Tchr Conferencing & Communicator Style; ice Tchr Ed for Working with Families; Several Articles Pub; Chptr book Pub; *office:* Clarion Univ Of PA 108 Stevens Hall Clarion PA

N, LORNA MAURIZ, Reading Teacher; *b:* Allentown, PA; *m:* J. l; *c:* Todd Arthur, Ryan Michael; *ed:* Moravian Coll (BS) Elem Ed Lehigh Univ (MED) Elem Ed, Rdng 1967; Orton-Gillingham ach Rdng, Writing, Spelling 18 Hrs; *cr:* Lehigh Lab Schl Tchr 7; Sellersville Carrie Downie 5th-6th Grd Tchr 1967-71; Monteith rton-Gillingham Tchr 1981-84; Saint Edmonds Acad Rdng Tchr *ai:* 4rh-5th Grd Prgm, Rdng, Lit Dept Coord; NEA 1984-; *office:* St d's Acad 2120 Veale Rd Wilmington DE 19810

'N, LOUISE ELAINE, English Teacher; *b:* Reading, PA; *m:* s; *ed:* Seton Hill Coll (BA) Eng 1964; Boston Univ (MED) Rdng 30 Addl Credit Hrs; *cr:* Belt Jr HS Rdng Tchr 1966-68; Kent Jr HS Tchr 1969-71; Gaithersburg Jr HS Rdng, Eng Tchr 1971-84; rsburg HS Eng Tchr 1984-89; Watkins Mill HS Eng Tchr 1989-; *ai:* chl Lit, Arts Magazine Spon 9 Yrs; NEA 1966-; Wood To Wonderful Treas; *office:* Watkins Mill HS 10301 Apple Ridge Rd Gaithersburg 0879

'N, LYNNE J., English Teacher; *b:* Providence, RI; *m:* Richard; *c:* ds, Stephen, Jennifer; *ed:* Rhode Island Coll (BE) Eng 1963; 36 Addl : Narragansett HS Eng Tchr 21 Yrs; *ai:* Scheduling Comm; NEA Grievance Bldg Rep; *office:* Narragansett HS 245 S Pier Rd ansett RI 02882

N, MARGARET MARY, English Teacher; *b:* Ashland, PA; *ed:* St 's Univ (BS) Eng 1969; Bloomsburg Univ (MS) Eng 1976; 30 Addl ; *cr:* North Schuylkill Jr Sr HS Eng Tchr 1969-; *ai:* Adv Newspaper; Adv Gifted Stdnts, SAT Coll Bound; AAUW; NEA, PSEA 1969-; Jrnlsm Ed Assn 1973-; Jrnslm Tchr of Yr; *office:* North Schuylkill Jr Sr HS Rt 61 RD 2 Box 47 Ashland PA 17921

BROWN, MARGUERITE J., Fifth Grade Teacher; *b:* Baltimore, MD; *ed:* Morgan St Univ (BS) Elem Ed 1973; Johns Hopkins Univ (MS) Ed 1980; *office:* Cross Country Elem Schl 247 6100 Cross Country Blvd Baltimore MD 21215

BROWN, MARK PATRICK, Fifth Grade Teacher; *b:* Hazleton, PA; *m:* Ana Echararria; *ed:* AZ St Univ (BS) Radio & TV Co 1974; Loras Coll (bA) Ed 1977; Beaver Coll (MS) Ed 1990; PA Alliance for Geog; IN Univ of PA; *cr:* St Marks Elem Tchr 1974-80; *office:* Rydal Elem Schl 1160 Huntingdon Pike Huntingdon Valley PA 19006

BROWN, MARY HELEN (SPEECH), English Teacher; *b:* Hagnesville, LA; *m:* Norris; *c:* Barre, Brock; *ed:* Grambling Univ (BA) Eng, Speech, Drama 1966; Univ of Dayton MS; *cr:* C. H. Iron HS Tchr 1966-70; Jefferson Jr HS Tchr 1970-82; Jefferson HS Tchr 1982-; *ai:* Frosh Class Adv; Fac Cncl; Jefferson Tchr Assn 1970-, Bldg Rep; OEA, NEA 1977-; Delta Sigma Theta 1963-; *office:* Jefferson Twp Schl 2701 S Union Rd Dayton OH 45418

BROWN, MARY RITA, Latin Teacher; *b:* Philadelphia, PA; *m:* James M.; *c:* Shannon, Rachel, Rebecca, Bryan, Michael; *ed:* Villanova Univ (BA) Fr, Philosophy 1971, (MA) Classical Lang 1974; PA K-12 Fr, Latin Cert, Assoc Stud Human Org Sci 18 Credits; Working Toward PHD in Cl Latin, Roman Archaeology at Bryn Mawr Coll; *cr:* Harriton HS Latin Tchr 1974-80, 1990-; Lower Merion HS Latin Tchr 1980-; *ai:* Natl Jr Classical League Spon; Phila Classical Soc 1995-; Amer Cl League 1978-; NEA, PSEA 1976-; Rosemont-Villanova Civic Assn Sports Prgm 1979-, Co-Dir; AP Stud Guide Grant; 3 Plays; Numerous Articles, Essays Pub; *office:* Lower Merion HS 245 E Montgomery Ave Ardmore PA 19003

BROWN, MAUREEN V. CASPER, Second Grade Teacher; *b:* Delaware, PA; *m:* Robert R. Jr.; *c:* Roseanne, Gregory, Daniel; *ed:* Mt St Mary Coll (BA) Elem Ed 1970; *cr:* St Mary's Elem First Grd Tchr 1966-67; Assumption Schl First Grd Tchr 1967-69; Clementon Elem Schl Fourth Grd Tchr 1969-71, Second Grd Tchr 1971-; *ai:* CEA Comm; Children of Substance Abuse Support Group; Rainbows for All God's Children Death Support Group; Children's Liturgy; CCD Firs Eucharist Preparation; NJEA, NEA 1969-; CEA 1969-, Treas; Girl Scouts of Amer, Ldr 5 Yrs; *office:* Clementon Elem Schl Audubon Ave Clementon NJ 08021*

BROWN, MERRY C., Business Education Teacher; *b:* York, AL; *m:* James Otis Jr.; *c:* Ceesha Wilson Hogg, Latanya M. Wilson; *ed:* Baldwin Wallace Coll (BS) Bus Ed 1978; Ashland Univ Certfd in Comp Sci, Certfd in Data Processing, 36 Credit Hrs Toward MS in Comp Ed; *cr:* Lorain Cty Comm Coll Bus Tchr 1978-; Elyria HS Bus Tchr 1979-; *ai:* OH Bus Tchr Assn 1980-; NAACP 1990-, Yth Adv 1994; Sodonia Lodge OES; Second Bapt Church, Mem, Musician; Asbury United Meth Church Minister of Music; Arch Angel Chrstn Assn 1973-, Chprsn, Outstdng Adv; Martin Luther King Jr Holiday Comm 1994-, Fundraiser.*

BROWN, MICHAEL G., Hlth, PE & Driver Theory Tchr; *b:* Greenville, PA; *m:* Diana Lynn Bish; *c:* Cari Marie, Erin Michele, Moira Ann; *ed:* Univ of Pittsburgh (BS) Hlth & PE 1975; Attnd Clarion & Penn St Univs; *cr:* Redbank Valley HS Hlth, PE & Driver Theory Tchr 1975-; Asst Athl Dir; *ai:* Head Coach Boys Bsktbl & Track; Asst Var Ftbl; Dept Head PE; NEA, PSEA, RVEA 1975-; Western PA Bsktbl Coachs Assn 1978-; Knights of Columbus 1990-; Clarion Cty Head of Yr 1980, 1991-92; Whos Who Among Coaches 1988.*

BROWN, MICHELLE DARLENE (WALLACE), Fourth Grade Teacher; *b:* Brooklyn, NY; *ed:* Hunter Coll CUNY (BA) Early Chldhd 1980, (MA) Elem Ed 1982; Kingsborough Comm Coll Elem Ed; *cr:* Kiddie Kollege 2nd Grd Tchr 1980-81; PS 244 2nd Grd Tchr 1982-83; PS 268 4th Grd Tchr 1984-; *ai:* Mentor Tchr; After Schl Rdng Coach; Spcl Act Coord; Chrldng Coach; UFT 1982-; Co-Authored an Awded Goals 2000 Grant; Co-Applied for Awded MacIntosh Tech Grant; *office:* PS 268 133 E 53rd St Brooklyn NY 11203*

BROWN, MILTON IRVIN, Principal; *b:* Baltimore, MD; *m:* Deborah; *c:* Milton Jr., Pamela, Michelle; *ed:* Columbia Union Coll (BA) Elem Ed 1974; Andrews Univ (MS) Admin 1990; Attnd Oakwood Coll 1982, Morgan St Univ 1962; *cr:* Allegheny East Conf Prin, Tchr 1966-76; South Cntrl Conf Prin, Tchr 1977-89; Allegheny East Conf Prin, Tchr 1990-; *ai:* 8th Grd Class Spon; 7th-8th Grd Bsktbl Coach; Comm Relations Committee; North Amer Div of Ed 1966-; Amer REd Cross 1966-, Water Safety Instr, Outstdng Svc Awd; Ministry of Tchng Awd 1981; *office:* Pine Forge 7th Day Advtst Elem PO Box 345 Pine Forge PA 19548*

BROWN, MIRIAM MAC DONALD, Third Grade Teacher; *b:* New London, CT; *c:* Mark P., Scott D., Jennifer E.; *ed:* Univ of NC (BA) Art His 1957; Cambridge Coll (MED) Ed 1993; Salem St Coll Cert 1969; *cr:* Mc Kay Schl Fifth Grd Tchr 1969-79, Third Grd Tchr 1979-; *ai:* Schl Improvement Cncl 1985-86; Fine Arts Curr Dev Comm 1991-93; Beverly Tchrs Assn 1969-, Prof Rights & Responsibilities Comm 1980-89, Governing Bd 1989-93; MA Tchrs Assn, NEA 1969-; North Shore Rdng Cncl 1980-; *office:* Mc Kay Schl 131 Mckay St Beverly MA 01915

BROWN, MITCHELL ROBERT, Health & Physical Ed Teacher; *b:* Philadelphia, PA; *m:* Donna; *c:* Leigh ann, Mitchell James; *ed:* Glassboro St Coll (BA) Hlth, PE 1982; Cert in Elem Ed; *cr:* Eastern Regnl HS Coach 1982-84; Lower Camdin Cty Schl Dist Tchr, Coach 1984-; *ai:* Asst Ftbl, Bsbl Coach; Head Frosh Bsbl, Wrestling Coach; NJ Ed Assn, South Jersey Coaches Assn 1984-; Lindinwood Little League Coach, Umpire; Articles Pub; Coached Group Champions in Ftbl, Wresting; Coached Conf Champions in Ftbl; *office:* Overbrook Jr HS White Horse Ave Lindenwold NJ 08021*

BROWN, MOLLY, English Teacher; *b:* Pittsburgh, PA; *m:* Roger Turk; *ed:* Dickinson Coll (BA) Eng, Art His 1987; Univ of PA (MS) Ed 1990; *cr:* Collingswood MS Eng Tchr 1990-91; Masterman Schl Eng Tchr 1991-; *office:* Collingswood MS 414 Collings Ave Collingswood NJ 08108

BROWN, NANCY GILBERT, 6th Grade Teacher; *b:* New Britain, CT; *c:* Scott, Tim; *ed:* CCSU (BS) Ed 1974; 30 Hrs Grad Stud; *cr:* Newington Schl System Kndgtn, 2nd-4th Grd Tchr 1974-78; Wethersfield Schl System 6th Grd Tchr 1989-; *ai:* Math Olympiad; Tech Comm; WFT 1989-; *office:* Alfred W Hanmer Elem Schl 50 Francis St Wethersfield CT 06109*

BROWN, NANCY KRAKOSKY, English Teacher; *b:* Kingston, PA; *m:* Edward Robert; *c:* Macawley Grace, Victoria Elizabeth; *ed:* Kings Coll (BA) Eng, Ed 1985; Wilkes Coll (MS) Ed 1988; 60 Addl Hrs; *cr:* Lackawanna Trail HS Eng Tchr 1986-; Luzerne Cty Comm Coll Adjunct Prof 1991-92; *ai:* Yrbk Adv; NEA 1986-; PSEA; LTEA; Music Box Dinner Playhouse 1981-.

BROWN, PAMELA TAYLOR, 10th-12th Grd Soc Stud Tchr; *b:* Rutland, VT; *m:* Arthur I.; *ed:* Univ of VT (BA) His with Tchr Cert 1972; Northern AZ Univ (MAE) His, Scndry Ed 1973; Post Grad 51 Credits Cooperative Learning, Curr Dev, Telecommunications, Cmptr Stud, Soc Stud Curr Dev, MS Tchng, Canadian Stud, Project TEACH, Glasser, Constitution, Alcohol & Drug Ed, Rdng Intnl Stud, VT His, Sociology Courses, Lesson Plan Dev; *cr:* Coconino HS Tutoring 1973-74; Kentucky Fried Chicken Managerial 1972-74; Castleton St Coll Adj Fac-Continuing Ed 1985; Vergennes Union HS Soc Stud Tchr 1974-; *ai:* Chprsn Fac, Prins Fac Advy Group, Block Scheduling Comm for Implementation 1996 Semester Courses; Adv Ukranian Exch; NEA, VT Ed Assn, Addison Northwest Tchrs Assn 1974-; Phi Delta Kappa 1995-; Rutland Cty Humane Soc 1993-; Natl Museum of Amer Indian, Smithsonian, Australian Geographic Soc 1994-; Natl Geographic Soc 1984-; Smithsonian Inst 1985-; Outstdng Vt Tchr; Nom VT Tchr of Yr; Chprsn Licensing Bd; Sr Yrbk Dedication 1990; Favorite Tchr Awd; *office:* Vergennes Union HS 50 Monkton Rd Vergennes VT 05491*

BROWN, PATRICIA LAINE, First Grade Teacher; *b:* Irvington, NJ; *m:* David S.; *c:* Debra King, Donna Cremin; *ed:* Grove City Coll (BA) Elem Ed 1964; Jersey City Coll (MA) Rdng; *cr:* Middletown Twp Bd of Ed Tchr 1964-66, 1971-; *ai:* Math Implementation Support Comm; Middletown Ed Assn 1964-; NJ Ed Assn 1964-; NEA 1964-; Westminster Pres Church 1960-, Elder, Church Choir & Asst Dir Yth Choir; Middleton Twp Ed Fndtn Grant 1992 & 1995; River Plaza Schl Tchr of Yr 1994; *office:* River Plaza Elem Sch 155 Hubbard Ave Red Bank NJ 07701*

BROWN, PATTY MOSLEY, High School English Teacher; *b:* Bartown Babson Pk, FL; *m:* Joseph Preston Jr.; *c:* Shamika, ELizabeth Milhouse; *ed:* FL A&M Univ (BA) Eng 1992; Attnd Jericho Chrstn Coll; *cr:* Griffin MS Intern 1992; FL A&M Univ Grad Asst Title III 1991-92; FL St Law Schl Stu Asst 1991-92; Huntington Learning Ctr Tutor 1993-94; Largo HS ENg Tchr 1992-; *ai:* YMCA Chrldr Coach 1991-92; Asst Track Coach 1992-93; Pom Pom Spon 1993-95; Chrldr Spon 1993-94; PGCEA, NEA 1992-; NCTE 1991-; Ladies of Distinction 1988-; Eng Lit Guild 1987-; Lake Wales Housing Authority 1988-, Bd Mem; Family, Child Svcs of D.C.; 2nd Place Oration Winner; Manor Care Nrsng Home; Melwood House; *home:* 1608 Brightseat Rd Landover MD 20785*

BROWN, PAUL GERALD,III, 7th & 8th Grade Teacher; *b:* New York City, NY; *ed:* Fordham Univ (BA) His, Philosophy 1973; Villanova Univ (MA) Amer His 1975; *cr:* Joseph P Kennedy Jr Home Chidl Care Worker 1976-77; St Luke's Schl 7th-8th Grd Tchr 1977-; Sportsmen Ctr Park Ranger 1988-; *ai:* Fresh Air Fund, Boys Ath League, Cath Yth Org Cnslr, Asst Dir, Dir 1970-83; Girls Bsktbl Coach; Peer-Tutoring Prgm Dir; St Luke's Ed Fnd Bd Mem; Stu Safety Patrol Moderator; IM Prgm Dir; FCT 1981-; Museum of Natural His 1979-; *office:* St Luke's Schl 608 E 139th St Bronx NY 10454

BROWN, PHYLLIS TAYLOR, Sixth Grade Teacher; *b:* Charleston, WV; *m:* Albert William; *c:* Sylveta Lynn, Katrina Jeanean; *ed:* Bluefield St (BS) Elem Ed 1963; Addl Credit Hrs at WV Univ, MD Univ, Bowie Univ; *cr:* Wright Denny Elem 2nd Grd Tchr 1963-68; Prince Georges Cty Pub Schls 6th Grd Tchr; *ai:* PGCEA 1976-, Schl Rep, Negotiating Team Mem; MSTA, NEA 1976-; Saint John United Bapt Church 1976-, Trustee & Chrstn Ed Comm; NAACP 1989-; *home:* 13904 Broomall Ln Silver Spring MD 20906

BROWN, RICHARD EARL, Technology Teacher; *b:* Watertown, NY; *m:* Donna Kay Tansey; *c:* Lindsay, Casey, Maggie; *ed:* SUNY at Oswego (BS) Indstrl Arts 1970, (MS) Tech 1988; Grad of Command & Gen Staff Coll 1983; Addl Grad Courses; *cr:* Mineto Schl MS Indstrl Arts Tchr 1970-71; Cicero HS Indstrl Arts Tchr 1971-87; North Syracuse Jr HS Tech Tchr 1987-; *ai:* Co-Adv Sci Olympiad Team; Phi Delta Kappa, AFT, NYSUT 1970-; Cntrl NY Tech Tchrs Assoc 1972-; 4-H Ldr 1992-94; US Army Reserves 1968-95, Lt Col; Natl Ski Patrol 1975-82; *office:* North Syracuse Jr HS 5353 W Taft Rd North Syracuse NY 13212*

BROWN, ROBERTA ANN, Fifth Grade Teacher; *b:* Cumberland, MD; *ed:* Potomac St Coll (AA) Jrnlsm 1985; Frostburg St Univ (BS) Elem, MS 1987, (MEd) Admin, Supervision 1993; *cr:* South Penn Elem 5th Grd Tchr 1988-; *ai:* Schl Improvement Team Mem 1993-; Amer Ed Week Chprsn; Past Cmptr Comm Mem 1989-94; NEA, MSTA, ACTA 1989-; Alpha Delta Kappa Phi Chapter 1994-, Treas; Western MD Rdng Cncl 1994-, VP; Australian Intnl Rdng Conf 1993; Presented Eisenhower Math, Sci MD Conf 1995; Presented SOMIRAC Wkshp 1994; *office:* South Penn Elem Schl 500 E 2nd St Cumberland MD 21502

BROWN, ROGER SCOTT, Asst Principal & Athletic Dir; *b:* Endicott, NY; *m:* Suzanne L. Reid; *c:* Kristen; *ed:* SUC at Cortland (BS) PE 1974, (MS) PE 1978, (CAS) Admin 1990; *cr:* Unatego Cntrl Schl PE Tchr 1974-94, Asst Prin & Ath Dir 1994-; *ai:* NYSAAA 1991-; SAANYS 1996-; *office:* Unatego Cntrl Schl Rd 1 Box 451-A Otego NY 13825

BROWN, RONALD, Music Department Chm & Teacher; *b:* Baltimore, MD; *ed:* Catholic Univ of Amer (BM) Music Ed 1992; *cr:* Basilica of the Natl Shrine Singer 1989-93 St Martin's Cath Chruch Dir of Music & Organist 79-92; Simpson Hamline United Meth Church Organist & Choirmaster 1992-; *ai:* Paul Hill Chorale/Washington Singer 1980-91; Fairfax City Concert Band Trumpeter 1993-; Washington Men's Camerata Asst Conductor 1988-90; Choir of the Washington Natl Cathedral 1978-79; Univ of Md Chorus 1981-81; Masterworks Chorus of Rockville, MD 1984-86; MENC, NEA 1992-; *office:* Friendly HS 10000 Allentown Rd Ft Washington MD 20744

BROWN, SANDRA COPELAND, 4th Grade Teacher; *b:* Dayton, OH; *m:* Kenton Lynn; *c:* Kassandra Jane, Kevin Lynn; *ed:* IN-Purdue Univ at Fr Wayne (BA) Ed 1984, (MS) Ed 1987; Addl Hrs Rdng, Sci; *cr:* Hicksville Elem Schl Grd 4 Tchr 1984-84, Grd 3 Tchr 1985-88, Chptr I Rdng Primary Tchr 1989-92, Grd 1 Tchr 1992-95, Grd 4 Tchr 1995-; *ai:* Hlth Prgm Comm 1987-88; Right-to-Read Comm 1989-; Sci Comm, Chair 1994-; NEA, OEA 1985-; Delta Kappa Gamma 1995-; OH Child Conservation League 1984-, Local Pres, Dist Pres, Many Local, St Offices; Village Player Theater 1988-90, Sec; Cntrl Mennonite Church 1987-; Who's Who Outstdng Women of Amer 1987; Who's Who in the Midwest 1996; *office:* Hicksville Elem Schl 200 W Arthur St Hicksville OH 43526

BROWN, SANDRA KING, 7th Grade Reading Teacher; *b:* Washington, DC; *m:* Daniel D.; *c:* Luis R. Ortiz, Andrew P., Amanda J.; *ed:* Millersville Univ (BS) Elem 1976; Addl Post Grad Work; *cr:* Penn Manor Schl Dist Tchr 16 Yrs; *ai:* 8-9th Grd Peer Helper Adv; Stu Assistance Team Mem; At-Risk Stu Mentor;Strategic Plan Comm; Co-Facilitator of Support Group; Tchr for Active Parenting of Teens Prgm; PA Peer Helpers Assn, St Sec, Newsletter Chprsn, Conf Chm 3 Yrs; PMEA, NEA; Millersville Women of Today 1978-, Pres, Directorship, Lifetime Achvmt Awd, Keywoman, Outstanding Young Women; St Pauls Luth Church 1980-, Tchr; Comm Drug & Alcohol Task Force 1993-, Recreation League Vlybl 1985-, Captain; Outstanding Tchr of Yr 1988; *office:* Penn Manor Schl Dist 2950 Charlestown Rd Lancaster PA 17603

BROWN, SANDRA MONTELEONE, Teacher & Counselor; *b:* Vineland, NJ; *m:* Raymond; *ed:* Glassboro State (BA) Home Ec Ed 1979, Voc Cert 1988; Rowan Coll of NJ (MA) Stu Personnell Svcs 1995; *cr:* Milleville Pub Schls Tchr 1979-, Tchr & Cnslr 1994-; *ai:* NJEA 1979-; AHEA 1979-86.

BROWN, SHARON K., Fr, Span Teacher & Dept Chair; *b:* Dayton, OH; *m:* Ronald Steven; *c:* Jason, Alyssa; *ed:* OH St Univ (BS) Fr 1975, (BS) Frgn Lang Ed 1988; *cr:* St Thomas Aquinas HS Fr, Span Tchr 1976-84; Studebaker Jr HS Fr, Span Tchr 1984-90; Wayne HS Fr, Span Tchr, Dept Chair 1990-; *ai:* Dept Chair; Fr Club; NCA Comm; Tchr, Co-Cnslr European Travel; NEA, OEA, OFLA 1984-; Tchr of Month Wayne HS; *office:* Wayne HS 5400 Chambersburg Rd Dayton OH 45424

BROWN, SHERYL BENITA, Math Liaison & Teacher; *b:* Boston, MA; *m:* Burl G.; *ed:* Fairleigh Dickinson Univ (BA) Elem Ed 1977; 33 Credits Math; *cr:* Hackensack MS Seventh Grd Math Tchr 1977-78; Passaic Vly HS Math Tchr 1978-95, Math Liaison, Tchr 1995-; *ai:* Math League; PSAT, SAT Review Course; Home Instr; Math Curr Comm; Site Coord for Tchng Night; Math Wkshp Coord; Tchr Facilitator for Passaic Vly Peer Resolve; ASCD; NCTM; Assn of Math Tchrs of NJ; Participated in 1994-95 Natl

Tchr Trng Inst; Nom for 1996 Presidential Awd for Excl in Sci & Math Tchng; Served on NJ Bds for Minimum Basic Skills Test; Appointed to US Army Summer Associateship Prgm for HS Sci & Math Fac; *office:* Passaic Valley HS East Main St Little Falls NJ 07424*

BROWN, STEPHEN C., Science Teacher; *b:* Bronx, NY; *m:* Lizandra Vega-Brown; *ed:* Fordham Univ (BS) Psych 1988; Working on Admin, Supervision MS Coll of New Rochelle; *cr:* Thomas C. Giordano MS 45 Eng Tchr 1988-90; *ai:* United Fed of Tchrs 1988-; Save a Generation 1994-, Ed Dir; Cardinal Hayes HS Alumni Assn, VP; Article Pub; *office:* William W. Niles MS 118 577 E 179th St Bronx NY 10457*

BROWN, STEVEN R., ESL Coordinator; *b:* Hayward, CA; *ed:* Univ of CA at Santa Cruz (BA) Politics, Modern Soc 1974; San Siego St Univ (MA) Amer Stud 1979; Univ of Pittsburgh PHD Frgn Lang Ed 1996; *cr:* Univ of Pittsburgh Instr 1986-88, Japan Prgm Dir 1988-91, Eng Lang Inst Admin 1991-95; Youngstown St Univ ESL Coord 1995-; *ai:* Japan Assn of Lang Tchrs 1982-, Natl Prgm Chair; IESOL 1982-; IRA 1992-; NCTE 1995-; Numerous Books Pub; *office:* Youngstown St Univ DEB 202 Youngstown OH 44555

BROWN, SUE HENDERSON, Chem, Physics & Calculus Tchr; *b:* Newport, ME; *m:* Keith R.; *c:* Nathan, Sarah; *ed:* Univ of ME at Farmington (BS) Math 1978; *cr:* Washburn Dist HS Math, Sci Tchr 1990-; *ai:* Soph Class, Stock Market Game Adv; Cert Support System Rep; NEA, ME Ed Assn 1990-; Washburn Tchrs Assn 1990-, Negotiating Team; Lidstone Meth Church 1980-, Past Treas; Washburn Zoning Bd 1995-; *office:* Washburn Dist HS Main St Washburn ME 04786

BROWN, SUSAN CAROL, Music & Chorus Teacher; *b:* Bellows Falls, VT; *ed:* Univ of MA (BA) Music Ed 1963, (MA) Music Ed; *cr:* UMass Women's Choir & Madrigal Singers Tchng Asst, Acting Dir 1973-74, Tchng Assoc, Acting Dir 1977-78; Amherst Coll Chorus Dir 1979-81; Smith Coll Asst to Dir of Choral Music, Assoc Dir Glee Club, Conducting Instr 1979-81; UMass Performing Arts Vocal Instr 1979-81; Agawam Jr HS Music Tchr, Chorus Dir 1981-; Chicopee Comm Chorus Dir 1982-83; Suffield Second Bapt Church Music Dir 1983-; Guitar Acad of Agawam Pvt Voice Tchr 1989-92; Cambridge Coll Guest Lecturer, Adj Fac Instr 1989-; Ludlow Schl System Pvt Voice Tchr 1995-; *ai:* Steering, Dist Coordinating Comms; Springfield Symphony Chorus; Wilbraham Madrigal Singers; MENC 1978-; MA Music Edctrs Assn 1981-, Western Dist Chprsn; MA Tchrs Assn 1981-; Amer Choral Dir Assn 1978-; Choristers Guild 1989-; ASCD 1991-; Amer Guild Eng Handbell Ringers 1994-; Agawam Ed Assn 1981-, Schl Rep; 1990 MMEA Western Dist Jr Treble Festival Chorus, 1993 Choristers Guild Childrens Festival Chorus, 1994 Amer Guild Organists Childrens Festival Chorus Conductor; Vocal Hlth Wkshp Presenter 1995- MMEA All St Conf; 1992 MMEA Lowell Mason Awd; *office:* Agawam Jr HS 1305 Springfield St Feeding Hills MA 01030*

BROWN, SUSAN DOUGLAS, Speech Teacher; *b:* London Ontario, Canada; *m:* Jeffrey Douglas; *c:* Laura, Craig; *ed:* Bowling Green St Univ (BS) Speech, Eng 1972; Akron Univ (MS) Scndry Ed 1979; *cr:* Faircrest Jr High Eng, Speech Tchr 1972-83; Canton South HS Speech Tchr 1985-; *ai:* Speech Club Adv; Drama Dir; NEA, OEA 1972-; CLEA 1972-, Sec, Bldg Rep; Meth Church, Youth Adv, Pastor-Parish Comm; Nom Twice for Ashland Oils Tchr Achvmt Prgm; *office:* Canton South HS 600 Faircrest St SE Canton OH 44707

BROWN, SUZANNE HYDE, English Teacher; *b:* Rockville, CT; *m:* Kurt F.; *c:* Ana Marie, Colton E.; *ed:* SUNT at Oneonta (BS) Scndry Ed Eng 1987; SUNY at Potsdam (MS) Scndry Ed Eng 1992; *cr:* Thousand Islands Cntrl Schl Eng Tchr 1987-; Family Cnslng Ctr Cnslr 1990-; *ai:* Drama Club; 8th Grd Grad, NHS Selection Comm; Coach, Adv; NCTE 1991-; *home:* PO Box 432 Clayton NY 13624*

BROWN, THOMAS JAMES, Physics Teacher; *b:* Brooklyn, NY; *m:* Sally Ann Jarvis; *c:* Christopher, Peter, David, Jennifer; *ed:* Cath Univ of Amer (BA) Physics 1960; Renssalaer Polytechnic Inst (MS) Phys Sci 1967; Univ of MD 30 Hrs 1972; Univ of MA 10 Hrs 1995; Boston Coll, Harvard, Rutgers, Tufts Credits; *cr:* LaSalle Acad Providence Math Tchr 1960-62; Walpole HS Physics, Chem Tchr 1962-; *ai:* Sr Class Adv; Sftbl Asst Coach; NEA 1962-; WTA 1962-, Past VP; NSTA; K of C 1965-, Past Sec; Univ of MD Flwshp; Colesca Outstdng Tchr; Presidential Awd Nom 8 Times; 3 Yrbk Dedications; Sigma Psi Scientific Tchr of Yr; *home:* 672 Common St Walpole MA 02081*

BROWN, VIRGINIA JUDITH, AP Biology Teacher; *b:* Baltimore, MD; *m:* Clinton H.; *c:* Christy, Jeremy, Jim, Michael, Robby, Trevor; *ed:* Mount Saint Mary's Coll (BS) Med Tech 1980; Univ of MD at Baltimore Cty (MA) Ed 1994; Intnl Baccalaureate Tchr Trng 1994; Intnl Baccalaureate Advanced Tchr Trng 1996; *cr:* Washington Hosp Ctr Med Technologist 1980-87; Montgomery Gen Hosp Med Technologist 1987-93; Richard Montgomery HS Bio Tchr 1992-; *ai:* Discipline Comm; NSTA 1992-; MD Assoc of Bio Tchrs 1995-; Phi Kappa Phi 1994-; Univ of MD at College Park Bio Inst 1995; *office:* Richard Montgomery HS 250 Richard Montgomery Dr Rockville MD 20852

BROWN, VIRGINIA LOUISE, Fourth Grade Teacher; *b:* Boston, MA; *c:* Daniel P.; *ed:* St Joseph Coll at Emmitsburg (BA) Elem Ed 1971; Mt St Marys Ecumenical Inst at Roland Park (MA) Theology 1975; *cr:* Trinity HS Theology Chprsn 1975-77; Memorial Elem 4th-5th Grd Tchr 1977-79; St Joseph Jr High Sci, Soc Stud Tchr 1979-85; H. W. Moore Elem 4th-5th Grd Tchr 1985-; *ai:* Curr, Fac Sunshine, Portfolio Comms; Mentor Prgm; NEA, NHEA 1985-; NHSTA 1980-; Census Taker 1971-72; Dir of Rel Ed 1973-75; Summer Camp Tutor 1973-75; Stu Tour Adv 1980-85; Big Brother, Big Sister 1990-94; *office:* Henry W. Moore Elem Schl 12 Deerfield Rd Candia NH 03034

BROWN, WANDA MAE (ATKINS), First Grade Teacher; *b:* West Portsmouth, OH; *m:* Roger L.; *c:* Nancy Stevens, Roger Dale, Paula Gauthreaux, Evanna Brown; *ed:* OH Univ (BS) Elem Ed 1973; 5th Yr; *cr:* 2-3 Grd Tchr 1966-69; 6-8 Grd Title I Tchr 1970-73; 1 Grd Tchr 1973-; *ai:* IBA Team; NEA; OEA; ELCTA, Sec; *office:* Stockdale Elem Schl PO Box 3 Stockdale OH 45683

BROWN, WILLIAM, Health Instructor; *b:* Buffalo, NY; *m:* Neila Maria Matia Lauretti; *c:* Christopher, Gina, Benjamin; *ed:* Brockport St (BS) Hlth & PE 1969; Syracuse Univ (MS) Hlth & PE 1970; Internship at Syracuse Univ Sports Medicine Dept 1980-82; Internship at Onondaga Sports Medicine & Rehabilitation 1991; Cortland St in Hlth & Sports Medicine Courses 1980; *cr:* Syracuse Univ Grad Asst 1969-70; Town of Cicero Recreation Parks & Spec Prgms Dir 1970-74; North Syracuse Schl Dist Hlth Instr & Sports Medicine Trainer 1970-; City of Syracuse Parks & Recreation Track & Field Dir 1979-83; *ai:* Hlth Ed Chprsn; We Care Crisis Hotline & Local Neighborhood Watch Dir; Sports Medicine Dept Head; NSEA 1970-; NATA 1982-; AATA 1987-; NYSATA 1988-; Optimist Club 1990-, Youth Svc Awd 1992; Eucharisitic Minister 1985-; Amer Red Cross 1967-, Instr 28 Yrs, Cert of Appreciation; SADD 1980-, Founder, Appreciation Awd Plaque 1990; North Syracuse Chamber of Commerce-Star News Man of Yr 1987; City of Syracuse/Onon Cty Drug & Alcohol Commission Awd 1993; Syracuse Moose Club Man of Yr-Work with Youth 1995; Comm Hero Torch Runner Olympics 1996; AATA Nom for Trainer of Yr Awd 1995; *office:* Cicero-North Syracuse HS Northstar Dr Cicero NY 13039

BROWN, WILLIAM, TV Production Teacher; *b:* Phila, PA; *m:* Joan C. Hermesman; *c:* William J., David John, James J.; *ed:* Temple (BS) Ed 1976, (MS) Admin 1981; St Apprenticeship Tool & Die Maker; *cr:* Tool & Die Maker Engr; Leeds Schl Indstrl Arts Tchr 1970-73; Lowell Schl Indstrl Arts Tchr 1973-76; Masterman Schl Indstrl Arts Tchr 1976-93; Roxborough HS TV Prod Tchr 1993-; *ai:* Sr Class Spon; Haddonfield Tennis Assoc, Pres; Mabel Kay Sr Citizens, Dir; Haddonfield Art League, Pres, Ch of Bd; Home School Chm; *office:* Roxborough HS 6498 Ridge Ave Philadelphia PA 19128*

BROWN, WILLIAM MORGAN, Professor of Commercial Art; *b:* Rochester, NY; *m:* Judith Warner; *c:* Heather; *ed:* Rochester Inst of Tech (BFA) Graphic Design 1964, (MFA) Graphic Design 1965; *cr:* North TX St Univ Art Instr 1965-67; Rochester Inst of Tech, Coll of Continuing Ed, Arts, Graphic Arts Dir 1967-72; Dutchess Comm Coll Art Dept Chm, Art Gallery Dir 1972-78; Genesee Comm Coll Commercial Art Prof 1978-; *ai:* Coord Commercial Art Prgm; Part-time Art Fac Mentor; Commercial Art Stdnts Adv; Guid Cnslr to Art Stdnts; Judge Scholastic HS Art Competition; NEA 25 Yrs; GEA 1978-; Genesee Cncl of Arts, Past Bd Mem; Genesee Wyoming BOCES 1985-, Advy Comm for Graphics Design; Fed Voc Ed Grants; Nom NY St Chancellor's Awd; George L. Herdle Meml Awd; Designer of Genesee Comm Coll Logo, Genesee Cncl of Arts Logo; One Man Shows; *office:* Genesee Comm Coll 1 College Rd Batavia NY 14020*

BROWN, WILLIAM PAUL, Phys & Learning Support Instr; *b:* New Kensington, PA; *m:* Justine Bartuccio; *c:* Maria Allison, Catherine Elizabeth; *ed:* Slipperty Rock Univ (BSEd) Physically Handicapped 1974, (MED) Spcl Ed 1975; Cert Slippery Rock Univ Spcl Admin & Supvr 1979; *cr:* Butler Area Schl Dist Scndry Phys & Learning Tchr 1975-, Support Instr 21 Yrs; *ai:* Mid Sts Accredidation Evaluation Comm Chrpsn; Teen Parenting Pgm Butler Area Schl Dist Tutor; NEA 1975-; Butler Ed Assn 1975-; Butler Twp Handicapped Advy Comm 1984-, Adv Architectural Accessibility; St Fidelis Parish Cncl 1995-, VP; *home:* 204 Williams Rd Butler PA 16001

BROWN, WILLIE CANNON, Asst Professor; *b:* West Point, MS; *c:* Samantha, Panzie Rene, Grent, Charles; *ed:* Temple Univ (BS) Bus Ed 1976; Wilmington Coll (MS) Mngmt 1995; *cr:* Peirce Coll Asst Prof 1976-; *ai:* Fac Mentor Early Employment Selection Prgm; Intnl Club Adv; Peirce Perkins Comm Mem; *office:* Peirce Coll 1420 Pine St Philadelphia PA 19102*

BROWN, WONDEL EVERETT, Chorus Teacher; *b:* Baltimore, MD; *m:* Gwendolyn Dyson; *c:* Everett, Erik, Ean, Megan; *ed:* Morgan St Univ (BS) Music Ed 1975; Univ of MD, Bowie St Univ, Morgan St Univ Working Towards Masters Equivalency; *cr:* G. Gardner Shugert MS Band Dir, Music Chm 11 Yrs; Potomac HS Band Dir, Music Chm 8 Yrs; Benjamin Stoddart MS Chorus Dir 1 Yr; *ai:* Tennis Coach; Bowie St Univ Jazz Ensemble Asst; USPTR 1984-; Kappa Alpha Psi 1971-, Reporter; WA Redskins Jazz Band Mem.

BROWN-BRECKENRIDGE, CHARLOTTE R., Distributive Education Teacher; *b:* Lynn, MA; *m:* Leon H.; *c:* Henry, Robert, Daniel; *ed:* Salem St Coll (BS) Bus Ed 1974; Attnd Suffolk Univ, Fitchburg St; *cr:* Lynn Eng HS Bus Tchr 1974-75, Distributive Ed Coord 1983; Lynn Voc Tech Inst Distributive Ed Tchr 1975-, Lynn Evening Education Bus Tchr 1994-; *ai:* Cultural Cncl Adv; Class Adv 1989 & 1995; Sunday Schl Tchr; NHS Comm; Teen Pregnancy Prevention; LVTI Mentor Pgm; Lynn Thcrs Union 1974-; AFT 1974-; MA Fed of Tchrs 1974-; Comm Minority Cultural Ctr 1968-; Brown Schl PTO 1988-, VP 1994-96; Whos Who in Amer Jr Coll 1968; *office:* Lynn Voc Tech Inst 80 Neptune Blvd Lynn MA 01902

BROWNE, DOUGLAS ALAN, Prof of Music & Dir of Choirs; *b:* Mineola, NY; *m:* Susan Evelyn Kamp; *c:* Joshua Douglas; *ed:* Houghton Coll (BSME) Music Ed 1968; West TX St Univ (MA) Music 1974; Univ of MO (DMA) Conducting 1984; *cr:* Elba Cntrl Schl Vocal Music Tchr 1968-69; Lee HS Choral Dir 1974-79; Grove City Coll Prof of Music 1981-; *ai:* Touring Choir Dir; Music Ed Natl Conf Adv; Amer Choral Dirs Assn 1974; MENC 1981; PA Music Ed Assn 1981; East Main Presbyn Church 1983-, Music Dir; *office:* Grove City Coll 100 Campus Dr Grove City PA 16127

BROWNE, HELEN DUH, Elementary School Educator; *b:* Bethlehem, PA; *m:* Leonard T.; *c:* Marisa Stewart, Brian Stewart, Sean; *ed:* Trinity Coll (BA) Bio 1968; St Univ of NY Coll at Buffalo (MED) Elem Ed, Philosophy of Ed 1974; Permanent Cert Elem Ed Cedar Crest Coll 1969; Master Catechist Diocese of Allentown 1993; DRE St Ambrose Parish Schulykill 1993-95, Sacred Heart Park 1995-; *cr:* Como Park Elem Schl 2nd Grd Tchr 1970-74; Holy Child Schl 7th Grd Tchr 1984-91; Sacred Heart Schl 2-8th Grd Tchr 1993-; *ai:* Sci Coord; PJAS 1984-, Sci Fair Spon; NCEA 1984-; *office:* Sacred Heart Schl 115 Washington St Bath PA 18014

BROWNE, JOSEPH BRADLEY, Mathematics Professor; *b:* Philadelphia, PA; *m:* Mary Sterling Marsden; *c:* George, James, Sarah Cox; *ed:* Bucknell Univ (BS) Math 1967; Northern MI Univ (MA) Math 1970; 57 Sem Hrs OK St Univ; *cr:* Mt Clemens Schls Math Tchr 1967-69; Northern MI Univ Math Instr 1970-72; Langston Univ Math, Physics Lecturer 1974-75; Onondaga Comm Coll Math Prof 1975-; *ai:* Math League Spon; Math Modeling Competition Coach; NYSMATYC 1976-, Sec, Pres, Outstdng Contributions Math Ed 1990; AMATYC 1984-; Math Assn of Amer 1971-, Comm, Conf Chair; NCTM, AFT; SPEBSQSA 1994-, Asst Dir; Chancellor's Awd for Excl in Tchng 1990; Articles Pub Prof Journals; *office:* Onondaga Comm Coll Onondaga Hill Road Syracuse NY 13215

BROWNE, OLIVENE FRIDAY, Math & Humanities Teacher; *b:* Antigua, West Indies; *m:* Lenroy; *c:* Cleon, Randy, Michael, Dimitri; *ed:* Lehman Coll (BA) Hum 1991, (MS) Eng 1995; Diploma in Bus Math, Union Stud; *cr:* Potters Primary Schl Tchr 1975-78; Clare Hall Scndry Schl Head Bus Dept 1979-83; St Angelamerici Schl Tchr 1983-94; Rice HS Tchr 1994-; *ai:* Mathathon Prgms for St Judes Hosp; St Marys Church Yth Adv, Warden; FCT 1983-; Family Math 1993-, Coord; Tchr of Yr 1985-86; Comm Svc Awd 1992, 1994; *office:* Rice HS 74 W 124th St New York NY 10027*

BROWNELL, ELAINE JORDAN, Mathematics Teacher; *b:* Lincoln, ME; *m:* William S.; *c:* John, Andrew; *ed:* Univ of ME at Orono (BA) Math 1970; Univ of Southern ME (MSEd) Scndry Ed 1980; Addl Credit Hrs; *cr:* Garland St Jr HS 7th-8th Grd Math Tchr 1970-72; Mahoney MS 8th-9th Grd Math Tchr 1973-79, Career Ed Tchr 1980-84; S Portland HS Math Tchr 1988-89; Cape Elizabeth HS Math Tchr 1989-; *ai:* Class Adv; Staff Dev Comm; NEA 1970-; MEA 1970-; Local Assn 1970-; NCTM 1994-; UCC Church 1973, Music Comm Chair & Organ Accompanist for Church Schl; *office:* Cape Elizabeth HS 345 Ocean House Rd Cape Elizabeth ME 04107

BROWNELL, MARK GRIFFEN, History Teacher; *b:* Cold Spring, NY; *m:* Judith Jones; *c:* Elizabeth, Jen; *ed:* Norwich Univ (BA) His 1972; Castleton St (MA) Ed 1980; Addl 37 Hrs Post Masters Ed; Harvard Graduate Schl of Ed 1994; *cr:* West Rutland HS His, Eng, Sci Tchr 1973-74; Green Mountain HS His Tchr 1974-75; Essex MS Jr HS Sci Tchr 1984-85; Mill River Union HS His Tchr 1976-; *ai:* AFT; Stratford Hall Monticello Summer Seminar 1986; Yale Hopkins Summer Seminar Russian Stud 1984; *office:* Mill River Union HS Box 6 Middle Rd N Clarendon VT 05759*

BROWNFIELD, ROBERT BEAUMONT,JR., Fifth Grade Teacher of Gifted; *b:* Akron, OH; *m:* Joan M. Bazelides; *c:* R. B., Jill; *ed:* Univ of Akron (BSEd) Soc Stud, Elem Ed 1970; Univ of Akron (MEd) 1993; Post Grad Work OH St, Bowling Green, Kent St, Ashland Univ; *cr:* Bissell Schl 5th Grd Tchr 1970-75; Twinsburg Elem Schl 4th Grd Open Class Tchr 1975-87; Twinsburg Elem Schl 4th Grd Tchr 1987-93; Bissell 5th Grd Gifted Tchr 1993-94; Gifted Cluster Grp Tchr 5th Grd 1994-; *c* Geography Club; Right to Read Week Co Chm; Recycle Comm; Hu Whale Adoption Project; Soc Stud Curr Comm; Schl Testing Tas NEA, OEA, NEOTA 1970-, Del Assembly 8 Yrs; TEA Past VP, Rep; Phi Delta Kappa; United Way 8 Yrs; Chm Math-a-Thon 4 Yr raternal Homeholding 1970-, Bd 2 Yrs; Jr Great Books Ld Classroom of the Future 1989-91; Martha Holden Jennings Writing 1988; Founder, First Chm TEA Schlsp; Math Curr Comm; *office* Middle Schl 10225 Ravenna Rd Twinsburg OH 44087

BROWNING, GLENN C., Social Studies Teacher; *b:* Pawtucke Linda Firth; *c:* Kyle, Ryan; *ed:* RI Coll (BA) Soc Stud 1969; Pr Coll (MED) Admin 1976; 30 Credit Hrs Univ of RI Ec; *cr:* Cumber Soc Stud Tchr 1969-; *ai:* Tech Comm; NEA 1969-; VP of New Educl Publishers Inc 1982-; 6 Titles Pub in Rdng Software Cumberland HS 2600 Mendon Rd Cumberland RI 02864

BROWNING, ROBERT J., Prof of Eng as Second Language; *b* Rapids, MI; *ed:* Harvard Divinity Schl (MA) New Testament St *cr:* Roxbury Comm Coll Prof ESL 1988-; *ai:* Chess Club; Tuto Right Brain, No Pain; *office:* Roxbury Community Coll 1234 Crossing Roxbury Xing MA 02120*

BROWN JENKINS, DAISY, Mathematics Teacher; *b:* Winnsboro Earnest L.; *c:* Kim Rechelle; *ed:* Southern Univ (BS) Scndry Ma Tulane Univ (MA) 1971; Attnd Loyola Univ, NJIT, Rutgers Univ; Orleans Pub Schls Math Tchr 1963-71; Newark Pub Schls Ma 1971-; *ai:* NHS Adv; New Tchrs Mentor; Calculator Consulta NCTM 1968-; AFT NJ 1971-; NJAMT 1980-; Delta Sigma Theta Linden Schlrshp 1973-; Outstdng Math Tchr Awd Dist; *office:* Sci 40 Rector St Newark NJ 07102

BROWNSTEIN, MICHAEL MARK, English Teacher; *b:* New CT; *ed:* Kenyon Coll (BA) Eng 1981; Syracuse Univ (MBA) Mrk Tchrs Coll at Columbia Univ (EDM) Curr, Tchng 1996; Wesley 7-12 Grds Eng Cert 1992; *cr:* Wilbur Cross HS Eng Tchr 1992-9 Annex Eng Tchr 1995-; *office:* Cross Annex School 45 Nash St Nev CT 06511*

BROZ, KENNETH STEPHEN, HS History Teacher & Co Streveport, LA; *m:* Janet Harris; *c:* Stephanie Linn; *ed:* Muskig (BA) Ed 1980; Univ of Dayton (MS) Admin 1982; *cr:* Cambridge C 6th Grd Tchr 1980-82; John Glenn Schl 8th Grd Tchr 1982-85; N Schl HS L D Tchr 1985-87; Logan Elm Schl HS His Tchr 1 Norwalk City Schl HS His Tchr 1990-; *ai:* Boys Var Bsktbl Coach; of Chrstn Ath Adv; NEA 1980-; *office:* Norwalk HS 80 E Main St N OH 44857*

BROZICK, JAMES R., English Dept Chair; *b:* Blairsville, PA; Univ of PA (BS) Eng Ed 1965; Univ of Pittsburgh (MED) Rdng Arts 1971, (PhD) Lang Comm 1976; Supvr of Comm; Prin Cert; Letter of Eligibility; *cr:* North Hills Schls AP Eng Tchr & Dept Chm Univ of Pittsburgh composition Instr 1976-78; *ai:* Mid St Evaluati Curr Cncl; Testing Comm; North Hill Ed Assn, PSEA, NEA 198 Cncl on Research in Eng 1976-; Making Thinking Visible Project C Mellon Univ 4 Yrs; Grant Univ of Pittsburgh Lang Arts Prgm; Promising Researcher Awd 1977; Review of Lit Journal of Aesth 1977; A Model for Tchng Composition Eng Journal 1979; *office* Hills Schls 53 Rochester Rd Pittsburgh PA 15229

BRUBACHER, ROBERT E., Fifth Grade Teacher; *b:* Kitchen Canada; *m:* Rebecca Jo Kaser; *c:* Jon, Jill; *ed:* Goshen Coll (BA) E 1965; IN Univ (MA) Elem Ed 1968; *cr:* Beardsly Elem 5th G Part-Time 1965; Milford Elem 4th Grd Tchr 1965-66; Melrose E Grd Tchr 1966-75; Wise Elem 7th-8th Grd Tchr 1975-77; Berlin E Grd Tchr 1977-; *ai:* NEA 1965-; OEA 1966-; WEA Tchrs Assn 1 Bldg Rep; EHTA Tchrs Assn 1975-, Bldg Rep; Martha Holden J Recipient; *home:* 5720 State Route 39 Millersburg OH 44654

BRUBAKER, ROY LESTER, Former Administrator & Teac McAlisterville, PA; *m:* Anita Hope Beidler; *c:* Angela, Roy D., Debra; *ed:* Eastern Mennonite Univ (BA) Elem Ed 1967; 45 Cr Hrs Mennonite Seminary; 8 Cr Hrs Arabic, Islam Daystar Comm Nair Somalia Mennonite Mission Tchr, Ed Dir 1967-75; Kenya Me Islamic Prgm Coord 1977-82; Juniata Mennonite Schl Admi 1983-89; *ai:* MACSA 1983-89; Lost Creek Mennonite Church 1 Pastor; Tuscarora Organic Growers 1993-, Bd Mem; Junia Ministerium 1983-92; *home:* RR 1 Box 209 Mifflintown PA 17059

BRUBAKER-SHOBER, GLORIA A., First Grade Teacher; *b:* La PA; *m:* Lee B.; *c:* Michael L., Mark A.; *ed:* Elizabethtown Coll (BS Ed 1961; Attnd Millersville Univ; *cr:* Ephrata Area Schl Dist Fou Tchr 1961-63; Cocalico Schl Dist First Grd Tchr 1964-; *ai:* NEA, CEA 1966-; Keystone St Rdng Assn 1990-; PTA 1966-; Jayne 1964-70, Pres, Outstdng Mem; St John Luth Church 1963-, Cnc *home:* 145 E Chestnut St Ephrata PA 17522

BRUCE, EUGENE WILLIAM, Social Studies Tchr & Co Rochester, NY; *m:* Sandra Lascell; *c:* Michael, Matthew, Megan; *e* of Rochester (AB) His 1965, (MA) Ed, His 1967; Addl 3 Grd Hrs; at Geneseo 27 Grad Hrs; SUNY at Brockport 6 Grad Hrs; *cr:* Brigh Soc Stud Tchr 1965-; *ai:* Detention Stud Hall Supvr; Ftbl & Bsk Announcer; NEA 1965-; Natl Rifle Assn, Mendon Conservation 1993-; Rochester Rifle Assn 1994-; Adirondack Mtn Club 1988-; Club, Greenpeace 1985-; *office:* Brighton HS 2035 Monroe Ave Ro NY 14618

BRUCE, RAE COTA, Eng Tchr & Write Rm Consultant; *b:* Wai VT; *m:* Rev. W. Ralph; *c:* Kenneth Stewart, Heather Stewart, Donna; *ed:* Univ of NH (BA) Eng Ed 1959; Rivier Coll (MA) Eng W Lit 1988; 22 Credit Hrs Poetry; *cr:* Winthrop Sr HS Eng Tchr, Dep 1959-64; Rundlett Jr HS Eng Tchr 1978-83; Merrimack HS Eng Write Room 1983-; *ai:* Lit Magazine Adv; NEA, NHEA 1978- England Writing Ctrs Assn 1989-, Bd Mem 1991; New England Ass Eng, NH Assn Tchrs Eng 1980-; St James United Meth Church L Meth; NH Poetry Soc 1984-, Bd Mem; Rising Rivers Poets 1993-; Who in Amer Ed 1990; Finalist NH Tchr of YR 1991; Awd Excl in E Outstanding Scndry Schl Educator, Clark Univ 1992; 5 Poems Pub; Pub; Co-Author Chptr in Bk; *office:* Merrimack HS 38 Mc Elw Merrimack NH 03054*

BRUCE, SANDRA WINDHAM, English Tchr & Dept Chp Grenada, MS; *m:* Woodson Larry; *ed:* Delta St Univ (BS) Eng, Scn 1973; Univ of MS (MED) Eng, Scndry Ed 1976; 30 Addl Hrs; 10 Hrs Univ of San Diego; 15 Credit Hrs Univ of MD; *cr:* Calhoun Ct Eng, Sci Tchr 1973-77; Oxford Municipal Schl Dist Eng Tchr 1 Dept of Defense Dependent Schls Eng Tchr 1981-; *ai:* AVID Outdoor Ed Spon; Schl Improvement Comm; Overseas Ed Assn 19 Delta Kappa 1976-; Schl Advy Comm 1985-86, Tchr Rep; Exce Tchr Awd 1989-95; Sustained Superior Tchr Awd 1991-95; *home:* PS 1005 Box 49 FPO AE 09593

BRUCIA, BENITA MARIA, Seventh & Eighth Grade Teach Brooklyn, NY; *ed:* St John's Univ (BS) Elem Ed 1970; Fordham Univ Elem Ed 1980; *cr:* St Benedict Joseph Labre Schl 3rd Grd Tchr 1 5th Grd Tchr 1971-73, 7th-8th Grd Tchr 1973-77, 4th Grd Tchr 1 7th-8th Grd Tchr 1981-; *ai:* Spec Events, Math, Math Bee, Confir Sacrament, Cmptr Ed Coords; Yrbk Ed; Lions quest Facilitator; M

Comm, Evaluation Team; Catechist Svc Awd; St Elizabeth Ann stinguished Tchr Awd; *office:* St Benedict Joseph Labre Schl 7th St Richmond Hill NY 11419

KEITH EUGENE, Mathematics Teacher; *b:* Somerset, PA; *m:* raby; *ed:* Univ of Pittsburgh at Johnstown (BS) Scndry Ed Math Parkside HS Math Tchr 1994-; *ai:* JV Math Team, JV Bsbl, Golf ach; 504 Comm; Attendance Review Comm; NEA, WCEA 1994-; 993-; *home:* 28350 Adkins Rd Salisbury MD 21801

ER, ELIZABETH GLEBA, Upper Elem Lang Arts Tchr; *b:* h, PA; *m:* Michael John; *c:* John Michael, Peter Gabriel; *ed:* oll (BA) Eng, Comm 1984; *cr:* St Joseph Schl Upper Elem Lang r 1994-95; All Saints Schl Upper Elem Lang Arts Tchr 1995-96; of Mount Schl Upper Elem Lang Arts Tchr 1996-; *ai:* Yrbk Adv; Moderator; WPCTE 1991-; NCEA 1985-; Youth Minister Maurice 990-, Spiritual Dir; Golden Apple Awd 1992; Elizabeth Strange Writing, Outstanding Leadership in Comm Arts Awd.

ROSELYN JENITA, 6th Grade Teacher; *b:* St Croix, VI; *ed:* WA BA) Ed 1989; *cr:* Cleveland Pub Schls 5th-6th Grd Tchr 1989-; PTA Liaison; Sunshien Comm Chprsn; Dress Code, Course of Stu Comms; Cleveland Tchr Union 1989-; OH Fed Tchrs, AFT; *office:* Longfellow Schl 650 E 140th St Cleveland OH 44110*

CHARLES JAMES, Secondary Mathematics Tchr; *b:* Jersey ; *m:* Carol Annette Benyo; *c:* Lt. Charles J. III, Debra Lynn ; *ed:* Saint Peters Coll (BS) Math 1967; Montclair St Univ (MA) & Supervision 1972; NJ Inst of Tech (MS) Cmptr Sci 1975; Univ (EDD) Math Ed 1994; Numerous Inservice Courses & Bergenfield HS Math & Cmptr Sci Tchr 1967-; Bergen Comm n & Cmptr Sci Adjunct Tchr 1990-; Bergenfield Summer Schl Prin Cmptr Team; Intnl Exch Coord; Staff Relations Comm; Alternate chr Mentor; NEA, NJEA, 1967-; BEA 1967-, Former VP, Bd of TM 1969-; ACM, SIGCSE 1990-, Task Force on Sec Schl; ISTE GCG 1980-, VP; BCEA 1967-; Skyliners Sr Drum & Bugle Corps Asst Dir; Skyline Alumni Drum & Bugle Corps 1995-, Dir; ACM Scndry Schls in Cmptr Scis Co-Author; Plane Goom C-Text or Interally Published; *office:* Bergenfield HS 80 S Prospect Ave eld NJ 07621*

, KATHRYN A., Soc Studies Dept Chprsn & Tchr; *b:* Queens, NY; Y at Albany (BA) Soc Stud-Cum Laude 1975; Iona Coll (MS) Ed, s 1981; *cr:* Nazareth Regnl HS Rel Stud Tchr 1975-77; Msgr HS Soc Stud Tchr 1977-84; Mary Louis Acad Soc Stud Chprsn, 84-; *ai:* Var Tennis Coach; Model UN Club Moderator; ASCD CEA 1975-; NCSS 1984-; *office:* The Mary Louis Acad 176-21 Terr Jamaica NY 11432

, THURZA, Second Grade Teacher; *b:* Pittsburgh, PA; *m:* ; *c:* Gretchen, Cody; *cr:* Easton Area Schl 2nd Grd Tchr 1970-; *ai:* 70-.

L, LILLIAN MANNINO, Fifth Grade Teacher; *b:* Bronx, NY; *m:* R.; *c:* Jennifer, Donald Jr.; *ed:* St Joseph's Coll (BA) Ed 1985; Coll (MS) Rdng 1989; 75 Post Grad Credits; *cr:* Frank P. Long iate Schl Fifth Grd Tchr 1985-; *ai:* Shared Decision Bldg Team *ome:* 3 Shade Tree Ln East Patchogue NY 11772

AGHIM, MERRY ELLEN E., English Teacher; *b:* Albany, NY; *m:* Gabriella, Dorian; *ed:* Skidmore Univ (BA) Eng 1989; St Rose S) Eng 1994; Russell Sage Tchng Cert Scndry Ed 1990; *cr:* Ft Plain oag Schl 6-8 Grd Eng Tchr 1989-90; Mayfield Cntrl Schl 8th Grd r 1990-; *ai:* Girls Sftbl Asst Coach; 8th Grd Builders Club, Jr Sr spaper Adv; Odyssey of the Mind Coach 2 Yrs; Wrote & Awded or an Author Festival; *office:* Mayfield Cntrl Schl School St l NY 12117

ACH, MARCIA A., Supvr of Wellness & Fitness; *b:* Pottstown, Concord Coll at Athens (BS) Hlth, PE 1971; West Chester Univ Hlth, PE 1980; Temple Univ Supvr of H PE Cert 1988; Penn St Univ t 1990; *cr:* York Vo-Tech Hlth, PE Tchr 1972-73; Boyertown Jr HS h, PE Tchr 1973-90; Boyertown Sr HS Tchr, Supvr H, PE 1990-; osse Coach; Comm Partnership; Rewriting Curr, Drug Testing PA St HPER, Amer Alliance of HPERD 1971-; USWLA, US e Selector; Kiwanis Club 1990-; YMCA, Swimming Prgm; *office:* wn Area Sr HS 4th & Monroe Sts Boyertown PA 19512*

BERG, JOHN CARL, Science Teacher; *b:* Du Bois, PA; *m:* Petak; *c:* John, Anna; *ed:* Clarion Univ (BS) Earth Space 1971, i Ed 1974; *cr:* Fox Chapel HS Sci Tchr 24 Yrs; *ai:* Planetarium Dir; ox Chapel Area HS 611 Field Club Rd Pittsburgh PA 15238

LL, ARTHUR B.,JR., Social Studies Teacher; *b:* Worcester, MA; E. Wynne; *c:* Anne, Catherine, Matthew, Elizabeth, Mary, John; Cross Coll (AB) His 1968; Assumption Coll (MA) His 1971; Over eyond Masters in Schl Admin & His; *cr:* Auburn HS Soc Stud Dept 58-; *ai:* Schl Bank Prgm, Sr His Scholars Prgm & Hum Scholars rative Prgm Moderator; NEA, MA Tchrs Assn 1968-; Auburn rs Assn 1968-, VP, PR&R Chm, Negotiator; Town of Shrewsbury, eeting Mem 1971-, Human Svc Needs Stud Comm Co-Chair 1995-; A Conf Ftbl Ofcls 1968-, 23 Yr Honorary Life Mem; New England legiate Ftbl Conf, Referee; MA Schl Bank Assn 1988-, St Sec; 2 h Fnd Fellowships; Insurance Inst of Amer 2 Week Stud Fellowship ounded Own Bus-Brunell Distributors-with Gross Sales in Excess 000 Annually; Auburn Schl Dept Tchr of Yr 1993-94; *office:* HS 99 Auburn St Auburn MA 01501*

LL, ROBERT HENRY, Professor of English; *b:* Gardner, MA; *w:* e Clark (dec); *c:* Lee, Martha; *ed:* Colby Coll (BA) Fr & Eng 1947; bury Coll (MA) Span & Eng 1950; Attnd Syracuse Univ Counseling *cr:* Little Falls HS Modern Langs Chair 1947-52; St Univ of NY At Lang & Eng Asst Prof 1952-54; Cayuga Comm Coll Prof of Eng *ai:* Honors, Writing & Collegewide Evaluation Comms; United Way ga Cty, Treas; Theatre Bd, VP; Arts Cncl; Chancellors Awd for Excl g 1974; CCC Outstanding Tchr of Yr 1990; *office:* Cayuga County Coll Franklin Street Auburn NY 13021

ELLE, CHARLES DAVID, Social Studies & PE Teacher; *b:* Price, Lilo Koss; *c:* Douglas C., Anthony G.; *ed:* Univ of UT (BS) Soc 73; Natl Louis Univ of IL (MED) 1996; Attnd Boston Univ Cmptr, fectiveness Trng; *cr:* Beatty HS Soc Stud Chprsn, Soc Stud, PE 73-80; Bamberg HS Soc Stod, PE Tchr 1980-, Soc Stud Chprsn Athletic Dir 1995-; *ai:* Ftbl Head Coach; NHS Comm Mem; as Educl Assn 1980-, Fac Rep; Comm Awd 1992-95; Achvmt Awd s of Foreign Wars; *office:* Bamberg American HS Dodds Unit 27539 564 APO AE 09139

ELLO, LAURA A., Art Teacher; *b:* Newark, NJ; *ed:* Kean Coll of) Fine Art Ed; Cnslr Ed Credit; *cr:* Woodbridge Bd Ed Art Tchr 17 Display Coord Barron Art Ctr 1996; 6th-8th Grd Art Club Adv; omm 1995; Elem, MS Track Meet Comm; Liaison Comm 1996; JEA 1977-; AENJ, NAEA 1995-; Art Work Printed Exxon Corp, ridge Democratic Org; *office:* Woodbridge MS 525 Barron Ave ridge NJ 07095

ER, GALE SNEED, Hlth & Physical Education Tchr; *b:* lphia, PA; *m:* Raymond C. Bruner, Jr.; *c:* Camille Wrae, Raymond II; *ed:* NC Cntrl Univ (BS) Hlth & PE 1964; Attnd NC Wesleyan *r:* Parker Jr HS Tchr 1964-69; Washington Twp HS Tchr 1969-70; Edgewood Jr HS Tchr 1971-; *ai:* Hlth & PE Dept Chprsn; Asst Ath Dir; Adv Natl Jr Honor Soc, Frosh Class; Chrldr Coach; Home, Schl Assn; NAHPERD: AAHPERD: NJ St Stdnf Cncl. Exec Advy Bd; NEA: NJEA: CCEA: NASAA: NABSE; NCCU Alumnus Assn; Jaycee's Wife, Comm Work; Winslow Twp Youth Assn, Chrldr Dir; CCU Missionary Chrch Bapt, Youth Dir; Overseas Orgs, Travel Cnslr; NJ St Grant; Tchr of Month 1988; Tchr of Yr; Tchr of Lower Camden Cty Dist #1 Who's Who Tchr Annual 1974; Guest Speaker; Model; Commercials; Governor's Grant; NJ Pageant Dir; EXCEL Telecommunications Rep; Pageant Judge; Middle Level Summit NASSP; *home:* 109 Arbor Meadow Dr Sicklerville NJ 08081*

BRUNER, JUDY VENTURELLA, Kindegarten Teacher; *b:* Oil City, PA; *m:* Daniel P.; *c:* Daniel Jr., Jayna, Jeffrey; *ed:* Clarion Univ of PA (BS) Elem Ed 1970, (MS) Elem Ed 1987; *cr:* Hasson Hts Elem Schl 6th Grd Tchr 1 Yr; Dakota Elem Schl 3rd Grd Tchr 2 Yrs; Lullaby Day Nursery Presch Tchr 1 Yr; Immaculate Conception Elem Schl Kndgtn Tchr 7 Yrs; Clarion Elem Schl Kndgtn Tchr 10 Yrs; *ai:* NEA; Seneca Rdng Cncl; Co-Presented Whole Lang Wkshps; Co-Wrote Article; *home:* 109 Crestmont Dr Shippenville PA 16254*

BRUNER, MICHAEL STEPHEN, English Teacher; *b:* Baltimore, MD; *m:* Patricia; *c:* Kara; *ed:* Univ of Baltimore (BA) Eng 1972; Loyola Coll (MED) Curr Dev 1987; *cr:* Sudbrook Jr HS Eng Tchr 1972-77; Pikesville HS Eng Tchr 1977-; *ai:* Bsbl Coach; *office:* Pikesville HS 7621 Labyrinth Rd Baltimore MD 21208

BRUNETTE, BEVERLY JANE, Biology Teacher; *b:* Lynn, MA; *m:* Thomas G.; *c:* TJ, Jeffrey; *ed:* 20 Credit Hrs at Salem St Coll; 8 Credit Hrs Norfolk St Coll; 8 Credit Hrs North Adams St Coll; 4 Credit Hrs Westfield St Coll; *cr:* Lenox Meml HS Bio Tchr 1967-; *ai:* Tech, Code of Conduct Comm; Lenox Tchrs Assn 1967-, VP; MTA, NEA 1967-; NABT 1970-; CoCurr Presentations at NSTA 1995, MABT 1996; Involvement in MCET Prgm on MesoAmer Stud; *office:* Lenox Memorial Jr Sr HS 197 East St Lenox MA 01240

BRUNETTI, AL, Assistant Principal; *b:* Queens, NY; *m:* Justine Morgan; *c:* Aldo Justin, Courtney Lynn; *ed:* Nassau Comm Coll (AS) PE 1970; SUNY at Cortland (BS) PE 1972, (MS) PE 1976; Cert of Advanced Stud in Ed Admin 1991; *cr:* Owego Appalachian Schls PE Tchr & Coach 1972-87; Auburn Enlarged City Dist PE Tchr & Coach 1987-92; Johnson City Schls 1992-; *ai:* Head Ftbl Coach; NEA 1972-; 2 Articles in Athletic Journal - Scholastic Coach; 1 Article in Bigger Faster Stronger Magazine; Coach of the Yr Owego Free Acad 1986; *office:* Johnson City Sr HS 666 Reynolds Rd Johnson City NY 13790*

BRUNETTI, STEVEN LUCIAN, Science Department Lead Tchr; *b:* Hartford, CT; *m:* Catherine Marino; *c:* Kevin, Erika, Matthew; *ed:* Eastern CT St Univ (BS) Ed, Geology 1974, (MS) Enviro Marine Sci 1979; Univ of CT 10 Credit Hrs Toward MA Geology; Sacred Heart Univ Intermediate Admin 24 Credit Hrs; *cr:* Westledge Schl Bio, Geology Tchr 1974-76; Norwich Free Acad Bio, Geology Tchr 1976-, Sci Dept Lead Tchr 1995-; *ai:* Jr HS Soccer Coach; NEA, CEA 1976-; NSTA 1988-; Best Team 1985-, Mentor, Co Tchr; Norwich Yth Soccer 1990-, Yth Soccer Coach; Police Ath League 1990-, Yth Soccer Coach; Curr Coordinating Cncl 1990-; Var Soccer Coach 1980-89; Selected for Flwshp Univ of CT 1991; *office:* Norwich Free Acad 305 Broadway Norwich CT 06360*

BRUNGART, ANN ASH, Math Teacher; *b:* Huntington, WV; *m:* Wayne A.; *ed:* Penn St Univ (MED) Math 1976, (PHD) Curr & Instruction 1987; *cr:* Bellefonte Area Mid Schl Tchr 1972-; *ai:* Math Dept Head; NCTM 1992-; PCTM 1992-; ASCD 1987-; Article PCTM Yrbk Pub 1993; *office:* Bellefonte Area MS 100 N School St Bellefonte PA 16823*

BRUNI, ANGELO G., Writing & Journalism Teacher; *b:* New Kensington, PA; *m:* Donna Lee Connors; *c:* Angelo, Samuel, Anthony, Rachel, Vincent, Christina, Benjamin; *ed:* St Vincent Coll (BA) Eng, Bio 1959; Univ of Pittsburgh (MED) Scndry Ed 1968; Penn St Univ (MS) Ed Psych 1976; Post Grad Stud Schl Psych at Indiana Univ of PA; *cr:* Highlands Schl Dist Tchr 1968-, Pub Relations Dir 1984-; *ai:* Stu Newspaper Adv; NEA, DSEA, HEA 1967-; AFM 1954-; Brackenridge Boro Cncl 1992-, VP; PA Schl Pub Relations Assn Awd of Excellence; *office:* Highland Schl Dist Idaho At Pacific Natrona Heights PA 15065

BRUNING, VICKI R. (SWENSON), French Teacher; *b:* Oak Park, IL; *m:* Donald H.; *ed:* IN Univ (AB) Fr 1977; St Univ of NY at Buffalo (EDM) Frgn Lang Ed 1980; Univ di Bologna 1974-75; Univ de Quebec Trois Rivieres 1989; *cr:* Lafayette HS Fr Tchr 1978; Mt Mercy Acad Fr Tchr 1980-83; St Francis HS Fr Tchr 1983-86; Orchard Park HS Fr Tchr 1986-; *ai:* AFS Intercultural Club Adv; Alternative Scheduling Comm; Attendance & Tech Comms; Stu Group Ldr Trip to France 1996; NYS Frgn Lang Tchrs 1979-, Sec 1987-90, Pres Awd 1990; WNYFLEC 1979-, Pres 1985-86; AATF, WNY Contest Admin 1984-86, Bd of Dirs 1980, 1982, 1984, 1986, Distngd Svc Awds; ASCD; Amer Cncl Tchrs Frgn Lang Nom Comm 1993, Del 1991-93, Newsletter Ed 1985-86; OPCS FCU 1990-, Ed 1993-; NYSED Schlsp Univ of Quebec Trois Rivieres 1989; NYSA FLT Awd Distngd Svc 1995; Pi Delta Phi Natl Fr Hnr Soc 1995; Numerous Articles Pub; *office:* Orchard Park HS 4040 Baker Rd Orchard Park NY 14127*

BRUNKOW, SHARON PARLOCK, Eighth Grade Teacher; *b:* Jersey City, NJ; *m:* Thomas C.; *c:* Sheila Venteicher, Christopher, Laura; *ed:* Mercyhurst Coll (BA) Elem Ed 1970; Credit Hrs John Carroll Univ, Drake Univ, Ursuline Coll; *cr:* Lechner Schl Fifth Grd Tchr 1970-71; St Raphael Schl Sixth Grd Tchr 1973-76; St Thomas Schl Remedial Math, Rdng Tchr 1979-82; St Mary Schl Eighth Grd Tchr 1982-; *ai:* /stu Cncl Adv; NCEA, OCEA 1981-; *office:* Saint Mary Schl 237 Fourth St Elyria OH 44036

BRUNNER, BETH K., First Grade Teacher; *b:* Akron, OH; *m:* Ford W.; *c:* Jay, Jeff; *ed:* Kent St Univ (BS) Early Chldhd & Elem Ed 1970; 18 Semester Post Grad; *cr:* Stow Pub Schls Kndgrtn & 1st Grd Tchr 1971-74; Southeast Local Schls 1st Grd Tchr 1979-; *ai:* OEA & NEA 1971-; United Presbyn Church 1972-, Elder; *office:* Southeast Primary Schl 8423 Tallmadge Rd Ravenna OH 44266

BRUNNER, REGINA BARON, Assoc Prof Math & Comp Sci; *b:* Orange, NJ; *m:* Carl E.; *c:* Brigitta Regina, Latissa Regina; *ed:* Montclair St Univ (BA) Math 1961, (MA) Math 1966; Syracuse Univ (MS) Math 1967, (PHD) Math 1971; *cr:* New Providence HS Math Tchr 1961-62; Irvington HS Math Tchr 1962-65; Syracuse Univ Math Tchng Asst 1965-71; Kutztown Univ Math Asst Prof 1982-83; Cedar Crest Coll Math & Comp Sci Assoc Prof 1983-; *ai:* Stu Chptr Of MAA Adv; NCTM 1958-; MAA 1970-; AMS, ACM & AWM, PA Reporter; LeHigh Cty Vo Tech Advy Comm on Comps; Allentown Schl Dist Transitional Outcomes Comm; Project Dir PA Eisenhower Grants; 1991 Sears Roebuck Found Awd for Tchng Excl & Campus Ldrshp; 1991 Alumnae Awd for Tchng Excl; Article Pub; Project Dir Math Coll; *office:* Cedar Crest Coll 100 College Dr Allentown PA 18104*

BRUNNER, STEVEN L., 8th Grade Language Arts Tchr; *b:* Fremont, OH; *m:* Susan H. Scarfo; *c:* Heather, Kristen, Jessica; *ed:* John Carroll Univ (BA) Eng 1970; 27 Hrs Post Grad Stud at John Carroll Univ, OH St Univ, Immaculata Coll; *cr:* St Agnes Schl Tchr, LA Coord 1989-; *ai:* Mid Sts Re-Accreditation Comm Co-Chprsn; Schl Newspaper Monitor; Poetry Contest Coord; NCEA 1990-; *office:* St Agnes Schl 211 W Gay St West Chester PA 19380*

BRUNNER, STEVEN NEAL, US History & Bible Teacher; *b:* Lebanon, PA; *m:* Nancy Frann; *c:* Gabrielle; *ed:* Phila Coll of Bible (BA) Bible & Scndry Ed 1987; *cr:* Holmsburg Chrstn Schl Lit, US His, Sci & Math Tchr 1987-90; Lancaster Chrstn Schl US His, Bible & AP US His Tchr 1990-; *ai:* Jr High Girls Sftbl Coach 1990-92, Sr High Girls Sftbl Coach 1992-94, Jr Var Bsktbl 1991-94, Sr High Boys Ice Hockey 1995-; ACSI 1987-, Mem; Ephata Bible Fellowship 1990-, Mem & Sunday Schl Supt; USA Hockey 1995-, Mem; *office:* Lancaster Christian Schl 651 Lampeter Rd Lancaster PA 17602

BRUNO, AUDREI MATAYA, Professor of Nursing; *b:* Pittsburgh, PA; *m:* Edward O.; *c:* Brent, Bradley; *ed:* CCAC (AD) Nrsng 1976; Penn St (BSN) Nrsng 1983; Univ of Pittsburgh (MSN) Nrsng 1988; *cr:* Visiting Nurse Assn P & MH Pgm Dir 1984-90; CCAC Nrsng Prof 1987-; *ai:* AFT 1990-; Coord of 2 Yr Comm Hlth Curr Grant; Article Pub; Book Chptr on Elder Abuse; Florence Nightengale of PA Tchng Awd Nom; NLN Convention Presenter; *office:* Comm Coll Algny Co Algny Cmps 808 Ridge Ave #M714 Pittsburgh PA 15212*

BRUNO, GAIL SUSAN, High School Guidance Counselor; *b:* Teaneck, NJ; *c:* Kara; *ed:* Elmira Coll (BA) Fr, Span, Scndry Ed 1971; KEan Coll (MA) 1979; 30 Addl Hrs Trenton St Coll, Rider Coll; *cr:* Terrill Jr HS Fr, Span Tchr 1971-76; West Windsor-Plainsboro HS Fr, Span Tchr, Guid Cnslr 1976-; *ai:* AFS, Intnl, Animal Rights Clubs Adv; Task Force Comm; NEA, NJEA 1971-; Amer Cnslng Assn 1984-; *office:* West-Windsor Plainsboro HS 346 Clarksville Rd Princeton Junction NJ 08550

BRUNO, JOANNE D'ALLESANDRO, 2nd Grade Teacher; *b:* Philadelphia, PA; *m:* Michael Nicholas; *c:* Michele Walsh, Renee, Daniele Livermon, Matthew; *ed:* Glassboro Coll (BA) Elem, Nursery Schl 1981; 12 Credits Elem Curr, Tchng Read, Elem Rdng, Slow Learner, Environmental Stud; Farleigh Dickinson 2.3 Educ Units Sci Stud; *cr:* St Nicholas Schl 2nd Grd Tchr 1958-60; Christ the King 3rd-4th Grd Tchr 1960-62; Strawbridge Elem Schl 2nd Grd Tchr 1984-; *ai:* Cultural Arts, Stu Cncl Co-Chair; Ecology Club Adv, Founder; Prof Improvement, Math, Lang, Arts, Spell Comms; HTEA, NJEA, NEA 1984-; Tchr of Yr 1992.

BRUNO, PHYLLIS GRODIN, 7th Grade Social Studies Tchr; *b:* Middletown, NY; *m:* Robert; *c:* Jessica, Heather; *ed:* Bamapo Coll of NJ (BA) Amer Stud 1976; Psych Courses at Rutgers Univ; *cr:* Franklin Twp HS Psych & Sociology Tchr 1987-90; Sampson G Smith Intermediate 7th & 8th Grd Soc Stud Tchr 1990-; *ai:* Acad Awds Comm Chprsn; NJEA, FTEA 1987-, Assoc Rep; NEA 1987-; NJ Commission of Hum Grant to Stud Constitutional Law; *office:* Sampson G Smith Interm Sch 1649 Amwell Rd Somerset NJ 08873*

BRUNO, ROBERT, English Teacher; *b:* Palisades Park, NJ; *m:* Phyllis; *c:* Jessica, Heather; *ed:* Ramapo Coll (BA) Amer Stud 1975; *cr:* Palisades Park HS Lang Arts Tchr 1976-; *ai:* Var Sftbl Coach; Sr Class & Yrbk Adv; NEA, NJEA, PPEA 1976-; Jr Olympics Sftbl Coach 1995; Awded First by Columbia Univ Yrbk 1991-93; *office:* Palisades Pk Jr Sr HS 1 Veterans Plz Palisades Park NJ 07650

BRUNO, ROSE MARIE, Second Grade Teacher; *b:* Bayonne, NJ; *ed:* Jersey City St Coll (BA) Elem Ed 1963; Addl 32 Credit Hrs Spec Ed; *cr:* Hopelawn Schl 2, 3 Grd Tchr; Mawbey St Schl 2 Grd Tchr, Summer Enrichment Arts, Crafts, Title I Rdng 4, 5 Grd Schl; *ai:* Pupil Asst Comm, Family Math; IALAC Facilitator; Middlesex Cty Rdng Assn 1975-; Woodbridge Tchrs Ed Assn, NJEA, NEA 1976-; Alpha Delta Kappa 1992-, Sargeant At Arms; PTO 1963-; Steel Violets 1970-, Treas; NJ Ed Grant; Woodbridge Mini Grant; Woodbridge Chamber of Commerce Tchr of Yr Awd 1989; *office:* Mawbey Street Elem Schl 1 428 School St Woodbridge NJ 07095

BRUNO, WILLIAM JOHN, Social Studies Teacher; *b:* Neptune, NJ; *m:* Margaret Ann Shields; *c:* Kyle, Eric; *ed:* Glassboro St Coll (BA) Psych, His 1975; Trenton St Coll Grad Schl (MA) Soc Stud 1978; Georgian Court Coll Schl of Admin Cert Supervision 1992; *cr:* Manalapan HS Soc Stud Tchr 1978-81; Chrstn Brothers Acad Soc Stud Tchr 1981-86; Asbury Park HS Soc Stud Tchr 1986-89; Pinelands Regnl HS Soc Stud Tchr 1989-; *ai:* Var Pep, His Clubs; Peer Ldrshp; Project Grad; Close Up Fnd; Head Indoor, Outdoor Track Coach; Asst Ftbl Coach; NJEA; NEA; Shore Track Coaches Exec, Sec; Shore Chptr St Track Ofcls; Ftbl Commissioner 1995-; Bsktbl Coach 1991-, Vol; Coach of Yr Track & Field, Ftbl; Tchr of Yr; Track Ofcl of Yr NJSIAA.*

BRUNS, ERIC W., Physics Teacher; *b:* Newport, VT; *m:* Lorraine; *c:* Ingrid, Paul; *ed:* Harvard Univ (BA) Physics 1968, (MAT) Scndry Sci 1970; *ai:* Acad Decathlon Coach; NEA 1986-; *home:* 10 Walnut St Sharon MA 02067

BRUNS, NANCY JAYNE (PERKINS), Spanish & French Teacher; *b:* Moniticello, IA; *c:* Darren R., Steven T.; *ed:* Cornell Coll at Mt Vernon (BA) Fr, Ed 1964; Univ of CO (MA) Ed 1970; Attnd Univ of Grenoble France, Kent St Univ; *cr:* Jefferson Co Schls Fr, Span Tchr1964-70, FL Dept Ch 1966-70; Stow City Schls Fr, Span Tchr 1976-; *ai:* Fr, Span Club Co-adv; Stu Cncl 1984-87; Peer Listeners; Co-operative Learning, Staff Dev Comms; NEA 1964-; OEA, STA, OMLTA, OFLA 1976-; PEO United Meth Church 1964-; *office:* Stow-Munroe Falls HS 3227 Graham Rd Stow OH 44224

BRUNS, SCOTT C., English & History Teacher; *b:* Toledo, OH; *m:* Jennifer Brown; *ed:* Bowling Green St Univ (BA) Eng & His 1991; *cr:* Clay HS Eng Tchr 1993-; *ai:* Co-Creator of Enriched Connections Pgm; Arts Festival Vol Coord; Organizer of Dist-Wide Young Authors Night; AFT 1993-; Golden Eagle Awd 1995; *office:* Clay HS 5665 Seaman St Oregon OH 43616

BRUNSMAN, PATRICIA DOWLING, 4th Grade Teacher; *b:* Cincinnati, OH; *m:* Thomas; *c:* Theresa, Sandra, Diane; *ed:* Coll of Mt St Joseph (BA) Elem Ed 1975; *cr:* Saint James White Oak Schl Elem Tchr 1970-; *ai:* Greater Cincinnati Fnd Awd; Scripps-Howard & Cincinnati Post for Spec Math Project; *office:* Saint James White Oak Schl 6111 Cheviot Rd Cincinnati OH 45247*

BRUNSON, DORIS HOLMES, Computer & Business Teacher; *b:* Mt Pleasant, SC; *m:* Talmadge O. II; *c:* Talmadge III, Tyrin; *ed:* SC St Coll (BA) Bus Ed 1973, (MS) Stu Prsnl Guid 1975; Jersey City St Coll Post Grad Stud Masters 15; *cr:* Cntrl Regnl HS Bus Ed Tchr 1975-81; Lacey HS Bus Ed Tchr 1981-; *ai:* After Schl Comp Lab Supvr; NEA 1975-; NJEA 1981-; NAACP 1980-; United Meth Church 1985-, Sunday Schl Tchr & Jr Church Tchr; *office:* Lacey Township HS Haines St Forked River NJ 08731

BRUNSON, JANE CASNER, French Teacher; *b:* St Louis, MO; *m:* John T.; *c:* Matthew, Michael; *ed:* Albion Coll (BA) Fr 1966; The CO Coll (MAT) Fr 1972; Attnd MI St Univ, Institut de Touraine, Universite de Poitiers France; *cr:* Fulton HS Fr Tchr; USAF Acad HS Fr Tchr; Kalamazoo Pub Schls Fr Tchr; *ai:* Adv; Fr Club; NYSUT; *office:* G Ray Bodley HS 6 William Gillard Dr Fulton NY 13069

BRUNSON, TIMOTHY MICHAEL, Social Studies Teacher; *b:* Albany, NY; *ed:* SUNY at Plattsburgh (BS) Scndry Ed, Soc Stud 1993; *cr:* Laurens Cntrl Schl Soc Stud Tchr 1994-; *ai:* Stu Cncl Adv; Girls Var Bsktbl, Boys Modified Bsbl Coach; Drama Club; Discipline Comm; Chprsn Soc Stud Dept; AFT, NYSUT 1994-; BSA 1995-, Merit Badge Instr; *office:* Laurens Central Schl PO Box 301 Laurens NY 13796*

BRUTICO, ROSEANN PIKULSKI, Learning Support Teacher; *b:* Scranton, PA; *c:* Allison, Robert; *ed:* East Stroudsburg St (BS) Elem Ed 1975; Marywood Coll (MS) Spec Ed 1980; Univ of Scranton Elem Prin Cert 1987; *cr:* Old Forge Schl Dist Kndgtn, Third & First Grd Tchr 1975-85, Learning Support Tchr 1985-; *ai:* Grds 7-12 Stu Cncl Adv; Primary Curr Coord; Elem Bldg, Strategic Planning Comms; Dist Curr

Cncl; Olde Forge Ed Assn 1975-, Treas, VP; PSEA, NEA 1975-; Jr League of Scranton 1987-, Treas; St Joseph's Ctr Auxiliary 1977-, Treas, Festival Co-Chair, Exec Bd; Komen Fnd 1991-, Comm Chairs, Race Co-Chprsn; PTA 1975-, Exec Bd; PA Assn of Stu Cncls Dist IX Adv of Yr 1995; ITEC Cmptr Grant; *office:* Old Forge Schl Dist 1 Marion St Old Forge PA 18518*

BRUTTO, PAUL ANTHONY, Eighth Grade Teacher; *b:* Shenandoah, PA; *m:* Victoria Ann Martin; *c:* Paul Jr., Pamela; *ed:* Bloomsburg Univ (BS) Scndry Ed, Soc Stud 1980; Attnd Wilkes Univ, Penn St Univ, Scranton Univ; *cr:* Mahanoy City Cath Schl Seventh, Eighth Grd Tchr 1981-; *ai:* Girls Var Bsktbl Coach Marian Cath HS; Acad Bowl CYO Team; *home:* 10 W Center Mahanoy City PA 17948

BRUZZO, PETER, Mathematics Chairman; *b:* Oceanside, NY; *m:* Denise Fellows; *c:* Peter, Melissa, Daniel; *ed:* St John's Univ (BS) Math 1970; Adelphi Univ (MS) Math 1974; Long Island Univ (PHD) Educl Admin 1983; *cr:* Freeport HS Scndry Math Tchr 1970-86, Math Chm 1986-; *ai:* Mathlete Coach; Math Magazine Adv; FTA 1970-, Del; NCTM, NCMTA 1970-; NCAMS 1976; Knights of Columbus 1990-; *office:* Freeport HS S Brookside Ave Freeport NY 11520*

BRYAN, BARNEY FREDERICK, Math Teacher, Work Study Coord; *b:* Melrose, MA; *m:* Pamela J. Chadwick; *c:* Meaghan E., Caitlin R.; *ed:* Merrimack Coll (BS) Ec 1960; Salem St Coll (MED) Ed 1965; 25 Addl Hrs; *cr:* Saugus Pub Schls Math Tchr, Coach 1961-; Fisher Coll Adj Instr Math 1978-; Front Runner Enterprises Owner 1980-; Bunker Hill Comm Coll Math Instr 1992-; *ai:* Interscholastic Bsktbl, Cross Cntry Coach 23 Yrs; Former Assoc Dept Head of Math; Dir Various North Shore Rd Races; MTA, NEA 1961-; SER 1961-, VP, Bd of Dirs, St Convention Del; Saugus Chamber of Commerce 1980-, Bd of Dirs, Recognition Awds; Saugus Bus Ed Collaborative 1989-, Bd of Dirs, Recognition Awds; Carol Dimati Stuart Fnd 1990-, Trustee; North Shore Regnl Employment Bd Work Subcommittee & Cncl 1994-; Article Pub; Natl Sci Fnd Grant 1969; *office:* Saugus HS Pearce Dr Saugus MA 01906

BRYAN, CATHERINE ANN, Chapter I & Title I Teacher; *b:* Erie, PA; *m:* Lee E.; *c:* Christy; *ed:* Slippery Rock Univ (BS) Elem Ed 1975, (MED) Rdng Specialist 1982, (MED) Early Chldhd 1982; Cmptr Courses; HOTS, Montessori Trng; *cr:* Montessori Tchr 1983-84; New Castle Area Schls Tchr 1985-90; Neshannock Twp Schl Tchr 1991-; *ai:* Robert Stevenson Fnd Mem, Bd; NEA 1991-; *office:* Neshannock Twp Schl Dist 301 Mitchell Rd New Castle PA 16105*

BRYAN, DOROTHY C., Drama Director; *b:* Brockton Hosp, MA; *ed:* Boston Conservatory of Music (BFA) Musical Theatre Stud 1991; Grad Work Cambridge Coll; *cr:* Terri's Schl of Dance Tchr 1990-93; Final Stage Productions Artistic Dir 1990-; Capachione Schl of Performing Arts Drama Dir 1993-; *ai:* Private Coach for Kristen Cockshaw; Best Directed Wkshp 1991; Boston Conservatory of Music Sunday in the Park with George 1988-; Directed, Choreographed 15 Musical Productions; *office:* Capachione Schl Of Perf Arts 4 W Union St East Bridgewater MA 02333*

BRYAN, HENRY C., Mathematics Teacher; *b:* Atlanta, GA; *ed:* Cheyney Univ (BSEd) Math 1962; Eastern Bapt Theological Seminary (MDiv) Theology 1968; Temple Univ Electrical Engrng 1960; Howard Univ Law Schl 1962-63; Univ of AK at Juneau Math Ed 1990; VA Union Theological Seminary Theology 1965-66; *cr:* Masterman Demonstration Schl Math Edctr 1968-71; Philadelphia HS for Girls Math Edctr 1971-; *ai:* Phila Fed of Tchrs 1968-, Bldg Comm; NCTM, Life Mem; NSTA, Life Mem; Phi Delta Kappa, Life Mem; NAACP, Life Mem; Assn Tchrs of Math Philadelphia, Life Mem; Alpha Phi Alpha, Chaplain, Life Mem; Zion Bapt Church 1967-70, Assoc Minister; Ordained to Ministry Amer Bapt Clergyman; Outstdng Young Men of Amer Awd 1971; Who's Who Among Stdnts in Univs & Colls 1962; *office:* Philadelphia HS For Girls 1400 W Olney Ave Philadelphia PA 19141

BRYAN, PAMELA ANN, English & Humanities Teacher; *b:* Bryan, OH; *m:* Thomas D.; *c:* Thomas, Michael; *ed:* Bowling Green Univ (BA) Eng 1970; Ashland Univ (MED) Curr, Instruction 1995; 18 Addl Grad Hrs Gifted Ed Oberlin, Cleveland St; *cr:* North Olmsted City Schls Tchr 1970-74; Firelands Local Schls Tchr 1977-84; Vermilion HS Tchr 1984-; *ai:* Saturday Schl; NHS; Tchr Directed, AP Seminars; VTA, OEA, NEA, Bldg Rep; United Church Christ Congregational 1978-, Confirmation Class 1979-89; Amnesty Intnl; ACLU; Erie Cty Excl in Ed Grant, Scndry Tchr of Yr; Most Influential Tchr; OH Conf Gifted Ed Speaker; *office:* Vermilion HS 1250 Sanford St Vermilion OH 44089*

BRYAN, THELMA JANE, Professor of English; *b:* Scotland, MD; *m:* David George Preston; *c:* Bryan David Preston; *ed:* Morgan St Univ (BA) Eng, Speech 1970, (MA) Eng 1974; Univ of MD at Coll Park (PHD) Eng 1982; *cr:* Coppin St Coll Eng Assoc Prof 1982-87, Chprsn, Lang, Lit, Jrnslm Dept, Assoc Prof 1987-90, Dean, Honors Division, Assoc Prof 1990-91, Dean, Arts & Sci, Prof 1991-; *ai:* Region II Alpha Kappa Mu Honor Soc Dir; Mu Beta Chapter Alpha Kappa Mu, Stu Honors Assn, Chi Sigma Chi Honor Soc Advs; Chair Coll Honors & Schlsp, Chprsn Stu Acad Review, Univ of MD System Financial Aid, Interinstitutional Enrollement & Registration Comms; Alpha Kappa Mu 1969-, Regnl Dir Outstanding Regnl Dir, Mu Beta Chapter Adv, Outstanding Adv 1989, 1991, 1994; MLA, CLA, NCHC, NE NCHC, NCTE, CCAS, AAHE, AACH; Prof for the Future 1994-, Advy Cncl; Alliance for Sucess 1991-, Steering Comm; MD Paper Box Schlsp Comm 1984-, Schlsp Comm; Governors Citation 1992; NEH Fellowship 1987; 9 Scholarly Articles on 20th Century African Amer Women Poets; Poem Pub; 19 Conf Presentations; Grants McNair 1989-, Univ MD System 1993, 1994, Title III 1992-97; *office:* Coppin State College 2500 W North Ave Baltimore MD 21216

BRYAN, THEODORE BENJAMIN, Social Studies Teacher; *b:* Camden, NJ; *m:* Josephine Mabel Barclay; *c:* Edward, Julia, Corann, Kassandra, Tedi; *ed:* Rowan St Coll (BA) Soc Stud Ed 1974; *ai:* Natl Honor Soc; Fac Adv Comm; Mock Trial Coach; NEA 1974-; NAACP 1973-; Tchr of Yr, Cape May Cty NAACP Image Awd 1992; *office:* Middle Township HS 212 Bayberry Dr Cape May Court Hse NJ 08210*

BRYANT, ANDREW L., MLT Pgm Dir & Prof Med Tech; *b:* Camalla, GA; *m:* Peggy J.; *c:* Andrea, Drew, Cliff, Desire; *ed:* Wagner Coll (BS) Bio, Chem 1959, (MS) Sci, Ed 1962; Rutgers Univ Geology, Ed 12 Semester Hrs; NY Univ Educl Admin 16 Semester Hrs; Worcester Polytechnic Inst Math, Physics for Tchrs 8 Semester Hrs; *cr:* USPHS Hosp Med Technologist, Hematology 1959-62; Port Richmond HS Bio Tchr 1962-66; Howell HS Physics, Earth Sci Tchr 1966-69; Brookdale Comm Coll Prof of Hematology, Clinical Chem Blood Bank & Nutrition 1969-; *ai:* Med Tech Org Adv; Division Promotion, Outstdng Stu Awd, Allied Hlth Admission Comms; ASCP 1962-; ASCLS 1993-; NJEA, NEA 1969-; Clinical Dir NCA; Bioanalytical Lab Dir St of NJ; Clinical Lab Supvr NYC; MT ASCP; *office:* Brookdale Comm Coll 765 Newman Springs Rd Lincroft NJ 07738*

BRYANT, APRIL DESIREE, Fourth Grade Teacher; *b:* Connellsville, PA; *m:* William Joseph; *c:* Jason Maloy, Kalee Maloy, Korey; *ed:* OH Univ (BA) Hlth, PE 1975, (BA) Elem 1978; Univ of Rio Grande Working on Masters Elem Ed; *cr:* Paint Valley Hlth, PE Tchr 1975-77; Waverly City 4th Grd Elem Tchr 1977-; *ai:* Var Track Coach 1977-; Past Var Bsktbl, Vlybl,Track Coach 1975-77, Jr High Vlybl Coach 1977; OEA 1975-; WCTA 1977-.

BRYANT, BERNARDINE ALTHEA, Mathematics Teacher; *b:* Washington, DC; *m:* Richard; *c:* Marc, Craig, Sharon; *ed:* DC Tchrs Coll (BS) Elem Ed 1971; Univ of MD (MS) Math 1984; *cr:* Arrowhead Elem Schl Tchr 1971-84; Du Val HS Math Tchr 1984-87; Martin L King MS Math Tchr 1987-; *ai:* Odyssey of Mind; Minorities Math, Sci; NCTM 1984-; NEA, MSTA, PGCEA 1971-; Delta Sigma Theta 1970-, Pres; Facilitor Equity 2000 Wkshps; Helping Tchr Saturday Acad; *office:* Martin Luther King Jr Acad Ctr 4545 Ammendale Rd Beltsville MD 20705*

BRYANT, DANIEL J., Computer Teacher & Coordinator; *b:* Portland, ME; *m:* Diane Kinney; *c:* Kevin, Kelly; *ed:* Univ of Southern ME (BS) Math 1969; *cr:* Nobleboro Cntrl Schl Math & Sci 6-8 1969-70; Rockland Dist MS Math 1972-94, Cmptrs 1994-; *ai:* Dist Cmptr Comm Chm; ME Tchrs Assn, NEA 1969-; Rockland Golf Club 1994-; *office:* Rockland Dist MS 38 Lincoln St Rockland ME 04841

BRYANT, DEBORAH PALMER, Span Tchr & Department Chair; *b:* Middletown, OH; *m:* Jerry; *c:* Jaime, Jacob; *ed:* Miami Univ (BS) Span 1980; Wright St Univ (MED) Ed 1995; *cr:* Glen Este HS Span Tchr 1981; Lakota HS Span Tchr 1981-83; Lebanon HS Span Tchr, Dept Chair 1988-; *ai:* North Cntrl Planning Comm; Frgn Lang Curr Chair; NEA, OFLA 1988-; AATSP 1990-; *office:* Lebanon HS 160 Miller Rd Lebanon OH 45036

BRYANT, ELEANOR SPURLOCK, Program Support Teacher; *b:* Philadelphia, PA; *w:* Ernest Leon (dec); *c:* Eric Lloyd; *ed:* Cheyney (BS) Elem Ed 1957; Antioch (MA) Elem Ed 1977; Attnd Temple; 30 Plus Hrs Univ of PA; *cr:* Coatesville HS Stu Future Tchrs of Amer 1952-53; Bonsall Elem Schl 4th Grd Tchr 1957-59; Meredith Elem Schl 1st Grd Tchr 1960-67; G. Washington Elem Schl 1st Grd Tchr 1968-88, Prgm Support Tchr 1988-; *ai:* Rdng Tutor; Crafts Kids Can Make; Order of Eastern Star 1991-, Dist Chprsn Ways & Means 1993-93, 1994-95 3rd Runner Up, 1995-of Ed, Nom for Rose Lindenbaum Awd 1985; Stu Tchr of Yr 1957; Excl Tchng Awd 1985; Commendations 1989, 1993; Commendable Performance 1989; Memorandum of Commendation 1988-, Prgm Support Tchr; Exemplary Attendance Awd 1989-90; Prin Commendation 1994-95; *office:* George Washington Elem Schl 5th & Federal Sts Philadelphia PA 19147

BRYANT, EMILY CATHERINE, Sixth Grade Teacher; *b:* Harrodsburg, KY; *c:* Mary Katherine Drummer; *ed:* Wilberforce Univ (BS) Elem Ed 1975; Ashland Univ 4 Grad Hrs; Walsh Coll 6 Grad Hrs; *cr:* Lorain City Schls Tchr 1984-; Lorain Family Y SACC Prgm Sup 1988-90; Lorain Bus Coll GED Instr 1991; Lorain Urban League Super Mentoring Summer Pro 1994; *ai:* Patrol Supvr; OEA, NEA LEA 1984-; Lorain Cty Black Edctrs Assn 1995-; NAACP 1989-; *office:* Homewood Elem Schl Goble & Charleston Lorain OH 44055

BRYANT, EUNICE EMILY, Fifth Grade Teacher; *b:* Catskill, NY; *w:* Bruce Richards (dec); *c:* Heather Anne; *ed:* Baruch Coll-CCNY (BBA) Bus Admin 1962; Hunter Coll (MS) Ed 1968; St John's Univ One Yr; *cr:* PS 9 Brooklyn Schl 2-6 GATE Tchr 8 Yrs; Sussex Ave Schl 5 Grd GATE Tchr 5 Yrs; Alexander Hamilton SChl 5 Grd Tchr 19 Yrs; *ai:* Grd 5 Level Chm; Fifth Grd Yrbk Comm; Exec Bd, Coorespondence Sec'y Morris Knolls; HS Marching Band Boosters; Chpaerone Competition Trips Around Cntry Marching Band; NEA, NJEA 1970-; UFT 1962-70; Dover Meml Presbyn Church 1977-, Adult Choirs, Bell Choir, Prepare for Homeless-Soup Kitchen, Fundraising; Best Tchr Awd Grd 5 1984; *office:* Alexander Hamilton Schl 24 Mills St Morristown NJ 07960

BRYANT, KAREN STRENZWILK, Business & Computer Teacher; *b:* Rochester, NY; *m:* Peter E.; *c:* Matthew, Jessica, Stephanie; *ed:* Nazareth Coll of Rochester (BS) Bus, Ec 1970, (MS) Ed 1973; *cr:* Victor Cntrl Schl Bus Tchr 1970-76; Strafford Bus Schl Bus Instr 1977-83; Brighton HS Bus, Cmptr Tchr 1983-; *ai:* Chess Team Coach; Natural Helpers Adv; Brighton Comm Planning Team Co-chair; Monroe Cty Bus Tchrs Assn 1970-; NEA; *office:* Brighton HS 1150 Winton Rd S Rochester NY 14618*

BRYANT, NANCY S., Retired Elementary Teacher; *b:* Marengo, OH; *m:* Roy B.; *c:* David; *ed:* Otterbein Coll (BSEd) Elem Ed 1965; Attnd OH Univ; *cr:* Big Walnut Local Schls Elem Tchr 1961-69; Westerville City Schls Elem Tchr 1969-95; *ai:* Rdng, Sci Comms; Tchrs Helping Stdnts Team; NEA, OEA 1964-; WEA 1969-, Tchr Rep; *home:* 800 E Walnut St Westerville OH 43081

BRYANT, ROBERT GUY, Peer Leadership Program Dir; *b:* Little Falls, MT; *m:* Linda; *c:* Elton, Sharon, Renell, Mike, Robert, Brandii, Brandon; *ed:* NC Cntrl Univ (MA) Soc Org 1968; OH Univ (MA) Ed 1975; Seton Hall Univ (EDD) Ed 1977; Attnd SC St, Montclair St, Duke Univ; *cr:* Orange HS Peer Ldrshp Prgm Dir, Asst Prin, Soc Stud Dept Chm, Assistance Prin 1968-; *ai:* Sr Class, Peer Ldrshp, Stu Cncl Adv; Tennis, Debate Team Coach; Future Tchrs of Amer; NHS; Orange Ed Assn 1971-; NEA; NJEA, Tchr of Yr 1989; Juvenile Conf Comm, Chm; Jaycees; North Jersey Philharmonic Glee Club, VP; Essex Chorale; Roundtop Dramatic Assn; Omega Psi Phi; A+ for Kids Flwshp Grant; Governor Tchr of Yr 1987-89; Articles Pub.*

BRYANT, ROBERT JOHN, Scndry Ed & Soc Stud Teacher; *b:* Allentown, PA; *m:* Laurie Jo; *ed:* Kutztown St Coll (BS) Scndry Ed & Soc Stud 1980; Kutztown Univ (MA) Scndry Ed & Soc Stud 1986; *cr:* Northampton Area Sr HS Scndry Ed & Soc Stud Tchr 1980-; *ai:* Track Asst Coach; Indoor Track Club Asst Adv; SADD Co-Adv; PSEA & NEA 1980-; Peer Helper Assn of Amer; *office:* Northampton Area Sr HS 1619 Laubach Ave Northampton PA 18067

BRYANT, STEPHANIE ELAINE, Social Studies Teacher; *b:* Hyattsville, MD; *ed:* Univ of MD (BA) Scndry Ed 1989, (MS) Human Resource Mngmt 1996; Attnd Univ Coll; *cr:* LaPlata HS Tchr 1989; Mc Donough HS Tchr 1990-; *ai:* Stu Govt Adv 1989-; Cross Cntry, Indoor Track Coach 1990-; Outdoor Track Coach 1993-; NEA 1991-; NASSP, EALL 1990-; Childrens Aid Soc 1993-; *office:* Maurice J. Mc Donough HS 7165 Marshall Corner Rd Pomfret MD 20675

BRYANT, THOMAS MARK, Jr High Science Teacher; *b:* Allentown, PA; *m:* Joanne L. Mc Goldrick; *ed:* Kutztown Univ (BS) Bio, Gen Sci 1986, (MS) Scndry Ed, Bio 1991; *cr:* Springhouse Jr HS Phys Sci Tchr 1987; Troxell Jr HS Life, Phys Sci Tchr 1987-; *ai:* Guitar Club Adv; NEA, PSEA, PEA 1987-; Amer Museum of Natural His 1996-; Lehigh Vly Blues Network 1995-; *office:* Troxell Jr HS 2219 N Cedar Crest Blvd Allentown PA 18104

BRYCKI, CATHERINE PROVENCHER, English Teacher; *b:* Norwich, CT; *m:* Paul; *c:* Amanda; *ed:* Eastern CT St Univ (BA) Eng 1974, (MS) Ed 1980; *cr:* Griswold Jr Sr HS Eng Tchr 1974-; *ai:* Soph Class Adv; CEU & MS Comm; Griswold Ed Assn 1974-; CT Ed Assn 1974-; NEA 1974-; Stonington HS Consultant; *home:* 484 Taylor Hill Rd Jewett City CT 06351

BRYER, PATRICIA GALE, HS Social Studies Teacher; *b:* Red Bank, NJ; *m:* David T.; *c:* Meredith, Allison, Daniel, Michael; *ed:* Univ of MD (BA) Soc Stud Ed 1971; St Peters Coll 9 Post Grad Credits; Nova Univ 30 Credits Post Grad Toward MA Ed; *cr:* Col Zadok Magruder HS Soc Stud Tch 1971-75; Holmdel HS Soc Stud Tchr 1979-; *ai:* NEA 1971-; HTEA 1979-; NCSS 1984-; Honor Soc Tchrs Awds 1990-; Human Rights Day Celebration 1988; Honor Soc Tchrs Awd 1990-; Univ of Chgo Frosh Tchr Recgntn Awd 1995; Renaissance Tchr of Mnth 1996; *office:* Holmdel HS 36 Crawfords Corner Rd Holmdel NJ 07733*

BRYK, RAYMOND T., Mathematics Teacher; *b:* Bridgeport, CT; *m:* Kathleen A. Tovish; *c:* Keith, Robert; *ed:* Cntrl CT St Coll (BS) Math Ed 1965; Univ of Bridgeport (MS) Sec Ed 1970, (6th Yr) Soc Ed & Math 1974; Univ of MD NSF Grant; Fairfield Univ Post Grad Stud; *cr:* Fairfield Woods JHS Math Tchr 1965-79; Fairfield HS Math Tchr 1979-; S Cntrl Comm Coll Part Time Lecturer Math & Statistics Prof 1988-90; *ai:* Yrbk & Fin Adv; Schl Newspaper; Bus Adv; NEA 1965-; CEA 1965-; FEA 1965-, Treas;

Apple Orchard Learning Ctr 1985-, Bd of Dirs; Bpt-Ffld FCU, B
office: Fairfield HS 755 Melville Ave Fairfield CT 06432*

BRYLA, THOMAS R., English Teacher; *ed:* Univ of Scranto
1973, (MA) Eng 1979; 12 Credit Hrs Wilkes Univ; *cr:* Lakelan
Eng Tchr 1973-, Eng Dept Chm 1979-84, Tchr of Gifted 1989-
ai: Lakeland's Art, Lit Magazine Adv; NEA 1973-; PSEA 1973-,
Educl & Comm Resources Inc 1981-82, Founding Bd Me
Lakeland Jr Sr HS RR 1 Box 313 Jermyn PA 18433

BRYMESSER, CONNIE CLEVENGER, Third Grade Te
Newville, PA; *m:* Steve F.; *ed:* Shippensburg St Coll (BS) Elem
(MED) Elem Ed 1972; *cr:* Plainfield Elem Schl Third Grd Tchr
BSEA, PSEA, NEA 1970-; *office:* Plainfield Elem Schl 7 Sprir
Carlisle PA 17013

BRYNER, PAULA HARTMANN, English & Reading Teacher; *b*
IL; *m:* James M.; *c:* Timothy Paul; *ed:* Univ of IL (BA) Eng
Wright St Univ (MS) Ed, Supervision, Admin 1987; C
Cooperative Learning, Cmptr Applications; *cr:* Fairborn Bake
Redng Tchr 1972-77; Ferguson Jr HS Eng, Rdng Tchr, Dept He
ai: Stu Cncl Adv; BEA,OEA, NEA 1987-; Beavercreek Swim Tea
1992-, Co-Pres 1994-; Article Pub; *office:* Ferguson Jr
Dayton-Xenia Rd Beavercreek OH 45434

BRZOZOWSKI, EDWARD JOSEPH,JR., Am Govt & Worl
Tchr; *b:* Baltimore, MD; *m:* Melisse Schelter Brzozowski; *ed:*
Univ (MS) His, Soc Stud 1974, (MED) Admin & Supervision
Hampstead Hill MS Tchr 1975-81; Lakeland MS Tchr 1981-84;
City Coll Tchr & Coach 1984-92; Patterson HS Tchr & Coach
Head Soccer, Jr Var Bsktbl & head Track Ladies Coach, JV Sft
AFT & Baltimore Tchrs Union 1975-; St Gerard YMA 1971-, Pr
of Dir; *office:* Patterson Sr HS 100 Kane St Baltimore MD 2122

BRZOZOWSKI, MARION SALOKY, American History & Gov
Brooklyn, NY; *m:* Richard F.; *c:* Mark, Cynthia, Paul; *ed:* Qu
(BA) His 1954; 32 Masters Credits in Ed & His 1965; Variou
Credit Hrs; *cr:* St Josephs HS World His Tchr 1955-58; Sewanh
HS Tchr of Soc Stud & Talented & Gifted 1968-; *ai:* NHS & Mo
Nations Club Adv; Pride of Prin & Fac Schlsp Comms; Sp
Challenge Contest; Fundraising for United Cerebral Palsy Ass
Comm Comms; NEA, NYSCSS & NCSS 1970-; LICSS 1992-
1993-; NYS Cncl for Hum Grant & Hum Tchr Inst; Tchr of Yr A
Park Mem HS; PTSA Lifetime Mem; 2 Supt Mini-Grants
Innovation; *office:* Flora Park Memorial HS 210 Locust St Flora
11001*

BUA, FRANK A., Social Studies Teacher; *b:* Syosset, NY; *ed*
Albany (BA) His 1991, (MS) Educl Admin 1994; *cr:* Chatham C
Soc Stud, Eng 1994-95; Great Neck Pub Schls Soc Stud 1
Entertainment Magazine Founder, Adv; Asst Coach Boys Tra
NYSSUt 1994-; Kiwanis Good Citizenship Awd; Phi Beta Kappa

BUB, WARREN, Football Coach; *b:* Bronx, NY; *cr:* NYNEX T
1988-95; Cardinal Spellman HS Ftbl Coach 1990-95; *ai:* VP M
Lions Ftbl Club 16 Yrs; *office:* Cardinal Spellman HS 1 Cardinal
Pl Bronx NY 10466*

BUBAR, THOMAS JOHN, Asst Prof of Medical Assisting; *b:*
NY; *m:* Judy Lau; *c:* Scott, Kelly, Lori; *ed:* St Univ of NY at Buf
Sociology 1973; Trocaire Coll (AAS) Nrsng; St Univ of NY a
(MS) Nrsng 1982; Ed Org Admin, Policy EDD Curr 6 Credit
Buffalo Veteran's Admin Med Ctr Registered Nurse 1977-78; Bu
Hosp Schl of Nrsng Instr 1978-80; Millard Fillmore Hosp Schl
Instr 1980-86; Brylin Hosps Nrsng Ed Coord 1986-87; Erie C
Asst Prof 1987-; *ai:* Med Assts Club Fac Adv; Blessed Sacra
Club, Former Ofcr, Bd of Dirs; Ken-ton Soccer, Blessed Sacram
Bsbl, Girls Sftbl Coach; AAMA 1988-; NEA, FFEC 1987-; Tro
Alumni Assn 1994-, Bd of Dirs; Amer Red Cross 1986-, CPR In
1972-, Lifetime Mem; Amer Red Cross 500 Hrs Cert.

BUBBINA, VINCENT S., English & Religion Teacher; *b:* Pittsb
ed: LaSalle Coll (BA) Eng 1984; West Chester Univ 15 Credits E
cr: St John Neumann HS Eng, Rel Instr 1984-91; North Catholic
Rel Instr 1991-95; Central Catholic HS Eng, Rel Instr 1995-
Council Moderator; Intramural Dir; Stu Cncl Moderator; Intram
office: Central Catholic HS 4720 5th Ave Pittsburgh PA 15213*

BUBNIS, JOYCE ANN, Jr High Teacher; *b:* New Brunswick,
Middlesex Cty Coll (AA) Lib Arts 1972; Farleigh Dickinson U
Elem Ed 1974; 15 Credits Trenton St Coll; *cr:* Our Lady of Lou
8th Grd Math tchr 1977; St Frances Cabrini 4th-8th Grd Tchr 1
Cheerleading Coach; Yrbk, Stu Cncl Moderators; Tutor; Lang
Cncl for Diocese, Curr Head; Outstndng Edctr of Yr Rcpnt 1991;
Cleveland Ave Milltown NJ 08850

BUBON, KIMBERLY TOLBERT, Teacher; *b:* Warren, OH; *m*
D.; *c:* Nicholas, Brianne; *ed:* OH St Univ (BS) Elem Ed 1982; Yo
St Univ (MS) Curr Ed 1988; Attnd Ashland Coll; *cr:* Weathersfie
Schls 2nd Grd Tchr 1983-; *ai:* Chrldng Adv; Schlsp & Strategic
Comm; TSAC Facilitator; Kappa Phi Kappa 1982-; WTA Tchr Ass
OEA 1983-; Trumbull Area Rdng Cncl 1990-; Delta Kappa Gamm
Martha H Jennings Grant; *office:* Seaborn Elem Schl 1600 Niles-C
Mineral Ridge OH 44440*

BUBONOVICH, CAROL HINES, Sixth Grade Teacher; *b:* Un
PA; *c:* Gerald David, Nicolas III; *ed:* CA Univ (BA) Elem Ed 19
Elem Ed 1974, (MS) Admin 1986; *cr:* R. W. Clark Elem Schl 6th
1969-; *ai:* Yrbk, Sixth Grd Class Spon; Homebound Instruction; W
CA Univ, Penn St Univ to Train Stu Tchrs; LHEA 1969-, Schls B
PSEA, NEA 1969-; Jr Achvmt 1985-; *office:* R W Clark Elem
Water St Uniontown PA 15401*

BUCCIO, DEBORAH K., Eleventh Grade English Teac
Wilmington, DE; *m:* Samuel A. Sr.; *ed:* Mount Saint Marys (BS
Ed 1968; 40 Extra Credit Hrs in Various Areas; Attnd LaSalle
Credit Hrs, Univ of DE 15 Credit Hrs; *cr:* Immaculate Concepti
Tchr 1958-66; Saint Bernadettes Elem Tchr 1966-67; Saint Jo
Brandywine Elem & MS Tchr 1967-68; Corpus Christi MS Tchr
Resurrection Parrish Adult Rel Ed Tchr 1969-72; Conrad Schl D
1972-78; Red Clay Schl Dist Tchr 1978-; *ai:* Stu Store Mgr; Stu Ne
Adv; Rdng Assn 2 Yrs; PDK 1980-; NCTE, DATE; *office:* Wilmin
100 N Dupont Rd Wilmington DE 19807

BUCCOSSI, VICTOR LOUIS, AP Psychology Instructor; *b:* P
NJ; *m:* Elizabeth; *ed:* Montclair St Univ (BA) Bio 1970; Montclai
(MA) Bio 1974; MSU Psych 1982; *cr:* New Providence Schl Dis
Bio, Physics Instr 1970-; *ai:* WrestlingCoach 1970-85; Ftb
1976-89; Vlybl Coach 1982-88; Bsktbl Coach 1985-92; Tenni
1993; NEA, NJEA 1970-; APA 1982-; Finalist Princeton Univ
Distngd Scndry Schl Tchng1994; Finalist Wilkes Univ Inspiratio
Awd 1994; NJ Star-Ledger Schlrs Tchr Awd 1992; Nom Olmsted
Excl Tchng Williams Coll; New Providence Tchr of Yr 1990; Boos
Awd Commitement to Excl 1988; Natl Endowment for Hum Gra
office: New Providence HS 35 Pioneer Dr New Providence NJ 07

BUCEY, KATHRYN ANN (KALIVODA), English & Speech Te
Steubenville, OH; *m:* John Morgan; *c:* Kristin Lynn Bucey-Paxton
Univ (BSEd) Eng, Speech 1966; OH St Univ Post Grad 1990-; C
Coll Grad Work; *cr:* Cuyahoga Falls HS Eng, Speech Tchr

lle S HS Eng, Speech Tchr 1982-; *ai:* Natl Forensic League, TV ıow, Schl Newspaper Adv; HS Reporter in Conjunction with n Coll; Career Ed Shadowing Day Coord; NEA, OEA 1966-; lle Ed Assn 1982-, Soc Comm, Dedicated Svc; Natl Cncl of Eng Career Ed Consortium Connection 1993-; Spearheaded Frosh Ed Shadowing Day Comm Involvement; WEA's 1993 Outstdng m; Excl in Tchng Profession Coll of Ed; OH St Univ Cooperating 94; Contributed, Co-Authored Section of Nationally Pub Speech k; *home:* 126 Buckeye St Westerville OH 43081

MARCIA, Art Teacher; *b:* Lancaster, PA; *m:* Jan Bennett; *ed:* Univ a (BFA) Fine Arts 1977; North GA Coll (MED) Learning ies 1981; *cr:* N Forsyth Jr HS Spec Ed Tchr 1981-83; Watkinson Tchr 1984-; *ai:* Safe, Ldrshp Adv; Robert Rauschenberg Fnd Art d; *office:* Watkinson Schl 180 Bloomfield Ave Hartford CT 06105

N, JAMES BRUCE, English Teacher; *b:* Pasadena, CA; *m:* Anne Shephard; *ed:* Univ of NC at Chapel Hill (ABEd) Eng Ed ttnd Loyola Coll of MD; *cr:* Sunset Park Jr HS Tchr 1979-80; HS Tchr 1981-82; Chesapeake HS Tchr 1982-; *ai:* Head Womens Coach; Womens Lacrosse St Comm Mem; Class of 1997 Adv; 85-; MSTA 1985-; TAAAC 1985-; ASCP 1990-; NCTE 1990-; hesapeake HS 4798 Mountain Rd Pasadena MD 21122*

NAN, MARVIN DARRELL, 7th Grade Math Teacher; *b:* San TX; *m:* Carol Sue Disterdick; *c:* Gregory, Brian; *ed:* OH St Univ m Ed 1984; Coll of Mt St Joseph (MA) Ed 1986; Grad Credits Coll; *cr:* Taft MS 8th Grd Math Tchr 1984-94; Marion City Schls dison MS 7th Grd Math Tchr 1994-; *ai:* Effective Schls Comm; ve Discipline Prgm Dir; Pre-Algebra Enrichment Prgm; Dev Math b; NEA, OEA, Marion Ed Assn 19840; OH St Univ Pres Schlsp nning's Scholar 1992-93; *office:* Edison MS 871 Chatfield Rd OH 43302

IT, KRISTINE ANN, 9th Grd PE & Hlth Teacher; *b:* Meadville, Michael; *ed:* Edinboro St Univ (BS) Hlth & PE 1973; Masters ncy Plus 30 Addl Grad Credits; *cr:* Conneaut Schl Dist 7th-12th & PE Tchr 1973-76; Greater Latrobe Schl Dist 9th Grd Hlth & 1978-; *office:* Greater Latrobe Schl Dist 410 Main St Latrobe PA

R, CARL, English Teacher; *b:* Columbus, OH; *m:* Janice gno; *c:* Jason, Jennifer, Jeremy, Justin; *ed:* OH St Univ (BS) Eng (MA) Eng Ed 1996; Attnd Franklin Univ; *cr:* Cedarville HS Eng 83-86; Sts Peter & Paul HS Eng Tchr 1986-90; Marion Cath HS r 1991-; *ai:* Sr Class Adv; NCTE 1983-; OCTELA 1987-; NRA *ffice:* Marion Catholic Schl 1001 Mount Vernon Ave Marion OH

R, CATHERINE STALTER, English Teacher; *b:* Columbus, OH; ard H.; *c:* Emily, Neal; *ed:* OH St Univ (BS) Eng Ed 1985; *cr:* Jr HS Rdng & Eng Tchr 1987-89; Fostoria HS Rdng & Eng Tchr iency Lab Instr 1989-; *ai:* Eng Dept Head; Mem of Curr Cncl; 87-; OCTELA 1991-; *office:* Fostoria HS 1001 Park Ave Fostoria 30

R, DENISE DRESCHER, Social Studies Teacher; *b:* Hollis, NY; ; *c:* Elyse, Charles; *ed:* SUNY at Geneseo (BA) His 1981, (MS) Ed 1985; *cr:* Honeoye Falls Schl Soc Stud Tchr 1981-82; Fairport ls Soc Stud Tchr 1982-86; Herricks MS Soc Stud Tchr 1986-; *ai:* clusion Prgm; Mentor Tchr; Long Island Cncl for Soc Stud; *office:* MS 7 Hilldale Dr Albertson NY 11507

R, MARK JAN, First Grade Teacher; *b:* Bluffton, OH; *m:* R. Essinger; *c:* Brittany R.; *ed:* Bluffton Coll (BA) Elem Ed, gy 1988; 2 Semester Grad Hrs Ashland Univ 1994; 3 Quarter Grad St Univ 1989; *cr:* New London Local Schls Fourth Grd Tchr Fifth Grd Tchr 1990-92; Fourth Grd Tchr 1992-95, First Grade 95-; *ai:* Ftbl, Track HS Coach; NEA 1988-; United Meth Church *office:* New London Local Schls 17 Park Ave New London OH

R, NANCY HOTTENSTEIN, Family & Consumer Sci Teacher; non, PA; *m:* James A.; *c:* Paul, Kristen, Sherry; *ed:* IN Univ of PA me Ec 1965; Masters Equivalence; *cr:* Eastern Lebanon Co Schl m Tchr 1965-69, Family & Consumer Tchr 1983-; *ai:* Yth Ed Assn, Little People Adv; Grad Requirements, Intensive Scheduling Lebanon Co Home Ec Club 1965-; PSEA, NEA 1983-; NEEA Neptune Fire Co Auxiliary 1980-; ELCO Tchr of Month; *office:* Lebanon County HS 180 Elco Dr Myerstown PA 17067

R, PATRICIA LAWRENCE, Math & Computer Teacher; *b:* gh, PA; *m:* Richard David; *c:* James, Kathryn, Suzette; *ed:* re Coll (BS) Music Ed 1972; Western Maryland Coll (MS) Math Ed) Addl Credit Hrs in Ed at Goucher Coll; *cr:* Hatboro-Horsham Schl sic Tchr 1972-74; Baltimore Cty Pub Schls Music Tchr 1974-76; Cty YMCA Fitness Instr 1982-85; Watkins HS Math, Cmptr Sci 89-; *ai:* Cty-wide Tchr Trainer for HS Level Preparation for a Curr, Former Coach Pom Squad 1990-95; NEA, NCTM, , MSMTA 1989-; Spec Parents Support Group 1980-, Pres; Carroll C 1976-; ACLD 1976-85, Prgm Dir; Wesley-Freedom United Meth 1976-, Chrprsn-Outreach Comm, Mem Bd of Ministries; Cntrl MD n Awd Vol of Yr 1983; *office:* Watkins Mill HS 10301 Apple Ridge hersburg MD 20879

R, RICHARD DAVID, Professor of Sociology; *b:* New Haven, Patricia Lawrence; *c:* James, Kathryn Gelin, Suzette Dubois; *ed:* Univ (BA) Sociology 1971; NY Univ (MA) Sociology 1974; Univ (PHD) Sociology 1983; *cr:* Rock Valley Coll Sociology Instr; ore City Comm Coll Sociology Prof; *ai:* Stdnts Organized for ty Awareness Fac Adv; Amer Sociological Assn 1974-; Southern gicla Soc 1986-; Soc for Disability Stud 1990-; Carroll Cty Comm s Commission 1990-, Chair 1990-91; Spec Parents Support Group Dir Baltimore Cty Comm Coll IIU 1991-; AACC Kellogg Beacon ant 1992-94; Fund For Improvement of Post Scndry Ed Grant); Excl Fac Awd 1993; Author Numerous Articles; Co-Author of 974, 1984; *office:* Baltimore City Community Coll 2901 Liberty Ave Baltimore MD 21215

HOLZ, GEORGE P., 7th Grade Science Teacher; *b:* Cleveland, Sandra Harnak; *c:* Jonathon, Megan; *ed:* Bowling Green (BSED) 9; Cleveland St (MED) Cnslng 1976; *cr:* Parma Pub Schls Sci Tchr *ai:* 7th Grd Team Ldr 1990-; NEA 1969-; OEA 1969-; NEOEA *home:* 6303 Rousseau Dr Parma OH 44129

KO, JOHN, Economics Teacher; *b:* Cleveland, OH; *c:* Scott K., J.; *ed:* Kent St Univ (BS) His, Govt 1963; Univ of MO (MS) Ec Hrs Am Stud Inst OH Northern Univ; 6 Hrs NDEA Grant Bradley *r:* Parma Pub Schl Sys Ec Tchr 1964-; Cuyahoga Comm Coll r, Ec Tchr 1972-; *ai:* Coalition Essential Schls Comm 1993-; Parma n, OH Ed Assn, NEA 1964-; *office:* Parma Sr HS 6285 W 54th St OH 44129

BARBARA MC KEE, English Teacher; *b:* Chester, PA; *m:* John Katherine R., Jonathan P.; *ed:* Univ of DE Coll of Arts & Scis (BA) 74; 30 Post Grad Hrs Eng, Ed; *cr:* Elkton HS Grds 9-12 Eng Tchr *ai:* Ski Club, Future Tchrs of MD Adv; Pupil Prsnl, Stu of Month, iterary Magazine Comms; Elkton Presbyn Church 1977-, Past Pres cons, Sunday Schl Supt; Elkmore Improvement Assn 1978-, Past Pres Bd; Women's Coll Club 1976-; Upper Chesapeake Ski Club 1972-, Past Sec; South Jersey Ski Club 1992-; Eastern Region of Amer Water Ski Assn 1972-, Jr Dev Comm; *office:* Elkton HS 110 James St Elkton MD 21921*

BUCK, JOSEPHINE CELANO, Mathematics Teacher; *b:* Philadelphia, PA; *m:* James H.; *ed:* Camden Cty Coll (AS) 1976; Temple Univ (BA) Math 1979, (MED) Math Ed 1983; Masters Degree +30 Grad Credits; *cr:* Cncl Rock HS Math Tchr 1980-; *ai:* Cmptr Tech & Strategic Planning Comms; NEA, PSEA, CREA 1980-; NCTM 1981-; New Tchr Mentor.

BUCK, JOYCE DAVIS, Professor of Ed & Spec Ed; *b:* Pawtucket, RI; *m:* Stephen C.; *c:* Kimberly Ferreira, Adam, Matthew W.; *ed:* RI Coll (BA) Elem Ed, Spec Ed 1967, (MED) Spec Ed, Learning Dis 1971, (MA) Educl Psych 1978; 9 Credits Educl Admin 1973-74, 9 Credits Cnslr Ed 1982-84; 3 Credits Anna Maria Coll Test Admin, Interp 1976; *cr:* Pawtucket Schl Dept Second Grd Tchr 1967; Woonsocket Schl Dept Tchr of Moderately Impaired Spec Needs 1967-70; Cntrl Falls Schl Dept Federal Grant Learning Disabilities Tchr 1971-72, Title III, Title I Federal Prgms Dir 1972-75; RI Schls Consultant, Wkshp Dev 1973-; Comm Coll of RI Prof of Ed, Spec Ed 1975-; *ai:* RI St Dept Task Force Tchr Asst Guidelines 1992-; NEA 1975-; Attleboro HS Voc Tech Child Care Prgm 1990-, Advy Bd; Co-Authored Stdnts Curr; *office:* Comm Coll of RI Flanagan Campus 1762 Louisquisset Pike Lincoln RI 02865

BUCK, LOU SPURLOCK, 6th Grade Teacher; *b:* Charleston, WV; *m:* Harold E.; *c:* Kenneth Alan, Sheila Jean; *ed:* Miami Univ (BS) Arts, Sci 1958; Kent St Univ (BS) Ed 1969; Edinboro Univ (MED) El Ed 1983; Attnd East Stroudsburg St Coll, Coll of Mount St Joseph on the Ohio, Goddard Coll; *cr:* Saybrook Elem Schl 6th Grd Tchr 1969-78, 5th Grd Tchr 1978-79, 6th Grd Tchr 1979-; *ai:* Coord Saybrook Natl Geography Bee; NEA, OH ED Assn, Northeast OH Ed Assn 1969-; Ashtabula Area Co Assn 1969-, II VP 1977-79; Saybrook United Meth 1958-, Lay Ldr 1987-91, Chm Adm Bd 1991-, Lay Speaker 1995-; Tchng Projects Cleveland Plain Dealer; Ldr Great Books Seminars; Wkshp Ldr Ashtabula Schls 1989-; Listed in Marquis Who's Who; *home:* 5719 N Ridge W Ashtabula OH 44004*

BUCK, RICHARD LESLIE, Fourth Grade Teacher; *b:* Bethlehem, PA; *m:* Connie Mae Sliker; *c:* Melissa Ann; *ed:* E Stroudsburg St Univ (BS) Elem Ed 1970; Lehigh Univ (MD) Ed 1974; Attnd US Army Command & Gen Staff Coll; *cr:* North PA Schl Dist Elem Tchr 1970-; US Army Active Dity Germany 1971-72, Haiti 1994; *ai:* Multi-Cultural Ed Comm; NEA 1970-; US Army Reserve 1972-, Pub Ed Ofcr; Humanitarian Svc Medal Work with Cuban Refuges 1981; Joint Svc Commendation Medal Svc as Adv Haitian Ed Ministry 1994; *office:* A. M. Kulp Elem Schl 801 Hatfield Valley Rd Hatfield PA 19440

BUCKENDORFF, ROSEMARY HAUSEMAN, Eng Dept Co-Chair & Teacher; *b:* Pottstown, PA; *c:* Jennifer; *ed:* Elizabethtown Coll (BA) Eng 1965; Kutztown Univ (MA) Eng 1978; Addl Credit Hrs; *cr:* Bayertown Sr HS Eng Tchr 1967-72; Exeter Twp Sr HS Eng Tchr, Dept Chair 1976-; *ai:* Quiz Bowl Team Coach; Lit Discussion Group Adv; ETEA, PSEA, NEA, NCTE 1976-; NEH Seminar Florence Italy 1994; Philadelphia Museum of Art Tchrs Adv Comm; *office:* Exeter Twp Sr HS 201 E 37th St Reading PA 19606

BUCKERT, GARY RICHARD, Biology & Chemistry Teacher; *b:* Rochester, NY; *m:* Sandra Donovan; *ed:* SUNY at Brockport (BS) Bio 1989, (MS) Ed, Bio 1995; *cr:* Greece Athena MS Tchr 1990-91; Greece Arcadia HS Tchr 1991-; *ai:* Frosh Ftbl Coach; Sci & Environment Club Adv; Sci Olympiad Adv & Coach; NSTA 1992-; NABT 1994-; AIBS 1995-; Cornell Inst Bio Tchrs 1994; Multimedia Tech Grant 1996; *office:* Greece Arcadia HS 120 Island Cottage Rd Rochester NY 14612*

BUCKEYE, CAROLE LYNN (OSBORNE), Health & PE Teacher; *b:* Abbyington, PA; *m:* Robert David Jr.; *ed:* Edinboro Univ (BS) Hlth, PE 1980; Crawford Cntrl Schl Dist Cert 1992; Edinboro, Shippensburg Univ Cert 1990-95; Edinboro Univ Elem Tchr Cert Post Grad Course Work 1996, MA Degree Finishing Post Grad Course Work 1996; Amer Red Cross Cert First Aid, CPR Trng 1995; *cr:* Saegertown HS Chrldng Coach 1980-82; Meadville & Vernon Twp Parks Playground Supvr, Act Coord 1980-84; Crawford Cntrl Schl Dist Elem Hlth, PE Tchr 1981-, Curr, Revision Comm Hlth Aids, PE OBE 1989, 1994-; Slippery Rock Univ Tchr Trainer Growing Healthy Prgm 1996; *ai:* Curr Revision Comm; Presenter Variety of Topics in Hlth, PE Seminars; NEA, PSEA 1985-; Autumn Hills Water Co 1983-, Treas; Tamarack Wildlife Rehabilitation Ctr 1993-; Spokestchr on Distngd Panel of 6 Profs for Stu Tchr Seminar on Classroom Mngmt, Discipline, Control 1985-95; Outstdng Young Edctr Awd 1991; Nom PA St Tchr of Yr 1991; Tchr 1996; Pub Svc Dev Successful For All Track, Field Day, Salt Water, Tropical Fish Hobbyist; *office:* Cochranton Elem Schl Rd 4 S Franklin St Ext Cochranton PA 16314*

BUCKHOLT, PAUL ALLAN, Chemistry Teacher; *b:* Charlenoi, PA; *m:* Helen L. McAdoo; *c:* Michael, Michele Buckholt Anderson; *ed:* CA Univ (BA) Chem, Phys Sci 1963; WVU 12 Hrs; *cr:* Trinity HS Chem Tchr 1963-67; McGuffey HS Chem Tchr 1967-; *ai:* Sr Class Spon; Track Coach; PSEA, NEA 1963-; MEA 1967-; Presbyn Trustee, Elder; W Alexander VFD.

BUCKINGHAM, KATHY RUBY, Fourth Grade Teacher; *b:* York, PA; *m:* Joe Eugene; *c:* Jami Sue; *ed:* York Coll (AS) Liberal Arts 1965; Shippensburg Univ (BS) Ed 1967, (ME) Ed 1970; Penn St at York 24 Credit Hrs; *cr:* Cntrl York Schl Dist 4th Grd Tchr 28 Yrs; *ai:* Title VI Comm Rep; Lang Arts Comm; NEA, PSEA, Cntrl York Ed Assn 1967-; Delta Kappa Gamma 1977-, Treas 2 Yrs; South Cntrl PA Girl's Vlybl Assn 1992-, Bd of Dirs, Ed Chprsn; Shippensburg Univ Outstanding Tchr, lecturer 1984; Exemplary Educator's Awd, Cmptr Math Excl Grant 1985; *office:* Cntrl York Schl Dist 775 Marion Rd York PA 17402

BUCKINGHAM, MARGO L., 6th Grade Teacher; *b:* Utica, NY; *m:* Richard C.; *c:* Scott C., Marla B.; *ed:* St Univ of NY at Cortland (BS) Elem Ed, Scndry Eng 1976; Syracuse Univ (MS) Elem Ed 1979; Grad Hrs; *cr:* Fayetteville Manlius Schl Dist Elem Tchr 1976-; *ai:* WA Chaperone Group; AFT, NYSUT 1976-; Onondaga Cty Tchrs Assn 1992-; Sec; Fayetteville Manlius Tchrs Assn 1976-, Pres, Former VP; Amer Field Svc 1981-, Former Pres; *office:* Wellwood MS F-M Road Rt 257 Fayetteville NY 13066

BUCKINGHAM, PATRICIA DOROTHY, Business Education Teacher; *b:* Baltimore, MD; *c:* Jamie Lynn; *ed:* Morgan St Univ (BS) Bus Ed 1993; 18 Credit Hrs Masters Admin Towson St Univ; *cr:* Brehms Lane Elem Schl #231 Schl Sec 1968-93; Mergenthaler Voc Tech HS #410 Tchr 1993-; *ai:* Voc Support Svcs; Schl to Work Transition, Drama Club Ticket Sales, FBLA Adv; MD Voc Assn 1995-, Outstdng New Tchrs Awd 1995; ASCD 1996; FBLA 1993-; Outstdng New Career & Tech Awd 1995; Stu Achvmt Awd Bus Ed 1993; *office:* Mergenthaler Voc Tech HS 3500 Hillen Rd Baltimore MD 21218

BUCKINGHAM, REBECCA SHELMIDINE, Biology & Life Science Teacher; *b:* Watertown, NY; *m:* Jeffrey H.; *c:* Lucas, Geoffrey, Jessica; *ed:* Saint Lawrence Univ (BS) Bio 1980, (MED) Ed 1984, (EdAd) Admin 1987; Addl Credit Hrs at St Univ of NY at Potsdam; *cr:* Lisbon Cntrl Schl Sci Tchr 1980-; Saint Lawrence Univ Sci Methods Tchr for Stu Tchrs 1992-; *ai:* Class & Photography Club Adv; Odessy of Mind Coach; Lisbon Tchrs Assn 1980-, VP; NYSUT, AFT 1980-; STANYS 1990-; ASCD 1991-; NSTA 1992-; PTSA 1993-, Sec; *office:* Lisbon Central Schl 6866 County Route 10 Lisbon NY 13658

BUCKLE, PETER ALEXANDER, Science Teacher; *b:* Williamsport, PA; *m:* Daryl Elizabeth Bixler; *ed:* Lycoming Coll (BA) Bio 1983; Wilkes Univ 9 Post Grad Hrs; *cr:* Peace Corps Agroforest 1984-86; Lycoming Coll Proctor 1987-90; Muncy HS Sci Tchr 1992-; *ai:* Jr Class & Environmental Club Adv; NHS, Staff Dev & Strategic Planning Comm; NEA 1992-; PSEA 1992-; MEA 1992, Exec Comm; Historical Soc 1995-; *office:* Muncy H S 200 W Penn St Muncy PA 17756

BUCKLER, JEANNE O'CONNOR, 6th Grade Reading Teacher; *b:* Scranton, PA; *m:* James Harold Jr.; *ed:* Cath Univ (BA) Elem Ed 1970; 18 Credit Hrs Univ of MD; 15 Credit Hrs George Washington Univ; *cr:* Seat Pleasant Elem Schl 4th-6th Grd Tchr 1970-81; Brandywine Elem Schl 5th-6th Grd Tchr 1981-; *ai:* Back to Schl Night Comm Chair; 5-6 Grd Level Chprsn 1982-; Schl Based Mngmt Comm; PGCEA, MSTA, NEA 1970-; Natl Basset Hound Club of Amer, Potomac Basset Hound Club 1985-; *office:* Brandywine Elem Schl 14101 Brandywine Rd Brandywine MD 20613*

BUCKLEY, BRIAN BURKE, Art Department Chair; *b:* Schenectady, NY; *m:* Susan Frances Horan; *c:* Olivia, Madeline; *ed:* Wesleyan Univ (BA) Studio Art 1978; Carnegie-Mellon Univ (MAT) Ceramics & Printmaking 1983, (MFA) Ceramics 1985; *cr:* Sewickley Acad Art Instr 1979-84; Roxbury Latin Art Dept Chair 1986-; *ai:* Jr Var Soccer Coach; Art Gallery Dir; Schl Dramatics Production Set Designer; Tibetan Schl Project Coord; Intnl Sculpture Source, Coll Art Assn 1983-; Pub Articles on Creativity in Sculpture for Young Children Arts & Act 1988, Line Drawing for Ind Schl Magazine 1991, Pottery for Boston Magazine 1991, Sculpture for Sculpting Clay By Leon Nigrosh 1992; Recognized By MIT as Significant Tchr 1995; *office:* Roxbury Latin Schl 101 Saint Theresa Ave West Roxbury MA 02132

BUCKLEY, DENISE, K-8th Grade Art Teacher; *b:* Cambridge, MA; *m:* Richard Fiorelli; *ed:* MA Coll of Art (BFA) Sculpture 1974; Syracuse Univ (MFA) Sculpture 1977; Attnd RI Schl of Design 1973, Tyler Schl of Art 1984, Haystack Mountain Schl of Crafts 1974; *cr:* Albertus Magnus Coll Art Instr 1977-80; Brockton Pub Schls Art Tchr 1980-82; Germantown Acad Art Instr 1983-86; Ruffing Montessori Schl Art Instr 1986-; Cleveland Inst of Art Adjunct Fac 1987-; *ai:* Set Design Plays; Art Club; College Art Assn 1990-; Natl Sculpture Assn 1986-; New Org of Visual Arts 1988-, Art Advy Comm; OH Comm for Pub Art Grant 1995; OH Arts Cncl Artists Grant 1992; Best of Show All Canton OH 1990; Summer Six Fellowship Skidmore Coll 1985; *office:* Ruffing Montessori Ingalls Sch 3380 Fairmount Blvd Cleveland OH 44118

BUCKLEY, EUGENE CHARLES, Adj Prof of Voice & Speech; *b:* Kearny, NJ; *ed:* Fordham Univ (BS) Eng, Speech 1955, (MS) Speech 1964; Montclair St Univ 38 Grad Credits; Cert Admin, Supervision; Seton Hall Univ Grad Stud; *cr:* Cerebral Palsy Schl & Treatment Ctr Speech Therapist 1958-60; Pvt Practice Speech Therapist 1958-65; Our Lady of Vly HS 9-12 Grd Eng, Speech Tchr 1960-63; Fairlawn HS Eng, Speech Tchr 1963-91; West Orange Adult Schl Oral Interp, rama, Composition, Intnl Speech Tchr 1963-67; Fairlawn Adult Schl Oral Interp, Drama, Composition, Intnl Speech Tchr 1963-67; *ai:* Coach Debate Team; Stu Cncl Moderator; Prepared Speaker Speech Contests Prgm; Speech Assn Eastern Sts; Speech Assn of NJ; NEA; NJEA; Bergen Co Ed Assn; Fairlawn Ed Assn; Spoke NJ Tchrs Convention Speech Assn of Eastern Sts, Mid Sts Evaluation; Comm Dinner Fairlawn Created, Dev Syllabus Intnl Speech Course; *office:* William Paterson Coll of NJ 300 Pompton Rd Wayne NJ 07470

BUCKLEY, GERALD F., Business Education Teacher; *b:* New York, NY; *m:* Sheila Kelly; *c:* Jerry, Colleen, Patrick; *ed:* Manhattan Coll (BBA) Ec 1964; St John's Univ (MBA) Ec 1969; Coll of New Rochelle, Coll of St Rose, Canesius Coll 60 Credits; *cr:* Nazareth HS Soc Stud Tchr 1964-73; Clarkstown North HS Bus Ed Tchr 1973-; *ai:* Distributive Ed Clubs of Amer Adv; Work Experience, Classroom In The Mall Coord; NYS Bus Tchrs Assn 1995-; Natl Bus Tchrs Assn 1990-; Manhattan Coll Alumni Spiked Shoe Club 1964-, Pres; St Augustine's CCD 1979-, Tchr, Svc Awd; Grants: Schl Store, Career Exploration InternshipPrgm; Nazareth HS Ath Hall of Fame Charter Mem; *office:* Clarkstown HS North Congers Rd New City NY 10956

BUCKLEY, JAMES MICHAEL, Secondary Science Teacher; *b:* Potsdam, NY; *ed:* SUNY ATC at Canton (AAS) Agrigultural Sci 1978; SUNY at Potsdam (BA) Bio 1982, (MA) Sci Ed 1987; NSF Projects Project Master & Project SPARC; St. Lawrence Univ & SUNY at BuffaloAdditional Coursework Completed; *cr:* Edwards Cntrl Schl Scndry Sci Tchr 1983-86; Edwards-Knox Cntrl Schl Scndry Sci Tchr 1987-; Sum Schl Sci Tchr; Gouverneur Cntrl Schl Sci 7,8, Gen Sci, Earth Sci, Biology & Chem; Adj Inst SUNY Coll at Canton Gen Bio Lecture & Laboratory; *ai:* Spec Ed & Labor & Mgmt Comms; Sci Olympiad Coach; Liberty Partnership Sci Club Adv; Fr Club Adv 1993-94; Sr Class Adv 1985,89, Jr Class Adv 1991; NEA 1988-; Sci Tchrs of NYS 1986-; NYS Sci Supvrs 1990-; Sec Oswegatchie Valley Amateur Radio Club 1992-93; Edwards Knox Central High Plng Tm 1993-; Effec Tchng Wrkshp 1991-92; Coop Lrng Wrkshp 1993; Alpha Tm 1995- 96; Amer Radio Relay League 1990-; Oswegatchie Valley Amateur Radio Club 1990-, Sec 2 Yr 1992-93, Treas 1996; St Lawrence Cty ARES & RACES; St Ed Dept Bio Regents Exam Question Writer; *office:* Edwards-Knox Jr Sr HS P O Box 630 Russell NY 13684

BUCKLEY, JOHN THOMAS, Math Teacher & Department Head; *b:* Chelsea, MA; *m:* Kathleen Margaret; *c:* John, Colleen, David; *ed:* Boston St Coll (BS) Elem Ed 1966, (MED) Guid 1969; Boston Univ (EDD) Curr, Instruction, Sci 1976; *cr:* Boston Univ Instr Sci Ed 1974-75; Natick Schl Tchr 1966-; *ai:* NCAA Soccer Referee 1969-, 65 Tourney, 6 Final Fours, Natl; NEA 1966-; Jiffy Lube Tchr of Yr 1991-; CYO 1974-, Dir, Lifetime Mem; NCAA Natl Referee of Yr Soccer 1986; *office:* Wilson MS 24 Rutledge Rd Natick MA 01760

BUCKLEY, KEVIN DALE, Chemistry & Physics Teacher; *b:* Salem, OH; *ed:* Youngstown St (BS) Ed 1987; Youngstown St & Miami of OH Post Grad Work in Curr & Dev; *cr:* Olentangy HS Phys Sci Tchr 1988-90; Southern Local HS Chem & Physics Tchr 1990-95; West Branch HS 1995-; *ai:* Asst Ftbl, Head Girls Track Coach, Boys Track Coach; Governors Awd in Sci 1993; Lake to River Sci Awd 1991-93; *office:* West Branch Local HS 14277 S Main St Beloit OH 44609

BUCKLEY, MARYANN DOLL, Science Teacher; *b:* Massillon, OH; *m:* Robert L.; *c:* Rayce Shelton; *ed:* Wright St (BS) Ed 1970; Univ of Dayton (MS) Ed 1980; 37 Addl Hrs Ed, Geology, Bio, Marine Bio, Marine Ecology, Spec Ed; *cr:* Youngstown & Cincinnati Diocese Tchr Grds 5th, 6, 7, 8th 12 Yrs; Centerville Pub Schls Sci Tchr Grd 6, 7, 8 2 Yrs; DOD Schls England & Quantico, VA Sci Tchr Grds 7 & 8 4 Yrs; Anne Arundel Pub Schls Sci Tchr Grds 7 & 8 13 Yrs; *ai:* Sci Dept Chprsn, Team Ldr; Odyssey of the Mind Coach; Yrbk, Stu Cncl, IM Sports, Chrldr Spon; Stu at Risk Mentor; MD Assn of Sci Tchrs; Tchrs Assn of Anne Arundel Cty 1994-, MS Comm; Phi Delta Kappa 1982-; NEA; Overseas Ed Assn, Treas, Sec; MD Stu Svc Alliance Fellow; Chesapeake Bay Trust Grant; MD Stu Svc Alliance Grant Astronomer for a Day; 2nd Intnl Conf of Meteorological & Oceanographic Ed Publication; *home:* 902 Forest Ter Annapolis MD 21401*

BUCKLEY, PAUL A., English Teacher; *b:* Ridley Park, PA; *m:* Ann M.; *ed:* Villanova Univ (AB) Eng 1959, (MA) Theatre 1962; *cr:* St James HS Eng Tchr 1962-64, Eng Dept Chair 1964-84, Eng Tchr 1985-93; Monsignor Bonner HS Eng Tchr 1993-; *ai:* Assn of Cath Tchrs 1967-; NCEA 1975-; Theatre Assistantship 1960; *office:* Monsignor Bonner HS 403 N Lansdowne Ave Drexel Hill PA 19026

BUCKLEY, ROBERT THOMAS, English Teacher & Dept Chm; *b:* New York, NY; *m:* Lesley Reardon; *c:* Robin, Holly; *ed:* Marist Coll (BA) Eng 1970; Central CT St Univ (MS) Eng 1974; Wesleyan Univ (CAS) Hum 1979; Central CT St Univ Supervision, Admin Cert 1984; Plethora of Trng in Ed Related Areas; *cr:* Newington HS Eng Tchr 1970; Avon HS Eng Tchr 1970-86; CT Comm Colls Eng Tchr 1977-; Hartford Pub HS Eng Tchr 1986-95; Shepaug Valley Schl Eng Tchr, Dept Chr Eng & Foreign Lang; *ai:* Youth Leadership Prgm; Toastmasters Intnl; NEA; CT Bus & Industry Assn Fellowship Distinguished Tchrs 2 Times; Nom Tchr of Yr 4 Times; Committed Adult to Children of Hartford Recipient; *office:* Shepaug Vally School 169 South St Washington CT 06793*

BUCKLEY, SUSAN E., Fifth Grade Teacher; *b:* Maldne, MA; *ed:* West Chester Univ (BSEd) Elem Ed 1968; Boston St Coll (MED) Elem Ed 1976; Post Grad Stud at Penn St Univ, Boston Univ, Boston Coll; *cr:* Primos Elem Schl Sixth Grd Tchr 1968-72; C. Coolidge Elem Schl Fifth-Sixth Grd Tchr 1972-80; T. Roosevelt Elem Schl Sixth Grd Tchr 1980-; *ai:* NEA 1968-; MEA, MTA 1972-; World Affairs Cncl, Appalachian Mt Club 1986-; Trustees of Reservations 1990-; Museum of Fine Arts 1985-; *office:* Theodore Roosevelt Elem Schl 253 Vinton St Melrose MA 02176

BUCKLEY-HARMON, MARY FRANCIS, English Teacher; *b:* Stamford, CT; *m:* Steven D.; *ed:* Coll of Holy Cross (BA) Eng, Span 1990; Boston Coll (MAT) Scndry Eng 1993; *cr:* Hartford Areas Rally Together Comm Organizer 1990-91; Dover HS Eng Tchr 1993-; *ai:* Span Club, Class of 1997 Adv; Tech Prep Curr Comm; NEA, Tchrs Union 1993-; Chrstn Fnd for Children, Aging 1995-, Spon; Most Spirited Staff Mem 1995; *home:* 51 Thornhill Dr Stratham NH 03885

BUCKMAN, JOHN FRANCIS, HS Phys Ed Teacher; *b:* Oceanside LI, NY; *m:* Janice Kowalski; *c:* Nicholas, Blair; *ed:* Bridgeport Univ (BS) PE 1968; Stony Brook Univ (MS) Lbrl Stud 1974; Hofstra Univ Cert of Advanced Stud Admin 1982; FL St Univ Communicating, Mktg 1989, Cmptrs I-II 1989, Drug & Alcohol 1976, Problem Solving 1975; *cr:* Longwood HS PE Tchr 1970-; East Coast Safety Prgm Defensive Driving Course Instr 1992-; Longwood HS Driver Ed Lecture 1993-; Pete's Brewing Co On-Premise Specialist 1994-; *ai:* Wrestling, Bsbl Coach; Supervision; Bill #4547 Headlight Legislation NY Senate 1993; Muscle Trng Illustrated 1976; Pete's Brewing Co Golden Tap Awd 1995; *office:* Longwood Sr HS 100 Longwood Rd Middle Island NY 11953

BUCKOVICH, MARJORIE BRANDS, Teacher for At-Risk Students; *b:* Cleveland, OH; *m:* Thomas Joseph; *c:* Mark Edwin, Paul Andrew, James Thomas, Suzy Ann, Tammy Buckovich Marchand; *ed:* Beaver Coll (BS) Elem Ed 1961; *cr:* 6th Grd Regular Tchr 1961-64; Spring Grove Sr High 10-12th Grd Rdng Specialist 1971-76; Spring Grove Intermediate 6th Grd Sci Tchr 1976-79, 6-7th Grd Low Eng, Rdng Tchr 1979-86, 6th Grd Tchr of At-Risk Stdnts 1986-95, 5-6th Grd Tchr of At-Risk Stdnts 1995-; *ai:* PSEA, MEA; *office:* Spring Grove Area Interm Sch 50 N East St Spring Grove PA 17362

BUCKS, SUSAN GOODMAN, Gifted Facilitator; *b:* Lakewood, OH; *m:* Barry E.; *c:* Jason, Erik, Amanda; *ed:* Hershey Jr Coll (AA) Fr, Eng 1963; Shippensburg Univ (BS) Fr, Eng 1965; PA St Univ (MA) Fr, Sequence Amer Lit 1967; Attnd L'Universite Laval Quebec 1965, L'Alliance Francais Paris France Cours Superieur 1966; *cr:* PA St Univ Grad, Research Asst 1965-67, Instr 1967-68; Shippensburg Univ Assoc Prof 1969-70; Cornwall-Lebanon Schl Dist Tchr 1973-86; Palmyra Area Schl Dist Gifted Facilitator 1986-; *ai:* Acad All Stars, Envirothon Coach; Dist Pub Relations; Coord Gifted Stdnts Vol Act; Math, Sci, Writing, Artistic Competitions; VFW Voice of Democracy Speech Contest, Lebanon Co His Fair, Natl Vol Day Coord; Elem Enrichment; Focus on Pride; PSEA, NEA 1973-; Lebanon Cty Ed Honor Soc 1983-; PA Gifted Ed Assn 1986-; Historical Soc, Dist Liaison 1992-; Leukemia Soc of Amer 1970's-, Vol; Phi Theta Kappa; Alpha Tau Delta; Kappa Delta Pi; Mu Pi Sigma; Drug Prevention Ed, Long Range Planning Comms; Lebanon Valley Chamber of Commerce Ed Excl; Ed Articles, Fr Poem Pub; Coord Dist Newsletter; Prof Model, Actress; Who's Who in Amer Colls & Univs 1965; Outstan ding Young Women of Amer 1966, Nom 1971; Gift of Time Tribute 1991; Organized Palmyra HS Gifted Prgm; Swatara Watershed Alliance Appreciation Cert; Mentor Tchr for Inductees; Lebanon Cty Environmental Edctr of Yr; *home:* PO Box 26 Colebrook PA 17015*

BUCKWALTER, JOHN DAVID, Professor of Biology; *b:* Strasburg, PA; *m:* Laurel Jo Grastorf; *c:* Janna, Rachel, Martha, Jewel, Esther; *ed:* Houghton Coll (BS) Bio 1973; SUNY at Geneseo (MA) Bio 1980; Addl Grad Hrs Alfred Univ, SUNY at Geneseo; NSF Summer Insts SUNY at Fredonia, SUNY at Oswego, Chesapeake Biological Lab of Univ of MD, Cold Spring Harbor Lab; *cr:* The Bible Acad Sci Tchr 1976-79; Andover Cntrl Schl Sci Tchr 1980-82; SUNY Coll of Tech Bio Prof 1982-; *ai:* Educl Technologies & Instructional Support Team Ldr; Environmental Tech Curr Coord; Amer Scientific Affiliation 1976-; Empire St Assn of Two Yr Coll Biologists 1983-; Alfred-Almond Schl Bd 1988-, Pres; Independence Mennonite Church 1963-, Elder; Alumni Assn Tchr of Yr Awd 1991; SUNY Chancellor's Excl in Tchng Awd 1992; NISOD Excl Awd 1993; NY Assn of Two Yr Colls Outstanding Tchr Awd Prgm Honorable Mention 1993; *office:* SUNY Coll of Tech Life Sciences Dept Alfred NY 14802

BUCKWALTER, LYDIA TAXIS, First Grade Teacher; *b:* Norristown, PA; *m:* H. Clinton; *c:* Kathryn K., Ross C.; *ed:* Beaver Coll (BA) Elem Ed 1970; 36 Credit Hrs Post Grad West Chester Univ; *cr:* Audubon Schl 2 Grd Tchr 1970-74; Boyer Schl 2 Grd Tchr 1974-75; Arrowhead Schl 1-3 Grd Tchr 1975-; *ai:* NEA 1970-; Methacton Ed Assn 1970-, Treas 1976-78; *office:* Arrowhead Elem Schl 232 Level Rd Collegeville PA 19426

BUCKWASH, ANTHONY JOSEPH, Physics Teacher; *b:* West Chester, PA; *ed:* Penn St Univ (BS) Scndry Ed 1992; 21 Hrs Towards Masters of Scndry Ed at West Chester Univ; *cr:* Coatesville Area Sr HS Physics Tchr 1993-; *ai:* 9th Grd Boys Bsktbl & Bsbl Coach; Girls Powder Puff Flag Ftbl Coach; NEA 1992-; Longwool Fire Co 1989-; Instructional Improvement Grant; *office:* Coatesville Area School Dist 1515 E Lincoln Hwy Coatesville PA 19320*

BUCZEK, ANN MARIE MARGARET, Mathematics Teacher; *b:* Lowell, MA; *ed:* Lowell St Coll (BS) Math 1975; Univ of Lowell (MEd) Curr, Instruction, Math 1982; 63 Credit Hrs Beyond Masters UMASS, Fitchburg St Coll, Lesley Coll, Boston Coll; *cr:* Greater Lowell Regnl Voc Tech HS Math Instr 1975-; *ai:* REMS2 Math Adv 1993-; Stu of Month, Curr Integration, Natl Voc Tech Honor Soc Selection Comms; Fac Cncl; Greater Lowell Tchrs Org, MA Tchrs Assn, NEA 1975-; St Stanislaus Schl 1994-, Advy Bd; MSCP Asst Dir 1987-91; Prof Dev Conf for Voc Tech Educators Presenter 1987-93; *office:* Greater Lowell Vo Tech HS 230 Pawtucket Blvd Tyngsboro MA 01879

BUDD, MARTHA H., Science Teacher; *b:* Cleveland, OH; *m:* David O.; *c:* Timothy, Carolyn; *ed:* Kent St Univ (BS) Elem Ed 1973; Credit Hrs in Audio-Visuals & Their Production & Use in Classroom, Earth Dynamics Since 1984;Computer Applications in Reading 1994; Using Apple II Computers & Sftwr 1994; *cr:* St Anthony of Pauda 7th Grd Tchr 7-8th Grd Sci Tchr 1973-77; Immaculate Conception 7th Grd Tchr 6-8 Sci Tchr 1984-94; 5-8 grd Sci Tchr 1994-; *ai:* Dir 5-8th Grds, Immaculate Conception, Coord to Portage Cty, Dist & St Sci Fairs; NCEA 1984-; Kappa Delta Pi 1973-; Gov Awrd for Excellence in Yth Sci Oppor 1993-1995; Outstanding Achvmt Awd Portage Cty Sci Fair 1991-92; Nom 1992 Presidential Awds for Exel in Sci & Math Tchng; Governor's Awd for Excl in Youth Sci Opportunities1992-93; *office:* Immaculate Conception Schl 225 S Sycamore St Ravenna OH 44266

BUDD, ROBERT MARSHALL, English Teacher; *b:* Brooklyn, NY; *m:* Alice Siegal; *c:* Lauren, Jason, Skyla; *ed:* C. W. Post Coll (BA) Eng 1965, (MS) Eng 1976; 60 Addl Credits; *cr:* Seth Low Intermediate Schl Eng Tchr 1967-69; Locust Vly HS Eng Tchr 1969-72; Miller Place HS Eng Tchr 1972-; *ai:* 4th-6th Grd After Schl GATE Theater Adv 1992-95; Former Newspaper Adv, Var Tennis Coach, Lit Magazine Adv, Drama Dir, SIT Comm; NYSUT 1969-; Established Shoreham Comm Yth Theater; Christa Mc Auliffe Flwshp Finalist, 1st Alternate 1990; CBE, NEH Flwshp for Ind Stud 1993; Long Island Writing Project Fellow 1994; NY St Eng Cncl NY Sec Edctr of Excl Awd 1994; NEH Summer Seminar Flwshp on Socrates; *office:* Miller Place HS North Country Rd Miller Place NY 11764*

BUDHOS, SHIRLEY, Retired HS English Teacher; *b:* Brooklyn, NY; *w:* Walter (dec); *c:* Philip Budhos Ashley, Marina Tamar; *ed:* Queens Coll at CUNY (BA) Eng 1967, (MS) Ed, Scndry Eng 1971; St Johns Univ at Jamaica (PHD) Eng 1980; Admin, Supervision Prgm at Queens Coll at CUNY 1989-92; *cr:* Robert Van Wyck Jr HS Eng Tchr 1968-70; Queens Coll CUNY Adj Lecturer Eng Dept 1971-75; NYC bd of Ed Per Diem HS Tchr 1975-78; Flushing HS Eng Tchr 1978-95; *ai:* Schl Newspaper, Lit Magazine Fac Adv; Coll Adv; SAT Prep; NEA; AFT; NCTE; Natl Endowment for Hum Grant at IN Univ 1984; UFT NYC Tchr Ctr Consortium Scholars Circle Honoree 1989-90; City Coll of CUNY Conf Presenter 1989-90; Article Pub.

BUDINE, ALAN L., English Teacher; *b:* Walton, NY; *m:* Barbara Y.; *c:* Matthew, Kyle; *ed:* Morrisville Ag & Tech (AAS) Auto Tech 1973; SUNY at Oneonta (BS) Scndry Eng Ed 1980, (MS) Scndry Eng Ed 1985; *cr:* Mt Upton Cntrl Schl Eng Tchr 1980-83; Walton Cntrl Schl Eng Tchr 1983-; *ai:* Jr Class Adv; NYS & NEA 1983-; Write Weekly Column for Local Paper; *office:* Walton Cntrl Schl 47-49 Stockton Ave Walton NY 13856*

BUDIWSKY, ANNA, Spanish Teacher; *b:* Germany; *ed:* Temple Univ (BA) Span 1968, (MED) Tchng Frgn Lang 1976; *cr:* Notre Dame HS Span Tchr 1969-81; Cardinal O'Hare HS Span Tchr 1981-; *ai:* Span Honor Soc Moderator; Homecoming Ct Coord; Act Office Asst; MLAPV 1969-, Sec; PSMLA 1970-; AATSP-GPA 1969-, Tchr of Yr 1994; Reader, Adv Scott Foresmans Texts; Grants: ACTFL Harverford Coll on Oral Proficiency 1983, PATHS Bryn Mawr Coll 1985, Pluma Project 1995; Commonwealth Partnership Scholar 1988; Tchr of Yr 1987; Presenter NE Conf Total Immersion Prgms 3 Models 1988; *office:* Cardinal O Hara HS 1701 S Sproul Rd Springfield PA 19064

BUEHLER, PEG TAUBKEN, Business Teacher; *b:* Lima, OH; *m:* James; *c:* Julia, Patrick, Jamie; *ed:* Bowling Green St Univ (BS) Bus Ed, Cmptr Sci 1973; Wright St Univ Lake Campus 25 Addl Hrs; *cr:* St Marys City Schls Bus, IOE Tchr 1973-74; Wapakoneta City Schls Bus Tchr 1974-78; Minster Local Schls Bus Tchr 1979-81; Botkins Local Schls Bus Tchr 1981-; *ai:* Sr Class Adv; Tech Comm; AFT 1987-, Sec, Treas; OH Bus Tchrs Assn 1973-; Copeland Grant 1995-; *office:* Botkins Local Schls Box 550 201 Sycamore Botkins OH 45306

BUELL, DONALD A., A P Biology Teacher; *b:* Framingham, MA; *m:* Claudette Jutras Buell; *c:* Rebecca, Catherine; *ed:* Framingham St Coll (BA) Bio Ed 1972; Boston St Coll MED) Scndry Ed 1974; Worcester St Coll (MS) Bio 1990; Frontiers of Bio; *cr:* Framingham HS Sci Tchr 1972-, Guest Lecturer 1989-91; *ai:* HS Accreditation Steering Comm; NEA 1972-; MTA 1972-; NABT 1992-; Full Schlsp To Study Frontiers of Bio at Boston Univ; Voted Most Outstdng Tchr by Stu Body at FHS; *office:* Framingham HS 115 A St Framingham MA 01701

BUENSALIDA, VICTORIA BALITAAN, Fourth Grade Teacher; *b:* Bauan Batangas, Philippines; *ed:* St Bridget's Coll (BSEE) Elem Ed 1962; Western Philippine Coll (BSE) Math 1974; Pamantasan Ng Lungsod Ng Maynila (MA) Math 1978; Episcopal Commission Ed, Reg Instr Level Two Cert Cath Schl Catechist; *cr:* Dept of Cty Schls HS Math Tchr 1975-81; Intnl Schl HS Math Tchr 1977-79; Govt Girls Sec Schl Educ Officer 1981-87; St Helena Schl ELem Classroom Tchr 1987-; *ai:* CCD Cathechist; NCEA 1987-; Pilipino Parish Ldrs 1995-; Acad Schlrsp; *office:* St Helena Schl 2050 Benedict Ave Bronx NY 10462*

BUERGERS, ERIC H., English Teacher; *b:* Bronx, NY; *m:* Andrea Schinas; *c:* John E., Alexa M.; *ed:* Wesleyan Univ (BA) Eng 1970, (MAT) Eng 1973; Addl 16 Post Grad Credits; *cr:* Berlitzsprachschule Lang Tchr 1970; Coginchaugreg HS Eng Tchr 1973-78; Arlington HS Eng Tchr 1978-; *ai:* Drama Dir; AFT, Arlington Tchrs Assn 1978-; *office:* Arlington HS North Campus 263 Rt 55 Lagrangeville NY 12540

BUETTNER, PAUL ELMER, Math Teacher; *b:* Cleveland, OH; *m:* Nancy J. Migot; *c:* Anne Marie, Katherine, Mary, Peter, Sarah; *ed:* OH St Univ (BS) Natural Resources 1976; Cleveland St Univ Cert Math, Sci 1989; Attnd Baldwin-Wallace Coll, Ursuline Coll, Cleveland Metro-Parks Ranger Acad; *cr:* St Paul Schl 7-8 Grd Math, 6-8 Grd Sci Tchr 1989-95; Villa Angela-St Joseph HS Math Tchr 1995-; *ai:* Jr Class, Stu Cncl Moderator; Respect, Discipline Comm; NCTM 1988-; GCCMT 1995-; NCEA 1989-; Selected to Stud Ocean as Ecosystem Spon by Ursuline Coll; *office:* Villa Angela St Joseph HS 18491 Lake Shore Blvd Cleveland OH 44119

BUETZOW, DAVID BENNETT, Band & Orchestra Director; *b:* Pittsburgh, PA; *m:* Debra Marietta; *c:* Mauri, Kim; *ed:* Carnegie Mellon U (BFA) Music 1974, (MFA) Music Ed 1976; *cr:* Bethel Park Schl Dist Tchr 1975-; *ai:* Marching Band Dir; Wind Ensemble & Orch Pit Conductor; Stage Crew Spon; PA Music Edctrs Assoc 1975-, Dist 1 Pres 1996; AFT 1975-; Music Edctrs Natl Conf 1975-; Cantelina Childrens Choir 1990-, Steering Comm; Amer Schl Band Dirs Assoc, Outstdng Band Dir 1983; Natl Schl Orch Assn; Phi Beta Mu; *office:* Bethel Park Sr HS 309 Church Rd Bethel Park PA 15102*

BUFWACK, MARLANE MARIE, Mathematics Teacher; *b:* Warren, OH; *ed:* OH Univ (BS) Math 1972; Youngstown St Univ (MED) Ed & Admin 1986; Attnd Kent St Univ, Univ of Dayton; *cr:* Edison Jr HS Math Tchr 1972-79; Niles McKinley HS Math Tchr 1979-; *ai:* NEA, OEA & NCTA 1972-, Bldg Rep; NCTM 1972-; St Jude Hosp 1970-; Amer Cancer Soc 1991-; Youngstown St Grad Schlsp; Trumbull Cty Mentorship Pgm; *office:* Niles Mc Kinley HS 616 Dragon Dr Niles OH 44446

BUGANSKI, PAMELA, Math Tchr & Dept Co-Chair; *b:* St Louis, MO; *ed:* Notre Dame Coll (BA) Ed 1980; Univ of Dayton (MS) Scndry Ed 1993; *cr:* St Mary Elem 7th-8th Grd Tchr 1980-82; Ladyfield Schl 7th Grd Tchr 1982-84; St Mary Elem 7th Grd Tchr 1984-86; St James Elem 8th Grd Tchr 1986-89; St Mary Cntrl Cath HS Algebra, Calculus, Cmptr Tchr, Math Dept Chair 1989-91; Notre Dame Acad HS Algebra, Calculus Tchr, Dept Co-Chair 1991-; *ai:* Jr, Sr Girl Retreat Ldr; Open House Comm; Area Univ Ed Majors Mentor; NCTM; OCTM; *office:* Notre Dame Acad 3235 Sylvania Toledo OH 43623

BUGANSKY, SUE A., Spanish Teacher; *b:* Warren, OH; *m:* James R.; *c:* Timothy, Elizabeth; *ed:* OH Univ (AB) Span 1968; OH St Univ (MS) Foreign Lang Ed 1974; 3 Addl Hrs; Ed Credits St of OH; Ashland Univ Courses at Marlington HS; *cr:* Moody Jr HS Span Tchr 1969-70; Colegio Bolivar Cali Colombia Eng & His Tchr 1970-72; OH St Univ Span Tchng Asst 1973; Worthington HS Span Tchr 1973-76; Cleveland St Univ Media Lab Resource 1977; Delaware City Schls Span Tchr 1983-85; Kent St Univ Span Instr 1986-87; Marlington Local Schls Span Tchr 1987-; *ai:* 4 Yr Adv Class of 1991; Span Club Adv; Odyssey of Mind Coach Grd 6 Team; Marlboro Schl Parent Involvement Grant Comm; Marlboro Schl, Span in the Elem 1992-; Adv Class of 1998; Foriegn Tours With Stu 1991, 1996 to Mexico, Costa Rica; Phi Sigma Iota 1969-; OH Ed Assn, NEA 1983-; OFLTA 1969, 1973, 1983-; Marlboro Twp Bd of Zoning Appea FROGS Exec Bd 1990-92; Marlboro Sftbl Assn Coach 1987-9 Marlington H S 10450 Moulin Ave NE Alliance OH 44601

BUGBEE, E. JOHN, Chemistry Professor; *b:* Springfield, MA; Cressotti-Bugbee; *c:* Shaun H., Timothy J.; *ed:* Amer Intnl (BA) I (MA) Ed 1966; Univ of CT Microbiology 1962-64; *cr:* Val Research Tech 1964-67; Springfield Tech Comm Coll Chem Pr *office:* Springfield Tech Comm Coll Armory Square Springfield M

BUHITE, WILLIAM RUSSEL,JR., Biology Teacher; *b:* Ridgwa Rita Bridgid Cregan; *ed:* Clarion Univ of PA (BS) Scndry Ed Credits Grad Bio Course; *cr:* Sherando HS Earth & Space 1992-94; Ridgway HS Bio Tchr 1994-; *ai:* Var Ftbl, Bsktbl Coa PSEA 1994-; Biscits Funded by Natl Sci Fnd; *office:* Ridgway 1403 Hill St Ridgway PA 15853

BUHLER, JAY WARREN, Music Teacher; *b:* Hollidaysburg Sandra Lee Goll-Buhler; *c:* Lisa Susan, Matthew Jay, Benjaman IN Univ of PA (BS) Music Ed 1972, (MA) Performing Arts Curwensville Tchr 1972-; *ai:* Stu Assistance Prgm Core Team; NEA, PSEA, MENC 1972-; PMEA 1972-, Cty Rep 1988-89; Accepted Mason 1986-, Sec, Past Master; *office:* Curwensville Dist 650 Beech St Curwensville PA 16833

BUHR, JANICE M. (HALL), Christian Education Director; *b:* I NY; *m:* Dennis Carl; *c:* Brian, Jeffrey, Kristin; *ed:* SUC at Gene Psych 1975; SUC at Buffalo (MS) Ed 1980; *cr:* Sodus Cntrl Schl Tchr 1976-79; Royalton Hartland Cntrl Schl First-Second C 1979-83; Ridgewood Bible Church Chrstn Ed Dir 1985-; *home:* Rd Lockport NY 14094

BUKSBAUM, RONALD WALTER, Professor of Fine Arts; *b:* IL; *m:* Rebecca Pizante; *c:* Aviva, Joshua, Samuel; *ed:* Univ of Fine Arts 1959; Univ of Cincinnati (MFA) Fine Arts 1961; Chicago Acad of Art 1955; Post-Grad Stud Studio Arts Cntrl CT *cr:* Herron Museum of Art Dir Museum Classes 1962-63; Lafayett Dir 1964-67; IN Univ Northwest Dept Chprsn, Prof Fine Arts Capital Comm Tech Coll Dept Chprsn Fine Arts 1971-76, Prof I 1971-; *ai:* Schl Cultural Comm; Acad Adv; Congress of CT Con 1975-; Art Exhibitions 1959-; *office:* Capital Comm-Tech Woodland Street Hartford CT 06105

BULGARIS, DALIA REGINA, Chemistry Teacher; *b:* Lithuania; *ed:* Marygrove Coll (BS) Chem 1958; Fordham Ur Organic Chem 1960; Addl 24 Credits Towards PHD 1960-66; Hu Ed Courses 1971-73; *cr:* Bronx Comm Coll Chem Instr & 1962-68; Hunter Coll Chem Instr & Lecturer 1962-68; Private Scl Tchr 1968-73; Brooklyn Tech HS Chem Tchr 1973-79; Stuyve Chem Tchr 1980-; *ai:* Chem Tchrs Club 1973-, Treas, Sec, Presidential Awd 1985; Amer ChemicalSoc 1957-88, ACS Av Polytechnic Inst of Brooklyn NSF 1971; SUNY at Purchase Sum 1987; *office:* Stuyvesant HS 345 Chambers St New York NY 102

BULINSKI, DANIEL GREGORY, Senior Army Instructor; *b:* Falls, NY; *m:* Susan; *c:* Katherine, Joseph; *ed:* Niagara Univ (BA 1973, (MS) Ed Admin 1974; Univ of CT (MA) Philosophy 1985; New Platz (CAS) Ed Admin & Supervision 1987; Command & C Coll at Ft Leavenworth; Logistic Exec Dev Course at Transportation Ofcr Advanced Course at Ft Eustis; *cr:* US Arm 1973-94; Coll of William & Mary Prof of Military Sci; USMA Point Asst Prof, Dept of Eng; XVIII Airborne Corps Logistics Pl Germany Co-Commander; *ai:* JROTC Color Guard & Drill Te Bronze Star Medal for Meritorious Svc During Desert Sto Meritorious Achvmt Medal with Two Oak Leaf Clusters; *office:* Penn Sr HS 101 W College Ave York PA 17403

BULIS, MARIA GEROSA, Science Teacher & Chairpe Manhattan, NY; *w:* Rudolph (dec); *c:* Eric J., Rudolf J.; *ed:* Coll Vincent (BS) Bio 1968; LIU (MS) Bio 1987; *cr:* Boyce Thomp Rsrch Assoc 1968-77; Acad Mt St Ursula Sci Tchr 1987; Fordh Schl Sci Tchr & Chrprsn 1988-; *ai:* Marine Bio Club; STANY Bronxville League for Svc 1978-; *office:* Fordham Prep Sch Fordham Rd Bronx NY 10458

BULKA, THOMAS MICHAEL, Computer Science Teacher; *b:* E NJ; *m:* Laurie Scott; *c:* Nicholas, Peter, Leah; *ed:* Pace Univ (BA 1977; Frostburg St Univ (MS) Cnslng Psych 1986, (BS) Cmptr S *cr:* Garrett Cty Hlth Dept Mental Hlth Therapist Addictions Cnslr Shalom at Benedicts Comm Asst Prgm Coord 1984-86; Washing Hlth Dept Mental Hlth Therapist 1986-87; Garrett Cty Bd of Ed C Tchr 1988-; *ai:* Stu System's Operator's Club Adv; MD Virtual Grant; *office:* Northern HS 86 Pride Pkwy Accident MD 21520

BULKLEY, ROBERT H., 7th Grade Social Studies Tchr; *b:* Berw *m:* Wendi Lynn Patacconi; *ed:* Bloomsburg St Coll (BS) Soc Stud Berwick MS 7th Grd Soc Stud Tchr 1984-; *ai:* Wrestling, Track Co Vly Track & Field Ofcl; NEA, PSEA, BAEA 1984-; Summerhill Fi 1979-; Outstdng Young Edctr 1984; Coach of Yr 1993-94; Men 1994-95; *office:* Berwick Area MS 1100 Evergreen Dr Berwick PA

BULLERS, JOSEPH, Instrctnl Support Pgm Tchr; *b:* Ridgway, Edinboro Univ (BS) Elem Ed 1976, (BS) Socially & Emotionally D 1976, (MED) Elem Ed Equivalency 1986; Saint Bonaventure Uni I Elem Guidance & Scndry Guidance 1995; *cr:* I U #9 Mixed Categ 1979-92; Saint Marys Area Schl Dist Instructional Support Treatment Prgm Tchr 1992-; *ai:* Stu Assistance Prgm; NEA, PSE Elk Cty Youth Advy Comm; Family Svc System Reform Bd; At-R Comm for IU #9; Alcohol & Drug Abuse Svcs 1995-, Bd Mer Comm; Animal Protection Agency 1994-; Elem Drug Abuse Svcs f Stackpole Hall Fnd & Schl Based Mental Hlth Svcs Grants; *offic* Saint Marys St Elem 370 S Saint Marys St Saint Marys PA 15857

BULLERWELL, LORNIE DAVID, Biology Teacher; *b:* Lynn, Univ of MA at Boston (BS) Bio 1965; Bridgewater St Univ (M 1979; Harvard Univ (CSS) Admin 1984; 60 Plus Hrs at Bowdoin, Boston Univ, MA Maritime, Brown, Framingham St, St Univ o Buffalo; *cr:* Danvers Jr HS Sci Tchr 1969-70; Dedham HS Sci Tch *ai:* Bsktbl Coach; Sci Olympiad Team Coach; Sci Club Adv; NE 1969-; Dedham Ed Assn 1971-, Exec Bd, Bargaining Bd; Natl A Tchr 1975-, Organizing Comm Convention, Outstanding Bio Tc Mother Brook Coalition 1995-, Exec Bd, Founder; Woodrow Fellow Princeton Univ; Boston Univ Sci Fellow; TEC Outs Educator Awd; Rotary Club Prof of Yr 1994; Contributing Wr Textbook; Pub in the Sci Tchr Journal & Sci Scope; *office:* Ded 140 Whiting Dedham MA 02026*

BULLOCK, BARBARA JEAN, Fifth Grade Teacher; *b:* Tulsa, Nathaniel Michael David; *ed:* Howard Univ (BA) Sociology 1970 Univ at New Orleans Elem Ed 18 Grad Hrs; Univ of MD at Colle 12 Credit Hrs; *cr:* Our Lady of Perpetual Help Schl Second, Fo Tchr 1970-71; St Thomas More Schl First, Second Grd Tchr 1 Charles Cty Pub Schl Fourth, Fifth Grd Tchr 1985-87; St Anthony C Fourth-Sixth Grd Tchr 1987-; *ai:* Advy Bd; Curr, Policy Dev Intermediate Level Coord; NCEA 1973-; Klutnik Museum 1994 Brith Ed Comm; Spec Olympics 1990-, Vol; Nom NCEA Distngd Yr 1995; *office:* St Anthony Grade Schl 12th & Lawrence Washington DC 20017*

CK, MAURA NESTOR, English Teacher; *b:* New York, NY; *m:* .; *c:* Elizabeth; *ed:* Notre Dame Coll of St John's Univ (BA) Eng niv of Notre Dame (MA) Eng 1972; Harvard Univ (CAGS) Human 8; Attnd Univ of London, Univ of Manchester; *cr:* Waterbury Cath Tchr, Eng Dept Chm 1967-69; Notre Dame HS Eng Tchr, Eng Dept 59-72; Stamford Cath HS Eng Tchr, 1972-74; Burlington HS Eng air, Eng Tchr 1974-; *ai:* Church Ldr, Children's Liturgy; Pub Eng AP Consultant; Reader AP Exam; *office:* Burlington HS 123 ge St Burlington MA 01803*

CK, PAULETTE GLADYS (BROWN), Elementary Educator; *b:* NY; *m:* Alex; *c:* Donya, Ahmid; *ed:* Oneonta NY (BS) Ed 1972; NY (MA) Math & Ed 1975; 30 Credits Post Grad Stud; *cr:* ad Elem Ed K-6th Grd Edctr 1972-; *ai:* AFT & NEA 1972-; Adult Group, Co-Yth Adv, Recognition Cert; CN Bus & Prof Church Schl Vol; Acknowledgements for Kwanzaa Presentations; Vith Grad.*

CK, TEDDI CALLAGHAN, Administrative Analyst; *b:* Cohoes, Paul; *c:* Chris, Dan, Andrew; *ed:* LeMoyne Coll (BS) Eng 1965; ussell Sage Coll, SUNY at Geneseo; *cr:* Newark St Schl Tchr ; Overbrook Ctr Tchr 1970-72; St Agnes Schl Jr High Tchr ; DMV Admin Analyst 1994-; *home:* 27 Barkwood Ln Clifton Park 55

TTA, DOMINICK MARK, Fifth Grade Teacher; *b:* Washington, Catherine Franz; *c:* Andrea, Megan, Corinne; *ed:* Coll of ville (BS) Elem Ed 1969; California Univ of PA (MA) Elem Ed Credits Admin Courses; *cr:* Cleveland Pub Schls Sixth Grd Tchr ; Trinity Area Schl Dist Fifth Grd Tchr 1973-; *ai:* Elem Girls 'oach; Schls Strategic Plan Mem; Sci Comm; PSEA, NEA, TAEA res 1990; St Hilary Church 1950-, Cncl Mem, Rel Ed Dir 1988-, Yr 1993; *office:* Trinity Area Schl Dist Park Ave Washington PA

N, LUCRETIA SCARDILLO, Mathematics Teacher; *b:* Albany, William; *c:* Victoria; *ed:* Russell Sage (BA) Math Scndry Ed 1973; (MA) Math Scndry Ed 1976; Attnd Union Coll Mechanical *cr:* Albany HS Math Tchr 1973-; *ai:* NCTM; *office:* Albany HS hington Ave Albany NY 12203

RNICK, BENIGNA,CDP, Retired Teacher; *b:* Johnstown, PA; uesne Univ (BA) Ed 1954.

UGH, SUSAN MORITZ, Asst Prof of Education; *b:* Lima, OH; T.; *c:* Michael, Lisa Vottero, Kathryn; *ed:* Bluffton Coll (BA) Elem Univ of Dayton (MS) Elem Schl Admin 1976; *cr:* Lima Pub Schls Tchr 1964-66; Weston Schl Dist 4th Grd Tchr 1966-68; Bath Schl th Grd Tchr 1968-79; Bluffton Coll Asst Prof Educ 1986-; *ai:* Acad Comm; Spec Stud, Hnrs Comm Chair; Am Univ Women; NAEYC; r Grant 1978; Fac Grant 1990, 1994; *home:* 2214 Wellesley Dr H 45804*

S, LAURIE CULVER, Mathematics Teacher; *b:* Riverhead, NY; en H.; *c:* Timothy, Daniel; *ed:* SUNY at Oswego (BS) Scndry Ed, 977; Grad Stud; *cr:* Solvay HS Math Tchr 1977-85; Onondago Ctr Adjunct Instr 1981-85; Liverpool HS Math Tchr 1985-; *ai:* Jr dv; Educator, Bus Partnership Prgm; SAT Prep Inst; AFT, NY St Tchrs 1977-; United Liverpool Fac Assn 1985-; Onondaga Cty Math 992-; PTO 1987-; *office:* Liverpool HS 4338 Wetzel Rd Liverpool 90*

DZYA, VANCE RICHARD, American Cultures Teacher; *b:* ahela, PA; *m:* Kathleen; *c:* Michael, Jennifer; *ed:* California Univ (BS) His 1968; Masters Degree at Duquesne Univ; *cr:* -Whitehall Schl Dist Classroom Instr 28 Yrs; *ai:* NEA, PA St Ed Natl Assn of Soc Stud 1968-; *office:* Baldwin HS 4653 Clairton Ave gh PA 15236

RY, RICHARD DAWSON, English Teacher; *b:* Johannesburg, frica; *m:* Anne Margaret French; *ed:* Univ of the Witwatersand ng Lit 1975, (HED) Eng Lit 1977; *cr:* Malvern Schl Eng Tchr ; Redhill Schl Eng Tchr, Rugby Coach 1976-78; York Howe Schl Eng Enriched Prgm, Class Tchr 1978-; *office:* York House Schl exandra St Vancouver BC V6J 2V6 Canada CN*

E, CAROL LANDES, Family & Consumer Sci Tchr; *b:* Pottstown, Donald E. Jr.; *c:* Janice Amico, Lori Amico, Stephen Amico; *ed:* PA (BS) Indvidual, Family Stud, Tchr Cert 1974, (MED) Home Ec Ed : Hinkletown Alternative Schl 6th-8th Grds Home Ec Ed, Pre Voc r Amish, Mennonite Stdnts 1974-84; Garden Spot Sr HS Family, er Sci Tchr 1984-; *ai:* Dist Strategic Planning Task Force Co-Chair Comm; Future Edctrs of Amer Club Adv; Mentor New Tchrs; Lit Coord Sr HS, Elem Schl Linkage; Dir, Coord Children's Corner Prgm; NEA, PSEA, E Lanco Ed Assn 1984-; Amer, PA, Lancaster Family, Consumer Svcs 1994-; St Stephen Handbell Choir 1981-; for Svc Learning, Planning 1993-94, Lit Corps 1994-96 Grant; PA Ed Train the Trainer Participant; Presentor: Back to the Family IU 1995; *office:* Garden Spot Sr HS PO Box 609 New Holland PA

, LARAINE ANNE (KOSCO), French Teacher; *b:* Uniontown, Jeffrey Paul; *ed:* Bowling Green St Univ (BS) Fr 1979; BGSU, Coll, Drake Univ & San Francisco St Univ Post Grad Stud; *cr:* Clay Tchr 1979-; *ai:* Intnl Club Adv; Strategic Planning; Instructional am; Toledo Area Foreign Lang Assn 1990-, Steering Comm; OH ng Assn; Bus & Prof Women 1989-, Pres, VP; Tchr-Cnslr for ACIS, NETC; Foreign Lang Dept Head; Fac Advy Comm; OFLA Treas; 129 Heathwyck Rd Maumee OH 43537

NS, KATHLEEN E., Teacher; *m:* Donald J.; *c:* Donald Jr., Jeffrey; ssboro St Coll (BA) Soc Stud 1972; Rutgers Univ Inst for Applied Tchng Tool; *cr:* Paulsboro HS Tchr 1972-80; Woodstown HS Tchr *ai:* Fac Alliance; Pupil Assistance Comm; Block Scheduling Dev; 72-; NJ Ed Assoc 1972-; Woodstown Ed Assoc 1984-; Woodstown ve Regnl Schl Dist Awd for Acad Excl for Outstdng Achvmt in S Jersey Debate League; *office:* Woodstown HS 140 East Ave own NJ 08098

, JOAN HOEHNE, Third Grade Teacher; *b:* Callicoon, NY; *m:* V.; *c:* Chris Morrison, Cynthia Morrison; *ed:* Mansfield Univ (BS) d 1964; *cr:* Franconia Elem 1st Grd Tchr 1964-66; Angelica Cntrl Tchr 1966-68; Wellsville Cntrl 3rd Grd Tchr 1968-; *ai:* Lang Arts Math Comms; NEA 1966-; WEA 1968-, Sec 1994-; NYEA 1968-; 7 Grove St Andover NY 14806

, ROBERT BRYON, 5th Grade Teacher; *b:* New Brighton, PA; *m:* Majestic; *c:* Kathleen, David, Elizabeth; *ed:* Slippery Rock Univ em Ed 1973; PA St 24 Hrs Ed Admin; *cr:* Hollidaysburg Area Schl , 3rd-5th Grd Tchr 1974-; *ai:* IST Team Mem; Stu Cncl Adv; NEA, 974-; MAEA 1974-, Rep; St Johns Youth Group 1994-, Adv; Parish 93-, Pres; Gift of Time Awd; *office:* Hollidaysburg Area Schl Dist of Ten Rd Duncansville PA 16635

, SAMUEL LEWIS, English & Mass Media Tchr; *b:* DuBois, PA; hia A. Yohe; *c:* Andrew, Elizabeth, Joshua; *ed:* Clarion Univ of PA ndry Ed & Commnctn Arts 1985; Addl 9 Credit Hrs; Clarion Univ Hrs; *cr:* USAF Technician 1976-80; Tri-County Broadcasting Co ir & Operations Mgr 1981-93; DuBois Area HS Eng & Media Tchr *ai:* Newspaper Adv; Sr Video Adv; Prins Advy Comm; Bus Network Comm; NHS Comm; NEA 1993-; PSEA 1993-; Hope for Victims of Violence 1992-, VP & Bd of Dirs; Soldier Wesleyan Meth Church 1973, Pres & Stewardship Comm; Dept of Hlth & Human Svcs Soc Security Admin Pub Svc Awd 1991; Outstdng Young Men of Amer 1986; Free Lance Writer; Articles Pub; *office:* Dubois Area Sr HS 400 Orient Ave Du Bois PA 15801

BUNDY, WILLIAM N., High School Math Teacher; *b:* Toledo, OH; *ed:* Univ of Toledo (BSEd) Math 1980; *cr:* Genoa Area HS Math Tchr 1980-; *ai:* Quiz Bowl Team Adv; Bsktbl Scoreboard Operator; Ftbl Team Videographer; NEA 1980-92; AFT 1992-; *office:* Genoa Area HS 2980 N Genoa Clay Center Rd Genoa OH 43430

BUNNELL, ROBERT, HS Mathematics Instructor; *b:* MT Vernon, OH; *c:* Mathew, Ashley; *ed:* OH St Univ (BED) Math Ed 1975; Ashland Univ (MED) Sports Sci 1993; *cr:* Lincolnview HS Math, Coach 1975-77; Margaretta HS Math, Coach 1977-80; East Knox HS Math, Coach 1980-81; Mt Vernon HS Math, Coach 1981-; *ai:* NEA, OEA 1975-; NCOEA, MVEA 1981-; *office:* Mount Vernon HS 300 Martinsburg Rd Mount Vernon OH 43050*

BUNTING, LARRY EUGENE, Mathematics Department Chair; *b:* Hicksville, OH; *m:* DiAnn Fetters; *c:* Taylor Leigh, Morgan; *ed:* Hillsdale Coll (BS) Math 1982; Bowling Green Univ Cmptr Class & Northwest Nine Mentor Prgm for Grad Credit; *cr:* N Cntrl HS Math Tchr Chprsn 1982-; *ai:* Var Cross Cntry, Var Girls Fast Pitch Sftbl Coach; Williams Cty Math Course of Stud, Williams Cty Compentcy Based Ed Comm; North Cntrl Eagles Bsktbl Team Announcer; Stu Cncl Adv; Dist Goals Comm to Form Bus Prtnrshp; N Cntrl Tchrs Assn, OEA, NEA, 5th Dist Umpires Assn 1982-; OH Cncl of Tchrs of Math; NCTM; Sons of the Amer Legion, N Amer Fishing Club 1992-; OH HS Ath Assn 1982-; North Cntrl Ath Boosters Club; *home:* 605 E Baubice St Pioneer OH 43554

BUONGIRNO, CAROL ARANCI, 6th Grade Tchr; *b:* New Haven, CT; *m:* John; *c:* David; *ed:* Southern CT St Coll (BS) Ed 1968, (MS) Ed 1971; *cr:* Montowese Elem Schl 5th Grd Tchr 1968-78; Bear Path Schl 6th Grd Tchr 1989-91; Alice Peck Elem Schl 1st Grd Tchr 1991-95, 6th Grd Tchr 1995-; *ai:* NEA, CEA, HEA & NHEA 1968-; Learning Disabilities Assn 1985-; *office:* Alice Peck Elem Schl 35 Hillfield Rd Hamden CT 06518

BUONO, FREDERICK J., Science Teacher; *b:* Syracuse, NY; *m:* Nancy Sykes; *ed:* Syracuse Univ (BS) Bacteriology 1961, (MS) Bacteriology Genetics 1984, (PHD) Microbiology 1967; *cr:* Roum & Haas Rsrch Scientist 1967-71; Tenneco Chemicals Inc Dir of Rsrch 1971-85; Lenape Regnl HS Sci Tchr 1986-; *ai:* SCi League Coach; Governor Schl Selection Comm; NEA, AARP, NJSTA 1986-; ASM 1962-; NIH Flwshp; Numerous Articles Pub.

BURA, CLAIRE PHILLIPS, Math Teacher; *b:* Audubon, NJ; *c:* Mary Jane, Jeffrey L.; *ed:* OH Wesleyan Univ (BA) Math 1967; Glassboro St Nursery Schl Cert 1977; *cr:* Collingswood HS Math Tchr 1967-69; Meth Pre-Kndgtn Tchr & Asst Dir 1976-79; Rancocas Valley Regnl Math Tchr 1979-; *ai:* Rancocas Valley Tchr of Yr 1992 Governors Recognition Prgm; *office:* Rancocas Valley Regional H S Jacksonville Rd Mount Holly NJ 08060*

BURACK, CAROLEE MIRSKY, Eng as Second Lang Tchr; *b:* Brooklyn, NY; *m:* Robert David; *c:* Paul, Glenn; *ed:* Brooklyn Coll (BA) Elem Ed 1960; Attnd Univ of Pittsburgh, PA St Univ; *cr:* PB 2272 Second Grd Tchr 1960-61; Buckingham Elem Schl Second Grd Tchr 1961-63; Highlands Elem Schl Second Grd Schl 1963-67; Assn for Children with Learning Disabilities Diagnostician, Tchr 1967-77; Allegheny Intermediate Unit ESAL Tchr 1979-; *ai:* ESL Vol Tutorial Prgm Organzer, Adv; PSEA 1995-; Beth Isreal Ctr 1967-, Sisterhood Bd; Children with Learning Disabilities Assn 10 Yrs Svc Awd; *home:* 327 Challen Dr Pittsburgh PA 15236

BURAN, DAVID S., Chemistry & Computer Teacher; *b:* Hamilton, NY; *m:* Bramble Jenkins; *c:* Bailey, Kasey, David; *ed:* Bowdoin Coll (AB) Biochem 1986; Dartmouth Coll MALS Pgm; *cr:* Kiski Schl Tchr & Admissions 1986-90, Tchr 1994-; Vermont Acad Dean of Stdnts 1990-94; *ai:* Head Wrestling & Asst Ftbl Coach; Vermont Acad Parents Assn Awd 1994; *home:* 1888 Brett Ln Saltsburg PA 15681*

BURATTI, CARMEL ANN, Itinerant Teacher of the Deaf; *b:* Dunmore, PA; *m:* Joseph A.; *c:* Juliann; *ed:* East Stroudsburg Univ (BS) Speech Correction 1971; Bloomsburg Univ (MED) Tchr of Hearing Imp 1975; Supvr of Spec Ed, Speech, Hearing; Post Grad Work in Rdng; *cr:* Northeastern Educl Intermediate Univ #19 Speech Therapist 1971-73, Tchr of Hearing Impaired 1973-75; Blast IU #17 PA Materials Ctr for Hearing Impaired Coord 1975-76; Northeastern Educl Intermediate Unit #19 Tchr of Hearing Impaired 1976-; *ai:* PA Speech & Hearing Assn 1973-; Northeastern Speech & Hearing 1973-, VP, Pres; PSEA 1975-; St John the Bapt Church, Ski Club Chaperone, Yth Group Adv; PA St Plan for Hearing Impaired Comm 1987-88; *home:* 530 Edgar St Throop PA 18512

BURBA, THERESA CATHERINE, 8th Grade Teacher; *b:* Pittsburgh, PA; *m:* Joseph Anthony; *c:* Catherine Elizabeth, Anthony Joseph; *ed:* IN Univ of PA (BS) Elem Ed 1982; *cr:* Northern Cambria Cath Schl 6-8 Grd Soc Stud Tchr 1983-; *ai:* Yrbk Adv; Girls Bsktbl Coach 1983-89; *office:* Northern Cambria Catholic Sch PO Box 249 Rt 271 S Nicktown PA 15762

BURBANK, ALICE M. K., High School English Teacher; *b:* Norwich, CT; *m:* Francis L.; *c:* Eliisa Winkel, Alison Letourneau; *ed:* Boston Coll (BS) Eng 1959; Univ of Hartford (MS) Sec Eng Ed 1974; *cr:* Griswold HS Eng Tchr 1959-61, 1963-64; Norwich Free Acad Eng Tchr 1961-62, 1968-70; Lyme Consol Schl Eng Tchr 1966-67; Old Lyme HS Eng Tchr 1970-; *ai:* Adv Lit Mag EDEN; NEA; CEA; NEATE; Old Lyme Shores Beach Assn, Pres 1989-91; *office:* Old Lyme HS Main St Old Lyme CT 06371*

BURBANK, BOULDIN GAYLORD,JR., Mathematics Teacher; *b:* Winchester, MA; *m:* Eloise Hills; *c:* Bradford G., Charlotte Fiorentino, Douglas, Timothy, Amy, Sarah; *ed:* Trinity Coll (BS) Math 1955; Syracuse Univ (MS) Math 1962; Harvard Grad Schl of Design 1955-56; *cr:* Tabor Acad Tchr & Coach 1956-61; Mercersburg Acad Tchr 1962-; *ai:* Stu Adv; Squash Coach; Seminar Comm; Comm for Arts; Honor Comm; Cum Laude; Learning Strategies Comm; NCTM 1980-; US Squash Racquets Assn 1975-, Jr Comm, Distinguished Svc Awd; Cub Scouts of Amer, Scout Master, Order of Merit Awd 1971; Natl Sci Fnd Grant; Established Bo Burbank Schlsp Fund 1994; Recipient of 1st Endowed Mercersburg Chair; Nom to Cum Laude.*

BURBANK-SCHMITT, PRISCILLA, High School Math Teacher; *b:* Manchester, NH; *m:* Daryl; *c:* Emma, Helen, Edith; *ed:* Carleton Coll (BA) Math 1969; Wesleyan Univ (MAT) Math 1970; *cr:* Hanover HS Math Tchr 1970-78; Winsor Schl Math Tchr 1978-83; Boston Coll Math Instr 1985-86; Brookline HS Tchr 1986-; *ai:* NCTM.

BURBINE, MARYLOU SUNDILSON, High School English Teacher; *b:* Hartford, CT; *c:* Thomas, Sara Lynn; *ed:* Univ of CT (BA) Eng 1964; *cr:* Poquonock Schl 3rd Grd Tchr; St Columbas Schl 5th Grd Tchr 1966; Fonda Fultonville CS 12th Grd Eng Tchr 1977-; *ai:* FFTA 1977-; AAUW 1964-; *office:* Fonda Fultonville Cntrl Schl 112 Old Johnstown Rd Fonda NY 12068

BURCH, BETH ANN STALNAKER, Third Grade Teacher; *b:* Akron, OH; *m:* Bradley D.; *c:* Seth, Sarah; *ed:* Bluffton Coll (BA) Elem Ed, Kndgtn 1982; Attnd Akron Univ, Ashland Coll; *cr:* St Peters Schl Second Grd Tchr 1982-83; Coventry Local Schls Tutor K-5 1983-85; Green Local Schls Third Grd Tchr 1985-, Tutor 1 Yr; *ai:* NEA, OH Ed Assn, Green Ed Assn 1985-; High St Chrstn Church 1973-, Chrstn Womens Flwshp Pres; Tallmadge Mothers Club 1994-, Sec; *office:* Green Local Schools 1900 Greensburg Rd Greensburg OH 44232

BURCH, REGINA L., Kindergarten Teacher; *b:* Buffalo, NY; *m:* Ralph S.; *c:* Aaron, Emily; *ed:* Medaille Coll (BS) Early Ed 1971; Post Grad Stud at Buffalo St Tchrs Coll, Niagara Univ & SUNY at Buffalo; *cr:* St Leo the Great Kndgtn Tchr 1970-73; Depew Pub Schls Kndgtn Tchr 1973-84, Third Grd Tchr 1984-86, Kndgtn Tchr 1986-; *ai:* NYSUT, AFT & Depew Tchrs Org 1973-; Girl Scouts 1988-, Asst Ldr, 5 Yr Awd; 4-H Club 1993-, Assisting Parent; *office:* Cayuga Heights Elem Schl 1780 Como Park Blvd Depew NY 14043

BURCHAM, DIANA G., Sixth Grade Teacher; *b:* Ironton, OH; *ed:* OH Univ (BSEd) Elem Ed 1984, (MED) Cmptr Sci 1995; *cr:* Symmes Valley Local Tchrs Aide 1976-85, 6th Grd Tchr 1985-; *ai:* OEA, NEA 1984-; SV Ed Assn 1985-, VP & Pres; OAPSE 1983-, Sec; Law Cty Democratic Comm 1988-, Cntrl Comm; Law Cty 4-H Comm 1985-, Sec; *office:* Symmes Valley Multi Level Schl 14860 State Route 141 Willow Wood OH 45696

BURCHETT, KAREN COPPESS, Kindergarten Teacher; *b:* Piqua, OH; *m:* Daniel W.; *c:* Jon Mardin, Brett, Ben; *ed:* Miami Univ (BS) Elem Ed 1972; Wright St Univ (MAED) Supervision, Curr 1991; 9 Credit Hrs Ec, Third Grd Guanrantee, 8 Credit Hrs Discovery Sci; Dayton Comm Ctr for Arts Muse Machine 3 Yrs; *cr:* Gettysburg Elem Schl Kndgtn Tchr 1972-86; Woodland Hghts Elem Schl First Grd Tchr 1986-95; East Elem Schl Kndgtn, Extended Day Kndgtn Tchr 1995-; *ai:* Invention Asst Team 4 Yrs; Math Curr Comm; Tutoring; GEA, OEA, NEA 1973-, Bdlg Rep; Phi Delta Kappa 1992-, Schlsp Comm; St Pauls Luth Church 1969-; St John's Luth Church 1994-; March of Dimes Coord of Wonder Walk for Greenville City Schls; Cancer Soc, Heart Fund; Who's Who Amer Ed 1994-95; Bldg Tchr of Yr 1995; *home:* 1185 Howard Dr Greenville OH 45331*

BURD, BARBARA KING, Math & Computer Science Tchr; *b:* New York, NY; *m:* James J.; *c:* James, Jason, Alicia; *ed:* Glassboro St Coll (BA) Math 1972, (MA) Math 1990; 20 Grad Credits Cmptr Sci Prgm; *cr:* Glassboro St Coll Dev Ed 1977-80, Math Adj Prof 1981-84; Gloucester Cty Coll Math Adj Prof 1983-84; Pitman HS Math Tchr 1984-; *ai:* Yrbk Bus Mgr; Tech Comm; Tech Action Team; NCTM 1980-; NEA, NJEA 1984-; *office:* Pitman HS 225 Linden Ave Pitman NJ 08071

BURDA, DIANA, English Teacher; *b:* Windber, PA; *ed:* Univ of Pittsburgh (BA) Comm 1983; Amer Univ (MA) Eng Ed 1989; *cr:* Forest Hills Jr HS Eng Tchr 1987; Cntrl Cambria HS Eng Tchr 1984-; Mount Aloysius Jr Coll Eng Instr 1991; *ai:* Asst Sftbl Coach; Schl Play Adv, Dir; CCEA, PSEA, NEA, NCTE, WPCTE 1984-; Allegheny Highlands Regnl Theatre 1981-; Allied Artists of Johnstown 1980-, Numerous Photography Awds; *office:* Central Cambria H S 206 Shoolhouse Rd Ebensburg PA 15931

BURDEN, MARTHA WILCOX, Fifth Grade Teacher; *b:* Allen County, OH; *m:* Gene E.; *c:* Gregory L.; *ed:* Bluffton Coll (AED) El Ed 1961, (BS) El Ed 1969; Attnd Bowling Green Univ; *cr:* Allen East Schls Sixth Grd Tchr 1961-77; Temple Chrstn Jr HS 1977-79, Fifth Grd Tchr 1979-; *ai:* Yrbk Adv 1977-; AEEA, VP 1972-73; AEEA, Pres 2 Yrs; OEA, Rep 2 Yrs; NEA 1969-76; West Cntrl OH Quilt Guild 1985-, Pres 2 Yrs; Cncl Arts 1985-, Bd 7 Yrs; Tchr of Month; Book Fun with Book Reports Unpld; *home:* 1970 Lutz Rd Lima OH 45801*

BURDEOS, MILA V., Science Teacher; *b:* Manila, PHillippines; *ed:* Natl Tchrs Coll (BSED) Sci Ed 1967, (MA) Guid, Psych 1980; Inst of Catechetics Rel Stud Theology 1982; Univ of St Tomas Christolog, Mariology 1986; First Aid Instrs Training Course; *cr:* Immaculate Conception Acad Tchr, Dept Head, E. C. Moderator 1968-75; Don Bosco Coll Tchr 1975-79; Lourdes Schl Tchr, Coord Acad 1979-89; St Anthony Schl Tchr 1987-89; Mary Help of Chrstns Acad Tchr 1989-; *ai:* Tchr In-change; Soph Chrldrs; NJ Sci Tchrs Assn 1995-; ASCD 1990-; Legion of Mary 1967-, Pres; NCEA 1987-; Cert of Merit in Physiology; Cert of Appreciation SCI Homeowners Assn, AP Yth Group; Seton Hall Univ Natl Sci Fnd Grant Bio; *office:* Mary Help Of Christians Acad 659 Belmont Ave North Haledon NJ 07508

BURDETTE, DAVID ANDREW, Sixth Grade Math Teacher; *b:* Warren, OH; *ed:* Kent St Univ (BA) Elem Ed 1981; Mt St Joseph (MS) Educl Competency 1988; Attnd Baldwin Wallace Coll, Coll of Mt. St. Joseph Prof Ed Courses; *cr:* North Royalton MS Sixth Grd Tchr 1981-; *ai:* Sixth Grd Team Ldr; Bowling Adv; Rep for C. V. Schl Career Project; NEA 1981-, Bldg Rep; OEA, NREA 1981-; N Royalton Bsbl Boosters 1981-, Purchaser; City of N Royalton 1985-, Asst Recreation Dir; *office:* North Royalton City Schls 6579 Royalton Rd North Royalton OH 44133

BURDICK, CAROL, Assistant Professor of English; *b:* Salem, WV; *c:* Peter Hudson, Christopher Hudson, Anna Pool; *ed:* Milton Coll WI (BA) Eng 1949; SUNY at Geneseo (BSE) Ed 1963; Univ of ME Addl 9 Credit Hrs Poetry; *cr:* Eden Cntrl Schl 5-6 Grd Lang Arts Tchr 1961-63; Hamburg NY Cntrl Schl 5-6 Grd Lang Arts Tchr 1963-67; Porland West Schl 5-6 Grd Lang Arts Tchr 1967-68; Yamouth HS 5-6 Grd Lang Arts Tchr 1968-73; Alfred Univ Coll Eng Prof 1973-; *ai:* Fac Resource Bd Trustees; Ed Coll Catalog; ASLE 1993-; Poetry Soc of Amer 1974-; Wee Playhouse, Historical Soc 1973-; Stop Calling Me Mr. Darling 1989, Woman Alone A Farmhouse Journal 1990 Books; *office:* Alfred University Seidlin Hall Alfred NY 14802*

BURDICK, ROSS MATTHEW, Teacher & Coach; *b:* North Adams, MA; *m:* Elizabeth Burdick Anderson; *ed:* Trinity Coll (BA) Latin Amer Stud 1988; *cr:* G Fox & Co Retail Mgr 1988-89; Trinity Coll Child Ctr Tchr 1989-90; Rockland Cntry Day Schl Tchr, Coach & Ath Dir 1990-93; Rye Cntry Day Schl Tchr & Coach 1993-; *ai:* Cross Cntry, Bsktbl, Sftbl Coach; Adv; *office:* Rye Country Day Schl Cedar St Rye NY 10580

BURDICK, SANDRA REITZELL, English Teacher & Dept Chair; *b:* Buffalo, NY; *m:* Robert; *c:* Julie T. Hewett, Blair N.; *ed:* Geneseo St Univ (BA) Ed & Eng 1975, (MS) Ed 1981; Attnd Penn St, Buffalo St Univ, St Bonaventure; *cr:* Cuba Cntrl HS Eng Tchr 1975-93; Cuba-Rushford Cntrl Schl Eng Tchr 1993-; *ai:* Schl Newspaper Adv; Dist Level Comm; NEA 1975-; Western NY Press Assn 1985-, Bd of Dirs; Allegany-Cutt Tchrs Resource Ctr 1992-, Bd of Dirs; Several Short Stories Pub; *office:* Cuba-Rushford Central Schl 15 Elm St Cuba NY 14727*

BUREK, LYNN ANGELICA, English, Speech & Theatre Tchr; *b:* Greenville, SC; *m:* Glenn J.; *c:* Jaclyn, Joseph; *ed:* West Chester Univ (BS) Ed & Eng 1981; William Paterson Coll 25 Credits Grad Work Writing & Theatre; *cr:* Lakeland Regnl HS Eng Tchr 1981-86; Haddonfield HS Eng Tchr 1986-88; Parsippany HS Eng, Speech & Theatre Tchr 1988-; *ai:* Drama, Forensics & UPBEAT Dir; Drama Club Adv; Speech & Theatre Assn of NJ 1982-; Anti-Defamation League Edctr Supporting Prejudice Reduction Recipient 1995; *office:* Parsippany HS 309 Baldwin Rd Parsippany NJ 07054*

BURESCH, PAMELA J., English Teacher & Dept Chair; *b:* Lewiston, NY; *ed:* SUNY at Buffalo (BA) Eng 1981, (EdM) Learning & Instruction 1983; SUNY at Brockport (CAS) Educl Admin 1991; Post Grad Stud Schl Bus Admin; *ai:* AFT 1981-; ASBO, ASCD 1988-; NY Jaycees 1995-, Comm Dir; Awded 10 Outstdng New Yorkers Ed Field; *office:* Batavia HS 260 State St Batavia NY 14020

BURFIELD, ROSEMARY HALLORAN, Mathematics Teacher; *b:* Saint Marys, PA; *m:* Daniel R.; *c:* Doug, Tom, Denise; *ed:* Edinboro Univ (BS) Scndry Math 1971; 30 Credits Towards Masters Equivalency Penn St Univ & Clarion Univ; *cr:* Brockway Area HS Math Tchr 1971-74; St Marys Area HS Math Tchr 1974-78 & 1985-; *ai:* NHS Comm; St Marys Area HS Prin

1991-; Advisory & Achvmt Related Tchng Comms 1991-92; SMAHS Tech Prep Comm 1991-; Mentor for 1st Yr Tchr 1995-; SMAEA 1974-; PSEA, NEA & NCTM 1971-; Little League Auxiliary 1988-94; Midget Ftbl Auxiliary 1990-92; ECCHS Athlecti Assoc 1990-; *office:* St Marys Area Schl Dist 977 S St Marys Rd Saint Marys PA 15857

BURGARD, MARY KENT, Readiness Teacher; *b:* Monroe, MI; *ed:* Mary Manse Coll (BA) Soc Stud 1974; Xavier Univ (MA) Montessori Ed 1984; 15 Hrs Early Integration Trng Project 1991; 15 Hrs Tchng Strategies for Young Children Drug Exposed & At Risk 1992; *cr:* St Johns 1st Grd Tchr 1966-67; St Joseph 1st Grd Tchr 1967-68; St Marys 1st Grd, Pre K & K Readiness Tchr 1968-78; St Martin de Porres Pre K & K Readiness Tchr 1978-80; St Marys 1st Grd, Pre K & K Readiness Tchr 1980-82; Lial Schl Pre K & K Readiness Tchr 1982-86; St Martin de Porres Pre K & K Readiness Tchr 1986-; *ai:* Toledo Assn for Young Children 1988-; Sister of Notre Dame 1963-; Began the 1st Readiness Prgm in Toledo Diocese 1970; Speaker at NCEA Conventions; Golden Apple Achiever Awd 1995; *home:* 1120 Horace St Toledo OH 43606*

BURGARELLI, CELINA JORDAN, Spanish Teacher; *b:* Mendoza, Argentina; *c:* Ramiro, Esteban; *ed:* Cath Univ of Santa Fe (MS) Professorship Span Lit 1970; SUNY at New Paltz (MS) MA Ed 1989; Photography 4 Cr Hrs; Cmptrs in Ed 3 Cr Hrs; Certifications From St of VA, SC, MA; *cr:* New York Military Acad Span Tchr 1984-; Sacred Heart Schl of Monroe Span Tchr 1987-; Mount Saint Mary Coll Lang Prof 1991-; Marist Coll Lang Prof 1993-; *ai:* Yrbk Photographer; Fac Friend Adv; *office:* New York Military Acad 96 Academy Ave Cornwall On Hudson NY 12520*

BURGATTI, JOSEPH C., Social Studies Teacher; *b:* Malden, MA; *ed:* St Anselm's Coll (BA) His 1968; Univ of NH (MA) His 1975; Plymouth St Coll (MED) Admin, Supervision 1979; Anti-Drug Curr Trng; *cr:* Southside Jr HS 8th Grd Amer His Tchr 1970, 7th Grd World Stud Tchr 1970-, Anti-Drug Prgm Tchr 1991-; *ai:* Prin Advy, Soc Stud Curr, Grading, Tracking Comms; Yrbk Adv 2 Yrs; NEA 1970-, Life Mem; NEA NH 1970-; Manchester Ed Assn 1970-, Bldg Rep 1987-90, 1994-; Save our Schls Comm 1994-; Natl Geographic Soc 1967-; Attnd 7th Annual Natl Geography Bee With St Champ; *office:* Southside Jr HS 140 S Jewett St Manchester NH 03103

BURGEI, KENNETH R., Elementary Guidance Counselor; *b:* Lima, OH; *m:* Connie M. Pohlman; *c:* Christopher, Kelly; *ed:* Findlay Coll (BA) PE 1972; Univ of Todelo Masters Degree Guidance, Supervision, Counseling 1986; *cr:* St Johns HS Bio, Sci Tchr & Boys JV Bsktbl Coach 1972-79; Menke Bros Construction Construction Supvr 1979-81; Four SEASONS Sales Dept 1982-83; Waseon HS PE Tchr, Head Boys Bsktbl Coach 1983-86; Waseon Elem St Schl, HS Guidance 1986-; *ai:* Head Boys Bsktbl Coach 13 Yrs; Summer Bsktbl Camps Supvr, Or Organizer; Intervention Comm Chprsn; Elem Stu Cncl Head; NEA, St Coaches Assn of OH 1972-; WEA 1983-; St Caspars Church Knights of Columbus 13 Yrs, Parish Cncl 4 Yrs; Division II Coach of Yr 1993; Dist 7 Coach of Yr 1992-94; *home:* 330 Cherry St Wauseon OH 43567

BURGER, JOSEPH V., Assoc Prof, School of Ed; *b:* Bronx, NY; *m:* Marsha J. Keller-Burger; *c:* Robert, Jordan, Daniel, Jamie, Cheryl; *ed:* Queens Coll (BA) Psych 1968; NY Univ (MA) Educl Psych 1971; IN Northern Univ (PHD) Human Relations 1973; *cr:* New York City Pub Schls Tchr 1968-71; Comsewogue Schls Dist Tchr 1971-75; Dowling Coll Ed Prof 1975-, Family, Individual Cnslng 1971-; *ai:* Stu Mentor; Schl of Ed Comms; AFT, NYSUT 1968-; Assn NYS Edctrs of Emotionally Disturbed 1980-; DARE, Northeast Regnl Ctr for Drug-Free Schls, NYS Impartial Hearing Ofcr, Reclaiming Yth, Spec Ed Trng, Resource Ctr Consultant; Articles Pub; *office:* Dowling Coll Idle Hour Boulevard Oakdale NY 11769

BURGER, LINDA RICE, HS Math Teacher; *b:* Schenectady, NY; *m:* John A.; *c:* Jacob, Andrew; *ed:* SUNY at Albany (BA) Math Ed 1974, (MA) Scndry Ed 1977; *cr:* Guilderland HS Math Tchr 1974-76; Schenectady HS Math Tchr 1976-; *ai:* NYSPOAC Treas; STF, AFT 1976-; NCTM, AMTNYS 1974-; Niskayuna Reformed Church; Nom Tchr of Yr 1992; *office:* Schenectady HS The Plaza Schenectady NY 12308

BURGER, RONALD MARK, Math Teacher; *b:* New York City, NY; *m:* Elyce H. Unger; *c:* Danielle Joy, Lauren Meredith, Jeffrey Russell; *ed:* Queens Coll (BA) Math, Ed 1970, (MA) Math 1973; St John's Univ (PD) Admin, Supervision 1977; *cr:* Woodside Intermediate Schl Math Tchr 1970-; St John's Univ Math Tchr 1973-85; Queensboro Comm Coll Math Tchr 1985-89; *ai:* Math Team Coach; Mentor Tchr; Math Tutor; Temple OR Elohim 1988-, Trustee, Sec 1992, Treas 1994; Tchr of Yr 1986; Arista Soc Honorary Mem 1985; Instituted HS Level Courses at Intermediate Schl 1980; *office:* Woodside Intermediate Schl 46-02 47th Ave Woodside NY 11377*

BURGESS, CRAIG EDWARD, Spanish Teacher; *b:* Camden, NJ; *ed:* Rutgers Univ (BA) Foreign Lang, Span, Ger 1967; Univ of PA (MS) Ed 1971; Natl Univ of Mexico Summer Sessions 1965; *cr:* Univ of PA Tchng Fellow, Span 1967-68; Cherry Hill HS East Span Tchr 1968-94, Foreign Lang Chprsn 1970-76; CCREA Pres 1995-; *ai:* Adopt-A-Grandparent Adv; Foreign Lang Lit Soc Founder & Adv; Passport Lit Magazine, Span Club Adv; NEA, NJEA 1968-; AATSP 1974-; ACTFL 1991-; Home & Schl Assn 1968-, Fac Rep 1991-; Haddon Heights Jaycees 1975-78; Intnl Soc of Poets 1991-, ISP Advy Panel, Lifetime Mem; Deputy Gov ABIRA 1995-; IBA Lifetime Mem; Pres AHS Alumni Assoc 1994-; Facilitator Audubon Poets 1995-; Audubon Lions' Club 1995-; Excl in Tchng of Modern Western European Lang Awd Johns Hopkins Univ 1991; Stu Govt Assns Outstanding Contributions to Schl & Comm 1991; Prof Reviewer of Educl Material 1991; Passport Magazine Fac Adv 1990-; NJ Assn of Hlth Care Facs Vol of Yr 1993; Pub 3 Collections of Poetry 1989, 1994, 1996; pub handbook on Adopt A Grandparent Prgm; *office:* Cherry Hill HS East 1750 Kresson Rd Cherry Hill NJ 08003

BURGESS, GILBERT G., 5th Grade Teacher; *b:* New Brunswick, NJ; *ed:* Monmouth Coll (BS) Elem Ed 1971; Trenton St Coll (MED) Elem Ed 1977; Early Chldhd Ed Admin, Supervisory Cert; *cr:* Hamilton Schl 3rd Grd Tchr 1971-72; Washington Schl 6th Grd Tchr 1972-83; Stelton Schl 4th Grd Tchr 1983-84; Martin Luther King Elem Schl 5th Grd Tchr 1984-; *ai:* Exec Bd Outdoor Environmental Educl Prgm; NEA, NJ Ed Assn, Middlesex Cty Ed Assn, Edison Twp Ed Assn 1972-; City of Hope 1993-, Educl Outreach; Article on Process of Decision Making; *office:* Martin Luther King Elem Schl Tingley Ln & Inman Ave Edison NJ 08820

BURGESS, N. JEAN BADIDA, 5th Grade Teacher; *b:* Spangler, PA; *m:* Ronald E.; *c:* Nicole, Bradford; *ed:* Caldwell Coll for Women (BS) His, Ed 1969; William & Mary One Half of Masters Ed 1970-72; *cr:* Bruton Heights Schl Grds 5 & 6 1969-72; Sickles Schl Grds 6,5,4,3 GATE 1972-95;Knollwood Schl Grd 5 Tchr 1995-; *ai:* Co-Head of Children of Alcoholics Grds 4-8; Personal Intervention for Acad Failing Stdnts; Grd Group Chm; Williamsburg James City Co Ed Assn 1969-72, Sec, Elected to Outstdng Amer Tchrs; Fairhaven Tchrs 1972-; Assn Cty Assn, NJEA; Elected to Outstdng Amer Tchr; Governor Florio's Outstdng Tchr Recognition Awd 1990; *office:* Knollwood Schl Hance Rd Fair Haven NJ 07704

BURGESS, NORMAN JOSEPH, 7th Grade Social Studies Tchr; *b:* Claremont, NH; *c:* Michael, Kerri; *ed:* Univ of NH (BA) His 1967; Continuing Stud at Rivier Coll; *cr:* Temple Street Schl 5th Grd Tchr 1967-75; Elm Street Schl 7th Grd Tchr 1976-; *ai:* AFT 1967-.

BURGESS, TERENCE DANIEL, Health & Science Teacher; *b:* Massena, NY; *m:* Kathleen O'Brien; *c:* Anthony, Michael, Sam; *ed:* Jefferson CC (AS) Math, Sci 1972; SUNY at Cortland (BSE) Hlth 1974; 30 Hrs Post Grad; *cr:* St Anthony's 5-8th Grd Sci Tchr 1974-76; Immaculate Heart Cntrl HS Hlth, Sci Tchr 1976-; *ai:* Dean of Men; Faith Comm Svc Prgm; Mystery Players; Women's Soccer Coach; NSCAA 1985-; ASHA 1993-; NCEA 1976-; Jefferson Cty Yth Bureau Awd; NY St Coaches Assn Hon Awd; Franklin Life Natl HS Coaching Awd; *office:* Immaculate Heart Central HS 1316 Ives St Watertown NY 13601

BURGHART, MARGARET D., Theology Teacher; *b:* Philadelphia, PA; *m:* Peter H.; *c:* Peter M., Megan E., Katherine E.; *ed:* St Josephs Coll (BS) Elem Ed 1974; St Charles Seminary (MA) Rel Stud 1989; *cr:* Notre Dame De Lourdes Fourth-Sixth Grd Tchr 1970-73; Natavity of Our Lord Dir of Rel Ed 1986-90; Little Flower HS Theology Tchr 1994-; *ai:* Respect Life Club Adv; NCEA, NCCL, NCDD 1986-; Booklet Pub Saints Summaries of Their Lives.

BURGIN, GEORGIANNA RANSOM, 5th Grade Teacher; *b:* Walton, NY; *m:* Marc; *c:* Brett, Miranda, Keith; *ed:* Oneonta Univ (BS) El Ed, Sci 1975, (MS) El Ed 1979; Critical Skills Trng; Cooperative Learning; Whole Lang; *cr:* Franklin Cntrl Schl 4th-6th Grd Tchr 1975-; *ai:* Created, Directed Elem Drama Club 5 Yrs; NEA 1975-; Compact for Learning Team 1993-; Cub Scout 1989-, Chprsn; Stone Hall Comm 1982-, Co-Chprsn; Sunday Schl Tchr 1987-; *office:* Franklin Central Schl Institute St Franklin NY 13775*

BURGINIA, NOREEN SACK, 4th Grade Teacher; *b:* Amsterdam, NY; *m:* James; *c:* Michelle, Jenny; *ed:* Wilkes Univ (BA) Elem Ed 1981; 24 Credit Hrs Permanent Cert; *cr:* St Jude Schl Tchr 1995-; *ai:* Mission Moderator; NCEAA 1982-; *office:* Saint Judes Schl 422 S Mountain Blvd Mountain Top PA 18707

BURGIO, LINDA D., Kindergarten Teacher; *b:* Albion, NY; *w:* Emanuel (dec); *ed:* SUNY at Brockport (BS) Elem Ed with Early Chldhd Emphasis 1968; Addl 30 Credit Hrs; *cr:* Waterport Elem Schl Kndgtn Tchr 1968-89; Albion Primary Schl Kndgtn Tchr 1989-; *ai:* AFT 1975-; *office:* Albion Primary Schl 324 East Ave Albion NY 14411

BURGOS, PETER J., Spanish, French Teacher & Adv; *b:* Bronx, NY; *ed:* SUNY at Brockport (BA) Span & Fr with Interdisciplinary Concentration in Multicultural Topics 1982; SUNY at New Paltz (MS) Scndry Span Ed 1994; Attnd Inst Fenix, Univ de Grenoble; *cr:* United Nations Information & Reception 1982-85; Realatron Realty Real Estate Mgr 1985-86; Strober King Hardware Sales Mgr 1986-89; Washingtonville Cntrl Schl Dist Tchr 1989-; *ai:* Sr Class Adv; Cnslr: Trip to Canada 1991, Trip to Spain & France 1993, Trip to Mexico 1994, Trip to PR 1995, Trip to Costa Rica 1996; Pit Musician in Musicals: Annie 1991, Grease 1992, Lil Abner 1993, Anything Goes 1994, Joseph & the Amazing Technicolor Dreamcoat 1996; Washingtonville Tchr Assn 1989-, Tchrs Views Ed; AFT 1989-; NYSUT 1989-; *office:* Washingtonville HS 54 W Main St Washingtonville NY 10992

BURIC, DANIEL ANDREW, Biology Teacher; *b:* Mc Keesport, PA; *m:* Rose; *c:* Michael, Melissa; *ed:* Edinboro Univ (BS) Bio 1972; CA Univ M Equiv Bio 1975; *ai:* Cty Envirothon Adv; Boy Scout Ldr; Driver Ed Tchr; Ind Stud in Schls Greenhouse; NEA 1972-; PSEA; VEA; BSA 1984-, Cubmaster, Asst Scout Master; *office:* Yough Sr HS 98 Lowber Rd Herminie PA 15131

BURK, JOHN H., Mathematics Teacher; *b:* Valencia, PA; *m:* Catherine R.; *c:* Melinda, Tim; *ed:* Slippery Rock Univ (BED) Math 1964; Univ Pittsburgh (MED) Math 1970; *cr:* HS Connlaut Lake Math Tchr 1964-67; Deer Lakes HS Math Tchr 1967-; *ai:* Math Dept Head; *office:* Deer Lakes Schl Dist Po Box 10 Russellton PA 15076

BURKARD, JOHN J., Bible Teacher; *b:* Brooklyn, NY; *m:* Barbara Ann Schmitz; *c:* Ken, Jessica; *ed:* Wagner Coll (BS) Math 1963; Rutgers Univ (MS) Math 1965; *cr:* IBM Various Sales & Mgmt Positions 1968-79, Branch Mgr 1980-91, General Mgr 1991; Dayton Chrstn Schls Asst Supt, Bus, Dev & Bible Tchr 1991-; *ai:* NHS Adv; ACSI Intnl 1991-; Dayton Engr Club 1985-, Bd of Governors; *office:* Dayton Chrstn Schls Inc 325 Homewood Ave Dayton OH 45405

BURKE, AARON HERBERT, Retired Teacher; *b:* Portland, ME; *m:* Ellen; *c:* Anita, Melissa; *ed:* Univ of ME (BS) Ed 1961; Univ of So ME (MS) Admin; *cr:* Lewistown MS Tchr, Team Ldr 1962-94; *ai:* MEA 1962-, LEA Rep; NEA 1962-.

BURKE, BARBARA A., Soc Studies Tchr & Act Coord; *b:* Scranton, PA; *m:* James D. Sr.; *c:* Anne, James Jr., Theresa, Joseph; *ed:* Immaculata Coll (BA) His 1966; Grad Credits Cnslng Pysch, Amer His; *cr:* Bishop Conwell HS Soc Stud Tchr 1966-68; St Basil Acad Soc Stud Tchr, Acts Coord 1988-; *ai:* Frosh Moderator; Acts Coord; NCEA 1988-; Woodrow Wilson Prgms; *office:* St Basil Acad 711 Fox Chase Rd Jenkintown PA 19046

BURKE, BARBARA KUSEK, Teacher of the Gifted; *b:* Warwick, NY; *m:* Robert J.; *c:* Christopher R., Corey P., Bryan C.; *ed:* Cntrl CT St Univ (BS) Eng 1970; Southern CT St Univ (MS) Gifted Ed 1988; Cntrl CT St Univ British Lit 6 Yrs; Educl Admin Univ of Hartford; *cr:* New Britain HS Eng Tchr 1970-78, Tchr of Gifted 1978-; *ai:* NBFT, AFT 1970-, Bldg Rep; Rho Delta Kappa 1976-; *office:* New Britain HS 110 Mill St New Britain CT 06051

BURKE, BARBARA RAMSEY, History Teacher; *b:* Albuquerque, NM; *m:* Edward Joseph III; *c:* Ramsey; *ed:* Vanderbilt Univ (BA) His 1971; Univ of Sydney (MA) European His 1981; *cr:* Boude Story Jr HS His Tchr 1974-75; Ursuline Acad His Tchr 1976-78, Vice Prin 1977-78; Salesianum Schl His Tchr 1988-; *ai:* START Team; Peer Cnslrs Spon; Spirituality Commission Chprsn; Music Ministry Team; NEA; AP Fac Consultant-Reader; *office:* Salesianum Schl 1801 N Broom St Wilmington DE 19802

BURKE, BARBARA S., Fifth Grade Math Teacher; *b:* Newark, NJ; *ed:* Seton Hall Univ (BS) Elem Ed 1968; Kean Coll of NJ (MA) Elem Tchng Processes 1975; K-12 Math Cert 1986; Rutgers Univ Ldrshp Prgm in Discrete Math 1993-94; *cr:* Woodrow Wilson Schl #19 3-4, 6 Grd Tchr 1968-78; William F. Halloran Schl #22 4-6 Grd Tchr 1978-; *ai:* Club Adv; GATE Advy, Mini-Stud Comm; NJEA, NEA, UCEA, EEA 1968-, Recording Sec 1973; AMTNJ 1988-; NCTM 1993-; St Mary's Food Pantry Vol 1991-; 1989 Governor's Tchrs Recognition Prgm; 1993 Edward F. Kappy Outstdng Edctr Awd; 1992 Honorable Mention NJ St Dept of Ed Presidential Awds Excl Sci, Math; *office:* William F. Halloran Schl #22 447 Richmond St Elizabeth NJ 07202

BURKE, CARLOS ALVINO, Mathematics Teacher; *b:* Philadelphia, PA; *m:* Lynda Donaldson; *c:* Carlos Jr.; *ed:* Cheyney Univ (BS) Math Ed 1975; Rowan Coll of NJ (MS) Math Ed 1993; Cert Supervision Math Ed 1993 Cheyney Univ; *cr:* Phila Schl Dist Math Tchr 1975-; Amer Fnd Negro Affairs Math Tchr 1982-94; Gloucester Cty Coll Math Instr 1994-; *ai:* Bsktbl, Bsbl Coach; Algebra Transition Project Team Participant; AFT, PFT, NCTM 1975-; Eisenhower, Paths-Prism Grant Awds; Dev Seminar.

BURKE, CAROL CONNOLLY, Fourth Grade Teacher; *b:* Scranton, PA; *m:* William V.; *ed:* Marywood Coll (BA) Elem Ed 1961; Univ of Scranton (MS) Elem Ed 1965; *cr:* Garfield Elem Schl 4th Grd Tchr 1961-65; John F. Kennedy Elem Schl 3rd-4th Grd Tchr 1965-; *ai:* NEA, PSEA, SEA 1961-; MU Chpt Delta Kappa Gamma 1966-, VP; Scranton Women Tchrs 1961-, VP; Marywood Seminary Alumni 1957-; Marywood Coll Alumni 1961-, Natl Pres; St Joseph's Ctr Auxiliary 1968-, Bd Mem; North Pocono Comm Ed 1992-, Cncl Mem; Marywood Coll Mentor Prgm; *offic* Kennedy Schl Prospect Ave & Saginaw St Scranton PA 18505

BURKE, DONALD ROBERT, Director of Bands; *b:* Norwich Jacqueline Gimson; *c:* Erin; *ed:* Duquesne Univ (BS) Music Ed Hrs Grad Credits at SUNY at Binghamton, St Univ Coll at Westchester Univ; *cr:* Mount Upton Cntrl Schl Music Dir Norwich HS Dir of Bands 1981-; *ai:* Brass Choir, Woodwi Percussion Ensemble & Marching Band Dir; Ret Jazz Ens Dir; NE NYSSMA 1976-; MENC 1976-; Lions Club 1976-; C Performances with Various Ensembles Over Past 21 Yrs; Served Conductor for Numerous Cty & Comm Music Festivals; *office:* HS Midland Dr Norwich NY 13815*

BURKE, DONNA L., Sixth Grade Math Teacher; *b:* Philadelphi John Edward; *c:* Adam, Jared; *ed:* West Chester St Coll (BS) 1974; Fairleigh Dickinson (MA) Human Dev 1982; 15 Addl Cr Belhaven Ave Schl Fifth Grd Self Contained Tchr 1974-82, Sixth Tchr 1983-; *ai:* NEA, NJEA, LEA 1974-; United Meth Women 19 Cub Scout Pack # 25 1993-, Treas; NJ Governor's Tchr Recogni 1994; *home:* 6 Saddle Ridge Ln Egg Harbor Tp NJ 08234

BURKE, DOROTHY R., High School English Teacher; *b:* Pate *ed:* Glassboro St Coll (BA) Comm 1986; Eng Cert 1988; *cr:* A. P. HS Eng Tchr 1988-89; Sacred Heart HS Eng Tchr 1989-; *ai:* New Class Adv; Bsktbl, Sftbl, Tennis Coach; Eng Tutor; NCTE, SCT NJISA 1988-, Coach; NJ Prof Umpires Assn 1983-, Umpire; Loc Teams News Articles Pub; *office:* Sacred Heart HS North Vineland NJ 08360

BURKE, ELIZABETH, HS Special Education Teacher; *b:* Flush *ed:* Siena Coll (BA) Eng 1988; SUNY at Albany (MS) Spec Ed 1 of St Rose Admin; *cr:* Shaker Jr HS Spec Ed Tchr 1990-91; Shaker Ed Tchr, Var Vlybl Coach 1991-; *ai:* Var Vlybl Coach; Spec Ed, At Comms; AFT, NCTA 1991-; USA Vlybl 1995-; AVCA 1992-; *offic* HS 445 Watervliet Shaker Rd Latham NY 12110

BURKE, FLORENCE LEE, Retired Latin Teacher; *b:* New York Pembroke Coll (BA) Classics 1956; Temple Univ (MED) Scndry *cr:* Sayre Jr HS Latin Tchr 1959-61; Atlantic City HS Latin Tchr

BURKE, JACK OLLIE,JR., Soc Stud & World His Tchr; *b:* B MD; *m:* Frances Charlotte Hambleton; *c:* Kathryn, Ashley; *ed:* F St Coll (BS) Soc Stud, His 1977; Attnd Johns Hopkins Univ, Un at College Park, Taft Inst of Amer Pol, Salisbury St Coll; *cr:* Moun HS Soc Stud Instr 1977-78; Hammond HS Soc Stud Instr 1978-; *ai* Interdisciplinary Team Chair; Var Bsktbl, JV Ftbl, Var Sftbl Coa Fantasy War Games Club; Vice Chair Stu Awds Comm; NEA NCEA 1977-, Bldg Rep; NCSS 1981-; St Annes Episcopal Chur Vestry; Howard Cty Talent Contest Cert of Appreciation; Baltin Howard Cty Coach of Yr 1989, 1993; *office:* Hammond HS 8800 Rd Columbia MD 21046

BURKE, JAMES VINCENT, High School Counselor; *b:* Sayre *ed:* Rutgers Coll (BA) Eng 1962, (MA) Eng 1963, (MED) Co Psych 1974, (EDD) Philosophy of Ed 1976; *cr:* Rutgers Coll Asst Stdnts 1968-70; Middlesex Cty Democratic Party Exec Dir Woodbridge Sr HS Cnslr 1971-73; East Brunswick Schls Cnslr 1 HS Hum, AP European His, Politics Class Lecturer; NJEA, NE Natl Assn Coll Admissions Cnslrs, NJ Assn of Coll Admission 1989-; Irish Amer Unity Conf 1983-; Sayreville Democratic Part Natl Democratic Comm 1970; Middlesex Cty Democratic Party 19 Dir; Doctoral Thesis, Numerous Articles, Letters Pub; *offi* Brunswick HS 380 Cranbury Rd E Brunswick NJ 08816

BURKE, JOAN A., English Professor; *b:* Ogdensburg, NY; *m:* F Yandon; *ed:* SUNY at Oneonta (BA) His 1966, (MA) Eng 1972; MD at Coll Park (PHD) Eng 1991; *cr:* Stamford Cntrl Schl E 1966-85; Univ of MD Eng, Master Tchr 1985-90; Georgetown U Instr 1990-91; SUNY at Fredonia Asst Eng Prof 1991-; *ai:* Pro Sv Eng Ed Comm Chair; Coll Comm for Womens His Month Mem; A Kappa Phi 1991-; NCTE 1970-; Sigma Tau Delta 1985-; Woodrov Natl Fellow 1990; Grad Sch, Research Fellow 1989-90; Prof D 1992; Scholarly Act Grant 1994; Pub Poems, Articles; *office:* S U At Fredonia Central Ave Fredonia NY 14063

BURKE, JOHN ANTHONY,III, English Teacher; *b:* Fall River, Robbie Morgan; *c:* Julie Ann Reitzas, Morgan Reitzas; *ed:* Elm (BA) Eng Lit 1975; Bridgewater St Coll (MAT) Eng; 24 Hrs Post G Theater & Drama; *cr:* Joseph Case Jr HS 7th & 8th Grd Eng Tch *ai:* MA Tchrs Assn, NEA 1973-; Swansea Tchrs Assn 1973-, Ne NCTE 1980-; Fall River Little Theatre 1973-, Actor, Dir, Moss H 1987; *office:* Joseph Case Jr HS 195 Main St Swansea MA 02777

BURKE, JORENE F., Learning Disability Specialist; *b:* Stamba *m:* Michael J.; *ed:* Northlan Coll (BA) Eng, Fr Sec Ed 1966; Stritch (MA) Learning Dis, Spec Ed 1981; Jersey City St Coll Resources 3 Credit Hrs; Georgian Court Coll Admin of Woodcock- Psychoed Battery Rev 3 Credit Hrs; Kean Coll Rdng Disabilities Hrs; *cr:* Ocean County Coll Learning Disab Specialist 9 Yrs; Mi Pub Schls LD Tchr 7 Yrs; Cedarburg HS LD Tchr 2 Yrs; DePere HS 7 Yrs; *ai:* Curr, Recruitment Comms; Speakers Bureau; NJ L Consultant Assn 1990-; Assn on Higher Ed & Disabilities, Cnc Children 1988-; NJEA, NEA 1992-, Sec, Treas; Brielle Learning C Bd 1990-; 2 Articles Pub; *office:* Ocean County Coll PO Box 2001 Dr Toms River NJ 08754*

BURKE, MARGARET CONNARTON, Fourth Grade Teac Medford, MA; *m:* Michael; *c:* Kimberly, Lisa, Christopher; *ed:* B Coll (BS) Elem Ed 1975; Univ of MA (MA) Critical & Creative T 1992; *cr:* Malden Pub Schls Tchr 1976-77; St Patrick Schl Tchr Stoneham Pub Schls Tchr 1988-; *ai:* Great Books Club Ldr; M Assessment Pgm Ldr-Scorer; Tchr Asst Team Mem; Lead Tchr Group Wkshp Ldr; Melrose Dev Pgm Wkshp Presenter; NEA Stoneham Drama Wkshp Dir 1980-87; Article Pub, MA Tchr of the 1995; *office:* Central Elem Schl 25 William St Stoneham MA 021

BURKE, MARILYN J. KEARNEY, Social Studies Teacher; *b:* E IL; *m:* Edward D.; *c:* Dennis, Erin; *ed:* Univ of MA (BA) His 1 East Longmeadow HS Soc Stud Tchr 1986-; *ai:* Key Club & Close- Adv; Clinical Site Pgm Comm; NEA 1986-; E Long Ed Assn 19 Alpha Theta His Honor Soc; Previous Whos Who Selection Dedication 1992; *office:* East Longmeadow HS 180 Maple Longmeadow MA 01028

BURKE, MARY CLARE, Mathematics Teacher; *b:* New York, Robert J.; *c:* Robert, Stephen, Clare Marie; *ed:* Hunter Coll (BA) 1966; Hofstra Univ (MS) Ed 1978; Addl 45 Credits Past MS Ed, M of CT, St Johns Univ, Nassau CC, LIU Cw Post; *cr:* P.S. 111 Q Tchr 1985-87, 6th Grd Tchr 1987-88; Acad for Intellectually Gifte 122 Q 6th-8th Grd Math Tchr 1988-; *ai:* Chess Club Adv; Prep Graders to Take SAT Through Johns Hopkins Univ Ctr for Talent AFT 1987-; UFT 1985-; NCTM 1990-; NYS Rdng Assn 1988-; Cat Assn 1988-, Del; Three Yr Flwshp Awd NSF to Stud Stan of 1990-93; *office:* Acad for Intellectually Gifted 21-21 Ditmars Blvd NY 11105

BURKE, MARY KATHLEEN, Social Studies Dept Chair; *b:* Prov RI; *ed:* RI Coll (BA) His 1971; Providence Coll (MA) His 1981, (P

: St Mary's Acad of Visitation Tchr 1971-76; Cranston-Johnston :hr, Soc Stud Coord 1976-86; St Raphael Acad Tchr, Dept Chair i: Moore Scholars Mentor; RI, Amer Historical Socs; Presidency ; NCEA; Providence Journal Bulletin Grant; *office:* St Raphael 3 Walcott St Pawtucket RI 02860*

, MARY L., 2nd Grade Teacher; *b:* Sharon, PA; *m:* David W.; *ed:*) Univ (BA) Ed 1967, (Masters) Ed 1970; *cr:* Mars Area Schl Dist Tchr 1967-69; West Middlesex Area Schl Dist 2nd Grd Tchr 1969-; 1967-; PSEA 1967-; WMEA 1969-, Sec; Tchrs Excl Awd 1987; 'est Middlesex Area Schl Dist 3591 Sharon Rd West Middlesex PA

, MARY ANNE MC CONNELL, Second Grade Teacher; *b:* phia, PA; *m:* Leo Joseph Jr.; *c:* Mary Anne, Christine, Leo III; *ed:* PA (BS) Elem Ed 1961; Villanova Univ (MS) Lib Sci 1968; 30 rs; Post Grad Stud in Ed; *cr:* Centennial Schl Dist Kndgtn, Grd 4 51-65; Abington Schl Dist Librn, Grd 2 Tchr 1969-; *ai:* NEA, 61-; AEA 1969-; *office:* Glenside-Weldon Elem Schl 423 N Easton side PA 19038

, MICHAEL J., Mathematics Teacher; *b:* Bronx, NY; *ed:* OCCC th 1972; SUNY New Paltz Math (BA) 1976, (MA) 1977; 8 Addl ad Credits SUNY Binghamton & Cornell Univ; *cr:* SVSD Math 77-; Bing SD Summer Schl Math Tchr 1990-; *ai:* Boys Var, Girls s Coach 10 Yrs; Ski Club Adv 19 Yrs; Section IV Tennis Coord 1 1977-; NYS Cmptrs & Tech in Ed Presenter.

, MICHAEL STEPHEN, Speech & Publications Teacher; *b:* OH; *m:* Jane Elizabeth Bayles; *c:* Timothy, Billy; *ed:* The Defiance) Eng & Speech Ed 1974; Eastern MI Univ (MA) Commncntn & ress 1975; Attnd Drake univ, Hamline Univ; *cr:* Napoleon HS Eng, & Jrnlsm Tchr 1975-; *ai:* Head Boys & Girls Tennis Coach; Girls sktbl & Speech Team Coach; Newspaper Adv; OHSSL 1975-, Dist NEA & OEA 1975-; Napoleon Fac Assoc 1975-; OH Tennis Assoc 1978-, Pres; SCAO 1980-; GLIPA 1980-; Elks 1980-; is Articles Pub; Prof Speaker at Clinics & Confs; Alumni Coach fiance Coll; *office:* Napoleon HS 701 Briarheath Dr Napoleon OH

, PATRICK MICHAEL, Dir of Physical Ed & Athletics; *b:* t, NY; *m:* Rebecca M. Bernat; *c:* Andrea, Bridgette, Lindsey; *ed:* Brockport (BA) PE 1980; Niagara Univ (MA) Educl Admin 1988; min Supvr 1989; Schl Dist Admin 1993; *cr:* Barker Cntrl SChl PE h Dir 1983-88; Medina Cntrl Schl Ath Dir, Asst HS Prin 1988-95; City Schl Dist PE, Ath Dir 1995-; *ai:* Boys & Girls Var Bsktbl, ol, Sftbl Coach; AP, Stu Govt Adv; AFT, NYS Tchrs Assn 1983-; n Admin Assn 1984-; SAANYS 1992-; Medina Parks, Orleans Co Rec Comm 1989-; Bsbl Coach of Yr; Womens Sports Fnd Grant *fice:* Lockport City Schl Dist 250 Lincoln Ave Lockport NY 14094

, SARAH RYAN, Sociology & Religion Teacher; *b:* Elmhurst, IL; larys Coll at Notre Dame (BA) Commnctns & Theology 1992; *cr:* HS Rel, Sociology & His Tchr 1992-95; *ai:* Head Var Vllybl Marching Band & 3-H Club Moderator; *office:* Aquinas HS 685 E Bronx NY 10457*

, THOMUS FRANCIS, History & Religion Dept Chair; *b:* MA; *m:* Kathleen Mahoney; *c:* Kaitlin Alice, James Collins; *ed:* ame Coll (BA) His 1972; *cr:* Calverton Schl His Tchr 1980-83; ndon Schl Dir of Stud 1983-87; Oak-Grove Coburn Schl Asst Head Stud 1987-90; Madeira Schl Dean of Stdnts 1990-91; The Masters ot Chair 1991-; *ai:* Bsktbl Head Coach; Field Hockey Asst Coach; 981-; ASCD 1983-; *home:* P.O. Box 1375 North Falmouth MA

, WILLIAM JOSEPH, Professor of Legal Stud Dept; *b:* ige, MA; *m:* Eva M.; *c:* Dorothy McCarthy, Ann Marie Swift, Jr., Eva M., Teresa R.; *ed:* Univ of MA at Amherst (BA) Ecs 1958; St Coll (MED) Ed 1963; Suffolk Law Schl (JD) Law 1968; *cr:* Tech Inst Instr 1961-64, Asst Prof 1964-68, Assoc Prof 1968-74; MA at Lowell Prof & Chprsn of Legal Stud Dept 1974-; *ai:* Pre-law Chprsn; MA Bar Assn 1968-; MTA 1975-; 5 Articles; 1 Instrs for Bus Law Textbook; US Army Armor 1959-61, Retired Capt 964; *home:* 37 Baniulis Rd Billerica MA 01821

:PILE, GERALD EUGENE,JR., Math, Sci Tchr & Dept Head; *b:* urg, PA; *m:* Annie Pearl Hostetter; *c:* Carol Claybaugh, Joni, Amos; *ed:* Harrisburg Area Comm Coll (AS) Math & Sci hippensburg Univ (BS) Math & Sci 1969, (MED) Math 1971; *cr:* ita HS Tchr 1969-81; Perry Chrstn Acad Supvr & tchr 1981-86; PA Labor & Industry PC Coord for Bus Research & Statistics 1986-89; irg Chrstn Schl Math & Sci Dept Head & Tchr 1989-; *ai:* Educl Comm; Church Tape, Sound & Music Ministries; Schl Supply Store :wport Assembly of God 1981-; *office:* Harrisburg Christian Schl ue Mountain Pkwy Harrisburg PA 17112

:T, GLENN ARTHUR,II, Computer Science Teacher; *b:* Roaring PA; *m:* Kim DoRee Giornesto; *c:* Glenn A. III, Lauren A..; *ed:* sburg Univ (BA) Bus Ed 1978, (MED) Admin 1980; Clemson Univ its; *cr:* Bedford HS Cmptr Sci Tchr 1981-; *ai:* Wrestling & AYSO Honor Soc Fac Cncl; Presbyn Church Bd of Trustees; Wrestling ; Drug Free Schl Comm; PAFPC, NEA & PSEA 1981-; Presbyn Bd of Teamsters 1992-, Sec; Bedford Cty Wrestling Ofcls 1975-; Bedford HS 330 E John St Bedford PA 15522*

:TT, JEFFREY O'HARA, Instrumental Music Teacher; *b:* , NE; *m:* Nancy Ann Mangel; *c:* Jessica, Alexander; *ed:* Clarion PA (BS) Music Ed 1980; West Chester Univ (MM) Music 1985; *cr:* dge Schl Dist Instrumental Music Dir 1980-; *ai:* Jr Class, Prom zz Ensembles Dir; IM Vlybl; NEA, PSEA, PMEA 1980-; BREA Rep; Blue Ridge Comm Band, Dir; *office:* Blue Ridge Schl Dist RR 20 New Milford PA 18834

:TT, RICHARD W., Social Studies Coordinator; *b:* Danville, PA; :e A. Whary; *c:* Richard W., Eric j.; *ed:* Bloomsburg Univ (BS) Ed 1965; Temple Univ (MED) Scndry Ed 1968; Attnd Univ of atic, Univ of IA, West Chester Univ, IN Univ of PA; *cr:* Lower id HS His Tchr 1965-70; Cntl Bucks HS East His & Soc Stud Coord *ai:* World Affairs Club Adv; CBEA 1970-, Bldg Rep, Sr High Rep :; PSEA & NEA 1965-; Hillown Twp Civic Assn 1975-; Grants from 1968 IN Univ of PA Geography Inst, NSF 1970 Univ of IA Scndry NSF 1972 Univ of Cincinnati Population Studies Inst; *office:* Buchs HS East Holicong Rd Buckingham PA 18912

:TT, RON L., Band Director; *b:* Tiffin, OH; *m:* Barbara Ann *c:* Aaron, Staci; *ed:* Heidelberg Coll (BM) Music Ed 1976; Toledo IED) 1976; *cr:* Tiffin Pub Schls Band Dir 1970-91; Benton, Carroll, & Oak Harbor Band Dir 1991-; *ai:* OMEA & MENC 1970-, Dist DEA & NEA 1970-; Tiffin Lions Club 1978-; *home:* 451 S Monroe n OH 44883

EY, MARILYN ELAINE, Second Grade Teacher; *b:* Warren, OH; :e Curtiss; *c:* David, Bryan; *ed:* St Univ of NY at Brockport (BA) 1973, (MA) Amer Stud 1978; *cr:* Spencerport Cntrl Schls Primary -3, 2nd 1973-; *ai:* NYSUT; *home:* 37 Berkshire Dr Rochester NY

HARDT, KATHY KENDALL, HS MH Teacher; *b:* Conneaut, OH; hew, Megan, Mackenzie; *ed:* Kent St Univ (BS) Spec Ed, Elem Ed 1976; Youngstown St Univ Kndgtn Cert 1992; *cr:* Happy Hearts Schl for Retarded Tchr 1976-81; Lads & Lasses Pre-Schl Tchr 1985-89; Boardman HS MH Tchr 1992-; *ai:* Work Lab Club Adv; Option IV Comm; OEA, NEO 1992-; *office:* Boardman HS 7777 Glenwood Ave Boardman OH 44512*

BURKHARDT, PAUL ERWIN, Dir of Adult & Vocational Ed; *b:* Hamilton, OH; *m:* Sherry Waer; *c:* Michelle Burkhardt Arnold, Kevin; *ed:* Miami Univ (BS) Bus Admin 1966; Zavier Univ (MS) Ed Admin 1968; Intnl Stud; *cr:* Hamilton City Schls Math Tchr 1966-81, Assoc Prin 1985-88, Dir of Adult & Voc Ed 1994-; Wilson Jr High Asst Prin 1982-85, Prin 1988-94; *ai:* Rotary Interact Fac Adv; Greater Cincinnati Tech Prep Consortium Mem; Greater Hamilton Chamber of Commerce Ambassador; Greater Cincinnati Yth Apprenticeship Comm; OASSA 1985-; NASSA 1985-; OH Voc Dir Assn 1994-; Hamilton Rotary Club 1994-, Fac Adv, Cert; Greater Hamilton Chamber of Commerce 1994-, Cert Awd; Pub Svc Awds: Adopt-a-Schl Pgm, PERT; Miami Univ Svc Awd; *office:* Hamilton HS 1111 Eaton Ave Hamilton OH 45013*

BURKHART, CAROL A., Science Teacher; *b:* Little Falls, NY; *m:* John M.; *ed:* St Univ of NY at Oneonta (BS) BIo Ed 1968, (MS) Bio ED 1973; St Univ at Albany (MS) Bio 1988; SUNYA Univ of Rochester Med Schl 1983; Univ Southern ME 1982; Robert Morris 1981; RPI 1979; Suny at Plattsburgh 1975; SUNY at Oswego 1971; *cr:* SUNY Albany Rsrch Asst 1986; Northeast Energy Corp Resource Agent, Solar Energy 1979-82; Elmira Coll Summer Instr 1979; St Johnsville Cntrl Coll Sci Tchr 1968-; *ai:* Sci Club Adv; St Johnsville TA 1968-, Pres, VP; NYSUT 1968-; AFT 1971-, SIGMA XI 1984-; Amer Photbiology Soc 1984-; AAUN 1981-; NABT 1972-; NSTA 1972-, Northeast ALOAL Soc 1991-; Douglas Ayres Meml Animal Shelter; Friends of Lib; FMCC Trustee; Greater Capitol Region Grants 1989-90; Honored Tchr 1988-89; Local Tchr of Yr 1988; U of Rochester 1983, DK6 1983 Schlsps; Publications 1978, 1990; USD Energy Patentee 1979; NSF Participant 1978-79, 1971; Permanent NYS Tchng; Poem Pub; *office:* St Johnsville Cntrl Schl 44 Center St Saint Johnsville NY 13452

BURKHOLDER, JON R., Math Teacher; *b:* Lancaster, PA; *ed:* Messiah Coll (BA) Math 1985; Millersville Univ (MED) Math 1991; *cr:* Grace Chrstn Schl Math Tchr 1985-88; Northern Lebanon Math Tchr 1988-; *ai:* Golf Coach; Inclusion Comm; NEA; NCTM; *office:* Northern Lebanon HS PO Box 100 Fredericksburg PA 17026

BURKHOLDER, ROGER OWEN, Orchestra Director; *b:* Salem, OH; *m:* Patricia Arlene Barnes; *c:* Kyle, Kevin; *ed:* Bluffton Coll (BS) Music Ed 1965; Bowling Green St Univ (MM) Music Ed 1976; *cr:* Lima City Schls String & Orch Dir 1965-73; Bryan City Schls Orch Dir 1973-; *ai:* Boys Tennis Coach; Pit Orch Dir; NEA, OEA, NWOEA 1965-; Lions Club 1973-, Pres; Stantons Sheet Music & OH String Tchrs Assn Tchr of the Yr; *home:* 2313 County Road 12C Bryan OH 43506*

BURKHOLDER, SUSAN RANAE, Health & Physical Ed Tchr; *b:* Millersburg, OH; *m:* Daryl Eugene; *c:* Brent Daniel, Jillian Ranae, Justine Elizabeth; *ed:* Eastern Mennonite Univ (BS) Hlth, PE 1981; *cr:* Locust Grove Mennonite Schl Hlth, PE Tchr 1987-; *ai:* Bsktbl, Sftbl, Track & Field Coach; ACSI 1996-; Forest Hills Mennonite Church 1984-, Youth Ldr; *office:* Locust Grove Mennonite Schl 2257 Old Philadelphia Pike Smoketown PA 17576

BURKHOUSE, ELLEN M., 5th Grade Teacher; *b:* Washington, DC; *ed:* Marywood Coll (BA) Elem Ed 1966, (MS) Lib Sci 1968; Attnd Lehigh Univ, LSU, Northern AZ Univ & Univ of Birmingham; *cr:* Robert Morris Schl 5th Grd Tchr 1966-; Marywood Coll Part-Time Lecturer 1968-; Wilkes Univ Lecturer 1988; *ai:* Tchr Rsrch Linker; Staff Dev In-Svc Comm; Mentor Tchr; AFT 1970-; NCTM 1990-; Jr League 1974-, Trng Chair; Skills in Scranton Grants 1991, 1993 & 1995; Dwight D Eisenhower Math & Sci Grant 1993; Local Woman of Distinction Awd from Girl Scout Cncl; Middlestates Evaluation Team Chair; *office:* Robert Morris Elem Schl 27 1824 Boulevard Ave Scranton PA 18509

BURKITT, JEFF F., Amer His & Urban Stud Tchr; *b:* Cleveland, OH; *m:* Trudi; *ed:* Cleveland St (BA) Soc Stud 1968; 30 Credit Hrs Post Grad Admin; Baldwin Wallace 15 Credit Hrs Post Grad Admin; Oberlin 5 Credit Hrs Post Grad Gen; *cr:* Cleveland Pub Schls Tchr 1967-; *ai:* Night Schl Tchr; AFT 1969-, Conference Comm, COPE; SDC 1985-; NCCC 1995-; Keoke Corp 1995-, Bd Mem; Tchr Effectiveness Trainer; Inst for Effective Integrated Ed; *office:* Martin L King HS 1651 E 71st St Cleveland OH 44103

BURKITT, LORI VULGAMORE, Fourth Grade Teacher; *b:* Chillicothe, OH; *m:* Michael Darrin; *c:* Kellyn M., Kyla A.; *ed:* Rio Grande Coll (BA) Elem Ed 1987; *cr:* Dublin City Schls 2nd Grd Tchr 1987-90; Piketon Elem Schl 6th Grd Tchr 1990-92; Piketon Jr HS 6th Grd Tchr 1992-94; Jasper Elem Schl 4th Grd Tchr 1994-; *ai:* OEA 1987-; Cotties Corner Church 1983-; *office:* Jasper Elem Schl 3185 Jasper Rd Box 51 Jasper OH 45642*

BURKLUND, VIRGINIA BEDELL, Retired Elementary Teacher; *b:* Freeport, NY; *m:* Carl Edwin; *c:* Bradford G. Leach, Jeffrey W. Leach; *ed:* Cedar Crest Coll (BS) Home Ec 1949; Adelphi Univ (MA) Ed 1969; 30 Credit Hrs Post Grad Stud; *cr:* Kings Point Cntry Day Schl 3 Yr Old Asst Tchr 1963, 3 Yr Old Tchr 1964-65; Guggenheim Schl Elem Tchr 1967-89; *ai:* NYSUT, AFT 1969-; PWTA RE Chptr 1989-; North Shore AAUW 1954-, VP; First Church Christ Scientist 1945-, Clerk; Manhasset Bay Assn 1960-, Rec Sec; Cow Neck Historical Assn 1980-; United Presbyn Res 1992-, Bd Mem; Set Up Math Curr for Port Washington Dist; North Shore AAUW Branch LEAP Awd; *home:* 10 Lynn Rd Port Washington NY 11050

BURKOWSKY, MITCHELL ROY, Speech Pathlgy, Audiology Prof; *b:* Cooperstown, NY; *m:* Diane Benowitz; *c:* Ruth, Joel, Rena; *ed:* SUNY at Albany (BA) Eng-Speech 1952; Wayne St U (PHD) Speech 1960; U of Paris 3 Cert Fr, Phonetics; Post-Doctoral Residency U of FL Coll of Hlth Related Profs 1965-66; Several Continuing Ed Prgm in Voice Disorders, Laryngectomy, Aphasia; *cr:* Detroit Inst of Tech Speech, Fr Asst Prof 1959-61; U of ND Assist Prof, Clin Dir 1961-65; Syracuse U Audiology, Sp Path Asst Prof 1966-72; SUNY Coll at Fredon ia Distngd Svc Prof Speech, Pathology, Audiology 1972-; *ai:* HS Swimming, Diving Ofcl; UUP 1972-; Am SP, Hrng Assn 1959-, St Del 1964, Cert of Clinical Competence; SPEBSQSA 1973-, Pres, Treas; Pub Books: Teaching American Pronunciation to Foreign Students, Parents' and Teacher Guide to Autistic Children, Orientation to Language & Learning Disorders, Contemporary Voice Therapy Children & Adults, Several Articles.

BURKS, PEGGY COLEMAN, Kindergarten Teacher; *b:* Parsons, KS; *m:* Luther; *c:* Reginald, Reigan; *ed:* Labette Comm Coll (AA) Lbrl Arts 1964; KS St Univ at Pittsburg (BS) Ed 1966; Attnd Univ of Dayton, Wright St Univ; *cr:* Dist #503 Kndgtn Tchr 1966-69; Dayton Cty Schls Kndgtn Tchr 1969-; *ai:* Kndgtn Unit Ldr; New Tchrs Mentor; Safety Patrol; DEA, OEA, NEA 1969-; South Dayton Lit Tchrs 1995-; Alpha Kappa Alpha 1964-; Order of Eastern Star 1966-; Revelation Bapt Church 1980-, Minister of Music; Dayton City Schls Tchr of Excl 1992; TV 2's Tchr of Week 1992; Impact II Grant 1993-94; MVH Grant 1994-95; *office:* Lincoln Ige Magnet Schl 401 Nassau St Dayton OH 45410*

BURLEY, CHRISTINE L. WARGO, Child Dev & Basic Foods Tchr; *b:* Windber, PA; *m:* Edward J.; *c:* Edward K., Patrick R.; *ed:* Fairmont St Coll (BED) Home Ec 1971; Indiana Univ at PA (MED) Child Dev 1974; Cert Early Chldhd Jersey City St Coll 1981; 30 Addl Credits Career Ed & Human Dev; *cr:* Cntrl Regnl HS Home Ec Tchr 21 Yrs; *ai:* Shore Shop Craftsman's Fair Coordinate Judging 15 Yrs; Ocean Co Coll Tech Prep Ed Advy Bd; NEA 1973-; AHEA, NJHEA 1974-90; PTA St Joseph Grd Schl 1986-; Monsignor Donovan HS PTA 1995-; Guest Speaker NJ Home Ec Conf 2 Yrs; Dev Child Dev Lab Curr, Implemented & Direct Nursery Schl in HS, HS Stdnts Assist Preschoolers & Plan Nursery Schl Experience 13 Yrs; Guest Speaker Voc Schl; *office:* Central Regional HS Forest Hills Pkwy Bayville NJ 08721

BURLINGAME, VIRGINIA KAY (JONES), Mathematics Teacher; *b:* Canton, OH; *c:* Jennifer Fraleigh, Janice; *ed:* Bowling Green St Univ (BS) Span, Math 1962; Ashland Univ (MS) Ed 1994; *cr:* Herbert Slater Jr HS Tchr 1963-65; Canton City Schls Sub Tchr 1966-76; Mc Kinley Sr HS Tchr 1976-; *ai:* Teen Bd; NCTM 1992-; OCTM 1987-; Order of Eastern Star 1968-; *office:* Mc Kinley Sr HS 2323 17th St NW Canton OH 44708

BURMEISTER, RICHARD, Physics & Chemistry Teacher; *b:* Ridgway, PA; *ed:* Penn St (BS) Chem Engrng 1959, (MED) Phys Sci 1963; *cr:* Glendale Jr-Sr HS Physics & Chem Tchr 37 Yrs; *ai:* Sr Class, Yrbk Staff & Class Adv; Sci Dept Head; NEA 1959-; PSEA 1959-; Coalport Lions Club 1959-, Pres & Sec; *office:* Glendale Jr Sr HS 1466 Beaver Valley Rd Flinton PA 16640

BURNASH, PETER THOMAS, Social Studies Tchr & Dept Chm; *b:* Watertown, NY; *ed:* Syracuse Univ (BA) Pub Relations, Jrnlsm 1980; St Univ of NY at Oswego (MS) Scndry Ed, Soc Stud 1992; Tchng of Sci, Tech, Soc Stud 1993; *cr:* South Jefferson Cntrl Schl Soc Stud Tchr 1989-, Soc Stud Dept Chair 1995-; *ai:* Class of 1997 Adv; AFT 1989-; NCSS 1995-; NY Palomino Exhibitors Assn 1975-, Past Pres, Lifetime Achvmt Awd 1992; Watertown Kawanis; Jefferson Cty NY Historical Assn; NYS Cncl for Hum Cert for Stud on Immigration in Amer His; *office:* South Jefferson Central Schl PO Box 10 Rt 11 Adams NY 13605

BURNE, JANET (SHARPE), English Teacher; *b:* Cambridge, MA; *m:* Alan R.; *c:* Rebecca Burne Harvey, Matthew R.; *ed:* Univ of MA at Amherst (BA) Eng 1966; Univ of MA at Boston (MA) Eng 1994; 20 Grad Credits Cmptrs, Tchng Strategies, Learning Styles; *cr:* Hale MS Eng, Rdng Tchr 1966-67; Littleton MS Rdng 1968-69; Reading Meml HS Eng 1980-; *ai:* Curr Dev Am Stud Pilot; RTA, NEA 1980-; *office:* Reading Memorial HS 62 Oakland Rd Reading MA 01867

BURNETT, BERNICE, 4th Grade Teacher; *b:* Detroit, MI; *c:* Erik Boller; *ed:* Olivet Coll (BA) Art 1959; Ball St Univ (MS) Early Chldhd Ed 1964; Attnd Eastern KY Univ; *cr:* Eastern KY Univ Lab Schl 2nd Grd Tchr 1964-67; Acad Elem Schl 2nd Grd Tchr 1967-70; Parkside Elem Schl Early Chldhd & Preschl Tchr 1974-81; Bemus Point Elem Schl 4H Grd Tchr 1981-; *ai:* Elem Ski Club Adv; Elem Planning Cncl; Stu Concerns & Dist Level Schl Improvement Comms; NEA 1959-; Chautaugua Cty Rdg Cncl 1986-; NY St Rdg Cncl 1989-; Headstart Wkshp Coord; *office:* Bemus Point Elem Schl Liberty Bemus Point NY 14712

BURNETT, ERNEST A., Instrumental Music Teacher; *b:* Miami, FL; *c:* Marvin, Rebecca Friend, Kevi, Shayna Donley, Brian Donely; *ed:* Miami Univ (BSME) Instrumental Music 1949; IN Univ (MME) Instrumental Music 1954; *cr:* Franklin Twp Schl K-12 Grd Music Tchr 1949-52; Paulding Exempted Village Schl 5-12 Grd Instrumental Music Tchr 1952-79; Oakwood Elem Schl 5th-6th Grd Instrumental Music 1982-; *ai:* NEA 1952-, Life Mem; MENC 1949-, Dist III Pres; OMEA 1949-; ASBDA 1960-; Superior Ratings at St Competitions; *home:* PO Box 187 108 N High St Oakwood OH 45873*

BURNETT, FREYA BERGLUND, VMT Instructor; *b:* Titusville, PA; *m:* Steven Paul; *ed:* Edinboro Univ (BS) Math 1973; Wilson Coll (AS) VMT 1985; Working on MS in Psych at Shippensburg Univ; *cr:* Cntrl PA Bus Schl Math Instr 1981-83; Westshore Veterinary Hosp Vet Technician 1985-86; Hershey Foods Corp Lab An Technician 1986-89; Wilson Coll VMT Instr 1989-; *ai:* Frosh, Soph & VMT Adv; Curr Comm Chair; Inst Animal Care & Use Comm; Wilson VMT Advy Bd; Vet Tech Asst Assoc of PA 1976-, Bd of Dirs, Job Opportunities & Newsletter Ed; Amer Assoc for Lab Animal Sci 1986-; NA Vet Tech Assoc 1988-, Bd of Dirs, Nominations Chair & Legal Comm; Assoc Vet Tech Edctrs 1990-; Amer Kennel Club 1979-; Dauphin Dog Club 1979-, Bd of Dirs; Helen O Kruse Animal Fndtn 1988-, Bd of Dirs & By-Laws Chair; *office:* Wilson Coll 1015 Philadelphia Ave Chambersburg PA 17201*

BURNETT, JEFFREY SCOTT, Science Teacher; *b:* Gallipolis, OH; *m:* Linda Marie Stiles; *c:* Heather; *ed:* Univ of Rio Grande (BA) PE 1986; 150 Addl Credit Hrs Univ of Dayton; *cr:* Eaton HS Sci Tchr 1986-; Warren HS Hlth Tchr 1995; *ai:* Var Track, Var Ftbl Asst Coach; SECO 1990-; OEA, NEA 1986-; First Bapt Church 1987-, Usher; *office:* Eaton HS 307 N Cherry St Eaton OH 45320

BURNETT, KAY (EGNER), Third Grade Teacher; *b:* Gallipolis, OH; *m:* Charles T.; *c:* Mary Katherine, Russ; *ed:* Morehead St Univ (BA) Elem Ed 1970; Akron Univ (MA) Elem Ed 1986; 15 Addl Hrs Elem Ed, Children's Lit; *cr:* Orville Cty Schls Rdng Tutor 1070-74, Librn 1974-81, First Grd Tchr 1981-84, Third Grd Tchr 1984-; *ai:* Lang Arts Curr Comm Level Ldr; Ed Assn of Orrville 1970-, Bldg Rep, Treas, Pres-Elect; AAUW; *office:* North Elem Schl 605 Mineral Springs St Orrville OH 44667

BURNETT, MARIAM ROBINSON, Retired Teacher; *b:* Gloucester, VA; *m:* Harold L.; *c:* Gayle Burnett Heyer; *ed:* West Chester St (BS) Elem Ed 1955; Penn St Univ (MED) Elem Ed Curr 1981; Temple Univ 20 Credit Hrs for Cert; *cr:* Wm Dick Elem Schl 2nd Grd Tchr 1955-58; David Landreth Elem Schl 1st & 2nd Grd Tchr 1959-74; Spec Assignment Inst Systems Curr Writer 1974-76; Fitler Acad Plus Schl 1st Grd Tchr 1976-87; *ai:* PFT 1975-87, Schl Rep; PASR 1990-; Alzheimers Assn 1983-, Bd Mem, VP, Pres; Natl Advy Cncl on Aging 1993-94, Comm Mem.

BURNETTE, CYKEITHIA, AP Biology & English Instr; *b:* Washington, DC; *ed:* St Augustines Coll (BS) Bio 1993; Calvary Bible Inst Working on BS; Amer Sign Lang Cert; *cr:* Suitland HS SAT Prep & Speech Tchr 1994-95, AP Bio Tchr 1994-; *ai:* Girls Vllybl Asst Coach; Daughters of Nandi Adv; Dist of Columbia Homeless Shelters Motivational Speaker; Home Church Sign Lang Interpreter; *home:* 4105 Southern Ave Apt 4G Capitol Heights MD 20743*

BURNEY, SKIP, HS Mathematics Teacher; *b:* Philadelphia, PA; *m:* Edith Randolph; *ed:* Comm Coll of Phila (AA) Math 1968; Southern IL Univ (BS) Math Ed 1971; Rosemont Coll (MA) 1993; *cr:* Reading Schl Dist Math Tchr 1971-73; Philadelphia Schl Dist Math Tchr 1977-; *ai:* Sr Tutorial Ldr; Asst Unit Head; AFT 1977-; NEA 1982-; *office:* Parkway Gamma HS 4901 Chestnut St Philadelphia PA 19139

BURNHAM, ROBERT J., English Teacher; *b:* Stafford Springs, CT; *m:* Gail B. Promboin; *ed:* Univ of MA (BA) Eng 1965; Westfield St Coll (MED) Eng Ed 1969; Syracuse Univ (MA) Jrnlsm 1976; *cr:* Westfield MS Eng Tchr 1969-71; Westfield HS Eng Tchr 1971-; *ai:* Lib Media & Tech Svcs Comm; Westfield Ed Assn 1978-, Negotiations Chair; MA Tchrs Assn & NEA 1978-; YMCA 1970-; Comm Research Articles Pub; *office:* Westfield HS 177 Montgomery Rd Westfield MA 01085

BURNHAUSER, ROMAINE BOLLINGER, Retired Fourth Grade Teacher; *b:* Palmerton, PA; *m:* James D.; *c:* Jeremiah, Rebecca Burnhauser Beidleman; *ed:* Kutztown Univ (BS) Elem Ed 1951; *cr:* East PA Schl Dist 4th Grd Tchr 1961-56, 1966-91; *ai:* PA St Ed Assn Retire, PA Assn of Schl Retirees 1991-; Monroe Cty Historical Soc 1991-; Lehigh Cty Historical Soc 1991-, Vol; Lehigh Gap Historical Soc 1991-, Restoration Comm Sec; DAR 1995-; Lehigh Vly Hosp Vol; Outstdng Tchr of Yr 1982-83; *home:* 7796 Bake Oven Rd Germansville PA 18053

BURNICH, RODGER, English Teacher; *b:* Youngstown, OH; *m:* Norma Roldan; *c:* Jeremy Scott; *ed:* Bowling Green St Univ (BS) Eng 1968; Univ of Bridgeport (MS) Eng 1972; Sarced Heart Univ (EDS) Admin 1994; Univ of Bridgeport 45 Credit Hrs Psych; Fairfield Univ 30 Credit Hrs Corporate, Pol Comm; Univ of Sarasota Candidate EdD Curr, Inst; *cr:* Cloonan Jr HS Tchr 1968-71; Rippowam HS Tchr 1971-85; Westhill HS Tchr 1985-; *ai:* Lit Review Adv; NEA 1980-; ASCD 1975-; NCTE 1985-; Stamford Tchr of Yr; First Runner Up CT Tchr of Yr; *office:* Westhill HS 125 Roxbury Rd Stamford CT 06902*

BURNS, DAWN MARIE, Business Teacher; *b:* Kenton, OH; *m:* Gordon J.; *c:* Chelsea, Logan; *ed:* Bowling Green St Univ (BA) Comprehensive Bus Ed 1985; Wright St Univ (MS) Ed 1988; Univ of Dayton Guid Cnslg; *cr:* Jonathan Alder HS Tchr, Coach 5 Yrs; Marysville HS Tchr 6 Yrs; *ai:* Newspaper Adv; OEA, NEA 1985-; AAVW 1987-93; Claiburne Meth Church Life Mbrshp; *office:* Marysville HS 800 Amrine Mill Rd Marysville OH 43040

BURNS, JAMES ARTHUR, Business Teacher; *b:* Poughkeepsie, NY; *m:* Kelly Mc Dermott; *ed:* Rider Univ (BS) Bus Ed 1971; Johns Hopkins Univ (MLA) Librl Arts 1978; 30 Hrs Fin Univ of Baltimore; *cr:* Parkville HS Bus Tchr 1971-90; Essex Comm Coll Acctng Prof 1980-; Towson St Univ Acctng, Fin Prof 1981-; Eastern Tech HS Bus Tchr 1990-; *ai:* SADD Adv; Grad Coord; Acctg Curr Chm; Sr Awds Comm; Who's Who in Amer Coll 1971; Delta Mu Delta Bus Hon Soc 1982; Outstdng Part-tine Acctng Prof Towson St Univ 1992; *home:* 947 Cromwell Bridge Rd Baltimore MD 21286

BURNS, JAMES EDWARD,JR., 5th Grade Teacher; *b:* Philadelphia, PA; *m:* Barbara Ann McPhee; *c:* Jennifer Ann, Brian Edward; *ed:* Lafayette Coll (BA) Ec 1967; West Chester Univ (MED) Cnslr Ed 1973; Temple Univ (EDD) Urban Ed 1986; *cr:* Stevens Schl 6th Grd Tchr 1967-75; Hamitlon Schl 6th Grd Tchr 1976-84; Greenfield Schl 5th Grd Tchr 1985-; *ai:* London Trip Spon 1996; Kickball Spon; Prof Bsbl Assn 1967-; PFT 1970-; PSEA 1990-; *office:* Albert M Greenfield Elem Sch 22nd & Chestnut Sts Philadelphia PA 19103

BURNS, JOYCE A., Sixth Grade Teacher; *b:* Peckville, PA; *m:* James C.; *c:* James Jr., Jason, Justin; *ed:* Bloomsburg Univ (BS) Elem Ed 1969; Masters Equivalency Plus 9 Credits; *cr:* Scranton-Hebrew Day Schl 6th-8th Grd Math Tchr 1982-85; LaSalle Acad 1st Grd Tchr 1985-88; Vly View Schl Dist 6th Grd Tchr 1988-; *ai:* Stu Cncl Act Chaperone; Rdng Comm; Peckville Bus & Prof Women 1983-, Past Pres & Past Recording Sec; NEA & PSEA 1988-; *office:* Valley View MS 1 Columbus Dr Archbald PA 18403

BURNS, KAY MARIE, Fifth Grade Teacher; *b:* Akron, OH; *m:* Robert S.; *ed:* Univ of Akron (BSEd) Elem Ed 1984; 30 Addl Hrs; Great Books Ldr Trng; *cr:* Silver Lake Elem Schl Fourth Grd Tchr 1984-85, Second Grd Tchr 1985-89, Fifth Grd Tchr 1989-; *ai:* Bldg Cmptr Coord 1988-; Cuyahoga Falls Ed Assn 1984-, Bldg Rep; OH Ed Assn, Northeastern OH Ed Assn, NEA 1984-; Cuyahoga Falls 2000 Tech Subcommittee 1992-93; Summit Cty Tech Acad 1994-95; *office:* Silver Lake Elem Schl 2970 Overlook Rd Stow OH 44224

BURNS, KIRBY L., Science & Physical Sci Tchr; *b:* Clarion, PA; *m:* Margaret J. Cooke; *ed:* Slippery Rock Univ (BS) Scndry Ed, Chem & General Sci 1983, (MA) Counseling Psych 1985; Addl 40 Credits Above Masters Post Grad Stud in Counseling, Ed & Theology; *cr:* Campus Crusade for Christ Intnl Missionary Candidate 1985-86; Slippery Rock Area Schl Dist Phys Sci Tchr 1986-; *ai:* Campus Crusade for Christ at Slippery Rock Univ Assoc Staff; Friends Against Drugs Adv, Interscholastic Track & Field Coach, Alternative Learning Ctr Coord at MS; PSEA, NEA, NSTA 1986-; Slippery Rock Alliance Church 1986-, Elder; *office:* Slippery Rock MS Keister Rd Slippery Rock PA 16057

BURNS, LAURA, 9th-12th Grd Soc Stud Teacher; *b:* Buffalo, NY; *c:* Julia Lennon, Christina Lennon; *ed:* Marygrove Coll (BA) His 1971; Buffalo St Coll (MS) Soc Stud Ed 1981; Cert of Qualification in Admin 1990; *cr:* Nardin Acad Soc Stud Tchr 1977-83; Mt St Josephs Acad Soc Stud Tchr & Asst Prin 1985-87; Immaculata Acad Soc Stud Tchr & Dept Chair 1987-; *ai:* Stu Cncl Adv; NCSS 1994-; Hamburg Cntrl Schl Bd 1988-, Pres & VP; Friends of Hamburg 1991 Chprsn; Hamburg Comm Svc Awd; *office:* Immaculata Acad 5138 S Park Ave Hamburg NY 14075*

BURNS, LYNN, Former Teacher; *b:* Toledo, OH; *ed:* Univ of Toledo (BA) Elem Ed 1972; *cr:* Walbridge Elem Schl Tchr 1972-93; *ai:* OH Theatre Vol; Toledo Fed of Tchrs, AFT 1972-; *home:* 3161 Maher St Toledo OH 43608

BURNS, MARIE T. (O'NEIL), 9th Grade English Teacher; *b:* Nashua, NH; *m:* Thomas M.; *c:* Ann M. Pelletier, Mary G. Powlowsky, Catherine L. Patten; *ed:* Regis Coll (BA) Eng 1957; Rivier Coll Grad Stud Ed; *cr:* Pelham Schl 7th Grd Eng Tchr; Spring St Jr HS 7th, 9th Grd Eng Tchr 17 Yrs; Pennichuck Jr HS 9th Grd Eng Tchr 7 Yrs; *ai:* Eng Curr Audit; Grouping Practices Comm; AFT 1972-; NCTE 1980-; New England Assn Tchr of Eng 1990-; NH Assn Tchrs of Eng 1993-; Mary A. Sweendy Home 1974-, Chair House Comm; Whos Who in The East; Whos Who of Amer Women; *office:* Pennichuck Jr HS 207 Manchester St Nashua NH 03060

BURNS, MARLENI BROWN, Social Studies Teacher; *b:* Port Lemon, Costa Rica; *m:* Garfield; *c:* Randell, Renita; *ed:* Univ of Bpt (BA) Ed 1980; 30 Addl Credits at Saint Joseph Coll 1983; *cr:* Multicultural Magnet Schl Grd I Tchr 1980-86, Grd 3 Tchr 1987-89; Grd 6-8 Soc Stud Tchr 1989-; *ai:* Native Amer Cncl 1990-, Bd Mem; Barnum Museum 1993-, Advy Comm for Kids Bridge; First Annual Statewide Mid Conf Presenter 1993; Article for Celebration of Excl 1990; Celebration of Excl Awd Project 1989; *office:* Multicultural Magnet Schl 700 Palisade Ave Bridgeport CT 06610

BURNS, MARY CATHERINE, Math, Physics Tchr, Dept Chair; *b:* Bridgeport, CT; *ed:* Hunter Coll (BA) Math 1966; Wesleyan Univ (MALS) Math 1975; Project UPDATE at Univ MA; Physics Coursework Evaluation Project; Natl Inst for Topics in Modern Physics; Lab Focus 1993; *cr:* Coyle & Cassidy HS Math, Physics Tchr 1965-; *ai:* Physics Olympics Adv; Mothers Club Moderator; NCTM 1987-; AAPT 1989-; NESAAPT 1992-, Treas; Math AP Calculus Consultant; Outstdng Contribution to AP Prgm 1990; *office:* Coyle & Cassidy HS 2 Hamilton St Taunton MA 02780*

BURNS, MARY KLEE, Supervisor of Student Teachers; *b:* Rochester, NY; *m:* John Hagerty; *c:* Jennifer Hart, Martin, Rachel, Laura; *ed:* Nazareth Coll (BS) Elem Ed 1982; St Bonaventure Univ (MSEd) Elem Ed 1995; *cr:* Imm Conception Schl 1st Grd Tchr 1956-58; Holy Rosary Schl 1st-2nd Grd, 6th Grd Tchr 1958-65; St Joseph Schl 4th-6th Grd Tchr 1982-91; St Bonaventure Univ Stu Tchr, Supvr, Adj Instr 1993-; *ai:* St Elizabeth Motherhouse Vol; Organizing Act for Infirmary Sisters; Stu Cncl Moderator.

BURNS, NOREEN CLARK, Mathematics Teacher; *b:* Salem, MA; *m:* Carey James Campbell; *c:* Clark, Nicole; *ed:* Salem St Coll (BA) Math 1971; *cr:* Georgetown HS Math Tchr 1971-82; Timberlane Regnl HS Math Tchr 1988-; *ai:* Sr Class Adv 1996; TSA Adv 1994-; AFT 1988-; *office:* Timberlane Regional H S 36 Greenough Rd Plaistow NH 03865

BURNS, RICHARD CRAIG, 6th Grade Teacher; *b:* Babylon, NY; *m:* Dorothy Rose; *ed:* Dakota Weslyan Univ (BA) Elem Ed 1970; Hofstra (MS) Elem Ed 1975; *cr:* West Babylon Jr HS 6th Grd Tchr 1970-; *ai:* Head Var LaCrosse Coach; West Babylon Tchrs Assn 1970-; Suffolk Cty LaCrosse Coachs Assn 1980-; *office:* West Babylon Jr HS 200 Old Farmingdale Rd Babylon NY 11704

BURNS, RICHARD J., Social Studies Teacher; *b:* Wilkes Barre, PA; *m:* Maria Ann Sindaco; *c:* Richard J. Jr., Tracey Ann; *ed:* Wilkes Univ (BS) Scndry Ed 1965; Univ of Scranton (MS) Scndry Ed & His 1971; Post Grad Stud Trenton St Univ, Penn St Univ, Carlow Coll & Coll Misericordia; *cr:* Montgomery Twp Tchr 1965-66; E L Meyers HS Tchr 1966-; *ai:* Natl Geographic Geography Bee Competition Coord; Long Range Planning Commission; Wilkes-Barre Area Ed Assn, PSEA & NEA 1966-; NJEA 1965; *office:* Elmer L Meyers HS 341 Carey Ave Wilkes Barre PA 18702

BURNS, STEPHEN MARK, Chem, Physics & AP Bio Tchr; *b:* Ashland, OH; *ed:* Wittenberg Univ (BA) Bio 1971; Ashland Univ (MS) Supervision 1984; Attnd Univ of Cincinnati, OH St Univ, Bowling Green St Univ, Mount St Joseph Univ, Kent St Univ; *cr:* Hillsdale HS Bio, General Sci, Advanced & Sci Tchr 1971-78, Chem & Physics Tchr 1979-, Advanced Bio Tchr 1992, 1993, Integrated Sci Tchr 1994 1995, Advanced Bio Tchr 1995-; *ai:* Cross Cntry Coach; NEA 1971-; OH Ed Assn 1971-; Hillsdale Ed Assn 1971-, Bldg Rep; Church Cncl Deacon, Sec; *home:* 758 Ellis Ave Ashland OH 44805

BURNS, TERRENCE PATRICK, English Dept Chair & Tchr; *b:* Scranton, PA; *m:* Elizabeth Corby; *c:* Rebecca C., Meghan E., Catherine G., Christopher T.; *ed:* Mt St Marys Coll (BA) Eng 1964; Univ of Scranton (MA) Eng 1973; Attnd Univ of London; *cr:* Stauton Military Acad Eng Tchr 1964-69; The Pennington Schl Eng Tchr, Eng Dept Chair 1969-; *ai:* Yrbk, NHS, Adv; Cultural Act Coord; Summer Session Dir; NJAIS; RL Church 1980-, Lector; Tchr of Yr Awd 1974; Selma Ott Awd for Outstanding Tchng 1989; Exemplary Tchng at United Meth Related Inst 1995; *office:* Pennington Schl 112 W Delaware Ave Pennington NJ 08534

BURNS, THOMAS, Social Studies Teacher; *b:* Potsdam, NY; *m:* Sheila Leone; *ed:* SUNY at Potsdam (BA) His, Sec Ed 1992; 24 Addl Grad Hrs; *cr:* Watertown HS Soc Stud Tchr 3 Yrs; *ai:* Key Club, Model United Nation Advs; Watertown Ed Assn 1993-; OP ED Article NY Tchr 1995; *office:* Watertown HS 1335 Washington St Watertown NY 13601

BURNS, THOMAS GARY, Instrumental Music Director; *b:* Danville, PA; *m:* Karen Louise Noll; *c:* Sean Thomas, Kristie Lynn; *ed:* Susquehanna Univ (BMUS) Music Ed 1973; *cr:* W Snyder HS Dir of Bands 7-12 Grd 1973-; *ai:* Stu Cncl Adv; Dir of Marching, Jazz, Susquehanna Vly Bands; PMEA Dist 8 1973-, Pres 1989-92; Phi Beta Mu 1993-; PSEA, NEA 1973-; Guest Conductor Bradford,Sullivan Cty Band; PA Music Edctrs Assn Dist 8 Pres 3 Yrs; Susquehanna Vly Band Assn Pres 3 Yrs; *office:* West Snyder HS RR 1 Box 292 Beaver Springs PA 17812

BURNS, THOMAS JAMES, English Teacher; *b:* Staten Island, NY; *m:* Kristina; *c:* Sadie Mae; *ed:* SUNY at New Paltz (BA) Eng 1988; Lehman Coll (MS) Eng Ed 1995; *cr:* Nyack HS Eng Tchr 1990-; *ai:* Lit Magazine; JV Girls Soccer; Amnesty Intnl; NCTE 1992-; NTA 1990-; *office:* Nyack Sr HS 361 Christian Herald Rd Upper Nyack NY 10960

BURNS, TIMOTHY D., English Teacher; *b:* Albany, NY; *m:* Catherine Gildea; *c:* Meghan, Brian; *ed:* St Bonaventure Univ (BA) Eng & Latin 1984; Syracuse Univ (MA) Eng 1987; Binghamton Univ (PHD) Eng 1996; *cr:* Liverpool HS Eng & Latin Tchr 1985-91; Le Moyne Coll Adj Instr 1991-; Fayetteville-Manlius HS Eng Tchr 1992-; *ai:* Prof Growth Comm; Eng & Lang Arts Curr Comm; Project Advance Cabinet Mem; NCTE 1985-; Dickens Soc 1988-; Edctr of the Yr 1988; NEH Cncl for Basic Ed Grant 1989; Eng Journal Article; Editing Work; *office:* Fayetteville-Manlius HS E Seneca Turnpike Manlius NY 13104*

BURNS, VIRGINIA ZIMMERMAN, Retired Elementary Teacher; *b:* Hartford, CT; *c:* Howard E. Bidwell, Marybeth Bender, Susan Williams, Tracy M. Bidwell; *ed:* William Jewell Coll (BA) Psych 1955; Eastern CT St Univ (MA) Early Chldhd 1972; Attnd Trinity Coll 1948, Brown Univ 1954; *cr:* US Military Schl 6th Grd Tchr 1955-56; Moosup Elem Schl Kndgtn Tchr 1969-88, Grd 1, Remedial Grd 1-2 Tchr 1989-93; *ai:* NEA, CEA, PEA 1969-, Bldg Rep, Treas; Early chldhd Edctrs 1975-; Windham Retired Tchrs Assn 1995-; Mc Sweeney Sr Cit 1995-; AARP, Women AGlow 1990-; Bapt Women of Amer Bapt Flwshp, VBS, Jr Church Tchr; *home:* 282 Gates Rd Lebanon CT 06249

BURNSIDE, WARREN LAVERNE, 7th Grade Social Studies Tchr; *b:* Salamanca, NY; *m:* Nancy Elaine Brown; *c:* Joel Mark, Jared Robert, Joelle Rae; *ed:* Houghton Coll (BA) His 1964; St Univ of NY at Geneseo (MED) Ed 1969; 9 Hrs Rdng Syracuse Univ; 9 Hrs Cmptr Sci; Elements of Instruction, Cooperative Discipline & Outcome based Ed; *cr:* Attica MS 7th Grd Soc St, Eng, Math & Cmptr Tchr 1964-; Attica Correctional Facility Remedial Rdng Tchr for Prisoners 1967; Attica Cntrl Schl GED Instr 1968; Genesee Comm Coll GED Instr 1984; *ai:* Retirement Del to NYSTRS; Fac Advy Comm; Stu Cncl Govt, Intnl Exch Group Canada & Acad Competition Knowledge Masters Open Adv; Ski Club; MS Comm of NY Cncl of Soc Stud; Testing Comm of NY Cncl of Soc Stud; Coach Vlybl; AFT & NYSUT 1964-; Attica Fac Assn 1964-, Pres & Treas; NY St Cncl for Soc Stud 1975-, Comm Mem; Attica Bapt Church 1965-, Deacon 16 Yrs & Youth Dir; Gidcon Intnl 1969-, Pres & Zoneleader; Attica Youth Assn 1984-87, Soccer Coach 4 Yrs; Attica Church Sftbl League 12 Yrs; Attica Cntrl Swim Coach 1970-; Article Pub Yesteryear Mag; Outstanding Career Svc to Youth Awd 1993 WY Cty Youth Bd; *office:* Attica Cntrl Schl 3338 E Main St Attica NY 14011*

BURO, WILLIAM MICHAEL, 6th Grade Eng & Soc Stud Tchr; *b:* Newark, NJ; *m:* Lucia A.; *c:* Ashley Christa, Vincent Patrick; *ed:* Kean Coll (BA) Elem Ed 1973, (BA) Spec Ed 1973; 12 Addl Credits Admin 1975, & 30 Credits Post Grad Stud; *cr:* Rosevelt Schl 6th Grd Tchr 1974-76, Tchr of GATE 1976-87, 4th Grd Tchr 1987-89, Eng & Soc Stud Tchr & Tchr of GATE 1989-; *ai:* Forensics Club Coach; Var Bsbl & Bsktbl Coach 1975-88; Grd Level Coord; Soc Stud Comm; Drama Dir; AFT, NEA, REA & NJEA 1974-; Natl Diabetes Assn 1974-; Monroe Cty Lib 1987-; Natl Autistic Soc 1988-; Fraternal Order of Police 1987-; Governor's Tchr Recognition Awd 1990; *office:* Lincoln/Roosevelt Schl 34 Hillside Ave Succasunna NJ 07876

BUROKER, DAWN (SPENGLER), 6th Grd Math & Phys Ed Tchr; *b:* Wauseon, OH; *m:* Waldo E.; *c:* Jessica, Tara, Alexa; *ed:* Bluffton Coll (BA) K-12 PE, Hlth 1977; Hrs Toward Scndry Math Cert 1981-81; Elem Ed Retraining 1983-84; Prof Certs Hlth, PE, Elem Ed with Math Specialty 1995; *cr:* Uppr Scioto Valley Schls Jr HS Sci, Math, Hlth, PE Tchr 1977-82; Bluffton Schls 3rd-4th Grd, 4th Grd, 6th Grd Lang Arts, Math, Jr HS Math Tchr 1984-; *ai:* Soc Comm; Bluffton Ed Assn Pres Elect; BEA Negtns Comm; Faclty Mngr; BEA 1984-, Bldg Rep, Exec Comm; OEA, NEA 1984-; OH Math League 1986-; Swim Team 1987-, Advy Comm; Et Cetera Shop, Bd Mem; Town & Cntry Mother's Club, Past Pres; Comm Nursery Schl, Past Bd Pres; St John Mennonite Church, Former Sr HS Youth Ldr; Elem, Jr HS Math Teams Awds; 6th Grd Math Team 1st Pl 4-Cty Region OH Math League 1993-95, State Lvl 1993-95; *home:* 9726 Hillville Rd Bluffton OH 45817

BURON, ROBERT W., Sixth Grade Teacher; *b:* Worcester, MA; *m:* Anne Marie Shea; *c:* John, Mary Anne, James; *ed:* Holy Cross Coll (BS) Pol Sci 1956; Worcester St Coll (MS) Ed 1962; Weather, Climate Assumption Coll; Cmptr Sci U MA; Math Sci COnsortium Amherst Coll; Sci, Internet Harvard & Smithsonian Astrophysical Observatory; NCTM Math Consortium; *cr:* Millbury HS Eng Tchr 1959; May Street Schl 5 Grd Tchr 1959-60; Petersham Ctr Schl 5, 6 Grd Tchr 1960-; *ai:* Advy Cncl; Natures Classroom Coord; Bldg Sr Tchr; MA Tchrs Assn, NEA 1986-; NCTM 1990-; U MA Med Ctr Blood Donor Group 1986-; Worcester Art Museum 1990-; Calvary Monastery 1984-, Vol.

BURR, CANDIE, Spanish Teacher; *b:* Beverly, NJ; *ed:* Univ of MD (BA) Span 2nd Ed 1973; 30 Addl Hrs; *cr:* Rollingcrest Jr HS Tchr, Dept Chair 1974-82; Northwestern HS Tchr, Chrldng Coach 1982-90; Eleanor Roosevelt HS Tchr, Chrldng Coach 1990-; *ai:* Span NHS; Feed The Children; SWAT; Cty Schl Calendar, Chrldng Comms; AATSP 19 CHrldng Coaches Assn 1995-; Concerned Women of Amer, Bo 1994-; GOPAC 1995-; Northwestern HS Coach of Yr.

BURRALL, CHARLES S., High School English Teacher; *b:* Gen *m:* Mary Bishop; *c:* Isaac, Samuel; *ed:* St Lawrence Univ (BA) E AK Bible Inst Prgm 1986; 3 Hrs Tchng Rdng on Scndry Leve Mainstreaming Univ of MD 1993; *cr:* Log Cabin Cafe Cook Thoms Marine Svc Deckhand 1982-84; Seward Fisheries Laborer Kibbutz Hazorea Forklift Operator 1987-88; Montgomery Cty P Tchr 1990-; *ai:* SAT Improvement Comm; *office:* Seneca Valley H Middlebrook Rd Germantown MD 20874

BURRELL, RICHARD STARR, 7th Grd Social Studies Teache Charlotte Hawkins; *c:* Jason, Richard Jr., Sara; *ed:* Union Schenectady (BS) Psych 1975; Nazareth Coll of Rochester (ME Ed 1980; *cr:* Cortland Jr Sr HS 7th Grd Soc Stud Tchr 1985-; *ai:* J Senate Adv; 8th Grd Class Trip Organizer; Block Scheduling Portfolio Assessment Comm; Natl Geographics; Natl Geog Bee Lo Cortland United Tchrs 1985-; NY St United Tchrs 1985-; *office:* Jr Sr HS 8 Valley View Dr Cortland NY 13045

BURRER, DARYL A., Social Studies Teacher; *b:* Columbus, Christine McElwain; *ed:* Binghamton Univ (BA) Pol Sci 1984; P Univ (MPIA) Intnl Affairs 1986; 18 Grad Hrs Ed Dowling Liverpool HS Soc Stud Tchr 1988-; *ai:* NHS Adv 1988-; A Decathlon Adv 1988-; CNYCSS 1988-; UFLA 1988-, Bldg Rep; 1989-; NYSUT; AFT; NY St Geographic Alliance 1989-, Tchr Co Grad Schl of Pub & Intnl Affairs Univ of Pittsburgh Flwshp 198 Star Awd 1992; *office:* Liverpool HS 4338 Wetzel Rd Liverpool NY

BURRIS, LYNETTE S., Choral & General Music Dir; *b:* Zanesv *m:* Jeffrey D.; *c:* Elijah, Zane; *ed:* Bowling Green St Univ (BM Voice 1983; Attnd Vandercook, Drake Univ; *cr:* Eastern Local C General Music Tchr 1983-85; Pleasant Local Choral & General M 1986-; *ai:* Show Choir, Muscial, Solo & Ensemble Dir; OMEA 1983-; ACDA 1996-; Marion Lecture Recital Club 1986-; Mari Chorus 1994-, Soloists; *office:* Pleasant Local Schls 1101 Owe Marion OH 43302

BURRIS, PAMELA JOY (KACZOR), Spanish Teacher; *b:* Norw *m:* Kenneth Jackson Jr.; *ed:* OH St Univ (BS) Span 1990; *cr:* Norv Span Tchr 1990-91; Fremont Ross HS Span Tchr 1991-; *ai:* Frgn L Adv; CEAI 1994-; OFLA 1990-; *office:* Fremont Ross HS 1100 Fremont OH 43420

BURRIS, SHEILA R., Assistant Prin & Math Teacher; *b:* Salem, Glassboro St Coll (BS) Math 1988; Rowan Coll (MA) Schl Adm Enrolled Widener Univ Doctorate Prgm Schl Admin; *cr:* Bridg Math Tchr, Asst Prin 5 Yrs, Math Tchr 3 Yrs; *ai:* Asst Girls Tenr Coach; Math Dept Co-Chair; NCTM, NASSP, NEA; Salem Cor Adjunct Fac; *office:* Bridgeton HS 111 N West Ave Bridgeton NJ

BURRITT, MARY ANN, Elementary Guidance Couns Springfield, MA; *ed:* Notre Dame Coll (BA) Ed, Psych, Soc 1972; Univ (MED) Cnslng 1974; 60 Addl Hrs Harvard Univ, MA Pharmacy, Assumption; *cr:* Westborough Pub Schls Guid Cnslr 1976-83, 1984-85, 1989-; Goffstown Pub Schls Schl Cnslr Keflavik DODDS Schl Cnslr 1983-84; Baumholder Schl Cnslr 198 SPED Chprsn; Multi-Cultural Asst; Fundraiser for UNICE Pantries; Natural Disaster Relief Funds; Schlsp Comm; Worc House, Mustard Seed Shelter; WTA, MTA, NEA, OEA 1974-; Suburban Guid Assn; MA Schl Cnslrs Assn, St Cnslr of Mon Suffolk Univ Flwshp 1972-74; NASA Tchr in Space Candidate Dept of Defense Exceptional Performance Awds 1985-89; U Poland Summer Tchr 1991; New England Multicultural Awd JFK L Anti-Defamation League A World of Difference Awd 1995; Hastings Elem Schl 111 E Main St Westborough MA 01581

BURROUGHS, LINDA SAPORITO, Learning Support Tea Warren, PA; *m:* Richard; *c:* Brodie, Jamie; *ed:* Edinboro Univ (B Ed Elem Ed 1973, MED) Spcl Ed 1992; *cr:* Warren Cty Schl Dist Tchr 1984-; *ai:* Pregnancy Support Ctr 1988-, Pres Bd of Dir Warren Area HS 345 E 5th Ave Warren PA 16365

BURROUGHS, RICHARD PHILO, 5th-6th Grade Teacher; Newbury, VT; *m:* Shirley Thompson; *c:* Richard B., Kerry White, Kendra B.; *ed:* Lyndon St (BS) ed 1963; Castleton St (MA) Ed Addl Hrs; *cr:* US Army SP4 1954-57; Readingtown Schl Prin Woodstock Elem Schl Tchr 1967-; *ai:* 10 Yr Fund Raiser St Judes C Hosp; Windsor Cent Tchr 1963-, Pres; NEA 1963-, Life Mem; N Mem; Boy Scouts Ldr; Windsor Orange Credit Union VP; Ford Fn Charter Mem Prof Standards Comm; Evaluated Masters Pgrm Cas Coll; Evaluation Team Mem VT Elem Schls, Pub Schls Approva 30 Barberry Hill Rd Woodstock VT 05091

BURROWS, JOHN W., Art Department Chairman; *b:* Providence Kathleen Denman; *c:* Brian, Jane; *ed:* Univ of MA (BFA) Paintin Attnd Coll of Santa Fe Art His 1963-64, Univ of RI, Salve Regina Coll; *cr:* Portsmouth HS Art Instr 1968-71; Newport art Museum Instr 1971-73; Portsmouth MS Art Instr 1971-90; Portsmouth H Chair, Painting, Ceramies Inst 1990-; *ai:* RIEA, NEA 1968-; Elk Exhibited Paintings; Participated in 2 Major Architectural Res Projects as Painter, Artist; *home:* 20 Park St Newport RI 02840

BURROWS, VELMA AVERY, Language Arts Teacher; *b:* Danvi *m:* James R.; *c:* Jan, Brian; *ed:* Bloomsburg Univ (BS) Eng 1972; Credits Penn St Univ, Wilkes Univ; Amer Acad Dramatic Arts Gr *cr:* Delhaas HS Lang Arts Tchr 1972-76; Cntrl Columbia HS La Tchr 1976-; *ai:* Parliamentary Procedure Coach FLBA; Occasio Forensic Team; Act 178 Prof Staff Dev Comm; Lead Tchr Coo Learning; NEA 1972-; NCTE 1976-; First Presbyn Church Sec-Pastor Nom Comm, Sunday Schl Tchr, Lay Reader; Turner Ad Learnings Electronic Field Trips, Tchr Trainer FldTrips, Onlin Presented Distance Learning Prgm PA Ldrshp Tchr St Conf; *office:* Columbia H S 4777 Old Berwick Rd Bloomsburg PA 17815*

BURSAW, NORMA KENYON, Biology Teacher; *m:* Richard C. Plymouth St Coll (BS) Bio Ed 1977; Univ of MA at Lowell (MS) 1983; 30 Credit Hrs; *cr:* Salem HS Sci Tchr 1977-; *ai:* St Environmental Action Adv; Cheer Comm Mem; NEA, NHEA NHSTA 1977-; NABT 1993-; Derry Conservation Commission *office:* Salem HS 44 Geremonty Dr Salem NH 03079

BURSI, MARIANNE MC MURRIN, Academic Resource Speci Columbus, OH; *m:* Steven William; *c:* Nicholas, Zachary; *ed:* AZ (BA) Elem Ed 1984, (MA) Admin, Supervision 1996; Gifted Endo St of AZ 1987; Sci Endorsement St of AZ 1994; Prin Cert OH 1 Chandler Unified Schls Sixth Grd Gifted Tchr 1984-85; Laveen S K-8 Gifted Coord, Instr 1985-87; Tempe Elem Schls Fifth G 1987-88, fourth, Fifth Grd Tchr 1988-89, Sixth, 7, 8 Hnrs S 1989-94; Shaker Hghts City Schls Acad Resource Specialist 1994-; Tech, Schl Recycling, Spec Events Comms; Stu Cncl Rep; Tchr in Staff Dev Cmptr Trng; Winter Lunch Clubs; Phi Delt Kappa 19 Kappa Phi 1996; National Assn for Gifted Children, OH Assn fo Children 1994-; NSTA 1990-; Best Paper Recycling Story Contest Natl Winner; Recycling Prgm, Tree Meml Mc Kemy MS; *office:* Schl 3115 Woodbury Rd Shaker Hts OH 44120*

CHRISTOPHER, Professor; *b:* Cambridge, MA; *m:* Mary Ann ; *c:* Christian, Justin, Nora; *ed:* Tufts Univ (BA) Eng 1965; Boston D) Amer Lit 1975; Warren Wilson Coll (MFA) Creative Writing Shaw Univ Asst Prof 1968-70; Buck Cty Comm Coll Prof 1971-; an Rights Club Adv; Advising Specialist; AFT 1974-; Woman's 72-, Bd of Dir, Comm Vol Svc; Bucks Cty Assn Corrections, ation Citizen of Yr; Natl Endowment for Arts 1987; Guggenheim ip Poetry 1984; PA Cncl Arts 1990; Capricorn Prize 1992; Pew ip in the Arts 1994-95; *office:* Bucks County Community Coll .d Newtown PA 18940

.IN, SHMUEAL L., Judaic Studies Teacher; *b:* New York, NY; *m:* edman; *ed:* Ner Israel Rabbinical Coll (BTL) Talmud 1978; St Univ (BS) Bus Admin 1978; Yeshiva Univ (MS) Jewish His I, Admin Post Grad Stud 1994-; Doctoral Candidate; Breuer's al Seminary Ordination 1982; *cr:* North Shore Hebrew Acad h-8th Grd Instr 1991-.*

DENNIS MICHAEL, History Teacher; *b:* Camden, NJ; *m:* Ann; *ed:* Glassboro St Coll (BA) His 1979; *cr:* Williamstown HS ub Tchr 1980-84; Eastern HS His Tchr 1985-; *ai:* Coach Asst Ftbl Head Track 1985, Asst Track 1980-; NJEA, NEA 1985-; l Military Impressions 1987-, Sec; *office:* Eastern Sr HS PO Box orhees NJ 08043

KENNETH W., Social Studies Teacher; *b:* Albany, NY; *m:* Ann Mc Mahon; *c:* Christopher; *ed:* St Univ of NY at Albany 1972; Cortland St Univ (MA) Soc Stud Ed 1981; *cr:* Holland ntrl Schls Soc Stud Tchr 1972-; *ai:* Var Ftbl Coach; AFT 1972-, , Negotiations Cncl; NCSS.

.UCILE D., English Teacher; *b:* Rochester, NY; *ed:* St Lawrence) Eng 1968; Boston Coll (MAT) Eng, Ed 1969; 30 Hrs Post Grad on Coll, Univ of MA at Amherst; *cr:* Arlington HS Eng Tchr : Lit Magazine Spon; Fac Adv Profiles in Diversity Project; NEA dctrs for Soc Responsibility 1983-, Bd of Dir 1984-87; Poems Pub; ing Wkshps for Tchrs; NEH Summer Seminars; NEH Ind Stud *ce:* Arlington HS 869 Massachusetts Ave Arlington MA 02174*

H, CHRISTOPHER JOHN, Economics & Amer History Tchr; *b:* , NY; *m:* Christine Marazsky; *ed:* Slippery Rock Univ (BA) d Soc Stud; Working Toward MA in His; *cr:* Slippery Rock Area Coach 1992-; *ai:* Girls Jr HS Bsktbl Coach; Boys Bsktbl Asst EA 1992-; Tchr of Yr 1993-94; *office:* Slippery Rock Area HS 201 .d Slippery Rock PA 16057

ETT, JAMES EDWARD, English Teacher; *b:* Hollidaysburg, PA; nia Nye; *c:* Kelly L.; *ed:* Shippensburg Univ (BS) Eng 1965, ng 1968; Western MD Coll Grad Courses, Admin for Scndry Prin nple Univ Grad Courses; PA St Univ Post Grad Courses; *cr:* Cedar Eng Tchr, Dept Head 1966-73; New Cumberland MS Asst Prin Red Land HS Asst Prin 1976-79; Cedar Cliff HS Field Experience d 1979-84; Messiah Coll Supvr of Cooperative Ed 1984-85; arg Area HS Eng Tchr, Prof Dev Coord 1986-; *ai:* Soph Class Adv; , Strategic Planning Comms; PA St Ed Assoc, NEA 1966-; MAEA *fice:* Millersburg Area HS 799 Center St Millersburg PA 17061

N, BECKY ALBERT, Fifth Grade Teacher; *b:* Landstuhl, ; *m:* James A. Jr.; *c:* Ashley; *ed:* Univ of DE (BA) Elem Ed 1985; on Coll (MS) Inst 1991; 18 Insvc Credit Hrs; *cr:* Georgetown hl 5th Grd Tchr 1985-; *ai:* PTA Pres; Soc Stud Curr Dev Comm s; Grd Level Chprsn 1985-; NEA 1985-; Harbeson United Meth Pastor, Parish Relations Comm 1995-, Sec; Order of Excl Awd *fice:* Georgetown Elem Schl 301 W Market St Georgetown DE

N, BERNADETTE NAPOLI, 5th Grade Teacher; *b:* New York , *m:* Donald Ernest; *c:* Chris, Patrick, Ronald, Jeff Steinwachs; *ed:* t Rose (BS) Elem Ed 1967; SUNY at Buffalo (MS) Rdng Ed 1971; rs Rd Schl 6th Grd Tchr 1967-69; West Jr High 6th Grd Tchr Northwood Elem 6th Grd Tchr 1975-85, 5th Grd Tchr 1985-; *ai:* Eng Cncl 1989-, Tchr of Excl 1989; Canadian Power Squadron ommander 1991-92; *office:* Northwood Elem Schl 250 Northwood Seneca NY 14224

N, JAMES J., Math Teacher; *b:* Rome, NY; *ed:* SUNY at Pottsdam th 1981, (MA) Math 1984; *cr:* Canastota HS Math Tchr 1981-84; Math Tchr 1984-; *ai:* Boys Vllybl Coach; Schl Improvement taff Dev Facilitator & Trainer; Madison Cty Childrens Camp amp Dir 1991-; *office:* VVS Cntrl HS Rt 31 Verona NY 13478*

N, JENNIFER DECELLES, Physical Education & Hlth Tchr; *b:* r, MA; *m:* Colin R.; *ed:* Springfield Coll (BS) PE 1992; *cr:* Sacred ad Ath Dir, PE & Hlth Tchr & Var Vlybl, Bsktbl & Sftbl Coach Wachusett Regnl HS PE & Hlth Tchr 1995-; *ai:* Girls Var Vlybl, Sftbl Coach at Sacred Heart Acad; Frosh Girls Bsktbl Coach; MA ssn 1995-; Womens Bsktbl Coaches Assn & AAHPERD 1992-; d Cross 1993-, First Aid, CPR, Aids Instr & WSI- Water Safety *ice:* Wachusett Regional HS 1401 Main St Holden MA 01520

N, KATHLEEN BONNER, Second Grade Teacher; *b:* Natrona PA; *m:* William Larry; *c:* Douglas, Marcy Sader; *ed:* Edinboro) Elem Ed 1967; Penn St Univ (MS) Elem Ed 1974; Addl 13 Credit otrs, Math, Sci Ed; *cr:* Pond Street Elem Schl First Grd Tchr Wood Street Elem Schl Second Grd Tchr 1969-74, Third Grd Tchr Fourth Grd Tchr 1975-76; Heights Elem Schl Second Grd Tchr *i:* Second Grd Level Ldr; Mentor for New Tchrs; Curr Cabinet; SEA, Highlands Ed Assn 1968-; BSA 1974-, Commissioner; of Presbyn Church USA 1985-, Pres; Elder of Presbyn Church USA ox-It, Bag-It Math Prgm Highlands Schl Bd Grant; *office:* ds School Dist 1415 Freeport Rd Natrona Heights PA 15065*

N, MARTHA L., Teacher; *b:* Winthrop, MA; *c:* Sherry Glascoe, *ed:* Slippery Rock St Univ (BS) Hlth, PE, Bio Sci 1960; NY cal Seminary (MRE) Rel Ed 1969; Southern CT St Univ Admin, ion, Spec Ed Prof Degree 1973; *cr:* Greenview HS Tchr 1960-62; n Chrstn Schl Tchr, Prin 1962-67; Harlem Vly St Hosp onal Therapist 1967-68; Walden Schl Tchr, Team Ldr 1968-76, n, Prin 1976-80; Mahopac Alternate HS Tchr 1980-93; Mahopac ource Room Tchr 1993-; *ai:* Bible Stud Group Spon; Women's peaker; Bible Tchr; Small Group Ldr; AFT 1980-; First Bapt 1970-, Choir Dir, Trustee; Outstdng Edctrs in Amer 1973-74, *office:* Mahopac HS Baldwin Place Rd Mahopac NY 10541

N, RAE LYNN, 8th Grade Math Teacher; *b:* Washington Crt Hou, James Dale; *ed:* Univ of Cincinnati (BA) Elem Ed 1987; Xavier slng; *cr:* Norwood MS 7th Grd Rdng Tchr 1987-90, 7th Grd Math 0-91, 8th Grd Math Tchr 1991-; *ai:* 7th & 8th Grd Vlybl Coach , Jr High, Sr High Play Stage Mgr 1992-95; NTA 1987-; NCTM *ffice:* Norwood MS 2060 Sherman Ave Norwood OH 45212

N, SHARON DELSIGNORE, Fourth Grade Teacher; *b:* Glens Y; *c:* Angela; *ed:* SUC at Potsdam (BA) Elem Ed 1969; SUNY at MA) Dev Rdng 1971; Syracuse Univ (MLS) Lib Sci 1993; Addl rad Courses; *cr:* Jackson Heights Elem Schl Tchr 1969-70; Solvay hl Tchr 1971-; Baldwinsville Pub Lib Part-time Reference Librn *i:* Schl Store; Head 4th Grd Sci; Solvay Tchrs Assn 1971-, Bldg Negotiations; NYSUT, AFT 1971-; Grants; *office:* Solvay Elem Woods Rd Syracuse NY 13209

BURWELL, BEVERLY KYLER, Adv Acad & Consulting Teacher; *b:* Baltimore, MD; *ed:* Morgan Univ (BS) Elem Ed 1967; Coppin St (MS) Ed 1977; Towson Univ Post Grad Stud 1970, 1990; *cr:* Hilton Elem Classroom Tchr 2nd Grd Tchr 1967-76, 3rd Grd Tchr 1976-86, 5th Grd Tchr 1986-87; 4th Grd Tchr 1987-95, Consulting, Advanced Acad Tchr 1995-; *ai:* Peer Tutoring; Conflict Resolution; Schl Improvement Team Mem 6 Yrs, Chair 1994-; After Schl Class Thinking Skills; AFT, NEA 1970-; Fund for Educl Excl Change Agent Grant; Hilton Elem Tchr of Yr 1990; Balto City Schl Thinking Skills Honor; *office:* Hilton Elem Schl 21 3301 Carlisle Ave Baltimore MD 21216

BURWELL, CAROLYN ROSE (HENRY), Kindergarten Teacher; *b:* Ironton, OH; *w:* Lloyd (dec); *c:* David, Karen, Nancy, Louis; *ed:* OH Univ (BA) Elem Ed 1951; Marshall Univ (MED) Early Chldhd 1986; *cr:* Dunkirk Schl 3rd Grd Tchr 1951-52; Blackfork Schl 3rd Grd Tchr 1952-53; Hanging Rock Schl 5th Grd Tchr 1954-56; Kingsbury Schl Kndgtn Tchr 1957-59; Campbell Schl Kndgtn Tchr 1963-64; Lawrence St Kndgtn Tchr 1967-; Whitwell Kndgtn Tchr 1967-; *ai:* NEA 1950-; BSA 1986-, Cubmaster; Beta Sigma Phi Rho Master 1956-, Sec; AAUW 1970-, Pres, Sec; Martha Holden Jennings Fnd Scholar Awd 1991-92; *home:* 2410 S 11th St Ironton OH 45638

BUSA, HEIDI WILSON, Science Teacher; *b:* Syracuse, NY; *m:* Steven L.; *c:* Kevan, Kathryn; *ed:* St Univ of NY Coll of Environmental Sci & Forestry (BS) Forest Bio 1980; Syracuse Univ (MS) Sci Ed 1983; Attnd Cornell Inst for Bio Tchrs 1990-91; *cr:* Fowler HS Sci Tchr 1983-91; Corcoran HS Sci Tchr 1991-92; Marcellus HS Sci Tchr 1992-; *ai:* Sci Dept Chair; Sr Class Adv; NYS Inst for Regents Bio Tchrs, NYS Inst for Sci & Math Instr; NSTA; ASCD 1993-; NYSUT 1983-; Project Learning Tree Edctr of Yr 1995; Onondaga Cty Tchrs Assn Svc Awd; *office:* Marcellus Sr HS 1 Mustang Hill Marcellus NY 13108*

BUSCH, CYNTHIA VOGT, First Grade Teacher; *b:* North Tonawanda, NY; *m:* Christopher; *c:* Megan Schasel, Zachary; *ed:* Buffalo St Coll (BS) Elem Ed 1982, (MS) Elem Ed 1992; *cr:* Lockport Cath Schls Kndgtn Tchr 1982-84, 2nd Grd Tchr 1985-86; Middleport Elem Schl Kndgtn Tchr 1986-94, K\1 Multiage Tchr 1994-95, 1st Grd Tchr 1995-; *ai:* Rdng Curr, Soc Stud Curr Comms; AFT, NYSUT 1986-; Designed, Implemented K\1 Multiage, Learning Centered First Grd Classroom; *home:* 1318 S Main St Medina NY 14103*

BUSCH, MARGARET HEMBERGER, Special Education Teacher; *b:* Orange, NJ; *m:* Dale C.; *c:* Daniel W., Michael C.; *ed:* Immaculata Coll (BA) Psych & Elem Ed 1965; Cert Tchr of Handicapped Monmouth Coll; *cr:* Pleasantdale Elem Schl First & Second Grd Tchr 1965-70; Harbor Schl Spec Ed Asst, Tchr 1979-83; Shrewsbury Boro Schl Spec Ed Tchr 1983-; *ai:* NEA, NJEA 1983-; Shrewsbury Tchrs Assn 1983-, Sec; Learning Disabilities Assn 1980-; Tchr of Yr 1992; *office:* Shrewsbury Boro Schl 20 Obre Pl Shrewsbury NJ 07702

BUSCH, RONALD J., Professor of Political Science; *b:* Cleveland, OH; *m:* Wendy Millar; *c:* T. Alexandra Kermode, Pamela Wehnes Jimenez; *ed:* Miami Univ (BA) Pol Sci 1961; Northwestern Univ (MA) Pol Sci 1962; OH St Univ (PHD) Pol Sci 1969; Attnd Philips Univ Marburg Germany, Freiburg IB Univ Germany; *cr:* IIT Research Inst Systems Analyst 1962-63; Allstate Insurance Co Systems Analyst 1963-64; Miami Univ Pol Sci Prof 1967-68; Cleveland St Univ Pol Sci Prof 1969-; *ai:* Pi Sigma Alpha, Tau Kappa Epsilon, Coll Republicans Fac Adv; Amer Surveys Polling Consultant; AAUP; OH Assn of Economist & Pol Scientists Exec Bd Mem; Midwest Pol Sci Assn; Pub Articles on Pub Opinion, Polling & Pol Parties; *office:* Cleveland State Univ 1983 E 24th St Cleveland OH 44115

BUSCH, STEVEN DANIEL, PE, Aquatics Tchr & Coach; *b:* Albany, NY; *m:* Lucille Anatriello; *c:* Stephanie; *ed:* Springfield Coll (BS) PE 1976; 30 Addl Hrs; *cr:* Chenango Forks Cntrl Schl Current 1977-; *ai:* Var Boys, Girls Swimming Coach; *office:* Chenango Forks HS 1 Gordon Dr Binghamton NY 13901*

BUSCHE, LEON FRANK, Social Studies Department Head; *b:* Elgin, IL; *m:* Alice Morrison; *c:* Karen Eileen, Susan Leigh; *ed:* The Amer Univ (BA) Govt 1967; Attnd Univ of MD, WA Coll of Law, Univ of Moscow, Cite Univ at Paris, Southampton Univ, London Schl of Ec; *cr:* T W Pyle Jr HS Soc Stud Tchr 1967-72; Amer Schl His Tchr 1972-73; T W Pyle Jr HS Soc Stud Tchr 1973-75; Ridgeview Jr HS Soc Stud Dept Head 1975-88; Quince Orchard HS Soc Stud Dept Head 1988-; *ai:* Stu Activity Spon; Grad Comm; Instructional Cncl; AFT 1988-; ACLU 1993-; Democratic Party 1964-; Parish Pastoral Cncl 1991-, Chair 1994-; Liturgical Life Cncl 1991-, Chair 1991-94; Outstanding Young Men of Amer 1975 & 1977; *office:* Quince Orchard HS 15800 Quince Orchard Rd Gaithersburg MD 20878

BUSCHTA, MARY SCHIMPF, Sixth Grade Teacher; *b:* Norristown, PA; *m:* Gary J.; *c:* Stephen, Kimberly, Mary Ann, Jacqueline, Michael; *ed:* St Josephs Coll (BS) Math 1974; 21 Grad Credits Permanent Cert; *cr:* Bishop Kenrich HS Math, Typing Tchr 1974-77; Christ the King Schl 5th Grd Math, Gym, Music, 8th Grd Tchr 1984-92; Allentown Cntrl Cath Math Tchr 1992-93; Christ the King Schl 6th Grd, Algebra Tchr 1993-; *ai:* Math Counts Coach; Liturgy Comm; Acad Bowl Coach; Math Coord; Diocesan Arts Comm; NCEA 1984-; PA Math Tchrs Assn 1993-; Parish Yth Group Moderator; *home:* 3234 Carbon St Whitehall PA 18052

BUSER, CATHERINE HERING, Second Grade Teacher; *b:* Baltimore, MD; *m:* Henry; *ed:* East Stroudsburg Coll (BS) Elem Ed 1976; 6 Grad Credits; *cr:* Chatham Boro Schl Dist Compensatory Ed, Math Grd 6-8 Tchr 1977; Kenilworth Schl Dist Math Title I Position 1977-78; Chatham Boro Schl Dist Rdng & Math Compensatory Ed Grds 1-4 Tchr 1978; Byram Twp Schl Dist 2nd Grd Tchr 1979-; *ai:* NEA 1978-; BEA 1979-; PTA 1979-, VP; NJ Governor's Tchr Recognition Grant; Tchr of Yr; *office:* Byram Twp Cons Elem Schl 55 Lackawanna Dr Stanhope NJ 07874*

BUSER, SALLY SCHOENBECK, Foreign Language Teacher; *b:* Cleveland, OH; *m:* Merle Franklin; *c:* Brandon Tyler, Garrett William; *ed:* Frostburg St Univ (BA) Fr Ed 1974; Masters Equivalent; *cr:* Northern HS Foreign Lang Tchr 1974-76; Northern HS Foreign Lang Tchr 1976-78; Allegany HS Foreign Lang Tchr 1981-; *ai:* Class of 97 Adv; Schl Improvement Team, Intnl Stud Prgm Bd of Dirs Mem; AATF 1974-; NEA, ACTA 1981-; Youth Group Adv 1995-; Chrstn Ed Comm 1981-; Tchr of Yr 1991-92; Presenter Current Pedagogical Topics at Cntry Wide Inservices 1981-; *office:* Allegany HS 616 Sedgwick St Cumberland MD 21502

BUSH, CHARLES A., English Teacher; *b:* Lackawana, NY; *ed:* SUC at Potsdam (BA) Eng Ed 1974; Permanent Cert; *cr:* Herkimer Cntrl Schl Eng Tchr 1974-81; Lowville Acad & Cntrl Schl Eng Tchr 1981-86; Sandy Creek Cntrl Schl Eng Tchr 1986-; *ai:* Yrbk, Soph Class, Newspaper Adv; NEA; *office:* Sandy Creek Cntrl Schl Salisbury St Sandy Creek NY 13145

BUSH, DEBORAH ANN, Fourth Grade Teacher; *b:* Defiance, OH; *m:* H. Russell; *c:* Corey, William; *ed:* Univ of Toledo (BA) Elem Ed 1971; St Francis (MS) Ed; *cr:* Whitehouse 4th Grd Tchr 1971-73; St Marys 5th-8th Grd Tchr 1973-76; St Lukes 6th Grd Tchr 1976-77; Ayersville Local 4th Grd Tchr 1979-95; *office:* Ayersville Elem Schl 28046 Watson Rd Defiance OH 43512*

BUSH, ELAINE HOPKINS, Fifth Grade Teacher; *b:* Philadelphia, PA; *m:* Terry Lee; *c:* Kijnanya, Asa; *ed:* Clark Atlanta Univ (BA) Elem Ed 1975; Univ of GA (MED) Elem Ed 1976; Spring Garden Coll Cmptr Programming; *cr:* Atlanta Tchr Corps Consortium Intern Tchr 1974-76; Philadelphia Bd of Ed Tchr 1976-77; Opportunities Industralization Cntrs Coord of Ed, Tchr 1977-81; Remedial Ed, Diagnostic Svcs Tchr 1981-85; Philadelphia Bd of Ed Tchr 1985-; *ai:* Yth Mngmt Assn; Rdng Club; Joint Comm Cncl; New Covenant Netcare Ministries Sec, Praise Worship Ldr; Mgr of R & B Soloist; Philadelphia More Beautiful Comm; AFT 1985-; Clark Atlanta Univ Alumni 1977-; Black Women's Educl Alliance 1988-; NAACP 1981-; Yth Motivational, Yth Exploration Svc, Career Intern Svc, Project New Pride Svc Awds; Tchr Corps Schlsp for Grad Schl; Nom for Tchr of Yr 1992; *office:* F S Edmonds Elem Schl Thouron Ave & Sedgwick St Philadelphia PA 19150*

BUSH, JODI M., 7th & 8th Grd Sci & Math Tchr; *b:* Worcester, MA; *ed:* Anna Maria Coll (BA) Ed 1992; Worcester St Coll 9 Credits; *cr:* Millbury HS Soccer & Bsktbl Coach 1990-; Saint Marys Schl Jr High Sci & Math Tchr 1992-; Anna Maria Coll Sftbl Head Coach 1995-; *ai:* SADD Adv; 3 Coaching Seasons; Tutor; MAST 1994-; *office:* St Mary's Catholic Schl 50 Richland St Worcester MA 01610*

BUSH, PATRICIA BULLOCK, Guidance Counselor; *b:* Canton, NY; *m:* Michael D.; *c:* Morgan A.; *ed:* SUNY at Potsdam (BA) Eng 1989; St Lawrence Univ (MED) Cnslng 1991; *cr:* Carthage Cntrl HS Guid Cnslr 1991-; *ai:* Jr Class, Teen AIDS Task Force Adv 3 Yrs; Jefferson-Lewis Cnslng Assn, Tchrs Assn 1991-; Grad Assistantship St Lawrence Univ 1992; *office:* Carthage Cntrl HS 36500 NYS Rt 26 Carthage NY 13619*

BUSH, ROBIN T., Science Teacher & Coach; *b:* Columbus, OH; *ed:* Otterbein Coll (BA) Hlth, PE, Recreation 1972; Xavier Univ (MA) Schl Admin; Ashland Hrs; *cr:* Lakewood Local Schls Tchr 1972-; *ai:* Var Track Coach; NEA, OEA 1972-.

BUSH, SAMUEL STEWARD, Social Studies Teacher; *b:* Gouverneur, NY; *m:* Julie Ann Manchester; *c:* Emily Ann; *ed:* Clinton Comm Coll (AS) Lbrl Arts 1990; SUNY at Plattsburgh (BS) Scndry Soc Stud 1992; 30 Addl Credits SUNY at Potsdam; *cr:* Hammond Cntrl Schl Soc Stud Tchr 1993-; *ai:* Ath Club Adv; Var Girls Soccer Coach; AFT, NYSUT 1993-; *home:* 2243 County Route 6 Hammond NY 13646*

BUSH, STEPHEN M., Instrumental Music Teacher; *b:* Jamestown, NY; *m:* Elizabeth L. Iacono; *c:* Ashton Elizabeth, Brittany Paige; *ed:* ON St Univ (BME) Music Ed 1978; Northern MI Univ (MME) Music Ed 1980; OH St Univ (PHD) Music Ed; Doctoral Candidate 1992; *cr:* RI Philharmonic Orch Prin Tuba 1980-82; Southwestern Cntrl Schl Music Tchr 1982-; *ai:* Marching Band Dir; Tech Crew Adv; Tchrs Assn Pres; AF Musicians 1978-; NEA-NY 1982-, Local Pres; MENC 1982-; Adjudicator in NY, OH, PA; *office:* Southwestern Cntrl Schl Dist 600 Hunt Rd Jamestown NY 14701

BUSHELL, ESTHER SIMON, High School English Teacher; *b:* Lawrence, MA; *m:* Michael; *ed:* Tufts Univ (MED) Scndry Ed 1967; 6th Yr Eng 1995; *cr:* Dracut Jr HS Eng Tchr 1965-67; Masconomet Regnl HS Eng Tchr 1967-68; Talcott Jr HS Eng Tchr 1969-70; Eastern Jr HS Eng Tchr 1970-89; Greenwich HS Eng Tchr 1989-; *ai:* Class of 1993 Adv; Frosh Class Adv & Speaker; Curr Dev; NCTE 1970-; Classical Assn of New England 1989-; NEA 1969-; Perrot Meml Lib 1973-, Bd Mem; Greenwich Womens Dem Club 1973-; NOW 1992-; Distinguished Tchrs Awd-Greenwich Pub Schls 1987; *office:* Greenwich HS 10 Hillside Rd Greenwich CT 06830

BUSHIKA, JOAN MAYNARD, Third Grade Teacher; *b:* North Adams, MA; *m:* George T.; *c:* Mark, Eric; *ed:* North Adams St Coll (BS) Ed 1965, (MED) 1990; Addl 24 Hrs; *cr:* Lanesborough Elem Schl 5th, 6th Grd Tchr 1967-70; North Adams St Coll Adult Learning Ctr Tchr 1992-94; Adams Cheshire Regnl Schl Dist 3rd Grd Tchr 1970-; *ai:* Schl Wide Discipline Comm Chm; Schl Cnsl, Curr Comm; NEA 1965-; ACTA 1972-; Adams Aggie Fair Comm; *office:* C. T. Plunkett Schl Commercial St Adams MA 01220*

BUSHMAN, DANIEL MCCLAIN, Latin Teacher; *b:* Gettysburg, PA; *m:* Catherine Crum; *c:* Susan Patricia May, George Daniel; *ed:* Gettysburg Coll (BA) Pol Sci 1954; 15 Hrs, 12 Hrs Shippensburg Univ, 8 Hrs PA St Univ; *cr:* Biglerville HS Lang Dept Head 1956-; *ai:* Ath Trainer; Attendance Officer; Trng Club; Arendtsville Fire Co 1950-; Eta Sigma Phi 1954-, Natl Classical Honorary Awd; PSEA, NEA 1956-; Classical League 1970-; Little & Pony Leagues 1969-77, Dir, Outstanding Svc Awd; Outstanding Tchr Awd Shippensburg Univ 1987-88; Bsktbl Sportsmanship Awd Southern PA Sportswriters 1960-61; Finalist PA Tchr of Yr Awd 1989; Outstanding Dedicated Svc Awd 1975; Excl in Tchng Awd Wooster Coll 1991; *office:* Biglerville HS N Main St Biglerville PA 17307

BUSKIRK, LORNA (COCKRELL), First Grade Teacher; *b:* Chillicothe, OH; *m:* Douglas A.; *c:* Alex D., Hilary E.; *ed:* Coll of Mt St Joseph (MS) Elem Ed 1986; *cr:* Huntington Elem Schl Chptr I, 1st & 2nd Grd Tchr 1983-84, 2nd Grd Tchr 1984-92, 1st Grd Tchr 1992-; *ai:* Tech Comm; HLEA, OEA & NEA 1983-; *office:* Huntington Elem Schl 188 Huntsman Rd Chillicothe OH 45601*

BUSS, ANGELA R., 11th Grade English Teacher; *ed:* Fitchburg St Coll (BS) Eng 1970; (MED) Eng 1972; *cr:* Gallagher Jr HS Tchr 1970-74; Leominster HS Tchr 1975-; *ai:* Yrbk Adv; LEA; MTA; NEA; *office:* Leominster HS 122 Granite St Leominster MA 01453

BUSS, DALE, Art Teacher; *b:* Allentown, PA; *m:* Donna; *ed:* Tyler Schl of Art Temple U (BFA) Fine & Graphic Arts 1981; Temple Abroad Fine & Graphic Arts Tyler Credits 1979; Kutztown Univ Art Ed Tchng Cert 1984; Attnd Southeastern MA Univ, Muhlenberg Coll; *cr:* Salisbury MS 9th Grd Art Tchr 1985-86; Lancaster Cath HS 9th-12th Grd Art Tchr 1986-; *ai:* Frosh St Cncl Adv 1986-92; NHS Adv 1992-95; NCEA 1986-; Guest Speaker at CLEWS Yth Conf 1988; *office:* Lancaster Catholic HS 650 Juliette Ave Lancaster PA 17601

BUSS, EDWARD WILSON, History, Geography & Govt Tchr; *b:* Quakertown, PA; *m:* Claire Christine Harpel; *c:* Audrey K., Constance C., Rebecca K.; *ed:* E Stroudsburg Univ (BS) Soc Stud & Geography in Scndry Ed 1963; Attnd Kutztown Univ 12 Hrs For Permanent Cert; *cr:* Parkland HS His, Geography & Govt Tchr 1963-; *ai:* Chess Team Coach 1972-; Chess Club Adv 1971-; Bsktbl Score Keeper 1978-; NEA, PSEA & Parkland Ed Assn 1963-; Penn-Jersey Chess League, Pres 1978-90; *home:* 842 Media St Bethlehem PA 18017

BUSSIERE, JOYCE GENTILE, 7th-8th Grade English Teacher; *b:* Providence, RI; *m:* Arthur T.; *c:* Deana E. DiBello, Steven A.; *ed:* RI Coll (BED) Ed, Fr 1964, (MED) Ed 1978; *cr:* Gilbert Stuart Elem Schl Fifth Grd Tchr 1964-1966; Kendrick Ave Schl Spec Ed Tchr 1966-69; Dr E. A. Ricci Schl Sixth Grd-Fr-Eng Tchr 1970-; *ai:* Natl Jr Hnr Soc Adv; Amer Fed of Tchrs 1964-; North Providence Fed of Tchrs 1970-; *home:* 4 Gladding Dr Cumberland RI 02864*

BUSSOLETTI, SUSANN RIGGI, Gifted Support Teacher; *b:* Latrobe, PA; *m:* William; *c:* Cameron, Chelsea; *ed:* Edinboro Univ (BA) Elem Ed 1972; Univ of Pittsburgh (MED) Elem Ed 1976; *cr:* N Warren Elem Schl Tchr 1973-74; Allegheny Vly Elem Schl Tchr 1973-74; Sugar Grove Elem Schl Tchr 1973-75; Allegheny Vly Elem Schl Tchr 1976-94; Beaty Warren MS Tchr 1994-; *ai:* Math Counts, Stock Market Game Adv; WCEA, PSEA, NEA 1972-; *home:* 31 Drumcliffe Dr Warren PA 16365

BUSTIO, DAISY, Sr Lab Technician & Span Instr; *b:* Pinar Del Rio, Cuba; *c:* Luis M. Montero; *ed:* F. H. LaGuardia CC (AA) Lbrl Arts 1974; Queens Coll (BA) Span Lit 1994; Attnd Universidad de Valencia Spain; *cr:* F. H. LaGuardia C Coll Asst 1975-77; Latin Amer Schl Fin Aid Dir 1980-84; NY Food & Hotel Mgmt Schl Fin Aid Dir 1984-87; F. H. LaGuardia C Coll Sr Lab Technician 1987-; *ai:* Dominican Club Fac Club Adv; Prsnl & Budget,

Sexual Harrasment Comms; CUNY Cncl Frgn Lang; Span Outstdng Awd; *office:* F. H. LaGuardia Comm Coll 31-10 Thomson Ave Long Island City NY 11101*

BUSTLE, ROD E., HS Social Studies Teacher; *b:* Cincinnati, OH; *m:* Lynne; *c:* Matthew, Andrew; *ed:* Wright St Univ (BS) Pol Sci, Soc Stud 1978; 15 Addl Hrs; 3 Hrs Drake Univ; *cr:* Milton-Union Schls HS Soc Stud Tchr, Coach 1979-80; Newton Schls HS Soc Stud Tchr, Coach 1980-84; Wilmington City Schls HS Soc Stud Tchr, Coach 1985-; *ai:* Coached Reserve Bsbl & Bsktbl; Bsktbl Head Coach 2 Yrs; Soccer Head Coach 3 Yrs; Frosh Class Adv; Wilmington Educ Assn, OH Educ Assn, NEA 1986-; *office:* Wilmington HS 300 Richardson Pl Wilmington OH 45177

BUTCH, JAMES VAN, HS Speech & Drama Teacher; *b:* Middletown, OH; *c:* Joel Anthony, Jodi Anne Butch Pitts, Jason Aaron; *ed:* OH Univ (BFA) Eng, Radio, TV & Theatre 1959; United Theogical Seminary (MARE) Chrstn Ed, Music & Worship 1984; *cr:* Middletown HS Eng, Speech & Drama Tchr 1963-82; Kettering Fairmont HS Eng, Speech, Drama & Debate Tchr 1987-; *ai:* Natl Forensic League Adv; NEA 1963-; OEA 1963-; KCTA 1987-; Christ United Meth Church 1946-, Asst in Ministry, Dir Music Worship, Chm Comm on Ed, Chm Cncl on Ministries, Sunday Schl Tchr & Chmn Comm on Worship; Natl Forensic League, Liftetime Mem; Intnl Thespian Soc, HS Theatre; W OH Conf United Methodist Church Diavonal Minister; Three-Diamond Coach Awd; OH HS Speech League Hall Of Fame Awd 1990; Founder Summer Yth Theatre Middletown 25 Yrs; *office:* Kettering Fairmont HS 3301 Shroyer Rd Kettering OH 45429

BUTCHER, JUANITA JAMES, Coop Coordinator; *b:* New York, NY; *m:* Reuben; *c:* Joelle Briggs, Jamal Jimoh; *ed:* Pace Univ (BBA) Bus Ed 1979; Hofstra Univ (MA) Educl Admin 1986, (CAS) Educl Admin 1988; *cr:* NYC BD of Ed Tchr 1980-1986, Coop Coord 1986-; Aux Svcs for HS Ctr Admin 1991-; *ai:* Lewis H. Latimer Yth Group; Baisley Park Club of NANBPWC; Thurgood Marshall Regular Democtatic Club; ASCD 1990-; Bus Ed Assn 1980-; NANBPW 1989-, Secy, Third Vice, First Vice; Thurgood Marshall Reg Dem Club 1994-, Secy; Awds L. H. Latimer Comm Svc, Baisley Park Club Prof; Appreciation; *office:* Beach Channel HS 100-00 Beach Channel Dr Far Rockaway NY 11694*

BUTCHER, NANCY JANE, High School Language Teacher; *b:* Valley Township, PA; *ed:* W Chester Univ (BSEd) Span, Langs 1992; Immaculata Univ (MS) Biling & Multicultural Stud; *cr:* Downingtown Area Jr HS Span Tchr 1992; Octorara Area HS Span Tchr 1993-; *ai:* Class of 1996 Adv 3 Yrs; Nationwide Insurance Prom Promise, Spirit Club Tribe, Bible Club Adv; PTO; Supt Advy Comm; Drug Alcohol Awareness Chm; Dist Yth Ed Assn Coord; NEA, AATSP 1993-; PSEA 1992-; OAEA 1993-, Bldg Rep, HS Grievance Chair; Red Cross Blood Dr 1987-, Gen; PA Black Caucus 1992-, Sec; Ikonawan Karate Inst 1991-, Gen, Natl 2nd & 1st Pl; Police Ath League 1994-, Gen, Tutor; Gift of Time Awd Amer Family Inst 1993; Alex Melton Schlsp Awd 1989, 1991; Articles Pub 1993-Tchr; *office:* Octorara Area HS Highland Ave PO Box 500 Atglen PA 19310*

BUTCHER, RALPH EDWARD,JR., Social Studies Teacher; *b:* Elizabeth, PA; *m:* Mary Elizabeth Donovan; *c:* Paul, Amy; *ed:* CA Univ of PA Ed 1991; *cr:* Mt Carmel Chrstn Schl Soc Stud Tchr 1992; Wilson Chrstn Acad Soc Stud Tchr 1992-; *ai:* Various Historical Clubs; Civil War, World War II Clubs; Kappa Delta Pi 1990-; Phi Alpha Theta 1992-; DAR; 1996 His Tchr of Yr; *home:* 811 N Penn St Penn PA 15675

BUTCHER, SANDRA JEAN, First Grade Teacher; *b:* Lorain, OH; *ed:* Bowling Green St Univ (MS) Ed 1963; 20 Addl Grad Hrs Ed; *cr:* Emerson Elem 1st-2nd Grd Tchr 1963-95; Longfellow Elem Schl 1st-2nd Grd Tchr 1995-; *ai:* K-3rd Grd Nature Club Adv; Portfolio Comm; Multi-Age Curr Dev Comm; NEA, OEA, LEA 1963-; Church First Chrstn 1963-, Deaconess; Amer Indian Ed Assn 1972-76; Church 1st Chrstn 1974-79, Yth Dir; Lorain Comm Choir 1972-75; Grant for Nature Club for Beautification of Schl Grounds at Emerson; *office:* Longfellow Elem 1800 Cleveland Blvd Lorain OH 44052

BUTEAU, ANTHONY PHILLIPPE, Science Teacher; *b:* Greenfield, MA; *m:* Elizabeth Haley; *c:* Joseph Haley; *ed:* St Anselm Coll (BA) Bio 1962; Univ of MA (MED) Counseling 1966; *cr:* Bedford Schl Dist 7th-8th Grd Sci Tchr 1962-65; Univ Of MA Upward Bound Project Assoc Dir 1968-74; Bedford Schl Dist 6th Grd Sci Tchr 1974-; *ai:* NEA, NHEA, NSTA, NHSTA 1974-; *office:* McKelvie Middle School 108 Liberty Hill Rd Bedford NH 03110*

BUTERA, PETER C., Professor of Psychology; *b:* Wilkes-Barre, PA; *m:* Irene Rykaszewski; *c:* Jackie, James; *ed:* Univ of Scranton (BS) Psych 1980; Purdue Univ (MS) Psychobiology 1983, (PHD) Neuroscience 1985; *cr:* Niagara Univ Asst Prof 1985-89, Assoc Prof 1989-93, Psych Prof 1993-; *ai:* Environmental Group Fac Moderator; Pre-Medical, Pre-Dental Advy Comm; Psych Dept Chprsn; Amer Psychological Assn, Amer Sci Advancement Assn 1985-; Neuroscience Soc 1983-; Residents Organized for Lewiston's Environment 1988-, VP; NIH, NIMH, Univ Research Cncl 9 Yrs; Scientific Journals Articles Pub; Wilkes-Barre Distinguished Svc Awd 1993; *office:* Niagara Univ PO Box 2208 Niagara Univ NY 14109

BUTHE, BETTY ANN HESS, Business Education Teacher; *b:* Englewood, NJ; *m:* Fred G.; *c:* Fred H.; *ed:* Montclair St Coll (BA) Secretarial Stud, Acctng 1964; St Univ of NY (MS) Advanced Classroom Tchng 1973; *cr:* Ridgefield Meml HS Bus Ed Tchr 1964-68; Berne-Knox-Westerlo HS Bus Ed Tchr 1972; Duanesburg Jr Sr HS Tchr, Bus Dept Chprsn 1972-; *ai:* Class Adv; NYS Bus Tchrs, NBEA 1980-; *office:* Duanesburg Jr Sr HS 163 School Dr Delanson NY 12053

BUTKUS, CHRISTINE STEPHENS, Rdng & Social Studies Teacher; *b:* Manchester, CT; *m:* J. Wayne; *c:* Stanley; *ed:* Elmira Coll (BA) Elem Ed 1971; Coll of St Rose (MA) Learning Disabilities 1976; *cr:* Cambridge Cntrl Schl 5 Grd Tchr 1971-76, 4 Grd Dev Lag Tchr 1976-78; 4 Grd Tchr 1978-90; 6 Grd Rdng & Soc Stud Tchr 1990-; *ai:* MS Coord 1994-95; Cambridge Fac Assn, NYSUT, AFT, NEA 1971-; *office:* Cambridge Central Schl 24 S Park St Cambridge NY 12816

BUTLER, ANA MARIA (CESPEDES), Biology Teacher; *b:* Elmhurst, NY; *m:* Peter; *c:* Peter Andrew; *ed:* Fordham Univ (BS) Sci 1988; Queens Coll (MS) Ed of Sci 1993; Summer Sci Rsrch Sci Prgm Columbia Univ; *cr:* Forest Hills HS Bio Tchr 1989-; *ai:* Astronomy Club 1990-91; Bio Ethics Club 1993-; Citation of Hnr by Clara Schulman Tchr of Yr Nom; *office:* Forest Hills HS 67-01 110th St Forest Hills NY 11375*

BUTLER, CATHERINE MARY, Second Grade Teacher; *b:* Lynn, MA; *m:* Joseph E. Jr.; *c:* Christie; *ed:* Salem St Coll (BS) Ed K-8th Grd Tchr 1973; Lesley Coll (MAED) Creative Arts in Ed, Soc Sci 1996; Skillful Tchr, Learning Styles, 4-Mat Trng Implementation in the Classroom; Cooperative Learning; Math a Way of Thinking Trng; Childrens Lit, Cmptr Courses; Creative Arts in Learning with Sci; Conflict Resolution Trng; Inquiry Bd Sci Courses; CPR, First Aid; *cr:* St Marys Annunciation Fifth Grd Tchr 1973-77; Cutler Schl 3rd, 5th Grd Tchr 1977-81; Winthrop Schl 3rd, 5th Grd Tchr 1977-81; Mrktg Rep Blue Cross Blue Shield 1981-84; Cutler Schl Fifth Grd Tchr 1984-89; Winthrop Schl Second Grd Tchr 1991-; *ai:* Taught Math Methods Course; Tchr Rep for Parents, Friends Grp 1994-; Dist Curr, Staff Dev Comm; Curr Review, Adoption Comm; NEA, MTA 1976-; Town Yth Soccer Coach; Spon Acord Food Pantry; *office:* Winthrop Schl Hamilton Wenham Schl Dist 325 Bay Rd South Hamilton MA 01982

BUTLER, CHARLOTTE C., Eighth Grade Social Stud Tchr; *b:* Gloversville, NY; *m:* George F.; *ed:* Skidmore Coll (BA) His 1967; Boston Univ (MED) Ed 1975; Univ of New Hampshire Post Grad Courses; *cr:* Northville Schl 9th, 11th Grd His Tchr 1967-68; Tenney HS 9th-10th Grd His Tchr 1969-70; Woodbury Schl 8th Grd Soc Stud Tchr 1970-; *ai:* Club Adv; MS Acad Bowl; AcadFair Chprsn; Curr Cncl Mem; *office:* Woodbury Schl 206 Main St Salem NH 03079

BUTLER, CHERYL LYNN, Earth Science Teacher; *b:* Buffalo, NY; *ed:* Fredonia St Coll (BS) Earth Sci 1993; Potsdam Coll 2 Credits Toward Masters; *cr:* Carthage HS Earth Sci Tchr 1994-; *ai:* Venture Tchr Adv; Venture Advy Comm 1994-; Co-Author St Ed Dept Variance to Implement Earth Sci Modification Prgm; Outstanding Rookie Team of Yr; *office:* Carthage H S 36500 NYS Rt 26 Carthage NY 13619

BUTLER, CYNTHIA HOUGLAN, Fourth Grade Teacher; *b:* Akron, OH; *m:* Harvey Andrews; *c:* Kirsten Marie Richie; *ed:* Otterbein Coll (BSEd) Elem Ed 1962; 30 Addl Hrs; *cr:* Windsor Elem 3rd Grd Tchr 1962-63; St Joseph Elem 2nd-3rd Grd Tchr 1963-65; Arongen Elem 2nd-4th Grd Tchr 1966-; *ai:* Shared Decision Making Team Chprsn; Shenendehowa Tchrs Assn Rep; Stu Cncl Adv; AFT, NYSUT, STA 1966-; Shenendehowa PTA 1966-, Lifetime Mbrshp; NYS Model Schl Grant 1995; Dev Interage Prgm Shenendehowa 1973; *office:* Arongen Elem Schl 489 Clifton Park Ctr Rd Clifton Park NY 12065

BUTLER, FLORENCE C., Fourth Grade Teacher; *b:* East Orange, NJ; *m:* Marshall A. III; *c:* Debra Susan Lacy, Donna Lee Gabelmann, Marshall A., Cheryl Lynn, Lori Jeanne; *ed:* Kean Coll (BA) Elem Ed 1958; Presch Cert Caldwell Coll 1976; *cr:* Belleville Pub Schls Tchr 1958-60; Comm Nursery Schl Tchr 1974-80; East Orange Pub Schls 4th Grd Tchr 1988; *ai:* Sci Facilitator; EOEA, NJEA, NEA 1988-; *office:* Lincoln Elem Schl 120 Central Ave East Orange NJ 07018

BUTLER, JACQUELINE JARVIS, Teacher; *m:* Leland N.; *c:* Leland T.; *ed:* Norfolk St Univ (BA) Elem Ed 1971; *cr:* Lanning Sq MS Grd 5 Tchr 1971-87; C. B. Hatch MS Tchr 1987-; *ai:* Natl Jr Hnr Soc Spon; 8th Grd Class Spon; NJEA, CCEA, CEA 1971-; NJ Black Alliance Edctrs; Govenors Recognition Awd Excl Tchng; Prins Appointee Tchr of Academically; *home:* 42 Dunhill Dr Voorhees NJ 08043*

BUTLER, JANE TICHO, Math Teacher; *b:* Brooklyn, NY; *m:* Frederick Lynn; *c:* Kimberly, Daniel; *ed:* Rosemont Coll (BA) Math 1966; Adelphi Univ (MA) Math-Ed 1970; Addl 70 Hrs Various Insts; Awded NSF Grant MS Ldrshp Prmg Hofstra UNv 1992, 1996; *cr:* Beach St MS 7-9 Grd Math Tchr 1966-73, 1982-; *ai:* Math Contest Club Mathletes Adv; Peer Group; NHS Cncl Mem; AFT 1966-; NCTM, NYSMA 1982-; RITEC Awd Excl Math 1985; Suffolk Cty Math Tchr of Yr 1994; Twice Nom Natl Tchr of Yr; NSF Grant Hofstra Univ Ldrshp in MS Math; *office:* Beach St MS Beach St West Islip NY 11795*

BUTLER, JANET JULIA, Science Teacher; *b:* Pawtucket, RI; *m:* Scott Matthew; *c:* Matthew, Mark; *ed:* Univ of RI (BS) Zoology 1982; RI Coll (MAT) Gen Sci 1985; RISD Natural Drawing; RIC Biochemistry; *cr:* Drayton Hall MS Sci Tchr 1985-88; Davies Career & Tech Sci Tchr 1988-; *ai:* NEASC Comm Sci Co-Chair; RI Project Aids Stu Adv; Negotiations Comm; NEA, RI 1988-; RIBT 1994-; Natl Geographic, Cousteau Soc 1982-; Nature Conservancy 1995-; Sierra Club 1988-; *office:* Davies Career & Tech HS 50 Jenckes Hill Rd Lincoln RI 02865

BUTLER, JULETT, Instructor; *b:* Jamaica, West Indies; *ed:* Coll of Arts, Sci & Tech (BA) Tech Ed 1986; Emerson Coll (MA) Commnctn Stud 1991; SUNY at New Poltz 9 Grad Credits; Marist Coll 6 Grad Credits; Adelphi Univ 3 Grad Credits; *cr:* Browns Town Comm Coll Instr 1981-88; Medical Inc Data Entry 1988-89; Emerson Coll Sec & Admin Asst 1989-91; Dutchess Comm Coll Instr 1991-; *ai:* Trained Mediator, Coll Equity Comm; Summer Yth Employment Pgm; HS Mediation Trng Wkshp Presenter; PACE Awds Guest Speaker; Fund Raiser Co-Chair & Team Captain; NBEA 1995-; DTSE 1991-; AAWCC 1994-; NYSATC & NEA 1993-; Minority Mentoring Dev Pgm 1993-; RAIN 1995-, Team Lrd, Cert of Svc; Numerous Poems Pub; Article Pub; Honors: Interfaith Vol Caregivers, Catherine St Comm Ctr, Dutchess Horizons & Non-Traditional Stdnts; Rep Dutchess Comm Col in The Poughkeepsie Journal; *office:* Dutchess Comm Coll 53 Pendell Rd Poughkeepsie NY 12601

BUTLER, KAREN ROWLEY, 7th-8th Grd Social Stud Tchr; *b:* Portsmouth, VA; *m:* David Austin Sr.; *c:* David Austin Jr., Kellie Christine; *ed:* Univ of DE (BSEd) Elem Ed 1989; Addl 18 Credits; Millersville Univ of PA 9 Credits; *cr:* St Peter Schl 6th-8th Grd Lang, Rdng Tchr 1990-91; Dallastown Area Schl Dist Sub Tchr 1991-92; West Shore Schl Dist 7th Grd Soc Stud, Sci, Math Tchr 1992-94, 7th-8th Grd Soc Stud Tchr 1994-; *ai:* Spirit Club, Peer Helpers, Mediators Adv; 8th Grd Career Day Coord; Stu Assistance Team; NEA, PSEA, WSEA 1994-; Prof Employee of Quarter 1995; *office:* Crossroads MS 535 Fishing Creek Rd Lewisberry PA 17339*

BUTLER, KEITH D., Biology & Computer Teacher; *b:* Ft Belvoir, VA; *m:* Jeanne M. Reinert; *c:* Kevin, Kristen; *ed:* Millersville St Coll (BA) Bio 1974; Univ of AZ (MS) Entomology 1976; Lehigh Co Comm Coll 21 Credits Alternate Energy Tech; Muhlenberg Coll 18 Credits Computer Tech; Lehigh Univ 4 Credits Computer Tech; Clarion Univ 1 Credit Microcomputer Lab Interfacing; Cedar Crest Coll DNA Tech; Univ of AL at Huntsville 3 Credits SOPE; Carbon-Lehigh IU 2 Credits; *cr:* Emmous Jr HS Bio, computer Tchr 1977-; *ai:* Computer Tech, Sci Curr Comm; PA Jr Acad of Sci Stu adv, Spon, Chaperone, Judge; Concept Mapping, Computer Applications, Multimedia, Internet Inservice Trainer; NEA, PSEA, NABT, NSTA 1977-; EPEA 1977-, Bldg Rep 1977-82; PSTA 1977-, Convention Comm 1992-95; Lehigh Valley assn Bio Tchrs 1988-; Lehigh Valley Audubon Christmas Bird Count 1976-; Leigh Valley Conservancy Butterfly Counts 1980-; Little Lehigh Watershed Task Force 1985-; Laurys Ath Assn 1987-, Asst Coach, Head Coach 1989, 1994, Sftbl Championship 1993; St Johns UCC Laurys 1986-, Cncl Mem 1989-95, Cncl VP 1993, Pres 1994-95, Family of Yr 1995; Charles Spotts Awd; Masters Thesis; Journal AZ Acad Sci 11:46 1976; Pestic Biochem Physiol 7:474-480 1977; Little Lehigh Watershed Curr 1988; PA Recycling, Waste Reduction Curr 1990; *office:* Emmaus Jr HS 660 Macungie Ave Emmaus PA 18049

BUTLER, LYNN GRANDY, Kindergarten Teacher; *b:* Gloversville, NY; *m:* Gary; *ed:* Fulton Mongt Comm Coll (AA) Liberal Arts 1968; Cedarville Coll (BA) Elem Ed 1970; 40 Credit Hrs & Post Grad Stud; *cr:* Fonda Fultonville Schl 2nd Grd Tchr 1 Yr, 1st Grd Tchr 12 Yrs & Kndgtn Tchr 13 Yrs; *ai:* PTA; Helping Children Learn with Whole Lang, Broken Families & Family-Related Act Comms; Church Related Act of Choirs & Childrens Work; Organist & Pianist Schl & Church & Comm Svc; Grd Chm 1995-; Yrbk Orgnzr 1995-; Local FFTA, NYSUT & AFT 1970-; *office:* Fonda Fultonville Central Schl Cemetery St Fonda NY 12068*

BUTLER, OBERIA BURGE, Mathematics Instructor; *b:* Rome, GA; *m:* Curtis William; *c:* Anita, Lori; *ed:* Morris Brown Coll (BA) Math 1960; Atlanta Univ (MS) Math 1961; Howard Univ (MDiv) Rel 1995; Post Grad Stud Math Ed Univ of MD at College Park; *cr:* Morris Brown Coll Grad Asst 1960-61; Bowie St Univ Math Fac 1961-.

BUTLER, PATRICIA A., English Teacher; *b:* Buffalo, NY; *m:* Patrick; *c:* Rebecca Pokorski, Carolyn Pokorski; *ed:* St Univ of NY at Buffalo (BS) Scndry Eng 1969, (MA) Eng 1973; *cr:* Lakeshore Cntrl HS Eng Tchr 1969-70; Pub Schl 52 Eng Tchr 1971-72; Pub Schl 76 Eng Tchr 1972-73; Riverside HS Eng Tchr 1975-81; Pub Schl 69 Eng Tchr 1981-89; Leonardo Da Vinci HS Eng Tchr 1989-; *ai:* Newspaper Adv; NEA 1969-; Poetry Pub; *office:* Leonardo Da Vinci HS 320 Porter Ave Buffalo NY 14201

BUTLER, RICHARD ARTHUR, 7th Grade History Teacher Bedford, MA; *m:* Sallie Mae Albro; *c:* Richard L., Dougla Bridgewater St Coll (BS) Elem 1973; *cr:* Bourne Schl Dept 1st 1973-74, 8th Grd His Tchr 1974-84; Lyle MS Asst Prin 1977-8 Prin 1984-85, 7th-8th Grd His Tchr 1986-; *ai:* Soc Stud Comm; F 1973-80; Washington DC Field Trip Coord 1995-; NEA, MA T 1974-; New England League of Mid Schls 1985-; Bourne Ed 1974-; VFW 1991-; Amer Legion 1986-; Bourne Recreatic 1967-68; Bourne Pigskins 1970-75, Charter Mem; WW II Interdis Grant; *home:* 7 Queens Bay Ln Buzzards Bay MA 02532

BUTLER, ROBERT DALTON, Resource & Social Stud Winchester, VA; *m:* Betsy A.; *c:* John Scott Stoer, Ryan MacLain; VA Univ (BA) His 1968; George Washington Univ (MA) Curr Richard Montgomery HS Soc Stud Tchr 15 Yrs; Walt Wh Resource & Soc Stud Tchr 11 Yrs; *ai:* Lorax Club Spon; MCE MSTA 1969-; Natl Capit His Soc 1990-; Numerous Curr Mo *office:* Walt Whitman HS 7100 Whittier Blvd Bethesda MD 208

BUTLER, ROBERT PETER, Spcl Resource Education Tchr; *b:* NY; *m:* Kathleen Mary Eletto; *c:* Sean, Michelle; *ed:* Westche Lbrl Arts 1973; Mercy Coll (BA) Psych 1975; Coll of New Roch Spec Ed 1980; *cr:* Commerce MS Tchr 1975-76; Longfellow Coach 1976-77; Roosevelt HS Tchr, Coach 1977-89; Tappan Zee Coach 1989-95; *ai:* Ftbl Coach Var Head, JV Head Roosevelt HS Roosevelt-Nyack HS; Spec Ed Comm; AFT, NYSUT 1975-; EAS Section 1 Coaches Assn 1976-; Coach of Yr 1991; Sons of Ita PTSA 1977-; PTA 1989-; NY Section 1 St Coach of Yr; O Recreation Supvr Jawonio Ctr for Disabled; *office:* Tappan Z Dutch Hill Rd Orangeburg NY 10962

BUTRYN, JEAN CRISPELL, 6th Grade Teacher; *b:* Newburgh Mark; *c:* Gregory, Meghan; *ed:* SUNY at New Paltz (BS) Elem (MS) Elem Ed 1980; *cr:* Circleville Elem Schl 5th, 3rd, Kndgtn 1975-89; Crispell MS 5th Grd Tchr 1990-92; Circleville MS 6th 1992-; *ai:* Var Chrldng Coach Pine Bush HS; Pine Bush Tchrs A NYSUT 1975-; *office:* Circleville MS PO Box 143 Circleville N

BUTT, BEVERLY L., Mathematics Teacher; *b:* Sharon, PA; *m:* F *c:* Jason, Nathan, Ryan; *ed:* Wilkes Univ 24 Hrs Toward Maste *cr:* Central Dauphin HS Math Tchr 1970-72; Donjegal HS M 1983-84; Dept of Commerce Census Bureau Field Supvr Manheim Twp HS Math Tchr 1989-; *ai:* TASK Club Adv; VISIC Chm; Tchr Mentor; PCTM, NCTM 1990-; Hempfield Church of 1991-, Deacon, Sunday Schl Tchr, Librn; Presented 2 Confs for Math; *office:* Manheim Twp HS 5134 School Rd Lancaster PA 1

BUTTELWERTH, JOHN W., Instr of Civil Engrng Tech; *b:* C OH; *m:* Cheryl Ann Dee; *c:* Tasha, Johnnie, Rhea, Julie; *ed:* Cincinnati (AS) Bldg Construction Tech 1978, (BS) Constructio 1980; Xavier Univ (MED) Ed 1985; *cr:* Dayton Power & Light C 1980-82; Catalytic Inc Project Controls Engr 1982-84; John Bu Construction Mngmt Consulting Bus Pres 1983-; Cincinnati S Comm Coll Instr 1984-; *ai:* Fac Senate Pres; OH Two Yr Coll Founder, Pres; Bd of Regents Chancellor's Fac Advy Comm; AAU CMAA, ASC 1993-; ACCE 1992-; House-Bruckmann Fac Excl A Cincinnati Enquirer Guest Columnist Twice; *office:* Cincinnati S Comm Coll 3520 Central Pky Cincinnati OH 45223

BUTTERFIELD, CAROL M., 3rd Grade Teacher; *b:* Jersey Ci Kenneth M.; *c:* Domenique B. Canino, Noreen T., Cori-Lynn E. *ed:* Jersey City St Coll (BA) Primary Ed 1964; 30 Credit Hrs in S SUNY at New Paltz; *cr:* Jersey City Schls 1st Grd Tchr 1964-65; Village Nursery Schl Tchr 1970-81; St Augustine Schl 3rd-8th Tchr 1981-; *ai:* Teach Guitar Lessons; *home:* 115 Vista Dr Hig 12528*

BUTTERFIELD, JOHN C., Science & Math Teacher; *b:* Bridg *m:* Barbara A.; *ed:* Glassbor St Coll (BA) Elem Ed 1970; 30 Credi Edgarton Meml Schl 4-8 Grd Tchr 1969-93; Dr. J. P. Cleary MS Sci & Math Tchr 1993-; *ai:* Dist Advy Comm Buena Regnl S NJEA, NEA 1970-; Atlantic Cty Ed Assn 1993-; Cumberland Co H Soc 1973-, Bd of Trustees 1990-; *office:* Dr. J. P. Cleary MS Hard Buena NJ 08310

BUTTERMORE, SIDNEY P., Seventh Grade Teacher; *b:* Charle *m:* Melissa; *c:* Kelly; *ed:* Southern CT (BS) Elem Ed 197 Environmental Sci 1975; *cr:* Colonel Ledyard Schl Tchr 1971-72 Heights Schl Tchr 1972-73; West Side Jr HS-MS Tchr 1973-; *ai:* Adv; Intramural; Amistad Friendship Soc Schl Ldr; Schl Imp Team; Groton Ed Assn, CEA, NEA 1971-, Treas, Membership Cha #2163 1972-, Exalted Ruler, Svc Awd; Previous Bsktbl & Sftb Have Trained 4 Stu Tchrs & Served as Mentor; *office:* West Side Brandegee Ave Groton CT 06340

BUTTERS, GLEN EDWARD, Computer Teacher; *b:* Wellsboro Mansfield Univ (BA) Math 1985, (MS) Cmptr Ed 1995; Second Cert 1987; *cr:* Micro Mrktg Intnl Sales, Cmptrs 1985-86; Troy A Dist 5-8 Grd Math, Cmptr Tchr 1987-; *ai:* Stu Asst Prgm; NEA TAEA 1987-; PTSO 1987-; PIAA 1980-, Wrestling Ofcl; *office:* King & High Sts Troy PA 16947

BUTTICH, FRANK, World History Teacher; *b:* Trenton, NJ; Muka; *c:* Mark, Michael, Matthew; *ed:* Trenton St Coll (BA) 1972, (MED) His, Pol Sci 1980; Addl 21 Hrs with Emphasis on Admin; *cr:* Dunn MS His, Eng Tchr 1972-84; Trenton Cntrl HS W Tch 1984-86; Alternative Ed Prog Eng Tchr 1986-88; Holland Ass't Prin 1988-89; Junior #5 Act Ass't Prin 1989-90; Trenton World Hist Tch 1990-; *ai:* Trenton Educ Assn, Mercer Cty Ed Ass NEA 1972-; Have Historical Researched on File Spec Collection L. West LIb Trenton St Coll; NJ for NASA TChr in Space Prog.

BUTTO, DANA GIANNETTI, Math Teacher; *b:* Belleville, Carmen; *c:* Danielle, Bryan; *ed:* Youngstown St Univ (BE) Indstr 1983, (MTS) Curr 1996; 90 Addl Hrs Scndry Ed; *cr:* Copperw Indstrl Engr 1983-86; Niles City Schls Sub Tchr 1986-89; Young Univ Part-time Math Tchr 1989-91; Niles Mc Kinley HS Math Tc *ai:* Key Club Adv; Stu Assistant Team; OCTM 1994-; *office:* Kinley HS 616 Dragon Dr Niles OH 44446*

BUTTOLPH, PATRICIA MC CARTHY, Mathematics Teache Jervis, NY; *c:* Catherine; *ed:* Nazareth Coll of Rochester (BA) M St Univ of NY at Albany (MS) Ed 1971; 36 Grad Hrs in Ed & of VT, Univ of MA, St Michael's Coll & Johnson St Carlton-Webster Math Tchr 1967-71; Palmyra Macedon Schls Cnslr 1971-73; Barre Voc Ctr Math Tchr 1973-75; Barre Gra Guidance Cnslr 1975-78; Lamville Union Schl Math Tchr 19 Scholars Bowl Coach; Facilitator Prof Dev; Admin Eisenhowe Guidance, Emergency Leade Comms; NEA 1967-; VT NEA LUHSTA 1978-, Various Offices; Hyde Park Recycling; Partic Woodrow Wilson Fnd Courses; Tchr of Yr 1990; *home:* RR 1 B Hyde Park VT 05655*

BUTTS, CLARA C., English Teacher; *b:* Brookhaven, MS; Butts; *c:* Radford D., Dierdre V.; *ed:* Alcorn St Univ (BA) E Southern IL Univ (MSEd) Eng 1968; Addl 12 Credit Hrs; *cr:* 1959-60; MS Vly St Eng Tchr, Dir, Frosh Eng 1967-75; Woodfor Eng Tchr 1976-82; Friendly HS Eng Tchr 1984-90; Crossland HS

· Soc Comm; MSTA 1984-; NEA 1960-; NCTE 1967-75, 1984-; Vol; *office:* Crossland HS 6901 Temple Hill Rd Temple Hills MD

JOHN FREDRICK, Biology Teacher & Sci Dept Chm; *b:* WV; *m:* Dawn Marie Martin; *c:* Khisha Jane Fallon, Kari Ruth West Liberty St Coll (BA) Bio, PE & Hlth 1964; Coll of Mount (MAEd) Tchr Effectiveness 1989; *cr:* Tuscarawas Vly Jr High oach 1964-66; Jewett HS Bio Tchr & Head Ftbl & Track Coach Coshocton HS Bio Tchr & Asst Ftbl & Head Track Coach Bio Tchr 1967-, Sci Dept Chm 1970-; *ai:* Sci Fair Coord; Eastern 'air & Seiko Yth Challenge Judge; Detention Supvr; NEA 1964-; ssn 1964-; Coshocton City Ed Assn 1967-; Sci Ed Cncl of OH ai Delta Kappa 1991-; Coshocton Elks Lodge 1972-; Coshocton Lodge 1987-; Tchr of the Yr 1973; Governors Awd for Excl in Yth rtunities 1992-94.

KENNETH EDWARD, Industrial Arts Teacher; *b:* Berkeley WV; *m:* Joy L. G.; *ed:* Fairmont St Coll (BS) Indstrl Arts Comp / Univ (MS) Safety Stud 1981; Tech Preparation Classes PDE; burg Univ Cmptr Ed; Natl Emergency Trng Ctr Prgm of Stud; *cr:* ood HS Indstrl Arts Tchr 1974-78; Southern Fulton Jr Sr HS rts & Tech Prep Tchr 1978-; *ai:* Southern Fulton Auto Club Class Adv; Strategic Planning, Discipline Handbook Comm; EA, Local 1979-, Negotiating Team; Burkeley Springs Vol Fire Co es; Morgan Cty Vol Rescue Svc 1972-, CPR Instr; Morgan Cty 985-; Morgan Cty Emergency Svcs 1981-, Dir; *office:* Southern Sr HS Rt 2 Box 45 Warfordsburg PA 17267*

SUSAN LEIS, Cooperative Bus Ed Coord; *b:* Greenville, OH; *m:* ts; *c:* Denea S., Alisa C., Ryan D.; *ed:* Cochise Comm Coll (AA) ; AZ St Univ (BAE) Bus Ed 1977; Grad Hrs Wright St Univ, Univ ı, Northern AZ Univ; *cr:* Greenville City Schls Mrktg Coord Computerized Bus Tech Instr 1980-95, Cooperative Bus Ed Coord : Bus Profs of Amer Adv; Dist-Wide Chrldr Coord; Bus Dept ports Cncl; Integrity Sportsmanship Comm; AVA, OVA 1993-; OH s Assn 1994-; Church 1977-, Bd of Chrstn Ed, Sub Sunday Schl *ce:* Greenville City Schls 100 Greenwave Way Greenville OH

AUM, ALVA JONES, Seventh Grade English Teacher; *b:* New LA; *c:* Kris, Kim, Nina; *ed:* Fisk Univ (BA) His 1957; Brooklyn) Ed 1983; 30 Credit Hrs Brooklyn Coll; *cr:* PS 398K Tchr PS 189K Bilingual Tchr 1986-; Brooklyn Coll Adjunct Tchr Adjunct Tchr 1994-; *ai:* Stu Govt Assoc Adv; AFT, UFT 1980-, Ldr 1990-94; Departmental Honors Brooklyn Coll 1983; *office:* Ctr PS 189 1100 E Ney York Ave Brooklyn NY 11212*

, JAMES MICHAEL, Social Studies Teacher; *b:* Hollis, NY; *m:* Anne Pratt; *c:* Brent, Neal, Alison; *ed:* Stonehill Coll (BA) Psych tioch Coll (MED) Counseling 1977; Attnd Univ of RI & RI Coll s in His & Pol Sci; *cr:* Browndale-Communities for People Schl 5-77; S Kingstown HS Soc Stud Tchr 1978-; *ai:* Soccer Coach Soccer Referee 1991-; Model United Nations Adv 1979-; Intnl Adv 1991-; RI Girls Soccer Assn, VP 1986-90; South Cty ccer Assn 1990-, Under 8 League Dir, Coaches Trng Dir 1990-; Girl Coach of Yr 1988; RI Model UN Conf 1991-; *office:* South n H S 215 Columbia St Wakefield RI 02879

D, LOUISE ANNTHONETTE, Second Grade Teacher; *b:* , PA; *ed:* Clarion Univ of PA (BS) Elem Ed 1966; Univ of ı (MED) Elem Ed 1970; *cr:* Burrell Schl Dist 1st & 2nd Grd Tchr Elem Dept Head 1989-92; BEA Schlshp Comm Schlshp Chprsn; Vlybl Coach; Bldg Rep; Mentor Tchr; Cooperating Tchr for Stu n St; NEA, BEA, PSEA 1966-; KDKA TV Thanks to Tchrs

L, JAMES RICHARD, Mathematics Teacher; *b:* Marlboro, MA; a Peprah; *c:* Jessica, James Jr.; *ed:* Mesa St Coll (BS) Geology iv of NH 45 Grad Hrs, St Cert; *cr:* US Coast Guard Electrician US Geological Survey Groundwater Hydrologist 1980-83; Akim cndry Math Tchr 1984-86; Nute HS Math Tchr 1986-; *ai:* Yrbk -95; NEA 1986-; *office:* Nute HS Elm St Milton NH 03851

DENISE A. STEWART, Mathematics Teacher; *b:* Philadelphia, obert Lee Jr.; *c:* Robert Lee III, Dominique Ashleigh; *ed:* Cheyney BA) (BS) Sec Ed Math 1976; Cheyney St Univ (MED) Adm, on 1986; *cr:* Yeadon HS Math Tchr 1976-82; Penn Wood HS Math 2-; *ai:* Sr Class Adv; PSEA, NEA 1976-; Alpha Kappa Alpha eadon Pub Lib Bd, Pres; *office:* Penn Wood HS 100 Green Ave ne PA 19050

DAWN MARIE (BRAWN), Mathematics Teacher; *b:* Coldwater, Russell; *ed:* Wright St Univ (BS) Sec Math Ed 1990, (MS) Tchr 95; *cr:* C. R. Coblentz Local Schl Jr HS, HS Math Tchr 1990-92; anan Local Schl Jr HS, HS Math Tchr 1992-95; Vandalia Nutler s HS Math Tchr 1995-; *ai:* WSUACTM, OCTM, NCTM 1990-; Tchr of Yr 1995; *home:* 126 Wickham Farm Rd Union OH 45322

LYNN MILLER, 8th Grade Language Arts Tchr; *b:* Sewickley, avid D.; *c:* Matthew, Katreine; *ed:* 18 Grad Credits Towards Lit New Brighton MS 7th Grd Soc Stud, Sci, 8th Grd Lang Arts Tchr 8th Grd Lang Arts Tchr 1993-; *ai:* Stu Cncl Spon; Homebound TE 1992-; Vanport Presbyn Church 1989-, Womens Assn; Caring ı Spon; *office:* New Brighton MS 901 Penn Ave New Brighton PA

RITA MYERS, Fourth Grade Teacher; *b:* Chambersburg, PA; *m:* ; *c:* Chad Glass, Rob, Nicole Glass, Julie; *ed:* Shippensburg Univ m Ed 1965, (MA) Elem Ed 1967; 52 Addl Grad Credits in Elem Waynesboro Schl Dist First Grd Tchr 1965-68; Headstart Tchr Educl Coord, Asst Dir 1978-80; Chambersburg Schl Dist Second, ird Tchr 1980-; *ai:* NEA, PSEA 1980-; CAEA 1980-, Large; Beta Sigma Phi 1967-, Pres, Sec; Outstdng Tchr 1994.

ON, DARLENE JOHNSON, Third Grade Teacher; *b:* St Louis, teven Byington; *c:* Juliet, Leslie; *ed:* Univ of MO (BS) Soc Stud, 1968; Univ of NY at Cortland (MS) Rdng 1992; *cr:* Fanning Elem ı Grd Tchr 1968-69; Blaine Sumner Elem Schl Fourth, Sixth Grd 9-72; Beaupre Elem Schl Fifth Grd Tchr 1972-73; Kemble Elem l Tchr 1986-; Hughes Elem Schl Third Grd Tchr 1986-; *ai:* Shared Making Team Fac, Magnet Schl Planning Team Mem; AFT 1986-; nts Utica Tchrs Ctr1994-; *office:* John F Hughes Elem Schl 24 St Utica NY 13501

SKI, MARIE, Latin Teacher; *b:* Pittsburgh, PA; *ed:* Duquesne) Ed 1958, (MA) Classics 1965; 18 Credits Span Carlow Coll; 15 cndry Schl Admin Univ of GA; *cr:* Pacelli HS Vice Prin 1972-74; San Antonio Asst Dir, Prin 1977-78; Colegio Nstra Sra del Dir, 3-81; Colegio Buen Pastor Dir 1979-81; Canevin HS Bus Mgr St Paul Seminary Instr Collegiate Level 1995-; *office:* Canevin H S 2700 Morange Rd Pittsburgh PA 15205

CAROL ANN TEN KATE, 7th & 8th Grade Teacher; *b:* Paterson, alph R. (dec); *c:* Kevin, Jeff, Gary, Christine; *ed:* Calvin Coll (BA) 1971; Addl Credit Courses; *cr:* Denver Chrstn Schls 5th Grd Tchr Eastern Chrstn Schl 7-8th Grd Tchr 1989-; *ai:* Stu Cncl Spon; ; MACSA; Wyckoff Fire Dept 1973-, Pres; 1 Ladies Aux, VP, Corres Sec; *office:* Eastern Christian MS 518 Sicomac Ave Wyckoff NJ 07481

BYRD, JEFFREY J., Asst Professor of Biology; *b:* Riverside, NJ; *m:* Elizabeth; *c:* Andrew; *ed:* Rutgers Univ (BS) Microbio 1983; Penn St U (MS) Microbio 1985; Univ of MD (PHD) Microbio 1991; *cr:* St Marys Coll Asst Prof of Bio 1990-; *ai:* Fac Adv; Beta Beta Beta Biological Hnr Soc; Fac Senate; ASM 1984-; CSTA 1991-; AAAS 1993-; Trinity Luth Church 1990-, Worship Asst; 2 Book Chapters; 6 Journal Articles; *office:* Saint Marys Coll Of MD Dept Of Bio St Marys Cy MD 20686

BYRD, LILLIAN ELIZABETH, History Teacher; *b:* Baltimore, MD; *m:* Richard Elsworth; *ed:* Morgan St Univ (BA) His 1965; Towson St, Morgan St, Coppin St (MA) Scndry Ed 1970; Project Mission Tchng Culturally Deprived Child; GATE; Providing Multicultural Ed; *cr:* Canton Jr HS Tchr 1966-71; Southwestern Sr HS Tchr, Admin 1972-77; Severna Park Sr HS Tchr 1978-; *ai:* Stu Tchr Mentor; Soc Stud Chprsn; Mid Sts Evaluation Comm; Ebony Cultural Club Adv; Stu Multi-Cultural Conf Facilitor; Human Relations Comm Chprsn; NEA, MSTA 1967-; TAAAC 1970-; MD Soc Stud Cncl 1987-; Bldg Learning Hierarchies, Dimensions of Learning Certs; *office:* Severna Park Sr HS 60 Robinson Rd Severn MD 21144*

BYRD, ROBERT EDWARD, Global Studies, Ec & Govt Tchr; *b:* Utica, NY; *m:* Mary Benson; *c:* Andy, Kevin; *ed:* Utica Coll of Syracuse Univ (BA) Soc Stud 1968; Post Grad Stud Cortland St, Syracuse Univ; *cr:* Waterville Cntrl Schl Tchr 28 Yrs; *ai:* Var Ftbl, Bsktbl, Jr Var Bsktbl, 7, 8 Grd Bsktbl, Girls Var Bsktbl, Track Coach; AFT 1968-; NY St Assn Soc Stud Tchrs 1985-, VP; Knights of Columbus 1968-; Skevendog Club 1987-; Brookside Ath Club 1995-; Won Sectional Title Girls Track 1988-89, Ctr St Conf Bsktbl 1970-71, West Div Girls Track 1993; Yrbk Dedication 1984-94; *office:* Waterville Jr Sr HS 381 Madison St Waterville NY 13480

BYRNE, JOHN JAMES, Dir of Evening & Weekend Coll; *b:* New York, NY; *m:* Marilyn Gilbert; *c:* Lisa Carol, John Jr.; *ed:* Manhattan Coll (BA) Langs 1962; Fordham Univ (MA) Fr 1963, (PHD) Romance Langs & Lits 1971; Attnd St Francis, Lehman Coll, William Paterson Coll, Trinity Coll, Columbia & Oxford Univ; *cr:* Dubois HS Eng Dept Chm 1963-74; Alfred E. Smith HS A.P.Guidance 1980; Bronx HS Superintendency Exec Asst 1982; John Dewey HS Curr Coord 1985-89; Bronx Comm Coll Evening & Weekend Coll Coord 1994-; *ai:* MLA 1993-; UFT, MENSA 1975-; Articles on Ed Pub.

BYRNE, KELLY ANN, HS Mathematics Teacher; *b:* Palmerton, PA; *m:* Kevin P.; *ed:* Kutztown Univ (BS) Scndry Ed, Math 1988; Rosemont Coll (MED) Tech in Ed 1995; Integrated Math & Sci Tchng; Commonwealth Partnership Initiative Grant; *cr:* Upper Darby HS Math Tchr 1990-; *ai:* 9th Grd Vlybl, Sftbl Coach; Adopt A Scholar Prgm Mentor; IAC, IPD; PSEA 1990-; *office:* Upper Darby HS 601 N Lansdowne Ave Upper Darby PA 19082

BYRNE, MICHAEL JOSEPH, Latin & Cmptr Appl Teacher; *b:* Waltham, MA; *m:* Katherine Ann O'Donnell; *c:* Elizabeth Ann, Charles Michael, Michael Jude; *ed:* Syracuse Univ (BA) Russian 1965; Boston St Coll (MED) His 1971; 30 Addl Credit Hrs Salem St Coll; *cr:* USAF Intelligence Specialist 1964-68; Andover HS Latin, Russian Tchr 1969-74; Andover East Jr HS Latin, Hum Tchr 1974-86; Andover Mid Schls Latin, Cmptr Applications 1986-; 6th Gr Exploratory Span 1993; *ai:* Assessment Team Chm; Taught Inservice Cmptr Courses; Andover Ed Assn 1969-, VP 1970-72; MA Tchrs Assn, NEA 1969-; BSA 1982-, Scoutmaster 1986-89, Troop Comm Chm 1989-, SM Merit Awd 1988, Scouters Key Awd 1989, Dist Merit Awd 1990, Scouters Trng Awd 1986; *office:* West MS Shawsheen Rd Andover MA 01810

BYRNE, PAMELA HYDE, 9th-12th Grd Mathematics Tchr; *b:* Kensington, CT; *m:* Stephen T.; *c:* Brian Edward, Aaron Douglas; *ed:* SCSC (BS) Math 1966; *cr:* Platt HS Math Tchr 1966-67; Swansboro HS Math Tchr 1967-68; Easton Jr HS Math Tchr 1968-69; Windsor HS Math Tchr 1969-70; Loomis Chaffee Schl Math Tchr 1981-; *ai:* Day Stndts Adv; NCTM 1994-; Jr Womens Club 1969-82, Pres; Windsor Shad Fest Bureau 1977-, Treas; Windor Shad Derby Co 1980-, Co-Chm; Herbert Savin Instructorship in Math; *office:* Loomis Chaffee Schl Batchelder Rd Windsor CT 06095

BYRNES, ANNE ELIZABETH, Director; *b:* Milwaukee, WI; *c:* Trea, Polly Vanderputten, Robin Vanderputten; *ed:* Coll of St Catherine (BA) Art 1962; Johnson St Coll (MA) GATE 1981; Montessori Tchr Trng Ctr Pre Primary Diploma 1970; *cr:* Wausau Montessori Schl Tchr 1970-71; Montessori Greenhouse Schl Tchr 1971-73; Neve Montessori Schl Tchr 1973; Highland Comm Schl Tchr of 5-7 Yr Olds 1974-76; Giving Tree Schl Head Tchr 1977-78; South Burlington Montessori Schl Dir 1981-; *office:* Sth Burlington Montessori Schl 1516 Williston Rd South Burlington VT 05403*

BYRNES, ROBERT WILLIAM, English Teacher; *b:* Morristown, NJ; *m:* Sherri Lyn Ackerman; *ed:* Newark St Coll (BA) Eng Ed 1970; Fairleigh Dickinson Univ (MA) Eng 1995; *cr:* Deptford Twp HS Eng Tchr 1971-72; Dover HS Eng Tchr 1972-; *ai:* NJEA, NEA 1972-; NCTE 1990-; NJ Cath Track Conf 1989-, Treas; *office:* Dover HS 100 Grace St Dover NJ 07801*

BYRNES, SUSAN KATHRYN, Sixth Grade Teacher; *b:* Marion, OH; *ed:* OH St Univ (BA) Elem Ed 1975, (MA) Ed, Children's Lit 1987; Attnd Odyssey Inst Georgetown Univ 1984; Metropolitan Opera Boston Coll Summers 1991-93; *cr:* St Rose Schl 6th Grd Tchr 1975-79; Our Lady of Peace Schl 6th Grd Tchr 1979-; *ai:* Safety Patrol Adv; Sixth Grd Opera Co Dir; Schl Musical Writer, Dir; CDEA 1980-; Soc of Children's Book Writers, Illustrators 1993-; Pub in Learning, Today's Cath Tchr; Amer Flwshp Tchrs Tour of Russian Schls 1989; *office:* Our Lady Of Peace Schl 40 E Dominion Blvd Columbus OH 43214*

BYRNES, THOMAS JAMES, Physics Teacher; *b:* New York, NY; *m:* Maryann Rosa; *c:* Thomas Jr., Timothy, Stephen, Peter, Andrew, James; *ed:* Marist Coll (BS) Physics 1965; Manhattan Coll (MS) Physics 1970; SUNY, Adelphi, RPI 60 Credit Hrs; *cr:* St Marys HS Tchr 1965-67; Deer Park HS Tchr 1967-; *ai:* Summer Schl Comm; Suffolk Cty Sci Tchr 1975-; NEA, AAPT 1967-; Parish Outreach 1994-, Bd Mem; NSF Grant 8 Credits RPI, 36 Credits Manhattan Coll; *office:* Deer Park HS 30 Rockaway Ave Deer Park NY 11729

BYRNES, WILLIAM ANDREW, English Teacher; *b:* Duquesne, PA; *m:* Helen Tasevich; *c:* Christopher, Martin, David; *ed:* Slippery Rock Univ of PA (BS) Eng & Speech 1961; IN Univ of PA (MED) Eng 1967; 9 Credit Hrs; *cr:* West Mifflin North HS Eng Tchr 1961-67; Beaver Cty Comm Coll Asst Prof of Eng 1967-74; Freedom Area HS Eng Tchr 1975-; *ai:* NEA & PSEA 1961-; PSEA Midwestern Region, Sec; NCTE 1961-76; Freedom Area Ed Assoc 1975-; Am Cancer Soc 1983-88, PR Chm, Cert Notable Svc 1984; Beaver Area Lib Bd 1983-, Pres; Beaver HS Soccer Boosters 1987-, Sec, Dedication Awd 1988; Beaver Co Task Force Drug & Alcohol 1987-; Sts Peter & Paul Church 1992-, Parish Cncl; Slippery Rock Univ of PA Alumni Assn Pres 1973-74, Distngd Svc Awd 1974 & Past Pres Svc Awd 1995; *office:* Freedom Area HS 1190 Bulldog Dr Freedom PA 15042*

BYRON, NANCY J., Eighth Grade Teacher; *b:* Fall River, MA; *m:* John; *c:* Keith, Jessica; *ed:* Univ MA at Dartmouth (BA) Math 1971; *cr:* Mt St Joseph's Schl 1st-3rd Tchr 1971-74; St Stanislaus Schl 5th-6th Grd Tchr 1984-89; St Jean Baptiste Schl 8th Grd, 6th-7th Grd Math Tchr 1991-; *ai:* Tchr in Charge; Yrbk Adv; Sci Fair Co-Coord; MS Dance Coord; HS, MS Liaison; NCEA; *office:* St Jean Baptiste Schl 64 Lamphor St Fall River MA 02721

BYTHEWOOD, LORRAINE M. GOMILLION, 6th Grade Teacher; *b:* Hempstead, NY; *m:* Charles Augustus; *c:* Debra Marie Bythewood-Ely, Charles Emerson, Susan Elizabeth; *ed:* SUNY at Oneonta (BA) Elem Ed 1957; 30 Hrs in Continuing Ed Curr Areas C. W. Post, LIU; *cr:* Saw Mill Schl 1 Grd Tchr 1957-58; Harrison Schl 1-2 Grd Tchr 1958-60; Meadow & Brookside Schls 1-3 Grd Tchr 1963-70; Shubert Schl K-6 Grd Tchr 1973-; Harbor Schl K-6 Grd Tchr 1973-; Plaza Schl K-6 Grd Tchr 1973-; Brookside Schl 6 Grd Tchr 1982-; *ai:* 6 Grd Grad Preparation, Ceremony Coord; 6 Grd Chprsn; Baldwin Tchrs Assn; Baldwin PTA; St Lawrence of Canberbury Episcopal Church Schl 1979-90, Supt, Tchr; Episcopal Church Women 1979-, Treas 1985-90; St John's Church 1990-; St John's Club 1994-; *office:* Brookside Elem Schl 940 Stanton Ave E Baldwin NY 11510

C

CABAUP, JOSEPH JOHN, Science Professor; *b:* Bronx, NY; *m:* Nancy Ann Peters; *c:* Joseph E., Jean M.; *ed:* Hunter Coll (BA) Physics 1962; Univ of NC (MS) Geology 1969; *cr:* Winthrop Coll Assist Prof Chem & Physics 1967-70; Franconia Coll Tchr 1970-71; Dartmouth HS Sci Tchr 1971-72; RI Jr Coll Assist Prof of Physics 1972-74; NH Tech Coll Sci Prof 1974-; *ai:* Alumni Relations, Competency Based, Safety Comms; ME Cert Geologist 1974-; AAAS 1971-; Geological Soc of Amer 1972-; Weeks St Park Assoc 1986-, Past Pres, Bd Mem; Conservation Commission 1984-93, Past Chair, Past Pres; *office:* NH Tech Coll At Berlin 2020 Riverside Dr Berlin NH 03570

CABLE, KATHLEEN M., Language Arts & Math Rdng Tchr; *b:* Binghamton, NY; *m:* Laurence Ray; *c:* Matthew, Catherine, Daniel; *ed:* St Univ Coll at Buffalo (BS) El Ed, Eng 1971; 34 Hrs St Univ at Binghamton; *cr:* Kenmore Jr HS 7th Grd Rdng, 8th Grd Eng Tchr 1971-75; Chenango Vly Cntrl HS 8th Grd Eng, Remedial Writing Tchr 1975-86; Deposit HS 9th Grd Eng, 12th Grd Critical Writing, Pub Speaking, Sci Fiction, Theatre Arts Tchr 1986-94; Deposit Elem Schl 6th Grd Tchr, Afton Consortium of Adult Ed GED Prgm 1994-; *ai:* Renaissance Faire Mime Performances; Stu Newspaper; Journals From Past; Echoes Play Project; Poetry Recitation; Jr Class, 6th Grd Class Adv; Co-Founder Deposit Past Prom Party 1989-; NYSUT 1971-; Kenmore Tchr Assn 1971-75; Chenango Vly Tchrs Assn 1975-85, 2nd VP 1 Yr; Deposit Tchrs Assn 1985-, Votel Cope Chprsn 1 Yr; DTA Action Comm 1 Yr; Deposit Effective Schls Comm 3 Yrs; Deposit Booster Club 1992-; Deposit Tchr of Yr Comm 1995; HS Tchr of Month; Tchrs Assn HS Tchr of Yr.*

CABLE, WILLIAM BRANT, Adult Basic & Literacy Ed Dir; *b:* Steubenville, OH; *m:* Marsha Powell; *c:* Ariana, Austin II, Courtney; *ed:* OH Univ (BSJ) Comms 1970; Attnd Kent St, Univ of Steubenville; *cr:* Edison Lcl Schl Adult Basic Ed Tchr 1977-88, Dir Adult Basic & Literacy Ed 1988-, Grds 7 & 8 His Tchr, Campground Mgr; *ai:* Selection Comm; Adult Ed Awds; Camp Edison Drug Awarenss Camp; Stu, Tchr Mentor; OAACE 1977-; NEA, OEA 1972-; Edison Lcl Ed Assn 1972-, Bldg Rep; Amer Forestry Assn, NCMT 1980-; OH Campground Owners 1985-; Assn St, Fed Private Dam Owners 1990-; Elks 1989-; Literacy Bd 1988-90; Amer Water Ski Assn 1995-; Edison Lcl Tchr of Yr 1988; Adult Basic & Literacy Ed Dir Awd; *office:* Edison Local Schl Dist PO Box 158 Hammondsville OH 43930*

CABRAL, ADELIO A., Mathematics Teacher; *b:* St Michael Azores, Portugal; *m:* Tracie Ann Poisson; *c:* Matthew, Timothy, Ryan; *ed:* RI Coll (BS) Scndry Ed, Math 1988; 24 Credit Hrs Math RI Coll; *cr:* Ponaganset HS Math Tchr 1988-89; Smithfield HS Math Tchr 1989-; *ai:* Girls Var Soccer Coach; Adv Math League Team; NEA 1988-; NCTM, RI Math Tchrs Assn 1990-; *office:* Smithfield HS 90 Pleasant View Ave Smithfield RI 02917

CABRAL, CATHERINE ELIZABETH (MELLO), Mathematics Teacher; *b:* Fall River, MA; *m:* Joseph M.; *c:* Christina Stevens, Colby Joseph; *ed:* RI Coll (BA) Elem Ed & Math 1979; 30 Addl Grad Credits at SMU Bridgewater St Coll; *cr:* Somerset Schl Dept Sub Tchr 1979; Norton Schl System Math Tchr 1980; Somerset HS 9th-12th Grd Math Tchr 1980-; *ai:* Math Curr Comm 1983-84, 1993-94; Math, Cmptr Curr Comm 1993-94; NEA, MA Tchrs Assn, Somerset Tchrs Assn 1980-; Cystic Fibrosis Fnd 1979-82; Golden Apple Awd 1993; *office:* Somerset HS Grandview Ave Ext Somerset MA 02726

CABRAL, EDWARD M., Mathematics Teacher; *b:* Taunton, MA; *m:* Mirella Gasparotto; *c:* Lisa Anne, Paula M.; *ed:* Bridgewater St Coll (BS) Ed 1959, (MS) Ed 1966; 15 Credit Hrs Univ of Conn NSF Grant; *cr:* Normandin Jr High Math Tchr 1959-60; Stoughton High Math Tchr 1963-70, Coord of Math 1970-83, Math Tchr 1983-; *ai:* Math Team Adv 1972-76; Hnr Soc Adv 1970-75; Various Schl Related Comm; NCTM 1963-; NEA, MTA, NCTA STA 1963-; NEMAM, ATMIM 1980-; *office:* Stoughton HS 232 Pearl St Stoughton MA 02072*

CABRAL, PAUL ANTHONY, Gen Music Teacher & Choral Dir; *b:* New Bedford, MA; *ed:* Univ of Lowell (BA) Music Ed 1982, (BA) Music Performance 1982; *cr:* Music on the Move 2-8 Grd Instrumental Tchr 1982-83; Allen P Keith Jr HS Gen Music Tchr, Choral Dir 1983-; *ai:* Cabaret Players, Allen Cabaret Players Dir; All City Jr HS Chorus; Schlsp Comm; Fac Advy Cncl; NEA, MTA, MENCA, NBEA 1983-, Bd Dirs 3 Yrs; St Julie Biliart Choir 1993-, Brass, Asst Conductor; St Marys Parish S Dart 1990-, Asst Choir Dir; Jubilate Chorale 1994-, Org Comm; *office:* Allen P Keith Jr HS 70 Hathaway Blvd New Bedford MA 02740

CACACE, IRINA R., Frgn Lang Dept Head & Teacher; *b:* Rome, Italy; *ed:* Univ of MA (BA) Span 1968, (MED) Ed 1993; NY Univ (MA) Latin Amer Lit 1970; *cr:* Coll Wegmann at Beirut Eng & Italian Tchr 1984-87; Amer Univ at Beirut Italian Instr 1986-89; Italian Embassy at Beirut Consular Ofcr 1987-89; Salem HS Span & Head Tchr 1990-; *ai:* Tchr Cert Bd of MA Examiner; Part-Time Instr; NHS Fac Adv; MAFLA 1990-; NEASC Evaluation Team Mem; *office:* Salem HS 77 Wilson Rd Salem MA 01970

CACCAMO, JOAN E., Business & Computer Teacher; *b:* Brooklyn, NY; *ed:* St Francis Coll at Brooklyn (BS) Mngmt 1983; Fordham Univ (MS) Ed 1988; Intership Admin, Supervision 6 Credits 1990-91; *cr:* Bishop Kearney HS Bus, Cmptr Tchr 1984-89; Catherine Mc Auley HS Bus, Cmptr Tchr 1989-; Brooklyn Coll Adjunct Prof Group Games Prgm 1993-; *ai:* Ath Dir; Yrbk Moderator; Var Bsktbl Coach; Kings Cty Amer Legion Auxiliary 1961-, Cty Pres; Newspapers Coach of Yr Awd 1989 Sftbl; Gatorade & Nom by Prin Coaches Care Awd 1992; *office:* Catherine Mc Auley HS 710 E 37th St Brooklyn NY 11203

CACCAVALE, BEVERLY ROSE (CARNISH), Biology Teacher; *b:* Passaic, NJ; *m:* Gaetano; *c:* Christopher, Tiffany; *ed:* Adelphi Univ (BA) Bio 1971; CW Post (MS) Bio 1972; 30 Addl Credits Beyond Masters; *cr:* Paramus HS Bio Tchr 1972-79 & 1984-; *ai:* Marine Bio Club & Fresh Class Adv; Faculty Rep; Curr Cncl & Negotiations Mem; Faculty Review Hnr Soc, Liaison, & Attendance Review Comms; Mid St Comm Chair; Final Exam Comm; Grad Reqrmnts Comm; NEA & BCEA 1972-; NJMEA, NABT, NMEA, NJSTA & ANJEE; Jr Womens Club 8 Yrs, Ed Chair; St Philips Schl Bd 5 Yrs, VP 1 Yr; Schl #15 6 Yrs VP, Recording Sec & Corresponding Sec; WWM Schl 3 Yrs Corresponding Sec; Little League 7 Yrs, Team Mother; Cert of Commendation Bd of Ed 1989; Outstanding Tchr Awd Univ of Chicago 1988; NJ Governors Tchr Recognition Awd 1990-91; *office:* Paramus HS 99 E Century Rd Paramus NJ 07652

CACCAVALE, SAL,JR., High School Mathematics Tchr; *b:* Brooklyn, NY; *ed:* Saint Francis Coll (BS) Math Ed 1972; NY Univ (MA) Math Ed 1976; *cr:* Msgr McClancy HS Math Tchr 1972-85, Dept Chair 1982-85; Mainland Reg Math Tchr 1985-; *ai:* Schl Newspaper Hoofprints; Math Club; NJEA 1985-; *office:* Mainland Regional HS 1301 Oak Ave Linwood NJ 08221

CACCIOLA, ANGELA N., Math Teacher & Dept Chprsn; *b:* Brooklyn, NY; *ed:* St Francis Coll (BS) Math, Elem Ed 1971; Wagner Coll (MS) Elem Ed 1975; *cr:* Sacred Heart of J&M Schl Tchr 1972-73; PS 104 Tchr 1973-76; Our Lady of Grace Schl 8th Grd Tchr 1976-84; The Mary Louis Acad Math Tchr 1984-; *ai:* Yrbk Moderator; NCTM 1984-; ATMNYC 1982-, Pres, VP, Cor Sec; *office:* Mary Louis Acad 17621 Wexford Ter Jamaica NY 11432

CACI, GERALD F., Social Studies Teacher; *b:* Teaneck, NJ; *m:* Marianne Gallagher; *c:* Dylan; *ed:* Glassboro St Coll (BA) His & Soc Stud 1984; *cr:* Manasquan Elem Schl 8th Grd Soc Stud Tchr 1986-89; Brick Twp HS Soc Stud Tchr 1990-; *ai:* Boys Bsktbl Head Coach; Law Class Mock Trial; NEA; *office:* Brick Twp HS 346 Chambersbridge Rd Brick NJ 08723

CACI, KATHRYN MARY, Third Grade Teacher; *b:* Leominster, MA; *m:* Gerald M.; *c:* Amy B., Jeremy L.; *ed:* Fitchburg St Coll (BA) Elem Ed 1970; 30 Credits Post Grad Stud; *cr:* Gardner Pub Schls Third Grd Tchr 26 Yrs; *ai:* Tchr Asst Team; Schl Advy Cncl; Prof Dev, Curr Comms; Mentor Tchr; NEA 1970-; MTA 1070-, Credential, Ballots Comm; GEA 1970-, Past Ex-Bd, Grievance Chair; WLTA 1985-; Article Pub; *office:* Waterford Street Schl 62 Waterford St Gardner MA 01440*

CACI, MARIANNE GALLAGHER, Art Teacher; *b:* Newark, NJ; *m:* Gerald F. Jr.; *c:* Dylan; *ed:* Georgian Court Coll (BA) Art Ed; Attnd Brookdale Comm Coll; *cr:* Manasquan Elem Art Tchr 1979-91; Manaskan HS Art Tchr 1991-; *ai:* HS Art Club; Elem Schl Newspaper; NJEA 1979-; Union Landing Historical 1992-, Mbrshp Ofcr; Tchr of the Yr 1988-89; *office:* Manasquan HS Broad St Manasquan NJ 08736*

CACIOPOLI, ROBERT A., English Teacher; *b:* New Haven, CT; *m:* Edith Lucille Lazaro; *c:* Lisa, Robert S., Laura, Victoria; *ed:* So CT St Univ (BS) PE 1961; So CT St Univ (MS) PE 1971; Fairfield Univ (CAS) Admin 1974; *cr:* Franklin Schl EMR Tchr 1961-62; Elias Howe Schl 7-8 Grd Eng Tchr 1962-69; Eastside MS 7-8 Grd Eng Tchr 1969-83; Paul Laurence Dunbar Schl 7-8 Grd Eng Tchr 1983-86; Cntrl Magnet HS Eng Tchr 1986-; *ai:* Boys Bsktbl, Boys Sftbl Coach; Westside Division Trophy 1966; City Championship 1966; BEA 1961-, Bldg Del 7 Yrs; CEA 1962-; NEA; Messiah Bapt 1978-, Dir Tutoring Prgm 1977-80; Flwshp Univ of CT 1966; Federal Rdng Grant 1972; Rdng Grant Classics in the Classroom 1982; Mini-Grant Asian Amer Newsletter 1991; *home:* 490 Woodside Ave Bridgeport CT 06606

CADDEAU, MEG M., English & History Teacher; *b:* CO; *m:* Patrick; *ed:* Brown Univ (BA) His 1986; Tchr Coll Columbia Univ (MA) His 1989; *cr:* Cate Schl Hum Tchr 1989-93; Convent of the Sacred Heart Hum Tchr 1993-; *ai:* Var Swim Team; Lit Magazine; NEH Summer Seminar 1992; Cncl for Basic Ed Ind Stud in Hum 1994; *office:* Convent Of Sacred Heart Schl 1 E 91st St New York NY 10128

CADDEN, TIM FRANCIS, English Teacher; *b:* Summit Hill, PA; *m:* Adele Kosciolek; *c:* Erin, Timothy; *ed:* Holy Cross (BA) Eng & Ed-Magna Cum Laude 1975; Univ of PA (MA) Eng 1977; 42 Credit Hrs beyond Masters; *cr:* Univ of PA Tchng Fellow 1976-79; Dept of Labor Mgr Yth Svcs 1980-82; Catasauqua HS Eng Tchr 1982-; *ai:* Lit Magazine, Sr Class & Ski Club Adv; Yrbk Past Adv 7 Yrs; NEA 1982-; PSEA 1982-; Phi Beta Kappa Hnr Soc; *home:* 1121 Sherwood Dr Laurys Station PA 18059

CADELINA, DAVID JONATHAN, Math Teacher; *b:* Boston, MA; *m:* Megan Anne; *ed:* Hamilton Coll (BA) Govt 1987; Fairfield Univ (MA) Scndry Ed 1994; *cr:* Barry Jr HS Math, Sci Tchr 1989-92; Bergen Cath HS Physics, Bio Tchr 1992-94; Harding HS Math, Cmptr Tchr 1994-; *ai:* Ftbl, Indoor Track, Head Track, Weightlifting Coach; Fac Cncl, Curr Dev Comm; Bsktbl Score Keeper; ID Card Technician; NEA, CEA 1994-; CT Coaches Assn 1987-; Woodbridge Recreation 1987-, Trng Staff, Mem of Yr 1992; ANPPC 1990-, MR CT 1992-93; *office:* Harding HS 1734 Central Ave Bridgeport CT 06610*

CADENA, AIDA DELGADO, Spanish Teacher; *b:* Santo Domingo, Dominican Repub; *m:* Enrique; *c:* Aida, Alexandra; *ed:* NY City Comm Coll (AA) Lbrl Arts 1972; Hunter Coll (BA) Span Lit, Ed 1974, (MS) Biling Ed 1990; *cr:* Elijah D. Clark Jr HS 149 Span Tchr 1974-85; Grover Cleveland HS Span Tchr 1985-86; Newtown HS Span Tchr 1986-; *ai:* FTA Club; AIDS Awareness, Regents Endorsed Diplomas Comms; AFT, UFT 1974-; Tchr of Yr 1994; *office:* Newtown HS 48-01 90th St Elmhurst NY 11373*

CADIGAN, JOANNE, History Teacher; *b:* Elizabeth, NJ; *ed:* Quinnipiac Coll (BA) His 1987; St Peter Coll (MA) Ed & Schl Admin 1991; *cr:* St Joseph Schl His Tchr 1987-91; Tobu Bd of Ed JET Pgm Eng Tchr 1991-94; Mt St Mary Acad His Tchr 1994-; *ai:* Yrbk, Jr St of Amer Club & Japanese Club Adv; NCEA 1987-; NEH Grant 4 Texts in Japan 1995; *office:* Mount St Mary Acad 1645 US Highway 22 Watchung NJ 07060

CADMAN, CHARLES ROBERT, Science Department Chairman; *b:* Mc Keesport, PA; *ed:* CA Univ of PA (BS) Chem 1966, (MED) Chem Ed 1972; *cr:* Monessen HS Tchr 1966-70; Mc Keesport HS Tchr 1970-; *ai:* Natl Honor Soc Comm; Planned Course-Strategic Planning Prgm; Facilitator In-Svc Prgm; NEA, PSEA 1966-; MAEA 1970-; *office:* Mc Keesport Area HS 1960 Eden Park Blvd Mc Keesport PA 15132

CAESAR, FRANKLIN NICHOLAS, Assistant Headmaster; *b:* St Georges, Grenada WI; *m:* MarthajeanBuchanan; *c:* Nicholas, Noah; *ed:* Grad Ctr CUNY (BA) Eng, Sec Ed 1977; Fordham Univ at L C (MS) K-12 Rdng 1984; Doctoral Candidate in Admin, Policy, Urban Ed; *cr:* Fordham Univ Lincoln Ctr Eng, Rdng Instr HEOP 1981-83; Xavier HS Dir HAP 1985-90, Eng Instr 1977-90, Chair Eng Dept 1984-90, Asst Headmaster 1990-; *ai:* Var Bsktbl Coach 1984-87; African-Amer Culture Club Moderator 1977-; Fin Aid, Schl Life of the Bd of Trustees Comms; ASCD, NASSP 1990-; Phi Delta Kappa 1988-; Coll Bd 1990-, Acad Assembly Del; CHILD 1995-, VP, Sec; AAPC Spence Chapin 1994-, Vice Chair; Holy Rosary R C Church 1980-, Trustee, Man of Yr 1992; Xavier Hall of Fame 1995-, Voted In Awd; Who's Who in Amer Ed 1988-89; Edctr of Yr Assn of Tchrs of NY 1990; Pub in Conversations 1993; Rep Fordham Univ with Doctoral Proposal at Grad Seminar of AERA 1995; *office:* Xavier HS 30 W 16th St New York NY 10011

CAEZZA, JOSEPH RICHARD, Biology Teacher; *b:* Syracuse, NY; *c:* Brian; *ed:* Onondaga Comm Coll (AA) Sci 1967; Univ of Toledo (BS) Bio 1970; ESF at Syracuse Advance Stud Forest Zoology 1982; Grad Work Cortland St, Oswego St; Schl of Environmental Sci & Forestry at SU; *cr:* Bristol Labs Microbiology Tech 1970; Shea MS Sci Tchr 1970; Corcoran HS Earth Sci, Bio Tchr 1982; *ai:* Site Based Planning Comm; NEA, STA, NYS 1970-; NYSGOA 1982-, Pres; CYNGOA 1980-, Sec; *office:* Corcoran HS 919 Glenwood Ave Syracuse NY 13207

CAFARELLI, MARY ELIZABETH, Teacher of the Handicapped; *b:* Dayton, OH; *c:* Tina; *ed:* East Stroudsburg Univ (BS) Spec Ed 1988; 30 Grad Credits Toward Masters in Spec Ed at Jersey City St Coll; *cr:* Lounsbury Hollow MS Tchr of the Handicapped 1988-94; Glen Meadow MS Tchr of the Handicapped 1994-; *ai:* Fac Senate; Core Team; Discipline Comm; CEC 1994-; NJEA 1988-; A Plus for Kids Grant 1990; Dist Spec Ed Tchr of Yr 1994; Dist Mini-Grant 1994; Whos Who in Amer Ed 5th Edition 1995; *office:* Glen Meadow MS PO Box 516 Vernon NJ 07462*

CAFFARO, PHYLLIS J., Fifth Grade Teacher; *b:* New York City, NY; *ed:* Southampton Coll (BA) Psych 1967; C. W. Post Coll (MS) Cnslng 1972; Permanent Cert K-6 1972, Guid Cnslng 1972; *cr:* Hauppauge Schls Elem Tchr 1967-87, Elem Sci Specialist 1987-93, Elem Tchr 1993-; *ai:* GATE Sci Specialist 1980-86, Coord 1989-93; Ed Mem Sci Rsrch Prgms 1989-93; Stu Cncl Adv 1994-; NSTA, CESO, Am Museum of Natural His 1988-; AFT, NYSUT 1967-; Alliance for Environmental Ed 1990-, Natl Conf Presenter; Comprehensive Instrl Mngmt System Statewide Comm for Sci Testing 1989-92; BOCES Wkshp Ldr 1990-91; *office:* Pines Elem Schl Holly Dr Smithtown NY 11787*

CAFFERTY, ANITA BIONDOLILLO, Music Tchr & Choral Conductor; *b:* St Albans, NY; *ed:* Hofstra Univ (BS) Music Ed 1965; C.W. Post LI Univ (MS) Music Ed 1981; *cr:* Sewanaka CSD Music Tchr 1965-66; Sachem CSD #5 Music Tchr, Choral Conductor; *ai:* 7-8th Grd Chorus; Select Show Choir; Musical Dir & Pit Conductor Sachem South HS; Suffolk Co Music Educators All Cty Chorus Div I & II; NYSSMA Solo Competition; Sagamore Jr HS Musical Dir; Sachem Cntrl TA 1966-, Bldg Rep, Tchr Ctr Bd 20 Yr Svc Awd; NYSUT 1966-, St Del 10 Yr Svc Awd; AFT 1971-, Natl Del Meritorious Svc Awd; NEA 1966-74, Alternate Del; Suffolk Cty Music Edctrs Assn; 99 Intnl Organ of Women Pilots 1973-, Aviation Educ Chm; Pilot Club Intnl 1982-90, Pub Relations, Distinguished Svc Awd; Civil Air Patrol 1976-80, Aerospace Ed Coord 2nd Lt; LI Vegetarian Soc 1992-, Animal Legislation Chm; 1993 Guest Choral Conductor Sachem Dist Elem Festival; NY St Schl of Music Adjudicator Voice; NASA Tchr in Space Applicant; *office:* Seneca Jr HS 850 Main St Holbrook NY 11741*

CAFFEY, KIMBERLY ANN, Secondary Education Teacher; *b:* Philadelphia, PA; *ed:* Ursinus Coll (BS) Hlth, PE 1986; Attnd Chestnut Hill Coll, Gratz Coll, Tchr Ed Inst; *cr:* Ancillae Assumpta Acad Tchr, Coach, Ath Dir 1986-91; Springfield HS Tchr, Coach 1991-; *ai:* Head Var Bsktbl, Head 9th Grd Field Hockey, Asst Var Sftbl Coach; Womens Ath Rep to Cntrl League; PSEA, SEA 1991-; AAHPERD 1986-; YAPB Ursinus Coll 1988-; Alumni Exec Bd Ursinus Coll 1994-, Alumni Rep; Pub Numerous Articles; *office:* Springfield HS 49 W Leamy Ave Springfield PA 19064

CAFFIER, JAMIE A., English & Public Speaking Tchr; *b:* Toledo, OH; *m:* Roger H.; *c:* Roger Justin, Brett Jamison; *ed:* OH Univ (BFA) Theater 1979; Penn St Univ (MA) Hum 1989; *cr:* Cntrl Dauphin East HS Eng, Pub Speaking, Drama Tchr 1986-; *ai:* Directing Schl Play; Coaching Pub Speakers for Events; Mid-St Steering Comm; Comm Task Force; Makup-Hair for Spring Musical; Directing Sr Showcase Play; Assorted Dist Comms; Cntrl Dauphin EA, NEA, PSEA 1986-; *office:* Central Dauphin East Sr HS 626 Rutherford Rd Harrisburg PA 17109

CAFFREY, DANIEL, Mathematics Teacher; *b:* Brooklyn, NY; *m:* Patricia Mc Court; *c:* Gerard, Christopher, Ellen Marie, Brendan; *ed:* Boston Coll (BS) Math 1965; 55 Credits Math, Ed Brooklyn Coll; *cr:* Bishop Ford HS Math Tchr 1965-76; S Brunswick HS Math Tchr 1976-; *ai:* Sr Class, Acad Team Adv; Asst to Dir Aths; NEA 1976-; SBEA 1976-, Pres; *office:* South Brunswick HS PO Box 183 Major Rd Monmouth Junction NJ 08852*

CAFISO, BONNA ZUCH, Fr Tchr & Foreign Lang Supvr; *b:* York, PA; *m:* Bruno; *c:* Danielle Marie; *ed:* Millersville (BSED) Fr 1968; Bloomsburg (MED) Fr 1972; Supvr Cert Foreign Lang 1980; Stud at Universite de Montpellier France; York, PA's Exchange Tchr to Arles France; *cr:* Schls of Arles France Exchange Tchr 1968-69; Shikellamy Jr HS Fr Tchr 1969-73; Shikellamy HS Fr Tchr 1973-; Shikellamy Schl Dist For Lang Supvr 1980-; Susquehanna Univ For Lang Methods Instr 1980-; *ai:* Fr Club, Societe Honoraine de Francais Advs; HS Scheduling, Curr Comms; NEA, PSEA, SEA 1969-; AATF 1972-; ACTFL 1982-; PSMLA 1980; ASCD 1994; Delta Kappa Gamma 1985-; Fellowship to Attend NEH Inst at Penn St Univ 1984; *home:* RR 2 Box 283K Sunbury PA 17801*

CAHALANE, CAROL, Health Educator & Dept Chair; *b:* Boston, MA; *m:* Wesley Coombs; *ed:* Univ of Lowell (BS) Hlth Ed 1988, (MED) Curr, Instruction 1991; *cr:* Westford Pub Schls Hlth Edctr 1988-89; Univ of Lowell Tchng Asst, Dormitory Resident Dir 1989-90; Phillips Exeter Acad Hlth Instr, Dorm Adv 1990-; *ai:* Dormitory Head; Club Adv; Peer Ed Coord; Ind Schl Hlth Assn 1990-; Amer Alliance of Hlth, PE, Recreation & Dance 1989-; Amer Schl Hlth Assn, Sexuality Infor & Ed Caucus of US, Amer Coll Hlth Assn 1993-; Sallie Mae Awd for Excl in First Yr Tchng 1989; Charles E. Ryberg Awd 1993; *office:* Phillips Exeter Acad 20 Main St Exeter NH 03833*

CAHALANE, JOAN A., 2nd Grade Teacher; *b:* Boston, MA; *ed:* Boston St Coll (BS) Ed 1969; Cambridge Coll (MEd) Integrated Stud 1992; 45 Addl Credits; Attnd Fitchburg St; *cr:* Mary Hemenway Schl 2nd Grd Tchr 1969-70; L. L. Damon Schl 1st, 3rd Grd Tchr 1971-81; L. M. Jacobs Schl 2nd Grd Tchr 1981-; *ai:* PR&R; Schl Cncl; Chld Stud Team Chair; NEA 1969-; HTA, PCEA 1971-; *office:* Lillian Jacobs Elem Schl 180 Harborview Rd Hull MA 02045

CAHAYLA, GREGORY, HS Guidance Counselor; *b:* Passaic, NJ; *m:* Kathleen; *c:* Kristin, Scott; *ed:* Lambuth Univ (BS) His 1970; Montclair St Univ (MA) Cnslng 1986; *cr:* Saddle Brook HS His Tchr 1972-93, Guid Cnslr 1993-; *ai:* Bsktbl & Tennis Coach; Class & Stu Cncl Adv; NJEA 1972-; SBEA 1972-; BCCA 1988-; NJ Natl Guard 1970-76; Outstdng Citizen Awd; BCSL Coach of the Yr Bsktbl; *office:* Saddle Brook HS 355 Mayhill St Saddle Brook NJ 07663

CAHILL, PATRICK WILLIAM, Physical Education Instructor; *b:* Malone, NY; *m:* Katheleen Mary DeCoste; *c:* Kelley, Kevin; *ed:* Brockport St (BS) PE 1972; 30 Credit Hrs Various Colls; *cr:* Sauquoit Vly Cntrl Schl PE Instr 1972-; *ai:* Head Ftbl Coach 1979-; Head Track & Field Coach 1976-; NYSUT, AFT 1972-; NFICA 1983-, Century Club; NYSAHPERD 1990-; Amer Legion 1986-; *home:* 15 Cedar Ln New York Mills NY 13417

CAHILL, WARREN, English Teacher; *b:* Bronxville, NY; *m:* Cathy; *c:* Brendan, Elizabeth, Michael; *ed:* Manhattan Coll (BA) Eng Lit 1970; SUNY at New Paltz (MAT) Eng Lit 1982; *cr:* Washington HS Scndry Eng Tchr 1979-; *ai:* Adv Mock Trial Team, Quiz Bowl Team, NHS; Washingtonville Tchrs Assn 1979-, Bldg Rep 1985-89; Natl Endowment for the Hum 1990 Flwshp; Tchr of Excl NY St Eng Tchrs Cncl 1991; *office:* Washingtonville HS 54 W Main St Washingtonville NY 10992

CAHN, GEOFFREY STEPHEN, History Dept Chairperson; *b:* London, England; *m:* Mary Z. Lichtenberg; *c:* Anna; *ed:* Rutgers Univ (BA) His 1969; Jersey City St Coll (MA) His 1971; St Johns Univ (PHD) His 1982; *cr:* Jersey City Bd of Ed Tchr 1969-71; Jersey City St Coll Adj Prof 1970-71; St Johns Univ Tchng & Rsrch Fellow 1971-73; Yeshiva Univ HS Chm 1988-, Dir of Coll Guid 1994-; *ai:* Coll Guid Dir; Planning & Curr Comms; Music Club; Field Trip Coord; AHA 1971-; OAH 1971 Culture Assn 1994-; Theodore Roosevelt Assn 1986-; Numerou Pub; *office:* Yeshiva Univ HS For Boys 2540 Amsterdam Ave New 10033*

CAIN, ALICE FARRELL, Assoc Prof & Phy Thrpst Dir; *b:* W MA; *m:* Howard Lorson Jr.; *c:* Julie Lorson, Tracy, Ian, Jacob L Russell Sage Coll (BS) Phys Therapy 1980; NDT-Bobath Tre Children with Cerebral Palsy 1994; Continuing Ed Courses; *cr:* Hosp Staff Phys Therapist 1980-86; Chapel Hill Comm C Therapist 1984-88, 1992-94; Stark Tech Coll Instr, Asst Prof Assoc Prof, Prgm Dir 1994-; *ai:* Advy Bd Walsh Coll Phys Thera Bd PTAT; Curr Dev Tech Prep Consortium; Amer Phys The 1980-, Dist Treas, Del Natl Conf; Outstdng Prof 1994 by Pub Therapy Stu; *office:* Stark Tech Coll 6200 Frank Ave NW C 44720

CAIN, BARBARA KRIEGER, 6th Grade Math & Rdng Te Brooklyn, NY; *c:* Douglas, Brian; *ed:* Brooklyn Coll (BA) Math (MS) Ed 1969; Addl 90 Credit Hrs; *cr:* PS 158 1st Grd Tchr 19 345 1st Grd Tchr 1966-69; Scraggy Hill Elem Schl 1st Grd Tchr Newfield HS Scndry Math Tchr 1980; Selden Jr HS Scndry 1980; Dawnwood MS Scndry Math 8th Grd Tchr 1984-, 6th Rdng Tchr 1988-; *ai:* Effective Schls Chair; Mentor-Intern P Compact Comm; Educl Issues Chair for Mid Cntry Tchrs Assn; L Site Coord AFT's Thinking Math; NCTM; AFT; NYSUT; Mid C Assn; Womens Amer ORT, Local Pres, Regnl.

CAIN, CHRISTINE MANTI, Middle Schl Soc Stud Te Schenectady, NY; *m:* Joseph; *c:* Sarah, Patrick; *ed:* SUNY at Bu Soc Stud & Ed 1972; SUNY at Albany (MS) Ed & Rdng 1974; Crane Cntrl Schl 5th Grd Tchr & Chprsn 1972-93, MS Tchr 19 Ed Dept Soc Stud Consultant 1987-; *ai:* Stu Cncl Adv; Discipli Educationally Able Comm; Math Comm; Soc Stud Curr Comm 1974-; IC Tchrs Assn 1974-; Capital Dist Cncl for Soc Stud 199 from Tchr Ctr & Ichabod Crane Grant Pgm; Pub Resources Stud; *home:* 268 Rapp Rd Valatie NY 12184

CAIN, HAROLD C., Eng Comms & Videography Tchr; *b:* Sewi *m:* Karen Lee Mowry; *c:* Shara Lynn, Erin Ashley; *ed:* CAliforni of PA (BSEd) Comms 1973; PA St Univ; *cr:* West Allegheny 1974-; *ai:* Comm Svc Club, Videography Club Adv; Safe & Schls Comm; HS Stu Assistance Prgm Coord; NEA, PSEA, WA Bldg Rep, VP; PASAP 1986-; NCTE 1989-; F & AM of PA 1986 Rite 1987-; TVT Consortium Western Region SAP 1993-; *off* Allegheny HS 205 W Allegheny Rd Imperial PA 15126

CAIN, JUDITH ANN, 5th Grade Teacher; *b:* Monongahela, PA Univ of PA (BS) Elem 1967; Information Tech Ed Commonwea Writing Process; Let Them Write; His Southwestern PA; *cr:* M Elem 5th-6th Grd Tchr 8 Yrs; Midway Elem 6th Grd Tchr 8 Yrs, 4 Yrs; Mc Donald Elem 5th-6th Grd Tchr 8 Yrs; Ft Cherry Ele Grd Tchr 5 Yrs; *ai:* Textbook 1970, 1974, 1979, 1974, 1989, 1992 Grading 1982, Discipline 1978, 1989-90 Comms; PSEA, NEA Cherry Ed Assn 1967-, Sec 1969, Bldg Rep 1967-74; ITEC G *home:* RR 1 Box 56 River Hill Monongahela PA 15063

CAIN, KENNETH ROBERT, 9th Grade English Teacher; Ravenna, OH; *m:* Jana Susan Hamrick; *c:* Elizabeth Bonnie, Sar Jennifer Grace, Gregory Scott O'Brien, Kenneth Robert II; *ed* Univ (BA) Eng 1987, (MAT) Ed 1989; *cr:* Ashtabula Area City & Hnrs Eng Tchr 1989-; *ai:* Advy Consultant for JOGS Sch to W Frosh Career Unit Coord; Frosh Writing Unit Coord; Frosh Seminar; NEOTA 1989-; NEA 1989-; ATA 1989-, Bldg Rep *office:* Ashtabula HS 401 W 44th St Ashtabula OH 44004*

CAIN, LEONA MARIE, 7th-8th Grade Math Teacher; *b:* Wa DC; *ed:* Mt St Mary Coll (BSEd) Eng 1966; *cr:* DE, MD, OK, Two-Eight Grd Tchr 1950-86; St Clement Mary Hofbauer Schl 1986-; *ai:* Math Comm; NCEA 1960-; *office:* St Clement Mary Schl 1216 Chesaco Ave Baltimore MD 21237

CAIN, ROSA MARIE, Assistant Professor; *b:* Baltimore, MD; Jr.; *c:* Deborah L., Michael T.; *ed:* Coppin St Coll (BSN) Nrsng 1 of MD (MSN) Nrsng 1984; Univ of MD Adult Nuse Practitic 1971; *cr:* Provident Hosp CCU Supvr, Cardiac Care Coo Practitoner 1968-82, Employee Hlth Coord 1982-84; Amer Ca Fac 1984-90; Coppin St Coll Asst Prof 1989-; Edmondson Wests Ctr Fac 1992-; *ai:* Chi Eta Phi Spon; ANA; MNA; Sigma Theta Bd of Amer Heart Assn 1975-85, Several Svc Awds; *office:* Copp Schl of Nrsng 2500 W North Ave Baltimore MD 21216

CAIN, SUSAN C., Math Teacher; *b:* Elmira, NY; *ed:* Nazareth Eng 1962; SUNY at Brockport (MS) Ed, Emphasis in Math 197 Lady of Mercy HS Math Tchr 1962-72; Notre Dame HS Math T *ai:* Sr Class Moderator; Treas Activity Fund; NCTM 1978-; 1978-; *office:* Notre Dame HS 1400 Maple Ave Elmira NY 1490

CAIN, TIMOTHY THOMAS, English Teacher; *b:* Niskayuna Cynthia Ann Nygren; *c:* Dylan Thomas; *ed:* Plymouth St Coll (B 1989; *cr:* Newport HS Eng Tchr 1989-95; Pinkerton Acad Eng T *ai:* Citizenship Comm; Yrbk Adv 1990-92; JC Sftbl Coach 1993- Ftbl 1994; NEASC Accreditation Eng Chprsn; NCTE 1989 Pinkerton Acad 5A Pinkerton St Derry NH 03773*

CAINE, DANA M., High School Mathematics Tchr; *b:* New Yor Stuart Sheinbaum; *c:* Emma S.; *ed:* Syracuse Univ (BA) Math Ed Univ (MA) Math Ed 1993; Montclair St Univ 12 Credit Hrs towar Cert; *cr:* GlenRock HS Math Tchr 1989-; *ai:* HS Bowl Adv Tr NCTM 1988-; NJEA & NEA 1989-; *office:* Glen Rock HS 400 Ave GlenRock NJ 07452

CAINE, LORRAINE SMITH, English & Literature Teache River, MA; *m:* Leo J. Caine III; *c:* Karyn Smith, Michael Smith MA at Dartmouth (BA) Eng Ed 1972; 30 Credit Hrs Beyond D Diman Regnl Voc HS Eng Lit Tchr 1973-; *ai:* Jr Class Adv; Curr Comm; Schedule Update Comm; Eng Courses Revision Com Tchr Assn, NEA, MTA 1973-; Fall River Little Theatre 19 Raising Chair Bd of Dir; Somerset Bowling Assn 1988-, Trea Diman Reg Voc Tech HS 251 Stonehaven Rd Fall River MA 027

CAIRNS, COLETTE D., Business Teacher; *b:* Greensburg, P Scott; *ed:* IN Univ of PA (BS) Bus Ed 1985; Penn St Univ C 1995; *cr:* Clarion-Limestone HS Bus Tchr 1986-89; Elizabeth HS Bus Tchr 1989-; *ai:* FBLA Adv; Elizabethtown Area HS T 1995; *office:* Elizabethtown Area HS 600 E High St Elizabet 17022

CAIRNS, KRISTEN SMITH, French & English Teacher; *b:* S IL; *m:* Bradley D.; *ed:* Wheaton Coll (BA) Fr, Sec Ed 1991; Comm Coll 3 Credit Hrs ESL Undergrad; Southern CT Univ 5 Grad Eng; *cr:* Woodlands Acad Houseparent, Dorm Mother 19 Tchr 1992-93; Chrstn Heritage Schl Fr, Eng Tchr 1993-; *ai:* Homeless Club 1993-95; Accreditation Team; ACTFL 199 Christian Heritage Schl 575 White Plains Rd Trumbull CT 0661

CAIRNS, ROGER A., Professor of Fine Arts; *b:* Ligouier, PA; Adams; *c:* Roger Louis; *ed:* Carnegie Inst of Tech (BFA) Paintin 1967; Univ of PA (MFA) Painting 1970; *cr:* Phila Museum of Childrens Prgm Tchr 1970-71; Phila comm col Adj Prof 1969-7 m Col Fine Arts Prof 1972-; *ai:* Art Club Spon; Print Prize Phillips odmere Gallery; HM Paints Phillips Mill; Exhibit Artists House; Montgomery County Comm Coll 340 Dekalb Pike Blue Bell PA

, SUZAN SIEKMANN, Biology Teacher; *b:* Buffalo, NY; *m:* .; *c:* Christopher; *ed:* St Lawrence Univ (BS) Chem 1962; SUNY brook (PHD) Molecular Genetics 1987; Adelphi Univ Sci Ed; *cr:* Anne HS Chem Tchr 1962-63; Walt Whitman HS Chem Tchr Ward Melville HS Sci Tchr 1966-; *ai:* NSTA 1963-; Sci Tchrs NY St 1963-; AAAS 1987-; Amer Bio Tchrs 1987-; Setauket Church 1981-, Ordained Elder & Deacon; NSF Flwshp 1966; SUNY at Stonybrook Chptr 1989; *home:* PO Box 2854 Setauket 3*

, THERESA ANN, Health Occupations Instructor; *b:* Pittsburgh, Duquesne Univ (BSN) Nrsng 1989; Grad Nrsng Ed; IN Univ of PA Cert 1995; *cr:* The Med Ctr RN, IMCU 1989-90; Comm Coll Lab, ept 1990-91; Univ of Pittsburgh Med Ctr Clinical Nurse III Beaver Cty AVTS Hlth Occupations Instr 1993-; *ai:* Voc Indstrl Amer Adv 1993-95; PEA 1993-; Beaver Cty AVTS EA 1993-, Sec; ada Sigma 1994-; John J. Thomas Schlsp Awd 1984-89; *office:* Cty AVT Schl 145 Poplar Dr Monaca PA 15061

, LORI CHASE CAIAZZO, Pre-K Teacher; *b:* Brooklyn, NY; *m:* *c:* Daniel, Richard, Jaimie; *ed:* Brooklyn Coll (BA) Early Chldhd (MS) Rdng Ed 1978; 30 Credit Hrs; *cr:* Assoc YM-YWHAs of ery Schl Tchr 1975-78 & 1983-84; NYC Bd of Ed Tchr 1985-; *ai:* r Adv; AFT 1985-; UFT 1985; Plumb Beach Civic Assn 1989-; S 194 Raoul Wallenberg 3117 Avenue W Brooklyn NY 11229

RESE, ALFRED J., US His, Govt & Economics Tchr; *b:* ille, NY; *m:* Mary Louise Higgins; *c:* Alfred, Richard, Mary Beth; St Mary's Coll (BS) Ec 1958; Siena Coll (MS) Ed 1966; *cr:* d-Halfmoon Schl Tchr 1959-; *ai:* Yrbk Co-Adv; *office:* d-Halfmoon Schl 125 Middletown Rd Waterford NY 12188

RESE, SAVINO ITALO BENITO, English Teacher; *b:* Jersey *m:* Carolyn Spice; *c:* Michele; *ed:* New England Coll (BA) Scndry g 1970; Adelphi Univ (MA) Eng 1973; Attnd Univ of Bridgeport, ost Grad Courses; Attnd RITA Inst 15 Addl Credit Hrs; *cr:* urst Pub Schls Eng Tchr 1971-; *ai:* Class of 1994 Adv; AFT, NEA 1971-; Islip Civic Assn 1989-, Histrcl Soc 1995-; Tchr of Yr urst Pub Schls 1994; *office:* Lindenhurst Sr HS 350 Charles St urst NY 11757

RO, SUSAN LEIGH, Spanish & French Teacher; *b:* Washington, Washington & Jefferson Coll (BA) Span, Bus Admin 1983; Span ert 1983, Fr Tchng Cert 1991; *cr:* Immaculate Conception HS el Tchr 1984-86; Canon-Mc Millan HS Sub Tchr 1986-88; Cath HS Span Tchr 1988-89; Burgettstown HS Span, Fr Tchr : Fr Club Adv; Sr Exit Interview Comm; PSMLA 1995-; PSEA nmaculate Conception Young Adults Group 1993-; Gift of Time *ice:* Burgettstown Area Jr/Sr HS 99 Main St Burgettstown PA

ESINA, SANARA LARSON, Math Teacher; *b:* Jamestown, NY; as; *c:* Sarah, Ryan; *ed:* Westminster Coll (BS) Math & Span 1973; Coll at Fredonia (MA) Math Ed 1978; Real Estate Courses; *cr:* stern Cntrl Schl Math Tchr 1973-; *ai:* Vllybl Coach 1974-77; NHS 5-; Ski Club Chaperone 1985-; Schlsp Comm 1990-; NEA 1973-; 3-, Bldg Rep; AAUW 1975-, Treas; Church Bd of Trustees Sec; Schl Tchr; Creche; Lakewood Womens Club Treas; Moon Brook ub Womens Assn Past Chm, Treas.

ITA, MARION VERMIGLIO, Kindergarten Teacher; *b:* New CT; *m:* Stephen F.; *c:* Nancy, Stephen, Paul; *ed:* Southern CT St m Ed 1974, (MS) Rdng Tchr 1980; CEU Kinder Facts 1 Credit; on, Suicide 1 Credit, Creating Thematic Units 1 Credit; Rainbow, Prgm 1 Credit; *cr:* Truman St Schl Sixth Grd Tchr 1975-76; St Schl Third Grd Tchr 1976-89, Kndgtn Tchr 1989-; *ai:* After Schl ; Rainbows for All God's Children Facilitator; lang Arts Coord; A 1976-; Women's Club 1994-; PTA 1984-; *office:* St Stephen Schl e Rd Hamden CT 06517*

CIBETTA, ROBERT ANGELO, In School Suspension Coord; *b:* ket, RI; *m:* Linda Diane Suffoletto; *c:* Brian, Alicia; *ed:* Boston) Hlth & PE 1970; Providence Coll (MS) Scndry Admin 1973; 16 s; *cr:* Woonsocket Schl Dept Tchr & Coach 1970-; *ai:* Ftbl Coach Asst 1980-; Girls Head Tennis Coach 1985-88; Asst Bsktbl Coach Head Bsktbl Coach 1994-; AFT 1970-; AAHPERED 1970-; IWC brshp Chm; Elks 1989-; *office:* Woonsocket Sr HS 777 Cass Ave ket RI 02895

, DOREEN R., English Teacher; *b:* Cleveland, OH; *ed:* Kent St Ed) Eng, Span 1967, (MED) Ed Admin 1977; 40 Addl Credit Hrs; eld Hts Jr HS 7th-8th Grd Eng, Span Tchr 1968-74; Garfield Hts 11th Grd Eng Tchr 1974-; *ai:* NEA, OEA 1968-; Garfield Hts ssn 1968-, Bldg Rep; *office:* Garfield Heights HS 12500 Maple field Heights OH 44125

R, LENDOL G., History Professor; *b:* Beaumont, TX; *m:* Kathy *c:* Abigail; *ed:* Univ of TX (BA) Psych 1980; Univ of Chicago s 1986, (PHD) His 1993; *cr:* Univ of WA Visiting Asst Prof Colby Sawyer Coll Asst Prof 1993-; *ai:* Dir of 1st Yr Collegium; storical Assoc 1992-; Org of Amer Historians 1992-; Phi Beta Univ of Chicago Von Holst Prize Lectureship 1992; *office:* Colby Coll 100 Main St New London NH 03257

RONE, ANTOINETTE BATTISTA, Asst Prof of Nursing Dept; , NY; *m:* James Michael; *c:* John Battista, Heather Calderone anette M. Battista; *ed:* Hunter Coll-Bellevue Schl of Nrsng of BS) Nrsng 1972; Coll Misericordia (MSN) Nrsng Ed, Adult Hlth idener Univ (DNSc) 1993; *cr:* Youville Hosp Schl of Practical c 173076; Upjohn Healthcare Svcs Field Supvr 1979-82; Luzerne m Coll Nrsng Dept Prof 1982-94; Coll Misericordia Nrsng Dept f 1994-; *ai:* NEA, PSEA 1984-94; Amer Nurses Assn 1984-; Co Dist Nurses 1984-, VP; Phi Kappa Phi 1983-; Sigma Theta Tau Ignatius Church 1976-, Lector, Euchristic Minister, Ldrshp, Soc omms; St Ignatius MS 1990-92, Bd of Dirs; Sigma Thera Tau Excl rch Awd 1993; Bellevue Nrsng Comm Maternal-Child Hlth Nrsng 2; Hunter Coll Nrsng Schlsp 1971; Publications: PA League for 94-95, Cmptrs in Nrsng 1994, The PA Nurse 1993, Nrsng Mngmt sng, Hlth Care 1989; *office:* Coll Misericordia 301 Lake St Dallas 2

RONE, JAMES MICHAEL, Assoc Prof of Soc Work; *b:* Newark, Antoinette Battista; *c:* John, Heather, Lanette; *ed:* Wilkes Univ g 1969; Univ of WI at MAdison (MSSW) Soc Work 1972; Temple D) Adult Ed 1992; *cr:* SUNY at Plattsburgh Instr in Soc Work Milford Family & Child Guidance Clinic Soc Work 1974-75; Counseling Svcs Supvr Comm Svc 1975-81; Coll Misericordia of of Soc Work, Chair Div of Behavorial Sci, Ed & Bus 1981-; *ai:* Club Adv; Coll Judicial Bd; Diversity Inst of Coll Misericordia; licies Comm; Fac Senate Chr; Natl Assn of Soc Workers 1972-; r Advance of Soc Work with Groups 1993-; Comm Counseling d of Dirs, VP; SHARE Advy Bd 1993; Acad of Certified Soc 1976-; Alpha Delta MU Soc Work Honor Soc 1985-; PENN Consultation Ed Cncl Awds 1980-81; Licensed Soc Worker 1989-; Tchr Excl Awd 1993; *office:* Coll Misericordia Lake St Dallas PA 18612*

CALDWELL, DEANNA MULDOON, Second Grade Teacher; *b:* Oil City, PA; *m:* James Roger; *c:* Matthew; *ed:* Clarion Univ of PA (BS) Elem Ed 1976; *cr:* Central Elem 2nd Grd Tchr 1979-80; Utica Elem 2nd Grd Tchr 1980-; *ai:* NEA, PSEA 1979-; *office:* Utica Elem Schl Academy St PO Box 128 Utica PA 16362

CALDWELL, EUGENE L., Machine Shop Teacher; *b:* Dayton, OH; *m:* Ellen Raye Dail; *c:* Debbie Jean Coterel, Rodney E., William E.; *ed:* ITT Tech Inst (AS) Engr 1975; 47 Credit Hrs Cincinnati Univ; 23 Credit Hrs Cntrl St Univ; 27 Credit Hrs OH St Univ; 12 Credit Hrs Wright St Univ; 8 Credit Hrs Sinclair Coll; *cr:* Chrylser Corp Machine Shop, Job Setter 1967-75; Trueblood Inc Designer 1975-76; Inland Gen Motors Process Engr 1977-79; Greene Cty Career Ctr Precision Machining Tchr 1979-; *ai:* VICA Club Adv; NEA 1979-, Second VP Local; OVA 1986-; VFW 1968-; Masonic Lodge 1969-; Scottish Rite 1979-; *office:* Greene Cty Career Ctr 2960 W Enon Rd Xenia OH 45385

CALDWELL, FREDERICK JACKSON,JR., Mathematics Tchr & Dept Chair; *b:* Beverly, MA; *m:* Cynthia Boutelle; *c:* Nathan T., Rachel D., Kimberly A.; *ed:* Salem St Coll (BA) Math 1967; Worcester St Coll (MA) Comp Sci 1985; *cr:* Gloucester HS Math Tchr 1967-72; Nauset HS Math Tchr 1974-75; Barnstable HS Math Tchr & Dept Chair 1975-; *ai:* Comp Lab Supvr; NCTM; NEA; MTA; BTA; *office:* Barnstable HS 744 W Main St Hyannis MA 02601

CALDWELL, JENNIFER J., Social Studies Teacher; *b:* Keene, NH; *c:* Robin; *ed:* Anna Maria Coll Keene St Coll (BSEd) His & Geog 1987; 2 Post Grad Courses His & Geog; *cr:* Keene HS Soc Stud, Western Civ & Global Stud Tchr 1987-; *ai:* Stu Assistance Pgm Fac Rep; NH Geog Bee Judge; NEA 1987-; Natl Geog Soc 1986-; NOW 1987-; Amnesty Intnl 1990-; Natl Geog Bee Question Author; *office:* Keene Sr HS 43 Arch St Keene NH 03431

CALDWELL, KELLEY M., 8th Grade Math Teacher; *b:* Cortland, NY; *ed:* SUNY Brockport (BS) Bus & Mrktg 1983; Lemoyne Coll Scndry Math Cert 1989; Syraucse Univ Masters Courses; *cr:* Homer Cntrl Schl Dist 8th Grd Math, Course 1 Tchr 1989-90; Jamesville Dewitt Schl Dist 8th Grd Math, Course 1 Tchr 1990-92, 1993-; Fayetteville Manlius Schl Dist 8th Grd Math, Course 1 Tchr 1992; *ai:* Girls Modified Lacrosse Coach; Jamesville Dewitt Tech Team Comm & Bldg Level Team; 8th Grd Ceremony Comm; NCMT 1990-; AMTNYS 1990-; *office:* Jamesville-Dewitt MS Randall Rd Jamesville NY 13078

CALDWELL, MARION MILFORD,JR., Former Instructor; *b:* San Antonio, TX; *m:* Priscilla; *c:* Priscilla, Marina; *ed:* DE St Univ (BS) Bus Admin 1978; Univ of DC (MBA) Mrktg 1983; *cr:* DE Tech & Comm Coll Instr 1984; DE St Univ Bus Dept Instr 1984-91; *ai:* Speech Comm Assn 1995-; Natl Black MBA Assn 1985-; Omega Psi Phi 1971-, Svc Awd; Prince Hall Mason Prudence Lodge 1981-; Who's Who Among Black Amers; Outstdng Young Men of Amer; Cert of Recognition for Svc; *home:* 106 Bertrand Dr Dover DE 19904

CALDWELL, PETER R., Social Studies Teacher; *b:* Hackensack, NJ; *m:* Dale Youngs; *c:* William, Amy; *ed:* Hobart Coll (BA) Amer His 1961; Rutgers Univ (EDM) Scndry Ed 1967; *cr:* Croydon Hall Acad Tchr 1961-62; Monmouth Regnl HS Soc Stud Tchr 1962-; *ai:* Stock Market Game Adv; Mid Sts Steering Comm; NEA, NJEA, MREA 1962-; *office:* Monmouth Regional HS 1 Norman J Field Way Tinton Falls NJ 07724

CALDWELL, ROBERT J., Social Science Teacher; *b:* Pittsburgh, PA; *m:* Patti Demar; *ed:* Univ of Pittsburgh (BA) His, Eng 1967, (MED) Comprehensive Soc Stud 1971; Grad Credits Geog; *cr:* Avalon Schl Dist Eng, His Tchr 1969-75; Northgate Schl Dist His Tchr 1975-78; North Allegheny Schl Dist His Tchr 1978-; *ai:* Head Boys Var Bsktbl Coach 1978-94; PSEA, NEA 1969-; AFT 1979-; Orchard Ave Presbyn Church 1964-68, Deacon; Masonic Lodge 1979-; Pittsburgh Steeler Media Spotter1988-, Pgh Statistician; Big East Bsktbl Ofcls 1993-; 1st Amer HS Bsktbl Ever to Coach Behind Iron Curtain; Coach of Yr; Winningist Coach in Bsktbl; Coached Bsktbl Soviet Union, China, Australia, Great Britain, Ireland; TV Commercial Model; *office:* North Allegheny H S 10375 Perry Hwy Wexford PA 15090

CALDWELL, ROSEMARY ELAINE, Fifth Grade Teacher; *b:* Columbus, OH; *m:* James Kenneth; *c:* Elizabeth; *ed:* OH St Univ (BA) Elem Ed 1967; 9 Credit Hrs; Ashland 10 Credit Hrs; *cr:* Indian Run Elem Schl 4th Grd Tchr 1967-71; Forest View Elem Schl 3rd Grd Tchr 1971-75; Greenbriar East Elem Schl 3rd-4th Grd Tchr 1975-77; Olentangy Elem Schl 5th Grd Tchr 1982-; *ai:* Lang Arts Dept Head; Staff Advy Cncl; Spelling Bee Adv; Author Comm; NCTM 1993-; IRA 1994-; OCTELA 1990-; Martha Holden Jennings Scholar; *home:* 79 Parkway Dr Delaware OH 43015

CALEY, RUTH P., Teacher of the Gifted; *b:* Brooklyn, NY; *m:* Richard J.; *c:* Joan; *ed:* Brooklyn Coll (BA) Sociology 1967; Coll of New Rochelle (MS) Gifted Ed 1988; 60 Addl Post-Grad Credits; *cr:* NYC Bd of Ed Tchr 1967-69; No Rockland Cntrl Schl Dist Tchr 1970-87, Tchr of Gifted 1988-; Coll of New Rochelle Grad Schl Adj Instr 1988-; *ai:* Odyssey of Mind Coach; Inservice Course Instr; Parent Ed Seminar Planner; AFT 1967-; No Rockland Tchrs Assn 1970-; US Figure Skating Assn 1971-, Ofcl Skating Judge, Silver Medal Ice Dancing; Rockland Cty Soc Svcs, Vol; *office:* North Rockland Cntrl Schl Dist 65 Chapel St Garnerville NY 10923*

CALF, PENELOPE SCHNEIDER, Latin Teacher; *b:* Boston, MA; *m:* John R.; *ed:* Mt Holyoke Coll(AB); Emory Univ (MAT); Attnd Amer Acad in Rome, Boston Univ Span Cert; *cr:* Walpole HS Latin & Span Tchr 1969-; *ai:* Latin Club Adv; Var Field Hockey Coach; Pres Fac Senate; NEA 1969-; MTA 1969-; WTA 1969-; Am Classical League 1969-; Field Hockey Coach of the Yr Boston Club 1990, 1994; *home:* 252 Baker St Walpole MA 02081

CALGARO, LOUIS A., Spanish Teacher; *b:* Pittsburgh, PA; *m:* Flora; *c:* Gavin; *ed:* Duquesne Univ (MA) Guid, Cnslng 1978; Spec Semester Abroad Universidad de Valladolid; *cr:* Swissvale HS Span Tchr 1972-81; Woodland Hills HS Span Tchr 1981-; *ai:* Mentor Tchr; Dept Chprsn; PA St Modern Lang Assn, Allegheny Cty For Lang Assn 1992-; WHEA, NEA 1972-; Swissvale Area EA 1972-, VP; Stu Assistance Prgm 1993-; *office:* Woodland Hills HS 2550 Greensburg Pike Pittsburgh PA 15221*

CALHOUN, ANTOINETTE CERVINO, Spanish Teacher; *b:* New York City, NY; *m:* Joseph; *c:* Christina Cervino, Matthew Cervino; *ed:* Adelphi Univ (BA) Span & Scndry Ed 1978; Saint Johns Univ (MS) Biling & Bicultural Ed 1981; 12 Credits Post Grad Stud in Ed Beyond Masters; *cr:* Our Lady of Mercy Schl Span Tchr 1987-91; East Meadow HS Span Tchr 1991-; *ai:* Class of 1998 Fac Adv; NYCFELT, LILT 1992-; *office:* East Meadow Sr HS 101 Carman Ave East Meadow NY 11554*

CALHOUN, CHRIS A., Park & Recreation Program Mgmt; *b:* Lock Haven, PA; *c:* Rachel; *ed:* Butler Co Comm Coll (AAS) Park, Rec Mgmt 1981; Slippery Rock Univ (BS) Resource Mgmt 1982, (MS) Recreation Admin 1989; *cr:* Butler Co Comm Coll Park & Rec Coord 1984-; Natl Park Svc Park Ranger 1984-86; PA St Parks Environmental Interpreter 1987-88; PA Fish & Boat Commission Boating Ed Specialist 1989-; *ai:* Adv Rcreation Outing Club; Fac Org 1995-, Pres; Amer Canoe Assn; Natl Assn for Search, Rescue, Fac Instr; Amer Red Cross, Chprsn Safety Svcs; Outstdng Alumni Slippery Rock Univ 1995; Achvmt Awd 1994; Appreciation Awd Natl Water Safety Congress 1993; Cert of Merit PA Comm Coll Awds of Excl 1992; *office:* Butler County Comm Coll PO Box 1203 Butler PA 16003

CALHOUN, JOHN TERRY, High School Teacher; *b:* Mobile, AL; *m:* Deborah K. Jackson; *c:* John II, Eric, J. Thomas; *ed:* Dillard Univ (BS) Sci & Bio 1969; Western CT St Univ (MS) Environmental Sci 1979; Southern CT St Univ 6 Yr Scndry Sci Specialist 1992; Hartford Univ Astronomy Class; *cr:* Western CT St Univ Pgm Adv 2 Yrs; Broadview Jr High Sci Tchr 6 Yrs; Alternative Ctr for Ed Bio Tchr 3 Yrs; Danbury HS Bio Tchr 18 Yrs; *ai:* Jr HS Bsktbl Coach; Minority Recruitment Comm; SWAT Adv; NAACP Schlsp Awd Comm; NEA 1969-; DMT 1985-; NABT 1990-; TOT 1991-; Calhoun Assn Inc 1995-, Chm of Bd; Danbury Comm on Arts; ISIS S CT St Univ; *office:* Danbury HS Beaver Brook Rd Danbury CT 06810

CALI, JOAN, Mathematics Teacher; *b:* Bridgeport, CT; *ed:* Saint Leo Coll (BA) Ed 1973; Jersey City St Coll (MA) Urban Ed 1987; Seton Hall Univ & Kean Coll Cert in Stu Prsnl Svcs; *cr:* Saint Michael Schl 2nd Grd Tchr 1973-75; Immaculate Conception Math Tchr 1975-79; Secaucus MS & HS Math Tchr 1980-; *ai:* Memory Book & Cmptr Club Adv; NEA & NJEA 1980-; Secaucus Ed Assn 1980-, Treas; NCTM 1991-; *office:* Seacaucus MS & HS 11 Mill Ridge Rd Secaucus NJ 07094

CALI, PAUL V., Principal; *b:* Medford, MA; *m:* Patricia Moriarty; *c:* Caitlin, Cristin; *ed:* Boston Boll (BA) Eng, Ed 1972; Univ of MA (MED) Comm Svc 1979; 31 Credits CAGS Prgm Bridgewater St Coll; *cr:* Medford HS Eng Tchr 1973-77; Falmouth HS Eng Tchr 1977-92, House Admin 1992-94, Prin 1994-; *ai:* NEA 1974-.

CALIENDO, RICHARD J., Instructor of Humanities; *b:* Brooklyn, NY; *m:* Lyn; *c:* Valerie Donoghue, Jennifer Zan Fardino, Richard F.; *ed:* Queens Coll (BA) Eng 1956; NY Univ (MA) Eng 1962; Queens Coll (MA) Admin, Supervision 1966; Fordham Univ (EDD) Admin, Supervision 1975; Norwalk Comm Coll Cert Paralegal 1993; *cr:* David Boody Jr HS Asst Prin 1965-72; Marlboro Elem Schl Prin 1972-76; Elmont HS Prin 1976-80; Elmont Schl Dist Supt of Schls 1980-89; Rocky Hill Schl Dist Supt of Schls 1989-92; Albertus Magnuss Coll Instr Hum 1993-; *ai:* Mngmt Trng; Ct Judicial Branch; Libretto Writer 4 Operas; Performed Metropolitan Opera Lib, Columbia Univ, Queens Coll, North Shore Symphony; Libretto Writer Children's Operetta; Performed NYC, Long Island.*

CALIFANO, RONALD, Chemistry & Physics Teacher; *b:* NJ; *ed:* Fairleigh Dickinson Univ (BS) Bio & Phys Sci 1973; NJ Inst Tech (MS) Chem & Phys Sci 1984; *cr:* Millburn High Tchr; Lyndhurst High Tchr 1987-90; Bloomfield High Chem & Physics Tchr 1991-; *ai:* Schl Improvement Comm; Former Ftbl Coach; NJSTA 1985-; ACS 1985-89; Local Comm Orch; *office:* Bloomfield HS Broad St Bloomfield NJ 07003*

CALIFORNIA, JOHN MARSHALL, Physics Teacher; *b:* Pittsburgh, PA; *m:* Judith Ann Papania; *ed:* PA St Univ (BS) Civil Engrng 1985; Univ of Pittsburgh(MED) Sci Ed 1995; *cr:* North Hills Sr HS Physics Tchr 1993-; *ai:* NEA, PSEA, PSTA 1995-.

CALIGARIS, SUSAN ROEBUCK, Dance Professor; *b:* New York, NY; *m:* David Peter; *c:* Christopher, Kyndle Marie; *ed:* Univ of AZ (BFA) Dance 1983; Univ of MI (MFA) Dance 1992; *cr:* Pikes Peak Comm Coll Dance Instr 1 Yr; CO Coll Guest Instr, Artist 2 Yrs; Alfred Univ Asst Dance Prof 4 Yrs; *ai:* Co-Dir Chiron Performing Arts Ensemble; Dance Team Adv; Lib Comm; NASDA, ACDFA 1992-; Natl Choreography Series IV Competition, Alternate; NEA Prof Dev Grant; Natl Fine Arts Video Competition Honorable Mention; Mini-Grant, Fac Research Grant; Scholarly Acts, Fac Fund Grants; Univ of MI Flwshp; *office:* Alfred Univ 26 N Main St Alfred NY 14802*

CALISE, JOSEPH EDWARD, English & Humanities Teacher; *b:* New York, NY; *ed:* Univ of CT (BA) Eng 1963; Western CT Univ (MS) Ed 1975; *cr:* John Pettibone Schl Eng Tchr 1965-70; Brookfield HS Eng Tchr 1970-76; Berlin HS Eng, Hum Tchr 1979-; *ai:* Lit Magazine Adv; Ind Stud Coord; SAT Prep Tchr; NEA, CEA 1965-; NCTE 1990-; Univ of CT Alumni, Celebration of Excl Awds; Tchr of Yr; *office:* Berlin HS 139 Patterson Way Berlin CT 06037

CALLAGHAN, CHRISTOPHER JOHN, 7th & 8th Grd Soc Stud Teacher; *b:* Painesville, OH; *ed:* Mercyhurst Coll (BA) Elem Ed 1988; Certfd in PA 24 Credits Hrs Beyond Degree; *cr:* St Patrick Schl 8th Grd Tchr 1988-90; St George Schl 7th-8th Grd Soc Stud Tchr 1990-; *ai:* Patrol Safety Adv; Cath Schls Week Comm; NCEA 1988-; *office:* St George Schl 1612 Bryant St Erie PA 16509

CALLAHAN, DOROTHY MONAHAN, Teacher & Coord of GATE; *b:* Bronx, NY; *m:* Robert; *c:* Christopher, Kathleen; *ed:* Coll Misericordia (BA) Eng, Jrnlsm Minor 1956; William Paterson Coll (MS) Rdng, Spec Ed 1971; Learning Disabilities Tchr, Consultant Cert; *cr:* Sussex Wantage Schls Remedial Rdng Tchr 1966-69; Lafayette Twp Schl Child Stud Team Coord, Tchr, Coord of GAT Prgm 1969-; *ai:* Girls Bsktbl Team Coach; Play Dir; Chess Team Adv; NEA; NJEA; Books: Under Christopher's Hat, Ruffian Thoroughbreds; Jimmy the Story of the Young Jimmy Carter, Julie Krone a Winning Jockey; *office:* Lafayette Township Schl 178 Beaver Run Rd Lafayette NJ 07848

CALLAHAN, EARL L., 8th Grade English Teacher; *b:* Hoosick Falls, NY; *m:* Nancy Forsythe; *c:* Daniel P.; *ed:* SUNY at Oneonta (BS) E S Eng 1968; 42 Post Grad Hrs; *cr:* A. S. Draper Schl Eng Tchr 1968-70; Norwich MS Eng Tchr 1970-; *ai:* Environmental Edctr Planning Ed Acts, Site Improvement 54 Acre Schl Owned Woodland; NEA 1968-; Enviromental Edctr Awd 1990-; Special Planning Awd 1992; *office:* Norwich HS Midland Dr Norwich NY 13815

CALLAHAN, EILEEN M., Social Studies Dept Chprsn; *ed:* Fordham Univ (BA) Amer Stud 1992, (MA) Amer His 1995; *cr:* St Jean Bapt HS Soc Stud Chprsn 1992-; *ai:* Stu Cncl Moderator; Gilder Lehrman Inst Seminar Yale Univ 1994; *office:* St Jean Baptiste HS 173 E 75th St New York NY 10021

CALLAHAN, ELAINE PASQUARIELO, Second Grade Teacher; *b:* Paterson, NJ; *m:* Bruce; *c:* Sean, Bradley, Tara; *ed:* William Paterson Coll (BA) Elem Ed 1964; 32 Addl Grad Credits Beyond BA; Cert Early Chldhd & Spec Ed; *cr:* Littleton Schl 4th Grd Tchr 1964-68, Spec Ed Tchr 1978-89, 2nd Grd Tchr 1990-; *ai:* ADK Historian; Tchr Mentor; NJEA, NEA 1978-; PTA 1968-; 3 Mini-Grants from Bd of Ed; Life Touch Grant; Governors Tchng Awd 1992; *office:* Littleton Elem Schl Brooklawn Dr Morris Plains NJ 07950*

CALLAHAN, GERALD FRANCIS, Social Studies Chairperson; *b:* New York, NY; *m:* Jean Hildebrandt; *c:* Christopher; *ed:* Marist Coll (BA) His 1968; St John's Univ (MA) Amer His 1972; Attnd Stony Brook Univ, Hofstra Univ; *cr:* Marist HS Soc Stud Tchr 1965-68; Bishop Reilly HS Soc Stud Chrprsn 1968-73; Miller Place HS Soc Stud Chrprsn 1973-; *ai:* NHS, His Club; Oratorical Adv; Swim Coach; Stu Govt Adv, Class Adv; NCSS, NYS Cncl of Soc Stud, Long Island Cncl of Soc Stud 1970-; Turnkey for NY St Regents Action Plan; US His Regents Evlntr; *office:* Miller Place HS 15 Memorial Dr Miller Place NY 11764*

CALLAHAN, JUDITH MURPHY, English Teacher; *b:* Philadelphia, PA; *c:* Meghan, Shannon; *ed:* Millersville Univ (BS) Ed 1962; Masters Equivalency; *cr:* Colonial Schl Dist Eng Tchr 1962-67; Neshaminy Schl Dist Eng Tchr 1967-68; Pennsbury Schl Dist Eng Tchr 1968-69; Neshaminy Schl Dist Eng Tchr 1979-; *ai:* Educl Support Team-Stud Assistance Prgm; AFT 1982-, Bld Comm; *office:* Neshaminy Schl Dist 2001 Old Lincoln Hwy Langhorne PA 19047

CALLAHAN, LEON E., Philosophy & Logic Teacher; *b:* New York, NY; *m:* Marcia; *c:* Katherine, Anna; *ed:* Providence Coll (BA) His 1958; Trinity Coll (MS) His 1968; Philosophical Stud; *cr:* Northwest Cath HS His, Hum

Tchr 1961-73; Hartford Convervatory of Music Jazz, Piano, Theory Tchr 1973-83; Quirk Ms Philosophy, Logic Tchr 1984-; *ai:* Hartford Fed of Tchrs 1984-; 4 Fllshps Natl Endowment of Hum Philsophical; *home:* 91 Davenport Rd W Hartford CT 06110

CALLAHAN, LISA A., Associate Prof of Sociology; *b:* Marion, OH; *m:* Mark T. Bryant; *c:* Jesse Callahan Bryant, Jackson Callahan Bryant; *ed:* OH St Univ (BS) Family Relations & Human Dev 1978, (MA) Soc 1981, (PHD) Soc 1983; Univ of WI at Madison Post-Doctoral Degree Sociology & Psych 1984-85; *cr:* Univ of Northern IA Asst Prof 1983-84; Univ of WI at Madison Post Doctoral Fellow 1984-85; NY St Office of Mental Hlth Project Dir 1985-88; Policy Research Assoc, Inc Research Assoc 1988-90; Russell Sage Coll Asst Prof 1990-95, Assoc Prof 1995-; *ai:* Coll Honors Prgm, Sociology Prgm Dir; Fac Senate Sec; Senate Exec Comm Mem; Am Soc of Criminology, Am Sociological Assn 1980-; Law & Soc Assn, Soc for Stud of Soc Problems 1982-; PEO 1978-, Local Chapter Pres; FIRST Awd NIMH Grant; Co Author of Book Before & After Hinckley; Author, Co Author of Over 10 Articles; Author of 2 Book Chapters; *office:* Russell Sage Coll At Troy Troy NY 12180

CALLAHAN, POLLY CLARK, Soc Stud Teacher & Yrbk Adv; *b:* Anchorage, AK; *m:* Richard; *c:* Ella; *ed:* Univ of VA (BA) Govt with Tchrs Cert 1977; Univ of MD (MA) Ed Admin 1983; *cr:* Thomas Stone HS Soc Stud Tchr 1977-; *ai:* Yrbk Adv; NEA, MSTA & EACC 1979-, Recording Sec; *office:* Thomas Stone HS 3785 Leonardtown Rd Waldorf MD 20601

CALLAHAN, RICHARD STUART, Earth Science Teacher; *b:* New York City, NY; *m:* Polly Penfield; *c:* Ella Grace; *ed:* Western CT (BA) Earth Sci 1979; Addl 24 Grad Credits Limnology, 9 Grad Credits Geology Loyola-Baltimore; *cr:* Washingtonville Jr HS 8th Grd Sci Tchr 1979-81; North Salem MS 8th Grd Earth Sci Tchr 1981-82; Thomas Stone HS 9th Grd Earth Sci Tchr 1982-; *ai:* Ftbl, Sftbl Coach 1982-; Video Yrbk 1989-; NEA 1982-; AFT 1979-81; MSTA 1982-; Cty Sci Fair Comm; NSF Meetings in Baltimore 1991; MD Dept of Ed Sci Reform 1989; MSTA Meeting 1992; *office:* Thomas Stone HS 3785 Leonardtown Rd Waldorf MD 20601

CALLAHAN, SEAN MICHAEL, Technology Teacher; *b:* Medford, MA; *ed:* Fitchburg St (BS) Tech 1991; New England Inst of Tech Studying CADD; *cr:* Woburn High Tech Tchr 1993-; *ai:* Hockey Asst Coach; MTA, WTA 1993-; Leo Club Adv 1993-, Adv, Float Cont 1st Pl 1993, 3rd Pl 1994, 1995; *office:* Woburn Sr HS 88 Montvale Ave Woburn MA 01801

CALLAHAN, SHARON LINDA, 8th Grd Language Arts Teacher; *b:* Sonoma, CA; *m:* Dan; *c:* Sean, Tara Callahan Clifford; *ed:* San Jose St Univ (BA) Soc Sci 1976; 15 Grad Units Towards Masters New England Stud Univ of So. ME; *cr:* St Paul's Luth Schl 4th Grd Tchr 1977-80; Newtown Rd Elem Schl 4th Grd Tchr 1980-81; Jordan Acres Elem Schl 2nd Grd Tchr 1982-83; Brunswick Jr HS 8th Grd Lang Arts Tchr 1983-; *ai:* Fall Tennis Coach; Church Choir; Bruns Music Theater Angel; NEH Seminar Participant 1994; *office:* Brunswick Jr HS 65 Columbia Ave Brunswick ME 04011*

CALLAHAN, THOMAS J., English Teacher; *b:* Ashland, PA; *m:* Dorota Walendzik; *ed:* Bloomsburg Univ (BSEd) Eng & Soc Stud 1981 & 1983; Grad Course in Eng; Course in Polish; *cr:* Canton Area Jr-Sr HS Eng & Soc Tchr 1986-88; Danville MS Eng Tchr 1988-; *ai:* NEA, DEA 1988-; *office:* Danville MS Rt 11 Danville PA 17821

CALLAN, SHARON MAIRS, Reading Specialist; *b:* Waseca, MN; *ed:* Univ of Rochester (BA) Psych 1976; SUNY at Geneseo (MS) Ed 1980; *cr:* Cr Nursery Schl Dir 1977-79; Livonia Cntrl Schl Rdng Tutor 1979-81; Pavilion Cntrl Schl Rdng Specialist 1981-; Genesee Comm Coll Psych, Sociology & Rdng Enrichment Pgm & Adj Fac 1990-; *ai:* Scholastic Bowl Coach; Effective Schls, Ways-&-Means & Bldg Comms; Ski Club Adv; MS Yrbk; Mary Jemison Chptr IRA 1980-, Recording Sec; Phi Delta Kappa 1980-, VP Projects; Pavilion Fac Assn 1981-, VP; Avon Group Home 1986-; Natl Assn Tole & Decorative Painters 1995-; Genesee Cntry Decorative Painters 1995-; Buffalo Snowbirds Dec Painters 1995-; Chosen to Teach Psych & Sociology for GCC Enrichment Pgm; Supervising Stu Intern from Univ of Rochester; *office:* Pavillio Central Schl 7014 Big Tree Rd Pavilion NY 14525*

CALLEBS, JOHN CECIL, High School Math Teacher; *b:* Barbourville, KY; *m:* Carolyn Asher; *c:* April Bentley, Lisa Brondhaver; *ed:* Berea Coll (BA) Math, Ger 1969; Xavier Univ (MED) PE 1975; *cr:* Moscow Elem Schl 4th-7th Grd Tchr 1969-74; New Richmond MS 7th-8th Grd Tchr 1974-93; New Richmond HS 9th-11th Grd Math Tchr 1993-; *ai:* 8th Grd Bsktbl, MS Track Coach; NEA, OEA, NREA 1969-; Moscow Lodge 1980-; *office:* New Richmond HS 1131 Bethel New Richmond Rd New Richmond OH 45157

CALLICOAT, DAVID LYLE, Science Department Chm & Tchr; *b:* Huntington, WV; *m:* Kathy Louise Maynard; *c:* John David; *ed:* Marshall Univ (BA) Chem, General Sci 1974, (MS) Phys Sci 1978; *cr:* Chesapeake HS Tchr, Dept Chm 1975-; *ai:* Head Golf Coach 1975-93; 10 Conf, 1 St Championships, 65 Winning Percentage; Chesapeake Ed Assn 1975-, Pres 1986; OHS Golf Coaches Assn 1975-; OEA 1994-; Jefferson Avenue Chruch of God 1981-, Elder 5 Yrs, Chm Chrstn Ed 1985-; Chrstn Ed Minister 1993-; 1990 Marshall Univ Schl of Medicine OH Sci Tchr of Yr; Mem Merrill Pub Co Advisory Cncl; Co-Author 1982 OH Scholastic Test of Achvmt in General Sci; *home:* 22 Valley Dr Chesapeake OH 45619

CALLINAN, CHRIS, Mathematics & Physics Teacher; *b:* Upper Darby, PA; *ed:* Cabrini Coll (BS) Math & Bus Admin 1993; Temple Univ Post Grad Work; *cr:* Sacred Heart HS Math, Comp & Sci Tchr 1993-; *ai:* Boys & Girls Head Cross Cntry, Girls Head Indoor Track & Head Outdoor Track Coach; Acad Team Adv; SCTO 1993-, Bd of Trustees; Cross Cntry Coach of Yr Canidate; *office:* Sacred Heart HS North East Ave Vineland NJ 08360*

CALLIS, JOHN ANDREW, Bio & Environmental Stud Tchr; *b:* West Islip, NY; *m:* Suzanne Yzonne Deutsch; *c:* Taylor, Stephen; *ed:* SUNY at Cortland (BS) Bio 1988; SUNY at Stony Brook (MALS) Sci, Ed 1992; *cr:* Half Hollow Hills Schl Dist Sub Tchr 1988-89; Island Trees HS Bio, Sci Tchr 1986-; *ai:* Sci Olympiad Adv-Coach; Stu Act Account Adv; Tchrs Union Treas; Schl Store Manager; NYSUT, AFT 1989-.

CALLO, LYNDA, English Teacher; *b:* White Plains, NY; *c:* Erik, Emily; *ed:* Cntrl CT St Coll (BS) Eng 1978, (MS) Rdng 1986; CT & PR Residential Inst; *cr:* Bulkeley HS Eng Tchr 1978-; *ai:* SAT Supvr; Discipline Comm Chprsn; CAPT Comm; NCTE, CT Cncl Tchrs of Eng 1976-; AFT, Hartford Fed of Tchrs 1978-; Fac Appreciation Awd From Stdnts; *office:* Bulkeley HS 300 Wethersfield Ave Hartford CT 06114

CALO, DOROTHY, Guidance Counselor; *b:* New York, NY; *ed:* Hunter Coll (BA) Theatre 1963, (MS) Cnslng 1989; Gestalt Ctr for Psychotherapy & Trng; 350 Credit Hrs; *cr:* NY Assn for New Amers Cnslr 1990-91; St Jean Baptiste HS Cnslr 1991-; *ai:* Soph Hnrs Group; NY St Assn for Cnslng & Dev 1989-; Natl Certfd Cnslr 1992-; *office:* St Jean Baptiste HS 173 E 75th St New York NY 10021

CALOGERO, CHRISTINE KING, Biology & Science Teacher; *b:* Oneida, NY; *m:* P Michael; *ed:* LeMoyne Coll (BS) Bio 1982; SUNY at Cortland (MS) Ed 1991; 36 Grad Credit Hrs Post Masters, 12 of Those Hrs Toward CAS Degree; *cr:* Staley Jr HS 7th-9th Grd Sci Tchr 1985-89; LV Denti Elem Schl 6th Grd Rdng & Math Tchr 1989-94; Rome Free Acad 10th-12th Grds Bio, & Sci Tchr 1994-; *ai:* Girls Bsktbl Games Announcer; NEA 1985-; Rome City Schl Dist Tchr of the Yr 1990-; Awarded Sabbatical at US Air Force Reliability Physics Rsrch Lab 1996; *office:* Rome Free Acad 500 Turin St Rome NY 13440

CALOMINO, GAIL ANN, Fourth Grade Teacher; *b:* Scranton, PA; *ed:* Marywood Coll (AB) Elem Ed 1975, (MS) Elem Cnslng 1981; 3 Credits Thematic Instr; Luzerne Intermediate 3 In-Svc Credits MS Math; Penn St 3 Ed Units Amer Constitutional Law; *cr:* Scranton Schl Dist Sub Tchr 1975-78; Hebrew Day Schl 3rd-5th Grd Tchr 1978-79; Epiphany Elem Schl 3rd Grd Tchr 1979-86, 4th Grd Tchr 1986-; *ai:* Sci Dept & Comp Comms Mem; NCEA 1979-; Marywood Coll Alumni Assn 1976-; Birthright Vol 1989-; Assn of Elem Schl Mid Sts Evaluator 1990 & 1993; *office:* Epiphany Schl 627 Stevenson St Sayre PA 18840*

CALTA, KAREN L., English & Religion Teacher; *b:* Elizabeth, NJ; *m:* Robert Calta; *c:* Kariane, Brett, Justin, Jonathan; *ed:* Fairleigh Dickinson Univ (BA) Eng Lit 1972; Addl 32 Credits Toward MA; *cr:* Wm Annin Jr HS Eng Tchr 1972-73; Fairleigh Dickinson Schl Grad Tchng Asst 1973-75; St Vincent DePaul Lang Arts, Lit Tchr 1990-93; Mt St Mary Acad Eng, Rel Tchr 1993-; *ai:* TLC Peer Cnslng; Acad Bowl Coach; Mercy Collaborative Curr Project; Fac Adv Comm; NCTE 1991-; NCEA 1990-; NJAIS 1993-; *office:* Mount St Mary Acad 1645 US Highway 22 Watchung NJ 07060

CALTAGIRONE, SILKE LORENZEN, HS German Teacher; *b:* Island of Fohr, N Germany; *m:* William; *c:* Kris William, Lauren Johanna; *ed:* Boston Univ (BA) Eng 1970; Fordham Univ (MAT) Eng 1971; *cr:* Mahopac HS German, Eng Tchr 1972-; *ai:* Beautification Comm Head; AFT 1972-; German Tchrs Assn 1972-; Meals on Wheels Vol; *office:* Mahopac HS Baldwin Place Rd Mahopac NY 10541

CALVANICO, JONNA, English & Drama Teacher; *b:* Hoboken, NJ; *m:* Robert; *ed:* Univ of DE (BA) Eng 1985; Montclair St Univ (MA) Counseling, Soc Work 1994; 3 Credits Early Amer Lit; *cr:* Saddle Brook HS Eng Tchr 1985-86; Becton Regnl HS Eng, Drama Tchr 1986-; *ai:* Play Dir; Stu Cncl Adv; Becton Ed Assn Sec; NJEA, NEA 1985-; *office:* Henry P Becton Reg HS Paterson Ave Cornelius E Rutherford NJ 07073

CALVERT, JAMES ALLEN, Art & Special Ed Teacher; *b:* Oak Park, IL; *m:* Sheryl Patrice Rast; *c:* Justin Allen, Carly Patrice; *ed:* IA Wesleyan Coll (BA) Art Ed 1975; Monmouth coll (MSED) Spec Ed 1988; Addl Hrs Monmouth Coll Spec Ed Cert 1979-80; *cr:* Monmouth Regnl HS Tchrs Aide, Aide to Handicapped 1977-80, Spec Ed Tchr 1980-94, Spec Ed, Art Tchr 1994-; *ai:* Head Wrestling Coach; Asst Boys Track & Field Coach; Art Club; peer Mediation; NEA, NJ Ed Assn, Monmouth Regnl Ed Assn 1980-; NJ Wrestling Coaches Assn Dist 22 Coach of Yr 1993-94; MRHS Educl Fnd Inc Grant Schl Beautification Project Wall Mural; *office:* Monmouth Regional HS 1 Norman J Field Way Eatontown NJ 07724*

CALVERT, KATHERINE RENO, Substitute Teacher; *b:* Valporaiso, IN; *m:* Charles B.; *c:* Shane A. Eversfied, Kevin T. W. Smith, Regan J. R. Smith, Darcy K. L. Austin; *ed:* Univ of MD (BS) Home Ec 1954; Loyola Coll (MS) Early Chldhd 1976; 48 Addl Credit Hrs; Towson St Univ Cert Early Chldhd 1954-84; Inservice Credits Balto Co Bd Ed Towson St Univ, Western MD Coll; *cr:* Montgomery Co Bd Ed 3rd Grd Tchr 1955-57; Church of Redeemer Parish Day Schl Tchr 5 Yr Olds 1966-68; Baltimore Cty Pub Schls Kndgtn, 3rd Grd Tchr 1968-95; *ai:* Supervising & Cooperating Tchr for 26 Stu Tchrs Towson St Univ, Morgan St Univ, Loyola Coll; Balto Co Ret Tchrs; MD St Retired Tchr; Natl Ed Assn Ret Tchrs; Delta Kappa Gamma Inst 1970-, Pres; PTA, Mbrshp Ch, Ways & Means Ch, Pres; Girl Scouts, Cookie Chm 1970-71; BSA Troop 35, Banquet Ch 1967-74; Amer Field Svc Chm Towson, Pres 1976-78; PTA Awd Life Mbrshp; Balto Co Outstdng Tchr 1989; *home:* 208 Murdock Rd Baltimore MD 21212

CALVIN, MATHIS ANTHONY,III, Special Education Teacher; *b:* Rochester, NY; *m:* Stacy Lynn; *ed:* Keuka Coll (BA) Spcl Ed-Cum Laude 1995; Credit Hrs at Brockport Univ; *cr:* Monroe Cty Handicapped Children Camp Dir 1989-95; DePaul Mental Hlth Residential Mgr 1994-95; RCSD #34 6th Grd Tchr 1995; RCSD #44 Spcl Ed Tchr 1995-; *ai:* Choir Dir; Promise Choir; Enrichment Afterschool Pgm; Minister Penecostal Miricle Deliverance Ctr Church; Orton Dsylexia Soc 1991-; Cncl for Exceptional Children 1991-, Intnl Rdng Assn 1991-; Rochester Yth Assn 1995-, Coord Team Chprsn; Sallie Mae 1st Class Tchr 1995; Keuka Coll Ministeral Outreach Awd; Rochester Telephone Schlrsp Flwshp Winner; Natl Friends of Frederick Douglass Ortorical Winner; *office:* Rochester City Schl Dist #44 820 Chili Ave Rochester NY 14611*

CALVO, MARITZA ACOSTA, Spanish Teacher; *b:* Havana, Cuba; *m:* Luis M.; *c:* Luis M. Jr., Leonardo M., Lorenzo M.; *ed:* Dowling Coll (BA) Span, Ed 1978; LIU, C W Post (MA) Span 1982; *cr:* LIU Grad Asst 1981-82; C W Post Grad Asst 1981-82; St Anthony's HS Span Tchr 1985-; *office:* St Anthony's HS 275 Wolf Hill Rd Melville NY 11747

CAMACHO, JAMES,JR., Mathematics Asst Professor; *b:* New York, NY; *m:* Suyi Yeh; *c:* James Yeh; *ed:* Polytechnic Inst of NY (BS) Physics 1978, (MS) Applied & Industrial Math 1980; Polytechnic Univ (PHD) Math 1987; *cr:* Polytechnic Univ Tchng Flwshp & Adj Lecturer 1982-87; Jersey City St Coll Asst Prof of Math 1987-; *ai:* Cncl of Hispanic Affairs; Mem of Math Dept; Prsnl, Search & Curr Comms; AMS 1982-; MAA 1985-; AFT 1987-; Genesis Pgm 1991-; Articles Pub in Journals; Contributed Problems & Solutions to Math Horizons Problem Section; Referee of Articles In Journals; Whos Who Among Hispanic Amers; *office:* Jersey City St Coll 2039 Kennedy Boulevard Jersey City NJ 07305*

CAMARA, JOAN ELLEN, Paralegal Studies Instructor; *b:* Fall River, MA; *m:* Charles J. Jordan; *c:* Alexander, Daniel; *ed:* Univ of MA (BA) Pol Sci 1973; Suffolk Univ Law Schl (JD) Law 1978; Legal Ed Courses; Criminal Practice, Family Law, Acctng Pub Defender Prgms, Civil & Trial Practice; Computerized Legal Rsrch; Lexis, Nexis & Westlaw Trng Prgms; *cr:* Clarin Waldron & Tucker Esq Jr Assoc 1979-80; Peppard Littman & Camara Esq Assoc, Partner 1981-85; Arbitrator T. Bornstein Rsrch Assoc 1989-95; Dean Coll Adj Fac 1996-; Fisher Coll Adj Fac 1992-; *ai:* Curr Adv Comm 1994; AAUP 1995-; MA Continuing Legal Ed 1995-, Legal Rsrch, Writing Prgm Fac; MA Bar Assn, US Dist Courts MA & RI, Supreme Judicial Court of MA 1979-; Parent Advocates for GATE 1995-; St Advocates for GATE 1994-; *office:* Fisher Coll 118 Beacon St Boston MA 02116

CAMARA, PAULINE FRANCOEUR, Business & Finance Acad Coord; *b:* Fall River, MA; *m:* Robert P. Jr.; *c:* Kalyn, Kyle; *ed:* Bristol Comm Coll (AS) Bus 1982-; Univ MA at Dartmouth (BA) Acctng 1985, (BA) Ed 1991; Bridgewater St Coll Master Prgm in Educl Ldrshp; Master in Oracle Database Mngmt; *cr:* Westport Acad HS Bus, Finance Acad Coord 2 Yrs; Our Lady of Fatima HS Bus Ed 1 Yr; Somerset HS Cheering Coach 6 Yrs; U Mass at Dartmouth Cheering Coach 5 Yrs; *ai:* Class, Cmptr Club Adv; HS Coach 11 Yrs; Coll Coach 5 Yrs; Schl to Work Tech Prep; MA Bus Edctrs Assn, AFT 1994-; PTO 1995-; Lib Comm 1995-, Co-Chair; *office:* Westport Academy HS 19 Main Rd Westport MA 02790

CAMARATA, LYN L., Social Studies Teacher; *b:* Atlantic City, NJ; *m:* Louis M.; *ed:* Fairleigh Dickinson U (BA) Psych 1978; Rowan Coll Cert Scndry Ed 1992; *cr:* Hartford Ins Group Casualty Underwriter 1978-82; Chubb Custom Market Underwriter, Trainer 1982-85; Surf Coaster Corp Risk Mgr 1985-92; Millville HS Soc Stu Tchr 1992-; *ai:* Conscious Living Club; NCSS 1996; IRA 1994-; NEA, MTA 1993-; USET 1990-; Hooved Animal Humane Soc 1996; *office:* Millville Sr HS 200 Wade Blvd Millville NJ 08332*

CAMASTRO, DOMINICK JOSEPH, Soc Stud, Cybertech Prgr *b:* New York, NY; *m:* Rose Marinello; *c:* Dominick III, Dear Divone, Dawn-Marie, Paula Divone, DeAnna; *ed:* SUNY at Stone (BA) Soc Scis 1979; Hunter Coll (MA) Soc Stud Scndry 1986; *c* Brooklyn Soc Stud Tchr 1979-88; Erasmus Hall HS Soc Stud Tch *ai:* Cybertech Prgm Creator, Coord; *office:* Erasmus Hall HS 911 Ave Brooklyn NY 11226*

CAMBARERI, MARGARET STEBELSKI, 3rd-6th Grd GATE Tchr; *b:* Cleveland, OH; *m:* Henry P.; *c:* Mitchell, Monica; *ed:* C St Univ (BS) K-8 Elem Ed 1971; Walsh Univ (MA) Ed 1990; 40 GATE; 36 Semester Hrs Elem Ed CSU, BW, AU, FPC, JCU, UA; V Tchng Gifted, Talented OH Permanent Tchng Cert; *cr:* Parma C 6th Grd Tchr 1971-80, GATE Pullout Prgm Tchr 1980-92, 3rd GATE Magnet Ctr Tchr 1992-; *ai:* Sci Fair Co-Chprsn; NEOEA Chprsn; NEA, OEA, PEA, NEOEA 1971-; Alpha Delta Kappa 198 NSTA 1989-; BEQ Xi Zeta Alpha 1970-, Pres; St Josaphat PTU 19 Treas, Fundraiser Chm; Nom Parma Master Tchrs Jennings Fr Renwood's Tchr of Yr 1989-90; Grants to Write Geology Curr 1 Writing Team Effective Schls Grant1991; *home:* 1606 Rustic Trl P 44134

CAMBELL, JANE ROSS, English & Film Arts Teacher; *b:* Mar *c:* Mark H. Graves, Eric C. Graves; *ed:* Penn St Univ (BA) Gene Sci 1972; Trinity Coll (APC) Ed 1989; Post Grad Work: PSU Anthr 1972-74, Eng 1976-77, Loyola Ed 1988-89; *cr:* St Coll Area HS 1977-85; Glenelg Sr HS Eng, Film Arts Tchr 1985-; *ai:* Tchr Ment NEA, HCEA 1977-.

CAMBERDELLA, KRISTEN LEIGH, Health Education Tea Lindenhurst, NY; *ed:* Cortland St Univ (BSE) Hlth Ed 1992; Dow (MSE) Spec Ed, Rdng 1995; Cert in N-6; *cr:* John Adams HS H Yrs; *ai:* Tutoring in Rdng; AFT, UFT 1993-; *office:* John Adams H Rockaway Blvd Ozone Park NY 11417

CAMDEN, KATHLEEN A., MS Mathematics Teacher; *b:* Columb *c:* Mark Sankey, Joan Sankey; *ed:* Daemen Coll at Amherst (BS) 1979; Duquesne Univ at Pittsburgh Elem Ed 1955-57; *cr:* St Patr 3rd-5th Grd Tchr 1957-64; St Teresa Schl 1st, 3rd & 7th Grd Tchr John F Kennedy Schl MS Math Tchr 1980-; *ai:* Math Counts & League Coach; PJAS Co-Spon; Covered Bridge Artesians 1980- Bd; All-Star Edctr 1995; *home:* 419 Old Hickory Ridge Rd Washir 15301*

CAMERA, WILLIAM J., Reading Teacher; *b:* Brooklyn, NY; *m* *ed:* Univ of MD (BA) Eng 1967; Fordham Univ (MAEd) Rdng Addl Credits; *cr:* Saint Bernadette Schl Lang Arts Tchr 1979-93 of Ed Rdng Tchr 1993-; *ai:* Comm Prgm After Schl Rdng Tchr; NY Assn, Queensboro Cncl of Rdng 1994-; *office:* Springfield Grdns Schl 132-55 Ridgedale St Springfield Gdn NY 11413

CAMERON, GLENN RICHARD, Music Teacher; *b:* New Castle Cheryl Sheely; *ed:* Grove City Coll (BM) Music Ed 1991; Phil Univ of the Arts 1994; Post Grad Stud in Music Ed in Conjunct Villanova Univ; *cr:* Conneaut Vly HS 7th-12th Grd Vocal & Instr Music Tchr 1991-; *ai:* Marching, Pep & Jazz Band; Woodwind Er Womens Trio; Mens Quartet; Show Choir; DJ Club; Dist, Reg & PMEA Festivals in Jazz, Concert Band & Chorus Jr & Sr High; MENC 1991-; PSEA & NEA 1991-; Conneaut Vly Bus Assn Pers Yr 1995; Keystone Intergrated Framework 1995; Co-Writer PMEA 1996 for PA Dept of Ed; *home:* RR 2 Box 376 Conneautville PA

CAMERON, JOHN WILSON, English Dept Head; *b:* Winslow, Judith Dunbar; *c:* Christopher A., Heather A.; *ed:* Colby Coll (1957; Wesleyan Univ (MA) Eng 1969; *cr:* Marshfield HS E 1959-64; Holderness Schl Head of Eng Dept 1964-76; Dana H Head of Eng Dept 1976-; *ai:* New England Assn of Tchrs of En Pres, Charles Swain Thomas Awd; NCTE 1970-; NEH Reader's Dig Scholar from MA 1989-90; NEH Summer Insts 1987, 1990; Klingenstein Fellow Tchrs Coll 1982-83; Fulbright Exchange England 1969-70; *home:* 141 Grove St Wellesley MA 02181

CAMERON, JUDY PHILLIPS, Sixth Grade Teacher; *b:* Fort Br *m:* John William; *c:* Alex Thomas, Christine Marie; *ed:* VA Te Mngmt Housing, Family Dev 1977; 6 Grad Hrs Learning Disabilit of VA; 12 Grad Hrs Math Ed Univ of MD; 18 Grad Hrs Sci Ed Loy *cr:* Town & Country Schl 4 Yr Old, 2-3 Grd Tchr 1977-79; St Ma Schl 3rd Grd Tchr 1979-81; Patuxent Elem Schl 3rd-6th Grd Tch *ai:* NEA 1984-; NCTM 1995-; Schl Math Coord; *office:* Patuxe Schl 4410 Bishop Mill Dr Upper Marlboro MD 20772*

CAMERON, JUDY REDDY, Sixth Grade Teacher; *b:* Reading, Gene; *ed:* Westchester Univ (BS) Elem Ed 1971; Penn St Univ Elem Ed 1977; 30 Addl Credits; *cr:* Clayton Elem Schl 6th C 1971-72; Gov Mifflin Intermediate Schl 6th Grd Tchr 1972-; *ai:* Adv 1973-91; New Tchr Mentor 1989-95; AAUW 1974-; NEA 19 Mountain Eagle Climbing Club, Prgm Chm 5 Yrs; *office:* Governo Intrmdt Schl 600 Governor Dr Shillington PA 19607

CAMERON, MOIRA, French & Spanish Teacher; *b:* Providence, RI Coll (BA) Fr, His 1976, (MAT) Fr 1981; 25 Credit Hrs Span; Credit Hrs Span; *cr:* Tolman HS Fr Tchr 1983-84; Ponaganset HS Tchr 1984-86; Burrillville HS Fr, Span Tchr 1986-; *ai:* NEAR AATSP 1991-, Exec Bd; AATF 1994-; RIFLA 1990-; *office:* Burri S 425 East Ave Harrisville RI 02830

CAMHI, PAUL J., Prof of Eng as a Second Lang; *b:* Brooklyn, Brooklyn Coll CUNY (BA) Linguistics 1968; CUNY Grad Ct Linguistics 1984; *cr:* Queens Coll Lecturer 1975-87; Laguardi Coll Adj Asst Prof 1984-94; NY Univ Adj Assoc Prof 1993-95; Bo Manhattan Comm Coll Asst Prof 1988-; *ai:* Linguistics Soc 1982-; Natl TESOL 1988-; NYS TESOL 1990-; NYS Assn of 2 1994-; ESL Consultant to NYC Bd of Ed; Ed of Fac Voices Articles Pub; Presentation at Prof Confs; Facilitate Tchr Trng ESL Coord of Pre-Frosh Immersion Pgms; *office:* Borough Of M Comm Coll 199 Chambers St Rm N420 New York NY 10007*

CAMILLI, DANIEL ANTHONY,JR., Social Studies Teacher; *b:* MA; *m:* Tandy M. Gold; *ed:* Boston St Coll (BA) His-Magna Cu 1978; Univ of MD (MA) Amer Stud 1981; Harvard Univ (EDM) *cr:* Arlington Cath HS Soc Stud Tchr 1987-94; Danvers Pub Sch Cultural Stud Dir 1994-95; Danvers HS Soc Stud Tchr 1995-; *ai:* Soc Stud Comm Chair; NEAS+C Assessment Comm; NCSS; AS Tchrs Assn; Phi Delta Kappa, Harvard Chapter; Keizai Koho Ctr to Japan; Fulbright Schlsp to China; Articles Pub; Book Revie Presentations; *office:* Danvers HS 60 Cabot Rd Danvers MA 0192

CAMMAROTO, JOYCE A., History Teacher; *b:* Philadelphia, Trinity Coll (BA) Cum Laude-Pol Sci & His 1973; *cr:* Overbook Jr Stud Tchr & Jr Honor Soc Adv 1973-82, Soc Stud Tchr 1982-; 1973-; NJEA 1973-; World Affairs Cncl 1993-; Trinity Coll Acad S *office:* Overbrook Regional Sr HS 1200 Turnerville Rd Pine Hill N

CAMP, DEBORAH SUE (REDMAN), Tchr of the Gifted & Tal Oceanside, CA; *m:* Fred; *c:* Kristopher, Molly; *ed:* OH St Univ (B Ed 1976, (MA) Gifted Ed 1990; *cr:* South-Western City Schls 4th-Elem Tchr 1976-87, Elem Enrichment & 4th & 5th Grd Tchr 1987-; *ai:* Tech Comm Mem; Gifted Prgm Travel Group Trip Ldr; of the Mind Coach, Tournament Dir, Regnl Tournament Dir & St in; NEA, OEA 1976-; OH Assn for Gifted Children 1987-; Natl Assn fted; Local Theatres 1993-, Vol; Grove City HS Orch Boosters 1995-, Pub Thesis Attitudes of Regular Classroom Tchrs Toward Gifted; a Holdings Jennings Scholar Recipient 1995-96; South-Western City Schl Bell Awds; Presenter Gifted Seminars at OH St Univ; *office:* Western City Schls 2975 Kingston Ave Grove City OH 43123

P, KRISTINA LYNN, German Teacher; *b:* Cincinnati, OH; *ed:* Univ yton (BA) Ger 1994; *cr:* Sidney HS Ger Tchr 1994-; *ai:* 8th Grd eading, Frgn Lang Adv; Jr HS Girls Track Coach; Schl Improvement Curr Cncl Yrbk Photographer; Sidney Ed Assn, OH Ed Assn, NEA Nom 1st Yr Tchr Awd St of OH; 6th Grd Parish Schl Rel Tchr; pated Red Glove Charity League of Sidney; *office:* Sidney HS 1215 ell Rd Sidney OH 45365

, VERNON PAUL,JR., Professor of Eng & Fine Arts; *b:* Bellevue, Charlotte Ruth Feldman; *c:* Amy Edith, Carrie Louise; *ed:* Comm Beaver Cty (AA) Liberal Arts 1973; Univ of PA (BA) Art His 1975; ry Rock Univ (MA) Eng 1988; MRA Schl Machinist Trng US Navy *cr:* Private Contractors Carpenter 1960-65; US Navy 3rd Class nist 1965-68; Kaufmanns Dept Store Displayman 1968-69; Comm Beaver Cty Prof 1969-; *ai:* Assoc Ed EMERGE; Facilities Planning, omms; Acad Cncl; Cultural Affairs Calendar; New Prgms; Speakers ; Art Club; Nea 1969-, Pres of Schls Chapter 1985 & 1989; Art ssions Narthex Stained Glass Window Cross Rds Presbyn Church Foyer Sculpture Comm Coll of Beaver Cty 1986; Various Private ssions & Portraits; *office:* Comm Coll Of Beaver County 1 Campus aca PA 15061

AGNA, ALVA SOBEL, Kindergarten Teacher of Gifted; *b:* yn, NY; *m:* Bruce; *c:* Daryn, Jason; *ed:* Brooklyn Coll (BA) Ed 1968, Ed 1970; 30 Grad Credit Hrs Various Courses Tchng Expertise; *cr:* Early Chldhd Classes Tchr 1968-74; PS 222 Tchr of Gifted Kndgtn *ai:* AFT, UFT, NYSUT 1968-; *office:* PS 222 Katherine R Snyder 301 Quentin Rd Brooklyn NY 11234*

AGNOLI, KATHY J., English Teacher; *b:* Baltimore, MD; *ed:* n MD Coll (BA) Eng 1982; Hood Coll (MA) Schl Admin 1987; 30 s Beyond Masters; *cr:* S Carroll HS Eng Tchr 1982-83; Gov Thomas n HS Eng ng Tchr 1983-; Wilson Coll Adjunct Ed Fac Mem, Ctr Dir hrs 1996-; *ai:* Tchrs Advy Comm Schl Rep Northern Region; NEA FCTA 1982-, Local Tchrs Union; NCTE 1982-; FMHA 1990-,Vol *office:* Governor Thomas Johnson HS 1501 N Market St Frederick 701*

ANA, THERESA (FIORINO), Science Teacher; *b:* New York, NY; nso N.; *c:* Francesco F., Maria Giuseppina; *ed:* Univ of Med & Dent PHD) Biochemistry 1955; Marymount at Manhattan (BS) Chem *r:* Columbia Univ Dept of Med Rsrch Technician 1952-62; Intnl Lab etics & Biophysics Rsrch Assn 1963-67; Yeshiva Univ Dept of Med ssc 1967-71; Univ Med & Dent of NJ Dept of Biochem Tchng Asst, c 1971-75; Sloan-Kettering Inst Rsrch Assoc 1975-78; Albert Coll of Med Rsrch Fac 1978-82; Birch Wathen HS Sci Dept Chair ; Acad of Mt St Ursula Sci Fac 1987-; *ai:* Asian Club; Assist with b; Grad Stu Assn Sec, Pres 1971-75; Grad Stu Alumni Assn Pres ; Cath Tchrs Assn 1987-; Sigma Xi 1975-; Salerno Club Ed Amici NY St Regents Schlsp 1955-59; Intnl Lab of Genetics Sci ant 1963-64; Articles Pub; *office:* Acad Of Mt St Ursula 330 Park Blvd Bronx NY 10458*

ANARO, MARIE JULIET, Spanish Teacher; *b:* Brooklyn, NY; *m:* chard; *c:* Camille, Benjamin; *ed:* SUC at Brockport (BA) Sec Educ, an 1976, (MS) Elem Ed, Biling Stud; Misc Courses for Prof Dev; CB Biling Multicultural Prgm Sec 1976-79; Cath Diocese of er MS Eng Tchr 1979-85; Spencerport Cntrl Schls Span Tchr *i:* Coord, Chaperone Trip to Spain; Liason to BCES II Second Lang on Ctr; MS Comm; Teaming Subcom; NYSAFLT 1991-; FLATRA NYPIRG 1991-; *office:* Cosgrove MS 2749 Spencerport Rd port NY 14559

ANELLA, NEALE, Mathematics Teacher; *b:* Jersey City, NJ; *m:* engler; *c:* Stephen David; *ed:* Kean Coll (BA) Math & Scndry Ed Credits Toward Masters at Trenton St Coll; *cr:* Iselin Jr HS Math 78-80; Conackamack MS Math Tchr 1980-81; Piscataway HS Math 81-; Middlesex Cty Coll Adjunct Prof 1993-94; *ai:* NJEA, NEA *office:* Piscataway HS 100 Behmer Rd Piscataway NJ 08854*

ANILE, MICHAEL, Mathematics Teacher; *b:* Plainfield, NJ; *m:* E. Laeske; *c:* Christine J., Michael John; *ed:* Eastern Nazarene Coll ath 1967; Western MI Univ (MA) Math 1972; Hofstra Univ Schl Prof Cert 1991; Attnd Columbia Univ Tchrs Coll, Fordham Univ, *v; cr:* Brentwood HS Math, Cmptr Tchr 1967-; SUNY Adj Instr of 76-81; Acad of St Joseph Dr Ed Instr 1986-90; Dowling Coll Adj ath Prof 1991-; LIU Curr, Instruction Adj Assoc Prof 1994-; *ai:* Jr uture Tchrs of Amer Adv; NCTM 1975-; AFT, NYSUT 1967-; e-Medford Yth Soccer League, IM Soccer Coach 1981-86, Travel occer Coach 1986-92; Tchr of Yr 1988, 1990, 1994; *office:* od HS Ross Center Brentwood NY 11772

NY, PATRICK MICHAEL, 5th Grade Teacher; *b:* Lowville, NY; orie J. Lathan; *c:* Eric Michael, Brian Patrick; *ed:* SUNY at (BA) Psych & Soc Sci 1961, (MS) Ed 1975; 27 Hrs in Admin & Disability; *cr:* Carthage Cntrl Schl 5th Grd Tchr 1961-66; Vly Cntrl Schls 5th Grd & Migrant Schl Tchr 1966-69; South Cntrl MS Tchr 1969-95; Jefferson Rehab Ctr Dir of Psychiatric atment 1975-76; *ai:* Coach: Yth Sports Adams NY 1975-90, Var th Jefferson Cntrl Schl 1976-86, Jr High 1970-75, JV 1986-90; Var ccer 1976-90, JV 1972-75, Jr High 1990-93, Frosh Bsktbl 1980-90 estling 1972-80; Co-Founder Harold Dunn Yth Soccer 1979 & SJ Club 1976-90; Sci Dept Chm Warwick Vly Cntrl Schl 1967-68; Cncl 1968-69; NEA 1961-70; AFT 1970-95; S Jefferson TA Ch Curr Dev Comm 1978; Comm Action Planning Cncl 1966-69, 8-69; Adams Vol Fire Dept 1973-80; S Jefferson Wrestling Club Exec Cncl; S Jefferson Lions Club 1976-81, Tailtwister 1980; unn Yth Soccer League 1979-85, Exec Cncl; Outstdng Elem Tchrs 1977; S Jeff Wrestling Club Hall of Fame 1990; *office:* South Central Schl Scholtz Elem Bldg Box 10 Institute St Adams NY

YO, KARIN POOLE, Spanish Teacher; *b:* Lynn, MA; *m:* Damian Campayo Romero; *ed:* West Chester Univ (BS) Span 1990, (MED) 5; 6 Post-Masters Credits; Univ of Madrid Lang & Culture Span *cr:* Amer Lang Acad ESL Tchr 1990-92; Coatesville Sr HS Span 2-; *ai:* Span Club Adv; Span Trip Dir; SAP Team Mem; New Tchr NEA, PSEA, CATA 1992-; Lionville Comm Meth Church 1994-, Bd; Tchr of the Yr Finalist 1995; *office:* Coatesville Area Sr HS incoln Hwy Coatesville PA 19320*

ELL, ABBY ANN, Bio & Human Physiology Tchr; *b:* arre, PA; *m:* Paul Lawrence; *c:* Jason Paul; *ed:* Coll Misericordia 1971; PA Dept Ed (ME) Ed 1988; Wilkes Univ Post Grad Stud; svc Credit Hrs; Dallas Schl Dist Staff Dev Insvc Credit Hrs; *cr:* S Bio, Human Physiology Tchr 1971-; *ai:* FTA Adv; Stu Records, ng, Discipline, Prin Advy Comms; Dallas Ed Assn 1971-, Bd Rep; EA 1971-.

ELL, BERNARD MARIE, Science Teacher; *b:* Joliet, IL; *ed:* Francis (AB) Math 1946; Univ of Notre Dame (MS) Chem 1962; Attnd NSF Summer Insts at American Univ, Univ of Detroit & OH St Univ; *cr:* St Peters HS Sci & Math Tchr 1946-55; Sacred Heart HS Sci & Math Tchr 1955-57; St Mary HS Sci Tchr 1957-59; SS Peter Paul HS Sci & Math Tchr 1959-63; St Peters HS Sci & Math Tchr 1963-; *ai:* Yrbk & Sports Photography; OH Cath Ed Assn & NSTA 1963-; Wooster OH Amer Chemical Soc Tchr of Yr 1990; *home:* 104 W 1st St Mansfield OH 44902

CAMPBELL, CAROL J., Business Instructor; *b:* Youngstown, OH; *m:* Charles E.; *c:* Carolyn; *ed:* Youngstown St Univ Bus (BSEd) 1971, (MAEd) 1974; Kent St Univ 1971 Voc Cert IOE COE; Spring, Summer 1995 Tech Prep Classes; *cr:* Struthers HS Bus Instr 25 Yrs; *ai:* Prep Club, Sr Class, Voc Club Adv; NEA, OEA, NEOEA, SEA 25 Yrs; Delta Kappa Gamma 10 Yrs, Treas; OBTA 25 Yrs; Poland Band Parents 1988-92; Struthers Fed Credit Union, Bd of Dirs; March of Dimes, Cancer, Heart Assn, Neighborhood Collections Collections; Martha Holden Jennings Scholar 1984-85; 3 Mini Grants from DKG; *office:* Struthers HS 111 Euclid Ave Struthers OH 44471*

CAMPBELL, CHARLES R., Cmptr Information Systems Prof; *b:* New Castle, PA; *m:* Mary Ann Drobezko; *c:* David, Anne; *ed:* Westminster Coll (BS) Math & Physics 1964; Indiana Univ of PA (MS) Math 1972; Attnd Univ of Dayton Chatauqua Courses, Univ of Pittsburgh Grad Courses; *cr:* Mohawk Area Schls Physics & Math Tchr 1964-68; Butler Cty Comm Coll Prof 1968-; *ai:* NEA 1993-; BCCCEA 1993-, Pres; PSEA 1993-; *office:* Butler County Comm Coll College Drive Oak Hills Butler PA 16001

CAMPBELL, CHRISTOPHER DOUGLAS, Director of Bands; *b:* Putnam, CT; *m:* Maria Hull; *c:* Andrew, Arden; *ed:* Clarion Univ of PA (BS) Music Ed 1988; Miami Univ OH (MM) Music Ed 1990; Post-Grad Work at Temple Univ & west Chester Univ; *cr:* Cedar Crest HS Dir of Bands 1990-; *ai:* Cedar Crest HS Marching Falcon Band; Music Educators Natl Conf, PMEA, NEA 1990-; *office:* Cedar Crest HS 115 E Evergreen Rd Lebanon PA 17042

CAMPBELL, DENISE BRYANT, First Grade Teacher; *b:* Sharon, PA; *m:* John E.; *c:* Matthew J., Katherine E.; *ed:* Clarion St Coll (BS) Elem & Early Chldhd Ed 1975; Slippery Rock Univ (MED) Rdng Specialist 1980; *cr:* Gamble Elem Schl Permanent Substitute 3rd Grd Tchr 1975-76; West Elem Schl Rdng Ctr Tchr 1976-77; Mercer Elem Schl 1st Grd Tchr 1977-; *ai:* Mercer Ed Assn & PSEA 1977-; Elem, PEP, Mercer Methodist Church, Suzanna Circle; *office:* Mercer Elem Schl 3001 Lamor Rd Mercer PA 16137

CAMPBELL, DORIS, English Teacher; *b:* Chicago, IL; *m:* Albert; *ed:* Univ of PA (AB) Eng 1967; PA St Univ (MA) Eng 1978; Rutgers Univ (EDD) Eng 1983; *cr:* Truman HS Eng Tchr 1969-; *ai:* NEA, PSEA 1969-; Books Pub: Given by the Day 1966, Fireflies 1970; Outstdng Young Woman of Amer 1978; *office:* Truman HS 3001 Green Ln Levittown PA 19057

CAMPBELL, ELLEN L., Fifth Grade Teacher; *ed:* Miami (BS) 1st-8th Elem Ed 1963, (MED) Elem Guid 1973; *cr:* Morrow Elem 1st Grd Tchr 1961-62; Wilmington 2nd Grd Tchr 1962-65; Waynesville 5th grd & Jr High Tchr 1966-; *ai:* NEA; OEA; WEA; Mary L Cook Pub Lib, Bd of Trustees; Project Excl Awd; *office:* Waynesville Elem Schl 659 Dayton Rd Waynesville OH 45068

CAMPBELL, ETHEL M., Lang Arts Tchr & Dept Coord; *b:* Norristown, PA; *m:* R. Kenneth; *c:* R. Scott, Cheryl Grier; *ed:* West Chester Univ (BS) Elem Ed 1959; Attnd Penn St, Lehigh Univ, Wilkes Coll, James Mason Univ; *cr:* Vly Forge Elem Schl 5th Grd Tchr 1959-61; High St Elem Schl 4th-5th Grd Tchr 1961-62; Wood Brook Elem Schl 5th-6th Grd Tchr 1970-71; Milton Hershey Schl 6th-8th Grd Remedial Tchr 1972-74, 8th Grd Frgn Lang Tchr 1974-75, 6th-7th Rdng Tchr 1975-92, Dept Coord 1982-92, 7th Grd Lang Arts Tchr 1992-; *ai:* NEA, PSEA, MHEA 1992-; KSRA, Capital Rdng Cncl 1987-; ASCD 1990-; Ed Excl 1989; *office:* Milton Hershey Schl Catherine Hall Hershey PA 17033

CAMPBELL, GEORGE ROBERT, Fifth Grade Teacher; *b:* Philadelphia, PA; *m:* Margaret Alice Trutt; *c:* Heather, Heidi; *ed:* Mansfield St Coll (BS) Elem Ed 1967; Attnd Bloomsburg St Coll, Penn St Univ, Cntrl Susquehanna Intermediate Unit 16; *cr:* Shikellamy Schl Dist Tchr 29 Yrs; *ai:* Outdoor Ed Coord; Asst HS Sftbl & JV Coach; Patrol Adv; NEA 1967-; PSEA 1967-; Shikellamy EA 1967-; *home:* 685 Water St Northumberland PA 17857

CAMPBELL, HARRIET LAVERNE, Math Teacher; *b:* Whitinsville, MA; *c:* Eric, Kim; *ed:* Worcester St Coll (BS) Math 1969; *cr:* Lakeside Lodge Schl for Boys Tchr 2 Yrs; Milford MS East Math Tchr 22 Yrs; *ai:* Pres Milford Tchrs Assn; Town of Milford CIP Steering Comm; MA Tchrs Assn, NEA 1972-; *home:* 14 Talbot Ter Uxbridge MA 01569

CAMPBELL, IVY MEADOWS, Sixth Grade Teacher; *b:* Flint, MI; *m:* W. Michael; *c:* Caroline, Will; *ed:* Morehead St Univ (AB) Elem Ed 1979; Univ of VA (MED) Curr, Instruction 1982; Univ of DE 4 Credit Hrs; *cr:* Perryville MS 6-8 Grd Rdng Tchr 1983-84; New Castle MS 6 Grd Tchr 1985-; Wilmington Coll Adj Fac 1992-; *ai:* Colonial Schl Dist Math Curr, Multi-Cultural Comms; Piloted Drop-Out Prevention Prgm; Peer Mediation Facilitator; NEA, PTA 1988-; Outstdng Amer Woman; Organized Feed the Children Prgm; Nom Tchr of Yr; New Tchrs Mentor; *office:* New Castle MS 903 Delaware St New Castle DE 19720*

CAMPBELL, JANE K., Mathematics Teacher; *b:* Pittsburg, CA; *c:* Cristin, Kelli, Katlyn; *ed:* Montclair St (BA) Math 1971; *cr:* Shore Regnl HS Math Tchr 1971-74, 1984-85; Marlboro HS Math Tchr 1985-86; Neptune HS Math Tchr 1990-; *ai:* Jr Class Adv; NEA, NJEA 1971-; NTEA 1990-; *office:* Neptune HS 55 Neptune Blvd Neptune NJ 07753

CAMPBELL, JEAN A., Tchr & Lwr Schl Head Asst; *b:* Brooklyn, NY; *c:* Jennifer L., Brian C.; *ed:* Southern CT St Univ (BS) Intermediate Ed 1962; Loyola Coll Admin; Univ of MD Post Grad Hrs; *cr:* Brushy Plain Schl 5th Grd Tchr 1962-64; Peshawar Air Station Schl Tchr, Ed Specialist 1965-67; Lamont Elem Schl 5th-6th Grd Tchr 1967-70; Traeger Park Schl 5th Grd Tchr 1976-78; Winward Prep Schl 6th-8th Grd Tchr 1980-84; Boys' Latin Schl 5th Grd Tchr, Admin 1985-; *ai:* Admissions Comm; K-8 Curr Coord, Tchr Stu Scheduler; Materials Purchasing Lower Schl; AIMS 1985-; Curr Assocs 1991-; ARGUS Tchr Evaluation 1994-; Assn of Ind MS Ford Fellow; Australian Amer Club Achvmt Awd; *office:* Boys' Latin Sch Of Maryland 822 W Lake Ave Baltimore MD 21210*

CAMPBELL, JOHN K., Telecommunications Professor; *b:* Reading, MA; *m:* Janet Forbes; *c:* Michael, Lisa; *ed:* 62 Credit Hrs Northeastern Univ; *cr:* Natl Teleco Operations Mgr 1970-76; IBM System Engr, Instr 1977-92; NH Tech Coll Telecom Prof 1992-; *ai:* Telecommunications Club Adv; Cmptr, Craft, Scheduling Comms; ASTD 1979-; *office:* NH Tech Coll 505 Amherst St Nashua NH 03061*

CAMPBELL, KATHERINE M. L., Language Arts Teacher; *b:* New York City, NY; *m:* Frederick Augustus Jr.; *c:* Julie A., Alicyn K.; *ed:* Univ of Bridgeport (BA) Lbrl Arts, His 1970; Cntrl CT St Univ (MS) Lang Arts, Rdng 1992; *cr:* Holy Rosary Parocial Schl Grd 3, Grd 5 Tchr 1968-71; Elisabeth M. Bennet MS Tutor 1986-87, Grd 8 Lang Arts Tchr 1987-; *ai:* Natl Jr Hnr Soc; Lang Arts Dept Head; Varous Comms; Presented Wkshps; IRA; CRA; AAUW; NCTE; CCTE; CT Writing Project Fellow, Consultent 1989; CT Celebration of Excl Winner 1992; Readers Digest Amer Heros Ed 1992; Natl Bd of Prof Tchng Standards COntent Validation Comms 1995; *office:* Elisabeth M Bennet MS 1151 Main St Manchester CT 06040*

CAMPBELL, KATHLEEN KIENER, English Teacher; *b:* Staten Island, NY; *m:* Patrick H.; *c:* Courtney, Meredith; *ed:* Wagner Coll (BA) Eng 1969, (MA) Eng 1975; 30 Credit Hrs Rdng Concentration, Cmptr; *cr:* Wagner Coll Eng Assistantship 1969-70; New Dorp HS Eng Tchr 1970-76; Tottenville HS Eng Tchr 1976-; *ai:* AFT, UFT, NYC Tchrs of Eng 1970-; Visiting Nurse Auxiliary Assn 1978-94; Friends of Snug, Harbor Cultural Ctr, Ed of Newsletter 1984-90; Notre Dame Acad Parents Guild, Class Rep 1987; IS 61 Parents Org, Sec 1991; *office:* Tottenville HS 100 Luten Ave Staten Island NY 10312

CAMPBELL, LINDA S., Third Grade Teacher; *b:* Youngstown, OH; *m:* Robert S.; *c:* Jennifer, Robert; *ed:* Bowling Green St Univ (BA) Elem Ed & Spcl Ed 1970; Youngstown St Univ (MS) Curr 1989; 3 Post Grad Credit Hrs; 15 Post Grad Credit Hrs at Walsh Univ; *cr:* Western Reserve Local 5th Grd Tchr 1971-74; Springfield Local 3rd Grd Tchr 1983-; *ai:* NEA & OEA 1983-; IRA 1983-; NCTM 1985-.

CAMPBELL, MANDLYN CERYSSE, Special Ed Paraprofessional; *b:* Hartford, CT; *cr:* Weaver HS Literacy Vol 1985-86; Barbour Schl Vision Impaired Para 1986-87; Martin Luther King Vision Impaired Para 1987-88; Quirk MS Vision Impaired Para 1989-; *ai:* Provide Cultural Awarenewss Pgm for Inner City Yth; AFT 1986-; *home:* 33 Deer Meadow Rd Bloomfield CT 06002

CAMPBELL, MARK ALLEN, Assistant Pastor; *b:* New Philadelphia, OH; *m:* April Joy Miles; *c:* Carrisa, Autumn; *ed:* TN Temple Univ (BA) Pastoral Stud 1990; Temple Bapt Seminary (MRE) Christian Ed 1992; *cr:* Carroll Christian Schls Tchr 1992-; *ai:* Soccer Coach; Rookie Tchr of Yr 1992; *office:* Carroll Christian Schl 550 Baltimore Blvd Westminster MD 21157

CAMPBELL, MARY HEBERT, English Teacher; *b:* Charles City, IA; *ed:* Winona St Univ (BS) Eng 1978; Ashland Univ (MA) Curr, Instruction 1988; *cr:* South Tama Cty Jr HS Eng Tchr 1978-79; West Jr HS Eng Tchr 1979-83; Westerville North HS Eng Tchr 1983-; *ai:* NEA 1978-; NCTE 1980-; OCTELA 1984-; Sr Class Adv 1986; Cheerleading Adv 1978-83; Brace II 1985-, Pres 1989, Service Awd, Sec 1987; Jr League Columbus 1988-; Leukemia Society, 1994; Comm for Night for Life Suicide Prevention Benefit, 1994; Jennings Scholar 1989-90; Article in English Journal 1980; Co-Editor Son of Heaven Newsletter 1988; *office:* Westerville North H S 950 Smothers Rd Westerville OH 43081

CAMPBELL, NANCY P., Kindergarten Teacher; *b:* Sodus, NY; *m:* Charles J.; *c:* Kevin, Jill Sill; *ed:* Potsdam St Tchrs (BS) Music Ed 1956; 32 Credit Hrs Elem Ed Perm Cert Oswego St Tchrs; *cr:* Newark Cntrl Schl K-3 Grd Elem Music Tchr 1956-58; Waterloo Cntrl Schl 2nd Grd Tchr 1958-59, Elem Music Tchr 1959-60; Sodus Cntrl 2nd Grd, Kndgtn Tchr 1962-; *ai:* HS Musical & Nyssma Festivals Accompanist; Team Ldr Kay; NEA 1962-; SFA Tchrs Assn; St John's Episcopal Church, Organist, Choir Dir; *office:* Sodus Cntrl Schl PO Box 220 Sodus NY 14551

CAMPBELL, PRISCILLA BARRY, Third Grade Teacher; *b:* Weymouth, MA; *m:* Robert A.; *c:* Ian, Colin; *ed:* Boston St Coll (BS) Early Childhd & Elem Ed 1970; 30 Hrs Post Grad Stud; *cr:* Penniman Elem Schl 3rd-5th Grd Tchr 1970-72; Hollis Elem Schl 3rd Grd Tchr 1972-81; Liberty Elem Schl 3rd Grd Tchr 1981-; *ai:* Schl Cncl Mem; Braintree Ed Assn 1970-; MTA 1970-; NEA 1970-; MA Audubon Soc; Braintree Historial Soc; New England Herpetological Soc; Madame Alexander Doll Club; *office:* Liberty Elem Schl 49 Proctor Rd Braintree MA 02184

CAMPBELL, ROBERT C., Coordinator & Assoc Professor; *b:* Maysville, KY; *m:* Lisa Ballew; *c:* Zachary, Kelsey; *ed:* Morehead St Univ (BS) Bus & Psych 1976, (MBE) Ed 1978; Kent St Univ (ABD) Curr & Instruction; *cr:* Mason Cty Bd of Ed Tchr 1977-79; Youngstown St Univ Prof 1979-; *ai:* Hospitality Mgmt Soc Adv; Consultant to Several Hospitality Related Bus; OH Bus Tchrs Assn 1979-; CHRIE 1993-; Natl Restaurant Assn 1993-; Amer & OH Hotel & Motel Assn 1993-; Outstdng Stu Org Adv; KY Col; NBEA Awd of Merit; *office:* Youngstown St Univ 410 Wick Ave Youngstown OH 44555

CAMPBELL, ROBERT LEWIS, Environmental & Earth Sci Tchr; *b:* Santa Ana, CA; *m:* Diana J. Rice; *ed:* Univ of PA at Edinboro (BA) Anthropology 1982; Salem St Coll (BS) Earth Sci Ed 1984; Attnd Harvard 4 Credits, Penn St 3 Credits & WV Univ 6 Credits; *cr:* Watertown HS Sci Tchr 1984-86; Burrell HS Sci Tchr 1989-; *ai:* Sci Olympic & Envirothon Coach; Sci Fair Coord; NEA 1989-; PSTA 1989-; Earth Sci Tchrs 1989-; Natl Geographic Soc 1982-; Key Person in the Comm & Innovative Tchng Awd PSTA; Allegheny Ludlum Grant; PA Tchr of the Yr Nom; *office:* Burrell HS Puckety Church Rd Lower Burrell PA 15068

CAMPBELL, ROY M., Sixth Grade Teacher; *b:* Dover-Foxcroft, ME; *ed:* Gordon Coll (BS) Elem Ed 1971; Providence Coll (MED) Ed Admin 1981; 30 Plus Credit Hrs; *cr:* Helen R Donaghue Elem Schl 6th Grd Tchr 1971-; *ai:* Schl Cncl Mem 3 Yrs; Schl Building Comm; NEA 1971-; MTA 1971-; Title Master Tchr & Merrimac Ath Assn Awds; Intramural Prog 25 Yrs; Little League Coach 9 Yrs; *office:* Helen R Donaghue Elem Schl 10 Union Street Ext Merrimac MA 01860

CAMPBELL, RUSSELL G., Mathematics Teacher; *b:* Pittsburgh, PA; *m:* Ellen; *c:* Mark, Allison; *ed:* Indiana Univ of PA (BS) Math 1977; *cr:* Ctr Area Schl Dist Tchr 1977-; *ai:* 8th Grd Bsktbl Coach; PSEA; NEA; Oakdaleborough Cncl 1987-, VP; *office:* Center HS 160 Baker Rd Monaca PA 15061

CAMPBELL, RUTH J., Fifth Grade Teacher; *b:* Philadelphia, PA; *ed:* Lock Haven Univ (BS) Elem Ed 1970; Commonwealth of PA Dept of Ed Masters Equivalency Elem Ed 1987; 54 Addl Hrs Ed; Buck Cty IU #22, Trenton St 16 Inservice Credits; *cr:* James Buchanan Elem Schl Permanet Sub Tchr 1970, First Grd Tchr 1970-88, Fifth Grd Tchr 1988-; *ai:* Dist Writing, Rdng Comms; NEA, PSEA 1970-; BTEA 1970-, Sec 2 Yrs; Bristol Twp Dem Comm 6 Yrs, Comm Person; Buchanan PTO 1970-, Fac Rep; BTEA 1970-, Alternate Rep; BTEA 1970-, Bldg Rep; Established Stu Cncl for Buchanan Stdnts; *office:* James Buchanan Elem Schl 2200 Haines Rd Levittown PA 19055*

CAMPBELL, SANDRA CARPENTER, Chemistry Teacher; *b:* Cincinnati, OH; *m:* Overton H.; *c:* Joseph, Alexander; *ed:* Cumberland Coll (BS) Bio, Chem 1974; 4 Semester Hrs Grad Credit Scndry Ed; CEU's Cmptr; *cr:* Marian HS Chem, Physiology, Life Scis, Geology Tchr 1974-80; St Ursula Acad Chem, Bio, Physiology, Phy Sci Tchr 1980-; *ai:* Sr Class Moderator 1987-; Prom Coord 1987-; Open House Chprsn 1985-; Marian HS Sci Dept Chprsn 1976-79; Sci Olympics Consultant; NSTA 1974-; Forst Hills PTO; Cub Scouts, Vol; Chem, Art, Soc Stud Cross Curricular Project; Natural Dyes & Fibers Presented at Cincinnati Art Museum, Schl Faculties; *office:* St Urusula Acad 1339 E Mcmillan St Cincinnati OH 45206

CAMPBELL, SHIRLEY A., Teacher; *b:* New York, NY; *ed:* Bronx Comm Coll (AA) Acctng 1975; Lehman Coll (BS) Acctng 1983; Working on MS Manhattan Coll Spec Ed; Monroe Bus Inst; *cr:* Treasury Dept Auditor 1975-81; Ethical Culture Schl Tchr 1981-85; NYC Bd of Ed Tchr 1985-; *ai:* Chess Club; After Schl Enrichment; UFT 1985-; BX Rdng Cncl 1989-; Tchr of Yr; *office:* The Throop Schl PS 121 2750 Throop Ave Bronx NY 10469

CAMPBELL, TAMITHA FISHER, High School English Teacher; *b:* Jackson, TN; *m:* Eric Jawara; *ed:* Howard Univ (BA) Eng 1992, (MED) Admin 1993; *cr:* Howard Univ Upward Bound Eng & Span Tchr 4 Yrs; Mount Jezreel Kiddie Coll Instr 1 Yr; Montgomery Blair HS Eng Tchr 3 Yrs; *ai:* Stu-to-Tchr Mentor Prgm; Sisters Club Spon; Blair Admin Comm; Stu Asst Prgm; Schl Improvement Comm; NEA 1993-; MCABSE 1994-;

Alpha Kappa Alpha Inc 1993-; Toastmasters Intnl 1989-, Pres; *office:* Montgomery Blair Sr HS 313 Wayne Ave Silver Spring MD 20910*

CAMPBELL, WILLIAM HARRY, Retired English Teacher; *b:* Erie, PA; *m:* Patricia Taylor Dahlstrand; *c:* Virginia, William, Cynthia, David, Carolyn; *ed:* Edinboro St Coll (BS) Eng, Speech 1956; 14 Addl Cdt Hrs; *cr:* Warren Schl Dist Eng Tchr 1956-70; Erie Schl Dist Eng Tchr 1956-70; Newspapers Reporter, Ed, Publisher 1960-73; Commonwealth of PA Press Ofcr 1974-80; PA St Ed Assn Media Specialist 1980-86; Millersburg Area Schl Dist Tchr 1986-95; *ai:* Writing, Producing 9th-12th Grd Composition Stud Course; Newspaper Adv; NEA, PSEA, Local EA's 1956-; Erie Regnl Theater 1960-65, Bd Mem; Cty Human Svcs 1980-82, Bd Mem; Wrote, Produced, Directed Two Musical Productions; Wrote Numerous Articles; *home:* 1186 Tourist Park Rd Halifax PA 17032

CAMPION, RICHARD PETER, Assistant Professor of English; *b:* New York City, NY; *c:* Maureen, Christine; *ed:* Manhattan Coll (BA) Eng, Modern Langs 1965; NYU (MA) Eng 1965; *cr:* Mt St Mary Coll Asst Prof 1966-; Orange Cty Comm Coll Adj Part-time 1974-88; *ai:* Adv, Asst Dir Stu Drama Group; Film Reviewer for Stu Newspaper; Performed in Schl Productions; Schl Concert Choir; Acad Stans, Admissions, Lib Comms; AAUP 1975-; Friends of the Lib; Amodeo Productions, Ticket Sales; Book Reviewer for Films in Review 1972-75; *office:* Mount Saint Mary Coll 330 Powell Ave Newburgh NY 12550

CAMPO, DAVID FRANK, History Department Chairperson; *b:* Vincennes, IN; *m:* Jane K. Copeland; *c:* Anne M., John D., Jennifer Pumphrey; *ed:* Manhattan Coll (BBA) Ec 1965; Indstrl Mngmt Air Force Inst of Tech; Attnd Squadron Ofcr Schl, Air Command & Staff Coll, Natl War Coll; *cr:* USAF Missile Operations Ofcr, Trng, Missile Operations Dir 1965-87; Madison Cty Historical Soc Archivist 1988-89; New Life Chrstn Schl His Tchr 1989-; *ai:* HS Cnslr; Career, Stamp Club Adv; Drum Instr; Textbook Evaluation Comm; NY St Historical Assn 1987-; *office:* New Life Christian Schl Rd 2 Box 248a River Rd Hamilton NY 13346

CAMPOLI, WILLIAM A.,SR., Adjunct Instructor of Psych; *b:* Binghamton, NY; *m:* Vonda L. Standish; *c:* Jennifer A., Melissa A., William A. Jr.; *ed:* Binghamton Univ (BA) Psych 1978; Marywood Coll (MA) Clinical Psych 1983; *cr:* Broome Developmental Svcs Psychologist 1975-; Broome Comm Coll Adjunct Instr 1984-; *ai:* Broome Developmental Svcs Outstanding Employee 1984; Lowes Syndrome Assn Wkshp Presenter 1989; *office:* Broome Community Coll PO Box 1017 Binghamton NY 13902

CAMPOLO, JAMES L., High Schl Business Ed Teacher; *b:* Newark, OH; *m:* Barbara A. Hanrahan; *c:* Kristine, Aaron; *ed:* Miami Univ Miami of OH (BS) Gen Bus, Pre-Law 1970; Attnd OH St Univ, Kent ST Univ Ed, Ashland Univ Sports Medicine; *cr:* Wickliffe Jr HS Indstrl Arts Tchr 1970-74; Newark HS Bus Ed Tchr 1974-; *ai:* Head Sftbl Coach; Asst Ftbl Coach, Offensive Coord; Newark Tchrs Assn, OH Ed Assn, NEA 1974-; OH Fastpitch Sftbl Coaches Assn 1987-, 2nd VP St, Dist Pres; Knights of Columbus, Des Newark Maennerchor 1980-; OH Insurance Inst Tchr of Yr 1994; *office:* Newark HS 314 Granville Rd Newark OH 43055

CAMPOPIANO, THOMAS, Mathematics Asst Principal; *b:* New York City, NY; *ed:* Queens Coll CUNY (BA) Math 1973, (MS) Ed 1977; St Johns Univ Prof Diploma Admin 1996; *cr:* Hillcrest HS Para Prof Tchr 1973-77; Far Rockaway HS Math Tchr 1977-95, Math Asst Prin 1995-; *ai:* AFT 1977-; Assn of Math Asst Prin, Supvrs of NYC 1995-; *office:* Far Rockaway HS 821 Bay 25th St Far Rockaway NY 11691

CAMPOS, PATRICIA S., History & Geography Teacher; *b:* Newark, NJ; *m:* Henrique Jr.; *c:* Kevin, Brian, Jeffrey; *ed:* Trenton St Coll (BA) Soc Stud Ed 1968; OH St Univ 5 Grad Credits; 6 Grad Credits Seton Hall; 3 Grad Credits VCU; 1 Grad Credit William Paterson Coll; *cr:* Kawameeh Jr HS His Tchr 1968-70; Mother Seton RHS His Tchr 1987-; *ai:* Yrbk Adv; Sr Class Adv & Homeroom Tchr; Curr Comm; NJCSS 1988-; NCSS 1989-; NCEA 1987-; Crane's Ford Chapter DAR Outstanding Tchr of Amer His 1990; *office:* Mother Seton Regional HS Valley Rd Clark NJ 07066

CAMPS, BRENDA KAY, First Grade Teacher; *b:* Wheeling, WV; *m:* Thomas James; *c:* Alaina Marie, Vincent James, Julia Lauren; *ed:* WV Univ (BS) Elem, Early Chldhd Ed 1983; Post Grad Courses in Cmptr, Lib Sci; *cr:* Red Jacket Elem Kndgtn Tchr 1983-84; East Franklin Elem 1st Grd Tchr 1984-; *ai:* NEA 1983-; PTA 1984-; *home:* 144 N Maiden St Waynesburg PA 15370

CANALE, LORRAINE DOUGHERTY, Fifth Grade Teacher; *b:* Jim Thorpe, PA; *ed:* East Stroudsburg Univ (BS) Early Chldhd, Elem Ed 1973, (MED) Elem Ed 1975; 36 Credit Hrs Sci; Spec Ed Cert; *cr:* Pocono Mt Schl Dist Sub Tchr 1974-80, Spec Ed Tchr 1980-89, 5th Grd Tchr 1989-; *ai:* Ski Adv; NEA, PMEA, PSEA 1980-; Tannersville Cranberry Bog Comm 1991-, Chprsn; *office:* Pocono Elem Ctr Warner Rd Tannersville PA 18372

CANALES, JOANNE CHRISTINE, 5th Grade Teacher; *b:* Harlem, NY; *c:* Andrea R.; *ed:* Lehman Coll (BA) Sociology, Ed 1976; Hunter Coll (MS) Ed 1983; 9 Credit Hrs Lehman Coll NY City Math Project; 17 Credit Hrs La Guardia Comm Coll; *cr:* PS 55 Bronx Classroom Tchr 1978-80; PS 11 Queens Classroom Tchr 1980-85; PS 7 Bronx Classroom Tchr 1985-; *ai:* AFT 1978-; NEA; NAACP; NY Urban League; *office:* PS 7 Bronx 3201 Kingsbridge Ave Bronx NY 10451

CANALES, MARIA-CRISTINA, Associate Professor of French; *b:* La Habana, Cuba; *ed:* Univ of PR (BA) Gen 1970; La Sorbonne (MA) Fr Lang & Lit 1972; Univ of MA (PHD) Fr Lit 1990; *cr:* colegio Puertorriqueno de Ninas Tchr 1975-81; Univ of MA TA 1981-87; Our Lady of the Elms Prof 1987-; *ai:* Dept Chair, Affirmative Action Comm Chair; AAUP Chptr Pres; Diversity, Fac Stans Comms; AAUP 1988-, Pres; MLA, ALA, MAFLA; Gracias Matiox Thanks Hermano Pedro Garland 1996; NEH Grants 1990-; Fac Dev Grants 1991, 1996; *office:* Our Lady of the Elms Coll 291 Springfield St Chicopee MA 01013

CANAVAN, MARY ANNE, Fifth Grade Teacher; *b:* New York, NY; *ed:* St Johns Univ (BS) Elem Ed 1963, (MS) Elem Ed 1973; *cr:* PS 67 Bronx Tchr 1963-85; PS 203 Queens 5th Grd Tchr 1985-; *ai:* UFT 1965-; *office:* PS 203 Oakland Gardens 53-11 Springfield Blvd Bayside NY 11364

CANCRO, JAMES RICHARD, Social Studies Teacher; *b:* Tarrytown, NY; *c:* Lance, Heather; *ed:* Ithaca Coll (BA) Soc Stud Ed 1973; Addl 30 Hrs in Ed at Oswego St Univ; *cr:* Cato-Meridian HS Soc Stud Tchr 1973-; *ai:* Sftbl Coach; Jr Class Adv; Restructuring & SIT Comms; master Tchr; Sport Boosters 1989-, Treas; Zoning Bd of Appeals 1993-; *office:* Cato Meridian HS Rt 370 Box 100 Cato NY 13033*

CANCRO, SUSAN MCCAFFERTY, Assistant Principal; *b:* Bronx, NY; *m:* Greg; *c:* Harrison; *ed:* Mercy Coll (AA) Liberal Arts 1978; Fordham Coll at Lincoln Ctr (BA) Theatre 1980; Cert Level I & II Catechist Formation Prgm Archdiocese of NY; *cr:* Saint Benedicts 4th Grd Tchr 1980-86; Mount Carmel 2nd & 4th Grd Tchr 1986-95, Asst Prin 1995-; *ai:* Lib Coord; Sci Fair Comm; *office:* Our Lady of Mt Carmel-Bronx 2465 Bathgate Ave Bronx NY 10458*

CANDIA, DIANE THERESA, Fourth Grade Teacher; *b:* Springfield, OH; *m:* Ramon; *c:* Alex, Ana Maria, Nicholas; *ed:* Miami U (BS) Elem Ed 1976; 20 Addl Hrs in Ed Admin Univ of Dayton; *cr:* Springfield City Schls 4th-5th Grd Tchr 1978-81; Peace Corps Math Instr at Tchr Trainer Coll 1981-82; Springfield City Schls 1st-2nd, 4th Grd Tchr 1982-; *ai:* NEA 1976-, Pub Relations Chair 1980-81; NCTM 1993-; Excl in Tchng Awd Rotary Club, Springfield News & Sun; *office:* Warder Park-Wayne Elem Schl 2251 Hillside Ave Springfield OH 45503*

CANDIOTTI, ORRIN, Mathematics Teacher; *b:* Brooklyn, NY; *m:* Ann Palladino; *c:* Derek, Kevin; *ed:* Brooklyn Coll (BA) Elem Ed 1972, (MS) Elem Sci 1979; Long Island Univ NSF; *cr:* CES 114 Tchr 1973-75; PS 172 Tchr 1977-; *ai:* Mentor; Testing Coord; *office:* PS 172 825 4th Ave Brooklyn NY 11232*

CANDLEN, FRANCES LARKIN, Third Grade Teacher; *b:* Boston, MA; *m:* Joseph T.; *c:* T. J., Lynne Dimond, Joanne Tocci; *ed:* Boston St Coll (BS) Scndry Ed, His 1959, (MS) Elem Ed 1972; 60 Addl Hrs; Lang Arts, Math, Sci, Spec Ed, Classroom Mngmt Courses; *cr:* Harris Schl Tchng Asst 1972-74; High Rock Schl 5th-6th Grd Classroom Tchr 1974-76; Broadmeadow Schl 4th-5th Grd Classroom Tchr 1976-82; Hillside Schl 3rd Grd Classroom Tchr 1982-; *ai:* NEA 1974-, Rep; NCTM 1991-; MTA 1974-; Parent, Staff Advy Comm 1990-93; Supt's Distngd Achvmt Svc Awd 1992-93; *office:* Hillside Schl 28 Glen Gary Rd Needham Heights MA 02194

CANDREVA, LAUREANN, Math Teacher; *b:* Rockville Centre, NY; *m:* Frank; *c:* Alexei; *ed:* SUNY at Cortland (BS) Scndry Ed 1985; Columbia U Tchrs Coll (MS) Math Ed 1988; 50 Credit Hrs Beyond MA; *cr:* West Windsor Plainsboro HS Math Tchr 1985-87; West Windsor Plainsboro MS Math Tchr 1987-88; East Meadow Schl Dist Math Tchr 1989-; *ai:* Jr HS Soccer 1987, Var, Frosh, Jr HS, Chrldng 1986-92, JV, Jr HS Tennis Girls, Boys 1991-94 Coach; East Meadow TA, NYSHTA 1989-; Locke Meml Awd 1985; *office:* East Meadow Sr HS 101 Carman Ave East Meadow NY 11554*

CANELL, BEVERLY J., Foreign Language Dir & Tchr; *b:* New Haven, CT; *m:* Edward; *c:* Brian; *ed:* Southern CT St Univ (BS) Scndry Ed, Fr Major, Span Minor 1971, (MS) Bilingual Ed 1974; 6th Yr Cert Admin & Supervision; *cr:* Hamden Pub Schls Foreign Lang ESOL Tchr 1971-, Foreign Lang Dir 1984-; *ai:* Intnl Stdnts Club Adv; Evaluation Comm Chair; CT Cncl of Lang Tchrs 1971-, Bd of Dirs; Phi Delta Kappa 1990-, Former VP; Univ of CT Alumni Assn Excl in HS Tchng Awd; *office:* Hamden Pub Schls 2040 Dixwell Ave Hamden CT 06514*

CANESTRARE, KIMBERLEY ANNE, Art Teacher; *b:* Syracuse, NY; *ed:* Syracuse Univ (BFA) Dual Enrollment in Art, Ed 1983, (MA) Studio Art, Art Ed 1991; *cr:* Syracuse Parks & Recreation Arts, Crafts Instr 1979-80; Canestrare Graphics Designer 1980-84; Woodland-Fremont Elem Schl Art Tchr 1984-85; Pine Grove Jr HS Sec Art Tchr 1986-; ES-M HS Sec Art Tchr 1986-; *ai:* Participation, Competition Scholastic Art Awds; Career Day, Tech Comms; Schl Advertising, Graphic Design; *office:* East Syracuse Minoa Schls 6400 Fremont Rd East Syracuse NY 13057*

CANFIELD, NANCY ARMSTRONG, English Teacher; *b:* Springfield, OH; *c:* Nicole, Phillip, Peter; *ed:* OH St Univ (BA) Eng Speech Ed 1969, (MA) Ed 1973; *cr:* Bexley City Schls Eng Tchr 1969-80; Olentangy Local Eng Tchr 1990-; *ai:* NHS Adv; NEA, OEA & OTA 1990-; NCTE 1990-; 4-H Adv 1985-; Book: Kids & the Law; Tchrs Manual to Accompany Bk; *office:* Olentangy HS 675 Lewis Center Rd Delaware OH 43015

CANFIELD BORDER, KAREN, Anthropology & His Professor; *b:* Pittsfield, MA; *m:* James Durning; *ed:* Univ of MA at Amherst (BA) Non-Western His 1963; Radcliffe Coll (AM) His 1964; Harvard Univ (AM) His & Athropology 1964; Amer Inst of Hyprotherapy DCH Clinical Therapy Expected 1996; Adams St Coll MA Cnslng Ed Summer 1996; *cr:* Miss Halls Schl Head His Dept 1964-69; Simons Nash & Bard Coll Prof of His & Anthropology 1967-75; Berkshire Comm Coll Prof of Anthropology & His 1971-; Skidmore Coll Adj Prof 1982-; *ai:* Selected Stud Lbrl Arts Pgm Head; Competetive Coll Adv; MTA & NEA 1976-, VP, Bershire Chptr; Woodrow Wilson Fellow; Ford Fdntn; Natl Endorsement for Hum Medicine Grant & Hum Educl Grant; *office:* Berkshire Comm Coll West Street Pittsfield MA 01201

CANGELOSI, ANTHONY,JR., Professor; *b:* Brooklyn, NY; *m:* Rhona Eve Popeil; *c:* Amie, Beth, Lisa Ann; *ed:* Nassau CC (AAS) Instrumental Tchr 1971; St Univ of NY (BS) Instrumentation Tech 1981, (MA) Bus & Policy 1986; *cr:* Taylor Instrument Cos Field Svc Tech 1972-75; Nassau Comm Coll Lab Asst for Electronics 1975-81, Electronics Instr 1981-; *ai:* Electrical Eng Tech & Telecommunications Tech Pgm Coord; Prsnl & Budget Comm Sec & Senator; ELT Club Adv 1981-91; Instrument Soc of Amer 1980-, Ed Chm; NY NJ Engr Tech Assn 1981-; Soc of Manufacturing Engr 1985-; Robotics Intnl 1985-; Apex Merrick Schls 1985-, Mentor; SUNY Fac Grants 1987-92; Evaluator; Amer Film & Video Assn 1990-93, Screening Juror; LI Sci Congress 1993-95, Judge; LI Solar Sprint 1995-, Judge; SUNY Improvement of Undergraduate Instruction & Robot Dev Grants; Assistance with Job Placement UL Labs; Lab Manuals Pub; *office:* Nassau Comm Coll 1 Education Dr Garden City NY 11530

CANGRO, MARILYN BINGHAM, Third Grade Teacher; *b:* Rahway, NJ; *m:* Joseph M.; *c:* Tracey Sarafin Jacey, Christopher Sarafin; *ed:* Westfield St Coll (BA) Elem Ed 1977, (MS) Educl Admin 1984; 18 Credit Hrs GATE Stud Univ of CT; 45 Addl Hrs; *cr:* Heritage Acad 4, 6-8 Grd Tchr 1977-84; Gateway Regnl Schl Dist Tchr of GATE 1984-91; Gateway Murrayfield Elem Third Grd Tchr 1991-; *ai:* Tech, Prof Dev Comms; MA Gateway Tchrs Assn 1977-; Outstdng Achvmt Heritage Acads Ed Comm 1983; *office:* Murrayfield Elem Schl 12 Littleville Rd Huntington MA 01050

CANIGLIA, ROSE A., Gifted & Talented Prgm Coord; *b:* Brooklyn, NY; *m:* Paul; *c:* Paul III; *ed:* Coll of Staten Island (AA) Lbrl Arts 1972, (BA) His 1974, (MS) Ed 1976; Brooklyn Coll Admin, Supervision Advanced Cert 1995; *cr:* Ft Green Cath Schl 8th Grd Tchr 1975-79; Coll of Staten Island Adj Prof 1978-80; Springfield Gdns IS 59 8th Grd Tchr 1980-82, 6th-8th Grd Tchr 1989-93, Coord of GATE 1993-; *ai:* Natl Jr Hnr Soc, Yrbk Adv; Grad Awds, Ceremony Coord; NYC Tchrs Assn 1989-; *office:* Intermediate Schl 59 132-55 Ridgedale St Springfield Garden NY 11413*

CANNAN, PATRICIA JEAN, High School Counselor; *b:* Buffalo, NY; *m:* Patrick; *c:* Sean, Colleen; *ed:* Buffalo St (BS) Criminal Justice 1980; Canisius Coll (MS) Cnslr Ed 1988; Advanced Cert in Cnslr Ed; Completed Work Towards Cert for Schl Admin; *cr:* Buffalo Alternative HS Coord 1990-93; Baker Hall Dir 1990-93; Frontier Hs Cnslr 93-; *ai:* Peer Listening; Post Prom Party, Futures & Concerned Individuals Comms; Peer Mediation; WNYCA 1991-; Mount Mercy Alumnai Assn 1977; St Marys HSA 1993-; Spec Ed 1995-; Hamburg Youth Fnd Grant for Alcohol & Drug Free Prgrmng; *office:* Frontier Sr HS 4432 Bayview Rd Hamburg NY 14075*

CANNATA, BEVERLY, 4th Grade Teacher; *b:* Passaic, NJ; *w:* Frank A. (dec); *ed:* William Paterson Coll (BA) Elem Ed 1969, (MS) Elem Ed, Lang Arts 1994; Addl 15 Credits; Stud Lib Media Specialist; *cr:* Elem Schl 3 Tchr 1969-; *ai:* Sci Rep, Comm; NEA, NJEA 1969-; NJ Governor's Tchrs Awd; Pub The Reading Instruction Journal NJ Rdng Assn; *office:* Elem Schl 3 365 Washington Ave Clifton NJ 07011

CANNATA, KATHLEEN, Teacher of Gifted & Talented; *b:* Passaic, NJ; *m:* Charles; *c:* Jennifer, Tara; *ed:* Kean Coll (MA) Supervision & Admin 1989; *cr:* Passaic Bd of Ed 3rd Grd Tchr 1969-74, 6th Grd Tchr, 5th Grd G&T Tchr 1983-; *ai:* Stu Govt Adv; Site Based Mgmt & Pupil Assistance Comms; EAP 1969-; NJEA 1969-; NEA 1969-; *office:* Jefferson Elem Schl 1 390 Van Houten Ave Passaic NJ 07055

CANNATTI, PATRICIA A. (STAMM), 7th Grade English Teacher; *b:* Garrettsville, OH; *m:* Philip A. Jr.; *ed:* Kent St Univ (BSEd) Eng, Speech 1971; *cr:* Windham Exp Village Schls 7th Grd Eng Tchr 1972-95; *ai:* Quiz Bowl, Lang Arts Festival Club Adv; NEA, OEA 1972-; Salem Hills Golf & Cntry Club 1989-; *office:* Windham Jr High 9530 Bauer Ave Windha 44288*

CANNAVALE, MICHAEL ANTHONY, English Instructor; *b:* City, NJ; *m:* Connie L. Culver; *c:* Dominic, Sarah; *ed:* Seton Hal (MA) Eng 1972; St John's Univ (DA) Eng 1989; Montclair St Coll Er 1974; *cr:* Seton Hall Univ Eng Instr 1970-72; Morris Cath HS Theology Instr 1972-74; Meml MS Eng Instr 1974-76; Vernon Twp H Instr 1976-; *ai:* CORE Team; In-Svc Courses Instr; NEA, NSEA *office:* Vernon Township HS PO Box 800 Vernon NJ 07462*

CANNELL, MARGARET M., English Teacher; *ed:* Manhattan Co Eng 1991; Addl Credits Publishing Penn St Univ; *cr:* Queen of Pea Eng Tchr 1991-; *ai:* Yrbk, Ski Club Adv; NCTE 1991-; *office:* Qu Peace HS 191 Rutherford Pl North Arlington NJ 07031

CANNELLA, JOSEPH JAMES,JR., Physics Teacher; *b:* Tampa, F Penn St Univ (BS) Physics 1990; Temple Univ (MED) Ed 1992; *cr:* Darby HS Physics Tchr 1992-; *ai:* Sci Club Spon, Supvr; Sci Oly Team Coach; Mem Bd of Dir DE Valley Sci Cncl; NEA, PSEA, PSTA, Del Val St, AAPT 1992-; Ebenezer United Meth Church 196 of Chrstn Ed; Lead Tchr HS Initiative in Computational Sci Rsrch P Ldr of Physics Instruction Comprehensive Concepted Curr in F Project; *office:* Upper Darby HS 601 N Lansdowne Ave Upper Da 19082*

CANNELLA, RICHARD ANTHONY, TV Commnctn & English T *b:* Pittston, PA; *m:* Penny A.; *c:* Ryan, David; *ed:* Univ of Scranto Eng & Comm 1973; Bloomsburg Univ (MS) Instructional Tech Wilkes Univ (BA) Eng Ed 1993; 45 Hrs, Cooperative Learning, Tc 21st Century, Pride, Computer Courses; *cr:* WVIA-TV Photographe Production 1974-76; Self Employed Bus 1980-92; Hazleton Area Sc Media Specialist 1977-93, Eng & Comm Tchr 1993-; *ai:* Multi C Club Adv; Tech Comm Mem; Media Coord; NEA, PSEA 1993-; L & Natl Photography Awds; *office:* Hazleton Area HS 1601 W 2 Hazleton PA 18201

CANNIFF, NANCY EVANS, Reading & English Teacher; *b:* Col OH; *m:* G. Brock; *c:* Kevin, Keith; *ed:* OH Univ Athens (AB) Ge (MSEd) Rdng 1984; Undergraduate Hrs OH St Univ, OH Dominic Univ; Post-Grad OH Univ, Natl Coll Ed; *cr:* New Lexington City K-12 Substitute Tchr 1975-82; Walnut Twp Local Schls Eng & Sp 1965-70, HS Eng & Libr 1971-73,10-12th Grd Eng, Rdng & Comp Tchr 1982-; *ai:* NEA, OEA, NCTE, OCTELA, SOCTE, WTEA 198 1990-93; Delta Kappa Gamma 1992, Chpt Sec 1994-; New Le Alumni Comm 1990-; Grandview Hgts OCCL 1978-; Venture Comm, Chprsn 1994-; CATO Partnership Advy Comm 1994-; WTE 1994-95; OH Arts Summer Media Wkshp 1990; Reg Judge NCTE Awds in Writing 1988-; Grant Author in Residence 1988; EPDA La 1969; Jennings Scholar 1967-68; *office:* Millersport H S P O B Millersport OH 43046

CANNING, KATHLEEN A., Latin Teacher; *b:* Pittsfield, MA; *m:* *c:* Christine, John E., Katheen E.; *ed:* North Adams St (MA) Scr Admin 1974, (BA) Eng 1984; *cr:* St Joseph HS Tchr 1974-; *ai:* NH Frosh Class Adv; Magazine Dr Co Chprsn; Under Grad Awds Ce Chprsn; NESCA 1974-.

CANNING, MARY GERRISH, Choral Director; *b:* Milo, ME; *m:* J. Jr.; *c:* Kathryn Bourgoin, Patricia Bourgoin, Robert, Don Farmington Tchrs Coll (BS) Elem Ed 1954; Northern Conserva Music (BM) Music Ed 1970; Univ of ME at Orono (MS) Choral M 1977; *cr:* City of Augusta Pub Schls Classroom & Vocal Mus 1963-77, Vocal Music Supvr 1971-77; Dexter Pub Schls Class Vocal Music Tchr 1977-; Northern Conservatory of Music Early Classes 1995-; *ai:* Girls Ensemble Singing; Barbershop Singing Early Chldhd Music Northern Conservatory Bangor, ME; MTA; N Music Ed; MENC; ACDA Choral Dirs; Dexter Area Comm Ch 1982-91; *office:* Dexter Regional HS 12 Abbott Hill Rd Dexter M

CANNISTRA, RONNIE DANELLA, Kindergarten Teacher; *b* NY; *m:* Patrick D.; *c:* Michael, Charlene Broccoli, Patrick; *ed:* Ut of Syr Univ (BA) Eng 1966; SUNY of Utica at Rome (MA) Elem *cr:* Conkling Schl 6th Grd Tchr 1966-67; Whitesboro Cntrl Schl S 1977-88; Sauquoit Vly Elem Schl Kndgtn Tchr 1988-; *ai:* Lang Art Comms; Fac Rep Kndgtn; NYSUT 1988-; *home:* 11 Ironwood Hartford NY 13413

CANNON, AUDREY MARIA PICONE, Social Science Tea Avellino, Italy; *m:* John R.; *c:* Peter John; *ed:* Frailegh Dickens (BA) Scndry Ed, Soc Sci 1969; William Paterson Coll (MA) Sc 1975, (MA) Learning Disabilities 1977; 30 Addl Hrs; *cr:* Wayne Soc Sci Tchr 1969-.*

CANNON, DENISE L., Bilingual Guidance Counselor; *b:* Newbu *ed:* Univ of Richmond (BA) Psych 1983; Columbia Univ Tchrs Co TESOL 1987; Long Island Univ (MS) Cnslng 1994; *cr:* Freeport Biling Sci Tchr 1987-94, Biling Guid Cnslr 1994-; *ai:* Adv Lati 1988-93, Spanish Club 1992-93 & Peer Leadership Org 1991-; NT 1988-; Assn for Biling Ed 1990-; Explorer Post 1 1991-, Adult Adv Masters Degree as a Federal Biling Grant; *office:* Freeport HS S B Ave Freeport NY 11520

CANNON, DONALD E., English Department Head; *b:* Boston, Laura; *c:* Courtney, Amy; *ed:* Harvard (BA) Govt 1968; Northeaste Eng 1974; 45 Credits; *cr:* Walpole Pub Schls Eng Tchr Dover-Sherborn Pub Schls Eng Tchr 1978-; *ai:* Lit Magazine; Soccer Coach; NCTE 1986-; E MA Girls Soccer Coaches 198 Distngd Svc, Coach of Yr; St Grant for Interdisciplinary Course Dover Sherborn Reg HS Junction St Dover MA 02030*

CANNON, GENEVA, Instruction & Cnslng Svcs Supv; *b:* Hornto *ed:* MD St Coll (BA) Eng 1966; Salisbury St Coll (Med) Ed 19 Stud at Univ of PA; Doctoral Stud Univ of MD; *cr:* Worcester 1966-70; Snow Hill HS Tchr 1970-76; Worcester Cty Bd of Ed S & Instr Coord 1976-89, Supvr Instruction & Cnslng Svcs 1989-; Peer Helpers Conf, Co-Chair; Phi Delta Kappa 1989-; Natl Bd for Cnslrs 1989-; Amer Cnslng Assoc 1989-; NCTE 1989-; Comm Fnd Eastern Shore Grants Review Comm 1989-; Salisbury Area Ch Commerce 1994-; MD Blue Cross Blue Shield Bd of Dir 19 Survival Guide for Sub Tchrs 1984; Chptr in Book 1984; MD S Cncl Pgm Awd 1991; Chesapeake Bay Girl Scouts Cncl Outstdn Awd 1993; *office:* Worcester Cty Bd of Ed 6270 Worcester Hwy MD 21841*

CANNON, LENORE RICHARDSON, English Teacher; *b:* N NY; *m:* Roland; *c:* Scott David, Leigh-Anne; *ed:* York Coll (B 1985; Adelphi Univ (MA) Elem Ed 1988; 30 Addl Credits; *cr:* S Halsey Jr HS 157 Eng Tchr 1985-; *ai:* Stu Adv St Mary's Hosp T AFT, UFT 1985-; Kappa Delta Pi 1982-; 1984-85 Edition Wh Among Stdnts Amer Univs & Colls; York Coll Hnr Soc, C Distinction Psych & African-Amer Assn 1985; *office:* Stephen A Jr HS 157 6400 102nd St Rego Park NY 11374

CANNON, LESLIE GALLE, Mathematics Teacher; *b:* Dayton George Dewey Jr.; *c:* Kimble C., Kristen Cannon Mondeaux, Geor *ed:* Miami Univ (BA) Math 1963; Fairleigh Dickinson Univ (M 1967; Post Grad Pre Doctorate NYU 1968; Tchng Inst Rutgers 1989-94; *cr:* Manasquan HS Math Tchr 1963-64; Neptune HS M

Fairleigh Dickinson Univ Math Tchr 1966-68; Manasquan HS · 1987-88; Ranney Schl Math Tchr 1988-; *ai:* Congression Awds s, Math League Adv; Alumni Club 1976-, Pres, VP, Treas; Phi a; *office:* Ranney Schl 235 Hope Rd Tinton Falls NJ 07724

, NIKKI IRENE (POLITES), Vocal Music Teacher; *b:* Akron, owell N. (dec); *ed:* Univ of Akron (BS) Music Ed 1968, (BA) g Arts 1971; 30 Credit Grad Hrs Masters Equivalency 1990; 18 1995; *cr:* Akron Pub Schls Vocal Music Tchr 1968-; *ai:* Drama ow Choir Vocal Dir & Choreographer; Pi Lambda Theta 1967-; : Edctrs Conf 1968-, 25 Yr Awd; Delta Kappa Gamma 1972-, m; Amer Choral Dirs Assn 1990-; Fred Warings US Chorus Admin Asst, Admin Cncl Mem; Akron Pub Schls OH Tchr of the 986 & 1987; Honored by HS Stu-Influenced His Life the Most , Honorary St Lifetime Memshp Awd 1996; *home:* 3310 Linden iontown OH 44685

, WILLIAM PATRICK, 11th Grade English Teacher; *b:* N; *m:* Loretta M. Shpuut; *c:* William, Corinne, Molly, John, Joe; etown Univ (BA) Eng Lit 1969; Univ of IA (MFA) Poetry Writing Gonzaga Schl Eng Tchr 20 Yrs; *ai:* Lit Magazine; Poetry Pub; of Arts Grant 1995; *office:* Gonzaga Coll HS 19 Eye St NW n DC 20001

MARY ELLEN SNYDER, Business Ed Tchr & Dept Chprsn; *b:* *m:* Albert E.; *ed:* Westminster Coll (BBA) Bus Ed 1960; IN Univ d) Bus Ed 1969; Word Processing Applications Using IBM PC Youngstown St Univ Sec Ed, Sec Plus; Essential Elements ı; Penn St Univ Office Procedures, Org for Sec; Classroom s Using Micro; Microcomputer Lit Using Apple II Cmptr; on Basic Operating Theory & Programming for Tandy Cmptr; *cr:* ings Co Switchboard, Teletype, Secretarial Summer 1956; er Coll General Office, Secretarial Summers 1957-63; Oil City d Tchr 1960-63; Callos-McCreary Temporaries, Inc Temporary rk 1979-80; Wilington Area HS Bus Ed Tchr 1963-; *ai:* Oil City sletter Editor; Spon, Regnl Future Bus Ldrs America Club; Exec ity Area Ed Assn; Amer Assn Univ Women; Rep Cncl of n Area Ed Assn; Oil City Area Ed Assn 3 Yrs; Wilmington Area 4 Yrs; PA St Ed Assn, NEA, Tri St Bus Ed Assn 34 Yrs; Chprsn Mid St Evaluation, Accreditation Comm, Seneca Valley HS 1977; s Stud Mid St Evaluation, Accreditation Comm, West Allegheny *office:* Wilmington Area H S 350 Wood St New Wilmington PA

O, ROBERT D., Tchr Asst of Culinary Arts; *b:* Syracuse, NY; ry Inst of Amer (AOS) Culinary Arts 1990; SUNY Oswego Cert Voc Ed; *cr:* Embassy Suites Line Chef 1990-92; OCM Boces 1990-; Delta Gamma Working Chef 1993-95; *ai:* AFT 1990-; M Boces Schl 6820 Thompson Rd P O Box 4754 Syracuse NY

O, ANTHONY L., 10th Grade Geometry Teacher; *b:* Scranton, anne Mc Cormick; *c:* Tony, Christopher; *ed:* Keystone Jr Coll Math 1972; Mansfield St Coll (BS) Scndry Ed, Math 1974; 15 s Post Grad Stud Ed, Math at Univ of Scranton; *cr:* Cardinal HS Tchng, Coaching Staffs 1975-78; Dunmore Sr HS Tchng, Staffs 1978-83; Scranton Preparatory Schl Tchng, Coaching 4-; *ai:* Soccer, Bsktbl, Bsbl Coach; NCEA 1985-; NPCTM 1992-; ion 1983-, Bsbl Coach; *home:* 1804 Dickson Ave Scranton PA

LI, STEPHEN J., 5th Grade Teacher; *b:* Boston, MA; *m:* Julie James, Katharine, Andrew; *ed:* Framingham St (BA) Ed 1972; Coll (MS) Ed 1976; *cr:* Pollard Schl 6th Grd Tchr 1972-82; ancock Schl 5th Grd Tchr 1982-; *ai:* Drama Coach; Parent Tchr Rep; Garden Club Dir; MA Tchrs Assn, NEA & Quincy Ed Assn incy Neighborhood Housing 1981, Bd of Dirs 11 Yrs; Ward 4 ood Assn 1981, Co-Chm 3 Yrs; Natl Gardening Assn Grant 1988; Awd 1989 & 1990; Scholastic News Kids Care Contest 1st 1988, Natl Winner 1992; Citizen of the Yr for Quincy, MA cted Granite Wrkrs Memrl 1994; *office:* Lincoln Hancock Schl e St Quincy MA 02169*

, SHARON JENKINS, Intervention Specialist; *b:* Ashley H; *m:* David Ray; *c:* Christopher Trent, Chad Tyson, Casey OH Univ (BS) 1st-8th Grd Elem Ed 1965; 30 Semester Hrs Yr; *cr:* Minford MS Tchr 1965-71; Vernon Elem Tchr 1971-93; rimary Title I Tchr 1993-; *home:* 6160 State Route 140 urg OH 45694

LO, THOMAS JOSEPH, Business Teacher; *b:* Glen Falls, NY; Barber; *c:* Louis, Joel, Jonathan; *ed:* St Univ of NY at Canton s Admin 1975; St Univ of NY at Albany (BS) Bus Ed 1977, (MS) room Tchng 1981; *cr:* Saratoga Springs Jr Sr HS Bus Tchr 1977-; ratoga Springs Jr Sr HS W Circular St Saratoga Springs NY

LUCILLE J.,CSC, Associate Prof of Education; *b:* r, NH; *ed:* Notre Dame Coll (BA) Latin, Scndry Ed 1969; Univ ED) MS Ed 1975; Boston Coll Univ (PHD) Curr, Instruction, 989; *cr:* Diocese of Manchester Elem Schl Tchr 1958-76; r E. Cath Regnl Schl Prin 1976-79; Notre Dame Coll Asst Prof 9-85, Dir of MED in Elem, Scndry Tchng 1989-94, Assoc Prof of 5; *ai:* Notre Dame Coll Concert Chair; 1st Yr Mentor Tchr; NH f Ed Mentor Trainer AH V; Assn of Tchr Ed 1979-; Assn for n & Curr Dev 1979-; Phi Delta Kappa 1984-, Fnd Rep, Honor a Sigma Nu; Sisters of Holy Cross Inc, US Region 1990-, Pres; Dwelling Place Inc 1990-, Trustee; NH Cath Charities Bd of Inc m; St Francis Fnd Inc 1990-, Trustee; *office:* Notre Dame Coll St Manchester NH 03104*

, PATRICIA ROGERS, Education Dept Instructor; *b:* Santa *m:* Alan M.; *c:* Rebecca Eliabeth, Max Nolan; *ed:* Harvard Coll Lit, Lang 1980; Plymouth St Coll (MED) Early Chldhd Stud nd Boston Univ Doctoral Prgm; Degree in Curr, Tchng, Early *r:* Plymouth St Coll Facilitating Tchr 1990-91, Instr 1991-, Dir , Family Ctr 1993-; *ai:* Acad Advising; Chair, Sidore Lecture mm; Svc on Dept Comms; NAEYC 1991-; CCDLA 1992-, Bd; 93-; NH St Child Care Advy Comm 1992-; Awarded Schlsp iv 1995-; *office:* Plymouth St Coll Education Dept Rounds Hall NH 03264

, SADELL FURMAN, Earth Science Teacher; *b:* Yonkers, NY; : Amy, Wendy; *ed:* Hunter Coll (BA) Geology-Cum Laude 1967; NY at New Paltz (MS) Earth Sci 1987; Master Tchr Status-90 eyond Bachelors 1995; *cr:* Lakeland HS Earth Sci Tchr 1967-70; HS Earth Sci Tchr 1970-71; Merchandise Dynamics Inc Mgr of -Tech Book Division 1981-86; North Jr HS Sci Tchr 1987-; *ai:* lub Spon; Newburgh Schls Alternative Assessment Act; Phi Beta 67-; NEA, AFT, NYSUT 1967-71, 1987-; Kappa Delta Pi 1967-; -; STANYS 1967, 1987-; 1969 NSF Grant Pace Coll Astronomy Empire Schlsp for Grad Work 1984-86; Orange-Ulster BOCES Sci Curr Writers Mem, Devng New St Curr; *home:* 111 Tillson Wallkill NY 12589

E-GREEN, JEAN MARIE, English Teacher; *b:* FT Belvoir, VA; Michael; *c:* Tommy, Jared; *ed:* SUNY Albany (BA) Eng 1974, , 1976; Albany Law Schl 1978-79; *cr:* Nisleayund HS Eng Tchr 1976-77; Columbia HS Eng Tchr 1977-78; SUNY Albany Writing Tchr 1979; Brighton HS Eng Tchr 1979-; *ai:* Sunshine Comm Dir, Schl Bus Safety Comm; Autism Soc of Amer 1993-; Phi Beta Kappa 1974-; NCTE, NEA; Phi Beta Kappa Tchr Recognition 1982, 1984; Outstanding Educator Award From Cornell Univ 1981; Tufts Univ Tchr of the Yr Award 1986; Outstanding Tchr Award Tufts Univ 1995; *office:* Brighton HS 1150 Winton Rd S Rochester NY 14618

CANTWELL, ELEANOR MARIANNE, Culinary Arts Teacher; *b:* New York, NY; *m:* John; *c:* ARchie, Mark, Paula, Sue Ann, Billy, John; *ed:* Marjorie Webster at WA DC (AAS) Merchandising; Cert Hotel Mngmt, Dining Room Operations, Wine & Spirit Mngmt, Front Office Operations, Hotel Motor Inn Operations, Catering, Cmptr Applications Hotel Industry Cornell Univ Schl of Prof Dev; *cr:* Highland Hotel Owner; Sullivan Cty Comm Coll Instr; Orange, Ulster Boces Tchr; *ai:* VICA Adv; BOCES Ldrshp Team; Schl Quality Review Initiative; HSMA; NRA; Orange Cty Citizens Fnd; Orange Cty Mediation; Two Manuals Pub; *office:* Orange-Ulster Boces 2 Gibson Rd Goshen NY 10924

CANTY, CHARLOTTE MARY, Third Grade Teacher; *b:* Addyston, OH; *m:* Andre Lamont; *c:* Errica Morehouse, Jay Goodlett; *ed:* Wright St Univ (BS) Elem Ed 1978; Univ of CT (MS) Cnslr Ed 1983; 23 Addl Gtr Hrs Various Ed Classes Evangelical Tchr Trng Assns Preliminary Tchrs Cert 1987; *cr:* Meredith Hitchens Elem Schl 4-5 Grd Tchr 1979-92; Charles T. Young Elem Schl 5th Grd Tchr 1992-93; Meredith Hitchens Elem Schl 4-5 Grd Tchr 1993-95; Miami Heights Elem Schl 3rd Grd Tchr 1995-; *ai:* U C Alumni Assn; Zion Temple Bible Inst 1988-, Tchr; Family Svc USAF 1970-72, 1974-, Vol, Appreciation; GEAT Bible Inst 1991-92, Asst Tchr; Local Schl Advy Comm 1985-86; Schl for Creative Perf Arts; Three Rivers Local Schl Dist Perfect Attendance Awds; Chrstn Yth Camp Cnslr 1991-93; GEAT Schlsp Comm 1992-93; Sunday Schl Tchr; *office:* Miami Hgts Elem Schl 7670 Bridgetown Rd Cincinnati OH 45248

CANZANESE, ROBERT PAUL, High School English Teacher; *b:* Camden, NJ; *m:* Diane Huminski; *ed:* Glassboro St Coll (BA) Eng Ed 1972; 9 Grad Credits Eng Villanova U; 6 Grad Credits Ed; *cr:* Cherry Hill HS East Eng Tchr 1977-; *ai:* Fac Adv Indian Culture Soc; Tchr In-Svc Pgrm Presenter for CPI Crisis Prevention Inst; CHEA 1988-; Rider Coll Dedication to Tchng Awd 1990; Western MD Coll Most Distngd HS Tchr 1991; Tufts U Tchng Excl Awd 1995; Governor's recognition Awd; *office:* Cherry Hill HS East Kresson Rd Cherry Hill NJ 08003*

CAOUETTE, ANNE M., Health, Human Development Tchr; *b:* Montague, MA; *ed:* Farmingham St Coll (BS) Home Ec Ed 1980; Bridgewater St Coll (MED) Hlth Promotion 1995; *cr:* North Adams MS 6-8 Grd Tchr 1980-81; Salem HS Home Ed Tchr 1981-83; Litteton HS Home Ed Tchr 1983-84; Mansfield HS Hlth, Human Dev Tchr 1984-; *ai:* Peer Ldrshp Prgm Adv; Prin Advy, Sexual Harassment Comms; Schl Cncl; Stu Asst Team; Chrldng Coach; MA Tchr Assoc, NEA 1980-; Schl Hlth Assoc 1994-; *office:* Mansfield HS 250 East St Mansfield MA 02048

CAPALARAN, AMELIA CORTEZ, High School Math Teacher; *b:* Samal Bataan, Philippines; *m:* Efren Ladia; *c:* Jemely, Jeffrey; *ed:* Univ of Manila (BSE) Math 1976; Jersey City St Coll MA Candidate Math Ed; *cr:* St Catherine of Sienna Acad Math Tchr 1976-79; Tomas Del Rosario Acad Math Tchr 1979-87; St Michael's Schl Math Tchr 1988-89; Our Lady of Good Counsel HS Math Tchr 1989-; *ai:* Stu Cncl Moderator; NEA 1988-; FACAGE 1992-, Sec; BATAAN Assn USA NJ Chptr 1990-; Eisenhower Grant; *office:* Our Lady Of Good Counsel HS 243 Woodside Ave Newark NJ 07104

CAPALDI, DAVID A., Mathematics Department Head; *b:* Providence, RI; *m:* Martha Mary Shea; *c:* Mary Angela, Elizabeth Anne, Philip Andrew; *ed:* RI Coll (BED) Ed & Math 1964, (MAT) Math 1967, (CAGS) Math Ed 1980; Attnd Univ of RI, Providence Coll, Brown Univ, Harvard Univ, U Cal at Berkeley; *cr:* Gorton Jr High Math & Sci Tchr 1964-72; RI Coll & Comm Coll RI Part-Time Instr 1970-; Winman Jr High Math Dept Head 1972-86; Toll Gate HS Math Dept Head 1986-; Interm Ecex 1995; RIMSEC Dir; *ai:* Co-Adv RI Math League, Adv Math Modeling & Odyssey Mind Teams; Stu Act Fund Coord; Chair of Fac; CAP, CAST Team; Chair TG Lit Comm; CCSSO-INTASC Project Team Mem; ATMNE Full Conf Gen Chr; RI Math Tchr Assn 1964-, VP & Pres; Assn Tchr Math NE 1964-, Pres; NCTM 1968-; Natl Cncl Super Math 1980-; Friends of Pub Lib; Kent Cty YMCA 1974-, Bd; Kent Cty Hospital 1988-, Bd Incorporators; RI NSF Presidential Math Tchng Awd 1986-87 & 1990-92; RI Math Tchrs Assn Recognition Prgm, RI Coll Alumni Honor Roll Awd Title IX Awd RI Comm on Women, RI Milken Family Fnd Awd 1992; DOE Tchr Res Assn.*

CAPALDO, PAUL STEPHEN, Biology Teacher; *b:* Providence, RI; *m:* Betty Jane Cameron; *c:* Alisa, Cathi; *ed:* Univ of RI (BS) Zoology 1968; FL Inst of Tech (MS) Bio, Envir Oceano 1976; *cr:* Riverside Jr High Bio Tchr 1970-; Barrington Coll Marine Bio Instr 1978-85; Roger Williams Univ Oceanography Instr 1986-93; Riverside Jr High Dept Chm 1989-; *ai:* Environmental Sci Club Adv; NABT 1988-, Regnl Rep; AAAS 1987-; RI Zoological Soc 1990-; East Prov Conservation Commission 1978-, Chm, Distinguished Leadership Citizen Planner; NE Bio Conf 1990-, Co-Chair; Articles Pub 1983, 1987, 1993; East Providence Outstanding Educator Awd 1983; RI Environmental Educator of Yr Awd 1981; *office:* Riverside Jr HS 179 Forbes St Riverside RI 02915*

CAPARELLI, FRANK PETER, Secondary Math Teacher; *b:* Mt Vernon, NY; *m:* Barbara Hoeymans; *c:* James, Andrew; *ed:* Iona Coll (BS) Physics, Math-Summa Cum Laude 1955; Columbia Univ (MA) Math 1958; 110 Hrs Math, Admin NYU, Manhattan Coll, Hofstra Univ, Fordham Univ; *cr:* Copiague Pub Schls Grds 7-12 Math Tchr 1956-62; Ardsley Pub Schls Grds 9-12 Math Tchr 1960-61; Valhalla Pub Schls Grds K-12 Math Coord 1962-90; Horace Mann Schl Grds 11-12 Math Tchr 1991-; Iona Coll Adj Prof of Math; *ai:* Math Team, Stu Adv; Prins, Governing Cncl; New Tchr Mentor; NCTM 1968-; MAA 1984-; NYSTU, AMTNYS 1962-; Republican Club 1955-; Parish Cncl 1990-; Knights of Columbus 1970-; Yrbk Dedications 1966, 1994; Grad Schlsps Brown Univ, Fordham, NYU, Univ of NC; *home:* 20 Edgewood Rd Ossining NY 10562*

CAPARRO, LOUIS EUGENE, 11th Grade US History Teacher; *b:* Norristown, PA; *m:* Mary Krepps; *c:* Louis Jr., Vincent, Lisa, Crouse; *ed:* West Chester Univ (BS) Soc Stud 1961, (ME) Soc Stud 1968; 12 Credit Hrs Penn St Univ; *cr:* Conestoga Sr HS US His Tchr, Coach 1961-62; Wissahickon Sr HS US His Tchr, Coach 1962-65; Downingtown Sr HS US His Tchr, Coach 1965-; *ai:* NEA, PSEA 1961-; Spring City Revitalization Comm 1988-, Sec; *home:* 265 Chestnut St Spring City PA 19475*

CAPELLO, LAURA ANNE FONDRAN, Art Teacher; *b:* Euclid, OH; *m:* Michael; *c:* Michael; *ed:* 22 Credit Hrs Post-Grad Work at Cleveland St, Kent St & Ursuline Coll; *cr:* Art Tchr Mayfield Schls; *ai:* MS Majorette Adv; MS Newspaper Adv 1984-86; Yrbk Adv 1986-90; Synchronized Swim Adv 1991, 1992 & 1994; Mayfield Educ Assoc 1979-; NEA 1979-; OH Art Ed Assoc 1979-; Scholastic Art Awds 1989-, Awds Advy Comm; *office:* Mayfield HS 6116 Wilson Mills Mayfield Vlg OH 44143*

CAPIK, MARIA D'AGOSTINO, Spanish Teacher; *b:* Buenos Aires, Argentina; *m:* John M.; *ed:* Kean Coll of NJ (BA) Scndry Ed Span 1980, (MA) Admin, Supv, Prin Cert; Bilingual Ed in Amer Soc 3 Credit Hrs; Career Psych 3 Credit Hrs; Substance Abuse Coord Cert 1995; *cr:* Our Lady of Mt Carmel 3rd Grd Tchr 1979-80; Carteret Bd of Ed Sub Tchr 1980; Newark Pub Schls Sub Tchr 1980-85; Newark Pub HS Span Tchr 1985-; *ai:* Sr Class, Span Club Adv; Newark Tchrs Union 1985-; *office:* East Side HS 238 Van Buren St Newark NJ 07105

CAPITO, ROBERT GREGORY, English Teacher; *b:* Warren, OH; *m:* Janet Lewis; *c:* Robin Webb, Eddie Sallusito, Greg, Bo; *ed:* Kent St Univ (BA) Eng 1984; Youngstown St Univ (MA) Eng 1992; Addl 30 Post Grad Semester Hrs Classroom Tchng, Theory, Technique; *cr:* John F. Kennedy HS Eng Tchr 1984-87; Memorial HS Eng Tchr 1987-; Youngstown St Univ Eng Composition Instr 1992-; *ai:* Class Adv; Campbell Ed Assn 1987-; NEA 1984-; Phi Kappa Phi 1992-; *office:* Campbell Memorial HS 280 6th St Campbell OH 44405

CAPLAN, JUDITH LANGER, English Teacher; *b:* Brooklyn, NY; *m:* Neil H.; *c:* Hillel, Baruch; *ed:* Brooklyn Coll (BA) Eng 1966; Syracuse Univ (MS) Commnctn & TV 1968; *cr:* Andries Hudde JHS Eng Tchr 1966-67; Wingate HS Eng Tchr 1969-72; Springfield Gardens HS Eng Tchr 1985-; *ai:* Lit Adv; UFT-NYC 1966-; Poets & Writers 1990-; Poet House Awd for Excl in Tchng of Poetry 1992; Numerous Poems, Short Stories & Articles Pub; *office:* Springfield Gardens HS 14310 Springfield Blvd Jamaica NY 11413

CAPODILUPO, PHILLIP, 5th-8th Grd Phys Ed Teacher; *b:* Lowell, MA; *ed:* Springfield Coll (BS) PE 1976; Cambridge Coll (MED) Scndry Ed 1990; *cr:* Andover West Jr HS Grd 8 Sci Tchr, Asst Track 1976-77; Georgetown Jr Grd 8 Sci Tchr, Grd 10 Hlth Tchr, Head Wrestling & Track 1977-79; Georgetown Sr HS Grd 8 Sci Tchr, Grd 10 Hlth Tchr, Head Wrestling & Track 1977-79; West Orange HS PE Tchr, Head Field Hockey, Wrestling, Asst Track Coach 1979-84; East Hanover MS PE Tchr, Head Soccer, Wrestling, Track Coach 1984-87; Ayer MS PE Tchr, Head Cross Cntry, Wrestling, Track Coach 1987-; Ayer HS PE Tchr, Head Cross Cntry, Wrestling, Track Coach 1987-; *ai:* Head Boys, Girls Var Cross Cntry Austin Prep Schl 1991-95; Asst Var Wrestling Coach Reading HS 1994-; Yth Track Coach Merrimack Vly 1989-; PE, Hlth Schl Newsletter Creator 1987-; NEA, Tchrs Assn 1976-; MA Wrestling Coaches Assn; MA Track & Field Coaches Assn; USA Wrestling Magazine Newsletter of Yr 1991-, Picture of Month 1996; USA Wrestling Magazine Selected Newsletter #1 1991, Accepted Nom of HS Coach Howard Crozier Natl Man of Yr 1991; Action Wrestling Photo Best of Month USA Wrestling 1996; *office:* Ayer MS Washington St Ayer MA 01432*

CAPOLINO, PAUL JOSEPH, Earth Science Teacher; *b:* Oceanside, NY; *ed:* Binghamton Univ (BA) Environmental Sci 1982; Adelphi Univ (MA) Ed 1986; 75 Credits; *cr:* Old Westbury Schl of Holy Child Grd 7 Gen Sci Tchr, Grd 8 Earth Sci Tchr, Grd 9 Bio Tchr 1985-86; Sachem-Sagamore Jr HS Grd 8 Phys Sci Tchr 1986-92; Sachem HS Grds 9-10 Earth Sci Tchr 1992-; *ai:* Var Track & Field, Sci Olympiad Coach; AFT, NYS United Tchrs 1986-; *office:* Sachem HS South 51 School St Lake Ronkonkoma NY 11779*

CAPOLONGO, ANDREA TERESA, Secondary School Art Teacher; *b:* New York, NY; *m:* Philip Anthony Capolongo, Jr.; *c:* Michelle, Michael, Jaclyn; *ed:* Univ of Bridgeport (BFA) Graphic Design 1977; 18 Credits Grad Studs; *cr:* Our Lady of Mercy Acad Scndry Art Tchr 1990-; *ai:* Yrbk; Photography Club; Set, Scenery Design Schl Play; Chprsn Fashion Show; NAEA, LIATA 1990-.

CAPONE, ADRIENNE M., English & Humanities Teacher; *b:* Philadelphia, PA; *c:* Heather Woodfield; *ed:* Goddard Coll (BA) Lbrl Arts 1981; Norwich Univ (MA) Eng 1989; Univ of VT Renaissance His, Ed Post Grad Stud 1990-94; *cr:* Barre Graded Schl Lang Arts Tchr 1989-90; Mt Mansfield Union HS Eng, Hum Tchr 1990-; *ai:* NHS Adv; Scholars Bowl Coach; NEA 1989-; *office:* Mt Mansfield Union HS RR 2 Box 120 Jericho VT 05465

CAPONE, PETER CHARLES, PE, Hlth & Drivers Ed Tchr; *b:* Teaneck, NJ; *m:* Pamela Jo Byrd; *c:* Vincent; *ed:* Montclair St Coll (BA) Hlth & PE 1984; Behind the Wheel Cert; First Aid, CPR & Pool Operator Certfd; *cr:* Hamilton North Tchr 1985-; *ai:* Coaching Ftbl 1984-92, Bsbl 1984-, Wrestling 1984-90; Chrldng 1995; Chprsn of Italian Amer Multicultural Group; Summer Camp Dir & Swim Pgm Coord; HTEA 1986-; NJEA 1986-; NJ Bsbl Coaches Assn 1986-; NJ Scholastic Coaches Assn 1995-; Conduct & Organize Bsbl Clinics; Scholastic Sporting Events Site Mgr; Screening Comm for Peer Ldrshp & Vol Internship Pgm; *home:* 1403 Richmond Ave Hamilton NJ 08619*

CAPONE, SANDRA P., English Teacher; *b:* Atlanta, GA; *m:* Michael; *c:* Cynthia, Michele Krissinger; *ed:* Muhlenberg Coll (BA) Ger & Eng 1963; Attnd Lehigh Univ & Wilkes Coll; *cr:* Bangor Area Jr HS 7th-8th Grd Eng Tchr 1962-65; Bangor Area Sr HS Eng Tchr 1967-; *ai:* Yrbk Adv; Fac Cabinet; Stu Assistance Prgm; PSEA & NEA 1962-; BAEA & Delta Kappa Gamma; Lehigh Valley Partnership.

CAPORASO, JO-ANN, Freshman Teacher; *b:* Newark, NJ; *ed:* Seton Hall Univ (BS) Eng & Scndry Ed 1969; *cr:* Saint Vincent Acad Tchr 1969-; *ai:* After Schl Tutoring; NCEA; NOW; Amnesty Intl; Greenpeace; Natl Dem Party; J Cousteau Soc; Tchr of Yr 1994; *office:* Saint Vincent Acad 228 W Market St Newark NJ 07103

CAPOZZI, ANN M., 7th Grade Teacher; *b:* Uniontown, PA; *m:* Vincent A.; *ed:* Indiana Univ of PA (BS) Elem ed 1982; WV Univ (MSW) Soc Work 1988; *cr:* St John Evangelist Tchr 1982-; *ai:* Chprsn Soc Stud Dept; Head Var Coach Girls Bsktbl; Soc Stud Curr Comm; NEA & NCEA 1982-; Jr Achvmt 1991-; *office:* Saint John The Evangelist Schl 88 Pennsylvania Ave Uniontown PA 15401

CAPPABIANCA, SILVANA PETRIZZELLI, French & Italian Teacher; *b:* Bari, Italy; *m:* Claudio; *c:* Marco, Giulia; *ed:* Coll of Mt St Vincent (BA) Fr-Italian 1968; Middlebury Coll (MA) Lit Stud in Fr 1969; Attnd Grad Schl of Fr, Universite' De Paris; *cr:* Aliatalia Airlines Group Desk Reservation Agent 1969-72; Sacred Heart HS Fr-Italian Tchr 1972-76; Hendrick Hudson HS Fr-Italian Tchr 1990-; *ai:* Alpha-Mu-Gamma 1972-; AATI 1992-; *office:* Hendrick Hudson HS 2 Albany Post Rd Montrose NY 10548

CAPPALLI, PAULA GARGANESE, Eng & Creative Dramatics Tchr; *b:* Providence, RI; *m:* Richard B.; *c:* Pia Paolino, T. J. Paolino; *ed:* RI Coll (BA) Eng 1962; Providence Coll (MED) Cnslng 1976; Attnd Villanna Univ, St Joseph's Univ; *cr:* Park View Jr HS Eng Tchr 1962-63; M Howard Schl Eng, Rdng Tchr 1963-67; Lincoln Sr HS Eng, Title I Rdng Tchr 1972-76; Lower Moreland MS Eng Tchr 1977-79; Bala Cynwyd MS Eng, Drama Tchr 1979-; *ai:* NEA 1979-; Alpha Delta Kappa 1995-; *office:* Bala Cynwyd MS 510 Bryn Mawr Ave Bala Cynwyd PA 19004

CAPPELLA, JOSEPH ALBERT, Mathematics Teacher; *b:* Philadelphia, PA; *m:* Karen Lynda Heaton; *c:* Amanda Heaton; *ed:* Temple Univ (BS) Ed 1972; Villanova Univ (BA) Math 1977; SAP Swap; 6 Credits Project TEACH Wilkes Coll; 2 Credits Outcome Based Ed Ottawa Univ; 1 Credit Macintosh Tool Allentown Coll; 2 CreditsEductr Trng Stu Assista nce Chester Co IU; *cr:* Jenkintown Schl Dist Math Tchr 1972-; *ai:* Church Camp, Brownie Troop Try-it Coord; NEA, PSEA, JEA 1972-; Rotary Intnl 1973-, Fac Spon Interact Club; *office:* Jenkintown Schl Dist 325 Highland Ave Jenkintown PA 19046

CAPPELLANO, DONNA M., Health Teacher; *b:* Albany, NY; *ed:* SUNY at Cortland (BS) Hlth Ed 1985, (MS) Hlth Ed 1990; *cr:* Cato-Meridian Cntrl Schl Dist Hlth Tchr 1985-; *ai:* Var Girls, Boys Cross Cntry, Jr HS Track Coach; Dir Stu Mediation Prgm; Cultural Exchange Club Adv; Cato Meridian Tchrs Union; AFT; NYFPHE; Syracuse Track Club; Florence Sherman Hlth Ed Schlsp.*

CAPPELLINI, LAURA RENO, 4th Grade Teacher; *b:* Peckville, PA; *m:* Ronald; *c:* Lauren; *ed:* Marywood Coll (BS) Elem Ed 1987; Loyola Coll

(MS) Curr & Instruction 1996; *cr:* Our Lady of Mount Carmel 3rd Grd Tchr 1987-89; Anne Arundel Cty Pub Schls Sub Tchr 1989-90; High Point Elem 4th-5th Grd Tchr 1990-; *ai:* Human Relations Comm; NEA, Tchrs Assn of Anne Arundel Co 1990-; NSTA, MD Sci Tchrs Assn 1994-; *office:* High Point Elem Schl 924 Duvall Hwy Pasadena MD 21122

CAPPIELLO, JANE ZAMEROSKI, Science Teacher; *b:* Ridgway, PA; *c:* Elizabeth; *ed:* Villa Maria Coll (BS) Chem 1969; Star Univ of NY at Albany (MS) Sci ed 1970; Rensselaer Polytechnic Ist (MS) Sci, Tech, Values 1982; *cr:* Bethlem Cntrl MS Sci Tchr 1971; *ai:* Mid Level Sci Tchng Club Adv; Sci Tchrs Ann of NY 1984-; Dir at Large; NSTA; Natl Mid Level Sci Tchr Assn; Finalist in Excl in Sci Tchng Shell Oil Co, NSTA, Journal Pub; Sci, Tech, Math Hands on Lesson on Saturday; Mid Level Sci Tchng Club; Bldg Ohms Law Apparatus for Interdisciplinary Unit of Sci, Tech & Math; NY St finalists in 1994; Presisdental Awd in Scndry Sci Tchng; *home:* 34 Douglas Rd Delmar NY 12054*

CAPP-SACCOCCI, CAROLE ANNE, French Teacher; *b:* Elizabeth, NJ; *m:* Joseph Saccocci; *c:* Michael, Robert; *ed:* Montclair St Coll (BA) Fr 1964; Attnd Sorbonne L'Universite De Paris, L'Universite De Laval Ste-Foy Quebec; *cr:* Iselin MS Fr, Ger Tchr 1964-86, Fr Tchr 1986-; Woodbridge MS Fr Tchr 1986-; JFK HS Part-time Fr Tchr 1986, Fr Tchr 1987-; *ai:* Natl Fr Hnr Soc Adv; AFT 1968-; NEA 1995-; FLENJ, AATF 1980-; Natl Notary Assn 1985-; Cub Scout Pack 77 1987-91, Den Mother; Notary Pub 1982-; Woodbridge Bd of Ed 3 Minigrants; 2 Articles Pub; REA Publishers Consultant; ETS Proctor; *office:* John F Kennedy Memorial HS Washington Ave Iselin NJ 08830*

CAPRIA, JOHN HUGO, High School Art Teacher; *b:* Syracuse, NY; *ed:* Onon Comm Coll (AAS) Graphic Arts 1987; SUNY at Cortland (BS) Ed 1989; SUNY at Oswego 3 Hrs Towards Master; *cr:* Onon Comm Coll Adj Prof 1990; Patuxent Pub Co Commercial Artist 1993; West Genesee HS Art Tchr 1993-; *ai:* NYSUT 1993-; Article Pub; *office:* West Genesee HS 5201 W Genesee St Camillus NY 13031

CAPRIGLIONE, TERESE MONTEFUSCO, HS Guidance Counselor; *b:* Neward, NJ; *m:* John; *c:* Joseph, James; *ed:* William Paterson Coll (BA) Art Ed 1972; Kean Coll (MA) Cnslr Ed 1986; Cert Dir Stu Prsnl Svc, Cert Soc Worker 1987; *cr:* Newark Bd of Ed; East Side HS; West Side HS; Mt Pleasant Annex; Marcus Garvey Art Tchr 1972-83; Self Employed Interior Decorator 1979-80; Fountain Realty Real Estate Agent 1984-85; East Side HS Guid Cnslr 1986-; *ai:* Crisis Intervention Cnslr; Safe Home Project; NTU 1972-; AFTU 1972-80, 1990-; Newark Guid Assn, Essex Cty Guid Cnslr Assn 1987-; Bi Centennial Ironbound Comm Svc Awd 1976.

CAPRIO, JOSEPH JAMES,JR., Science Teacher; *b:* Pittston, PA; *m:* Nancy Mc Cabe; *c:* J. J., Michael; *ed:* Mansfield St Coll (BA) Gen, Earth, Space Sci 1973; Penn St Univ Marine Bio; Wilkes Coll Credits Towards Nrsng Degree; *cr:* Wilson Borough Schl Dist Sci Tchr 1973-74; Pittston Hosp Schl of Nrsng Chem Tchr 1978-83; Pittston Area Schl Dist Sci Tchr 1978-; *ai:* Soccer Asst Coach; AFT, LCSTA 1978-; NSTA 1973-; BSA 1993-, Asst Scoutmaster; Friendly Sons of St Patrick 1991-; Wyoming Vly Coin Club 1960-; *home:* 54 Searle St Pittston PA 18640

CAPRIO, JUDITH ANN (CYNA), 9th-10th Grade Math Teacher; *b:* Buffalo, NY; *m:* Nicholas; *c:* Anthony & Thomas; *ed:* St Univ Coll of NY at Buffalo (BS) Scndry Ed Math 1972; 30 Grad Hrs for Permanent Cert in NY St; *cr:* West Seneca East Sr HS Math Tch 1972-; *ai:* Inclusion Model & Comm; Lib Advy Comm; AFT, West Seneca Tchrs assn & NYSUT 1972-; Hemophilia Ctr of WNY 1979-, Svc Awd 1987; Nom Local Tchr of Yr 1993; *office:* West Seneca East Sr HS 4760 Seneca St West Seneca NY 14224*

CAPSOURAS, JOHN DAVID, Business Education Teacher; *b:* New York City, NY; *m:* Barbara; *c:* Janine, Cristina, Alexi; *ed:* Trenton St Coll (BA) Accounting 1970; Seton Hall Univ (MA) Admin & Supv 1980; Attnd St Peter's Coll, Montclair St Coll; *cr:* Parsippany HS Bus Ed Tchr 26 Yrs; *ai:* Frosh Class Adv; Ctr Curr Planning, Prejudice Reduction, Stu Assessment Comms; Weightlifting, Boys Track Coach; Dist Instrl Cncl; PTHEA 1970-, Pres; NEA, NJEA, NJBEA, MCBEA, FBLA 1970-, MCCEA; Publ Ed Week; NJ Acad for Advancement of Tchng & Mngmt; NJEA St Tech Comm; *home:* 2 Cedar Ter Randolph NJ 07869*

CAPUANO, JEFFREY A., Biology Teacher; *b:* Albany, NY; *ed:* The Kings Coll (BA) Bio 1990; Coll of Saint Rose (MS) Ed 1992; St Univ of NY at Albany Doctoral Stu; Dept of Educl Admin & Policy Stud; *cr:* Ballston Spa MS 6th-8th Grd Sci Tchr 1990-91; Mayfield HS Bio Tchr 1993-; *ai:* Soph Class Adv; Section 504 Planning Comm; HFM Workforce; Preparation Steering & Block Scheduling Comms; ASCD 1992-; *home:* 9 Kniskern Ave Mechanicville NY 12118*

CAPUTO, CARYN PATRICE, Social Studies Teacher; *b:* Bronx, NY; *ed:* Dickinson Coll (BA) Amer Stud 1990; NY Univ Soc Stud Ed 1994; *cr:* Stuyvesant HS Soc Stud Tchr 1994-; *ai:* Model United Nations Club Adv; UFT 1994-; Gilder-Lehman Inst of US His Mem; Amer Culture Inst; Article Pub; *office:* Stuyvesant HS 345 Chambers St New York NY 10282

CAPUTO, JANET E., Reading Teacher; *b:* Belle Vernon, PA; *m:* Richard S.; *c:* Denise Fundy, Jennifer Utterdyke; *ed:* CA St Coll (BS) Early Chldhd, Elem 1982; CA Univ of PA (MA) Rdng Specialist 1984; *cr:* Jefferson-Morgan Schl Dist Tchr 1984-; *ai:* Stu Asst Prgm Team; Discipline Cncl; NEA, PSEA, JMPA 1984-; *office:* Jefferson-Morgan Jr Sr HS Greene St Jefferson PA 15344*

CAPUTO, JOHN RICHARD, Business Dept Chair & Teacher; *b:* Worchester, MA; *m:* Donna Ray C. Olson; *c:* Dawn Marie Mignault, Jeffrey John; *ed:* Nichols Coll (BA) Accounting 1968; Worchester St Coll (ME) Ed 1975; 15 Credit Hrs Cmptr Sci; *cr:* Grafton HS Tchr Bus 1968-, Dept Head 1978-; Own Accounting Bus Accounting 1983-; *ai:* Ftbl Coach 1969-94; Bus Dept Head 1978-; Intra-Sports Adv 1990-; MTA, GTA 1975-; MA Bus Teachers Assn 1985-; MA Bus Dept Head Assn 1988-; Schl Cncl 1994-; New England & MA Bus Tchrs Assn 5 Time Nom for Outstanding Bus Tchr; *office:* Grafton Memorial HS 24 Providence Rd Grafton MA 01519*

CAPUTO, JOSEPH FRANK, Stu Activities, Dev & Adv Dir; *b:* Scranton, PA; *m:* Mary Ann Williams; *ed:* Marywood Coll (BA) Comm 1977; St Univ of NY (MA) Theatre 1990; Attnd Univ of MN at Deluth, Amer Univ at WA DC, Carnegie Mellon Univ; *cr:* Bishop O'Hara HS Tchr 1980-82; Marywood Coll Instr Eng, Comm 1987-; Keystone Coll Inst Intensive Eng 1987-; S H Jr Sr HS Eng, Comm, Jrnlsm Tchr 1993-; *ai:* Drama; Jrnlsm; Co-Chair Middle Sts Eval Comm; NTE, NCTE 1990-; Standing Room Only Comm Theatre, Bd 1980, Artistic Dir, Pres 1990; Drama-Critic; *office:* Sacred Heart Jr Sr HS 44 S Church St Carbondale PA 18407

CAPUTO, KATHLEEN ANN, Elementary Art Teacher; *b:* Wilmington, DE; *ed:* West Chester Univ (BA) Painting 1992; Moore Coll of Art, Design Tchng Cert 1993; Tyler School of Art 6 Grad Credits Art His, Painting; West Chester Univ 6 Grad Credits Ceramics; *cr:* North Brandywine MS Grd 6-8 Art Tchr 1993; Kenneth MS Grd 6-7 Art Tcher 1993-94; Mary D. Lang Elem Schl Grd 1-6 Art Tchr 1994-; *ai:* Kennett HS Jr Var, Var Chrldng Coach; Set, Production Designer; NAEA, PA Art Ed Assn 1992-; NEA, PA Ed Assn 1994-; *office:* Mary D Lang Elem Schl Center & Mulberry St Kennett Square PA 19348*

CAPUTO, MARY THERESA GALLAGHER, 5th Grade Teacher; *b:* Philadelphia, PA; *m:* Louis A. Jr.; *c:* Donna L., Theresa A.; *ed:* St Joseph Univ (AS) Acctng, (BA) Theology 1996; *cr:* St Timothy Schl 5th Grd Tchr 1989-; *ai:* Rel Comm; Math Coord 1992-95; Video Club 1993-94, Christmas Pageant 1990-95, Easter Pageant 1992-95 Moderator; NCEA 1989-; *home:* 19 Sherin Dr Newark DE 19702

CAPUTO, NANCY BARTON, Math Teacher; *b:* Freeport, NY; *m:* Tony; *c:* Christine, Nicole; *ed:* SUNY at New Paltz (BA) N-9 Ed & Math 1973; SUNY at Stony Brook (MS) Ed 1977; *cr:* Bayshore MS Math Tchr 1974-78, 1985-; *office:* Bay Shore MS 393 Brook Ave Bay Shore NY 11706

CAPUZZI, JUDY, Accounting & Finance Professor; *b:* Philadelphia, PA; *m:* Bernard Havard; *ed:* Drexel Univ (BS) Bus Admin 1975; St Josephs Univ (MS) Ed & Bus 1986; *cr:* US Bureau of Labor Statistics Economist 1975-78; Self-Employed Art Dealer & Consultant 1978-82; Self-Employed Consultant & Adj Prof 1982-85; Peirce Coll Prof 1985-; *ai:* Acctng Soc Spon; Chair of Comms to Dev Intnl Bus & Arts Admin Major; *office:* Peirce Coll 1420 Pine St Philadelphia PA 19102

CARACCIO, ALANA GENE REINER, English Teacher; *b:* New York City, NY; *m:* Joseph Anthony; *c:* Ariel Mariya; *ed:* Queensborough Comm Coll (AA) Liberal Arts 1965; Queens Coll (BA) Eng 1968; New York Univ (MA) Eng 1972; MacMillian Univ Grant; Stratford Ontario Shakespeare Festival; 45 Addl Hrs Educl Credits; *cr:* Lawrence Jr HS Eng, Theatre Arts Tchr 1968-81; Lawrence HS Eng, Theatre Arts Tchr 1981-; Shakespeare 1981-; *ai:* Jr HS Drama Coach 11 Yrs; LTA, NYSUT 1970-; Chamber of Commerce 1984-; Oyster Bay Arts Cncl 1980-; 25 Yrs Recognition Awd; Owner, Producer, Dir, Actress Long Islands Leading Touring Theatre Troupe; The Other Vic Theatre Co; *office:* Lawrence HS Reilly Rd Cedarhurst NY 11516

CARAGIANES, WILLIAM JAMES, Mathematics Teacher; *b:* Boston, MA; *m:* Valerie Seidel; *c:* James, Clay; *ed:* Boston Univ (BS) Ed 1972; Attnd Northeastern Univ, Boston Coll Math Courses; *cr:* Fletcher Elem Schl Eng Tchr 1974-78; Cambridge Rindge & Latin HS Title I Math Tchr 1978-79; Fitzgerald Elem Schl Soc Stud Tchr 1979-81, Math Tchr 1981-; *ai:* Project Zero Coordinating Comm; Chess Club & Stu Govt Advs; Mentor Prgm; Homework Help Club; Cmptr Organizing Comm; Stu Support Team; Mini Course Coord; NEA, MTA, CTA 1974-; CTA Tchr Rep 1982-83; Cambridge Little League 1985-91; *office:* Fletcher Elem Schl 89 Elm St Cambridge MA 02139

CARANDO, PETER MICHAEL, Biology Teacher; *b:* New Bedford, MA; *m:* Amy Jo Labi; *ed:* Slippery Rock Univ (BS) Bio 1972, (MS) Bio 1979; Multiple Grad Credits in Biological & Educl Fields; *cr:* New Castle Sr High Bio 1972-; *ai:* PA Jr Acad Spon; Sci Region 9 Co-Dir; Bio Dept Chprsn; NSTA & AFT; PA Hunter Ed Staff 1988-; NRA Trout Unlimited Lifetime Mem; Have Presented Wkshps at Regnl & Natl Levels for NSTA; Previous Whos Who Nomination; Presidential Awd of Excl Nomination.*

CARANESE, ELLEN E., Teacher of Bus Ed & Gifted; *b:* Mc Keesport, PA; *m:* Lee A.; *c:* Erica Bailey, Amanda Bailey; *ed:* Univ of Pittsburgh (BS) Bus Ed, Acctng 1986; 24 Grad Credits Robert Morris Coll, IN Univ of PA, Allegheny Intermediate Unit; *cr:* Westinghouse Electric Corp Acctng 1980-84; South Allegheny HS Full-Time Sub, Bus Tchr 1990-; Forbes Rd East AVTS Cmptr Tech Tchr 1992-93; Elizabeth Forward Sr HS Bus Ed 1993-; *ai:* SADD Spon; VITA Instr & Spon; NEA 1990-; PBEA 1995-; NBEA 1992-; Provided Free Income Tax Preparation for Stdnts Through VITA Prgm Enrolled Acctng II; *office:* Elizabeth Forward Sr HS 1000 Weigles Hill Rd Elizabeth PA 15037

CARANFA, JANICE CHASE, Accounting Teacher; *b:* Plymouth, MA; *m:* Lawrence A. Jr.; *c:* Michael; *ed:* Acquinas Jr Coll (AS) Exec Sec 1969; Salem St Coll (BS) Bus Ed 1972; Suffolk Univ (MED) Scndry Ed 1973; *cr:* Northeast Met Reg Voc Schl Acctg Tchr 1972-; *ai:* Tech Prep, VICA Adv; Schl to Work Comm; MTA 1972-; NEA 1974-; NTA 1972-, Acad VP; Voc Ed Cert of Appreciation 1994; *office:* Northeast Metro Reg Voc Schl 100 Hemlock Rd Wakefield MA 01880

CARAPELLA, DAVID A.,JR., HS Media Communications Tchr; *b:* Rochester, NY; *c:* Andrew; *ed:* Monroe Comm Coll (AAS) Audio Visual Tech 1983; Empire St Univ (BS) Commnctns 1996; Oswego Univ 24 Credits; *cr:* Edison Tech & Occupational Ed Ctr Tchr Media Commnctn 1990-; *ai:* Frosh Orientation Comm; Video Production Club Adv; WXXI-TV Grant for Stu Produced Video Production; *office:* Edison Tech & Occupational Ctr 655 Colfax St Rochester NY 14606

CARAVELLA, JAYNE FIORELLA, English Teacher; *ed:* Montclair St Coll (BA) Eng Ed 1989; *cr:* Brick Memrl HS Eng Tchr 1989-; *ai:* JV Field Hockey Coach 4 Yrs; Spring Track Coach 5 Yrs; Class of 1995 Adv; Peer Mediation Adv; NEA 1989-; NJEA 1989-; *office:* Brick Twp Mem HS 2001 Lanes Mill Rd Brick NJ 08724

CARAZO, JANINE SNYDER, English & German Teacher; *b:* Palmerton, PA; *c:* David II; *ed:* Temple U (BA) Ger 1971, (MFA) Theatre, Comm 1973, (MED) Eng as Second Lang 1989; Attnd Goethe Inst, Univ of Gottingen 1992-93; *cr:* Comm Coll of Phil Eng, ESL Instr 1980-85; Franklin Learning Ctr ESL Tchr 1980-85; Univ City HS ESL Tchr 1985; Phil HS for Girls Ger, ESL Tchr 1986-; *ai:* Ger Club Spon; Bldg Comm; AATG 1990-; Fulbright Tchr Exchange 1989-90; DeWitt-Wallace Grant 1993-; *home:* 923 S 10th St Philadelphia PA 19147

CARBALLO, DEBORAH ANN, Spanish Teacher & Dept Chprsn; *b:* Buffalo, NY; *ed:* Buffalo St Coll (BS) Scndry Ed Eng 1973, (MS) Scndry Ed Eng 1976; 30 Credit Hrs Span Linguistics at SUNY at Buffalo; *cr:* St John the Evangelist Schl 3 Grd Tchr 1973-74; Immaculata Acad 9-12 Grd Eng, Span Tchr 1974-76; Nardin Acad 6-8 Grd Eng, Soc Stud Tchr 1976-77; Mt St Joseph Acad 9-12 Grd Eng, Span, Drama Tchr 1977-78; Starpoint Cntrl Schl 9-12 Grd Eng, Span Tchr 1978-; SUNY at Buffalo ESL Instr 1995-; *ai:* Effective Schls Bldg Team; Dept Chair Frgn Lang; Drama Club Dir; Span Club, Culture & Travel Club Adv; Chprsn Frgn Exch Stu Comm; NY St Theatre Edctrs Assn 1995-; Lake Tree Village Bd of Mgrs 1988-, Pres; Mini-Grants Tchr Ctr at BOCES for Cross Curricular Tchng Units with Soc Stud; Peace Grant for Venezuelan Exch Prgm 1994; *office:* Starpoint Cntrl Schl 4363 Mapleton Rd Lockport NY 14094

CARBONE, CINDY SEEHAFER, English Composition & Lit Prof; *b:* Marshfield, WI; *m:* Ralph Edward; *c:* Rachael E, Rebecca A.; *ed:* Univ of WI at Oshkosh (BS) Scndry Ed, Speech, Eng 1978; Butler Univ (MA) Eng 1988; *cr:* IN Univ Adj Fac 1986-89; Purdue Univ at Indianapolis Adj Fac 1986-89; Marian Coll Adj Fac 1987-89; Butler Univ Adj Fac 1988-89; Marietta Coll Adj Fac 1989-90; *ai:* Phi Theta Kappa Adv; Eng Composition & Lit Dept Lead Fac; Transfer Module Del OH St Wide Comm; SCA 1980-; CSCA 1984-, Vice Chair; OATYC 1992-; Telesis 1991-; Children's Prgms Dir 1984-; Short Story: If We Shadows Have Offended; Outstdng Adj Fac of Yr 1989; *office:* Washington State Comm Coll 710 Colegate Dr Marietta OH 45750*

CARBONE, NANCY MOODY, Fourth Grade Teacher; *b:* Farmington, ME; *m:* Andrew Frederick Jr.; *c:* Adam, Megan; *ed:* UMF (BS) Elem Ed 1975; *cr:* Mark Emery Elem Schl Kndgtn Tchr 1975-81, Third Grd Tchr 1981-94, 4th Grd Tchr 1994-; *ai:* Dist MDI Prgm; Schl Coord; Cmptr Comm; Booster Club & Math Curr; NEA, MTA 1975-; Lib Trustee 1993-; 2 Sci & 1 Soc Stud Grants Awded; *office:* Mark Emery Elem Schl PO Box 187 Main North Anson ME 04958

CARBONETTI, LARRY S., English Teacher; *b:* Brooklyn, NY; *m:* Jeanne A. Leone; *ed:* Juniata Coll (BA) Eng 1971; Antioch Univ (MED) Scndry Ed 1989; 30 Addl Hrs Film Stud, Lit, Ed; *cr:* Bernards HS Eng Tchr 1972-82; Springfield HS Eng Tchr 1984-; *ai:* NEA 1972-; Regnl Ed Lab 1992-95, Bd of Overseers; Dist Tchr of Yr 1974-75; VT Outstdng Tchr 1988; Antioch, Norwich Univs Grad Instr; *office:* Springfield South St Springfield VT 05156*

CARBOY, BEVERLY, English Teacher; *b:* Pompton Plains, William Paterson Coll (BA) Eng 1965; Seton Hall Univ (MA) Svcs 1969; William Paterson Coll (MA) Eng 1977; *cr:* Morris Hil Tchr 31 Yrs; *ai:* Hnr Soc Selection, Fac Advy & Interdiscipl Comms; Morris Hills Regnl Ed Assn 1965-, VP; Morris Cty Ed As Rep; NJEA 1965-; NEA 1965-; Intnl Dickens Flwshp 1990-; Dodg Grant 1986; Morris Hills Tchr of Yr 1991; *office:* Morris Hills H Main St Rockaway NJ 07866

CARCHEDI, THEODORE, Amer History & Govt Tea Youngstown, OH; *m:* Mary Jo Mahoney; *c:* Alex, Charles, Mary *ed:* Youngstown St Univ (BS) Ed 1976, (MS) Ed 1986; 15 Hrs P *cr:* Holy Family Schl Soc Stud Instr 1977-79; Leetonia HS Soc S 1979-; *ai:* Intnl Affairs Club Adv; Ftbl, Bsktbl & Bsbl Coach; OH 1979-; NEA 1979-; Leetonia Ed Assn 1979-, Negotiations Team of Columbus 1992-; *office:* Leetonia HS 181 Walnut St Lee 44431*

CARD, AMY CLAY, Former 2nd Grade Teacher; *b:* Syracuse Matt; *c:* David, Molly, Andrew; *ed:* Univ of NH (BA) Soc Stud, 1978, (MED) Rdng, Elem Ed 1981; 30 Addl Credit Hrs; *cr:* Bra Schl 5-6 Grd Tchr 1979-81; Writers Unlimited Writing Co 1988-89; Wheelock Coll Writing Co-Taught 1989; Sippican Schl Tchr 1981-; *ai:* NEA, MA Tchrs Assn, Marion Tchr Assn 1981-.

CARD, KENNETH ROBERT, Biology Teacher; *b:* Teaneck Maureen; *c:* Timothy, Allison; *ed:* Forkham Univ (BS) Bio 1971; Montclair St Univ; *cr:* Bloomfield HS Bio Tchr 1985-; *ai:* Bio Te NSTA; *office:* Bloomfield HS 160 Broad St Bloomfield NJ 0700

CARDEA-WEISSMANN, BARBARA ANN, French Teacher; York, NY; *m:* Richard; *ed:* Queens Coll, CUNY (BA) Fr; Que (MA) Fr; Attnd Sorbonne Univ Cert, Stony Brook Univ Docto Franco-Forum Post Grad Stud; *cr:* H. Frank Carey HS Fr T Heurtey Eng Tchr; Lynbrook HS Fr Tchr; Half Hollow Hills Fr Fr Hnr Soc, Fr Culture Club Advs; Amer Assn of Tchrs of Fr; Lo Lang Tchrs Assn; Bellport-Ste Maxime Co-Dir; Sister-City Stu of Intercom Magazine; *office:* Half Hollow Hills HS East 50 Va Pkwy Dix Hills NY 11746*

CARDELL, GRACE CASSIDY, Hlth Occupations Tchr & C Elizabeth, NJ; *m:* Emid Francisco; *c:* Loretta G., John Arthu Timothy; *ed:* Jersey City St (BA) Hlth Ed & Schl Nursing 1971 Paterson (MA) Spec Ed 1979; Nursing Diploma from Passaic Hospital Schl of Nursing 1957; Cert Courses for Coord; Cert Co Tchr of Deaf & Early Chldhd Ed at Kean Coll; Montclair St & Univ Various Liberal Arts Courses; *cr:* United Cerebral Palsy Pre-K Handicapped 1985-87; Paterson Pub Schls Tchr o Handicapped 1987-89; Elizabeth Schl #1 Tchr of Comm Han 1989-90; Cedar Grove Schls Schl Nurse & Tchr of Handicapped Clifton HS Tchr & Coord 1992-; *ai:* Hlth Occupations Stdnts of A Adv & Competition Events Judge; NJ Ed Assn 1987-; Essex Nurses Assn 1990-; Pi Lamda Theta 1978-; Passaic General Hos of Nursing Alumnae Assn 1957-; Parents Assn of Eastern Chrstn Retreat 1974-; Commonwealth Club Womens Bowling Leagu Essex Cty Medical Assn Auxiliary Nursing Schl Schlsp 195 Clifton HS 333 Colfax Ave Clifton NJ 07013

CARDELLA, FRANCIS PAUL, Third Grade Teacher; *b:* Roche *m:* Paula Moccia; *c:* Kathryn, Daniel; *ed:* St Univ of NY at Brockp Elem Ed & Sociology 1972; Addl 30 Hrs Grad Stud; *cr:* William Schl Classroom Tchr 1972-95; *ai:* Planning Team Mem; Turnk Trainer; Career Ed Cncl Assoc; AFT, Spencerport Tchrs Ass Habitat for Humanity 1995-; Saint Josephs Church 1984-; Roy B Received for Excl in Tchng & Supervision at St Univ of NY at B 1992; *office:* William C Munn Elem Schl 2333 Manitou Rd Sp NY 14559*

CARDILLE, KATHLEEN REEHER, History Teacher; *b:* Sharo Stephen F.; *c:* Jeffrey, Stacia, Gregory; *ed:* Youngstown St Univ 1970, (MA) Eng 1987; Continuing Post-Grad Stud; *cr:* Young Univ Composition Tchr 1983-87; Liberty HS Eng Tchr 1988-9 City HS His Tchr 1992-; *ai:* CCC; NCTE 1970-; NEA 1970-; P Phi 1987-; DKG 1989; Grants: St of OH, Liberty Endowment & Area Rdng Cncl; NEH Sponsoring Tchr for Rsrch on Thoreau Grove City Sr HS 511 Highland Ave Grove City PA 16127

CARDILLO, ANTONIO, High School ESL Teacher; *b:* Formia, Lucia Amenta; *c:* Kristian, Juliau; *ed:* Univ of MA (BA) Eng, Ital 21 Credit Hrs ESL; *cr:* Somerville Schls Biling Tchr 1980-83, F Tchr 1983-88, ESL Tchr 1988-; *ai:* NEA 1980-; US Army 1970-93, Veteran of Desert Storm; *office:* Somerville HS Hig Somerville MA 02143*

CARDILLO, GIULIANA G., Guidance & Athletic Director; *b:* B NY; *ed:* St Francis Coll (BA) Psych 1993; St Johns Univ (MS) S 1997; *cr:* St Savious HS Guid & Ath Dir 1994-; *ai:* Fund Rais Tutoring; Ath Newsletters; Ath Dept; GHSCAA 1994-; *office:* S HS 588 6th St Brooklyn NY 11215

CARDILLO, KAREN ADACK, Associate Professor; *b:* Schenec *m:* Thomas S.; *c:* Andrew, Nicholas; *ed:* Alfred Univ (BS) Nrs Univ of Rochester (MS) Nrsing 1979; *cr:* Highland Hosp Sta 1975-79; Keuka Coll Instr 1979-80; Monroe Comm Coll Fac 1980 Nurses Assn Adv; Mem of Coll Stu Success Comm; Senator of Fa Chprsn of Dept of Nrsng Curr Comm; GVNA 1980-, Awd for N 1995; Western NY League for Nrsng 1992-; NYSNA 1995-; Monr Coll Hanson Awd 1993 & NISOD Awd 1994 for Tchng Excl; Co-A 4 Comp Assisted Instr Pgms CAI for Nrsng Ed; *office:* Monroe Co 1000 E Henrietta Rd Rochester NY 14623*

CARDINALE, LOUISE MARIE, Science Teacher; *b:* Brooklyn Joseph; *c:* Frank, Lauren; *ed:* Kingsborough Comm Coll (AA) 1981; Brooklyn Coll (BA) Elem Ed 1983, (MS) Ed 1985; St Joh (PD) Instrl Ldrshp Learning Styles 1987; Long Island U Supervision, Admin 1994; *cr:* The Bensonhurst Schl IS 128 3, 5-6 1983-95; The Brooklyn Studio Schl IS 280 6-7 Grd Sci, Family Tchr 1995-; *ai:* Sci Tchr of Yr 1990-92; Tchr of Yr 1991-92; Excl Awd 1991; *office:* Brooklyn Studio Schl 2075 84th St Brooklyn N

CARDONE, PATRICIA BRENNAN, Chrstn Ethics & Psych Te New York, NY; *m:* Michael V.; *c:* Elizabeth; *ed:* Brentwood Coll 1960; Providence Coll (MA) Rel Ed 1966; Hofstra Univ (CAS Admin 1987; *cr:* Holy Family HS Dept Chair Rel Stud 1967-73; HS Dept Chair Rel Stud 1975-81; St Agnes HS Dept Chair 1981-87; St Agnes Acad HS Rel Stud Tchr 1987-; *ai:* Stu Govt M PDK, ASCD 1987-; TOPSS 1995-; *office:* Saint Agnes Academic 124th St College Point NY 11356

CARDONI, AGNES TOLOCZKO, English Instructor; *b:* Wilk PA; *m:* John Jr.; *c:* Christopher Swantek; *ed:* Coll Misericordia 1969; Wilkes Univ (MSED) Eng 1974; Lehigh Univ (PHD) Eng Writing Project West Chester Univ; Bad Inst Writing, Thinking U at Urbana-Champaign; *cr:* Wilkes-Barre Area Schls Instr En King's Coll Part-time Fac 1986-; *ai:* NEA 1969-; Phi Delta Kap Kappa Gamma 1985-; WY Vly Oratorio Soc 1992-, Fundraisir

Mertz Awd; Delta Kappa Gamma Rsrch Grant; Co-Authored *office:* J. M. Coughlin HS 80 N Washington St Wilkes Barre PA

CCI, DONALD JOSEPH, Band Director; *b:* Syracuse, NY; *ed:* t Fredonia (BM) Music Ed 1977; Ithaca Coll (MM) Music Ed 1990; rpool Cntrl Schls MS Band Dir 1977-82; West Genesee Cntrl Schls and Dir 1982-89; Oswego City Schls HS Band Dir 1989-90; Dryden hls HS Band D ir 1990-91; Orchard Park Cntrl Schls HS Band Dir *i:* Music Educators Nation Conf, NY St Schl Music Assn 1977-; Band Dirs Assn 1982-, Sec; Natl Band Assn 1989-; Quaker Arts Bd 1994-; *office:* Orchard Park HS 4040 Baker Rd Orchard Park 27

JCCI, ELEANOR WHALEN, Assistant Professor of English; *b:* e, PA; *m:* Joseph Jr.; *c:* Erin; *ed:* East Stroudsburg St Coll (BS) 4; Seton Hall Univ (MA) Ed 1968; Rutgers Univ (PHD) Eng, Ed der Coll Amer Lit Summer Inst; Montclair St Psych Grad Courses; er Pub Schls Eng Tchr 1964-80; Centenary Coll Assoc Prof Eng ; Sussex Cty Comm Coll Asst Prof Eng, Lbrl Arts Coord 1992-; *ai:* estern NJ Acad Collaborative Curr Comm; Fac Dev Comm; Fac Dev ., Exec Bd; NCTE; Phi Delta Kappa; Rutgers Univ Grad Fellow for ng Stud; Outstdng Ldrshp Awd Natl Chair Acad 1996; Natl Tchng d Natl Inst of Staff, Orgnl Dev 1994; Sears Tchng Excl, Campus Awd 1994; *office:* Sussex County Comm Coll College Hill Newton 0

ILLO, MARIA ANN, Sci Dept Chairperson & Teacher; *b:* Boston, Emmanuel Coll (AB) Chem 1963, (AB) Bio 1964; Boston Coll o 1967, (PHD) Bio 1971; *cr:* Christopher Columbus Cath HS Sci prsn, Bio, Chem Tchr 1977-90; Cath Meml HS Bio, Chem Tchr ; Savio Prep HS Sci Dept Chprsn, Bio, Gen Sci Tchr 1994-; *ai:* Sci ace Festival Moderator; Sigma Xi 1967-; NCEA 1977-, Outstdng aywoman HS Edctr 1984; Archdiocesan Acad Quality Comm ; Alcohol & Drug Referal Team 1988-89, Chprsn; Publications; avio Prep HS 145 Byron St E Boston MA 02128

ESS, ROBERT XAVIER, Earth Science Instructor; *b:* Audubon, Jean Susan Saudhofer; *ed:* Univ of OR (BS) Sci & His 1984; St Coll (MS) Admin of Intnl Schls 1992; *cr:* Univ of OR General ma Instr 1981-84; Smith MS Earth Sci Instr 1984-88; Curundu MS i Instr 1988-; *ai:* Tennis Coach; Yrbk; MS Team Ldr; Pan Amer ub 1988-, Pres; Balboa Dive Club 1988-, Pres; Killeen Daily Herald ding Educator; Dept of Defense Depts Schls Panama Region ding Educator 1992; *home:* PSC Box 2 Box 1736 APO AA 34002*

, PHILIP STEPHEN, Seventh Grade Mathematics Tchr; *b:* , MA; *m:* Carolyn Cutter; *c:* Alison C., Diana J., Stephanie R.; *ed:* er St Coll (BS) Scndry Ed 1967; Thirty-Six Post Grad Credit Hrs; hborough Jr HS Math Tchr 1967-70; Marlborough MS Math Tchr *ai:* NEA; MA Tchrs Assn; *office:* Marlboro MS Bolton St ough MA 01752

, DALE MAXSON, Fifth Grade Teacher; *b:* Northampton, MA; ell E.; *ed:* Univ of MA (BA) Ed 1970; Grad Credits; *cr:* Amherst ls Elem Tchr 1971-; *office:* Wildwood Schl 71 Strong St Amherst 02

, ANNE, Science & Religion Teacher; *b:* Brooklyn, NY; *m:* Joseph; *c:* Steven, Julie, Maureen, Timothy, Joanne; *ed:* Paine Hall T) Med Tech 1949; Jackson St Univ (BA) Sci, Ed 1960; Rel Ed Middlesex Cty Voc Tech Evening Schl Tchr 5 Yrs; Middlesex Cty Extension Prgm Asst 7 Yrs; St Frances Cabrini Sci Tchr 21 Yrs; *ai:* Philosophy Accrediation Comm; Metuchen Diocesan Cncl of Curr d Grds Dept Chprsn; Stu Cncl Co-Adv; NJSTA 1980-; FACMT NJCEA; Who's Who in Ed; Who's Who in the World; Tchr of Yr ood Housekeeping Invent Amer Awd; *office:* St Frances Cabrini 0 Cooper St Piscataway NJ 08854

, DONNA VASQUEZ, Sixth Grade Teacher; *b:* Philadelphia, PA; am; *c:* Victoria, Abigail; *ed:* Rowan St Coll (MA) Elem Ed 1991; Harbor Twp Schls Tchr 1983-; *ai:* NJEA; *office:* Egg Harbor Twp diate 25 Alder Ave Egg Harbor Twp NJ 08234*

, ELIZABETH CATHERINE, English Teacher; *b:* Provicence, ames A.; *ed:* RI Coll (BA) Eng, Scndry Ed 1992; 3 Post Grad Cnslng Bridgewater St Coll; 3 Post Grad Credits Skillful Tchr g St Coll; *cr:* North Attleboro HS Sub Tchr 1989-91; Attleboro HS eld Hockey Coach 1990-92, Summer Schl Instr 1993-95; Fisher Jr r 1993; North Attleboro HS Eng Tchr 1992-; *ai:* Vol Attleboro Ctr; Jr Class Adv 1994-95; Peer Mediator 1994-; Sr Class Adv urr Comm for Level 3 Eng; AFT 1993-; North Attleboro Teen Ctr -, Bd of Dir, Clerk; *office:* North Attleboro HS Landry Ave North MA 02760*

, JAMES M., Earth Science Teacher; *b:* New York, NY; *ed:* St NY at Oneonta (BA) Geology 1984, (BA) Sci Ed 1991; 11 Credit ward Masters in Environmental Sci at Plymouth St Univ; *cr:* berger Inc Offshore Geologist 1984-86; US EPA Geologist & r 1986-89; Canajoharie Cntrl Schls Sci Tchr 1992-; *ai:* Ski Club panese Exch Prgm Coord; Ftbl, Bsktbl & Bsbl Coach; NSTA, 1993-; Mohawk River Watch, Dir; Montgomery Cty Soil & Water ation Dist Environmental Tchr of Yr; Toshiba Corp $2500 Grant er Quality Testing of Local Waterways; Natl Diffusion Network neonta St Sci Discovery Ctr Schlsp; *office:* Canajoharie Cntrl Schl Blvd Canajoharie NY 13317

, LILLIAN TORKELSEN, Spanish & French Teacher; *b:* n, NY; *m:* Richard Allen; *c:* Christopher, Melissa, Kevin; *ed:* Stony Brook (BA) Fr & Scndry Ed 1974, (MA) Fr 1977; Cert to an; Post Grad Courses in ESL; *cr:* Schreiber HS Fr & Span Tchr Accompsett Intermediate Fr & Span Tchr 1978-79; Smithtown chl Fr & Span Tchr 1993-; *ai:* Natl Span Honor Soc Adv; *office:* vn Chrstn Schl Higbie Dr Smithtown NY 11787

, THOMAS P., Professor of Allied Health; *b:* Hudson, NY; *m:* . Lagowski; *c:* Shannon, Allison, Connor; *ed:* Hudson Vly Comm AS) Respiratory Care 1978; SUNY Upstate Med Ctr (BS) ory Care 1982; UMASS (MPH) Pub Hlth 1990; *cr:* Berkshire Med ff Respiratory Therapist 1982-92; Berkshire Med Ctr Staff ory Therapist 1982-92; Hillcrest Hosp Staff Respiratory Therapist *i:* Mass Soc of Resp Care Stu Schlsp Comm 1987-90; Pres Mass Resp Care Chptr V 1988-93; NEA, MA Tchrs Assn 1982-; Amer Resp Care 1989-; Cystic Fibrosis Fnd Vol of Yr 1984, 65 Roses Awd 1986; Wrote Several Grants; *office:* Berkshire Comm Coll st St Pittsfield MA 01201*

, WALTER HENRY,III, Anatomy & Physiology Professor; *b:* MA; *m:* Sandra Teresa Caron; *ed:* Univ of MA (BS) Animal Sci MS) Reproductive Physiology 1967, (PHD) Reproductive gy 1975; Univ of NH Photo Micrography & Macrugraphy Cert; *cr:* eld Tech Comm Coll Prof 1975-; *ai:* Audio Visual Media & Safety ept of Biological Scis; Jr HS Metrics Prgm Instr 1987-94; MTA res Awd for Meritorious Svc 1984; STCC Fnd Incentive Grant for 84; Commonwealth of MA Citation for Outstdng Performance *fice:* Springfield Tech Comm Coll One Armory Sq Springfield MA

CARFAGNO, URSULA, Assoc Prof of English; *b:* Nuremberg, Germany; *m:* Vincent R.; *c:* Manfred, Roland; *ed:* Columbia Univ (MA) Eng & Comparative Lit 1962; Univ of Erlangen Germany Frgn Langs 1956; Goshen Coll Lbrl Arts 1957; Tempel Univ 9 Post Grad Credit Hrs; Beaver Coll 12 Post Grad Credit Hrs; *cr:* Montgomery Cty Comm Coll Assoc Prof of Eng 1970-; *ai:* Lit & Hnrs Comms; AFT; Choral Soc of Montgomery Cty 1982-, Soprano; *office:* Montgomery County Comm Coll 340 Dekalb Pike PO Box 400 Blue Bell PA 19422

CARFORA, ANNMARIE MAZZACCO, First Grade Teacher; *b:* Archbald, PA; *m:* Gori J.; *c:* Tracey, Gori L.; *ed:* Fairleigh Dickinson Univ (BA) His, Govt 1964; Post Grad Stud Ed; *cr:* Secaucus Pub Schl Fifth, First Grd Tchr 1964-68; South Bound Brook PS Third, Kndgtn, First Grd Tchr 1969-; *ai:* Math, Lang Curr Planning Comms; IRA, Young Authors 1990-; Natl Org for Women 1978-; Tchr of Yr 1995; *home:* 794 Watchung Rd Bound Brook NJ 08805

CARFORA, LOLITA S., Spanish Teacher; *b:* Jersey City, NJ; *ed:* Juanita Coll (BA) Span 1954; Wichita St Univ (MA) Span 1969; Rutgers Univ, Columbia Univ, NY Univ Summer Courses Anthropology, Archeology, Art, Culture, His, Lang, Linguistics, Lit, Methods in Mexico, Ecuador 1961-94; *cr:* Cntrl Regnl HS Span Tchr 1960-; Ocean Cty Coll Adj Span Instr 1990-; *ai:* Span Schlsp Fund Adv; Chaperone Field Trips, Acts; Schl Comms; AATSP 1962-, East Coast Culture Unit Dir; Frgn Lang Edctrs of NJ 1976-, VP, Mbrshp 8 Yrs; Outstdng Contribution FL Ed; ACTFL 1987-, Charter; NEA, NJEA, OCCEA, CREA 1960-; Sigma Delta Mu 1990-; NJ St Dept of Ed 1995-, Panel Dev Content Stans World Langs; Co-Author Supplementary Text, Culture Units Aspects Mexican Life; NDEA Grant; Prins Awd Tchr of Yr 1984; Toms River HS Hall of Fame 1993; *office:* Central Regional H S Forest Hills Pkwy Bayville NJ 08721

CARGILE, ROSIE SMITH, Mathematics Teacher; *b:* Pine Bluff, AR; *m:* James; *c:* Sanford, Garry, Christopher; *ed:* Univ of AR at Pine Bluff (BA) Mathematics 1953; Case Western Reserve (MS) Ed 1967; *cr:* Case Western Reserve Medical Schl Research Asst 1956-60; Cleveland Bd of Ed Math Tchr 1960-; *ai:* Math Dept Chprsn; Math Club Spon; NHS Bd; Citizen Bee Club Spon; Union COnf Comm; Greater Cleveland Cncl of Tchrs of Math 1960-; Cleveland Collaborative for Math Ed 1989-, Advy Bd; NCTM 1989-; Phi Delta Kappa 1985-; St James AME Church 1967-, Sunday Schl Tchr, Chrstn Bd of Ed, Choir, Church Nursery; Univ of AR at Pine Bluff Alumni; North Coast Tech Prep Consortium of Cuyahoga Comm Coll; *office:* Jane Addams Bus Careers Ctr 2373 E 30th St Cleveland OH 44115*

CARGILL, SANDRA E., Secondary Social Studies Tchr; *b:* Teaneck, NJ; *m:* Michael; *ed:* Montclair St Univ (BA) Soc Sci 1969, (MA) Rdng 1979; Addl 45 Credits Post Grad Stud; *cr:* Paramus Bd of Ed Tchr 1969-; *ai:* Mock Trial; Lincoln Ctr Fellow; Svc & Schlrsp Awds; NEA; BCEA; Ed Assn of Par; NCSS; NJ Tchrs Governors Recognition Awd; *office:* Paramus HS 99 E Century Rd Paramus NJ 07652

CARINI, DOMINIC JOSEPH,JR., Social Studies Department Chm; *b:* Waterbury, CT; *m:* Mary Albanese; *ed:* Univ of New Haven (BA) Pol Sci 1976; Southern CT St Univ (MS) Soc Stud Ed 1980; 6th Yr Admin & Supervision 1985; *cr:* City of Waterbury Sub Tchr 1976-77; Holy Cross HS Soc Stud Tchr 1977-, Dept Chm 1985-; City of Naugatuck Adult Ed Tchr 1989-93; *ai:* Prin Advy Comm; ASCD 1985-; NCEA 1977-; NCSS 1980-; Natl Geographic Soc 1967-; *office:* Holy Cross HS 587 Oronoke Rd Waterbury CT 06708

CARINI, MARY ALBANESE, English Teacher; *b:* Waterbury, CT; *m:* Dominic J. Jr.; *ed:* Southern CT St Univ (BS) Scndry Ed 1983, (MS) Eng 1987; Trinity Coll 6th Yr CAS Ed 1994; *cr:* Our Lady of Mt Carmel Schl 7th Grd Tchr 1983-84; Holy Cross HS Eng Tchr 1984-89; Wilby HS Eng Tchr 1989-90; Kennedy HS Eng Tchr 1990-92; Crosby HS Tchr for Gifted 1992-94, Eng Tchr 1994-; *ai:* Peer Helpers Org Adv; New England Assn of Eng Tchrs 1984-; NCTE 1984-; Waterbury Tchrs Assn 1989-; *office:* Crosby HS 300 Pierpont Rd Waterbury CT 06705*

CARINO, DONNA MARIE RITTER, 5th Grade Teacher; *b:* St Marys, PA; *m:* David; *c:* Michelle, Stacey, Matt; *ed:* Villa Maria Coll (BS) Elem Ed 1969; *cr:* St Marys Parochial 4th Grd Tchr 1969-71; St Gabriel Schl 6th Grd Tchr 1971-74; Notre Dame Elem 5th Grd Tchr 1984-; *ai:* Spirit, Advy, Strategic Planning Comms; *office:* Notre Dame Elem Schl 13000 Auburn Rd Chardon OH 44024

CARIOTI, DANIEL VINCENT, Director of Bands; *b:* Warren, OH; *m:* Karen Margret Baker; *c:* Dominic, Julian; *ed:* Youngstown St Univ (BM) Ed 1987; *cr:* Springfield Local Schls Band Dir 1987-88; Brookfield Local Schls Band Dir 1988-; Mt Union Coll Saxophone Instr 1991-, Jazz Ensemble Dir 1992-; *ai:* Marching Band; AFT 1988-; Music Educatros Natl Assn & OH Music Ed Assn 1987-; Amer Fed of Musicians 1980-; WFMJ-TV21 Tchr of Week 1995; *office:* Brookfield H S 7000 Grove St Brookfield OH 44403

CARITHERS, JAMES FRANKLIN, Mathematics Teacher; *b:* Springfield, MA; *m:* Denise Marie Quenneville; *c:* Amy ELizabeth, Brian James, Jason Matthew, Julie Marie; *ed:* Clark Univ (BA) Math 1970; Westfield St Coll (MED) Math Ed 1975; *cr:* Forest Park Jr HS Math Tchr 1970-82; Classical HS Math Tchr 1982-86; Springfield Cntrl HS Math Tchr 1986-; *ai:* Schlsp Comm; NEA, MA Tchrs Assn 1972-; Springfield Ed Assn 1972-, Exec Bd 1978-81; Cub Scout Den Ldr 1992-; *office:* Springfield Central HS 1840 Roosevelt Ave Springfield MA 01109

CARL, CATHERINE (WALSH), Mathematics Teacher; *b:* Hartford, CT; *m:* Scott; *c:* Brendan, Sam; *ed:* Univ of Lowell (BS) Civil Engrng 1982, (MS) Ed 1983; Working Towards CAG Bridgewater St Coll; *cr:* Westford Acad Scndry Math Tchr, Track Coach 1983-85; Littleton HS Scndry Math Tchr, Track Coach 1985-88; Silver Lake Regnl HS Scndry Math Tchr, Track Coach 1988-; *ai:* NEA 1995-; *office:* Silver Lake Reg HS-Kingston 132 Pembroke St Kingston MA 02364

CARL, ETHEL ELIZABETH, Second Grade Teacher; *b:* Taunton, MA; *m:* Edward Frederick; *c:* Yvette Reed, Yvonne; *ed:* Worcester St (BS) Elem Ed 1966; 30 Hrs Post Grad Stud Elem Ed; *cr:* Town of Mansfield 2nd-4th Grd Tchr 28 Yrs; *ai:* Systemwide, Bldg Based Prof Dev Comms; NEA, MTA, Mansfield Tchrs Assn 1967-; DAR 1992-;Insurance Advy Bd 1991-; Outstdng Svc Awd 1987; *office:* Jackson Elem Schl 255 East St Mansfield MA 02048*

CARL, HERMAN E., Chemistry & Physics Teacher; *b:* Spangler, PA; *m:* Judith Ann Cooper; *c:* Robert, Michelle; *ed:* Saint Francis Coll at Loretto (BS) Chem 1976; Indiana Univ of PA (MA) Chem 1988; Prin Cert Prgm; *cr:* Mount Alyosius Jr Coll Chem Instr 1975-77; Columbia Borough Schl Dist Chem & Physics Tchr 1977-81; Portage Area Schl Dist Chem & Physics Tchr 1981-; Mount Alyosius Jr Coll Chem Instr 1989-90; *ai:* 10th-12th Grd Class Adv; Organizer of Schls Comm Svc Project; Alliance for Tchng of Sci 1989-, Treas; Amer Assn of Physics Tchr 1993-; Amer Nuclear Soc 1992-; NEA, PSEA & PAEA 1977-; Mem PA St Team for Systematic Sci & Math Reform, Mid-Atlantic Eisenhower Consortium; Holy Name Schl & Home Assn 1989-; NSF Grant Nuclear Concepts at Penn State Univ; NSF Grant Chemical Instrumentation Univ of AZ; Spectroscopy Soc of Pittsburgh Grant for ATS, PAHS 1995; *office:* Portage Area Schl Dist 800 High St Portage PA 15946

CARLACCI, MICHAEL, Math Teacher; *b:* Mt Kisco, NV; *ed:* Manhattan Coll (BS) Math, Ed 1982, (MS) Math, Ed 1996; *cr:* Pearl River HS Math Tchr 1993-; *ai:* JV Soccer, Frosh Bsktbl, JV Bsbl Coach; Mu Alpha Theta Adv; *office:* Pearl River HS 275 E Central Ave Pearl River NY 10965

CARLIN, MARY O'NEILL, 2nd Grade Teacher; *b:* Philadelphia, PA; *m:* Joseph J.; *c:* Brian J., Stephen J., Teresa M.; *ed:* Drexel Univ (BS) Acctng 1981; *cr:* St Raymond Schl 2nd, 3rd Grd Tchr 1954-59, 2nd Grd Tchr 1981-; *ai:* Stu Tchrs 5 Yrs; NCEA 1981-; *office:* St Timothy Schl 3033 Levick St Philadelphia PA 19149

CARLIN, PATRICIA MYERS, Global Studies Teacher; *b:* Rome, NY; *m:* Edward; *c:* Maurene Frank; *ed:* Syracuse Univ (BA) His 1965, (MA) Ed 1985; *cr:* Rome St Schl Spec Ed Tchr 1966-68; Solvay MS 6 Grd Tcher 1968-71; Solvay HS Soc Stud Tchr 1971-; *ai:* Staff Dev; Site-Base Team; Tech, Means & Stan Comms; Solvay Tchrs Assn 1968-, VP, Grievance, Cprresponding Sec; AFT, NYSUT 1968-; *office:* Solvay HS 600 Gertrude Ave Solvay NY 13209

CARLINA, ROBERT F., Dean & Social Studies Teacher; *b:* Brooklyn, NY; *c:* Marianne, Thomas, Dominic; *ed:* Brooklyn Coll (BA) His 1969; Long Island Univ (MS) Guid 1975; 12 Credits Ethnic Stud Queens Coll; 6 Credits Medieval His Brooklyn Coll; 18 Credits Supervisory Prgm Coll of Staten Island; *cr:* JHS 263 Soc Stud Tchr 1970-73; South Shore HS Soc Stud Tchr 1973-74; JHS 223 Soc Stud Tchr 1974-75; IS 43 Tchr, Dean 1977-; *ai:* Schl Drama Club Dir, Law Stud Prgm, Fac Sftbl Team Coach, Founder; AFT, UFT 1970-; ATSS 1975-; *home:* 7201 4th Ave Brooklyn NY 11209*

CARLISLE, JAMES EDWARD, English Teacher; *b:* Amar, AL; *m:* Deborah Ann Carter; *c:* Connie, Phillip; *ed:* Youngstown St Univ (BA) His, Eng 1967; Bowling Green St Univ (MED) 1978; Toledo Coll of Law (JD) Law 1985; *cr:* Perkins Jr HS Lang Arts Instr 1967-69; Lincoln Schl 6th Grd Tchr 1969-70; Stewart Jr HS 7th-8th Grd Eng Tchr 1970-71; Waite HS Eng Tchr 1971-; *ai:* Chess Team, Swim Club, Afro-Amer Club Adv; Bsktbl, Asst Ftbl Coach; Reynolds Corners Redskins; NUBIA 1979-, Rdng Coord, Coord of Yr 1979; Aft 1969-; TEA 1969-71; Natl Bar Assn; Fair Housing Project 1993-, Exec Bd; Big Brothers of Amer 1971-; YUBIA Yth Adv 1995-96; Outstdng Eng Tchr Northwest OH 1993-94 Nom.

CARLISLE, MARCIA R., History Instructor; *b:* Bismarck, ND; *ed:* Univ of ND (BA) Lit 1968; IN Univ (MA) Creative Writing 1972, (MS) Admin of Higher Ed 1975; Rutgers Univ (PHD) His 1982; *cr:* Rutgers Univ, NY Univ & Bennington Coll Visiting Asst Prof 1982-88; Phillips Exeter Acad His Instr 1989-; *ai:* Amer Historical Assn; Numerous Articles Pub in Both Prof His Journals & The Poplar Press; Mellon PostDoctoral Fellow NY Univ 1985; Dissertation Fellowshi Amer Assn of Univ Women 1980; *office:* Phillips Exeter Acad 20 Main St Exeter NH 03833

CARLO, ALICIA MARIA, 1st Grade Teacher; *b:* Carbondale, PA; *ed:* Keystone Jr Coll (AA) Early Chldhd Ed 1985; West Chester Univ (BS) Elem Ed 1988; 10 Grad Credits Marywood Coll; *cr:* Our Lady of Mt Carmel Kndgtn Tchr 1988-89, 6th Grd Tchr 1990-92, 8th Grd Tchr 1992-93, 1st Grd Tchr 1993-; *ai:* Chrldng Adv; Mission Moderator; Earth Week Coord; Stu of the Month Coord; NCEA 1990-; Lockawanna Cty Humane Soc 1993-; Amer Soc for Prevention of Cruelty to Animals 1996; *home:* 130 Westgate Dr Apt F-11 Carbondale PA 18407*

CARLO, RICHARD THOMAS, Assoc Prof of Architecture; *b:* Buffalo, NY; *m:* Diane Mulkin; *c:* Allison, Nicholas; *ed:* SUNY at Alfred (AAS) Archiectural Tech 1975; Univ of Buffalo (BPS) Arch 1978, (MArch) Arch 1980; *cr:* SUNY Assoc Prof 1980-; *ai:* Amer Inst of Architects 1986-; Town of Alfred Zoning & Planning Bd 1989-, Chprsn; Prof Architect; *office:* S U N Y Coll Of Tech At Alfred Engineering Tech Bldg Alfred NY 14802

CARLONE, JOANNA INSANA, History Teacher; *b:* Providence, RI; *m:* Michael P.; *c:* Ariana, Nathan; *ed:* River Coll (BA) His 1972; Attnd Rhode Island Coll, Brown Univ, Providence Coll; *cr:* North Providence HS Tchr 1972-; Rhode Island Coll Adj Prof Hnrs Hum 1992-94; *ai:* Critis Tchr for Stu Tchrs; AFT, RISSA 1972-; RICITE 1972-90; *office:* North Providence HS 1828 Mineral Spring Ave North Providence RI 02904

CARLSON, BRITA K., First Grade Teacher; *b:* Bath, NY; *ed:* SUNY at Geneseo (BA) His, Elem Ed 1980, (MS) Rdng; *cr:* Northstar Chrstn Acad First Grd Tchr 1983-86, Fourth Grd Tchr 1987-89; First Grd Tchr 1989-; *ai:* Quality Kid Rep; Field Day Chprsn; Accelerated Reader Comm; *office:* Northstar Christian Acad 332 Spencerport Rd Rochester NY 14606

CARLSON, DANIEL T., AP Chemistry Teacher; *b:* Elmhurst, IL; *m:* Carla E. Kreamer; *c:* Robert, Leigh; *ed:* OH St Univ (BS) Chem 1970; Northwestern Univ (MA) Ed 1977; Ashland Univ 12 Post Grad Hrs; *cr:* ME Twp HS West Tchr 1970-79; Dublin Coffman HS Tchr 1982-; *ai:* NEA & OEA 1984-; SECO 1985-; Pres Awd for Excl Nom 1996; Cntrl OH Chem Tchr of Yr Nom 1996; *office:* Dublin Coffman HS 6780 Coffman Rd Dublin OH 43017

CARLSON, DAVID ARTHUR, PE Teacher & Swimming Coach; *b:* Kane, PA; *m:* Linda Messineo; *c:* Marisa, Erik, Krista; *ed:* Slippery Rock Univ (BS) Hlth, PE, Recreation 1970; 30 Hrs Grad Work Azuza Pacific; *cr:* Rome Cty Schl Dist PE Tchr, Swimming Coach 26 Yrs; *ai:* Cross Cntry Coach Rome Free Acad 12 Yrs; Swimming Coach Rome Free Acad 26 Yrs; AFT, NYSUT 1970-; NISCA 1982-; SCANYS 1987-; *home:* 6660 Harvey Ave Rome NY 13440

CARLSON, DEE ANN, Vocal Music Teacher; *b:* San Leandro, CA; *m:* Dr. William R.; *ed:* Univ of CO (BME) Music Ed 1968; Baldwin-Wallace Coll (MAEd) Learning Disabilities 1984; *cr:* Boulder Valley Schls K-6 Vocal Music Tchr 1968-70; Berea City Schls K-6 Vocal Music Tchr 1970-71; Parma City Schls K-8 Vocal Music Tchr 1971-; Baldwin-Wallace Coll Undergrad Instr 1989-; *ai:* Dir Jr HS Show Choir; Jr HS Bldg Advy Comm Mem; Choir Dir; Alpha Delta Kappa 1981; Sigma Alpha Iota; Music Educators Natl Conf 1968-; OH Music Ed Assoc; Baldwin Wallace Coll Women's Comm 1981-, Adv; Martha Holden Jennings Schlsp Prgm 1989; *office:* Greenbriar Jr HS 11810 Huffman Rd Cleveland OH 44130

CARLSON, DONNA, English Teacher; *b:* Teaneck, NJ; *m:* James O'Rourke; *c:* Ryan, Devon; *ed:* Northeast MO St Univ (BS) Eng Ed 1969; William Paterson Coll (MA) Eng 1977; Attnd New Schl for Soc Research, Manhattan Coll & LaSalle Univ; *cr:* Ramapo Coll Adjunct Eng Prof 1981-86; William Paterson Coll Adjunct Eng Prof 1986; Secaucus HS Eng Tchr 1987-; *ai:* Acad Quiz Team Adv; NEA 1987-; NCTE 1989-; NJEA 1987-; Bogota PTO 1981-, Exec Bd, Grd Rep; Have Written & Pub 2 Books, Both Adaptions of Classics for Children; *office:* Secaucus HS Mill Ridge Rd Secaucus NJ 07094*

CARLSON, FRANNI LEE, 5th-8th Grd PE Tchr; *b:* Jamestown, NY; *ed:* SUNY Coll at Brockport (BS) PE 1983; SUNY Coll at Fredonia (MS) Curr & Instr 1990; Working Toward Cert of Advanced Stud at Fredonia State Coll; *cr:* Cassadaga Valley Cntrl Schl Sub Tchr 1983-85; Jamestown Pub Schl Var Bsktbl Coach 1985-94; Var Vlybl Coach & PE Tchr 1985-; *ai:* Var & Middle School Vlybl Coach; Member of Schl Shared Decision Making Comm; NEA 1985-; Chautauqua Striders Mentoring Program 1994; *office:* Jefferson MS 195 Martin Rd Jamestown NY 14701*

CARLSON, LINDA DEROSE, Guidance Counselor; *b:* Bridgeport, CT; *m:* Robert B.; *c:* R. Ryan, Nicolas B.; *ed:* Central CT St Univ (BS) Elem Ed 1971, (MS) Guid, Cnslng 1973; Univ of CT 6th Yr Admin 1984; *cr:* Holy Angels Schl Elem Tchr 1972-75; Sykes Schl 6 Grd Math Tchr 1975-88; Courthouse Plus Exercise Instr, Dir 1980-; Vernon Ctr MS Guid Cnslr 1988-; *ai:* Vernon Drug, Alcohol Cncl; Phi Delta Kappa 1990-; Phi Kappa Phi 1982-; VEA, CEA, NEA 1975-; Yth Svcs Bureau 1994-; Outstdng Svcs Awd 1989; Edctrs Awareness Awd 1991-92; *home:* 194 Hany Ln Vernon Rockville CT 06066

CARLSON, LISA ANNE, Foreign Language Teacher; *b:* Norwood, MA; *ed:* Wheaton Coll (BA) Hispanic Stud 1994; *cr:* East Bridgewater HS Frgn Lang, Span & Fr Tchr 1994-; *ai:* Chrldng Team Vol Adv; Schl Act Chaperone; MTA, MAFIA 1994-; *home:* 228 Mill St Mansfield MA 02048

CARLSON, LORRAINE E., Mathematics Teacher; *b:* Troy, MI; *m:* Richard W.; *ed:* Hartwick Coll (BA) Math 1972; SUNY at Albany (MA) Math Ed 1976; *cr:* Lansingburgh HS Math Tchr 1973-76; *ai:* NCTM, AMTNYS 1982-.

CARLSON, PATRICIA BELDEN, English Teacher; *b:* Amsterdan, NY; *m:* Paul C.; *ed:* Univ of RI (BA) Eng 1968; Wesleyan Univ 12 Grad Credits; 30 Addl Grad Hrs; *cr:* Univ of RI Spec Instr 1968-69; East Greenwich HS Eng Tchr 1969-; *ai:* NHS Adv 1986-93; Class Adv 1992-; NEASC Steering Comm 1990; Schl Climate Comm Chair 1990-92; Kappa Delta Pi, NCTE & NEA 1969-; Lib Bd 1982-, Treas, Pres 1991; Literacey Vols of Amer 1992-, Bd Mem; Book Reviewer The RI Churchman 1970-72; *office:* East Greenwich HS 300 Avenyer Dr East Greenwich RI 02818

CARLSON, RICHARD CARROLL, Eng, Greek His & Drama Tchr; *b:* Mojave, CA; *m:* Paulette Laufer; *ed:* NM St Univ (BS) Eng Ed 1969; Univ of IA (MFA) Theater 1977; *cr:* Albuquerque Pub Schls Eng Tchr 1969-72; Edmund Burke Schl Eng, Greek Hist & Drama Tchr 1986-; *ai:* Schl Plays Dir; NCTE 1989-; *office:* Edmund Burke Schl 2955 Upton St NW Washington DC 20008

CARLSON, ROBERT PRATT, Industrial Arts Teacher; *b:* Kane, PA; *c:* Wendy Carlson Gee, Michelle; *ed:* CA St Coll (BS) Ed 1968; Penn St Assoc Drafting & Design 1965; 24 Advanced Credit Hrs; *cr:* St Marys HS Ind Arts Tchr 1968-69; Sheffield Area Jr Sr High Ind Arts Tchr 1969-; *ai:* Track Coach; Filming Ftbl Games; Drama Stage Sets; Schl Fund Raising Act; Mentor Tchr; Curr Adv; NEA 1968-; PSEA 1968-; WCEA 1969-; Sheffield Twp Planning & Zoning 1974-, Chm; Sheffield Municipal Auth 1975-, Bd Chm; Warren Cty Solid Waste 1992-, Fin Chm; Masonic 1993-, Jr Warden; BSA Eagle Scout; *home:* 154 Kinzua Rd Warren PA 16365

CARLSON, TIMOTHY A., Director of Bands; *b:* Ashtabula, OH; *m:* Elizabeth Helwig; *c:* Katherine; *ed:* Otterbein Coll (BME) Music Ed 1989; VanderCook Coll (MMEd) Instrumental Music 1993; *cr:* Elmwood Local Schls Dir of Bands 1989-91; Grand Vly Local Schls Dir of Bands 1991-; *ai:* Jazz & Marching Band; Solo, Ensemble & Band Contest; Music Ed Natl Conf 1989-; OH Music Ed Assn 1989-; *office:* Grand Valley HS 44 N School St Orwell OH 44076

CARLTON, CECILE M., Mathematics Educator; *b:* Adams, MA; *m:* William F.; *c:* Trevor W., Chad M N; *ed:* Coll of Our Lady of Elms (BA) Math 1969; North Adams St Coll (MED) Scndry Ed Math 1974; Attnd UNH Ldrshp Insts, Boston Coll Discrete Math Inst, Rivier Coll; *cr:* Adams-Cheshire Regnl HS Math Tchr 1971-79; Northbrook HS Math Tchr 1979-81; Cy-Fair HS Math Tchr 1981-83; Elm St JHS 9th Grd Math Tchr 1983-87; Nashua HS 7th-12th Math Coord & Tchr 1987-95; Elm St JHS 8th Grd Math Tchr 1995-; *ai:* ESJH: Math Counts Adv, Math Dept Liaison, New England Math League Coord; Dist Level: Curr, Assessment Task Force; NH St Assessment Comm; NCTM 1979-; NH-ATMNE 1983-, MBRSHP Chair, Conf Chair; NCSM 1992-; AFT 1995-; NHIEAP 1993-, Comm Mem; Dev Mentorship Pgm with HS & Area Bus; *office:* Elm St Jr High 117 Elm St Nashua NH 03060

CARLTON, JOHN RYLAND, Sci Dept Chm & Biology Tchr; *b:* Wilmington, DE; *ed:* Univ of DE (BM) Biological Sci 1969, (MS) Cellular Bio 1972, (MED) Admin 1976; *cr:* St Mark's HS Sci Tchr 1971-76, Chm Sci Dept 1976-; Univ of DE Lab Instr 1985-; *ai:* Adv NHS; Dir Work Schlsp Prgm; DE Tchrs of Sci 1973-, Pres; NSTA 1989-; Sigma Xi 1972-; De Acad Sci 1985-; Civic Assn 1985-, VP 1987-89; DE Bio Tchr of Yr 1989-90; *office:* St Marks HS Pike Creek Rd Wilmington DE 19808

CARLTON, LAURIE SULLIVAN, English Teacher; *b:* Portland, ME; *m:* James D.; *c:* Nicholas, Ryan, Jordan; *ed:* Evangel Coll (BS) Eng Ed 1984; Goddard Coll (MA) Spirituality in Ed 1993; *cr:* Bethel Chrstn Acad Eng Tchr 1984-85; New Castle Schls Homebound Tutor 1985-86; Notre Dame HS Eng Tchr 1986-87; Lockport, Caribou Schls Homebound Tutor, Adult Ed Tchr 1987-88; Clymer Cntr Schls Eng Tchr 1990-; *ai:* Class of 1999 Adv; NEA 1990-, Gifts, Pub Relations Chair; Clymer Ed Assn 1990-; New Compact for Learning Comm 1993-; New Compact Team 1995-, Pub Relations; *office:* Clymer Central Schl PO Box 580 Clymer NY 14724*

CARLTON, MARGARET HELEN, Jr High Language Arts Teacher; *b:* Cincinnati, OH; *m:* Richard J.; *c:* Maggie, Michael; *ed:* OH Univ (MSEd) Eng & Commnctns Arts 1965; Xavier Univ Master Rdng Ed; *cr:* Norwood HS Eng Tchr & Debate Coach 1965-69; St Bernard Elmwood Pl Jr HS Lang Arts Tchr 1969-72, 1985-; Bethany 1st-8th Grd Rdng Tchr 1981-85; *ai:* Homework Asst Ctr Operator; Pub Speaking Contest Coach; OH Ed Assn 1965-72, 1982-; NEA 1965-; St Bernard Elmwood Pl Ed Assn 1969-72, 1985-; Glendale Village Cncl 8 Yrs; Glendale Historical Soc 20 Yrs; Glendale Garden Crafters 20 Yrs; St Bernard Elmwood Distngd Svc Awd; Glendale Village Cncl Proclamation; *office:* St Bernard Elmwood Pl Pub Sch Tower Ave St Bernard OH 45217

CARLUCCI, MICHAEL, Mathematics Teacher; *b:* Teaneck, NJ; *m:* Jeanene; *ed:* William Patterson Coll (BA) Elem Ed 1988, (MA) Math Ed 1992-; *cr:* Moonachie Schls Math Tchr, Chprsn 1988-91; Ridgefield HS Math Tchr 1992-; *ai:* Head Soccer, Asst Track Coach; Ski Club Adv; NEA; NJEA; *office:* Ridgefield Meml HS 555 Walnut St Ridgefield NJ 07657*

CARMAN, LINA T., Biology Teacher; *b:* Brooklyn, NY; *m:* Gregory W. Jr.; *c:* Gregory III; *ed:* SUNY at Farmingdale (AS) Lbrl Arts, Sci 1982; Univ of AZ (BSE) Biological Ed 1985; Hofstra Univ (MA) Scndry Ed 1989; *cr:* Walt Whitman HS Sci Tchr 1985-; *ai:* Awd Winning Sci Project LILCO Energy Contest Adv 1989; NY Sci Tchrs Assn, NEA, NSTA 1985-; NABT 1988-; Author, Co Author Curr Guides; *office:* Walt Whitman HS 301 W Hills Rd Huntingtn Sta NY 11746

CARMEL, RANDALL ANTHONY, 10th Grade Sci Teacher; *b:* Mansfield, OH; *m:* Joan Marie Alberico; *c:* Olivia; *ed:* Hocking Tech Coll (AAS) Natural Resources 1982; OH St Univ (BS) Earth Sci Ed 1987; 3 Credit Hrs Akron Univ; *cr:* OH Dept Nat Resources Seasonal Naturalist 1982-87; Columbus & Franklin Cty Parks Part-Time Park Ranger 1986-87; Wooster HS Sci Tchr 1988 -; *ai:* Sci Club Adv; Enrichment Acad Instr; NEA 1988-; Sci Ed Cncl of OH 1988-; 2 Rotary Club Tchr Schlsps; *office:* Wooster HS 515 Oldman Rd Wooster OH 44654*

CARNABUCI, CATHERINE SOLOMITA, Music Department Head; *b:* Brockton, MA; *m:* Joseph S.; *c:* Joseph, Christopher, Anthony; *ed:* Trinity Coll (BA) Music 1957; Lesley Coll (MEd) Music 1988; Attnd Boston Univ Grad Schl of Music; *cr:* Roosevelt Pub Schls Music Supvr 1958-61; Montgomery Cty Pub Schls Music Supvr 1961-62; Quincy Pub Schls K-12 Grd Music Tchr 1968-88, System Dept Head 1988-; *ai:* Dir Jazz, Show, Concert Choirs North Quincy HS; MMEA, MENC 1968-; MA Alliance for Arts Ed, Outstdng Tchr Awd; Brockton Italian Schlsp Club 1968-, Sec; Brockton Symphony Orch Guild, Sec, Treas; Metropolitan Opera Guild; North Quincy HS Renaissance Brochure, Video; Arts Lottery Grants; *office:* Quincy Pub Schls 316 Hancock St Quincy MA 02171

CARNAHAN, AMY MARTIN, Assistant Professor; *b:* Richmond, VA; *m:* Robert Earl; *c:* Jonathan, Brian; *ed:* VA Polytechnic Inst & St Univ (BS) bio 1975; Univ of MD at College Park (MS) Microbiology 1990; 20 Addl Credit Hrs Grad Course Work, Rsrch Marine Environmental, Estuarine Stud Univ of MD at College Park; *cr:* Southern MD Hosp Ctr Clinical Microbiologist 1985-87; MD Med Lab Inc Asst Clinical Microbiology Supvr 1987-88; Anne Arundel Med Ctr Med Technologist III 1990-95; Univ of MD at Baltimore Schl of Med Asst Prof 1992-; *ai:* Fac Practice Lab Consulting Comm 1993-; Ad Hoc Strategic Planning Comm 1995-; Sr Class DMRT Adv 1993-95; Amer Soc for Microbiology, Amer Soc of Clinical Pathologists 1986-; Grad Stu Flwshp Univ of MD at College Park 1989-90; Chairs Awd 1994; Co-Author Lab Manual Pathogenic, Clinical Moicrobiology 1995; Co-Author Microbiology Textbook, Reference Book 1996; First Author Various Peer-Reviewed Pub Articles 1989-; *office:* Univ of MD Schl of Med Dept of Med & Research Tech 100 Penn St Allied Health Bldg Baltimore MD 21201

CARNAHAN, PEGGY STENKEN, Fourth Grade Teacher; *b:* Abington, PA; *m:* Harry; *c:* Jason N., A. Josh, Brett H.; *ed:* Shippensburg Univ (BS) Elem Ed 1971; Penn St Univ (MEq) Elem Ed 1992; *cr:* Stony Brook Elem Schl 6th Grd Tchr 1972-82, 4th Grd Tchr 1984-89; North Hills Elem Schl 4th Grd Tchr 1991-; *ai:* Hlth Curr Writer; Schlsp Fundraiser Comm Chprsn; NEA, PSEA 1991-, Bldg Rep 1991-92; Delta Kappa Gamma 1991-; York Cty Conservation Dist 1985 Outstdng Conservation Edctr; *office:* North Hills Elem Schl 1330 N Hills Rd York PA 17402

CARNES, ERNEST RUSSELL, Physics Tchr & Sci Dept Head; *b:* Akron, OH; *m:* Lois Anne; *c:* E. Russell, Stacey Joy; *ed:* Univ of Akron (BA) Sci & Psych 1966, (MAEd) Guidance & Counseling 1971, (PHD) Physics Scndry Ed 1985; Addl 2 Hrs Cmptr Sci Course at Ashland Coll; *cr:* Litchfield Jr HS Sci Tchr & Dept Head 1966-72; Hudson HS Sci Tchr & Dept Head 1972-; *ai:* North Cntrl Accreditation Steering, Schedule & Bus Advy Comms; NEA, OEA 1966-; HEA 1972-, VP 2 Yrs; AAPT; SECO; Evangel Temple Church 1990-, Deacon; Jennings Scholar; Summer Sci Intern at Liquid Crystal Inst Kent St Univ; Photograph Used on Cover of The Physics Tchr 1992; Article Pub in Journal of Research in Sci Tchng; Numerous Presentations at Prof Meetings; *office:* Hudson HS 2500 Hudson Aurora Rd Hudson OH 44236

CARNES, MARY ELIN KORCHINSKY, Global Studies Teacher; *b:* Newburgh, NY; *m:* Mark Christopher; *c:* Stephanie Lauren; *ed:* SUNY at Albany (BA) Fr 1973; 12 Credit Hrs Coll of New Rochelle; 24 Credit Hrs SUNY at New Paltz; 3 Credit Hrs NYU; *cr:* N Jr HS Fr Tchr 1973-76; Newburgh Free Acad Lib Consultant 1976-79, Soc Stud Tchr 1979-; *ai:* Mid Sts Philosophy Comm Chprsn; AFT, NYSUT, NTA 1973-; Mid-Hudson Soc Stud Cncl 1985-, Outstdng Tchr; NY S Soc Stud Cncl 1985; St Thomas Episcopal Church Vestry 1993-; Fulbright Flwshp Recipient for Stud in Netherlands; NEH Yth Grant Recipient; *office:* Newburgh Free Acad 201 Fullerton Ave Newburgh NY 12550

CARNEVALE, DANIEL K., Art Teacher; *b:* Buffalo, NY; *ed:* Buffalo St Coll (BS) Design 1985, (MS) Art Ed 1994; Art Ed Cert at Buffalo St Coll 1989; *cr:* Appliance Parts Dist Art Dir 1986-89; Rushford Cntrl Schl 3rd-12th Grd Art Tchr 1989-91; Elba Cntrl Schl 7th-12th Grd Art Tchr 1991-; *ai:* Yrbk Adv; NYSATA 1989-; *office:* Elba Central Schl 57 S Main St Elba NY 14058

CARNEVALE, DIANE DEBIASE, 7th-8th Grade Math Teacher; *b:* Staten Island, NY; *m:* Anthony; *c:* Lynn Gilreath, Jill, Susan; *ed:* Wagner Coll (BS) Elem Ed 1967; Richmond Coll (MS) Ed 1970; Post Grad Work Georgian Ct Coll Supervision; *cr:* PS 26 Schl 3rd Grd Tchr 1967-69; PS 25 Annex Spec Ed Tchr 1969-70; St Ambrose Schl 6-8 Grd Math Sci Tchr 1984-88; St Benedict Schl 7-8 Grd Math Tchr 1988-; *ai:* Safety Patrol, Math Team, Math Peer Tutoring Moderator; Math Curr Coord; Diocese Curr Dev Comm; NJ Math Tchrs Assn; NMTA; NCEA; NJ Sci Tchrs Assn; St Marys Choir 1987-; Outstdng Cath Edctr Awd Trenton Diocese 1995; *office:* St Benedict Schl 165 Bethany Rd Holmdel NJ 07733*

CARNEVALE, PATRICIA A., Foreign Language Teacher; *b:* Newark, NJ; *m:* Norman J. Kuhn; *c:* Adam J. Kuhn; *ed:* Hofstra Univ (BA) Span 1978, (MA) Scndry Ed, (EDD) Ed Admin 1994; *cr:* Massapequa HS Span, Italian Tchr 1978-81; The Wheatley Schl Span Tchr 1981-82; HS West Span, Italian Tchr 1982-83; Baldwin HS Span, Italian Tchr 1983-; *ai:* Curr Cncl; Italian Club Coord; Districtwide Shared Decision Making Comm; AAFLT; AATSP; AATI; ASCD; Doctoral Fellow; Span Hnr Soc Pres; *office:* Baldwin HS 841 High School Dr Baldwin NY 11510*

CARNEY, BRITT MARIA, Mathematics Teacher; *b:* Washington, DC; *m:* Edward Leo; *c:* Arlene D., Dustin R.; *ed:* Frostburg St Univ (BS) Elem Ed 1981; Bowie St Univ Admin & Supervision Courses; Western MD Coll Credit Hrs; *cr:* Margaret Brent MS Spcl Ed Tchr 1981-87, Math Tchr 1987-; *ai:* Yrbk Adv; Sign Lang Interpreter; Conflict Resolution & Peer Mediation Comms; Crisis Intervention Team; Safety & Security Task Force Cty & Schl; NEA 1981-; MSTA 1981-; Tchr of Yr Margaret Brent MS 1994-95; *office:* Margaret Brent MS Rt 5 Helen MD 20635

CARNEY, BRUCE N., Physics Teacher; *b:* Pittsburgh, PA; *m:* Barbara; *c:* Matthew, Jason; *ed:* Clarion Univ (BS) Math 1967; Clarkson Univ (MS) Physics 1974; Attnd PA St, Case-Western, Pitt, Robert Morris; *cr:* Upper St Clair HS Physics Tchr 1968-; *ai:* JETS Teams Coach; Schl Dist Strategic Planning Comm; AFT; Local Physics Assn; *office:* Upper Saint Clair HS 1825 Mclaughlin Run Rd Pittsburgh PA 15241

CARNEY, J. E., History Instructor; *b:* Rochester, NY; *m:* Gwendolyn C. Castleman; *c:* C.B., Rocky, Elvis, Doobie, Spunk; *ed:* Bowling Green St Univ (BA) His 1984, (MA) His 1986; NY Univ at Buffalo Cert Ed 1988; *cr:* The Menninger Fnd Arch for Karl Menninger M.D. 1986-87; Fairport Cntrl Schls His Instr 1988-89; Maryvale Schls His Instr 1989-91; Fairport Cntrl Schls His Tchr 1991-; *ai:* Researching & Pub Historical Articles; Articles Pub in Acad Historical & Psychological Journals, Newspapers & Encyclopedia Entries; *office:* Martha Brown MS 665 Ayrault Rd Fairport NY 14450

CARNEY, MARY O'LEARY, Fifth Grade Teacher; *b:* Darby, PA; *m:* Dennis P.; *c:* Matthew; *ed:* Neumann Coll (BA) Behavioral Sci 1983; Early Chldhd Ed Level I Cert 1983; Archdiocese of Philadelphia Cert; *cr:* St Madeline-St Rose Schl 6th Grd Tchr 1985-87, 8th Grd Tchr 1989-93, 5th Grd Tchr 1993-; *ai:* Schl Yrbk Ed; Sftbl Asst Coach; Adopt A Family Coord; Math Club Adv; NCEA 1985-; *office:* Saint Madeline Saint Rose Schl Tome & Rodgers Sts Ridley Park PA 19078

CARNEY, MARY TUPTA, 7th Grade Teacher; *b:* Cleveland, OH; *m:* Timothy J.; *c:* Sharon, Katie, Chrissy; *ed:* Notre Dame Coll (BS) Bio 1968; John Carroll Univ (MST) Physics 1971; OH Math-Sci Project Discovery 1995; *cr:* Wasburne Jr HS Sci Tchr 1968-69; Monticello Jr HS Sci Tchr 1969-76; St Clare Schl Sci Tchr 1988-; *ai:* Sci Fair; NSTA 1988-; *office:* St Clare Schl 5655 Mayfield Rd Cleveland OH 44124

CARNEY, NANCY, French & Spanish Teacher; *b:* Earlville, NY; *m:* Franklyn; *c:* Holly Carney Pearsall; *ed:* Old Dominion Univ (BS) Ed 1965; Grad Hrs Colgate Univ, Western Ct St Univ; Lang Immersion SUNY New Paltz; *cr:* Carmel HS Frgn Lang Tchr 1965-; *ai:* Adv Fr Club; NHS Selection, Schlsp Comms; Carmel Tchrs Assn, NY St Tchrs Assn 1965-; *office:* Carmel HS 30 Fair St Carmel NY 10512

CARNEY, SUELLEN, Computer Science Teacher; *b:* Beaver Falls, PA; *c:* Emily, Michael; *ed:* Comm Coll of Beaver Cty (AAS) Data Processing 1984, (AAS) Bus Mngmt 1985; Geneva Coll (BS) Human Resource Mngmt 1990; Working Toward MS Mngmt Information Systems Robert Morris Coll; *cr:* Comm Coll of Beaver Cty Asst Dir Cmptr Ctr 1986-, Part-time Instr 1990-; *office:* Comm Coll Of Beaver County 1 Campus Dr Monaca PA 15061

CARNEY, SUSAN MACEWEN, HS Home Economics Teacher; *b:* Erie, PA; *m:* William H.; *c:* Jonathan, Betsy; *ed:* Mansfield St Coll (BS) Home Ec Ed 1979; Elmira Coll (MS) Ed 1983; *cr:* Horseheads Cntrl S[...] 1980-; *ai:* Dist Home Ec Dept Chprsn; Early Chldhd Comm Chprs[...] Parenting Ed Instr; Nutrition Clinic Nutrition Ed; NYSFCSA 19[...] Coord 1988-90; Nutrition Cncl 1995-; First United Meth Churc[...] NYSFCSA Tchr of Yr 1989; *office:* Horseheads HS 1 Ra[...] Horseheads NY 14845

CARNICELLI, ANNE MARIE, Middle School Reading Te[...] Auburn, NY; *ed:* Alfred Univ (BA) Bio 1966; St Univ of NY at [...] (MS) Rdng Ed 1975; Cooperative Learning; Learning Styles; C[...] *cr:* Dept of Soc Svcs Soc Worker 1966-71; Auburn Schls Soc[...] 1971-75, Elem Rdng Tchr 1976-82, MS Rdng Tchr 1982-; *ai:* Sp[...] Assistance Prgm Facilitator; Dist Shared-Decision Making Te[...] Strategic Planning Team; AFT, NEA 1972-; Mid-Lakes Rdng Co[...] Pres; NY St Rdng Assn 1978-; *office:* East MS Franklin St Au[...] 13021*

CARNICOM, CONNIE, Media Specialist; *b:* Fremont, OH; *ed:* [...] Green St Univ (BS) Scndry Ed 1978, (MED) Lib & Educl Media 1[...] Grad Stud in Scndry Ed; *cr:* Saint Joseph Cntrl Cath HS Bio Tchr [...] 1981-89; Terra Comm Coll Librn 1989-90; Fostoria HS Media S[...] 1990-; *ai:* Musical & Drama Dir; Youth to Youth Curr Cncl [...] Assistance Team; Cmptr Coord; OEA, NEA, FEA 1990-; OELM[...]

CAROCCI, ALBERT E., Seventh Grade Science Teacher; *b:* [...] NY; *m:* Lois Ann Dawson; *ed:* Uni of Scranton (BS) Bio 1967 [...] Univ (MED) Ed 1969; West Chester Univ 60 Credits Earth, S[...] Intermediate Unit Courses; *cr:* E. T. Richardson MS Sci Tchr [...] Coach Sci Olympiad Team, 8th Grd Boys Bsktbl, Asst Var Ftbl; [...] Team Ldr; NEA, PSEA, PSTA, NSTA 1967-; Thomas Mass[...] 1989-91, Trustee; PA Commonwealth Flwshp Bio Initiative; Art[...] *office:* E T Richardson MS 20 W Woodland Ave Springfield PA [...]

CAROCCI, GERTRUDE,OSF, Math Teacher; *b:* Philadelphia, [...] Villanova Univ (BA) Eng 1969; Millersville Univ (MA) Math 19[...] Coll Cert Admin & Supervision 1984; 21 Grad Hrs Cmptr, Math P[...] of Textile & Sci; 12 Credit Hrs Ldrshp Discrete Math 1993-95; *cr* [...] of Lima Schl Elem Schl Tchr 1956-68; St Anthony Schl Jr H[...] 1968-71; Lancaster Cath HS 9-12 Grd Math Tchr 1971-75; Bishop [...] HS Math Tchr, Chprsn 1975-93; Conwell Egan HS Math Tchr [...] Schl Community, Fac Schlsp, Math Curr Comms; Frosh Class M[...] Father-Daughter Dance Chprsn; Joint Elem, Scndry Math Cur[...] NCSM 1988-; NCTM 1972-; PA Cncl Tchr of Math, Assn Tchrs [...] Phila 1975-; GTE Gift Fellow Grant 1990; PA Citation Commitm[...] 1991; Excl in Tchng Math 1992; Tandy Tech Natl Tchng Aw[...] Commendation for Professionalism 1993; PA Awd Excl 1994; Pre[...] Awd Excl Tchng Math 1994; *office:* Conwell-Egan Cath HS 611 V[...] Fairless Hills PA 19030

CAROFF, CAROL HENIKMAN, Math Teacher & Dept C[...] Cleveland, OH; *m:* Glen; *c:* Craig; *ed:* Heidelberg Coll (BA) 1972 [...] Univ (ME) Ed 1976; 30 Hrs beyond Masters Various Colls & U[...] Solon HS Math Tchr 1972-, Math Dept Chm 1994-; *ai:* Vision Te[...] Multicultural, Portfolio, K-12th Grd Math Curr Comms; Alternati[...] Strategies Comm chair; NCTM, OCTM; Greater Cleveland Cncl [...] of Math Outstanding Tchr of Yr 1994-95; Math Portfolios, Spre[...] Wkshps Presenter; *office:* Solon HS 33600 Inwood Dr Solon OH [...]

CAROLAN, JOSEPH PATRICK, 5th Grade Teacher; *b:* Phil[...] PA; *m:* Anne; *ed:* Temple Univ (BA) His 1991; Saint Joseph Univ [...] Cert in Elem Ed, and Secondary Soc Stud 1994 & 27 Grad Cred[...] *cr:* Resurrection of Our Lord 8th Grd Tchr 1990-94, 5th Grd Tc[...] *ai:* Cath Youth Org Fac Rep; After Schl Prgm Cnslr & Tuto[...] Resurrection Of Our Lord Schl 2020 Shelmire St Philadelphia PA[...]

CAROLAN, JOSEPHINE M., Guidance Counselor; *b:* Elizabet[...] John (dec); *c:* Anne M.; *ed:* Seton Hall Univ (BS) Soc Stud 19[...] Cnslng 1976; Immaculate Conception Seminary (MA) Pastoral [...] 1990; NYU Credit Hrs; *cr:* EHS Eng Tchr 1961-78, Guid Cnslr [...] NEA, NJEA, EEA, UCEA 1961-; St Mary's Church 1987-, Truste[...] Ministries 1950-; *office:* EHS Jefferson House 27 Martin Luthe[...] Plaza Elizabeth NJ 07201*

CAROLAN, MARYANN CARROLL, High School English Te[...] Elizabeth, NJ; *m:* Kevin; *ed:* Montclair St Univ (BA) Theatre 19[...] Hall Univ MAEd in Progress; *cr:* Union Cath RHS Eng Tchr, Pe[...] Arts Dir 1990-; *ai:* Performing Arts Co Dir; Intl Thespian Soc M[...] Troupe 3673; NCTE, ASCD 1990-; *office:* Union Catholic Reg [...] Martine Ave Scotch Plains NJ 07076

CARON, ALBERT W.,JR., English Teacher; *b:* Taunton, MA; *m*[...] Soucy; *c:* Stephanie, Andrea; *ed:* Univ of MA at Dartmouth (BA [...] 1969; 30 Addl Credit Hrs in Eng Univ of MA at Dartmouth; [...] Information Schl of Jrnlsm Ft Benjamin 1971; *cr:* Congressional [...] Inc Researcher 1969-73; Newspaper Assn of Amer Spec Projec[...] 1973-79; The New Bedford Standard Times Mrktg & Promo[...] 1979-80; Mfg Jewelers and silversmiths of Amer Dir of Pub [...] 1980-83; Saint Marys Schl Eng & Soc Stud Tchr 1984-90; New[...] Pub Schls Eng Tchr 1990-; *ai:* Schl Newspaper The Normandin [...] Jrnl Adv; Bee Buddies Spelling League Asst Coord 1993-95, Coo[...] Schl Cncl 1994-; New Bedford Educators Assn, MA Tchrs Ass[...] 1990-; Univ of MA at Dartmouth Alumni Assn Bd 1987-, Pres [...] Alumni Svc Awd 1992; Marion Planning Bd 1983-, Elected [...] Southeastern MA Regnl Planning & Ec Dev Dist Bd 1993-, Comm[...] Exec Comm 1995-; Distinguished Citizen Awd Prince William [...] Whos Who Among Stu in Amer Colls & Univs 1968-69; *office:* N[...] Jr HS 240 Tarkiln Hill Rd New Bedford MA 02745*

CARON, ELAINE M., Assistant Prof of Nursing; *b:* Portland, [...] Ronald J. Stuart; *ed:* St Joseph's Coll (BSN) Nrsng 1983; Univ [...] (MS) Nrsng 1989; *cr:* St Joseph's Coll Clinical Instr 1984-86; J. [...] & Co Ed Coord 1987-90; Univ of So ME Clinical Instr 1991; Uni[...] England Asst Prof 1991-; *ai:* Acad Curr, Appeals Comm; Acad Ad[...] Theta Tau 1984-, Charter Mem Kappa Zeta; ME Cncl of Assoc De[...] Prgms, Sec, Treas 1995-; ME Affiliate Assn of Diabetes Edctrs [...] Newsletter 1988-90; Am Heart Assn, Vol; ME Chptr Am Diabet[...] Vol; ME Amputation Prevention Prgm, Advy Comm; Am Diabe[...] Educl Lit Dev ME Diabetes Control Project.

CARONE, MARGARET LEE, Sixth Grade Language Tea[...] Ridgway, PA; *m:* Thomas A.; *ed:* Post-Grad, In-svc Credits [...] Edinboro, Millersville, Clarion Univs, Northwest, MidWest Inte[...] Units; *cr:* Diocese of Erie Tchr 1967-70; Erie Co Day Care Sr[...] Tchr 1970-82; Ft LeBoeuf Substitute Tchr 1983, Tchr 1984-; *ai:* [...] Habitat Activity; PTA Bd; NEA, PSEA, Erie Rdng Cncl 1984-; [...] Cncl 1990-; Natl Wildlife 1974-; Pub in Sunday News Magazine; [...] LeBoeuf MS Cherry St Waterford PA 16441

CAROPRESE, ANN, 6th-8th Grade Teacher; *b:* Phillipsburg, [...] Northampton Cty Comm Coll (AA) Early Chldhd Ed 19[...] Stroudsburg Univ (BS) Elem Ed 1978; 16 Addl Credits Towar[...] Rdng; *cr:* The Nursery Schl Presch Tchr 1974-76; Saint Philip [...] James Schl 6th-8th Grd Rdng, Lang Arts & Soc Stud Tchr 1978-8[...] Schl 6th-8th Grd Rdng Tchr 1986-93, 4th Grd Tchr 1993-, 6th [...] Rdng & Soc Stud Tchr, 7th Grd Sci Tchr, 8th Grd Eng Tchr; [...] Comm; Stu cncl Adv 4 Yrs; Adult Ed GED Tutor; NJEA 1986-, S[...] NEA 1986-; Tchrs Applying Whole Lang 1992-; Warren Hospital [...] Vol; St of NJ Governors Awd; Alpha Schl Tchr of Yr 1990; Stdnts[...]

:dng Writing Connection; *home:* 937 Wilbur Ave Phillipsburg NJ

CIO, MARY ANN, First Grade Teacher; *b:* Elmira, NY; *ed:* Comm Coll (AS) Liberal Arts 1968; St Univ of NY at Geneseo n Laude Ed 1970; Elmira Coll (MS) Elem Ed 1974; Directed Stud Broadway Test Admin 3 Grad Hrs; *cr:* Edward D. Hardy Schl First 1970-82; Broadway Elem First Grd Tchr 1982-; *ai:* Elmira Tchrs YSUT & AFT 1970-; Delta Kappa Gamma 1981-; Spencercrest & ood Nature Ctrs; Clemens Cntr YWCA; *office:* Broadway Elem 0 Broadway Elmira NY 14904

CIO, WILLIAM J., Mathematics Teacher; *b:* Elmira, NY; *m:* Crump; *c:* Karen, Elizabeth; *ed:* Corning Comm Coll (AS) Math JNY at Geneseo (BS) Math Ed 1971; Elmira Coll (MS) Math Ed ttnd Syracuse Univ; *cr:* Ernie Davis Jr HS Math Tchr 1971-73; Southside HS Math Tchr 1973-; Corning Comm Coll Adjunct 1974-; Elmira Coll Adjunct Faculty 1980-; *ai:* AFT & NYSUT; Tchrs Assn 1971-, VP 2 Yrs; AMTNYS Elected Pres, MAA & 971-; NYSAMS VP; NCSM; Math Tchrs Assn of NY St Past Pres; lmira Southside HS 777 S Main St Elmira NY 14904

HERS, JILL WHITE, Fourth Grade Teacher; *b:* Columbus, OH; Dean; *c:* Zachary; *ed:* Capital Univ (BA) Elem Ed 1977; Wright (MED) 1995; Heidelberg Coll Elem Ed 1 Yr; Urbana Univ Elem land Coll Wkshp Way; *cr:* Monroe Elem 6th Grd 1977-78 Tchr; Elem 6th Grd Tchr 1978-89; Plain City Elem 4th Grd Tchr 1989-; & Soc Stud Curr; Textbooks Selection Comm; Handwriting Spelling Bee Adv; NEA, OEA 1987-; JAEA 1987-, Bldg Rep OH His Book Roblen Publishing 1994; *office:* Plain City Jr HS Main St Plain City OH 43064

HERS, KIMBERLY RENEE, Administrator & Teacher; *b:* ocha, Peru; *m:* Brent Alan; *c:* Zakary Tyler; *ed:* John Brown Univ Eng 1985; *cr:* Akron Chrstn Schls Span Tchr 1985-86, 7th-8th Grd m Tchr 1986-87, Eng, Span, Home Ec Tchr 1987-95, Eng, Span, , Admin 1995-; *ai:* Vlybl, Bsktbl Coach; Homcmng, Sr Class Adv; nce Comm; Head Librn; *office:* Akron Christian Schools 508 St Tallmadge OH 44278

ILLANO, LINDA PALADINI, Fourth Grade Teacher; *b:* Newton, isa, Michael; *ed:* William Paterson Coll (BA) Elem Ed & Psych (ED) Lang Arts 1977; Credit Hrs in Sup & Admin; *cr:* Stillwater 3rd-5th Grd Tchr 1974-; *ai:* Discipline & Environmental Comms; 974-; NEA 1974-; Stillwater Ed Assn 1974-; PTA 1974-; *office:* r Twp Elem Schl PO Box 12 Stillwater NJ 07875

ZA, NICHOLAS ANTHONY, Sixth Grade Teacher; *b:* Bronx, Herbert H. Lehman Coll (BA) Comm 1989; 21 Addl Hrs; *cr:* Day Care Ctr Group Tchr 1988-90; Our Lady of Mt Carmel Schl & Eighth Grd Tchr 1990-91; St Barnabas Elem Schl Seventh & Grd Tchr 1991-95; IS 192 Pub Schl Sixth Grd Tchr 1995-; *ai:* , Asst Sports Coord; NCTE 1992-; Herbert H. Lehman Coll 1993-, Donor; Golden Poet Awd 1990; Cert of Recognition Cath League Civil Rights; *office:* IS 192 650 Hollywood Ave Bronx NY 10465

NTER, BRIAN WELLS, Acctng Assoc Prof & Dept Chair; *b:* , PA; *m:* Dona M. Rinaldi; *c:* Emily, Brian; *ed:* Penn St Univ (BS) 79, (PHD) Acctng 1987; Univ of Scranton (MBA) Acctng 1982; Mgmt Accountant; *cr:* Penn St Univ Grad Tchng Asst 1982-85; Univ Asst Prof of Acctg 1985-87; Univ of Scranton Asst Prof of 987-92, Chprsn & Assoc Prof 1992-; *ai:* BSA Guest Speaker; Scis Inst Reviewer; Very Spcl Arts Pgm Vol; Amer Acctg Assoc ist of Mgmt Accts 1985-; Admin of Acctg Pgms 1991-, Acad Comm; March of Dimes 1988-; Amer Heart Assoc 1990-; Multiple Soc 1995-; Numerous Articles Pub.

NTER, CALVIN L., History Teacher; *b:* Norwood, MA; *m:* A. Pierce; *c:* Krystin, Katelyn; *ed:* Univ of MA (BA) His 1971, ng 1974; Third Yr Doctoral Candidate, Nova Southeastern Univ 6; *cr:* Medford Pub Schls Soc Stud Tchr 1971-; Lesley Coll Grad unct Fac & Cmptrs in Ed 1989-; *ai:* NEA 1971-; MTA 1971-; Tchrs Assn 1971-, Rep Cncl; ISTE 1994-; Bedford Minuteman Co apt; MassCUE 1986-; Named Governor John Hancock Fellow by monwealth of MA 1987; Grade Point Grant Awd from Pinpoint g Co 1989; Named to MA Coalition Tchr Advy Comm by Educl y Cncl 1991; Articles Pub 1992 & 1996.

NTER, CARL EMERSON, Mathematics Teacher; *b:* Johnson ; *m:* Frances Paula Hulse; *c:* John; *ed:* Bob Jones Univ (BS) Math Y Univ (MA), (MS) Math 1970; *cr:* Chester HS Math Tchr Maine Endwell Sr HS Math Tchr 1970-; *ai:* Mathletes Adv; NEA; NSF Grants; 1 NYS Stud Grant; *office:* Maine Endwell Sr HS To Market Rd Endicott NY 13760

NTER, CAROL MARIE, Second Grade Teacher; *b:* New York ; *m:* Gailey; *c:* Sherri Whitely, Kristi Amend, Lorri Avery, Judi cott Ehrig; *ed:* Queens Coll (BA) Elem Ed 1961; *cr:* PS 48 Q Tchr 1961-62; Alfred Almond Cntrl Schl 1st Grd Tchr 1962-67; lem Schl 2nd Grd Tchr 1983-; *ai:* Genesee Valley Developmental 1988-; United Meth Church 1977-, Various Offices, Orgs; Silver t 1993-, Bd of Trustees; Educl Trip to New Zealand; *home:* 52 k Dr Rochester NY 14624*

NTER, CATHY F., Third Grade Teacher; *b:* Ticonderoga, NY; *ed:* aint Rose (BS) Elem Ed 1972; Attnd Coll of Saint Rose, Russell l; *cr:* Ravena-Coeymans-Selkirk Cntrl Schl Dist First-Third Grd 2-; *ai:* Lang Arts Task Force; NY St United Tchrs, AFT 1972-; Supervision & Curr Dev 1995-; *office:* Ravena-Coeymans-Selkirk Box 248 Selkirk NY 12158

NTER, ELIZABETH WIXTED, Physics Teacher; *b:* Winchester, Timothy P.; *c:* Robert Peter, Margaret Honor; *ed:* US Military Acad Engr Mgmt 1987; Syracuse Univ (MS) Sci Ed 1995; *cr:* Loch S Physics Tchr 1992-; *ai:* SADD Adv; Sci Bowl Coach; *office:* ven HS 1212 Cowpens Ave Baltimore MD 21286

NTER, ERNA L., Math Teacher; *b:* Youngstown, OH; *m:* Gary R.; Greg; *cr:* Yough Sr HS Math Tchr 1993-; *ai:* PSEA 1993-; PCTM ffice: Yough Sr HS 97 Lowber Rd Herminie PA 15637

NTER, JEAN M., Math Teacher; *b:* New York, NY; *m:* Roger A.; J., Kristin M.; *ed:* Coll of White Plains of Pace Univ (BS) Math NY at Stony Brook (MA) Math Ed 1982; Addl 40 Credit Hrs; *cr:* Bapt HS Math Tchr 1978-84; West Islip HS Math Tchr 1984-; Vest Islip HS Lion's Path West Islip NY 11795

NTER, LORAINE KELLY, Art Teacher; *b:* Drexel Hill, PA; *m:* W.; *c:* Charles W., William E.; *ed:* Rosemont Coll (BA) Studio ma Cum Laude 1988; Univ of the Arts; *cr:* padua Acad Art Tchr Arichbisoph Prendergast HS Art Tchr 1990-; Schl of the Holy Tchr 1991-94; *ai:* Drama Club Moderator; Alpha Sigma Lambda; rchbishop Prendergast HS 401 N Lansdowne Ave Drexel Hill PA

NTER, N. DARLENE MILLER, Adv English & Reading *b:* Marietta, OH; *m:* Phillip Mercer; *c:* A Noelle; *ed:* OH Univ Eng 1969; Attnd OH Univ, Univ of Dayton, Muskingum Coll, acific Univ, Loyola Mary Mount; *cr:* Pickerington Local Schl Eng chr 1970-71; Olentangy Local Schl Eng Grd 8 Tchr 1973-75; Cambridge City HS Eng Grd 9 & 10 1993-; *ai:* Works Independently with Talented & Gifted Stdnts; NEA, OEA, Cambridge Assn of Classroom Tchrs 1993-; Batesville UM Church 1957 Adult SS Tchr, Trustee, Auditor; *home:* 705 McKinley Ave Cambridge OH 43725*

CARPENTER, PHILIP M.,JR., MS Social Studies Chairperson; *b:* White Plains, NY; *m:* Marjorie J.; *c:* Jennifer, Philip III, Susan, Elizabeth; *ed:* St Univ of NY (BA) Ed 1964, (MA) His 1967; Attnd Long Island Univ, NY Univ, Hofstra Univ, NY St Univ at Stoney Brook; *cr:* Bay Shore School System 6th Grd Tchr 1964-66, Soc Stud Tchr 1966-79, Soc Stud Chprsn 1979-; *ai:* Home Bound Stdnts Alternative Schl Tchr; AFT, NY St United Tchrs 1964-; Bay Shore Classroom T A 1964-, Negotiator; Long Island Cncl for SS 1968-; NAACP 1966-, Pub Relations; *office:* Bay Shore School System 393 Brook Ave Bay Shore NY 11706*

CARPENTIERI, PAMELA A., 9th-12th Grade English Teacher; *b:* Montclair, NJ; *m:* Frank; *c:* Austin; *ed:* Ithaca Coll (BA) Eng 1991; 21 Credit Hrs toward MA in Eng at Western CT St Univ; *cr:* Ossining Union Free Schl Dist Tchrs Asst 1991-92; Archbishop Stepinac HS Eng Tchr 1992-; *ai:* Jr Prom Coord 1993-94; Semi-Formal Coord 1994-95; *office:* Archbishop Stepinac H S 950 Mamaroneck Ave White Plains NY 10605

CARPER, JEFFREY RHODES, Asst Professor of Accounting; *b:* Charleston, WV; *m:* Lisa; *c:* Anne, Daniel; *ed:* Marshall Univ (BA) Acctng 1972; Marshall Univ (MBA) Mngmt 1977; Phil Cosby Schl of Quality Grad; *cr:* Union Carbide Corp Various Acctng Positions 1972-78; PPG Industries Inc Financial Analyst 1978-90; Triad Communications Inc VP Mkt, Finance, Co-Owner of Bus 1991-; Pt Park Coll Asst Prof of Acctng 1990-; *ai:* Elder, Sunday Schl Tchr in Westminster Presbyn; Yth Soccer Coach; PA Soc of Pub Accountants, Natl Tax Practitioners Assn 1994-; Greater Pittsburgh Bus Assn 1996; *office:* Point Park Coll 201 Wood St Pittsburgh PA 15272

CARPINELLI, DONNA, Chemistry Teacher; *b:* Passaic, NJ; *ed:* Montclair St Coll (BS) Chem 1985, (MA) Supervision 1989, (MED) Sci Ed 1992; *cr:* Clifton HS Chem Tchr 1985-; *ai:* Conservation Club; Sci Curr Writer; Affirmative Action Officer; Schl Beautification Comm-Tchr Organizer; Sci Cmptr & Recycling Coord; Spec Ed Resource Person; Dist Curr Comm; Fac Advy Bd; Showcase Decorator; NSTA & NJ Sci Tchr Assn 1986-, Reviewer; Environmental Ed Task Force; NEA & NJ Ed Assn 1985-, Negotiator; Amer Chem Soc 1983-; ACTS 1985-, Founder & Organizer; Giuaudan CAP 1992-; Christmas Toy Dr 1987-, Organizer, Raised $1700 in Donations; Hugh O'Brien Schlsp Comm 1986-; Tech Grant 1996; NJ Outstanding Recycle Award; Governors Awd 1993; A for Kids Awd 1992; NJ BISEC Internship 1989 & 1992; Merrill Outstanding Chem Tchr Finalist 1991 & 1993; Antarctic Curr Project Winner; Commissioners Tchr Candidate Awd 1985; Book: And Not A Drop To Drink; *office:* Clifton HS 333 Colfax Ave Clifton NJ 07013*

CARPINO, ELVIRA ANN, English Teacher; *b:* Lyndhurst, NJ; *ed:* Anna Maria Coll (BA) Fr, Eng, Ed; Seton Hall Univ (MA) Testing, Philosophy; Post Grad Fr Lafayette Inst; *cr:* RCA Stock Records Clerical; LHS Eng Tchr 1970-; *ai:* Yrbk Class Spon; Cheering; Schl Trips; Acad Awds Comm; NJEA, LEA, AFE 1970-; CCD, Tchr; Acad Advancement of Tchng, Mngmt NJ St Dept of Ed 1989.*

CARR, ENZO ANTHONY, High School English Teacher; *b:* Syracuse, NY; *m:* Heidi Gayle Hinsdill; *c:* Vincenzo; *ed:* Onondaga Comm Coll (AA) Hum 1980; Lemoyne Coll (BA) Eng 1982; SUNY at Cortland Scndry Eng 1987; *cr:* Solvay HS Eng Tchr Grd 9-12 1982-; *ai:* NY St United Tchrs, AFT 1982-; *office:* Solvay HS 600 Gertrude Ave Solvay NY 13209

CARR, GEORGE THOMAS,III, Industrial Arts Teacher; *b:* Neptune, NJ; *m:* Linda Jo Chapman; *c:* George T. IV, Ryan T.; *ed:* William Penn Coll (BA) Industrial Arts Ed 1973; *cr:* Wal HS Industrial Arts Tchr 1973-; *ai:* Odyssey of Mind Coach; Set Construction & Stage Crew Adv for Schl Musical; Yrbk Adv; NEA & WTEA 1973-; Shore Shop Tchrs Assn of Monmouth & Ocean Counties 1975-; Belmar 1st Presby Church, Elder; Monmouth Cty Blind Assn, Bd of Trustee; *office:* Wall HS 18th Ave & New Bedford Rd Wall NJ 07719

CARR, JAYNE MEIER, Kindergarten Teacher; *b:* Detroit, MI; *w:* Donner; *c:* Donner Dowd, Thomas Erikson, Elizabeth Meier Martell; *ed:* MI St Univ (BA) Early Ed 1946; Several Tchng Courses; *cr:* Grosse Pointe Pub Schls 3rd & 4th Grd Tchr 1946-57; Windsor VT Pub Schl 4th Grd Tchr 1980-83, 1st Grd Tchr 1983-86; Kndgtn Tchr 1986-; *ai:* NEA; *office:* State Street Elem Schl 127 State St Windsor VT 05089

CARR, JOHN W., Fourth Grade Teacher; *b:* New Haven, CT; *m:* Elaine B.; *ed:* Univ of New Haven (BS) Bus Admin 1967; Fifth Yr Elem Ed Southern CT St 1971; *cr:* Ferrara Schl Fourth Grd Tchr 1983-87; Deer Run Schl Fifth Grd Tchr 1967-83, Fourth Grd Tchr 1987-; *ai:* NEA-CEA 1967-; *office:* Deer Run Schl Rt 80 East Haven CT 06512

CARR, JOYCE (LUTSON), Fourth Grade Teacher; *b:* Kingston, PA; *m:* Bruce; *c:* Desiree; *ed:* Wilkes Coll (BA) Bus Ed 1969, (BA) Elem Ed 1970, (MBA) Elem Ed 1976; 59 Addl Hrs; *cr:* Monticello HS Bus Ed Tchr 1969-70; Rural Hlth Corp Exec Sec, Prsnl Dir 1970-71; WY Vly West Schl Dist Fourth Grd Tchr 1972-; *ai:* Soc Stud, Christmas Food & Clothing Drive Comms; PSEA, NEA 1972-; *office:* WY Vly West Schl Dist Maple Ave Kingston PA 18704

CARR, LAURIE ANNE, 8th Grade Physical Sci Teacher; *b:* Newport, VT; *ed:* Lyndon St Coll (BS) Scndry Sci Ed 1988; 60+ Credit Hrs; *cr:* Woodsville HS Summer Sci Tchr 1988; Waterford Elem 6th-8th Grd Sci Tchr 1988-89; Lancaster Schl 7th-8th Grd Sci, Math & Lang Tchr 1990-; *ai:* EIS; Stu Action Club; 6th-8th Grd Bsktbl Coach 1991-; White Mts Regnl HS Track Coach 2 Yrs; NEA 1990-; NHSTA 1991-; Ct River Advy Bd 1993-; Trailmasters Advy Bd 1995-; *office:* Lancaster Elem Schl Bridge St Lancaster NH 03584*

CARR, MARLENE (THOMAS), Fifth Grade Teacher; *b:* Akron, OH; *m:* Dewey Jr.; *c:* D. J., Brian C.; *ed:* Univ of Akron (BS) Ed 1975; Cmptr Sci & Early Elem Ed Courses; *cr:* St Matthew Schl 2nd, 3rd & 5th Grd Tchr 1968-; *ai:* Right to Read Week Coord 1996; Cmptr Coord 1990-95; NEOTA 1970-; NCEA 1968-; St Matthew Federal Credit Union 1995-, Sec; MADD 1989-; Received the First Outstanding Cath Educator Awd-Cleveland Diocese Southern Region 1988; Tchr of Yr 1987-88; *office:* St Matthew Schl 2580 Benton Ave Akron OH 44312

CARR, MATTHEW JAY, English Teacher; *b:* New York City, NY; *m:* Joan Mary Dorfmann; *c:* Joshua D., Zachary D.; *ed:* CCNY (BA) Eng 1969; Univ of NH (MA) Eng 1974; 30 Credit Hrs Temple Univ; *cr:* NYC Pub Schls Tchr 1969-72; Westbrook Coll Instr 1973-74; Deer Island Prison Tchr GED 1975-; Cherry Hill HS E Eng Tchr 1977-; *ai:* Yrbk 1977-85, 1990-; Far East Soc 1985-86; Odyssey of Mind 1989-91; Music Meaning Metaphor Club 1986-88; Standing Comm Eng Curric 1987-90; Asst Ed NJ Eng Journal 1987-90; Staff Dev Comm 1989-92; Asian Culture Club 1992-93; NEA, NJEA 1977-; BSA 1985-, Advancement; NJ Governors Recognition Awd Excl Tchng 1987; NEH Summer Seminar Grants 1989, 1991, 1993; Cncl Basic Ed Flwshp Ind Stud 1990; NEH Travel Grant 1992; Publications; Cert of Commendation, Univ of Chicago, Univ of VA, Tufts Univ, Rutgers Univ, MIT; Amer Scholastic Press Assn Most Outstdng Yrbk 1995; *office:* Cherry Hill HS East Kresson Rd Cherry Hill NJ 08003*

CARR, OYESHIKU BURGESS, History Teacher; *b:* Geneva, Switzerland; *ed:* Wesleyan Univ (BA) His 1992; *cr:* Catlin Gabel Schl His Tchr & Summerbridge Dir 1992-94; City on a Hill Public Charter His Tchr 1995-; *ai:* Founding Tchr; Fac Rep to Judicial Hearing Bd; 9th Grd Adv; His Dept Chair; Boston Do Something Vol Tutor; Pub in Black Stus Guide to Coll Success; *office:* City on Hill Pub Charter Schl 320 Huntington ave Boston MA 02115*

CARR, PETER EDWARDS, Bandmaster; *b:* Lebanon, NH; *m:* Suzanne Marie Forbes-Carr; *c:* Joshua, Jennavieve; *ed:* Univ of NH (BS) Music Ed 1969; *cr:* Timberlake HS Asst Dir of Music 1969-72; Newmarket HS Dir of Music 1972-76; Southern Aroostook Comm Schl Asst Dir 1985-91; Saint Marys Schl Dir of Music 1987-94; Salvation Army Houlton Corps Y P Bandleader 1986-; Salvation Army Divisional Music Inst Bandmaster 1990-; *ai:* Private Instruction in Comm; NBA 1991-; NMMEA 1984-; Awd Winning Bands & Stdnts; *home:* RR 1 Box 136 Houlton ME 04730*

CARR, ROBERT LANCE, Chemistry Teacher; *b:* Philipsburg, PA; *m:* Holly J. Owens; *c:* Adam, Joshua, Caleb, Rachel, Leah; *ed:* Mansfield St Coll (BS) Ed Chem 1978; *ai:* Graham Twp 4-H Club 1973-, Ldr; *home:* RR 1 Box 288B Morrisdale PA 16858

CARR, SALLY SPRAGUE, Assoc Professor of Psychology; *b:* Buffalo, NY; *c:* Melissa Lee, Dennis Dorsey; *ed:* Middlebury Coll (AB) Psych 1959; Univ of MI (MA) Ed, Psych 1962; *cr:* Lake Erie Coll Adj Fac 1975-85; Kent St Univ Adj Fac 1978-85; Cleveland St Univ Adj Fac 1980-85; Lakeland Comm Coll Assoc Prof 1985-; *ai:* Psi Beta Spon; Behavioral Soc Sci Dept Chair; Tchng Excl, Degree Review Comms; VP Acad Affairs Comm; Enrollment Mngmt; OEA, NEA 1985-, Local Treas, Pres; Amer Psy Soc, Amer Psy Assn Division II 1990-; Family Planning Assn 1992-, Bd of Trustees Pres; Ldrshp Lake Cty 1991-, Alumni Rep; Mental Hlth Ctr, Mooreland Restoration, Bd of Trustees; Western Reserve Sr Svc League, Sustainer 1980; OH Assn of 2 Yr Colls Tchr of Yr 1992; Lakeland Speakers Bureau; Amer Assn of Higher Ed Mem of Acad Awd 1994; *office:* Lakeland Comm Coll 7700 Clocktower Dr Kirtland OH 44094*

CARR, SUSAN L., Guidance Counselor; *b:* New York, NY; *m:* Ronald S.; *c:* Lindsay, Adam; *ed:* West Chester Univ (BS) Elem Ed 1970; Syracuse Univ (MS) Guidance & Counseling 1972, (CAS) Admin 1996; *cr:* Etta J Wilson Elem Tchr 1970-71; Liverpool HS Guidance Cnslr 1975-77; West Genesee HS Guidance Cnslr 1979-; *ai:* Class Adv 1992-; Dept Chprsn; Curr Cncl; ASCD 1992-; WGTA 1979-; ACA 1970-; Whos Who Among Coll Stdnts 1970; *home:* 108 Feldspar Dr Syracuse NY 13219*

CARRA, FRANK ANTHONY, Science Teacher; *b:* Bronx, NY; *m:* Diane; *c:* Frankie, Steven, Justine; *ed:* Fordham Univ (BS) Bio 1979; Iona Coll (MS) Bio Ed 1984; *cr:* Mt St Michael Acad Bio & Chem Tchr 1979-86; Island Trees HS Bio & Chem Tchr 1986-88; Herricks HS Bio, Forensic Sci & Chem Tchr 1988-; *ai:* Jr High & Frosh Bsktbl, Weight Trng Coach; Intramural Moderator; *office:* Herricks HS 100 Shelter Rock Rd New Hyde Park NY 11040

CARRANTI, THOMAS ANDREW, Band Director; *b:* Syracuse, NY; *m:* April Marie; *c:* Pio Peter, Joseph Henry; *ed:* Onondaga Comm Coll (AAS) Music 1984; Syracuse Univ (BMEd) Music Ed 1989, (MM) Music Theory 1991, (MM) Music Composition 1992; *cr:* Syracuse Univ Adj Instr 1989-92; Mexico HS Band Dir 1993-; *ai:* Marching Band, Pit Band, Pep Band Dir; AF of M #78 1983-; AFT, Mexico Tchrs Assn 1993-; *office:* Mexico H S Main St Mexico NY 13114*

CARRAS, BETSY BRITTON, HS English Teacher; *b:* Cincinnati, OH; *m:* Evan; *cr:* Fred J. Miller Clinics Admin, Instr 1978-90; Meja-Mideast Judging Assn Auxiliary Judge 1983-; Wayne HS Eng Tchr, Drill Team Adv 1985-91; Lakota HS Eng Tchr, Drill Team Adv 1991-; *ai:* Marching Band Auxiliary; Diversity Cncl Ldrshp Prgm; Working to Educate Better Fac Ldrshp Cncl; NEA 1986-; *office:* Lakota HS 5050 Tylersville Rd West Chester OH 45069*

CARRASCO, MICHAEL A., Span, Eng & Soc Studies Tchr; *b:* Lowell, MA; *ed:* Binghamton Univ (BA) Philosophy, Politics & Law 1994; Post Grad Credits Queens Coll, Coll of Saint Rose; *cr:* NYC Bureau of Citywide Equal Employment Staff Analyst, Resrchr 1992-93; Bureau of Legal Affairs & Employment Staff Analyst 1993-94; Hillcrest HS Soc Stud Tchr 1994-; *ai:* Latin Amer Club Adv; Schl Tone Comm; Tutor Span, Soc Stud, Ec; AFT, NYSUT, UFT 1994-; Tchr of Yr Awd 1994-95; *office:* Hillcrest HS 16005 Highland Ave Jamaica NY 11435*

CARREL, MARION L., Band Director; *b:* Wheeling, WV; *c:* Michael D., Eric S.; *ed:* Bowling Green St Univ (BM) Music Ed 1974; Kent St Univ (MM) Music Ed 1983; 30 Semester Hrs Ashland Coll, Kent St Univ; *cr:* River HS Band Dir 1974-78; Geneva HS Band Dir 1983-; Chippewa HS Band Dir 1983-89; *ai:* Marching, Bsktbl Pep Bands; OH Music Ed Assn, MENC, NEA, OEA 1974-; Masonic Lodge 1975-; *office:* Geneva HS 839 Sherman St Geneva OH 44041*

CARRELL, ANTHONY JOSEPH, Social Studies Teacher; *b:* Hazleton, PA; *ed:* East Stroudsburg Univ (BS) Scndry Ed 1987, (MA) US His 1989; *cr:* East Stroudsburg Univ Grad Asst 1988-89; Hazleton Area Schl Dist Tchr 1988-91; Brandywine Schl Dist Tchr 1991-; *ai:* Mock UN Adv; Bsbl Coach; Discipline, Multi-Cultural Comms; NEA 1989-; DE Cncl for Soc Stud 1992-; Masters Thesis 1989; *home:* 114 Congressional Dr Apt C Greenville DE 19807

CARRERA, ROSELY X., Second Grade Teacher; *b:* Belem, Brazil; *m:* Arnaldo; *c:* Jonathan, Thomas, Christopher, Jessica; *ed:* Rutgers Univ (BA) Ed 1981; Master's Equivalency Newark Bd of Ed; *cr:* Ridge St Schl Second Grd Tchr 1983-; *ai:* Tutoring; AFT 1983-; *office:* Ridge Street Schl 735 Ridge St Newark NJ 07104

CARRIER, CELINE ANN (GEORGE), Seventh Grade English Teacher; *b:* Plattsburgh, NY; *m:* Paul A.; *c:* Jonathan P., Justin P.; *ed:* Notre Dame Coll (BA) Eng & Scndry Ed 1972, (MED) Schl Counseling 1995; *cr:* Meml HS Eng Tchr 1985-86; Cntrl HS Eng Tchr 1986-87; Meml HS Eng Tchr 1987-89; Southside Jr HS Eng Tchr 1989-; *ai:* Drama & Speech Coach; Parent Group Fac Liaison; Manchester Ed Assn, NH Ed Assn, NEA 1985-; *office:* Southside Jr HS 140 S Jewett St Manchester NH 03103

CARRIERO, KEVIN J., Physical Education; *b:* Buffalo, NY; *ed:* Univ of Buffalo (BED) PE 1969; 37 Addl Grad Hrs; *cr:* Lancaster Como Park Elem Schl PE Tchr 1969-78; Lancaster HS PE Tchr 1978-; *ai:* Asst Jr Var Ftbl, Var Boys & Girls Indoor Track, Var Boys Outdoor Track Coach; NY St United Tchrs, NEA 1969-; Boys Indoor Track 1978-, Chm 1984-; Amer Casting Assn 1969-, Pres 1984-85; 25 Yr Svc Awd for Coaching Erie Cty Interscholastic League; World Casting Championship 1984 Gold Medal; Listed in Guiness Book of World Records Longest Double Hand Cast; 1995 World Assn of Veteran Ath Championships Track & Field Competition Dir; *office:* Lancaster HS 1 Forton Dr Lancaster NY 14086

CARRINGTON, BARBARA CIRIELLO, Vice Principal; *b:* Waterbury, CT; *m:* James R.; *c:* James Richard; *ed:* Western CT St Univ (BS) Soc Scis 1972; Cntrl CT St Univ (MS) Soc Scis 1976; 6th Yr Admin & Supervision 1992; Cert from Johns Hopkins Univ 1981; *cr:* Wilby HS Soc Stud Instr 1972-76; North End MS Soc Stud Instr 1976-83; J F Kennedy MS Soc Stud Instr 1983-92, Soc Stud Dept Chair 1992-94, Vice-Prin 1994-; *ai:* Advanced Placement Coord; Public Relations Comm Chprsn; Soc Stud Curr Revision Comm Chprsn; Schl Admins of Waterbury 1994-; Partners in Ed 1990-; Our Lady of Loreto 1970-, Sec; Ladies Guild; CIAC 1990-; Classroom Mgmt Wkshp Presenter; Drug & Substance Abuse Trng Presenter 1990; Mellon Grant for AP Trng 1991; Olympian Club of Waterbury Tchr of Yr 1993; Wilby HS Yrbk Dedication 1975; *office:* Kennedy HS 422 Highland Ave Waterbury CT 06708*

CARRINGTON, RICHARD JAMES, AP US History Teacher; *b:* Holyoke, MA; *m:* Katherine Deutsch; *c:* Liese, Keith; *ed:* WA Coll (BA) His 1967; Bowie St Univ (MA Eq) Admin 1977; *cr:* Belair Jr HS Govt & His Tchr 1967-81; Eleanor Roosevelt HS US His Tchr 1981-; *ai:* Jr Civitan Co-Spon; Schl Awds Comm Mem; Cooperating Tchr for Stu Tchr; NEA 1967-; MSTA 1967-; PGCEA 1967-; VOMCA 1971-, Corresponding Sec; Millersville Sports Assn 1980-; Knights of Columbus 1990-; Belair Jr High Tchr of Yr 1975; Ray A Kroc Tchr Achvmt Awd 1991; City of Bowie Outstdng Edctr Awd 1992; *office:* Eleanor Roosevelt H S 7601 Hanover Pky Greenbelt MD 20770

CARRION, KATHLEEN PATRICIA, Sixth Grade Teacher; *b:* West Islip, NY; *m:* Daniel Joseph; *c:* Spenser Lee; *ed:* SUNY at Oswego (BA) Theatre & Eng 1986; LIU at CW Post (MS Ed) Early Chldhd 1995; Tchng Cert SUNY at Stonybrook; *cr:* Bay Shore HS Eng & Theatre Tchr 1986-88; Island Park Schls Theatre Arts Dir 1987-, 5th Grd Tchr 1990-93, 6th Grd Tchr 1993-; *ai:* Theatre Arts Dir; AFT 1989-; PTA-Island Park 1989-, Rep; *office:* Lincoln Orens MS Trafalgar Blvd Island Park NY 11558*

CARRION, RICHARD PETER, Earth & Environmental Sci Tchr; *b:* ELkton, MD; *ed:* Salisbury St Univ (BS) Bio 1973, (MS) Environment 1983; *cr:* Elkton HS Sci Tchr 1973-; *ai:* Conservation, Ecology Club Adv; Classic Yacht Restoration Guild Inc 1984-, Pres, Founder; Pres George Bush Pres Awd; Govenor Donald Schaffers Environment Achvmt EPA Awd; *office:* Elkton HS 110 James St Elkton MD 21921

CARRIUOLO, RALF EUGENE, Professor of Humanities; *b:* Brockton, MA; *m:* Nancyann Elizabeth Munzert; *c:* Matthew; *ed:* Yale Univ (BA) Music Theory & Comp 1963; Hartt Conservatory (MM) Music Theory 1967; Wesleyan Univ (PHD) Ethnomusicology 1974; Attnd Harvard Organic Chem, NYU Telecommunications, Univ of Bridgeport British Lit; *cr:* Univ of New Haven Exec Dir UNH Fdn 1984-90, Schl of Arts & Sci Tchr, Acting Dean 1980-82, Schl of Prof Stud Dean 1983-89; Endicott Coll VP 1990-93; Univ of New Haven Prof of Hum 1994-; *ai:* Orch New England Admin; Soc for Ethnomusicology 1970-, Pres, 1975-76; NADE 1982-, Chm 1984-86; AFT 1970-, Pres 1972-73; ACLS Rsrch, Smithsonian Inst Travel, NEH Prgm, HUD Dev Grant; Articles Pub; 2 Radio Braodcasting Series; 5 Musical Compositions; *office:* Univ Of New Haven 300 Orange Ave West Haven CT 06516

CARRO, ANN SORANNO, Law Instructor; *b:* Brooklyn, NY; *m:* John P. Jr.; *c:* Joyce Phillips, John P. Jr., J. Dean, P. Michael; *ed:* Ladycliff Coll (BA) Soc Stud 1964; Niagara Univ (MA) His 1967; St Johns Univ (MA) Ed 1970; Taft Inst of Govt at Tufts Univ; US Constitution SUNY at Old Wesbury; Grad Schl of Econ UCLA; Presidential Classroom American Univ; Assertive Discipline Drake Univ; *cr:* North Babylon SR HS Grd 11, 12 Soc Stud Tchr 1965-68; Half Hollow Hills HSE Grd 9-12 Law Instr, Gr 12 Govt, Ec Tchr 1968-; *ai:* Adv; Trail Adversary CLub; Future Lawyers; Legal Eagles; Hills Dixettes Kickline; NY St Mock Trial Team; Long Island Cncl of Soc Stud 1965-, Portfolio Assessment 1993; NY St Cncl of Soc Stud 1965-, Half Hollow Hills Tchr Assn 1068-, Union Rep, Distngd Merit; Ny St United Tchrs 1968-; Schl Based Mngmt 1995-, Chprsn; Tchrs Bldg Comm 1968-; Natl Bicentennial Competition on Constitutional Bill of Rights 1986-, Long Island Regnl Coord 5 US Congressional Dists; NY St Bar Assn 1995 Tchr of Law Achvmnt Awd; *office:* Half Hollow Hills HS E 50 Vanderbilt Pky Dix Hills NY 11746

CARROLL, ANNE MARIE, Finance Professor; *b:* Columbus, OH; *m:* Patrick Davish; *c:* Max Davish; *ed:* Miami Univ (BS) Fin 1982; Univ of PA (MA) Risk Mngmt, Insurance 1986, (PHD) Risk Mngmt, Insurance 1991; *cr:* Rider Univ Adj Asst Prof 1986-90, Asst Prof 1990-; *ai:* AAUP 1986-; Amer Risk & Insurance Assoc 1984-; Articles Pub; *office:* Rider Univ 2083 Lawrenceville Rd Lawrenceville NJ 08648

CARROLL, ANN LOUISE L., 8th Grade English Teacher; *b:* Pittsburgh, PA; *m:* Richard; *c:* Richard, Reigh Anne, Bradley; *ed:* East Stroudsburg (BS) PE, Eng 1962; Various Univs (ME) Eng 1990; *cr:* North Penn Schl Dist Tchr 20 Yrs; Easton Schl Dist Tchr 3 Yrs; *ai:* Field Hockey, Sftbl, Chrldrs Coach; NCTE 1995-; AAUW 1987-; *office:* Pennbrook MS 1201 E Walnut St North Wales PA 19454

CARROLL, BARBARA ANN, Math, Cmptr Tchr & Dept Head; *b:* Bronx, NY; *ed:* Nassau Comm Coll (AS) Math 1972; Molloy Coll (BA) Math, Scndry Ed 1974; Adelphi Univ (MS) Math 1977; 3 Credit Hrs Univ of VT; *cr:* Sacred Heart Acad Math Tchr, Cmptr Dept Head 1974-; *ai:* Folk Group; Math Team; Newspaper, Yrbk Cmptr Consultants; Exam Comm; Regnl Meetings of NCTM Comm Work; Newsltr Layout Ed; Tech Comm; NCTM 1975-; NCMTA 1993-; Honored 20 Yrs Svc 1994; Honored by Ath Dept for Spirit & Support 1990-95; *office:* Sacred Heart Acad 47 Cathedral Ave Hempstead NY 11550

CARROLL, BARBARA BOTTO, Mathematics Teacher; *b:* Hackensack, NJ; *m:* Charles; *c:* Jeffrey, Kevin; *ed:* Paterson St Coll (BA) Math 1970; *cr:* Franklin JHS Math Tchr 1970-74; Lyndhurst HS Math Tchr 1987-; *ai:* Class of 1999 Co-Adv; Fac Senate Treas; NEA, NJEA & NCTM; *office:* Lyndhurst HS Weart & Fern Ave Lyndhurst NJ 07071

CARROLL, FRANCES M., French Teacher; *b:* Philadelphia, PA; *ed:* Beaver Coll (BA) Fr 1964; L'Ecole Francaise de Middlebury (MA) Fr Lang, Lit 1978; Attnd Sorbonne Univ of Paris; Temple MA Equivalency Fr Lang, Lit; *cr:* Kennett sautre Schl Dist Fr Tchr 1965-68; Council Rock HS Fr Tchr, Foreign Lang Coord 1968-; Council Rock Schl Dist 1968-; *ai:* NEA, PSEA 30 Yrs; ATF, MLA 15-30 Yrs; BCTFL 5 Yrs; *office:* Council Rock Schl Dist 301 Twining Ford Rd Richboro PA 18954*

CARROLL, GLORIA CRAUGH, Superintendent; *b:* Dallas, TX; *m:* Roger Wescott; *c:* Debra, Mrs. Thomas J. Patton (dec), Christopher, John; *ed:* Keuka Coll (BA) Pol Sci, Scndry Ed 1974; Elmira Coll (MS) Ed 1976; SUNY at Brockport (SDA) Schl Dist Adm 1985; Ed Adm at Columbia Univ 1996; *cr:* Penn Yan Cntrl Schls Soc Stud Tchr 1974-86, Asst Supt 1989-91, Supt 1991-, Dir Gifted Programming 1985-86, Admin Curr, Instruction 1986-89; *ai:* Prevention of Substance Abuse Task Force; NEA 1974-89; ASCD 1989-; NYSCOSS 1991-; Yates Cty Tomorrow 1992-; St Michaels Endowment Comm; Pres Circle 1993-; Supts Work Conf at Columbia Univ 1993; *office:* Penn Yan Cntrl Schl Dist 1 School Dr Penn Yan NY 14527

CARROLL, GRETCHEN SCHWOPPE, Business Management Instructor; *b:* Graton, MA; *m:* Paul E. III; *c:* Jonathan, Christina, Cody, Cameron; *ed:* Purdue Univ (BS) Mgmt 1981; Univ of Toledo (MBA) Mrktg 1983; *cr:* Fresh Products Natl Mktg Mgr 1983-86; Carroll Consulting Pres 1986-; Sanitary Supply Wholesalers Assn Exec Dir 1986-; Owens Comm Coll Bus Instr 1993-; *ai:* Alpha Beta Gamma Fac Adv; Bus Mgmt Advy Comm Chm; ASAE 1991-; ASTD 1996-; Alpha Phi Alumni Exch Club 1981-, Pres; Dale Carnegie Human Relations Awd Winner; Dale Carnegie Sales Talk Champion; Numerous Articles Pub; *office:* Owens Comm Coll PO Box 10000 Toledo OH 43699*

CARROLL, JAMES JOSEPH, 7th-8th Grade Science Teacher; *b:* Jersey City, NJ; *m:* Patricia Eileen Jessup; *c:* James, Christopher; *ed:* Springfied (BS) PE 1964; Adelphi (MS) Hlth 1974; 10 Addl Hrs; *cr:* Neptune HS PE Tchr 1964-65; Oceanside HS PE Tchr 1968-69; Baldwin HS Driver Ed Tchr 1969-76, Sci Tchr 1976-; *ai:* Var Wrestling Scorer, Timer; BTA 1969-; *office:* Baldwin Jr HS 3211 Schreiber Pl Baldwin NY 11510

CARROLL, JOSEPH ALOYSIUS, Seventh Grade Teacher; *b:* Philadelphia, PA; *m:* Margaret Gray; *c:* Bridget, Jennifer, Theresa; *ed:* DE Vly Coll (BS) Bus 1970; Post Grad Stud Gwynned Mercy Coll Rel; Credits Prof Cert; *cr:* Our Lady of Good Counsel Seventh Grd Tchr 1985-95; Resurrection of Our Lord Schl Seventh Grd Tchr.

CARROLL, KATHLEEN MARY, English Teacher; *b:* Utica, NY; *ed:* St Univ of NY at Plattsburgh (BA) Eng 1986, (MST) Scndry Ed 1991; *cr:* Churchill Livingston Inc Copy Ed 1987-89; Thomas R Proctor HS Eng Tchr 1991-; *ai:* Class of 1996 Adv; Colgate Seminar Adv; Mock Trial Adv; Tech Prep Eng Comm Rep; Coll Transition; Utica Tchrs Assn 1991-; *office:* T. R. Proctor Sr HS Hilton Ave Utica NY 13501

CARROLL, KENNETH ALLEN, Studies Teacher; *b:* Hammond, IN; *m:* Christine M. Denault; *ed:* Kutztown Univ (BA) His 1985; Ed Tchr Cert West Chester Univ 1993; *cr:* US Army Captain 1985-89; Pocono Mtn Schls Dist Tchr 1993-; *ai:* Asst Rifle Coach; Moch Team Coach; Nature Conservancy 1994-, Vol; *office:* Pocono Mountain Schl Dist PO Box 200 Swiftwater PA 18370

CARROLL, MARY ANNE KENNEY, Fifth Grade Teacher; *b:* Cleveland, OH; *m:* James P.; *c:* James, Megan, Elizabeth; *ed:* Univ of Steubenville (BS) Elem Ed 1969; John Carroll Univ (MA) Cnslng & Human Resourses 1993; LSW St of OH 1992; 30 Grad Semester Hrs Past Masters; CEU in Soc Work & Ed; *cr:* St William Schl 4th Grd Tchr 1969-70; Ridgebury Elem Schl 5th Grd Tchr 1986-90; Greenview Upper Elem Schl 5th Grd Tchr 1990-; *ai:* Coord, Facilitator & Trainer of Conflict Mediation Pgm; Core Team Coord; Intervention Assistance Team Tchr Rep; NEA & OEA 1986-; Chi Sigma Iota 1993-; CHEMAM 1987-; *home:* 4745 Anderson Rd Cleveland OH 44124

CARROLL, MAUREEN FITZMAURICE, English & Social Studies Tchr; *b:* Waterbury, CT; *m:* James E.; *c:* Maura, Macaire, Siobhan; *ed:* Nazareth Coll of Rochester (BA) Eng Lit 1968; Fairfield Univ (MA) Amer Stud 1981; Univ of CT (CAS) Educl Leadership 1991; *cr:* Waterbury Cath HS Alternate Schl Eng Tchr 1974-75; Holy Cross HS US His Tchr 1980-85; Naugatuck HS Eng, Social Stud Tchr 1985-; *ai:* NHS Comm; Worked in Class on Natl Bicentennial Competition on Constitution 1987-92; NEA, CEA 1985-; AAUW 1983-; CT Soc of Genealogists 1980-; CT Trainer Law Related Ed NICEL; Univ of CT Alumni Assn Excl Tchng Awd 1989; *office:* Naugatuck H S 543 Rubber Ave Naugatuck CT 06770

CARROLL, RICHARD L., Eighth Grade Science Teacher; *b:* Boston, MA; *m:* Margaret L. Kurtz; *ed:* Univ of MA at Amherst (BA) Geology 1984, (MED) Instructional Ldrshp in Sci Ed 1989; 60 Addl Credits; *cr:* Mohawk Trail REgnl Schl 9 Grd Sci, Math Tchr 1984-85; Marshall Simonds MS 8 Grd Sci Tchr 1990-; *ai:* Community of Learners, Sci Fair Comms; NEA, MA Tchrs Assn 1984-85, 1990-; NSTA 1990-; Greater Boston Earth Sci Tchrs 1990-, Sec; Natl Earth Sci Tchrs Assn 1994-; Christmas in the City 1993-, Vol; Sci Ed through Experiments, Demonstrations Federal Grant 1994; Palms Grant 1993-94.

CARROLL, STUART H., High School English Teacher; *b:* Germantown, PA; *c:* Sean; *ed:* Fairleigh Dickinson Univ (BA) Ed 1974; Wroxton Coll (MA) British Lit 1976; 15 Grad Credits in Ed; *cr:* Calis Schl Rdng Tchr 1972-73; Gill St Bernards Schl Eng, Rdng Tchr 1974-83; Montville HS Eng Tchr 1983-; *ai:* Soccer, Lacrosse Coach; NEA; *office:* Montville HS 100 Horseneck Rd Montville NJ 07045

CARROLL, SUSAN ELLIOT, English Teacher; *b:* Hartford, CT; *m:* Edward; *c:* Jennifer, Michael; *ed:* Albertus Magnus Coll (BA) Eng 1970; Univ of MA at Boston 3 Credit Hrs; *cr:* Matignon HS Eng Tchr 1971-77 & 1984-; *ai:* Pub Relations Club Adv; NHS Fac & Discipline Comm; BATA; NCTE 1984-; Town PAC; Tufts Univ Commended Tchr; Tchr of Yr; *office:* Matignon HS 1 Matignon Rd Cambridge MA 02140

CARROLL, THOMAS JOHN, Math Teacher; *b:* Peekskill, NY; *m:* Jennifer Mancini; *c:* Christine, James, Leann; *ed:* Cornell Coll (BA) Math Ed 1977; Western CT St Univ (MS) Math Ed 1985; Long Island Univ 45 Credits Beyond Masters; *cr:* Peekskill HS Math Tchr 1977-; *ai:* Girls Var Soccer & Boys & Girls Var Bowling Coach; NYSUT 1977-; AFT 1977-; Wappingers United Soccer Club 1993-, Coach; Hudson Vly Natl Bank Tchr of Yr 1991; Tandy Scholar Nom 1995; *office:* Peekskill H S 1072 Elm St Peekskill NY 10566

CARROLL, THOMAS RICHARD,OFM, Acad Dean & Spanish Teacher; *b:* Concord, NH; *ed:* OH Dominican Coll (BA) Span, Rel Stud 1976; 30 Hrs Towards Pastoral Ministry MA; *cr:* Marion Cath HS Span, Rel Tchr 1976-78; Holy Name Grd Schl Jr HS Tchr 1978-79; Franciscan Order Novice, Candidate, Formal Stud 1979-84; Padua Franciscan HS Span, Rel Tchr, Campus Ministry 1984-86; St Jude Parish Dir of Rel Ed 1986-90; Padua Franciscan HS Span Tchr 1990-, Acad Dean 1993-; *ai:* OH St Proficiency Test Prgm Coord; Bldg Mgr; NCEA 1994-; Jesuit Retreat House 1990-, Bd of Trustees; *office:* Padua Franciscan H S 6740 State Rd Parma OH 44134*

CARROLL, VIRGINIA SCHAEFER, Associate Professor of English; *b:* Buffalo, NY; *m:* Allan D.; *c:* Emily Alison, Caitlin Elizabeth; *ed:* SUNY at Buffalo (BA) Eng 1978; Kent St Univ (MA) Eng 1979, (PHD) Eng 1984; *cr:* Kent St Univ at E Liverpool Campus Asst Prof Eng 1985-92; Shimane Univ of Japan Visiting Prof Eng 1992-93; Kent St Univ at Stark Campus Assoc Prof Eng 1993-; *ai:* KSUs Stratford Pgm Co-Dir; Stu Groups Adv; AAHE; Modern Lang, NCTE & CCC, Childrens Lit, Midwest Modern Lang & Medieval Assn of Midwest; Medieval Acad; KSU Alumni Assn Distinguished Tchng Awd 1991; Book Pub; Numerous Articles Pub; *office:* Kent St Univ 6000 Frank Ave NW North Canton OH 44720*

CARROLL, ZEFFIE LUCAS, 7th-10th Grade English Teacher; *b:* Washington, PA; *m:* Clinton; *ed:* Duquesne Univ (BS) Scndry Ed 1989, (MS) Rdng Specialist 1995; 12 Addl Credit Hrs; *cr:* Canon-Mc Millan Schl Dist Sub Tchr 1989-90; Steel Valley Schl Dist 7th Grd Lang Arts Tchr 1990-93; Carlynton Schl Dist 7th, 10th Grd Eng Tchr 1993-; *ai:* Past Cheerleading Spon, Stu Cncl, Natl Jr Honor Soc, Dance Chaperone; Prof Dev Comm; Read Marathon; AFT 1993-; NCTE 1996-; IRA 1995-; Muscular Dystrophy Assn 1989-, Vol; Thanks to Tchrs Awd 1990-91; *office:* Carlynton Jr Sr HS 435 Kings Hwy Carnegie PA 15106*

CARROLL-PARKER, MARGARET ANN, Second Grade Teacher; *b:* Philadelphia, PA; *c:* Angela D Parker Jones, Danielle J. C. Parker; *ed:* Comm Coll (AA) Early Child Ed 1982; Antioch (BA) Early Child Ed, Elem Ed 1985; *cr:* Our Lady of the Rosary Tchr 11 Yrs; *ai:* Med Records Trancriptionist 1979.

CARROW, VICTORIA A., Spanish Teacher; *b:* Poughkeepsie, NY; *m:* David; *ed:* SUNY at Cortland (BS) Scndry Ed 1986; SUNY Oswego Masters in Scndry Ed 1994; *cr:* Liverpool HS Span Tchr 1986-; *ai:* NYSUT, NYSAFLT, FLACNY 1986-; *office:* Liverpool Cntrl Schls Wetzel Rd Liverpool NY 13090*

CARROZZA, FRANK PAUL, Physical Ed & Athletics Dir; *b:* Brooklyn, NY; *m:* Shawn M. Cox; *c:* Michele, Frank Jr.; *ed:* Orange Cty Comm Coll (AAS) Hlth, PE 1967; West Chester St Coll (BS) PE, Hlth 1969; SUNY at New Paltz (MS) Ed 1974; Admin, Supvr Cert; East Stroudsburg St Coll NY St Perm Cert; *cr:* Minisink Valley HS Hlth, PE Tchr 1969-70, Ath Dir, PE Tchr 1971-74, PE, Ath Dir 1974-; *ai:* Var Club Adv; NYSAAA 1974-, Admin of Yr 1975; NYS Section 9 Ex Cncl; Orange Cty Ath League; M V Youth Wrestling; Montgomery Little League; *office:* Minisink Valley HS Rt 6 Box 217 Slate Hill NY 10973

CARRUTHERS, STEPHANIE, Science & Health Teacher; *b:* Gary, IN; *m:* Richard; *c:* Richard Jr., Omer, Tivani; *ed:* Allen Univ (BA) Elem Ed; C. W. Post (MA) Elem Ed; *cr:* Martin L. King Elem 2nd Grd Tchr 19 Yrs, 3rd Grd Tchr 3 Yrs, Sci, Hlth K-3 Grd Tchr 2 Yrs; *ai:* Enrichment Club Sci, Hlth; Family Sci, Hlth Wkshp; Sci Fair; NEA 1970-; *office:* Dr M King Elem Schl Straight Path Adm Wyandanch NY 11798

CARSLEY, JAMES FREDERICK, History & Humanities Tea Bastrop, TX; *m:* Cynthia Louise Hobbs; *c:* Michael, Cheryl, Joel; *e* of NH (BA) His 1968; Boston St Coll (MED) His 1972; Retail Mg Grossmans 1969; VT Geographical Inst Stud 1993; *cr:* Grossmans Co Mgmt 1968-69; Hartford Schl Dist Tchr Vice Prin & Coach 19 Sftbl Coach; Dev Hum Curr for Dist; NEA, VEA, HTA 197 Geographical Inst 1993-; Attnd VT Geographic Seminars; Tchr Goodwill Ambassador for Rotary Spent Five Weeks in Philipp Group Stud Exchange Prgm Flanagan White Svc Awd for Com League Prgms; *home:* Weston Heights Windsor VT 05089

CARSON, DIANNE BUPP, Fifth Grade Teacher; *b:* York, PA; *m:* L.; *c:* Gordon L. Jr., John Edward; *ed:* Shippensburg St Coll (B 1968; Master's Equivalency Elem 1974; *cr:* Spring Grove Elem Tchr 1968; Wyndmoor Elem 5th-6th Grd Tchr 1968-76; Hillcrest 1976-78; Enfield MS 6th Grd Tchr 1978-81; Gifted-Talent 1982-83; Enfield Elem 5th Grd Tchr 1985-95; Springfield MS 5th C 1995-; *ai:* Soc Stud Curr Comm; Instructional Support Team, Te NEA, PSEA 1968-; STEA 1968-, Pres, Pres-elect, VP, Sec, C Negotiator; Whitpain Recreation Assn 1991-; Soccer Comm, Dir 570 School Rd Blue Bell PA 19422

CARSON, FRANK, World Cultures Teacher; *b:* Monongahela, Debra M. Roberts; *c:* Mandy, Erick; *ed:* Slippery Rock (BS) Sec Stud 1972; CA Univ (MED) M Ed, Soc Stud 1976; *ai:* Interact Clu PSEA, NEA 1973-; Masonic Lodge 1982-; *office:* Ringg Monongahela PA 15063

CARSON, JANITA DECHVAN, Mathematics Teacher; *b:* Suffc *ed:* Hampton Univ (BS) Math 1990; *cr:* Ferguson HS Math Tchr Largo HS Math Tchr 1994-; *ai:* Chrldr Coach; NEA 1991-; MTS Alpha Kappa Alpha 1988-; *office:* Largo HS 505 Largo Rd Upper M MD 20774*

CARSON, MARGARET MULKEY, Teacher; *b:* Statesville, Lester; *c:* Gary, Lisa; *ed:* Howard Univ (BA) Ed, Art 1952; Trin (MAT) Ed Graphic Art 1973; Attnd Cath Univ, Univ of DC, Univ *cr:* Banneker Tchr 1952-53; Hine Jr HS Tchr 1955-56; K. Miller Jr Chm of Fine Arts Coord for GTE 1956-; *ai:* Smithsonian Edu DCPS; Yrbk; AFT; Natl Geographic; Curr Writer for Hum Vis DCPS; Tchr of Yr 1986, 1996; Participant & Proposal Writer Afr Approach to Hum Spon Rockfellow.

CARSON, MELISSA ANN, 4th-5th Grade Teacher; *b:* Peterborou *ed:* St Lawrence Univ (BS) Environmental Bio 1983; SUNY at Pla (BS) Elem Ed 1985; Trinity Coll Grad Pgm; *cr:* Williamstown El 4th-5th Grd Tchr 1986-; *ai:* 5th-6th Grd Spelling Team Coach; SA NEA 1987-; *office:* Williamstown Elem Schl Brush Hill Rd Willia VT 05679

CARSON, PATRICIA FAY, Kindergarten Teacher; *b:* Massillon, Malone Coll (BS) Elem Ed 1973; Attnd LaVern Coll, Grand Rap Bible & Music; *cr:* Allen Elem Schl Kndgtn & 3rd Grd Tchr 1960 Elem Schl Kndgtn Tchr 1980-; *ai:* NEA, OEA 1962-; Bus & Prof 1970-, Pres; *home:* 162 Jerrol Ct Elyria OH 44035

CARTA, JOSEPH RAYMOND, Assistant Professor; *b:* Waterbury Shari Leigh Fackler; *c:* Joseph Michael, David Matthew, Christopher, Aaron Daniel, Rebecca Leigh; *ed:* Southern CT St U Bio 1966, (MS) Bio 1969; *cr:* Saint Francis Hospital Schl of Nurs of Microbiology 1969-89; Greater Hartford Comm Coll Microbiology & Anatomy 1988-91; Manchester Comm Coll Microbiology & Anatomy 1989-92; Briarwood Coll Asst Prof o Hlth Division 1992-; *ai:* Tutorial Assistance at Learning Resou United Meth Church, Nursery Schl Bd 1996; Literacy Vols 1990- Southern CT St Univ Tchng Fellowship 1966; Article Pub in Jo Infection Control; Numerous Inservice Prgms, Confs & Seminars Briarwood Coll 2279 Mount Vernon Rd Southington CT 06489*

CARTAINA, JOHN JOSEPH, Social Studies Teacher; *b:* Jersey *m:* Gloria Costa; *c:* Diane Christine, John Andrew; *ed:* Montclair (BA) Soc Stud 1969, (MA) Soc Stud 1975; 6 Credits Columbia Tc 40 Credits Admin & Supervision; *cr:* Paterson Pub Schls Sixth C 1969-80, Sci Resource Tchr 1981-82, Eighth Grd Tchr 1983-89, Stud Tchr 1990-; *ai:* Sr Class, SADD Adv; Acad Decathlon Coac NJEA, PEA 1969-; NJ Cncl His Ed 1990-; Governor's Tchr Rec Awd 1985, 1990; *office:* Rosa Parks Schl/Fine/Perf Arts 413 1 Paterson NJ 07514

CARTECHINE, KATHRYN ANN (KUBAT), Assistant Professor Castle, PA; *m:* Alfred; *c:* Michael A., Mark S.; *ed:* Saint John Cleveland (BSN) Nrsng 1970; Univ of Akron (MSN) Nrsng 1 Aultman Hosp Emergency Dept Staff Nurse 1970; Aultman Hosp Nrsng Instr 1970-74, 1982-90, Level II Coord 1990-91; Stark Te Nrsng Instr 1991-92; Kent St Univ Asst Prof, Nrsng Recruiter, Ad *ai:* Fac Cncl, Distngd Tchng Awd Comm, Search Comm; Tus Campus Stu Act, Budget Comm, Wellness Screening; Kent Camp Baccalaureate Fac Group, Peer Review of Tchng Group, Visio Sigma Theta Tau 1989-; Canton City Schls 1992-, Advy Bd Practical Nrsng; CPR Instr 1992-; Stop Smoking Instr 1989-; R Distngd Tchng Awd 1994; Cert of Recognition for Grantmanshi CARHEN Grant; *office:* Kent St Univ Stark Cmps Schl of Nrs Frank Ave NW North Canton OH 44720*

CARTER, ALAN R., Professor of Pol Sci & History; *b:* Schenecta *c:* Dan, Cindy; *ed:* Hope Coll (BA) Pol Sci 1965; Univ of WY (Sci 1966; Addl Pol Sci Stud at Univ of MO; *cr:* Hope Coll Instr Schenectady Cty Comm Coll Prof 1969-; *ai:* NEA 1969-; Fac Comm Colls, Vice-Chm; Chancellors Awd for Excl in Tchg 198 Fnd Awd for Excl in Tchng 1980; *office:* Schenectady County Co 78 Washington Ave Schenectady NY 12305

CARTER, AYANNA-PATRICIA TAYLOR, Teacher & C Specialist; *b:* Washington, DC; *m:* Clarence P. Jr.; *c:* C. Parrin, Vi Christopher S.; *ed:* Hiram Coll (BA) Ed 1973; *cr:* Agnon Schl M 1972-73; Georgetown Day Schl HS Staff 1973-74, 1st-3rd Grd M 1974-77; Univ of DC Ed Skills Specialist, Instr 1977-88; Wa Chrstn Schl Tchr, Cmptr Specialist 1988-93, 1995-96; *ai:* Com Stud 1993-, Core Ldr; NEA, DCNEA Trng Team Ldr, Womens Ldr Prgm; NEA Instrl, Prof Dev Wrkshp Ldr; *office:* Washington School 1820 Franwall Ave Silver Spring MD 20902*

CARTER, CAROLE HANSHUE, Guidance Counselor; *b:* New *ed:* Wittenberg Univ (BA) Eng 1964; The OH St Univ (MED) Cnsl Attnd Univ of VT, Univ of Western IL; *cr:* Licking Vly HS E 1967-72, Guid Cnslr 1973-; *ai:* NEA, OEA & COTA 1967-; LVE Past Pres; Licking Cty Cnslrs Assn 1973-, Past Treas; Licking Fndtn Sec; Mental Hlth Assoc 1976-, Bd of Dir 1976-82; Lick Humane Soc 1987-; *home:* 775 Smithfield Dr Newark OH 43055

CARTER, DIAN (A.) LEAKE, English Teacher; *b:* Brooklyn, Kevin Harvey; *ed:* Univ of MD at Coll Park (BA) Eng Ed 1993; Hrs Hampton Univ; 3 Credit Hrs Univ of FL; *cr:* Hyattsvill MS 1993; Eleanor Roosevelt HS Stu Tchr 1993; DuVall HS Eng Tch *ai:* JV & Var Chrldng Coach; Yrbk Adv; Jr Class Co-Spon; NE PGCEA 1993-; SECME 1995-, Tchr Participant & Summer Tech cipant; Shakespeare Theatre Tchr Participant 1994-95; *office:* Du S 9880 Good Luck Rd Lanham MD 20706

R, EVELYN ADKINS, English Tchr; *b:* Boykins, VA; *m:* Herman Jarrett, tamelah, Jason; *ed:* VA St Univ (BA) Eng Ed 1976; Bowie MS) Admin, Supervision 1990; Trinity Coll Writing 3, Univ of VA 3, Univ of MD Staff Dev 3 Hrs Grad Work; *cr:* Rustburg HS Eng r; King George HS Eng Tchr 3 Yrs; Friendly HS Eng Tchr 1 Yr; MS Eng Tchr 1 Yr; Suitland HS Eng Tchr 13 Yrs; *ai:* Heather m, Kenmoor MS PTA; Multi-cultural Comm; 2 New Tchrs, George on Grad Stu Mentor; MSTA, PGCEA 1981-; Alpha Kappa Alpha Heather Hills Vol Work; Whos Who in Amer Ed 1989, 1996; ultural Gallery Walk; Dept of Ed Exemplary Schl Awd.*

R, GEORGE ANN FLAITZ, 8th Grd Social Studies Teacher; *b:* NY; *m:* James A.; *c:* Jeff, Todd, Heather; *ed:* SUNY at Geneseo Stud 1969, (MA) His 1972; Attnd St John's Univ at Philadelphia; Cntrl Schls Tchr 1969-; *ai:* NHS Adv; HS Bldg Comm; 8th Grd r; Perry Tchrs Assn, NYSUT, AFT 1969-; Delta Kappa Gamma nited Church of Warsaw 1981-, Trustee; Warsaw Soccer Boosters eas; Warsaw Summer Soccer 1970's-, Sec; 1992 Yrbk Dedication; r of Yr; Univ of Rochester Excl in Secondary Teaching Awd 1994; erry Central HS 33 Watkins Ave Perry NY 14530

R, GLENNA CAROLE, English Teacher; *b:* Pittsburgh, PA; *m:* Morgan; *c:* Joshua, Christopher; *ed:* Geneva Coll (BA) Comm Arts A Univ 6 Credit Hrs; *cr:* Trinity HS Eng Tchr 1981; Faith Comm chl Eng Tchr, Pub Speaking 1983-85; Central Chrstn Acad Eng ub Speaking 1990-; *ai:* Drama Team; Forensic Moderator; stern PA Forensic League 1990-, Exec Bd of Dirs; Washington outreach, Vol; *office:* Central Christian Acad 145 Mcgovern Rd PA 15342

R, JAMES R.,II, 9th Grade Russian His Teacher; *b:* Boston, MA; Beebe; *c:* Juliet, Alison, Stephanie; *ed:* Univ of PA (BA) Fr Lit fts Univ (MED) Ed 1970; *cr:* Robert Acad Istanbul Turkey Tchr 1965-69, Lang Dept Chm 1966-69; Fenn Schl Tchr His & Eng Admissions Dir 1979-95, Fiancial Aid Dir 1991-95; *office:* Fenn Monument St Concord MA 01742

R, JOHN WILLIAM, Ninth & Tenth Grade Teacher; *b:* Buckland, Dorathea Upson; *c:* David, Glenn, Joanna; *ed:* Atlantic Union Coll igion 1963; Andrews Univ (MA) Bio 1972; *cr:* Pine Tree Acad Sci 72-75; Riverview Meml Schl 9th & 10th Grd Tchr 1975-; *ai:* Awd; *office:* Riverview Memorial Schl RFD 2 Box 245 wock ME 04957

R, LISA BROWNLEE, Second Grade Teacher; *b:* Janesville, WI; ny; *c:* Hailee, Hillary; *ed:* Miami Univ (BA) Elem Ed 1982; Grad ology, Environmental Stud, Cmptr; *cr:* Miami Univ Asst Visiting est Clermont Schls Second Grd Tchr; *ai:* Clermont Cty Curr Forest Hills Sci Consultant; NEA, OEA 1982-; NSTA, NCTM rof Dev Comm for Math & Sci; Phi Kappa Phi 1994-; Jennings Ford Motor Co Grant; Miami Univ Excl Awd for Sci Ed; NSF rd Ecology; *home:* 6459 Sandric Ln Middletown OH 45044*

R, MARVIN L.,JR., Director; *b:* Philadelphia, PA; *m:* Tracey; *c:* tha, Michael; *ed:* FL A&M Univ (BS) Hlth, PE 1974; *cr:* on HS Tchr Present; *ai:* Germantown Acad Bsbl, Ftbl Coach; AFT reater Exodus Church 1995-, Minister; Hossana Family Flwshp inister; *office:* WA Alternative Learning Ctr 9707 Bustleton Ave hia PA 19116*

R, MARY KENNEDY, Social Studies Teacher; *b:* Franklin, OH; d Wesley Sr.; *c:* Donald Jr., Keith; *ed:* OH St Univ (BSC) Elem s; Columbia Univ (MA) Curr & Tchng 1964; Attnd Univ of San Diego St Univ, Univ of Buffalo; *cr:* Canon Lawrence Tchrs & Supvr 1964-66; McGraw Hill Book Co Ed & Writer 1967-69; t Pub Schls Tchr & Consultant 1969-72; SSMS Soc Stud Tchr Prejudice is Not Kool Club Adv; RVC Schl Dist Grad Task Force Relations Comm Mem; NY St Tchrs Assn 1983-; Rockville Ctr 3; Long Island Cncl for Soc Stud 1985-; NY St Cncl for the Soc 5-; Stearns Park Civic Assn 1976-; Concerned Parents of Baldwin aldwin Human Relations Adv Cncl 1989; Baldwin Continuing Ed dvy Bd; Chrstn Bible Inst MPC 1993-, Tchr; Afro-Anglo-Amer Sojourner Truth Svc Awd; Svc Awd; Pi Lambda Theta Honorary; for the Hum Grant; Mem NY St Soc Stud Syllabus Review Comm; outh Side MS 67 Hillside Ave Rockville Centre NY 11570

R, MICHAEL RAYMOND, Physical Education Teacher; *b:* NY; *m:* Michelle Mc Donald; *c:* Joshua, Jessica; *ed:* WV Weslyan 1977; Univ of VT Grad Schl; TN St Univ Grad Credit Hrs; Coll, Westchester Coll Undergrad Hrs; *cr:* Winchenden Schl Soc r 1983-84; Penquis HS PE Tchr 1984-85; Bucksport MS PE, E Tchr 1985-; *ai:* Vars Wrestling Head Coach 10 Yrs; MS IM Yrs; MAHPERD, MEA 1984-; NEA 1979-; ME Coaches Assn oach of Yr 1990; Natl Coaches Assn 1988-, 1990 Coach of Yr; ME Wrestling Alliance 1991-, Dir; 2nd Marine Division Assn 1990-; Career Victories Head Wrestling Coach.

R, OLIVER THOMAS, Science Teacher; *b:* Pittsburgh, PA; *c:* , Damara, Tawnya, Tia, Shaunna; *ed:* Cntrl St Univ (BAS) y, Bio 1968; Univ of Pittsburgh (MAT) Ed 1970; 18 Credit Hrs d Duquesne Univ; Interface I & II Univ Johnston; 9 Credit Hrs Sci Carlow Coll; Attnd Grove City Coll; 9 Credit Hrs Enter 2000 *cr:* Pittsburgh Bd of Ed Tchr 1968-; Project Rediscovery Tutor, 4-; Stu OZANAM Site Supvr, Bsktbl 1964-; M. L. Steel Corp, Pol Co, St Regis Paper Co Summer Employment; *ai:* Bsktbl Coach Instutional Rep BSA; PFT, AFT 1969-; NSTA, PSTA 1984-; Natural Gas 1990-, Tchr Adv, TAP; Amer Gas Assn 1992-, Natl stdng Tchr Awd 1986; Comm Svc Awd 1987-89; PHEAA Grants *office:* Crescent Elem Schl 8080 Bennett St Pittsburgh PA 15221*

R, RALPH DONALD, Asst Prof of His & Soc Sci; *b:* Detroit, MI; M.; *c:* Landon, Aislyn; *ed:* Highland Park Coll (AA) Lbrl Arts ayne St Univ (BS) His, Sci 1957, (MED) Ed, Scndry 1964; Clark A) His, Colonial Amer 1972, (PHD) His, Amer, African 1974; orp Headquarters Job Accomodation Specialist 1990; Rutgers man Resource Mngmt 1986; Bell Laboratories Natl Trng Lab Oakland Comm Coll Chprsn, Asst Prof 1968-69; Rutgers Univ 1972-82; Wabash Coll Visiting Prof 1982-83; Univ of MD Asst 2-; *ai:* Soc Sci Tchr Evaluator; Frosh Adv; St of MD Bd of Ed Soc ent Team; Worcester Cty Bd of Ed Soc Sci Core Team; Amer al Assn; Assn for Stud for Afro-Amer Life; Org of Amer s; Most Outstdng Prof, UMES, Peoples Choice Awds 2 Yrs; One of Ten Best Tchrs in Detroit Pub Schl System; Trained Corp Employees to Acclimate Time to Corp Culture; *office:* Univ astern Shore Backbone Rd Princess Anne MD 21853*

R, REBECCA D., Facilitator & Teacher; *b:* Charleroi, PA; *m:* Paul Carter II; *ed:* Wilberforce Univ (BS) Elem Ed 1971; Univ of h (MED) Elem Ed 1976; Post Grad Stud Univ of Pittsburgh; *cr:* h Bd of Pub Ed Sub Tchr 1972; Beechwood Elem Schl Tchr Millions MS Grd 7 Soc Stud Instrl Tchr Ldr 1976-80, Grd 8 Soc rl Tchr Ldr 1980-93; Restructuring Comm 1991-93, Restructuring Team 1993-, Growth & Achvmt Acad Facilitator, Tchr Grd 7-8 *i:* Homework, Modeling Club; Field Trips 8th Grd Stdnts; ng Club; AFT, PFT 1972-; ASCD 1995-; Excl in Tchng Awd Langley HS Tchng Acad; MAP Writing, Testing Comm for Soc Stud; Rep Pittsbugh Pub Schls FIPSE Comm.*

CARTER, RENEE L., Computer & Reading Teacher; *b:* Orange, NJ; *ed:* Kean Coll of NJ (BA) Elem Ed 1976; Addl 15 Grad Credits; *cr:* Abraham Clark HS Cmptr, Rdng Tchr 1977-; *ai:* Grils Track & Field Team Asst Coach; Peer Mediation Adv; NEA, NJEA, Roselle Ed Assn 1977-; *office:* Abraham Clark HS 122 E 6th Ave Roselle NJ 07203

CARTER, ROBERT THOMAS,JR., World His & Morality Tchr; *b:* New York, NY; *m:* Deborah Lynn; *ed:* Loyola Univ (BA) His 1990; 9 Hrs Northern IL Univ; Infantry Ofcr Basic, Airborne, TOW Ldr, Battalion Motor Ofcr, Infantry Ofcr Advance Courses, Lions-Quest Skills For Adolescence Appalachian Mountain Club Mountain Ldrshp Schl; *cr:* Haines Jr Sr Schl Amer His Tchr 1990-91; St Charles HS Amer & World His Tchr 1992; Haine Jr HS Amer His, Geography Quest Tchr 1992-93; Cedars Acad Sci, Soc Stud Tchr 1993-94; St Thomas More Schl Geography, World His, Morality Tchr 1994-; *ai:* Cross Country Coach 1995; Swimming Pool; IMS; First Aid; Lifeguarding; CPR Instruction; Camping Trips; Phi Delta Kappa 1989-; Phi Alpha Theta 1988-; NCSS 1995-; Assoc of US Army 1988-; Reserve Ofcrs Assn 1992-; Appalachian Mountain Club 1993-; Amer Red Cross Vol Instr 1990-; 500 Hrs Vol Svc Amer Red Cross; 1993 Cert of Merit Asst Coach Boy's St Swimming Champions 1992-93; *office:* St Thomas More Schl 45 Cottage Rd Oakdale CT 06370*

CARTER, SHEILA M., Sixth Grd Social Studies Tchr; *b:* Rochester, PA; *m:* Raymond Douglas; *c:* Devin, Logan; *ed:* Attnd Carlow Coll Elem 1974, Penn St, Villanovia; *cr:* Our Lady of Lourdes Schl 6th Grd Tchr 1968-70; St Ignatius Schl 4th Grd Tchr 1970-74; Ft Cherry Elem Schl K-6th Grd Tchr 1975-; *ai:* FCECAB Liason Between Bd & Tchrs; NEA 1975-; PSEA 1975-, Exec Comm; NCEA; St Mary's Parish Cncl 1975-, Sec; Chrstn Mothers 1986-; Turning Point; Gift of Time Tribute 1991, 1992, 1996; *office:* Ft Cherry Elem Ctr 110 Fort Cherry Rd Mc Donald PA 15057

CARTER, T. LEE, Agriscience Teacher; *b:* Washington, PA; *ed:* Penn St Univ (BS) Ag Ed 1964; Masters Equivalency; *cr:* Ft Cherry Jr, Sr HS Agriscience Tchr 1964-; *ai:* FFA Adv; NEA, PSEA 1964-; Ft Cherry Ed Assn 1964-, Sec; PVATA 1964-, Regnl VP; Hickory Up Church 1956-, Elder; Church Adult Choir 1974-, Pres; Honorary Amer FFA Degree 1982; Outstdng Tchr Voc Ag PA St Winner 1989; *office:* Fort Cherry Jr Sr HS 110 Fort Cherry Rd Mc Donald PA 15057

CARTER, WILLIAM R., Associate Professor; *ed:* North Shore Comm (AS) Sci 1971; Curry Coll (BA) Physics 1981; Tufts Univ (EDM) Chem Ed 1985; Cornell (CSS) Nutrition 1994; CA Coast Univ EDD Candidate; *cr:* Don Bosco HS Instr 1987-88; Saint Johns Prep Instr 1988-89; Mount Ida Coll Assoc Prof 1989-; Bunker Hill Comm Coll Adj Prof 1991-; *ai:* Soccer & Tennis Coach; Pgm Dir; MA Tchrs Assn 1992-; Somerville Portuguese Amer League 1993-94, Bd dir; *office:* Mount Ida Coll 777 Dedham St Newton MA 02159*

CARTIER, PENNY WELDON, First Grade Teacher; *b:* Boston, MA; *m:* Raymond B. Jr.; *c:* Wendy T.; *ed:* Bridgewater St Coll (BS) Elem Ed 1969; *cr:* Cntrl Schl First Grd Tchr 1969-72; Hoxie Schl Fifth Grd Tchr 1980-81; Stone Schl Sixth Grd Tchr 1981-82; Peebles Schl Third Grd Tchr 1982-83, First Grd Tchr 1983-; *ai:* Lang Curr, Prof Stans Comms; Fine Arts Comm Chm; MA Tchrs Assn, NEA 1969-; Bourne Edctrs Assn 1980-, Sec; Jonathan Bourna Pub Lib 1982-, Bd of Trustees, Chm; Cape Cod Cncl on Ed Grant; *office:* James Peebles Elem Schl 70 Trowbridge Rd Bourne MA 02532

CARTISANO, MARK CARMEN, History Teacher; *b:* Peekskill, NY; *m:* Su Allen; *c:* Teodora, Carmen; *ed:* East Stroudsburg Univ (BS) 2nd Ed & His 1979; SUNY at New Paltz (MS) 2nd Ed & His 1987; *cr:* Morgan City HS His Tchr 1980-84; Pine Bush HS His Tchr 1984-; *ai:* Weightroom Strength Coach; Alternative Ed Night Schl Tchr; Grading Comm Co-Chair; AFT 1984-; Prin Awd for Excl in Ed 1995; *office:* Pine Bush HS Rt 302 Pine Bush NY 12566*

CARTWRIGHT, M. JEAN, Health & Physical Ed Teacher; *b:* Hershey, PA; *m:* Ronald; *c:* Sean; *ed:* Lock Haven St Coll (BS) Hlth & PE 1967; Scranton Univ Scndry Cnslng 1987; Attnd Mansfield Univ, Penn St Univ, Lock Haven Univ; *cr:* Williamsport HS Hlth & PE Tchr; Towanda HS Hlth & PE Tchr; *ai:* TAEA 1971-, Treas; pSEA 1971-; NEA 1971-; *office:* Towanda Area HS High School Dr Towanda PA 18848

CARTWRIGHT, WILLIE QUINTON, Vice Chair & Assistant Prof; *b:* Camden, NC; *m:* Nora Williams; *c:* Wanda D., Wendy A., Willie Q. Jr.; *ed:* Howard Univ at Washington (BS) Zoology 1959; St Univ of NY at Buffalo (MS) Med Tech 1972; Post Grad Stud at Cath Univ of Amer at Washington; *cr:* Malcolm Grow Hosp Spec Hematology Technologist 1962-65; D. C. Gen Hsop Chief Technologist, Hematology 1966-70; Univ of MD Instr, Asst Prof 1971-89, Vice Chair, Asst Prof 1990-; *ai:* Adopt-A-Schl Prgm; Balt City Pub Schls Tech Prep, Howard Univ Dept of Med Tech Advy Comm; Dept of Med, Rsrch Tech Fac Practice Plan; Amer Soc of Clin Pathology 1965-, Cert; Specialist in Hematology ASCP 1973-, Cert; Amer Soc Clin Lab Sci 1991-; Natl Assn Med Minority Edctrs 1995-; Willowoods Civic Assn 1980-, Block Capt; BioTECh Advy Bd Largo HS 1993-, Ltr of Appreciation; Charity Champaign 1990-, Coord, Governors Plaque; Frederick Douglass HS Mentoring Prgm 1993-, Svc Awd; Kellog Flwshp; 4 Book Chptrs, Article Pub; St of MD Minority Admin Internship; Univ of MD Office of Stu Affairs Exemplary Svc Awd; Recruitment, Retention Allied Hlth Trng Grant Coord; Hlth Careers Opportunity Prgm Grant Co-Dir; *office:* Univ Of MD At Baltimore Dept of Med & Research Tech 100 Penn St Rm 340F Baltimore MD 21201

CARUANA, ANTHONY FRANCIS, Jr High English Teacher; *b:* Buffalo, NY; *m:* Diane E. Gilcrist; *c:* Jennifer, Brian; *ed:* Niagara Univ (BA) Eng 1969, (MS) Ed 1974; Post Masters Courses in Ed, Admin & Supervision Niagara Univ, St Univ of NY at Buffalo, St Univ of NY Coll at Buffalo, US Army Inst of Admin, US Army Command & Gen Staff Coll; US Army Natl Security Course Natl Defense Univ, US Army War Coll; *cr:* Depew MS Eng Tchr 1969-; *ai:* Sertoma Essay & Speech Contest Adv, Coord; NCTE Promising Young Writers Prgm Judge; Dist Staff Dev, MS Dist Substance Abuse Comms; Crisis Response Team; Acting Eng Dept Chm; Area Colls Cooperating Tchr; NCTE 1975-, Recognition for Svc; NY St United Tchrs 1972-; Depew Tchrs Org 1969-, TEPS Comm, Edctr of Yr 1981-82; AFT 1972-; US Army Reserve 1969-, Commanding Officer, US Army Legion of Merit; Reserve Officer Assn 1979-; Sr Army Reserve Commanders Assn 1987-; Army Engr Assn 1988-, Silver De Fleury Medal; Adjutant Gen Regimental Assn 1988-; St John's Church, Eucharistic Minister; Depew Pub Schls Edctr of Yr 1981-81; Nom NY St Tchr of Yr 1982; Pub Rsrch Paper; *office:* Depew MS 5201 S Transit Rd Depew NY 14043

CARUSELLO, RICHARD JAMES, Earth Science Teacher; *b:* Waterbury, CT; *ed:* Unif of CT (BS) Voc Ag 1970; Ratcliffe Hicks 2 Yr Cert Horticulture 1966; 30 Credit Hrs Beyond Bachelors in Voc Ed; *cr:* Waterbury Chamber of Commerce VP of Ed & Bus Consortium 1978-80; Trumbull HS Earth Sci Tchr 1983-; *ai:* Horticulture Club; Class Adv 3 Yrs; NEA, CT Ed Assn, Trumbull Ed Assn 1983-; *home:* 219 New Haven Ave Waterbury CT 06708

CARUSO, CARMELINA SIENA, Second Grade Teacher; *b:* New Haven, CT; *m:* Daniel; *c:* Donna Marie Mazzucco, Lisa Marie Pataky, Cynthia Marie; *ed:* Southern CT St Univ (BS) Elem Ed 1955; *cr:* Hamilton St Schl Second Grd Tchr 1955-59; Benjamin Jepson Schl Second Grd Tchr 1959-61; Branford Pub Schls Sub Tchr 1974-76, Instrl Aide 1976-77; Mary R. Tisko Schl Second Grd Tchr 1977-; *ai:* NEA, BEA, CEA 1977-; *home:* 21 Queach Rd Branford CT 06405

CARUSO, CAROLYN V., Health & Physical Ed Teacher; *b:* Wilkinsburg, PA; *ed:* Fairmont St Coll (ABEd) Hlth & PE 1970; 27 Grad Credits; *cr:* Penn-Trafford Schl Dist HPE Tchr 26 Yrs; *ai:* Head Bsktbl Coach 1970-83; Head Sftbl Coach 1976-83; Jr High Vllybl Coach 1994-; Ski Club Co-Spon 1995-; NEA 1970-; PA St Tchrs Assn 1970-.

CARUSO, JOSEPH PETER, Mathematics Tchr & Dept Chprsn; *b:* Philadelphia, PA; *ed:* LaSalle Univ (BA) Math 1971; Temple Univ (MA) Math Ed 1974; Grad Courses in Advanced Placement Calculus BC & Calculus AB; *cr:* Cardinal Dougherty HS Math Tchr 1971-, Math Dept Chprsn 1984-; LaSalle Univ Adjunct Math Tchr 1991-; *ai:* ATMOPAV 1980-; Holy Cross Parish 1950-, Eucharistic Minister 1987-; DE Valley Engrs Week Outstanding Math Tchr Awd 1993; Philadelphia Chapter PSPE Outstanding Math Tchr Awd 1993; *home:* 7138 Bryan St Philadelphia PA 19119

CARUSO, MADELINE THERESA, Teacher & Admin; *b:* Troy, NY; *ed:* Russell Sage Coll (BS) Ed, Psych 1978; Coll St Rose (MS) Rdng 1980; *cr:* Little Red Schoolhouse Tchr, Adm 1978-; *office:* Little Red School House 49 N Greenbush Rd Troy NY 12180*

CARUSO, RENA TARDELLI, Fourth Grade Teacher; *b:* Seneca Falls, NY; *m:* Thomas John; *c:* Kayci Jo, Talia Lynn; *ed:* VT Coll (AA) Liberal Arts 1973; SUNY at Potsdam (BA) Eng Ed 1975, (MA) Ed N-6 1976; 9 Hrs Ed Courses; *cr:* Potsdam Cntrl Kndgtn, 4th Grd Tchr 1976-; *ai:* Soc Comm; Dist Planning, Bldg Planning Team; Delta Kappa Gamma 1986-; AFT 1976-; Potsdam Tchrs Assn 1976-, Sec.*

CARUSO, ROBERT F., Social Studies & Drama Dir; *b:* New York, NY; *ed:* Rugers Univ (BA) His 1966, (EDM) Soc Stud Ed 1974; Attnd William Paterson Coll, Seton Hall univ & Amer Univ; Post Grad Work & Flwshps; *cr:* West Essex HS Soc Stud Tchr 1969-; *ai:* Drama Dir; NHS Adv; NEA & Affiliates 1969-; NCSS 1975-; Friends of NY Theatre 1993-, Sec & Nominating Comm; Phi Beta Kappa; 5 Yrs Reader for AP Exam in US His; *office:* West Essex Sr HS W Greenbrook Rd North Caldwel NJ 07006

CARUSO, SHARON MARIE, Social Studies Teacher; *b:* Fairfax, VA; *ed:* Montclair St Univ (BA) Psych 1985; Monmouth Univ (MAT) Ed 1992; Northern KY Univ Clinical, Comm Psych in London Summer 1995; TX A&M 4 Grad Credits Summer Prgm AP Psych 1994; *cr:* Freehold Twp HS Soc Stud, Psych Tchr 1987-; *ai:* After Schl Tutor Prgm; TOPPS 1994-; Rutgers Univ Tchr Recognition Awd 1995-; *office:* Freehold Township High School 281 Elton Adelphia Rd Freehold NJ 07728

CARVELL, PETER EDWARD, Former Arts Dept Head; *b:* Leicester, England; *ed:* Exeter Univ (BA) Eng, Music 1973; Royal Soc of Art (FRSA) Svcs to the Arts 1995; *cr:* Chiswick Schl Head of Arts 1973-78; Cooper Schl Head of Arts 1978-80; London Borough of Ealing Schl Head of Arts 1981-84; Anglo Amer Schl Head of Arts 1984-88; Friends Acad Head of Arts 1988-95; *ai:* Dept of Ed & Sci United Kingdom 1974-; Various Piano & Orchestral Works; *home:* 300 W 12th St Apt 6G New York NY 10014*

CARVER, JOHN PRESTON, Varsity Basketball Coach; *b:* Manchester, NH; *m:* Lisa Ciccotelli; *ed:* Lyndon St Coll (BS) Soc Sci 1992; Work Towards MA Ed Candidate Univ of NH; *cr:* St Mary Acad PE Tchr, Ath Dir 1993-94; Dover HS Spec Ed 1994-95; *ai:* Var Boys Bsktbl Coach 1993-; Dover HS Var Ftbl Coach 1992-, JV BSbl Coach 1993-; NHNEA 1992-; NFICA 1990-; *office:* Nute HS Elm St Milton NH 03851

CARVER, JON CAMERON, Social Studies Tchr & Dept Chm; *b:* Sandusky, OH; *m:* Lisa Arkett; *c:* Erin, Camille; *ed:* Bluffton Coll 18 Hrs Towards MS Soc Stud; Bowling Green St Univ 24 Hrs; OH St Univ 20 Hrs; NJ Inst of Tech 4 Hrs; Bluffton Coll 18 Hrs Towards MS Soc Stud; Bowling Green St Univ 24 Hrs; OH St Univ 20 Hrs; NJ Inst of Tech 4 Hrs; *cr:* Lima Sr HS Tchr 1976-77, 1985-86, Tchr, Dept Chair 1985-, Tchng AP Amer, AP Eropean, Russian, Reg, Achvmt World His; *ai:* North Cntrl Evaluation, Fac Tech, Soc Stud Curr Improvement Comms; Soc Stud Dept Chair; Head Soccer, Asst Swim Coach; World His Assn 1992-; United Way 1993-, Appr Bd; Bluffton Coll Tchr Ed Steering Comm 1993-; Woodrow Wilson Flwshp, Princeton Univ World His Inst, St PTSA Dist Tchr of Yr 1992; *office:* Lima Sr HS 600 S Pierce St Lima OH 45804

CARY, DOREEN KAY, Language Arts Teacher; *b:* Woodsville, NH; *m:* Robert W. Sr.; *ed:* Lyndon St COll (BS) Ed 1965; Trinity Coll (MA) Mid Grds Ed 1995; *cr:* Enosburg Falls Schl 5th-6th Grd Tchr 1965-66; Marshfield Elem Schl 5th-8th Grd Tchr 1966-69; Barre Town Elem Schl 8th Grd Lang Arts Tchr 1969-; *ai:* BTEA 1969-, Pres 1995-; Local Standards Bd, Chprsn 1992, 1993; NEA, VEA; Amer Legion Auxiliary 1976-; BPOE #1535 1996; Article Pub.

CARY, PAUL FRANCIS, Electronics Technology Teacher; *b:* Allentown, PA; *m:* Eleanore Marie Kurter; *c:* Julie Ann, Amanda, Michael; *ed:* Lincoln Tech Inst (AD) Electronics Tech 1971; Temple Univ Indstrl Ed Cert 1978; *cr:* Lincoln Tech Inst Tchr Asst 1965-71, Tchr 1971-; *ai:* Stu Affairs Dept Cnslr; Stu Cncl Adv; Men's Bsktbl Coach; Inst Electrical Electronics Engr 1982-; Intnl Soc of Certfd Electronic Technicians 1993-; Mens Soc of Sacred Heart 1985-, Pres; Bath Federal Credit Union 1989-, Exec Comm; Carbon Cty Vo-Tech Advy Comm 1990-, Chm; VICA 1988-, Event Mgr, Svc Excl; Knights of Columbus 1980-, 3rd Degree; ISCET Certfd in Indstrl Electronics, Consumer Electronics; Svc Excl Awd; Employee of Yr; *office:* Lincoln Tech Inst 5151 W Tilghman St Allentown PA 18104*

CARY, THOMAS DAVID, Mathematics Teacher; *b:* N Adams, MA; *m:* Diane; *c:* Christina Marie Cary-Cummings; *ed:* N Adams St Coll (BA) Math 1970, (MS) Scndry Schl Admin 1975; *cr:* Berlin Cntrl Math Tchr 1970-; *ai:* AFT, NYSUT, BTA 1970-; *office:* Berlin Cntrl Jr Sr HS Rt 22 Berlin NY 12022

CASABIAN, JOAN ANDO, PE Tchr & Field Hockey Coach; *b:* Stoughton, MA; *m:* Edward K. Jr.; *c:* Mary, Edward III; *ed:* Bridgewater St Coll (BSEd) Hlth, PE 1966, (MSEd) Counseling; *cr:* Bridgewater-Raynham Regnl HS Tchr, Coach 1966-; *ai:* Field Hockey Coach; NEA, MTA, BRRTA, AAHPERD, MAHPERD 1966-; Natl Fed 1990-; MA St Field Hockey Assn 1992-; MA South Sectional Field Hockey Assn 1987-, VP; New Agenda Northeast Women's Hall of Fame; Boston Globe Division 1 Field Hockey Coach of Yr 1992; *office:* Bridgewater Raynham Reg HS 166 Mt Prospect St Bridgewater MA 02324

CASACCIO, FRANK M., Sixth Grade Teacher; *b:* Bronx, NY; *m:* Victoria Rea; *c:* Christine, Michael, Julie Ann; *ed:* St Joseph's Seminary & Coll (BA) Philosophy, Eng 1969; Herbert H. Lehman Coll (MA) Eng 1973; *cr:* Rice HS 10th Grd Eng Tchr 1969-70; St Anthony Schl 7th-8th Grd Rdng, 6th Grd Tchr 1970-; *ai:* Fed of Cath Tchrs 1970-, Union Del; Poetry Pub; *office:* St Anthony Schl 4520 Matilda Ave Bronx NY 10470

CASAGRANDE, LOUIS ANGELO,JR., History & Social Studies Tchr; *b:* Springfield, MA; *m:* Sally Ann Mastalerz; *c:* Katriona Jeanette, Joseph Luigi; *ed:* Providence Coll (BA) Amer Stud & Gen Soc Stud 1984; Cntrl CT St Univ (MS) His 1995; Univ-Coll Dublin Semester Abroad 1983; Westfield St Coll Scndry Ed & His Cert 1986; *cr:* Ludlow HS Long Term Sub Tchr 1985-86; Nonnewaug HS His & Soc Stud Tchr 1987-; *ai:* Nonnewaug HS Var Bsbl & Frosh Bsktbl Coach; NHS Class of 1999 Co-Adv; NEA & CT Ed Assoc 1987-; CT HS Coaches Assoc 1987-; *office:* Nonnewaug HS 5 Minortown Rd Woodbury CT 06798

CASALS DIAZ, ZAIDA E., ESL Teacher; *b:* Arroyo, PR; *c:* Ivan Ramos Casals; *ed:* Univ of PR (BS) Psych, Sociology 1968; Bridgeport Univ (MA)

Instrl Media 1979; Attnd Immaculata Coll, Interamerican Univ; *cr:* Dept of Educ PR His, Sociology Tchr, Audio-Visual Specialist 1968-79; W Chester Area Schl Dist Multiethnic Specialist 1979-82, ESL Tchr 1982-; *ai:* Hispanic Stu Group Adv; NEA 1968-; PABE 1979-; Immaculata Coll Acad Dev Prgm 1990-; Bd Mem; Drug & Alcohol Comm 1992-; Bd Mem; Latin Hispanic Force 1989-; YMCA 1991-, Exec Bd; Prof Bus women Assn 1974-, VP; *home:* 12 Edgewood Rd West Chester PA 19380*

CASANO, SALVATORE, High School Chemistry Teacher; *b:* Brooklyn, NY; *m:* Veronica; *c:* Vincent, Michael, Catherine, Steven; *ed:* Long Island Univ (BS) Chem 1964, (MS) Scndry Ed, Chem 1970; Adelphi Univ (MS) Natural Sci, Chem 1974; Nassau Comm Coll (AS) Nursing 1992; *cr:* A.G. Berner HS Chem Tchr 1969-88; SUNY at Farmingdale Casual Asst Chem Prof 1975-; Massapequa HS Chem Tchr 1989-; *ai:* ACS Chem Olympiad; NSTA 1966-; AFT 1967-; STANYS 1970-; Amer Chem Soc 1993-; NY St Nursing Assn 1993-; Holistic Nurses Assn; Natl Cert in Chem NSTA; Pub Lab Manuals; NSF Grant 1970-74; *office:* Massapequa HS 4925 Merrick Rd Massapequa NY 11758*

CASCIERO, THOMAS, Associate Professor; *b:* Baltimore, MD; *m:* Meliss Bunce; *c:* Larken; *ed:* Towson St Univ (BA) Psych 1977; Union Inst (MA Eq) Theatre 1993, (PHD) Theatre 1996; CMA 1988; *cr:* Towson St Univ Part-Time Instr 1986-90, Sr Instr 1990-95, Assoc Prof 1996; Webster Movement Inst Guest Artist 1994-; Casper Coll Guest Artist 1995; *ai:* Mid-Atlantic Movement Theatre Festival Liason; Movement & Voice Coach; 22 Theatre Majors Adv; AAUP 1990-; ATHE 1993-; ATME 1993-; VASTA 1994-; *office:* Towson State Univ 8000 York Rd Baltimore MD 21204

CASCIO, JUDITH A., 6th Grd Teacher & Team Leader; *b:* Port Chester, NY; *m:* 10573; *ed:* St Univ Coll at Oneonta (BS) Elem Ed, Math 1971; Coll of New Rochelle (MS) Spec Ed, Learning Disabilities 1976; *cr:* Corpus Christi Schl Grds 6-8 Tchr 1972-84; Greenwich Cath Schl Grd 8 Tchr, Math Dept Chprsn 1984-88; Port Chester MS Grd 6-7 Tchr 1988-; *ai:* Team Ldr 1993-; Scheduling Comm; *office:* Port Chester MS 113 Bowman Ave Port Chester NY 10573

CASE, DANIEL HAROLD, Health & Physical Ed Teacher; *b:* Peckville, PA; *m:* Diana Alden; *c:* Tiffany; *ed:* Temple Univ (BS) PE, Hlth 1975; 36 Credit Hrs; *cr:* Bishop OHara HS PE Tchr 1975-78, Head Ftbl Coach 1975-77; Lakeland HS PE, Hlth Tchr 1978-, Head Ftbl Coach 1985-88, 1990-91; *ai:* Asst Ftbl Coach 1978-84; Head Ftbl Coach 1975-78, 1985-88, 1990-91; PSEA, NEA 1978-; *office:* Lakeland Jr-Sr HS Rd 1 Jermyn PA 18433

CASE, JAMES H., Lead Residential Administrator; *b:* Pittsfield, MA; *m:* Robin Elaine Brantley; *c:* Tyeas, Brittany, Indira; *ed:* PA St (BS) Behavioral Sci 1994.

CASE, MOLLY ELIZABETH, Reading & Science Teacher; *b:* Lockport, NY; *ed:* St Univ Coll at Brockport (BS) Elem Ed 1974; 30 Post Grad Hrs St Univ Coll at Brockport, St Univ Coll at Buffalo; *cr:* John Bayne Elem Schl 4th Grd Tchr 1970; De Witt Clinton Elem Schl Pre 1st, 1st-2nd Grd Tchr 1970-89; North Park MS Rdng, Sci Tchr 1989-; *ai:* MS Team Ldr; Dramatics Club Adv, Dir; Lkpt Ed Assn, AFT, NEA 1970-; YWCA 1975-, Bd of Dir; Kenan Ctr 1980-, Bd of Dir; Intnl Womens Decade Honoree; Distngd Employee Recognition Lkpt Schl Dist; Kenan Ctr Outstdng Vol; *office:* North Park MS 160 Passaic Ave Lockport NY 14094

CASE, RUTH BURTON, District Librarian; *b:* Edgefield, SC; *m:* Kevin R.; *ed:* Lander Univ (BA) Eng 1973; Xavier Univ (MEd) Rdng Specialist 1981; OH Univ Lib, Media Cert 1984-86; *cr:* Aiken HS Eng Tchr 1 Yr; Abbeville HS Spec Ed Tchr 2 Yrs; Eastern HS Eng Tchr 4 Yrs; Greenfield Expt Village Eng Tchr 1 Yr; Western Schl Dist Librn, Rdng Tchr 15 Yrs; *ai:* Jr Class Adv; OEA, NEA 1981-, VP 1987; *office:* Western Local Schl Dist 8640 St Rt 124 Latham OH 45646

CASELLA, ANN JANET WARK, Kindergarten Teacher; *b:* Brooklyn, NY; *c:* Brian Michael; *ed:* SUNY at New Paltz (BA) Elem Ed 1968; Hofstra Univ (MA) Elem Ed 1972; 60 Credits Beyond MS; *cr:* Cntrl Blvd Schl 2nd-4th Grd & Kindgtn Tchr 1968-; *ai:* NYSUT 1968-; AFT; John Masino Chldrn & Yth Awd 1993; Natl PTA Honorary Life Mbrshp Awd; *office:* Central Blvd Elem Schl 60 Central Blvd Bethpage NY 11714

CASELLA, MARY JOANN, 5th Grade Teacher; *b:* Woodbury, NJ; *c:* Katherine; *ed:* Glassboro St (BA) Elem Ed 1974; *cr:* P. W. Carleton Schl Fifth Grd Tchr 1974-; *ai:* Homework Bound Stud; Discipline Comm; *office:* Paul W. Carleton Schl Penns Grove-Carney's Pt Smith & Maple Ave Penns Grove NJ 08069

CASEY, DIANE R., Guidance Counselor; *b:* Passaic, NJ; *m:* Bruce P.; *c:* Bruce Jr., Susan D.; *ed:* Salem Coll (BS) PE, Hlth 1968; Montclair St Univ (MA) PE 1985; Stu Prsnl Svcs Cert 1987; *cr:* Christopher Columbus Jr HS PE, Hlth Tchr 1968-72; Clifton HS PE, Hlth Tchr 1971-72, 1980-81; Woodrow Wilson MS PE, Hlth Tchr 1981-90; Clifton HS Guid Cnslr 1990-; *ai:* Schlsp, Awds Chprsn; Schl Stud Comm; Children of Cancer Patients Support Group Co-founder 1994-; Ath Cnslr; NEA, NJEA, PCEA, CTA 1968-; Coll Bd 1990-, Sec Schl Del Fin Aid; ACA, NJCA, PCCA 1990-; Clifton Jr Womens Club 1972-80, Pub Relations; Church Mem 1956-, Sunday Schl Bd 1972-80; Curr Dev in Comprehensive Cnslng; Cnslr Recognition of Yr 1994; *office:* Clifton HS 333 Colfax Ave Clifton NJ 07013

CASEY, DOROTHY FLOYD, Computer & Secretarial Teacher; *b:* Mullins, SC; *c:* Darrell; *ed:* Barber-Scotia Coll (BS) Bus Ed 1966; Montclair St Coll 18 Grad Credits; Cmptr Cert Newark Bd of Ed In-Svc Trng3 Grad Credits; *cr:* Newark Pub Schls Tchr 1970-; Amer Bus Inst Part-time Tchr 1984-89; Seton-Hall Upward Bound Tchr Summers 1985-86; *ai:* Jr Class; Black His Comm; NBEA 1985-; Outstdng Commitment, Svc Cert of Appreciation; *home:* 1442 Compton Ter Hillside NJ 07205

CASEY, KATHLEEN LOUISE, Fr Tchr & Frgn Lang Dpt Chrpsn; *b:* Baltimore, MD; *m:* Paul K.; *c:* Meghan K. Evan J.; *ed:* Coll of Notre Dame (BA) Fr 1970; Univ of VI (MA) Fr Lit 1973; Attnd Institut De Touraine, Loyola Coll, Johns Hopkins Univ; *cr:* Lycee De Grandmont Tchng Asst 1970-71; Univ of VI Tchng Asst 1971-72; Arch Keough HS Fr Tchr 1972-74; Mt St Joseph HS Fr Tchr 1984-88; IND Fr Tchr, For Lang Chair 1988-; *ai:* Acad, Fr, Fac Comm Natl Honor Soc, Stu Govt; ACTFL, AATF 1984-; MFLA 1984-, 1st VP; Res St Paul Schl Bd 1992-; Howard Co Advy co For Langs 1993-; Balt Co Intnl Vistors 1979-; Fulbright Tchng Assistantship France; Kappa Gamma Pi; Pi Delta Phi; *office:* Inst Of Notre Dame 901 Alsquith St Baltimore MD 21202

CASEY, RICHARD MICHAEL, Sixth Grade Teacher; *b:* Luzerne, PA; *m:* Marjorie Kaszubski; *c:* Richard Jr.; *ed:* Wilkes Coll (BA) Elem Ed 1971; Masters Equivalency Plus 30 Addl Credits; *cr:* Pine Run Elem 4th Grd Tchr 1971-73, 3rd Grd Tchr 1973-75, 5th Grd Tchr 1975-81, 4th Grd Tchr 1981-85, 6th Grd Tchr 1985-; *ai:* Math Chprsn; PTO Rep; Schl Store Adv; Frin Advy; Chapter I Math Coord; Cntrl Bucks Ed Assn 1971-, Bldg Rep; PSEA & NEA 1971-; BSA 1989-, Pub Relations; Jaycees 1975-77; Pine Run Comm Tchr of the Yr Awd 1985; *office:* Pine Run Elem Schl 383 W Butler Ave New Britain PA 18901*

CASEY, ROBERT A., English Teacher; *b:* Danville, PA; *m:* Michele Baker; *c:* James, Kathlene; *ed:* Bloomsburg Univ (BS) Ed 1972; 30 Grad Hrs; *cr:* Cumberland Vly Schl Dist Eng Tchr 1972-78; West Shore Schl Dist Eng Tchr 1978-80; Brookside Enterprises Actor & Dir 1980-84; Diocese of Harrisburg Eng Tchr 1984-; *ai:* Drama & Forensics Dir; Stage Mgr; PA HS Speech League 1978-, Dist Chair; Natl Cath Forensics League 1986-; PA Speech & Debate Assn 1989-; Kiwanis Intnl 1992-, VP.

CASEY, RUTH STETLER, Home Economics Teacher; *b:* Washington, DC; *m:* George Walter; *c:* Elizabeth, Denise; *ed:* Albright Coll (BS) Ed, Home Ec 1970; St Mary's Coll of MD Home Ec Ed; 35 Hrs; *cr:* Francis Scott Key Jr HS Home Ec Tchr 1970-76; Samuel Ogle Jr HS Home Ec Tchr 1976-81; Walker Mill MS Home Ec Tchr 1981-88; Prince Georges Cty Bd of Ed Part-time Consultant for Home Ec Supvr 1988-93; Oxon-Hill HS Home Ec Tchr 1993-95; Bowie Sr HS Home Ec Tchr 1995-; *ai:* MS Sts Evaluation Hospitality Comm; Prince Georges Cty Tchrs Assn 1970-; Dev Home Ec Enrichment Act for Greenbelt Ctr After Schl Care Prgm; Wrote Gender Harassment Curr, Dev Learning Styles Inventory for MS Home Ec; *office:* Bowie HS 15200 Annapolis Rd Bowie MD 20715

CASEY, TIMOTHY FRANK, Librarian; *b:* Beaver Falls, PA; *ed:* Clarion Univ of PA (BSED) Lib Sci, His 1969, (MA) Lib Sci 1972; *cr:* Northampton HS Librn 1969-70; Beaver Falls Area HS Librn 1970-83; Kane Area HS Librn 1983-; *ai:* Flwshp of Chrstn Aths; *office:* Kane Area HS 300 Hemlock Ave Kane PA 16735*

CASEY, WALTER J., English Instructor; *b:* Glenolden, PA; *ed:* Widener Univ (BA) Eng 1964; Villanova Univ Post Grad 30 Hrs Eng; *cr:* Widener Univ Instr 1968-69, 1977-79; CEI Instr 1969-79; Berean Inst Instr 1979-; *ai:* Drama; Newspaper; Oratorical; AFT 1977-, Pres Local; *office:* Berean Inst 1901 W Girard Ave Philadelphia PA 19130

CASHIER, BARBARA R., Resource Room Teacher; *b:* Syracuse, NY; *c:* Nora L. Mc Cabe; *ed:* LeMoyne Coll (BS) Sociology 1959; Syracuse Univ (MS) Ed, Speech, Lang Pathology 1962; Tchr of Deaf, Instrl Media, 7-12 Soc Stud Certs; *cr:* St Joseph's Schl for Deaf Prgm Dev, Tchr 1963-72; Horace Mann Schl for Deaf Educl Programmer, Lang, Speech Evaluator 1972-73; Pelham Schl Dist Resource, Tchr of Deaf 1977-88; West Genesee HS Resource Tchr 1988-; *ai:* Hospice; A. G. Bell 1970-; NY St A. G. Bell 1995-; Mu Phi Epsilon 1957-; Pub: NY St Bureau of Physically Handicapped Children Spec Stud Inst; Tchr of Yr, Personalities of Amer, Who's Who in the East, Citizen Ambassador Prgm Awds.

CASHMAN, DAVID H., English Teacher; *b:* Morgantown, WV; *c:* Eleanor; *ed:* Brown Univ (BA) Eng 1970; *cr:* Grand River Acad Eng Tchr 1970-72; St Michaels Schl Eng Tchr 1976-78; Providence Cntry Day Schl Eng Tchr 1978-; *ai:* Cycling Coach; Dept Chair; Cultural Awareness Club Adv; Haiku Soc of Amer; Sierra Club; Short Stories Pub; *office:* Providence Country Day Schl 2117 Pawtucket Ave East Providence RI 02914

CASHWELL, JEANNE WILLERT, Eighth Grade Teacher; *b:* Chester, PA; *ed:* Delaware Cty Comm (AAS) Criminal Justice 1982; West Chester Univ (BS) Criminal Justice 1984; Post Grad Stud at Neumann Coll; *cr:* Del Cty Juvenile Court Juvenile Probation Officer 1984-87; Tri-St Abstract Settlement Agent 1987-89; Saint Cyril of Alexandria Schl Tchr 1989-; *ai:* Yrbk Adv; Safety Moderator; Stu Cncl Adv; Christmas Show & Spring Musical Dir; Sci Coord; Mathlete Moderator; NCTA 1990-; NCTM 1994-; Ridley Twp Swim Club 1990-, Corresponding Sec; *office:* Saint Cyrils Of Alexndria Schl 716 Emerson Ave East Lansdowne PA 19050*

CASLIN, EUGENE H., 8th Grade US History Teacher; *b:* Columbus, OH; *m:* Teri D.; *c:* Patrick, Angela; *ed:* OH St Univ (MA) Ed Admin 1993; Capital Univ (BA) His 1975; Fnd of Banking Diploma Columbus St Univ 1986; Working on (PHD) in Ed & Hum Fnd OH St Univ; *cr:* Cambridge HS His Tchr 1975-78; Eastmoor HS His Tchr 1978-82; Whetstone HS OWE Tchr 1990; Westmoor MS His Tchr 1990-; *ai:* NEA 1975-; OEA 1975-; CEA 1978-; Eastmoore HS 1971-, Hall of Fame; Capital Univ Alumni Assn 1975-; NAACP 1988-; Columbus Urban League 1988-; Grand Marshall Eastmoor HS 25th Anniversary 1980; *office:* Westmoor MS 3001 Valleyview Dr Columbus OH 43204*

CASNER, BRIAN LANCE, Earth Science Teacher; *b:* Tachikawa AFB, Japan; *m:* Marla Jo; *c:* Brandy, Christa; *ed:* OH St Univ (BS) Earth Sci 1985; *cr:* US Navy Submarine Sonar Tech 1973-81; Columbus Metro Parks Park Ranger 1983-85; COSI Planetarian Supvr 1983-85; Fairfield Union Jr HS Earth Sci Tchr 1985-; *ai:* Stu Cncl, Sci Olympiad Adv; OH Earth Sci Tchrs Assn Newsletter Ed; Adult Sunday Schl Tchr At Grace Bible Church; OESTA 1988-, Ed 4 Yrs; *office:* Fairfield Union Jr H S 6401 Cincinnati-Zanesville Rd Lancaster OH 43130*

CASS, SARAH MUMFORD, 8th Grd Amer His Teacher; *b:* Vienna, MD; *m:* William F.; *c:* Holly E., William B. P.; *ed:* Washington Coll (BA) His 1964; Univ of MD (MA) Diplomat His 1967; 15 Credit Hrs West Chester Univ, Univ of DE, Wilkes Coll; *cr:* Federalsburg Jr HS Tchr 1964-65; Avon-Grove HS Tchr 1966-67; Fayetteville-Manlius HS Tchr 1967-70; Eagle Hill Jr HS Tchr 1970-71; Peirce MS Tchr 1986-; *ai:* Curr Comm; Site-Based Mngmt Team; Musical Pgrms Assistance; West Chester ATA, PA St Assn, NEA 1986-; Chester Cty Hist Soc 1994-; United Meth Church 1972-, Chprsn; Greenleigh Music Comm, Choir Mem, Sunday Schl Tchr; Diamond Jubilee Prize Best Undergraduate Paper; Phi Alpha Theta His Honorary; DAR Outstdng Amer His Tchr Chester Cty 1995-; PA St DAR Outstdng Am His Tchr 1996; *office:* Peirce MS 1314 Burke Rd West Chester PA 19380

CASSADY, LINDA E., 10th-12th Grades Soc Stud Tchr; *b:* Philadelphia, PA; *m:* Charles D.; *ed:* East Stroudsburg Univ (BS) His, Govt 1970; Beaver Coll (MAEd) His 1980; 45 Addl Hrs; 24 Credit Hrs Penn St Univ Ed; Bloomsburg Univ Supervisory Cert Soc Stud; *ai:* NEA 1970-; NCSS, Supvrs, Curr 1982-; Upper Moreland Ed Assn 1970-, Sec; *office:* Upper Moreland HS 3000 Terwood Rd Willow Grove PA 19090

CASSANDRO, JAMES ANTHONY, Drafting Teacher; *b:* Pittsburgh, PA; *m:* Beth George-Cassandro; *c:* Cara Patricia; *ed:* California Univ of PA (BS) Indstrl Tech 1988; *cr:* Greenville Schl Dist Indstrl Tech Tchr 1988-92; North Hills Schl Dist Architecture, Autocad, Tech Drawing Drafting Tchr 1992-; *ai:* Ftbl Coach; TEAP 1986-; *office:* North Hills Sr HS 53 Rochester Rd Pittsburgh PA 15229

CASSELLA, BARBARA A. (HEERAN), Social Studies Teacher; *b:* Troy, NY; *m:* Joseph L.; *c:* Michael, Dominic; *ed:* Russell Sage Coll (BA) His, Govt, Dr Ed 1963; SUNY (MA) Soc Stud 1969, (MS) Cnslng, Guid 1972; 24 Addl Hrs; *cr:* Avenell Park Schl Dist Tchr 14 Yrs; St Augustine Schl 6-8 Grd Soc Stud Tchr 7 Yrs; Cath cntrl HS Jr HS Dean, 8, 11 Grd Soc Stud Tchr 8 Yrs; *ai:* Stu Cncl; Curr, Litergy Comms; NYS Soc Stud 1963-, Sec; AAUP 1987-; Jr Achvmt 15 Yrs, 10 Yr Svc Awd; St Augustine's Church Parish Cncl Pres 1996-, Chair 1995-; DAR 1959-; Elks Women's Aux 1978-, Sec; NY St Grant 1976-77; NY St Historical Soc Grant 1967-68; Boston Coll Fellowship Grant 1969-70; *home:* 28 Mockingbird Ct Waterford NY 12188*

CASSELLA, JOSEPH L., Business Education Teacher; *b:* Troy, NY; *m:* Barbara Ann Heeran; *c:* A. Michael, Dominic J.; *ed:* SUNY at Albany (BS) Bus Ed 1963, (MS) Bus Ed 1968; *cr:* Averill PK HS Tchr 1963-, Dept Chm Bus Ed 1983-89; *ai:* Club Adv FBLA; Averill Pk Tchrs 1963-, Treas; NYS United Tchrs, AFT 1963-; *home:* 28 Mockingbird Ct Waterford NY 12188

CASSIDY, ANNE V., General Music Teacher & Dir; *b:* Utica, NY; *c:* Ian Michael Baxter; *ed:* Coll of St Rose (BS) Studio Music, Music Ed 1984, (MS) Music Ed 1990; *cr:* Fonda-Fultonville Cntrl Schl 6-12 Grd Gen Music Tchr, Choral Dir 1985-; *ai:* Boys Ensemble, All Cty Chorus, Girls Ensemble, Grad Ceremony Choral, Combined Ensembles Dirs; Sr Class Adv; AFT, MENC 1985-; Montgomery Cty Music Tchrs Assn 1985-, Sec; *office:* Fonda-Fultonville Cntrl Schl 112 Old Johnstown Rd F
12068

CASSIDY, CATHERINE, History Teacher; *b:* Hackensack, NJ; *e*
City St Coll (BA) His, Ed 1993; Post Grad Stud St Peter's Co
Mary's HS His Tchr 1993-; *ai:* Var Vlybl, JV Sftbl Coach; Mock T
Adv; Curr Advy Comm; BCWCA, NCEA, NCSS 1993-; ASC
NFICA, NJSCA 1995-; Wood Ridge Democratic Org 1990-, Sec

CASSIDY, DEBORAH K., Social Studies Teacher; *b:* Cleveland
IN Univ (BS) Soc Stud, Eng & Scndry Ed 1983; John Carroll Uni
1991; Numerous Courses Taken; 45 Addl Hrs, John Carroll Wrkr
(MA) Hum; *cr:* Charles F Brush HS Soc Stud & Eng Tchr 1988-;
Dept Chprsn 1993-; *ai:* Girls Bsktbl Asst Coach 1989-90; Yrbk
1990-92; Conflict Mediation 1990-; Sr Project 1988-; Malcolr
Schlsp Comm Mem 1993; Schl & Dist Problem Solving Com
Advncd Plcmnt Conferences; NCSS & OCSS 1989-; NEA & C
ASCD 1990-; Mid East 2 Hrs & Issues 90s 1 Hr Seminars; Free
Summer Seminar Schlsp 1990; Jennings Scholar 1993-94; Ge
(OH Dept of Educ & BGSU) 1993; Monticello- Straford hall Sm
for Tchrs 1994; *office:* Charles F Brush H S 4875 Glenlyn Rd
OH 44124

CASSIDY, MICHAEL OWEN, History Teacher; *b:* Kearney
Marilyn; *c:* Marissa; *ed:* William Paterson Coll (BA) Soc Sci 19
Ed, Admin 1987; Rutgers Univ Working Toward MA Matriculate
cr: Rutherford Schl Dist Soc Stud Tchr 1977-; *ai:* Ftbl, Bsbl, Trac
Stu Cncl Adv; NEA, NJEA, REA 1977-; Governors Tchr Recogn
1995; Bd of Ed Employee Recognition Awd 1995; *office:* Ruthe
56 Elliott Pl Rutherford NJ 07070

CASSIDY, ROBERTA KELLY, Principal; *b:* Holyoke, MA; *m:*
J.; *c:* E. J., Robert; *ed:* Our Lady of Elms Coll (BA) Soc Work,
Working on Masters; *cr:* Joseph Metcalf Schl 3 Grd Tchr 1972-7
Sacrament Schl 2 Grd Lang Arts Tchr 1981-92, Prin 1992-; *a*
1981-; ESPA 1992-; Cath Women's Club 1980-, Treas, Sec, VP; W
Young Amer Execs; *office:* Blessed Sacrament Schl 21 Wes
Holyoke MA 01040

CASSIDY, SUZANNE RUTH, Biology Teacher; *b:* Alfred
William L.; *c:* Erin Johnson, Shannon; *cr:* Cntrl Sq HS Eng T
Malcolm MS Eng Tchr 1 Yr; St Peters Schl Sci & His Tchr 13 Y
McNamara HS Bio Tchr 3 Yrs; *ai:* Sci Fair Coord; Womens V
Coach; MAST 1989-; MABT 1992-; MAOE 1994-; NSTA 1
Governors Acad for Sci & Math 1989; Martin Marietta Gra
1993-95; Operation Pathfinder Participant 1995; *office:* Bi
Namara HS 6800 Marlboro Pike Forestville MD 20747

CASSIDY, TERRY LAWRENCE, High School Math Teacher; *b.*
NJ; *m:* Crystal J.; *c:* Liza Jo, Blaine, Mackenzie; *ed:* Glassbor
(BA) Math Ed 1975; Jersey City St Coll (MA) Ubran Ed Supervis
cr: Halstead MS Math Tchr 1975-76; Camden Jr HS Math Tchr
High Point Reg HS Math Tchr 1977-79; Vernon Twp HS Math T
ai: PAL Ski Club, Jr & Sr Asst Class Adv; Faculty Senate 19
VTEA; NCTM; Branchville Presbyn Church 1978-, Elder.

CASSUTTO, GEORGE HENRICUS, Secondary Soc Studies T
Passaic, NJ; *m:* Teresa Deavours; *c:* Grace, Gabriel; *ed:* Hoo
Frederick (MA) Contemporary Govt 1991; Maryville Coll (BA)
cr: Frederick HS Soc Stud Tchr 1983-86; Oak Hill House Ed Dir
North Hagerstown HS Soc Stud Tchr 1992-; *ai:* Cmptr Club; S
Club; Schl Improvement Team; Neighborhood Inclusion
Interdisciplinary Team Org; Frederick Presbyn Church 198
Deacon; Nominated for Christa Mc Auliffe Flwshp; Holocaust E
1994; Presented Seminar at Connected Classroom Conf 1996;
Hagerstown Jr Coll; *office:* North Hagerstown HS 1200 Pennsyl
Hagerstown MD 21742*

CASTAGNA, ROBERT CHARLES, Math Tchr & Athleti
Clairton, PA; *m:* Dana Casoli; *c:* Daniel, Kristen; *ed:* Clarion
Scndry Math 1967; Slippery Rock Univ (MEQ) Scndry Math 1
St Univ 24 Credit Hrs; Masters in Scndry Ed Admin Youngstow
Scndry Prin Cert YSU; *cr:* West Mifflin Jr HS Math Tchr 196
Army Specialist 4 1970-72; Aliquippa HS Math Tchr & Ath Dir
NCTM 1976-; NEA & PSEA 1967-; Aliquippa Alumni As
Aliquippa Recreation Bd 1988-; *office:* Aliquppa HS Har
Aliquippa PA 15001

CASTALDI, JEFFREY M., 10th Grade Biology Teacher; *b:* V
CT; *m:* Beth Lassen; *c:* Jason, Lauren; *ed:* Western CT St Univ
1986; *cr:* Hillhouse HS Phys Sci Tchr 1976-83; New Fairfield HS
1983-; *ai:* Head Bsbl, Asst Ftbl, Frosh Bsktbl Coach; CEA 197
1983-; CIAC Coaches Assn 1990-; *office:* New Fairfield MS 54 C
New Fairfield CT 06812

CASTANZO, BARBARA THERESE, Fifth Grade Teacher; *b:*
NY; *ed:* Fordham (BS) Elem Ed 1970; SUNYA (MS) Dev Rdng
Albany Schls 5th Grd Tchr 1970-72; Schalmont Schls 5th Grd T
ai: NSVT; NEA; STA Exec Bd; Sci Mentor 1986-91; Arts in
1993-94; Tech Pilot Classroom 1995.

CASTEEL, BRENDA SUE, English & Reading Tchr; *b:* Parm
Michael Aaron; *c:* Corryn Marie, Carrah Michelle; *ed:* Slippery
(BA) Ed 1985; Attnd Cleveland St Univ, Ashland Coll; *cr:* North
City Schls Tchr 1985-; *ai:* Sftbl Coach; OEA, NEA, NREA 198
1993-, Chprsn; Educl Fnd Grant; *office:* North Royalton MS 14
Rd North Royalton OH 44133

CASTELINO, AMY D'SOUZA, Sixth Grade Teacher; *b:* M
SIndia; *m:* Frederick Vincent; *c:* Ruben, Rennie; *ed:* St Agnes
Botany, Zoology 1962; St Anns Tchr Coll (BED) Ed 19
Enrichment Courses at Xavier, Cincinnati & Miami Univs in Ma
Sci 1969-; *cr:* St Peter & Paul Schl Jr HS Sci Tchr 1970-81; St
Sales Schl 4th & 6th Grd Tchr 1981-89; Hays Elem Schl 6th Gr
Sci Tchr 1989-; *ai:* Rep on Sci Curr Cncl; Mem of SC Steeri
Intermediate Promotional Standards Team; Team Mem of M
1990-; Learning Links Grants, Awded by Greater Cincinnati Fn
& 1996; *office:* Hays Elem Schl 1035 Mound St Cincinnati OH

CASTELLANA, DOUGLAS FRANK, Indstrl Ed, Tech Tchr &
Englewood, NJ; *m:* Deanna L. Haggerty; *c:* Christin, Cath
Glassboro St Coll (BA) Indstrl Arts 1972; Montclair St U
Environmental Stud 1979; Supvr Cert Jersey City St Coll
Blackwood Schl Tchr; Chas W. Lewis MS Indstrl Arts Tchr
Franklin Ave MS Indstrl Arts Tchr 1973-78; Vernon Twp HS
Arch, Cmptr Aided Drafting Tchr 1978-; *ai:* Asst Boys Tennis C
Tying Club; Hnr Roll, Schl Expansion Comms; Vernon Twp Ed A
Sec, Chm Negotiations; Sussex Cty Ed Assn 1978-, NEA 1972
Twp Zoning Bd 1991-, Vice-Chm; Vernon Meth Church 1978
1980-82; NJ Governor's Tchr Awd 1987-88; Citizen of Yr 1989;
Yr 1980-81, 1986, 1988; *office:* Vernon Township HS PO Box 8
NJ 07462

CASTELLANO, JOHN J., Physical Education Teacher; *b:* P
NY; *m:* Donna Maloney; *c:* Nicholas, Erica, Kristin, Mark; *ed:*
Univ (BS) PE 1976, (MS) PE 1979; *cr:* Mamaroneck HS PE
Gorton HS Hlth Ed 1983-86; Roosevelt HS Hlth Ed 1986-88; Nya
1988-; *ai:* Head Ftbl, Asst Track Coach; Strength Club Adv; AF
1983-; Section I Ftbl Coach of Yr 1989; Rockland Cty Coach of

eague II C Coach of Yr 1988-91, 1994-95; *office:* Nyack HS 360 ı Herald Rd Nyack NY 10960

LLANO, MARIE CATHERINE, 2nd Grade Teacher; *b:* an, NY; *m:* Angelo; *c:* Philip, Julie; *ed:* Mount St Vincent Coll at (BA) Eng 1962; SUNY at New Paltz (MS) Ed 1964; 30 Credit Hrs Supervision; *cr:* Honey Hollow Schl Kndgtn Tchr 1962-65; Pines l Grd Tchr 1966-; *ai:* Hauppauge Tchrs Assn, NY St United Tchrs ımer Assn of Women in Arts 1990-; *office:* Pines School Holly Dr wn NY 11787*

LOT, WILLIAM LAWRENCE, HS & Coll Mathematics Tchr; *b:* ort, CT; *m:* Annette Mary Carreau; *c:* Lynn Marie, Nicole, Alicia; of New Haven (AS) Math 1967, (BA) Math 1968; Attnd Univ of ort with 30 Grad Credits in Math, Univ of Fairfield with 12 Grad in Math; SCSU St Tchng Cert & Cmptr Courses; *cr:* Notre Dame ı Tchr 1969-; Univ of New Haven Adjunct Math Tchr 1969-; SCSU Math Tchr 1985-; Univ of New Haven Math Ctr Tutor 1989-; *ai:* 990-; NSF Grant 1973-74; Nom Tchr of Yr Cunn HS 1985.

RLINE, JEAN M., English Teacher; *b:* Wilkes Barre, PA; *m:* F.; *c:* Amie Beth, Brittany Blair; *ed:* Cedarville Coll (BA) Soc Stud 'oll Misericordia Eng Cert 1981; 36 Hrs of Addl Credits; *cr:* nnock Area Soc Stud, Eng Tchr 1977-; *ai:* Class, NHS Adv; Grad ment Comm; NEA, PSEA 1977-; Friends of Lib 1992-; Tyler Show & Auxiliary 1982-, Chm; *office:* Tunkhannock Area Schl W Tioga St Tunkhannock PA 18657

ELLO, FRANCES DOBEK, Fifth Grade Teacher; *b:* Derby, CT; ıas; *c:* Thomas, Michael; *ed:* Southern CT St Univ (BA) Eng 1972, lng 1979; 6th Yr Fairfield Univ 1989; *cr:* Irving, Bradley, Lincoln ı-6th Grd Tchr 22 Yrs; *ai:* Co-Chair Tech Comm; NEA, CEA, DEA /P; Phi Delta Kappa 1989-, Ed Assn 1994-95; Hartford Critical, Thinking Ctr 1993-, Bldg Rep 1990-; Cub Scouts 1988-94, Treas; chr of Yr 1989; *office:* Irving Schl 9 Garden Pl Derby CT 06418*

GLIE, JOSEPH PAUL, Chemistry Instructor; *b:* Brooklyn, NY; *m:* ; *c:* Joseph III, Alison, Michael; *ed:* Univ at Stony Brook (BA) Space Sci 1979, (MA) Librl Stud 1987; Hofstra Univ (MS) PE : St Anthonys HS Chem Instr 1980-81; Univ at Stony Brook Head Coach 1984-91; Miller Place HS Chem Instr 1982-; *office:* Miller S 15 Memorial Dr Miller Place NY 11764*

GLIE, MARY THERESE (BUCKLEY), Mathematics Educator; ose, NY; *m:* Joseph D. Jr.; *c:* Joseph Paul, Alison Mary, Michael *ed:* St Johns Univ (BS) Ed & Math 1981; SUNY at Stonebrook brl stud & Math 1989; *cr:* Sacred Heart Acad Scndry Math Tchr ; Miller Place HS Scndry Math Tchr 1984-; *ai:* Future Tchrs of *ffice:* Miller Place HS 15 Memorial Dr Miller Place NY 11764

LLO, CONSTANTINO ALEXANDER, Auto Body Repair ; *b:* New York, NY; *m:* Flor; *ed:* Sub Voc Asst Prgm Ed City Coll Assocs in Ed, Occupational Ed; *cr:* Alfred E. Smith HS Sub Tchr , Tenured Tchr 1991; Alfred E. Smith HS Safety Coord 1992-93, Stdnts 1992-; *ai:* VP Ju-Jutsu Martial Arts Prgm; *office:* Alfred E S 333 E 151st St Bronx NY 10451*

LLO, IBIS NADAL, Business Education Teacher; *b:* New York, ose V. III; *c:* Jose IV, Ricardo; *ed:* Pace Univ (BBA) Bus Ed 1973; v (MA) Bus Ed 1975; *cr:* The Irving Trust Co Trng Specialist & ınt 1974-80; The Kelly Org Inc Coord of Trng & Dev 1981-82; ecretarial Schl Bus Ed Tchr 1982-83; Roosevelt Jr-Sr HS Bus Ed 83-87; Elmont Memrl HS Bus Ed Tchr 1987-; *ai:* Key Club Adv 3TA 1973-; NEA 1983-; NCBEA 1983-; *office:* Elmont Meml HS ge Rd Elmont NY 11003

NE, PATRICIA DOOLEY, Third Grade Teacher; *b:* Brooklyn, NY; ald M.; *ed:* St Univ of NY at Cortland (BS) Ed & N-9 Conc Sci owling Coll (MS) K-12 Rdng Ed 1992; *cr:* Brentwood East Jr HS h Grd Industrial Arts Tchr 1987-88; Parliament Place Elem 3rd Grd 88-; *ai:* Bldg Sci Contact Person; IRA 1995-; AFT, NYSUT 1987-; abylon Tchrs Org 1988-; *office:* Parliament Place Elem Schl 80 ent Pl Babylon NY 11703

E, SONDRA SULLIVAN, Kindergarten Teacher; *b:* Potsdam, NY; H.; *c:* John M., Christopher M.; *ed:* SUNY at Potsdam (BS) Elem s 1960; 18 Credit Hrs; *cr:* Onondaga Cntrl Schl K-3rd Grd Tchr , 1961-62; Norwood Norfolk Elem 3rd Grd Tchr 1962-63; Brasher ntrl Kndgtn Tchr 1964-; *ai:* NYSTA 1960-; *home:* 8715 US 11 Potsdam NY 13676

ER, DEBORAH O'MALLEY, Sixth Grade Teacher; *b:* Kingston, ennifer S., Kyle D.; *ed:* Coll Misericordia (BS) Elem Ed 1978; REI 1995; 4 Grad Credits in Cooperative Learning Marywood Coll; 19 Luzerne Intermediate Unit; *cr:* Wyoming Vly West Schl Sub Tchr; ild Schl 6th Grd, 7th-8th Grd Soc Stud, 5th Grd Eng Tchr 1988-; W Aquatics Club 1994-; *home:* 13 Willow St Plymouth PA 18651

ER, PRISCILLA COOPER, English Department Chairperson; *b:* stle, PA; *m:* James A.; *c:* Melissa, Kathryn; *ed:* Allegheny Coll g 1972; Post Grad Work; *cr:* Cleveland Pub Schls Tchr 1972-73; Cty Voc Tech Adult Ed 1974-75; Wilmington Area Tchr 1985-; *ai:* Adv; WAEA, PSEA, NEA 1985-; *office:* Wilmington Area Sr HS ıd St New Wilmington PA 16142

, STEVEN EUGENE, Social Studies Teacher; *b:* Marietta, OH; *m:* rrick; *c:* Elizabeth; *ed:* Marietta Coll (BA) Interdisciplinary, Soc 30, (MA) Ed 1993; *cr:* Washington Co Joint Voc Schl Soc Stud, Eng 80; Swiss Hills Voc Schl Soc Stud Tchr 1981-; *ai:* NEA 1980-; 75 Lewisville Rd Woodsfield OH 43793

R, KARL FREDRICK, Track & Conditioning Coach; *b:* n, PA; *m:* Margaret Anne Bevard; *c:* Michelle L., Douglas F.; *ed:* Rock St Univ (BS) Hlth & PE 1973; *cr:* Hatboro-Horsham HS Boys Track Coaching Asst & Conditioning Instr 1988-; *ai:* phia Masters Track Assn 1988-, Exec VP 1992-, Person of Yr 1994; ays 1992-, Masters Coord; *office:* Hatboro Horsham Sr HS 899 ı Rd Horsham PA 19044

RO, NORAH SCHWARTZ, Mathematics Teacher; *b:* Amityville, Daniel J.; *c:* Daniel Jr., William; *ed:* Queens Coll (BA) Elem Ed MS) Scndry Ed, Math 1986; *cr:* St Johns Prep Math Tchr 1985-87; k North Jr HS Math Tchr 1987-88; Woodland Jr HS Math Tchr eansburg HS Math Tchr 1989-90; W. Tresper Clarke HS Math Tchr *i:* 1994 Class Adv; NCTM 1987-; NCMTA 1995-; EM Tchrs Assn *ffice:* W Tresper Clarke HS 740 Edgewood Dr Westbury NY 11590

ONOVO, BERNADINE MARRO, Music Teacher; *b:* Peekskill, Charles; *ed:* Western CT St Univ (BS) Music Ed 1971, (MS) Music ; *cr:* Austin Rd Elem Schl Music Tchr, Chorus Dir 1971-75; e HS, Music Tchr, Chorus Dir 1975-86; Mahopac Falls ELem Schl chr, Chorus Dir 1975-77; Lakeview Elem Schl Music Tchr, Chorus 7-80; Mahapoc Jr HS Music Tchr, Chorus Dir 1980-86; Mahapac sic Tchr, Chorus Dir 1986-92; Lakeview Elem Schl Music Tchr, Dir 1992-; *ai:* Music Edctrs Natl Conf, Music Tchrs Assn, NYSUT, O 1971-; Western Conn St Univ 1975-, Alumi Assn; Ruth DeVilla Music Awd 1971; Mahopac HS Chorus Performs Carnegie Hall *ffice:* Lakeview Elem Schl 112 Lakeview Dr Mahopac NY 10541

ONOVO, JACQUELINE ANN, Special Education Teacher; *b:* n, NY; *m:* Santo; *c:* Dorotea, Francesco; *ed:* Trenton St Coll (BS) Ed, Spec Ed 1985; *cr:* Home Away from Home Child Care Ctr Owner 1991-95; Sayreville War Meml HS Tchr 1992-; *ai:* Var Chrldng Coach; MCEA, NJEA, NEA 1992-; PTA 1993-; *office:* Sayreville War Memorial HS 820 Washington Rd Parlin NJ 08859

CASWELL, CAROLINE JOHNSON, Mathematics Teacher; *b:* Newport, RI; *m:* James William; *ed:* Grove City Coll (BS) Engrng & Math 1988, (MS) Math 1994; *cr:* Rogers HS Tchr 1990-; *ai:* Jr Class Adv; 1st Presbn Church, Praise Team, Pastoral Comm; Drama Adv; Communion Steward; Travel with Stu; PRR-TAN Union 1991-, HS Rep; Industrial Fellowship Raytheon SSD; Math Watch; *office:* Rogers HS 15 Wickham Rd Newport RI 02840*

CASWELL, RICHARD H.,II, History Tchr & Faculty Advsr; *b:* Bennington, VT; *m:* Maria Napolitano; *c:* Ricky, Mark, John, James; *ed:* Middlebury Coll (BA) His 1977; North Adams St Coll (MA) Ed 1989; Grad Credit in Eng & His from Univ of VT; Comp Stud Univ of VT; *cr:* Rice Mem HS His Tchr, Coach 1977-83; Mt Anthony Union HS His Tchr, Coach, Adv 1983-; *ai:* Fac Adv NHS, Model United Nations Debate Club; Natl Cncl of Soc Stud 1983-; Peace Resource Ctr of Bennington 1987-95, Bd of Trustee; Adv to St Acad Model United Nations Comm 1989-; *office:* Mount Anthony Union HS Park St Bennington VT 05201

CATALANO, CONCETTA BARBAGALLO, 4th Grade Teacher; *b:* Syracuse, NY; *m:* George; *c:* George III, Peter, Paul Joseph; *ed:* LeMoyne Coll (BBA) General Bus 1961; OSWEGO Permanent Tchng Rdng Cert 1970; Binghampton 4 Hrs Physics 1992; *cr:* Holy Trinity Schl Elem Tchr 1 Yr; St Margaret's Schl Elem Tchr 4 Yrs; N Syr Schl Dist Elem Tchr 20 Yrs; *ai:* Bldg Planning, Bldg Based Budget, Acad Teams; Sci Rep; Sci Exhibit Chprsn; Twn of Sabra Civic Cntr Advsy Comm; NSEA, NYSUT 1976-; STANYS 1984-; CNY Rdng Cncl, CNY Soc Stud Cncl 1989-; St Margaret's Altar & Rosary 1964-, Corresponding Sec; Pub Booklet on Mattydole; N Fyr Schl Dist Winner 4 Grants Through Tchng Ctr; *office:* Roxboro Elem Schl 200 Bernard St Syracuse NY 13211

CATALANO, RICHARD L., Guidance Director; *b:* Greenville, PA; *m:* Kathy Wasser; *c:* Michael, Amy Altemose, Marci; *ed:* Youngstown St Univ (BA) Math Ed 1968; Kent St Univ (MED) Counseling 1971; Univ of Scranton Supvrs Cert 30 S H; *cr:* Sandy Valley HS Math Tchr 1968-71; Meadville HS Math Tchr 1971-74; Pocono Mountain HS Scndry Cnslr 1974-93, Dir Guidance 1994-; *ai:* Asst Ftbl Coach; PSEA, NEA, & PMEA 1971-; *office:* Pocono Mtn Intermediate School PO Box 200 Swiftwater PA 18370

CATALANO, ROSELEEN WARD, 2nd Grade Teacher; *b:* Boston, MA; *m:* Harold; *c:* Kimberly, Matthew, Janine; *ed:* Boston St Coll (BA) Ed 1961; 9 Credit Hrs Fitchburg St; 6 Credit Hrs Bridgewater St; *cr:* City of Boston Grd 1 Tchr 1961-66, Town of Stoughton Grd 2 Tchr 1975-; *ai:* STA 1975-, Bldg Rep; MTA, NEA 1975-; *office:* North Elem Schl 131 Pine St Stoughton MA 02072

CATALANO, THEA, Social Studies Teacher; *b:* Smithtown, NY; *m:* Ralph A.; *c:* Ralph C.; *ed:* SUNY at Stony Brook (BA) Soc Sci 1987; Hofstra U (MS) Sec Ed 1989; 15 Cred Hrs Adelphi U; *cr:* Walt Whitman HS SS Tchr 1988-; *ai:* S Hunt Tchrs Assn, LI Cncl fo SS 1988-; Kappa Delta Phi 1987-; *office:* Walt Whitman HS 301 W Hills Rd Huntingtn Sta NY 11746

CATALDO, LINDA ROMANO, High School Math Teacher; *b:* Rome, NY; *m:* F. Paul II; *c:* Chip, Eric; *ed:* SUNY at Potsdam (BA) Math 1969; SUNY at Utica (BS) Cmptr Sci 1987; 120 Grad Hrs ED; *cr:* Strough Tchr 1969-92; H&R Block Instr, Preparer 1981-84; Rome Free Acad Tchr 1993-; *ai:* Mock Trial Team, Class of 98 Advs; Math Coach; AFT 1969-; RFA Alumni Assn 1986-, Pres; *office:* Rome Free Acad 500 Turin St Rome NY 13440

CATALDO, PATRICK J., Sixth Grade Teacher; *b:* New Bedford, MA; *m:* Eileen Phillips; *c:* Maryanne, Patrick Jr., Kathleen, Kevin, Megan, Bryan; *ed:* John Carroll Univ (BA) Elem Ed 1976; *cr:* Saint Margaret Mary 7th Grd Tchr 1 Yr; Saint Joan of Arc 8th Grd Tchr 1 Yr; Saint Piux X 6th Grd Tchr 6 Yrs; Newbury Elem 6th Grd Tchr 10 Yrs; *ai:* Elem Stu Cncl Adv; Ski Club Adv; Sci Curr Dir; Newbury Ed Assn 1986-, Treas, Treas of Yr; Cub Scouts Pack 197 1990-, Cub Master; *home:* 14824 S Cheshire St Burton OH 44021*

CATALFOMO, JOSEPH ROCCO, Social Studies Teacher; *b:* Providence, RI; *ed:* St Joseph's Coll (BA) His, Sec Ed 1990; Providence Coll (MA) His 1993; *cr:* Rondout Vly MS 7-8th Grd Soc Stud Tchr 1993-; *ai:* Coach 7-8 Grd Girls Track, 5-6 Grd Flag Ftbl; Asst Coach 7-8 Grd Boys Bstkbl.*

CATALLOZZI, JOHN JOSEPH, Professor of Educl Psychology; *b:* Worcester, MA; *ed:* Lowell St Coll (BS) Ed 1964; Boston Univ (ME) Psych, Ed 1966, (EDD) Psych, Ed 1970; Post Grad Stud NY Univ, Tufts Univ, Northeastern Univ; *cr:* Boston Univ Tchng Fellow 1967-70, Asst Prof 1970-73; Univ of Lowell Asst Prof 1973-79; Univ of MA Assoc Prof 1979-; *ai:* Chief Test Admin; Psychological Corp Fac Adv; Pi Lambda Theta; Philosophy of Ed Soc, John Dewey Soc, NEA 1970-; Licensed Psychologist; *office:* Univ Of MA At Lowell 1 University Ave Lowell MA 01854

CATALUCCI-NICOSIA, LINDA, Third Grade Teacher; *b:* Groton, MA; *m:* Anthony Nicosia; *c:* Gia Catalucci; *ed:* Salem St Coll (BS) Ed 1969; Lesley Coll (MA) Creative Arts 1992; *cr:* Barnstable Schl System 4th Grd Tchr 1969-70; Callahan Schl 4-5th Grd Tchr 1970-92; Shoemaker ESL, K-3rd Grd Tchr 1992-93, 3rd Grd Tchr 1993-; *ai:* AFT 1970-; *office:* Shoemaker Schl 26 Regina Rd Lynn MA 01904

CATANIA, PATRICIA A., Kindergarten Teacher; *b:* Jersey City, NJ; *m:* Joseph; *c:* Christopher; *ed:* Jersey City St Coll (BA) Gen Elem Ed 1966; *cr:* Cordero Schl Tchr Grds K-6 1966-; *ai:* Tchr Recognition Comm; Schl Improvement Team; Sunshine Club Treas; JCEA, HCEA, NJEA, NEA 1966-; NJAKE 1994-; Cordero Tchr of Yr 1993-94; Hudson Co Tchr Recognition Prgm 1994; Merrill Lynch, Mc Graw Hill Tchr Recognition Prgm 1994.

CATAPANO, FRANK ANTHONY, Eighth Grade Teacher; *b:* Brooklyn, NY; *m:* Patricia; *c:* Denise, Vincent; *ed:* St Johns Univ (BA) His 1968, (MA) His 1971; Hofstr & CUNY 30 Grad Credits; *cr:* St Rita Schl 6th & 8th Grd Tchr 1966-74; Resurrection Ascension 8th Grd Tchr 1974-; *ai:* CYO Bsktbl Coach; Math League & Advanced Math Moderator; *office:* Resurrection Ascension Schl 85-25 61st Rd Flushing NY 11374

CATENA, CHRISTINE LYNNE, Guidance Counselor; *b:* Bronxville, NY; *ed:* Siena Coll (BA) Psych 1988; Univ of MA (MED) Cnslng Psych 1991; 6 Addl Credit Hrs; *cr:* Albany City Schl Career Cnslr 1991-92; Albany HS Guid Cnslr 1992-; *ai:* NHS Induction Supvr; Coll Information Nite & Fin Aid Pgms Organizer; Wrote 3 Yr Grant for Dist Career Cnslr Funding; *office:* Albany HS 700 Washington Ave Albany NY 12203

CATER, AMELIA PANZICA, High School Biology Teacher; *b:* Brooklyn, NY; *m:* Glenn John; *ed:* SUNY at Stony Brook (BS) Bio 1992; Attnd Coll of St Rose at Albany, CUNY at Staten Island; *cr:* Lafayette HS Bio Tchr 1992-; *office:* Lafayette HS 2630 Benson Ave Brooklyn NY 11214

CATES, JOYCE M. DENT, First Grade Teacher; *b:* Philadelphia, PA; *c:* Dawn Elizabeth; *ed:* West Chester Univ (BS) Elem Ed 1960; Villanova Univ (MA) Elem Ed 1982; 12 Credit Hrs Rdng Temple Univ; 3 Credit Hrs Cmptr Delaware Cty CC; 3 Credit Hrs Cmptrs in Ed West Chester Univ; *cr:* Upper Dublin Schl Dist Second Grd Tchr 1960-64; Chester-Upland Schl Dist First Grd Tchr 1971-; *ai:* NEA, PSEA, CVEA 1971-; Kappa Delta Pi 1982-; Suburban UNCF 1983-; Phila NCWA 1981-, Treas; *home:* 904 Deer Rd Bryn Mawr PA 19010

CATLIN, KATHY, School Social Worker; *b:* El Segundo, CA; *ed:* Boston Univ (BA) Psych 1982; St Univ at Albany (MSW) Soc Work 1987; *cr:* Hudson City Schls Soc Worker 1987-89; Guilderland Cntrl Schls Soc Worker 1989-; *ai:* Prevention of Sexual Harrassment Comm Co-Chair; Safe Schls Comm; Dist Crisis Response Team; Alliance Club; NYSUT 1987-; Guilderland Tchrs Assn 1989-; Capital Region Assn for Eating Disorders 1993-95, Bd Mem; *office:* Guilderland Cntrl Schls St Farm Rd Guilderland NY 12084*

CATONE, JOSEPH R., Mathematics & Inclusion Tchr; *b:* Youngstown, OH; *ed:* Youngstown St Univ (BA) Soc Stud 1983, (BA) Spec Ed 1989; Post Grad Classes LD-SBH Accounting & Math; *cr:* Carl Wharehouse Produce Clerk 1983-88; Youngstown Bd of Ed DH & Math Inclusion Tchr 1984-; Giant Eagle Produce Clerk 1988-93; ACLD Math Tutor 1988-; *ai:* Young People Inc; Sr Adv; NEA, YEA 1989-; *office:* Rayen HS 250 Benita Ave Youngstown OH 44504*

CATRILLO, MICHAEL, Assistant Principal; *b:* Jersey City, NJ; *m:* Ann Mc Govern; *c:* Matthew; *ed:* Seton Hall Univ (BS) Scndry Ed, Eng 1983; Montclair Univ (MA) Eng 1991; East Stroudsburg Univ (MED) Educl Admin 1994; 6 Credits at Marywood Coll; *cr:* Queen of Peace HS Eng Tchr 1983-86; Livingston HS Eng Tchr 1986-87; Parsippany Hills HS Eng Tchr 1987-90; East Stroudsburg HS Eng Tchr 1990-93; J. T. Lambert Intermediate Schl Asst Prin 1993-; *ai:* Phi Delta Kappa 1995-; NASSP, ASCD 1993-; *office:* J T Lambert Intermediate Schl 2000 Milford Rd E Stroudsburg PA 18301

CATRON, VICKIE CLAUDE, HS Spanish I, II, III Teacher; *b:* Dayton, OH; *m:* Gary; *c:* Kimberlee, Andrea; *ed:* Bowling Green St Univ (BS) Eng, Span 1972; Grad Hrs Univ of Dayton, Wright St Univ; *cr:* Continental Local Schls Eng, Span Tchr 2 Yrs; Carlisle Local Schls Eng, Span Tchr 1974-78, 1984-; *ai:* Span Club; Carlisle Credit Union Bd; OEA, NEA 1984-; Project Excl Tchr of Yr; Jennings Scholar; *office:* Carlisle HS 250 Jamaica Rd Carlisle OH 45005

CATTANI, CAROLINE MANCINI, Third Grade Teacher; *b:* Trenton, NJ; *m:* Eugene J.; *c:* Mary G., Eugene Jr., Katherine M.; *ed:* Temple Univ (AB) Ec 1950; Cert Prsnl Mngmt NY Univ 1959; 9 Grad Cr Rdng Specialization Kean Coll; 9 Cr Perception & Play Brookdale Comm Coll; Edu Kinesthesiology Cert Course; *cr:* Radio Corp of Amer Trng Mgr 1952-61; Matawan Aberdeen Schl Dist Remedial Rdng Tchr 1966-68; St Benedict R. C. Schl Remedial Rdng, Admin Tchr 1968-72; St Joseph R. C. Schl 2nd-3rd Grd Tchr 1977-; *ai:* Mid Sts Accreditation Chprsn; Rainbows for God's Children, Chrstn Svc Moderators; St Benedict Comm Parish Cncl Ed Chprsn, Parish Cncl Rep, VP; NCEA 1977-; AAUW 1965-, Yrbk Chprsn; Prsnl Club of NY 1954-59; Temple Univ Alumni 15 Yrs; League of Women Voters 1965-; 3rd Grd Class Won Senator Bill Bradley Geography Contest; Articls Pub Prnsl & Trng Magazines; Nom Who's Who Amer Women in Industry 1960; Non-Pub Schl Tchr of the Yr St Awd 1995-; *home:* 140 Idlebrook Ln Matawan NJ 07747

CATTELL, DAVID F., Physics & Math Asst Professor; *b:* Woodbury, NJ; *ed:* Drexel Univ (BS) Physics 1972; Temple Univ (MA) Physics 1974, (PHD) Physics 1981; *cr:* Temple Univ Grad Asst 1972-81; Comm Coll of Phila Phsics & Engr Math Asst Prof 1983-; Chm of Physics Dept 1996; *ai:* Helped Maintain CCP Video Message System; Franklin Inst 1968-; Article Pub in Journal of Mathematical Physics 1979; *office:* Community Coll Of Philadelphia 1700 Spring Garden St Philadelphia PA 19130

CATTOGGIO, GERALDINE, 8th Grade Teacher; *b:* New York City, NY; *m:* Anthony P.; *c:* Nicholas, Anthony J.; *ed:* Hunter Coll of the City Univ of NY (BA) Classics 1968; Advanced Cert from the Brooklyn Diocese for Tchng Rel; Trng in Ministry Pgm for Rel Ed at Immaculate Conception Seminary in Douglaston NY; *cr:* St Anthony of Padua Tchr 1968-74; St Francis of Assisi Tchr 1981-, Rel Ed Pgm Prin 1993-; *ai:* Rel Coord; Yrbk & Math League Moderator; Mid Sts Steering Comm; NCEA 1982-; NCTM 1985-; NCTE 1996-; St Francis of Assisi Parish 1989-, Lector & Eucharistic Minister; Seton Awd from Diocese of Brooklyn 1992; *office:* St Francis Of Assisi Schl 21-18 46th St Astoria NY 11105

CATTRAN, DAVID FRANK, Sr Govt & Social Psych Teacher; *b:* Lancaster, OH; *m:* Judith Lynn Graham; *c:* Doug, Kevin; *ed:* The OH St Univ (BS) Soc Stud, Ed 1972, (MA) Guid, Cnslng 1977; 9 Sem Hrs Prof Ed Drake Univ; 3 Sem Hrs Prof Ed Ashland Univ; 3 Sem Hrs Prof Ed Walsh Univ; *cr:* Amanda Clearcreek HS Soc Stud Tchr 1972-73; Sheridan HS Soc Stud Dept Head, US Govt, Soc Psych Tchr 1973-; *ai:* Sr Soc Stud Schlsp Team Spon; OH Ed Assn, NEA, OH Cncl for Soc Stud 1973-; *home:* 765 Carpico Dr NE Lancaster OH 43130

CATTRELL, KATHY WILSON, Biology Teacher; *b:* Warren, OH; *m:* Mitch; *c:* Ben, Adam; *ed:* WV Univ (BS) Bio, General Sci & Math 1975; Working on Masters at Franciscan Univ; *cr:* Saint Francis HS Algebra Tchr 1975-76; Ripley HS Math, Bio & General Sci Tchr 1977-79; Columbiana Co Career Ctr Math & Cmptrs Tchr 1988-92; Crestview HS Bio & Geometry Tchr 1992-; *ai:* Sci Olympiad & Envirothon Teams Spon; CEA, OEA, NEA 1992-, Negotiating Team; NSTA 1994-; *office:* Crestview H S 44100 Crestview Rd Columbiana OH 44408

CAUCHI, PATRICK JOSEPH, High School English Teacher; *b:* Manhattan, NY; *m:* Catherine Anne; *c:* Patrick John, Matthew Paul, Paul Christopher; *ed:* Queens Coll (BA) Eng, Anthropology 1975, (MA) Eng 1979; St John's Univ (PD) Ed Adm, Superv 1985; Farmingdale Univ (RN) Nrsng 1988; Tchng Cert Eng, Soc Stud, Gen Sci, Bio, Hlth, Schl Dist Admin, Supvr, Admin; *cr:* Holy Trinity Grammar Schl 7-8 Grd Bio, Sci Tchr 1976-77; Holy Cross HS 9-12 Eng Tchr 1977-83; Longwood Sr HS 9-12 Eng, Sci, Hlth Tchr 1989-94, 9-12 Grd Eng Tchr 1983-, Asst Dir LAP 1994-; Nassau Comm Coll Asst Adj Eng Prof 1978-; Farmingdale Univ Asst Adj Eng Prof 1978-; Dowling Coll Asst Adj Eng Prof 1978-; *ai:* Asst Ath Dir; Ath Trainor; Frosh, JV, Var Boys, Girls Tennis Coach; Class Adv 1984-88; Schl Newspaper Adv 1978-83; Photography Club Moderator 1978-83; Dow Jones Flwshp Judge; Amer Nurses Assn 1988-; Aft 1983-; Amer Tennis Assn 1980-; Natl Geographic 1976-; Amer Museum of Natl His 1985-; Rosedale Vol Ambulance 1975-78, EMT, Driver; BSA 1989-, Den Ldr, Svc Awds; Dow Jones Jrnlsm Flwshps 1983; PR Natl Theatre Play Awd 1988; Most Popular Play; 1000 Poems Pub; Working on Novel; *office:* Longwood Sr HS 100 Longwood Rd Middle Island NY 11953*

CAUGHEY, BARBARA HODGE, Second Grade Teacher; *b:* Chicago Heights, IL; *m:* Robert E.; *c:* Rob, Jon; *ed:* Penn St Univ (BS) Elem Ed 1963; Post Grad Stud 12 Credits; Several Prof Dev Courses; *cr:* Penn Hills Schl Dist Elem Tchr 1963-; *ai:* Gifted Task Force Comm; PTA 2 Yrs Tchr Rep; NEA, PSEA, PHEA 1963-; PTA 1963-, Membership Chm, Other Comm; Tchr of Yr 1992-93; Light of Inspiration Awd 1995; *office:* Penn Hebron Elem Schl 102 Duff Rd Pittsburgh PA 15235

CAUL, JUNE MARIE, Fourth Grade Teacher; *b:* Fort Frances, Canada; *m:* Ken Dick; *c:* Jacuqline, Jeff; *ed:* Ontario Tchrs Elem Schl Cert 1971; Jr Ed Specialist 1992; *cr:* F. H. Huffman Schl 2nd, 4th Grd Tchr 1971-75; Robert Moore Schl 2nd Grd Tchr 1975-76; Sixth Street Schl 1st, 3-5th Grd Tchr 1980-88; Alexander MacKenzie Schl 4th Grd Tchr 1988-; *ai:* Acting Prin, Vice Prin; Asst Coach of Yth Soccer, Bsbl; FWTAO 1971-; Fort Frances Minor Hockey Assn 1995-, Sec; *office:* Alexander Mac Kenzie Schl 408 Portage Ave Ft Frances ON P9A 2S7 Canada CN*

CAULEY, MICHAEL, Industrial Technology Instr; *b:* Columbus, OH; *ed:* OH Northern Univ (BA) Indstrl Tech 1977; Ashland Univ (MS) Sports Sci 1990; *cr:* Col. Crawford Schls Instr, Coach 1977-; *ai:* Head Ftbl, Strength, Asst Track Coach; OEA, NEA, OH HS Coaches Assoc 1977-; N Cntrl OH Coach of Yr 1992; *office:* Colonel Crawford HS St Rt 602 North Robinson OH 44856

CAUSEY, MARION,JR., Assistant Principal; *b:* Colubmus, OH; *ed:* Central St Univ (BS) His Ed 1969; Univ of Cincinnati (MA) Spec Ed 1979; OH St Univ (PHD) Educl Admin 1992; *cr:* Columbus Pub Schls His Tchr 1973-79, Spec Ed Tchr 1979-87, HS Schl Admin 1987-.

CAVAGNARO, SUSAN VANHOOK, Social Studies Teacher; *b:* Newfield, NJ; *m:* Raymond; *c:* Jeannine, Raymond, Mark; *ed:* Villanova Univ (BS) Eng & Soc Stud 1971; Attnd Glassboro Coll, Camden Cty Coll, Rutgers Univ; *cr:* Our Lady of Mercy Acad Soc Stud Tchr 1974-; *ai:* Yrbk; Sr Homeroom; Show; NCEA.

CAVALCANTE, CAL JOSEPH, 7th-8th Grade English Teacher; *b:* Masontown, PA; *m:* Dorothy Jane Bank; *c:* Thomas, James, Autumn Mendel; *ed:* CA St Coll (BS) Eng 1962; Kent St Univ (MED) Eng 1968; Youngstown St Univ Counseling Cert 1974; Tulane Univ Eng; *cr:* East Jr HS Eng Tchr 1962-65; West Jr HS Eng Tchr 1965-69; Warren Western Reserve HS Eng Tchr & Cnslr 1969-76; Mineral Ridge MS Eng Tchr 1976-; *ai:* Book Adoption Comm; Spelling Bee Coord; Weathersfield Ed Assn 1976-, Schlsp Comm; OH Ed Assn, NEA 1962-; Dist 13 Sftbl 1994-, Commissioner; Trumbull Cty Umpires Assn 1978-; Trumbull Cty Bsktbl Assn 1979-, Pres; Bsktbl Article Pub in Scholastic Coach; 2 Poems Pub; Trumbull Cty Tchr of Yr 1993-94; Nom for Warren City Schls Tchr of Yr 3 Times; Martha Holden Jennings Scholar; *home:* 8686 Bayberry Dr NE Warren OH 44484

CAVALIER, MICHAEL JEFFREY, 12th Grade Eng Tchr; *b:* Ellwood City, PA; *ed:* Washington & Jefferson Coll (BA) Eng 1986; Univ of Pittsburgh Schl of Law (JD) Law 1989; Addl Grad Courses in Eng at; *cr:* Beaver HS Eng Tchr 1993; Neshannock HS Eng Tchr 1993-; *ai:* Dir & Choreographer of Schl Musicals Riverside HS 1990-; Dir & Choreographer of Musicals 1993-; PSEA, NEA 1993-; Vagabond Repertory Co 1989-92, VP; New Castle Playhouse 1993-; Best Dir Awd 1994-95 Henry Mancini HS Musical Theatre Awds; *home:* 940 Skyline Dr Ellwood City PA 16117*

CAVALIERE, CATHERINE COANE, History Teacher; *b:* Teaneck, NJ; *c:* Catherine Marie; *ed:* Caldwell Coll (BA) His & Pol Sci 1966; Jersey Cit St (MA) Urban Ed 1984; Principal Cert; Holocaust Stud; *cr:* Cliffside Park Pub Schl System His Tchr 1966-; *ai:* NJ Cncl for Soc Stud; Holocaust Museum; Tchr of the Yr 1988; *office:* Cliffside Park HS 64 Riverview Ave Cliffside Park NJ 07010

CAVALIERE, ROBERT JOSEPH, High School English Teacher; *b:* Plainfield, NJ; *m:* Jacquelyn A.; *c:* Allison; *ed:* Rider Coll (BA) Eng 1969; Trenton St (MED) Urban Ed 1977; Eng Doctoral Stud at Rutgers; *cr:* Hubbard MS Tchr 1969-74; Plainfield HS Tchr 1974-; *ai:* Wrestling Coach; Drama & Poetry Clubs Adv; Strength Coach; Mid Sts Steering Comm; PEA, NJEA & NEA 1969-; A A Halden Grad Fellowship; Kappa Delta Pi Honor Soc; Articles Pub in NJEA Review & Bank Street Journal; Rutgers Symposium on Intnl Ed; Poetry Pub.

CAVALIERO, CHERYL FUHRER, Mathematics Teacher; *b:* Frederick, MD; *m:* Brad; *c:* Zachary; *ed:* Butler Cty Comm Coll (AA) Math, Pre-Engrng 1982; Univ of Pittsburgh (BS) Math 1984; Indiana Univ of PA (MS) Math 1989; Scndry Ed Cert, Math Slippery Rock Univ 1985; *cr:* New Castle Area Schls Eighth Grd Math Tchr 1985-86; Monteau Schl Dist Long-term Sub 1986; Butler Area Schl Dist Long-term Sub 1987; Indiana Univ o fPA Full-time Temp 1991-92; Butler Cty Comm Coll Part-time Tchr 1984-85, 1987-89, Full-time Temp 1989-91, Part-time Tchr 1992-93, Full-time Tchr 1993-; *ai:* Mid States Self Stud Subcommittee Co-Chair; Planning Cncl Rep; Ethnic Luncheon Comm Co-Chair; Discipline Articulation Assembly Math; Butler Cty Comm Coll Ed Assn 1993-; Math Assn Amer 1995-; LaLeche League 1992-; St Peter's Parish Family Choir 1995-; Grad Assistantship Indiana Univ of PA 1987, 1988; *office:* Butler County Comm Coll PO Box 1203 Butler PA 16003*

CAVALLARO, ROBERT A., Guidance Counselor; *b:* Providence, RI; *c:* Jennifer A., Alexandra J., Robert P.; *ed:* RI Coll (BA) Scndry Ed 1974; Providence Coll (MED) Guid, Cnslng 1978; *cr:* East Providence Sr HS Fr, Math Tchr 1974-93, Guid Cnslr 1993-; *ai:* NEA, NEARI, EPEA 1974-; RICA 1993-; *office:* East Providence Sr HS 2000 Pawtucket Ave East Providence RI 02914

CAVALLI, CHRISTINE MARIE, English Teacher; *b:* New York, NY; *m:* Nicholas J.; *c:* Erica, Nicholas; *ed:* Coll of Mt St Vincent (BA) Eng 1972; Iona Coll (MS) Ed & Eng 1993; *cr:* Cardinal Spellman HS Eng Tchr 1986-; *ai:* NCTE 1987-; *office:* Cardinal Spellman HS 1 Cardinal Spellman Pl Bronx NY 10466

CAVALLO, FRANK,JR., Teacher of Gifted & Talented; *b:* Garfield, NJ; *ed:* Paterson St Coll (BA) Ed 1959; Fairleigh Dickinson Univ (MA) Human Dev 1980; 18 Credits Aesthetic Ed at Julliard & Columbia; 16 Credits Gifted Ed at Coll of New Rochelle & Montclair St; 12 Credits Applied Scis at NJIT & Rutgers; Over 30 Miscellaneous Credits; *cr:* Paramus Elem Schl 7th Grd Tchr 1959-63; East Brook Jr HS 7th-8th Grd Tchr 1963-69, Open Classroom Tchr 1969-79; East Brook MS Tchr of Gifted & Talented 1980-; *ai:* Yrbk Lit Magazine; Renaissance Soc; Gourmet Club; Ski Club; Lincoln Ctr Coord; Dist Fairs; Strategic Quality Planning Coord; Olympics of Mind Coach; Math Counts & Math Olympiad Coach; NCEA, NEA, EAP Tchrs Assn 1959-; NJ Governors Recognition Awd 1985; Articles on Open Classroom in NJEA Review & Other Journals; Linking Industry, Nature, Knowledge & Systems Pub Svc; *home:* 407 Lafayette Ave Westwood NJ 07675

CAVANAGH, ELIZABETH, English Teacher; *b:* Boston, MA; *m:* Roderick; *c:* Christine, Scott; *ed:* Manhattanville Coll (BA) Eng 1967; Boston Coll (MAT) Eng, Ed 1968; 3 Hrs Tchng Writing on Scndry Level; Adoles Psych; 3 Hrs Rdng in Content Areas; 3 Hrs Writing Project; 2 Hrs Advanced Writing Project; Natl Endow for Hum Focus Groups; 20 Cen Liter of Displacement; *cr:* St Sebastian C D Schl 8th, 12th Grd Eng Tchr 1967-68; M. E. Curley Jr HS 7th Grd Eng Tchr 1968-69; Lincoln Schl 7th, 9th-10th Grd Eng Tchr 1970-75; St Mary Acad 9th-12th Grd Eng Tchr 1992-; *ai:* Journal, Musical Groups Adv; Jr Class Assoc; 10th Grd Writing Assess RIDE; Acad Decathlon Lecturer, Compos Reader; NCTE; RICTE; Chamber Music Festival 1988-95, Sec; Poet Competition Honorable Mention 1994-95; *office:* St Marys Acad Bayview 3070 Pawtucket Ave Riverside RI 02915

CAVANAGH, JACQUELINE WELTNER, Eng, World Lit & Adv Comp Tchr; *b:* Pittsburgh, PA; *ed:* IN Univ of PA (BS) Ed Eng 1969, (MED) Eng 1977; *cr:* United HS 11-12th Grd Eng Tchr, World Lit, Adv Comp 1969-; *ai:* Spon Lit Magazine Kaleidoscope; UEA, PSEA, NEA 1969-, Exec Bd 1970-; NCTE 1970-; Ldr of Scndry Ed; Honary PA Farmer Degree FFA; *office:* United HS PO Box 168 Armagh PA 15920*

CAVANAGH, PAUL T., Fourth Grade Teacher; *b:* Thompson, OH; *m:* Mary Lynne Spaude; *c:* Michael, Jonathan, Matthew; *ed:* Bowling Green St Univ (BS) Ed, Lang Speech 1968, (MS) Supervision, Admin 1988; *cr:* Toledo Pub Schls Tchr 1968-72; OTSEGO Local Schls Tchr, Prin, Dir of Migrant Ed 1972-; *ai:* NEA 1972-; Lions Club; Cub Scout Ldr; Lit Cncl; *home:* 319 W Poe Rd Bowling Green OH 43402

CAVANAUGH, JOHN CHARLES, Interim Assc Provost Grad Stud; *b:* Terre Haute, IN; *m:* Patrice Newman; *ed:* Univ of DE (BA) Psych 1975; Univ of Notre Dame (MA) Psych 1977, (PHD) Psych 1978; Postdoctoral Flwshp Univ of MN; *cr:* Bowling Green St Univ Asst, Assoc Prof 1980-92; GA Inst of Tech Visiting Prof 1989-90; Univ of DE Prof, Chair 1992-94, Interim Assoc Provost Grad Stud; *ai:* Amer Psychological Assn 1980-, Pres, Division 20, Flwshp; Amer Psychological Soc 1988-, Charter Flwshp; Gerontological Soc Amer 1980-, Flwshp; Wilmington Sr Ctr 1993-, Bd Pres; DE Commission Natl, Comm Svc 1994-, Chair; Natl Inst on Aging Grant; Author Adult Development and Aging; Co-Author Human Development; Author, Co-Author Numerous Articles, Chptrs; *office:* Univ Of DE 234 Hullihen Hall Newark DE 19716*

CAVANAUGH, JUDITH A., Assistant Prof of Humanities; *b:* Grafton, OH; *m:* Rodney A.; *ed:* Bowling Green St Univ (BS) Scndry Ed Eng & Speech 1974; Ashland Univ (MS) Curr & Instruction Ed 1989; Post Grad Hours OH St Univ; *cr:* DE JVS Eng Tchr 1976-84; Gahanna Lincoln HS Eng Tchr & Dept Chair 1984-92; Chazy Cntrl Schl Eng Tchr 1992-93; Clinton Comm Coll Asst Prof of Hum 1993-; *ai:* Adv: Art & Literary Magazine & Phi Theta Kappa; Comms: Curr, Retention & Prof Dev; NCTE St Judge; Division Sub Comms: Assessment & Prog Dev; Natl Cncl of Tchrs of Eng; Phi Delta Kappa; NY St Assn of 2 Yr Colls; Amer Assn Univ Women; Clinton Comm Coll Faculty Assn Treas; Arts Cncl for Clinton Cty; Presentations: Career Ed, Portfolio Assessment, Comp Assisted Writing Instruction; *office:* Clinton Comm Coll 136 Clinton Point Dr Plattsburgh NY 12901*

CAVANAUGH, PATRICIA ANN, Adjunct Instructor of English; *b:* Pottsville, PA; *c:* Elaine Wilson Cook, Diane Elizabeth Wilson; *ed:* Millersville Univ (BS) Eng, Span 1960, (MA) Eng 1992; 60 Credits Assoc Interior Design LaSalle Univ; 23 Grad Credits Jrnlsm, Ed; *cr:* Palmer Bus Schl Instr 1989-90; Reading Area Comm Coll Instr 1990-; Penn Coll of Tech Instr 1995-; HACC Instr 1992-; *ai:* Constitutional Review Comm; Numerous Articles Pub as Stringer for Lancaster Newspapers Inc; *office:* Harrisburg Area Comm Coll 1 HACC Dr Harrisburg PA 17110

CAVANAUGH, VIRGINIA WATERMAN, Social Studies Teacher; *b:* Bridgeport, CT; *m:* Joseph; *c:* Joseph, Brian, Shawn; *ed:* Southern CT St Coll (BA) Elem Ed 1975, (MS) Rdng 1978; Univ of Bpt 30 Credits Ed 1996; *cr:* Wilbur Cross Schl Math Tchr 1975-76; Elias Howe Schl 7th Grd Tchr 1977-84; J. J. Curiale Schl 8th Grd Tchr 1984-; *ai:* Soccer, Bsktbl Coach; St Jude Rel Schl 5th-6th Grd Tchr; NEA 1975-; *office:* James J. Curiale Schl 300 Laurel Ave Bridgeport CT 06605

CAVE, TIMOTHY J., European & Global History Tchr; *b:* Columbus, OH; *ed:* OH St Univ (BS) Scndry Soc Stud 1991; Post Grad Stud in Slavic & East European Stud; Intensive Russian Lang Harvard Univ 1993; *cr:* Worthington Kilbourne HS Behavioral Scis Tchr 1992-93, Global His Tchr 1992-, Advanced Placement European His Tchr 1993-; Thomas Worthington HS Global His Tchr 1996; *ai:* Girls Lacrosse Head Coach; Boys Golf Asst Coach; Model United Nations Adv; NEA, OH Ed Assn, Worthington Ed Assn 1992-; City of Columbus, Firefighter 1987-92, Battalion Chiefs Commendation; *office:* Worthington Kilbourne HS 1499 Hard Rd Columbus OH 43235

CAVETT, PHILIP A., Mathematics Teacher; *b:* Pittsburgh, PA; *ed:* Geneva Coll (BS) Math 1989; Robert Morris Coll (MS) Bus Ed 1994; *cr:* Riverside MS Math, Cmptr Sci Tchr 1989-; *ai:* Photography Staff Spon; Tech Planning Comm; NEA, PSEA 1989-; Delta Pi Epsilon 1994-; Amer Family Inst Gift of Time Awd 1990; *office:* Riverside MS RR 2 Box 4010 Ellwood City PA 16117

CAVOLI, DANIEL JOSEPH, Latin Teacher; *b:* Cleveland, OH; *ed:* Coll of Holy Cross (BA) Classical Lang Latin, Greek, Rel Stud 1980; Attending John Carroll Univ MA Classics; *cr:* Marion Cath HS Rel Tchr 1980-81; St Ignatius HS Latin Tchr 1981-86; St Christopher Parish Pastoral Minister 1987-88; St Edward HS Latin Tchr 1989-; *ai:* Natl Jr Classical League Knights Tibur Adv; Hiking Retreat Club Moderator; Natl Jr Classical League 1996; NCEA 1980-86; OH Cath Ed Assn 1989-; Natl Endowment Hum Grant Seminar Harvard Univ 1986; *office:* Saint Edward HS 13500 Detroit Ave Lakewood OH 44107*

CAWLEY, LORI AWENOWICZ, 7th Grade Language Arts Tchr; *b:* Pittsburgh, PA; *m:* Joseph; *ed:* Univ of Pittsburgh (BA) Eng 1990, (MAT) Scndry Ed 1991; *cr:* Woodland Hills Schl Dist Lang Arts Tchr 1992-; *ai:* Lib & Rdng Club, Pep Club, Dance Club Spons; NEA, NCTE 1992-; Women of the Moose 1990-; Woodland Hills Mini Grant Prgm 1995-96; *office:* Woodland Hills Schl Dist 7600 Evans St Pittsburgh PA 15218

CAYEA, KRISTA B., Choral & Music Director; *b:* Syracuse, NY; *m:* Kenneth Peter; *c:* Daniel K., Nathan W.; *ed:* Syracuse Univ (BA) Music Ed 1984; Ithaca Coll (MS) Music Ed 1988; *cr:* Onteora Cntrl Schls 7-12 Grds Choral Dir 1984-, K-12 Grds Music Dir 1992-; *ai:* Vocal Jazz Ensemble, HS Musicals Coach; NYS United Tchrs 1984-; MENC 1984-, All-St Selection Comm; Ulster Cty Music Edctrs Assn 1984-, All-Cty Vocal Jazz Ensemble Chprsn; *office:* Onteora Cntrl Schl Dist Rt 28 Boiceville NY 12412

CAYEA, LANCE W., Dean of Students; *b:* Batavia, NY; *m:* Amy Maddigan; *c:* Mitchell; *ed:* Coll of Wooster (BA) His 1988; Buffalo St Coll (MS) Soc Stud 1992; *cr:* Attica Central Schl Soc Stud Tchr 1988-92; Batavia HS Tchr, Dean of Stu 1993-; *ai:* Jr Var Vlybl, Ftbl Coach; AFT 1988-; Batavia Tchrs Assn 1992-, Rep; *office:* Batavia HS 260 State St Batavia NY 14020

CAYER, JANE, English Teacher; *b:* Baltimore, MD; *ed:* Coll of Notre Dame of MD (BA) Eng 1972; Johns Hopkins Univ (MLA) Liberal Arts 1981; Attnd Towson St Univ, Loyola Coll; *cr:* St Patrick Schl Eng Tchr 1968-71; Notre Dame Preparatory Eng Tchr 1972-85; Inst of Nore Dame Eng Tchr 1985-; *ai:* Frosh Class Moderator; Eng Dept Chprsn; NCTE, ASCD; *office:* Institute Of Notre Dame 901 N Aisquith St Baltimore MD 21202

CAYWOOD, MELISSA ROSE MARY, Instrumental Music Teacher; *b:* Cobleskill, NY; *ed:* Coll of St Rose (BS) Music Ed 1984; IN Univ (MME) Music Ed 1992; *cr:* Cherry Valley-Springfield CS Instrumental Music Tchr 1987-90 Berlin Cntrl Schl Instrumental Music Tchr 1990-; *ai:* Sr HS Jazz Ensemble; Pep, Marching Band; Co-Musical Adv; All Cty Mgr, Conductor; Colorgrd Adv; MENC, NYSSMA 1981-; NBA 1986-; *office:* Berlin Central School Rt 22 Cherry Plain NY 12022*

CAZES, ARLINE HERZ, ESL Teacher; *b:* New York City, NY; *m:* Jack; *c:* Jessica, David; *ed:* Queens Coll (BA) Span 1972; CW Post LIU (MS) Admin, Supvr 1984; 30 Grad Credits Hunter Coll CUNY ESL 1975; 3 Grad Credits Hofstra Univ Biling Theories 1986; 3 Grad Credits Fordham Spec Ed 1989; *cr:* IS 125 Woodside Span Tchr 1974-76; August Martin HS Span Tchr 1977-81; Hawthorne Comm Ctr Span & ESL Tchr 1982-83; MS 67 Louis Pasteur ESL, Comm Arts Tchr 1984-; *ai:* Peer Mediator-Conflict Resolution Coord, Parents Advy Comm Coord; Schl Based Mngmt, Tchrs Interest Comms; UFT, AFT 1972-; Jewish Tchrs Assn 1984-, Bldg Rep; NYSTESOL 1986-; Temple Emanuel 1982-, Fin Sec, Bd Trustee, Sisterhood; North Lakeville Civic Assn 1985-; NYS ISS, LEP Grant 1990-93, 1995; Article Pub in NYSTESOL Idiom Journal; *office:* MS 67 Louis Pasteur 51-60 Marathon Pkwy Little Neck NY 11362

CEBULA, JAMES E., Professor of History; *b:* Dupont, PA; *c:* Anne, Judith; *ed:* East Stroudsburg Univ (BS) Soc Stud 1963, (MED) His 1965; U of Cincinnati (PHD) His 1972; *cr:* Univ of Cincinnati His Prof 1969-; *ai:* His, Philosophy & Art Dept Chair;Amer Assn of Univ Profs Pre Org of Amer Historians 1966-; Amer Historical Assn 1968-; OH His 1969-; Sylvis Soc 1984-, Pres 1990-95; Glory & Despair A His Molders Union 1976; James M Cox Jounalist & Politician 198 Build The City The Working People of Cincinnati Exec Producer & Dir 1989; *office:* Univ Of Cincinati 9555 Plainfield Rd Cincin 45236

CEBULA, MARY ANN ANTOINETTE, Special Ed Teacher; *b:* NJ; *m:* Charles M.; *c:* Jessica; *ed:* Newark St Coll (BA) Elem E Georgian Court Coll (MA) Spec Ed 1991; Certs LDTC, Spec Ed, Handicapped; *cr:* Belleville Schls Speech Therapist 1972-73; St A Elem Tchr 1973-78; Our Lady of Mt Carmel Schl Elem Tchr 1981- Family Schl Elem Tchr 1986-88; Mc Kinley Ave Schl NI Tchr Oxycocus Elem Schl Spec Ed Tchr 1989-; *ai:* Spec Olympics; T Play; CCD; Fac Advy Comm; NEA, NJEA, STEA 1988-; PTA 1988-; T. R. North Marching Mariners Boosters 1992-; Tchr c 1992-93, Month Local; Classroom Garden Grant 1993-94; Oxycocus Elem Schl Rt 9 Manahawkin NJ 08050*

CEBULA, MARY LOU THERESA, Dean of Students; Brunswick, NJ; *m:* Frank; *c:* Christopher, Craig; *ed:* Trenton St C Elem Ed 1971, (MA) K-12th Grd Rdng 1983; Prin Cert Adm Rutgers Univ 3 Grad Credits Writing Process; St Peters Coll Credits Admin & Supervision; *cr:* Hillsborough Schl 5th-7th C 1971-83, Rdng Specialist 5th-7th Grds 1983-87; Warren M Specialist 6th-8th Grd 1987-95, Dean of Stdnts 1995-; *ai:* Stu G Act Dir; Kappa Delta Phi 1984-; PSA 1995-; Manville Bd of Ed Pres; Somerset Cty Schl Bds Assn 1983-, Pres & VP; Somerset C Svcs Commission 1985-, Pres & VP; *office:* Warren MS 100 Old Rd Warren NJ 07059*

CEBULA, RAYMOND J., 7th Grd Math Teacher; *b:* Youngstown, Sondra J. Herman; *c:* Jane3 V., Suzanne M., Leslie A.; *ed:* Wes Coll (BA) Elem Ed 1967, (MS) Ed 1972; *cr:* New Bedford Elem 1967-70; Wilmington Jr Sr HS Math Tchr 1970-; *ai:* Chm Stu A Prgm; Boys Var Trakc Coach; Yo-Yo Club Adv; NEA, PSEA, Wi Each 1967-; St Camillus Parish 1970-; Wilmington Twp 1988 Authority; Youth League Sftbl 1985-, CCd Instr 1977-88; Par 1982-86; *office:* Wilmington Area MS 350 Wood St New Wilmir 16142

CECCHETTI, MARIO EUGENE, Computer Technology Profe Arnold, PA; *m:* Bridget T. Hoak; *c:* Jon M., Diane L., Merle J., Da Point Park Coll (BS) Information Sci; Pittsburgh Univ (MS) Infe Sci, (CAS) Information Sci; Penn St Univ (AA); *cr:* WCCC Prof 1 Club Adv; Am Legion; TROA; VFW; *office:* Westmoreland Coun Coll Armburst Rd Youngwood PA 15697

CECCOLI, CHRISTOPHER JOHN, English Teacher; *b:* Clevela *ed:* Univ of Dayton (BA) Eng & Ed 1992; *cr:* St Mary Cntrl Cath 1992-94, Eng Tchr 1993-; *ai:* Eng Dept Chprsn; Var Girls Vllybl Boys Bsktbl Coach; SADD, Great Books Club & Sr Class Adv 1992-; Tri-Parish Yth Ministry 1993-, Vision Team Mem; CYC 1995-, Adv & Referee; Dr Harry Hand Memrl Awd for Excl in E *office:* St Mary's Ctl Cath HS 410 W Jefferson St Sandusky OH 4

CECIL, ROBERT ANTHONY, Sixth Grade Teacher; *b:* Chestert *ed:* Univ of MD (BS) Ed 1972; Unv of VA His, Eng; Post-Grad Earned for Quality Advanced Prof Cert; *cr:* Wm Paca Elem Sc Tchr 1972-76; J. Enos Ray Elem Schl 5-6 Grd Tchr 1976-80; L Elem Schl 6 Grd Tchr 1980-92; Montpelier Elem Schl 4-6 Grd Tch *ai:* Tchr in Charge in Prins Absence; Grd Level, Soc Stud Dept Ch Stu Govt; Schl-Based Mgmt Team; NEA, MSTA, PGCEA 1972-, *office:* Montpelier Elem Schl 9200 Mirkirk Rd Laurel MD 20708

CEGLIA, GLENN A., Instrumental Music Teacher; *b:* Locust Va *m:* Shelley Wolcott; *c:* Christopher; *ed:* Nassau Comm Coll (AA 1979; Crane Schl of Music SUNY at Potsdam (BM) Music Ed 198 Music Ed 1988; *cr:* Dolgeville Cntrl Schl Instrumental Music Tch *office:* Dolgeville Ctnrl Schl 38 Slawson St Dolgeville NY 13329

CEGLIA, SHELLEY (WOLCOTT), Chorus Teacher; *b:* Camden Glenn A.; *c:* Christopher; *ed:* SUNY at Potsdam Coll (BM) Music (MM) Music Ed 1989; *cr:* Frankfort Schuyler CS Vocal Music Tch *ai:* Womens Select Chorus, Show Choir Dir; Musical Producti *office:* Frankfort-Schuyler HS Palmer St Frankfort NY 13340*

CELECKI, MARK ALBERT, Physical Education Teacher; *b:* Co NY; *m:* Kimberly Ann Myers; *ed:* St Univ of NY at Cortland (BS) (MS) PE 1988; *cr:* Moriah Cntrl Schl 2-12 Grd PE Tchr 1983-88; Patent Cntrl Schl 9-12 Grd PE Tchr 1988-; *ai:* Coaching Var Girls Swimming & Diving Teams 12 Yrs; Coaching JV Girls Sftbl NYSAHPERD 1995-; NISCA 1996-; *office:* Holland Patent Ce Thompson Rd Holland Patent NY 13354

CELENTANO, SANDRA, Intervention Specialist; *b:* Brooklyn, Richard; *c:* Brian, Sheri; *ed:* Natl Drug Research Inst 450 Hrs; E Coll Guidance Dept 180 Hrs; Office of Alcoholism & Substanc Svcs Certified Substance Abuse Cnslr Substance Abuse Counseli *cr:* IS 228 Substance Abuse Prevention Intervention Specialist 1 Cncl for Unity Advy Comm; Stu Mentor; Youth Expo Peer Le Coord; *office:* IS 228 David A Boody 228 Avenue S Brooklyn NY

CELESTE, JEAN KANE, Guidance Counselor; *b:* Newark, NJ; Nicky; *ed:* Kean Coll (BA) Psych & Sociology 1976, (BA) Spcl (MA) Cnslr Ed 1990; SAC Coursework Completed; Cnslr & Spcl 1987 & 1990; *cr:* Linden HS Spcl Ed Tchr 1987-89; Colonia MS Tchr 1989-90; Avenel MS Guid Cnslr 1990-; *ai:* Talent Show Coo Ed Night Schl Tchr-in-Charge; NJEA & NEA 1987-; Middlesex C Assoc 1990-; Governors Recognition Awd 1995; *office:* Av Woodbine Ave Avenel NJ 07001

CELI, JANET LYN, Spanish Teacher; *b:* Tampa, FL; *m:* Peter; of South Fl at Tampa (MA) Span & Eng Ed 1968; Boston St Co Biling Ed 1978; Salem St Coll (CAGS) Innovative Practices 1 Marlborough HS Eng & Speech Tchr 1969; Acton-Boxboro Re Span Tchr 1970-73; Woburn High Span Tchr 1973-; *ai:* Span E Prgm Coord; Span Natl Soc Adv; Fac & Schl Cncl; Prof Dev Chprsn; MA Assn Biling Ed, WTA, MTA, NEA & Assn Super C Horace Mann Grants 1987-88; MA St Dept Svc to Ed Awd 20 Yrs; Bus Assn Ed Awd for Svc 20 Yrs; *office:* Woburn HS 88 Mont Woburn MA 01801*

CELIDONIO, RALPH JOSEPH, Asst Principal & Math Philadelphia, PA; *m:* Elizabeth Adams; *c:* Therese Sawaya, Donn Michael, Albert, Linda; *ed:* St Joseph Univ (BS) Eng 1960; Tem (MED) Educl Admin 1965; 18 Math Credits Villanova Univ 196 MSGR Bonner HS Math Tchr 1960-, Asst Prin Acad Affairs, Cns *ai:* IM Prgm; NCEA 1960-; NAMTCV 1970-; Knights of Columbu 3 Natl Sci Fnd Grants; *office:* Monsignor Bonner HS 403 N Lansdo Drexel Hill PA 19026*

CELLA, ELVIRA KOHLHAMMER, Mathematics Teac Hackensack, NJ; *m:* Thomas; *ed:* Montclair St Coll (BA) Math 19 Math 1980; Supvr Cert 1989; *cr:* Kearny HS Math Tchr 1978-; *ai:* HS PTA 1978-; KEA 1978-; NJEA & NEA 1977- NCTM 19 Hummel Club 1977-; Natl Audubon Soc 1993-; Natl Wildlife Fn or Day Fnd 1990-; NYZS the Wildlife Conservation Soc 1987-; earny HS 336 Devon St Kearny NJ 07032

, **JEAN DEMMA,** Instructor of Legal Studies; *b:* Framingham, Albert A.; *c:* Mark, Lisa, Beth; *ed:* Becker Coll (AS) Med al 1952; Boston Univ (BS) Bus Ed 1955, (MS) Bus Ed 1961; Cert Bentley Coll 1983; *cr:* Rockland HS Tchr, Dept Chair Becker Coll Instr 1959-62; Holliston Adult Ed Instr 1969-75; Jr Coll New England Ed Ctr Instr, Prgm Coord 1969-79; Aquinas r 1979-; *ai:* Legl Stdnts Assn Club Adv; Keyboarding Competition Curr Revision Comm; MA Bus Tchrs; Natl Assn of Legal ies; Italian Culture 1988-; Wrote Workbook for Procedural Law *office:* Aquinas Coll At Newton 15 Walnut Park Newton MA

, **MICHAEL ANDREW,** Physical Education & Hlth Tchr; *b:* , MA; *m:* Pamela Corbett; *c:* Stephanie, Steven; *ed:* Northeastern) Hlth, PE & Spcl Ed 1974; Attnd Kents Hill Prep; *cr:* Abraham Schl Spcl Needs Tchr 1974-78; All Schls in City Traveling PE Tchr 1978-90; RIF 1990-93; Revere HS Hlth & PE Tchr *i:* Head Ftbl & Babe Ruth Bsbl Coach; MA Track & Field Ofcl 74-, Head Timer & Starter Judge; MA Tchrs Assn 1974-; MA Ftbl Assn 1974-; Sons of Italy 1974-; Kiwanis 1974-; Greater Boston or Retared 1974-; Revere Spcl Olympics Founder Since 1978; MA mpics; *office:* Revere HS 101 School St Revere MA 02151

R, THOMAS K., School Counselor; *b:* Columbus, OH; *m:* Tamera ngham; *c:* Chelsea, Adam; *ed:* Capitol Univ (BA) Eng Ed 1975; Dayton (MS) Schl Cnslng 1988; MS +36 Semester Hrs OH St Univ, Coll & Drake Univ; *cr:* Cols Whetstone HS Eng Tchr 1975-77; Hayes HS Schl Eng Tchr 1977-88, Schl Cnslr 1988-91; Thomas gton HS Schl Cnslr 1991-; *ai:* Dept Chprsn; Career Ed Dist Ldr; is Dist & Bldg Comms; NEA, OEA & Local 1975-, Bldg Rep; OH slrs Assn 1988-; OH Assn of Coll Cnslrs 1988-; First Presbyn 988-, Elder, Various Comms; OH Peer Helpers Assn 1988-, Bd, St Coord; OH Swim Coaches Assn Svc Awd; Amer Red Cross, nal Vol Awd; *office:* Thomas Worthington HS 300 W Granville Rd gton OH 43085

JOHN ROBERT, Biology & Environment Sci Tchr; *b:* Barre, PA; *m:* Kathleen Sceski; *c:* Emily, Christopher; *ed:* urg Univ Bio (BS) 1971, (MED) 1975; *cr:* Pequea Valley HS Tchr *i:* Portfolio, Restructuring Comms; Stu Assistance Team Mem; ich, Tchr Trng Mentor; NEA 1971-; *office:* Pequea Valley HS 4033 ort Rd Kinzers PA 17535*

I, ALVA VICTORIA, Assoc Prof of Modern Languages; *b:* Piura, : St Bonaventure Univ (BA) Modern Langs 1973; Binghamton NY (MA) Romance Langs 1976; St Bonaventure Univ (MS) Ed nghamton Univ SUNY (PHD) Comparative Lit 1988; *cr:* Fillmore al Span Tchr 1976-79; St Bonaventure Univ Assoc Prof of Modern 979-; Binghamton Univ SUNY Lecturer Romance Langs 1986-88; Senate; Refounding Comm; Campus Ministry; Asociacion onal De Hispanistas; Northeast Modern Lang Assn; Amer Assn Span, Portuguese; Xi Delta; Pi Delta Pi; Assn for Advancement , Rsrch, Dev in Third World 1990-, Regnl Advy Mem; Tchng Fac Tchng Excl Recognition Awd 1992; Fac Summer Grants 1990, ublications Translations 1990, 1993; *office:* Saint Bonaventure Box 78 Saint Bonaventure NY 14778

I, DOROTHY B., Chemistry Teacher; *b:* Trenton, NJ; *ed:* Court Coll (BA) Chem 1960; Villanova Univ (MA) Chem 1971; d City Univ of NY, Trenton St Coll, Rider Univ; *cr:* Notre Dame m Tchr 1960-69; Pennsbury HS Chem Tchr 1969-; *office:* ry HS 705 Hood Blvd Fairless Hills PA 19030

R, JANICE MUELLER, Elementary Teacher & Vice Prin; *b:* NJ; *m:* Lawrence; *c:* David; *ed:* Trenton St Coll (BS) Ed 1959; *cr:* Schl 1st Grd Tchr 1959-67; St Clare Schl 1980-; *ai:* NCEA 1980-; Clare Schl 39 Allwood Rd Clifton NJ 07014

R, LAWRENCE PETER, Ninth Grade Reading Teacher; *b:* vn, PA; *ed:* Univ of Pittsburgh at Johnstown (BS) Elem Ed 1987; g Univ & Saint Francis Coll (MA) Ed 1996; 18 Credit Hrs Admin ion Prgm; *cr:* Forest Hills Elem 3rd Grd Tchr 1989; Forest Hills th Grd Rdng Tchr 1989-; *ai:* Awds Comm Chm; Var Ftbl Asst 0th Grd Class Adv; Jaycee-Jayceette Adv; PSEA, NEA, FHEA ummerhill Twp Fire Co 1978-; *home:* PO Box 192 Salix PA 15952

E, JIM, High School Mathematics Tchr; *b:* New Haven, CT; *m:* ravich; *c:* Christina; *ed:* Yale Univ (BA) Pol Sci & Intnl Relations Sacred Heart Univ Math Instr 1992-93; East Haven HS Math Tchr ; West Haven HS Math Tchr 1994-; *ai:* Chess Club Adv; USCF oach; Math Assn of Amer, MENSA 1993-; Master Captain US it Marine; Prof Assn of Diving Instrs Divemaster; Eagle Scout; ant Stud Nuclear Physics at Univ of PA 1978; *office:* West Haven rcle St West Haven CT 06516*

OLA, THOMAS, Industrial Arts & Tech Tchr; *b:* Hackensack, NJ; h Katherine Scoccimarro; *c:* Matthew; *ed:* Montclair St Coll (BA) & Tech 1971, (MA) Ind Arts & Tech 1973; Paramedic Ed Union Jackson Twp HS Industrial Arts Tchr 1971-72; Montclair St Coll st, Ind Ed & Tech Tchr 1972-73; Bloomfield HS Ind Arts, Tech 73-; *ai:* Ski Club; Auto Mechanics Club; Anti DWI Prgm Coord; EA, Essex Co EA, Bloomfield EA 1973-; Rochelle Park FD 1978-, Officer, Fire Fighter of Yr 1992; Chilton Mem Hospital 1986-, ic; Montclair St Coll MA Fellowship; Bergen Cty 200 Club Unit Rescue; *office:* Bloomfield HS 160 Broad St Bloomfield NJ

DEBORAH PREISS, Business Teacher; *b:* Buffalo, NY; *m:* d J.; *c:* John, Robert, Joseph; *ed:* D'Youville Coll (BS) Scndry Bus ; Canisius Coll (MS) Bus Ed 1983; Alderson-Broaddus Coll; *cr:* Erectors & Haulers Staff Accountant 1977-80; Pioneer Cntrl Schl s Tchr 1980-88; Panama Cntrl Schl Dist Bus Tchr 1989-; *ai:* Stu ss; NHS Co-Adv; NEA, CCBTA 1989-; *office:* Panama Cntrl Schl North St Panama NY 14767

FANTI, CYNTHIA L., Business Teacher; *b:* Alexandria Bay, NY; d M.; *c:* Francesca, Dominic; *ed:* SUNY at Oswego (BS) Bus Ed SUNY at Potsdam (MS) Inst Tech, Media Mngmt 1993; *cr:* burg Correctional Facility Summer Bus Tchr 1989; Potsdam Sr HS r 1989-; *ai:* FBLA, Modified Girls Bsktbl Coach 1989-92; Sr Class 90-; Kappa Delta Phi 1988-; Organized, Instructed Cmptr tions Mini-Courses; *office:* Potsdam Sr HS 29 Leroy St Potsdam 76*

KAS, LYNN DUFFY, English Teacher; *b:* Pittsburgh, PA; *m:* A.; *c:* Holly, Luke; *ed:* Boston Coll (BA) Eng 1979; NH Writing *r:* Stoughton Jr HS Eng Tchr 1979-80; Newman Jr HS Eng Tchr ; D C Heath Publishing Co Ed, Lang Arts Tchr 1983-87; Hartford Tchr 1987-89; St Pius Schl Eng Tchr 1989-90; Mascoma Vly Regnl Tchr 1990-; *ai:* Grd 9-12th Curr Facilitator; Stu, Tchr Supvr; NHS n Comm; 9th Grd Oratorical Contest; NCTE 1987-; NHATE 1994-; 90-; Childrens Ctr of Upper Vly 1994-, VP; *home:* 94 Wellington anon NH 03766*

IIC, NANCY A., Program Director; *b:* Roaring Spring, PA; *m:* *c:* John, Michael; *ed:* Penn St (BS) Medical Tech 1978; *cr:* Nason Hospital Medical Technologist 1978-82; Roxborough Meml Hospital Medical Technologist 1982-83; Medical Coll Hospital Medical Technologist 1985-92; Manor Jr Coll Educl Coord 1989-94; Prgm Dir 1994-; *ai:* Amer Soc of Clinical Pathologists Certified Medical Technologist 1978, Hematologist 1982; *office:* Manor Jr Coll 700 Fox Chase Rd Jenkintown PA 19046

CERASO, JOHN W., Guidance Counselor; *b:* New Kesington, PA; *m:* Paulette Gestl; *c:* Mark J., Lisa, Gina; *ed:* Washington & Jefferson (BS) Chem 1966; IN Univ of PA (MA) Cnslng 1974; *cr:* Penn-Trafford S Dist Sci Tchr 1966-68; Kiski Area S Dist Phys Sci Tchr 1968-74, Guid Cnslr 1974-; *ai:* Career Day, Fin Aid Night Dir; PSEA, NEA, KAEA 1968-; Gift of Time Tribute 1995; Umbrella Soc Agency Bd of Dir; YMCA Bd of Dir.

CERASO, MICHAEL MATTHEW, English & Magnet Resource Tchr; *b:* New Haven, CT; *m:* Jody Lynn Kamens; *c:* Melissa L., David A.; *ed:* Southern CT St Univ (BS) Ed, 9-12 Eng 1973, (MS) Eng 1982; 6th Yr Admin, Supervision 1986; Yale Child Stud Ctr Comer Schls Ldrshp Dev Prgm 1995-; JCC Anti-Defamation League Holocaust Ed Project 1986-92; *cr:* Richard C. Lee HS 9th-12th Grd Eng Tchr 1974-75, Rdng Prgm Coord 1976-86; Career HS Eng, Jrnlsm, Lead Tchr 1986-94, Eng, Magnet Resource Tchr 1995-; *ai:* Summer Enrichment Prgm Coord; Educl Ldrshp Team Chm; HS, 2 Elem Schls Cooperative Tutorial Prgm Coord; Schl Planning, Mngmt Team, Yale-New Haven Hosp Partnership Comms; AFT, NHFT 1974-, Steward; Admin, Supervision Assn 1985-; Sleeping Grant St Park Assn 1988-; Amer Philatelic Soc 1975-; Yale Child Stud Ctr Ldrshp Dev Prgm Cert of Achvmt 1996; PTSO Cert of Appreciation 1995; Hill Cntrl Schl Cert of Appreciation 1995; New Haven Fnd Excl Grant 1986; *office:* Career HS 21 Wooster Pl New Haven CT 06511

CERAULO, LARRY, Physical Education Teacher; *b:* Jamaica, NY; *m:* Ellen; *c:* Larry Jr., Michael; *ed:* CCNY (BS) PE 1973, (MS) Hlth Ed 1976; Queens Coll Prof Diploma in Admin & Supervision 1983; *cr:* Townsend Harris HS PE Tchr & Coach 8 Yrs; South Shore HS PE Tchr & Coach 4 Yrs; JHS #324 PE Tchr 6 Yrs; Springfield Gardens HS PE Tchr & Coach 3 Yrs; *ai:* Girls Var Bsktbl, Sftbl & Boys Var Bowling Team Coach 8 Yrs; Summer Camp Big Apple Games 12 Yrs; NYC Coaches Assoc 1988-; Vly Stream Little League 1973-83; Girls Bsktbl Coach of Yr 1987-88; Girls Sftbl Coach of Yr 1993-94; *office:* Townsend Harris HS 149-11 Melbourne Ave Flushing NY 11367

CERBONE, DWAYNE JOSEPH, HS Mathematics Teacher; *b:* Ronkon Koma, NY; *m:* Noreen Krieser; *c:* Aaron; *ed:* SUNY at Gereseo (BA) Math, Scndry Ed 1992; 12 Addl Credits; *cr:* Churchville-Chili CSD Math Tchr 1994-; *ai:* Jr HS Steering, HS Staff Dev Comm; Instr Support Team Mem; NCTM 1992-; NEA 1994-; *office:* Churchville-Chili Cntrl Schl Buffalo Rd Rochester NY 14428

CERCONE, JOSEPH MICHAEL, Secondary Mathematics Teacher; *b:* Buffalo, NY; *m:* Kathleen Rose Milletello; *c:* Joseph John; *ed:* Canisius Coll (BS) Acctng 1965; 60 Grad Hrs Above BA in Math Buffalo St Tchr Coll 1970-77; *cr:* PS #1 7-8 Grd Math Tchr 1967-76; PS #77 7-8 Grd Math Tchr 1976-78; West Hertle Schl 7-8 Grd Math & Remedial Math Tchr 1978-80; Lafayette HS Math Tchr 1980-82; Cmapus West-Buffalpo St Tchrs Coll Gen Math, Pre-Algebra, Regents Course I Tchr 1982-91; Buffalo Alternative-St Gerards Schl Transition Math Tchr 1991-; *ai:* Weight Trng, Sunshine Club; NEA, BTF 1967-; NCTM 1985-; Cert of Recognition & Achvmt from Buffalo Alternative-St Gerard's, Campus West-Buffalo St Tchrs Coll, PS #1, Buffalo Bd of Ed, Lafayette HS; Math Team Awd 1989; *office:* St Gerards Schl 2515 Bailey Ave Buffalo NY 14215*

CERICOLA, SHARON HARRISON, Third Grade Teacher; *b:* Syracuse, NY; *m:* Harold D.; *c:* Harold, Paula, Amy; *ed:* Auburn Comm Coll (AA) 1967; Oneonta St Coll (BS) Elem Ed 1969; Cortland Coll (ME) Rdng Ed 1971; Addl 6 Hrs; *cr:* Lakeland Elem Schl K, 2-3 Grd Tchr 1969-; *ai:* Lakeland Compact Site based Comm Tchr 1994-, Compact Bienniel Review Comm 1996; Intl Rdng Assn 1969-1995; Solvay Tchrs Assn 1971-73, Bldg Rep, 1994-, Retirement Alternate, 1995-, Retirement Del, 1993-96, Bldg Rep; AFT, NEA 1969-; TAWL Assoc of C.N.Y.; Lakeland PTA 1970-75, Sec; Order of Eastern Star 1972-; Girl Scouts of CNY 1986-, Ldr of Troop 264, 267; Kasaog Lake Assn 1978-, BSA 1988-92, Adult Comm Troop 72; Cmptr Classes 1980; Mini Grant 1993; ITIP Trng, Cooperative Staff Dev 1993; Cmptr Classes 1996; NY St Cmpct Site Bsd Tm Mem; *home:* 440 Horan Rd Solvay NY 13209

CERINO, RUTH ANN O'HARA, Fourth Grade Teacher; *b:* New Haven, CT; *m:* Matthew L.; *c:* Elizabeth Anne; *ed:* Southern CT Univ (BA) Intermediate Upper Ed 1969; Fairfield Univ (MA) Media 1973; Inservice Courses 21 Hrs; *cr:* Race Brook Schl 6th Grd Tchr 1969, 4th Grd Tchr 1969-74, 5th Grd Tchr 1974-79, 4th Grd Tchr 1979-84, 6th Grd Tchr 1984-92; Turkey Hill Schl 6th Grd Tchr 1992-94, 4th Grd Tchr 1994-; *ai:* Stu Cncl 1974-79; Caring Hands Comm 1994-; Staff Dev Comm 1992-94; Orange Tchrs League 1969-, Prsnl Policy Comm 1979-80, United Fund; CEA, NEA 1969-; Cath Charity League 1973-, Treas, VP, Pres.

CERNE, GERALD JOHN, Adjunct Biology Professor; *b:* Amsterdam, NY; *m:* Elaine; *c:* Michael, Diana Cunningham, Maryanne Hammund; *ed:* SUNY at Albany (BS) Bio, Sci 1962, (MS) Ed, Bio 1966; 60 Hrs past MS in Sic, Ed Through St, Federal Prgms; *cr:* South Colonie Cntrl Schls Bio, Sci Tchr 1962-95; NYS Ed Dept Adj Consultant, Writer, Editor 1968-75; Schenectady Co Comm Coll Adj Bio Prof 1969-; *ai:* NYSUT 1962-; AFT; STANYS, Co-Dir of NYS Sci Congress; BALSA 1992-; BPO Elks USA 1988-.*

CERNIGLIA, ROBERTA KROMBAR, English & Public Speaking Tchr; *b:* New London, CT; *m:* Donald J.; *c:* David, Adam; *ed:* Ea Nassau Comm Coll (AA) Lbrl Arts 1966; Eastern MI Univ (BA) Eng, Ed 1968; SUNY New Paltz (MA) Eng, Ed 1974; *cr:* Gen Douglas Mc Arthur HS Eng Tchr 1968-69; John F. Kennedy HS Eng Tchr 1969-70; Arlington HS Eng Tchr, Pub Speaking 1970-; *ai:* AFT, NY St United Tchrs 1970-; Toast Masters Intnl 1988-95, VP of Ed; *office:* Arlington HS North Campus 263 State Route 55 Lagrangeville NY 12540*

CERONE, ROBERT ALEXANDER, Sociology, Govt & Psych Tchr; *b:* Rochester, NY; *m:* Linda Howie; *c:* Robert, Elizabeth; *ed:* St Univ Coll at Buffalo (BS) Soc Stud 1965, (MS) Soc Stud 1968; *ai:* Stu Cncl Adv; AFT 1973-, Del 6 Yrs; NYSUT 1973-, Del 8 Yrs; Credit Union Bd of Dirs, VP; *office:* N Tonawanda Sr H S 405 Meadow Dr North Tonawanda NY 14120

CEROW, JACQUES ANTOINE, Business Tchr & Computer Coord; *b:* Alexandria Bay, NY; *m:* Cynthia Rae Norton; *c:* Michelle Hodge, Jay; *ed:* Jefferson Comm Coll (AAS) Acctng 1966; North TX Univ (BBA) Bus Ed 1970; Certfd Driver Ed Tchr; 48 Credit Hrs Grad Work; *cr:* Sackets Harbour Cntrl Schl Bus Tchr 1971-; *ai:* Dist Treas; Extracurricular Act Auditor; Cmptr Coord; NEA 1990-; Local Tchrs Assn 1971-.

CERRA, LINDA STRASBURGER, Spanish Teacher; *b:* Scranton, PA; *m:* John; *c:* Selena Rose; *ed:* Marywood Coll (BA) Span 1978; Univ of Scranton (MA) Scndry Schl Admin 1985; *cr:* Scranton Cntrl HS Span Tchr 1979-92; West Scranton HS Span Tchr 1993-; *ai:* Peer Tutoring Club Adv; AFT 1979-.

CERRETO, LUCILLE J., Cosmetology & Voc Ed Teacher; *b:* Newark, NJ; *m:* Joseph Sr.; *c:* Carmen, Dominic, Joseph Jr.; *ed:* Montclair St Univ (BA) Eng 1989; 24 Addl Hrs; *cr:* Belleville Sr HS Cosmetology Tchr 1984-; *ai:* Cosmetology Club Adv; Crisis Intervention Mediator; Curr Revision Comm; NEA, NJEA 1984-; VCEA, VEA 1993-; Montclair St Univ Grant 1995; *home:* 136 Carpenter St Belleville NJ 07109

CERULLO, MICHAEL PETER, 7th-12th Grade Technology Tchr; *b:* Lawrence, MA; *m:* Fay Levine; *c:* Ryan Lee, Dillon Avery; *ed:* Suffolk Cty Comm Coll (AA) Gen Stud 1970; SUNY at Oswego (BS) K-12th Industrial Arts Ed 1973; New York Inst of Tech (MS) Commnctn Arts 1980; Sullivan Co & Orange Co Comm Colls E Sci, Physics & Gen Sci 1995; *cr:* Uniondale HS 9th-12th Grd Industrial Arts Tchr 1973; Pierson HS 9th-12th Grd Industrial Arts Tchr 1974-85; Roscoe Cntrl Schls 7th-12th Grd Tech & Sci Tchr 1988-; *ai:* Tech Comm Chm; Internet Distance Learning; Amateur Radio Club; NYSTEA 1975-; STTEA 1988-; ROSTEA 1988-; STANYS 1993-; SCARS 1990-; EMUG 1990-; 3 NYSEG Grants; NSF Grant; Carl Perkins Federal Grant; *office:* Roscoe Central Schl Academy St Roscoe NY 12776

CERVELLO, ALPHONSE ADEN,SR., 5th & 6th Grade Principal; *b:* Bedford, England; *c:* Al Jr., Amy Joy; *ed:* Youngstown St U (BS) Ed, Math, Soc Stud 1969; Westminster Coll (MS) Admin 1972; Attnd Azusa Pacific Coll, Seattle Pacific Coll; *cr:* Lakeview HS Tchr 1967-69; Frank Ohl MS Tchr, Coach 1969-95, Asst Prin 1995-; *ai:* Family Math Night; Handicapped Children Fishing Derby; Punt, Pass, Kick Contest; OEA, NEA, NEOTA 1969-; Austintown Optimist 1993-, VP; BSA Order of Arrow, Life Scout; *home:* 5260 Pine Tree Ln Boardman OH 44512

CERVINO, FRANCESCA DIANE, Math Teacher; *b:* Cambria Heights, NY; *ed:* St John's Univ (BS) Ed, Math 7-9 1992, (MS) Scndry Ed 1993; *cr:* Bishop Loughlin Meml HS Math Tchr 1993-, Rel Tchr 1994-95; *ai:* NCTM 1990-; LIMACON 1994-; *office:* Bishop Loughlin Meml HS 357 Clermont Ave Brooklyn NY 11238*

CERVONE, CARMELA REALMUTO, 6th Grade Teacher; *b:* Brooklyn, NY; *m:* Ray J.; *c:* Ray, Lisa; *ed:* Monmouth Univ (BS) Elem Ed 1989; *cr:* Woodmere Elem Schl 6th Grd Tchr 1989-; *ai:* Ed Advy Comm 2 Yrs; NEA 1989-; Phi Delta Kappa Most Promising Educator Awd 1988-89.

CESARE, MELODY ANN EIERMANN, 7th-12th Grade Math Teacher; *b:* Bay Shore, NY; *m:* Peter; *c:* Nicholas, Alexander; *ed:* SUNY at Cortland (BS) Elem Ed 1986; L. I. Univ (MS) Cmptr Ed 1990; *cr:* Copiague UFSD 7-12 Grd Math Tchr 1986-; *office:* Copiague UFSD Schl 1100 Dixon Ave Copiague NY 11716

CESCA, SHARON ANN, Second Grade Teacher; *b:* Danbury, CT; *ed:* Western CT St Univ (MS) Elem Ed 1989; 30 Addl Credit Hrs; *cr:* Great Plain Schl Grd 1 Tchr 1975-76; Shelter Rock Schl Grd 2 Tchr 1976-77; Mill Ridge Int Schl Grd 5 Tchr 1977-79; Hayestown Ave Schl Grds 2, 3 Tchr 1979-; *ai:* Parents Rdng, Writing Wkshp Ldr; Ed Fair Co-Chair; Pitney Bowes After Schl Prgm Tchr; NEA 1976-, Bldg Rep, Chprsn; Alpha Delta Kappa 1980-; Federal Grant Executor; *office:* Hayestown Ave Schl Hayestown Ave Danbury CT 06810*

CEZUS, JOSEPH JAMES, 9th, 11th & 12th Grd Eng Tchr; *b:* Hartford, CT; *m:* Maria Irene Schulewsky; *c:* Kate, Larissa; *ed:* Univ of Hartford (BA) Eng & Ed 1974, (MA) Rdng & Ed 1976; *cr:* Sagepark MS Stu & Sub Tchr 1973-74; East Windsor MS Permanent Sub Tchr 1974; East Windsor Jr-Sr HS Eng Tchr 1974-; *ai:* Class, NHS, Newspaper & Yrbk Adv; Drama Coach; GED & Eng as 2nd Lang Instr; Magazine Drive Coord; Assessment & Portfolio Comm; EWEA 1974-; NCTE 1974-; CEA 1974-; 21st Century Tchr of Yr 1994; Article Pub; *office:* East Windsor Jr Sr HS 76 S Main St East Windsor CT 06088

CHABE, ALEXANDER MICHAEL, Adjunct Professor of Education; *b:* Gary, IN; *m:* Mary Janice Gilbert; *c:* Daniel Stafford, David Gilbert; *ed:* MI St Coll (AB) His 1948; IN Univ (MS) Ed 1950, (EDD) Ed 1959; Norwich Univ (MA) Russian Lang, Lit 1993; 12 Credit Hrs San Francisco St Coll; 6 Credit Hrs Univ of CA at Berkeley; 3 Credit Hrs KS Univ; *cr:* MI St Coll Russian Instr 1948-49; Calumet Twp Schls 4 Grd Tchr, K-6 Grd Prin 1950-51; San Bruno Park Schl System 3 Grd Tchr 1951-52; Benton Harbor MI Schl System 5-6 Grd Tchr 1952-54; Ottawa Cty Bd of Ed K-8 Grd Cty Supvr of Schls 1954-56; Park Coll Ed Asst Prof 1956-58; SUNY Coll Ed Prof 1959-; *ai:* Kappa Delta Pi, Ed Club Adv; NEA 1950-; United Univ Professions 1959-; Kappa Delta Pi; Phi Delta Kappa; Delta Tau Kappa; Norwich Univ Russian Schl Soc Sci Rsrch Cncl Flwshp; NY Fac Scholar in Intnl Stud; Outstdng Edctrs of Amer; Democracy and Communism; How People Live in the USSR; How People Live in France; Numerous Articles Pub; Sound Film Strips; Sound Slide Sets.

CHACE, JOEL EDWARD, English Teacher; *b:* Walton, NY; *m:* Candace Louise Benjamin; *c:* Larissa, Logan, Brechyn, Tristan; *ed:* Colgate Univ (BS) Philosophy, Religion 1972; Syracuse Univ (MA) Creative Writing 1976; *cr:* O'Neal Schl Eng Tchr 1979-80; Stavanger Amer Schl Norway Eng Tchr 1980-82; King Schl Eng Tchr 1982-85; Mercersburg Acad Eng Tchr 1976-79, 1985-; Schl Yr Abroad France Eng Tchr 1989-90; *ai:* Lit Magazine Adv; Peer Group Adv; Var Womens Tennis Coach; NEH Fellowship; The Harp Beyong The Wall Poetry Book 1984; Red Ghost Poetry Book Winner 1992 Persephone Press Book Awd; Pushcart Prize Nom; Pub Poetry Books, Court of Ass-Sizes 1995, Twentieth Century Deaths 1996; Poetry Ed of Antietam Review 1996-; *office:* The Mercersburg Acad Mercersburg PA 17236

CHADOWSKI, THERESE C., Guidance Counselor; *b:* Cleveland, OH; *ed:* Indiana Univ of PA (BS) Bus Ed 1979; Cleveland St Univ (MED) Guid, Cnslng 1995; *cr:* Villa Angela Acad Bus Tchr 1979-89; Beaumont Schl Asst Treas, Tchr 1989-92; Notre Dame Cathedral Latin Guid Cnslr 1992-; *ai:* Stu Cncl Co-Moderator; *office:* Notre Dame Cathedral Latin Sch 13000 Auburn Rd Chardon OH 44024*

CHADWICK, CHRISTINA PAGE, Teacher for the Deaf; *b:* Worcester, MA; *m:* Benjamin W.; *ed:* Springfield Coll (BS) Elem Ed 1990; Smith Coll (MED) Tchr for the Deaf 1991; *cr:* F. J. Mc Grath Schl Tchr for the Deaf 1991-; *ai:* Project Lift Tutor; Comm Ed Vol; NEA, MA Teach Assn, Educl Assn of Worc, Cncl for Educ of Deaf 1991-; Smith Church, Yth Comm; Grace Coolidge Flwshp; *office:* Francis Mcgrath Elem Schl 51 Chadwick St Worcester MA 01609

CHADWICK, DONNA MC COWAN, Assoc Professor of Accounting; *b:* Cincinnati, OH; *m:* Robert Allen; *ed:* Wright St Univ (BFA) Theater Arts Mngmt 1984, (MBA) Acctng 1986; *cr:* NCR Corp Fin Specialist, External Reporting Analyst 1986-88; Wright St Univ Acctng Instr 1988-90; Sinclair Comm Coll Asst Prof of Acctng 1990-94, Assoc Prof of Acctng 1994-; *ai:* Stu Act Prgm Bd Fac Rep; Learning Excl Task Force; Campus Bible Flwshp Fac Spon; Inst of Mngmt Accountants 1986-, Bd of Dir; Amer Inst of Certfd Pub Accountants 1988-; Certfd Pub Accountant; Certfd Mngmt Accountant; Robert Beyer Silver Medal 1990; Author Instrs Manual for Acctng Prins Manual; *office:* Sinclair Comm Coll 444 W 3rd St Dayton OH 45402

CHADWICK, JOY CARPENTER, Kindergarten Teacher; *b:* New York, NY; *m:* Benjamin; *c:* Alden, Laura, Katherine; *ed:* 45 Credit Hrs in Early Chldhd Dev, Ed Emphasis on Whole Lang; *cr:* Billerica Co-op Tchr 1971-73; Tyngsboro Pub Schls Tchr 1973-; *ai:* Steering Comm for Accreditation; Assessment Rdng, Math Curr Dev; Initiated Grandparents Day, Pen Pal Yearly Prgms; Tyngsboro Tchr, MA Tchr Assn 1973-; Chalmsford Friends of Music 1974-80, Pres; Chelmsford Cultural Cncl 1986-88; AFS 1974-82, Host Family, Cnslr; Bell Ringer 1988-, Asst Dir; *office:* Winslow Schl Middlesex Turnpike Tyngsboro MA 01879

CHADWICK, SAMANTHA P., Social Studies Teacher; *b:* Bronx, NY; *m:* Walter W. III; *ed:* Iona Coll (BA) His 1990, (MS) Scndry Ed 1991; Addl

Courses, Grants Admin, Rel; *cr:* Adelphi Acad Tchr 1991-92; Herbert H. Lehman HS Soc Stud Tchr 1992-; *ai:* Mock Trial Coach; AFT, UFT; Endowment for Hum NY St Grant.

CHAFFEE, LINDA JANE, Science Department Head; *b:* Westerly, RI; *m:* Kenneth F.; *c:* Kenneth B., Christopher Allen, Susan, Jennifer Allen; *ed:* Brown Univ (BA) Chem 1967; RI Life Cert Math, Gen Sci, Chem, Physics; NSTA Cert Chem, Physics; *cr:* Westerly HS Math, Sci Tchr 1978-93, Sci Dept Head 1993-; *ai:* Fac Collabortive; Instructional, Schl Improvement Team; Site Cncl; NSTA 1985-; AAPT 1986-; ASCD 1995; Incorporator Westerly Pub Lib 1990-; Presidential Scholars Distinguished Tchr 1990; St Presidential Awd Excl Tchng Sci 1993; *office:* Westerly HS 23 Ward Ave Westerly RI 02891*

CHAFFEE, MICHAEL ANTHONY, English & Humanities Teacher; *b:* Youngstown, OH; *m:* Kathy Brown; *c:* Jonathan (dec), Scott, Keeley; *ed:* Youngstown St Univ (BA) Eng 1982, (MA) Eng 1990; *cr:* Windham HS Eng Tchr & Vllybl Coach 1982-; *ai:* Girls Vllybl & Girls Track Coach; Jr Class & Prom Adv; NEA & OEA 1982-; WTA 1982-, Pres; OH Vllybl Coaches Assoc 1990-, Dist Dir; Akron Touchdown Club Vllybl Coach of Yr 1992 & 1995; Portage Cty League Vllybl Coach of Yr 1992 & 1995; Dist III Vllybl Coach of Yr 1993 & 1994; Ashland Oil Co Golden Apple Awd Winner; *office:* Windham HS 9530 Bauer Ave Windham OH 44288*

CHAGNON, DEBORAH BOWEN, Sixth Grade Teacher; *b:* Medina, NY; *m:* Roger G. Jr.; *c:* Heather, Roger III; *ed:* SUNY at Fredonia (BA) Elem Ed 1972; 30 Addl Hrs 1976, 6 Hrs Cmptr Lit 1987; *ai:* Bldg Level Teams Mem 1994-; Tech, Stu Assistance Team Mem; Impact; NEA 1981-; Ripley Tchrs Assn 1972-; Delta Kappa Gamma 1988-, Research Dir; Westfield Meml Hospital Auxiliary; Tchr of Yr 1993-94; *home:* 53 Elm St Westfield NY 14787

CHAHDA, ISABEL JIMENEZ, Spanish Teacher; *b:* Cleveland, OH; *m:* Mario; *c:* Marisa, Mario, Carena; *ed:* Cleveland St Univ (BA) K-12 Span 1975; Addl 12 Quarter Hrs Elem Ed 1975; *cr:* Magnificat HS Span Tchr 1976-83, 1990-; *ai:* Span Conversational for Advanced Stdnts Seminar; Strongsville Chandler Commons Swim Team 1995-, Sec; Ashland Tchr Achvmt Awds Eastern KY Univ; *office:* Magnificat HS 20770 Hilliard Blvd Rocky River OH 44116

CHAIET, CARL K., Art Teacher; *b:* New York, NY; *m:* Lynn Kearcher; *c:* Max; *ed:* Hunter Coll (BA) Fine Arts, Ed 1973; Herbert Lehman Coll (MA) Printing, Drawing 1976; NY Univ Aesthetics 1980-82; *cr:* Mercy Coll Art Ed Instr 1988-90; N Rockland HS Art Tchr 1973-; *ai:* Curr Coordination Comm Chm 1980; Soccer Coach 1973-78; *office:* North Rockland HS Hammond Rd Thiells NY 10984*

CHAINEY, DOLORES MANCUSO, Biology Teacher; *b:* Utica, NY; *m:* Hendrick J.; *c:* Maryellen; *ed:* Hamilton Coll (BA) Bio 1972; SUNY Sci-Hlth Ctr 30 Grad Hrs Clinical Pathology; SUNY at Cortland CAS in Educl Admin; *cr:* Univ Hosp SUNY Sci-Hlth Ctr Hematology Instr 1975-78; Roosevelt Schl Sci-Math Tchr 1978-87; Donovan Jr HS Sci Dept Chair, Bio Tchr 1987-94; Proctor Sr HS Sci Tchr 1994-; *ai:* Yrbk Adv; Sci Fair Coord; Bio Mentor; PDK 1989-; NYSUT, NABT, STANYS, UTA 1978-; Cath Schl Bd 1994-; BPW 1996; AAUW 1975-; AFCEA Awd Excl Sci Ed; Woodrow Wilson Bio Outreach Prgm Selected for Participation in; *office:* T. R. Proctor Sr HS 1203 Hilton Ave Utica NY 13501*

CHAISSON, MAUREEN, Biology Teacher; *b:* Chester, PA; *m:* Ronald Paul; *c:* Matthew John; *ed:* Bloomsburg Univ (BS) Scndry Ed, Bio, Chem 1984; St Univ of NY at New Paltz (MS) Scndry Ed, Bio 1988; *cr:* Kingston City Schls HS Sci, Bio Tchr 1984-91; Highland Cntrl Schl Dist HS Sci, Bio Tchr 1991-; *ai:* Ulster Cty Math, Sci Schl Industry Cncl Adv; Bldg Ldrshp Team; Interdisciplinary Conf Day Comm; Adv, Helper Sci Olympiad; STANYS, Phi Kappa Phi, NABT 1984-; Highland Parent-Tchrs Assn, Sci Fair Coord HPTA 1991-; Empire St Schlsp Recipient Grad Level; *office:* Highland HS 320 Pancake Hollow Rd Highland NY 12528*

CHAKEMIAN, K. KENNETH, Foreign Language Instructor; *b:* Fitchburg, MA; *ed:* Tufts Univ (AB) Double Major Classics Latin & Greek, Fr 1967; Harvard Univ (AM) Classical Philology 1969, (PHD) Classical Philology 1974; *cr:* Harvard Univ Tchng Fellow in the Classics 1969-71; The Winsor Schl Instr of Latin, Greek 1974-75; Meml Jr HS Foreign Lang Instr 1975-81; Fitchburg HS Foreign Lagn Instr 1981-; *ai:* Chprsn of Foreign Lang Dept 1987-89; General Excl Comm, NHS Comm, Schlsp Comm 1981-; Chprsn For Lang Dept at Meml Jr HS 1980-81; Classical Assn of New England 1965-; Amer Classical League 1975-; Fitchburg Tchrs Assn 1976-; MTA 1976-; NEA 1976-; Finalist for Warren Litsky Distinguished Tchr Awd 1995; Distinguished Tchr Awd 1993; Curr Grant 1980, 1987; Harvard Univ Graduate Prize Fellow 1967-72; Fellowships 1972-74; Tufts Univ Summa Cum Laude 1967; Phi Beta Kappa 1966; Deans List 8 Semesters 1963-67; Boston Greek Prize 1965; Honorable Mention for Woodrow Wilson Natl Fellowship 1967; Who's Who Among Armenians in N Amer 1994; Around the World in Fitchburg Vol II 1975; Dictionary of Intnl Biography 1973; Comm Ldrs of Amer 1971; General Excl Prize 1963; Spec Honor Grad 1963; Gold F Recipient 1963; Winner of Numerous First Prizes in Latin, Fr, Advanced Algebra 1960-63; Winner Fitchburg, Dist Elks Youth Leadership Contest, Honorable Mention St Competition 1963; Editor in Chief of Schl Publication 1962-63.

CHALIFOUR, LINDA POLINSKY, English Teacher; *b:* Boston, MA; *m:* Clark; *c:* Lisa Webber; *ed:* Jackson Coll in Tufts Univ (BA) 1961; St Univ of NY at Oswego 30 Credits Rdng Ed; *cr:* George Fishburne Schl His Tchr 1962-64; South Jr HS Eng Tchr 1964-69; Oswego HS Eng Tchr 1969-76; Hamilton HS East Eng, Jrnlsm Tchr 1976-; *ai:* Newspaper Adv; NJEA, NEA, HTEA 1976-; Barnegat Sail Club 1985-; Sunrise Beach Club 1986-; *office:* Hamilton HS East 2900 Klockner Rd Hamilton Square NJ 08690

CHALMERS, JOAN BOVE, Mathematics & Science Teacher; *b:* Philadelphia, PA; *m:* Joseph; *c:* David, Stephen; *ed:* Pace Univ (BS) Bio 1965; St Josephs Univ (MA) Ed 1968; Rutgers Univ Cert Ed 1980; *cr:* Temple Medical Schl Research 1965-71; Gloucester Cath HS Math & Sci Tchr 1979-; *ai:* Jr Class & Environment Club Adv; NSTA; Colwick Civic Assn 1975-, Past Pres; Woodbine Swim Clb Past Pres; *office:* Gloucester Catholic HS 333 Ridgeway St Gloucester City NJ 08030

CHAMBERLAIN, ROBERT J., Asst Prof of Clncl Radiography; *b:* Dover, NJ; *m:* Jeri Mandel; *c:* Brett, Max, Jonathan; *ed:* Fairleigh Dickinson Univ (BS) Bio 1969; Montclair St Univ (MA) 1980; Currently Enrolled at Univer of Med & Dentistry of NJ in biomedical Informatics; *cr:* Middlesex Cty Coll Asst Prof of Radiography 1969-88; Univ of Med & Dentistry of NJ Asst Prof of Radiography 1988-; *ai:* appointments & Promotions Comm; Comm on Comms; ARRT 1965-; ASRT 1994-; AERS 1990-; *office:* Univ Of Med & Dentistry Of NJ 65 Bergen St Newark NJ 07107*

CHAMBERLAIN, ROBIN RENEE WALK, Vocal Music Teacher; *b:* Defiance, OH; *m:* Jay; *c:* Shaile, Jayla; *ed:* The Defiance Coll (BS) Vocal Mus Ed 1989; BGSU; IUPU; *cr:* Antwerp Local Schl Vocal Music Dir 1990-; *ai:* Sixteeners Dir; Sr Class Adv; Girls JV Coach; OMEA 1991-; NEA 1991-; Sherwood Comm Church 1994-, Music Dir; *office:* Antwerp Local Schls Archer Dr Antwerp OH 45813*

CHAMBERLAND, ROSE MARIE M.,CSJ, 5th Grade Teacher; *b:* Schenectady, NY; *ed:* Coll of St Rose at Albany (BS) Elem Ed 1960, (MS) Elem Ed, Rdng 1973; *cr:* St Bernard's Acad 5th Grd Tchr 1960-62; St Ann's Schl 5th Grd Tchr 1962-63; St Paul's Schl 1st Grd Tchr 1963-64; St Peter's Acad 1st Grd Tchr 1964-65; Cathedral Acad Kndgtn, 4th Grd Tchr 1966-70; St Mary's 7th-8th Grd Eng Tchr 1970-72; St Peter's 7th-8th Grd Eng, Soc Stud Tchr 1972-73; St Francis 7th-8th Grd Lang Arts Tchr 1973-74; Sacred Heart Schl 5th Grd, 6th-8th Grd Lang Arts Tchr 1974-79; Cath Cntrl HS 9th-12th Grd Rdng Tchr 1979-84; Sacred Heart Schl 1st Grd, 7th-8th Grd SAT Prep Tchr 1984-87; St Joseph's Schl 1st Grd, 7th-8th Grd SAT Prep Tchr 1984-87; Saint Ambrose Schl 3rd, 1st, 5th Grd Tchr 1987-; *ai:* After Schl Prgm; NCEA 1987-.

CHAMBERS, BETTYE THOMAS, Italian Teacher; *b:* Lynchburg, VA; *m:* Samuel Allen Jr.; *ed:* Sweet Briar Coll (BA) Fr 1962; Univ of VA (MA) Fr 1969; George Washington Univ (PHD) Fr 1979; *cr:* George Washington U Lecturer 1969-83; Georgetown Univ Adj Instr 1977-; *ai:* First, Second Yr Italian Lang Courses Coord; Cine Club Italiano Organizer; AATI 1993-; NEH Flwshp 1981-82, 1987-88, 1995-; *office:* Georgetown Univ 37th & O Sts NW Washington DC 20057

CHAMBERS, GERRY SZPANKA, Chem, Physics Tchr & Dept Chm; *b:* Mc Keesport, PA; *m:* George Mark; *c:* Mark, Jeffery; *ed:* Clarion (BS) Comprehensive Sci, Bio 1968; Attnd Kent St, Boston Univ, Case Western Reserve, Youngstown St; *cr:* West Miffin Lebanon Phys Sci Tchr 1968; Warren Western Reserve Phys Sci Tchr 1969-70; Bristol HS Chem Tchr 1971-72; Girard HS Chem, Physics, Bio Tchr 1972-; *ai:* Dept Chm; Stu Sci Assn; Sci, Physics Olympiad; Sci Fair; GEA 1972-, Sec, Bldg Rep; OEA, NEA 1969-; AAPT 1992-; Christ Episcopal Church 1969-, Sunday Schl Tchr; *office:* Girard HS 31 N Ward Ave Girard OH 44420

CHAMBERS, JACQUELINE MARIE, High School Math Teacher; *b:* Olean, NY; *m:* Jery Kenneth; *c:* Amy Michelle; *ed:* Univ of Buffalo (BS) Scndry Math 1968; Canisius Coll (MA) Scndry Guid, Cnslng 1973; 9 Addl Hrs; *cr:* Depew HS Math Tchr 1968-; *ai:* Depew Tchrs Org, NYSUT, AFT 1968-; *office:* Depew HS 5201 S Transit Rd Depew NY 14043

CHAMBERS, JOANNE PERKINS, English Teacher; *b:* Glens Falls, NY; *m:* James S.; *c:* Thomas A., Jennifer A.; *ed:* Green Mountain Coll (AA) Liberal Arts 1962; Keuka COll (BA) Eng 1964; SUNY at Albany (MA) Eng 1982; 30 Addl Grad Hrs; *cr:* Queensbury HS Eng Tchr 3 Yrs; Schalmont HS Eng Tchr 1 Yrs; Shenendohowa HS Eng Tchr 14 Yrs; Itinerant Sub Tchr; Hudson Valley Comm Coll Instr 3 Yrs; *ai:* Prin Selection Comm; Shared Decision Making Tm; NCTE, Outstanding Tchr of Composition; NY St United Tchrs 1964-; Amer Assn of Univ Women 1967-; Delta Kappa Gamma 1989-; Lib Bd 1986-, VP, Treas; Amer Assoc of Univ Women; Pub in Eng Journal; Dist Excl in Tchng Awd; Tchr of Yr 1994-95; *office:* Shenendehowa HS 970 Rt 146 Clifton Park NY 12065*

CHAMBERS, MARY JANE E., Social Studies Teacher; *b:* Philadelphia, PA; *ed:* St Joseph Univ (BA) His 1978, (MS) Ed 1986; 6 Hrs World Perspectives; 3 Hrs World After Cold War; 6 Hrs WW II; SAC 1994; *cr:* Blessed Virgin Mary Schl 8th Grd Tchr 1980-85; Gloucester Cath HS Soc Stud Tchr 1985-; *ai:* Play Dir; Drama Club Moderator; Liturgical Music Group; Rainbows; Peer Mediation; NCEA 1980-; SCTO 1985-; NCSS 1995-; PA Historical Soc 1993-; NEH Grant Eleanor & Franklin Roosevelt Inst Pub Article 1990; Grant World After Cold War 1991; *office:* Gloucester Catholic H S 333 Ridgeway St Gloucester City NJ 08030

CHAMBERS, OPAL T., Second Grade Teacher; *b:* Middletown, OH; *m:* Gary L.; *ed:* Miami Univ (BA) Elem Ed 1970; 20 Addl Hrs Terrific Toys in Sci; *cr:* Poasttown Elem Schl 1st Grd Tchr; Garfield Elem Schl Kndgtn Tchr 1974-; Taft Elem Schl Second Grd Tchr; Wilson Elem Schl Second Grd Tchr; *ai:* Math Club Organizer, Adv; OEA, NEA 1971-; MTA 1974-, Rep; Girl Scouts 1976-79, Ldr; BSA 1980-82, Asst Ldr; Salvation Army 1960-85, SS, Bible Schl Ldr, Scouting; Grant Tetons Geology Field Stud Grant; Martha Holden Jennings Fnds Schlsp; *home:* 1912 Baltimore St Middletown OH 45044*

CHAMBERS, REGINA MONTGOMERY, High School English Teacher; *b:* Cincinnati, OH; *m:* D. Brentley; *c:* Elizabeth; *ed:* Morehead St Univ (BA) Eng 1984; Xavier Univ (MED) Ed Rdng 1995; 9 Hrs Miami Univ OH Writing Project 1990-91; *cr:* Clermont Northeastern MS Eighth Grd Tchr of Eng, Rdng, Gifted 1985-94; New Richmond HS Eng, Creative Writing Tchr 1994-; *ai:* Acad Team Coach; NCTE 1984-; NEA 1994-; Mt Carmel Church of Christ 1992-; *office:* New Richmond HS 1131 Bethel New Richmond Rd New Richmond OH 45157*

CHAMBERS, SHARON SMITH, Office Technology Asst Prof; *b:* Fulton, NY; *c:* Melissa, Mark; *ed:* NY St Univ at Albany Bus Ed (BS) 1966, (MS) 1967; *cr:* Gloversville HS Bus Tchr 1967-69; Lee Pub Advertising Sales 1980-82; Contel Admin Asst 1982-86; Liberty Enterprises Bus Tchr 1986-87; Fulton Montgomery Comm Coll Bus Tchr 1987-; *ai:* Schlsp, Mission & Vision, Tech Prep Coll & HS Comms; NEA, Office Tech Secretarial Educators 1987-; Hospice of Fulton Cty 1994-, Vol; Comm Meals 1995-, vol; *office:* Fulton Montgomery Comm Coll 2805 State H 67 Johnstown NY 12095

CHAMBERS, VIRGINIA EILEEN, 7th Grade Life Science Teacher; *b:* Sandusky, OH; *m:* Bennett G.; *c:* Robert T., Matthew T.; *ed:* Bowling Green St Univ (BSED) Elem Ed 1972, (MED) Guidance & Counseling 1982; 50 Hrs Past Masters Sci & Cmptrs; *cr:* Bowling Green City Schls Learning Disability Tutor 1975-79, 7th Grd Sci Tchr 1979-; Bowling Green St Univ Instr 1989-91; *ai:* Project Star Eisenhower Grant; Intramurals; Violence Task Force; NEA, OEA, BGEA 1978-; NSTA, SECO 1980-; Gleams 1989-, Treas; NMSA, OMSA 1991-; Toledo Zoo 1987-; AAUW 1993-; Wood Cty Soil & Water Advy 1995-; Wrote Stud Lab Manual; Outstanding Educator; Bulletin Bd Pub in Sci Scope; Co-Pl & Field Instr NSF Grant; NSF MS Sci Summer Inst Honoree; *office:* Bowling Green MS 215 W Wooster St Bowling Green OH 43402*

CHAMBLESS, SYLVIA, Piano Instructor; *b:* Delhi, LA; *m:* Lawrence Pratt; *c:* Susan Worters, David Worters; *ed:* Juilliard Schl of Music (BA) 1965; New England Conservatory (MS) Piano 1978; *cr:* New England Conservatory Piano Instr 1979-; Walnut HIll Performing Arts Schl Piano Instr 1990-; *ai:* New England Piano Tchrs Assn 1965-, Pres 1995-; MS Music Tchrs Assn 1975-; *office:* New England Cnsrvtry Prep Schl 290 Huntington Ave Boston MA 02115

CHAMBON, MARY TWEEDLIE, 7th Grade Social Studies Tchr; *b:* Wheeling, WV; *m:* C. Kenneth; *c:* Kenneth, Kerry; *ed:* West Liberty St Coll (BA) Soc Stud 1975; Attending Duquesne Univ Masters Prgm Ed; *cr:* South Fayette Twp Schl Dist Soc Stud Tchr 11 Yrs; *ai:* Jr NHS Spon; Girls Sftbl, Cheerleading Coach 5 Yrs; *home:* 502 Jeana Ln Bridgeville PA 15017

CHAMP, VALJEAN JEFFREYS, Third Grade Classroom Teacher; *b:* Meyersdale, PA; *m:* Ronald Albert; *c:* Warren A., Bethany L., Tamatha J. Boice; *ed:* Slippery Rock Coll (BS) Elem S 1963; IN Coll, Clarion Coll, Duquesne, Midwestern Univ IV, Pittsburgh Univ 34 Credits; *cr:* Penn Hills Schl 1st Grd Tchr 1963-65; Butler Areas Schl Sub Tchr 1975-77; Butler Areas Schl 3rd Grd Tchr 1977-; *ai:* IPD Cncl; Lead Tchr; NEA, PSEA, BEA 1986-; *office:* Meridian Elem Schl 135 Sparks Ave Butler PA 16001*

CHAMPAGNE, DAVID JOHN, English Department Chairperson; *b:* Woonsocket, RI; *m:* Karen Donna Rocheleau; *ed:* RI Coll (BA) Scndry Ed, Eng 1989; *cr:* Woonsocket Sr HS Tchr 1989-90; Woonsocket Jr HS Eng Tchr 1990-91; Wm M. Davis Career, Tech HS Eng Tchr 1991-95, Eng Dept Chprsn; *ai:* Head Coach Var Bsbl; Eng NEASS Comm Chprsn; Sr Class Adv; CAST Comm; TEEN Ctr Coord; Saturday Schl Supvr; Arts Talk; ASCD 1994-; NEA 1990-; Awds Rotary Club 1982, Stdnts Tchr Appreciation 1995; Yrbk Dedication 1995; *office:* William M Davies Voc Tech Sch 50 Jenckes Hill Rd Lincoln RI 02865*

CHAMPAGNE, GRAHAME, Automotive Instructor; *b:* Saratoga NY; *m:* Patricia A. Crandall; *c:* Patrick, Tracey, Yvette Ryan, Josep Crandall, Jackie Brown; *ed:* Attnd SUNY at Utica, Rome, Oswego St Coll, Adirondack Comm Coll, Ctr Automotive Tech, Trng, Ge Schl Product Svc; *cr:* Ctr Automotive Tech, Trng Lead Instr Donald Myers Ed Ctr Automotive Instr 1979-; *ai:* Curr Design Media, Tech Cncl; Master Trainer; Saratoga BOCES TA 1979-, 1984-90; Corinth Fire Dept 1966-, Asst Chief 1977; *home:* 43 Ave Corinth NY 12822*

CHAMPAGNE, GREGORY JOHN, Business & Computer Tea Portland, ME; *ed:* Thomas Coll (BS) Bus Ed 1981; Bowling Green (MED) Bus Ed 1983; *cr:* Bloomsburg Univ Bus Instr 1983-84; St Bus Instr 1984-85; Amity Regnl HS Bus & Mrktg Tchr 1985-86 Acad Bus, Comp & Commnctns Tchr 1986-; *ai:* FBLA Club; Y Prof Staff Dev; NBEA 1981-; CBEA 1986-, Pres; NEBEA 198 CSFT 1986-, 2nd VP; AIDS Project Hartford 1991-, Bd of Di Telecommnctns Grant 1993; Colchester Tchr of the Yr 1995; Proje Grant 1995; *office:* Bacon Acad 611 Norwich Ave Colchester CT

CHAMPAGNE, NORMAN EDWARD, Middle School Teacher; Plains, NY; *m:* Janet Martin; *c:* George, David, Lauree Gilmore; *e* Williams Univ (AS) Bus Mngmt 1964; Gordon Barrington Coll Theology 1970; Univ of RI 15 Hrs; RI Coll 15 Hrs; Salve Regin Credit Hrs; Roger Wm's Univ 12 Credit Hrs; *cr:* Pocasset Schl 1970-76; Tiverton MS Sci, Soc Stud, Lang Arts Tchr 1976-; *ai:* 5 Sci Coord; Chicago Acad of Sci 1994; Church 7-12 Grd Sub Tc 1970-; Tiverton Ed Assn 1970-, Blue Cross, Blue Shield Comm; R 1970-; NSTA 1970-, Group Ldr; First Presbyn Church 1957 Deacon, Pastor's Chrstn Svc Awd; Outstdng Elem Tchrs of Am NSTA St of RI Sci Ed Awd 1982; RI St Sci Geology Awd H Mention; Norman Bird Sanctuary Tchr of Geology; Guest Lectu Regina Univ; Oceanography HS Level; *office:* Tiverton MS 10 Q Tiverton RI 02878*

CHAMPAGNE-JONES, MARLENE, First Grade Teacher; *b:* NH; *m:* Richard C.; *c:* Ashley; *ed:* River Coll (BA) Elem Ed 1979 Elem Ed 1985; Gesell Cert 1984; *cr:* Lanchaster Elem Sch 4th 1979-80; Lamprey River Elem Schl 1st Grd Tchr 1980-; *ai:* Rdn 1995-; NEA 1980-; Rivier Coll Alumni Assn 1979-; *office:* Lampr Elem Schl 33 Old Manchester Rd Raymond NH 03077*

CHAMPAGNE-MYERS, MARY DZIUBA, German Teac Rochester, NY; *m:* Thomas E.; *c:* Erika Marie; *ed:* Nazareth Rochester (BA) German 1973, (MS) Ed 1979; St Univ of NY at B (CAS) Educl Admin 1991; *cr:* Greece Arcadia HS Foreign L Teacher 1977-; SUNY at Brockport Adjunct Ger 1979-85; *ai:* Dresden Exchange Adv; Keep the Peace, Social Skills, Human Comms; NEA 1977-; ACTFL 1991-, NYSAFLT Rep; NYSAFL Pres, NYSAFLT 1992; AATG 1977-, AATG Rochester Chap 1986-88; ASCD 1995; Tchr Preparation Task Force; Regents Assessment Lang Other Then Eng; NYSAFLT DI Bartalo Ldrshp Awd 1992, Papalea Outstndg Article Awd, Service Awd 1993 House Awd Otstndg Tchr of German in NYS 1983, Travel Grant to 1992; *office:* Greece Arcadia HS 120 Island Cottage Rd Roche 14612*

CHAMPIGNY, DAVID PAUL, English Teacher; *b:* Lynn, MA; *n* O'Brien; *ed:* Saint Anselm Coll (BA) Eng 1990; Franklin Pie Scndry Cert Eng 1990; *cr:* Bishop Fenwick HS Eng Tchr 199 Middlesex Regnl HS Eng Tchr 1991-; *ai:* Class, Newspaper Ad Bsktbl, Spring Track Coach; *office:* North Middlesex Regnl HS 19 Townsend MA 01469*

CHAMPION, JOHN S., Retired PE Teacher; *b:* South Kingstow Marie Pucella; *c:* Jennifer Gray, Carol Bard, James, Amy; *ed:* U (BS) PE 1961, (MA) Continuing Adult Ed 1967; 36 Addl Credit Hazard Elem Schl Tchr 1961-63; HS Bsktbl Coach 1961-8 Kingstown Jr HS PE Tchr 1964-94; JH Bsbl Coach 1965-90; *ai:* Jr & Boys & Girls Bsktbl Game Supvr; HS Bsbl, Girls & Boys Socc Wrestling, Field Hockey & Gymnastics Game Supvr; NEA S South Kingstown Tchrs Assn 1961-, Chm 1970-71, Negotiations AAHPERD 1964-94; Article Pub in RI Cncl on Ec Ed 1981.

CHAMPION, RICHARD G., History Teacher; *b:* Neptune, Bethann Miller; *c:* John; *ed:* Fairleigh Dickinson Un Tchr (BS) His 1974; St Peter's Coll, Jersey City St Admin & Supervision; St Spec Ed; *cr:* Bergen Cty Spec Svcs Sr Corrections Ofcr, Yt 1975-85; South Orange Municipal Pool Mgr 1986-92; Irvington Stud Tchr 1986-; Indian Trl Club Beach Supvr 1994-; *ai:* Class Class 1995 Adv; Head Coach FDU Bsktbl, Sftbl 1972-76; Ath D Cty Spec Svcs 1975-80; IEA 1975-, Rep; NJEA, NEA 1974-; 1976-; NJSIAA Ofcl 1973-, 20 St Championships; NISOA Socc NCAA Championship; Amer Red Cross 1968-; IAABO Bd 1973-; NJBUA 1973-, Clinician; CBOA 1986-; 20 Yr Svc Awd Yrs Svc Awd Bsbl, Soccer, Bsktbl; Swimming Coach of Yr Referee of Yr 1988-89; *office:* Frank H Morrell HS 1253 Clir Irvington NJ 07111

CHAN, FERNADINA HOW-CHING, Dance Program Dir & Te Hong Kong, Hong Kong; *m:* Albert Y. C. Wong; *ed:* Southern IL U Physics 1970; Univ of IL (MA) Dance 1972; Harvard Univ (M 1993; Attnd Martha Graham Schl of Contemporary Dance, Summer Dance Ctr, Fuhsing Peking Opera Schl Taiwan; *cr:* St Un Asst Prof 1972-76; Free Lance Choreographer, Performer 197 West Dance Theater Founder, Artistic Dir 1977-1987; English H Tchr 1978-; *ai:* All City Dance Co Founder, Artistic Dir; MA De Curr Framework, Assessment Comm; Boston Arts Acad Plannir Boston Tchrs Union 1978-; Boston Dance Alliance 1994-, Bd of Dance Umbrella 1994-; Conant Fellow Harvard Univ; Choreographer Boston Move Spon Dance Umbrella; Panelist, Natl Endowment Arts; MA Cultural Cncl; *home:* 499 Dutton Rd MA 01776

CHAN, M. DONALYN, Third & Fourth Grade Teacher; *b:* New *ed:* Hunter Coll CUNY (BA) Theatre Arts 1976, (MS) Elem Ed Pub Schl 130M Educl Assoc 1970-82; On Stage Children St Scenic, Lighting Designer 1976-85; Pub Schl 126M Educl Assoc Tchr 1986-; *ai:* NSTA 1991-; Presenter at IRA, Natl Assn of B NY St Assn of Biling Ed, NY City Bd of Ed, Hunter Coll, CUN for Tchrs & Parents; *office:* PS 126M Jacob Riis Comm Schl 80 St New York NY 10038

CHANCE, MARY A., Asst Professor of Accounting; *b:* Johnst *m:* Edward F. Rogan Jr.; *c:* Kara Rogan, Edward Rogan III; *ed:* S Coll (BS) Accounting 1976; Long Island Univ (MS) Taxation 199 Cert Pub Accountant License 1980; *cr:* Price Waterhouse 1976-83; St Joseph's Coll Accounting Asst Prof 1983-; Long Isl MS Tax Coord 1993-; Acctng & Tax Prac, Own Account; *ai:* A Comm; Accounting Soc Moderator; Advy Cncl; Accounti Internship Coord; AICPA, NYSSCPA 1980-; Natl Assn Practitioners; Tax Inst of Long Island Univ; St James Church Y Bd; Pub Article 1980; *office:* Saint Josephs Coll W Roe Blvd P NY 11772*

CHANDLER, CLIFTON EDISON,JR., Technology Instrl Spec Oswego, NY; *m:* Christine M. Long; *ed:* SUNY at Oswego (BS)

(S) Tech, Design Ed 1985, (SDA) (CAS) Admin Ed 1992; Certfd
d; cr: Syracuse City Sch Sub Tchr 1980-81; Bryne-Knox-Westerlo
ign Instr 1981-82; Fayetteville-Manlius Sch Tech, Design Tchr
i: Bus, Schl Partnership; Tech, Kiry & Kiry Archs; Hands Across
m Dir; Curr Chm; Comprehensive Research NY St Schl, Bus
nips; Stu Work Manuel Small Engine Repair; Musical Recording
of Early Amer Music; *office:* Fayetteville-Manlius HS Rt 173
NY 13104

LER, JAY, Science Teacher; *ed:* Univ of NH (BA) Psych 1978;
MA Boston (BS) Chem 1986; Masters in Ed Candidate
ham St Coll; *cr:* Blue Hills Regnl Vocation Tech HS Sci Tchr
Uxbridge HS Sci Tchr, Dept Head 1987-90; Wayland HS Sci Tchr
: Stud Cncl Adv; Fac Comm; NEA; MA Assoc of Sci Tchr; *office:*
HS 264 Old Connecticut Path Wayland MA 01778

LER, JOHN S., Professor of Biology; *b:* Fairbanks, AK; *c:* Bree,
Brendan, Jesse; *ed:* Northern AZ Univ (BS) Zoology 1972; Univ of
)) Bio Chem 1982; *cr:* Letterman Army Inst Rsrch Asst 1976-77;
AZ Grad Res Assoc 1980-82; Cornell Univ Rsrch Assoc 1982-;
Pittsburg at Bradford Asst Prof 1992-; *office:* Univ Of Pittsburgh
ord 300 Campus Dr Bradford PA 16701*

LER, MERRY LEE, Fourth Grade Teacher; *b:* San Diego, CA;
; *c:* Kacee Lee, Michael Vincent; *ed:* FL St Univ (BS) Elem Ed
iv of MI (MS) Elem Ed 1993; *cr:* Robins AFB Elem 1st Grd Tchr
Russell Elem 1st Grd Tchr 1974-75; Twin Ridge Elem 4th Grd
6-80; Cedar Lake Elem 5th Grd Tchr 1985-86; Oscoda Elem 5th
1986-87; Titus Elem 5th Grd Tchr 1987-93; Kutz Elem 5th Grd
3-; *ai:* Dist Math, Rdng, Tech, Math Curr Comm; CBEA 1987-;
71-; PA St Tchs of Yr 1991-, Founding Charter Mem; Amer Lung
2-, Bd Mem; PA Tchr of Yr 1992; Founder & Initiater Geography
; Host 1st Annual Pa Tchr of Yr Forum; *office:* Kutz Elem Schl
k Rd Doylestown PA 18901*

LER, SCOTT GORDON, Technology Education Teacher; *b:*
Springs, CT; *m:* Patricia Lynn Harvey; *ed:* Erie Comm Coll North
riminal Justice 1975; Buffalo St Coll (BS) Ed 1978, (MS) Ed 1981;
nce Jr HS Tech Tchr 1978-79; West Seneca Cntrl Schls Tech Tchr
1985-86; Eastern Scientific Inc Tech Rep 1984-85; North
da City Schls Tech Tchr 1986-89; Clarence Sr HS Tech Tchr, Dept
89-; *ai:* Stage Crew Adv; Tech Club; Districtwide Tech, Schlsp,
ch, SAC Comms; Dept Chair; AFT, NY St Tchrs Assn 1978-;
NY Tchrs Ed Assn 1979-, Mbrshp Chm, Tchr of Yr 1994; Clarence
sn 1989-; *office:* Clarence Central HS 9625 Main St Clarence NY

LER, TIMOTHY J. L., Assoc Prof of Exercise; *b:* London,
m: Margaret P.; *c:* Stephanie, Christopher; *ed:* Loughborough
D) PE, Eng 1976; Dalhousie Univ (MSC) PE 1981; Stanford Univ
s 1984, (PHD) PE 1984; *cr:* Syracuse Univ Asst, Dept of Hlth, PE
soc Prof 1984-91; Kent St Univ Exercise, Leisure, Sport Assoc
1-; *ai:* Adv Cricket Club; ISCPES 1984-, Treas; NASSH, BSSH
ent Soccer Club 1993-, Bd; 30 Articles; Book: Making Men 1996;
Vendien Scholar 1982; *office:* Kent St Univ Dept Exercise, Leisure
Kent OH 44242*

, RICHARD LEO, Curriculum Coordinator; *b:* Beverly, MA; *m:*
A. Colburn; *ed:* Tufts Univ (BA) Ger 1963, (MA) Ger Stud 1969;
id Marburg, Heidelberg, Munich Germany, Strassburg France,
Coll; *cr:* Gloucester HS Ger, Eng Tchr 1969-73, Dept Head
Kennett Jr-Sr HS Curr Coord, Eng, Frgn Lang Tchr 1993-; *ai:*
ub; NHAT of Eng 1994-; MAFLA 1971-; Tchr of Yr Kennett HS;
ennett Jr-Sr HS 170 Main St Conway NH 03818

, ANNE MIKULAS, Adjunct Professor; *b:* Milwaukee, WI; *m:*
; *ed:* Marquette Univ (BA) Eng Major, Elem Ed Cert Prgm 1981;
ll at Columbia Univ Curr, Tchng (MA) 1982, (MED) 1984; Work
EDD Curr, Tchng; *cr:* The Episcopal Schl in City of NY Early
Head Tchr 1982-85; Westchester Comm Coll Adjunct Prof 1986;
ll at Columbia Univ Project Coord, Research Asst 1987-90; Anne
hotographer Photo Artist 1991-; Ramapo Coll of NJ Adjunct Prof
: Exceptional Contribution to Extra Curr by Fac, Staff Mem 1993;
1 Ramapo Valley Rd # 713 Mahwah NJ 07430

, PING-HAN, Mathematics & Science Teacher; *b:* Pingtung,
m: Hsin-Chia Wang; *c:* Mai-Liang, Shirley; *ed:* Chinese Military
S) Civic Engrng 1973; Univ of MS (MS) Cmptr Sci 1986; Cntrl
iiv Cmptr Sci; PHD Prgm City Univ of NY Cmptr Sci; *cr:* Engrng
r 1973-83; Drug Store Asst Mgr 1987-88; NYC Pub Schl System
9-; *ai:* Before Schl Tutoring Selected Stdnts; After Schl Tutoring
n Stdnts; Team of Martial Arts Adv; AFT 1989-; United Fed of
Y St United Tchrs 1989-; *office:* JHS 56 Anthony Corlears 220
New York NY 10002*

, CHRISTOPHER DAVID, Social Studies Teacher; *b:* N
da, NY; *m:* Shelly Hebert; *ed:* St Rose Coll (BA) His, Pol Sci &
d 1993; 12 Addl Credit Hrs; *cr:* Notre Dame-Bishop Gibbons Schl
d Tchr 1993-; *ai:* Fac Liason Comm; Ski Club, Cinema
ation Club Coord; *office:* Notre Dame-Bishop Gibbons Schl 2600
St Schenectady NY 12304

, NANCY A., Honors English Teacher; *b:* Syracuse, NY; *c:* Arden;
ell Sage (BS) Eng Ed 1967; RPI (MS) Communication 1972; *cr:*
lenville HS Honors Eng & Advanced Placement Tchr 1967-; *ai:* Sr
Lit Magazine Adv; NYSUT 1967-; SGTA 1967-, Jrnlsm Dir,
a 1st Place; NY St Cncl of Eng Tchrs; Octavo Singers 1989-, Pres,
; GE Star Awd & Grant; Golub Recognition Awds & Influential
5-95; CASDA Recognition Awd 1996; Columbia Jrnlsm 1st Place,
wspaper, Union Newsletter; *office:* Scotia Glenville HS 1 Tartan
tia NY 12302*

LLE, ERIC R., Assoc Pastor of Secondary Ed; *b:* Flint, MI; *m:*
vonne; *c:* Nolan R., Alyssa Y.; *ed:* Hyles-Anderson Coll (BA)
1989; *cr:* Berean Bapt Church Assoc, Yth, Children's Pastor
Intnl Bapt Church Assoc Pastor, Scndry Ed Tchr 1992-; Chrstn
r, Yth Pastor; *ai:* Yth Cnslng; Bus Ministry; Said Church Assoc
rganizing Comm Outreach; Soph Class Adv; *office:* International
Schl 302 Vanderbilt St Brooklyn NY 11218

I, BRECKINRIDGE, Volunteer Services Coordinator; *b:*
, NY; *w:* Barbara Roop (dec); *c:* Sarah Schweizer, Lauren Edsall,
Mary Grebe; *ed:* Brown Univ (BA) Liberal Arts 1955; SUC
gh (MS) Ed Admin 1968; Attnd SUNY Postdam; *cr:* Lake Clear
ng Prin 1962-68; Bloomingdale Schl; Saranac Lake Cntrl Schl
ng Prin 1968-87; Petrova Schl Cntrl Dist Academically Talented
37-; *ai:* Butterfly House Project Coord; Volunteer Services Coord;
1968-; Amer Legion, BPOE; Cornell Cooperative Extension
Bd Dir; North Star Industries 1993-, Bd Dir.

I, PAUL ROBEERT, Science Teacher; *b:* Meadville, PA; *m:* Kim
ed: Allegheny Coll (BS) Physics 1985; SUNY at Oswego 30 Hrs
rk; Working on Masters; *cr:* Meadville HS Sci Tchr 1989-91; CNS
chr 1992-95; *ai:* Sci Olympiad Coach; NSTA 1994-; *home:* Rt 31
Y 13039

I, RICHARD R., Social Studies Teacher; *b:* Union City, PA; *m:*
Huston; *c:* Richard; *ed:* Grove City Coll (BA) Scndry Ed 1965;
v (MA) Ed 1974; Attnd Univ of CO, Slippery Rock Univ; *cr:*
Mercer Area HS Tchr 1966-; *ai:* MEA, PSEA, NEA 1966-; Jaycees 1967-, Pres, VP, Sec-Treas, Dir, Citizen of Yr; *office:* Mercer Area HS 545 W Butler St Mercer PA 16137

CHAPLA, WILLIAM MARK, 12th Grd Language Arts Teacher; *b:* Pittston, PA; *m:* Catherine Stancampiano; *ed:* Univ of Scranton (BS) Bio, Med Tech 1977, (MA) Eng 1983; *cr:* PA St Univ Part-time Fac 1987-; Bishop O'Hara HS Lang Arts Tchr 1984-; *ai:* NCEA 1984-; Book, Film Reviewer; *office:* Bishop O'Hara HS 501 E Drinker St Dunmore PA 18512*

CHAPLICK, MARY VIRGINIA GOODHUE, English Teacher; *b:* Buffalo, NY; *m:* Daniel A.; *c:* Gail, Daniel; *ed:* Emmanuel Coll (BA) Eng 1962; Addl Women's Stud; Cath Univ of AMer Eng; Harvard Coll Fr; *cr:* Hart Jr HS Eng Tchr 1962-64; Warren Jr HS Eng Tchr 1964-66; Whittier Jr HS Eng Tchr; Girls Cath HS Eng Tchr, Chair 1983-92; Our Lady of Nazareth Acad Eng Tchr 1992-; *ai:* Jr Class Adv; Schl Newspaper; Lit Magazine; Fac Adv Voice of Democracy Contest; MCTE 1992-; NCEA 1983-; St Rose Church 1977-, CCD Tchr; Emmanuel Coll Alumnae 1962-, Treas of Class 62 1982-92; Woman of Yr Girls Cath HS 1990; VFW Awds for Meritorious Svc 1990-91, 1995; *home:* 37 Brookside Rd Topsfield MA 01983*

CHAPLIN, HATTIE DANIELS, Proj Dir of Tutorial Vol & LiB; *b:* Columbia, SC; *m:* Edmund M.; *c:* Russell D., Lisa L. Chaplin-Hobbs; *ed:* Winston-Salem St Univ (BA) Ed 1947; The Univ of Dist of Columbia (MA) Lib Sci 1969; George Washington Univ Cnslng, Guid 1972; Cath Univ Ed 1983; Trinity Coll Ed 1985; *cr:* Pittsylvania Cty Schl Prin 1947-48, Tchr 1948-50; Surgeon Gen USA Sec, Statistical Coder 1950-53; DC Pub Schls Elem Tchr 1955-; *ai:* Girls, Boys Are People Spon, Adv; Ebonymuse Adv; Art from the Heart Dir; First Come the Children Mentor; NEA 1947-, Mbrshp Comm, Hororarium; AFT, Honorarium Svc; Women in Arts 1993-; WTU, Honorarium; Natl Lib Assn 1985-, Plaque Outstdng Svc; NRA 1970-; DC Rdng Assn; DC Assn of Librns; NAACP, Life Mem; DC Commission on Arts, Hum, Pub Svc; AFT Honorarium Quilt of Pub Svc; Chaperoned Tour Moscow Russia; *home:* 5133 33rd St NW Washington DC 20008

CHAPMAN, CHRIS PRISCILLA, Art Teacher; *b:* Damariscotta, ME; *ed:* Univ of South ME (BS) Art Ed 1969; Tchrs Coll at Columbia Univ (MA) Art Ed, Craft Design 1978; NM St Univ (MA) Ceramics, Art Ed 1986; Attnd Haystack Mt Schl of Crafts; *cr:* Boothbay Harbor Elem Schl Art Tchr 1970-75; Boothbay Region HS Art Tchr 1970-75; Mt Ararat HS Art Tchr 1975-; *ai:* Steering Comm; New England Assn Schls & Colls Accreditation; ME Art Ed Assn 1968-, VP, ME Art Tchr of Yr; ME Alliance of Arts Ed 1984-, Vice-Chprsn; ME Craft Alliance 1987-; Watershed Ctr for Ceramic Arts 1989-, Advy Bd; Natl Recognition Studio Potter Fnd Nom; *office:* Mt Ararat HS Rt 201 Topsham ME 04086*

CHAPMAN, DANA L., Spanish Teacher; *b:* Hamilton, OH; *m:* Kenneth Ray; *c:* Rachel, Lauren; *ed:* Miami Univ (BS) Span Ed 1989; Post Grad Stud at Univ of Cincinnati, Ohio & Calvin Coll in MI; Working Towards Masters Degree in Hispanic Civilation; *cr:* Fairfield City Schls Span Tchr 1990; Lakota Local Schls Span Tchr 1991-; *ai:* OFLA 1990-, Spec Events Comm; NEA, DEA, LEA 1990-; Towne Boulevard COG 1989-; *office:* Lakota H S 5050 Tylersville Rd West Chester OH 45069

CHAPMAN, DANIELLE RENEE, Spanish Teacher; *b:* Trenton, NJ; *ed:* WV Univ (BA) Span 1990, (BA) His 1991, (MA) Scndry Ed 1992; *cr:* Warrenton Jr HS Span Tchr 1992-94; Edgewood HS Span Tchr 1994-95; Be Air HS Span Tchr 1995-; *ai:* Multicultural Club Spon; Bsktbl, Vlybl, Track, Schl Fac Advy Comms; Scndry Schl Advy Comm; Harford Cty 1994-; VA Ed Assn 1992-94; MD Ed Assn 1994-.

CHAPMAN, DEBORAH L., Guidance Counselor; *b:* Buffalo, NY; *ed:* Baldwin Wallace Coll (BS) Home Ec 1975; Cleveland St Univ (MED) Cnslng 1988; 15 Credit Hrs; *cr:* Collinwood HS Home Ec Tchr 1975-77; H. E. Davis Jr HS Voc Home Ec Tchr 1977-84; F.D.R. Jr HS Dept Chair, Voc Home Ec Tchr 1984-89; Willson MS Guid Cnslr 1989-; *ai:* Greater Cleveland Home Ec Assn 1977-, Treas, Sec, Awds Chair; Cleveland Tchrs Union, AFT 1975-; OH Schl Cnslng Assn 1995-; Cleaveland Mediation Ctr 1989-, Sec; Forest Hill Church Presbyn 1995-, Bd of Trustees; *office:* Willson MS 1625 E 55th St Cleveland OH 44103*

CHAPMAN, DONALD CHARLES, Administrator; *b:* Cheserville, OH; *m:* Louella F. Mast; *c:* Galen, Glenda, Gary; *ed:* Goshen Coll (BS) Bio 1963; OH St Univ (MA) Admin 1989; *cr:* Northmor HS Bio, Sci, PE Tchr 1963-65; Fredericktown HS Bio, Sie Tchr 1965-77; Gilead Chrstn Schl Admin 1986-; *ai:* Ftbl, Bsktbl Coach; FCA Adv; Intramural Dir; ACSI 1986-; Gideons Intnl 1975-, VP; REA Bd 1984-85; OH Farm Bureau 1975-; *home:* 6493 State Route 95 Mount Gilead OH 43338

CHAPMAN, DOROTHY, Business Teacher; *b:* Queens, NY; *ed:* NY Tech Coll (AAS) Exec Sec Sci 1983; Bernard Baruch Coll (BBA) Office Admin & Tech 1989; Long Island Univ (MS) Comps in Ed 1993; *cr:* Metropolitan Life Insurance Exec Sec 1982-89; Brooklyn Tabernacle Church Admin Asst 1989-91; Paul Robeson HS Bus Instr 1991-; *ai:* Former Sr & Yrbk Advs; Girls Handball & Bowling Coach; AFT 1991-; NEA 1993-.*

CHAPMAN, JACKLYN MARIE, French Teacher; *b:* Newburgh, NY; *c:* Jeffrey R.; *ed:* SUNY at Albany (BA) Fr 1968; SUNY at New Paltz 33 Grad Credits Fr, Ed; *cr:* Chester Schl Dist Fr Tchr 1968-71; Newburgh Schl Dist Fr Tchr 1984-85; C. J. Hooker MS Fr Tchr 1985-; Orange-Ulster BOCES Schl ESL Tchr 1992-; *ai:* Frgn Lang Coord; Montreal, Quebec Trip Spon; E-Mail Stu Project Co-Spon; NYSUT 1968-; AFT; NYSAFLT 1989-; Alliance Francaise 1992-; Bd of Dirs; Planned Parenthood Inc; Mc Quade Fnd; Friends of Lib; *office:* C J Hooker MS Lincoln Ave Goshen NY 10924*

CHAPMAN, JANET ANDERSON, Art Teacher; *b:* Lake Charles, LA; *m:* Gary C.; *ed:* Miami Univ at Oxford OH (BS) K-12th Grd Art Ed 1976; Grad Hrs at Craftsummer 3 Yrs; *cr:* Miamisburg Schls Art Tchr 1976-; *ai:* Lit & Art Magazine & Art Club Adv; Fine Arts & Practical Arts Dept Chair; Miamisburg Classroom Tchrs Assn 1976-; Bd of Ed Grant for Lit & Art Magazine; Excl in Ed Grant for Fine Arts Day-Dayton Fnd; *office:* Miamisburg HS 1860 Belvo Rd Miamisburg OH 45342

CHAPMAN, JUDITH ANN (POLAK), English Teacher; *b:* Adams, MA; *m:* Ronald Kim; *ed:* North Adams St Coll (BA) Eng 1968; URI (MA) Eng 1970; 27 Credits Post Masters in Ed; *cr:* Adams-Cheshire Regnl Schl Dist Eng Tchr 27 Yrs, Eng Chprsn 2 Yrs; *ai:* Jr Prize Speaking Coach; NCTE 1994-; *office:* Hoosac Valley HS 125 Savoy Rd Rt 116 Adams MA 01220

CHAPMAN, KATHLEEN PASCHAL, Mathematics Teacher; *b:* Atlanta, GA; *c:* Michael; *ed:* Univ of MD at Coll Park (BS) Math Ed 1989, (MED) Math Ed 1995; *cr:* Bates MS Math Tchr 1990-92; Arundel Sr HS Math Tchr 1992-; *ai:* NEA 1991-; NCTM 1988-; Numerous Articles Pub.

CHAPMAN, MARGARET ELIZABETH, Elementary Education Teacher; *b:* Haverstraw, NY; *c:* Jennifer Woska; *ed:* St Thomas Aquinas Coll (BS) Elem Ed 1975; Grad Stud Fairfield Univ, Coll of New Rochelle, City Coll of NY, Long Island Univ; *cr:* Haverstraw Schl Sub Tchr 8 Yrs, 4 Grd Tchr 14 Yrs; *ai:* Elem Hlth Coord; Youth at Risk Cnslr; Dist Hlth Advy Bd Co-Chprsn; Multi-Cultural Comm Chprsn; ASCD 1988-; Local Tchrs' Assn 1995-, Bldg Rep; Impact II Grant Dev 1987, Adaptor 1989; AIDS Mini Grant Regnl Hlth Ctr 1989; Business Week Magazine Grantee 1990; Dist Summer Curr Grants; *office:* West Haverstraw Elem Schl 71 Blauvelt Ave West Haverstraw NY 10993

CHAPMAN, MARY ANN SRODE, Sci, Hlth, Soc Stud, Math Tchr; *b:* Dayton, OH; *m:* Dennis C.; *c:* Denise; *ed:* Univ of Dayton (BS) Ed 1968; Wright St Univ (ME) Ed 1991; *cr:* Prescious Blood Schl 4th Grd Tchr; St Andrew Schl 3rd Grd Tchr; St Margaret Mary Schl Unpraded Primary; NCR Intnl Acctg; St Luke Schl 5th Grd Tchr 1979-; *ai:* Hlth, Sci Dept Chprsn; Rosary Club Moderator; OH Acad of Sci 1985-; WS Math Org, NCEA 1980-; NSTA 1982-; Winning in Sci Ed Grant Wright St; Excl in Youth Sci Opportunities Governors Awd; Tchr of Excl Awd Archdiocese of CT; Outstanding Kids Voting Tchr 1995; *office:* Saint Luke Schl 1442 N Fairfield Rd Dayton OH 45432

CHAPMAN, PAMELA, English Teacher; *b:* Newark, NJ; *ed:* Upsala Coll (BA) Eng 1970; West CT St Univ (MS) Ed & Eng 1973; 60 Credits Beyond MS; *cr:* Danbury Pub Schls Sub Tchr 1970-73; Bethel HS Eng Tchr 1973-; *ai:* NHS Adv; Drama Production Producer; NEA, CEA & BEA 1973-; NOW 1979-, Feminist Awds Recipient; Womens Ctr of Greater Danb 1982-, Pres Bd of Dir; *office:* Bethel HS Educl Park Bethel CT 06801

CHAPMAN, PATRICIA, Eighth Grd Mathematics Tchr; *b:* Kearny, NJ; *ed:* William Paterson Coll (BA) Ed 1977; 15 Addl Credit Hrs; Amer Acad of Dramatic Arts NY 1972; *cr:* Paterson Bd of Ed 2nd-4th, 6th, 8th Grd Tchr, Grd 8 Math Tchr 1978-; *ai:* Peer Cnslng Tchr; Yrbk Ed; Math Chprsn, Fund Raising Chprsn, Prom Spon, Textbook Selection Comms; Teach for Amer Prgm Mentor; PEA, NJEA 1995-; Kappa Delta Pi, Hnr Soc; Girls Club of Amer, Vol Supvr; Frederick L. Hipp Fnd Grant 1996-; *home:* 227 Elbert St Ramsey NJ 07446*

CHAPMAN, PHYLLIS, 3rd Grade Teacher; *b:* Pittsburgh, PA; *m:* David; *c:* David Jr., Jennifer Chapman Bell; *ed:* Duquesne Univ (BS) Elem Ed 1967; Univ of Pittsburgh (MS) Elem Ed 1972; *cr:* Baxter Elem Schl 2nd Grd Tchr 3 Yrs; Linden Elem Schl 1st-3rd, 5th & 6th Grd & ITL Tchr 25 Yrs; *ai:* Schl Vol Liaison; Coord Coll Tutoring Pgm; Curr Writer of Schls Commnctn Pgm; Dev Performance Standards for New Standards; AFT 1967-; 1984 PA Tchr of the Yr Finalist; *office:* Linden Elem Schl 725 S Linden Ave Pittsburgh PA 15208*

CHAPMAN, RAYMOND, History Teacher; *b:* Newark, NJ; *m:* Lois VanDyk; *c:* Andrew R., Stephanie J.; *ed:* Montclair St Univ (BA) Soc Stud 1968, (MA) Amer His 1975; Addl 32 Credits NJ Administrative, Supervisory Cert 1977; *cr:* Nutley HS His Tchr 1968-89, His Tchr, Testing Coord, Attendance Asst 1989-; *ai:* AP US His Comm Chair; NEA, NJ Ed Assn 1968-; Smithsonian Assoc 1983-; Current His Assn 1975-; Hamilton Club 1978-; Nutley Crew Boosters Awd 18 Yrs Coaching 1985; Dist Svc Awd for Ed Nutley Jaycees 1989; Nutley Crew Boosters Assoc Named a Shell in Hnr 1993; *office:* Nutley HS 300 Franklin Ave Nutley NJ 07110

CHAPPELL, JUDY A., Biology Teacher; *b:* Lewisburg, PA; *m:* William E. Jr.; *c:* William III, Justin, Jonathan, Nathan; *ed:* Bloomsburg Univ (BS) Bio, Sec Ed 1972; Wilkes Univ (MS) Bio 1980; 36 Credit Hrs Beyond MS from Several Insts; *cr:* Plains Jr HS Gen Sci Tchr 1973-94; Coughlin HS Bio Tchr 1972-73, 1994-; *ai:* Coach Coughlin Sci Olympiad Team; Judge PA Jr Acad of Sci; PSEA, NEA, WBAEA 1972-; *office:* Coughlin HS 80 N Washington St Wilkes-Barre PA 18702

CHAPUT, JACQUES ANDRE, 3rd-4th Grd Multi-Age Tchr; *b:* Montreal, Canada; *m:* Lorraine; *c:* Helen Closs, Celeste, Christopher; *ed:* Rhode Island Coll (EDB) Ed 1963, (MAT) Sci 1966; SUNY at New Paltz Rdng Curr; *cr:* Providence RI 6th Grd Tchr 1963-66; Arlington Cntrl Schl 3-5th Grd Tchr 1966-; *ai:* MORE Prgm Tchr; Audio-Visual, Cmptr Specialist, Sci Advy & Tech Comm; ATA, NYSTA 1966-; Mid Hudson Astronomy 1993-; Childrens Comm Theater 1986-; Holy Trinity Church1966-; Poughkeepsie Ham Radio Club 1994-; NSF Grant Physics, Astronomy; NY St Cncl for Soc Stud Tchr of Yr; NSF NY Hall of Sci Grant Astronomy; Texaco Grant Lego Logo; *office:* Arlington Elem Schl Raymond Ave Poughkeepsie NY 12601

CHARLESWORTH, CHRISTINE, German Teacher; *b:* Philadelphia, PA; *m:* Gene; *c:* Alexander, Stephanie; *ed:* Millersville St Univ (BS) Ger 1976; Jr Yr Abroad Prgm Marburg Germany 1974-75; 3 Grad Courses Rider Univ Curr & Supervision, Methods of Tchng, Tchng of Rdng; *cr:* William Penn HS Ger Tchr 1976-77; Timberlane Jr HS Ger Tchr 1988-89; Hamilton North HS Ger Tchr 1989-94; Hamilton West HS Ger Tchr 1989-94; Hamilton East HS Ger Tchr 1994-; *ai:* Ger Club Spon 1991-; Mid Sts Comm on Frgn Lang; NEA, NJEA 1989-; St Marks Luth Church 1992-, Chrstn Ed Comm; *office:* Nottingham HS 1055 Klockner Rd Trenton NJ 08619

CHARNAS, FRAN E., Theatre & Musical Theatre Prof; *b:* Cleveland, OH; *ed:* OH Univ (BFA) Theatre; Emerson Coll (MA) Theatre, Directing 1981; *cr:* Shaw HS Tchr; Lakeland Comm Coll Instr; St Mary's Coll Visiting Asst Prof 1981; The Boston Conservatory Prof 1980-; *ai:* New England Theatre Con; Directed, Choregraphed, Co-Authored Musicals & Live Theatre; Various Directing Credits NY, Regnl, Boston; *office:* The Boston Conservatory 8 The Fenway Boston MA 02215

CHARNEY, SANDRA LEE ANN (BEGLIOMINI), 4th-5th Grd Math & Sci Tchr; *b:* Kingston, PA; *m:* Patrick J.; *c:* Donald Joseph, Stephen Patrick, ColleenMarie; *ed:* Coll Misericordia (BS) Elem Ed, Eng 1964; 6 Credit Hrs Cooperative Learning; Credits Scranton Univ; *cr:* WY Area Schl Sub Tchr 1967-69; WY Vly West Schl Permanent Sub Tchr 1976-80; Co-Owner Cookie Corner Nursery Schl Tchr 1980-85; St Mary's Assumption Schl 4th-5th Grd Tchr 1985-; *ai:* Stu Cncl Adv; Mid Atlantic St-Liturgy Comm; Nom Tchr of Yr 1994; *home:* 50 Slocum St Forty Fort PA 18704

CHARNOCK, FELICIA PERSINGER, 4th Grade Teacher; *b:* Gassaway, WV; *m:* J. Donald; *c:* Donna; *ed:* Glenville St Coll (BA) Elem 1-8, PE, Soc Stud 1968; Univ of MO 45 Grad Hrs; *cr:* Elizabeth Vaughn Elem Schl 4th Grd Tchr 1968-70; Vly View Elem Schl 4th Grd Tchr 1970-; *ai:* Sci Fair Comm; Fac Advy Comm; Discipline Comm; PGCEA, MSTEA 1970-; NEA 1968-; *office:* Valley View Elem Schl 5500 Danby Ave Oxon Hill MD 20745

CHARNOCK, JAMES TALBERT, Eighth Grade Teacher; *b:* Baltimore City, MD; *ed:* Philadelphia Coll of Bible (BS) Religion 1963; Temple Univ (MED) Elem Ed 1975; Cert Rdng Specialist at Univ of PA 1981; Admin Cert 1981; *cr:* Charles Drew Pub Schl 8th Grd Tchr 1969-; *ai:* Staff Dev Ldr; Educl Conf Speaker; Mentor Tchr; AFT 1969-, Bldg Rep, Chprsn in Local Schl; Local Habitat for Humanity 1990-, Bldg Comm Mem, Building Hands Awd 1990, 1991; Listed in Whos Who in the East; 11 Articles Pub in Instr, The Rdng Tchr, Tchr, AZ Eng Bulletin; Geography Game & Lit Kit Pub by Educl Insights; Philadelphia Tchr of Yr Semi-Finalist 1995; NCTE Journal Lang Arts Advy Review Bd 1977-78; IRA Journal Feature Writer for The Rdng Tchr 1984-87; *office:* Charles R Drew Elem Schl 38th St & Powelton Ave Philadelphia PA 19104

CHARNY, KRIS VECCHIO, Third Grade Teacher; *b:* Pittsburgh, PA; *m:* Daniel Timothy; *c:* Ellen, Nathan; *ed:* Slippery Rock St Coll (BA) Elem Ed 1970, (MA) Environmental Ed 1976; *cr:* Fox Chapel Area Schls Elem Tchr 1970-82; Beechwood Farms Nature Reserve Naturalist Tchr 1982-84; Fox Chapel Area Schls Gifted Support, Elem Tchr 1985-; *ai:* Sci Curr Comm; NEA 1970-; Audubon Soc of Western PA 1972-; Write Childrens Page for Audubon Soc; *office:* Fox Chapel Area Schls 115 Cabin Ln Pittsburgh PA 15238

CHARTIER, KAREN MOTTA, Fifth Grade Teacher; *b:* Springfield, MA; *m:* Gary L.; *ed:* Westfield St Coll (BSEd) Elem Ed 1972; Springfield Coll (MED) Elem Ed 1981; *cr:* Elias Brookings Elem Schl 6 Grd Tchr 1970-87; Frank H. Freedman Elem Schl 5-6 Grd Basic Skills Tchr 1987-94;

Frederick Harris Elem Schl 5 Grd Tchr 1994-; *ai:* Stu Cncl; NEA; *office:* Frederick Harris Elem Schl 58 Hartford Terr Springfield MA 01118

CHARTRAND, DAVID JOSEPH, Computers & Engineering Tchr; *b:* Lowville, NY; *m:* Beverly Yousey; *c:* Dana, Jacob, Ryan; *ed:* St Univ of NY at Oswego (BS) Ed 1987, (MS) Ed 1991; *cr:* R. W. Shank Inc Drafter, Foreman 1979-83; Liverpool MS Cmptr, Engr Tchr 1987-; *ai:* Environmental Club, Engineering, Cmptr Club, Stu Cncl Adv; Cntrl NY Tech Assn 1987-, Pres; NY St Tech Assn, Intnl Tech Ed Assn, Elipson Pi Tau 1987-; Awded 2 WCNY-TV Innovations with Video Tech in Classroom Grants; Nom Twice Tchr of Yr 1990-92; *home:* 985 Gilbert Mills Rd Fulton NY 13069

CHARUHAS, JEFFREY MAURY, Chemistry Teacher; *b:* Washington, DC; *m:* Birgit Maria Schock; *c:* Anna Maria; *ed:* Univ of MD (BS) Sci Ed 1980; 68 Hrs of Grad Work Beyond BS; *cr:* Montgomery Cty Pub Schl Sci Tchr 1980-; *ai:* Girls Vlybl Coach; Natl Hnr Soc Comm; *office:* Seneca Valley HS 12700 Middlebrook Rd Germantown MD 20874

CHASE, BARRY A., Dept Chairperson & Teacher; *b:* Scranton, PA; *m:* Donna Dylo; *ed:* Bloomsburg Univ (BS) Bus Ed, Acctng 1974; Univ of Scranton (MBA) Mrktg, Acctng 1977; 64 Grad Credits Bus, Tech Penn St Univ, Marywood Coll, Wilkes Univ; *cr:* Wayne Crushed Stone Inc Acctng Dept, Safety Instr for Employees 1977-83; Quarkertown Schl Dist Bus Ed Tchr 1974-75; Abington Heights Schl Dist Bus Dept Chprsn, Tchr 1975-; *ai:* Adult Ed, Cmptr Instr; Past Vlybl Coach; Tech, Curr Revision Comm; AHEA Tchr Union 1975-, Past Treas; Pi omega Pi, PSEA, NEA 1975-; *office:* Abington Hghts Schl Dist Noble Rd Clarks Summit PA 18444*

CHASE, CYNTHIA SARGENT, Assistant Athletic Director; *b:* New York, NY; *m:* Tyler Earl; *c:* Spencer Lawton, Corey Benjamin; *ed:* St Lawrence Univ (BA) Sociology, PE 1979; *cr:* Hopkins Schl Asst Ath Dir, Var Sftbl Coach 1979-; *ai:* Stud Adv; Coach Asst Var Boys, Girls Swimming, Var Sftbl; *office:* Hopkins Schl 986 Forest Rd New Haven CT 06515

CHASE, HAZEL VALLIANT, Retired Elementary Teacher; *b:* Corinth, VT; *m:* Lloyd G.; *c:* Cynthia Perry, Kimberlee Horton; *ed:* Lyndon Normal Schl Ed 1946; *cr:* Pike Hill Schl Grds 1-8 Tchr 1946-48; Waits River Schl Grds 1-8 Tchr 1948-57; West Topsham Schl Grds 6-8 Tchr 1957-58; St of VT Spec Ed Tchr 1959-63; Orange Ctr Schl Grds 5-6 Tchr 1963-64; Waits River Schl Grds 1-3 Tchr 1964-69; East Topsham Schl Grds 1-3 Tchr 1969-71; Corinth Schl Grds 1-3 Tchr 1971-81; Topsham Schl Grds 1-3 Tchr 1971-81; *ai:* Orange Cty Retired Tchrs Assn 1981-, Sec, Comm Svc Cert Appreciation 1991; NRTA, AARP 1981-; U-36 Schl Vol 9 Yrs, Sub Tchr 9 Yrs; *home:* Box 319 West Topsham VT 05086

CHASE, HELENANN, 9th Grade English Teacher; *b:* Pittsburgh, PA; *m:* David; *ed:* Slippery Rock Univ (BS) Eng 1968; 36 Post Grad Hrs; 9 Credit Hrs in Ed; 12 Credit Hrs Univ of Pittsburgh Prsnl Mngmt; *cr:* Penn Hills Schl Dist Eng Tchr 1964-; *ai:* NEA 1968-; PSEA 1968-, Regnl Office Pol Lobbyist 1970-80; Local Affiliate 1968-, Sec; *office:* Linton MS 250 Aster St Pittsburgh PA 15235*

CHASE, JOSEPH DUANE, Physics Teacher; *b:* Sharon, CT; *m:* Mary Beleca Komeyan; *c:* Yarpilah, Josephine, Sianay; *ed:* Univ of VT (BS) Physics 1987; Completing Masters in Physics; *cr:* US Peace Corps Ed, Vol 1987-90; Univ of VT Grad Tchng Fellow 1990-92; Bellows Free Acad Sci Tchr 1992-; *ai:* Multi-Cultural Diversity Group Adv; AAPT 1992-; *office:* Bellows Free Acad 71 S Main St Saint Albans VT 05478*

CHASE, MARY HAMMOND, Strings Tchr & Orch Conductor; *b:* Spangler, PA; *m:* Thomas; *ed:* IN Univ of PA (BS) Music Ed 1970; PA St Univ (MED) Music Ed 1976; *cr:* Gettyburg Area Schls Strings Tchr 1970-73; Wyalusing Area Schls String Tchr, Orch Dir 1975-; *ai:* NHS Selection Comm; MENC 1977-; NEA 1970-.

CHASE, MARY FRAN, Choir Dir & Piano Lab Tchr; *b:* Jersey City, NJ; *m:* Calvin L.; *c:* Danielle, Ryan; *ed:* Jersey City St Coll (BA) Music 1970; Trenton St Coll (MA) Music 1989; Cntrl CT St Univ 3 Credits; Kean Coll 3 Credits; *cr:* Nutly Schl Dist HS & Elem Music Tchr 1970-71; Berkeley Twp Schl Dist Vocal & Gen Music Tchr 1971-72, 1983-85; Bay Head Schl Dist Voc & Gen Music Tchr 1978-82; Lacey Twp Schl Dist Vocal & Gen Music Tchr 1982-83; Fair Haven Schl Dist Vocal & Gen Music Tchr 1985-86; Jackson Memrl HS Choir Dir 1986-; *ai:* Dir: Concert Choir, Chorus II, Chorus I, Madrigal Singers, Chorale & Select Ensemble for Male & Female Voice, HS Musical; Vocal Coach; MENC 1970-; NJEA 1970-; NJMEA 1971-; ACDA 1986-; Cert of Merit in Recognition of Dedication to the Success of Vocal Music Stdnts in Jackson Schl Dist; *office:* Jackson Memorial HS 101 Don Connor Blvd Jackson NJ 08527

CHASE, MARY MAY (DIONNE), Health Occupation Instructor; *b:* Madawaska, ME; *m:* Daniel L.; *ed:* St Louis-Maillet Coll (AS) Registered Nurse 1983; Univ of Southern ME 18 Credits Voc Ed; Univ of ME at Orono 72 Credits RN, BSN Prgm; *cr:* High View Manor Staff, Charge Nurse 1983-; Madawaska HS Certfd Nurses Aid Instr 1984-90; High View Manor Nrsng Dir 1989-93; St John Vly Tech Ctr Health Occupations Instr 1993-; *ai:* Staff Dev Comm 1994-96; HOSA Adv 193-; Attendence Comm 1993-94; NEA 1993-; MHOEA 1994-; MSAD #33 Ed Assn 1993-, VP 1994-; ME St HOSA Adv of Yr 1994; *office:* St Johns Valley Tech Ctr PO Box E US Rt #1 Upper Frenchville ME 04784*

CHASE, RAYMOND EARL, Eighth Grade Science Teacher; *b:* Rumford, ME; *m:* Lisa Belanger; *c:* Anna, Emily; *ed:* Univ of ME (BS) Scndry Ed & Bio 1980; 26 Credit Hrs Grd Stud Univ of VT Master of Sci for Tchrs Prgm; *cr:* Jay MS 8th Grd Sci Tchr 1980-; *ai:* Sci Curr Chprsn; Sci Olympiad Coach; Sftbl Coach; ME Sci Tchrs Assn 1980-; Coach of ME St Sci Olympiad Championship Team 1988-95; *office:* Jay MS 3 School St Jay ME 04239*

CHASE, WARREN JOHN, English Teacher; *b:* Springfield, MA; *m:* Margaret Lecak; *c:* Rebecca, Julie; *ed:* Fairfield Univ (BA) Eng 1969; Seton Hall Univ (MA) Amer Stud 1972; Jersey City St Coll Admin Cert; Attnd Marywood Coll, East Stroudesburg Univ; *cr:* Hopateong HS Eng Tchr 1969-75; Kittatinny Reg HS Eng Tchr 1975-84, Ath Dir 1984-91, Eng Tchr 1991-; *ai:* Jr High Cross Cntry Coach; Dist Articulation Comm; Natl Fed of Soccer Ofcl 1991-; Natl Fed Of Track Ofcl 1980-; NEA 1970-; Western Hills Chrstn Church 1984-, Sunday Schl Tchr, Elder; HS Cross Cntry Coach of Yr 3 Yrs; Lions Club, March of Dimes, Swim Coaches Assoc Recognition Awds; *office:* Kittatinny Regional Schl 77 Hasley Rd Newton NJ 07860*

CHASKES, STUART JAY, Assoc Prof of Med Lab Tech; *b:* Brooklyn, NY; *ed:* OH St Univ (BA) Microbiology 1964; Syracuse Univ (MS) Microbiology 1968; *cr:* Oakridge Associated Univ Rsrch Assoc 1969-74; Montefiore Hosp Anaerobic Microbiologist 1974-80; SUNY Assoc Prof 1980-; *ai:* Med Lab Tech Club Adv; Campus Blood Drive Coord; ASCP 1983-, St Adv; ASM 1969-; MMSNY 1978-; US Navy, Amer Soc for Engrng Ed Grant for Summer Rsrch Naval Med Rsrch Inst at Bethesda 1989; *office:* St Univ of NY at Farmingdale Rt 110 Farmingdale NY 11735

CHASON, DAVID BEN, Physics Teacher; *b:* White Plains, NY; *m:* Sheilah Gould; *c:* Molly, Keith; *ed:* Binghamton Univ (BS) Geology 1982; Syracuse Univ (MS) Hydrogeology 1984; Sci & Ed 60 Plus Credit Hrs; *cr:* Dames & Moore Engrs Geologist 1984-86; Sacred Heart HS Ecology, Chem Tchr 1986-87; Ardsley MS Earth Sci, Phys Sci Tchr 1987-94; Ardsley HS Physics, Earth Sci Tchr 1994-; *ai:* Cmptr Club Adv; AFT, Sci Tchrs Assn of NY St 1986-; AAPT 1994-; *office:* Ardsley MS 300 Farm Rd Ardsley NY 10502

CHATEAUNEUF, JOHN E., English Teacher; *b:* Lowell, MA; *m:* Alison; *c:* Cameron, Evan, Graham; *ed:* Univ of MA (BA) Eng; Attnd Breadloaf Schl of Eng, Middlebury Coll & Harvard Univ; *cr:* Concord Schl of Philosophy Dir 1976-80; Hollis Area HS Eng Tchr 1980-82; Acton-Boxborough Regnl HS Eng Tchr 1982-; *ai:* Schl Newspaper Spectrum Adv; Intnl Stdnts & Exch Prgm Area Coord; Thoreau Soc; NEA; MA Tchrs Assn; Eng Lunch Club; Acton-Boxborough Youth Hockey Assn, Bd of Dirs Mem; Film Reviews Pub in Newspapers; Poetry Pub in Acad & Historic Publications; *office:* Acton Boxborough Regional HS 96 Hayward Rd Acton MA 01720*

CHATKIN, DOROTHEA CARBAUGH, 12th Grade English Teacher; *b:* Frederick, MD; *m:* William C.; *c:* Aaron David, Elizabeth Ann; *ed:* Hagerstown Jr Coll (AA) Eng 1962; Shepherd Coll (BA) Lang Arts 1972; Western MD Coll (MLA) Theater, Lit 1981; Attnd Penn St 1993; *cr:* North Hagerstown HS Grd Twelve AP Eng Tchr 1978-; *ai:* Fac Rep Community Action Comm; Hnr Awd Comm; WA Co Tchr Assn, MD St Tchr Assn, NEA 1979-; NCTE 1986-; Alpha Delta Kappa 1988-; *office:* North Hagerstown HS 1200 Pennsylvania Ave Hagerstown MD 21742

CHATLAND, BRADLEY J., Social Studies Teacher; *b:* Malone, NY; *m:* Tamara J. Smallman; *c:* Joseph, Erynn; *ed:* St Univ of NY at Potsdam (BA) Soc Stud 1973; Addl 38 Hrs; *cr:* Franklin Acad Soc Stud Tchr 1973-; *ai:* Whiz Quiz Team Adv; Union Rep for Bldg; NYSUT, Malone Fed of Tchrs 1973-; *office:* Franklin Acad State St Malone NY 12953

CHATTERTON, RAYMOND EDWARD, Economics Professor; *b:* Springfield, MO; *m:* Pauline Ramsey; *c:* Paul Allen, Robert Emerson, Douglas Howard; *ed:* Southwest MO St Coll (BA) Ec 1968; WA St Univ (PHD) Ec 1980; *cr:* Randolph-Macon Woman's Coll Ec Asst Prof 1975-80; Lock Haven Univ Ec Assoc Prof 1982-88, Ec Prof 1988-; *ai:* Amer Ec Assn 1975-; Lock Haven Rotary Club 1982-, Pres; H. L. Mednick Fnd Recipient; Numerous Articles; *office:* Lock Haven Univ Lock Haven PA 17745

CHAUVIN, PAULINE M., Guidance Counselor; *b:* RI; *m:* Raymond Lebel; *ed:* Univ of RI (BS) Home Ec Ed 1969, (MA) Cnslng 1973; *cr:* Smithfield HS Home Ec Tchr 1969-89, Guid Cnslr 1990-; *ai:* RI Cnslng Assn 1992-; *office:* Smithfield HS 90 Pleasant View Ave Smithfield RI 02917

CHEATLE, JAMES MICHAEL, Elementary Art Teacher; *b:* St Marys, PA; *m:* Katherine Giordano; *c:* Zachary, Noah; *ed:* Edinboro Univ (BS) Art Ed 1971, (ME) Art Ed 1975; *cr:* Fox Twp Elem Schl Art Tchr 1971-; Bennetts Vly Elem Schl Art Tchr 1971-; *ai:* PSEA, NEA 1971-; *office:* St Marys Area Schl Dist 977 St Marys Rd St Marys PA 15857

CHEESMAN, KERRY LEE, Assoc Prof & Chm of Biology; *b:* Santa Barbara, CA; *m:* Sara Day; *c:* Ian, Nathan; *ed:* Univ of CA (BA) Zoology, Geology 1976; Univ of IL Med Ctr (PHD) Physiology 1981; IN Univ (MS) Sec Ed 1987; *cr:* Northwestern Univ Med Schl Asst Prof 1983-85; St Francis Coll Asst, Assoc Prof 1986-92; IN Univ Adj Assoc Prof 1988-92; Capital Univ Assoc Prof, Dept Chair 1993-; *ai:* Chief Premedical, Pre-Ed, Premed Adv; Mem Several Coll Curr comms; NSTA, Soc Coll Sci Tchrs 1991-; Amer Assn Adv Sci 1981-; Nat Assn Ads Hlth Prof 1994-; BSA 1966-, Exec Bd, Several Awds; Amer Bapt Churches 1977-, St Pres; Pub 21 Articles, 32 Abstracts; Several Grants forEquipment; Curr Dev Rsrch; *office:* Capital Univ 2199 E Main St Bexley OH 43209*

CHEKOW, MARY TANZA-LUPO, Dance Teacher, Artistic Dir; *b:* Jamaica, NY; *m:* Jeff Alan; *c:* Michael, Lupo; *ed:* Nassau BFA Dance; Attnd Orlando Schl of Ballet, Seiskaya Ballet Schl; *cr:* Amer Ballet Tour of South America Prof Dancer, TV Commercials 1973; Ballet Long Island Prin & Prof Dancer, Tchr 1978; Airport Playhouse Featured Dancer 1982; *ai:* Sacred Hearts Dance Club Artistic Dir; Annual Fine Arts Festival; Multicultural Assemblies; Open House; *office:* Sacred Heart Acad 47 Cathedral Ave Hempstead NY 11550

CHELEWSKI, RAY EDWARD, Agriscience Instructor; *b:* Broken Bow, NE; *m:* Paula Kay Robinson; *c:* Dale, Julie; *ed:* CO Mountain Coll (AS) Farm Mngmt 1973; CO St Univ (BS) Voc Ag Ed 1975; NM St Univ (MA) Ag, Extension Ed 1985; Post Grad Stud Univ of ME, Presque Isle ME, NM St Univ; *cr:* Golden HS Ag Tchr Sub 1973-75; Career Dev Ctr Ag Tchr 1975-82; Raton HS Ag Tchr 1982-90; Presque Isle Tech Ctr Agriscience Tchr 1990-; *ai:* USDE Natl Work Group Prgm Planning, Mrktg; Natl FFA TAsk Force Natl Ldrshp New Millenium; Natl Ag Literacy Task Force; FFA Spon; ME Ag Tchrs Assn 1990-, Pres, Distngd Prof 1994-95; ME Voc Assn 1990-; Natl Ag Tchrs Assn 1975-; NMTC Advy Bd 1993-; Adj Fac NMTC 1993-, Instr; Adj Fac UMO 1994-, Instr; Adj Fac UMPO 1995-, Instr; Outstdng Aquaculture Tchrs NVATA 1989; Tchr of Yr SW Regnl Soil & Water Conservation Dist 1989; Tchr of Yr NM Wildlife Fed 1989; Natl Agriscience Tchf or Yr Finalist 1988-89; *office:* Presque Isle Regnl HS 79 Blake St Ste 3 Presque Isle ME 04769

CHELTE PH.D., JUDITH SEGZDOWICZ, English Teacher; *b:* Springfield, MA; *m:* Raymond J. Sr.; *ed:* Westfield St Coll (BA) Eng 1973; Smith Coll (MAT) Eng 1974; Amer Intnl Coll (CAGS) Eng 1980; Univ MA at Amherst (PhD) Eng 1994; *cr:* Chicopee Comprehensive HS Eng Tchr 1974-; *ai:* Evaluation 1988 Steering Comm to Organize Individual Comms to Prepare for What Was a Successful Accreditation 10 Yrs; Chicopee Ed Assn, MA Tchr Assn, NEA 1974-; Chicopee Bus & Prof Womens Club 1975-; Springfield Smith Coll Club 1974-, Pres 2 Yrs, VP 2 Yrs; Frnds of the Chicopee Pub Lib Sec; Articles Pub in Eng Journal 1986, 1990 & 1995; Chicopee Comprehensive HS Tchr of Yr 1987; Yrbk Dedication 1986; Smith Coll Grad Stud Full Tuition Schlsp 1973-74; AP Rdr 1993, 1996; Est Eng Wrtng Course; *office:* Chicopee Comprehensive H S 617 Montgomery St Chicopee MA 01020

CHEMERKA, WILLIAM RONALD, Amer History & Ec Teacher; *b:* Jamaica, NY; *m:* Deborah Brooman; *ed:* Bloomfield Coll (BA) Amer His 1972; Montclair St U (MA) Soc Sci 1978; Post Grad Stud Montclair St Univ; *cr:* N Waren Regnl HS His Tchr 1972-73; Madison HS His & Ec Tchr 1973-; *ai:* Stu Cncl Adv 1979-; Yth in Govt Adv 1994-; Var Vlybl Coach 1977-80; Class Adv 1976, 1980; NEA, NJEA 1972-; Madison Educ Assn 1973-; NJ Historical Soc 1980-; Morris Cty Historical Soc 1984-; Alamo Soc 1986-; Geraldine Rockefeller Dodge Grant 1987, 1995; DAR His Tchr of Yr 1987; NJ Governor's Tchr Awd 1992; Golden Apple Tchr Awd 1989; Yrbk Dedication 1980, 1991; *office:* Madison HS 170 Ridgedale Ave Madison NJ 07940

CHEN, CHUEN-CHIN HSU, Science Teacher; *b:* China; *m:* Robert H. K.; *c:* Tzu-Yi, Tzu-Mainn; *ed:* OK St Univ (PHD) Chem 1968; Univ of Chicago Post-Doctor Biochemistry 1968-71; *cr:* Highland Park HS Sci Tchr 1986-88; West Windsor-Plainsboro HS Sci Tchr 1988-; *ai:* NJEA 1986-; NJSTA; *office:* West Windsor-Plainsboro HS 346 Clarksville Rd Princeton Jct NJ 08550

CHENEY, LEREN WILLIAM, Professor of Psychology; *b:* Meridan, CT; *m:* Kathleen F.; *c:* Elizabeth, Stephen, Jonathan; *ed:* Oberlin Coll (BA) Psych 1960; Univ of MA (MED) Cnslng 1966, (EDD) Guid, Cnslng 1970; *cr:* Oberlin Coll Asst Dean of Men 1963-65; RI Coll Dir of Residence Halls 1970-73; CCRI Coll Cnslr, Instr 1973-80, Dir Cnslng Ctr 1980-81, Prof of Psych 1981-; *ai:* Spon Psi Beta NHS; Comms Adj Fac Trng, Stu Success, Course, Tev Learing Team, Bachelor Bound Prgm; Adv Psych Club; EPA, NEPA 1985-, Co-Chair of Conf; Psi Beta 1991-, Eastern Regnl VP; CTUP 1995-; NEA 1973-, Exec Comm; Greenwood Comm Church 1973-, Elder 7 Yrs, Deacon 6 Yrs, Pres Men's Assn 3 Yrs; Narregarsett Cty BSA 1980-, Comm Chm, Dist Chm Quequaduct; Narregarsett Bay Barbershop Chorus 1974-, VP; Distngd Lecturer Awd 1987; Natl Excl Tchr Awd 1988; Pub Career Information Stud Guide; Served on Accreditation Team Comm Coll Of RI Flanagan Camps 400 East Ave Warwick RI 02

CHENEY, LES, Weight Training & Health Tchr; *b:* Ashtabula Cynthia Hahlen; *c:* Amy, Kim; *ed:* Kent St (BS) Comp Hlth, Akron 18 Sem Hrs 1982; *cr:* Pymatuning Vly Schl Bio, Earth 1966-68; Springfield HS Weight Trng, Hlth, PE Tchr 1968-; *ai:* Be Head Cross Cntry, Powerlifting Team Coach; Boys Head Track Co Spartan Gym; NEA, OEA 1966-; SLACT 1968-; NEOEA 1968- Media Image Awd 1991-92; Spoke Natl Clinics U of TN, San Fitness Convention, Un of Waterloo; Natural Aths Strength A Masters I; Powerlifter of Yr 1991; Natural Natl Champion; Intnl C Against Russia 1990; Amer Drug Free PLA Natl Champion 19 Natl, 4 St Records; Dapper Dan Awd 1992; *office:* Springfield Sanitarium Rd Akron OH 44312

CHENOWETH, OKEY EVERETT, Drama & English Teache Lick Run, WV; *m:* Jane Aeschbach; *c:* Carol Constance, Thomas L *ed:* Davis & Elkins Univ (BA) Eng & Drama 1951; WV Univ (M. Drama; Attnd Stella Adler Theatre Conservatory, Pasadena Playh of Theatre Arts, Harold Clifton Assocs; *cr:* US Armed Forces 1953-54; Mark Keppel High Tchr 1955-60; Clifford Scott 1960-61; Glen Rock HS Tchr & Supvr 1961-; William Pate Part-Time Tchr; Bergen Comm Coll Part-Time Tchr; *ai:* Dir of Drama; Drama Club; NEA 1955-; NJEA 1960-; Dramatics Guild Theatre Edctrs Coalition 1993-; On-Stage Inc., Bd of Dir; Prince Distngd Tchr; Bergen Cty Tchr of the Yr; NJ Tchr of the Yr 1st Ru NJ Cncl of the Arts Grant; Numerous Poems Pub; Natl Endowme Hum Grant.

CHEO, LI-HSING S., Professor of Computer Science; *b:* Tainan *m:* Bernard R.; *c:* Louise Cheo Lasota, Lin-Wen Wayne; *ed:* Na Kung Univ (BS) Electrical Engineering 1955; Univ of CA at Berk Electrical Engineering 1959; NY Univ (PHD) Math 1970; VA Po Inst at Blacksburg Physics 1957-58; *cr:* Taiwan Power Co Jr Engr Univ of CA Research & Tchng Fellow 1957-60; NY Univ Re Tchng Fellow 1968-70; NY Inst of Tech Math Asst Prof 1970-72 Paterson Coll of NJ Math Asst, Assoc Prof 1972-78, Cmptr Sci Full Prof 1978-, Cmptr Sci Chprsn 1985-93; *ai:* Fac Adv SGA C 1974-, Chinese Stu Assn 1993-, ACM Stu Chapter 1974-, U Epsilon Cmptr Sci Honor Soc Chapter 1988-; Assn for C Machinary 1972-; AFT 1972-, Exec Cncl; NJ Bergen Cty Human Commission 1993-; Teaneck Presbyn Church 1975-, Cho Nomination Comm; Org of Chinese Amer NJ Chapter Pres 1995, Pres 1994, 1995; NY Univ Funder's Day Awd; Sigma Xi Natl H of Sciences; NJ Dept of Higher Ed Grant; GRE Cmptr Sci T Research Papers; VPE Natl Comp Sci Honor Soc1988-; *office:* Paterson Coll of NJ 300 Pompton Rd Wayne NJ 07470

CHERILL, ANTHONY F., Global Studies Teacher; *b:* Hazleto Roberta Birnbaum; *c:* Randi, David; *ed:* Bloomsburg U Anthropology & Pol Sci 1970; Trenton St Coll (MS) His & A 1976; Attnd OH St Univ, Princeton Univ, Rider Coll; *cr:* Pennsb Dist Classroom Tchr 1969-, Dept Chair 1988-; *ai:* Stu Cncl Adv Drama Producer 1980-; NEA, PSEA & PEA 1969-, Bldg Rep; L Ath Assn 1986-; USTA 1991-; *office:* Medill Bair HS 608 S C Fairless Hills PA 19030

CHERMAK, MARK ALLEN, HS History & Government Allegan, MI; *m:* Diane Marie Darling; *c:* Timothy Michael; *ed:* ((BA) Soc Stud 1971; SUNY at Oswego (MS) Ed 1981; Addl Grad of IA at Iowa City; *cr:* North Syracuse Cntrl Schls HS Soc Stud T *ai:* Band Parents Inc Bd Mem; AFT 1972-; NYSUT 1975-; Andre United Meth Church 1972-, Bd of Trustees Chr; *office:* Cice Syracuse HS Route 31 & Northstar Dr Cicero NY 13039

CHERNESKY, EDWARD JOSEPH, 5th Grade Teacher; *b:* King *m:* Mary Ann; *c:* Edward, Chris, Michele; *ed:* Kings Coll (AB) Scranton Univ (MS) Ed 1968; Univ of Pittsburgh, Wilkes U Misericordia, Bloomsburg Univ, Princeton Univ, & NY Univ 1 Credits Beyond Masters; *cr:* Towanda Area Schls Tchr; WY Semi Schl Tchr & Summer Schl Dir; Kingston Schl Dist Tchr; WY Vly Dist Tchr & Head Tchr; *ai:* Standing, Bldg, Testing Pgm & Selection Comms; Curr Chm; Negotiator; WUWEA, PSEA, NE Bldg Rep, Negotiator; LUZ & WY Soc Stud Cncl 1964-, B WUWEA 1980-, Chm Prof Rights & Response; Phi Delta Kappa; Osterhout Lib; Won 5 NEH Flwshps to Princeton Univ; NSF Schl Coll; Winner PA Governors Club Schlsp to Freedom Fndtn; C Largest Contributor in Cntry to Vietanm Memrl.*

CHERNICK, JONATHAN, Mathematics Teacher; *b:* Bronx, SUNY at Oneonta (BS) Bus & Ec 1988; City Coll (MA) Math & Ed Admin Credits; *cr:* IS 192 Math Tchr 1989-91; Truman HS M 1991-; *ai:* AFT 1989-; UFT 1989-; NCTM 1992-; Articles Pu Harry S. Truman HS 750 Baychester Ave Bronx NY 10475*

CHERNOFF, SALLY, 7th & 8th Grd Math & Sci Tchr; *ed:* Radcliffe (AB) Phys Sci; *ai:* NSTA, NCTM, St Level Math & Design & Dev of 7th Grd Life Sci Prgm; Educl Consultant Writ Guides for ADAM Software Atlanta, GA; *office:* Far Brook Schl Hills Rd Short Hills NJ 07078*

CHERRY, KENNETH JAMES, Fifth Grade Teacher; *b:* Butle Lu Ann Kennedy; *c:* Jason, Justin; *ed:* Slippery Rock Univ (BS) 1973, (MED) Elem Ed, His 1976; Post-Grad Hrs Villanova Univ Univ; *cr:* Butler Area Schl Dist Kndgtn-6th Grd Tchr 1975-; *a* Supvr 9 Yrs; Eng, Rdng, Soc Stud Comms; Dept Chair Soc St PSEA 1975-; Butler Cty Historical Soc 1990-; Captain WIlliam T 1990-, Extra Movie Last of the Mohicans; Golden Tornado Mi *office:* Mc Quistion Elem Schl 210 Mechling Dr Butler PA 1600

CHERRY, TARAH S., 4th Grade Teacher; *b:* Cincinnati, OH; *m:* *c:* David Evans, Brett Evans, Christopher Evans; *ed:* Salem St T (BS) Elem 1974; *cr:* New Haven Schl System 2nd & 4th Grd Tc *ai:* Construct Mentor Tchr, NSF; Mentor Tchr, GLOBALEARN NSTA 1989-; Amer Assoc Univ Women 1991-, Fellow, Eleanor F Awd; Delta Sigma Theta 1962-, Sec; Excl in Ed Grant, LUSTMA Ed Awd 1992-; Amer Assn Univ Women Eleanor Roosevelt Fell Soutwen CT Telephone Cos Telecommunication Incentive Gra *home:* 22 Pine Ridge Rd Woodbridge CT 06525*

CHERUNDOLO, JOHN JOSEPH, 6th Grade Math Tea Binghamton, NY; *m:* Cheryl Hunter; *c:* Christina, Joseph, (Mansfield Univ (BS) Elem Ed 1976; Temple Univ (ME) Montrose Area Schl Dist Kndgtn Fourth-Sixth Grd Tchr 1979-; *a* Soccer, Head Boys, Jr High Boys Bsbl Coach; 4th-6th Grds I Bskbl Supvr; Math Curr Advy Team; NEA 1979-; NCTM; NEPCTM; LD Assn of Susquebanna Co, Area P Special Olymp PA Assessment Team for Math Testing, Dept of Ed Scorer, St Assessment, Dept of Ed Mem; *office:* Montrose Area School Lathrop St Montrose PA 18801

CHESKO, RICHARD LEE, History Tchr & Bsktbl Coach; *b:* City, PA; *m:* Judy Mirkovich; *c:* Beth Ann, Stephen Richard; *ed:* Rock Univ (BS) His 1969; Attnd Edinboro Univ; *cr:* Linesville Tchr 1969-; *ai:* Jr HS & Var Girls Bsktbl Coach; Var Girls Sftbl C Dept Chm; NEA, PSEA 1969-; Little League, Umpire 1969-; Line

Yr 1986; *office:* Linesville HS RR 3 Box 135e E Erie St Linesville 4

EY, KATHRYN, English & Theater Arts Teacher; *b:* Buffalo, NY; ne; *c:* Adam; *ed:* SUNY at Buffalo (BA) Commnctn & Theatre Coll at Buffalo (MS) Multidisciplinary 1975; Credit Hrs in Drug & Alcohol Issues, Eng as a Second Lang & Writing; *cr:* West chls Eng & Theatre Tchr 1970-; *ai:* Drama Club Adv; Sr Play Adv; ation Adv; Schl Musical Adv; Lit Magazine Adv; West Seneca ssn 1970-, Bldg Rep, Tchr of the Yr; WNY Writing Project 1985-, r; NYS Eng Cncl 1987-, Tchr of Excl; NYS Theatre Edctrs Assn omm Intervention 1986-; Actress in Awd Winning Production; Pub & Poems; Tchr Mentor & Trainer; *office:* West Seneca East Sr HS neca St West Seneca NY 14224*

EY, ROBERT VINCENT, Social Studies Teacher; *m:* Claudia g; *c:* Vincent, Robert, Nicholas; *ed:* Lycoming Coll (BA) gy, Anthropology 1971; Credits Bloomsburg Univ, Penn St, Santa Azusa Pacific Soc Scis; *cr:* North Schuylkill Schls Elem Ed , Scndry Ed 1976-; *ai:* Coach Head Ftbl, Asst Bsktbl; NEA, PSEA A Coaches Assn 1980-; Knights of Columbus 1990-, Recorder; St s Bd, Pres; St Casimir's Holy Name, Pres; Polish Club; East End ; Dev Alternative Ed Prgm Disciplinary Stdnts; *office:* North ll Jr Sr HS RD 2 Box 47 Ashland PA 17921

IC, THOMAS J., Math Teacher; *b:* Canonsburg, PA; *ed:* CA St S) Scndry Ed 1964-67; Grad Courses in Math 1971-73; Grad Penn St Univ 1968-69; *cr:* Syracuse City Schl Dist Tchr 1967-68; urg Jr HS Tchr 1968-89; Canonsburg MS Tchr 1989-90; Canon Mc HS Tchr 1990-; *ai:* Math Dept Chprsn 1994-; Bsbl, Wrestling Wrestling Tournaments Comm Co-Chm; CMEA 1968-; NEA, PSEA m; NCTM, PCTM, MCWP 1994-; *office:* Canon-Mc Millan Sr HS Ext Canonsburg PA 15317

ER, PHILLIP JEROME, English Teacher; *b:* Washington, DC; *m:* y K. Rainer; *c:* Paul, Amy Chesser Brock, Emily; *ed:* Univ of RI g 1975, (MA) Eng 1977; *cr:* Northwestern HS Eng Tchr 1980-89; HS Eng Tchr 1989-; *ai:* NEA 1995-; Fleet Reserve Assn 1993-; or Christmas 1986; From Boyhood to Manhood on a Pungy 1988; otomac HS 5211 Boydell Ave Oxon Hill MD 20745*

ER, DEBORAH L., High School English Teacher; *b:* Medina, OH; nas; *ed:* Mt Vernon Nazarene Coll (BA) Eng 1992; Grad Course Univ of Dayton at Capital Univ; *cr:* World Harvest Chrstn Acad Tchr 1992-; *ai:* Sr, Stu Cncl Adv; Prom Coord; Dept Head; LA 1992-; *office:* World Harvest Christian Acad 4595 Gender Rd inchester OH 43110

IG, SHIRLEY MUI, Bilingual Teacher; *b:* Toyshan Guangdong, n: Frank Sau; *ed:* The Chinese Univ of Hong Kong (BA) Chinese ; Seton Hall Univ (MA) Scndry Ed 1979; Diploma of Ed 1976; *cr:* ng MS Tchr 1970-77; Immigrant Soc Svc Prgm Coord 1979-80; PS Desoto Schl Tchr 1980-; *ai:* Garden Diplomat, Docent NY al Garden; AFT 1980-; Asian, Pacific Islander Coalition on HIV, ol, Interpreter; *office:* PS 130 The Desoto Schl 143 Baxter St an NY 10013

NAK, KATHLEEN HELEN, AP Biology Teacher; *b:* Passaic, NJ; stopher, Jason; *ed:* Montclair St Univ (MA) Bio 1986; William Coll Credits in Biotechnology; *ai:* NABT 1980-; *office:* Lakeland l H S 205 Conklintown Rd Wanaque NJ 07465

RETTE, HELEN,SSA, Religion & Math Teacher; *b:* Central Falls, Anna Maria Coll (BA) Ed 1967; St Bonaventure Univ (MA) y 1973; Attnd St Joseph Tchrs Coll 1958; Rel Cert Diocese of nce 1983; *cr:* Queen of Angels Acad Grd 4-5 Tchr 1953-56; Luke n Meml Schl Grd 7 All Subjects Tchr 1956-57, 1958-59; Indian ation Kanawakee Grd 7 All Subjects Tchr 1959-61; Indian ation St Regis Grd 6-7 Rel, Math, Lang Arts Tchr 1961-63; St Pius rd 9-10 Rel, Algebra & Latin I, II Tchr 1963-64; Noranda Cath HS 0 Rel, Algebra I & II, Geometry, Latin Tchr 1964-66; Bishop HS Grd 9-10 Rel, Algebra & Latin I, II Tchr 1966-67; St James chl Grd 7-9 Rel, Algebra I, Lang Arts, Sci Tchr 1966-68; Notre IS Grd 9-10 Rel, Eng Latin Tchr 1968-70; St Matthew Schl Prin ; Notre Dame Elem Schl Grd 7-8 Rel, Math, Lang Arts Tchr ; St Matthew-Notre Dame Consolidated Schl Grd 6-8 Lang Arts, 8 Math, Grd 8 Rel Tchr 1977-80, Prin 1980-81, Grd 6-8 Lang Arts,; Rel Coord 1977-; Plant Comm 1994-95; RI Mid Level Edctrs St Matthew Parish, Eucharistic Minister 1980-, Lector 1980-, Cncl 1980-94, Ed Comm 1980-94, Parish Festival Vol 1993-.

, DONALD P., Mathematics Teacher; *b:* Cape May, NJ; *m:* Jane; *c:* Jason; *ed:* Eastern Nazarene Coll (BA) Math 1975; *cr:* Mid Twp h Instr 1988-; *office:* Middle Township HS 212 Bayberry Dr Cape urt Hou NJ 08210

LBERT YU-MING, Professor; *b:* Shanghai City, China; *m:* Sari ; *c:* Heidi Yen-Mei, Suvi Bettina, Cynthia Yen-Mei, Henry Kaifu; Tsng-Hua Univ (BA) Math 1969; KS St Univ (EDD) Math 1974; Univ (PHD) Statistics 1979; *cr:* Emporia St Univ Asst Prof 1979-80; n Vly Coll Asst Prof 1980-82; Bowie St Univ Asst Prof & Assoc 82-89; Univ of MD Univ Coll Prof 1989-; *office:* Univ of MD Univ ad Schl Univ Blvd at Adelphi Rd College Park MD 20742*

ING-CHUNG, Computer Science Professor; *b:* Kao-Hsiung, n: Lin W.; *ed:* Natl Taiwan Univ (BS) Math 1977; Univ of MD at re Cty (MS) Applied Math 1984; Univ of Maryland at College Park Cmptr Sci 1988; *cr:* Catholic Univ of America Asst. Prof 1988-94; St. Univ Asst. Prof 1994-; *ai:* Cath Univ of Amer Asst Prof 1988-94; St Univ Asst Prof 1994-; Cell Group Ldr Comm Church; Amer Assn al Intelligence 1977-; ACM 1996; Articles Pub; Panelist Prof Conf; Cmptr Softwares Tchng, Learning; *office:* Bowie St Univ Jericho ad Computer Science Dept Bowie MD 20715*

ESE, MERIGO CARROLL, Language Arts Teacher; *b:* New Y; *m:* Tony; *c:* Bizzy, Meg, John; *ed:* Manhattanville Coll (BA) ost Grad Ed Credits Coll of New Rochelle; *ai:* Xmas Play Dir; of Charity; *office:* Blessed Sacrament Elem Schl 24 Maple Ave New e NY 10801

PELLI, DONALD FRANCIS, Health, PE Tchr & Dept Coord; *b:* lle, PA; *m:* Nancy Caliari; *c:* Barbara Fortunato, Robert, Bryan; *ed:* Univ (BS) Hlth & PE 1958; Attnd Carlow Coll, Saint Francis s Equivalency; *cr:* St Marys Cntrl Tchr 1958-59; Bennetts Vly Tchr h 1959-67; St Marys Area Schl Dist Tchr 1967-; *ai:* Outdoor Club D Adv; NEA & PSEA 1959-; Bennetts Vly Kiwanis 1970-; Pres & c Awd; Bennetts Vly Little League 1970-80, Pres; St Joseph Church 85-, Pres; *home:* PO Box 61 Force PA 15841*

A, JANINE LONGSTREET, Fourth Grade Teacher; *b:* Perth , NJ; *c:* Vance, Jeffrey; *ed:* Trenton St Coll (BA) Elem Ed 1969; Glassboro St Coll; *cr:* Willett Elem Schl Third Grd Tchr 1970-71; ell Elem Schl Fourth Grd Tchr 1971-79, Fifth Grd Tchr 1980-82; Schl GATE Tchr 1983; Campbell Elem Schl GATE Tchr 1983; MS GATE Tchr 1983; Willett Schl Second Grd Tchr 1983-88, Grd Tchr 1988-89; Campbell Schl Second Grd Tchr 1989-91, Fourth hr 1991-; *ai:* Math Curr, Bell Act, Sci Fair Comms; Prins Cabinet; , NJEA, NEA, SREA 1971-; *office:* William Campbell Schl 22 St South River NJ 08882

CHIARA, LIESL MUNDORFF, Mathematics Teacher; *b:* Yonkers, NY; *m:* Joseph C.; *ed:* Univ of DE (BAAS) Psych 1988; Pace Univ (MBA) Human Resources Mngmt 1990; *cr:* Alexander's Inc Prsnl Mgr 1990-92; Lakeland Schl Dist Math Tchr 1993-; *ai:* Alumni Assn Pres; FBLA Adv; Discovery Rsrch Team; Turnkey; LFT 1993-; *home:* 8 Winterberry Ct Peekskill NY 10566

CHIARELLA, CAROL L., Chprsn & Assoc Prof of Acctng; *b:* Weissbaden, Germany; *m:* Joseph L.; *c:* Jonathan, Anna Marie; *ed:* SUNY Coll at Plattsburgh (BS) Mrktg 1983; SUNY at Albany (MS) Acctng 1985; *cr:* Urbach Kahn & Werlin CPA's Accountant 1985-87; NYS Dept of Labor Accountant 1987-88; Schenectady Cty Comm Coll Asst Prof 1990-94, Assoc Prof 1994-; *ai:* Phi Beta Lambda Campus Chptr Adv 1991-95; Fac-Stu Assn Chprsn; AICPA 1990-; Inst of Mngmt Accountants; Womens Club of Luther Forest 1992-, Corresponding Sec 1995; CPA; *office:* Schenectady County Comm Coll 78 Washington Ave Schenectady NY 12305

CHIARIELLO, JOAN SZEWCZYK, English Teacher; *b:* Passaic, NJ; *m:* Ronald G.; *c:* Michael; *ed:* Montclair St (BA) Eng 1962, (MA) Eng 1963; 30 Addl Post Grad Stud Eng, Rdng, Ed; *cr:* Clifton HS Eng Tchr 1962-63; Pascack Vly HS Eng Tchr 1963-69; Rockville HS Eng, Soc Stud Tchr 1969-71, Eng Tchr 1976-; *ai:* Mentor Comm; Ninth Grd Transition Comm; St Francis Church 1994-; *office:* Rockville HS 2100 Baltimore Rd Rockville MD 20851

CHICK, ANN HOLOWATY, 4th Grade Teacher; *b:* Norwich, CT; *m:* Robert K.; *c:* Joseph B.; *ed:* Univ of CT (BA) Eng 1965; Eastern Ct Univ 5th Yr Ed 1971; *cr:* Norwich Bd of Ed Elem Tchr 1965-78; Oakdale Elem Schl 4, 5 Grd Tchr; Murphy Jr HS Sci, Eng Tchr; Tyl MS Sci Tchr 1991-94; Oakdale Elem Schl Tchr 1994-; *ai:* Mentor, Co-Operating Tchr; CEA 1965-; MEA 1981-; *office:* Oakdale Elem Schl 30 Indiana Cir Oakdale CT 06370*

CHICKERING, SUSAN HERNDON, Guidance Counselor; *b:* Peterborough, NH; *m:* John Ayers; *c:* Lars, Gabriel, Silas; *ed:* Univ of VT (BS) Human Svc 1978, (MS) Cnslng 1983; Vasterbergs Folk HS Sweden Creative Dramatics Tchr Cert; Natl Bd of Cert Cnslrs Cert 1984-; *cr:* Kingsland Bay Schl Residential Cnslr, Case Worker 1980-83; U-32 Jr, Sr HS Guid Cnslr 1983-87; Cabot HS Guid Cnslr 1987-93; Spaulding HS Guid Cnslr 1993-; *ai:* Soccer Club Coach 1986-87; Parent Support Groups 1983-95; NEA 1981-; NBCC 1984-; Conservation Comm 1988-, Chprsn; VT Prevention Trng Team 1986-90; *office:* Spaulding HS Ayers St Barre VT 05641*

CHIDESTER, JOSEPH PAUL, Physical Science Teacher; *b:* Mt Pleasant, PA; *c:* Joedy, Paul, Laurie, Stephen; *ed:* Carnegie Inst of Tech (BSEE) Electrical Engrng 1957; *cr:* Bendix Radio Prin Engr 1958-70; Jemicy Schl Phys Sci Tchr 1972-; *home:* 11 Celadon Rd Owings Mills MD 21117

CHIEFSKY, SUSAN J., English & Amer Stud Teacher; *b:* Bridgeport, CT; *ed:* Univ of RI (BA) Eng 1974; Goddard in VT (MA) Spec Ed 1979; Tchr Cert in Eng 1976; 30 Plus Post Credit Hrs Pertaining to Counseling, Tchng Methods Such as Cooperative Learning, MS Philosophy & Art for Tchrs of Other Subjects; *cr:* Woodstock Union HS Spec Educator 1978-81, Eng Tchr 1981-92; Woodstock Union MS Eng & Soc Stud Tchr 1992-; *ai:* NCTE 1975-; NEA & VEA 12 Yrs; ASCD 6 Yrs; NELMS 1992-; Pentangle Arts Cncl 3 Yrs; Recreation Bd 4 Yrs; NELMS Outstanding Curr Dev Awd 1996; *office:* Woodstock Union MS Rt 4 W Woodstock VT 05091*

CHIERO, NANCY TAGLIA, Special Education Teacher; *b:* Waterbury, CT; *m:* John; *c:* John, Jennifer; *ed:* Cntrl CT St Univ (BS) Spec Ed, Elem Ed 1975; Southern CT St Univ (MS) Learning Disabilities 1979; 9 Credits Toward 6th Yr Degree; *cr:* Laurel Ledge Schl K-5 Resource Room Learning Disabilites Tchr 1975-86; St Margaret Mc Ternan Schl Tutor, Evaluator 1991-94; Southington HS Learning Disabilites Tchr 1994-; *ai:* Run Marathons; Quality Plus Q Comm 1995-; Triathlete; CEA, NEA 1975-86, 1994-; Catechism Tchr 1992-94; YMCA 1994-, Bd of Dir Southington; Classroom Highlighted in CT Ed Assn Magazine; *office:* Southington HS 720 Pleasant St Southington CT 06489

CHIKEKA, CHARLES DHIRI, Associate Professor; *b:* Emii Owerri, Nigeria; *m:* Rita Ngozika; *c:* Chiamaeze, Chiedozi, Enyinna, Ijeuru, Kelechi, Kemjika; *ed:* Univ of MN (BA,MPA) Pol Sci 1963, 1964; Columbia Univ (MA) Intnl Relations, His 1966, (MPHD) Pol Sci, His 1978, (PHD) Pol Sci 1982; Grad Prgm Pol Sci Cath Univ of Amer; *cr:* Jackson St Univ Asst Prof 1967-68; FL A&M Univ Asst Prof 1968-69; Morgan St Univ Assoc Prof 1970-; *ai:* Dept Comm, Stu Recruitment; Supervising Undergraduate Sr Comprehensive Examinations; Amer Historical Assn, Amer Pol Sci Assn, African Stud Assn 1970-; AAUP 1995-; Britain, France, New African States 1990; Africa, EFC 1993-; *home:* 600 Tunbridge Rd Baltimore MD 21212 *

CHILDS, ALICE MEISER, Retired Kindergarten Teacher; *b:* Genesee Cty, NY; *m:* Marvin F.; *c:* Marval, Denise C. Lynk, Donald, Darla C. Jaszko; *ed:* Geneseo St Univ (BA) Elem Ed 1953; *cr:* Painted Post Schl Kndgtn Tchr 1953-56; Lincoln Schl Kndgtn Tchr 1956-57; Jackson Schl Kndgtn Tchr 1956-57; Oakfield Schl Kndgtn Tchr 1968-95; *ai:* NY St United Tchrs 1968-95; AFT 1968-95; *home:* 7591 Alleghany Rd Basom NY 14013

CHILDS, MICHAEL, Economics Teacher & Dean; *b:* Queens, NY; *c:* Michael, Tarrell; *ed:* Bronx Comm Coll (AA) Lbrl Arts 1978; York Coll (BA) Pol Sci 1980; City Coll of NY (MS) Ed 1993; New York & The World Project Intnl Ed 1995; City Coll Telecommunications in Global Instruction 1994; Columbia Univ Conflict Resolution Cert 1993; NY Stock Exch Teach the Tchr Prgm 1992; *cr:* William H. Taft HS Tchr 1985; Alfred E. Smith HS Tchr, Dean, Negotiation Specialist 1985-; *ai:* Supervising Tchr of After Schl Peer Tutoring Prgm; Red Cross Club Adv; ASCD 1989-; UFT, NYSUT 1985-; IAMAA 1987-; Schomburg Ctr, ASALH 1993-; Smithsonian 1991-; Conflict Resolution Awd of Excl 1995; Peer Mediators Advy Cncl Excl Awd 1994; Citizenship Excl Awd 1992; Parent Ldrshp Awd 1991; IBM Awd of Excl 1991; *office:* Alfred E Smith HS 333 E 151st St Bronx NY 10451*

CHILDS, MICHAEL D., Social Studies Teacher; *b:* St Charles, AR; *m:* Karla Windham; *c:* Michael D. Jr., Jann H.; *ed:* MS St Univ (BS) Soc Stud 1976, (MED) Schl Admin 1971; 45 Addl Hrs; *cr:* Greenville HS Study Hall, Ftbl, Tennis 1967-69; Walton Co HS PE, Ftbl 1971-73; BainGridge HS SS, Ftbl, Tennis 1973-74; DODDS SS, PE, Ftbl, Tennis, Track 1974-; *ai:* Soph Class Spon Wrestling, Ftbl, Vlybl, Track; DEA 1982-; AFCENT Historical Soc 1987-; AFCENT Chapel 1982-; M Club MS St Univ 1964-; MS St Alumni Assn 1971-.

CHILDS, PHILIP MICHAEL, 8th Grade Science Educator; *b:* New York City, NY; *m:* Jo Michael; *c:* Jessie Anna, Andrew Joseph, David Benjamin; *ed:* Queensborough Comm Coll (AA) Lbrl Arts 1964; City Coll of NY (BS) Geology 1967; Binghamton Univ (MA) Geology 1970; 60 Addl Hrs ASU, Boston Coll, LIU, SUNY at Albany, SUNY at Buffalo; *cr:* Orangeburg Cntrl Schl Dist Earth Sci, Chem Tchr 1969-70; Union-Endicott Schl Dist Earth, Phys Sci Tchr 1970-; Binghamton Univ Adj Prof 1995; *ai:* Curr Frameworks Comm; K-8 Sci Frameworks; Mentor Elem Sci; STANY, NSTA 1990-; Endicott Tchrs Assn 1970-; NY United Fed Tchrs, AFT 1969-; BSA 1987-, Cubmaster; USTA 1986-; Presenter STANYS, NSTA, SAR Wkshp; Natl Tchr Trng Inst Master Tchr 1995; NSF Grant; Douglas Mc Arthur Yth Awd; *office:* Jennie F Snapp MS 101 S Loder Ave Endicott NY 13760*

CHILDS, SALLY JOHNSTON, Choir, Band & Orchestra Dir; *b:* Dover, OH; *m:* James W.; *c:* Dylan, Karrin; *ed:* Baldwin-Wallace Coll (BME) Music Ed 1971; OH St Univ (MA) Music Ed 1973; Univ of Akron (EDD) Admin 1991; Univ of Ashland Cooperative Learning, Alternatives to Violence, Cmptrs Credit Hrs; *cr:* Crestview Local Schls 5th-12th Grd Band Dir 1977-83; East Holmes Local Schls 5th-12th Grd Band Dir 1984-85; Green Local Schls 5th-12th Grd Choir, Music Dir 1985-88; Akron Pub Schl Band, Orchestra Dir 1988-; *ai:* OH Music Educators Assn 1971-; Midwester Educl Research Assn 1991-; Kappa Delta Pi Ed Honorary 1970-; Pi Lambda Theta Ed Honorary 1989-; ASCD 1988-; Mu Phi Epsilon Music Honorary 1970-; Bath-Richfield Kiwanis; Articles Pub; Crestview Schls Tchr of Yr 1981; Akron Schls Ambassador Awd 1992-93; Akron North Tchr of the Yr 1995; *office:* North HS 985 Gorge Blvd Akron OH 44310*

CHILELLI, CHRISTOPHER JAY, 6th Grade Teacher; *b:* Wiesbaden, Germany; *c:* Matthew J., David R.; *ed:* Univ of VT (BS) Wildlife Bio 1977; Univ of AZ K-8 Tchng Cert 1983; Univ of ME Masters Prgm Coll of Natural Resources, Environmental Ed in Progress; Masters Pgm Univ of Miami, Sci Curr & Assessment in Middle Schl in Progress; *cr:* Univ of AZ Veterinary Sci Lab Tech 1979-83; Asa C. Adams Schl 5th Grd Tchr, Sci Club Coord 1983-89, 6th Grd Tchr, Greenhouse 1989-93; Orono MS 6th Grd Tchr 1993-; *ai:* ME Ed Assessment Comm, St-Wide Sci for 4th, 8th & 11th Grds; EQUALS, Project Learning & Project Wild Facilitator; Univ of ME Tchng Sci in Elem Schl Instr; Univ of ME Math & Sci Acad for Tchrs Presenter; St Sci Portfolio Assessment Pilot Project 1995; NSTA 1985-; ME Sci Tchrs Assn 1989-; NEA, ME Tchrs Assn 1985-; MSTA Sec 1995; Pres Awd for Excl in Elem Sci Tchng 1992; Blaine House Schlsp 1990-92; Pulp & Paper Fnd Grant 1991; ME Innovative Educl Grant 1985; *office:* Orono MS 14 Goodridge Dr Orono ME 04473*

CHILLA, BENIGNA, Professor of Art; *b:* Hamburg, Germany; *c:* Milena; *ed:* SUNY at Albany (MA) Painting, Printmaking 1972; U MA at Amherst (MFA) Painting, Printmaking, Sculpture 1974; Acad of Fine Arts Germany (MA) Painting 1968; Bezalel Schl of Art Jerusalem Israel 1962-63; *cr:* Univ of MA at Amherst Tchng Assistantship 1973-74; Brown Univ Visiting Asst Prof of Art 1977-79; Cornell Univ Visiting Artist in Residence 1979-80; RI Schl of Design Visiting Artist, Guest Lecturer 1979-81; Tel Aphek Excavation Israel Artist, Staff 1979; Berkshire Comm Coll Fac Art Dept 1980-; Univ of MA Guest Lecturer, Printmaking Wkshp 1981; Tel Aphek Excavation Israel Artist, Staff 1982-85; Berkshire Comm Coll Visual Arts Prgm Chprsn 1982-87; Natl Inst Design Guest Artist, Lecturer 1990; Kanuria Ctr for Arts & Schl of Arch Guest Artist, Lecturer 1990; Berkshire Comm Coll Full Prof 1990-; SUNY at Albany Speaker for Arts & Math Conf 1993; *ai:* Art Gallery Dir; Coll Art Assn 1979-; NEA 1980-; Numerous Flwshps 1969-94, One Person & Group Shows Exhibits 1967-, Collections 1971-92; *office:* Berkshire Comm Coll West Street Pittsfield MA 01201

CHILTON, SUSAN STROHMENGER, 6th Grade Reading Teacher; *b:* Long Branch, NJ; *m:* James A.; *c:* Elizabeth, James Jr.; *ed:* Lycoming Coll (BA) His 1969; 24 Post Grad Hrs in Educl Fields from Various Colls ie Wilkes Coll; *cr:* Conover Rd Elem Schl 3rd Grd Tchr 1969-70; Overlook Elem Schl 4th Grd Tchr 1970-71; Bel Air Elem Schl 3rd Grd Tchr 1971-72; St Peter's Nursery Schl 3-4 Yr Olds Tchr 1979-86; Eagle View MS 6th-7th Grd Tchr 1986-; *ai:* Instrl Support Team; Gateways Comm, Grant to Implement Inclusion Practice; EDS Bus Schl Partnership, Cumberland Vly Ath Fac Comms; NEA; PSEA, CVEA 1988-; Jr League of Harrisburg 1980-83; Church Bd of Trustess 1990-; Parent Coord HS Swim Team; *office:* Eagle View MS 6746 Carlisle Pike Mechanicsburg PA 17055

CHIMATO, DOLORES E., Spanish Teacher; *b:* Haines Falls, NY; *m:* Paul C.; *c:* Korisa Mullenix, Paul A.; *ed:* St Coll at Albany (BA) Span & Fr 1960; St Univ of NY at New Paltz St Cert in English as Second Lang 1995; 3 Credits Grad Stud from NY Univ; 6 Credits from Columbia Tchrs Coll; Addl 36 Credits; *cr:* H Frank Carey Jr Sr HS Fr & Span Tchr 1960-63; Hunter- Tannersville Cntrl Fr & Span Tchr 1965-66; Windham-Ashland-Jewett Span Tchr 1969-; *ai:* Span Club Adv; Exchange Stdnts Coord; NY St Assn Foreign Lang Tchrs 1965-, Bd of Dirs; WAJ Tchrs Assn 1970-, Pres, Co-Pres; AATSP 1980-; ACTFL 1995-; World Heritage 1991-; Outstanding Tchr Awd from St Univ of NY at Albany 1986; Jr Prom Comm & Class Adv 1995; *home:* PO Box 321 Hunter NY 12442

CHIMERA, CHARLES C., Religion Teacher; *b:* Buffalo, NY; *m:* Sandy Jedrysik; *c:* Lisa, Charles, Gary, Kristin; *ed:* St Bonaventure Univ (BA) Philosophy 1959; Canisius Coll (MS) Ed 1965, (MA) Rel Stud 1973; Post Grad Univ of Buffalo, Univ of Innsbruck, Albright Coll; *cr:* Baker HS Math Tchr 1961-62; Canisius HS Eng, Latin, Ger, Religion Tchr 1962-; Canisius Coll Adjunct Prof 1971-95; *ai:* Ignatian Scholars Co-Moderator; Network, Fac Life Comms Chm; NEA 1970-; Nursing Home Svc Awd; NEH Seminars 1989, 1995; *office:* Canisius HS 1180 Delaware Ave Buffalo NY 14209

CHIN, DEBORAH LAU, Computer Teacher; *b:* Canton, China; *m:* Check K.; *c:* Diana, Steven; *ed:* Westchester Comm Coll at Valhalla (AAS) Bus Secretarial 1970; Lehman Coll at Bronx (BA) Bus Ed 1972; Hunter Coll at NY (MS) Bus Ed 1974; Yonker Tchrs Ctrs 12 Inservice Credits; Westchester Tchrs Ctr Inst 2 Inservice Credits; Iona Coll & Elizabeth Seton Coll 3 Undergrad Credits; *cr:* Yonkers Pub Schls Bus & Comp Tchr 1972-; *ai:* Comm Svcs Coord; Comp Club; NHS; NYS Assn for Comps & Tech in Ed 1989-; Westchester Educl Coalition Inc 1993-; Delta Pi Epsilon Alpha Xi Chptr 1975; Yonkers Pub Schls Innovator Mini Grant 1990-91; Yonkers Comm Svc Awd Sharing Comm 1990-91; Neighborhood Yth Corps Comm Svc Awd; *office:* Ralph Waldo Emerson Jr HS 160 Bolmer Ave Yonkers NY 10703*

CHIN, STEVE HAN-HOY, Engineering Prof & Asst Dean; *b:* Bronx, NY; *m:* Jacqueline Mae Perkins; *c:* Elena, Victor; *ed:* Rutgers Univ (BS) Electrical Engrng 1979; Johns Hopkins Univ (MS) Electrical Engrng 1982; Rutgers Univ (PHD) Electrical Engrng 1987; *cr:* Westinghouse Elec Corp Engr 1979-82; Rutgers Univ Tchng, Rsrch Asst 1982-87; Amer Systems Corp Tech Staff, Consultant 1987-; Cath Univ of Amer Electrical Engrng Prof, Asst Dean 1988-; *ai:* Core Curr 1994-, Undergraduate Lab 1989-Comms; Cmptr 1992-, Undergraduate Awds 1994- Comm Chprsn; IEEE 1978-; IASTED 1993-; Prof Engr 1992-; NSF Grant Connections Prgm 1994; Numerous Publications; Numerous Grants; Ed Summer Fac Fellow 1988-89; *office:* The Catholic Univ Of America 620 Michigan Ave NE Washington DC 20064

CHINN, TERESA L., Physical Science Teacher; *b:* Russell, KY; *m:* Jeffrey Daniel; *c:* Hillary, Meredith; *ed:* Univ of KY (BS) Bio 1987; Slippery Rock Univ Scndry Guid, Cnslng; *cr:* Freedom Area HS Alternative Ed Tchr 1990-91, Phys Sci Tchr 1991-; *ai:* Homecoming Coord; Teen Ldrshp, STOP Adv; NEA 1987-; PSEA, FAEA 1991-; PSTA 1990-; *office:* Freedom Area HS 1190 Bulldog Dr Freedom PA 15042

CHIODO, REBECCA BACKSTETTER, English Teacher; *b:* Coatesville, PA; *m:* George G.; *c:* Michael, Laura, John; *ed:* West Chester St (BS) Scndry Eng 1971; Villanova (MA) Tchng Eng 1975; 30 Addl Hrs; *cr:* DJHS Eng Tchr 1971-; *office:* Downingtown Jr HS 335 Manor Ave Downingtown PA 19335

CHIOTT, JUDITH WOODARD, 6th Grd Math & Science Teacher; *b:* Barton, VT; *m:* Richard Edgae; *c:* Glenn, Darren, Starlan; *ed:* Univ of VT (BS) Ed 1961, (MED) Foundational Stud 1991; 5th Yr Ed 1975; Johnson St Coll Sci Institute; St Michael's Coll Mid Level Institue; *cr:* Riverside

MS 7-8 Grd Math Tchr 1961-62; Overlake Day Schl 7-8 Grd Math Tchr 1968-69, Grd 2 Tchr 1969; John F. Kennedy MS 7-8 Grd Math Tchr 1970-80; Winooski MS 6th Grd Math Tchr 1981-; *ai:* Spelling Bee Team; NEA 1970-; WEA 1970-, Pres, Grienance; NCTM 1973-; VAMLE, NMSA 1985-; Delta Kappa Gamma 1991-, Sec; AARP 1989-; AAVW 1992-; Coll St Church 1968-, Deacon, Missions Bd, Ed Chm; Wesleyan Coll Flwshp; VT Standards Bd for Prof Ed; *office:* Winooski MS 80 Normand St Winooski VT 05404

CHIPONIS, MICHAEL ANTHONY, 4th Grade Classroom Teacher; *b:* Pittsburgh, PA; *c:* Michael Eric, Christine Lynn; *ed:* Penn St (BA) Elem Ed 1966; Mc Keesport Campus 28 Cred Hrs Permanent Cert; *cr:* New England Elem Schl 4th Grd Classroom Tchr 1966-; *ai:* 4th Grd Drug Awareness Prgm Instr; NEA, WMFT 1966-; AFT 1970-; *office:* New England Elem Schl 2000 Clairton Rd West Mifflin PA 15122

CHIRAS, CAROLE AMOUR, Principal; *b:* Worcester, MA; *m:* John Wm.; *c:* John A., Stefanie R.; *ed:* Worcester St Coll (BS) Elem Ed 1964, (MED) Urban Stud 1982; Clark Summer Inst for Prins; Cert MA SUpvr, Dir; Gifted Prgm Coll Acad; *cr:* Gillbury Pub Schls Tchr, Coord, GT Prgm, Prin 8 Yrs; El Paso-Isletta Dist Grd 3 Tchr 1987-; St Ginatias Schl Grd 2 Tchr 1966-; Arlington Jr HS Grd 9 Algebra Tchr 1968; Coll Acad Cood 1988-93; *ai:* Blackstone Natl Heritage Active in Establishing; Coord MA, RI; NEA; MA Tchng Assn; Millbury Tchng Assn; Delta Kappa Gamma 1986-, 1st VP; MA, AIP Awd Comm Svc; Millbury Historical Soc, Trustee 8 Yrs; Millbury Historical Comm 6 Yrs; Blackstone Valley Edctrs, Pres 2 Yrs; MA Elem Schl Prin Assn 2 Yrs; Presently on Redevelop Comm for Downtown Millbury; Top 5 MA Tchr of Yr 1982; Blackstone Vly Edctr 1988; Alliance for Ed Many Grants, Spokesperson at Confs on G-T; *office:* Elmwood Street Schl 40 Elmwood St Millbury MA 01527*

CHIRBAN, JOHN T., Psych Prof, Human Dev Dept Chm; *b:* Chicago, IL; *m:* Sharon A.; *c:* Alexis Georgia, Anthony Thomas; *ed:* Hellenic Coll (BA) Soc, Behavioral Sci 1973; Holy Cross (THM) 1975; Harvard Univ (THM) Applied Theology 1976, THD) Applied Theology 1980; Boston Univ (PHD) Clinical Psych, Oral Histories 1990; Harvard Med Schl Internship Behavioral Med, Biofeed-back 1993-95; *cr:* Hellenic Coll Prof, Chm Hum Dev 1978-; Holy Cross Prof, Chm Hum Dev 1978-; Cambridge Cnslng Assn Co-Dir 1983-; Harvard Med Schl Psych Behavioral Med 1993-; *office:* Hellenic Coll/Holy Cross 50 Goddard Ave Brookline MA 02146*

CHIRCH, FRANCES ROSS, Spanish Teacher; *b:* New York, NY; *m:* Phillip; *c:* Lisa, Laurence; *ed:* Carnegie-Mellon Univ (BA) Eng 1968; Columbia Univ Tchrs Coll (MA) Span 1969; Univ of Madrid 1966-67; SUNY of St Rose 36 Grad Credits; *cr:* Argo Comm HS Span & ESL Tchr 1969-72; New Trier Twp HS Span Tchr 1973-74; Suffolk Co Comm Coll Adj 1974-82; Patchogual Medford Schl Dist ESL Tchr 1975-77; Westhampton Beach HS 1977-78; Miller Place HS Span Tchr 1983-; *ai:* Span Club Adv; Group Ldr for Trips to Spain; AATSP 1983-; NYSAFLT 1983-; LILT 1983-; *home:* 11 Meroke Trl Port Jefferson NY 11777

CHIRICO, ANTHONY J., Guidance Counselor; *b:* Herkimer, NY; *ed:* SUNY at Genesco (BA) Amer Civilaztion 1971; SUNY at Albany (MS) Guid & Personal Svc 1972; *cr:* Burnt Hills-Ballston Lake Jr HS Soc Stud Tchr 1972-82; United Cerebral Palsy Asst Dir 1976-90; Burnt Hills-Ballston Lake Jr HS Guid Cnslr 1982-85; Burnt Hills-Ballston Lake HS Guid Cnslr 1985-; *ai:* Burnt Hills Ballston Lake Tchrs Assn 1972-; Capital Dist Cnslng Assn 1991-; Phi Delta Kappa 1993-; Tchr of Yr 1973; Rotary Club, Citizen of Yr Awd 1990; *office:* Burnt Hills-Ballston Lake HS 88 Lake Hill Rd Burnt Hills NY 12027

CHIRLIN, LARRY E., High School Math Teacher; *b:* Philadelphia, PA; *m:* Susan D. Feldman; *c:* Joshua; *ed:* Penn St Univ (BA) Lib Arts 1972; Beaver Coll (MA) Sec Ed & Math 1981; St Joseph Univ Tchng Cert 1980; *cr:* Gillespie Jr High Math Tchr 1982-87; Parkway CC Math Tchr 1988-; *ai:* SAT Prep Tutor; *office:* Parkway Ctr City 46 S 11th St Philadelphia PA 19107

CHISAMORE, DONALD RAYMOND, Fifth Grade Teacher; *b:* West Carthage, NY; *m:* Patricia Ann DeCaprariis; *c:* Barbara Cohen, Brian; *ed:* SUNY at New Paltz (BSEd) Ed 1963, (MSEd) Educl Admin & Supervision 1968; 19 Addl Sem Hrs Doctoral Prgm SUNY at Albany; *cr:* Brinckerhoff Elem Sch 5th Grd Tchr 5 Yrs; Vassar Rd & Sheafe Rd Schls Tchr & Coord 4 Yrs; Wappingers Cntrl Summer Schl Prin Elem 3 Yrs; Vassar Rd Elem 5th & 6th Grd Tchr 22 Yrs; Kinry Rd Elem 2 yrs; *ai:* Civic Oration & Drama Club Advs After Schl; Wappingers Congress of Tchrs 1980-; Amer Legion Bowling League 1992-; Whos Who Biographical Record-Schl Dist Ofcls 1976; Fellowship Bay Area Writing Prgm & Co-Dir Bay Area Writing Prgm E Pace Univ; Fellowships Chem Tchng Marsfield Univ & Energy SUNY at Odeonta; Writing, Listening & Speaking Act for K-6th Grds; Whos Who in the E 1979-80; Outstndng Educator in Amer 1973-74 by Acad of Amer Educators; *office:* Vassar Road Elem Schl 100 Vassar Rd Poughkeepsie NY 12603*

CHISELKO, BERNADETTE PANZA, Math Teacher; *b:* Bayonne, NJ; *m:* Dennis; *c:* Maira, Stephen; *ed:* Glassboro St Coll (BA) Ed, Math 1969; Rutgers (MA) Ed, Math 1973; Supervisory Cert 1980; *cr:* Middlesec HS Tchr 1969-71; North Plainfield HS Tchr 1971-81; Koinonia Acad Tchr 1984-.

CHISESI, CHERI SWEENEY, Math Teacher; *b:* Hazleton, PA; *m:* James; *c:* Anthony; *ed:* Bloomsburg Univ (BS) Ed & Math 1987; Allentown Coll 18 Credit Hrs Grad Level; *cr:* Nativity BVM HS Math Tchr 1987-91; Notre Dame HS Math Tchr 1992-; *ai:* Peer Listener Group Moderator; Stu Cncl Co-Moderator; Stu Assistance Team Mem; NCEA 1987-; ADLTA 1987-; NCTM 1992-; *home:* 1320 Wayne St Easton PA 18045

CHISHOLM, SHAWNTEL MARIE, Substitute Teacher; *b:* Coldwater, MI; *m:* Stephen William; *c:* Heather, Kaitlyn, Christopher; *ed:* Bob Jones Univ (BS) Eng Ed 1987; *cr:* Centre Cty Chrstn Acad Eng, Speech Tchr 1988-95; Dublin Chrstn Acad Eng, Speech Tchr 1996; *ai:* Drama Coach; *office:* Dublin Chrstn Acad PO Box 521 Dublin NH 03444

CHISHOLM, TERESA AIKEN, Reading Teacher; *b:* Wellsville, NY; *m:* Terry M.; *c:* Shauna, Andrew, Aaron; *ed:* SUC at Geneseo (BA) Elem Ed 1976; Alfred Univ (MS) Ed Rdng Specialization 1979; *cr:* Immaculate Conception Schl 2dn Grd Elem Tchr 1976-82; St Bonaventure Schl Admin 1982-84; Oswayo Vly HS Rdng Tchr 1986-; *ai:* Adv Stu Cncl, Sr Class; Stu Assistance Prgm Core Team; PSEA, NEA 1986-; Girls Scouts 1993-, Ldr; *office:* Oswayo Valley Jr Sr HS Oswayo St Box 610 Shinglehouse PA 16748

CHIUMENTO, ARLENE DIMEGLIO, Third Grade Teacher; *b:* Philadelphia, PA; *m:* James M.; *c:* Jodi, Jayme; *ed:* Glassboro St Coll (BA) Elem Ed 1971; 3 Credit Hrs Tchng Gifted, Talented Stdnts; 3 Credit Hrs Curr Dev in Elem Schl; *cr:* Berlin Comm Schl Tchr 1971-; *ai:* Natl Jr Honor Soc Tchr Rep; Dist Math Comm; Family Math Prgm Instr; NEA, NJEA CCCEA 1971-, BTA 1971-, Mbrshp Chprsn; *office:* Berlin Cmty Elem Schl 215 S Franklin Ave Berlin NJ 08009

CHIVERS, JOHN PATTEN, German Teacher; *b:* GLencoe, IL; *m:* Mary; *c:* Elizabeth, John, Nicholas, Alexandra, Peter; *ed:* Wesleyan Univ (AB) Ger 1956; Middlebury Coll (MA) Ger 1962; Attnd Univ of Murrick, Univ of Innsbruck, Boston Univ; *cr:* Brooks Schl Ger Tchr 1957-60; Phillips Acad Ger Tchr 1960-; *ai:* Hockey, Soccer Coach; Acad Adv; AATG 1965-; Kenan Grant to Write Poetry; *office:* Phillips Acad S. Main St Andover MA 01810

CHIZEK, ANDREA WAGNER, 5th & 6th Grade Teacher; *b:* Elkhart, IN; *m:* Mark D.; *ed:* DePauw Univ (BA) Ed 1973; IN Univ (MBA) Mrktg 1980; *cr:* Brownsburg Schls Tchr 1973-78; Hamilton City Schls Tchr 1980-; *office:* Buchanan Elem Schl 263 Hancock Ave Hamilton OH 45011

CHIZMAR, CHRISTINE HUTZELL, Fourth Grade Teacher; *b:* Johnstown, PA; *m:* Robert; *c:* Tyler, Jordan, Chelsea; *ed:* Univ of Pittsburgh (BS) Elem Ed 1979; *cr:* Forest Hills Elem Tchr 1981-; *ai:* Stu Cncl Adv; NEA, PSEA 1981-; *office:* Forest Hills Elem Schl 547 Locust St PO Box 156 Sidman PA 15955

CHIZMAR, STEPHEN JOHN, Senior English Teacher; *b:* Pittsburgh, PA; *m:* Angela C. Lazzaro; *c:* Christine, John; *ed:* Enboro Univ (BA) Eng 1963-67, MS Eng 1968-70; *cr:* Girard HS Tchr 28 Yrs; *ai:* Head Ftbl Coach; AFT 1976-, VP 1978-79, Pres 1979; Knights of Columbus 1981-; *office:* Girard HS 1135 Lake St Girard PA 16417

CHMARA, VAN, American History Teacher; *b:* Naliboki, Poland; *m:* Roseanne Bemben; *cr:* John P. Stevens HS Class Adv 1968-71, Soccer Coach 1969-81; *ai:* CORE Team 4 Yrs; NEA, NJEA, MCEA, ETEA 1967-; Who's Who Among Stdnts in Colls & Univs; *home:* 139 Dey Rd Cranbury NJ 08512

CHMELIK, SUSAN M., Music Educator; *b:* Cleveland, OH; *ed:* Bowling Green St Univ (BM) Music Ed 1979, (MED) Guid, Cnslng 1986; St Thomas Univ (MED) Music 1996; Orff Cert; Orff Masters Class, Kodaly, Dalcroze; *cr:* Baldwin-Wallace Coll Music Ed, Conservatory of Music Tchr 1995-; Strongsville City Schls K-6 Grd Music Edctr 1979-; *ai:* Guitar, Dulcimer, Recorder Clubs; NEA; Amer Orff Schulwerk Assn 1980-; MENC; Holy Martyrs Cath Church 1980-, Children's Music; Tchr of Yr Awd 1985-86; *office:* Helen Muraski Elem Schl 20270 Royalton Rd Strongsville OH 44136

CHMIEL, RHOANN JONES, Fourth Grade Teacher; *b:* Scranton, PA; *m:* George J.; *c:* David, Mark, Richard, Megan; *ed:* West Chester Univ (BS) Elem Ed 1960; Attnd East Stroudsburg Univ, Lehigh Carbon Comm Coll, Quest Intnl, Perfomance Learning Systems Inc; *cr:* Charlie Brown Nursery Schl Tchr 1972-74; St John Neumann Schl Kndgtn Tchr 1974-81; Delaware Elem Sch First Grd Tchr 1981-83; Franklin Elem Sch Fourth Grd Tchr 1983-88; S.S. Palmer Elem Sch Fourth Grd Tchr 1988-; *ai:* Rdng, Steering, Discipine Comms; PSEA, PTO 1981-; Palmerton Meml Park Assn 1992-, Bd Mem; *office:* S S Palmer Elem Schl 3rd & Lafayette Palmerton PA 18071

CHMIEL, THOMAS JOHN, Bus Tchr & Bus Dept Staff Ldr; *b:* Bayonne, NJ; *ed:* Fairleigh Dickinson Univ (BA) Elem Ed 1967; Kean Coll (MA) Admin & Supervision 1977; Cert Cooperative Mrktg Ed, Data Processing, General Bus; *cr:* Matthew Jago Elem Schl 5th Grd Tchr 1981-83; Woodbridge HS Mrktg, Data Processing Tchr 1983-90; Woodbridge MS 6th Grd Tchr 1990-93; Colonia HS Mrktg Ed, Data Processing Tchr 1993-; *ai:* Coach Boys Cross Cntry, Girls Bsktbl; DECA Adv; Colonia Girls Bsktbl Camp Dir; AFT 1968-; NJEA, NEA 1990-; NJBEA 1980-; Natl Parks Assn 1987-; Natl Wildlife Fed 1989-; Assn for Preservation of Civil War Sites 1990; *office:* Colonia HS East St Colonia NJ 07067

CHMIELAK, JAMES J., History Teacher; *b:* Newark, NJ; *m:* Morina; *c:* James Jr., Christopher M.; *ed:* Seton Hall Univ (BA) His 1968; Rutgers Univ (MA) His 1991; *cr:* Linden HS His Tchr; Seton Hall Univ Western Civ AP Tchr 1971-; *ai:* Schl Newspaper; Mid Sts Evaluation Comm; NEA 1971-; LEA; NJEA; Westfield Jaycees 1976-; *office:* Linden HS 121 W Saint Georges Ave Linden NJ 07036*

CHMIELENSKI, ANGELA LA NEVE, Social Studies Teacher; *b:* Utica, NY; *m:* Thomas R.; *c:* Thomas Edward; *ed:* Utica Coll of Syracuse Univ (BA) Soc Sci 1969; NY St Cert Syracuse Univ; 30 Grad Hrs SUNY at Cortland; Integrated Thematic Tchng Courses; *cr:* St Francis de Sales HS 9-10 Grd Soc Stud Tchr, Dept Chm 1969-76; Cntrl Jr HS Grd 7 Soc Stud Tchr 1976-77; St Patrick MS 5-8 Grd Soc Stud Tchr 1986-; *ai:* Yrbk, Natl Jr Hnr Soc Adv; Southern Tier Cncl for Soc Stud; Svc Awd De Sales Comm Svc Project; *office:* St Patrick MS 58 Oak St Binghamton NY 13905*

CHOCIEJ, HELEN R., Sixth Grade Teacher; *b:* Buckhannon, WV; *m:* Vincent P.; *c:* Eric Paul; *ed:* West Liberty St Coll (BA) Elem Ed 1972; Univ of Dayton (MS) Ed 1981; *cr:* Wayne Elem Schl Sixth Grd Tchr 1977-85; Buchanan Jr HS Lang Arts Tchr 1985-95; Wintersville Elem Schl Sixth Grd Tchr 1995-; *ai:* NEA, OEA 1977-, Bldg Rep; AFT 1995-; Mastery Learning Consortium 1982; *home:* 476 Gregg Ave Bloomingdale OH 43910

CHOI, NAMKEE GANG, Assoc Prof of Schl Soc Work; *b:* Korea; *c:* Bryan; *ed:* Ewha Womens Univ (MA) Soc Work 1981; Univ of MN (MSW) Soc Work 1983; Univ of CA at Berkeley (PHD) Soc Welfare 1987; *cr:* SUNY at Buffalo Asst Prof 1987-94, Assoc Prof 1994-; *ai:* Mentoring Minority Stdnts; Assisting Soc Svc Agencies Improve Their Accountability; The Gerontological Soc of Amer, Cncl of Soc Work Ed 1988-; Buffalo Coalition for Adolescent Pregnancy Prevention 1995-, Bd Mem; Pub Articles; *office:* S U N Y At Buffalo 359 Baldy Hall Buffalo NY 14260

CHOJNACKI, BARBARA PECHER, Reading Specialist; *b:* Waynesboro, PA; *m:* Eugene R.; *c:* Darin, Bryan, Casey; *ed:* St Joseph Coll (BA) Eng 1965; Trenton St Coll (MED) Dev, Rdng 1977; Univ of DE 9 Credit Hrs; Rowan St Coll NJ 15 Grad Credits; *cr:* Caesar Rodney Schls 7-12 Grd Eng Tchr 1969-72; Hamilton West Schl 9-12 Grd Eng Tchr 1973-78; Atlantic Comm Coll Eng Instr 1980-87; Mainland Regnl HS 9-12 Grd Rdng Specialist 1987-; *ai:* Co-Chair Mid Sts Steering, Staff Dev Comms; IRA 1990-; Amer Assn Univ Women 1980-, Treas, Pres Cty Group; NEA 1969-; ASCD 1993-; BSA 1985-90, Chprsn; Girl Scouts of Amer 1990-, Troop Ldr; *office:* Mainland Regional HS 1301 Oak Ave Linwood NJ 08221

CHOJNACKI, DANIEL, Eng as Second Lang Teacher; *b:* Erie, PA; *m:* Mary Michele Price; *c:* Amanda, Ali, Joshua; *ed:* Clarion Univ (BS) Mrktng, Mngmt 1980; Edinboro Univ (BA) Scndry Ed 1989; *cr:* Gridley MS Soc Stud Tchr 1988-89; Wilson MS Soc Stud 1989-92; East HS Eng as Second Lang Tchr 1992-; *ai:* Ath Dir; PSEA, NEA 1988-; *office:* East HS 1151 Atkins St Erie PA 16503*

CHOLLOCK, DONNA REED, Biology Teacher & Dept Chmn; *b:* Du Bois, PA; *m:* Ronald Steven; *c:* Ronda Anne; *ed:* Clarion Univ (BS) Bio 1969; 36 Post Grad Credits Wilkes Univ; *cr:* Du Bois Cntrl Chrstn HS 1969-; *ai:* Western PA Moderator Sci Olympiad; Sci Fair Project Coord; EF Tchr, Stu European Tours Moderator; Sci Dept Chprsn; NHS Asst; NCEA 1970-; Former United Way Dir, Bd; PA STEP, PHEAA Sci Tchrs of PA, HIgher Ed Assistance Grants; Clarion Univ Biotechnology Asst for Other Tchrs; *office:* Du Bois Cntrl Chrstn HS 204 Hospital Ave Du Bois PA 15801*

CHOME, REBECCA SNYDER, Elementary Computer Specialist; *b:* Washington, PA; *m:* Larry Conrad; *c:* Christopher, Elizabeth; *ed:* West Liberty Coll (BA) Elem Ed 1968; 36 Post Grad Credits Towards Masters; *cr:* Fort Cherry Schl Dist Elem Tchr 1968-89, Elem Cmptr Coord 1990-; *ai:* Chm Christmas Food, Toy Drive; NEA, PSEA, Fort Cherry Ed Assn 1968-; Vol Pilots Assn 1990-, Sec, Treas; *office:* Fort Cherry Schl 110 Fort Cherry Rd Mc Donald PA 15057

CHONTOS, JOHN ALBERT, American History Teacher; *b:* Mc Keesport, PA; *m:* Jane Louise Clohessy; *c:* Jennifer Lynn Crider, Jessica; *ed:* Shippensburg Univ (BSEd) His 1966, (MED) His 1969; 45 Credit Hrs; *cr:* Susquenita Schl Dist Elem Tchr 1966-67; Scotland Schl for Veteran's Children Amer His Tchr 1967-; *ai:* JV Bsktbl Coach; NEA, PSEA 1967-; Scotland Schl Ed Assn 1967-, Pres, VP; *office:* Scotland Sch Children 3583 Scotland Rd Scotland PA 17254

CHORBA, CARRIE C., Spanish Instructor; *b:* Perth Amboy Robert Shein; *ed:* Duke Univ (BA) Comparative Area Stud 198 Univ (MA) Hispanic Stud 1993; Working on PHD; *cr:* Univ de De Compostela Eng Tchr 1991-92; Brown Univ Tchng Fello 1990-95; El Colegio de Mexico Researcher 1995-; *ai:* Chilrea Patron to Child; 2 Articles Pub; Awded Presidential Awd for Excl 1993; Fulbright Flwshp to Colombia 1989; *office:* Brown Univ Providence RI 02912

CHOUINARD, DONALD PETER, English Teacher; *b:* Brock *m:* Lisa Martin; *c:* Olivia; *ed:* Univ of ME at Ft Kent (BS) Eng & *cr:* Comm HS Eng Tchr 1992-, Adult Ed Tchr 1995-; *ai:* Jr Class A 1992-; NCTE 1994-; *office:* Fort Kent Community HS 55 Pleasar Kent ME 04743*

CHOVINARD, DONALD RAYMOND, Counselor; *b:* Fall River June Whalley; *c:* Paul, Timothy; *ed:* Bridgewater St (BA) His 197 Ed Cnslng 1973; 30 Addl Hrs; *cr:* Mc Donough Schl Soc S 1970-78; Kuss MS Soc Stud Tchr 1978-84; Henry Lord MS Cns *ai:* Bsktbl Coach at Bishop Connolly 1973-85, Durfee HS 1996; H Coach Bishop Connolly HS 1973-; MTA, FRAA 1970-; ELKS 19 1968-, Tchr; Notre Dame Church Lector; St Title Div III Bsbl Coa

CHOW, CAROL, Assistant Principal; *b:* China; *ed:* Taiwan Nat Univ (BA) Ed 1961; Phillip Univ (MA) Ed & Psych 1963; Hunte NY City (MA) Math 1973; Pace Univ (MA) Admin & Supervisi *cr:* Long Island City HS Tchr 1967-85, Asst Prin 1985-; *ai:* Asia Math Team Adv; AFT 1967-; PDK 1985-; CSA 1985-.

CHOW, OIYIN PAULINE, Associate Professor of Math; *b:* Ho *ed:* SUNY at Stony Brook (BS) Math 1973, (MS) Applied Math 19 Candidate Ordinary Differential Equations 1974-78; *cr:* Philadel of Pharmacy, Sci Instr 1978-82; Thomas Jefferson Univ Part-time 1980; Harrisburg Area Comm Coll Assoc Prof 1984-; *ai:* Local El Presentations to Promote Cultural Diversity; Local, Natl Co Wkshps, Cmptr Tech Presenter; PA St Math Assn of Two-Yr Coll Amer Math Assn of Two-Yr Colls 1991-; Math Assn of Amer 1993-; Natl Sci Fnd Cmptr Equipment Grant Prin Investigator Solutions Manuals Author; Comm Coll Consortium Fac Recogniti Cert 1992; Crhistian R., Mary F. Linback Fnd Distinguished Tc 1982; Martha J. Stauffer Math Awd 1991; *office:* Harrisburg Are Coll 1 HACC Dr Harrisburg PA 17110

CHOW, SUNG GAY, English Professor; *b:* China; *m:* Amelia Turner; *c:* Silas, Holly; *ed:* MS St Univ (BA) Eng 1972, (MA) E Univ of AL (PHD) Eng 1989; *cr:* Univ of HI Asst Prof 1989-90; of PA Asst Prof 1990-; *ai:* Eng Majors Adv; Dept Comms; MLA PA Coll Eng Assn, Treas; St System of Higher Ed Grant; Tchng A Articles Pub; *office:* Indiana Univ Of PA Dept of Eng Indiana PA

CHRESOMALES, HARRIET, Computer Teacher; *b:* New York *m:* Gus; *ed:* Queens Coll (BS) Elem Ed 1983, (MS) Cmptr Ed, Ma UFT Tchrs Consortium Ctr 30 Credit Hrs; *cr:* Pub Schl 139Q Fo Tchr 8 Yrs, Cmptr Tchr 4 Yrs; *ai:* Fac Adv Stu Newspaper; UF *office:* Pub Schl 139Q 93-06 63rd Dr Rego Park NY 11374

CHRETIEN, ELLEN MASI, 5th Grade Teacher; *b:* Manhattan, Edward F.; *c:* Virginia Smith, Ellen Kara Hill, Anne; *ed:* Coll Rochelle (BA) His 1959; Georgian CT Coll Curr Dev & Su Masters Stud; *cr:* Holy Family Schl 1st Grd Tchr 1959-61; Wm H Schl 1st Grd Tchr 1961-63; Robin Hill Schl Preschl Tchr 196 Agnes Schl 1st Grd Tchr 1970-75; St Agnes Parish CCD Prin 197 Pius X Schl 1st Grd Tchr 1985-87; Keyport Cntrl 5th Grd Tchr 1 Stu Mentor; Yrbk Adv; Keyport Tchrs Assn 1987-, VP; ASC Middletown Bd of Ed 1982-85, Rec of Svc; *office:* Keyport C Union & Division St Keyport NJ 07735*

CHRISENTON, VIRGINIA HOEPER, Computer Teac Levingtown, NY; *m:* Thomas G.; *ed:* Univ of NH (BA) Math 1 Milford MS Math Tchr 1972-74, Comp Tchr 1985-; Keene Jr HS 1974-84; Milford HS Math Tchr 1984-85; *ai:* Coach Comp Team Club; NEA 1972-, Local Exec Bd; NHSTE 1984-; Tree Farme NHTOA 1990-, Bd of Dir; Co-Presenter of Multi-Disciplinary Uni Television; *office:* Milford MS 33 Osgood Rd Milford NH 03055

CHRIST, ARLINE SAND, Visual Arts Teacher; *b:* Lakewood, Donald Harold; *c:* Kirk Bryn (dec), Kira Ayn; *ed:* Kutztown St (BS 1964, (ME) Art Ed 1968; *cr:* Perkiomen Vly Schl Dist Art Tchr Earl & Cole Brookdale Elementaries Art Tchr 1972-74; Boyertow West Visual Arts Tchr 1974-; *ai:* Calligraphy Club; NEA, PSEA 1965-; Arts & Acts Article 1985; Nom PA Tchr of Y Bogodukiv-Ukraine Tchr Exch 1992; Awd of Excl NAEA 1995 1082 Mitch Rd Pottstown PA 19464

CHRIST, ROBERT B., English Teacher; *b:* Red Bank, Elizabethtown Coll (BA) Comm 1986; Rowan Coll of NJ (MST) E Eng Cert; *cr:* Gateway Regnl HS Eng Tchr 1993-; Lenape Regnl H Schl Eng Tchr 1995-; *ai:* Soph Class Adv; Track, Head Bsbl Coa Drama Dir; Weighlifting Club Adv; Ftbl Games Announcer; Young Conf; NJEA, NEA 1993-; *home:* 505 Westerly Dr Marlton NJ 080

CHRISTEN, DAVID ROBERT, Instr of Computerized Engine; OH; *m:* Rebecca Epling; *c:* Laura, Abbie, Cayla; *ed:* Northwest (AA) Appled Sc, Automotive 1991; U of CT BS Fire Sci P Attending; Gen Motors Trng Ctr Detroit, Cincinnati; GM Trng I Owens Coll, Vantage Voc Schl; *cr:* Bolkey Motor Sales Inc Tech 1 Delphos Nrsng Homes Maintenance 1979-89; Delphos Fire D Fighter, Rescue Scuba Squad 1990-; Northwestern Coll Instr 1989- Diesel, Fac Advy Bds; Retention, Acad Assesment Comms; North of Regents; Automotive Svc Excl 1978-, Various Certs; Delphos Van Wert Moose 1986-; Northwest Vol Fire Fighters Assn 199 Hydraulics, AG Courses Northwestern Coll, Extrication Class Rescue Divsion Trng Delphos Fire Dept; *office:* Northwestern Coll Cable Rd Lima OH 45805

CHRISTEN, TONI KALLMEYER, 5th Grade Teacher; *b:* Cin OH; *c:* Keith R., Melissa E., Camilla M. Diesel, Bradley F.; *ed:* Univ (MED) Ed 1985; Xavier Univ Admin Cert 1994; 16 Credit H Admin Work Oxford Univ, England; 6 Credit Hrs 1995 Italian Ren Art, Lang His Urbino Univ Italy; *cr:* Adams Elem Schl LD Tchr 1 Fairfield West Elem Schl 5th Grd Tchr 1988-; *ai:* Dist Lan Mentoring, Core Lit Comms; Phi Kappa Phi 1975-; Delta Kappa 1993-95; Ed Cncl 1990-92; Cncl for Children with Dev Disorders 1 Bd Mem; 3 Acad Schlsps Miami Univ, Oxford OH; *office:* Fairfie Elem Schl 4700 River Rd Fairfield OH 45014

CHRISTENSEN, BETTY JANE, 5th & 6th Grd Math Teacher; *b:* NJ; *ed:* Jersey City St Coll (BA) Early Chldhd Ed 1976; *cr:* Linc First Grd Tchr 1978-82; Columbus Schl Kindergarten Tchr 1 Jefferson Schl First Grd Tchr 1983-86, Fifth, Sixth Grd Lang Arts 1 Roosevelt Schl Fifth, Sixth Grd Math Tchr 1991-; *ai:* NEA, NJEA 1978-; Lyndhurst Ed Assn 1978-, Rec Sec; United Presbyn Church Deacon & Ruling Elder; *home:* 344 Kingsland Ave Lyndhurst NJ 0

CHRISTENSEN, DAVID ALAN, Vocal Activities Director; *b* Amboy, NJ; *m:* Judith M. Midthassel; *c:* Brian, Kurt; *ed:* Wagner C Music Ed 1970; Rutgers Univ (MA) Music Ed 1978; *cr*

-Plainsboro HS Vocal Act Dir 1977-; *ai:* Head JV Ftbl Coach; Head irls Var Golf; Head of Ski Club; NEA, NJEA, NJMEA, MENC ACDA 1977-; Richard E. Dupre Awd; *office:* West Windsor ro HS 346 Clarksville Rd Princeton Jct NJ 08550

TENSEN, DIANE MARIE, Choir Director; *b:* Corry, PA; *ed:* St NY at Fredonia (BME) Piano 1984; Univ of CO At Boulder MS Work in Choral Conducting; *cr:* Kingston City Schls Jr High Choral Music Tchr 1984-87; Boulder Vly Pub Schls Jr High Choral Tchr ; Riverdale Local Schls Jr-Sr High Choral Tchr 1989-94; Fairlawn City Schls Sr High Choral & Band Tchr 1994-; *ai:* Show Choir; MENC 1984-; NEA 1984-.

TENSEN, EDWARD R., Math Teacher; *b:* Jersey City, NJ; *m:* Steven, David; *ed:* Wagner Coll (BS) Math 1967; Univ of NH (MS) 69; 30 Addl Credits; *cr:* Port Richmond HS Math Tchr 1968-72; l Jr HS Math Tchr 1972-84; East Brunswick HS Math Tchr 1984-; S, HS Track Coach 16 Yrs; Jr HS Soccer Coach 2 Yrs; Math Team rs; Math Curr Writing; NEA 1972-; NJMTA, NCMT 1980-; *office:* nswick HS 380 Cranbury Rd East Brunswick NJ 08816

TENSEN, HEIDI S., Fourth Grade Teacher; *b:* Erie, PA; *m:* Tom : Tommy; *ed:* Edinboro Univ (BA) Elem Ed, Early Ch 1981; 20 Irs PLS Courses Edinboro Theatre; *cr:* N E Schls 4th Grd Tchr *i:* Lang Arts Comm; NEA, PSEA 1985-; Rainbow Girls 1970-; eard Schl 40 N Lake St North East PA 16428

TENSEN, HOWARD G., US History Teacher; *b:* New London, CT; e Thomson; *c:* Mark, Paul, Karen Day, Edith Thompson, Janice; v of VT (BA) His 1953; Tufts Univ (MAT) His, Ed 1957; *cr:* rd HS His Tchr 1957-, Dept Head 1970-83, Cooperative Tchr, 1989-; *ai:* Asst Bsbl Coach 1958-85; Class Adv 1962, 1964; Rifle iv 1962; WEA, CEA, NEA 1957-; Phi Delta Kappa 1967-; East l of Fin 1986-92.

TENSEN, MITCH, Athletic Trainer; *b:* Reading, PA; *m:* Terese; St Univ (BS) Hlth & PE 1984; Gannon Univ (MS) Hlth Admin *r:* Hamot Medical Ctr Head Ath Trainer 1985-93; Gannon Univ th Trainer 1985-93; McDowell HS Head Ath Trainer 1993-; *ai:* Scis Ind Stud Assoc; Stu Ath Trainer Adv; NATA 1993-, NFL PATS 1994-; PTA 1993-; Hlth & Fitness Video Series; *office:* ell HS 3580 W 38th St Erie PA 16506

TIAN, DAN, Science Department Chairman; *b:* Ada, OK; *m:* rew; *c:* Lisa; *ed:* Bowling Green St Univ (BS) Chem 1971; Addl at Akron Univ; Attnd Kent St Univ & John Carroll Univ; *cr:* New ales Sci Tchr 1972-74; Solon City Schls Physics Tchr 1974-; *ai:* 978-; Reader for Physics AP Exams 1990-94; Consultant for AP 1993-; *office:* Solon HS 33600 Inwood Dr Solon OH 44139

TIAN, DREW MITCHELL, Secondary English Teacher; *b:* re, MD; *m:* Debbie Ann Davenport; *c:* Anna Helen, Nathaniel ; *ed:* Elon Coll (BA) Eng & His 1989; Salisbury St Univ (MA) Eng Credit Hrs Univ of DE; *cr:* Salisbury St Univ Eng Tchr 1990-91; MD Eastern Shore Eng Tchr 1990-91; Woodbridge HS Eng Tchr *ai:* FEA Adv; Eng Lang Arts Frameworks Commission; Asst Var Coach; Bethesda Meth Church 1992-, Lay Speaker & Sunday Schl rticle Pub; *office:* Woodbridge Sr HS 307 S Laws St Bridgeville DE

TIAN, EDWARD HENRY, English Tchr & Head Ftbl Coach; *b:* Barre, PA; *m:* Margaret Born; *c:* Edward III, Patti; *ed:* Kings Coll g 1967; *cr:* East Stroudsburg Eng Tchr 1968-; *ai:* Ftbl Head Coach; s Adv; NEA 1968-; Knights of Columbus 1965-; *office:* East burg HS N Courtland St East Stroudsburg PA 18301*

TIAN, JAMES ROBERT, Chemistry Teacher; *b:* West Islip, NY; n Volz; *c:* Trevor, Connor; *ed:* Univ of Notre Dame (BS) Bio 1982; v (MBH) Fin 1985; Dowling Coll Post Grad 30 Hrs; *cr:* Amityville S Bio, Chemistry Tchr 1986-; *ai:* NHS Adv; Cross Cntry, Winter g Trach Coach; AFT 1986-; *office:* Amityville Memorial HS 250 Rd Amityville NY 11701

TIAN, JOHNATHON ANTHONY, Mathematics Tchr & Dept : Syracuse, NY; *m:* Lisa Lucia Epifani; *ed:* Onondaga Comm Coll ath, Sci 1985; St Univ of NY at geneseo (BA) Math 1988, (MS) d 1993; Scndry Certification 1988; *cr:* Angelica Cntrl Schl Dist chr 1988-92; West Genesee Cntrl Schl Dist 1992-, Dept Chair *ai:* Math Learner Outcomes, Tech Initiative, Curr Cncl Comms; 88-92; AFT 1992-; NCTM 1990-; Onondaga Cty Math Tchrs Assoc Assn of Math Tchrs of NY 1990-; *office:* West Genesee Cntrl Schl 1 W Genesee St Camillus NY 13031

TIAN, JUDY ANN, Asst Dean, Coll of Arts & Sci; *b:* Washington, Howard Univ (BA) Sociology, Psych 1968; Federal City Coll (MA) d, Curr, Admin 1970; The Cath Univ of Amer (EDD) Admin, Curr Higher Ed 1982; DC Tchrs Coll Tchr Cert Scndry Ed 1972; 30 Addl Hrs of Prof Dev post Grad Stud; *cr:* Univ of DC Assoc Dean for ffairs 1983-85, Dean, Prof Coll Ed & Human Ecology 1985-89, , Prof-Chrprsn of Accreditation 1989-94; Asst Dean for Acad, Stu Scheduling 1994-; *ai:* Commissioner; Ed Licensure Comm DC; Ed omm; Fac Adv; Adult Ed Grad Stu Assn; Phi Delta Kappa 1982-83, ns, Mbrshp, Outstdng Ldrshp Awd 1989-, Karygan of Yr 1991-, s Svc Key Awd 1993-; Alumni Assn 1970-, Outstdng Alumna; Delta Pi Hnr Soc 1995-; DC Mayor's Transition Task Force on Pub ; Educl Specialist on Accreditation Teams for Natl Assn of Trade, hls; Proposal Reviewer, Selection Panelist, Consultant for US Dept Amer Assn of Colls of Tchr Ed; Amer Assn on Aging; Cafritz Fnd; d for Improvement of Ed; *office:* Univ Of The Dist Of Columbia onnecticut Ave NW Bldg 48 Rm 7410 Washington DC 20008*

TIAN, SANDRA HART, Visiting English Lecturer; *b:* Baltimore, Mitchell; *c:* Drew, Daric; *ed:* Salisbury St Univ (BA) Eng 1987; v (MA) Eng 1989; *cr:* OH Univ Tchng Asst 1987-89; Salisbury St str 1989-91; Univ of MD at Eastern Shore Visiting Lecturer 1991-; sh Composition Adv; Textbook Comm; Lambda Iota Tau 1986-; ry-Wicomico Arts Cncl 1991-; Poetry Pub in Tar River Poetry, is St Review, Poetry Miscellany, OH Woman, MD Review; *office:* MD Eastern Shore Princess Anne MD 21853

TIANSEN, TONI ISAACSON, Science & Chemistry Teacher; *b:* , MI; *m:* Glenn H.; *ed:* Cedarville Coll (BA) Eng, Chem 1990; *cr:* Chrstn Schls Sci, Math, Cmptrs Tchr 1990-; *ai:* Jr HS Vlybl , JV Vlybl 1993- Coach; NHS Spon 1993-; Sci Fair 1990-92, Coord *home:* 8219 Woodbrier Ct Grand Rapids OH 43522

TIE, KATIE BABCOCK, HS Special Education Teacher; *b:* Lynn, Stephen; *c:* Tyler, Jenna; *ed:* Univ of ME at Farmington (BA) Spec 7; *cr:* Salem HS Spec Ed Tchr 1987-94, Spec Ed Team Ldr 1994-; Var Vlybl Coach 1987-92; Jr Var Sftbl Coach 1988-90; Chrldng 1987-89; NEA 1987-; *office:* Salem HS 44 Geremonty Dr Salem NH

TIE, MADELEINE B., Second Grade Teacher; *b:* Brooklyn, NY; old D.; *c:* Sean R., Ryan C.; *ed:* St Univ of NY at Stony Brook (BS) l; St Univ of NY at New Paltz (MS) Ed 1974; Addl 9 Post Grad ; *cr:* Violet Avenue Elem Schl 5th Grd Tchr 1971-78, 2nd Grd Tchr *ai:* AFT, NYSUT 1971-; Hyde Park Tchrs Assn 1971-, Educl Action Saint Johns Luth Church, Comms Vol; *office:* Violet Avenue Elem l Violet Ave Poughkeepsie NY 12601

CHRISTIE, SUZANNE M., Music & Drama Director; *b:* Norwood, MA; *ed:* Emmanuel Coll (BA) Music 1985; Bridgewater St Coll (MAT) Creative Arts 1992; *cr:* Pelham Meml Schl Music, Chorus Tchr 1985-90; Bishop Stang HS Music, Drama Tchr 1991-; *ai:* Drama Club; Music Ed Natl Conf 1985-; MA Music Edctrs Assn, NCEA 1992-; *office:* Bishop Stang HS 500 Slocum Rd North Dartmouth MA 02747

CHRISTIE, THOMAS WILLIAM,JR., Middle School Teacher; *b:* Bremerhaven, Germany; *m:* Linda Longfellow; *c:* Nicholas; *ed:* Univ of ME at Machias (BS) Elem Ed 1979; Addl Credit Hrs Geog, Cmptrs, Lang Arts, MS, Admin; *cr:* Rose M. Gaffney Schl Chap I Tutor 1979; Dedham Elem Schl Grd 4-5 Tchr, Tutor 1981-83, MS Math, Lang Arts, Soc Stud Tchr 1983-; Asst Prin 1994-; *ai:* Girls, Boys Cross Cty, OM, Boys Bsktbl, Bsbl Coach; GAG Players Comedy Troupe, 7th Grd Adv; NAESP 1995-; MAMLE 1992; Schl Improvement Team; Soc St Curr Coord; Stud Assistance Team; IASA Dist Team; *office:* Dedham Elem Schl RR 3 Box 330 Holden ME 04429

CHRISTIN, CARMELA PALAZZOLO, Third Grade Teacher; *b:* Cincinnati, OH; *c:* Beth Rampa, GiGi, Susan Foy, Amy Hollingsworth, Kathleen, Tina Wolfer; *ed:* St Mary of Springs (BS) Elem Ed 1956; 42 Credit Hrs Ed, Psych Xavier Univ, Univ of Cincinnati; *cr:* Cincinnati Pub Schls Tchr 1956-57; Columbus Pub Schls Tchr 1957-59; Forest Hills Pub Schls Tchr 1970-; *ai:* Stage Dir 8 Productions; Camp Kern Dir 4 Yrs; Soc Comm 8 Yrs; Curr Comm 15 Yrs; Mentor; YMCA 1980-, Day Camp Dir; *office:* Maddux Elem Schl 943 Rosetree Ln Cincinnati OH 45230

CHRISTMAN, BARBARA L., HS Mathematics Teacher; *b:* Hamilton, OH; *m:* Wayne Jr.; *ed:* Bowling Green St Univ (BSEd) Math 1973, (MAT) Scndry Math Ed 1984; Courses OH St Univ, OH Univ, Grand Vly St Univ, Wayne St Univ, Bowling Green St Univ, Univ of Delaware; *cr:* Fraser HS Tchr 1973-78; Defiance Jr HS Tchr 1978-79; Leipsic Jr HS Tchr 1979-81; Bowling Green St Univ Grad Asst, Instr 1981-84; North Baltimore HS Tchr 1984-; *ai:* NHS, Math Club, M&O, Sr Class Adv; NCTM 1982-; OCTM, NW OH Outstdng Sec Math Tchr 1993; GTCTM; NEA, OEA, NBEA 1984-, Treas; Amer Red Cross, Vol Swimming Instr 20 Yrs; GTE Gift Fellow 1993; Nom 3 Times Pres Awd; *office:* North Baltimore HS 124 S 2nd St North Baltimore OH 45872*

CHRISTMAN, ROBERT L., 1st-12th Grade Music Teacher; *b:* Dayton, OH; *m:* Michelle M. Skapik; *c:* Jacob, Zachary; *ed:* Lindsay-Wilson Coll (AA) Liberal Arts 1969; Berklee Coll of Music (BSME) Music Ed 1978; Piano & Percussion Stud; *cr:* Haverhill Pub Schls 1st-6th Grd General Music Tchr 1978-80; Newton Pub Schls 1st-6th Grd Vocal & Instrumental Music Tchr 1980-81, 4th-12th Grd Percussion Specialist 1981-87; Brookline Pub Schls 1st-12th Grd Vocal & Instrumental Music Tchr 1987-; *ai:* Bsbl Coach; Intnl Assn Jazz Educators 1995-; NEA 1978-; Boston Musicians Assn 1977-; Brookline Ed Assn 1989-; Jazz Improvisation Wrksps-Aebersold Piano With Michael Marra & Percussion With Alan Dawson Arthur Press-BSO; Prof Freelance Percussionist; The Brookline Fnd Contribution Honor; *office:* Brookline Pub Schls 115 Greenough St Brookline MA 02146

CHRISTMAN, SANDRA K., Spanish Teacher; *b:* Galion, OH; *ed:* Bluffton Coll (BA) Span & Eng 1967; Kent St Univ (MA) Span Lit 1973; Attnd EPDA Inst & Murray St 1969; *cr:* Chillicothe HS Span Tchr 1967-; Ohio Univ Span Inst 1974-89, 1990-; *ai:* Dept Coord; Spon Span NHS; N Cntrl Evaluation Co-Chair; Mentor for 1st Yr Tchrs; CEA, OEA & NEA 1967-; OFLA 1967-; AATSP 1974-, St Rep for SHH; Sister City 1992-, Arrange Educl Exch; *office:* Chillicothe HS 381 Yoctangee Pky Chillicothe OH 45601*

CHRISTOFF, ELLEN BALNIS, Mathematics Teacher; *b:* Doylestown, PA; *m:* George; *c:* ALexis, Chelsea; *ed:* East Stroudsburg (BS) Scndry Ed 1970; Beaver Coll (MA) Math 1981; Credit Hrs Trenton St, Temple Univ, Bucks Cnty Comm Coll, Lehigh Univ; *cr:* Central Bucks HS East Tchr 1970-; *ai:* NEA, PSEA, CBEA 1970-; *office:* Central Bucks H S East Holicong & Anderson Rd Buckingham PA 18912

CHRISTOFIL, WILLIAM STEVEN, Social Studies Teacher; *b:* Youngstown, OH; *m:* Beth Ann Williams; *c:* Chaz William; *cr:* Rayden HS 9th & 11th Grd Soc Stud Tchr 1994-; *ai:* Former Jr High Girls Track Coach, 2 Championships & Former Var Ftbl Coach; Girls Sftbl Coach; NEA 1993-; YEA 1993-, Bldg Rep; *office:* Rayen HS 250 Benita Ave Youngstown OH 44504

CHRISTOPH, MARGARET S., Chemistry Teacher; *b:* Cleveland, OH; *m:* Frank; *c:* Diane Herbert, Paula Yanik, Mark, Ross, Neal; *ed:* Ursuline Coll (BS) Chem 1943, Case Western Reserve Univ (MS) Chem 1949; 30 Hrs Case Western Reserve, Univ of DE; *cr:* Standard Oil Co Chemist 1943-50; Mt Aviat Acad Tchr 1963-70; St Mark's HS Tchr 1970-; *ai:* Sci Olympiads Dir; Jr, Sr HS DE Sci Olympiads Mbrshp Chm, Even Supvr; Natl Sci Olympiad Event Supvr; Outreach Sci Prgms; NSTA 1980-; ACS DE Section, Alternate Cnclr, Stay Chm, Sci Tchrs Affiliate Group, Svc Awd 1984; NCEA; Sci Tchng Presidential Awd 1987; Chamber of Commerce Superstar Awds 1990, 1994; Hall of Hnrs 1993; *office:* St Mark's HS Pike Creek Rd Wilmington DE 19808

CHRISTOPHEL, PAUL WILLIAM, Science Teacher; *b:* Greencastle, PA; *m:* Shirley J. Rockwell; *c:* Fred Buterbaugh, Paul N., Kelly Buterbaugh, Lori Christophel-Hummer, Joel D.; *ed:* Shippensburg Univ (BSEd) Chem 1963; Master Equivalency Cert; *cr:* Morrison Cove Jr HS Sci Tchr 1963-66; James Buchanan HS Sci Tchr 1966-72; Mc Connellsburg HS Sci Tchr 1977-; *ai:* Satellite Club Adv; Produce Morning Announcements TV; NEA 1963-, Life Mem; PSEA 1963-, Treas 5 Yrs, Life Mem; MMPW Vol Ambulance 1980-, Chief; Squad, Asst, Deputy Chief, Life Mem; BSA, Asst Scoutmaster 18 Yrs; *home:* 3520 Mountain Rd Mercersburg PA 17236*

CHRISTOPHER, CAROL MARIE, Sixth Grade Teacher; *b:* Buffalo, NY; *m:* Frank Ross; *c:* William Glodzik, Paul Glodzik, Jeffrey Glodzik; *ed:* Hilbert Coll (AA) Lbrl Arts 1968; Medaille Coll (BS) Elem Ed 1972; Canisius Coll (MS) Elem Ed 1976; 24 Grad Hrs Spec Ed St Univ Coll at Buffalo; *cr:* St Bernard's Schl 1st Grd Tchr 1968-70; St Casimir's Schl 5th Grd Tchr 1971-72; Lackawanna Schls Sub Tchr 1972-81; Buffalo Schl #40 Spec Ed Tchr 1981-82; Buffalo Schl #3 Spec Ed Tchr 1982-88, 5th-6th Grd Tchr 1988-; *ai:* Site Based Comm; Tutoring Prgm; NEA, NEANY, Women Tchrs Assn, Buffalo Tchrs Fed 1981-; *office:* PS 3 D'Youville-Porter Schl 255 Porter Ave Buffalo NY 14201

CHRISTOPHER, DONNA L., 12th Grade Music Teacher; *b:* Scranton, PA; *m:* Paul; *ed:* Bob Jones Univ (BS) Music Ed 1987; Marywood Coll (MA) Music Ed 1995; *cr:* Canaan Chrstn K-12th Grd Music & 4th-6th Grd Math Tchr 1987-88, K-12th Grd Music & 7th-10th Grd Eng Lit Tchr 1988-95, K-12th Grd Music 7th Grd Eng & 7th-12th Grd Speech Tchr 1995-; Bapt Bible Coll Voice Prof; *ai:* Choir Festival & Drama Coord; Spcl Music & Competition Coach; Pvt Voice & Pvt Piano Instr; Natl Assn Tchrs of Singing 1995-; Schlsp for Grad Credits; *home:* RR 2 Box 538 Honesdale PA 18431*

CHRISTY, CHARLES W.,III, Dept Chm Ind Engineering Tech; *b:* Wilmington, DE; *m:* D. Jean Cullmann; *c:* Richard, Chip, Mike; *ed:* Widener Univ (BS) 1973; Temple Univ (MBA) 1980; *cr:* DE Tech & Comm Coll IE Tech Chm 1970-; Pierpont Industries Inc Prin; *ai:* Phi Theta Kappa & IET Stu Org Adv; Amer Inst Industrial Engrs 1970-, Pres; ASQC; Opportunity Ctr Inc Dir, Past Pres; *office:* Delaware Tech & Community Coll 400 Stanton-Christiana Rd Newark DE 19713

CHRISTY, KATHRYN MANGAN, Fifth & Sixth Grade Teacher; *b:* Rutland, VT; *m:* David L.; *ed:* Keene St Coll (BSED) Elem Ed 1982; Trinity Coll (MED) 1994; 15 Addl Credit Hrs; *cr:* Cntrl Elem Schl 6th Grd Tchr 1982-84; Deerfield Comm Schl 4th-5th Grd Tchr 1984-89; E. Montpelier Elem Schl 5th-6th Grd Tchr 1989-; *ai:* Blue Ribbon Comm; NEA 1982-, Local Offices 1984-89; *office:* East Montpelier Elem Schl PO Box 190 Vincent Flats Rd East Montpelier VT 05651*

CHRONISTER, JAMES BRADLEY, Technology Education Teacher; *b:* Columbia, PA; *m:* Jacqueline M. Cassel; *ed:* Millersville Univ (BSEd) Indstrl Arts, Tech Ed 1989; Principles of Tech Course Cert; *cr:* Cntrl Dauphin Schl Dist Tech Edctr 1989-; *ai:* CADD, Electric Car Design Clubs Adv; PSEA 1989-, Bldg Rep; Tech Ed Assn of PA 1985-; BSA 1991-, Scoutmaster, Asst Scoutmaster; Tech Ed Assn of PA Schlsp; Who's Who Among Amer Univs & Colls; Burl N. Osborn Outstdng Tech Awd; Deans List; Cum Laude; *office:* Central Dauphin East Sr HS 626 Rutherford Rd Harrisburg PA 17109*

CHRZANOWSKI, CHRYSTENA ANN, English Teacher; *b:* Englewood, NJ; *c:* Margaret Mei; *ed:* Wm Paterson Coll (BA) Eng 1977, (MA) Eng Composition 1986; Supvrs Cert 1992; *cr:* Westfield HS Eng Tchr 1978-80; Dumont HS Eng Tchr 1984-85; No Arlington HS Eng Tchr 1985-; Wm Paterson Coll Eng Tchr, Adj Prof 1986-; *ai:* Acad Decathlon, Class of 1998 Co-Adv; NJCEA 1990-; NEA 1985-; Numerous Wkshps Presented at Writers Roundtable; Presented Papers at NSCEA Spring Confs 1990-, Assn of Tchrs of Eng 1991-92.*

CHULICK, PATRICE MARIE (YONISH), Biology Tchr & Sci Dept Chprsn; *b:* Somerset, PA; *ed:* Penn St Univ (BS) Bio 1980; Univ of Pittsburg at Johnstown Bio, Post Baccalaureate Scndry Sci Ed 1981; Univ of CA at Santa Cruz Biological Field Stud; Clarion Univ Grad Stud; *cr:* US Forest Svc Field Fisheries Biologist 1980; Bishop McCort HS Tchr 1982-83; Forest Hills HS Tchr 1985-; United Way Field Cnslr, Instr 1994-95; *ai:* Sci Dept Chrprsn; Environmental Olympics Team Adv; NEA, PSEA, Amer Bio Tchrs, PA Sci Tchrs Assn 1986-; Girl Scouts 1980-, Past Camp Dir, Girl Scouting Pin; PA Environmental Grant; Univ of Pittsburg at Johnstown Sci on Saturday Prgm Wkshps Tchr; *office:* Forest Hills Sr HS 489 Locust St PO Box 325 Sidman PA 15955

CHURBA, MARY ANN WHITE, Elem Cnslr & Computer Coord; *b:* Cleveland, OH; *c:* Jeff, Susan, Laurie; *ed:* Bucknell Univ (BS) Elem Guid 1964; Penn St Univ (MED) Instrl Systems 1987; Bloomsburg Univ (MED) Spcl Ed & Elem Ed 1989; *cr:* Lycoming Bd of Sch Dirs Spcl Ed 1964-69; So Williamsport Sch Dist Elem Tchr, Cnslr & Comp Coord 1973-; *ai:* NEA 1964-; SWEA 1973-, VP.

CHURCH, BOB J., Physical Education Teacher; *b:* Penn Yan, NY; *m:* Abbie; *c:* Tim, Kerri; *ed:* SUNY at Cortland (BS) PE 1970, (MS) PE 1976; *cr:* Fairfax Schl PE Tchr 1970-74; Penn Yan Acad PE Tchr 1975-; *ai:* Girls Bsktbl Coach; Var Club & Sr Class Adv; NEA 1975-; Elks Club 1976-; Fire Dept 1983-, Treas; Numerous Local & Regnl Coach of Yr Bsktbl; NYS Coach of Yr 1986; *office:* Penn Yan Acad 305 Court St Penn Yan NY 14527

CHURCH, JUDITH FOX, English Teacher; *b:* Lock Haven, PA; *m:* William H.; *ed:* Lock Haven Univ (BS) Eng & Math 1963; Shippensburg Univ MED) Eng 1977; Masters +30 Credit Hrs Penn St Univ; *cr:* Phoenixville Area HS Eng Tchr 1963-69; Willoughby-Eastlake HS Eng Tchr 1969-73; Cumberland Vly HS Eng Tchr 1973-; *ai:* Adult Ed Drama Club Co-Spon; NEA 1973-; PSEA 1973-; CVEA 1973-; NEH Seminar 1987 & 1991; *office:* Cumberland Valley HS 6756 Carlisle Pike Mechanicsburg PA 17055

CHURCH, KEITH WAYNE, Math Teacher; *b:* Buffalo, NY; *ed:* Erie Comm Coll (ASS) Metallurgy 1964; Buffalo St Coll (BE) Math; Addl Grad Work; *cr:* General Motors Metallurgy Lab 1964-67; Grand Island HS Math Tchr 1967-70; Kenmore-Tonawanda Schls Math Tchr 1970-; *ai:* Schl Planning Team; AFT & KTA; FA Masons of NYS 1974-, DDGM; Shriner Ismailia Temple 1976-, on Divan; York Rite 1986-; Rite Mason 1976-; *office:* Ben Franklin MS 540 Parkhurst Blvd Buffalo NY 14223

CHURCHILL, DEBORAH JEAN, Music Teacher; *b:* Syracuse, NY; *ed:* Credits Westminster Choir Coll; *cr:* Calvary Chrstn Schl Fourth Grd Tchr; Lan-Chester Chrstn Schl Fifth-Sixth Music Tchr; *ai:* Chrldng; HS Play.

CHURCHILL, PAUL G., Latin & French Teacher; *b:* Washington, DC; *w:* JoAnn Grammer (dec); *c:* Mark, Gregory; *ed:* Univ of MD (BA) Latin 1967; Towson St Coll (MED) Tchng of Rdng 1975; 1-8th Grd Elem Tchng Cert; K-12th Grd Rdng Spec Cert; 8-12th Grd Latin Tchng Cert; *cr:* Longfellow Elem Schl 3-4th Grd Tchr 1972-80; Centennial HS Latin & Eng Tchr 1980-83; Centennial & Haymond HS Latin Tchr 1983-85; Centennial HS Latin & Fr Tchr 1985-; *ai:* NEA, MSTA, HCEA 1972-; Amer Classical League 1980-; MD Public Television, WETA WA PBS 1974-; Fellowship NEH Summer Latin Inst 1991-92, 1994; Sherlock Holmes Course Tchr at Local Comm Coll.

CHURCHILL, SUSAN SCHUTTE, Fourth Grade Teacher; *b:* Cincinnati, OH; *m:* Rex; *c:* Jennifer, Sarah; *ed:* Edgecliff Coll (BS) Elem Ed 1975; *cr:* St Veronica Schl 4th Grd Tchr 1975-77, 1985-; *ai:* Youth Advy Bd 3 Yrs; Bereavement Ministry 1985-; Adopted-Grandparent Prgm Coord 1986-; NCEA 1985-; *home:* 775 McClelland Rd Milford OH 45150

CHURCHWARD, RICHARD A., Social Studies Teacher; *b:* Baraboo, WI; *m:* Sylvia Colwell; *c:* Paul L., Laura L.; *ed:* Bapt Bible Coll (BS) Elem Ed 1976, (MS) Chrstn Schl Ed 1995; *cr:* Arlington Bapt Schl Elem, Jr HS Soc Stud Tchr 1976-90; Cntrl Bapt Acad Jr HS Soc Stud Tchr 1990-; *ai:* Bsbl Coach; Ath Dir; Summer Schl Coord; *office:* Central Baptist Christian Acad 1606 NY Rt 12 Binghamton NY 13901

CHUROVIA, ROBERT M., History Teacher; *b:* Aliquippa, PA; *m:* Janice; *c:* NIck, Chris, Brian; *ed:* Geneva Coll (BSEd) Elem, Scndry Ed 1968; Slippery Rock Univ (MSEd) Soc Stud 1971; Univ of Pittsburgh (PHD) Higher Ed Admin 1978; *cr:* Somerset Daily Amer Sports Ed 1965-66; Hopewell Schl Dist Elem Tchr 1967-68; Ambridge Schl Dist His Tchr 1969-71; Beaver Cty Times Copy Ed 1966-78; Southside Schl Dist His Tchr 1971-; *ai:* Track & Field Coach; SSEA 1971-, Pub Relations & Negotiator; PSEA, NEA 1967-; Natl Achvmt Newsletter; Boosters, Ftbl, Track & Field, Bsbl Club 1976-, Numerous Offices Held; Ftbl Conf 1971; Beaver Cty Sports Hall of Fame; Ftbl, Bsbl Boosters, St Sports Writing Awds; World, Natl, Amer, St Bench Press Record Holder Champion; *office:* South Side Schl Dist 4949 St Rt 151 Hookstown PA 15050*

CHUY, DEANNA J., Language Arts Dept Head; *b:* Newark, NJ; *m:* Paul S.; *c:* Elyse Christina, Paul Michael; *ed:* Montclair St Coll (BA) Eng & Psych 1971; 15 Credit Hrs; *cr:* South Jr HS Lang Arts Tchr 1971-84; Cntrl MS Lang Arts Tchr & Dept Head 1987-; *ai:* Var Soccer Booster Assn Exec Bd; Var Sftbl Booster Assn; NEA, NJEA, MCTA & PTHEA 1971-; NCTE 1971-; NJCTE 1971-; PTA; PTA Tchr 1971, Rep; Giving Tree 1993, Chm; *office:* Central MS RR 46 Parsippany NJ 07054*

CIAFRE, DAVID A., Guidance Counselor; *b:* Pittsburgh, PA; *m:* Donna L.; *c:* David, Dawn; *ed:* Univ of Pittsburgh (BA) Lang Comm 1975, (MED) Sec Guid 1986; *cr:* Penn Circle Comm HS Eng, Psych Tchr 1975-85; Alleg Vly Cnslng Ctr Child & Adolescent Therapist 1986-90; So Fulton Jr-Sr HS Guid Cnslr 1990-92; Sharon HS Guid Cnslr 1992-; *ai:* Head Wrestling Coach; Dir Outdoor Adventure Prgm; NEA 1990-; *office:* Sharon HS 1129 E State St Sharon PA 16146

CIAMILLO, MARIE ELEANOR, First Grade Teacher; *b:* Orange, NJ; *ed:* St Elizabeth Coll (BS) Elem Schl Tchr 1970; 18 Credit Hrs Lib Sci Cert; *cr:* Archdiocese of Trenton, Hartford, Pittsburgh, New York City,

Newark 1st Grd Tchr 1949-; *ai:* Tutor Children; Sacrament Classes; Teach Music; Altar Servers; NCEA 1949-; Catechetical Awd 1992; Tchr Recognition Awd as Outstdng Cath Schl Edctr 1994; *office:* St Joseph Schl 115 Telford St East Orange NJ 07018

CIANCI, SCOTT D., Mathematics Teacher; *b:* Camden, NJ; *ed:* Valparaiso Univ (BA) Math 1985; Rowan Coll (MA) Math Ed 1992; Post Baccalaureate Stud Leading to NJ St Tchr Cert in Math Completed 1987; *cr:* Burlington Twp HS Math Tchr 1988-90; Burlington Cty Coll Math Adjunct Instr 1991-95; Faith Chrstn Schl Math Tchr & Dept Head 1991-; *ai:* Class 1977 Adv; Transportation Asst; Free & Accepted Masons 1992-, Sr Deacon; Scottish Rite 1994-; *home:* 151 Chelsea Cir Clementon NJ 08021*

CIANCIOLO, ANTHONY JAMES, Technology Education Instr; *b:* Bridgeport, CT; *m:* Gayle Fournier; *c:* Anthony James, Caitlyn Marcella, Corynn Marie; *ed:* Cntrl CT St Univ (BS) Indstrl Arts 1974; Southern Ct St Univ (MS) Instrl Tech 1984; Attnd Various Univs 6th Yr Equivalency 1987; St Joseph's Coll, Enivornmental Stud, Astrological Stud; *cr:* Masuk HS Tech Edctr 1975-; *ai:* Photography Club Adv 1982-; Graphic Arts Club Adv 1085-89; Sr Class Adv; Expo Comm 1983-; Liaison to Monroe Courier Stu Freelance Photographer Cooperative 1994-; Monroe Ed Assn, CT Ed Assn, NEA 1982-; Tech Ed Assn 1985-; Monroe Bd of Ed Staff Dev Awd 1988; Philadelphia Coll of Textile & Sci Centennial Edctr Awd 1993; Monroe Bd of Ed Edctrs Crystal Apple Awd 1995.

CIANCIOSA, CAROLYN LUCY, Asst Prof of Radiologic Tech; *b:* Gowanda, NY; *m:* Robert; *ed:* Jamestown Comm Coll (AA) Psych 1976; SUNY at Fredonia (BA) Psych 1980; SUNY at Buffalo (MS) Allied Hlth Tchng 1981; WCA Schl of Radiologic Tech Radiologic Tech Cert 1975; *cr:* Millard Fillmore Hosp Tech Dir, Acad, Clinical Instr 1981-88; Picker Intnl Account Exec 1988-91; Niagara Cty Comm Coll Asst Prof, Prgm Coord 1991-; *ai:* Fac Senate; Advisement, Radiologic Tech Advy Comms; Fac Resource Ctr Bd; NEA, Radiologic Tech Educators Assn 1991-; Radiologic Tech Niagara Frontier Soc 1992-; *office:* Niagara County Comm Coll 3111 Saunders Settlement Rd Sanborn NY 14132*

CIANI, THOMAS FREDERIC, History Instructor; *b:* Staten Island, NY; *m:* Susan A. Curitore; *c:* Geoffrey S.; *ed:* City Coll of NY (BA) His, Anthropology, Classical Lit 1970, (MA) His 1976; *cr:* William Paterson Coll Adj Instr 1990-; Bergen Comm Coll Adj Instr 1990-; Ocean Cty Coll Adj Instr 1991-; Raritan Vly Coll Adj Instr 1991-; *ai:* AFT 1996; Hazlet Yth Ath League 1986-92, Bsbl Commissioner, Coach; *office:* Ocean County Coll College Drive Toms River NJ 08753

CIANO, JACK E., Health Teacher; *b:* Brooklyn, NY; *m:* Jacqueline Varone; *c:* John, Joseph, James; *ed:* St Francis Coll (BS) PE 1983; Coll of Staten Island (MS) Spec Ed 1987; Queens Coll (SDE) Admin, Supervision 1992; *cr:* JHS 51K Hlth, PE Tchr 1983-86; Grover Cleveland HS Hlth, PE Tchr 1987-; *ai:* Var Head Ftbl Coach Bayside HS; Girls Bsktbl, Bsbl Var Coach; NYCCA 1993-, Bd; *office:* Grover Cleveland HS 2127 Himrod St Ridgewood NY 11385*

CIAO, FREDERICK J., President; *b:* Philadelphia, PA; *ed:* La Salle Univ (BA) Psych 1962; Villanova Univ (MA) Math 1973; Southwest Univ (PHD) Ed 1990; Temple Univ (MED) Counseling; *cr:* Northeast Cath HS Math Chprsn, Guidance Dir 1962-73; Archbishop Wood HS Vice Prin 1973-86; Bishop McDevitt HS Prin 1986-93, Pres 1993-; *ai:* Var Mathletes Coach; Acad Decathalon Mentor; NCEA 1980-; NASSP 1975-; MAA 1986-; NCTM 1975-; ASCD 1986-; Phila Orch Ed Adv Cncl; Mid States Assn Reader, Chair; Millay Club Educator of Yr; Chapel of Four Chaplains Legion of Honor; *office:* Bishop Mc Devitt Schl 125 Royal Ave Wyncote PA 19095

CIARROCO, RALPH ANTHONY, 8th Grade Teacher; *b:* Philadelphia, PA; *ed:* Holy Family Coll (BA) Elem Ed, Math, Rel Stud 1979; Villanova Univ Cath Schl Admin, Grad Stud; *cr:* Our Lady of Calvary Schl 5th-8th Grd Tchr 1979-86; St Joan of Arc Schl 6th & 8th Grd Tchr 1986-; *ai:* Yrbk Comm; CAT Testing Coord; Grad & HS Placement; NCEA 1979-; Brookville Campground 1979-; Whos Who Among Amer Coll and Univ 1979; Kappa Mu Epsilon; PSEA Officer; *home:* 3116 Nesper St Philadelphia PA 19152

CICACCI, FRED CARL, Social Studies Teacher; *b:* Pittston, PA; *m:* Barbara Ann Dente; *c:* Josette, Carlo; *ed:* Mansfield St Coll (BA) His & Comprehensive Soc Stud 1971; Kutztown St Coll (MED) Scndry Cnslng 1977; Cheyney St Coll Prin Cert Scndry Ed 1985; Intnl Stud Inst Westminster Coll 1972; Post Grad Stud Penn St & West Chester Univ; *cr:* Wyoming Area HS Jr High Soc Stud Tchr 1972-; Souderton Area HS Scndry Soc Stud, Global Stud, Consumer Ec, Geog & Practical Law Tchr 1972-; *ai:* Golf Coach; NEA 1972-; PA St Ed Assn 1972-; Souderton Area Ed Assn 1972-; *office:* Souderton Area HS 41 N School Ln Souderton PA 18964

CICALA, KATHLEEN M. BLANK, 7th-8th Grade Spanish Teacher; *b:* Jamaica Queens, NY; *c:* Nicholas Charles, Steven Joseph, Caitlin Maura; *ed:* Marist Coll Span Sec Ed 1974; SUNY at New Paltz Span Sec Ed 1977; Undergrad Semester at Univ of Madrid; Post Grad Credit Hrs at Coll of St Rose, Drake Univ; *cr:* LaGrange Jr HS 7-9 Grd Span Tchr 1974-79; Titusville MS 7-8 Grd Span Tchr 1979-; *ai:* Record HS Bsktbl Stats; Jump Rope for Heart Event; Stu Tchr Prgm; Budget, Constitution, Pub Relations, Crisis Comm; Grievance Rep; Children Xmas Party Chprsn; AFT, NYSUT 1974-; ATA 1974-, Sr Bldg Rep 1979-; Arlington Tchrs Assn 1982-, Negotiating Team Mem, Sec; *office:* Titusville MS Green Meadow Pk Poughkeepsie NY 12603*

CICALI, THERESA ANNE, Social Studies Teacher; *b:* Audubon, NJ; *m:* Michael; *c:* Brian, Kevin; *ed:* Stockton Coll (BA) Psych 1985; Soc stud Cert; Glassboro St Coll 17 Grad Credits; *cr:* Egg Harbor Twp HS 9th-12th Grd Soc Stud Tchr 10 Yrs; *ai:* NEA 1985-; NJEA 1985-; NJ Cncl on His Ed 1995-; Literacy Vols of Amer 1990-; *office:* Egg Harbor Twp HS 24 High School Dr Egg Harbor Townshi NJ 08234

CICCARELLI, CHARLES JOHN, Health, PE Teacher & Coach; *b:* Brooklyn, NY; *m:* Pia Scali; *c:* Charles, Kelly, Tatiana; *ed:* Univ of Charleston (BA) Hlth, PE 1967; Brooklyn Coll (MA) Hlth 1970; *cr:* Dyker Hghts Jr HS Tchr, Coach 1967-74; Tottenville HS Tchr, Coach 1974-84; New Utrecht HS Tchr, Coach 1984-; *ai:* Alumni Founder, Pres; Var Ftbl, Girls Sftbl, Bsktbl Coach; PSAL Games Comm; UFT, AFT 1967-; NYC Coaches Assn 1967-; Head Var Ftbl Coaches 1974-, Sportsmanship Awd; Pres Cncl Phys Fitness 1984-, Schl Rep; Alpha Sigma Phi 1964-; Newspapers Coach of Yr 1977-85; *home:* 826 Rathbun Ave Staten Island NY 10309*

CICCO, AUDREY WOMERSLEY, Second Grade Teacher; *b:* Pittsburgh, PA; *m:* John A. Jr.; *c:* Whitney Lynn; *ed:* Univ of Pittsburgh (BS) Elem Ed 1959; License Accredidation Credits Univ of Pittsburgh, Penn St Univ; *cr:* Penn Hills Schls Second Grd Tchr 1959-60; Waco Ind Schls Third Grd Tchr 1960-62; Falmouth Schl Dist Third-Fourth Grd Tchr 1962-65; New York City Pub Schls first Grd Tchr 1966-68; Private Schl Sub Tchr 1970-73; Franklin Regnl Schls Pre-First-Third Grd Tchr 1977-; *ai:* Site-Based Mngmt Team; Budget-Package Mem; Soc Comm Co-Chm; NEA, PSEA, Franklin Regnl Ed Assn 1977-; *office:* Franklin Regnl Schl Dist 3170 School Rd Murrysville PA 15668*

CICCO-KUPER, MARY A., Retired Art Teacher; *b:* Scranton, PA; *m:* Felix Kuper; *ed:* Kutztown St Univ (BA) Art Ed 1959, (MS) Art Ed 1965; Summer Grad Courses 1961, 1972; Attnd Instituto Allende; *cr:* Walton Elem Schls Elem Art Tchr 1959-63; Binghamton Schls Elem Art Tchr 1963-64; ME Endwell Schls Elem Art Tchr 1964-81, MS Art Tchr 1981-94; *ai:* Pvt Magic Lessons; Art Adult Ed, Tchrs Wkshps; Summer Camp Magic Tchr; NY St Art Tchrs Assn 1959-; Intnl Brotherhood of Magicians 1979-, Recognition Promoting Jr Magicians; Woodcarvers Assn 1995-; Ret Tchrs Assn 1994-; 2 Excl in Painting Awds; Photography, Jewelry Making Awds; Excl in Tchng Magic Awd; *home:* 3601 Matthews Dr Endicott NY 13760

CICCONETTI, YVONNE ELIA, Instr & Coord of Allied Health; *b:* Bayonne, NJ; *m:* Victor R.; *c:* Gregory, Richard; *ed:* Jersey City St Coll (BS) Hlth & Voc Ed 1987; Amer Heart Assn CPR Instr 1993; *cr:* Hudson Cty Schls Tech Med & Dent Instr 1976-92, Instr & Allied Hlth Coord 1992-; Univ of Med & Dentistry of NJ Clinical Instr 1994-; *ai:* Allied Hlth Tech Prep Advy Bd & Curr Comm; Hlth Occupations Stdnts of Amer Class Adv; NEA 1976-; Vietnam Vet of Amer 1980-; Marine Acad of Sci & Tech 1988-; PTA; *office:* Hudson Cty Schls of Tech W 30th St Bayonne NJ 07002

CICHOCKI, SHARON ANN, Scndry Math Coord & Teacher; *b:* Buffalo, NY; *m:* Ronald; *c:* Gregory, Cynthia; *ed:* SUNY at Buffalo (BA) Math, His 1977, (MA) Math Ed 1982; 9 Hrs OH St 9 hrs Tchr Center Both Grad Schl Classes; *cr:* Hamburg HS Scndry Math Coord, Math Tchr 1979-; Buffalo St Coll Math Prof; *ai:* NHS, Service Club Adv; Run School Bookstore; AMTNYS, NCTM 1987-, AFT, NEA, Hamburg Tchrs Assn 1979-; NCSM; Recognized by Hamburg Schl; Dist Board of Ed for Leadership in Math Ed; *office:* Hamburg HS 4111 Legion Dr Hamburg NY 14075*

CICHOWICZ, ANN MARIE, Science Teacher; *b:* Baltimore, MD; *m:* Jerome J.; *c:* Mary Kay Barrick, Suzanne Jones, Joann Antoszewski, Amy Corbett; *ed:* Coll of Notre Dame of MD (BA) Biological Sci 1957; Loyola Coll Physics, CEU Time & Stress Mgmt; *cr:* Roland Park Jr HS Sci Tchr 1957-60; Mt de Sales Acad Sci Dept Chair & Tchr 1970-80, Prin 1980-85; Madonna Cath Sci Tchr 1989-; *ai:* Jr High & Sci Coord; 8th Grd Homeroom Class Adv; Curr & Admissions Comms; MSTA 1970-; NSA 1970-; NCEA 1970-; NEA 1970-; Ind Alum Assn 1953-; Cnd Alum Assn 1957-; Westview Pk Womens Club; YMCA 1996; Westview Park Woman of Yr 1975; St Agnes Hosp NFP Advy Comm; Teen Crossroads Co-Ed; Outstdng Prin Awd 1985; *office:* Madonna Catholic Schl 3601 Old Frederick Rd Baltimore MD 21229

CICKAVAGE, WILLIAM JOHN, Mathematics Teacher; *b:* Frackville, PA; *m:* Elaine R. Bevan; *ed:* Penn St Univ (BS) Ed 1971; MA Equivalency Cert issued PA Dept of Ed 1995; *cr:* Williams Vly Jr Sr HS Math Tchr 1971-; *ai:* Cmptr Applications Club; NEA, PSEA, WVEA 1972-; NCTM 1994-; Frackville Elks 1971-; *office:* Williams Valley Jr Sr HS Rt 209 Tower City PA 17980

CICON, MELANIE ANN, Chemistry Teacher; *b:* Johnstown, PA; *ed:* Elms Coll (BA) Bio & Chem 1976; Attnd Univ of MS Pharmacognosy Grad Assistantship 1976-77 & Cardinal Stritch Coll Post Baccalaureate Cert in Scndry Ed 1981; *cr:* Dominican HS Chem Tchr & Sci Dept Chprsn 1977-86; Milwaukee Area Tech Coll Adult Ed Instr 1982-85; Purchase Line HS Chem Tchr 1986-; *ai:* Prof Dev Comm; Cooperating Mentor Tchr; SADD Moderator; NSTA; PA Sci Tchrs Assn; Alliance for the Tchng of Sci; NEA; ACS; Arin Intermediate Unit & Spectroscopy Soc of Pittsburgh Equipment Grants; Presidential Awd for Excl in Sci Tchng Nom 1992; Excl Foundation Tchr of Yr 1994; *office:* Purhcase Line H S Purchase Line Schl Dist RD 1 Box 374 Commodore PA 15729

CICONE, CARL, 6th-7th Grd Social Stud Tchr; *b:* Baltimore City, MD; *ed:* UMBC (BA) Psych 1976; Towson St Univ (MA) Scndry Ed 1981; Hood Coll; *cr:* Sykesville Mid Soc Stud Tchr; *ai:* Comp Coord at Sykesville Mid; NEA 1978-; CCEA 1978-; *office:* Sykesville M S 55 N Court St Westminster MD 21157

CIELAKIE, ANTONINA MARY, 6th Grade Teacher; *b:* Lowell, MA; *ed:* Mt St Vincent Univ at Halifax NS (BS) Ed 1962, (BA) Ed 1965; Salem St Coll (MAT) His 1972; *cr:* St Sebastian Schl Grd 1, 3-4, 7 Tchr 1959-67; St Patrick Schl Grd 6 Tchr 1967-71; Washington Schl Grd 6 Tchr 1971-76; Daley MS Gr 5-6 Tchr 1976-; *ai:* AFT; *office:* Daley MS 150 Fleming St Lowell MA 01851

CIEREMANS, BARBARA MILLS, HS Social Studies Teacher; *b:* Long Beach, CA; *m:* Gerard; *c:* Lauren, David; *ed:* CA St Univ at Long Beach (BA) Phys Geography 1971; Univ of Southern CA (MS) Educl Psych 1974; Psychological Stud Inst 15 Credits; CA St Univ 6 Credits; Willim Paterson Coll 6 Credits; *cr:* DODDSEUR Soc Stud Tchr 3 Yrs; Hebrew Acad Soc Stud Tchr 1 1/2 Yrs; Revlon Inc Sr Dir of Merchandising 11 Yrs; East Orange HS Soc Stud Tchr 5 Yrs; *ai:* Sr Issues Group Ldr; Girl Scout Ldr; Montclair St Univ Adjunct Prof; NEA, NJEA, EOEA 1991-; Roseland Historical Soc 1995-; Univ of Southern CA Educl Alumni Assn Outstdng Educator Awd 1974; *office:* East Orange Schl Dist 715 Park Ave East Orange NJ 07017

CIESIELKA, GERALDINE ANN, History Teacher; *b:* Johnstown, PA; *ed:* St Francis Coll (BA) His 1976, (MED) Ed 1986; *cr:* Forest Hills Schl Dist Soc Stud Tchr 1991-; *ai:* NEA, PSEA 1985-; FHEA 1991-; Fatima Soc 1981-, Sec, Treas; RCIA 1990-, Dir; *office:* Forest Hills Sr HS 489 Locust St Sidman PA 15955

CIESLA, BETTY E., School Assistant Professor; *b:* Baltimore, MD; *m:* Dennis G.; *c:* Marci, Melissa, Meagan; *ed:* Phil Coll of Pharmel Sci (BS) Med Tech 1973; Towson St Univ (MS) Prof Writing 1990; *cr:* Good Samaritan Hosp Staff Tech 1973-80; Univ of MD Schl of Medicine PT Instr 1980-90, Schl Asst Prof 1990-; *ai:* Recruiting, Detention Comm Chair; Writing Grant; Strategic Planning Comm; Rsrch, Fac Adv; Comm Outreach Prgms; Amer Soc of Clinical Pathologist 1973-; Amer Clinical Lab Scientist 1990-; MD Soc of Clinical Lab Scientist Bd Mem 1993-; Tchr of Yr 1982, 1992-93; Deans Flwshp 1990; Baxter Hlth Care Grad Schlsp 1989; *office:* Univ of MD-Schl of Med Medical & Research Tech Dept 100 Penn St Allied Hlth Bldg Baltimore MD 21201*

CIFELLI, CHRISTOPHER T., Social Studies Teacher; *b:* Portland, ME; *ed:* Purdue Univ (BA) Soc Stud Ed 1993; *cr:* Leavitt Area HS Soc Stud Tchr 1993-; *ai:* Var Soccer, Mock Trial Coach; Soph Class Adv; P A Announcer Bsktbl; NEA, MEA, Natl Soccer Coaches of Amer Assn 1993-; YMCA 1993-, 5th-6th Grd Bsktbl Coach; *office:* Leavitt Area HS RR 1 Box 1251 Turner ME 04282

CIFELLI, NICHOLAS JOSEPH, Secondary Mathematics Teacher; *b:* South Amboy, NJ; *ed:* Rutgers Univ (BA) Math 1986; Jersey City St Coll 36 Credits; *cr:* Manchester Twp HS Scndry Math Tchr 1986-93; Sayreville War Memrl HS Scndry Math Tchr 1993-; *ai:* Asst Var, Jr Var Girls Soccer, Frosh Bsbl Coach; Class of 1999 Adv; NEA 1986-; NJEA 1986-; NCTM 1986-; *office:* Sayreville War Memorial HS 820 Washington Rd Parlin NJ 08859

CIGNETTI, GLORIA NOVAK, English Teacher; *b:* Greensburg, PA; *m:* James J.; *ed:* Thiel Coll (BA) Latin, Eng 1968; Indiana Univ of PA (MA) Eng 1973; *cr:* Yough Schl Dist Tchr 1968-; *ai:* Stu Assistance Prgm; NEA, Yough Educl Assn 1968-; Cmptr Specialist; Mentor Prgm; PMET Cert; Cooperative Learning Cert; Conflict, Resolution Cert; *office:* Yough Sr HS 99 Lowber Rd Herminie PA 15637*

CIHIWSKY, ANGELA LOCKETT, English Teacher; *b:* NY; *m:* Timothy; *c:* Nicole, Allison; *ed:* Binghamton Univ Eng & Lang Arts 1973; SUC at Cortland K-12 Grd Stud; *cr:* Lockport Sr HS Eng Tchr 1970; Vestal Schls Eng & Lang Arts Tchr 1971-; *ai:* Var Ftbl Cheerleading Coach; *office:* Vestal Sr HS 205 Woodlawn Dr Vestal NY 13850

CIHY, CHARLENE F. (KAVEC), Third Grade Teacher; *b:* C[illegible] OH; *m:* Joseph; *ed:* St John Coll (BSE) Ed 1968; Cleveland St Uni[illegible] Ed 1971; Attnd John Carroll Univ, Baldwin-Wallace Coll, LaVe[illegible] *cr:* Dentzler Elem 6th Grd Tchr 1968-73; Dag Hammarskjold Ele[illegible] Grd Tchr & Team Ldr 1973-75; Arlington Elem 3rd, 4th & 6th [illegible] 1975-82; Greenbriar Jr HS 7th-8th Grd Rdng Tchr 1982-94; Parkvi[illegible] 3rd Grd Tchr 1994-; *ai:* Cleveland St Univ Cooperating Tchr; S[illegible] United Way & Green Cross Drive Co-Chrpsn; NEA, OEA, PEA, [illegible] & UTP 1968-; IRA, Past Mem; GCCTE, Past Mem; St Richar[illegible] 1968-, Worship Comm Mem, Recorder & Choir Mem; Kappa G[illegible] 1968-; Amer Elem Ed Ldr 1971; Parma Tchr of the Yr Nom 1987 [illegible] Parma PTA Flwshp Awd 1989; *office:* Parkview Elem 5210 Lo[illegible] Parma OH 44134

CILIBERTI, VICKI HOLEWINSKI, English & Drama Tea[illegible] Toledo, OH; *m:* Greg; *c:* Joseph, Katharine; *ed:* OH St Univ (BS[illegible] & Speech 1971; Northern KY Univ (MED) Scndry Ed 1983; Attn[illegible] Univ, Univ of Cincinnati; *cr:* Amelia HS Tchr 1971-; *ai:* Video Pr[illegible] Dir; Dramas Co-Dir; WCEA, OEA & NEA; Kindervelt 199[illegible] Anderson & Union Cable Television 1995-, Bd of Dirs; Reader [illegible] Inst Sponsored by Natl Endowment for Hum; Entry Yr Tchr Mento[illegible] Amelia HS 1351 Clough Pike Batavia OH 45103

CILLO, RICHARD JOSEPH, Mathematics Teacher; *b:* Rutland[illegible] Margaret Simonds; *c:* Paul, Lori; *ed:* Catleton St Coll (BA) Math [illegible] Univ of Toledo (MS) Math 1972; NFS Discrete Math Prgm; W[illegible] Coll Graphing Calculator Inst; Dartmouth Coll Cmptr Lit[illegible] Information Processing; *cr:* Otter Valley Union HS Math Tchr 23[illegible] Bsktbl & Sftbl Coach; *office:* Otter Valley Union HS Rt 7 Bra[illegible] 05733

CIMINO, DAVID M., Guidance Counselor; *b:* Philadelphia, [illegible] Beverly June Shull; *c:* Sarah Mas, Emily Mas; *ed:* Bucks Cty Co[illegible] (BA) Elem Ed 1969; West Chester St Univ (BS) Elem Ed 1971; T[illegible] Coll (MA) Stu Prnsl Svcs 1975; *cr:* Pemberton Twp Schl Dist [illegible] Guidance Cnslr 1971-; *ai:* Stud Skill Class Tchr; College Fair Co[illegible] Burlington Cty Guidance Assn 1984-; Saint James Church, Usher-[illegible]

CIMINO, JAMES LOUIS, Automotive Teacher; *b:* Scranton, PA; [illegible] Hoffman; *ed:* (MS) Voc Ed 1996; Temple Univ Voc I 1987, Voc II [illegible] Susquehanna Cty AVTS Automotive Mechanics Tchr 1984-; *ai:* Vo[illegible] Clubs of Amer Adv; NEA, PSEA 1984-; VICA 1985-; Moscow Vol[illegible] 1993-, VP, Ambulance LT; Vol Pilots Assn 1991-; Natl Registry o[illegible] 1995-; Natl Inst of Auto Svc Tech 1981-, Master Auto Tech; Be[illegible] Bureau Tech Adv; *office:* Susquehanna Cty Area Voc Tech PO [illegible] Dimock PA 18816

CIMINO, MARYANN DIETRICH, High School Art Teacher; *b:* [illegible] PA; *m:* John L.; *c:* Christina, Gina; *ed:* Northampton Comm C[illegible] Commercial Art 1975; Kutztown Univ (BS) Art Ed 1977; Post Gra[illegible] *cr:* Wilson Area HS Art Tchr 1982-; *ai:* Drama Club Asst Dir; NE[illegible] Ed Assn, Wilson Area Ed Assn 1982-; SPCA, March of Dimes, Vol[illegible] Wilson Area HS 424 Warrior Ln Easton PA 18042

CIMO, ANGELO, Fourth Grade Teacher; *b:* Jamestown, NY; *m:* C[illegible] Lamantia; *c:* Matthew, Carrie Ann; *ed:* SUNY at Fredonia (BS) Sc[illegible] Bio 1972, (MS) Elem Ed 1975; Edinboro St Coll (MED) Spec [illegible] Completed Clinical Field Supvr Prgm at Fredonia St Tchrs Coll; [illegible] NY 1974-; Southwestern Tchrs Assn 1979-, Treas; Rotary [illegible] Lakewood 1990-, Treas, Sec & Pres; *office:* Southwestern Cntrl S[illegible] Hunt Rd WE Jamestown NY 14701

CIMOCHOWSKI, EILEEN MARIE, Third Grade Teacher; *b:* [illegible] NJ; *m:* S. William; *c:* William, Andrew, Thomas, Karen, Jennine; [illegible] St (BS) Elem Ed 1966; MS Equivalency 1991; *cr:* Clara Barton [illegible] Tchr 1986-87; Lafayette 3rd Grd Tchr 1987-; *ai:* NEA 1986-[illegible] 1986-; *office:* Lafayette Elem Schl 4201 Fayette Dr Bristol PA 19[illegible]

CIMPKO, DENISE, English Teacher; *b:* Somerville, NJ; *ed:* Rutg[illegible] (BA) Eng 1988; Rutgers Inst for Scndry Tchrs 28 Credit [illegible] Bridgewater Raritan HS Eng Tchr 1990-; *ai:* Peer Mediation, Poe[illegible] Adv; Teen Arts Festival Coord; Homebound Instr; Forensics Tou[illegible] Judge; SAT Proctor; NJEA, NEA, BREA 1990-; NCTE 1990-; [illegible] Apple Awd 1994-95; *office:* Bridgewater-Raritan HS PO B[illegible] Garretson Rd Bridgewater NJ 08803

CINNAMOND, JUDITH ANN, Mathematics Teacher; *b:* Paterson [illegible] Thomas W.; *c:* Michael, Kelly; *ed:* Trenton St Coll (BA) Math 1[illegible] Pemberton Twp HS Math Tchr 1980-; *ai:* Instrl Advy Comm; [illegible] Cmptr Club; Mentor Tchr; Rel Ed Instr; Math Tutor; NEA, NJEA, [illegible] AMTNJ 1980-; 2 NSF Cmptr, Math Curr, Math, Sci, Tech Gr[illegible] Governors Tchr Recognition Prgm Tchr of Yr 1988-89; *office:* Pe[illegible] Township HS Arneys Mt Rd Pemberton NJ 08068*

CINQUE, JOSEPH JOHN, Biology Teacher; *b:* Hoboken, NJ; *m*[illegible] Ann DelDuca; *ed:* Fairleigh Dickinson Univ Bio (BS) 1979, (MS[illegible] *cr:* Bergen Comm Coll Adjunct Instr 1983-86; WNY Pub Schl 3 [illegible] Tchr 1987-88; WNY Meml HS Bio, Chem, Sci Tchr 1988-; *ai:* Ba[illegible] Instr; Color Guard Coach; Alter Ego Color Guard Dir; NJEA, NEA[illegible] WNYEA 1988; WNYEA 1990-, Exec Bd; Natl Judges Assn Color [illegible] 1996-, Exec Bd; Biological Scis Tchng Fellowship 1981-83; [illegible] Memorial HS 5501 Park Ave West New York NJ 07093*

CINQUE, MARY ANN DEL DUCA, Sci Dept Supervi[illegible] Hackensack, NJ; *m:* Joseph J.; *ed:* Fairleigh Dickinson Univ ([illegible] 1979, (MAT) Ed 1980; Addl 51 Grad Credits Cmptrs, Gifted & T[illegible] Ed, Admin, Supervision St Peter's Coll, Jersey City St, F[illegible] Dickinson; *cr:* Paramus Cath Girls HS Chem, Sci Tchr 1979-83; PS[illegible] Tchr 1983-85; PS #5 Sci Tchr 1983-85; PS #2 Tchr of Gifted, T[illegible] 1985-87; Meml HS Bio Tchr 1987-, Sci Dept Supvr 1995-; *ai:* Color[illegible] Majorettes Coach; Dir of Alter Ego ColorGuard; NJEA, NEA [illegible] WNYEA 1983-, Exec Bd; Moonachie Bd of Hlth 1984-, Pres; [illegible] Mem of Mid-Atlantic Indoor Network "Main"; Princeton [illegible] Distinguished Tchr Awd Nom 1993; *office:* Memorial HS 5501 P[illegible] West New York NJ 07093*

CINTAVEY, KATHLEEN OTTERSON, High School Teac[illegible] Manchester, NH; *m:* Albert; *c:* Christopher, Elizabeth; *ed:* Colby C[illegible] Fr 1972; Bowling Green St Univ (MED) Rdng 1989; Cleveland [illegible] (PHD) Urban Ed, Learning & Dev 1995; Attnd Universite de Caen [illegible] *cr:* Lorain City Schls Tchr 1984-; Oberlin Coll Adj Prof Ed Psyc[illegible] Cleveland St Univ Adj Prof Instrl Dev 1995-; *ai:* Culture Club Adv[illegible] Intnl Travel with Stdnts 1988-89, 1992, 1994; Originating Mem[illegible] Omega Cleveland St Univ; NEA, OEA 1984-; Phi Delta Kappa [illegible] Venture Capital Grant 1995-; Lorain Endowment Fund 1989, 1[illegible] Who's Who in Amer Edctrs 1995-; ERIC Stud Document; *home:* [illegible] Wellington Dr North Olmsted OH 44070*

CIOCCA, CAMELLIA KURT, High School Art Instructor; [illegible] Augustine, FL; *c:* Robert, Camellia Rose, Christina; *ed:* Univ [illegible] (BFA) Printmaking 1963; VT Coll (MA) Art Ed 1992; MA Coll [illegible] Advanced Drawing Cert Credits; Framingham St Coll, Tufts Univ D[illegible] Credits; *cr:* Marian HS Art Instr 1978-; Town of Framingham Swim [illegible] Prgm Dir, Instr 1979-; Keefe Regnl Tech HS Art, Swim Instr [illegible] Newbury Coll Art His, Art Instr 1983-; *ai:* Natl Art Hnr Soc Spo[illegible] Red Cross Water Safety Instr, Trainer; Natl Cath Tchrs Assn 1978-; [illegible] 1990-; DAR 1963-, St Conservation Chm, Chptr Regent, Regen[illegible] n Mosquito Control Comm; Amer Red Cross Vol 40 Yrs; *office:* HS 273 Union Ave Framingham MA 01701

K, DEBI MC LAUGHLIN, Computer Literacy Teacher; *b:* Bronx, Fred; *c:* Glenn, Scott; *ed:* Univ of Albany (BS) Bus Ed 1976, (MS) 1980; In-Svc Cmptr Trng; *cr:* Columbia-Greene Comm Coll Instr ; Columbia HS Perm Sub, Part-time Bus Tchr 1982-83; Amsterdam Ed Tchr 1983-84; Gullderland Cntrl Schls Bus Ed Tchr 1984-87; a Springs Cntrl Schl Bus Ed Tchr, Cmptr Lit Tchr 1987-; *ai:* Past CA, FBLA; Adv Cmptr Club; Creative Arts, Fac Status Comms ssn Bd of Dir; AFT, NEA 1977-; SSTA 1984-; Guilderland PTA Dev Curr for AAS Degree Word Processing Prgm; VEA Grant; Saratoga Springs Maple Ave Sch 515 Maple Ave Saratoga Springs 66*

I, CAROL A., First Grade Teacher; *b:* New Rochelle, NY; *m:* G.; *c:* Geoffrey, Christopher, Stacey; *ed:* St U of NY at Cortland em Ed 1971; Univ of Southern CA (MSEd) Ed 1979; Montgomery Schls Tech Acad 1995; *cr:* St Peter's Schl 6-8 Grd Math, Sci Tchr ; Mill Creek Towne Elem Schl 1 Grd Tchr 1985-88; Goshen Elem Grd Tchr 1988-; *ai:* Tech, Math Comms; MCTM 1988-; AYCE res; Presenter MCTM Conf 1995; Mimosa Math Consultant 1994-; Goshen Elem Schl 8701 Warfield Rd Gaithersburg MD 20882

LINI, DANIEL JOSEPH, Teacher; *b:* Norristown, PA; *m:* n O.; *c:* Michael; *ed:* Montgomery Cty Comm Coll (AS) Ed 1979; hester Univ (BS) K-8 Ed 1981; Masters Equivalency in Ed 1990; 45 s; *cr:* C. F. Patton MS Earth Sci Tchr 15 Yrs, Pre-Algebra Tchr 15 ptr Tchr 10 Yrs, Amer His Tchr 12 Yrs; *ai:* Team Ldr; 8th Grd Girls Sftbl Coach; NMSA; NSTA; MS Svc Awd; *office:* Charles F Patton Unionville Rd Kennett Square PA 19348*

RONE, FRANK C., Social Studies & Lit Teacher; *b:* Phila, PA; *m:* n Klesitz; *c:* Frank S., Katie, Laura; *ed:* Penn St (BA) His 1968; Univ (MED) Soc St Ed 1979; 36 Hrs Ed, Child Psych Temple Univ; um Phila Coll; *cr:* Alcorn Elem Schl 6th Grd Tchr 1969-88; W.S. MS 7th & 8th Grd Soc Stud Tchr 1988-; *ai:* Soc Stud Chm; Textbook Comm; Natl Endowment for Hum Fellow 1989; Nom Rose aum Excl in Tchng Awd 1994; *office:* W.S. Peirce MS 24th & n Sts Philadelphia PA 19146

ANI, JOSEPH ANTHONY, Assistant Professor; *b:* Nanticoke, PA; en Marie; *c:* David, Michael; *ed:* Wilks Coll (BA) Psychology 1980; St Univ (MA) Psychology 1982; Coll Misericordia (BS) tional Therapy 1988; Candinate EDD Higher Ed Nova-SE Univ; *cr:* Svc for the Handicapped Occupational Therapy Therapist 1988-91; Misericordia Asst Prof 1991-; *ai:* Mid St Accreditation Comm; Fac c; Amer Occupational Therapy Assn 1988-; PA Occupational Assn 1983-, Financial Officer Dis III, 5 Yr Svc Awd; AAUP; Pub Amer Journal of Comm Psychology, Prevention in Human ook Reviewer; AJOT, Wrote Revision Geriatrics Occ Ther; *office:* sericordia Lake St Dallas PA 18612*

ANO, JULIA MARY, First Grade Teacher; *b:* Brooklyn, NY; *m:* J.; *c:* Angela Scianni, Joseph Anthony; *ed:* Packer Collegiate Bus 1960; Brooklyn Coll (BA) Ed 1978; *cr:* St Jude Schl Sub Tchr 4, Tchr 1974-75; St Rose of Lima Schl Tchr 1978-; *ai:* Primary Math 994-; Primary Unit Ldr 1992-94; NCEA 1978-; Tchr of Yr 1995; In y Monitor Diocese of Trenton 1988; *home:* 38 Birch Hill Rd d NJ 07728

CH, CYNTHIA P., Mathematics Teacher; *b:* Philadelphia, PA; *ed:* ville Univ (BSE) Scndry Ed & Math 1990; *cr:* Various Schl Dist in er & Bucks Cty Sub Tchr 1990-92; Lancaster Cath HS Math Tchr *ai:* Frosh Stu Cncl; Moderator Bowling Club; NCEA 1993-.

ESI, JO-ANNE K., Chemistry Teacher; *b:* Plainfield, NJ; *c:* Chad, *ed:* Montclair St (BS) Chem 1967; *cr:* PIscataway HS Tchr 1967-; League Chem Coach; NIST, NJEA, PTA 1968-.

LO, CHRISTINE TULOTTA, Science Department Chairperson; York City, NY; *m:* Anthony; *c:* Daniella; *ed:* Manhattan COll (BS) 87; Fordham Univ (MS) Ed, Specialization 1989; 3 Credit Hrs omy; *cr:* Sacred Heart Sci Tchr 1988-89; Good Counsel Acad Sci hprsn 1989-; *ai:* Earthwatch Mentor; NHS Comm; Sci Olympiad; S 1989-; NSTA 1994-; Fordham Univ Stu Asst Grad Level; *office:* L Good Counsel HS 52 N Broadway White Plains NY 10603

LO, LOUIS, Advanced Placement Bio Tchr; *b:* Yonkers, NY; *ed:* ester Comm Coll (BA) Soc Sci 1974; Long Island Univ (MS) Ed Attnd SUNY at Albany; Post Grad Stud in Bio, Educl Admin; *cr:* t H. Lehman HS Tchr 1983-; *ai:* HS Acad Olympics Team Coach; l of New York City 1990-; NY Bio Tchrs Assn 1990-; AFT, NYSUT, 983-; New York Acad of Sci 1993-; Amer Museum of Natural His Physician's Comm for Responsible Medicine 1992; People for the Treatment of Animals 1992; Assn for Prevention of Cruelty to s 1990-; Cert of Appreciation for Wkshp in Tchng AP Bio Bronx Dev Day 1994; Cert of Appreciation for Tutorial Svc in Bio in the Prgm Under the Auspices of Albert Einstein Coll of Medicine 1995; lace Cert, Trophy Spec Ed Acad Olympics 1985.*

LIA, DENNIS T., Occupational Ed Teacher; *b:* Jamaica, NY; *m:* Greco; *c:* Joseph; *ed:* NY Inst of Tech (BA) Architecture 1970; City BS) Ed 1981; 150 Credit Hrs Autocad Trng; *cr:* Sewanhaka HS ecture Instr 1979-, Carpentry Instr 1983-85; *ai:* PA Club Adv; haka Fed of Tchrs, PTSA 1979-; Citizens Advy Cncl Occupational 79-; Electric Vehicle Contest Adv, Schl Honorable Mention; Stdnts St Architecture VICA Awds; *office:* Sewanhaka HS 500 Tulip Ave Park NY 11001

LLI, EILEEN MARY, 10th Grade Language Arts Tchr; *b:* Reading, John Michael; *c:* Joshua M.; *ed:* Kutztown Univ (BS) Comm 1978; f Ed MEq Equivalency 1992; 3 Post Grad Credits West Chester Univ; hlenberg Sr HS Lang Art Sub Tchr 1978-; Kutztown Area HS Lang Tchr 1978-; *ai:* Sr Class Play Adv 1978-79; NEA, PSEA 1978-; ng Yng Edctr Awd Kutztown Jaycees 1989; *office:* Kutztown Area Trexler Ave Kutztown PA 19530

R, JOSEPH P., Special Ed Dept Chairman; *b:* Passaic, NJ; *m:* lle Venutolo M.; *c:* Michael; *ed:* William Paterson Coll (BA) Ed Kean Coll (MA) Admin, Supervision 1973, (MA) Spec Ed 1980; *cr:* c Bd of Ed Tchr, Spec Ed Supvr Grds 7-12 1969-; *ai:* Bsktbl Coach 30; Spec Edtrs Club 1985-; Frosh Class Adv 1970-85; NJEA, NEA, 1969-92; NJ Prins & Supvrs 1993-; Passaic Cty Coaches Assn 30; CEC 1988-; Passaic Recreation Dept Chm 1969-70, Pres; Yth 972-73, Pres; Rainbow Fnd 1985-, Assisting Cancer Victims; Jason n Liver Transplant Fund 1983-85; Monmouth Yth Hockey Assn aiser, Treas; Bsktbl Coach of Yr 1977, 1972; BYAA Sports ipation Awd; Humanitarian Awd Rainbow Fnd 1986; *office:* Passaic Ed 101 Passaic Ave Passaic NJ 07055

R, SUSAN MARIE, Social Service Instructor; *b:* Cleveland, OH; *ed:* tta Coll (BA) Ed 1980; Attnd WV Grad Coll; *cr:* O'Neill Sr Ctr 1981-85; Washington Cty Children Svcs Case Worker 1985-91, 990-; Braley & Thompson Inc Soc Worker 1993-; *ai:* Zonya Intnl 95; *home:* 713 3rd St Marietta OH 45750

O, TINA ZDROJEWSKI, Mid & HS Home Economics Tchr; *b:* *m:* Tod; *c:* Jacob; *ed:* Buffalo St Coll (MS) Multidisciplinary Stud 1990, (BA) Ed in Sci; *cr:* Lake Shore Cntrl Tchr 1992-; *ai:* NYSHETA 1989-; *office:* Lake Shore Cntrl Schl 8855 Erie Rd Angola NY 14006

CISZEK, LEONARD R., Social Studies Teacher; *b:* Shenandoah, PA; *m:* Marcia Sincavage; *ed:* Penn St Univ (AA) Bus 1969; Mansfield Univ (BS) His 1972; Bloomsburg Univ (MED) Soc Stud 1978; *cr:* Shenandoah Vly HS Soc Stud Tchr 1972-; *ai:* Cross Cntry Coach 1972-; Track & Field Coach 1972-90; Ath Dir 1994-; NEA 1972-; PIAA 1969-; *office:* Shenandoah Valley Jr Sr HS 805 W Centre St Shenandoah PA 17976

CITARELLI, VINCENT E., Mathematics Teacher; *b:* Upper Darby, PA; *ed:* Penn St Univ (BS) Ed 1991; St Joseph's Univ Stud for Masters in Ed; *cr:* Upper Darby Hs Math Tchr 1992-; *ai:* Asst Ftbl Coach; NCTM 1990-; *office:* Upper Darby HS 601 N Lansdowne Ave Upper Darby PA 19082*

CITINO, DONNA, Social Studies Teacher; *b:* Boston, MA; *ed:* Emmanuel Coll (BA) Pol Sci 1979; *cr:* Farley MS Soc Stud Tchr 1985-90; Walsh MS Soc Stud Tchr 1990-; *ai:* Curr Integration Comm; NEA; MA Tchrs Assn; NCSS; New England His Tchrs Assn; *office:* Walsh MS 301 Brook St Framingham MA 01701

CITINO-FUSCO, SANDRA, English Teacher; *b:* Riverside, NJ; *ed:* 3 Credits Soc Agencies Grad Level in Scndry Guid Degree; *cr:* St Cecilia's Schl Eng, Rdng, Rel Tchr 1985-86; Stella Maris Schl Eng, Rdng, Rel Tchr 1987-88; Sylvan Learning Ctr Writing, Rdng Tchr 1988; Samuel S. Yellin Schl Eng Tchr 1989-; *ai:* Inter Dist Meetings Eng Dept Rep; Soc Dev After Schl Prgm 1991-92, 1994-95; Peer Mediation Prgm Adv; NJHS Adv 1992-93; 7-8 Grd Spelling Objective Comm 1995-; Curr Comm 1989-; NCTE 1991-; *office:* Samuel S Yellin Elem Schl 111 Warwick Rd Stratford NJ 08084*

CITRANO, ROBERT MITCHELL, Guidance Counselor; *b:* Bethpage, NY; *ed:* SUNY at Stony Brook (BA) His 1987; Long Island Univ C. W. Post (MS) Cnslng 1990; Fifteen Post Masters Credits; *cr:* US Merchant Marine Acad Midshipmen Cnslr 1990-92; Half Hollow Hills HS East Guid Cnslr 1993-; *ai:* Amer Cnslng Assn, NY St Cnslng Assn 1988-; AFT 1993-; Editorial Review Bd Journal for Prof Cnslr; Article Pub; Nassau Cnslrs Assn Outstdng Grad Stu Awd 1993; *office:* Half Hollow Hills HS E 50 Vanderbilt Pkwy Dix Hills NY 11746

CITRO, ANTHONY RALPH, Social Studies Teacher; *b:* Springfield, VT; *m:* Carmen Anne Melanson; *c:* Monique, Brian, Nicole, Renee Shedd; *ed:* Castleton St Coll (BSED) Scndry 1960; St Michaels Coll (MA) His 1970; Addl 15 Credit Hrs Prof Dev; *cr:* Bristol HS Soc Stud Tchr 1960-64; Otter Vly Union HS Sox Stud Tchr 1964-66; Jericho HS Prin 1966-67; Mt Mansfield Union HS Soc Stud Tchr, Dept Chm 19 Yrs, 1967-; *ai:* NEA, VEA 1961-; Tchr of Yr 1984; *home:* 34 Countryside Dr Essex Junction VT 05452

CITRO, PATRICIA H., Science Teacher; *b:* Darby, PA; *m:* Thomas F.; *c:* Thomas F. Jr., Suzanne P.; *ed:* Immaculata Coll (BA) Bio 1962; *cr:* Archbishop Prendergast HS Sci Tchr 34 Yrs; *ai:* Soph Dance Moderator; Comm Svc Corps Projects; NCEA 1962-; DE Cty Sci Tchng Assn 1962-; Tchr of Yr 1995; *office:* Archbishop Prendergast HS 401 N Lansdowne Ave Drexel Hill PA 19026

CITRON, MERLE, 12th Grade English Teacher; *b:* Hoboken, NJ; *m:* Murray Gottfried; *c:* Chad Breitenfeld; *ed:* Douglass Coll (BA) Eng 1965; VT Coll (MA) Tchng of Writing 1988; Jersey City St Coll K-12 Tchr Cert Eng 1969; Trenton St Coll Educl Media Cert 1976; *cr:* Hoboken HS Speech, Drama Tchr 1966-72; Lecturer, Group Trainer 1972-77; Cogent Assocs Project Dir 1972-77; Hillside Annex Remedial Rdng Tchr 1973; Writer, Media Consultant 1977-; Hopewell Vly Cntrl HS Eng Tchr 1979-82; Ewing HS Eng Tchr 1985-; *ai:* Yrbk, Newspaper Adv; Environmental Club; NJEA, NEA 1985-; Artsbridge 1993-, Pres; Friends of Lambertville Lib 1994-; Articles Pub; Grants; Governor's Tchr Recognition Prgm 1990-91; Created, Managed USOE Nationally Validated Prgm, Career Ed Project; *home:* 72 York St Lambertville NJ 08530*

CIUFERRI, RICHARD DAVID, Music Teacher & Band Director; *b:* Taylor, PA; *m:* Marie Ann Pero; *c:* Maria R., Gina E.; *ed:* Wilkes Univ (BS) Music Ed 1971; Post Grad Stud Wilkes Univ, Marywood Coll, Penn St Univ, Utah St Univ & West Chester St Univ; *cr:* North Pocono MS Music Tchr & Band Dir 1971-; *ai:* MS Concert Band; PSEA, NEA 1971-; *office:* North Pocono M S Church St Moscow PA 18444

CIUFFETELLI, ANTHONY, Spanish & Italian Teacher; *b:* Wilmington, DE; *ed:* Univ of DE (BA) Intnl Relations, Span 1993, (MA) ESL 1995; *cr:* Univ of DE Span Tchng Asst 1993; St Mark's HS Span, Italian Tchr 1995-; *office:* St Mark's HS Pike Creek Rd Wilmington DE 19808

CIUFFREDA, LILLIAN CHRISTINE, Teacher of Gifted & Talented; *b:* Perth Amboy, NJ; *m:* Mark Poiani; *c:* James; *ed:* Newark St Coll (BA) Eng, Elem Ed 1969; Kean Coll of NJ (MA) Rdng Specialization 1977; Admin, Supervision Cert 1977; *cr:* Avenel Jr HS Eng Tchr 1968-71; Colonia HS Eng Tchr 1971-81; J. F. K. HS Eng Tchr 1981-85; Iselin MS GATE Tchr 1985-; Colonia MS GATE Tchr 1985-; *ai:* Creative Writing Club 1969-71, Newspaper 1971-75, Frosh Class 1981-85, Photography Club 1989- Advs; Curr Comms 1980, 1985, 1987, 1995; NEA 1969-; Woodbridge Twp Lib Bd, Trustee 1982; Consultant Educl Testing Svc 1975; Lecturer NJCTE 1977; Consultant Coll of Optometry SUNY 1981; Screen Play 1983; Childrens Book Listen, Kids 1989; *office:* Woodridge Twp Schl Dist School St Woodbridge NJ 07095

CIULLA, KARIN CASTELLI, History Teacher; *b:* Brooklyn, NY; *m:* Christopher; *ed:* Farleigh Dickinson Univ (BS) Hotel, Restaurant Mngmt 1990; 36 Undergraduate Credits Coll Staten Island Scndry Ed, 16 Grad Credits Scndry Soc Stud; *cr:* Francis Schl Sci, His Tchr 1992; Tottenville HS His Stu Tchr 1992-93, Sub Tchr 1993; St John Villa Acad His Tchr 1993-; *ai:* JV Sftbl Asst Coach; Stu Adv, Mentor; Interdisciplinary Prgm Chprsn; Schl Tracking Task Force; NCEA 1994-; *office:* St John Villa Acad-Richmond 26 Landis Ave Staten Island NY 10305

CIULLA, LOUISE MARCELLE, Fourth Grade Teacher; *b:* New York, NY; *m:* Robert K.; *c:* John, David; *ed:* Coll of Mt St Vincent (BA) Fr 1963; Fairfield Univ (MA) Ed 1985; Hunter Coll CUNY 9 Credits, Masters Prgm in Ed; Wesleyan Univ 1 Credit, Continuing Ed Prgm; *cr:* PS 149 Second Grd Tchr 1963-64; Conte Schl Fourth Grd Tchr 1964-65; St Thomas Day Schl Asst Kndgtn Tchr 1976-79; Hamden Hall Cntry Day Schl Kndgtn, Fourth Grd Tchr 1980-; *ai:* In Service Coord; Ed Comm Lower Schl Rep; Afterschool Enrichment Classes Fr Tchr; CT Cncl for Soc Stud 1995-; Elizabeth Doyle Meml Schlsp Fund Comm, Chair 1990-; Alliance Francaise de New Haven 1986-, Chair of Prgm Comm 1 Yr; Summer Sabatical Grant Hamden Hall; YWCA of Greater New Haven Awd Women in Ldrshp 1991; *office:* Hamden Hall Country Day Schl 1108 Whitney Ave Hamden CT 06517*

CIZENSKI, RICHARD ANTHONY, 6th Grade Teacher; *b:* Syracuse, NY; *m:* Julie C. King; *c:* Matthew, Mark, Michael; *ed:* SUNY at Cobleskill (AAS) NED 1970; SUNY at Oneonta (BA) Elem Ed 1972; 30 Credit Hrs Grad Work; Coaches Cert; *cr:* 4th Grd Tchr 1972-84; 6th Grd Tchr 1984-; *ai:* Coach for 16 Yrs; Site Base Cty; CT Tchrs Assn 1972-; AFT & NYSOT 1972-.

CIZON, LINDA RZEGOTA, 8th Grade Teacher; *b:* Passaic, NJ; *c:* Michael, Nicholas, Kristin; *ed:* Jersey City St (BA) Elem Ed 1972; *cr:* St Stanislaus Kostka Schl 4th, 5th, 6th Grd Tchr 1972-79; St Anthony of Podua 4th Grd Tchr 1979-84; St Stanislaus Kostka Schl 8th Grd Tchr 1990-; *ai:* Sci Co-Ord; Schl Jeopardy Co-Chrpsn; 8th Grd Sacramental Prgm; NCEA 1972-; PTA 1995-; Garfield PTA 1979-; Outstndng Tchrs Awd 1972; Newark Diocese Tchr of Yr 1994.

CLAAR, LORI L., Math Teacher; *b:* Alum Bank, PA; *m:* David G.; *c:* Matthew; *ed:* Univ of Pitts at Johnstown (BS) Sec Math, Gen Sci 1983; 32 Addl Credit Permanent Cert; *cr:* Conemaugh Vly SD Math Tchr 13 Yrs; *ai:* Scholastic Quiz, Math Counts Coaches; Jr Class Adv; Prom Coord; Laurel Highlands Math Alliance 1992-; CVEA, NEA, PSEA 1985-, Bldg Rep; *office:* Conemaugh Valley Jr Sr HS 1342 William Penn Ave Johnstown PA 15906

CLADWELL, NANCY CLAYTON, Social Studies Teacher; *b:* Reno, NV; *c:* Mathew, Jenny Deitrick; *ed:* CA St U at Los Angeles (BA) His 1970; Post Grad Work Eng, Soc Stud, Methodologies, Curr 78 Semester Units Various Univs; *cr:* St Louis of France Schl 8th Grd Tchr 1974-75; St Stephen Schl 8th Grd Tchr 1975-76; Carson HS Eng, Soc Stud Tchr 1976-88; Vilseck Am HS Soc Stud Tchr 1988-; *ai:* NHS Spon; Tchr Trng Facilitator; Soc Stud Dept Chair; AVID Trng Cadre; Federa Ed Assn 1988-; Ormsby Cty Teach Assn 1974-88, Bldg Rep; Phi Delta Kappa 1982-87; Warberg Dist Tchr of Yr 1996; Avid Soc Stud Cadre 1993-; *office:* Vilseck American HS Unit 28041 CMR 411 APO AE 09112*

CLADY, LINDA SAUNDERS, Accelerated Program Teacher; *b:* Cleveland, OH; *w:* Robert (dec); *c:* Kimberly Clady Schreck, Kristen M.; *ed:* OH St Univ (BA) Ed 1969; Gifted Ed Post Grad Stud Wright St Univ, Ashland Univ; Addl Courses OH St Univ Masters Pgm, Bowling Green St Univ; *cr:* Pearl St Schl Tchr 1969; Bucyrus MS Rdng Tchr 1981-82; Carlisle Elem Schl Tchr 1982-84; Bucyrus MS Accelerated, Enriched Prgm Tchr 1984-; *ai:* Chess Club, Magazine Adv; Strategic Planning Comm; NEA, OEA, BEA 1982-; OCTELA 1991-; CEC 1994-; Christa Mc Auliffe Tchng Excl Awd; Jennings Schlr; Natl Schl Bd Assn Conf Presenter 1996; *office:* Bucyrus MS 245 Woodlawn Ave Bucyrus OH 44820

CLAFFEY, NEIL EVERETT, HS Social Studies Teacher; *b:* Boston, MA; *m:* Renae Lias; *c:* Elias; *ed:* Univ of NC at Chapel Hill (BA) Ec 1985; Harvard Univ (MED) Tchng & Curr 1989; *cr:* US House of Representatives Doorman 1985-88; Nashua Sr HS Tchr 1989-; *ai:* Granite St Challenge Club, Sr Class Play Ticket Sales Adv; Var Bsktbl Statistician; AFT 1989-; Outstanding Tchr Recognition Awd Tufts Univ; Stock Market Game Outstanding Participant Awd Securities & Exch Commission; *office:* Nashua Sr HS 36 Riverside Dr Nashua NH 03060

CLAGETT, WENDY MORRIS, Spanish Teacher; *b:* Warren, OH; *m:* Wayne Lee; *c:* Wayne Alan, Neil Evan; *ed:* OH St Univ (BS) Span 1976; Univ of Dayton (MS) Guidance 1981; Attnd Drake Univ, Seattle Pacific Univ Masters Plus & Youngstown St Univ Ger; *cr:* Mathews HS Span & Eng Tchr 1976-; *ai:* Span Club Adv; HS Drug Policy Comm; Organized Various Trips to Spain; Delta Kappa Gamma 1988-; Church Youth Group-KICK 1993-, Co-Adv; *office:* Mathews HS 4429 Warren Sharon Rd Vienna OH 44473

CLAIN, JANICE LEE, Spanish Teacher; *b:* Milo, ME; *ed:* Univ of ME (BA) Fr 1971, (MED) Ed 1980, (CAS) Tchng 1991; Deutsche Sommerschule at Atlantikuri 1993 & 1994, Goethe Inst at Munich 1995; *cr:* Cntrl HS Fr & Span Tchr 1971-74; Bangor HS Fr & Span Tchr 1974-75; Georges Valley HS Fr & Span Tchr 1975-80; Hermon HS Fr & Span Tchr & Fine Arts Dept Chair 1980-; *ai:* Sr Class & Span Club Adv; Hiking Club Spon; AATF 1988-, Sec 1988-94; AATSP 1994-; FLAME 1988-; Article in ME Scholar; *home:* PO Box 89 Levant ME 04456*

CLAIR, ANNE LANTZ, Second Grade Teacher; *b:* Baltimore, MD; *m:* George Barry; *c:* Sarah Anne, Amanda Louise, Elizabeth Anne; *ed:* Lynchburg Coll (BA) Sociology & Psych 1960; Westchester Univ Tchr Cert Ed; Varied Courses at Grad Level & Ed Inservice Courses; *cr:* PA Dept of Welfare Caseworker 1960; Blue Ball Elem 1st Grd Tchr 1962-64; Nitrauer Elem 1st Grd Tchr 1964-69; Intermediae Unit #13 Gifted Pgm 1973-75; Manheim Twp MS Gifted Pgm 1982-93; Reidenbaugh Elem 2nd & 4th Grd Tchr 1993-; *ai:* Sci Curr Comm; NEA & Penn St Edctr 1962-, Local Assn Sec; Lynchburg Coll Alumni 1960-, Class Co-Chm; St James Episcopal Church 1979-, Sec Vestry & Vestry Mem; *office:* Reidenbaugh Elem Schl 1001 Buckwalter Rd Lititz PA 17543*

CLAIR, KATE, Assoc Prof in Comm Design; *b:* Teaneck, NJ; *ed:* Elmira Coll (BFA) Sculpture & Printmaking 1983; Binghamton Univ (MA) Art His 1986; Tyler Schl of Art (MFA) Graphic Design 1989; *cr:* Art Dept Dir 1987-90; Kutztown Univ Prof 1991-; *ai:* Art Test Coord; Pa-SSHUE Womens Consortium Campus Contact; Adv Essence Literary & Fine Arts; Commissions Status of Minorities & Women; Soc of Scribes 1990-; Binghamton Art Directors 1990-, Multiple Recognition Awd; Stud Work Included in Intnl Typographic Annual #4; Design Work Selected for IABC Award; Financial World Mag Bronze for Annual Report Financials; *office:* Kutztown Univ Communication Design Bldg College Ave Kutztown PA 19530

CLAIR, REGINA A., Guidance Counselor; *b:* Pittsburgh, PA; *ed:* Duquesne Univ (BA) Psych, Sociology 1990, (MSEd) Schl Cnslng 1992; *cr:* Steel Vly HS 8-10 Grd Guid Cnslr 1993-; *ai:* Stu Assistance Team; SADD, Teen Inst Peer Cnslr Adv; JV, Var Girls Vlybl Coach; Americorp Liaison; Fin Aid Wkshp Instr; Supvr Guid Interns; NEA, PSEA, Allegheny Cty Cnslrs Assn 1993-; Mon Vly Ed Consortium 1993-95, Stu Action Comm; First Annual Mock Crash Demonstration Organized & Held 1995 Through SADD Org Pub Svc, Comm Svc; *office:* Steel Valley HS 3113 Main St Munhall PA 15120

CLAIRE, DENNIS DANIEL,JR., English Teacher; *b:* Port Jefferson, NY; *m:* Janice Marie Larcheveque; *c:* Dennis P., Ryan J., Patrick J.; *ed:* Marist Coll (BA) Eng 1974;(MS) LIU, Eng Ed 1992; Credit Hrs SUNY at New Paltz, SUNY at Plattsburg, SUNY at Stony Brook & LIU at Southampton; Doctoral Fellowship St John's Univ; *cr:* Rhinecliff Union Free Schl Dist Eng Tchr 1974-77; Self Employed Electrical Contractor Master Electrician 1977-79; Greenport Union Free Schl Dist Eng Tchr 1979-; *ai:* Schl Lit Magazine Shorelines Adv 1981-; Schl Newspaper Quill Adv 1989-90; Var Wrestling Coach 1980-84; Jr Var Ftbl Coach 1980-88; AFT Greenport Tchrs Assn 1979-, Local Pres 1988-90; AFT Rhinecliff Tchrs Assn 1974-77, VP; NAPPS, NCTE, NYSEC; Suffolk Times Educator of Yr 1990; Pub Story La Mispocha Hebrew Lang Magazine; 2 Views on Ed Pub in Viewpoints Newsday; 1992 NY St Engl Cncl Tchr of Excl; *office:* Greenport H S Front St Greenport NY 11944*

CLANCY, BRIAN PAUL, High School Band Director; *b:* Manhasset, NY; *ed:* Nassau Comm Coll (AAS) Music Performance 1982; Potsdam Coll (BM) Music Ed 1985, (MM) Music Performance 1987; *cr:* Deer Park Schls Band Dir 1987-90; Hauppauge Pub Schls Band Dir 1990-; *ai:* 1995 Class, Tri-M Honor Soc Adv; HS Jazz Emsemble Instr, Conductor; Suffolk Cty Music Educators Assn 1987-, Exec Bd; Percussive Arts Soc 1983-, Ed Comm 1995; Music Educators Natl Conf, NY St Schl Music Assn 1987-; *home:* 19 Balsam Dr Medford NY 11763

CLANCY, ELLEN M., English Teacher & Chairperson; *b:* Bronx, NY; *ed:* Lehman Coll (BA) Eng 1972, (MA) Eng 1981; Pace Univ (MS) Ed Admin, Supervision 1985; *cr:* Mother Cabrini HS Eng Tchr, Dept Chprsn 1972-; *ai:* Adv Stu Cncl, Yrbk, Shakespeare Oratory Contest; Dir Talent Show; Curr Comm; Media Edctrs Assn 1990-; NCEA 1973-; *office:* Mother Cabrini HS 701 Fort Washington Ave New York NY 10040

CLANCY, JAMES P.,JR., Junior High Mathematics Teacher; *b:* Gloucester, MA; *ed:* St Anselm Coll (BA) Ec 1968; Plymouth St Coll (MED) Admin

1975; *cr:* Manchester Mem HS Math Tchr 1968-84; Hillside Jr HS Math Tchr 1984-; *ai:* NEA, NHEA, MEA 1968-.

CLANCY, PAMELA JANE, Sci & Soc Stud Tchr; *b:* Hornell, NY; *ed:* Plymouth St Coll (BS) Elem Ed 1980; *cr:* NH 4-H Camps Unit, Prog, Camp Dir 1979-90; Acad of Holy Names Tchr 1980-; *ai:* After Schl Care Dir, Supvr 1984-; Summer Day Camp Prgm Dir 1991-; NCEA 1980-; Distngd Tchr of Yr 1995; *office:* Acad Of The Holy Names 1065 New Scotland Ave Albany NY 12208

CLANCY, THOMAS GERALD, Business Education Teacher; *b:* New York, NY; *m:* Maryalyce O'Neill; *c:* Justin; *ed:* Iona Coll (BBA) Mrktg & Finance 1970; Baruch Coll (MSED) Voc Ed 1975; Montclair St Guidance Cert 1989; Jersey City St Coord of Work Stud Prgms 1981; *cr:* Bishop Dubois HS Bus Ed Tchr 1970-74; Northern Valley Reg HS Bus Ed Tchr 1974-; *ai:* Girls Soccer & Track Coach; NEA, NJEA, NJ Bus Ed Assn 1974-; Dumont Elks 1980-, Crippled Children & Schlsp Comms Chm; Whos Who Among Stdnts in Amer Colls & Univs 1970; Outstanding Coll Aths of Amer 1970; *office:* Northern Valley Regional HS 100 Central Ave Old Tappan NJ 07675*

CLANTON, BARBARA LYNN, Mathematics Teacher; *b:* Bay Shore, NY; *m:* Jackie Weathers; *ed:* Princeton Univ (BSE) Electrical Engrng 1984; SUNY at Stony Brook (MA) 1989; Attnd Pace Univ; *cr:* The Masters Schl Math Tchr 1985-91; Horace Greeley HS Math Tchr 1991-94; The Masters Schl Math Tchr 1994-; *ai:* Var Sftbl Coach; Yrbk Adv; NCTM, AMTNYS 1986-; *office:* The Masters Schl 49 Clinton Ave Dobbs Ferry NY 10522

CLANTON, PATRICIA DICKENS, Language Arts Teacher; *b:* Falkland, NC; *m:* Donald R.; *ed:* Bennett Coll (BA) Eng 1971; Credits for Me at Coppin St, Morgan St, Univ Coll at Univ of MD; *cr:* Lake clifton Sr HS Eng Tchr 1971-74; Herring Run MS Eng Tchr 1974-93; Thurgood Marshall #171 Lang Arts Tchr 1993-; *ai:* 8th Grd Team Ldr, Articulation Chprsn; Schl Improvement Team Co-Chprsn; AFT 1994-; NEA 1992-; First Mt Olive FWB Church 1971-, Ministry Pres, Comm Chprsn; Presenter MD MS conf, Natl MD Assn, Urban Initiatives Conf 1996; *office:* Thurgood Marshall MS #171 5000 Truesdale Ave Baltimore MD 21206

CLAPP, KATHLEEN LYONS, Math Teacher & Dept Chair; *b:* Little Falls, NY; *m:* John M.; *ed:* UMPI (BS) Math 1978; Addl 36 Hrs; *cr:* Bucksport HS Tchr, Dept Chair 1989-; *ai:* Math Team Coach; Climate, Aspirations & G-T Comms; Tech Comm; NEA, ME Tchrs Assn, Bucksport TA 1979-; *home:* RR 1 Box 1015 Blue Hill ME 04614

CLAPS, MARIA, 7th-12th Grade Math Teacher; *b:* Larchmont, NY; *ed:* St Univ of NY at Albany (BS) Math 1977; Herbert H. Lehman Coll (MA); Westchester Tchr Ctr In-Service; *cr:* Mamaroneck Schl Dist Part-time Tchr, TA in ESL; Pope Pius XII Regnl HS Math, Bus Tchr 1978-80; Acad of the Resurrection Math, Cmptr Tchr 1980-85; Woodlands HS Math Tchr 1985-; Manhattan Coll Adjunct Prof, Cmptr Sci; *ai:* Unit Rep Greenburgh Tchr Fed; Mini-Cusp; African-Amer Comm; Buddy Prgm Adv; New Tchr Mentor; Coord New Tchr Mentor Prgm; NCTM, COMAP, AMTNYS, GTF 1985-; 10 Cty 1985-, Bd of Dir; MAA 1989-; NYSAMS 1995-; Compute, Bd Mem; WIBC of Westchester Cty 1977-; Westchester Tchr Ctr Grant Recipient; Wkshp Presenter 10 Cty Math Conf 1994, SUNY at Purchase 1993 Presenter; LImacon Wrkshp Presenter 1996; *office:* Woodlands HS 475 W Hartsdale Rd Hartsdale NY 10530*

CLAPSADDLE, DAVID E., 7th-12th Grd Vocal Music Tchr; *b:* Toledo, OH; *m:* Rachel; *ed:* Bowling Green St Univ (BA) Vocal, Choral Ed 1990; Attnd Harmony Coll, MO Western St Univ Barbershop; *cr:* Anthony Wayne Schls Elem Music Tchr 1991-; Paulding Exempted Vlg Schls Choral Dir 1991-; *ai:* Asst Dir Northwesternaires Barbershop Chorus; Worship Ldr Bryan Alliance Church; Swing Choir Dir; NEA, OMEA, MENC, OCDA, ACDA 1991-; SPEBSQSA 1993- Prgm VP Barbershopper of Yr 1995; *office:* Paulding HS 405 N Water St Paulding OH 45879*

CLARE, ELLEN J., Fourth Grade Teacher; *b:* New York, NY; *ed:* Fordham Univ (BA) Ed 1945; Columbia Univ Post Grad Stud; *cr:* All Saints Parochial Schl 4th Grd Tchr 1945-46; Saint Thomas Parochial Schl 3rd-5th, 8th Grd Tchr 1946-60; Ralph Bunche Schl 3rd-5th Grd Tchr 1960-76, Asst Prin 1976-78, Tchr 1978-; *ai:* After Schl Tutoring Prgm; Tchr Trng; Tchr in Charge; AFT, UFT 1965-; Tchr of Yr 1980, 1993-94; Dedicated Svc Awd 1990-91; Dist Outstdng Tchr Awd 1994-95; *office:* PS 125 Ralph Bunche 425 W 123rd St New York NY 10027*

CLARK, ANN FRANCES, Health Teacher; *b:* Elmira, NY; *ed:* St Univ of NY at Cortland (BSEd) Hlth 1990; *cr:* Broadway Jr HS Part-Time Hlth Tchr 1990-92; Peace Corps Assignment 1992-93; Ernie Davis Jr HS Part-Time Hlth Tchr 1993-95; Elmira Free Acad Summer Schl Hlth Tchr 1994-95; Twin Towers MS Hlth Tchr 1995-; *office:* Twin Towers MS 223 Wisner Ave Ext Middletown NY 10940

CLARK, BARBARA TURKETT, 1st Grade Teacher; *b:* Seneca Falls, NY; *m:* James F.; *c:* Michael; *ed:* Geneseo SUNY (BS) Elem Ed 1963; *cr:* West Street Schl 2nd Grd Tchr 1963-64; West Irondequoit 1st, 2nd Grd Tchr 1964-71; Lakewood Elem Schl 1st Grd Tchr 1971-85; Celoron Primary Schl 1st Grd, Lib Tchr; *ai:* Bus Supvr; NEA; NYSTA; STA; *office:* Celoron Primary Schl Dunam Ave Celoron NY 14720*

CLARK, BRIAN, Biology Teacher; *b:* South Weymouth, MA; *m:* Tammy Strout; *c:* Alaina; *ed:* Univ of ME at Orono (BS) Bio 1980; Univ of Southern ME (MS) Educl Admin 1993; *cr:* Lake Region HS Sci Tchr 1980-; *ai:* Var Sftbl, Girls Soccer Coach; IM Adv; NEA 1980-; *office:* Lake Region HS Rt 302 Bridgton ME 04009

CLARK, BRIAN S., Humanities & US History Instr; *b:* Warren, OH; *m:* Melanie L.; *ed:* Youngstown St Univ (BS) Scndry Ed, Soc Stud 1993; *cr:* Carrollton HS Hum & US His Tchr 1994-; *ai:* Head Boys Bsktbl Coach; Fed Chrstn Aths, Stu Cncl Adv; Carrollton Ed Assn 1994-; OEA, NEA 1993-; OH HS Bsktbl Coaches Assn 1992-; Natl Fed Interscholastic Coaches Assn 1986-; Fed of Russian Orthodox Clubs 1990-, OH Sports Dir 1994-95; *home:* 418 McKinley Ave NW # B Carrollton OH 44615

CLARK, BROOKS ALEXANDER, English Teacher; *b:* Brookfield, IL; *m:* Tina Pelletier; *ed:* Univ of ME (BA) Ed & Eng 1984; *cr:* Mattanawcook Acad Eng Tchr 1985-91; Bonny Eagle HS Eng Tchr 1991-; *ai:* Asst Var Ftbl & Wrestling Coach; ME Tchrs Assn 1995-; *office:* Bonny Eagle HS 700 Saco Rd Standish ME 04084

CLARK, CAROL S., Orchestra Conductor & Coord; *b:* Cleveland, OH; *ed:* OH St Univ (BS) Music Ed 1961; Trenton St Coll (MA) Conducting 1969; Attnd Eastman, Oberlin, MI, Univ of WI & Rutgers; *cr:* Columbus Pub Schls Instrumental Music Tchr 1961-63; Franklin Twp Schls Instrumental Music Tchr 1963-72; Boardman Schl Dist Orch Dir 1972-; *ai:* Orch Prgm Coord; OH Music Ed Assn 1961-; Natl Schl Orch Assn 1972-; Natl Bd Mem at Large; Amer String Tchrs Assn 1972-; OH String Tchrs Assn 1972-, Tchr of Yr; Boardman Orchs Have Won Superior Ratings at St Contest for 23 Yrs & 18 First Place Natl Titles Including 5 Grand Natl Championships; *office:* Boardman HS 7777 Glenwood Ave Youngstown OH 44512

CLARK, CHERYL LYNNE, K-12 Grd Art & Technology Tchr; *b:* Syracuse, NY; *c:* Elissa, Lauren; *ed:* SUNY Coll at Potsdam (BA) Studio Art 1988, (MSEd) Instrl Tech, Media Mngmt 1992; St Lawrence Univ NYS K-12 Art Tchng Cert 1987; *cr:* Parishville-Hopkinton Cntrl Schl K-12 Grd Art, Tech Tchr 1988-; *ai:* Class Adv; Semestering, Shared Decision Making, Stans Comms; AFT, NYSUT 1988-; Phi Delta Kappa 1995-; One of Three Art Specialist Yearly Projects Liaisons Clarkson Univ, Xerox Corp Schl Bus Rural, Urban Schls Partnership; *office:* Parishville Hopkintn Ctrl Schl School St Parishville NY 13672

CLARK, CHRISTOPHER ROY, Band Director; *b:* Akron, OH; *m:* Tami Lynne Kee; *c:* Benjamin Roy, Jacob Edward, Alice Catherine; *ed:* Univ of Akron (BSME) Music Ed 1989; *cr:* Open Door Chrstn Schl Band Dir, Music Dept Head 1990-; *ai:* Handbell, Schl Musical, Marching Band Dir, Jazz Band; MENC & OMEA 1989-; *office:* Open Door Christian Schl 8287 W Ridge Rd Elyria OH 44035

CLARK, DALE J., Assoc Prof of Business Div; *b:* Bath, NY; *ed:* Suny at Geneseo (BA) Pol Sci-magna cum laude; Suny at Buffalo (JD) Commercial Law & Taxation-cum laude 1981-; *cr:* Corning Comm Coll Assoc Prof 1981-; *ai:* Fac Governance Comm; NYS Bar Assoc 1982-; Steuben Cty Bar Assoc 1982-; Southern Tier Legal Svcs 1993- Dir; Bath Bapt Church 1986- Trustee; *office:* Corning Comm Coll 1 Academic Dr Corning NY 14830

CLARK, DANIEL R., 5th Grade Teacher; *b:* Corry, PA; *m:* Martina M. Consolo; *c:* Nathan, Casey; *ed:* Edinboro Univ (BS) Elem Ed 1973; 24 Post Grad Hrs in Elem Ed; *cr:* Columbus Elem Schl 5th Grd Tchr 1973-88; Wright Elem Schl 5th Grd Tchr 1989-90; Sparta Elem Schl 5th Grd Tchr 1991-; *ai:* Ftbl Asst Coach; Bsbl Head Coach; Rdng, Writing & TQM Comms; Corry Area Ed Assn 1973-, Building Rep; PSEA 1973-, NEA 1973-; Little League Corry 1985-95, Pres 1993; *home:* 14900 Stewart Rd Corry PA 16407*

CLARK, DEBORAH BEST, French Teacher; *b:* New Castle, PA; *m:* Thomas Royd; *ed:* Clarion St Coll (BS) Fr-Cum Laude 1975; *cr:* Clarion-Limestone Area Schl Fr Tchr 1981-; *ai:* Fr Club Adv; NEA, PSEA 1981-; Southern Clarion Cty Vol Ambulance Svc 1978-, Emergency Medical Technician; *office:* Clarion-Limestone Jr, Sr HS Rd 1 Box 205 Strattanville PA 16258

CLARK, DONNA MARIE SAVONA, Science Teacher; *b:* Brownsville, PA; *m:* Bill Gordon; *c:* Crystal, Tanya; *ed:* California Univ (BA) Bio 1974, (MS) Bio 1981, (MS) Elem 1993; *cr:* Univ of Southern CA Sec 1974; Berkeley Springs WV Bio Tchr 1975-76; Mon Vly Hlth Ctr Sec 1 Yr; Frazier Schl Dist Sci Tchr 1977-; *ai:* Ski Club Spon, PA Jr Acad of Sci, Pittsburgh Regnl Schl Sci & Engrng Fair Spon; PSEA, NEA, FEA 1977-; Pittsburg Geological Soc Tchr's Awd 1980; Nom Keivin Burns Awd 1982; Fayette Cty Drug & Alcohol Commission's Comm Svc Awd 1987; Nom Thanks to Tchrs Excl Recognition 1990; *home:* PO Box 53 Stockdale PA 15483

CLARK, EMMA L., Fifth Grade Teacher; *b:* Central Falls, RI; *ed:* RI Coll (BS) Elem Ed 1972; Masters Equivalency 1989; *cr:* Mendon Road Schl 4th Grd Tchr 1972-77; Cumberland Hill Schl 4th Grd Tchr 1977-81; B. F. Norton Schl 5th Grd Tchr 1981-84; St Patrick Pub Schl 5th Grd Tchr 1984-94; B. F. Norton Elem Schl 5th Grd Tchr 1994-; *ai:* RI Coll, Comm Coll of RI Cooperating Tchr; Hlth Curr, Rdng Texts, New Bldg Liason Comms; SCRAPS Parent-Tchr Group; Rdng Bee Organizer; NEA, Cumberland Tchr Assn 1972-; Calvin Presbyn Church, Amer Guild Eng Handbell Ringers 1985-, Choir 1984-, Worship Comm 1985-; *office:* B F Norton Elem Schl 364 Broad St Cumberland RI 02864

CLARK, GEORGE A.,JR., Biology Teacher; *b:* Weymouth, MA; *ed:* Bridgewater St Coll (BA) Bio 1971, (MED) Guidance Admin 1972; 45 Addl Grad Hrs Beyond Masters; *cr:* East Jr HS 7th-8th Grd Gen Sci Tchr 1971-82; Great Esker Park Summer Nature Prgm Dir 1976-; Weymouth HS Honors Bio Tchr 1982-; Weymouth Evening HS Dir 1985-89; *ai:* Ski Club Dir 1971-83; Outward Bound Club Coord 1971-83; Drivers Ed Tchr; NEA, MA Tchrs Assn & Weymouth Tchrs Assn 1971-, mem; MA Assn of Bio Tchrs 1993-, Mem; Korean War Veterans Comm 1992-; Apple Awd 1992 an Awd to Outstanding Tchrs Presented by The Quincy Patriot Ledger; *office:* Weymouth North HS 1051 Commercial St Weymouth MA 02189

CLARK, GREGORY L., 4th Grade Teacher; *b:* Pittsburgh, PA; *ed:* Erie Comm Coll (AS) Child Care 1984; Medaille Coll (BS) Elem Ed 1987; Working on Master Empire St; *cr:* Build Acad 6th Grd Tchr 1987-88; Olmsted 67 4th Grd Tchr 1988-; *ai:* Stu Cncl Adv; MACK Buffalo 1990-, Del.

CLARK, HELEN MADDEN, Fifth Grade Teacher; *b:* Altoona, PA; *w:* Raymond J. (dec); *c:* Michael Wm., Matthew R., Marjorie A. Thomas, Andrew F.; *ed:* Indiana Univ of PA (BSEd) Elem Ed 1953; 33 Addl Credit Hrs Elem Ed Frostburg Univ; *cr:* Penn Ave Schl 2nd Grd Tchr 1953-55; Cresoptown Elem Schl 2nd Grd Tchr 1966-68; St John Newmann Schl 5th Grd Tchr 1968-; *ai:* Chprsn of Math Dept; NCTM 1985-; NCEA 1975-; *office:* St John Neumann Schl 109 S Fayette St Cumberland MD 21502

CLARK, JAMES A., English Teacher; *b:* Rochester, NY; *ed:* Univ of Dubuque (BA) Eng 1968; Boston Coll (MA) Eng, Am Lit 1978; Increment Courses; Ed; Tech Prep; *cr:* Stoughton HS Eng Tchr 26 Yrs; *ai:* The Gathering Club Adv; MA Tchrs Assn 1970-; Stoughton STA 1970-, Negotiations Team; *home:* 1254 Bay Rd Stoughton MA 02072

CLARK, JAMES EDWARD, Guidance Cnslr & US Govt Tchr; *b:* New York City, NY; *m:* Brenda Jean; *c:* Chrishawn, Vanetta, Teri; *ed:* Andrews Univ Seminary (MDIV) Theology, Cnslng 1981; *cr:* Greater NY Conf of SDA Pastor 1992; Greater NY Acad Pastor, Guid 1995; *ai:* Adventist Yth for Better Living Spon 10 Yrs; Smithsonian, Natl Guid Tchr Assn 1994-; *office:* Greater New York Acad 4132 58th St Flushing NY 11377

CLARK, JOSEPH THEODORE, English Teacher; *b:* Washington, DC; *m:* Dawn Maria Reeves; *c:* Paige Elice, Austin Joseph; *ed:* Univ of MD (BS) Eng Ed 1974, (MED) Rdng 1979; *cr:* Northwestern HS Eng Tchr, Eng Intern 1974; Kent Jr HS Eng Tchr, Dept Chair 1975-76; Bowie HS Eng Tchr, Coord 1976-92; Calvert HS Eng Tchr, Jrnlsm Adv 1992-; *ai:* Yrbk, Newspaper Adv; Asst Cross Cntry Coach; Outdoor Track Coach; NEA, NCTE 1980-; Calvert Cty Edctrs Assn, ASCD 1992-; Agnes Meyer Outstdng Tchr Awd 1995; Prince George's Cty MD Outstdng Edctr Awd 1991; MD St Track Coaches Assn Cross Cntry Coach of Yr 1984; *office:* Calvert HS 600 Dares Beach Rd Prince Frederick MD 20678

CLARK, KAREN HALLAM, Spanish Teacher; *b:* Pittsburgh, PA; *m:* William W.; *c:* Ryan C., Lauren E.; *ed:* Baldwin Wallace Coll (BA) Span 1969; Coll of Mt St Joseph (MED) Rdng 1990; *cr:* Valley Forge HS Span Tchr 1969-81; Parma Sr HS Span Tchr 1982-; *ai:* OEA, NEA 1969-, OMLTA; PTA 1982-; Lake Erie Girl Scouts 1990-94; Jennings Scholar 1993-94; *office:* Parma Sr HS 6285 W 54th St Parma OH 44129

CLARK, KATHLEEN MULHERN, Prof of Foreign Lang & Lit; *b:* Philadelphia, PA; *m:* Robert L.; *c:* Matthew, Kelly; *ed:* Immaculata Coll (AB) Fr 1970; Villanova Univ (MA) Fr 1981; Univ Laval at Quebec 10 Credits; Post Grad Work Ecole Francaise des Attaches de Presse, Rassias Fnd Dartmouth Coll; *cr:* Great Vly HS Scndry Fr Tchr 1971-72; Conestoga HS Scndry Fr Tchr 1970-71, 1972-78; Immaculate Coll Instr 1973-89; Asst Prof Frgn Lang, Lits 1989-; *ai:* Dir Lang Lab; oral Proficiency Interviewer; Intnl Stud Stdnts; Coll Cncl; Core Coord Comm Co-Chair; Stu Acad Adv; Selection Comm Svc Medal; Stud Abroad Schlsp Test Admin; AATF 1970-, Exec Bd; Modern Lang Assoc Phila 1970-, Exec Cncl; AAUP 1973-, Exec Bd; AmCncl Tchng of Frgn Lang, Alliance Francaise 1970-; AA Univ Women 1995-; Immaculata Coll Alum 1971-, Class Rep; Immaculata Coll Assoc 1971-, Bd of Governors 1996; St Ann's R C Church 1972-; Who's Who of Amer Women 1993-94, 1995-; Pi Delta Phi; Lamda Iotq Tau; Pew Meml Trust Grant; Co-Designer of Core Curr in Ldrshp; *office:* Immaculata Coll 17 Faculty Ctr Immaculata PA 19345

CLARK, KIMBERLY BRENNAN, Social Studies Teacher; *b:* Boston, MA; *m:* Douglas; *ed:* Salem St Coll (BA) His 1993; McIntosh Coll (BA) Bus Mgmt; Univ of NH Cultural Anthropology; *cr:* Plymouth N Soc Stud Tchr 1993-94; Raymond HS Soc Stud Tchr 1994-; *ai:* 1998 & Peer Outreach Adv; Schl Improvement Prgm & Schl Comms; Phi Alpha Theta, Org Amer Historians 1993-; Nom Tc 1995 Raymond HS Stdnts; *office:* Raymond HS 45 Harriman Raymond NH 03077*

CLARK, LAWRENCE THOMAS,JR., Assistant Professor o Orange, NJ; *ed:* Slippery Rock Univ (BA) Ec 1979; KS St Univ (1984; Post-Doctoral Fellowship Ec Northwest Coll, Univ Assn NORCUS at Richland WA 1984-85; *cr:* Battelle Pacific Northw Research Economist 1984-85; NJ Dept of Labor Research Ec 1985-87; Expert Witness, Consultant Asst Prof of Ec 1988-; C Court Coll Asst Prof of Ec 1992-; *ai:* Moderator Delta Mu Delta H in Bus Admin; Bus Club Chprsn; Mem of Bus Advy Council; NAE 1984-; NJ Private Industry Council 1988-, Bd of Dirs; South Jers Plan Coalition 1988-, Exec Comm; Numerous Awds, Grants, Fell Pub Over 100 Reports, Articles; Book Pub on Casino Gambling Georgian Court Coll 900 Lakewood Ave Lakewood NJ 08701

CLARK, LINDA DARUS, 7th & 8th Grd Soc Stud Tchr; *b:* Cl OH; *m:* Gary C.; *c:* Kevin, Christopher; *ed:* Cleveland St Univ (1982; *cr:* Saint Thomas More Soc Stud Tchr 1989-; *ai:* NCSS 19 Cncl of Soc Stud 1989-, Historian; Greater Cleveland Cncl of S 1989-, Pres; Natl Cncl for His Ed 1992-; Disney & McDonalds An Awd 1995-96; Television Channel 8 Feature Tchr 1995; McGi Grant 1992; *office:* St Thomas More Schl 4180 N Amber Dr Brook 44144*

CLARK, LYNN LAUX, Physics Teacher; *b:* Williamsport, PA; *m:* Ladendecker; *c:* Tyler; *ed:* IL Inst of Tech (BS) Physics 1972 Internat Coll (MS) Sci Tchng 1985; 2 Courses at Univ of MA in U Pgm; *cr:* Westfield Pub Schls Tchr 1972-; *ai:* Stans Steering Comm Support & Involvment Comm Chair; Westfield Ed Assn 1972-; M Assn 1972-; NEA 1972-; West St Soccer League 1975-, Pres; Westf Soccer 1994-, Coach; Univ of Chicago Outstdng Tchr Awd 1995; *h* Farnham Ln Westfield MA 01085

CLARK, LYNN S., English Teacher & Coordinator; *b:* Atlantic C *m:* Roy; *c:* Christopher, Bryan (dec), Bradley; *ed:* Glassboro St Co Elem Ed 1968; *cr:* Hamilton Twp Schls 6th Grd Tchr 1968-74, 5th G 1978-82; Wm Davies MS 8th Grd Eng Tchr 1975-78, 1984-, Co Dept 1988-; *ai:* Adv Natl Jr Honor Soc; Grad, Dinner Dance Planning Team; Hamilton Twp Ed Assn 1968-, VP, Sec 15 Yrs; NJE 1968-; NCTE 1993-; Negotiations Chr 1994-; March Dimes 1974 Events Chprsn, Vol of Week; Northfield Cultural Comm 1992-; Cle Clinic 1974-, Parent Coord; Telethon/ March of Dimes Comm 199 1994; Grant Stud Bard Coll Seminar; *office:* William Davies MS Ave & Rt 40 Mays Landing NJ 08330*

CLARK, MARION J., Guidance Counselor; *b:* Totowa, NJ; *m:* Ja *ed:* Paterson St Coll (BA) Jr HS 1964; Seton Hall Univ (MA) A Supervision 1973; 45 Hrs Stu Prsnl Svcs William Paterson Coll; Schl Admin Jersey City St; *cr:* Meml Schl Grd 8 Math Tchr 1 Brooklawn Jr HS Grd 8 Eng, Soc Stud Tchr 1965-69; Parsippany 10 Eng Tchr 1969-70, Grds 9-12 Guid Cnslr 1970; *ai:* SChlsp NEA, NJEA, MCEA, PTHEA 1965-; PDK Montclair St Chptr 1974 Parsippany Chptr 1972-, VP 1972-73; NJCA 1973-; NJACES; NJ Kiwanis of Parisppany 1992-, Bd of Dirs, Charter; Parsippany Distngd Svc Awd Outstdng Edctr 1988; *home:* 590 Lynne Dr Morris NJ 07950

CLARK, MARSHA MUSICK, English Teacher; *b:* Latrobe, Robert M.; *ed:* Grove City Coll (BA) Eng 1963; 36 Grad H Northwestern Univ; *cr:* Norwin Sr HS Eng Tchr 32 Yrs; *ai:* NEA Tchrs Assn 1964-; Heritage United Meth Church 1991-, Lib Bd; Norwin Sr HS 251 Mcmahon Dr North Huntingdon PA 15642

CLARK, MARY DONALDSON, Biological Sciences Teac Camden, NJ; *m:* Douglas C.; *c:* Adam, Matthew, Tyler; *ed:* Rosemo (BA) Bio 1993; *cr:* Lower Cape May Regnl HS Sci Tchr 1993-; *ai:* S Adv; Marching Band Asst; NJEA 1993-; NJ Sci Tchrs Assn, Natl Sc Assn 1995-; *office:* Lower Cape May Reg HS 687 Route 9 Cape N 08204

CLARK, MATT CHARLES, Social Studies Teacher; *b:* Freeport, Stacey Bertsch; *c:* Jacob Xavier; *ed:* Syracuse Univ (BA) Soc S Sociology 1991; 18 Credits at Dowling Coll; *cr:* Miller Place HS S Tchr 1994-; *ai:* Jr HS Coach Boys Soccer, Boys, Girls Bsktbl; Cl Debate; Long Island Cncl for the Soc Stud 1994-; NYS Cnsl for S 1995-; *office:* Miller Place HS 15 Memorial Dr Miller Place NY 1

CLARK, MELANIE S., Third & Sixth Grade Teacher; *b:* Baltimor *m:* Keith; *c:* Thomas, Michelle, Amanda, Benjamin; *ed:* Roberts W Coll (BA) Elem Ed 1977; SUNY at Geneseo (MS) Spcl Ed 1981; Line Childrens Home 5th-9th Grd Spcl Ed Tchr 1977-80; Monroe B Sub Spcl Ed Tchr 1980-81; St Lawrence-Lewis BOCES Tchr of Emot Hand 1981-84; Rainbow Chrstn Acad Elem Tchr 1986-; *ai:* Wesleyan Church 1982-, Tchr; 4-H 1987-, Ldr; *home:* 181 Poll Canton NY 13617

CLARK, NORMAN GRANT, Chemistry Teacher; *b:* Boston, M Mary Ellen Steer; *c:* Thomas Hunter II, Kevin Robert; *ed:* North Univ (BS) Bio, Ed 1983, (MED) Sci Ed 1986; 120 Hrs Trng Microsc Techniques, Merrimack Coll; *cr:* Nauset Regnl HS Bio Tchr 1 Alpine Ski & Sports Corporate Trng Coord 1986-91; Pentucket Re Sci, Chem Tchr 1991-; Northern Essex Comm Coll Part-time Che 1995-; *ai:* Sci Fair Coord 1991-; MASCD 1995-, Peter Farrelli Aw 1994-; NEA; MTA; *office:* Pentucket Regional HS 22 Main S Newbury MA 01985*

CLARK, RANDALL HOWARD, Music Director; *b:* Cincinnati, Melinda J.; *c:* Ryan, Robert; *ed:* Morehead St Univ (BME) Music E (MME) Music Ed 1976; *cr:* Univ of Breckridge Music Dir 1975-7 Bremen Local Schls Music Dir 1976-; *ai:* HS Marching, Concert Ba Choir; Jr HS Band; OH Music Ed Assn 1976-, St Adjucicated Event 12 Yrs; Natl Band Assn 1976-; Phi Beta Mu 1992-; Amer Schl Ba Assn 1992-; St Paul United Church of Christ 1993-95, Deacon; Alpha Sinfonia 1972-; Pi Kappa Lamda Music Honorary 1976- Bremen Schls Jennings Prgm Rep; OH Music Ed Assn Dist Pres; A Pub; 18 Superior Rating Band Performance St Level Band Compe *home:* 136 Bear Dr New Bremen OH 45869*

CLARK, ROBERT DONALD, Biology Teacher; *b:* Erie, PA; *m:* M Timashenka; *ed:* Edinboro Univ of PA (BS) Scndry Ed Bio 1968, Scndry Ed Bio 1974; Attnd FL St Univ, Gannon Univ, PA St Univ, Univ; *cr:* Penncrest Schl Dist Bio Tchr 1968-; Edinboro Univ Co-Operating Tchr 1972-; *ai:* NEA, PSEA 1968-; ASIH 1983-; Phi Kappa 1991-; Penncrest Ed Assn 1968-, Pres 1986-87; Penncrest Mngmt 1990-; Penncrest Rep to NEA 1983-86; Herpetologists' Lea 1994-; *office:* Penncrest Schl Dist RD #1 Mook Rd Saegertown PA

CLARK, RODNEY LYNN, Biology Teacher; *b:* Cedar Rapids, Christine McCaffrey-Clark; *ed:* IA St Univ (BS) Bio 1988; 15 Addl Hrs Towards ME at Fitchburg St Coll; *cr:* US Peace Corp Africa V 1989-91; Hillside Jr High Sci Tchr 1991-92; Merrimack HS Bi 1992-; *ai:* Earth Svc Corp Club, Acad Decathalon Adv; NEA 1991-; Merrimack HS 38 Mcelwain St Merrimack NH 03054*

, ROGER W., Elementary PE Teacher; *b:* Utica, NY; *m:* Rita L.; L., Elizabeth A.; *ed:* St Bonaventure Univ (BS) Ed & Sci 1967; of NY at Cortland Grad Stud 31 Hrs in Hlth Ed; *cr:* Brookfield Tchr & Coach 1967-68; Mount Markham Cenral Tchr & Coach Richfield Springs Cntrl Tchr, Coach & Ath Dir 1971-74; Lyons l Tchr & Coach 1975-; *ai:* Boys Var Track Coach; Intramural Dir; del NY St Tchrs Retirement System; NYSUT 1967-; Lyons Tchrs 5-, VP 1980; St Michaels Roman Cath Church 1975-; Coach of Yr / Boys Track 1993; *home:* 22 Cherry St Lyons NY 14489

, ROSS JAMES, Soc Studies Tchr & Dept Chrpsn; *b:* Washington, Christina Manos; *ed:* Amherst Coll (BA) Psych 1981; *cr:* en Schl Asst Dir of Admissions 1982-83, Tchr & Coach 1982-87; hl Tchr & Coach 1988-, Soc Stud Dept Chrpsn 1992-; *ai:* Yrbk rls Soccer Coach; Assn of Ind MD Schls, Acad Adv Cncl 4, Bd of Dir 1995; NCSS 1992-; ASCD 1993-; MD Assn 1995-; nd MD Schls 1991; Assn of Ind Schls of Greater WA 1992; *office:* hl 10601 Falls Rd Potomac MD 20854*

, STEPHEN LYNN, 7th Grd Lang Arts Teacher; *b:* Augusta, ME; Davies; *c:* Kevin, Kristopher, Korey; *ed:* Plymouth St Coll (BED) FL Atlantic Univ (MED) Eng Ed 1971; +30 Credit Hrs Beyond *cr:* Barre Town Elem Schl 7th & 8th Grd Lang Arts Tchr 1966-; Adv; Staff Dev Rep; Svc Club Adv; NEA 1966-; Credit Union es 2 Terms; Barre Town Tchrs Assoc VP 3 Terms; VT Tchrs 1995-; R 1 Box 28 East Montpelier VT 05651*

, SUSAN, Music Department Chair; *b:* Cleveland, OH; *ed:* Notre ll of OH (BA) Music 1966; Bowling Green St Univ (MM) Music onducting 1981; Univ of UT at Salt Lake City, Univ of Dayton, rroll Univ, Baldwin Wallace Coll Conservatory of Music, d St Univ Addl Credit Hrs; *cr:* Notre Dame Acad Choir Dir, Tchr Cleveland Cntrl Cath HS Choir Dir, Tchr 1970-74; Regina HS ept Chair, Choir Dir 1974-89; Cleveland Cntrl Cath HS Music air, Choir Dir 1989-94; Elyria Cath HS Music Dept Chair, Choir -; *ai:* Dept Chair Comm; Extra Curr Music Ensembles Adv, Dir; Cath Church Music Dir; MENC 1968-, 25 Yr Awd; ACDA 1967-; 94-; Diocese of Cleveland Music Commission 1977-, Sec 1979-81, c Awd; Ed for Aesthetic Awareness Grant 1977-79; Tchr of Yr Awd *fice:* Elyria Catholic HS 725 Gulf Rd Elyria OH 44035

, SUSAN JESSIE, Family & Consumer Sci Tchr; *b:* Middletown, ames E.; *c:* D'Artagnan, Jennifer, Katelin, Shannon; *ed:* Univ of Ed 1977; Eastern CT St Univ (MS) Human Relations 1987; *cr:* S Home Ec Tchr 1977-81; Windham High Food Svc Instr 1983-89; High Family, Consumer Scis Tchr 1989-; *ai:* FHA, Home Ec Occupations Club, St Adv; Fac Cncl; Amer Assn of Family, er Scis 1977-, Grant Awd; CT Ed Assn 1989-; Natl Assn of Young 1994-; Lighthouse Schl Bd 1985-, Fundraiser Chair; Girl Scouts Cookie Chprsn; Voc Improvement Awd; Excl in Ed Honorable 2 Times; *office:* Coventry HS 78 Ripley Hill Rd Coventry CT

, THOMAS C., History Teacher; *b:* Urbana, IL; *ed:* Messiah Coll s 1988; Working Towards Masters PA St Univ in Amer Stud; *cr:* csburg Area Sr HS Tchr 1988-89; Chrstn Schl of York Tchr 1989-; na Dept Tech Adv; Bsbl & Mock Trial Team Coach; Continental a 1986-91, Asst Dir 1990; *office:* Christian Schl Of York 907 ar Rd York PA 17404

, WALTER T., English Teacher; *b:* Potsdam, NY; *m:* Lynn Moore; elle; *ed:* SUNY at Potsdam (BA) Eng Ed 1970; Grad Stud nt Cert 7th-12th Grd Eng Ed; *cr:* Massena HS 7-12th Grd Eng Tchr *i:* AFT 1970-, Pres, Pride of Union 1988, 1990; NYSUT 1970-, assena Fed of Tchrs 1970-; NYSUT Cadre, Shared Decision Schl Reform; Massena Rescue 1974-, Chief 1979-81, ships Outstanding Leadership Awd; Town of Massena EMS , Advy Bd; *home:* 6 Prospect Cir Massena NY 13662

, ZENDE LARMAR, Mathematics Teacher; *b:* Scotland Neck, Kean Coll of NJ (BA) Elem Ed 1977, (MA) Rdng Specialist 1983; St Math Cert Prgm; *cr:* Hillside Bd of Ed Tchr 1979-; Passaic Cty j Rdng Instr 1988-93; *ai:* Minorities in Engrng Instr; Rainbows or; NEA 1979-; Alpha Delta Kappa, Chaplain; Hillside Ed Assn P, Pres; Lions Club 1994-, Corresponding Sec; Alpha Kappa Alpha rammateus, Fin Sec; Tchr of Yr 1990; Masters Thesis Pub; *home:* h St Newark NJ 07103

APEL, JOANNE M., 7th Grade Teacher; *b:* Lowell, MA; *m:* . Apel; *c:* Alexis; *ed:* Boston Univ (BS) Ed, Psych 1971; Lesley A) Cmptr Ed 1982; *cr:* Vestal Schl Dist Non-Graded 2-8 Grd Math 71-73; Amherst Schl Dist 8 Grd Math Tchr 1973-82; Lowell Schls d tchr 1986-88, 7-8 Grd Math Tchr 1988-; *ai:* United Tchrs of 1986-; NCTM 1988-; *office:* Bartlett MS 79 Wannalancit St Lowell 54

E, DARLENE ANN, Nursing Instructor; *b:* CLeveland, OH; *m:* riffith; *ed:* Univ of Akron (BSN) Nrsng 1990; Kent St Univ (MSN) Functional Ed 1992; Fairview Gen Hosp Nrsng Deg 1979; cal in England, Exploration of Nrsng in the Hlth Care, Nrsng Ed in Kingdom 1989; 24 CEU's Every Two Yrs to Maintain OH Nrsng ; *cr:* Para Comm Gen Hosp Staff Nurse 1979-85, O R Circulator , Asst Head Nurse Surgery 1986-89, Pre Admission Testng Coord , Charge Nurse Surgery 1991-92; Ursuline Coll Nrsng Instr 1992-; or of Sigma Theka Taw Intnl, Ioka Psi Chptr Newsletter; Vol for Nrsng 1994-; Amer Nurses Assn, OH Nurses Assn, Greater nd Nurses Assn 1992-; Sigma Theta Tau 1988-, Linnea Henderson xcl Awd 1992; Ehlers-Damlos Natl Fnd 1995-; Ehlers-Damlos Natl OH Branch 1996, Branch Org 1996-; Nightingale Soc 1990; Excl in Teaching Awd 1994; Merit Level Stipend Awd 1994; Tchng d Soph Level 1995; *home:* 10561 Aaron Dr Parma OH 44130

E, ILENE IDELL, English Teacher; *b:* Pittsburgh, PA; *m:* Daniel aime Eiler; *ed:* Bugler Comm Coll (AA) Gen Stud 1990; Slippery niv (BS) Scndry Ed, Eng 1992; Attnd FL Jr Coll Practical Nrsng ost Bac Grad Schl Ed Courses; *cr:* N Allegheny Schls Eng, Jrnlsm *ai:* Newspaper Adv; AFT 1994-; Sigma Tau Delta, Delta Kappa Pi Phi Theta Kappa 1989-; *office:* North Allegheny HS 350 land Rd Pittsburgh PA 15237

KE, KAREN-CHRISTINE FELICITY, Third Grade Teacher; *ed:* land Univ (BS) Ed 1987; Brooklyn Coll (MA) Scndry Ed Lit 1991-; d Instrl Tech Prgm Under NY Inst of Tech MA; *cr:* John JaY Coll al Justice Inmate Ed Prgm Queens Correctional fac for Men GED Yr; Icicle Seafood Seward Fisheries Packer in Neichirel Eggroom 1 d in Icicle Eggroom 1 Yr; P.S. 91 Tchr 3rd Grd 8 Yrs; *ai:* Brooklyn ncl; Edctrs for Gateway; Amer Canoe Assn; Sebago Canoe Club; YSUT 1988-; Brooklyn Rdng Cncl 1994-.*

KE, KEITH, Counselor; *b:* Panama City, Panama; *m:* Kathleen lez; *c:* Jahni, Amanda, Lisa; *ed:* NC A&T (BS) PE 1966; Queens UNY (MED) Cnslr 1972; Boston Univ (PHD) Counseling Psych *r:* Barnstable Schls Cnslr 1989-; *ai:* Girls Var Bsktbl Head Coach MA Tchr Assn 1989-; NAACP 1975-; Bd Cape Cod Hospital 1983-; logist NBA Rookie Orientation Prgm 1986-92; *office:* Barnstable Barnstable-Osterville Marstons Mills MA 02648*

CLARKE, LINDA J., Adjunct Prof of Philosophy; *b:* Melrose, MA; *ed:* Univ of NH (BA) Lit 1988; Bank Street Coll (MED) Ed 1990; Columbia Univ Tchrs Coll (EDD) Philosophy & Ed 1993; *cr:* Kate Millett Artists & Writers Colony Co-Founder 1983-93; Ulster Cty Comm Coll Prison Ed Prgm 1993-95; Mount Saint Mary Coll Philosophy Prof 1993-; *ai:* Philosophy of Ed Soc 1994-; Essay in On The Lores Magazine Spring 1996; Included in Best Sockport Scholars Conf 1995; Best Paper Women & Soc Conf 1994 & 1995; *home:* 6 Hassel Pl New Paltz NY 12561

CLARKE, MADELINE FLEMING, 6th Grd English & Reading Tchr; *b:* Quincy, MA; *m:* Clyde C.; *ed:* Mt St Mary Coll (BA) Elem Ed 1968; Bridgewate St Coll (MED) Spec Needs 1979; *cr:* Willard Elem Schl Third Grd Tchr 1968-78; Montclair Elem Schl First, Third Grd Tchr 1979-87; Atlantic MS Sixth Grd Tchr 1988-; *ai:* Comm Svc Stu Adv for Long Island Hosp for Terminally Ill 1990; Adv for Intnl Photo Exch, Photography Wkshp 1994-95; Adv for Tchng Tolerance, Lifestyle, Cultures Prgm 1996; Adv for Stu, Sr Citizen Pen Pal Prgm 1994; NEA, MTA 1968-; QEA 1968-, Rep 1974-75, 1982-83; Awded Numerous Arist in Resident Grants MA Cultural Cncl; Consultant with Young Arts Prgm Wang Ctr for Performing Arts, Boston MA; *office:* Atlantic MS 86 Hollis Ave Quincy MA 02171

CLARKE, MARY HAWLEY, Social Studies Teacher; *b:* Warsaw, NY; *m:* Stephan P.; *c:* Erin Elizabeth; *ed:* SUNY Coll at Geneseo (BSEd) Soc Stud Ed 1966, (MSEd) Soc Stud Ed 1970; Credit Hrs at SUNY Coll at Brockport; *cr:* Spencerport Cntrl Schl Dist HS Soc Stud Tchr 1966-; *ai:* Spencerport Tchrs Assn Schlsp Comm; AFT; NY St United Tchrs; Natl Soc DAR 1994-; Gen Soc of Mayflower Descendants 1996; *office:* Spencerport HS 2707 Spencerport Rd Spencerport NY 14559

CLARKE, STEPHAN PAUL, High School English Teacher; *b:* Waterton, NY; *m:* Mary Elizabeth Hawley; *c:* Erin Elizabeth; *ed:* SUNY Coll at Geneseo (BSEd) Scndry Eng Ed 1966; OH St Univ at Bowling Green (MA) Speech 1968; Post-Grad Hrs OH St Univ at Bowling Green, SUNY Coll at Brockport; *cr:* US Navy Reserve Lieutenant, Staff of Commander 1969-70; Spencerport Cntrl Schls HS Eng Tchr 1970-; *ai:* Coord Xerox AWD Hum, Soc Sci; AFT; NY ST United Tchrs 1970-; NY ST Eng Cncl 1975-, Conf Speaker 1974; NCTE 1975-, Conf Speaker 1978; Mystery Writers of Amer 1978-, Edgar Allan Poe Spec Awd 1985; US Naval Inst Life Mem; Dorothy L. Sayers Soc 1978-, Conf Speaker 1985; Stratford Shakespearean Festival Fnd 1975-; Natl Soc of Sons of Amer Revolution; Crimes & Clues Prentice Hall 1978; Lord Peter Wimsey Companion Mysterious Press 1985; Various Articles Pub; Biogs Listed Who's Who in Amer, Contemporary Authors, Who's Who in Amer Ed, Who's Who in the East; *office:* Spencerport HS 2707 Spencerport Rd Spencerport NY 14559

CLARK-KEVAN, MARGERY ANN (CLARK), Biology & Chemistry Teacher; *b:* Bethesda, MD; *m:* Jeffrey M.; *c:* Meghan, Katherine, Joshua; *ed:* Chatham Coll (BS) Bio 1980; Franklin Pierce HS Bio Cert, Ed Cert 1991; *cr:* Pelham Meml MS 8th Grd Sci Tchr 1982-87; Conant HS Bio, Chem Tchr 1987-; *ai:* Var Swim Team Coac 1987-; Envirothon Coach 1992-; Class of '90 Adv; NEA 1982-; Vol of Yr Amer Red Cross CPR Instruc 1982; *office:* Conant HS 3 Conant Way Jaffrey NH 03452

CLARKSON, LUANN DAVIS, Spanish Teacher; *b:* Newark, NJ; *m:* Donald G.; *c:* Patricia, Leigh Ann; *ed:* Seton Hall Univ (BA) Span 1976; 42 Addl Credits; *cr:* Salt Brook Schl Tchr 1976-85; Marlboro MS Tchr 1985-87; Howell Twp Schl Tchr 1987-; *ai:* NEA, NJEA 1976-; FLENJ 1980-.

CLARK-WARNE, BRENDA RUTH, Track & Cross Country Coach; *b:* Grand Haven, MI; *m:* Nicholas; *c:* Christopher, Sarah; *ed:* Eastern MI Univ (BS) Microbiology & Biochemistry 1984; Purdue Univ (MS) Molecular Bio 1986; Ed Cert 1988; *cr:* Crawfordvill HS Sci Tchr 1988-90; Exter HS Sci Tchr 1990-92; Methuen HS Track & Cross Cntry Coach 1991-; *ai:* Methuen HS Track & Cross Cntry Coach; Andover HS Winter Track Coach; *office:* Methuen HS 1 Ranger Rd Methuen MA 01844

CLARY, RHONDA OWENS, Sixth Grade Teacher; *b:* Cuba, NY; *m:* Kevin R.; *c:* John P., Emily M.; *ed:* SUC at Geneseo (BS) Elem Ed 1983, (MS) Elem Ed 1993; *cr:* Pavilion CS Sub Tchr 1984-87; Elba CS Sub Tchr 1984-87; Attic CS Sub Tchr 1984-87; Pavilion Cntrl Schl Sixth Grd Tchr 1988-; *ai:* MS Comm; Lang Arts Framework, Compact for LearningComms; Spelling Bee Coord; NCTM, NCSS 1993-94; AFT, NYSUT 1988-; Friends of Lib 1992-; BSA 1992-, Parent Vol, Ldr Asst; PTO 1990-, Treas 1994-95; *office:* Pavilion Central Schl 7014 Big Tree Rd Pavilion NY 14525

CLARY, WILLIAM ARTHUR, Art & Theatre Teacher; *b:* Sharon, PA; *m:* Carol Jean Pancione; *c:* Scott Allen, Todd Allen; *ed:* Youngstown Univ (BSBA) Mrktg & Satistics 1964, (BSEd) Art 1966; Slippery Rock Univ (MAEd) Elem Guid 1970; Attnd Point Park Coll, Art Inst, Ithica Coll, CLO; *cr:* Sharon Steel Corp Mrktg & Statistics Analy 1962-64; Freelance Art & Theatre Comm Art & Theatre 1964-66; Sharon City Schls Tchr 1966-; *ai:* Drama, Spring Musical & Crisis Theatre Dir; NEA, PSEA & STA 1966-, Treas; ETA Tap 1970-; ETC 1970-; BSA 1975-, Advy Bd; *home:* 5090 Schwartz Ln Sharpsville PA 16150

CLAUS, LARRY E., Science & Cmptr Sci Tchr; *b:* Bellevue, OH; *m:* Mary Elva Trevino; *c:* Katherine, Lauren; *ed:* Bowling Green St Univ (BS) Chem 1970; Penn St Nuclear Concepts 1978; Individualized Instruction 1980, Project Teach 1977, Desktop Publishing 1992; OH Northern Univ Chem Inst; Ashland Univ Grad Course Work 1983; Attnd Miami Univ of OH Terrific Sci Prgms Inst Tchng Sci with Toys 1992; *cr:* Bellevue Sr HS Physics, Chem, Phys Sci Tchr 1970; North Coll Hill Schl Dist Physics, Chem, Phys Sci Tchr 1970-72; St Joseph Elem Schl Jr High Sci Tchr 1973-75; Bellevue Sr HS Physics, Phys Sci I & II, CHem, Chem II, Intro to Comp, Cmptr Programming, Comp Applications 1975-; *ai:* Cmptr Coord & Tech; Independent Stud Tchr; Tech Comm 1994-; NEA, OEA Bellvue Ed Assn 1971-; NSTA 1971-, Life Mem; Amer Nuclear Sci Tchrs Assn 1978-; Sci Ed Cncl of OH 1979-, Charter Mem; Sci Cncl at Heidelberg 1975-95; Firelands Area Physics Alliance 1991-; Amer Assn of Physics Tchrs; OH Section Amer Assn of Physics Tchrs; Flat Rock Comm Cncl 1975-83, Sec, Pres 1978; Organ Historical Soc 1993-; SECO Dist II Rep 1994-; Main Speaker at SECO Conventions 1979; Energy Ed Presenter Leadership of The 80's Conf 1981; Letter of Recommendation from Dr Wm Jester, Penn St to Mac Millan Publ for Tech Writer; OH Edison's Tchr Seminar Dinner Speaker 1978; BGSU Energy Wkshp Presenter, Tchr Panal 1981; Ashland Univ Taught Cmptr Course; Adult Ed Tchr; Presented Local Inservice on Cmptrs & Software Helped Implement Grant; *office:* Bellevue Sr HS 200 Oakland Ave Bellevue OH 44811

CLAUS, MICHELLE ROVNER, Math Teacher; *b:* Waterloo, IA; *m:* Joseph H.; *c:* Christopher, Jonathan; *ed:* Rosary Hill Coll (BA) Elem Ed 1972; Canisius Coll (MS) Elem Ed & Rdng 1976; Univ of Buffalo Grad Work; *cr:* Hamburg Jr HS 7th Grd Math Tchr 1977-78; Springville GICSD 8th Grd Math Tchr 1978-; *ai:* MS Stu Cncl Adv; JV Girls Soccer Coach; Dist Staff Dev & Dist Shared Decision Making Comms; AFT 1978-; NYSUT 1978-, Treas & Bldg Rep; NYS Curr 1995-; Springville Yth Inc 1991-, Soccer Coach; Hamburg YASC 1992-, Soccer Coach; Springville CSD Tchr of Yr Awd 1985; *office:* Griffith Institute CSD Schl 267 Newman St Springville NY 14141*

CLAUSEN, ANGLEA COMETTO-BARTRAM, Spanish Teacher; *b:* Buffalo, NY; *m:* George Roeser; *c:* Eric Bartram, Patrick Bartram, Carla, Andrea; *ed:* Rosary Hill Daeman Coll (BA) Span 1973; Univ of NY at Buffalo (MED) Span Ed 1977; Univ of Valencia Spain; Certified Eng & Fr Tchr; *cr:* Akron Cntrl HS Span Tchr 1973; East Aurora MS Span Tchr 1973-74; Depew HS Span Tchr 1974-75, Eng Tchr 1975-85, Eng & Span Tchr 1985-86, Span Tchr 1986-; *ai:* Span Club Adv-Annual Trips to Mexico; Honor Soc Adv; Bldg Cncl Mem; NYSUT 1974-; Depew Tchrs 1975-, Tchr of Yr 1989-90; WNYFLEC, NYSAFLT; Saint Johns Church 1974-, Eucharistic Minister, Rel Ed Instr, Confirmation Facilitator; Cub Scouts 1984-88, Den Mother, Fund Raising Chprsn; *office:* Depew HS 5201 Transit Rd Depew NY 14043

CLAUSS, DEBRA LYN, Spanish Teacher; *b:* Marion, OH; *m:* William B.; *c:* Amy, Bryan, Betsy; *ed:* OH St Univ (BS) Span, Fr Ed 1977; Post Grad Stud Foreign Lang Ed Ashland Univ, Cmptr Lit Schl Stud Cncl of OH; *cr:* Marion Cath HS Span, Fr Tchr 1977-80; Mount Gilead HS Span, Fr Tchr 1980-; *ai:* Span Club Adv; Venture Comm Chprsn, St Dept Liaison; OH Ed Dept Tchr Scholar; Block Schedule Spokesperson, Presenter; OH Foreign Lang Assn, OEA, NEA 1980-; Ashland Foreign Lang Alliance 1991-, Co-Founder; OH HS Ath Assn 1979-, Class 1 Vlybl Ofcl; Marion Vlybl Assn 1979-, Rules Interpretor; Pine Lakes Golf Club 1982-, Women's Club Champ; Co-Author, Recipient Effective Schls Grant, Venture Capital Grant, Venture Friends Grant; Natl Milken Tchr of Yr Awd; *home:* 3880 Shaw Ln Cardington OH 43315*

CLAUSS, SANDRA RYAN, Second Grade Teacher; *b:* Bristol, CT; *m:* Wesley Joseph; *c:* Mark; *ed:* Cntrl Comm St Univ (BA) Elem Ed 1967, (MS) Rdng 1969; 6th Yr 1990; *cr:* Northeast Schl First Grd Tchr 1967-74; Greene Hills Schl Pre-Kndgtn Tchr 1975-77; O'Connell Schl Kndgtn Tchr 1978; Edgewood Schl Kndgtn, 2nd Grd Tchr 1979-; *ai:* BFT 1979-; Second & Third Graders Lit & Cooking After Schl Prgm Grant; *office:* Edgewood Schl 345 Mix St Bristol CT 06010

CLAY, ETTA STEIN, English Teacher; *b:* Baltimore, MD; *m:* Crawford; *c:* Jeffrey, Mitchell; *ed:* Towson St Univ (BS) Ed 1963; Loyola Univ (MED) Ed 1975; *cr:* Southern HS Eng Tchr 1963-81; Dunbar HS Eng Tchr 1981-; *ai:* Courtesy Fund, Mid Sts, Attendance Comms; Proofreader Newspaper; Balto Tchrs Union; Synagogue Sisterhood 1980-; MADD 1990-; *office:* Paul L. Dunbar HS 1400 Orleans St Baltimore MD 21231

CLAY, JOYCE HOLMES, 7th Grd Sci, 8th Grd Rdng Tchr; *b:* Youngstown, OH; *m:* Russell Thomas; *c:* Thomas, Tricia, Erin; *ed:* Youngstown St Univ (BS) Elem Ed 1980, (MS) Rdng Specialist 1985; Univ of UT Learning Disabled, BD; Classes on Spec Needs; Working on Tchng in Quality Classroom; *cr:* Trumbull Cty Schls Sub Tchr 1980; Champion Local Schls Fifth, Sixth Grd Tchr 1980-82; Newton Falls Schls SLD Tutor, Tchr 1982-93, 7th Grd Sci, 8th Grd Rdng Tchr 1993-; *ai:* AFT; NFCTA 1982-; Nom Golden Apple Awd for Spec Ed 3 Yrs; *office:* Newton Falls Exempted Vlg Schl 907 Milton Blvd Newton Falls OH 44444*

CLAY, SCOTT LEE, 7th & 8th Grd Science Teacher; *b:* Reading, PA; *m:* Luanne Evelyn Kern; *c:* Katie Ellen, Heather Anne; *ed:* Kutztown Univ (BS) Bio & General Sci 1965, (MED) Bio 1968; *cr:* Tulpenocken Area Schls 7th & 8th Grd General Sci Tchr & Coord of Gifted 1965-; *ai:* Stu Assistance Prgm; Model Rocket Club Adv; NEA, PSEA, TEA 1965-; Heidelberg Cemetery Assn Bd 1987-, Sec, Treas; Saint Pauls USG Church Consistory 1965-78; Tulpenocken Area Schl Tchr of Yr Nom 1986; Berks Cty Intermediate Unit Blue Ribbon Awd for Outstanding Contribution to Career Ed Prgms 1985; *home:* 1000 Conrad Weiser Pkwy Womelsdorf PA 19567

CLAY, SUSAN GEITGEY, Chemistry Teacher; *b:* Atlanta, GA; *c:* Julie Anne, Victoria L.; *ed:* Univ of Toledo (BS) Chem 1971, (MED) Educl Statistics 1987; Tchr Cert 1979-80; *cr:* Evergreen HS Sci Tchr 1980-88; Cuyahoga Hills Boys Schl Sci Tchr 1988-92; Maple Hghts HS Chem Tchr 1992-; *ai:* After Schl Tutoring; NSTA 1981-; NEA, OEA 1980-; SECO 1986-; Order of Eastern Stars 1981-, Worthy Matron; US Figure Skating Assn 1989-; *office:* Maple Heights HS 5500 Clement Ave Maple Heights OH 44137

CLAYPOOLE, JOAN LOUISE, Fine Arts Teacher; *b:* Youngstown, OH; *ed:* Youngstown St Univ (BFA) Drama, Theatre K-12 1991; *cr:* Ursuline HS Fine Arts Tchr, Dir of Theatre, Forensics 1991-; *ai:* ITS Spon; Theatre Dept is Listed in Who's Who Among HS Prgms; *office:* Ursuline HS 750 Wick Ave Youngstown OH 44505

CLAYS, MICHELE LASALA, Art Teacher; *b:* New Brunswick, NJ; *m:* Eric; *cr:* Valley Rd Elem Schl Art Tchr 1989-90; Washington Elem Schl Art Tchr 1990-91; South River MS Tchr of Spcl Ed 1991-92, Art Tchr 1992-; *ai:* Newspaper Adv; Project Discovery Comm; NJEA 1991-; NEA 1991-; NJAE 1992-; SREA 1992; *office:* South River MS Thomas St South River NJ 08882

CLAYTON, BARBARA ANN, Special Education Teacher; *b:* Jersey City, NJ; *m:* Brian Keith; *ed:* Ocean Cty Coll (AA) Lbrl Arts 1988; Ball St Univ (BA) Deaf Ed 1992; *cr:* Howell HS Spec Ed Tchr 1993-; *ai:* Asst Girls Gymnastics, Spring Track Coach; NEA, NJEA 1993-; *office:* Howell HS 405 Squankum-Yellowbrook Rd Farmingdale NJ 07727

CLAYTON, BETTY LEE, First Grade Teacher; *b:* Syracuse, IN; *ed:* Manchester Coll (BS) Elem Ed 1972; *cr:* Paulding Elem 1st Grd Tchr 27 Yrs; *ai:* Paulding Ed Assn 1969-; OH Ed Assn 1969-; NEA 1969-; *home:* 4333 Evard Rd Fort Wayne IN 46835

CLAYTON, BUDDY, Math Teacher; *b:* Long Branch, NJ; *c:* Kyle, Kieran; *ed:* Montclair St Coll (BA) Math 1974; *cr:* Shore Regnl HS Math Tchr 1974-84; West Point Military Acad Math Tchr 1984-90; Holmdel HS Math Tchr 1990-; *ai:* Frosh, JV Soccer, Girls Frosh Soccer; Head Track Coach Boys, Girls; Girls Head Cross Cntry Coach; Powder Putt Ftbl; Math, Sci Competitions Adv; Chrldr Adv; *office:* Holmdel HS 36 Crawfords Corner Rd Holmdel NJ 07733

CLAYTON, DELBERT EUGENE, Social Studies Teacher; *b:* Toledo, OH; *m:* Lynn Marie; *c:* Casey Tyler, Cody Nicholas; *ed:* Adrian Coll (BA) PE 1981; Univ of Toledo (BA) Soc Stud 1991; ME Pgm Still in Progress; *cr:* Toledo Pub Schls Sub Tchr 1983-88; Rossford HS Soc Stud Tchr 1991-; *ai:* Asst Var Bsktbl & Jr High Ftbl Coach; Frosh Class Adv; Soc Stud Curr Mem; Block Scheduling Comm; NEA 1990-; OEA 1990-; NCSS 1995-; Pres List 1989-90; Phi Alpha Theta 1990-, Natl Historical Hnr Soc; Phi Alpha Kappa 1990-, Univ of Toledo Historical Hnr Soc, Citizenship Comm 1992-; *home:* 2232 Vistamar Rd Toledo OH 43611*

CLAYTON, JULIE PENDERGAST, Social Studies Teacher; *b:* Syracuse, NY; *m:* Bruce C.; *ed:* Colgate Univ (BA) Intnl Relations, Fr 1990; Iona Coll 6 Credit Hrs His; LeMoyne Coll Scndry Tchr Cert Prgm 1992-93; *cr:* St Catharine Acad Soc Stud Tchr 1993-; *ai:* A World of Difference Moderator; Anti-Bias Prgm; *office:* St Catharine Acad 2250 Williamsbridge Rd Bronx NY 10469

CLAYTON, MATTHEW W., Chemistry Teacher; *b:* Buffalo, NY; *m:* Christina Corey; *c:* David, Kristen, Colin; *ed:* SUNY at Geneseo (BA) Speech Comm 1984; *cr:* Hard Rock Cafe Asst Kitchen Mgr 1989-91; Stadium Svcs Inc Concessions Supvr 1992-; Local Dists Sub Tchr 1993-94; Springville- G. I. HS Chem Tchr 1994-; *ai:* Jr Class Adv; Coach Girl's Mofified Soccer, Sci Olympiad; AFT, NYSUT, GIFA 1994-; NSTA, STANYS 1995-; Cub Scout Pack 583 1993-, Webelos Den Ldr; *office:* Springville-Griffith Inst 290 N Buffalo St Springville NY 14141

CLAYTON, PATRICIA RAE, Social Studies Consultant; *b:* Akron, OH; *ed:* Kent St Univ (BA) Soc Stud, Eng 1969; Univ of Akron (MA) Soc Stu 1977, (MA) Supervision 1992, (MA) Rdng 1994; *cr:* Mogadore HS Soc Stud, Eng Tchr 1969-94; Summit Cty Educl SC K-12 Grd Soc Stud Consultant 1994-; *ai:* NHS, Chrldng Adv; Sec for Fac-Stu Senate; Boys Ath Dir; Chprsn Annual Magazine Drive; Statistician for Ftbl Team;

Sponsored Red Cross Blood Drives, Holiday Food Baskets; Phi Delta Kappa 1990-, Nu Conclave Sec; NCSS 1990-; NSDC 1994-; Martha Jennings Scholar Awd 1987-88; 1st Woman Recipient O. H. Somers Awd, Portage Cty Prins Assn Lifetime Pass; Yrbk Dedication; *office:* Summit Cty Educl Svc Ctr 420 Washington Ave Cuyahoga Falls OH 44221*

CLAYTON, THOMAS FRANCIS, AP English Teacher; *b:* Montclair, NJ; *m:* Joan Mc Cormack; *c:* Jack, Katie; *ed:* Boston Coll (BA) Eng, Philosophy 1981; Rutgers (MA) Eng 1989; *cr:* St George's 10-11 Grd Eng Tchr 1981-83; St Anthony's 10th Grd Eng Tchr 1984; Highbridge Comm Ctr GED Tchr;1988-90; *ai:* Yrbk, Sr Class Adv; NCTE 1991-; *office:* Schoharie Central HS Main St Schoharie NY 12157

CLAYTOR, DAVID LEE, Speech & English Teacher; *b:* Akron, OH; *m:* Susan Carol Allison; *c:* Christopher, Catheryn, John; *ed:* Univ of Akron (BA) Scndry Ed 1971; Kent St Univ (MED) Scndry Admin 1979; Addl Credit Hrs Ashland Univ, Walsh Univ, Akron Univ; *cr:* Southeast HS Eng, Speech Tchr 1971-75, Dir Comm Ed 1975-76, Eng, Speech Tchr 1976-; *ai:* North Cntrl, Venture Capital Time Allocation Comm; NEA, OH Ed Assn, Southeast Local Tchrs Assn 1971-; Hawthorne Soc, Thoreau 1992-; Hogar de Ninos Huerfanos Inc 1991-, Dominican Republic Vol; Charles Stewart Mott Flwshp; Martha Holden Jennings Scholar; Grant: GAR Fnd, Effective Schls, Venture Capital Schls.

CLAYTOR, WANDA JEANNE, Resource Teacher; *b:* Cleveland, OH; *c:* Dwayne; *ed:* Cntrl St Univ (BSEd) Elem Ed 1970; Ashland Theological Seminary (MA) Chrstn Ed 1983; John Carroll Univ (MA) Cmptr Ed 1990; *cr:* Blue Cross Receptionist, Prsnl Asst 1967; Cleveland City Schls Elem Tchr, Afrocentric Coord 1970-; *ai:* Tutorial Prgm Coord; Math TEEM Lead Tchr; Afrocentric Planning Team Chprsn; AFT 1970-; Liberty Hill Bapt Church 1956-, Chrstn Ed Dir, Sunday Schl 1966-67, 1970-, Bible Stud Tchr 1975-, Vacation Bible Schl Dir 1977-93; Write Sunday Schl Lessons for Natl Bapt of Amer; Wkshp Presenter in Churches; *office:* Miles Elem Schl 11918 Miles Ave Cleveland OH 44105

CLEARY, BARBARA KESSLER, English Teacher; *b:* Brooklyn, NY; *m:* Richard L.; *c:* Melissa Bompiani, Kevin, Teresa; *ed:* Millersville Univ (BS) Eng 1968; *cr:* Dallastown HS Eng Tchr 1968-70; Sub Tchr 1970-83; York Cty Day Schl Eng Tchr 1983-; *ai:* Yrbk, Sr Class Adv; Stu Assistance Prgm; NCTE 1992-; Christ Luth Church of Dallastown Sunday Schl Tchr, Bible Schl Tchr; *office:* York Country Day Schl 1071 Country Club Rd York PA 17403

CLEARY, BERYL BOARDMAN, Retired Instructor; *b:* Sayre, PA; *m:* James G.; *c:* Michael (dec); *ed:* Univ of PA (BSN) Nrsng 1951; Univ of PA (MS) Ed 1953; Diploma Robert Packer Hosp Nursing 1947; *cr:* Univ of Pa Instr 1951-58; Schl Nursing Univ of Pa Instr 1966-72; Robert Packer Hosp Schl of Nursing Instr 1972-89; *ai:* Amer Nurses Assn Treas; Sigma Theta Tau; Amer Nurses Assn 1947-, LIfe Mem; Sigma Theta Tau 1970-, Archivist; Sayre Historical Soc 1989-, Sec; Bradford Co Historical Soc 1994-, Bd Mem; Book: Robert Packer HospitaL Schl of Nursing A History 1901-1989; *home:* 107 West St Sayre PA 18840

CLEARY, DENISE, Science Teacher; *b:* Rahway, NJ; *m:* Brian; *c:* Samantha; *ed:* Rutger's Univ (BS) Environmental Sci, Tchr Ed 1988; Kean Coll (MA) Admin, Supervision 1995; *ai:* Stu Cncl, MIE Adv; Asst Chrldng Coach; NEA, NJEA, VCEA 1988-; *office:* Linden HS 121 W Saint Georges Ave Linden NJ 07036

CLEARY, EDWARD DELLON, English Teacher; *b:* Elmira, NY; *m:* Maryann Davis; *c:* Megan, Matthew, Molly; *ed:* King's Coll (BA) Eng 1972; Elmira Coll (MS) Eng Ed 1977; Brockport St 15 Credits; *cr:* St Patrick's Jr HS Eng Tchr 1975-77; Washington & Lee HS Eng Tchr 1977-85; Odessa Montour HS Eng Tchr 1985-86; Elmir Free Acad Eng Tchr 1986-; *ai:* Cross Cntry, Boys Spring Track Coach; NYSUT 1985-; Southport Recreation 1989-, Bsbl Coach; St Mary's Church, Parish Cncl 1995; *home:* 408 Fairway Ave Elmira NY 14904*

CLEARY, MARY ELIZABETH, Sixth Grade Teacher; *b:* Newark, NJ; *m:* James H.; *c:* James Mark, Elizabeth, Pierce, Patricia; *ed:* Caldwell Coll (BA) Eng 1968; Post Grad Stud Montclair St, Jersey City St; *cr:* Kearny Bd of Ed Third Grd Tchr 1968-73; St Anthonys Schl Rdng Tchr 1982-85; Rutherford Bd of Ed Sixth Grd Tchr 1989-; *ai:* NJEA 1989-; *office:* Pierrepont Elem Schl 70 E Pierrepont Ave Rutherford NJ 07070

CLEARY, WILLIAM JOSEPH, Health, PE & Business Teacher; *b:* Wilkinsburg, PA; *m:* Maureen Ann Schmidt; *c:* Brandon, Jordan; *ed:* California St Coll at PA (BSEd) Scndry Ed 1975; 24 Credits at Comm Coll of Allegheny Cty; 21 Credits at California Univ of PA; *cr:* St Regis Schl Tchr 1976-79; Mon Vly Cath HS Tchr 1979-80; Serra Cath HS Tchr, Ath Dir, Head Girls Bsktbl Coach 1980-; *ai:* Head Bsbl Coach; NCEA 1976-; Dist 7 ADs Assn, PIAA ADs Assn 1982-; DAR His Tchr of Yr; Coach of Yr; *office:* Serra Catholic HS 200 Hershey Dr Mc Keesport PA 15132

CLEARY-TODD, DEBRA L., Secondary Social Studies Tchr; *b:* Elmira, NY; *ed:* SUNY at Cortland (BA) Scndry Soc Stud 1983; NY Univ (MA) Latin Amer His 1987; *cr:* Elmira City Schl Dist Summer Schl Tchr 1984-87 & 1991; Elmira Southside HS Soc Stud Tchr 1987-; *ai:* Class of 1990-1994 Adv; Sr Level Ind Stud in Historical Rdng Coord; Tchr Ldr; People to People Stu Ambassador Prgm; Elmira Southside HS Stu Comm Vol Prgm Initiator, Organizer & Coord; Bldng Planning Tm Mem 1996; Tchr & Admin Liason Comm Mem 1994-95; NY St Cncl for Soc Stud 5 Yrs; NY St United Tchrs Assn & Elmira Tchrs Assn 2 Yrs; Phi Kappa Phi, Phi Alpha Theta & Kappa Delta Pi; Jr League of Greater Elmira-Corning Inc 1989-, Exec Bd Mem 1991-, Pres-Elect 1993-94, Pres 1994-; NY Cncl for Hum Grant 1991; Natl Endowment for Hum Grant 1990; NY Univ Grad Research Assistantship 1985-87; Article Pub in NY Univ Law Assn Journal of Intnl Affairs 1987; Outstanding Young Women of America 1987; *home:* 321 Glen Ave Elmira NY 14905

CLEAVALL, MARILYN A., Special Educator; *b:* Springfield, MA; *m:* Paul J. Jr.; *c:* Katherine, Daniel, Elizabeth; *ed:* Westfield St Coll (BS) Ed 1974; Amer Intl Coll (MA) Spec Ed 1982; Attnd MA Gen Hosp LD Clinic, Univ of MA at Boston Creative, Critical Thinking; *cr:* Springfield Schl System Spec Edctr 1966-67; East Longmeadow Schls Spec Edctr 1985-; *ai:* Univ of MA Prof Dev Tchr Trng, Educl Reform, Bldg Level, Accredidation, Reform Frameworks Comms; Frosh, Soph Class Adv; NEA, MTA 1986-; Smithsonian Assoc 1990-; Amer Museum Natural His; Univ of MA Field Experience Manual Mentor Tchrs, Internships; Mentor Tchr; Grant Univ of MA Field Experience Stud Alternative Tchng, Assessment; *office:* East Longmeadow HS 180 Maple St East Longmeadow MA 01028*

CLEAVER, ANN ELIZABETH, Second Grade Teacher; *b:* York, PA; *ed:* Shippensburg Univ (BS) Elem Ed 1972, (MS) Elem Ed 1974; 32 Addl Hrs; *cr:* Leaders Hghts Schl Fourth Grd Tchr 1972-80; York Township Schl Second Grd Tchr 1981-; *ai:* Elem Sci Comm Co-Chair; Curr Cncl Comm; New Tchr Mentor; NEA 1972-; Lehman Ctr Vol; *office:* York Township Schl 2500 S Queen St York PA 17402

CLEEMPUT, MARSHA ANN, Mathematics Teacher; *b:* Lima, OH; *ed:* Bowling Green St Univ (BS) Math Ed 1985, (MED) Guid, Cnslng 1988; 12 Semester Hrs Ed, Cnslng, Discipline, Classroom Mngmt, Drug Consulting; *cr:* Sylvania City Schls Math Tchr 1985-; *ai:* Sr Class, Cat's Meow Adv; 24 Hr Relay Steering, Inservice, Bldg Comms; Soc Comm Chprsn; *office:* Sylvania Northview HS 5403 Silica Dr Sylvania OH 43560*

CLEES, PAMELA CRESSMAN, Art Teacher; *b:* Camden, NJ; *m:* Larry J.; *ed:* Keystone Jr Coll (AA) Liberal Arts 1975; Edinboro Univ (BS) Art Ed 1977; Mansfield Univ (MEd) Art Ed 1983-; Philadelphia Coll of Textiles, Sci Post Baccalaureate Degree Interior Architecture 1991; *cr:* Coudersport Elem Schl K-6th Grd Art Tchr 1977-83; Palmerton Area Schl Dist K-8th Grd Art Tchr 1983-84; Coatesville Area Intermediate HS 9th-12th Grd Art Tchr 1984-; *ai:* SAP; Peer Mediation Group; NEA 1977-; Chester Cty Art Assn 1990-; Coatesville Area Tchr Assn 1994-; *office:* Coatesville Area Inter HS 1425 E Lincoln Hwy Coatesville PA 19320

CLEGGETT, LILY THOMAS, Fifth Grade Teacher; *b:* Youngstown, OH; *w:* Stanley H (dec); *c:* Sheryl C. Blakemore; *ed:* Cleveland St Univ (BS) Ed 1973, (ME) Cnslng 1978; Kent St Univ 10 Addl Hrs Post Grad 1976; *cr:* Cleveland HS Univ Hts Bd of Ed 4th & 5th Grd Tchr 1973-; *ai:* Bethany Bapt Church 1950; Bd of Chrstn Ed; Sunday Schl Tchr; Sunday Schl Supvr Jr Dept; Blvd Schl Improvement Comm 1993; AFT 1974-; Hghts Alliance Black Sc Ed 1976-, Historian, Appreciation; Intnl Trng in Comm 1984-, Pres & Sec, 2nd Pl Speech Cont; Woodmere Civic League, Pres & Sec; Sigma Gamma Rho 1982-, Sec & Treas, svc; Eta Phi Beta 1976-, Sec & Historian, Chaplain 1992-- Soror of Yr; Natl Cncl Negro Women 1985-, Comm Chair; Intnatl Trng in Commnctn Del to Cncl; Martha Holden Jennings Schlr 1978-79; *home:* 3900 Maplecrest Rd Beachwood OH 44122

CLELAND, THOMAS EDWARD,JR., Aerospace Sci Dept Chairman; *b:* Holyoke, MA; *m:* Patricia Helen Deitz; *c:* David T., Donna Cleland Worthy, Todd R. Cleland; *ed:* Univ of MA (BA) Librl Arts 1965; Troy St Univ (MS) Guid & Cnslng 1976; USAF Command Pilot 500 Hrs; Distngd Grad USAF Squadron Ofcr Schl 1972, USAF Command & Staff Coll 1978; Grad Air War Coll 1982; *cr:* USAF Ofcr Command & Staff Positions 1965-91; Air Univ Instr & Dept Chair 1974-78; Army Command & Staff Coll Instr 1990-91; Pine Bluff HS Aerospace Sci Instr 1991-93; Cntrl HS Chm Aerospace Sci Dept 1993-; *ai:* AFJROTC Drill Teams Spon; CHS Aerospace Club Adv; AFJROTC Acad Hnr Soc Adv; Instr Pvt Pilot Ground Schl; Air Force Assn 1965-; Amer Legion 1991-; Red River Vly Fighter Pilots Assn 1991-; Deacon-United Congregational Church 1948-; CHS Dept Chm Comm 1993-; MA Air Force Assn 1993-, VP Aerospace Ed; Springfield Veterans Comm 1996-; 393 Combat Missions in Vietnam 1969-70; Military Trng Instr of Yr 1974; Letter of Appreciation from Pres Bush for Career Achvmt as a USAF Ofcr 1991; CHS Aerospace Sci Dept Rated Top 20%; *office:* Springfield Central HS 1840 Roosevelt Ave Springfield MA 01109

CLEM, VICKI KEARTON, French Teacher; *b:* Laurel, MD; *m:* David Kirk; *c:* Vicki Clem Leimbach, Anthony Kirk; *ed:* Univ of MD at College Park (BA) Fr 1963, (MA) Fr Lit 1971; 6 Credits Span; St Dept Course Spec Ed; *cr:* Ellicott City Jr HS Fr, Math Tchr 1965-66; Mt Hebron HS Fr Tchr 1972-77; Centennial-Wilde Lake Schl Fr Tchr 1977-80; Mt Hebron HS Fr Tchr 1980-; *ai:* NHS Adv 1985-; Fr Club Adv 1980-; Stdnts for Environmental Action Adv 1993-; Societe Honoraire de Francais Spon; AATF, NEA, MD St Trs Assn, Howard Co Edctrs Assn 1972-; MD For Lang Assn; Article Art, Frgn Langs Pub MD Art Edctrs Newsletter; Howard Comm Coll, Howard Co Pub Schls Tchng Excl Awd 1989; *office:* Mount Hebron HS 9440 State Route 99 Ellicott City MD 21042*

CLEMENS, CYNTHIA FERRELL, American History Teacher; *b:* Columbus, OH; *c:* Jessica, Benjamin; *ed:* Kent St Univ (BA) 1981; OH St Univ Jrnlsm, Eng; Jrnlsm, Poetry, Creative Writing, Comms, Shakespearean Courses; *cr:* Fournier Supply Cmptr Operator Accounts Payable 1975-78; Cardinal MS 7th Grd OH His, Geog, 8th Grd Amer His Tchr 1993-; *ai:* Stu Cncl, Chrldng, Drill Team Adv; NEA; Wrote Poetry Books.*

CLEMENS, DEBORAH SHERMAN, French Teacher; *b:* Lancaster, PA; *m:* Thomas Michael; *c:* Benjamin Groff, Ann, Jessica Groff, Kevin, Melora Groff, Caitlin Groff, Carol; *ed:* Lebanon Vly (BA) Frgn Langs 1970; Middlebury Coll (MA) Fr 1973; Attnd Franklin & Marshall Coll; *cr:* Lebanon HS Fr Tchr 1969-; *ai:* Fr Club Adv; NEA, PSEA, LEA 1985-; Mt Gretna Arts Cncl, Music at Gretna 1988-; Mt Gretna Lib Bd 1994-, Treas; *office:* Lebanon Sr HS 1000 S 8th St Lebanon PA 17042

CLEMENS, KAREN CONNORS, Physical Education Instructor; *b:* Camp Lejeune, NC; *m:* Jeffrey; *ed:* Burlington Cty Coll (AA) Nursing 1978; Trenton St Coll (BS) Hlth Ed 1981; *cr:* St Joan of Arc Schl Sixth Grd Tchr 1981-95, PE Tchr 1995-; *ai:* Head Age Group Swimming Coach; Jersey Wahoos Swim Club; Two-time Qualifier for Boston Marathon; NCEA, USS Swimming 1981-; Mid Atlantic Age Group Coach of Yr 1993-94, 1995-96; *office:* Saint Joan Of Arc Schl 101 Evans Rd Marlton NJ 08053

CLEMENS, THOMAS G., History Professor; *b:* Summit, NJ; *m:* Mary Jo; *c:* Sarah, Joseph; *ed:* Salisbury St Univ (BA) His 1972, (MA) His 1984; George Mason Univ (CAS) Comm Coll Ed 1995; *cr:* Salisbury St Univ Asst Instr 1974-78; Hagerstown Jr Coll Instr, Asst Prof 1978-; *ai:* Fac Assembly Chair; Ruritan 1988-, VP; Save Historic Antietam 1986-, Pres; 5 Articles Pub; *office:* Hagerstown Jr Coll 11400 Robinwood Dr Hagerstown MD 21742

CLEMENS, TIM A., Mathematics Teacher; *b:* Paulding, OH; *ed:* OH Northern Univ (BA) Math 1976, (JD) Law 1979; *cr:* Lebanon City Schls Math Tchr 1980-86; Antwerp Local Schls Math Tchr 1986-; *ai:* Asst Athletic Dir; *office:* Antwerp Local Schls Archer Dr Antwerp OH 45813

CLEMENS, TRACIE LEE-MOYER, 5th-6th Grd Classroom Tchr; *b:* Lebanon, PA; *m:* Raymond Arthur Jr.; *c:* Andrew Brandon, Alex Benjamin; *ed:* Lebanon Valley Coll Sci Ed, Partnerhsip 1995; Millersville Univ (MA) Ed 1988; Lebanon Vly Coll Post Grad Stud; *cr:* Helping Hand Daycare, Nursery Schl Head, Early Chldhd Tchr 1981-85; T. L. C. Consulting Inc Private Tutoring 1982-85; Northern Lebanon Schl Dist Elem Tchr 1985-; *ai:* Asst IM Dir; Environmental Club Adv; Sci Partnership Ldr; Peer Tutor Coord Class Mentor; NEA, Northern Lebanan Ed Assn 1985-, Gen Comm; Millersville Univ Alumni 1981-, Gen Comm; Lebanan Jr Womens Club 1951-, Ed Chm Ways & Means; Museum Scientific Discovery Asst Coord for Sat Nite Live; Covenant United Meth Church 23 Yrs, Ed Comm; Pub Svc; Local Advocate of Children, Ed; *office:* Lickdale Elem Schl RR 1 Box 1324 Jonestown PA 17038*

CLEMENT, JOHN THOMAS, Mathematics Teacher; *b:* Merrick, NY; *ed:* LeMoyne Coll (BA) Math 1993; *cr:* Mother Cabrini HS Math, Cmptr Sci Tchr 1993-; *ai:* Newspaper Adv; Cmptr Consultant; Peer Tutoring Prgm Co-Coord; ASCD 1993-; *office:* Mother Cabrini HS 701 Fort Washington Ave New York NY 10040*

CLEMENT, MARC A., Prof of Social Sciences Dept; *ed:* Villanova Univ (BA) Psych 1966; Univ of MA (MS) Child Psych 1973, (PHD) Child Psych 1976; *cr:* Colby-Sawyer Coll Prof 1974-; *ai:* Outing Club Adv; Court Appointed Spec Advocate 1989-; *office:* Colby Sawyer Coll New London NH 03257

CLEMENT, NANCY GLAHN, 1st Grade Teacher; *b:* Hartford, CT; *m:* Robert B.; *c:* Robert Jr., Stephen, Betsey; *ed:* Univ of Ct (BA) His 1963; Cntrl CT St Univ BA +30 in Ed 1982; *cr:* Northeast Schl 3rd Grd Tchr 1963-68; Whiting Ln Sch Primary Tchr 1976-78; Squadron Line Schl Primary Tchr 1978-; *ai:* Partners in Sci Founding Mem; CEA 1963-; NEA 1963-; NSTA 1995-; *office:* Squadron Line Schl 44 Squadron Line Rd Simsbury CT 06070*

CLEMENT, PHILOMENA WARD, Eng Instr & Dept Chprsn; *b:* Belfast, N Ireland; *m:* Paul Edward; *c:* Geoffrey, Jacqueline, Valerie, Terence; *ed:* St Marys Coll of Ed (BSC) Ed 1958; Long Island Univ (MA) Eng Lit 1981; SUNY at Stony Brook Eng Lit; Post Grad Credits in PHD Prgm; *cr:* St Patricks Schl Elem Instr 1958-60; Pan Amer World Airways Flight Supvr 1960-63; Hauppauge Mid HS Eng Sub Tchr 1978-79; Holy Famil Tchr, Home Ec Chair 1979-81; St Anthony's HS Eng Instr, Chp *ai:* Shades of Gray Lit Magazine Adv; Mid Sts Evaluation Cor NCTE 1994-; NY St Eng Cncl.*

CLEMENTE, CARMEN, ESL & Modern Langs Lab Dir; *b:* San *c:* Jessica Reid, Ruben, Alexander, Cynthia; *ed:* Hostos Comm (Early Chldhd Ed 1977; Herbert H. Lehman Coll (BA) soc W Hunter Coll (MSW) Soc Work 1983; Addl Hrs 1984-85; *cr:* Pue Comm Dev Project Comm Worker 1966-68; PS 83 Comm Worker John Jay Coll Prof 1986-94; Hostos Comm Coll Chief Proctor, Dir, Prof 1978-; *ai:* Bronx Second Chance Project; Bronx F. (Work Consultant; Practicum Placement Coord for Admir Mentoring Prgm for Incoming Frosh Stdnts; Natl Assn of Soc 1984-; Natl Assn of Puerto Rican Women 1993-; ASCD 1994-; Chance 1982-, Soc Work Consultant, Cnslng Awd; NYC Mi 1989-; Cert of Appreciation DEA; Exemplary Work for Advan Women Plaque; Assembly St of NY Citation for Comm Svcs; Recognition of Outstdng Work with Stdnts; *office:* Hostos Com CUNY 500 Grand Concourse Bronx NY 10451*

CLEMENTS, GLEN G., High School Mathematics Tchr; *b:* Bal NY; *m:* Kathleen Ehler; *c:* Jamie, Renee; *ed:* St Univ of NY at (BA) Math Ed 1974; St Univ of NY at Albany (MA) Math Ed Shenendehowa HS 10th-12th Grd Math Tchr 22 Yrs; *ai:* Math T 1988-; Our Lady of Grace Church 1956-; Chancellors Awd fo Tchng 1974; Price Chopper Scholars Recognition; *office:* Shene HS Rt 146 Box 970 Clifton Park NY 12065

CLEMENTS, PATRICIA BOWERS, English Teacher; *b:* Lit NY; *m:* Richard Dennis; *c:* Jordan Nicole, Karyn Noel; *ed:* Herk Comm Coll (AA) Lbrl Arts 1976; SUC at Potsdam (BA) Eng, S 1978; Coll of St Rose (MA) Eng 1984; 1994 Hum Tchr Ins Johnsville Cntrl Schl Eng Tchr 1978-79; SUNY EOP Summ 1981-88, Adj Instr 1986-88; Middleburgh Cntrl Schl Eng Tchr Natl Jr Hnr Soc Adv; Eng Dept Curr Coord 1994-; Alpha Psi, Natl Act Advs 1993-; NCTE 1992-; NY St United Tchrs 1978- Middleburgh Cntrl Schl 181 Main St Box 400 Middleburgh NY

CLEMENZ, KATHLEEN M., English Teacher; *b:* Southampton Peter M.; *c:* Colin, Keenan; *ed:* SUNY at Geneseo (BA) Eng Credit Hrs at Grad Level; *cr:* Geneseo Cntrl Eng Tchr 1975; Wes Beach HS Eng Tchr 1975-; *ai:* Jr Class Adv; Stu of Month, Sr Schlsp & Attendance Comms; NYSEC 1986-, Tchr of Excl; LILA Westhampton Beach HS 49 Lilac Rd Westhampton Beach NY 11

CLEMMER, PAUL M., Fifth Grade Teacher; *b:* Royersford, Ronda Jean Shank; *c:* Janelle Ferne Miller, P. Martin, J. Wen Eastern Mennonite Univ (BS) Soc Sci 1966; Shippensburg Uni Elem Ed 1972; *cr:* Inglewood Elem Schl 4th-6th Grd Tchr 1966-6 Hill Dev Schl 4th-6th Grd Tchr 1968-69; Greencastle Elem Sch Tchr 1969-; *ai:* Head Tchr 1976-78; Grade Level Chair 1991-; NE GAEA 1969-; Fr Cty Beekeepers 1980-, Pres; Fr Cty 4-H S 1980-82, Pres; Marion Mennonite Church 1972-79, Pastor; Shalo Acad 1976-, Bd Chm; *home:* PO Box 383 5116 Main St Marion P

CLEMMONS, KATHLENE MAYERS, 2nd Grade Teacher; *b:* City, CA; *m:* Steven Randale; *c:* Whitney Marie; *ed:* Northwest Coll (BA) Elem Ed 1977; *cr:* Nampa Schl Dist 3rd & 5th Grd E 1977-85; Dept of Defense Schls 4th-6th Grd Tchr 1985-89, 2nd & Tchr 1989-; *ai:* HS Vllybl, Tennis, Swim Team & Yth Svcs Co Choir Dir; Tchr Inservice Facilitator; Natl Hnr Soc Spon; Jr Ldrs Point Bapt Church 1995-, Church Pianist; *office:* Amberg Elem S 28218 APO AE 09173*

CLEMSON, CANDY, Art, Gifted Ed & Hum Teacher; *b:* Clevela *ed:* Notre Dame Coll (BA) Art Ed 1970; Attnd Cleveland Inst c Credit Hrs Drawing, Kent St 28 Hrs Scndry Ed, OH Univ 10 C Italian Renaissance & Akron Univ 20 Credit Hrs Craft & Commer *cr:* Charles F Brush HS Art, Gifted Ed & Hum Tchr 1970-; Joh Intern Prgm Media Instr; *ai:* Stu Congress Adv; Powderpu Homecoming; Holiday Family Food Drives; United Way Drive; S Prgm; Strategic Planning Comm; Vision Comm 2000 Mem; S Mntrshp Comm; OEA 1970-; OAEA 1980-; SELTA 1970-, VP Cleveland Museum of Art; PTA 1982-, Life Membership Awd 199 HS & S Euclid Lyndhurst Schl Dist Tchr of Yr; Bd of Ed Bell Rin for Service to Schl Dist; Breakfast of Champions Awd; Martha Jennings Tchr 1990, 1994, Master Tchr Candidate; Ashland (Achvmt Awd Nom; Nom Wlt Disney Amer Tchr Awd; *office:* C Brush HS 4875 Glenlyn Rd Lyndhurst OH 44124

CLESCERI, LENORE STANKE, Professor of Biochemistry; *b:* (IL; *m:* Nicholas L.; *c:* Pamela Kaiser, Kristine Wood, Craig, Erika, *ed:* Loyola Univ (BS) Chem, Bio 1957; Marquette Univ (MS) 1959; Univ of WI (PHD) Biochem 1963; Post Doctoral Fellow S Inst of Tech Zurich Switzerland; *cr:* Univ of WI Instr 1957-59; M Med Schl Rsrch Asst 1957-59; Univ of WI Rsrch Asst 1959-64; Svc Rsrch Fellow 1964-66; Rensselaer Prof 1966-; *ai:* Confrate Chrstn Doctrine; Children's Museum Exhbitor; Carrer Guid Wkshp Environment Fed 1982-, Bd of Dir; Achvmt 1984, 1987, 1990, 199 AAUP 1970-; SETAC 1985-; AWWA 1984-; EPA Sci Advy Bd 197 Siting Comm 1994-; USPHS Flwshp; NSF, EPA, Indstrl Grants; S Publications, Books; *office:* Rensselaer Polytechnic Inst M Research Ctr Troy NY 12181*

CLEVELAND, C. DIANE, Kindergarten Teacher; *b:* Jacksonville David A.; *c:* Christian, Brittany; *ed:* OH St Univ Elem Ed 1977; Louisville (MED) 1978; *cr:* Mt Hope Elem Title I Rdng Tchr 1 Walnut Creek Elem Title I Rdng Tchr 1981-83, 2nd Grd Tchr 1 Kndgtn Tchr 1993-; *ai:* Delta Kappa Gamma 1987-; Sci Ed Cnc 1992-; Grad Asst Univ of Louisville 1977-78; 5 Mini Grants S Planning Comm; *office:* Walnut Creek Elem Schl 4840 Olde Pum Box 145 Walnut Creek OH 44687

CLEVELAND, JOELITA C., Librn & 8th Grd Earth Sci T Cambridge, MA; *m:* Thomas; *c:* Nicolas, Christopher; *ed:* Boston (BA) Eng, Scndry Ed 1970; 48 Prof Dev Points; *cr:* Western Jr HS Eng Tchr 1970-81; Powderhouse Comm Schl 8 Grd Eng Tchr 1 Lincoln Park Comm Schl 8 Grd Eng Tchr 1983-85; St Agnes Schl Grd Sci Tchr 1989-; *ai:* NCEA 1989-; *office:* Saint Agnes Schl 39 St Arlington MA 02174

CLEVELAND, MAXINE LEHRMAN, Fifth Grade Teacher; *b:* Br NY; *c:* Andrea; *ed:* SUNY at Cortland (BA) Elem Ed 1964; 45 A *cr:* PS 183 Second Grd Tchr 1964-65; De Ruyter Cntrl Schl Sixth G 1965-66, Fifth Grd Tchr 1966-; *ai:* Awds, Superspeller, Spelli Chprsn; NEA 1965-, Resolutions Comm; NEA NY 1965-, Bd c Cortland Meml Hosp Auxilliary 1992-, Vol; *office:* De Ruyter Cn 711 Railroad St De Ruyter NY 13052

CLEVELAND, STEPHEN, Sixth Grade Teacher; *b:* Bennington, Darlene; *c:* Gregory; *ed:* North Adams St Coll (BA) Elem Ed Castleton St Coll (MA) Elem Ed 1978; Post Grad Cert Educl Appli of Comps 193; *cr:* Brookside Elem Schl 5th Grd Tchr 1971-73; Mo Elem Schl 6th Grd Tchr 1973-79; Catamount Elem Schl 6th G 1979-; *ai:* Dist Tech & Schl Comp Comms; NEA 1971-; SWVEA BPOE 1982-; *office:* Catamount Elem Schl 230 School St Benning 05201

LAND BOYLE, JANET HAWTHORNE, Jr High Math Teacher; use, NY; *c:* Ryan, Shannon; *ed:* Univ of MA at Amherst (BA) Ed ent Univ (MA) Math Specialist 1993; Drake Univ 15 Semester Hrs sters; *cr:* Surrarrer 2nd & 6th Grd Tchr 1982-90; Albion 7th-8th th Tchr 1990-; *ai:* Weight Club; NEA & NCMT 1982-; *office:* Schl Webster Rd Strongsville OH 44136

DENCE, RICHARD HERBERT, Instr of Learning Disabilities; *b:* H; *m:* Kathie Anne Ashbaugh; *ed:* Kent St Univ (BS) Ed 1975; ad Courses in Spec Ed at Akron Univ; Post-Grad work in Curr & on at Ashland Univ; *cr:* Medina HS Small Group Instr & Spec Ed, Soc Stud Tchr 1975-; *ai:* Girls Gymnastics Coach 17 Yrs; Curr EA 1975-; OH Ed Assn 1975-, Franklin B Walter Outstanding r Awd; Medina City Tchrs Assn 1975-, Dow Chemical Outstanding d; *office:* Medina HS 777 E Union St Medina OH 44256

ELL-PARKER, SHARON LEIGH, Teacher of the Gifted; *b:* t, PA; *m:* Ricahrd Charles Parker; *c:* Matthew David Parker, er Michael Parker; *ed:* IN Univ of PA (BS) Spec Ed, Elem Ed 1977; niv (MED) Educl Admin 1987; PA Cert Principalship; Millersville *cr:* Cntrl Elem Schl Tchr 1977-80; Blanche Neville Schl for Deaf 80-81; Cntrl Elem Schl Tchr 1981-82; Charles W. Longer Elem r 1982-; *ai:* Spec Ed, Strategic Planning Sci Comm; PSEA, NEA ast Local Rep; PA Assn Gifted Educ 1982-, Affiliate Rep, Past VP; Tchrs of Yr 1995-; YWCA 1992-, Bd Mem; Altoona Comm Theatre Past Production, Mgr, Actress, Makeup, Props; PA St Tchr of Yr 1987; Gift of Time Tribute Honoree 1994-; *office:* Charles W. Elem Schl 1320 Union St Hollidaysburg PA 16648*

ORD, BARBARA O'NEIL, Stu Assistance & Guid Cnslr; *b:* CT; *m:* John J. Jr.; *c:* William Brown, Brian Brown, John, Mark; *ed:* n CT St Univ (BS) Scndry Ed, Soc Stud 1973; Boston Univ s (MED) Cnslng 1986; 6th Yr Cnslng 1994; *cr:* Lafayette Elem slr 1987-92; Sunnyside Elem Schl Cnslr 1990-92; Shelton HS Stu nce, Guid Cnslr 1992; *ai:* Class of 1995, SADD Adv; Amer Cnslng 84-; CT Cnslng Assn, CT Edctrs Assn 1987-; Vly Advocates Aids ess 1995-, Bd of Dir; Vly Substance Abuse Action Comm 1993-, g Comm; Dev & Implemented System-wide 5th Grd Career ess Prgm; K-12 System Guid Curr Comm; K-6 Early Intervention Chprsn; 9-12 Stu Assistance Team; Facilitator Yth Svc Bureau ng Classes.

ORD, DAYLE MARCHESANI, High School AP Art Teacher; *b:* , NJ; *m:* James N.; *c:* Seth James, Sacha Clare; *ed:* William n Coll (BA, BFA) Fine Art Ed 1972; AP Studio Art 3 Credits gh Dickinson Univ; *cr:* Valleyview Schl Art Tchr 1972-76; ield Art League Art Tchr 1982-83; Courtime Meadowlands RB Club Artist 1983-87; Morris Knolls HS AP Art Tchr 1991-; Frogmore's d Cntry Store Prof Artist 1992-; *ai:* Staff Dev, Alternatives in nent Steering Comms; Block Scheduling Task Force; Adult Ed g Instr; Natl Art Hnr Soc Adv; Art Svc Club; ASCD; MHRD Ed 91-; NEA 1972-; NAEA 1991-; AENJ 1996; Bloomfield Art League , 1st Place Watercolor; Blackwell Gallery 1992-; Morris Knolls 91-; Dist Tchr of Yr 1995; Bloomfield Pub Lib, Florham Park Pub ogmore's Lily Pad, The Country Store, San Francisco Boutique Art Sales; Article Pub; *office:* Morris Knolls HS 50 Knoll Dr Rockaway 66*

ORD, PATRICK JAMES, Guidance Counseling Director; *b:* New CT; *ed:* Fairfield Univ (BA) Psych 1979, (MA) Schl Cnslng 1983; n CT St Univ (CAS) Admin & Supervision 1990; *cr:* Notre Dame r 1979-81, Schl Cnslr 1981-90, Guid Dir 1990-; *ai:* Admin Cncl; d; Admissions Comm; Co-Moderate of Minority Stu Union; Team anti Drug Alcohol Group Moderator; ASCA, ACA, CSCA 1980-; St ce Schl Bd 1980-, Comm Chprsn; Seth Haley Schlsp Fund 1985-; d of Certfd Cnslr; Natl Bd of Schl Cnslr Cert; Pub Book Catholic chol Ministry: Training Student Leaders; *office:* Notre Dame HS 24 St West Haven CT 06516

ORD, VICTORIA CHIECO, American Literature Teacher; *b:* NY; *c:* John Ryan; *ed:* Manhattan Coll (BA) Eng 1981; 30 Credits in Ed, Counseling; *cr:* Monsignor Scanlan HS Tchr 1981-; *ai:* Jr ord; Fashion Show, Yrbk Consultant; NCTEA, UFT 1981-; De La chlsp; Magna Cum Laude Grad 1981; Phi Beta Kappa; *office:* nor Scanlan H S 915 Hutchinson River Pky Bronx NY 10465

ON, CHARLES H., English Professor; *b:* Syracuse, NY; *m:* *c:* Charles, Suzanne; *ed:* Univ of IA (BA) Eng 1960, (PHD) Eng *r:* San Bernardino St Univ Asst Prof 1964-70; Coe Coll Visiting 71-72; Univ of Pittsburgh Prof 1972-; *ai:* Dramatist's Guild 1991-; s Cncl Grants in Poetry & Fiction; Story in Pen Short Story ion; Chancellor's Tchng Awd.

, BRUCE,PH.D Prof & Photography Dept Chair; *b:* Cleveland, Constance Wolfe; *ed:* Kent St Univ (MA) Art 1978; OH Univ Ed 1994; Cooper Schl of Art Printmaking Art Diploma 1971; Great Retreat Hocking Tech Coll 1995; *cr:* Cooper Schl of Art Instr, Fine pt 1971-80; Lakeland Comm Coll Photography Prof 1980-; *ai:* Chair Tchng Comm; Amer Soc of Media Photographers 1996-; Prof & v Network 1994; Amer Educl Research Assoc 1995; Pub Article; sn of Two Yr Colls Tchr of Yr Nom 1994-95; Co-Author, Prof Bus es Photography; *office:* Lakeland College 7700 Clocktower Dr d OH 44094*

, CHERYL ANN SUTTON, Third Grade Teacher; *b:* Steubenville, Darl Edwin; *ed:* Kent St (BS) Elem Ed 1969; 30 Hrs Post Grad *cr:* Richmond Elem 3rd Grd Tchr 1969-95; *ai:* NEA, OEA 1969-; ond Lioness Club 1989-, Treas, 7 Yr 100 Percent Perfect Attendance *ome:* RR 1 Box 645 Castner Dr Richmond OH 43944

, DAVID SHANE, Art Teacher; *b:* Urbana, OH; *ed:* Urbana Coll E, Hlth Ed, Art 1981; Dayton Univ (MS) Admin 1992; Wright St 0 Hrs; Ashland Coll 4 Hrs; *cr:* Springfield Shawnee Local Schls chr 1992; Logan Cty Juvenile Court Probation Office 1993-; Indian ocal Schl Art Instr; *ai:* Asst Boys Var Bsktbl; Art Club; NEA 1993-; Indian Lake Local Schl System 6210 State Route 235 N Lewistown 333

KSCALES, CLAUDETTE RICHARDSON, Math Teacher of Program; *b:* Youngstown, OH; *m:* Lucius; *c:* Nichole rdson-Adams, Dwaylon Richardson; Lucian; *ed:* Youngstown St AAS) Child Care Tech 1977, (BS) Elem Ed 1987, (MS) Spec Ed, d 1992; 11 Hrs Towards Ed Admin Cert; 6 Hrs Curr Compacting; *cr:* ays to Better Living Inc Prgm Monitor 1982-95; Youngstown City -6th Grd Math, Gifted Tchr 1987-, Chrldng Adv 1995-; *ai:* Lake Sci Assn Sci Fair Judge 1993-; Math Course of Stud Comm 1993; stown City Sci Fair Judge 1996; North Jr HS Chrldng Adv 1995-; On 992; Hnrs Pol Comm 1992-93; Math Textbook Selection Comm 94; Odeyessey of Mind Coach 1989-; Chess Coach 1989-; Oral His ttant Tchr 1995-; Quiz Bowl Coach; Yo City Strategic Planning 1995-; West Elem Yrbk Adv 1989-92; OCTM 1991-; North East OH f Tchrs of Math 1990-, Math, Elem Contest Comm; OH Assn for Children 1991-; Youngstown Assn for Gifted Children 1990-; YEA, 1987-; NAACP 1991-; West PTO 1987-, Bldg Liaison; Friends of side Lib 1994-; Youngstown Area Alliance of Black Schl Edctr 1991-; Young Scholars Bldg Liaison 1993-; Tchr Innovative Ec Ed Grant 95; Jennings Scholar 1993; Impact II Grant 1993, 1995; Impact II Disseminator Grant 1994-95; Math Movers TV Channel 45 Presenter 1993; *home:* 3142 Glenwood Ave Youngstown OH 44511*

CLINT, L. EARL, High School Teacher; *b:* Toronto, Canada; *m:* Katherine Helen Graham; *c:* Bradley Earl, Andrea Katherine; *ed:* Univ of Western Ontario (BA) Geog 1979, (BAE) Geog 1980; Honours Specialist Qualifications Geog at Univ of Toronto 1987; Cooperative Ed Qualification at Brook Univ 1988; *cr:* Great Lakes Chrstn Coll Full Time Tchr 1980-; London Bd of Ed Summer Schl Tchr 1980-81; Lincoln Cty Bd Of Ed Night Schl Tchr 1988-; Self Employed Facilitator of Human Resource Seminars 1988-; *ai:* Yrbk Staff Spon; Asst Coach Boys Hockey; Ontario Assn for Geographic & Environmental Ed 1980-; *office:* Great Lakes Christian Coll 4875 King St Beamsville ON L0R 1B0 Canada CN

CLINTON, DANA GAIL, Fr Tchr & Frgn Lang Dpt Chprsn; *b:* Lawrence, KS; *c:* Dorothee; *ed:* Univ of KS (BA) Fr-Hnrs 1970, (MS) Fr-Honors 1972; MI St Univ (ABD) Fr 1980; Univ de Bordeuna France 1968-69, Diploma Superieur d'Etuded Frangaises; Ecole Normale Superieure de Saint Cloud France Fr Govt Fellow 1979-80; *cr:* Olivet Coll Fr Instr 1981; Alma Coll Resident Dir, Paris Prgm 1982-87; Berwick Acad Fr Tchr, Dept Chair 1987-; *ai:* Stud Abroad Paris Summer Prgm; Chess Club; Drama; Discipline, Acad Affairs Comm; AATF 1980-, Natl Fr Contest Coord St of ME 1989-; FLAME 1987-; NEH Summer Seminar 1990; Fr Govt Flwshp 1979-80; Hinman Flwshp MI St Univ 1979-80; Excl in Tchng Citation MSU 1982; *office:* Berwick Acad 31 Academy St South Berwick ME 03908

CLINTON, PEGGY ANN,OP, Religious Studies Teacher; *b:* Jersey City, NJ; *ed:* St Peters Coll (BA) Elem Ed 1981; Providence Coll (MA) Rel Stud 1992; *cr:* Lacordaire Acad Primary Dept Tchr 1984-88; Aquinas Acad Resource Room Dir 1988-90; Mount St Dominic Acad Rel Stud Dept 1990-; *ai:* Spectrum Prgm Dir; Moderator, Lectors; Amnesty Intnl; *office:* Mount St Dominic Acad 3 Ryerson Ave Caldwell NJ 07006

CLIPPINGER, STEVEN L., Amer His, AP Govt & Ec Teacher; *b:* Lima, OH; *m:* Jennifer Davis; *c:* Caroline, Rebecca; *ed:* OH St Univ (BS) Ed 1976; Univ of Dayton (MS) Schl Admin 1982; *cr:* Thomas Ewing Jr HS OH His Tchr 1978-82; Lancaster HS Soc Stud Tchr 1982-; *ai:* Var Girls Bsktbl Coach; NEA 1984-; DOR Amer His Tchr Awd; *office:* Lancaster HS 1312 Granville Pk Lancaster OH 43130*

CLISSOLD, JOHN RICHARDSON,II, HS Chem, Bio & Physics Tchr; *b:* Bronxville, NY; *m:* Gabrielle J.; *ed:* Univ of NC at Wilmington (BA) Environmental Sci Bio 1982; Bio Tchrs Cert at Univ of NC at Greensboro 1991; Attnd Kean Coll Earth Sci Ed 19 Hrs towards Master; *cr:* Rochester Midland Corp Salesman 1982-89; High Point Pub Schls 8th Grd Sci Tchr 1991-93; Solomon Schechter Day Schl Bio, Chem & Physics Tchr 1993-; *ai:* Sr Class Adv; Stu-Fac Liason for CORE; NJ Bio Tchrs 1994-; NJ Geology Assn 1994-; Audubon Schlsp; *office:* Solomon Schechter Day School 1418 Pleasant Valley Way West Orange NJ 07052

CLITES, ROBIN RAE, Chemistry Teacher; *b:* Martinsburg, WV; *m:* Gary Lee Jr.; *c:* Rachel Ann, Mallory Christine; *ed:* WV Univ (BS) Scndry Ed 1982; Advanced Prof Cert 30 Hrs Scndry Ed 1991; *cr:* Allegany Cty Schls Chem Tchr 1983-88; Calvert Cty Pub Schls Chem Tchr 1989-; Charles Cty Comm Coll Adj Prof 1990-; *ai:* Tchr Liason Consultant MD St Bd of Ed; Hnr Sci Seminar Spon; Sci Fair Coord; Chemathon Coach; *office:* Northern HS 2950 Chaneyville Rd Owings MD 20736

CLOSE, BRUCE ALLAN, PE, Cmptr Literacy & Hlth Tchr; *b:* Little Falls, NY; *ed:* SUNY at Plattsburgh (BS) Hlth Ed 1978, (BS) Elem Ed 1979, (BS) PE 1981, (MA) Lbrl Stud, Ed 1983; *cr:* Parishville-Hopkinton Schl Hlth Tchr 1978; Morristown Cntrl Schl Hlth Tchr 1979; Williamsburg HS Jr HS Math Tchr 1979-80; Peru Cntrl Schl Hlth, PE Tchr 1980-; *ai:* Girls Var Soccer, Boys Var Golf Coach; Dir Drug Free Open Gym; Yth Bureau Recreation Supvr; NEA, Peru Assn of Tchrs 1980-; Williamsburgh Cty Tchr of Yr 1980; Who's Who Among Stdnts in Amer Colls 1978; *office:* Peru Cntrl Schl 17 School St Peru NY 12972

CLOSE, JOSEPH MANLEY, Jr & Sr HS History Teacher; *b:* Wellsville ; *ed:* Villanova Univ (BA) His 1981; Alfred Univ (MS) Ed 1983; *cr:* Andover Central Jr & Sr HS His Tchr 1983-; *ai:* 7th Grd Class Adv; Acad Remediation Coord; NEA 1983-.

CLOSE, RICHARD A., Science Teacher & Coord; *b:* Pittsburgh, PA; *m:* Virginia Mac Neill; *c:* Barbara Close Moyer, Constance Anne; *ed:* Houghton Coll (BS) Gen Sci 1968; Westchester St Univ (MED) Ed 1971; Penn St Univ Sci Supvr Cert 1991; Attnd Marywood Coll, Bloomsburg St Univ 48 Grad Credits; *cr:* Indian Vly MS Sci Tchr 1968-, Sci Chm 1980-95; Souderton Area SD K-7th Grd Sci Coord 1995-; *ai:* Montgomery Cty Sci Rsrch Competition & Region 1B PA Jr Acad of Sci Dir; DE Vly Sci Fair Exec Comm Mem; Energy Ed Advy Cncl; Mont Cty Ecomeet, Envirothon & Gifted Ed Task Force Co-Dir; Souderton Area Ed Assn 1968-; PSEA & NEA 1968-; Montgomery Cty Sci Tchrs 1968-, Exec Comm, Tchr of the Yr; NSTA 1975-; Grace Bible Church 1968-, Elder & Tchr; NASA Newmast Scholar; Rohm & Haas Project Labs Intern; Article Pub; *office:* Indian Valley MS 130 Maple Ave Harleysville PA 19438

CLOSS, JANICE HOLMAN, 9th Grade English Teacher; *b:* Corbin, KY; *c:* Alison, Ann; *ed:* Cumberland Coll (BS) Soc Stud 1966; Xavier Univ (MS) Ed 1990; *cr:* Campbell Cty HS Tchr 1966-73 & 1978-79; Pendleton Cty GED Tchr 1978-83; Withrow HS Tchr 1983-; *ai:* Proficiency Test Intervention Classes; CFT 1985-; *office:* Withrow HS 2488 Madison Rd Cincinnati OH 45208

CLOSSER, BARRY JOSEPH, Media Specialist & Schl Librn; *b:* Martins Ferry, OH; *ed:* OH Univ (BA) Ed 1972; WV Univ (MA) Ed & Field in Lib Sci 1974; 3 Grad Hrs; 10 Grad Hrs Andrews Univ; 6 Grad Hrs Dayton Univ; *cr:* Buckeye West HS Librn 1972-88; Buckeye Southwest HS Librn 1988-90; Buckeye Local HS Media Specialist & Schl Librn 1990-; *ai:* HS Sftbl & Frosh Ftbl Coach; Diamond Club Adv; Lib Club Co-Adv; NEA; OEA; OVAC 1988-, Sftbl Dir; *office:* Buckeye Local HS Rd 2 Box 475 Panther Dr Rayland OH 43943

CLOSSER, BLAIR N., Occupational Work Adjust Coord; *b:* Martins Ferry, OH; *m:* Patricia A. Orizczak; *c:* Douglas, Derek, Darin; *ed:* OH Univ (BS) Elem 1974; Dayton Univ (MS) Admin 1977; *cr:* Mt Pleasant Elem 5th Grd Tchr 1974-76; Buckeye South Jr HS 7-8th Grd Rdng His Tchr 1976-90; Buckeye Southwest MS OWA Coord 1990-; *ai:* Var Asst Ftbl, 7th Grd Boys Bsktbl Coach; Buckeye Local Classroom Tchrs Assn, OEA, NEA 1974-; Belmont Cty Work Coord Assn 1992-; Yorkville Fire Dept 1970-, VP, Fire Captain; Village of Yorkville Cncl 1990-, Councilman, Cncl Pres 1995-; *office:* Buckeye Southwest MS 100 Walden Ave Tiltonsville OH 43963*

CLOSSER, CHARLES E.,JR., Prof of Oral Communication; *b:* Marshall, MO; *m:* Etta Louisa Jett; *ed:* Univ of MO at Columiba (AB) Speech & Drama 1964, (MA) Speech & Drama 1966; Ball St Univ (MA) Musical Theatre 1974; *cr:* Univ of MA Speech Instr 1966-67; Ball St Univ Theatre Tech Dir 1967-72; Univ of ME at Fort Kent Oral Communication & Performing Arts Prof 1975-; *ai:* Performing Arts Club, The Web Club, Le Club Toile Adv; Theatre Stage Dir; NEA 1980-; ME Arts Spons Assn 1985-, Pres; Fort Kent Lions Club 1976-, Pres; Fort Kent Chamber of Commerce 1988-, Pres, Merit Awd; univ of ME at Fort Kent Outstanding Fac Awd; Arts Leadership Inst Grant Univ of MN 1989; *office:* Univ Of ME At Fort Kent 25 Pleasant St Fort Kent ME 04743*

CLOSSER, ELAINE BARNO, Music Teacher; *b:* Johnson City, NY; *m:* Thomas G.; *ed:* Seton Hill Coll (BM) Piano 1968; Ithaca Coll (MM) Music Ed 1981; Attnd Duquesne Univ, Peabody Conservatory of Music, St Univ of NY at Potsdam, St Univ Coll NY at Brockport; *cr:* ME-Endwell Cntrl Schls Music Tchr 1968-74, 1977-; *ai:* 6th-8th Grd Chorus; MS Musical Dir; NEA 1968-; MENC; NYSSMA; BCMEA; *office:* Maine Endwell MS 1119 Farm To Market Rd Endicott NY 13760

CLOSSICK, JAMES J., Social Studies Teacher; *b:* Philadelphia, PA; *m:* Maryanne Roche; *c:* Rebecca; *ed:* Widener Univ (BA) Pol Sci Ed 1973; Villanova Univ (MA) Cnslng 1976; Univ of PA Post Grad Cert Scndry Admin 1981; *cr:* Beverly Hills Jr High Soc Stud Tchr & Guid Clslr 1973-76; Upper Darby High Guid Cnslr 1976-86, Soc Stud Tchr 1986-; *ai:* HS Var Golf Coach; NEA 1973-; PA Schl Cnslrs 1973-; PSEA 1973-; Vietnam Vets 1966-; Committeeman 1992-, DE Cty; US Navy Submarine Svc 1966-68; Honorable Discharge; Active Duty USS Henry Clay & USS Cutlass; *office:* Upper Darby Sr HS Lansdowne & School Ln Drexel Hill PA 19026

CLOSSON, CHESTER ROBERT,JR., World His & Geog Teacher; *b:* Trenton, NJ; *c:* Christianna; *ed:* Glassboro St (BA) Soc Stud 1969; 11 Addl Credits; *cr:* Willingboro Pub Schls Soc Stud Tchr 1969-; *ai:* Var Girls Winter, Spring Asst Field Events Coach; NEA 1969-; Willingboro Ed Assn 1969-, Head Bldg Rep, Dist Grievance Team; *office:* Meml Jr HS Van Sciver Pkwy Willingboro NJ 08046

CLOUD, ELIZABETH WILLIAMS, Spanish Teacher; *b:* Burlington, NC; *m:* William R.; *c:* William R. Jr.; *ed:* East Carolina Coll (BS) Span 1961; West Chester Univ (MA) Span 1977; NDEA Inst Appalachian St 1963; Grad Courses Span Univ of NC at Chapel Hill 1974-75; AP Span Lang Course Ridgeway Inst 1995; *cr:* Wicomico HS Span Tchr 1961-64; Chichester Sr HS F L Dept Moderator, Span Tchr 1964-; *ai:* Spon Sociedad Honoraria Hispanica; Dist Curr Restructuring, Site-Based, HS Restructuring Comm; Chprsn Frgn Lang Curr Comm; CEA, PSEA, NEA 1964-; AATSP 1962-; ACTFL 1974-; ASCD 1990-; Aston Pres Church 1979-, Elder; *home:* 120 Blackthorne Ln Aston PA 19014

CLOUGH, KARIN ELISABETH, English Teacher; *b:* New London, NH; *m:* Dr Kurt A. Weber; *ed:* Dartmouth Coll (BA) Eng 1988; Univ of TN Coll of Law (JD) Law 1992; Summer Stud at Univ of NH 1994; *cr:* Gould Acad Summer Schl Eng Tchr 1990 & 1992; Deerfield Acad Eng Tchr 1993-95; Oxbow HS Eng Tchr 1995-; *ai:* Var Girls Ice Hockey & Jr Var Girls Field Hockey Coach 1993-95.

CLOUGH, RUSSELL DEAN, Science Teacher; *b:* Norwood, MA; *m:* Stephanie Crea; *c:* Marie, Dean, Courtney; *ed:* Bridgewater St Coll (BS) Bio 1978; Post Grad Stud Scndry Admin; *cr:* O'Donnell MS Sci Tchr 1978-; *ai:* Girls Var Tennis Coach 1982-95; Systemwide Tch Task Force; Ski Trip Coord; NEA, MA Tchrs Assn, Stoughton Tchrs Assn 1978-; *office:* Robert G O'Donnell MS 211 Cushing St Stoughton MA 02072*

CLOUSE, NANCY L., Business Teacher; *b:* Miami Cty, IN; *m:* Thomas L.; *c:* Jodi K. Lange, Mike M., Tami R., Luke T.; *ed:* Manchester Coll (BS) Bus 1968; Wright St Univ (MA) Tchr, Ldr 1986; *cr:* Celina Sr HS Bus Tchr 1968-70; Parkway Local HS Bus Tchr 1975-; *ai:* Co-Adv FBLA, Stu Cncl; Parkway Ed Assn 1975-, Sec, Treas; Zion United Brethren Church 1970-, Fin Sec, SS Tchr; *office:* Parkway Local Schls 401 S Franklin St Rockford OH 45882*

CLOUSE, TOM LEE, Mathematics & Science Teacher; *b:* Mercer Cty, OH; *m:* Nancy L. Livengood; *c:* Jodi K. Lange, Mike M., Tami R. Luke T.; *ed:* Manchester Coll (BS) Math & Sci Ed 1966; St Francis Coll (MS) Ed 1970; *cr:* Lincolnview HS Study Hall Monitor & Tutor 1966; Parkway Local HS Math, Sci & Drivers Ed Tchr 1966-; *ai:* Var Ftbl 13 Yrs; Jr Var Bsbl 8 Yrs; 7th Grd-Jr Var Bsktbl 8 Yrs; Sci & Math Curricula; Mentor Prgm; FCA Adv; NEA, OEA, PEA 1966-, Pres, VP; WOEA 1966-; Rockford Recreation 1975-78; Zion United Brethren 1947-, Trustee, Sunday Schl Tchr, Financial Sec; Selected as Commencement Speaker for Class of 1993; *office:* Parkway HS 401 S Franklin St Rockford OH 45882

CLOUSER, ANNE FRANCES, English Teacher; *b:* Chambersburg, PA; *ed:* Wilson Coll (BA) Eng 1972; Master's Equivalency; Attnd Shippensburg Univ, Millersville Univ, Clarion Univ, Marywood Coll, Wilkes Coll; Univ of Nairobi at Kenya Stud African Lit, Music, Art, dance; *cr:* Manheim Twp HS Eng Tchr 1972-; *ai:* Comm, Work Prep Comms; PCTE, NCTE Writing Adv; Acad Teams Coach, Dir; Quiz Bowl; Knowledge Master Open; Quiz Net; PSEA, NEA 1972-; MTEA 1972-, Ed of Contact, PA Ed of Yr 1988; Federation of Acad Coaches & Team Sponsors; Lancaster New Era's Red Rose Awd Exceptional Achvmt Acad Team Coaching Reaching Natl Competition 1992-; *office:* Manheim Twp HS Box 5134 Schl Rd Lancaster PA 17606*

CLOUTIER, CYNTHIA HENDRICKSON, Foreign Language Dept Chairman; *b:* New York, NY; *m:* Robert A.; *c:* Melissa, Andrew; *ed:* OH Wesleyan Univ (BA) Psych, Span 1964; Fairfield Univ (MA) Ed 1969; *cr:* West Rocks MS Span Tchr 1964-70; Norwalk HS Span Tchr 1970-73; Ridgefield HS Span Tchr 1980-81; Brookfield HS Span Tchr 1981-, Dept Chm 1995-; *ai:* NHS Adv; Attendance, BEA Schlsp Comms; NEA, CEA, BEA 1980-; Comm Org Lang Tchrs 1990-; *office:* Brookfield HS 45 Long Meadow Hill Rd Brookfield CT 06804

CLOUTMAN, ARTHUR RHODES, Mathematics Teacher; *b:* Lynn, MA; *m:* Susan Frost; *c:* Darcy Cloutman Nelson, Kristi; *ed:* Salem St Coll (BS) Scndry Math 1964; Fairfield Univ (MATM) Tchng Math 1975; *cr:* South Windsor HS Math Tchr 1967, Math Tchr 1969-84, 1995-, Math Dept Head 1984-95; US Army Comp Programmer 1967-69; *ai:* Sr Class & Outing Club Adv; Drama Club Technical Adv & Dir; NEA 1969-; SWEA 1969-, Pres 1975-76; NCTM 1969-; *office:* South Windsor HS 161 Nevers Rd South Windsor CT 06074

CLOVER, SUSAN E., Instr of Practical Nurse Pgm; *b:* Montclair, NJ; *c:* Samuel, Jessica; *ed:* Boston Coll (BS) Nursing 1982; Orange Meml Hospital Schl of Nursing Diploma 1976; Working Toward Masters in Nursing at Regis Coll; *cr:* Orange Meml Hospital Staff Nurse 1976-79; Newton Wellesley UNA Staff Nurse 1979-80; Ind Nurse Consultant Self Employed 1980-; Quincy Coll Instr of Practical Nurse & Assoc Degree Registered Nurse Prgms 1991-; *ai:* Acad Procedure, AD to BSN Steering, Stu Svcs, Admissions, Curr & Fac Comms; Practical Nurse Prgm Class Adv 1995 & 1996; Amer Nurses Assn 1976-, Mem; MA Tchrs Assn 1993-, Mem; Sigma Theta Tau Intnl 1982-, Mem; Alpha Chi Chapter; Hull Yacht Club 1990-, Jr Race Comm; *office:* Quincy Coll 34 Coddington St Quincy MA 02169

CLUFF, GREG BRUCE, US History Teacher; *b:* Lewiston, ME; *m:* Lynn Turner; *c:* Amy, Brett; *ed:* Lafayette Coll (BA) Govt 1968; Univ of VT (MAT) His 1978; Univ of MA (MA) Sport Stud 1985; 15 Post Grad Credits U VT; *cr:* Champlain Vly Union HS US Hist Tchr 1969-; *ai:* Head Boys Tennis, Yth Bsktbl Coach; NEA 1970-; CVU Univ of VT NEA 1970-, Pres, VP; Town of Charlotte Bd of Civil Authority 1984-, Justice of the Peace; Chittenden Solid Waste Dist 1992-94, Town Rep to Bd of Dir; Tchr of Yr 1993; *office:* Champlain Valley Union HS RR 2 Box 160 Hinesburg VT 05461*

CLUKEY, SUE HARTFORD, Fifth Grade Teacher; *b:* Littleton, NH; *m:* Douglas Francis; *c:* Diane, Rebecca, Nathan; *ed:* Gorham St Coll (BS) Ed 1963; Univ of Southern ME (MA) Amer, New England Stud 1995; 18 Grad Credits Spec Ed; 33 Grad Credits His Univ of ME; 9 Yrs Archaeological Field Work; 20 Grad Credits Art, Rdng; *cr:* MSAD #51 Fourth Grd Tchr 1963-67, Sub Tchr 1967-70; Project Mainstream Graphic Artist, Presenter 1975-80; Sacred Heart Church Dir Rel Ed 1976-80; MSAD #51 Art Tchr 1976-80; MSAD #62 Grd 5 Spec Ed, GATE Tchr 1981-; *ai:* Sci Curr Comm; Archaeological Enrichment Group Facilitator; NEA, ME Tchrs Ed

Assn 1981-, Pownal Tchrs Assn 1981-, Sec; ME Archaeological Assn 1985-; Southern ME Volksmarch Assn 1984-; Spring Point Museum 1987-95, Vol Conservator; Nom ME Tchr of Yr 1987-89; Accepted as One of 15 ME Tchrs NEH ME-MS Region Project; Kathryne Sturtevant Moore Awd Incorporating Local His into Curr 1990; *office:* MSAD #62 587 Elmwood Rd Pownal ME 04069

CLUM, ALLEN J., AP Calculus & Psychology Tchr; *b:* Lima, OH; *m:* Nancy K. Lloyd; *c:* Matthew, Corey; *ed:* OH Northern Univ (BA) Psych 1980; Univ of Dayton (MS) Sch Cnslng 1989; Kent St Univ Inst for Scndry Math, Cmptr Sci Tchrs; Addl Hrs Drake Univ; *cr:* Elida HS Math Tchr, Ftbl, Track Coach 1981-, Math Dept Chair 1989-94, Psych Tchr, Guid Cnslr 1994-; *ai:* Asst Ftbl, Track Coach; NEA 1981-; NCTM 1985-88; TOPPS 1995-; Elks 1995-; *office:* Elida HS 101 E North St Elida OH 45807

CLUNEY, THOMAS EDWARD, 12th Grade English Teacher; *b:* Buffalo, NY; *m:* Patricia Mary Peacock; *ed:* Canisius Coll (BA) Philosophy 1977, (MA) Eng 1985; 12 Addl Hrs Ed 1986; Lehman Coll 3 Hrs Ed 1993; *cr:* Riker's Island Ed Facility Eng Tchr 1988; Bushwick HS Eng Tchr 1989; Laguardia Comm Coll Eng Instr 1990; Evander Childs HS Eng Tchr 1991-; *ai:* Fac Adv Lit Magazine; Multicultural Dir; AFT 1991-; UFT 1987-, Del Assembly; Tchr of Yr; Bronx PTO 1995.

CLUTTER, BARBARA MARY, 7th-8th Grade Teacher; *b:* Honolulu, HI; *m:* John B.; *c:* Kaitlin; *ed:* CA St Coll (MS) Ed 1982; *cr:* McGuffey MS 6th-8th Grd Tchr 15 Yrs; *ai:* MEA 1985-; *office:* McGuffey MS 86 McGuffey Dr Claysville PA 15323

CLUTTER, MARIANNE, Third Grade Teacher; *b:* Columbus, OH; *ed:* OH St Univ (BS) Child Dev 1983; Grad Hrs in Ed, Theory, Practice Tchr Cert; *cr:* St Brendon Schl Sixth Grd Tchr 1987-91, Third Grd Tchr 1991-; *ai:* Spelling Bee Organizer; Phi Upsilon Omicron 1983-; Pi Beta Phi 1979-; *office:* St Brendan Schl 4475 Dublin Rd Hilliard OH 43026

CLUTTER, TIMOTHY JOHN, English Teacher; *b:* Cincinnati, OH; *ed:* OH St Univ (BSEd) Lang Arts 1976; Yale Univ (MA) Linguistics 1980; *cr:* Olentangy Schl Dist 8th Grd Eng Tchr 1976-78; Forest Hills Schl Dist HS Eng Tchr 1982-; *ai:* Moderator; Acad Team Adv; Spectrum Lit Magazine; Phi Kappa Phi, Kappa Phi Kappa 1975-; Yale Alumni Assn 1980-; *office:* Anderson HS 7560 Forest Rd Cincinnati OH 45255

CLUVER, BARBARA CHANTRY, English Teacher; *b:* Pocatello, ID; *m:* Henning; *c:* Cathryn, Annette; *ed:* Univ of OR (BA) Ger 1962, Univ of Co (MA) Ger 1964; Univ of Ct GATE 16 Hrs, Univ of WA 30 Hrs Eng; *cr:* Gen H. H. Arnold HS Ger, Eng Tchr 1965-72, Gifted Specialist 1972-; *ai:* NHS, Acad Games Spon; Schl Improvement Steering Comm; OFT 1965-, PDK 1987-; *office:* General H H Arnold HS Unit 29647 APO AE 09096

CLYMER, KAREN LYNN, Psychology Teacher; *b:* Phillipsburg, NJ; *m:* Earl C. III; *ed:* Shippensburg Univ (BS) Soc Stud, Psych, Ed 1989; Lehigh Univ (MEd) Scndry Ed 1996; *cr:* Hunterdon Cntrl Reg HS Psych Tchr 1989-; *ai:* NJEA & NEA 1989-; *office:* Huntedon Central Regional HS 84 State Route 31 Flemington NJ 08822

CLYONS, KATHERINE HELFRICH, Kindergarten Teacher; *b:* Danbury, CT; *m:* Thomas J.; *c:* Carolyn, Elizabeth; *ed:* The Coll of New Rochelle (BA) Ed, Psych 1986; Sacred Heart Univ (MAT) Elem Ed 1995; *cr:* Roosevelt Schl Bpt Ct 3rd Grd Tchr 1986-87; Jane Ryan Schl 2nd Grd Tchr 1987-92, Kndgtn Tchr 1992-93, 2nd Grd Tchr 1993-94, Kndgtn Tchr 1994-; *ai:* CEA, NEA 1986-; *office:* Jane Ryan Elem Schl 190 Park Ln Trumbull CT 06611

COAKLEY, JANE MAZZA, Reading Facilitator; *b:* Elizabeth, NJ; *m:* John F. X.; *ed:* Newark St Coll (BA) Gen Elem 1967; Kean Coll (MA) Early Chldhd 1987; 6 Credits FL St Conjunction with Disney Univ; *cr:* Elizabeth Bd of Ed 4th-6th Grd Tchr 1967-93, Success for All Rdng Facilitator 1993-; *ai:* Ldrshp Team Site Based Mgr 1993-; Family Support Team 1993-; NEA, UCEA, EEA 1967-; Alpha Delta Kappa 1983-, Pres, VP, Treas; Chi Delta 1964-; NJ Governors Grant Recipient; Americanism Awd NJ Veterans; *office:* Christopher Columbus Schl #15 511 3rd Ave Elizabeth NJ 07202*

COAKLEY, LORI ANN, Asst Prof of Management; *b:* San Diego, CA; *m:* Steven John; *c:* Joseph Alexander; *ed:* Univ of CA at Santa Cruz (BA) Amer Stud 1984; Univ of MA at Lowell (MBA) Orgnl Stud 1989; Univ of MA at Amherst (PHD) Orgnl Stud 1993; *cr:* Enterprise Leasing Mgmt & Customer Svc 1986-87; Univ of MA Rsrch Asst 1987-93; Bryant Coll Asst Prof 1993-; *ai:* Fac Adv; SAM; Fac Coord; Visiting Execs Pgm; EAM 1988-; Acad of Mgmt 1990-; NAFE 1992-; CIBED & DOD Grant; Acad Stipend-Dev & Execution of Frosh Ldrshp Seminar; Fac Merit Awd for Outstdng Svc.*

COAKLEY, SUSAN GANTZ, ESL Teacher; *b:* Pawtucket, RI; *m:* James F.; *c:* Lynn, Beth, John; *ed:* Smith Coll (BA) His 1970; Notre Dame Coll (MED) TESL 1992; *cr:* Milford Schl Dist ESL Tchr 1990-; Notre Dame Coll Acting Dir 1995-; *ai:* After Schl Prgm Coach; Tchng Bosnian Lang; TSSOL 1990-; NNETESOL 1990-, NH Rep; AATG 1989-; ASCD 1991-; NCTE, NEA 1990-; NH ESL Network 1992-, Founding Mem, Chair; Presenter at NNETESOL Conventions & TESOL; NH Tchr Trainer; *office:* Milford HS 100 West St Milford NH 03055*

COATE, CHARLENE DINARDO, Fifth Grade Teacher; *b:* Cleveland, OH; *m:* David Russel; *c:* Brian, Laura, Kevin, Anne Zrenda, Katherine Zrenda; *ed:* John Carroll Univ (BA) His, Ed 1970, (MED) Ed 1986; Eco Chalk Talk 3 Hrs 1995; Eco Ed 4 Hrs 1993; Media Tech Ed 3 Hrs 1987; *cr:* Univ Schl Grd 1, 3 Apprentice 1985-86; Chambers Elem Schl 6th Grd Tchr 1987-92, 5th Grd Tchr 1992-; *ai:* Mental Hlth Intervention Team; Fifth Grd Chprsn; NEA, OEA, NEOEA 1987-; ECEA 1987-, Bldg Rep; Jr League of Cleveland 1985-, Provisinal Rep; Effective Schl Grant Prgm Chprsn; *home:* 3148 Belvoir Blvd Shaker Heights OH 44122

COATES, DAVID B., Social Studies Teacher; *b:* Coatesville, PA; *c:* Carol Hall, Kelly Daily, Rebecca; *ed:* IN Univ of PA (BS) Soc Scis 1970; Masters Equivalency West Chester Univ 1973; *cr:* South Brandywine 6th Grd Soc Stud Tchr 1970-73; North Brandywine Soc Stud Tchr 1973-76; Coatesville Area Sr HS Soc Stud Tchr 1973-76; North Brandywine 7th Grd Soc Stud Tchr 1973-; *ai:* 8th Grd Coach Bsktbl, Soccer, Track & Field; PSEA, NEA 1970-; NCSS; Outstanding Svc, Outstanding Tchr, Outstanding Tchr Team Awds; *office:* North Brandywine MS 200 Reeceville Rd Coatesville PA 19320

COATES, PATRICIA WALSH, Social Studies Teacher; *b:* Philadelphia, PA; *m:* Robert D.; *ed:* Westchester Univ (BA) Amer His 1984; Widener Univ (MeD) Soc Stud Ed 1989; Lehigh Univ (PhD) Colonial Amer His; *cr:* Natl Park Svc Ranger 1985-88; DE Cty Comm Coll Adjunct Instr 1989-92; Conestoga HS Soc Stud Tchr 1991-92; Spring Ford HS Soc Stud Tchr 1992-; *ai:* Stu Cncl, 1996 Class Cncl, Thespain Soc, Pep Club Adv; NEA, PSEA 1991-; Spring Ford Ed Assn 1992-; Chester Cty SPCA 1986-; *office:* Spring-Ford HS Lower Lewis Rd Royersford PA 19468

COBAU, PENNY KARABEDIAN, Science Teacher; *b:* Augusta, GA; *m:* Charles D. Jr.; *c:* Daniel, Thomas; *ed:* Duke Univ (BS) Psych, Bio 1979; Univ of Toledo (MED) Spec Ed 1981; 3 Quarter Hrs Grad Rdngs Bio 1995, 3 Quarter Hrs Astronomy II 1987, 6 Post Grad Hrs NSF Hnrs Tchrs Rsrch Prgm 1984-85; *cr:* Mc Cord Jr HS LD Tutor 1981-82, Sci Tchr 1982-87; Sylvania Southview HS Sci Tchr 1987-; *ai:* Critical Thinking Comm 1993-; OH Jr Sci & Hum Symposion Comm 1987-; Northwest Dist Sci Day Cncl 1991-; AAAS 1988-; NSTA 1991-; SEA, OEA 1981-; Syliania Acad Excl Fnd 1985-88, VP, Pres; Duke OH Alumni Admin 1979-, Chprsn 1978-81; St Michaels Church 1978-, Altar Guild, Choir; Univ of Toledo Outstdng HS Tchr Awd 1995; Sigma Xi Awd 1994; Jr Acad of Sci, OH Jr Sci Symposion Col George Leist Distngd Tchr Awd 1992, 1994-95; Sylvania Edctr of Yr 1991; *office:* Sylvania Southview HS 7225 Sylvania Ave Sylvania OH 43560

COBB, GARY R., Physical Science Teacher; *b:* Towanda, PA; *m:* Mary E. Lawrence; *c:* Michele Matylewicz, Bridget Van Houten, Stacie Rosengrant, Matthew, Jason; *ed:* Bloomsburg St Univ (BS) Phys, Earth Sp Sci 1967; Attnd Wilkes Coll, Penn St Univ; *cr:* Scotch Plains Schl Dist 9th Grd Sci Tchr 1967-70; Fanwood Schl Dist 9th Grd Sci Tchr 1967-70; Tunkhannock Area Schl Dist 8th Grd Sci Tchr 1971-; *ai:* MS Schl Sci Dept Coord; TASD Long Range Plan, Environmental Ed Comms; NSTA, PSEA, NEA, TAEA 1971-; PTO 1970-; PA Conservation Edctr of Yr 1986; Acid Base Chem Prentice Hall Allyn & Bacon 1986; *office:* Tunkhannock Area Schl Dist Franklin Ave Tunkhannock PA 18657

COBB, JOAN E., Dir, Acad Adorsement Center; *b:* Washington, DC; *c:* Joseph Wilson Jr., Jon Wilson; *ed:* Howard Univ (BA) Ed 1966; Univ of MD (MED) Ed 1975, (PHD) Ed 1978; *cr:* DC Pub Schls Classroom Tchr 1966-71; Rosemary Hills Children's Ctr Tchr, Ed Dir 1972; US Educ Dept DCPS Right Read Dir 1976; Howard Univ Asst Prof ECE, Dir Lab Presch 1978-82; Montgomery Co Govt Child Care Prog Dev Officer 1984-88; Balt City Comm Coll ECE Prof 1988-; *ai:* Curr Comm Chair; Balt Area Cncl Stu Tchng; NWP MD Writing Project, USN Tchr Research Group; TC Cncl Facilitator; AAUW 1993-; NAEYC 1980-; ACEI 1991-; ATE, MD ATE 1990-; AFT 1988-; Phi Delta Kappa 1994-; MD Comm for Children, Bd of D, VP Pub Policy 1989-91; R. Lourie Ctr Infants, Children 1986-, Co-Chair Prsnl; Montgomery Child Day Care Assn 1975-85, Sec, B of D; MD Commission Children, Youth, Chair; Univ of WI Madison Schl of Ed Natl Tchr Corps Leadership Dev Fellowship 1979; Gov Appointment Children & Youth Awd Silver Spring Links 1985; BCCC Excl Awd 1995; NISOD Tchng Excl Awd 1996; *office:* Baltimore City Community Coll 2901 Liberty Heights Ave Baltimore MD 21215*

COBB, MARTHA E., Science Teacher; *b:* Waterville, ME; *m:* Bill; *ed:* Univ of ME (BA) Zoology 1985; *cr:* Waterville Sr HS Sci Tchr 1989-90, Sci Tchr 1990-92, Sci Tchr 1992-; *ai:* Co-Adv Key Club, Sci Olympiad; ME Ed Assn, NSTA 1989-; Waterville Tchrs Assn 1989-, Sec; *office:* Waterville Sr HS 1 Brooklyn Ave Waterville ME 04901

COBB, MILAGROS MARIA, Second Grade Teacher; *b:* New York City, NY; *m:* Stephen Christopher; *ed:* Coll of Staten Island (BA) Lit, Soc Stud, Ed 1989; Working Towards MS Early Chldhd City Coll; *cr:* St Gregory The Great 4th Grd, 8th Grd Rel Tchr 1989-93, 2nd Grd Tchr 1993-; *ai:* After Schl Prgm; CCD Rel Ed Prgm Vol; Sacrament Class; St Peter's Choir; IRA 1990-; Manhattan Cncl; Fed Cath Tchrs 1989-; Hispanic Coalition 1990-; Rockland Cty 1995-, Exec Bd.

COBER, KAY ANN LICHVAR, English Teacher; *b:* Myersdale, PA; *m:* William R. Cober Jr.; *c:* Elizabeth, Christa, William John; *ed:* CA Univ (BS) Elem Ed 1970; Cert CA Univ; Attnd Penn St, Univ of Pittsburgh at Johnstown, Frostburgh St Univ; *cr:* Berlin Brothersvalley Schl Dist Elem Tchr 1970-73; Eng Tchr 1987-; *ai:* Track Coach; PSE-NEA 1970-; MAEA 1987-; Natl Cncl Tchrs Eng 1989-; Honorary Chapter Farmer Meyersdale Area FFA; *office:* Meyersdale Area HS Rd 3 Meyersdale PA 15552

COBERLY, KATHERINE KOLANKO, Third Grade Teacher; *b:* McKeesport, PA; *m:* Jack; *c:* Bree; *ed:* Penn St Univ (BS) Elem Ed 1970; *cr:* South Allegheny Schl Dist Kndgtn Tchr 10 Yrs, 1st Grd Tchr 1 Yr, 2nd Grd Tchr 11 Yrs, 3rd Grd Tchr 4 Yrs; *ai:* PSEA, NEA, SAEA 1970-.

COBLE, NANCY LOU (DAVIS), Fourth Grade Teacher; *b:* Newark, OH; *w:* James L. (dec); *c:* Amy, Alan, Alice Money Penney, Abby, Andrew; *ed:* OH Univ (BS) Elem Ed 1974, (MS) Curr, Instruction 1984; Post Grad Work; *cr:* Northern Local Schl Dist Sub, Title I Tchr 1968-70; Lakewood Local Schl Dist 4th Grd Tchr 1970-; *ai:* Safety Patrol Adv; Dist Soc Stud Comm; Cluster Tchr for Gifted Prgm; Lakewood Tchr Assn, OH Ed Assn, NEA 1970-; Natl Org Tchrs of Eng 1995-; *office:* Jacksontown Elem Schl 9100 Jacksontown Rd S E Jacksontown OH 43030

COBLENTZ, WAYNE ALBERT, Social Studies Teacher; *b:* Bell, CA; *m:* Kathryn Mae Koehler; *c:* Brian Wayne; *ed:* Coll of Emporia (BA) His, Pol Sci 1972; Emporia St Univ Media Specialist Cert; *cr:* Kansas City Pub Schls Soc Stud Tchr 1973-82; Frederick Cty Pub Schls Soc Stud Tchr 1982-; *ai:* Schl Improvement Team; Stdnts of Color and Others Club Spon; MD St Tchrs Assn, NEA 1982-; Natl Fed Interscholastic Ofcl Assn 1983-; Frederick Cty Civil War Roundtable 1989-, VP, Bd of Dir; Friends of Monocacy Battlefield 1991-; Western MD Track Ofcls 1985-; USA Track & Field Certfd Ofcls 1984-; Frederick Cty Tchr Historian Awd 1988; US Capital Historical Soc Tchr-Historian Awd 1988; *office:* Linganore HS 12013 Old Annapolis Rd Frederick MD 21701

COBURN, BARBARA PUPPEL, 9th-12th Grd Soc Stud Teacher; *b:* Hartford, CT; *w:* Kimball R. (dec); *ed:* N Adams St Coll (BA) His 1974; *cr:* Pittsfield Pub Schls 10th-12th Grd Soc Stud Tchr 1974-81; Albuquerque Pub Schls Sub 1981-82; Littleton Pub Schls 9th-12th Grd Soc Stud Tchr 1984-; *ai:* Peer Ldrshp Adv; Co-Adv Peer Mediation; NEA 1984-; Littleton Edctrs Assn 1984-, Sec 3 Yrs; Amer Psychological Assn 1984-; *office:* Littleton Jr Sr HS 55 Russell St Littleton MA 01460

COBURN, LYNN ANN, English Teacher; *b:* Cumberland, MD; *m:* Robert E.; *c:* Meghan; *ed:* Frostburg St Univ (BS) Scndry Ed, Soc Sci 1987, (MED) Curr, Instr 1992; Cert Eng 1990; *cr:* Frostburg St Univ Upward Bound Writing Tchr 1989-94; Northern Garrett HS Eng Tchr 1987-; *ai:* Rdng Club; Schl Improvement Team Mem; Eng Dept Chm; Yrbl Adv 1987-93; *office:* Northern Garrett HS 86 Pride Pkwy Accident MD 21520

COCCA, WILLIAM P., Music Teacher & Band Director; *b:* Buffalo, NY; *m:* Wendy Sutton; *c:* Christina, Will; *ed:* SUC at Fredonia (BA) Music Ed 1974; Ithaca Coll (MM) Music Ed 1987; (SAS) Educl Admin 1992; Addl Coursework SUC Potsdam, Eastman Schl of Music & Syracuse Univ; *cr:* LeRoy Central Schl 7-12th Grd Instrumental Music Tchr 1974-76; Greene Central Schl 7-12th Grd Instrumental Music Tchr 1976-85; Springville-Griffith Inst 9-12th Grd Instrumental Music Tchr 1985-; *ai:* Music Dept Coord; NYSUT, MENC, NYSSMA 1974-; ECMEA 1986-; *office:* Springville-Griffith Inst 290 N Buffalo St Springville NY 14141*

COCHENOUR, LINDA FEICK, 6th Grd English & Reading Tchr; *b:* Charleroi, PA; *m:* Robert J.; *ed:* CA Univ of PA (BS) Elem Ed 1969, (ME) Ed 1973; *cr:* Carroll Elem Schl 5th Grd Tchr 1969-80; Ginger Hill Elem Schl 5th Grd Tchr 1981-85; Finley MS 6th Grd Eng, Rdng Tchr 1985-; *ai:* Stu Cncl Spon; Sci Olympiad Team, Cheerleaders 1988-91 Co-Spon; Ringgold Ed Assn, PA St Ed Assn, NEA 1969-; Finley PTA 1989-; Nom PTA for Pheobe, Apperson, Hurst Outstanding Educators Awd 1990; *office:* Finley MS Rt 88 Finleyville PA 15332

COCHEO, VICTOR PAUL, Special Education Teacher; *b:* Staten Island, NY; *m:* Susan; *ed:* William Paterson Coll (MA) Spec Ed 1973; *cr:* Parsippany Bd of Ed Tchr, Coach 1970-; *ai:* Boys JV Soccer Coach; Head Bsbl Coach 1981-95; NJ Cncl for Soc Stud 1993-; NJEA, NEA 1970-; NJ Scholastic Coaches Assn 1995-; Randolph Little League Bsbl 1996-.

COCHRAN, FREDERICK HAYDEN, Technology Education Teacher; *b:* Ephrata, PA; *m:* Radeen Mann; *ed:* Millersville St Coll (BS) Ed 1978; 84 Grad Credits Cmptr & Tech Ed Penn St, Wilkes Coll; *cr:* Northeastern Jr HS Indstrl Arts Tchr 1979; Perkiomen Vly Sr HS Tech Ed Tchr 1980-; *ai:* NEA, PSEA, PVEA 1979-; Tech Ed Assn of PA 1980-; Rock Hill Island Packet Fleet 1991-; Selected to Participate Tech Showcase in St Capitol PAECT 1994, 1996; *office:* Perkiomen Valley HS 502 Gravel Pike Collegeville PA 19426

COCO, NANCY (NAWROCKI), 8th Grd Language Arts Te Stroudsburg, PA; *m:* Franklin E.; *ed:* East Stroudsburg Univ (BS 1987; PA St Univ Lehigh Vly Writing Project Inst, Advanced Pocono Mountain Schl Dist Jr HS Eng Tchr 1988-; Monroe Vo-Tech Schl Adult Ed Fr Tchr 1988-92; *ai:* Lancaster Assessm Mid-Atlantic Retreat Comms; NEA, PSEA, NCTE 1987-; Natl Project 1993-, Fellow; St Ann's Cath Churhc, Organist, Choir Adopt-a-Hwy Prgm; Articles Pub; NCTE Conf Presenter.

COCOMAN, KATHLEEN, First Grade Teacher; *b:* Queens, Franklin Pierce Coll (BS) Psych, Elem Ed 1972; Long Island Southampton (MS) Rdng 1984; 45 Addl Hrs; *cr:* St Martin of T First Grd Tchr 1972-85; Locust Schl Tchr 1985-87; Hemlock S Grd Tchr 1995-; *ai:* Head Tchr; Site Base, Dist Ed Comm Hemlock Schl 78 Bayberry St Garden City South NY 11530

CODDAIRE, ANN ROMILDA, Music Teacher; *b:* Haverhill, John W. III; *c:* Katherine Ann, John IV; *ed:* Bridgewater St Coll 1963; *cr:* Tilton Schl Elem Tchr 1963-64; Acad Notre Dame Mu 1984-; *ai:* Glee Club Dir; Spring Musical Dir; Chm NEASC Liturgical Music Dir Instrumentalists & Soloists; Parents Music Center 1984-; Music Ed Natl Conf 1984-; NCEA, Natl Music Soc 1984-; Natl Assoc of Pastoral Musicians 1992; Old Ch Garrison House Assn 1975-; St Mary's Church 1968-, Woemns Clu Kathy Nisco Mem Awd Outstanding Service & Commitment; *offi* Of Notre Dame 180 Middlesex Rd Tyngsboro MA 01879

CODDING, ELAINE (SIMPSON), Fifth Grade Teacher; *b:* Bos *m:* David W.; *c:* Sheila M.; *ed:* Keene St Coll (BED) Elem Ed 19 of Lowell (MED) Rdng 1972; Univ of NH 30 Hrs Post Grad Work *cr:* Barron Elem Schl Fifth Grd Tchr 1968-80; North Salem E Fifth Grd Tchr 1980-; *ai:* PTA Fac Rep; 5th Grd Spelling, Math Organizer; NEA, NH-NEA 1968-; Salem Educ Assn 1968-, Fac R of Yr Nom; Girl Scouts USA 1985-, Assoc Ldr; Timberlane Mu 1994-, Sec; Timberlane Bsktbl Boosters 1995-; North Salem PT Timberlane HS PTA 1994-; *office:* North Salem Elem Schl 140 Rd Salem NH 03079*

CODER, HILARY HALL, PE Teacher & Track Coach; *b:* Attleb *m:* Kenneth James; *c:* Kelly Anson, Vaughan William; *ed:* PA St U Hlth, PE 1983; *cr:* Phillips Exeter Acad PE Tchr, Track Coac Combine Dir for Reebok 1994-; *ai:* Head Boys, Girls Indoor & Track Coach; Var Girls Soccer Coach; Individual Stu Adv; Appoir Leaves, Curr Review Comms; USATF 1990-; USWTFC, USHSTF Brown Awd 1991; Level II Cert 5 Areas Track & Field; Clinic P *office:* Phillips Exeter Acad 20 Main St Exeter NH 03833*

CODERRE, BETTE-JEAN, Junior High Teacher; *b:* Pawtucket Our Lady of the Elms (BA) His 1965; St Michaels Coll (MAT) R 33 Credit Hrs Undergraduate Ger; *cr:* Sacred Heart Elem Tchr 196 Louis Schl Elem, Jr High Tchr 1968-71; St Patrick Schl Jr H 1971-; *ai:* Educating People on Native Amer Culture, Tradition; Intertribal & Grand Entry Dances; Mohegan Tribal; Sister of S 1960-; Appear in New England Native Amer Calender Helps Foste Amer Legacy; *office:* St Patrick Schl 125 Montgomery St Chico 01020

CODERRE, FRANCIS JOHN, Band Director; *b:* New York, Christopher, Kimberly; *ed:* Univ of VT (BS) Music Ed 1962; Lon Univ (MS) Music Ed 1967; *cr:* Mayfield Cntrl HS Band Dir Sachem South HS Band Dir 1965-; *ai:* Jaycee Bsbl, PAL Hocke League Bsbl Coach; Marching Band, Stage Band Dir; AFT, SCTA Bldg Rep; NYSUT 1962-, Delegate; MENC, SCMEA 1962-; NEA Delegate; US Navy 4 Yrs; NROTC Schlshp; *office:* Sachem Sout School St Ronkonkoma NY 11779

CODY, JOHN J., Earth Science Teacher; *b:* Bronx, NY; *c:* Ki Robyn; *ed:* SUNY at Brockport (BS) Ed 1964; Hofstra Univ (MA) Sci Ed 1971; 45 Addl Hrs; *cr:* Connetquot Pub Schls Jr HS S 1964-65; Bay Shore Union Free Schls HS Sci Tchr 1965-; *ai:* B Soccer, Jr Var La Crosse Coach; Awareness Weekends Stdnts Cnslr Clinics for Kids; Soccer Coaching Courses For Adults; AFT, NE Shore Classroom Tchrs Assn 1964-; Natl Soccer Coaches Assn o 1976-; Bay Shore Youth Soccer Club 1980-; Suffolk Cty Soccer Assn 1975-, Sec, Treas; Natl Sci Fnd Inst Geology; Writte Workbooks, tchr Lecture Notes 2 Sci Courses; *office:* Bay Shore Free Schl Dist 75 W Perkal St Bay Shore NY 11706*

CODY, MICHAEL THOMAS, 8th Grade Mathematics Teac Salisbury, MD; *m:* Linda Faye Griffen; *c:* Michael Joshua & Rache *ed:* Bob Jones Univ (BS) Elem Ed 1985; 21 Grad Credit Hrs West Coll; *cr:* Victory Chrstn Acad Classroom Tchr 1985-86; Somerset C System 6th-8th Grd Math Tchr 1986-92; Wicomico Cty Schl Sys Grd Sci Tchr 1992-93, 8th Grd Math Tchr 1993-; *ai:* Stu Cncl Spo Ldr; Schl Improvement Team Mem; TASCO 1986-; MSTA 1986-; Boys Sunday Schl Tchr 5 Yrs; Bible Bapt Church 20 Yrs; Greenw Tchr of the Yr 1990-91 & 1991-92; *office:* Woodson MS 281a W School Rd Crisfield MD 21817*

CODY, PATRICIA ANN, Eighth Grade Teacher; *b:* Philadelphia, LaSalle Univ (BA) Ed, Soc Stud 1982; *cr:* St William Schl S 1981-82; King of Peace Sixth Grd Tchr 1982-89; Epiphany of O Schl Eighth Grd Tchr 1989-; *ai:* Yrbk, Stu Cncl, Safety Patro League Moderator; NCEA 1982-; Soc Stud Cncl 1995-; Geograp 1994-; Parish Pastorial Cncl 1994-; Soc Stud Chprsn; *office:* Epiph Our Lord Schl 1248 Jackson St Philadelphia PA 19148

CODY-HOWE, PATRICIA A., Resource Center Teacher; *b:* Br NY; *m:* James E. Sr.; *c:* James Jr., Patrick; *ed:* Monmouth Coll (B Ed 1982; *cr:* Asher Holmes Elem Schl Resource Sped Ed Tchr 1 Marlboro MS Selfcontained Spec Ed Tchr 1984-86; Robertsville Ele Selfcontained Spec Ed Tchr 1986-88; Central Schl Selfcontained S Tchr 1991-92; Robertsville Elem Schl Resource Spec Ed Tchr 19 NEA, NJEA 1982-; Eisenhower Grant; *office:* Robertsville Elem S Menzel Ln Morganville NJ 07751*

COE, HELEN M., Math Teacher; *b:* Elizabeth, NJ; *m:* Robert Montclair St Coll (BA) Math 1970; *cr:* Westfield HS Math Tchr 19 NEA, NJEA & WEA 1970-; NCTM; *office:* Westfield HS 550 Do Westfield NJ 07090

COE, MAURENE ANN, Lang Arts Tchr of GATE; *b:* Mt Clemens, Gerald Edward; *ed:* Western MI Univ (BA) Elem Ed 1968; Grad W St Univ, Kent St Univ; *cr:* Grand Ledge Pub Schl Tchr 1970-7 Kennedy Schl for Gifted Tchr 1982-86; The Boardman Acad for Tchr 1986-90; Youngstown Pub Schls Tchr 1990-; *ai:* Odyssey of Future Problem Solving; YEA, OEA, NEA & OH Assn for Gifted C 1990-; Inter Rdng Assn 1993-; NCTE, ASCD 1994-; IMPACT II 1992; *office:* West Elem Schl 134 N Hazelwood Youngstown OH 4

COEN, ELIZABETH ANNE (BOWLEY), HS Social Studies Teac Newport, RI; *m:* Timothy; *c:* Liam; *ed:* RI Coll (BA) Soc Sci 1990 Regina Univ 60 Credits Bus Mgmt; Comm Svc Learning Summ 1994; *cr:* South Kingstown HS Soc Stud Tchr 1993-; *ai:* NEA *home:* 31 Spencer Ct Wakefield RI 02879*

COENE, MARY CARMELLA, Sci & Team Physics Teach Rochester, NY; *ed:* St Bonaventure Coll (BA) Math, Sci StBonaventure Univ (MS) Bio 1955; Union Coll (MST) Chem,

Addl Credit Hrs; *cr:* St Patricks Schl Third Grd Tchr 1927; Holy hl Sixth Grd Tchr 1929-30; Mercy HS Math, Sci Tchr 1931-33; ath HS Math, Sci 1033-40; Mercy HS Math, Sci Tchr 1940-51; mily Schl Math, Sci Tchr 1951-53; St Ann's HS Frosh Courses St Mary's Schl Eighth Grd Tchr 1954-55; Nortre Dame Schl i Tchr 1955-; *ai:* Quiz League, Schlsp Challenge, Chem Group for tion Coaching; Mentor for Physics Tchr; NSF Federal Grants; St andy Outstdng Tchr Awd1988-89; Outstdng Edctr Awd 1994; Twin tstdng Edctr Awd 1994; *office:* Notre Dame HS 1400 Maple Ave IY 14904

Y, FRANCIS G., Fifth Grade Teacher; *b:* Milford, MA; *m:* Linda : Jennifer Lynn, Francis G. IV; *ed:* Fitchburg St Coll (BS) Elem ; Worcester St Coll (MS) Ldrshp & Admin 1983; *cr:* Cntrl Elem Tchr 1974-79; Brookside Elem 5th Grd Tchr 1979-95; Stacy Mid Tchr 1996; *ai:* Coached Bsbl 1986-; NEA 1973-; MTA 1974-; tacy MS 66 School St Milford MA 01757

Y, MELISSA ANN, English Teacher; *b:* Buffalo, NY; *ed:* Saint iture Univ (BA) Eng 1993; *cr:* East Aurora HS Sub Tchr 1993-94; Park HS Sub Tchr 1993-94; Immaculata Acad Eng Tchr 1994-; *ai:* azine, Schl Newspaper Adv; *office:* Immaculata Acad 5138 S Park nburg NY 14075

N, BRUCE METCALF, English Teacher; *b:* Woodstock, VT; *m:* artog; *c:* Elizabeth, Jonathan; *ed:* Univ VT (BA) Eng 1965; NY A) Eng 1969; Wesleyan Univ CAS Intellectural His 1985, Univ Trinity Coll Dublin Eire 1963-64; *cr:* Passaic Collegiate Schl Eng 65-69; Amer Comm Schl London Eng Tchr 1969-71; Amer Schl Eng Tchr 1976-77; Malvern Coll Eng Tchr 1986-87; Westover Schl ır 1972-; *ai:* Adv Literary Magazine; Admissions Comm; Adv rs Club; Informal Group Eng 1976-; RG Collingwood Soc Lftme T Quarterly 1988; Wesleyan Alumni Mag 1993; CBE Fello 1995; O Box 847 Middlebury CT 06762

NET, MARIA PAZ, French & Spanish Teacher; *b:* LaAlberca, ı: Emmanuel Louis; *c:* Marguerite, Marianne; *ed:* Dominican Coll Span 1974; Iona Coll Grad Schl (MS) Span 1977; *cr:* Nyack HS ı Tchr 1974-; *ai:* Span Hnr Soc; Span Club; AATSP, NYSFLT *ffice:* Nyack HS 360 Christian Herald Rd Upper Nyack NY 10960

IAN, BILLIE A., Early Childhood Ed Asst Prof; *b:* Altoona, PA; glas; *c:* Michelle L. Crowell; *ed:* Lock Haven Univ (BS) Early Educ 1977; PA St Univ (MED) Curr, Instruction 1988; Doctorate Work IN Univ of PA; *cr:* Blair Cty Head Start Tchr 1978-86; Child es of Blair Cty Child Dev Assoc Trainer 1986-89; Mount Aloysius Early Chldhd Instr 1986-89; Penn Coll of Tech Early Ch Ed Asst 39-; *ai:* Co-Pres, Stu Adv Natl Assoc for Educ of Young Children; tor NAEYC Accreditation; CSAEYC, NAEYC 1990-, Co-Pres; Wkshps at Local, St, Natl Confs for St Child Care Agencies, Natl art Assn; *office:* PA Coll Of Tech 1 College Ave Williamsport PA

IAN, JOHN DODSON, Social Studies Tchr & Dept Chm; *b:* gh, PA; *m:* Claudine Foltz; *c:* Renee Cuffman Riggs, Tara Coffman James Dodson; *ed:* Clarion UNiv (BS) Soc Stud, Geog 1956; IN PA (MED) Geog 1962; 6 Grad Hrs Penn St Univ; 6 Grad Hrs Univ ourgh; 8 Grad Hrs Univ of Costa Rica; *cr:* Marion Ctr HS Soc Stud 56-62; US Dept of St Frgn Svc Ofcr 1962-65; Edinboro Univ Geog ept Chair 1965-70; US Dept of St Frgn Svc Ofcr 1970-8; US Naval ol Sci Prof 1986-87; Marion Ctr HS Soc Stud Tchr, Chm, Gifte 987-; *ai:* Mock Trial Team Coach; Chess Club Spon; PSEA, NEA Amer Frgn Svc Assn 22 Yrs; Planning Commission 1988-, VP; of White Words 1995-, Pres; IN Univ Comm 1985-; NSC Rsrch Costa Rica 1968; Superior Honor Awd Dept of St; Various Articles *ice:* Marion Ctr Jr Sr HS Box 156 Marion Center PA 15759

LL, MONICA ELISE, Science Teacher; *b:* New Britain, CT; *m:* . Jr.; *c:* Christopher, Emily; *ed:* Salisbury St Univ (BS) Bio 1990, Educl Admin 1993; Univ of MD at Baltimore Cty DNA Tech Course alisbury St Univ Admin Courses 1995; Loyola Coll at Baltimore ing Thinking Course 1994; *cr:* Stephen Decatur HS Sci, Family Life 991-; *ai:* Schl Improvement, Pupil Svcs Teams; Phi Delta Kappa NEA, MSTA, WCTA, NSTA, MAST 1991-; ASCD 1995-; Kappa i; Phi Kappa Phi; Beta Beta Beta; *office:* Stephen Decatur HS 9913 k Rd Berlin MD 21811

O, JOSEFINA GONZALEZ, Frgn Lang Chprsn & Span Tchr; *b:* , Cuba; *m:* Roberto Gonzalez; *c:* Roberto, Isabel, Eduarbo, Felipe ez, Finita Cofino Kilby; *ed:* Havana Tchrs Coll (AA) Span His Jniv of Havana (BA) Span Lang & Lit 1955; Amer Frgn Svc Inst chng One Semester 1969; Amer Univ Span Tchng Course with Field ı Oyster Schl One Semester 1986; *cr:* Holy Redeemer Schl Chprsn Tchr, Frgn Lang Dept 1969-; Schl of the Holy Child HS Span Tchr ; Our Lady of Good Counsel HS Span Tchr 1986; Holy Cross Elem pan Tchr 1986-89; *ai:* Judge Frgn Lang Tournament HS Level y Schl VA 1983-; Amer Assn of Tchrs of Span & Portuguese, Greater sn of Tchrs of Frgn Langs, MD Frgn Lang Assn, NEA, Amer Cncl rs Frgn Lang 1970-; Rock Creek-Byforde Highlands Assn 1981-; s of Columbus Outstdng Tchr Awd 1991; Main Speaker Frgn Lang of Archdiocese of WA Annual Convention 1989, 1992; Dev First chng Curr of Paroch ial Primary Schls in Archdiocese of Washington *fice:* Holy Redeemer Schl 9715 Summit Ave Kensington MD 20895

INS, ROSE B., Magnet Resource Teacher; *b:* South Hill, VA; *m:* E.; *c:* Cleven W., Brycee L.; *ed:* Norfolk St Univ (BS) Bus Ed 1975; ırn CT St Univ (MS) Instrl Tech 1979; *cr:* Hillhouse HS Bus Ed Tchr 3; Career HS Bus Ed Tchr 1983-95, Magnet Resource Tchr 1995-; v Sr, Jr Class, FBLA, Cmptr Club; Yale Univ Tchrs Inst Extended gm, Gospel Choir Coord; Educl Ldrshp Team; AFT 1976-; CBEA, 1978-; NAASP; Alpha Kappa Alpha 1990-, Corresponding Sec; Natl Bus, Prof WOmen's Club Inc 1978-, Pres, Outstdng Presidential; Church Ushers 1980-, VP, Outstdng Svc; *office:* Career H S 21 er Pl New Haven CT 06511*

LAN, ROSEMARIE MAMMELE, Dean of Students & Eng Tchr; oy, PA; *m:* Raymond J. III; *c:* Raymond IV, Brigid Ann; *ed:* Chestnut oll (BA) Eng 1971; Villanova Univ (MA) Eng 1977; OH St Univ 6 s; *cr:* St Huberts HS Eng Tchr 1971-72; DE Cty Comm Coll Eng Tchr 3; Villa Maria Acad HS Eng Tchr 1983-; *ai:* Lit Magazine; NCTE PCTE 1985-; Brandywine Ballet Auxiliary 1990-93; Incentive s Grant for Writing Center West Chester Area Schl Dist 1979; *office:* Maria Acad HS Green Tree Malvern PA 19355

N, SANDRA LEE, French Teacher; *b:* Madison, WI; *m:* Robert; *ed:* of WI at Whitewater (BA) Fr 1968; Univ of Cincinnati (MED) 1986; Alliance Francaise 1971; Centre De Perfectionnement Linguistique Univ of Avignon 1983; Inst in Alsace & Savoie 1991; *cr:* Delta HS g Tchr 1968; Bowling Green HS Fr Tchr 1968-69; Schwab Jr HS Eng 970; Lyon Jr HS Fr, Eng Tchr 1970-76; Walnut Hills HS Fr Tchr *ai:* Fr Club; Fr Natl Honor Soc; AFT, CFT, 1986-; AATF 1976-; OH n Lang Assn 1980-; Dept Chprsn; Dist Wide Lead Tchr; Citywide Appreciation Day Rep; OH Foreign Lang Assn Most Outstanding n Lang Dept in St 1995; Mayerson Awd for Comm Svc 1994; *office:* t Hills HS 3250 Victory Pkwy Cincinnati OH 45207*

EN, BLANCHE RUBIN, Science Teacher & Dept Chprsn; *b:* hstan, USSR; *m:* Michael L.; *c:* Howard Swett; *ed:* Wilkes Univ (BS) Scndry Ed, Bio 1964; SUNY at New Paltz (MS) Scndry Ed 1990; Cold Spring Harbor Learning Ctr Exploring Human Genetics Lab Course, Word Processing, Authentic Portofolio Assessment, Peer Mediation In-Svc courses; *cr:* Fallsburg Cntrl Schls Sci Tchr 1964-69, 1975-76, 1978-, Sci Dept Chprsn 1980-; Liberty Cntrl Schls Sci Tchr 1977-78; *ai:* Sr Class Adv; Super Team; Shared Decision Making Comm; Dinner Co-Chair, Sec Comm Schlsp Comm; NYSUT, AFT 1978-; Sullivan Cty Tchrs Cncl 1989-; Fallsburg Tchrs Assn 1978-, Bldg Rep, VP, Exec Cncl, Pres, Negotiations Team; Delta Kappa Gamma Society Intl; B'Nai B'Rith Women 1974-, Tres, Sec, Prgm Chair; Lions 1993-, Executive Comm 1995-; NEA Grant 1969; Fallsburg Cntrl Comm Schlsp Dinner Honoree 1987; SADD Hall of Fame Inductee 1989; Yearbook Dedication 1994; *home:* PO Box 432 Woodridge NY 12789*

COHEN, DAVID ALEXANDER, Former Asst Prof of Mrktg; *b:* Suffern, NY; *m:* Susan H. Foster-Cohen; *c:* Avram, Naomi; *ed:* UCLA (BA) Psych 1974; USCAL (MA) Sociology 1981, (PHD) Sociology 1983; OK St Univ Mrktg Post Doctoral Stud; *cr:* OK St Univ Visiting Asst Prof 1986-88; WA St Univ at Vancouver Mrktg Asst Prof 1988-90; Northern AZ Univ Mrktg Asst Prof 1990-95; Pispolino Consulting, Managing Dir; *ai:* Alpha Epsilon Pi, Assn des Etudiants en Sci Economiques et Commerciales Fac Adv; AMA 1986-; ACR 1988-; Delta Sigma Pi Outstanding Prof 1993.

COHEN, DEBBY MOYER, Spanish Teacher; *b:* Pittsburgh, PA; *m:* Ted; *c:* Jeffrey, Andrew; *ed:* Mt Union Coll (BA) Span; Master's Equivalency Ed Framingham St Coll, Indiana Univ of PA; Attnd Gannon Coll, Coll of St Rose, Carlow Coll, Indiana Univ of PA, IN Wesleyan Univ; *cr:* Gateway Sr HS Span Tchr; *ai:* Span Play; NEA; PSEA; *office:* Gateway Sr HS Mosside Blvd Monroeville PA 15146

COHEN, GAIL STEINBERG, Business Education Teacher; *b:* Queens, NY; *m:* Harvey; *c:* Ian Joshua, Melissa Beth; *ed:* Hofstra Univ (BBA) Bus Ed 1970; Western CT St Coll (MS) Counseling & Guidance 1981; 15 Post Grad Credits; *cr:* Joel Barlow HS Part-time Bus Ed Tchr 1979-81; Carmel HS Bus Ed Tchr 1981-; *ai:* Sr Class, Yrbk Co-Adv; Work Co-op Coord; FBLA 1990-; Natl Cncl of Jewish Women 1975-; *office:* Carmel HS 30 Fair St Carmel NY 10512*

COHEN, HARVEY JAY, Teacher & Ice Hockey Coach; *b:* Brookling, MA; *c:* Charlie Gayle, Matthew; *ed:* Manhattan Comm Coll (AA) Bus Admin 1970; Brooklyn Coll (BA) Ec 1972; NY Univ (MA) PE 1981; *cr:* Chatham Twp HS Bus, His, PE Tchr, Ath Dir 1973-88; Chatham HS His, PE Tchr 1989-; *ai:* Ice Hockey Coach 1973-; NEA, NJ Coaches Assoc 1973-; NJ Ice Hockey Coaches Assn, Sec; Article Pub 1990; *office:* Chatham HS 255 Lafayette Ave Chatham NJ 07928

COHEN, JACK A., Psychology Professor; *b:* San Francisco, CA; *ed:* Princeton Univ (AB) Psych 1966; Univ of PA (MS) Psych 1967, (PHD) Psych 1976; *cr:* Camden Cty Coll Prof of Psych 1971-; *ai:* Psi Beta Adv; Phi Beta Kappa 1966-; Sigma Xi 1966-; *office:* Camden County Coll PO Box 200 Blackwood NJ 08012

COHEN, JACQUELINE G., Mathematics Chairperson; *b:* New York City, NY; *m:* Melvin H.; *c:* David, Michael; *ed:* NY Univ (BS) Math 1964; Iona Coll (MS) Educl Computing 1984; Coll of New Rochell Admin & Supervision Cert; *cr:* Lehman Coll Adjunct Math Instr 1980-84; Scarsdale HS Math Tchr 1982-84; Byram Hills HS Math Tchr 1984-94, Math Chprsn 1994-; *ai:* Sr Options, Scheduling Comms; Past Jr Adv; NCTU 1964-; NCSM 1994-; AMTNYS 1984-; MAA 1990-; *office:* Byram Hills HS 12 Tripp Ln Armonk NY 10504*

COHEN, JAY VICTOR, Mathematics Teacher; *b:* Providence, RI; *ed:* URI (BS) Math 1967; Brown U (MSC) Applied MAth 1970; RI Coll 18 Credits Ed; *cr:* Perry MS Math Tchr 1972; Warren HS Math Tchr 1972-73; Paths Schl Mat Tchr 1973-80; ALP Schl Math Tchr 1980-; *ai:* PACE, Scheduling Comms; AFT 1984-, Bldg Rd; *office:* Alternate Learning Project 582 Elmwood Ave Providence RI 02907

COHEN, KENNETH, Dean & Science Teacher; *b:* Brooklyn, NY; *m:* Lynne R. Dolinger; *c:* Randy, Rayna; *ed:* Queens Coll CUNY (BS) PE 1970, (MS) Exercise Sci 1972; The OH St Univ (PHD) Exercise Physiology 1975; *cr:* Lehman Coll CUNY Asst Prof 1975-80; Brooklyn Coll CUNY Asst prof 1985-90; Kingsborough Comm Coll Asst Prof 1990-; IS 211 Dean 1990-; *ai:* UFT 1990-; ACSM 1975-, Pres, NY Chptr; Full Flwsp OH St Univ; 2 Pub Articles; 2 Grants; Grad Tchrs Awd; *office:* John Wilson IS 211 1001 E 100th St Brooklyn NY 11236

COHEN, MAXINE ALICE, Nursing Teacher; *b:* Brooklyn, NY; *c:* Marcel Blum, Jesse Blum; *ed:* Hunter Coll (BS) Nrsng; Adelphi Univ (MS) Comm Hlth Nrsng 1976; 3 Credits TEACH for Exceptional Stdnts Coll of St Rose; 3 Credits Spec Ed Learning Disabilities Brooklyn Coll; *cr:* Rutgers Univ Instr 1077-78; Wagner Coll Instr 1978-82, Adj 1983, 1990; Curtis HS Nrsng Tchr 1992-; *ai:* UFT, NYSTA, AFT 1992-; Sigma Theta Tau 1981-; Who's Who in Amer Nrsng 1986-87; Awd of Recognition from Mozzini Sr Ctr 1981; Federal Nrsng Traineeship HEW 1975-76; Educl Grant Brooklyn VNA 1974-75; *office:* Curtis HS 105 Hamilton Ave Staten Island NY 10301

COHEN, MERYL, Chemistry Teacher; *b:* New York City, NY; *m:* Harmon; *ed:* Hunter Coll-CUNY (BS) Chem 1966; Syracuse Univ (MS) Sci Ed 1969; Long Island Univ (PD) Educl Admin 1980; Madeleine Hunter Trained; Cmptr In-Svc Courses; *cr:* Julia Richman HS Chem Tchr 1966; Jericho Jr Sr HS Sci Tchr 1966-67; Syracuse Pub Schls Sci Tchr 1967-70; Riverhead HS Chem Tchr 1970-; *ai:* Field Trip, Assembly Comm, Liason Tchr for Proj WISE (NSF); AFT, NYSUT, NYSTA 1967-; RCFA 1970-, Bldg Rep, Exec Bd, Tchr of Yr 1990; Suffolk Cty Sci Tchrs Assn; Dist Tchr of Yr 1990; *office:* Riverhead HS 700 Harrison Ave Riverhead NY 11901

COHEN, MILTON R., Retired English Teacher; *b:* Hartford, CT; *c:* Karen Beth, Stephen Erik; *ed:* Syracuse Univ (BA) Eng; Univ of MI (MA) Fr; Cert Tchng Univ of Hartford; Eng Brandeis Univ; Attnd Univ of CT Schl of Law; *cr:* Milford Acad Eng, Fr Tchr 1956-57; Brandeis Univ Assistantship Eng 1957-58; Amity Regnl Sr HS Fr, Eng Tchr 1958-94; *ai:* Outstdng Blood Drive Coord 1985-86; Newspaper Spon 1958-71, 1991-93; Stu Cncl Spon 1976, 1973; Ftbl Refreshments Stand Coord 1975-77,1979; Attendance, Schlsp Comms; Drama Club Asst Adv 1980-81; Jr Class Spon 1963-66; Adult Ed Tchr; Group Ldr Stu Tours England; Governor's Advy Cncl for Spcl Ed 1979-80; Spcl Olympics World Games Vol 1995; AEA 1958-, Exec Bd 1980-, PR, Prsnl Comm Policies; CEA, NEA 1958-; CT Cncl Eng Tchrs; Amity Players Org 1963-, Pres 1965; Recording for Blind, Dyslexicc 1994-, Monitor, Reader; New Haven Jewish Historical Soc 1981-, Exec Bd; US Army 1956; Shakespeare Lectures; Mentor, Master Tchr Prgm 1981; *home:* 297 Fountain St New Haven CT 06515*

COHEN, MIRIAM KRISTEIN, Capping & Art Cluster Teacher; *b:* Long Island City, NY; *m:* Walter; *c:* Jonathan K., Matthew D.; *ed:* Hunter Coll (BA) Eng 1959, (MS) Ed; *cr:* 5th Grd Tchr 1961-63; 4th Grd Tchr 1963-64; PS 220 Edward Mandel 2nd-3rd Grd, Sci, Art Clusters Tchr 1964-; *ai:* ESSA; NYCATA; Murray Hill Comm 1988-; Impact II Grant 1988-89; *office:* Edward Mandel Schl PS 220 62-10 108th St Forest Hills NY 11375

COHEN, MYRA WASSERMAN, 6th Grade Teacher; *b:* Brooklyn, NY; *m:* Norman; *c:* Pamela, Jason; *ed:* Brooklyn Coll (BA) Elem Ed 1972, (MS) Lang Arts 1974; C W Post (MS) Educl Admin 1992; St Certfd Licenses; *cr:* PS 16 Brooklyn 4th Grd Tchr 1972-75; Levittown Schl Dist Chptr I Math Tchr 1988-89; Hebrew Acad of Nassau Cty 6th Grd Sci & Soc Stud Tchr 1989-; *ai:* Report Card Comm; Math Olympaid; Fund Raising Adv; NEA 1972-; Nassau Cty Rdng Assn 1985-; Hadassah 1980-, VP; NYS Edctr of Excl Awd 1996; Federal Grant NY Univ Study of Comparison of Rdng & Self-Esteem 1984-88; *office:* Hebrew Acad Of Nassau Co 25 Country Dr Plainview NY 11803

COHEN, NORMAN E., Asst Prof of Cmptr Science; *b:* Louisville, KY; *m:* Jessica Field; *c:* Geoffrey; *ed:* Cornell Univ (BA) Lbrl Arts, Cinema 1969; VA Tech (MS) Cmptr Sci 1980; *cr:* Genigraphics Corp Software Mgr 1980-86; Paralogix Corp Software Mgr 1986-89; The Foxboro Co Software Mgr 1989-92; SUNY Asst Prof 1992-; *ai:* ACM, IEEE Cmptr Soc 1980-; *office:* S U N Y Coll Of A & T Morrisvl Lab Class Bldg Morrisville NY 13408

COHEN, PHYLLIS, English Teacher; *b:* Brooklyn, NY; *ed:* St Univ of NY (BA) Eng 1968; 32 Credit Hrs in Ed Amer Univ 1988; *cr:* Damascus HS Eng Tchr 1990-91; Seneca Valley HS Eng Tchr 1992-; *ai:* Lit Magazine Spon; Eng Curr Revision Comm Mem; NCTE, NEA, MSTA 1987-; Montgomery Cty Cert of Excl; *office:* Seneca Valley HS 12700 Middlebrook Rd Germantown MD 20874*

COHEN, RICHARD L., AP Eng, Gifted Education Tchr; *b:* Williamsport, PA; *m:* Mary Beth; *c:* Sean (dec), Allison, Meredith; *ed:* Hamilton Coll (BA) Eng Lit 1970; Villanova Univ (MA) Eng Lit 1974; Educl Admin, Supervision 30 Post Grad Credit Hrs; *cr:* Upper Moreland Jr HS Eng Tchr 1970-77; Upper Moreland Sr HS Eng Tchr, Tchr of Gifted Ed 1977-; *ai:* Boy's Tennis Coach; PA Tchrs Assn, NEA 1970-; Montgomery Cty Gifted Ed Cncl 1987-; Nom Twice PA Tchr of Yr; Muhlenbourg Coll Scndry Schl Tchng Excl Awd; Nom OLMSTEAD Prz, Williams Coll; *office:* Upper Moreland HS 3000 Terwood Rd Willow Grove PA 19090

COHEN, ROBERTA, Advanced Work Class Teacher; *b:* Boston, MA; *ed:* Mass Bay Comm Coll (AA) Lbrl Arts 1963; Univ of MA at Amherst (BA) Eng 1967; Univ of MA at Boston (MACCT) Critical Thinking 1980; 65 Addl Grad Credits; *cr:* Boston Schls Sub Tchr 6 Months; Roger Wolcott Elem Schl Grd 5 Tchr 1968-80; Bradford Annex Elem Schl Grd 5 Tchr 1968-80; Holland Elem Schl Grd 5 Tchr 1968-80; M. L. King MS AWC, Grd 6, Lang Arts, Rdng, Math Tchr 1980-; *ai:* AICUM-ADHOC Kids to Coll Evaluation Comm; Boston Tchrs Ctr Evaluation Comm; AFT, Rollins Griffith Tchr Ctr 1968-; Boston Women's Heritage Trl 1994-; Various Mini-Grants From Boston Schls, Pvt Funding; *office:* Martin Luther King MS 77 Lawrence Ave Dorchester MA 02121

COHEN, RUTH ALICE, Assistant Principal; *b:* New York City, NY; *ed:* CCNY (BA) Bio, Psych1967; Lehman Coll (MS) Elem Ed 1972; Coll of New Rochelle (PHD) Schl Admin, Supervision 1988; Lehman Coll Spec Ed, Rdng, Art His, Photography; CCNY Schl Psych; Pratt Inst Photography, Ceramics; *cr:* PS 61X First, Third Grd Tchr 1967-71; PS 126X Fourth Grd Tchr, Cluster, Rdng Tchr 1971-77; Dist Office 9 Tchr Trainer 1977-80; PS 95X Spec Ed, Rdng Tchr 1980-81; SETRC Tchr Trainer 1981; JHS 135X Rdng, Sci Tchr 1981-82; PS 160X Spec Ed, Rdng Tchr 1982-83; PS 148Q Second Grd, Media Tchr 1983-91; PS 76Q Interim Acting Asst Prin 1991-92; PS 148Q Media Tchr, Adm Asst 1992-93, Asst Prin 1993-; *ai:* Sr Class Adv; Schl Fund Raiser; Chprsn; Curr Comm; CSA, AAP 1993-; UFT, AFT 1967-93; Bronx Rdng Cncl 1975-83, Recording Sec; *office:* PS 148Q 8902 32nd Ave East Elmhurst NY 11369

COHEN, RUTH LYNN (GOLDBERG), Chemistry Teacher; *b:* New York, NY; *m:* Kenneth; *c:* Dana, Samara; *ed:* City Coll of NY (BS) Jewish Area Stud & Sci 1966, (MA) Chem Ed Scndry 1970; NY Univ (MA) Jewish Stud 1970; Yeshiva Univ Modern Jewish His PHD Stud; *cr:* JHS 143X Sci Tchr 1966-67; HS of Fashion Industries Sci Tchr 1967-71; Lehman HS Chem Tchr 1974-75; Truman HS Chem Tchr 1977-79; Bronx HS of Sci Chem & Hebrew Tchr 1979-; *ai:* Judaic Culture Soc Adv 1992-; AFT 1966-; Chem Tchrs of NY 1978-; Hadassah 1971-; ORT 1975-; Project Dorot 1986-; Wouk Schlsp at Hebrew Univ 1963-64; Bernard Revel Grad Schl Yashina Univ 1976-78; Memrl Fndtn for Jewish Culture 1977-78; Woodrow Wilson Summer Inst 1987-88, 1990 & 1995; Summer Flwshp Mentor Pgm at Hebrew Univ 1988.

COHEN, VICTOR S., Natural Science Professor; *b:* Madison, WI; *m:* Sandra Maia-Cohen; *c:* Libby Maia; *ed:* St Univ of NY at Buffalo (BA) Bio 1980; Marshall Univ (MS) Physics, Phys Sci 1987; *cr:* North Yonawanda Pub Schl 7-9 Math Tchr 1980-81; Marshall Univ Grad Asst Chem 1983-89; OH Dept of Hlth, Hlth Physicist 1990; Columbus St Comm Coll Natural Sci Prof 1989-; *ai:* Distngd Tchng Awd Finalist 1995, Nom 1990; *home:* 6994 Scottsford Pl Columbus OH 43235*

COHN, ARLENE MANGINELLI, Spanish Teacher; *b:* Brooklyn, NY; *m:* Robert A.; *c:* Robert, David, Cari Ann; *ed:* SUNY at Albany (BA) Span, Ital Ed 1972; Long Island Univ (MS) Span 1975; Tchng Eng to Speakers of Other Langs Cert; 60 Post Grad Credits Educl Related Areas; *cr:* Commack HS South Span, Ital Tchr 1972-77; Commack HS Span Tchr 1988-; *ai:* Schl Mediation Adv; Multi Cltrl Comm, Frgn Lang Fetival Chrpn; AATSP 1990-; *office:* Commack HS Scholar Ln Commack NY 11725

COHN, SHERYL A., 4th Grade Teacher; *b:* Bronx, NY; *ed:* Hofstra (BA) Elem Ed 1973, (MA) Elem Ed 1975; 60 Hrs Post Grad Stud; *cr:* SUNY at Farmingdale Instr of Sociology 1973-; Port Washington Pub Schls Elem Tchr 1973-; *ai:* Sci Mentor; Admin NYS ESPET; PWTA & NYSUT 1973-; SCOPE; SSBPOA 1984-88 Sec; NGA & NPC & Several Racing Orgs; Won Several Female Car Racing & Bodybuilding Titles; *office:* John Philip Sousa Elem Schl 101 Sands Point Rd Port Washington NY 11050

COIA, LOU V., Seventh Grade Mathematics Tchr; *b:* Philadelphia, PA; *m:* Gracelyn Lisi; *c:* Lisa DeCesero, Marisa, James; *ed:* Glassboro St (BA) General Elem Ed 1964; 18 Credits in Span; *cr:* Dr J P Cleary Jr HS 7th Grd Math Tchr 1964-65; Caroline L Reutter Schl 6th Grd Tchr 1965-66; Delsea MS 7th Grd Math Tchr 1966-; *ai:* 7th Grd & Jr Atheneum League Adv; NEA, NJEA, GCEA, DEA 1964-; Buena Little League; Newfield Youth Soccer League; Buena Wrestling Boosters Club; Tchr of Yr 1987; Governors Tchr Recognition Awd; *office:* Delsea Regional Middle Schl Blackwoodtown Rd Franklinville NJ 08322

COKER, SUSAN, Fourth Grade Teacher; *b:* Massillon, OH; *ed:* Bowling Green St Univ (B S) Sec Ed Soc Stud 1970; Akron Univ (BS) El Ed 1972; *cr:* Tuslaw Local Schls Elem Tchr 1970-; *ai:* NEA & OEA 1970-; Phi Delta Kappa 1994-; W Lebanon Unit Meth Admin Cncl 1986-, Chprsn; *office:* Moffitt Heights Elem Schl 12035 Moffitt St SW Massillon OH 44647

COKINES, ELLEN MARIE, Art Teacher; *b:* Brooklyn, NY; *ed:* Brooklyn Coll (BA) Fine Arts & Classics-Magna Cum Laude 1975; Fordham Univ (MA) Medieval Church His 1982; Working Towards MFA; MA Grad Flwshp; *cr:* Bd of Ed City of NY Tchr 1982-; Crafts On The Average Owner 1986-93; *ai:* AP Art His; Phi Beta Kappa 1975-; Grad Flwshp Fordham Univ; Phi Beta Kappa Brooklyn Coll; *office:* Fort Hamilton H S 8301 Shore Rd Brooklyn NY 11209

COLABELLA, THOMAS CHARLES, Music Teacher; *b:* Mineola, NY; *m:* Christine M. Kuchta; *c:* Jennifer, Thomas Jr.; *ed:* Long Island Univ at CW Post Ctr (BA) Music Ed 1971, (MS) Elem Ed 1976, (PD) Educl Admin 1978; 60+ Credits Past Masters; *cr:* Kings Park Cntrl Schl Dist Music Tchr 1971-; Prof Musician Percussionist 1963-; *ai:* Band; Orch; Chorus; NY St Adjudicator for NYSSMA Solos & Ensembles; AFT, NYSUT, NYSSMA, SCMEA, MENC, KPCTA, FSSO & Local 802 AFM 1971-; Most Distngd Tchr of Yr 1978; Recording Artist & Musician Prof for Alfred Publishing; *office:* Fort Salonga Elem Schl 39 Sunken Meadow Rd Northport NY 11768

COLACHICO, RONALD CHARLES, Chemistry Teacher; *b:* Medford, MA; *ed:* Merrimac Coll (BS) Chem & Bio 1974; Salem St (MED) Scndry Ed 1982; *cr:* Pope John XXIII High Chem Tchr 1975-; *ai:* Amer Chem Soc 1976-; *office:* Pope John Xxiii Ctl HS 888 Broadway Everett MA 02149

COLAIANNI, MARY LINDA, Cmptr Sci & Bus Dept Chair; *b:* St Johns NF, Canada; *m:* David Lee Brady; *c:* Jennifer, Toni, Daniel; *ed:* Univ of Pittsburgh (BA) Pol Sci 1979; Troy St Univ (MS) Bus 1987; USAF Squadron Ofcrs Schl; St Certfd Adv Prof; *cr:* USAF Intelligence Ofcr 1979-89; Archbishop Spalding HS Comp Sci, Bus Tchr 1990-93, Comp Sci, Bus Chair 1993-; *ai:* ASHS Mock Trial Team Coach; SADD Moderator; Soph Class Moderator; USAFR Major; Air Force Assn 1979-; *office:* Archbishop Spalding H S 8080 New Cut Rd Severn MD 21144*

COLAIO, GERARD J., Guidance Department Chairman; *b:* New York, NY; *ed:* Iona Coll (BA) His, Ed-Cum Laude 1968; Tchr Coll, Columbia Univ (MA) Guid & Cnslng 1971; Manhattan Coll Post Grad Credits; *cr:* Emerson Jr HS Soc Stud Tchr 1968-69; Burroughs Jr HS Soc Stud Tchr, Guid Cnslr 1969-74; Roosevelt HS Guid Cnslr 1974-; *ai:* Grad Requirement Comm; Fashion Club; AFT, Yonkers Fed of Tchr 1968-; Southern Westchester 1980-; Coll Conf Comm 1972-; Iona COll Advy Bd; West Putnam Rockland Cnslng Assoc; Roosevelt HS 1968-, Co-Pres 1991-93; PTA; NY St PTA Jenkin's Awd Svc to Yth 1973, Outstdng Svc to Yth Awd 1987; Tchr of Yr 1990; Yrbk Fac Dedication 1987; St Univ of NY Partnership Educl Grant Nestle Foods; *office:* Roosevelt HS 631 Tuckahoe Rd Yonkers NY 10710

COLANERI, AGNES, 9th Grd English Teacher; *b:* Jersey City, NJ; *ed:* Seton Hall Univ (BS) Eng, Scndry Ed 1969; Jersey City St Coll (MA) Rdng 1975; 17 Post Grad Credit Hrs Spec Ed; 28 Post Grad Credit Hrs ESL Cert; 6 Post Grad Credit Hrs Rdng Specialist Cert, Trng Ed Tech; *cr:* Emerson HS Tchr 1969-; *ai:* Project Explore Bell Atlantic; Scndry Lang Arts Standing, Revising Lang Arts Curr Comms; Mid Sts Evaluation Philosophy, Goals, Lang Arts Comms; UECA, HCEA, NJEA, NEA 1969-; Big Brothers, Big Sisters Hudson Cty 1991-, Outstdng Big Sister 1993; Tchr Recognition Awd Spon by Douglass Coll 1994; *office:* Emerson HS 318 18th St Union City NJ 07087

COLANGELO, PATRICIA ANN, Fourth Grade Teacher; *b:* Neptune, NJ; *ed:* Monmouth Coll (BS) Elem Ed 1969; *cr:* Woodmere Schl 4th Grd Tchr 1969-; *ai:* NJEA 1969-; NEA; ETA; Governors Tchr of Yr Recognition Awd 1990; *office:* Woodmere Elem Schl 65 Raleigh Ct Eatontown NJ 07724

COLANGELO, PATRICIA JO (BARNS), Senior High Chemistry Teacher; *b:* Pittsburgh, PA; *m:* Joseph Peter; *ed:* Univ of Pittsburgh (BS) Chem 1992, (MAT) Scndry Sci Ed 1993; *cr:* Fox Chapel Schl Dist Intern Chem Tchr 1992-93; Boyertown Area Schl Dist Chem & Bio Tchr 1993-; *ai:* Sci Olympiad Spon & Coach; NEA, PSEA, BAEA 1992-, 1993; NSTA, PSTA 1992-; Amer Chemical Soc 1992-, Stu Affiliate Mem 1991; Kappa Kappa Gamma 1993-, Alumni & Adv; Home Schl Network 1994-, Exec Bd Mem; Enrichment Honors Course Seminar Instr; *office:* Boyertown Area Sr HS 500 E 4th St Boyertown PA 19512

COLANGELO, PETER JOSEPH, Music Director; *b:* Camden, NJ; *m:* Patricia; *c:* Peter, Perry; *ed:* Glassboro St Coll (BA) Music 1965; Trenton St Coll (MA) Music 1976; *cr:* Stratford Schl Dist Music Dir 1965-; *ai:* Concert & Stage Band; NEA 1965-; NJEA 1965-; MENC 1965-; AFM Local 77 1960-; Prof Working Musicians; *home:* 1 Liberty Ln Cherry Hill NJ 08002

COLANNINO, ANTHONY, French, Spanish & Italian Tchr; *b:* Panni, Italy; *m:* Mary Cotoia; *c:* Nicholas, Paula M. Karach; *ed:* Montclair St Univ (BA) Fr 1966; Span 1977; Fairleigh Dickinson Univ; *cr:* New Mildord HS Tchr 1966-69; New Milford MS Tchr 1969-81; New Milford HS Tchr 1981-94; David E. Owens MS Tchr 1994-; *ai:* 6th Grd After Schl Prgm; NEA, NJEA, NMEA, BCEA 1966-; AATF 1978-; NBFLEA 1970-; *office:* David E Owens MS Roselyn & Marion Ave New Milford NJ 07646

COLASANTI, JAMES NICHOLAS, Teacher & Dept Chairperson; *b:* Pottstown, PA; *m:* Lori Lynn Mcbride; *c:* Ryan, Andrew, Marie, Julie; *ed:* Ursinus Coll (BA) Fr 1964; West Chester Univ (MA) Fr & Ed; *cr:* Perkiomen Schls Tchr 1964-65; West Chester Schls Tchr 1965-70; Boyertown Schls Supvr & Tchr 1970-; *ai:* Curr & Textbook Selection Comms; Dept Chprsn; NEA & PSEA 1964-; BAEA 1988-; *office:* Boyertown Sr HS 4th & Monroe Sts Boyertown PA 19512

COLAVECCHIO, ANTHONY PHILLP, Physical Education Teacher; *b:* Winsted, CT; *ed:* Northwestern CT Comm Coll (AS) Phys Ed & Rec 1973; Cntrl CT St Univ (BS) Phsy Ed & His 1976, (MS) Phys Ed 1978; Cooperating & Mentor Tchr St of CT; Project Adventure Training; *cr:* Winsted Schl System Spec Ed Aid & Adapted PE Tchr 1976-78; Eastern CT St Univ Asst Bsktbl Coach 1978-89; Glastonburg HS Boys Bsktbl Coach 1989-95; Elmer T Thienes Elem Schl Phys Ed & Adapted PE 1978-; *ai:* Co-Chm Phys Ed Curr Comm; HS Boys Bsktbl Coach; Bsktbl Clinician; Summer Camp Admin & Adv; CT Assn for Hlth, Pys Ed, Rec & Dance 1980-; CT Assn of Bsktbl Coaches 1990-; DARN, Pgm Vol 4 Yrs; Celebration of Excl Recipient 1987; Articles Pub Irish Bsktbl Coaches Assn; Celebration of Excl & the CT Assn for Hlth, Phys Ed, Rec & Dance; *office:* Elmer T Thines Elem Schl 25 School Dr Marlborough CT 06447*

COLAVECHIO, MARYELLEN E., Eighth Grade Teacher; *b:* Philadelphia, PA; *ed:* St Norbert Coll (BA) Elem Ed 1975; St Joseph Univ 14 credits Towards Masters; *cr:* St Richard Schl 2nd Grd Tchr 1975-86, 4th Grd Tchr 1987-93, 8t Grd Tchr 1994-; *ai:* Stu Cncl; CYO, Math Club, Yrbk Adv; Tchr, Mentor Prgm; NCEA 1990-; Distinguished Cath Educator Awd 1987; *office:* St Richard Schl 1827 Pollock St Philadelphia PA 19145

COLAVITO, ARLENE DAHL, English & Social Studies Tchr; *b:* Yonkers, NY; *m:* Joseph Anthony; *ed:* Mt St Vincent (BA) His 1973; Fordham Univ (MA) His 1975; Union Theological Seminary (MDIV) Pastor Cnslng 1979; *cr:* Our Lady of Victory Schl 5th-6th Grd Eng, Soc Stud Tchr 1973-74; Fordham Prep Schl 7th-11th Grd Soc Stud Tchr 1974-77; Our Lady of Fatima Schl 4th-8th Grd Eng, Soc Stud Tchr 1977-81; St Hilda's, St Hughs's Schl 7th Grd Eng, Soc Stud Tchr 1981-84; Immaculate Conception Schl 5th-8th Grd Eng, Soc Stud Tchr 1984-87; The Lenox Schl 6th-8th Grd Eng, Soc Stud Tchr 1987-91; Iona Prep Schl Eng, Soc Stud Tchr 1991-94; Our Saviour Luth Schl Eng, Soc Stud Tchr 1994-; *ai:* Drama Club; NCSS 1973-; NCET 1991-; Region II Yth Team 1988-; Region II Chrstn Ed Team 1989-; Who's Who in Colls, Univs; Who's Who in Women in Westchester Cty; *office:* Our Saviour Lutheran Schl 1734 Williamsbridge Rd Bronx NY 10461*

COLBERT, DAVID CHARLES, Fourth Grade Classroom Teacher; *b:* Conemaugh, PA; *m:* Carol M. Flook; *c:* Lindsay Carol, Carrie Lynn; *ed:* Indiana Univ of PA (BS) Elem Ed 1972; Commonwealth of PA (MS) Elem Ed 1987; Attnd Univ of Pittsburgh for PA Sci Tchr Prgm 6 Credits, & ITEC Cmptr Lit 7 Credits; Addl Drug & Alcohol Trng Prgm 16 Credits; *cr:* Conemaugh Valley Schls 4th-6th Grd Tchr 1972-; *ai:* Dist 6 Championship Girls Sftbl Coach With Citation from PA House of Reps; Profiles in Survival Amer Cancer Soc Part 1992; Appointed to TAP 1993; Dist 6AA Sftbl Championship Coach with Schl Bd Recognition Letter 1993; Letter of Congratulations from Congressman; Hd Coach Girls Sftbl Conf Chmpnshp 1993-94, 1994-95; Vic's Blue Room Girls Bsktbl Coach 2nd Place 1994-96; PSEA & NEA 1972-; Conemaugh Valley Ed Assoc 1972-, VP; Conemaugh Twp Zoning Hearing Bd 1991-, Sec 2 Yrs; Conemaugh Twp Planning Commission, Sec 2 Yrs, Recognition Awd from Twp Supervisors 1990; Pegasus Sewer Auth, Sec; Outstanding Effort in Interscholastic Competition Awd from Conemaugh Valley Schl Bd 1984; *home:* 1295 Clapboard Run Rd Johnstown PA 15904

COLBERT, LISA GARRISON, Religion Tchr & Dept Chprsn; *b:* San Diego, CA; *m:* Timothy E.; *c:* Meghan, Caitlin; *ed:* Barry Univ (BA) Rel Stud 1981; Univ of Dayton Educl Ldrshp Credit Hrs; *cr:* Lasalle HS Rel Tchr 1981-83; Madonna Acad HS Rel Tchr, Campus Minister 1983-89; Chaminade-Madonna HS Rel Tchr, Campus Minister 1989-93; Chaminade-Julienne HS Rel Tchr 1993-; *ai:* Dept Chprsn; Pastoral Team; LIFE Prgm Moderator; NCEA 1981-; Chaminade-Madonna Alumni Hall of Fame Induction; *office:* Chaminade-Julienne Cath HS 505 S Ludlow St Dayton OH 45402

COLBURN, DEVRA L., Mathematics Teacher; *b:* Willimantic, CT; *c:* Jennifer, Jonathan, Jesse; *ed:* Eastern CT St Univ (BA) Psych Ed 1983; Univ of CT (MA) Ed Curr, Instruction 1991; *cr:* D. A. Kramer MS Home Ec Tchr 1983-84, Math Tchr 1984-85; Woodstock Pub Schl 6th-8th Grd Math Tchr 1985-91, 7th Grd Sci Tchr 1985-91, 7th-8th Grd Math Tchr 1991-94; Woodstock MS 8th Grd Math Tchr 1994-; *ai:* Math Team Ldr; NEA; *office:* Woodstock MS 147 Rt 169 Woodstock CT 06281

COLBURN, MELISSA STRAYER, English Teacher; *b:* Toledo, OH; *m:* Tony; *ed:* Univ of Toledo (BE) Eng Ed 1992; *cr:* Cardinal Stritch HS Eng Tchr 1992-; *ai:* Past Jr Class Moderator 1993-94, Frosh Cheerleading Adv 1992-93; Sr Class Moderator 1994-; Stu Assistance Team Dir 1994-; NCEA 1992-; *home:* 524 Independence Dr Waterville OH 43566

COLBY, ELISABETH, Volunteer Latin Teacher; *b:* Little Falls, NY; *ed:* Coll of St Rose (BS) Piano & Mus Ed 1953; Cath Univ of Amer (MA) Music Ed 1958; Crane Schl of Music at Potsdam Music Therapy 1967; *cr:* Cath Schls in Syracuse & Albany Dioceses Music Tchr 1941-94; Rome Cath Jr & Sr HS Music & Latin Tchr 1974-; *office:* Rome Cath Jr & Sr HS 800 Cypress St Rome NY 13440

COLBY, REBECCA MORRILL, Special Education Teacher; *b:* Concord, NH; *m:* Paul W.; *c:* Rachel, Megan; *ed:* Keene St Coll (BS) General Spec Ed, Elem Ed 1981; *cr:* Nizhoni Elem Schl Level 3 Spec Ed Tchr 1981-82; Merrimack Valley Schl Dist 1st-4th Grd Itinerent Spec Ed Tchr 1982-86; Coe Brown Northwood Acad Spec Ed Tchr 1987-; *ai:* Sr Portfolio Adv; Epsom Bapt Church 1994-, Teen Ldr; *home:* 76 Concord Hill Rd Pittsfield NH 03263*

COLE, CAROLINE, 7th Grade Teacher; *b:* Have De Grace, MD; *m:* Ronald; *c:* Cathleen Johnson, Eric; *ed:* Empire St Coll (BS) Elem Ed 1990; SUNY at Stony Brook (MS) Lib Stud, His 1995; *cr:* Faith Acad Tchr, Adm Cnslr 1984-.

COLE, CHRISTINE LILIAN, English Teacher; *b:* Marietta, GA; *ed:* Augustana Coll (BA) Eng 1980; Univ of AR (MA) Eng 1982; Post Grad Stud in Cmptrs, Writing Assessment, Multi-Cultural Stud & Advanced Placement; *cr:* Univ of AR Grad Tchng Asst 1980-82; Jack R. Kearns Amer Schl HS Eng, Music 1982-87; Shape Amer Elem Schl Music Specialist 1987-93; Shape Amer HS Eng Tchr 1993-; *ai:* Multi-Cultural Coord, Schl Improvement Team Chprsn; Fed Ed Assn 1987-; Kappa Delta Pi 1996; Tch of Yr 1996; *office:* Shape American HS Cmr 451 Box 0005 APO AE 09708*

COLE, DEBBIE GOLIBER, Biology Teacher; *b:* Dover, DE; *m:* Michael; *ed:* NY St Univ at Albany (MS) Curr Dev & Instrl Tchng 1994; *cr:* Mohanasen HS Summer Schl Sci Tchr 1988; South Colonie Cntrl Schls Sub Tchr 1991-93; Bishop Maginnn HD Bio Tchr 1993-95; Shaker HS Bio Tchr 1995-; *ai:* Comm Adressing 9th Grd Issues; Greater Capital Reg DNA Sci Pgm 1994-; NSTA 1994- NABT & BALSA 1994-, Mem; Greater Captial Reg Tchng Ctr 1994-, Bldg Ambassador; *office:* Shaker HS 99 Slingerland St Albany NY 12202*

COLE, DELYSIA LASSITER, Chem, Anatomy, Physiology Tchr; *b:* Baltimore, MD; *m:* Freddie; *c:* Shannon, Delysia Maria; *ed:* VA St Coll (BS) Bio 1973; Morgan St Univ (MS) Urban Ed, Sci 1980; Guid, Cnslng Prgm at Loyola Coll; *cr:* Baltimore City Pub Schls Tchr 1973-; *ai:* Staff Dev, Multicultural Comm; Balto Tchrs Union 1983-; Alpha Kappa Alpha 1971-; *office:* Patterson Sr HS 100 Kane St Baltimore MD 21224

COLE, EDMUND JOSEPH, Chemistry Instructor; *b:* Ogdensburg, NY; *m:* Nicole L.; *c:* David, Gayla, Shannon, Erin; *ed:* St Univ of NY (BA) Sci, Scndry Ed 1965; 45 Grad Hrs; PE Cert; *cr:* Parishville Cntrl Sci Instr 1966; Morristown Cntrl Sci Instr 1967-69; St Laurence Univ Grad Stu 1970; Lisbon Cntrl PE Instr 1970-73; Ogdensburg Free Acad Sci Instr 1974-; *ai:* Ftbl, Soccer, Bsktbl, Hockey Coach; Chess Club; Yth Act; NEA 1966-; NYSTA 1974-; Kiwanis 1973-; Ogdensburg Minor Hockey 1971-; Prescott Minor Hockey 1970-, Treas; *office:* Ogdensburg Free Acad 1100 State St Ogdensburg NY 13669

COLE, FRED J., Business Education Dept Chm; *b:* Florence, SC; *m:* Virginia Adams; *c:* Fred Jeffrey, Gregor Edward, Michelle Denise; *ed:* Duquesne Univ (BED) Bus Ed, (MED) Scndry Ed; *cr:* West Mifflin HS Bus Ed Tchr 1969-; *ai:* Stud Secretarial Spon; Former Girls Vlybl Coach; Assessment Comm Cho-Chair; WMAFT 1969-; *office:* West Mifflin Area HS 91 Commonwealth Ave West Mifflin PA 15122

COLE, GWENDOLYN, Ninth Grade English Teacher; *b:* Cincinnati, OH; *c:* Latisha D.; *ed:* Univ of Cincinnati (BS) Eng 1973; *cr:* Aiken HS Eng Tchr 1973-; *office:* Aiken HS 5641 Belmont Cincinnati OH 45224

COLE, JANET ANN, HS Mathematics Teacher; *b:* Columbus, OH; *m:* Van Richard; *c:* Kenneth, Bonnie; *ed:* Bowling Green St Univ (B S) Ed & Math 1973; Heidelberg in Tiffin (MA) Ed 1991; *cr:* Lakewood Local Schls Jr High Math & Sci Thcr 1973-74; St Francis HS Math & Sci 1974-76; Seneca East Local Schl Math Tchr 1976-; *ai:* Quiz Bowl Adv; Venture Capital Grant Chprsn; NEA, OEA & SEEA 1976-; OCTM 1978-; NCTM 1989-; Delta Kappa Gamma 1992-; Republic UCC 1974-, Sunday Schl Supt; Martha Holden Jennings Scholar; Jennings Grant & Mini Grants Recipient; *office:* Seneca East HS PO Box 462 Attica OH 44807*

COLE, JANICE DEENA (JONES), Fifth Grade Teacher; *b:* Sneedville, TN; *m:* Edward Russell; *c:* Jeffrey Edward, Jennifer Jill; *ed:* Grace Coll (BS) Elem Ed 1969; Univ of Akron Credit Hrs for Renewal; *cr:* Akron Elem Schl 1st Grd Tchr 1969-70; Chapel Hill Chrstn Schl N 2nd Grd Tchr 1970-71, 4th Grd Tchr 1974-76; Chapel Hill Chrstn Schl S Rdng Specialist 1982-85, 5th Grd Tchr 1986-; *ai:* Golden Apple Achiever Awd Ashland Oil Co 1993; Books: A Child's Guide to Historical Places, A Child's Guide to Natural Wonders 1993; *home:* 2429 Foxboro Ave Akron OH 44305*

COLE, JOANN SHERMAN, Eng Dept Chairperson & Tchr; *b:* Gettysburg, PA; *m:* William F. Jr.; *c:* Timothy W., John A., Carolyn A.; *ed:* Gettysburg Coll (BA) Eng 1958; Attnd Duke Univ; *cr:* New Oxford HS Eng Tchr 1958-59; Southern Lehigh HS Eng Tchr 1959-61; Bethlehem Cath HS Eng Tchr 1983-, Eng Dept Chprsn 1987-; *ai:* NCTE; Allentown Diocese Lay Tchrs Assn; PTA; Former Pres; Former CCD Tchr; Church, Lector; Excl in Tchng PA St Univ; *office:* Bethlehem Catholic HS 2133 Madison Ave Bethlehem PA 18017

COLE, JOHN DAVID, Mathematics Dept Chairman; *b:* Darby, PA; *m:* Jeanne Gramer; *ed:* Drexel Univ (BS) Chem Engrng 1974; Univ of PA (MA) Scndry Math, Sci Ed 1976; Supervisory Cert Widener Univ; Masters Level Course Work at Widener Univ, Temple Univ, Univ of VT, Phila Coll of Textiles & Sci; *cr:* Upper Darby Schl Dist Sci Tchr 1976-77; Chichester Sr HS Math Tchr 1977-93, Math Dept Chm 1993-; *ai:* Scott's HI-Q Acad Team Adv 1979-; NEA, PSEA 1977-; NCTM 1978-; *office:* Chichester Sr HS 3333 Chichester Ave Boothwyn PA 19061*

COLE, LISA SABLE, First Grade Teacher; *b:* Perth Amboy Andrew John; *ed:* Morrisville Coll (AS) Bus Admin 1984; Keuka C Elem Ed 1991; Elmira Coll (MS) Gen Ed, Early Chldhd Ce Southeastern Acad Travel Career Trng Diploma; *cr:* House of Trav Agent 1985-91; Hammondsport Cntrl Schl Kndgtn, 1st Grd Tchr 1 Var Chrldng Coach 3 Yrs; NEA, HTA 1992-; Cert of Excl Sou Acad; *home:* 10472 Cross St Hammondsport NY 14840

COLE, MARY COLLINS, Business Education Teacher; *b:* Wave *m:* John D.; *ed:* Univ of Scranton (BS) Hospital Admin 1987 Production & Operations Mngmt 1989; Elmira Coll (MS) Elem & Bus Ed 1994; *cr:* Univ of ScrantonGrad Asst 1987-89; Athens & Sa Dist Sub Tchr, Cmptr Consultant 1989-91; Chemung Cmpt Consultant 1991-94; Sayre Area HS Bus Ed Tc hr 1994-; Penn Adjunct Prof 1995-; *ai:* FBLA, Stu Cncl, 8th Grd Adv; Strategic Comm; NEA, PSEA 1995-; Prof FBLA 1994-; Sayre Comm E Instr; *office:* Sayre Area HS 331 W Lockhart St Sayre PA 18840

COLE, NANCY CLIFFORD, Early Chldhd Occupations Instr; *b:* ME; *m:* Melvin Jr.; *c:* Beth, Ellen, Brian; *ed:* Univ of ME at Far (BS) Home Ec 1969; *cr:* Bath Voc Ctr Early Chldhd Occ Tchr Capital Area Tech Ctr Early Chldhd Occ Tchr 1984-; *ai:* Voc Inds of Amer Adv, St Exec Bd; NEA, MEA, AEA 1984-; ECOE 19 Challenge Fnd Bd 1993-; Oak Hill HS Boosters 1989-, Sec, Pr *office:* Capital Area Tech Ctr RR 7 Box 2520 Augusta ME 04330

COLE, NANCY J., Physical Education Teacher; *b:* Northport, Ithaca Coll (BS) PE 1969; SUNY at Stony Brook (MA) Liberal Stu *cr:* Middle Cty Schls Tchr & Coach 1969-; *ai:* Var Field Hockey MCTA 1969-; USFHA 1970-, Bd of Dir; NYSUT 1970-; SCFHC Pres; #1 HS Field Hockey Coach in Amers Greatest Coaches; NF Field Hockey Coach of Yr 1995; Selected to Coach US Olympic 1993 & 1995; NHSACA Natl Merit awd; Nom Natl HS Coach of & 1985; *office:* Centereach HS 14 43rd St Centereach NY 11720

COLE, RICHARD L., PE, Ec Tchr & Var Ftbl Coach; *b:* Waterto *m:* Cheryl Barnard; *c:* Barret, Jonathan, Seth, Emily; *ed:* Norwi (BS) PE, His 1971; Potsdam St 30 Hrs Educl 1975; *cr:* Liverpoo Tchr, Coach 1971-72; Black River Nursery Landscaping A 1972-74; Carthage Cntrl HS Soc Stu Tchr 1975; Lowville Acad Schl PE, Ed, Ec Tchr, Coach 1976-; *ai:* Var Ftbl Head Coach Coach; LTA Tchrs Assn 1976-; Section III Ftbl Comm 1986-, R Lodge 1605 1971-, House Comm Chprsn, Elk of Yr 1992-93; Tch Yr 1994-95; 100 Career Ftbl Wins Awd; *office:* Lowville Acad & C 7668 State St Lowville NY 13367

COLE, SUSAN LETZLER, Eng Prof & Dramatic Stud Washington, DC; *m:* David Stuart; *ed:* Duke Univ (BA) Eng L Harvard Univ (MA) Eng Lit 1963, (PhD) Eng Lit 1968; Yale U Grad; *cr:* Univ of VA Eng Instr 1964-66; Harvard Univ Eng Tutor Cleveland St Univ Asst Eng Prof 1968-96; Yale Univ Eng Tutor 1 Southern CT St Coll Eng Lecturer 1969; Quinnipiac Coll Eng A 1970-71; Albertus Magnus Coll Eng Prof 1971-; *ai:* Acad Concentration in Dramatic Stud; Fac Adv to Coll Lit Magazine, Er Fac Status Comm; Dramatur for Coll Theatre Productions; MLA NY Shakespeare Soc, Columbia Univ Seminars in Shakespeare Shakespeare Assn of Amer 1971-; Woodrow Wilson Tchng, Yale Fac Fellowship; Nom for AAHE Fac Salute; Pub Books.

COLE, THOMAS A., Physical Education Teacher; *b:* Oxford, Dale Cross; *c:* Kathleen, Michael; *ed:* Ithaca Coll (BS) PE 1965; Pc Stud PE at SUNY at Brockport; *cr:* Pittsford PE & Wrestling 1965-78, PE & Track Coach 1966-88, PE & Cross Cntry Skiing 1983-90, PE & Cross Cntry Running Coach 1978-92; *ai:* Many Se Wins, St Competitions & 1 Olympian Pete Pfitzinger 1984 & NYSHPERD 1965-, 100 Wins in Track; *office:* Pittsford Central S W Jefferson Rd Pittsford NY 14534

COLE, TODD SCOTT, First Grade Teacher; *b:* Albany, N Westminster Coll (BA) Elem Ed & Music 1983, (MA) Rdng Sp 1990; *cr:* Laurel Elem 1st Grd Tchr 1983-; *ai:* PSEA 1983-; Lawre Rdng Assn 1986-; PTO 1983-, Pres & Inspiration Chprsn; Presbyn 1985-, Deacon Pres, Choir & Bell Choir Mem; Alumni C Westminster Coll 1993-, Internship Chprsn; Young Educator Lawrence Cty; Top 10 Finalist for PA Tchr of Yr; Disney Tc Honoree; Pub 10 Articles in Newspaper Concerning Ed Issues; Laurel Elem Schl Rd 4 Box 52 New Castle PA 16101

COLEFIELD, BERNICE, Principal; *b:* Paterson, NJ; *m:* Aston Al Carrie; *ed:* Glassboro St (BA) Elem Ed 1968; Montclair St (MA) A Supvrsn 1992; *cr:* Birches Schl 4th Grd 1968-70; Haskell Schl Kn 6th-8th Grds 1971-86; Haskell Schl Tchr of Gifted 1986-94; Hask Prin 1994-; *ai:* ASCD 1994-; NJ Prin Assn 1994-; NAESP 199 1971-, Honorary VP 1994-; Gov Regognition Awd 1989; *office:* Elem Schl 973 Ringwood Ave Haskell NJ 07420

COLELLA, ALBERT C., High School Band Director; *b:* New Cas *m:* Georgeann Cappuzzello; *c:* Jeneane, Phillip, Christine, Alai Youngstown St Univ (BME) Instrumental Music 1971; The Catholi of Amer (MM) Music Preformance 1974; 30 Grad Hrs Past Masters; Naval Acad Band Clarinetist 1971-75; Warren City Schls Jr High B 1975-78; Poland Local Schls HS Band Dir 1978-81, 1983-; Pr Industries Sales Consultant 1981-82; *ai:* Marching Band, Jazz En Dir; OMEA Music Judge; Amer Fed of Musicians 1965-; OH Mu Assn, OH Ed Assn 1975-; Amer Schl Band Dirs Assn 1990-; *office:* Seminary HS 3199 Dobbins Rd Youngstown OH 44514

COLELLA, ROSEMARY LYNN (MOSCIPAN), 3rd Grade Teac New Castle, PA; *m:* John; *c:* Matthew; *ed:* Youngstown St Univ (BS Ed 1969; Slippery Rock Univ (MA) Rdng 1973; *cr:* Riverside Ele 3rd Grd Tchr 1969-73; Shenango Elem Schl 3rd Grd Tchr 1973-; *a* Strategic Planning Comm; PA St Tchr Assn 1969-; Shenango Area E 1973-, VP; Shenango Garden Club 1980-, Pres; Gift of Time; *home* Old Pittsburgh Rd New Castle PA 16101

COLEMAN, ANTOINETTE KNOWLES, Kindergarten Teach Spokane, WA; *c:* Alisha J.; *ed:* AL A&M Univ (BS) Elem Ed 197 of AL at Birmingham (MA) Early Chldhd Ed 1979; *cr:* Mitchell El Grd Tchr 1974-84; Schenck Elem 2nd Grd Tchr 1984-91; L. Farrel Kndgtn, Extended Day Tchr 1991-93; Schenck Elem Kndgtn Tchr *ai:* Early Chldhd Comm; Franklin City Schls Summer Schl Coord, M FEA 1984-; NEA 1974-; Delta Sigma Theta 1980-; Phi Delta Kappa Outstanding Young Women of Amer 1981; Gadsden Jaycees Outst Educator 1979; OH St Early Chldhd Dept Grant Reader 1991-93; 1065 Parklane Apt B Middletown OH 45042*

COLEMAN, CHARMAINE N. YANEK, English Teacher; *b:* DuBo *c:* Shawn; *ed:* PA St Univ (BS) Eng 1964; Attnd Clarion St Univ, Ed St Univ; *cr:* DuBois Area Sr HS Eng Tchr 1960-63; Our Lady of Vall Tchr 1978-92; East Orange HS Eng Tchr 1992-; *ai:* NJEA 1992- 1992-; EOEA 1992-.

COLEMAN, CRAIG WAYNE, High School Math Teacher; *b:* Yor *m:* Beth Ann Sellers; *c:* Tyler, Callie; *ed:* Shippensburg Univ (BA Ed 1987; 31 Grad Credits; 27 Credits Ed Admin; *cr:* Bermudian S HS Math Tchr 1987-; *ai:* Var Track Coach 8 Yrs; Jr HS Ftbl Coach Bible Club Adv; NEA 1987-; Mt Holly Springs United Meth Church

·; *office:* Bermudian Springs HS 7335 Carlisle Pike York Springs

·N, JOHANNE EPIFANIO, G&T Teacher & Coordinator; *b:* NJ; *m:* Raymond; *c:* Shawn, Craig; *ed:* Trenton St Coll (BA) 965; Widener Univ (MED) Ed 1992; Grad Stud Columbia Univ; ·n Pub Schls 6th Grd Tchr 1966-68; Galloway Twp Schls Elem ·-83; Pomona Schl G&T Tchr 1983-; Galloway Twp Schls Dis ·rd 1996; *ai:* Comm of 21; Mid St Team 1991-94; Phi Delta A G&T; NJaET, ACE G&T, VP 1993-95; NEA, NJEA; Governors ·gnition Awd 1991; Numerous Articles Pub; *office:* Galloway ·chls 101 S Reeds Rd Absecon NJ 08201*

·N, JOHN M.,JR., High School History Teacher; *b:* Malden, ·ndrea Desmarais; *c:* Cara, Cristen, Cailin; *ed:* Boston Univ ·cndry Ed 1964; Salem St Coll (MAT) Non-Western His 1971; ·Coll (MED) Schl Admin 1980; *cr:* Belmont Pub Schls His Tchr ·*i:* Schlsp Comm; MA Cncl for Soc Stud 1994-; MTA, ·Educ Assn 1964-; Phi Alpha Theta 1980-; Amer Legion #2073 ·amed Christa Corrigan Mc Auliffe Ctr for Ed & Tchng Excl ·Tchr; *office:* Belmont HS 221 Concord Ave Belmont MA 02178

·N, JOSEPH, HS Social Studies Teacher; *b:* Levittown, PA; *m:* Rachel, Aidan; *ed:* 18 Credit Hrs Temple Univ Pol Sci; *cr:* ·e Jr Sr HS Soc Stud Tchr 1986-89; Cherokee HS Soc Stud Tchr Delran HS Soc Stud Tchr 1990-91; Northern Burlington Regnl ·tud Tchr 1991-; *ai:* Debate Coach; 11th Grd Class Adv; NEA ·EA 1989-; NJ Cncl for Soc Stud 1995-; Holmeville Recreation ·; *office:* Northern Burlington Reg HS 160 Mansfield Rd E ·NJ 08022

·N, JOYCE JEFFERSON, 2nd Grade Teacher; *b:* Kane, PA; *m:* ·Jr.; *c:* Sarah Coleman Shobert, Rebecca Coleman Sorensen, Coleman Gordon; *ed:* OR St Univ Ed 12 Credit Hrs; *cr:* Coos 1st Grd Tchr 2 Yrs; Corvallis Pub Schls 1st Grd Tchr 1 Yr; ·e Chrstn Acad Lower Elem Grds Tchr 7 Yrs; Warren Cty Chrstn ·gtn Tchr 13 Yrs, 2nd Grd & Span I Tchr & Librn 1 Yr; *ai:* Lib ·r Comm; *office:* Warren Co Christian Schl Rt 6 W Youngsville PA

·N, JULIE PELKAN, English Tutor & Teacher; *b:* San ·, CA; *m:* Jeffrey Alan; *c:* Katherine Anne; *ed:* Dartmouth Coll ·1988; Working on MA Degree Middlebury Coll Bread Loaf of ·eo Burnett Advertising Client Svc 1988-90; Dartmouth Coll Dev Hackley Schl Tchr 1991-; *ai:* Girls Var Lacrosse Coach 1993-; ·wimming Coach 1991-95; *office:* Hackley Schl 293 Benedict Ave ·NY 10591

·N, LINDA MINOR, Library Media Specialist; *b:* Dunkirk, NY; ·L.; *c:* Robert J., Julie J.; *ed:* OH St Univ (BSEd) Eng, Latin 1969; ·Univ (ME) Supervision 1995; Grad Hrs Wright St Univ; Credit ·Univ, OH Dominican Coll; *cr:* Westfall Local Schls K-12 Grd ·hr 1970-71; Teays Valley Local Schls 9-12 Grd Eng Tchr 1971-72; ·e City Schls LD Tutor 1974-75; Dublin City Schl s K-12 Grd ·Media Specialist 1980-; *ai:* Bldg & Dist Tech Team; Dist Tech ·nm; Dept Chair; Right-to-Read Comm; Dist Rep to Cntrl OH ·nsortion; DEA, OEA, NEA 1980-, DEA Newsletter Ed, Bd Mem ·H Educl Media Assoc 1980-, Ldrshp Conf Chair 1993, St Conf ·; Phi Delta Kappan 1990-; Ashland Telesis Cncl 1996; Upper ·Luth Church 1975-; OH Genealogical Assn 1985-; OH Historical ·; OH Yth Choir Alumni Assn 1963-; Excl In Ed Awds, Grants; ·Celebration of Excl Honoree; Articles Pub; *office:* Dublin Scioto Hard Rd Dublin OH 43016*

·AN, LORI ANN, Biology Teacher; *b:* Erie, PA; *ed:* Marquette ·) Broad Field Sci Ed 1990; Grad Classes Wilkes Univ, Manhattan ·rently Working on Master's Theis in Natural, Environmental Sci ·illa Maria Acad Bio, Chem Tchr 1990-91; Fairview HS Bio, Chem ·1-; *ai:* PA Jr Acad of Sci; Class Adv; PA Sci Tchrs Assn 1992-; ·airview HS 7460 Mccray Rd Fairview PA 16415

·AN, NANCY LOUISE, Interdisciplinry Resource Tchr; *b:* ·r, MA; *ed:* Univ of MA (BA) Elem Ed 1967; Western MD Coll ·Media 1979; 6 Credits St Hilda's Coll, Oxford Univ 1967; 12 ·Eng Georgetown Univ 1984, 1987; *cr:* Montgomery Cty Pub Schls ·hr 1967-77, MS Tchr 1978-89, Tchr of the Gifted 1980-85, Staff ·nings Summers 1983-88, MS Tchr 1985-; *ai:* GATE Comm Chair; ·chr Rep; NEA 1970-; Patient Astronomer Ltd 1993-, VP; NEH ·omer's Oddyssey 1984, Theatre East & West 1988, 1989; *office:* ·Scott Key Mid Schl 910 Schindler Dr Silver Spring MD 20903

·AN, WILLIAM W., Sixth Grade Teacher; *b:* Waterloo, NY; *m:* ·ewman; *c:* Sherry Sacco, Jill Eberle; *ed:* Hamilton Coll (BA) Ec ·Univ of Geneseo (MS) Elem Ed 1966; *cr:* Victor Central Schl ·d Tchr 1960-62; RAF Fairford Sixth Grd, PE Tchr 1962-63; Victor ·Schl Sixth Grd Tchr 1963-83; Asir Acad Sixth Grd Tchr 1983-85; ·entral Schl Sixth Grd Tchr 1985-; *ai:* Boys Tennis Coach 32 Yrs; ·nis Coach 15 Yrs; Victor Tchrs Assn 1960-, Pres; AFT 1960-; US ·ssn; St Davids Soc, Pres; BHV Bd of Dir; NYSPHSAA 15 Yrs; ·Leave Wales 1971-72; Tchr Awd Amsterdam 1989; *office:* Victor ·iate Schl 953 High St Victor NY 14564

·AN KOHN, ANN P., World Geography & History Tchr; *b:* ·NJ; *m:* Eric D.; *ed:* Rowan Coll (MA) Scndry Ed-Magna Cum ·990; Grad Classes Spec Ed; *cr:* Washington Twp Schls Sub Tchr ·Lenape HS Soc Stud Tchr 1993-; *ai:* Core Team; Interact Adv; ·NEA 1996; *office:* Lenape HS 235 Hartford Rd Medford NJ 08055

·FRANKLIN, English Teacher; *ed:* Adelphi Univ (BA) Eng 1971; ·CT St Univ (MS) Env Sci 1987, (MA) Oceanography, Limnology ·Chem; *cr:* Lakeland Cntrl Schl Dist Eng, Phy Sci Tchr 1974-; *ai:* ·Track, X-C Coach; Weather Club, SADD Adv; NYS Bd of Regents ·hp; *office:* Lakeland HS E Main St Shrub Oak NY 12571*

·NATALIE MOON, Reading Specialist; *b:* Connellsville, PA; *m:* ·V.; *c:* Jerel W., Tre A.; *ed:* California Univ of PA (BS) Early Chldhd ·MS) Rdng Specialist 1981; 1 Credit Hrs Tchng Basal Reader; 2 ·Hrs Memory Dev & Application; 1 Credit Hrs Dev Stud Skills & ·*cr:* Uniontown Beauty Acad Cosmetologist 1984-; *ai:* NEA, CAEA ·Fayette Cty NAACP 1986-, Former Sec; Ladies Auxiliary Amer ·1986-; *office:* Bullskin Twp Elem Schl 125 Pleasant Vly Rd ·sville PA 15425

·TOCK, JULIE CONRAD, Hlth & PE Instructor; *b:* Camp Hill, ·David H.; *ed:* James Madison Univ (BS) Hlth & PE 1986; Cert Natl ·iner Acad 1993; 30 Credit Hrs Post-Grad; *cr:* Camp Hill HS Tchr ·1987-; *ai:* ATC; Sr Class Adv; Field Hockey Coach; Stu Asst Team; ·& PATS; PSHERD & APPHERD; CHEA & NEA; ARC Standard ·d & CPR Instr 1988-; *office:* Camp Hill HS 100 S 24th St Camp ·17011

·, HELEN ALSTON, Math & Science Coordinator; *b:* Raleigh, ·Alvin B.; *c:* Jessica, Justin; *ed:* NCCU (BA) Elem Ed 1979; ·g on Ed Admin Univ of MD; Grad Level Ldrshp, Multiculture Ed ·ourses; *cr:* Hanau Amer Preschool Tchr 1979-82; A.V. Baucom ·chl Tchr 1983-84; Ptomac Landing Elem Schl Tchr, Sci, Math ·1984-; Prince Georges Staff Dev, Math Dept Fac 1995-; *ai:* ·lture Comm Friends for Sci Club; NEA, MD St Tchrs Assn 1984-; ·1995-; Ebenezer AME Church 1984-; Math Dept 1994-, Math Facilator, Nom Presidential Tchrs Awd; Tchr in Charge When Prin Absent; Outstdng Tchng Evaluations; Outstdng Tchr Plague; Schl Panning Mngmt Team Chprsn; *office:* Potomac Landing Elem Schl 12500 Fort Washington Rd Fort Washington MD 20744*

COLGAN, LINDA L., 7th Grd Language Arts Teacher; *b:* Indiana, PA; *m:* Michael Sahlaney; *c:* Sarah Sahlaney; *ed:* Indiana Univ of PA (BS) Eng 1975, (MS) Rdng 1981; 12 Credit Hrs Amer Univ; *cr:* Leary Schl LD & ED Tchrs 1977-79; Bishop Mccort HS 10-11th Grd Eng Tchr 1979-80; United HS 11th Grd Eng Tchr 1980-81, Rdng Internship 1981-82; *ai:* Mentor to HS Tchrs; Mem of PA Geographic Alliance; NEA, PSEA, Phi Delta Kappa 1992-; IN Rdng Cncl 1982-, Pres Elect; Great Bks Ldr;S & T Edctr of The Yr 1994; IN Rdng Cncl Past Pres; United Meth Church 1985-, Childrens Coord; Blue Ribbon Grant; YAC Awd Winner; *office:* United Schl Dist Box 168 Armagh PA 15920

COLL, KATHY ANN KNITTER, English & Leadership Dev Tchr; *b:* Rochester, NY; *m:* Edward A.; *c:* Edwawrd C., Erik R.; *ed:* Point Park Coll (BS) Eng Ed 1973; Univ of Pittsburgh (MS) Comm 1976; Post Grad in Leadership Stud at Portland St Univ & Western OR St Univ; *cr:* Girl Scouts of SW PA High Adventure Camp Dir Summer 1973-; N Allegheny Schl Tchr 1973-; *ai:* Act Dirl; Stu Cncl & Fresh Class Adv, Prin Adv Comm; Dist Strategic Mgmt Team Mem; Peer Mediation Team; PA Assn of Stu Cncl 1983-, Dist Dir, Asst Exec Dir, 1st PA Stu Cncl Adv of Yr; AFT 1973-; NCTE 1974-; NASAA 1984-; Girl Scouts 1957-, Every Level; March of Dimes 1983-, Steering Comm for Walk Amer; N Hills Food Bank 1983-, Vol; St Teresa Choir & CCD Tchr 1991-, Vol & Tchr; 1993 1st Ever Wolf Awd for Tchr of Excl; 1992 Univ of Pittsburgh All Star Ed; 1992 Finalist in Vol Prgm Organizer Natl Assn of Partners in Ed; 1985 Present Vol Awd for Extra Effort March of Dimes; Nom for PA Tchr of Yr 4 Times; *office:* N Allegheny Intermediate Schl 350 Cumberland Rd Pittsburgh PA 15237*

COLL, LEA (HOCK), Physics Teacher; *b:* Zagreb, Croatia; *m:* Hans; *c:* Fiona M., Elizabeth I.; *ed:* Univ of Zagreb (BS) Bio Tech 1975; SUNY at Brockport (MS) Ed 1994; *cr:* Our Lady of Mercy HS Sci Tchr 1989-95; Spencerport HS Physics Tchr 1995-; *ai:* AFT 1995-; *office:* Spencerport HS 71 Lyell Ave Spencerport NY 14559

COLLAGE, PATRICIA KARAVAS, Social Studies Teacher; *b:* Chios, Greece; *m:* Jack B.; *c:* William Nicholas; *ed:* Waynesburg Coll (MA) His-Cum Laude 1962; Carnegie-Mellon Univ Masters Equivalency; Fordham Univ NEH Scholar; Univ of Pgh Asian Stud; *cr:* Avonworth HS Tchr 1962-68; Rochester Inst of Tech Instr 1970-72; Villa Maria Coll Instr 1974-78; FAirview HS Tchr 1978-85; Mt Lebanon HS Tchr 1988-; *ai:* Speech, Debate Coach; NEA, PSEA 1962-; Jr League 1972-, Pres; YWCA 1974-, Bd; Tchr Consultant Mc Dougal-Little Publishers Ec Textbook; Tchr of Yr Nom 1984; *office:* Mt Lebanon Sr HS 155 Cochran Rd Pittsburgh PA 15228

COLLAND, RONALD D., History Teacher; *b:* Connellsville, PA; *m:* Jacqueline A. Tyke; *c:* Deborah A., Michael G.; *ed:* Clarion St Coll (BS) His 1970; CA St Coll (MA) His 1975; *cr:* Hempfield Area Tchr, Coach 1972-; *ai:* Head Boys & Girls Cross Cntry, Track & Field Coach; PSEA, NEA 1972-; Westmoreland Cty Coaches Assn 1973-; *office:* Hempfield Area Schl Dist Rd 6 Box 77 Greensburg PA 15601

COLLAR, CORINNE MELINDA (CAPANO), First Grade Teacher; *b:* Boston, MA; *m:* Brent Herbert; *c:* Keith, Kristen Collar Willand; *ed:* Northeastern Univ (BSEd) Elem Ed 1962; Lesley Coll (MSEd) Spcl Needs 1980; 60 Grad Credits Beyond Masters; *cr:* Augustine C Whelan Schl 1st Grd Tchr 1962-63, 1964-66; Abraham Lincoln Schl 2nd Grd Tchr 1973, 1st Grd Tchr 1973-76, 1983-90, 1991-, Spcl Needs Tchr & Resource Room Coord 1976-83, Tchr of Young Children with Spcl Needs 1990-91; *ai:* Rdng & Lang Arts Curr Comm; Co-Tchng After Schl Enrichment Pgm Integrating Lit & Math 1st Grd; Piloted Organisms Sci Kit; Mentor Tchr; Bldg Based Support Team Mem; Assn for Supervision & Curr Dev 1995-; Revere Tchrs Assn; MA Tchrs Assn; NEA; Whole Lang Tchrs Assn; St Anthonys Schl of Rel 1971-90, 1st & 6th Grd CCD Tchr, Conducted Instrl Wkshps for Vol Tchrs, Pageants & Spcl Needs Dir; CCD Ctr & Chapel Comm; Work in Cooperative Ed & Classroom Work Cited in Magazine Publications 1961 & 1974; Resource Room Team Mem Selected as St Model 1978; MA Tchr of Yr Nom 1992-93, 1996-; Presidential Awds for Excl in Sci & Math Tchng 1993; Thanks to Tchrs Nom; Article Pub; *office:* Lincoln Elem Schl 68 Tuckerman St Revere MA 02151*

COLLAZO, JANET, 8th Grade Teacher; *b:* Suffern, NY; *ed:* St Thomas Aquinas Coll (BS) Soc Stud 7-12, Ed 1991; Iona Coll (MS) Soc Stud, Ed 1995; *cr:* St Joseph's Schl 8th Grd Tchr 1991-; *ai:* 8th Grd Class Adv, Supvr; Grad Coord; *office:* St Joseph's Schl 245 N Main St Spring Valley NY 10977

COLLAZO, LINDA CHARAK, Second Grade Teacher; *b:* Bridgeport, CT; *c:* Lynore, Maris, Kyle; *ed:* Western CT St Coll (BS) Elem Ed 1973; Southern CT St Coll Environmental Ed 1978; *cr:* Eli Whitney Schl 2nd Grd Tchr 1973-; *ai:* NEA 1973-; Stratfords Small TAWL; CoOperating Tchr BEST Pgm; Mini Grant Soc Stud; *office:* Eli Whitney Elem Schl 1130 Huntington Rd Stratford CT 06497

COLLAZO, PAULA PISARSKI, High School Math Teacher; *b:* Newfane, NY; *m:* Alex; *ed:* Hougton Coll (BA) Math, Chem 1985; St Univ of NY at Cortland (MAT) Math Ed 1993; *cr:* Nichibei Eng Svc ESL Instr 1985-89; George Jr Republic Resource Room Tchr 1990-91; Manhatton Chrstn Acad Math, Sci Tchr 1993-; *ai:* Stu Govt Adv; NCTM 1992-; Challenger Flwshp Math 1991; *office:* Manhatten Christian Acad 401 W 205th St New York NY 10034*

COLLER, BARRY S., Prof of Medicine & Dept Chm; *b:* New York, NY; *m:* Barbara Gelfand; *c:* Hilary, Alyssa; *ed:* Columbia Coll (BA) Govt 1966; NY Univ (MD) 1970; *cr:* Natl Insts of Hlth Sr Staff Physician 1974-76; SUNY at Stony Brook Schl of Medicine Asst Prof & Prof of Medicine & Pathology 1976-93; Mt Sinai Schl of Medicine Prof & Chm Dept of Medicine 1993-; *ai:* Am Soc Hem 1973-, Treas & VP; Am Heart Assoc; Am Soc Clin Insts; Am Prof Medicine 1993-; Natl Insts of Hlth Rsrch Grants 1976-; 8 US Invention Patents; *office:* Mount Sinai Schl of Medicine 1 Gustave L Levy Pl New York NY 10029

COLLERAN, ANDRA M. JAREMKA, Fr Tchr & Frgn Lang Dept Chair; *b:* Buffalo, NY; *m:* John F.; *c:* Evan W., Claire L.; *ed:* St Univ Coll Buffalo (BSEd) Fr, Ed 1972; NY Univ (MA) Fr 1975; La Sorbonne Paris Diplome de Langue et Civilisation Francaises 1971; Post Grad Stu GATE Ed; Cert Elem Frgn Lang Ed Grds N-6; Credit Hrs Cmptr Applications; *cr:* Buffalo Pub Schls 5-12 Grd Fr Tchr 1972-76; City Hnrs Schl 5-12 Grd Fr Tchr 1976-, Frgn Lang Dept Chair 1987-; *ai:* Fr Club Adv; AFS Schl Contact; Chair Textbook Review, Curr Dev, Testing Prgm Comms; NEA, NYEA, BTF, AATF, NYSAFLT, WNYFLEC 1972-; Pi Delta Phi 1989-; Staff Mem, Translator WNY World Univ James; Presenter Lang Conf; *office:* City Honors Schl Masten & North Sts Buffalo NY 14204*

COLLETTE, JUDITH DOE, First Grade Teacher; *b:* Worcester, MA; *m:* Roderick E.; *c:* Michael, Jennifer Wilson, Peter; *ed:* Univ of VT (BA) Psych, Bio 1958; 375 Inservice Hrs Powling Elem Schl Mid Hudson Tchr Ctr; Post Grad Stud Western CT St Coll, Sacred Heart Univ, SUNY at New Poltz, Boston Univ; *cr:* Powling Elem Schl First Grd Tchr 1980-; *ai:* PTA Liaison; Instrl Cncl; Early Chldhd Curr Dev; Rdng Curr Comm; Child Study Team; Family Math Night; AIDS Curr Comm; NEA 1982-; Christ Church 1960-, Trustee, Bldg Comm, Choir; YMCA 1970-, Bd of Mgrs, Triatholon Comm; West Mountain Mission 1978-, Trustee; *office:* Pawling Elem Schl 7 Haight St Pawling NY 12564*

COLLETTI, PETER T., Fourth Grade Teacher; *b:* Brooklyn, NY; *m:* Diane Impagliazzo; *c:* Christopher, Andrew; *ed:* SUNY at Brockport (BA) His & Ed 1976; Stony Brook Univ (MA) Soc & Behavioral Scis 1986; 30 Credit Hrs Post Grad Stud; *cr:* Deer Park Schls Soc Stud Tchr 1979-90, 4th Grd Tchr 1991-; *ai:* Girls Soccer & Vllybl Coach; NEA 1979-; *office:* Deer Park Schl Dist 1881 Deer Park Ave Deer Park NY 11729

COLLEY, STEPHEN JOHN, Art Instructor; *b:* New Haven, CT; *m:* Ann Marie Griffith; *c:* Gavin, Joshua; *ed:* Swam Schl of Design (BFA) Painting 1984; Parsons Schl of Design (MFA) Painting 1986; *cr:* Colley Studio of Fine Arts GED 1995-; Univ of Scranton Art Instr 1995-; Marywood Coll Art Instr 1995-; *ai:* Drawing; Sculpture Colley Studio of Fine Arts; Annmarie g Colley Co Owner; Exhibition of Work Miesora Cordia Coll 1996; Natl Acad of Design Show 1993; *home:* RR 5 Box 181 Tunkhannock PA 18657*

COLLIER, CYNTHIA ANN, Social Studies Teacher; *b:* Cleveland, OH; *ed:* OH St (BS) Scndry Ed 1972; Atlanta Univ (MA) His 1975; Attnd Kent St; *cr:* Cleveland Bd of Ed Tchr 1975-78; Cleveland Hghts Tchr 1978-; *ai:* Excl in Stu Performance Adv; Phi Delta Kappa 1986-; Martha Holden Jennings Scholar; *office:* Monticello MS 3665 Monticello Blvd Cleveland OH 44118

COLLIER, ELISE HERRINGTON, Special Education Teacher; *b:* Balto, MD; *ed:* Coppin St Coll (BS) Spec Ed 1975; Loyola Coll of Balto (APC) Ed 1984; Cmptr Sci Comm Coll of Baltimore; *cr:* Deep Creek Elem Schl Camp Cnslr 1982-84; Jade Fitness Inc Fitness Instr, Chief Operational Ofcr 1984-90; Edmondson-Westside Adult Ctr Areobics Instr 1994-95; Guide Shelter Cnslr; *ai:* Var Girls Bsktbl; Badminton; Fr Class Adv; Stu Govt; Grad Comm; Mentor to Young Ladies; AFT 1975-; Amer Fed of Exceptional Children 1989-; Zeta Phi Beta 1972-, Fin Sec, Zeta of Yr; NAACP; Balto Metro Coaches Assn 1993-; Coppin St Alumni Assn 1986-; Tchr of Yr; Woman of Yr; Coach of Yr; Women's League Outstdng Svc; Outstdng Young Women of Amer.

COLLIER, JOHN P., Professor of Engineering; *b:* Albany, NY; *m:* Nancy Clifton; *c:* Thomas John, Robert John; *ed:* Dartmouth Coll (AB) Engrng 1972; Thayer Schl of Engrng (BE) Biomedical Engrng 1973, (ME) Biomedical Engrng 1975, (DE) Biomedical Engrng 1976; *cr:* Thayer Schl of Engrng Rsrch Assoc 1976-84, Dir R&D, Cook Engrng Des Ctr 1978-87, Rsrch Assoc Prof 1984-93, Prof Engrng 1993-; *ai:* Sigma Xi Honorary; Soc for Biomaterials; Orthopaedic Rsrch Soc; The Hip Soc; Amer Acad of Orthopaedic Surgeons; Bd of Overseers, Hanover Inn; Winner of Otto Aufranc Awd for Most Outstndng Paper Submitted to Hip Soc 1994; Numerous Articles Pub; *office:* Dartmouth Coll Thayer Schl of Engrng Cummings 8000 Hanover NH 03755

COLLIGAN, ELIZABETH ANN (BENSON), English Teacher; *b:* Akron, OH; *m:* Timothy Patrick; *c:* Christopher, Courtney; *ed:* Anderson Coll (BA) Eng 1977; Addl Credit Hrs Kent St Univ, Univ of Akron; *cr:* Stow-Munroe Falls HS Eng Tchr 1977-; *ai:* NEA, OEA, STA 1978-; NCTE; Martha Holden Jennings Schlr 1978; Who's Who Amer Edctrs; *office:* Stow-Munroe Falls HS 3227 E Graham Rd Stow OH 44224

COLLIGAN, MARGARET M., English Teacher; *b:* Jamaica, NY; *m:* James; *c:* Megan, Tricia, J. P.; *ed:* Niagara Univ f(BA) Eng 1970; Hofstra Univ (MS) Rdng 1980; 60 Credits Ed NYSUT, Coll of St Rose; *cr:* St Frances de Chantal Schl Eng Tchr 1970-72; Carle Pl HS permanent Sub Tchr 1977-87; Manhasset HS Rdng, Eng Tchr 1987-88; Huntington HS Eng Tchr 1988-; *ai:* Disciplinary Comm; Portfolio Comm Chair; Yrbk Adv; Lang Arts Cncl; NCTE 1990-; Carle Place Citizen of Yr 1987; *office:* Huntington HS Oakwood & Mc Kay Rds Huntington Sta NY 11746

COLLINS, ANNE LOUISE, US History Teacher; *b:* Salisbury, MD; *ed:* Madison Coll (BS) Soc Stud, His, Psych 1967; VA Commonwealth Univ (MEd) Admin, Supervisory 1974; James Madison Univ (MA) 1978; *cr:* Chesterfield Cty 7th-12th Grd Tchr 1967-76; James Madison Univ Tchng Asst 1976-78; Wicomico Cty 7th-12th Grd Tchr 1978-; *ai:* Local Ed Assn 1967-76, Bldg Rep; NEA 1978-; *office:* Parkside HS 1015 Beaglin Park Dr Salisbury MD 21801

COLLINS, ANNUNCIATA, History & Religion Teacher; *b:* Watertown, NY; *ed:* SUNY at Potsdame (BS) Soc Stud 1970; Providence Coll (MA) Biblical Stud 1980; SUNY at Plattsburgh 18 Hrs; *cr:* St Joseph's Tchr 1967-69; Holy Name Tchr 1970-74, Tchr, Admin 1974-81; Holy Family Admin 1981-89; Immaculate Heart Cntrl Schl Tchr 1990-; *ai:* Lib Rsrch Asst; Spiritual Life Comm; Forensics Asst; NCEA 1969-; Delta Kappa Gamma 1994-; *office:* Immaculate Heart Central HS Ives Street Rd Watertown NY 13601

COLLINS, CAROL YEAGER, Religion Teacher; *b:* Sandusky, OH; *m:* Howard L.; *c:* Lisa, Christopher; *ed:* Bowling Green St Univ (BA) Elem Ed 1972; *cr:* Immaculate Conception Elem Schl 3rd Grd Tchr 1972-77; St Marys Cath Church Pastoral Assoc 1977-82; St Marys Cntrl Cath HS Religion Tchr Jr & Sr 1994-; *ai:* Sr Internship Projects Coord; Intervention Team Facilitator; OCEA 1995-; NDEA 1995-; Bishops Ed Cncl 1989-95, VP 1992-95; Lifetouch Increase the Peace Awd 1996; Tchr of Yr Awd 1994; *office:* St Mary's Ctl Cath HS 410 W Jefferson St Sandusky OH 44870

COLLINS, DENNIS CHARLES, PE & Health Teacher; *b:* Middletown, OH; *m:* Judi Lindsay; *c:* Jeanette, Jeffrey; *ed:* Lamar Comm Coll (AA) 1967; Adams St Coll (BA) 1971; *cr:* Dayton Dunbar HS Tchr, Coach 1971-83; Dayton Jefferson HS Coach 1982-84; Lemon Monroe HS Tchr, Coach 1984-95; *ai:* Coach Asst Kettering Alter HS Bsktbl; OHSBCA 1971-; Dist 15 BCA 1971-95, Treas, Coach of Yr 1980; OEA, NEA 1971-; 2 League Championships; 2 Tournament Dist Championships; OHBCA Hall Famae Cert; Whos Who Outstanding Coll Aths of Amer 1971; *home:* 413 Early Dr W Miamisburg OH 45342

COLLINS, GLORIA MICHALSKI, Second Grade Teacher; *b:* Battle Creek, MI; *ed:* Lowell Univ (BMEd) Music Ed 1967; Univ of MA (MED) Elem Ed 1971; Springfield Coll (CAGS) Guid, Physchological Stud 1972; Attnd Westfield St Coll; *cr:* Chicopee Schl System Elem Music Tchr 1967-70, 2 Grd Tchr 1970-; *ai:* Chicopee Educl Assn Schl Rep; Chicopee Ed Assn, MTA, NEA 1967-; St Patrick Church 1982-, Choir; *office:* Bowie Meml Schl 180 Broadway St Chicopee MA 01013

COLLINS, JAKE HENRY, Housemaster; *b:* Boston, MA; *m:* Kathy A. Connors; *c:* Ryan, Katelyn; *ed:* North Adams St Coll (BA) His 1973; Bridgewater St Coll (MA) Schl Admin 1980; 30 Credit Hrs; 15 Credit Hrs Fitchburg St Coll; *cr:* Plymouth Comm Int Schl 7-8 Soc Stu Tchr 1976-95, Housemaster 1995-; *ai:* Bsktbl, Bsbl, Soccer Coaches; NEA, MA Tchrs Assn, Plymouth Cty Tchrs Assn 1976-; Sagamore Beach Civic Assn 1982-; *office:* Plymouth Cmty Intermediate Sch 117 Long Pond Rd Plymouth MA 02360*

COLLINS, JOAN P., Math & Homeroom Teacher; *b:* White PLains, NY; *ed:* NY Univ (BS) Math, Mngmt Ed 1954; Seton Hall (MA) Ed 1973; 30 Addl Hrs FDU; *cr:* St Clare Schl Grd 3 Tchr 1969-71, Grd 5 Tchr 1971-74, Grd 8, 6-8 Grd Math Tchr 1974-85, Grd 7, 6-8 Grd Math Tchr 1985-; *ai:* Math Dept Chprsn 1980-; Yrbk Adv 1975-85; NCEA 1969-; NCTM 1990-; Diocese of Paterson Fac Advy Cncl 1986-, Chm 2 Yrs; Salary & Benefits Comm 1986-; *home:* 117 Woodward Ave Rutherford NJ 07070

COLLINS, JOHN EDWARD, High School Math Teacher; *b:* Wilkinsburg, PA; *m:* Kathleen S. Rearick; *c:* Heather S. Kidd, Kimberly S., Matthew E.; *ed:* Lancaster Bible Coll (BS) Bible 1985; Attnd USN Nuclear Power Schl 1969; *cr:* Grace Ind Church Pastor 1984-86; Salina Bible Church Pastor

1987-91; Open Door Chrstn Acad Tchr 1994-; *office:* Open Door Chrstn Acad 970 N Main St Greensburg PA 15601

COLLINS, JOHN FRANCIS,JR., Director of Instructional Svcs; *b:* Worcester, MA; *m:* Darlene Wales; *c:* Sarah; *ed:* Worcester St Coll (BS) Ed 1974; Lesley Coll (MED) Cmptr Curr, Instruction 1991; Cntrl New England Coll Classroom Application of Cmptr Tech Cert 1987; *cr:* Marlborough Pub Schls 4th Grd Tchr 1974-75, 5th Grd Tchr 1975-85, 3rd Grd Tchr 1985-91, Curr Coord 1991-95, Instrl Svcs Dir 1995-.

COLLINS, JOHN JAMES, Prof of Anthropology & Rel; *b:* Niagara Falls, NY; *m:* Mary Ann; *c:* Rebecca Ann, Christopher Jon; *ed:* Univ of Buffalo (BA) Anthropology 1960; SUNY at Buffalo (MA) Anthropology 1964, (PHD) Anthropology 1969; *cr:* Hobart William Smith Instr 1964-65; Southern Meth Instr 1966-67 Jamestown Comm Coll Asst Assoc & Full Prof 1967-; *ai:* Hnrs Comm Chm; Curr Comm; Local Hnr Soc Chptr Founder; Phi Theta Kappa; Amer Anthropological Assoc 1960- Fellow; Prendergast Lib Bd 1973-78,Sec; Jamestown City Cncl 1974-75 Councilman; Fenton Historical Soc 1990-91, Trustee; Awds: NYS Chancellors for Excl in Tchng & Natl Inst for Staff & Orgnl Dev Natl Winner 1993; Fac Awd for Excl (Twice); 5 Books & 13 Articles Pub; 20 Book Reviews; *office:* Jamestown Comm Coll 525 Falconer St Jamestown NY 14701*

COLLINS, KATHLEEN ADAMS, English Teacher; *b:* Suffern, NY; *m:* Jeramie A. Collins; *ed:* Binghamton Univ (BA) eng 1984; SUNY at New Paltz (MS) Eng Ed 1995; *cr:* Will Rogers Inst Pub Relations Dir 1985-89; Volvo North Amer Pub Relations Specialist 1989-90; New Paltz HS Eng Tchr 1990-; Syracuse Univ Adj Instr 1992-; *ai:* Acad Awds, Assessment Comm; *office:* New Paltz HS 196 Main St New Paltz NY 12561

COLLINS, KATHY IMOBERSTEG, Elementary Counselor; *b:* Salem, OH; *c:* Megan; *ed:* Kent St Univ (BS) Elem Ed 1971; Youngstown St Univ (MS) Guid & Cnslng 1976; 45 Credit Hrs; *cr:* Boardman Local Schls 3rd Grd Tchr 1971-74, Career Ed Supvr 1974-76, Elem Cnslr 1976-79, 6th Grd Lang Arts Tchr 1979-89, Elem Cnslr 1989-; *ai:* Boardman Local Safety, Drug & Gifted Identification Comms Mem; Boardman Ed Assn 1971-, Past VP; OEA & NEA 1971-; IRA 1971-; Jennings Scholar 1974.

COLLINS, LAUREL L., English Teacher; *b:* Pittsburgh, PA; *ed:* Edinboro Univ (BSEd) Comprehensive Eng 1970; PA St Univ Comm, Marketing; Univ of Pittsburgh Curr & Supervision; *cr:* PA Jr HS Core Tchr 1970-74; Linton MS Eng Tchr 1974-; *ai:* Eng, Rdng Dept Chair; Implementor of Portfolio Assessment; New Standards Lead Tchr; NCTE 1980-; NEA 1968-; PA St EA 1970-; Career, Acad Passport 1995-, Commissioner, Lead Tchr; Pymatuning Lake Assn 1981-, Dir; DAR 1974-; Dimensions of Learning Awd; Who's Who Amony Intnl Bus Women Nominated; Consultant Work; *office:* Linton MS 250 Aster St Pittsburgh PA 15235

COLLINS, LAURIE BOYLE, Second Grade Teacher; *b:* Medford, MA; *m:* Michael A.; *c:* Allison; *ed:* Plymouth St Coll (BS) Elem Ed 1978; Attnd Notre Dame Coll; *cr:* South Range Schl 2nd Grd Tchr 1979-80; Ellis Schl 2nd Grd Tchr 1980-81; Derry Village Schl 3rd Grd Tchr 1981-86; East Derr Mem Schl 2nd Grd Tchr 1986-; *ai:* Staff Dev, Crisis Intervention Comm; 100th Day Comm Chprsn; NEA 1979-; Spec Ed Classroom Tchr Awd 1984; *office:* East Derry Memorial Elem Sch 18 Dubeau Dr Derry NH 03038*

COLLINS, MARC STEVEN, High School Science Teacher; *b:* Collingdale, PA; *m:* Denise Romano; *ed:* Westchester Univ (BSEd) Bio, Sci Scndry Ed 1974; 30 Post Grad Credits PA St Univ, DE Cty Intermediate Unit; *cr:* Dynamic Springs Prep Sci Tchr 1974-76; Deverevx Manor Schl Sci tchr 1977-80; Chichester Jr High Sci Tchr 1987-90; Chichester Sr High Bio, Sci Tchr 1990-; *ai:* Sci Olympiad Coach; PA Envirothon Coach; NEA, PSEA, CEA 1987-; *office:* Chichester HS PO Box 2100 Boothwyn PA 19061*

COLLINS, MAUREEN, Fourth Grade Teacher; *b:* Jamaica, NY; *ed:* St Johns Univ (BS) Elem Ed 1973; Long Island Univ (MS) Elem Ed 1979; *cr:* Cath Schls in Diocese of Brooklyn 1st-8th Grd Tchr 1956-60; Cath Schls in Diocese of Rockville Centre 1st-8th Grd Tchr 1960-.

COLLINS, MAUREEN KENNEDY, English Teacher; *b:* Pittsburgh, PA; *m:* Leo W.; *ed:* Clarion St Coll (BS) Eng, Comm Arts 1976; Duguesne Univ (MS) Rdng Specialist 1979; *cr:* South Fayette HS Eng Tchr 1976; Forest Hills Jr HS Eng Tchr 1977-79; Chartiers Vly HS Eng Tchr 1979-80; South Park HS Eng Tchr 1980-; *ai:* Girls Var Tennis Coach; 9th Grd Class, Ski Club Spons; NEA 1980-; NCTE 1977-; USPTR 1993-; *office:* South Park HS 2178 Ridge Rd Library PA 15129

COLLINS, MICHAEL, Mathematics Teacher; *b:* Westbury, NY; *ed:* SUNY at Westbury (MS) Math 1992; *cr:* St Demetrios HS Math Tchr 1992-; Harriet Eisman Comm Schl Math Tchr 1992-95; Uniondale HS Math Tchr 1995-; *ai:* Sr Class Adv; Sftbl, JV Bsktbl Coach; *home:* 520 Lowell St Westbury NY 11590*

COLLINS, PATRICIA A. (WORNOM), Choral Director; *b:* Hampton, VA; *m:* Paul Dennis; *ed:* Longwood Coll (BA) Music 1971; *cr:* Bethlehem Elem Schl Music Tchr 1971-73; Fair Oaks Elem Schl Music Tchr 1971-73; Schor MS Choral, Music Tchr 1973-76; Johnson & Johnson Prsnl Admin, Trainer 1976-80; Taylor Bus Inst Schl Dir 1980-81; Quibbletown MS Choral Dir 1981-83; Piscataway HS Choral Dir 1983-; *ai:* Small Ensemble; Show Choir; NJEA, NEA, NJMEA, ACDA 1973-; Piscataway Fnd Tchr of Yr 1993; Small Ensemble Performed for Gov. Whitman 1994; Choir Performed for St Legislature 1985, Declared Official Choir NJ Legislature;Numerous Natl, Intl Choral Festivals 1st Pl, Grand Championships with Superior Ratings 13 Yrs.

COLLINS, PATRICK M., HS Tech Ed Teacher; *b:* Ballston Spa, NY; *ed:* Schenectady Cty Comm Coll (AA) Soc Sci 1989; SUNY at Oswego (BS) Tech Ed 1991, (MS) Tech Ed 1996; *cr:* CEI Inc Installation, Fabrication Tech 1983-89; Riverside Cemetery Technician, Supt 1990-91; Pre-Press Technician Quad Graphics 1992; Carthage Cntrl HS Tech Ed Tchr 1992-; *ai:* Stu At Risk Team; Venture Prgm Tchr Adv; Epsilon Pi Tau, Kappa Delta Pi 1990-; BPOE 1993-; *office:* Carthage Cntrl HS 36500 NYS Rt 26 Carthage NY 13619*

COLLINS, PAULA GOVONI, 1st Grade Teacher; *b:* Plymouth, MA; *m:* Robert; *c:* Kevin, Katherine; *ed:* (BA) Elem Ed 1973; 15 Addl Hrs Fitchburg Coll, Bridgewater Coll; *cr:* Cold Spring Schl Grade One Tchr 1973-; *ai:* NEA 1973-; 375th Comm for Town of Plymouth & Schl 1995-; Working on Hlth Grant 1990-; SS Comm 1994-; *office:* Cold Spring Schl 25 Alden St Plymouth MA 02360

COLLINS, PETER, Social Studies Teacher; *b:* Bayside, NY; *m:* Christina Villano; *ed:* Oneonta St U (BS) Soc Stud Ed 1991; *cr:* HS of Tchng Soc Stud Tchr 1993-; *ai:* 11th Grd Cncl Adv; AFT 1993-; *home:* 3931 211th St Bayside NY 11361*

COLLINS, RONNIE LEON, Linguistics Professor; *b:* Pocomoke City, MD; *m:* Rachelle Large; *c:* Ronnie Jr., Jared Arbye, Isabelle Janae; *ed:* Bowie St Univ (BA) British Amer Lit 1974; Univ of Edinburgh Scotland (SPG Gen Linguistics 1975; Georgetown Univ (MS) Sociolinguistics, Theoretical 1977; Working Toward PHD Sociolinguistics; *cr:* Intercultural Comm Sr Linguist 1975-77; Bowie St Coll Eng Prof 1978-83; Coppin St Coll Dean of Arts & Sci 1984-89, Linguistics Prof 1990-; *ai:* Queens Chapel Male Chorus VP; Historic Mt Royal Civic Assn VP; Eng Major Advising Comm Chair; Queens Chapel United Meth Church Prgm DirUn; Modern Lang Assn 1985-; Linguistic Soc of Amer 1988-; Rhodes Schlsp Finalist; Danforth Flwshp; Fulbright Schlsp; India Stud Tour Grant; *office:* Coppin St Coll 2500 W North Ave Baltimore MD 21216*

COLLINS, SANDRA PETRUCCI, Third Grade Teacher; *b:* Scranton, PA; *m:* Robert J.; *c:* Jason; *ed:* Marywood Coll (BA) Elem Ed 1972, (MS) Rdng Ed 1975; 70 Addl Credit Hrs Cmptr Ed; *cr:* North Pocono Schl Dist Third Grd Tchr 1973-; *ai:* New Tchr Mentor; Cmptr Comm; NEA 1973-; NP Woman's Tchr Assn 1980-; NCMT Math Tchrs Assn 1991-; NP Booster Assn 1992-; *office:* Moscow Elem Center Church St Moscow PA 18444

COLLINS, SCOTT GORDON, American Government Teacher; *b:* Cleveland, OH; *m:* Deborah; *ed:* Youngstown St Univ (BS) Sec Soc Stud 1989; Working Towards Masters in Admin; *cr:* Girard HS Summer Schl Sub 1989-90; Maplewood HS DPPF, Stud Hall ISS 1990-91; Ashtabula HS 9-12 Grd Soc Stud Tchr 1991-; *ai:* Asst Var Girls Bsktbl, Asst VarFtbl, Head Track Coach; Sr Class, Pep Club Adv; Church Youth Vol; Sunday Schl Tchr; NEONEA 1991-; *home:* 308 Beverly Dr Jefferson OH 44047

COLLINS, WILLIAM J., Social Studies Teacher; *b:* Passaic, NJ; *m:* Constance Melomo; *c:* Edward, Bridget, Brian, Michael; *ed:* St. Francis Coll (BA) His 1966; Montclair St Coll (MA) Soc Stud 1972; Seton Hall Law Schl; *cr:* Pope Pius XII HS Tchr & Dept Chair 1967-83; Paul VI HS Tchr 1983-90; DePaul HS Tchr 1990-; *ai:* NCEA 1967-; Alpha Phi Theta, Natl Honor Historical Soc 1966-; *office:* DePaul HS 1512 Alps Rd Wayne NJ 07470

COLLINSWORTH, JANE FLEMING, Music Teacher; *b:* Wichita, KS; *m:* David A.; *ed:* Friends Univ (BM) Vocal Performance 1984, (BME) Music Ed 1986; *cr:* St Anne Schl Music Tchr 1988-90; Bishop Leibold Schl Music Tchr 1990-; Miamisburg HS Musical Dir 1994-; *ai:* 4-8 Grd Choir; St Anne Schl 7 & 8 Grd Choir; Dayton Philharmonic Orch Chorus 1991-; Performed Music Theatre of Wichita 1988-94; Dayton Playhouse 1994; Crown Uptown Dinner Theater; Empire House Melodrama Theatre; *office:* Bishop Leibold Schl 24 S 3rd St Miamisburg OH 45342

COLLISHAW, JUDITH ANN AHLIN, Social Studies Teacher; *b:* Bronx, NY; *m:* William T.; *c:* Denise, Keith; *ed:* Concordia Jr Coll (AA) Ed 1963; Concordia Tchrs Coll (BA) His & Ed 1966; Dartmouth Coll (MALS) His 1979; Univ of NH Russian Lang & Lit; Dartmouth Alumni Coll; Natl Geographic Alliance; Facing His & Ourselves; *cr:* Grace Luth Schl 4th-6th Grd Tchr 1965-67; Lebanon Jr High 8th Grd Tchr 1973-75; Mascoma Jr High 7th Grd Tchr 1977-80; Frances C Richmond Schl 7th & 8th Grd Tchr 1986-; *ai:* Stu Recycling Pgm Adv; NEA 1986-; HEA 1986-, VP; HS Grad Speaker 1994; *office:* Francis C Richmond Schl Lebanon St Hanover NH 03755

COLLOM, MARY IRENE PALMER, Foreign Language Teacher; *b:* Burlington, VT; *m:* Roger E.; *ed:* Univ of VT (BA) Fr, Scndry Ed 1978; St Michael's Coll (MED) Ed 1988; Certfd Mid Level Ed; Tchr Mentor; Attnd Univ of Nice France; *cr:* Camels Hump MS Fr, Span, Exploratory Frgn Lang Tchr 1978-; *ai:* Mentoring Comm; 8th Grd Montreal Trip Spon; NEA 1978-; *office:* Camels Hump MS RD 1 Jericho Rd Richmond VT 05477*

COLLWARD, LAURIE, HS Special Education Teacher; *b:* Clifton Springs, NY; *ed:* Finger Lakes Comm Coll (AAS) Human Svcs 1983; Nazareth Coll (BS) Psych, Spcl & Elem Ed 1987, (MS) Ed & Rdng Ed 1991; Rochester Inst of Tech 6 Hrs Sign Lang; *cr:* Red Jacket Cntrl Schl Spcl Ed & Consultant for Scndry Ed 1987-; *ai:* Comprehensive Schl Hlth & Wellness, Assessment Design & Spcl Ed Advy Comms; NY St United Tchrs & AFT 1987-; *office:* Red Jacket Central Schl Lehigh Ave Shortsville NY 14548

COLMAN, MARCIA JANNARONE, 8th Grade Teacher; *b:* Newark, NJ; *m:* Dale; *c:* Michael, Patrick; *ed:* Rowan St Coll (BA) Ed 1965; LaSalle Univ 28 Credits Grad Theology; *cr:* Egg Harbor City Schls Kndgtn Tchr 1965-66; Pleasantville Pub Schls Second Grd Tchr 1976-81; St Peters Schl 3, 6, 7-8 Grd Tchr 1981-; *ai:* Rel Ed Yrbk Dir; NEA 1965-; Cath Schls Tchrs Assn 1981-; Atlantic Cty Environmental Cncl; Pax Christi Intnl; *office:* St Peters Schl Decatur & Chestnut Sts Pleasantville NJ 08232*

COLODIN, JOSEPH FELIX, Program Consultant & Writer; *b:* Red Bank, NJ; *ed:* Union Coll (AA) Criminal Justice 1977; Rutgers Univ Voc Ed Cert Prgm; Unio Co Tech Inst Cmptr Sci Prgm; *cr:* Union Co Voc-Tech Inst Auto Mechanics Tchr 1979-83; Lincoln Tech Inst Auto Mechanics Tchr 1984-86; Union Co Regnl HS Auto Mechanics Tchr 1986-90; Monmouth Co Voc Schl Auto Mechanics Tchr 1990-93; Linden HS Voc Automotive Tech Tchr 1993-95.

COLOMBO, MARIA CARMELA, Teacher of the Gifted; *b:* Lakewood, OH; *ed:* Kent St Univ (BA) Psych 1979, (BS) Elem Ed 1986; Ashland Univ (MED) Curr 1990; Addl Hrs Kent St Univ, St Bonaventure Univ; *cr:* St Vincent Elem Schl 3, 4, 5 Grd Tchr 1979-82; Immaculate Conception Schl Primary Grds Tchr 1982-87; Pleasant View Schl 4-8 Grds Gifted, 6th Grd Rdng Tchr 1987-; *ai:* NEA 1987-; Sisters of St Dominic of Akron 1993, Assoc Mem; East Cntrl OH MENSA Excl Tchng Awd 1990; Contributing Author Tchr Resource Books 1990; *office:* Pleasant View Sch For The Arts 3000 Columbus Rd NE Canton OH 44705

COLON, CARMEN MARIA, Spanish Teacher; *b:* Utuado, PR; *m:* Juan; *c:* Lisandra, Cyndia; *ed:* Univ of PR, Cleveland St Univ (BA) SPan 1973; Addl 24 Credits Bowling Green St Univ, Ashland Univ, Univ of Findlay 1982-; Enrolled in Curr & Instruction Master's Pgm at Ashland Univ 1995-; *cr:* Whittier Jr HS 7-8th Grd Span Tchr 1973-77, Permanent Sub Tchr 1982-83; Southview HS 9-12th Biling Tchr 1983-89; Admiral King HS 9-12th Grd Span Tchr 1987-; *ai:* Foreign Lang Club Adv; OEA 1973-77; NEA 1982-; LEA; *office:* Admiral King HS 2600 Ashland Ave Lorain OH 44052

COLON, EDWINA, Instructional Support Teacher; *b:* Reading, PA; *ed:* PA St Univ (BS) Elem Ed 1991; 3 Credits Temple Univ; Presently Attending Kutztown Univ; *cr:* Glenside Schl 2nd-5th Grd Biling Tchr 1992-93; Amanda E. Stout Schl 2nd Grd Tchr 1993-94, Instrl Support Tchr 1994-; *ai:* After Schl Migrant Tchr; Asst Coord Schl Show; Dance Instr for AES Stdnts; Schl Wide, Culturally Diverse Stdnts Comms; NEA, PSEA 1992-; Cncl on Chemical Abuse 1993-, Sec; Puerto Rican Latin Assn 1992-94; Ldrshp Round Table 1992-93; *office:* Amanda E. Stout Reading Schl 321 S 10th St Reading PA 19602

COLON, MARYBELLE B., Bilingual Special Ed Teacher; *b:* Brooklyn, NY; *m:* Fernando J.; *c:* Jose F., Tania M.; *ed:* Pace Univ (BA) Psych, Span 1985; Hunter Coll at CUNY (MS) Spec Ed 1990; NY Univ PHD Candidate Bilingual Spec Ed; NY St Educl Evaluation Cert Prgm 72 Addl Credits; Working on Doctorate; *cr:* Bushwick HS Spec Ed Tchr 1986-92; Brooklyn HS Educl Diagnostician, Evaluator 1991-92; New Haven Pub Schls Bilingual Spec Ed Tchr 1992-94; New Britian Pub Schls Bilingual Resource, Inclusion Specialist 1994-; Cntrl CT St Univ Adjunct Prof 1994-; *ai:* After Schl Prgm Dir; Parish Cncl; Parish Folk Group Dir; AFT 1986-; Psi Chi NHS 1984-, Pace VP 1984, 1986; AAUW 1994-; Jornada Movement NYC 1981-; Church of Holy Family 1994-, Parish Cncl; Bi Sep Grant Title VI Dept of Ed 1986-90; NYU, Dept of Ed Title VII Flwshp 1990-93; psi Chi NHS Certs 1984, 1986; *home:* 69 Chesterfield Rd Amston CT 06231*

COLON, RICARDO, Span Tchr & Girls Track Coach; *b:* Patchogue, NY; *m:* Ellen Murphy-Colon; *ed:* Univ of SD (BA) Span, PE 1983, (MA) PE 1990; *cr:* Gayville-Volin Schl Dist Span, Driver Ed, PE 1984-85; East Hampton Union Free Schl Dist Span Tchr, Track Coach 1985-88; Longwood Cntrl Schl Dist Span Tchr, Track Coach 1988-; *ai:* Head Var Cross Cntry, Winter Track Coach; Suffolk Cty Track, Field 1985-, Pres 1993; *office:* Longwood Cntrl Schl Dist 198 Longwood Rd Middle Island NY 11953*

COLONNA, ELIZABETH A. (MOTTO), High School Ma Tchr; *b:* Pottsville, PA; *m:* Philip S.; *ed:* Villanova Univ (BS) Beaver Coll at Glenside Masters Degree Math Stud; *cr:* Souderto Math Tchr 1992-; *ai:* Sr Class Adv; NEA 1992-; NCTM 199 Souderton Area HS 41 N School Ln Souderton PA 18964

COLOSI, RONALD J.,SR., Bio, Anatomy & Physiology Tchr; MA; *m:* Gloria M. Catalano; *c:* Ronald Jr., Carissa, Christopher; St Coll (BA) Bio 1975; Boston Univ Working Toward MA; Nc Univ Math Tchr Cert; *cr:* Littleton HS Math, Sci Tchr 1976-77; Bio Tchr 1977-; *ai:* SICK League Bank Comm Chair; Everett T Stu Rsrch Adv; NEA, MA Tchrs Assn 1977-; NH Lakes As Governors Inprovement Assn 1984-, VP; Vol Lake Assessment Pr *home:* 127 Grover St Everett MA 02149

COLOZZI, DIANE M., Foreign Language Dept Head; *b:* S MA; *ed:* Emmanuel Coll (BA) Fr 1976; Lesley Coll (MED) Ed Mission Church HS Frgn Lang Dept Head, Fr & Span Tchr Bishop Fenwick HS Frgn Lang Dept Head, Fr & Span Tchr Accreditation of Schl Steering Comm 1982, 1992; Schls Open Tour Guide Coord; Class of 2000 Schlsp Comm; Fac Meetings F NHS Selection Comm; MAFLA 1982-; AATF 1985-89; AATS Essex Cty Frgn Lang Assn of MA, Greater Boston Wc Collaborative 1994-; Article Pub; Svc Awd 1980; Perfect A 1976-94; Initiated & Taught AP Fr 1994-95; *office:* Bishop Fenw Margin St Peabody MA 01960*

COLTON, THOMAS ALLEN, Latin & English Teacher; *b:* N NY; *m:* Nancy A. Green; *c:* Brian, James, Christopher; *ed:* Qu (BA) Classics 1966; Iona Coll (MS) Ed 1989; CUNY Grad Ctr Trinity Coll at Hartford 1968; Cath U of Milan 1969; *cr:* Sleep HS Latin, Eng, Italian & ESL Tchr 1966-; *ai:* Tchrs Assn Tarryto NYSUT 1966-; Classical Assn Empire St 1968-, Regents Cor Latin Pgm, NYS Hnrs 1989; BSA 1950-, Troop Comm, Eagle Sc St Boniface Church 1982-, Parish Cncl; Rockland Co Jr Bow 1994-, Comm; Numerous Articles Pub 1988-89; Regents Comm

COLUCCI, COLLEEN JENNIE, Art Teacher; *b:* Rockville Ct Catholic Univ of Amer (BA) Art & Ed 1993; Working on (MA) *cr:* Holy Trinity HS Art Tchr 1993-; *ai:* Sr Stu Cncl; Ski Club M Grad Asst Adelphi Univ; *office:* Holy Trinity Diocesan HS 98 (Hicksville NY 11801*

COLUMBIA, MICHAEL MATTHEW, Foreign Langua Chairman; *b:* New York City, NY; *m:* Rosemary Keenan; *c:* S Nancy, Nicole, Michael; *ed:* Fordham Univ (AB) Eng 1966; Col (MA) Eng 1967; Attnd St Univ of NY 30 Credits, New York Univ Long Island 16 Credits, Univ of Rochester 6 Credits; *cr:* Su Comm Coll Assoc Prof of Eng 1967-; Patchogue HS Eng Tchr Ward Melville HS Eng Tchr 1970-90, Foreign Langs Chm 1 Foreign Lang Task Force; AFT, NYSUT 1966-; SANYS 199 Fellowship in Medieval Stud 1984; *office:* Ward Melville Sr HS Town Rd East Setauket NY 11733

COLUSSI, DONALD R., English Teacher; *b:* Cincinnati, OH; *m* Osterholt; *c:* Dave, Dan, Dea, Dawn; *ed:* Xavier Univ (BA) A 1959, (MA) Eng 1963; Attnd Miami Univ & Univ Cincinnati; Oak Jr HS Eng Tchr 1961-65; Colerain SR HS Eng Tchr 1966-; Bsbl & Ftbl Coach; NEA, OEA, NEWA 1962-; OH Bsbl Coac 1967-; Southwestern OH Bsbl Assn 1967-, Coach of Yr 1968, 19 1984, 1990; OH Ftbl Coaches Assn 1970-; PTA 1962-; OH Bsb Fame 1990; Hamilton Cty Hall of Fame 1993; *office:* Colerain Sr Cheviot Rd Cincinnati OH 45251

COLVARD, MARY PAGE, Biology & Research Teacher; *b:* Sid *m:* John Bartsch; *c:* Jeffrey, Craig, Matt; *ed:* SUNY at Gene Scndry Bio 1968; SUNY at Oneonta (MS) Scndry Bio 1984; Bir Univ & Cornell Univ Post Grad Courses; *cr:* Sidney HS Sci Tch Chair 1969-89; Cobleskill-Richmondville HS Bio & Rsrch Tchr 1 Sci Club & Sci Olympiad Team Adv; Shared Decision Making Co NYSUT 1968-, Assn Local Sec & Grievance Comm; STANYS 19 Bio & DAL Wkshps; NABT 1990-, Region II Coord, Outstdng NY St; NSTA 1990-; NABT Outstdng Bio Tchr NY St; Sigma Xi Sci Tchr for Tri-Cty Area; Access Excl Genentech Fellow; NAB Coord; Sci Tchrs Assn of NY Dir for Bio; Co-Author of NYS Bi Assessment Guide; Books: People & Animals Working Together Review in Biology; *office:* Cobleskill-Richmondville HS Wa Heights Cobleskill NY 12043

COLVIN, LINDA BENEDICT, Computer Education Coordir Norwalk, CT; *m:* Neil J.; *ed:* Wellesley Coll (BA) US Stud 1971; Univ (MA) Tchng Rdng 1972; Lesley Coll (CAGS) Cmptr in Ed Walpole Schls Lang Dev Specialist 1972-78, 3rd Grd Tchr 1978-8 Coll Adj Fac 1990-; Walpole Schls Cmptr Ed Coord 1985-; *ai:* S Pre K-12 Cmptr Ed Lang Range Planning, Principals & Coord Boston Cmptr Soc, Intnl Soc Tech in Ed 1984-; Phi Delta Kappa, N Tchr Assn, Norfolk Cty Tchr Assn 1972-; MA Cmptr Using Edct Bd Mem 7 Yrs; Nepanset Choral Soc 1975-, Bd Mem 9 Yrs; Resources Trust fo Easton 1975-, Bd Mem 16 Yrs; Easton Histor Friend of Boulevard 1974-, Life Mem; Acrri Collabrative 1987-, Mem; TEC Supt Distinguished Traveling Awd 1993; Horace Ma 1988; Cert of Merit Electronic Learning Ed of Yr Awds 1984; Kappa Grants 1987, 1988., 1990, 1995; Articles Pub; Book Pu 1986; *office:* Walpole Pub Schls School St Walpole MA 02081

COLVIN, MARK THOMAS, Fifth Grade Teacher; *b:* Watertown, Jo Elaine; *c:* Matthew, Kellie; *ed:* Oswego St (BS) Elem Ed 1975; Post Grad Credit Hrs; *cr:* Mexico Acad, Cntrl Schl 5th Grd Tchr 1 Var Boys Soccer, Var Girls Sftbl, Boy, Girls Modified Socce Modified Sftbl Coach; AFT, NY St United Tchr 1975-; *office:* Mexi & Cntrl Schl Rt 104 Mexico NY 13114

COLVIN, SUSAN PUGLIESE, Asst Prof of Pediatric Nur Pittsburgh, PA; *m:* Gerald C.; *c:* Michael, David, Anne; *ed:* Duques (BSN) Nrsng 1965; Univ of Pittsburgh (MS) Pediatric Nrsn Doctoral Prgm 18 Credits; *cr:* Natl Insts of Hlth Rsrch Staf 1965-67; Presbyn Univ Hosp Schl of Nrsng Instr 1967-70; Comm Allegheny Co Asst Prof 1982-87; Children's Hosp of Pittsburgh A Practice Nurse 1984-; Duquesne Univ Asst Prof 1987-; *ai:* Sr Cla Sigma Theta Tau Intnl 1982-; Three Rivers Rowing Assn 1993 Safety Comm; Articles Pub; 3 Rsrch Grants; Certfd Pediatric Nurse Trauma Nurse Cert; *office:* Duquesne Univ School of Nursing For Pittsburgh PA 15282

COLVIN, WILLIAM DOLQUEST, English & Theater Tea Connellsville, PA; *m:* Judith Katherine Reed; *c:* Bridget, Megan Alan; *ed:* Coll of Wooster (BA) Theatre & US His 1970; Univ of Pi Eng; PA St Ed & Cmptr; *cr:* Connellsville Area Sr HS Tchr 1973- Class Play Producer, Broadway Musical Tech Dir; Camera Club Ad Thespian Soc Spon; CAEA, PSEA, NEA 1973-, Bldg Rep, Newsle Natl Guard Assn US 1971-; Natl Guard Assn PA 1970-, Bd Di Brotherhead of Magicians 1968-, Order of Merlin; PA Army Nat 1970-, Bn Cdr, Bde & Div, MSM W/OLC, Staff Officer ARCOM AAM W/3OLC; Laurel Highlands VHF Soc 1970-, Bd of Dirs; Imm Conception Church Parish Cncl 1990-, Pres 1992-93; Fayette Yth Assoc, Bd of Dirs; Tm Coach, Bantams & Squirts; Honor Grad U

Jeneral Staff Coll at Ft Leavenworth KS; *office:* Connellsville IS 201 Falcon Dr Connellsville PA 15425*

.L, LARRY WINFRED, English Teacher; *b:* Washington, DC; Irene Preston; *c:* Annel C. Cooke, Dennis J.; *ed:* DC Tchrs Coll , Fr 1967; Trinity Coll (MAT) Eng, Rdng 1975; Univ of DC (MA) upervision 1982; *cr:* Francis Jr HS Tchr 1967; Evans Jr HS Tchr Sr Class Spon; Writing Coord; Testing, Schl Chptr Advy Comm; ; WA Tchr Union 1967-; DC Coun Tchr of Eng; Omega Psi Phi; ill Kiwanis, Ed of Newsletter, Plaque; Dev Eng Unit; Awd from ponents Packages Pgrm in Eng 1970-71; *office:* Evans Jr HS 5600 St NE Washington DC 20019

ATO, NATALIE GATTO, Second Grade Teacher; *b:* Brooklyn, ouis; *c:* Christopher, Diana; *ed:* Trenton St Coll (BS) Elem Ed Fairmount Elem Schl 2-5 Grd Basic Skills Tchr 1990-92; Nellie Elem Schl 2nd Grd Tchr 1992-96; *ai:* Pupil Assistance, Whole nl Level Planning, Women in His, Schl Hospitality Comm; Math ; Multicultural Acts, Presentations; PTA; NJEA, NEA 1990-; Dev al Tchng Strategy Awd Winner by NJ St Dept of Ed 1995; *office:* Parker Elem Schl 261 Maple Hill Dr Hackensack NJ 07601*

:, DAVID, Latin, Fr & Ancient Greek Tchr; *b:* Norwood, MA; *ed:* wn Univ (BS) Linguistics 1970, (MS) Linguistics 1971; *cr:* Faith S Latin, Fr, Ancient Greek Tchr 1988-; *ai:* Amer Classical Phi Beta Kappa; *office:* Faith Christian Schl Faith-Haddon Ave & Blvd Collingswood NJ 08108

CAROL REZANKA, Secondary Teacher; *b:* Bayonne, NJ; *c:* no Hee; *ed:* Douglass Coll (BA) Math, Eng 1968; Univ of AK at ge (MA) Ed 1984; *cr:* Terrill Jr HS 7th-9th Grd Math Tchr Am Horse Day Schl 7th Grd Tchr 1975-76; Savoonga Elem Schl 3rd Tchr 1977-83; UAA Adjunct Math Tchr 1988-93; East HS ır 1993-95; Yorketown Area Schl Scndry Math, Exch Tchr 1996; ncl, Cheerleaders, Ski Club Adv; NEA, ASCD; PTA.

LANDA DARLENE, Home Ec, Fmly & Cnsmr Sci Tchr; *b:* N; *ed:* Ball St Univ (BS) Home Ec 1969; Xavier Univ (Med) ri Ed 1973; +15 Credit Hrs Over Masters; *cr:* Southeastern Jr r 1969-70; Colerain HS Tchr 1970-; *ai:* Teens in Action Adv; NEA WOEA 1970-; NAE 1970-; DAR 1981-; *office:* Colerain HS 8801 Rd Cincinnati OH 45251

U, KATHERINE SULLIVAN, Third Grade Teacher; *b:* :, MA; *m:* Richard D.; *c:* Richard M., Jonathan D.; *ed:* ater St Coll (BS) Elem Ed 1961; Fitchburg St Coll (MS) Educl 3; 19 Addl Credits; *cr:* Scituate Pub Schls 3rd Grd Tchr 1961-64; le Pub Schls 3rd Grd Tchr 1974-; *ai:* MA Tchrs Assn 1961-; le Cty Tchrs Assn, NEA 1974-; *office:* Barnstable West Elem Schl arnstable MA 02630

ETZ, MARIAN, German & Spanish Teacher; *b:* Boston, MA; *m:* : Jacob; *ed:* Smith Coll (BA) Fr 1965; Harvard (MAT) Ed & Fgn 56; Middlebury Coll (MA) Fr 1971; Cert in Span; *cr:* Lexington of Fr Ger, Span 1966-; *ai:* German Fest; Fgn Lang Awds Night; TA & LEA 1966-; MAFLA 1966-; AATG 1983-; *office:* Lexington Waltham St Lexington MA 02173

, CORA ANN, K-1 Multi Age Teacher; *b:* Portsmouth, OH; *m:* ..; *ed:* OH Univ (BS) Elem Ed 1964; Coll of Mt St Joseph (MA) 30 Post-Grad Stud; *cr:* Union Elem Schl Third Grd Tchr 1962-64; em Schl First-Second Grd Tchr 1964-93, K-1 Grd Multi Age Tchr : NEA, Cntrl OH Tchrs 1970-; OH Ed Assn 1962-; Chillicothe Ed 34-, Sec; Delta Kappa Gamma 1975-, Corresponding Sec 8 Yrs; Holden Jennings Scholar; Spokesperson Educl Luncheon Rep; entral Elem Schl 40 W 5th St Chillicothe OH 45601

:, DIANA HOUDE, Dir of Early Childhood Ed; *b:* Worcester, MA; ıas John; *c:* Elisabeth, Katherine, Thomas, Robert; *ed:* Worcester BESd) Kndgtn, Primary 1971; Cambridge Coll (MED) Admin Ed, 1984; Effective Use Paraeducators 3 Credits; Univ of MA New Sci, Soc Stud 3 Credits; Northeastern Univ Behaviorally d Children Practicum 6 Credits; *cr:* Worcester Pub Schls Kndgtn 71-74; Worcester St Coll Lead Tchr, Dir Lab Schl 1975; Becker sch Dir 1976-81, ECE Dir 1981-; *ai:* Worcester Voc HS ECE Adv Vorcester St Coll Tchr Prep Adv 5 Yrs; Goddard Schl, Hiatt Ctr, er Pub, Clark U ECE Adv; WAAEYC 1980-; ASCD 1990-; NEA; er Bus & Prof Women; YMCA Advy ECE Bd 3 Yrs; Coll Worcester um 5 Yrs, Chprsn Tchr Ed Prep Group 3 Yrs; Books: Developing kills for the Young Child 1985, Growing Up with Literature 1985; ant Work Cntrl DSS Foster Care, Headstarts, Presch, Daycares.*

R, JERRY BYRON, Science Teacher; *b:* Bellefontaine, OH; *m:* ayne Stahler; *c:* Andrew, Matthew; *ed:* Bowling Green St Univ 1972; John Carroll Univ 30 Hrs Schl Admin; *cr:* Parma City Schl andy Chem, & Earth Sci Tchr 1972-; *ai:* Var Girls Sftbl Coach; Educl Assoc 1972-; OH Educl Assoc 1972-; NEA 1972-; Boggs 292 F&AM 1972-, 32 Degree; Northeast OH Fastpitches Assoc Pres; OH Coaches Assoc 1979-; BSA 1990-, Asst Scoutmaster; Normandy HS 2500 W Pleasant Valley Rd Parma OH 44134

R, JONATHAN A., High School English Teacher; *b:* Springfield, Michelle Dawson; *ed:* OH St Univ (BS) Eng Ed 1990; OH Univ Coll Stu Prsnl 1992; Working Toward Schl Guidance Cnslr Cert at Dayton; *cr:* Western HS Eng Tchr 1993-; *ai:* Sr Class Play Adv; g Bee Coach; Career Night Spon; NEA, OEA, WEA 1993-; ed Career Fair as Result of Strategic Planning Initiated through Capital Grant Process; *office:* Western Pike Cty HS 8640 St Rt 124 OH 45646

RFORD, DANIEL J.,III, Social Studies Teacher; *b:* Brooklyn, Kathie Wiener; *ed:* SUNY at New Paltz (BA) His & Ed 1968; at Stony Brook (MA) Soc Issues & Black His 1970, (MA) His & Ed Y Univ (EDD) Scndry Ed & Evaluation 1983; Cornell Univ; Cert ract Admin 1991; *cr:* Three Village CSD Soc Stud Tchr, House Plan gm Evaluator & Prsnl Assoc 1968-; SUNY at Stony Brook Grad str 1988-; *ai:* 2000 Steering Comm; Sexual Harassment Task Group ir; House Plan & Interdisciplinary Planning Comm; Three Village ssoc Grievance Co-Chair; Early Amer Industries Assoc 1971-, Pres; EERA, NEERO & NCSS 1982-, NEERO Best Paper 2nd Place; Phi Kappa 1982-, Young Scholar 1982; NOLPE 1988-; ETC, ATTIC, , MWTCA, LIATCA & SWTCA 1972-; Amer Red Cross 1977-, Drive Chair; Three Village CSD Tchr of Yr 1979-80 & 1972-73; ecognition 1987; Whos Who in Amer Ed 1988-90, 1994 & 1996; Y St Outstdng Tchr of Amer His 1990; Numerous Presentations & Pub; Book: The Hammer-The King Of Tools; Consulting Ed onian; *office:* Robert C. Murphy Jr HS Oxhead Rd Stony Brook NY

RFORD, JOAN K., Biology Teacher; *b:* Richmond, VA; *ed:* St Univ (BS) Bio 1968; VA Commonwealth Univ (MED) Bio 1975; ts at Univ of MD 1990; *cr:* Essex Cty Pub Schls Tchr 1968-78; Georges Pub Schls Tchr 1978-; *ai:* Frosh Class Spon; Bio Club; 969-; *office:* Oxon Hill HS 6701 Leyte Dr Oxon Hill MD 20745

Y, JAMES HUGH, Academic Services Director; *b:* Drexel Hill, Patricia A. Borda; *c:* Jennifer, Colleen (Dec), James Jr.; *ed:* West Univ (BS) Eng & Ed 1969, (MEd) Eng 1973; Univ PA (EdD) zation Leadership in Curr & Instruction 1995; Neuro-Linguistic Programming Certified Master Practitioner; *cr:* DE Cty Comm Coll Instr in Eng Evening 1976-84; Kennett Consolidated SD Eng Tchr 1969-74; Upper Darby Schl Dist Eng Tchr 1974-86; Wallingford-Swarthmore SD Dir of Acad Svcs 1990-; *ai:* Coord of Gifted Talented Prgm; NEA 1969-, Citaton in Natl Newsletter; PSEA 1969-; Authors Guild 1975-, Cited in Natl Newsletter; Novel Pub; Co-Founder of Natl Recognized Childrens Theater Co Wrote 7 Issues Based on Childrens Musical Plays; Writing Recognized by Southern Poverty Law Ctr & PA Ctr; Grants from PA Cncl on Arts; *office:* Strath Haven MS 203 S Providence Rd Wallingford PA 19086

COMIRE, GARY CHARLES-JOSEPH, Soc Stud Tchr & Dept Chm; *b:* Woonsocket, RI; *m:* Susan Katherine Defond; *ed:* Assumption Coll (BA) European His 1976; Providence Coll (MA) Amer His 1988; 22 Hrs CAGS; *cr:* William Davies Voc Tchrs Aide 1976; Woonsocket Cath Regnl Soc Stud Tchr 1976-77; Saint Joseph Schl Soc Stud Tchr 1977-78; Mount Saint Charles Acad Soc Stud Tchr & Dept Chair 1978-; *ai:* North Smithfield HS Var Soccer Coach 14 Yrs; Sr Class Tchr Asst; Acad Cncl; RI Soccer Coaches Assn 1976-, Sec, Coach of Yr 1989; NEA 1980-; Org of Amer Historians 1988-; Natl Cncl for His Ed 1990-; GENIP 1989-; NCSS 1990-; NCEA 1980-; RI Labor Inst 1990-; RISS Assn 1991-; NEHTA 1989-; Freedoms Fnd Stud Grant; 2 Educator of Yr; CALL Coach of Yr; NSCAA Regnl Diploma; 2 RI Governor Citations; 2 RI Legislature Citations; North Smithfield Town Citation for Coaching Soccer Teams; *office:* Mount Saint Charles Acad 800 Logee St Woonsocket RI 02895

COMMISSO, ROSA, Elem Italian Lecturer & Coord; *b:* Glosia Marina, Italy; *ed:* Univ of Akron (BA) Span 1980, (MA) Span 1981; Latin Amer Stud Cert 1980; Liscenced Real Estate; *cr:* Kent St Univ Lecturer & Coord of Elem Italian 1981-; Univ of Akron Span Instr 1983-; *ai:* Teach Continuing Ed Courses for Stow Parks & Rec, Wayne Coll; OH Bd of Realtors 1993-; Pi Delta Phi; Sigma Delta Pi; Phi Alpha Pheta; Reviewed Text Books; *office:* Kent St Univ Kent OH 44242*

COMMITO, ANN E., Associate Prof of Mathematics; *b:* New York, NY; *m:* John; *c:* Gianna, Angela; *ed:* Cornell UNiv (BS) Child Psych 1971; Hood Coll (BA) Math 1983, (MS) Cmptr Sci 1987; *cr:* Pub Schl Tchr 1971-80; Hood Coll Adj Instr 1981-88; Frederick Comm Coll Assoc Prof Math 1988-; *ai:* Moderator Amatyc Stu League Team; Math Club Adv; Vice Chair Fac Assn; MMATYC 1985-, VP; MAA, Phi Kappa Phi 1983-; PTSA, Exec Comm; NISOD Excl Tchng Awd 1994; *office:* Frederick Comm Coll 7932 Opossumtown Pike Frederick MD 21702

COMMOSS, SUSAN HARRIET, 5th Grade Teacher; *b:* Belmont, MA; *ed:* Jackson Coll Tufts Univ (BA) Eng 1962; Tchrs Coll at Columbia (MA) Elem Ed 1966; Boston Univ (CAGS) Rdng 1973; *cr:* Amherst NH Brick Schl Tchr 1962-63; Center Moriches Pub Schl Tchr 1965-69; Garden City Pub Schl Tchr 1969-72; Belmont Pub Schl 1973-; *ai:* Care for AV Equipment; NEA 1962-; 2 Articles Pub.

COMOLLI, DAVID MICHAEL, Junior Schl Dir & English Tchr; *b:* Burlington, VT; *m:* Pebbles Drum; *c:* Morgan; *ed:* Norwich Univ (BS) El Ed 1982; Pursuing Grad Degree U of Southern MS; *cr:* Carson Long Military Acad Tchr 1982-, Jr Schl Dir 1991-; *ai:* Bsktbl, Bsbl Head Coaches; NCTE 1989-; *office:* Carson Long Military Acad 200 N Carlisle St New Bloomfield PA 17068*

COMOLLI, TIMOTHY DOYLE, Imaging Lab Director; *b:* Montpelier, VT; *ed:* Johnson St (BS) Ed 1965; Norwich Univ (MA) Comm 1985; 36 Credit Hrs Beyond Masters; *cr:* S Burlington HS Tchr 1965-; *ai:* Tech Cncl Dist & Local; New England Evaluation; Pep Club; Class Adv & Model UN Adv for Tech; NEA & VEA 1965-; SBEA 1965-, VP; VT Assn of Cable Casters 1992-; Planning Commission 1985-; Microsoft Bill Gates Road Ahead Grant; Alias, Warefront grant; Henderson Fnd Grant; Pepsi; Silicon Graphics Educators Grant; Autodesk Grant; St of VT Drug Free Schls Grant; Chapter 3 Minigrants 2; Resolution Video Grant; Media Group Gift; *office:* South Burlington HS 550 Dorset St South Burlington VT 05403*

COMPANY, KELLE CAMPBELL, High School English Teacher; *b:* Lubbock, TX; *m:* Carlos; *ed:* TX Tech Univ (BA) Eng, Compartitive Lit 1990; Addl 30 Hrs Lit; *cr:* Balboa HS Jr-Sr Eng Tchr 1992-93, Sr Eng Tchr 1993-94, AP & Sr Eng Tchr 1994-95, Frosh Hnrs, Sr Eng Tchr 1995-; *ai:* Frosh Class, Letterman Club Spon; Schl Improvement Team; Phi Delta Kappa 1996; AFT 1992-; *office:* Balboa HS DODDS Panama Region Unit 925 APO AA 34002

COMPEAU, JOHN DAVID, Mathematics & Computer Teacher; *b:* Watertown, NY; *m:* Carol Wiswell; *c:* Michael, Jennifer; *ed:* SUNY at Albany (BS) Math 1969; 30 Grad Hrs Ed; 24 Grad Hrs Cmptr; *cr:* LaFargeville Cntrl Schl Math, Cmptr Tchr 1972-; Immigration & Naturalization Inspector 1982-; *ai:* Hnr Soc Selection Comm; NYSUT; LaFargeville Tchrs Assn; Turnkey Trainer HS Math 1988; *office:* La Fargeville Central Schl PO Box 138 La Fargeville NY 13656

COMSTOCK, BARBARA LYNN (FITCH), Fourth Grade Teacher; *b:* Utica, NY; *m:* Gary R.; *c:* Aaron, Audrey; *ed:* SUNY at Potsdam (BA) Psych 1978; SUNY at Cortland (MA) Elem Ed; *cr:* Sauquoit Vly Elem Schl 4th Grd Tchr 1978-; *ai:* Delta Kappa Gamma 1992-; NUSUT 1979-; *home:* PO Box 12 Bridgewater NY 13313

COMSTOCK, EDITH ANN, Mathematics Teacher; *b:* Natrona Heights, PA; *m:* Bruce M. Jr.; *c:* Megan Cramer, Matthew; *ed:* Univ of Pittsburgh (BS) Math, Fr 1962; *cr:* Har Brack Union Schls Math Tchr 1962-65; New Kensington Arnold Schl Dist Chptr I Math Tchr 1975-85, Tells Tchr 1985-89, Math Tchr 1991-; *ai:* Schlsp Comm; NEA, PSEA, NKAEA 1985-; *office:* Valley HS 703 Stevenson Blvd New Kensington PA 15068

COMSTOCK, WALTER C., Biology Teacher; *b:* Chicago, IL; *m:* Mary Beth Lederer; *c:* Kimberly, Matthew; *ed:* Coll of Emporia (BS) Bio & Ed 1970; Attnd Univ Cincinnati, Xavier Univ; *cr:* Turkeyfoot Jr HS 8th Grd Sci Tchr 1971-72; Anderson HS Sci & Bio Tchr 1972-76; Turpin HS Sci & Bio Tchr 1976-; *ai:* Sci Club Spon; Coach Odyssey of the Mind, Acad Quiz Team & Sci Olympiad; Natl Sci Bowl Coach; Confirmation Ldr; FHTA, OEA, NEA 1972-; Anderson Hills Meth Church 1980-, Chm Comm 2 Yrs; Turpin HS Tchr of Yr 1984-85; Acad Coach of the Yr 1992-94; *office:* Turpin H S 2650 Bartels Rd Cincinnati OH 45244*

CONAHAN, JEANNE SHOBER, Home Economics Teacher; *b:* Coaldale, PA; *m:* John; *c:* Michael, Timothy, Daniel; *ed:* Marywood Coll (BS) Foods & Nutrition & Home Ec Ed 1982; MS Equiv 1994; *cr:* Jim Thorpe HS Home Ec Tchr 1989-92; *ai:* PSEA 1989-; *office:* Hazleton Jr HS 900 N Wyoming St Hazleton PA 18201

CONAN, JOELLE, HS Biology & Geology Teacher; *b:* Brest, France; *ed:* Baccalaureat-Lycee Rotrou Dreux 1980; Univ Orleans Licence of Bio & Geology 1983, Naitrize of Bio & Geology 1984; ENS St Cloud Agregation of Scis Naturelles 1986; Agregation of Scis Post Grad Stud; *cr:* Lycee Jeanne d'Arc France Tchr 1987-93; Lycee Francais de NY Tchr 1993-; *ai:* 1 Yr Research at INSERM in Immunology; Adv for New Tchrs While in France; *office:* Lycee Francais De New York 3-5 E 95th St New York NY 10128

CONANT, JUDITH N., Mathematics Teacher; *b:* San Francisco, CA; *ed:* Western Coll (AB) Math; Johns Hopkins Univ (MS) Biostatistics; Stanford, NYU, NAU Post Grad Stud; *cr:* Madeira Schl Math Tchr; Brearley Schl Math Dept Chm 1968-91; Pvt Math Tutoring Bus 1990-; Rye Cntry Day Schl Math Tchr 1991-; *ai:* Adv; Multivariable Calculus Ind Stud Tchr; AP Awd; Brearley Schl Tchng Excl Chair, Sandra Lea Marshall Awd; AP Grader; *office:* Rye Country Day Schl 10580 Cedar St Rye NY 10580*

CONATY, DONNA M., Associate Professor of Oboe; *b:* Elliot Lake ON, Canada; *m:* Brigham J. Cooley; *ed:* Univ of Northern CO (BM), (BME) Music 1981; Yale Univ (MM) Music 1984; *cr:* SUNY Purchase Affiliate & Music Fac 1985; Univ of Evansville Adj Fac 1985-89; Evansville Philharmonic Prin Oboe 1985-89; Owensboro Symphony Prin Oboe 1985-89; OH Univ Assoc Prof of Oboe 1989-; Promusica Chamber of Orch Prin Oboe 1990-; *ai:* Amer Fed of Musicians 1989-; Music Edctrs Natl Conf 1990-; Intnl Double Reed Soc 1991-; MTNA 1993-; The OH Univ Tchng Fund Grant 1994; Univ of OH Schl of Music Distngd Tchng Awd 1995; *office:* OH Univ Schl of Music 440 Music Bldg Athens OH 45701*

CONCANNON, MARY T., 5th Grade Teacher; *b:* Manchester, NH; *m:* Gerald; *c:* Jerry, Tim; *ed:* Lesley Coll (BS) Ed 1966; *cr:* Norwood Schl Elem Tchr 1966-70; Marshfield Pub Schl Elem Tchr 1974-75; Cary Pub Schl Elem Tchr 1979-82; Penfield Pub Schl In Schl Elem Tutor 1982-84; St Joseph Schl Elem Tchr 1984-; *ai:* Soc Stud Chprsn; *home:* 56 Willowhurst Dr Penfield NY 14526

CONCILIO, ALAN J., Teacher & Dist Science Coord; *b:* New Haven, CT; *m:* Sandra M. DiLisio; *c:* Amy Lynn, Jon; *ed:* Fairfield Univ (BS) Mrktg 1966; Univ of Bridgeport (MS) Elem Ed 1971; 6th Yr Southern CT St Univ Educl Admin 1975; *cr:* Mead Schl Sixth Grd Tchr 1967-69; Prendergast Schl Sixth Grd Tchr 1969-71; Beecher Road Schl Fifth Grd Tchr 1971-90, Sci Coord, 5th Grd Tchr 1990-; *ai:* Dist Sci Coord; Woodbridge Sci Comm; BOWA Sci Comm; CT Journal of Sci Ed Assoc Ed; CSTA 1980-, CSTA Awd of Excl; NSTA 1980-, Presidential Awd in Sci Ed 1995; Trout Unlimited 1994-; Beacon Falls Recycling 1989-; CYO 1991-; Articles Pub; *office:* Beecher Road Elem Schl 40 Beecher Rd Woodbridge CT 06525

CONCILIO, M. ALPHONSA,IHM, Assistant Professor of Voice; *b:* Bethlehem, PA; *ed:* Marywood Coll (BA) Music 1965, (BM) Piano 1969; St Louis Univ (MA) Fr 1975; Marywood Coll (MA) Music Ed 1977; Courses at Univ of ID; Gonzaga U; U of WA; Manhattan Schl of Music; U of MN; Amherst; *cr:* Various HS Lang, Music Tchr 1954-61; IHM Acad Lang, Music Tchr 1961-71; IHM HS Lang, Music Tchr 1971-75; Marywood Coll Asst Prof of Voice 1975-; *ai:* Club Moderator St Cecelia Music Soc; Vocal Coach, Musicals, Other Musical Presentations; Campus Ministry Advy Bd; Liturgy, Mid Sts Comms; NATS 1976-, St Governor 1982-86.

CONCOVIA, TRACY TISCHER, English & Journalism Teacher; *b:* Baltimore, MD; *m:* Brian; *ed:* Georgetown Univ (BA) Eng 1986; Tchng Cert Hood Coll; Master's Equivalency Scndry Ed Western MD Coll; *cr:* Smithsburg HS Tchr 1986-87; South Hagerstown HS Tchr, Adv 1991-; *ai:* Schl Improvement Team; Discipline Comm; Newspaper Adv; Rebel Spirit Awd; *office:* South Hagerstown HS 1101 S Potomac St Hagerstown MD 21740*

CONDELLA, JAMES FRANK, American History Teacher; *b:* Jamestown, NY; *ed:* Kent St Univ (BS) His, Govt, Scndry Ed 1973; Attnd St Bonaventue Univ, Fredonia St; *cr:* Southwestern Cntrl Schl His Tchr 1973-, Dir Aths 1991-; *ai:* Dir Aths; Coach Var Bsktbl, Sftbl; NEA 1973-, Prof Negotiation; NY Coaches Assn 1975-; Loyal Order Moose 1992-; NY Lakewood Rod, Gun 1990-; *office:* Southwestern Central H S 600 Hunt Rd WE Jamestown NY 14701

CONDELLO, CHARLES ANTHONY, Instrumental & Gen Music Tchr; *b:* Dunkirk, NY; *m:* Ann Theresa Musto; *c:* Paul A., John P., Deborah A.; *ed:* Boston Conservatory of Music (BM) Applied Clarinet 1974; Cambridge Coll (MED) Scndry Ed 1990; Integrated Stud; Eastern Nazarene Coll Scndry Ed Tchng Cert 1976; *cr:* Lynn Pub Schls 5th-12th Grd Instrumental Music Tchr 1976-77; Bedford Pub Schls 9th-12th Grd Instrumental Music Tchr 1976-77; North Andover Pub Schls K-12th Grd Instr, Gen Music Tchr 1977-91; Fryeburg Pub Schl 4th-8th Grd Instr, Gen Music Tchr 1991-; *ai:* Regnl Hnrs Music Festivals, Competitions; MENC; MEA; NEA; World Vision Amateur Ham Radio 1976-, Advanced License; Boston's Symphony Hall Solo Clarinet 1974; WCRB Concert Radio Station Boston Solo Clarinet 1975; Boston Conservatory Orch Solo Clarinet 1970-74; Natl Tchrs Exam; *office:* Molly Ockett MS 10 Bridgton Rd Fryeburg ME 04037*

CONDELLO, JOHN A., Mathematics Teacher; *b:* Philadelphia, PA; *m:* Ellen E. Cassidy; *c:* Maura, Sarah; *ed:* St Bernard Coll (BA) Elem Ed, Philosophy 1970; LaSalle Univ Cert Spec Ed; Temple Univ Cert Math Ed; *cr:* DeLaSalle in Towne Reading, Soc Stud & Math Tchr 1973-88; E Spencer Miller Math Tchr 1988-93; Horace Furness HS Math Tchr 1993-; *ai:* Stu Assistance Prgm; AFT 1988-, Del; PAFT 1993-, Asst Sec Exec Cncl; PFT 1988-, Bldg Rep 1990-92; Friends Cianfrani Park 1990-, Chm Design Comm; Tree Tenders 1995-; *office:* Horace Furness HS 1900 S 3rd St Philadelphia PA 19148

CONDON, EARL ARTHUR, Teacher of Learning Support; *b:* Ridgway, PA; *ed:* Edinboro St Univ (BS) Elem Ed 1970, (MED) Spec Ed 1972; Addl Grad Credits Wilkes Univ 3, Bloomsburg St Univ 6, East Stroudsburg 3, Gannon Univ 9; 20 Undergraduate Credits at Pitt Univ; *cr:* Elk Cty Schl System Tchr of Living Support 2 Yrs; Seneca Highlands IU #9 Tchr of Living Support 14 Yrs, Tchr of Learning Support 10 Yrs; *ai:* Stu Assistance Prgm 1995-; NEA, PSEA, SHEA 1972-, Pres; *office:* Seneca Highlands IU #9 119 Mechanic St Smethport PA 16749

CONDON, GAIL ANN, English Teacher & Dept Chair; *b:* Roselle, NJ; *m:* Thomas J.; *c:* Michael, Christopher, Craig; *ed:* Douglass Coll (BA) Eng 1964; Univ of Louisville (MED) Rdng 1978; *cr:* St Leonard Schl Tchr 1978-80; MacArthur MS Tchr 1981-82; Cntrl MS Tchr 1982-; *ai:* NEA 1981-; Governor's Cncl on Women's Hlth Issues 1994-95; *office:* Central MS 221 Central Ave E Edgewater MD 21037

CONDON, PHYLLIS STICCO, Fourth Grade Teacher; *b:* Brooklyn, NY; *m:* Bernard Francis; *c:* Jeanmarie O'Regan, Bernard Francis; *ed:* Brooklyn Coll of City Univ of NY (BA) Ed 1961; Queens Coll of City Univ of NY (MS) Ed, Rdng 1976; *cr:* St Thomas Aquinas Schl First Grd Tchr 1957-59; NY City Pub Schl Third Grd Tchr 1961; Fort Leonard Wood Army Schl Second Grd Tchr 1961-62; Our Lady of Victory Schl Fourth Grd Tchr 1971-; *ai:* Grds 1-6 Rdng Dept Chprsn; NACST; Amer Assn of Univ Women; Sewanhaka Continuing Ed 1980-, Advy Bd; Argo-Valmont Civic Assn, Bd Mem; Brooklyn Coll Cum Laude; Yeshiva Univ Flwshp; Kappa Delta Pi Adopt-A Tchr Awd; Natl Assn for Advancement of Humane Ed Awd; *office:* Our Lady Of Victory Schl 2 Bellmore St Floral Park NY 11001

CONDRY, FLORENCE M., English Professor; *b:* Boston, MA; *ed:* Boston St Coll (BA), (BS) Eng, Scndry Ed 1966; St Coll at Boston (MAT), (MS) Eng, Cnslng Ed 1968; 49 Addl Hrs; *cr:* Girls HS Eng, Soc Sci Tchr 1966; Jamaica Plain HS Eng, Jrnlsm, Guid Tchr 1967-72; Boston Bus Schl Eng, Soc Sci Tchr 1972-81; Hyde Pk HS Eng, AP Tchr 1981-84; Roxbury Comm Coll Eng, ESL, Soc Sci Prof 1984-; *ai:* Acts Adv; Stu Advisement; Facilities Comm; ESL Journal Publication; MTA, NEA, MEATE, NEATE, NCTE 1984-; Project Discovery, Young at Arts, Bostonian Soc 1994-; Museum of Fine Arts 1986-; Internship Grad Schl; Grammar & Punctuation for Bus Schls; Who's Who Coll Tchrs; *office:* Roxbury Comm Coll Boston Business Campus 989 Commonwealth Ave Boston MA 02215

CONDY, DAWN E., Science & Biology Teacher; *b:* Bayshore, NY; *ed:* The King's Coll (BS) Elem Ed 1988; SUNY at Stony Brook (MALS) Sci Ed 1991; *cr:* South Shore Chrstn Schl 7th-8th Sci, Bio Tchr 1988-; *ai:* Vlybl, Bsktbl, Sftbl Coach; *office:* South Shore Christian Schl Farmedge Rd Levittown NY 11756

CONELY, JOHN L., English Teacher; *b:* Brockton, MA; *m:* Paul B.; *c:* James M., Katherine A.; *ed:* Tufts Univ (BA) Eng 1973; Boston Coll (MA) Eng 1977; Participant in Trng of Trainers Tufts Univ; *cr:* Kennedy Jr HS Eng Tchr 1973-83; Milton Acad Summer Writing Inst Tchr 1978-82; Sharon HS Eng Tchr 1983-; *ai:* Adv Stu Newspaper; Advy Bd for Comm Svc Learning Initiatives; Sharon Tchrs Assoc 1983-; MA Tchrs Assoc, NEA 1973-; *office:* Sharon HS 180 Pond St Sharon MA 02067*

CONES, JOAN PLANSON, Third Grade Teacher; *b:* Columbus, OH; *m:* William George; *c:* Robert, Douglas; *ed:* OH St Univ (BA) Elem Ed 1959; *cr:* Whitehall-Etna Rd 1st Grd Tchr 1959-60; Sidney Schls Sub Tchr 1961-67; Lebanon Schls Sub Tchr 1967-70; River Vly Schls Sub, 3rd & 5th Grd Tchr 1970-; *ai:* PTO Sec; NEA; OEA; RUTA; *office:* Claridon Elem Schl 3938 Marion Mount Gilead Rd Caledonia OH 43314

CONFER, CAROL SIMON, Third Grade Teacher; *b:* Northampton, PA; *m:* Bruce G.; *ed:* Kutztown Univ (BS) Elem Ed 1973; Instrl II Cert 24 Credit Hrs; *cr:* St John The Bapt Schl Kndgtn Tchr 1974-83; Christ The King Schl Third Grd Tchr 1983-; *ai:* Chprsn Schl Self-Evaluation Process Mid Sts Assn Commission Elem Schls 1989-; Mission Coord 1991-94; Rel Dept Coord 1990-; Co-Dir Annual Schl Curr Musical; NCEA 1983-; Allentown Diocese Lay Tchrs Assn 1985-; Holy Trinity RC Church 1993-, Eucharistic Minister, Children's Catechist.

CONFER, LESLIE ANNE (KULHA), Fifth Grade Teacher; *b:* Lehighton, PA; *m:* Dean Randolph Sr.; *c:* Dean Jr.,Rachel; *ed:* Kutztown Univ (BA) Elem Ed 1983; Instrl Level II Cert; *cr:* Annunciation Schl 5th Grd Tchr 1986-88; St Jerome Regnl Schl 5th Grd Tchr 1988-; *ai:* NCEA 1988-; *office:* St Jerome Regional Schl 250 W Broad St Tamaqua PA 18252

CONFESSORE, ROBERT JOSEPH, Prof & Exercise Sci Pgm Coord; *b:* Brooklyn, NY; *ed:* Brooklyn Coll-CUNY (BS) PE 1977; Univ of MT (MS) Exercise Sci 1980; Univ of MD (PHD) Exercise Sci 1990; *cr:* Cardio Fitness Systems Exercise Physiologist 1980-82; Univ of MT Instr 1982-84; Univ of MD Instr 1986-90; NH Tech Coll Prof 1992-; NH Musculoskeletal Inst Bd of Dir; *ai:* Phi Theta Kappa Adv; Amer Red Cross CPR Instr; ACSM 1983-; NSCA 1994-; ACSM Certified Hlth, Fitness Instr; Grad Cum Laude; Phi Alpha Epsilon Univ of MD; Fellow; Amer Coll Sports Med; Certified Strength Conditioning Specialist; National Strength Conditioning Assoc; *office:* NH Tech Coll at Manchester 1066 Front T St Manchester NH 03102

CONFOY, JANE K., English Teacher; *b:* Trenton, NJ; *c:* Casey, Karen, Kevin, Craig; *ed:* Trenton St Coll (BS) Scndry Ed, Eng, His, Elem Ed; Attnd Coll of St Elizabeth, Mercer Co Comm Coll; *cr:* Hopewell Twp Tchr Jr HS Core Curr; Diocese of Trenton, Hopewell Twp, City of Trenton Schls Elem, Spec Ed, Comm Handicapped Tchr; Diocese of Trenton Jr, Sr HS Eng, His Tchr; Notre Dame HS Tchr 1978-; *ai:* Moderator ND Chptr NHS; NSTE, NCEA 1979-; Natl Assn Stu Act Adv 1987-; Natl Historical Soc 1992-; Nat Geneological Soc, Nat Pres Trust 1993-; Friends of NJ St Museum; *office:* Notre Dame HS 601 Lawrenceville Rd Lawrenceville NJ 08648

CONGDON, CATHY CARR, 1st Grade Teacher; *b:* Wilkes-Barre, PA; *m:* Thomas H.; *c:* Tom, Elizabeth; *ed:* Jamestown Comm Coll (AA) 1973; SUC at Fredonia (BS) Elem Ed 1975, (MS) Early Chldhd Ed 1980; *cr:* Randolph Cntrl Schl Elem Tchr 1976-; *ai:* Shared Decision Making Team; NYSUT 1976-; Randolph Presbyn Church 1983-; *office:* Randolph Cntrl Schl Main St Randolph NY 14772

CONGDON, CHRISTOPHER, Lecturer in English; *b:* Norwich, CT; *ed:* Colby Coll (BA) Eng 1981; Univ of CT (MA) Eng 1990; *cr:* Univ of CT Tchng Asst 1988-90; Univ of CT Lecturer 1990-; *ai:* Asst Acad Adv; UCAP Ath Dept; Ct Assn of Eng Tchrs 1991-; Univ of CT Alumni Assn 1990-; *office:* Univ Of Connecticut-Avery Pt 1084 Shennecossett Rd Groton CT 06340

CONGDON, JUDY ANN, Professor of Organ; *b:* Bismarck, ND; *ed:* Wheaton Coll (BMus) Organ 1975; Univ of CO (MMus) Organ 1977; Eastman Schl of Music (DMA) Organ Performance, Lit 1990; Music Stud Hochschule fur Musik Frankfurt Germany 1977-79; Summer Courses Regent Coll at Vancouver 1981-82; *cr:* First Presbyn Church Organist 1979-85; Bapt Temple Music Dir 1986-91; Mansfield Univ Organ Instr 1990-91; Houghton Coll Organ Assoc Prof 1991-; *ai:* Fac Affairs Comm Chair; Spiritual Life comm; Amer Guild of Organists 1980-, Allegheny Chptr Dean; St Stephen's Episcopal Church, Interim Organist; Fulbright Grant 1977-78; Eastman Schl of Music Distngd Tchng Awd 1990; *office:* Houghton Coll Music Dept Houghton NY 14744*

CONGDON, SHERRY DUNLAP, Second Grade Teacher; *b:* Harrisburg, PA; *m:* Gary R.; *c:* Douglas, Liza; *ed:* Mansfield Univ (BS) Elem Ed, Eng 1971; Elmira Coll (MS) Elem Ed 1989; Elem Ed, 7-12 Eng Certs; *cr:* V. E. W. Primary Schl 2nd Grd Tchr 1971-76; Chrstn Learning Ctr 3rd-6th Grd Tchr 1983-89; V. E. W. Primary Schl 2nd Grd Tchr 1989-; *ai:* Dist Fine Arts Curr Steering Comm Bldg Coord; Soc Stud Curr; New Tchrs Mentor; NYSUT, AFT, Haverling Tchrs' Assn 1989-; Common Time Choral Group 1990-; Heart Soc 1992-, Vol; HS Play 1988-, Vol; Grd Chm; Helped Write K-12 Wide Dist Fine Arts Integration Grant; *office:* V E Wightman Primary Schl Maple Heights Bath NY 14810*

CONGDON, SUSAN BLIGH, Fifth Grade Teacher; *b:* New York City, NY; *m:* Mark A.; *c:* Michael, Andrew, David; *ed:* St Univ of NY at Geneseo (BS) Elem Ed 1982, (MS) Rdng 1986; *cr:* Geneseo Elem Schl 5th Grd Tchr 1982-; *ai:* AFT, NYSUT, GFA 1982-; Mentor Tchr 1991-; *office:* Geneseo Central Schl 4050 Avon Rd Geneseo NY 14454*

CONGER, GRACE L. (DEMAREST), Retired 5th Grade Teacher; *b:* Glen Ridge, NJ; *m:* Richard; *c:* Amy Demarest; *ed:* Trenton St Coll (BS) Elem Ed 1957; Rutgers Univ (MED) Supervision & Curr 1962; Wm Paterson Coll Supvr Cert, Prin License; Jersey City St Coll Cmptr Ed; *cr:* Washington Schl Grd 6 Tchr 1957-84; West Orange Bd of Ed Cmptr Resource Tchr 1984-86; Hazel Avenue Schl 5 Grd Tchr 1986-95; *ai:* Cmptr Lab Coord; NEA, NJEA, WOEA 1957-; Bloomingdale Bd of Ed, Pres 9 Yrs, Mem 2 Yrs; Bloomingdale Planning Bd 11 Yrs; Bloomingdale GATE Steering Comm; Glenwild Lake Bd of Dirs, Pres 2 Yrs, 8 Yrs Mem; NJ Govenors Tchr of Yr 1993; *home:* 12 Club House Rd Bloomingdale NJ 07403*

CONGI, ANTHONY J., Math Teacher; *b:* Clarksburg, WV; *m:* Maryann Chiulli; *c:* Christina, Rebecca; *ed:* Wheeling Jesuit Coll (BS) Theolgy & Philosophy 1977; Univ of Bridgeport (MA) Ed 1989; 43 Hrs of Post Grad Work Beyond Masters in Ed & Math; *cr:* Cardinal Stritch HS Theology & Philosophy Tchr 1977-81; Young Life Outreach Area Dir 1981-83; Louis M. Klein MS 7th-8th Grd Math Tchr 1984-; *ai:* Soccer, LaCrosse Ofcl; Youth Ldr at Fishkill Bapt Church; Club Ldr for East Fishkill Young Life; Pub Music in 12 Different Pub Companies; NYSUT 1984-; NCTM 1986-; Pub an Article on Cooperative Learning in an Acad Publication; *office:* Louis M Klein MS 50 Union Ave Harrison NY 10528

CONGLETON, JOHN MICHAEL, Math Teacher; *b:* Washington, DC; *m:* Christine Denise; *ed:* Univ of MD (BS) Scndry Math Ed 1993; *cr:* Eleanor Roosevelt HS Math Tchr 1993-; *ai:* Class of 1997 Spon; Cedar Ridge Comm Church 1993-, Jr-Sr HS Yth Group Ldr; *office:* Eleanor Roosevelt HS 7601 Hanover Pky Greenbelt MD 20770

CONKLIN, ALAN W., Science Teacher; *b:* Deposit, NY; *m:* Sharon; *c:* Cristy, Jill, Joshua; *ed:* Broome Comm Coll (AAS) Engrng Physics 1965; SUC at Oneonta (BS) Chem & Ed 1968; SUC at Oswego (MS) ed 1987; *cr:* Ichabod Crane Cntrl Sci Tchr 1969; Liverpool Cntrl Sci Tchr 1969-; *ai:* Soccer & Bsktbl Coach; Natl Assn for Research in Sci Tchng; *home:* 15 Nectarine Ln Liverpool NY 13090

CONKLIN, DAVID CHARLES, Speech & English Instructor; *b:* Oberlin, OH; *m:* Rubyleen Miralo; *c:* Abigail, Rachel, Calvin; *ed:* Kent St Univ (BS) Ed 1984; *cr:* US Peace Corps ESL Instr 1988-91; Wellington HS Eng, Speech Instr 1992-; *ai:* Cross Cnty Coach; Comm Theatre Stage Crew Adv; Percussion Adv; NEA 1992-; St Patricks Church 1993-, Cantorer; Brighton United Meth Church 1974-, Choir Dir; *office:* Wellington HS 629 N Main St Wellington OH 44090

CONKLIN, HENRY A., Chemistry & Physics Teacher; *b:* Brooklyn, NY; *m:* Judyth Ann Shaffron; *c:* Andrew, Richard; *ed:* Manhattan Coll (BS) Sci Ed 1969; City Coll (MA) Sci Ed 1974; 60 Credits Sci Ed Numerous Schls; *cr:* Wisdom Lane JHS Sci Tchr 1969-70; Hempstead HS Sci Tchr 1970-75; A. Hamilton HS Chem, Physics Tchr 1975-79; Sleepy Hollow HS Chem, Physics Tchr 1981-; *ai:* HS Track & field Ofcl; Tarrytown Tchrs Assn 1981-, Corr Sec, Bldg Rep; NYSUT, AFT 1981-, Natl Conv Del; Nat Fed Intr Schl Ofcls Assn 1987-; Amer Chemical Soc 1987-; Amer Chem Soc Mid Atlantic Regnl Awd HS Chem Tchrn 1995; Nichols Awd Chem Tchng ACS NY Section 1993; Manhattan Coll Outstdng Sci Tchr Awd 1992; NSF Summer Hnrs Prgm HS Chem 1984; Presentations ChemEd Biennial Confs 1989, 1991, 1993, 1995; *office:* Sleepy Hollow HS 210 N Broadway North Tarrytown NY 10591*

CONKLIN, JAMES C., Science Teacher & Coordinator; *b:* Middletown, NY; *ed:* Coll of Holy Cross (BS) Sci, Philosophy 1959; Syracuse Univ (MS) Guid, Cnslng 1967; 40 Grad Hrs Sci St Univ Coll at Oneonta; *cr:* Chittenango HS Mid Level Sci Tchr 1959-91, HS Sci Chm 1980-91; Chittenango MS Mid Level Sci Tchr 1991-, Sci Curr Coord 1991-; *ai:* Stu Cncl Adv; AFT, Chittenango Tchrs Assn 1959-; *office:* Chittenango MS 1732 Fyler Rd Chittenango NY 13037

CONKLIN, LEE B., Social Studies Tchr; *b:* Ridgewood, NJ; *m:* Ann Marie; *c:* Jenna; *ed:* Villanova Univ (BS) Ed 1982; SUNY At Albany (MA) Ed 1989; *cr:* Shaker HS 9-10th Grd Tchr 1984-88; Saratoga Springs HS Soc Stud Tchr 1988-; *ai:* Bus Mgr of Schl Yrbk; Coached Track Shaker HS; Chaparone Schl Activities; Active Mentor Prgm; Bldg Plnng Tm; NEA, NYSUT 1984-; *office:* Saratoga Springs Sr HS W Circular St Saratoga Spgs NY 12866*

CONKLIN, WARREN GEORGE, Ec & Criminal Justice Teacher; *b:* Brooklyn, NY; *ed:* Hobart Coll (BA) His 1976; Elmira Coll (MS) Ed 1982; 45 Post Grad Hrs; *cr:* Horseheads Cntrl Schl Tchr 1976-; Corning Comm Coll Adj Prof 1990-94; *ai:* Girls Var Sftbl Coach 1977-; Boys Var Soccer Coach 1981-; Site Based Team Mem 1992-; NY St United Tchrs 1976-; Tchr of Yr 1991; Coach of Yr 1991 & 1993; *office:* Horseheads HS 1 Raider Ln Horseheads NY 14845

CONKO, COLLEEN STAINES, Mathematics Teacher; *b:* Connellsville, PA; *m:* Stephen P. III; *c:* Caitlin; *ed:* California Univ of PA (BS) Ed 1989; 18 Credits in Grad Prgm in Math, Cmptr Sci Ed; *cr:* CWCTC Math Tchr 1991-; *ai:* PSEA, NEA 1989-; *office:* Cntrl Westmoreland Career Tech 240 Arona Rd New Stanton PA 15672*

CONLAN, PATRICIA M., Computer Teacher; *b:* Brooklyn, NY; *c:* Kaitlyn, Erin; *ed:* NY St Tchrs Coll at Oneonta (BS) Ed & Math 1967; Richmond Univ (MS) Spcl Ed 1971; 30 Credits Above Masters; *cr:* PS 314 Comps Tchr 1967-; *ai:* Tech Resource Specialist; Yrbk; New Compact for Learning & Annenberg Advy Comm Mem; UFT 1967-; St Pats & St Eparems Swim Team 1993-, Coach; Tech Grants; *office:* PS 314 Luis Munoz Marin 330 59th St Brooklyn NY 11220*

CONLEE, JAMES RICHARD, Social Studies Teacher; *b:* Worcester, MA; *m:* Peggy; *c:* Katie, Jane; *ed:* Worcester St Coll (BA) His; Fitchburg St Coll (MED) His 1975; 6 Credit Hrs Ed Admin, 3 Credit Hrs Juvenile Law Tufts Univ; *cr:* Fitchburg HS Soc Stud Tchr 1972-82, 1986-93; *ai:* Schl Cncl; Schl Improvement Renew Team; Class of 1993-94 Adv; NEA 1986-; Litsky Tchr of Yr Finalist 2 Yrs; Class of 1994 Schlr Tchr of Yr; Litsky Tchr of Yr 1994-5; *office:* Fitchburg HS 98 Academy St Fitchburg MA 01420*

CONLEY, JOSEPH JOHN, Communications Teacher; *b:* Painesville, OH; *ed:* OH St Univ (BA) Communicology 1970; Garfield Comm Coll (BFA) His of Theatre 1976; 20 Hrs Early & Mid Chldhd Dev, 20 Hrs Spec Ed, 50 Hrs Masters Prgm Ed Post Grad Stud OH St Univ; Post Grad Stud Interpersonal Comm Trinity Coll Dublin; *cr:* OH St Univ Tchg Asst 1977-78; Jones Jr HS Comm Tchr 1980-83; Upper Arlington HS Lang Arts, Comm Tchr 1984-; *ai:* Jr HS Ftbl Coach 1982-83; Drama Club Adv 1980-83; WARL Broadcasting Club Adv 1984-; North Cntrl Evaluation Chprsn 1991-; Upper Arlington Ed Assn 1980-, VP 1988-92; Cntrl OH Tchrs Assn 1980-, Mem Rep 1985-90; Intnl Speech, Comm 1980-, Chm Dublin 1991 Conf; Speech Comm Assn of OH 1980-, Mem Rep 1985-; NEA 1980-; Ed 25 Access Channel 1986-, Trustee Original Bd Mem, Chprsn 1990; Shamrock Club of Columbus 1976-, Sec, Treas, VP, Pres, Irishman of Yr 1996; Wrote & Directed Musical Play 1986; CNN Broadcasting Video Achvmt 1995; *office:* Upper Arlington HS 1650 Ridgeview Rd Upper Arlington OH 43221*

CONLEY, KAREN BRAGG, Computer Education Teacher; *b:* Oberlin, OH; *m:* Kevin; *c:* Kyle, Kory; *ed:* Ashland Univ (BSEd) Bus, Hlth Ed 1976, (MSEd) Curr & Instruction, Cmptr Ed 1992; *cr:* Oberlin Municipal Court Head Civil Clerk 1972-76; Wellington HS Tchr 1976-; *ai:* Jr Var Vlybl Coach; Co Adv NHS; Wellington Educ Assn 1976-, Pres 1993-; OEA, NEA 1976-; Local Endowment Grants 3rd Grd Elem Keyboarding, HS Telecommunications, 3rd Grd Desktop Publishing, HS Graphics Projects; Comp in the Comm; *office:* Wellington HS 629 N Main Wellington OH 44090*

CONLEY, KIMBERLY SWEIGART, Kindergarten Teacher; *b:* Lewistown, PA; *m:* Vernon Keith; *c:* Megan, Keith; *ed:* Bob Jones Univ (BA) Early Chldhd 4 Yrs; *cr:* Granite Bapt Church Schl Kndgtn Tchr 7 1/2 Yrs; *home:* 210 Pinewood Dr Pasadena MD 21122

CONLEY, MARIA JO (ROSE), Mathematics Teacher; *b:* Canton, OH; *m:* Nicholas W. Jr.; *ed:* Muskingum Coll (BS) Math 1990; *cr:* Carrollton HS Math Tchr 1992-; *ai:* SADD Adv; NEA, OEA, OH Cncl of Math Tchrs 1992-; Sons of Italy 1995-; *office:* Carrollton HS 252 3rd St NE Carrollton OH 44615

CONLIN, MARY, Theology Teacher; *b:* Amsterdam, NY; *ed:* St Josephs Coll Brooklyn (BA) Child Stud 1977; Seminary of Immaculate Conception (MTH) Theology 1988; *cr:* Sts Cyril Methadius Elem Tchr 1977-80; Our Lady of Mercy Acad Psych & Theology Tchr 1980-; *ai:* Stu Cncl Adv; Fac Advy, Weighted Grd Review Comm; Comm to Stu Infusion of Womens Issues & Multiculturalism; NCEA 1977-; Amer Assn Univ Women 1994-; *office:* Our Lady Of Mercy Acad 815 Convent Rd Syosset NY 11791

CONLOGUE, RUTH A.,RSM, Science Department Chair; *b:* Houlton, ME; *ed:* St Joseph's Coll (BA) Bio 1971; Attnd Univ of NH Grad Schl, ME Conservation Schl; *cr:* Elem Schl Tchr 1959-69; Jr HS Tchr 1959-69; Catherine Mc Auley HS Anatomy, Physiology Tchr, Dept Chair 1969-, Asst Prin 1977-79; *ai:* Acad Review, Tech, St ME Recertification Steering Comms; Purposes, Objectives Reaccreditation Stud Chair; NCEA 1980-; Mercy Hlth System of ME 1993-, Dir, Nom Comm Chair; St Joseph's Coll 1984-, Trustee, VP; Cath Hlth Assn 1994-; NSF Grant; *office:* Catherine Mc Auley HS 631 Stevens Ave Portland ME 04103

CONLON, BARBARA A., Math Teacher; *b:* New York City, NY; *ed:* St John's Univ (BS) Ed 1969, (MS) Curr, Tchng 1971; Long Island Univ (MS) Educl Admin 1981; *cr:* Sachem Schls HS Math Tchr 1975-, Sur Prin 1987-90; *ai:* Asst Marching Band Dir; Schl Photographer Video; NYSUT 1977-; Edited 2 Math Books 1980-82; *office:* S South Campus 51 School St Lake Ronkonkoma NY 11779

CONLON, JAMES G., Social Studies Teacher; *b:* Belfast, N I Jane De Bernardo; *c:* Seamus, Leo; *ed:* Queen's Univ (BA) Hi Philosophy 1969; 30 Addl Hrs Johns Hopkins Univ; *cr:* Freepo Stud Tchr 1970-76; Wilde Lake HS Soc Stud Tchr 1977-92; 1992-93; Patuxent Vly MS Grd 7 Tchr; *ai:* Speech & Deba Outward Bound Advocate Instr; NEA 1977-; *office:* Wilde Lake Clarksville MD 21044

CONLON, NANCY MARY KELLEY, English Teacher; *b:* Stan *c:* Michael, Matthew, Meghan; *ed:* Annhurst (BA) Eng, Elem Fairfield Univ (MA) Amer Stud 1974; Long Island Univ (MA) Sc 1990; St John's Univ Working on DA; 55 Hrs Past Masters Whole Lang; *cr:* Stamford Pub Schl 1-2nd, 4-5th Grd Tchr 1971- Manor Writing Coord 1983-, 7-10th Grd Eng Tchr 1976-; *ai:* Natl Soc Club Adv; 3 Day Ski Trip, Whaling, Canoeing, Rafting; NE Local Union Pres 1980-81; NYSUT.*

CONN, MARY ALICE, Former Eng & Lit Teacher; *b:* Morehea Archie Clifford; *c:* Mark, Cheryl Pursselley, Robert; *ed:* Bapt C (BA) Scndry Ed; Cmptr Literacy, Clothing Structure & Design 3 Counseling 2 Hrs; *cr:* Jonesboro Chrstn Schl Sec, Home Ec, Gram 1977-80; Tabernacle Chrstn Acad Home Ec, Grammar Tchr 198 Valley Chrstn Schl Tchr 1989-; *ai:* 2 Poems; 1 Story; *home:* 9 Route 7 S Gallipolis OH 45631

CONN, VALERIE ANN, Fifth Grade Teacher; *b:* Freeport, NY; *c:* Tyler James, Shane David; *ed:* SUNY Coll at Oneonta (BA) 1984; Adelphi Univ (MS) Spcl Ed 1987; *cr:* St Nichols Elem Sch Tchr 1984-86; Sacred Heart Elem Schl 4th Grd Tchr 1986-87; P Schl 2nd-3rd & 5th Grd Tchr 1987-; *ai:* PTA Tchr Rep; AFT 198 Tchrs of Northport 1987-; *office:* Pulaski Rd Schl Ninth Ave East NY 11731

CONNAR, MEREDITH LYNN, Teacher of Gifted Students; *b:* ND; *m:* Thomas N.; *c:* Thomas Jr., Theresa, Matthew; *ed:* Towso (BS) Ed-Magna Cum Laude 1981; Hood Coll (MA) Ed 1985; 25 *cr:* Wesley Grove Schl Head Dir 1974-77; Frederick Cty Pub S Tchr 1981-85, Magnet Tchr 1985-; *ai:* Sci Fair Judge; Odyss Mind; Team Ldr Six Yrs; Children's Poetry Publishing Ment MSTA, Frederick Cty Tchrs Assn 1981-; Women's Club 1986 Meth Women 1972-; Bus, Prof Women 1983-; Natl Historic Tr Pub Guides; *office:* Urbana Elem Magnet Schl 3554 Urbana Pike MD 21704

CONNELL, JOAN ELIZABETH, First Grade Teacher; *b:* Wi CT; *ed:* Eastern CT St Univ (BA) Ed 1974; UCONN (MA) Ed 19 ECSU; *cr:* Horace Porter Schl 3rd Grd Long-Term Sub Tchr 1976; Elem Schl Kndgtn Classroom Tchr 1976-79, 2nd Grd Classro 1977-78, 1st Grd Classroom Tchr 1979-; *ai:* Grds K-8 Sci Fair Co Curr, Scheduling Comms; Negotiations Comm 1995; Franklin CEA 1976-, Treas; IRA 1989-; Assn for Superivison & Curr De 7 Russ Rd Willimantic CT 06226

CONNELL, ROYAL W., Naval Science Instructor; *b:* Kansas C *m:* Melinda Anne Rathbun; *c:* Royal W. III, Alan L., David B; *ed:* Acad (BS) Operations Analysis 1970; George Washington Uni Prsnl Mngmt 1980; *cr:* US Navy Career Ofcr 1970-93; US Na Navigation Course Dir 1977-80, Prnsl Ofcr, Instr 1989-93; Ann HS Naval Sci Instr 1993-; *ai:* Drill Team; Air Rifle Tean Attendance Review Comm; Fac Cncl; BSA 1977-, Asst Dist Comm Order of the Arrow 1984-, Brotherhood; Dist Awd of Merit; Auth Ceremonies, Customs & Tranditions 1980; Wood Badge Traine Annapolis Sr HS 2700 Riva Rd Annapolis MD 21401

CONNELL, WALTER GLEN, Professor & Coordinator; *b:* Phil PA; *m:* Roseann; *c:* Glen, Gregory; *ed:* Temple Univ (AS) Bus 19 Distributive Ed 1966, (EDM) Distributive Ed 1967; Rutgers Uni Voc Ed 1977; *cr:* Eastern Montgomery Cty Voc Tech Schl Tch 1966-69;Montgomery Cty Comm Coll Instr 1969-72, Asst Prof Assoc Prof 1975-78, Prof 1978-, Curr Coord 1983-; St Josep Adjunct Fac 1984-92; *ai:* Delta Pi Epsilon 1971-; Kappa Delta AFT 1980-, Treas 1978-79; Philip M. Mc Kenna Fellowship Ma Duquesne Univ 1984; Admin Inter to Robert D. Joy St Dir Dept of *office:* Montgomery County Comm College 340 De Kalb Pike Blue 19422*

CONNELL-HARPER, PHYLLIS CLAIRE, Social Science Te Yonkers, NY; *m:* William; *ed:* Rutgers Univ (BA) Soc Sci 1971; K Elem Cert 1973; Jersey City St Coll Grad Credit Hrs Ed; *cr:* Our Good Counsel 3rd Grd Tchr 1971-73; Our Lady of Lourdes 6th 1982-84; Bethel Chrstn Acad Jr Sr High His Tchr 1984-88; Kearny Stud Tchr 1988-; *office:* Kearny HS 336 Devon St Kearny NJ 070

CONNELLY, ANGELA MARIE, Third Grade Teacher; *b:* Brook *m:* Robert; *c:* Michael, Matthew; *ed:* Fairleigh Dickinson Univ (B Ed K-8 1972; Montclair St (MA) Rdng Specialist 1991; *cr:* Memo 4th Grd Tchr 1972-78; T. Baldwin Demarest Schl 4th Grd Tchr 3rd Grd Tchr 1987-; *ai:* Recycling Coord; Tech, Dist Ad-Hoc OTTEA, BCEA, NEA 1985-, Bldg Rep; OTPTA 1985-; Northern V Parents 1991-; Governor's Tchr Recognition Awd 1992; *office:* T. Demarest Schl 1 School St Old Tappan NJ 07675

CONNELLY, BRUCE R., English Teacher; *b:* Moultrie, GA; Kay Frey; *ed:* Duquesne Univ (BSED) Eng 1967; *cr:* South Alleg Eng Tchr 1967-68; Easy Meth Driver Trng Schl Instr 971; Cntrl Eng Tchr 1971-; *office:* Central Catholic HS 4720 5th Ave Pittsb 15213

CONNELLY, DENISE LORRAINE, Fifth Grade Teacher; *b:* Coa PA; *ed:* PA St Univ (BS) Elem Ed 1977; Millersville St Univ (ME Ed 1983; Lincoln Univ (MS) Rdng 1996; *cr:* Oxford Area Schl D 1978-; *ai:* Chorus Co-Dir; Prof Dev & Induction Comms; Team L 1977-; PSEA 1977-, OAEA 1978-, Rep; Tchr of Yr Nominatio *office:* Elk Ridge Elem Schl 2 Reisler Rd Oxford PA 19363

CONNELLY, EDMUND JAMES,JR., Senior Marine Instructor; York City, NY; *m:* Carol Cassino; *c:* Christopher, Patrick, Theresa, Colleen, Catherine, Edmund III, Margaret, Mary; *ed:* St Coll (BA) Sociology 1959; Wichita St Univ (MA) Criminal Justic Northern VA CC Law Enforcement, Security 1977; Post Grad Stud VA, Univ of Houston, Clear Lake Cath Univ; *cr:* US Marine Corp 1959-86; Willow Ridge HS Sr Marine Instr 1986-90; Elizabeth Marine Instr 1990-; *ai:* Marine Corps Jr ROTC Adv; Marine Corps Air Rifle Coach; NEA 1990-; Marine Corps League 1990-, Advocate; VFW, Amer Legion 1990-; 1st Marine Div Assn 199 Awds; *office:* Elizabeth HS 600 Pearl St Elizabeth NJ 07202

CONNELLY, KEVIN M., Computer Sci & Biology Tchr; *b:* New *m:* Tacie K.; *ed:* Univ of DE (BA) Bio 1975; Columbia Univ (MA Ed 1989; Univ of MD 6 Hrs Geology; Loyola Coll 18 Hrs Supervision,; Univ of DE 20 Yrs Ed; *cr:* Rising Sun HS Tchr 1 Perryville HS Tchr 1986-; *ai:* NHS Adv; Tech Use Comm; Mid Visitation Team; NEA, MSTA, CCCTA 1981-; MICCA 1986-; NAS dor Prgm; Westinghouse Space Initiative; *office:* Perryville HS ryville Rd Perryville MD 21903

LLY, MARY ANN, Spanish Teacher; *b:* Buffalo, NY; *m:* c: Carl, Kevin; *ed:* SUNY at Buffalo (BA) Fr Ed 1969, (EdM) 1988; *cr:* Maryvale Schl System Fr, Span Tchr 1969-71; ville Cntrl Schls Span Tchr 1980-82; North Tonawanda Schl Span Tchr 1982-83; Royalton-Hartland Cntrl Schls Span Tchr Frgn Lang Dept Chprsn 1985-; Sr HS Frgn Lang Club Adv 1984-; Rep 1989-; NYSUT, AFT, NYSAFLT, WNYFLEC 1981-.

LLY, MARYANN BARRY, Eighth Grade Teacher; *b:* Jersey City, hilip Connelly; *ed:* Jersey City St Coll (BA) Elem Ed 1981, (MA) d, Admin 1991; *cr:* Theodore Roosevelt Schl Tchr 1984-91; Comm Schl Tchr 1996; *ai:* Grd 8 Peer Ldrshp Adv; Fac Comms Shared Decision Making Team; NJASCD 1985-, East Regnl Del; Tchrs Assn 1984-; Ireland's 32 1982-, Pres, VP, Sec; Bayonne St Parade Comm 1988-, Chprsn; NJ Governor's Tchr Recognition ; *office:* Midtown Comm Schl 550 Avenue A Bayonne NJ 07002*

LLY, NEIL, Math Teacher; *b:* Buffalo, NY; *m:* Patricia Kelleher; opher, Sean; *ed:* SUNY at Oswego (BA) Math 1971; Canisius Coll 1977, (MBA) Bus 1987; 21 Credit Hrs Admin Prgm; *cr:* Depew Tchr 1973-; *ai:* Math Club Adv; AFT, NYSUT 1973-; NCTM raternal Order Eagles 1994-; Boys, Girls Club Alumni 1972-; der Moose, Little League Coach 1990-; Bsktbl, Bsbl Coach 10 e: Depew MS 5201 S Transit Rd Depew NY 14043

LLY, PATRICIA KELLEHER, Social Studies & English Tchr; o, NY; *m:* Neil; *c:* Christopher, Sean; *ed:* Rosary Hill Coll (BA) Canisius Coll (MS) Ed 1980; *cr:* St Mary's Elem Schl Tchr 1988-; *ai:* Lancaster Garden Club 1985-; *office:* St Mary's Elem Marys on the Hill Lancaster NY 14086

R, DAVID JAMES, Social Science Instructor; *b:* Olean, NY; *m:* Marie Carpenter; *c:* Brandon, Aaron; *ed:* St Bonaventure Univ Sci 1990, St Bonavewture Univ (MS) Ed 1994; (SAS) 1996; *cr:* shford Soc Sci Instr 1990-; *ai:* Sr Class Adv; Partnership Coord; 90-; Lions Club 1990-, Bd of Dirs; Soc of Military Engineers; uba-Rushford Cntrl Schl 15 E Elm St Cuba NY 14727

R, DENNIS HOWARD, Mathematics Teacher; *b:* Bluefield, WV; Wesleyan (BS) Math 1971; Emporia St U (MS) Curr, Instr 1973; on Vly HS Math Tchr 1971-87; Brussels Amer Schl Math Tchr Notre Dame Acad Math Tchr 1995-; *ai:* Bsktbl, Cross Cntry, Math Counts; AAE 1995-; Pres Awd; *home:* 20 Winslow St MA 02360

R, MARY-ANNE NUFRIO, Spanish & ESL Teacher; *b:* , NJ; *m:* James; *c:* Jimmy, Brett; *ed:* Fairfield Univ (BA) Modern 74, (MA) Biling, Bicultural Ed 1980; *cr:* Fairfield Woods Jr HS ar 1974-77; Roger Ludlowe HS Span Tchr 1977-87; Sacred Heart Prof 1981-82; Fairfield HS Span, ESL Tchr 1987-; *ai:* Span Hnr ss Adv; AATSP; TESOL; CT COLT; Shelton PTA; Pack 24 Cub Goal Club; Pecylak Comm; Diamond Club; *office:* Fairfield HS ville Ave Fairfield CT 06432

R, NANCY SWARTZLANDER, English Teacher; *b:* Beaver ; *m:* Jeffrey D.; *c:* Jason; *ed:* Geneva Coll (BA) Eng 1964; Univ (MS) Eng Ed 1976; Attnd Lake Erie Coll; *cr:* Madison 9-10, 12 Grd Eng Tchr 1964-69; Kenmore East Sr HS 10-12 Grd 1969-71; Cicero N Syracuse HS 10-11 Grd Eng Tchr 1972-; *ai:* ecathlon Lang Arts, Lit Coach; NYSUT, NSEA 1972-; NCTE; Meth Church 1970-; Software Grant; Articles Pub; *office:* orth Syracuse HS Rt 31 Cicero NY 13039

R, PAMELA PROVINS, 6th Grd Language Arts Teacher; *b:* oro, NC; *c:* Jeffrey, Rachel; *ed:* Towson St Univ (BA) Eng, Scndry Masters Equivalency 1988; Western MD Coll Masters Ed Prgm; ern HS Eng Tchr 1973-79; Southampton MS Lang Arts Tchr 1989-; A, MSTA, HARCO 1989-; Piloted Collaborative, Cooperative rgm; Summer Wkshps for Schls; *office:* Southampton MS 1200 Mill Rd Bel Air MD 21014

RS, BETTY A., English Teacher; *b:* St Marys, PA; *c:* Catherine CA Univ of PA (BSEd) Eng 1962; Millersville Univ of PA; *cr:* Heart Acad Grd 4 Tchr 1962-64; Clearfield Area Schls Spec Ed 6-68; St Rose of Lima Music Tchr 1969-74; Bishop Guilfoyle HS r 1987-; *ai:* Mock Trail Club Adv; Music Private Piano Lessons; NEA 1964-; AJCSTA 1987-; *office:* Bishop Guilfoyle HS 2400 Valley Blvd Altoona PA 16602

RS, LISA JANE (MELLEN), Spanish Teacher; *b:* Providence, argaret, Charlotte; *ed:* Trinity Coll (BA) Span 1975; Scndry Tchng 0; Span 1990; Soc Stud 1993; Universidad de Madrid 1973-74; ad Span 1995; *cr:* Anne Arundel Cty Schl Long Term Sub HS Art 1979-81; St Mary Acad at Bay View Span Tchr 1984-86; URI eld Ctr Rsrch Asst, Prgm Dev 1986-88; Portsmouth HS Span Tchr *i:* Span Club Adv 1984-85; SADD Adv 1990-91; Acad Decathlon Adv 1993-95; NEA-RI, RIFLA 1990-; AAVW 1995-; Parents of & Girls' Club of Cumberland-Lincoln 1995-; New Swimming 1988-; Fullbright Tchr Exchange Applicant 1996; ortsmouth HS Education Ln Portsmouth RI 02871

LLY, BREEDA WALSH, Eighth Grade Teacher; *b:* Jamaica, NY; oy Coll (BA) Elem Ed, His 1976; C. W. Post (MS) Elem Ed 1981; cumencial Inst at Jerusalem Biblical Stud 1992; Fordham Univ d 3 Credits Admin 1995; *cr:* Long Beach Cath Schl 2nd Grd Tchr ; US Trust Co Asst VP 1981-90; Our Lady of Grace Schl 8th Grd 0-; *ai:* Stu Cncl Adv; Rel 5 Yrs, Soc Stud Curr 3 Yrs Coord; Natl ctrs Assn 1990-; Distngd Grad Awd Dept Elem Schls Natl Cath ssn 1994; *office:* Our Lady Of Grace Schl 158-20 101st St Howard Y 11414*

LLY, EILEEN M., Guidance Counselor; *b:* Brooklyn, NY; *ed:* St Univ (BS) AAD 1979; Fordham Univ (MSEd) Cnslng, Prsnl Svc John's Univ (PD) Cnslr Ed 1986; 30 Credit Hrs Advanced Cert & Supervision CUNY at Brooklyn, CUNY at Staten Island & NYU : St Francis de Sales Schl 7-8 Grd Tchr 1979-81; Stella Maris HS nslr 1981-85; Baldwin Union Free Schl Dist SHS Guid Cnslr , JHS Guid Cnslr 1989-; *ai:* Stu Act Adv; JHS Sftbl Coach; SHS ockey Asst Coach; Lifetime Achvmt Awd Baldwin SHS PTA 1989; onin Meml Awd Tchr of Yr PTA 1991; NY St Cncl PTAs Awd 1992; gnition Excl 1995; *office:* Baldwin Jr HS 3211 Schreiber Pl NY 11510*

LLY, GERALD FRANCIS, Reading Teacher; *b:* Albany, NY; *ed:* Valley Comm Coll (AA) Bus 1958; Rochester Inst of Tech (BS) 0; Coll of Saint Rose (MS) Ed 1965; Cortland St Ed 3 Hrs Past MS; Falls Jr HS 7th-9th Grd Eng, Math, & General Bus Tchr 1961-81; lls MS Dev Rdng Tchr 1981-; *ai:* Frosh Jr Var Bsktbl, Jr HS Ftbl 961-81; Numerous Clubs, Sponsorships, & Comms; Annual Schl Feed Poor 1961-81; NYSTA, NEA 1961-; Glens Falls Elks #82 Glens Falls Schl Dist Tchr of Yr 1989; Childreach Spon for 8 in 3rd World Countries 1965-; Head of Albany & Glen Falls Vol Group 1982-92; Childreach Natl Vol Comm 1985-90; *office:* Glens Quade St Glens Falls NY 12801*

LLY, GERARD J., Sixth Grade Teacher; *b:* Boston, MA; *m:* ry Lesinski; *c:* Jill, Kevin; *ed:* SUNY at Fredonia (BA) Elem Ed 1972; SUNY at Buffalo (MS) Ed 1976; *cr:* West Seneca Cntrl Schls Tchr 1972-; *ai:* WSTA 1972-; NYSTA 1972-; *office:* Allendale Elem Schl 1399 Orchard Park Rd West Seneca NY 14224

CONNOLLY, JONI HERSCHENHORN, Student Assistance Counselor; *b:* Pittsfield, MA; *m:* Charles Christopher; *c:* Cheryl Ann Kwalick, Steven Benjamin Kwalick; *ed:* Monmouth Univ (BS) Ed 1960; Trenton St Coll (MED) Cnslng 1981; 12 MA Credits Substance Awareness Coord; Certfd Alcohol, Drug Cnslr, Stu Prsnl Svcs, Presch-8th Grd Tchr; *cr:* HI, TX, NJ Pub Schls Presch-4th Grd Tchr 1960-77; NJ Dept of Hlth Trainer, Edctr in Drug-Alcohol Cnslng 1977-80; Treatment Alternatives to Street Crime Court Evaluator 1980-82; Monmouth Chemical Dependency Treatment Ctr Cnslr 1982-84; Nalt Cncl of Alcoholism Ed Coord 1984-85; Keyport Schl Dist Stu Assistance Cnslr 1985-; *ai:* Coord Life Line Prgm; Frosh Class Adv; Anti Drinking, Druging, Suicide Club Adv; NJEA, NEA 1985-; Assn of Stu Assistance Prof; Keyport Drug Alliance 1987-; Numerous Schl Drug & Alcohol Grants; *office:* Keyport Schl Dist 351 Broad St Keyport NJ 07735

CONNOLLY, MICHAELA, Dean of Students; *b:* New York, NY; *ed:* Dominican Coll (BSEd) Elem Ed 1968; Fordham Univ (MS) Admin 1973; *cr:* Holy Spirit Schl 1 Grd Tchr 1967-68; St Luke Schl 8 Grd Tchr 1968-72; Dominican Coll PR Dir 1972-73, Dev Dir 1973-87; St Margaret's Parish Patoral Asoc 1987-93; St Raymond Acad Dean of Stdnts 1993-; *ai:* Stu Cncl Moderator; CSAANYS, NCEA 1993-; Dominican Coll Bd of Trustees 1988-; Sisters of St Dominic 1994-, Formation Team; *office:* Saint Raymond Acad For Girls 2380 E Tremont Ave Bronx NY 10462

CONNOLLY, THADDA DELIA, 8th Grade English Teacher; *b:* New York, NY; *ed:* Kent St Univ (BS) Eng Ed 1991; Cleveland St Univ 20 Credit Hrs Towards MA Rdng; *cr:* Greenbriar Jr High Eng Tchr 1992-; *ai:* Track Coach; NCTE 1990-; NEA, OH Ed Assn 1992-; *office:* Greenbriar Jr HS 11810 Huffman Rd Cleveland OH 44130

CONNOR, BARBARA, 3rd-6th Grd Title I Math Tchr; *b:* Carbondale, PA; *m:* William; *ed:* Bloomsburg Univ (BS) Elem Ed 1966; Univ of Scranton (MS) Elem Ed 1971; Math Cert 1987; 44 Grad Credit Hrs; *cr:* Susquehanna Comm Schls Elem Tchr 1966-67; Wayne Highlands Schl 3rd Grd Tchr 1967-90, Title I Math Tchr 1990-; *ai:* Wayne Highlands Ed Assn 1967-; NEA 1967-; PSEA 1967-; NCTM 1995-; Forest City BPW 1972-, Pres 1977-78; *office:* Wayne Highlands Schl Dist 474 Grove Honesdale PA 18431

CONNOR, DOROTHY EDWARDS, Second Grade Teacher; *b:* Jersey City, NJ; *m:* Robert Connor; *ed:* Newark St Coll (BA) Elem Ed Rdng 1972; Kean Coll of NJ (MA) Advanced Specialization Elem Ed 1974; 32 Credits Seton Hall Univ, Jersey City St 1988; Acad Advancement Tchrs Mngnt 1985; Instrl Theory Practice, Coop Learning 1994; Supvr, Prin, Rdg Tchr Certs 1988Cert; *cr:* Roosevelt Schl 1st Grd Tchr 1 Yr, 4th Grd Tchr 1 Yr, 2nd Grd Tchr 1972-; *ai:* Curr Writing Eng Adv Lit Magazine; Curr Selection Math Soc Comm; Curr Selection Rdng Organizer of Ordering Supplies; Supvr Stu Interns; Alpha Delta Pi 1980-, Treas; NSEA, NEA 1972-; Contemporary Club 1990-, Treas; Ho-Ho-Kus Svc Org Comm Acts; *office:* Roosevelt Elem Schl 733 Kearny Ave Kearny NJ 07032*

CONNOR, MARGUERITE PEZZULLO, French & Spanish Teacher; *b:* New Haven, CT; *m:* James Joseph; *c:* Kristen, Erin; *ed:* Albertus Magnus (BA) Fr 1969; 30 Hrs Quinnipiac Coll Accounting; *cr:* Jonathan Law Fr, Span Tchr 1969-70; Cheshire High Fr, Span Tchr 1970-72, 1984-; Lyman Hall Span Tchr 1980-84; *ai:* Fr Club; NEA 1969-.

CONNOR, TIMOTHY J., Mathematics Tchr & Comp Coord; *b:* Jamaica, NY; *c:* Bryan; *ed:* Salem Coll (AS) Comp Sci 1982; SUNY at Oneonta (BS) Math Ed 1984; NY Inst of Tech (MS) Instrl Tech 1990; *cr:* Sarah J Hale HS Tchr 1986-92; Robert F Wagner Jr Inst for Arts & Tech Tchr & Comp Coord 1992-; *ai:* Bsktbl Coach; *office:* Robert F Wagner Jr Inst 47-07 30th Pl Long Island Cty NY 11101

CONNORS, CAROLE SULZER, Guidance Counselor; *b:* Camden, NJ; *m:* William L.; *c:* William Jr., Scott, Jeffrey, Craig; *ed:* Trenton St Coll (BA) Eng 1965; Rowan Coll (MA) Stu Prsnl Svcs 1994; *cr:* Pitman HS Eng Tchr 1965-69; Haddon Heights HS Eng Tchr 1969-70; Triton Regnl HS Eng Tchr 1986-94, Guid Cnslr 1994-; *ai:* Staff Dev, NHS Selection & In-Svc Comms; Core Team Mem; Mentor Tchr; NEA & NJEA 1965-70, 1986-; Black Horse Pike Ed Assn 1986-; NJ Schl Cnslrs Assn 1994-; Camden Cty Schl Cncl Assn 1994-; 1st United Meth Church 1970-; PTA 1971-; Triton HS Tchr of Yr 1989-90; Courier Post Newspaper Best Tchr of South Jersey 1994; Whos Who in Amer Ed 1996; *office:* Triton Regional HS 250 Schubert Ave Runnemede NJ 08078

CONNORS, JEAN HOHMAN, 5th Grade Teacher; *b:* Pittsburgh, PA; *m:* Daniel J.; *c:* Sean, Colleen, Ryan, Patrick, Danny; *ed:* IN Univ of PA (BS) Elem Ed 1966; Univ of Pittsburg (MS) Rdng, Lang Arts 1969; *cr:* Gateway Schl Dist Elem Tchr 1966-72; St Colman Schl Elem Tchr 1987-; *ai:* Troop 220 BSA Chprsn; St Francis Coll Parent Rep; ST Bernadette Church Tchr Childrens Liturgy; NEA 1987-; Girl Scouts of Amer 1980-90, St Anne Awd; BSA 1983-, Chprsn; St Bernadette Church 1976-; *home:* 199 Shackelford Dr Monroeville PA 15146*

CONOVER, TERRY L., 9th-12th Grd Hlth & PE Tchr; *b:* Lebanon, NJ; *m:* Tenna K. (Miller); *c:* Josh, Tyke; *ed:* Western MD Coll (BS) PE 1970, (MED) Ed 1974; *cr:* Hanover HS 9th-12th Grd Hlth & PE Tchr 1971-; *ai:* Head Wrestling, Bsktbl, Asst Ftbl Coach; Hlth & PE Dept Head; Boys Intramurals; PIAA Wrestling Ofcl 1982-, Past Pres; Western MD Athl Hall of Fame 1993; Dist III Wrestling Coaches Hall of Fame 1992; PA Wrestling Coaches Hall of Fame 1996; Coach of Yr Awds; *office:* Hanover HS 401 Moul Ave Hanover PA 17331

CONOVER, VICKI L., Computer & Business Teacher; *b:* Pittsburg, CA; *c:* Zachariah, Joshua; *ed:* Univ of ME (BA) Acctng 1986; *cr:* Univ of ME Accountant 1980-89; Islesboro Cntrl Schl Cmptr Tchr 1989-; *ai:* Girl Var Bsktbl, Odyssey of Mind Coach; Odyssey of Mind St Champions 1987, 1989, 1995; *office:* Islesboro Central Schl PO Box 118 Alumni Dr Islesboro ME 04848

CONRAD, BETH BURRIS, 7th Grade Language Arts Tchr; *b:* Kenosha, WI; *m:* Mike; *c:* Alexandra; *ed:* Bowling Green St Univ (BA) Eng 1989; *cr:* Tri Valley MS 8th Grd Lang Arts Tchr 1989-95, 7th Grd Lang Arts Tchr 1995-; *ai:* Stu Cncl Adv; *office:* Tri-Valley MS 35 E Muskingum Ave Dresden OH 43821

CONRAD, ELLEN CRITCHFIELD, Latin Teacher; *b:* South Charleston, WV; *ed:* WV Univ (BA) His 1982; Univ of Pittsburgh Grad Stud & Classical Stud; Marshal Univ Tchr Cert; *cr:* Winchester Thurston Schl Latin Tchr 1989-93; Bethel Park HS & Independence MS Latin Tchr 1993-; *ai:* Frgn Lang Club Spon; AFT 1993-; *office:* Bethel Park Sr HS 309 Church Rd Bethel Park PA 15102*

CONRAD, JAY RICHARD, Fifth Grade Teacher; *b:* Lancaster, PA; *m:* Betty Hess; *c:* Matthew (dec); *ed:* Millersville Univ (BS) Elem Ed 1966; Temple Univ (MS) Ed 1970; Elem Admin Cert 1973; *cr:* Quarryville Elem 5th Grd Tchr 1966-69; Bart-Colerain & Quarryville Elem Prin 1969-82; Providence Elem 5th Grd Tchr 1982-; *ai:* Phi Delta Kappa 1981-; NEA 1982-; *office:* Providence Elem Schl 137 Truce Rd New Providence PA 17560

CONRAD, JEANETTE REED, Fourth Grade Teacher; *b:* Kingston, PA; *m:* Arthur Conrad; *c:* William, Steven, Barbara; *ed:* William Paterson Coll (BA) Elem Ed 1976; *cr:* Haledon Pub Schl 3rd, 4th Grd Tchr 1977-; *ai:* NEA, PCEA, NJEA 1977-; Hadelon Ed Assn 1977-, VP 2 Yrs; PTA 1977-; *home:* 15 Whippany Ave West Paterson NJ 07424

CONRAD, JOSEPH PATRICK, Cross Country Coach; *b:* Ft Wayne, IN; *m:* Madonna Grzelak; *c:* Johanna; *ed:* Univ of Toledo (BS) Psych 1972, (MS) Exercise Physiology 1973, (PHD) Exercise Physiology 1983; *cr:* Univ of Toledo Asst Prof 1983-86; Notre Dame Acad Coach 1986-; Owens Tech Coll Inst 1996; *ai:* Amer Red Cross Vol Instr; ACSM 1976-; AACVPR 1994-; *office:* Notre Dame Acad 3535 W Sylvania Ave Toledo OH 43623

CONRAD, JULIE BARRICK, French & Spanish Teacher; *b:* Alliance, OH; *m:* David; *c:* Robert, Andrew; *ed:* Mt Union Coll (BA) Fr 1968; Post Grad Kent St Span, Eng; Mentoring Class Ashland; *cr:* East Canton HS Fr, Span Tchr 1968-75, 1980-; *ai:* Lang, Ski Clubs; SADD; Direction Leadership Camp Dir; Mentor Trainer; Spnsrd 8 Stu Trips to Europe & 1 to Quebec; NEA, OEA, ECTA, FLA 1968-; First Presbyn, Elder, Deacon, Sunday Schl Tchr; Delta Kappa Gamma 1975-, Pres; Alpha Chi Omega Alumni; *office:* East Canton HS Browning St East Canton OH 44730*

CONRAD, MARGARET STRINGER, Literature Teacher; *b:* London, England; *m:* Richard; *c:* Anjanette Stauffer, Allison; *ed:* Saffron Walden Coll (BA) Ed 1967; *cr:* Cath Diocese 2nd, 3rd Grd Tchr 1967-71; St Martin's Church Dir of Chrstn Ed 1982-86; Greater Works Acad MS Lit Tchr 1986-; *ai:* St Alban's Church 1994-, Bible Stud; St Martin's Church 1977-, Women's Bd; *office:* Greater Works Acad 301 College Park Dr Monroeville PA 15146

CONRAD, MARION T. (MCPOLIN), Mathematics Teacher; *b:* Brooklyn, NY; *m:* Walter David; *c:* Erin, Elizabeth; *ed:* Douglas Coll (BA) Math 1983; Georgian Court Coll (MA) Ed 1992; *cr:* Spotswood HS Math Tchr 1983-89; Jackson HS Math Tchr 1991-; *ai:* NEA 1983-; OCEA & JEA 1991-; NJEA 1983-; Girl Scouts 1990; Saint Raphaels 1990-; *office:* Jackson Memorial HS 101 Don Connor Blvd Jackson NJ 08527

CONRAD, MICHAEL D., Earth & Space Science Teacher; *b:* Hagerstown, MD; *m:* Elizabeth A.; *c:* Christopher, Jeremy; *ed:* Dickinson Coll (BS) Geology 1968; 40 Hrs Post Grad Earth Scis; *cr:* Cumberland Valley HS 9th Grd Earth Sci Tchr 1968-; *ai:* Harrisburg Geological Soc 1990-; *office:* Cumberland Valley HS 6746 Carlisle Pike Mechanicsburg PA 17055

CONRAD, MILLIE L., Math Teacher; *b:* Mason City, WV; *m:* Tod T.; *ed:* OH Univ (BSEd) Math 1975; Attnd Mt ST Joseph Coll, Ashland Univ, Univ of Cincinnati; *cr:* Teays Vly Schl Dist 7th Grd Math Tchr 1975-79; Northwest Schl Dis 7th-9th Grd Math Tchr 1979-86; Logan Elm HS 9th-12th Grd Math Tchr 1986-; *ai:* Proficiency Tutor; OEA & NEA 1975-; LECTA 1986-, Treas 1987-88; *office:* Logan Elm HS 9575 Tarlton Rd Circleville OH 43113*

CONRAD, PAULETTE ASHCRAFT, Fifth Grade Teacher; *b:* Kingston, PA; *c:* Jeremy, Jaime; *ed:* Mansfield Univ (BS) Elem Ed 1968; *cr:* Wyalusing Schls 3rd Grd Tchr 1968-71, 4th Grd Tchr 1971-74, 3rd Grd Tchr 1977-94, 5th Grd Tchr 1995-; *ai:* Head Tchr; NEA; PSEA; WHEA; *office:* Wyalusing Area Schls Main St Wyalusing PA 18857

CONRAD, SHARON (SLOAN), 5th & 6th Grade Teacher; *b:* Toledo, OH; *m:* Brian L.; *ed:* BGSU (BA) Elem Ed 1973; Univ of Toledo (MS) Recreation 1993; *cr:* Park Elem Schl 5th, 6th Grd Tchr 1973-; *ai:* Site Based Ed Comm; Former Vlybl Coach; SEA, OEA, NEA 1973-; *office:* Park Elem Schl 100 Elton Pky Swanton OH 43558

CONRAD, STEPHEN EDWARD, Social Studies Teacher; *b:* Philadelphia, PA; *m:* Lynne Hutnik; *c:* David; *ed:* Gettysburg Coll (BA) His 1970; Temple Univ (MA) His 1980; 30 Hrs Beaver Coll, Bloomsburg Univ; 6 Hrs His; *cr:* Athens Coll Tchng Fellow 1970-71; Philadelphia Schl Dist Longterm Sub Tchr 1973-79; Cncl Rock Schl Dist Soc Stud Tchr 1979-; *ai:* Bldg Rep Cncl Rock Ed Assn 2 Yrs; Performance Assessment Dev Project 1994-95; NEA, PSEA, CREA 1979-; NCSS 1980-; Amer Red Cross 1966-, Lifeguard Trainer; Historical Commission 1982-, Exec Comm 10 Yr Svc Awd; 2 Articles Pub; *office:* Holland Jr HS 400 E Holland Rd Holland PA 18966*

CONRADS, URSULA MARGARETHE, German Teacher; *b:* Riesa Elbe, Germany; *ed:* Kutztown Univ (BA) Ger, Ed 1969; Millersville Univ (MA) Ger 1988; 11 Credit Hrs Modern Germany Reunification; *cr:* Old Bridge Bd of Ed Ger Tchr 1970-80; Midd-West Schl Dist Ger Tchr 1981-; *ai:* Project DIPLOMA Stu-Tchr Mentor Prgm; NEA, AATG 1970-; PSEA 1981-; *office:* Midd West Schl Dist 568 E Main St Middleburg PA 17842*

CONROY, PATRICK JOSEPH, Social Studies Teacher; *b:* New York, NY; *m:* Sheila A. Furner; *c:* Kieran, Craig; *ed:* Fordham Univ (BA) His 1966; Howard Univ (MA) His 1968; 60 Hrs Soc, Natural Sci, Ed Pace, Ramapo, St Thomas Aquinas, Fordham, New Paltz, Potsdam, Rockland CC, Orange CC, Empire St Coll, St Rose, New Rochelle; *cr:* St Paul's Sec Schl His, Fr Tchr, Librn 1968-70; Tappan Zee HS Soc Stud Tchr 1970-72; Leonia HS Soc Stud Tchr 1972-73; Clarkstown South HS Soc Stud Tchr 1973-; Mt St Mary Coll Adj Prof His 1992-; St Thomas Aquinas Coll Adj Prof His 1996-; *ai:* Coll Bd Admissions Testing Prgm Supvr; NYSUT, AFT, NCSS, NY St Cncl Soc Stud 1970-; Rockland Cncls Soc Stud 1990-; US Peace Corps 1968-70, Vol; Woodbury Comm Ambulance 1982-87, Vol; BSA 1994-, Asst Scout Master; Grad Assistantships Howard, Duquesne Univs; Howard Univ Flwshp 1966-68; Fullbright Travel Flwshp India 1972; *office:* Clarkstown South HS 31 Demarest Mill Rd West Nyack NY 10994*

CONROY, TIMOTHY LEE, Math, Science & Cmptr Teacher; *b:* Caribou, ME; *m:* Heidi J. Griffeth; *c:* Amber Lori; *ed:* Univ of ME at Presque Isle (BS) Scndry Ed, Math 1990; *cr:* Schenck HS Math, Sci, Cmptr, Tchr 1990-; *ai:* Coach Var Bsbl, Cross Ctry Running, Skiing; NEA, ME Sci Tchrs Assn, ATOMIN 1990-; Millinocket Elks 1992-; *office:* Schenck HS 33 41 North St E Millinocket ME 04430*

CONSALVO, MARILEE O., Latin & English Teacher; *b:* Waldoboro, ME; *c:* Ruth, Elizabeth; *ed:* Bates Coll (BA) Eng 1974; 18 Credit Hrs Latin St Joseph's Coll; Attnd Cane Summer Inst at Dartmouth; *cr:* Kangaru Schl Eng Tchr 1974-79; Sacopee Vly HS Eng, Latin Tchr 1987-; *ai:* Amer Classical League, CANE 1988-; ME Classical Assn 1995-, Sec; Miller Flwshp; *office:* Sacopee Valley Jr Sr HS RR 2 Box 5166 Hiram ME 04041

CONSER, JAMES ANDREW, Chair of Criminal Justice Dept; *b:* Salem, OH; *m:* Linda S. Maris; *c:* Nicole, Jodi, Jami; *ed:* Youngstown St Univ (BA) Law Enforcement Admin 1971; MI St Univ (MS) Criminal Justice 1974; Kent St Univ (PHD) Higher Ed Admin 1980; *cr:* Youngstown St Univ Asst Dean 1986-89, Asst Prof 1989-91; Kent St Univ Asst Prof 1991-93; Youngstown St Univ Assoc Prof 1993-; *ai:* Instr & Fire Inspector; Acad Senate; Acad of Criminal Justice Scis, Amer Soc for Industrial Security 1976-; OH Assn of Criminal Justice Educators 1975-, Past Pres, Bd Mem; World Future Soc 1988-; United Schlsp Fnd 1990-, Pres; Winona United Meth Church 1965-, Admin Bd Chair; Winona Vol Fire Dept 1977-, VP; Certified Protectional Prof; Police Personnel Systems Co-Ed, Co-Author; Articles, Book Chapters Pub; *office:* Youngstown St Univ 410 Wick Ave Youngstown OH 44555

CONSIDINE, MARY ANN, Third Grade Teacher; *b:* Albany, NY; *ed:* SUNY At Central (BA) Ed 1968; SUNY At Brockport (MA) Ed 1973; *cr:* Plank North Schl 1-3rd Grd Tchr 1968-79; Klem Rd North Schl 2-3rd Grd Tchr 1979-; *ai:* Webster Tchr Asst 1968-, Rep, VP; AFT, NYSUT 1968-; *office:* Klem Road North Elem Schl 1015 Klem Rd Webster NY 14580

CONSIGLI, BEN L., Asst Principal for Academics; *b:* Brooklyn, NY; *ed:* Queens Coll (BA) His 1984; Rutgers Univ (MAT) His 1993; MA Candidate Educl Admin; *cr:* Archbishop Molloy HS Eng, His Tchr 1984-87, 1989; Roselle Cath HS His, Hum Tchr 1989-91; Archbishop Molloy HS Tchr, Admin 1991-; *ai:* Acad Excl Comm; Acad Advy Bd; Extra-Curricular Act Supvr; NCAANYS 1995-; Phi Beta Kappa; NEH Recipient; *office:* Archbishop Molloy HS 8353 Manton St Briarwood NY 11435

CONSOL, DANIEL A., 7th Grade Social Studies Tchr; *b:* Johnson City, NY; *ed:* St Univ of NY at Cortland (BA) Scndry Soc Stud 1973; SUNY at Binghamton Post Grad Stud; *cr:* Union-Endicott Cntrl Schls Sub Tchr 1973-74, 7th Grd Soc Stud Tchr 1974-; *ai:* Var Asst Ftbl & Track Coach; NYSUT 1974-; NFICA 1980-; NYSHSFCA 1993-; Alhambra Sidona #212 1980-; Sons of Italy 1993-; PTA Founders Day Awd; *office:* Jenny F Snapp Schl 101 Loder Ave Endicott NY 13760*

CONSTAIN, SALLY WAHL, Staff Developer; *b:* Brooklyn, NY; *m:* Edward; *c:* William F.; *ed:* St Univ Coll of Cortland (BS) Early Chldhd Ed 1966; CUNY at Hunter Coll (MS) Biling Ed 1979; *cr:* PS 171 Queens Early Chldhd, Biling Tchr 1966-85; PS 166 Queens Kndgtn, Grd 2, Biling, Writing, Rdng Tchr, Staff Developer 1986-; *ai:* Adj Prof Fordham Univ Curr Dev, Rdng, Lang Arts for Biling, ESL Classroom; UFT 1966-; Numerous Reviews Pub; *office:* PS 166 Queens 33-09 35th Ave Long Island Cty NY 11106*

CONSTANT, WILLIAM PAUL, Math Teacher; *b:* New Bedford, MA; *m:* Kristine Frates; *c:* Kathrine, Sarah; *ed:* St Anselms (BA) His, Math 1967; Fitchburg St (MS) Ed, Admin 1989; *cr:* St Theresas Tchr 1967-68; GNBRVT Tchr 1968-; *ai:* Ftbl Coach 23 Yrs; Voke-Vol-Tech Hall of Fame Comm; Mentor, Summer Bilingual Math Tchr; Math Tutorial Admin; New Bedford Racing Pigeon Club 1967-, Pres, Presidents Cup Best Loft in USA.*

CONSTANTINE, KATHRYN A., High School Math Teacher; *b:* Kingston, NY; *m:* David; *ed:* SUNY at Oneonta (BS) Scndry Ed Math 1979; SUNY at Binghamton (MS) Math Ed 1984; *cr:* Oxford Acad HS Math Tchr 1979-; Norwich HS HS Math Tchr Summer Schl 1981-; *ai:* Grad Adv; Mat Boname Schlrshp Comm Pres; NEA 1979-; Oxford Dollars for Schls 1991-, Sec; *office:* Oxford Acad & Cntrl Schl S Washington Ave Oxford NY 13830

CONSTANTINEAU, ERIC ROBERT, High School English Teacher; *b:* Methuen, MA; *m:* Abigail Schlichting; *c:* Aian; *ed:* St Anselm Coll (BA) Eng 1983; IL St Univ (MA) Eng 1986; *cr:* IL St Univ Grad Asst, ESL Tchr 1984-86; Triton Regnl HS Long Term Sub 1986; Timberlane Reg HS Eng Tchr 1987-; *ai:* Amnest Intnl Schl Chapter Creator; Dramatic Arts Dir; Co-Enrichment Coord; Television Production Class, Amer Stud Class, Ethics Prgm Co-Creator; AFT 1992-; Wrote, Produced Holocaust Play; Nom NH Tchr of Yr Awd; Created Comm Theater; *office:* Timberlane Regional HS 36 Greenough Rd Plaistow NH 03865*

CONSTANTINO, ADELE MARIE, K-2nd Grade Teacher; *b:* Camden, NJ; *ed:* Camden Cty Comm Coll (AA) Librl Arts 1973; Glassboro St Coll (BA) Elem Ed 1975; *cr:* Laurel Springs Elem Schl 5th Grd Tchr 1976-84, 2nd Grd Tchr 1984-85; Mary E. Volz Schl K-2 Grd Tchr 1985-; *ai:* 7 Class Plays; Safety Patrol 1981-85; Phillies Day 1980; Eagles Day 1981; K-2 Grd Circus 1987; K-2 Grd Talent Show 1988; Christmas Shows 1990-93; K-2 Grd Fashion Show 1993; K-2 Grd Grad, Yrbk 1987-; Laurel Springs Ed Assn 1976-85, Pres 1981-83; NEA, NJEA 1976-; Runnemede Ed Assn 1985-; Laurel Springs PTA 1976-85; Runnemede 1985-; NJ Governors Tchr Recognition Awd 1991; Citation Womens Club Runnemede Loyal Support 1993; *office:* Mary E. Volz Schl 505 W 3rd Ave Runnemede NJ 08078

CONSTANTINOU, GUS, 7th & 8th Grd Soc Stud Teacher; *b:* Larnaca, Cyprus; *m:* Patricia Lennstrom; *ed:* St Univ of NY at Oswego (BS) Ed 1974; 31 Addl Grad Credits St Univ of NY at New Paltz; 9th Addl Grad Credits Coll of St Rose; *cr:* RVMS 5th & 6th Grd Tchr 1974-87, GATE Tchr 1984-85, Crisis Cnslr 1987-89, 7th & 8th Grd Soc Stud Tchr 1989-; *ai:* Artists for Pub Ed Group Adv; AFT & NYSUT 1974-; Rondout Vly Fed 1974-, 2nd VP; 1987-91 Del NYS Tchrs Retirement Sys; 1983-85 Grd Chprsn; 1977-79 Team Chprsn; *home:* PO Box 83 Hurley NY 12443*

CONTE, DONNA, English Teacher; *b:* Uniontown, PA; *m:* Donald J.; *c:* Michael, Melanie, Christian; *ed:* California Univ of PA (BS) Eng 1965, (MA) Eng 1972; *cr:* Connellsville HS Eng Tchr 1965-67; Bentworth HS Eng Tchr 1969-70; Brownsville Area HS Eng Tchr 1975-; *ai:* Annual Coal Queen Contest Coord; Lucostic Meml Schlsp Comm; Judge for Hugh O'Brian Outstanding Soph; BEA; PSEA; NEA; Duquesne Univ Recognition Tchng Excl Cert; *office:* Brownsville Area HS Brashear Ave Brownsville PA 15417

CONTE, JAMES E., Music Teacher; *b:* Upland, PA; *ed:* Temple Univ (BA) Music Ed 1969, (MA) Music Ed 1973; Penn St Univ Supvr of Music Cert 1982; Drexel Univ Arts Admin Prgm; Attnd Eastman Schl of Music, IN Univ, Peabody Conservatory & Hartt Schl of Music Summer Stud Credits; *cr:* Tredyffrin-Easttown Jr HS Music Tchr & Coach 1969-76; Upper Darby HS Band Dir 1977-85; Penncrest HS Music & Band Tchr 1986-; *ai:* Competitive Marching Band & Band Front, Wind Ensemble & Jazz Band Dir; Chamber Ensembles Coach; MENC 1969-; PMEA 1969-, Pres Dist 12 1988-89; Natl Band Assn 1977-; Rose Tree Media Schl Dist Svc Awd 1994; Inducted into the Media Old Times Sports Assn for Track 1995; Columbus 500th Assn 2 Svc Awds; *office:* Penncrest HS 134 Barren Rd Media PA 19063

CONTE, LORRAINE F., Substitute Teacher; *b:* Newark, NJ; *ed:* Rutgers Univ (BA) His 1995; *cr:* Ridge Street Schl 1980-; *ai:* Ridge St Girls Sftbl Coach; NEA; Friends of Newark Lib 1992-; Block Watch Assn 1993-, Ldr; North Ward Prtnrshp 1992-; *office:* Ridge Street Elem Schl 735 Ridge St Newark NJ 07104

CONTE, NICK, Guidance Counselor; *b:* Utica, NY; *m:* Jean Hobbs; *c:* Joseph, Kerry; *ed:* Univ at Albany (BA) Sociology 1972, (MS) Guid & Cnslng 1981; Univ Cert Cnslng 1981; *cr:* Albany HS Tchr 1974-75, Attendance Tchr 1975-83, Guid Cnslr 1983-; *ai:* Bsktbl Referee; Club Adv Natural Helpers & CEASE; Sftbl Umpire; Yth Bsktbl Coach; APSTA, NYSUT & AFT 1974-; Cap Dist Cnslng Assn 1983-, Treas, Trustee; NYS Cnslr Assn 1985-; Cap Dist Bd Womens Sports Ofcls 1975-; St Catherine Siena 1989-; NYS ACAC Grant 1988; *office:* Albany HS 700 Washington Ave Albany NY 12203*

CONTE, SUSAN ANNE, Counseling Department Chair; *b:* Astoria, NY; *ed:* Coll of New Rochelle (BA) Eng, Italian 1973; Fordham Univ (MA) Rel Ed 1974, (MSW) Soc Work 1991; Advanced Clinical Cert Prgm New York Univ; *cr:* Archbishop Williams HS Rel Ed Tchr 1974-76; Ursuline Schl Rel Ed, Italian Tchr 1976-77; Acad of Mt St Ursula 1977-78; Ursuline Schl Rel Ed, Italian Tchr 1979-87; Ursuline Companions in Mission Founding Dir, Natl Vol Prgm 1987-92, 1989-92; Ursuline Schl Chair, Cnslng Dept 1992-; *ai:* Dir Peer Cnslng Prgm Awd Natl Cncl of Chrstns & Jews for Yth Ldrshp 1995; Substance Abuse Ed Core Team; NASW 1991-, Clinical Practice Comm; Amer Orthopsychiatric Assn 1991-; Coll of New Rochelle Bd of Trustees 1992-, Chair, Stu Svcs Comm; Acad of Mt St Ursula Bd of Trustees 1985-86; Companions in Mission Bd of Dir 1987-92, 1995-; Fordham Univ Full Schlsp Rel Ed 1973; Natl Cncl on Alcholism Trng in Substance Abuse Cnslng Schlsp 1986; Fordham Univ Partial Schlsp Grad Soc Work Ed 1988; Kappa Gamma Pi Schlsp 1988; *office:* The Ursuline Schl 1354 North Ave New Rochelle NY 10804*

CONTI, ALEXANDRIA RODRIGUEZ, ESL Head Teacher; *b:* Jersey City, NJ; *m:* Daniel M.; *c:* Derek, Danielle; *ed:* Jersey City St Coll (BA) Elem Ed 1976; ESL Tchng Cert; Biling & Bicultural Tchng Cert; *cr:* Thomas A Edison Schl Tchr 1976-93, ESL Head Tchr 1993-; *ai:* Extended Schl Day Pgm Asst Coord; Comm Svc Adv; NJEA 1976-; NEA 1976-; TESOL 1993-; NABE 1994-; *office:* Thomas A Edison Schl 507 West St Union City NJ 07087

CONTI, DANIEL R., English Teacher; *b:* Plymouth, MA; *ed:* Coll of the Holy Cross (BA) Eng 1992; Tufts Univ (MAT) Tchng Eng 1994; *cr:* Lincoln-Sudbury Regnl HS Eng Tchr 1994-; *ai:* Stu Senate, Clas of 1999 Steering Comm Advs; Girls Jr Var Sftbl Coach; NCTE 1995-; NEA 1994-; St Brigid's Parish Youth Ministry 1995-, Youth Commission Mem; *office:* Lincoln Sudbury Reg HS 390 Lincoln Rd Sudbury MA 01776*

CONTI, JOAN NOEL, School Social Worker; *b:* Rome, NY; *m:* Stewart Bowman Whitney; *c:* Stewart Bowman II; *ed:* Niagara Univ (BA) Sociology 1980; Univ of Buffalo (MSW) Child & Family Therapy 1987; 30 Post Grad Hrs Psychotherapy; Credit Hrs in Reality Theory & Control Theory; *cr:* Erie, Boces Schl Soc Worker 1987-88; Cheektowaga Cntrl Schl Dist Soc Worker, EAP Coord 1988-; Pvt Practice Psychotherapist 1990-; *ai:* Challenge Prgm Co-Chprsn; NASW, WNYSSWA, NYSTA 1985-; Amer Sociological Assn 1980-; Cheektowaga Action Partnership 1988-, Schl Partnership Worker of Yr; Univ of Buffalo 1985-, Bd Mem, Ed of Newsletter; 2 Comm Svc Awds 1987, 1995; Article Pub; Grants for Working with Children & Adolescents; *office:* Cheektowaga Cntrl Schl Dist 3600 Union Rd Cheektowaga NY 14225

CONTI, JOYCE A., Hum & Social Studies Teacher; *b:* Woonsocket, RI; *m:* Olivio B.; *c:* Jonathan, Jason; *ed:* Univ of RI (BA) His 1965; Providence Coll (MA) His 1971; 6 Post Grad Credits; Georgetown Univ 3 Post Grad Credits; RI Coll 3 Post Grad Credits; *cr:* Albert Einstein HS Soc Stud Tchr 1967-70; Bellingham HS Eng Tchr 1970-72; Woonsocket HS Soc Stud Tchr 1978-82; Lincoln HS Tchr, Soc Stud Dept Ch 1982-; *ai:* NHS Exec, RI Skills Commisson For Educl Reform-Chair of Soc Stud Curr Comms; AFT 1965-; RI Com for Hum 1994-, Exec Bd; Hum Forum of RI 1990-; RI Soc Stud Assn 1982-; Parent Advy Cnc on Ed 1990-; 3 Natl Endowment for Hum Grants; *office:* Lincoln SR HS Old River Rd Lincoln RI 02865*

CONTI, LINDA DETULLIO, Social Studies Teacher; *b:* Brooklyn, NY; *m:* Douglas; *c:* Douglas, Richard; *ed:* St John's Univ (BA) Soc Stud 1975; Adelphi Univ (MA) His 1980; *cr:* St Sylvester's Schl 7th-8th Grd Soc Stud Tchr 1975-79; Holy Trinity HS 9th, 11th Grd Soc Stud Tchr 1979-81, 11th Grd Soc Stud Tchr 1987-; *ai:* NHS Selection Comm; Voice of Democracy Essay Contest Coord; NCSS, NYS Cncl Soc Stud 1987-; *office:* Holy Trinity HS 98 Cherry Ln Hicksville NY 11801

CONTI, NEIL ALVIN, English Teacher; *b:* Springdale, PA; *m:* Judith Hogan; *ed:* IN Univ of PA (BA) Eng Scndry Ed 1975; 36 Post Grad Hrs; *cr:* Lower Burrell HS Tutor & Tchr 1975-76; Cntrl Chrstn HS Tchr 1977-78; *ai:* STAR Pgm; IM Dir; NEA 1979-; *office:* Punxsutawney Area Sr HS N Findley St Punxsutawney PA 15767

CONTINI, MARIE E., Voc Info Processing Tchr; *b:* Dover, OH; *ed:* Kent St Univ (BS) Bus, Voc Ed 1974; Coll of Mount St Joseph (MA) Scndry Ed 1985; *cr:* Coshocton HS Bus Tchr 1974-79; Harrison Hills Voc Schl Clerk, Stenography Tchr 1980-81; Newcomerstown HS Bus Tchr 1992-83; New Philadelphia HS Voc Bus Tchr 1984-; *ai:* Young Bus Ldrs Club Adv; NBEA 1990-, OH Bus Ed Assn, NEA 1975-; Natl Cncl on Ec Ed, Intnl Paper Co Fnd Honorable Mention Awd Sr High Level 1992; Oh Cncl on Ec Ed, BP in Amer Excl in Ec Ed 1st Place Awd Sr High Level 1992; *office:* New Philadelphia HS 343 Ray Ave NW New Philadelphia OH 44663

CONTINO, LINDA GATTI, Coral Director; *b:* Brooklyn, NY; *c:* Michael, Leanne, Jessica; *ed:* Ithaca Coll (BM) Voice & Music Ed 1984; SUNY Stonybrook & CW Post (MA) Lbrl Stud & Music Ed 1987; *cr:* Three Village Elem & Jr High Elem Gen Music & Choir Tchr 1984-86; Ward Melville HS Choral Dir 1986-; *ai:* Musical Dir; Musical Production 3 Choirs; NYSSMA 1986-; MENC 1986-; SCMEA 1986-; ACDU 1986-; NY St Vocal Jazz; Exec Bd; SCMEA; Cty Jazz Choir; Outstndg Tchr 1987, 1988 & 1994; *office:* Ward Melville HS 380 Old Town Rd Setauket NY 11733

CONTOS, CAROL DEMETRO, Speech, Eng & Parenting Tchr; *b:* New York City, NY; *m:* Demetrios; *c:* George, Nicole; *ed:* NY Univ (BS) Speech Day HS 1960; Columbia Univ (MS) Speech Day HS 1964; Post Grad Work at Queens Coll; *cr:* George Washington HS Tchr, Prgm Planner 1960-; *ai:* Pregnant & Parent Linkage Coord; Cathedral Church Philoptohos Soc 1968-, Pres; Natl Philoptohos Soc 1972-, VP; Prof UFT 1962-, Mem; *office:* George Washington HS 549 Audubon Ave New York NY 10040

CONWAY, CONSTANCE J., High School English Teacher; *b:* Batavia, NY; *m:* James T.; *c:* Ryan, Erin, Meghan; *ed:* SUNY at Brockport (MA) Eng, Ed 1979; *cr:* Attica HS Eng Tchr 1977-; *ai:* Class Adv; Tchr of Yr 1993.

CONWAY, DEAN JOSEPH, English & Social Studies Tchr; *b:* Syracuse, NY; *m:* Cynthia Rowley; *c:* Sarah, Megan; *ed:* Georgetown Univ (AB) Eng 1970; *cr:* Linden Hill Schl Tchr 1973-76; Eaglebrook Schl Tchr 1976-79; The Park Schl Tchr 1979-; *ai:* Soccer Coach; *office:* Park Schl 171 Goddard Ave Brookline MA 02146

CONWAY, JANET SUSAN, High School Mathematics Tchr; *b:* New York, NY; *m:* John Sinclair; *c:* Eric, Jania; *ed:* Kean Coll (BA) Math Ed 1966; 60 Hrs; *cr:* Eastside HS Math Tchr 1966-68; Passaic Valley HS Math Tchr 1968-74; Hopatcong HS Math Tchr 1980-; *ai:* Project Quest; Project Adventure, Class Adv; Motivation Comm; NJEA, NEA 1966-; NCTM 1981-; Jr Woman's Club 1975-, Pres, Diamond Dozen Club; Women's Club 1985-, Pres, Excl for Creating New Branch; Governor's Awd for Excl Tchng Prof; Commendation from St of NJ for Writing Curr Linking Metric System; Grant to Teach Metric System 3 Yrs; *office:* Hopatcong HS PO Box 1029 Hopatcong NJ 07843*

CONWAY, KATHRYN MARIE, Science Teacher; *m:* Joseph D. Jr.; *ed:* Potsdam Univ (BA) Bio, Ed 1987; St Univ of Albany (MS) Ed 1994; *cr:* Rensselaer Mid, HS Earth Sci, Bio Tchr 1989-95; South Colonie Schl 8th Grd Earth Sci Tchr 1995-; *ai:* Vlybl, Bsktbl, Track Coach; *home:* 2165 Swampscott St Schenectady NY 12306

CONWAY, MARIA TREMENTOZZI, Social Studies Teacher; *b:* Washington, DC; *m:* Gerald Jr.; *cr:* Damascus HS Soc Stud, Eng Tchr 1992-; *ai:* DOCCS Prgm Team Ldr; Stu Mentor; NEA 1992-; MCEA; Sea Explorers 1993-; *office:* Damascus HS 25921 Ridge Rd Damascus MD 20872

CONWAY, PHYLLIS AUDREY NETTERBLADE, Stu Assistance Coord, Bus Tchr; *b:* Wood, PA; *m:* Wallace R.; *c:* Jon, Scot; *ed:* Elizabethtown Coll (BS) Bus Ed 1968; Temple Univ Masters Equivalency Coop Ed 1990; Alvernia Coll Cert Addiction Stud 1989-90; *cr:* Lower Dauphin Schl Dist Stu Assistance Coord, Cooperative Ed Dir & Bus Tchr 1968-; *ai:* Staff Dev Comm; High on Kids Comm Advy Comm Schl Liason; PA Assn Stu Assistance 1989-, Bd of Dirs, Sec; Trinity United Meth Church 1976-; Outstanding Scndry Classroom Tchr Awd 1979; Stu Acts Recognition Awd 1983; Dauphin Cty Dept of Drugs, Alcohol Comm Service Awd 1993; *office:* Lower Dauphin Sr HS 201 S Hanover St Hummelstown PA 17036*

CONWAY, SUSAN DUPONTE, 4th Grade Teacher; *b:* New Bedford, MA; *m:* Michael F.; *c:* Erin, Richard; *ed:* Framingham St Coll (BS) Elem Ed 1970, (MED) 1976; *cr:* Holliston Schl System Elem Tchr 1970-; *ai:* AFT 1970-; Nobsoot Rdng Cncl 1970-, Membership Chair 1989-90; Assn; Friends of Lib Hopkinton; Framingham St Coll Alumni A & Means Chm 1980-81; *office:* Flag Adams MS 100 Linden St MA 01746

CONWAY, TERESA J., English Teacher; *b:* Cincinnati, OH Booker; *ed:* Univ of Cincinnati (BA) Eng 1978, (MED) Rdng & S 1982; Xavier Univ (MA) Eng 1989; *cr:* Indian Hill HS Eng & R 1979-80; Amelia MS Eng Tchr 1980-81; Amelia HS Eng Tchr North Cntrl Steering Comm; Bldg Coord; Cty Gifted Prgm; N 1980-, Pres, VP & Negotiator; Delta Kappa Gamma 1987-; West C Ed Assn 1980-, Pres; Play Review Pub in Eng Journal; *office:* A 1351 Clough Pike Batavia OH 45103

CONWAY, WALLACE R., Mathematics Teacher; *b:* Grassfla Phyllis Audrey Netterblade; *c:* Jon, Scot; *ed:* Shippensburg U Elem Ed 1960; Temple Univ (MED) Ed 1965; Penn State Univ Su Cert Ed 1971; *cr:* Milton Hershey Schl 5th Grd Tchr 1960-66, 6t Math Tchr 1967-88, 9th-12th Grd Math Tchr 1989-; *ai:* Coopera Penn St Univ; Central PA Tchrs Math 1966-; PA Cncl of Tchrs M NCTM 1966-; Trinity United Meth Church 1976-; BPOE 1988- Excl Awd 1990; *office:* Milton Hershey Schl PO Box 830 He 17033*

CONYNE, SALLY B., High School English Teacher; *b:* Philadel *ed:* Beaver Coll (MS) Eng Ed; *cr:* Cncl Rock Schl Dist 6-12 Grd 1972-; Acad of Natural Scis Ornithological Ed Dir 1996; *home:* Rd Rushland PA 18956

CONZO, ROSEMARY MCDONALD, Second Grade Teacher; PA; *m:* Daniel; *ed:* PA St Univ (BS) Individual Family Stud 197 Univ of PA 24 Addl Credits; *cr:* St Marys Schl Second Grd Tchr NCEA 1971-; *office:* St Marys Schl 1005 Caroline St Nanty Glo

COOGAN, JOAN CANAN, Sixth Grade Teacher; *b:* Hornell, Patrick, Colleen Kratzer; *ed:* PA St Univ (BS) Scndry Ed 1958; Univ NY at Geneseo; *cr:* Hornell Intermediate Schl Sixth Grd Tc Steuben-Allegany Cty BOCES GED Tchr, Coord 1976-; *ai:* Ski C Sixth Grd Level Chprsn; NEA 1967-; Hornell Tchrs Assn 19 Cncl; Hornell Civic Comm for Yth Rec 1975-, Treas, Prgm Dir; 1956-.

COOGAN, MARY ELLEN, 2nd Grade Teacher; *b:* Yonkers, N St Mary Coll (BA) Eng 1980; SUNY at New Paltz (MS) Elem Ed Sacred Heart Schl 2nd, 3rd Grd Tchr 1980-93; Sacred Heart St Fra 2nd Grd Tchr 1993-; *ai:* NCEA 1980-; Cherish the Ladies T Music & Dance Performing Ensemble 1987-, Musician; Gree Records Recording Artist; *office:* Sacred Heart-St Francis S Robinson Ave Newburgh NY 12550

COOK, ADREN M., English Teacher; *b:* Cleveland, OH; *m:* C. *c:* Mark, Brian, John, Matthew; *ed:* Geneva Coll (BA) Speech Wesleyn MED; *cr:* Greensburg Salem Tchr 1970-; *ai:* Arts Drama Club Spon; PSEA & NEA 1970-.*

COOK, ANNE (DURANTE), Second Grade Teacher; *b:* Brookly Kermie D.; *c:* James D., John M.; *ed:* St Johns Univ (BS) Ed 19 Courses SUNY at Oswego; *cr:* Cuba Hill Schl 4th-5th Grd Tchr Harley Avenue Schl 4th Grd Tchr 1966-67; Pulaski Acad, Cntrl Grd Tchr 1971-; *ai:* Alpha Delta Kappa 1972-, Charter Mem; Rdng Cncl; NYSTRS, Rep; *office:* Pulaski Acad & Cntrl Schl 2 H Pulaski NY 13142

COOK, BARBARA HELMS, Kindergarten Teacher; *b:* Monroe James Bradford; *c:* Steven Bradford, Brian Hartsell; *ed:* Univ of Bus Admin 1963; Attnd Converse Coll Lbrl Arts 1949-51; 30 C Early Chldhd Ed Univ of MD, Univ of DE, Salisbury St Univ; *cr:* Elem Schl Kndgtn Tchr 1966-67; Preston Elem Schl Summer Stdnts Kndgtn Tchr 1975-81; Greensboro Elem Schl Kndgtn Tc *ai:* Schl Improvement Team Kndgtn Rep; Soc Comm; NEA, MST 1967-; Alpha Delta Kappa 1970-, Treas, Pledge Chm, Chaplain; Hlth Svcs Inc 8 Yrs, Bd Mem; Tri-Cty Educl Conf, MD St Bds of Speaker; Nom Tchr of Yr Awd; Caroline Cty PTA Tchr of Yr A *office:* Greensboro Elem Schl 625 N Main St Greensboro MD 21

COOK, BEATRICE R., Spanish Teacher; *b:* Cincinnati, OH; *m:* Jennifer; *ed:* Kent St Univ (BS) Span, Eng 1970; Grad Credit Estudios Iberoamericanos, Xavier Univ, Wright St Univ, Cincinnati; Bowling Green Univ Mentor Trng; *cr:* Little Miami Tchr 1970-; Little Miami Local Schls Elem Span Tchr 1985-95; Club; Span Schlsp Team Coach; OEA, NEA, OFLTA, LMTA 1970- Excl Outstdng Tchr Awd 1991; *office:* Little Miami HS 605 W Morrow OH 45152*

COOK, CAROL A., Director of Curriculum; *b:* Marlborough, N H.; *c:* Heather Graves, Jennifer Colley, Barry, Martin, Denise S Keene St Coll (BE) Elem Ed 1963; Univ of NH (MED) Rdng 197 Dame Coll (MED) Learning, Lang Disability 1980; *cr:* Superv Spec Ed Coord, Trainer for Vols, Curr Design, Rdng Specialist, C Tchr, Supvr of Fac, Grant Writer 1963-80; Learning Svcs U Founder, Adovcate-Assessment Intergration, Curr Planning 1980-85; Learning Skills Acad Founder, Curr Coord, Dir, Staff 1985-; *ai:* Curr Dir; Fields Stud Co-Operative Cncl; Drama, Coach; Applied Comm, Prgm Comm Svc Projects; LDA 1970-, P Sam Kirk Spec Edctr of Yr 1990; Orton Gillingham Soc 1987- 1989-; CHADD 1992-; Portsmouth Chamber of Commerce Taxpayer's Assn 1992-; NH Assn for Partnership in Ed 1990- Information Ctr Outstdng Tchr of Yr 1990; Grants Fuller Fnd 19 Barber Fnd 1985, 1995; Who's Who Among Amer Coll Stdnts 196 Learning Skills Acad 35 Sherburne Rd Portsmouth NH 03801*

COOK, DAVID A., HS History & Bible Teacher; *b:* Pittsburgh, Carol Ann Wireback; *c:* Kristin Lee, David Jeremiah; *ed:* TN Tem (BA) His, Bible & PE 1973; *cr:* FL Chrstn Schl Jr HS Sci & Bi 1974-75; Gold Coast Chrstn Schl Jr HS His & Bible Tchr Heritage Chrstn Schl HS His & Bible Tchr 1979-; *ai:* Var Bsktbl & Coach; Vice Prin; Sr Spon; Past Ath Dir; Chrstn Schls of OH Cleveland Bapt Church 1979-; Deacon & Sunday Schl Tchr Heritage Christian Schl 4403 Tiedeman Rd Cleveland OH 44144

COOK, DEBORAH FERRA, Assistant Principal; *b:* Norwich, Richard H.; *c:* Kevin P., Kerry Cook Edwards; *ed:* Coll of St Jose Elem Ed 1968; Eastern CT St Univ (MA) Rdng 1975; *cr:* Led Schls 2 Grd Tchr 1968-72; John Moriarty Schl 4 Grd Tchr 1976- Tchr 1989-92, 5 Grd Tchr, Vice Prin 1993-; *ai:* Bldg Instrl, Planning, Budget Comm; NEA, CT Ed Assn, Norwich Tchrs Leagu Delta Kappa Gamma 1986-, Sec 1990-92; Crescent Beach Assn 1 of Dirs, VP; VFW Auxiliary 1990-; *office:* John M Moriarty Elem Lawler Ln Norwich CT 06360

COOK, DONALD M., English Dept Chairperson, Tchr; *b:* Nyack, Jane Tanner; *c:* Christopher D.; *ed:* Albany Univ (BA) Eng, Elmira Coll (MS) Eng, Ed 1971; 30 Addl Credit Hrs; *cr:* Horseh Eng Tchr 1968-; Corning Comm Coll Adj Eng Instr 1979-; *ai:* N Schl Site-Based Team; AFT, Horseheads Tchr's Assn 1968- Horseheads HS 401 Fletcher St Horseheads NY 14845*

COOK, ELIZABETH BRUCE, Ninth Grade English Tea Lowville, NY; *m:* Oren Francis; *c:* Catherine P., Cynthia Ackerman G., Anne Frances, Stephen Michael; *ed:* Mohawk Valley Comm C

·ts 1988; Utica Coll of Syracuse Univ (BA) Eng 1990; St Univ of ·tland (MS) Rdng 1995; Univ of NH Writing Prgm 6 Credit Hrs; d Patent MS Sub Stu Tchr 1989-90; Carthage Cntrl Schl Dist Sub ·-90; South Lewis Cntrl Schl 9th Grd Eng Tchr 1990-; *ai:* Rdng Groups; NCTE 1989-; NY St United Tchrs 1990-; Girl Scouts 971-, Ldr; BSA 1975-, Den Mother, Day Camp Dir; *home:* 7188 St Lyons Falls NY 13368*

ANE JANE, Speech & English Teacher; *b:* Dayton, OH; *m:* Roy Sarah; *ed:* Wright St Univ (BS) Speech & Eng Scndry Ed 1976, Ldrshp 1994; Attnd Morehead St Univ; *cr:* Ferguson Jr HS Eng Tchr 1976-; *ai:* Svc Awd Optimist Club & Downtown ptimist Club; *office:* Ferguson Jr HS 2940 Dayton Xenia Rd H 45434

EAN THOMANN, English Teacher; *b:* New Haven, CT; *w:* G. (dec); *c:* Robin, Andrew; *ed:* Western Coll (BA) Rel 1968; Univ (MAT) Eng 1974; Dutchess Comm Coll (AAS) Nrsng 1985; Cmptr His Bard Coll; Lit Criticism SUNY at Albany; *cr:* wn Cntrl Schl Eng Tchr 1974-80; Bard Coll Writing Adj Instr, Ctr Coord, Memoir Writing Instr, Elder Hostel Prgm, Writing -92; Pine Plains Cntrl Schl Eng Tchr 1987-; *ai:* Bldg Level Team ist Level Team Rep; NHS Adv; NCTE 1988-; NYSUT 1987-; dvy Comm to Bd of Ed Chprsn; Mid Level Ed Comm; AIDS Ed m; St John's Church 1975-, Bd of Trustees 1993; *office:* Stissing IS 3731 State Route 199 Pine Plains NY 12567*

AREN ATWOOD, First Grade Teacher; *b:* Waterville, ME; *m:* ; *c:* Brittany, Samuel; *ed:* Univ of ME at Orono (BS) Child Dev Grad Courses in Childrens Lit; *cr:* Central St Schl 1st Grd Tchr 2nd Grd Tchr 1982-83; Rockport Elem Schl 1st Grd Tchr Pre-1st Grd Tchr 1986-87; Boothbay Region Elem Schl 2nd Grd -94, 1st Grd Tchr 1994-; *ai:* Discipline, Soc Stud Curr Comms; Lang Arts Dev; NEA 1978-; BREA 1993-, Mem; Early Chldhd 86; *office:* Boothbay Region Elem Schl 156B Townsend Ave ME 04856*

KATHLEEN DOYLE, Art & Interdisciplinary Tchr; *b:* Long NJ; *ed:* SUNY at New Paltz (BS) Art Ed 1971; Lake Shore Tchrs 1967; *cr:* Ouden Schl Tchr 1967-69; St James Tchr 1969-71; HS Tchr 1972-; *ai:* Art Club; NEA, MTA 1972-; *office:* Andover sheen Rd Andover MA 01810*

KENNETH E., Religion & Social Studies Tchr; *b:* Fulton, NY; le Univ (BA) His, Ed 1962; (MA) Theology 1964; Rel Ed 35 Hrs; Mary at Winona, Coll of Santa Fe; *cr:* West Cath Boys Schl Tchr La Salle Coll HS Tchr 1970-71; Trinity HS Tchr 1971-73; op Carroll HS Tchr 1973-78; West Cath Boys Schl Tchr 1978-86; HS Tchr 1986-; *ai:* NCEA 1964-; Philadelphia Human Relations hdiocese of Philadelphia 25 Yr Tchng Awd.

LEAH HUTTEN, Computer Science Teacher; *b:* Schenectady, Marvin F.; *ed:* U of WI (BA) Psych 1968; U of MA (EDD) Rsrch ement 1981; Tchr Cert Scndry Level Math Boston U 1990; *cr:* Coll Instr Computing Coord 1979-80; Tufts Univ Dir of Analytic -84; Natl Ctr Higher Ed Mngmt Sr Rsrch Assoc 1985-86; The useum Exhibit Developer 1987; Boston Latin Acad Cmptr Sci -; *ai:* Cmptr Club Adv; Former Jrnlsm Club, Jr Class, Scrabble ; Phi Delta Kappa 1990-, Newsletter Ed; Intnl Soc for Tech in Ed, f Tech in Ed 1991-; AFT 1988-; Arsenal Park Condominiums Treas; Mellon Grant 1991; 6 Publications; Presentations at Amer rch Assn, Assn for Institutional Rsrch, EDUCOM, Natl Educl onf, MA Cmptr using Edctrs; *office:* Boston Latin Acad 205 St Boston MA 02121

INDA G., Second Grade Teacher; *b:* Clarks Mills, PA; *m:* David vid B., Aaron D.; *ed:* Edinboro St Univ (BS) Elem & Special Ed Credits Special Ed Masters Prgm; 6 Intermed Unit Credits; *cr:* y Spec Ed Elem Tchr 1967-70; West Middlesex Special Ed Scndry 2-73; Com Perry Special Ed Elem Tchr 1973-75, 2nd Grd Tchr Generations Together Prgm; CPEA 1973-, Pres 1975; United TA; PFA Spokesman for Ag in Classroom; *home:* 47 Tripplewood r PA 16137*

MARIANNE, 4th-5th Grade Teacher; *b:* E St Louis, IL; *ed:* Univ rgh (BS) Ed 1970; *cr:* Our Lady of Grace Schl 4th-8th Grd Tchr Rel Moderator; Liturgy Coord; NCEA 1967-; Natl Pastoral s 1980-; Music Minister 1967-; Choir Dir 1972-; Outstdng Elem Amer 1975; *office:* Our Lady Of Grace Schl 1734 Bower Hill Rd h PA 15243

MARY ANN FARINA, Third Grade Teacher; *b:* Plainfield, NJ; *m:* *ed:* Keane Coll (BA) Elem Ed 1962; Rowan Coll (MA) Admin, on 1979; Addl 6 Credit Hrs; *cr:* Plainfield Schl Dist Second, Tchr 1962-71; Upper Twp Schl Dist Tchr, Prgm Coord 1971-81; f Ed Schl Prgm Coord, Cty Supts Office 1981-82; Upper Twp Schl ond, Third Grd Tchr 1982-; *ai:* Lang Arts, Scheduling Comm; EA 1962-; Upper Twp Tchrs Assn 1971-, Sec, VP; Cape Educl 1-, Sec; Upper Twp PTA 1971-; Instituted Upper Twp Comm Ed; 's Awd Outstdng Tchr; Div Chprsn United Way Campaign; *office:* vp Schl Dist 50 Old Tuckahoe Rd Marmora NJ 08223*

NANCY M., Hotel & Restaurant Mgmt Instr; *b:* Buffalo, NY; *ed:* Coll (AAS) Hotel & Restaurant Mgmt 1991; Cambridge Coll Ed 1992; St Univ of NY at Albany Bus 1972-74; Certified ty Educator by Educl Inst of AH&MA; *cr:* Holiday Inn Randolph ffice Mgr 1984; Ritz-Carlton Front Office Mgr & Exec Asst eper 1984-87; Appleton Inn General Asst Mgr 1987-88; Newbury r 1988-; *ai:* Fac Dev Comm Chprsn; Acad Stans & Curr Comms; roup on Acad Resource Ctr; NECHRIE 1989-, Bd of Dirs; or Ethics in Hospitality Mgmt A Book of Rdngs; *office:* Newbury Fisher Ave Brookline MA 02146*

ROBERT W., Physical Education Teacher; *b:* Camden, NJ; *m:* *ed:* Morgan St Univ (BS) PE 1966; Rowan St Coll (MA) Schl 975; Chrstn Cnslng, Educl Fnd Philadelphia Coll of Bible; *cr:* rt Elem Schl PE Tchr 1967-, Prins Designee 1975-; *ai:* HS Aths onal Speaker; Phi Delta Kappa 1975-; NJEA, NEA 1966-; PTO overnors Recognition Tchr of Yr 1989; Hall of Fame HS Aths *ice:* Hainesport Elem Schl 211 Broad St Hainesport NJ 08036

ROBIN LAVERNE, Principal; *b:* Washington, DC; *ed:* Univ of Scndry Math Ed 1984, (MS) Math Ed 1987; *cr:* Holy Temple cad Tchr 1983-92, Head Tchr 1992-95, Prin 1995-; Univ of DC Math Dept 1984-; *ai:* Yth Choir Adv; Yth Praise Team Coord; Yth Tchr of the Yr 1986 & 1987; Outstndg Svc Awd 1993-94; *office:* nple Christian Acad 439 12th St SE Washington DC 20003*

RONALEE A., English Teacher; *b:* Johnstown, PA; *c:* Kathleen; cuse Univ (BS) Sci 1965, (MA) Eng Ed 1979; 43 Addl Grad Hrs d, Cmptr, Hlth; Attnd SUNY at Cortland; *cr:* Jamesville DeWitt 1967; Onondaga Eng Tchr 1968-; *ai:* Grievance Chm Assn; Advy NEA 1970-; NYSUT 1974-, VP; Kappa Delta 1965-; NCTE 1968-; ague; Womens Bowling Congress; Scuba Intnl; *office:* Onondaga 4479 S Onondaga Rd Nedrow NY 13120*

TED, Visual Arts Teacher; *b:* Spring Lake, NJ; *m:* Kathleen *c:* JOshua; *ed:* Univ of South FL (BA) Fine Arts 1969, (MA) Art ; 30 Post Grad Hrs Rutgers Univ, PA Acad Fine Arts, USF; Visual Arts, Photography, Ceramics, Supervisory Certs; *cr:* Cherry Hill HS East Art Dept Chm 1984-86; Rutgers Univ Photography Prof 1988; Camden Co Coll Photography Prof 1989; Haddonfield Meml HS Art, Digital Photography Tchr; *ai:* Art, Lit Magazine, NAHS, Teen Arts Adv; Performing, Visua Arts Soc Adv, Acting Dir; NEA 1974-; NAEA, NJAEA 1992-; Medford Bus Assn 1990-; ATT Tech in Classroom Awd 1996; Fac Show Rutgers Univ; Amer Crafts Cncl Shows 10, 11; USF Permanent Collection; USF One Man Show, Work Reviewed in Magainzes; *office:* Haddonfield Memorial HS 401 Kings Hwy E Haddonfield NJ 08033

COOK, TERRI-LEE MORRIS, Art Teacher; *b:* Philadelphia, PA; *m:* William A.; *ed:* Bucks Cty Comm Coll (AA) Art 1983; Temple Univ (BFA) Art 1989; *cr:* Downintown Area Schl Dist Art Tchr 1993-; *ai:* Fine Art Sculptor; Exhibitor Yellow Springs Art Stud Of Chester Cty PA; US Patent Holder #5167586 Issued December 1 1992; Restore Antique Carousel Animals Carved by Grandfather E Joy Morris C 1895-1906; *home:* PO Box 786 Philadelphia PA 19105

COOKE, CYNTHIA LOU, High School English Teacher; *b:* Kansas City, MO; *m:* Tom Schaefer; *c:* Jennifer Bryant, Kelly Schaefer; *ed:* OH Univ (BS) Ed, Eng 1975; Univ of Dayton (MS) Scndry Ed 1988; Attnd Univ of East Anglia in Norwich 1973-74; *cr:* Studebaker Jr HS Eng Tchr 1975-86; Wayne HS Eng Tchr 1986-; *ai:* NEA, OEA, HHEA, NCTE 1975-; Christ Epsicopal Church 1981-, Vestry Mem; Tchr of Yr 1977; *home:* 5565 Short Rd New Carlisle OH 45344

COOKE, DIANE O'BRIEN, Instructor of Nursing; *b:* Kingston, NY; *m:* John A. Jr.; *ed:* Ulster Cty Comm Coll (AS) Lbrl Arts 1974; Mt St Marys Coll (BSN) Nrsng 1980; NY Univ (MA) Nrsng Ed 1982; Benedictine Hosp Schl of Nrsng Diploma 1967; *ai:* Sigma Theta Tau 1980-; NYS Nurses Assn; *office:* Ulster County Comm Coll Stone Ridge NY 12484

COOKE, EDWARD JAMES, Mathematics Dept Chairman; *b:* Middlebury, VT; *c:* Maria, Sara; *ed:* Dartmouth Coll (BA) Math 1973; 30 Addl Hrs; *cr:* Woodstock Elem Schl 4th Grd Tchr 1973-75; Hudson Meml Schl 5th Grd Tchr 1976-77; Alvirne HS Math Tchr 1978-81; Hartford HS Math Dept Chm 1981-; *ai:* Golf Coach; Jr Class Adv; *office:* Hartford HS 28 Highland Ave White River Juncti VT 05001

COOKE, ELIZABETH PATRICIA, Business Teacher; *b:* Brooklyn, NY; *ed:* Baroch Coll (BSEd) Bus Ed 1993; Working on MSED Bus Ed; *cr:* NY Life Insurance Co File Clerk 1988-91; Marian Polovy Esquire Legal Asst 1991-93; Sarah J Hale HS Bus Tchr 1993-; *ai:* FBLA Adv; BEA; BTA; *home:* 507 Lenox Rd Brooklyn NY 11203

COOKE, PATRICIA FENNELLY, Science Teacher; *b:* Point Pleasant, NJ; *m:* Peter; *c:* Peter Jr., Shaun; *ed:* Rutgers Coll (BA) Psych, Bio 1984; Georgian Court Coll, Post Grad Stud Ed; *cr:* Brick Twp HS Sci Tchr 1986-; *ai:* CORE Team; NEA 1986-; *office:* Brick Township HS 346 Chambersbridge Rd Brick NJ 08723*

COOKE, RALPH CHARLES, Comm, Eng & TV Production Tchr; *b:* Glenn Ridge, NJ; *m:* Kathleen S.; *c:* Lucas E., Ana Leigh; *ed:* Alfred Univ (BA) Eng 1971; Universidad Autonoma de Madrid(Maestro) ESL 1974; William Paterson Coll (MA) Comm 1989; 30 Addl Hrs in Effective Tchng, Comm, Directing, Mngmt, Creative Writing, Tchng Rdng; *cr:* Alfred Univ Tchng Asst 1970-71; Tupper Lake HS Tchr 1971-73; Ctr of Modern Langs Tchr, ESL Supvr 1973-75; West Milford Twp HS Eng, Comm Tchr 1975-; *ai:* Directing & Producing Plays, Musicals 8 Yrs; Adv Highland News Team 14 Yrs; Dir Dist Television Production; NEA, WMEA 1975-, Rep; NJ Television Educators Consortium 1989-, Passaic Co Chm; NJ Cable Users Assn 1991-; Assn of Prof Videographers; Cable Franchise Comm 1992-, Rep; Passaic Co Tech Comm, West Milford Tech Comm 1993-; Vernon Little League 1984-, Coach; Pub Svc Awd Cable in Classroom TKR Cable Co, Distributive Ed Clubs of Amer; NJ Teen Arts Festival Excl in Production; Passaic Cty Nom for Outstanding Classroom Practices; *office:* West Milford Township HS 67 Highlander Dr West Milford NJ 07480

COOKE, SUSAN LIVERMORE, Computer & Technology Teacher; *b:* Utica, NY; *c:* Holly Cooke Sellers, Sarah, Amy; *ed:* SUNY at Morrisville (AAS) Secretarial Sci 1976; SUNY at Oswego (BA) Voc-Tech Ed & Bus & Dist 1985, (MS) Voc-Tech Ed & Bus & Dist 1988; SUNY at Utica Post Grad; MUCC Courses in Tech; *cr:* Waterville Cntrl Schl Comp & Tech Tchr 1 Yr, Bus Tchr 9 Yrs; Madison Cntrl Schl Bus Tchr 1 Yr; *ai:* Tech Comm Chprsn; Jr Class Adv; NYSUT & AFT 1985-; Waterville Tchrs Assn 1986-; Sports Boosters; *office:* Waterville Cntrl Schl Madison St Waterville NY 13480*

COOK-HUFFMAN, DANIEL JAY, Adj Instr, Sociology & Pol Sci; *b:* Wabash, IN; *m:* Celia B.; *ed:* Manchester Coll (BA) Peace & Conflict Sutd 1986; Maxwell Schl of Citizenship & Pub Affairs at Syracuse Univ (MA) Pol Sci 1991; PHD Coursework Completed; *cr:* Colgate Univ Adj Lecturer Sociology, Peace Stud 1991; Juniata Coll Adj Instr Sociology 1992-93; Penn St Univ Adj Instr Sociology, Peace, Conflict Sutd 1991, 1995-; St Francis Coll Adj Instr of Sociology, Pol Sci 1992-; *ai:* Consortium on Peace Rsrch 1989-; Intnl Stud Assn 1991-; Borough of Huntington PA 1994-, Shade Tree Commissioner; Huntington Revitalization Dev & Industry 1994-, Appearance Comm; Articles Pub; *office:* Saint Francis Coll Dept Of Political Science Loretto PA 15940

COOLEY, ANN KELLY, Fifth Grade Teacher; *b:* Flushing, NY; *m:* Robert F.; *c:* Erin, James; *ed:* St Univ of NY at Oswego (BS) Elem Ed 1966; Queens Coll (MS) Pol Sci 1970; *cr:* Burnt Hills-Ballston Lake Schls Tchr 1966-; *ai:* Hlth & Personal Dev Curr Chprsn; AFT, NYSUT 1966-; Saratoga Springs Figure Skating Club 1985-, Pres, VP; Saratoga Winter Club 1987-, VP, Sec; NY St PTA Fellowship Awd; *office:* Burnt Hills-Ballston Lake Schl 50 Cypress Dr Scotia NY 12302

COOLEY, CHERYL LYNNE, Title I Teacher; *b:* Kenton, OH; *c:* Eric D., Craig A., Shawn L.; *ed:* OH Northern Univ (BSEd) Elem Ed 1965; Univ of Dayton (MSEd) Lit & Whole Lang 1993; Rdng Recovery Cert OH St Univ 1989; Attnd Ashland Univ, Drake Univ; *cr:* North Union Schls Third Grd Tchr 1965-67, Kndgtn Tchr 1967-1968, 1983-84, Second Grd Tchr 1984-89, Title I Tchr 1970-77, 1989-, Rdng Recovery Tchr 1989-; *ai:* NEA, OH Ed Assn, North Union Ed Assn 1965-; Tri-Rivers Voc Advy Bd; United Meth Church; Master's Thesis; *office:* North Union Schl Dist 401 N Franklin St Richwood OH 43344

COOLEY, PATTY LYNN, 5th-12th Grade Art Teacher; *b:* Youngstown, OH; *m:* Roger; *c:* Seth, Sara; *ed:* Youngstown St Univ (BS) Art Ed 1964, (MS) Scndry Curr 1996; *cr:* Western Reserve Schl Art Tchr 1964-65; South Range Schl Art Tchr 1965-70; Austintown Schl Art Tchr 1986-87; Crestview Schl Art Tchr 1988-; *ai:* Art Club Adv; OEA, NEA 1988-; OAEA 1993-; Scholastic Arts Exec Comm 1990-95; *office:* Crestview H S 44100 Crestview Rd Columbiana OH 44408

COOLEY, ROBERT JACOBS, English, Greek & Latin Tchr; *b:* Oberlin, OH; *m:* Vera Parry; *c:* Karin Melissa, Jessie Eleanor, Ryan Thomas; *ed:* Miami Univ of OH (BA) Classics-With Honors 1973; Antioch New England (MED) Org & Mgmt 1985; Bard Coll Narrating, Essay, Poetry & Fiction Courses; Univ of MA at Amherst Amer Stud; Amer Schl of Classical Stud at Athens Greece Stud in Classical Greek Lit, Art, Archaeology & His; *cr:* Northfield Mount Hermon Schl Classics Tchr 1973-, Head of Dorm 1978-85, Campus Dean 1987-88; Eng Tchr 1987-, Summer Schl Ath Dir 1990-93, Upward Bound Writing & Lit Tchr 1992-; Antioch New England Grad Schl; Nais Diversity Inst; *ai:* Lacrosse Coach 1974-82; Wrestling Coach 1974-84; Ftbl Coach 1988-91; Cross Cntry Coach 1992-; Stu Govt & Multi Cultural Stdnts Group Adv; Diversity Wkshps Facilitator; Seeking Equity & Educl Diversity Seminar for Tchrs; NCTE 1989-91; *home:* 23 Winchester Rd Northfield MA 01360*

COOLEY, SANDRA ELIZABETH, General Science & Geology Tchr; *b:* York, PA; *m:* William Clayton; *c:* Jason, Laura; *ed:* West Chester Univ (BS) Bio & Ed 1965, (MED) Ed 1970; 45 Post-Grad Credits; *cr:* Baltimore Cty MD Schls Bio Tchr 1967-69; Susquehannock Sr HS Bio, Chem & Earth Sci Tchr 1972-73; West York Jr HS 8th Grd Sci Tchr 1973-74; Red Lion Area Sr HS General Sci & Geology Tchr 1976-; *ai:* Envirothon Club Adv; Envirothon Team Coach; NEA 1965-; NSTA 1980-; Natl Wildlife Fed 1985-; York Cty Parks & Recreation Bd 1990-, VP, Pres, Sec; Outstanding Earth Sci Tchr; Environmental Educator Awd; Outstanding Tchr & Shippensburg Univ Lecturer; Outstanding Achvmt in Field of Conservation & Ecology Twice; WGAL Earth Angel; Coached Winners of Natl Envirothon; *office:* Red Lion Area Sr HS 200 Horace Mann Ave Red Lion PA 17356

COOLEY, SHIRLEY SCOTT, Assistant Professor of Nursing; *b:* Columbus, OH; *m:* Gale Allen; *c:* Isaac, Jonathan; *ed:* the OH St Univ (BSN) Nrsng 1973; the Cath Univ of Amer (MSN) Maternal & Newborn Nrsng 1978; Working on PHD in Nrsng; *cr:* GA St Univ Nrsng Instr 1978-80; Howard Univ Nrsng Inst 1981-85; The OH St Univ Nrsng Instr 1985-86; Mt Carmel Coll of Nrsng Asst Prof of Nrsng 1990-; *ai:* Sigma Theta Tau 1978-; Amer Nurses Assn Minority Flwshp; *office:* Mt Carmel Coll Of Nrsng 127 S Davis Ave Columbus OH 43222*

COOLIDGE, CLINTON A., Mathematics Teacher; *b:* Alexandria Bay, NY; *m:* Kathleen M. Ryan; *c:* Zachary, Bridget; *ed:* St Univ of Oswego (BS) Scndry Ed 1970; Addl Hrs Ed, Math; ST Univ of Potsdam Cmptr Grad Course 1995; *cr:* Indian River HS Scndry Math Tchr 1970-; Jefferson Comm Coll Part-Time Coll Algebra Instr 1993-; *ai:* Bldg Compact Team; NYSUT, AMTNYS 1970-, Exec Cnsl; Theresa Town Bd 1983-91; *office:* Indian River Central H S Rt 11 Philadelphia NY 13673

COOLIDGE, RICHARD F., Lead Social Studies Teacher; *b:* Springfield, MA; *m:* Marjorie R. Spurr; *c:* Brian, Scott, Andrew; *ed:* Northeastern Univ (BS) Ed, Soc Stud 1969; Salem St Coll (MA) US His 1975; *cr:* Breed Jr HS Tchr 1969-, Lead Tchr Soc Stud 1994-; *ai:* Various Curr Stud Comm; Oversee Audio Visual Dept; Annual Ski Trip; AFT, MA Fed Tchrs 1969-; Prof Ski Instr of Amer 1994-; Troop 51 BSA 1984-, Scout Comm Chm; Georgetown MA Historial Comm 1978-83; *office:* Breed Jr HS 90 O'Callaghan Way Lynn MA 01905*

COOLIDGE, ROBERT M., English Teacher; *b:* Springfield, MA; *m:* Betty O'Brien; *c:* Christopher, Rebecca; *ed:* North Adams St Coll (BSEd) Eng, Ed 1965; Salem St Coll (MAT) Eng 1970; Attnd Boston Univ, Plymouthy St Coll; *cr:* Pinkerton Acad Eng Tchr 1965-70; Kingswood Regnl HS Eng Tchr 1970-; Educl Testing Svc Test Supvr 1976-; *ai:* Stdnt Cncl, NHS Adv; NCTE 1990-; NHATE 1979-, Treas, Exec Bd Mem; GWEA, NHEA, NEA 1970-; 1st Congregational Church, Deacon; Eng Dept Chair 1978-95; *office:* Kingswood Regional HS 396 S Main St Wolfeboro NH 03894

COON, BARBARA RIGGLE, Second Grade Teacher; *b:* Mansfield, OH; *m:* Jerrold J.; *c:* Julianne; *ed:* OH St Univ (BS) Ed 1972; Ashland Univ (MA) Curr, Instruction 1990; LaVerne Coll 15 Hrs; *cr:* Madison Local Schls Elem Tchr 1969-, Math Dept Chprsn 1973-78; Mansfield Cty Schls Adult Ed Tchr 1981-84; Madison HS Adult Ed Tchr 1983; *ai:* Family Math Night Co-Chprsn; Picture Lady Prgm Spon; NEA, OEA 1969-; Chrstn Day Schl Bd 1991-; Friends of OH St Univ Mansfield 1994-; Tchrs Amer Enterprise OH Cncl Ec Ed Awd; Madison Local Schls Fac Awd; *office:* Wooster Heights Schl 1419 Grace St Mansfield OH 44905*

COON, NANCY RAUSCHMEIER, 4th Grade Teacher; *b:* Binghamton, NY; *c:* Derek, Stacy; *ed:* SUC at Cortland (BA) Elem Ed 1972; SUNY at Binghamton Harpur Coll (MA) Elem Ed 1977; *cr:* Cedarhurst Elem Schl 4th Grd Tchr 1973-; *ai:* Elem Curr Cncl; NEA 1973-; *office:* Cedarhurst Elem Schl 1605 NY Rt 11 Kirkwood NY 13795

COON, WILLIAM AARON, Guidance Counselor; *b:* Clairton, PA; *m:* Yvonne Marie Moragne; *c:* William, Keith, Diedrin, Stephen and Eric Johnson; *ed:* Westminster Coll (BS) Behavorial Sci 1979; Cntrl MI (MA) Bus, Prsnl Mgmt 1981; Bowie St Univ (MED) Spec Ed 1986; Psychotherapy Cert 1995; Guid, Cnslng 36 Credit Hrs; Cert Asst Aerospace Sci Instr; Grad of Dept of Defense Race Relations Inst; *cr:* USAF Flight Engr 1966-68, Career Develp, Proficency Tng 1969-71, Human Relations Instr 1971-83; E. Roosevelt HS Asst Aerospace Sci Instr 1983-94, Guid Cnslr 1994-; *ai:* Tchrs Advy Comm Chm 1987-90; Prince George Comm Coll Part-time Fac Instr 1981-; USDA Grad Schl Part-time Instr 1990-; NEA 1983-.

COONEY, ANITA GLACY, English Teacher; *b:* Queens, NY; *m:* Hank; *c:* Sean, Kevin; *ed:* Saint Johns Univ (BA) Eng 1966, (MS) Ed 1971; *cr:* Calhoun HS Eng Tchr 1967-74; Merrick Ave Jr HS Eng Tchr 1976-77; Grand Ave Jr HS Eng Tchr 1979-; *ai:* Girls Cross Cntry & Track Coach; Grand Ave Parent Tchr Stu Assn Honorary Life Membership; *office:* Grand Ave Jr HS 2301 Grand Ave Bellmore NY 11710

COONEY, CHARLENE D'AGOSTINO, Former English Dept Chair; *b:* Brooklyn, NY; *m:* Robert J. Sr.; *c:* Robert Jr., Stephen; *ed:* STAC (BA) Eng 1977; CUNY (MS) Ed, Rdng 1985; *cr:* Fontbonne Hall Acad Eng Dept Chprsn 1982-94; *ai:* IRA; NCTE; PPODS 1994-; PODS 1995-.

COONEY, FRIEDA DIGIORGIO, Home Ec & Health Educator; *b:* Trenton, NJ; *m:* William J. Jr; *c:* Natalie, William, Veronica; *ed:* Drexel Univ (BS) Home Ec, Human Behavior & Dev 1973; 28 Hrs Spec Ed; 15 Hrs Cert Hlth Ed; 18 Hrs Home Ec, Gen; *cr:* Howell Twp Schls Home Ec Tchr 1974; Berkeley Cty Schls Spec Ed Tchr 1975; Clinton Cty Schls Spec Ed Tchr 1976; Mont Cty Schls Spec Ed Tchr 1976; Bldg Blocks Day Care Ctr Owner, Dir 1977-84; Montgomery Cty Schls Home Ec Tchr 1986-; *ai:* Teen Pregnancy Support; Hlth Ed Curr Dev; Stop Teen Pregnancy Club Adv; NEA, MCEA 1985-; Cert Home Economist 1987-; 4-H 1992-, Ldr, Club Founder; St Nutrition Curr Awd 1995; Alternative Curr Author, Hlth Ed 1995; Home Ec Tchr of Yr 1992; *office:* Richard Montgomery HS 250 Richard Montgomery Dr Rockville MD 20852

COONEY, JAMES HENRY, 5th Grade Teacher; *b:* Worcester, MA; *m:* Paula Jean Stringer; *c:* Garrett, Megan, Trevor; *ed:* Worcester St Coll (BS) Ed 1961, (MED) Ed 1968; 12 Credit Hrs; 3 Credit Hrs Anna Maria Coll; *cr:* Allen L. Joslin Fifth Grd Tchr 1961-64; Woodward Schl Sixth Grd Tchr Head Tchr 1965-70; Clara Barton Schl Asst Prin, Fifth Grd Tchr 1970-80; Alfred Chaffee Schl Asst Prin, Fifth Grd Tchr 1981-87; Allen L. Joslin Schl Asst Prin, Fifth Grd Tchr 1988-93, Fifth Grd Tchr 1994-; *ai:* Dimensions of Learing Comm; NEA 1961-; Oxford Ed Assn 1961-, Bd of Dirs; NESPA; Amer Legion 1990-; Experiment, Use of Cmptrs With Gray's Meth of Dev Writing Skills.

COONEY, JOANNE, English Teacher; *b:* New York, NY; *m:* James; *c:* Brendan, Christopher, Megan; *ed:* The Cath Univ of Amer (BA) Eng 1971, (MA) Cnslng 1974; To Complete MA Eng; Supvrs Cert 1995; *cr:* The Cath Univ of Amer Assoc Dir Admissions 1971-74; Adelphi Univ Assoc Dir Admissions 1974-75; Ridgefield Park HS Eng Thcr 1983-89; Fair Lawn HS Eng Tchr 1989-; *ai:* Adv Interact Club, Shakespeare Troupe; NEA, NJEA 1983-; *office:* Fair Lawn HS 14-00 Berdan Ave Fair Lawn NJ 07410

COONLEY, DON E., Dir of Comm Stud & Prof of Hum; *b:* Grand Island, NE; *m:* Nancy Serrell; *c:* Whitney Serrell, David Serrell; *ed:* Stetson Univ (BA) Eng 1964; Univ of South FL (MA) Eng 1969; Univ of MI Doctors of Arts Eng 1972; *cr:* Sacred Heart Univ Chair, Prof of Media Stud 1973-89;

Colby-Sawyer Coll Comm Stud Dir 1989-; *ai:* Multiple Comms; WSCS-FM Radio Weekly Discussion Prgm Host; Univ Film, Video Assn 1989-; NH Hum Cncl, Media Advy Comm; NH Pub Radio, Comm Advy Bd; 2 Nature Conservation Groups; 2 Tchng Excl Awds 1992-94; Natl Educl Film, Video Festival Bronze Apple 1993; Best Locally Produced Drama Corp for Pub Broadcasting Awd 1981; Regnl Emmy Noms 2 in 1992, 2 in 1981; Cncl for Intnl Non-Theatrical Events Golden Eagle 1980; *office:* Colby Sawyer Coll 100 Main St New London NH 03257*

COONS, ADRIENNE, Associate Professor of Biology; *b:* Philadelphia, PA; *m:* Thomas; *ed:* Rutgers Univ (BS) Nrsng 1975; Univ of PA (MSN) Nrsng 1980; Rutgers Univ (EDD) Ed 1986; *cr:* Camden Cty Coll Nrsng Coord 1980-82, Asst Dean of Sci, Allied Hlth 1982-87, Dean of Sci, Allied Hlth 1987-94, Assoc Prof of Bio 1994-; *ai:* Acad Affairs, Safety, Mid Sts Steering Comms; Friends of the Fnd; NEA 1994-; Soc of Allied Hlth Professions Charter, Mem; NJ Pub Hlth Licensing Bd 1989-94; Our Lady of Lourdes Schl of Nrsng 1987-94, Bd of Trustees; Camden Cty Commission on Women 1993-94, Women Who Have Made a Difference; Prof Svc Awd Univ of Med & Dentistry of NJ; *office:* Camden County Coll PO Box 200 Blackwood NJ 08012

COONS, KARIN HOERUP, 6th Grade Resource Room Tchr; *b:* Yonkers, NY; *m:* Thomas J.; *c:* Seamus, Michaela; *ed:* Mercy Coll (BS) Psych & Spcl Ed 1986; Univ of CT (MS) Adolescent Ed 1990; Mulitple Intelligences; Learning Styles; Dimensions of Learning; Authentic Assessment; Math their Way of Thinking; *cr:* PVC MS Croton Self Contained Spcl Ed Tchr 1987-91, 6th Grd Sci Tchr 1990-92, Resource Room Tchr 1991-; *ai:* 6th Grd Team Ldr; Critical Friend Group Mem; Tech & Ldrshp Comm; Sftbl Coach; AFT 1986-; CTA 1987-, BTF Ofcr; Taught Classes to Other Edctrs at BOCES Northern Westchester; *office:* Pierre Van Cortlandt Schl Larkin Pl Croton On Hudsn NY 10521*

COOPER, ALANA GAIL (WARTELL), Sixth Grade Teacher; *b:* Malden, MA; *c:* Jennifer Lyn, Jonathan Lee; *ed:* St Coll at Boston (BS) Elem Ed 1967, (MED) Elem Ed 1972; In-Svc Credits at Lincoln-Filene Ctr of Tufts; *cr:* Belmont Schl 4th Grd Tchr 1966-68; Elem Schls Tchr of Learning Disabilities 1968-69; Salemwood Schl 6th Grd Tchr 1977-81; Browne Jr HS 6th Grd Tchr 1981-82; Maplewood Schl 6th Grd Tchr 1982-88; Browne MS Eng Tchr 1988-90; Linden Schl 6th Grd Tchr 1990-; *ai:* Cncl Mem; NEA, MA Tchrs Assn 1966-; NCTE 1989-; Temple Tifereth Israel 1979-, Youth Commission, Bd Mem 1986-88; Agudas Achim Sisterhood 1969-; Grant to Attend Summer Inst for Learning Disabilities at Boston Coll to Start Prgm in Malden MA 1968; 6th Grd Cluster Ldr 1988-90; Maldens Lang Arts Curr Frameworks Stud Group 1994-95; Eng Curr Comm 1988-89; Report Card Comm 1979-80; *office:* Linden Elem Schl 29 Wescott St Malden MA 02148

COOPER, ARVELA ODD, Art Education Teacher; *b:* Philadelphia, PA; *w:* James Arthur Sr. (dec); *c:* James A., Karima A.; *ed:* Phila Museum Coll of Art (BFA) Art Ed 1965; Antioch Univ (MA) Admin 1986; Cheyney St Univ Elem Prin Cert 1987; Attnd Penn St Univ, Tyler Temple Schl of Art, Marwygod Coll, Temple Univ Schl of Ed; *cr:* Schl Dist of Phila Elem Art Ed Tchr 1965-93: Wharton Rec Ctr 1965-70; Messiah Coll Facilitator, Wkshp Ldr, Art Consultant 1973; Antioch Univ Facilitator, Wkshp Ldr, Art Consultant 1988; Schl Dist of Phila Multicultural Arts Inservice Instr for Tchr 1992-, Acting Art Supvr NW, SW Regions of Phila 1993-94, MS Art Ed Tchr 1994-; *ai:* Artistically Talented Club Spon; Bldg Rep; Facilitator Mem Arts Empower Team; Coord Arts In Ed Inst; Stu Tchr Trng Prgm, Mentor Beaver Coll, Temple & Moore Coll of Art; Phila Fed of Tchrs 1968-, Bldg Rep 1995; Women in Ed 1994-, Art Ed, Ad Book Chprsn; Minority Arts Resource Cncl 1986-, Co-Founder; Alpha Kappa Alpha 1988-; Arts Consultant, Global Affairs Mem; 2nd Place North Atlantic Regnl Display; Gwynedd Mercy Coll 1990 Advy Bd; Parent Rep Stu Welfare Cncl 1988-; Arts in Ed Flwshp Finalist 1993; Tcher of Yr Celebration Excl Semi-Finalist 1992; Women in Ed Awd 1991; PA St House of Rep Excl Tchng Svc to Young 1991; City Cncl Phila Citation 1991; Numerous Awds Prof Art Work; *home:* 6701 Crittenden St Philadelphia PA 19119

COOPER, BARBARA ANN (YONEK), Fifth Grade Teacher; *b:* Leechburg, PA; *m:* Michael C.; *ed:* Slippery Rock Univ (BS) Elem Ed 1973; Penn St Univ, Masters Equivalency; *cr:* Our Lady of Lourdes Schl First Grd Tchr 1974-90, Fifth Grd Tchr 1991-; *ai:* SAP Team; NCEA; Historical Soc Western PA; *office:* Our Lady Of Lourdes Schl 620 S Main St Burgettstown PA 15021

COOPER, CECELIA CHESLEY, Consulting Teacher; *b:* Baltimore, MD; *m:* Tancil; *c:* Traci (dec), Treya; *ed:* Coppin St Coll (BS) Elem Ed 1964; Advanced Prof Degree; *cr:* Mildred Monroe Elem Schl Classroom Tchr 1964-; Towson St Univ Tchr Consultant 1988-; Mildred Monroe Elem Schl Consulting Tchr 1995-; *ai:* Spec Events Comm, Self Esteem Team Coord; Schl Improvement Team; Par Schl Rep; AFT 1988-; Mt Ararat Bapt Church 1991-, Bd of Chrstn Ed; Outstdng Tchr Awd 1989; *office:* Mildred D. Monroe Elem Schl 1634 Guilford Ave Baltimore MD 21202

COOPER, CHARLES C., English Teacher; *b:* Brooklyn, NY; *m:* Marjorie L.; *c:* Amy; *ed:* Dowling Coll (BA) Eng 1968; Adelphi Univ (MA) Eng 1975; Addl 75 Credits; *cr:* Bellport HS Eng Tchr 1970-78, Eng Dept Chprsn 1978-94, Eng Tchr 1994-; *ai:* Script Writer, Dir for Annual Variety Show; NCTE 1980-; *office:* Bellport HS Beaver Dam Rd Brookhaven NY 11719

COOPER, DALE E., Physics Professor; *b:* Red Lion, PA; *m:* Harriet J. Godfrey; *c:* George L.; *ed:* Millersville (BS) Phys Sci 1961; Temple Univ (MS) Sci Ed 1965; 70 Grad Hrs ABD PE; *cr:* Hempfield HS Physics Instr 1961-64; Temple Univ Tchg Fellow 1965-68; Lockhaven Univ Assoc Prof 1968-; *ai:* Lock Haven Univ Assessment Comm; AAPT; Amer Solar Energy Soc 5 Yrs; Assn of PA St Coll & Univ Fac 24 Yrs; Clinton Cty Solid Waster Authority 1970-; Lockhaven Area Flood Protection Project 1985-, Chm; NSF Inst 1964-65; *office:* Lock Haven Univ Dept Of Hpe Lock Haven PA 17745*

COOPER, DAVID A., Fifth Grade Teacher; *b:* Newark, NJ; *m:* Doris Berman; *c:* Steven; *ed:* Jersey City St Coll (BA) Elem Ed 1968; *cr:* Littleton Schl 5th Grd Tchr 1968-; *ai:* Bsktbl Coach Hoptalong HS; Adv Continental Math League; Dir Willow Lake Day Camp; Tchr Mentor; PTHEA, NJEA, NEA 1968-; Amer Cncl Math Tchrs 1993-; Kaved Awd Morristown Jewish Ctr.

COOPER, DORIS SUE, Fifth Grade Teacher; *b:* Brooklyn, NY; *m:* David; *c:* Steven; *ed:* Trenton St Coll (BA) Elem Ed 1969; 30 Addl Credit Hrs; *cr:* Lakeview Schl 4th Grd Tchr 1969-73; Hopatcong MS 5th Grd Tchr 1981; Lincoln Roosevelt Schl 4th-5th Grd Tchr 1081-; *ai:* PTA Cultural Arts Chprsn; Sci Curr, Soc Comms; Denville Ed Assn 1969-73; Roxbory Ed Assn; NJEA, NEA 1969-73; Governor's Tchr Recognition Prgm Recipiant 1992; *home:* 109 Conklin Ave Stanhope NJ 07874

COOPER, EARL HOWARD, Health Educator; *b:* Lackawanna, NY; *m:* Linda L. Agthe; *c:* Darci, Eric; *ed:* Niagara Cty Comm Coll (AA) Sci 1968; St Univ of NY at Buffalo (BS) Hlth, PE & Rec 1971, (MS) Ed 1982; 12 Credit Hrs; *cr:* West Seneca Cntrl Schls Hlth Edctr 1971-; *ai:* Bldg Budget Comm; Mod Ftbl Coach 19 Yrs; Var Womens Track Coach 4 Yrs; Mens Var Track Coach 2 Yrs; Child Study Team; AFT 1971-; WSTA 1971-; Eden Emergency & Rescue Squad 1978-, Pres, Asst Chief, Bd of Dir; Amer Red Cross 1979-, CPR & First-Aid Instr; W Seneca Yth Bureau Yth Advocate Awd 1989; *office:* West Seneca West MS 395 Center Rd West Seneca NY 14224

COOPER, ELIZABETH ANNE, Social Studies Dept Chprsn; *b:* Oakland, CA; *ed:* George WA U (BA) His 1969, (MA) Scndry Educ 1971; *cr:* Immaculate Conception Acad Phys Educ Tchr 1969-70; Garnet Patterson JHS Soc Stud Tchr 1971; Lincoln Jr HS Soc Stud Tchr 1971-93; Phelps Career Sr HS Soc Stud Dept Chair 1993-; *ai:* Amenities Comm Co-Chprsn; Mem Career Day, Black His Month Comms; WA Tchrs Union 1971-, Lincoln Jr HS SCAC 1975-84; DC Geographic Alliance 1993-; IAS 1988-, Tchng TEam for Teen Peer Facilitation; Natl Geographic Summer Seminar 1993; Tchr of Yr 1994-95; *office:* Phelps Career Sr HS 24th & Benning Rd NE Washington DC 20009

COOPER, GARRY, Marketing Education Coord; *b:* Dayton, OH; *c:* Garry Jr., Chad, Brittany; *ed:* Bowling Green St Univ (BS) Mrktg Ed 1976; Univ of Dayton Post Grad Stud in Schl Admin; Knowledge Link Co Cmptr Trng; *cr:* Viacom Cablevision Telemarketing Coord 1980-83; Dayton Bd of Ed Mrktg Ed Coord 1976-; *ai:* Past Head Bsktbl, Soccer Coach; DECA Chapter, Stu Cncl Adv, Prgm Coord; NEA 1976-; DEA 1976-, Pub Rel Comm Chair; OMEA 1980-; DECA 1976-, Dist Chprsn; Amer Legion SAL 1985-, Commander, Achvmt Awd; PHFAM 1983-, Class Pres; NAACP 1988-; OH Bsktbl Coaches Assn 1980-86; *office:* Patterson Cooperative HS 441 River Corridor Dr Dayton OH 45402*

COOPER, GARY OWEN, Fourth Grade Teacher; *b:* Newark, NJ; *m:* Mary Ann Ross; *c:* Meredith; *ed:* William Paterson Coll (BA) Early Chldhd Ed 1970; Montclair St Coll (MA) Guidance 1973; Funded Grant Writer 1977; *cr:* Essex Cty Coll Intern, Rdng Instr 1970-71, Stu Act Coord 1971; Red Bank Regnl HS Rdng Instr 1971-72; Paterson Schl System Elem Schl Tchr 1972-, Internal Change Agent 1978-79; *ai:* Coach Boys Bsktbl 1973-74; Stu Safety Patrol 1982-88; Adv Stu Govt; Paterson Ed Assn, NJEA, NEA 1975-; Essex Cty Coll Natl Fellowship 1970; *home:* 331 Boyle Ave Totowa NJ 07512*

COOPER, GERALD LEE, Math Teacher; *b:* Huntington, PA; *m:* Margaret E. Peighlal; *c:* Pamela, Geri; *ed:* Shippensburg Univ (BS) Math 1975; *cr:* Bishop Guilfoyle HS Tchr 1975-; *ai:* CSTA 1986-, Treas, Tchr of Yr; Knight of Columbus 1980-; Tchr of Yr 1990; *office:* Bishop Guilfoyle HS 2400 Pleasant Valley Blvd Altoona PA 16602*

COOPER, GLEN LAWRENCE, Health & Physical Ed Teacher; *b:* Greenville, PA; *m:* Lisa Marie Higgins; *c:* Sara Aileen, Molly Ann; *ed:* Univ of Pittsburgh (BS) Hlth, PE 1983; George Mason Univ Driver Ed 1986; Thiel Coll Bus Admin; Video Correspondence, Cmptr Courses; Instrs, CPR Certs; *cr:* Duquesne Univ Head Womens Bsktbl, Ath Trainer 1983-84; Arlington Cty Pub Schls Hlth, PE Tchr, Certfd Ath Trainer 1984-91; East Suburban Sports Med Ctr Head Ath Trainer 1991-93; Penn-Trafford Schl Dist Hlth, PE Tchr, Certfd Ath Trainer 1993-; *ai:* East Suburban Sports Med Ctrs Stu Ath Trainer Wkshp Coord 1991-; Natl Ath Trainesr Assn 1983-; PA Ath Trainers Soc 1983-, Mbrshp Chair 1993-95; PA St Assn Hlth, PE, Rec, Dance 1991-; Northern VA Sports Med Assn 1984-, VP, PR Chprsn, Schlshp Comm; VA Ath Trainers Assn 1985-, Regnl Rep; Amer Heart Assn 1988-, Instr; Author Elem PE Curr, MS Handbook for IMS & Interscholastic Sports 1990, Video REview in Journal of Ath Trng 1993; NVSMA Stu Trainer Symposium Asst Dir 1991; Arbor Day Chm 1987-88; Grantee Say No to Drugs Calendar Arlington Cty Pub Schls, Washington Post; *office:* Penn-Trafford Schl Dist Rt 130 Harrison City PA 15636

COOPER, GRANT, Music Professor; *b:* Wellingotn, New Zealand; *m:* Margaret Chapman; *c:* jessica, Rachel; *ed:* Univ of Auckland (BSC) Pure Math 1974; Univ of Tulsa (MM) Trumpet Performance 1981; *cr:* Yale Univ Asst Dir of Bands 1976-79; SUNY at Fredonia Prof of Trumpet & Orch Conductor 1982-93; Ithaca Coll Dir of Orchs 1993- 1993-; *ai:* Fredonia Chamber Players Music Dir Penfield Symphony Orch; Presidents Awd Excellence in Tchng 1990; William T Hagan Awd for Creative Activity 1993; *office:* Ithaca Coll Danby Rd Ithaca NY 14850

COOPER, IRA J., Mathematics Teacher; *b:* Brooklyn, NY; *ed:* Hunter Coll (BA) Pol Sci 1972; Brooklyn Coll (MA) Cmptr Sci 1982; 24 Credits in Supervision & Admin; *cr:* Lafayette HS Math Tchr 1978; Automotive HS Math Tchr 1979; Alexander Hamilton TVHS Math Tchr 1979-82; W. E. Grady TVHS Math Tchr 1991-; *ai:* Voc Indstrl Clubs of Amer Adv; Work Stud Internship, Comm Svc Ldrshp Coord; UFT, AFT 1978-; SURDNA Fnd Grant for Comm Svc; *office:* William E. Grady Voc Tech HS 25 Brighton 4th Rd Brooklyn NY 11235

COOPER, JOAN BERTON, Math Teacher; *b:* Neptune, NJ; *m:* Robert; *c:* Kristen Truex, Keith Truex; *ed:* Glassboro St Coll (BA) Elem Ed 1964; Georgian Ct Coll (MA) Ed 1984; Jersey City St Coll (MA) Math 1990; *cr:* Ocean Twp Schl 4-5 Grd Tchr 1964-65, 1973-89, Math Tchr 1986-; *ai:* Acad Team, Odyssey of Mind Coach; Class Adv; NEA, NJEA, MCEA 1973-; AMTNJ, NCTM 1986-; TOEA 1973-, VP; Wrote Cmptr Prgm for Magazine; *office:* Ocean Twp Intermediate Schl 1200 W Park Ave Ocean NJ 07712

COOPER, JOHN ARTHUR,JR., 9th Grade Science Teacher; *b:* Clarksburgh, WV; *m:* Barbara Bowen; *c:* Lisa A.; *ed:* Slippery Rock St Univ (BS) Earth, Space Sci 1968; St of PA Ed Dept (ME) 1990; *cr:* Manheim Twp HS Sci Tchr 28 Yrs; *office:* Manheim Twp HS 5134 School Rd Lancaster PA 17601

COOPER, JUDITH BUCKNER, Fifth Grade Teacher; *b:* Toledo, OH; *m:* Martin Christopher; *c:* Jacquelyn; *ed:* Univ of Toledo (BE) Elem Ed 1972, (ME) Early Chldhd 1975; Addl Post Grad Hrs Lang Arts, Supervision, Guiding Stu Tchrs; Bowling Green St Univ 16 Hrs Learning Disabilities; *cr:* Rosary Cathedral Schl 2nd Grd Tchr 1968-72; Collingwood Learning Ctr Primary Multi-Unit Tchr 1972-73; Birmingham Schl Kndgtn Tchr 1973-75; Martin Elem Schl 2-4 Grd Tchr 1975-85; Fall-Meyer Elem Schl 3-5 Grd Tchr 1986-; *ai:* AFT, Toledo FT 1972-; Delta Kappa Gamma 1980-; Jr League of Toledo 1985-; *office:* Fall Meyer Elem Schl 1800 Krieger Dr Toledo OH 43615*

COOPER, KENNETH PETER, Religion Teacher; *b:* New York City, NY; *m:* Jacalyn Kalin; *ed:* Manhattanville Coll (BA) Sociology 1980; Boston Coll (MA) Spec Ed 1982; Cath Univ (MA) Theology 1988; IA Coll Ed Cert 1984; *cr:* Cardinal Hayes Schl Tchr, Coach 1984-86; Br Rice HS Tchr, Coach 1986-90; Cardinal Spellman Schl Tchr, Coach 1990-93; St John's Schl Tchr, Coach 1993-; *ai:* Bsktbl Coach; Chrstn Svc Project Vol Prgm; NCEA 1984-; Mayor Dinkins Vol Awd; George Bush 1000 Points of Light; Tchr of Yr; *home:* 3737 Legation St NW Apt 107 Washington DC 20015

COOPER, KEVIN CHARLES, Electronics Instr; *b:* Torrington, CT; *ed:* Oliver Wolcott Tech Schl Grad Electronics 1983; CT Schl of Broadcasting Grad Radio Broadcasting 1984; Tech Careers Inst Grad Electronics 1985; Taking Courses Cntrl CT St Univ Voc Tech Ed; *cr:* WSNG Radio Chief Engr 1985-95; Tech Careers Inst Electronics Dept Head 1989-93; Oliver Wolcott Tech Schl Electronics Instr 1993-; *ai:* Amateur Radio Club Adv; Tech Careers Inst Instr of Yr 1991; *office:* Oliver Wolcott Voc Tech Schl 75 Oliver St Torrington CT 06790

COOPER, LARRY L., Third Grade Teacher; *b:* Pittsburgh, PA; *m:* Jill Ann; *c:* Lisa, Eric; *ed:* CA Univ (BS) Elem Ed 1974; Univ of Pittsburgh (MS) Elem Ed 1980; *cr:* Penn Elem Schl Third Grd Tchr 1974-; *ai:* Dist Cmptr & Tech Comm; JV Soccer Coach; PSEA 1974-; Tchr PA Gift of Time Awd; *office:* Penn Elem Schl 199 Airport Rd Butler PA 16001

COOPER, PHYLLIS VIALL, Third Grade Teacher; *b:* St Albans, VT; *m:* Harold; *c:* Diane Rowe, David; *ed:* Univ of MA at Amherst (BA) Elem Ed & Sociology 1964; Univ of MA at Boston (MA) Critical, Creative Thinking 1988; Addl 30 Hrs Rdng, Spec Ed, Sci; *cr:* Job Corps Cnsl Adams Schl 3 Grd Tchr 1968-73; Cotuit Schl 4 Grd Tchr Collegiate Schl 4 Grd Tchr 1975-79; Allen Schl Title I Tchr 197 Baker Schl 4 Grd Tchr 1978-90, 3 Grd Tchr 1990-; *ai:* Schl Im Cncl; Dennis Schl Bldg Comm; Piloting New Math Prgm; P Prgm Regular Classroom 1995-; NEA 1968-; MRA 1993-; De Gamma 1985-, Pres, VP, Sec; Participated Writing Curr Barnst Career Ed System Pub 1980; Co-Authored Act Book; *office:* Ez Schl 810 Main St West Dennis MA 02670

COOPER, RICHARD P., English Teacher; *b:* Boston, MA; *m* Stuart; *c:* Jesse, Paul; *ed:* Univ MA at Amherst (BA) Eng Williston HS Eng Tchr 1969-70; Lakeside Schl Houseparent Kennedy MS Eng Tchr 1971-; *ai:* Chess Club; Schl Store; NEA Tchrs Assn 1971-, Local Pres (2 Times) 1979-81; Boston Writi 1987-; Newspaper Columnist; Novel: Wasted Lives; *office:* Ke Middle St Woburn MA 01801*

COOPER, SCOTT MEREDITH, Assistant Music Director; OH; *m:* Kimberly Anne Lupco; *c:* Jaynie, Mark; *ed:* Bowling Univ (BM) Music Ed 1980; Kent St Univ (AA) Cmptr Tech 1992 Cty Schls Sub Tchr 1983; Warren Music Ctr Pvt Music Instr Trumbull Cty Schls Sub Tchr 1992-93; Word of Life Chrstn A Tchr 1993-95; *office:* Believer's Chrstn Flwshp 2577 Schenle Warren OH 44483

COOPER, STEPHANIE BARTON, 9th Grade English T Hornell, NY; *m:* John W.; *c:* Tara, John; *ed:* SUNY at Brockp Admin; SUNY at Albany (MA) Eng Ed 1975, (BA) Eng Ed 1 Quality Mngmt Confratute; Effective Tchng; Classroom Mngmn Supervision; *cr:* Guilderland Cntrl Dist HS Eng Tchr 1969- Cntrl Dist 8 Grd Eng Tchr, GATE Facilitator 1980-85; Fairport Eng Dept Ldr, Mentor, Eng Tchr 1985-92, MS GATE Coord 1992 Tchr, GATE Facilitator 1994-; *ai:* Helping Hands Adv; Prof Ad Day Co-Chprsn; Phi Beta Kappa 1986-; NYSUR 1969-; IDEA 1 NYSEC Gifted Ed 1985; *home:* 5110 Butler Rd Canandaigua N

COOPER, VALERIE LANETTE, Health Teacher; *b:* Ayer, M Univ of PA (BS) Hlth, PE 1980, (MS) Sports Sci 1982; 12 Und Credits in Advanced Ath Trng West Chester Univ; *cr:* West N Acad Hlth Tchr 1982-85; Bel Air HS Hlth Tchr 1985-; *ai:* Head Bsktbl, Head Var Sftbl Coach; Var Club Spon; Stu Assisted Prg AAHPERD 1985-; ASHA 1994-; Girls Bsktbl Coach of Yr 1 Coach of Yr 1993-94; *office:* Bel Air HS 100 Hieghe St Bel Air

COOPER, WAYNE M., Elementary Teacher; *b:* Mishawak Temple Univ (BS) Elem Ed 1967; Glassboro St Coll 9 Credit Univ 6 Credits; *cr:* Merchanville Pub Schls Elem Tchr 1966-6 Cty Pub Schls Elem Tchr 1967-69; Cherry Hill Pub Schls Elem T *ai:* NEA; NJ Ed Assn; Cherry Hill Ed Assn; Jaycee of FL Mos Young Edctr; NJ Governor's Tchr Recognition Prgm 1990-91 Media Act Monthly; *office:* Cherry Hill Pub Schls Browning Ln Cherry Hill NJ 08034*

COOPER, WILLIAM THOMAS, Humanities Teacher; *b:* Itta *m:* Joan Schulhafer; *c:* William Thomas Jr., Teryl Catherine Jonathan Gregory; *ed:* LA Tech Univ (BA) Jrnlsm 1962; Univ of (MA) Pol Sci 1970; 250 Undergrad, Grad Credit Hrs Southwe Univ of OK, Northeastern Univ; *cr:* USAF 2Lt, Col 1962-86; R Internal information in Pentagon; Montclair Kimberly Hum Tchr Tech, Discipline, Lib Comms; Fac Choir; Triad of Knives Novel Moon Novel 1987; *office:* Montclair Kimberley Acad 201 Montclair NJ 07042

COOPER-FROTRIK, JULIE, Writing Instructor; *b:* Philadelph Susan Abtouche, Tina Frotrik Duffy, Carol Tykainski, Goddard-VT Coll (MFA) Poetry 1983; Beaver Coll (MA) Hum A Womans Pl Cnslr & Legal Advocate 1985-91; Bucks Cty C Writing Instr 1991-; *ai:* Adj Fac Comm Chprsn; Lang & Lit Di Organizing Comm Pres; Acad of Amer Poets; Poetry Soc of Am & Fiction Pub; *home:* 521 Street Rd New Hope PA 18938

COPE, DAVID JAMES, High School Teacher; *b:* Berwick, PA; Van Allen; *c:* Matthew David; *ed:* Bloomsburg St Col COmprehensive SS 1973, (MED) His 1975; Edinboro Univ Pr Chair Certs 1986; *cr:* Titusville Jr High 9th Grd Team Tchng Titusville Sr high 1-12th Grd Tchr 1983-, 10-12th Grd Honors T Dept Chair 1992-; *ai:* Sr Class Play Dir; Musical Dir; Drama C Trial, Model UN & Oratorical Adv; NCSS 1983-; Emanuel Lu 1979-, Organist & Choir Dir; Titusville Summer Theatre Dir & Scholastic Search & Scholastic Update Adv; Pubished; Coa Champions in Natl His Day; *office:* Titusville Sr High 302 E Titusville PA 16354

COPE, LYNN E., 7th Grd His & 8th Grd Geo Tchr; *b:* Easto Danita M.; *c:* Kyle E.; *ed:* East Stroudsburg St Univ (BS) His & G 1963; *cr:* Bangor Area Schl Dist 7th & 8th Grd Tchr 1 Principal-Fac Adv Comm; Alternative Ed Prgm 7th Grd Rep; Comm; NEA & PSEA 1963-; BAEA 1963-, Pres & VP; *office:* Ba Schl Dist 44 S Third St Bangor PA 18013*

COPE, VICTORIA WARDZWSKI, English Instructor; *b:* Phi PA; *m:* Lyle Stuart Sr.; *c:* Daniella, Cory, Tristan, Stuart; *ed:* Mo Cty Comm Coll (Assoc) Gen Eng 1980; Univ of Pittsburgh (BA) IN Univ of PA (MA) Lit 1991; PHD in Lit & Criticism Cou Completed; *cr:* Allegheny Cty Comm Coll Adj Instr 1991; Moun Coll Eng Instr 1991-95; St Francis Coll Eng Instr 1994-; Penn St a Eng Instr 1995-; *ai:* Mount Aloysius Creative Journal D Subsequent Ed; Fac Adv; SUP Assistantship; Numerous Arti *home:* 160 Macridge Ave Johnstown PA 15904*

COPELAND, CAMILLE CARPENTER, Asst Prof, Dept of Co *b:* Wills Point, TX; *m:* Ned B. Cash; *c:* Colette Copeland Courtney C., Candy R. Cash, Carla Cash Peace; *ed:* Univ of TX (Arts, Applied Art 1963; Duquesne Univ (MSEd) Cnslr Ed 1975 Pittsburgh (PHD) Cnslr Ed 1989; *cr:* Colgate Elem Schl 1st 1964-65; Chartiers Mental Hlth, Mental Retardation Ctr Thera Mgr 1975-79; Western Ctr for Mental Retardation Admin, Psy 1979-85; Duquesne Univ Fac, Admin 1985-; *ai:* Assn for Cn Supervision 1990-, Exec Bd; North Atlantic Regnl Assn of Cn Supervision 1990-, Pres; PA Assn of Cnslr Ed & Supervision 19 Past Pres Svc Awd; United Mental Hlth 1994-, Bd Mem; Chartie Hlth, Mental Retardation Ctr 1993-, Bd Mem; Who's Who in A & Univs 1995; Numerous Articles Pub; *office:* Duquesne Univ P PA 15282

COPELAND, MARION WILSON, Professor of English; *b:* Nor *ed:* Drew Univ (BA) British Lit 1958; Syracuse Univ (MA) Amer UMass at Amherst (PHD) Eng 1973; *cr:* Syracuse U Part-time 1961-62; Holyoke Comm Coll 1962-; *ai:* Visiting Lecturer, Inst Ctr Animals & Pub Policy Tufts Veterinary Schl; Natl Comm An Delta Soc; Nature in Lit & Soc 1990-, Bd of Dirs; AISLE 1995-; 1985-, Natl Stud Comm; Frienda of Amherst Stray Animals 198 Dirs; NEH Seminar 1973, Yr in Residence 1975-76; Elaine Ma Tchng Excl 1993; Mass Cncl for Hum Adult Rdng Seminar Tr *office:* Holyoke Comm Coll 303 Homestead Ave Holyoke MA 01

, CARLA SUE, Art Teacher; *b:* Lexington, KY; *m:* James; *c:* d: Miami Univ (BSEd) Elem Ed 1977, (MAEd) Art Ed 1990; 21 Grad Hrs Studio Areas Printmaking, Ceramics; *cr:* Hopewell 3rd Grd Tchr 1978-88, 1-6 Grd Art Tchr 1988-89, 3rd Grd Tchr Shawnee Elem Schl 1-6 Grd Art Tchr 1990-; *ai:* Grant, Discipline omms; NEA, Lakota Ed Assn 1978-; OH Art Ed Assn 1990-; Edctr 1992; Pub 2 Articles; *office:* Shawnee Elem Schl 9394 Dr Cincinnati OH 45241

, ROBERT A., Mathematics Teacher; *b:* Youngstown, OH; *m:* Borman; *ed:* Univ of Cincinnati (BS) Math 1989; OH St Univ ath Ed 1992; *cr:* Woodland Hills HS Math Tchr 1993-; *ai:* Asst Coach; NEA, PSEA 1993-; NCTM 1992-; *office:* Woodland Hills 50 Greensburg Pike Pittsburgh PA 15221

ACQUELINE D., 6th Grade Teacher; *b:* Burlington, VT; *m:* .; *c:* Courtney, Christopher; *ed:* Univ of VT (BA) Elem Ed 1973; Michael's, UVM, Trinity Coll, Univ of ME, St Joseph's Coll, Essex Elem Schl 4th Grd Tchr 1973-76; Spec Ed Tutor, Sub K-6 1977-87; Champlain Elem Schl 5th Grd Tchr 1986-88; Hunt MS Tchr 1988-; *ai:* Mentoring Prgm; Carnegie Grant Mid Grds Advy Cncl; Peer Mediation; Co-Starter Pilot Prgm 1996; Natural Prgm; Strategegic Planning Comm; VT, NEA, BEA 1986-, Rep PEO 1974-, Pres, VP, Sec R; Article Newsletter; *office:* Lyman C dle Schl 1364 North Ave Burlington VT 05401*

GER, ANDREW JAMES, Soc Stud Tchr & Asst Principal; *b:* NJ; *m:* Joanne K. Roberts; *c:* Abigail Katherine; *ed:* Merrimack His 1984; Univ MA at Lowell (MA) Ed 1989; 11 Hrs Admin Cert mouth St Coll; *cr:* Stratford Pub Schl Soc Stud Tchr 1989-, Asst -; *ai:* Cross Cntry Coach 1994-; JV Boys Bsktbl Coach 1990-94; m; Peer Cnslng, Steering Comms Chm; Outing Club Adv; NEA es; ASCD 1994-; Lancaster Conservation Comm 1994-; *office:* Public Schl Rt 3 North Stratford NH 03590

A, ANNETTE M., High School Spanish Teacher; *b:* Mount NY; *m:* Rick A.; *c:* Christina M.; *ed:* Iona Coll (BA) Span, Math S) Ed 1989; *cr:* Mt Vernon HS Span Tchr 1986-; *ai:* Adv Span dergraduate Recognition Comm; Phi Beta Kappa 1989-, Honoree Mbrshp; NYSAFLT, ACTFL 1986-; NYS Schlsp Tchrs of Frgn ce: Mt Vernon HS 100 California Rd Mount Vernon NY 10552*

A, ELAINE M., English Teacher; *b:* Buffalo, NY; *c:* er; *ed:* St Univ of NY at Fredonia (BA) Scndry Eng 1969; SUC (MS) Multidisciplinary Stud 1987; *cr:* Frontier Cntrl HS & Jr HS Eng Tchr 1969-70; Royalton-Hartland Cntrl Eng Tchr AFT Distinguished Tchr Fellow 1988; Royalton-Hartland Tchr 8; *office:* Royalton-Hartland Cntrl Schl State St Middleport NY

ELLA, BIAGIO, Assoc Professor of Accounting; *b:* Bridgeport, hyllis A. Kaminski; *c:* Mark, Dan, Karen; *ed:* Univ of Bridgeport ng 1959; NY Univ (MBA) Acctng 1963; *cr:* Univ of Bridgeport of of Acctng, Dept Chprsn 1963-; *ai:* Amer Inst of CPA, CT Soc 972-; Amer Acctng Assn 1975-; Knights of Columbus 1995-; Outstdng Tchr Awd; Parents Assn Outstdng Fac Awd; Milton Endowed Professorship; Book: Computer Problems for al Accounting; CPA; *office:* Univ Of Bridgeport 230 Park Ave t CT 06601

, JOSEPH, Technology Teacher; *b:* Kansas City, MO; *m:* Jane : Caitlyn, Alyssa; *ed:* SUNY at Oswego (BS) Industrial Arts Ed ster CT Univ (MS) Comm, Scndry Ed 1989; *cr:* Manopac HS Tech 3-; *ai:* Var Lacrosse, JV Ftbl Coach; Intnl Tech Ed Assn 1993-; Yr Gannett Newspaper 1995; NYNEX Sci, Tech Awd; *office:* HS Baldwin Place Rd Mahopac NY 10541

LORI GINGERELLA, Reading Specialist; *b:* Westerly, RI; *m:* .; *c:* Steven, Christine; *ed:* Univ of RI (BS) Early Chldhd Ed uthern CT St Univ (MS) Rdng 1986; *cr:* Bishop Mc Vinney Schl chr 1980-81; St Pius Schl 5th-8th Grd Tchr 1982-85; Westerly HS g Tchr 1986-95; Babcock MS 8th Grd Rdng Tchr 1995-; *ai:* Schl er Adv; Class of 91 Adv; Staff Dev, Discipline Comms; IRA; ARI 1986-; WT Assn 1986-, Recording Sec; *office:* Babcock MS Ave Westerly RI 02891*

LO, ELEANOR KLINGERMAN, Instrumental Music Teacher; nd, PA; *m:* Charles J.; *c:* Charles S.; *ed:* Susquehanna Univ (BS) 1964; Attnd Trenton St Coll, Temple Univ, Univ of VT, Ithaca uesne Univ; *cr:* Neshaminy Schl Dist K-6 Grd Vocal Music Tchr Trenton Schl Dsit Title I Elem, Secord Music Tchr 1968-69; hl Dist K-6 Grd Music Tchr 1969-70; Westampton Schl Dist K-8 c Tchr 1976-79; Medford Twp 6-8 Grd Instrumental Music Tchr : Jazz, All S Jersey Bands; Music Ensemble; Recitals; NEA usic Educators Natl Conf 1979-; All S Jersey Band & Orch Dirs 9-, Mgr; *office:* Medford Memorial MS 55 Mill St Medford NJ

LO, NICHOLAS WARREN, Music Teacher; *b:* Lackawanna, ulia A. Smith; *ed:* SUNY at Buffalo (BFA) Music 1986; Working AH Music Ed; Daemen Coll Music; *cr:* Buffalo Pub Schls Music d Dir 1988-; *ai:* Dir of Bands; Yrbk Adv; NEA, NYSSMA, MENC me: 331 Saint Lawrence Ave Buffalo NY 14216

, CARY DOUGLAS, Math & Physics Teacher; *b:* Sunbury, PA; : Morrow; *c:* Karen, Carol; *ed:* Bloomsburg Univ (BS) Ed, Math Addl Hrs; *cr:* Spencerville Jr Acad Math Tchr 1974-81; Adelphian th, Physics, Cmptr Tchr 1981-86; Blue Mt Acad Math, Physics 6-; *ai:* Stu Assn Spon; NCTM 1993-; Excl in Tchng Awd 1991; 3 Packages Written, Marketed; Articles Pub; *office:* Blue Mountain 3 Box 3642 Hamburg PA 19526*

, IVAN JEFFREY, Social Studies Teacher; *b:* Columbus, OH; H St Univ (BS) Soc Stud 1975; Mt St Joseph (MA) 1987; *cr:* Cols s Tchr 1975-; *ai:* Stu Cncl; Assn Sr Fac Rep; NEA 1975-, Fac Rep, Rep 1991-; Cols Ed Assn 1975, Conventation Del; OH Ed Assn fice: South HS 1160 Ann St Columbus OH 43206

, STEPHANIE ANN, English & Journalism Teacher; *b:* DuBois, Grove City Coll (BA) Lit, Comms, Scndry Ed 1992; Loyola Coll ore 9 Hrs Towards Rdng Specialist MA; *cr:* Aberdeen HS 10th Tchr, Jrnlsm Adv 1992-; *ai:* Newspaper Adv 4 Yrs; Spon Var, JV 2 Yrs; NCTE 1992-; Grace United Meth Church 1993-, Sunday r; Article Pub.

T, J. NATHAN, Assoc Prof of Music Comm; *b:* Fort Worth, TX; e Crotts; *c:* Heather Crutchfield, Zachary, Laura; *ed:* Mars Hill E) Music Ed 1971; Southern Bapt Theological Seminary (MCM) tion 1977, (DMA) Musicology 1985; Univ of AL at Tuscaloosa tion Stud, Baptist Lang Schl in Kenya Swahili Proficiency Stud, Univ in Kenya Grad Comm Stud; *cr:* Macon Cty Schls Band & Dir 1979-79; Intnl Bd SCB at Africa Cross Cultural Comm t 1981-92; Kenyatta Univ at Kenya Music Lecturer 1986-87; Coll Assoc Prof of Music & Comm 1992-; *ai:* Fac Senate, ltural Advy Bd; Friends of Arts; ICA 1995-; Sietar 1994-; Pub on Music, Comm & Missions; Curr Author for Cross-Cultural Stud rgraduate & Grad Level; Cross-Cultural Trainer, Consultant; ng Ethnomusicologist.

CORBOSIERO, SUSAN (BACHOFNER), Math & Business Dept Head; *b:* Boston, MA; *m:* Louis J. Jr.; *c:* Kristen, Karen; *ed:* Boston Univ (BA) Math 1970; Northeastern Univ (MED) Math Ed 1973; Framingham St Coll (MED) Spec Ed 1982; 12 Addl Hrs Scndry Admin Northeastern Univ; *cr:* Newman Jr HS Math Tchr 1970-78, Dept Head Math 1978-81; Needham HS Math Tchr 1981-87; Westbrough HS Math Tchr 1987-92, Math Dept Head 1992-; *ai:* Class Adv; NEA, MTA, ATMIM 1970-; Westborough Tchrs Assn 1987-, Sec; NCTM 1990-; *office:* Westborough HS 90 W Main St Westborough MA 01581

CORBRAN, EILEEN DEWAN, 6th Grade Reading & Math Tchr; *b:* Jersey City, NJ; *m:* Harold Joseph Jr.; *c:* Harold III, Matthew; *ed:* Jersey City St Coll (BA) Elem Ed 1973; William Paterson St Coll (MED) Elem Ed & Cmptrs 1990; 36 Credits beyond Masters in Supervision, Curr Dev & Tech; *cr:* Jersey City Pub Schls 2, 3, 5, 8th Grds Tchr 1973-77; Secaucus Adult Schl GED Instr 1979-86; Rutherford Pub Schls 6th Grd Tchr 1986-; *ai:* Acad Coach of Knowlege Masters, Thinking Cap Quiz Bowl; REA Union Sec; Cmptr Specialist; IRA, NEA, NJEA, REA, ASCD, NCTM; *office:* Union Schl 359 Union Ave Rutherford NJ 07070*

CORCORAN, ANDREW JOSEPH, Chemistry Teacher; *b:* Boston, MA; *ed:* Northeastern Univ (BS) Chem 1963; Univ of NC (MS) Organic Chem 1966; Boston St (MED) Sec Schl Admin 1972; Northeastern Univ (MS) ClinicalChem 1978; Post Masters Tufts Univ 1966-68; *cr:* Univ NC Tchng Asst 1963-66; Tufts Univ Tchng Asst 1966-68; Dedham HS Chem Tchr 1968-; MA Gen Hosp Med Technologist 1977-; *ai:* Curr, Scholastics Awd Comms; NHS Fac; Dedham Ed Assn Exec Bd; Amer Chem Soc 1957-; New England Assn Chem Tchrs, Northeastern Ach Soc 1972-; NEA, MTA, DEA 1968-; *office:* Dedham HS 140 Whiting Ave Dedham MA 02026

CORCORAN, VIRGINIA MC DERMOTT, Asst Prof of Nutrtn & Diet; *b:* Wilkes-Barre, PA; *m:* John P.; *c:* John P., Michael J.; *ed:* Coll Misericordia (BA) Dietetics 1968; Marywood Coll (MS) Nutrition 1982; Mercy Hosp Traineeship, RD Cert; Temple Univ ABD Ed 1996; *cr:* Dairy Cncl Nutrition Ed Dir 1981-87; Wilkes-Barre Gen Hosp Nutrition Edctr 1987-88; Hazleton Gen Hosp Prgm Dir 1988-93; Marywood Coll Asst Prof 1983-; *ai:* Moderator Marywood Stu Dietetic Assn; Comm Mem Mid St Evaluation; PA Dietetic Assn 1978-, Pres, Keystone Outstdng 1982; Amer Dietetic Assn 1978-, Dietitian 1996; NE Dietetic Assn 1974-, Pres, Anita Owen Awd; Middleby Schlsp Acad Excl; Author 2 LoFat Cook Books; *office:* Marywood Coll 2300 Adams Ave Scranton PA 18509*

CORCORAN, WILLIAM C.,JR., American History Teacher; *b:* Medford, MA; *m:* Robin Bunting; *c:* William III, Blair Ann; *ed:* West Chester St Coll (BS) His 1969; Penn St Univ (MED) 1986; Post Grad Stud & Cert Safety in Industry & Society; *cr:* Haverford Sr HS Amer His Tchr 1969-; *ai:* Sr Thesis Project Mentor; Amer His Curr Dev Comm; Haverford Twp Ed Assn 1969-, VP 1993-95; NEA 1969-; E Brandywine Yth Assn 1988-, Bsbl Coach, Indoor, Outdoor Soccer; *home:* 9 Sussex Pl Downingtown PA 19335

CORDEK, CYNTHIA LEE, Second Grade Teacher; *b:* Johnstown, PA; *ed:* Univ of Pgh at Johnstown (BS) Elem Ed 1981; Grad Courses on Spcl Ed; *cr:* St Joseph Schl 2nd Grd Tchr 1981-; *ai:* Dir of Plays & Musicals; NCEA 1981-; Portage Area Station Museum 1993-; Tchrs Mentor; *office:* St Joseph Schl 511 Caldwell Ave Portage PA 15946

CORDERO, ALICIA, Sixth Grade Bilingual Teacher; *b:* Brownsville, TX; *ed:* St Univ Coll at Buffalo (BS) Scndry Ed, Span 1980; St Univ of NY at Buffalo (MED) Frgn Lang, Span 1974, (MED) Elem Ed 1980; *cr:* Bishop Neumann HS Span Tchr 1969-75; Herman Badillo Biling Acad 6th Grd Biling Tchr 1975-; *ai:* Buffalo Tchrs Fed Inc, NEA 1975-; Outstdng Tchr Awd 1986; *office:* Herman Badilla Biling Acad #76 300 S Elmwood Ave Buffalo NY 14201

CORDERO, PATRICIA WILMOT, Fifth Grade Teacher; *b:* Montclair, NJ; *m:* Robert L.; *c:* Robert Kennedy; *ed:* Jersey City St (BA) Elem Ed 1972; *cr:* Holy Cross Schl Grd 4 Tchr 1973-77; Queen of Peace Grd 7 Tchr 1977-94, Grd 5 Tchr 1994-; *ai:* Math Coord; Cath Schls Week Celebration; NCEA, Natl Assn of Cath Tchrs 1977-; NCTM; NJ Math Coalition; Mid St Soc Stud Assn 1990-; Amer Legion Auxiliary; JFK PTA; Boys & Girls Club; *office:* Queen of Peace Elem Schl 21 Church Pl North Arlington NJ 07031

CORDERO, THOMAS,JR., High School English Teacher; *b:* Middle Village, NY; *m:* Amy; *ed:* Queens Coll CUNY (BA) Drama, Theater 1985; 15 Credits toward MA St John's Univ; 10 Yr Cert Manhatton Schl of Music; *cr:* Our Lady of Miraculous Medal Schl Gr 6 Eng Tchr 1986-88; St Aloysius Schl 7-8 Grds Eng Tchr 1989-94; *ai:* Schl Plays Music Dir; Rel Act Comm; Natl Assn Pastoral Musicians 1993-; *office:* The Mary Louis Acad 176-21 Wexford Terr Jamaica NY 11432

CORDES, JENNIFER ANN, Engineering Professor; *b:* York, PA; *m:* Jerald Leibovitz; *c:* Maria, Murilo; *ed:* Rutgers Coll of Engrng (BS) Engrng 1978; Rutgers Coll (BA) Math 1978; Stevens Inst of Tech (ME) Mech Engrng 1985, (PHD) Mech Engrs 1989; *cr:* Enertech Corp Engr 1978-81; Western Union Engr 1982-85; Stevens Inst of Tech Asst Prof 1986-95; *ai:* ASME; *office:* Stevens Inst Of Tech Castle Point On The Hudson Hoboken NJ 07030

CORDISCO, MARY ELLEN FULLER, Substance Awareness Coord; *b:* Dover, NJ; *c:* Meghan, Micah; *ed:* Georgian Court Coll (BSW) Soc Work 1989; Substance Awareness Coord Cert Rutgers MSW Prgm; *cr:* Toms River Schls Stu Assistance Cnslr 1988-90; Barnegat Twp Schls Substance Awareness Coord 1990-; *ai:* Peer Ldrshp, Peer Mediation, Mentor Prgm Adv; AFT, NJ Assn of Stu Assistance Prof 1990-; NEA 1995-; Girl Scouts of Amer 1986-, Ldr; Barnegat Municipal Alliance 1990-; *home:* 39 Hadley Ave Toms River NJ 08753

CORDLE, NANCY ARCHER, Earth Science & Lang Arts Tchr; *b:* Circleville, OH; *m:* Terry Allan; *c:* Aaron William, Joshua Allan, Emily Lou; *ed:* Miami Univ (BA) Elem Ed 1985, Ashland Univ (MA) Curr & Instruction 1993; Ashland Univ Statistics 3 Hrs, Tchng Writing Systematic Approach 1 hr, Curr & Dev 4 Hrs, Intro to Computers; *cr:* Pickaway Co Schls Substitute Grd 1-8 1985-86; Fairfield Co Schls Substitute Grd 1-8 1985-86; Amanda Clearcreek Jr HS 7th Grd Earth & Life Sci, 8th Grd Eng 1986-, 7th Grd Lang Arts Tchr; *ai:* 8th Grd Bsktbl Coach; Schl Sci Fair Coord; Soc Comm; Stu Cncl Adv; 7th & 8th Grd Vlybl Coach & Referee; Ladies Ensemble; NHS Jr Spon; NEA, OH Ed Assn 1986-; OHSVA; Church Ed Comm 1985-91, Chm 1986-88; Pastor Parish Comm, Nominating Comm 3 Yrs; Sunday Schl Bd; Women's Ministries Cncl; *office:* Amanda Clearcreek Jr H S 9096 Walnut St Stoutsville OH 43154

CORDLE, TERRY ALLAN, Math & Industrial Arts Tchr; *b:* Lancaster, OH; *m:* Nancy Jo Archer; *c:* Stephanie D. Cordle Davis, Timothy V., Jeffrey W., Aaron W., Joshua A., Emily Lou; *ed:* Rio Grande Univ (BA) Elem Ed 1977; Marshall Univ (MS) Elem Ed 1979; Attnd OH St Univ; *cr:* Amanda Clearcreek Jr HS Tchr 1979-; *ai:* Hosler Fndtn Comm; Natl Jr Hnr Soc; NEA 1979-; OH Ed Assn 1979-; NCTM 1979-; New Hope Chrstn Schl Bd 1995-, Curr Cncl; OH St Univ Partnership Grant in Sports Physics; *office:* Amanda Clearcreek Jr H S 9096 Walnut St Stoutsville OH 43154

CORDNER, DIANE ATKIN, Reading Teacher; *b:* Youngstown, OH; *m:* Donald Paul; *c:* Heidi Lynne; *ed:* WV Wesleyan (BA) Elem Ed 1968; Post Grad Stud Youngstown St Univ; *cr:* Warren City Schl Third Grd Tchr 1968-73; Austintown Schls Third-Fourth Grd Tchr 1979-81, Rdng Tchr 1981-87; Youngstown City Schls Rdng Tchr 1987-; *ai:* Rdng Dept Chprsn; AEA Bldg Rep 1980-81; OH Rdng Assn; Band Parents; Tutoring; Girl Scout Ldr; Canfield Jr Leag; OEA, NEA, YEA 1987-; Amer Assn of Women 1981-; Alpha Gamma Delta Alum 1968-; Sociology Club 1968-; *home:* 495 Greenmont Dr Canfield OH 44406*

COREY, DEBRA, Spanish Teacher; *b:* Penn Yan, NY; *m:* William Craig; *c:* Erin, Neil, Jordan, Justin, Hannah, Mallory, Megan, Cheryl, Joe, Mark; *ed:* SUNY at Oswego (BA) Sociology 1974; SUNY at Brockport (MS) Biling Ed 1992; *cr:* Our Lady of Mercy HS Span Tchr 1986-87; Dundee Cntrl Schl Span Tchr 1987-; Finger Lakes Comm Coll Span Instr 1996; *ai:* Jr Class Adv; NYS Challenger Flwshp 1988, 1990; Tchr of Yr 1992; *home:* 1536 Friend Rd Penn Yan NY 14527

COREY, DIANE GEARY, Learning Specialist & Educator; *b:* Providence, RI; *m:* Michael; *c:* Devin, Keil; *ed:* Greensboro Coll (BA) Spec Ed 1969; Univ of VT (MED) Spec Ed 1978; Addl 30 Credit Hrs; *cr:* Ira Allan Elem Schl Spec Edctr 1976-79; So. Burlington MS Spec Edctr 1979-85; So. Burlington HS Spec Edctr 1985-89; Middlebury Union Jr HS Spec Edctr 1989-; *ai:* Cath Yth Org Adv; Tchr Relicensing Bd; NEA, VT Ed Assoc 1979-; Cncl for Exceptional Children; New England Rdng Assn; Children with Attention Deficit, Chptr, Advy Bd; Outstdng Tchr of Yr South Burlington MS 1985; Outstdng Tchr of Yr 1995; *office:* Middlebury Union Jr HS Charles Ave Middlebury VT 05753

COREY, GORDON ROGER, English & Music Teacher; *b:* Terre Haute, IN; *m:* Claudia Tamblyn; *c:* Anna Maclean, Samuel Tye, George Asher; *ed:* Cntrl MO St Univ (BME) Music 1973, (BSE) Eng 1978; Univ of KS (MS) Jrnlsm 1987; *cr:* Kansas City MO Schl Dist Eng Tchr 1987-89; Dominion Chrstn HS Eng, Jrnlsm, ESL Tchr 1989-91; Bad Kreuznach HS Eng, Jrnlsm Tchr 1991-92; Spangdahlem MS Eng, Music Tchr 1992-; *ai:* Tchr of Writing Consultant for Rhine Eifel Schl Dist 1992-95; Mem of Writing Assessment Test Scoring Group 1995; DODDS Europe Lang Arts Curr Task Group 1994; Advanced Prof Dev Presentations 1992-95; OEA 1995-; Club Beyond 1993-, Ldr; Outstdng Achvmt Awd 1995; Article Pub 1995; *office:* Spangdahlem MS Unit 3640, Box 45 APO AE 09126*

COREY, KAREN POWERS, Vocational Work & Family Tchr; *b:* Milton, WV; *m:* John C. Jr.; *c:* Chris, Michael; *ed:* Marshal Univ (MA) Guid & Cnslng 1976; Voc Home Ec 1971; *cr:* Rock Hill Mid Voc Home Ec Tchr 1971-91; Rock Hill High Voc Work & Family Tchr 1991-; *ai:* Peer Cncl; Teen Inst; Voc Tchr Ldr Cadre; Venture Captial Comm; NEA 1971-; Drugwatch 1992-, Sec & Pres; Project Taking Change Pilot Tchr; *office:* Rock Hill HS 2171 Cty Rd 26 Ironton OH 45638*

CORGEL, NIKKI, District Art Dept Chairperson; *b:* Binghamton, NY; *m:* Thomas R.; *c:* Carrie, Kate; *ed:* Fashion Inst of Tech (AAS) Fashion Illustration 1970; Buffalo St Univ (BS) Art Ed 1971; Attnd Binghamton Univ, Syracuse Univ; *cr:* Vestal Cntrl Schls Art Tchr 1971-88, Dist Art Dept Chprsn 1989-; *ai:* Level III Odyssey of the Mind Coach; NY St Art Tchrs Assn 1971-; Discovery Ctr 1995-, Bd Mem; Vestal Schl Fndtn Grant; *office:* Vestal Sr HS 205 Woodlawn Dr Vestal NY 13850

CORIELL, JOHN GERALD, Mathematics Tchr & Dept Chprsn; *b:* Portsmouth, OH; *m:* Deborah Lynn Shoemaker; *c:* John M.; *ed:* OH Univ (BS) Math 1972; Marshall Univ (MA) Educl Admin 1976; Attnd Shawnee St Univ & Miami Univ; *cr:* Portsmouth East HS 9th-12th Grd Math Tchr 1972-, Math Dept Chprsn 1979-; Shawnee St Univ Adjunct Fac Math 1980-; *ai:* Sr Class Adv; Coach Various Sports; NEA & OEA; OCTM, SE Dist Tchr of Yr 1987; OH Cncl of Tchrs of Math Southeastern Dist Tchr of Yr 1987; Porstmouth City Tchrs Assn, Tchr of Yr 1993; *office:* Portsmouth East HS 224 Marshall Portsmouth OH 45662*

CORIGLIANO, JAMES VINCENT, High School Band Director; *b:* New York, NY; *m:* Jo Ann Shedina; *c:* Antoinette, Melissa; *ed:* SUNY at Fredonia (MS) Music Ed 1968; *cr:* Brocton Cntrl Schl Music Tchr 1968-69; Draper Cntrl Schl Music Tchr 1969-72; Guilderland Cntrl Schl Music Tchr 1972-; *ai:* Jazz Ensemble; Pep Band; HS Musical; NEA, AFT, MENC, NYSSMA 1968-; Guilderland Tchrs Assoc 1972-; Serenade & Rondo Shawnee Press; Reverie for String Orch Shawnee Press; Clarinet Caprice Ethos Press; *office:* Guilderland HS PO Box 37 Guilderland Center NY 12085

CORIGLIANO, LYNN RAE (BYRNES), English as Second Lang Tchr; *b:* Jersey City, NJ; *m:* Frank; *c:* Casey; *ed:* Jersey City St (BA) Elem Ed 1868, (MA) Rdng; Certs LDTC Tchr of Handicapped, Supvr ESL; Adj Fac Montclair St Univ; *cr:* Union City Schl ESL Tchr 1968-79; Mt Lakes Schl ESL Tchr 1980-84; Parsippany Troy Hills Schl ESL Tchr 1985-; *ai:* Yrbk Adv 1994-; Boys Var Tennis Coach 1970-72; NJ TESOL, BE 1985-; NEA, NJEA 196j8-; NJAET 1996; Mini Grant Closed Captioned TV Improve Eng, Rdng Skills Limited Eng Speakers; *office:* Parsippany HS 309 Baldwin Rd Parsippany NJ 07054

CORKER, MARTHA STACK, Third Grade Teacher; *b:* Lorain, OH; *w:* Paul Dowd (dec); *c:* Mary Williams, Grat, Robert, Anne Lindeman; *ed:* St Mary's Coll of Notre Dame (BS) Ed 1952; Coll of Mt St Joseph (MA) Ed 1987; 15 Hrs Toward PHD OH Univ; *cr:* Kayley Elem Schl Third Grd Tchr 1952-53; Western Elem Schl First Grd Tchr 1963-64; Worthington Elem Schl Third Grd Tchr 1966-; *ai:* CEA, OEA, NEA 1966-; Jr Civil League, Retired Pres; AAUW, Retired; Hopewell Investment Club; Martha Holden Jennings Schlr; *home:* 193 Church St Chillicothe OH 45601

CORKERY, ANTOINETTE JUGON, High School English Teacher; *b:* Prince Bay, NY; *m:* Dennis F.; *c:* Michael W., Dennis A.; *ed:* Middlebury Coll (BA) His 1965; Brown Univ (MAT) Eng 1966; Middlebury Coll at Bread Loak (MA) Eng 1971; 45 Addl Credits Post Grad; *cr:* Johnsburg Cntrl Schl HS Eng Tchr 1966-70; Danvers HS Eng Tchr 1970-; *ai:* Yrbk Bus Mgr; Amnesty Intnl Chpt Adv; NEA 1966-; MTA 1970-; NCET 1980-; Gloucester Sawyer Nee Lib Bd, Saint Vincent de Paul 1995-; Writing Across Curr NSCC Journal of Rdng 1994; *office:* Danvers HS 60 Cabot Rd Danvers MA 01923*

CORLE, TRISHA A., Asst Girls Vars Bsktbl Coach; *b:* Johnstown, PA; *ed:* IN Univ of PA (BA) Criminology 1985; *cr:* Appalachian Yth Svc Case, Prgm Mgr 1986-95; Christian Home of Johnstown Exec Dir 1995-; *ai:* Yth Svc Alliance of PA 1995-; Co-Author Ind Living Skills Workbook; *office:* Ferndale Area HS 600 Harlan Ave Johnstown PA 15905

CORMAN, EDWARD ROBERT, Fifth Grade Teacher; *b:* Brooklyn, NY; *m:* Shelley Berger; *ed:* Hunter Coll (BA) His 1970; Brooklyn Coll (MS) Ed 1975; Addl 30 Credits; *cr:* PS 156 4 Grd Tchr 1970-73; PS 181 4 Grd Tchr 1973-88; PS 235 5-6 Grd Tchr 1988-92, 1994-, Tchr in Charge of Annex 1992-94; *ai:* UFT, AFT 1970-; No MA Civic Assn 1983-; Cert Appreciation NYC Police Dept; To Sir With Love Awd 1978; *office:* PS 235 525 Lenox Rd Brooklyn NY 11203*

CORMAN, NED W., Commission Project Director; *b:* Bellefonte, PA; *m:* Linda Q.; *ed:* Univ of Rochester (BM) Ed 1959; Penn St Univ (MA) Musicology 1965; Eastman Schl of Music; Post Grad ESM U of R; *cr:* Greece Cntrl Schl Dist Music Tchr 1959-63; Penn St Univ Musicology 1963-65; Fred Waring Pennsylvanians Lead Woodwind 1965-67; Freelance Musician 1963-; Penfield Schl Dist Music Tchr 1068-94, Dept Chair 1980-86; *ai:* AF of M 1957-; AFT 1968-; MENC 1959-; Soc for Chamber Music Rochester 1985-, Chair, Nom Comm; Periuton Comm Band 1990-; Penfield Sym Orch 1985-90; Commission Project 1994-, Dir; Discography, Soloist.

CORMIER, ANNE, English Teacher; *b:* Stone Aylesbury, England; *m:* James J. Jr.; *c:* Jake, Sarah, Katie, Jesse; *ed:* Wellesley Coll (BA) Eng 1968; Brandeis Univ (MA) Eng 1969; *cr:* Milton Acad Eng Tchr 1969-70; Hoosac Schl Eng Tchr 1980-83; Mount Anthony Union HS Eng Tchr 1985-; *ai:* Mount Anthony Messenger Newspaper Adv; Millennium III- Studying

New Grad Requirements; NEA 1985-; WHIPS-Preservation Trust 1993-; Goals 2000 Grant Writer To Stud Grad Requirements; *office:* Mount Anthony Union HS Park St Bennington VT 05201*

CORN, ALAN MITCHELL, Latin Teacher; *b:* Detroit, MI; *m:* Shelly Elizabeth Wechter; *c:* Rachel, Leah; *ed:* Franklin & Marshall (BA) Classics & Eng 1970; OH St Univ (MA) Classics 1971, (PHD) Classics 1975; *cr:* Bexley HS Latin, Eng Tchr 1974-; OH St Univ Adj Asst Prof of Classics 1985-; *ai:* Lit Magazine Adv; Fin & Negotiations Comm Ed Assn Chair; NEA, OEA, BEA 1975-; Amer Philological Assn 1974-; Amer Classical League 1976-, MacKinlay Awd 1990-; OH Frgn Lang Assn 1980-; Sci-Mat Flwshp 1994; NEH Seminar 1984, 1988, 1993; Ind Stud in Hum Flwshp 1985; Numerous Articles Pub; *office:* Bexley H S 326 S Cassingham Rd Bexley OH 43209*

CORNELL, CATHY CAMPBELL, Kindergarten Teacher; *b:* Long Branch, NJ; *m:* Robert Barry Jr.; *c:* Robert, Andrew, Douglas; *ed:* Rider Univ (BA) Early Chldhd, Elem Ed 1982; *cr:* Long Branch COE Kndgtn Paraprofessional Tchr 1983; Keyport Cntrl Schl Kndgtn Tchr 1983-; *ai:* NJ Tchrs Assn, NEA 1983-; *office:* Keyport Central Schl 335 Broad St Keyport NJ 07735*

CORNELL, JANET BURCH, French Teacher; *b:* Albany, NY; *m:* R. James; *c:* Timothy James; *ed:* St Lawrence Univ (BA) Fr 1960; Attnd Various Colls & Univs for Addl Credits Hrs; *cr:* E Greenbush Jr HS Fr Tchr 1960-69; Hamagrael Schl K-5 Grd Tchrs Aide & Room Mother 1977-83, Kndgtn Fr Tchr 1983-84; Goff Schl Fr Tchr 1984-89; Coxsackie-Athens Mid Sr HS Fr Tchr 1989-; *ai:* AATF 1960-69 & 1984-; NY St Assn of Foreign Lang Tchrs 1984-; NY St United Tchrs, AFT & Local Tchrs Assn; Bethany Reformed Church 1986-, Deacon & Mission Comm Chm 1990, Vacation Bible Schl Tchr 1988; Village Stage Drama Group 1991-; La Fed Franco-Americanine du NY 1987-; Bethlehem Parent-Faculty Act 1983-89, 6th Grd Team Parent, Membership Chm 1983 & Sec 1984-88; Bethlehem Pub Lib 1983-, Storyteller; Westminster Presbyn Church 1969-71, Sunday Schl Tchr; United 4th Presbyn Church 1979-80; Heldeberg Wkshp Tchng Aide 1979-84; Bethlehem Comm Church Chrstn Wkshp Tchr 1979-81, 1984 & 1986-88; *office:* Coxsackie-Athens Mid Sr HS 24 Sunset Blvd Coxsackie NY 12051

CORNELL, JEFFREY L., Business Department Chair; *b:* Dalton, PA; *m:* Mary Ann L.; *c:* Sarait; *ed:* Western New England Coll (BS) Bus Admin 1970; Mary Wood Coll Grad Schl for PA Tchr Cert 1971; *cr:* Montrose HS Tchr 1972-; *ai:* Head Boys Tennis, Asst Girls Tennis Coach; Adv Entrepreneural Skills Team; NEA, PSEA, MEA 1972-; Montrose Bd Planning Comm 1978-88; *office:* Montrose Jr Sr HS RR 3 Box 28 Montrose PA 18801

CORNELL, MARIBETH, Business Teacher; *b:* Framingham, MA; *ed:* Quinsigamond Comm Coll (AS) Bus Admin 1975; Salem St Coll (BS) Bus Ed 1977; NH Coll (MS) Bus Ed 1985; Cnslng Strategies Tchrs; Wellness VT Schls; Interdisciplinary Ed; Amer Airlines Sabre Trng; *cr:* Comm Coll of VT Bus Tchr 1980; Greenfield Comm Coll Word Proces Instr 1995; Southeastern VT Career Ed Ctr Bus Tchr 1977-; *ai:* Adv DECA, Natl Voc Tech Honor Soc; WSESU Wellness Coord; NBEA 1979-; VT Bus Ed Assn 1977-, Past Pres; New England Bus Ed 1980-, Dir VT; Eastern Bus Ed Assn 1979-, Mbrshp Dir; VT Bus Tchr of Yr; *office:* Southeastern VT Career Ed Ctr Fairground Rd Brattleboro VT 05301

CORNETT, BRIGITTE BIBIANA, French Tchr & French Club Spon; *b:* St Veit Karnten, Austria; *m:* Jackie Lane; *ed:* Univ of Vienna Austria (MS) Math, Fr 1982; *cr:* Real Gymnasium 4 Fr, Math Tchr 1982-83; Handelsakademie Vienna Fr Tchr 1983-84; Lakota HS Fr Tchr, Fr Club Spon 1984-; *ai:* AATF 1993-; *office:* Lakota HS 5050 Tylersville Rd West Chester OH 45069

CORNETT, MARGARET KERSHNER, Retired Fourth Grade Teacher; *b:* Clear Spring, MD; *m:* Fred; *c:* Catherine Dobrzanski, Michael; *ed:* Frostburg St (BS) Elem Ed 1956; Western MD (MS) Elem Ed 1974; *cr:* Lincolnshire Elem Schl 5th Grd Tchr 1956-59, 1964-65; Indianspringss Elem Schl 1st & 2nd Grd Tchr 1959-60; Clearspring Elem Schl 1st & 2nd Grd Tchr 1960-61, 1970-89; Conacocheague Elem Schl 3rd, 4th, & 5th Grd Tchr 1966-67; *ai:* Comm Mem Trying to Secure Lib, Sr Ctr & Sr Housing For Clear Spring; MD Retired Tchrs, Wash Cty Retired Tchrs 1989-; Clear Spring Dist Historical Assn 1989-, Bd Mem, VP; Amer Legion Auxiliary Post 222 1990-, Historian, Chaplain; Extensive Stud on Mile Markers Along Natl Pike from Baltimore to Vandalia IL.

CORNETT, SUSAN BACHUS, Sixth Grade Teacher; *b:* Cincinnati, OH; *m:* Russell G.; *c:* Genevieve, Adam, Lucia; *ed:* Eastern KY Univ (BS) Elem Ed & Spec Ed 1974; Coll of Mount Saint Joseph (MS) Rdng Ed 1991; 18 Post Grad Hrs in Various Educl Areas; *cr:* Saint Antoninus Schl Tchr 1974-77; Saint John the Bapt Schl Tchr 1977-79; Mount Saint Joseph Coll Lab Schl Tchr 1979-80; Our Lady of Victory Schl Tchr 1980-81; C O Harrison Elem Tchr 1988-; *ai:* Schl-Fac Media Rep; OHEA, OEA, NEA 1989-, Schl Rep; C O Harrison PTA, Bd Mem; Learning Links Awd Grant for Soc Stud Project Oriental Expression; *office:* C O Harrison Elem Schl 585 Neeb Rd Cincinnati OH 45233

CORNISH, ANNETTE HOLLIDAY, HS Counselor & Student Advisor; *b:* Greenville, SC; *m:* William Roy; *c:* William Roy Jr., Ursula Denise; *ed:* Allen Univ (BS) PE 1963; Morgan St Univ (MS) PE 1977; EDD Stu Educ Ldrshp 1986-87; Hood Coll Head Start Cert 1966; Wilmington Coll, St Joseph Univ Educ, Cnslng Credits 1989-94; Univ of DE Admin Cert 1984-88, Grad Credits PE; *cr:* Salisbury HS PE Tchr 1963-64; Anna P. Mote Elem Schl Head Start Dir 1966-67; Delawarr HS PE Tchr 1967-69; George Gray Elem Schl PE Tchr 1969-78; Shue MS PE Tchr 1978-91; Newark HS Cnslr, Stu Adv 1991-; *ai:* NHS Conflic Mediation Prgm Coord; Chrstn Schl Dist Trainer Conflict Mediation; Step-Group Adv; NEA, DSEA 1967-; DEAHPERD 1967-, Prof Hnr 1982; ASCD 1976-; DCA 1995-; Alpha Nu Sigma, Eta Zeta Sigma 1971-, Basileus, Adv, Who's Who Sigma Gamma Rho; City of Newark 1991-, Bd of Elections; Nat Assn Univ Women 1990-, Chprsn Nominations Comm; Phi Delta Kappa 1995-; Frank DeCosta Flwshp Morgan St Univ 1986; Inspiring Tchr Recognition Awd 1994; Spec Recognition Awd Amer Heart Assn 1987; DE PE Tchr of Yr 1986; *office:* Newark HS 750 E Delaware Ave Newark DE 19711*

CORNISH, DAVID FREEMAN, Director; *b:* Boston, MA; *m:* Caroline Eshbach; *c:* Caroline L., John S.; *ed:* Harvard Coll (AB) Bio 1974; Boston Coll (MED) Educ Admin 1985; *cr:* Dexter Schl Tchr, Admin 1974-; *ai:* Coach Ftbl, Bsktbl, Bsbl; *office:* Dexter Schl 20 Newton St Brookline MA 02146

CORONA, CAROL F., Special Education Teacher; *b:* Sterling, CO; *m:* Vincent J.; *c:* Vincent Jr., Rhonda Connors, Michael; *ed:* SUNY at Geneseo (BS) Elem, Spec Ed N-6 1975; Nazareth Coll of Rochester (MS) Spec Ed, Learning Disabilities 1977; 30 Hrs Grad Spec Ed, Admin Courses; *cr:* Genesee, Wyoming Boces Spec Ed Tchr 1975-77; Oakfield-Alabama Cntrl Schl Spec Ed Tchr 1977-; *ai:* Rdng Prgm Improvement Comm; NYSUT, NEA 1975-; Batavia City Cncl 1983-87; Batavia Youth Bd 1978-80; *home:* 8421 Stringham Dr Batavia NY 14020*

CORONEL, VICTOR FELIPE, Physics Professor; *b:* La Oroya Junin, Peru; *m:* Cecilia Moreno; *c:* Felipe, Claudia; *ed:* Haverford Coll (BS) Physics 1971; Columbia Univ (MS) Materials Sci 1979, (PHD) Materials Sci 1983; *ai:* United Nation Adv; AFT; Numerous Papers Written on Refered Journals 1982-; NSF Grant 1991-1993; United Nation Expert Biosignals & Med Imaging 1996; *office:* Rockland Comm Coll Sci Dept 145 College Rd Suffern NY 10901

CORONIS, SCOTT J., Dean of Students; *b:* Newport, NH; *m:* Shari Sue Searcy; *c:* Kassandra, Ariel; *ed:* Dartmouth Coll (BA) Drama 1980; *cr:* Montclair Kimberly Acad Drama Tchr 1983-, Chair, Fine, Performing Arts Dept 1985-, Talent Explosions Summer Prgm Dir 1992-, Dean of Stdnts 1994-; *ai:* Tech Dir; Ftbl, Vlybl Coach; *office:* Montclair Kimberley Acad 201 Valley Rd Montclair NJ 07042

CORPORA, JEFFREY ALLEN, Social Studies Teacher & Coord; *b:* Phillipsburg, NJ; *m:* Cynthia Sakasitz; *c:* Mark, Ryan, Ty; *ed:* Kutztown Univ (BS) Scndry Ed 1985; 12 Hrs Wilkes Univ of PA; 12 Hrs Carlow Coll of PA; 3 Hrs Univ of AK SE; 3 Hrs Allentown Coll of PA; *cr:* Easton Area HS 11th Grd Soc Stud Tchr 1985; Tannersville Learning Ctr Alternative Ed Tchr 1986; Easton Area MS 7th Grd Soc Stud Tchr 1987-; *ai:* Var Coach HS Girls Vlybl; Asst Var Coach HS Girls Sftbl; NEA, PSEA, EAEA 1987-; Easton Coaches Assn 1985-; *office:* Easton Area MS 1221 Northampton St Easton PA 18042

CORPUS, DEBORAH P., 10th Grade English Teacher; *b:* Royal Oak, MI; *m:* Charles W. Jr.; *c:* Andy, Hadley; *ed:* Mount Holyoke Coll (BA) Eng 1971; Univ of Dayton (MA) Eng 1979; Addl Grad Hrs; *cr:* Oakwood HS Eng Tchr 1973-80; Sinclair Comm Coll Composition Instr 1988; Miami Vly Schl Eng Tchr 1991; Oakwood HS Eng Tchr 1993-; *ai:* Newspaper Adv; NEA 1993-; OTA 1993-, Bldg Rep; Dayton Philharmonic Womens Assn 1984-, Exec Bd, Ed Prgms; *office:* Oakwood HS 1200 Far Hills Ave Dayton OH 45419

CORR, CHERIE ANNE PASH, Assoc Prof of Mathematics; *b:* Tonawanda, NY; *m:* D. Joseph; *c:* Chelsea, Daniel, Kendra; *ed:* SUNY at Albany (MA) Math 1971; 27 Grad Hrs Cmptr Sci; *cr:* Tamarac MS 8th Grd Math Tchr 1971-78; Tamarac HS Math Tchr 1978-79; HVCC Instr 1979-; *ai:* Stu Life, Chancellor's Awd, Math Lecture Comms; NYSMATYC 1980-; Delta Kappa Gamma 1978-; E Greenbush Schls 1993-, Spec Ed Comm; Belltop Schl PTO 1989-; Holy Spirit Choir 1994-; Tchng Excl Awd; Not a Bit of Difference Awd Disabled Stdnts Club; SUNY Two Yr Colls Consortium Capital Region Fac Dev Grant; *office:* Hudson Valley Comm Coll 80 Vandenburgh Ave Troy NY 12180

CORR, JOHN F., English Teacher; *b:* Kings Park, NY; *m:* Clare; *c:* John Henry, Mary Ellen; *ed:* SUNY at Stony Brook (BA) Eng 1969, (MA) Eng 1972; *cr:* Longwood HS Eng Tchr 1969-; *ai:* Bootstraps Traditional Music 1985-, VP; Recorded Tape; *office:* Longwood Sr HS 100 Longwood Rd Middle Island NY 11953*

CORRADO, DONALD L., Dean of Students; *ed:* Mount Saint Marys Coll (BS) Ed 1964; Saint Johns Univ (MS) Admin & Supervision 1967; *ai:* Honor Soc Adv; NYSUT 1968-; SAANYS 1975-; LICSS 1964-; *office:* Lincoln Orens Schl Trafalger Blvd Island Park NY 11558

CORRADO, MARILYN S., Instructor of Finance; *b:* Youngstown, OH; *c:* Amy Shoenberger, Tod Shoenberger; *ed:* Youngstown St Univ (BABS) Accounting 1983, (MBA) Finance 1986; Kent St Univ PHD Prgm Finance; *cr:* Home Savings & Loan Co Staff Accountant 1983-86; Youngstown St Univ Asst Prof of Finance 1986-89; Westminster Coll Finance Instr 1989-; *ai:* Curr Dev Comm; Adv Theta Chi; Stu Life Comm; Coord Bus Jeopardy Game; Financial Mngmt Assn 1988-; *office:* Westminster Coll New Wilmington PA 16142

CORRAO, DIANA, Math Teacher; *b:* Brooklyn, NY; *m:* John E. Thompson; *c:* Alexander Thomson, Jenna Thomson; *ed:* SUNY at Cortland (BA) Early Scndry Math 1972; SUNY at Stony Brook (MA) Lbrl Stud 1976; 60+ Post Grad Credit Hrs; *cr:* Robert Frost JHS & Deer Park HS Math Tchr 1974-; *ai:* NEA; Suffolk Cty Math Tchrs Assn; Finley PTA; Habitat for Hum; Sunday Schl Tchr & Various Comm in Church; Suffolk Cty Supt Valedictorian Luncheon Fac Rep.

CORRARO, DOMINIC J., Foreign Language Dept Chair; *b:* New Haven, CT; *m:* Tina DiSalvatore; *c:* Elisabetta, Angela, Dominic A.; *ed:* Southern CT St Univ (BS) Italian, Span, Fr 1983, (MS) Biling Ed, Fr & Italian 1989; *cr:* West Haven Adult Ed Italian, Span Tchr 1984-94; Notre Dame HS Fr, Italian, Span Tchr 1984-, Dept Chair, Frgn Lang Tchr 1989-; Albertus Magnus Coll Span Tchr 1995-; *ai:* Fr Hnr Soc; Italian Hnr Soc; Frgn Lang Club; COLT 1984-; AATSP 1990-; AATF, AATI 1985-; Knights of Columbus 1987-; Blessed Sacrament Church 1986-, Music Dir; AFM 1982-; UCONN Almuni Assn Excl in HS Tchng Awd1993; *office:* Notre Dame HS 24 Ricardo St West Haven CT 06516*

CORRELL, LINDA CONWAY, Advertising Professor; *b:* Pawtucket ; *m:* Stephen F; *c:* Shannon Conway Tompkins; *ed:* Mt Holyoke Coll (AB) Music 1960; Hunter Coll CUNY (MA) Music Composition, Theory 1968; Attnd NY Coll of Music, NYU; *cr:* Young & Rubicam Agency Copywriter, Supvr 1960-73; Mc Cann, Daniel & Charles Agency Copywriter, Supvr 1960-73; Cunningham & Walsh Agency Copywriter, Supvr 1960-73; Keller Crescent, Bozell, Bloom VP, Group Head, Assoc CD 1977-85; Fitzgerald & Co VP, Creative D 1985-88; Northeastern Univ Asst Prof 1991-; *ai:* Ad Club, Head Schl of Jrnlsm Adv; Core Curr, Centennial PR, Evaluate Fac & Staff Comms; AAA 1993-; New England Tech 1990-, Prof Adv, 5 Yr Svc Awd; NCIS 1994-, Bd of Dir; *office:* Northeastern Univ Schl of Journalism 360 Huntington Ave Boston MA 02115

CORRENTE, WILLIAM F., Social Studies & English Tchr; *b:* Johnstown, PA; *m:* Bettina M. Wingard; *c:* Brielle Marie; *ed:* Slippery Rock Univ (BA) Ed 1987; 4 Credits St Francis Coll; *cr:* St Francis Xavier 8th Grd Math Tchr 1988-89; Cntrl Cambria7th, 8th Grd Eng, Soc Stud Tchr 1989-; *ai:* HS Ftbl Offensive Coord; HS Weight Trng Coach; MS IM Weight Trng; NEA, PSEA 1989-; *office:* Central Cambria MS 205 W Highland Ave Ebensburg PA 15931*

CORRIDAN, PAULA MARIE, Science Teacher; *b:* Boston, MA; *m:* Brian Q.; *c:* Kevin, Colin, Kathryn; *ed:* Stonehill Coll (BS) Bio 1970; Springfield Tech Comm Coll 45 Credits Comp Classes; *cr:* Holy Name Schl Tchr 10 Yrs; Mulberry Orthopaedic Assn Sec 9 Yrs; MA Gen Hosp Chief of Orthopaedics Sec 3 Yrs; Brockton Schls Jr High Tchr 2 Yrs; *ai:* Local Chicopee St Patricks Colleen Contest Worker; NCEA 1985-; *office:* Holy Name Elem Schl 63 South St Chicopee MA 01013

CORRIGAN, BRUCE WILLIAM, Jr High Band Director; *b:* West Palm Beach, FL; *m:* Julie Matney; *c:* Megan, Craig; *ed:* IN Univ (BM) Music Ed 1983; IN Univ at Bloomington (MM) Music Performance 1990; Attnd Tanglewood Inst at Lenox 1979; Bowling Green St Univ 9 Hrs; Capital Univ at Columbus 2 Hrs; *cr:* Alexandria HS Band Dir 1984-86; Marion HS Band Dir 1986-88; IN Univ Assoc Instr 1988-90; Bowling Green City Schls Band Dir 1990-; *ai:* Jazz, Marching Bands; Composers Club; Scheduling, Levy Comms; Natl Band Assn 1985-; MENC 1986-; OH Music Edctrs Assn, All St Band Selection Comm; Percussive Arts Soc 1981-; Cub Scouts 1995-, Tiger Cubs Ldrshp; Little League Coach 1995-; Band, Percussion Ensembles, Trumpet, Woodwind, Clarinet Quartets Compositions; Band, Cmptr Grants; *office:* Bowling Green Jr HS 215 W Wooster St Bowling Green OH 43402*

CORRIGAN, MARY EVE BARRETT, Middle School Science Teacher; *b:* Frankfort-Am-Main, Germany; *m:* Richard W.; *ed:* OH St Univ (BS) Ed 1970; Post Grad Work Otterbein Coll; *cr:* Westerville City Schls Tchr 1970-76; Columbus Acad Tchr 1976-; *ai:* Prof Dev Comm; ISACS Fac Rep; Phi Delta Kappa; ASCD; OASCD; NSTA, SECO, NMLSTA, Sci Mbrshps; Life Care Alliance 1991-, Meals on Wheels; Immaculate Conception Parish; Who's Who Among Young Amer Prof 1989; NASA Name Orbiter Competion 1st Place Winner OH; Joule Awd OH Natl Energy Ed Dev 1994; OH House of Rep Citations 1994-95; *office:* Columbus Acad 43 Bottom Rd Gahanna OH 43230*

CORRIGAN, PATRICIA WALSH, Language Arts Teacher; *b:* (OH; *m:* Neil C.; *c:* Honora, Erin Martin, Elizabeth, Paul Lean; Dame Coll (BA) Eng 1963; *cr:* St Mary Schl Elem Tchr 19 William Schl Lang Arts Tchr 1991-; *ai:* Safety Patrol; Stu Co Yrbk; OCEA 1991-; OCTELA 1991-; Parish Cncl 1990-; TOPS 1 Lifescope Players 1995-; *office:* St William Schl 351 E 260th St 44132

CORRIGAN, WENDY (OTT), Art Teacher; *b:* Troy, NY; *m:* M *c:* Kelsey Jaye, Graeme Kiley; *ed:* SUC at Potsdam (BA) Painti 1979; UMASS at Amherst (MED) Instrl Media 1982; 41 Credits Stud; Art Ed Cert St Lawrence Univ 1978; 18 Credits Grad Cour Rose Coll; North Adams St Coll Educl Admin 1986-90; *cr:* Turn Schl Rdng Asst 1979080, Art, Long Term Sub Tchr 1983-84; Bc Schls Elem Art Tchr 1984-86; Burnt Hills-Ballston Lake HS 1986-; *ai:* Bldg Planning Cncl; HS Staff Dev Rep; Auditorium, Adv; Project Team Participant; Schl Drug, Alcohol Abuse Refe Procedures, Restructuring Comms; NY St Art Tchrs Ass Rensselaer Cty for Arts 1975-; Hudson Mohawk Hand Weav 1983-; NYSUT, AFT 1986-, Negotiation Team; NY St Uni BH-BLTA 1988-89; BH-BL Tchrs Assn 1986-, Chprsn, Pro 1992-93; Children's Books Illustrator, Graphic Designer; R Person Show Alternate Spaces Prgm 1980; Art Shows Exhib Recipient; Adjudicator Sage Jr Coll Stu Art Show 1993; *offi* Hills-Ballston Lake HS Lakehill Rd Burnt Hills NY 12027

CORRIVEAU, BEATRICE HATFIELD, English Tea Minneapolis, MN; *m:* Kevin D.; *c:* Garth, Alexandra; *ed:* Keer (BED) Scndry Eng 1970; Fine Arts & Writing; *cr:* Conant HS E *ai:* Granite St Challenge Coach; Dist Staff Dev Comm Rep; Tchrs Eng; NEA; NHEA; JREA; *office:* Conant H S 109 Stratton NH 03452*

CORRIVEAU, KEVIN D., HS English Teacher; *b:* Mancheste Beatrice H.; *c:* Garth, Alexandra; *ed:* Keene St Coll (BEd) Eng Attnd Univ of NH Content Area Rdng & Writing Post Grad, M Coll Writing Prgm & Rural Tchrs, Elem & Intermediate Convers *cr:* Hinsdale HS Intership 1971; Mascenic Regnl HS 5th-12th Tchr 1972-; *ai:* Curr Dev 3rd-12th Grd Dist Writing Prgm, 9th Outcome Based Ed Prgm; Facilitator for Curr & Instruction R Project; Eng & Music Dept Chprsn; NCTE, NHATE, ASDC & N Educl Video Review & Freelance; Recipient of Rockefell Middlebary Coll Studng the Writing Process; Mutiple H Differentiated Staffing Grants-Curr Dev; *office:* Mascenic Reg Turnpike Rd New Ipswich NH 03071

CORSETTI, SANDRA ESPEJO, Social Studies Teacher; *b:* M NY; *m:* James M.; *c:* Darren J., Damien P., Deana M.; *ed:* Syra (BA) Soc Stud Ed 1965; Tchrs Coll at Columbia Univ (MA) So 967; Attnd Hum Inst at Williams Coll; *cr:* Newburgh Free Acad Tchr 1967-72; Alternative Ctr for Ed Soc Stud Tchr 1985-90; Magnet MS Soc Stud Tchr 1990-91; Newburgh Free Acad Soc 1991-; *ai:* NCSS 1995-; NY St Cncl for Soc Stud 1995-; Mid-Hu Stud Cncl 1987-, Pres; Served on Curr & Mid Sts Evaluation Band Boosters Club; Various In-Svc Courses Including Multicult the Holocaust; *office:* Newburgh Free Acad 201 Fullerton Ave NY 12550

CORSO, GAIL SHANLEY, Asst Prof Of Commnctn Arts; *b:* NY; *m:* Charles M.; *c:* Christopher, Gina; *ed:* Brooklyn Coll (B Ed 1971; SUNY at Albany (MA) Eng 1972; Bowling Green St Ur Eng with Rhetoric & Comp 1991; SUC at Oswego 24 Credits Tow *cr:* Oswego HS Eng Tchr 1973-78; Onondaga CC Adj Instr Syracuse Univ Writing Coord, Consultant & Instr 1984-89; Bowl SU Rsrch & Tchng Fellow 1989-91; Neumann Coll Asst Prof Core Revision Chair 1995-; ETS Writing Consultant 1994-; WPA ATAC; NADE; AAUW; RRAA; NCTE 1971-, Media Liasion; Assn of Tech Writing 1993-, Rsrchr; WICI 1993-, Bd Mem; AAUP Jersey Rdng Assn 1995-, Bd Mem; Clearview Comm Schl Comm Mem & Recording Sec; Teagle Grant Awd 1995; Neumann PA Grant 1993; Bards Collaborative Learning Wkshp Schlrshp 198 Writing Pgm at Syracuse Univ Merit Bonus 1988; NYS Rege Schlrshp 1967-71; Rsrch & Tchng Flwshp & Grant Bowling 1988-90; *office:* Neumann Coll Concord Rd Aston PA 19014

CORSON, NANCY LYNN, 8th Grade Literature Teacher; *b:* P PA; *ed:* Working on Scndry Counseling Masters at Shippensburg Mount Union HS Tchr 1992-; *ai:* Girls Elem, Jr HS & Jr Var Bskt Yrbk & SADD Adv; Drama Coach; First Meth Church; *office* Union Area HS 706 N Shaver St Mount Union PA 17066

CORTAZZO, DIANE (DREISBACH), German Teacher; *b:* Nort PA; *m:* Charles P. Jr.; *c:* Jamie, Kurt; *ed:* Kutztown St Coll (BS) Lang 1976; Millersville St Coll Rdng Spec Cert 1977; *cr:* Parklan Tchr 1977-81, 1993-; Springhouse Jr HS Rdng Specialist 198 NEA 1977-; *office:* Parkland HS 2675 Rt 309 Orefield PA 18069

CORTEN, SYLVIE MARTINA, French & Spanish Teacher; *b* Provence, France; *m:* Albert John; *c:* Timothy, Amandine, D SUNY at Purchase (BA) Span, Ed 1987; Manhattanville (MA) F 1993; 15 Addl Hrs; *cr:* Chappaqua HS Fr Tchr 1987-88; New Roc Fr, Span Tchr 1988-89; Blind Brook HS Fr Tchr 1989-90; Ardsle Span Tchr 1990-; *ai:* Environment & Soc Awareness Club, Span Exchange Adv; Spon Fr 1, 2 Ind Stud; AATF 1990-; AATSP 1994- 1988-; Ardsley PTA 1990-; FASNY PA PTA 1991-; *office:* Ardsle Farm Rd Ardsley NY 10502*

CORTES, JULIO, Computer Science Teacher; *b:* New York, NY Asta; *c:* Joseph; *ed:* Borough of Manhattan C C (AAS) Data P 1970; Hunter Coll (BS) Med Cmptr Sci 1975; City Coll (MS) C 1986; 27 Post Grad Credits; *cr:* BMCC Sr Lab Tech 1969-83, Adj 1977-; Gould Inc Systems Analyst Prog 1980-81; BMCC F Lecturer 1983-; *ai:* Prof Staff Congress 1969-, Assembly Del; Ho Cornell Univ 1968; *office:* Borough Of Manhattan Comm Chambers St New York NY 10007

CORTESE, KRYSTAL KAY, 2nd Grade Teacher; *b:* Detroit, David W.; *c:* Scott, Jeremy; *ed:* UNC (BS) Elem Ed 1980; Mansfi (MS) Cmptr Ed 1989; *ai:* NEA 1980-; *office:* Big Flats Elem Maple Ave Big Flats NY 14814

CORTESE, RICHARD PHILIP, Social Studies Teacher; *b:* New *m:* Patricia Williams; *c:* Melissa; *ed:* Kean Coll (BA) Scndry Montclair St Univ (MA) Admin, Supervision 1980; *cr:* Union HS Tchr 1973-; *ai:* NEA, NJEA 1973-; UTEA 1973-, VP 1988-94 Stud Cncl 1985-; Mentor Tchr 1993-94; NJ Governors Tchr Rec Awd 1991.

CORWEL, PAUL PETER, English Teacher & Dept Lia Bridgeport, CT; *ed:* Fairfield Univ (BA) Eng 1974, (MA) Amer St (CAS) Educl Tech 1987; Georgetown Univ Amer Stud Inst f Flwshp; *cr:* Assumption Schl Eng Tchr 1976-78; Fairfield Woo Eng Tchr 1978-79; Andrew Warde HS Eng Tchr 1979-87; Fairfiel Tchr 1987-; *ai:* Key Club Adv; Eng Curr Revision Comm; NE FEA, CT Cncl of Tchrs of Eng, New England Assn of Tchrs of Er

76-; Arts Cncl of Greater New Haven 1995-; *office:* Fairfield HS ille Ave Fairfield CT 06432

LL, GEORGE V., Adjunct Instr Language & Lit; *b:* Philadelphia, nne Marie Mc Donnell; *c:* Melissa, Candace; *ed:* La Salle Coll 1967; Univ of PA (MA) Eng 1968; La Salle Univ (MA) Rel Ed nple Univ (MED) Curr & Instruction 1975; Lehigh Univ (EDD) 1984; Post Grad Work Philosophy Villanova Univ; *cr:* West Cath oys Eng, Rel, Music Tchr, Dept Chair 1968-75; West Cath Girls Prin 1975-85; Bucks Cty Comm Coll Adj Prof 1981-; Bishop Mc Vice Prin 1985-88; NJ Cath Conf Dir of Ed 1988-; La Salle Univ 1990-; *ai:* NCEA 1985-; CACE 1988-; Permanent Deacon OL Of l Church; Wilson Fnd Flwshp Univ of PA; Natl Endorment Schlsp oll; *office:* Bucks County Community Coll Swamp Rd Newtown

I, NORMA BAUM, Band & Choral Director; *b:* New Castle, PA; Rabeneck; *ed:* Westminster Coll (BME) Instrumental & Piano bert Morris Coll (MBA) Bus Ed 1985; Attnd Penn St Univ & y Intermediate Unit, Ed Credits; *cr:* New Castle Schls Elem hr 1962; Montour Schls General Music Tchr, Band & Choir Dir Marching Band; Jazz Ensemble; Montour Fine Arts Appreciation Music Educators, MENC, Natl Orch Assn, PSEA & NEA 1969-; ontour Schl Dist Grant St Coraopolis PA 15108

A, ANN MARIE (GRABLE), Lang Arts Tchr & Jr HS Coord; *b:* , PA; *m:* Gerald L.; *c:* Ann Marie, Sheree Trainham, Shelly, annizzo, Kathy Gural; *ed:* St Bonaventure Univ (BS) Elem Ed sdam coll (MS) Elem Ed 1970; *cr:* Sacred Heart 4th Grd Tchr Gregory the Great 7th, 8th Grd Lang Arts Tchr 1971-74; St Peter's ligion Coord 1974; Ft Drum NY Clerk 1974-83; Sacred Heart Jr Arts Tchr 1986-; *ai:* Jr HS Coord; NCEA 1993-; Kappa Delta Pi; eart Church 1978-; *home:* 609 Meriline Ave Watertown NY 13601

IUS, PAULINE HOLLOS, Science Teacher; *b:* Belleville, NJ; en; *ed:* Plymouth St Coll (BS) Environmental Sci 1981; Univ of Botany 1984; *cr:* Woodsville HS Sci Tchr 1985-; NH Tech Coll 1992-; *ai:* Class of 1999 Adv; Costa Rica Trips 1991 & 1995; ip 1992; New England Botanical Club 1980-; Kappa Delta Pi gma Xi 1984-; Haverhill Wetland Bd 1989-, Clerk; NH-VT Joint ommission 1994-; *office:* Woodsville HS High St Woodsville NH

, WAYNE ANTHONY, Chemistry Teacher; *b:* Revere, MA; *m:* n; *c:* Gina Maria, Christina, Anthony; *ed:* Merrimack Coll (BS) 75; Salem St Coll (MED) Schl Admin 1978; 15 Credits in Cmptr Chelmsford HS Chem Tchr 1975-78; Revere Schl System Data g Mgr 1988-92; Revere HS Chem Tchr 1978-88, 1992-; *ai:* NEA, nerican Chem Soc 1975-; Wakefield Elks 1986-; Mentor Tchr; Briarwood Ln Wakefield MA 01880*

TINI, MARIANNA RETTURA, Italian & Spanish Teacher; *b:* ne, Australia; *m:* Francesco; *c:* Sonya M., Adriano G., Daniela R.; cuse Univ (BA) Frgn Lang Ed 7-12, Italian Lang & Lit 1977; St Coll (MA) Elem Ed 1995; Addl Post Bacc Elem Ed 1-6 1992; d 3 Credits Each Intro to Educ Admin, Rsrch in Ed, Schl elations, Exper Curr Dev, Schl Prin; *cr:* Mt Carmel Schl K-8 Grds hr 1986-89; West Spfld HS 9-12 Grd Italian, Span Tchr 1990-; *ai:* ning & Understanding Through Cultural Exch Club; MA Tchrs A Italian Tchrs Assn; *office:* West Springfield HS 425 Piper Rd ngfield MA 01089

TINO, RICHARD VINCENT, Science Teacher; *b:* Steubenville, iana; *ed:* W Liberty St Coll (BA) Bio & Sci Comprehensive 1970; niv (MSEd) Ed 1981; *cr:* US Coast Guard BM 2nd Class 1970-74; a Jr HS 7th Grd Life Sci & 8th Grd Earth Sci Tchr 1974-95; Indian HS 7th Grd Life Sci & 8th Grd Earth Sci Tchr 1995-; *ai:* Sci f Stud Comms 1988 & 1996; NEA, OEA, ICEA 1974-; *office:* eek Jr HS 110 Steuben St Mingo Junction OH 43938

OVE, DANIEL J., 8th Grd US History Teacher; *b:* Waterville, Vendi, James; *ed:* Univ of ME at Orono (BS) Soc Stud 1971; 27 s in Ed, His & Geography; *cr:* Waterville Jr HS Geography & His 2-; *ai:* Soc Stud Curr Comm Chair; Girls Var Bsktbl Asst Coach; Girls Bsktbl Coach; NEA, ME Tchrs Assn, Waterville Tchrs 1972-; dication 1992; *office:* Waterville Jr HS Gilman St Waterville ME

R, BARBARA S., Math Teacher; *b:* Hartford, CT; *m:* Norman W.; Douglas; *ed:* Eastern CT St Coll (BS) Ed 1965; Univ of CT (MA) 90 Credit Hrs Beyond MA; *cr:* East Hartford Pub Schls 5th-7th 1965-69; Hartford Pub Schls 7th-8th Grd Math Tchr 1973-; *ai:* rtford Fed of Tchr 1973-; Union Schl Comm 1993-, Chprsn; CT stry Assn Grant; *office:* Lewis Fox MS 305 Greenfield St Hartford 2

R, JANET EHLERT, English Teacher; *b:* Dallas, TX; *m:* ; *c:* James Martis, Theodora Martis, Tim, Jennifer; *ed:* Kent St U g & His 1971; Cleveland St Univ Grad Courses; Case Western U; *cr:* Euclid Forest Park Jr HS Eng Tcher 1971-78; Cwy Comm nan Dev Inst 1981-83; Cleveland Hts HS Eng Tchr 1989-; Ctr for Writing Wkshp Presenter 1994-; *ai:* Schl of New Heights Lead for Adolescent Hlth 1995-; Books: Real People at Work & Laser ngineer; Jennings Scholar 1994; OH Dept of Ed Talent Pool; Pub s Articles Tchr of the Week; Channel 8 Apple Awd-Plain Dealer; Cleveland Heights HS 13263 Cedar Rd Cleveland Heights OH

R, STEPHEN EDWARD, Electronics Instructor; *b:* Oakland, MD; Knepp; *c:* Emily, Sarah, Jennifer; *ed:* WV Univ (BS) Engrng 1983; Courses Univ of MD, Frostburg St Univ & West VA Univ; *cr:* Garrett HS Electronics Instr 1983-; *ai:* VICA Adv; Boys Track EA & GCTA 1992-; St Johns Luth Church 1988-, Cncl.

EDWARD JAMES, 6th Grd Math Tchr & Team Ldr; *b:* Toledo, Debra; *c:* Ben, Brittany; *ed:* Univ of Toledo (BA) Ed 1976; OH St A) His 1984; Working on PHD Military His; *cr:* Finland Mid stern City Schls 6th Grd Tchr 1977-87; FBI US Govt Spec Agent rk St MS 6th Grd Tchr, Math Dept Team Ldr 1988-; *ai:* Bsktbl Natl League Math League Adv; 6th Grd Natl Champions 1995; EA 1977-, Bldg Rep; La Sabertache 1993-; Napoleonic Soc of 992-, Mentor, Achvmt Awd; 6 Dist Schl Bell Awds Tchng Excl; 2 ist Awds; ABCD of Yr Golden Bell Awd 1994; Numerous Articles Sts Rep to 1st Wellington Congress 1987, Iberian Congress 1992; ark Street MS 3191 Park St Grove City OH 43123*

BOON, JUDITH RENNE, Health & PE Teacher; *b:* Bridgeton, Vinfield; *c:* Brent; *ed:* Glassboro St Coll (BA) Hlth & PE 1973; *cr:* lloways Creek Elem Schl Hlth & PE Tchr 1973-; *ai:* Field Hockey, Sftbl Coach; Stu Cncl Adv; Pupil Assistance, Family Life Ed NEA, NJEA, NJSIAA Field Hockey Ofcl 1973-; PTA Stowcreek ec; Bd of Ed, Deacon of Church 1990-; Tchr of Yr 1994; *office:* lloways Creek Schl 967 Main St Salem NJ 08079

DOROTHY GROCH, Sixth Grade Teacher; *b:* New Brunswick, onn; *c:* Donn Jr., Debbie; *ed:* Amer univ at Washington (BA) Eng ttnd Newark St Tchrs Coll, OH Univ; *cr:* Western Elem Schl 4th ır 1983-90; Southeastern Elem Schl 6th Grd Tchr 1990-93; Bellefontaine MS 6th Grd Tchr 1993-; *ai:* Delta Kappa Gamma 1995-; NCSS 1994-; NEA, BEA 1983-; Kaizei Kobo Flwshp Awd to Japan; Article Pub; *office:* Bellefontaine MS 509 N Park St Bellefontaine OH 43311

COSTA, CAROL A., School Psychologist; *b:* Ludlow, MA; *ed:* Hartwick Coll (BA) Eng 1972; Amer Intnl Coll (MA) Educl Psych 1980, (CAGS) Schl Psych 1984; MAT Eng Prgm 27 Credits; Ed, Rdng 12 Credits; *cr:* Roscoe Cntrl Schl Eng Tchr 1972-74; HS of Commerce Eng Tchr 1974-83; Classical HS Eng Tchr 1984-85; Springfield Cntrl HS Eng Tchr 1986-95; Schl Psychlgst 1995-; *ai:* AWARE Club Adv, Drama Club Adv, Yrbk Adv; AFT, NEA, MTA 1974-; DKG 1981-; Amer Psych Assn 1989-; Mass Schl Psychologists Assn 1992-; NCTE 1976-; Horizon Shelter Bd 1989-95, VP & Pres; Natl Org for Women 1985-, Past VP & Pres; *office:* Springfield Central HS 1840 Roosevelt Ave Springfield MA 01109

COSTA, DONNA MARIE, Electronics Tchr & Dept Head; *b:* Peabody, MA; *c:* Dawne Marie Phelan, Brian Michael Phelan II; *ed:* North Shore Comm Coll (AS) Electro Mechanilal 1982; Univ MA at Boston (BA) Mngmt Human Svcs 1986; Saicm St Coll (MED) Schl RDM 1988; Harvard Grad Schl Educl (CAS) Tech Ed 1991; Cert Cmptr Aided Design Tech 1980, Electronic Tech 1989, Tech Writing 1986 North Shore Comm Coll; *cr:* Super Sub Shop Owner 1987-90; Peabody Schl System Elec Tchr, Dept Head 1981-; North Shore Comm Coll Site Facilitator 1993-; *ai:* Phi Delta Kappa, Sec 1990-92, Treas 1992-; MA Tchrs Assn 1981-, Tchr; PTA 1981-, Tchr; MA Voc Assn 1981-, Tchr; Amer Red Cross 1984-, CPR, First Aid Instr, 10 Yr Svc Pin; Curr Dev Horace Mann Tchr 1988-89; 25th Anniversary Brochure North Shore Comm Coll; *home:* 8 Monroe St Peabody MA 01960*

COSTA, ELIZABETH BARRETT, Vocal Music Teacher; *b:* Hartford, CT; *w:* Ronald Frank (dec); *c:* Deborah Ann; *ed:* Attnd Dowling Coll, Banks Street Coll 1962-63, Hartt Coll of Univ of Hartford 1960-61; Post Brentwood Ext 2 Courses in Ed; *cr:* East Hartford Pub Schls Vocal Music Tchr 1960-62; Church of All Nations Asst Tchr 1962-63; Manhattanville Day Care Ctr Asst Tchr 1962-63; Convent of the Sacred Heart Vocal Music Tchr 1963; Fort Wayne Pub Schls Vocal Music Tchr 1964; Town of Babylon Summer Music Prgm Dir, Piano Tchr 1973-82; Lindenhurst Pub Schls Vocal Music Tchr 1973-; *ai:* MENC 1991-; SCMEA, NYSSMA 1973-; NYSUT 1973-, Union Rep; Grace United Meth Church 1978-, Choir Dir, Organist; St Sylvesters 1972-, Organist, Choir Dir; Temple Sinai 1986-, Choir; St Johns Church 1964-67, Organist, Choir Dir; St Mark's Church 1964-67, Organist, Choir Dir; Congregational Church 1959-62, Soloist; PTA Life Mbrshp Awd 2 Times, Schlsp for 6 Coll Credits; Local Civic Awds; Wurlitzer Piano Course Self Tchng Tape & Books; *office:* Lindenhurst Pub Schls 350 Daniel St Lindenhurst NY 11757

COSTA, JAKE FRANCIS, Vice Principal; *b:* Fall River, MA; *m:* Joyce Silvia; *c:* Craig, Katelyn; *ed:* Fitchburg St (MED) Ed 1988; 18 Post Grad Hrs Ed; *cr:* Somerset North MS Soc Stud Tchr 1977-89; Berkley Comm Schls Soc Stud Tchr 1989-94, Dept Head 1990-94, Vice-Prin 1994-; *ai:* Soc Stud Curr Comm; Schlsp Comm 1984-, Pres; St Vincent De Paul Soc 1988-, Pres; Mass Reform Ed Grant; Staff Person of the Month; Commended for Saving a Childs Life-Heimlech Manuever; *office:* Berkley Cmty Schl 159 S Main St Berkley MA 02779*

COSTA, JOYCE, High School Math Teacher; *b:* Fall River, MA; *m:* John F.; *c:* Craig, Katelyn; *ed:* Bridgewater St Coll (BA) Math 1975; Grad Credits at Worcester Polytechnic inst; *cr:* North Attleboro HS Math Tchr 1975-80; Bishop Connolly HS Math Tchr 1982-; *office:* Bishop Connolly HS 373 Elsbree St Fall River MA 02720*

COSTA, MARY ANN T., High School English Teacher; *b:* Portland, ME; *ed:* Boston Univ (BS) Eng, Soc Stud 1973, (EDM) Rdng, Lang 1975; 22 Credits Grad Courses Problems Tchng Rdng Tufts Univ; CAGS Prgm cnslng Bridgewater St Coll; Critical Thinking, Cooperative learning Univ of MA; Tchr Effectiveness Trng Fitchberg St Coll; *cr:* Boston Pub Schls Sub Tchr 1975; Bridge Fund Inc Head Instr, Prgm Dir 1975-77; Avon Pub Schls Eng, Rdng, Soc Stud Tchr 1977-83; Southeastern Regnl HS Eng, Soc Stud Tchr, Curr Dev 1983-; *ai:* Lit Magazine Adv; Schl Conflict Mediation; Curr Dev; Integration project Mgr; Tech-Prep Eng Curr Specialist; NHS Fac Adv; Eng Dept Self-Evaluation Comm Chm; Stu Govt Day Adv; Southeastern Regnl Tchrs Fed, Amer Fed of Tchrs, AFL-CIO 1983-; Horace Mann Tchr 1988-89; Poem Pub Natl Lib Poetry Anthologies 1990, 1995; *office:* Southeastern Reg Voc Tech Sch 250 Foundry St South Easton MA 02375*

COSTA, ROXANNE FERREIRA, Social Studies Teacher; *b:* Fall River, MA; *m:* Arthur J.; *c:* Anthony, Andrew; *ed:* Bridgewater St Coll (BA) His 1972, (MED) Scndry Ed 1973; 30 Addl Credit Hrs; *cr:* Somerset HS Soc Stud Tchr 1973-; *ai:* Prep-Tech Comm; Somerset Tchrs Assn 1973-, Bldg Rep; MA Tchrs Assn, NEA 1973-; *home:* 24 Arruda Ave Somerset MA 02726

COSTABILE, JAMES NICHOLAS, 5th-8th Grade Teacher; *b:* Long Branch, NJ; *ed:* Montclair St Coll (BA) Soc & Behavioral Sci 1971; Monnmouth Coll (MA) Ed 1974; Glassboro St Univ 17 Hrs Elem Cert; Univ of DE 15 Hrs Pupil Personnel Svcs; Amer Univ 9 Hrs Child Psych; *cr:* Frank Antonides Schl 7th Grd Soc Stud Tchr 2 Yrs; Youth Horizons of Long Branch Ed Svcs Dir 3 Yrs; Elsinboro Twp Schl Tchr, Admin Asst 20 Yrs; *ai:* Tchr in Charge; Soc Stud Curr Chprsn; Team Instruction Ldr; Acad League Adv; NEA 1971-, Resolutions Comm; NJEA 1971-, Exec Comm; Amer Cancer Soc 1979-, Local Vol; Salem Cty Tchr of Yr 1985; Ed Articles Pub; *office:* Elsinboro Twp Schl Dist 631 Salem Fort Elfsborg Rd Salem NJ 08079

COSTABILE, MARY JO CROCE, Fifth Grade Teacher; *b:* Bridgeport, CT; *w:* Gino (dec); *c:* Gino; *ed:* Western CT St (BS) Elem Ed 1968, (MS) Elem Ed 1978; 75 Addl Credit Hrs Grad, Inservice Stud; *cr:* Veteran's Park Schl First Grd Tchr 1968-69; Cranbury Schl Fourth Grd Tchr 1969-71; Jefferson Schl Fourth, Fifth Grd Tchr 1971-84; Silvermine Schl Fifth Grd Tchr 1985-; *ai:* Tchr in Charge; Fac Cncl; Sci Fair Comm; Norwalk Fed Tchrs, AFT 1969-; Sweet Adelines Intnl Yankeemaid Chapter 1992-, Treas; Kappa Delta Pi; *office:* Silvermine Schl 157 Perry Ave Norwalk CT 06850

COSTAGLIOLA, THOMAS WILLIAM, Italian & Spanish Teacher; *b:* Mineola, NY; *m:* Graziella Faggiano; *c:* Ralph, Mario, Thomas Jr.; *ed:* City Univ NY (BA) Ed 1957, (MA) Italian, Span 1965; 18 Credits City Univ, Brooklyn Coll 1985; *cr:* Dyker Hts Jr HS Tchr 1960-70; Barnes Jr HS Tchr 1970-89; Moore Cath HS Tchr 1990-; *ai:* Lang Lab, Coord; UFT 1960-; Columbia Assn 1960-, Corresponding Sec; Natl Defense Ed Act Grant Cntrl CT St Coll 1961; Natl Defense Ed Act Grant Italy 1967; *office:* Moore Catholic HS 100 Merrill Ave Staten Island NY 10314*

COSTANTINI, FRANK JOHN, Horticulture & Lndscp Teacher; *b:* Mount Vernon, NY; *m:* Linda Cannito; *c:* David, Frank Jr.; *ed:* SUNY at Farmingdale (AAS) Ag 1960; City Coll of NY City Univ (BSEd) Occupational Ed 1987, (MSEd) Schl Admin 1991; Spec Ed Post-Grad Stud at City Coll of NY City Univ; *cr:* Carmine Labriola Inc General Supt 1962-72; Sitex Industries Inc Pres & Owner 1972-89; Mount Vernon HS Horticulture & Landscaping Tchr 1985-; *ai:* FFA Adv; Project Pals Coord; FFA Natl Mentoring Prgm; Mount Vernon Fed of Tchrs 1986-; Amer Horticultural Therapy Assn 1994; Village of Ardsley Comm Ctr 1986-87, Founder, Jenkins Awd; Ardsley Youth Comm 1985-88, Chprsn; Ardsley Planning Bd 1983-85; Ardsley Landscape Consultant 1982-90; Emotional Stability & Horticulture Research Accepted for Pub in Amer Journal of Therapeutic Horticulture 1994; Book to be Pub; *office:* Mount Vernon HS 100 California Rd Mount Vernon NY 10552*

COSTANZA, JOHN THOMAS, Mission Commander; *b:* Rochester, NY; *m:* Paulette M. Aube; *c:* Amy, Matthew; *ed:* Nazareth Coll (MS) Ed 1974; Certs K-6, 7-12 Math, 7-12 Soc Stud, Driver Ed; *cr:* West Ave Schl 4-6 Grd Tchr 1972-83; Jefferson Ave Schl 4-6 Grd Tchr 1983-89; Martha Brown MS 6th Grd Tchr 1989-95; Challenger Learning Ctr Mission Commander 1995-; *ai:* Pub & Private Groups Mission Commander; Challenger Simulated Space Missions Curr Dev; Stock Market Game Coord; Cross Cntry Coach; NYSUT 1972-; Certfd Fin Planners 1992-, CFP Degree; Fairport Bsbl 1985-, Umpire; Red Cross 1980-, Yth First Aid Instr; NY St Semifinalist Edctr of Yr 1992; Nom Local Edctr of Yr 1988-89; Acad Decathlon Awd 1995; *home:* 1525 Ayrault Rd Fairport NY 14450*

COSTEIN, IKE JOHN, Applied Physics & Chem Instr; *b:* Willard, OH; *ed:* Bowling Green St Univ (BS) Chem 1974; 30 Credit Hrs Heidelberg Coll; Working on MA Schl Cnslng; *cr:* Shelby Hosp Clinical Chemist ASCP 1973-80; Providence Hospital Chief Med Technologist ASCP 1980-86; Pioneer CTC Applied Sci, Physics, Chem Instr 1986-; *ai:* Adv Teams 1 Yr, VICA 9 Yrs, Asst 1 Yr; Tech Comm 2 Yrs; Tech Prep Advy Comm 5 Yrs; NEA, OEA 1986-; OVA, AVA 1986-, Applied Sci Tchr of Yr; NSTA 1986-, Top 10 in Nation 1996; OVA Ashland Oil Tchr Achvmt Awd-Team Category 1988; 1st Place Stdnt Winners Principles of Tech Natl VICA Contest 1992, 1995; Team USA Intnl Schl Olympics 1995; Pioneer Tchr of Yr 1995; NCTA Top Ten Sci Tchr of Yr 1996; *office:* Pioneer Career & Tech Ctr 27 Ryan Rd Shelby OH 44875*

COSTELLO, AMELIA FUSCO, English & Theater Teacher; *b:* Schenectady, NY; *m:* Thomas Michael; *c:* Jason Sean; *ed:* Russell Sage Coll (BA) Eng 1971, (MS) Elem Ed 1973; N Adams St Coll (Cert) Admin 1996; Attnd SUNY at Plattsburgh, St Rose Coll, SUNY at Albany; *cr:* St Madeleine Sophie 4th Grd Tchr 1970; Averill Park Cntrl Eng, Theater Tchr 1971-1996, Eng & Admin Asst 1995-; *ai:* Drama Club; Sr Awds Night; Study Skills Comm; Staff Dev; District Shared Decision Making Team; Sched Comm; NYSUT 1971-, Convention Comm, VOTE, COPE; AFT 1971-; Averill Park Tchr Assn 1971-, VP; Troy Area Labor Cncl 1981-82, Pres, Labor Person of Yr 1982; Phi Delta Kappa Capitol Dist Assn for Women in Admin; St Jude's Rosary, Altar Soc 1990-, Lector, Eucharistic Minister; Pub Articles; Intnl Biography; Who's Who, Amer Ed, Amer East, Emerging Leaders, Ed; Intnatl Bio; *office:* Averill Park HS 16 Gettle Rd Averill Park NY 12018*

COSTELLO, BRIAN PATRICK, English Teacher; *b:* Albany, NY; *m:* Patricia Rockette; *c:* Jacqueline, Patrick, Cara; *ed:* North Adams St Coll (MED) Eng 1971; Credit Hrs Univ of VT, Castleton St, Coll of St Joseph; *cr:* Adams Jr HS Eng Tchr 1969-71; Rutland Jr High Eng Tchr 1971-87; Rutland HS Eng Tchr 1987-; *ai:* 7th Grd Bsktbl Coach 1974-77; Jr Class Adv, Eng Dept Chm 1994-; NEA 1971-; Knights of Columbus 1982-; Parish Cncl 1980-90, Mem; Curr Advy Bd 1985-; *home:* 16 Howard Ave Rutland VT 05701

COSTELLO, CAROLYN, Curr & Spcl Project Acting Dir; *b:* Syracuse, NY; *c:* Saralyn, Rob, Keri, Joshua; *ed:* SUNY at Oswego (BS) Elem Ed 1987, (MS) Rdng 1990, (CAS) Educl Admin 1993; 21 Credit Hrs Math Instruction; Ctr for Innovation in Ed Instr; *cr:* Hastings Mallory Elem Schl 4th & 5th Grd Tchr 1988-90, 6th Grd Tchr 1990-93; Cntrl Sq Intermediate Schl Curr Consultant 1993-95; Cntrl Sq Schl Dist Curr Acting Dir 1996; *ai:* IRA; CNYRC; ORC; Article Pub 1990; Facilitated Formulation of Comp-Generated 5th Grd Report Cards with Inclusion of Whole Lang Philosophy; Conducted Stud on Retention Policies & Practices for Cntrl Sq Schl Dist; Led Math A Way Of Thinking Follow-Up for Tchrs; Dev Summer Rdng & Writing Pgm for Onondaga Comm Coll for Kids Pgm; Presentations: Univ of AZ, CIMS Trng, Whole Lang Umbrella Conf, SUNY Oswego, HILL Trng, Pulaski Supt Conf Day; *home:* 37 Brooks Pl Baldwinsville NY 13027

COSTELLO, CECILIA LONCZAK, English Teacher; *b:* Springfield, MA; *m:* Edward J. III; *c:* Edward IV, Jason, Nathan; *ed:* Amer Intnl Coll (BA) Eng 1964; *cr:* Chicopee Comprehensive HS Eng Tchr 1978-; *ai:* Class 1994 Adv; Pro Merito NHS 1988-90; NEA, MTA, CEA 1978-; Bus, Prof Women's League 1991-; *office:* Chicopee Comprehensive HS 617 Montgomery Rd Chicopee MA 01020

COSTELLO, FRANK T., Director of Community Ed; *b:* Hoboken, NJ; *m:* Claire Wraga; *c:* Lauren, Cynthia; *ed:* Jersey City St Coll (BA) Music Ed 1967, (MA) Music Ed 1971; NJ Dept of Ed Educl Admin, Supervision Cert 1975; *cr:* Secaucus Pub Schls Elem Music Tchr 1971-75, Mid-Scndry Music Tchr 1976-; Dir of Comm Ed 1995-; *ai:* Concert, Jazz Bands Dir; Audio Visual Coord; Musical Theatre Productions Orch Conductor; Secaucus Ed Assn 1971-, First VP; Hudson Cty Ed Assn, Second VP; NJEA, NEA Third VP; Music Ed Natl Conf; Comm Arts 1989-, Dir; Schlsp Theatre, Musical Dir; Who's Who 1991-92; *office:* Secaucus Mid-Scndry Schls 11 Millridge Rd Secaucus NJ 07094

COSTELLO, GUY W., High School Social Stud Tchr; *b:* Youngstown, OH; *ed:* Youngstown St Univ (BS) Comprehensive Soc Stud 1991; OH Coll of Massotherapy Massotherapist License 1995; *cr:* Leetonia HS Soc Stud, World Geog, His, Ec, Psych, Civics, Rdng 1992-; *ai:* Teen Inst Adv; JV Head, Asst Var Bsktbl Coach; Soc Stud Dept Chair; NEA, Leetonia Ed Assn 1992-; Yth Ministry Instr 1986-; Weight Trng Facility Owner 1987-; Outstdng Geog Tchr of Dist 1993; *office:* Leetonia HS 181 Walnut St Leetonia OH 44431

COSTELLO, JAMES FRANCIS, ESL Teacher; *b:* Methuen, MA; *m:* Ingrid Reyes DeLeon; *c:* Santiago F., James Miguel; *ed:* Univ of MA at Amherst (BA) Ed 1984; Tchrs Coll at Columbia Univ (MA) TESOL 1992; *cr:* US Peace Corps in costa Rica Comm Developer 1985-87; Henry K. Oliver Schl ESL Tchr 1987-88; Northern Essex Comm Coll ESL Tchr 1992-; Andover Pub Schls ESL Tchr 1990-; *ai:* Comm Svc Tutors Adv; NEA 1990-; MATSOL 1991-; *office:* Andover HS Shawsheen Rd Andover MA 01810*

COSTELLO, JEANNE RUSS, Integrated Language Arts Tchr; *b:* Philadelphia, PA; *m:* John A.; *c:* John C., Bryan F.; *ed:* Holy Family Coll (BA) Elem Ed 1976; Beaver Coll (MA) Rdng Disabilities & Difficulties 1978; *cr:* Immaculate Conception 2nd Grd Tchr 1976; St Benedict 2nd & 4th Grd Tchr 1976-79; Our Lady of Consolation 5th-8th Grd Tchr 1980-81; Our Lady of Calvary 6th Grd Tchr 1989-; *ai:* Integrated Lang Arts Coord 4th-8th Grd; NCEAA 1989-.

COSTELLO, JOAN F., High School Guidance Cnslr; *b:* Teaneck, NJ; *m:* Thomas E. Rubin; *ed:* Fordham Univ (BS) Ed 1965; New York Univ (MA) Guidance 1971; Columbia Univ (MS) Soc Work 1981; Inst for Mental Hlth Ed Cert 1984; *cr:* Holy Rosary Schl 6th-7th Grd Tchr 1962-64; Our Lady of Grace Schl 8th Grd Tchr 1965; Holy Rosary Acad HS Math Tchr 1966-70; North Bergen HS Guidance Cnslr 1971-; *ai:* AFT, North Bergen Fed of Tchrs 1972-; Friends of Franklin Lakes Lib 1994-; *office:* North Bergen HS 7417 Kennedy Blvd North Bergen NJ 07047*

COSTELLO, LYNN HAMMER, English & Drama Teacher; *b:* Jersey City, NJ; *m:* Louis J.; *ed:* Jersey City St Coll (BA) Eng 1970; Montclair St Univ (MA) Speech & Theatre 1977; Attn Georgetown Univ; 6 Hrs Fr Dijon Univ 1971; 32 Hrs Theatre Montclair Univ; *cr:* Kearny HS Eng & Drama Tchr 1970-; *ai:* Spring Drama Presentations Dir; NEA, NJEA 1970-; NCTE 1970-78, 1996; Contact Hotline 1987-89, Vol; Holy Family Parish 1995-, Song Ldr at Mass; One of 50 Tchrs Geraldine R. Dodge Fnd Theatre Prgm Tchrs & Playwrights 1991; Original Poetry Presenter Dodge Poetry Festival 1988; Mid Sts Mem Visiting Comm 1981; NEH Shakespeare Inst Indiana Univ 1987; NJ Environmental Issues Seminar Selectee 1990;

Selected to Sing Choir for John Paul II 1995; *office:* Kearny HS 336 Devon St Kearny NJ 07032*

COSTELLO, MARSHA SIMS, Latin Teacher; *b:* Huntington, WV; *m:* Andrew J. Jr.; *c:* Michael, Patrick; *ed:* Univ of Richmond (BA) Latin 1966; Univof VA (MED) Cnslr Ed 1970; Attnd St Bernard Coll, Univ of AL; *cr:* Wilson HS Latin, His Tchr 1966-67; Henley Jr HS Latin, His Tchr, Guid Cnslr 1971-72; Wyoming Seminary Latin Tchr 1980-; *ai:* Stud Skills Coord; SAT Admin Asst Guid Cnslr; Disciplinary Comm Fac Rep; Amer Classical League; Church of Christ Uniting, Ed Task Force Co-Chair, Choir; *office:* Wyoming Seminary Upper Schl 201 N Sprague Ave Wilkes Barre PA 18704

COSTELLO, MONICA, Principal; *b:* Brooklyn, NY; *ed:* Marywood (BS) Ed, Eng 1976, (MS) Rel 1980; Attnd NY Univ 1983; Cmptr Update Classes; *cr:* Tchr Grds 1-2, 4-5 1959-83; Olph Schl Prin, Tchr 1976-83; Holy Rosary Schl Prin 1983-85; Our Lady of Lake Verona Prin 1985-88; St Mary's Elem Schl Prin 1988-; *ai:* Long Term Planning, Prin Search Comms; Mid States Evaluator; NCEA 1956-; Church, Rel Comm 1956-, Various Comms, Working Woman Awd; Albany Lobbyist; *office:* Saint Marys Elem Schl 1340 Northern Blvd Manhasset NY 11030*

COSTELLO, STEVEN, Soc Stud Tchr & Var Bsbl Coach; *b:* Queens, NY; *m:* Donna Lyn Trapanese; *c:* Keelyn, Zachery; *ed:* Albany St Univ (BA) Pol Sci 1982; Stoney Brook Univ (MA) 1995; Hofstra Univ Law Schl 1983-84; *cr:* Jonas Salk MS Permanent Sub 1985-86; New Covenant Chrstn Schl Scndry Tchr 1986-89; Mac Arthur HS Soc Stud Tchr 1989-; *ai:* Coach Jr Var Bsktbl, Var Bsbl; NHS Admission Bd; Aths Helping Aths Peer Leadership Group Supvr; AFT, NYSUT 1989-; Nassau Cty Bsbl Coach of Yr 1993-94; Coached 1993-94 Long Island Bsbl Champions; *office:* General Douglas Mac Arthur HS Old Jerusalem Rd Levittown NY 11756*

COSTELLO, SUSAN MARIE, English Teacher; *b:* Utica, NY; *m:* Robert M.; *ed:* Nazareth Coll of Rochester (BA) Eng 1968, (MA) Scndry Ed 1975; *cr:* Penfield Schl Dist Seventh Grd Eng Tchr 1968-; *ai:* Co-Ed Lit Magazine Penprints; Site-Based Shared Decision-Making Team; NCTE; ASCD; NYSUT; Co-Author of Basic Business English 1986; Tchr of Excl Awd NYS Eng Cncl 1989; *office:* Bay Trail MS 1760 Scribner Rd Penfield NY 14526

COSTELLO, WILLIAM JOHN, Science Teacher; *b:* Hartford, CT; *c:* Erick, Casey, Emma; *ed:* Cntrl CT St Univ (BA) Bio, Chem 1979; Post Grad 60 Credit Hrs; *cr:* Otter VLy HS Sci Tchr 1980-86; Champlain VLy UHS Sci Tchr 1986-; *ai:* System Dynamics Stud Group; NSTA 1980-; VSTA 1987-; ASCD 1990-; Make a Wish Fnd 1992-, Town Planning Commision; Tech Grants; Guest Speaker 1994 Goals 2000; Outstdng VT Tchr 1988; NHS Tchr of Yr 1991; Tandy Tech Scholar 1992; *office:* Champlain Valley Union HS RR 2 Box 160 Hinesburg VT 05461*

COSTELLOE, PAUL KEVIN, Ec, Govt & His Insight Tchr; *b:* New York City, NY; *m:* Helga A. Skelka; *c:* Claire-Ellen, Meredith-June Jude; *ed:* Manhattan Coll (BA) Arts 1963; Hofstra Univ (MA) Ed 1970; Stony Brook Univ (MLS) Lbrl Stud 1978; 6 Credit Hrs Towards PHD; Black Belt Shotokan Karate; Brown Belt Aikido; *cr:* Patchogue Sr HS His Tchr 1963-65; US Marine Corps Lt 1965-68; Westhampton Beach HS His Tchr 1968-; *ai:* Karate Instr; Aikido Stu; Suffolk Inst of Eastern Stud St James NY; NYSUT 1968-; NY St Educl Dept Grant 1975-76; Book: Tears of the Moon 1978; *office:* Westhampton Beach HS 49 Lilac Rd Westhampton Beach NY 11978

COSTELLO-KUHNER, MARY CECILIA, Librarian; *b:* Bronx, NY; *m:* Vincent; *c:* Vance, John, Mary Kate; *ed:* York Coll (BA) Art His 1986; John Jay (MA) Criminal Justice 1992; Queensbo Cert Comp Sci 1984; *cr:* PS 66 Tchr 1986-95, Librn 1995-; *ai:* Story Tellers Club Moderator; Ruth Eilenberg Awd for Environmental Edctr 1994; *office:* PS 66 The Oxford Schl 8511 102nd St Richmond Hill NY 11418

COSTER, ELIZABETH PEISS, High School Art Teacher; *b:* Madison, WI; *c:* Lisa Marie, Michael Walter, Angela Patricia; *ed:* OH St Univ (BEA) Art Ed 1979, (MA) Ed Admin 1981; 30 Post Grad Credits; *cr:* Groveport Madison Schls Elem Art Tchr 1979-81, MS Art Tchr 1981-91, HS Art Tchr 1991-; *ai:* GMLEA Exec Bd; Taught GATE Ger; Scheduling, GATE, LEVY Comm; Art Graded Course of Stud Participant, Originated, Revised CCD Tchr; NEA 1979-; OAEA; PTA, Treas; Bd of Ed St Mary's Ger Village; Jennings Scholar; *office:* Groveport Madison Local Schls 5500 S Hamilton Rd Groveport OH 43125

COSTNER, BARBARA M., Latin & Mathematics Teacher; *b:* London, England UK; *m:* Dale; *c:* Lesley Hildebrand, Angela McTaggart, Ivan McTaggart, Adrienne Hudson, Ingrid McTaggart; *ed:* St Andrews Univ (MA) His 1955; AZ St Univ (MED) Rdng 1980; Diploma of Ed 1956; 30 Grad Hrs for Math Endorsement; 24 Grad Hrs for Media Specialist Endorsement; 30 Grad Hrs for Elem Endorsement; 9 Grad Hrs for Latin Endorsement; *cr:* Assunta Convent at Petaling Jaya Geog & His Tchr 1963-65; Garden Scndry at Kuala Lumpur Prin & His Tchr 1966-71; Higley Elem 5th-8th Grd Tchr 1973-79; Corona del Sol HS Rdng & Latin Tchr 1979-86; Haberdashers Schl at Monmouth Latin Tchr 1986-87; Chopticon & Leonardtown HS Latin & Math Tchr 1988-; *ai:* Latin Club Spon; Amer Classical League; AWANA Childrens Group 1993-, Team Ldr; *office:* Chopticon HS Rt 242 Morganza MD 20660

COTE, DIANE NEWMAN, Fourth Grade Teacher; *b:* Springfield, MA; *m:* Richard J.; *c:* Mark, Brian; *ed:* Our Lady of Elms Coll (BA) Sociology, Soc Work & Ed 1960; 35 Credits Toward Masters; *cr:* Ludlow Pub Schl 1st Grd Tchr 1960-65; Saint Thomas the Apostle 1st, Kndgtn & 4th Grd Tchr 1979-; *ai:* Sunshine Comm Chprsn; Meal Chain Chm; NCEA 1979-; NEA, MTA 1960-65; *home:* 24 Autumn Rd West Springfield MA 01089

COTE, PATRICIA C., ESL Teacher; *b:* Bronx, NY; *c:* Paul Marc; *ed:* Manhattan Coll (MA) Rdng 1969; Iona Coll (MS) Urban Ed 1983; CNR Coll of New Rochelle Post Grad Stud; *cr:* Lincoln Elem Schl 1st-3rd Grd, 6th Grd Tchr 1962-, ESL Tchr 1978-; Our Lady of Lourdes 6th Grd Tchr 1965-66; *ai:* Schl Productions Participation; TESOL 1978-; MT Vernon Fed of Tchrs 1970-; Jenkins, PTA Awds 1986; *office:* Lincoln Elem Schl 170 E Lincoln Ave Mount Vernon NY 10552*

COTE, PAUL D., Social Studies Teacher; *b:* Fall River, MA; *m:* Nancy Ann Viveiros; *c:* Marc, Megan; *ed:* U of MA at Amherst (BA) Sociology 1973; Bridgewater St (MAT) Behavioral Scis 1983; *cr:* Joseph Case Hs Soc Stud Tchr 1973-; *ai:* Girls Tennis Coach; SWansea Tchrs Assn 1973-, Bldg Rep; Amer Legion 1980-; MA Archaeological Soc Inc 1983-; *office:* Joseph Case HS 70 School St Swansea MA 02777

COTE, SUSAN L., Home Economics Teacher; *b:* Biddeford, ME; *m:* Donald R.; *c:* Lydia, Emily; *ed:* Univ of ME (BS) Home Ec 1975; Attnd Southern ME Tech Coll; *cr:* Belfast Area HS Home Ec Tchr 1975-76; Biddeford HS Home Ec Tchr 1976-, Dept Head Home Ec 1988-90; *ai:* JV Chrldng Coach 1976-77; Adv Support Team 1990-; Class Adv 1982-83; AVA, MHEA 1994-; Svc Awd Culinary Arts 1994; *home:* 4 Hillview Avenue Ext Saco ME 04072

COTE-CROSSKILL, SCOTT ANDREW, Life Science Teacher; *b:* Lewiston, ME; *m:* Nicole Cote; *c:* Mitchell, Ashley; *ed:* Univ of ME (BA) Zoology 1974; Finishing MA Degree in Ed 1996; *cr:* Fryeburg Acad Life Sci Tchr 1976-; *ai:* Extended Tchr Ed Prgm; NEA; NSTA; NABT; Knights of Columbus 1994-; Bd Mem of Overseers for the Regional Lab for the Improvement of ED in Northeast, Islands; NEWMAST Participant; *office:* Fryeburg Acad 152 Main St Fryeburg ME 04037*

COTHRAN, MARY MC CAA, Nursing Instructor; *b:* Fairmont, PA; *ed:* Mary Baldwin Coll (BA) Bio 1970; Univ of TN at Knoxville (BS) Nrsng 1977, (MS) Nrsng 1980; PhDc Nrsng Univ of Pittsburgh; *cr:* Park West Hosp ICU Staff Nurse 1977-78; Planned Parenthood Family Nurse Practitioner 1982-84; Knox Cty Hlth Dept Family Nurse Practitioner 1980-82, 1984-86; Univ of Pittsburgh Nurse Pracitioner, Edctr 1988-; *ai:* Doctoral Nrsng Stu Org Pres 1995-; Sigma Theta Tau 1977-, Chptr Pres 1978, Rsrch Eta Chptr; AANP 1989-; NPASP 1989-, VP 1993-95; ASPO 1978-; Planned Parenthood Med Comm; Pub Article 1995; Rsrch Awd Sigma Theta Tau Eta Chptr 1994; *office:* Univ Of Pittsburgh 440 Victoria Bldg 3500 Victoria St Pittsburgh PA 15261

COTTEN, ANNE BOYER, Associate Prof of Art & Design; *b:* Phoenix, AZ; *m:* Robert R. II; *c:* Kimberly Martin, John, Matthew; *ed:* Drexel Univ (BS) Applied Arts in Interior Design 1962; Cornell Univ (MA) Preservation Planning, His of Architecture 1987; Rural Preservation Prgm; *cr:* Vestal Cntrl Schl Jr HS Art Instr 1962-63; The Fair Store Head of Interior Design Dept 1963-67; Ind Designer Boyer Cotten Interiors Designer, Owner 1967-82; First Presbyn Church Dir Music 1986-91; The Madrigal Choir ArtisticDir 1978-; Broome Comm Coll Adjunct Instr 1978-84, Assoc Prof Art, Design 1985-; *ai:* Fine Art, Design Club Adv; Comm Coll Cncl on The Arts, Exec Mem; Fac Coord Annual Stu Art Exhibition; OFLA Div Fac Assn Rep; Comm Outreach Comm; FATE 1992-; NEA 1980-; AGO 1986-; Preservation Assn of Southern Tier 1980-, Pres, VP, Consultant; Honor for Enrichment Prgm Elem Schls; Broome Cty Historical Soc 1985-, Speaker; First PResbyn Church 1979-, Co-Historian; Binghamton Museum of Fine Arts 1991-, Exec Comm, Acting Sec; Fine Arts Assn 1975-, Pres; Research Grant John Nolen Collection Fnd in Rare, Manuscript Collections; Three Part Article Broome Cty Historical Soc Newsletter; Spec Architectual Consultant Awd Winning Fourth Grd Enrichment Prgm; Grant NYSCA All Women Composers Concert, Grant Recipient for Dave Brubeck Concert; *home:* 13 Jutland Rd Binghamton NY 13903*

COTTER, CARMELA MARIE, English Teacher; *b:* Middletown, OH; *m:* Michael; *c:* Sean; *ed:* Univ of Notre Dame (BA) Eng & Theater 1984; James Madison Univ (MS) Dance 1986; Xavier Univ Cert Scndry Ed 1991; Univ of Dayton & Wright St Univ Post Grad Stud; *cr:* James Madison Univ Tchng Asst 1985-86; Blue Ridge Coll Instr 1986; Fenwick HS Eng Tchr 1987-91; Lemon Monroe Hs Engl Tchr 1991-; *ai:* Soc Comm; Ohion Ed Assn 1991-; Middletown Tchr Assn 1991-; Tri-Arts Assn 1992-, Pres; Article Pub; *office:* Lemon Monroe HS 101 W Elm St Monroe OH 45050*

COTTER, JAMES, Professor of English; *b:* Boston, MA; *m:* Emily Kerrick; *c:* Anne, James, John; *ed:* Boston Coll (BA) Classics 1954, (MA) Philosophy 1955; Fordham Univ (MA) Eng 1958, (PHD) Eng 1963; *cr:* Fordham Univ Asst Prof 1960-63; Mount Saint Mary Coll Assoc & Full Prof 1963-; *ai:* Fac Dev Comm; Intnl Hopkins Assn 1969-, Pres 1989-; Dante Soc 1989-; Friends of Newburgh Lib 1979-, Pres; NEH 1968, 1984 & 1989; Fulbright-Hays Lecturer 1970-71; Author of Inscape Univ of Pittsburgh 1972, The Divine Comedy Thousand Element 1990; Articles & Poetry in SP, VP, HQ, ELS, Hudson Review Amer; *office:* Mount Saint Mary Coll 330 Powell Ave Newburgh NY 12550

COTTER, JAMES PATRICK, Science Teacher; *b:* Williston Park, NY; *m:* Nicole Wagner; *c:* Emily Rachel; *ed:* Washington & Lee Univ (BA) Bio 1988; Adelphi Univ (MA) Scndry Ed 1991; *cr:* Chaminade HS Sci, Bio, Earth Sci, Cmptrs Tchr 1990-; *ai:* Woodworking Club Asst Supvr; Swimming Pool Supvr; Sci Olympiad Adv; Diocese of Brooklyn Sci Cncl 1990-; NY St Tchrs Assn 1991-; Phi Gamma Delta 1985-, VP 1988; *office:* Chaminade HS Jackson Ave Mineola NY 11501

COTTERMAN, M. SCOTT, Mathematics Teacher; *b:* North Baltimore, OH; *ed:* Univ Findlay (BA) Math 1989; Grad Stud Cmptrs & Curr Ashland Univ; *cr:* South Cntrl HS Math Tchr 1989-; *ai:* Jr Class Adv; 8th Grd Girls Bsktbl Coach; NEA, OEA, SCEA 1989-; *office:* South Central HS 3305 Greenwich-Angling Rd Greenwich OH 44837*

COTTIER, ELEANOR BRALEY, Substitute Teacher; *b:* New York City, NY; *m:* Edward John; *ed:* Marymount Coll (BA) Eng & Elem Ed 1956; Hunter Coll (MA) Eng Ed 1964; Assumption Coll (CAGS) 20th Century Lit & World Lit 1984; Anna Maria Coll 6 Credit Hrs; St Michaels 12 Credit Hrs; Worcester St Coll 9 Credit Hrs; Cath Univ 6 Credit Hrs Guid; Vassar Coll 6 Credit Hrs; *cr:* St Bridgets Elem Schl 1st-2nd & 6th-8th Grds Tchr 1951-60; Mother Butler Mem & Acad Sacret Heart of Mary 1961-70; Algonquin Regnl HS Tchr 1971-; *ai:* MTA 1971-; NCTE 1971-; NEA 1971-; Camp Cnslr & Dir 1960; Marriage Encounter 1975-84; Pre-Cana Marriage Prep 4 Yrs; Evenings for Couples 2 Yrs; Schl Spon Week at DIGITAL 1980's; Horace Mann Grant; ELS to Corps Frgn Adults 80 Hrs; *office:* Algonquin Reg HS 79 Bartlett St Northborough MA 01532*

COTTLE, SHIRLEY DARLENE (FODOR), Computer Office Tech Teacher; *m:* Steven; *c:* Deanna D., Brett C.; *ed:* Wright St Univ (BS) Comprehensive Bus Ed, Data Processing 1988, (MS) Classroom Tchr 1991; Attnd INFOCOMM Intnl Washington DC 1992; *cr:* Miami Vly PCA Sec, Bookkeeper 1971-73; Society Bank Sec, Supvr, Loan Processor 1973-79; Self Employed Child Care Attendant 1980-85; Greene Cty Career Ctr Bus Ed Tchr 1988-; *ai:* Stu Svcs Advy Comm 1988-; Tech Task Force Comm 1990-; Wright St Univ Search Comm for Bus, Mrktg Tchr Edctr 1990-91; OVA, AVA 1988-; OEA, NEA GCCC EA Div 1988-, Sec 1980-91, Treas 1993-94; OBTA-NETEA 1988-; Bus Prof of Amer 1986-, Adv; *office:* Greene Cty Career Ctr 2960 W Enon Rd Xenia OH 45385

COTTON, MARTINE BINDLER, French Teacher; *b:* Paris, France; *m:* Paul Robert; *c:* Paul, Benjamin; *ed:* Univ of MA at Dartmouth (BA) Fr 1979; Lesley Coll (MA) Ed 1994; *cr:* Falmouth Acad Fr Tchr 1977-81; Falmouth HS Fr Tchr 1981-; *ai:* Fr Club, HS Stdnts Tchng in Elem Schls Adv; SC Mem 1994-; Supt Awd 1985; *office:* Falmouth HS Guifford St Ext Falmouth MA 02540

COTTON, TAYLOR H., Librarian; *b:* Shippenville, PA; *m:* Donna Bashline; *c:* Taylor Jr.; *ed:* Clarion Univ (BSEd) Soc Stud, Eng, Lib 1962; Post-Graduate Stud Univ of Pittsburgh, Slippery Rock Univ, Gannon Univ; *cr:* Univ of MD Tchr 1962-64; Beaver Falls Schl Dist Tchr 1964-69; Lakeview Schl Dist Librn 1969-; *ai:* Lit Guild Club Adv; Curr Cncl; Strategic Planning Comm; Schl Assessment Team; NEA, PSEA 1964-; PSLA 1969-; MEFA 1978-; Access PA Consortium, Lintel 1984-; Mercer Co Sheep & Wool Growers 1974-, Dir; Mercer Co Wheel Patrol 1988-, Past Pres; Clydesdale Breeders of USA 1992-; Articles Pub; *office:* Lakeview Schl Dist 2482 Mercer St Stoneboro PA 16153*

COTTONE, GLORIA LIPSCOMB, Sixth Grade Math Teacher; *b:* Lynchburg, VA; *m:* Richard Edward; *c:* Stacia Elizabeth; *ed:* Western Carolina Univ (BS) Elem Ed 1969; Cntrl CT St Univ (MS) Ed 1979; Univ of Hartford Sixth Yr Educl Admin 1984; 12 Credits Toward EDD Ed Ldrshp Univ of Sarasota 1995; *cr:* Charlotte-Mechlenburg Schls Grd 5 Tchr 1969-70; Newington Pub Schls Grd 1-3, 5-8 Math, Soc Stud Tchr 1972-; *ai:* Schl Newspaper; Walking Club; Aerobics Club; Cooking Club; CT Ed Assn, Newington Tchrs Assn 1972-; Hartford Jaycees 1975-85, Soc Comm, Food for Needy; Suffield CC 1979-88, Tennis Comm, Children's Prgm; Suffield Bapt Church 1980-85, Yth Dept Tchr; Nom Newington Tchr of Yr; *office:* John Wallace MS 71 Halleran Dr Newington CT 06111

COTTONE, JOSEPH RAUOL, Physical Education Teacher; *b:* Hanover, NH; *m:* Cindy Lou; *c:* Danielle Leigh, Alexander Joseph; *ed:* Norwich Univ (BS) Bus Admin 1971, (MED) Admin of PE 1977; 15 Semester Credit Hrs Educl Ldrshp; *cr:* Norwich Univ Asst Ftbl, Head Track Coach, Assoc PE Prof 1977-81; Plymouth St Coll Head Ftbl Coach, PE Instr 1981 of MA Asst Ftbl Coach 1986-88; William H Hall HS PE, Hlth T Ftbl Coach 1988-; *ai:* Curr Comm; Peer Mediation; Stu Assts Tea Harrassment Comm; Frosh Girls Lacrosse Coach; Head F 1988-95; HS Evaluation Team; NEA, WHEA, CHSCA, NFF *office:* William H Hall HS 975 N Main St W Hartford CT 0611

COTTREL, WILLIAM RUSSELL, Naval Science Instructor; OH; *m:* Pamela Ann Frazier; *c:* Katherine, Elizabeth, Erin; *ed:* G (BS) Ed 1971; Naval War Coll (MS) Military & Intnl Affairs 19 Navy Ofcr & Naval Aviator 1971-93; Belmont HS Naval Sci In *ai:* Rifle Team Coach; Marksmanship & Orienteering Instr Schl for Ldrshp Experience; Orientation Visits to Military Installatio Ed Purposes Spon; NEA 1993-, Area Del; OEA, WOEA Prospective Change, Goal III Comm; Process Comm PCP 1993- Area 9 1993-, Spon Instr for New NJROTC Units in Western O Belmont HS 2323 Mapleview Ave Dayton OH 45420*

COTTRELL, DANIEL A., 5th Grade Teacher; *b:* Glen Falls Monelle Allison Weeks; *c:* Christopher, Jordan Renee; *ed:* Potsdam (BA) Iss, Economics, Ed 1977; SUNY at Plattsburgh Elem, Sec Ed 1982; *cr:* Hadley Luzerne Central Schl 3rd, 5th Grd 9th Grd Tchr 1977-86; Queensburg Schl 5th Grd Tchr 1986-; Bsktbl Coach; NYSUT, NEA 1977-.

COTTRILL, CHERYL LYNN, Second Grade Teacher; *b:* G OH; *ed:* OH Univ (BS) Elem Ed 1973; Coll of Mt St Joseph Specialty 1988; *cr:* Westfall Local Schl Dist Remedial Rdng T Darby Elem Schl First Grd Tchr 1973-83; Monroe Elem Schl Tchr 1984-93, Second Grd Tchr 19930; *ai:* Tch Comm Dist Care NEA, Cntrl OH Ed Assn 1973-; Westfall Local Ed Assn 197 *home:* 85 N High St Chillicothe OH 45601

COTTRILL, MICHAEL DAVID, Accounting Professor; *b:* We *m:* Peggy Fletcher; *c:* Alexandra; *ed:* WV Univ at Wesleyan Admin 1970; VA Tech (MS), (mAC) Accounting 1975; CPA Arthur Young & Co CPAs Staff Auditor 1970-73; Thiel Coll A 1975-85; Northeastern Univ Lecturer CBA 1985-; *ai:* Betas Alp Adv Natl Honorary Accounting; Amer Inst of CPAs 1977-, PA Ins 1977-, Outstanding Contg Prof Ed Instr; MA Soc of CP Outstanding Contg Ed Instr; Beta Gamma Sigma, Natl Honorar Majors in Bus, Fincance, Accounting Tchr of Yr 1993-95; No tchng Hall of Fame (bA 1995; *office:* Northeastern Univ 404 Ha 360 Huntington Ave Boston MA 02115

COUCH, CAROL DIEDRICH, Mathematics Teacher; *b:* Akro Howard C. Jr.; *c:* Benjamin, Peter; *ed:* OH St Univ (BSEd) Math Ashland Univ (MEd) Educl Admin 1994; *cr:* Elyria HS Math Tch N Canton Jr HS Math Tchr 1974-78; Hoover HS Math Tchr 1988 Growth Comm Chprsn 1993-; Tchr Mentor 1995-; NEA; OEA; *office:* Hoover HS 605 Fair Oaks Ave SW North Canton OH 447

COUCH, PHILIP GEORGE, Technology Teacher; *b:* Secaucu Karen M.; *c:* Devyn, Dane; *ed:* CO St Univ (BS) Indstrl Arts Credits Towards MED; *cr:* Bayshore MS Indstrl Arts Tchr Middletown HS South Tech, Indstrl Tchr 1990-; *ai:* Ski Club; Re Tech Comms; NEA, NJEA, MTEA 1981-; Shore Shop Tchrs A Citizens Ad-Hoc Referendum Comm 1995-; Whithycomb G Portion of Book: A+ for Excellence; *office:* Middletown HS Nutswamp Rd Middletown NJ 07748

COUCHE, JUNE MC LORIE, Sixth Grade Teacher; *b:* Philade *m:* Richard; *c:* Krista Mc Lorie Reber, Mark Mc Lorie; *ed:* W Univ (BS) Elem Ed 1970; Penn St at Marywood Masters Equiv Ward Elem Schl Fifth Grd Tchr 1972-91; Bradford Hghts Elem Grd Tchr 1972-; *ai:* Instrl Support Team; NEA, DAEA 197 Bradford Heights Elem Schl 1330 Romig Rd Downingtown PA

COUDEN, LINDA BURNS, Eighth Grade Teacher; *b:* New Have Theodore L. Jr.; *c:* Janice C. Surato, Susan C. Hitchcock, Micha Southern CT St Coll (BS) Elem Ed 1960; *cr:* Mary L. Tracy Sch Tchr 1960-61; St Aedan Schl 8th Grd Tchr 1971-, Vice Prin 1992 Chprsn; Moderator Jr High Discussion Seminar; Schl Newspa Times & Fac Adv; Stu Cncl; NCEA 1971-; *home:* 228 Alden Haven CT 06515

COUFAL, CAROL ANN (ROOT), English Teacher; *b:* Syracus James E.; *c:* Laura, Eric; *ed:* Syracuse Univ (BS) Speech, Dra SUNY at Albany (MS) Comm, Inst Tech 1975; Attnd SUC at Syracuse Univ; *cr:* Clifton Fine Cntrl Schl Eng, Sub Tchr Fayetteville Manlius HS Eng Tchr 1984-85; LaFayette Jr Sr HS 1985-; *ai:* Syracuse Univ Eng Acad Chair, Eng Ed Host Tchr; LaFayette Tchrs Assn 1985-, Bldg Rep; NEA; Cazenovia Ambulance Corp 1994-, Dispatcher, Communications Comm Ch Assn of NYS 1980-84, Hosp Aux Northern Region Exec Mem; Fayette Jr Sr HS RR 11 N La Fayette NY 13084*

COUGHENOUR, REETA COLTON, Instrumental Music Te Hanover, NH; *m:* Ronald Lee; *c:* Carrie Lee, Gabrielle, Claire; *e* VT (BS) Music Ed 1974; 30 Credit Hrs; NFIMA Certfd Adjudi Proctor Elem Schl 4-6 Grd Instrumental Music Tchr 1974-78; Pr HS 7-12 Grd Instrumental, Choral Music Tchr 1974-82; Stockbri Schl 1-6 Grd Instrumental, Classroom Music Tchr 1982-83; Rutl Schl 4-8 Grd Instrumental Music Tchr 1983-; *ai:* Jazz, Marchi Hlth Curr Comm; Dist Festivals; St Dist Sec; NIFMA 1992- MENC 1974-; Pittsfield Federated Church 1963-, Organist, C Sunday Schl Tchr; Proctor Summer Band; Greater Rutland Co VT Tchr of Yr 1991; All-Male Big Band Ldr 3 Yrs; *office:* Rutl Schl Post Rd Rutland VT 05701*

COUGHENOUR, SALLIE EILEEN, Chemistry & Math Te Windber, PA; *m:* Thomas; *c:* Benjamin A.; *ed:* PA St Univ (B Math & Ed 1970; Masters Equivalent 1995; Post Grad Work at U Penn St, Univ of Pittsburgh at Johnstown, IN Univ of PA & W *cr:* Conemaugh Twp Tchr 1970-75; Forrest Hills Tchr 1980-81; N 1981-; *ai:* NEA, PA Tchrs Assn & NSTA 1981-; Mellon Gr Fellow.

COUGHLAN, BARBARA ANN JUNG, German Teacher; *b:* *m:* Edward J.; *c:* Christine, Jeffrey; *ed:* Montclair St (BA) Ger Paterson St 1991; Bus & WP Morris Cty 1994; *cr:* Kinnelon HS Ger Tchr 1982-93; Morris Hills Adult Schl 1987-; Morris Cty G AP Tchr 1989-; Iberia Lang Schl Adult Tutor, Translator 1992- Club; Hnr Soc; AATG 1983-; Comm Club Telemark Sec Geraldine Dodge Awd; Gregg Bus Awd; Translated Diary From re Bosnia Ger to Eng; *office:* Vernon Twp HS PO Box 800 Vernon

COUGHLIN, HEIDI SCHIFFERLI, English Teacher; *b:* Roche *m:* Patrick J.; *ed:* Clarion Univ 25 Credit Hrs Eng; *cr:* Marathon Eng Tchr 1990-93; Brookville Area HS Eng Tchr 1993-; *ai:* B Area Ed Assm 1993-; DuBois Comm Theater 1994-, Bd; *office:* B Area HS Jenks St Brookville PA 15825

COUGHLIN, JACK A., Guidance Counselor; *b:* Boston, MA; Maloney; *c:* Colleen Kilfoil, Susan, Caroline, Seana, Cathleen; *ed* Coll (AS) Accounting 1959; Suffolk Univ (BS) Accountir Bridgewater St Coll (MS) Counseling 1965; *cr:* Bourne S Guidance Cnslr & Tchr 1962-; *ai:* Bourne Educators Assn, MA T 1962-; *home:* 25 Olney Rd Buzzards Bay MA 02532

ƷHLIN, JOAN DAMON, Fourth Grade Teacher; *b:* Northampton, : William, Lisa C. Hayes, Kevin, Timothy; *ed:* North Adams St (BS) 55; Sacred Heart Univ (MA) Tchng Ed 1989; *cr:* Fawn Hollow Elem ·rd Grd Tchr 1967-69; Booth Hill Elem Schl 4th Grd Tchr 1985-; *ai:* Patrol Adv; Acad Excl, Nutrition Comms; NEA, CEA 1985-; TEA Schl Rep; Phi Delta Kappa 1988-.

HLIN, PATRICIA LAMBERT, 7th-8th Grd Soc Studies Tchr; *b:* lyn, NY; *m:* Robert Joseph; *c:* Patricia Coughlin Boyle, Mary, ., Kathleen Coughlin De Meo, Cecelia, Maureen; *ed:* Suffolk Comm AA) Liberal Arts 1980; SUNY at Old Westbury (BS) N-6th Ed 1981; hi Univ (MS) Rdng LD Background 1987; Cert Math & Rdng gh 12th Grd, Elem Ed N-6; *cr:* St Benedict Joseph RC 4th Grd Tchr -Cont 1983-85; St Ladisluas RC 5th Grd Tchr of Self-Cont 1985-86; amily RC 5th & 6th Gr Tchr Math 1986-88; PS 231 Springfield Gard d Math Tchr 1988; Maria Regina RC 7th-8th Grd Soc Stud, LA Tchr Holy Family RC 7th-8th Grd Soc Stud Tchr 1989-; *ai:* nalization Tchrs Rep 1991-; Forum Rep & Head Comm 1991-; san Rep 1993-; SACPES Rep 1993-; *office:* Holy Family R C Schl 25 m Ave Hicksville NY 11801

HLIN, ROBERT CHARLES, US History Teacher; *b:* Quincy, MA; li Dill; *c:* Michael, Kevin, Laura; *ed:* Westfield St Coll (BA) Amer 80; Salem St Coll (MA) Amer His 1988; *cr:* Melrose HS AP US His 1984-; Northern Essex Comm Coll Part-time His Instr 1993-; ry Coll Part-time His Instr 1995-; *ai:* Girls Tennis Coach 1991-93; Vinter Track Coach 1989-92; NEA 1984-; *office:* Melrose HS 360 ills Pkwy Melrose MA 02176

IBALY, SALIF, Spanish Teacher; *b:* Bamako, Mali; *ed:* Temple BBA) Fin, ECO, Intnl Bud 1991; The Franco-Amer Centero, Mngmt iploma Bus Admin 1990; *cr:* Washington Cty Bd of Ed Span Tchr 2 ncoln Univ Fr Tchr 1 Yr; *ai:* Article Published 'You and Frgn Lang'.

L, PENNY PRUETT, High School Art Teacher; *b:* Philadelphia, Curtis E.; *ed:* Univ of NC at Greensboro (BFA) Art Ed 1965; Drexel MS) Rdng 1988; Addl 6 Post Grad Credits; 21 Post Grad Credits at t Univ; 12 Post Grad Credits at Temple Univ; 22 Post Grad Credits Other Insts; *cr:* Anne Arundel Jr HS Art Tchr 1965-69; Wordsworth Art Tchr 1970-71; Upper Merton Area Jr & Sr HS Art Tchr 1971-; *ai:* r Project & Dept Assts Comms; NEA, PSEA 1971-; UMAEA 1971-, *ffice:* Upper Merion Area HS 435 Crossfield Rd King Of Prussia PA

STON, THERESA AURIEMMA, Sixth Grade English Teacher; *b:* ne, NJ; *c:* Scott Anthony; *ed:* Jersey City St Coll (BA) Elem Ed 1968; dits Towards Masters; Cmptr, Peer Ldr Courses; *cr:* Vroom Schl rd Tchr 1968-77; Bailey Schl First, Second, Sixth Grd Tchr 1979-; lti-Cultural, Citywide Testing, Pupil Assistance, Hlth, & Safety s; Peer Ldr; NJEA, Bayonne Tchrs Assn 1968-; St Henrys Rosary chr of Yr Awd 1988; *office:* John M Bailey Elem Schl 12 75 W 10th onne NJ 07002

TER, CHRISTINE WILSON, Business Teacher; *b:* Pittsburgh, PA; rey L.; *c:* Brandon, Jordan; *ed:* IN Univ of PA (BS) Bus Ed 1978, Bus Ed 1983; *cr:* Somerset Area Vo-Tech Schl Shorthand Instr); Somerset Area HS Bus Tchr 1980-; *ai:* Bus Ed Coord; FBLA Adv 5; PA Bus Ed Assn, NBEA 1980-; Somerset Ed Fnd 1995; *office:* et Area HS 835 S Columbia Ave Somerset PA 15501

TER, GERTRUD PEUKERT, German Teacher; *b:* Leitmeritz, Republic; *m:* Edward A.; *ed:* SUNY at Albany (BA) Ger, Eng 1962; se Univ (MA) Ger Ed 1967; *cr:* C. W. Baker HS Ger Tchr 1962-; *ai:* 3 1963-; *office:* Baldwinsville Cntrl Schl 29 E Oneida St nsville NY 13027

TRIP, MARSHA LOUISE, Health & Physical Ed Teacher; *b:* k, OH; *ed:* Lorain Cty Comm Coll (AS) 1976; OH Univ (BS) Hlth, 8; Ashland Coll (MS) Sports Sci 1988; 15 Addl Hrs toward Cert Ashland Univ; *cr:* Wellington Exempted Village Schls 9th & 10th E Tchr 1979-; *ai:* Head Var Vlybl 15 Yrs, Jr Var Sftbl 7 Yrs Coach, bl Assn, Vlybl Dir 2 Yrs; NHS Adv 1995-, Wellington High Schl; gton Ed Assn 1979-, Pres 1989, Treas 1985; Lorain Cty Vlybl s Assn 1981-, Treas 1985-, Pres 1992-93; Appointed Hlth Curr by OH St Dept of Ed; *office:* Wellington Sr HS 629 N Main St gton OH 44090

CIL, MARILYN WILLIAMS, Fourth Grade Teacher; *b:* oro, NC; *w:* Charles Sr. (dec); *c:* Jonathan, Adrienne, Charles Jr.; Cntrl Univ (BS) Bus Ed 1971; Univ of Bridgeport (MS) Scndry Ed th Yr Elem Ed 1987; *cr:* Gimbels Dept Store Sales Clerk 1972-80; for Bridgeport Comm Dev Sec 1980-83; Univ of Bridgeport Sec, Cnslr 1983-85; Longfellow Schl Fourth Grd Tchr 1987-; *ai:* Chrldr EA, NEA 1986-; Alpha Kappa Alpha 1986-; Coalition of 100 Black 1992-; Negro Bus, Prof Women 1993-, Financial Sec; Phi Delta *ffice:* Longfellow Schl 139 Ocean Terr Bridgeport CT 06605

ELL, SHERRY PHILLIPS, Instructor of Hlth Occupations; *b:* , DE; *m:* William Sherman III; *c:* Angela, Nathan; *ed:* Univ of MD Nrsng 1991; Macqueen Willis Schl of Nrsng Grad 1977; Tchng Cert Attnd Univ of MD at Coll Park, Loyola Coll; *cr:* CA Nrsng Home red Nurse 1977-; Dr Christian Jensen Registered Nurse 1977-80; ctine Convent Registered Nurse 1980-; CA Hlth Svc Hlth Ed, red Nurse 1980-91; CA Career & Tech Cntr Hlth Occ Instr 1991-; Cty Chptr Hlth Occupations Stdnts Amer Adv; Yr Long Comm Hlth ss Project Local, St, Natl Lead Stdnts; Sigma Theta Tau 1991-; Girl of Amer 1992-, Assist With Troop Act; Amer Red Cross 1992-, Instr; ccupations Stdnts of Amer Mems Competed St & Natl Levels First 1995; *home:* PO Box 52 Goldsboro MD 21636

HAN, DARLYN JOYCE, Magnet Mathematics Teacher; *b:* land, MD; *m:* Mark W. Chambre'; *ed:* Hood Coll (BA) Math 1970, chl Admin 1982; Univ of MD Math 12 Credit Hrs 1971, Ed 3 Credit 2; Loyola Coll 3 Hrs 1982; Montgomery Cty Pub Schls Inservice 25 Hrs 1971-86; Amherst Coll 6 Hrs 1992; *cr:* Cabin John JHS chr 1970-75; Takoma JHS Math Resource Tchr 1975-77; Ridgeview ath Resource Tchr 1977-81; John F. Kennedy HS Math Tchr ; Takoma Park MS Magnet Math Tchr 1984-; *ai:* Math Team Magnet Team; AFT 1972-, Albert Shanker Awd 1993; MCMTA, 1976-; NCTM 1975-; CPAM 1990-; VFW Auxilliary 1411, 1976-; MD Math Counts Comm 1991-93; MD Mathalon Comm ; David W. Taylor Sigma Xi Math Recognition Awd 1993; Phi Phi; NSF Grant 1971-72, 1990, 1992; Natl Dean's List 1982-83; Who of Amer Women 1981-82, 1983-84; Presidential Awd in Math 990; Wrote 2 Chapters of Geometry Textbook; Women in Ed Awd tanding Achvmt Math 1986; *office:* Takoma Park MS 7611 Piney Rd Silver Spring MD 20910*

CELLE, WANDA HARWOOD, Sixth Grade Teacher; *b:* ton, VT; *m:* Lawrence J Jr.; *c:* Jeffrey, Sarah; *ed:* Castleton St Coll em Ed 1972, (MA) Curr & Instruction 1985; 25 Addl Credits Hrs Masters; *cr:* Shaftsbury Elem Schl 3rd Grd Tchr 1972-73; VT Ctr Tchr Asst for Multihandicapped 1973-74; Castleton Elem Schl th Grd Tchr 1974-87; F D Barstow Meml Schl 2nd & 4th-6th Grd 87-; *ai:* Asst Prin; Stu Cncl Adv; NEA 1974-; VT-NEA 1974-; 1987-; BEA 1987-, Past Pres; Federal Grant for Photography Click; Selected by VT Dept of Ed for Promising Practice in VT; ding Young Women of Amer; ARSU Tchr of Yr; Presidential Scholars Distinguished Tchr; *office:* Barstow Meml Schl Chittenden VT 05737

COURCHESNE, MICHEL MAURICE, 8th Grade French Teacher; *b:* Lewiston, ME; *m:* Elizabeth A. Dube; *c:* Aimee; *ed:* Univ of Southern ME (BS) Industrial Arts Ed 1979, (MS) Instructional Leadership 1989; *cr:* Holy Cross Elem Schl 8th Grd Soc Stud Tchr 1980-84; Lewiston MS 8th Grd French Tchr 1985-; *ai:* Intramural Sports Coach; City Wide Staff Dev Comm, Schl Wide Prof Dev Comms; Pride Comm Chm; Adv-Advisee Comm Sec; End of Yr Comm Chm; Mentor for New Tchrs; NEA, Lewiston Ed Assn 1985-; *office:* Lewiston MS 75 Central Ave Lewiston ME 04240

COUREY, MARIA REGINA, Jr High Instructor; *b:* Roanoke, VA; *ed:* Nazareth Coll (BS) Elem Ed 1964; Eastern KY Univ (MA) Eng 1973; OH Dominican Coll (BA) Theology; 3 Hrs Span, 3 Hrs Theology Thomas More Coll; Attnd Xavier Univ; *cr:* St Anthony Schl Jr HS Instr 1965-69; St Joseph Schl Acting Prin 1969-70; St Matthias Schl Jr HS Instr 1970-71; John XXIII Schl Jr HS Instr 1971-73; St Agnes Schl Jr HS Instr 1973-75; Bishop Ready HS Eng, Theology Tchr 1975-77; Holy Spirit Schl Rel Ed Coord 1977-80; St Pius X Schl Jr HS Instr 1980-; *ai:* Shakespearean Residency; CDEA 1976-; Prin Advy Comm 1995-; Diocesan Liturgical Commission 1984-88; Eastern KY Univ Grant 1968; NSF Grant 1978; Distngd Tchr Awd 1986; *office:* St Pius X Schl 1061 Waggoner Rd Reynoldsburg OH 43068

COURSEY, LEON N., Health & Physical Ed Prof; *b:* Queens, NY; *ed:* Queens Coll (BS) Hlth & PE 1968, (MS) PE 1969; OH St Univ (PHD) PE & Ed Admin 1971; Addl Post Doctoral Stud in Sports Medicine, Athletic Trng, Kinesiology, Law & Ath, Piano, Glass Cutting, Fr & Adapted Spec Ed; *cr:* Queens Coll Tchng Asst 1969; OH St Univ Instr 1970-71; Brockport St Coll Asst Prof & Bsktbl Coach 1971; Univ of MD Eastern Shore Assoc Prof, Athletic Dir & Prof Stud Dean 1972, Hlth & PE Prof; *ai:* PE Majors Acad Adv; Stu Org Adv; MAHPERD 1975-, Pres; MATE 1980-, Treas; MSTA 1975-, Exec Bd; MAHE 1980-, Exec Bd, Mentor Awd; AAHPERD 1971-, Ethnic Affairs Comm; DELMARVA Bus League 1994-, Exec Bd; Phys Fitness Commission, Exec Bd; MD St Games 1977-, Exec Bd; AAHPERD- Eastern Dist 1975-, PE VP; Book The Prof Contributions of Edwin Bancrot Henderson, The Prof Contribution of Black PE Educators; Sponsored Womens Bsktbl Team & Stdnts to Local & Dist Prof Meetings; *office:* Univ Of MD Eastern Shore Backbone Rd Princess Anne MD 21853*

COURTEMANCHE, MARGOT SUZANNE, Ninth Grade English Teacher; *b:* Washington, DC; *ed:* Assumption Coll (BA) Eng 1994; Bowie St Univ Grad Pgm; *cr:* Tiffanys Bakery Cake Decorator 1986-94; Potomac HS Eng Tchr 1994-; *ai:* Co-Spon of Art Club & Lit Magazine; JV Girls Vllybl Coach; Swim Team Head Coach; NEA 1994-; *office:* Potomac HS 5211 Boydell Ave Oxon Hill MD 20745

COURTOIS, MICHAEL GEORGE, Biology Teacher; *b:* Worcester, MA; *m:* Kathleen Hamel; *c:* Mary Beth, Patrick; *ed:* Coll of the Holy Cross (BA) Bio 1981; Worcester Polytechnic Inst (MNS) Natural Sci 1990; Grad Courses Univ of MA, Lowell & Worcester St Coll; *cr:* Salem HS Bio Tchr 1981-; *ai:* Dist Summer Schl Dir 1988-; Stu Cncl Adv 1984-; Stu Expectations Comm; NEA, NEA-NH 1981-; Salem Ed Assn 1981-, Bldg Rep, Negotiator; NSTA, NHSTA, NABT 1982-; Natl Assn of Stu Cncls, Warren Schull NH Stu Cncl Adv of Yr 1994; *office:* Salem HS 44 Geremonty Dr Salem NH 03079*

COURTRIGHT, JANICE L., English Teacher; *b:* Flushing, NY; *c:* Jennifer Durner, John Durner; *ed:* Salem Coll (BA) Eng 1974; 9-12 Grd Post Grad Classroom Mngmt 9 Credits; *cr:* Belvidere HS Eng Tchr 1975-; *ai:* Fac Adv AIDS Awareness Comm, Partnership in Ldrshp 1994-; NEA, NJEA 1974-; *office:* Belvidere HS Oxford St Belvidere NJ 07823

COUSENS, JAMES BLAINE,JR., Visual Arts Teacher; *b:* New Bedford, MA; *m:* Leslie Paula Kelly; *ed:* Univ of MA at Dartmouth (BA) Art Ed 1992; *cr:* Mansfield Kids Lead Presch Tchr 1992-93; Attleboro HS Visual Arts Tchr 1993-; *ai:* SADD Adv; ACT Asst; Saturday Breakfast Club Supvr; Teen Ctr Art Instr; Summer Schl; SMARTS; MS Tchrs Assn 1993-; Teen & Family Outreach Prgm 1993-, Staff, Art Instr, Grant; Attleboro Museum 1993-, Staff; Attleboro Cultural Cncl Art Grant; *office:* Attleboro HS 100 Rathbun Willard Dr Attleboro MA 02703*

COUSIN, KIM FANT, Physical Education Teacher; *b:* Fostoria, OH; *m:* Arthur Darnell; *c:* Nelson Jermain De'Angleo, Andre Duvall; *ed:* OH St Univ (BA) Spec K-12 PE 1984; Drivers Ed Tchr; Working on Cnslrs Degree; *cr:* Fostoria City Schls PE Tchr 1987-; *ai:* Var Vlybl 6 Yrs, Var Asst Track 8 Yrs Coach; Drivers Ed Instr 1 Yr; NEA 1987-; Recreational Bd 1994-; Bureau of Concern 1990-; 1995 Working Women; *office:* Fostoria City Schls 1202 H. L. Ford Dr Fostoria OH 44830

COUSINEAU, GERALD E., Social Studies Dept Chairman; *b:* Providence, RI; *m:* Pauline M.; *c:* Michele; *ed:* Providence Coll (AB) Ed, His 1967, (MA) Amer His 1969; *cr:* Pilgrim HS Class Rm Tchr 1968-90; Winman Hr HS Soc Stud Dept Chair 1990-93; Toll Gate HS Soc Stud Dept Chair 1993-; *ai:* Mock Trial Team RI Model Legislature Adv; AFT 1968-; NCSS 1993-; RISSA 1968-; *office:* Toll Gate HS 575 Centerville Rd Warwick RI 02886*

COUTURE, DAWN TITUS, Govt & Criminal Justice Instr; *b:* Weymouth, MA; *m:* Paul G.; *c:* Timothy, Nicole; *ed:* Univ of MA at Boston (BA) Govt, Law 1981; New England Schl of Law (JD) Law-Summa Cum Laude 1986; *cr:* Rivkind, Baker & Golden Paralegal 1979-85; MA St Senate Legislative Dir 1985-87; Wheaton Coll Exec Asst to Pres 1987-90; Quincy Coll Instr 1991-; *ai:* Coll Senate; Phi Theta Kappa Fac Adv; MA Bar 1986-; MA Bar Assn 1993-, Criminal Justice, Family Law Sections; Acad of Criminal Justice Scis 1995-; New England Schl of Law Scholar 1982-86; Phi Delta Delta Prize 1986; Amer Jurisprudence Book Awds; *office:* Quincy Coll 34 Coddington St Quincy MA 02169

COUTURE, LINDA JANE, Fourth Grade Teacher; *b:* Manchester, NH; *ed:* Notre Dame Coll (BA) Elem Ed 1972; Math Their Way; *cr:* Our Lady of Perpetual Help Cath Schl Fifth Grd Tchr 1972-73; Maynard Schl Second Grd Tchr 1973-74; Beech St Schl Second Grd Tchr 1974-93, Fourth Grd Tchr 1993-; *ai:* NYNEX-Beech Partnership; Attendance Chprsn; Chair Spec Projects Comms; MEA, NHEA, NEA 1972-; Anselmian Ath Club 1986-, Bd of Dir 1990-92; *office:* Beech Street Schl 333 Beech St Manchester NH 03103

COVE, ANNE-MARIE, Guidance Counselor; *b:* Washington, DC; *ed:* Loyola Coll (BA) Eng 1985; Univ of MD (MED) Schl Cnslng 1993; *cr:* Marriott Intnl Human Resource 1985-90; Cntry Day Schl of Sacred Heart Asst to Dean of Stdnts 1990-91; Montgomery Blais HS Guid Cnslr 1993-; *ai:* Montgomery Cty Coll Fair Comm; Adv Black Achvmt Through Support & Ed; AP Coord; Amer Cnslng Assoc, Amer Schl Cnslrs Assoc 1992-; Montgomery Cty Cnslrs Assoc 1994-; NEA, MD St Tchrs Assoc 1993-; *office:* Montgomery Blair HS 313 Wayne Ave Silver Spring MD 20910

COVEY, THOMAS C., Biology Teacher; *b:* Lockport, NY; *m:* Pamela Ross; *c:* Laura, Thomas, Rachael, Daniel; *ed:* Univ of Steubenville (BA) Bio 1967; Univ of Buffalo (MS) Sci Instruction 1973; 60 Addl Hrs Univ of Buffalo, Canisius Coll, Niagara Univ, Long Island Univ; *cr:* Adena HS Bio, Physics Instr 1967-70; Wilson HS Bio, Chem Instr 1970-; *ai:* Asst Ftbl Coach 1967-70; Head Var Bsbl, Bsktbl Coach; Var Ftbl, Bsbl Head Coach 1970-81; Asst Var Ftbl Coach 1982-; Wilson Tchr Assn; AFT, NYSUT 1970-; NYS Bio, Mentor Network 1990-, Local Mentor; NYS Coach's Assn 1970-, Coach of Yr Div VII 1975, 1977; Participant in DNA Summer Seminar 1992; *office:* Wilson Cntrl HS 412 Lake St Wilson NY 14172*

COVINGTON, LEATRIZ DELLAHOUSSAYE, History Teacher; *b:* Queens, NY; *m:* Anthony Bruce Sr.; *c:* Anthony, Domonique; *ed:* SC St Univ (BA) His 1984; Howard Univ (MA) Ed 1990; 24 Credit Hrs Above Masters; *cr:* Comm Coll of Air Force Ed Specialist 1988-89; Howard Univ Eng & Rdng Tchr 1989; Univ of MD Coord of Admissions 1990; High Point High His Tchr 1990-; *ai:* Alpha-Omega, Nia-Imani & Pep Squad Spon; Multicultural, Philosophy, Steering for Mid-Sts Evaluation Comms; NEA 1990-; PGCEA 1990-; PG Cty Soc Stud 1996-; *office:* High Point HS 3601 Powder Mill Rd Beltsville MD 20705*

COWAN, ANDREA STOCK, Home Economics Educator; *b:* Wheeling, WV; *m:* Gerald L.; *c:* Christopher, Timothy, Andrea, Christine; *ed:* West Liberty St Coll (AB) Scndry Ed 1971; WV Univ (MA) Comm Stud 1990; Ashland Coll Voc Home Ec 1974; Addlt Credit Hrs West Liberty St Coll 1975-78; Addl Enrichment Classes 1972-75 Stifel Fine Arts Ctr, WV Northern Comm Coll; 15 Semester Hrs Beyond Masters 1990-93 WV Univ; *cr:* Buckeye Local Schl Dist Home Ec Tchr 1971-; *ai:* Self Esteem Class Instr; NEA, OEA, BLCTA 1971-; Finalist in 17th Annual Pillsbury Bake Off 1966; Ashland Oil Tchr Achvmt Awd Nom 1994; *home:* RR 3 Box 199A Wheeling WV 26003

COWAN, FRANCES HEADLEY, Vice Principal; *b:* New York, NY; *ed:* Univ of MD (BS) Ed, Distributive Ed 1977; Trinity Coll (MS) Admin, Supervision; *cr:* Cntrl HS Cooperative Voc Ed Tchr 1977-90; Largo HS Vice-Prin 1990-; *ai:* Oasis Prgm Vol; Peer Mediator Admin; ASBA 1990-; NEA 1978-; NAFE 1995-; Prince Georges Cty of PTAs Svc Awd.

COWAN, MAYBELLE ELLEN, English Teacher; *b:* Newark, NJ; *ed:* 16 Credits Towards Masters in Tchng; *cr:* Immaculate Conception Eng Tchr 1990-; *ai:* Stu Cncl, Soph Class & Amnesty Intnl Fac Adv; Disciplinary Bd Chm; NCTE; Natl Assn of Arts & Letters Theatre Awd 1993; Dodge Flwshp 1995; Archdiocese of Newark Tchr Awd 1996; *office:* Immaculate Conception HS 258 S Main St Lodi NJ 07644

COWAN, THOMAS L., Health & Physical Ed Instr; *b:* Batavia, NY; *m:* Linda S. Stratton; *c:* Kimberly, Mikki, Casey; *ed:* SUNY at Brockport (MS) Hlth & PE 1964, 1971; *cr:* Alden Cntrl HS Instr 1964-; *ai:* Var Bsktbl, Jr Var Bsbl Coach; NYSUT, NEA 1964-; Elected Councilman 1987-; Dist Hlth & PE Dept 1978-, Chprsn.

COWAN, WILLIAM F., Scndry Social Studies Teacher; *b:* Bangor, ME; *m:* Jane Bartley Kennison; *c:* Emily; *ed:* Univ of ME (BS) Ed 1988; *cr:* John Bapst Schl Soc Stud Tchr 1989-; *ai:* Head Var Ftbl & Bsbl; Girl Frosh Bsktbl; Young Democrats Adv; Jr Class Adv; Listen to the Stdnts Aids Awareness Adv; *office:* John Bapst Memorial HS 100 Broadway Bangor ME 04401

COWIE, ESTELLE MARIE, Family & Consumer Science Tchr; *b:* Boston, MA; *ed:* Framingham St Coll (BS) Clothing, Textiles 1977; John C. Stalker Inst Nutrition; *cr:* Bicknell Jr HS Family Consumers Sci Tchr 1978-81; Weymouth HS Family Consumer Sci Tchr 1982-; *ai:* Curr, Grad Comms; NEA, MA Tchrs Assn, Framingham St Alumni 1978-; Phi Upsilon Omicron 1976-; *office:* Weymouth HS 1051 Commercial St Weymouth MA 02189*

COWLE, DONNA ANN LAGRANDE, English Teacher; *b:* Mt Vernon, NY; *m:* Rick; *c:* Jessica; *ed:* IA Coll (BA) Eng 1976; Coll of New Rochelle (MS) Ed 1982; Syracuse Univ Eng 3 Credits; *cr:* Holy Trinity Schl 7-8 Grd Tchr 1976-77; St Jude Schl 7-8 Grd Tchr Sci, Rdng 1977-82; Westchester Comm Coll Adj Prof Eng 1982-87; Port Chester HS Eng Tchr 1982-; Syracuse Univ Adj Prof Eng 1984-88; *ai:* Jr Class Adv; NYSUT 1982-; PCTA; Tchr of Yr 1987; *home:* 16 Cornish Rd Carmel NY 10512

COWMAN, VICKI HUTZELL, HS Science & Chemistry Teacher; *b:* Hagerstown, MD; *m:* Donald F.; *c:* Andrew Lawrence, Jessica Elaine; *ed:* Hagerstown Jr Coll (AA) Gen Stud 1975; Shepherd Coll (BS) Bio 1977; WV Univ Coll of Law Dr of Jurisprudence 1983; *cr:* Hymes & Coontz Law Firm Attorney 1983-85; WV Wesleyan Coll Bus Law Prof 1985-92; Grace Acad Grammar Tchr 1992-93, Sci & Chem Tchr 1994-; *ai:* WV St Bar 1983-; Bus & Prof Women 1983-85; Amer Assn Univ Women 1983-83, Pres; *office:* Grace Acad 530 N Locust St Hagerstown MD 21740

COX, BARRY A., Physical Education Teacher; *b:* Canastota, NY; *m:* Renee Weber; *c:* Aimee, Alyson, Bryan; *ed:* SUNY at Cortland (BS) PE 1961; AZ St (MA) Hlth Ed 1969; *cr:* Middletown City Schl PE 1965-70; AZ St Grad Asst 1970; Middletown City Schl Hlth Ed 1971-76; Private Bus Owner 1977-94; East Hampton UFSD Adapted PE 1994-95; Ross Schl Wellness Coord 1995-; *ai:* Var Girls Bsktbl; JV Girls Vllybl; JH Ftbl; AFT 1965-; AAHPERD 1965; Disabilities Band 1995-, Bd; Games for Physically Challenged 1995-; AZ HPER; Sport Muscle Dev; *office:* Ross School 18 Goodfriend Park East Hampton NY 11937

COX, CAROL W., Former English Teacher; *b:* Wilson, NC; *m:* Larry V.; *c:* Renee, Stephanie, Larry Jr.; *ed:* Bob Jones Univ (BA) Eng 1964; Attnd Univ of TN at Chattanooga & E Carolina Univ Post Grad Stud; *cr:* Ringgold HS Eng & Jrnlsm Tchr 1964-67; Farmville Cntrl HS Eng Tchr 1970-78; Fellowship Chrstn Acad Eng Tchr 1978-79; Carrington Jr HS Eng Tchr 1979-80; Mountain View Chrstn Schl Eng Tchr 1982-83; Emmanuel Bapt Chrstn Acad Eng Tchr 1984-87; Mt Calvary Chrstn Schl Eng & Jrnlsm Tchr 1987-94; *ai:* Accreditation Curr Comm; Newspaper Adv; Alumni Newsletter Ed; NCTE 1991-.

COX, CYNTHIA ANN, English Teacher; *b:* Philadelphia, PA; *m:* William Wright Abbot IV; *c:* Will Abbot, Catherine Abbot; *ed:* Princeton Univ (BA) Eng 1984; Univ of MD at Coll Park (MA) Eng 1988; Credit Hrs in Grad Level Eng Courses; *cr:* McDonogh Schl Eng Tchr 1985-; *ai:* AP Eng Lit Exams Reader 1992-; Yrbk Adv; Schl Madrigals Group Mem; New Tchr Mentor; Klingenstein Summer Inst Flwshp 1985; Univ of MD Flwshp to Pursue MS Degree; *office:* Mc Donogh Schl PO Box 380 Owings Mills MD 21117

COX, DAVID EMERY, Hlth & Physical Education Tchr; *b:* Rumford, ME; *c:* Pamela, Daniel, Erin; *ed:* Univ of ME at Presque Isle (BS) Hlth, PE, Recreation 1982; Univ of ME at Orono Working Towards Masters in Educl Admin; *cr:* Peru Schl Dept Hlth, PE Tchr 1984-, Acting Prin 1994-95; *ai:* Girls Sftbl, Boys Bsbl, Soccer Coach; Schl Improvement Comm; Stu Asst Team; NEA, ME Ed Assn, ME Assn Hlth, PE, Recreation & Dance 1984-; IAABO 1984-, Awds Comm; ME Assn of Soccer Ofcls 1985-, Pres 2 Yrs, Ofcl of Yr 1990-91; Natl Assn Securities Dealers 1987-; Wrote, Dev Grant to Purchase Hlth Curr; Presenter at Annual Hlth, PE St Assn Meeting; *office:* Peru Schl RR 1 Box 80 Peru ME 04290

COX, GRADY L., First Grade Teacher; *b:* Ennis, TX; *ed:* East TX St Univ (BA) Elem Ed 1964; Southwestern (MS) Ed 1969; 60 Credit Hrs Temple Univ, St Josephs Univ, Trenton St Univ; *cr:* Edna ISD First Grd Tchr 1964-67; TN Bapt Convention Missions Dir 1969-70; Bristol Twp Schl Dist First Grd Tchr 1970-; *ai:* BTEA, NEA 1970-; Bus & Prof Women 1970-; AARP 1986-; *office:* James Buchanan Elem Schl 2200 Haines Rd Levittown PA 19055

COX, JACOB THOMAS, Science Teacher; *b:* Ft Hood, TX; *m:* Kathleen; *c:* Lauren; *ed:* West VA Univ (BS) Scndry Ed 1988; Grad Schl Towson St Univ Cmptr Sci; *cr:* Cable & Wireless Comm Network Analyst 1989-91; Patterson HS Tchr 1991-; *ai:* Tech Comm; Baltimore Tchrs Union 1991-; MD Space Grant Consortium; Space Sci Internship Prgm Ctr Excl Math & Sci Ed; Summer Physics Inst; *office:* Patterson Sr HS 100 Kane St Baltimore MD 21212

COX, JOHN ANTHONY, Health & Physical Ed Teacher; *b:* Wilton, CT; *ed:* West Chester Univ (BS) Hlth, PE 1983, (MS) Hlth Scis 1985; *cr:* Bart Gray Inc Roofer 1980-85; WJTV Reporter 1985-87; Merrell Lynch Stock Broker 1987-90; Penncrest HS Tchr 1990-; *ai:* Golf Coach; Jr Variety Show Dir; Shakers Club Adv; NEA 1993-; PSEA 1990-; Parrot Club 1994-, Pres; Four Dog Club 1995-, VP; Burke Hollow Club 1981-; West Chester Univ Dance Dept Grad Assistantship; *office:* Penncrest HS 134 Barren Rd Media PA 19063*

COX, JOHN W., English & Social Studies Tchr; *b:* Buffalo, NY; *m:* Judith Lauffenburger; *c:* Nicole; *ed:* Allegheny Coll (AB) Eng 1966; Clarion Univ of PA (BS) Ed 1989; 12 Grad Credits at Gannon Univ; 12 Grad Credits at E Stroudsburg Univ; *cr:* Warren Natl Bank Mrktg Officer 1968-82; Marine Bank Asst Operations Officer 1982-84; PNCISC Sales Rep 1984-86; Johnsonburg Area Jr & Sr HS Eng & Soc Stud Tchr 1989-; *ai:* Ind Stud Groups & Advanced Lit Adv; NEA & PSEA 1987-; BPOE 1968-; F&AM 1975-, PM; *office:* Johnsonburg Area Jr & Sr HS Elk Ave Johnsonburg PA 15845

COX, JOHN WARREN, History Teacher; *b:* Waltham, MA; *ed:* Boston Coll (BA) Scndry Ed, His 1976, (MA) Scndry Ed, His 1980; *cr:* South Jr HS His Tchr 1976-81; Waltham HS His Tchr 1981-; *ai:* Jr Var Boys Bsktbl Coach; NHS Adv; NEA, MTA, Waltham Edctrs Assn 1976-; Waltham Historical Soc 1980-, Treas; Waltham Historical Commission 1986-, Chm; Waltham Babe Ruth League 1980-, Sec; Reagle Players Bd of Dir 1993-; Brandeis Univ Comm Involvement Awd 1992; *office:* Waltham High School 617 Lexington St Waltham MA 02154

COX, JUDITH ANN, Fifth Grade Teacher; *b:* Wheeling, WV; *m:* Edward V.; *ed:* Duquesne Univ (BA) Ed; Attnd St Mary's Coll of MD, St John's Coll of Cleveland OH, George Washington Univ, Maryland Univ, Trinity Coll; *cr:* Thomas Schl Tchr 1958-63; Bristol Schl Tchr 1963-66; Clarksburg Schl Tchr 1966-68; Wheeling Schl Tchr 1968-70; Indianapolis Schl Tchr 1970-71; *ai:* Schl Improvement Team; Rdng Assn; Drug Abuse Prevention; NEA; St Mary's Cty Ed Assn; St Mary's Cty Nursing Home, Bd of Dirs; Christmas in April; St Mary's Cty Alliance Against Alcohol, Drug Abuse; *office:* Banneker-Loveville Elem Schl RR 2 Box 165e Loveville MD 20656

COX, KENNETH MERVIN, Prof of Hlth, PE & Recreation; *b:* Williamsport, PA; *m:* Glenda Gay Garrett; *c:* K. Michael, Richard M., David E., Deborah D. Desmond, Daniel J., Lawrence G.; *ed:* East Stroudsburg Univ (BS) Hlth, PE 1955; Univ of WA (MS) PE 1960; CA St Univ at Northridge (MA) Elem Ed 1961; Univ of WA (EDD) Curr, Instruction 1969; 30 Addl Hrs Comparative Ed, PE, Sport Sci Moscow-Lenin St Cntrl Inst of Phys Culture & Sport Russia 1976-93; *cr:* Simi Valley Unified SD Tchr, Coach 1957-60; Eastern OR Coll Instr, Coach 1961-62; MI tech Univ Asst AD, Instr, Coach 1962-63; St Cloud St Univ Asst Prof, Coach 1963-67; WI St Univ Assoc Prof, Coach 1969-70; Lock Haven Univ of PA Prof, Coach 1970-; *ai:* Fac Adv, Head Coach Boxing Club Team 1977-; Chm Eastern Collegiate Boxing Assn 1980-; Dir Natl Collegiate Boxing Assn 1994; Sec Dev, Ed Comm USA Boxing Inc 1993-; Grp Ldr to Russia, 32 Trips; PA AAHPERD 1976-, Intnl Relations Comm; USA Boxing Inc 1985-, Intnl Coaches Comm; Phi Delta Kappa 1968-; Clinton Cty Hall of Fame Sports 1993-; Lock Have Salvation Army 1985-, Bd of Dirs; Kirkland Quebec AICEP 1976-, Bd of Dirs; Alpha Omega Phi Beta Delta Soc Intnl Scholars 1993-; Reserve Officers Assn USAR 1988-, Ret Ltc USAR; Medal of Leningrad St Cncl Russia 1988; Champions Awd Downtown Ath Club NYC 1987; Inducted Hall of Fame: Wrestling Coaches Hershey PA 1991, NAIA Wrestling Butte MT 1993, East Stroudsburg Univ Ath 1989; Lvl III Intrntl Boxng Coach, USAB 1995; *home:* RR 2 Box 149 Mill Hall PA 17751

COX, PAULYN, Retired Third Grade Teacher; *b:* Oberlin, OH; *ed:* St Univ at Cobleskill (AAS) Nursery Ed 1953; Ithaca Coll (BA) Citizenship Ed 1957; Coll of Saint Rose Grad Stud 1969; *cr:* East Carlisle Schl 5th Grd Tchr 1964-65; Midview Sch Dist 8th-9th Grd Rdng Tchr 1966-67; St Colombas Schl 5th Grd Tchr 1968; Fonda-Fultonville Cntrl Schl 3rd Grd Tchr 1969-94; *ai:* Brown Schl Mentor 1995; NY St United Tchrs 1964; NY St Retired Tchrs Assn Inc, Montgomery Co Retired Tchrs 1994-; AARP 1986-; YWCA, Crop Annual Walker; Hamilton Hill Arts Ctr 1990-; Bed & Breakfast City Mission 1987-; Bapt Retirement Nrsng Home Vol 1977-; Barbara Gray Awd of Merit for Excl in Comm Svc; Spon 3 Children.

COX, ROSEMARY COLEGROVE, 5th Grade Gifted Class Tchr; *b:* Portsmouth, OH; *m:* David O. Jr.; *c:* Cara Sue, Christi Mills, Cindi Lou, David Ogden III; *ed:* Kent St Univ (MS) Educl Admin 1993; Attnd Cleveland St, Baldwin Wallace, Ashland Coll, Lake Erie Coll, Akron Univ; *cr:* Ransom Barr Schl 3rd Grd Tchr 1969-70; Madison Local Schls 7th Grd Math Tchr 1977-78, 5th Grd Tchr of the Gifted 1978-; *ai:* Challenge Selection Comm; Parent-Tchr Challenge Org; Delta Kappa Gamma 1988-, Legislative; Madison Garden Club 1986-, VP; Chapel Meth Church; *office:* North Madison Elem Schl 6735 N Ridge Rd Madison OH 44057

COXON, ROBBIE L., Education Coordinator; *b:* Pittsburgh, PA; *m:* Nicholas; *c:* Nicholas, Eric, Dennis; *ed:* Point Park Coll (BS) Medical Tech 1980; *cr:* Children Hospital of Pittsburgh Medical Tech 1980-81; St. Francis Medical Ctr Medical Tech 1981-89; Mercy Hospital of Pittsburgh Medical Tech 1989-92; Penn St Univ Instr, Ed Coord & Medical Lab Tech 1992-; *ai:* Amer Soc of Clinical Pathologists 1976-; *office:* PA St Univ N Kensington Cmps 3550 7th Street Rd New Kensington PA 15068

COXON, WILLIAM GEORGE, Fourth Grade Teacher; *b:* Greenwich, CT; *c:* Laurence, Alan; *ed:* Dickinson Coll (BA) Lbrl Arts 1968; Univ of Hartford (MA) Ed MED 1972; *cr:* Kosciusko Jr HS 7th-8th Grd Tchr 1968; Eli Whitney Elem Schl 4th-6th Grd Tchr 1968-; *ai:* Tutoring; NEA, CEA, ETA 1968-; Various Sports Teams.*

COYLE, BERNADETTE DOWNES, Social Studies Teacher; *b:* New York City, NY; *m:* Dennis P.; *c:* Delia, Deirdre, Logan, Joseph, Bernadette; *ed:* Marymount Coll at Tarrytown (BA) His 1971; Seton Hall Univ (MED) Ed 1991; Supvr Cert 1994; *cr:* Cathedral HS Soc Stud Tchr 1971-74; Moore Cath Soc Stud Tchr 1974-76; Hillsborough HS Soc Stud Tchr 1989-; *ai:* Var Boys Tennis, Var Girls Tennis Coach; NJ Educl Assoc; Hillsberingh Educl Assoc; Supervision/Curr Dev Assoc; Natl Cncl of Soc Stud Tchrs; Tchr of Yr 1993-; Hillsborough Research Grant World Cultures Art Project; Home News Coach of the Yr 1995; *office:* Hillsborough HS Raider Blvd Belle Mead NJ 08502*

COYLE, MARILYN ALICE, Math Dept Coord & Teacher; *b:* Kearny, NJ; *m:* William J.; *c:* William, Heather, Christopher, Daniel; *ed:* Georgian Ct Coll (BA) Math 1976; Grad Courses Math, Ed; *cr:* Msgr Donovan HS Tchr Math 1984-, Curr Coord 1991-; *ai:* Frosh Class Adv; Curr Comm; Var Chrldng, Asst Var Sftbl Coach; NCTM, NJTNJ 1991-95; NCEA 1984-; NJCCA 1994-; Consortium of Math Supvrs Diocese of Trenton 1991-; Island Jr Bsbl League, Sec 1982-90; Intnl Thespian Soc 1993-; *office:* Msgr Donovan HS 711 Hooper Ave Toms River NJ 08753*

COYLE, MARY LOUISE A., Jr High Teacher; *b:* Riverside, NJ; *ed:* Georgian Ct Coll (BA) Elem Ed 1953; Seton Hall Univ (MS) Elem Ed 1971; *cr:* St Paul Schl Jr HS Tchr 1952-60, Elem Prin 1960-66; St Francis Elem Schl Tchr 1966-70; St James Elem Schl Tchr 1970-76; St Joseph 5th-8th Grd Tchr; *ai:* Stu Cncl Adv; Curr, Mid Sts Comms; NEA, NCEA 1960-; Metuchen Diocese Tchr of Yr 1991; *office:* St Joseph Schl 101 Westervelt Ave Plainfield NJ 07060

COYLE, NANCY TOMASSO, 7th Grade Teacher; *b:* Elizabeth, NJ; *m:* John J.; *c:* John M., Allyson E.; *ed:* Georgian Court Coll (BA) Elem Ed 1984; *cr:* Osbornville Schl Supplemental Tchr 1984-85; Manchester MS 5th Grd Tchr 1985-86, 7th Grd Tchr 1986-; *ai:* Lang Arts, Soc Stud Comm; NEA 1985-; *office:* Manchester TWP MS 121 Rt 539 Whiting NJ 08759

COYLE, SANDRA, Kindergarten Teacher; *b:* Phila, PA; *m:* Joseph; *c:* Joseph, Christine Mazzola, Stephanie Micua; *ed:* Edison St Coll (BA) Psych 1980; *cr:* St Thomas Schl 2nd, 4th Grd Tchr 1960-65; St Gabriel Schl K, 1st, 3rd Tchr 1977-; *ai:* NCEA 1977-; Campfire Girls 1978-, Ldr, Elizabeth Ann Seton Awd; *office:* St Gabriel Schl 2916 Dickinson St Philadelphia PA 19146

COYNE, CECELIA EBLE, Biology Teacher; *b:* Abington, PA; *ed:* Chestnut Hill Coll (BS) Bio 1967; Beaver Coll (MA) Ed 1978; *cr:* Bishop McDevitt HS Sci Tchr 1967-; Gwynedd Mercy Coll Staff 1993-; *ai:* Spon Montgomery Cty Sci Fair; PA Jr Acad of Sci Spon, Judge; Chprsn Fac Coordinating Comm; ACT 1967-, Nom Tchr of Yr 1991; Montg Cty Sci Tchrs 1967-; NAUI 1982-; NAIC 1987-; Northwoods Comm Assn 1976-; Bd Mem for Grey Nuns Acad 1994-; *office:* Bishop Mc Devitt HS 125 Royal Ave Wyncote PA 19095

COYNE, GARY, Art Teacher; *b:* Red Bank, NJ; *m:* Susan; *c:* Andrew, Cory, Mollie; *ed:* Trenton St Coll (BA) Art Ed 1974; *cr:* Hamilton Twp Elem Schl Art Tchr 1974-87; Hamilton West HS, Grice MS Art Tchr 1987-89; Hamilton West HS, Nottingham HS North Art Tchr 1989-92; Nottingham HS North, Reynolds MS Art Tchr 1992-94; Hamilton West HS Art Tchr 1994-; *ai:* Stagecraft Set Design; NEA, NJEA, HTEA, Art Edctrs of NJ 1974-; *office:* Hamilton HS West 2720 S Clinton Ave Trenton NJ 08610

COYNE, HENRY FRANCIS,JR., History Teacher; *b:* Fort Knox, KY; *m:* Linda K.; *c:* Hank; *ed:* Juniata Coll (BA) Pre-Law & Scndry Ed 1984; Villanova Univ (MED) Scndry Ed 1988; Penn St Univ Prin Cert Admin 1991; Cushing Acad Post Grad 1979-80; *cr:* Phoenixville Area Schl Dist Tchr & Coach 1984-; *ai:* Asst HS Ftbl Coach; Head Wrestling & Bsbl MS Coach; Weight Lifting Coach; Class 1999 Adv; Vol Coach Yth Wrestling; NEA 1984-; Jaycees Young Fitness Ldr 1989; *office:* Phoenixville Area HS Gay St & City Line Ave Phoenixville PA 19460*

COYNE, MARY, 2nd Grade Teacher; *b:* Philadelphia, PA; *m:* Anthony Green; *c:* Aviva Coyne-Green, Max Coyne-Green; *ed:* Univ of PA (MS) Ed 1976, (EDD) Rdng, Lang Specialist 1981; *cr:* Lower Merion Schl Dist 4th Grd Tchr 10 Yrs, 2nd Grd Tchr 14 yrs; *ai:* Lang Arts, Math Task Force, Sci Comms; NEA 1972-; Honorable Mention Prof Best Awds; Helped Write Application Won Schl US Dept Ed Blue Ribbon Awd; *office:* Cynwyd Elem Schl 101 W Levering Mill Rd Bala Cynwyd PA 19004*

COZZE, BONNIE CARY, College Prep & English Teacher; *b:* Chattaroy, WV; *m:* Frank Clark; *c:* Kari Viland, Kelley Eaton; *ed:* Marshall Univ (BA) Scndry Ed, Hlth, PE, Eng 1961; Ohio St Univ (MA) Scndry Ed 1967; 45 Hrs Post Grad Ed Ashland Univ; *cr:* Warren Cty Schls MS Hlth, PE Tchr 1961-64; Mifflin Twp Schls HS Hlth, PE Tchr 1964-68; Olentangy Schls HS Eng Tchr 1976-; *ai:* Interscholastic Vlybl Fac Adv; Bsktbl Asst Ath Dir; NEA, Olentangy Tchrs Assn 1976-; NCTE 1990-; Tchr of Yr 1990; Amorak Flwshp Grant 1990; OH Tchr Selected to Speak Holocaust Meml St of OH Observance 1992; *office:* Olentangy HS 675 Lewis Center Rd Lewis Center OH 43035

COZZI, DIANNE, Middle School Math Teacher; *b:* New York, NY; *ed:* SUNY at New Paltz (BA) Scndry Ed & Math 1971; Iona Coll (MS) Math Computing 1983; *cr:* Nyack MS Math Tchr 1971-; *ai:* Site Based Mgmt; PTA Tchr Liaison, Math League Adv; NYSUT 1971-; AFT 1971-; NCTM 1982-; AMTNYS 1982-; *home:* 215 Washington St Apt 23 Tappan NY 10983

CRABTREE, GLENDA WILSON, Fifth Grade Teacher; *b:* Thomaston, GA; *c:* Michelle Hamilton, Chris Seidleck, Jason; *ed:* Tift Coll (BS) Elem Ed 1964; Wilkes Univ (MS) Elem Ed 1974; Addl 49 Credit Hrs Beyond Masters; *cr:* Spaulding Jr HS 8th Grd Math Tchr 1964-65; Zebulon Elem Schl 6th Grd Tchr 1965-66; Thomaston Cty Schls 6th Grd Tchr 1966-68; Dallas Schl Dist 5th & 6th Grd Tchr 1968-; *ai:* PSEA, NEA, DEA 1968-; PTO, Bylaws Comm; Jaycees Outstanding Educator Awd 1967; *home:* 231 Overbrook Rd Dallas PA 18612

CRADLE, RONALD JOTEZ, 7th-8th Grd English Teacher; *b:* Richmond, VA; *ed:* Wilberforce Univ (BSEd) Ed, Eng 1994; Princeton Ctr Ldrshp Trng 1995; *cr:* Xenia Brd Ed 7th & 8th Grd Sci Tchr 1975-76; Muskegon Hts Brd Ed 10th Grd Eng Tchr 1976-82; Elizabeth Brd Ed 7th, 8th, 9th, 12th Grd Eng Tchr 1982-; *ai:* 8th Grd Class Adv; Ldrshp Team 1994-95; Instrl Partners 1994-95; Elizabeth Ed Assn, NJ Ed Assn 1992-; *home:* 1550 Schley St Hillside NJ 07205

CRADLE, TONI J., Guidance Counselor; *b:* Chicago, IL; *m:* James C.; *c:* Kevin L. Hamilton, Karla E. Hamilton; *ed:* Southern IL Univ (BA) Eng 1964, (MA) Scndry Ed 1966; *ai:* Black Awareness Club & Big Brother-Big Sister Adv; Bsktbl Cheerleading Coach; *office:* Brookline HS 115 Greenough St Brookline MA 02146

CRAFT, JAMES ROGER, English Teacher; *b:* Gallipolis, OH; *m:* Gwen Ellen Blair; *c:* Nicholas, Lehanna, Caleb, Joel; *ed:* Univ of Rio Grande (BS) Comm 1987; 8 Credit Hrs Univ of Dayton; 6 Credit Hrs; *cr:* Logan Elm HS Eng Tchr 1988-94; Gallia Acad HS Eng Tchr 1994-; *ai:* Eighth Grd Ftbl Asst Coach; 7-8 Jr HS Track Head Coach; NEA, OEA, NCTE, OHSFCA 1988-; Christ United Meth Church; Logan Elm HS Tchr of Yr Awd Excl in Career Achvmt 1989; Thomson Consumer Electronics Outstdng Tchr Awd 1993; *home:* 1981 State Route 218 Gallipolis OH 45631*

CRAFT, LINDA SUE, Kindergarten Teacher; *b:* Lima, OH; *m:* Arthur E.; *c:* Robert, Bryan, Nathan; *ed:* OH St Univ (BS) Elem Ed 1966; Recertified to Teach Kndgtn; 12 Addl Hrs at OSU Lima Branch K-8th; *cr:* Whittier Elem Schl 4th Grd Tchr 1966-67; Chicago Elem Schl Spec Ed Tchr 1967-69; Ninth Ave Elem Schl Spec Ed, 3rd, 2nd Grd Tchr 1969-72; Gomer Elem Schl Kndgtn Tchr 1983-; *ai:* North Cntrl Targets, Elida Elem Kndgtn Rsrch Comms; Elida Elem Ed Task Force; NEA, OEA 1966-; Elida Ed Assn 1983-, Mbrshp Chm; St Paul United Meth Church 1972-, Yth Cnslr, HS Sunday Schl Tchr; Achvmt in Sci Instrucion Grant 1990; Elida Local Schls See For Yourself Prgm 1994; Sci Enhancement for Sci Advancement Grant 1995; *office:* Gomer Elem Schl 4040 W Lincoln Hwy Gomer OH 45809

CRAGLE, WYANITA M., Biology Teacher; *b:* Philadelphia, PA; *ed:* Bloomsburg Univ (BS) Scndry Ed & Bio 1989; 12 Credit Hrs Post BS; *cr:* Berwick HS Long-Term Sub of Bio 1993; Northwest HS Half Day Bio Tchr 1994-; *ai:* Class of 1996 Class Adv; Bio Club Adv; Sci Olympiad Coach; Prom Comm Moderator; PSEA, NEA 1990-; NAEA 1994-, Bldg Rep 1995-; *office:* Northwest Area Jr Sr HS RR 2 Box 2271 Shickshinny PA 18655

CRAIG, BETSY J., Asst Prof of Communications; *b:* Steubenville, OH; *m:* Robert P.; *c:* Gordon; *ed:* Grove City Coll (BA) Eng, Comm 1977; NY Univ (MA) Educl Theater 1981, (PHD) Educl Theater; *cr:* North Allegheny Schl Tchr 1977-81; Grove City Coll Prof 1981-; *ai:* Theater Dir; Stu Tchr, Childrens Theater Supvr; NCTE; Intnl Rdng Assn; Literacy Cncl Bd Mem 1993-; YMCA Bd Mem 1994-; Shakespeare Club.*

CRAIG, CHARLES ROBERT, Director of Bands; *b:* Pittsburgh, PA; *m:* Ruth Louise Hogle; *c:* Matthew, Kathryn; *ed:* Coll of Wooster (BMEd) Music Ed 1985; Kent St Univ (MMEd) Music Ed 1992; Grad Stud OH St Univ; *cr:* Covington Schls Band Dir 1985-88; Ashtabula City Schls Band Dir 1988-93; Kettering City Schls Band Dir 1993-; *ai:* Concert, Marching, Jazz Ensemble, Pep Bands; MENC, NEA, OEA 1985-; OH Music Ed Assn 1985-, 1996 All-St Chprsn; Article Pub; Outstdng Young Men in Amer; Who's Who in Amer Ed; Guest Conductor Cleveland & Yth Symphony; OMEA Adjudicator; *office:* Kettering Fairmont HS Shroyer Rd Kettering OH 45429*

CRAIG, CORINNE ANN, Mathematics Teacher; *b:* Wilkes Barre, P Wilkes Univ (BS) Math 1989; Scranton Univ (MS) Human Res 1992; *cr:* Wilkes Barre Area Schl Dist Math Tchr 6 Yrs; *ai:* SADD Adv; 7th Grd Mentor; Track Officiating; PCTM 1990-; LCTM NCTM 1993-; Church Cantor 1994-; *office:* GAR Memorial Jr/Sr H S Grant St Wilkes Barre Towns PA 18702

CRAIG, DOUGLAS, Business Management Instructor; *b:* Philade PA; *m:* Patricia Lawrence; *c:* Shari, Shawn; *ed:* Mercy Coll (BS) M Psych 1986; Fordham Univ (MS) Adult Ed 1989; *cr:* Westchester B Instr 1992-; *ai:* Orientation Seminars for New Stdnts; Stu Coa Tutoring, Cnslng; Curr Enhancement Comm; Toastmasters 1988- Ofcr.

CRAIG, GWENDOLYN OLIVIA (STEELE), 5th Grade Teacher; *b* Christian, MS; *c:* Deirdre Kym Gibson; *ed:* Clarke Coll (BS) Bio Adelphi Univ (MA) Elem Ed 1974; (PHD) Arts, Sci 1991; *cr:* Wyan Day Care Ctr Dir 1973-76; So Cntry Schl Dist Edctr 1978-; Patc Medford Schl Dist GED Instr 1984-; St Joseph Coll Instr 199 Conduct African & African Amer His Seminars, Multicultural Ed W Holistic Hlth Seminars; Bellport Tchr Assn 1978-; Intl Assn of Cr Therapists 1980-; Delta Sigma Theta 1958-; 100 Black Women of LI Treas; *office:* So Cntry Schl Dist Brookhaven Ave Bellport NY 117

CRAIG, JAN D., Technology Coordinator; *b:* Dover, OH; *m:* Ka Porterfield; *c:* Carrie Boyd; *ed:* Mount Union Coll (BA) Ec 1969 Work Ed Kent St Univ, Cmptr Sci Ashland Univ; *cr:* Claymount MS Algebra, Cmptr Tchr 1967-95; Claymont City Schls Tech Coord 199 Natl Jr Hon Soc Adv 20 Yrs; NEA, OEA 1970-; Claymont Ed Assn Pres 1979-80; Tuscarawas Co Tech Coord 1995-; Math Dept Chm 19 *office:* Claymont City Schls 115 N 3rd St PO Box 111 Dennison OH

CRAIG, JENNIFER LYNN SCAIFE, Teacher; *b:* Burlington, V Kenneth J.; *ed:* Amherst Coll (BA) Neuroscience 1990; Yale Univ Neuroscience 1993; *cr:* Hebron Acad Tchr 1992-; *ai:* Soccer, Bs Tennis Coach; Acappella Singing Group Hebron Hebeejeebies; Womens Group; Hebron Acad Distinguished Tchr Awd 1994 & *office:* Hebron Acad PO Box 309 Hebron ME 04238*

CRAIG, JOAN E., 5th & 6th Grade Teacher; *b:* Buffalo, NY; *c:* Craig-Redding, Kristen Braun; *ed:* St Univ of NY at Buffalo (BS) E 1958, (EDM) Remedial Rdng 1980; *cr:* Kenmore Pub Schls 3rd Gr 1958-65; Royalton-Hartland Cntrl Schls Kndgtn, 5th & 6th Remedial Rdng Tchr 1980-; *ai:* AFT, NYSUT, RHTA, NFRA 1980-; Gasport Elem Schl 4500 Orchard Pl Gasport NY 14067

CRAIG, JUDITH LEWIS, Kindergarten Teacher; *b:* Wheeling, V John D.; *c:* David, Joseph; *ed:* Muskingum Coll (BS) Elem Ed 1961 St Mary's, OH Univ; *cr:* St Clairsville Schls 1st Grd Tchr 19 1969-70, Kndgtn Tchr 1972-; *ai:* OEA, NEA 1961, 1972-; Tuesda Club, Sec, Pres; *office:* St Clairsville-Richland Schls 120 Norri Clairsville OH 43950

CRAIG, KATHLEEN CARNEY, Guidance Counselor; *b:* Acka NY; *m:* Robert Emerson; *c:* Kenneth, Joanne; *ed:* Daemen Coll (B & Soc Stud; St Univ at Buffalo (Med) Guid & Cnslng; *cr:* Rivers His Tchr; MA Bay Comm Coll Stu Prsnl Asst; Arlington HS Guid Falmouth HS Guid Cnslr; *ai:* NEA; MTA; NEACAC; Cape & Islanc Assoc; *office:* Falmouth HS 874 Gifford Street Ext Falmouth MA (

CRAIG, KEITH, English Teacher; *b:* Laurel Springs, NJ; *ed:* FL (BS) Media Comm 1983; NJ Tchrs Cert Glassboro St Coll 1990; Harbor Twp HS Eng Tchr 1990-; *ai:* Asst Swim Team Coach; Fros Adv; EHTEA, NJEA, NEA 1990-; *office:* Egg Harbor Township High School Dr Egg Harbor Townshi NJ 08234

CRAIG, KENNETH L., Teacher & Math Dept Chprsn; *ed:* Concorc (BA) Ed & Behavioral Sci 1986; *cr:* Immanuel Luth Schl 6th G 1988-90; St Matthew Luth Schl 7th Grd Tchr 1990-; *ai:* Bsktbl Coa Dir; *office:* St Matthew Lutheran Schl 875 Eggert Dr North Tonawa 14120*

CRAIG, LANA ROBB, Spanish Teacher; *b:* E Liverpool, OH; *m:* *ed:* SUNY at Cortland (BA) Span 1970; CA St Univ at LA (MA) Spa Lit 1987; *cr:* Livonia HS Span 1-3 Jr, Sr HS Tchr 1970-73; Alve Span 1-3, AP Tchr, Chprsn FLD 1975-88; Upland HS Span 2-3, A 1988-90; Ithaca HS Span 1-5, AP Tchr 1990-; *ai:* Span Club Ad Cabinet, Pub Relations; NYSAFLT, AATSP 1990-; NEA 1988-; Span Rvw Text 1995; *office:* Ithaca HS 1401 N Cayuga St Ithaca NY

CRAIG, MARVA MIGOL, Speech & Communications Prof; *b:* J West Indies; *m:* Anthony M. Foster; *c:* Toni Ashlie Foster; *ed:* Hun (BA) Speech, Comm 1984; NY Univ (MA) Speech, Comm 1986; B of Manhattan CC (AA) Lbrl Arts 1991; Working on Curr, Tchr Columbia Univ; *cr:* Borough of Manhattan CC Registrar 1979-, A 1988-95; NY Inst of Tech Adj Prof 1988-; Coll of New Rochelle A 1991-93; *ai:* AACRAO; NACADA 1991-; AACRAO, NACAD Presentations; *office:* Borough Of Manhattan Comm Coll 199 Cham New York NY 10007

CRAIG, MARY A., English Teacher; *b:* Meridian, MS; *c:* Trav Aisha; *ed:* Buffalo St Coll (BS) Ed, Eng 1973, (MS) Ed 1981; Cert 1996; 45 Hrs Summer Yth Mngmt Trng; *cr:* Univ of Buffalc Opportunity Ctr Instrl Staff 1990-92; Hutch Tech Schl Eng Tchr 1 CMAK-Buffalo Pub Schl Eng Tchr 1994-; CMAK-STEP Lead Tchr 1995-; *ai:* Debate Team Adv; Field Trip Coord; Speaking African-Amer His Month Prgm Chprsn; Yrbk Adv; Buffalo Tchr Fe Alternate; NEA 1974-; BTF Conf, Del; *office:* Career Mag Kensington 319 Suffolk St Buffalo NY 14215*

CRAIG, MARY ACKER, 5th Grade Teacher; *b:* Scranton, PA; *m:* B. Jr.; *c:* John; *ed:* Bridgewater Coll (BA) Sociology 1970; Grad Cr Salisbury St; *cr:* Talbot Co Pub Schls 2nd-3rd Grd Tchr 1970-74 Annes Co Pub Schl Homebound Tchr 1974-75; The Cntry Schl Tchr 1975-; *ai:* Lit Magazine Co-Chm; Theme Comm; Co-Chair La Self Stud Comm; Assn of Ind MD Schls 1975-; Friends of Talbot 1992-; Talbot Soccer Club 1990-; Support Our Sports Easton HS

CRAIG, MAUREEN, Art Teacher; *b:* Buffalo, NY; *ed:* Rosary H (BS) Art Ed 1973; Canisius Coll (MS) Ed 1978; *cr:* West Seneca C Art Tchr 1974-; *ai:* Art Dept Ldr 1980-; Art Club 1980-93; IMS CSIP 2 Yrs; WSTA, AFT, NYSUT 1974-; NYSATA 1990-; Natl A Assn 1995-; Preservation Cncl of Erie Cty 1994-; Albright-Knox 1985-; Buffalo Historical Soc 1995-.

CRAIG, RICHARD FRANKLIN, Sixth Grade Teacher; *b:* Ellwo PA; *m:* Michelle Bendick; *c:* Renee Craig Reeder, Shawn Jeffer Geneva Coll (BS) Ed 1966; Slippery Rock Univ (ME) Ec Westminster Coll Elem Prins Cert 1976; *cr:* Bell Comm Ctr Part-T 6 Yrs; Ellwood City Area Schl Dist Summer Recreation Dir Riverside Beaver Cty Schl Dist 5th Grd Tchr 1 Yr; Ellwood City A Dist 6th Grd Tchr 29 Yrs; *ai:* PSEA, NEA 1966-; North Sewickley Church 1978-, Elder, 4th-6th Grd Sunday Schl Tchr, Jr & Sr HS Yc *home:* RR 1 Box 385W Ellwood City PA 16117

CRAIG, TONI G., Secondary English Teacher; *b:* Middletown, Tiffany Michael, Scott Michael; *ed:* Miami Univ (BS) Ger, Eng 19

(MS) Ed, Cooperative Grouping 1990; *cr:* Edgewood HS Tchr Middletown HS Tchr 1978-79; West Carrollton HS Tchr 1980-; isciplinary Tchng Block; Cooperative Tchng Instr; Strategic Comm; Dist European HS Group Tour Dir; Chess Club; NEA, 0-; Martha Jennings Scholar Univ of Dayton; Significant Tchr Articles Copperative Tchng; *office:* West Carrollton H S 5833 Dayton OH 45449*

TRISHA ANN VARISH, English Teacher; *b:* Corry, PA; *m:* evin; *ed:* Univ of Pittsburgh (BA) Eng Lit 1992; 6 Credits Admin Masters Prgm; Gann Univ 34 Ed Credits PA Scndry Tchng Cert *cr:* Ft Cherry Schl Dist Eng Tchr, Spon 1993-; *ai:* Yrbk, Lit , Sr Class Spon; NEA, PSEA 1993-; NCTE 1992-; *office:* Fort hl 110 Fort Cherry Rd Mc Donald PA 15057

WILLIE EDWARD, Mathematics Teacher; *b:* Baltimore, MD; *c:* -Barney, William; *ed:* Morgan St Univ (BS) Bus Admin 1968; 24 S Pub Admin at NY Univ 1968-69; *cr:* US Army Medical 1962-65; Port Authority of NY & NJ Admin Asst of Real Estate 3-72; US Army Medical Specialist, Army Ed Instr in Germany *ai:* Class Club Coach; Tchng & Counseling At-Risk Stdnts; inquapin MS 46 900 Woodbourne Ave Baltimore MD 21212

, CARTER WALKER, Retired Professor; *b:* Richmond, VA; *m:* an; *c:* Jenny Kathryn; *ed:* Williams Coll (BA) Eng 1960; Univ of Folklore, Folklife Stu8d 1967, (PHD) Folklore, Folklife Stud Montgomery Cntry Day Schl 5th Grd Tchr 1960-65; Cabrini Coll -95; *ai:* Chm Soc Sci Dept, Cncl of Coll Affairs; Soccer Coach; Photography Club, Kappa Sigma Omega Svc Soc; Frosh Adv; klore Soc; Paoli United Meth Church 1989-, Various Comms; icles Pub; *home:* 5 Faggs Manor Ln Paoli PA 19301

WALTER J., Math Teacher & Dean of Stdnts; *b:* New York, NY; M.; *c:* Walter III, Roger, Adrienne; *ed:* SUNY at Brockport 1960; NY Univ (MSEd) Ed 1963; *cr:* NY City Bd of Ed Math -70; The Hotchkiss Schl Math Tchr & Dean of Stdnts 1970-; *ai:* ar Bsktbl & Mens & Womens Var Track Coach; Discipline Comm g Advy Comm; Stu Fac Cncl; NAIS 1970-; CAIS 1970-; Math 86-; Ambulance Svc 1980-, Treas; Salisbury Vol; *home:* 53 Rd Lakeville CT 06039*

, ANN M., Social Studies Teacher; *b:* Findlay, OH; *ed:* OH St Comp Soc Stud 1971; Bowling Green St Univ (MA) Geography d Hrs in Bus; *cr:* Hopewell Loudon Schl Tchr 23 Yrs; *ai:* NEA; Assn 1986-; *office:* Hopewell Loudon Schl Box 400 Bascom OH

, CHRISTOPHER MICHAEL, 7th Grade Science Teacher; *b:* Y; *m:* Amy Bellows; *c:* Zachary, Ian, Jesse; *ed:* LeMoyne Coll 977; SUNY at Oswego (MS) Sci Ed 1989; *cr:* Fulton Jr High 7th chr 1985-; *ai:* Red Cross Bd of Ed 1993-, VP; Eisenhower Math nt 1994-95, 1995-96; *office:* Fulton Jr HS 129 Curtis St Fulton

, DAVID JAMES, Biology Teacher; *b:* Indiana, PA; *m:* Alice jocha; *c:* Janell Marie; *ed:* Indiana Univ of PA (BS) Scndry Ed dits of Univ of Pittsburgh 28, Duquesne Univ 6 Grad Schl; *cr:* Area HS Bio, Earth Sci Tchr 1970-; *ai:* PSEA, NEA, Hopewell 966-; Duquesne Univ 1970-, Roble Team Coach; LTC Ret 26 Yrs ny Reserve; *office:* Hopewell Area Schl Dist 1215 Longvue Ave PA 15001

, EUGENE DALE, School Guidance Counselor; *b:* d, MD; *m:* Sandra Kay Truly; *c:* Andrew F.; *ed:* Allegany Comm Gen Stud 1974; Frostburg St Coll (BS) Elem Ed 1975, (MA) 1978; 12 Addl Hrs; *cr:* John Humbird Elem Schl 5th-6th Grd -79; South Penn Elem Schl Guid Cnslr 1980-84; Bel Air Elem Cnslr 1984-; Cresaptown Elem Schl Guid Cnslr 1986-; Westside Guid Cnslr 1986-; *ai:* Allegany Cty Cncl of PTAs Schlsp Chm; Cty Tchrs Ass 1976-, Schl Rep; MD St Tchrs Assn, NEA 1976-; for Cnslng & Dev; Loyal Order of Moose 1976-; MD Congress & Tchrs Inc 1976-, Tchrs Relations, Honorary Life Mbrshp; chr Magazine 1982; Instr Tchr Plus Awd; Article Pub; *home:* vada Ave NW Cumberland MD 21502

, GAIL (WALCZAK), English Teacher; *b:* Hammonton, NJ; *m:* : Adam, Aaron, Rachel; *ed:* Trenton St Coll (BA) Eng 1978; 15 Work in Ed; Tchng Cert 1992; Garden St Bible Schl ACSI Cert; m Acad First Grd Tchr 1979-80, Eng, Jrnlsm, Speech Tchr 1990-; *ai:* Schl Newspaper Adv; Lit Magazine Founder, Adv; oach; ACSI 1990-; PTF 1979-, Co-Pres 1988-90; Tri Sigma Soc 1990; Local Newspapers Freelance Journalist; *office:* Pilgrim Box 322 Egg Harbor City NJ 08215

, GAYLE, Sixth Grade Math Teacher; *b:* Cincinnati, OH; *m:* . Thompson; *c:* Susan; *ed:* Univ of Cincinnati (BA) Elem Ed t Grad Stud Miami of OH; *cr:* Summerside Schl First-Second, Tchr 1974-88; Glen Este MS Sixth Grd Tchr 1988-; *ai:* Miami t of Math & Statistics OH Problem Solving Consortium; NEA; OEA; NCTM 1993-; *office:* Glen Este MS 4342 Glen Este ille Rd Cincinnati OH 45245

, LONA LEE, Biology & Chemistry Teacher; *b:* Youngstown, BS) Comprehensive Sci 1982; (MA) Biological Scis 1987; *cr:* eserve HS Bio, Chem Tchr 1983-; *ai:* Var Vlybl, Asst Track dg Cncl for Tchrs; NEA, OEA, TOWR 1983-; Mahoning Valley ssn 1987-, Pres 2 Yrs, 3 Times Coach of Yr; Dist I Vlybl Coaches -, VP 2 Yrs, 3 Times Coach of Yr; *office:* Western Reserve HS Akron Canfield Rd Berlin Center OH 44401*

I, GREGORY PETER, Music Teacher & Dir of Bands; *b:* , CT; *m:* Constance Mary Stoll; *ed:* Cntrl CT St Univ (BSEd) -Magna Cum Laude 1989, (MSED) 1995; *cr:* St Paul Schl General Music Tchr 1987-89; Canton Jr-Sr HS Music Tchr & Band Dir Northwestern Region #7 Music Tchr & Band Dir 1992-; *ai:* HS zz Ensemble; Pit Orch & Chamber Ensembles Coach; MENC, 84-, Northern Reg HS Fest Dir 1991-92; Kappa Delta Pi 1986-; E, NBA 1989-; NEMFA 1992-; CMEA, Stu Affairs Comm 1995-; Mu; CT Assn of Schls, Music Dir Comm; Dist Tchr of Yr Finalist st Conductor MS Northern Region Festival Jazz Ensemble 1992; azz Festival Honorable Mention 1990-91, 1994, 1995; Guest for 1992 CMEA All St & MENC Stu Chapter Conf, Cntrl CT St l Fnd of Advancement in Arts Tchr Awd 1991-92; World Spcl Mrchng Band Prtcptn; *office:* Northwestern Regnl #7 MS & HS Dr Winsted CT 06098*

LL, MAUREEN NADEAU, First Grade Teacher; *b:* Holyoke, ed D.; *c:* Brendan D.; *ed:* Westfield St Coll (BSE) Elem Ed 1970; a Maria Coll 1992-94; *ai:* MTA 1970-; *office:* Anna E Barry Schl t Chicopee MA 01020

LL, CAROLYN G., Adjunct Instructor of Math; *b:* Troy, NY; *m:* .; *c:* Bradford, Donald; *ed:* William Smith Coll (BA) Math 1961; Univ (MA) Math 1963; *cr:* LeMoyne Coll Instr 1963-67; m Coll Instr 1967-69, Fin Aid Dir 1971-72, 1976-81, Instr WA St Comm Coll Adj Instr of Math 1991-; *ai:* MAA; OASFAA agur of Women Voters; *office:* Washington State Comm Coll 710 Dr Marietta OH 45750

CRANDOL, CYNTHIA MORINGS, Business Education Teacher; *b:* Eure, NC; *m:* Gregory L.; *ed:* East Carolina Univ (BS) Bus Ed, Admin Svcs 1990; 24 Hrs Toward MS; *cr:* East Carolina Univ Admin Asst 1989-91; Woodlawn HS Bus Ed Tchr 1991-; *ai:* Future Edctr of Amer Co-Spon; NHS; NEA, MBEA 1991-; Participated in Wkshp Presentation Intnl Bus; *office:* Woodlawn HS 1801 Woodlawn Dr Baltimore MD 21207*

CRANE, DAVID WILLIAM, Chemistry Teacher; *b:* Marion, NY; *m:* Donna Leno; *c:* Heather, Kristen Crane Kiley; *ed:* St Univ of NY at Buffalo (BA) Chem 1967; Univ of Rochester (MA) Sci Ed 1969; SUNY Coll at Brockport, Rochester Inst of Tech Addl Courses; *cr:* Monroe Comm Coll In-Svc Eastman Kodak Co Instr 1988-90; Univ of Rochester Early Connection Opportunity Instr 1989-90, Chem 100 Instr 1983-; Greece Arcadia HS, AP Chem Instr 1968-; *ai:* Sci Olympiad Chem Adv; Sci Exploration Days Coord; ACS 1970-, Mem at Large, Rochester Section Chem Tchr of Yr 1979, Spec Recognition 1993, Northeast Regnl HS Chem Tchng 1984 Awds; NYS Ed Dept Regents Chem Advy Comm 1978-83; Excl in Scndry Schl Tchng, ACS Phoenix Natl Chem Day Prgm Awds 1987; Articles Pub 1981-82; *office:* Greece Arcadia HS 120 Island Cottage Rd Rochester NY 14612

CRANE, ELAINE MARIE (KAZANJIAN), Secondary English Teacher; *b:* Methuen, MA; *m:* Eugene F. Jr.; *c:* Jacqueline Cloutier, Eugene F. III; *ed:* Merrimack Coll (BA) Hum 1964; Salem St (MA) Rdng; 3 Credit Hrs Learning Styles; 3 Credit Hrs Skillful Tchr; 3 Credit Hrs Cmptr Use of IBM Microsoft Prgms; *cr:* Central Jr HS Eng Tchr 1964-70; Methuen HS Scndry Eng Tchr 1971-; *ai:* New England Assn of Schls & Colls Eng Comm; Curr Revision Comm; NHS; NCTE, NEATE 1988-; MTA 1970-.

CRANE, LINDA L., Second Grade Teacher; *b:* Martins Ferry, OH; *m:* Gregory L.; *c:* Kyle, Travis, Deena; *ed:* Baldwin-Wallace Coll (BS) Elem Ed K-8 1983; Univ of Akron (MA) Elem Ed; *cr:* Our Lady of Perpetual Help 4th Grd Tchr 1965-67; Applewood Elem 5th Grd Tchr 1968-69; Memorial Elem Kndgtn, 2nd & 4th-6th Grd Tchr 1983-; *ai:* 3R Comm; Stu Tchr Cooperating Tchr; Consulting Tchr to Other Dists on Inclusion; NEA, OEA, BEA 1983-; Natl Tchrs of Eng 1992-; Comm Action 1990-, Fund Raiser, Vol of Yr Awd; Saint Ambrose Chrldrs 1980-, Fund Raiser, Family of Yr Awd; Dist Tchr of Yr 1986-87; Plain Dealer Crystal Apple Nom; Sex Equity Grant; Martha Holden Jennings Awd; NASA Tchr Prgm at Lewis Research Ctr; *office:* Memorial Elem Schl 3845 Magnolia Dr Brunswick OH 44212*

CRANEY, JOAN BOOMHOWER, Fifth Grade Teacher; *b:* Troy, NY; *m:* John Patrick; *c:* Dawn Finewood, Brenda, John Patrick Jr., Krisann; *ed:* SUNY at Oswego (BS) Elem Ed 1965; Attnd Coll of St Rose; *cr:* Brittonkill Cntrl Schls Elem Tchr 1965-; *ai:* Class Fundraising; Yrbk; Comm for Alternative Assessment; Compact 2000, Strategic Action Planner; Crisis, Staff Dev, Effective Schls Comms; NYSUT 1965-; PTA 1965-, Pres 1966; Garfield Lib Bd 1992-, Prsnl Com; Ath Booster 1970-; U. Meth PPR Bd 12 Yrs; WMHT Educl TV Grant; SUNY Oswego Hnrs Convocation Guest Speaker 1994; Article Pub.

CRAST, JULIE GORDINIER, Sixth Grade Teacher; *b:* Watertown, NY; *m:* Patrick M.; *c:* Jamieson P., Jared M., Jonathan R; *ed:* SUNY Coll at Cortland (BS) Elem & Early Scndry Ed 1985, (MS) Rdng Ed 1988; *cr:* South Jefferson Cntrl Schl Sixth Grd Tchr 1986-; *ai:* Elem Peer Tutor Prgm Coord; S Jeff Tchrs Assn 1986-, Recording Sec; NYSUT 1986-; *office:* South Jefferson Central Schl 10 Institute St Adams NY 13605

CRAUDERUEFF, MICHAEL L., Spanish Teacher; *b:* Elkhart, IN; *m:* Elaine J.; *c:* Robert, Mary; *ed:* St Josephs Univ (MS) Ed 1989; LaSalle Univ (MA) Biling & Bicultural Stud 1993; RI Univ Grad Stud; *cr:* Lake Forest Cntry Day Schl Fr Tchr 1978-80; Freinds Cntrl Schl Span & Fr Tchr 1980-; *ai:* 10 Grd Dean; JV Bsbl Coach; AATSP 1989-; *office:* Friends Central Upper Schl 1101 City Ave Wynnewood PA 19096

CRAVER, CHERYL CHRISTINA (DENNISON), Biology Teacher; *b:* Ft Wayne, IN; *m:* Bruce A.; *c:* Erica, Sean; *ed:* IN Univ (BS) Bio Ed 1969; Purdue Univ (MS) Sci Ed 1973; Attnd Univ of Dayton & Wright St Post Grad Stud; *cr:* Lafayette Schl Corp Jr HS Sci Tchr 1969-78; Greenview Schl Corp HS Bio, Anatomy, Physiology & Honors Bio Tchr 1980-; *ai:* N Cntrl & Strategic Planning Comms; NHS; NEA, OEA & GEA 1980-; Amer Bio Tchrs 1986-; Phi Delta Kappa; Childrens Medical Ctr Womens Auxiliary 1978-, Sec 1982; Valedictorian & Salutetorian Excl in Tchng Awd 1987, 1988, 1990, & 1991; *office:* Greeneview H S 53 N Limestone St Jamestown OH 45335

CRAVOTTA, NICOLENE FAYE, Language Arts Tchr & Dept Chr; *b:* Indiana, PA; *ed:* IUP (BA) Eng Ed 1969, (MED) Eng 1975; *cr:* Saltsburg Jr, Sr HS Eng Tchr 1969-71; Blairsville MS Eng Tchr 1971-; *ai:* Assessment, Writing Comms; Budget; Origami, Introductory Ger, Lit Magazine Spon; ASCD, PMSA 1991-; PSEA, BSEA, NEA 1969-, Local Sec, PR Chm, Rep at Large; Church Admin 1996, Bd; *office:* Blairsville MS 104 School Ln Blairsville PA 15717*

CRAW, TERENCE L., US History Teacher; *b:* Bridgeport, CT; *m:* Justine C. Edyk; *c:* Tricia, Terence; *ed:* Western CT Univ (MS) Scndry Ed, Soc Sci 1972; 30 Addl Hrs Art His; *cr:* Broadview MS 8th Grd US His Tchr1967-; *ai:* After Schl Tutoring Prgm; Hispanic Tutoring 1994-95; CEA, NEA, DEA 1967-; *home:* 75 Rita Dr New Fairfield CT 06812

CRAWFORD, EILEEN WILKOS, Music Teacher; *b:* Hartford, CT; *m:* Kevin Bradway; *ed:* Univ of Hartford Hartt Schl of Muisc (BM) Music Compsition 1983; 29 Credit Hrs Prof Cert 1985-87; Post Grad 15 Credit Hrs; *cr:* Glastonbury United Meth Church Choir, Instrumental Dir 1985-92; Glenbrook MS Music Tchr 1987-89; Timothy Edwards MS Music Tchr 1989-; *ai:* Entertainers Drama Club Music Dir 1989-95; Chocolate Cake Orch Music Dir 1993-; Organizing Stdnts to Perform Concerts, Bake Sales to Benefit Homeless, Hungry 1993-; NEA, MEA 1987-89; NEA, CEA 1989-; MENC, CMEA 1991-93, 1995-; Glastonbury United Meth Church 1975-; South Windsor Tchrs Recognition of Excl Awd 1991-; Composed Music for 3 Musicals; *office:* Timothy Edwards MS 100 Arnold Way South Windsor CT 06074

CRAWFORD, FREDERICK L., 2nd Grade Teacher; *b:* Ford City, PA; *m:* Georgenia L. Startzell; *c:* Dacia R. Como, Triste L., Manda S.; *ed:* IN Univ of PA (BSEd) Math 1970; Univ of Dayton (MST) Math 1974; IUP at Slippery Rock (BSEd) Elem Ed 1980; 24 Addl Credits; Permanent Cert; *cr:* Butler Area Schl Dist Math Tchr 1970-80; St. Michael's Schl 2nd Grd Tchr 1980-; *ai:* Stu Cncl Adv; After Schl Tutoring; Drug & Alcohol Task Force; Middle States Stu Assistance Program; Strategic Planning Comm; NEA, PSEA, BEA 1970-; NCEA 1980; PCTM 1985-; NCTM 1985-; NASSP 1989-; West End PTG 1980-, Pres; St Michael's Eucharistic Ministers 1985-; *office:* St. Michael's Schl 130 Glenn Ave Butler PA 16001*

CRAWFORD, JOAN BIELAU, Dir of Enrllmnt Dev & Eng Prof; *b:* Pittsburgh, PA; *m:* William E.; *c:* Susan, Mikal; *ed:* Univ of Pittsburgh (BA) Retail Trng & Eng 1944; Frostburg St Univ MA Equivalent Eng 1972; *cr:* Castle Shannon Jr HS Eng Dept Head 1960-64; Keystone Oaks HS Eng Dept Chprsn 1965-71; Garrett Comm Coll Asst Eng Prof, Chprsn Hum Div 1976-85; Enrollment Dev Dir 1986-; *ai:* Retention Comm Chmn; Writers Guild; Galaxy Pgm; Admin Cncl; Tenure Comm; Beacon Pgm for Adults; Transition Team for Unemployed Workers; NCTE 1965-; NCMPR 1989-; MCCPRO 1993-; Garrett Cty Arts Cncl Bd 1979-, Publicity Chmn; Delta Kappa Gamma Honorary 1982; Habitat for Hum Bd 1988-91, Publicity Chrmn; Numerous Articles Pub; *office:* Garrett Comm Coll 687 Mosser Rd Mc Henry MD 21541

CRAWFORD, JOANNE,SSJ, First Grade Teacher; *b:* Kane, PA; *ed:* Villa Maria Coll (BS) Primary, Early Chldhd 1965; Temple Univ Early Chldhd; Edinboro Univ Lib Sci; Behrend Univ Lib Sci; *cr:* St Bernard Schl Tchr 1960-61; Sacred Heart Schl Tchr 1961-63; Blessed Sacrament Tchr 1963-65; St John Tchr 1965-67; Villa Maria & Maryvale Presch Prin & Tchr 1967-70; Holy Rosary Schl Tchr 1971-; *ai:* Curr Comm; PTO 1971-; Holy Rosary Parish Litury Planning 1985-; Parish Lector & Commentator 1983-; Parish Life 1995-; Schl Bd 1995-; *office:* Holy Rosary Schl 605 Market St Johnsonburg PA 15845

CRAWFORD, JUNE MACIOROWSKI, Second Grade Teacher; *b:* Yonkers, NY; *m:* Harold A.; *ed:* SUNY at New Paltz (BA) Elem Ed 1969, (MS) Elem Ed 1974; *cr:* Fulmar Rd Elem Schl 1st Grd Tchr 1969-79, 2nd Grd Tchr 1979-; *ai:* Mahopac Schl Dist Lit Review Comm; Enrichment Comm; Mahopac Tchrs Assn, NYSUT, AFT 1969-; Sweet Adelines Women's Barbershop Chorus 1981-, Corresponding Sec, Show Chprsn; Multinational, Comparatiave Ed Schlsp New Zealand Univ of NY St Ed Dept; *office:* Fulmar Road Elem Schl 55 Fulmar Rd Mahopac NY 10541

CRAWFORD, RODNEY GENE, Social Studies Teacher & Chair; *b:* York, PA; *m:* Linda Lee Thomas; *c:* Michael, Jeanie, Amanda; *ed:* Shippensburg Univ (BS) Soc Stud 1972, (MED) His 1975; Western MD Coll (MS) Admin 1993; Admin Cert; *cr:* Chambersburg Schl Dist Tchr, Cross Cntry Coach 1973-89; Spring Grove Schl Dist Tchr, Dept Chair 1989-; *ai:* Soccer Club, Military His Club Adv; Phi Delta Kappa 1994-; Mid Sts Cncl 1980-; PA Cncl for Soc Stud 1985-; NEA 1973-; Dover Lions Club 1990-, Bd of Dir; Spring Grove Historical Soc, Zeredatha Lodge #451 1989-; York Rd Runners 1980-; Lions Club Sportsman of Yr 1986; Natl HS Coaching Awd 1988; Schl Bd Recognition 1986; *office:* Spring Grove Area MS RD #4 Box 4621 Spring Grove PA 17362

CRAWFORD-JONES, CAROL, Business Education Instructor; *b:* Morristown, NJ; *c:* J. Michael, Charles T.; *ed:* Montclair St Coll (BA) Bus Ed 1964; Attnd Rider Univ, Trenton St Coll, Jersey City St Coll, Local In-Svc 36 Credit Hrs; *cr:* Katharine Gibbs Schl Tchr 1964-66; North Hunterdon-Voorhees HS Dist Job Placement Coord 3 Yrs, Bus Ed Instr 1975-; *ai:* FBLA Club Adv; SATI & SATII Test Ctr Coord; Discipline, Attendance & Grading Comm Assn Rep Cncl; NJBEA 1975-; Church of the Holy Spirit 1990-, Altar Guild Treas; *office:* North Hunterdon HS 1445 Rt 31 Annandale NJ 08801

CRAWLEY, MARGARET BAILEY, Third Grade Teacher; *b:* Rogersville, TN; *m:* James Winston Jr.; *c:* Allyson Joy, James Winston III; *ed:* Carson Newman Coll (BS) Elem Ed 1969; Shippensburg Univ (MED) Elem Ed 1984; Post Grad Classes Coll of William & Mary, Wilson Coll, Univ of TN, PA St Univ; *cr:* Yorktown Elem 4th Grd Tchr 1969-72; Alcoa Elem 1st Grd Tchr 1972-74; James Burd Elem 3rd-4th Grd Tchr 1982-; *ai:* Local Audubon Act; NEA, PSEA, SAEA 1982-; Shippensburg Pub Lib Bd, 5 Yrs; St & Natl Nature, Conservation Orgs; *home:* 700 Brad St Shippensburg PA 17257

CRAWN, LINDA K., Health & Physical Ed Teacher; *b:* Newton, NJ; *ed:* Concord Coll (BS) PE 1973; East Stroudsburg Univ (MS) PE 1991; 15 Grad Credits; *cr:* Franklin HS PE, Math Tchr 1973-75; Kittatinny Regnl HS Hlth, PE Teacher 1975-; *ai:* Var Field Hockey Coach 19 Yrs; NEA, SCEA 1973-; Kitt Tchrs Assn 1975-, VP; North Jersey Coaches Assn 1978-; Coach of Yr 1994; *office:* Kittatinny Regnl HS 77 Kalsey Rd Newton NJ 07860

CRAY, DANA L., English Teacher; *b:* Paterson, NJ; *m:* W. Kelly; *ed:* Castleton St Coll (BA) Eng, Ed 1992; *cr:* West Rutland Schl Scndry Eng Tchr 1993-; *ai:* SADD, Class of 1997 Adv; NEA 1993-; VT Outstdng Tchr Awd 1995.*

CRAYTON, CAROL, English Teacher; *b:* Brooklyn, NY; *ed:* William Paterson Coll (BA) Eng, Scndry Ed 1972; Montclair St Coll (MA) Human Svcs & Cnslng 1983; Post-Grad Stud Rutgers Univ; *cr:* St Joseph HS Eng Tchr 1972-75; Eastside HS Title I Rdng Tchr 1975-79; John F. Kennedy HS Compensatory Ed Rdng Tchr 1979-83; Private Industry Cncl Adult Ed Instr 1983-85; Neptune MS Eng Tchr 1985-88; Raritan HS Eng Tchr 1988-; *ai:* Teen Inst of Garden St Adv 1992-95; Facilitator of Stress Mngmt Wkshps Rutgers Univ; Private Industry Cncl; SAT Instr; NEA, NCTE, NJEA 1972-; Grant 1971; *office:* Raritan HS 419 Middle Rd Hazlet NJ 07730

CREAGER, DARWIN LAMAR, Professor of Accounting; *b:* Waynesboro, PA; *m:* Barbara Joann Ulrich; *c:* Kellie Sue Reiber, Jonathan Ulrich; *ed:* Shippensburg Univ (BED) Bus & Accounting 1959, (MED) Bus & Accounting 1969; *cr:* Quincy HS Bus Tchr 1959-63; Waynesboro Sr HS Bus Tchr 1963-69; Hagerstown Jr Coll Prof of Accounting 1969-; *ai:* Division Asst for Accounting; NEA 1985-; *office:* Hagerstown Jr Coll 11400 Robinwood Dr Hagerstown MD 21742

CREAMER, CHRISTINA, First Grade Teacher; *b:* Mansfieldd, OH; *ed:* Bowling Green St Univ (BS) Elem Ed 1971; 30 Credit Hrs Grad Ashland Univ; *cr:* Mansfield St Peters 1st & 3rd-4th Grd Tchr 1971-74; Shiloh Jr High Schl 7th Grd Tchr 1974-75; Plymouth Elem 2nd Grd Tchr 1975-86; Shiloh Elem 1st Grd Tchr 1986-94; Plymouth Primary 1st Grd Tchr 1994-; *ai:* OEA & NEA 1974-, Past Pres; Ashland Cty Historical Soc 1986-; Experiment Aircraft Assoc 1989-; Ninety-Nine 1989-; *office:* Plymouth Primary Schl 48 W Broadway St Plymouth OH 44865

CREAN, ANNA DEMICHELE, Second Grade Teacher; *b:* Brooklyn, NY; *m:* James A.; *c:* Michele M., Jennifer A., Bridget A.; *ed:* Westfield St Coll (BSEd) Elem Ed 1961; *cr:* Town of Agawam 1st Grd Tchr 1961-64, 4th Grd Tchr 1978-84, 1st Grd Tchr 1984-85, 3rd Grd Tchr 1985-87, 2nd Grd Tchr 1987-; Town of Colonie 1st Grd Tchr 1964-65; *office:* Robinson Park Elem Sch 65 Begley St Agawam MA 01001

CREECH, W. ANGELA, Business Teacher; *b:* Middlesborough, KY; *ed:* Wright St Univ (BS) Bus Ed 1977, (MEd) 1994; Addl Hrs at Univ of Dayton; *cr:* Spinning Hills Jr HS Bus Tchr 1981-82; Beavercreek HS Bus Tchr 1984-; *ai:* Yrbk Adv; Chrstns in Action HS Grp Adv; Kappa Delta Pi 1977-; NEA 1981-; BEA 1984-; Northridge Freewill Bapt Church, Sunday Schl Tchr, Church Clerk, Youth Music, Drama Dir; Most Outstanding Yrbk 1993 Amer Scholastic Press Assn 1993, 1994; First Class Rating Mark of Distinction Natl Scholastic Press Assn; First Place Rating All Columbian Honor Columbia Scholastic Press Assn; 1994 Classroom Tchr of Yr; Tech Grant; *office:* Beavercreek HS 2660 Dayton-Xenia Rd Beavercreek OH 45434

CREEDON, VINCENT J., Business Education Teacher; *b:* Somerville, MA; *ed:* Salem St Coll (BS) (BED) Scndry Bus Ed 1965; Bridgewater St Coll (MED) Bus & Schl Admin 1976; 45 Hrs Beyond Masters in Schl Prsnl & Cmptr; *cr:* East Jr HS Bus Ed & His Tchr 1972-80; Weymouth South HS Bus Ed Tchr 1980-88; Weymouth Jr HS Eng Tchr 1988-90; SIS Eng Tchr 1990-94; Weymouth HS & VTHS Bus Ed Tchr 1994-; *ai:* Yrbk Staff Bus Mgr; NEA, WTA, MTA 1972-; Weymouth Elks 1980-; Schl Yrbk Adv 1980-88; *office:* Weymouth HS 1051 Commercial St East Weymouth MA 02189

CREGAN, BRENDAN PATRICK, World Cultures Teacher; *b:* New York, NY; *m:* Kimberly; *ed:* Mansfield Univ of PA (BS) Scndy Ed 1989; *cr:* Kennard Dale HS Soc Stud Tchr 1990-; *ai:* Head Soccer, Jr Var Bsbl & Jr High Bsktbl Coach; NEA 1993-; NCSS 1990-; Natl Soccer Coach Assn Amer 1992-; Timber Hill Comm Assn 1989; YAIAA Soccer Coach of Yr 1992, 1994, 1995; *home:* 735 Saint Johns Pl Dallastown PA 17313*

CREIGHTON, SHERRY SANTILLI, 12th Grade Teacher; *b:* Youngstown, OH; *m:* Ralph Michael; *c:* Jacquelyn, Jonathan, Ryan; *ed:* Youngstown St Univ (BS) Bus Ed 1979; Coll of Mt St Joseph (MSEd) Instruction 1988; *cr:* Trumbull Cty JVS Data Processing Tchr 1980-81; Mahoning Cty JVS Data Processing Tchr 1981-83; Trumbull Cty JVS Data Processing, Internet Tchr 1983-; *ai:* Bus Profs of Amer Club Adv 1980-95; AVA 1994-; *office:* Trumbull County Joint Voc Schl 528 Educational Hwy NW Warren OH 44483

CREMONINI, MICHAEL P., English & Theater Arts Teacher; *b:* Springfield, MA; *ed:* Amer Intnl Coll (MAT) Eng 1975, (BA) Eng 1972; Attnd Amer Stud Inst, Tufts Univ 4 Credit Hrs & The Univ of MA at Boston 6 Credit Hrs; *cr:* Our Lady of Mt Carmel Schl 5th Grd Tchr 1972-78; Cathedral HS Tchr 1978-86; Springfield Cntrl HS Tchr 1986-; *ai:* Springfield Cntrl HS Annual Shakespeare Performance & Musical Productions Dir; NCTE & NEA 1986-; Springfield Symphony Chorus 1980-, Pres 1987-88; NEH Summer Inst Amer Stud 1983; NEH Summer Tchng Inst Shakespeare & Co 1988; Shakespeare & Co NEH Inst Asst Tchr 1990-91; Shakespeare & Co NEH Inst Core Faculty 1992 & 1994; New England Wkshps on Tchng Shakespeare; NCTE Conv Spkr 1995; Shakespeare & Co Assoc Dir of Ed; *office:* Springfield Central H S 1840 Roosevelt Ave Springfield MA 01109*

CRENNAN, LINDSAY ANN, Kindergarten Teacher; *b:* Syracuse, NY; *m:* Randy G.; *c:* Meredith, Marc, Matthew; *ed:* Syracuse Univ (BS) Early Chldhd, Elem Ed & Human Dev 1972; 45 Credit Hrs Southampton Long Island Univ Grad Stud 1976; *cr:* Eastport Union Free Schl Dist Kndgtn Tchr 1972-84, 2nd Grd Tchr 1984-88, Kndgtn Tchr 1988-; *ai:* Kndgtn Liaison Spcl Ed; Kndgtn Coord; AFT 1972-; NYSUT 1972-; Eastport Tchrs Assn 1972-, Treas 1990-92; ETA 1986-89; VOTECOPE; Eastport Elem Coop 1984-; PTSA 1993-; SEPTA 1995-; *office:* Eastport Union Free Schl Dist 390 Montauk Hwy Eastport NY 11941

CRESCENZI, JOANNE BINKS, English Teacher; *b:* Milford, MA; *m:* David A.; *c:* Adam, Joshua; *ed:* Worchester St Coll (BS) Scndry Ed, Eng 1969; Attnd Black Hills St of SD, Emerson Coll, Fitchburg St Coll, Framingham St Coll, Leslie Coll, Anna Marie Coll, A World of Difference; *cr:* Milford HS Eng Tchr 1969-; *ai:* Cooperating Practitioner Simmons Coll Dept Ed; Mentor Tchr; Acad Decathlon 1995-; Diversity 1994-, Prins Search 1994, Substance Abuse Prevention Ed 1985-92, Staff & Admin Self Evaluation, Schl & Community Comms; Team Harmony Event MA 1994-; MS Task Force 1993-94; Schl Improvement Cncl 1991-93; Prin Advy Comm Chprsn & Vice Chprsn; NEA, MTA 1969-; NCTE, NARAL, MADD 1983-; Holocaust Mus 1995-; Town Govt 1982-92, Precint Mem; Union Evangelical Church 1987-91, Sunday Schl Tchr; Horace Mann Grant Multicultural Approach to Curr Receipent; *home:* 32 Congress Ter Milford MA 01757

CRESCO, CAROLYN CATTO, English Teacher; *b:* Auburn, NY; *m:* John P.; *c:* Holly, John Jr.; *ed:* Auburn Comm Coll (AA) Lib Arts 1961; St Univ at Albany (BA) Eng 1963; Syracuse Univ (MS) Eng Ed 1967; 12 Addl Grad Hrs; *cr:* West Genesee Jr HS 8th Grd Eng Tchr 1963-67; Cntrl HS 11th, 12th Grd Eng Tchr 1967-69; Auburn HS 11th, 12th Grd Eng Tchr 1969-74, 9th, 10th Grd Eng Tchr 1987-89; East MS 6th-8th Grd Eng Tchr 1989-92; West MS 7th, 8th Grd Eng Tchr 1992-; *ai:* Auburn Tchrs Assn 1967-74; NY St United Tchrs, AFT 1987-; Auburn Coll Club, Schlsp Chm 1968-70, Pres 1970; St Mary's Church 1972-, Vol Catechist Several Yrs; Outstdng Young Edctr Cayuga Cty 1967; *office:* West & East MS West Genessee St Auburn NY 13021

CRESPO, STELLA POURNARAS, Spanish Teacher; *b:* Beaver Falls, PA; *m:* Michael; *c:* Lauren Tomasula, John Tomasula; *ed:* Univ of CA at PA (BA) Span, Elem Ed 1975; 9 Credit Hrs Span Univ of Valencia 1973; *cr:* Beaver Vly Chrstn Acad 3rd Grd Tchr 1976-81; New Brighton HS Span Tchr 1990-; *office:* New Brighton HS 3200 43rd St New Brighton PA 15066

CRESSMAN, LYNN JOHNSON, English Teacher; *b:* Corry, PA; *m:* Barry Edward; *c:* Tye J., Leigh E., Toby J.; *ed:* Westminster Coll (BA) Eng, Ed 1975, (MA) Ed, Rdng Specialist 1980; 12 Grad Hrs in Supervision Edinboro Univ; *cr:* Maplewood HS Eng Tchr 1971-73; Titusville HS Jr High Eng, Rdng Tchr 1973-76, Eng Tchr 1976-; *ai:* Coord UPT Poetry Contest; Creative Writing Project Vol Coord; *home:* RR 1 Titusville PA 16354*

CRESSMAN, PAMELA GEISERT, High School Librarian; *b:* Philadelphia, PA; *m:* John R.; *c:* Jennifer, J. Robert; *ed:* West Chester Univ (BS) Scndry Eng 1967; Villanova Univ (MSLS) Lib Sci 1968; Attnd Beaver Coll & Univ of the Arts; *cr:* Abington Friends Schl Librn & Eng Tchr 1968-70; Holicong Jr HS Tchr of the Gifted 1978-80; Central Bucks HS West Librn & Philosophy Tchr 1980-; *ai:* Scholars Bowl Coach; Poetry Discussion Group Ldr; Lib Aides; Schl Restructuring Comm; Amer Lib Assn; Pennridge Schl Dir 1976-87, Pres; *office:* Central Bucks HS West W Court & Lafayette St Doylestown PA 18901

CRESSOTI-BUGBEE, ELSA, Chem Prof & Dept Chairman; *b:* Springfield, MA; *m:* E. John Bugbee; *c:* Matthew Cressotti; *ed:* Amer Intnl (BA) Chem 1968, (MST) Chemical Ed 1973; *cr:* Springfield Tech Comm Coll Chem Prof 1968-; *office:* Springfield Tech Comm Coll Armory Square Springfield MA 01105

CRESSOTTI, DEANNA RAY, French Teacher; *b:* Holyoke, MA; *ed:* Coll of the Holy Cross (BA) Fr 1991; Univ of MA (MAT) Fr Presently in Prog; Stu Tchr Ed Prgm St Cert; *cr:* CAthedral HS Fr Tchr 1994-; *ai:* JV Soccer Coach Holyoke Cath HS; Drama Dir; Stu Travel Dir; MAFLA, AATF 1994-; Boston, Strasbourg Sister City Assn 1994-, Trustee, Stu Exch Dir; *office:* Cathedral HS 260 Surry Rd Springfield MA 01118*

CREWSAW, CHARLES L., Social Studies Teacher; *b:* Carlisle, PA; *m:* Darrie J.; *c:* Daon, Ra'Sean, Charles III, Charlei, Chonte; *ed:* Penn St Univ (BSS) Soc Scis 1979; OH St Univ (MA) Ed Psych 1980; Still Attending Shippensburg Univ for Principalship; *cr:* Cols Tech Inst Behavioral Scis Instr 1981-87; Harrisburg HS Soc Stud Tchr 1991-94, Acting Asst Prin 1994-95; *ai:* Track & Field Head Coach; NEA 1991-, Mem; NAACP & Urban League; Outstanding Young Men of Amer 1985-; 4 Newspaper Articles About Cencus Awareness; OH St Univ Grad Schl Fellowship; *home:* 3543 N 6th St Harrisburg PA 17110

CRILLEY, JAMES PATRICK,JR., History & Social Studies Tchr; *b:* Bridgeton, NJ; *ed:* Lock Haven Univ of PA (BS) Ed 1990; 3 Hrs Manhattan Coll; *cr:* Cumberland Regnl HS His, Soc Stud Tchr 1991-92; Bridgeton HS His, Soc Stud Tchr 1992-; *ai:* Peer Leadership Trng, Jr Class Advs; Mid Sts Steering Comm; NEA, NJEA, NJ Cncl of Soc Stud 1991-; Natl Exchange Club 1992-, Sec; Bridgeton Area Jaycees Outstanding Young Educators of Yr Awd 1995; Mellon Grant Tchrs of Advanced Placement 1995; *office:* Bridgeton HS 111 N West Ave Bridgeton NJ 08302*

CRIMMINS, THOMAS F., Guidance Counselor; *b:* New York, NY; *m:* Catherine M.; *c:* Thomas, Michael, Kathleen, Mary, Megan; *ed:* Marist Coll (BA) Soc Stud 1967; St Johns Univ (MA) His 1972, (MS) Schl Guid 1975; *cr:* Resurrection-Ascension Schl Tchr, Coach 1967-69; Christ The King HS Tchr, Coach 1970-74; Maria Regnl HS Tchr, Coach 1974-77; Christ The King HS Guid Cnslr, Coach 1977-81; Elmont HS Guid Cnslr, Coach 1982-; *ai:* Coaching; Evening Schl Cnslr; NEA, Nassau Cnslrs Assn, PTA 1982-; Floral Pk Indians 1984-; Mended Hearts Inc 1995-; *office:* Elmont Meml HS 555 Ridge Rd Elmont NY 11003

CRISCI, DOMINICK JAMES, Social Studies Teacher; *b:* Newburgh, NY; *m:* Bonnie Ann Rinck; *c:* Jillian; *ed:* Marist Coll (BA) His 1981; SUNY at New Paltz (MS) Elem Ed & Scndry Soc Stud 1995; *cr:* Sacred Heart Schl 5th-8th Grd Soc Stud Tchr 1991-92; Vly Cntrl HS Summer Pgm 9th-12th Grd Soc Stud Tchr 1992-94, 9th-12th Grd Soc Stud Tchr 1993-; *ai:* Mock Trial Team Coach; AFT 1989-; NYS Assn Tchrs 1989-; Vly Cntrl Tchrs Assn 1993-; Walkill Little League 1994-, Coach; *office:* Valley Central HS 1175 Rt 17k Montgomery NY 12549

CRIST, DANIEL THOMAS, Sixth Grade Teacher; *b:* Roaring Spring ; *m:* Elaine Carol Doran; *c:* Matthew, Erin, Danelle; *ed:* Penn St Univ (BA) Elem Ed 1977; *cr:* Claysburg Kimmel Schl Dist Elem Tchr 1977-; *ai:* Jr Hs Girls Bsktbl, Var Girls Bsktbl, Girls Sftbl Coach; Elem Girls Bsktbl Coord; PSEA 1977-; NEA 1977-; Sunday Schl Supt 1980-, Supt; Church Bd 1977-, Deacon, Elder; Amer Legion Band 1970-, Pres; Rotary Club Citizen of Month Awd 1987; Jaycees Young Edctr of Yr Awd 1988; *home:* RR 1 Box 241 Imler PA 16655*

CRIST, DIANNE SHELDON, Computer Literacy Teacher; *b:* Warren, OH; *c:* Jason Patrick, Jared Lewis; *ed:* Kent St Univ (BA) DH 1st-12th Grd 1975, (BA) Elem Ed 1st-8th Grd 1975; Attnd Younstown St, Kent St, Ashland Univ; *cr:* Niles Schls at Jefferson 2nd Grd Tchr 1975-78; Niles Schls at Washington 6th Grd Tchr 1978-88; Niles Schls at Garfield 4th-6th Grd Math Tchr 1988-93; Niles Schls at Edison Jr High 7th-8th Grd Cmptr Lit Tchr 1993-; *ai:* NEA, OEA, NCTA 1975-; Phi Delta Kappa 1974-; North Mar Church 1979-, Bible Schl, Sunday Schl Tchr, Gal, Pal Prgm 1982-; Ctr for Innovation in Ed Educl Facilitator 1994-; Trumbull Cty Math Wkshp Co-Leader; OH Acad for Schl Improvement Strategies Participant 1993; *office:* Edison Jr HS 36 W Church St Niles OH 44446

CRISTOFARO, CORRINNE ELIZABETH, Business Education Teacher; *b:* Elmira, NY; *ed:* Corning Comm Coll (AAS) Secretarial & Word Processing 1988; Buffalo St Coll (BS) Bus Ed 1991; 12 Grad Hrs Toward NY St Coaching Cert; *cr:* Lakeshore Cntrl Schls Bus Ed Tchr 1993-; Hilbert Coll Womens Bsktbl Head Coach 1995-; *ai:* Girls Modified Bsktbl Coach; NY St Bar Assn Mock Trial Adv; Teen Action Group Adv; Stu Fac Forum Adv; Schl Musical Publicist; Go Out & Lead Somebody Adv; Girls Var Track & Field Asst Coach; Phi Beta Lambda 1989-; AFT 1992-; NBEA, Bus Tchrs Assn of NY St 1996; Empire St Challengers Tchrs Schlsp 1988-91; Intnl Prof Secretaries Awd 1988; Elmira Womens Bus Org Awd 1986; Elmira Free Acads Highest Bus Average Awd 1986; *office:* Lakeshore Cntrl Schl 959 Beach Rd Angola NY 14006*

CRISWELL, WILLIAM G., Guidance Counselor; *b:* Coatesville, PA; *m:* Pamela J. Rostron; *c:* William David, Matthew Andrew; *ed:* Philadelphia Coll of Bible (BS) Soc Work 1977; West Chester Univ (MED) Cnslr Ed 1980; Various Post Grad Courses; *cr:* First Bapt Church of Coatesville Youth Dir 1976-79; Riverside Brandywine Counseling Ctr Substance Abuse Therapist 1983-87; Downingtown Schl Dist Guidance Cnslr 1987-; Private Practice Psychological Therapist 1987-; *ai:* Stu Assistance Svc 8 Yrs; Chrstn Youth Fellowship Group Spon; NEA, PA Schl Ed Assn, Downingtown Area Ed Assn 1987-; Cntrl Presbyn Church 1983-, Elder, Church Schl Tchr, Youth Group Ldr; *office:* Downingtown Jr HS 335 Manor Ave Downingtown PA 19335

CRITELLI, RALPH JOSEPH, Science Teacher; *b:* Kenmore, NY; *m:* Wendy Ann Beiring; *c:* Nicolette; *ed:* Univ at Buffalo (BA) Geology 1984; Buffalo St Coll (MSEd) Geo Sci & Interdisciplinary 1990; *cr:* Erie I Boces Sci, Bus & Hlth Tchr 1985; Kenmore Schls Earth Sci Tchr 1985-; *ai:* IM Vllybl, Bsktbl & Sftbl Coach; Var, Radio, Sci & Ping Pong Clubs & Bookstore Adv; NY St Sci Tchrs Flwshp Awd 1984; NY St Tchr of Yr Semifinalist 1994; PTSA Tchr of Yr 1994; Adv of Yr Var Club Awd 1993; *office:* Kenmore East Sr HS 350 Fries Rd Tonawanda NY 14150*

CRITTENDEN, JACQUELINE LAPAZE, Math Teacher; *b:* Youngstown, OH; *m:* Jerry R.; *ed:* Youngstown St Univ (BS) Ed 1990, (MS) Curr, Instruction 1996; *cr:* Cardinal Mooney HS Math Tchr 1990-91; Poland Seminary HS Math Tchr 1991-; *ai:* SADD 1991-92 Adv; Acad Challenge Team 1991- Adv; NEA, OEA, Poland Ed Assn, NEOEA 1991-; Eisenhower Grant for Math 1992; *office:* Poland Seminary HS 3199 Dobbins Rd Youngstown OH 44514

CRIVELLO, RITA LEVINE, Chemistry Teacher; *b:* Newark, NJ; *m:* James A.; *c:* Renee; *ed:* Newark St Tchrs Coll (BA) Sci 1968; Kean Coll of NJ (MA) Stu Prsnl Svcs 1975; 32 Addl Credits Union Cty Coll 1990; *cr:* Kearny HS Chem Tchr 1968-; *ai:* KEA, HCEA, NJEA, NEA, NJ Sci Tchrs Assn 1968-; Alpha Delta Kappa 1985-; *office:* Kearny HS 336 Devon St Kearny NJ 07032*

CROCETTI, CATHERINE FUSILLO, Science Teacher; *b:* North Tarrytown, NY; *m:* Emidio; *c:* Christopher, Lauren; *ed:* Stony Brook Univ (MA) Liberal Stud 1976; Hofstra Univ (MBA) Bus Admin; 75 Hrs of Credit Beyond Masters in Ed Classes; *cr:* Holland Patent Sr HS 10th Grd Bio Tchr 1972-73; Pomona Jr HS 7th Grd Bio Tchr 1973-74; West Hollow MS 7th-9th Grd Sci Tchr 1974-; *ai:* Natl Jr Honor Soc Comm; AFT 1972-; NEA 1972-; HHH Tchrs Assn 1972-; Recently Inducted as Honorary Mem of Natl Jr Honor Soc; *office:* West Hollow MS 250 Old East Neck Rd Melville NY 11747*

CROCK, DONNA E., French Teacher; *b:* Bellefonte, PA; *ed:* Lock Haven Univ (BS) Fr 1975, (MEQ) 1995; *cr:* Bellefonte HS Fr Tchr 1975-; *ai:* Fr Club Adv; AATF 1994-; Kappi Delta Pi 1974-; PSEA, NEA 1975-; *office:* Bellefonte Area HS 830 E Bishop St Bellefonte PA 16823*

CROCKER, ELLI BARBARA, Assistant Professor; *b:* Boston, MA; *m:* John Morse; *c:* Alexander, Brittany, Evan; *ed:* Smith Coll (BA) Art, Sociology 1977; Tufts Univ (MFA) Painting 1981; *cr:* Montserrat Coll of Art Part-time Instr 1988-89; Art Inst of Boson Part-time Instr 1989-91; Clark Univ Part-time Asst Prof 1982-94, Full-time Asst Prof 1994-; *ai:* Coll Bd; Phys Plant Comm; Adv; St Botolph Club 1995-; League of Women Voters 1995-; Unitarian Universalist Soc of Newton 1985-; St Botolph Club Fnd Grant 1992; Finalist New England Fnd for the Arts Drawing Flwshp 1994; Cummineton Arts Colony Resident 1993; Finalist Artists Fnd Drawing Flwshp 1991; *office:* Clark Univ 950 Main St Worcester MA 01610

CROCKER, LAURIE L., Sixth Grade Teacher; *b:* Youngstown, OH; *c:* Brandi, Kasey, Tyler, Carlie; *ed:* Working Towards Masters Kent St Univ Child Guidance; Summit Cty Bd, Ashland Univ Trainers 94-95; *cr:* Indian Trl Stow City Schls 1st Grd Tchr 1989-90, 5th Grd Tchr 1990-92; Lakeview Stow City Schls 6th Grd Tchr 1992-95, Schl Coord 1995-; *ai:* Supts Advy Cncl, Mem 2 Dist Wide Comms; Coord of Lakeview Intermediate Schl; Helped Design & Coordinate 5th-6th Grd Bldg; Lang Arts Trainer Tots; NEA 1989-; Stow Tchrs Assn 1989-; Ladies Soccer Assn 1990-, Team Rep; Kent Soccer Club 1994-, Sec; Corp Challenge Ath of Yr 1993; *office:* Lakeview Intermediate Schl Lakeview Intermediate Schl Stow OH 44224*

CROCKER, STUART, Chemistry & Computer Teacher; *b:* Baltimore, MD; *m:* Germaine Troxell; *c:* Katherine; *ed:* Rochester Inst of TEch (BS) Chem 1983; IN Univ of PA Towards Cert in Ed; St Francis Coll Cert in Ed; *cr:* Bishop Carroll HS Chem Tchr 1990-93; Bishop Guilfoyle HS Chem, Sci, Cmptr, Tchr, Cmptr Dept Head 1993-; *ai:* Coach Head Track, Field, Cross Cntry; Ski, Video Clubs Moderator; *office:* Bishop Guilfoyle HS 2400 Pleasant Valley Blvd Altoona PA 16602

CROCKETT, BEVERLEY ANNE, 7th Grade English Teacher; *b:* Washington, DC; *c:* Stephanie, Shawn, Stephen; *ed:* DC Tchrs Coll (BA) Eng & Spec Ed 1969; 18 Hrs Toward Cnslng Degree; Drug Awareness, Books Project, Rdng in Content Areas & Comp Literacy Stud; *cr:* Lincoln Jr HS Eng Tchr 1969-93; Eliot Jr HS Eng Tchr 1993-; *ai:* 7th Grd Team Ldr; Spon of School-Wide Act; WTU 1973-, Bldg Rep; NCT *office:* Eliot Jr HS 1830 Constitution Ave NE Washington DC 2(

CROFT, DANIEL THOMAS, Band Director; *b:* Pittsburgh Dawna LaRae Ainsworth; *c:* Daniel Jr., LaRae M.; *ed:* CLari (BS) Music Ed 1973; Attnd Univ of PA Scndry Admin; Conducti Duquesne Univ; *cr:* North Star Schl Dist Dir of Bands 1973-; *ai:* Band Dir; Strategic Planning Task Force Comm; Time Keep Prgm; Tennis Club Founder, Benefactor; SCMEA 1973-, Pres 19 Conf; PMEA, NEA, PSEA, NSEA 1973-; MENC 1969-; AF Somerset Yth Bsktbl Org 1983-, Bd, Head Referee; Somerset C Band 1988-, Founder, Dir; Somerset Alliance Church Band Former Dir; Laurel Highlands Church Sftbl League 1979-, Mgr Music Ministry in Area Churches; Local Schl Musical Musiciar Miller Awd Recipient 1994; Somerset Cnty Chamber of Commer Yr; Clarion Univ Summer Band Clinic Fac Mem 15 Yrs; Guest for Festival Bands Throughout Western PA; *office:* North Star HS St Boswell PA 15531*

CROMWELL, PAMELA ANN, Elementary Teacher; *b:* New NY; *c:* Scott Wilson, Melinda Wilson; *ed:* Amer Univ (BA) Elem George Washington Univ (MA) Spec Ed 1975; MCPS, Montogo 45 Addl Credit Hrs; *cr:* Montgomery Co Pub Schl Elem Tchr Young Astronaut Cncl, Schl Chptr Ldr NASA Mem; Speaker for Schls Active Mem; Grd Level Chprsn; GAT Comm; NEA, MC Young Astro Cncl; LIFO, Trained to Tch; PTA; BSA, Merit Bad Greater Damascus Schl Comm Action Team; MD NASA Tchr Prgm 1985-86; Montgomery Cty Partnership Awd Drug Abuse P Curr Coord; *office:* Cedar Grove Elem Schl 24001 Ridge Rd Ge MD 20876

CRON, MARC C., Secondary Science Teacher; *b:* Atlanta, GA; Gehring; *c:* Lauren; *ed:* Miami Univ (BS Comp Sci Ed 1990, (B Ed 1990, (MAT) Bio 1995; Minor Botany 1990; *cr:* Harrison HS 1990-; *ai:* JV Boys Bsktbl; Fernald Environmental Mgmt Pro 1992; *office:* William Henry Harrison HS 9860 West Rd Ha 45030

CRONAN, BEVERLY M., English Teacher; *b:* Cambridge, Robert R.; *c:* Susan Ryan, Dana, Todd; *ed:* Emmanuel Coll (BA) Univ of MA at Lowell (MED) Curr, Instruction 1985; Salem S Boston Univ Rdng; *cr:* Lynch Jr High Eng Tchr 1968-79; Winche Eng Tchr 1979-83; Rath & Strong Systems Products Trng Dir Winchester High Eng Tchr 1986-; *ai:* Winchester Tchrs Assn; NC Rdng; *office:* Winchester HS 80 Skillings Rd Winchester MA 0

CRONAN, EDWARD L.,JR., Guidance Department Head; *b:* P RI; *m:* Mary-Ellen Mercurio; *c:* Patrick, Jarrett; *ed:* Univ of Scndry Ed 1972; Cnslng, Guid 1976; RI Coll Scndry Adm Providence Coll; *cr:* East Providence Sr HS Soc Stud Tchr 1972 Cnslr 1976-80, Guid Dept Head 1980-; *ai:* Class Day awds, Seminar, Schlsp, Grant Directory Coord 1981-; RI Regnl Col 1978-; Townie Pride Bsktbl Camp Dir 1995-; Ed Assn 1972-; NE 1973-; Amer Cnslng Assn 1981-; RI Cnslng Assn 1981-, Sc Citizen Schlsp Fnd 1981-, Bd Mem; St Martha's CYO Bsktbl 198 East Providence Cntrl Little League 1986-, Coach, Umpire 1986 1990-94; RI Cross Cntry Coach of Yr 1985; East Bay Women's of Yr 1986; New England Assn Cnslr of Yr 1989; Natl Yth Sport Assn Awd 1995; Natl Distngd Svc Registry 1989-90; *off* Providence Sr HS 2000 Pawtucket Ave East Providence RI 0291

CRONAUER, DONNA, Language Arts & Religion Tchr; *b:* Spa *ed:* Carlow Coll (BS) Ed 1973; Duquesne Univ (MS) Elem Continual Upgrading New Educl Prgms, Trends, Act; *cr:* St Ra 1st-3rd Grd Tchr 1966-75; St Angela Merici Schl 2nd Grd Tchr St Benedict the Moor Schl 1st-2nd Grd Tchr 1976-; *ai:* Church A Church, Comm Outreach Act; NCEA 1976-; Pittsburgh Dioces Apple Awd 1993; Recognition for Dev Learning Ctrs in Classroo St Benedict The Moor Schl 2900 Bedford Ave Pittsburgh PA 15

CRONE, ALETA KAY, Vocal Music Teacher; *b:* York, PA; *ed:* Coll (BS) Music Ed 1987; Instructional II Cert 23 Credit Hrs We Univ, Duquesne Univ, Wilkes Univ; *cr:* Dover Area Schl Dist E Music Long-Term Sub 1987-88; Central York Schl Elem, MS Vo Tchr 1988-93; Christian Schl of York MS, HS Vocal Music Tchr MENC 1984-; WCTU 1987-; *home:* 1155 Baish Rd Mechanic 17055

CRONE, THOMAS G., Band & Orchestra Director; *b:* Homstea Mary Mc Laughlin; *ed:* Duquesne Univ (BSME) Music Ed 19 Music 1973; *cr:* Woodland Hills Schl Dist HS Band, Orch Dir 2 Music Dept Chprsn; Producer, Dir HS Musicals; Marching Band Mgr; NEA; PSEA 1980-, Treas; Best Stage Dir Awd; PSL Ci Opera Gene Kelly Awds 1991-93, 1995; *office:* Woodland Hills Greensburg Pike Pittsburgh PA 15221

CRONIN, PATRICIA K., Vice Principal; *b:* Malden, MA; *m:* F Ryan, Kristin; *ed:* Salem St Coll (BS) Bus Ed 1970; Suffolk Un Ed 1975; Attnd Westfield St Coll, Salem St Coll, Fitchburg St Northeast Metro Tech Schl Bus Ed Tchr 1970-91, Vice Prin 1991 Ed Week Co-Chm; Peer Mediation Coord 1 Yr; NASSP, MSSA 1990-; Tewksburg Girls Sftbl 1994-, Treas; *office:* NE Metro R Schl Dist 100 Hemlock Rd Wakefield MA 01880

CRONIN, PATRICK LAWRENCE, English Teacher & Curr C Weymouth, MA; *m:* Brenda Joyce Young; *c:* Jennifer Cronin Patrick Kevin; *ed:* St Michaels Coll (BA) Eng 1970, (MED) S 1971; Addl Grad Credit Hrs at Bridgewater St Coll; *cr:* Weeks Tchr 1971-72; East Bridgewater Jr High Eng Tchr 1972- Bridgwater HS Eng Tchr 1978-90, Eng Coord & Tchr 1990-; *a* Magazine Adv; Co-Adv Lions Club Yth Speech Contest; Var Bskt MTA 1972-, Prof Dev Liaison; NCTE 1990-, St Ldr Pgm to Recog in Stu Lit Magazines; MCTE 1990-, Exec Bd; Holy Ghost Parish Spirit Times Newsletter; Received Hnrs for Various Articles & Po Horace Mann Grant Tchr; *office:* East Bridgewater HS 11 Plymou Bridgewater MA 02333

CROOKS, ANNELOUISE PETERSON, 5th Grade Teacher; PA; *m:* Robert M.; *c:* Kaci G., Kevin R. F.; *ed:* West Chester U Elem Ed, Eng 1969; Master's Credits Lit, Linguistics; Scndry Ed Eng; Post Grad Credits in Educ Trends; *cr:* West Chester U Adminis 1969-70; Coatesville Sch Dist Tchr 1970-71; Marple Sch Dist Tchr 1971-; *ai:* Prof Dev Comm; Partner Writing Men NEA, PSEA 1969-; MNEA 1971-; Women in Crisis 1991-, Cns 1989-; AAUW 1981-; Natl Merit Schlr; Wilson Flwshp; LSAT La Periodic Articles for Local Newspapers; *office:* Charles H Russ Schl Sproul & New Ardmore Ave Broomall PA 19008

CROOKS, KATHLEEN MYERS, 1st Grade Teacher; *b:* DuBoi Kevin; *c:* Jaime, Jeffrey; *ed:* Clarion Univ (BS) Elem Ed 1973, (M Ed 1977; *cr:* Luthersburg Elem Schl 3rd Grd Tchr 1974, 1st 1975-; *ai:* Rdng Comm; DAEA, NEA 1974-; Delta Kappa Gam *home:* RR 2 Box 369 Reynoldsville PA 15851

CROOKSHANK, MARTHA ERMLICH, Art Teacher; *b:* Allia *m:* James E.; *c:* Anne Rackley; *ed:* Mt Union Coll (BA) Art Ed Hrs Specific Learning Disabilities Cert; *cr:* Marlington Local S 1980-84; Stanton MS Art Tchr 1985-; *ai:* Unified Arts T

: Pgm Planning Comm; Incentive Comm Chm; OH Art Ed Assn :sign Winner for Alliance City Flag; *office:* Stanton MS 311 S e Alliance OH 44601

STON, JOHN PAUL, Physics Teacher; *b:* Johnstown, PA; *ed:* 'ittsburgh at Johnstown (BS) Scndry Math Ed 1986; Drummers : NYC 10 Week Cert Pgm 1989; IN Univ of PA Physics Cert 1991; Hills HS Long Term Sub Physics Tchr 1987, Physics Tchr 1993-; :cCort HS Physics & Math Tchr 1987-92; Lyons Twp HS Physics '-93; *ai:* Intensive Scheduling Comm; NEA 1993-; AAPT; Ldr of nstruction Mentor; Univ of Dallas C3P Project 1996; *office:* ls HS 489 Locust St Sidman PA 15955

'HOMAS J., Social Studies Supervisor; *b:* Kingston, PA; *m:* an; *c:* Colleen, Kathleen; *ed:* Wilkes Coll (BS) His 1966; Trenton MA) His 1972; Montclair Coll; Kean Coll Supvrs Cert; *cr:* HS Soc Stud Tchr 1966-70; Bridgewater-Raritan Soc Stud Tchr Soc Stud Chm 1981-88, Soc Stud Supvr 1988-; *ai:* NJ Cncl for 1980-, Pres Elect & VP; NJ Prins & Supvrs Assoc 1981-; Flwshps: :y Assn & Arthur K Watson; *office:* Bridgewater-Raritan HS PO Bridgewater NJ 08807

THOMAS IRWIN, French Teacher; *b:* Danville, PA; *m:* Diana ; *c:* Debra Fox, Stacy Anderson, Steph Derugen; *ed:* Bloomsbury Fr 1967, (MED) Fr 1975; Addl 9 Hrs Univ of ME; *cr:* Jersey l Fr Tchr 1967-; *ai:* French Club, Ski Club; NEA, PSEA, DDTF *ice:* Jersey Shore Area Sr HS 701 Cemetery St Jersey Shore PA

:, WILLIAM F., Math, Science Tchr & Dept Head; *b:* Worcester, anice Moon; *c:* Kathleen Richard, Nancy, Stacy; *ed:* Worcester St ED) Math Ed 1965; 30 Credit Hrs Beyond Masters; *cr:* David ; Tchr & Dept Head 1962-; *ai:* Bsktbl & Bsbl former Coach; Comms; NEA & MTA 1962-, Pres MTA 1960; NCTM; NCTS; ts: WPI, Univ MA, Holy Cross & Syracuse; *office:* David Prouty lain St Spencer MA 01562

, ANDREA M., Business Education Teacher; *b:* Rochester, NH; C.; *c:* James, Joyce; *ed:* Grahm Jr Coll (AS) Bus Law 1973; Univ A) Arts 1977; NH Coll (BS) Bus Ed 1984; *cr:* Dept of Labor nfo Specialist 1977-81; Sanford HS Adult Ed Tchr 1980-84; ic HS Bus Ed Tchr 1985-; *ai:* BEAM; FBLA; NEA 1985-; *home:* 53 Springvale ME 04083

, ANNE CORDELL, High School English Teacher; *b:* Quincy, iv of NE (BS) Eng 1964; Wilkes Univ (MED) 1990; *cr:* Bellevue : Tchr 1964-65; Willingboro Schl Dist Eng Tchr 1968-70; / Schl Dist Eng Tchr 1971-; *ai:* Curr Comm for Mentally Gifted; SEA 1971-; *office:* Medill Bair HS 608 S Olds Blvd Fairless Hills

, DEBORAH KAWALKO, Mathematics Teacher; *b:* Hancock, aniel; *c:* Ryan, Kyle; *ed:* Mansfield Univ (BS) Math Tchr 1975; d Coll (BS) Elem Ed 1978; 60 Addl Credit Hrs; *cr:* Wayne ; MS 7-8th Grd Math Tchr 1976-; *ai:* NEA, WHEA 1976-; Mt atrol 1992-; *office:* Wayne Highlands MS 482 Grove St Honesdale *

, LINDA ESTES, Special Education Teacher; *b:* Plymouth, MA; .; *c:* Katherine; *ed:* Bridgewater St Coll (BA) Elem Ed 1964; Spec :; Post Grad Courses at Boston St Coll; *cr:* Silver Lake Schl Dist Tchr 1964-67; Weymouth Pub Schls Kndgtn & 1st Grd Tchr Tchr of Spec Needs 1978-; *ai:* Weymouth Tchrs 1967-; NEA rmer Intramural Track Coach 4 Yrs; *office:* Weymouth Jr HS 360 st South Weymouth MA 02190

, LUANN S., Mathematics Teacher; *b:* Lancaster, PA; *m:* M.; *ed:* Juniata Coll (BS) Math 1975; PA St Univ (MED) Math st Grad Stud Rosemont Coll; *cr:* Ridley Schl Dist Math Tchr NEA, REA, PSEA 1975-; New Tchrs Mentor; Ridley Impact ; DE Cty Impact Awd 1992; *office:* Ridley HS 1001 Morton Ave A 19033

R, SANDRA KAY, Mathematics Teacher; *b:* Oakland, CA; *m:* ; *c:* Jennifer; *ed:* Salisbury St (BS) Math, Ed 1969; Masters ce 1979; *cr:* Severna Park Jr HS Math Tchr 1969-72, Dept Chair Annapolis Sr HS Math Tchr 1986-; *ai:* Jr Class Adv; Schl nent Team; Human Relations, Discipline, Annapolis Pride Fac Cncl Pres; NCTM 1969-; MCTM 1986-; Admiral Heights dmiral Heights Swim Club, Sec, Team Rep; A Plus Tchr Awd *ce:* Annapolis Sr HS 2700 Riva Rd Annapolis MD 21401

Y, MARY ANNE, Professor of Nursing; *b:* New York City, NY; Y at Stony Brook (BS) Nrsng 1972; Adelphi Univ (MS) Nrsng NY at Stony Brook (MALS) Lib Stud 1990; Maryview Hosp Schl RN 1964; *cr:* Army Nurse Corps 1st Lt 1966-68; Brunswick Hosp , Discharge Planner 1968-77; Nassau Physicians Review Org Dir iews 1977-79' Suffolk Comm Coll Coord Nrsng 1982-87, Dept n Sci 1987-92, Prof of Nrsng 1979-; *ai:* Coord Tchng, Learning tr, Schlsp Comms; Cmptr Cncl; ANA, NYSNA 1979-; Sigma 1986-; NANDA 1982-; Amer Assn Critical Care Nurses 1975-; ncer Soc 1982-, Bd, Nurse of Hope; NY Long Island 1982-, Pres; agnosis Assn Treas; VATAE Grants Awded; Pub Articles; Wrote n Questions; *office:* Suffolk Comm Coll Western Cmps Crooked Brentwood NY 11717

ARTHUR BURTON,JR., Physical Education Instructor; *b:* ME; *m:* Catherine Elaine Kenney; *c:* Shannon, Caryn, Cheyenne; of ME at Presque Isle (BS) HPER & Dance 1978; *cr:* Lon Buker E Tchr 1978-86; Mt View HS PE Tchr 1986-; *ai:* Var Boys Soccer etter Club Adv; Former Var Wrestling Coach; Part-Time Asst

BARBARA ANN, Mathematics Teacher; *b:* Cincinnati, OH; *ed:* m Coll (BA) Math 1970; Attnd Xavier Univ, Univ of Cincinnati; Jr HS Math Tchr 1970-74; Gamble MS Math Tchr 1974-; *ai:* s in Math Sci & Eng, Brotherhood, Tchrs Bldg Comms; AFT eater Cincinnati Fnd Grant 1986.

CHRISTINE ANNE, Social Studies Teacher; *b:* Utica, NY; *m:* M.; *ed:* St Gregory's Coll (AA) Lbrl Arts 1969; St Leo Coll (BS) 30 Credits MA Syracuse Univ Ed 1980; *cr:* Bronson HS 9, 10, 12 'chr 1973-74; St Joseph Schl 6, 8 Grd Sci, Soc Stud Tchr 1975-78; field Schl System 7th Grd His Tchr 1979-82; Baldwinsville Schl h Grd Soc Stud Tchr 1982-; *ai:* Discipline, Mentor Comms; NEA ycees Women 1975-80; *office:* Donald S Ray MS 7650 Van Buren insville NY 13027

DEBRA DUGAN, Multi-Age Classroom Teacher; *b:* Montclair, ark Anthony; *c:* Neil Thomas, Jessica Dugan; *ed:* SUAY at Canton ursery Ed 1972; SUNY at Geneseo (BS) Speech Pathology 1974; /T 52 Grad Credit Hrs; *cr:* Hinesburg Elem Schl 5th Grd Tchr; Elem Schl 4th-6th Grd Tchr; *ai:* Addison NE Supervisory Dist nsing Bd Mem; Staff Dev & Lang Arts Comms; NEA 1975-; VT Rdng; St Catherines Pre-Cana Trainer 1992-; Addison NE ry Dist Tchr of the Yr 1993; *office:* Beeman Elem Schl Box 3 New Haven VT 05472

DEE FICHTER, LaCrosse Coach; *b:* Norristown, PA; *m:* Sumner ison, Amy, Kelly; *ed:* Shippensburg Univ (BSBA) Bus Mngmt 1981; Temple Univ (MED) Bus Ed 1988; *cr:* Abington Schl Dist Bus Tchr 1984-85, 1987-95; Abington HS Girls Lacrosse Coach 1984-; *ai:* Flwshp Chrstn Aths Co-Spon; NEA, PSEA 1984-; PASLA 1984-, League Rep; USWLA 1983-, Beth Allen Awd; PWLA 1981-, Treas; US Women's Lacrosse Team 9 Yrs; World Cup Team Silver Medalist Lacrosse 1986; World Cup Champion Lacrosse Team Capt 1989; US Squad Asst Coach 3 Yrs; *office:* Abington Sr HS 900 Highland Ave Abington PA 19001

CROSS, ERVIN, Retired History & Science Tchr; *b:* Lamberton, PA; *m:* Rose Marie King; *c:* Chris, Deborah, Robin, Ervin Lee; *ed:* California Univ of PA (BS) Elem 1975; 18 Hrs Grad Stud; *ai:* Girls Sftbl Coach 2 Yrs; PA St Ed Assn, NEA, CA Area Ed Assn 1976-; B'ville Masonic Lodge 1979-; *home:* 409 Washington Ave West Brownsville PA 15417*

CROSS, ROBERT EDWARD, 8th Grade Mathematics Teacher; *b:* Leonard Town, MD; *m:* Donna Marie Owens; *c:* Jodi C. Stanalonis, Kathy J., Amanda E.; *ed:* Wheeling Coll (BS) Math 1968; George Wash Univ (MS) Scndry Ed 1974; *cr:* Calvert Jr HS Tchr 1968-71; Esperanza MS Tchr 1971-; *ai:* Math Dept Chprsn; Cty Cmptr, Cty Book Review Comms; Smeco Math Tchr of Yr; MS Tchr of Yr; *office:* Esperanza MS 201 Maple Rd Lexington Park MD 20653*

CROSS, SALLY BARIGHT, Biology Teacher; *b:* Poughkeepsie, NY; *m:* Thomas K.; *c:* Jeffrey T., John D.; *ed:* SUNY at Cortland (BS) Scndry Ed, Sci 1964; Vassar Coll (MS) Bio 1965; *cr:* Arlington Jr HS Sci Tchr 1965-69; LaGrange Schl Tchng Asst 1978-86; Arlington HS Bio Tchr 1986-; *ai:* Frosh, Soph Class Adv; Arlington TA, NYS United Teach, AFT 1986-; Sci TA of NYS 1987-; LaGrange Soccer League 1981-86, Pres 1984-86; Trinity Nursery Schl Bd 1971-86, Treas; Cub Scout Comm 1981-84, Sec; *office:* Arlington HS-S Campus 110 Stringham Rd Lagrangeville NY 12540*

CROSS, THOMAS MICHAEL, Cmptr Assisted Drafting Tchr; *b:* Cincinnati, OH; *c:* Kathryn, Sarah; *cr:* Diamond Oaks CDC Cmptr Assisted Drafting Tchr 12 Yrs; *ai:* AVA 1985-; OH Voc Assn 1985-, Tchr of Yr 1995; *office:* Diamond Oaks Career Dev Campus 6375 Harrison Ave Cincinnati OH 45247

CROSS, THOMAS R., Coll Prep 9th Grd Eng Tchr; *b:* Lansing, MI; *m:* Susan M. Fleming; *ed:* OH Univ (BSEd) Eng & Rdng 1988, (MED) Coll Admin 1996; *cr:* Newark City Schls 9th Grd Eng Tchr 1989-; *ai:* Frosh Eng Honours Prgm; 9th Grd Coll Acad Team Eng Rep; Reflections Lit Magazine Former Adv; OCTELA 1988-; NCTE 1990-; Lang Arts Curr Dev Comm 1990-; Crisis Mgmt Team-Newark HS 1994-, Comm Mem; Awded Newark City Schls Tchr of the Month September 1995; Presenting at the OCTELA Spring Conf March 1996; *office:* Newark HS 314 Granville Rd Newark OH 43055*

CROSSAN, KATHERINE THERESA, Retired Teacher; *b:* Jersey City, NJ; *ed:* Jersey City St Coll (BS) Kdg-Primary Ed 1952; Seton Hall Univ (MA) Admin, Supervision; 30 Addl Credits Ed; *cr:* Roselle Bd of Ed Kndgtn Tchr 1952-57; Paramus Bd of Ed Kndgtn Tchr 1958-93; *ai:* Schl Lib Vol; NJEA, NEA, BEA 1953-; EAP; NJKEA; *home:* 176 Thomas Dr Paramus NJ 07652

CROSSON, MARK ALLEN, Civics, Geography, PA His Tchr; *b:* Lewistown, PA; *m:* Sherri Renae; *c:* Jesse M., Dylan N; *ed:* PA St Univ (MED) Curr, Instruction; PA St Univ (BA) His 1987; Masters in Curr, Instruction Being Sought; Cum & Admin; *cr:* Indian Valley HS World Cultures, Soc Problems Tchr 1990-91; Mifflin Cty Schl Dist Alternative Ed Tchr 1992-; Mt Union Jr, Sr HS World Cultures, Psych, Sociology Tchr 1993-94; Cvcs, PA His, Geogrphy Tchr at Mt Union 1994-; *ai:* Adv Sr HS Stu Cncl; Fac Advy, Prof Growth, Comm LINK Comm, Internal Faclitor for Stragic Plnng Process; NEA 1990-; Local MU Tchr Assn 1993-; Asst Pastor of Bethel AMI Church 1990-; *home:* 1 Woodland Cir Reedsville PA 17084*

CROTEAU, NANCY ROBERTS, Eng, Art Instr & Asst Prin; *b:* Concord, VT; *m:* Albert; *c:* Celina, Ethan; *ed:* Notre Dame Coll (BA) Art & Eng 1976; Lyndon St Coll (MED) Instruction & Curr 1994; Prins Cert 1996; *cr:* Sacred Heart HS Art & Eng Tchr 1976-77, Permanent Sub 1978-79; Concord HS Art & Eng Tchr 1984-; *ai:* Advisor Sr Class, Yearbook, Prom; Chair Arts Comm; Coord Project Grad; NEA; Lyndon Town Schl Bd 1993-, Clerk; *office:* Concord HS RR 1 Box 1b Concord VT 05824

CROTTI, ROSE MARIE LEITZA, Learning Support, Spec Ed Tchr; *b:* Scranton, PA; *m:* John; *c:* Michelle, Joseph, John Michael; *ed:* Marywood Coll (BA) Spec Ed, Elem Ed 1974; Marywood Coll (MS) Spec Ed, Counseling 1984; Educl Initiatives Trng; Curr Based Assessment; Curr Adaptations for Mildly Handicapped; Assertive Discipline; 9 Credits Univ of SC; 24 Credit Sch Ldrshp Marywood Coll; Elem, Sec Prin Cert; *cr:* Northeastern Educl Intermediate Unit #19 Severely & Profoundly Mentally Retared Trainable, Partial, Hospitalization Socially & Emotionally Disturber Tchr 1975-88; PA Dept of Ed Instructional Support Consultant 1990-91; NEIU #19 Learning Support Consultant 1991-; Marywood Coll Instr Pt-time 1991-; *ai:* SADD 7th-8th Grd Chrldr Adv; Peer Mediator; Fac Adv; Adv Peer Tutor Prog; NEA, PSEA 1975-; CEC 1975-, Sec, VP, Pres; Marywood Coll Family Festival, Chprsn; Northeast Woman of Yr 1989-; Elkview Cntry Club 1991-; Natl Conf 1989-, Co-chm; Children Without Conscience Handicapped Awareness Day 1992-, Co-chm; Bishop O'Hara HS Parent Org, Pres 1995-; Who's Who in Amer Ed; Who's Who in Intnl Women; Intnl Platform Speakers Assoc; Who's Who in Amer Coll & Univ; Co-authored Parent to Parent Handbook; Presenter Fed CEC St Conf; Who's Who in East; Who's Who in World; Who's Who of Amer Women; *home:* 24 Green Grove Hills Rd #1 Olyphant PA 18447*

CROUCH, ROBERT WILLIAM, HS History Teacher; *b:* Boston, MA; *m:* Petricia Conroy; *c:* Suzanne, Ellen; *ed:* Bridgewater St Coll (BA) His 1967; Providence Coll (MA) Amer His 1974; Bridgewater St Coll (MAt) His 1980; *cr:* Somerset HS His Tchr 1967-; Bristol Comm Coll West Cir Instr Div of Cont Ed 1975-81; Bridgewater St Coll Amer Govt Instr Div of Cont Ed 1981; *ai:* Comm to Restructure HS; NEA, MTA, STA 1967-, Chm of Negotiations Comm 1985-86; Mass Cncl for the Soc Stud 1993-, Tchr of Yr; New England His Tchr Assn 1993-; Bridgewater St Coll Bd of Trustees 1990-95 Trustee; Bridgewater St Coll 1988-89 Presidential Search Comm; New England Assn of Schls, Colls 1989-94 Evaluator; Cncl of Basic Ed Flwshp for Ind Stud in Hum 1995; Outstdng Tchr Awd 1989; Natl Endowment of Hum Flwshp 1992; John Hancock Flwshp 1987-88; Brown Univ Flwshp 1986-87; Robert A. Taft FLwshp 1979; Rsrch on Mass Convention to Ratify Consitution in Mass Archives; *office:* Somerset HS Grandview Ave Ext Somerset MA 02726*

CROUSE, MARSHA (KIRTLEY), Reading & Science Teacher; *b:* Kendalville, IN; *m:* David R. Mann; *c:* Theodore Crouse-Mann; *ed:* IN Univ (BS) Ed 1970, (MS) Ed 1972; *cr:* Rogers Elem 6th Grd Tchr 1970-72; North Muskegon Elem & Jr High Tchr 1972-78; Sugg MS Tchr 1989-; *ai:* Adv & Advisee Facilitator; LEA 1989-; MEA 1989-; NEA 1989-; *office:* Sugg MS Rt 196 Lisbon Falls ME 04252

CROUSE, MICHAEL THOMAS, History & English Teacher; *b:* Baltimore, MD; *ed:* Gods Bible Schl & Coll (BA) Eng 1990; Attnd Lancaster Bible Coll, Catonsville Comm Coll; *cr:* Epworth Chrstn Schl Jr-Sr HS Eng, His Tchr 1990-; Worcester-Wicomico Comm Coll Eng Prof 1991-; *ai:* Var, JV Soccer Coach; Var Sftbl Coach; JV Bsktbl Coach; Asst Ath Dir; Jr-Sr Banquet Adv; Sr Adv; YELL Coord; Prom Promise Adv; Nanticoke Yth Soccer Coach; 3rd Place Overall Prom Promise Scrapbook 1995; *office:* Epworth Christian Schl Rt 1 Box 65 1-2 Laurel DE 19956

CROUTHAMEL, JANE MARIA, 3rd Grade Teacher; *b:* Allentown, PA; *c:* Casey R., Madison J.; *ed:* Shippensburg Univ (BS) Elem Ed 1980; 24 Credits; *cr:* Jefferson Elem Schl 5th Grd 1980-81; Central Elem Schl 4th Grd 1981-83; Dodd Elem Schl 2nd & 3rd Grd 1983-; *ai:* Discipline Comm Chprsn; AEA 1980-, Fac Rep; NEA 1980-; *office:* Hiram W Dodd Elem Schl 1944 Church Rd Allentown PA 18104

CROUTWATER, CHARLES HARRY, Educl Television Specialist; *b:* Springfield, OH; *m:* Barbara; *c:* Nita, Laura, Kyle; *ed:* Bowling Green St Univ (BS) Music Ed 1964, (MA) Piano Performance 1972; *cr:* Willard City Schls MS Band Dir 1964-66; Fiverside Local Schls Music & Band Dir 1966-68; Bellefontaine City Schls HS Choral Dir 1968-85, Educl Television Specialist 1985-; *ai:* Production Mgr; Rotary 1975-; *home:* 3827 County Road 1 Bellefontaine OH 43311

CROVAK, MARK ERIC, Social Studies Teacher; *b:* Pittsburgh, PA; *m:* Kathryn Hensberger; *c:* Nicholas, Robert; *ed:* Univ of Pittsburgh (BA) Scndry Ed 1986; Penn St at Monroeville 24 Credit Hrs Permanent Cert; *cr:* Penn Trafford HS Soc Stud Tchr 1987-89; Trafford MS Soc Stud Tchr 1989-92; Penn Trafford Soc Stud Tchr 1992-; *ai:* Boys & Girls Var Track Head Coach; NEA, PSEA, PTEA 1987-; Police Rod & Gun Club 1994-; *office:* Penn Trafford HS PO Box 530 Harrison City PA 15636*

CROWE, BARBARA J., 2nd Grade Teacher; *b:* Como, MS; *m:* Lawrence A. Sr.; *c:* Traci L. Gregory, Lawrence A. Jr.; *ed:* Tougallo SC Coll Bio; MS Ind Coll Ed; Cleveland St Univ Ed 1974; Attnd Univ of Toledo; *cr:* Cleveland Pub Schl Tchr 1968-83; Toledo Pub Schls Tchr 1986-; *ai:* Cleveland Tchrs Union 1968-83; Toledo Fed of Tchrs 1986-; *home:* 2057 W Alexis Rd Apt D11 Toledo OH 43613

CROWE, MARCELLA E., Language Arts Teacher; *b:* Massapequa, NY; *ed:* Brookdale Comm (AA) Lbrl Arts 1979; Glassboro Rowan Coll (BA) Commnctn & Jrnlsm 1981; Pursuing MS in Principalship & Supervision at Monmouth Univ; ALT Pgm Elem Cert 1987; *cr:* Thorne MS His Tchr 1987-88; Bayshore MS 7th Grd His & Lang Arts Tchr 1988-90; Thompson MS 8th Grd Lang Arts Tchr 1990-; *ai:* 7th & 8th Grd Girls Bsktbl & Soccer Coach 6 Yrs; NEA 1987-; NJEA 1987-; *office:* Thompson MS 1001 Middletown Lincroft Rd Middletown NJ 07748

CROWE, NADINE SENECAL, Mathematics Instructor; *b:* Worcester, MA; *m:* Robert; *c:* Ashleigh Ann, Amanda Paige; *ed:* Worcester St Coll (BS) Math, Sec Ed 1973; Anna Maria Coll (MA) Clinical Psych 1977, (CAGS) Cnslng Psych 1978; Working Toward EDD Child, Yth Stud, Educl Ldrshp Nova Southeastern Univ; MIT Engrng Prgm; Worcester St COll Cert Prgm Educl Admin; *cr:* Keefe Tech Schl Math Instr 1973-; Newbury Coll Math, Psych Instr 1988-; *ai:* Prof Dev Comm; Var Bsktbl Coach 1973-78; NEASC Steering Comm; MTA, NEA, Keefe Tech Tchrs Assn 1973-, Treas, Del; Alpha Delta Kappa 1990-, Pres-Elect; New England Sci Tchrs at MIT 1992-, St Rep; United Parish of Upton 1985-, Deaconness; MIT Grant; Author Measurement-An Applied Integrated Workbook For Voc-Tech Stdnts.*

CROWELL, ARTHUR PAUL, Chemistry Tchr & Dept Head; *b:* Jamaica, NY; *c:* Joy Kouloheras, Paul, Christopher; *ed:* Farmington St Coll (BS) Sci 1963; Univ of ME (MED) Physics 1965; Colby Coll (MST) Chem 1968; *cr:* A D Ingalls Schl Tchr 1963-66; Skowhegan Area HS Chem Tchr & Dept Head 1966-; *ai:* NEA, MTA 1963-; SAD 54 Tchrs Assn 1966-; Elks 1985-; Mensa 1995-; NSTA Excl in Sci Ed 1982; Presidential Awd for Excl in Sci Tchng 1985; *home:* RR 3 Box 4066 Skowhegan ME 04976

CROWELL, DIANNE E., Director of Musical Theatre; *b:* Providence, RI; *m:* Robert Freeman; *c:* Marcia, Jonathan, Robert Jr., James; *ed:* Roger Williams Univ (BA) Theatre 1982; Attnd Univ of RI & Oberlin Conservatory; *cr:* Roger Williams Univ Dir of Musical Theatre 1973-; *ai:* Club Adv; Stage Co; Search Comm; NETC 1979-; NEA 1983-; ATHE 1983-, Panel Mem 1989; Compiled, Arranged & Directed over 25 Original Musical Revues; Prof Actress; Listed in Whos Who in Entertainment; Pub Svc Awds; *office:* Roger Williams Univ Old Ferry Road Bristol RI 02809*

CROWL, APRIL ANN, English Teacher; *b:* Hagerstown, MD; *c:* Christy Dicken, Adam, Beth Zentmeyer, Jessica Zentmeyer; *ed:* Towson St Univ (BS), (MA) Ed 1974-82; Shippensburg St Univ (MA) Counseling 18 Hrs; Univ of S FL (PHD) Curr & Instruction 18 Hrs; *cr:* Baltimore City Schls Tchr 1974-78; Annearundel Cty BOE Tchr Specialist 1978-82; Zentmeyer Electronics Pres, CEO 1982-90; Tampa Airways VP 1982-86; Center for Vein Medicine RN 1990-92; Washington Cty BOE Tchr 1992-; *ai:* Jr Class, Yrbk, Video Adv; Odyssy of Mind Coach; WC Tchrs Assn, MSTA, NEA 1993-; NTE 1994-; COBACE 1995-; Miss Wash Cty Schlsp 1991-,Bd; Brownsville Church of the Brethren, Chrstn Ed Dir; *office:* Boonsboro HS 10 Campus Ave Boonsboro MD 21713

CROWL, VAUGHN DANA, Professor of Psychology; *b:* Hagerstown, MD; *c:* Christianna Noelle Crowl Dicken, Adam Christopher; *ed:* Frostburg St Univ (BS) Psych 1968; Johns Hopkins Univ (MS) Cnslng & Therapy 1978, (MED) Cnslng & Therapy 1974, (CAS) Cnslng & Therapy 1972; Amer Univ (PHD) Cnslng & Dev 1987; Attnd Natl Fed Bureau of Investigation Acad; *cr:* South Hagerstown HS Psych Tchr 1968-70; Hagerstown Jr Coll Prof of Psych 1970-; *ai:* Choral Ensemble Dir; Racquetball Coach; Curr Comm Chm; Amer Psychological Assn 1980-; MD Psychological Assn 1985-; Citizens Aiding & Sheltering Abused 1988-, Bd of Dir; Domestic Violence Coalition 1994-, Bd of Adv; Big Brothers of Washington Cty 1970-, Bd of Dir; Washington Cty Schlsp Fdn 1989-, Bd of Dir; Intnl Mngmt Cncl 1995-; Church of the Brethen Chm Bd of Deacons; Cited & Honored by FBI for Work in Police Psychological Svcs; Fac Assembly Chair; Behavioral & Soc Sci Division Chair; Cert Prof Cnslr; Washington Cty Hlth Dept Spec Psychological Consultant; *office:* Hagerstown Jr Coll 11400 Robinwood Dr Hagerstown MD 21742*

CROWLEY, DONALD CHRISTOPHER, Sixth Grade Science Teacher; *b:* Waterbury, CT; *ed:* Western CT St Coll (BS) Elem Ed 1970; Univ of Bridgeport (MS) Elem ed 1977; St of CT 120 Continuing Ed Units; *cr:* Southbury Trng Schl Voc Instr 1970-72; Cider Mill Schl 6th Grd Tchr 1972-93; Middlebrook Schl 6th Grd Sci Tchr 1993-; *ai:* Adv-Advisee, Let's Talk Sci & Instructional Ldr Model Comms; NSTA 1992-; NEA, CEA, WEA 1972-; NSF Grant for CT Sci Museum Collaborative; *office:* Middlebrook Schl 131 School Rd Wilton CT 06897*

CROWLEY, KENNETH B.,JR., Medical Lab Science Professor; *b:* Concord, NH; *m:* Deborah A. Grenier; *ed:* St Anselm Coll (AB) Bio 1968; Anna Maria Coll (MA) Bio 1981; Burbank Hosp Schl of Med Tech MT 1972; *cr:* Burbank Hosp Med Tech 1972-74, Hematology Supvr 1974-79; Burbank Hos Schl of MT Ed Coord 1979-82; Middlesex Comm Coll MLT Pgm Dir 1982-; *ai:* ASCP 1972-; ASCLS 1972-; NEA 1982-; AMT 1990-; Temple Vol Fire Dept 1980-, Clerk; *office:* Middlesex Comm Coll Springs Road Bedford MA 01730

CROWLEY, OSMOND E., 7th Grade Math Teacher; *b:* Bangor, ME; *c:* Shannon, Crystal, Charles; *ed:* Univ ME at Machio (BS) Elem Ed 1978; Univ ME AT Orono Grad Prgm; *cr:* Hartland Jr HS 7-8th Grd Tchr 1978-, Asst Prin 1991-95, Ath Dir 1979-95; *ai:* NEA, MTA 1978-; ASCD 1994-; Washington Cty Tchrs Assn Schlsp; *office:* Hartland Jr HS 48 Academy St Hartland ME 04943*

CROWLEY, SHERYL E., Secondary Guidance Counselor; *b:* Providence, RI; *m:* Robert A.; *ed:* Bryant Coll (BS) Bus Ed 1960; Providence Coll (MED) Guid, Cnslng 1974; Attnd RI Coll, Univ of RI; *cr:* Ponaganset HS Bus Instr, Dept Chair 1960-66; Bryant Coll Evening Instr 1969-70; Ponaganset HS Guid Cnslr `976-; *ai:* Co-Adv NHS; NEA RI

1960; NEA Ponaganset 1960; RI Cnslng Assn 1974-, Bd; RIAAD, RI Assoc of Admissions Ofcrs 1992-; New Eng Assoc of Coll Admissions Ofcrs 1992-; Outstdng Cnslr of Yr 1995 by RI Assn of Admissions Ofcrs; *office:* Ponaganset HS 137 Anan Wade Rd North Scituate RI 02857

CROYLE, ALLYSEN TODDSEN, English Professor; *b:* Charleroi, PA; *m:* Richard Allen; *ed:* Bethany Coll (BA) Eng 1977; Duquesne Univ (MA) Eng 1980; Univ of Pittsburgh (PHD) Admin Policies, Higher Ed 1990; *cr:* Wilson Chrstn Acad Eng Tchr 1979-82; Comm Coll Allegheny Cty Adj Eng Fac 1982-84, Assoc Prof of Eng 1984-, Eng Dept Chair 1991-95; *ai:* Retention Comm, Chair; Mid Sts Strategic, Acad Planing Comm; *office:* Comm Coll Algny Co Algny Cmps 808 Ridge Ave Pittsburgh PA 15212*

CROZIER, LOIS STAHL, Science Teacher; *b:* Plainfield, NJ; *m:* Steven M.; *c:* Kyle S., Alyssa N.; *ed:* Clarion Univ (BS) Ed, Scndry Bio 1986; 27 Credits; *cr:* Johnsonburg HS Sci Tchr 1987-; *ai:* Environmental Club; SAP Team; Girl Scout Ldr 1995-; *office:* Johnsonburg Area Jr & Sr HS Elk Ave Johnsonburg PA 15845*

CROZIER, NANCY STOTZ, Science, Health, Spelling Tchr; *b:* Prescott, AZ; *c:* Steven Marsh, David Lawrence; *ed:* Edinboro Univ (BSEd) Elem Ed 1971; Clarion Univ (MS) Elem Ed 1975; *cr:* Irvinedale Elem 6th Grd Tchr 1971-73; Sheffield Elem 6th Grd Tchr 1973-94; Sheffield Area Mid Sr HS 7th-8th Grd Tchr 1994-95, 6th Grd Tchr 1995-; *ai:* Curr Comm Mem; PA Writing Assessment Scorer; NEA, PSEA, WCEA 1971-; Bethany Luth Church 1956-, Church Bd, Sunday Schl Tchr, Youth Group Ldr; Honor Convocation Speaker; Summa Cum Laude Edinboro, Clarion; *home:* RR 1 Box 1250-F Clarendon PA 16313*

CROZIER, SCOTT W., 4th Grade Teacher; *b:* Elyria, OH; *m:* Becky Boving; *c:* Emily, Olivia; *ed:* Malone Coll (BS) Elem Ed 1983; Univ of Dayton (MS) Ed 1989; *cr:* Lakewood Local Schl Dist 6th Grd Tchr 1984-85, 5th Grd Tchr 1985-86, 1st Grd Tchr 1986-88, 5th Grd Tchr 1988-92, 4th Grd Tch 1992-; *ai:* Guidance & Yrbk Comms; Stu Cncl Adv; Crisis Intervention Comm; Grace Bible Church 1988-; *office:* Hebron Elem Schl 709 Decon St Hebron OH 43025

CRUCS, BARBARA WISE, Mathematics Tchr & Dept Chm; *b:* Carey, OH; *m:* William A.; *c:* Kevin Michael, Jennifer Crucs Rice; *ed:* OH St Univ (BSEd) Comp Sci 1965; Masters Equiv; *cr:* Columbus Pub Schls Math, Sci Tchr 1965-67; Isidore Newman Schl Math Tchr 1967-68; Copley-Fairlawn Schls Perm Math Sub Tchr 1983-84; Akron Pub Schls Math, Sci Tchr 1984-; *ai:* NHS Adv; Math Contest Review for OH Proficiency Test; Intnl Baccalaureate Coord; Field Test Tchr Core Plus Math Project; Core Plus Tchrs Trng; OCTM, NCTM 1986-; OMELC 1994-; Akron Jr League 1974-; Presenter St OCTM Meetings, Natl, Regnl IJ Confs; SMART Grant Co-Recipient FLOW Project; Golden Apple Achiever Awd; *office:* Firestone HS 333 Rampart Ave Akron OH 44313

CRUDALE, ALFRED ROBERT, Italian & Spanish Teacher; *b:* Providence, RI; *m:* Barbara Jean Delemontex; *c:* Frederick Charles, Matthew James; *ed:* RI Coll (BA) Scndry Ed, Span 1985; Univ of RI (MAEd) Scndry Ed, Italian 1991; Attnd Universita di Perugia Italy; *cr:* Toll Gate HS Italian, Span Tchr 1985-; Comm Coll of RI Span Prof 1994-; *ai:* Class of 1992, Class of 1995, Italian Club, Fine Arts Club Adv; RI Tchrs of Italian, RI Frgn Lang Tchrs, AFT 1985-; Assn of Amer Tchrs of Italian1995-; St Mary's Holy Name Soc 1981-, Past Pres; Commitato Festa di Maria SS Della Civita 1980-, Past Pres, Outstdng Benefactor; Exeter Grange #12 1991-, Asst Steward; *home:* 3243 S County Trl West Kingston RI 02892

CRUIKSHANK, DAVID EARL, Attorney, Private Practice; *b:* Painesville, OH; *m:* Nancy K.; *c:* Robert Slotta, Edward Slotta; *ed:* DePauw Univ (BA) His 1967; Case Western Reserve Univ (JD) Law 1973; *cr:* Painesville Harvey HS Legal Adv, Coach, Mock Trial Team 1990-95; *ai:* Am Bar Assn 1973-, Foreman; OH St Bar Assn 1973-, Chm, Ins Law Comm; Fellow OH Bar Fnd 1988-; Lake Cty Grand Jury 1976-, Foreman; John D'Angelo Schlsp 1994-, Trustee; Coach, Legal Adv Mock Trial Team St Championship Qualifiers 1992, 1993, 1995, Dist Champions 1992, 1995, St Honorable Mention 1992; Awd of Merit OH Legal Ctr Inst 1985; *home:* 30 Wintergreen Hill Dr Painesville OH 44077

CRUM, JAMES ROBERT, Math Teacher; *b:* Carlisle, PA; *m:* Barbara Marlene Moffit; *c:* Kimberly, Matthew; *ed:* Bucknell Univ (BS) Math Ed 1969; Temple Univ (MS) Math Ed 1972; *cr:* Boiling Springs HS Math Tchr 1969-; *ai:* Golf Coach; Ftbl Statistician; NEA 1969-; PSEA 1969-; SMEA 1969-; Carlisle Areas Finest Edctr Evening Sentinel Awd 1987; *office:* Boiling Springs Jr Sr HS 4 Forge Rd Boiling Springs PA 17007

CRUM, JOHN WILLIAM, History Department Chairman; *b:* Mapleton Depot, PA; *m:* Karen E. Enck; *c:* Laurette, Leslie; *ed:* Univ of DE (MA) His 1972, (PHD) His 1980; *cr:* Mt Pleasant HS His Tchr 1964-; Univ of DE Adjunct Prof 1976-; *ai:* Class, Honor Soc; NEA, NCSS & DE Ed Assn 1964-; Mid Sts Cncl for Soc Stud 1980-, Bd of Dirs 2 Yrs, Distinguished Service Awd 1990; Democratic Party 1964-, Committeeman 10 Yrs; DE Historical soc 1988-; DE Hum Forum 1985-; White House Commission on Pres Schlrs Distinguished Tchr 1991; DE His Tchr of Yr 1984; DE Tchr-Historian of Yr 1990; Brandywine Schl Dist Tchr of Yr 1983; Various Articles Pub; Ap Exam Author; *office:* Mount Plesant H S Washington St Ext Wilmington DE 19809

CRUM, SEAN CHRISTIAN, Art Teacher; *b:* Pasadena, CA; *m:* Gail; *c:* Adam; *ed:* Cleveland St Univ (BA) Art 1974; Case Western Reserve (MA) Art Ed 1977; *cr:* North Ridgeville City Schls Art Tchr 1978-; *ai:* Yrbk Adv; OEA 1978-; Chptr II Grants 1995-; *office:* N Ridgeville Sr HS 7000 Pitts Blvd North Ridgeville OH 44039

CRUM, WILLIAM LEE, Chemistry Teacher; *b:* Harpers Ferry, WV; *ed:* Shepherd Coll (BA) Chem 1991; Grad Courses Nuclear Chem, Chem; Working Toward MS Hood Coll; *cr:* Essex HS Chem, Bio, Physics Tchr 1991-92; Linganore HS Chem Tchr 1992-; Shepherd Coll Chem Instr 1992-; *ai:* Tennis Coach; Amer Chemical Soc 1987-; *office:* Linganore HS 12013 Old Annapolis Rd Frederick MD 21701*

CRUMBAKER, DEBRA ELLIOTT, Primary Multi-Age Teacher; *b:* Hamilton, OH; *m:* Thomas Neil; *c:* Jeremy, Joshua, Daniel; *ed:* Miami Univ (BSEd) Elem Ed 1971, (MSEd) Elem Ed, Math Emphasis 1985; Attnd Portland St Univ; *cr:* Preble Shawnee Camden Elem Schl Tchr 1971-72, 1975-; *ai:* 4th Grd Proficiency Test Totor; Inservice, Venture Capital Grant, Eisenhower Grant, Svcs Delivery Comms; CERT; Mentor for Tchrs; NEA, OEA 1971-72, 1975-; PSLEA 1971-72, 1975-, Bldg Rep; Delta Kappa Gamma 1987-, 2nd VP, Intnl Flwshp Comm; Martha Holden Jennings Scholar; Nom Presidential Awd 1995-; Presented Multiage at WRPDC Meeting; Jennings Scholar Awd Grant Nom; *office:* Camden Elem Schl 124 Bloomfield St Camden OH 45311

CRUMLEY, KRISTIE CALDWELL, Mathematics Teacher; *b:* Philadelphia, PA; *m:* Michael Jr.; *ed:* The Amer Univ (BS) Math 1993; *cr:* Damascus HS Math Tchr 1994-; *ai:* JV Field Hockey Coach; Girls Lacrosse Coach; Stu Govt Assn Spon; NEA 1994-; *office:* Damascus HS 25921 Ridge Rd Damascus MD 20872

CRUMLISH, JANE, Science Dept Chprsn & Tchr; *b:* Phildelphia, PA; *ed:* West Chester St Univ Bio (BS) 1962, (MEd) 1971; Master Plus 45 Credits; *cr:* Woodrow Wilson HS Bio Tchr 1962-65; Great Valley HS Bio Tchr 1965-67; Neshaminy HS Bio Tchr 1967-, Sci Dept Chprsn 1993-; *ai:* Curr Restructuring Comm; NEA, NABT 1962-; NSTA 1992-; DE Valley Bio Tchrs Network; Newtown Library Assn 1979-, Book Selection Comm; Newtown Historical Assn 1979-; Commonwealth Partnership Bio Initiative Fellow; Book Reviews the Amer Bio Tchr; Article Sci Act; *office:* Neshaminy HS 2001 Old Lincoln Hwy Langhorne PA 19047*

CRUSEY, BETH HOCKLEY, Developmental Reading Teacher; *b:* Mt Holly Sprgs, PA; *m:* Frank W.; *c:* Nathan S., Shem A., Jessica m.; *ed:* Shippensburg Univ (BS) Elem Ed 1978, (ME) Rdng 1986; *cr:* Plainfield Elem 2nd & 5th Grd Tchr 1981-83; Big Spring MS 6th Grd Lang Arts Tchr 1983-84, 6th Grd Sci Tchr 1984-86, 7th Grd Rdng Tchr 1986-, 7th Grd Team Ldr 1994-; *ai:* Creative Storywriting Club Adv; NEA 1981-; Trinity Day Care Bd 1995-; *office:* Big Spring Schl Dist 45 Mount Rock Rd Newville PA 17241

CRUSH, HENRY KENNETH, Mathematics Teacher; *b:* Abington, PA; *m:* Deborah Ann (Palmer); *c:* Elizabeth Joy, Amy Lynn, Henry James, Sarah Marie, Allana Kendra; *ed:* Pinebrook Jr Coll (AA) 1975; Bloomsburg Univ (BS) Scndry Ed & Math 1978; Kutztown Univ (MED) Scndry Ed & Math 1988; *cr:* Lehigh Valley Chrstn HS Math Tchr 1978-93; *ai:* Drama Club & Sci Fair Dir; Mentor Prgm for Tchrs; NCTM 1978-; Faith Evangelical Free Church 1983-, Pioneer Boys Dir; *office:* Lehigh Valley Christian HS 1414 E Cedar St Allentown PA 18103

CRUSIUS, THERESA D'ARMINIO, English Teacher; *b:* Hackensack, NJ; *m:* Kenneth; *c:* Elsbeth, Jennifer, Lee; *ed:* Montclair St Coll (BA) Eng, Span 1970, (MA) Eng Lit 1974; Supervision Cert 1970; 30 Addl Credit Hrs; Post Grad Stud Curr, Supervision 1974-79; *cr:* Ridgefield Meml HS Eng Tchr 1970-76; Edward Williams Coll Frosh Composition Tchr 1977; Slocum Skewes MS 7th, 8th Grd Eng Tchr 1979-81; Berkeley Schl Comm Tchr 1981-83; Ridgefield Meml HS Eng Tchr 1984-; *office:* Ridgefield Memorial HS Walnut St Ridgefield NJ 07657

CRUZ, CAMILO, Chemistry Professor; *b:* Bogota, Columbia; *m:* Shirley; *c:* Richard; *ed:* Jersey City St Coll (BS) Chem; Seaton Hall Univ (MS) Analytical Chem, (PHD) Analytical Chem; *cr:* Jersey City St Coll Chem Prof; *ai:* Amer Chem Soc; Authored 3 Books; *home:* 3 Bucknell Ct Kendall Park NJ 08824

CRUZ, YOLANDA PAJE, Professor of Biology; *b:* Albay, Philippines; *c:* Elsa Cruz Pearson; *ed:* Univ of the Philippines (BS) Ag 1971, (MS) Entomology 1974; Univ of CA at Berkeley (PHD) Entomology 1982; Univ of CA at San Francisco Postdoc Fellow 1982-84; Postdoc Fellow 1984-86; *cr:* Oberlin Coll Asst Prof 1986-92, Assoc Prof 1992-; *ai:* Mem of Neurology B Stud Section, Elected Mem of Natl Insts of Hlth; Electorate Nominating Comm; Amer Assn for Advancement of Sci; Soc for Developmental Bio 1982-; Amer Soc for Cell Bio 1982-; Amer Assn for Advancement of Sci 1977-; Entomological Soc of Amer 1980-; Soc for Study of Fertility 1993-; Natl Inst of Child Hlth & Human Dev Research Grants 1988-90, 1994-; Book: Lab Exercises in Developmental Bio 1993, Acad Press; Book Chapters, Research Papers; *office:* Oberlin Coll Dept Of Biology Oberlin OH 44074

CSEHOSKI, HELEN TRIMBLE, Math & Cmptr Programming Tchr; *b:* Johnstown, PA; *m:* Robert; *c:* Stephen; *ed:* Bucknell Univ (BA) Math 1964; Indiana Univ of PA (MED) Math 1971; *cr:* Johnstown HS Math, Cmptr Programming Tchr 1966-; *ai:* Scholastic Quiz Coach; Math League Spon; PSEA 1966-; NEA 1968-; *office:* Greater Johnstown HS 222 Central Ave Johnstown PA 15902

CSER, AUDRY J., Marketing Ed Teacher & Coord; *b:* Philadelphia, PA; *ed:* Trenton St Coll (BS) Mrktg Ed 1990, (MA) Office Systems Admin 1992; Schl Bus Admin at Rowan Coll; *cr:* Eastern Sr HS Tchr 1992-; *ai:* DECA, Schl Store & Class Adv; Schl Musical Bus Dir; Career Advy Comm; NJ Mrktg Ed Assn 1992-, Sec, Region Tchr of Yr; NJEA 1992-; Southern NJ Mrktng Ed Tchr of Yr 1992-93 & 1993-94; *office:* Eastern Senior High School 1306 Laurel Oak Rd Voorhees NJ 08043*

CUCCI, SUSAN RUFF, 5th Grade Teacher; *b:* Pasadena, TX; *c:* Joseph Scott, Michael Todd; *ed:* Trenton St Coll (BS) His, Ed 1987; *cr:* Rosenauer Elem Scl Fift Grd Tchr 1987-93; C. Mc Auliffe MS Fift Grd Tchr 1993-; *ai:* NJEA, NEA 1987-; Governor's Outstdng Tchr Candidate 1987; *office:* Christa Mcauliffe MS 35 Hope Chapel Rd Jackson NJ 08527*

CUCCINIELLO, DAWN GRACE, Teacher; *b:* Brooklyn, NY; *ed:* Bklyn Coll (BS) Adm, Sup Ed 1969, (MS) Adm, Sup Ed 1971; Supervisory License 6th Yr Cert Adm, Sup Ed 1989; 60 Credits Beyond Masters; Cmptr, Child Abuse, Gifted Courses; *cr:* PS 221 Grd 5 Tchr, Grd Ldr, Gifted Prgm 1969-; *ai:* Church Act, SI Cncl for Animal Welfare Vol; Elem-Coll Subjects Prof Tutor; AFT, UFT 1969-; ASCD 1988-; Italian-Amer Tchrs Comm; Cath Tchrs Comm; SI Cncl An Welfare 1980-, Vol, Number 1 Fundraiser 1992-95; Holy Family RC Church 1971-; Articles to be Pub; Who's Who of Am Women.*

CUCCIO, CAROL ANN SAMELA, Math & Science Teacher; *b:* Scranton, NJ; *c:* Michael, Christina, Anthony, Daniel; *ed:* Montclair St Univ (BA) Math 1972; 32 Credits Grad Schl; *cr:* Teaneck HS 10th-12th Grd Math Tchr 1972-77; Frisch HS 9th-11th Grd Math Tchr; Hampton Schl 6th-8th Grd Math, Sci Tchr 1989-; *ai:* Chrldng Adv; Sci Fair Dir; North Hunterdon Math & Sci Articulation Comms; NEA, NJEA 1972-; NCTM 1990-.

CUFF, EDWARD THOMAS, Fourth Grade Teacher; *b:* Shamokin, PA; *m:* Louise Ann LaCrosse; *c:* Lori Ann Reed, Edward Thomas III; *ed:* Bloomsburg St Univ (BS) Scndry Ed, Soc Stud 1969, (ME) Elem Ed 1973; *cr:* Lincoln Elem Schl Fourth Grd Tchr 1969-79; Frackville Elem Schl Fourth Grd Tchr 1979-81; Ashland Elem Schl Fourth Grd Tchr 1981-; *ai:* NEA, PSEA 1969-; NSEA 1969-, Bldg Rep 1970-; Knights of Columbus 1986-, Fourth Degree Knight; West End Fire Co 1989-, Chauffeur, Vol Firefighter, Trustee; *office:* Ashland Area Elem Schl 1 Broad St Ashland PA 17921*

CUFFIA, JAMES A.,JR., French Teacher; *b:* Hyde Park, PA; *m:* Joyce Mc Clellan; *c:* Brigette, Jessica; *ed:* Edinboro St Coll (BSEd) Fr 1966; Temple Univ (MSEd) Educl Media 1970; Post Grad Stud Slippery Rock Univ, PA St Univ; *cr:* Seneca Valley Schl Dist Fr Tchr 1966-; *ai:* Stu Cncl Co-Adv; Seneca Valley Ed Assn 1966-, Bldg Rep, Comm Ch; PSEA, NEA 1966-; Zelie-Harmony Lib, Bd Mem 6 Yrs; Zelienople Nursery Schl, Bd Mem 4 Yrs; St Ferdinand R C Church, Parish Cncl 4 Yrs.

CUILTY, JEFFREY L., Business Ed Teacher & Coach; *b:* Ardsley, NY; *m:* Carolyn; *c:* Britny, Bryan; *ed:* Lehigh Univ (BS) Acctng, Fin 1979; Lehman Coll (MS) Bus Ed 1989; SUNY at New Paltz (CAS) Ed Admin 1994; 60 Addl Credits Beyond MS; *cr:* Pace Bus Schl Bus Ed, Dept Chair 1981-84; Simmons Bus Schl Acct Chair 1985-87; Ardsley HS Recreation Dir, Coach 1981-88; Newburgh Free Acad Acct Tchr, Coach 1987-; *ai:* Var, JV Wrestling 17 Yrs, Girls Soccer 7 Yrs Coach; Delta Pi Epsilon 1989-, Bus Ed Hnr Soc; *home:* 17 Cardinal Ct Newburgh NY 12550*

CUITE, GERRY NAWROCKI, Teacher of Gifted & Talented; *b:* Elizabeth, NJ; *m:* Thomas F.; *ed:* Fordham Univ (BS) Speech 1964; SUNY (MS) Lbrl Stud 1988; Amer Montessori Soc Cert Early Chldhd 1965; Brookdale Ctr on Aging Treatment Non-Verbal Patient 1987; *cr:* Montessori Schl Dir, Tchr 1965-85; BOCES Tchr of Gifted 1985-; Javits Grant Dept of Ed Curr Dev, Lecturer 1992-; *ai:* Portfolio Publications; Am Montessori Soc; NAGC; AGATE; Curr Column AGATE Newsletter; Natl Convention Speaker; NAGC Grant Javits Dept of Ed; *office:* Saratoga/Warren County BOCES Henning Rd Saratoga Springs NY 12866*

CUK, JOHN C., Director of Choirs; *b:* Bronx, NY; *m:* Celia Daniels; *c:* Emily, Sarah; *ed:* Manhattan Coll (BMus) Ed 1977; Manhattan Schl of Music (MM) Piano 1982; Post Grad Stud at Westminster Choir Coll; *cr:* Somers HS-Jr HS Choir Dir & Vocal Music Tchr 1985-; Manhattanville Coll Dir of Choirs 1994-; *ai:* Chamber Choir Dir; Vocal Coach; F Co Music Dir; MENC, NUSSMA, WCSMA 1982-; Coll Music ACDA 1989-; Chorus Amer 1992-; AGO 1995-; *office:* Somers 640 Lincolndale NY 10540*

CULBERTSON, GORDON LEE, Mathematics Coord Baltimore, MD; *m:* Susan; *c:* Keith, Kevin; *ed:* Towson St Univ Ed 1969; Rutgers Univ (MS) Math Ed 1973; *cr:* Old Court JHS 1969-77; Pikesville Mid Math Dept Chm 1978-85; Gilman Coord 1986-; *ai:* Ftbl, Bsktbl, LaCrosse Coach; Bsbl Card C MCTM, NCTM; Dunn Fellow, Meritorious Tchng Awds, Gra Gilman Schl 5407 Roland Ave Baltimore MD 21210

CULBERTSON-STARK, MARY, High School Art Teacher; *b:* NJ; *m:* Gary S. Stark; *ed:* Univ of SC (BFA) Art Studio & Ar Univ of Pittsburgh (MED) Art Ed 1979; Duquesne Univ Disabilities Grad Courses; Cmptr Ed; *cr:* Bethel Park Schl Dist Art Tchr 1975-87; Peters Twp SD MS Art Tchr 1987-88; Bethel Dist Tchng Admin 1988-; *ai:* Art Dept Chm 6th-12th Grd; Pub Comm; Tchr Mentor; Stu Adv; AFT 1975-; Assoced Artists of 1987-, VP, Bd Mem; NAEA 1990-; Pittsburgh Watercolor Soc Mem; St Clair Art League 1995; South Hills Art League 1986-; Cultural Trust 1993-, Consultant & Advy; Theos Fnd 1993-, South Hills Art League 1985-, Bd Mem; Pittsburgh Print Gr Artists Equity 1990-; Master Visual Artists of PGH; Educl Outr 1994-; Hugh O'Brien Ldrshp Fndtn 1993; Carnegie Museum of Consultant 1994-; Commendation of Achvmt PA Senate 19 Finalist Scndry Tchr of Yr PA 1992; Commendation PA Hou 1992; Thanks to Tchrs Awd 1991; Semifinalist Top Working W Glamour Magazine; Top Awd Painting Assoced Artists of Pittsb Outstanding Women in Amer 1982; Tchr Mentor 1983-; Fir Practices in PA Ed/Visual Art Awd 1995; Awd of Distinction H Art 1995; Who's Who in Amer Ed 1996; Who's Who of Amer W *office:* Bethel Park Sr HS 309 Church Rd Bethel Park PA 1510

CULL, CHRISTOPHER JOHN, Acting Teacher; *b:* Salamanc Sherrill Duchteme; *ed:* Bethany Coll (BA) Eng 1977; Cert Acti Drama Studio in London; Neighborhood Playhouse NY; St Studios NY; *cr:* MO Rep Co Actor 1985, 1988, 1992; Walnut Actor 1986, 1991; Cincinatti Playhouse Actor 1990; OR S Festival Actor 1990-91; *ai:* Fac Affairs Comm; Theatre Produ Actors Equity Assn, Screen Actors Guild 1981-.

CULLARI, CLAUDIA, Business Teacher; *b:* Montclair, NJ; *ed:* St Coll (BS) Bus Ed 1992, (MS) Bus Ed 1996; *cr:* Fair Lawn H 1992-; *ai:* FBLA; Mock Trial Team; Fac Treas; NEA, NJEA 199 1990-; Delta Pi Epsilon, Yth Advy Cncl 1995-; *office:* Fair Lawn Berdan Ave Fair Lawn NJ 07410*

CULLEN, CHRIS FREDERICK, Physical Education & Hlt Sandusky, OH; *m:* Debra Lee; *c:* Ashlee, Jordan; *ed:* Garrett C (AS) PE, Hlth 1977; Davis & Elkins Coll (BS) PE, Hlth 198 Univ (MS) Sports Sci 1995; Bowling Green St Univ Drivers Ed *cr:* Sandusky HS Drivers Ed Tchr 2 Yrs; Margaretta HS Drivers Months; Sandusky St Marys Cntrl Cath Schl PE, Hlth 6 Yrs; Pl PE, Hlth 3 Yrs; *ai:* Head Coach Sandusky Bay Stars Collegia Ashland Univ Asst, Pitching Coach Ashland Univ 3 Yrs; H Sandusky St Marys Cntrl Cath; Asst Ftbl Coach; SADD Adivora NEA 1993-; Amer Legion Bsbl 10 Yrs Pres of League; *ho* Washington St Castalia OH 44824

CULLEN, DAVID PETER, Chem Dept Chairperson & Sommerville, NJ; *m:* Hak Yon Park; *c:* Colleen; *ed:* LaSalle Univ & Chem 1964; Troy St Univ (MA) Ed; Univ of NH Natl Sci Fnd Mater dei HS Chem Tchr & Dept Chair 1964-68; Delaware Va Schl Chem Tchr 1968-76; Charlotte Amalie HS 9th Grd Sci Tch MC Perry Schl Japan Sci Tchr 1978-80; Seoul Amer HS Korea & Dept Chair 1980-; *ai:* Sci Dept Chprsn; Ladies Jr Var Bsktbl C Sci Fnd Grant; DOE-TRAC Summer Research at Natl Lab; *off* American HS Unit 15549 # 27 APO AP 96205

CULLEN, LOIS CARTER, 6th Grd Lang Arts & Rdng Pawtucket, RI; *m:* Robert K. Jr.; *c:* Glenn, Mark, Brenda; *ed:* Coll (BA) Elem Ed 1967; Fitchburg St Coll (MED) Elem Post-Grad Work Cmptr Course Pagemaker Prgm, 24 Cre H Masters Degree; *cr:* Richardson Schl Tchr Grd 4, 1967-69; S Elem Schl Tchr Grd 3 1969; St Michaels Elem Schl Grd 4 Tch C. G. Mc Donough City Magnet Schl Grd 6 Tchr 1986-; *ai:* Homework, Tutoring Club; AFT 1986-; ASCD 1993-.

CULLEN, ROSEMARY CRAWFORD, High School English T Belfast, North Ireland; *m:* James Edward; *c:* John, David, Ramapo Coll (BA) Eng 1980; Fairleigh Dickinson Univ (MAT) Cost Accounting Cert Belfast North Ireland; 30 Post Grad Credit of North Ireland Cost Accountant; Cliffside Park HS Eng Tch Dumont HS Eng Tchr 1982-; *ai:* Lit Magazine Adv; NCTE 198 Bible Chapel 1980-; Poetry Pub; Conf Speaker; *home:* 30 Ca Woodcliff Lake NJ 07675*

CULLERTON, CAROL L.,SSJ, Secondary Mathematics T Philadelphia, PA; *ed:* Chestnut Hill Coll (BS) Elem Ed 1984; Univ (MA) Math 1995; 24 Addl Credits Chestnut Hill Coll 19 Cecilian Acad 4th Grd Tchr 1973-75; St Catharine's Schl 6th 1975-80; Nativity of Our Lord Schl 8th Grd Tchr 1980-84; St Assisi Schl 6th-8th Grd Tchr 1984-85; St Helena's Schl 7th-8th 1985-86; Chestnut Hill Coll Payroll Mgr 1986-90; Archbishop P HS Math Tchr 1990-; *ai:* NCEA 1990-; *office:* Archbishop Prend 401 N Lansdowne Ave Drexel Hill PA 19026

CULLIN, JANE BUSSON, Health & Physical Ed Teacher; *b:* OH; *m:* Kerry Lee; *c:* Kipp Anthony, Zachary Arthur; *ed:* OH Univ (BA) Hlth, PE Tchr 1979; Univ of Akron (MA) PE Tchr 19 *cr:* Buckeye HS Hlth, PE Tchr 1979-; *ai:* Jr HS Vlybl Coach; S Core Team Substance Abuse Resistance Group; OFT, AFT 1987- Local Ed Assn 1979-, Bldg Steward; OEA, NEA 1979-87, Bldg & Light Handicapped 1987-; Annual Recognition for Work Substance Use Prevention; *office:* Buckeye HS 3084 Columbia R OH 44256*

CULLIN, MICHAEL JOSEPH, Physics Teacher; *b:* Allentow Elizabeth Marion Strohmeier; *ed:* Kutztown Univ (BS) Physics Sec Ed, Physics 1989; 21 Addl Grad Credits Sec Ed, Curr East St Univ; *cr:* Blue Mt HS Physics Tchr 1989-92; Freedom HS Ph 1992-; *ai:* Freedom Environmental Awareness Team Adv; AA NEA, PSEA 1989-; *office:* Freedom HS 3147 Chester Ave Beth 18017*

CULLINAN, PATRICIA A. (MARTIN), Social Studies Teache York City, NY; *m:* Martin J.; *c:* Sean M., Mary Margaret; *ed:* Coll (BA) His 1962; St Johns Univ (MA) Amer His 1967; 30 Credits St Johns Univ, Long Island Univ; *cr:* All Saints Comm World, Amer His Tchr 1962-63; Mac Arthur HS Soc Stud Tchrs Division Ave HS Soc Stud Tchr 1965-72; Gen Douglas Mac Arth Stud Tchr 1975-; *ai:* Renaissance Comm; AFT 1964-, Bldg Rep; United Tchrs, Rep; New York CIty Historical Soc Summer Flw Mentor Tchr, Intern Tchr Prgm 1988-89; Honorary Life Mbrs 1995-; *office:* General Douglas Mac Arthur HS Old Jerus Levittown NY 11756

'G, NANCY L., Earth Science Teacher; *b:* Batavia, NY; *m:* Larry ic S.; *ed:* SUNY Coll at Brockport (BS) Zoology 1973, (MA) ud 1991; Addl 60 Hrs; *cr:* Cuyahoga Falls HS Bio Tchr 1973-75; IS General Sci Tchr 1985-87; Batavia HS Earth Sci Tchr 1987-; Curr Sr Adv, Examgen Inc 1994-; *ai:* 25 Neediest Fund Comm; ecision Making Tm; Regents Earth Sci Tchrs of WNY 1991-; AFT 1985-; GLOW Recycling Comm 1993-, Neighborhood *office:* Batavia HS 260 State St Batavia NY 14020

UDITH WILLIAMS, Educational Technology Teacher; *m:* John Sr.; *c:* John Jr., Cynthia A. Foxworth; *ed:* Cheyney Univ (BS) 9; Temple Univ (MED) Math 1972; Temple Univ Cert Cmptr Sci n St Univ 12 Credits; Marywood Coll 6 Credits; Gratz Coll 12 chl Dist of Philadelphia Inservice 6 Credits, Schl Dist 12 Credits; ova Univ Grad Asst 1969-70; Shaw Jr HS Math Tchr 1970-71; wn HS Math Tchr 1971-72; Martin Luther King HS Math Tchr Germantown-Lankenau HS Math, Cmptr Sci Tchr 1973-; *ai:* EACH Coord; Newspapper Spon; Cmptr Club Adv; Frosh Coord; Bldg Resource Tchr; Dean of Stdnts; AFT, PAFT, NCTM ndry Cmptr Users, EPECC, NAVG 1987-; Alpha Phi Sigma 1965-; Vomen For Justice 1982-; NSF Scndry RETCS; Project Flwshp, rant; Acad Excl Scroll 2nd Scholar of Yr High Hnrs; *office:* wn-Lankenau Mtvtn Schl 201 Spring Ln Philadelphia PA 19128

ADELYN MOORE, 5th Grade Teacher; *b:* Birmingham, AL; *m:* DeLise, Otis III; *ed:* TN St Univ (BS) Elem Ed 1968; Cleveland Soc Admin Cert 1974; Attnd John Carroll Univ, OH St Univ, Coll, Notre Dame for Addl Course Work; *cr:* Cleveland City Schls -; *ai:* Drug Liaison; After Schl Tutor; Passage Elder; Sunday Schl Level Chprsn; *home:* 4697 E 178th St Cleveland OH 44128

IARILYN ELIZABETH (SAMSON), Chemistry Teacher; *b:* nswick, NJ; *m:* Lawrence W.; *ed:* Montclair St Coll (BA) Chem A) Chem 1986, (MA) Admin & Supervision 1991; *cr:* Kearny HS r 1972-; *ai:* Sci Competition Coord; Chem Teams Coach; Schl m Mem; NSTA 1977-; Phi Kappa Phi 1985-; NTSSA 1987-; ACS K 1990-; *office:* Kearny HS 336 Devon St Kearny NJ 07032

PER, JUDITH A., Fifth Grade Teacher; *b:* Savannah, GA; *c:* Breslin, James Scott, John Spence, Martha Allison, Richard Kent; ian Court Coll (BS) Elem Ed 1986; *cr:* West Dover Schl 4th-5th 1986-; *ai:* Pep Club; TREA Schlsp Comm; NEA, NJEA, TREA urch Ushering Guild 1995-; Alpha Delta Kappa 1991-; *office:* er Elem Schl Blue Jay Dr Toms River NJ 08755*

, SUSAN JANE, Second Grade Teacher; *b:* Connellsville, PA; *c:* Adam, Gregg; *ed:* CA Univ (BS) Elem Ed 1974; 33 Post-Grad Hrs; llsville Area Schl Dist Elem Classroom Tchr 1974-; *ai:* Stu Cncl O Former Sec; Connellsville Area Ed Assn 1974-, Pres 1989-; ille Chamber Commerce 1995-; Bus & Prof Womens Club 1988-; ar Chrstn Church 1972-, Elder, Worship Ldr, Sunday Schl Tchr, Tchr; *office:* Dunbar Borough Elem Schl Rd 1 Dunbar PA 15431*

T, EDWARD ROSS, Prof of Soc Science & History; *b:* New York *m:* Sylvia Evans; *c:* Marcus, Willis, Gregory, Lisa, Sherree, icole; *ed:* TX Bapt Coll (BA) Music, Ed 1956, (MA) Ed 1957, el 1958; Thomas Edison Coll (BA) Soc Sci, His; City Coll (MA) ; CUNY Grad Ctr (PHD); *cr:* Lehman Coll Prof 10 Yrs; CCNY rs; *ai:* NAACP NY Branch Bd of Dir; African Free Soc Founder; arish Assoc Pastor; Amer Sociological Assn; NY St Labor Bd First Black Chm; Omega Psi Phi; Martin Luther King Club naplin NYC Police Dept 23 Yrs; Book: Malcolm X; Toured ly 1994.

RLAND, KATHLEEN CASCIO, Fifth Grade Teacher; *b:* on, DC; *m:* Robert Antony; *c:* Annie; *ed:* Hood Coll MA Elem oly Cross Schl Jr High Tchr 1980-83; IBM Corp Bus Control 984-90; St Peter's Schl 5 Grd Tchr 1990-; *ai:* Mem Mid Sts Chprsn Arts, Lib Media, Admin Comms; MD Cncl for Soc Stud *ice:* St Peter's Schl 2900 Sandy Spring Rd Olney MD 20832

CLARKE, ANITA GRIFFIN, 8th Grd Eng Tchr & Dept Chprsn; , AL; *m:* Walter M.; *c:* Robyn Cumbo Mullen, Stewart B. Cumbo, III; *ed:* Bowie St Univ (BS) Elem Ed 1972; 45 Plus Credit Hrs ing; Certfd Conflict Resolution Univ MD; 25 Credit Hrs Ldrshp US Info Agency Newswriter 1959-63; Prince George's Cty MD Supvr Stu Tchr, Schl Based Mngmt Chprsn 1987-89, Eng Dept l Based Mngmt Team 1990-, Tchr 1972-; *ai:* PGCEA Tchr Rep; r Adv; Drama Club Spon; NEA 1972-; *office:* Benjamin Tasker Collington Rd Bowie MD 20715*

G, MARY K., Fourth Grade Teacher; *b:* New York City, NY; *m:* : Hunter Coll (BA) His 1971; Richmond Coll (MS) Ed 1974; Coll Island (MS) Ed 1987; *cr:* St Christopher's Schl 4th Grd Tchr PS 41 3rd Grd Tchr 1986-87; PS 1 4th Grd Tchr 1984-; *ai:* 4th After Schl Chorus Choral Dir 1987-89; UFT, AFT 1984-; Conf n 1992-, Sec, Bd of Dirs; Lynne Robbins Steinman Fnd 1988-, Treas, Bd of Dirs; Amer Heart Assn, Lynne Robbins Steinman s; *office:* Pub Schl 1 58 Summit St Staten Island NY 10307

IG, WILLIAM GORDON, Chemistry Tchr & Fin Aid Dir; *b:* Manitoba, Canada; *m:* Sandra Susan Maki; *c:* Ailsa, Glynis; *ed:* Calgary (BSc) Chem 1978, (BED) Scndry Sci 1982; *cr:* a-Tweedsmuir Schl Fac 1979-86; Deerfield Acad Fac, Fin Aid Dir Var Girls' Hockey, Cycling Coach; Amer Chemical Soc 1979-; Fire Dept 1986-, Lieutenant; Deerfield Rescue 1990-, EMT; low Univ of MA at Amherst 1988-89; Fin Aid Ofcrs Assn Chair Schl Fin Aid Svcs Comm Mem; Natl Ind Schls Fin Aid Comm; erfield Acad 7 Boyden Ln Deerfield MA 01342*

IGS, CYNTHIA HUGGINS, Third Grade Teacher; *b:* , MD; *m:* Charles Parker; *c:* Jeffrey P., Jennifer C. Marcus; *ed:* St Coll (BS) Elem Ed 1963; Post Grad Work for Advanced al Cert Western MD Coll, Hood Coll; *cr:* Lutherville Elem 4th 1963-66; Charles Carroll Elem 4th Grd Tchr 1978-91; Carroll Cty res 1991-95; Taneytown Elem 3rd Grd Tchr 1995-; *ai:* Instrl, Prof Relations Comms; Carroll Co Ed Assn 1978-, Pres; MD St Tchrs A 1978-; Kappa Delta Pi; Democratic Cntrl Comm 1990-, Sec; Women Voters 1990-, PTA, PTO 1978-; Appt to Prof Stan & Tchr of MD 1993-; Appt Governor's Ed Transition Team 1994; Articles

IGS, DEL F., Indstrl Envrnmtl Mgt Asst Prof; *b:* Syracuse, NY; *ed:* Alfred Univ (BS) Ceramic Eng 1980; Rensselaer Poly Tech erials Eng 1985; Univ of CT (MS) Environmental Eng 1996; *cr:* Production Supvr 1982-87; Atmi Inc Team Ldr, Semiconductors Univ of CT Res Assoc 1992-93; Naugatuck Vly Comm-Tech Coll 1993-; *ai:* Learning Resources Ctr Comm; Amer Water Works l Groundwater Assn 1995-; Silver Lake Assn 1984-, Pres; Two ts; *office:* Naugatuck Vly Comm Tech Coll 750 Chase Pky CT 06708*

IGS, DOROTHY LACERDA, Special Needs Educator; *b:* rough, MA; *m:* Michael Dennis; *c:* Devon Shimkus, Andrea *ed:* Keene St Coll (BED) Spec Ed & Elem Ed 1972; Antioch Univ pec Ed 1977; Research for Better Tchng I & II Fitchburg St *cr:* Lakeview Acad Tchr of Spec Needs 1984-86; White s Reg HS Tchr of Spec Needs 1986-88; Silver Lake Reg HS Tchr of Spec Needs 1988-91; Falmouth HS Tchr of Spec Needs 1992-; *ai:* Class of 1999 Adv; NEA 1982-; MTA 1988-; FEA 1992-; Plymouth Cty 4-H 1988-, Ldr, Schlsp Comm; Falmouth HS Band Parents, Sec; Town of Falmouth, Inclusionary Practices Comm; *office:* Falmouth HS 847 Gifford St Ext Falmouth MA 02540*

CUMMINGS, GLEN A., Social Studies Teacher; *b:* Rochester, NY; *m:* Julie Hoag; *c:* Ashley, Matthew; *ed:* Empire St Coll (BA) Music 1992; *cr:* Northfield Music Private Music Instr 1976-88; Roxy's Music Private Music Instr 1988-; Empire St Coll Tutor, Evaluator 1994-; Eastridge HS Ec, Amer His, Participation in Govt Tchr 1995-; *ai:* NY St United Tchrs 1995-; ASCAP 1985-, Writer; NAACP Cert Achvmt for Performance Attica St Prison; Pub Article 1995; *office:* Eastridge HS 2350 Ridge Rd Rochester NY 14622

CUMMINGS, JANET ARNOLD, Language Arts Tchr of Gifted; *b:* Cincinnati, OH; *m:* Charles; *c:* Cathy Davis, Charles Jr., Carolyn St John; *ed:* Heidelberg Coll (BA) Elem Ed 1958; Post Grad Work Xavier Univ, Mt St Joseph, Univ of Cincinnati; *cr:* Columbus Pub Schls 6 Grd Tchr 1958-61, Sub Tchr 1962-64; cincinnati Pub Schls Sub Tchr 1969-70; Northwest Local Schsl Elem Grd Tchr 1977-; *ai:* Ed Commision; Cheviot United Meth Church Hosp Visitor; Gifted Prgm Comm Writing New Materials Assoc with Curr; NEA, OEA 1980-; OAGC, OVATAG 1985-; West Hills Music Club 1968-, Performing Mem; Jennings Scholar 1989-90; Golden Apple Achiever Awd 1994; Chorus Dir 1993-94; *office:* Monfort Hts Schl 3661 W Fork Rd Cincinnati OH 45247*

CUMMINGS, MARJORIE B., Fifth Grade Teacher; *b:* Westerly, RI; *m:* F. Glenn; *ed:* RI Coll (BS) Ed & Eng 1963; 34 Hrs Grad Stud at St Univ of NY at Albany, Saint Rose at Albany, Russell Sage; Various Inservice Courses in Portfolio Assessment, Assessing Writing & Self Esteem; *cr:* Westerly Pub Schls 6th Grd Tchr 1963-67; Niskayuna Schl 3rd Grd Tchr 1967-70; Schoharie Elem 5th Grd Tchr 1971-; *ai:* AFT; Schoharie Tchrs Assn 1971-; NYSUT 1967-; Duanesburg Voluntary Ambulance Corps 1985-, Emergency Medical Technician of Yr 1993-94; Christ Church, Vestry 2nd Term, Altar Guild 1984-; Schenectady Animal Shelter-Humane Soc; Duanesburg Planning Bd, Sec 1971-75; *home:* 997 Cole Rd Delanson NY 12053

CUMMINGS, MARY MC GOWAN, Agriculture Teacher; *b:* White Plains, NY; *m:* Wilbert J.; *c:* Cody, Kasey; *ed:* SUNY (AAS) Horticulture, Ag Bus Mngmt 1984; PA St Univ (BS) Ag Ed 1987; *cr:* Salem HS Ag Tchr 1987-; *ai:* FFA, Frosh Class, Jr Class, SADD Adv; Discipline Comm Spon Jr-Sr Prom; Bldg Rep; NEA, NJEA 1987-; Salem Tchrs Assn 1987-, Sec Bldg Rep; Natl Vol Ag Tchrs Assn, NJ Ag Tchrs Assn 1987-; *office:* Salem HS 219 Walnut St Salem NJ 08079*

CUMMINGS, SHEILA L., Biology Teacher; *b:* Brooklyn, NY; *c:* Shataye, Oneika; *ed:* Queens Coll (BA) Home Ec 1974; City Coll (MA) Environmental Sci 1988; *cr:* Seward Park HS Paraprofessional 1978-82, Lab Specialist 1982-90; Wm H. Maxwell Voc HS Bio Tchr 1996; *ai:* HOSA Co-Adv; *office:* Wm H Maxwell Voc HS 145 Pennsylvania Ave Brooklyn NY 11207

CUMMINGS, SONDRA LOUISE (GERMANIO), Kindergarten Teacher; *b:* Centerville, IA; *m:* Joseph C.; *c:* John J.; *ed:* Rowan Coll (BA) Elem Ed 1964; *cr:* Oak Vly Schl 3rd Grd Tchr 1964-67; Pershing Schl Kndgtn Tchr 1971-74 & 1981-90; Broad St Schl 1st Grd Tchr 1974-76 & 1979-81; West Harmony St Schl 1st Grd Tchr 1976-79; Lafayette-Pershing Schl Kndgtn Tchr 1990-; Woodstown Schls Summer Schl Tchr; Penns Grove-Carneys Point Summer Schl Tchr; *ai:* Grievance, Liaison & Curr Comm; Schl & Tchr Learning Ctr Liaison 6 Yrs; Schl Planning Comm 1994-; Kndgtn Comm & Stu of Month Chprson 1994-95; Penns Grove-Carneys Point Tchrs Assn 1971-, Rep; NEA 1971-; NJEA 1971-; PTA 1971-, Sec 2 Yrs; Kndgtn Tchrs Assn 1971-, VP 2 Yrs, Sec 2 Yrs; AARP 1993-; Queen of Apostles Church 1979-, Summer Fair Comm; Xi Alpha Lambda Beta Sigma Phi Chptr, Sec, VP & Comms, Girl of Yr Awd; September Fest Comm Day 1985-95; Toys for Tots Campaign 1990-95; Neighborhood Cancer Dr 1993-95; Dist Tchr of Yr 1986; Gov Kean Grant; *office:* Lafayette Pershing Elem Schl 237 Shell Rd Carneys Point NJ 08069

CUMMINGS, SUSAN, Third Grade Teacher; *b:* New York, NY; *m:* Robert; *c:* Tully; *ed:* Pembroke Coll in Brown Univ (BA) Psych 1964; Boston Univ (MED) Schl Psych 1966; Attnd Bridgewater St Coll, Johnson St Coll; *cr:* Brockton Pub Schls 1st Grd Tchr 1966-70, Guid Cnslr 1970-72; Middleboro Pub Schls 3rd Grd Tchr 1984-; *ai:* Co-Chm Bldg Based Support Team; Schl Cncl Mem; Brockton Ed Assn, Bldg Rep; Middleboro Ed Assn; MA Tchrs Assn 1987-; NEA; Adopted Tchr of Cabot Club; GFWC in a Pgm of Natl Assn for Humane & Environmental Ed; *office:* Mayflower Schl 31 Mayflower Ave Middleboro MA 02346

CUMMINGS, SUSAN G., Associate Professor of Biology; *b:* Montclair, NJ; *ed:* Montclair St Coll (BA) Bio 1967; American Univ (MS) Invertebrate Zoology 1973; Univ of CA at Irvine (PHD) Cell, Dev Bio 1983; *cr:* So IL Univ Rsrch Assoc 1973-76; Mycogen Corp Staff Scientist 1983-86; Georgian Court Coll Bio Dept Chm 1990-; *ai:* Pre-Hlth Adv; Undergraduate Acad Cncl; Campus Pastoral Cncl; Identity Comm; AAAS; NJ Acad of Sci; Natl Inst of Hlth Traineeship, Dev Bio; NSF Traineeship; Grad Fellow US Natl Museum of Natural His; *office:* Georgian Court Coll 900 Lakewood Ave Lakewood NJ 08701

CUMMINGS, TIMOTHY, Global Studies II Teacher; *b:* Staten Island, NY; *m:* Debra Ann Sinclair; *ed:* St John's Univ (BS) Soc Stud 1990; *cr:* New York City Police Dept Police Ofcr 1974-88; Monsignor Farrell HS Tchr, Asst Dean 1990-; *ai:* Asst Ath Dir; Jr Prom, JV Bsktbl Team Moderator; Europe Easter Trips Head Tchr; *office:* Msgr Farrell HS 2900 Amboy Rd Staten Island NY 10306

CUMMINGS, WENDY ELIZABETH, Mathematics Teacher; *b:* Scranton, PA; *m:* Michael S.; *ed:* Wilkes Univ (BA) Math 1990; Penn St Univ Ed Credits 1985-87; *cr:* Dunmore HS Sub Tchr 1990-95; Lakeland HS Sub Tchr 1990-95; Wolff Group Learning Ctr Tutor 1993-95; Old Forge HS Math Tchr 1994-; *ai:* Newspaper Adv; PSEA, NEA 1995-; Transplant Awareness & Group Support 1989-; *office:* Old Forge HS 1 Marion St Old Forge PA 18518*

CUMMINS, ALEXIS KECHRIS, 9th Grade Social Studies Tchr; *b:* Quincy, MA; *m:* Richard Albert; *c:* Theodore K., Richard K., Nyssa A.; *ed:* Boston Univ (BA) Psych 1968; Bridgewater St Coll (MED) Guidance Counseling 1972; Eastern Nazarene Coll Tchrs Cert Courses 1968; Northeastern Univ Adjustment Counseling Cert; *cr:* New Bedford Pub Schls Federal Testing & Tutoring on Bussing 1 Yr, Tchr of Spec Ed 1 Yr, Soc Stud Tchr 1 Yr; Jr Colls Part-Time Psych Tchr; Weymouth Pub Schls Home Tchr for Physically Handicapped 16 Yrs; Weymouth Voc HS & Alternative HS Adjustment Cnslr 3 Yrs; Weymouth Jr HS Soc Stud Tchr 3 Yrs; *ai:* Transition Prgm; Peer Mediation & Mentoring; Crisis Caring Team; WTA, MTA; Courses & Wkshps in Violence Prevention, Peer Mediation, Crisis Intervention; *office:* Weymouth Jr HS 360 Pleasant St Weymouth MA 02190

CUNEO, ANTHONY LEO, Jr High Language Arts Teacher; *b:* Baltimore, MD; *ed:* Neumann Coll (BA) Eng 1970; Loyola Coll (MED) Educl Planning, Supervision 1981; 12 Post Grad Credit Hrs; *cr:* St Joseph on the Bradywine Schl Elem Tchr 1961-71; St Peter Elem Schl Prin 1971-76; St Peter MS Prin 1971-76; Holy Spirit Elem Schl Prin 1976-79; Holy Spirit MA Prin 1976-79; St Elizabeth Elem Schl Prin 1979-87; St Elizabeth MS Prin 1979-87; Our Lady of Fatima Jr HS Lang Arts Tchr 1987-; Essex Comm Coll Part-time Eng Tchr 1991-92; *ai:* Stu Cncl, Safety Patrol Adv; Eng Curr Coord; NCEA 1961-; Mid Sts Assn for Five Schls Team Mem; St Matthew Schl, St Mary Schl, St John Schl, Roosevelt Pub Schl Team Visitor 1981-84; St Mary Schl Assembly Visitor 1981-84; *office:* Our Lady Of Fatima Schl 6400 E Pratt St Baltimore MD 21224*

CUNEY, GEORGE CHARLES, Assoc Prof of Automotive Tech; *b:* Georgetown, NY; *m:* Barbara E.; *c:* Deborah A. Mitchell; Sandra L. Groves; *ed:* Suny Morrisville (AAS) Automotive 1962; Suny Oswego (BS) Indstrl Arts 1966, (MS) Ed 1971; 40 Addtl Credit Hrs Trng Ctr Buffalo NY, Anderson IN; *cr:* Gilbertsville CS Indstrl Arts Tchr 1964-67; SUNY Morrisville Assoc Prof Auto Tech 1967-; *ai:* UUP; Sae; Faith Bapt Church Treas, Trustee; Chancellors Awd Excl in Tchng; ASE Certfd 1990; *office:* S U N Y Coll Of A & T Morrisvl Main St Morrisville NY 13408

CUNFER, ELAINE B., Graphic Design Professor; *b:* Levittown, PA; *ed:* Kutztown Univ Comm Design 1983; Tyler Schl of Art at Temple Univ Visual Design 1991; *cr:* The Times Leader 1983-84; The Washington Times 1984-85; The Morning Call 1985-89; Kutztown Univ Prof 1991-; *ai:* Comm Arts, Tech Group Club Adv; Coll, Univ Curr Comms; Graphic Design Ed Assn 1995-; Articles Pubs; The Soc of Newspaper Design Annuals; Included in Book Fresh Ideas in Letterhead, Bus Card Design by North Light Press; *office:* Kutztown Univ Of PA Kutztown PA 19530

CUNHA, ANN MARIE BURKE, 8th Grade Lang Arts Teacher; *b:* Lowell, MA; *m:* Paul D.; *c:* Allyson, Matthew, David; *ed:* Lowell St Coll (BS) Elem Ed 1972; Post Grad Stud & Credits Univ of MA, Lowell St Coll, William Paterson Coll; *cr:* Hugh J. Molloy Schl Remedial Rdng Tchr 1972-76; Meml Schl 8th Grd Tchr 1977-82; St Clare Schl Lang Arts, 8th Grd Tchr 1991-; *ai:* Yrbk Adv; 8th Grd Testing Coord; Steering Comm; Mid Sts Accrediation; NCEA 1991-; *office:* St Clare Schl 39 Allwood Rd Clifton NJ 07014

CUNNINGHAM, BETTY SIKINOW, English Teacher; *b:* Carolina, WV; *m:* Richard Rex; *c:* Richanne Cunningham Mankey, David, Mark; *ed:* Fairmont St Coll (BA) Eng, Home Ec 1958; Attnd Heidelberg Coll, Bowling Green St Univ; Lee Canter Correspondence; *cr:* Upper Sandusky HS Voc Home Ec Tchr 1958-66; Hopewell-Loudon HS Voc Home Ec Tchr 1970-71; Tiffin Columbian HS Voc Home Ec Tchr 1971-84, Eng Tchr 1984-; *ai:* Venture Capital Attendance Comm; Princ Advy; Frosh Mentor; TEA Rep; Eng Dept Chair; United Way Chair; NEA, OEA, TEA, NWOEA 1971-; AAUM, SCHEA, OHEA, AHEA 1971-; Cancer Drive; Easter Seals; Microwave Classes; Microwave Annual at Demonstration; *home:* 55 Lelar St Tiffin OH 44883

CUNNINGHAM, DAVID E., Computer Teacher; *b:* Haverhill, MA; *ed:* Univ of MA at Amherst (BA) Geosciences 1979; Lesley Coll (MA) Tech in Ed 1990; Univ of MA at Lowell Post Grad; *ai:* Tech, Comm Dept Chprsn; Bsktbl Coach; Key Club, Jr Class Adv; Tech Prep Faciliator; Tech Comm; MA Tchrs Assn 1987-; MA Cmptr Using Edctrs 1993-; *office:* Whittier Reg Voc Tech HS 115 Amesbury Line Rd Haverhill MA 01830

CUNNINGHAM, DEBORAH (DOVICSAK), Math Teacher; *b:* Mc Keesport, PA; *m:* Kim Alan; *c:* Kaci L., Kari L.; *ed:* Muskingum Coll (BS) Math 1976; Coll of Mt St Joseph (MA) Ed 1988; *cr:* Buckeye Trl HS Math Tchr 1976-; *ai:* Yrbk; NCTM 1985-; *office:* Buckeye Trail HS 65555 Wintergreen Rd Lore City OH 43755

CUNNINGHAM, DEBORAH MAY, Kindergarten Teacher; *b:* Pittsburgh, PA; *ed:* Duquesne Univ (BA) Elem Ed 1973, (MED) Elem Guid, Cnslng 1975; *cr:* Adlai Stevenson Elem Schl Third Grd Tchr 1973-96, Kindergarten Tchr 1986-; *ai:* NEA, PSEA, Plum Borough Ed Assn 1973-; *office:* Adlai E Stevenson Elem Schl 313 Holiday Park Dr Pittsburgh PA 15239

CUNNINGHAM, H. WAYNE, Crafts Teacher; *b:* New Salem, PA; *m:* Karen M. Guyton; *c:* Bradley W., Kristen A.; *ed:* Waynesburg (BA) Art 1965; Attnd WV Univ & Edinboro Univ of PA; *cr:* Uniontown Schls Tchr 1965-68; Millcreek Schls Art Tchr 1968-; *ai:* Ski Club; NEA 1965-; PSEA 1965-; *home:* 612 Oregon Ave Erie PA 16505

CUNNINGHAM, J. KEVIN, Band & Chorus Director; *b:* Lewistown, PA; *m:* Laura Ann Stuck; *c:* Ashley, Jonathan; *ed:* IN Univ of PA (BS) Music Ed 1980; Post Grad Stud Masters Equiv West Chester Univ, Hartt Schl of Music, Vandercook Coll of Music; *cr:* Juniata HS Band, Chorus Dir, 4th & 5th Grd Instrumental Music Instr 1980-; *ai:* Marching Band, Jazz, Stage, Sr Class Play Music Dir; Tri-M Music Hnr Soc Adv; PA Music Edctrs Assn 1980-, St Exec Bd 1992-94, Dist 4 Pres 1992-94, Region III Chprsn 1993-94; NEA, PSEA, MENC 1980-; Port Royal Luth Church 1971-, Cncl 1985-87, Cncl Sec, Choir Dir; *office:* Juniata HS RR 4 Box 99 Mifflintown PA 17059

CUNNINGHAM, JAMES FRANKLIN,III, Math Teacher & Dept Chairman; *b:* East Liverpool, OH; *m:* Dee Anna McAfoose; *c:* James Franklin IV; *ed:* Regis Univ (BS) Bus Admin Ec 1984; Univ of CO (BA) Math 1988; OH Univ (MED) Curr & Instruction 1993; *cr:* USAF Prsnl Specialist 1981-84; Janitell Jr HS Math Tchr 1988-89; Belpre City Schls Math Tchr & Dept Chm 1989-; *ai:* Asst Track Coach; Competency Based Ed & Partner in Ed Comms; Part-Time Instr Evenings; NCTM 1987-; ASCD 1989-; Sunday Schl Tchr Cath CCD 1994-; Chptr 2 Grant Initate the Use of Graphing Calculators in the Classroom; Eisenhower Grant Prof Growth Trng for Math Tchrs Evolve Toward NCTM Stans; *office:* Belpre HS Stone Rd Belpre OH 45714*

CUNNINGHAM, JAMES THOMAS, English Teacher & Dept Chair; *b:* Dayton, OH; *m:* Sally; *c:* Tyler, Adrienne Ault, Jacob Ault; *ed:* Wright St Univ (BS) Eng 1978; *ai:* Xenia HS Ten Coach; W OH League Coach of the Yr 1995; *office:* Greene Cty Career Ctr 2960 W Enon Rd Xenia OH 45385*

CUNNINGHAM, JOSEPHINE A., Civics & Economics Teacher; *b:* Punysutawnay, PA; *m:* Carl G.; *c:* Samuel, Aaron; *ed:* IN Univ of PA (BS) Soc Stud, His 1973, (MA) Eng, Amer Lit 1981; *cr:* IN Jr HS Soc Stud Sub Tchr 1974-82, Soc Stud Tchr 1983-; *ai:* His Club Spon 1987-90; Strategic Plan ActionComm 1995-; NEA 1983-; PSEA 1983-, Bldg Rep Twice; IN Free Lib 1983-, Pres, VP; IN Cty Historical Soc 1979-, Past VP; IN Hospice Assn 1985-, Vol; IN Cty Municipal Svc 1991-, Bd Mem; IN Arts Cncl 1979-88, Bd; Commonwealth Partnership Grant 1986; Carnegie-Mellon Univ IN Area Schl Dist Grant; Fellow Civil Inst Gettysburg Coll 1987-94; *office:* Indiana Jr HS 245 N 5th St Indiana PA 15701*

CUNNINGHAM, KAREN GUYTON, Fine Arts Teacher; *b:* Stoneboro, PA; *m:* H. Wayne; *c:* Bradley W., Kristen A.; *ed:* Penn St Univ (BS) Art Ed 1965; Attnd Univ of Pittsburgh & Edinboro Univ; *cr:* Bethel Park Schls Art Tchr 1965-68; JSW MS Art Tchr 1978-92; McDowell HS Fine Arts Tchr 1992-; *ai:* Ski & Art Clubs; NEA 1965-; PSEA; *home:* 612 Oregon Ave Erie PA 16505

CUNNINGHAM, LISA ANNE, Middle School English Teacher; *b:* Albany, NY; *m:* William J. III; *c:* Jacob William; *ed:* George Mason Univ (BA) Eng Lit 1992; Currently Pursuing St Cert; Towson 3 Hrs Grad Stud; PG Comm Coll 15 Addl Subject Hrs; *cr:* Queen Anne Schl MS Eng Tchr 1993-, Asst to MS Head 1994-; *ai:* 7th Grd Class Spon; 6th Grd & Newspaper Club Adv; Prof Dev Comm Mem; NCTE 1993-; *office:* Queen Anne Schl 14111 Oak Grove Rd Upper Marlboro MD 20774

CUNNINGHAM, LOIS CRAWFORD, Human Ecology Teacher; *b:* New Kensington, PA; *m:* James; *c:* Cory; *ed:* Mansfield Univ (BS) Home Ec 1975, (MS) Home Ec 1990; 40 Credit Hrs; *cr:* Elmira Free Acad Home Ec Tchr 1990-; *ai:* Childcare Stud Team; AFT 1990-; NYSUT 1990-; ETA

1990-; Mansfield Univ Grad Assistantship; *office:* Elmira Free Acad 933 Hoffman St Elmira NY 14905

CUNNINGHAM, MAUREEN BREY, Secondary English Teacher; *b:* Ft Dix, NJ; *m:* Terence; *c:* Kevin, Ryan; *ed:* Marist Coll (BA) Eng 1977; SUNY at New Paltz (MS) Scndry Eng Ed 1988; *cr:* Rhinebeck HS Scndry Eng Tchr 1983-; Dutchess Comm Coll Adjunct Lecturer 1989-91; *ai:* NCTE 1985-; Wood Shoes Nursery Schl 1990-, Bd Mem; *office:* Rhinebeck HS PO Box 351 Rhinebeck NY 12572*

CUNNINGHAM, PATTY LYNN (ROTTA), Spanish & English Teacher; *b:* Pittsburgh, PA; *m:* Tom; *c:* Christy, Craig; *ed:* Slippery Rock St Coll (BS) Span, Eng Tchr 1968; Attnd Pitt, Penn St, IN; *cr:* Churchill Area SD Tchr 1968-78; Comm Coll of Allegheny Cty Adj Fac 1978-; Gateway Schl Dist Tchr 1987-89; Carnegie Mellon Univ Part-time Instr 1993-; Penn Trafford Schl Dist Tchr 1994-; *ai:* PSMLA; AFLA; PSEA; NEA; PTEA; NNELL; APPLES; *office:* Penn Trafford Schl Dist Rt 130 Harrison City PA 15636*

CUNNINGHAM, PAUL FRANCIS, Psychology Professor; *b:* Orange, NJ; *m:* Suzanne L. Fournier; *ed:* Our Lady of Providence Seminary (BA) Philosophy 1971; Purdue Univ (MS) Educl Psych 1975; Univ of TN (PHD) Gen-Experimental Psy 1986; Multiple Personality Disorder Seminar; Advances in Behavioral Medicine & Animal Welfare Information Ctr Wkshps; *cr:* Mount St Mary Coll Ed Adj Instr 1975-78; Western CT St Univ Psych Adj Instr 1978-80; Univ of TN Psych Tchng Asst; Rivier Coll Behavioral Sci Chprsn 1986-94, Assoc Prof Psych 1994-; *ai:* NEPA & Alternatives to Dissection Table Spon; NH Coll & Univ Cncl Fac Rep; Rivier Coll Heritage Day Comm; APA 1986-; EPA 1987-; Psych for the Ethical Treatment of Animals 1994-, Bd of Dirs & Treas; R-AIDd Day 1986-; Friends of Wadleigh Memrl Lib 1986-; Annual Earthday Celebration 1990-, Coord of Coll Event; The Great Amer Meatout 1993-, Coord of Coll Event; COMPEER 1993-, Advy Bd; Essay Pub in Riviers Fac Publication Insight 1992; Papers Presented at APA 1992, NEPP 1993 & EPA 1994; Acad Investiture Address 1992; Comment Pub in Amer Psych 1996; Article Pub Soc & Animals; *office:* Rivier Coll Behavioral Sci Dept 420 Main St Nashua NH 03060

CUNNINGHAM, RICHARD, Math Teacher; *b:* Marion, IN; *ed:* East Strandsburg Univ (MS) Ed 1984; *office:* Frankford Township Schl Pines Rd Branchville NJ 07826

CUNNINGHAM, SANDRA ANN, Second Grade Teacher; *b:* Boston, MA; *ed:* MA Bay Comm Schl (AA) Lib Arts 1964; U MA (BA) Ed 1966; 36 Post Grad Hrs; *cr:* Weymouth Pub Schls Grd 2 Tchr 1966-; *ai:* NEA; Wey T Assn; MTA; Golden Apple Awd 1988-95; *home:* 67 Union St South Weymouth MA 02190*

CUNNINGHAM, SEAN THOMAS, Physical Education Teacher; *b:* Cornwall, NY; *c:* Erinn Elizabeth; *ed:* Orange Co Comm Coll (AAS) Recreation 1965; Concord Coll WV (BS) PE, Elem Ed 1968; SUNY at New Paltz (MS) Elem Ed 1973; St Marys Coll Elem Ed; NY Univ Elem Ed; *cr:* NYS Dept of Mental Hygiene Sr Recreation Therapist 1969-73; Assoc Help of Retarded Children Prgm Dir 1974-75; Minisink Vly CSD PE Tchr 1973-; *ai:* JV Soccer, Bsktbl, Modified Track Coach; AFT 1973-; AAHPER, NASO 1985-; Elks Club 1990-; Eagles Club, NISOC 1987-; FIFA 1985-, Instr; Middletown Jaycees Sportsman of Yr; Middleton Yth Soccer 15 Yr Svc Awd; Minisink Yth Soccer 15 Yr Svc Awd; *office:* Minisink Vly Cntrl Schl School St Otisville NY 10963

CUNNINGHAM, TERENCE RICHARD, Earth Science Teacher; *b:* Paterson, NJ; *m:* Maureen Brey; *c:* Kevin, Ryan; *ed:* Queens Coll (BA) Earth, Environmental Sci 1975; Univ of Northern CO (MA) Earth Sci 1976; Addl Stud in Local Hudson River Environment, Curren Educl Issues; *cr:* Wappingers Cntrl Schl Dist Sci Tchr 1976-; Dutchess Comm Coll Adj Lecturer 1980-; *ai:* Wappingers Dist Ldrshp Team; Ldrshp Team; Coaching; STANYS; Wappingers Congress of Tchrs, Pub Relations Comm; Dutchess Cty United Tchr Cncl; Rhinebeck Schl Dist Strategic Planning Team 1994-; Little League 1994-, Trustee, Coord & Coach; Catechist for Rel Instruction 1994-; Cub Scout Den Ldr; Toshiba Tech Grant; *office:* John Jay HS Rt 52 Hopewell Junction NY 12533*

CUOCO, MARION, Language Arts Teacher; *b:* Peabody, MA; *m:* Albert A.; *c:* Alicia; *ed:* Salem St Coll (BA) Eng, Ed 1985; Grad Work at Kent St Univ 1988-91; *cr:* St Charles Schl Lang Arts Tchr 1985-88; Woburn HS Lang Arts Resource Tchr 1988-89; St Monica Schl Lang Arts Tchr 1989-; *ai:* Natl Assn of Stu Act Adv; NHS Selection Comm; Kids to Kids Intnl Book Prog Spon; 8th Grd Grad Coord; Jr High Yrbk, Class Trip Adv; NCTE 1992-; Salem St Coll Alumni Assn 1985-; Wilmington Comm Schls Comm 1980-, Fac; Wilmington Gifted Prgm 1985-, Mentor; *office:* St Monica Schl 212 Lawrence St Methuen MA 01844

CUOMO, MARY ELLEN M., Learning Disabilities Teacher; *b:* Rockville Center, NY; *m:* Paul; *ed:* Boston Coll (BA) Elem, Spec Ed 1974; Hofston Univ (MA) Rdng Specialization 1982; Mc Gill Univ Rdng Cert 1977; 16 Addl Credits Admin Degree Prgm; *cr:* Montreal Cath Schl Commission Spec Ed Tchr 1974-76; Baldwin Cartier Schl Commission Spec Ed Tchr 1976-78; Glen Cove Pub Schls Kndgtn, Resource Room Tchr 1978-; *ai:* SEPTA Tchr Rep; GCTA 1978-; *office:* Glen Cove HS 150 Dosoris Ln Glen Cove NY 11542

CUPELLI, LILLIAN DESANCTIS, Child Development Teacher; *b:* New York, NY; *m:* Frank; *ed:* Queens Coll (BA) Family & Consumer Sci 1989; Adelphi Univ (MA) Hlth Stud 1993; *cr:* H Frank Carey HS Tchr 1989-92; Port Washington Schl Dist Tchr 1992-93; Elmont Meml HS Tchr 1993-; *ai:* Cheerleading & FHA Club Adv.

CUPOLO, NANCY T., Assistant Professor; *b:* Troy, NY; *m:* Frank; *c:* Lisa, Andria; *ed:* Russell Sage Coll (MS) Spec 1977; *cr:* NY St Ed Dept Ed Asst 1978-80; Flower Hill Nursery Dir 1980-91; Russell Sage Coll Instr 1977-90; Hudson Valley Comm Coll Asst Prof 1989-; *ai:* Early Chldhd Club Adv; Muscular Dystrophy Assn Spon, Fund Raiser; Woman & Minority Issues, Mid Sts Accreditation Comms; Assn Retarded Citizens, VP 1971-; Assn Ed Young Children 1980-; CEC 1975-; Spec Ed Comm 1985-, Surrogate Parent; Brittonkill Schl Dist 1991-, Strategic Planning Comm; Cath Schls Acad Comm 1992-; Hudson Valley Girl Scout Cncl, Ldr 1991-; Arts in Spec Ed Video Production 1993; Exc in Tchng Pres Awd 1994; Elizabeth Ann Seton Awd 1995; *office:* Hudson Valley Comm Coll 80 Vandenburgh Ave Troy NY 12180

CUPPETT, JEANNE J., Asst Prof of Nursing; *b:* Johnstown, PA; *m:* Cary J.; *c:* Randi, Chris; *ed:* Univ of Pittsburgh (BSN) Nrsng 1972; Indiana Univ of PA (MSN) Nrsng 1985; St Cert Emergency Med Technician; Continuing Ed Prgms; *cr:* Greater Johnstown Area Vo-Tech Schl Nrsng Instr 1972-76; Mount Aloysuis Coll Nrsng Instr 1976-79; Conemaugh Vly Meml Hosp Schl of Nrsng Term Coord 1979-90; Saint Francis Coll Asst Prof Nrsng 1990-; *ai:* Stu Nurse Org Adv; Curr, Fac Org, Fac Dev Comms; Sigma Theta Tau 1985-; NAACOG 1972-; Investigational Review Bd 1989-; East Hills Emergency Med Svcs 1986-; Reviewer for W. B. Saunders, Addison-Wesley, Elsiever Sci Publishing Cos; Who's Who Among Human Svc Profs 1988; *office:* Saint Francis Coll Don Schwab 107 Loretto PA 15940*

CUPPETT, PATRICIA OLDLAND, 3rd Grade Teacher; *b:* Uniontown, PA; *m:* Donald V.; *c:* Courtney, Carrie Lee, Christina; *ed:* CA Univ (BA) Elem Ed 1971, (MS) Elem Ed 1974; *cr:* R. W. Clark Schl Music, Art Tchr 1971-74, Rdng Tchr 1974-76, 3rd Grd Tchr 1976-; *ai:* Girls Bsktbl JV Coach 1976-78; JR HS Track Coach 1994-; NEA, LHEA 1971-; *office:* R W Clark Elem Schl 200 Water St Uniontown PA 15401

CURIEL, JUDITH, Spanish Teacher; *b:* West Chester, PA; *m:* Harvey Harr; *ed:* West Chester Univ (BS) Span, Elem Ed 1977; Immaculata Coll (MA) biling Ed 1981; 1 Semester Univ of the Andes at Bogota; *cr:* Colegio Bolivar Schl 2nd Grd Tchr 1978-79; West Chester Schl 1st Grd Tchr 1979-80; Norristown Schl ESL Tchr 1980-81; Chester Co IU Migrant Ed Tchr 1981-82; Downingtown Schl Span Tchr 1984-85; Coatesville Schl Dist Span Tchr 1984-86; Octorara HS Span Tchr 1986-; *ai:* Span Club, Stdnts with Drug & Alcohol Problems Tchr Adv; AATSP 1989-; *office:* Octorara HS Rt 41 & Highland Rd Box 501 Atglen PA 19310*

CURL, KATHRYN CHATHAM, English Teacher; *b:* Greenville, SC; *m:* James; *c:* Jason, David; *ed:* Queens Coll (BA) Eng 1966; UNC-CH (MAT) Eng 1969; Univ of Pittsburgh (SPD) Curr & Supervision 1976; *cr:* Bethel Park HS Eng Tchr 1968-71; Wade Hampton HS Eng Tchr 1974-75; Greenwood HS Eng Tchr 1976-80; Alfred-Almond HS Eng Tchr 1980-; *ai:* Yrbk Adv 1968-94; NCTE 1980-, Presenter Fall Conf 1995; Wellsville Town Planning Bd 1989-, Bd Mem; St Johns Episcopal Church 1994-, Warden; Southern Tier Traveling Tchr Bd 1995-, Bd Mem; *office:* Alfred Almond Schl Rt 21 Almond NY 14804

CURLEY, ANN CREHAN, Third Grade Teacher; *b:* Boston, MA; *c:* Susan Curley Clancy, Ellen L.; *ed:* Bridgewater St Coll (BS) Elem 1968; *cr:* A. T. Morrison Schl Second Grd Tchr 1968-74, Third Grd Tchr 1974-; *ai:* BEA, MTA, NEA 1968-; Golden Apple Awd from Previous Stdnts 1990-93.

CURLEY, MARY DWYER, 8th Grade Science Teacher; *b:* Kingston, PA; *m:* Joseph M.; *c:* Neil, Colleen, Joseph, Kevin (dec), Kathleen; *ed:* Masters Equivalency + 18 Credit Hrs; *cr:* Wilkes Barre Area 9th Grd Sci Tchr 1963-66; Bishop O'Reilly HS Bio Tchr 1969; Our Lady of Peace 7th & 8th Grd Sci Tchr 1984-91; Wyoming Area Scndry Ctr 8th Grd Sci, Earth & Phys Sci Tchr 1991-; *ai:* 7th-9th Grd Sci Olympiad Coach; NEA 1991-; WAEA 1991-; *office:* Wyoming Area Scndry Ctr Memorial Ave Exeter PA 18643*

CURLIS, DEBORAH JEAN, Medical Careers Instructor; *b:* Tiffin, OH; *m:* David Lee; *c:* Bryan, Amy Curlis Kozel; *ed:* Marion Tech Coll (RN) Nrsng 1981; Univ of Toledo (BA) Soc Sci 1996; *ai:* Voc Industrial Clubs of Amer Adv; VICA Opening & Closing Team Coach; Amer Voc Assn 1982-; OH Voc Assn 1982-; Golden Key Natl Hnr Soc 1993-; United Church of Christ 1974-, Edctr; Order of Eastern Stars 1970-, Star Point; *office:* Sentinel Vocational Schl 793 E Township Road 201 Tiffin OH 44883

CURNOW, GARY W., Teacher of Gifted & Talented; *b:* Dover, NJ; *m:* Barbara Shubert; *ed:* East Stroudsburg Univ (BS) Hlth & PE 1966; Montclair St (MA) Environmental Mgmt 1984; 30 Grad Credits Elem Ed; *cr:* Parsippany Elem Schls PE Tchr 1966-70; Northvail Schl 5th Grd Tchr 1970-95; Knollwood & Intervale Schls Tchr of Gifted & Talented 1995-; *ai:* Morris Area Sci Alliance Steering Comm; PTHEA 1966-; MCCEA 1966-; NJEA 1966-; NEA 1966-; Rotary Club Comm Schl Man of Yr 1986; NJ Governors Recognition Awd 1987; *office:* Knollwood Schl Knoll Rd Parsippany NJ 07054

CURRAH, JOEY A., Business Teacher; *b:* Lackawana, NY; *m:* Jeffrey Scott; *ed:* St Bonaventure Univ (BBA) Mngmt 1991; Working Toward Masters Bus, Ed 6 Credits; *cr:* Frewsburg Cntrl Schl Bus Tchr 1993; Private Industry Cncl Schl-To-Work Instr 1993; Cassadaga Vly Cntrl Schl Bus Tchr 1994-; *ai:* Var Chrldng Coach 1992-; Tech Comm 1995-; Chaut Co Bus Tchrs Assn 1994-, Treas; Chaut Co Chrldng Coaches Assn 1992-; Fac Assn, NYSUT 1994-; *office:* Cassadaga Valley Cntrl Schl PO Box 540 Sinclairville NY 14782

CURRAN, AUDREY HARWELL, Assoc Professor of Psychology; *b:* Cleveland, OH; *m:* Robert C.; *c:* Robert C., Michaelann, Aline, Audrey B.; *ed:* Seaton Hill Coll (BA) Lit 1965; Fielding Inst (MA) Psych 1983, (PHD) Clinical Psych 1986; Three Yr Post Doctoral Stud Gestalt Inst of Santa Barbara; *cr:* Notre Dame Coll Prof of Psych 1989-; John Carroll Univ Adj Prof of Psych 1991-94, Grad Schl Adj Prof Psych 1995-; *ai:* Psych Club Adv; Acad Cncl; Lib Comm Dir; Psych Stu Practicum Chair; Acad Cncl Comm Fac Promotions; APA 1991-; OPA 1992-; Natl Fed of Blind, Amer Cncl for Blind Grants; *home:* 27020 Cedar Rd Ph 6-1 Beachwood OH 44122

CURRAN, BARBARA A., 8th Grade Language Arts Tchr; *b:* West Point, NY; *m:* Frank E.; *c:* Teresa Colon, Joanne Horsfall, Geraldyne Colon, Troy Milne; *ed:* Univ of Lowell (BSEE) Elem Ed 1964; *cr:* Sacred Heart Schl 8th Grd, 6-8 Grds Lang Arts Tchr 5 Yrs; St Patrick's Schl 5-8 Grds Lang Arts Tchr 7 Yrs; Bartlett Schl 6th Grd Lang Arts Tchr 5 Yrs; Arts Magnet Schl Jr High Lang Arts Tchr 1 Yr; *ai:* Yrbk Adv; Class Trip Organizer; Fund-raiser Coord; Rainbows for All God's Children Facilitator; NCEA 1979-; Neighborhood Crime Watch 1992-; Parish Org, Home Schl, Choir, Etc; *office:* Sacred Heart Schl 122 Andrews St Lowell MA 01852

CURRAN, BERNADETTE FOLEY, Journalism Teacher; *b:* Troy, NY; *m:* Stephen M.; *c:* Christoper Fumarola, Jeffrey Fumarola, Susan Kelts, Daniel Fumarola, David Fumarola, Michael Fumarola, Erin Fumarola, Kelly; *ed:* SUNY at Albany (AS) Jrlsm 1975; Attnd Hudson Valley Comm Coll; Jrnlsm; Anatomy; Physiology; *cr:* Folsom Telegraph Reporter 1968-70; Albany Diocese Theology Tchr 1971-93; Free-Lance Writer 1970-86; Troy Record Correspondent 1986-94; Catholice Cntrl HS Tchr 1994-; *ai:* Class, Club Moderator; Newspaper Adv; Jrnlsm Club; NCEA, Prof Women's Org 1994-; Ancient Order of Hibernians 1960-89, Sec; Outstdng Svc Scouting Awd; NY St Writing First Pl; Second Pl Nation Writing Irish in Amer; Articles Pub Various Newspapers, Magazines; *office:* Catholic Central HS 625 7th Ave Troy NY 12182

CURRAN, KATHLEEN ROSETTI, Prof of Human Services; *b:* Milford, MA; *m:* Daniel J.; *c:* Kaitlyn, Kolby, Kallen; *ed:* Univ of Bridgeport (BS) Dental Hygiene 1979; Notre Dame Coll (MED) Cnslng & Comm Agency Cnslng 1986; Post Grad Stud & Clinical Supervision; Family Systems Therapy; Continuing Ed Credit in Cnslng, Therapy & Family Work; *cr:* Univ of Bridgeport Instr 1979-80; Quinsigamond Comm Coll Instr 1980-81; NH Tech Inst Asst Prof 1981-, Dept Head 1996; *ai:* Human Svcs Stu Org Adv; Stdnts Information Wkshps; Numerous Comms; Natl Acad of CCMHC 1991-; NCC 1993-; NHCMHC 1995-; Sanbornton Pub Lib Vol, Storytime Coord; Sanbornton Cntrl Elem Schl Vol; Article Pub; *office:* NH Tech Inst 11 Institute Dr Concord NH 03301*

CURRAN, LAWRENCE WILLIAM, Eng Tchr & Asst Advancmnt Dir; *b:* Bronx, NY; *m:* Linda Sadlo; *ed:* Fordham Univ (BA) Commnctns 1981, (MA) Commnctns 1992; *cr:* Tiffany & Co Receiving Supvr 1978-86; KH Macy Receiving Supvr 1986-88; Fordham Prep Schl Dir of Alumni & Pub Relations & Tchr 1988-; *ai:* Alumni Magazine Ed; *office:* Fordham Prep Schl E Fordham Rd Bronx NY 10458

CURRAN, MARY DENISE D., Mathematics Teacher; *b:* Philadelphia, PA; *m:* Vincent; *c:* Vincent, Denis; *ed:* Rosemount Coll (BA) Math 1969; Villanova Univ (MA) Ed 1987; *cr:* Schl of the Holy Child Tchr 1969-70; Archbishop Carroll Tchr 1972-74, Tchr & Math Chprsn 1980-95; Archbishop Ryan Tchr 1974-80; Archbishop Prendergast Tchr 1995-; *ai:* Math Curr Comm; NCTM 1989-; NCSM 1990-; Tandy of Tech Scholar Honorable Mention 1995-; NSF Grants to Smith Coll & Swarthmore Coll; *office:* Archbishop Prendergast HS 401 N Lansdowne Ave Drexel Hill PA 19026*

CURRAN, MELODIE WHITLING, Math Teacher; *b:* Oil Ci Ryan; *ed:* Clarion St Coll (BS) Math & Physics & General S Clarion Univ (MS) Sci Ed 1985; 22 Credit Hrs for Clarion Univ AL, & Boston Univ; *cr:* Redbank Valley Scl Dist Physics & M 1981-82; Oil City Area Schl Dist Math Tchr 1982-; *ai:* Young Club Adv; Yrbk Adv; PSTA 1982-; MCWP 1982-; *office:* Oil Ci Spring St Oil City PA 16301

CURRENS, LANCE WILLIAM, Health & PE Instructor; *b:* Me *m:* Lisa Barieter; *c:* Ashley, Brett, Luke; *ed:* Baldwin-Wallace C Hlth, PE 1984; OH St Univ (MA) Ath Admin 1987; Post C Cleveland St Univ Admin Cert; *cr:* North Olmsted City Schls K-10th Grd Tchr 1984-86, 1988-; *ai:* FCA Adv; Ftbl, Track Co Chm Hlth, PE; OEA, NEA 1988-; *office:* North Olmsted HS 57 Rd North Olmsted OH 44070*

CURRIE, OLIVE, English Teacher; *b:* Passair, NJ; *m:* Ronald; *c:* Megan; *ed:* Seton Hall Univ (BS) Eng, Scndry Ed 1962; Kean C Chldhd Cert; *cr:* Woodrow Wilson Schl Eng Tchr 1962-69; Child Group Tchr 1980-84; Our Lady of Blessed Sacrament Eng Tchr Clifton HS Eng Tchr 1988-; *ai:* Alternative Ed Eng Tchr; Peer Adv; NEA, NJEA 1962-; NJ Alt Ed Tchrs 1989-; Brownie Ldr CCD Tchr 1980-83; *home:* 8 Vale Dr Mountain Lakes NJ 07046

CURRIE, WALTER ERICH, Math Teacher; *b:* Point Pleasant Richard Stockton Coll (BS) Math 1994; *cr:* Pt Boro HS Math T Toms River HS South Math Tchr 1994-; *ai:* Peer Ldrshp; Conflic Co-Adv; Asst Ftbl, Bsbl Coach; NEA, TREA, NCTM 1994-; *offi* River HS South Hyers St Toms River NJ 08753

CURRIER, JILL ANNE, English Teacher; *b:* Albany, NY; Pfaffenbach; *ed:* SUNY at Albany (BA) Eng 1992, (MA) Ed South Colonie HS Eng Tchr 1992-; *ai:* Class Adv; Mediator; Var Chrldng Coach; NYSUT 1992-.

CURRIER, KATHERINE A., Prof & Dept Chair of Paralegal; *b:* MI; *m:* Gary K. Booth; *c:* Eric Booth, Kristin Booth; *ed:* Carlton Pol Sci 1971; Univ of CA at Berkeley (MA) Pol Philosop Northeastern Univ Law Schl (JD) Law 1979; *cr:* Suffolk Law S 1979-81; Western New England Coll of Law Asst Prof 1981-84; Prof 1985-; *ai:* Pre-Law Adv; Fac Parliamentarian; AAFPE 198 Dirs, Publications Chair; Articles Pub; *office:* Elms Coll 291 Sp St Chicopee MA 01013

CURRY, BRUCE OXLEY, Aerospace Science Instructor; *b:* G NY; *m:* Marian Grabski; *c:* Alison, Andrea Curry Posey, Am Rutgers Univ (BA) Pre-Law 1970; Embry-Riddle Univ (MAM) Mngmt 1979; USAF Air War Coll, Air Command & Staff Coll, Ofcr Schl, Inspector Schl, Undergrad Pilot Trng; Instr Schls, Schls; *cr:* USAF Assignments 1970-82; Clarkson Univ Prof of A Stud 1982-85; Pope AFB Asst Operations Ofcr, C-130 Pilot 1985 Mildenhall Dir of Operations 1988-92; Maxwell AFB Deputy Gen 1992-93; Polytech HS Aerospace Sci Instr, Head of AFJRO 1993-; *ai:* Jr ROTC Related, Charity Act; Float Construction Chp Team, Yth Bsktbl Coach; Cath Yth Org 1993-; Air Force Assn 198 of Medalians 1980-; Variety of Air Force Awds, Accomplishmen Polytech HS PO Box 97 Woodside DE 19980

CURRY, CLARE ANITA, 8th Grade Math & Religion Philadelphia, PA; *ed:* Chestnut Hill Coll at Philadelphia (BS) 1970; 10 Credits Theology from LaSalle Univ; *cr:* St Gabriels 5t Tchr 1966-68; Holy Angels 7th-8th Grd Tchr 1968-72; Blessed S 8th Grd Tchr 1972-76; St Luke Prin 1976-82; St Mary of the La 8th Grd Math & Religion Tchr 1982-; *ai:* Math Chprsn; Yrbk; S Adv; Natl Cncl of Math 1991-; Natl Cath Ed Assn 1970-; Mid S Chprsn; *office:* St Mary Of The Lakes Schl R R 70 Medford NJ (

CURRY, ELLEN ANNE MARIE, English & Writing Specialis Mountain Lake, NY; *ed:* Saint Bonaventure Univ (BA) Mass Cor SUC at Potsdam (MA) Eng Lit 1989; 19 Addl Hrs Scndry En Hamilton Cty News Contributing Reporter 1982-89; Torrington Date TV Listing Ed 1983-84; Glens Falls Post-Star Stringer Herkimer Cty Comm Coll Learning Ctr Specialist 1989-; Disability Awareness Comms; ARCT Task Force Intervention Mc Comm; Art-Lit Magazine Adv; Dev Eng Position Selection NYSUT 1989-; NYCLSA 1991-; Natl Tutoring Assn Newslette Church Choir 1974-; Altar, Rosary Soc 1989-; 4-H 1971-, A Animal Husbandry; College Newspaper 1980-, Copy Ed; NYCL 1991, 1992, 1995; Natl Tutoring Assn Symposium 1993; St Bo Univ Schlrsp 1980; Cntrl NY Writing Skills Conf 1989; Croati Clothing Drive Co-Chair 1993; *office:* Herkimer County Comm Reservoir rd Herkimer NY 13350*

CURRY, JANE ELISE, Fourth Grade Teacher; *b:* New Bruns *ed:* Bennett Coll (BA) Elem Ed 1972; William Paterson Coll (M Ed 1981; Kean Coll 6 Credit Hrs; *cr:* Bayard Schl 3rd Grd Tchr Roosevelt Schl 4th Grd Tchr 1973-; *ai:* African-Amer Culture Cl 1972-; NJEA 1972-; NBEA 1972-; *home:* 201 Fulton St New B NJ 08901

CURRY, JANICE SCHIAVI, English Teacher; *b:* Queens, NY; J.; *c:* Julia; *ed:* Hunter Coll (BA) Eng 1970; Richmond Coll (1974; *cr:* Manhattanville JHS Eng Tchr 1970-71; Mc Kee Voc & Eng Tchr 1971-88; Staten Is Tech HS Eng Tchr 1988-; *ai:* Lit M Amnesty Intnl Moderator; United Fed of Tchrs 1970-; Meals or 1986-; Contributor Armchair Companion Agatha Christie; *offic* Island Technical HS 485 Clawson St Staten Island NY 10306

CURRY, JEAN ANN, Guidance Counselor & Art Tchr; *b:* New Y *ed:* Fordham Univ (BS) Ed 1957; St John's Univ (MS) Cnslr Ed 19 Ed Prgm 60 Hrs; Theology Course 30 Hrs; Group Dynamics 30 Cardinal Mc Closkey Home House Mother, Tchr 1946-52; St C Schl Tchr 1952-67; St Martin's Schl Tchr 1952-67; Our Lady of Help Tchr 1967-70; St Helena Schl Guid Cnslr 1970-90; St Bren Guid Cnslr 1970-90; Annunciation Schl Guid Cnslr, Art Tchr 1 After Schl Prgm; Caligraphy; Art Projects; Prsnl & Guid Ass 1970-; Amer Red Cross Poster Contests, Natl Schl Traffic Safe Prmg Outstdng Entries Recognition Certs; *office:* Ann School-Crestwood 465 Westchester Ave Yonkers NY 10707

CURRY, JOSEPH L., English & Journalism Teacher; *b:* Pittsto Rosemary Revak; *c:* Sean, Brian, Kathryn; *ed:* Univ of Scranton 1966; Attnd Marywood Coll; *cr:* Oxford Acad Tchr 1966-67; La Jr Coll Instr 1975-81; Pittston Area Sr HS Tchr 1967-; *ai:* Jrn Moderator; AFT 1968-; Lacka Co Swim Ofcls 1970-, VP, Exe Vanner Awd; WY Vly Track Ofcls 1970-, Pres, VP, Sec, Ex Comm Twp Zoning Ofr; Ancient Order of Hibernians 1992-, Sec; Tc *office:* Pittston Area Sr HS 5 Stout St Pittston PA 18640

CURRY, LEE MARTIN, Outdoor Education Director; *b:* Morrist *m:* Sandra Sehbaugh; *c:* Valeri Asbury, Charissa Asbury, Micha Asbury, Bruce; *ed:* Washington Coll (BA) Ec 1961; Loyola C Pastoral Cnslng 1986; *cr:* Soc Security Admin Claims Adj 1961-63; Severn Schl Eng Tchr, Coach & Ath Dir 1964-70; The Eng Tchr, Coach, Cnslr, Dean of Stdnts, Dir of Outdoor Ed 19 Woods Memrl Presbyn Church 1950-, Elder; Severn Schl Ath Hall Washington Coll Ath Hall of Fame; *office:* The Key Schl 534 Hill Annapolis MD 21403

MAUREEN C., Math & Computer Science Tchr; *b:* Meriden, niv of Miami (BS) Systems Analysis 1987; Southern CT Univ Ed 1991, 39 Credits Towards MS Math Ed; *cr:* OH Platt HS omp Sci Tchr 1991-; *ai:* Chief Spon Class of 1998; Var Girls ach; Stu Asst Team; AFT; NCTM; *office:* Platt HS 220 Coe Ave 'T 06451

ROBERT A., English Teacher; *b:* Pittsburgh, PA; *m:* Marcia; *c:* r, Susan; *ed:* Westminster Coll (BA) Speech, Eng 1967; Slippery D) Eng 1991; Univ of Pittsburgh 12 Credit Hrs 1967; *cr:* Union peech, Eng Tchr 29 Yrs; *ai:* Past Head Ftbl Coach; NEA, PSEA, a Ed Assn 1967-; *office:* Union Area HS 2106 Camden Ave New 16101

SANDRA LAMBERT, 6th Grade Teacher; *b:* Ferrellsburg, WV; s; *c:* Melissa, Melinda; *ed:* Marshall Univ (BA) Voc Home Ec) Elem Ed 1983; Attnd OH Univ; *cr:* Wayne Elem 5th Grd Tchr /inson HS Home Ec Tchr 1970-71; Symmes Vly Elem 5th & 6th 984-93; Symmes Vly Multi Level 6th Grd Tchr 1993-; *ai:* OEA A 1984-; SVEA 1984-, Schl Rep for Fac Cncl 6 Yrs; Chesapeake 1992-, Vol; Nom for Ashland Oil Tchr Awd.

DIANE M., Fourth Grade Teacher; *b:* Northampton, MA; *ed:* St Coll (BA) Elem Ed 1978, (MS) Elem Ed 1993; Great Books racy Network; *cr:* Easthampton Pub Schls Sub Tchr 1978-80, Tchr 1980-81, Fourth Grd Tchr 1985-; *ai:* Curr, Staff Dev chl Improvement Cncl; MTA, NEA 1985-; *home:* 10 Spring St on MA 01027

MICHELLE BLAHUT, High School Biology Teacher; *b:* , NY; *m:* Daniel J.; *ed:* LeMoyne Coll (BS) Bio 1994; 9 Credit d Masters; *cr:* Cntrl HS Bio Tchr 1994-; *ai:* Sci Club; Sci Fair sn of Women in Sci 1993-; MD St Assn Bio Tchrs 1995-; NABT nt Physiology Lab Book; *office:* Central HS 200 Cabin Branch Heights MD 20743*

TERESA MARY, Social Studies Teacher; *b:* Jamaica, NY; *ed:* Jniv (BA) His 1953; Hunter Coll (MA) His 1970; Attnd Cath ner, China Inst in Amer, South Africa at United Nations Wkshp, r Wkshp at Manhattan Coll; *cr:* St Mary's Acad 7th-8th Grd Tchr it mary Gate of Heaven Schl 7th-8th Grd Tchr 1964-74; Christ HS 9th-10th Grd Soc Stud Tchr 1974-79; Bishop Ford HS rd Soc Stud Tchr 1979-; *ai:* Liturgy, Honor Stdnts Field Trip CEA 1974-; Mid Sts Cncl for Soc Stud, Cncl of Long Island Soc s 1990-; 3rd Place Amer Express Geography Competition ng Achvmt Supporting Stu Initiative in Geography; Travel *me:* 7101 Colonial Rd Brooklyn NY 11209

CAROLE CUTLIFFE, Music Teacher; *b:* Bangor, ME; *m:* latthew Gilley, Brandon Gilley; *ed:* Univ of ME at Orono (BA) 1982, (MS) Ed Admin 1996; Eastern ME Voc Tech Inst Med Tech 1985; *cr:* Tremont Elem Schl Music Tchr 1983-85; Ausic Tchr 1988-90; Waterville Pub Schls Music Tchr 1990-; *ai:* Adelines; NEA, ME Music Edctrs Assn 1988-; Waterville Tchrs -; ACDA 1994-; Dir Kennebec Vly Jr Hnrs Chorus 1994, Dist IV norus 1995; *office:* Waterville Sr HS 1 Brooklyn Ave Waterville *

JANE ANN (KANE), Tchr of Deaf & Hard of Hearing; *b:* PA; *m:* Stephen Albert; *c:* Greg; *ed:* (MA) Masters Equiv 1992; redits Cmptrs, Writing; *cr:* Bucks Cty IV #22 Itinerant Hearing 1985-90; Cntrl Bucks Schl Dist Tchr of Deaf, Hard of Hearing Organize Soc Events Deaf, Hard of Hearing Stdnts; Sign Lang NEA; *office:* Central Bucks-East HS Holicong Rd Buckingham

JOHN LOUVILLE,JR., Sixth Grd Language Arts Tchr; *b:* ME; *m:* Elizabeth; *ed:* Univ of ME (BS) Elem Ed 1988; *cr:* Camp or Boys Owner & Dir 1988-; Hudson Meml Schl Lang Arts Tchr Boys Soccer Team Head Coach; Ski Club Coord; Discipline & Comms; AFT, ME Youth Camp Dirs 1988-; *office:* Hudson M S 1 Memorial Dr Hudson NH 03051

MARTHA LOUISE, Sci, Rel Tchr & Librarian; *b:* Selma, NC; T St Univ (BS) His 1966; Univ of DC (MA) Admin, Supervision vard Univ 30 Hrs Towards MA Modern European His; *cr:* Harrison Schl Tchr 1966-69; Howard Univ Grad Cnslr 1969-70; Schl Tchr 1971-72; Brook-Wein Bus Inst Ltd Tchr 1974-75; DC Sub Tchr 1975-79; Taft Jr HS Tchr 1979-80; Sacred Heart Schl 1982-; *ai:* Schl Patrol Adv; NCEA 1982-; ASCD 1994-; Cath 995-; Eastern Stars 1982-; UDC Alumni Assn 1993-; Howard Flwshp; Who's Who Among Stdnts in Amer Univs & Colls Vho's Who in Amer Ed 1994-96; Grad Cncl Cert of Appreciation

PATRICIA TREVELISE, Mathematics Supervisor; *b:* Jersey : William; *c:* Christie; *ed:* Jersey City St Coll (BA) Math 1970; s Coll (MA) cmptrs, Supervision, Admin 1987; *cr:* Ridgefield ath Tchr 1970-88; Ridgefield Park Jr-Sr HS Math Supvr 1988-; ev Ldr; St Project Facilitator in Math Ed; Grant Reader for St ; Tech Comm Chprsn; Math Consortium Coord; Sunshine Comm CTM, AMTNJ 1970-; PSA 1988-; ASCD 1994-; Parent 1993-, VP; Eastern Star 1978-; Presented Wkshps on Math ves & Learning Styles; *office:* Ridgefield Park Jr-Sr HS 1 Ozzie Ridgefield Park NJ 07660

RHONDA LEE, 7th-8th Grade Math Teacher; *b:* Oswego, NY; Floyd; *ed:* SUNY at Plattsburgh (BS) Scndry Math Ed 1983; Oswego (MS) Secd Curr, Inst 1990; *cr:* Bound Brook HS 9-12 Tchr 1983-85; Fulton Jr HS 7-8 Grd Math Tchr, Remedial Math 5-; *ai:* Soccer, Sftbl, Vlybl Coach; Stu Cncl, Yrbk Adv; Tech Dir Club; Mathcounts, Jr Class Adv; Challenger Flwshp.*

ROBERT KERN, Physics Teacher; *b:* New York, NY; *m:* Meadows; *c:* Phyllis; *ed:* Fordham Univ (AB) Physics 1964; Coll (PHL) Philosophy 1965; Fordham Univ (MSEd) Physics, ach 1970; Seton Hall Univ (JD) Jurisprudence 1985; NSF Inst ysics at RPI 1975, Physics & Microcomputers at Seton Hall Brooklyn Prepatory Schl Geometry & Phys Sci Tchr 1965-67; & Mission Bureau Dir 1967; Xavier HS Geometry & Phys Sci -69; Hackensack HS Physics Tchr 1969-; *ai:* Philosophy, Ham hess Clubs; NHS Chapter; Tchr-Admin Liason Comm; k Ed Assn 1969-, Pres 1979-80; Amer Phys Soc 1975-; AAPT mstead Schl 1986-, Bd Mem; Physcis Articles Pub The Physics *e:* Hackensack HS First & Beech Sts Hackensack NJ 07601

ROBERT L., 6th Grd Rdng & World His Tchr; *b:* Wilmington, oseanna Wills; *c:* Megan Kylene, Brian Nicholas; *ed:* Wright St Ed 1975; Attnd Miami Univ, Mt St Joseph; *cr:* Martinsville 4th-6th Grd Tchr 10 Yrs; East End Schl Rdng, Math, Soc Stud ; Wilmington MS Rdng, World His Tchr 3 Yrs; *ai:* Enrichment minology Tchr 1995-; Sponsorship Awd to Purchase Text Books; -, Bldg Rep; Career Ed, 1986-87, Bldg Rep;Tchrs Advy Comm 88-; Sftbl Coach 1993-95; Vol in Ed 1994; *office:* Wilmington norne Ave Wilmington OH 45177

ROSEMARY PALMUCCI, Lang Arts & Soc Stud Tchr; *b:* J; *m:* Richard P.; *c:* Suzanne Frisch, Renee Ann Frisch Phillips, Frisch; *ed:* Farleigh Dickinson Univ (BS) Ed 1957; 28 Grad Credits in Lit, Testing Assessments, Discipline, Sci Notre Dame Coll; *cr:* Branford CT Pub Schls Tchr 1957-59; Mont Vernon Village Schl Tchr 1969-; *ai:* Intergrated Lang Arts Comm; MVEA 1990-, VP; NEA, NHEA 1990-; NH Cncl for the Soc Stud 1995-; *office:* Mont Vernon Village School Harwood Rd PO Box 98 Mont Vernon NH 03057

CURTIS, RUSSELL GLENN,JR., Social Studies Teacher; *b:* Maysville, KY; *ed:* OH univ (BGS) Justice, Gen Stud 1985; Morehead St Univ (BA) His, Govt 1990; Currently Enrolled in Master of Soc Sci Prgm OH Univ; Natl Geographic Soc Summer Geog Inst 1995; *cr:* Mason Cty Schls Sub Tchr 1990-91; Ripley-Union-Lewis-Huntington HS Soc Stud Tchr 1991-; *ai:* HS Acad Team Coach, Spon; HS Mock Trial Spon, Tchr Adv; NCA Steering, Soc Stud Curr Comms; NCSS 1994-; OH Cncl for Soc Stud 1992-; Amer Psych Assn 1995-; OH Geographic Alliance 1993-; Brown Cty Historical Soc, Natl Geographic Soc 1995-; Univ of Cincinnati Ctr for Ec Ed 1995-, Assoc; Ashland Oil Tchr Achvmt Awd Nom 1993-; Golden Apple Tchr Achvmt Awd 1994-; Taft Fellow 1994; *office:* Ripley-Union-Lewis-Hntngtn HS 1317 S 2nd St Ripley OH 45167*

CURTIS, SHIRLEY HAUBNER, Fourth Grade Teacher; *b:* Hamilton, OH; *m:* Steven D.; *c:* Shannon E., Sarah E.; *ed:* Miami Univ (BS) Elem Ed 1987; Xavier Univ (MED) Schl Counseling 1992; Attnd Univ of Cincinnati Doctoral Prgm; *cr:* Sacred Heart Schl Jr HS Math Tchr, 4th Grd Tchr 1988-93; Freedom Elem 4th Grd Tchr 1993-; *ai:* NEA 1993-; NCTM 1992-; OCTM 1993-; OH Certified Schl Cnslr 1992; UC Univ Grad Schlsp 1991-95; Olive Flower Schlsp 1987; James P. Ryan Schlsp 1987; *home:* 125 Meadowview Ct Fairfield OH 45014*

CURTIS, TIMOTHY J., Physics & Chemistry Teacher; *b:* Chillicothe, OH; *m:* Jan Elise Shanks; *c:* Kerri, Denise Curtis-Smith; *ed:* OH Univ (BSEd) Bio Scis 1980; Miami Univ 21 Hrs; *cr:* Sheffield-Sheffield Lake Schls Physics, Chem, Gen Sci Tchr 1980-81; Union-Scioto Local Schl Dist Jr High Sci, TAG, Chem, Gen sci 1981-86; Huntington Local Schl Dist Physics, Chem, Gen Sci 1986-; Ohio Math, Sci Project Discovery; OH EPA Southern OH Lakes Water Quality Project Co-Coord; *ai:* Co-Coord Jr & Sr HS Sci Day; NASA Project Inspire Adv; Voc Home Ec Adv Comm; NEA, OEA, HLEA 1982-, Pres 2 Yrs, Schlsp Chprsn 2 Yrs; NSTA 1989-; Sci Ed Cncl of OH 1991-, Bd Mem & Dir Dist Ten; AAPT 1989-; Amer Chem Soc 1989-96; NSTA; AAPT 1989-; Governors Awd Excl in Youth Sci Opportunities 1985, 1991; Unioto HS Educator of Yr 1986; Huntington HS Educator of Yr 1988; Chillicothe-Ross Cty Chamber of Commerce 1991 Charley Awd; Dept of Energy, Shawnee St Univ, Recognition as Instr Math Sci Acad 1991; Outstanding Support of Schls; Nominee for Pres Awd Excl in Sci Tchng-92; Chillicothe-Ross Cty Chmbr of Comm 1992 Charley Awd; WBNS 10 TV Cntrl Ohio Tchrs Assoc Tchr of Week 1993; *office:* Huntington Local Schl Dist 188 Huntsman Rd Chillicothe OH 45601

CURTOLO, ROBERT LEONARD, Mathematics Teacher; *b:* Easton, PA; *m:* Lorna V. Sabatine; *c:* Philip, Matthew; *ed:* East Stroudsburg St Coll (BS) Scndry Ed, Math 1974; 27 Post Grad Credits; *cr:* United Engrs & Constructors Inc Field Inspector 1974-75; Bangor Area Schl Dist Math Tchr 1976-; *ai:* MS Curr Comm; MATHCOUNTS Coach 1993-95; Mental Gymnastics Club Adv; NEA, PSEA 1978-; NCTM; Roseto Borough Park Bd 1988-, Pres 1992-; *office:* Bangor Area Jr HS Rd 2 Box 2071 Bangor PA 18013

CURTS, GARY R., Physical Science Teacher; *b:* Fort Gorden, GA; *m:* Holly Irvin; *c:* Clayton; *ed:* Otterbein Coll (BA) Geology, Bio 1974; OH St Univ (MS) Sci Ed 1993; Attnd Akron Univ, OH St Univ; *cr:* Oleutangy HS Sci Tchr 1977-88; Dublin Coffman HS Sci Tchr 1988-; *ai:* Strength Trng Coach; NEA 1977-; Sci Ed Cncl of OH 1987-, Bd of Dirs; Natl Advy Bd Eisenhower Sci, Math Clearinghouse 1993-; Hall of Fame 1993; Tchr of Yr 1992; *office:* Dublin Coffman HS 6780 Coffman Rd Dublin OH 43017*

CUSATIS, LORRAINE A., Family & Consumer Sci Educator; *b:* Hazleton, PA; *m:* Anthony; *ed:* Coll Miserlcordia (BS) Home Ec 1969; Penn St Univ (MED) Home Ec 1972; 67 Addl Credits; 75 PDU Credits Every 2 Yrs to Maintain Cert; *cr:* D. A. Harman Jr HS Home Ec Tchr 1969-92; Hazleton Area HS Family, Consumer Sci Tchr 1969-92; West Hazleton Jr HS Family, Consumer Sci Tchr 1995-; *ai:* Cert Family, Consumer Sci Assoc 1989-; AHEA, PHEA, NEA, PSEA 1969-; Eckley Miners Vlg Assoc 1995-, Sec; Outstdng Edctr of Yr Phila Coll Textiles, Sci 1995; *home:* RR 3 Box 620 Drums PA 18222

CUSATO, DAREN, Biology Teacher; *b:* Ellwood City, PA; *ed:* Geneva Coll (BS) Bio 1992; *ai:* Var Club, SADD, Teen Ldrshp Corps Spon; North Way Chrstn Comm 1989-; *office:* South Side HS 4949 St Rt 151 Hookstown PA 15050

CUSH, BARBARA JO, Fifth Grade Teacher; *b:* Trafford, PA; *ed:* IN Univ of PA (BS) Elem Ed 1971; Doquesne Univ (MS) Elem Ed 1974; *cr:* PA Trafford Schl Dist Elem Tchr 1971-; *ai:* Prof Dev Comm; PSEA, NEA 1971; Mc Keesport Coll Club 1979-, VP; *office:* Level Green Elem Schl 650 Cypress Ct Trafford PA 15085

CUSHING, ALAN DAVID, Social Studies Teacher; *b:* Brockton, MA; *c:* Ruth, Anna, Nathaniel; *ed:* Suffolk Univ (BA) US His 1966; Univ of MA (MA) Medieval His 1970; Grad Course 60 Credit Hrs; *cr:* Wahconeh Reg HS Soc Stud Tchr 1966-70; King Philip Reg HS Soc Stud Tchr 1970-71; Bridgewater Raynham Reg HS Soc Stud Tchr 1971-; *ai:* MTA; NEA; PCEA.

CUSHING, JUDITH FEIL, Physics Teacher; *b:* New York, NY; *m:* John W.; *c:* James D., Janet L. Parsons; *ed:* OH St Univ (BS) Food Tech 1955, (MA) Sci Ed 1981; OH Univ (BA) Electronics Tech 1991; *cr:* OH Dept of Hlth Analytical Chemist 1957-62; Lancaster City Schls Asst Food Svc Dir 1974-80; New Lexington City Schls Physics, Chem, Earth Sci & Algebra Tchr 1981-; *ai:* Scndry Sci, Sci Fair Chprsn; Sci Olympiad Coach; Dist X Sci Olympiad Dir; Dist Sci Fair Steering, Scholastic Comms; NSTA 1980-; ACS 1985-; AAPT 1995-; Fairfield Cty Regnl Planning Comm 1972-, Past Pres, VP, Sec; Hospital Twig 14 1962-, Past Pres, VP, Treas; League of Women Voters 1970-75, Past Pres; North Hocking Water Shed 1975-90, Chprsn; Fairfield Cty Transportation Comm 1995-; Governors Awd of Excl in Sci 2 Times.

CUSICK, THOMAS P., HS Guidance Counselor; *b:* Red Bank, NJ; *m:* Valerie; *c:* Nicole, Sean; *ed:* Montclair St Coll (BA) Eng 1972; Kean Coll (MA) Cnslr Ed 1986; *cr:* Christian Brothers Acad Eng Tchr 1972-76; Thorne Jr HS Eng Tchr 1976-79; Middletown HS South Eng Tchr 1979-88; Middletown HS North Eng Tchr 1988-; *ai:* Little Silver Recreation Bsbl Commissioner; Monmouth Cty Schl Cnslr Assn 1988-, Exec Bd; *office:* Middletown HS North 63 Tindall Rd Middletown NJ 07748*

CUSTEAD, NANCY LOU, 6th Grade Teacher; *b:* Conneaut, OH; *ed:* Kent St Univ (BS) Elem Ed 1968; Edinboro (MA) Elem Ed 1973; Attnd Baldwin Wallace Coll, Univ of CT, Kent St Univ; *cr:* Ashtabulta Area City Schls 4th, 6th-7th Grd Lang Arts, 7th-8th Grd Cmptr, 4th-6th Grd Tchr 1968-; *ai:* Stu Assistance Prgm Bldg Coord; Peer Mediation Adv; NEA, OEA 1968-; AATA 1968-, Sec; Delta Kappa Gamma 1975-, Pres; Rebekahs 1970-, Noble Grand, Sec; East OH Gas; *office:* Mc Kinsey Elem Schl 1113 Bunker Hill Rd Ashtabula OH 44004*

CUSTER, HAROLD RICHARD,JR., HS & MS Art Teacher; *b:* Dayton, OH; *m:* Eva L. Kuhn; *c:* Shawn D., Heather L.; *ed:* Wright St Univ (BA) Visual Arts K-12th Grd 1974; Wester KY Univ 3 & Half Yrs music; Dayton Art Inst 1 & Half Yrs Art; Wright St Art Therapy; *cr:* Natl Trail K-6th Grd Art Tchr 1974-79; Natl Trail HS 9th-12th Art Tchr 1980-86; Ansonia HS Jr High & HS Art Tchr 1986-; Ansonia Migrant Prgm 6th Grd Music Dir 1995-; *ai:* Art Club, Photo, Stu Cncl, Art Club Adv; Advy, Multi Culture, Intervention Comms; Migrant Dir; OH Tchrs Assn 1974-; Phi Mu Alpha 1964-; Castine Town Cncl 1984-; Preble Cty Art Assn 1985-, Pres 1985; Bible Study Fellowship; White Water Prof Art Most Outstanding Tech Wd; Dark Cty Art Show Best of Show; NCR Best of Show; Randolph Cty Art 1st, 2nd in Outstanding Pastels; Grumbacker Art Aawd; *home:* 3572 N Creekd Wayne Lakes Greenville OH 45331

CUSUMANO, CHRISTOPHER R., English & Humanities Teacher; *b:* New York City, NY; *ed:* CW Post Coll (BA) Span 1966, (MA) Eng 1982; Stony Brook Univ Grad Level Span Courses 1973-; *cr:* Huntington HS Span Tchr 1966-82, Eng Tchr 1983; *ai:* Key Club Adv 1969-; Sr Class Adv; AFS Adv; Stu Govt Adv; AFT 1966-; Amer Guild of Organists 1965-; *office:* Huntington HS Oakwood Rd Huntington NY 11743*

CUTAIA, TONY J., Physics Instructor; *b:* New York, NY; *m:* Patricia; *c:* Christopher, Jennifer; *ed:* St Francis Coll (BA) Chem 1973; Adelphi Univ (MS) Geophysics 1977; NY Univ Engrng; Fordham Univ Educl Admin; *cr:* White Plains HS Physics Instr 22 Yrs; *ai:* Jr Engrng Club Adv; AFT 1974-; AAPT 1977-; Cortlandt Little League; Cortlandt Sftbl; *office:* White Plains HS 550 North St White Plains NY 10605

CUTCHALL, CRAIG C., Health & PE Teacher; *b:* Mc Connellsburg, PA; *m:* Barbara Black; *c:* Cortney, Corryn; *ed:* Slippery Rock (BS) Hlth, PE 1973, (ME) Elem Ed 1990; *cr:* Forbes Road Schl Tchr 1975-; *ai:* Ath Dir; Var Girls Bsktbl Coach; PSEA; AAPERD; PSAHPERD; Fairview Meth Church 1966-; Lions Club; *office:* Forbes Road HS HC 01 Box 222 Waterfall PA 16689

CUTE, WILLIAM JOSEPH,JR., Social Studies Dept Chair; *b:* Providence, RI; *m:* Wendy Hamilton; *c:* James; *ed:* OH Wesleyan Univ (BA) His 1973; Providence Coll (MED) Scndry Admin 1985; 20 Hrs Plus in Supervision & Evaluation Techniques; *cr:* Dighton-Rehoboth Regnl HS Soc Stud Tchr & Golf Coach 1973-80, Soc Stud Dept Head Golf Coach 1980-; *ai:* Golf Coach; Character Ed Comm; Comm Svc Learning Comm; NEA, MA Teachers Assn, Dighton-Rehoboth Regnl Teachers Assn 1973-, Treas 1978-80; Segregonsett Cntry Club 1965-, 3 Time Club Champion; St Senate Intern 1978; *home:* 89 Hillside Ave Rehoboth MA 02769*

CUTHBERT, SAMUEL STEWART, English Teacher; *b:* New Milford, CT; *m:* Elizabeth Valerie Juka; *c:* Elizabeth Pascal, Thomas; *ed:* Hobart Coll (BA) Eng 1976; *cr:* Grand River Acad Librn, Eng Tchr 1976-77; Hoosac Schl Eng, Latin, Math Tchr 1986-88; St James Schl Eng, Latin Tchr 1988-93; St Maria Goretti Schl 11th-12th Grd Eng Tchr 1993-; *ai:* Yrbk Adv; Outstdng Male Tchr 1995; Author of Novels, Poetry, Essays; Numerous Articles Pub; *office:* Saint Maria Goretti HS 1535 Oak Hill Ave Hagerstown MD 21742*

CUTLER, CAROL SMITH, Band Director; *b:* Corinth, NY; *m:* James; *c:* Seamus; *ed:* Skidmore Coll (BS) Music Ed 1988; Coll of St Rose at Albany (MS) Music Ed 1994; *cr:* North Warren Cntrl Schls K-6th Grd Music Tchr 1989-90; Hartford Cntrl Schl 5th-12th Instrumental Music Tchr 1990-; *ai:* Color Guard Marching Band; MENC 1989-; Hartford Faculty Assoc 1990-; NYSBDA 1995-; *office:* Hartford Central Schl PO Box 79 Hartford NY 12838

CUTLER, ELAINE COOPER, Fifth Grade Teacher; *b:* Baltimore, MD; *m:* Robert B.; *c:* Howard Andy, Michelle Mindy; *ed:* Univ of MD (BS) Ed 1962; John Hopkins Univ (MED) Ed 1966, (CASE) Ed 1971; 36 Credit Hrs; *cr:* Ft Garrison Elem Schl Tchr 1962-70; Bannockburn Elem Schl Tchr 1970-71; Wayside Elem Schl Tchr 1971-72; Woodley Gardens Tchr 1972-78; Georgetown Hill Elem Schl Tchr 1978-84; Beverly Farms Elem Schl Tchr 1984-; *ai:* Safety Patrol Spon; Schl Store; Instrl Ldrshp, Schl Soc, MECA Liaison Comm; Exec Bd PTA; Tutoring Prgm; Baltimore Cty Tchrs Assn 1962-70; Montgomery Cntry Ed Assn 1970-; MD St Tchrs Assn, NEA 1962-; Washington Hebrew Congregation 1970-; PTA 1984-, Tchr Rep; Georgetown Hill Elem Schl PTA 1978-84, Tchr Rep; *home:* 8715 Postoak Rd Potomac MD 20854

CUTLER, JODY L., Drama & Vocal Music Teacher; *b:* Hempstead, NY; *ed:* Univ of Rochester (BA) Music 1989; Natl Shakespeare Conservatory Summer Intensive; Studio Theatre Acting Conservatory Classes; *cr:* Arts for the Aging Music Instr 1989-90; Barrie Schl Dir of Drama & Vocal Music Depts 1990-95; *ai:* Drama Club, Drama Mamas & Papas Spons; Dir All Productions Plays, Musicals, Concerts; Intnl Thespian Soc Chptr Spon, Adv.

CUTLER, LEONARD M., Public Law Professor; *b:* Brooklyn, NY; *m:* Sheila Rona Moscovice; *c:* Julie, Heidi; *ed:* City Coll of NY (BA) Pol Sci 1965; (MA) Pol Sci 1967; New Schl for Soc Research (PHD) Pol Sci 1970; *cr:* Seton Hall Univ Pol Sci Instr 1965; Notre Dame Coll of SI Pol Sci Asst Prof 1965-67; Siena Coll Pre-Law Adv & Pub Law Prof 1970-; Rockefeller Inst at St Univ of NY-GSPA Pub Law Adjunct Prof 1982-90; *ai:* Albany Law Schl Advy Bd of Dirs; Empire St Performing Arts Ctr Bd of Dirs; Cncl of St Govt Exec Comm; Natl Law Advs Assn 1992-, Mem; Anderson Awd Amer Acad of Criminal Justice; Outstanding Men & Women of Sci Pi Gamma Mu; Kennedy Schl of Govt Fellow; Nelson A Rockefeller Inst Policy Leadership Fellow; *office:* Siena Coll 515 Loudonville Rd Loudonville NY 12211

CUTRO, FRANCIS JOSEPH, Biology Teacher; *b:* Oswego, NY; *m:* Carol; *c:* Michele, Marie, Maureen; *ed:* SUNY at Oswego (BS) Elem & Scndry Ed Sci 1962, (MS) Elem & Scndry Ed Sci 1968; *cr:* JC Birdlebough HS Sci & Bio Tchr 1962-; *ai:* Sr Class Cap, Gown & Grad; Phoenix Tchrs 1962-, VP; NEA; AFT; Yrbk Dedication 3 Times; *office:* John C Birdlebough HS 470 Main St Phoenix NY 13135

CUTTER, DONNA JOE, Business Education Teacher; *b:* Cumberland, MD; *ed:* Frostburg St Univ (BS) Bus Ed 1989; (MSEd) Curr, Instruction 1994; *cr:* Salisbury-Elk Lick Schl Dist 9-12 Grd Bus Ed Dept Chprsn, Tchr 1991-; *ai:* Bus Club Adv 1994-; Ed Assn Sec 1995-; Salisbury Area Family Ctr Adult Ed Instr 1994-95; Sr Portfolios Dir 1994-; NEA 1991; PA Bus Ed Assn 1994-; *home:* PO Box 312 Midlothian MD 21543

CUTULI-BLOCK, DEBORAH A., English Teacher; *b:* Norwalk, CT; *m:* Joel W. Block; *ed:* Univ of CT (BA) Eng & Scndry Ed 1976; Fairfield Univ (MA) Media 1986; *cr:* St Thomas the Apostle Eng Tchr 1977-79; Brian McMahon HS Eng Tchr 1979-84; Norwalk HS Eng Tchr 1984-; *ai:* Former Dir & Choreographer of Musical Theatre Dept 1980-90; Norwalk Fed of Tchrs 1977-; *office:* Norwalk HS 23 Calvin Murphy Dr Norwalk CT 06851

CUTY, JAMES MICHAEL, Business Education Teacher; *b:* Bayshore, NY; *m:* Ellen; *c:* Ashleigh; *ed:* Suffolk Cty Comm Coll (AAS) Mrktg, Mngmt 1963; Adelphi Suffolk Coll (BBA) Bus Admin 1966; Hotstra Univ (BS) Scndry Ed 1973; Addl 52 Credits; *cr:* Grumman Aerospace Corp Contracts Admin 4 Yrs; West Babylon Pub Schls Bus Ed Tchr 25 Yrs; *ai:* Mid St Evaluation Steering Comm 1993-94, 1973-74; Former Ski Club Adv 1974, DECA Adv St Competion 1973; West Babylon Tchrs Assn, NYSTA 1971-; Parkwood Civic Assn 1990-, Bd of Dir.

CYBAK, EDWARD JOHN, HS Social Studies Teacher; *b:* Youngstown, OH; *m:* Amber Dawn; *ed:* Kent ST Univ (BS) Scndry Ed 1990; Ashland Univ (ME) Admin 1995; *cr:* Ridgedale HS Soc Stud Tchr 1992-; *ai:* Asst Var Ftbl Coach; Ridgedale Tchrs Assoc 1992-, VP 1995-; OH Ed Assoc, NEA 1992-; Local HS Rep That Helped Dev the Requirements for Soc Stud Schlshp Awd; *office:* Ridgedale HS 3165 Hillman Ford Rd Morral OH 43337

CYBURT, MARIAN (HOSTENSKY), Jr High Science Teacher; *b:* Johnstown, PA; *m:* Kevin; *ed:* Univ of Pittsburgh (BS) Soc Sci, Elem Ed 1976; 30 Addl Grad Credit Hrs; *cr:* Visitation B.V.M. Schl Tchr 1977-82; St. Benedict Schl Jr HS Sci Tchr 1982-; *ai:* PA Jr Acad of Aci Schl Spon; Regnl & St Meeting Organizer; Instrl Support Team; NCEA 1977-; PA Sci Tchrs Assn 1988-; Amer Artists Prof League 1985-; PA Jr Acad of Sci 1982-; Visitation Preschool Bd 1991-; Math on Saturday, Sci on Saturday Partricipant & Presenter; Rel Curr Dev Diocesan; *office:* St Benedicts Schl 2306 Bedford St Johnstown PA 15904

CYLAR, WILLIAM J., Mathematics Teacher; *b:* Attalla, AL; *m:* Marilyn Yvette Baker; *c:* Calvin L., Colby L.; *ed:* Damen Coll (BS) Bus Admin 1981; Canisus Coll (MS) Cmptr Instruction 1987; Buffalo St Coll Schl Dist Admin; *cr:* NY St Div for Yth Math Tchr 1984-93, Ed Supvr 1993-94; Buffalo Bd of Ed Math Tchr 1994-; *ai:* Natl Inner City Yth Org Little League Bsbl Coach, Bd Mem; Parents for Quality Ed Bd Mem; NEA 1993-; *office:* Seneca Voc HS 666 Delavan Ave Buffalo NY 14211

CYPHERT, HENRY,JR., Earth Science Teacher; *b:* Clarion, PA; *m:* Nola Curtis; *c:* Rayne Hammond, Summer Hammond; *ed:* Clarion Univ (BS) Ed & Bio 1964; SUNY at Geneseo (MS) Ed & Bio 1972; Attnd Bucknell Univ, Edinboro Univ, Syracuse Univ & Finger Lakes Comm Coll; *cr:* Riverside HS Gen Sci Tchr 1964-66; Midlakes HS Earth Sci Tchr 1966-; *ai:* Hlth & Saftey Comm; PCSFA 1966-; NYSUT 1975-; AFT 1975-; NSF Grants 1967 & 1981; *office:* Midlakes HS Rt 488 Clifton Springs NY 14432

CYR, ELAINE MARIE, Secondary Resource Teacher; *b:* Edmundson NB, Canada; *m:* Philip; *c:* Scott, Erica; *ed:* Univ of ME at Farmington (BS) Home Ec & Spec Ed 1974; *cr:* Wisdom Mid & HS Resource & Home Ec Tchr 1974-; *ai:* Frosh Class Adv; Tenure Licensure Comm Mem; MTA, MEA 1974-; *home:* 165 Cleveland Rd Saint Agatha ME 04772*

CYR, GILMAN JOSEPH, Science Teacher; *b:* Waterbury, CT; *m:* Sarah McGuinness; *c:* Kaitlin, Timothy, Patrick, Peter; *ed:* Univ of WI at Madison (BS) Botany 1976; Univ of New Haven (MBA) Finance 1982; Working on 6th Yr Degree Prgm at Southern CT St Univ; *cr:* Shearson Lehman Brothers Financial Consultant 1982-87; CT Hlth Facilities Dir of Mrktg 1987-93; Kennedy HS Sci Tchr 1993-; *ai:* Hamden HS Boys & Girls Diving Coach & Swim Asst Coach; Waterbury Tchrs Assn, CT Ed Assn, NEA 1993-; US Diving 1992-, VP of USD-CT; New England Womens Intercollegiate Swimming & Diving Coach of Yr 1992-93, Diving Coach of Yr Awd 1992-93; *office:* Kennedy HS Highland Ave Waterbury CT 06708

CYR, KAREN MARY, 1st-2nd Grade Teacher; *b:* Attleboro, MA; *m:* Patrick; *c:* Jessica, Heather; *ed:* Univ of ME at Orono (BA) Spec Ed 1982; *cr:* Head Start Tchr 1983-84; Mallett Resource Room 1986-90; Mallett 1st & 2nd Grd Tchr 1990-; *ai:* Wellness Comm Chm; ME St Tchr Assn 1986-; *office:* W G Mallet Schl 1 Quebec St Farmington ME 04938

CYR, PAUL RONALD, English Teacher; *b:* Boston, MA; *m:* Irene M.; *c:* David, Andrew, Jaclyn; *ed:* Boston Coll (BA) Eng 1970; Salem St Coll (MED) Admin 1977; *cr:* Winthrop HS Eng Tchr 1970-; *ai:* Supvr Security Bsktbl; Track Ofcl; Curr Reform Comm; NEA, WTA, PTA 1970-; BSA 1985-, Scoutmaster; Melrose Bandaiders 1992-, Fundraiser; Governors Citation for Work with United Way; *office:* Winthrop HS 400 Main St Winthrop MA 02152*

CYR, RODERICK J., Retired Counselor; *b:* Fort Kent, ME; *m:* Linda Kleinsmith; *c:* Debra Pattison, Douglas, Diane Federico, Donna Szestakow, Dorothy Vittner, John; *ed:* Univ of ME (BSEd) Bio, Chem 1956; Boston Univ (MS) Guid Cnslr 1960; *cr:* ME Cntrl Inst Chem, Physics, Math Tchr 1956-59; Biddeford HS Chem, Bio, Guid Dir 1959-60; Wethersfield HS Chem, Bio Tchr 1961-68, Guid Cnslr, Active Fac Mgr Aths, Golf Coach 1969-93; *ai:* Ftbl, Golf Coach; CT Sci Fai, Golf Coache's League, Sr Prom Chm; Fac Mgr Aths; CCD Dir; Prof Dev Comm; AFT 1965-; CT Coaches Assn 1962-, CCC & CCIL Chm; Knights of Columbus 1970-, Fin Sec; CT Golf Coach of Yr 1986; Natl Golf Coach of Yr 1990; *home:* 61 Rivermead Blvd East Hartford CT 06118

CYR, TRACI JANE, 8th Grade Mathematics Teacher; *b:* Easton, PA; *m:* Lewis C.; *ed:* Univ of Scranton (BS) Mrktg 1990; Lehigh Univ (MED) Scndry Ed 1993; Addl Five Credits; *cr:* Notre Dame HS Head Bsktbl Coach 1990-; Northeast MS 8th Grd Math Tchr 1993-; *ai:* MS Field Hockey Coach; HS Head Bsktbl Coach; NCTM 1992-; *office:* Northeast MS 1110 Fernwood St Bethlehem PA 18018*

CZACHOR, THOMAS ANTHONY, Computer Maintenance Tech Tchr; *b:* Scranton, PA; *m:* Kathy Lee Kapuscinski; *c:* Jerome Thomas; *ed:* Penn St Assoc Electrical Engr 1985; Temple Univ Voc Ed; *cr:* Lacka Cty Area Votech Instr 1988-; *ai:* AFT 1989-; Skills in Scranton; *office:* Lackawanna Co Avt School-Dende 3201 Rockwell Ave Scranton PA 18508

CZARNECKI, DORIS CHRISTIE, Soc Stud & Lang Arts Teacher; *b:* Brooklyn, NY; *m:* John Walter; *c:* Stefka, John III., Felicity, Anne; *ed:* Fairleigh Dickinson Univ (BA) His, Eng 1961; Seton Hall Univ (MA) Ed Admin 1969; 33 Post Grad Credit Hrs; *cr:* Brick Twp Bd of Ed Seventh Grd Soc Stud, Lang Tchr 1963-68; Woodbridge Twp Bd of Ed Supvr Adult Basic Ed 1969-72; Brick Twp Bd of Ed Seventh Grd Soc Stud, Lang Tchr 1985-89, Adult Ed Dir 1988-94, US His, World His Tchr 1989-94, 7th Grd Tchr 1994-; *ai:* NEA, NJEA 1963-; OCCEA 1963-, Rep; BTEA 1963-, Bldg Rep, Secy; NJALL 1968-, St Sec; COABE 1988-; *office:* Veterans Memorial MS 105 Hendrickson Ave Brick NJ 08724

CZARNIEWICZ, MARGARET C., 6th Grade Teacher; *b:* Syracuse, NY; *m:* Casimir M.; *c:* Anne Robison, Stephen, Joseph, Andrew, Helen E.; *ed:* LeMoyne Coll (BS) Eng 1955; Maria Regina Coll (AB) Rel Stud 1980; *cr:* LeMoyne Coll Asst Dean of Women 1955-57; St Rose of Lima Schl Tchr 1971-; Roman Cath Dio of Syr Wkshps Presenter 1977-80; Maria Regina Coll Lecturer, Tchr 1979-80; *ai:* NCEA 1972-; Assn Curr Dev 1994-; NYSSSTA 1989-; St Rose Lima Parish 1962-, Trustee, Cncl Pres; *office:* St Rose Of Lima Schl 411 S Main St Syracuse NY 13212

CZAYA, ALLAN JOSEPH, Health & PE Teacher; *b:* Newark, NJ; *m:* Janice Angelo; *c:* Michael, Jeffrey, David, Karen; *ed:* Montclair St Univ (BA) PE, Hlth 1969; *cr:* David Brearley Reg HS PE, Hlth, Driver Ed Tchr 1969-93; Arthur L. Johnson Reg HS PE, Hlth Tchr 1993-; *ai:* Var Soccer, Var Golf Coach; Class Adv; Cty Soccer Chprsn; Union Cty Soccer Tournament Dir; AFT, Natl Soccer Coaches Assn 1969-; NJ Soccer Coaches Assn 1969-, Exec Bd Mem; IAABO Bd 33 Bsktbl Assn 1975-; Kenilworth Yth Soccer Assn 1969-93, Founder; Clark Yth Soccer Assn 1993-, Clinician; NJ Governor's Outstdng Tchr of Yr Awd 1993; Natl Soccer Coaches Assn Region #3 Coach of Yr 1995; NJ Soccer Coaches Assn Coach of Yr 1995; Union Cty Soccer Coach of Yr 1989-90, 1995; Harrison HS Hall of Fame 1994; *home:* 621 Sheridan Ave Roselle Park NJ 07204

CZEKAJ, ROBERT, Health & PE Instructor; *b:* Everson, PA; *m:* Jean M. Brown; *c:* Bob, Rick, Lori Lynn; *ed:* PA St Univ (BS) Hlth, PE, Coach 1976; Frostburg St Univ (ME) Hlth, PE 1987; *cr:* Penn Hall Acad HS Hlth, PE Tchr, Coaching 7 Yrs; Berlin Brothersvalley HS Hlth, PE Tchr, Coaching 18 Yrs; *ai:* SADD Adv; FFA, Vlybl, Boys & Girls Bsktbl, Ftbl, Sftbl, Bsbl Coach; BBEA, NEA, PSEA 1978-; Somerset Cty Bsbl Assn; Jr & Sr Legion Bsbl; Little & Pony League Bsbl; Grd Schl Bsktbl & Ftbl; Levelgreen Ath Assn, Pres; Somerset Cty Bsbl Coach of Yr 1982, Girls Bsktbl Coach of Yr 1992-93; Hlth & PE Chprsn; 250 Var Bsktbl Wins; 175 Var Bsbl Wins; *office:* Berlin Brothersvalley HS 1025 E Main St Berlin PA 15530

CZELUSNIAK, JUDITH TYMINSKI, Spanish Teacher; *b:* Springfield, MA; *m:* A. George; *c:* Alyson, Shelly; *ed:* Our Lady of the Elms Coll (BA) Span 1967; *cr:* Ludlow HS Span Tchr 1967-68; Chicopee Comprehensive HS Span & Eng Tchr 1968-; *ai:* Past Span Club Adv; NEA, MTA & CEA 1968-; *office:* Chicopee Comprehensive H S 209 Rolf Ave Chicopee MA 01013

CZEPIEL, DIANE MORELLE, English Teacher; *b:* Utica, NY; *ed:* Mohawk Valley Comm Coll (AAS) Liberal Arts 1973; Utica Coll of Syracuse Univ (BA) Eng 1975; NY St Permanent Cert Scndry Eng; SUNY Cortland, SUNY Coll of Tech 60 Addl Hrs; *cr:* Kennedy HS Eng Tchr 1976-; Proctor HS Eng Tchr 1976-; Donovan MS Eng Tchr 1976-; *ai:* Drama Club Adv; NYSUT, AFT 1976-.

CZERWIEC, IRENE THERESA (MATUSZEK), 6th-8th Grd Tchr of Gifted; *b:* Holyoke, MA; *m:* Stanley Joseph; *c:* Keith John, Daniel Paul; *ed:* U Mass at Amherst (BS) Math 1969, (MED) Gifted & Cmptr Ed 1987, (EDD) Ed, Educl Leadership 1992; *cr:* Holyoke Cath HS Math, Physics Tchr 1969-71; Chicopee Pub Schls Sub Tchr 1979-85, Tchr of Gifted 1985-, Math Tchr 1990-92, Cmptr Tchr 1992-; *ai:* Future Problem Solving Teams Coach; After Schl Logo Instr; NEA, MTA, Chicopee Educ Assn 1986-; CEC 1988-; Amer Assn Univ WOmen, ASCD, World Future Soc 1993-; Natl Space Soc; Pub TV 1993-95, Advy Comm Tchr; Stdnts, Future Scientist Engr Prgm 1993-; NSF Fellowship Spacemet 1990-91; Coor Chicopee Centennial Looking Forward Project, Merit Awd Chicopee Cncl Parents & Tchrs 1990; Educl Ldrs Math 1987-89; Cert Excl Coaching Team Intnl Future Problem Solving Conf 1987 & 1988; Cert of Merit MA Bar Assn 1988 & 1989; NSTA Natl Convention 1992, MA Future Problm Solving Conf 1994, World Future Soc Conf 1994, Dev Amer Talent: A New England Response, 2nd Annual Conf on GATE, Presenter; *home:* 4 Plainville Cir South Hadley MA 01075*

CZUCHRA, BRENDA LEE, Kindergarten Teacher; *b:* Springfield, MA; *m:* Theodore John Jr.; *c:* Shawn, Laurie; *ed:* Fitchburg St Coll (BS) Elem Ed 1974; 2 Grad Courses at Westfield St Coll; *cr:* Our Lady of Perpetual Help Schl 4th Grd Tchr 1986-90, Kndgtn Tchr 1990-; *ai:* NCEA 1986-; *office:* Our Lady Of Perpetual Help Sch 261 Chestnut St Holyoke MA 01040*

CZYRYCA, MICHAEL THOMAS, Principal; *b:* Norwood, MA; *m:* Stephanie Siblo; *c:* James; *ed:* St Coll at Boston (BS) Elem 1968, (MED) Elem Ed & Admin 1977; 30 Addl Hrs Elem Sci Courses; *cr:* F A Cleveland Schl 6th Grd Tchr 1968-89; Norwood Sci Ctr 1st- 5th Grd Sci Res Specialist 1989-94; F A Cleveland Schl Prin 1994-; *ai:* NEA; NSTA; MME; MAST; Natl Assn of Rocketry; AARP; Sci Educator of Yr Norfolk Cty MAST 1995; *office:* F A Cleveland Schl 33 George F Willett Pkwy Norwood MA 02062*

D

DAALIYA, SHAREEF AKBAR, Computer Science Teacher; *b:* Oklahoma City, OK; *m:* Delphine Hinson; *c:* Bahjah, Nadiyah, Yakita, Jibriah; *ed:* Langston Univ (BS) Bus Ed, Acctng; Rowan Coll Grad Stud Cmptr Sci; *cr:* Camden Cty Coll Cmptr Stud Instr 7 Yrs; Camden HS Cmptr Sci Tchr 20 Yrs; *ai:* Head Coach Woodrow Wilson Girls Track, Camden City Track Club; NEA, NJEA, NJ Bus Teach 1976-; Black Data Processors Assn 1994-; Alpha Phi Alpha 1969-; *office:* Camden HS Park & Baird Blvd Camden NJ 08103

DABROWSKI, ELIZABETH MARIE, Chemistry Teacher; *b:* Cleveland, OH; *ed:* John Carroll Univ (BS) Chem 1972; Case Western Reserve Univ (MS) Chem 1974; Physics for Tchrs; *cr:* Hebrew Acad of Cleveland Sci Tchr 1973-74; St Ignatius HS Chem Tchr 1974-76; Cuyahoga Comm Coll Part-Time Chem Instr 1990-; Magnificat HS Chem Tchr 1979-; Science Dept Chair 1995-; John Carroll Univ Part Time Chem Instr 1995-; *ai:* Moderator Math, Sci Club, Chem Club; Amer Chemical Soc 1974-, HS Affairs Co-Chair 1994-; Iota Sigma Pi 1985-; NSTA 1984-; Amer Inst of Aeronautics, Astronautics 1993-; John Carroll Univ Sci Across Amer Prjct 1996; Playhouse Sq Ctr 1984-, Head Usher; Parma Rose Soc 1992; Northeastern OH Iris Soc 1993-; MENSA 1988-; Authored Portion Addison Wesley's 1995 Chem Packet; OH Tchr to Amer Vacuum Soc Wkshp; Cert Appreciation Amer inst of Aeronautics & Astr; *office:* Magnificat HS 20770 Hilliard Rd Rocky River OH 44116

DABROWSKI, LAWRENCE JOHN, Science Teacher; *b:* Baltimore, MD; *ed:* Towson St Coll (BA) Bio 1969, (MED) Scndry Ed 1977; Loyola Coll Guid, Cnslng Courses; *cr:* Baltimore City Pub Schls Sci Tchr 1969-78, Sci Dept Head 1978-84; Anne Arundel Cty Pub Schls Sci Tchr 1983-; *ai:* Challenge Rocket, Green Thumb Clubs; Hum Relations Comm; Nat Sci Tchrs Assn 1985-; Tchrs Assn of Anne Arundel Co 1993-; Amer Soc Microbiology Commendation; *office:* Severn River Jr HS 241 Peninsula Farm Rd Arnold MD 21012

DABULEWICZ, JOHN R., Secondary English Instructor; *b:* Oneonta, NY; *m:* Florretta Thomas; *c:* David B., Stefin J., Mary E., Julie McKee; *ed:* Pacific Coast Bapt Bible Coll (BS) Elem Ed, Schl Admin 1981; Univ of Buffalo Nursing; Temple Univ Liberal Arts; Radiologic Tech Registered 1965; Advanced Rdng & Writing; Advanced Ed Admin; *cr:* Montrose General Hospital Radiologic Svcs Admin 1965-76; Marina Chrstn Schl Admin 1981-83; Grace Bapt Schl Admin 1983-84; Riverside Bapt Schls Admin 1984-88; Oneonta Comm Chrstn Schl Admin 1988-; *ai:* Yrbk, Fundraising Adv; Guidance Cnslr; ASCI 1988-; *office:* Oneonta Cmty Christian Schl 3200 Chestnut St Oneonta NY 13820

DACHOWSKI, THOMAS JOSEPH, Science Teacher; *b:* Springfield, MA; *m:* Rosemary Regan; *ed:* Nasson Coll (BA) Bio 1969; American Intnl Coll (MST) Sci Ed 1974; Attnd Westfield St Coll, Univ of MA & Worcester Polytechnic Inst; Boston Coll Doctoral Candidate Curr & Instr; *cr:* Sweeney Schl Jr High Sci Tchr 1969-74; Chicopee HS Sci Tchr 1974-93, Head Tchr Sci Dept 1993-94; Sci Supvr 1994-; *ai:* Curr Cncl, Cmptr Lab & Alternative Assessment Sci Comms; Sci Frameworks Facilitator Pre K-12; NEA & MTA; CEA, Bd of Dir; NSTA 1990-; Dwight D. Eisenhower Tchr Trng Grant; NDEA Grant Sci Ed in Jr High; Tech Grant; *office:* Chicopee HS 650 Front St Chicopee MA 01013

DA CRUZ, SUSY, Guidance Counselor; *b:* Elizabeth, NJ; *ed:* Saint Peter's Coll (BA) Psych, Ed 1993; Jersey City St Coll (MA) Cnslng 1995; *cr:* Queen of Peach HS Guid Cnslr 1992-; *ai:* Moderator Stdnts Against Substance Abuse, Drinking & Driving, Comm AIDS Awareness Prgm; NJ Cnslng Assn 1992-, Awd for Outstdng Cnslng Prgm; Bergen Cty Prof Cnslrs Assn 1992-; Comm Action Prgm 1993-; *home:* 95 Sunset Ave North Arlington NJ 07031*

DACUS, JUDY MCLELLAN, Science Dept Chair & Prof Bi
Bluff, AR; *m:* Darin Michael; *c:* Michelle Lesley, Katherine Ne
St Univ (BS) Bio-Chem 1965; Univ of AR Medical Ctr (MS)
1967; NM St Univ (PHD) Curr & Instr 1982; *cr:* NM St Univ
1977-81; Mesilla Valley Christian Schls Bio & Math Tchr 1983-
Univ Project Evaluator 1987-89; Frederick Comm Coll Sci Ch
Chem Prof 1989-; *ai:* Coll Senate Chair; Research Cncl,
Planning Cncl, Pres Cabinet, Fac Assn Mem; Amer Soc for Mic
1992-, Scientist Educator Team; Southview Bapt Church 1995
Schl Tchr; MD Higher Ed Comm Grant for Improving Sci Ed;
Awd; Master Tchr NISOD; *office:* Frederick Comm C
Opossumtown Pike Frederick MD 21702

DADDIO, MARLENE BERGAMASCO, Second Grade Te
Meadville, PA; *m:* Anthony Jr.; *c:* Tae, Ryan; *ed:* Edinboro Univ
1969, (MS) Elem 1972; Credit Hrs Cmptrs, Arts Infusion in C
Project Adapt Courses, Math; *cr:* First Dist Schl 1st Grd Tchr
Third Dist Schl 2nd Grd Tchr 1970-76; East End Schl 1st
1977-78, 2nd Grd Tchr 1979-; *ai:* PA St Ed Assn, NEA 1969-
Cntrl Ed Assn 1969-, Exec Cncl; *office:* East End Schl 640
Meadville PA 16335

DADEY, MARGARET R., American History Teacher; *b:* Syra
ed: LeMoyne Coll (BA) His 1989; SUNY Coll at Cortland (M
Soc Stud 1993; *cr:* Mexico Acad & Cntrl Schl Soc Stud Tchr 19
Girls Vlybl Coach; NYSUT 1989-; CNYCSS, NCSS 1995-; *offic*
Acad & Cntrl Schl Main St Mexico NY 13114

DADOURIAN, MELISSA HOLLY, Art Teacher; *b:* Clevland
Pratt Inst (BFA) Painting 1991; Hunter Coll (MFA) Painting 199
Dwight School Art Tchr 1995-; *home:* 40 Sidney Pl # 2B Bro
11201

DADSON, WILLIAM KWAME, Economics, Bus Dept Chm
Arkra, Ghana; *m:* Gladys L.; *c:* Faustina, Thato, Nankofi; *ed:*
Univ (BA) Advertising 1976, (MSBA) Fin 1978; Univ of Den
Tech, Pub Policy 1980, (MIM) Intnl Mngmt 1981, (PHD) Intnl
cr: Univ of Southwestern LA Asst Prof 1984-85; Morgan St Univ
1985-89, Acctng, Fin Dept Chm 1986-89; Lincoln Univ Prof 1
1992-; *ai:* Soc for Free Enterprise Campus Dir; AAUP 198
Awareness Soc 1991-, Sec; Eastern Ec Assn 1986-91; Herita
Corp, Bd Mem; Assn for Advancement of Rsrch Dev 1988-, Ex
for Pub Policy, Diplomacy 1989-95, Bd Mem, Ldrshp Aw
Baltimore Headstart Prgm 1988-89; Fulbright, Hayes 1987; Nis
1994; *office:* Lincoln Univ Lincoln University PA 19352*

DAESCHNER, ROLF EMIL, Frgn Langs Dept Chr & Ger
Karlsruhe Baden, Germany; *m:* Janice Elaine Schiefferle; *c:* Ke
Diane; *ed:* Gannon Univ (BA) Ger 1968; 24 Credit Hrs Ed, Guid
Maria Coll Ger Tchr 1977-79; Cathedral Prep Schl Dept Chm,
1968-; Mercyhurst Coll Ger Tchr 1994-; *ai:* Ger Club Adv; NC
PSMLA 1968-; Erie Diocesan Mentor Tchr Awd; PSMLA Conf
office: Cathedral Prep Schl 225 W 9th St Erie PA 16501

DAFFNER, BEVERLY A., History Teacher; *b:* Schenectady
SUNY at Oneonta (BS) Ed 1966; CW Post (MA) Admin 1980; U
NYU, SUNY at Stony Brook 60 Credit Hrs 1975-79; *cr:* Smitht
Schl Dist His & Rdng Tchr 1966-; *ai:* AFT, NEA NYSUT; Smit
Schl Rep, Negotiator 1980-81; *office:* Smithtown MS 10 Schoo
James NY 11780*

DAGANYA, ROSE A., Physical Education Teacher; *b:* Staten Is
m: Lawrence E. Reynolds; *ed:* Trenton St Coll (BS) PE 1977;
Instr; *cr:* Cheesequake Elem Schl PE Tchr 1977-78; Cooper Ele
Tchr 1978-79; Madison Cntrl, Cedar Ridge HS PE Tchr 1979-
Salk MS PE Tchr 1980-; *ai:* Old Bridge HS Field Hockey He
Sftbl Asst Coach; OBEA, NJEA, NEA 1977-; Old Bridge Coa
1994-; Amer Cancer Soc, Pet Therapy Vol; *office:* Jonas Sa
Greystone Rd Old Bridge NJ 08857*

DAGATA, HOLLIE WILLIAMS, Instructional Support Te
Wilkes Barre, PA; *m:* Ernest; *c:* Carie, Manda; *ed:* Elmira Col
1965; Marywood Coll (MS) Rdng Ed 1989; 18 Inservice Cred
Tunkhannock Schls 1st Grd Tchr 1979-82, 2nd Grd Tchr 1983-
Tchr 1984-85, TELLS & Gifted Tchr 1985-92, IST Tchr 199
NEA; Northeastern PA Rdng Assn; Keystone St Rdng Assn; Cla
Church 1992-, Ed Comm; *office:* Roslund Elem Schl 99
Tunkhannock PA 18657

DAGENAIS, DANIEL G., History Teacher; *b:* Claremont, NH;
Kelley; *c:* Adam; *ed:* Keene St Coll (BA) His; Univ of VT (MA)
Univ of CT (PHD) Amer His Pending; *cr:* Cheshire Acad
1984-87; Worcester Acad His Tchr 1987-89; Plymouth Regnl H
Tchr, Dept Head 1990-93; Emma Willard Schl His Tchr 1993-;
Coach, 3 Regnl Championships; Model Congress, Forensics,
Adv; Amer Historical Assoc 1991-; Org of Amer Historians
Alpha Theta 1990-; NEH Flwshp 1985; Predoctoral Flwshp 19

D'AGOSTINO, ANNE DONNELLY ROGERS, Second Grade
b: Providence, RI; *m:* Alan G.; *ed:* Brown Univ (AB) Eng
Fitchburg St Coll (MED) Educl Tech 1989; *cr:* Palmer River S
Tchr 1964-; *ai:* NE Assn of Schls & Colls Visiting Team
Enrichment Curr Task Force 1991-93; Schl Cncl 1993-95; NEA,
Assn 1970-; Dighton-Rehoboth Regnl Tchrs Assn 1964-.

D'AGOSTINO, LORRAINE ANN, Third Grade Teacher;
NY; *c:* Lisa Kremyar; *ed:* SUNY at Oswego (BA) Elem Ed 1976;
Comm Coll (AAS) Lbrl Arts 1965; Attnd Southampton Coll L
St Rose Elem Ed; *cr:* St Margarets Schl 2nd Grd Tchr 1967-74;
Rd Elem Schl 3rd Grd Tchr 1977-; NY St United Tchrs In
Onondaga Madison BOCES Consultant 1980-82; *ai:* Hlth
Lakeshore Rd Advy Comm; Cntrl NY Tchng Ctr liaison; NY
Tchrs 1977-, Consultant; North Syracuse Ed Assn 1977-, Cncl R
Assn Tchr Ed 1980-; AFT 1977-; Ed Ctr Publication 1982; Cntrl
Ctr Mini Grants; North Syracuse Schl Dist Excl Tchng Awd
Best Ldrshp Awd 1990; *home:* 311 Brookhaven Rd North Syr
13212*

D'AGOSTINO, NANCY FADEL, Fifth Grade Teacher; *b:* Elms
c: Robert, Donna, Ellen; *ed:* Gettysburg Coll (BA) Psych 198
MD Coll (MLA) Lbrl Arts 1983; 30 Hrs Post Grad Stud; *cr:* Keef
6 Grd Tchr 1980-92, 5 Grd Tchr 1992-; *ai:* Peer Mediation
Shakespeare; Instr Lincoln Intermediate Unit Summer Acad Boo
Illustrating; NEA 1980-, Sec, PR Person; Character Ed Partners
ASCD 1990-; Delta Kappa 1988-; Mediation Svcs of Adams Cty
Phi Beta Kappa; Natl Fellow Ind Stud in Hum 1990; Martin L
Curr Dev Awds; Articles Pub; *office:* Keefauver Elem Schl
Gettysburg PA 17325

DAGOSTINO, PEGGY SMITH, Basic Skills Teacher; *b:* Norv
m: Joseph A.; *c:* Anthony, Frank, Joseph John; *ed:* Glassboro St
Elem Ed 1966, (MA) Rdng Specialist 1975; Supervisory Cert
Cert HOTS Prgm; *cr:* Leuchter Schl Fourth Grd Tchr 1966-70;
Maurice Fels Schl Remedial Rdng Specialist 1971-72; Reber
Remedial Rdng Specialist 1972-80; Memorial MS Basic Skills
Chprsn 1980-; *ai:* Girls Bsktbl Coach Sacred Heart HS 1964-
NJEA 1966-; Vineland Ed Assn 1966-, Chm, Soc Comm; A
Kappa 1977-, Pres, Pres Elect, Historian; Tiny Tim Fund 1975-,

nts Coord; Governors Tchr Recognition Awd 1986; *home:* 2270 Vineland NJ 08360

INO, R. ALFREDO, 9th-12th Grade Science Teacher; *b:* Y; *m:* Therese A.; *c:* Joseph, Maria; *ed:* Univ of Buffalo (BA) (EDM) Sci Ed 1970; Canisius Coll (MS) Admin 1989; *ai:* Sftbl oach; ASCD; NEA; *office:* Sweet Home Schl Sweet Home Rd Y 14228

WILLIAM C., English Teacher; *b:* Pittsburg, PA; *m:* Patricia : Michael, Melissa, Erin; *ed:* Allegheny Coll (BA) Eng 1968, 974; *cr:* J F Kennedy HS Eng Tchr & Coach 1968-71; Carteret hr & Coach 1972-79; Freehold HS Eng Tchr & Coach 1979-87; Eng Tchr & Coach 1987-; *ai:* Howell HS Ath Hall of Fame EA 1995-; NEA 1995-; MCEA 1995-; FRHSEA 1995-; Howell the Yr 1995-96; *office:* Howell HS Squankum-Yellowbrook Rd le NJ 07727

ANEY, Retired Mathematics Teacher; *b:* Staten Island, NY; *m:* Matthes; *ed:* 40 Credits in Cmptr Sci at Coll of Staten Island; in Math Ed at Belfer Grad Schl at Yeshiva Univ; *cr:* Curtis HS nptr Tchr 1963-1995; *ai:* Math Team Adv; SIGMA 1977-, Pres; -, Past Recording Sec; NCTM & NYCTM 1963-; VFT; Curtis ni Assn 1980-, Bd of Dir; Our Saviour Luth Church 1941-, Past on Pres, Vacation Bible Schl Dir; Staten Island Continuem of Yr 1988; Coll of Staten Island Outstanding Tchng of Math 1988.

ANCY VODREY, English Teacher; *b:* East Liverpool, OH; *c:* ., Brandon V.; *ed:* Wilson Coll (BA) Pysch 1962; Youngstown St 1976; *cr:* North Elem Title Rdng Tchr 1972-80; East Liverpool hr 1980-; *ai:* NEA, OEA & ELEA 1972-; *office:* East Liverpool aine Blvd East Liverpool OH 43920

VINTHROP H.K., Latin Teacher; *b:* Attleboro, MA; *ed:* Univ (BA) Classics & Coll of Letters 1984; *cr:* Portsmouth HS 1986-90; Nashoba Regnl HS Latin Tchr 1991-; *ai:* Amesty Intnl E 1986-; NEH Summer Seminar; *office:* Nashoba Regional HS Rd Bolton MA 01740*

EN, JEAN GARVEY, Associate Professor; *b:* Ticonderoga, NY; W.; *c:* Kathryn E., Laura J.; *ed:* St Univ of NY at Oswego (BA) 1978, (MA) Fine Arts 1983; *cr:* Sage Jr Coll of Albany Assoc aphic Design 1988-; *ai:* Graphic Artists Guild 1994-; NY St Ed EA Grant 1992-93; Albany Advertising Club Nori Awd Winner Kerox Ventura Publisher Design for Excl Awd 1988; *office:* Sage Albany 140 New Scotland Ave Albany NY 12208*

ROM, DENISE ELAINE REEM, Music Teacher; *b:* Galesburg, ris Alfred Dahlstrom; *c:* Roger, Philip, Rebekah; *ed:* Univ of IL ign/Urbana (BS) Music Ed 1971; Miami Univ (MM) Music Ed Addl Credit Hrs; *cr:* Madison Schl Dist Music Tchr 1971-73; n Chrstn Schl Music Tchr 1981-83; Lakota Schl Dist Music Tchr Frosh Ensembles; OMCA Solo & Ensembles Competition pt Head; OMEA, MENC 1971-; ACDA, OCDA 1990-; Church 973-83; Church Choir Dir 1985-87.

BRUCE JOHN, English & Social Studies Tchr; *b:* Manchester of ME at Orono (BSEd) Scndry Ed & Soc Stud 1969; 30 Hrs in 971-72; *cr:* US Army Military Police Vietnam 1969-71; VT St mp Abnaki Cnslr & Asst Dir 1967-69 & 1972-86; Southeastern Acad Eng, Soc Stud, Fr & Art Tchr 1973-; *ai:* US Army Vietnam r Medal; *office:* Southeastern NH Chrstn Acad 12 Rocky Hill Rd rth NH 03878

AIL SWANK, 7th & 8th Grade Teacher; *b:* Shelby, OH; *m:* arles; *c:* Keith, Melissa Speelman, Rebecca Lomax, Michael : Bowling Green St Univ (BS) Elem Ed 1967; Ashland Univ sic Classes; *cr:* Shelby City Schls 3-5 Grd Sub Tchr 1967-82; St l 6-7-8 Grd Tchr 1982-; *ai:* Power of Pen Coach, Judge; Chime NCEA 1982-; Lang Arts Ldrshp Cncl 1993-; First Luth Church lsp 1988, Chime Choir Dir 1982; For God, Youth Awd; *office:* St l 26 West St Shelby OH 44875

KI, NANCY CARPENTER, Family & Consumer Sci Teacher; npton, MA; *m:* Arthur W.; *c:* Kimberly J., Robert T.; *ed:* Univ of d, Home Ec 1964; Attnd Univ of MA; *cr:* Ridgefield HS Home 64-65; South Hadley Intermediate Schl Home Ec Tchr 1965-69; ley MS, HS Home Ec Tchr 1984-85, 1988-92; Turners Falls HS onsumer Sci Tchr 1993-; *ai:* NTA, NEA 1994-; Phi Upsilon 963-; *office:* Turners Falls HS Turnpike Rd Turners Falls MA

DAVID C., Mathematics Teacher; *b:* Dover, NH; *m:* Catherine athan D., Olivia C.; *ed:* Univ of NH (BS) Math 1985; *cr:* n Acad Math Tchr 1986-; *ai:* Class Adv; Coach Frosh Boys 85-89, Boys JV Bsktbl 1989-; NCTM, NHATMNE 1988-; NH ssn 1986-; *office:* Coe-Brown Northwood Acad Rt 4 Northwood

DONALD PAUL, Mathematics Teacher; *b:* El Paso, TX; *m:* Connolly; *c:* Thomas, Elizabeth, Amy; *ed:* Univ of South AL 1972; Auburn Univ (MS) Math 1973; Post Grad Enrichment ath, Cmptrs, Ed George Mason Univ, Univ of VA; *cr:* Bishop Connell HS Math Tchr 1974-76; Bishop Mc Namara HS Math -78; Georgetown Visitation Math Tchr 1978-; Georgetown Univ 987-95; *ai:* Stu Mentor; Soph Class Moderator; NCTM 1980-; ilon; St James Church 1974-; Amer Heart Assn Vol 1995-, Area office: Georgetown Visitation Prep Sch 1524 35th St NW n DC 20007*

MELODY ANNE, Sixth Grade Teacher; *b:* ME; *m:* Richard J.; *ed:* Trinity Coll (BA) Spec Ed & Eng 1988; 15 Grad Credit Hrs; IS 6th Grd Tchr 1988-; *ai:* Newshunt Schl Paper Adv; At-Risk m Mentor; Responsible Inclusion & Diversity Comms Mem; ation Prgm Mem; NEA 1988-; Natl Tchrs Schlsp Undergraduate drens Story Pub in Childrens Magazine; *home:* 570 S Willard St VT 05401

JAMES M., OWA Coordinator; *b:* Royal Oak, MI; *m:* Marilyn ; *c:* Megan, Erin, Matthew; *ed:* Bethany Coll (BA) His 1973; ayton (MS) Child & Yth Guid 1986; *cr:* St Vincent de Paul Grd Stud & PE Tchr 1975; Bridgeport HS OWA Coord & Soc Stud -; *ai:* Head Bsktbl Coach; Bridgeport Ed Assn 1976-, VP; OH Ed -; NEA 1976-; West VA Coaches Assn 1990-; Grad of Ldrshp 1989; *office:* Bridgeport HS 501 Bennett St Bridgeport OH

DIANE BUTH, Special Education Teacher; *b:* Lockport, NY; *m:* SUC Potsdam (BA) Psych 1969; SUC Buffalo (MS) Spec Ed Camden Cntrl Schl Spec Ed Tchr 1970-72; Ogdensburg City Schl Ed Tchr 1972-78; St Lawrence Lewis BOCES Spec Ed Tchr Citizenship, Playground, Fund-Raising Comms; BOCES Tchrs ; NYSUT 1970-; Madill PTA 1980-; *home:* 205 Cemetary Rd g NY 13669

MARTHA LA CROIX, History Teacher; *b:* Bennington, VT; *m:* .; *c:* Jennifer Melissa, Jacqueline M. Le Blanc, Timothy, *ed:* Coll of St Rose (BA) His 1961; North Adams St Coll (MS) Univ of MA (MA) Amer His 1983; Univ of NM (PHD) Amer Stud d AZ St Univ, SUNY at Albany, Antioch Grad Schl of Mngmt; *cr:* NY Ave MS Tchr 1961-62; Northport HS Tchr 1964-65; Shenendehowa Cntrl Schl 1966-67; Window Rock Regnl Tchr 1978; Univ NM Tchr 1983-84, 1989-91; Mount Greylock Regnl HS Tchr 1970-95; *ai:* USIP, NEH Essay Contest; Supt Round Table on Prof Dev; NEA, MTA 1970-; MGFA 1970-, Pres; NCSS 1970-, Racism & Soc Justice Comm; Bridgs for Peace; MA Right to Life 1974-; CCD Coord, PIUS X Awd; Wiliams Coll Olmsted Awd; B'nai B'rith World of Difference Awd; CBE Flwshp; NEH Flwshp UNM & Italy; Korean Cultural Soc Fellow Korea; John F. Kennedy Awd for Tchng; Fulbright to Pakistan; Fulbright to India; Japan Fellow to Japan; Russia Linkage Flwshp; Outstdng Tchr Univ of Chicago; US Distngd Tchr 1984-86; *office:* Mount Greylock Regnl HS 1781 Cold Spring Rd Williamstown MA 01267*

DAILEY, THOMAS, Assoc Professor of Theology; *b:* Bensalem, PA; *ed:* Allentown Coll (BA) Theology 1981; Pontifical Gregorian Univ (STD) Biblical Theology 1986, (STL) Biblical Theology 1988, (STD) Biblical Theology 1993; *cr:* Northeast Cath HS Fac 1981-83; Allentown Coll Instr 1988-91, Asst Prof 1993-95, Assoc Prof 1996-; *ai:* Fac Steering Comm Chair; De Sales Honors Prgm Dir; Cath Biblical Assn, Coll Theology Soc, Soc of Biblical Lit 1988-; Flwshp of Cath Scholars 1994-; De Sales Schl of Theology 1995-, Bd of Trustees; Berman Ctr for Jewish Stud 1995-, Acad Advy Bd; 3 Books, 17 Articles, 2 Chptrs Pub; 2 Books Translated; *office:* Allentown Coll Of St Francis 2755 Station Ave Center Valley PA 18034

DAILEY HYLKEMA, PATRICIA A., Applied Communications Teacher; *b:* Zanesville, OH; *m:* Donald R.; *c:* Scott Madigan, Jay Madigan, Holley Madigan, Leigh; *ed:* OH Univ (BA) Eng 1989; Interpersonal Comm; *cr:* Mid-East OH Voc Schl Dist Adult Instr 1977-87; OH Univ Writing Tutor 1987-89; Mid-East OH Voc Schl Dist Eng Tchr 1989-; *ai:* Yrbk Career Classics, NHS Adv; Schl Improvement Advy Comm; Network Cmptr, Tech Task Force; NEA, MEEA, AVA, OVA 1990-; SOCTE 1988-; Zanesville Comm Theater 1973-, VP, St OCTA, Pres 1983, Awd Costuming Awd, Acting; Rdng Hall of Fame Awd 1994; Natl Red Ribbon Week Awd 1993; *office:* Mid East OH Voc Schl Dist 57090 Vocational Rd Senecaville OH 43780

DAILY, CHERYL A., Spanish & French Teacher; *b:* Broctkon, MA; *c:* Erin, Meghan; *ed:* Emmanuel coll (BA) Span 1975; *cr:* North Reading HS Span Tchr 1975-77; North Reading Jr HS Span, Fr Tchr 1977-84; Whitman-Hanson HS Span, Fr Tchr 1991-; *ai:* Frgn Lang Club, Stu Cncl Adv; NEA, MTA 1975-; MaFLA 1994-; AATSP 1992-; Saftlers Quilt Guild 1994-, Exec Bd, Vice Chprsn; *office:* Whitman Hanson Regnl HS Franklin St Whitman MA 02382

DAILY, ROSWITHA BURKEY, German Teacher; *b:* Milstatt, Austria; *m:* James A.; *c:* Michelle A. Burkey; *ed:* OH St Univ (BS) Ed 1967, (MA) Frgn Lang Ed 1971; *cr:* Grove City HS Ger & Fr Tchr 1967-; *ai:* Ger Exch Club Adv; Exch Pgm with Ger HS Coord 23 Yrs; OFLA 1968-; AATG 1970-; Grove City HS Tchr of the Yr 1990; Ger Reader Pub Der Weg Zum Lesen 1978, 1982; OH St Univ Ger Dept Distngd Tchng Hnr Roll 1981; *office:* Grove City HS 4665 Hoover Rd Grove City OH 43123

DAISLEY, ELLIE GLASSMIRE, Biology Teacher; *b:* Coodersport, PA; *ed:* PA St Univ (BS) Bio 1975; St Bonaventure Univ (MS) Ed 1991; 6 Post Grad Hrs Cornell Univ 1992-93; *cr:* Port Allegany HS Bio Tchr 1984-86; Cuba-Rushford Cntrl Bio Tchr 1986-; *ai:* Stu Cncl, NHS Advs; CRCS Bldg Level Team; NYS Compact For Learning; NEA, CRTA 1986-, Past Pres 1991-93; *office:* Cuba-Rushford Central Schl 15 Elm St Cuba NY 14727

DAKOS, MINAS JAMES, Seventh Grade Soc Studies Tchr; *b:* Peabody, MA; *m:* Maria Christina Kazogles; *c:* Frances Shaheen, Theodora D'Angelo, James; *ed:* Boston Univ (BA) His 1961; Salem St Coll (MED) Ed 1969; Attnd Univ of MA; *cr:* Pentucket Reg Schl Dist Tchr, Dept Head 1963-; *ai:* Stu Cncl Adv 1966-93; NEA 1963-; Jordan Lodge of Masons 1969-; AHEPA 1973-; *office:* Pentucket Regnl Schl Dist 22 Main St West Newbury MA 01985

DALBEC, DANIELLE CHRISTINE, French Teacher; *b:* Cornwall ON, Canada; *ed:* Potsdam Coll (BA) Fr, Early Chldhd Ed 1985; St Lawrence Univ (MED) Gen Ed 1989; 18 Hrs Span; Laval Univ 6 Hrs Fr Masters; *cr:* J. W. Leary Jr HS Fr Tchr 1985-86; Bolton Cntrl Schl Fr Tchr 1986-87; Edwards-Knox Cntrl Schl Fr Tchr 1987-; *ai:* Fr Club Adv; NEA 1987-; St Etienne France Fulbright Tchr Exch 1992-93; Laval Univ Multi Natl, Cultural Exch Schlsp 1991; *office:* Edwards-Knox Central Schl PO Box 630 Russell NY 13684

D'ALBERTO, ADELE DALOIA, Retired Teacher; *b:* Mechanicville, NY; *m:* Ernest; *c:* Jolie O'Brien, David, Janine Welcome; *ed:* Coll of St Rose (BS) Early CH to 6th Grd 1956; *ai:* NYSUT 1956-; NYS Ret Tchrs 1990-; *home:* 28 Route 146 Mechanicville NY 12118

DALE, LINDA B., Math Teacher; *b:* Cincinatti, OH; *ed:* OH Wesleyan Univ (BA) Math 1994; *cr:* Riverdale HS Math Tchr 1994-; *ai:* After Schl Math Proficiency Review Sessions; NCTM 1993-; NEA 1994-; Kappa Delta Pi 1994-; Chrysalis Emmaus Comm 1989-, Chrysalis Bd of Dir 1993-; *home:* 950 King St Kenton OH 43326

D'ALESSANDRO, DENNIS ANTHONY, Math Teacher; *b:* Brooklyn, NY; *m:* Connie Berry; *c:* Jontomas, Dennis, Toni; *ed:* Suffolk Cty CC (Assoc) Math 1970; SUNY at New Paltz (BA) 7th-12th Grd Math Ed 1972, (MA) K-6th Grd Elem Ed 1975; 21 Grad Credits Beyond BA in Math Ed; *cr:* Temple Hill Schl Math Tchr 1972-79; North Jr HS Math Tchr 1980-; *ai:* Union Bldg, NYSUT & AFT Del; Newburgh Tchrs Assn Bd of Dir; Tchr Ctr Bd of Dir; Newburgh Tchrs Assn 1972-, Del Profile in Unionism; NYSUT 1972-, Del; AFT 1972-, Del; *office:* Newburgh Enlrgd City Schl Dist 124 Grand St Newburgh NY 12550

DALESSIO, ELIZABETH BAILEY, Fifth Grade Teacher; *b:* Salem, NJ; *m:* Michael J. III; *ed:* West Chester Univ (BS) Elem Ed 1982; Rowan Coll (MS) Comm 1994; *cr:* Absegami HS Rdng Tchr 1983-89; Brigantine North MS Seventh-Eighth Lit, S Stud Tchr 1990-93, Fifth Grd Eng Tchr 1993-; *ai:* Strategic Planning, Sunshine, GATE Comm; NEA 1983-, Pub Media Comm NJEA; Brigantine Ed Assn 1990-, Sec; NCTE 1995-; Egg harbor Twp Ed Fnd 1992-; Ranch Hope Inc 1994-, Bd Mem; NJ Governors Awd Tchr Recognition 1995; Thesis-Tuition Vouchers; *office:* Brigantine North MS Lafayette Blvd Brigantine NJ 08203*

DALEY, ANN MARY, Fourth Grade Teacher; *b:* Haverhill, MA; *ed:* Salem St Coll (BS) Elem Ed 1970; 40 Grad Credit Hrs; *cr:* Dr. Elmer S. Bagnall Elem Schl Fourth Grd Tchr 1970-; *ai:* Bsktbl Coach 1 Yr, Vlybl Coach 2 Yrs; Founded Environmental Schl Nature Trl; Child Stud Team Mem; Multicultural Comm; MTA, NEA, Pentucket Assn of Tchrs 1970-; Louise Mills Credit Union 1970-, Sec 2 Yrs, Bldg Rep 12 Yrs; MA Audubon Soc 1991-, Mem; Runner-up Tchr of Yr MA Audubon Soc 1993; Nom for Presidential Awd in Sci; *office:* Bagnall Schl 253 School St Groveland MA 01834

DALEY, DANIEL DAVID,III, Acad Counselor & Math Instr; *b:* St Johnsbury, VT; *m:* Kathryn Anne Hubbard; *c:* Connor, Cameron; *ed:* Lyndon St Coll (BS) Math & (AS) Physics 1981, (BS) Meteorology 1982, (MED) Curr & Instruction 1993; *cr:* Lyndon Inst Math Instr 1982-; Lyndon St Coll Adjunct Math Instr 1986-, Acad Cnslr 1992-; *ai:* Asst Mens Cross-Cntry Coach; Lyndonville Town Band 1972-, Mgr; AHEAD 1993-; NEAOPP, VEOP 1994-; Tchng Fellowship Univ of VT 1985-86; Articles Pub New England Math Journal 1994 & 1995; *office:* Lyndon St Coll Vail Hill Lyndon Center VT 05850

DALEY, JAMIE T., English Professor; *b:* Huntington, NY; *m:* Roger; *c:* Kristin, Ryan, Meghan; *ed:* IN Univ (BA) Eng 1976; Univ of Notre Dame (MA) Eng 1978, (PHD) Eng 1983; *cr:* Marian HS Eng Instr 1979-82; Rutgers Univ Eng Instr 1983-92; Shoreless Lake Schl Eng Instr 1993-95; Middlesex Cty Coll Eng Instr 1993-; *ai:* Instruction, Eng I & II, Stu Relations & Developmental Writing Comms; AAUP 1985-, Sec; NJ Coll Eng Assn, NJ Consortium on Higher Ed 1994-; Saint Bartholomew Church, Rel Ed Tchr 1983-; *home:* 103 Farms Road Cir East Brunswick NJ 08816

DALEY, KATHLEEN DETRICK, 8th Grd Language Arts Teacher; *b:* Springfield, OH; *m:* Bert A.; *c:* Paul W., Dana M.; *ed:* OH St Univ (BS) Elem Ed 1983; Univ of Dayton (MS) Guid Cnslr 1992; 15 Post-Grad Credit Hrs Writing, Eng Wright St Univ; *cr:* Indian Lake Elem Schl Learning Disability Tutor 1983-84; Indian Lake MS Sixth Grd Tchr 1984-92, Lang Arts Tchr 1992-; *ai:* Crisis Support Team Mem; NEA, OEA, ILEA 1983-; Selected Change Course Participation; Tchr Ldr Network Rep West Central OH; West Region Lang Arts Network Inst Rep; *office:* Indian Lake MS 8144 Road 54 Lewistown OH 43333

DALEY, PATRICIA, Health Careers Teacher; *b:* Fall River, MA; *ed:* Univ of MA at Darthmouth (BSN) Nrsng-Highest Distinction 1981; Union Hosp Schl of Nrsng Diploma 1966; Fitchburg St Coll 36 Credit Hrs; Roger Williams Univ 6 Credit Hrs; *cr:* Charlton Meml Hosp Emergency Dept, Intensive Care, Telemetry Univ Dir 1966-90; Travelers Insurance Co Rehabilitation Consultant 1990-91; Diman Rgnl Voc Tech HS Hlth Careers Tchr 1991-; *ai:* Amer Heart Assn CPR Instr; Amer Cancer Soc Liason; Great Amer Smokeout; Advy Bd; Safety Comm; Walk-a-Thon; Red Cross Blood Drive; Sigma Theta Tau 1981-, Highest Distinction; NEA, MTA, DTA 1991-; Amer Assn Critical Care Nurses 1980-; RI Schl Nurses Assn 1995-; Big Brothers, Sisters 1980-; FR Emergency Med Svcs Bd 1980-; Critical Care Ed Grant at Boston Univ; *office:* Diman Reg Voc Tech HS 251 Stonehaven Rd Fall River MA 02723*

DALLARA, RALPH ANTHONY, HS Mathematics Teacher; *b:* Jamaica, NY; *m:* Priscilla Gugliotti; *c:* Eric, Paul; *ed:* SUCO at Oneonta (BS) Scndry Math 1970; St Univ of NY at Albany (MS) Scndry Math 1976; *ai:* Gymnastics; Unatego Cntrl Schl Wrestling; NYSUT 1970-; *home:* 17 Turnberry Ln Clifton Park NY 12065

DALLARI, ELAINE DANNER, Resource Room Teacher; *b:* Long Beach, NY; *m:* Richard; *c:* Gregory; *ed:* SUNY at Oswego (BS) Elem Ed 1965; Adelphi (MS) Spec Ed 1976; C. W. Post; Hofstra; Univ of Vienna; *cr:* Baldwin Schls Classroom Tchr 1965-83, Resource Room Tchr 1983-; *ai:* Elem Rep Dist Hlth, Safety, Prof Dev Comms; Site Base Team; Union Rep; Baldwin Tchrs Assn 1965-, VP, NYSUT Cert of Recognition; Pub Spelling Prgm Called Spelling Box.

D'ALOISIO, TRACEY JEAN, 2nd Grade Teacher; *b:* Providence, RI; *ed:* RI Coll (BS) Elem Ed, Lang Arts 1984, (MA) Lang Arts 1990; MS Endorsement 1993; *cr:* North Providence Schl Dept Gifted Resource Tchr 1985-87; Greystone Schl Advanced 8th Grd Tchr 1987-89, 4th Grd Tchr 1989-90, 7th-8th Grd Tchr 1990-94; Centredale Schl 2nd Grd Tchr 1994-; *ai:* Stu Cncl Adv 1992-93; CAST 1992-; Ldrshp Team for Math & Sci; AFT 1985-, Del, Alternate; MS After Dark 1986-; *office:* Centredale Schl 41 Angell Ave North Providence RI 02911*

D'ALONZO, ROBERT F., Physical Education Teacher; *b:* New Brunswick, NJ; *m:* Mary Lynn Mc Closkey; *c:* Christopher, Jeffrey, Daniel; *ed:* Middlesex Coy Coll (AA) Lbrl Arts 1972; Trenton St Coll (BS) Hlth, PE 1974; *cr:* St Peter's HS Hlth, PE, Drivers Ed Tchr 1975-77; Readington MS PE Tchr 1977-; *ai:* Staff Dev, Curr Dev, Prin Search Comm; IM Coord Track & Field, Cross Country Coach; Stu Cncl Adv; NEA, NJEA, Readington Ed Assn 1990-; AAHPERD, NJAHPERD 1977-; Natl Fed of St HS Assn 1976-; Intnl Assn Approved Bsktbl Ofcls 1976-; BPOE #254 Elks 1988-; Knight of Columbus 1975; East Brunswick Soccer Club 1990-, Coach; East Brunswick Bsbl League 1984-, Coach; Outstdng Svc Awd Stu Cncl 1993-94; *office:* Readington MS PO Box 2 Readington NJ 08870

DALPE, LEO PAUL, American History Teacher; *b:* Woonsocket, RI; *m:* Loretta Coppinger; *c:* David, Stacy; *ed:* Framingham St Coll (BA) His & Ed 1974; 33 Credit Hrs towards Masters from RI coll & Boston St Coll; *cr:* Bellingham Jr Sr HS Soc Stud Tchr 1974-; *ai:* Class Adv 1980-; Stu Cncl Adv 1990-; NEA 1974-; MA Tchrs Assn 1974-; Bellingham Tchrs Assn 1974-; Bellingham Girls Sftbl 1992-, League Dir; *office:* Bellingham Mem Jr Sr HS Blackstone St Bellingham MA 02019

DALTON, JOAN FITZGERALD, Second Grade Teacher; *b:* Boston, MA; *ed:* Suffolk Univ (BA) Elem Ed 1968; Worcester St (MA) Rdng 1978; *cr:* Dyer Schl 3rd Grd Tchr 1968-72; Proctor Schl 2nd Grd Tchr 1972-; *ai:* Hlth Frameworks & Lib Comm; NEA 1968-; MTA 1968-; Anna Seaver Awd Northboro; *office:* Proctor Schl 26 Jefferson Rd Northborough MA 01532

DALY, DANIEL JAMES, Hotel & Restaurant Mgmt Coord; *b:* Winthrop, MA; *m:* Virginia Feraco; *c:* Elizabeth, Daniel; *ed:* Univ of MA at Amherst (BS) Hotel, Rest & Travel Admin 1973; Bryant Coll (MBA) Mngmt 1986; CHA Certified Hotel Admin Educl Inst of AHMA; CHAE Certified Hospitality Accountant Exec IAHA; *cr:* Driftwood Restaurant & Motor Inn General Mgr 1975-78; Johnson & Wales Univ Asst Prof & Acad Coord 1978-84; Endicott Coll Asst Prof & Dept Chair 1984-85; Quinsigamond Comm Coll Prof & Prgm Coord 1985-; *ai:* Chair Acad Affairs Comm; Adv Hotel & Restaurant Mngmt Assn; Ed Mer-Chrie Newsletter; CHRIE Past Dir; Ner-Chrie Past Pres; ACE; *office:* Quinsigamond Comm Coll 670 W Boylston St Worcester MA 01606

DALY, DORIS CHRISTENSON, Fourth Grade Teacher; *b:* Bridgeport, CT; *m:* William Thomas; *c:* Scott F.; *ed:* Southern CT St Univ (BA) Elem Ed 1957; Univ of Bridgeport (MA) Elem Ed 1964; *cr:* Bd of Ed Bridgeport Tchr 1957-67; Bd of Ed Fairfield Tchr 1967-68; Spec Tutor 1972-74; Bd of Ed Fairfield Paraprofessional Spec Ed 1980-86; Diocese of Bridgeport Tchr 1986-; *ai:* NCEA 1986-; Bridgeport Hosp Auxiliary 1994-; United Congregational Church 1993-, Music Bd; *home:* 118 Larkspur Rd Fairfield CT 06430

DALY, JAMES JOSEPH, Fourth Grade Teacher; *b:* Oswego, NY; *c:* Sean; *ed:* SUNY at Oswego (BS) Elem Ed 1969, (MS) Ed 1974; SUNY at Geneseo (MLS) Lib & Information Sci 1978; *cr:* Syracuse City Schls 6th Grd Tchr 1969-70; Fairport Cntrl Schl Syst Intermediate Grds Tchr 1970-; Fairport Cntrl Schl Syst Librn 1984-85; *ai:* AFT 1973-; Irish Northern Aid 1984-, Co-Chm; *office:* Jefferson Avenue Elem Schl 303 Jefferson Ave Fairport NY 14450

DALY, JEAN M., Fifth Grade Teacher; *b:* New York, NY; *m:* Joseph T.; *c:* Christopher, Matthew; *ed:* SUNY at New Paltz (BS) Bio, Western Civilization 1960; SUNY at Stony Brook (MALS) Lbrl Arts 1976; 75 Credits Hrs; *cr:* Setauket Schl 4 Grd Tchr 1960-63; Nassakeag Schl Grd 4 Tchr 1963-64; Arrowhead Schl Grd 5 Tchr 1965-74; Setauket Schl Grd 5 Tchr 1975-; *ai:* Peer Mediation Team; Tchrs as Readers Coord; Family Math Ldr; CW Post Stu Tchr Seminars Lectorer; AFT, NYSUT, IRA 1964-; Three Vlg Tchrs Assn, Bldg Rep 2 Yrs; Habitat for Hum 1990-; Worker, Bldr, Fundraiser; Mestrac Grant for Interdistrict Tchrs Lit Discussion Group 2 Yrs; Hodge Podge Soc; Tchr of Yr; NYSEC Tchr of Excl; *home:* 8 Center Ct Rocky Point NY 11778*

DALY, MARY WELLINGTON, German Teacher; *b:* El Reno, OK; *m:* Richard David; *c:* Kristin, Eric, Laura; *ed:* Cornell Univ (BA) German Lit 1966; Harvard Univ (MAT) German 1967; 18 Post Grad Credit Hrs from Lewis & Clark Coll at Portland, Cambridge Coll, Univ of CT at Storrs; *cr:* Darien HS German Tchr 1967-69; Newton N HS German Tchr 1969-70;

Pentucket Regnl Jr Sr HS German Tchr 1970-72; Spofford Pond Elem Schl German Tchr 1984-92; Masconomet Regnl Jr Sr HS German Tchr 1992-; *ai:* AATG 1967-; MA Frgn Lang Assn, Essex Cty Lang Assn of Tchrs 1992-; Second Congregational Church 1974-, Many Offices; *office:* Masconomet Regnl Jr Sr HS 20 Endicott Rd Topsfield MA 01983

DALZELL, KENNETH F., Jr HS Science Teacher; *b:* Milton, MN; *m:* Diane M. Riordan; *c:* Kimberly Harper, Keith, Kristi, Kendra, Michell Harper, Stacey Harper; *ed:* Bridgewater St Coll (BS) Ed 1967; Credit Hrs Boston St Coll, Boston Coll; *cr:* Norwood Jr HS Sci Tchr 1967-; *ai:* Coach HS JV Sftbl, Frosh Bsbl 1969-88, Frosh Ftbl 1969-90; Club Adv Ski, Ping Pong, Bsbl, Bsktbl; NEA, MTA 1967-; NSTA 1989-.

D'AMARIO, URSULA A., Mathematics Teacher; *b:* Providence, RI; *m:* Daniel; *ed:* Boston Univ (BS) Math 1965; Purdue Univ (MAT) Math 1972; Coursework Univ of RI 1992, Providence Coll 1988, Mt Holyoke Coll 1987, Univ of FL 1985, Taft Schl 1984, Rhode Island Coll 1983; *cr:* Scituate HS Math Tchr 1965-69; Annandale HS Math Tchr 1969-70; East Greenwich HS Math Tchr 1970-; *ai:* Chrldr, Math Team Adv, Sr Class Adv; Admin Intern; NCTM, NEA 1965-; NEA, RI 1980-; Dist Cmptr Task Force Chprsn; Instr Governors Iniative on Cmptrs; Co-Manage Regnl MECC Software Ctr; *office:* East Greenwich HS 300 Avenger Dr East Greenwich RI 02818

DAMATO, BERNADETTE (DANILEWICZ), 4th Grd Tchr & Asst Principal; *b:* Jersey City, NJ; *m:* James Vincent; *c:* Helene M., Charlene R.; *ed:* Fordham Univ (BS) Elem Ed 1960; *cr:* St Clemens Mary 1st, 4th, 6th Grd Tchr 1960-69; Holy Cross 1st Grd Tchr 1969-74; St James Sub Tchr 1978-83, 4th Grd Tchr 1983-, Asst Prin 1990-; *ai:* Coord Rainbows for all Children Inc; Columbiettes 1978-; St James Schl Bd 1992-; Outstanding Educator 1993; *home:* 43 Baltusrol Way Springfield NJ 07081*

D'AMATO, PHILIP, Modern Languages Dept Chprsn; *b:* Cold Spring, NY; *m:* Patricia Ann Helbock; *c:* Maria, Philip; *ed:* Marist Coll (BA) Span 1977; St Univ of NY at New Paltz (MS) Span, Ed 1985; Marist Abroad Prgm at Universidad Complutense de Madrid 1975; *cr:* Marist HS Span Tchr 1977-80; Crittenden MS Span Tchr 1980-81; Mahopac Jr HS Span, Fr Tchr 1981-82; Haldane Jr Sr HS Span, Fr Tchr, Dept Chprsn 1982-; *ai:* NHA, Grad Awds Cmms; Schl Improvement Team; Coach Ftbl, Soccer, Track, Field, Cross Cntry; AFT, NYSAFLT 1980-; Little League Coach 1995-; Two Schlsps NYSAFLTS Summer Wkshp Skidmore Coll; Grant Mini Lessons Frgn Langs; *home:* 38 Pine St Nelsonville NY 10516

DAMBACH, EDWARD CHARLES, Secondary Math Teacher; *b:* New Castle, PA; *m:* Diana Gail Hillard; *c:* Gretchen; *ed:* Westminster Coll (BS) Math Ed 1971, (MED) Scndry Admin 1976; Scndry Prin Cert 1989; *cr:* Highland Jr HS 8th-9th Grd Math Tchr 1971-73; Blackhawk HS Math Tchr 1973-89; Geneva Coll Evening Instr 1986-; Riverside HS Asst HS Prin 1989-91, Math Tchr 1991-92; Blackhawk HS Math Tchr 1992-; *ai:* Stu Assistance Team; NEA, PSEA 1971-; Blackhawk Ed Assn 1971-, Mbrshp Chm; Chippewa Twp Planning Commission 1994-, Asst Chm; Blackhawk Federal CU 1976-, Loan Officer; Coll Hill Pres Church 1979-, Elder; Tchr of Yr 1985-87; Stu Cncl; Nom Excl Ed in PA 1986; *office:* Blackhawk HS 500 Blackhawk Rd Beaver Falls PA 15010*

D'AMBOLA, JOSEPH, Industrial Ed & Tech Teacher; *b:* Newark, NJ; *m:* Patricia Carlin; *c:* Michele, Lori; *ed:* Montclair St Univ (BA) Industrial Ed, Tech 1967, (MS) Industrial Ed, Tech 1987; *cr:* East Side HS Industrial Arts Tchr 1967-71; Belleville HS Industrial Ed, Tech Tchr 1971-; *ai:* Var Ftbl Defensive Coord, Coach; NJEA, NEA 1971-; *office:* Belleville HS 100 Passaic Ave Belleville NJ 07109

D'AMBOLA, TOBY, High School Math Teacher; *b:* Newark, NJ; *m:* Judith A. Krais; *c:* Denise, Lisa, Dana; *ed:* Montclair St Univ (BA) Math 1968, (MA) Math 1972; 6th Yr Educl Supervision; *cr:* Nutley HS Math, Fin & Comp Prog Instr 1968-; Essex Cty Coll Adjunct Prof 1974-75; Bloomfield Coll Adjunct Prof 1976-81; Union Cty Coll Adjunct Math Prof 1992-; *ai:* Sr Class, Am Field Sci, Stock Investment Club Advs; NJEA, NEA 1968-; Natl Cncl Teach of Math; Clark Bd of Ed 1985-88, VP 1987-88; Project Grad 1992-93, Chprsn; Stock Investment Club 2 Grand Championships in Stock Game Competition 1991, 1995; Numerous Articles Pub; *office:* Nutley HS 300 Franklin Ave Nutley NJ 07110*

D'AMBRA, JOHN R., High School English Teacher; *b:* Brooklyn, NY; *m:* Irene Regan; *ed:* Manhattan Coll (BA) Eng & Ed 1967; Montclair St (MA) Amer Lit 1972; Addl Courses at Syracuse Univ, NYU, Fordham Univ, Northeastern Univ, Jersey City St; *cr:* Northern Valley Eng Tchr 1967-; *ai:* Lit Magazine Co-Adv; Retired Tennis Coach; Northern Valley Ed Assn 1967-, Past Pres, Past Chief Negotiator; Chosen by Stdnts Tchr of Yr; Nom by Schl as Candidate for Cty Tchr of Yr; Governors Awd for Excl in Tchgng; *office:* Nrthn Vly Reg-Demarest HS 150 Knickerbocker Rd Demarest NJ 07627*

DAMBROGIO, KIMBERLY A., Chemistry Teacher; *b:* Youngston, OH; *ed:* Univ of Akron (BA) Ed, Chem 1987; Cleveland St Univ (MS) Chem 1995; *cr:* Chanel HS Chem Tchr 1988-89; Cleveland Schl of Sci Math Tchr 1989-91; Nordonia HS Chem Tchr 1991-; *ai:* NEA, Amer Chem Soc 1991-; Sci Ed Cncl of OH 1993-; *office:* Nordonia HS 8006 S Bedford Rd Macedonia OH 44056*

D'AMBROSIO, JUDITH REGA, Kindergarten Teacher; *m:* Anthony L.; *c:* Joseph; *ed:* Ursuline Coll (BA) Elem Ed 1963; NY UNiv (MA) Early Chldhd 1967; *cr:* Ridgecrest Schl First Grd Tchr 1963-65; William St Schl Second Grd Tchr 1965-67; Highland View Elem Schl First Grd Tchr 1968-69; Silver Spring Learning Ctr Presch Tchr 1972-76; St Andrew Apostle Schl Kndgtn Tchr 1976-84, 4th Grd Tchr 1987-94, Kndgtn Tchr 1994-96; *ai:* Curr Review Chprsn; Level Coord; Mentor Tchr; NCEA 1976-; ASCD 1987-; *office:* St Andrew Apostle Schl 11602 Kemp Mill Rd Silver Spring MD 20902

D'AMBROSIO, MADELINE, 1st Grade Teacher; *b:* Fall River, MA; *m:* Anthony John; *c:* John A., Thomas A.; *ed:* RI Coll (BA) Elem Ed 1966; 15 Credits Addl; *cr:* Fall River Schl Dept Kndgtn Tchr 1969-80, 1st Grad Tchr 1980-; *ai:* NEA 1969-; Tchr Apple Awd.

D'AMBROSIO, MICHAEL ANTHONY, English Teacher; *b:* Brooklyn, NY; *ed:* Fordham Univ (BA) Eng 1969; NY Univ (MA) Eng 1971, (MA) Admin & Supervision 1979; 30 Addl Credits; *cr:* Ft Hamilton HS Eng Tchr 1969-, Asst Prin Eng 1990-92, IA; *ai:* Adv NHS; Honors Acad Bd Governors; AFT 1969-; UFT 1969-; Nom Reliance Awd Excl Ed 1991; Tchr of Yr 1988, 1990; Pub Articles Eng Journal, Eng Record; *office:* Fort Hamilton H S 8301 Shore Rd Brooklyn NY 11209

D'AMBROSIO, SANDRA ANN, Seventh Grade Teacher; *b:* New Haven, CT; *ed:* Sacred Heart Univ (BS) His 1976; *cr:* St Raphael Schl Tchr 1970-76; Conn Area Cath Tchr 1977-82; Santa Maria Schl Tchr 1983, 1985; Sacred Heart Schl Tchr 1984; Sacred Heart St Peter Schl Tchr 1985-, Vice Prin 1993-95; *ai:* NCEA 1985-; Parish Cncl 1986-, Past Pres; *office:* Sacred Heart St Peter Schl 208 Columbus Ave New Haven CT 06519

DAMERON, GEORGE WILLIAMSON, Assoc Professor of History; *ed:* Duke Univ (BA)-Summa Cum Laude 1975; Harvard Univ (AM) His 1979, (PHD) His 1983; *cr:* St Michaels Coll Asst Prof of Hum 1983-87, Asst Prof of His 1987-; Assoc Prof His 1991-; *ai:* Amer Historical Assn; Medieval Acad of Amer; Soc for Italian His Stud; Renaissance Soc of Amer; New England His Assn; Amer Assn of Univ Profs; Numerous Articles, Essays Pub; Numerous Book Reviews; Numerous St Michaels Coll Fac Dev Grants; Amer Philosophical Assn 1991; Natl Endowment for Hum Travel to Collections Grant 1991; Harvard Lehman Fund Grad Schl Flwshp 1980-81; Book: Episcopal Power and Florentine Society.

DAMIAN, PATRICIA M. (RE), Lang Arts Tchr & Dept Chair; *b:* Somerville, MA; *m:* Antonio J.; *c:* Andrea, Mark, Christopher, Robert, Steven, Carla, Luke; *cr:* St Clement 5th Grd Sub Tchr 1972-76; Six Acres Nursery Schl Tchr of Gifted & Talented 1978-82; St Clement LA Tchr 1982-; *ai:* 8th Grd Outreach Prgms, Chrstn Svc Act Advs; Mentor Tchr; NCEA 1982-; Malden Cath PTA 1990-, Comm Chair; Greater Boston Rdng Cncl; *office:* Saint Clements Elem Schl 589 Boston St Somerville MA 02144*

DAMIAN, RADU ALEXANDRU, Visiting Assistant Professor; *b:* Bucharest, Romania; *m:* Roxana Zoica Graur; *c:* Sandra; *ed:* Polytechnic Inst at Bucharest (BS) (MS) Manufacturing, Design 1982; Mc Gill Univ (MBA) Admin 1994; Polytechnic Inst at Bucharest (PHD) Mechanical Vibrations 1994; *cr:* Heavy Equipment Inc Plant Engr 1982-84; Polytechnic Inst Assoc Prof 1984-90; Tecsult Inc Power Plant Design Engr 1991-93; SR-FN Fin Network Mrktg-Investment VP 1993-94; Worcester Polytechnic Inst Visiting Asst Prof 1994-; *ai:* Romainian Engr Assn 1982-; Ordre Des Ingenieurs Du Quebec, Canadian Bd of Engrs 1992-; Pub 4 Books, 14 Articles; *office:* Worcester Polytechnic Inst 100 Institute Rd Worcester MA 01609

DAMIANI, ETTORE,III, Physical Education Teacher; *b:* Buffalo, NY; *m:* Lori A. Damiani; *c:* Ettore, Alyssa; *ed:* Mt Union Coll (BA) PE 1982; IN St Univ (MS) PE & Sports Medicine 1983; *cr:* St Gregory The Great Schl PE Tchr 1984-85; West MI Sports Medicine Clinic Ath Trainer 1985-86; Depew Cntrl PE Tchr, Coach & Ath Ctr 1986-89; Wilson Cntrl PE Tchr & Coach 1989-; *ai:* Var Ftbl, Var Wrestling & Var Girls Track Coach; Sports Medicine & Ath Trainer; NATA 1985-, Mem; *office:* Wilson Central Schl 412 Lake St Wilson NY 14172

DAMIAN-MARVIN, LISA M., Science Teacher; *b:* Pittsburgh, PA; *m:* Nathan Marvin; *c:* Zachary; *ed:* Boston Univ (BA) Chem 1989; Carnegie Mellon Univ (MS) Chem 1990; Univ of ME Post Grad Stud Sci Ed; *cr:* Univ of ME Teaching Fellow 1991-92; Georges Valley HS Sci Tchr 1992-; *ai:* Acad Decathlon; Jr Class Adv; MSTA 1992-; Amer Red Cross Diaster Relief 1992-; *office:* Georges Valley HS Valley St Thomaston ME 04861

D'AMICO, ANNE-MARIE, Instrumental Music Teacher; *b:* Southington, CT; *ed:* Baldwin Wallace Conservatory of Music (BM) Performance 1985; Univ of KY (MM) Performance 1989; Univ of MA at Amherts (MMED) Music Ed 1991; *cr:* Great Salt Bay Cmty Schl Instrumental Music Tchr 5 Yrs; *ai:* Sftbl Coach; Jazz Band Dir; Casco Bay Tummlersklezmer Band 1991-, Musician; New Womens Ensemble 1994-, Dir; *office:* Great Salt Bay Cmty Schl PO Box 937 Damariscotta ME 04543*

DAMICO, CHARLES ALFRED,JR., English Teacher; *b:* Philadelphia, PA; *m:* Kathleen Susan Mc Kenzie; *c:* Mary, Charles; *ed:* Rowan Coll (BA) Eng 1975, (BA) Eng 1992; 24 Credits Scndry Schl Tchng of Eng; Univ of MD European Division 30 Credits; *cr:* US Air Force Jet Engine Mechanic-Tech 1967-72; Transfiguration Schl Seventh Grd Tchr 1975-77; Burl Co Inst of Tech Eng Tchr 1977-; *ai:* Grad Coord; NEA 1977-; Assoc Rep; Amer Legion 1985-; Voted Farvorite Tchr Fourteen Consecutive Yrs 1983-; *office:* Burl County Inst Of Tech 695 Woodlane Rd Mount Holly NJ 08060

D'AMICO, FRANCES CLARE, Hlth & Physical Education Prof; *b:* Jamaica, NY; *ed:* Brooklyn Coll (MS) Ed 1967; Saint Johns Univ (MS) Admin 1974; NY Univ (PHD) Higher Ed 1982; VA Schl of Massage Therapeutic Massage 1994; *cr:* JHS 73Q Hlth & PE Tchr 1964-67; New Hyde Park Meml HS Hlth & PE Tchr 1967-70; Queensborough Comm Coll Hlth & PE Prof 1970-; *ai:* Acad Advisement; AAUP, AAHPERD 1970-; Articles JUCO Review 1976, AERA Proceedings 1983; *office:* Queensborough Comm Coll 222-05 56th Ave Attn Nursing Dept Flushing NY 11364

DAMICO, JOHN PATRICK, Social Studies Teacher; *b:* Phoenix, AZ; *m:* Francine Lorenz; *c:* Gian; *ed:* Rutgers (BA) His 1965; Glassboro ROAN (MA) Scndry Ed 1968; Attnd Temple, Acad for the Advancement of Tchng & Learning; Traditional Ideas in Amer His Grad Course; *cr:* Triton Regnl Schl Soc Stud Tchr 1968-; *ai:* Track, Distance Runners, Midget Wrestling Coach; BHPEA, NJEA, NEA 1967-; Animal Welfare Assn 1969-; South Jersey Wrestling Hall of Fame 1987-; Triton Midget Wrestling 1976-, Pres, Coach.*

D'AMICO, KATHLEEN SUSAN, Social Studies Teacher; *b:* Syracuse, NY; *m:* Anthony F.; *c:* Lynne, Steven, Kurt, Lauren; *ed:* Alfred Univ (BA) His, Pol Sci 1962; SUNY at Oswego (MS) Ed 1992; *cr:* Onondaga Co Dept of Soc Svcs Soc Worker 1962-66; Plaza Square Owner, Mgr 1966-86; Cntrl Square Cntrl Schls 9-12 Grd Soc Stud Tchr, Global Stud, Ec Tchr 1987-; *ai:* Adv Mock Trial Teams Spon by Onondaga Co Bar Assn 1987-; Adv Stdnts with a Motive 1995; Fac Comm on Scheduling 1992-94; NYSUT, AFT 1987-; Cntrl Square Lib 1966-, Bd of Trustees 1988-90; Area 29 Spec Olympics 1990-, Vol, Coach of C Sp Olympians; St Michaels Church Choir 1983-94; *office:* Paul V Moore HS Caughdenoy Rd Central Square NY 13036

D'AMICO, VALERIE GROWDEN, Math Teacher; *b:* Canonsburg, PA; *m:* Joseph Anthony; *ed:* Franciscan Univ of Steub (BS) Math 1992; Credit Hrs Cooperative Learning, Graphing Calculators; *cr:* Toronto City Schls Math, Alg I, Geom, Precalc Tchr 1992-; *ai:* Math Club Spon; NEA 1992-93; AFT 1996; *office:* Toronto City Schls 3rd And Myers St Toronto OH 43964*

DAMON, GRETCHEN F., Biology Teacher; *b:* Leominster, MA; *ed:* Johnson St Coll (BS) Scndry Ed 1968; Fitchburg St Coll (MED) Sci Ed 1976; Marine Sci Inst NSF Salem St Coll 1980; Credit Hrs in Bio Field; *cr:* Ticonderoga MS 6-7th Grd Sci Tchr 1969; Lamoille Union HS 7th Grd Sci Tchr 1969-88, Bio Tchr 1988-; *ai:* New Tchr Mentor; Research at Bermuda Biological Research Station 1987, 1989; *office:* Lamoille Union HS PO Box 304 Hyde Park VT 05655

DAMON, MICHAEL SCOTT, Spanish Teacher; *b:* Erie, PA; *m:* Machelle M. Biangone; *c:* Joshua, Marissa; *ed:* Geneva Coll (BA) Span 1992; *cr:* Kennedy Chrstn HS Span Tchr 1992-93; St Marys HS Span Tchr 1993-; *ai:* Jr HS Ftbl, Boys Track Head Coach; Soph Class Adv; PSEA 1993-; *office:* St Marys Pub HS 977 S Saint Marys Rd Saint Marys PA 15857

D'AMORE, CARMELO V., Guidance Counselor; *b:* Gloversville, NY; *m:* Susan Rathburn; *c:* David, Daniel; *ed:* SUNY at Oswego (BS) Industrial Arts 1967; SUNY at Oneonta (MS) Cnslr Ed 1973; *cr:* Oppenheim Ephuatah CS Ind Arts Tchr, Guidance Cnslr 1967-81; Johnstown HS Guidance Cnslr 1981-; *ai:* SADD Adv; Vidiographer for Ftbl & bsktbl; AFT 1968-; NYSUT 1968-; Tri Cty Cnslrs 1979-, Tres; Comm Svcs Bd 1993-, Mem; Alcohol & Substance Abuse Subcommittee of CSB 1988-, Co-Chm; *office:* Johnstown HS 2 Wright Dr Johnstown NY 12095

DAMORE, RICHARD, HS Physical Education Teacher; *b:* Queens, NY; *m:* Kim Jamison; *c:* Casie, Dean; *ed:* Adelphi Univ (BA) PE 1975; Stonybrook Univ (MS) Ed 1980; *cr:* Bayshore HS PE Tchr 1975-; *ai:* Head Coach Boys Lacrosse; Bayshore Classroom Tchrs Assn 1975-; AFT; Coach of Yr 1988, 1992; *office:* Bay Shore HS Perkal St Bay Shore NY 11706*

DAMPIER-COOK, JULIE, Former English Teacher; *b:* Kansas City, MO; *m:* Thomas W. Cook; *c:* Joshua, Anna; *ed:* Univ of CA at Davis (BA) Eng 1986; Univ of AK at Anchorage (MA) Eng Lit 1993; Univ of CA at Davis Tchng Cert Scndry Eng 1987; Addl Hrs Women's Lit, Tchng of Grammar, Linguistics; *cr:* Fairfield HS Eng Tchr 1987-90; Univ of AK Adj Instr 1990-91; Bartlett HS Eng Tchr 1991-95; *ai:* NEA 1987-, Union Rep; NCTE 1987-; AK Women's Book Group 1993-, Founder; *h* Brighton Ave Linwood NJ 08221

DAMPMAN, DIANNE I., First Grade Teacher; *b:* Ashlan Millersville Univ (BS) Elem Ed 1969; Penn St Univ, Villa Chestnut Hill Coll Post Grad Stud; *cr:* Pennsbury Schl Dist Elem Tchr 1969-; *ai:* PSEA 1969-; NEA 1969-; Pennsbury EA Ofcr at Large 1981-88 & 1994-, Sec 1988-94; *office:* Oxford Schl 430 Trenton Rd Fairless Hills PA 19030*

DANA, GREGORY SCOTT, Mathematics Teacher; *b:* Saler Anita K. Boston; *c:* Hana, Alexander; *ed:* Univ of ME(BA) Salem St Coll (MED) Sec Sch Adm 1978; Addl Credit Hrs Univ; *cr:* Marblehead Jr HS 8th Grd Math Tchr 1974-81; Marb Math Tchr 1981-; *ai:* Yrbk; Tech Theatre Dir; Phi Kappa Marblehead Ed Assn 1974-, Negotiation VP; MA Tchrs Assn, N NCTM 1975-; *office:* Marblehead HS Duncan Sleigh Sq Marb 01945

DANA, JANET NOREAULT, High School English Teacher; NY; *m:* Donald C.; *c:* Jeff, Alan, Beth; *ed:* Univ of VT (BS) En Grad Credits SUNY at Potsdam; *cr:* Brushton-Moira Cntrl 1965-68, 1978-; *ai:* Stu Cncl, Class Adv; NCTE; NY Tchrs NYSEC Outstndng Tchr.

DANAHER, JAMES P., Head of Philosophy; *b:* Jersey Ci Kathleen; *c:* Kathleen, Kerry Nicholson; *ed:* Montclair St Sociology 1976; New Schl for Soc Research (MA) Philosophy Univ of NY (MPHIL) Philosophy 1989, (PHD) Philosophy Berkeley Coll Head of General Ed 1980-; Nyack Coll Head of Dept 1990-; *ai:* Amer Philosophic Org 1986-; Intnl Berkeley New Covenant Church, Elder; Philosopher in Residence at Wh Home of The Irish Philosopher George Berkeley; *office:* Ber West Red Oak Lane White Plains NY 10604

DANAHER, JANE WINFIELD, First Grade Teacher; *b:* Bridg *m:* Francis L.; *c:* Cynthia, Patrice Neifert, Douglas, James; *ed* Green St Univ (BS) Ed 1963; Southern CT St Univ (MS) Spe 6th Yr Rdng 1990; Attnd Sacred Heart Univ at Bridgeport & Wes at Middletown; *cr:* Turkey Hill Schl 5th Grd Tchr 1977-78; Ni & Booth Hill Schl Tchr of Learning Disabilities Resource 197 Ryan Schl Tchr of Learning Disabilities Classroom; Daniels Fa Grd Tchr 1981-; *ai:* CT Ed Assn, NEA, Trumbull Ed Assn 197 Electric Educl Grant Twice; *office:* Daniels Farm Schl 710 Da Rd Trumbull CT 06611*

DANCE, ANNE GABRIEL, Mathematics & Science T Cleveland, OH; *m:* Randy; *c:* Richard, Mariann, Randi; *ed:* C Univ (BS) Math 1977; *cr:* St Augustine Acad Math Tchr 1977 Math, Sci Tchr 1989-; *ai:* SADD Moderator; NCEA 1993-; Augustine Acad 14808 Lake Ave Lakewood OH 44107

DANCHENKO, HALINA, Russian Teacher; *b:* Graven, Ge Frank Bishop; *ed:* Kutztown Univ (BA) Russian 1968; Mount Coll (BS) Nrsng 1985; Attnd Fordham Univ, Herzen Inst at St Moscow Univ, Bryn Mawr Coll, Rutgers Univ; *cr:* Arlington Sch Lang Tchr 1969-; Montrose Hosp RN 1987-89; *ai:* Russian Chair NY Olympiada of Spoken Russian; ACTR 1975-; ATSEEL 1969-; NEH Russian Lang; CIES Leningrad Pr Exchange Moscow; NEH, CORLAC Bryn Mawr; *office:* Arling Rt 55 Lagrangeville NY 12540

D'ANDREA, ELLEN DEMARCO, Science Teacher; *b:* Bror David M.; *c:* Dennis, Karen, Elaina; *ed:* Manhattan Coll (BS) B 1979; Cmptr Courses; 15 Credits Bus Mgmt Lehman Coll Catharine Acad Sci Tchr 1979-; *ai:* Fac Soc Comm; New Mentor; Manhattan Coll Cooperating Tchr-Stu Tchr; STAN *office:* Saint Catharine Acad 2250 Williamsbridge Rd Bronx N

D'ANDREA, ROBERT MICHAEL, Social Studies & Cmptr Passaic, NJ; *m:* Anne Robbolino; *c:* Robert, Matthew, Jennie, C Bethany Coll (BA) Elem Ed 1971; William Paterson Coll (MA Soc Sci 1976; *cr:* A. S. Faust Intermediate Schl 6th Grd Tch Boys & Girls Bsktbl Coach 1972-, 7th Grd Soc Stud Tchr 1981- Soc Stud, Math Tchr 1983-86, 7th-8th Grd Soc Stud Tchr 198 Stud Comm Chprsn; NEA, BCEA, NJEA 1971-; IAABO Bd *office:* Alfred S Faust Interm Sch Grove & Uhland Sts E Rut 07073

D'ANDREA, WILLIAM R., Language Arts Instructor; *b:* Newa Montclair St Coll (BA) Eng, Scndry 1971; *cr:* Passaic Connt 1971-73, 1984-90; Clifton HS Eng 1990-; *ai:* Drama Dir 1990-94 Harness Horse Trainer, Driver; Bsbl Coach; NEA, NJEA 1 1990-; Represented Screenwriter; *office:* Clifton HS 333 C Clifton NJ 07013

DANDRIDGE, VALARIE COOPER, Guidance Cour Philadelphia, PA; *m:* Albert S. III; *c:* Kyle, Stephen; *ed:* Villa (BA) Lbrl Arts 1974; Univ of PA (MS) Cnslng & Human Rela *cr:* Cheltenham HS Guid Cnslr 1993-; *ai:* NEa; CEA 1993-; A Alpha 1974-, Sec; *office:* Cheltenham HS Rices Mill Rd Wyncote PA 19095

DANEKER, SARAH MASTERSON, Frgn Lang Dept Chair New York, NY; *m:* David C.; *ed:* Bryn Mawr Coll (BA) Ger 196 Grad Schl of Ed (MAT) Ger 1966; Johns Hopkins Span; L Ldrshp Admin; *cr:* Roland Park Schl Ger, Fr, Span, Russian Tch Baltimore Coll Ger, Fr, Latin Tchr 1984-, Frgn Lang Dept Chair Coord 3 Frgn Lang Prgms; NHS Adv; AATG 1985-; Baltimore Coll 1995 Outstdng Awd; *office:* Baltimore City College HS 48 Alameda Baltimore MD 21218

DANESE, SYLVIA PAULETTE, English Teacher; *b:* Jacksonv Andrea Marie Moore, Cynthia Louise Moore; *ed:* FL Jr Coll (A 1967; Univ of North FL (BS) Eng Ed 1977, (MED) Spec Ed 197 Schl Psychologist Cert, Guid & Cnslng Credits; *cr:* Windsor Tchr 1969-71; Morgan Local Schl Dist LD Tutor 1979-80; Learning Disabilities Tutor, Eng Tchr 1983-; *ai:* Sr Class, Newspaper Adv; NHS Comm; NEA, OEA, MLEA 1983-, Transitions 1994-, Bd Mem; Tchr Mentor 1992-; Peer Media Adv; *office:* Morgan HS 800 Raider Dr Mc Connelsville OH 4

DANFORTH, PETER GREGORY, Chemistry Teacher; *b:* Au *m:* Mona Jane Charest; *c:* Kate E., Megan E.; *ed:* Univ Farmington (BS) Bio, Chem 1981; Univ of Southern ME Immun Hrs, Calculus Math 7 Cr Hrs; Woodrow Wilson Chem Insts 9 Biddeford HS Bio Tchr 1982-86, Chem Tchr 1982-; Biddeford Chem Tchr 1987-95; *ai:* Schls Sci Curr; HS Math, Sci Integ Comms; ME Ed Assn 1983-, VP 1993-94; NSF Fellowship 1992 Wilson Chem Inst Eisenhower Funding 1990-91; *office:* Bid Maplewood Ave Biddeford ME 04005

D'ANGELO, LAREM KEAM, School Counselor; *b:* Warsav Adirondock Coll (AAS) Correction Admin 1972; Oswego St (1974; Castletan St (MED) Schl Cnslr 1980; 60 Hrs Post Gra Brockport to Receive NYS Cert 1991; *cr:* NYS Dept of Corre Svcs 1976-77; NYS Dept Mental Hygiene Alcohol Cnslr Wyoming Cty Probation Kirby Co Sales 1979-80; Restart C Substance Abuse Cnslr 1980-85; VA Med Ctr Alcoholism Cnsl Thomas Jefferson MS Cnslr 1987-93; John Marshall HS Cnslr ympics Vol; Habitat for Humanity Vol; AFT, NYSUT 1987-; Naval Assn 1977-; *office:* John Marshall HS 180 Ridgeway Ave er NY 14615*

ELO, LOUIS PHILLIP,JR., Mathematics Teacher; *b:* phia, PA; *m:* Carol Fusco; *c:* Michele L., Mark D.; *ed:* Boston Coll ath 1968; Brandeis Univ (MA) Math 1969; Credit Prgms Cheyney niv of Northern IA, Rutgers Univ; *cr:* Boston Coll Math Inst Rsrch 72-75; Regis Coll Adj Fac 1975; Archmere Acad Math Tchr 1975-; n Coll Adj Fac 1984-92; Widener Univ Adj Fac 1990-; *ai:* NHS ath League; NCTM 1972-; MAA 1966-; DE Cncl Tchr of Math Pres 1984-85, HS Rep 1979-84; CPAM 1986-; Woodrow Wilson SF 1968-71 Grad Flwshps; Presidential Awd Excl Sci, Math Tchng andy Tech Scholar Outstdng Tchr 1991-92; Presidential Scholars ommended Tchr 1983; *office:* Archmere Acad 3600 Philadelphia ymont DE 19703

ELO, RITA, Pre-Kindergarten Teacher; *b:* Newark, NJ; *ed:* MD of Art (BFA) Art Tchr 1971; Kean Coll (ECC) Early Chldhd 1980; Schl of Fine & Indstrl Art Diploma Art Illustration 1965; *cr:* Magic Day Care Schl Pre-K Tchr 1980-82; St Peter's Schl Pre-K Tchr

ELO, TINA M., Kindergarten Teacher; *b:* Staten Island, NY; *m:* c: John P., Douglas M., Robert J., Laurie Costa, Debra Monaco; er Coll (BA) Early Chldhd Ed 1959; Wagner Coll (MA) Ed 1976; Vly Coll 30 Addl Credits; *cr:* Pub Schl #8 K-1st Grd Tchr 1967-81; l #36 Kndgtn Tchr 1981-; *ai:* UFT 1968-; *home:* 717 Hart Dr ater NJ 08807

LO, WILLIAM NICHOLAS, English Dept Chair; *b:* Trenton, Patricia Ann Gervasoni; *ed:* Trenton St Coll (BA) Eng & ntal Music Ed 1973; Grad Stud at St Univ of NY at Stonybrook & ning Inst; *cr:* Arthur J Holland MS Eng Tchr 1975-84, Eng Dept 1984-, Work-Stud Tchr & Coord 1994-; *ai:* Spelling Bee Coord; kins Planning Comm; TEA 1975-; NJEA 1975-; NEA 1975-; ASCD DAV 1985-, Commanders Club; Yrbk Dedication 1990; *office:* Holland MS 1001 W State St Trenton NJ 08618

O, MARY ANN, Physical Education Teacher; *b:* Brooklyn, NY; klyn Coll (BS) PE 1975; Long Island Univ (MS) Rehabilitation) Addl Hrs; *cr:* Chase Manhattan Bank Remittance Bank Supvr ; Court Stenographer 1982-86; UBS Securities Admin Asst ; Wm C. Bryant HS PE, Hlth Tchr 1988-; *ai:* Girls Var Bowling HIV-AIDS Team Ldr; NDEITA 1995-, Aerobics Instr; Black Belt ee Shotokan Karate; *office:* William C Bryant HS 48-10 31st Ave and City NY 11103

, DEBORAH K. FRYMAN, English Teacher; *b:* Toledo, OH; *m:* C.; *c:* Hilary, Christina; *ed:* Ashland Univ (BSEd) Eng 1994; Marion Tech Coll; *cr:* Plymouth HS Eng Tchr 1994-; *ai:* Acad ge Adv; Career Planning Comm; NEA, NCTE, OEA 1994-; *office:* h HS 184 Sandusky St Plymouth OH 44865

, JOHN LAWRENCE, Health Teacher; *b:* Southbridge, MA; *c:* s, Nathan; *ed:* Univ of MA at Amherst (BS) PE 1980; Attnd er St Coll Hlth Stud Ed; *cr:* Southbridge HS Sci Tchr 1986-87; Jr Sr HS Hlth Ed Coord 1987-93, Hlth Educator 1987-; *ai:* Head ner; Jr HS Bsktbl, Sftbl Coach; Stu Ath Trainer Club Adv; NEA, rs Assn 1986-; Webster Educators Assn 1987-, Bd of Govs 1993-; Trainers Assn 1981-; Webster Substance Awareness Comm 1988-; ster Cty Teen Pregnancy Prevention Coalition 1993-, Exec Bd; artlett Jr Sr HS Lake Pkwy Webster MA 01570

, PAUL EDWARD,JR., English Teacher; *b:* Windber, PA; *m:* (Bencie); *c:* Ryan, Breanne; *ed:* Univ of Pittsburgh at Johnston Ed, Comm 1980; Attnd Univ Pittsburgh, IUP 24 Credits; MATE Univ of PA; *cr:* Conemaugh Vly HS Eng Tchr 1980-81; Windber Eng Tchr 1981-82; Meyersdale Area HS Eng Tchr 1982-87; Area HS Eng Tchr 1987-; *ai:* NEA, PSEA 1980-; WAEA 1987-; drens Lit Grad; Fellow of South Cntrl PA Writing Project.

, SABRINA RUSSELL, Science Teacher; *b:* Valdosta, GA; *m:* *c:* Kawana, Rashida; *ed:* Hunter Coll (BS) Hlth Ed 1982; City A) Sci Ed 1995; 30 Addl Credits Sci; Telecommunications 15 Credits; ville Medical Group Med Asst 1974-79; Group Hlth Incorporated laims Approver 1983-84; Harlem Dowling Children's Svc ker 1984-86; NY City Dept of Hlth Resource Coord 1986-88; NY of Ed Tchr 1988-; *ai:* Act Planning Comm of Yth Act; Exec Comm for Coop Children's Ctr; Educl Planning Comm for Harlem Children's Svc; AFT, UFT 1984-; CCNY Alumni Assn 1995-; Amer Assoc of Co-op City 1989-; NAACP 1995-; Flwshp Bapt 1989-, Sec Bldg Fund; *office:* Arturo Toscanini Comm Jr HS 1000 ve Bronx NY 10456*

LS, ANNE MARIE, Language Arts Teacher; *b:* Brighton, MA; *m:* *c:* Julianne, Kay, Meghan; *ed:* Merrimack Coll (BA) Eng 1966; oethe Inst for Ger Culture 1966; Post Grad Work Rivier Coll, Univ owell, Brown Univ, Notre Dame, St Anselm, Keene St, Plymouth on Univ, Simmons Coll, Univ of NH for Eng Lit, Scndry Ed, hy; *cr:* Andover East Jr HS Eng Tchr 1967-68; Nashua HS Eng 68-69; Mt St Mary HS Eng Tchr, Dept Chair 1981-89; Hudson chl Lang Arts Tchr 1989-; *ai:* 7-8 Grd Stu Act Cncl; Citizenship AFT 1989-; NCTE 1980-; YMCA 1990-; St Christophers Church ucharistic Minister; NELMS Grant 1990; NH Cncl of Hum Tchrs 86, 1991; Dev & Implementing Prgms for Stdnts 1992; *office:* Memorial Schl 1 Memorial Dr Hudson NH 03051

LS, CARMEN, English Teacher; *b:* Auyana, South America; *c:* Dionne; *ed:* Univ of Guyana (BA) Eng 1982; Adelphi Univ (MS) Cyril Potter Coll Ed, Eng Cert in Ed 1972; 30 Credith Hrs Various ; *cr:* St Johns Coll Eng Tchr 17 Yrs; Bough of Manhatten CC al Eng Tchr 2 Semesters; Maggie Walekr J HS Lang Arts Tchr 3 ra Barton HS Eng Tchr 6 Yrs; Kingsborough Comm Coll Schl to oll Now; *ai:* Barton Leo Club Adv; UFT Exec Comm; Lehman arning Core Charter Mem; Guyana Tchr Assn 1969-; Rugby Lions 94-, Treas, VP, Leo Club Adv, Cert of Merit; Best Graduating Eng ril; Potter Coll of Ed Cuyana 1973; Adult Ed Prise Soc Stud 1973; Clara Barton HS 901 Classon Ave Brooklyn NY 11225

LS, CHARLES R., Biology Teacher; *b:* Schenectady, NY; *c:* Sarah zabeth L.; *ed:* NYS Ag & Tech at Cobleskill (AAS) Animal dry 1977; PA Coll of Pharmacy & Sci (BS) Pharmacy 1984; Temple ED Scndry Ed 1994; Stu Pilot Cert; *cr:* Sterling Drug Co Sr Rsrch 1987-90; Archbishop Wood HS Chem Tchr 1990-91; Chestnut sp Pharmacist 1990-; Upper Merion Area HS Bio Tchr 1991-; *ai:* Spon; PSEA 1991-; APHA 1984-; Ambler Cath 1987-, Tchr CCD; ay; STAR AWD Martin Marietta; *office:* Upper Merion Area HS ld Rd King Of Prussia PA 19406

LS, CHERYL STONE, President; *b:* Hartford, CT; *c:* Jeffrey; *ed:* Hartford (BA) Sociology 1976, (MED) Ed 1981; 90 Addl Hrs; *cr:* Fed of Tchrs Pres 1 Yr; South MS 6-7th Grd Soc Stud Tchr 3 Yrs; ooker Schl 6th Grd Tchr 4 Yrs; D. F. Burns Schl 6th Grd Tchr 9 Yrs; Environmental Club; CT St Fed of Tchrs 1978-, VP, COPE Awd; Fed of Tchrs 1978-, Pres 1995-; Greater Hartford Labor Cncl Del; *office:* Hartford Federation of Tchrs 355 Washington St CT 06106

DANIELS, EDGAR ROTH, 8th Grade English Teacher; *b:* Flushing, NY; *m:* Jessica Radcliffe; *c:* Jed, Megan; *ed:* Widener Univ (BA) His 1970; Long Island Univ (MS) Scndry Ed 1976; SUNY at Stony Brook (MA) Liberal Stud 1982; 60 Addl Hrs; *cr:* Smithtown Cntrl SD Tchr 1973-; Long Island Univ Spec Lecturer in Continuing Ed 1987-89; Long Island Schl Dist Consultant, Presenter 1989-; SUNY at Stoney Brook Lecturer 1991-; Smithtown Cntrl SD Staff Dev 1994-95; *ai:* AFT, NYSUT, Smithtown Tchrs Assn 1973-; Levittown Schl Bd 1985-87, Sec; Levittown Lib Bd 1983-88, Pres 1987; Articles, Booklets, Coll Workbook; *office:* Smithtown MS 10 School St Saint James NY 11780

DANIELS, GORDON, Principal; *b:* Johnson City, NY; *m:* Natalie Burgin; *c:* Cameron, Russell; *ed:* Hudson Vly Comm Coll (AA) PE 1973; SU Coll at Cortland (BS) PE 1975, (SDA) Admin 1990; St Univ Coll at Oneonta 24 Credit Hrs; 6 Credit Hrs; *cr:* Afton Cntrl Schl Elem Tchr 1975-78, Phys Edctr 1978-84; Greene Cntrl Schl Phys Edctr 1984-90, MS Prin 1990-; *ai:* 7th Grd Modified Bsktbl Coach; NYS MS Assn 1990-, Region IV Co-Dir; Natl Fed of Schl Admins 1990-; NASSP 1990-; Chenango Cty Yth Bureau 1995-, Bd Mem; St Ed Liaison for BOCES MS; *office:* Greene MS 40 S Canal St Greene NY 13778*

DANIELS, HARRY A., Mathematics Department Chair; *b:* Pittsburgh, PA; *m:* Lorene Reinhold; *c:* Stephen, Marc; *ed:* Wagner Coll (BA) Math 1963; Fairfield Univ (MA) Math, Ed 1968; Boston Univ Advanced Stud Math 1970-71; *cr:* Rye HS Math Tchr 1963-68; Wayland HS Math Tchr 1969-70; Boston Univ Math, Ed Instr 1970-79; Newburyport Schls Math Curr Coord, Dept Chair 1980-; Hamilton-Wenham HS Math Tchr, Dept Chair; *ai:* Math Team Adv; Scheduling Admin Asst; MTA, NEA 1969-; NCTM 1970-; HP-OSU Calculus Project, Calculator Prgm; Calculator Wkshps Trainer; *office:* Hamilton-Wenham Regnl HS 775 Bay Rd S Hamilton MA 01982*

DANIELS, JOSEPH R., Second Grade Teacher; *b:* Ridley Park, PA; *m:* Marlene A. Pawlush; *ed:* West Chester St Univ (BS) Elem 1971; Temple Univ (BA) Horticulture 1993; *cr:* Dewey Mann Elem Schl Third Grd Tchr 1971-80; William Penn Elem Schl Fourth, Second Grd Tchr 1980-; *ai:* Safety Patrol Adv; A-V Coord; Tchr Mentor; Primary Ctr Chair; Interview Comm Chair; PSEA, NEA 1971-; CUEA, 2nd VP; PA Horticulture Soc 1988-, Flower Show Comm; Scott Arboretum 1988-, House Tour Comm; Temple-Hort Alumni Assn 1993-, Adv, Coord; Lansdowne Civic Assn 1975-, Tree Beautif Comm; *office:* William Penn Schl Highland Ave & Twp Line Rd Chester PA 19013

DANIELS, LANA DIANE CHILDRESS, 7th Grade Math Teacher; *b:* Portsmouth, OH; *c:* Brent; *ed:* OH Univ (BA) Elem Ed 1978; 8 Grad Hrs Miami Univ; *cr:* Minford MS 7th Grd Art, Rdng, Eng, Math Tchr 1978-; *ai:* Jr HS Vlybl Coach 10 Yrs; HS Sftbl Coach 10 Yrs; NEA, OEA 1978-; NCTM 1994-; SE Dist Coaches Assn 1988-, Sec, Treas; USTA 1988-; *office:* Minford MS PO Box 204 Minford OH 45653

DANIELS, MARLENE ALEXIS, Guidance Counselor; *b:* Chester, PA; *m:* Joseph R.; *ed:* West Chester Univ (BS) Elem Ed 1971, (MED) Cnslng & Elem 1993; Certfd for Scndry Cnslng 1993; *cr:* Columbus Elem 1st Grd Tchr 1971-79; Stetser Elem 2nd Grd Tchr 1979-89; Main St Elem 6th Grd Tchr 1989-95; Showalter Mid Guid Cnslr 1996; *ai:* Stu Cncl & 8th Grd Adv; PYEA Coord; Tchr Mentor; PSEA 1971-; NEA 1971-; CUEA 1971-, Treas & Bldg Rep; Lansdowne Civic Assn 1975-, Treas; Phi Betta Kappa 1992-; Apple Grant Awds 1989 & 1990; *office:* Showalter MS 1000 W 10th St Chester PA 19013

DANIELS, NANCY LOCH, English Teacher; *b:* Meshoppen, PA; *m:* Robert; *c:* Gretchen; *ed:* Mansfield Univ (BS) Eng 1972; Wilkes Univ, Penn St & Allentown Coll Credit Hrs; *cr:* Mountain View Schl Dist Eng Tchr 1972-75; Tunkhannock Area Schl Dist Eng Tchr 1984-; *ai:* NEA & PSEA 1984-; *home:* 1405 Spyglass Ln Clarks Summit PA 18411

DANIELS, PAMELA BRYANT, German Teacher; *ed:* Miami Univ (BA) Ger 1970; Penn St (MA) Ger Lit 1972; Grad Work at William Paterson, Jersey City Coll & Marywood; *cr:* Penn St Univ Grad Asst 1971-72; High Point HS Ger & His Tchr 1975-79; Pope John XXIII His & Ger Tchr 1989-91; Newton HS His & Ger Tchr 1991-; *ai:* Class Adv; Ger Club Spon; Ger Hnr Soc Adv; AATG 1975-; NEA & NJEA 1975-; Lake Mohawk Ski Hawks 1989-, Sec 1991-93.

DANIELS, ROBERT ARTHUR, Math Teacher; *b:* Columbus, OH; *m:* Tamara Elaine Christian; *c:* Katelyn; *ed:* OH St Univ (BA) Math Ed 1988; *cr:* Buckeye Vly MS Math Tchr 1988-; *ai:* NCTM 1989-; NEA, OEA, BVTA 1988-; Classroom Act Pub in Glencoe Course 3 Math Book 1994; *office:* Buckeye Valley MS 4230 State Route 203 Radnor OH 43066

DANIELS, ROBERT G., Physical Education Teacher; *b:* Scranton, PA; *m:* Nancy L.; *c:* Gretchen; *ed:* Penn St, BYU, Wilkes East Stroudsburg, NC St Master's Equivalency PA, 72 Credit Hrs 1975; *cr:* Abington Heights PE Tchr 25 Yrs; *ai:* Boys & Girls Var Track & Field, Cross Cntry Head Coach; Lackawanna Cross Cntry League 1972-, Pres; Abington Heights Coaches Assn, Pres; USA Track & Field Level II Certificated Endurance Events; Sport for Understanding Track Coach Intnl Exch; Amer Coaching Effectiveness Ldr Level Certificated; Pub in Journal Magazine; PA St Championship Class AAA Boys Cross Cntry 1981; *home:* 1405 Spyglass Ln Clarks Summit PA 18411

DANIELSEN, CLIFFORD ALLEN, House Parent of Sr Div Boys; *b:* Englewood, NJ; *m:* Edna Harn; *c:* Stephen, Kevin; *ed:* Montclair St Coll (BS) Industrial Arts Ed 1985; *cr:* Providence MS Tech Ed Tchr 1988; Meadowbrook HS Mechanical Drawing Tchr 1988-94; Milton Hersey Schl House Parent of Sr Division Boys 1995-; *home:* PO Box 830-Uc Hershey PA 17033

DANIELSON, ANDREW E.,II, Technology Coordinator; *b:* Mckeesport, PA; *m:* Cynthia W. Gilbert; *c:* Drew, Ada, Danielle, Dawn, Chase, Sara; *ed:* Edinborough of PA (BS) Elem Ed 1968; PA Dept of Ed (MEE) Elem Ed 1985; *cr:* Waterford Elem Schl Classroom Tchr 1968-80; Mill Village Elem Schl Classroom Tchr 1980-88; Waterford Elem Schl Classroom Tchr 1988-90; Ft LeBoeuf Schl Dist Tech Coord 1990-; *ai:* Adult Ed Classes; PSEA 1968-; NEA 1968-; PAECT 1991-; *home:* 122 Harrison Dr Edinboro PA 16412

DANIEU, MICHAEL JOSEPH, English Teacher; *b:* Buffalo, NY; *ed:* Univ of Buffalo (MA) Hum, Eng, Psych & Eng Cultural Stud 1978; John Carroll Univ Eng & Fr 1973; Doctorate in Eng; SUNY at Buffalo Modern Fiction & Cultural Stud 1986-90; *cr:* Allendale Jr High Tchr 1973-78; SUNY at Buffalo Composition 1978-79; West Sr High Eng Tchr 1979-91, Sr Eng Tchr 1996; East & West Sr High Traveling Tchr 1991-95; *ai:* Interdisciplinary Sr Projects; Block Scheduling Comm for Dist; AFT 1973-; NSTA 1973-, Bldg Rep 1978-80; Tchr of Yr Nom; Pres Stud Cncl SUNY at Fredonia for Mention Several Times by Incoming Frosh as Most Influential Tchr; Salutorian of East Sr Outstdng Tchr Nom; *office:* West Sr HS 3330 Main West Seneca NY 14224

DANIS, DIONE L., English Teacher; *b:* New York, NY; *w:* Joseph (dec); *c:* Susan, Gordon; *ed:* Simmons Coll (BS) Journals 1952; Queens Coll (MA) His 1966; Fairleigh Dickson Univ (MS) Guid 1980; Syracuse Univ Journals 1951; 60 Credit Hrs Ed, Eng, Soc Stud, Cmptr Tech; *cr:* Eng, His Tchr 29 Yrs; *ai:* Stu Org Adv 1983-88; NCTE 1982-; TEA 1970-, Recording Sec; Tchr of Yr Awd 1992, Citizens Group 1983; *office:* Tenafly HS 500 Columbus Dr Tenafly NJ 07670*

DANISH, GASPER JOSEPH, Social Studies Teacher; *b:* Mount Union, PA; *m:* Teresa Mary Brown; *c:* Andrew; *ed:* IN Univ of PA (BS) Soc Stud Ed 1968; Masters Equivalancy from IN Univ of PA & PA St Univ; *cr:* Mount Union Area Soc Stud Tchr 1970-; *ai:* Jr Class, Jr HS Stu Govt, Prom & Hobby Club Adv; Ftbl Statistician; Jr & Sr HS Bowling Spon; Mount Union Area Ed Assn, PA St Ed Assn, NEA 1970-; BSA 1978-, Scout Master, Round Table, Act & High Adventure Comms, Awd of Merit; Lepidopterist Soc 1972-; *home:* 1017 2nd Ave Altoona PA 16602

DANKS, CAROL NICKLES, English & Journalism Teacher; *b:* Effingham, IL; *m:* Joseph H.; *c:* Mark, David; *ed:* Rutgers Univ (BA) Eng 1968; Kent St Univ (MAT) Eng 1969; Attnd Haifa Univ, Stanford Univ, Univ of Chicago; *cr:* Stow HS Eng Tchr 1969-72; Kent HS Eng, Jrnlsm Tchr 1979-; *ai:* Schl Newspaper Adv; Kent Ed Assn 1979-, Comm Chair; Jrnlsm Ed Assn; Franklin Twp Bd of Zoning Appeals 1988-, Vice-Chair; Kevin Coleman Fnd 1993-, VP; OH Cncl on Holocaust Ed 1992-; Natl Endowment for Hum; The Holocaust & Jewish Resistance Seminar; Articles Pub; Co-Ed of Holocaust Curr; Rdng, Writing Wkshp Grant; Designated by JEA as Certfd Jrnlsm Edctr; *office:* Theodore Roosevelt HS 1400 N Mantua St Kent OH 44240

DANKULICH, CHERYL WYSONG, Language Arts & Reading Tchr; *b:* Burlington, VT; *m:* George P.; *c:* Sara, Adam; *ed:* Univ of MD (BS) Elem Ed & Spcl Ed 1974; 30 Grad Credit Hrs; *cr:* Anne Arundel Co Pub Schls Spcl Ed Tchr 1974-77; St Marys Co Pub Schls Spcl Ed & Reg Lang Arts 1979-; *ai:* 8th Grd Team Ldr, Discipline Comm; Safety Comm; Assn of Amer Edctrs 1994-; Southern MD Soccer League, Mgr; Northern St Marys Soccer League, Coach; *office:* Margaret Brent MS Helen MD 20635

DANN, JOHN M., English Teacher; *b:* Elmira, NY; *m:* Susan Aspinwall; *c:* Kelly, Alex; *ed:* Alfred Univ (BA) Eng Lit 1972; SUNY at Oswego (MS) Eng & Ed 1981; Syracuse Univ Post Grad Courses; *cr:* Lyons Eng Tchr 1972-; *ai:* Eng Dept Chair; NYS & Univ of Rochester Tchr Excl Awd; Numerous Articles Pub.

D'ANNA, MICHAEL DOMINICK, English & Theater Teacher; *b:* Alexandria, VA; *m:* Mary Ellen; *c:* Dominique, Danielle; *ed:* Univ of MD (BA) His 1968, (MA) Eng Ed 1973; *cr:* Good Counsel HS Eng, His Tchr 1968-73; Tilden Jr HS Eng, Theatre Tchr 1973-78; Woodward HS His Tchr 1978-79; Magruder HS Eng, Theatre, TV Production Tchr 1979-; *ai:* Artistic & Stage Dir; Asst Var Ftbl Coach; Educl Theatre Assn 1987-, MD St Dir, Regnl Dir, Oustdng Scholar; All Amer HS Theatre Assn, Exec Dir; Presented Productions 1989-90; Theatre Prgm Recognized by Natl Assn of Scndry Schl Prin; Invited to Represent US HS Theatre Edinburgh Festival Fringe 1995; *office:* Colonel Zadok Magruder H S 5939 Muncaster Mill Rd Rockville MD 20855

DANNAKER, CYNTHIA ARMITAGE, Eng Teacher & Activity Adv; *b:* Upland, PA; *m:* Scott K.; *ed:* Villanova Univ (BA) Eng, Comm Arts 1983, (MA) Eng 1987; Scndry Ed Cert Scndry Eng 1985; *cr:* Cty Press Newspaper Journalist, Sales Rep 1983-88; Villanova Univ Frosh Eng Tchr, Grad Asst 1985-87; Springfield HS Eng Tchr, Act Adv 1987-; *ai:* Stu Helping Stu, Amnesty Intnl, Stdnts Towards Animal Rights & Environment, After Schl Comm Ed Adv; NEA 1987-; Grad Assistantship; Phi Kappa Phi; Kappa Delta Pi; Pub Photographs, Feature Hard News Articles; *office:* Springfield HS 49 W Leamy Ave Springfield PA 19064

DANNER, CAROL A., Assistant Prof of Biology; *b:* Schenectady, NY; *m:* Paul; *ed:* Coll of Saint Rose (BA) Bio 1965; SUNYA (MA) Sci Ed 1967; Russell Sage (MA) Hlth Ed 1983; *cr:* Sand Creek Jr HS Sci Tchr 1967-77; Albany Med Coll Diabetic Admin, Instr 1978-83; Albany Diocese Drug Abuse Coord, Tchr 1983-88; HVCC Sci Tchr 1988-; *ai:* Course Coord; Environmental, Hnrs Comms; NEA 1988-; NYS Tchrs Assn 1967-; Diabetic Trng Awd; Great Lakes Ecosystem Seminar Trng; Park Trail Guide Production.

DANOWSKI, CATHERINE KOS, English Teacher; *b:* Patchoque, NY; *m:* Robert Thomas; *c:* Melissa Danielle; *ed:* SUNY at Oneonta NY (BS) Eng Ed 1980; SUNY at Cortland NY (MS) Rdng Ed 1984; SUNY at Stony Brook 9 Credit Hrs; BOCES 9 Credit Hrs; *cr:* Skaneateles Cntrl Schl Eng Tchr Grd 9, 10, 12 1980-81; SUNY at Cortland Summer Inst Composition Instr 1982; Fabius Pompey Cntrl Schl Eng Tchr Grd 9, 9 Skills 1982-83; Middleville Jr HS Eng Tchr Grd 9, Rdng Tchr Grd 7-9 1983-85; Miller Place HS Eng Tchr Grd 9-10 1985-; *ai:* NCTE 1979-; AFT 1980-; NY St Eng Cncl 1985-; *office:* Miller Place H S 15 Memorial Dr Miller Place NY 11764

DANSDILL, JOHN P., English Teacher; *b:* Oklahoma City, OK; *m:* Dorothy Newton; *c:* John, Catherine; *ed:* Coll of Holy Cross (BA) Eng 1970; Western CT St Univ (MS) Ed, Eng 1976, (MA) Eng 1981; Univ of CT (PHD) Eng; *cr:* New Milford HS Eng Tchr 1972-77; Bethel HS Eng Tchr 1977-; *ai:* Arts Magazine; Golf Team; NEA, CEA, NCTE 1972-; CCTE, CT Poet of the Yr 1986; Poems Pub in English Journal 1981, 1994; Article Pub in English Journal 1993; *office:* Bethel HS Educational Park Bethel CT 06801*

D'ANTONA, JOSEPH PETER, Science Teacher; *b:* Brooklyn, NY; *m:* Karin Headlee; *c:* James, Kathryn; *ed:* Southern CT St Coll (BS) Intermediate Upper Ed 1968, (MS) Sci Ed 1972; Fairfield Univ 6th Yr Admin Supervision 1978; *cr:* Eastern Jr HS 8th Grd Sci Dept Chair 1968-77, 9th Grd Admin 1977-81; Western Jr HS 8th Grd Admin 1981-84; Eastern MS 6-8 Grd Sci Tchr, Dept Chair 1984-; *ai:* Hook Line & Sinker Club; Gator Olympics Eastern MS, Trumbull Babe Ruth Bsbl All Star Coach; Fac Senate EMS; Human Relations Comm; Greenwich Tchr Assn, CT Ed Assn, NEA 1968-; Trumbull Babe Ruth Assn 1994-; Trumbull Little League Assn 1990-; NSF Grant ISCS Sci Univ of VA 1973; *office:* Eastern MS 51 Hendrie Ave Riverside CT 06878

DANZI, ANGELA D., Assistant Professor; *b:* Brooklyn, NY; *c:* Daniel, Camille, Anthony, Mark, Christopher; *ed:* SUNY at Old Westbury (BA) Urban Stud 1984; NY Univ (MA) Sociology 1987, (PHD) Sociology 1993; *cr:* NY City Bd of Ed Research Consultant 1988-90; SUNY at Old Westbury, Queens Coll Adjunct Asst Prof 1988-92; SUNY at Farmingdale Asst Prof 1990-; *ai:* Sociology, Anthropology Club Adv; Amer Italian Historical Assn 1985-, Long Island VP, Natl Exec Cncl; Encyclopedia of Italian Amer His & Culture, Bd of Advs; United Univ Profs, Amer Sociological Assn, Eastern Sociological Soc; Amer Assn of Univ Women 1985-; UFT, UUP Research Grants; Hlth, Ethnicity Articles Pub; Book From Home to Hospital Jewish & Italian Amer Women & Childbirth 1920-40; *office:* S U N Y Coll Of Tech At Frmgdl Melville Road Farmingdale NY 11735

DAOUST, RICHARD JOSEPH, Social Studies Teacher; *b:* Oceanside, NY; *m:* Mary Ann Kassick; *c:* Michelle, Danielle, Suzanne; *ed:* St John's Univ (BA) Scndry Ed 1968; Hofstra Univ (MA) Ed 1972; Addl 60 Hrs Soc Stud Disciplines; *cr:* John F. Kennedy HS Soc Stud Tchr 1968-; *ai:* Boys Var Soccer, Girls Var Bowling, Boys Var Vlybl Coach; NYSUT, Bellmore-Marrick United Sec Tchrs 1968-; Natl Soccer Coaches Assn 1973-; PTA Tchr of Yr 1993; Sr Class Tchr of Yr 1994; *office:* John F Kennedy HS 3000 Bellmore Ave Bellmore NY 11710*

D'APOLITO, KIMBERLY ANN WOOLF, Spanish Teacher; *b:* Bridgeton, NJ; *m:* Drew M.; *ed:* Indiana U of PA (BS) Ed, Span 1983; *cr:* Egg Harbor Twp HS Span Tchr 1983-86; Rumson-Fair Haven HS Span Tchr 1986-88; Howell HS Span Tchr 1988-; *ai:* Span Club; Renaissance Comm; Frgn Lang Edctrs of NJ 1988-; Span Embassy Schlsp Univ of Salamanca 1994; *home:* 1012 Gully Rd Neptune NJ 07753*

DAPORE, MARY NAVEAU, Kindergarten Teacher; *b:* Greenville, OH; *m:* Robert; *c:* Benjamin, Alex, Joel; *ed:* Bowling Green St Univ (BS) Elem

Ed 1983; Univ of Dayton (MS) Elem Ed 1992; 15 Addl Hrs; *cr:* Amos Mem Lib Asst Children Librn 1983-84; Russia Local Schl Kndgtn Tchr 1984-; *ai:* OEA, NEA 1984-; Kinder Korner 1995-, Preschl Bd Sec; Copeland Grant; *office:* Russia Local Schl 110 Main St Russia OH 45363

DAPRA, ELAINE MARIE (BURLEY), 7th & 8th Grd English Teacher; *b:* Brooklyn, NY; *m:* George DeBerlle; *c:* Catherine, Theresa; *ed:* Cntrl Ct St (BS) Eng 1972; CW Post (MS) Rdng 1993; 30 Credit Hrs in Ed; *cr:* Highland Falls ONeill 7th & 8th Grd Eng Tchr 1972-; *ai:* Chrldr Coach; Newspaper Adv & After Schl Readers Club Spon; NYSUT 1972-; Highland Fralls Tchrs Assn 1972-, Negotiator 1978, Chair of Fund Raising 1992 & 1995; Friends of the Lib 1992-; Parent Tchr Council 1994-; Pub Relations 1994; PTA Sec 1988; Sacred Heart Church Lector 1990-; Orange Cty Apple Grant for Art Cart for Writing; *office:* ONeill HS Rt 9 W Highland Falls NY 10928

D'ARCY, ERIC WINSTON, Global Studies I Teacher; *b:* Buffalo, NY; *m:* Leslie Griffin; *c:* Collin, Ryan, Katia; *ed:* SUNY at Oswego (BS) Scndry Ed, Soc Stud 1989; SUNY at Cortland (MS) Scndry Ed, His 1995; *cr:* North Rose Wolcott HS 9-11 Grd Soc Stud Tchr 1990-92; Newark Vly HS 9 Grd Global Stud I Tchr 1992-; *ai:* Coach for Wrestling 1989-, Cross Cntry 1990-, Track 1993-; Natl Wrestling Coaches Assn 1994-; NYSUT 1990-; St John's Church 1992-, Eucharistic Minister; Mat Rat Wrestling Club 1993-, Pres; Democratic Party 1995-, Dist Rep; *office:* Newark Valley HS Wilson Creek Rd Newark Valley NY 13811

DARCY, JANET LUTZ, Social Studies Teacher; *b:* Boston, MA; *m:* James B. Jr.; *c:* Jennifer, Timothy; *ed:* Newton Coll of the Sacred Heart (BA) Amer Stud 1970; Rowan St Coll 3 Grad Credits; St Joseph's Univ 6 Grad Credits; *cr:* Upper Township MS 7th-8th Grd Tchr 1986-; *ai:* Core Team Comm Mem 1989-; Strategic Planning Team 1996; NEA 1986-; NJ Cncl for Soc Stud 1992-; Tchr of Yr 1995; Cape May Cty Tchr of Yr 1995; *office:* Upper Twp MS Box 159 Perry Rd Tuckahoe NJ 08250

DARCY, MAVIS JOAN, Latin & English Teacher; *b:* Elyria, OH; *ed:* Miami U of OH (BS) Ed 1968, (MAT) Eng 1969; Millersville U (MA) Latin 1988; U of Toledo 1995 Tchng Irish Culture; *cr:* Clearview HS Tchr 1969-; *ai:* Amer Classical League 1980-; Natl Org for Women; Disabled Am Vets, Commander; Emily's List; Exhibit on Sheppard Murder Case.

DARDECK, JUDY SIMPSON, Social Studies Teacher; *b:* San Mateo, CA; *m:* Stephen Alan; *c:* Adam, Aaron; *ed:* Foothill Coll (AA) His 1967; Univ of CA at Berkeley (BA) His 1969; Tchng Credential Ed 1970; Post Grad Work Univ of VT, Castleton ST Coll; *cr:* Otter Vly HS Tchr 1973-; *ai:* Jr Class Adv; NEA 1984-; *office:* Otter Vly Union HS RR 1 Box 1115 Brandon VT 05733

DARE, DELISE K., 7th & 8th Grade Math Teacher; *b:* Millville, NJ; *m:* Rocky; *c:* Tarah Gilson, Kyle Gilson; *ed:* Cumberland Cty Coll (AA) Elem Ed 1973; Rowan Coll (BA) Elem Ed 1975; Rowan Coll of NJ, St Peter's Coll of NJ Grad Courses; *cr:* Lawrence Twp Elem Schl 7-8 Grd Sci Tchr 1975-86; LAC Elem Schl 7-8 Math Tchr 1989-; *ai:* Safety Patrol Adv; Musical Productions Pianist; NJEA, NEA 1975-; NCTM; AMTNJ; Centre Grove ME Church 1964-, Pianist; EPRHA 1994-, Bd Mem; *home:* 6 Acton Station Rd Salem NJ 08079*

DARE, JOHN S., History Teacher; *b:* Cleveland, OH; *m:* Jean Trainor-Dare; *c:* Christopher, Jason; *ed:* Kent St Univ (BS) Ed, Soc Stud 1959, (MED) His 1963; *cr:* Carl F. Shuler Jr HS Soc Stud Tchr 1959-64; J. Marshall Sr HS Soc Stud Tchr 1964-90; Cuyahoga Comm Coll Part-time His Tchr 1969-79; Lake Erie Coll His Tchr 1988; Hebrew Acad of Cleveland Soc Stud Tchr 1991-; *ai:* M. H. Jennings Schlsp 1963, Master Tchr 1978; Fulbright Scholar 1964.*

DARENSOD, MELANIE BURNS, Fifth Grade Teacher; *b:* Mahopac, NY; *m:* Joseph; *c:* Michelle Mullaly, Leslie Weber; *ed:* SUNY at New Paltz (BS) Elem Ed 1966; *cr:* Mahopac Pub Schls Third Grd Tchr 1966-70, Remedial Math Tchr 1974-78; St Lawrence O'Toole Schl 6-8 Grd Math, Soc Stud Tchr 1978-89, Fifth Grd Tchr 1989-; *ai:* Fed Cath Tchrs 1981-, Schl Rep; SUNY New Paltz Alumni Assn 1966-, Sec, Chptr Dev Chair, 1989 Distngd Alumni Svc Awd; St Joseph's Parish 1981-, Parish Cncl, Yth Group Dir; Capuchin Yth, FamilM inistry 1986-, Retreat Rector Ldrshp Comm; *home:* 12 Hillandale Rd Yorktown Heights NY 10598*

DARGAN, CAROL WIANT, Reading, Eng & Soc Stud Tchr; *b:* Parkersburg, WV; *m:* Stephen McLynn; *c:* Patrick, Westley, Stephanie; *ed:* WV Univ (BS) Elem Ed 1973; George Washington Univ (MA) Elem Ed 1982; *cr:* Lincoln Elem Schl 1st Grd Tchr 1973-74; Parole Elem Schl 4th Grd Tchr 1974-78; Huntingtown Elem Schl 2nd-5th Grd Tchr 1978-95; Plum Point MS 6th Grd Tchr 1995-; *ai:* NEA 1974-; MSTA 1978-; Calvert Co His Fair 1995-, Judge; U Meth Church 1995-, Commission on Ed; Chesapeake Investment Club 1995-; *office:* Plum Point MS 1475 Plum Point Rd Huntingtown MD 20639

D'ARGENIO, RON ANTHONY, English & Journalism Teacher; *b:* Allentown, PA; *m:* Debra Young; *c:* Thurman, Sam; *ed:* East Stroudsburg Univ (BS) Eng 1971; Masters Equivalency in Ed 39 Credits; *cr:* Dieruff HS Eng Tchr, Bsbl Coach 1972-73; Whitehall HS Eng Tchr, Bsktbl Coach 1973-75; Northwestern HS Eng, Jrnlsm Tchr 1993-; *ai:* Allentown Coll Bsktbl Coach; PSEA, NWLEA 1993-; Allentown Jaycees 1978-; *office:* Northwestern Lehigh HS 6493 Route 309 New Tripoli PA 18066*

DARLAK, DARRYL FRANK, Adapted Physical Ed Teacher; *b:* Wilmington, DE; *m:* Karen Ann Uzzo; *ed:* West Chester St Coll (BS) Hlth, PE 1980; West Chester Univ (MED) Hlth, PE 1986; Admin, Elem-Sec Principalship, Supervisiory Certs Hlth, PE Penn St Univ; Elem Ed Cert Immaculata Coll; *cr:* Devereux Fnd Adapted PE Tchr 1980-82; Chester Co Intermediate Unit Adapted PE Tchr 1982-85; Coatesville Area Schl Dist MS PE Tchr 1985-86; Devereux Fnd Adapted PE Tchr 1986-88; Downingtown Area Schl Dist Adapted PE Tchr 1988-; *ai:* Downingtown HS Spec Olympics Vol Club Adv; Ski Club Vol; Head Ftbl, Head Track & Field Coach Downingtown Jr HS; NEA, PSEA, DAEA 1982-, Rep Cncl; Kappa Delti Pi; Spec Olympics Advy 1982-, Cty Coord, Sports-Competition Events Dir; Big Brother-Big Sisters 1993-, Big Brother Vol; Outstdng Svc Awd 1984; *office:* Downingtown Area Schl Dist 445 Manor Ave Downingtown PA 19335

DARLING, JILL ANN, Home School Teacher; *b:* Long Branch, NJ; *m:* Eugene B.; *c:* Greg, Keith; *cr:* Homeschool Tchr 1982-; *ai:* Writing Act Adv; Sr HS Guid Cnslr, Schlsp Coord; PA Homeschoolers 1983-; NYS LEAH 1985-, NE PA Chptr Ldr; Home Schl Legal Defense Assn 1995-; Faith Chrstn Flwshp 1991-, Children's Minister, Area Yth Skate Nite Coord; Articles Pub; Group Speaker Homeschool Wkshps; Contact Person for Homeschooling Information; Attnd Confs NYS Loving Ed at Home, Region #6 1990-; *home:* HC 34 Box 27-C Warren Center PA 18851

DARLING, MARSHA JEAN TYSON, History Professor; *b:* New York City, NY; *ed:* Staten Island Coll (AA) Lbrl Arts 1971; Vassar Coll (BA) Interdisciplinary Stud 1973; Duke Univ (MA) His 1975, (PHD) His & Oral His 1982; Imperial Coll of London Film 1970; Newberry Lib Statistical Methods Cert 1975; *cr:* Wellesley Coll Asst Prof of Black Stud 1980-87; Hunter Coll Asst Prof of Womens Stud 1987; Hood Coll Assoc Prof of His 1991-92; Univ of Md Fac Rsrch Assoc 1990-91; Georgetown Univ Assoc Prof of Interdisciplinary Stud 1992-; *ai:* Black Womens Artistic Resource Collective 1990-; Org of Amer Historians; Assn for Stud of Afro-Amer Life His; Phi Alpha Theta 1993-; Natl Black Womens Hlth Project, Bd of Dirs 1983-88; MA Endowment for Arts, Bd of Dirs 1982-88; Fulbright Scholars Awd to India; Smithsonian Inst Fac Awd; Rockefeller Fdntn Post-Doctoral Flwshp; Wellesley Coll Pinanski Awd; Articles Pub; *office:* Georgetown Univ 624 Intercultural Centre Washington DC 20057*

DARLING, MARY LOUISE, Math Teacher & Dept Chair; *b:* Marion, OH; *m:* Mark Paul; *c:* Andrew, Peter; *ed:* Otterbein Coll (BS) Math 1970; Ashland Univ (MA) Curr & Instruction 1992; Attnd OH St Univ; *cr:* Gahanna Lincoln HS Math Tchr 1970-75 & 1987-88; New Albany HS Math Tchr & Dept Chair 1988-; *ai:* NHS Adv; Scndry Curr Cncl; NCTM & OCTM 1988-; Martha Holden Jennings Scholar 1993; *office:* New Albany HS 6425 New Albany Condit Rd New Albany OH 43054

DARLING, STANTON GIRARD,II, Professor of Law; *b:* Camp Blanding, FL; *m:* Judy A. Carpenter; *c:* Stanton G. III, Stephen M.; *ed:* OH St Univ (BA) Soc Sci-Summa Cum Laude 1965; Georgetown Univ of Law Ctr (JD) 1968; *cr:* Univ of Santa Clara Schl of Law Asst Prof of Law 1974-81; Capital Univ Law Schl Visiting Prof of Law 1981-83, Prof of Law 1984-; *ai:* Fac Adv; Acad Success Prgm; Amer Bar Assn 1969-; OH St Bar Assn, Columbus Bar Assn 1984-; Dr Martin Luther King Jr Image Awd Black Law Stdnts Assn 1991; Prof of Yr 1983; Book: Ohio Civil Justice Reform Act 1987; *office:* Capital Univ Law Schl 665 S High St Columbus OH 43215

DARLING, WILLIAM WEBB, Assoc Prof of Mechanical Engr; *b:* Niskayna, NY; *ed:* Clarkson Coll of Tech (BS) Civil & Environmental Engr 1977, (ME) Civil & Environmental Engr 1979; Rensselaer Polytechnical Inst 1978-80; *cr:* Rensselaer Polytechnical Inst Instr 1982-84; Hudson Valley Comm Coll Assoc Prof Mechanical Engrng & Industrial Tech 1984-; *ai:* Transfer Adv; NY St Engrng Tech Assn 1984-, Pres, VP; ATEA 1993-; CETNYS 1995-; Kiwanis Intnl 1986-; NYTECH Grant PI; GAD Consultant NYMEP; HVCC Meritorios Svc Awd; *office:* Hudson Valley Comm Coll 80 Vandenburgh Ave Troy NY 12180*

DARMENTO, RALPH J.,FSC, Mathematics Department Head; *b:* Brooklyn, NY; *ed:* Manhattan Coll (BS) Math, Classical Langs 1973; Columbia Univ (MA) Mathematical Ed 1976; Univ of San Francisco (MA) Pvt Schl Admin 1980; 6 Credits Ed Providence Coll; Fordham Univ PHD Candidate Ed Admin, Supervision; *cr:* Bishop Loughlin HS Math Tchr 1973-76; LaSalle Acad Math Dept Chair, Vice Prin 1976-84; St John's Coll Vice Prin, Math Tchr 1984-87; LaSalle Acad Math Dept Head 1987-88; LaSalle Military Acad Math Dept Chair, Coll Cnslr 1988-89; Arch Bishop Carroll HS Prin 1989-92; St Raphael Acad Prin 1992-93; LaSalle Acad Math Dept Head 1993-; *ai:* Math Team Coach; Prins Advy, Acad Cncls; NHS Selection Comm; NCTM 1972-; NCEA 1976-; ASCD 1980-93, 1995-; Pro Ecclesia et Pontifice 1991; *office:* LaSalle Acad 44 E 2nd St New York NY 10003*

DARMSTADTER, LEO J.,JR., Junior High Math Chairperson; *b:* Millville, NJ; *m:* Elizabeth; *c:* Daria, Marcy, Lee; *ed:* Glassboro St Coll (BA) Elem Ed 1970; 15 Grad Credits; *cr:* Vineland Bd of Ed Adult Migrant Ed 1 Yr, Summer Migrant Schl 4 Yrs; Deerfield Twp Schl Tchr 27 Yrs; *ai:* Bowling, IM Bsktbl, Soccer, Chess Club & Natl Jr Hnr Soc Adv; NEA 1969-; NJEA 1969-; CCEA 1969-; PTTA 1969-, Negotiations Chair 18 Yrs; St Francis Church 1967-; BSA 1967-, Cnslr, Eagle Scout; NJSIAA Ofcl 1982-, Examiner; *office:* Deerfield Township Schl Morton Ave Rosenhayn NJ 08352

DARNER, ROBERT JOSEPH, History Teacher; *b:* Dayton, OH; *m:* Debra Lynn Greiner; *c:* Ryan, Brent, Kelli; *ed:* Denison Univ (BA) Pol Sci 1971; Wright St Univ (MA) Ed 1977; *cr:* Johnstown-Monroe HS Amer His, W His Tchr 1971-72; High St Elem Schl Tchr of Learning Disabled 1973-76; Washington Elem Schl Tchr of 6th Grd Learning Disabled 1976-79; South St Elem Schl 6th Grd Tchr 1979-85; Wilder Jr HS Amer His, OH His Tchr 1985-; *ai:* Miami Vly Vikings Boys AAU Bsktbl; Intervention Assistance Team; NEA 1973-; *office:* Wilder Jr H S 1120 Nicklin Ave Piqua OH 45356

DA ROSA, LUIS GONZAGA, Span Tchr & Dept Head; *b:* Faial Horta, Portugal; *m:* Marie Bento; *c:* Zachary; *ed:* Univ of MA at Dartmouth (BA) Portuguese, Span 1978; Brown Univ (MA) Biling, Port, Brazilian Stud 1983; Universidad Internacional (MS) Span, Amer Lit 1987; *cr:* New Bedford HS Portuguese Tchr 1978-81; MA Migrant Ed Prgm Comm Liaison 1981-84; Case HS Span Tchr 1984-87, Dept Head 1987-; *ai:* Iberian Club; MTA, NEA 1979-; ACTFL 1994-; AATSP 1993-; Coast Guard Auxiliary 1984-; Fincom Vice, Vice Chm 1991; Schl Comm Chm 1995-; *office:* Joseph Case HS 70 School St Swansea MA 02777

D'ARPINO, LENORE M., Spanish Teacher; *b:* Rochester, NY; *m:* John Angelo; *ed:* SUNY at Geneseo (BA) Span 1994; 12 Credit Hours; *cr:* Key Bank of NY Asst Branch Mgr 1990-91, Fin Planner 1992-93; Churchville-Chili Control Schls Span Tchr 1994-; *ai:* Jr Class Adv; Bldg Staff Dev Comm; Dist Staff Dev Comm; NEA 1994-; NYSAFLT 1993-; Phi Theta Kappa; Sigma Delta Pi; Sylvia Haseltine Awd for Excl in Span; Natl Deans List; *office:* Churchville-Chili Sr HS 5786 Buffalo Rd Churchville NY 14428

DARRAGH, JANINE S., 9th & 10th Grd English Teacher; *b:* Middletown, OH; *ed:* OH Univ (BSEd) Eng Ed 1994; Working on Masters Curr, Instruction, Scndry Eng Ed; *cr:* Waterford HS Eng Tchr 1994-; *ai:* Chrldng, Soph Class, Bible Club Adv; OCTELA 1993-; YMCA 1995-; OH River Road Runners 1990-; *office:* Waterford HS PO Box 67 Main St Waterford OH 45786

DARSON, DONNA JEAN, 7th Grade Social Studies Tchr; *b:* Bay Shore, NY; *ed:* Cortland St Univ (BS) Early Scndry Ed & Soc Stud 1977, (MS) Rdng 1981; MS +75 Credit Hrs; *cr:* Longwood Cntrl Schls 6th Grd Soc Stud & Eng Tchr 1978-81, 7th Grd Rdng Tchr 1981-85, 7th Grd Rdng & Soc Stud Tchr 1985-91, 7th Grd Soc Stud Tchr 1992-; *ai:* Yrbk Adv 1982-95; AFT 1978-; NEA 1978-; *home:* 97 Leeward Ln Port Jefferson NY 11777

DART, PETER M., 8th Grd Science & English Tchr; *b:* Augusta, GA; *m:* Karen Christianson; *ed:* Lyndon St Coll (BA) Elem Ed 1987; CT Coll (MAT) Arts in Tchng 1994; *cr:* Jack Jacter Elem Schl 4th Grd Tchr 1987-93; Colchester Intermediate Schl 4th Grd Tchr 1993-94; Wm J. Johnston MS 8th Grd Eng, Sci Tchr 1994-; *ai:* Outing Club Adv; At-Risk Prgm Coord; Sci Curr Comm; AFT 1987-; Yth Svc Bureau 1990-92, Chm; *office:* William J. Johnston MS Norwich Ave Colchester CT 06415*

DARYTICHEN, FRANK JOSEPH, Biology Teacher; *b:* Perth Amboy, NJ; *ed:* Ft Hays St Univ (MS) Bio 1973; KS Wesleyan Univ (BA) Bio; Attnd Kean Coll, Coll of Atlantic; *cr:* Hays HS Bio Tchr 1973-75; Tri Cty HS Bio Tchr 1975-76; Oakley HS Bio Tchr 1976-78; Woodbridge Twp Schls Bio Tchr & Sci Rsrch 1978-; *ai:* Sci League; Sci Rsrch Coord; NEA 1973-; NJ Sci Tchrs Assn 1978-; NJ Bio Tchrs Assn 1993-; Governors Grant for Excl in Sci & Math; Sigma Xi Rsrch Soc Awd for Excl in Sci Tchng; NJ Finalist for Pres Awd for Excl in Sci & Math Tchng; 3 ECO Lab Grants for Creative Curr; *office:* John F Kennedy Memorial H S Washington Ave Iselin NJ 08830*

DAS, ASSUNTA, Spanish Teacher; *b:* Vallata Avellino, Italy; *m:* Jagdish; *c:* Alita, Liana; *ed:* Montclair Univ (BA) Span, Fr & Italian 1967, (MA) Span 1972; In-Service & Grad Credits Earned; *cr:* Union Regent Schl System Span Tchr 1967-71; Wappinger Schl Dist Span, Fr & Italian Tchr 1978-; *ai:* NSFLT 1978-; Modern Lang Assn 1978-; ALM 1978-; Sons of Italy; El Nido; *office:* John Jay HS PO Box 38 Hopewell Junction NY 12533

DAS, MITRA, Professor of Sociology; *b:* Delhi, India; *ed:* Univ of Rajasthan (BA) Sociology, Philosophy 1962, (MA) Sociology 1964-; Univ of MA at Amherst (MA) Sociology 1972, (PHD) Sociology 1975; of Lowell Asst Prof 1974-80, Assoc Prof 1981-86; Univ of MA Pr *ai:* Laotian Stu Org Adv; NEA, MTA 1975-; Books: Technology Society, Nation to Nation A Case Study of Bengali Intependence, Pub; *office:* Univ Of MA At Lowell 1 University Ave Lowell MA

DASENBROCK, ALICE FRANK, Spanish Teacher; *b:* Cincinn *m:* Lawrence; *c:* Jeffrey, Julie; *ed:* Univ of Cincinnati (BA) E 1972, (BS) Ed 1972; Xavier Univ (MA) Eng 1976; 45 Semester C Eng, Span, Ed; *cr:* St Bernard-Elmwood Place HS Eng, Span Tchr Northwest HS Eng, Span Tchr 1984-; *ai:* NEA, OEA 1995-; AATS OFLA 1984-; *office:* Northwest HS 10761 Pippin Rd Cincinnati O

DASILVA, ELIZABETH MARTIN, Biology & Chemistry Te Waterbury, CT; *m:* Joseph; *c:* Joseph, Michael; *ed:* Univ of Clinical Dietetics 1986; Cntrl CT St Univ (MS) Scndry Sci Southern CT St Univ Sci Ed Cert 1989; Currently Pursuing 6th Y Ed; *cr:* Crosby HS Sci Tchr 1993-; *ai:* Soph Class Adv; TQE Subc on Positive Discipline; NEA, CEA 1993-; CSTA 1995-; East Er Club 1994-, Sec; Home & Schl Assn 1990-, Carnival Co-Chprs Crosby HS 300 Pierpont Rd Waterbury CT 06705

DA SILVA, MIMI, Adjunct Instructor of Psych; *b:* Pawtucket, R A. Randolph-Macon Coll (BA) Philosophy 1975; NY Univ (MSW Soc Work 1984; Seton Hall Univ (PHD) Cnslng Psych 1996; Practitioner 1986-; Monmouth Univ Adj Instr Psych 1991-; *ai:* 1981-; APA 1984-; *office:* Monmouth Univ Cedar Ave West Lon NJ 07764

DATES, ELAINE ZAK, Latin Teacher; *b:* Hartford, CT; *m:* Ste *ed:* Univ of VT (BA) Classics 1964; Wayne St Univ (MA) La Middlebury Coll (MA) Italian 1981; Continuous Courses Classica New England's Summer Inst at Dartmouth, Cambridge Inst, Am *cr:* Essex Junction HS Eng Tchr 1964-65; Spaulding HS Eng, L 1965-66; Warren HS Eng, Latin Tchr 1966-70; Burlington HS E Tchr 1972-; *ai:* Latin Club; Interdisciplinary; Strategic Planni Revision; VCLA 1972-, Pres, Sec Prog; CANE 1972-, Ed Auxi Dir; VFLA 1979-, Sec; Northeast Conference 1989-, Sec; BEA Bd; Odyssey of the Mind 1990-, Ex Bd; First Congregational 1956-, Yth Minist; Pierson Lib 1990-, Vol; Amer Assn of Univ Wor Tchr of Yr 1985; Yrbk Dedication 1975, 1985; Univ of VT Outst Awd 1988; Rockefeller Fellow 1989; Pub Articles; Present Amer League; *office:* Burlington H S 52 Institute Rd Burlington VT 05

DATTILO, JERRY M., 7th Grade Social Studies Tchr; *b:* Pittsbu *m:* Monica Zaremba; *c:* Matthew, Laura; *ed:* Univ of Notre Da Sociology 1973; Westminster Coll (MS) Counseling 1976; *cr:* Bl HS Scndry Soc Stud Tchr 1973-89; North Allegheny Schls Scndry Tchr 1989-; *ai:* Beaver Boys Pony League Team, 4th Grd Girls Bsktbl & Girls Sftbl Coach; AFT 1989-; St Blaize Church 1985- Stu Assistance Team 1989-, Cnslr; Runner-Up Wolf Endowme *office:* North Allegheny Schl Dist 5145 Wexford Run Rd We 15090

DATTILO, MONICA K., English Teacher; *b:* Rochester, PA; *m:* Matthew, Laura; *ed:* Clarion St (BS) Comm Arts 1974; Credit H Cert; *cr:* Hopewell Sr HS 9-12th Grd Eng Tchr 1974-; *ai:* Ass Scorekeeper for Beaver Elem Bsktbl, SS P & P Bsktbl Teams; Sco For Beaver Bsbl, Sftbl Teams; NEA, PSEA, NCTEA 1974-; SS P PTG 1992-, Bd Mem.

DATZ, ALAN, Government & Soc Sci Teacher; *b:* Philadelphia Alyson; *c:* Michele, Nicole, Danielle; *ed:* Temple Univ (BS) 1965; Beaver Coll (MS) Ed 1976; Widener Univ Supvr Cert 1991; Credit Hrs; *cr:* George Washington HS Tchr 1966-; *ai:* Stu Govt Chapter Spon; Red Cross Bloodmobile Coord; AFT 1965-; Soc S 1966-; Philadelphia Fed of Tchrs 1965-; PA Bd of Realtors 1974 Cty Bd of Realtors 1991-; St Ct System Lesson Plan Pub for Wa Univ; *office:* George Washington HS Bustleton Ave & Ve Philadelphia PA 19116*

DAUBENMIRE, JEFFREY ALAN, Director of Choral Activ Logan, OH; *ed:* OH Univ (BM) Music Ed 1990, (MED) Educl Adm *cr:* Logan-Hocking Schls Dir of Choral Acts 1990-; *ai:* Sho Choraliers Dir; Producer Annual HS Musical; Amer Choral 1990-; Phi Delta Kappa 1995-; ASCD 1995-; The Bowen Hous Exec Dir; *office:* Logan HS 50 North St Logan OH 43138

DAUBENSPECK, NORA J., Third Grade Teacher; *b:* Oil City, Westminster Coll (BA) Elem Ed 1972; 18 Hrs Edinboro Univ; 12 St Univ; 12 Hrs Millersville Univ; Inservice at Shippensburg Bloomsburg Univ; *cr:* Starbrick Elem Schl Third Grd Tchr Jefferson Elem Schl Third Grd Tchr 1972-; *ai:* Mentor Tchr; Comm; PTA; Dist Transitional Outcomes; Co-Op Learning Netwo PSEA, WCEA 1972-; Delta Kappa Gamma 1974-, Sec 5 Yrs; E Cncl 1985-; United Meth Church 1974-; Assn of Coll Women 197 Yrs; Warren Art League 1972-; Hospice 1990-.*

DAUBNEY, THOMAS JAMES, Project Adventure Coord & Tonawanda, NY; *m:* Patricia; *c:* Tamara, Amy, Thomas Jr. Tricia Timothy; *ed:* Boston Univ (BA) PE 1963; Univ of RI PE 1972; *cr* Univ Ftbl Asst Coach 1963-68; Barnstable HS Tchr Coach 1968- of RI Asst Ftbl Coach 1969-70; Portsmouth HS Tchr & Coach 19 NEA, NHAPEHRR 1970-; PTO 1986-; Moose 1973-; Coach of Y 1981; *office:* Portsmouth HS Alumni Cr Portsmouth NH 03801*

DAUGHERTY, DENISE MENDENHALL, HS Math Teacher Chprsn; *b:* Akron, OH; *m:* Daniel M.; *c:* Danette Waddle, Michelle Lewis, Paul Lewis; *ed:* Univ of Akron (BA) Scndry 1976, (MA) Scndry Admin & Supervision 1983; Attnd Drake Univ Univ, Ashland Univ, Baldwin-Wallace Coll, OH St Univ; *cr:* Univ Comp Lab & Math Asst 1972-76; North Royalton HS Math Tchr Chair 1976-; *ai:* Ski Club Asst; Outdoor Ed Class Chaperone; CAR Drug Intervention Facilitator; Proficiency Intervention Team; Equ Assertive Discipline Team; NCTM 1972-; NEA, OEA & NEOE GCCTM & OCTM 1976-; Cantor at Church 1968-; BSA 1987-, Merit Badge Cnslr; Brunswick PAC 1994-; Brunswick Schls Planning Comm 1996-; Brunswick & N Royalton Levy Comm; N PTA; Classroom of the Future Project Mem; Tchr of the Yr; Equals Coord; Jennings Grant; Wkshp Presentor; Jennings Scholar; Jer Outstdng Tchr Awd 1989-90; Eisenhower Grant; Title II Grant; Woman on Campus; *office:* North Royalton HS 14713 Ridge R Royalton OH 44133*

DAUGHERTY, HELEN GINN, Professor of Sociology; *b:* Wyo PA; *m:* G. Thomas; *ed:* Univ of SC (BA) Sociology 1974; Univ Greensboro (MA) Sociology 1977; Univ of MD (PHD) Sociology Univ of NC at Greensboro Research Asst 1974-76; Univ of MD Research Asst 1977-82; Univ of MD Coll Instr & Research Asst *ai:* Amer Sociological Assn, Population Assn of Amer 1982-; S for Women in Soc 1976-; Bd of Soc Svcs 1992-, Chair; Co-Au Introduction to Population with Kenneth Kammeyer Interdisciplinary Congress of Women Del 1987, 1990, 1993 & 199 Saint Marys Coll Of MD Dept of Sociology St Marys Cy MD 20

DAUGHERTY, KAREN JANE (OLMSTEAD), Mathematics Te Canton, OH; *m:* Earl; *c:* David Scott LeGates, Jeffrey Paul Michael Carl Elijah LeGates; *ed:* OH St Univ (BS) Elem Ed 1971;

MA) Ed Tech 1988; Enrolled in Doctoral Prgm; Project Discovery; Scndry Math, Cmptr Sci Ed Andover-Dartmouth Inst; *cr:* Toledo s Home Instr 1982-94, Classroom Tchr 1984-, Dial-A-Tchr 1990-; a Class, Youth-to-Youth Adv; Jefferson Madison Ldrshp Mentor oledo Hands-On Museum Adv 1992; Greater Toledo Cncl of Tchrs OH Cncl of Tchrs of Math, NCTM 1990-; Natl Cncl of Supvrs of 95-; Ed Symposium 1988-, Registration Chm 1995-; Impact II 93; Outstdng HS Tchng Awd 1995; Nom Amer Tchr Awds 1996; sidential Awds for Excl in Sci & Math Tchng 1996; *office:* Roy C. 2100 Tremainsville Rd Toledo OH 43613

ERTY, LORI PERRY, Psychology & Sociology Teacher; *b:* on, DC; *m:* Kevin; *ed:* James Madison Univ (BBA) Bus Mgmt iv of MD at College Park (MED) Scndry Soc Stud Ed 1994; *cr:* HS Soc Stud Tchr 1994-; *ai:* Stu Cncl Co-Spon; MD Substance gm Comm; NEA 1994-; MSTA 1994-; *office:* Northern HS 2950 ille Rd Owings MD 20736

ETY, JOHN MARK, Principal; *b:* Port Huron, MI; *m:* Mary Beth Brandon, Nathan; *ed:* Harding Univ (BA) Elem Ed 1988, (MS) 1992; *cr:* Barlow-Vincent Elem 7th & 8th Grd Sci Tchr 1988-94; Elem Prin 1994-; Cutler Elem Prin 1994-; *ai:* Warren Local Tech EASA 1994-; *office:* Warren Local Schl Dist PO Box 26 Vincent 4*

NAIS, DONNA M. (FRANCIUSI), Science Teacher; *b:* ter, MA; *m:* Raymond; *c:* Matthieu; *ed:* Fitchburg St Coll (BS) y 1986; Currently Working Toward Masters in Sci Ed; *cr:* Apache HS Sci Tchr 1986-89; Notre Dame Preparatory Schl Sci Tchr North Middlesex Regnl HS Sci Tchr 1990-91; Keene HS Sci, raphy & Earth Sci Tchr 1991-; *ai:* Peer Mediation Adv; NEA STA 1993-; Natl Marine Educators Assn, Gulf of ME Maritime s Assn 1995-; Project Oceanology Boston Harbor Marine Prgm for Tchrs; Marine Awareness Research Expedition 1993 & ice: Keene Sr HS 43 Arch St Keene NH 03431*

, JOHN JOSEPH, American History Teacher; *b:* Jamestown, Phyllis A. Knable; *c:* Michelle, Rachel, David; *ed:* Kent St Univ Stud 1962; 40 Credit Hrs Cleveland St Univ; 15 Credit Hrs Akron St Michaels Schl 6th Grd Tchr 1963-66; Brecksville-Broadview hls Classroom Tchr 1966-; *ai:* IM; Bsktbl Coach; Tchr Mentor; r; Soc Stud Text Review; Curr Writing Projects; NEA 1966-; OH 1966-; Brecksville Ed Assn 1966-, Pres of Local Assn (Twice); 6-, Pres; OH Tchr Cert Commission 1980-84; St Standards Comm 1982-84; Dist Tchr of Yr 1978; OH Tchr of Yr 1979.*

A, JOSEPH P., Social Studies Teacher; *b:* Brooklyn, NY; *m:* Michael, Joseph, Nicholas; *ed:* SUNYat Stony Brook (BA) His A) Lbrl Stud 1989; 45 Addl Credit Hrs; *cr:* Sachem HS Soc Stud 6-92; Island Tree HS Soc Stud Tchr 1992-; *ai:* Sr Class Adv; JV Ftbl Coaches; NYSUT 1986-; UTIT 1992-; *office:* Island Trees raight Ln Levittown NY 11756*

SHARON LEE, Professor of Nursing; *b:* Buffalo, NY; *ed:* SUNY o (BSN) Nrsng 1967, (MS) Tchng, Nrsng 1973; *cr:* Niagara Cty oll Instr 1969-70; Buffalo Gen Hosp Clinical Supvr 1980-95; Erie oll N Nrsng Prof 1970-; *ai:* Amer Nurses Assn; Natl League for NY League for Nrsng, Bd of Dirs 1993-95; Contributing Author, on, Pharmacotherapeutics for Nurses; *office:* Erie Comm Coll mps 6205 Main St Williamsville NY 14221

ANSKY, FANNY PAPA, Retired 8th Grade Tchr; *b:* New York, William (dec); *c:* Anthony; *ed:* Hunter Coll (BA) Ed; *cr:* ate Conception Tchr 1959-88; *ai:* Schl Lib Named in Her Honor.

DONIS, MARY HAVILAND, Sixth Grade Teacher; *b:* Elizabeth, Anthony J. Jr.; *c:* Gregg, Jill; *ed:* Ladycliff Coll (BA) Eng 1967; iams St (MED) Ed; Addl 36 Plus Grad Hrs; *cr:* Hoosick Falls Cntrl d Tchr 1967-; *ai:* NY St United Tchrs, AFT 1970-; NYSUT Comm 990-; Hoosick Falls Tchrs Assn, Pres, Sec; *office:* Hoosick Falls l PO Box 192 Hoosick Falls NY 12090

PORT, ANTHONY WYATT, Art Instructor; *b:* New York, NY; *m:* ; *c:* Michelle Rogers, David, Ben, Marc; *ed:* Princeton Univ (BA) ure 1971; St Univ of NY (MFA) Ceramics & Sculpture 1977; Ed e Paris France Primary & Scndry Ed; *cr:* OH Univ Art Instr 1977-; Cncl Artist in Residence 1981-84; Northwood Univ Dir, Term in 984-; *ai:* OH Univ Fac Rsrch Grants 1979-83; Louis Comfort Apprenticeship Grant 1978-79; Numerous Exhibitions in USA & *home:* 131 E Chestnut St Lancaster OH 43130*

PORT, GLORIA, Second Grade Teacher; *b:* Chattanooga, TN; *m:* a Sanyika; *c:* Kimberly; *ed:* Cntrl St Univ (BS) Ed 1976; Credit ght St Univ; *cr:* Spfld City Schls Elem Tchr 1979-; *ai:* Drug Comm; Rafiks Cnsl; NEA; *office:* Snyder Park Elem Schl 1600 Ln Springfield OH 45504

PORT, STEPHEN F., Fourth Grade Teacher; *b:* Wilkes-Barre, PA; Scott, Kevin; *ed:* Lycoming Coll (BA) Sociology, Anthropology & hy 1979; Attnd Mansfield Univ; *cr:* Towanda Area MS Tchr J A Morrow Elem Schl Tchr 1986-95; Wysox Elem Schl Tchr *ai:* Summer Sports Camp Dir; Towanda Area Ed Assn 1980-, or; Towanda Presbyn Church 1980-, Elder; *home:* 223 N 4th St PA 18848*

LYNN F., Psych Prof & Dept Chair; *b:* Falls Church, VA; *ed:* Univ Dame (BA) Psych 1986; Cath Univ (MA) Human Dev 1991, uman Dev 1993; *cr:* Saint Josephs Coll Asst Prof of Psych 1992-, Asst Dean of Stdnts 1996; *ai:* Educl Standards & Tech Advy Intnl Stu & SGA Adv; Fac Senate VP; Stu Act Coord; Vol Svcs Amer Psychological Assn 1992-; Soc for Research in Child Dev, Research on Adolesence 1991-; *office:* Saint Josephs Coll 278 ridge Rd Standish ME 04084

GERALD ALVIN, English Teacher; *b:* Glen Ridge, NJ; *c:* Peter, *ed:* Bates Coll (BA) Eng 1960; Univ of Chicago (MA) Eng 1961; r St Coll, Seton Hall Univ Addl 30 Hrs; *cr:* Fairleigh Dickinson g Instr 1963-65; West Orange Mountain HS Tchr 1965-82, Dept 72-82; West Orange HS Eng Tchr 1982-; *ai:* NEA, NJEA, WOEA etropolitan Assn of Sea Kayakers 1993-; Numerous Articles Pub; Vest Orange HS 51 Conforti Ave West Orange NJ 07052

JENN, Middle School English Teacher; *b:* New York, NY; *cr:* rep Schl MS Math & Sci Tchr 1991-94; Providence Summerbridge & Dir 1991-95; Wheeler Schl 7th-9th Grd Eng Tchr 1994-; *ai:* Schl CDC Cncl on Diversity & Comm; Samuel Huntington Pub l; Freedom Torch Awd for 6 RI Women for Notable Achvmts in vc; *office:* Wheeler Schl 216 Hope St Providence RI 02906

HOFER, CLAIRE H., French Instructor; *b:* Bouake, Ivory Coast; liam J.; *c:* Kristine, Erik, Claudine; *ed:* Universite d Provence, France (BA) 1968 Eng, (MA) Eng 1969; *cr:* Judd Schl Fr Lecturer 1966-67; Presque Isle HS Fr Tchr 1969-80; Univ of resque Isle Fr Lecturer 1980-90, Fr Instr 1990-; *ai:* Univ of ME Task Force on Foreign Lang, Culture, Real Lang Subcommitte rganizing Foreign Lang Culture Day for Area Schls; PAFTA 1980-, eFlect 1989-91, 1995-, Mem; Zippel PTO 1986-, Mem; PRISM Mem; Mini Grant Awd for Traveling, Researching in France 1992; s, Stories Pub in Univ Times, Fort Kent St John Valley Times, Edmunston,New Brunswick Madawaska; *office:* Univ Of ME At Presque Isle 181 Main St Presque Isle ME 04769

DAVIDSON, BARBARA TANA, Spanish Teacher; *b:* Harrington, DE; *m:* Joel Frank; *c:* Lev Hillel; *ed:* C. W. Post Coll (BA) Span 1969; Temple Univ (MEd) Scndry Ed 1971; Villanova Univ (MEd) Scndry Schl Cnslng 1977; *cr:* Leeds MS Span Tchr 1969-80; J. R. Masterman Schl Span Tchr, Frgn Lang Dept Chair 1980-; *ai:* Span Club Spon; Philadelphia Pub Schls Frng Lang Hnrs Convocation; AATSP 1980-; MLA 1990-.*

DAVIDSON, DALE A., Instrumental Music Director; *b:* Canton, OH; *m:* Karen K.; *c:* Chad & Amanda; *ed:* Kent St Univ (BM) Music Ed 1977; Univ of Akron (MA) Music Ed 1987; Ashland Coll & Kent St Univ, Post-Grad Work; *cr:* St Vincent-St Mary's HS Music Dir 1977-81; Springfield Local Schls Instrumental Music Dir 1981-94; Green Local Schls Instrumental Music Dir 1994-; *ai:* Marching Band Dir; Pep Band, Jazz Ensemble, Concert Bands; Instrumental Music Dept Supvr; OH Music Educators Assn; Music Educators Natl Conf; OH Ed Assn; Natl Band Assn; NEA 1981-; Natl Band Dirs Assn 1985-; Green Local PTA; Green Ed Assn; Jefferson Co Historial Soc & Tuscarawas Co Historical Soc 1991-; Comm Christian Church N Canton OH; Kent St Univ Post Grad Wkshp 1990; Marching Band Cotton Bowl Performance Dallas TX 1992; OMEA Dist 6 Solo & Ensemble Contest Chm 1982, 1983 & 1990; OMEA Dist 6 Jr HS Large Group Contest Chm 1991; PTSA Springfield Local Schls Outstanding Educator, Tchr of Yr 1992; Akron Beacon Journal Readers 5 Cty Region Most Popular Band 1991; Univ of Chicago Educator Citation 1993; OMEA Dist 6 HS Large Group Contest Chm 1994; Summit County Tchr of Yr Fnlst 1992; Natl HS Band Dir Hall of Fame Inductee; *office:* Green Local Schls Green H S 1737 Steese Rd PO Box 218 Green OH 44232*

DAVIDSON, EDWARD P., Latin, Spanish & French Tchr; *b:* Clinton, MA; *m:* Hester A. Thompson; *c:* Kelly, Christine; *ed:* Worcester St Coll (MED) Scndry Ed 1995; Assumption Coll 30 Addl Credits Fr; Tufts Univ 12 Credits in Latin; *cr:* Athol HS Fr, Span TChr 1974-79; Clinton HS Latin, Span Tchr 1980-85; Firestone of Leominster Owner 1985-90; Athol HS New Latin Prgm Started, Span, Fr Tchr 1990-; *ai:* CVG Vlybl Coach; Leo Club Adv; Schl Store Adv, Revived Prgm 1992-; Intnl Club Adv 1993-; Fac Advy Comm 1993-; Time, Restructuring Comm 1995-; NTA; Athol Teach Assn 1974-; MAFLA 1990-; Clinton Lions Club 1989-, Sec, Zone Chm; St John's Church 1990-, Lectors Grp; *office:* Athol HS 2363 Main St Athol MA 01331*

DAVIDSON, EVELYN C., AP Biology Teacher; *b:* Montreal, Canada; *m:* Mitch D.; *ed:* Northern KY U (BS) Bio 1987; Miami Univ (MAT) Scndry Ed 1990; *cr:* Miami Univ Tchng Asst 1987-89; West Clermont Schls Sub Tchr 1990-91; Ursuline Acad Bio, AP Bio Tchr 1991-; *ai:* Sci Club; Odyssey of the Mind; NABT 1989-; OH Acad of Sci 1991-; NSTA 1995-; Articles Pub; GTE GIFT Fellow; *office:* Ursuline Acad of Cincinnati 5535 Pfeiffer Rd Cincinnati OH 45242

DAVIDSON, FRANK EDWARD, Special Education Teacher; *b:* Brockton, MA; *m:* Lee Aldrich; *ed:* Fitchburg St Coll (BA) Spec Ed & Elem Ed 1978, (MED) Spec Ed 1984; *cr:* Fitchburg-Leominster Rehabilitation Ctr Spec Ed Tchr 1978-81; Peterboro MS Spec Ed Tchr 1981-84; Contoocook Valley Regnl HS Spec Ed Tchr 1984-; *ai:* Spec Olympic Vlybl, Skiing, Bsktbl, Sftbl, Soccer & Track-Field Coach; Boys Var Bsktbl Coach 1986-; NEA 1981-; Advent Luth Church 1986-; NH Spec Olympic Coach of Yr 1990; Contoocook Valley HS Bsktbl Coach of Yr 1995; NH Class I Var Bsktbl Coach of Yr 1989; NH Charitable Trust Matilda Mandrey Awd 1991; NH Spec Olympics Gold Medal Club 1985; *office:* Contoocook Valley Regnl HS Rt 202 N Peterborough NH 03458*

DAVIDSON, HARRY LEE,JR., Assoc Prof of Music & Dir; *b:* Cleveland, OH; *m:* Heidi Kankaanpaa; *c:* Heather, Melissa; *ed:* Case Western Reserve Univ (BA) Music 1978; Pacific Luth Univ (MM) Conducting 1983; *cr:* Tacoma Youth Symphony Music Dir & Conductor 1981-95; Tacoma Comm Coll Music Dept Chair 1985-95; Bremerton Symphony Orch Music Dir & Conductor 1992-95; Univ of Akron Assoc Prof of Music & Dir of Orchestras; *ai:* Lakeland Civic Orch Music Dir & Conductor; Cleveland Inst of Music Prep Orchestras; ASOL 1980-; CMS 1980; AFT 1992-; Tacoma Comm Coll Fac Achvmt Awd 1993 & Fac Excl Awd 1991; Tacoma Arts Commission Achvmt 1984; KSTW TV "Class Act Awd" 1993; *office:* University of Akron S School of Music Akron OH 44325

DAVIDSON, JAMES HARRY, 6th Grade Teacher; *b:* Oneonta, NY; *ed:* St Tchrs Coll at Oneonta (BA) Ed 1966; *cr:* Point Schl 5th Grd Tchr 1966-67, 6th Grd Tchr 1968-75; Oxford Rd Elem 6th Grd Tchr 1976-; *ai:* Adult Ed; Bsktbl Classes; Natl Level Boy Scouts Waterfront Dir 1988-; NYSUT 1966-; AFT 1966-; BSA 1951-, Asst Scout Master God & Cntry, DA Lodge Adv, Eagle 3 Palms; OA Ceremonial Adv, Silver Beaver, Waterfront Dir 1966-; *home:* 11282 OBrien Rd Remsen NY 13438*

DAVIDSON, JAN O'BRIEN, Fourth Grade Teacher; *b:* Hagerstown, MD; *c:* John Wesley, Jodi Lynne; *ed:* Towson St (BS) Elem Ed 1971; Western MD Coll Masters; Hood Coll Equivalency 1980, Spec Ed Cert 1981-82; *cr:* Norwood Elem Schl 3 Grd Tchr 1971-74; Pangborn Elem Schl 3 Grd Classroom Tchr 1974-75; Fountain Rock Elem Schl 4 Grd Tchr 1979-82; Boonsboro Elem Schl Media Spec, Resource Tchr 1982-86; Lincolnshire Elem Schl 3 Grd Tchr 1986-87, 4 Grd Tchr 1987-; *ai:* Cooperating Tchr; Schl Improvement Team Facilitator; Soc Stud Liason; Beginning Tchr Mentor; Sunday, Bible Schl Tchr; WCTA, NEA 1974-; Citizens Advy Comm 1993-; Private Tutoring; PTA VP; Noland Village Comm Ctr, Summer Schl Tchr; Awd Excl Ed Local Chamber of Commerce 1995; *office:* Lincolnshire Elem Schl 17545 Lincolnshire Rd Hagerstown MD 21740*

DAVIDSON, JEFFREY HOWARD, High School Choral Director; *b:* Philadelphia, PA; *ed:* Wittenberg Univ (BME) Voice 1980; Temple Univ (MM) Choral Conducting 1982; *cr:* John F. Kennedy HS Choral Dir 1982-85; Walt Whitman HS Choral Dir, Music Dept Chm 1985-; *ai:* All Vocal Music Act; Spring Musical Productions; Music Edctrs Natl Conf, Amer Choral Dirs Assn 1977-; Guest Lecturer Cath Univ Choral Techniques; MD Music Edctrs Assn Outstdng Scndry Schl Vocal Music Tchr 1996; *office:* Walt Whitman HS 7100 Whittier Blvd Bethesda MD 20817*

DAVIDSON, KENNETH W., Chemistry & Physics Teacher; *b:* Shippensburg, PA; *m:* Gloria J. Ginter; *ed:* Shippensburg Univ (BS) Chem 1966; Morgan St Coll (MS) Chem 1970; Post-Grad Stud Univ of DE, Univ of FL; *cr:* Pikesville HS Chem, Physics Tchr 1966-; *ai:* Honor Soc, Grad Comm; NEA, MSTA, TABCO 1966-; *office:* Pikesville HS 7621 Labyrinth Rd Baltimore MD 21208

DAVIDSON, NANCY DELINSKY, Spanish & Latin Teacher; *b:* Terre Haute, IN; *c:* Cindi, Karen, Kathy; *ed:* IN St Univ (BA) Foreign Lang 1966; Bloomsburg St Univ (MED) Span 1973; 48 Credits Beyond MS; *cr:* Laporte Jr HS Span Tchr 1966-67; Lebanon HS Span Tchr 1967-68; Abington Heights Jr HS Span Tchr 1968-71; Tunkhannock HS Span, Latin Tchr 1987-; *ai:* Latin Club; Stu Asst Team; NEA, ISTA 1966-68; NEA PSEA, TAEA 7 Yrs; Philharmonic Chorus 1983-; Wyoming Valley Orotario Soc 1986-; Amici Cantus 1993; Participant NDEA Foreign Lang Inst 1966, 1967; *office:* Tunkhannock HS 120 W Tioga St Tunkhannock PA 18657

DAVIDSON, ROBERT L., Social Studies Teacher; *b:* Brooklyn, NY; *ed:* Fordham Univ (BA) His & Soc Sci 1978; NY Univ (MA) His 1982; 30 Credits Beyond Masters at NY City Tchrs Consortium & NY St United Tchrs; *cr:* Martin Luther King Jr HS Soc Stud Tchr 1978-80; Queens Voc & Tech HS Soc Stud Tchr 1983-; *ai:* Prgm Chprsn; Testing Coord; Debate & Mock Trial Coach; We the People Schl Coord; Assn of Tchrs of Soc Stud 1983-; Population Reference Bureau 1977-; *office:* Queens Vocational HS 3702 47th Ave Long Island City NY 11101

DAVIDSON, RONALD, Sixth Grade Teacher; *b:* Grey Hawk, KY; *m:* Amy Louise Frauenkuecht; *c:* Dwight P., Kimberly Helterbrant; *ed:* Kent St Univ (BA) Corrections 1975; TX Chrstn Univ (MLA) Lbrl Arts 1978; Post-Grad Stud Elem Ed Xavier Univ; *cr:* USAF Captain Flight Crew Mem 1971-81; Little Miami Schl Dist 5th Grd Tchr 1968-70, 6th-7th Grd Tchr 1981-; *ai:* Bldg Discipline Comm Chair; Bldg Sci Curr Adv; Prof Dev Ldr Sci; NEA, OEA, LMTA 1981-; Bapt Church; Stu of Yr Corrections 1975; Air Force Commendation Medal 1981; Project Excl Nom 1992, 1993; *office:* Morrow Elem Schl 10 Miranda St Morrow OH 45152

DAVIDSON, SYLVIE G., Assoc Prof, Romance Lang & Lit; *b:* Nimes, France; *m:* Stephen Barber; *c:* Sarah, Sophie; *ed:* Univ of Montpellier (MA) Fr & Italian Lit 1968, (PHD) Comparative Lit 1978; Fr, Italian Lit License 1967; *cr:* Yale Univ Italian Instr 1969-70; Univ of MN Italian Instru 1973-74; Dickinson Coll Assoc Prof Fr & Italian 1979-; *ai:* Modern Lang Assn 1984-; Renaissance Soc of Amer 1990-; Recipient of 3 NEH Grants; Pub in Fr & Italian Lit; *office:* Dickinson Coll Carlisle PA 17013*

DAVIDSON-ROTH, JUDITH ANN, Spanish & ESOL Teacher; *b:* Allentown, PA; *m:* Ronald N. Roth; *c:* Julie Davidson Keiffer, Kristina Roth, Kurt Davidson, Timothy Roth, Nathan Davidson; *ed:* Kutztown Univ (BSEd) Span 1967; Attnd Univ of MD, Wilkes Univ, Multi Cultural Inst; *cr:* John Hanson Jr HS Span Tchr 1967-69; Emmaus HS Span Tchr 1969-70; Louis E Dieroff HS Span, ESOL Tchr 1987-; *ai:* Safety, Portfolio Comm; Peer Mediation, Conflict Resolution Coach; PSEA, NEA, AEA 1987-; Pilot Prgm Allentown Schl Dist; *office:* Louis E. Dieruff HS 815 N Irving St Allentown PA 18103*

DAVIE, LOIS LEMMON, K-Jr HS Substitute Teacher; *b:* Brownsville, PA; *w:* William R. (dec); *ed:* Geneva Coll (BS) Bio, Scndry Ed, Elem Ed 1948; *cr:* Hopewell Elem Schl Tchr 1960-92; Hopewell Area Schl Dist Sub Tchr 1992-; *ai:* 4th Grd Hike Farm Trips; NEAR, PSEAR 1992-; NNGA, PNGA 1960-, Dir; ONGA 1989-, Pres; Hopewell Comm Park 1993-, Dir; Meals on Wheels 1994-, Driver; Beaver Co Cncl of PTA Cert of Appreciation Svc Comm Children; Tchr of Yr Founders Day PTA; *home:* 3100 Kane Rd Aliquippa PA 15001

DAVIES, DIANE OLIVER, English & Computer Teacher; *b:* Baltimore, MD; *m:* Hugh S.; *c:* Christopher H., Thomas R.; *ed:* Amer Univ (BA) Eng 1965; Johns Hopkins Univ (BS) Cmptr Ed Tech 1989; Attnd Towson St, Mongomery Coll; MD In-Svc Trng; Quest Instr; *cr:* Prince George's Co Schls Tchr 1965-68; Medford Schls Bd of Ed 1975-76; Montgomery Co Pub Schls Interdisciplinary Resource Tchr 1976-; *ai:* Cmptr Coord & Chprsn; Receipt Chprsn; NEA; MICCA; BSA 1976-, Treas.

DAVIES, GARRIE LYNN, English & Speech Teacher; *b:* Aliquippa, PA; *m:* Christine Frank; *c:* Damian, Vanessa, Daria; *ed:* IN Univ of Pa (BS) Eng 1968, (MS) Ed, Rdng 1989; Duquesne Univ Cnslng 1994; *cr:* Punxsutawney HS Eng, Speech Tchr 1969-80; Freeport HS Eng, Speech Tchr 1980-; *ai:* Var Boy's Bsktbl Coach; HS Morning Television Prgm Broadcast Dir, Producer; Stu Assist Team; PA St Ed Assn, NEA 1969-; NCTE 1988-; Natl Rdng Assn, Freeport Food Bank Vol 1990-; Western PA Bsktbl Assn 1990-, Sec; Amer Running & Fitness Assn 1996; All Star Tchr Pittsburgh Univ 1995.*

DAVIES, HARRY RUSSELL, Counselor & Chairperson; *b:* Avoca, PA; *m:* Sandra; *c:* Brian, Keith; *ed:* Lackawanna Jr Coll (AS) Acctng 1962; Bloomsburg St Coll (BS) Bus Ed 1967; West Chester St (MS) Cnslr 1972; Fully Certfd Schl Cnslr 1972; *cr:* Conrad HS Tchr & Cnslr 1967-76; Wilmington HS Cnslr 1976-78; Newark HS Cnslr 1978-; *ai:* Head Bsbl Coach; Head Girls Cross Cntry Coach; Chprsn; Stu of Month Coord; SAT Supvr; NEA & DSEA 1967-; Amer Bsbl Coaches Assn 1987-, 200 Career Hits; Tchr Recognition Awd (3 Times); *office:* Newark HS 750 E Delaware Ave Newark DE 19711

DAVIES, JULIE LYN, Learning Disabilities Teacher; *b:* Saginaw, MI; *m:* David C.; *c:* Hilary J., Hannah E., Hope K.; *ed:* Cntrl MI Univ (BA) Spec Ed 1982; Attnd Walsh Univ, Ashland Univ, Bowling Green Univ, Heidelberg Coll; *cr:* Findlay City Schls Sub, LD Tutor 1983-84; Seneca East HS LD Tchr 1984-; *ai:* Chrldng Adv 1985-86; NEA, OEA 1984-, Bldg Rep; Vacation Bible Schl 1995-, Co-Chm; Joint Yth Group Ldr 1994-94, Co-Chm; *home:* 20 Lelar St Tiffin OH 44883

DAVIES, KATHLEEN, Chemistry Teacher; *b:* Alexandria, LA; *c:* Brian; *ed:* Reed Coll (BA) Bio 1967; Univ of AL at Fairbanks (MAT) Bio & Ed 1970; 60 Addl Grad Credits; *cr:* Lathrop HS Bio Tchr 1970-72; Nyack Jr HS Sci Tchr 1975-76, Nyack HS Bio & Chem Tchr 1976-78; Clarkstown South HS Chem & Bio Tchr 1978-; *ai:* NJ Sci League Team Adv; Mary Beth Hall Meml Schlsp Comm Chprsn; STANYS 1986-; NSTA 1985-; NYSUT 1975-; Elmwood Playhouse 1975-, Pres, VP; Cty Choral Soc 1975-; Appalachian Mt Club 1984-; Adirondack Mt Club 1976-; NY NJ Trail Conf Life Mem; AICHE HS Environmental Sci Ed Awd of Merit for Outstanding Service 1991; Pub in The Sci Tchr 1985 & Amer Tchr 1992; *office:* Clarkstown Sr H S South Demarest Mill Rd West Nyack NY 10994*

DAVIES, LINDA PILHOFER, Teacher of Gifted & Talented; *b:* Kew Gardens, NY; *m:* Roy; *c:* Cheryl, Brian; *ed:* St Univ of NY at Albany (BA) Eng 1969, (MA) Eng, Ed 1975; *cr:* Greenville Cntrl Schl Eng Tchr 1969-74, Sub Tchr 1974-84; Eng Tchr 1984-90; GATE Tchr 1990-; *ai:* Schl Newsletter Adv; NHS Adv 8 Yrs; NYSUT, NEA 1969-; Bethlehem Luth Church 1984-, Bd, Comms; *office:* Greenville Cntrl Jr Sr HS PO Box 129 Greenville NY 12083

DAVIES, NANCY ANN, First Grade Teacher; *b:* Concord, MA; *m:* David W.; *c:* Adam, Sarah; *ed:* IN Univ PA (BS) Elem Ed 1979; Univ of Pittsburgh (Masters) Early Chldhd 1986; *cr:* Franklin Regnl Schls 2nd Grd Tchr 1979-81; Greater Works Chrstn Acad 2nd Grd Tchr 1981-85; New Brighton Area Elem 1st Grd Tchr 1985-; *ai:* PSEA 1979-; PTA 1979-; Cub Scouts 1993-95, Exec Bd Mem; New Brighton Jr Womens Club 1994-, Ed Chm; Girl Scouts Asst Ldr 1995-; Phonetic-Approach Rdng Crt Grant; *office:* New Brighton Elem Schl 3200 43rd St New Brighton PA 15066

DAVIES, TREVOR WELDON, Biology Teacher; *b:* Fairview Park, OH; *m:* Lori K. Mc Donald; *ed:* Bowling Green St Univ (BA) Bio 1993; Working on BA Comprehensive Sci Cleveland St Univ; *cr:* Trinity HS Bio, Ecology, Botony Tchr 2 Yrs; *ai:* Frosh Ftbl 2 Yrs; Var Wrestling 2 Yrs; Var Bsbl 1 Yr; *office:* Trinity HS 12425 Granger Rd Garfield Heights OH 44125

DAVIGNON, PAUL MAURICE, French Teacher; *b:* Central Falls, RI; *m:* Mary Ann Postava-Davignon; *c:* Laure-Jeanne, Christi-Anne, Marielle; *ed:* Cath Univ (BA) French-Summa Cum Laude 1964; Manhattan Coll (MA) Theology 1969; Columbia Tchrs (MA) Fr 1973; New Schl for Soc Research 12 Credits in Anthropolgy 1970; Montclair St 6 Credits in Span 1995; *cr:* LaSalle Military Fr & Theology Tchr 1964-67; LaSalle Theology Tchr & Chm 1969; Saint Cecilia Fr, Span & Theology Tchr 1970-72; Acad of Saint Aloysious Fr Tchr & Chair & Theology Chm 1973-80; Dwight Morrow HS Fr Tchr & Subject Area Ldr 1984-; *ai:* NJEA, NEA 1984-, Local Eng Tchrs Assn VP; Phi Beta Kap pa 1964-; Noyes Fellowship in Environmental Ed at Columbia 1970; Columbia Univ Grant to Stud at Sorbonne Paris France Summer 1971; *office:* Dwight Morrow HS 274 Knickerbocker Rd Englewood NJ 07631

DAVIS, ADRIENNE, Science Teacher; *b:* Huntington, NY; *m:* Charles; *c:* Chuckie, Arianna; *ed:* Molloy Coll (BS) Bio 1983; SUNY at Stony Brook

(MALS) Sci Tchng 1987; *cr:* St John the Bapt DHS Sci Tchr 1985-87; Amityville HS Sci Tchr 1987-91; Brentwood HS Sci Tchr 1991-; *office:* Brentwood HS Ross Center Brentwood NY 11717

DAVIS, ANGELA LENTINI, Retired First Grade Teacher; *b:* Scranton, PA; *m:* Ralph George; *c:* Theodore L., Roslyn A.; *ed:* Marywood Coll (BS) Elem Ed 1974; PA Dept ED MS Equivalency Elem Ed 1985; Received Instructional II Cert; Fifteen Credit Hrs; *cr:* Moses Taylor Hospital Stdnt Grad & Registered Nurse 1948-52; East Stroudsburg Hosp RN 1954-56; Scranton St Hospital RN 1965-70; Moscow Elem Schl North Pocono Schl Dist First Grd Tchr 1974; *ai:* SCOLA Vol; Elem Tutor; Mem of Moscow Library Board; NEA-R, PSEA-R, NPEA 1974-.

DAVIS, ANN L., Mathematics Teacher; *b:* Marysville, OH; *ed:* OH St Univ (BS) Math Ed 1976, (MA) Math Ed 1981; Addl 9 Hrs; OH Univ 7 Grad Hrs; Drake Univ 3 Grad Hrs; *cr:* Buckeye Vly Local Schl Jr HS Tchr 1976-81, HS Tchr 1981-; *ai:* Flwshp of Chrstn Aths Huddle Coach; Math Team Adv; Math Dept Head; NEA, OEA, NCTM, OCTM 1976-; BVTA 1976-, Treas; First United Meth Church, Lay Ldr; Panelist ACT Test Review; OH AP Girls Bsktbl Coach of Yr 1993, Dist 1993; *office:* Buckeye Valley HS 901 Coover Rd Delaware OH 43015

DAVIS, ANN S., Seventh Grade Teacher; *b:* Long Island City, NY; *m:* Thomas E.; *ed:* Trenton St Coll (BS) Elem Ed 1971; *cr:* Sacred Heart Schl Tchr 1972-78; Roosevelt Elem Schl Tchr 1987-; *ai:* NEA, NJEA, NBEA 1987-.

DAVIS, ANNETTE T., Latin & Reading Teacher; *b:* Fort Yates, ND; *m:* David C.; *c:* David D., Samuel D., Jonelle D., Kathleen D.; *ed:* Thiel Coll (BA) His, Elem Ed 1971; Elem Ed Edinboro Univ; Latin Westminster Coll; *cr:* Greenville Elem Schl 3rd-5th Grd Tchr 1971-86; Greenville HS Latin, Rdng Tchr 1986-; *ai:* Club Adv Latin Club; Greenville Ed Assn 1971-, Pres, Negotiator; NEA; CAAS, CAPV 1991-.

DAVIS, BARBARA DEESE, 9th-12th Grd ESL Teacher; *b:* Concord, NC; *c:* Paul B. III, Cameron Wilkerson, Taylor Allen (dec); *ed:* Univ of NC (BS) Eng 1967; Wright St Univ (MS) Master Tchr 1987-, (MS) Lib, Media 1992; TESOL Validation 1987; Univ of Dayton 8 Hrs; Univ of OK 12 Hrs; *cr:* Warner Robbins Pub Schl Eng Tchr 1968-69; Moore Pub Schls Eng Tchr 1977-79; Dayton Pub Schls ESL, Eng Tchr 1979-; OH ST Univ Young Scholars Prgm 1992; Greene Cntry Career Ctr Adult ESL, Night Schl Tchr 1994-; *ai:* Intnl Club Adv 1991-; Stdnts Summer European Trips Cnslr 1993-; Frgn Lang, ESL Dept Chprsn 1993; PCP Admin Team 1995-; Kappa Delta Psi 1987-; TESOL 1987-, Socio, Pol Rep K-12; NEA, OH Ed Assn 1979-; Red Cross 1975-, Publicity Dir; Notary Pub 1991-; Handicap Olympic Vol 1992-; Military Ofcr Wives Club 1969-78, Pres, Magazine Ed; Tchr in Excl Finalist 1993; Martha Holden Jennings Scholar 1995-; Impact II Grant Winner 1992, 1994, 1995; Tchr Initiative Grant 1986, 1990, 1992; OH Dept of EdValidation Team TESOL Testing 1991; Pub Intnl Cookbook 1989; *office:* Colonel White H S For The Arts 501 Niagara Ave Dayton OH 45405*

DAVIS, BARRY K., Social Studies Teacher; *b:* Hamilton, NY; *ed:* Syracuse Univ (BA) SS, Ed 1985; SUNY at Potsdam (MS) Ed 1990; *cr:* Lyme Cntrl Schl Soc Stud Tchr 1985-; *ai:* Stu Cncl, Sr Class, Ski Club Adv; Jeff-Lewis Tchr Ctr 1985-, Exec Sec; NYSUT, NYSCSS 1985-; Cape Vincent United Church; *office:* Lyme Central Schl PO Box 219 Academy St Chaumont NY 13622*

DAVIS, BELINDA WALSH, 7th Grade Math Teacher; *b:* Hamilton, OH; *m:* Jeffrey Hughes; *c:* Cory, Jay; *ed:* Miami Univ (BA) Elem Ed 1973; Post Grad Stud 45 Hrs; *cr:* Hamilton City Schls Tchr 1973-; *ai:* Facilitator of Core Team 8 Yrs; Discipline Comm; *home:* 314 N Dick Ave Hamilton OH 45013

DAVIS, BERNARD BYRON, Biology Teacher; *b:* Sewickley, PA; *m:* Christine Allenson; *c:* Carolynne, Anna, Sarah; *ed:* Geneva Coll (BS) Bio 1975; Univ of PA at Edinboro (MS) Bio 1983; *cr:* Lakeview HS Tchr & Coach 1976-; Theil Coll Asst Ftbl Coach 1981-85; Grove City Coll Asst Ftbl Coach 1995; *ai:* Asst Track Coach; Bio Club Adv; Stu Asstance Team; PSEA, NEA, LEA 1976-; Sandy Lake Wesleyan Church 1978; Lakeview HS Tchr of Yr 1985; *home:* PO Box 71 Sandy Lake PA 16145

DAVIS, BETH ANN, Religion Teacher; *b:* Lackawanna, NY; *m:* Thomas P.; *c:* Kenneth, Scott, Kellie; *ed:* Daemen Coll (BS) Ed 1969; Buffalo St Coll (MS) Ed 1975; *cr:* W Seneca Cntrl Schl Tchr 1969-71; St Thomas Aquinas Schl Tchr 1980-89; St Gregory the Great Schl Asst Prin 1990-92; Mt Mercy Acad Tchr 1992-; *ai:* Frosh Class Moderator; NCEA 1980-; *office:* Mt Mercy Acad 88 Red Jacket Pkwy Buffalo NY 14220

DAVIS, BETTY LOUISE, English Professor; *b:* Greenville, SC; *ed:* Morgan St Univ (BA) Eng 1982, (MA) Eng 1990; *cr:* US Army First Lieutenant Platoon Ldr 1982-85; The Chimes Prgm Supvr 1986-90; Morgan St Univ Eng Prof 1990-; *ai:* Adv: Eng Club 1990, Tutors 1992; Women of Morgan 1990; St Vincent Orphanage Spec Friends, Cnslr 1988; Frosh Writing Prgm Comm Chm; Friends of Friendless 1990; Mid Atlantic Writers Assn 1993-; Goldseker Fellowship 1989; *office:* Morgan State Univ Cold Spring Ln & Hillen Rd English Dept Baltimore MD 21239

DAVIS, BRUCE, Technology Education Teacher; *b:* Brooklyn, NY; *m:* Wendy Lee Boxer; *c:* Joel Owen, Stephen Corey; *ed:* Staten Island Comm Coll (AAS) Mechanical Engrng 1967; City Coll of NY (BS) Ed 1969, (MS) Ed, Indstrl Arts 1974; Attnd Iona Coll, Westchester Comm Coll; *cr:* John Burroughs Jr HS Indstrl Arts Tchr 1969-75; Hawthorne MS Indstrl Arts Tchr 1975-77; Gorton HS Indstrl Arts Tchr 1977-80; Ossining HS Tech Ed Tchr 1992-; *ai:* Theatrical Arts Set Design, Construction, Yrbk Adv; Yrbk Bus Coord; AFT, NYSUT 1969-; OTA 1992-; Knights of Pythias 1990-; *office:* Ossining HS 29 S Highland Ave Ossining NY 10562

DAVIS, BRYAN SCOTT, Protective Services Instructor; *b:* Erie, PA; *m:* Kay Partch; *ed:* Univ of New Haven (AS) Fire & Occupational Safety 1992, (BS) Fire Sci Admin 1993, (BS) Arson Investigation 1993; 10 Grad Hrs Temple Univ Voc I; PA Cert Voc I Instr; *cr:* Lackawanna Cty Area Voc Tech Schl Protective Svcs Instr 1993-; *ai:* AFT 1993-; Keystone Chptr of Fire Svc Instrctrs 1994-; Crescent Hose Co 1989-94, Fireman of Yr; Dickson City Fire Dept 1994-, EMS Capt; Old Forge Fire Dept 1996; PA St Fire Instr; NFPA 1001 Firefighter III; Natl Registry of Emergency Medical Tech; PA St Emergency Medical Svcs Instr; *office:* Lackawanna County Vo-Tech 3201 Rockwell Ave Scranton PA 18505

DAVIS, CAROLYN J. SMITH, Eng, Lang Arts & Drama Tchr; *b:* Baltimore, MD; *m:* Marvin E.; *c:* Nicole Melanie; *ed:* Wilber Force Univ (BA) Eng, Jrnlsm 1973; Univ of MD at Baltimore Cty (MA) Ed, Eng 1978; MD Inst Coll of Art at Baltimore MD Post Grad Stud Continuing Ed; *cr:* Hochschild Kohn Advertising Copywriter 5 Yrs; Hutzler's Dept Store Credit Mgr New Accounts 4 Yrs; Baltimore City Pub Schls Eng, Lang Arts Tchr 8 Yrs; *ai:* Natl Jr Hnr Soc, Schl Awds Comm Spon; Stu Cnl, Mentor Parent Liason Comm Adv; PTO Westport Elem Schl #225 6 Yrs, Pres, Awds PTO Pres, Mayor's Citation, Pres of City Cncl Citation; Baltimore City Perfect Attendance Awd; Outstdng Citizenship Awd Mayor City of Baltimore; Natl Tchrs Corps 11th Cycle Awd; *home:* 628 N Eutaw St Baltimore MD 21202*

DAVIS, CHERYL ROSE, Computer Teacher; *b:* Camden, NJ; *m:* Russell W.; *c:* Ryan, Brendan, Dana; *ed:* Glassboro St (BA) Elem Ed 1981; 15 Credit Hrs Comp Ed 1984; Internet Trng; *cr:* Berlin Comm Schl 1st Grd Tchr 8 Yrs, Gifted & Comp Tchr 2 Yrs, Comp Tchr 5 Yrs, Staff Comp Trainer 2 Yrs; *ai:* Berlin 2000 Goals; Cub Scout Ldr; BCSHA Parent & Tchr Assn; NEA 1981-; NJEA 1981-; Cub Scouts 1995-, Co-Ldr; Tchr of the Yr; *office:* Berlin Cmty Elem Schl 215 S Franklin Ave Berlin NJ 08009

DAVIS, CHET JOHN, Art Teacher; *b:* Ashland, PA; *m:* Sandra E. Parks; *c:* Jacob, Eric; *ed:* Penn St Univ (BS) Art Ed 1973; Univ of Hartford (MA) Art Ed 1980; Bloomsburg Univ 6 Grad Credits in Painting; *cr:* Shamokin Area Art Tchr 22 Yrs; *ai:* Stu Art League Adv; Strategic Planning & Chair Schl to Work Comm; NEA 1973-; PAEA 1984-, Bd of Dir, Tchr of the Yr 1986; PCAE 1988-, Treas 1989-93; PA Wildlife Fed 1990-, Charter Mem Speakers Bureau; Shamokin Area Ministries 1989-94, Church Camp Dir; Natl Tchrs Exam Visual Arts Evaluation Panel, PA Dept of Ed PCRP II Rdng Pgm Consultant; PA Arts Curr Project Adv; PA Arts Ed Advy Cncl; Kings Gap Arts Ed Symposium III, Presenter & Art Pub.

DAVIS, CHRIS FRANCIS, Seventh Grade Science Teacher; *b:* Glen Falls, NY; *m:* Judith Joan Singleton; *c:* Tyler J., Ryan J.; *ed:* St Univ Coll at Fredonia (BS) Ed 1986; Nazareth Coll of Rochester (MS) Elem Ed 1991; Attnd Adirondack Comm Coll 1979-81; *cr:* Burgoyne Ave Elem Schl Sith Grd Tchr 1986-88; Churchville-Chili MS Seventh Grd Sci Tchr 1988-; *ai:* Cert Coach; Sports Stud Hall Supvr; Tech, Sprucewood Nature Ctr Comms; Sprucewood Summer Sci Prgm Tchr; NEA 1988-; *office:* Churchville Chili MS 139 Fairbanks Rd Churchville NY 14428*

DAVIS, CLAUDIA MARY (FRAMPTON), Sixth Grade Teacher; *b:* Malden, MA; *m:* Richard W.; *c:* Sharon, Jennifer; *ed:* Boston St Coll (BS) Ed; Cambridge Coll (MS) Ed 1994; Post Grad 30 Credit Hrs; *cr:* Burke Schl 1st Grd Tchr 1967-68; Northfield Falls Elem Schl 1st Grd Schl 1968-69; South Schl 2nd Grd 1969-70; Amer Schls Kndgtn Tchr 1972-73; Wakefield Schl System 1st, 4th 6th Grd Tchr 1987-; *ai:* WTA, MTA 1987-; *office:* Atwell-Galvin Schl 485 Main St Wakefield MA 01880

DAVIS, D. LYN, English & Speech Teacher; *b:* Decatur, IN; *m:* Robert R.; *c:* Alicia, Katie, Rob, Nathan, Maggie, Luke; *ed:* Findlay Coll (BA) Fr, Eng 1978; Coll of Mt St Joseph (MA) Ed 1987; Elem Course Univ of Aix-en-Provence, France 1970; Tchng Multi Cultural Lang Arts OH Northern Univ; *cr:* United Meth Nursery Schl Tchr 1979-80; Hardin Cty Schls Sub Tchr 1978-80; Ada Exempted Village Schls Tchr 1980-; *ai:* Yrbk, Quiz Bowl, Senior Class, Interclass Advs; Eng Dept Chair; NEA, OEA 1980-; Ada Ed Assn 1980-, Sec, St Conv Rep, Bldg Rep, Negotiation Ldr; Univ Women 1989-, Sec; Natl Music Club 1990-, VP; Emmaus Comm 1993-, Speaker; Jennings Scholar of OH; Wrote & Filmed Educl Video; Outstanding Tchr Univ of Chicago 1989; *office:* Ada HS 500 Grand Ave Ada OH 45810

DAVIS, DELIA MYERS, 7th Grade Reading Teacher; *b:* Mc Kees Rocks, PA; *m:* Wayne Michael; *c:* Elizabeth Ann Vingin, Jeffrey Alan Vingin; *ed:* Edinboro St Univ (BA) Elem Ed 1970; Duquesne Univ (MS) Tchng of Rdng, Rdng Specialist 1974; *cr:* Penn Hills Schl Dist Elem Ed 1970-74, MS Rdng Tchr 1974-; *ai:* PSEA, NEA 1970-; *office:* Linton MS 250 Aster St Pittsburgh PA 15235

DAVIS, DIANE ROGERS, Art Teacher; *b:* Dayton, OH; *m:* Mark E.; *c:* Colin, Shelby; *ed:* Wright St Univ (BA) Art Ed 1970, (MA) Art Ed 1972; Attnd CA Polytechnic Inst, Munson Williams Proctor Art Inst, Mohawk Vly Comm Coll; *cr:* Fairborn HS Art Tchr 1970-73; Holland Patent HS Part-Time HS Art Tchr 1974-81; Poland Elem Part-Time Art Tchr 1981-83; Upland HS Art Tchr 1986-87; Adirondack Cntrl Schl 1988-; *ai:* Annual Musical Production Set Design; NY St Art Tchrs; AFT & NYSUT; BSA Den Mother, Advy 1978-95; *office:* Adirondack Sr HS Rt 294 Boonville NY 13309

DAVIS, DONALD A., Science Teacher; *b:* Fort Totten, NY; *m:* Debra L. Gilman; *c:* Meredith, Matthew, Lindsey; *ed:* Ithaca Coll (BA) Psych 1970; Long Island Univ (MS) Ed 1973; Meteorology Topics 3 Credit Hrs; Presentation Techniques 2 Credit Hrs; Environmental Change 2 Credit Hrs; Sci Methods 2 Credit Hrs; *cr:* Westmoreland Schl Sci Tchr 1986-; Antioch New England Grad Schl Adj Fac 1992-; *ai:* Stu Cncl, Sargent Camp Adv; Tech Comm; Project Atmosphere; NEA 1986-; NSTA 1988-; NESTA 1993-; Natl Meteorological Soc 1993-, Atmospheric Ed Resource Agent; Presidential Awd for Excl in Sci, Math Tchng 1992; Environmental Tchr of Yr Runner Up; Chosen One of 20 Nation Wide Tchrs Featured AAAS Book; *home:* PO Box 515 Walpole NH 03608*

DAVIS, DONALD LEE, Math Tchr & Interim Dept Chair; *b:* Woodbury, NJ; *m:* Hayley Padilla; *c:* Jackson, Jamison; *ed:* West Chester Univ (BS) Scndry Ed, Math 1986; Penn St Univ (MS) Curr, Instruction 1993; *cr:* Coatesville Area Sr HS Math Tchr 1986-; *ai:* Math Dept Interim Chm; New Tchr Prgm Mentor; Stu Tchr Cooperating Tchr; NEA, PSEA, CATA 1986-; Marsh Creek Church 1995-, Music Dir; Appt to West Point by Hon James Florio 1980; *office:* Coatesville Area Sr HS 1445 E Lincoln Hwy Coatesville PA 19320*

DAVIS, DORIS RELEFORD, Social Studies Teacher; *b:* Manasas, GA; *m:* Ernest T. Jr.; *c:* Ernest T. III (dec), Michelle Johnson; *ed:* Temple Univ (BS) Scndry Ed, Soc Stud 1972; Master's Equivalency 38 Post Grad Hrs Scndry Ed, Soc Stud PA St Cert 1990; *cr:* Darby Twp HS 11-12 Grd Soc Stud Tchr 1972-79; Acad Park HS 11-12 Grd Soc Stud Tchr 1979-; *ai:* Stu Assistance Prgm; Black His, Comm Involvement, Multicultural Awareness Comms; SEDELCO Tchrs Assn, NEA 1972-; Delco Cncl for Soc Stud Tchr Excl Awd; *office:* Academy Park HS 300 Calcon Hook Rd Sharon Hill PA 19079*

DAVIS, EDWARD RONALD, Biology & Limnology Teacher; *b:* Haverhill, MA; *m:* Betsey Anne Lamie; *c:* Daniel Peter, Christopher, Susan D. Dempsky, Katharine A., Aimee D.; *ed:* Bates Coll (BS) Pre-Med Bio 1965; Middlebury Coll (MS) Environmental Stud 1968; *cr:* The Hotchkiss Schl Tchr, Coach, Adv 1967-; *ai:* Var Ftbl Defensive Coord, Var Wrestling Head Coach 1967-; ARC Life Guard Trainer for Schl Life Guards; Sex Ed Curr Comm; Schl AHA, ARC Cpr Trainer; Town Lake's Commission; St of Emergency Med Tech 1975-; St of Ct Emergency Med Instr 1976-; ARC First Aid Instr 1994-; CT Sci Tchrs Assn 1967-; Salibury Vol Ambulance 1972-, Pres, VP, Trng, Trustee 1975-; Outstdng Coach NEISWA 1982, WNEISWA 1983; Judy Larsen Awd 1989; 2 Limnological Articles Pub; Sabbatical Grant 1985, 1991; *office:* The Hotchkiss Schl PO Box 800 Lakeville CT 06039

DAVIS, EVE LORRAINE, English Instructor; *b:* Wyatt, MO; *c:* Timberlawn Simpson; *ed:* Wilberforce Univ (BA) Eng 1989; Old Dominion Univ (MA) Literature 1991; OH St Univ; *cr:* Cntrl St Univ Eng Instr 1991-; *ai:* Herstory, Lebanon Correctional Fac Lib Comms; Speakers Bureau Mem; OH Hum Cncl; HAUD 1991-; Alpha Kappa Mu 1995-; CLA 1992-; OH Hum Cncl Grant 1995; Pub Review Paper, Presented at 1995 CLA Conf; *office:* Central St Univ Brush Row Rd Wilberforce OH 45384*

DAVIS, EVERETT DREW, Technology Teacher; *b:* Queens Village, NY; *m:* Cynthia Ann Viscotha; *c:* Emma Lee, Katlin Bess; *ed:* SUNY at Oswego (BS) Tech Ed 1982, (MS) Tech Ed 1984; *cr:* Groton Jr Sr HS Tech Tchr 1982-; *ai:* NEA 1982-; Article Pub; *office:* Groton Jr Sr HS 400 Peru Rd Groton NY 13073

DAVIS, FRANCES JONES, Language Arts Teacher; *b:* Richmond, VA; *m:* Roy A. Sr.; *c:* Roy A. Jr.; *ed:* Hampton Univ (BS) Elem Ed 1967; VA St Univ (MS) Ed 1972; Rutgers Univ Post Grad Stud; *cr:* Richmond Pub Schls Tchr 1967-72; Reading Schls Tchr 1972-74; Hanover Twp Schls Tchr 1974-75; Henrico Cty Schls Tchr 1975-78; New Brunswick Schls Tchr 1978-; *ai:* Schl Newspaper Adv; Partners in Learning Mid Grds Project Staff Mem; NJEA, NEA 1979-; NBEA 1979-, Schl Rep; Delta Sigma Theta 1986-; CNK Jack & Jill of Amer 1979-, Teen Adv; Raritan Vly Chptr The Links Inc 1986-, Yth Svcs, Conf Chair; New Brunswick Tchr of James E. Burke Tchng Excl Awd 1991; *office:* Lord Stirling Elem Carman St New Brunswick NJ 08901

DAVIS, GINA PAGLIA, 5th-6th Grade Teacher; *b:* Danvers, Darryl; *c:* Michael; *ed:* Northeastern Univ (BS) Ed 1987; *cr:* St Schl 5-6th Grd Tchr 1987-88; St John the Bapt Schl 5th-6th 1988-95; St Mary of the Annunciation Schl 5th,6th Grd Tchr 1 Chrldng Coach 1987-94; 5th & 6th Grd Sci Fair Coord; *office:* St Annunciation Schl 14 Otis St Danvers MA 01923

DAVIS, HOWARD KEASBEY,JR., 6th Grd Math Tchr & Team Salem, NJ; *m:* Virginia Richie; *ed:* Glassboro St Coll (BA) Elem Grd 1973; Salem Tech Coll Electronics 2 Yr Degree 1964; *cr:* De Elem Schl 3rd & 6th Grd Tchr 1973-82; Pennsville MS 6th Grd M & Team Ldr 1982-; *ai:* Team Ldr; Schl Discipline Comm; Penns Assn, NJEA & NEA 1973-; Elsinboro Twp Planning Bd 1988-; T NJ Governors Tchr Recognition Prgm 1989-90; *office:* Pennsv William Penn Ave Pennsville NJ 08070

DAVIS, HUGH H., History Professor; *b:* Findlay, OH; *m:* Jea Andrew, Mark, Jenny, Kate; *ed:* OH Wesleyan Univ (BA) His, E OH St Univ (MA) His 1965, (PHD) His 1969; *cr:* OH Univ A 1968-69; SCSU Prof 1969-; *ai:* Chair Univ Lib Comm, Acad Comm, His Dept Curr Comm; Cultural Diversity Comm; OA AAUP 1976-, Treas; SHA 1980-; North Haven Conservation Com Chair; Killam's Point Conf Ctr 1983-, Pres; North Haven Citize 1995-; Joshua Leavitt Evangelical Abolitionist 1990; Outstdng Bo Numerous Articles, Chptrs of Books Pub; Fac Scholar Awd; Ar Learned Socs Grant; *office:* Southern CT St Univ 501 Crescent Haven CT 06515

DAVIS, JAMES RICHARD, Reading Teacher; *b:* Mc Kees Rocks Janet Ross; *c:* Jonathan; *ed:* Edinboro Univ of PA (BS) Elem Ed 19 of Pittsburgh (MED) Rdng, Lang Arts 1972; Rdng Specialist, S Montour Schl Dist 7th Grd Rdng Tchr 1969-74; North Allegheny 7th Grd Rdng Tchr 1974-; *ai:* Help Spon Readers for Ldr Vol Pr 1975-; BSA 1990-, Advancement Chm; Iroquois Dist Advancemen *office:* Carson MS 200 Hillvue Ln Pittsburgh PA 15237

DAVIS, JAMES WAYNE, Machine Trades Instructor; *b:* McMech *m:* Carol Shimp; *c:* Janell McDaniel, Joycelyn Zanclron, Doug Gr Green; *ed:* OH Univ Voc 1987; *cr:* Belmont-Harrison Voc Machin Instr 1984-; *ai:* Machine Trades VICA Adv; Alpha Gamma Iot Sigma 1992-; Marine Corps League 1990-; Veterans of Foreign Wa Legion 1976-, Post Commander, St Vice Commander; Belmont-Harris Voc Schl 110 Fox Shannon Pl Saint Clairsville O

DAVIS, JEFFRY DENNET, 8th Grade Science Teacher; *b:* New *m:* Barbara Lois Smith; *c:* Crane, Ardea; *ed:* Columbia Univ (B Lit 1967; Montclair St Univ (MAT) Sci Tchng 1973; Princt Pre-Med, Eng; Cert for Regents Earth Sci SUNY at New Paltz Roosevelt Jr HS Sci Tchr 1967-69; Minisink Vly MS Sci Tchr 1 Tech Crew Group of Hnr Stdnts Responsible for Running Prof Le for Schl & Comm Productions; NEA 1967-; AFT, Sci Tchrs As 1969-; Kiwanis 1970-, Yth Svc Chm, Cert of Merit; Boy Scout Chm; SPEBSQSA 1988-, Treas, Barbershopper of Yr; *office:* Valley MS Rt 6 Slate Hill NY 10973

DAVIS, JENNIFER SUE, Teacher of Gifted; *b:* Dayton, OH; *m* W.; *c:* Andy, Tony, Jeremy, Casey; *ed:* Miami Univ (BA) Ed 1973 St Univ (MS) Gifted Ed 1991; *cr:* West Elkton Elem Schl Tchr of Disabled1973-74; Newton Local Schls Tchr of Learning Disabled Troy City Schls Tchr of Learning Disabled 1978-79; Northrid Schls Tchr of Learning Disabled 1979-90, Tchr of Gifted 4th, 1979-; *ai:* Odyssey of Mind Coord, Coach; Kids Against Environments Adv, Founder; Miami Vly Astronomical Soc Jr Adv; OH Ed Assn, NEA 1983-; OH Assn of Gifted Children 1990 Vly Astronomical Assn 1991-, Bd Mem; Partners for Terrific Sci 1991-92; *office:* Esther Dennis MS 5120 N Dixie Dr Dayton OH

DAVIS, JERRY D., Sixth Grade Teacher; *b:* Middleport, OH; *m* Morris; *ed:* Univ of Rio Grande (BA) His, Pol Sci, Ed 1969; Marsh (MA) His 1976; 15 Credit Hrs Beyond Masters; *cr:* Green El 1969-; *ai:* Curr Comm; Goverance Bd Mem, S Regnl Prop Dev C OEA 1969-; NCTE 1986-; Operation Liftoff of OH 1986-, Pres, Mem; Nom by Local Dist for OH Tchr of Yr 1987; *office:* Green E 113 Centenary Church Rd Gallipolis OH 45631

DAVIS, JOAN MC INERNEY, English Dept Chprsn & Tea Flushing, NY; *m:* William G.; *ed:* Coll of Saint Rose (BA) En Binghamton Univ (MST) Eng 1976; 12 Credits 1994; Syracuse Credits; Elmira Coll 4 Credits 1995; *cr:* Owego Free Acad Eng Tc Syracuse Univ Adj Instr 1988-; Owego Free Acad Eng Dept Cha *ai:* Supts Budget Advy, Prins Educl Advy, Cmptr Comm; Bldg NCTE 1981-; NY St Eng Cncl, Tchr of Excl 1991-; Delta Kappa 1993-; Owego Apalachin Tchrs Assn 1970-; Owego-Apalachin Apple Awd; Copy Ed 1990; *office:* Owego Free Academy George S NY 13827

DAVIS, JODEE, Music Professor; *b:* Marshalltown, IA; *ed:* Northern IA (BM) Music Ed 1980, (MM) Trombone Performance Univ (DM) Brass Lit & Performance 1995; *cr:* Eastern WA Univ Low Brass 1987-92; Kent St Univ Prof of Trombone & Euphoniu *ai:* PRISMA Mem; Schl Music Fac Advy Comm; Schl Music Cu Coll of Fine Arts & Prof Arts Curr Comm; Delta Chi Chapter of Lambda Pres; Amer Fed of Musicians 1983-; Intl Trombone As TUBA 1987-; Unity Chapel of Light 1993-, Bd of Trustees Sec Bd Mem 1994-; Creative Activity Appointment 1995; Outstn Tchng Awd for Kent St Univ Frosh Orientation 1993; *office:* Kent H A Glauser Schl of Music Kent OH 44242

DAVIS, JODI S., Guidance Counselor; *b:* Tupper Lake, NY; Owen; *c:* Pierce, Jyliann; *ed:* SUNY at Brockport (BA) Dance, 1984; Syracuse Univ (MS) Educl Psych 1986; Attnd Fordham Univ at New Paltz, Coll of New Rochelle; *cr:* Merrimack Coll Resi 1986-87; Pine Plains Cntrl Schls Guid Cnslr 1987; Wappingers Cn Guid Cnslr 1987-90; Washingtonville HS Guid Cnslr 1990-; *ai:* Mime Soc Adv; Schlsp Talent Show Dir, Producer, Choreograph Career Day, Mental Hlth Comms; NHS, Voice of Democracy S Schlsps Coord; AFT; NYSUT; NYSSCA; The Fourth Wall Playe Bd of Dirs; Just Off Broadway 1988-, Performer, Dir, Choreo Washingtonville Centennial Comm 1995-, Vol; Leukemia So Raising Vol; Above and Beyond Call of Duty ABCD Awd Washingtonville HS 54 W Main St Washingtonville NY 10992

DAVIS, JOHN WANDEL, Professor of Biology; *b:* Far Rockaway Maria Antonia Milan; *c:* Matthew, Peter; *ed:* Univ of Notre Dame (1967; St John's Univ (MS) Bio 1970, (PHD) Biological Sci 1975; Hosp Post Doctoral Stud Clinical Micro Bio; *cr:* Long Beach Jr Sci Tchr 1967-68; Bronx Comm Coll Bio Prof 1970-; *ai:* Socce Referee; Intnl Org for Mycoplasmology 1980-, Mbrshp Sec 199 Soc for Micro Biology 1975-, Div G Chair 1990-91; NY Acad of S White Plains Yth Soccer Assn 1986-, Pres 1991-92; White Plains P Post Rd Schl 1989-91, Ldrshp Cncl; Rsrch Fnd CUNY 1994-, E NSF Fac Dev 1978-79, NIH Minority Biomedical Rsrch Support NIH Bridge to Baccalaureate 1993- Awd Grants; CUNY Fac

988; Articles Pub; *office:* City Univ Of NY Bronx Comm Col W Jniversity Ave Bronx NY 10453

JDITH L., Sci, Math & Language Arts Tchr; *b:* OH; *m:* Denver sa Shull, Lisa Linville, Denise Reeves, Jerry, Jeff; *ed:* Defiance Elem Ed 1988; *cr:* Preschl Tchr 10 Yrs; St Joseph Schl Jr HS ; St Patrick Jr HS Tchr 3 Yrs; *ai:* 8th Grd Class, Stu Cncl Adv; r Ldr; NSELA, NSTA 1994-, Master Sci Ldr; OAEYC 1988-, :s; OCEA 1988-; HCA 1988-, Chrprsn, Recognition Awd; ASCD 'kview Nrsng Ctr, Outstdng Svc; Civic Achvmt 1993-, Instr, l; *home:* 06-384 Cr 4-50 Edgerton OH 43517

AREN ANN, 3rd Grade Teacher; *b:* Bangor, ME; *m:* Rodney Rachel Marie, Robert Rodney; *ed:* Bapt Bible Coll (BS) Elem Ed Twin City Chrstn Schl, K-4, 3rd GrdTchr 1982-; *ai:* AACS *ce:* Twin City Christian Schl 194 Electric Ave Lunenburg MA

AREN POWELL, First Grade Teacher; *b:* Youngstown, OH; *m:* Marsh; *c:* Kathryn, Sandy, Sunny; *ed:* Mt St Joseph's (MS) Ed s Malone Coll; 6 Hrs Aust Schls; *cr:* Noble Cty Schls Grd 4 Tchr Austintown Schls Grd 3 Tchr 1974-82, Grd 1 Tchr 1982-; *ai:* OH NE OH Ed Assn, Natl Rdng Assn 1972-; Women's Hlth on Network 1992-, Bd Mem; Hospice of Youngstown 1992-; United Meth Church 1994-, Educ Comm; *office:* Lloyd Elem Rd Austintown OH 44515

AREN TAUFFENER, Business Education Teacher; *b:* Dunkirk, obert L.; *c:* Jeffery, Kora; *ed:* Alfred St Coll (AAS) Exec Sci 1970; Buffalo St Coll (BS) Bus Ed 1987, (MS) Bus Ed 1992; Union Cnslr; Cmptr In-Svc Trng; *cr:* Fredonia Cntrl Schls Tchng -74; Westfield Acad Bus Ed Tchr 1987-89; Central Schl Bus Ed -89; Fredonia Cntrl Schls Bus Ed Tchr 1989-91; Dunkirk Pub Ed Tchr 1991-; *ai:* FBLA Adv; Tech, Multi-Cultural Ed Comms; s Hnrs Night Chprsn; Chautauqua Cty Bus Tchrs Assn 1987-, Dunkirk Tchrs Assn 1991-; AFT, Kappa Delta Pi, NY St Bus 1 1987-; St Joseph's CYO 1993-, Adv; St Joseph's Caring Clowns v; Fredonia Parks & Recreation Commission 1983-, Chprsn; Yth omm 1988-, Chprsn; *home:* 126 Pulaski St Fredonia NY 14063

ATHLEEN GAINES, English Teacher; *b:* Greenville, SC; *m:* 1; *c:* Emily Louise, Victoria Coleen, Olivia Anne; *ed:* Bob Jones Eng Ed 1985; Addl Hrs Univ of MD, Bob Jones Univ; *cr:* MD Chrstn Acad Eng, Family Living Tchr 1985-, Yrbk Adv 992-95, Chrldng Coach 1985-91, Drama Tchr 1987-91, Banquet 5-93; *ai:* Yrbk Consultant; First Bapt Church of Waldorf; Yrbk n; Chrldng Awds as Coach; Awd-Winning Drama at Folger ar Festival, Coach; Articles Pub; *office:* Southern Maryland ad 9805 Faith Bap Chruch White Plains MD 20695

IMBERLY LYNNE, Fifth Grd Lang Arts Tchr; *b:* Dayton, OH; Univ (BSEd) Elem Ed 1988; Wright St Univ (MED) Tchr Ldr Lebanon City Schls Tchr 1988-; *ai:* Fr Magnate Prgm; Soc Stud it to Read Week; LEA, OEA, NEA 1988-, Local Rep; *office:* ntermediate Schl 401 Justice Dr Lebanon OH 45036

A DEVA MAUREEN, Dance Teacher; *b:* Philadelphia, PA; *ed:* e Arts (BME) Music Ed Voice & Piano 1965; 30 Addl Hrs Temple c Ed, Urban Ed, Dance Ed; *cr:* Bartlett Jr HS Music, Dance Tchr Creative & Performing Arts HS Dance Co Dir, Modern Tap, z Tchr 1978-; *ai:* Dance Co Dir 1987-; AFT 1965-; Amer Fed of io Artists, Screen Actors Guild 1982-, Emmy 1990-91; 100 Black 993-; Choreographer of WPVI TV Thanksgiving Parade 1988-; Anielewicz Awd for Choreography 1990-91; Melon PSFS Awd Svc 1995; Concerned Black Men Awd Artistic Dir of Yth 1986; re Artistic Dirs Awd Choreographer 1995; Hostess of Nationally d Show What's Cooking 1975-77; *office:* HS Creative & g Arts 11th & Catherine St Philadelphia PA 19147

AURA E., French & Spanish Teacher; *b:* Bridgeport, CT; *ed:* H (BA) Fr 1970, (MAT) Ed 1971; *cr:* Sunapee Mid HS Frgn Lang 1-; *ai:* Yrbk, Jr Class & NHS Adv; Fr Exch Coord; Grad NEA; Sunapee Tchrs Assn 1971-, Past VP & Past Sec; AATF Sec 2 Yrs; *office:* Sunapee Mid HS 10 North Rd Sunapee NH

AURIE ANN, Fourth Grade Teacher; *b:* Binghamton, NY; *ed:* Cortland (BS) Ed 1970; 30 Addl Credits SUNY at Binghamton; Cntrl Schls 4th-5th Grd Tchr 1970-; *ai:* NEA, NYSTA 1970-; enwood Elem Schl 401 Jones Rd Vestal NY 13850

EWIS N., Automotive Technology Teacher; *b:* Chicago, IL; *m:* letrich; *c:* Sarah, Luke; *ed:* Temple Univ Voc II Voc Ed 1988; e Svc Excl Technician Cert; *cr:* Bell Telephone of PA Contract hanic 1973-79; Berks Career & Tech Ctr Tchr 1979-; *ai:* Voc ubs of Amer Stu Adv 10 Yrs; YMCA Yth Bsktbl Coach 2 Yrs; p Athl Assn Minor League Coach 3 Yrs; NEA, PSEA 1979-, VP AA Auto Club 1986-, Hnr Mem, Safety Ed Awd; West Lawn eth Church 1990-; Natl Amer Cncl of Automotive Tchrs 1995-; A Automotive Tchr Excl Awd 1989; Mitsubishi Natl Automotive r, Valvoline Natl Tchr of Yr 1995; Valvoline St Tchr of Yr 1992; Excl Natl Second Place Schl 1995; *office:* Berks Career & gy Ctr R D 1 Box 1370 Leesport PA 19533

INDA J., 6th Grade Teacher; *b:* Bryn Mawr, PA; *ed:* Master's cy, 60 Credits; *cr:* East Ward Elem Schl 6th Grd Tchr 1975-90; ford Elem Schl 6th Grd Tchr 1990-; *ai:* NEA, PSEA 1975-; Big & Big Sisters Chester Cty 1974-, VP, Sec, Bd Mem of Yr; *home:* irch St West Chester PA 19382

INDA KAY, Spanish Teacher; *b:* New London, CT; *c:* Davis M. : Bowling Green St Univ (BS) Span 1987; Univ of Dayton (MS) 1990; Certfd Span K-12th, Elem & HS Prin; *cr:* Wellsville HS 3rd Span Tchr 1987-; *ai:* Yrbk & Newspaper Spon; Spirit Club & Adv; Fall & Spring Plays Dir; NHS Fac Comm; NEA 1987-; 87-; Potter Players Comm Theater, Bd Mem; *office:* Wellsville enter St Wellsville OH 43968

INDA WITMER, Science Teacher; *b:* Fall River, MA; *c:* Aaron; *ed:* Endicott Jr Coll (AS) Bus 1964; Franklin Coll (BA) IN Univ 15 Hrs Towards MA; Bridgewater St Tchrs Coll 9 Hrs; MA at Dartmouth 9 Hrs; *cr:* St Louis de France 6th Grd Tchr Case Jr HS 7th Grd Sci Tchr 1982-; *ai:* Sci Curr Frameworks; ll Comm; NEA, SWansea Ed Assn 1972-; NSTA 1982-; Ducks 1990-; Westport Watershed Alliance 1991-; Precint One, Amer rse Assn 1980-; *office:* Joseph Case Jr HS 195 Main St Swansea 7

OUANNE BURG, 5th Grade Elementary Teacher; *b:* Pittsburgh, illiam Paul; *c:* Jeffrey, Nicole; *ed:* Thiel Coll (BA) Elem Ed & y 1983; 24 Credit Hrs Permanent Cert in PA; *cr:* Resurrection 5th Grd Tchr 1983-; *ai:* Talent Show & Mini-Soc Dir; Coord for win Borough Lib Bd 1986-, Sec; *home:* 200 Conrad Dr Pittsburgh

MARIE KIELBASA, 4th Grade Teacher; *b:* Salem, MA; *m:* R.; *c:* Mark, Allison Goble, William Jr.; *ed:* Emmanuel Coll (BA) 960; *office:* Witchcraft Heights Elem Sch 1 Lielinsky Way Salem 0

DAVIS, MARLENE SOKOL, 2nd Grade Teacher & Trainer; *b:* New York City, NY; *m:* Roger William; *ed:* PA St Univ (BS) Elem Ed 1971; Temple Univ (MED) Ed 1974; Inservice Credit Hrs Cmptr Instruction; *cr:* Local Colleges & Univs Cooperating Tchr 1972-; Lower Merion Schl Dist Mentor Tchr 1987-89, Math Consultant 1989-91; Ctr Statistical Ed in PA Tchng Fac 1994-; *ai:* Tchng Inservice Course for Tchrs; Math Task Force; George WA Carver Sci Fair Judge; Strategic Planning Comm; NEA, PSEA, LMEA 1971-; Wynnewood Civic Assn 1983-; Natl Assn Female Exec 1995-; Penn St Alumni Assn 1971-; Outstdng Tchng Awd Penn St Univ 1995; Publication Educl Ldrshp 1988; The World Who's Who of Women; *home:* 710 Greythorne Rd Wynnewood PA 19096

DAVIS, MARY PITT, Biology Teacher; *b:* Johnson City, TN; *m:* Ted Carlyle; *c:* Hugh Allan, Leland Dathan, David Ander; *ed:* Univ of WA (BA) Span Lit, Ed 1966; Univ of WA (BS) Botany, Bio 1967; Johns Hopkins Univ (MS) Adult Ed 1984; Courses at Univ of MD at Coll Park; *cr:* Cambridge High & Latin Schl Tchr 1968-70; Schl of Sacred Heart Tchr 1972-74; DODDS Tchr 1985-87; Howard Cty Pub Schls Tchr 1977-; *ai:* Howard Comm Coll Evening Tchr; Sunday Schl Tchr; NEA 1978-; MABT 1978-, Trustee, Bio Tchr of Yr; MAST 1978-; Pub 2 Books; Georgetown Medical Schl Biotechnology Fellowship 1988; Amer Soc for Biochemistry & Molecular Bio Fellowship 1989; Amer Soc of Clinical Investigation Fellowship 1991; MAST Outstdng Sci Tchr 1994; Howard Cty Tchr of Yr 1995 & 1996; *office:* Glenela HS 14025 Burnt Woods Rd Glenelg MD 21737*

DAVIS, MARY ANN YOKITIS, Fourth Grade Teacher; *b:* Johnstown, PA; *m:* Carl E.; *c:* Dane Jonathan; *ed:* Univ of Steubenville (BS) Elem Ed 1970; Indiana Univ of PA (MS) Elem Ed 1974; 15 Credit Hours Univ of Millersville; *cr:* Cambria Heights Schl Dist Second Grd Tchr 1970-71; Cntrl Cambria Schl Dist Fourth Grd Tchr 1971-; *ai:* MADD Participant Poster Essay Contest Stdnts; Cntrl Cambria Ed Assn 1971-, 1978-79, Sec; NEA 1971-; Phi Mu Delta Rho Chapter 1968-, Greek Women of Yr 1970; Cambria Cty Conservation Tchr of Yr 1988-89; *home:* 297 Rose Branch St Johnstown PA 15909

DAVIS, MARY BETH HURLEY, Mathematics Teacher; *b:* Manhattan, NY; *m:* Peter; *c:* Peter, Christine, Maureen; *ed:* Manhattan Coll (BS) Math 1977; *cr:* St Nicholas of Tolentine HS Math Tchr 1977-79; GMAC Programmer 1979-82; Msgr Scanlan HS Math Tchr 1993-; *ai:* Cardinal Spellman HS Ath Hall of Fame 1995; *office:* Monsignor Scanlan H S 915 Hutchinson River Pky Bronx NY 10465

DAVIS, MARY BETH KAIN, Third Grade Teacher; *b:* Pittsburgh, PA; *m:* Lawrence A.; *ed:* High Point Univ (ABT) Elem Ed 1970; *cr:* Pomona Elem Schl Second Grd Tchr 1970-74, Fifth Grd Tchr 1974-80, Fourth Grd Tchr 1980-88, Third Grd Tchr 1988-; *ai:* NEA, NJEA, ACEA, GTEA 1970-; Alpha Delta Kappa 1984-; Galloway Twp Tchr of Yr 1983; NJ Governors Recognition 1989; *office:* Pomona Elem Schl 4005 Genoa Ave Pomona NJ 08240

DAVIS, NADIS A., Fourth Grade Teacher; *b:* Cleveland, OH; *m:* James A.; *ed:* Ashland Coll (BA) Fr 1966; Natl Louis Univ (MEd) Curr, Instruction 1991; *cr:* Chrstn Clemens Elem Schl 4th-6th Grd Tchr 1966-69; Fallon HS Fr Tchr 1969-71; West End Elem Schl 6th Grd Learning Disabilities Tchr 1972-74; Kaiserslautern Amer Elem Schl 4th Grd Tchr 1975-; *ai:* Budget Comm Chprsn; Safety Comm; NEA, ASCD 1989-; Alpha Kappa Alpha; *home:* PSC Box 3 Box 2537 APO AE 09021

DAVIS, NANCI N., Fourth Grade Teacher; *b:* Berea, OH; *m:* John E.; *ed:* Kent St Univ (BS) Spcl & Elem Ed 1973; Xavier Univ (MS) Educl Admin 1985; *cr:* New South Wales Dept of Ed Tchr 1974-75; Cambridge City Schls Tchr 1975-78; Finneytown Local Schls Tchr 1978-; *ai:* NEA & OEA 1975-; FEA 1978-; *office:* Cottonwood Elem Schl 8513 Cottonwood Dr Cincinnati OH 45231

DAVIS, NORMAN EUGENE, Coach; *b:* Erie, PA; *c:* Nanette, Monsanto, Tony, Ebony, Jennifer, Cordero; *ed:* Intnl Coorespondence Schls (AD) Fitness, Nutrition 1995; Western Psychiatric Inst & Clinic Cocaine Addiction 6 CEU, Mental Hlth Issues 5 CEU, Peer Support & Consumer Advocacy 5 CEU, Sexual Abuse of Women-Rape & Incest 5 Ceu, Dual Diagnosed Patient's & Families 6 Ceu; Criminal Justice & Mental Illness 5 Ceu; *cr:* Stairways Inc Rehabilitation Specialist 1986-; Villa Maria Acad Track, X-Country Coach 1986-; *ai:* Personal Wellness Trainer; *home:* 2332 Prospect Ave Erie PA 16510

DAVIS, OLGA NATSIOS, French Teacher; *b:* Lowell, MA; *m:* Jeffrey Randolph; *c:* Nicholas, Gregory; *ed:* Lowell St Coll (BA) Fr 1974; 23 Credit Hrs Fitchburg St Coll; *cr:* Dracut MS Fr Tchr 1977-81; Englesby Jr HS Fr Tchr 1981-92; Greenmont Ave Schl Sixth Grd Tchr 1992-93; Englesby Jr HS Fr Tchr 1993-; *ai:* Frgn Lang Club Adv; DTA, MTA, AATF, MAFLA 1977-; Middies-Lettermens Club 1993-, Ath Hall of Fame; *office:* George H Englesby Jr HS 1580 Lakeview Ave Dracut MA 01826

DAVIS, PATRICIA ANN, Spanish & Latin Teacher; *b:* Huntington, WV; *ed:* Georgetown Univ (BS) Span 1976; Univ of MD 6 Credits ESOL 1983, Ind Stud in Latin 1984; Coll of Notre Dame Orbis Romanus Summer Prgm in Latin 1989; Cert Fr, Latin; *cr:* Archbishop Keough HS Span, Latin Tchr 1977-84; Glenelg HS Span, Latin Tchr 1984-90; Howard HS Span, Latin Tchr 1990-; *ai:* Site Based Mngmt Team; Ninth Grd Team; NEA, MD For Lang Assn, Amer Classical League 1984-; Amer Assn Tchrs of Span & Portuguese 1992-; *office:* Howard HS # 108 8700 Old Annapolis Rd Ellicott City MD 21043

DAVIS, PATRICIA CHARNEY, Assoc Professor of Acctng; *b:* Newark, NJ; *m:* Albert Sterling III; *c:* Gretchen, Jennifer, Suzanne, Amber, Albert IV, Adam; *ed:* Keystone Jr Coll (AA) Gen Bus 1980; Wilkes Coll (BS) Bus Admin 1981; Univ of Scranton (MBA) Acctng 1984; Marywood Coll 3 Credits Pub Admin; *cr:* Keystone Coll Asst, Assoc Prof, Bus Dept Chair 1984-; *ai:* Adv Phi Theta Kappa, Stu Senate; Strategy Team; Presidential Evaluation Comm; NEBEA 1987-; Ldrshp Lackawanna 1986-, Pres; PA for Human Life 1980-; Northeast Woman of Week; *office:* Keystone Jr Coll Harris Hall 204 La Plume PA 18440

DAVIS, PATRICIA MURPHY, Mathematics Teacher; *b:* Adams, MA; *m:* Robert J.; *c:* Brandon; *ed:* North Adams St Coll (BA) Math 1969; Fairfield Univ (MA); *cr:* Hillcrest Jr HS Math Tchr 1969; Madison Jr HS Math Tchr; Trumbull HS Math Tchr; *ai:* TEA, CEA, NEA 1969-; *office:* Trumbull HS 72 Strobel Rd Trumbull CT 06611

DAVIS, RICHARD, Physical Education Teacher; *b:* South Charleston, WV; *ed:* Morris Harvey Coll (BS) PE 1967; Western CT St Univ Ed 1975; Univ of CT (PHD) Ed, Anthropology 1990; *cr:* City of Los Angeles Housing Project Recreation Dir; Huntington Schls Tchr 1969-70; Mahopac Schl System Tchr 1970-; Peace Corps Tchr 1980-82; *ai:* IMS; AFT, Mahopac Tchrs Assn 1970-; Peace Corps Niger West Africa; *office:* Fulmar Road Elem Schl 55 Fulmar Rd Mahopac NY 10541

DAVIS, ROBERT ARTHUR, Eighth Grade Teacher; *b:* Chester, PA; *ed:* Neumann Coll (BA) Elem Ed 1983; *cr:* Resurrection of Our Lord Schl Third, Fifth Grd Tchr 1973-81; Holy Saviour-St John Fisher Schl Fifth, Sixth, Eighth Grd Tchr 1981-; *ai:* Drama Coach; Stu Cncl Moderator; Literature, Fine Arts Curr Coord; Master Tchr PA Tchr Induction Prgm; NCEA 1973-; *office:* Holy Saviour-St Jhn Fisher Sch 122 E Ridge Rd Marcus Hook PA 19061*

DAVIS, ROGER WILLIAM, Science Teacher; *b:* Dover, DE; *m:* Karen S. Argo; *c:* Molly Kate, Karelenn, Leonard, Emerald, Roger; *ed:* Univ of DE (BS) Bus, Physics 1971; DE St Ed, Scndry 1992; Grad Working Physics, Chemical Engrng, Electronics; 100 Addl Hrs Occupational Stud Machinest, Welder, Applied Sci, Applied Math; *cr:* David Cycle-Roger Davis & Son Owner, Operater 1972-; Polytech HS Phys Sci, Chem Tchr, Tech Prin 1993-; *ai:* Acad Coaching; Prof Svcs Acad Mem; DE Sci Olympiad DE St Univ 1995-; NEA 1991-; US Army Reserve Otho Assn 1992-; Hartly Vol Fire Co 1967-, Trustees Chain, Deputy Chief; US Army Reserves 1972-; *home:* 1671 Peach Basket Rd Felton DE 19943

DAVIS, ROSEMARY BODKIN, Fifth Grade Teacher; *b:* Buffalo, NY; *m:* Kendall W.; *c:* Rosemary K., Mary E.; *ed:* SUNY (MS) Elem Ed; 60 Credit Hrs Post-Grad Stud Elem Ed; *cr:* Buffalo Pub Schls 5th-6th Grd Tchr 1982-87; North Tonawanda Pub Schl 5th Grd Tchr 1987-; *ai:* Shared Decision Making Comm Facilitator; Lang, Math & Stud Skills Comms; NTUT 1987-; Republican Comm Person 1976-; Co-Author of District Human Growth & Development; *office:* Gilmore Elem Schl 789 Gilmore Ave North Tonawanda NY 14120

DAVIS, RUBY C., Physical Education Teacher; *ed:* Winston-Salem St Univ (BS) Hlth & PE 1965; Bowie St Coll Grad Stud; *ai:* Girls Bsktbl; Super Ldr Org; NEA 1985-; PGCEA 1985-; *home:* 2017 Chadwick Ter Temple Hills MD 20748

DAVIS, SARAH OLINDA, Fourth Grade Teacher; *b:* Woodbury, NJ; *m:* Glenn C.; *ed:* Bob Jones Univ (BS) Elem Ed 1985; Credit Hrs Univ of DE Ed; *cr:* New Castle Bapt Acad Fourth Grd Tchr 1985-; *ai:* Math League Coord, Coach; Project 301 Bldg Rep; Elem Sci Fair Coord; DCTM 1993-; *office:* New Castle Baptist Acad 901 E Basin Rd New Castle DE 19720

DAVIS, SHIRLEY RAE (SIMS), Vocational Business Ed Tchr; *b:* Greencastle, IN; *m:* John Henry III; *c:* Aaron D., John Barnett, Joshua Wayne; *ed:* In St Univ (BS) Bus Ed 1971, (MS) Bus Ed 1980; *cr:* Vigo Co Dept of Welfare Caseworker 2 Yrs; Terre Haute North HS Tchr 13 Yrs; Duval County Schl Bd Tchr 3 Yrs; Cleveland Heights HS Tchr 7 Yrs; *ai:* Bus Profs Amer Club Spon; Treas Nonprofit Org; AFT 1985-; *office:* Cleveland Heights HS 13263 Cedar Rd Cleveland Heights OH 44118

DAVIS, THELMA DUNCAN, English Teacher; *b:* Jamaica, West Indies; *w:* Gumbridge Jr. (dec); *c:* Alethea, Eric; *ed:* Boston Coll (BA) Scndry Ed 1971; 21 Credit Hrs Educl Admin Univ of MA; *cr:* Highland Park Free Schl Tchr 1971-74; English HS Tchr 1974-75; Boston Trade HS Tchr 1975-76; South Boston HS Tchr 1977-; *ai:* NHS Adv 1988-93; ASCD 1996; Local 66 AFL-CIO 1974-; Newton Chptr Jack Jill of Amer 1988-; *office:* South Boston HS 95 G St South Boston MA 02127*

DAVIS, VICKIE RAE, High School English Teacher; *b:* Cincinnati, OH; *m:* Donald David; *c:* Casey, Kelly; *ed:* Univ of Cincinnati (BS) Ed 1974; Univ of Dayton (MA) Ed 1979; *cr:* Miamisburg Jr SR HS Eng Tchr 1974-; *ai:* Class & Bowling League Adv; NEA 1974-; OEA 1974-; MCTA 1974-, Bldg Rep Commnctn Person; *office:* Miamisburg Sr HS 1860 Belvo Rd Miamisburg OH 45342

DAVIS, WALTER C., Principal; *b:* Canton, OH; *m:* Aimee L.; *ed:* Univ of Akron (BA) Ed 1988, (MA) Ed Admin 1994; Addl 16 Hrs Post Grad Work; *cr:* Plain Local Schls Tchr 1988-89; Roberts MS Tchr 1989-95; Newberry Elem Prin 1995-; *ai:* OAESA 1995-; ASCD 1992-; Tchr of Month; PTA Tchr of Yr Nom 1994; *office:* Newberry Elem Schl 2800 13th St Cuyahoga Falls OH 44223

DAVIS, WANDA ANDERSON, Eng, Speech & Drama Teacher; *b:* Dade City, FL; *m:* Thomas A.; *c:* Eric; *ed:* Univ of FL (BA) Speech 1978, (MA) Eng 1983; Nova Univ 30 Credit Hrs in Admin & Supervision; *cr:* Lincoln MS Eng Instr 1978-80; Buccholz HS Eng & Speech Tchr 1980-86; Boca HS Eng & Speech Tchr 1986-93; Crossland HS Eng, Speech & Drama Tchr 1993-; *ai:* Debate & Mock Trial Spon; Broadcast Team Spon; Drama Spon; Alpha Kappa Alpha 1988-; Article Pub 1982; *office:* Crossland HS 6901 Temple Hill Rd Temple Hills MD 20748*

DAVIS, WILLIAM G., Social Studies Teacher & Coach; *b:* Holyoke, MA; *m:* Judith Nicholson; *c:* Jeffrey A., Susan J.; *ed:* Amer Intnl (BA) His 1967, (MAT) Ed 1978-79; 30 Credits Above Masters; *cr:* Chicopee Comprehensive HS Soc Stud Tchr 1967-, Var Soccer Coach 1968-, Var Track & Field Coach 1968-; *ai:* Var Boys Soccer & Track & Field Coach; Summer Schl Soc Stud Tchr; Chicopee Tchrs Assoc 1967-; MA Tchrs Assoc 1967-; New England Tchrs 1967-; Horace Mann Tchr 2 Yrs; MA Track & Field Coaches Hall of Fame Nom; *office:* Chicopee Comprehensive HS Rolf Ave Chicopee MA 01020*

DAVIS, Z. HAROLD,JR., French & Spanish Teacher; *b:* Jonestown, MS; *m:* Minnie; *c:* Barbara, Avril, Harriette, Z. Harold III; *ed:* John Caroll Univ (AB) Fr 1967; OH St Univ (MA) Foreign Lang Ed 1976; L'Alliance Francaise; Cleveland St Univ 24 Hrs; Kent St Univ 2 Hrs; *cr:* Addison Jr HS Fr Tchr 1967-69; John F. Kennedy HS Fr, Span Tchr 1969-80; James Ford Rhodes HS, Fr, Span Tchr, Dept Chair 1980-; *ai:* Radio Broadcast Adv; Staff Lead Team, Guidance & Recognition Comms; La Maison Francaise DE Cleve, AFT 1967-; AATF, AATSP 1968-; PDK 1978-; ASCD 1990-; Amer Field Svc 1994-; Holy Grove Bapt Church 1949-; Natl Endowment for Hum Grant; Martha Holden Jennings Scholar; BSA Awd of Merit; *office:* James Ford Rhodes HS 5100 Biddulph Rd Cleveland OH 44144

DAVIS-GEIST, RITA MARIE, 4th Grade Teacher; *b:* Pittsburgh, PA; *m:* David A. Geist; *ed:* IN Univ of PA (BSEd) Elem Ed 1966, (MED) Elem Ed 1972; Basic Cmptr Programming 3 Credits; PA St Dept of Ed Eng Acad Sessions; Apple An Instrl Skills Prgm; *cr:* IN Cty of PA Head Start Tchr 1966; Chandler Elem 5 & 6 Grd Tchr 1966-71; Oakhurst Elem Grd 6 Tchr 1971-76; Johnstown MS Grd 6 Tchr 1976-93; Roxbury Elem Grd 4 Tchr 1993-; *ai:* Roxbury Microsociety Project Svc Bus Spon; GJSD Lang Arts Curr Comm; NEA, PA St Ed Assn 1966-; GJEA 1966-, Fac Rep; Johnstown Schl Employees Federal Credit Union 1966-, Bd Sec; Comm Arts Ctr 1975-; Greater Johnstown Alumni of IUP; Johnstown Comm Concert Assn 1988-; *home:* 1641 Sunshine Ave Johnstown PA 15905

DAVISON, MARK WARREN, Social Studies Teacher; *b:* Buffalo, NY; *m:* Pamela J. Messer; *c:* Matthew, Kevin; *ed:* Canisius Coll (BA) Hum 1972; St Univ of NY at Buffalo (MED) Soc Stud Ed 1996; *cr:* East Aurora HS Soc Stud Tchr 1988-91; Iroquois Cntrl HS Soc Stud Tchr 1991-; *ai:* Club Adv: Ace Ldrshp, Model UN & Master Minds; AFT & NYSUT 1989-; ASCD 1992-; NY St Cncl Soc Stud 1993-; *office:* Iroquois HS Girdle Rd Box 32 Elma NY 14059

DAVISON, ROBERT IRWIN, Educl Missionary HS Teacher; *b:* Maldes, MA; *m:* Ellen Muth; *c:* Rebecca Fay, Daniel Robert; *ed:* Univ of MA (BSCE) Civil Engrng 1966; Tufts Univ (MS) Environmental Engr 1968; US Army Med Svc Corps; St of NH Fire Fighter Level I Trng; *cr:* US Army Med Svc Corps Capt & Preventive Med Ofcr 1969-71; Dana F Perkins & Sons Inc Design Engr 1971-74; Hamilton Engrng Project Engr & Assoc 1974-78; Self-Employed Consulting Civil Engr 1978-83; Allan Swanson Inc Project Engr 1984-87; Chrstn Bible Church Acad HS Tchr & ACE Curr 1987-95; Centro Educativo Chrstn Bilingue HS Tchr & ACE Curr 1995-; *ai:* Prof Engr MA 1974-; Prof Engr NH 1974-; Hollis Planning Bd 1971-93; Hollis Fire Dept 1975-95, 2nd Lt, Capt & Deputy Chief; Hollis Conservation Commission; Master Thesis Pub Presented at Industrial Waste Conf Purdue Univ 1968; *office:* Centro Ed Chrstn Bilingue Av Villazon Km2 Cochabamba Bolivia XX

DAVISON, SANDRA (PRUTZMAN), Fourth Grade Teacher; *b:* Newark, NY; *m:* Gerald J.; *c:* Deborah Davison Finan, John R.; *ed:* St Univ at Geneseo (BS) Sped Ed, Elem 1961; St Univ at Buffalo (MS) Prin, Supervision 1964; *cr:* Brighton Elem Second Grd Tchr 1961-64; Kadimah

Schl of Buffalo Sixth Grd Gifted Class Tchr 1964-65; Grand Island Kaegebein Elem Sixth Grd Tchr 1965-69; Ridgewood MS Vice Prin 1969-70; Palmyra Elem Schl Supvr 1970-71, 2nd, 4th, 5th Grd Tchr 1971-1995; *ai:* Wellness, AIDS Comms; Core Team; Just Say No Club; Tchr of The Gifted & Talented, Invent Amer, History Bowl, debate adv; Great Bks Instr; (NERC) Super Team; NEA 1961-69; NYSASSA 1969-70; NYSUT, Wayne Cty Tchrs Assn 1970-; Palmyra Fac Assn 1970-, Bldg Rep; Jaycees, Women of the Moose 1965-69; Western NY Communities Against Drug Abuse Bd 1984-94; Citizens Alliance to Prevent Drug Abuse 1988-91; Comm Anti-Drug Coalitions 1992-; Prevention Partners Bd 1994-; Yth to Yth, RAYS; Subustance Abuse Prg Consultant; *home:* 511 Fishers Rd Fishers NY 14453*

DAVISON, THOMAS EDWARD, AP & Precalculus Teacher; *b:* Williamsport, PA; *ed:* Univ of PA (BSE) Decision Sci 1986; Bloomsburg Univ (BSE) Scndry Math 1990; *cr:* Sayre HS Math Tchr 1991-; *ai:* Alth, Strategis Planning Comms; Ftbl, Soccer Vol; Tutor; Sayke Area EA 1990-, Pres; PSEA, NEA 1990-; *office:* Sayre Area Jr Sr HS 331 W Lockhart St Sayre PA 18840

DAWE, JOSEPH RANDALL,III, Social Studies Teacher; *b:* Boston, MA; *m:* Kathryn Penardi; *ed:* Bates Coll (BS) Pol Sci 1983; MA Tchr Cert 27 Credit Hrs; *cr:* North Jr High Brockton Soc Stud Tchr 1985; Austin MS US His Tchr 1986; Silver Lake Regnl Jr HS Math Tchr 1987; Southeastern Regnl Voc HS Soc Stud Tchr 1991-; *ai:* Head Ftbl, Girls Track Coach; MTA 1985-; AFT 1991-; *office:* Southeastern Reg Voc Tech HS 250 Foundry St South Easton MA 02375

DAWIDOFF, MARIA GERSCHENKRON, English Teacher; *b:* Vienna, Austria; *c:* Nicholas, Sarah; *ed:* Harvard Radcliffe (BA)Eng Lit 1960; Attnd Columbia Univ 1962; *cr:* Day Prospect Hill Schl Eng, Am His, Eur His Tchr 1960-62, 10th-12th Grd Eng Tchr 1966-72, Eng Dept Chm 1969-72; Hopkins Schl 10th-12th Grd Eng Tchr 1972-, Eng Dept Chm 1977-80; *ai:* Summer Rdng Coll Fac Adv; 11th Grd Adv; Recording for the Blind 1989-, Reader, Monitor; Church of the Redeemer 1970-; Meetinghouse in Francestown 1980-; Sabbatical Flwshp 1987; Books Pub: Between the Frames, Thinking About Movies; *office:* Hopkins Schl 986 Forest Rd New Haven CT 06511

DAWSON, CHRISTINE, Reading, Math & Algebra Tchr; *b:* Atlantic City, NJ; *m:* Peter; *ed:* Chestnut Hill Coll (BS) Elem Ed 1973; *cr:* Green Bank Schl Rdng, Math, Algebra, Tchr 23 Yrs; *ai:* Yrbk Adv; Bsbl Coach; NEA, NJEA 1975-; Green Bank Educ Assn 1975-, Pres, Sec, Treas; *office:* Green Bank Elem Schl 2436 Route 563 Egg Harbor City NJ 08215

DAWSON, GEORGE E., English Teacher; *b:* Cumberland, MD; *m:* Gail Kesner; *c:* Marsha Schaffer, Dr.Michele Overtoom; *ed:* Frostburg St Tchrs Coll (BSED) PE, Sci 1958; Frostburg St Coll (MED) Eng, Lang Arts 1965; Admin, Cmptr Tech, Tech Prep, Tchr Supervision, Group Relationships, Leadership, Pol Lobbying, Project TEACH, Schl Law Classes; *cr:* Greenbelt Jr HS Eng, Soc Stud, Sci Tchr 1958-59; Fort Hill HS Eng Tchr, Ftbl, Track Coach 1959-86; Alleg Co Bd of Ed Amin Asst Supt 1986-88; Career & Tech Ed Ctr Eng, Work Stud Skills Tchr 1988-; *ai:* Local Tchr Assn Pres Five Terms; Yrbk Comm; Internet Project Supervision; NEA 1959-, St RA Rep; PDK 1980-, Exec Bd; MATE 1978-, Exec Bd; NCTE 1959-; Church Christ Luth 1959-; CALM 1992- Exec Bd; Alleg Co Tchrs Credit Union 1986-, Exec Bd; Runner Up Supervising Tchr of Yr MATE; Schl Policy Manual Author; Prof Stans Bd Tchr Ed Mem Governor Appointee; Cert Bd for MD Chair; *office:* Ctr For Career And Tech Educ 14211 Mc Mullen Hwy SW Cresaptown MD 21502*

DAWSON, GERALDINE YARNAL, Assistant Professor; *b:* Huntingdon, PA; *ed:* PA St Univ (BA) Psych 1967; Smith Coll (MSW) Soc Work 1969; Albert Einstein Coll of Med (MD) Medicine 1988; Columbia Univ Pre-Med Cert 1982; Harvard Med Schl Rsrch Flwshp 1980-82; All India Inst of Med Sci Rsrchl Flwshp 1987-88; Natl Inst of Mental Hlth Trng Flwshp 1967-69; *cr:* Albert Einstein Coll of Medicine Clinical Instr 1975-79; Smith Coll Schl Soc Work Clinical Instr 1972-79; Cornell Univ Med Intern 1988-89; Marywood Coll Schl of Soc Work Asst Prof 1993-; *ai:* Natl Assn of Soc Workers 1991-, St Rep Natl Del Assembly 1994-; 6 Journal Publications.

DAWSON, PENELOPE BALDWIN, Asst Prof & Dir of Equine Mgmt; *b:* Bridgeport, CT; *ed:* Western CT St Univ (BS) Ed 1971, (MS) Ed 1978; Ed Grad Courses Fairfield Univ; Silvermine Coll of Art 1964-65; Silvermine Coll of Horsemanship Cert 2 Yrs; Cornell Coll of Veterinary Medicine Equine Cert in Early Foal Care, Equine Nutrition & Equine 1st Aid; *cr:* Oxford Schl 2nd Grd Tchr 1972-73; Redding Elem Schl 3rd Grd Tchr 1973-78; Teikyo Post Univ Dir Equine Stud 1978-79, Fac 1979-; *ai:* Initiated Membership in Intercollegiate Horse Shows Assn; Equestrian Team Coach 1980-89; Equestrian Club Adv 1989-94; Equine Stud & Mgmt Dir & Admin; NEA, CEA 1973-78; CT Dressage Assn 1980-89; CT Horse Cncl 1980-88; Redding Trails Assn, Pres 1984-86; Whitewood Rehab Hospital, Weekly Vol in Pet Share Prgm 1986-91; New Leash on Life Inc 1989-, VP 1994-; 3 Articles Pub in Horses of CT; *office:* Teikyo Post Univ 800 Country Club Rd Waterbury CT 06708

DAWSON, PERRY J. E., Business Ed Dept Chair; *b:* Butler, PA; *m:* Debora Cosentino; *c:* Jeremy, Stephanie; *ed:* IN Univ of PA (BS) Bus Ed 1969, (MED) Bus Ed 1973; *cr:* Knoch Sr HS Tchr, Bus Ed Chair 1969-; *ai:* PSEA, SBCEA, NEA 1969-, Sec, Treas; Knights of Columbus 1990-; Fourth Degree K of C 1994-; Order of Arrow 1990-; *office:* Knoch Jr-Sr HS PO Box 628 Saxonburg PA 16056*

DAWSON, SANDRA J., Agriscience Instructor; *b:* Great Barrington, MS; *ed:* Cornell Univ (BS) Horticulture 1976, (MAT) Ed 1977; Cntrl Ct St Univ 6th Yr Inter Super & Admin Tchr Cert Voc Admin 1986; *cr:* Saratoga-Warren BOCE Tchr 1977-81; Waterburg Regnl Voc Ag Schl Tchr, Coord 1981-89; Trumbull Agriscience Schl Tchr, Dept Head 1989-; *ai:* FFA Adv; NUATA 1981-, Alternate VP; CUATA 1981-, VP, Pres; CEA, NEA 1981-; Jaycees, Prospect; *home:* 198 Straitsville Rd Prospect CT 06712*

DAWSON, SANDRA PETTY, Teacher; *b:* Newton, NJ; *m:* Steven P.; *c:* Aaron, Sarah; *ed:* Chesapeake Seminary (MMin) Ministry 1994; *cr:* Hope Elem Schl Eng Tchr 1977-78; Arnold Chrstn Acad Elem Tchr 1979-81; New Covenant Chrstn Acad 2nd-12th Grd Tchr 1983-; *ai:* Drama Stu Convention Coord; Book Published; *office:* New Covenant Christian Acad 7401 Main St Queenstown MD 21658

DAWSON, WILLIAM BRUCE, Chemistry & Physics Teacher; *b:* Cleveland, OH; *m:* Dalette Jean Kay; *c:* Ronald, Thomas, Kenneth; *ed:* U of Akron (BA) Comprehensive Sci 1973; Ashland Univ (MA) Curr, Instruction 1996; Post-Bac 20 Hrs; 21 Grad Hrs; 21 Grad Hrs Kent St Univ; *cr:* Medina Highland Schl Gen Sci Tchr 1972-75; Warrensville Hgts HS Bio, Gen Sci Tchr 1975-77; Wellington HS Bio, Gen Sci Tchr 1977-79; Harshaw Chemical Co Production Supvr 1979-84; Midview HS Bio, Gen Sci, Chem, Physics, Geology Tchr 1984-; *ai:* Asst Ftbl, Wrestling Coach; Lorain Cty Schls Sci Curr Comm; NEA, OEA SECO 1973-; AAPT 1994-; Cleveland Regnl Area Bio 1991-; West Side Alliance Physics Tchrs 1996; Brunswick Yth Sports 1989-, Little League Coach, League Champions; St Ambrose Wrestling 1985-, Coach, City Champions; Grad Asstantship 1970; Grad Schl Schlsp 1978; Interscholastic Wrestling Ofcl 19 Yrs; Voted by Coaches Officiate Sectional, Dist Tournaments; *office:* Midview HS 38199 Capel Rd Grafton OH 44044*

DAY, CAROL CRIDER, Art Teacher; *b:* Lancaster, OH; *m:* James R.; *ed:* OH Univ (BFA) Art, Ed Painting 1972; 6 Hrs Printmaking; 3 Hrs Cmptr Ed; 2 Hrs CD Rom Video Tech, Ed; 2 Hrs Appleworks Ed; *cr:* Elyria HS Art Instr 1972-; *ai:* NHS, HS Cmptr Tech Comms; NEA; OEA; *office:* Elyria HS 6th St & Middle Ave Elyria OH 44035

DAY, CATHERINE BARKER, Third Grade Teacher; *b:* Rochester, NY; *m:* Jeffrey H.; *c:* Justin, Jeremy; *ed:* Baldwin-Wallace Coll (BSEd) Ed 1969; Grad Credit Hrs at Cleveland St Univ; *cr:* Willoughby-Eastlake Schls Elem Tchr 1969-; *ai:* Annual Schl Field Day, Father-Daughter Dance, Bike Rodeo Comms; ONEA 1969-; Willoughby-Eastlake Tchrs Union 1970-; PTA Millridge Elem 1992-; PTA Washington Elem 1969-, Staff Rep 1990; Selected as Martha Holden Jennings Scholar 1991; Lesson Plans Pub in The Plain Dealer as Part of OH Right to Read Week 1990 & 1992; *office:* Washington Elem Schl 503 Vegas Dr Eastlake OH 44095

DAY, CHRISTOPHER DANIEL, Humanities Teacher; *b:* Stamford, CT; *m:* Cynthia White; *ed:* Univ of NH (BA) His 1988, (MED) Scndry Ed 1990; *cr:* Dublin Schl His Tchr 1991-94; Rye Cntry Day Schl Hum Tchr 1994-; *ai:* Var Boys Ice Hockey, Var Bsbl Coach; *home:* 23 Fairfield Rd Apt B Greenwich CT 06830*

DAY, DEBORAH JEAN, PE Teacher & Coach; *b:* Niagara Falls, NY; *m:* Elwin A.; *ed:* Russell Sage Coll (BS) PE 1976; Niagara Univ (MS) Admin & Supervision 1983; Inservice Credit Hrs for PE; *cr:* Williamsville East HS Tchr 1977-; *ai:* Field Hockey Coach; Indoor Track & Field, Spring Track & Field; USFHA, Natl Dance Exercise Instrs Trng Assn; NFICA, NYSHPERD; Jaycees, Jr Miss 1972; Coach Hall of Fame Awd Winner 1992; Sportsmanship Field Hockey Team Awd 1992; Scholar Ath St Field Hockey Team Coach 1994; *office:* Williamsville East H S 151 Paradise Rd East Amherst NY 14051

DAY, DENISE M., Eng as a Second Lang Teacher; *b:* Sanford, ME; *c:* Emily Kavanaugh; *ed:* Rutgers Coll (BA) Eng 1986; Kean Coll Cert ESL 1993; 30 Credits Toward MA, ESL; *cr:* Ocean Twp HS ESL TChr 1991-95; Wayside Elem Schl ESL Tchr 1995-; *ai:* NJEA, NJTESOL 1991-; *office:* Wayside Elem Schl 733 Bowne Rd Wanamassa NJ 07712

DAY, ELAINE M., Assistant Professor; *b:* Providence, RI; *m:* Robert E.; *c:* Alyssa Marie; *ed:* Johnson & Wales Univ (BS) Court Reporting 1991; Candidate MA Tchng; *cr:* Reporting Assoc Freelance Court Stenographer 1975-78; St of RI Admin Asst 1978-88; Johnson & Wales Univ Asst Prof 1988-; *ai:* Notary Public, Cert Shorthand Reporter; Cert Reporting Instr NCRA; RISRA, RIBEA 1988-, NCRA 1988-, Assoc; Jr Achievement Vol 1996; *office:* Johnson & Wales Univ 8 Abbott Park Pl Providence RI 02903

DAY, ELIZABETH PONZILLO, Sixth Grade Teacher; *b:* Troy, NY; *m:* John F.; *c:* Sarah Elizabeth; *ed:* Siena Coll (BA) 7th-12th Grd Eng Ed 1976; Coll of St Rose (MS) Spec Ed 1977; NY St Theatre Inst Edctrs in Residence 1989-90; *cr:* Mechanicville Pub Schls Sixth Grd Tchr 1977-; *ai:* Archeological Dig Simulation Coord; Visual Arts Club Adv; MS Comm; Friday Night Prime Time Rdng Project Coord; Spring Show Dir; Intnl Day Chprsn; Big Heart Theatre Mem; Delta Kappa Gamma 1990-; Albany Musicians Assn 1972-; Catskill Whole Lang Conf Presenter; NYS Cncl Soc Stud Presenter; 3 Articles Pub; Dwight D. Eisehower Math, Sci Ed Act Grants.

DAY, GARY ALAN, Math Teacher; *b:* Middletown, NY; *ed:* Attnd Coll of St Rose & SUNY at New Paltz; *cr:* Middletown Schl Dis Tchr 1975-; *ai:* Middletown Tchrs Assn 1975-, Pres & Treas; Middletown Federal Credit Union 1975-, Pres.

DAY, JOHN T., HS Math Teacher; *b:* Fulton Cty, OH; *m:* Margel Sue Baker; *c:* Kenneth, Susan Day Karg, Steven, Sandra Day Ober; *cr:* W Liberty-Salem Math Tchr 1964-; *ai:* Bsktbl & Golf Coach.*

DAY, MICHAEL PAUL,SR., Mathematics Teacher; *b:* Cincinnati, OH; *m:* Deborah Busam; *c:* Michael Paul, Kyle Timothy; *ed:* Univ of Cincinnati (BS) Sociology 1984, (MS) Math & Ed 1993; Math Cert 1986; *cr:* Reading Jr Sr HS Math Tchr 1987-; *ai:* Var Sftbl & Jr HS Boys Bsktbl Coach; Frosh Class Spon; LaSalle Alumni Bd 1979-, Dir; *office:* Reading Jr Sr HS 810 E Columbia Ave Reading OH 45215*

DAY, SANDRA FULTON, Family & Consumer Sci Tchr; *b:* Wilmington, DE; *m:* William A.; *c:* Michael; *ed:* James Madison Univ (BS) Home Ec Ed 1973; Univ of DE (MS) Textiles, Clothing 1980; 14 Credit Hrs Penn St Univ; 6 Credit Hrs Temple Univ; 3 Credits Hrs Drexel Univ; 3 Credit Hrs West Chester Univ; *cr:* Oxford Area Schl Dist Family, Consumer Sci Tchr 1973-; Adult Ed Quilting Tchr 1988-94; *ai:* Stu Assistance Team; Ronald MC Donald Quilt Club Spon; Coached Girls IM Field Hockey; NEA, PSEA, OAEA, Amer Assn of Family, Consumer Scis 1973-; Oxford United Meth Church 1961-, Worship Comm Chprsn; Friendship Quilters 1984-, Pres, Vp, Prgms Chair; Elk Creek Spinners, Weavers 1980-; NQA, AQS; Vol in Textile Conservation Lab at Winterthur Museum; Traveled During Sabbatical YR 1994-95, to 15 States & 8 Frgn Countries Focusing on Textiles, Foods, Lu Hual Diversity; *office:* Penn's Grove Schl 602 Garfield St Oxford PA 19363

DAY, STANLEY CURRIER,JR., US History & POTC Teacher; *b:* Auburn, ME; *ed:* Prince Georges Comm Coll (AA) His 1969; Univ of MD (BA) Ed 1971; Inservice Prgm Advanced Prof Cert; *cr:* US Air Force Navigational Equipment Instr 1961-65; Cmptr, Software GSFC Satellite Quality Control 1967-70; Montgomery Cty Pub Schls Electronics Tchr 1971-90, His Tchr 1982-; *ai:* Speech, Debate & Mock Trial Coach; NEA 1971-; MCEA 1971-, Chm Negotiation Cncl; Natl Forensic League; Double Diamond Coach Awd; MD Forensic Assn; Coach of Yr 1984, 1987; WACFL; Montgomery Cty Debate League; Outstanding Tchr MCPS 87; VFW Citation for VOD Prgm; Nomination Agnes Myers Tchr of Yr, Finalists in MD Tchr in Space Prgm; *home:* 1714 Sams Creek Rd Westminster MD 21157*

DAY, VICTORIA LYNN, Music Teacher & Orchestra Dir; *b:* Philadelphia, PA; *m:* Scott R.; *ed:* Crane Schl of Music SUNY Potsdam (BM) Music Ed 1987, (MM) Music Ed 1992; *cr:* Gouverneur Cntrl Schls 4th-12th Grd Music Tchr, Strings, Orch Dir 1987-; *ai:* Elem, MS, HS Orchs; MENC, ASTA, NSOA, GTA 1987-; Crane Alumni Assn 1995-; NYSSMA 1987-, Orch Chair; SLCMEA 1987-, Pres; *office:* Gouverneur Jr Sr HS 133 E Barney St Gouverneur NY 13642*

DAYE, SARAH MILES, K-6th Grade Music Teacher; *b:* Washington, DC; *ed:* Howard Univ (BME) Music Ed 1965; 30 Credit Hrs; *cr:* Calvert Cty Bd of Ed Music, Eng Tchr 1965-66; DC Bd of Ed Music Tchr 1966-; *ai:* Glee Club; Piano Tchr; MENC; *office:* Bowen Elem Schl Delaware Ave & M Street SW Washington DC 20024

DAYHOFF, GLENDA HESS, Second Grade Teacher; *b:* Chambersburg, PA; *m:* Theron Sterner Jr.; *ed:* Shippensburg Univ (BS) Elem Ed 1964, (MED) Elem Ed 1967; *cr:* Keefauver Elem Schl Second Grd Tchr 1964-; *ai:* Elem Math Curr Comm; Primary Ed Comm; Coll Stdnts Mentor, Cooperating Tchr; Action Team; NEA, PSEA 1964-; GAEA 1964-, Mbrshp Chrpsn; Delta Kappa Gamma 1970-, Pres; Outstdng Tchr Awd Shippensburg Univ 1985-86; Unger Awd Tchr Recognition Gettysburg Area Schls 1994; Outstdng Svc to Yth, Comm Awd 1984; *office:* Keefauver Elem Schl Lefever St Gettysburg PA 17325*

DAYTON, AUDREY HALLIER, Third Grade Teacher; *b:* Marblehead, OH; *m:* Lloyd J.; *c:* Timothy, Thomas, Diane Alden, Edward; *ed:* Bowling Green SU (BS) Elem Ed 1953; 36 Hrs Ed, 5 Hrs Math; 6 Hrs Children Lit, 2 Hrs Sci Univ of Toledo; 2 Hrs Math, 2 Hrs Sci Ashland Univ; 3 Hrs Math Portland St Univ; 3 Hrs Sci BGSU; *cr:* Columbus Pub Schls First Grd Tchr 1953-54; Catawba Island Schls Second Grd Tchr 1955-56; Danbury Local Schls First Grd Tchr 1952-53, EMR 1956-57, Third Grd Tchr 1973-; *ai:* Math & Sci Cty Curr, Right to Read Comm; North Cntrl Acc Team; OEA, NEA, DEA 1973-, Bldg Rep; NCTM 1989-; IRA 198 1993; OCESS; Sr Choir St Paul Luth Church 1975-, Dir 6 Yrs; C Famers Dir; Farm Bureau; Eisenhower Grant Ottawa Cty; *office:* Elem Schl 9451 E Harbor Rd Lakeside Marble OH 43440

DAYTON, CHARLENE FAIRCHILD, Secondary English Te Sharon, PA; *m:* David Bonney; *c:* Heather Lea; *ed:* Roberts Wes (BA) Tchng-Eng 1968; Post Grad Stud Cert Credit 42 Brockport Col, John Carroll Univer, Baldwin Wallace Col; Cleve Museu Continuing Ed Units; *cr:* Brockport High Sc Eng Tchr 1968- Angela-St Joseph HS Eng TChr 1983-; *ai:* Writers Club Adv: Pu of Lit, Art Magazine; MEA 1983-; *office:* Villa Angela St Joseph Lake Shore Blvd Cleveland OH 44119

DAYTON, CONSTANCE ELLEN, English Teacher; *b:* Rockvil NY; *m:* Richard E.; *ed:* Sacred Heart Univ (BA) Eng, Ed 1971; Coll (MS) Ed 1984; *cr:* St Brigid Schl 1st Grd Tchr 1968-69; In Schl 6-8 Grd Eng Tchr 1972-; *ai:* Newsletter, Spelling Bee, 6-8 C Lang Arts Coord; Tchr Forum Rep; Staff Dev Comm 1993; NCT NCEA 1972-; Cousteau Soc, Nature Conservancy 1984-; Gr Open Space Cncl 1988-; NCEA Dstngshd Tchr Aw Nom 1995; *o* Lady of Wisdom 110 Myrtle Ave Port Jefferson NY 11777

DAYTON, KIMBERLY ANN, 8th Grade Teacher; *b:* Oregon, Bowling Green St Univ (BS) Elem Ed 1985; Working on MA Guic *cr:* St Stephen Schl 6th Grd Tchr 1985-86, 5-6 Grd Tchr 1986- Tchr 1987-93, 8 Grd Tchr 1993-; *ai:* Quiz Bowl Team; Sci, Soc OCEA 1995-; *office:* St Stephen Schl 2018 Consaul St Toledo O

DEADY, LINDA AUGUSTO, Mathematics Teacher; *b:* Fall R *m:* Michael E.; *c:* Lisa Augusto, Justin Augusto; *ed:* Southeastern (BS) Math 1981; *cr:* Coyle & Cassidy High Dept Head & M 1982-92; Southeastern Reg Voc Tech Math Tchr 1992-; *ai:* Sr C Fac Adv for Peer Mediation; AFT 1992-; Tchr of Yr Nom (Twic Southeastern Reg Voc Tech HS 250 Foundry St South Easton M

DEAGUIAR, SUSAN P., Fourth Grade Teacher; *b:* Somerville Ricardo F.; *ed:* Bridgewater St Coll (BS) Elem Ed 1972, (ME 1978; Math A Way of Thinking; Project Read Writing Strand; Applications of the Apple & IBM Cmptr, DOS Platform; Rep Meets the Writing Proces s; Spec Topics in Elem Sci; *cr:* Danie Elem Schl Librn 1972-81, Grd 3 Tchr 1982-93, Grd 4 Tchr Progress Report Comm; Former Tech Comm; MTA, NEA 1972-, Bldg Rep; Plymouth Cty Ed Assn 1972-, Hnr Awd Significant Svc Profession 1995; *office:* Daniel Webster Elem Sch 1456 Marshfield MA 02050

DEAKIN, PATRICIA SMITH, 6th Grade Language Arts Tchr ME; *m:* Frank A.; *ed:* Univ of ME at Farmington (BS) Eng, His Credit Hrs; *cr:* Cushing Schl 4th Grd Tchr 1969-74, 6th Grd Tchr Gates Intermediate Schl 6th Grd Lang Arts Tchr 1985-; *ai:* Lang Frameworks Comm; Plymouth Cty, Scituate Tchrs Assn Rep; Outdoor Ed; Fac Senate; NCTE 1985-; NEA, MTA 1969-; STA, Past Sec; Patriot Ledger Golden Apple Awd; MS Conf, inservic Area Schl Inclusion Presenter; St of MA Inclusion Mentorin *office:* Gates Intermediate Schl 327 First Parish Rd Scituate MA

DEAKINS, JESSICA STAHL, English Teacher; *b:* Somerse Thomas S.; *c:* PA St Univ (BS) Scndry Eng Ed 1991; *ed:* PA St U Sndry Eng Ed 1991; Pursuing Masters at Frostburg St Univ; *cr:* Elklik HS Eng, Jrnslm Tchr 1991-93; Meyersdale Area HS Eng Tc *ai:* Head Sftbl Coach 1991-; Jrnlsm, Newspaper Adv 1991-93 Club Adv; Ski Club Chaperone; NEA, PSEA 1991-; *office:* M Area HS Rd 3 Meyersdale PA 15552

DEAL, EDWIN E., English Instructor; *b:* Butler, PA; *m:* Mar Jonathan, David; *ed:* Westminster Coll (BA) Eng 1962; Ad Slippery Rock Univ Grad Schl 20 Hrs; *cr:* Shenango Area HS Ch Tchr 1962-; *ai:* NHS Adv 10 Yrs; Book Club Adv; Shenango Are 1962-, Pres 2 Yrs; PSEA, NEA 1962-; Deacon Church 6 Yrs; Ame Tchr of Yr 4 Times; Outstanding Scndry Educators of America 2 of Eng Dept 12 Yrs.

DEAL, JANET L., Social Studies Teacher; *b:* Martins Ferry, C Robert; *c:* Kermit, Heather; *ed:* OH Univ (BS) Soc Stud Comp Xenia City Schl Tchr 1961-63; Talawanda Local Schls Tchr Ithaca City Schls Tchr 1965-69; Clay Local Schls Tchr 1988-; Adv; CEA, OEA, NEA 1988-, Pres; Natl Soc Stud Cncl 1989-; Women Voters 1993-; *office:* Clay Local Schls 44 Clay High St Po OH 45662

DEAL, JOHN C., 8th Grade Mathematics Teacher; *b:* Greensbur Bonnie Best; *c:* Jeffrey B., Lori S., John W.; *ed:* Slippery Rock St His & Geography Ed 1963; Univ of DE (MS) Ed 1967; 25 Addl C *cr:* Townsend Schl Dist 7th & 8th Grds Math & Soc Stud Tchr Middletown Schl Dist 5th, 7th & 8th Grds Math Tchr 1966-69; Be Schl Dist 8th Grd Math, Algebra I & Geometry Tchr 1969-; Leader; Algebra I Contest Spon; Bus Proctor; Western PA Cncl Tchrs 1991-; PA Cncl of Mathm Tchr; Masons 1986-, Area C-2 1990; Baldwin Comm United Meth Church; Demolay 1989-, Honor; Ch of Demolity Advy Cncl; ACT Testing Involvement; Outstanding Tchr 1964; *home:* 1003 Dallett Rd Pittsburgh PA 15

DEAMER, PATRICIA MULVANY, Third Grade Teacher; *b:* B *m:* Donald; *c:* Deborah Gustafson; *ed:* Northeastern Univ (BS) 1967; Various Courses 1967-; *cr:* Ayer Pub Schls 3rd Grd Tchr 1 NEA, ATA; *office:* Page Elem Schl Washington St Ayer MA 014

DEAN, ALAN ROSS, Associate Prof of Education; *b:* Mobile Pamela Jacobs; *ed:* Univ of Southern MS (BS) Geog & Scndry (EDD) Scndry Ed & Soc Stud 1980; Univ of Southern AL (MED Ed & Soc Stud 1975; Univ of KY 8 Credit Hrs in Ec; Morehea Credit Hrs in Ed Admin; *cr:* Mobile Cty Pub Schl Soc Stud Tchr Alice Lloyd Coll Prof Ed 1981-85; Univ Rio Grande Prof Ed Future Edctrs Org Adv; Tenure & Fin Comm; Gallia Animal Welfa Dir; *office:* Univ Of Rio Grande Rio Grande OH 45674*

DEAN, JANE AMOSS, Assistant Principal; *b:* Fallston, MD; *m* Powell; *c:* Gregory A., Amy E.; *ed:* Towson St Univ (BS) Elem (MED) Elem Ed 1971; *cr:* Havre de Grace Elem Schl 4th & 5th 1966-68; Rogers Forge Elem Schl 6th Grd Tchr 1968-70; Homest Schl 6th Grd Tchr 1970-73; Forest Hill Nursery Schl Pre S 1979-82; St Margaret Schl 3rd & 5th Grd Tchr & Asst Prin 1982- Jr Beta Club & Span Club Spon & Adv; Admissions Dir; Pub Re Assembly Coord; SOMIRAC 1990-; NCEA 1992-; Arch Catechist; WBAL-TV Class Act Tchr 1991; Harford Cty Child Awd 1991; St Margaret Schl Tchr of the Yr 1992; *office:* St Marg 205 N Hickory Ave Bel Air MD 21014

DEAN, JANICE KIMMICH, Science Teacher; *b:* Cortland William F.; *c:* Kristofer, Meghan, Jaime Lynne; *ed:* St Univ Albany (BS) Medical Tech 1983; St Univ of NY at Cortland (MA Ed 1990; CORD Applied Bio-Chem Trng 1995; 3 Credits at St Ur at Oneonta 1 Week Summer Inst in Chem TORCH Prgm 1993; WS Tchr Trng Inst in Video & Tech 1996; *cr:* Owego Free Acad Sci Tc *ai:* Drama Club Adv 2 Yrs; Curr Tech Writing for Goals 2000 Educ Act; NSTA, NY St Tchrs Assn 1990-; Wrote 2 Currs Modern Ea Modern Bio; *office:* Owego Free Acad George St Owego NY 13

MARGARET MULLEN, Spanish Teacher; *b:* Elmira, NY; *m:* G.; *c:* Connor, Kevin, Ellen; *ed:* Elmira Coll (BA) Fr, Scndry Ed S) Ed 1992; *cr:* Notre Dame HS Lang Tchr 1975-80, Span, Fr Tchr : Stu Cncl Moderator; NYSAFLT.

REBECCA KAY, Assoc Prof of Spch, Prgm Coord; *b:* Charleston, Univ of Pittsburgh (BA) Eng 1981, (MA) Comm 1984; Doctoral e Eng; *cr:* Hillsborough Comm Coll Visiting Prof Speech & Eng Pasco-Hernando Comm Coll Visiting Prof Speech & Eng Lafayette Coll Visiting Prof Speech & Eng 1990-91; pton Coll Assoc Prof of Speech 1991-; *ai:* Acad Policy Comm earning Resources Comm; League of Women Voters 1990-, Bd ner Assn of Univ Women; Rdng, Writing Lab Grants Hillsborough oll; Review of Speech Comm Txt; *office:* Northampton Comm 5 Green Pond Rd Bethlehem PA 18017

RICHARD MARSHALL, Assistant Professor of Art; *b:* Boston, Mary Anne Sullivan; *c:* Geoffrey, Christina; *ed:* Tufts Univ Schl useum of Fine Arts (BFA) Fine Arts Painting 1972, (MFA) Fine ting 1976; *cr:* Dean Coll Asst Prof of Art 1976-, Coord of Visual n 1992-95; *ai:* Dept Rep & Former Chm Honor & Awds Comm; Chm Family Weekend Comm & Mem Fac Prsnl Policy Comm; Exhibit Tufts Univ; Creiger Assocs Boston, Premier Image Ashland, Piper Galley Lexington & Dean Coll Exhibits; *home:* 14 Franklin MA 02038

HARON L. WELCH, Professor; *b:* Lowell, MA; *m:* Ronald; *c:* Emily; *ed:* Univ of NH (BA) Eng 1965, (MA) Eng 1969, (PHD) 3; *cr:* Chelmsford Jr HS Tchr 1966; Del Rio HS Tchr 1966-67; oll at UNH Manchester Adjunct Fac 1973-82; Rivier Coll Asst of 1982-; *ai:* Dept Chair of Eng & Comm 1992-; Evaluation MLA; NCTE; NEMLA; Author of Scholarly Articles; Project & Presenter; NH Hum Cncl Presenter Acad Confs; *office:* Rivier S Main St Nashua NH 03060

HIRLEY RUTH, Mathematics Teacher; *b:* Waynesburg, PA; *ed:* Coll (BS) Math 1965; Univ of Pittsburgh (MEd) Curr, Supervision nptr Courses Penn St, Pitt; *cr:* Ctr Area Schl Dist Tchr 1966-; Coll Calculus Tchr 1979-85; *ai:* CAEA, PSEA, NEA 1966-; Women 1980-, Area Pres, Dist Exec Comm 1993-95; Airport Area y Care Ctr 1995-, Exec Bd Mem; Brodhead C&MA Church 1959-, d Dir; *office:* Ctr HS Baker Rd Ext Monaca PA 15061*

THOMAS EUGENE, Choral & Asst Band Director; *b:* on, DC; *m:* Trisha A. Ferko; *c:* Heather, Holly; *ed:* West Chester (BS) Music Ed 1982; West Chester Univ (MM) Music Ed nce 1993; *cr:* The Eisenhower Schl K-12th Grd Music Tchr Twin Spring Farm Day Schl Presch-4th Grd Music & General 3-84; Dover HS Choral Dir & Asst Band Dir 1989-; *ai:* Mens & Choir; Gospel Ensemble; Musicians in Visual & Performing Arts Gifted Prgm Adv; NEA, DEA & CEA 1984-; MENC 1980-; DE l Assn 1984-, All St Chorus Chair; KCMEA 1984-, Treas; Amer irs Assn 1990-; Editor DE Music Ed Assoc 1995-; DE ACOA Sr Chair; Visual & Performing Arts Curr Framework Comm for DE lem Ldrshp Team for VPAC Framework Comm; Tchr Standards es for DE 1995; Elected Membership The Soc of Pi Kappa Lamda Music Honor Soc 1993; *office:* Dover HS 625 Walker Rd Dover *

R, MARJORIE VAUGHAN, First Grade Teacher; *b:* Meyersdale, ynn Richard; *c:* Douglas Levi; *ed:* Edinboro St Coll (BS) Elem Ed Grad Hrs Masters Equivalency Various Inst; *cr:* Conemaugh Twp Second Grd Tchr 1972-76; Meyersdale Area Schl Dist Kndgtn D Classroom Tchr 1985-86; Berlin Brothersvalley Schl Dist First, Third, Fourth Grd Tchr 1986-; *ai:* Phi Delta Kappa 1992-; 86-; PSEA, NEA 1972-; Plus Spring Womens Club 1986-, Various Somerset Cty Womens Club 1986-, Pres 1993-95; Trinity United f Christ, Deacon; *office:* Berlin Brothersvalley Schl 1025 E Main 15530*

ELIS, GUY R., Retired Third Grade Teacher; *b:* Schenectady, Catherine; *c:* David, Lorene DeAngelis Holmes, Timothy; *ed:* ll (BA) Ec, Eng 1963; St Univ Coll at Oneanta (MS) Ed 1967; 9 s Elem Supervision, Admin; *cr:* Mohonasen Cntrl 6th Grd Tchr 7 almont Cntrl 3-5th Grd Tchr 26 Yrs; *ai:* Own, Operate Beef, Calf ecialize Hay Production; NEA 1970-; AFT; *home:* 457 Swart Hill erdam NY 12010

ELIS, JOSEPH F., Fifth Grade Teacher; *b:* Philadelphia, PA; *m:* d: West Chester Univ (BS) Elem Ed, Rdng 1978, (MS) Elem Ed, & Dev 1991; Addl 60 Credit HRs AAS Cmptr Sci 1983; *cr:* Alco Accident Co Cmptr Operations 1982-85; William Penn Schl Dist 3rd Tchr 1985-87; Upper Darby Schl Dist 4th-5th Grd Tchr 1987-; age Computerized Electronic Message Bd for Bywood Schl ing Spec Act, Concerts, Etc.; Ran an After Schl Cmptr Club at Schl; Chrstn Svc Brigade 1980-, Prgm Ldr, Dir; *office:* Bywood l 330 Avon Rd Upper Darby PA 19082

ELIS, LEONARD A., Scndry Eng Tchr & Dept Chair; *b:* Boston, Monica Lin; *ed:* St Coll at Boston (BSEd) His & Eng 1963; Boston) His 1965; 47 Addl Hrs Beyond MA; *cr:* Dedham High Sub 1967; IS Eng & His Tchr 1968-80; Middletown High Scndry Eng 1980-; Hist Coach Bowl 1995; NEA 1968-; NCTE 1980-; Buddy-RI AIDS 1989-; Tchr of Yr 1989; RI & Disney Feature Tchr of Yr ice: Middletown HS Valley Rd Middletown RI 02840*

ELO, JOSEPH, Social Studies Teacher; *b:* Shenandoah, PA; *m:* ne Steibler; *c:* Anthony, John, Michael; *ed:* Bloomsburg (BS) d, Soc Stud 1979; 24 Post Grad Credits; *cr:* Marian HS Soc Stud 0-90; St Michael Schl Soc Stud Tchr 1990-; *ai:* Schuylkill Haven Var Asst Bsktbl Coach; Marian HS Var Asst Bsbl Coach; ADLTA oach of Yr Berks Cty Section III 1987, Schuylkill League Division Hazleton Stan Speaker Newspaper 1992; *office:* St Michael Schl ater St Lansford PA 18232

NI, GEORGE, Drama Director; *b:* Paterson, NJ; *ed:* Seton Hall) Ed 1973; Montclair St (MA) Speech & Theatre 1977; 30 Addl rs 1993; *cr:* PS #25 Eigth Grd Tchr 1973-86; Rosa Parks Arts HS ir 1986-; *ai:* Thespian Spon; Positive Impact Ensemble Theatre Dir, Equity Ensemble Dir Theatre Troupe; Sr Class Adv; NJEA el, Human Rights Awd; NEA 1973-, Human Rights Awd 1994; ccordion Assn 1970-, Bd; NJ Accordion Assn 1968-, Pres, Contest chr of Yr 1993 & 1995; Disney Outstanding Tchr Nom; Tchrs Hall Nom; *office:* Rosa Prks Schl Fine & Perf Art 413 12th Ave NJ 07514

NG, DAVID RICHARD, English Teacher; *b:* Pittsburgh, PA; *m:* offman; *c:* Julie, Brent, Caitlin; *ed:* Edinboro Univ of PA (BS) Eng rad Stud NY Univ, SUNY at Fredonia, SUNY at New Paltz; *cr:* rg HS Eng Dept Chair 1968-71; The Henley Schl Eng Tchr Windham Ashland Jewett Cntrl Schl Eng Dept Chair 1972-; *ai:* ki Coach; Drama Dept; NYSUT 1972-; NCTE 1980-; Lions Intnl Fulbright Exch Tchr London 1983; British Theatre Exch 1986, *me:* HC 1 Box 22 Durham NY 12422*

NG, SUSAN HOFFMAN, French & German Teacher; *b:* Vienna, *m:* David Richard; *c:* Brent, Caitlin; *ed:* Middleburg Coll (BA) Fr SUNY at Buffalo (MED) Frgn Lang Ed 1974; *cr:* Windham-Ashland-Jewett CS Fr, Ger Tchr 1974-91; Hunter-Tannersville CS Fr, Ger Tchr 1991-; *ai:* Asst Yrbk Adv; Co-Adv Class of 1999; Fr Club Adv; NYSUT 1974-; NYSAFLT 1974-, Svc, Regnl Meeting Chprsn; Cairo-Durham Booster Club 1995-, Sec; *office:* Hunter-Tannersville Cntrl Schl Main St Tannersville NY 12485*

DEARTH, SHERRY CHILCOTE, 6th Grade Teacher of Gifted; *b:* Buffalo, NY; *m:* Richard; *c:* Richard, Heather, Suzanne; *ed:* Findlay Coll (BA) Sociology 1971; Cleveland St (MS) Curr Instruction 1989; Gifted Validation; Permanent Cert; *cr:* North Ridgeville City Schls Tchr 1984-; *ai:* Young Authors Coord; Outdoor Ed Tchr; Ventur Capital Planning Comm; NEA 1986-; Continental Cable Tchr of the Yr for OH; *office:* North Ridgeville MS 35895 Ctr Ridge Rd North Ridgeville OH 44039

DEATRICK, SARAH ANN, Spanish Teacher; *b:* Ft Wayne, IN; *ed:* Working Toward MED; Cnslng Cert; *cr:* Old Ft Local Schls Span Tchr 1991-; *ai:* Chrldng Coach; Jr Class Adv; NEA 1991-; CFLEA Tchrs Assn 1991-, Bldg Rep, Sec; *office:* Old Fort Local Schls 7635 N County Road 51 Old Fort OH 44861

DE BACCO, JANE OLIVER, German Teacher; *ed:* Univ of Vienna (Zeugnis) Ger 1971; Indiana Univ of PA (BSEd) Ger 1972, (MA) Eng 1976; Univ of Pittsburgh (MSIS) Information Sci 1984; PA Cert in Elem Ed; Oral Proficiency Trng; *cr:* Greensburg Salem Schl Full-Time Ger Tchr 1972-80; Westmoreland Cty Comm Coll Eng & Cmptr Adjunct Instr 1976-90; Univ of PA Information Sci Adjunct Prof 1984-86; Greater Latrobe Sr HS Full-Time Ger Tchr 1980-; *ai:* Ger Club Adv; Delta Epsilon Phi Spon; Sr HS Retirement & Prins Advisory Comm; Latrobe Ger Exch Prgm Coord; AATG 1987-; GLEA, PSEA, NEA; PMLA; ACTFL; *office:* Greater Latrobe Sr H S Country Club Rd Latrobe PA 15650

DEBANY, BETH M., Science Teacher; *b:* Watertown, NY; *m:* Warren H. Jr.; *c:* Warren, Christopher; *ed:* Russell Sage Coll (BA) Bio & Scndry Ed 1983; Syracuse Univ (MS) Bio & Sci Ed 1990; *cr:* Rome Cath Jr & Sr HS Sci Tchr 1984-87, 1992-; Notre Dame HS Sci Tchr 1989-90; HRH Lab Technician 1990-92; *ai:* Sci Fair Coord; NHS Moderator; Tech Comm; NABT 1990-; Rome Acad of Sci 1995-, Trustee; *home:* 6659 Williams Rd Rome NY 13440

DEBAYLO, BARBARA ANNE (SCHRAVEN), Art Teacher; *b:* Astoria, NY; *m:* Paul William; *ed:* Queens Coll (BA) Art 1969; Attnd Western MD Coll, Middlesex Cnty Coll, Mercer Cty Coll; *cr:* William M. Carr Jr HS Art Tchr 1969-69; Montgomery Village Jr HS Art Tchr 1970-75; Highland Village MS Art Tchr 1975-77; Highland Park HS Art Tchr 1977-; *ai:* Mentor Prgm; Mural Club; Fac Soc Co-Chprsn; NEA, Art Edctrs of NJ 1975-; NJ Governors Tchr Recognition Tchr of Yr 1995; Princeton Univ Distinquished Edctrs Awd Nom; 1st Runnerup League of Amer Pen Women Awd; NEH Grant Leonardi Inst; *office:* Highland Park HS N 5th Ave Highland Park NJ 08904

DEBELL, BETTINA POLLARD, Special Education Teacher; *b:* Uniondale, NY; *m:* Joseph; *ed:* St Univ of NY at Geneseo (BS) Spec Ed & Theater 1987, (MS) Rdng 1992; *cr:* Rochester City Schls Spec Ed Tchr 1987-90; Geneseo Cntrl Elem Spec Ed Tchr 1990-; *ai:* Drama Club Adv; Colorguard Coach.

DEBERDINE, FAYE B., Retired Teacher; *b:* Lancaster, PA; *m:* Michael F.; *c:* Jennifer Faye Goldbach, Michael III; *ed:* Millersville Univ (BS) Elem 1963; Temple Univ (MS) Elem 1971; *cr:* Manhiem Twp 3rd Grd Tchr 1963; Martic Twp 3rd Grd Tchr 1956-59; Solanco MS Lang Arts 8th-9th Grd, Block Stud 6th Grd, Block Rdng 6th-8th Grd Tchr 1972-92, Lead Tchr 7th Grd 1992-93; *ai:* PSEA, LEA, SEA 1993-, Retired; Quarryville Chamber Commerce 1993-, Dir; Robert Fulton Ch Eastern Star 1949-; St Paul's Church of Christ 1956-; Dir of SECA in Quarryville; *home:* 50 Oak Ridge Dr Quarryville PA 17566

DEBETTA, ROY EDWARD, 4th Grade Teacher; *b:* Jamaica, NY; *m:* Lorraine; *c:* Michele, Amy; *ed:* Adelphi Univ (BA) Bus Ed 1965, (MA) Ed 1970; *cr:* YMCA Mgr 1960-63; Longwood HS Gen Math Tchr 1964; Coram Elem Schl 5th & 6th Grd Tchr 1965-75; Longwood Jr High 6th Grade Tchr 1976; West Mid Island 4th & 5th Grd Tchr 1977-87; Ridge Elem 4th Grd Tchr 1988-; *ai:* BaNam Orphanage Thailand Charity Pgm 1970; Diagnosis Eval Comm 1971; Report to Parents Comm 1975; Instrl Imp Comm 1975; Elem Sci Comm 1988-94; Hlth Resource Pgm 1995-; NYSUT & AFT 1965-; MITA.

DEBICH, NATALIE LONG, Teacher of Gifted Students; *b:* Greensburg, PA; *m:* John G.; *c:* Larisa Anna; *ed:* IN U of PA (BS) Ed 1973; WV Univ (MA) Cnslng, Guid 1976; *cr:* Hempfield Area Schl Dist Third Grd Tchr 1973-78, Enrichment Prgm Tchr K-5 Grd 1978-; *ai:* Teach Coll for Kids at Westmoreland Cty Comm Coll; NEA 1973-.

DEBIEC, DAVID ANTHONY, 6th Grade Teacher; *b:* Reading, PA; *m:* Sandra Ann; *c:* Eric, Russell, Daniel; *ed:* Kutztown St Coll (BS) Spec Ed, Elem Ed 1974, (MS) Elem Ed 1980; 15 Hrs Prins Cert Temple Univ; *cr:* Wilson Schl Dist Spec Ed Jr HS 1975-85, 6th Grd Tchr 1985-; *ai:* Jr HS Bsbl Coach 20th Season; NEA, PSEA, WEA 1975-; *office:* Wilson Schl Dist 2300 Grandview Blvd West Lawn PA 19609

DEBLASE, HELEN, First Grade Teacher; *b:* Jersey City, NJ; *ed:* Caldwell Coll (BA) Ed, Bio 1967; Attnd Seton Hall Univ 15 Credit Hrs, Montclair Univ 3 Credit Hrs, William Paterson 11 Credit Hrs; *cr:* Parochial Schl Tchr 1956-69; North Dover Elem Tchr 1970-; *ai:* NJEA, NEA, MCCEA 1970-; Tchr of Yr 1988; Right to Read Dir 1976.

DEBLASIO, MARY ABATE, Italian & Spanish Teacher; *b:* Hackensack, NJ; *w:* Vito A. (dec); *ed:* Fairleigh Dickinson Univ (BA) K-12 Frng Lang Ed 1974; 12 Addl Credits Italian Lang, Lit Montclair St Univ; Univ Degli Studi at Roma Italia Italian Lang, Lit 27 Credits; Univ di Urbino Italy Italian 6 Credits; Univ Per Stranieri at Siena Italy 3 Credits; Jersey City St Coll Supervision 12 Credits; *cr:* Palisades Park HS Italian, Span Tchr 1974-; *ai:* Var Chrldng Coach; Fall, Winter Sports Head Coach; NHS Fac Review Comm; Stu Assistance Team Interpreter; Child Stud Team Interpreter, Translator; NEA, NJEA 1974-; Voice of Italian Tchrs 1988-, VP 2 Yrs, Pres 2 Yrs; FLENJ, AATI 1993-; Ctr for Ital, Amer-Ital Culture 1991-, Bd of Trustees, Culture, Ed Comms, Frgn Affairs Ministry, Italian Govt, Vice Consul of Italy, NJ & NY 1994-; Italian Reception Comm, Chprsn Poster Contest; World Cup 1994, NJ Stu Participation; *office:* Palisades Pk Jr Sr HS 1 Veteran's Plaza Palisades Park NJ 07650*

DEBONIS, DONNA MARIE, Supvr of Curr & Instruction; *b:* Sharon, PA; *ed:* Edinboro St Univ (BSE) Elem Ed 1971, (ME) Rdng 1974; Univ of Pittsburgh (PhD) Lang Comm 1987; Rdng Specialist, Supervision Cert; Information Sci Post Grad Work; *cr:* St Anthonys Schl Tchr 1971-76; Farrell Area Schl Dist Cmptr Coord, Tchr 1976-89; PA St Univ at Shenango Consultant, Instr 1980-95; Sharon City Schl Dist Supvr, Curr, Instruction 1989-; *ai:* Interact Club Co-Adv; Hudson Charitable Fnd Dir; ASCD 1991-, Mem; Rotary 1995-, Mem; Sharon Lifelong Learning Cncl 1989-, Mem; Shenango Valley Performing Arts Cncl 1993-, Mem; Numerous Grants, Articles; *office:* Sharon City Schl Dist 215 Forker Blvd Sharon PA 16146

DEBORD, TIMOTHY A., English & Speech Teacher; *b:* Chillicothe, OH; *m:* Tina G.; *c:* Sarah; *ed:* Morehead St Univ (BA) Eng, Speech 1971; Coll of Mt St Joseph (MA) Comm 1984; *cr:* Huntington HS Tchr 1971-; *ai:* Huntington Local EA, OH EA, NEA 1971-; *office:* Huntington Local Schl Dist 188 Huntsman Rd Chillicothe OH 45601

DEBORD, TINA ELLIOTT, Business Teacher; *b:* Colcord, WV; *m:* Timothy; *c:* Sarah; *ed:* Morehead St Univ (BS) Bus Ed 1972; Coll of Mt Saint Joseph (MS) Ed 1985; *cr:* Southern HS Bus Tchr 1972-79; OH Univ at Chillicothe Bus Tchr 1979-; Pickaway-Ross JVS Bus Tchr 1979-; *ai:* Bus Profs of Amer Adv; OH Ed Assn, OH Bus Tchrs, NEA 1972-; OH Voc Assn 1986-; *office:* Pickaway Ross Co Jt Voc Schl 895 Crouse Chapel Rd Chillicothe OH 45601

DEBREUIL, TERRILYNN BARDEN, Lit Teacher & French Tutor; *b:* Portland, ME; *m:* Kerry Robert; *c:* Christyn, Deanna; *ed:* Univ Southern ME (BFA) Fine Arts-Summa Cum Laude 1978; Attnd Portland Schl of Art; Addl Hrs Lit, Frgn Lang, Philosophy; *cr:* ME Broadcasting System Commercial Artist 1979-83; Private Instruction Fine Arts Instr 1982-; Windham Schl Dept Adult Ed Instr 1988-; *ai:* Newspaper Adv; Drama Coach; Fine Arts Instr; Windham Assembly of God 1978-, Board, Cnslr, Youth Ldr, Music Co-Dir; *home:* 80 Windham Center Rd Windham ME 04062

DEBROSSE, MARTHA HELEN,CPPS Retired Teacher; *b:* Piqua, OH; *ed:* Athenaeum of OH (BSE) Elem Ed 1952; Univ of Dayton (MSE) Elem Ed, Admin 1967; 10 Post-Grad Credits Curr Design, Tchng Strategies, Soc Stud; *cr:* Archdiocese of Cincinnati 1st-8th Grd Tchr 1943-91, Prin Elem Schl 1963-64, 1970-74; *ai:* K-6th Grd Sub Tchr; Tchr of Yr Awd; *home:* 120 S Buckeye St Celina OH 45822

DECAPRIO, DOROTHY TORELLO, 6th-8th Grade Math Teacher; *b:* New Haven, CT; *m:* M. Philip; *c:* Paul, Mary, Antonetti, David; *ed:* Albertus Magnus Coll (BS) Soc Stud, His Ed 1962; Southern CT St Univ (MS) Upper Elem Ed 1990; *cr:* East Haven HS His Tchr 1962-65; St Rita Schl 6-8th Grd Math Tchr 1980-90, 1992-; Barry Jr High Math, Geography Rdng Tchr 1991-92; *ai:* Asst Prin; Jr Honor Soc Moderator; Rainbow Children Facilitator; NEA 1980-; Hamden Womans Club 1991-, Treas.

DECAPRIO, JOHN ANTHONY, Freshman Social Studies Tchr; *b:* New Haven, CT; *m:* Sarah Greenhalgh; *c:* Michael, Matthew; *ed:* Trinity Coll (BS) Psych 1986; Southern CT St Univ 30 Credits in His; *cr:* Notre Dame HS Tchr, Coach 1987-; *ai:* Asst Var Ftbl Coach; Head Fresh Bsbl Coach; CHSCA 1987-.

DECAPRIO, JUDITH LAVORGNA, 8th Grade Social Studies Tchr; *b:* New Haven, CT; *m:* John A.; *c:* John, Jeffrey, Jenine, Joseph; *ed:* SCSC (BS) Ed & His 1961, (MS) Spec Ed 1971; Credit Hrs for Master Tchr & Best Prgm; *cr:* Pine Orchard 4th Grd Tchr 1961-63; Brandford Intermediate Schl 8th Grd Soc Stud Tchr 1978-; *ai:* Best, Prin Advisory & Schl Improvement Comm; Stu Asst Team; NEA 1978-; Branford Ed Assn 1978-, Rep; BEA Exec Bd; Faculty Excl Awd 1984.*

DECARO, BARBARA ANN, Teacher; *b:* Rockaway, NY; *m:* Laurence T.; *c:* Laurence, Scott; *ed:* Montclair St Coll (BA) Hlth, PE 1970, (MA) 1977; Natl Cncl Family Rel Certfd Family Life Educ; Natl Assn Mediation Educ Certfd Mediator; Supervision Cert; *cr:* Pascack Vly Regnl HS Tchr 1970-; *ai:* Stu Govt, Model Un Adv; Peer Mediation Coord; NCFR 1983-; NEA, NJEA 1970-; ASCD 1986-; Hillsdale Bd of Hlth 1991-, VP; Schl, Family Task Force 1982-, Chair; Natl Conf Chrstn Jews 1982-, Adv; Prof Achvmt Awd 1995; *office:* Pascack Hills HS 225 W Grand Ave Montvale NJ 07645

DECARO, LAURENCE T., Health Teacher; *b:* Springfield, MA; *m:* Barbara Ann M. Stilwell; *c:* Larry Jr., Scott; *ed:* Montclair St Coll (BA) Hlth, PE 1968, (MA) Hlth Prof 1976; 24 Credits Supvr, Admin, 22 Credits Hlth Prof; *cr:* Pascack Vly Regnl HS Stu Asst Coord 1983, Lead Tchr 1983-86, Tchr l971-; *ai:* Dist Tech Comm; P U's Hall of Fame Ath Comm; NEA, NJEA 1971-; Natl Family Conf 1988-; Amer Cancer Soc 1989-, Man of Yr; Cub Scouts 1985-, Cubmaster; Nationally Cert Family Life Educator; Who's Who in Ed in East; Co-Pres Task Force Crimes Against Children; Clinical Fac Montclair St Univ; *office:* Pascack Vly Regnl HS 200 Piermont Ave Hillsdale NJ 07642*

DE CARVALHO, MARIA-FILOMENA FIDALGO, Spanish Teacher; *b:* Coimbra, Portugal; *ed:* Coll of Our Lady Of Elms (BA) Modern Lang 1975; Univ of MA at Amherst (MA) Span 1980; *cr:* Indian Orchard Elem Schl Portuguese Bilingual, ESL K-4th Grd Tchr 1975-76; Kennedy Jr HS Portuguese Bilingual, Span Tchr 1976-84; MA Migrant Ed Prgm Span & Portuguese Bilingual Tchr 1977; Classical HS Span Tchr 1984-86; Springfield Cntrl HS Span Tchr 1986-; *ai:* Chrldr Coach; Philosophy, Scholarship Comms; Confirmation Tchr; NEA, Springfield Ed Assn 1979-; MA Foreign Lang Assn 1979-; Amer Cncl Tchng Foreign Langs; MA Assn of Bilingual Educators 1975-85, Sec 1976-77, Treas 1977-80, Tchr of Yr 1983; Delta Kappa Gamma Soc Intnl 1987-; Alpha Upsilon Chapter 1987-; Western MA Collaborative of Foreign Lang Tchrs 1989-; Natl Assn of Bilingual Educators 1976-86; Amer Assn Tchrs of Span & Portuguese 1975-88; Springfield Tchrs Club 1975-; Kappa Gamma Pi 1975-, VP 1977-79, Pres 1981-83; Confraternity of Chrstn Doctrine 1976-, Tchr; Cath Womans Club Diocese of Springfield 1978-, Sec 1992-; Cath Youth Club Adv 1980-92; Eucharistic Minister 1981-; Spiritual Life Comm 1979-92; Coll of Our Lady of Elms Alumnae Assn 1985-; Schlsp Comm 1978-84, Chprsn; MA Citizens for Life 1978-; World Apostolate of Fatima 1976-, Chapter Pres 1984-86; MA Mutual Insurance Co Tchr Recognition 1990-92; Outstanding Young Women of Amer 1984; Intl & Pioneer Valley Rdng Cncl Lit Awd 1984; Tchr Svc Awd 1988; Presenter & Panelist For MA Bilingual Bicultural Symposium Univ of MA at Amherst; MA Foreign Lang Assn Annual Conf Presenter; *office:* Springfield Central HS 1840 Roosevelt Ave Springfield MA 01109*

DECATUR, PHYLLIS, Mathematics Teacher; *b:* New York, NY; *c:* Scott, Deborah, Jonathan; *ed:* Queen Coll (BA) Psych 1963; Stony Brook SUNY (MA) Math 1984; 75 Credits Past Masters Degree; *cr:* PS 69 Bronx 4th Grd Tchr 1963-66; Bellport HS Math Dept Chair 1991-94, Math Tchr 1980-; *ai:* Math Team Adv; Scorekeeper Girls Bsktbl; NCTM, AMTNYS, SCMTA 1980-; *office:* Bellport HS Beaver Dam Rd Brookhaven NY 11719

DECATUR, STEVEN ROBERT, High School Art Teacher; *b:* Columbus, OH; *c:* Heather, Ashley; *ed:* Marietta Coll (BA) Art 1975; Ashland Univ (ME) Admin 1985; Attnd AP Advanced Instr Inst; *cr:* Northland HS Tchr 1975-; *ai:* Head Girls Fastpitch Sftbl Coach; NEA 1975-; OEA 1975-; CEA 1975-; Northland Boosters 1975-; Disciplined Based Arts Ed Coalition of Essential Schls Comm Chm; Adopt A Dozen Group Ldr; *office:* Northland HS 1919 Northcliff Dr Columbus OH 43229

DECEDER, KIMBERLY FOLINO, Business Education Teacher; *b:* Pittsburgh, PA; *m:* Brian W.; *ed:* IN Univ of PA (BS) Bus Ed 1992; Elem Cert; *cr:* Montour Schl Dist Bus Ed Tchr 4 Yrs; *ai:* Jr High Chrldng Spon; NEA, PBEA, PSEA 1991-; *office:* Montour HS 90 Clever Rd Mc Kees Rocks PA 15136

DECESARE, GARY THOMAS, Administrator; *b:* Bronxville, NY; *m:* Pamela Sulzer; *ed:* Iona Coll (BBA) Mrktg 1984; Working Toward MS in Admin at Saint Johns Univ; *cr:* Saint Raymonds Cmptr Tchr 1984-88, Cmptr Chprsn 1987-89, Asst Prin 1990-92, Assoc Prin 1992-; *ai:* Maintenance Dir; Bldg Supvr; Var Bsktbl Head Coach; ASCD; Natl Assn of Bsktbl Coaches; NCEA; Natl Assn of Interscholastic Coaches; NY Cath Coaches Assn, Pres; Adidas ABCD Bsktbl Camp, Dir; Saint Raymonds Bsktbl Camp, Dir; CHSAA Pre-Season Bsktbl Camp, Dir; Kodak & Downtown Athletic Club Coach of Yr; CHSAA Coach of Yr; Saint Raymonds HS Hall of Fame; Saint Helena Parish Vol Awd; *office:* St Raymond HS For Boys 2151 Saint Raymonds Ave Bronx NY 10462

DECESARE, VINCENT EDWARD, Math Teacher; *b:* Bridgeport, CT; *m:* Theresa Provenzano; *c:* Michael, Nicholas, Anthony; *ed:* Southern CT St Coll (BS) Intermediate Upper Ed 1972, (MS) Ed 1974; *cr:* Madison MS Tchr 1972-; *ai:* Sr Babe Ruth Bsbl Coach; Boys & Girls HS Bsktbl Ofcl; NEA 1972-; CT Ed Assoc 1972-; Trumbull Ed Assoc 1972-; Monroe

Jaycess 1982-86, VP; Masur HS Booster Club 1993-, Pres; *home:* 43 Old Castle Dr Monroe CT 06468

DECHEINE, PHYLLIS J., 8th Grade Teacher; *b:* Tupper Lake, NY; *ed:* Annhurst Coll (BA) Elem Ed 1968; Fairfield Univ (MA) Private Schl Admin 1985; Ed for GATE, Geometry for Everybody, Hand on Algebra Credit Hrs; *cr:* Our Lady of Grace Schl 8 Grd Tchr 1966-72; St Rita Schl Prin, 8th Grd Tchr 1972-76; Saints Peter & Paul Schl Prin 1976-87; Blessed Sacrament Schl 8th Grd Tchr 1987-; *ai:* Sci Fair Dir; Mathcounts Coach; NCEA 1966-; Church of Epiphany 1988-, Lector; Marin Cty CA Parochial Schl Prins 1972-76, Chprsn; Hartford Diocese Math Comm 1985-92; Amer Cancer Soc; Spec Olympics; Waterbury CT Parochial Schl Prins Chprsn 1984-87; Hartford Diocese Family Life Comm 1978-; *office:* Blessed Sacrament Schl 386 Robinwood Rd Waterbury CT 06708

DECKER, DANIEL EDWARD, Civics & PA History Teacher; *b:* Lock Haven, PA; *m:* M. Elizabeth Pokorney; *c:* Lori, Leslie; *ed:* Lock Haven Univ (BA) Scndry Ed 1975; Univ of PA Ed; *cr:* Nazareth HS Drivers Ed 1975-77; Lock Haven Univ Asst Ftbl Coach 1977-81; Bald Eagle Nittany Ftbl Coach 1987-1993; Jersey Shore Civics, PA Hist Tchr, Coach 1993-; *ai:* Head Var Ftbl Coach; Landscaping Bus Owner, Operator 20 Yrs; PSEA, NEA 1993-; CPCA 1987-, Coach of Yr 1992; PA Jaycees 1980-, Pres, Treas, St Sports Dir, US Ambassador Awd; Outstanding Young Men of Amer 1985; Outstanding Young Amer Educator 1987; Univ of PA Grant 1970; *home:* 121 Cardinal Dr Lock Haven PA 17745

DECKER, DELORES KROUSE, First Grade Teacher; *b:* Mount Union, PA; *m:* Richard M. Decker Jr.; *c:* Gretchen E. Decker-Pierce, R. Michael Decker Jr.; *ed:* Shippensburg Univ (BA) Elem Ed 1970, (MS) Elem Ed 1973; *cr:* Mercersburg Elem Schl 1st Grd Tchr 1970-; *home:* 10847 McFarland Rd Mercersburg PA 17236

DECKER, GEORGE R., English Teacher; *b:* Curwensville, PA; *m:* Diane; *c:* Jennifer, Janessa; *ed:* Clarion St Coll (BS) Eng 1967, (MS) Ed 1994; *cr:* Upper St Clair SD Eng & Rdng Tchr 1967-68; Curwensville Area SD Eng Tchr 1968-; *ai:* Annual Essay Contest; NEA, PSEA 1967-; CAEA 1968-; Curnwensville Lions Club 1986-, Sec & Treas; *office:* Curwensville Area Schl Dist 650 Beech St Curwensville PA 16833

DECKER, JUDY MARSH, Fourth Grade Teacher; *b:* Gorman, TX; *m:* Ronald Charles; *c:* Jennifer, Lisa, Zachary; *ed:* CA St SB (BA) His 1971-; Webster Univ (MS) Mgmt 1976; K-8th Tchng Credentials Univ of Dayton; Post-Grad Stud Geog OH St Univ; *cr:* Wright St Univ Admissions Cnslr 1983-84; St Peter Elem 4th Grd Tchr 1988-; *ai:* Archdiocese of Cincinnati Soc Stud Curr Review Comm Mem 1992-93; Served Southwest OH Soc Stud Acad to Articulate the New OH Model; NCEA 1988-South Whole Lang Support Group 1988-; OH Geographic Alliance 1992-, Tchr Asst; OH Cncl for Soc Stud 1995-; IRA 1995-; St Peter Parish 1977-, Eucharist Minister; Presenter for OH Geographic Alliance; Involved with the St Competition of Natl Geographic Geog Bee Held Annually; Selected Tchr Finalist in the Call to Value Excl Pgm for Cath Schls 1992; Article Pub; *office:* St Peter Schl 6185 Chambersburg Rd Dayton OH 45424

DECKER, MADELINE S., Spanish & French Teacher; *b:* Eagle Lake, ME; *m:* James N.; *c:* Christopher J., Matthew A.; *ed:* Univ of ME (BA) Math 1968, (MA) Fr, Span 1989; UMO Continuing Ed to Renew Cert for Tchng in ME; *cr:* Orono HS Tchr 1967-68; Penquis Vly HS Tchr 1968-; *ai:* Sr Class Adv; Mentor for New Tchrs; FLAME 1995-; NEA, MEA 1968-; Church Lector 1968-; ME Tchr Summit on Learning Results Participant, Local Facilitator; *office:* Penquis Valley HS 35 W Main St Milo ME 04463*

DECKER, MICHAEL GEORGE, Coll Prep Tech Dept Instr; *b:* Buffalo, NY; *m:* Phyllis; *c:* Gregory, Brandy; *ed:* St Coll at Buffalo (BA) Latin & Classics 1971, (BS) Tech Ed 1983; St Univ of NY at Albany (MS) Curr Dev 1987; *cr:* Chevrolet Motors Auto Worker 1978-80; Schenectady HS Tchr 1983-; *ai:* Vlybl & Sftbl Asst Coach; Dept Tchr Ldr; UAW 1980-; AFT 1983-; *office:* Schenectady HS 1401 The Plz Schenectady NY 12308*

DECKER, WALTER STUART, Chemistry Teacher; *b:* Paterson, NJ; *m:* Ann Monzione; *c:* Kristen, Michael; *ed:* Fairleigh Dickinson Univ (BA) Ed & Chem 1969; Montclair St Coll (MA) Ed & Chem 1972; Addl 30 Credits in Admin & Supervision; *cr:* Clifton HS Chem Tchr 1968-; *ai:* Chem Lab Assts Club; NJEA 1968-; *office:* Clifton H S 333 Colfax Ave Clifton NJ 07013

DECKER-LOMBARDI, CAROLE, English & Pub Speaking Teacher; *b:* Newton, KS; *m:* Ralph; *c:* P.J. Lombardi-Frankel, Maximillan Frankel; *ed:* KS Univ at Emporia (BSE) Speech & Eng 1967; Stony Brook Univ (MALS) Eng & Lbrl Stud 1973; St Johns Univ (PD) Supervision & Admin Ed 1989; 30 Credit Hrs Ed Inst of Long Island; CW Post Coll; 12 Credit Hrs Antiques Appraisal Inst; *cr:* Salina Jr High Tchr 1967-68; Commach HS Tchr 1968-69; Kings Park HS Tchr 1969-; *ai:* Prin Cncl Portfolio Comm; Yrbk Adv; Forensics, Speech & Debate Coach; Block Scheduling Comm; Coll Bd Testing Dir; NYSUT 1968-; KPRTA 1968-, Negotiator, VP; NCTE 1969-; Amer Assn of Univ Women; Long Island Scholastic Press Assn, Sec; Rotary, Interact & Amer Legion Certs Of Achvmt & Merit; *office:* Kings Park HS Kohr Rd Kings Park NY 11754*

DECONDO, ANTHONY PAUL, 4th Grade Teacher; *b:* Paterson, NJ; *m:* Camille DeRosa; *c:* Louis, Michael, Anthony; *ed:* Seton Hall Univ (BA) Ed 1962; William Paterson Coll (MA) Admn, Supervision; Montclair St Coll Cert Pupil, Prsnl Svcs 1968; *cr:* Midland Schl Tchr 1962-64; Broadway Schl Elem Tchr, Cnslr 1964-71; Nellie K. Parker Schl Elem Tchr, Cnslr 1971-; *ai:* Archaeology Club Stu Cncl Adv; Homework Assistance Group; NJEA, NEA, BCEA 1962-; Archaeological Soc of NJ 1985-; *home:* 119 E 24th St Paterson NJ 07514*

DECONINCK, MARYBETH SCHNITTKER, Instructor of Marketing & Mgmt; *b:* Independence, MO; *m:* James B; *ed:* Central MO St Univ (BS), (BA) Mgmt 1983, (MBA) Human Resources 1984; *cr:* Western IL Univ Mrktg Instr 1988-89; Cntrl MO St Univ Mgmt Instr 1989-92; Univ of Dayton Mrktg & Mgmt Instr 1993-; *ai:* Delta Sigma Pi Outstanding Tchr of Year 1991-92; *office:* Univ Of Dayton Dept of Mrktg & Mgmt 300 College Park Dayton OH 45469

DECOOK, HAROLD JACOB, Math Teacher & Department Chm; *b:* Clifton Springs, NY; *m:* Jill Breimer; *c:* Timothy, Douglas; *ed:* SUNY at Geneseo (BS) Math Ed 1973; SUNY at Brockport (MS) Ed; Educl Admin; *cr:* Lyons Jr-Sr High Tchr & Dept Chair 1973-; *ai:* Sftbl, Bsbl & Track Coach; Class Adv; Peer Observation Comm; AMNYTS 1973-; NYSVT 1973-; LTA 1973-, VP, Tchr of the Yr 1992; UR Tchr of the Yr 1987, 1996; LTA Tchr of the Yr 1992; *office:* Lyons Jr Sr HS 10 Clyde Rd Lyons NY 14489*

DE CORTE, ANNETTE ACQUAVIVA, Kindergarten Teacher; *b:* Newark, NJ; *m:* Fredrick Sr.; *c:* Fredrick Jr.; *ed:* Kean Coll of NJ (BA) Early Chldhd Ed 1982; *cr:* St James 1st Grd Tchr 1982-88, 3rd Grd Tchr 1992-94, Kndgtn Tchr 1994-; *ai:* NCEA.*

DECOSTA, LINDA MARIE (DONAHUE), Scndry English & Comm Teacher; *b:* Sonlerville, MA; *c:* Joseph, David, Jennifer; *ed:* Salem St Tchrs Coll (BS) Eng 1971; Coursework Univ MA at Lowell 1976, Rivier Coll 1983; *cr:* Pinkerton Acad Scndry Eng, Comm Tchr 1973-; *ai:* Co-Adv Class of 98; Peer Partners, PALS Adv; NASSPA 1992-; NCTE 1980-; NEATE, NHATE 1975-; Baton Boosters-Red Star Twirlers 1987-, Chair Comms; Local, St Spelling Bees 1980-91, Pronouncer, Elks Svc Awd; Finalist 1996 NH Tchr of Yr Prgm; Stu Cncl of Yr 1989; Shepard Fac Awd 1980; *office:* Pinkerton Acad 5a Pinkerton St Derry NH 03038*

DECTER, FRED R., Foreign Language Dept Chairman; *b:* Newark, NJ; *m:* Susan; *c:* Scott, Tracey; *ed:* Montclair SC (BA) Span 1964, (MA) Span 1972; Univ of Madrid 1968-69; *cr:* Hackensack Pub Schls Tchr 32 Yrs; *ai:* Natl Span Honor Soc Spon; Amer Assn Tchrs Span & Portugese 1963; NEA & NJEA 1964-; Bergen Cty EA; Hackensack EA; Shomrei Torah 1979-, Treas 1985-88; *office:* Hackensack HS 1st & Beech St Hackensack NJ 07601

DECUBELLIS, KENNETH, HS Guidance Counselor; *b:* Providence, RI; *m:* Gloria Girard; *c:* Maria, Julie; *ed:* RI Coll (BS) Elem Ed 1966; Providence Coll (MED) Elem Admin 1971, (MED) Guid Cnslng 1976; *cr:* Harris Schl 6th Grd Tchr 1966-77; Woonsocket Elem Schl Guid Cnslr 1977-88; Woonsocket HS Scndry Guid Cnslr 1988-; *ai:* AP Pgm Coord; New England Assns of Schls & Coll Steering FollowUp Comm; RI Real Estate Brokers 1973-; Woonsocket Tenant Bd of Affairs 4 Yrs, Chm; Real Estate Broker 1973-; *office:* Woonsocket HS 777 Cass Ave Woonsocket RI 02895

DEDERICK, WAYNE F., Chemistry Teacher; *b:* Saugerties, NY; *m:* Barbara Flores; *c:* Heather, Mya, Caitlyn; *ed:* SUNY at New Paltz (BS) Bio & Chem 1970; 30 Hrs; *cr:* Red Hook HS Sci 1970-95; *ai:* Stanis; AFT; Amer Chem Soc Tchr of the Yr Mid Hudson; Spcl Tchr Recognition Union Coll; *office:* Red Hook HS W Market St Red Hook NY 12571

DE DOMINICIS, PAULA J., Second Grade Teacher; *b:* Augusta, ME; *m:* Salvatore; *ed:* Gorham St Tchrs (BA) Elem Ed 1965; Univ of Miami Coll (MED) Spec Ed 1971; Addl Hrs Westfield St Coll, Cntrl CT St univ, Univ of Hartford, Eastern CT St Univ Gen Ed 1992; CT Ed Units 1989-94; Natl Wildlife Fed Summits 1994-95; *cr:* Simsbury Bd of Ed 4th Grd Tchr 1965-66, 3rd Grd Tcher 1966-70, Spec Ed Tchr 1971-75, 2nd Grd Tchr 1975-; *ai:* Elem Cncl Chm; Elem Rep Evaluation, Math Curr Dev, Soc Stud Curr Comm; Bd of Ed SEA Rep; Simsbury Ed Assn 1965-, VP, 25 & 30 Yrs Svc Awds; CT Ed Assn, NEA 1965-; St Mary's Church 1989-, Lector; Univ of Miami Flwshp; *office:* Tariffville Elem Schl 42 Winthrop St Tariffville CT 06081

DEDOSZAK, STEVEN JOHN, 5th Grade Teacher; *b:* Buffalo, NY; *m:* Michele Van Cise; *ed:* Genesee Comm Coll (AAS) Criminal Justice 1976; SUC Geneseo (BA) Speech Comms 1983, (BA) Elem Ed 1986, (MS) Elem Ed 1991; *cr:* Dairy Farmer 1986; St Josephs Schl Elem Tchr 4th-7th Grd 1986-88; Letchworth Cntrl 5th Grd Tchr 1988-; *ai:* Boys Var Soccer, Jr High Bsktbl, Girls Var Sftbl coach; NEA 1986-; Fullbright Tchr Exchange Prgm; *home:* 2096 Perry Rd North Java NY 14113

DEDRICK, DAVID LEE,SR., Civics & Geography Teacher; *b:* Cleveland, OH; *m:* Linda Valentino; *c:* David Jr.; *ed:* Mercer Cty Comm Coll (AA) Soc Sci 1968; Trenton St Coll (BA) Soc St 2nd Ed 1970; *cr:* Hammonton HS Drivers Ed, Trng, Soc St Tchr 1970-79; Hammonton MS Civics & Geog Tchr 1979-; *ai:* NEA, NJEA, ACEA, HEA 1970-; Batsto Citizens Comm 1987-, Vice Chprsn; Retired Air Force MSGT NJANG; *office:* Hammonton MS Central Ave & Vine St Hammonton NJ 08037

DEE, CLARE, Art Teacher; *b:* Hempstead, NY; *m:* John Staudenraus; *c:* Caroline; *ed:* SUNY at Stony Brook (BA) Drawing & Printing 1983; Hofstra Univ (MA) Art Ed 1987; MA +30 Credit Hrs; *cr:* Portledge Schl Art Tchr 1987-89; Half Hollow Hills Cntrl Schl Dist Elem Art Tchr 1989-90; Locust Valley Mid & Sr Schl Dist HS Art Tchr 1990-; *ai:* Yrbk Adv; Art Club Adv; Long Island Art Tchrs Assn 1992-; NY St Art Tchrs Assoc 1993-; Western Suffolk Tchrs Assoc Grant; Article Pub; *office:* Locust Valley Jr-Sr HS Horse Hollow Rd Locust Valley NY 11560

DEEGAN, JAMES W., Mathematics Teacher; *b:* Hornell, NY; *m:* Therese Mento; *c:* Mary Roseberry, Daniel, Jennifer Sullivan, Anne Marie; *ed:* St Bonaventure Univ (BS) Math 1961; Syracuse Univ (MS) Math Ed 1965; Attnd Oswego St Coll; *cr:* Cntrl Tech HS Math Tchr 1961-64; Onondaga Comm Coll Adj Math Tchr 1965-; Nottingham HS Math Tchr 1965-; *ai:* Syracuse Tchrs Negotiating Team; Onondaga Cty Math Tchrs Assn, NYSMTA, NCTM, NYSUT, AFT 1965-; Syracuse Tchrs Assn 1961-, Second VP, Outstdng Svc Awd; Christ the King Church 1971-; Outstdng Tchr Awd 1988; *office:* Nottingham HS 3100 E Genesee St Syracuse NY 13224*

DEEGAN, NANCY O'CONNELL, Music Director; *b:* Philadelphia, PA; *m:* Francis William; *c:* Daniel, Kathleen Deegan Dickson, Mary Deegan Haff, Maureen; *ed:* Immaculata Coll (BA) Soc, Music 1963; Post Grad Stud Univ of PA Schl of Soc Work; *cr:* Delaware Cty Juvenile Court Probation Ofcr 1963-64; Nassau Cty Dept of Welfare Caseworker 1965-66; St Christopher Ottilie Home Adoption, Foster Home Caseworker 1967-76; Harbor Village Realty Inc Owner, Broker, Appraiser, Pres 1076-87; St Dominic HS Music Dir 1988-; *ai:* Long Island Singers; HS Musical Dir; MENC, NMEA, Nassau Music Ed Assn, NY St Musical Assn, Amer Choral Dir Assn 1990-; Chrstn Edctr of Yr 1995; *office:* Saint Dominic HS 110 Anstice St Oyster Bay NY 11771

DEELEY, JO-ANNE MARIE, Biology & Chemistry Teacher; *b:* Brockton, MA; *m:* John M.; *c:* Michael, Jay; *ed:* Bridgewater St Coll (BA) Bio 1967; *cr:* Middleboro HS Gen Sci Tchr 1967-68; Enrichment Prgms Inc Sci Tchr 1980-84; Oliver Ames HS Bio Tchr 1985-88; Boston Latin Acad Bio Tchr 1988-89; Arlington Cath HS Bio, Chem Tchr 1991-; *ai:* Multicultural Comm Chm; Fac Dev Comm; NABT; MA Assn Sci Tchrs; NEA; Seton Manor-AIDS Hosp, Hospice 1991-93, Vol; Horace Mann Grant; *office:* Arlington Catholic HS 16 Medford St Arlington MA 02174*

DEEP, ANNORA R., 4th Grade Teacher; *b:* Pittsburgh, PA; *m:* Donald; *c:* Colleen, Kelly Leigh, Don; *ed:* Duquesne Univ (BA) Elem 1964; Post Grad Hrs PA St, Duquesne Univ; *cr:* North Hills Elem 5th, 6th Grd Tchr 1964-67; Ridgewood Jr HS 9th Grd Eng Tchr 1975-79; South Side Elem 4th, 5th Grd Tchr 1980-; *ai:* Wole Lang Trainer, Coord; Authentic Assessment Comm; Total Inclusion Team; NEA, PSEA, SSEA 1980-; Moon Twp Lib Bd 1993-; *office:* Southside Schl Dist 4949 St Rt 151 Hookstown PA 15050

DEERING, LESLIE ELLEN, English Teacher; *b:* Ossinning, NY; *m:* John; *c:* Todd Liebman, Jennifer Liebman; *ed:* City Coll of NY (BA) Eng 1965, (MA) ENg 1970; Montclair St Coll 45 Credit Hrs Rdng Specialist 1981; Rowan Coll Strategies Planned Curr 3 Grad Credits 1994; *cr:* Bergen Cty Vo-Tech HS Rdng Tchr 1979-83; Eastside HS Rdng Tchr 1983-85; Bergenfield Schl System Tchr of Gifted, Talented1985-87; Edgewood Jr HS Eng Tchr 1987-; *ai:* Publish Stu Writing, Cooperative Learning Comms; Coord Shakespearean Street Fair; NEA 1979-; Governor Grant Awd 1992.

DEERING, NANCY ANN, German Teacher; *b:* Niagara Falls, NY; *ed:* SUNY at Albany (BA) Ger 1966; Univ of Rochester (MA) Ger Lang & Lit 1970; Attnd Univ of Wurzburg Germany, Goethe Inst in Munchen, Trier & Warendorf Germany, Fulbright Schlr in Germany, Univ of Scranton & SUNY at Buffalo; *cr:* Niagara Falls HS Ger Tchr 1966; Starpoint Cntrl Schl Ger Tchr 1966-68; West Seneca Schls German & Span Tchr 1969-, Dept Chm 1969-75; *ai:* Ger Club & Ger NHS Adv; Amer Assn of Tchrs of Ger 1966; NYS Assn of Frgn Lang Tchrs 1966-; Western NY Frgn Lang Edctrs Cncl 1970-; NYS United Tchrs; AFT; W Seneca Tchrs Assn; Modern Lang Assn & Amer Cncl on the Tchng Frgn Lang; SUNY at Albany Valedictorian; Lang & Ed Honoraries Mem; Signum Landis Pres; Univ of Rochester & NDEA Flwshp; Goethe Inst & Fulbright Schlshp; West Ger Govt Grant; *office:* West Seneca West Sr HS 3330 Seneca St West Seneca NY 14224

DEETJEN, JOHN H.,SR., Math, Reading Tchr & Ath Dir; *b:* ME; *m:* Carol Comber; *c:* John Jr., William, Bobby; *ed:* Univ of Ed 1972; Addl 30 hrs Beyond BS; *cr:* Boothbay Harbor Grammar Grd Tchr 1972-78; Boothbay Region Elem Schl 7-8 Grd Tchr 1 Ath, IM Dir; Bsktbl, Sftbl, Math Counts Coach; Store Mgr; Glee C Math Comm; MTA, NEA, ME Math Tchrs 1972-; NELMS 1989 Boothbay Region Elem Schl 156B Townsend Ave Boothbay Ha 04538

DEFAZIO, JOHN M., Mathematics Teacher; *b:* Johnstown, PA; of Pittsburgh (BS) Math 1975; St Francis Coll Instrl Cert 1993; Cath Schl Math Tchr 1976-79; Bishop Mc Cort HS Math Tchr 1 Head Bsbl Coach; *home:* 29 Irene St Johnstown PA 15905

DEFAZIO, KIT, Secondary Social Stud Teacher; *b:* Elyria, OH Kathleen; *ed:* Notre Dame Coll (BA) Soc Stud 1967; Kent St U Lib Sci 1995; *cr:* Euclid Bd of Ed Jr High Soc Stud Tchr Willoughby Eastlake Bd of Ed Sr High Soc Stud Tchr 1983-; *ai:* Dept Chair; WETA, NEOEA & OEA 1983-; NEA; *office:* Wi South HS 5000 Shankland Rd Willoughby OH 44094*

DE FELICE, HUGO, Retired Social Studies Tchr; *b:* New Ke PA; *m:* Audrey Tantlinger; *c:* Pamela Sawhook, Deborah M Krantz; *ed:* Clarion St Univ (BS) Geog, Soc Stud 1953; Univ of Soc Sci 12 Credit Hrs; Penn St Univ Drivers Ed 9 Credit Hrs; *cr:* 82nd Airborn Div 1953-55; Pittsburg Plate Glass Co Lab Tech Highlands Schls Tchr, Coach 1959-94; *ai:* Var Ftbl, Track & Fie Cntry Coach; Highlands Educl Assoc, NEA 1959-; Arnold Ch Commerce 1976-; Teleflora Bd of Dir Western PA.

DE FELICE, LINDA, Assoc Prof of Lib Media Svcs; *b:* Philadel *ed:* Shippensburg Univ (BS) Eng & Lib Sci 1973; Rowan Coll (Ed 1980; Drexel Univ Cert of Advanced Stud 1987, Information Post-Grad Credits; *cr:* Highland Regnl HS Librn 1973-81; Xe Mrktg Rep 1981; Pittman HS Media Ctr Dir 1981-82; Gloucester Assoc Prof Lib Media Svcs 1982-; *ai:* Fac Fed Schlsp, SJRLC R & Interlib Loan & NJLA Schlsp Comm; NJ Lib Assn 1983-; NCT GCC Allegro Soc Bd 1992-; SJRLC Reference Guidelines; NJ Lib Pub; NJLA Schlsp Recipient; *office:* Gloucester County Coll 1400 Rd Sewell NJ 08080

DEFENDIS, DAVID WILLIAM, Sixth Grade Teacher; *b:* Roche *c:* Megan E., Christopher; *ed:* Univ of Dayton (BS) Elem Ed 1970 of NY at Brockport (MS) Curr & Dev 1976; *cr:* Andrew Townson Tchr of Gifted & Talented 1970-84; Francis Parker Schl #23 A Prgm Tchr 1984-; *ai:* Jr Math Olympiad, Natl Current Events Leag & Knowledge Master Open Contest; Rochester Tchrs Assn Membership Chm, Svcs Comm Awd; NYSUT, AFT 1970-; NCTM *office:* Francis Parker Schl #23 170 Barrington St Rochester NY

DEFEO, JAMES VINCENT, English Teacher; *b:* Bridgeport, Lucille Menosky; *c:* Marc, Jonathan; *ed:* Univ of Bridgeport (1962, (MS) Scndry Ed 1973; 6th Yr Scndry Ed 1975; Hunter C Degree Eng; *cr:* Stamford HS Tchr 1971-; *ai:* Yrbk, Chrldng Adv Outdoor Asst Coach; Ath Cncl Pres; CSFT 1975-, VP, Grievan *office:* Stamford HS 55 Strawberry Hill Ave Stamford CT 06902

DEFEO, PETER JOHN, Mathematics Teacher; *b:* Philadelphia Jacqueline Rofrano; *ed:* Rutgers Univ At Camden (BA) Math 1990 Coll 6 Grad Credits; *cr:* Paul VI HS Math Tchr 1990-94; Eastern R Math Tchr 1994-; *ai:* Girls Var Soccer Asst Coach; NCTM 199 1994-; *office:* Eastern Regnl HS Laurel Oak Rd Voorhees NJ 080

DEFFNER, JOSEPH JOHN, English Tchr & Guidance C Pittsburgh, PA; *m:* Sarah Olney Martel; *ed:* Univ of Dayton (BS) 1987; Plymouth St Coll 12 Credits Grad Stud Cnslr Ed; Salem St C Ed Grad Stud 6 Hrs; *cr:* Peace Corps ESL Tchr 1987-89; The L Schl Spec Ed Tchr Tutor 1990-91 & 1992-93; South Royalton HS 1993-94; Thetford Acad Eng Tchr & Guidance Cnslr 1991-92 & 1 Cross Country & Girls Bsktbl Coach; Sr Adv; Dartmouth Old Boy Club 1991-; *office:* Thetford Acad PO Box 190 Thetford VT 0507

DEFILIPI, JANICE ANN, English & Reading Teacher; *b:* Spr MA; *m:* Robert; *c:* Susan, Mike; *ed:* Westfield St Coll (BSE) (MA) Ed 1983; 33 Addl Credits; *cr:* Granger Elem Schl Tchr Grd 1972-88; Agawam MS Grd 6 Tchr Eng, Rdng 1988-; *ai:* Acad Team; Summer Inst Team for Schl Reform; Dist Coordinating Imagination Team; Lang Arts Curr Comm; Coord of MS Lit M NEA, AEA 1972-; *office:* Agawam MS 68 Main St Agawam MA

DEFILIPPO, CYDNEY A., Social Studies Teacher; *b:* Washing *m:* Wallace; *c:* Lauren; *ed:* Clarion St Univ (BS) Scndry Ed 197 City St Coll (MA) Cnslng Psych 1996; Stu Prsnl, SAC Eligibility Bayonne Bd of Ed 7-8th Grd Tchr 25 Yrs; *ai:* Yrbk Adv; Resolution Cnslr; Peer Prgm Coord; Lunch Supvr; Mary J. Dono 75th Anniversary Comm; Mentoring Prgm; NJEA 1980-; Bayon Cleaner & Greener 1994-, Schl Rep; St Henry's Rosary Soc 198 Sec; JC Boys & Girls Club 1995-, Ed Dir; NJ Tchr Recognition Prg St Peter's Coll Urban Comm Svc Grant; *office:* Mary J Donohoe E 4 38 E 5th St Bayonne NJ 07002*

DEFILIPPO, DANA H., Coach; *b:* Lowell, MA; *m:* Vincent J.; *c:* *ed:* U MA at Lowell (BA) Hlth Ed 1982; G. R. Lowell Voke (LP 1983; *cr:* G. R. Lowell Voke Schl Sci, Hlth Tchr 13 Yrs; *ai:* V Coach 14 Yrs; Sports Television Commentator, Winter & Spring E R. Lowell Voke; NEA 1983-; Boston Globe Vlybl Coach of Yr 19

DEFILIPPO, DENNIS ANTHONY, Ec & American Government Pittsburgh, PA; *m:* Mary Julia Scanlon; *c:* James, Coleman, Ai Duquesne Univ (BA) Sociology 1973, (MA) Sociology 1976; P Cert 1979; Inst on Amer Ec; Advanced Placement Trng; Rdng, T Writing Across the Curr; *cr:* St Mary of the Mt HS Tchr 1973-82 Heart HS Tchr 1982-89; Oakland Cath HS Tchr, Dept Chair 1990 Class Moderator; Pittsburgh Fed of Diocesan Tchrs 1973-; *office:* Catholic HS 144 N Craig St Pittsburgh PA 15213*

DEFINA, GEORGE A., Fourth Grade Teacher; *b:* New York City Jennifer, Geoffrey; *ed:* SUNY at New Paltz (BS) Elem Ed 1968, 1971; 60 Addl Post-Grad Hrs; *cr:* Onteora Cntrl Schl 5th-6th Grd L Specialist 1989-95, 3rd-6th Grd Tchr 1968-, GATE Coord 1986-; GATE, Dist Shared Decision Making, Portfolio Assessment Onteora Tchrs Assn 1968-, Sec, Pres; AFT, NY St United Tchrs Daily Bread Soup Kitchen 1994-; Parent Tchrs Club 1980-, Pre *home:* 7 Manor Dr Woodstock NY 12498

DE FINA, GERARD LEWIS, 6th Grd Math & Lang Arts Tchr; York City, NY; *ed:* Hofstra Univ (BA) Psych 1961; Queens Coll (M Ed 1965; St Cert Elem Schl, Admin, Supervision 1974; Univ of Gifted Ed; Oxfordshire England Stud Primary, Intermediate Inter *cr:* Plainview Pub Schls 4-5 Grd Tchr 1961-66; Garden City Pub Grd Tchr 1966-69, 4-6 Grd Tchr, Designed Prgm 1969-80, 2-6 G Designed GATE Prgm 1980-85, 6 Grd Common Branch, Math Tch *ai:* Gifted, Talented Comm Prgm Evaluation; Tchrs Assn 1966-, S Rep; Founded, Co-Chm Open Ed Soc 1969-79; *office:* Garden Cit Cherry Valley Ave Garden City South NY 11530*

DEFLORIO, PATRICIA ANN, ESL Teacher; *b:* Lawrence, MA; Ann, Christine; *ed:* Merrimack Coll at Andover (AB) Amer St, Salem St Coll, Univ of MA at Lowell Adolescent Psych ESL Ce Patrick's Schl 3rd Grd Tchr 1968-69; Salem Schl 2nd Grd Tchr 19

ael's Schl 2nd Grd Tchr 1970-72; St Monica's Schl 5th Grd Tchr -84; Greater Law Tech Schl ESL Tchr 1984-; *ai:* Tech Prep ulation Coord; Integration Steering Comm; ESL Curr Dev; AFT -; Gardner Museum 1995-; Natl Geographic 1993-; Newspaper les; Curr Dev; Articulation Agreements; Adult Ed; *office:* Greater ence Technical Sch 57 River Rd Andover MA 01810

LYER, EDWARD W., Criminal Justice Instructor; *b:* Canandaigua, *m:* Margaret Miceli; *c:* Clifford Poehlmann, Julia Poehlmann; *ed:* re St Coll (BS) Criminal Justice 1978; Oswego St Coll 18 Hrs Voc Ed; ntario Co Sheriff Dept Chief of Detectives 28 Yrs; Mid-St Security cy Pres 7 Yrs; Finger Lakes Voc Ctr Instr 5 Yrs; *ai:* Criminal Justice Law Enforcement Explorer Scout Troup 399 Advs; NY St Tchrs Assn ; Amer Post #34 1952-, Commander; *office:* Finger Lakes Area Voc 501 County Road 20 Stanley NY 14561*

ONCE, RICHARD PAUL, Guidance Supervisor; *b:* Jersey City, NJ; aureen Dolan; *c:* Christopher, Paul; *ed:* Seton Univ (Ba) Soc Stud (BS) Sci 1963, (MA) Scndry Cnslng 1966; Addl 15 Hrs ological Cnslng; *cr:* Archbishop Walsh HS Sci Tchr 1963-65; Elroy Schl Sci, Soc Stud Tchr 1965-66; Point Pleasant Borough HS Sci 1966-67, Guid Cnslr 1967-72, Dir Stu Personnel svcs 1972-78, Sci 1978-88, Guid Supvr 1988-; *ai:* Monmouth Univ Women's Ath Staff; NJEA 1965-; OCPGA 1967-, Pres 1973; New Jersey Schl Cnslng , Cnslr of Cty 1992-94; *office:* Point Pleasant Borough HS Laura rt Dr Point Pleasant Bea NJ 08742

RANCISCO, JOHN P., English Teacher; *b:* Derby, CT; *m:* Nancy De Francisco; *c:* Jessica, Jennifer; *ed:* Fairfield Univ (BA) Eng (MA) Scndry Ed 1971; 6th Yr Admin 1977; 15 Credits Toward rate Fordham Univ; *cr:* Derby HS Eng Tchr 1968-; Adult Basic Ed Tchr 1980-92; Sacred Heart Univ Adj Prof Bridge Prgm, Eng Tchr Credit Diploma Prgm Eng Tchr 1992-; *ai:* Var Bsbl Coach; Jr Var oach; Prom Adv; NCTE 1994-; ASCD 1993-; DEA, NEA 1968-; CT es Assn 1990-; Derby Little League 1988-, Bd of Dir; Greater New Diamond Club Area Coach of Yr 1991; Support Tchr BEST Prgm *office:* Derby HS 8 Nutmeg Ave Derby CT 06418

RANCISCO, MICHAEL ANTHONY, Guidance Counselor; *b:* town, NY; *m:* Darlene Suzanne Hill; *ed:* Jamestown Comm Coll (AA) 1974; St Univ of NY at Oneonta (BA) Eng Ed 1976; St Bonaventure (MS) Ed Cnslng 1981; 51 Grad Hrs Advanced Cert Specialization Cnslng 1981; *cr:* Panama Cntrl Schl Eng Tchr 1978-79; Falconer Cntrl Guid Cnslr 1982-85; The Leelanau Schl Homelife Cnslr 1986-87; ord Cntrl Schl Guid Cnslr 1987-88; Jamestown HS Guid Cnslr 1988-; chlsp Chprsn; NEA NY 1978-; Kappa Delta Pi 1981-; *office:* town HS 350 E 2nd St Jamestown NY 14701

ANZO, FRANCES INZANO, Assistant Principal; *b:* New wick, NJ; *ed:* Coll of St Elizabeth (BS) Ed 1967; Seton Hall Univ Ed 1969, (EDS) Admin, Supervision 1984; *cr:* Our Lady of Victories st Grd Tchr 1960-64; Holy Trinity Schl 7th-8th Grd Tchr 1964-68; t Hoover Jr HS 7th-8th Grd Tchr 1968-82; Woodrow Wilson MS Grd Tchr 1982-; *ai:* NEA, NJEA, AMTNJ, ACTM, MCEA, ETEA ASCD 1970-; Natl Honor Soc Kappa Delta Pi 1983-; Comm Woman 37 1969-; *office:* Woodrow Wilson MS 50 Woodrow Wilson Dr NJ 08820

REEST, KEVIN A., Band Director; *b:* Paterson, NJ; *m:* Nancy ield; *c:* Lauren, Melissa, Timothy; *ed:* Trenton St Coll (BA) et, Music Ed 1976; Montclair St Coll (MA) Trumpet, Music Ed *cr:* Clayton HS Band Dir 2 Yrs; Oakland Pub Schl Instrumental Tchr 6 Yrs; Indian Hills HS Band Dir 11 Yrs; *ai:* Pep Band; Jazz ble; Wrestling Coach; NEA, MENC 1976-; Natl Band Assn 1988-; Indian Hills HS 97 Yawpo Ave Oakland NJ 07436

EITAS, ROBERT JOSEPH, Biological Science Teacher; *b:* town British, South America; *c:* Danielle A. Passon, David, l; *ed:* Univ of Scranton (BS) Pre-Med 1968, (MS) Cnslr Ed 1973c; 0 Credit Hrs; *cr:* Scranton Sr HS Sci Tchr 1968; *ai:* Private Martial oach; AFT 1968-; FOE 1986-; Natl Fnd Grant; Univ of Scranton ential Schlsp; Mainstreaming Stdnts Awds; *office:* West Scranton HS uzerne St Scranton PA 18504

N, DAVID MICHAEL, Baking & Pastry Arts Teacher; *b:* Quincey, : Maryellen Martin; *c:* Lisa McKay; *ed:* Cape Cod Comm Coll (AS) & Restaurant Mgmt 1980; Working on Bachelors at Fitchburg St Certified in Sanitation at NIFI 1980; Cert of Attainment at Henry O ly in Culinary Arts 1978; *cr:* Henry O Peabody Schl Sub Tchr 2; Massasoit Comm Coll Night Schl Baking Instr 1984; astern Regnl Voc Tech HS Baking & Pastry Arts Instr 1985-; *ai:* MA Mgmt Team 1988-, Skills Events Asst Dir 1994-; Southeastern VICA 87-; Epicurean Club of Boston 1989-; Amer Culinary Fed 1989-, Medal; Natl Retail Bakers Assn, MA Retail Bakers Assn 1992-; MA Tchrs 1985-; 2nd Place Awds Boston Culinary Salon 1978, 1979, Outstanding Decorating in Pastry CT Hotel Show 1978; Outstanding al Design in Pastry Boston Hotel Show 1980; Natl VICA Baking Chair 1990; *office:* Southeastern Reg Voc Tech Sch 250 Foundry St Easton MA 02375

NESTE, LESLIE C., Science Teacher; *b:* Newark, NJ; *c:* Kyhara; trl St Univ (BS) Psych, Ed 1967; Kean Coll Post Grad Stud onal Child 15 Credits; *cr:* James Madison Elem Schl 2-3 Grd Tchr 9, 4th Grd Tchr 1980-82, 6th Grd Tchr 1983-85; Woodrow Wilson , Soc St Tchr 1986, Sci Tchr 1987-; *ai:* Art, You Clb Adv; Odysee d Judge; NEA, NJEA, MCEA 1967-; NJST 1989-; No Edison Svc 975-90; Governor's Tchr of Yr Awd 1992-93; *office:* Woodrow MS Woodrow Wilson Dr #50 Edison NJ 08820*

NHARDT, ANNE PALMER, Kindergarten Teacher; *b:* Batavia, Frederick; *c:* Meredith Kelly; *ed:* Daemen Coll (BS) Elem Ed 1970; ort St Coll, Canisus Coll Post Grad Work; *cr:* Jackson Schl 1-2nd r 1970-75, Resource Rm Tchr 1976-78, Pre-1st Grd Tchr 1979-81; Morris Schl 1st Grd Tchr 1982-86, Kndgtn Tchr 1987-; *ai:* de Inclusion Comm; Parent Group Comm Tchr, Rep for Parent s; City-Wide Comm Redoing Kndgtn Report Cards; ny St Tchrs Batavia Tchrs Assn, AFT, NEA 1970-; YMCA 1983-, Bd Mem; al Womenas Bd, Pres; Crop Walk for Hunger Tchrs Group Org; Nursery Schl Annual Speaker; Tchr Selected First Inculsion Tchr for rticles Pub; *home:* 5213 E Main Batavia NY 14020

NNARO, ALFRED JOSEPH, Math & Computer Science Tchr; *b:* nd, OH; *m:* Sarah Louise Barker; *c:* Alfred Isaac Andrew, Daniel rittany Rose; *ed:* Cleveland St Univ (BA) Math, Philosophy 1981, Math 1986, (MS) Cmptr Information Sci 1987; Workings Towards min Doctorate; *cr:* Cleveland Heights HS Math, Cmptr Sci Tchr Cleveland St Univ Math, Cmptr Lecturer 1986-; *ai:* Cmptr Club H Aerospace Inst Intern 3 Yrs; NASA Lewis Rsrch Ctr Cmptr st; Shuttle Mission Ground Rsrch Team; *office:* Cleveland Heights 53 Cedar Rd Cleveland Heights OH 44118*

NNARO, DOROTHY JACOBSON, Jr HS Language Arts Teacher; ken, NJ; *m:* Vito J.; *c:* Sasha, Heather; *ed:* St Peters Coll (BA) -Magna Cum Laude 1984; *cr:* St Peters Coll Ed Dept Part-time 84; Lacordaire Acad Jr HS Lang Arts Tchr 1988-; *ai:* Grad Memory oderator; NJCEA 1988-; Mayors Comm Against Alcohol & Drug 993-; Parents Supporting Parents 1993-, Chair; *home:* 207 Forest n Ridge NJ 07028

DEGENNARO, RAYMOND PETER, High School Mathematics Tchr; *b:* New Haven, CT; *m:* Cheryl Anne Grappi; *c:* Timothy, Caitlin Rose; *ed:* Fairfield Univ (BS) Math 1972, (MA) Ed 1976, (CAS) Ed 1988; *cr:* Stamford HS Math & Career Assessment Prgm Tchr 1972-76; Westhill HS Math Tchr 1976-; *ai:* Bowling Club & Key Club Adv; Math Reevaluation Comm Chprsn; Schl Dev Comm Sec; Discipline & Attendance Comm Facilitator; SEA, CEA, NEA 1972-; *office:* Westhill HS 125 Roxbury Rd Stamford CT 06902*

DEGENNARO, STEVEN DAVID, Physical Education & Hlth Tchr; *b:* Brooklyn, NY; *m:* Anita Batson; *c:* Steven M.; *ed:* St Univ of NY at Buffalo (BS) PE 1978; NY Univ (MA) Ed for Handicapped 1981; 30 Credits Above Masters at Kingsborough Comm Coll 1981-84; *cr:* Pub Schl 371 PE Tchr & Tchr Coord 1979-86; Lafayette HS PE & Hlth Tchr 1986-, PE Dept Coord 1988-90, Var Ftbl Asst Coach & Jr Var Ftbl Head Coach 1987-92; *ai:* Boys Var Vlybl Coach 1987-; Project LIRA Adv; Multicultural Comm; NFICA 1987-; AFT, UFT, NYSUT 1979-; Amer Red Cross 1987-, Cardiac Pulmonary Resuscitation & First Aid Instr; Cncl for Unity 1992-, Lafayette Adv, Inductee 1992; Kids for Life US of Amer 1993-, Lafayette Adv, Honoree 1995; NY Heart Assn Awd for Excl 1982-83; NYC Cert of Appreciation Mayors Awd 1994; Kids for Life US of. Amer Cert of Appreciation 1994; Honored in UFT Newspaper & The Crusaders Television News Magazine for Work With Children 1994; *office:* Lafayette HS 2630 Benson Ave Brooklyn NY 11214

DEGENNARO, VIRGINIA WOLFE, 6th Grd Language Arts Teacher; *b:* Scranton, PA; *w:* Stephan (dec); *c:* Stephan, Timothy; *ed:* Western CT St Univ (BS) Elem Ed 1974; *cr:* Assumption Schl Tchr 1989-; *ai:* Yrbk Adv; NCEA 1989-.

DEGHETT, VICTOR JOHN, Professor of Psychology; *b:* New York City, NY; *m:* Stephanie Coyne; *c:* Torie Rose; *ed:* Univ of Dayton (BA) Psych 1964, (MA) Psych 1966; Bowling Green St (PHD) Animal Behavior 1972; *cr:* St Univ of NY Instr 1971-72, Asst Prof 1972-77, Assoc Prof 1977-86, Full Prof 1986-; *ai:* Animal Behavior Soc 1966-, Editorial Bd, Chair Ed Comm; Amer Soc of Mamalogists 1968-; Chancellors Awd Excl Tchng 1982; Books, Articles, Papers; *office:* St Univ of NY Potsdam NY 13676

DE GIAU, BETTE J., High School Counselor; *b:* Paterson, NJ; *m:* Peter D.; *c:* Heather, Melissa, Aimee; *ed:* William Paterson Coll (BA) Elem Ed 1972, (MED) Cnslng 1996; 12 Hrs Spec Ed 1972-73; *cr:* Bogota Bd of Ed Grd 4 & 6 Tchr 3 Yrs; Clifton Bd of Ed MS BSI Tchr 3 Yrs, Alternative Ed Prmg 7 Yrs, HS Cnslr; *ai:* Head Chrldng Coach 1990-95; NEA, NJEA, Clifton Tchrs Assn 1986-; Amer Cnslng Assn 1995-; Passaic Cty Unity 2000 Grant; Master's Thesis Pub Educa Resource Info Ctr Univ of NC; Pi Lambda Theta; Kappa Delta Pi; *home:* 31 Piaget Ave Clifton NJ 07011

DEGIORGIS, JACQUELINE MAILHOT, Biology Teacher; *b:* Huntington Station, NY; *m:* Ernest F.; *c:* Travis, Jason, Samantha Therrien; *ed:* U MA at AMherst (BS) Bio 1985; Westfield St Scndry Ed 1993; Enrolled Master's Prgm North Adams St Coll; *cr:* Silvio O. Conte MS 8th Grd Sci Tchr 1993-94; Drury HS Bio Tchr 1994-; *ai:* Mural Comm Adv; MTA 1988-; NATA 1993-.

DEGON, NANCY MCGOWAN, High School Chemistry Teacher; *b:* Danbury, CT; *m:* David R.; *c:* Brenda Jean, Brian David; *ed:* Clark Univ (BA) Math 1970; Worcester Polytechnic Inst (MNS) Sci 1984; Attnd Univ of CT, Univ of Hartford, Boston Univ, Framingham St Coll, Worcester St Coll 31 Credit Hrs Scis; *cr:* Worcester Pub Schls Math Tchr 1976-82; Auburn Jr HS Math Tchr 1982-85; Auburn HS Chem Tchr 1985-; MA Acad of Math & Sci Chem Tchr 1992-93; *ai:* Sci Fair Coord 1987-; Stdnts for Environment 1995-; MA Tchrs Assn 1976-; NEA 1976-; Auburn Ed Assn 1982-; NSTA 1985-; Worcester Regnl Sci & Engrng Fair 1990-, Sec; Horace Mann Grant 1987; Alliance for Ed Grant 1991; *office:* Auburn HS 99 Auburn St Auburn MA 01501

DEGRABA, MICHAEL JOSEPH, Mathematics Teacher; *b:* Takoma Park, MD; *m:* Gina Marie Lehman; *c:* Logan, Zachary, Olivia; *ed:* Univ of MD (BS) Math Ed 1975; Montgomery Cty Pub Schls (MEq) Ed 1985; *cr:* Belt Jr HS Math, Drama Tchr 1975-83; Parkland Jr HS Math, Cmptr Programming Tchr 1983-86; John F. Kennedy HS Math, Drama Tchr 1986-94; Damascus HS Math Tchr 1994-; *ai:* Forensics Speech Team Spon; Stage Dir; Stage Crew Spon; Drama Dir Kennedy HS; Night Schl Tchr Einstein HS; *office:* Damascus HS 25921 Ridge Rd Damascus MD 20872

DEGRANDIS, RONALD WAYNE, Instrumental Music Teacher; *b:* Drexel Hill, PA; *ed:* Temple Univ (BMEd) Viola Performance 1973; West Chester Univ (MMEd) Music Ed, Viola 1978; 9 Addl Hrs Jazz Improv, Cmptr Music, String Pedagogy; Vandercook Coll Jazz Improv, Elect Music; Villanova Univ 40 Addl Hrs Sequencing, Jazz Arranging, Cintemp Band Dir, Instrumental Pedagogy, Tchng Improv; *cr:* Great Vly HS 9-12 Grd Instrumental Music Tchr 1973-74; Tower Hill Schl 5-12 Grd Instrumental Music Tchr, Coord 1974-79; Schl Music Svc 3-8 Grd Inst Music Tchr 1979-80; Shawnee Intermediate Schl 8-9 Grd Band, Orch, Jazz Dir 1980-; *ai:* Band, Orch, Jazz Band, Pit Orch, Strolling Strings, Jazz Improvisation, Percussion, Music Theory, Instrumental Music Lessons; NEA, PSEA, EAEA 1980-; MENC, PMEA 1973-; AFM Local 561 1980-; Allentown Symphony 1980-, Prin Violist; St Thomas Moore Folk Group 1986-95, Guitarist; Tri-Cty Orch Conductor 1989-; Amer Yth Chamber Orch 1974, 1979, Asst Conductor; Chansonette Musical Theater 1993, 1995, Musical Dir; *office:* Shawnee Intermediate Schl 1010 Echo Trl Easton PA 18040

DEGREGORIO, DAVID JON, Health & Physical Ed Teacher; *b:* Willamantic, CT; *m:* Amy; *ed:* Univ of Pittsburgh (BA) Hlth, PE & Recreation 1987; James Madison Univ 9 Credit Hrs; *ai:* Var Bsktbl Coach.

DEGRENDELE, JULIA WALTON, Prof of Reading & Study Skills; *b:* Abington, PA; *m:* Arthur Edward; *c:* Dawn DeGrendele Harris, Arthur William; *ed:* Lehigh Univ at Bethlehem (MED) Rdng 1967; Temple Univ at Phila (MED) Cnslng Ed 1976; Western IL Univ Stu Tchr Supervision; *cr:* Quakertown Comm Schl Dist Rdng Specialist 1966-69; Palisades Schl Dist dir of Vols for Delayed 2nd Grd Readers 1970-71; Montgomery Cty Comm Coll Adult Ed, ESL, LD, Children's Lit, Study Skills Tchr 1969-; *ai:* Founded, Spon MCCC Meridians 1969-94; Dev Stud Comm; Advy Comm for Title III; Advy Bd for New Choices; AFT, PAAFT, MCCC-AFT 1983-; IRA 1969-; PA Assoc of Dev Edctrs 1985-; Delta Kappa Gamma 1985-, 1st VP, Pres; Grand View Hosp Hospice 1995-, Vol; Chapel of Four Chaplains Legion of Hnr Awd; France E. Bowers Awd; Meridians Mug Awd for Svc to Older Stdnts; Alumni Fac Awd; Contributor to Master Plots II for Young Adults; Who's Who in Amer Ed; *office:* Montgomery County Comm Coll 340 Dekalb Pike Blue Bell PA 19422

DEGUZMAN, PATRICIA WHOLIHAN, Lang Arts & Humanities Teacher; *b:* Carlisle, PA; *m:* N. Enrique; *c:* Cristina, Katalina, Miguel; *ed:* Barnard Coll (BA) Eng 1970; Framingham Coll-U of MA (MA) Rdng & Lang 1988; Boston Writing Project; Natl Endowment for Hum; U MA Lowell; *cr:* Asociasim Escuelas Lincoln Tchr 1971-72; Tarrytown Pub Schl Tchr 1972-73; Natuck HS Tchr 1973-; Weaver Clinic Therapeutic Tutor 1990-; *ai:* Eng as a Second Lang HS Coord; Accredit Comm; Eng Curr Revision; Writing Project; NEA 1975-; Natl Assn Eng; Natl Endowment for Hum Awd; *office:* Natick HS 15 West St Natick MA 01760

DEHNBOSTEL, NANCY L., 4th-5th Grd Gifted Stdnts Tchr; *b:* Indianapolis, IN; *ed:* Ball St Univ (BS) Ed 1966; Xavier Univ (MSEd) Elem Ed; 30 Addl Semester Hrs Gited Ed from Univ of Cincinnati, Wright St Univ; *cr:* Marion Comm Schls 2-3 Grd Tchr 1966-69; Nowrthwest Local Schls 3 Grd Tchr 1969-80, 4-6 Grd Tchr of Gifted 1980-; *ai:* NEA, OEA, Northwest Assn Edctrs 1969-; OH Assn for Gifted Children 1980-, Dist Rep, Cert of Merit, Cert of Achvmt; OH Vly Assn for GATE 1980-, Trustee; Delta Kappa Gamma 1982-; Christ Luth Church 1980-, Bd of Chrstn Ed; Numerous Articles Pub; *office:* Pleasant Run Elem Schl 11765 Hamilton Ave Cincinnati OH 45231

DEI, KOJO A., Assistant Professor; *b:* Kyebi, Ghana; *m:* Beatrice Earle-Dei; *ed:* Philipps Univ (MA) Ethnology 1975; Columbia Univ (MPhil) Anthropology 1994, Tchrs Coll (PHD) Anthropology, Ed 1996; *cr:* Narcotic, Drug Rsrch Inc Predoctoral Fellow 1986-90; John Jay Coll of Criminal Justice Instr 1991-95, Asst Prof 1996-; *ai:* Drug, Alcohol Abuse Cnslr for Neighborhood Yth in Mount Vernon; PSC 1991-; Acad for Hum, Sci 1992-; Amer Anthropological Assn 1988-; Rsrch Initiative Awd 1993; Rsrch Awd 1994, 1995; SSRC Dissertation Flwshp 1990; *office:* City Univ Of NY John Jay Coll 445 W 59th St Ofc New York NY 10019*

DEICHLER, JAMES K., Math Teacher; *b:* Pittsburgh, PA; *m:* Karen Weber; *c:* Kimberly, Jason, Kristin, Karl; *ed:* Univ of Pittsburgh, California Univ of PA Grad Stud; *cr:* South Fayette HS Math Tchr 1971-; Comm Coll of Allegheny Cty Math Adj Prof 1974-; Univ of Pittsburgh Math Adj Prof 1981-87; *ai:* NHS Spon; NCTM 1990-; PSEA, NEA, SFEA 1971-; *office:* South Fayette HS 2254 Old Oakdale Rd Mc Donald PA 15057

DEIGHAN, MARY ELLEN DUGAN, Assoc Professor; *b:* Albany, NY; *m:* Gerard Donovan; *c:* Caitlin Dugan; *ed:* Coll of St Rose (BA) Sociology 1969; SU Schl of Soc Work (MSW) Soc Work 1971; PhD Soc Work SUNY @ Albany; *cr:* SUNYA Schl of Soc Welfare Foster Care Unit Coord 1978-80; NY ST Dept Soc Svc Child Welfare Specialist IV 1980-82; Various Orgs including NY Dept of Soc Svc Consultant 1982-88; Hudson Valley Comm Coll Assoc Prof 1985-; *ai:* Human Svc Club Adv; Trainer for Renn Co DSS through HVCC; Stu Adv; Acad Sen; Stu Life Comm; Natl Assoc of Soc Workers 1971-; Acad of Certified Soc Workers 1973-; NYS Certified Soc Workers 1971-; Safe at Home Initiative 1994-, Domestic Violence Coalition; HVCC Rep on Rubin Comm Fellows Prgm; PTA 1989-94; Rubin Comm Fellowship Recipient 1991-93; Past Recipient of Excl in Tchng Awd; Past Publication Towards Collaboration of Foster Care Author 1980; Author of Other Publications; *office:* Hudson Valley Community Coll Human Svc Dept 80 Vandenburgh Ave Troy NY 12180

DEITCHMAN, JEFFREY ALAN, English Teacher; *b:* Baltimore, MD; *ed:* Univ of MD (BA) Eng Ed 1971; Stud in Neurolocical Bases of Learning Disabilities, Freedom & Ed, Multicultural Ed, Supervisiing Stdnt Tchr; Assoc Discipline, Mainstreaming Stdnts with Spec Needs, Succeeding with Difficult Stdnts, Peer Mediation; *cr:* Sherwoow HS Eng Tchr 1992-; *ai:* Lit Magazine, Philosophy Club, Creative Writing Club Spons; Peer Mediation Adv; Discipline Comm; MCEA 1993-; NHS Awd; Article Pub; WA Post Poetry Awd; *office:* Sherwood HS 300 Olney Sandy Spring Rd Sandy Spring MD 20860

DEITZ, ALLAN, High School Band Director; *b:* Catskill, NY; *m:* Carol Brandifino; *c:* Philip, Robert; *ed:* Hartwick Coll (BS) Music Ed 1975; LIU CW Post (MS) Music Ed 1986; *cr:* Half Hollow Hills CSD Sub Music Tchr 1978-80; Amityville Pub Schls Orch Tchr 1980-86, HS Band Dir 1986-; *ai:* NY St Schl Music Assn Cert Adjudicator in Brass & Piano; Suffolk Cty Music Ed Assn, Exec VP for Festivals; Amityville Tchrs Assn Bldg VP; NEA; NYSUT; MENC, NYSSMA 1980-; SCMEA 1980-; NY St Band Dir Assn; *office:* Amityville Memorial HS Merrick Rd Amityville NY 11701

DEITZ, KAREN LAFENE, First Grade Teacher; *b:* Sandusky, OH; *m:* Robert William; *c:* Matthew William; *ed:* Bowling Green St Univ (BS) Elem Ed 1973; Exemplary Ctr Rdng Instruction Rdng Techniques Trng; *cr:* Monroeville Schl First Grd Tchr 1968-; *ai:* MTA, OEA, NEA 1968-; Althea Chptr OES 1970-; Wkshp Consultant; Nom Tchr of Yr Awd; Martha Holden Jennings Fnd Awd 1976-77; *home:* PO Box 2321 3216 Stonewood Dr Sandusky OH 44871

DE JESUS, CHRISTOPHER, Bilingual Mathematics Teacher; *b:* New York, NY; *c:* Inez, Evita; *ed:* Rider Coll (BA) Scndry Ed, Math 1984; MA Candidate Educl Admin at Rider Univ; *cr:* Grace A. Dunn Jr HS Math Tchr, Gifted & Talented 1983-90; Trenton St Coll Math Instr 1989-; Trenton Cntrl HS Bilingual Math Tchr 1990-; *ai:* Sftbl Coach; Trenton Ed Assn, NJ Ed Assn, NEA 1983-; ASCD 1992-; Ike Grant Awd 1990; Cert Awd Outstanding Accomplishment & Excl Math Trenton Pub Schls 1990; Cert of Appreciation Comm Watch Prgm 1992; EOF Pgm Recognition Awd to Trenton St Coll; *home:* PO Box 1219 Levittown PA 19058*

DE JONCKHEERE, MARCEL,S.C. Sixth Grade Teacher; *b:* Detroit, MI; *ed:* Coll of Mt St Joseph (BS) Dietetics 1965; MI St Univ (MS) Inst Admin 1968; *cr:* St Vincent Hosp Chief Dietitian 1968-72; Coll of Mt St Joseph Assoc Prof 1972-76; Sisters of Charity Dir of Affiliates 1976-81; St Dominic Schl Tchr 1981-; *ai:* Just Say No Club Adv; Environmental High IQ Bowl Coach; Sci Dept Chprsn; Sci Ed Cnlc of OH & NSTA 1993-;d Sci Alliance 1988-; Boys Hope 1992-, Vol; Ronald McDonald House 1994-, Vol; Cincinnati Zoo Vol 1988-; Curr Writer; Greater Cincinnati Fnd Scripps Howard Grant Winner; *office:* Saint Dominic Schl 371 Pedretti Cincinnati OH 45238

DEJOSEPH, ALBERT,III, Soc Stud Tchr of Gfted & Tlntd; *b:* Philadelphia, PA; *ed:* Glassboro St Coll (BA) His 1982; Post-Grad Soviet His 3 Credits; *cr:* West Deptford Sr HS Tchr 1988-91; Edgewood Sr HS Tchr 1991-; *ai:* AVA Club, Gifted & Talented Club Adv; Stu of Month Comm; NJEA 91-, Mem.

DEJOY, MARIA CHRISTINE, Secondary Social Studies Tchr; *b:* Jamestown, NY; *ed:* Jamestown Comm Coll (AAS) Bus Admin 1981; SUNY Coll at Fredonia (BA) Sec Soc Stud 1991; MS Scndry Soc Stud SUNY Coll at Buffalo; *cr:* Montgomery Wards Inc Area Presentation Mgr 1984-87, Asst Buyer 1987-88; Jamestown HS Sec Soc Stud Tchr 1994-; *ai:* Co-Adv Class of 1999; Ninth Grd Task Force, Comm Chada Koin River Project Class of 1999 Comms; NEA, JTA 1994-; *office:* Jamestown HS 350 E 2nd St Jamestown NY 14701*

DEJOY, NANCY C., Asst Prof of Eng & Prgms Dir; *b:* Rochester, NY; *m:* Timothy C. Lord; *ed:* Nazareth Coll of Rochester (BA) Eng 1987; Purdue Univ (MA) Eng 1989, (PHD) Eng 1993; *cr:* Nazareth Coll of Rochester Asst Prof 1993-, Summer Seminar Rhetoric & Composition Dir 1994-, Writing Prgms Dir 1995-; *ai:* Eng Hnr Soc, Women's Rape Awareness Prgm Fac Adv; Writing Across Curr, Elections Comms Chair; Women's Stud Comm; Modern Lang Assn, NCTE 1989-; Coll Eng Assn 1993-; Numerous Fac Grants; Articles Pub; Reviewer of Numerous Books; Bibliographer for Coll Composition & Comm Bibliography; Schl of Criticism & Theory Fellow; *office:* Nazareth Coll Of Rochester 4245 East Ave Rochester NY 14618

DEJULIO, PATRICIA DIAMOND, Intermediate & Jr HS Sci Tchr; *b:* Pittsburgh, PA; *m:* Leslie Frank; *c:* Michaelangelo, Dominic; *ed:* Univ of Pittsburgh (BS) Elem Ed 1978; PA Permanent Cert Allegheny Intermediate Unit Credits, Carlow Coll; *cr:* Saint Stephen Schl Intermediate Sci Tchr 1979-; Diocesan Summer Space Experience Instr, Ed 1992-; *ai:* Stu Assistance Prgm Coord; Diocesan Summer Space Experience Steering Comm; Diocesan Sci Curr Comm; Mid Sts Cert Chprsn; Schl Assembly Prgms Coord; NCEA 1979-; Pi Lambda Theta 1978-; Parent Tchr Guild 1979-; Concerned Parents Group 1993-; Spectroscopy Soc of Pittsburgh Elem Sci Tchr of Yr 1993; *home:* 311 Winston St Pittsburgh PA 15207

DEKALB, FRANCIS L.,III, Health & Physical Ed Teacher; *b:* Lowell, MA; *m:* Kathleen Wright; *ed:* Niagara Univ (BS) PE 1974, (MS) Ed 1979;

cr: Port Arthur Ind Schls Hlth & PE Tchr 1980-85; West Canada Vly Cntrl Hlth & PE Tchr 1985-; *ai:* Ftbl Coach & Frosh Class Adv; NYSUT 1985-; WCVTA 1985-; Elks 1988-; *office:* West Canada Valley Schl PO Box 360 Newport NY 13416

DE KALB, KATHLEEN WRIGHT, Business Education Teacher; *b:* Niagara Falls, NY; *m:* Francis L. III; *c:* Kari, Francis, Daniel; *ed:* Niagara Cty Comm Coll(AAS) Secretarial Sci 1975; Lamar Univ (BBA) Bus Admin 1986; St Univ of NY at Albany (MS) Curr Dev Instructional Tech 1991; *cr:* Port Arthur Indep Schls Sec, Sub Tchr 1980-85; Mayfield Jr Sr HS Bus Ed Tchr 1986-91; Fort Plain HS Bus Ed Tchr 1991-; *ai:* FBLA, Schl Store Adv; NYSUT 1986-; Fort Plain TA 1991-; Bus Tchrs of NYS, NBEA 1987-; BMEA 1993-; *office:* Fort Plain Central Schl 1 West St Fort Plain NY 13339*

DEKOFF, ROBERT S., Tech Ed Teacher & Dept Head; *b:* New York, NY; *m:* Myrna Davids; *c:* Sherri; *ed:* NY Univ (BS) Ed 1967, (MA) Ed 1971; Queens Coll Diplomate Ed Admin 1974; *cr:* NY City Schls MS Indust Arts Tchr 1967-69; Great Neck South HS Tech Ed Tchr 1969-, Tech Ed Dept Head 1981-, Dean of Spcl Pgms 1984-; *ai:* Tech Ed Club & Vista Yrbk Adv; AFT 1970-; Comprehensive Ed Assn 1995-; *office:* Great Neck South HS 341 Lakeville Rd Great Neck NY 11020*

DE LAAT, JACQUELINE, Assoc Prof of Political Sci; *b:* Chicago, IL; *m:* R. Michael Smith; *c:* Meghan Dilley, Michelle Smith; *ed:* Univ of IA (BA) Pol Sci 1965; Univ of MN (MA) Pol Sci 1967; Univ of Pittsburgh (PHD) Pub Admin 1982; *cr:* US Information Agency Mngmt Trng, Research 1968-71; Day Care & Child Dev Agency Admin, Lobbyist 1971-72; WA Youth Seminars Dir 1973-76; Waynesburg Coll Prof, Pub Admin 1979-82; Bethany Coll Prof of Pub Policy 1982-88; Marietta Coll Prof of Pol Sci & Leadership 1988-; *ai:* Young Democrats; Honors House Adv; Pol Internships Coord; Amer Soc for Pub Admin; Southern Pol Sci Assn; Midwest Pol Sci Assoc; Girl Scout Ldr 1987-; Luth Church; Articles Pub; Phi Beta Kappa; *office:* Marietta Coll Marietta OH 45750

DELAHUNTY, GEORGE, Prof of Biological Sciences; *b:* Darby, PA; *m:* Katherine Henneberger; *ed:* Duquesne Univ (BS) Bio 1974; Marquette Univ (PHD) Physiology, Endocrinology 1979; Guest Worker Diabetes Branch, NIDDK, NIH 1985-86; *cr:* Johns Hopkins Med Schl Visiting Assoc Prof 1992-93; Goucher Coll Asst Prof 1979-85, Assoc Prof 1985-91, Prof 1992-; *ai:* Pre-Med Adv Undergraduate Prgm; Acad Adv Post Bac Pre-Med Prgm; Co-Dir Howard Hughes Undergraduate Biological Sci Initiative Awd; AAAS 1979-; Endocrine Soc 1985-; Amer Soc Zoologists 1977-; Numerous Articles Pub; 2 Awds NSF, ILI Prgm; NIH-AREA Prgm Grant; NRSA, NICHD, NIH; Sci Grant; *office:* Goucher Coll 1021 Dulaney Vly Rd Baltimore MD 21204

DELAMER, PATRICIA ANN, English Instructor; *b:* New York, NY; *m:* John; *c:* Kevin, Brian, Michael; *ed:* Univ of Dayton (BA) Eng 1994; Working on MA, Eng-Composition & Rhetoric; *cr:* Univ of Dayton Eng Instr, Second Yr Tchng Asst 2 Yrs; *ai:* Signa Tau Delta 1993-; Golden Key Nat H S 1994-; Archbishop Alter Ed Comm 1994-, Comm Mem; US Naval Acad Parents Club 1986-, Pres; Composition Comm; Fac, Stu Dialogue Comm Appreciation Awd for Excl in Tchng 1994; *office:* Univ Of Dayton 300 College Park Ave Dayton OH 45469

DELANCEY, DONALD E., 7th Grade Social Studies Tchr; *b:* York, PA; *m:* Ann Majorie Lebo; *c:* Richard, Catherine; *ed:* Salem Coll (BA) Scndry Soc Stud 1970; *cr:* Dallastown MS Soc Stud Tchr 26 Yrs; *ai:* NEA; Penn St Ed Assn; *office:* Dallastown Area MS 700 New School Ln Dallastown PA 17313*

DELANCEY, MICHAEL P., Social Studies Teacher; *b:* Miami Beach, FL; *m:* Darlene A. Mitchell; *c:* Erin, Regan; *ed:* Franklin & Marshall Coll (BA) His 1977; St Univ of NY at Albany (MS) Curr & Instruction 1988; *cr:* St Marys Schl Tchr 1978-79; CBA at Albany Tchr 1979-85; Middleburg HS Tchr 1985-87; Saratoga Springs Sr High Tchr 1988-; *ai:* Ftbl, Wrestling & LaCrosse Coach; *office:* Saratoga Spgs Sr HS 186 West Ave Saratoga Springs NY 12866

DELANEY, HELEN ELIZABETH, Sixth Grade Science Teacher; *b:* Auburn, NY; *ed:* Auburn Comm (AA) Lbrl Arts 1971; Nazareth Coll (BA) Sociology, Elem Ed 1972; Elmira Coll (MS) N-8 Ed 1976; Addl Post Grad Local His Stud Long Island Univ; *cr:* Holy Family Elem Schl 6th-8th Grd Tchr 1966-71; Saint Mary's Elem Schl 7th-8th Grd Sci, Math Tchr 1972-82; Cayuga Cty Soc Svc Case Worker, Child Protective 1983; Union Springs Cntrl Schl 4th, 6th Grd Sci Tchr 1984-; *ai:* Stu Govt Co-Adv; United Way, Cancer Soc Rep; NYSUT 1984-; Union Springs Tchrs Assn 1984-, VP; Liturgy Comm Holy Family Church; Co-Chprsn Drug Task Force Fun Fair; *home:* RR 5 Auburn NY 13021

DELANEY, JACQUELINE HARMS, Kindergarten & Spanish Teacher; *b:* Pittsburgh, PA; *m:* Timothy; *c:* Brendan, Katy; *ed:* Clarion (BS) Elem Ed 1973; Univ of Pittsburgh Prin Ldrshp Class; *cr:* St Joseph Schl 6-7-8 Grds Lang Arts Tchr 1974-78; St Anthony Schl PE Tchr 1979-81; St Ann Schl 3rd Grd Tchr 1982-89; Holy Spirit Schl Kndgtn, Span Upper Tchr 1989-; *ai:* Frosh Chrldng Moderator; Handbook Comm; Mid Sts Chprsn 6 Yrs; Reach Alliance; NCEA 1975-; PSBA 1989-, Gift of Time; Shaler Schl Bd 1989-, Pres; PTA 1990-, Pres; Church Cncl 1988-; North Cath Ath Assn 1993-, Rep; Mc Donald's Tchr Awd; Golden Appla Nom; *home:* 218 Karen Dr Pittsburgh PA 15209*

DELANEY, MARC WILLIAM, Social Studies Teacher; *b:* Rome, NY; *m:* Susan J. Burkle; *c:* Philip; *ed:* NC Wesleyan Coll (BA) His 1968; Frostburg St Univ (MED) Rdng K-12 Rdng Specialist 1979; Towson St Univ Elem Ed 21 Credit Hrs; Bowie St Univ Scndry, Elem Ed 12 Credit Hrs; *cr:* Ralph J. Bunch, Cntrl Schl 6th Grd Tchr 1968-73; John Humbird Schl 6th Grd Tchr 1973-76; Parkside Schl 6th Grd Tchr 1976-83; Columbia St Schl 4th Grd Tchr 1983-84; Washington MS 8th Grd Soc Stud Tchr 1984-; *ai:* Stu Cncl Advl Fort Hill HS Marching Band Asst Dir; NEA, MSTA 1968-; ACTA 1973-, Treas 1989; Loyal Order of Moose 1990-; Cumberland Chamber of Comm Tchr of Yr 1978; *home:* 542 Rizer Ave Cumberland MD 21502

DELANEY, MATTHEW MICHAEL,III, Instructor of Fine Arts; *b:* Boston, MA; *m:* Patricia Louise Tirrell; *c:* Sara Linde, Elizabeth Kerrin; *ed:* MA Coll of Art (BS) Art Ed 1970; Bridgewater St Coll (MED) Scdnry Ed, Creative Arts 1974; Boston Coll (MA) Amer Stud, His 1981; Cmptrs Ed, Apple Cmptr Ed Tech; Rochester Inst of Tech Photography Ed; Kodak Mrktng Ed Ctr; *cr:* Brockton East Jr HS Art Instr 1970-74; Brockton Pub Schls Comm Schl Coord 1971-74; Whitman-Manson Regnl HS Art Instr 1974-, Dept Chm Fine Arts, Instr of Fine Arts 1989-92, PK-12 Curr Coord, Instr Fine Arts 1993-; *ai:* Newspaper, Photography Club Adv; Curr Stud, Tech Stud, Alternative Schl Ruling, Block Scheduling Comms; Sailing, Cmptr Graphics Instr; Instrl Advy Cncl; NEA, MTA, PCEA, WHEA 1970-, MTA Distngd Svc Cert; NAEA, MAEA 1970-, ASCD 1992-; MA Coll of Arts Alumni Assn 1970-; Boston Coll Alumni Assn 1980-; Abington Music Parents Assn 1991-; Abington Lib Bldg Support Comm 1993-; Abington Cncl 1996; Natl Endowment for Hum Grant; Elizabethian Theatre Horace Grant 2 Times; Articles Pub; *office:* Whitman Hanson Regional HS 600 Franklin St Whitman MA 02382

DELANEY, PATRICIA MORRIS, Mathematics Teacher; *b:* Fall River, MA; *w:* Frederick A. (dec); *ed:* NCA&T St Univ (BS) Ec 1967; Long Island Univ (MA) Ec 1978; Bethel Bible Inst 18 Credits; *cr:* IBM at Harrison Programmer Trainee 1967; Equitable Life Assurance Co Rate Analyst 1967-70; IS 49 6th-8th Grd Math Tchr 1970-78, 1984-; Nobel JHS 7th-8th Grd Math Tchr 1979-84; *ai:* St Judes Hosp Math-a-Thon 1991; Annual Black His Pgm Fac Asst; Combined Charities Coord at Worksite; UFT 1984-; AFT 1984-; Bethel Gospel Tabernacle 1987-; Widows & Widowers Flwshp 1987-, Sec; Camp Joharie 1987-; Missionary Dept Outreach 1993-; *office:* IS 49 William Gaynor 223 Graham Ave Brooklyn NY 11206

DELANEY, SHIRLEY BOOTH, Education Specialist; *b:* St Louis, MO; *c:* Susan White, Barbara Brown, Erica L.; *ed:* DC Tchrs Coll (BS) Ed 1972; Attnd Trinity Coll; *cr:* Alex Dept of Substance Abuse Prevention Psychological Cnslr 1986-89; Browne Jr HS Sci Tchr 1989-91; Hine Jr HS Sci Tchr 1991-95; George Washington Univ Ed Specialist 1995-; *ai:* Phi Delta Kappa 1990-; Whos Who Among Stdnts, Colls & Univs 1972-; Lawrence Hall of Sci Flwshp; *home:* 1811 24th St NE Washington DC 20002*

DE LA PUENTE, MARIA, 8th Grd Bilingual Teacher; *b:* Habana, Cuba; *c:* Michale DeLorenzo, Tahlia DeLorenzo; *ed:* Jersey City St Coll (BA) Elem Ed 1977; Biling Cert; ESL Cert; *cr:* Thomas A Edison Biling Tchr 1990-; *ai:* Pan Amer Show Co-Coord; NJEA 1990-.

DELAURIER, DOREEN GIACONA, Third Grade Teacher; *b:* Elizabeth, NJ; *m:* David W.; *c:* Davis, Kiernan; *ed:* Kean Coll (BA) Elem Ed 1971; Attnd St Peters Coll; *ai:* Pupil Assistance Comm; NJEA 1971-; NEA 1971-; UTTA 1971-; *office:* Connecticut Farms Schl 711 Stuyvesant Ave Union NJ 07083

DELAY, KATHLEEN M., Commercial Art Instructor; *b:* Winchester, MA; *m:* John L.; *c:* Brendan S., Melissa M., Kara M.; *ed:* Emmanuel Coll (BA) Art 1966; Working on MED Art Ed Univ of Toledo; *cr:* Four Cty Voc Schl Commercial Art Instr 1991-; *ai:* NEA 1991-; OH Art Ed Assn 1992-; *office:* Four Cty Voc Schl Box 245-A 22-900 SR 34 Archbold OH 43502*

DELAY, RICHARD JAMES, PE Teacher & Coach; *b:* Lexington, MA; *m:* Susan Mary HIggins; *c:* Amy, Cora, Debra, Kelly; *ed:* Northeastern Univ (BS) PE, Hlth Sci 1968; *cr:* Zervas, Lincoln Eliot Schl PE Tchr 1968-72; Franklin Elem Schl PE Tchr 1972-93; Bigelow MS PE Tchr 1993-; *ai:* Boys Soccer, Bsktbl, Bsbl Coach; NEA, Newton Tchrs Assn, MAPHERD 1968-; *office:* Bigelow MS 42 Vernon St Newton MA 02158

DELCASTILLO, VINCENT, Prof of Law & Police Sci Dept; *b:* Brooklyn, NY; *m:* Mary Alice Craver; *c:* John, Doris, Rose; *ed:* Empire St Coll (BS) Labor Stud 1982; John Jay Coll (MPA) Pub Admin 1984; Fordham Univ (PHD) Sociology, Criminology 1992; FBI Natl Exec Inst Grad 1989; *cr:* NYC Transit Police Dept Ofcr, Asst Chief 1963-87, Chief of Police 1987-90; John Jay Coll Prof 1990-; *ai:* Stu Adv; Fac Senate; Coll Cncl; Amer Soc of Criminology 1991-; Police Exec Rsrch Forum 1987-; Commission on Accreditation for Law Enforcement Agencies 1988-, Assessor; Intnl Assn of Chiefs of Police 1984-; Phi Kappa Phi 1994-; Nassau Cty Legal Aid Soc 1991-, Sec; NY Comm Mayors 1987-, Honorary Mayor; Numerous Articles, Conf Lectures; *office:* City Univ Of NY John Jay Coll 899 10th Ave New York NY 10019*

DEL CIOPPO, VICTOR, 8th Grade Math Teacher; *b:* Waterbury, CT; *m:* Julene M. Kosowicz; *c:* Jennifer, Scott Biondi, Mark Biondi; *ed:* Southern CT St Coll (BA) His 1967; 30 Addl Hrs Math Cntrl CT St Coll 1974; *cr:* Alcott MS Math Tchr 1967-; *ai:* Bsktbl Coach; 8th Grd Class, Stu Cncl, Natl Jr Hnr Soc Adv; Math Ldrshp Comm; Washington DC Coord; *office:* Alcott MS 1497 Woodtick Rd Wolcott CT 06716

DELEO, JOHN DANIEL, Professor; *b:* Scranton, PA; *m:* Teresa H.; *ed:* PA St (BA) Pol Sci 1976; Loyola Univ of New Orleans Schl of Law (JD) Law 1984; Paralegal Cert at Long Island Univ; *cr:* Cntrl Penn Bus Schl Prof 1987-; *ai:* PA Bar Assn 1987-; Article Pub; Tchr of Yr 1991, 1993.

DELEO, JOHN L., Science Teacher; *b:* Brooklyn, NY; *m:* Juliann M. Solghan; *c:* Christopher, Danielle; *ed:* SUNY at New Paltz (BA) Bio Sec Ed 1969, (MS) Scndry Ed 1972; Kingston City Schls Various Inservice Courses; *cr:* Miller Schl Tchr & Sci Liaison 1969-95, Tchr, Liaison & Grd Level Coord 1995-; *ai:* Natl Jr Hnr Soc & Chess Club Adv; Bus Supvr; 8th Grd Level Coord; AFT 1969-, 2nd VP 1970; STANYS 1975-; New Paltz Travel Soccer Club 1989-, Past Pres; New Paltz CYO 1993-, Bd of Dirs; New Paltz Ath Assn 1994-, VP; Task Force for Kids 1995-, Bd of Dirs; Whos Who in Amer Colls & Univs 1968; STANYS Southeast Region Outstdng Sci Tchr Awd; *home:* 8 Elyse Dr New Paltz NY 12561

DELEO, LOUIS, Developmental Rdng & Lit Tchr; *b:* Scranton, PA; *m:* Cindy Eyet; *c:* Corey, Ashlie; *ed:* Keystone Jr Coll (AA) Ed 1974; E Stroudsburg St (BA) Elem 1976; Masters in Ed; *cr:* Tunkhannock Area Schl Dist 8th Grd Dev Rdng, Lit, Vocabulary & Spelling Tchr 1977-; *ai:* Stu Cncl Adv; Jr HS Bsktbl Coach; NEA 1977-; *office:* Tunkhannock Area MS 41 Philadelphia Ave Tunkhannock PA 18657*

DELEO, MICHAEL G., Social Studies Teacher; *b:* Fall River, MA; *m:* Bonita; *c:* Kristen Deleo Swist, Steven M.; *ed:* Providence Coll (BA) Ed, Soc St 1966, (MED) Admin 1971; Attnd Univ of RI, Bridgewater Coll, RI Coll; *cr:* Warren HS Soc St Tchr, Stu Act Coord 1966-93; Bristol Cty Adult Schl Tchr, Guid 1969-91; Mt Hope HS Soc St Tchr, Stu Act Coord 1993-; *ai:* Adv Class of 1973, 1981, 1985, 1988; Stu Act Coord 1984-94; Stu Cncl, Yrbk Adv; Head of GATE Prgm; NEA 1966-, VP, Rep Cncl; RIA Soc St Tchr 1990-; RIA of Adult Ed 1969-91; Robert Taft Flwshp Scholar; Tchr of Yr; *office:* Mount Hope HS Bristol-Warren Regnl Schl Dept 151 State St Bristol RI 02809

DELEO, VIRGINIA ANN, Biology Teacher; *b:* Queens, NY; *m:* Stephen Peter; *c:* John Christian, Timothy Stephen, Evan Michael; *ed:* Molloy Coll (BS) Bio, Scndry Ed 1976; Adelphi Univ (MA) Bio, Scndry Ed 1980-81; *cr:* St Peters of Alcantara Jr High Sci Tchr 1976-81; Maria Regina HS Bio Tchr 1981-84; Malverne HS Bio Tchr 1984-; *ai:* Supvr Jr Var, Var Bsktbl; Tutor; Project HELP Grant 1977; Master Tchr Awd 1990; *office:* Malverne HS 80 Ocean Ave Malverne NY 11565*

DELEONE, JOSEPH JOHN, Physics Professor; *b:* Elmiro, NY; *m:* Carrie M.; *ed:* Clarkson Univ (BS) Electrical Engrng 1988, (MS) Electrical Engrng 1993; *cr:* Corning Comm Coll Physics Prof 1993-; *ai:* Cmptr Lab Supvr; NY St Sci Olympiad Reg Dir; Tech Guild Adv 1994-95; NYS Engrng Tech Assn 1994-; Pub Articles; Planetarium Presentations Local Groups; Tchnlgy Ed NSF Grant; *office:* Corning Comm Coll 1 Academic Dr Corning NY 14830*

DELEVO, DORIS BRITTON, Developmental Reading Teacher; *b:* Holyoke, MA; *m:* Felix R. Sr.; *c:* Kathryn Ekmalian, Felix R. Jr., David F., Janine Marshall, Jeffrey A.; *ed:* Westfield St (BSED) Ed 1973, (MSEd) Rdng 1976; 33 Hrs Above Masters in Ed & Psych 1983; Paralegal Cert 1988; *cr:* Agawam Schl System Tchr 1976-; *ai:* Taught CCD 1974-78; Non Users Club AJHS Adv 1993-94; MTA & Agawam Tchrs Assn 1976-; *office:* Agawam Jr HS 1305 Springfield St Agawam MA 01001

DEL GAUDIO, RICHARD, Dean of Business; *b:* Medford, MA; *m:* Dianne E. Stapleton; *c:* Damon, Elwe, Jessica, Daryl; *ed:* Northwestern Univ (BS) Accounting 1964, (MBA) Finance 1966; *cr:* Arthur Andersen Co CPA Sr Auditor 1966-72; Merrimack Coll Asst Prof Accounting 1972-90, Full Prof Accounting & Dean of Bus 1990-95; *ai:* Beta Gamma Sigma NHS Bus; Prof of Yr 1994; *office:* Merrimack Coll 315 Turnpike St North Andover MA 01845*

DELGIUDICE, JOHN MICHAEL, Ice Hockey Coach; *b:* New Haven, CT; *m:* Lisa Ann Saucier; *c:* Matthew, Christopher, Nathan; *ed:* Univ of NEW England (BA) Phys Therapy 1988; *cr:* Messalonskee HS Ice Hockey Coach 1990-; *ai:* Tutoring; *office:* Messalonskee HS 62 Oak St Oakland ME 04963

DELGREGO, ELIZABETH, Elem Gifted Support Teacher; *b:* Darby, PA; *c:* Nicholas, Kaes; *ed:* Penn St Univ (BS) Elem Ed 1976; Widener Univ (MED) Gifted & Talented 1989; 30 Post Grad Credits at Temple Univ; Southeast Delco Schl Dist Kndgtn Tchr 1979-82, Gifted Support 1987-; *ai:* Schl Newspaper; Spelling Bee; Career Day; NEA, SDEA 1 PSEA 1979-, Legislative Contact Team Mem; Norwood Pub Lib 1 Treas, Bd of Dirs; Impact Awd; *office:* Southeast Delco Schl Dist De Dr Folcroft PA 19032

DELGROSSO, PRISCILLA ANN, Health Educator; *b:* Buffalo, N Glenn; *c:* Cassie; *ed:* SUC at Cortland (BS) PE 1970, (MS) Hlth 197 Univ of NY at Albany (MLS) Lib Sci 1987; Tchng Methods C Essential Elements of Instruction; *cr:* West Sand Lake & Poestenkill Schls PE Tchr 1970-71; Addison Cntrl Schl 7th-12th Grd PE Tchr 197 Northside-Blodgett MS 7th Grd Hlth Tchr 1974-76; Saratoga Springs Schls 8th Grd Hlth Tchr 1977-80, HS Hlth Tchr 1981-; *ai:* Peer Med Team; AIDS Cncl; Drug Free Schls Cncl; AFT 1970-; Saratoga Sp Tchrs Assn 1977-; *office:* Saratoga Spgs Sr HS 186 West Ave Sar Springs NY 12866

DELIA, JAMES NICHOLAS, Global Studies Teacher; *b:* Seneca NY; *m:* Judith Powell; *c:* Nicholas, Kimberly, Laurie; *ed:* Niagara (BA) His 1966; St Univ of NY at Cortland (MS) Soc Stud 1970; Attnd of Rochester; SUNY at Brockport; *cr:* Romulus Cntrl Schl Soc Stud 1966-; *ai:* K-12 Soc Stud Dept Coord, TEAM Ldrshp Cncl, NYSUT Chrmn; NYSUT & AFT 1966-; NYSSSC, NYSSSC 1988-; Wayne-F Lakes Soc Stud Cncl 1988-, Bd of Dirs; Diocese of Rochester S Commission, Mem 1989-; Woodrow Wilson World His Fellowship Fulbright Summer Seminar Schlsp to Italy 1987; Cncl for Bas Fellowship 1985; NY St Soc Stud Cncl Schlsp 1968; NYS MCES S to Germany 1993; *office:* Romulus Central Schl Main St Romulu 14541*

DELIER, DEBORAH LYNNE, Physical Ed & Health Teach Frankfurt, Germany; *ed:* Univ of MO Columbia (BS) PE & K-12th 1988; *cr:* St Bernard CCHS PE & Hlth Tchr 1989-92; John Stark Reg PE & Hlth Tchr 1992-; *ai:* Jr Var Soccer, Sftbl Coach; Var Asst C NHAPERHD 1992-; NH Soccer Assn 1992-, 1994 Class M-S JV Co Yr; *office:* John Stark Regional HS 618 N Stark Hwy Weare NH 032

DELILLI, CHARLES N., Soc Stud Teacher & Dept Chm; *b:* Glovers NY; *m:* Sue L.; *c:* Laurie, Joe, Lynne; *ed:* SUNY at Plattsburgh Scndry Ed & Soc Sci 1975; SUNY at Oneonta 30 Grad Credit Hrs S 1980; *cr:* Estee MS 8th Grd Soc Stud Tchr 1976-, 6th-8th Grd Dept 1988-; *ai:* 7th-8th Grd Soccer Coach; Dist Advy Cncl; Discipl Grading & Bldg Design Comms; AFT & NYSUT 1976-; Gloversville Assn 1976-; *office:* Estee MS 90 N Main St Gloversville NY 12078

DELILLI, FAYE STANTON, Multi-Age Classroom Teacher; *b:* Ilio *m:* Michael Nicholas; *c:* Anthony, Michael; *ed:* Adirondack Comr (AS) Lbrl Arts 1981; SUNY at Plattsburgh (BA) N_L, &th-12th G Stud 1983; Coll of St Rose (MS) Elem Ed 1989; 1 Credit Cmptr Lit Trng; *cr:* Dr. A. J. D'Errico Med Sec 1973-83; Fulton Cty Elem Sch Tchr 1983-85; Mayfield Elem Schl 5th Grd Tchr 1985-95, 4th-5 Multi-Age Tchr 1995-; *ai:* Costum, Arts In Ed, Writing, Rdng Comr Sports Booster Club; Drama Club; Mayfield Tchrs Assn, NYS Tchrs, AFT, AF of CIO 1985-; Mayfield Historical Soc 1993-; PTA Extra Spec Tchr Awd 1994; *office:* Mayfield Elem Schl N Main St M NY 12117*

DE LILLI, MICHAEL N., 6th Grade Math Teacher; *b:* Gloversvill *m:* Faye Stanton; *c:* Anthony, Michael; *ed:* Adirondack Comm Co Lbrl Arts 1972; SUNY at Plattsburgh (BA) Grds K-6 Elem Ed 1974; at Oneonta (BS) 1979; 30 Addl Hrs; *cr:* Greater Amsterdam Schl Di 2-6 Tchr 23 Yrs; *ai:* Peer Mediation; Sports Booster Club Ma Mayfield Drama Club; Amsterdam Tchrs Assn, NYS United Tchrs Fed Tchrs 1974-; AFFLCIO; Forrester Club 1986-; Amsterdam Fr JV Ftbl Coach; Mayfield HS Soccer Coach Modified 5 Yrs; *home:* 229 Rd Gloversville NY 12078

DELILLO, RICHARD JOSEPH, Mathematics Teacher & Chair; York, NY; *ed:* Iona C. (BA) Soc 1972; St Thomas Aquinas C (BS) Ec Fairfield Univ (MS) Ed 1978; 3 Grad Credits Guidance & Counseli S Orangetown CSD Elem Tchr 1973-76; Don Bosco Prep Math Tchr *ai:* Pom Squad Coach; NCEA & NJMTA 1976-; NJCCA 1992; *offic* Bosco Prep 492 N Franklin Tpk Ramsey NJ 07446

DELINE, ALAN CHARLES, Criminal Justice Teacher; *b:* Syracus *m:* Diane Diluzio; *c:* Michael, Kathleen, Susie; *ed:* MI St (BS) C Justice 1982; SUNY Oswego (BA) Pub Justice 1983; 18 Credit Voc-Tech Ed; *cr:* Ramer Tech Career Ctr Criminal Justice Tchr 19 Law Enforcement Explorer Adv; HS Bsktbl, Coll Swimming Oswego Cty Sheriffs Dept Spec Deputy; Criminal Justice Edctr 1986-; Amer Soc of Law Enforcement Trainers, Intnl Assn of C Police 1988-; VFW 1986-; Marine Corps League 1987-; FBI USM 1995; Police Marksman Assn 1990; Police Acad Instr; Who's Wh Law Enforcement; MI St Univ Grad Fellow 1985; BSA Awd of Mer Art Rivers Meml Police Acad Awd 1995; *office:* Ramer Tech Car Oswego Cty BOCES Campus Mexico NY 13114*

DELINSKY, JOSEPH L., Spanish Teacher; *b:* Nanticoke, PA; *c:* C Karen L., Kathy J.; *ed:* King's Coll at Wilkes-Barre (BA) Eng Bloomsburg Univ (MED) Span 1969; 6 Credits Knox Coll 1965, 9 Wichita Univ; 6 Credits Univ of Madrid 1971; *cr:* Edwardsvill H Eng Tchr, Head Ftbl Coach 1962-66; WY Vly West HS Span Tchr *ai:* NEA, PSEA, WVW Tchrs Assn 1966-; WY Vly West Fed Emp Union 1986-, Advy Bd; *home:* 116 Green St Edwardsville PA 1870

DELISE, THOMAS J., English Teacher; *b:* Copiague, NY; *ed:* S Brockport (BS) Eng 1977; Towson St Lbrl Stud; *cr:* Waycross Jr Tchr 1978-81; LaGrange HS Eng Tchr 1981-88; Liberty HS E 1988-; *ai:* Liberty High Discipline Comm; Girls Bsktbl Coach NEA 1978-; Star Tchr Awd LaGrange HS 1987; Region GAA Bsktbl Coach of Yr 1985, 1988; Carroll Cty Times Girls Bsktbl C Yr 1991; LaGrange Dailey News Girls Bsktbl Coach of Yr 198 Yrbk Dedication Sr Class 1988; *office:* Liberty HS 5855 Bartho Sykesville MD 21784

DELISLE, DEBORAH SMITH, Language Arts Specialist; *b:* Wa CT; *m:* James; *c:* Matt Tremaglio; *ed:* Springfield Coll (BS) E Psych 1994; Kent St Univ (MED) Gifted Ed; Post Grad Stu Instruction; *cr:* Crestwood Local Schls Coord of Gifted Prgms 1 Shaker Hts City Schls Coord of Gifted Prgms 1987-89; Kent Visiting Instr 1989-94; Orange City Schls 6th Grd Lang Arts Tch *ai:* Lang Arts Comm Chair; Schl Newspaper; Continuous Impr Comm; NAGC 1986-, Treas for Div of Global Awareness; ASCD 1990-; NEA, OTA, OEA 1981-; Portage Cty Hospice Cncl 199 Greeter; Walsh Jesuit HS Mothers Club 1991-, Pres; Prof Best Ldrs 1990; OH Dept of Ed Master Tchr Awd 1995; OH St Tchr of Yr 1991; Eisenhower Grant Recipient; *home:* 519 Earl Ave Kent OH

DELISLE, JAMES ROBERT, Professor; *b:* Methuen, MA; *m:* Ann Smith; *c:* Matthew; *ed:* Univ of ME (BS) Elem & Spec E Millersville Univ (MED) Emotional Disturbances 1975; Univ of C Ed Psych Gifted Children 1981; *cr:* Gorham Pub Schls Spec 1975-78; univ of CT Instr 1979-82; Kent St Univ Prof 1983-; So Schls 5th-6th Grd Tchr 1991-; *ai:* SENG Co-Dir; Bd of Dirs, Natl Gifted Children; Bd of Trustees, Roeper Schl for Gifted; Natl Gifted 1980-, Bd of Dirs; Assn for Supervision & Curr Dev 1987-; Gifted 1978-, Pres; Cncl for Exceptional Children 1978-, Bd of Go

ds Survival Guide Team Handbook, Guide the Soc & Emotional ifted Youth, Open Minds Caring Hearts Act to Enrich Stu, , & Gifted Kids Speak Out; *office:* Kent State University 405 l KSU Kent OH 44242

, LUCILLE FORTUNATO, Assistant Professor of History; *b:* A; *m:* Harold F.; *ed:* Bridgwater St Coll (BA) His 1974, (MA) ston Coll (PHD) His; Grad Courses in Italian Lang, Lit y Coll; Audited Grad Classes HisUniv of CT; *cr:* Weymouth Soc Stud Tchr 1974-81; Miss Porter's Schl His Tchr, Dept Chair, chrs 1981-93; Univ of CT NEH Tchng Fellow 1990; Bridgewater st His Prof 1993-; *ai:* Weymouth South HS His Club Adv; Miss hl Model UN Amnesty Intnl, Equestrian Adv; Phi Alpha Theta; Adv; New England Historical Assn 1989-, Nominating Comm; ce Soc of Amer; Amer Historical Assn; Soc Italian Historical SS; NEHTA; NEH Summer Seminar Petrarch Arignon France; ner Inst Model Western Civilization Univ of CT at Storrs; NEH Scholar's Awd; Article Pub 1995; *office:* Bridgewater St Coll er MA 02325*

ARRELL D., Retired Teacher; *b:* West Milton, OH; *m:* Jennie adden, Velvet; *ed:* Manchester Coll (BS) Ed, Psych 1961; Attnd niv of Oxford, Lake Forest Coll; *cr:* Deer Path Jr HS Tchr Trotwood-Madison Pub Schls Tchr 1962-68; Northmont Jr HS -93; *ai:* OH Ed Assn, Lifetime Mem.

AMERA, PAULA MARIA, High School Italian Teacher; *b:* New T; *ed:* Southern CT St Univ (BS) Italian, Span 1993; Working asters in Italian at Middlebury Coll in VT; *cr:* Fairhaven MS an Culture Tchr 1992; East Haven HS Sub Tchr 1993; Hamden Tchr 1993-; *ai:* Italian Club Adv; NEA, CEA, 1993-; COLT, 4-; *office:* Hamden H S 2040 Dixwell Ave Hamden CT 06514*

ORINO, BENNY, 7th Grd Social Studies Teacher; *b:* on, NY; *m:* Sylvia; *ed:* Fresno St Coll (BA) His 1966; Scranton) Scndry Schl Admin 1975; 41 Credits & Fresno St 45 Credits -67 Credits; *ai:* NEA 1968-; Johnson City Tchrs Assn 1968-; red Johnson MS 100 Albert St Johnson City NY 13790

NO, RALPH ANTHONY, Dean of Men; *b:* Montclair, NJ; *m:* nne Will; *c:* Paul Anthony, Mark Andrew; *ed:* Seton Hall Univ Stud 1980; Immaculate Conception Grad Schl of Theology SHU eology; *cr:* St Cecelia's HS Rel Tchr 1981-82; Essex Cath Boys hr 1986-88; Seton Hall Prep Schl Theology Tchr 1988-; *ai:* Var, ng Coach; Cuisine & Card Club Moderator; Schl Diversity CEA 1987-; Catechist, RCIA, St Francis Cathedral 1994-; Call to Mem 1995-; *office:* Seton Hall Prep 120 Northfield Ave West 07052

ENTA, PATRICIA CIPUZAK, Assistant Professor of Science; eg, Canada; *m:* Dennis W; *c:* Heather, Troy; *ed:* Hofstra Univ 1967; SUNY at Buffalo (MA) Microbiology 1970; Post Grad Ed Rutgers Univ, Kean Coll; *cr:* Niagara Cty Comm Coll Asst Prof 74; SUNY at Stony Brook Rsrch Asst 1975-81; Hydron Labs st 1975-81; Carter Wallace-Wampole Labs Production Mgr Warren Comm Coll Asst Prof Sci 1992-; *ai:* Curr & Instr, Schlsp Phi Theta Kappa; Numerous Publication Pub; Patent Pending Vampole Labs Cryopreservation of Toxoplasma Gondi; Phi Beta Y St Regents Schlsps; gold Key Ath Awd; Grad Tchng hip; NY St Jr Coll Rep; *office:* Warren County Comm Coll 475 Vashington NJ 07882

IETRA, JOHN, English Teacher; *b:* New Haven, CT; *m:* Joan Lynn, Cheryl; *ed:* Fairfield Univ (BA) Eng 1964, (MA) Admin East Haven HS Eng Tchr 1964-; *ai:* CEA, NEA, EHEA 1964-; st Haven HS 200 Tyler St East Haven CT 06512

ROCCO, FELIX CARLO, Sixth Grade Teacher; *b:* Derby, CT; Lee Carboni; *c:* Julie Lynn Iannotti; *ed:* Southern CT St Univ mediate Upper 1964; Univ of Bridgeport (MS) Early Chldhd Ed Units 90 Hrs; *cr:* Peck Pl Schl 7th-8th Grd Tchr 1964-66; l 6th Grd Tchr 1966-70; First Ave Schl 6th Grd Tchr 1970-83; Mackrille Schl 6th Grd Tchr 1983-; *ai:* Stu Asst Team Chm; AFT l Fed of Tchrs 1969-, Ret Chm, Stewart; Tchr of Yr 1995; West ar of Yr Nom 1995; *home:* 395 Hilltop Rd Orange CT 06477*

ANTA, LOUIS RICHARD, Assistant Principal; *b:* Winchedon, Mary K. Mc Donough; *c:* Mark, Erik; *ed:* Springfield Coll (BS) MI St Univ (MS) Anatomy 1964; 45 Grad Credits Brandeis, iv, Fitchburg St; *cr:* Lexington HS PE Tchr 1964-66; Wakefield hr 1966-68; Dedham HS Bio Tchr 1968-70; Murdoch HS PE, Tchr, Asst Prin 1970-; *ai:* Ftbl, Bsktbl Coach; NEA, MTA 1964-;)-, Pres; BSA 1982-, Asst Scout Master; IAABO 1983-, Chair omm; Credit Union 1980-, Bd; *office:* Murdock Mid HS 3 Dr Winchendon MA 01475

OVI, BETSY MARY, Associate English Professor; *b:* Hartford, Roger Stephenson; *ed:* St Univ of NY at Buffalo (BA) Eng 1982, 1987, (PHD) Eng Ed 1993; *cr:* Grand Island HS Eng Tchr Canisius Coll Eng Prof 1989-; *ai:* Frosh Adv; Fac Mentor; Peer ab Supvr; Fac Senate; Fac, Stu liaison Comm; MLA, NCTE, NY g Skills Assn 1990-; Bay Area Writing Project Fellow; on; Article Pub; *office:* Canisius Coll 2001 Main St Buffalo NY

ONACHE, CARLENE, Business Teacher; *b:* McKees Rocks, Univ of PA (BS) Bus Ed 1991, (MED) Bus 1992; *cr:* Langley hr 1991; Conneaut Schl Dist Bus Tchr 1992-93; Titusville Area Bus Tchr 1993-; *ai:* Key Club Adv; Strategic Planning & Tech BLA Co-Adv; NEA, PSEA 1992-; Titusville Ed Assn 1993-; 1993-, Key Club Chprsn; Grad Assistantship; Continuing Ed Titusville Area Schl Dist & IN Univ of PA Yearly Wkshps; *office:* H S 302 E Walnut St Titusville PA 16354

BA, STEPHEN GUY, Fourth Grade Teacher; *b:* Utica, NY; *m:* Castano; *c:* Stephen III, Thomas; *ed:* Mohawk Vly Comm Coll rl Arts 1969; SUNY at Oneonta (BA) Elem Ed, Early Scndry Grad Hrs, SUNY Cortland; *cr:* New Hartford Schl Sys Elem Ed -; *ai:* Shared Decision Making Team; New Hartford Tchrs Assn g Rep; NEA, NYSUT 1972-; Jaycees, Past Mem, Sec; US Army 1971-93, Major, Army Achvmt Medal, Army Commendation fice: Myles Elem Schl 110 Clinton Rd New Hartford NY 13413

ELD, DENNIS L., Band Conductor; *b:* Oberlin, OH; *m:* Marilee *c:* David, Jonathan; *ed:* Bluffton Coll (BA) Music Ed 1971; Univ (MS) Music Supervision & Curr 1974; Post Grad Stud Univ of of Dayton; *cr:* Bluffton HS Asst Marching Band Dir 1967-68; Asst Marching Band Dir 1968-71; Allen East HS Conductor of 1-; *ai:* Jr Class Play, Musical Dirs; Jr Class Adv; Tchr Ed Comm Coll; MENC, OMEA 1967-; NBA 1971-; Allen Cty Outstndng Bluffton Coll Outstndng Alumni; *office:* Allen East HS 105 N n St Lafayette OH 45854*

GER, WILLIAM EARL,III, Social Studies Teacher; *b:* Lima, nn L. Bowsher; *c:* Jamie, Adam; *ed:* Bluffton Coll (BA) His, Soc ndry Ed 1981; *cr:* Marion Pleasant HS Soc Stud Tchr 1981-82; rstown HS Soc Stud Tchr 1982-84; Cardington-Lincoln HS Soc r 1984-87; Wapakoneta HS Soc Stud Tchr 1987-; *ai:* Lima HS Var Ftbl Asst Coach; Jr Var Girls Sfbl Coach; NEA 1981-, Bldg Rep; OHSAA Bsktbl 1993-, Ofcl; OHSAA Ftbl Coaches Assn 1996; *office:* Wapakoneta HS 1 Redskin Trl Wapakoneta OH 45895*

DELLI SANTI, DOLORES D., Drama Dir & English Teacher; *b:* Passaic, NJ; *ed:* Coll of St Elizabeth (BA) Eng 1966; Goucher Coll (MED) Ed 1967; Attnd Banff Schl of Fine Arts 1970-71; 27 Credit Hrs Univ of WA Masters Theatre; NY Univ Performance Art Doctoral Prgm; *cr:* Bedwell Elem Schl 5th Grd Tchr 1967-70; Bernards HS Eng Tchr, Drama Inst 1970-80; Bernards HS Drama Dir, Theatre Tchr, Eng Instr 1980-; *ai:* Drama Dir, Fall Repertory, Spring Musical Acting Troupe of 14 Stdnts; Tchrs Assn 1967-; Hunterdon Arts Ctr 1978-80, Theatre Dir; Black River Playhouse 1974-76, Dir, Showcase Producer; Foothill Playhouse 1983-87, Artistic Dir 1987; Tchr of Yr 1992; Yrbk Dedication 1982, 1995; Womens His Month Outstdng woman in Field of Arts by Somerset Cty Comm on Status of Women 1996; *home:* 128 Hacklebarney Rd Long Valley NJ 07853*

DEL LLANO, PATRICIA A., Art Teacher; *b:* Lowell, MA; *m:* Luis A.; *c:* Brian, Michael, Erin; *ed:* Emmanuel Coll (BA) Fine Arts 1965; Univ of MA at Lowell (MED) Ed 1969; 30 Addl Credits Ed, Tech Fitchburg St; *cr:* Lowell Pub Schls K-8 Grd Art Tchr 1965-87; Lowell HS 9-12 Grd Tchr 1987-; *ai:* Curr Dev Wkshps; AFT; MFT; UTL; NAEA; Museum of Fine Arts 1982-; Amer Craft Cncl 1994-; *office:* Lowell HS 50 Fr Morrissette Blvd Lowell MA 01852

DELLOLIO, LAWRENCE, Associate Art Professor; *b:* Paterson, NJ; *m:* Rosanna Dinice; *c:* Larry, Lauren DiVello; *ed:* Art Stdnts League Painting 1958-60; Paterson St (BA) Art Ed 1968; Rutgers (MA) Art 1970; 45 Post Grad; *cr:* Allendale High Art Tchr 1967-68; Red Bank Regnl Art Tchr 1968-72; Camden Cty Comm Art Prof 1972-; *ai:* Specializing Ceramic Tchng 20 Yrs; NEA, NJEA 1968-; NJAEA, CAA 1972-; Burlington Cty 1980-90, Commissioner; Cultural Heritage Comm; Young Sculptors, USA 1968-69; Various St, Natl Shows 1960-74; *office:* Camden County Coll PO Box 200 College Dr Blackwood NJ 08012

DELO, DIRK ANDREW, Mathematics Teacher; *b:* Washington, DC; *m:* Sarah; *ed:* Amherst Coll (BA) Math, Eng 1989; Columbia Univ (MA) Math Ed 1990, (MS) Math Ed 1993; PHD Candidate Math Ed Columbia Univ Tchrs Coll; *cr:* Greenwich HS Math, Eng Fac Tchr 1989-90; Gstaad Intnl Schl Math, Eng, Sci Fac Tchr 1990-91; Ethel Walkers Schl Math Fac Tchr 1991-; *ai:* Class Adv; Var Crew Coach; Dir of Computing; Farmington Vly Rowing Assn 1992-, Treas; Amer Red Cross 1978-, Woodrow Wilson Natl Svc Awd 1985; Woodrow Wilson Natl Fellow Math 1993; GTE Gift Fellow 1996; *office:* Ethel Walker Schl 230 Bushy Hill Rd Simsbury CT 06070

DELOFF, DOLA COUGHENOUR, English Teacher; *b:* Fredericksburg, VA; *m:* Francis R.; *c:* Jeffrey Francis, Daniel Patrick; *ed:* Penn St Univ (BA) Eng 1984; St Univ of NY at Oswego (MS) Ed 1993, (MA) Eng 1994; *cr:* MX Acad & Cntrl Schls Eng Tchr 1986-; St Univ of NY at Oswego ESL Pgm Coord 1993-, Adj Eng Prof 1994-, Pre-Coll Pgm Coord 1996; *ai:* Yrbk Adv 1986-; AFT & NYSUT 1988-, 3rd VP Pub Relations; *office:* MX Acad & Cntrl Schls Main St Mexico NY 13114*

DELONG, LINDA DILUZIO, 6th Grade Teacher; *b:* Keene, NH; *m:* Paul; *c:* Matthew, Meghan; *ed:* Keene St Coll (BED) Elem Ed 1971; *cr:* Winchester Elem Schl Grd 5 Tchr 1971-72; Hinsdale Elem Schl Grd 4 Tchr 1972-88, Grd 6 Tchr 1988-; *ai:* HFT, NHFT, AFT, HFT, NEANH, NEA, Pres; *home:* 98 Fox Run Rd East Swanzey NH 03446

DELONG, PATRICIA WIEGAND, Guidance Counselor; *b:* Piney Point, MD; *m:* Robert J. Jr.; *c:* Robert J., Michelle J.; *ed:* Oswego St Coll (BS) Scndry Ed Eng 1967, (MEd) Scndry Guid & Cnslng 1980; *cr:* Liverpool HS Scndry Eng Tchr 1967-71, Guid Cnslr 1971-79; Onondaga Jr, Sr HS Guid Cnslr 1979-; *ai:* Grds K-12 Dir of Guid; Jr Class Adv; Chprn Bldg, PPS, Bldg Adv Comms; *office:* Onondaga Cntrl Jr, Sr HS 4479 S Onondaga Rd Nedrow NY 13120

DE LONG, ROBERT J.,JR., Guidance Counselor; *b:* Erie, PA; *m:* Patricia Wiegand; *c:* Robert J., Michelle; *ed:* Edinborough Univ (BS) Scndry Ed Soc Stud 1970, (MED) Scndry Guid & Cnslng 1973; *cr:* Corry HS Soc Stud Tchr 1970-72; Liverpool HS Guid Cnslr 1973-; *ai:* Head JV Ftbl Coach 12 Yrs; Natl Fed Interscholastic Coaches Assn 13 Yrs; *office:* Liverpool HS 4338 Wetzel Rd Liverpool NY 13090

DELONG, ROBERT LEE,JR., Biology Teacher & Head Coach; *b:* Oregon, OH; *m:* Lisa M.; *ed:* Wright St Univ (BS) Comprehensive Sci Ed 1987; *cr:* Toledo Pub Schls Sci Tchr, Coach 1987-91; Fairborn City Schls Sci Tchr, Coach 1991-92; Tecumseh Local Schls Sci Tchr, Head Ftbl Coach 1993-; *ai:* Head Ftbl Coach; Weightroom Supv; FLA Group Adv; Chosen for Project SHAPE; 1995 Southwest Dist Co Coach of Yr; Miami Valley Ftbl Coaches Assn Coach of Yr; *office:* Tecumseh HS 9830 W National Rd New Carlisle OH 45344*

DELONTI, JAMES JOSEPH, 4th Grade Teacher; *b:* Scranton, PA; *m:* Elizabeth Duffy; *c:* Norina, Angela; *ed:* Mansfield Univ (BS) Elem Ed 1973; Univ of Scranton (MS) Elem Ed 1978; Drug, Alcohol Abuse Cnslng Courses; *cr:* Vly View Schl Dist Elem Tchr 1973-; *ai:* Head Var Sftbl Coach; Soc Stud Curr Comm; Fac Advy Bd; PSEA, NEA 1973-; Cougarette Sftbl 1990-93, Pres; Jessup Yth Sports 1995-, Diamond Club 1995-; *home:* 383 Virginia Ave Peckville PA 18452*

DELORENZO, CARL S., 12th Grade History Teacher; *b:* Jersey City, NJ; *m:* Annette Tagliareni; *c:* Carl Julian, Gerard Alexander; *ed:* Fordham Univ (MA) His 1992; *cr:* St Peters Prep Tchr 1972-; *ai:* Bd of Trustees Fac Adv; Lyons Club 1991-, Past Pres 1994; *office:* St Peters Prep 144 Grand St Jersey City NJ 07302

DELORME, DANIEL E., Physics Teacher; *b:* Barbourville, KY; *ed:* Univ of Buffalo (BA) Phys 1992; Elmira Coll (MS) Math Ed 1996; Cornell Univ Inst on Sci, Enviromen; SUNY at Oswego, Energy Inst; Rsrch Assoc Continous Electron Beam Accelerator Facility CEBAF; Woodrow Wilson Inst Statistics, Probability; *cr:* Corning Incorporate Tech 1990; Northville Cntrl Schl Sci Tchr 1992-93; Horseheads MS Phys Sci Tchr 1993-94; Horseheads HS Physics Tchr 1994-; *ai:* AFT 1993-; Continuous Election Beam Accelerator Facility Follow on Awd; Bd of Cooperative Educl Svcs Grant 1993, 1995; *office:* Horseheads HS 401 Fletcher St Horseheads NY 14845*

DELPIANO, DOREEN O'NEILL, 7th Grade Teacher; *b:* Jersey City, NJ; *m:* Ralph; *c:* Christian; *ed:* Jersey City St Coll (BA) Elem Ed 1967; *ai:* NEA, NJEA 1967-; JCEA 1967-, Bldg Dir.

DELPLATO, JOAN, Instructor of Art History; *b:* Batavia, NY; *c:* Jilla Benson; *ed:* SUNY at Buffalo (BA) Art His 1975; UCLA (MA) Art His 1980, (PHD) Art His 1987; *cr:* CA St Univ at Long Beach Part-time Lecturer 1985-86; Loyola Marymount Univ Acting Asst Prof 1987; Simon's Rock Coll Art His Instr 1987-; *ai:* Chair Arts Div; Historian of Bristish Art 1993-; Woodrow Wilson Natl Flwshp Fnd Women's Stud Rrsch Grant 1986; Yale NEH Seminar 1988; Articles Pub; Local, Natl Lectures Delivered; *office:* Simons Rock Coll Of Bard 84 Alford Rd Gr Barrington MA 01230

DEL PRETE, MICHELE PIERRE, High School Choral Director; *b:* Scranton, PA; *m:* William; *ed:* Marywood Coll (BM) Music Ed 1991; 12 Credits Towards Masters in Ed; *cr:* Dunmore Schl Dist K-12th Grd Long-Term Sub 1992-93; North Pocono Schl Dist 9th-12th Grd Choral Dir 1993-; *ai:* Strategic Planning Comm; Pit Orch Dir for Musicals; PMEA 1991-; MENC 1991-; PSEA & NEA 1992-; Childrens Choir & Summer Bible Schl 1993-, Church Vol; *office:* North Pocono HS 701 Church St Moscow PA 18444

DEL RIO, ANTONIO FRANCISCO, Director of Religious Affairs; *b:* Gary, IN; *ed:* Marquette Univ (BA) His & Philosphy 1974; Edinboro Univ (MED) Educl Psych 1992; Attnd WA Theological Union, Univ of Brideport; Working on Pastoral Ministry at Gannon Univ; *cr:* St Johns Elem His & Rel Tchr 1977-78; Conn-Area Cath Math & Rel Tchr 1978-79; Sacred Heart Elem Sci & Rel Tchr 1979-81; Cathedral Prep Schl Dir of Rel Affairs 1981-; *ai:* Key & Photo Club Adv; Yrbk Asst Adv; Utilization Comm; NCEA 1981-; Phi Sigma Tau 1973-, Philosophy Hnr Soc; Alpha Sigma Nu 1974-, Jesuit Hnr Soc; Jaycees Uniontown 1977-79, Sec; Grad Schl-Schl Psych Club 1990-91, Pres; Kiwanis 1991-; Who's Who in Colls & Univs 1974; Grad Assistantship at Edinboro Univ; Poetry Pub; Lectures on Behavior Disorders & Ed Approaches; Lib Corps Coord; Rsrch Project Lib System for At-Risk-Kids; *home:* PO Box 520 Edinboro PA 16412*

DELSANDRO, BETTY BARLE, French Teacher; *b:* Finleyville, PA; *m:* Charles; *c:* Charles; *ed:* California Univ of PA (BA) Fr 1963; Univ of Bucknell 12 Credits; Universite de Toulouse France 12 Credits; *cr:* Finley Jr HS Fr, Span Tchr 1963-69; Bethel Park HS Fr Tchr 1973-; *ai:* AFT 1973-; Govt Grants; *office:* Bethel Park HS 309 Church Rd Bethel Park PA 15102

DE LUCA, DENISE BERNARD, 6th Grade English & Rdng Tchr; *b:* Berea, OH; *m:* Daniel R.; *c:* Matthew; *ed:* Bowling Green St Univ (BA) Elem, Spec Ed 1976; Attnd Coll of Mt St Joseph, Baldwin Wallace, Drake Univ; *cr:* North Royalton City Schls 6th Grd Eng, Rdng Tchr 1976-; *ai:* Team Ldr; NEA, OEA 1976-; NREA 1976-, Pol Action Comm; NCTE 1993-; North Royalton Bsbl Boosters 1990-; Martha Holdings Jennings Schlr; Cuyahoga Vly Joint Voc Schl Lit Grants 1981-84; *office:* North Royalton MS 14725 Ridge Rd North Royalton OH 44133*

DELUCA, LINDA (BENNA), Computer Coordinater; *b:* Brooklyn, NY; *m:* Philip; *c:* Christine, Philip, Nicholas, Thomas, Stacey; *ed:* Attnd Ulster Cty Comm Coll,Empire St Coll at New Paltz; *cr:* IBM Cmptr Technician, Supvr; Dance Tchr 10 Yrs; Yoga Tchr 3 Yrs; Kerhonkson Elem Schl Sub Tchr; Roundout Valley Schl System Cmptr Instr, Coord; *ai:* Peer Mediator.

DELUCA, LYNDA ANN, Sixth Grade Teacher; *b:* Albany, NY; *ed:* Cazenovia Jr Coll (AAS) Liberal Arts 1967; Cortland SUCC (BS) Psych 1969, (MS) Elem Ed 1972; Addl 30-40 Grad Hours; NYSSILR Cornell Cert Labor Relations; NYSUT Effective Tchr Cert Teach Grad Level Courses; Admin Internship Scranton Univ; *cr:* Union-Endicott CSD Elem Tchr 4th-6th Grd 1969-; *ai:* Effective Tchng Prgm, Teach Grad Courses LIU & St ROSE; Presenter SUNY Binghamton, NYSCATE, More Math More Females, Endicott Tchr Ctr; Dist Planning, Peer Partnering, Instruction Strategies Team; NYSUT, AFT 1969-, Local Pres ETA, Chief Negotiator; Phi Delta Kappa 1980-, Pres, VP, Newsletter; Delta Kappa Gamma 1983-, Pres, Legislative Chair; PTA 1969-, VP, 2nd VP, Life Membership; Bing Area Rdng Cncl, NYS Rdng Cncl 1969-; Natl Schl Excl Recognition 1988; Outstanding Sci, Tech Tchr 1994; Macmillian Publishing Comp Tchr Roundtable Discussion; ABC Inside Schl Frost Valley; *office:* Ann G Mc Guinness Schl 1301 Union Center-Maine Hwy Endicott NY 13760

DELUCA, RICHARD S., Dir Cntr for Educl Leadership; *b:* Pittsburgh, PA; *m:* Margaret Killian; *c:* Lauren, Anthony; *ed:* St Vincent Coll (BA) His 1961; DuQuesne Univ (MED) Admin 1965; Univ of Pittsburgh (PHD) Ed Admin 1985; *cr:* West Deer Jr-Sr HS Tchr 1961-65; Burrell Sr HS Tchr, Dept Head 1966-72; Hempfield Schl Dist Asst Prin, Asst Dir of Curr, Asst Supt 1972-1990; Johnstown Schl Dist Supt 1990-93; Clarion Univ Dir of Cntr for Ed Leadership 1993-; *ai:* NASSP 1972-; ASCD, Schl Bd Assn 1978-; Lions 1994-; St Barbanas RC Church 1993-; 2 NDBA Fellowships; St System of Higher Ed Grant of PA; *office:* Clarion Univ Of PA B-66 Carlson Clarion PA 16214

DELUCCIA, KATHRYN EMILY, Fine Arts Teacher; *b:* New York, NY; *m:* Robert J.; *c:* Carmen; *ed:* NY Univ (BS) Art Ed 1968, (MS) Art Ed 1971; Schl of Visual Arts 4 Courses; United Digital Artists Apple Multimedia Cert; *cr:* Northern Vly Reg HS Tchr 25 Yrs; *ai:* Theater Graphics Set Design 1971-94; Color Guard Adv 1972-76; Class Adv 1977-79; Aviation Club 1978; Northern Vly Dist Graphic Designer 1995-96; NVEA 1971-, Negotiations Com 1993, Grievance Comm 1996; NJEA 1971-; NURHS Tchr of the Yr 1976; *office:* Northern Valley RHS-DEMAREST 150 Knickerbocker Rd Demarest NJ 07627*

DE LUCCO, DEBORAH CORTESE, French Teacher; *b:* Niagara Falls, NY; *m:* Gary; *ed:* SUNY at Albany (BA) Fr 1971, (MA) Advanced Classroom Tchng 1976; 3 Grad Credits Shakespeare Empire St Coll; 3 Credits Italian SUNY at Albany; 9 Credits Univ of Grenoble; 9 Credits Univ of Avignon; 25 Credits Span SUNY at Brockport & at Albany, Schenectady Comm Coll; Cert Span; Cert Eng; *cr:* Schuylerville Cntrl Schl Fr Tchr 1971-; *ai:* Fr Club Adv; Coord of NYS Dept of Ed's PEACE Prgm; Natl Fr Contest Coord; NYSAFLT, AFT 1971-; NYSUT, STA 1971-, Local Pres, Sec Negotiator; PLDELTA PHI 1971-, Election Dist Rep, Mem of Exec Bd; AATF 1971-, Full Schlsp to Study in France 1976; Saratoga Flyers Inc 1995-, Pres; Saratoga Labor Cncl 1975-; Civil Air Patrol 1987-; AOPA 1985-; AATF Schlshp Univ of Avignin; Sabbatical Leave to Achieve Fluency, Cert in Span in Mexico; *office:* Schuylerville Cntrl Schl 18 Spring St Schuylerville NY 12871

DE LUCCO, GARY, Global Studies Teacher; *b:* Dolgeville, NY; *m:* Deborah; *ed:* SUNY (BA) His 1971, (MA) Ed 1974; *cr:* Shenendehowa Cntrl Schl 7-12th Grd Tchr 1971-; *ai:* Ski Club Spon; NUSUT, AFT 1971-, Del; Shenendehowa Tchrs Assn 1971-, VP 1978-93; HS Partnership Tm 1996; *office:* Shenendehowa HS 970 Rt 146 Clifton Park NY 12065*

DELUCIA, MAUREEN MURPHY, Kindergarten Teacher; *b:* Meriden, CT; *m:* Tony; *c:* T.J., Drew; *ed:* Cntrl CT St Univ (BS) Elem Ed 1973; Southern CT St Univ (MS) Early Chldhd; 6th Yr Classroom Specialist; *cr:* Rock Hill Elem Schl, Moses Y Beach Elem Schl, Stevens Elem Schl, Yalesville Elem Schl, Parker Farms Elem Schl Kndgtn Tchr 1974-; *ai:* Advy Cncl; Soc Stud Mgmt Team; EIP Mem; NEA 1974-.

DELUCIA, VINCENT RICHARD, English Teacher; *b:* Hackensack, NJ; *m:* Elizabeth Wheeler; *c:* Gregory A., D. Richard; *ed:* Wagner Coll (BS) Ed 1972; Attnd Trenton St Coll Cnslng, Rider Univ Educl Admin, Rutgers Univ Literacy Inst; *cr:* Crossroads Eng Tchr, Stu Affairs Coord 1972-81; Meade-Johnson Pharmaceuticals Sales Trainer 1981-84; Q-Med Inc Sales Mgr 1984-89; Crossroads Schl Eng Tchr 1989-; *ai:* Peer Mediation, Lit Magazine Adv; Soccer, Bsbl, Recreation Coach; NEA, MCEA, NJEA 1972-; SBEA 1972-, PR&R Rep; Middlesex Cty Conf of Maoyrs, NJ Assn of Planning Ofcls 1991-; NJ League of Municipalities 1988-; S B Twp Comm 1988-91, Mayor 1991, Committeeman 1989-90; Natl Bd Cert in Eng Lang Arts 1995; US Dept of Ed Blue Ribbon Schl Awd for Excl 1993; Who's Who in NJ 1992; *office:* Crossroads MS Georges Rd Monmouth Jct NJ 08852*

DELUISI, MARIA (PELUSO), Third Grade Teacher; *b:* Newark, NJ; *m:* Nicholas; *c:* Nicholas, Neal, Margo; *ed:* William Patterson Coll (BA) Elem Ed 1969; *cr:* South Eighth Schl Elem Tchr 1969-71; Schl Number Two Elem Tchr 1971-80; Schl Number Four 3 Grd Elem Tchr 1982-; *ai:* NJEA, NEA 1969-; BEA 1971-; Home & Schl #4 1982-; Home & Schl MS 1987-; Home & Schl HS 1989-; Silver Lake Assn 1994-; Governor's Tchr Recognition Awd, Excl Ed Awd Belleville Chamber of Commerce 1994; *office:* Schl Number Four 30 Magnolia St Belleville NJ 07109

DELVECCHIO, SUSAN LOMBARDI, Second Grade Teacher; *b:* Hartford, CT; *m:* Robert R.; *c:* Kristin Madden, Erinn; *ed:* Saint Joseph Coll at West Hartford (BA) Early Chldld, Spec Ed 1969, (MA) Spec Ed 1982; *cr:* Wallingford Bd of Ed 1 Grd Tchr 1969-70, Spec Ed Tchr

1970-71; Regnl Dist #13 Spec Ed Tchr 1977-89, 2 Grd Tchr 1989-; *ai:* Grd 2 Unit Coord 1989-; CEA, NEA 1977-; Riverview Hosp for Children 1995-; Spec Ed Fair Presenter; Dist 13 Spec Educator Awd 1985; Early Chldhd Conf Presenter; *office:* Brewster Elem Schl PO Box 310 Tuttle Rd Durham CT 06441

DELZINGARO, ANTHONY ROBERT, American Studies Teacher; *b:* Abington, PA; *c:* Brigitte Marinos, Vanessa; *ed:* Shippensburg Univ (BS) Soc Stud 1959; 36 Credit Hrs Western MD Coll, Penn St Univ, Eastern Bapt Coll; *cr:* Fairfield Schl System Tchr 1959-63; Penn Hall Jr Coll Instr 1963-71; Littlestown Schl Dist Tchr 1971-; *ai:* Mock Trial Competition Team Adv, Coach; Awds & Recognition Task Force; NEA, PSEA, LEA 1959-; Torch Club 1976-86; Jaycees 1960-66; Gettysburg Boro Cncl 1976-84; Adams Cty Lib Bd 1985-86; Adams Cty Human Relation Cncl 1991-; Coe Fnd Grant to Stud Amer Stud Eastern Bapt coll; Wrote Several Articles; *office:* Littlestown HS 200 E Myrtle St Littlestown PA 17340*

DELZOPPO, GERALD PAUL, 6th Grade Teacher; *b:* Niagara Falls, NY; *m:* Gail Marie; *c:* Ben, Tessa, Noelle; *ed:* NCCC (AA) Lib Arts 1978; Buffalo St Coll (BA) El Ed 1982, (MS) Read 1986; 48 Addl Hrs; *cr:* 79th St Schl 6th Grd Tchr 2 Yrs; LaSalle MS 6th Grd Tchr 7 Yrs; *ai:* Head JV, Asst Var Ftbl, Track Coach; AFT 1987-; *office:* La Salle MS 76th St & Buffalo Ave Niagara Falls NY 14304

DEMAGISTRIS, CHERYL GURGA, Mathematics Teacher; *b:* Gloversville, NY; *m:* Anthony; *c:* Megan, Timothy; *ed:* NY St Univ at Potsdam (BA) Math 1974; NY St Univ at Albany (MS) Math 1978; *cr:* Saratoga Springs Jr HS Math Tchr 1974-75; Cntrl Square HS Math Tchr 1975-76; Shaker HS Math Tchr 1976-77; Saratoga Springs HS Math Tchr 1977-; *ai:* Pi Mu Epsilon 1972-; NY St Tchrs Assn; AFT; *office:* Saratoga Spgs Sr HS 186 West Ave Saratoga Springs NY 12866

DEMAIO, BARBARA KOLENOVSKY, Jr High Math Teacher; *b:* Manhattan, NY; *m:* Vincent A.; *ed:* Queens Coll (BA) Eng Ed 1984; Brooklyn Diocese 15 Credit Hrs; Brooklyn Coll 9 Grad Credits; Fordham Univ 3 Grad Credits; *cr:* St Cecilia Schl Jr High Tchr 1984-89; Most Precious Blood Jr High Tchr 1989-; *ai:* Schl Play; 8th Grd Fac Vllybl Game; Mid Sts Steering Comm Chair; HS Fair; 8th Grd Grad Act; NCEA 1984-; Immaculate Conception Church 1989-, Eucharistic Minister; Astoria Folk Group 1989-, Singer; *office:* Most Precious Blood Schl 3252 37th St Long Island City NY 11103

DE MAIO, RON, Director of STAC; *b:* New York, NY; *ed:* Adelphi Univ (BA) Eng, Ed 1969, (MA) Eng 1971; Queens Coll; *cr:* Herricks HS Eng Tchr 1969-79, Dir STAC 1979-; *ai:* Thespian Soc 1990-92; Herricks Repertory Co 1969-73; NYSTA 1993-, NYSUT 1969-; Fulbright Exchange 2 Yrs London 1973-75; *office:* Herricks HS 100 Shelter Rock Rd New Hyde Park NY 11040*

DEMARCO, CARLA ANN, English Teacher; *b:* Berwick, PA; *ed:* Juniata Coll (BA) Ed & Eng 1986; IN Univ of PA (MA) Tchng Eng 1987; 15 Credit Hrs Towards Guid Cnslng Degree; *cr:* Aberdeen HS Eng Tchr 1988-92; Susquehanna Region Pvt Industry Cncl Inc Basic Ed Specialist 1992; Harford Tech HS Eng Tchr 1992-; *ai:* Forensics Coach; ARD Comm; NEA 1988-; NCTE 1988-94; MSTA 1988-; Toastmasters 1991-92; Numerous Articles Pub; *office:* Harford Technical HS 200 Thomas Run Rd Bel Air MD 21015*

DEMARCO, HELEN KINDER, Literature & Lang Arts Tchr; *b:* Plainfield, NJ; *m:* Raymond P.; *c:* Nancy, Susan; *ed:* Univ of DE (BA) Eng 1961; Attnd Banff Schl of Fine Arts, Kean Coll; *cr:* Courier News Reporter 1961-63; Wm Woodruff Schl 4th Grd Tchr 1965-69; Holy Cross Pre-Kndgtn Head Tchr 1978-82; St Josephs K-8th Grd Art Tchr 1982-84; OLMV 7th-8th Grd Lit & Lang Arts Tchr & Chprsn 1984-; *ai:* MS Lit Magazine; NMSA 1 Yr; NCEA 1984-; *office:* Our Lady Of Mt Virgin Schl Drake Ave Middlesex NJ 08846

DEMARCO, JILL ESTHER, Music Teacher; *b:* Euclid, OH; *m:* Samuel; *c:* Alyssa; *ed:* Coll of Wooster (BME) Music & Voice 1987; Spliipery Rock Univ 6 Credit Hrs; DuQuesne Univ 15 Credit Hrs; *cr:* Wooster City Schl Dist Elem & Jr High Music Tchr 1987-88; St John the Bapt Elem & Jr High Music Tchr 1989-90; Rhema Chrstn Schl Elem & Jr High Music Tchr 1989-90; Western Beaver Schl Dist Jr & Sr HS Vocal Music & Gen Music Tchr 1990-; *ai:* Show Choir; Chamber Choir; Schl Musical; NEA 1990-; MENC 1990-; Chrstn Assembly Church 1989-, Yth Ldr; *office:* Western Beaver Co Jr Sr HS 216 Engle Rd Industry PA 15052

DEMARCO, PETER GEORGE, Mathematics Teacher; *b:* Queens, NY; *ed:* Fairfield Univ (BS) Math 1983; Montclair St Univ (MA) Math 1988; *cr:* Greenwich HS Math Tchr 1983-84; Immaculate Heart Acad Math Tchr 1984-85; Monroe-Woodbury HS Math Tchr 1985-88; Minisink Valley HS Math Tchr 1988-; *ai:* Head Var Boys Soccer Coach, Frosh Boys Indoor Soccer Coach; Soph Class Adv; ATF 1983-; *office:* Minisink Valley HS PO Box 217 Slate Hill NY 10973

DEMARCO, ZONIA S., Guidance Counselor; *b:* Nanticoke, PA; *m:* Robert; *c:* C. J., Lindsey; *ed:* East Stroudsburg Univ (BS) Hlth & PE 1971, (MS) Hlth & PE 1979; Kean Coll Stu Prsnl Cert 1983; *cr:* Salk MS Hlth & PE Tchr 1971-83; Carl Sandburg MS Guidance Cnslr 1983-93; Old Bridge HS West Guidance Cnslr 1993-; *ai:* NEA, MCEA, OBEA 1971-; MC Prsnl & Guidance Assn 1983-; *office:* Old Bridge HS West Campus 363 Route 516 Old Bridge NJ 08857

DEMAREST, ROBERT A., Earth Science Teacher; *b:* Hackensack, NJ; *m:* Shirley Anne Phillips; *c:* Daniel D., Jonathan M., Laurie Lynn Demarest Jordan; *ed:* William Paterson Coll (MA) Field Natural His 1966, (BA) Bio, Gen Sci 1967; 65 Addl Credits Earth Sci Univ of Southern IL, Earth, Field Sci Montclair St Coll, East Stroudsburg Univ, Penn St Univ; *cr:* Essie Olive Abeel Pvt Schl Dorm Headmaster, Sub Tchr 1958-62; Hackettstown Elem Schl Sci Dept Head, 8th Grd Sci Tchr 1962-67; Pocono Mtn Jr Sr HS Earth Sci, Bio, Phys Sci 1967-; *ai:* Pocono Mtn Ed Assn 1967-, Negotiations Comm 1970-80; PSEA, NEA 1967-; Emply Summer Nat Pk Sev Ranges 1983-; Mn Cnty Planning Comm 1976-88; Poc Twsp Planning Comm 1976-, Vice-Chair, Chm; Poc Mtn And Soc 1974-82, Pres; Messing Nature Ctr Bd Dir 1976-84, Vice-Chair, Bd Mem; Millbrook Village Soc 1978-, Pres; Millbrook Village Demonstrator Woodworking Skills 1800 Village; NSF South IL Univ 1968; Tchr of Yr 1972; *home:* HC 1 Tannersville PA 18372

DEMARRO, ANGELA E., Music Teacher & Choral Dir; *b:* Saxton, PA; *m:* Vincent J.; *ed:* 9 Credit Hrs Towards M Mus Ed; *cr:* Upper Merion Area HS Music Tchr 1992-; *ai:* Show Choir, Schl Musical Dir; PMEA 1988-; Schl Dist Recognition Awd; *office:* Upper Merion Area HS 435 Crossfield Rd King Of Prussia PA 19406

DEMARS, JANE, Sixth Grade Teacher; *b:* Defiance, OH; *m:* Philip B.; *c:* Kimberly, Stacey; *ed:* Univ of Toledo (BA) El Ed 1976; 28 Grad Hrs El Ed; *cr:* Meadowvale Schl 5th Grd Tchr 1977; Monac Schl 5th Grd Tchr 1977-79; Shoreland Schl 5th Grd Tchr 1979-80, 7th Grd Tchr 1980-81, 6th Grd Tchr 1981-; *ai:* NEA, TAWLS 1977-; *office:* Shoreland Schl Suder & E Harbor Toledo OH 43611

DEMARSE, JOY A., English Teacher; *b:* Malone, NY; *c:* Jaclyne Marcil, Jorja Marcil; *ed:* SUNY at Plattsburgh (BA) Eng & Scndry Ed 1976, (MS) Scndry Ed & Eng 1979; 45 Post Grad Hrs Eng & Educl Admin; *cr:* SUNY at Plattsburg Eng & Ed Instr; Plattsburgh HS Eng Tchr 1977-; *ai:* Drama Club Adv; Past Yrbk & Future Edctrs Adv; NYSUT 1977-; Plattsburgh Tchrs Union 1977-; NCTE; Goals 2000 Comm SUNY Plattsburgh 1995-; St Josephs Church 1977-94, Lector, Parish Cncl Sec & Pres; Wrote One Act Plays for Children; Articles Pub; *office:* Plattsburgh Sr HS Ste 102 1 Clifford Dr Plattsburgh NY 12901*

DEMAS, SANDRA (NIDER), Fifth Grade Teacher; *b:* Binghamton, NY; *c:* Daphne Anne; *ed:* St Univ of NY at Cortland (BS) Elem Ed 1963; Grad Work Univ of CO at Boulder, Southampton Coll; *cr:* Daniel S. Dickinson Schl 1st Grd Tchr 1963-64; Benjamin Franklin Schl 2nd Grd Tchr 1964; Sunrise Drive Schl 1st Grd Tchr 1964-68; Sycamore Ave Schl Kndgtn Tchr 1970-76; Cherokee Street Schl K, 2, 5th Grd Tchr 1976-; *ai:* Connetquot Tchrs Assn Bldg Rep; Grd Level Tchr Rep; Rdng Textbook Selection, Report Card Revision Comms; Supervising Mentor Tchr; AFT, NEA 1970-; CTA 1970-, Bldg Union Rep; *office:* Cherokee Street Elem Schl 130 Cherokee St Ronkonkoma NY 11779*

DEMATTE, ANTOINETTE PARO, Eighth Grade English Teacher; *b:* Steubenville, OH; *c:* Tracy; *ed:* West Liberty St Coll (BA) Eng & Ed 1969; Baldwin Wallace Coll (MA) Ed & Rdng 1981; *cr:* Avon Lake Schls 7th & 8th Grd Eng Tchr 1969-; *ai:* First Yr Tchr Mentor; Lang Arts & ALEA Schlsp Comms; NEA, OEA, ALEA 1969-; Learwood Tchr of Yr 1986; Attnd Various Wkshps in Cooperative Learning, Whole Lang Instruction, Interdisciplinary Planning, Cmptr Introduction; *office:* Learwood MS 340 Lear Rd Avon Lake OH 44012*

DEMATTEIS, ROBERT JOSEPH, Secondary Math Teacher; *b:* Rochester, NY; *m:* Barbara Jean Smith; *c:* Jennifer DeMatteis Simmons, Jeffrey, Elizabeth, Rebecca; *ed:* St John Fisher Coll (BS) Math 1968; Univ of Rochester (MA) Ed 1971; *cr:* Rochester City Schl Dist Math Tchr 1968-71; Webster Cntrl Schl Dist Math Tchr 1971-; *ai:* Bible Stud Adv; Natural Helpers Adv; Webster Tchrs Assn 1991-; New Covenant Fellowship 1989-, Home Fellowship Pastor 20 Yrs; Cntrl Western NY Bd of Women Sports 1991-93, Referee Bsktbl 2 Yr; *office:* Webster HS 875 Ridge Rd Webster NY 14580*

DEMATTEO, LORI (FRANK), Second Grade Teacher; *b:* New Castle, PA; *m:* Gregory S.; *ed:* Slippery Rock Univ (BS) Elem Ed 1988; 24 Credit Hrs; *cr:* St Vitus Elem 3rd Grd Tchr 1989-90; Neshannock Memrl 4th Grd Tchr 1990-91, 2nd Grd Tchr 1991-; *ai:* Curr Comms; PSEA & NEA 1990-; *office:* Neshannock Memrl Schl 299 Mitchell Rd New Castle PA 16105*

DEMATTIES, MARY MC KONE, 4th Grade Teacher; *b:* Geneva, NY; *m:* Michael; *c:* Molly; *ed:* SUNY at Geneseo (BS) Elem Ed 1973, (MS) Elem Ed 1975; 7-12 Soc Stud, Lang Arts Perm Certs; *cr:* Border City Schl K-1 Grd Tchr 1973-74, 1-2 Grd Tchr 1974-76, 7-8 Grd Tchr 1977-88, 5 Grd Tchr 1988-94; LaFayette Elem Schl 4 Grd Tchr1994-; *ai:* Yrbk, Yorker Adv; Soc Stud Curr, Sci Comm Coord; NEA 1976-, Local Pres, VP; Hosp Vol 1973-, 10 Yr Awd; Ec Ed Awd; Border City Schl 20 Yr Tchr Appreciation Awd 1994; *office:* LaFayette Schl 71 Inslee St Waterloo NY 13165

DEMAYO, BETTE J., Mathematics Teacher; *b:* Concord, NH; *m:* Robert E.; *c:* Gary, Robin DeMayo Pollock, Kristen; *ed:* Cntrl CT St Coll (BS) Math 1971; Cntrl CT St Univ (MS) Math 1974; Credit Hrs Acctng, Cmptr Sci, Eng; *cr:* North Haven HS Math Tchr 1971-; *ai:* Class Adv 1996; Chm of Cert of Employability Prgm; Adv of Math Team; Math Rep for Fac Cncl; MAA, NCTM, NEA, NHEA 1971-; Lit Vols 1992-, Tutor of ESL; United Church of Christ 1971-, Asst Treas, Bd of Chrstn Ed; Ulbrich Distngd Tchr Flshp Prgm, Educating for High Performance 1994; Delio J. Rotondo Tchr of Yr 1988; Goals 2000 Rep; Tech, Ldrshp Prgm; GRASP Interdisciplinary Prgm; *office:* North Haven HS 222 Maple Ave North Haven CT 06473*

DEMAYO, DONNA MARIE, High School English Teacher; *b:* Bronx, NY; *ed:* Univ of CT (BA) Eng 1989; Cert Prgm Western CT St Univ 1993; *cr:* Our Lady of Assumption Schl Rdng Tchr 1993; Danbury HS Eng Tchr 1994-; *ai:* Key Club Adv; Curr Cncl Mem; NEA 1994-; 1st Yr Sallie Mae Tchr of Yr Nom; *office:* Danbury HS 47 Clapboard Ridge Rd Danbury CT 06811

DEMCZYK, JILL SCHUE, Chemistry Teacher; *b:* Silver Springs, MD; *m:* Mike; *ed:* Muskingum Coll (BS) Bio 1993; 28 Grad Hrs In Counseling at Univ of Dayton; 6 Grad Hrs in Chem at Miami Univ; *cr:* Edgewood City Schls Chem Tchr 1993-; *ai:* Yrbk Adv; Stu Responsibility Comm; Schl Efficiency Comm; NEA, OEA, SECO 1993-; Church, Sunday Schl Tchr 1995-; *office:* Edgewood HS 5005 Oxford State Rd Trenton OH 45067*

DEMELLIER, MARY ANN TUCKER, 3rd Grade Teacher; *b:* Norwich, NY; *m:* Mark F.; *c:* Sarah, Robert, Molly; *ed:* SUC at Oswego (BS) Elem Ed 1975; 38 Grad Hrs; *cr:* Norwich City Schls Tchr 1976-; *ai:* NEA 1976-; *office:* Stanford J Gibson Elem Schl Ridgeland Dr Norwich NY 13815

DE MELLO, MARY ANN, HS Sci Tchr & MS Curr Coord; *b:* Fall River, MA; *ed:* Springfield Coll (BS) PE, Bio Minor 1982; Bridgewater St Coll (MS) Exercise Sci 1985; Addl 60 Credit Hrs Sci, Schl Admin; *cr:* Rockland Pub Schls Sci Tchr 1983-; Massasoit Comm Coll Sci Tchr Continuing Ed 1987-91; Bridgewater St Coll Advanced Stud Prgm, Sci Tchr 1991-; *ai:* Var Girls Sftbl Coach; NST 1985-; Horace Mann Promising Practice; *office:* Rockland Pub Schls 34 Mac Kinlay Way Rockland MA 02370

DEMENT, MARTHA MALLOTT, Mathematics Teacher; *b:* Defiance, OH; *m:* Norman Hall Jr.; *c:* Matthew Grafton; *ed:* Bowling Green St Univ (MS) Ed 1987; *cr:* Bryan HS Eng & Math Tchr 1982-87; Defiance HS Math Tchr 1987-; *ai:* Math Team & Club Adv; Math Dept Chair; Track Coach; NEA 1982-; Defiance City Ed Assn 1987-, Pres; OCTM, Site Supvr; NCTM; Saint John UCC 1971-, Deacon, Consistory Sec; Defiance Zoo 1994-, Comm Mem; *office:* Defiance HS 1755 Palmer Dr Defiance OH 43512*

DEMEO, KATHLEEN AGNES, Retired Teacher; *b:* Bronx, NY; *m:* Donald J.; *c:* Teresa, Donald, Edward; *ed:* Notre Dame (BA) Eng Ed 1961; Coll of Staten Is (MS) Eng Ed 1970; 30 Credit Hrs Women's Lit, Creative Writing; NYC Consortium Writing 3 Terms; *cr:* Port Richmond HS Sub Eng Tchr 1961-69, Reg Eng Tchr 1970-95; *ai:* UFT 1968-; Poetry Pub Amherst Soc 1989; Tchr of Yr 1987.*

DEMEO, MICHAEL, Social Studies Teacher; *b:* Cambridge, MA; *m:* Kathleen; *c:* Joseph, John; *ed:* Providence Coll (BA) Ed 1960, (MED) Ed 1971; *cr:* Jamestown Soc Stud Tchr 1960-63; Warren HS Soc Stud Tchr 1963-93; Mt Hope High Soc Stud Tchr 1993-; *ai:* Class Adv 1963-67; NEA 1960-; Warren Ed Assn 1963-93, Pres 1968; NSF 1967; *office:* Mount Hope HS 166 Chestnut St Bristol RI 02809

DEMERS, ANN MARIE KRESGE, Related Cosmetology Teacher; *b:* New Bedford, MA; *m:* James M.; *ed:* Voc Cert Fitchburg St Coll; *cr:* Fantastic Sam's Salon Mgr 1987-92; J.C. Penney Styling Salon Mgr 1992-94; LaBaron Hairdressing Acad Cosmetology Instr 1990-94; Gr NB Reg Voc Tech HS Cosmetology Instr 1994-; *ai:* Cosmetology Assn 1987-; Clairol Prof Hair Colorist 1990-, Color Cnslr; *office:* Greater New Bedford Reg Voc HS 1121 Ashley Blvd New Bedford MA 02745

DEMERS, BONNIE SMITH, First Grade Teacher; *b:* Amerstdam, NY; *w:* Peter (dec); *ed:* SUC at Oneonta (BS) Elem Ed 1968; SUC at Plattsburgh (MS) Elem Ed 1976; 71 Post Grad Hrs; *cr:* Lamberton Elem Schl First Grd Tchr 1968-70, 1973-80, Kndgtn Tchr 1970-72; Harison Elem Schl First Grd Tchr 1972-73; St Joseph Comm Schl Second Grd Tchr 1988-89, First Grd Tchr 1989-; *ai:* Star Schls Lead Tchr 2 Yrs; Stu Cncl Adv 8 Yrs; Schl Improvement Comm 2 Yrs; Cmptr Tchr, Consultant 16 Yrs; Union Rep 1968-, Schl Rep; Malone Fed of Tchrs, NEA 1968-; Girl Scouts 1968-88, Ldr, Prgm Coord; Project Outreach 1990-, Minister to Elderly Homebound; St John Bosco CCD 1992-, Tchr & Coord Prek-8, Layminister 1995-, Yth Ministry; *office:* St Josephs Elem Schl 111 Elm St Malone NY 12953*

DEMERS, DAVID P., Teacher in Charge; *b:* Glens Falls, NY; Block; *c:* Gregg; *ed:* SUNY at New Paltz (BA) Eng & Scndry (MA) Eng & Ed 1972; *cr:* Saugerties HS Eng Tchr 1967-69; W Falls Jr High Eng Tchr 1969-86, Tchr in Charge 1986-; Ulster C Coll Adj Prof 1985-87; *ai:* Newspaper & IM Adv; Stu Mentor; Instr; Educl Dev, Discipline & Curr Comm; AFT 1969-; NYSI NCTE; New Paltz Rescue Squad Past Mem; New Paltz Friends in Help Past Mem; Memrl Lib Bd of Trustees Past Mem & VP *office:* Wappingers Jr HS 90 Remsen Ave Wappingers Falls NY

DEMERS, ROBERT A., Professor of Chemistry; *b:* Taunton Helen Callahan; *c:* Kelly, John; *ed:* Bridgewater St Coll (BS) E Boston coll (MS) Chemistry 1965; Post Grad Courses Bridgewat Lowell Univ, SMU, Northeastern Univ; *cr:* K. J. Quinn Inc Chemist 1965-67; MaSSASOIT Comm Coll Prof of Chemis Satuit Chem Co Consultant 1970-; *ai:* ACS 1985-; MTA, NI *office:* Massasoit Comm Coll 1 Massasoit Blvd Brockton MA 0

DEMETRICIAN, CAROL ANN SESTERAK, Soc Stud & Lang Tchr; *b:* Perth Amboy, NJ; *m:* William John; *c:* Elizabeth Glassboro St Coll (BA) Gen Elem Ed 1965; 22 Credit Hrs; *cr:* Twp Bd of Ed Tchr 1965-72; Lyndhurst Bd of Ed Tchr 1972-; NJEA 1965-; LTA 1972-; *office:* Jefferson Schl 336 Lake Ave NJ 07071

DEMETRIOU, DIANTHA KATHRYN, Teacher & Arts Dept New York, NY; *m:* Edward Raymond Simpson III; *ed:* Adelphi Eng 1978; NY Univ (MA) Eng & Amer Lit 1983; *cr:* St Demetrio Schl Eng Tchr 1978-80; Liz Claiborne Inc Acct Rep 1990-91; D Acad Music, Drama, Eng Tchr 1985-89, Dean of Stu Concerns, D Accompanist of Liturgical Chorus 1991-; *ai:* Glee Club Music I Dir of Schl Musicals; Dir of One Act Plays; Proofreader Con Blue Ribbon Schls Document; Collegiate Chorale 1985-94, Singer; NY Christmas Revels 1986-, Asst Music Dir, Sing Dominican Acad 44 E 68th St New York NY 10021

DEMKO, JOSEPH ANDREW, Science Teacher; *b:* Punxsuta *ed:* IN Univ of PA (BS) Bio 1985; Robert Morris Coll MBA Prg Hrs; *cr:* Punxsutawney Area HS Sci Tchr 1986-88; United 7th Int Sci Tchr 1988-91; Aliquippa HS Sci Tchr 1992-; *ai:* Sci Club NEA 1986-; Aliquippa Ed Assn 1992-; Fraternal Order of Eag Benevolent & Protective Order of Elks 1986-; *office:* Aliq Harding Ave Aliquippa PA 15001*

DEMO, CARL FRANCIS,JR., High School English Teacher; *b.* YR; *m:* Dianne Mary Downer; *c:* Jeffrey, Scott; *ed:* Univ of (BA) Psych 1965; 44 Addl Credit Hrs at SUNY at Oneonta & Cortland; *cr:* Little Falls HS Eng Tchr & Boys Jr Var Bsk 1965-71; Immaculate Heart HS Eng Tchr & Boys Var Bsk 1971-74; Hilton HS Eng Tchr & Boys Var Bsktbl Coach 1974-8 Advy Cncl Chm; Immaculate Heart HS Coached Sectional Cham Bsktbl 1972-73; NYSUT 1974-; Hilton HS Tchr of Yr 1992-93; Fredonia "Exceptional Tchr" Awd 1992; NYS Coaches Assn Cer Awd; *office:* Hilton Central HS 400 East Ave Hilton NY 14468*

DE MONIC, BETTY L., Music Teacher; *b:* Hinton, WV; *m:* Ja *ed:* Concord Coll (BS) Music Ed 1971; WV Univ (MM) Music 32 Credit Hrs Stud in Voice, Opera Theater; *cr:* Morgantown Jr Music Tchr 1973-74; Sabraton Jr HS Vocal Music Tchr 1974 Dickinson HS Vocal Music, Drama Tchr 1975-83; Franklin Music Tchr, Musical Theater 1983-; Amer Acad of Dramatic A Vocal Production, Adj Fac 1988-; *ai:* Spring Musical, Fall Drama Dir; Madrigal Singers, Concert Choir Dir; Stage Mgr; NE NJMEA, CJMEA 1983-; MENC 1967-; Governor's Excl in T 1992; *office:* Franklin HS 415 Francis St Somerset NJ 08873*

DEMOS, BRENDA SUZANNE, Visual Arts Educator; *b:* Colun *c:* Olivia Suzanne Kearns; *ed:* Capital Univ (BA) Arts Ed 1976; Hrs OH St Univ; *cr:* Worthington Schls HS Art Tchr 1976-78, Tchr 1978-83, MS Art Tchr 1983-84, HS Art Tchr 1984-; *ai* Mngmt Comm; Art Shows & Competitions Art Dept Contact; C & Fine Artist Work on Commission; Worthington Educ Assn 19 Yrs, Bldg Rep 11 Yrs; Scholarship Fundraising 2 Yrs; Negotiatic 3 Yrs; P.A.C. Comm 3 yrs, Chair 1 Yr; N.E.A. Convention Local 4 Yrs; OEA Rep Assembly Del 8 Yrs, Election Chair 5 Yrs; O 1976-; OH Art Ed Assn 1976-, Secondary Div Chr Bd of Outstdng Art Tchr Awd Central Div; Conf Comm-Mailer & Adde 2 Yrs; Kiwanis 1991-; Eastern Star 1976-; Bexley Area Art Gu Sec Second Pl Oils & Acrylics H M Graphite & Drawing; Worthin Cncl 1983-85, Bd of Dirs; New Albany First Church of Nazaren Pres 1993-94; Order of Amaranth 1995-; Sr Recognition Prgm Ce Stu Appreciation Day Thomas Worthington HS; Outstandi Women of Amer 1988; Outstdng Art Tchr Awd; *office:* W Kilbourne HS 1499 Hard Rd Columbus OH 43235*

DEMOS, ROGER D., Physics Teacher; *m:* Barbara J. Rock; *c:* Matthew; *ed:* Drexel Inst of Tech (BS) Civil Engrng 1968; Dr (MS) Civil Engrng 1970; Train Mechanical Universe HS Adapta Operation Physics Trained Instr; 48 Addl Post Grad Credits; *c* Newton Sr HS Physics Tchr 1970-84; Haverford Sr HS Physics T *ai:* Sci Olympiad Coach; Haverford HS Fac Advy; Cncl Chm; Planning, Sci Dept Outcome Base Ed, Awds Comm; PTO; NE 1970-; NSTA 1985-; AAPT 1986-; Wallingford Presbyn Chur Elder, Trustee, Deacon; Rose Tree Fire Co 1966-, VP, Sec; Operation Physics Wkshps Elem Tchrs; *office:* Haverford HS 20 Havertown PA 19083*

DE MOTT, BERNADETTE, Secondary English Teacher; *b:* Li NY; *c:* Scott, Erica; *ed:* SUNY at Oswego (BA) Eng, Writing (MS) Scndry Ed 1994; *cr:* Syracuse City Schls Eng Tchr 1992-; *a* Adv; Girls Var Swimming Coach 7 Yrs; Amer Red Cross Aquati Henninger HS 600 Robinson St Syracuse NY 13206

DEMOUGIN, KATHLEEN S., Science Teacher; *b:* Cincinnati Univ of Cincinnati (BS) Elem Ed 1986; Northern KY Univ (M 1989; Attnd Miami Univ, Univ of Dayton; *cr:* Glen Este MS 1986-; *ai:* CORE Team; Sci Ed Cncl of OH, NSTA 1986-; Tchr L Glen Este MS 4342 Glen Este Withamsville Rd Cincinnati OH 4

DEMPSEY, DOUGLAS MARK, Fifth Grade Teacher; *b:* Atlant Jill Schlegel; *c:* Luke M., Hannah L., Abigail G., Sarah C.; *ed:* Univ (BS) Elem Ed 1988; Loyola Coll (MS) Guidance & Counsel *cr:* Bel Air HS Ftbl Coach 1985-; Homestead Elem Schl 5th 1988-; *ai:* Var Ftbl Coach 1985-; *office:* Homestead-Wakefield 900 S Main St Bel Air MD 21014

DEMPSEY, LANCE, World Studies Teacher; *b:* Yonkers, NY; B.; *c:* Ryan, Katie; *ed:* Univ of MD (BS) Elem Ed 1974; Western (MS) Curr & Instruction 1995; Grad Work 9 Credits in Ge Working on MS in Admin & Supervision; *cr:* St Michaels Cath S 6th Grd Tchr 1976-78; Chevy Chase Elem 3rd & 5th Grd Tchr Earle B. Wood MS 7th & 8th Grd World Stud Tchr 1989-; Geographic Geography Bee Spon; Adopt-A-Ship Prgm; MD Ge Alliance, MD Cncl for Soc Stud 1991-; NCSS 1992-; MD MS As Assoc for Supervision & curr 1993; Flower Valley PTA 1985-, Scouts of Amer 1985-90, Brownie Ldr; Early Adolescence, Soc Cert; Soc Stud Exemplars Project; World Heritage Curr Writer; for Argus, Japan Inst 1995; World Heritage Youth Forum US

›lo MD Rep 1993; *home:* 15105 Westbury Rd Rockville MD

Y, LESLIE MC COY, Fifth Grade Teacher; *b:* Trenton, NJ; *m:* isa, Steven, Marc; *ed:* West Chester Univ (BS) Elem Ed 1969; Jniv (MS) Eng, Lang Arts 1990; Rosemont Coll Six Credit Hrs; ster Univ Three Credit Hrs; *cr:* Ridley Schl Dist Elem Tchr 10 mptr Tech Lead Tchr; Lang Arts Redirection Comm; Yrbk Ed; IM strl Support Team Mem; PSEA, NEA, REA 1986-; ATMOPAV ıer Heart Assn 1990-, Vol; Exec Comm 1995-; St John's Day Care ıcl 1995-, Sec; *office:* Edgewood Elem Schl 525 8th Ave Folsom

ER, DAVID ALLAN, Amer Govt & Economics Teacher; *b:* CA; *ed:* Trenton St Coll (BA) His Ed 1973; *cr:* Hamilton HS Stud Tchr 1974-82; Hamilton HS North Soc Stud Tchr 1982-; *ai:* Boys Soccer, Asst Wrestling, Baseball Coach; NEA, NJEA, 75-; Ancient Order of Hibernians 1987-; *office:* Hamilton HS 5 Klockner Rd Trenton NJ 08619

O, RICHARD RAY, Business Teacher; *b:* Adrian, MI; *m:* :.; *c:* Amanda Hitchcock, Samantha Leigh; *ed:* Indiana Univ of 3us Ed 1969; *cr:* Riverside Jr Sr HS Bus Tchr 1 Yr; Nationwide Co Claims Adjustor 3 Yrs; North East HS Bus Tchr 22 Yrs; *ai:* 74-, Treas, Pres; NEA 1974-; *office:* North East HS North East North East PA 16428

RI, ALEXANDER G., Eighth Grade Teacher; *b:* Paterson, NJ; *m:* venzale; *c:* Alex; *ed:* William Paterson Coll (BA) Elem Ed 1985; Hrs; *cr:* Paterson Pub Schls #5 Eighth Grd Tchr 10 Yrs; *ai:* ol Pgrm; Paterson Ed Assn, NJ Ed Assn, NEA 1986-; Passaic Cty 986-, Del; *home:* 4 Midland Ave Hawthorne NJ 07506*

LA, ALBERT JOSEPH, Fifth Grade Teacher; *b:* New k, NJ; *m:* Geraldine; *c:* John, Courtney; *ed:* Monmouth Coll (BS) 1968; Trenton St Coll (ME) Elem Ed 1978; *cr:* Somerville Pub Grd Tchr 1969-74, 6th-8th Grd MS Tchr 1974-93, 5th Grd Tchr Ecology Club & IM Adv; NEA, NJEA & SEA 1968-; Somerville soc 1968-, VP & Chief Negotiator; *office:* Somerville Pub Schls t Somerville NJ 08876

LA, ANNE CALATE, Social Studies Teacher; *b:* New York City, Michael; *c:* Matthew, Stephanie; *ed:* St Francis Coll (BA) His n Paterson Coll (MA) GATE 1983; Tchng Certs, Post Grad Stud Eng as a Second Lang; *cr:* Union City Bd of Ed 5th Grd Tchr Bergen Ctr for Child Dev Tchr Asst 1978-79; Univ City Bd of Ed c Stud 1979-; *ai:* Schl Improvement Team; Mini Model Congress Cncl; NEA, NJEA 1979-; NCSS 1989-; Intnl Brotherhood of s Labor Stud Schlsp; Consultant for Search Magazine.

)LA, DESIREE DIANE, College Prep & AP Eng Teacher; *b:* A; *ed:* Kutztown St Coll (BS) Eng, Speech 1969; 24 Addl Credits; Coll Lehigh Valley Partnership 1988; Lehigh Univ, Allentown gh Valley Partnership 1991; Grad P.L.S., Wilkes Coll; *cr:* Bangor S 8th Grd Eng 1969-77, 7th Grd Eng 1977-84, 9th CP Eng, 8th 84-91, 9th CP Eng, 9th General, 8th Grd Eng 1991-93; 8th & 9th ng; *ai:* Jr HS Drama Dir; Spec Security Police for Schl Ath, Soc Verbal Review Educator, Instr; NEA, BAEA 1969-; PSEA 1969-, ip Dev Comm 1972-76; Delta Kappa Gamma 1988-; 2nd VP Pres 1996-; Bethlehem Spec Olympics 1989-94, PR Coord 3 Yrs, end 1991; US Army Reserve 1977-84, SP5 7 Yrs, Commanders ip 1980; WLVT-TV Ch 39 PBS 1988-, Co Chair of Mem Drive Burnside Plantation 1990-94, Guide, Historic Interpreter; Lehigh artnership Shakespear in Performance Fellow 1988; PA Adopt a gle Participant Pub Ed Partners, Promoters Awd 1987; Lehigh ıs Educ Partnership Summer 1993, 1994, Day Times Inc Product Stud Planner; AT & T Allentown Works P.R. Dept; Lihigh Valley ip Native Amer Lit Lenni Lenape Fellow 1991; Someone Special utstdng Service to Comm 1994; *office:* Bangor Area Jr H S 401 ıts/Richmond Rd Bangor PA 18013*

LO, PATRICIA NOCETTI, First Grade Teacher; *b:* New York *m:* Lloyd A.; *c:* Lloyd D., Marina; *ed:* Fordham Univ (BS) Elem 6 Credit Hrs Scndry Ed; 6 Credit Hrs Theology; 7th-12th Grd Cert *cr:* PS 41 NYC 2nd-3rd Grd Tchr 1962-64; PS 91 NYC 5th Grd 4-66; *ai:* Schl Talent Show; NCEA 1982-; Ascension Schl Bd adies Aux BPOE 1984-, Fund Raising; Outstdng Edctr Arch of 1995; Poem Pub; *home:* 265 Monmouth Ave New Milford NJ

RIS, PETER RICHARD, Fourth Grade Teacher; *b:* Brooklyn, NY; D.; *ed:* SUNY at Genesco (BS) Elem Ed 1970; SUNY at Brockport Admin 1973, (SAS) Ed Admin 1994; *cr:* Gates Chili Cntrl Schls 70-; *ai:* K-6 Math Comm Chprsn 1992-; NYSUT 1970-; PDK CTM 1992-, Curr; *office:* Neil Armstrong Elem Schl 3273 Lyell ester NY 14606*

, AMY PATRICIA, 3rd Grade Teacher; *b:* Detroit, MI; *ed:* St Univ (BS) Early Chldhd Ed 1984, (MED) Rdng 1990; 60 Credit ond Masters; *cr:* Kingsville Elem Tchr 1984-; *ai:* Coach Odyssey Iind 1986-, 3 World Finals Winner; MSTA 1984-; Winner Jack Awd 1991; Baltimore Cty Chamber of Commerce Excl in Ed 1991 & 1993; *office:* Kingsville Elem Schl 7300 Sunshine Ave le MD 21087

, NILES K., Instrumental Music Teacher; *b:* Louisville, NY; *m:* oyer; *c:* Jeffery, Brian, Scott, Brett; *ed:* SUNY at Fredonia (BM) 1 1970, (MM) Music Ed, Performance 1973; *cr:* Univ of Buffalo 93-; East Sr HS Band Dir 1970-; *ai:* NVSSMA Festival Chm 1993; ECMEA Jazz Ensemble Chm 1992-93; NYSSMA, MENC CMEA, NYSTA 1970-; Eric Cty Wind Ensemble 1979-, Prsnl Mgr, 1 of Dir; Amer Legion Band of Tonawondus Post 264 1973-, Bd of falo Silver Band 1992-; East Sr HS Tchr of Yr 1994; *office:* West East Sr HS 4760 Seneca St West Seneca NY 14224*

)N, JOHN FRANCIS, English Teacher & Drama Dir; *b:* r, NY; *m:* Martha Thigpen; *c:* Tara L., Tyler J.; *ed:* Univ of er (BA) Eng 1964, (MA) Ed 1969; Eastman Schl of Music Scndry ert 1974; Univ of Rochester Scndry Admin, Supervision Cert; g Univ of Rochester EDD Prgm 1990; *cr:* Pittsford HS Eng Tchr ; Pittsford Mendon HS Eng Tchr, Drama Dir 1972-; Univ of er Stu Tchrs Eng Supv 1991-; *ai:* Prod, Dir Plays & Musicals; AFT, NYSUT 1966-; Pittsford Dist Tchrs Assn 1964-; NY St PTA Flwshp d; NY St Eng Cncl Excl in Tchng Drama Awd; Pittsford PTSA Life Awd; *office:* Pittsford Mendon HS 472 Pittsford Mendon Rd NY 14534

E, DONNA EMILE MARIE, English Teacher; *b:* Worcester, MA; ıehill Coll (BA) Eng & Scndry Ed 1977; Howard Univ (MA) ance Drama 1985; Attnd Middlebury Coll Breadloaf Schl of Eng; ard Univ Grad Asst 1978-82; Foxcroft Schl 10th-12th Grd Eng 82-87; St Albans Schl 9th & 11th-12th Grd Eng Tchr 1987-; *ai:* St Diversity Comm Co-Chprsn; Schl Lit Magazine for Stdnts Fac Adv; Comm; Poetry Comm for Greater WA 1986-, Bd Mem; Poets & 1995-; Friends of the Folger 1991-; Dayspring Bahai Schl Chair & ıair; Grants: Folger Tchr Inst Shakespeare 1984 & 1988-89, ury Coll, Breadloaf Lincoln Coll & Oxford Univ 1986, Johns Hopkins Writers Conf 1986; Appt By Gov Robb to St Advy Bd on Voc Ed; *office:* Saint Albans HS Mt Saint Alban Washington DC 20016

DENKENBERGER, CHARLES DEAN, Math Teacher & Dept Chair; *b:* Elmira, NY; *m:* Martha Holcomb; *c:* Sean S., Nate S., David D., Thomas D.; *ed:* Mansfield St Coll (BA) Math Ed 1970; Wilkes Univ (MS) Math Ed 1975; Attnd Penn St, Marywood Coll; *cr:* Elk Lake HS Math Tchr 1970-; *ai:* Tennis Coach 18 Yrs; Chess Club Adv; NEA, PSEA 1970-; NCTM 1993-; Nature Conservancy 1985-, Bd; Montrose Camera CLub 1980-, Pres 2 Yrs; *office:* Elk Lake HS PO Box 100 Dimock PA 18816

DENKEWALTER, LORI KATHLEEN, Spanish Teacher; *b:* Urband, OH; *c:* Murphy Ritter; *ed:* Marietta Coll (BA) Span, Ed 1983; Univ of Dayton (MA) Educl Admin; Middleburg Coll (MA) Span; Univ of Northern IA; Summer Spain; OH St Univ Ecuador Stud Prgm; *cr:* Springfield South HS Span Tchr 1985-; Wittenburg Univ Span Instr 1994-95; *ai:* Span Club, Hlth Insurance Comms; OFLA 1990-; Soroptimist, Sec; Champaign Cty Humane Assn 1992-; *office:* Springfield South HS 700 S Limestone St Springfield OH 45505*

DENMAN, THOMAS CHARLES, Science Teacher; *b:* Toledo, OH; *c:* Christopher L., Gregory T.; *ed:* Univ of Toledo (BS) Bio 1966; MI St Univ (MS) Biological Sci 1972; *cr:* Libbey HS Sci Tchr 1968-91; Univ of Toledo Comm & Tech Coll Part-time Instr 1976-87; Owens Comm Coll Part-time Instr 1980-84; Roy C. Start HS Sci Tchr 1991-; *ai:* Jefferson-Madison Ldrshp Team; Cross Cntry Coach 1976-78; Bldg Comm 1981, 1986-87; Textbook Comms; Environ Sci Club Adv; Area Water Quality Testing Prgm 1990-94; AFT, OFT, Toledo Fed of Tchrs 1975-; Investigating Solid Waste Curr OH Dept of Natural Resources; Partner in Excl 1990-91; Outstdng HS Sci Tchr Awd Sigma XI Univ of Toledo 1995; Presidential Commendation 1991; *office:* Roy C. Start HS 2100 Tremainsville Rd Toledo OH 43613

DENNER, DAVID THOMAS, Earth Science Teacher; *b:* Painesville, OH; *m:* Therese Ann Kish; *c:* Katie, Sarah, Matthew, Rebecca, Joshua; *ed:* OH Univ (BSEd) PE, Bio 1975; Coll of Mt St Joseph (MS) Ed 1987; *cr:* Painesville Twp Elem Schls K-5 PE, Adaptive PE Tchr 1985-93; Riverside HS Bio Tchr 1993-94; Riverside Elem Schls K-5 PE Tchr 1994-95; John R. Williams 8th Grd Earth Sci Tchr 1995-; *ai:* Var Defensive Line Ftbl Coach; Head Var Boys Track; Jr HS Girls Bsktbl; FCA Adv; NEA, OEA 1985-; Riverside Comm Ath Fnd 1994-, VP; Riverside #1 Club; *office:* Riverside HS 585 Riverside Dr Painesville OH 44077*

DENNEY, CAROL MARGARET, English Teacher; *b:* Evanston, IL; *m:* Michael Baxter; *c:* Jacqueline, Kate, William; *ed:* Denison Univ Ed, Eng 1985; OH St Univ (MA) Eng Ed; 6 Credit Hrs; *cr:* Westerville North HS Eng Tchr 1985-; *ai:* Boys & Girls Tennis Coach 1985-87; Ski Club 1985-86; Choreographer 1987-89; NEA, OEA, WEA 1985-; Northpointe Neighborhood Assn 1995-, Comm Chprsn; *office:* Westerville North HS 950 County Line Rd Westerville OH 43081*

DENNING, NANCY H., Home & Career Skills Teacher; *b:* Schnectady, NY; *m:* Kevin G.; *c:* Mairanne, Michael; *ed:* Vermont Coll (AA) Liberal Arts 1972; SUNY at Oneonta (BSEd) Home Ecs Ed 1974, (MSEd) Home Ecs Ed 1977; *cr:* West Jr HS Home Ecs Tchr 1974-77; West MS Home, Careers Tchr 1977-85; East MS Home, Careers Tchr 1986-; *ai:* Shared Decision Making Team; Schl-to-Work, Outcomes Comms; NYSHETA, BTA, NEA 1974-; Northminster Presby Church 1988-, Chrstn Spec Events Chm; *office:* East MS 167 E Frederick St Binghamton NY 13904

DENNIS, JUDITH E., English Teacher; *b:* New Britain, CT; *m:* Roger W.; *ed:* Douglass Coll (AB) Eng 1962; Wesleyan Univ (MALS) Lbrl Stud 1972; *cr:* Conard HS Eng Tchr 1962-66; Walnut HS Eng Tchr 1967-69; Druid HS Eng Tchr 1969-74; Lewis Mills HS Eng Tchr 1975-; *ai:* Tchr of Yr 1995-.

DENNIS, MICHAEL LEE, Physical Ed & Health Instr; *b:* Loudonville, OH; *m:* Denise Lynn Lortz; *c:* Aysha R., Michael A., Megan A.; *ed:* Ashland Univ (BS) PE, Hlth, LD 1983; Univ of Findlay (MS) Ed 1996; *cr:* Hillsdale HS PE, Hlth Tchr 1984-85; Lexington HS Learning Disabilities Tutor 1986-87; Carey HS Tchr of Learning Disabilities 1988-89; Hardin Northern HS PE, Hlth Tchr 1989-; *ai:* Care Team; Asst Var Ftbl, Asst Var Bsktbl Coach; Prom Promise; OH Ftbl Coaches Assn, NW OH Ftbl Coaches Assn 1986-; OH Bsktbl Coaches Assn 1988-; Loudonville HS Ath Hall of Fame; *office:* Hardin Northern HS 11589 State Route 81 Dola OH 45835*

DENNIS, NANCY CLEMONS, Specialist; *b:* Nashua, NH; *m:* Robert; *c:* Cynthia Baker, Kerry Willett, Robert IV; *ed:* Regis Coll (BA) Latin 1962; Notre Dame Coll (MA) Learning Disabilities 1990; Post Grad Stud in Emotional & Behavioral Disorders; *cr:* Manchester Cntrl Asst Tchr of Learning Disabilities 1978-88; Manchester West Specialist of Learning Disabilities 1989-; *ai:* Curr Comm; Comm of Caring; Assessment Comm; NEA, ASCD, LDA, NH Classical Assn 1989-; NH Hum Assn 1993-; CBM 1993-, Dir; Coffey Post Amer Legion 1960-; Lions Club, Bean Fnd & Veterans of Foreign Wars Grants; *office:* Manchester HS West 9 Notre Dame Ave Manchester NH 03102*

DENNIS, ROGER W., English Teacher; *b:* Gadsden, AL; *m:* Judith E.; *ed:* Jacksonville Univ (AB) Eng 1961; Univ of AL (MA) Eng 1963, (PHD) 1972; Univ of London 3 Addl Credit Hrs 1966; Exeter Coll at Oxford 3 Addl Credit Hrs 1967; *cr:* Univ of AL Eng Instr 1967-73; Central CT St Univ Part-Time Eng Instr 1974-; Avon HS Eng Admin 1975-89, Eng Tchr 1989-; *ai:* SCTE, ACLU 1977-; 3 Articles Pub; *home:* 38 Greenwood St New Britain CT 06051

DENNIS, SHERRIE (BICKSLER), Art Teacher; *b:* Akron, OH; *m:* Bill L.; *ed:* KS City Art Inst (BFA) Painting 1972; Amer Univ (MFA) Painting 1975; Univ of Akron Ed Cert Art Ed 1976; *ai:* Art Club; Dept Head; OH Alliance for Arts Ed 1987-, Bd Mem; OH Art Ed Assn 1978-, Regnl VP, Tchr of Yr; OEA, NEA, TLCTA 1978-, Pres, Distinguished Svc Awd; One Woman, Group Art Shows; *office:* Triway HS 3205 Shreve Rd Wooster OH 44691

DENNIS, SUSAN SELENA, Social Studies Teacher; *b:* Tallashassee, FL; *ed:* FL A&M Univ (BS) Home Ec Ed 1967; Howard Univ (MS) Home Ec 1972; Univ of DC Nutrition, Sci ed; *cr:* Broward Cty FL Pub Schls Tchr 1968-71; DC Pub Schls Tchr 1973-; *ai:* Schlsp Comm; Acad of Law, Justice, Security; AFT, DC Tchr Univ 1975-; Delta Sigma Theta 1966-; Kappa Omicron Nu 1972-; Burke Ed Project Achvmt Awd 1988; SE Neighborhood House Cert of Appreciation 1990; Howard Univ Schl of Bus, Small Bus Dev Ctr Cert of Appreciation 1994; *office:* Anacostia Sr HS 16th & R Sts SE Washington DC 20020

DENNIS, TIMOTHY DAVID, Professor & Construction Tech; *b:* Albany, NY; *m:* Marcia Shelmidine; *c:* Kimberly, Kelly; *ed:* Hudson Vly CC (AAS) Construction Tech 1966; Buffalo St (BS) Ind, Voc Ed 1969; SUNY at Albany (MS) Ed Commun 1974; *cr:* Washington-Warren-Hamilton Cty Boces Schls Instr 1969-71; Hudson Vly CC Prof 1971-; *ai:* Construction Club Adv; Bsbl Coach; Construction Cert Prgm Coord; Major Curr Change Proposals; Asst Project Mngmt Team; NYS Assn Two-Yr Colls 1984-; Prof Estimator Org; Colonie Jaycees; United Way-Kiwanis-Rotary Sunnyside Day Care Ctr Project; TD2 Construction Consulting Firm Established & Active 1973; HD & S Dev Pres 1981-; *office:* Hudson Valley Comm Coll 80 Vandenburgh Ave Troy NY 12180

DENNISON, DEBORHA WILAND, Fourth Grade Teacher; *b:* Tewskbury, MA; *m:* Raymond William; *c:* Michele Rene, Raymond E.; *ed:* Univ of MA (BA) Ed 1974; *ai:* You Inc 1975-82; Young Amer Bowling Alliance 1989-90, VP; Worcester Cty Womens Bowling Assn 1995-, VP; Jr Bowlers Auburn Ten Pin 1987-, Pgm Dir; *office:* New Ludlow Elem Schl 1407A Main St Worcester MA 01603

DENNISON, MARGARET ANN MC GUIRE, Principal; *b:* Rochester, NY; *m:* James C.; *c:* James P., Thomas M., Sarah A. Luger, Margaret F.; *ed:* Mercyhurst Coll (BA) Sociology, Soc Stud 1951; Edinboro Univ (MA) Elem Ed Adm 1987; Attnd Univ of Buffalo, Schl of Soc Wk, Kent St Univ, Villa Maria Coll; Edinboro Univ Retraining in Ed; Ursuline Coll Rel Ed; *cr:* NY St Dept of Mental Hygiene Soc Worker 1951-58; St Frances Cabrini Comm Tchr 1970-91, Prin 1991-; *ai:* Consultative Cncl; Finance & Advy, Mrktg & Tech Comms; Dir of Pub Relations; NCEA 1971-; ASCD, Natl Assn Tchrs of Soc Stud 1985-88; St Frances Cabrini 1987-88; Parish Cncl 1991-; Altar, Rosary Soc 1980-88; Knights of Columbus Tchr of Yr Awd 1990; *office:* St Frances Cabrini Comm Schl 734 Mill St Conneaut OH 44030

DENNISTON, MARY ANN BONK, Fourth Grade Teacher; *b:* Toledo, OH; *m:* Thomas G.; *c:* Jean Wasikowski, Michael, Karen Gensbechler, Thomas; *ed:* Mary Manse Coll (BA) Ed 1963; 12 Credit Hrs Toledo Univ 1978-79; *cr:* Saint Hedwig 2nd Grd Tchr 1963-65, 4th Grd Tchr 1965-67; Saint Agnes 4th Grd Tchr 1979-; *ai:* CCD; Labels for Ed Coord; NCEA, Toledo Cncl of Math Tchrs, IRA 1979-; *office:* St Agnes Schl 3891 Martha Ave Toledo OH 43612

DENNO, GEORGE RAYMOND, 6th Grade Teacher; *b:* Danvers, MA; *ed:* Northern Essex Comm Coll (AA) Liberal Arts 1963; Salem St Coll (BS) Math & Sci J H Ed 1967; 30 Addl Credit Hrs in Elem Ed & Cmptr Courses; *cr:* Matthew Thornton Elem Schl 5th & 6th Grd Tchr 1967-72; Londonderry Jr High-MS 6th Grd Tchr 1972-77; South Londonderry Elem Schl 6th Grd Tchr 1977-; *ai:* Outdoor Enviromental Ed Prgms; NEA, NHEA & LEA 1967-; Project Adolescence 1976-80; *office:* South Londonderry Schl 88 South Rd Londonderry NH 03053

DENNY, DAVID FRANK, Fifth Grade Teacher; *b:* Salem, OH; *m:* Charlene Kay Brooks; *c:* Marcie, Philip; *ed:* Mount Union Coll (BA) Elem Ed 1967; Univ of Akron (MA) Elem Ed 1971; Attnd Malore Coll, Ashland Coll, OH St, Kent St; *cr:* Alliance City Schls 5th Grd Tchr 1967-68, 6th Grd Tchr 1968-72; Lake MS Asst Prin 1972-76; Uniontown 4th Grd Tchr 1976-79; Lake Elem Schls 5th Grd Tchr 1979-; *ai:* Tech, Dist Math, Dist Seeds Sci Rep, Comms; NEA, OEA, ALEA 1967-72; NEA, OEA, LLEA 1972-; Phi Delta Kappa 1972-, Historian; Damascus Puritan 1978-, Bd Officer, Prgm, Chprsn; Damascus Friends Organist 1991-; Jaycee Young Educator Awd; Jenning Scholar; *office:* Lake Elem Sch 225 W Lincoln St Hartville OH 44632

DENONCOUR, MARK T., 5th & 6th Grade Teacher; *b:* Franklin, NH; *m:* Theodora; *c:* Ellen, Adam; *ed:* Plymouth St Coll (BS) Ed 1976; Univ of HI (MA) Pacific Stud 1980; Attnd Univ of NH; *cr:* Peace Corps 6 Grd Tchr 1977-78; Winnisquam Regnl 6 Sci Tchr 1978-79; Rowell Schl 5-6 Grd Math, Sci Tchr 1980-89; Beaver Meadow 5-6 Grd Tchr 1989-; *ai:* Tech Comm Chair; Work With Stu Actors Prgm; Sci Tchr Enhancement Prgm in Cntrl NH; NEA 1978-; NSTA 1994-; NH Pub Radio 1995-; Comm Advy Bd; Town of New Hampton 1992-, Selectman; New Hampton Historical Soc 1984-; Outstdng Tchr Awd Franklin 1985; Chubb LifeAmerica, Christa Mc Aullife Flwshp 1991; NH Environmental Tchr of Yr 1994; NH Excl in Ed Edie Awd 1995; Interactive Lake Ecology Prgm for Scientific Understanding of Fresh Water Lakes, Ponds Author; *home:* PO Box 212 New Hampton NH 03256

DENOS, GLORIA, Religion & Health Teacher; *b:* Toledo, OH; *ed:* Notre Dame Coll (BA) PE, Hlth 1974; John Carroll Univ (MA) Rel Ed 1985; Cooperative Ed, Bldg Stdnts Self-Esteem Courses; Multiple Intelligences; *cr:* Cardinal Mooney HS PE Tchr, Coach 1974-75; Villa Angela Acad PE, Religion Tchr, Coach, AD 1976-84; St Edward HS Religion Tchr, Coach 1985-89; Notre Dame Acad PE, Religion Tchr, Sr Class Adv, Svc Prgm Coord 1989-; Sr Project Coord; *ai:* NCEA; ASCD 1992-; Religion Tchr's Journal Article Pub.*

DENT, PHAIDRA ANN, Teacher of Hearing Impaired; *b:* Canton, OH; *c:* Lauren Shirin; *ed:* Gordon Coll (BS) Elem Ed 1975; Smith Coll (MED) Deaf Ed 1979; 40 Addl Credit Hrs; *cr:* Beverly Schl for the Deaf Dorm Cnslr, Supvr 1975-78; Lakewood City Schls Tchr of Hearing Impaired 1979-; *ai:* Tchr Adv Peer Medication Prgm 1995; IA Team 1993-94; Report Card Comm 1993-95; Project Ready, Set, Go 1993-95; LTA, OEA, NEA 1979-; OH Camp Cherith Staff Bd 1970-87, Cnslr, Division Dir, Cnslr in Trng, Riflery Instr, Treas, VP; N Olmstead Evangelical Friends Church 1985-, Ldr, Coord Pioneer Clubs, VP Ladies Flwshp; Choir; Jr Church Tchr; Del to Yearly Meeting; *office:* Hayes Elem Schl 16401 Delaware Ave Lakewood OH 44107

DENTI, SANDRA M., Mathematics Teacher; *b:* Mt Pleasant, PA; *m:* Joseph P.; *c:* Joseph R., Suzanne M.; *ed:* Waynesburg Coll (BS) Math 1968; Post Grad Stud Penn St Univ; *cr:* North Allegheny Schl Dist Ingomar Mid 8th Grd Math Tchr 1968-70; Penn Hills Schl Dist Linton Intermediate Algebra I Tchr 1970-71; Millcreek Schl Dist Westlake Algebra I Tchr 1972-76; South Fayette Schl Dist 7th Grd Math Tchr 1993-; *ai:* NEA 1993-; Nom Outstdng Tchr of Yr KDKA 3 Times; Nom Walt Disney Presents Amer Tchrs Awds; Gift of Time Amer Family Inst; *office:* South Fayette Jr Sr HS 2254 Old Oakdale Rd Mc Donald PA 15057

DENTINGER, JAMES ANTHONY, Reading Specialist; *b:* Rochester, NY; *c:* Shannon, Shane; *ed:* Univ of Rochester (BA) Eng 1970, (MED) Ed 1973; *cr:* Rush Henrietta HS Tchr Intern 1972-73; Rochester Inst of Tech Adj Fac 1973-87; Spencerport HS Rdng Specialist 1973-; St John Firher Coll Adj Fac 1983-84; *ai:* Schl Improvement Comm; Dist Ldrshp & Child Stud Teams; Certfd Effective Schls Trainer; Effective Schls Consultant; *office:* Spencerport HS 2705 Lyell-Spencerport Rd Spencerport NY 14609

DENTINO, ALFRED WILLIAM, Director of Bands; *b:* Chelsea, MA; *m:* Christine Herbst; *c:* Corey, Jaclyn; *ed:* OH St Univ (BMEd) Music Ed 1976; Harvard Univ (ALM) Fine Arts 1991; *cr:* Columbus Pub Schls Instrumental Music Tchr 1976-79; Wachusett Regnl HS Dir of Bands 1979-80; Concord Pub Schls Instrumental Music Tchr 1980-92; Concord-Carlisle HS Dir of Bands 1992-; *ai:* Pep Band & Pit Orch for Annual Broadway Musical Dir; NEA 1976-; MNEA 1979-; MA Instrumental Cond Assn 1980-, VP; Harvard Univ Crite Prize Winner; *office:* Concord Carlisle HS 500 Walden St Concord MA 01742*

DENTITH, DIANE BARLEIB, Mathematics Teacher; *b:* Easton, PA; *m:* Thomas G.; *c:* JoLynn; *ed:* Cedar Crest Coll (BA) Math 1974; Grad Credits in Ed From Marywood Coll & East Stroudsburg Univ; *cr:* Pen Argyl Schl Dist Tchr Aide 1974-76; Pleasant Valley Schl Dist Math Tchr 1976-78; Faith Chrstn Schl Math Tchr 1982-; *ai:* Individual Tutoring; Supporting Sports Act; Class of 1996 Adv; House on the Rock Flwshp 1994-; Childrens Ministry Accompanist; *office:* Faith Christian Schl 122 Dante St Roseto PA 18013

DENTON, SANDRA ELIZABETH, English Instructor; *b:* Kansas City, KS; *ed:* Univ of Missouri at Kansas City (BA) Eng Lang, Lit 1969, (MA) Scndry Ed 1976; Rdng Cert OH St Univ 1991; *cr:* KC MO Pub Schls Eng Tchr 1969-84; Merrill Publishing Co Lang Arts Ed 1984-86; East HS Eng Tchr 1986-; Columbus St Comm Coll Adj Eng Instr 1992-; *ai:* Rangefinder Comm 12th Grd Proficiency Test Writing; NCTE 1969-; NEA 1986-; Alpha Kappa Alpha 1969-; Ed Spelling For Word Mastery; Contributor Today's Great Poems; Tchr of Yr; Edctr of Yr; *office:* East HS 1500 E Broad St Columbus OH 43205

DENUTTE, BARBARA ALLEN, Fourth Grade Teacher; *b:* Highland Park, MI; *m:* Peter III; *c:* Megan M., Tyler Allen; *ed:* Alma MI Coll (BA) Elem Ed, PE 1979; Notre Dame Coll Working on MA Cmptrs in Ed; *cr:* Webster Elem Schl TESOL Aide 1979-80; Nashua Cath Jr HS Amer His, Span, Geography, PE Tchr 1980-83; Thorntons Ferry Elem Schl 3rd-4th Grd Tchr 1983-; *ai:* Schl Soc Stud Facilitator 1989-; Schl Duty, Scheduling Comms; NEA-NH 1983-95, VP, Treas, Mbrshp Chair; Bedford Taxpayers for Quality Ed 1994-; *office:* Thorntons Ferry Elem Schl 134 Camp Sargent Rd Merrimack NH 03054

DEOLIVEIRA-KASHTAN, PAULETTE, Private Piano Teacher; *b:* Taunton, MA; *m:* Robert J.; *ed:* RI Coll (BA) Music Ed 1985; *cr:* Paulettes Studio Piano Tchr; *ai:* Miss America Preliminary Schlsp Pageant Winner; City of Attleboro, Greater Attlebor St Level Rep.

DEPACE, WILLIAM FREDERICK, Secondary Math & Bible Teacher; *b:* Wilmington, DE; *m:* Melody Jones; *ed:* Univ of DE (BA) Math 1983; Bob Jones Univ (MDIV) Divinity 1989; *cr:* Concord Chrstn Acad 3rd Grd Tchr 1989-91, Math, Bible Tchr 1991-; *office:* Concord Christian Acad 2510 Marsh Rd Wilmington DE 19810

DEPALMA, FREDRIC RAYMOND, Science Dept Chair & Teacher; *b:* Yonkers, NE; *m:* Susan Ann Cook; *c:* Amanda K., Mario C., Kristina A.; *ed:* Manhatten Coll (BS) PE, Sci 1977; Iona Coll (MS) Educl Computing 1992; 27 Post-Grad Credits Sci, Safety Ed; *cr:* Sacred Heart HS Tchr, Dept Chair 1977-; *ai:* Bluejacket Shipcrafters Craftsperson, Consultant; Sacred Heart Driver Ed Prgm Dept Chair, Instr; NCEA 1977-; NHSTA 1980-; Astronomical Soc of Pacific 1984-; Tandy Scholar Awd Math, Sci; Japan Automobile Ed Fnd; *home:* 13 Aqueduct Rd Cortlandt Manor NY 10566

DEPALMA, GINNY BARONE, 8th Grade English Teacher; *b:* Brooklyn, NY; *ed:* Fairfield Univ (MA) Ed 1977; 77 Post Grad Hrs; *cr:* Suffern Jr High Librn 1972-73, 7th Grd Core Tchr 1973-81, 8th Grd Eng Tchr 1981-; Suffern MS 8th Grd Eng Tchr & Team Ldr 1995-; *ai:* Team Ldr of MS Reorganization; AFT 1972-; Ramapo Tchrs Assn 1972-; NYSUT 1972-; *office:* Suffern Jr HS Hemion Rd Suffern NY 10901

DE PALMA, GREGORY A., Mathematics Teacher; *b:* New Kensington, PA; *m:* Linda Pugliese; *c:* Gregory B., Aaron M., Beth L.; *ed:* IN Univ of PA (BS) Math 1970, (MED) Math 1975; St Vincent Coll Natl Sci Fnd 1986-88; Penn St Univ Eisenhower Grant Rsrch; *cr:* Natl Tooling, Machine Assn Math Instr 1978-; *ai:* Math Bowl Spon Strongland Chamber of Comm; NEA, PSEA, NKAEA 1971-; MCWP 1989-, Del at Large; PCTM 1989-, Mbrshp Comm; ASCD 1992-; BSA 1983-, Comm Chm; St Margaret Mary Church 1980-, Parish Cncl; Natl Sci Fnd Rsrch Grant St Vincent Coll 1986-88; All Star Achiever Tchr of Yr 1995; *office:* Valley HS 703 Stevenson Blvd New Kensington PA 15068

DEPALMA, JOSEPH WILLIAM, English Teacher; *b:* Pittsburgh, PA; *m:* Judith Ann Kvorjak; *c:* Jennifer, Gary; *ed:* Slippery Rock Univ (BS) Ed 1965; Univ of Pittsburgh (MA) Eng 1973; *cr:* North Braddock HS Tchr 1965-66; US Army Infantry Captain 1966-70; Upper St Clair HS Tchr 1971-; *ai:* Boys Soccer Head Coach; Asst Fac Mgr; AFT 1971-; Natl Soccer Coaches Assn of Amer; Western PA Soccer Coaches Assn, Pres 1987-93; Western PA Cncl of Tchrs of Eng; USC Soccer Boosters 1984-; Spon of St Wide Writing Contest Stu Winner 1989; *office:* Upper Saint Clair HS 1825 Mclaughlin Run Rd Pittsburgh PA 15241

DEPALMA, JUDY ANN (LAZZARO), Prof of Business Office Tech; *b:* Rochester, NY; *m:* Joseph; *c:* Joseph C., Melissa, Anthony; *ed:* Nazareth Coll of Roch (BS) Bus, Ec 1963; Syracuse Univ (MS) Bus Ed 1968; Post Grad Work Robert Morris Coll at Coraopolis; SUNY at Buffalo, Rider Coll at Trenton, SUNY at Brockport; *cr:* Ben Franklin HS Bus Tchr 1963-67; West HS Bus Tchr 1963-67; Greece Arcadia HS Bus Tchr 1967-69; Manpower Dev Ctr Instr Adult Office Skills 1969-71; Genesee Comm Coll Prof Bus, Office Tech 1971-; *ai:* Acad Senate 1988-, Pres; NEA 1978-; NBEA, EBEA 1992-94; Office Tech, Secretarial Edctrs of SUNY, CUNY 1965-, Pres, VP, Sec; Delta Pi Epsilon 1967-; Genesee Ed Assoc 1971-; Scottsville Free Lib 1994-, Trustee; Mumford Vol Fire Dept 1985-, Dir, VP, Sec, First Responder; Town of Wheatland Solid Waste Task Force Comm 1992-93; Calendonia-Mumford Variety Show Assoc 1988-91; NY St Chancellors Awd for Excl in Tchng 1985; Stu Govt Educl Svc Awd 1987; NISOD Medallion for Excl in Tchng 1989; pres Dist Svc Awd 1985; *office:* Genesee Comm Coll 1 College Rd Batavia NY 14020

DEPALMA, MARIA CERNARO, 5th-8th Grd English Teacher; *b:* Bronx, NY; *m:* Michael J.; *c:* Stephanie; *ed:* Fordham Univ (BS) Psych 1985; Lehman Coll (MA) Spec Ed 1988; *cr:* Manhattan Internal Medicine Med Sec 1982-85; Lachmi Montessauri Presch Tchrs Asst 1985; St Theresa Schl Tchr 1985-; *ai:* FCT 1986-.

DEPAOLA, DOMINIC PHILIP, High School Music Teacher; *b:* New York City, NY; *m:* Diane Hart; *ed:* Queens Coll (BA) Music Ed 1979, (MS) Music Ed 1984; 5 Credit Hrs NY St Tchr Ctrs; *cr:* Carle Place Jr & Sr HS Music Tchr 1986-88; North Babylon HS Music Tchr 1988-; *ai:* Asst Marching Band Dir; HS Musical Orch Dir; NYSSMA 1986-; MENC 1986-; NBTO 1988-, Bdlg Rep; Long Island String Festival Assn 1988-; Music Tech in Classroom OWL Tchr Ctr Grant; *office:* North Babylon HS 1 Phelps Ln North Babylon NY 11703

DEPAOLA, GEORGENE HELEN, Seventh Grade Teacher; *b:* Bethlehem, PA; *m:* Michael A.; *c:* Michael J., Michele M. Williams; *ed:* West Chester Univ (BS) K-8 Ed 1957; Muhlenberg Coll 6 Credit Hrs 1959; *cr:* Bethlehem Area Schl Dist Tchr 1957-60; Aurora Schl Dist Parochial Schl 4th Grd Tchr 1960-61; Bethlehem Area Schl Dist MS K-8th Grd Rdng, Soc Stud Tchr 1967-; *ai:* Curr Writer; LA Rdng Clb; After Schl Act Writing Comm; Glassworks Act Tchr; Stu Asst Prgm; NEA 1957-60; PSEA 1967-; Bethlehem Ed Assn 1967-; Childrens Theatre Bd Pres; YWCA Nursery Schl Bd Mem; Westchester Alumni Club; Jr Wmns Club Mbrshp Chm; Outstdng Elem Tchrs of Amer 1973; Outstdng Performance Awd 1982; *office:* East Hills MS 2005 Chester Ave Bethlehem PA 18017

DE PAOLA, WILLIAM, Science Teacher; *b:* Bayonne, NJ; *m:* Corinne Koplick; *c:* Michelle, Laura; *ed:* Jersey City St (BA) Geoscience 1972; *cr:* Thomas Jefferson Jr HS Sci Tchr 1972-77; Memrl MS Sci Tchr 1977-; *ai:* Girls Bsktbl Coach; in Charge of Outdoor Ed Pgm; Fac Treas; NEA & NJEA 1972-; Fair Lawn Ed Assn 1972-, Negotiating Team; *office:* Memrl MS 1st St & Lambert Rd Fair Lawn NJ 07410

DEPASSE, COLLEEN MC DERMOTT, Principal; *b:* Jamaica, NY; *m:* Gari J.; *c:* Justin, Allison; *ed:* Annhurst Coll at Woodstock (BA) Span, Elem Ed 1977; UCT at Storrs (MA) Curr, Instr 1987; *cr:* St Mary Schl Fourth Grd Tchr 1977-82; St James Schl Fourth Grd Tchr 1989-91, 1992-94, Principal 1994-; *ai:* NCEA 1989-; *office:* St James Schl 120 Water St Danielson CT 06239

DEPEW, MARGO CRAWFORD, 2nd Grade Teacher; *b:* Glens Falls, NY; *m:* Jon Scott; *c:* Bree, Jessica, Matthew; *ed:* Adirondack Comm (AAS) Eng 1972; Castleton St (BS) Elem Ed 1974; 30 Grad Hrs; *cr:* Argyle Cntrl Schl 5th Grd Tchr 1974-75, 2nd Grd Tchr 1975-; *ai:* AFT & NEA.

DEPICE, DOUGLAS JOSEPH, Art Teacher; *b:* Jersey City, NJ; *m:* Marilyn Antinori; *c:* Cynthia Rose; *ed:* Fairleigh Dickinson Univ (BA) Art 1970; NY Univ (MA) Painting 1972; Montclair St Coll Cert K-12 Tchr Art 1974; NY Acad of Art Classes Painting, Drawing 1994-95; Art, Ed Courses Jersey City St Coll, Schl of Visual Arts, New Schl; *cr:* North Bergen HS 9-12 Grd Art Tchr 1974-76; Secaucus HS 9-12 Grd Art Tchr 1976-78; Vailsberg MS 5-8 Grd Art Tchr 1988; Secaucus HS 9-12 Grd Art Tchr 1989-91; Schl #15 Visual & Performing Arts HS K-12 Grd Tchr 1991-92; Secaucus HS K-12 Grd Tchr 1992-; Clarendon Grammar Schl K-12 Grd Tchr 1992-; *ai:* Yrbk Adv; NEA, Secaucus Ed Assn, NJEA 1976-; Geraldine R. Dodge Schlsp Awd 1995; *office:* Secaucus HS Mill Ridge Rd Secaucus NJ 07094*

DEPINA, BARBARA L., Social Studies Teacher; *b:* New Bedford, MA; *c:* Judy Dufour, Joyce Santos, Joseph Gomes, Jo Ann Roberts; *ed:* Bristol Comm Coll (BA) Mental Hlth 1972; Univ of MA (BA) Sociology 1976; His 1977; *cr:* New Bedford Schl Dept Tchrs Aide 1972-75; New Bedford Police Dept Emergency Phone Operator 1975; New Bedford Schl Dept Sub Tchr 1977-78, Tchr 1978-; *ai:* His Club Adv; NEA 1978-; Black Profs Assn; Merchant Mariners Soc Club Inc.*

DEPINHO, MARY VOEGELI, French & Literature Teacher; *ed:* Sarah Lawrence Coll (AB) Fr 1964; The Amer Univ (MA) Ed 1984; John Hopkins Univ Schl of Advanced Intnl Stud 4 Hrs 1991; The Smithsonian Inst Art His Cert 1996; *cr:* St Timothy's Schl Fr Lang, Lit Tchr 1964-66; The Potomac Schl Fr Lang Culture, Civiliz Tchr 1966-69; The Holton-Arms Schl Fr Lang & Lit, His of Art Tchr 1966-; The Amer Univ Fr Lang Adj Prof 1983-84; *ai:* Fac Rep Dept of His, Soc Sci Curr Comm; Sr Projects Comm Chair; AATF 1966-; MLA 1989-; ACTFL 1994-; Recording for Blind, Dyslexic 1993-, Vol Ldr; CEEB-ETS 1994-, Fr Lang & Lit AP Exam Reader; *office:* The Holton-Arms Schl 7303 River Rd Bethesda MD 20817

DEPIRRO, JO-ANN LOUISE, English Teacher; *b:* Detroit, MI; *m:* Michael Joseph; *ed:* Mary Grove Coll (BA) Soc Scis 1963; SUNY at Stony Brook Gen Stud 1973; New York Inst of Tech (MS) Labor & Industrial Relations 1990; 60 Hrs Beyond Masters Degree in Effective Tchng Courses & Comp Literacy; *cr:* Livonia Pub Schls Elem Tchr 1963-68; Christ the King Schl Elem Tchr 1969; Harborfields Cntrl Schls Elem Tchr 1970-77, Eng & Soc Stud Tchr 1978-; *ai:* 7th Grd Class Adv; Team Ldr; Lang Arts & Pgm Evaluation Comm; AFT 1970-; United Tchrs of Harborfields 1976-, Exec VP 1984-93; NCTE 1978-; NMSA 1984-; ASCD 1985-; Our Lady Queen of Martyrs R C Church 1970-, St Pius X Medal; Anita Messinger Memrl Awd for Outstdng Svc; Co-Authored Soc Stud Units.*

DEPLER, NANCY SCHULL, Kindergarten Teacher; *b:* Shelby, OH; *m:* Thomas A.; *c:* Sarah K., Kyle A.; *ed:* (BS) Ed, (BA) Elem Ed 1972; Addl Hrs Cmptr Classes, TEACH, PRIDE, TESSA, Ec; *cr:* Bath Local Schls Second Grd Tchr 1972-74; Shelby City Schls Kndgtn Tchr 1975-; *ai:* Soc Stud Curr Comm; Planning Comm to Recognize Grds in Elem Bldgs; NEA, OEA 1972-; SEA 1972-, Bldg Rep; Shelby Hosp Guild 1976-, Mbrshp Chm 1990-93; Shelby V Bd 1975-78, Bd Men; *office:* Auburn Elem Schl 109 Auburn Ave Shelby OH 44875*

DEPOE, CYNTHIA K., Mathematics Teacher; *b:* Dayton, OH; *m:* Stephen P.; *c:* Aaron, Andrew; *ed:* Ft Hays St Univ (BS) Math 1981; Univ of Cincinnati (MAT) Meth 1990; Physics for Tchrs of AP Calculus 3 Credit Hrs 1995; Tchng Math as Interdisciplinary Subject 3 Credit Hrs 1994; *cr:* Junction City HS Math Tchr 1981-84; Chase Cty HS Math Tchr 1984-86; Woodward HS Math Tchr 1986-87; Sycamore HS Math Tchr 1987-; *ai:* Math Club Spon; NCTM 1986-; NEA, SWOEA, SEA 1987-; GTE Gift Grant 1995-; *office:* Sycamore HS 7400 Cornell Rd Cincinnati OH 45242

DE POLO, ROBERT JOHN, Chemistry Teacher; *b:* Windber, PA; *m:* Kathleen Pierre; *c:* Kristine L., Robert P.; *ed:* IN Univ (BS) Chem & Phys Sci 1962, (MED) Chem & Phys Sci 1969; *cr:* Zelienople HS Chem Tchr 1962-64; Seneca Valley HS Chem Tchr 1964-; *ai:* SVEA 1962-, Pres 1970-71; PSEA & NEA 1962-; *office:* Seneca Valley HS 124 Seneca School Rd Harmony PA 16037

DEPPE, CHARLES THOMAS, Social Studies Teacher; *b:* Bakersfield, CA; *m:* Barbara Wawrzyniak; *c:* Allison, Jacquelyn, Amanda, Michelle, C. Todd; *ed:* Nassau Comm Coll (AA) Lang, His 1965; SUNY at New Paltz (BS) US His 1968; Addl 36 Credit Hrs US His; *cr:* Wappingers Jr HS 7th Grd Soc Stud Tchr 1968-; *ai:* JV Field Hockey Coach; Ski Club Adv; NYSTA, AFT, Wapp Congress of Tchrs 1968-; Town of East Fishkill Sftbl Coach 1985-; Rel Ed Instr 1990-; *office:* Wappingers Falls Jr HS 90 Remsen Ave Wappingers Falls NY 12590

DEPPEN, CATHERINE CUMMINGS, Fifth Grade Teacher; *b:* New Haven, CT; *m:* John T.; *ed:* Southern CT St Univ (BS) Ed 1970, (MS) Rdng Ed 1976; *cr:* First Avenue Schl 5th Grd Tchr 1970-82; Forest Elem Schl 5th Grd Tchr 1982-; *ai:* Univ Ldr-Coord of Tchng Act for Grd Level Collegues 1984-; Master Tchr; West Haven Fed of Tchrs 1970-; Cath Charity League 1989, Placement Chprsn, Recording Sec; West Havens Tchr of Yr Nom 1995-96.*

DE PRILLE, MICHELE ANNE, Tchr of Multi-Hndcppd Support; *b:* Butler, PA; *ed:* Edinboro Univ of PA (BS) Spec Ed, Elem Ed 1968; St Coll of Victoria at Burwood (BED) Spec Ed 1977; 30 Addl Grad Credit Hrs; *cr:* Lawrence Cty Schls Life Skills Support Tchr 1968-71; Midwestern Intermediate Univ IV Schl Life Skills Support, Multi-handicapped Support Tchr 1971-; *ai:* Stdnts Helping Stdnts Adv 1993-; Regnl Very Spec Arts Show Comm 1989-; PA St Ed Assn, NEA 1968-; Rotary Fnd Tchr of Handicapped Awd 1976; Annie Sullivan Awd 1991; Presenter at Wkshp PA Statewide Conf on Inclusion 1994; Panelist St Teleconference on Inclusion in Arts 1995.*

DE PROFIO, JAMES A., Health Teacher; *b:* Lowell, MA; *m:* Pamela Merrill; *ed:* Plymouth St Coll (BS) Hlth, PE 1984; Grad Stu Fitchburg St Coll; *cr:* Chelmsford HS Tchr, Coach 1984-87; Lowell HS Tchr, Coach 1987-; *ai:* A Stu Assn Adv; IM Coord; Indoor, Outdoor Track & Field Coach; UTL, MFT, AFT 1984-; Fac Advy Cncl 1995-; No Chelmsford Congregational Church1978-, Sunday Schl, Supt; *office:* Lowell HS 50 Fr Morrissette Blvd Lowell MA 01852*

DEPUY, DEBORAH LUCIANO, Spanish Teacher; *b:* Elizabeth, NJ; *m:* Robert Scott; *ed:* Western MD Coll 6 Grad Credits Curr, Instruction; *cr:* Glasgow HS Span Tchr 1990; Easton HS Span Tchr 1990-; *ai:* Span Club Adv; Mentor Tchr; Stu Tchr Supervising Tchr; Co-Chair Mid Sts Comm; *office:* Easton H S Mecklenburg Ave Easton MD 21601

DEPUY, KATHY N., Business Education Teacher; *b:* Pittsburgh, PA; *m:* Meade; *c:* Jane; *ed:* Carnegie Mellon Univ (BS) Bus Ed 1963; Univ of Pittsburgh (MED) Bus Ed 1965; *cr:* IBM Corp Educl Rep 1964-65; Wilkinsburgh HS Tchr 1967-68; Robert Morris Coll Tchr 1975-82; South Park HS Tchr 1982-; *ai:* Stu Cncl, Prom Promise Adv; DPE 1965-; Tri St Bus Ed 1963-, Pres, Life Mem; NEA; NBEA 1975-; Borough of Whitehall 1989-, Councilperson; YMCA 1992-, Chprsn; *office:* South Park HS 2178 Ridge Rd Library PA 15129*

DERAMO, DONALD P., American History Teacher; *b:* Meadville, PA; *m:* Gail Buxton; *c:* Eliza Arrow, David; *ed:* Slippery Rock Univ (BS) Soc Stud 1963; Attnd Univ of Pittsburgh & Univ of Youngstown; *cr:* Lakeview Schls Tchr 1963-66; Mahoning Valley Voc Schl Tchr 1966-69; Girard City Schls Tchr 1969-; *ai:* NEA 1963-; *office:* Girard HS 31 N Ward Ave Girard OH 44420

DE RAMOS, AIDA FERNANDEZ, Spanish Teacher; *b:* San Juan, PR; *m:* Hector M.; *c:* Shakira Aida, Yamil Francisco; *ed:* Univ of CT (BA) Span, Italian 1978; NY Univ (MA) Biling Ed 1981; 6th Yr Prgm Cntrl CT St Univ 1983-87, Cert Prgm Admin, Supervision; Hartford Bd Ed 1988-92; 90 Addl Hrs; *cr:* Burr Schl Biling Tchr 1978-84; Batcheldor Schl Frgn Lang Tchr 1984-89; Univ of Hartford Dept of Continued Ed Span Tchr 1991-93; Bulkeley HS Frgn Lang Tchr 1989-92, Frgn Lang Tchr 1989-; *ai:* Present Statewide Frgn Lang Poetry Recitation Comm 1986; Chrldr Coach 1995; Club Adv Cancun Club 1994-95; CT Cncl Lang Tchrs 1984-, Pegasus Pride Awd 1994; CT Italian Tchrs Assn 1992-; Southend Comm Svc Sec; *office:* Bulkeley HS 300 Wethersfield Ave Hartford CT 06

DERBAUM, MERCEDES A., Librarian; *ed:* Clarion Univ (BS) Univ of Pittsburgh (MLS) Lib Sci 1974; Cert Lib Sci Advanced Rdng Specialist 1985; *cr:* Highlands Jr HS Librn 1972-83, High Math Tchr 1985-95, Highlands HS Librn 1995-; *ai:* Dist Tech Co Reviewer; NEA, PSEA 1972-; HEA 1972-, Former Trea; PSLA Afterschool Congregation Cncl 1994-, Coord; First Luth Chur Sec; *office:* Highlands Sr HS 1500 Pacific Ave Natrona Heights

DERBY, PAUL HARRIS, Art Teacher; *b:* Milwaukee, WI; *ed:* Geneseo (BA) Art 1980; Coll of St Rose (MSEd) Art Ed 1989; Springs Cntrl Schl Art Tchr 1989-92; Middleburgh Cntrl Schl 1992-; *office:* Middleburgh Central Schl Main St Middleburgh N

DEREMER, RENETTA FOLK, Mathematics Teacher; *b:* Alt *m:* William J.; *c:* Renetta A., Krista M.; *ed:* IN Univ of PA (BS 1971; PA St Univ (MED) Math Ed 1974; Addl 2 Credit Hrs Credit Hrs IN Univ of PA; *cr:* Hollidaysburg Area Schl Dist M 1971-75, 1982-; *ai:* NEA, PSEA, HAEA 1971-; NCTM 198 1993-; St James Luth Church; Statistics Ed Quantitative Litera 1992, 1994; Coll in HS Prgm Univ of Pittsburgh 1993-; PA Dept o Assessment Advy Comm; Sequal Villanova Univ 199 Hollidaysburg Area Sr HS 1510 N Montgomery St Hollidaysburg

DEREMER, WILLIAM JAY, Orchestra Director; *b:* New Par Renetta Louise Folk; *c:* Renetta Ann, Krista Michelle; *ed:* IN U (BS) Music Ed 1968, (MED) Music 1971; *cr:* Pennsbury Schls 1968-69; Hollidaysburg Area Schls Orch Dir 1970-; *ai:* Orch Dir Dir for Annual Musical; NEA, PSEA, MENC, NSOA 1968 Holidaysburg Area Schl Dist 1510 N Montgomery St Holliday 16648

DERES, ALICE SEREGHY, Art Teacher; *b:* Mount Kisco Robert; *ed:* Alfred Univ Schl of Art & Design (BFA) Painting, Ce Art His & Ed 1977; Attnd St Univ of NY at Geneseo, Penlan Crafts & Syracuse Univ; *cr:* Rushford Cntrl Schl Art Tchr Allegany BOCES Enrichment Prgm Tchr 1982-87; Arkport Cntr Tchr 1989-; *ai:* Art Club; Odyssey of Mind; AFT, NEA & NYSA Adirondack Mountain Club; Nature Conservancy; Appalachian Club; Natl Wildlife Fed; *office:* Arkport Central Schl 35 East Av NY 14807

DE RIGGI, CATHERINE IANNOTTA, Senior Academic Cou Pittsburgh, PA; *m:* Carl J.; *c:* Marc; *ed:* Duquesne Univ (BA) 1974, (MS) Cnslng Ed 1977; Post Grad Stud; Certs in Elem, Scn Cnslng Supervision; *cr:* Arsenal MS Tchr, Team Ldr 1974-84; La Acting Cnslr 1987-; Belmar-East Hills Elem Acting Dev Ac Greenway MS Cnslr 1988-92; Langley HS Acad Cnslr 1992- Educl Ctr Acad Cnslr 1992-; *ai:* BRIDGES Co-Spon; Co Discipline Comm; AFT 1974-, Del St-Natl Conventions, Bldg Re Langley HS 2940 Sheraden Blvd Pittsburgh PA 15204

DERIGGI, JEAN SKINDER, Home Economics Teacher; *b:* R NY; *m:* Louis A.; *c:* Joyce DeLany, John Skinder, Barbara Me Suny at Buffalo (BS) Home Ec Scndry Ed 1957; Hofstra Univ (M Ed 1973; 60 Post Grad Credit Hrs; *cr:* Wayne Cntrl Schl Tchr Lindenhurst Pub Schls Tchr 1969-; *ai:* Chefs Club Adv; Adult Title 9 Comm Memter; NEA, NYSHETA, SCHETA, NYSUT, T PTA 1969-; Outstdng Svc Awd Lang Dept; Writer, Curr Home Tchr of Yr Rotary Club; Tchr of Month; Implementation of Placement Coll of Credit Course; *office:* Lindenhurst Pub Schls Lindenhurst NY 11757

DE RISO, THERESA PATTERSON, High School English Te Providence, RI; *m:* Stephen A.; *ed:* Boston Univ (BA) Eng 198 (MAT) Scndry Eng 1992; Post Grad Eng, Drama Courses at RI Endorsement 1995; *cr:* Lincoln HS Eng Tchr 1992-; *ai:* Class of Drama Tchr; New England Assn Tchrs of Eng, RI Cncl Tchr NCTE, Lincoln AFT 1992-; Lit Vol of Amer 1991-93, Tutor Fellow for Natl Writing Project; Story Pub 1994; *office:* Lincol Old River Rd Lincoln RI 02865

DERLAN, SHARON E., English & Theater Teacher; *b:* Cumberl *m:* William David Jr.; *c:* Benjamin; *ed:* Bellarmine Coll (BA) Co 1974; Frostburg St Univ (MA) 20th Cent Lit 1982; Stud in Irela Comm Coll Irish Stud; *cr:* Bishop Walsh HS Eng, Theatre Tchr Wayside Theatre Various Positions 1976-80; Allenberry Theatre Positions 1976-80; Hartman Theatre Various Positions 1976-80; St Univ Grad Asst 1980-81; Allegany Comm Coll Eng Instr Northern HS Eng, Theatre Tchr 1987-; *ai:* Drama Coach; Play Di Adv; Writing Club Moderator; Supvrs Grant 1989; Theatre A Cumberland Times News 1986-; *office:* Northern HS 86 Pri Accident MD 21520*

DEROMEDI, CHRIS M., Business Education Teacher; *b:* Danv *m:* John; *ed:* Bloomsburg Univ (BS) Bus Ed 1971, (ME) Ed 197 Clair Schl Dist Tchr 1971-86; Mt Carmel Area Schl Dist Tch Relations Coord 1986-; *ai:* Coord for Adopt a Schl Partnership Northumberland Cty Area Agency on Aging; Adv Bus Club; Prin of in Schl Pub; Comm for OBE Pub Relations; Dir of Schl TV Stat on Inclusion; NEA & PSEA 1971-; Alpha Tau Delta 1968-; *home:* Dr Shady Acres Kulpmont PA 17834

DEROMEDI, GARY LEE, Mathematics & Cmptr Sci Tchr; *b:* D OH; *m:* Diane L. Mc Allister; *ed:* Kent St Univ (BS) Math Ed 19 Cmptr Tech 1982; Ashland Coll (MED) Cmptr Sci 1988; Post Grad Cmptr Sci; *cr:* Glenoak HS Math Tchr 1978-79; Lakeland HS Mat Sci Tchr 1979-; Buckeye Joint Voc Schl Cmptr Sci Tchr 1982-89; Coll Cmptr Sci Tchr 1989-91; Kent St Tuscarawas Campus Ad Math, Cmptr Sci 1989-; *ai:* Soph Class Adv; OEA, NEA, OCTM 1978-; OSTA 1989-; Masters Thesis; *office:* Lakeland HS Rt 3 Fre 43973*

DEROO, HELEN PYNN, English & Language Arts Tchr; *b:* Tako MD; *m:* David C.; *ed:* Univ of MD (BA) Eng 1967; George Wa Univ (MA) Ed 1979; Numerous Personal Interest & Prof Dev Including 2 Yrs Russian, 2 Semesters Comp Programming, Trave Russia & Ancient Mediterranean World; *cr:* DuVal HS Eng, Spee & Home Ec Tchr & Eng Dept Chprsn 1967-; *ai:* NEA, MSTA & 1967-; Delta Kappa Gamma 1988-, 1st & 2nd VP; U MD Alum Life Mem 1970-; Amer Sewing Guild 1993-; MD Speech Coach of Metropolitan WA Ear Reader; *office:* Duval HS 9880 Good Lanham Seabrook MD 20706

DEROSA, ANTHONY MARK, Foreign Language Resource Johnstown, PA; *m:* Ruth Rander; *c:* Catherine Mc Govern, Amy, F IN Univ of PA (BA) Ger 1969; Johns Hopkins Univ (MAT) Tchng Lang & Lit; Span Lang; Ed; Cmptrs; *cr:* Thomas S. Wooten HS Tchr 1 Yr; Robert Frost MS Ger, Fr Tchr 17 Yrs; Thomas S. Wo Foreign Lang Resource Tchr 9 Yrs; *ai:* Sister City Stu Exch Co Hon Soc Adv; Cmptr Programming Club Spon; NEA 1970-; AAT Newsletter Ed; MD For Lang Assn 1972-, Pres, Outstanding Tc Frederick Humane Soc 1990-; Fredericktowne Players 1994-; R Sister City Corp 1988-, Exch Coord; Mid Sts Steering Comm *office:* Thomas S Wootton HS 2100 Wootton Pky Rockville MD 2

, HEIDI LOUISE, Travel & Tourism Tech Teacher; *b:* Boston, Salem St Coll (BS) Bus Ed Scndry 1979; Suffolk Univ (MS) Bus Trng 1994; Lesley Coll (MED) Cmptrs in Ed 1995; 162 Addl Hrs d Ctr; *cr:* Julie Billart Cntrl HS Bus Tchr 1979-80; Tewksbury Bus Tchr 1980-92; Fisher Coll Adj Instr, Bus 1983-84, 1992-93; on HS Travel, Tourism Tech Tchr 1993-; *ai:* Mock Trial Adv; Schl r Travel, Tourism Pathway; Tech Planning Comm; AFT, BTU EA 1980-92; Amer Field Svc 1986-88 Sec; *office:* East Boston HS St East Boston MA 02128

, MARLYCE PEDERSEN, Vocal Music Teacher; *b:* Fairmont, Richard; *ed:* Gustavus Adolphus Coll (BMus) Pipe Organ, Vocal ion Theol Sem Schl of Sacred Music (SMM) Scared Music, Pipe ocal 1967; Wm. Patterson Coll (BED) Vocal Music Ed K-12 1972; Credits Multi-Natl Music, Soc Stud, Children's Musical Theatre; rove Schl K-6 Grd Vocal Music Tchr 1968-69; Shongum Schl K-6 l Music Tchr 1969-75; Ctr Grove Schl K-6 Grd Vocal Music Tchr K-5 Grd Vocal Music Tchr 1994-; *ai:* Grd 3 Choir; Grd 4-5 ; Grd 4-5 Girls' Chorus; Organist, Choirmaster; NEA, NJEA EA 1968-, Rep Cncl; MENC, NJMEA 1987-; AGO 1975-; J 1995-; OAKE 1996; PTA 1969-; Smithsonian Assoc 1993-; seum of Natural History 1992-; MADD 1989-; Natl Audubon Soc, ongress Assoc 1995-; Tchr of Yr 1988; NJ Governor's Grant Awd; al to Collect Childrens Gamesongs for Natl Music Curr in 1993-94; 20, 25 Yr Svc Awd; 10 Yr Achvmt Awd Gustavus s Coll; Outstdng Yng Women of Amer 1975; Author Recorder Curr *fice:* Ctr Grove Schl 25 Schoolhouse Rd Randolph NJ 07869*

, RENO F., Art Teacher; *b:* Marigliano, Italy; *m:* Luz De Rosa; Andre; *ed:* St Univ Coll at New Paltz (BS) Art Ed 1963, (MS) Art *cr:* Roy C Ketcham Sr HS Art Tchr 1964-; *ai:* NYSUT 1968-; 68-; NYSATA 1968-; *office:* Roy C Ketcham Sr HS 99 Myers Rd Wappingers Falls NY 12590

E, JENNIFER RAUSCH, Eighth Grade Physical Sci Tchr; *b:* NY; *m:* Garret; *ed:* Columbia Greene Comm Coll (AS) Chem Univ of NY at Plattsburgh (BS) Scndry Ed Chem 1992; 12 ad Credits Physics, 6 Grad Credits Ed St Univ of NY at Albany; ament Mountain Reg HS Chem, Algebra HS Tchr 1993-95; Ravena as Selkirk MS 8th Grd Phys Sci Tchr 1995-; *ai:* Kappa Delta Pi Regents, Presidential Schlsps; *office:* Ravena-Coeymans-Selkirk W Ravena NY 12143

AMY S. (MOORE), 8th Grade American His Teacher; *b:* gh, PA; *m:* Randy T.; *c:* Samantha M., Madison R.; *ed:* Theil Coll ciology 1988; 24 Credits Towards MA; *cr:* Lebanon MS 7th Grd ud 1988-95, 8th Grd Amer His 1995-; *ai:* Past Jr High Bsktbl Head 988-92; NEA 1988-; LEA 1988-, Legislative Chprsn; *home:* 2 n Lititz PA 17543

PENNY MOTTO, Second Grade Teacher; *b:* Bloomsburg, PA; *m:* en; *c:* Charissa Leigh, Madelyn Quinn; *ed:* Bloomburg Univ (BA) 1987; Williamsport Area Comm Coll Assoc Comp Sci Tech 1984; d Credit Hrs; *cr:* GC Hartman Elem Ctr Comp Tchr 1987-88, Comp Kndgtn Tchr 1988-89, 2nd Grd Tchr 1990-; *ai:* NEA 1987-; PSEA Southern Columbia Ed Assoc 1987-; Excl in Composition Awd *fice:* G C Hartman Elem Ctr RR 2 Box 372c Catawissa PA 17820

LL, CRAIG ANTHONY, High School Religion Teacher; *b:* vorth, KS; *ed:* Coll of the Holy Cross (BA) Rel Stud 1993; *cr:* Holy ntrl Cath HS Rel Tchr, Coach & Ski Club Coord 1993-; *ai:* Asst st Girls Bsktbl & Head Track Coach; Sr Class Moderator; Pep Club *ffice:* Holy Name Central Catholic HS 144 Granite St Worcester 04*

COTTE, MARK LAMONT, Teacher & Coordinator; *b:* phia, PA; *ed:* Millersville St (BA) Psych 1979; Antioch Univ Spcl Ed 1981; *cr:* Phila. Schl Dist Tchr 1982-83; George gton Acad Tchr 1983-, Hotel, Restaurant & Tourism Coord 1991-; te Catering Caterer 1986-; *ai:* Class of 1991 Spon; Class Reunion er; PFT 1982-; CHRIE 1991-; MAC 1992-; Kappa Alpha Psi ville St Coll 1979-, Achvmntment Awd; Kappa Alpha Psi own Alumni Chptr 1995-; *office:* George Washington HS Bustleton Verree Rd Philadelphia PA 19116

YTER, CAROL ANN, 8th Grade Mathematics Teacher; *b:* ville, NJ; *ed:* Elizabeth Coll (BS) Math 1970; Fairleigh Dickinson A) Human Dev 1985; Supervision Cert from Rutgers Univ; Grad Gifted & Talented, Ed Admin & Career Ed at Glassboro St Coll, St Coll & Temple Univ; NS-LTI Inst on Gifted & Talented 1980; loway Twp Bd of Ed 8th Grd Math Tchr 1970-; Southern NJ ium for Gifted Talented Coord 1994-; *ai:* Natl Jr Honor Soc Adv; ounts Coach; Johns Hopkins Talent Search Adv; Math Curr & k Review Comms; Rep from Galloway Twp Regnl HS Articulation Cmptr Tchr Southern NJ Consortium for Gifted-Talented; Summer str; Phi Delta Kappa 1986-, Sec; Assn of Math Tchrs of NJ 1975-; 1970-; AAAS 1980-; NEA 1970-; NJ Math Coalition 1994-; Alpha appa 1978-, Pres, VP, Sec; Delta Kappa Gamma 1989-; Egg Harbor an Church 1964-, Elder, Trustee; Galloway Twp Tchr of Yr 1985; overnors Tchr Recognition Prgm Awd 1986; St Awd Presidential Awd for Excl in Math & Sci Tchng 1985; NJ Math Panel; Wkshp Presenter Problem Solving, Cmptrs, Math & Talented; *office:* Arthur Rann MS 515 S 8th Ave Absecon NJ 08201

IN, ELEANOR DECAPUA, English Teacher; *b:* CT; *c:* Liz; *ed:* s Magnus Coll (BA) Eng, Italian 1968; Fairfield Univ (MA) Ed CAS) Supervision, Admin 1995; *cr:* Equitable Life Assurance t Specialist, Tech Writer 1968-70; Joel Barlow HS Eng Tchr 1975-; atre Tour of London Designer, Chaperone 1994; Austria, Italy Choir Chaperone 1990, 1993, 1995; TAC; JBEA Exec Bd; CCTE 1985-; CEA, JBEA 1976-; *office:* Joel Barlow HS 100 Black Rock Tpke g CT 06896*

.VO, DARIENNE ANNE, Student Assistance Counselor; *b:* ide, NY; *m:* William Dickson III; *ed:* St Univ of NY at Albany (BA) 1986, (MSW) Clinical Soc Work1989; Credentialed Alcoholism 990-; Certfd Schl Soc Worker; Certfd Soc Worker; *cr:* Hope House ent Clinic Therapist Grad Intern 1988-89; Mental Hlth Assn Albany erapist 1989-90; Tamarac Mid & HS Stu Assistance Cnslr 1990-; *ai:* ediation Prgm Trainer & Consultant Safe & Drug-Free Schls Comm; ide Crisis Planning Team; Natl Assn of Social Workers 1995-; Tamarac MS & HS RD 3 Box 200A Troy NY 12180

LVO, DAVID PAUL, Mathematics Teacher; *b:* Winchester, MA; *m:* Gardner Park; *c:* Andrew, Richard; *ed:* Univ of the South (BA) Eng Univ of NH (MST) Math 1991; Univ of AR Math Ed, Math 12 Hrs; N St Univ PASCAL 3 Hrs; Univ of South Schl of Theology 9 Hrs gy; *cr:* Sewanee Acad Dorm Cnslr, Math Tchr 1979-81; Saint w's Schl Eng Tchr 1981-87, Math Tchr 1981-; *ai:* 1997 Class w; JV Bsbl Head Coach; Schl Cnslr; Chaplaincy Team; Fac Meeting u Life Comm Co-Chair; NCTM 1987-; *office:* St Andrew's Schl 350 own Rd Middletown DE 19709*

NTIS, JOHN W., Mathematics Teacher; *b:* Pittsburgh, PA; *m:* Zupancic; *c:* Nicole, Brian; *ed:* Case Western Reserve Univ (BA) 970; Cleveland St Univ (MA) Math 1972; *cr:* Eastlake N HS Math 970-; Lakeland Comm Coll Math Instr 1973-78; John Carroll Univ Coach 1977; Lake Erie Coll Math Instr 1978; *ai:* Advanced Placement Coord; Acad Competition Adv; Soccer Coach; Willoughby-Eastlake Tchrs Assn 1970-, VP; OEA 1970-; OH Cncl Tchrs of Math 1970-; NEA 1973-; Mayfield Soccer Club 1988-, Yth Soccer Coach; Natl Sci Fndtn Grant; Martha Holden Jennings Tchr Scholar; *office:* Eastlake North HS 34041 Stevens Blvd Eastlake OH 44095

DESANTIS, NICK CHARLES, 6th-8th Grade Science Teacher; *b:* Erie, PA; *m:* Rita Therese; *c:* Susanne; *ed:* Mercyhurst Coll (BA) Elem Ed 1978; Gannon Coll (BA) Gen Sci 7-12 1989, (MA) Environmental Sci 1989; Edinboro Univ; *cr:* Saint George Schl 6 Grd Sci Tchr 1975-77; Villa Maria Schl 6-8 Grd Sci Tchr 1977-78; St Boniface Schl 4-8 Grd Sci Tchr 1978-89; Roosevelt Schl 6-8 Grd Sci, Math Tchr 1989-92; Harding Schl 6-8 Grd Sci Tchr 1992-; *ai:* Dir PA Jr Acad of Sci; Head Coach Girls Bsktbl Cntrl HS, Bsbl Seneca HS; Coord Governors Energy Awd St Boniface 1989; 1st City of Erie Pub Schl to Become Involved in PA Acad of Sci; *home:* 352 E 35th St Erie PA 16504

DE SANTO, SUSAN WEST, English & French Teacher; *b:* Elmira, NY; *m:* Michael; *c:* Jennifer; *ed:* Fr, Eng Mansfield Univ 1968; 36 Credit Hrs Eng, Ed Penn St; *cr:* Millville HS Eng, Fr Tchr 1968-69; Hughesville HS Eng, Fr Tchr 1969-; *ai:* Fr Club Adv; NEA, ELEA 1980-; *home:* 1557 Overbrook Rd Williamsport PA 17701*

DESARRO, JENNIFER TANGORRA, 5th Grade Teacher; *b:* Ilion, NY; *m:* Joseph James Jr.; *ed:* Mohawk Vly Comm Coll (AAS) Word Processing, Secretarial Sci 1988; Coll of St Rose (BS) Elem Ed 1990; SUNY at Cortland (MS) Rdng 1994; *cr:* Frankfort-Schyler Cntl Schl Dist 5th Grd Tchr 1992-; *ai:* Ftbl, Bsktbl JV, Var Chrldng Adv; *office:* Reese Road Elem Schl Reese Rd Frankfort NY 13340

DESAUTELS, PETER F., 9th-12th Grade Technology Tchr; *b:* Nashua, NH; *m:* Pauline G.; *c:* Daniel P.; *ed:* Univ of Lowell (BS) Bus Admin 1973; Univ of NH (MOE) Occupational Ed 1978; Bus Mngmt Cert 1983, Peoples Law Schl 1993 Northeastern Concord NH; Keene St Summer Inst 1993-95; *cr:* Nashua HS Tchr 1974-85; Nashua Tech Coll Dean Comm Ed 1986-88; Nashua HS Head Tchr, Assc Voc Dir 1989-91; Nashua Schl Dist Sub Tchr, Consultant 1991-93; Pelham HS Tech Tchr 1993-; *ai:* Tech Stu Assn, AT&T Rube Goldberg Contest Advs; Tech Comm; Sr Project Mentor; NEA, NHSTE 1993-; AVA, NHVA 1975-; NHTEA 1990-; Am Legion 1986-; ACA 1991-; Pelham Comm Tech 1994-; Tchr of Yr 1983; NH Legislative Commendation 1983; *office:* Pelham HS 85 Marsh Rd Pelham NH 03076

DESCH, EUGENE MICHAEL, World Cultures Teacher; *b:* Swissvale, PA; *m:* Alberta Kradel; *c:* Natalie, Adrianne; *ed:* Clarion Univ (BS) Comprehensive Soc Stud 1965; Westminster Coll (MED) His 1967; Communism & Constitutional Democracy Inst; *cr:* New Castle Area Schls World Culture Tchr 1965-; *ai:* Soc Stud Curr & Daily Attendance Comm; NEA 1965-70; AFT 1970-; Jaycees 1960-; New Castle Credit Union 1970-, Bd Mem; Eintracht Maennerchor 1975-, Pres; Westminster Coll Grant 1970; Kerygma Pgm Awd 1978; Thanks to Tchrs WestingHouse Electric Awd 1996; *home:* 4 W Clen Moore Blvd New Castle PA 16105

DESCHAMPS, JANET ELLEN, Second Grade Teacher; *b:* Mount Kisco, NY; *m:* Richard Carl; *c:* Eric, Christopher; *ed:* SUNY at Oneonta (BA) Elem Ed 1971; Western CT St Univ at Danbury (MA); *cr:* Millerton Elem Schl Second Grd Tchr 1971-; *ai:* Webutuck Tchrs Assn 1971-, Bldg Rep, Sick Bank Comm; NY St United Tchrs 1971-, Tchrs Retirement Del; Ladies Auxiliary Ancram Fire Dept 1991-; *office:* Millerton Elem Schl PO Box L Millerton NY 12546

DESCHAMPS, KARIN, German Teacher; *b:* Doylestown, PA; *ed:* Millersville St Coll (BS) Scndry Ed & Ger 1982; Deutsche Sommerschule Master Prgm 16 Credits; PA St Univ & Goethe Inst Ger Pedagogical Series 12 Credits; *cr:* Lawrence MS & HS Ger & FLEX Tchr 1982-; *ai:* German Club Adv; Delta Epsilon Phi Spon; Intnl Club Adv; German Tour Chaperone; NEA, NJEA, LTEA & AATG 1982-; FLENJ 1992-; *office:* Lawrence HS 2525 Princeton Pike Lawrenceville NJ 08648*

DESCHENEAUX, ERNEST JOSEPH, English Teacher; *b:* Lowell, MA; *ed:* Univ of Lowell (BA) Eng Scndry Ed 1977; Univ of MA at Lowell (MED) Admin 1995; Rivier Coll 3 Eng Courses at Grad Level; *cr:* Lowell HS Eng Tchr 1984-; *ai:* Jr Var Bsbl Coach; AFT 1984-; NCTE 1985-; Yth Bsbl 1973-, Pres; Yth Bsktbl 1978-.

DESENA, MARY ELIZABETH, High School English Teacher; *b:* New York, NY; *c:* Suzanne Pisano, Leslie Masuzzo, Richard DeAgazio, Christopher DeAgazio; *ed:* Coll of White Plains (BA) Eng 1959; Rutgers Univ Grad Schl (MA) Eng 1973; Eng Ed 35 Doctoral Credits; Christ Church Oxford, England Mini-courses Summer 1991, 1992, 1995; *cr:* Rutgers in Newark Eng Tchng Asst 1972-73; Woodrow Wilson Jr HS Eng Tchr, Dept Head 1973-78; John P. Stevens HS Eng Tchr 1978-; Middlesex Cty Coll Eng Adjunct Prof 1980-84; *ai:* NEA, MCEA, ETEA 1973-, Newspaper Ed 1987-89; Thomas Hardy Soc 1994-; NJ Poetry Soc 1991-; Phi Delta Kappa 1982-; PTSA 1978-, Exec Bd 1991-; NJ Eng Journal 3 Articles Pub 1994-96; NEH Fellowship for Stud Abroad 1989 & 9994; Amer Bus Womens Assoc Wkshp & Presentation 1993; NJ Teen Arts Festival 1981; NJ Cncl of Tchrs of Eng 1981; *office:* John P Stevens HS 855 Grove Ave Edison NJ 08820

DESENBERG, DAVID ARTHUR, High Schl Social Studies Tchr; *b:* Lima, OH; *m:* Catherine; *c:* David, Kathayrn, Kristina; *ed:* Bowling Green St Univ (BS) Scndry Ed 1978; Grad Stud 1989-93; Attending Univ of Dayton 1993-; *cr:* Huron City Schls Scndry Soc Stud Tchr 1978-83; Elida Local Schls Scndry Soc Stud Tchr 1983-; *ai:* Var Ftbl, Track Coach 1978-; Soc Stud Dept Chprsn; NEA, OEA, EEA, OH Ftbl, Track Coaches Assns 1978-; OH Track & C C Ofcls 1980-, Pres; *office:* Elida Local HS 101 E North St Elida OH 45807

DESHAIES, JAMES J., Retired Social Studies Teacher; *b:* Massena, NY; *m:* Barbara Brogan; *c:* Michelle Bartelotte, Brian, Robert, Rene' Berwick; *ed:* SUNY at Potsdam (BS) Ed 1962, (MS) Ed 1965; Post-Grad Stud Clarkson Coll, St Lawrence Univ; *cr:* South Lewis Cntrl Schl Jr HS Soc Stud Tchr 1962-95; *ai:* Var Bsbl, JV Bsktbl Coach; Var Club Adv; South Lewis Tchrs Assn 1962-, Mbrshp, Negotiations; NY St Tchrs Assn 1962-; Knights of Columbus 1970-, Grand Knight; Elks 1975-; Village Bd Boonville 1975-85, Deputy Mayor.

DESHAIS, THOMAS FRANCIS, Science Teacher; *b:* Springfield, MA; *m:* Cynthia A. Clute; *c:* Meghan, Brigette; *ed:* Westfield St Coll (BSE) General Sci 1969; Wesleyan Univ (MALS) Earth Sci 1973; Addl 60 Hrs at Cntrl CT St Univ; *cr:* Sage Park MS Sci Tchr 1969-; *ai:* Environmental Club Adv; NEA 1969-; Windsor Soccer Club 1990-; Windsor Exemplary Tchr Awd 1986; Windsor Educator of Yr 1990; UCONN Hlth Ctr Exemplary Sci Tchr 1996; *office:* Sage Park MS 25 Sage Park Rd Windsor CT 06095*

DESHIELDS, CHARLENE CALDWELL, First Grade Teacher; *b:* Cambridge, MD; *m:* Vernon L.; *c:* Demond, Kendra, Vernon II; *ed:* Bowie St Univ (BA) Early Chldhd Ed 1977; Western MD Coll (MS) Curr & Instruction 1990; Credit Hrs Salisbury St Univ; *cr:* Easton Elem Schl 1st Grd Tchr 1977-; *ai:* Schl Improvement Comm; NEA 1977-; TCEA 1977-; MSTA 1977-; PTA-Local 1977-; YMCA 1994-; Habitat for Humanity 1995-; Midshore Comm Fndtn 1995-; Alpha Kappa Alpha Inc Local Chptr, VP; Talbot Cty Tchr of Yr 1993-94; NAACP Local Comm Awd; *home:* 115 Parris Ln Easton MD 21601*

DESHIELDS, JUNE M., Fifth Grade Teacher; *b:* Baltimore, MD; *c:* Derek; *ed:* Bowie St Coll (BS) Elem Ed 1970; Bowie Univ (MS) Educl Admin, Supervision 1977; *cr:* High Point Elem Schl Sixth Grd Tchr 1970; Waugh Chapel Elem Schl Fifth Grd Tchr 1970-73; Four Seasons Elem Schl Fifth Grd Tchr 1973-; *ai:* NEA, MSTA, TAAAC 1970-; *office:* Four Seasons Elem Schl 979 Waugh Chapel Rd Gambrills MD 21054

DESIDERIO, PATRICIA ANN (DI BARTOLO), Science Teacher; *b:* Philadelphia, PA; *m:* Frank J. Jr.; *c:* Lisa, Frank; *ed:* Gwynedd-Mercy Coll (BA) Bio 1969; 200 Hrs NJ Alternate Rt to Cert Stockton St Coll; *cr:* Notre Dame HS Sci Tchr 1969-73; Holy Spirit HS Sci Tchr 1986-; *ai:* Soph Class Moderator; Bio Lab Asst Adv; Schl Play Make Up Crew Moderator; Fac Soc Coord; NCEA, SCTO & NJSTA 1986-; Mullica Twp PTA 1984; *office:* Holy Spirit HS California & New Rds Absecon NJ 08201*

DESILETS, BRIAN HENRY, Professor; *b:* Leominster, MA; *m:* Kathleen R.; *c:* Frances, Kathleen, Brian; *ed:* Marist Coll (BA) Math 1950; St John's Univ (MA) Math 1954; NYU (MS) Physics 1958; Cath Univ (PHD) Physics 1964; *cr:* Bishop DuBois HS Tchr 1950-54; Marist Coll Asst Prof 1954-60; Cath Univ Lecturer 1963-64; Marist Coll Prof 1964-74; IBM Rsrch Mgr 1974-91; Marist Coll Prof 1991-; *ai:* Acad Computing, Core Curr Comm; AAPT 1964-; Articles Pub; 7 Patents in Semi Conductors; *office:* Marist Coll D 107 82 North Dr Poughkeepsie NY 12601

DESIMONE, ELIZABETH, Family & Consumer Science Tchr; *b:* Fall River, MA; *m:* Michael R.; *c:* Michael, Matthew; *ed:* Georgian Ct (BS) Home Ec 1965; *cr:* Brick HS Tchr 1965-66; Lake Riveria MS Tchr 1966-67; Jackson Meml HS Family, Consumer Sci Tchr, Creative Cooking, World Cuisine 1967-; *ai:* NEA, NJEA, OCEA 1965-; JEA 1967-; Dev, Field Test St Curr Guide Meeting Needs Schl Age Stdnts; *office:* Jackson Memorial HS 101 Don Connor Blvd Jackson NJ 08527*

DESIMONE, MARIE STABILE, First Grade Teacher; *b:* New York, NY; *m:* Salvatore Robert; *c:* Andrea, Michael; *ed:* SUNY at New Paltz (BS) Behavioral Sci 1964; C W Post Coll (MS) Schl Guid & Cnslng 1983; 69 Grad Credit Hrs at Columbia Univ; *cr:* Belmont Elem Schl 2nd Grd Tchr 1964-68; William Sidney Mount Elem Schl 1st-4th Grd Tchr 1969-; *ai:* AFT 1964-; S Village Tchrs Assn 1969-; Northeast Awd for Innovative Lit Pgm Grant Issued by Advocates of Lit for Young People 1993; Awded 4 Mini-Grants; *office:* William Sidney Mount Elem Sch 50 Dean Ln Stony Brook NY 11790*

DESIMONE, MICHAEL PAUL, Social Studies Teacher; *b:* Cambridge, MA; *m:* Marie E.; *ed:* U MA (BS) His 1971, (MED) Soc Stud 1975, (CAGS) Scndry Rdng 1978; *cr:* Cambridge Rindge & Latin Schl Tchr 1971-; *ai:* MA Tchrs Assn; Cambridge Tchrs Assn; NEA; *office:* Cambridge Rindge & Latin HS 459 Broadway Cambridge MA 02138

DESJARDINS, PHILIP A., Science Teacher; *b:* Reading, PA; *m:* Anne Marie Lohmann; *c:* Robert, John, Chris, Ashley; *ed:* Villanova Univ (BS) Bio Ed 1967; Post Grad Stud Temple Univ, Salisbury Univ; *cr:* Welsh Vly Jr HS Sci Tchr 1967-72; Wicomico MS Sci Tchr 1973-; *ai:* Admin Advy Comm; IM Coach; Soccer; Flag Ftbl; Bsktbl; Sftbl; Dept Chair; Sci Fair Coord; Bowling Club Adv; WCEA, MSTA, NEA 1973-, Convention Del 1992-93, 1995; Salis Little League 1987-, Mgr, Umpire; MS Tchr of Yr 1990; *office:* Wicomico MS 635 E Main St Salisbury MD 21801

DESKEVICH, PAUL, Associate Professor of Math; *b:* Johnstown, PA; *m:* Mary Gloria Mc Carthy; *c:* Michael Paul, Nicholas Peter; *ed:* St Francis Coll (BS) Math 1965; WV Univ (MS) Math 1967; 40 Credit Hrs PA St Univ; *cr:* WV Univ Grad Asst 1965-67; St Francis Coll Math Prof 1967-; *ai:* Stu Adv; Medical Schl & Tech, Fac Salary & Benefits, Curr Comms; Act 101 Bd; MAA 1980-; Part-time Prof PA St Univ Altoona Campus Several Yrs; Awded St Francis Coll Honor Soc Fac Citation 1979; Sears Roebuck Fnd Tchng Excl, Campus Leadership Awd 1991; *office:* St Francis College Loretto PA 15940

DES LAURIERS, EILEEN ROBERTSON, English Teacher; *b:* McKeesport, PA; *m:* Ronald H.; *c:* Nicole, Christopher, Joshua; *ed:* IN Univ of PA (BS) Commnctns Ed 1975, (MA) Eng 1984; *cr:* Franklin Regional Inter HS Eng Tchr 1975-84; Kaplan Learning Ctr SAT, ACT & GRE Tchr 1987-90; Belleville Area Comm Coll Composition Tchr 1989-90; Chapmanville Jr HS Eng Tchr 1990-91; Gateway HS Eng Tchr 1991-; *ai:* Sr Class Adv & Cncl; NHS Selection Comm; NEA 1975-; NCTE 1975-; PSEA 1975-; Hillcrest UP Church 1965-, Deacon; PTSA Plum Schl Dist 1991-; Plum Wrestling & Soccer Boosters 1991-; Gift of Time Honoree; *office:* Gateway Sr HS 2629 Mosside Blvd Monroeville PA 15146

DESMARAIS, GERALD, High School History Teacher; *b:* Nashua, NH; *m:* Jan Perry; *ed:* Univ of NH (BA) His 1979, (MAT) Scndry Soc Stud 1982; 30+ Credit Hrs; *cr:* Berwick Acad Tchng Intern 1980-81; Grove Schl Eng Tchr 1982-83; Oxford Acad His Dept Chair 1983-87; Spaulding HS His Tchr 1987-; *ai:* Scholars Bowl; Barre Ed Assn & NEA 1987-, Sec; New Eng His Tchrs Assn 1990-; VT Labor Hist Soc 1991-; Natl Endowment for Hum, Cncl on Basic Ed, Ind Study Flwshp 1992; Article Pub; *office:* Spaulding HS 154 Ayers St Barre VT 05641*

DE SMITH, DENISE FILIPPONI, Spanish Teacher; *b:* Huntington, NY; *m:* Daryl Wayne Smith; *ed:* SUNY Brockport (BA) Span 1992; Working on Masters Elem Rdng Ed; *cr:* Hornell HS Span Tchr 1993-; *ai:* Span Club Adv; NEA, NY St Assn Frgn Lang Tchrs 1993-; *office:* Hornell HS Maple City Pk Hornell NY 14843

DESMOND, ELIZABETH M., English Teacher; *b:* Brooklyn, NY; *ed:* St Johns Univ (BS) Speech Ed 1971; Adelphi Univ (MA) Theatre Arts 1973; NY Inst of Tech (MA) Comm 1983; *cr:* West Hollow Jr HS Comm Skills Tchr 1979-91; H. H. H. Schl East Eng Tchr 1991-; *ai:* Play Productions; Newspaper; NY St United Tchrs, H. H. Hills Tchrs Assn 1971-; ASCD; Church Comms; BMT Theatrical Co 1980-; Nom Woodrow Wilson Schlsp; Univ Key St Johns Univ; *office:* Half Hollow Hills HS East 50 Vanderbilt Pky Dix Hills NY 11746

DESMOND, JOHN EDWARD, Science Teacher & Team Leader; *b:* New Haven, CT; *m:* Elaine Mellon; *c:* John, Jill; *ed:* Southern CT St Univ (BS) Intermediate & Upper Ed 1965, (MS) Sci Ed 1972; 6th Yr Degree in Admin & Supervision 1977; *cr:* Bungay Schl 6th Grd Sci & Math Tchr 1965-76; Seymour MS Team Ldr, Sci & Math Tchr 1976-; *ai:* Evaluation Revision & Jr Honor Soc Screening Comms; SEA 1965-, VP 1979-85, Bldg Rep 1978-86; CEA & NEA 1965-; New England League of MS 1988-; Seymour Tchr of Yr 1990-91; *office:* Seymour M S 20 Pine St Seymour CT 06483*

DESMOND, MABEL J., State of Maine Representative; *b:* Lower Southampton, Canada; *m:* Jerry R. Sr.; *c:* Jerry R. Jr., Jed Carey, Ronnee Beth Johnston, Jennifer Shea York; *ed:* Aroostook St Coll (BS) Elem Ed 1964; Univ of ME (MED) Ed 1975; Advanced Degree Credits in Ed Admin; Prins Cert K-12; *cr:* Bridgewater Elem Sch V Grd Tchr 1949-50; Ashland Schl IV Grd Tchr; MSAD #1 Schl K-8 Grd Tchr 1950-; Univ of ME at Preque Isle Ed Dept Fac 1991-; St of ME Rep 1994-; *ai:* Ed, Cultural Affairs Comm 117th ME Legislature; MEA; NEA; DKG Sec, Treas, Pres, St Parliamentarian; Univ ME at Preque Isle Alumni Assn 1949-, Sec, Treas, Pres Twice; Exec Bd, Distngd Aluni Awd; Univ of ME at Preque Isle Tchr Ed Advy Bd 1996; Numerous Newspaper Columns; Pub Articles; *home:* Main St Mapleton ME 04757

DESMOND, REBECCA C., Art Teacher & Dept Chair; *b:* Montgomery, PA; *m:* H. Parry; *ed:* Kutztown St Coll (BS) K-12 Art 1961; PA Acad of Fine Arts 54 Credits; Weidner Univ 6 Grad Credits; Millersville Univ 9 Grad Credits; West Chester Univ 3 Grad Credits; *cr:* Downingtown Area Schl Dist Art 1961-, Dept Chair 1983-; *ai:* Tennis Coach Girls 1968-, Boys 1983-; Art Assts Club; Schl Dist Strategic Planning, Act 178 Comms; NEA, PSEA 1961-; DAEA 1961-, Tchr of Yr 1985; USPTA 1980-, Div Pres, Coach of Yr 1983, 1995; USTA 1970-, Section VP, Coach of Yr 1994; PIAA

Dist I Tennis Steering Comm 1973-, Chair; Downingtown Jr Tennis Assn 1972-, Chair; DATT Comm 1994-; PA HS Tennis Coaches Assn 1996, Pres; Chester Co Intermediate Unit 24 Grant 1976; Articles Pub; Coaching Tennis Successfully Co-Author; Seminar Presentations; Coaches Wkshps, Conventions; *office:* Downingtown Sr HS 445 Manor Ave Downingtown PA 19335*

DESOL, PAUL P., 7th Grade Math Teacher; *b:* Middletown ; *ed:* Cortland St (BA) Scndry Math Ed 1980; City Coll (MA) Math Ed 1988; *cr:* John S. Burke Cath HS Math Tchr 1980-83; Orange Cty Comm Coll Math Tchr 1986-; Wallkill MS Math Tchr 1983-; *ai:* Soccer & Sftbl Coach; Wallkill Tchrs Assn & NYSUT 1983-; Middletown Babe Ruth 1974-, Coach & Bd of Dir; Middletown Soccer 1990-, Coach; *home:* 51 Ogden St Middletown NY 10940

DESORGHER, RICHARD PAUL, US History Teacher; *b:* Boston, MA; *m:* Virginia Park; *c:* Matthew, Michael, Amy; *ed:* Univ of MA (BA) His 1975, (MA) Amer Civilization 1986; Masters +30 Credit Hrs; *cr:* Medfield MS Tchr & Team Ldr 1976-95; Medfield HS Tchr 1995-; *ai:* MS Stu Cncl Adv; IM Dir; Stu Cncl Mem; Yth Hockey Coach; Little League Coach; MA Tchrs Assn 1976-; Norfolk Cty Tchrs Assn 1976-, Laura Warcup Distngd Edctrs Awd; MA Cncl of Soc Stud 1980-, William Spratt Excl in Tchng Soc Stud Awd; Medfield Park & Recreation Commission 1976-, Chm; Medfield Yth Advy Commission 1976-84, Vice-Chm; Medfield Historical Soc 1976-, Curator, Pres; Medfield Bd of Selection 1980-83, Chm; Medfield Historical Commission 1983-, Chm; Medfield Comm to Stud Memrls 1988-, Chm; Natl Soc Daughters of Colonial Wars Tchr of the Yr Awd; DAR Tchr of the Yr Awd; Medfield Lions Club Citizen of Yr Awd; Book Pub; Outstdng Young Men of Amer Awd; WCVB Ch 5 Spotlight on Tchng Awd; *home:* 4 Carmen Cir Medfield MA 02052

D'ESPOSITO, RITA A., Fifth Grade Teacher; *b:* Passaic, NJ; *m:* Vincent N.; *c:* Marc Edward; *ed:* Georgian Ct Coll (BA) Ed 1986; *cr:* Walnut St Elem Schl Basic Skills Math Tchr 1986, 5th Grd Tchr 1986-; *ai:* NEA 1986-; Garden St Philharmonic Designer Showcase 1995, Spec Events Chprsn; Sandcastle Early Learning Ctr, Advy Bd; *office:* Walnut Street Elem Schl 50 Walnut St Toms River NJ 08753

DESPRES, GINA LOUISE, English Teacher; *b:* New Bedford, MA; *ed:* Univ of MA at Dartmouth (BA) Eng, Writing Option 1987; 30 Addl Grad Credit Hrs; *cr:* Old Colony RVTMA Eng Tchr 1987-; Newbury Coll Part-time Eng Bus Comm, Lit Instr 1989-92; *ai:* Voc Industrial Clubs of Amer Adv; Environmental Partnership Comm; Implementor with Other Select Tchrs in Inclusion Tchng System SOC; NCTE 1992-; MA Cncl Tchrs Eng 1996-; Nom MA Tchr of Yr 1995-; *office:* Old Colony Regnl Voc Tech HS 476 North Ave Rochester MA 02770*

DESROCHES, DANIELLE, Associate Professor of Biology; *b:* Haiti, WI; *ed:* Hunter Coll NY (BA) Bio 1974; City Univ of NY (MPHIL) Bio 1978, (PHD) Bio 1981; *cr:* Hunter Coll Adjunct Lecturer 1978-81; William Paterson Asst & Assoc Prof 1981-; *ai:* SSMSS Dir; AMPS Learning Ctr Coord; Project AMP; AFT, AAAS, Sigma XI & NY Acad Sci; Lab Books Anatomy & Physiology Human Bio; Research Articles In Drug & Alcohol Research & In Alcohol; *office:* William Paterson Coll 300 Pompton Rd Wayne NJ 07470

DESROSIERS, PHILIP CHARLES,S.C. Music Teacher; *b:* Woonsocket, RI; *ed:* RI Coll (BS) Music Ed 1975, (MAT) Music Ed 1981; Working Toward Masters in Worship & Music at Univ of Portland; 18 Credits in Rel Ed From Saint Michaels Coll; *cr:* Mount Saint Charles Acad Music Dir 1977-81; Nashua Cath Jr HS Music Dir 1983-89; Mount Saint Marys Acad Band Dir 1985-91; Bishop Guertin HS Music Dir 1985-; *ai:* Liturgical Music Ministry; Ski Club; Music Educators Natl Conf 1971-, Nationally Registered Music Educator Awd; NH Music Educators Assn 1983-; Natl Band Assn 1977-; Natl Pastoral Musicians 1983-; Saint Joseph Church Choir 1985-, Dir; *office:* Bishop Guertin HS 194 Lund Rd Nashua NH 03060

DESSEREAU-KOCH, APRIL, Art, Photography Tchr & Chrmn; *b:* Port Chester, NY; *m:* Kevin H. Koch; *ed:* SUNY at Oswego (BA) Art, Art His 1975; Univ of Bridgeport (MS) Art Ed 1978; Manhattanville Coll (MA) Hum 1992; *cr:* Port Chester HS Adult Ed, Calligraphy Tchr 1979-83, Art, Photography Tchr 1982-; *ai:* Art Chair 1989-; Art, Music, Culinary Arts Liaison 1990-; AFT, NEA 1982-; NAEA 1989-; Childrens Book Illustrator; Tchr of Month 1991; *home:* 66 College Ave Port Chester NY 10573

DESSNER, LINDA ECKHARDT, Adjunct Professor of ESL; *b:* Haddonfield, NJ; *m:* Murray; *ed:* American Univ (BS) Pol Sci 1967; Univ of PA (MS) TESOL 1983, (PhD) Educl Linguistics 1991; *cr:* Phila Coll T&S Adjunct Prof of ESL 1983-; Univ of PA Lecturer 1993-; *office:* Phil Coll of Textile & Science 4201 Henry Ave Philadelphia PA 19144

DESTEFANIS, GIANCARLO, French Teacher; *b:* Tocco Casauria, Italy; *m:* Maria Marini; *c:* Alessandra, Laura, Carla; *ed:* Southern CT St Univ (MS) Italian, Fr, Span 1975, (MS) Modern Lang 1982; Sixth Yr Prgm Educl Ldrshp; *cr:* Sacred Heart Univ Adj Prof Italian 1983-85; East Haven HS Frgn Lang Tchr 1975-; *ai:* Var Soccer Coach 1978-83, 1985-94; Ski, Fr, Travel Club Adv; Prof Dev Comm; Schl Senate; Frgn Lang Stu for Comm Svc Dir; CITA 1975-; TOFEL 1980-; NIAF 1987-; *office:* East Haven HS 200 Tyler St East Haven CT 06512

DESTEFANO, ELENA BARBIERI, Kindergarten Teacher; *b:* Brooklyn, NY; *m:* Ralph Joseph; *c:* Jennifer, Ralph Martin; *ed:* Wagner Coll (BS) Elem Ed 1971; 18 Addl Credits in Ed, Catechetical Stud; *cr:* St Patrick's Schl First-Second Grd Tchr 1971-72; St Bernadette Schl First Grd Tchr 1979-80; Sacred Heart Schl First-Second Grd Tchr 1980-85, Kndgtn Tchr 1985-; *ai:* Kndgtn Coord; Fed of Cath Tchrs 1980-; *office:* Sacred Heart Schl 301 N Burgher Ave Staten Island NY 10310*

DESTEFANO, KAREN MARIE, Fourth Grade Teacher; *b:* Cambridge, MA; *ed:* Lowell St Coll (BS) Elem Ed 1970; 60 Credit Hrs; *cr:* Shamrock Schl 5th Grd Tchr 1970-79, 4th Grd Tchr 1979-90; Reeves Schl 4th Grd Tchr 1990-91; Malcolm White Schl 4th Grd Tchr 1991-; *ai:* Main Curr Comm Co-Chair 1994-95; Lang Arts Comm Co-Chair 1994-95; WTA Comm Co-Chair 1995; NEA 1970-; MA Tchrs Assn 1970-; Woburn Tchrs Assn 1970-, Fac Rep 1992-; Woburn Lioness Club 1992-93; *office:* Malcolm White Elem Schl Bow St Woburn MA 01801

DE STEFANO, MARK PAUL, English Teacher; *b:* Washington, DC; *ed:* James Madison Univ (BA) Eng, Comms 1993; *cr:* Springbrook HS Eng Tchr 1994-; *ai:* Newspaper Adv; Jr Var Boys Bsktbl & Coed Vlybl Coach; Quill & Scroll Spon; NEA, MSTA & MCEA 1993-; Sweepstakes Winner In-Depth Reporting Individual Adv; given By Natl Newspaper Assn & Quill & Scroll; *office:* Springbrook HS 201 Valleybrook Dr Silver Spring MD 20904

DE STEFANO, PATRICE NEVITT, English Teacher; *b:* Brooklyn, NY; *m:* Louis; *c:* Matthew, Andrew, Patrice, Jaclyn; *ed:* Queensborough Comm Coll (AA) Eng 1971; Queens Coll (BA) Eng 1973, (MS) Ed, Eng 1976; *cr:* St Margaret Schl 6-8 Eng, Rdg Tchr 1974-76; Eng, Rdng, Math, SAT Prep Tutoring Tchr 1976-; Queens Elem Schls Sub Work 1980-91; Our Lady of Mercy Acad Amer Lit, World Lit, Comm Techniques Tchr 1991-; *ai:* SADD Adv; NYSUT 1974-; AAUW 1991-; CAth Daughters Ladies Auxiliary 1993-, Ed Comm Chprsn; St James Fire Dept 1994-.

DESTEPHANO, JOHN ANTHONY, Junior High Math Teacher; *b:* York, PA; *ed:* Elizabeth Coll (BS) Acctng 1960; Millersville Elem Ed 1962; *cr:* St Rose of Lima Schl Elem Math Tchr 1960-92; York Cath High Jr High Math Tchr 1992-; *ai:* Jr High Girls Bsktbl Coach; *home:* 426 Pacific Ave York PA 17404

DESTINO, ALICE L., 2nd Grade Elementary Teacher; *b:* Niagara falls, NY; *m:* Louis P.; *c:* Paul, Ann Marie; *ed:* Buffalo St (BS) Ed 1989; Niagara Univ (MA) Fnds of Ed 1993; *cr:* Lewiston-Porter Elem Tchr 1989-; *ai:* Phi Delta Kappa 1990-; *office:* Lewiston-Porter Cntrl Schl 4061 Creek Rd Youngstown NY 14174*

DESUE, ERNIE, Industrial Arts Tech Teacher; *b:* McKeesport, PA; *m:* Susan L. Davis; *c:* Robert James, Christipher Lee; *ed:* CA St Coll (BS) Industrial Arts 1970; Automobile & Small Engine Repair; Voc Ed; *cr:* Grove City MS Tchr 1984-; *ai:* MS Yrbk Adv 9 Yrs; MS Video Yrbk Adv 3 Yrs; Sr HS Head Soccer Coach 9 Yrs; PSEA 1993-; NEA 1993-; Exemplary Tchr Awd Grove City Area Schl Dist 1984; Stu Assistance Team Mem Awd 1994; Class Act Tchr Awd WFMJ TV 21 1994; *home:* 408 College Ave Grove City PA 16127

DESZO, CARMEN LIND, Medical Lab Assisting Teacher; *b:* Jamestown, NY; *m:* Robert; *c:* Eric; *ed:* Baldwin-Wallace Coll (BS) Bio 1972; Cleveland St Univ (MS) Curr & Instr 1986; *cr:* Hlth Careers Tchr 1984-; *ai:* Voc Dept Co-Chprsn; Work Keys Test Coord; ASCP 1974-; *office:* Health Careers Ctr 1740 E 32nd St Cleveland OH 44114

DETERDING, CHRISTOPHER DAVID, Mathematics & Cmptr Sci Tchr; *b:* Chicago, IL; *m:* Patti S. Parkinson; *c:* Amy, Stephen, James; *ed:* VA Polytechnic Inst & St Univ (BS) Math Ed 1973; Towson St Univ (MED) Scndry Ed 1979; Attnd George Washington Univ, Univ of MD; *cr:* Annapolis HS Tchr 1973-; Anne Arundel Co Pub Schls Staff Dev Instr 1980-92, Cmptr Specialist 1993-; Anne Arundel Comm Coll Adj Prof 1993-; *ai:* NHS Adv; Math Club Adv; Cmptr Liaison; Phi Kappa Phi; Broadneck Evangelical Presbyn Church 1990-, Clerk of Session; Outstdng Tchr Awd Univ of Chicago; Outstdng Edctr Awd Cornell Univ; Outstdng Tchr Awd Tandy Tech Scholars; *office:* Annapolis Sr HS 2700 Riva Rd Annapolis MD 21401

DETOFSKY, LOUIS BENNETT, Biology & Earth Science Tchr; *b:* Philadelphia, PA; *ed:* Rutgers Univ (BA) Geology & Bio 1968; Rowan Coll (MA) Geology & Bio 1976; 60 Hrs Ed in Geology & Bio at Univ of AK at Anchorage, Portland St Univ, William Patterson St Coll, Univ of PA, Trenton St Coll, West Chester Univ; *cr:* Washington Twp HS Geology, Bio & Anthropology Inst 1968-; *ai:* Geology Club 1968-; NEA 1968-; NSTA 1976-; Natl Assn of Geology Tchrs 1980-; Natl Earth Sci Tchrs Assn 1980-; Geological Assn of NJ 1984-, Cnslr at Large 1985; NJ Earth Sci Tchr Assn 1984-; Bnai Brith 1987-; Geology Explorer Post 8 1988-, Adv; Tchr of the Yr 1990-91; Have Writen Six Books; *office:* Washington Township HS 509 Hurffville-Crosskeys Rd Sewell NJ 08080*

DETORE, PHILIP G., Jr HS American History Teacher; *b:* Greensburg, PA; *m:* Rita A.; *c:* Vincent, Shane, Amy; *ed:* Clarion St Univ (BS) His 1970; Univ of Pittsburgh, Penn St Univ Grad Credits; *cr:* Southmoreland Jr Sr HS Amer His Tchr 1971-; *ai:* Wrestling Coach 1971-78; Gifted Tchr 1990-93; New Tchrs Mentor 1993-; PA St Ed Assn 1971-; *home:* 1615 Elm St Greensburg PA 15601

DETORO, JIM, 8th Grade Math Teacher; *b:* Youngstown, OH; *m:* Susan Blystone; *c:* Michael, Carla, Thomas; *ed:* Youngstown St Univ (BA) Comp Soc Stud 1977; Scndry Math Cert 1978; *cr:* Liberty HS Math Tchr 1978-81; W S Guy Schl 7th Grd OH His Tchr 1987-91, 8th Grd Math Tchr 1981-; *ai:* Asst Ftbl Coach 1978-; Math Counts, TAPS & Stu Tchr Adv; NEA 1978-; Trumbull Cty Coaches Assn 1978-; OH HS Ftbl Coaches Assn 1978-; E OH Tchrs of Math 1983-; Austintown PTA 1988-; Liberty PTA 1988-; Austintown Yth Bsbl 1991-, Ath Dir for PeeWees, Coach & Mgr; LEAF Grants 1990-93; Golden Apple Achiever Awd 1993; *home:* 423 Forest Hill Dr Youngstown OH 44515*

DETTBARN, SHIRLEY JOSEPH, First Grade Teacher; *b:* Berlin, MD; *m:* Carl Leverne; *ed:* Mt St Agnes Coll (BA) Elem Ed 1970; Masters Equivalency Salisbury St Coll; Real Estate Course; *cr:* Pittsville Schl 1st-4th Grd Tchr 1970-92; Willards Primary Schl 1st Grd Tchr 1991-; *ai:* SIT Team; Mentor; Cooperating Tchr Stu Tchrs; Fac Rep PTA; NEA, WCEA 1995-; Moose WOTM, Amer Legion 1995-; VFW 1992-; *home:* 36416 Poplar Neck Rd Willards MD 21874*

DETTORRE, ALBERT JOSEPH, Health & PE Teacher; *b:* Latrobe, PA; *m:* Lujean Boving; *c:* Jacquelyn, Nicholas; *ed:* (BS) Hlth & PE 1976; (MS) Sports Sci 1985; *cr:* Blairsville Sr High Tchr & Coach 1978-; *ai:* Head Ftbl & Asst Track Coach; Var Club Spon; Blairsville Vol Fire Dept 1976-, 2nd VP; *office:* Blairsville HS 100 School Ln Blairsville PA 15717*

DETWEILER, CARL WRIGHT, Student Act Dir & Math Teacher; *b:* Abbington, PA; *m:* Brenda Lynn Harris; *c:* Jesse Ryan, Jeremy Lee, Jaclyn Rose; *ed:* Bob Jones Univ (BS) Elem Ed 1983; *cr:* Faith Chrstn Acad Math Tchr, Elem Supt 1987-; *ai:* 8th Grd Adv; Var Soccer Coach; AACS 1987-; *office:* Faith Christian Acad 700 N Main St Sellersville PA 18960

DETWEILER, KAREN HOLLERAN, English Teacher; *b:* Sayre, PA; *m:* John; *c:* Jessa, Jeptha; *ed:* Mansfield Univ (BS) Scndry Ed 1974; Elmira Coll (MS) Ed 1982; *cr:* Mansfield Jr-Sr HS Tchr 1974-; *ai:* NHS; Lang Arts Comm; NEA, PSEA 1974-; Southern Tioya Ed Assn Pres 1992-; Founding Mem W. L. Miller PTO & Pres 1991-92; Girl Sct Ldr.

DETWILER, DOROTHY WYNN, Mathematics Teacher; *b:* Phoenixville, PA; *ed:* Ursinus (BS) Math 1952; Penn St (MED) Ed 1959; Courses at Univ of CO 6 Credits; Course in Cmptr BCCC 3 Credits; *cr:* George Schl Tchr of Math 1952-81, Tchr of Math & Registrar 1981-95, Registrar 1995-; *ai:* Adv; NCTM 1952-92; Delta Kappa Gamma 1993-; United Meth Church 1960-, Lay Ldr, Have Held Many Other Offices; Independence Chair at George Schl 1981-95; *office:* George Schl Box 4203 Newtown PA 18940*

DETWILER, MELISSA MANN, Spanish Teacher; *b:* Morenci, MI; *m:* Jon; *ed:* Bluffton Coll (BA) Elem Ed k-8th Grd Ed with Span 7th-12th Grd Cert 1989; Univ of Findlay (MA) TSEOL & Biling Ed 1995; 2 Semester Hrs at OH St Univ in Span Phonology; *cr:* Fremont Jr HS Jr High Span I,II, III, Lang Arts & Rdng Tchr 1989-; Fremont City Schls Summer Migrant Schl Tchr 1991-94; Terra Tech Coll Span Instr 1992; *ai:* Jr High Yrbk 1993-95, Span Club Adv 1989-; HS Amer Field Svc Club Adv 1990-95; NEA 1989-; OH MS Assn 1993-; *home:* 1900 Riverbend Pkwy Fremont OH 43420

DETWILER, PATRICIA AURENTZ, Fourth Grade Teacher; *b:* Lebanon, PA; *m:* John P.; *ed:* Millersville Univ (BS) Elem Ed 1963; 36 Post-Grad Credits; *cr:* Henry Houck Elem Schl Elem Tchr 1963-68; Southwest Elem Schl Elem Tchr 1969-; *ai:* Post Office Spon; Southwest Exec Cncl; NEA, PSEA 1963-; Lebanon Cty Educl Hnr Soc 1985-; Good Samaritan Hosp Auxiliary; Amer Heart Assn Vol; *home:* 414 Edgewood Dr Lebanon PA 17042

DETZ, JOSEPH ANTHONY, Mathematics Teacher; *b:* Newburgh, NY; *m:* Cynthia Rainey; *c:* Joseph, Suzanne, Lori-Lynn; *ed:* Univ of SC (BS) PE, Math 1973; Attnd SUNY at New Paltz, Pace; *cr:* Meadow Hill Schl Math Tchr 1973-80; South Jr HS Math Tchr 1980-82; Marlboro MS Math, Math Lab Tchr 1982-83; Marlboro HS Math Tchr, Bsktbl Coach 1983-; *ai:* Boys Var Bsktbl Coach 13 Yrs; MFA 1982-; NYSUT, AFT 1973-; Bsktbl Coaches Assn of NY 1983-; Our Lady of Fatima R.C. Church 1982-; *office:* Marlboro HS 50 Cross Rd Marlboro NY 12542

DETZEL, CARL W., Mathematics Teacher; *b:* Erie, PA; *m:* Judith Kravenrath; *c:* James, Kelly; *cr:* Shaler Area Schl Dist Math Tchr 1971-95; *ai:* Math Club; WWW, Allegheny Projects; PSEA; NEA; NCT Shaler Area HS 381 Wible Run Rd Pittsburgh PA 15209

DEUTSCH, RICHARD ALAN, Social Studies Department Taunton, MA; *m:* Lena; *c:* Paul, Jason; *ed:* RI Coll (BA) His & 1970, (MED) Scndry Admin 1976; *cr:* Cntrl HS Tchr 1970; Greene MS Soc Stud Tchr 1970-74; Classical HS Soc Stud Tc Dept Head 1996-; *ai:* Close-Up Adv WA DC Pgm; Yrbk Adv; Bc Coach; Innovative Tchr of the Yr; Nom Providence Tchr of the & Beyond Awded by Parents; *office:* Classical HS 770 Westn Providence RI 02903

DEUTSCH, WARREN NEAL, Professor of Social Studies Ed; FL; *m:* Shirley Hess; *c:* Bryan, Michael, Kevin; *ed:* Valley Forge (AA) Liberal Arts 1967; SUNY at Buffalo (BA) Anthropology 19 Univ (MA) Anthropology 1972; Rutgers St Univ (EDD) Soc Stud *cr:* Georgian Court Coll Anthropology, Sociology Chm 1977-; Antropological Assn, Fellow; Amer Archaeology Soc, Anthropol Cncl, Voting Mem; Lakewood Bd of Ed 1989-, VP; Phi Beta K Theta Kappa VP; Kappa Delta Pi; Who's Who in East; Archaelogical Research Mini-Grant 1990; *office:* Georgian Cour 900 Lakewood Ave Lakewood NJ 08701*

DEVALVE, DIANNE GRACE, Professor of Counseling; *b:* Free *ed:* Seton Hall Univ (BA) Psych 1976, (MA) Rehabilitation C 1980; Gestalt Therapy Trng Philadelphia Family Counseling Family Stud Family Therpy, Rutgers Advanced Alcohol Stud Essex Cty Coll Adjunct Prof of Counseling 1986-, Substance Abu 1993-95; Turning Point Inc Clinical Dir 1995-; *ai:* NJ Assn of Drug Cnslrs 1980-, Bd Mem 1993-96, St Conf Chprsn 1994-; A Counseling & Human Dev, NJ Prof Cnslrs, Amer Mental Hlt Kappa Delta Pi 1980-; Natl Distinguished Svc Registry Coun Human Dev 1990; Publications Natl Soc Sci Perspectives Journa 1990, Spec Problems in Counseling-Chemically Dependent A Haworth Press Inc NY 1991, Journal of Adolescent Chemical De Vol 1 #4 1991; Certified Alcoholism Cnslr NJ 1979, 1981, 19 1987, 1989 & 1991; Natl Certified Alcohol & Drug Abuse Cn 1992, 1994 & 1996; Natl Certified Cnslr 1995; Certified Dependency Supvr 1993; Certified Rehabilitation Cnslr 1980, 1995; *office:* Essex County Coll 303 University Ave Newark NJ

DEVAN, ROBERT JAMES, Guidance Coordinator; *b:* Plattsbur Bonnie Bridge; *c:* Megan, Michael, Matthew; *ed:* Univ of Ste (BA) Soc Stud 7-12 1972; SUNY at Plattsburg (BS) Ed 1977, (C Stud Cnslng 1984; SUNY at Cortland (CAS) Educ Admi Continuing Ed Credits; *cr:* St Joseph Schl Soc St, Sci 6-8th 1972-77; Saranac Cntrl Schl Cnslng Intern 1997; Peru Jr Sr 1977-78; Neward Vly Cntrl Dir Guid 1978-95; Dryden Cntrl Schl Guid 1995-; *ai:* Var Soccer Coach 13 Yrs; Modified Bsbl Coach Bsbl 4 Yrs; JV Soccer 1 Mod; Bstbl 9 Yrs; Acad Adv; TC3 HS C Team 9 Yrs; JETS Team 8 Yrs; WAVR/WATS Challenge Team 4 Indoor Soccer 6 Yrs; NYS Cnslr Assoc 1978-; Amer Assoc of C 1980-; NYS United Tchr 1978-95; Broome-Tioga Coun Assoc Treas 10 Yrs; BPOE 1990-, Schlsp Chm; Tau Kappa Epsilon 196 Cty B&G Club Coach 1990-; St Patricks Schl Bd; *office:* Dryden C PO Box 88 Dryden NY 13053

DE VELVIS, LINDA HARP, Social Studies Teacher; *b:* Sidney, David E.; *c:* Keri, Joshua, Jason; *ed:* Wright St Univ (MS) Su 1987; Gifted Cert 1987; *cr:* Sidney City Schls Elem Spec Ed Tchr 7th-8th Grd Soc Stud Tchr 1983-; *ai:* Bridgeview Play Dir; S Assn, Soc Comm; SEA, OEA, NEA 1983-; OH Cncl for Soc Stu Shelby Cty Historical Soc 1993-, VP; Grants from OH Ame Auxilliary for Freedom Wkshps; Dev 2 Living His Persons Bridgeview MS 320 E North St Sidney OH 45365*

DEVENEY, CHARLES LOUIS, Social Studies Teacher; *b:* Cam *m:* Linda E. Bull; *c:* Blaise L.; *ed:* PA St Univ (BS) Scndry Ed 19 Chester Univ (MA) His 1993; *cr:* St James HS His Tchr 1986-88 X HS His Tchr 1988-89; Pottsgrove Intermediate Soc Stud Tchr 1 Asst Womens Bsktbl Coach Ursinus Coll; NEA 1993-; Adult Liter Tutor; Article Pub; *office:* Pottsgrove Intermediate Schl 1329 Bu Pottstown PA 19464

DEVENEY, DOROTHY A. GIARDINO, Mathematics Tea Dorchester, MA; *m:* John W.; *ed:* Boston St Coll (BS) Math, S Cambridge Coll (MED) Ed 1994; Attnd Salem St Coll. UMA Fitchburg St Coll; Univ of Lowell; *cr:* North Jr HS Math, Sci Tc Nahant Jr HS Math, Sci Tchr; Northeast Metro Reg Voc Math, Tchr; *ai:* NHS, Natl Voc, Tech Hnr Soc Adv; Adult Ed Tchr; Recr Mediation, Peer Ldrshp, Voc Ed Wk, Tech Prep, Schl to Work NEA; MA Tchrs Assn; Northeast Tchrs, Sec; NCTM; Horace Ma NSF Grant; Sci Fair Judge; Math League Adv.*

DEVENEZIA, ANN M. (LUPARDI), English Teacher; *b:* Florha NJ; *m:* Richard F.; *c:* Marie Gebbia, Debra, Richard A., Nicholas Chmiel, John; *ed:* Coll of St Elizabeth (BA) Eng 1956; Drew Univ Western Civilization in Liberal Stud 1990; *cr:* Westwood HS E 1956-59; Parsippany HS Eng Tchr 1979-; *ai:* Arts, Diversity Com NEA 1956-, Vol Reader; NCTE 1980-; Mountain Lakes Bd of Ed 1982-85 Pres; Drew Univ Michael Ellis Writing Awd 1990; Mid S Assembly Coll Bd Advanced Placement Recognition Awd 1994; D Grant 1995; *office:* Parsippany HS 309 Baldwin Rd Parsippany N.

DEVENNEY, ANNE CONNELLEE, Spanish Tchr & Director o Plainfield, NJ; *m:* John J. Jr.; *ed:* Dickinson Coll (BA) Span, Er Weidner Univ (MED) Admin 1982; Univ of PA Principalship 1 Darby Colwyn Sr HS Eng, Span Tchr, Dept Chair 1972-82; Penn V Span Tchr, Dept Chair, Act Dir 1982-; *ai:* Dir All Non-Athletic Strategic Planning Steering, Tech, Reorganization All Dist Level New Tchr Induction Mentor 1993, 1995-; NEA, PSEA, WPEA AATSP, ACTFL 1980-; Commonwealth Tchng Fellow 1988; 2 Gift Tributes Am Family Inst 1993, 1995; Tchr of Yr Nomination 19 Penn Svc Awds 1977, 1982; *office:* Penn Wood HS 100 Gr Lansdowne PA 19050*

DEVER, CHERIE ANN (COX), Third Grade Teacher; *b:* Chicago Ramon; *c:* Michael Carmoney, Shannon Carmoney Benton; *ed:* Univ (BS) Ed 1982, (MA) Curr, Instr 1990; Post Masters 10 Hr Edward's Schl 1-2nd Grd Tchr 1982-85; Hillside Elem Schl 3rd C 1985-; *ai:* Bldg Rep HEA; Assembly Comm; Earth Day Comm; NE 1985-, Bldg Rep; Sci Cncl of OH 1989-; Hillsdale PTO 1992-; Alp Kappa 1987-, Sec; Women's Symphony League 1995-; Humane So Ashland YMCA 1983-; Hillsdale Acad Boosters 1989-; OH Mini-Grant; Career Grant; *office:* Hillsdale Elem Schl County Rd Hayesville OH 44838*

DEVESTERN, HAROLD, Fourth Grade Teacher; *b:* Brooklyn, Irene Kyguolis; *c:* Michael, William; *ed:* Fairleigh Dickinson Un Elem Ed 1973; *cr:* USMC Sgt 1956-60; Tenneco Chemicals C Operator 1960-73; Woodbridge Bd of Ed Tchr 1973-74; Roselle B Tchr 1974-; *ai:* Head Tchr; NEA, NJEA, REA 1974-; Woodbridge 1973-; *office:* Polk Elem Schl 1100 Warren St Roselle NJ 07203

DEVINCENTIS, BRENDA KORDISH, Earth & Space Science T *b:* New Castle, PA; *m:* Richard Arthur; *c:* Richard Alexanc Westminster Coll (MS) Chem, Math 1985, (MED) Ed 1987; Po Credits in Physics in Ed, Wallops Island Oceanography, Cmptr

HS Chem Tchr 1985-86; Mercer HS Chem, Sci, Math, Cmptr 5-93; Neshannock HS Earth Space Sci Tchr 1993-; *ai:* Jr Acad of d; Environmental Meet Coord; Ski Club Adv; PSEA 1986-, VP; 3-; AKT 1986-; *office:* Neshannock Jr-Sr HS 301 Mitchell Rd le PA 16105*

'ENTIS, NICHOLAS ALBERT, Science Teacher; *b:* Langley ; *c:* Lori Renee Strong, Kristin Marie; *ed:* CA Univ of PA (BS) 1967; PA St Masters Equivalency Elem Ed 1976, Post Grad Stud; son Park Elem Schl 5th-6th Grd Modified Self-Contained Tchr Trafford MS 6th-7th Grd Math, Sci Tchr 1972-95; Jeannette Dist sp Paramedic, Advanced Life Support 1986-; Penn MS 7th-8th Chr 1995-; *ai:* NEA, PA St Ed Assn 1967-; Penn-Trafford Ed Assn hief Negotiator, Dist Grievance; Penn Twp Rescue 6 1979-, Capt, North Huntingdon Rescue 8 1985-.

'ENTIS, RICHARD ARTHUR, Mathematics Teacher; *b:* Sharon, renda Sue; *c:* Richard; *ed:* Westminster Coll (MS) Ed 1993; *cr:* le Bus Schl Tchr 1986-88; Mohawk HS Tchr 1988-89; Chancy HS 9-; *ai:* Chess Club; NEA, NEOEA 1989-; NCTM 1992-; *office:* HS 731 S Hazelwood Ave Youngstown OH 44509*

ENZO, MADELYN MILLER, Basic Skills Teacher; *b:* Jersey *m:* Richard; *c:* Jennifer, Danielle; *ed:* Jersey City St Coll (BA) 1969; *cr:* Franklin Schl Grd 1 Tchr 1969-73, Grd 3 Tchr 1973-88, d 1-8 Tchr 1988-; *ai:* Chrldng Coach; PAC Comm; Quality e Comm; Math Comm Chprsn; Stu Selection Comm; AFT 1969-, nding Sec; Franklin PTA 1969-, VP, Life Mbrshp; *office:* Franklin 1 Columbia Ave North Bergen NJ 07047

, ELIZABETH LANE, Soc Studies Tchr & Dept Chair; *b:* , NY; *m:* John F. Jr.; *c:* Mari-jean Cerney, Timothy, Kevin; *ed:* St Coll (BA) His 1964; C. W. Post (MS) Soc Stud Ed 1984; Attnd Coll, Empire St Coll, Nassau Comm; *cr:* St Brendan Soc Stud 54-67; St Joseph HS Soc Stud Tchr 1976-77; St Raymond Schl Grd Soc Stud, Eng Tchr 1977-78; St John the Baptist Soc Stud m 1980-; *ai:* Hockey, Stu Cncl Moderator; NEA 1964-; LISSC Francis Coll Alumni 1964-, Pres; Amer Vision Arts 1995-, Bd of ice: St John the Bapt HS 1170 Montauk Hwy West Islip NY 11795*

, GERARD PAUL, Fourth Grade Teacher; *b:* Scranton, PA; *m:* ane Duda; *c:* Kelly, Colleen; *ed:* Mansfield Univ (BS) Elem Ed nn St & Wilkes Univ St Masters Equivalency in Elem Ed 1975; 48 ond Masters Equivalency in Ed; *cr:* Northeast Bradford Elem Schl Tchr 25 Yrs; *ai:* Sincere Sportsman Club Spon; Head of Dist Big ntest; Schl Lib Mounted Wildlife Prgm Founder; PSEA, NEA eRaysville-Pike Fire Co 1976-; Natl Rifle Assn 1971-; Natl Wild ed 1990-; PA Trappers Assn 1985-; BSA Troop 89, Comm 1978-; ortheast Bradford Elem Schl RR 1 Box 211b Rome PA 18837

, WILLIAM T., Art Teacher; *b:* Springfield, MA; *m:* Elaine Ann ian; *c:* Elizabeth, Luke; *ed:* Westfield St (BA) Art 1974; ion Coll (MAT) Art 1981; Attnd Springfield Tech Comm Coll, gh Coll of Arts & Design; *cr:* Monson Jr-Sr HS Art Tchr 1974-; *ai:* r Cross Cntry, Bsktbl, Track & Field Coaches; Class, NHS Advs; Tchr Assn 1974-, Tchr of Yr 1995; NEA, NAEA 1974-; MA Bsktbl Assn1980-, Dist Rep West, Div III Coach of Yr 1994.

A, CARMEN V., Learning Assistance Chprsn; *b:* Germany; *m:* J.; *c:* Jennifer, Jason, Julie; *ed:* St Univ of NY at Oswego (BA) Ed Univ of NY at Binghamton (MS) Ed, Rdng 1980; 15 Grad Cr Hrs St Univ; 6 Grad Cr Hrs Ed Psych St Univ of NY at Binghamton; Manor Elem Schl Second-Third Grade Tchr 1970-74; Binghamton dng Spec, Educl Op Prgm 1984-86; Broome Comm Coll Assoc Prof, 986-94, Chair, Assoc Prof Learning Assistance Dept 1994-; *ai:* ecial Populations Coordinating, Retention, Lang Learning Across ciplines, Registration Procedures Comm; NY St Coll Learning ssn, IRA 1980-; Binghamton Area Rdng Cncl 1980-; Binghamton ampus Presch Bd 1977-84; Cert Recognition Outstandg ance in the Master of Sci Ed, Rdng Spec; *office:* Broome Comm Box 1017 Binghamton NY 13902

A, JOHN VINCENT, Math, Physics & Soc Stud Tchr; *b:* Brooklyn, Barbara Ryan; *c:* Michael, Megan; *ed:* Brooklyn Coll (BA) Ec & 6, (MA) His 1980; *cr:* Natl Cncl on Ec Ed Aide to Dir 1976-81; ate Schl Tchr & Asst to Headmaster 1981-; *ai:* Key Club Adv; Acad Adv; Natl Assn of Stu Act Adv; Phi Kappa Phi 1980-; Alpha Sigma 1985-; Kiwanis Club 1986-, Pres; Cub Scout Pack 3005 1991-, ter; Seymour Shapiro Awd 1980; Collegiate Schl Stdnts Awd 1987; ollegiate Schl Passaic Ave & Kent Ct Passaic NJ 07055*

O, JAMES JOHN, 7th Grade Soc Studies Teacher; *b:* Mt Vernon, Meghan; *c:* Susan, Janna; *ed:* Mercy Coll (BS) His 1972; Western MS) Environmental Stud 1978; Grad Courses Coll of New Rochelle, St Rose; *cr:* Brewster Cntrl Schls 7th-8th Grd Soc Stud Tchr for 21 Var Ftbl Coach 23 Yrs; JV & Var Lacrosse Coach 15 Yrs; JV & Var Coach 18 Yrs; NYST 21 Yrs; AFCA 8 Yrs; Amer Ftbl Coaches Assn; Yrs; Girl Scouts of Amer 8 Yrs; Brewster Educl Fndtn Grants; Henry H Wells MS RR 312 Brewster NY 10509

O, TINA MARIE, Scripture Teacher; *b:* Bronx, NY; *m:* Michael Georgian Court Coll (BA) Rel Stud, (BA) Span 1988; LaSalle Univ Theology 1995; *cr:* Red Bank Cath HS Religion, Morality, Soc Tchr 1988-; *ai:* Liturgical Choir Dir; Chrstn Svc Adv; NJ Cath ors Assn 1988-; Joyful Spirit Music Ministry 1988-, Liturgist; Red Bank Catholic H S 10 Peters Pl Red Bank NJ 07701

T, WILLIAM PATRICK, Physical Education Teacher; *b:* ter, NY; *m:* Donna Marie Pask; *c:* Kari, Morgan, James, Holly; *ed:* a Coll (BA) PE, Hlth 1981; US Sports Acad (MS) Sport Sci 1991; St Univ of NY at Brockport; *cr:* City Schl Dist of Rochester ent Sub Tchr 1981-85; St Ambrose Schl PE Tchr 1985-87; Perry chl PE Tchr, Coach 1987-; *ai:* Head Ftbl 1989-95; Head Track 5; NYSUT 1987-.*

'O, SARAH, Fr, Bus & Social Studies Tchr; *m:* Ronald; *ed:* IN Univ BSEd) Fr, Span Minor, Bus Ed, (BS) Soc Stud; Cooperative Ed Cert; lub Spon; Tchr Advy Prgm; PA St Modern Lang Assn 1990-; Tri-St ucators Assn 1983-; NEA; PSEA; HCEA; Pi Omega Pi; DAR 1989-; Club 1990-, Chairwoman; VFW 1977-; DKG Women Educators Bus, Prof Woman's Club 1989-, Chairwoman; St Vincent Coll Tchr ition Awd 1992; *office:* Homer Ctr Schl Dist 20 Wildcat Ln Homer 15748

IN, EDWARD JOHN, United States History Teacher; *b:* elphia, PA; *m:* Mary Jane Weingartner; *c:* Michael, Megan; *ed:* Saint s Univ (BA) His 1970, (MA) His & Ed 1975; Attnd Bloomsburg A St Post Grad Stud; *cr:* Charles Boehm HS US His Tchr 1970-90; Bair HS US His Tchr 1990-; *ai:* Instructional Support Team 1995-; PSEA, PEA 1970-; Phi Alpha Theta 1969-; Saint Michael the ngel 1974-, Joy for Needy Svc Org; Seminars Taken from Harvard *office:* Medill Bair HS 608 S Olds Blvd Fairless Hills PA 19030*

IN, JUDI CALLANAN, Assistant Principal; *b:* Baltimore, MD; *m:* Thomas; *c:* Andrew, Christopher, Jack; *ed:* Towson St Univ (BS) Pathology 1977, (MS) Speech Pathology 1979; 30 Addl hrs; *cr:* Ctr Schl Speech, Lang Pathologist 1 Yr; Oakleigh Elem Schl SLP Loch Raven MS SLP 10 Yrs; Winand Elem Schl Asst Prin 6 Mos; Cancer Soc, Gilman Schl, Roland Park Swim Team Vol; MSTA, NEA, Amer Speech Hearing & Lang Assn 1979-; Bd of Dir of St Elizabeth;s Schl 1991-, Sec; *office:* Winand Elem Schl 8301 Scotts Level Rd Baltimore MD 21208

DEVLIN, PATRICIA CONRAD, Fourth Grade Teacher; *b:* Weymouth, MA; *c:* Danielle; *ed:* Salem St Coll (BS) Elem Ed & Eng 1974; Attnd Boston Univ, Univ of MA At Boston; *cr:* East Jr HS 8th Grd Math Tchr 1981-82, 7th & 8th Grd Math Tchr 1982-85; Pingree Schl 6th Grd Head Tchr 1985-91, 4th Grd Head Tchr 1991-; *ai:* Schl Based Mgmt Team Co-Chprsn 1992-; Curr Dev Team Mem 1993-95; NEA 1974-; MTA 1974-; WTA 1974-; St Helens Parish CCD Tchr; MA Dept of Ed Worker; *home:* 10 Old Oaken Bucket Rd Norwell MA 02061

DEVLIN, ROBERT W., HS Tchr of Special Education; *b:* Pittston, PA; *m:* Diane Cebula; *c:* Robert Jr., Jade; *ed:* East Stroudsburg Univ (BS) Scndry Ed 1974; Marywood Coll Grad Cert in Spec Ed 1976; Luzerne Intermediate Unit 18 Masters Equivalency in Ed 1995; 10 CEVs in Various Continuing Educl Subjects; *cr:* Saint Michaels Schl Tchr of Spec Ed 1974-78; Luzerne Cty Children & Youth Svcs Soc Worker-Caseworker 1978-86; Luzerne Cty Prison Supvr of Cnslrs 1986-94; Pittston Area HS Tchr of Spec Ed 1994-; *ai:* Stu Cncl & Stu of Month Adv; Luzerne Cty Spec Olympics Adv & Judge; AFT 1994-; YMCA 1974-, Bd of Dirs; Pittston Area HS Cert of Recognition for Outstanding Svc & Commitment 1995; Key Club Intnl Cert of Recognition 1996; *office:* Pittston Area Schl Dist 5 Stout St Shenandoah PA 17976

DEVLIN, SIOBHAN ANNE, Health & Physical Ed Teacher; *b:* Summit, NJ; *ed:* Eastern KY Univ (BS) K-12 Hlth, Phy Ed 1986; Oh Univ (MA) Phy Ed, Admin 1987; St Peters Coll 9 Hrs; *cr:* Cedar Hill Schl Elem Hlth, PE Tchr 1989-; Ridge HS Scndry Hlth, PE Tchr 1987-89, Head Field Hockey Coach 1991-; *ai:* Frosh Girls Bsktbl, JV Sftbl Coach Ridge HS; NJEA, BTEA, NJAPHERD 1987-; *office:* Cedar Hill Schl 100 Peachtree Rd Basking Ridge NJ 07920*

DE VOE, THOMAS ELLIOTT, History Teacher; *b:* Phillipsburg, NJ; *m:* Gayle Renee Abrom; *c:* Mandee Marteen, Amber Danielle, Charyl Amanda; *ed:* IA Wesleyan Coll (BA) Scndry Ed, Soc Stud 1967; Fairleigh Dickinson Univ (MA) Human Dev 1981; Attnd Cty Coll of Morris, Univ of MD Continuing Ed Extention Courses; Jersey City St Coll; *cr:* West Morris Regnl HS His Tchr 1967-68; Mt Olive MS His Tchr 1972-; *ai:* Cross Cntry Coach; NEA, NJ Ed Assn 1972-; Educl Assn of Mt Olive 1972-, Fac Rep; Company of Military Historians 1973-; Bermuda Maritime Museum; WA Bicentennial Comm 1975-76, Historian; Mt Olive Historic Preservation Comm 1976-79, Historian, Chevalier, Noble Companion of the Swan; Joseph Sloat His Awd 1962; Outstanding His Tchr of NJ 1988; Co-Author of Book 1991; Mentioned or Thanked in 19 Books; *home:* PO Box 377 Flanders NJ 07836

DEVOLLD, MARYANN (SPITZNAGEL), Eng & Publications Teacher; *b:* Rochester, NY; *m:* Stewart E.; *ed:* Muskingum Coll (BA) Eng, Theater, Scndry Ed 1973, (MA) Ed 1990; *cr:* John Glenn HS Eng, Speech Tchr 1973-74; Millcreek Twp Schls Eng Tchr 1974-75; Zanesville City Schls Lang Arts Tchr 1975-78; East Muskingum MS Lang Arts Tchr 1978-82; John Glenn HS Eng, Publications Tchr 1982-; *ai:* Schl Newspaper, Yrbk, Lit Magazine Adv; TREK Team Coalition of Essential Schls; North Cntrl Steering Comm; NCTE; OCTELLA; Muskingum Coll Ed Dept Site-Based Supvr; *office:* John Glenn HS 13115 John Glenn School Rd New Concord OH 43762*

DE VOOGT, MICHELLE KRISTEN, English Teacher; *b:* Westminister, MD; *ed:* SUNY at Geneseo (BA) Eng 1994; Grad Schl SUNY at Brockport; *cr:* Williamson Cntrl Schl Eng Tchr 1994-; *ai:* Girls Var & Jr High Bstkbl Coaches; WTA 1994-; *office:* Williamson Cntrl Schl 1 South Ave Williamson NY 14589

DEVORAH, STEPHEN RICHARD, 12th Grade English Teacher; *b:* Kansas City, MO; *m:* Janice Zoe; *c:* Shira Malka; *ed:* Univ of KS (BSE) Eng, Soc Studies 1985; Baltimore Cty Pub Schls MS Equal; Grad Credit MS Writing Project Tauson St Univ, Dimensions of Learning Loyola Univ; Ohr Somayach Rebbinical Coll Jerusalem 1984; Monsey NY 1986-87; *cr:* Center Schl Dist 8 Grd Soc Stud Tchr 1985; Shawnee Mission East Schl 11 Grd His, 12 Grd Amer Govt Tchr 1985-86; Johnnycake MS 6 Grd Eng, Rdng Tchr 1989-92; Parkville HS 12 Grd Eng, Yrbk Tchr 1992-; *ai:* Odyssey Yrbk 1992-; Acad Team Co-Spon; NEA 1989-; North West Citizens Patrol 1992-, Deputy Watch V Commander; Baltimore Cty Pub Schls Bd of Ed Recognition Outstdng Contributions 1996; *office:* Parkville HS 2600 Putty Hill Ave Baltimore MD 21234*

DEVORE, CAROLYN VANCE, Dean & Dance Teacher; *b:* St Albans, NY; *w:* Van Heusen (dec); *c:* Rashaad, Kahlil; *ed:* Brooklyn Coll (BS) Dance, Scndry Ed 1976; Adelphi Univ (MS) Spec Ed 1992; UFT Courses; *cr:* Erasums Hall HS Tchr 2 Yrs; Andrew Jackson HS Tchr, Dance Club Dir 6 Yrs; Andrew Jackson HS Prep Coord; Benjamin Cardozo HS Dean, Dance Tchr 10 Yrs; *ai:* Apprentice Dance Ensemble, Performance Tour Dir; UFT, AFT 1979-; Brooklyn Coll Alumni 1976-; B N Cardozo Alumni 1994-; DeVore Dance Ctr 1992-, Exec Dir; Bernice Johnson Cultural Arts Ctr 1975-91, Tchr, Coreographer; Boys & Girls Club of Amer 1990-92, Performing Arts Specialist; Police Athletic League 1976-80; Brooklyn Coll Black Family Achvmt Awd; Book: Dance World; Articles Pub; Re-Design Comm Andrew Jackson HS; *office:* Benjamin N Cardozo HS 5700 223rd St Flushing NY 11364*

DEVORE, JANET PRESSMAN, Business Ed Tchr & Coordinator; *b:* Cumberland, MD; *m:* Chester A.; *c:* Mark A., Denise DeVore Mc Harg, Christie DeVore Mc Mullen; *ed:* Univ of MD (BS) Bus Ed 1975, (MS) Bus Ed 1980; Johns Hopkins Univ (MS) Cmptr Ed 1988; *cr:* Allegany Ballistics Lab Sec 1962-63; Univ of MD Sec 1963-67; Old Mill HS Bus Ed Tchr, Coord 1976-; *ai:* FBLA Adv 1976-; Tchrs Assn of Anne Arundel Co, MD St Tchrs Assn, NEA 1976-; Nichols-Bethel United Meth Church 1968-, Chprsn, Pastor, Parish Relations Comm; Office Skills for the 90's Textbook Contributer; Numerous Curr Writing Activities; *office:* Old Mill Sr HS 600 Patriot Ln Millersville MD 21108*

DEVORE, JANICE FICHTNER, English Teacher; *b:* Steubenville, OH; *m:* Kenneth E.; *ed:* Kent St Univ (BS) Ed, Eng Educl Media 1974; 36 Credit Hrs Ed; *cr:* Nordonia Eng Tchr 1974-; *ai:* Girls Track & Field Coach 1977-81; NCTE 1993-; NEA, OEA, Nordonia Hills Educators Assn 1974-; *office:* Nordonia HS 8006 S Bedrford Rd Macedonia OH 44056

DEVRIENDT, MARY LOU MC INTIRE-WELCH, Choral Music Director; *b:* Toledo, OH; *m:* Galen; *c:* Laureen Welch, James Welch, Robert Welch, Diana Welch; *ed:* Mary Manse Coll (BM) Music 1972; *cr:* Mc Auley HS Music Tchr 1973-79; Cntrl Cath HS Choral Music Dir 1991-; *ai:* Producer Sounds of Christmas, Spring Musical Acad Advy Comm; OMEA 1991-; Kappa Delta Pi 1994-; *office:* Central Catholic HS 2550 Cherry St Toledo OH 43608

DEWALD, DAN WILLIAM, Geology Teacher; *b:* Massillon, OH; *m:* Judy K. Martin; *c:* Debra Spearman; *ed:* Lindsey Wilson (AA) Pre-Dentistry 1964; Eastern KY Univ (BS) Bio, Chem 1967; Xavier Univ (MED) Admin 1978; OH St Univ, Columbus St Univ 6 Hrs; *cr:* Highland Schls Tchr 1967-71; Mt Vernon Schls Tchr 1971-; *ai:* OEA, NEA 1967-; MVEA 1971-; Jaycees 1971-; Kawanis 1988-; Tchr of Yr 1994; *office:* Mount Vernon HS 300 Martinsburg Rd Mount Vernon OH 43050*

DEWALD, JUDY KAY, First Grade Teacher; *b:* Portsmouth, OH; *m:* Daniel William; *c:* Debra Spearman; *ed:* Mt Vernon Nazarene Coll (BA) Elem Ed 1979; 20 Grad Hrs Ashland Univ; 7 Grad Hrs Mt St Joseph; *cr:* Highland West Elem Schl 3rd Grd Rdng Tchr 1968-70, 1st Grd Tchr 1979-81; Highland East Elem Schl 1st Grd Tchr 1981-; *ai:* HEA, OEA NEA 1979-; Jaycees Wives; Ashland Oil Grant Nom; *office:* Highland East Elem Schl PO Box 69 Sparta OH 43350

DEWEY, PAUL H., Natural Resources Teacher; *b:* Buffalo, NY; *m:* Kathleen M. Hedrick; *c:* Jacob, Bethany; *ed:* Geneseo St Coll (BS) Bio 1980; Univ of Buffalo (EDM) Admin 1985; Conservation Ed Prgm Cortland St Coll; *cr:* North Tonawanda Schls Sci, Metrics Instr 1981-82; Niagara Educl Ctr Natural Resources Instr 1982-; *ai:* Voc Indstrl Clubs of Amer, FFA Adv; Niagara Cty Envirothons Coach; Conservation Ed Club, High Adventure of NCCGS Adv; Site Fac Chm; Niagara Cty Wilderness Parks Vol; NYS Conservation Assn 1989-; NYS Tchrs Assn 1982-; Niagara Cty Natural Resources Dist 1989-, Vice Chm, Educl Awds 1990-91, 1993; Ontario Lake Plains Resource Conservation & Dev 1994-; NCCC Bd for Animal Mngmt & Horticultural Sci 1990-; NYS Conservation Cncl Edctr of Yr 1994; Hydroponics Rsrch & Dev Ed Grant; *office:* Niagara Educl Ctr 3181 Saunders Settlement Rd Sanborn NY 14132*

DEWEY, PAULETTE BAKER, English Teacher & Dept Chair; *b:* Evansville, IN; *m:* John C.; *c:* Joel, Rachel, Joshua; *ed:* Univ of Evansville (BA) Eng 1968; Univ of Toledo (MA) Eng 1975; 48 Addl Post-Grad Hrs Eng Lit & HS Composition & Curr; *cr:* Washington Catholic HS Eng & Ger Tchr 1968; DeVilbiss HS Eng Tchr 1972-74; Rogers HS Eng Tchr 1974-; Univ of Toledo Part-Time Frosh Composition Tchr 1990-; *ai:* NHS; Future Tchrs of America; Scholars by Design; AFT 1985-; PDK 1989-, Educator of Yr 1990; NCTE 1984-; Toledo Area Writing Project 1988-, Co-Dir 1988-; NEHI Summer Seminars 1985 & 1988; Toledo Career Ladder Tchr Awd; Rogers HS Eng Dept Chprsn 1983-; NEH Summer Seminar 1993, London; *office:* Robert S Rogers HS 5539 Nebraska Ave Toledo OH 43615*

DEWEY, ROBERT THOMAS, Seventh Grd Soc Stud Teacher; *b:* New Bedford, MA; *m:* Susan Bianchi; *ed:* Holy Cross Coll (BA) His 1969; Bridgewater St (MA) Tchng 1975; 12 Credits in His; *cr:* Mulcahy Schl 6th Grd Elem Tchr 1969-72; Taun HS World His Tchr 1972-74; Cohannot & Martin MS 7th Grd Geography Tchr 1975-; *ai:* Taunton HS Track & Cross Cntry Coach 1969-74; MATA, NEA 1969-; *office:* Martin MS 131 Casewell St Taunton MA 02718

DEWEY, THOMAS MICHAEL, High School English Teacher; *b:* Brooklyn, NY; *m:* Grace Voelker; *c:* Denise, Lauren; *ed:* St Joseph Univ (BA) Eng 1965; Brooklyn Coll (MA) Ed 1969; NYS Cert Eng; Attnd Azusa Pacific Coll, St Johns Univ; *cr:* Boro Hall Acad Eng Dept, Fr Tchr 1965-66; St Augustine HS Eng Dept, Fr Tchr 1966-69; Nazareth HS Engl Dept Coord 1969-; Fordham Univ Head Track Coach 1981-; *ai:* Stu Fundrasing; Boys & Girls Track Coach Fordham U; NCET; UST&F Assoc 1981-; Metropolitan T&F Assn 1981-, Pres; Articles Pub; Coach of Yr Fordham U 1982, 1995; Ath Hall of Fame; *home:* 250 Cochran Pl Valley Stream NY 11581*

DEWITT, KATHY STEWART, Math Instructor; *b:* Washington, PA; *m:* Terry W.; *c:* Amy, Michael; *ed:* OH St Univ (MA) Math Ed 1992; IN Univ of PA (BSED) Math Ed 1975; *cr:* King George MS Math Tchr 1976-77; Riverview MS Math Tchr 1977-79; Columbus St Comm Coll Math Instr 1988-; *office:* Columbus St Comm Coll Spring St Columbus OH 43216

DEWITT, PAMELIA METCALF, 4th Grade Teacher; *b:* Wilkes-Barre, PA; *c:* Hunter Shaw, Susan Reigle; *ed:* Mansfield Univ (BA) Elem Ed 1960; 24 Addl Credits Penn St; *cr:* Wyalusing Schl Dist 2nd Grd Music Tchr 1960-62; Tunkhannock Schl Dist K-1st Grd Swimming Tchr 1963-74; Hanover Pub Schl Dist 4th Grd Specialized Rdng, 7-8th Grd eng Tchr 1975-; *ai:* HEA 1974-; PSEA 1961-; NEA 1974-; *office:* Hanover Public Schl Dist 403 Moul Ave Hanover PA 17331

DEXTER, CAROLINE ELIZABETH, Asst Professor of Classics; *b:* Midland, MI; *m:* James H. Mann; *c:* Elizabeth Mann, Theodore Mann; *ed:* Manhattanville Coll (BA) Classics 1969; Duke Univ (MA) Classics 1970, (PHD) Classics 1975; *cr:* Georgetown Univ Asst Prof 1979-80, 1982-83 & 1994-; Univ of MD at Coll Park Asst Prof 1980-81; Howard Univ Asst Prof 1992-94; *ai:* Univ Hnrs Pgm Asst Dir; Archaeological Inst of Amer 1975-; Classical Assoc of Atlantic Sts 1978-; WA Classical Soc 1980-; Woodrow Wilson Dissertation Flwshp 1972-73; 2 NEH Summer Seminars 1981 & 1991; UMCP Tchng Excl Awd 1990; Articles Pub; *office:* George Washington Univ 2138 G Street NW Washington DC 20052

DEYO, STEPHEN ALLEN, Sixth Grade Teacher; *b:* Hackensack, NJ; *m:* Suzanne Butynes; *c:* Stephen, Sarah, Shane; *ed:* Glassboro St Coll (BS) Elem Ed 1974; *cr:* Little Egg Harbor Intnl Schl Sixth Grd Tchr 1974-; *ai:* Spelling Bee; 6th Grd Boys Bsktbl; NJEA 1974-; *office:* Little Egg Harbor Int Schl 305 Frog Pond Rd Tuckerton NJ 08087

DHAMOON, MANMOHAN SINGH, Chemistry Teacher; *b:* Karachi, Pakistan; *m:* Leela; *c:* Neeta, Neena, Indermohan; *ed:* Khalsa Coll-Univ of Bombay (BS) Chem 1956, (MS) Inorganic Chem 1958; Queens Coll (MED) Sci Ed 1992; *cr:* Khalsa Coll Demonstrator in Chem 1957-61; Diff Insts E Nigeria Sci Ed Ofc 1961-66; Diff Insts Rep of Zambia Tchr, Prin, Regnl Insp of Schls 1967-85; Susan Wager HS Tchr 1986-88; Staten Island Tech HS Tchr 1988-; *ai:* Asian Amer Club of Schl Coord, Adv; Sci Tchrs Assn of NY, Brooklyn Queens Section SC Teac Assn 1986-; Chem Tchrs Club of NY 1987-; Cath Sci Cncl 1988-; Victoria Falls Lodge 5327 EC 1979-, Past Master, Life Mem; Rotary Club 1980-, Past Pres; Sci Cncl NYC Sci Ed Awd Outstdng Contributions to Sci Ed 1995; *home:* 3835 147th St Flushing NY 11354*

DHARM, BEN, Science Teacher; *b:* Bangkok, Thailand; *m:* Elizabeth; *c:* Matthew; *ed:* Hunter Coll (BS) Chem 1967; Columbia Univ (PHD) Biochemistry 1967; Woodrow Wilson Summer Instr Physics, Chem, Bio, Sci, Soc, Tech; *cr:* Cornell Univ Med Ctr Biochemist 1979-82; Rockfeller Univ Plant Molecular Biologist 1982-84; Pace Univ Sci Tchr 1980-86; White Plains Pub Schls Sci Tchr 1985-86; Yonkers Pub Schls Sci Tchr 1986-; *ai:* Flagship Acad Bowl Coach; Stu-Tchr Relation Comm, Sci Club, Sci Olympiad, Jr NY Acad of Sci, After Schl Homework Help & Cmptrs Spons; Sigma Xi 1970-; Harvey Soc 1978-; Columbia Univ Sci Lit Group 1987-; AFT 1985-; Tri Centennial Commission 1988-; Yonkers Fed of Tchrs 1986; Various Museums; Hudson River Museum 1982-; NY Hall of Sci 1984-; Staff Dev Grants; Innovation Grants; New Rochelle City Cncl Commendation; SCOR Grant Natl Inst of Heart, Lung & Blood; Sci Literacy Group Wkshp Grants; *office:* Museum Jr HS 365 Warburton Ave Yonkers NY 10701*

DHEMBE, ALBERT FRANK, Physical Education Instructor; *b:* Southbridge, MA; *m:* Zarri Rose Hougasian; *c:* Alexis Zarri; *ed:* Boston Coll (BA) Scndry Ed, Soc Stud 1972; Hlth, PE; *cr:* Boston Eng HS Civics Tchr 1972-73; Shepherd Hill HS Sub Tchr 1973-74; Tantasqua HS Alternative Ed Tchr 1975; Bay Path Voc HS PE Instr 1976-; *ai:* Head Ftbl Coach; IM Weightlifting Adv; MA Tchrs Assn, NEA 1977-; Natl Ftbl Fnd Hall of Fame 1991-; Friends of Joshua Hyde Library 1991-; Armenian Church of Our Saviour 1975-; Asst Coach Shriners Game MA 1991; Head Coach Hall of Fame Game Cntrl MA 1992; Tri Comm Exch Club Svc Yth Awd; *office:* Bay Path Reg Voc Tech HS 57 Old Muggett Hill Rd Charlton MA 01507

DIACONESCU, ILEANA, French Teacher; *b:* Bucharest, Romania; *m:* Tudor Stancu; *c:* Bogdan-Ionut, Madalina; *ed:* HS #32 (BA) 1974; Univ of Bucharest Romania (MS) Fr 1978; Credit Hrs Italian, Ed; *cr:* Bucharest Tchr 1978-89; 22 Magazine Journalist 1990-92; Phoenix HS Sub Tchr 1992-93; ASU Law Lib Librn 1992-93; Fontbonne Hall Acad Fr Tchr

1993-; *ai:* Amnesty Intnl; Dance Club; Rel Stud Comm; AATF 1993-; Romanian Journalists 1992-93; War Reporter Former Soviet Union, Yougoslavia 1992; Lecture AZ St Univ; Authored 80 Feature Articles; *home:* 2520 30th Rd Long Island City NY 11102

DIACONIS, LINDA, Nursing Instructor; *b:* Port Arthur, TX; *m:* John N.; *c:* Nicholas, Pamela; *ed:* Univ of MD (BS) Nrsng 1992, (MS) Nrsng Admin 1994; Hendrick Meml Hosp Schl of Nrsng Diploma 1968; Doctoral Stu College Park Dept of Ed Policy, Planning, Admin; *cr:* Univ of MD Hosp Primary Nurse 4 Yrs; Kaiser-Permanente Advice Nurse 4 Yrs; Villa Julie Coll Instr 1 Yr; *ai:* Sigma Theta Tau 1992-; AERA 1996; Kappa Delta Pi 1995-; *office:* Villa Julie Coll Green Spring Valley Road Stevenson MD 21153

DIAMOND, JEAN ROSENBERG, Art Teacher; *b:* Revere, MA; *m:* Gary W.; *c:* Jennifer Anne, Gerri Elaine, Rebecca Elizabeth; *ed:* Tufts Univ (BS) Ed & Spcl Ed 1969; MD Inst Coll of Art (MFA) Gifted, Talented & Painting 1985; The Schl of Museum of Fine Arts Commercial Art 1964-69; The Corcoran Schl of Art 1963-64; In-Svc Pgm; Masters Equivalency 1979; Masters +30 Credit Hrs 1984; Phase I & Ii Admin & Supvr; *cr:* Robert Frost Jr-Mid Head of Dept 1974-78; Albert Einstein High Summer Pgm Gifted-Talented Visual Arts Ctr Tchr 1978-85, Visual Arts Ctr Tchr 1979-80; Head of Dept 1979-85; North Chevy Chase Elem Tchr 1979-80; Charles Woodward HS Tchr 1985; Damascus High Tchr 1987-88; Luxmanor Elem Schl Tchr 1989-93; Walt Whitman High Art Instr, Art ed Supvr 1993-; *ai:* Stu Govt Adv; Frosh & Soph Class Spon; B Rep Tilden Woods Swim Club 1993-95; MAEA; NAEA; Alumni Assoc; MD Inst Coll of Art; Temple Sinai Rel Schl, Art Coord; RI Schl of Design Hnrs Seminar; Yrbk Adv Columbia Scholastics Won 1st Place 1979-85; *office:* Walt Whitman HS 7100 Whittier Blvd Bethesda MD 20817*

DIAMOND, MARK A., Ballet Instr & Choreographer; *b:* Cincinnati, OH; *m:* Kathryn Moriarty; *c:* Erika; *cr:* Milwaukee Ballet Co Prin Dancer 1974-78; Hamburg St Opera Ballet Demi-Soloist Ballet Ensemble 1978-83; Schl for Creative Perf Arts Dance Fac 1983-96; Chautauqua Inst Resident Choreographer 1994-; *ai:* Intnl Ballet Competition Japan Coach; AGMA 1967-; Full Schlsp Duquesne Univ, Point Park Coll; OH Arts Cncl Individual Artist Flwshp; Greater Cincinnati Fnd Grant; *office:* Schl Creative & Performing Art 1310 Sycamore St Cincinnati OH 45210

DIAMOND, PAUL R., Social Studies Teacher; *b:* New York, NY; *m:* Macy Whafir; *ed:* Pealthers Coll & Columbia Univ (MA) His Ed 1986; SUNY at Stony Brook (BA) Amer His 1980; Addl 24 Credits Coll of New Rochelle Admin & Supervision, 12 Credits His; *cr:* Clarkstown Schls Tchr 1981-; *ai:* Debate Team Coach; Clio Adv; Russian Amer Stu Exchange Prgm Coord; NYSUT 1981-; Clarkstown TA 1981-, Neogotiations Comm; NCSS, Soc for His Ed 1982-; Natl Endowment for Hum 1991 Fellowship; Yrbk Dedicatee 1992; *office:* Clarkstown North HS 151 Congers Rd New City NY 10956

DIANGELO, JOSEPH A.,JR., Dean & Professor of Management; *b:* Philadelphia, PA; *m:* Frances DiAngelo; *c:* Deana, Kristen, Joseph III; *ed:* Saint Josephs Univ (BS) Mgmt 1970; Widener Univ (MBA) Mgmt 1975; Temple Univ (EDD) Ed 1986; *cr:* Saint Josephs Univ Instr 1978-80; Widener Univ Asst Dean & Asst Prof 1980-85, Dean & Asst Provost Grad Stud 1985-88, Dean Schl of Mgmt 1988-, Prof of Mgmt 1995-; *ai:* Amer Arbitration Assn 1986-; Soc for Human Resource Mgmt 1984-; Mid Atlantic Assn of Colls of Bus Admin 1988-, 1st VP; Columbus Quincentennial Fnd 1992-, Ed Comm Chprsn; Private Industry Cncl 1990-, Monitoring Comm Chair; Soc for the Advancement of Mgmt Distinguished Tchr of Yr 1980; 6 Articles Pub in Natl & Intnl Journals; *office:* Widener Univ 1 University Pl Chester PA 19013

DIANGELO, LOUIS PHILIP, English Teacher; *b:* Jersey City, NJ; *ed:* St Peter's Coll (BA) Eng 1978; *cr:* Cath Comm Svc Tchr Aide 1979; Jersey City Pub Schls Tchr 1979-; *ai:* JCEA, NJEA, NEA 1979-; Holy Name Soc of Holy Rosary Church 1973-; *office:* James J Ferris HS 35 Colgate St Jersey City NJ 07302

DIANGI, DICK ANGELO, Amer His & World Culture Tchr; *b:* Greenville, PA; *m:* Rhonda Mossman; *c:* Joel, Jared; *ed:* Edinboro Univ of PA (BSEd) Soc Stud 1971, (ME) Guidance & Counseling 1981; *cr:* Joseph Badger Schl Dist Soc Stud Tchr 1972-78; Greenville Schl Dist Soc Stud, Alternative Ed Prgm Tchr 1978-82; Crawford Cntrl Schl Dist Soc Stud Tchr 1982-; *ai:* Cochranton HS Head Ftbl Coach 10 Yrs; Head Track Coach; NEA, Local Ed Assn 1972-; PSEA 1978-; *office:* Meadville Area Sr HS 930 North St Meadville PA 16335

DIAS, JEFFREY E., Special Education Teacher Aide; *b:* Boston, MA; *ed:* St Lawrence Univ (BA) Sociology 1992; Boston Coll (MED) Spec Ed 1996; *cr:* Newton South HS Spec Ed Tchr 1992-; *ai:* Crisis Mngmt Team; Gymnastics Coach; NTA, MTA, NEA 1992-; *home:* 1783 Massachusetts Ave Cambridge MA 02140*

DIAZ, CONSUELO ANTONA, Spanish Teacher; *b:* Santa Clara, Cuba; *m:* Emiliano; *c:* Emil Joseph, Maria de Lourdes Diaz Campbell; *ed:* Univ of MA at Boston (BA) Span 1973; Grad Courses in Span Lit & Span Ed; *cr:* Brookline HS Span Sub Tchr 1968-70; Barnstable HS Span Tchr 1970-; *ai:* Fac Senate; Mentor; Translator & Interpreter; Barnstable Tchrs Assn 1970-; MA Tchrs Assn 1970-; NEA 1970-; Tufts Univ Spcl Recognition by Former Stdnts 1994; *office:* Barnstable HS 744 W Main St Hyannis MA 02601

DIAZ, EDWARD L., Art & Business Teacher; *b:* Pueblo, CO; *c:* Brett, Stacy Oberly, Derek; *ed:* Univ of Northern CO (BA) Indstrl Arts 1969; Adams St Coll (MA) Indstrl Arts 1974; 30 Semesters Youngstown St Univ, Cleveland St Univ, Kent St Univ; *cr:* Jefferson HS Ind Arts Tchr 1966-73; Grand Vly Schls Ind Arts Tchr 1974-78; Maple Heights Schls Ind Arts Tchr 1980; Ashtabula HS Art, Bus Ed Tchr 1981-; *ai:* Wrestling Coach; Chm Jr Prom; Book Evaluation Comm; Phi Delta Kappa 1978-; Delta Phi Delta 1960-; Amer Indust Arts Assn 1966-; OH Ed Assn 1973-; Ashtabula Area Tchr Assn 1982-; Pub Article; *office:* Ashtabula HS 401 W 44th St Ashtabula OH 44004

DIAZ, LIZA CRUZ, Spanish Teacher; *b:* New York, NY; *m:* Javier; *c:* Tiffany, Jonathan, Kaylynn; *ed:* Bernard Baruch Coll (BS) Spcl Ed 1988; Adelphi Univ (MS) Spcl Ed 1994; *cr:* PS #111 & IS 70 Biling Resource Room 1989-90; PS #111 Spcl Ed Tchr 1990-93; PS #111 & PS #11 Biling Resource Rm 1993-95; OCHS Acad Span Tchr 1995-; *ai:* Chrldng & Span Club Adv; UFT 1994-, Grievance Liaison; Grant for Grad Stud; *office:* Ochs Acad 440 W 53rd St New York NY 10019*

DI BARI, DENNIS PHILIP, Dean of Stdnts, Soc Stud Edctr; *b:* Brooklyn, NY; *m:* Maria Seibel; *c:* Maria, Dennis; *ed:* St Johns Univ (BA) Soc Stud 1977, (MBA) Mngmt, Comp Sci 1980; Horstra Univ (MS) Scndry Ed 1982; Long Island Univ (PHD) Admin 1994; *cr:* Jamaica HS Dean, Edctr 1985-91; Forest Hills HS Dean, Edctr 1991-; *ai:* Bus Ed Assn 1992-; Dedicated Edctr Awd Jamaica HS Gateway Prgm 1990; *office:* Forest Hills HS 6701 110th St Forest Hills NY 11375

DIBARI, JOSEPH VINCENT, Science Teacher; *b:* Bronx, NY; *m:* Maria Razzano; *ed:* Lehman Coll (BA) Bio 1978; Iona Coll (MS) Sci Ed 1988; Attnd St Univ of NY at Albany with 7 Credits Bio, 3 Credits Ed; *cr:* Evander Childs HS Sci Tchr 1985-89; Hudson Valley Comm Coll Adjunct Instr of Bio 1989-94; Troy HS Sci Tchr 1992-; Coll of Saint Rose Adjunct Instr of Ed 1994-; *ai:* Key Club Adv; Liberty Partnership Sci Tutor; Connie Mack Bsbl Team Coach; AFT, NYSUT 1985-; Woodrow Wilson Fnd 1988-; New York City Writing Project 1986-; Rensselaer Cty Childrens Museum 1993-, Vol; Woodrow Wilson Awd for Physics Tchrs; Various Articles in Anthology of New York City Tchrs; Article on Minority Access to Higher Ed Sponed by CASDA; *office:* Troy HS 1950 Burdett Ave Troy NY 12180*

DIBARTOLO, COSMO, Mathematics Teacher; *b:* New York City, NY; *m:* Cathleen Engel; *c:* Brian, Kevin, Sean; *ed:* St Peters Coll (BS) Math 1964; Attnd Mountclair St Coll, Univ of CT; *cr:* Bergenfield HS Math Tchr 1964-69; Pascack Vly Regnl HS Math Tchr 1969-; *ai:* Retired Wrestling Coach; NEA 1964-; NJEA 1964-; Bergen Cty Ed Assn 1964-; Pascack Vly Ed Assn 1970-; Hillsdale Italian Amer Club, Past Pres; Boy Scout Asst Ldr; Bergen Cty Wrestling Coach of Yr 1971; *office:* Pascack Valley HS 200 Piermont Ave Hillsdale NJ 07642

DIBARTOLOMEO, KEVIN MICHAEL, US History & Psych Teacher; *b:* Amsterdam, NY; *m:* Deborah Lampros; *c:* Nicholas, Alexis; *ed:* St Univ Coll at Fredonia Scndry Soc Stud 1969; 45 Non-Degree Grad Hrs; *cr:* Schendehowa CS Jr High Soc Stud Tchr 1969-70; Unatego CS 11th Grd Soc Stud Tchr 1970-; *ai:* HS Advy Comm; AFT, NYS United Tchrs 1969-; Unatego Tchrs Assn 1970-, Pres, Chief Negotiator; Oneonta Parks & Recreation Comm 1985-, Chm; Tchr of Yr 1992; *office:* Unatego Cntrl Schl RD 1 Box 451A Otego NY 13825

DIBELLA, VINCENT BRUNO, Chemistry Teacher; *b:* Englewood, NJ; *m:* Isa Petrizzelli; *c:* Vincent Jr., Maria Elena; *ed:* Iona Coll (BS) Bio 1960; St John's Univ (MA) Pol Sci 1966; St Mary's Coll (MS) Bio 1969; Attnd Univ of Bologna Italy, Hunter Coll; *cr:* Cardinal L. Spellman HS Bio Tchr 1964-66; Bronx Comm Coll Anatomy, Physiology Tchr; Seton Coll Anatomy, Physiology Tchr; Clarkstown HS Sci Tchr 1966-; *ai:* CTA 1980-; NSF Grant 1966-69.

DIBENEDETTO, ROBERT THOMAS, US His & Government Teacher; *b:* Peekskill, NY; *m:* Carolyn Brennan; *c:* Jason, Nicholas; *ed:* St Univ of NY at Plattsburg (BA) Scndry Ed 1965, (MS) Scndry Ed 1968; *cr:* South Lewis Cntrl Schls Soc Stud Tchr 1965-; *ai:* Fac Adv Falcon Vision; Var Wrestling Coach 12 Yrs; Sr, Jr Class Adv 1965-90; NY St Cncl for Soc Stud 1968-; NY St United Tchr, South LewisTchrs Assn 1970-; Elizabeth Strong Meml Lib Bd 1984-85, Pres; *office:* South Lewis Central Schl East Rd Turin NY 13473

DIBIASE, DAVID ALAN, Fourth Grade Teacher; *b:* Latrobe, PA; *m:* Lori Grimshaw; *c:* Michael, Becky; *ed:* IN Univ of PA (BS) Elem Ed 1974; Morgan St Univ (MS) Admin & Supervision 1980; 9 Credit Hrs Post-Grad Stud; *cr:* Joppatowne HS 7th Grd Math Tchr 1974-79; Magnolia MS 6th Grd Soc Stud & 7th Grd Math Tchr 1979-84; Prospect Mill Elem Schl 5th Grd Tchr 1984-94, 4th Grd Tchr 1994-; *ai:* Historical Interpreter for MD St Park Svc 6 Yrs; Sunday Schl Tchr; Eucharistic Minister; Parlimentarian for Comm Advy Comm; Mem of Parent Advy Comm; Mem of Historical Soc Comm of Delta; Curr, Fac Advy, Safety & Discipline Comms; NEA 1974-; MSTA 1974-; HCEA 1974-, Rep; Delta Boro Cncl 1994-, Cncl Mem & VP; Team Ldr; *office:* Prospect Mill Elem Schl 101 Prospect Mill Rd Bel Air MD 21015

DIBIASI, ROSE LAUDICINA, Retired Kindergarten Teacher; *b:* Passaic, NJ; *m:* Vincent; *c:* Jennifer; *ed:* Fairleigh Dickinson Univ (BS) Elem Ed 1960; William Paterson Coll (MA) Elem Ed 1968; *cr:* Windsor Schl 2, 5 Grd Tchr 1960-66; Rockaway Meadow Schl 1-2 Grd Tchr 1966-71; Allamuchy Twp Schl Basic Skills, Kndgtn Tchr 1977-95; *ai:* NJEA, NEA 1960-; Tchr of Yr Governor's Tchr Recognition Prgm 1990.

DIBILIO, MICHAEL PATRICK, Spanish Teacher; *b:* Easton, PA; *m:* Jessica Susan Antonioli; *ed:* Kutztown UNiv (BS) Ed 1992; 80 Post Bachelor Credit Hrs; *cr:* Pocono Mountain Schl Dist Span Tchr 1993-; *ai:* Jr High Boys Bsktbl Coach; Grading Policy Comm; IM Bsktbl Adv; PSEA, NEA 1993-; El Hnr Soc 1991-; *office:* Pocono Mountain Sr HS PO Box 200 Swiftwater PA 18370*

DIBLER, EILEEN MC CAULEY, English Teacher; *b:* Upper Darby, PA; *m:* Jack M.; *c:* Beth, Jeffrey; *ed:* Penn St Univ (BA) Eng 1972; Univ of DE (MED) Rdng 1974; *cr:* Mary MC Leod Bethune Jr HS Eng Tchr 1974-80; Northwestern HS Eng Tchr 1980-83; Largo HS Eng Tchr 1983-88; High Pt HS Eng Tchr 1988-; *ai:* Co-Spon It's Acad; Acad Coach Sports Teams; TAG Coord; Schlrshp Comm; NEA 1974-; *office:* High Point HS 3601 Powder Mill Rd Beltsville MD 20705

DIBLING, CHRISTINA M., Spanish Teacher; *b:* Philadelphia, PA; *ed:* Carlow Coll (BA) Span 1970; Trenton St Coll (MED) Urban Stud 1978; NJ Prin & Supvr Cert; *cr:* Shor MS Span Tchr 1970-73; Piscataway HS Span Tchr 1973-; *ai:* NEA, NJEA, PTEA 1970-; *office:* Piscataway HS 100 Behmer Rd Piscataway NJ 08854

DI BONAVENTURA, INES MARIE,OP, Asst Prin & HS Music Teacher; *b:* Boonton, NJ; *ed:* Caldwell Coll at Caldwell (BA) Soc Stud 1960; LaSalle Univ at Philadelphia (MA) Rel Ed Admin 1980; Montclair St Undergraduate Course His 1970; Paterson St Guid 1980-82; Seton Hall Advanced Ldrshp 1984; William Paterson People Programming 1984; *cr:* Archdiocese of Newark Schl K-12th Grd Tchr 1947-77; St Catherine of Siena Schl Prin 1977-83; Holy Rosary Church Pastoral Assoc 1983-90; St Mary's HS Vice Prin, Music Dir 1991-; *ai:* Mid Sts Chprsn; Glee Club Concerts Music Dir; NCEA 1977-; ASCD, Affiliate; NHS 1995-, Moderator; Archdiocese of Newark Adult Ed Courses 1977-, Coord, Certs; Archdiocese of Newark Evaluation Teams 1977-, Chprsn, Certs; Rutherford Museum 1965-69, Bd of Dirs; Dominican Comm, Papal Visit, Synod Facilitator Certs; Archdiocese of Newark Pro Meritas Medal; Distinguished Persons Awd Plaque, Cert; Mayor of Bertone of Rutherford Proclamation Awd Cert; *office:* St Marys H S 64 Chestnut St Rutherford NJ 07070*

DIBONGRAZIO, DONNA LACY, Third Grade Teacher; *b:* Trenton, NJ; *m:* William; *c:* Lacy, Ashley, Amy; *ed:* Trenton St Coll (BA) Elem Ed 1979; *cr:* Wilson Schl 3, 5 Grd Tchr 1979-80; Mc Galliard Schl 4 Grd Tchr 1980-84; Sayen Schl 3, 5 Grd Tchr 1984-; *ai:* Sci Fair Coord; Cmptr Rep; Family Math Tchr; NEA, NJEA, HTEA, Kappa Delta Pi 1979-; Governor's Tchr of Yr 1988-89; *home:* 631 Perrineville Rd Hightstown NJ 08520

DIBURRO, JOSEPH P.,JR., 8th Grade Social Studies Tchr; *b:* Lawrence, MA; *m:* Sheila Kalil; *c:* Tiffany, Kimberly, Kelley; *ed:* Framingham St (BA) Scndry Ed 1971; Working on MA Lowell St; 36 Hrs Post Grad; 12 Credits Cmptrs; *cr:* Vol Probation Officer Lawrence Dist Ct 2 Yrs; Di Burro's Auto Schl Instr 17 Yrs; Haverhill Schls 8th Grd Tchr 25 Yrs; *ai:* Chrldng Adv; NEA 1971-; Garabaldi Club 1991-; *home:* 3 Williams St Salem NH 03079

DI CANDIA, ANTHONY, Italian Teacher; *b:* Atena Lucana, Italy; *m:* Evelyn M.; *c:* Alessandro, Nicol; *ed:* Suffolk Comm Coll (AA) Italian & Span 1969; Hofstra Univ (BA) Italian & Span 1971; Rutgers Univ (MA) Italian 1975; 60 Credit Hrs Toward PHD; *cr:* Kean Coll Tchr of Italian 1973-76; Ryder Coll Tchr of Italian 1975-77; Notre Dame HS Tchr of Latin 1977-78; Easton Area Schls Tchr of Italian 1979-; *ai:* Italian Cultural Comm Adv; AATI 1973-, Cert of Appreciation; PSEA 1979, Bldg Rep; Knight of Columbus 1992-, Pgm Dir; NEH Grant; Article Pub; *office:* Easton Area HS 2601 William Penn Hwy Easton PA 18045

DI CAPRIO, ELIZABETH ANNE (GARGIULO), Retired 5th Grade Teacher; *b:* Amsterdam, NY; *m:* Robert C. Sr.; *c:* Lisa Mc Coy, Mara Buchanan, Robert C. Jr., James F., David J.; *ed:* Coll of Saint Rose (BS) Music Ed 1958, (MS) Elem Ed 1976; Children's Lit Rdng Depts 1986-; *cr:* Gloversville Elem Schls Pre-K-6th Grd Music Tchr 1958-59; New Hanover Twp Schls K-8th Grd Part-time Music Tchr 1961-62; Fonda-Fultonville Cntrl Schl K-6th Grd Music Tchr 1966-68; Estee MS 6th-8th Grd Music Tchr 1972-74; Fonda-Fultonville Cntrl Schl 4th Grd Tchr 1974-81 Lit Tchr 1981-95; *ai:* Author Selection Comms; MS Rdng D 1992-93; FFMS Natl Jr Hnr Soc Adv; Hodge Podg Montgomery-Fulton Rdng Cncl 1974-, Prgm Comm; NY St Rc 1974-; Coll of St Rose Alumnae Assn 1958-, VP; SOFCO Bc 1983-94; Parish Cncl 1981-90; Children's Lit Adjunct Prof FM(1995-; Presented Whole Lang Rdng Prgm Seminars at Lit Co Wkshps 1989, 1990, 1994-.

DICARLO, RITA SCARAMUZZO, Foreign Languages Tea Castel Del Giudice, Italy; *m:* Philip; *c:* Daniel, Paul, Mark; *ed:* E Coll (BA) Italian, Math 1976; Attnd Salem St Coll; *cr:* St Peter S Tchr 1976-78; Medford Pub Schls Sub Tchr, Home Instr, 1979-92; Medford Comm Schl ESL Tchr, Night Schl 1980-92; Me Italian, Span Tchr 1992-; *ai:* MA Frgn Lang Tchrs Assn 1992-, N Commendation 1995; MA Italian Tchrs Assn 1992-; *office:* Mec 489 Winthrop St Medford MA 02155

DICESARE, JEFFREY ETTORE, Band Director; *b:* Pittsburgh Jacqueline Cunat; *ed:* Youngstown St (BA) Music Ed 1988; Ashl (MED) Ed Admin 1996; *cr:* East Palestine City Schls Band Di Massillon City Schls Band Dir 1 Yr; South Euclid Lyndhurst C Band Dir 2 Yrs; *ai:* Marching, Pep, Jazz Bands; MENC, NTA 198 Tchr of Month; Author Director's Choice Software; *office:* East HS 360 W Grant St East Palestine OH 44413*

DI CHIARA, FREDERICK JOHN, Health & Physical Ed Tea Dobbs Ferry, NY; *m:* Harriet Lee Merwin; *c:* Laura Caryl Lipka, F J., Deborah Anne; *ed:* Springfield Coll (BS) Hlth, PE 1964; Wes Univ (ME) Hlth, PE 1968; 40 Hrs Penn St, E. Stroudsburg, Wi Huntingdon Jr HS Tchr 1964-66; Klinger Jr HS Tchr 1966-67; Lo HS Tchr 1967-77; William Tennent HS Tchr 1977-; *ai:* Curr Coo Tennis Coach; Curr Resource Team; PSPHERD 1994-; Ivyland Pa Bd 1967-; Centennial Kiwanis Club 1974-; Area Wrestling Coac Times; Tennis Coach of Yr 2 Times; USTA Mid Sts Tennis Coa 1994; *office:* William Tennent HS 333 Centennial Rd Warminster P

DICHIARO, CATHERINE BARBARIU, Math Tchr & Stu Ac Woonsocket, RI; *m:* William; *c:* Gregory, Leah, Mark, Meredith; *e* Regina (BA) Math 1970; Boston Coll; *cr:* Smithfield Jr HS Ma Tchr 1970-72; North Providence HS Math Tchr 1972-74; Smith Math Tchr & Dir of Stu Act 1976-; *ai:* NEA, Natl Assn of Tchrs 1976-; Smithfield HS Booster Club 1988-, Pres, Dedication Aw Adv 1987-91; Stu Cncl Adv 1991-94; *office:* Smithfield HS 90 View Ave Smithfield RI 02917

DICICCO, DOMINICK WILLIAM, Technology Teacher; *b:* CT; *m:* Judith L. Grimaldi; *c:* Michele Augeri, Dominick W. Jr.; *e* CT St Univ Voc Ed 1972; *cr:* Bulkeley HS Tchr 1972-85; Weaver 1985-94; Bulkeley HS Tchr 1994-; *ai:* Tae Kwon Do Class; AF Union Schl Comm; Arabian Horse Club NE 1969-, Intnl Del; Horse Club CT 1969-, Former Pres; Bass Anglers Sportsmen So Pub BASS LOG Book; *office:* Bulkeley HS 300 Wethersfield Ave CT 06114

DICICCO, MARK LOUIS, Soc Studies, Sci & Art Teac Philadelphia, PA; *m:* Mary G. Marrazzo; *ed:* Camden Cty Coll (AS Svcs 1974; Glassboro St Coll (BS) Sociology 1976; Inst of Cmptr at Philadelphia Cmptr Mngmt Prgm 1967; Univ FL at Gainsville Svcs 1970; *cr:* Vols of Amer Comm Liaison 1974-75; Progressiv Svcs Educl, Curr Consultant 1976-; Holy Saviour Schl Soc Stud, Tchr 1976-, Soc Stud, Sci, Art Chprsn 1980-, After Schl Care P 1983-; *ai:* Diocese of Camden Soc Stud & Sci Curr, Peer V Comms; NCEA 1976-; *office:* Holy Saviour Schl Cambridge & Aves Westmont NJ 08108

DICICCO, ROSEMARIE PETROCIK, 8th Grade English Tea Philadelphia, PA; *m:* Stephen DiCicco; *c:* Anna, Stephen, Nicholas *ed:* LaSalle Coll (BA) Eng Ed 1977; Temple Univ (EdM) Eng Ed 1 West Catholic HS Girls 10th-12th Grd Bus Tchr 1978; Arch Pre HS 9th Grd Eng Tchr 1978; Lower Moreland HS 9th-11th En 1978-79; Holy Cross Schl 8th Grd Tchr 1979-85; Resurrection of C Schl 8th Grd Eng Tchr 1985-; *ai:* Lit Magazine Ed; *office:* Resurre Our Lord Schl 2020 Shelmire Philadelphia PA 19152

DI CIOCCIO, GARY F., Chemistry Teacher; *b:* Beaver Falls, Gannon Univ (BS) Chem 1985; Attnd Univ of Pittsburgh & PA Univ of Miami, La Roche Coll, Wilkes Univ; *cr:* West Mifflin A Chem & Earth Sci Tchr 1986-88; INMETCO Chemist 1988; Roy F Inorganic Chemist 1989-90; West Schl Schl Distnct 1990; West Area HS Chem Tchr 1990-; *ai:* Drama Club; Musical; Boys Tennis AFT 1987-; NSTA 1986-, Manual Script Reviewer; PSTA 1986-, PA Rep; AFI 1986-; AFI 1986-; ACS 1984-; Bucknell Univ Organic Chem Research 1990; AFI Kennedy Art Ctr 1991; Penn Nuclear Concept 1992; ASCI West Penn Hospital Rheumatoid A 1993; DOE Argonne Natural Lab 1994; Univ of Miami Global Fellowship 1995; Univ of CA Berkley Sci & Soc Fellowship 1995 Accelerator Natl Lab Tchrs Fellowship 1996; *office:* West Mifflin 91 Commonwealth Ave West Mifflin PA 15122*

DICIOCCIO, JOSEPH NICHOLAS, Mathematics Teacher; *b:* O NY; *m:* Eleanore; *c:* Katherine, Joseph; *ed:* St Bonaventure Un Math 1973; Western Ct St Univ (MS) Math Ed 1978; *cr:* Mahopa Math Tchr 1973-86; Mahopac HS Math Tchr 1986-; *ai:* JV Bsbl Harmon HS 1978-85, Asst Var Bsbl 1986-94; JV Soccer 1974- Piano Accompanyist Chorus Mahopac Jr HS 1976-85; AMTNYS NCTM 1980-; *office:* Mahopac HS Baldwin Place Rd Mahopac N

DICK, ALEXANDER C.,JR., Mathematics Teacher; *b:* Wilmingt *m:* Margaret Sue; *c:* Emily, David; *ed:* Washington Coll (BA) Mat Univ of MD (MED) Math 1973; *cr:* Peace Corp Math Tchr & Cor 1965-68; Ardmore JHS Math Dept 1968-69; Garrison Forest Sch Dept 1969-73; Friends Acad Math Dept 1973-; *ai:* Math Dep 1981-83; Coach: Tennis, Bsktbl, Lacrosse, Soccer; Sr Class Adv; 1981-; *office:* Friends Acad Duck Pond Rd Locust Valley NY 1156

DICK, MATTHEW ROBERT, Physics Teacher; *b:* Toledo, (Catherine Roether-Dick; *c:* Christina, Sara; *ed:* Bowling Green (BS) Sci Ed 1989; Univ of Toledo (MS) Psych 1994; *cr:* Delta HS Physics Tchr 1989-92; Maumee HS Physics Tchr 1992-; *ai:* T Engrng Coach; SECO, NSTA 1989-; *office:* Maumee HS 1147 S Maumee OH 43537*

DICK, ROSEANNE VITALE, Fifth Grade Teacher; *b:* New York, Steven; *c:* Joshua, Evan; *ed:* Queens Coll (BA) Ed 1970, (MA) E 30 Credits Post Grad Stud; *cr:* PS 81 Q 5th Grd Tchr 1970-78, 198 UFT 1970-; *office:* PS 81 Queens 559 Cypress Ave Flushing NY 1

DICKEN, DANIA HALLER, Business Teacher; *b:* Oakland, MD; *c:* Mark Haller, Kim Haller; *ed:* Univ of MD (BS) Secretarial Ec Montgomery Cty Pub Schl Masters Equivilency Secretarial Ed 19 Credit Hrs Inservice Courses; *cr:* Gaithersburg HS Bus Tchr 19 Paint Brush HS Bus Tchr 1977-79; Magruder HS Bus Tchr 1979-; *a* Store Spon; Magruda Soc Comm; Chprsn for MS Evaluation fc Cmptr Sci; NEA, MSTA, MCEA 1982-; MCBETA 1990-; Teach A Courses, Montgomery Cty Systemwide Trng Word Perfect for Winc Adults in Comm & Prof Staff in Cty; *office:* Colonel Zadok Magruc 5939 Muncaster Mill Rd Rockville MD 20855

ON, DAVID ALAN, Health Teacher; *b:* Norwich, CT; *ed:* ' St Univ (BS) Hlth, PE 1988; 15 Credits Hlth Ed, Southern CT *r:* Dr. Helen Baldwin Schl 4th-8th Grd PE, Hlth Tchr 1989-90, .edyard MS 7th-8th Grd Hlth Tchr 1994-; *ai:* Boys Bsktbl, JV Coach; Adv, Advisee Comm Co-Chair; NEA, CEA 1989-; LEA ss 1990 Yrbk Dedication; *office:* Ledyard MS 1860 Rt 12 Gales 6335

ON, MARTIN, Mathematics Teacher; *b:* Fort Smith, AR; *m:* er; *c:* Beau, Brian; *ed:* Univ of Cntrl AR (BS) Math 1971; Attnd ific Univ, Bowie St Univ; *cr:* Kingman HS Math Tchr 1971-72; HS Math Tchr 1972-78; Montgomery Blair HS Math Tchr Walt Whitman HS Math Tchr 1981-; *ai:* Head Ftbl Coach; Past bl, Asst Ftbl, Asst Bsktbl, Golf, Cross-Cntry, Tennis Coach; Asst EA; MCEA; PTSA, VP, Pres; Mont Co Recreation Dept, Vol 13 sktbl, Bsbl Coach; Recognized as Inspirational Tchr; Whitman's 1992-93; Nom for Mont Co Tchr of Yr; Mont Co Boys Bsktbl Yr 1985-86; *office:* Walt Whitman HS 7100 Whittier Blvd MD 20817

ON, MAXINE MORRIS, English Teacher; *b:* Philadelphia, Anford D. Sr.; *c:* Catherine; *ed:* Howard Univ (BA) Eng 1969; A Rdng Cert, Courses in Adolescent Psych & Testing; *cr:* St Sales Schl Lang Arts Tchr 1970-74; St Hubert HS Eng Tchr Archbishop Prendergast HS Eng Tchr 1994-; *ai:* NHS Cncl; Scholar Cncl; Fac Coordinating, Retention Recruitment Comms; ath Tchrs, NCTE, Natl Cncl of Cath Schl Tchrs 1974-; NAACP Governor's Awd for Tchr, Mentor 1990; *home:* 504 Holly Rd A 19050*

SON, STEVEN EDWARD, Industrial Technology Teacher; *b:* H; *m:* Sherri Ann Schilling; *c:* Eric, Andrew; *ed:* OH St (BS) ch Ed 1983; *ai:* Ftbl, Bsktbl, Bsbl Coach; Class Adv; Tchr Advy DEA, NEA; *office:* Lucas HS 5 First Ave Lucas OH 44843

T, PAMELA, HS Special Education Teacher; *b:* Jersey City, NJ; oro St Coll (BA) Tchr of the Handicapped 1980; *cr:* Buena Regnl & Coach 1980-; *ai:* Var Sftbl & Asst Field Hockey Coach; NEA 1980-; BREA 1980-; CIE 1979-; S Jersey Sftbl Coaches Assn hr of the Yr 1984-85; Atlantic City Press Coach of the Yr Awd vernors Awd 1986-; *office:* Buena Regional HS Weymouth Rd 08310

, IRENE SICOUTRIS, English Teacher; *b:* Baltimore, MD; *c:* ristine Dickey Hutchinson; *ed:* Glassboro St Coll (BA) Jr HS Ed van Coll (MA) Pub Relations 1994; *cr:* Upper Pittsgrove Schl 8th 1966-67; Junction City Jr HS Eng Tchr 1968; Carleton Schl 8th Tchr 1968-70; Penns Grove MS 7th Grd Eng Tchr 1972-86, Eng -; *ai:* Pub Relations Coord; Co-Producer HS Play; FTA Co-Adv; heduling, Five Yr Planning Comms; SRA Panel; NEA, NJEA -CP Tchrs Assn 1966-, Treas; PRSA 1994; NCTA 1979; *office:* ove HS 334 Harding Hwy Carneys Point NJ 08069*

, SARAH COWGILL, English Teacher & Yrbk Adv; *b:* Dover, Matthew, Sarah; *ed:* Univ of MD (BA) Eng 1970; Salisbury St) Ed 1979; *cr:* Newport News HS Eng Tchr 1971-72; Milford MS s Tchr 1972-74; Dela Tech & Comm Coll Eng Tchr 1974-75; r HS Eng Tchr 1975-76; Bowie HS Eng Tchr 1977-82, 1987-; *ai:* ; PGCEA 1995-; MSTA 1995-; NEA 1995-; Calvary United Meth 985-; *office:* Bowie HS 15200 Annapolis Rd Bowie MD 20715

, JOY SIEBLER, Guidance Counselor; *b:* Brooklyn, NY; *m:* SUNY at New Paltz (BA) Eng, Scndry Ed 1965; Long Island Univ idance & Counseling 1970; Post Grad Stud Hofstra Univ, Long niv; *cr:* Roosevelt Jr-Sr HS Eng Tchr 1966; Westbury HS Eng Tchr Guidance Cnslr 1969-79; Westbury Jr HS Guidance Cnslr Westbury HS Guidance Cnslr 1986-; *ai:* Class of 76, ding 1966-75, Honor Soc 1993- Advs; Acad Awds 1989-, Class 89- Coords; LIPGA 1969-; WTA, NYSUT, AFT 1966-; SUNY at z Alumni Assn 1985-; *office:* Westbury HS 1 Post Rd Old NY 11568

SON, DONALD C., Eng Tchr & Dir of Forensics; *b:* arre, PA; *m:* Linda Naugle; *c:* Matthew, Todd, Beth; *ed:* burg Univ (BS) Eng, Speech 1970; Addl 24 Credits; *cr:* sburg Sr HS Eng Tchr 1970-73; Faust Jr HS Eng Tchr 1973-84; sburg Sr HS Eng Tchr, Forensics Dir 1984-; *ai:* Forenscis Dir; ea 1988-; Natl Forensic League 1986-, Degree of Exel 1990; burg Comm Food Bank 1971-93, Sec-Treas 21 Yrs; Messiah Choir Dir Handbell Choir 1991; Wkshp Spkr Natl Cncl Tchrs of Conv 1993; Educl Consltnt, United St Memrl Musm; *office:* sburg Area Sr HS 511 S Sixth St Chambersburg PA 17201

SON, JANET KEROHER, 8th Grade Language Arts Tchr; *b:* San A; *m:* Evan; *ed:* UT St Univ (BS) Eng, Bus Ed 1967; Montclair St nl Svcs, Counseling 1975; *cr:* Boonton HS Eng Tchr 1967-69; Mt per Elem Eng Tchr 1969-73; Long Valley MS Eng Tchr 1973-; *ai:* Enrichment Prgm Dir; 14 Yrs Abroad With Stu Groups; NJ Field er Cncl of Intnl Stud; Guest Tchr in Russia 1991; Geraldine ler Dodge Grant 1990; *office:* Long Valley MS 51 W Mill Rd Long J 07853

SON, JEANNE MARIE, Mathematics Teacher; *b:* Queens, NY; ty Coll (BA) Ed 1981; *cr:* Mater Dei HS Math Tchr, Coach 1981-; Hockey, Bsktbl Asst Coaches; Sftbl Var Coach; AFT 1981-, Treas; ater Dei HS 538 Church St New Monmouth NJ 07748

SON, KARLYN (EBERHARDT), German & Spanish Teacher; *b:* NY; *m:* Alfred H.; *ed:* Olivet Coll (BA) Ger, His 1967; Canisius S) Ed, Ger 1969; 60 Addl Credits Frgn Lang, Span, Fr, Ger; *cr:* Cntrl Schls 7th-9th Grd Am His, Ger, Fr, Span, Tchr 1968-; *ai:* er Clubs; Dept Chair MS Frgn Lang; NYSAFLT, WNYAFLC, FCTA 1968-; *office:* Frontier MS 2751 Amsdell Rd Hamburg NY

SON, ROBERT PAUL, Principal; *b:* Phila, PA; *m:* Donna Earley; , Bryan; *ed:* Trenton St (BS) Elem Ed 1971; Rider Univ (MA) dmin 1982; Post Grad 60 Credit Hrs; *cr:* Lower Bucks Joint Bd Tchr 1970-72; Sierra Leon Peace Corps Vol 1972-74; Bensalem l Dist 4th, 5th Gifted Tchr 1974-94, Prin 1995-; *ai:* Sci Comm; urr Supvr; NSTA, NCTM 1992-; NAEP 1995-; AIMS Ldrshp ; *home:* 184 Bridgeton Rd Elmer NJ 08318

ER, PAUL DENNIS, History Teacher; *b:* New York City, NY; *c:* Jesse; *ed:* Wharton Schl (BS) Pol Sci 1970; Univ of PA (MS) His DD) Curr & Instruction 1976; Post-Doctoral Stud at Saint Andrews , Princeton Univ, Trenton St Coll, Haverford Coll & Univ of Ca; adelphia Public Schls Tchr 1969-71; Neshaminy Schls Tchr 1971-; Policy Research Inst 1991-; Coll Bd Consultant 1991-; Univ of PA Fac 1993-; *ai:* Stu Govt Adv; Forensics Head Coach; His Club; 73-; ECSSS 1987-; NCSS 1992-; NEH Grants; Keza-Koho Fnd hip; His Insts; *office:* Neshaminy HS 2001 Old Lincoln Hwy ne PA 19047

IAN, MARGARET L., Sixth Grade Teacher; *b:* Continental, OH; st; *c:* Ann Ellerbrock, Mark, Dean, Tracey, Jill; *ed:* Mary Manse A) Elem Ed 1964; Attnd Bowling Green St Univ; *cr:* Sts Peter & hl Grd 4 Tchr 1964-65, Jr HS Soc Stud Tchr 1968-73, Grd 4 Tchr , Grd 3 Tchr 1978-93, Grd 6 Tchr 1993-; *ai:* Level Coord 1995-; Jr Cath Daughters of Amer Adult Adv 1981-95; Cath Schls Week Comm 1995-; OH Cath Ed Assn, NCEA 1975-; IRA 1975-, Recording Sec, Bldg Rep; Amer Legion Aux 1980-95, Veterans Affairs Chprsn; Cath Daughters of Amer 1968-, Pres, Sec, Fin Sec; Elizabeth Ann Seton Awd 1990.

DICKSON, AUDREY ELVA, Magnet Coordinator; *b:* Washington, DC; *m:* Aubrey Leon; *c:* Everett E. Washington Jr; *ed:* Howard Univ (BA) Elem Ed 1971; 45 Hrs Beyond BA Masters Equivalent, 30 Hrs Beyond That Towards Masters Degree Loyola Coll; *cr:* Middleton Vly Elem Schl 1st-2nd Grd Tchr 1971-90, 2nd-3rd Classroom Tchr 1990-93; Owens Rd Elem Schl 3rd Grd Math Sci Tchr 1993-94, Magnet Coord 1994-; *ai:* Sci Bowl Team Spon; Globe Lead Tchr; Sci, Math, Testing Coord; Drug Ed Advy Bd; Stu Act Chprsn; Kids for Sci Steering, Christie McCuliffe Awds, Sci Trek Steering Comms; PGCEA 1971-, Former Del; MSTA, NEA 1971-; NSTA 1995-; NCTM 1994-; Cntrl HS PTSA 1993-, Sec; Owens Rd PTA 1993-, Tchr Liaison; Peace Bapt Sunday Schl 1989-; Middleton Vly Tchr of Yr 1991; Cty Proclamation Tchr of Yr 1991; Prince Georges Cty Outstndng Edctr 1992; Washington Post Grant 1993-94; Kids for Sci Steering Comm Awd 1995; Chesapekae Bay Trust 1995; MAST Presenter 1995-; Math Tchr Resource Book 1990; *office:* Owens Road Elem Schl 1616 Owens Rd Oxon Hill MD 20745*

DICKSON, CHRISTOPHER SCOTT, Music Teacher & Dept Chair; *b:* Rochester, NY; *ed:* Hartwick Coll (BS) Music Ed 1993; *cr:* Mc Quaid Jesuit HS Music Tchr 1993-; *ai:* Band Dir; Var Vlybl, Track & Field Asst Coach; NCEA 1993-; Phi Mu Alpha 1990-; Epsilon Pi Pres Chptr 1992-93; NYSSMA 1993-; BSA 1985-89, Eagle Scout; *office:* Mc Quaid Jesuit HS 1800 S Clinton Ave Rochester NY 14618

DICKSON, DAVID PAUL, Social Studies Teacher; *b:* St Charles, IL; *m:* Pamela; *c:* Joshua, Caleb; *ed:* (MA) Soc Stud Engl; *cr:* Pavilion Jr Sr HS Soc Stud Tchr 1988-; *ai:* Amer Field Service, Close Up Washington Adv, Europe Trip Facilitator; NY Cncl for Soc Stud 1990-; *home:* 24 Highview Cir Brockport NY 14420

DICKSON, DONALD SCOTT, Industrial Tech Ed Tchr; *b:* Cleveland, OH; *m:* Loreen Kay; *c:* Gregory, Alicia; *ed:* Lorain Cty Comm Coll (AS) Leneral Stud 1984; Bowling Green St Univ (BSE) Industrial Tech Ed 1986; Ashland Univ (MA) Sports Sci 1995; *cr:* Marion L Steele HS Industrial Tech Tchr 1986-87; Avon HS Industrial Tech Tchr 1987-; *ai:* Var Ftbl Coach 1986-95; Building Advy Team Coord; NEA, OEA, OH Industrial Tech Assn 1986-; *office:* Avon Lake HS 175 Avon Belden Rd Avon Lake OH 44012*

DICKSON, DOROTHY LOUISE RICE, Third Grade Teacher; *b:* Meridian, MS; *m:* Silas; *c:* Marlon C., Errol D., Silas C.; *ed:* MS Vly St (BAA) Bus Ed 1966; Temp Cert Elem St John Coll 1968; Credit Hrs Notre Dame, Cleveland St, Ursuline Coll; *cr:* Epiphany Cath Schl Tchr 1967-70; Holy Family Schl Tchr 1970-72, St Cecilia Schl Tchr 1973-; Mt Pleasant Cath Tchr 1996; *ai:* Sunday Schl Tchr 25 Yrs; Asst Pastor's Needs Choir; Chrstn Women's Auxiliary; Faithful Church; Multiple Intelligence; St Tchrs Assn 1973-; Awd Excl Outstdng Tchr; Tchr of Yr 1991; Nom Ashland Oil Tchr Achvmt Awd 1994-; *home:* 13115 Christine Ave Garfield Heights OH 44105

DICKSON, JANET MC CLINTOCK, Retired First Grade Teacher; *b:* Zanesville, OH; *c:* Kevin, Eric; *ed:* OH Univ at Athens (BS) Ed 1963; Ashland Coll Post Grad Work; *cr:* Newton Elem Schl 4th Grd Tchr 1961-63; Bethel Manor Elem Schl 3rd, 5th Grd Tchr 1963-65; Conesville Elem Schl 1st Grd Tchr 1965-95; *ai:* RVEA, OEA, NEA 1965-; OH REACT Dresden Village Assn 1994-; *home:* PO Box 232 Dresden OH 43821

DICKSON, MELINDA SUE (HENDERSON), Spanish & Psychology Teacher; *b:* Dayton, OH; *m:* Jeffrey Robert; *c:* Braden Jeffrey; *ed:* OH Univ (BS) Span Ed 1991; Working Towards Masters in Schl Cnslng; *cr:* Madison HS Span & Psych Tchr 1991-; *ai:* Jr Class Adv; Span Club Spon; NEA 1992-; OFLA 1992-; Crystal Apple Nom; *home:* 2829 Shartle St Middletown OH 45042

DICKSON, STEPHEN W., Earth Science Teacher; *b:* Bronx, NY; *m:* Maureen E. McAllister; *c:* Jennifer, Lesley, Stephanie; *ed:* Southampton Coll LIU (BS) Marine Sci 1972; Adelphi Univ (MS) Hydrology 1991; 30 Credit Hrs in Ed at St Johns Univ; *cr:* St Marys Manhasset Sci Tchr 1972-78; Half Hollow Hills Schl Dist #5 Earth Sci Tchr 1978-; *ai:* Sci Explorers Club; AFT 1978-; *office:* Half Hollow Hills HS East 50 Vanderbilt Pky Dix Hills NY 11746

DICLEMENTE, LORIE CVIJIC, Eighth Grade Math Teacher; *b:* Hershey, PA; *m:* Gary J.; *ed:* Clarion Univ (BS) Actuarial Sci 1982; Millersville Univ Scndry Tchng Cert 1985; Credits in Cmptr Related Courses & Psych; *cr:* Harrisburg Schl Dist Tchr 1983-84; Susquehanna Twp HS Tchr 1984-90; Susquehanna Twp MS Tchr 1991-; *ai:* Bldg Cmptr Coord; Stu Assistane Team; Team Ldr; NEA 1983-; STEA 1984-, Bldg Rep; Hershey Italian Lodge 1985-; *home:* 542 W Granada Ave Hershey PA 17033*

DIDION, SUSAN ANN, Sixth Grade Teacher; *b:* Cleveland, OH; *ed:* Bowling Green Univ (BSE) Ed 1973; Ashland Univ (ME) Ed, Curr, Instruction 1994; *cr:* Parma City Schls 3-6 Grd Tchr 1973-; *ai:* Team Ldrshp Venture Capital Grant; Assessment Liason; Safety Patrol Adv; NEA; OEA; PEA; NEOEA; *office:* John Muir Elem Schl 5531 W 24th St Cleveland OH 44134

DIDONATO, MICHELE PENNISI, School Librarian & Dept Coord; *b:* Brooklyn, NY; *c:* Stephen, Andrea; *ed:* SUNY at New Paltz (BS) Ed 1970, (MS) Ed 1975; Long Island Univ (MLS) Schl Lib Media 1990; *cr:* Maybrook Elem Schl Elem Tchr 1977-90; Chester Elem Schl Elem Librn 1990-91; Pine Tree Elem Schl Elem Librn 1991-95; Monroe-Woodbury HS Librn 1995-; *ai:* Dist Lib, Media Coord; ALA, NYLA 1990-; SLMSSENY, NYLA 1990-, Pres 1995-; AFT, NYSUT 1970-; Grant Recipient 1991 Area Fund of Orange Cty; *office:* Monroe-Woodbury Sr HS Dunderberg Rd Central Valley NY 10917

DIEDRICHSEN, RICHARD PETER, English Teacher; *b:* Lordship, CT; *m:* Julia R. Glad; *c:* Nickolaus, Lena, John; *ed:* Assumption Coll (BA) Eng 1971; Marquette Univ(BA) Eng 1978; 6th Yr Eqv Gr 1987 Yale, Southern CT St; Tech Ed, Writing; Theater Techniques Ed; *cr:* Johnson Jr HS Lang Arts Tchr 1975-78; Bunnell HS Eng Tchr 1978-; *ai:* Var Soccer Coach 1983-93; St Soccer Comm 1991-93; CT Interscholastic Ath Conf; Comm Chair NEASC Evaluation 1984, 1994; NEA 1975-; Natl Soccer Coaches Assn, Amer 1980-; CT Soccer Coaches Assn 1983-; Sterling House Comm Ctr 1980-, Coach Dir, Debbie Diaz Awd; Who's Who Amer Ed 1989-90; Co-Author Soccer Coaching Books; Coach of Yr 1992; *office:* Bunnell HS 1 Bulldog Blvd Stratford CT 06497

DIEFFENBACH, JODIE WALMER, Second Grade Teacher; *b:* Lebanon, PA; *m:* Dale J.; *ed:* West Chester St Univ (BS) Elem Ed 1976; PA St Univ (MS) Tchng & Curr 1991; *cr:* Naschitti Pub Schl Kndgtn Tchr Navajo Children 1976-78; Myerstown Elem Schl Kndgtn Tchr 1979; Annville Elem Schl Transitional First & 4th Grd Tchr 1979-80; East Hanover Elem Schl 1st & 2nd Grd Tchr 1980-; *ai:* Asst After Schl Intramural Prgm 4-6 Grds; NEA, PSEA 1989-.

DIEHL, ALTA A., Second Grade Teacher; *b:* Lurgan, PA; *m:* Jack E.; *c:* Wanda Frank, Lesa, Janeen Roe, Carla Rahrig; *ed:* BGSU (BS) K-8 Elem Ed 1973, (MS) K-8 Elem Ed; 45 Addl Post Grad Hrs; *cr:* South Main Kndgtn Tchr 1974-75, Second Grd Tchr 1975-; *ai:* Bowling Green Educ Assn 1973-, Schl Rep; Martha Weber Rdng Cncl, Pres, VP; OH Rdng Cncl; IRA; United Meth Church, Choir, Educ Comm; Storytelling Techniques for Tchrs, Enrichment Classes at Lit Wkshps; Martha Holden Jennings Scholar 1988-89; *home:* 702 E Gypsy Lane Rd Bowling Green OH 43402

DIEHL, JAN A., Dir of Bands & Gen Music Tchr; *b:* Cincinnati, OH; *m:* Elaine M. Furlong; *c:* Valerie, Faith; *ed:* Univ of Cincinnati CCM (BME) Music Ed, Saxophone 1977; Jazz Stud-Fender Bass 1981-82; Orff-Schulwerk Cert Levels 1, 2 & 3; *cr:* Bethel-Tate HS Dir Bands, Chorus, Music Theory & Supvr of Instrumental Stud 1977-81; Self-Employed Prof Musician 1982-87; Guardian Angels Schl Dir of Bands & General Music Tchr 1987-; *ai:* OMEA, MENC 1977-.*

DIENHART, JOHN, Chairman; *b:* Lafayette, IN; *m:* M. Diane Lemm; *c:* Stacie Gascho, Timothy, Mark; *ed:* Purdue Univ (BA) Institutional Mgmt 1964, (MS) Restaurant & Hotel Mgmt 1984; KS St Univ (PHD) Institutional Mgmt 1991; *cr:* Dienhart & Milligan Pres; Purdue Univ Asst Prof & Hotel & Restaurant Mgmt 1984-88; KS St Univ Instr & Hotel & Restaurant Mgmt 1988-92; Univ of MD Eastern Shore Chm & Hotel & Restaurant Mgmt 1992-; *ai:* Amer Soc of Mgmt 1992-; Cncl Hotel Restaurant, Institutional Mgmt Educators 1985-; Natl Restaurant Assn 1984-; H J Heinze Fellowship Awd; Authored & Co-Authored 25 Plus Articles Related to Hospitality Industry; *office:* Univ Of MD Eastern Shore Princess Anne MD 21853

DIENI, DOMINICK JOSEPH, American Government Teacher; *b:* Springfield, MA; *m:* Phyllis M.; *c:* David, Alicia Dieni Furgueson; *ed:* Amer Intnl Coll (BA) His, Govt 1968, (MA) Soc Sci; Univ of MA Cert of Advanced Grad Stud; *cr:* Southwick-Tolland Rengl HS Soc Stud Tchr, Dept Head 1970-; *ai:* Debate Coach Ct Vly Debate League; Model Congress, Stu Govt Day Adv; Southwick Ed Assn 1970-, Negotiations Comm; MA Tchrs Assn, NEA 1970-; NCSS 1975-; CT Vly Debate League 1970-, Pres 1973-75; Boston Univ Psych Grant; *office:* Southwick Tolland Reg HS 93 Feeding Hills Rd Southwick MA 01077*

DIERKSHEIDE, MARY ELLEN, 7th & 8th Grade Math Teacher; *b:* Bowling Green, OH; *m:* Kenneth William; *c:* Julie, Douglas, Jeffrey, Michael, Sara; *ed:* Bowling Green St Univ (BSE) Math, Eng 1967; 20 Sem Hrs Bowling Green St Univ; 3 Sem Hrs Heidelberg Coll; 15 Quarter Hrs Univ of Toledo; *cr:* Bowling Green Jr HS 8th Grd Math, Algebra I Tchr 1967-72; Vanguard Voc Ctr Math Tchr 1985-86; Elmwood MS 7th-8th Grd Math Tchr 1987-; *ai:* Math Counts Coach; 8th Grd Farewell Dinner Chprsn; Discipline, Venture Capital Grant Comms; Regnl Prof Dev Ctr Subregion 5 Bldg Rep; Mentor Tchr; Stu Tchrs Supvr; Elmwood Ed Assn 1987-, Treas, OEA Outstdng Treas; OEA, NEA, NCTM, OCTM, GTCTM 1987-; Math Assessment Comm 1993-; Discovery Tchr 1993; Participated in Tchr Facilitators Ldrshp for Sustained Improvement of Math; Co-Write Wood Cty Math Competency 8th Grd Test; *home:* 15374 Silverwood Rd Pemberville OH 43450*

DIEROLF, EVELYN LAURA, Physical Education Teacher; *b:* Newark, NJ; *ed:* Newark St Coll (BA) PE, Hlth 1973; Kean Coll (MA) PE, Spec Ed 1990; Supvrs Cert; 30 Addl Credits Jersey City St Coll, Montclair Univ; *cr:* Walter O. Krumbiegel Schl PE Tchr 1973-; Hillside HS Girls Track, Field Var Coach 1978-92; *ai:* MS Field Day Coord; Schl Safety Comm; Town-Wide Educl Cncl; IM Adv; NJEA, NEA, HEA 1973-; AAHPERD 1980-; Governor's Cncl Tchr of Yr 1992-93; *office:* Walter O Krumbiegel MS 145 Hillside Ave Hillside NJ 07205

DIETEMANN, CHANTAL M., Mathematics Instructor; *b:* Corning, NY; *ed:* Columbus Univ (AB) Ec 1985; SUNY Albany (MA) Math 1993; NY St Cert HS Math Tchng; *cr:* Jefferson CC Instr 1994-; *ai:* Environmentally Concerned Group of Stdnts Adv; NYSMATIC 1994-; SU-Tech Ctr 1995-, Bd; North Cntry Bird Club 1996; Watertown Historial Soc 1995-; *office:* Jefferson Comm Coll Outer Coffeen Street Watertown NY 13601

DIETERLE, JEFF, Instrumental Music Teacher; *b:* Montclair, NJ; *m:* Marie Farese; *ed:* MI St Univ (BA) Music Ed 1988; Post Grad Stud Music Performance; *cr:* Charles Selzer Schl Instrumental Music Tchr 1989-92; Bloomfield HS Instrumental Music Tchr 1992-; *ai:* Marching, Jazz Band Dir; MENC, NJMEA, NEA 1988-; Played on Fox Cartoon; *office:* Bloomfield HS 160 Broad St Bloomfield NJ 07003

DIETRICH, ANNE CARLEY, Earth Science Teacher; *b:* Saranac Lake, NY; *m:* David; *c:* Michelle, Aaron; *ed:* SUNY at Potsdam (BA) Ed & Sci 1970; Coll of St Rose (MS) Ed 1991; SUNY at Plattsburgh 9 Credit Hrs Post Grad; Brooklyn Coll 3 Credit Hrs Post Grad; *cr:* Morrisville-Eaton CS Elem Ed Tchr 1970-71; St Michaels Schl Sci & Math Tchr 1971-73; St Marys Sci & Math Tchr 1973-74; Broadalbin-Perth HS Sci Tchr 1986-; *ai:* Sci Hnr Soc & Sci Bowl Adv; Sci Dept Chprsn; Broadalbin-Perth Tchrs Assn 1986-, VP; AFT 1986-; STANYS 1986-; NESTA 1995-; Tandy Outstdng Tchr Awd; Presented Article at Amer Educl Rsrch Assn; BP Bd of Ed Excl In Tchng Awd; *office:* Broadalbin Perth HS 100 Bridge St Ext Broadalbin NY 12025

DIETRICH, DENNIS EDWARD, Social Studies Teacher; *b:* Buffalo, NY; *m:* Linda A. Helmer; *c:* Timothy, Leigh Ann; *ed:* NE St (BS) Ed 1968; Buffalo St (MS) Soc Stud 1973, (SDA) & (SAS) Admin 1991; *cr:* Schl 43 7th & 8th Grd Tchr 1968-78; Buffalo Traditional Magnet 9th-12th Grd Tchr 1978-88; Buffalo St Coll & St Univ of NY at Buffalo Staff Developer Local, St & Natl Level 1985-; Hutch-Tech HS 9th-12th Grd Tchr 1988-; Adj Prof 1989-; *ai:* NEA 1968-; ASCD 1988-; NCSD 1988-; NYSUT 1990-; Mem Natl Blue Ribbon Schls Panel Wash DC; Site Reviewer Schls of Excl Pgm; *office:* Hutchinson Central Tech HS 256 S Elmwood Ave Buffalo NY 14201*

DIETRICH, GEOFFREY ARTHUR, Chemistry Teacher; *b:* Westfield, NY; *m:* Diane Lynn Hewes; *c:* David, Steven; *ed:* McGill Univ (BS) Zoology 1971; Attnd SUC at Fredonia, SUNY at Buffalo; *cr:* Peace Corps the Gambia Vol & Logistics Coord 1971-74; SUC at Fredonia Grad Asst 1974; Envir Resources Ctr Rsrch Assoc 1974-79; Salamanca HS Sci Instr 1979-; *ai:* Sr Class Adv; Tech Rep; Sigma Xi 1979-, Assoc; NEA 1979-; STANYS 1981-; Kiwanis 1989-; Co-Author of Limnology Journal Articles; *office:* Salamanca HS 50 Iroquois Dr Salamanca NY 14779

DIETRICH, MARLYN ROSE, Eng, Spelling & Math Teacher; *b:* Baltimore, MD; *m:* John L. Sr.; *c:* John L. Jr., Sharon L. Stoekly Dietrich, Patricia R. Hood; *ed:* Towson St Univ (BS) Elem Ed 1987; *cr:* St Clare Schl 6th-8th Grd Math, Soc Stud, Sci Tchr 1979-86; St Elizabeths Schl 4th Grd Rdng, Math, Soc Stud Tchr 1986-88; St Clements Schl 6th-8th Grd Math, Eng, Spelling, Rel Tchr 1988-89; St Ritas Schl 6th-8th Grd Math, 5th Grd Eng, Spelling Tchr 1989-; *ai:* Chprsn Math, Philosophy, Fifth Grd Schl Newspaper, Acad Bowl, Acad Young Poets; Math Coach Class Tutor; NCTM, NCEA 1994-; ESTA 1989-; Stu Cncl 1981-84, Fac Rep; Schl Bd 1992-, Fac Rep; *home:* 4708 White Marsh Rd Baltimore MD 21237

DIETRICH, WILLIAM EDWARD,JR., Professor of Biology; *b:* Easton, PA; *m:* Patricia Gortner; *c:* Eric M., Rebecca L., Samantha J.; *ed:* La Salle Coll (BA) Bio 1964; Univ of PA (PHD) Bio 1970; Grad Stud Syracuse Univ 1964-65; *cr:* Brookhaven Natl Lab Rsrch Assoc 1969-71; Indiana Univ of PA Asst Prof 1971-76, Assoc Prof 1976-80, Prof 1980-, Coord Biochemistry Prgm 1995-; *ai:* Biochemistry Club Co-Adv; Outing Club Reunion Organizer; AAAS 1971-; Amer Soc Plant Physiologists 1968-; Assoc PA St Coll & Univ Fac 1971-, St Pub Relations Chair; PA Acad of Sci 1971-; IN Cty Botanical Soc 1980-, Pres, VP, Newsletter Ed; *office:* Indiana Univ Of PA Biology Dept Indiana PA 15705

DIETZ, DAVID L., Band Director; *b:* Mt Wolf, PA; *m:* Donnamarie Dilabio; *c:* Julianna Micnezze, Christina Marie; *ed:* Indiana Univ of PA

(BS) Music Ed 1972; Temple Univ (MS) Music 1986; *cr:* Harrisburg HS Band Dir 1973-78; Bermudian Springs HS Band Dir 1978-82; Spring Grove Area Sr HS Band Dir 1982-; *ai:* Marching, Jazz Bands; Small Instrumental Ensembles; NEA, MENC 1972-; *office:* Spring Grove Area Sr HS Hanover & Jackson Sts Spring Grove PA 17362*

DIETZ, ELIZABETH ANN, Music Teacher; *b:* Bethlehem, PA; *ed:* West Chester St Univ (BS) Music Ed 1968; Addl Grad Stud; *cr:* Boyertown Schl Dist Jr HS Vocal & General Music 1968-; Boyertown Sr HS Music Theory Tchr, Choral Directory; *ai:* Chorus Dir; Show Choir Dir; Schl Musical Dir; Stu Assistance Prgm Team Mem; Music Educators Natl Conf 1968-; Amer Choral Dirs Assn 1988-; PA Ed Assn 1968-; YMCA 1991-; Cedarville United Meth Church; Vocal VP of Berks Cty Music Educators; *office:* Boyertown Area Sr HS 500 E 4th St Boyertown PA 19512

DIETZ, KAREN S., Retail & Fashion Teacher; *b:* Washington, DC; *m:* Richard L.; *c:* Melissa, James; *ed:* Radford Univ (BS) Home Ec, Retailing 1973; St Univ of NY (MSEDC) K-12 Rdng 1995; *cr:* K-Mart Apparel Mgr 1973-77; Marshall's Store Mgr 1979-84; Dutchess BOCES Retail & Fashion Tchr 1989-; *ai:* Effective Schls Chprsn 1992-93; Co-Chaired 25th Anniversary Mall Show for Schl 1992; Wappinger Nursery Schl 1987-, Sec, Treas; *office:* Dutchess Co BOCES Tech Ctr 578 Salt Point Tpke Poughkeepsie NY 12601

DIETZ, KATHLEEN HURLEY, Math Dept Chair; *b:* Baltimore, MD; *c:* Robert, Geoffrey; *ed:* Mt St Agnes Coll (BA) Math 1969; Univ of Dayton (MS) Math 1971; Addl 2 Semester Hrs; Wright St Univ Addl 17 Qtr Hrs; Addl 3 Semester Hrs OR St Univ; *cr:* Univ of Dayton Grad Tchng Asst 1969-71; Miami Valley Schl Math Dept Chair 1971-74; Wright St Univ Adjunct Math Tchr 1982-83; Carroll HS Math Dept Chair 1983-; *ai:* MU Alpha Theta Chapter Spon; JETS Coach; NCTM 1983-; OH Tchrs Cncl of Math 1987-, Outstanding Scndry Tchr West Dist 1991; Wright St Univ Area Tchrs Cncl of Math 1987-, Treas 7 Yrs; Math Assn of Amer; Assn for Suprvsn & Curr Dev; Beavercreek Friends of Lib 1977-, Sec 1979; Univ of Dayton Schl of Ed Tchr Awd 1990; Recipient of $8500 Calculator Grant Hewlett Packard Co; Outstanding Building Tchr Miami Valley Cncl on Cath Ed 1990; Honorable Mention Tandy Tech Scholars Awd 1994; Outstanding Tchr Eng & Sci Hall of Fame 1995; *office:* Carroll H S 4524 Linden Dayton OH 45432*

DIETZ, RAYMOND JON, English Teacher; *b:* Niagara Falls, NY; *m:* Suzanne Marie Simon; *c:* Olivia, Jessica, Aaron; *ed:* Edinboro St Coll (BS) Scndry Soc Stud 1973; Niagara Univ (MS) Ed 1978; *cr:* Southwestern Cntrl Schl Soc Stud Tchr 1973-74; Lewiston Porter Cntrl Schl Soc Stud & Eng Tchr 1974-; *ai:* Ftbl Announcer; Attendance & Discipline Comm Co-chm; Mid Sts Accreditation Comm Mem; Supts Quality & Advy Teams; LPUT 1974-, VP; St Bernard RC Church 1982-94, Church Schl & Catechism Tchr; Heart & Soul, Driver; *home:* 1301 Lutts Rd Youngstown NY 14174

DIETZ, ROCHELLE ERB, Kindergarten Teacher; *b:* Lexington, PA; *m:* Ronald L.; *c:* Christopher David; *ed:* Westminster Choir Coll (BMus) Music, Voice 1958; 50 Ed Credits Various Colls, Millersville Univ; *cr:* Conestoga Vly Schl Dist Kndgtn Tchr 1959-62; Red Lion Area Schl Dist Kndgtn Tchr 1963-; *ai:* Red Lion Area Ed Assn, PSEA 1962-; NEA 1970-; Alpha Delta Kappa 1986-, Chaplain, Altruism Chm; York Symphony Chorus 1970-, Librn; St Paul's United Church of Christ 1965-, Dir of Choirs; 25 Yr Svc Awd; 30 Yr Svc Awd Red Lion Area Schl Dist; *home:* 4275 Evergreen Rd Felton PA 17322

DIETZ, SUSAN BALL, 8th Grd Lang Arts & Grad Instr; *b:* Corydon, IN; *m:* Steven; *c:* Amelia, Jeffrey; *ed:* OH Univ (BSEd) Scndry Eng Ed 1979; Coll of Mount Saint Joseph (MA) Ed 1987; *cr:* Athens Chrstn Schl 5-8 Grd Lang Arts Tchr 1979-81; Logan-Hocking Dist Lib Childrens Librn 1981-83; Bowling Green St Univ Grad Schl Instr 1992-; Logan-Hocking Schls Eighth Grd Land Arts Instr 1983-; *ai:* Drama Co, Babysitter Club, Power of the Pen Adv; In-service Presenter; Festival of the Arts Comm; NEA 1983-; OH MS Assn 1992-, Presented at St Conf; Phi Delta Kappa 1994-; Delta Kappa Gamma 1995-; Hocking Valley Industries 1988-, Bd Mem; Presbyn Church 1985-, Elder, Commissioned to General Assembly; Bowen House 1992-, Comm Chairperson; Young Businesswoman of Yr 1986; Jaycees Outstanding Young Educator 1987; Jennings Scholor 1988-89; Ashland Oil Golden Apple Awd 1995; Co-Authored Guide OH Univ 1994; *office:* Logan Hocking MS 1 Middle School Dr Logan OH 43138*

DIETZEL, SHARON LAKE, Dean of Students; *b:* Bridgeport, CT; *m:* Alfred S.; *c:* Jill Alles, Scott Esposito; *ed:* St Joseph Coll (BA) Bio, Math 1964; Columbia Univ (MA) Ed 1989; *cr:* The Vail Deane Schl Math Dept Head 1972-75; Columbus Schl for Girls Asst Head 1977-84; The Brearley Schl Math Fac 1986-88; Greenwich Acad Upper Schl Head 1989-; *ai:* nAIS; Sandra Lee Marshall Tchng Awd; Sharon Lake Dietzel Cup Awded in Honor Each Yr Since 1982.*

DIEUGENIO, DAVID GUY, Biology Teacher; *b:* Downington, PA; *m:* Mary Lou Parker; *c:* David Jr., Stephen, Kevin; *ed:* Ursinus Coll (BS) Bio 1964; West Chester Univ (MED) Bio Ed 1969; Addl 60 Credit Hrs Cmptrs in Sci Tchng; *cr:* Henderson Sr HS Bio Tchr 2 Yrs; Downingtown Jr HS Hlth Ed Tchr 4 Yrs; Southern Regnl HS Bio, AP Bio Tchr 21 Yrs; Ocean Cty Coll Prof Anatomy, Physiology Adj Evenings 15 Yrs; *ai:* Ftbl Coach; Career Day Chm; SREA 1970-, Negotiations; NJEA 1970-, NEA 1964-; Environmental Mental Comm 1986-; Forked River Mts Env Group 1991-, VP; *office:* Southern Regional HS 75 Cedar Bridge Rd Manahawkin NJ 08050

DIEVENDORF, JANE WELCH, School Counselor; *b:* Plattsburgh, NY; *m:* Charles; *c:* Margaret, Anna; *ed:* St Lawrence Univ (BA) Eng 1983; St Univ of NY at Plattsburg (MS) Ed 1987, (CAS) Schl Cnslng 1987; *cr:* Malone Cntrl Schls Elem K-6 Cnslr 1988-89; Franklin Acad Grds 9-12 Schl Cnslr 1989-; *ai:* AIDS Advy Comm; Internship Supvr; NYSUT 1988-; Yth Bureau Advy Bd 1992-; *office:* Franklin Acad State St Malone NY 12953

DIFABBIO, ANTHONY B., English Teacher; *b:* New Rochelle, NY; *m:* Marian Coppola; *c:* Justin, Benjamin; *ed:* Iona Coll (BA) Speech 1970; Adelphi Univ (MA) Drama 1975; 40 Hrs Drama NY Univ; *cr:* Hillcrest Ctr for Children Speech, Lang Therapist1970-76; Adelphi Univ Adj Prof, Drama 1976-81; Somers HSEng, Drama Tchr 1976-; *ai:* Drama Dir; HS Drama Club 1976-; NCTE 1990-; Awd Bringing Performing Arts Stdnts 1991; *office:* Somers HS PO Box 640 Lincolndale NY 10540*

DIFABIO, MICHAEL JOSEPH, Mathematics Teacher; *b:* Syracuse, NY; *m:* Lenora Lorece Crouch; *c:* Christopher Michael, Michael Joseph, Alexa Leigh; *ed:* Onondaga Comm Coll (AA) Math & Sci 1976; Oswego St Univ (BS) Scndry Ed & Math 1980, (MS) Scndry Ed & Math 1985, (CAS) Ed Admin 1995; *cr:* Hannibal Jr & Sr HS 7th-12th Grd Math Tchr 1980-; *ai:* Jr High Ftbl & Track Coach; Tech Prep & Work Force Prep Coord; Half Day Asst Prin; Curr Dev; HFA, NYSUT & AFT 1980-; NYSTEN 1995-, Mentor; *office:* Hannibal Jr Sr HS 928 Cayuga St PO Box 66 Hannibal NY 13074*

DIFAZIO, SUSAN E., Third Grade Teacher; *b:* Callicoon, NY; *m:* Santo; *c:* Jessica, Lindsay; *ed:* State Univ of NY at Oswego (BS) Ed 1968; Adelphi Univ (MS) Ed 1975; 75 Addl Credit Hrs His, Ed 1988; *cr:* Sachem Cntrl Schl Dist 1972-; *ai:* AFT, NEA, SCTA 1972-; *home:* 10 Mineola St Holtsville NY 11742

DI FELICE, CHRISTY ANNE, Biology Teacher; *b:* West Chester, PA; *ed:* Immaculata Coll (BA) Bio, Scndry Ed 1991; Scndry, Guid Cnslng West Chester Univ; Stu Assistance Prgm 1995, Co-Tchng; *cr:* Owen J. Roberts MS 7th Grd Sci Tchr 1992-93; Coatesville Intermediate HS Bio Tchr 1993-; *ai:* Peer Mediation Adv 1994-; JV Lacrosse Coach 1993-; Spain Trip Adv 1995; Coatesville Tchrs Assn 1993-; NEA, PSEA 1992-; Instrl Improvement Grant 1994-95; *office:* Coatesville Intermediate HS 1515 E Lincoln Hwy Coatesville PA 19320*

DI FERDINANDO, FRANK ANTHONY, Mngmt & Mrktg Dept Coord, Inst; *b:* Philadelphia, PA; *m:* Carmela R.; *c:* Dana, Frank; *ed:* Rutgers Univ (BS) Bus Mngmt 1974; Fairleigh Dickinson Univ (MBA) Mngmt, Fin 1977; *cr:* Dana Marie Fashions Pres 12 Yrs; Silver Star Fabrics Asst G Mgr 2 Yrs; Merrill Lynch & Co AVP Corp Credit 10 Yrs; Passaic Cty Comm Coll Asst to VP Fin 2 Yrs, Adj Prof 14 Yrs; Hudson Cty Comm Coll Mngmt, Mrktg Coord 2 Yrs; *ai:* Chair Self Stud, Admin, Planning, Sabbatical Comms; Acad Cncl; NJEA 1992-; AMA 1980-; *office:* Hudson County Comm Coll 25 Journal Sq Jersey City NJ 07306

DI FRANCO, TIMOTHY S., 5th Grade Teacher; *b:* Geneseo, NY; *m:* Kathleen Caverly; *c:* Margaret Merica, Theresa Versage, James C.; *ed:* St Univ of NY at Geneseo (BS) Spec Ed 1966; St Univ of NY at Buffalo (MS) Spec Ed 1969; Various in Service Courses; Advanced Courses in Counciling St Univ of NY at Brockport; *cr:* Rush-Henretta Cntrl Schl 7th & 8th Grd Spec Ed Tchr 1966-67; Geneseo & Wyoming BOCES Spec Ed Tchr for Mentally Retarded 1967-68; Le Roy Cntrl Schls 5th Grd Tchr 1970-; *ai:* Gifted Comm; Photography Club Adv; 5th Grd Chprsn; AFT & NYSUT 1966-; Le Roy Tchrs Assn 1969-; Le Roy Jaycees 1966-68; Assn for Retarded 1966-69; Kennedy Fnd Fellow Spec Ed St Univ of NY at Buffalo 1969-70; *home:* 9285 South St Rd Le Roy NY 14882

DI GAETANO, F. THOMAS, Chemistry Teacher; *b:* Rochester, NY; *ed:* St John Fisher Coll (BS) Bio 1983; Nazareth Coll (MS) Ed 1986; *cr:* Pittsford Sutherland HS Sci Edctr 1983-; *ai:* Chair of Cert of Mastery; Co-Chair of Umbrella Comm for the HS; Steering Comm for Sci Stans; Tchr Mentor 1995-; Soph & Sr Class Adv 1984-94; STANYS 1985-; U of Rochester Excl in Tchng Awd 1987; Tchr of the Yr at Pittsford Sutherland 1987; PTSA Life Mbrshp Awd 1992; *office:* Pittsford Sutherland HS Sutherland St Pittsford NY 14534*

DIGEL, SETH RICHARD, Fourth Grade Teacher; *b:* Bradford, PA; *m:* Carolyn Moening; *c:* Ursula, Antoinette; *ed:* Moravian Coll (BA) Sociology 1965; Saint Bonaventure Univ (MS) Ed 1974; Post Grad Stud at Penn St Univ; *cr:* Smethport Area Schl Dist Bldg Prin 1973-74, Asst Elem Prin 1975-80, Bldg Prin 1980-81; *ai:* Comm Long Range Planning Comm Co-Chair; PA Ed Assn, NEA 1969-; Smethport Area Ed Assn 1969-, Pres 2 Yrs; Smethport Area Jaycees 1975-, Treas, VP; Smethport United Way 1975-, Treas, Dir; Hamlin Meml Lib 1993-, Dir; Saint Lukes Episcopal Church 1943-, Vestery Mem, Treas; *office:* Smethport Area Elem Schl 414 S Mechanic St Smethport PA 16749

DIGERLANDO, SALVATORE MICHAEL, Art Teacher; *b:* Newark, NJ; *m:* Jackie; *c:* Alex, Tara; *ed:* NYU (MA) Creative Art 1964; Montclair Univ Art 1989; 36 Credit Hrs Comp Jersey City St Coll; *cr:* Barringer HS Art Tchr 32 Yrs, Comp Coord 15 Yrs; Salem Craftsmens Guild Potter & Tchr 15 Yrs; *ai:* Yrbk 26 Yrs; Newspaper 8 Yrs; Video, Historical Archives, Photography & Comp Graphics Publications Clubs; NJAEA 1966-; NAEA 1967-; AFT 1968-; Boy Scouts 1959-, Asst Scoutmaster; Perkins Grant Comps 1989; Historical Commission Grant 1991; *office:* Barringer HS 90 Parker St Newark NJ 07104*

DI GERONIMO, LINDA JANE (SERETTO), Dean of Students; *b:* Fitchburg, MA; *m:* John; *c:* Corey; *ed:* Fitchburg St Coll (BS) Ed 1969, (MS) Ed 1973; 45 Hrs Lang Arts, Tech; *cr:* Oakmont Regnl HS Eng & Rdng Tchr 1969-74, Rdng Dept Dir 1975-93, Eng Tchr 1993-95, Dean of Stdnts 1995-; *ai:* Class Adv 14 Yrs; Odyssey of the Mind Prgm, Rdng Dist Coord; NASC Accreditation Co-Chair; NEA, MTA 1969-; Ashburton-Westminster Tchrs Assn 1969-, Pres 8 Yrs; NCTE, MA Rdng Assn 1969-; Tchr of Yr 1990.

DIGERONIMO, RICHARD ANTHONY, Algebra Teacher; *b:* Cleveland, OH; *m:* Leslie Belli; *c:* Alyssa, Anthony; *ed:* John Carroll Univ (BA) His, Scndry Ed 1977, (MED) Cmptr Sci, Prof Tchr 1992; ECCO Cmptr Tech Fairs 1991-93; *cr:* Benedictine HS Tchr 1977-; *ai:* Math Tutor; Asst to Transportation Dir; Bus Office Cmptr Operator; Greater Cleveland Cncl Tchrs of Math 1993-; Ed Cmptr Consortium of OH 1992-; Tchr of Yr 1983; *office:* Cleveland Benedictine HS 2900 Martin Luther King Jr Dr Cleveland OH 44104

DIGESARE, JOHN, Art Teacher; *b:* Schenectady, NY; *m:* Mary Jane Purcino; *c:* Kathleen, Christine; *ed:* Syracuse Univ (BFA) Art 1959, (MS) Art Ed 1963; *cr:* Roxboro MS Art Tchr 1960-77; No Syracuse HS Art Tchr 1977-83; Cicero North Syracuse Hghts HS Art Tchr 1983-; *ai:* Yrbk; Modified Girls Track Outdoor; Var Girls Track Indoor; AFT; No Syracuse Art Guild; *office:* Cicero-N Syracuse HS Northstar Dr Cicero NY 13039

DIGGS, NANCY GOODWIN, Education Professor; *b:* Charleston, SC; *m:* Richard; *c:* Rich, Erick, Leah; *ed:* SC St Univ (BS) Elem Ed-Cum Laude 1977; The Citadel (MED) Rdng 1980; Attnd Univ of SC, Morgan St Univ; *cr:* Conder Elem Schl 3rd Grd Tchr 1984-89; James Simons Elem Schl 4th Grd Tchr 1989-90; Explorer Elem Schl Whole Lang Specialist 1990-91; Morgan St Univ Instr 1991-; *ai:* Space Telescope Sci Inst Consultant; Tchr Ed Advy Bd; Stu Recruitment, Retention; Univ Cncl; IRA 1996; Amer ASCD 1992-; NSTA 1985-; Long Reach Curr Dev 1991-, Consultant; Soc of Future Edctrs Medallion, Friends, City Cncl of Baltimore, Citation from Mayor of Baltimore; *office:* Morgan St Univ Cold Spring La-Hillen Rd Baltimore MD 21239

DIGGS, VANESSA JUANITA, Fourth Grade Teacher; *b:* Baltimore, MD; *ed:* Goucher Coll (BA) Elem Ed, Psych 1985, (MA) Ed At Risk Cert, Admin 1996; *cr:* Deep Creek Elem Tchr 1985; St Paul Apostolic Church Supt 1994-; COGICJ Apostolic Dist Supt 1992-; *ai:* Mentor Tchr of Grad Stu Pursuing MAT; Coord Monthly Dist Tchr Training Wkshps; NEA, MSTA, Tabco 1985-; COGICJ Apostolic Intnl Yth, VP; *office:* Deep Creek Elem Schl 1101 E Homberg Ave Baltimore MD 21221

DIGIACOMO, DONALD SCOTT, Physical Ed & Health Teacher; *b:* Cincinnati, OH; *m:* Mollie Anne Schneider; *ed:* Univ of Cincinnati (BS) PE, Hlth 1986; Xavier Univ (ME) Sports Admin 1996; *cr:* Mid-West Educl Svcs PE K-8th Grd Tchr 1986-88; St Xavier HS PE, Hlth Instr, Ftbl, Bsbl Coach 1988-; *ai:* Asst Dir of Ath Internship; SW OH Ftbl Coaches Assn 1986-; SW OH Bsbl Coaches Assn 1989-; Natl Assn for Sports & PE 1986-; Natl Amer soc for Sports Mgmt 1995-; The Paul Lammermeier Fnd 1996, Comm; Guest Speaker 1992 St of OH Ftbl N S Coaches Clinic; *office:* St Xavier Schl 600 W Northbend Rd Cincinnati OH 45224

DIGIANDO, JULIO JOSEPH, Resource Teacher; *b:* Newton, MA; *c:* Nicholas, Dana; *ed:* Bates Coll (BA) His 1970; RI Coll (MED) Spec Ed 1975; Attnd Providence Coll, Boston Univ; *cr:* Pilgram HS Sp Ed Tchr 1971-79; RI Coll Adj Staff 1976-83; RI Dept of Ed Consultant 1980-89; Toll Gate HS Sp Ed Tchr 1979-; *ai:* Yrbk, Newspaper, Lit Magazine Adv; Jamestown Soccer Assn; Jamestown RI Schl Comm 1993-, Clerk; *home:* 63 Clarke St Jamestown RI 02835

DIGIESI, JOHN V., Eighth Grade Teacher; *b:* Philadelphia, PA; *ed:* La Salle Univ (BA) Eng, Ed 1982; Holy Family Coll (MA) Elem, Ed 1997; *cr:* North Cath HS 9th-10th Grd Tchr 1982-83; Father Judge HS 9th-10th Grd Tchr 1983-84; Ascension of Our Lord Schl 6-8th Grd Tchr 1984-91; St Hilary of Poitiers Schl 7th-8th Grd Tchr 1991-; *ai:* Stu Cncl, Writing, Art Moderator; Mid Sts Chprsn; NCEA 1982-; NSTA 1985-; Distngd Cath Educator Philadelphia Awd 1991; Fox Television Tchr of M *office:* Saint Hilary Of Poitiers Schl 920 Susquehanna Rd Ryda

DIGIORE, KATHLEEN A., Fifth Grade Teacher; *b:* Buffal Rosary Hill Coll (BS) Elem Ed 1973; St Univ Coll at Buffalo Ed 1975; Addl 18 Credit Hrs; *cr:* Heim Elem Schl 4-5 Grd Tch Heim MS 5th Grd Tchr 1989-; *ai:* Performance Assessment Co Williamsville Tchrs Assn 1973-; *office:* Heim MS 175 Lawren Williamsville NY 14231

DI GIOVANNA, AUGUSTINE GASPAR, Professor of B Brooklyn, NY; *m:* Linda Lee Arnold; *c:* Gaspar Russell, Christin St John's Univ (BS) Bio 1965; Univ of MD at College Park (MS 1970, (PHD) Bio 1972; *cr:* Univ of MD College Park Instr 1972 St Univ Bio Prof 1972-; *ai:* Fac Dev Comm; Univ Judicia Accreditation Working Comm; Phi Kappa Phi 1970-, Chptr P 1988-; Geront Soc of Amer 1990-; MD Consort Geront Higher Treas; Assn Geront Higher Ed 1992-; St Francis de Sales Chu Fnd Grants; Distngd Fac Awd 1995; Book: Human Aging: Perspectives 1994; *office:* Salisbury State Univ 1101 Ca Salisbury MD 21801

DIGIULIO, DANIEL ARTHUR, Director & Tchr of Voc Meriden, CT; *m:* Theresa Magnano; *c:* Kristin; *ed:* Univ of CT Production 1963, (MA) Ed 1969; Ag Ed Cert 1966; *cr:* Univ of Asst, Farm Mgr 1963-65; Glastonbury HS Ag Ed Tchr Middletown HS Dir, Tchr Ag Ed 1973-; *ai:* FFA Adv; NEA, C 1966-; Natl, CT Voc Ag Tchr 1996, Pres, VP, Treas, Outst Middlesex Cty Farm Bureau 1975-, Pres, VP, Bd Dir; US Arm Natl Guard 1963-, Ofcr, Col, Meritorious Svc; Degrees Honor Honorary St FFA; Tchr of Tchr Awd; Adv of Yr FFA; Conservation Tchr; Outstdng Voc Educator; 30 Minute Awd; NVATA Tchr Awd, St Winner; *office:* Middletown HS Middlet Voc Ag Ctr Hunting Hill Ave Middletown CT 06457

DIGIULIO, JOAN FERRY, Chair & Prof of Social Work; *b:* Jo Katrina Carleton; *ed:* Coll of St Francis (BA) Sociology 195 Chicago (MA) Soc Work 1962; Case Western Reserve Univ (Work 1986; *cr:* Tipecano Co Mental Hlth Ctr Psychiatric S 1967-69; Family Svc Agency Clinical Soc Worker 1969-; Privat Marriage, Family Therapist 1973-94; Youngstown St Univ Soc Chair 1976-; *ai:* Acad Events, Hlth Enhancement, Lib, Admissi Goals Comms; NASW 1962-, Treas, Outstdng Svc; AAMFT 19 OEA 1976-, Treas, Sec; Burdman Group 1986-, Pres; Chil Flwshp; Articles Pub; *office:* Youngstown St Univ Dept of So Youngstown OH 44555*

DIGREGORIO, ROBERT EUGENE, Fifth & Sixth Grade T Taylor, PA; *m:* Constance Campbell; *c:* Andrea, Donna; Stroudsburg Univ (BS) Ed 1972; *cr:* Stillwater Twp Schl Spec 1972-79; Fredon Twp Clem Schl Spec Ed, 5th-6th Grd Tchr 1 NEA, NJEA 1972-; Northwest Jersey Rdng Cncl 1992-; Italia Benefit Assn 1981-, Bd of Dirs; Governor's Awd for Excl in Ed 19 RR 6 Box 6778 East Stroudsburg PA 18301

DI GREGORY, NICHOLAS A., Social Studies Teacher; *b:* Phi PA; *m:* Kathleen Mc Namara; *c:* Megan, Sarah, Evan; *ed:* East St Univ (BS) Scndry Ed 1976; West Chester Univ (MA) His 1991; S Rowan Coll 1993; *cr:* Interboro HS His Tchr 1979-80; Ridley N His Tchr 1980-81; Paxon Hollow Jr HS His Tchr 1981-82; Del HS His Tchr 1982-; *ai:* Advl Class 1994, His Club; Coach G Tennis; Edu Comm Chrm; NEA, NJEd Assn, NCSS 1987-; USTA; Alpha Theta 1990-; US Achvmt Acad All Amer Scholar 1990; W in Amer Ed 1994-; *office:* Delsea Regional HS Blackwood Franklinville NJ 08322

DILELLO, ANTOINETTE MARIE, Vice Principal & 5th Grd Yonkers, NY; *ed:* Manhattan Coll (BA) Fr, Italian, Religion 19 Rdng 1983; *cr:* St Paul the Apostle Schl Fifth Grd Tchr 1981-, 1988-; *ai:* IRA 1989-; Enrico Fermi Educl Fund 1976-, Co-Chpr Breakfast, Chprsn Schlsp Recipient Comm, Advy Bd, Bd of *office:* Saint Paul The Apostle Schl 77 Lee Ave Yonkers NY 107

DILG, JUDITH SOLBERG, Fifth Grade Teacher; *b:* Port Jeffe *m:* Joseph H.; *c:* Elisa; *ed:* Adelphi Suffolk Univ (BS) Elem Ed Connetquot Cntrl Schl Dist Elem Tchr 1964-66, 1968-; *ai:* Overnight Class Trip; AFT; NYSTA; PTA; Jenkins Meml Awd 19 Dedication 1994; *office:* Sycamore Avenue Elem Schl 745 Syca Bohemia NY 11716

DILL, ALISHA HILL, First Grade Teacher; *b:* Fremont, OH; Lee; *c:* Michael; *ed:* OH Northern Univ (BA) Elem Ed K-8, R 1986; *cr:* Upper Scioto Vly Schls Tchr of 6th Grd, Jr HS Dev Han 1986-88; St Joseph's Cath Schls 2nd Grd Tchr 1988-89; Madis Local Schls Kndgtn, 1st Grd Tchr 1989-; *ai:* Jr HS & Reserve Va Coach; MPEA, OEA 1989-, Bldg Rep; *office:* Mt Sterling Elem S Main St Mount Sterling OH 43143

DILLAH, KENRICK L., HS Mathematics Teacher; *b:* Trinidad West Indies; *m:* Angela Mohansingh; *c:* Karen, Jillian, Dane; *ed.* West Indies (BA) Math 1975, (DPEd) Math 1976; City Col (MAEd) Math 1988; Tchng Scndry Schl Math; *cr:* Rosary Boys Boys Math Tchr 1963-69; Tchrs Coll Trinidad Math Tchr Baratoria Sr compr Math Tchr 1977-83; Manhattan Ctr for Sci Math Tchr 1984-; *ai:* Peer Tutoring; MAA, ASCD, NCTM ATMNYC 1984-.*

DILLAHUNT, HERBERT A., Music Teacher; *b:* Springfield, Duquesne Univ (BSME) Music Ed 1978; *cr:* Presentation Schl Mu 1978-85; Good Shepherd Schl Music Tchr, Handbells 1991-; Music Dir; Adult Choir, Funerals, Weddings Organist; Liturgy Cor Liturgies, Musicals; 3-8 Grd Classroom Music; NPM 1979-, Cha NPM-ME 1990-; NPM-DMMD 1985-; AGO 1974-; *office:* Good S Catholic Schl 1025 S Braddock Ave Braddock PA 15104

DILLANE, DEBORAH A., Piano Music Teacher; *b:* Reading, Robert J.; *c:* Erin E., Kristen M.; *ed:* Lebanon Vly Coll (BS) M 1977; Post Grad Stud Westminster Choir Coll, West Chester Univ Piano Instr 1977-; Milton Hershey Schl Piano Instr 1989-; *ai:* H Choirs Accompanist; Advise Carillon Performers; NEA, PSEA, 1994-; AGO 1977-; Church Comms 1977-; *office:* Milton Hershey Box 830 Senior Hall Hershey PA 17033

DILLEN, WILLIAM C.,JR., Biology Teacher; *b:* Natrona Hts, Sandra K. Swartzlander; *c:* Erik A., Brooke R., Cari Jo; *ed:* Allegh Hosp (AS) Radiology 1970; Butler Comm Coll (AS) Radiolog Slippery Rock Univ (BS) Bio 1975; Penn St Grad Work Sports M Univ Pitts Post Grad Cell Bio; *cr:* Allegeghney Vly Hosp Ra Technologist 8 Yrs; Freeport Area Schls Bio Tchr, Coach 20 Yrs; Track Coach; Stu Instrl Support Team; NEA, PSEA 1976-; NSTA NABT 1988-; Western PA Bio Tchrs 1985-; Howard Hughes Wksh Cell Bio; Who's Who Among Amer Edctrs 1994; Marquis Wh Among HS Tchr 1995; *office:* Freeport Sr HS PO Drawer H Fre 16229

DILLEY, TERRA E., 8th Grade Teacher; *b:* North Canton, OH; *c:* Justin, Erin; *ed:* Walsh Univ (BA) Math 1974; *cr:* Madison Jr Grd Math Tchr 1974-81; St Vincent de Paul Schl 8th Grd Tchr 1 Civics Club Adv; Sci Fair Coord; Asst Track Coach; Schl Newspa

994-; *office:* St Vincent de Paul Schl 206 E Chestnut St Mount
H 43050

AN, PEGGY LOU LIMLEY, Fourth Grade Teacher; *b:* Mc
, PA; *m:* Richard Guy; *c:* Pamela Sue; *ed:* IN St Coll (BS) Music
Clarion Univ (MED) Sci Ed 1986; Elem Ed Cert 1980; 10 Addl
Mars Area Joint Schl Sys Elem Vocal Music Tchr 1961-64; South
n Joint Schl Sys Elem Vocal Music Tchr 1964-65; Pittsburgh Pub
n Vocal Music Tchr 1965-66; Brookville Area Schl Sys 3rd, 4th,
Tchr 1980-; *ai:* Arts, Hum Comms; BAEA 1980-, Sick Bank
PSEA, NEA 1980-; Alpha Delta Kappa 1985-, Pres 1992-94;
k Environmental Ctr 1990-; Choir Dir Presbyn Church; *home:* 161
Ave Brookville PA 15825

, ALEXIS, Visual Arts Instructor; *b:* Mt Pleasant, PA; *ed:* 20
Seton Hall Coll; 24 Addl Hrs Penn St; *cr:* Hempfield Area Schl
al Arts Edctr 1973-; *ai:* Photo Club; HAEA, PSEA, NAEA 1973-;
h Assoc Artists 1990-; HSUS 1988-; ASPCA 1989-; PETA 1990-;
or 1995, Photographer or Yr 1992 Westmoreland Arts & Heritage
bit; Westmoreland Cty Comm Coll Photography Exhibit Best of
91; New Growth Arts Festival Best of Show 1993; Westmoreland
s First Merit Awd 1990, Jurers Awd 1989; One-Person Show
h Ctr for Arts 1994, Greensburg 1987; *office:* Hempfield Area Sr
Box 77 Greensburg PA 15601*

N, BRENDAN EDWARD, High School History Teacher; *b:*
mond, Ireland; *m:* Mary Ann DeJaeger; *c:* Alanna; *ed:* Natl Univ
d (BA) His, Gaelic 1967; Univ of MA (MA) His 1988; H Dip in
; *cr:* Grand Bahama Cath Schl Soc Stud Tchr 1968-75; Shellsburg
Stud Tchr 1975-78; Regis HS Soc Stud Tchr 1978-84; Xaverian
His Tchr 1984-91; Westwood HS His Tchr 1992-; *ai:* 9th Grd
r; Chess Team Moderator; MTA, NEA 1992-; NEH Grant 1995;
Mentor 1993-; *office:* Westwood HS 200 Nathan St Westwood MA

N, CAROLYN HENDERSON, English Teacher; *b:* Johnstown,
Willard; *ed:* IN St Coll (BS) Eng 1963; IN Univ of PA (MS) Eng
: Mt Lebanon Jr HS Eng Tchr 1963-67; Hempfield HS Eng Tchr
: Greater Latrobe HS Eng Tchr 1969-; *ai:* NEA, PSEA 1963-;
968-; *home:* 734 Highland Ave Latrobe PA 15650

N, KIMBERLY M., Title I & Reading Specialist; *b:* Washington,
Richard L.; *ed:* California Univ of PA (BS) Scndry Ed, Eng 1990,
Rdng Specialist Prgm 1992; *cr:* Baldwin HS Eng Tchr 1993-94,
g Tchr 1994-95, Title I, Rdng Specialist Tchr 1995-; *ai:* Eng Curr
Outcomes Based Ed Comm; NEA, PSEA, BWEA 1993-; *office:*
HS 4900 Curry Rd Pittsburgh PA 15236

N, LOIS A., 8th Grd Language Arts Teacher; *b:* Meriden, CT; *m:*
c: John, Mary Beth Stearns, Bevin, Lauren; *ed:* Albertus Magnus
g 1963; 33 Hrs Ed Cert; *cr:* Dr. Elizabeth C. Adams MS 8th Grd
s Tchr 1980-; *ai:* Fac Cncl; NEA 1981-; GEA 1981-, Rep; Church
stors 1995-, Pres; *office:* Dr. Elizabeth C. Adams MS Church St
CT 06437

N, MARY LOU L., US History & Pub Policy Tchr; *b:* Suffern, NY;
rt I.; *ed:* Ashland Coll (BS) His 1970; NY Univ (MA) His 1979;
New Schl for Soc Rsrch, Boston Univ, Oxford Univ; *cr:* North
d HS Tchr 1971-; Orange Comm Coll Adj 1985; Syracuse Univ Adj
i: Soc Stud Hnr Soc, His Day Competition Adv; AFT 1971-; NYS
ant Recipient 1991; Nat Endow Hum Grant Recipient 1984, 1988;
United for Sep of Church, St Grant Recipient 1987; Schl Dist Grant
nt 1988, 1993; *office:* North Rockland HS 106 Hammond Rd
NY 10984*

N, P. MATTHEW, Soccer Coach & Kndgtn Teacher; *b:* Nyack, NY;
coa Falls Coll (BS) Missiology 1984; Columbia Univ (MA) Curr &
Elem Ed 1986; USSF Natl B License; *cr:* Nyack Pub Schls Boys JV
Coach 1988-90, Elem Tchr 1986-, Head Girls Soccer Coach 1991-;
SF 1990-; NSCAA 1991-; *office:* Nyack Pub Schl System Christian
Rd Nyack NY 10960

N, RICHARD LAWRENCE, Biology & Adv Biology Tchr; *b:*
sville, PA; *m:* Sheila; *c:* David, Donald, Richard Jr.; *ed:* CA Univ
BS) Bio, Chem 1960; West VA Univ (MA) Bio 1965; 40 Addl Hrs;
fornia Sr HS Bio Tchr 1960-; *ai:* Campus Life Spon; Yth for Christ;
t Chair; NEA, PSEA 1960-; Campus Life 1993-, Bd Dir; Yth Cncl
Adv; Tchng Flwshp 1960; Naturalist OH Pyle St Pk 1960-68; Pub;
California Area HS 239 Malden Dr Malden Rd Coal Center PA

N, SANDRA BOWDEN, Instrumental Music Director; *b:*
ille, ME; *ed:* Boston Univ (BM) Clarinet, Music Ed 1962; Temple
MMEd) Music Ed 1974; *cr:* Monadnock Reg Schl Dist Elem Instr,
Music Dir 1962-63; Lisbon HS Vocal, Inst Music Dir 1963-66; Phila
st Woodwind Specialist, Band Orch Cond 1966-73; ME Schl Dist
Band Dir 1973-82; Phila Schl Dist Woodwind Specialist, Band,
ond 1982-86; Girard Acad Music Prgm Inst Music Dir 1986-; *ai:* HS
t, Marching, Jazz, Dixieland, MS Spirit Bands; Jr Wind Ensemble;
Jazz Bowl; MENC 1962-, Phila Fed of Tchrs 1992-; PA Music Ed
1982-, Regional Band Host; Music Festival Conductor Band,
tra; *office:* Girard Acad Music Program 22nd & Ritner St
lphia PA 19145*

N, SUSAN, English Teacher; *b:* Monongahela, PA; *ed:* California
f PA (BS) Comm 1975, (MA) Eng 1983; *cr:* CA Area MS Lang Art
976-90; CA Arean Sr HS Eng Tchr 1990-; *ai:* Stu Cncl, Yth & Govt,
f 1996, Class of 1998 Spons; PSEA 1976-, WA Cty Pres 1994-96;
1976-, Pres 1986-90; NEA 1976-, PA St Rep for NEA RA 1990-;
ly Educl Consortium 1990-. Bd of Dir, Schl Action Team Chprsn;
n PA Caring Prgm for BC, BS Spokesperson 1990-; Democratic
of PA; Amer Cancer Soc Schl Spon 1985-; United Cebral Palsy Schl
995-; Mon Vly Consortium Grant; Amer Legion Recognition Awd
office: California Area HS 293 Malden Dr Coal Center PA 15423*

N, SUSAN BRESLOW, 6th Grade Teacher; *b:* Brooklyn, NY; *m:*
P.; *c:* Eleanor Petigrow, Alice; *ed:* Cornell Univ (BS) Early Chldhd
7; Long Island Univ C. W. Post Campus (MS) GATE Ed 1984; 60
rad Credit Hrs; *cr:* NYC Pub Schl 209 Grd 3-6 Tchr 1957-67;
k Pub Schls Elem Sub Tchr 1975-79; Merrick Pub Schls GATE Tchr
0; Bellmore Merrick HS Night Prgm Tchr for Hancapped, Home
1978-80; Copiague Pub Schls GATE Tchr 1980-81; Vly Stream Schl
GATE Tchr 1981-91, 6th Grd Tchr 1991-; *ai:* Grd Chprsn; Spelling
ord; VSTA, AFT 1981-; PTA 1973-, Pres Elem, Jr HS, Cncl, Life
; NY St PTA Tchrs Flwshp; Odyssey of Mind First, Second, Third
Teams Coach; *office:* Wheeler Ave Schl 1 W Wheeler Ave Valley
NY 11580

, LINDA BAYES, Sixth Grade Math Teacher; *b:* Dayton, OH; *m:*
Lee; *c:* Leslie, Amy; *ed:* Wilmington Coll (BS) Hlth & PE 1973;
d Univ (MED) Curr & Instruction 1996; Elem Ed OH Univ 1982;
stfall HS Hlth & PE Tchr, Coach 1973-79; Westfall MS Sixth Grd
982-; *ai:* Math Tchr Ldr; Sigma & Math League Spon; Discussion
Rep; PBS Mathline Tchr WOSU: Cty, City Inservice Comm Rep;
ll Ed Assn 1982-, Assn for Supervision & Curr Dev 1995; OH Ed
NEA 1982-; Nation Cncl Tchrs of Math 1995-; OH Cncl Tchrs of
1995; Delta Kappa Gamma 1988-, Recording Sec; Emmanuel United
Church 1981-, Sunday Schl Tchr, Fin Sec; WOSU-TV Master Tchr
Tech in Classroom; *office:* Westfall MS 19545 Pherson Pike Williamsport
OH 43164*

DILULLO, ANITA M., Instrumental Music Teacher; *b:* Camden, NJ; *ed:* Boston Conservatory (BM) Music Ed 1989; Temple Univ (MMed) Music Ed in Progress; *cr:* Private Studio Flute & Piano Instr 1989-; Brigantine Pub Schls Music Edctr 1989-; *ai:* Chamber Music Ensembles, Concert, Pep & Jazz Band Dir; NEA, NJEA & BEA 1989-; NJMEA & MENC 1989-; ASJBODA 1989-; Sigma Alpha Iota 1987-, VP, Sword of Hnr; Brigantine PTA 1989-, Corresponding Sec; NJ Governors Tchrs Recognition Awd 1993; Conductor of the 1995 All South Jersey Jr High Band; Citizen Ambassador to Vietnam as part of a Music Ed Del; *office:* Brigantine North Schl 301 E Evans Blvd Brigantine NJ 08203

DILULLO, DAVID S., Fine Art Dept Chr & Drama Dir; *b:* Providence, RI; *ed:* Univ of RI (BFA) Theatre 1992; Amer Musical, Dramatics Acad Acting, Musical Theatre; *cr:* Univ of RI Theatre Dept Instr 1992-, Theatre Dept Tchr of Record 1993-94; *ai:* Soph Class Moderator; Fac, Admin Advy Bd Comm; Amer Fed Television & Radio Artists; RI Theatre Ed Assn; Theatre Coord RI Scholar Ath Games Theatre Arts Division; Attnd H B Studio New York City Acting; *office:* The Prout Schl 4640 Tower Hill Rd Wakefield RI 02879*

DIM, ISAAC, History Teacher; *b:* Okigwe, Nigeria; *m:* Dorothy; *c:* Chu; *ed:* Buffalo St Coll (BA) Jrnlsm, (MS) Jrnlsm 1980; Univ of Buffalo (PHD) Comparative Ed 1985; *cr:* SUNY Old Westbury Frgn Stdnts Adv 1986-88; Long Island Univ Sociology Instr 1988-; August Martin HS 9-12 Grd His Tchr 1989-; *ai:* UFT, AFT 1989-; Review on Nigeria Universal Primary Ed 1984; *home:* 76 S Bergen Pl Freeport NY 11520

DI MAIO, JOSEPH ROBERT, Health Educator; *b:* Jamestown, NY; *m:* Cheryl Mary Carr; *c:* Joseph R. Jr., Sara Ellen; *ed:* Jamestown Comm Coll (AAS) Sci 1970; Brockport St Coll (BS) Hlth Sci 1972; Penn St Grad Courses; St Bonaventure Grad Work; *cr:* Lincoln Jr HS Hlth Educator 1972-83; Jefferson MS Hlth Educator 1980-83; Jamestown HS Hlth Educator 1980-; *ai:* Asst Ftbl Coach; Dist Equity Review Comm; Weightlifting Club Co-Adv; Home, Schl, Comm Advy Comm; NY Educl Assn 1976-; NEA 1972-; Western NY Coaches Assn 1985-; St James Cath Church 1973-; Western NY 9th Grd Coach of Yr 1979; *home:* 5 Juliet St Jamestown NY 14701

DIMAIO, PATRICIA ANN, English & Theater Arts Teacher; *b:* Chicago, IL; *ed:* Univ of Md Baltimore Cty (BA) Eng 1975; Various Places MA Equivalency Scndry Ed 1984; Variety of Courses Scndry Ed, Theatre Arts; *cr:* Lansdowne HS Eng Tchr 1975-, Theatre Arts Tchr 1987-; *ai:* Producer of Schl Musical; Pom Pon Squad Adv; Baltimore Symphony Orch partnership, Assembly Comms; NEA 1975-; MCTELA 1988-; ST Agnes Hosp Hospice Vol 1994-; Lector at Church of the Crucifixion 1995-; Nom by Fellow Fac Mems TABCO Tchr of Yr; *office:* Lansdowne HS 3800 Hollins Ferry Rd Baltimore MD 21227*

DIMAIO, VICKY P., French & Spanish Teacher; *b:* Campodipietra, C. Basso Italy; *m:* John; *c:* Jennifer, Michael; *ed:* Cntrl CT St Univ (BS) Fr, Italian 1969, (MA) Fr 1973; Manhattanville Coll Span Cert 1987; Attnd NDEA Inst at Fairleigh Dickinson Univ 1968, Tunxis Comm Coll 1982-84; Sorbonne Paris Summer 1969; *cr:* Windsor Locks HS Fr Tchr 1969-72; J. F. Kennedy MS Fr, Span Tchr 1973-; *ai:* Prof Dev, Curr Comms; SEA 1973-; CEA, NEA, COLT 1969-; PTO 1980-; YMCA 1982-; *office:* John F. Kennedy MS 1071 S Main St Plantsville CT 06479

DIMANNO, DORRIA L., Communications Professor; *b:* Manchester, CT; *c:* Dorria Marsh, Danielle; *ed:* Housatonic Comm Coll (AA) Gen Stud 1976; Sacred Heart Univ (BA) Media Stud 1978; Boston Univ (MS) Mass Comm & PR 1991; *cr:* WTNH TV Dir of Promotion & Pub Affairs Producer 1978-81; CT Pub Television Dir of Programming & Promotion 1981-83; Praxis Media Inc Pres Creative Svcs & Sr Producer 1983-; Colby Sawyer Coll Asst Prof 1993-95; Curry Coll Adj Fac, Commnctns Producer & Consultant 1995-; *ai:* Univ Film & Video Assn 1995-; Intnl Film & Video Assn 1996; Numerous Awds for Broadcast & Non-Broadcast Video Pgms; CINE Golden Eagle Winning Film Assoc Producer; Nom Tchr of Yr Colby Sawyer Coll 1994-95; Whos Who Global Bus Ldrs; Whos Who in CG; Whos Who Amer Jr Colls; *office:* Curry Coll 1071 Blue Hill Milton MA 02186

DI MARTINO, ROBERT,JR., Reading & Learning Specialist; *b:* Queens, NY; *m:* Lynn V. Romaine; *c:* Kristin, Lauren-Kate, Dayna-Renee; *ed:* Dowling Coll (BA) Soc Scis 1973, (MS) Elem Ed 1974; Long Island Univ at Southampton (MS) Rdng 1979; *cr:* Comsewogue HS 9th-10th Grd Soc Stud Tchr 1973-74; Mount Sinai Elem 6th Grd Tchr 1974-77; Sachem Jr HS 9th Grd Soc Stud Tchr 1977-79; Longwood Cntrl Schls Rdng, 7th-9th Grd Learning Specialist 1979-; *ai:* Schl Act, Stu Govt Adv; JV & Var Ftbl, Wrestling, Girls Sftbl Coach; NY St United Tchrs 1973-; Mid Island Tchrs Assn 1979-; AFT 1973-; PTA 1979-; Natl Schl of Excl Fac Mem; Longwood Jr HS Tchr of Yr 1988; *office:* Longwood MS Middle Island-Yaphank Rd Middle Island NY 11953

DI MASI, FRANK S., Social Studies Teacher; *b:* Providence, RI; *m:* Joanne H.; *c:* Domenic, Andrea, Nina; *ed:* Windham Coll (BA) Amer Govt 1969; Providence Coll (MA) Amer His 1976; Southern New England Schl of Law (JD) Law 1993; *cr:* Winman Jr HS Soc Stud Tchr 1972-79; Ponaganset MS & HS Lang Arts & Soc Stud Tchr 1985-; *ai:* MS & HS Mock Trial Adv; AFT 1972-79; NEA 1985-; *office:* Ponaganset MS 91 Anan Wade Rd North Scituate RI 02857*

DIMATTEO, CANDIDA, Italian Teacher; *b:* Latina di Baia, Italy; *m:* Anthony; *c:* Ralph, Maria Lorenzna Calley, Joe; *ed:* Salvatore Pizzi Capua (BA) Elem Schl Diploma 1962; Youngstown St Univ (BA) Italian 1984, (BA) Latin 1985; *cr:* Latina di Baia Elem Sch Italian Tchr 1963-64; Lowellville HS Italian Tchr 1985-; Sons of Italy Italian Tchr 1989-94; Warren Italian Cmt Club Ital Tchr 1994-; *ai:* Italian Club Adv; Frgn Lang Chairwoman; NEA, OEA 1985-; Youngstown Opera Guild 1995-; *home:* 72 Terrace Dr Boardman OH 44512

DIMATTIA, PHILIP ANTHONY, Assoc Prof & Dir of Education; *b:* Boston, MA; *m:* Geraldine Sophia Pilch; *c:* Deborah, David, Paula, Gerilyn; *ed:* Boston Coll (BS) Ed 1954, (MED) Ed 1956, (PHD) Ed Admin 1974; Harvard Schl Pub Hlth Comm Mental Hlth 1969-71; *cr:* Medford Pub Schls Tchr 1954-56; Gaebler Schl Tchr 1956-62, Prin 1962-88; Boston Coll Assoc Prof 1962-88; Boston Coll Campus Schl Assoc Prof & Dir 1988-; *ai:* Phi Delta Kappa VP; Harvard Med Schl Fac Fellow 1978-88; CEC 1970-; MA Assn Sp Ed Admin 1987-; ASCD 1988-; AASA 1988-; Book: Effective Management Special Education Programs; Numerous Articles Pub; *office:* Boston Coll Chestnut Hill Newton MA 02167*

DIMAURO, PATRICIA ANN OBRIEN, Pre-School Teacher; *b:* Middletown, CT; *c:* Reina Dyan, Erin Fay; *cr:* Bonanaza & Lord Cromwell Waitress 3 Yrs; Queens Convalescent Home Nurses Aide 2 Yrs; Crystal Lake Life Guard 2 Yrs; Farm Hill Schl Playground Instr; The Little Peoples House Tchr 28 Yrs; *ai:* Gymanstics Tchr, Coach, Cert Judge; First Aide 1980-, First Aide Cert; *office:* The Little Peoples House 616 Long Hill Rd Middletown CT 06457*

DI MEGLIO, DANIEL, Dean of Discipline; *b:* New York City, NY; *m:* Blanca Pedraja; *c:* Amy, John; *ed:* St John's Univ (BA) Ed 1971, (MS) Ed 1976; Admin, Sci Credits; *cr:* IS 52 Tchr 1972-79, Sr Dean of Discipline 1980-; *ai:* AFT, NEA 1972-; Controling Gang Activity Expert; Instrumental in Solving Major Crimes; *office:* IS 52 Manhattan Dist #6 650 Academy St New York NY 10034

DIMENTO, PETER R., Principal; *b:* Boston, MA; *m:* Noreen; *c:* Patrick, Michael, John, Daniel; *ed:* Salem St (BS) Elem Ed 1958; Hofstra Univ (MA) Ed 1961; C. W. Post; *cr:* Brentwood Schls 4th Grd Tchr 1958-61, Math Specialist 1961-64, Prin 1964-; *ai:* Dist Math & Cmptr Comms Chm; NEA 1958-; SANNYS; Brentwood Lions Club 1961-, Pres; Brentwood Prins Org 1964-91, Pres; Suffolk Cty Outstanding Prin 1991; *office:* Southwest Elementary 1095 Joselson Ave Bay Shore NY 11706

DI MEZZA, LINDA SUSAN, 8th Grd Language Arts Teacher; *b:* Paterson, NJ; *m:* Martin P.; *c:* Robert, Martin, Michael, Steven, Nadine Accurso, Dean; *ed:* William Paterson Coll (BA) General Elem 1970, (MA) Lang Arts 1977, (MA) Admin 1993; Supervisory Cert 1992; Eng Tchr Cert 1977; *cr:* Wanague Schl Curr Coord 1989-92, 8th Grd Tchr 1970-, Tchr-In-Charge 1992-; *ai:* 8th Grd, HS Coord; 7th-8th Grd Scheduling Comm; Grad Coord; Cnsltnt NJ Dept of Ed, EWT Wrng Test Dev 1994-; Tchr Eval Comm 1994-95; Dist Budget Comm 1994-95; Princ Advsy Comm 1995-; Coord 8th Grd Activities; NEA, NJEA, PCEA 1970-; WBEA 1970-, VP; ASCD, NCTE 1992-; Pi Lambda Theta; *office:* Wanaque Elem Schl 1st St Wanaque NJ 07465*

DIMICK, MARK S., English Teacher; *b:* Bryn Mawr, PA; *ed:* Lebanon Vly Coll (BA) Eng, Scndry Ed, (BMus) Sacred Music, Organ 1993; 4 Grad Hrs in Church Music Westminster Choir Coll; 24 Hrs towards MA in Eng Millersville Univ; *cr:* Annville-Cleona HS Frosh Eng Tchr 1993-95, Jr Amer Lit, Bus Comm Tchr 1995-; *ai:* Jr Class, Key Club, Horizons Lit Magazine Adv; Tech Prep, Acad Booster, Renaissance Comm; NCTE 1995-; NEA, PSEA, MENC, PMEA 1992-; AC Kiwanis 1993-; LVC Alumni Chorale 1993-, Sub Bus Mgr; Leb-Lanc Lit Cncl 1994-95, Tutor; PA Huguenot Soc 1993-; UM Church of the Good Shepherd 1989-, Organist; *office:* Annville Cleona Jr Sr HS 500 S White Oak St Annville PA 17003*

DIMICK, MELODY DEAN, English Teacher; *b:* Plattsburgh, NY; *m:* Barry Andrew; *c:* Barry Albert; *ed:* Castleton St Coll (BA) Ed 1970; St Univ of NY at Plattsburgh 60 Addl Hrs Liberal Stud; *cr:* Northern Adirondack Cntrl Eng Tchr 1970-; St Univ of NY at Plattsburgh Lecturer & Adjunct Tchr 1979-; *ai:* Sftbl Coach; Class Adv; Variety Show Dir; Dept Chair; Scholars for Dollars & Drama Club Adv; Mentor Prgm; UUp 1979-; NYSUT 1970-; AFT; Delta Kappa Gamma Intnl Honor Soc for Women Tchrs, Held Every Office of Local Chapter & Present Pres; *home:* 7 Independence Dr Plattsburgh NY 12901*

DIMIERO, PHYLLIS ANN, Fourth Grade Teacher; *b:* Oswego, NY; *ed:* SUC at Oswego (BS) Elem Ed 1970; SUC at Buffalo (MS) Ed 1987; *cr:* Lyndonville Cntrl Schl 3rd Grd Tchr 1971-72, 4th Grd Tchr 1970-71 & 1972-; *ai:* Delta Kappa Gamma 1987-; AFT & NYSUT 1970-; PTA 1989-; Outstanding Educator Awd PTA; *office:* Lyndonville Central Schl Housel Ave Lyndonville NY 14098

DIMMICK, MARY ELLEN (LOCOCO), French & English Teacher; *b:* Bellaire, OH; *m:* Charles Allen; *c:* Christopher, Michelle; *ed:* West Liberty St (BA) Eng, Fr 1962; Univ of Dayton (MS) Ed, Cnslng 1986; Cnslng Cert; OH Univ Ed, Supervision Mentor Prgm Post Grad Stud; *cr:* Moundsville HS Eng Tchr 1962-63; Shadyside HS Eng Tchr 1965-68; Bishop Donahue HS Eng, Fr Tchr 1982-85; Union Local HS Eng, Fr Tchr 1985-; *ai:* Fr Club, Frosh Class Adv; NEA, OEA 1962-; Delta Kappa Gamma 1985-; Cert Achvmt; *office:* Union Local HS 66859 Belmont-Morristown Rd Belmont OH 43718*

DIMOCK, CRANDALL W., Physics Teacher; *b:* Perth Amboy, NJ; *m:* Barbara; *c:* Christopher, Heather; *ed:* (BS) Bio & Chem 1971, (MS) Microbiology & Chem 1975; Tchng Cert Physics, Chem & Bio 1981; *cr:* Smithfield HS Tchr 1981-82; Groton HS Tchr 1983-84; South Kingstown HS Tchr 1984-; *office:* South Kingstown HS 215 Columbia St Wakefield RI 02879

DIMODICA, KATHLEEN ANNE (MURPHY), High School Science Teacher; *b:* Framingham, MA; *m:* Paul; *ed:* Univ of RI (BS) Microbiology 1983; Providence Coll (MED) Scndry Admin 1991; *cr:* Davies Voc Schl Sci, Math Tchr 1984-85; Cumberland HS Sci Tchr 1985; Providence Hebrew Day Schl Sci Tchr 1985-86; Norton HS Sci Tchr 1986-; Coll Acad Chem Tchr 1990-94; *ai:* Sci Olympiad Coach; Yrbk Adv; Sr Class Adv; NSTA 1983-; Assn for Curr Dev 1988-; NEA 1985-; NEST-1995; MA Sci Olympiad 1987-, St Dir; *office:* Norton HS 66 W Main St Norton MA 02766*

DIMOND, MAHLON U., Music Teacher; *b:* Altoona, PA; *m:* Jane Shoemaker; *c:* Katherine, Marcie; *ed:* Valley Forge Military Coll (AA) Lbrl Arts 1967; Indiana Univ of PA (BS) Music Ed 1970; PA St Univ (MED) Music Ed 1976; *cr:* US Army 1970-73; Bedford Area Schl Dist Music Tchr 1973-; *ai:* Band Dir; Strategic Planning, Elem Bldg Comms; PSEA, NEA 1973-; PFCJ 1975-; ARRL 1976-; Bedford Vol Fire Dept 1975-, Soc Sec; BCVVA 1990-, Treas, Emir; Article, Picture in QST; *office:* Bedford Area Schl Dist 330 E John St Bedford PA 15522

D'IMPERIO, CHARLES JAMES, Assistant Principal; *b:* Mt Morris, NY; *m:* Terry Leigh Estelle; *c:* Charles Patrick, Emily Rose; *ed:* Alfred St Coll (AS) Cmptr Sci 1984; Potsdam St Coll (BA) Cmptr Sci 1986; Brockport St Coll (MS) Counseling 1993, (CAS) (SAS) (SDA) Admin 1996; *cr:* Oatka Residential Ctr Tchr, Cnslr 1989-91; Bishop Kearney HS Tchr, Cnslr 1991-93; Rush Henrietta Sr HS Stu Adv 1993-95, Asst Prin 1995-; *ai:* Natl Helpers Co-Adv; Stu Act Supvr; SAANYS 1995-; *office:* Rush-Henrietta Sr HS 1799 Lehigh Station Rd Henrietta NY 14467*

DIMUZIO, SALLY ANN (MOSER), Scndry Math Tchr & Dept Chm; *b:* Cincinnati, OH; *m:* Michael J.; *c:* Stacey; *ed:* Univ of Cincinnati (BS) Hlth, PE, Rec, Ed 1972; Math Ed 1980; 10 Hrs GA St Univ; 5 Hrs Xavier Univ; 18 Hrs Prof Growth & Dev; *cr:* Dekalb Cty Schl Elem Tchr 1973-76; Oak Hills Schl PE Tchr 1977-78; MariemontSchl Math Tchr 1779-; *ai:* NCTM 1988-; Gen Electric of Cincinnati Grant; *office:* Mariemont HS 3812 Pocahontas Ave Cincinnati OH 45227

DINABURG, ROBERT, Teacher; *c:* Anna, Dave; *ed:* St Univ of NY at Fredonia (BA) US His 1968; St Univ of NY at Binghamton (MST) His & Foreign Policy 1971; Attnd St Univ of NY at Cortland Educl Admin, Univ of MD, Saint Lawrence, Hofstra; *cr:* Union-Endicott CSD Tchr 1970-; BOCES Night Side Supvr 1989-; *ai:* His Club Adv; AFT, NYSET 1970-, Comm of 100; NCSS 1970-, Legislative Chair; NYS Archives & Record 1990-, Region 6 Bd of Dirs; Amer Legion 1992-; Robert Taft Fellowship in Amer Govt from Lehigh Univ; 1991 Kesai Koho Fellowship to Japan; *office:* Union Endicott HS 1200 E Main St Endicott NY 13760

DINARDO, ROBERT A., Social Studies Teacher; *b:* Brooklyn, NY; *m:* JoAnn Piazza; *c:* Michael, Thomas, Annmarie; *ed:* Baruch Coll (BA) Ed & Sociology 1974; Lehman Coll (MA) Ed 1982; *cr:* Our Lady Queen of Angels Tchr 1974-80; Monsigner Sconlon Tchr & Coach 1980-; *ai:* Var Bsbl & Bsktbl Coach; Recruitment Comm; FCT, NCEA & Bsktbl Coaches Assn of NY 1980-; Natl Fed of Interscholastic Coaches 1980-; 100 Career Victories Bsbl & Bsktbl; *office:* MSGR Scanlan HS 915 Hutchinson River Pkwy Bronx NY 10465*

DINEEN, SUSAN GILWOOD, English Teacher; *b:* Brooklyn, NY; *m:* William; *ed:* George Washington Univ (BA) Anthropology 1969; Rutgers St Univ (EDM) Eng Ed 1971, (PHD) Eng Lang & Lit 1978; *cr:* Rutgers Univ Adj Visiting Lecturer 1972-83; The Hun Schl Eng Tchr 1983-90; The Pingry Schl Eng Tchr 1990-; *ai:* Stu Newspaper Adv; Interdisciplinary Comm Chair; Justin Soc Creative Writing Pgm Coord; NCTE 1984-; Dodge Fndtn, Wellesley Coll Seminar Flwshp 1986-87; Cncl Basic Ed & Natl

Endowment for Hum Tchng Fellow 1988; Pingry Summer Flwshp 1996; *office:* The Pingry Schl Martinsville Rd Martinsville NJ 08836

DINGLE, DONNA VICTORIA, Elementary Teacher; *b:* Bryn Mawr, PA; *c:* Jarrod B.; *ed:* Millersville Univ (BS) Elem Ed 1973; Post Grad Stud Cheyney Univ, West Chester Univ; *cr:* Philadelphia Schl Dist Sub Elem Tchr 1974-76, 1977-82; Delawware Cty Head Start Tchr Coord 1984-86; Walnut St El Schl Elem Tchr 1986-; *ai:* NEA, PSEA, WPEA 1987-; Zion Bapt Church 1962-, Schl Tchr, Beginners Tchr, Tchr of Yr 1989, 1992, Gospel Chorus 1988-, Pres 1995, The Jewels little Peopls Choir 1984-, Music Dir & Pianist; Fellow PA Writing Project 1987; Who's Who in US Writers Eds & Poets 1989-90; *office:* Walnut Street Elem Sch 6th & Spruce Sts Darby PA 19023

DINGLE, FRANK JOSEPH, Prof of Printing Mgmt & Comm; *b:* Brooklyn, NY; *m:* Kendall Diane Fuhrman; *c:* Joan Marie Hite, John Francis, Bridget Mary Mather, Michael Joseph, Kevin Thomas, Patrick Gorman; *ed:* Univ of Baltimore (AA) Pre-Law 1966; Morgan St Univ (BS) Ed 1973; Intnl Typographical Union Apprenticeship Typographers Journeyman Card 1960-65; MD St Dept of Ed Masters Equivalent Voc Tec Ed 1969, Master plus 30 Equivalent Adult Ed 1976; *cr:* Northwestern Sr HS Voc Ed Printing Instr 1966-68; Howard Voc Tech Ctr Voc Ed Printing Instr 1968-77; Catonsville Comm Printing Mgmt Asst Prof 1977-81, Printing Mgmt Assoc Prof 1981-86, Printing Mgmt & Comp Graphic Assoc Prof 1986-92, Printing Mgmt & Comp Graphic Prof 1993-96, Visual Commnctn & Media Production Prof 1996-; *ai:* Printing Task Force Comm 1985-; Acad Computing Comm 1981-93; Voc Ed Advy Comm Serving on at Least 2 Yearly for the Following Ctys: Anne Arundel, Baltimore City & Cty, Frederick, Howard & Hartford 1978-; Various MD St DACUMs on Printing Tech Ed; Intnl House of Printing Craftsmen 1973-; Baltimore Club of Printing House Craftsmen 1973-; Intnl Graphic Arts Ed Assn 1976-; 1993 Van Hanswyk-Jasser Outstdng Achvmt Awd for Efforts in Improving Commnctn between Industry & Ed & Improved Curr in Graphic Arts Ed by the Intnl Assn of Printing House Craftsmen Inc; *office:* Catonsville Comm Coll 800 S Rolling Rd Catonsville MD 21228

DINGLE, PATRICIA ANN, High School Art Teacher; *b:* Washington, DC; *ed:* CT Coll (BA) Studio Art, Dance 1976; RI Schl of Design (MAT) Art Ed 1977; Univ of MD (PHD) Curr, Instruc Poss 1996; Cartographer Course 1987; Army Pre Commission Course 1985; Primary Ldrshp Dev Course 1985; Graphic Specialist Course 1984; Graphics Introduction Univ Coll 1981; *cr:* RI Schl of Design Young Artist Summer Prgm Instr 1978; City of East Providence Schl 7th-9th Grd Art Tchr 1978-79; US Army Illustrator 1983-87; PG Co Pub Schls 9th-12th Grd Art Tchr 1987-; MD Natl Capital Park, Planning Commission Dance Specialist Tchr 1990-92; *ai:* Crossroads; Amer Craft Cncl 1996; Ding La Gift Studio 1995-, Proprietor; Amazing Grace Bapt 1992-, Assoc Minister; Park View Bapt 1966-85, Assoc Minister; Pacific Garden Mission 1995-, Supporter; Thru the Bible Radio 1993-, Supporter; Family Radio in Touch Ministries 1995-, Supporter; Coll of Ed Schlsp 1990; Grad Flwshp 1989; Army Commendation 1st Oakleaf Cluster 1987; Army Achvmt Awd 1986; Subject Article Providence Journal 1986; Grad Assistantship 1976; Anna Lord Strauss Awd 1976; Subject Article The Day 1976; Artwork Cover Peacock Poems 1975; Print Smithsonian Christmas Card 1973; Schlsp CT Coll 1971-76; *home:* 1614 Pacific Ave Capitol Heights MD 20743*

DINGMAN, DONALD LEE, Mathematics Teacher; *b:* Chardon, OH; *ed:* Kent St Univ (BSEd) Math 1991; Working on Cert in Physics & Masters Degree in Admin; *cr:* Geauga Cty Schls K-12th Grd Sub Tchr 1991-93; Grand Vly Schls 9th-12th Grd Math Tchr 1993-; *ai:* JV Vllybl Coach; Acad Challenge Adv; Marching Band, Pep Band & Choir Asst; Mentor Tchr; Bsktbl Annoucer; TILT Comm; NEOCTM 1994-; AFT 1995-; Geaug Lyric Theater Guild 1992-, Artistic Dir; Geauga Highland Pipes 1995-, Band Mem; Peoples Choice Best Math Tchr 1995-; *office:* Grand Valley HS 44 N School St Orwell OH 44076*

DINGMAN, ROBERT A., Social Studies Teacher; *b:* Glens Falls, NY; *c:* Rosemary, Robert M., Deidre; *ed:* Castleton St Coll (BS) Eng 1966; Attnd Springfield Coll Soc Stud, SUNY at Potsdam Soc Stud, SUNY at Albany Soc Stud, 50 Grad Hrs; *cr:* Hudson Falls HS Eng & Soc Stud Tchr 1966-, Soc Stud Tchr & Dept Chair 1975-; *ai:* Sr High Stu Cncl & NHS Adv; Capital Dist Cncl Soc Stud, NY St Tchrs Assn & AFT 1966-; Hudson Falls Tchrs Assn 1966-, Bldg Rep, Chief Negotiator; Phi Delta Kappa; NY St Cncl on Soc Stud; North Cty Arts Cntr 1990-, Treas; Knights of Columbus 1986-; *home:* 140 E Hunter St Glens Falls NY 12801*

DINIACO, GEORGIANN, Safe & Drug Free Schls Coord; *b:* Steubenville, OH; *ed:* Kent St Univ (BA) Individual, Family Stud 1983; OH St Univ (MA) Hlth Ed 1989; Working on Ed Theory, Practice PHD; *cr:* Maryhaven Alcoholism, Family Cnslr 1983-86; OSU Assistantship 1986-88; Dublin City Schls Safe, Drug-Free Schls Coord 1988-; *ai:* Drug-Free Ldrshp Prgm Teen Inst Adv; OEA, NEA Dublin EA 1990-; Amer Schl Hlth Assn, Amer Hlth PE & Recreation 1993-; Alumni Assn Phys Hlth Educ Recreation & Dance 1989-; Certfd Alcoholism, Chemical Dependency Cnslr III, OH Prevention Specialist; Ath Mngmt Excl Awd 1995; *office:* Dublin City Schls 6780 Coffman Rd Dublin OH 43017

DINI-ADAMS, ELISSA A., Second Grade Teacher; *b:* Freeport, NY; *w:* M. Edward Adams (dec); *c:* Allyson Gardener, Allysa Adams, Allayne Martinolli; *ed:* SUNY at New Paltz (BA) Anthropology 1968, (MS) Ed 1972, (CAS) Ed Admin 1984; Multiple Intelligences; Cooperative Discipline; Whole Lang; Interdisciplinary Planning; Talents Unlimited; *cr:* Lindbergh Schl Kndgtn Tchr 1968-70; Sophie Finn Elem K, 2, 4 Grd Tchr 1972-83; Ernest C. Myer Elem Schl 1-2 Grd Tchr, Tchr in Charge 1986-88; Kingston Schl Dist GATE, Testing, Evaluation Coord 1988-89; Ernest C. Myer Elem Schl Grd 2 Tchr, Tchr in Charge 1992-; *ai:* Parental Vols for Rdng; Stu Review Team; Bldg Ldrshp Team; GATE After Schl Act; AFT, NEA, NYSUT 1968-; STANYS 1986-; Amer Assn of Univ Women 1994-; ASCD 1988-; Hurley Lib Assn; King Tchrs Golf League; Mid Hudson Wine Soc; Gold's Gym; Mid Hudson Tchrs Ctr Grant; *home:* 231 Evergreen Ln Hurley NY 12443*

DINICOLA, KATHLEEN CADY, Fifth Grade Teacher; *b:* Pittsfield, MA; *m:* Eugene A. Jr.; *c:* Gary, Brian; *ed:* North Adams Coll (BS) Elem Ed 1976, (MS) Elem Ed, Rdng 1986; Needs, Alternative Assessment; Whole Lang, Sci & Math Hands-On Classroom Techniques; Cooperative Learning; Strategies For Children with Spec Needs; *cr:* Cntrl Berkshire Regnl Schl Dist 3-5 Grd Tchr 1976-; *ai:* Former 3-4 Grd Human Sexuality Tchr; Bldg Based Curr Comms; NEA, MTA 1976-; St Agnes Parish 1986-, Schl Bd Chprsn, Cncl; BSA 1992-, Group Asst; Schl Accreditation 1993; *office:* Craneville Elem Schl 71 Park Ave Dalton MA 01226

DINING, JANET TAYLOR, English Teacher; *b:* Franklin, NH; *c:* Mark Taylor D., Timothy Bruce D., Elizabeth Joy D.; *ed:* Univ of NH (BA) British Lit-Magna Cum Laude 1958, (MAT) Ed 1984; Addl Post-Grad Credit Hrs; *cr:* North Hampton Elem Schl Fifth Grd Tchr 1958-59; Exeter Jr HS Permanent Sub Eng Tchr 1975, 1979; Epping HS 9-11 Grds Eng Tchr 1982-84; Rye Jr HS Eng, Stud Skills Tchr 1984-; *ai:* Phi Beta Kappa 1958; Phi Kappa Phi 1958; NEA 1984-; NCTE 1982-; Natl Endowment for Hum Georgetown Univ 1983; W. H. Governor's Initiative GATE Stud Summers 1986, 1987; *office:* Rye Jr HS 501 Washington Rd Rye NH 03870

DININO, ROSLYN, Pre-K Teacher; *b:* Passaic, NJ; *m:* William Paterson St Coll (BA) Elem Ed 1972; *cr:* St Brendan Schl 4-6 Grd Tchr 1968-75, 4-5 Grd Tchr 1975-89, 5 Grd Tchr 1989-92, Pre Kndgtn Tchr 1992-; *ai:* Schl Exec Bd 1995-; Schl Art Consultant; NAEYC 1992-; NCEA 1968-; Mid Sts Assn of Colls & Schls 1991-, Team Mem.*

DINNELL, PATRICIA CONWAY, Librarian; *b:* Brookly, NY; *m:* Ralph; *c:* Andrew, Karen, Scott; *ed:* St Joseph (BA) Elem Ed, His 1967; Addl 12 Credits Jersey City St Coll; *cr:* Bd of Ed NYC Hlth, PE, Summer Tchr 1965-67; St Augustine's Schl 4th Grd Tchr 1966-68; Bd of Spec Svcs Compensatory Ed Tchr 1983-85; Our Lady of Victories Asst Prin, 6-8 Grd Rdng, Soc Stud Tchr 1991-95, Librn 1996-; *ai:* HSA Tchr Rep; Mid Sts Steering Comm; Coord Candy Sales Fund Raisers; Cmptr club Asst; NCEA 1986-; Intnl Rdng Assn 1991-; NYS Rdng Assn; Intnl Rdng Soc 1991-; Our Lady of Victories 1988-, Neighborhood Parish Rep; Cath Daughters 1985-; 1995 Outstdng Educator Awd; Diocese of Newark; *office:* Holy Family Interparochial Sch 200 Summit St Norwood NJ 07648

DINNIE, CRAIG D., English Teacher; *b:* Springfield, MA; *m:* Cathleen Marchese; *c:* Justin; *ed:* Western New England Coll (BA) Eng 1971; Springfield Coll Masters in Guidance & Psycholgical Svcs; Amer Int Coll Tchng Cert; *cr:* Van Sickle Jr HS Eng Tchr 1972-75; Classcial HS Eng Tchr 1976-86; Spfld Cntrl HS Eng Tchr 1987-; *ai:* Yrbk Adv; NEA 1973-; SEA 1973-, Exec Bd; Guest Lecturer Yrbk Seminars New England Staffs Bryant Coll RI & North Adams St Coll MA; *office:* Springfield Ctl HS 1840 Roosevelt Ave Springfield MA 01109*

DI NOBILE, CYNTHIA A., Seventh Grade English Teacher; *b:* Providence, RI; *m:* Louis R.; *c:* Kate, Rachel; *ed:* RI Coll (BA) Eng 1974; Life Time Cert in Eng, Speech & Theatre Scndry Ed 7-12; *cr:* Smithfield Schl Dept 7th-12th Grd Scndry Eng 1975-; *ai:* Feinstein Fnd Coord for Youth Brigade Against Hunger; Prins Advy Bd; NEA 1975-; Class Adv 1975-85; Cheerleading 1975-80.

DINOLA, ANGELA JACANGELO, Eighth Grade Teacher; *b:* Newark, NJ; *m:* Gerald A.; *c:* Gerard, Nicholas; *ed:* Jersey City St Coll (BA) Elem Ed K-8 1971; 27 Grad Hrs at Seton Hall Univ; *cr:* 13th Avenue Schl Third Grd Tchr 1971-74; Ridge Street Schl Seventh, Eighth Grd Tchr 1974-; *ai:* Mentor to New Tchrs; Yrbk, Stu Cncl Adv; Amer Fed of Tchrs; Ladies of Unico 1989-, Treas; Governor's Tchr Recognition Awd 1995; *home:* 72 S Prospect St Verona NJ 07044*

DINOLA, JANICE MEMERING, Language Arts Teacher; *b:* Vincennes, IN; *m:* James; *c:* Jill, Jaclyn, James III; *ed:* Murray St Univ (BA) Elem Ed 1963; Grad Credit Hrs; *cr:* Tecumseh Schl Kndgtn Tchr 1963-64; Marshall Cty Schls 2-3 Grd Tchr 1964-66; Rockaway Valley Schl Grd 1 Tchr 1966-69; Mt Lakes Schl Supplemental 1976-79; Rockaway Valley Schl Tchr 1979-; *ai:* Newspaper Adv; NEA 1966-; *office:* Rockaway Valley Schl 11 Valley Rd Boonton NJ 07005

DINOWITZ, MICHAEL, Biology Teacher; *b:* Kew Gardens, NY; *m:* Linda Mc Allister; *c:* Jonathan, Laura, Jennifer; *ed:* SUCNY at New Paltz (BS) Sci, Bio 1971; 45 Post Grad Credits Adelphi, Hofstra, SUNY at Stony Brook; *cr:* Smithtown Schls MS Sci Tchr 1973-74; So Cntry Schls Bio Tchr 1974-; *ai:* Stu Cncl Adv; Bellport Tchrs Assn 1974-, Pres; AFT, NYSUT 1974-.

DINSE, DEBRA POPPY, Classical Ballet Instructor; *b:* Cleveland, OH; *m:* R. Michael; *cr:* Cleveland Civic Ballet Prin Dancer 1971-81; North Coast Ballet Theatre Prin Dancer 1985-93; Dance by Gloria Classical Ballet Instr 1993-; *ai:* Bd of Trustees North Coast Ballet Theatre 1981-93, Sec.

DINSMORE, DAVID RAYMOND, Physics Teacher; *b:* New York, NY; *m:* Sue Ann Young; *c:* Shawn, Megan; *ed:* USMA at West Point (BS) 1970; UC at Berkeley (MS) Nuclear Engrng 1976; 21 Hrs Cert Ed; Naval War Coll Naval Command & Staff Course; *cr:* USMA at West Point Exec Officer, Assoc Prof 1987-93; O'Neill HS Physics Tchr 1993-; *ai:* Jr Class Adv; Asst Ski, Golf Coach; NYSTU 1994-.

DINUNZIO-HALL, BARBARA ANN, Third Grade Teacher; *b:* Proidence, RI; *m:* Charles D. Hall; *c:* Brandon, Jason; *ed:* RI Coll (BS) Elem Ed 1971, (MS) Elem Ed 1975; 30 Hrs Beyond MA; *cr:* Stone Hill Elem Schl 3rd, 5th, 6th Grd Tchr 1971-; *ai:* Local Union Rep 1973-; AFT 1971-; *office:* Stone Hill Elem Schl 21 Village Ave Cranston RI 02920

DIODATO, SHERRY FARWELL, Eighth Grade English Teacher; *b:* Red Bank, NJ; *m:* Dr. Louis F. III; *ed:* Monmouth Coll (BS) Elem, Spec, Nursery Schl Ed 1984; Working Toward Prin, Admin Cert Monmouth Univ 1995-; *cr:* Forrestdale Schl TMR Class Tchr's Aide 1984-86; Little House Riverview Med Ctr Presch Tchr 1986; Navesink Schl 2nd Grd Tchr 1989-90; Thompson MS 8th Grd L A Tchr 1986-; *ai:* NEA, NJEA 1984-; MCEA, MTEA 1986-; Kappa Delta Pi 1984; Celebration of Tchng Star Tchr 1992; *office:* Thompson MS 1001 Middletown Lincroft Rd Middletown NJ 07748

DION FAUST, DEBRA, English Teacher & Drama Adv; *b:* Pottstown, PA; *m:* Joseph E. Dion; *c:* Andrea R., Joanne T. Dorgan; *ed:* Moravian Coll (BA) Music, Fr 1973; Boston Univ (MFA) Theatre Ed 1978; 34 Grad Credits; *cr:* Saugus HS Eng Tchr, Drama Adv 1979-81; Manchester Jr, Sr HS Eng Tchr, Drama Adv 1982-83; Ipswich HS Eng Tchr, Drama Adv 1983-; *ai:* MA Tchrs Assn, NEA 1979-81, 1982-; Ipswich Tchrs Assn 1983-, VP; NCTE 1985-; Educl Theatre Assn, New England Theatre Conf 1992-; MA HS Drama Guild 1979-; Tchr of Yr MA Alliance for Arts Ed 1993-94; Article Pub in Eng Journal 1995; *office:* Ipswich HS 136 High St Ipswich MA 01938

DIPASQUALE, MARY LEE, Eng, Mythology & Writing Tchr; *b:* New York City, NY; *m:* Louis; *c:* Douglas, Karen; *ed:* Vassar Coll (BA) Eng Lit 1983; NYS Tchrs Coll at New Paltz (MA) Eng Lit 1988; *cr:* John S. Burke HS Eng Tchr 1983-; *ai:* Schl Newspaper Adv; NCTE 1983-; *office:* John S Burke Catholic HS Fletcher St Goshen NY 10924

DIPETRILLO, DIANE C., Science Teacher; *b:* Paterson, NJ; *m:* John Anthony; *c:* Marissa, Ashley; *ed:* Paterson St Coll (BA) Ed, Bio 1966; Fairleigh Dickinson Univ (MA) Bio 1969; 45 Credits Univ of Boston, Univ of Bridgeport, Jersey City St Coll; *cr:* Waldwick Jr Sr HS Bio, Introductory Phys Sci, 7th Grd Life Sci, Stud Skills Tchr 1966-; *ai:* 7th Grd Team & Curr, Dist Wide Evaluation Comms; Class Adv 6 Yrs; WEA, BCEA, NJEA, NEA 1966-, Bldg Rep 3 Yrs; NJSTA 1966-; Project Lovematch Vol 2 Yrs; Ramapo HS & Summer Drama Prgms Costume Dir Vol 2 Yrs; Tchr of Yr; Letter of Appreciation & Cert of Awd Tchr Who Made a Difference Univ of Chicago; *office:* Waldwick Jr Sr HS 155 Wyckoff Ave Waldwick NJ 07463

DI PIAZZA, KATHRYN BRUNETTI, First Grade Teacher; *b:* Passaic, NJ; *m:* Frank; *ed:* Jersey City St Coll (BA) Kindergarten, Primary Ed 1968; William PattersonColl (MAEd) Rdng, Lang Arts 1982; 24 Credits Rdng & Lang Arts for Elem Ed; *cr:* Mark Twain #3 1-3 Grd Tchr 1968-80; Roosevelt Schl #7 Second Grd Tchr 1980-92, First Grd Tchr 1992-; *ai:* Dist Rdng Comm; Fac Liason Rep; Schl Base Mngmt Team; PAC Comm; NJEA, BCEA, NEA 1968-; GEA 1968-, Sec; Holy Name Church 1968-, CCD Tchr; St John Baptist Church 1983-, CCD Tchr; NJ Tchr of Yr Awd 1993; *office:* Roosevelt Schl #7 225 Lincoln Pl Garfield NJ 07026

DIPIETRA, HELEN WALKER, Second Grade Teacher; *b:* New York City, NY; *m:* Frank; *c:* William; *ed:* St John's Univ (BA) Fr 1970; Rutgers Univ (MA) Fr 1974; Univ of Grenoble France Summer Stud 1969; *cr:* Rutgers Univ Fr Tchng Asst 1970-71; Holy Trinity Schl 7th-8th Grd Tchr 1972-73; St Elizabeth Schl Kndgtn Tchr 1981-86, 2nd Grd Tchr 1987-; *ai:* Yrbk Moderator; Art Exhibit, Testing Coord; Pub Relations; NCEA 1981-; *office:* Saint Elizabeth Schl 9401 85th St Ozone Park NY 11416

DIPIETRO, THOMAS G., 6th Grade Math Teacher; *b:* Aliquippa, PA; *m:* Liz Wosotowsky; *c:* Anthony, Amy; *ed:* Univ of Pitt (MS) Supervision 1980; Univ of Steubinville El Ed 1976; *cr:* Pgh Pub Schls Tchr 1978-; *ai:*

Time & Score Keeper Boys & Girls Bsktbl, Wrestling; PFT 197[illegible] of South Hills 1982-, Dir of Camp AIM.

DIPILATO, NANCY M., World Language Teacher; *b:* Worceste[illegible] Michael J. Martin; *ed:* Univ of MA at Amherst (BA) Span 1987; St Coll (MED) Scndry Ed 1995; *cr:* Millbury Meml HS Span Tch[illegible] Belchertown HS World Lang Tchr 1990-; *ai:* Span Club Adv; 1986-; MTA, NEA 1987-; *office:* Belchertown HS 62 N Wash[illegible] Belchertown MA 01007

DIPINO, FRANK, Professor of Biology; *b:* Syracuse, NY; *m:* J[illegible] Stiles; *ed:* St Univ of NY at Oswego (BA) Zoology 1981; Marq[illegible] (PHD) Molecular Bio 1991; *cr:* Coll Misericordia Dept of Biol, [illegible] Sci Div Chair 1992-; *ai:* AAAS, Sigma Xi, Alpha Sigma Nu 19[illegible] 1996-; Marquette Univ, Denis J. O'Brien Flwshps; *off*[illegible] Misericordia 301 Lake St Dallas PA 18612*

DIPIPPO, ELIZABETH ANNE, Math Instr & Algebra C[illegible] Providence, RI; *ed:* Marquette Univ (BS) Math 1966; Provid[illegible] (MA) Rel Stud 1974; St Univ of NY at New Paltz (MS) Math & [illegible] 1975; Attnd Regina Mundi Rome Italy Theology 1967-68, Inst De[illegible] Fr 1982, Inst Catholique Fr 1982-83; *cr:* Notre Dame HS Math & Tchr 1966-67; John A Coleman HS Math & Rel Stud Tchr 1968-8[illegible] & Asst Prin 1978-82; St Univ of NY at New Paltz Math Ins[illegible] Algebra Coord 1992-93 & 1994-; *ai:* Delta Kappa Phi Adv; Task Educl Outcomes Assessment; NCTM, AMTNYS 1992-; MAA 19[illegible] Joseph Parish Cncl 1994-; NSF Grant to Prism Prgm Lawrence H[illegible] Univ of CA at Berkeley; *office:* S U N Y Coll At New Paltz 75 S Blvd New Paltz NY 12561*

DIPOCE, DORIS LEE, Assistant Principal; *b:* New Brunswic[illegible] Vincent; *c:* James, Jason; *ed:* Wm Paterson Coll (BA) Elem Ed 19[illegible] Soc Sci 1974; 15 Hrs Prin & Supvr; *cr:* Byram Intermediate Sch[illegible] Tchr 1971-75; Rockaway Twp Schls 5th-8th Grd Tchr 1976-; *ai:* 1995-; NJ Tchrs Governor Awd 1989; *office:* Copeland MS 100 L[illegible] Dr Rockaway NJ 07866

DIPOFI, KATHLEEN JEAN, French Teacher; *b:* Toledo, OH; of Toledo (BA) Fr 1987; OH St Univ (MA) Fr 1990; 33 Hrs Span[illegible] Cert; *cr:* OH St Univ Tchng Asst 1988-90; Columbus Schl for Girl[illegible] 1991-92; Saint Francis DeSales HS Fr Tchr & Dept Chair 1992-[illegible] Advy Bd; Fr Club Adv; Homecoming Comm; Big Brothers Bi[illegible] 1994-; Columbus Literacy Cncl 1995-; Columbus Merrick S[illegible] *office:* St Francis De Sales HS 4212 Karl Rd Columbus OH 4322[illegible]

DIPOLLINO, PATRICIA ANNE, High School Business Te[illegible] Westerly, RI; *ed:* Cntrl CT St Univ (BS) Secretarial Stud 1986, (MS) Ed, Guid 1990; Credits at Univ of RI at Kingston, Johnson Univ at Providence; *cr:* Chariho Regnl HS Bus Tchr 1986-; *ai:* A[illegible] of 1992, 1995, 2000, YMCA Yth Ldrs, FBLA; RIBEA 1988-, Tre[illegible] NEA, NEARI 1986-; NE Regnl Conf Participant for Drug Fr[illegible] *office:* Chariho Reg HS 453 Switch Rd Wood River Junctio RI 02[illegible]

DI POMPEI, GERALDINE C., Soc Stud Teacher & Dept Coord[illegible] York, NY; *m:* Vincent; *c:* Alicia Sasser; *ed:* Hunter Coll (BA) H[illegible] Lehman Coll (MA) His & Ed 1973; Coll of New Paltz (CAS) Adm[illegible] *cr:* Mt Vernon Pub Schls Soc Stud Tchr 1968-70, Sub Tchr Manhattanville Coll Stu Tchr Supvr 1973-75; Arlington Cntrl [illegible] Stud Tchr 1977-, Part-Time Asst Prin 1994-95; *ai:* NHS Adv; Mid[illegible] Soc Stud Cncl 1987-, Sec, Outstdng Scndry Tchr of 1991; NYS [illegible] Cncl 1988-; NYSHA 1995; Church of Our Lady of Mt Carmel 19[illegible] Cncl; *office:* Arlington HS-N Campus 263 State Route 55 Lagra[illegible] NY 12540

DIPPO, JEANETTE POTTER, Health Education Teacher; *b:* Mi[illegible] *m:* Walter Allen; *c:* Julie Lynn, Kimberly Michelle; *ed:* St Luke's Schl of Nursing (RN) 1964; St Univ of NY at Cortland (BS) Hlth [illegible] (MS) Hlth Ed 1969; Cert Self-Exam, Trained Drinking Driver Prg[illegible] Natl Ctr Sub Abuse Trng; NYS Ed Dept Turnkey Trainer Nutrition Drug & Alcohol Initiative, Comprehensive Sch Hlth & Wellne[illegible] Courses in Coop Learning, Sexuality, Personal Self-Empowerm[illegible] Cortland Meml Hospital RN 1964-66; Cortland City Schls Hlth ed, Hlth Supv 1966-73; Cortland-Madison BOCES Hlth, Drug E[illegible] 1973-75; Cortland City Schls Hlth Ed, Wellness Coord 1975-; *ai:* Tobacco Prevention Coalition; Healthy Options Will Work Tas[illegible] Liberty Partnership Mentor Tchr; Cooperating Master Tchr Wit[illegible] Coll & SUCC; Coord Hlth Promotion Prgm; Hlth Ed Dept Chair; Advy, Dist Wellness Comms; Bldg Cabinet, Cortland HS Share[illegible] Mkng Team; Cortland United Tchrs, NYSUT, NEA, Amer Schl H[illegible] 1966-; NYS Fed of Prof He Educ 1973-, Pres 1976, NYS Outstand[illegible] Teach Past Pres Awd; Amer Cancer Soc 1968-, Past Pres, Lifesav[illegible] Distinguished; First United Meth Church 1986-, Sunday Confirmation Class Tchr; Seven Valleys Cncl Alcohol & Substanc[illegible] 1987-, Founders' Comm; Cortland CARES Aids Resources, [illegible] Support 1988-; Delta Kappa Gamma Intnl 1991-; Articles & Newsletters Pub; Keynote Speaker Wkshp, Conf Presenter; Dar[illegible] Tobacco-Free, Zero Adolescent Pregnancy, Metropolitan Lif[illegible] Comprehensive Schl Hlth Ed Demonstration Prgm Grants; 197[illegible] Dedication, Peer Recognition, Eleanor Schwartz, #1 Club Fac, Coop Ext Recognition Awds; Cortland Cty Legislature Commer[illegible] AAHPER Who's Who in Hlth Ed 1976; CBS 30 Minutes, SED N[illegible] Ed Syllabus Dev Task Force Consultants; *office:* Cortland Enlarg[illegible] SD 8 Valley View Dr Cortland NY 13045*

DIPPOLITO, LILLIAN RUSSELL, Dean of Junior High; *b:* Bro[illegible] *m:* Charles; *c:* Charles Jr., Joseph; *ed:* Mercy Coll (BS) Eng & S[illegible] 1981; Adelphi Univ (MS) Spec Ed 1987; *cr:* Saint Frances de Chan[illegible] 1981-87; Mt Saint Michael Acad Tchr 1987-, Tchr & Dean 19[illegible] Rainbow Prgm Moderator; *office:* Mt St Michael Jr HS 4300 Murd[illegible] Bronx NY 10466

DIPRIMA, ANNE, Physical Ed & Health Teacher; *b:* Brooklyn, [illegible] Adelphi Univ (BS) PE, Hlth 1970; Hofstra Univ (MS) Hlth Ed 197[illegible] Stud C. W. Post Univ Prof Diploma Schl Admin, Supvr 1986; *cr:* Kennedy MS Tchr, Ath Coord 1970-; Bethpage HS Coach 1970-; Vlybl, Var Sftbl Coach; Nassau Cty Div Rep for Vlybl, Exec Bd fo[illegible] PTA, NY Shaper 1970-; Phi Delta Kappa 1986-; Amer Vlybl Coache[illegible] Natl HS Ath Coaches Assn; Natl Sftbl Coaches Assn; Nassau Ct[illegible] Coaches Assn, Exec Bd; Nassau Cty Vlybl Coaches Assn Div Rep; Cty Bd of Vlybl Ofcls Girls & Boys Div; NY St Ath Assn; Bruce [illegible] Awd 1988; Outstdng Coach 1988; Svc Awd 1993; Natl Regnl Vlyb[illegible] of Yr 1994; Div Coach of Yr 1990; Coach of Yr 1993; Awd for O[illegible] Prof Svc 1993-94; 1995 Crown Trophy Awd; 1996 Female Coach 1995- Inducted Into Hall of Hnr Amateur Sftbl Assn; *office:* [illegible] Kennedy MS Broadway Bethpage NY 11714

DIPRIMA, GERALDINE GAUDIOSI, Kindergarten Teacher; *b*[illegible] York, NY; *m:* Joseph; *ed:* Queens Coll (BA) Ed 1968; Hunter co[illegible] Early Chldhd Ed 1971; *cr:* PS 19 First Grd Tchr 1968-83; PS 319 [illegible] Tchr 1983-; *ai:* UFT 1968-; *office:* Public Schl 319 360 Keap St Br[illegible] NY 11211

DIRADO, LINDA MARIE (WILLIAMS), Mathematics Teac[illegible] Danville, PA; *m:* Anthony; *c:* Amber Wynn, Shannon Lyn[illegible] Bloomsburg St Coll (BSEd) Scndry Math 1973; Johns Hopkin[illegible] (MSEd) Guid & Cnslng 1978; *cr:* Joppatowne Jr-Sr HS 8th Grd Ma[illegible] I Tchr 1974-78; Magnolia MS 8th Grd Math, Alg I Tchr 1978-79; S[illegible] Cty Jr-Sr HS Math Tchr 1979-84; Benton Area Jr-Sr HS Math Tchr

1974-84, 1993; PSEA 1979-84, 1993; BAEA 1993-; Stillwater urch 1965-, Sunday Schl Tchr; *office:* Benton Area Jr-Sr HS Park Benton PA 17814

OR, MARIA GIANNETTA, Math Teacher; *b:* Malverne, NY; *m:* *ed:* Univ at Albany (BA) Math 1993; Working Masters Math, d Queens Coll; *cr:* Nassau Boces TAP, CAC Prgms Math, Span 4; Hempstead HS Math Tchr 1994-95; Bethpage HS, MS Math 5-; *ai:* NCTM, AFT 1994-; NCMTA 1995-; *office:* Bethpage H S ve Bethpage NY 11714

O, CAROL GARVINE, Communication Arts Teacher; *b:* ter, PA; *m:* Carman Jr.; *ed:* Shippensburg (BS) Eng & Fr 1971; urg Univ (MS) Eng 1982; *cr:* C. W. Rice MS Eng Tchr 1972-; *ai:* tance; PSEA & NEA 1972-; *office:* CW Rice MS 4th & Hanover umberland PA 17857

, STEVEN JOSEPH, Math Instructor; *b:* Philadelphia, PA; *ed:* niv (BS) Ed 1989; Rosemont Coll (MS) Educl Tech 1996; *cr:* eet Schl Math Dept 1989-; *ai:* IMS Sports Coach; Eighth Grd Adv; er Coord; NEA, NCTM, CVEA 1989-; *office:* Main Street Schl St Upland PA 19015

O, ANNETTE CESONE, 6th Grade Teacher; *b:* New York City, ohn A.; *c:* Doreen Maroney, Michael; *ed:* Hofstra Univ (BS) Ed ny Brook Univ (MALS) Soc Scis 1988; Addl 45 Credits Dowling NY at New Paltz, SCOPE; *cr:* Alleghany Ave Schl 4 Grd Tchr Albany Ave Schl 2, 5, 6 Grd Tchr 1971091; Lindenhurst MS 6 Grd 91-; *ai:* GATE, Curr Dev, Rdng, Lang, Spelling Curr Comm; AFT; Cornell Home Extension Svc; 4-H Club Ldr; OWL nt; *office:* Lindenhurst MS 350 S Wellwood Ave Lindenhurst NY

ATINO, PHILLIP ANTHONY,JR., Physical Ed & Health *b:* Canton, OH; *m:* Kathryn Stephens; *c:* Kira Marie, Andrew *l:* DE Tech Coll (AA) Criminal Justice 1972; Univ of DE (BA) PE, 3; *cr:* St Mark HS PE, Hlth Tchr 1983-87; Stanton MS PE, Hlth Dir 1987-91; Sussex Cntrl HS PE, Hlth Tchr 1991-; *ai:* Head Ftbl Dfcl Boys Bsktbl Scorer; NEA 1987-; DIFCA, NFICA 1980-; 988-; Lower Sussex Little League 1992-, Coach; Outstdng Svc v Castle Cty Parks & Rec.

/O, CAROLE FAIRCHILD, Language Arts Teacher; *b:* Newark, atrick R.; *c:* Lisa, Laura; *ed:* Jersey City St (BA) Elem Ed 1968; ll (MA) Rdng Specialization 1994; *cr:* Walnut St Schl 5 Grd Tchr Middletown-Lincroft Schl Tchr 1980-; Port Monmouth New th 2 Grd Tchr; Thompson MS 6-8th Grd Tchr 1996; *ai:* Alpha ppa Upsilon 1994-; Kappa Delta Phi 1993-; Middletown Ed Assn NJEA; NEA; *office:* Thompson MS Middletown-Lincroft Rd own NJ 07748*

TE, ANGELO, 7th-12th Grade Art Teacher; *b:* Sewickeley, PA; *m:* e Baker; *ed:* Edinboro Univ (BS) K-12th Grd Art 1967, (MED) Art Hrs of Post Grad Stud From Penn St & Comm Coll of Beaver Cty; ory Schl 1st-9th Grd Art Tchr 1967-68; Rochester Area Schl Grd Art Tchr 1968-; *ai:* Young Artists Club Spon; Art Judge; NEA 1967-; Rochester Area Ed Assn 1968-; PA Art Ed Assn 1985-; 985-; Beaver Cty Humane Soc 1989-; Animal Welfare Org 1985-; ochester Area Schl 540 Reno St Rochester PA 15074

TIS, PAUL ANTHONY, Science Department Chairman; *b:* d, OH; *m:* Patricia J. Murray; *c:* Kristen, Karen, Paul; *ed:* OH St S) Sci Ed 1961; Kent St Univ (MS) Ed Admin 1966; Attnd Akron Cleveland St Univ; *cr:* Mt Carmel Schl Elem Ed 1961-62; Harry HS Sci Tchr 1962-64; Charles Mooney Jr HS Sci Dept Chm Cleveland Schl of Sci Sci Dept Chm 1979-; *ai:* Schl & Bus hip Coord; Schl Advisory Comm; Illuminating Cty Ed Advisory FT 1961-, Del; Cleveland Cncl of Sci Tchrs 1961-, Pres; Holy oc 1976-; Martha Holden Jennings Scholar; Rotary Club Tchng d; BP America Acad Excl Awd; Schl of Sci Outstanding Tchr Awd; of Sci Text & Article for NSTA Sci & Children; Rec by St House *home:* 6974 Anthony Ln Parma OH 44130*

RO, NICHOLAS, Mathematics Teacher; *b:* Plainfield, NJ; *ed:* Univ (BA) Math 1976, (MED) Math Ed 1992; *cr:* Sci HS Math 76-77; Westfield HS Math Tchr 1977-78; Union Cty Regnl Dist HS chr 1978-80; Carteret HS Math Tchr 1980-; *ai:* Future Tchrs of lub, Cntrl Jersey Math League, Acad Club Adv; NEA 1976-; NJ Ed 76-; Carteret Ed Assn 1980-; Assn of Math Tchrs of NJ 1976-; Univ Alumni Assn 1976-; Rutgers Univ Alumni Assn Grad Schl of 2-; Most Promising Scndry Schl Tchr Rutgers Univ; Inducted in elta Pi; *office:* Carteret HS 199 Washington Ave Carteret NJ 07008

AFANI, BEVERLY, Third Grade Teacher; *b:* Ballston Spa, NY; *m:* ; *c:* Santo, Vincent; *ed:* St U at New Paltz (BS) Elem Ed 1965; *cr:* k Schl Third Grd Tchr 1965-68; Corona Ave Denver Schl Second r 1968-69; Clara H. Carlson Schl Kndgtn Tchr 1984-85, Third Grd 85-; *ai:* Tchng Math Tutorial; Elmont Elem Tchrs Assn, Clara H. Tchrs Assn 1985-; Delta Kappa Gamma 1991-, Soc Sec; New Paltz Assn 1986-; AFT, NYSUT 1984-; St Vincent De Paul Parish 1968-, First Communion Classes; *home:* 349 Lehrer Ave Elmont NY

AFINO, MARY ANN MATHAUER, Retired 4th Grade Teacher; shawauka, IN; *m:* Rick; *c:* Paul, Susan LeBhun, David; *ed:* alata Coll (BS) Ecs 1951, (ME) Elem Educ 1984; 36 Credit Hrs ME n Ed; *cr:* Tredyffrin-Easttown Sch Dist Sub Elem Tchr 1965-71; n Park Elem Schl 4th Grd Tchr 1972-93; *ai:* While Employed At n Park Served on Numerous Curr Dev Comms in Lang Arts, Math, tics, Cmptr Tech, Major Soc Stud Revision; Volunteering Local chl Cmptr Lab; Part-time Vol in Local Schl Accrediated Rdng Prgm; g Math, Lit for Migrant Workers; NEA, PSEA 1972-1993; Currently d in Writing Children's Lit Course Hope to Publish.

ROON, RICHARD ALAN, Music Dept Chair; *b:* Balto, MD; *w:* Kaye Patzkowsky (dec); *c:* Kerry Sue, Sherry Lynn; *ed:* Towson (BS) Elem Ed 1962; Tchrs Coll Columbia Univ (MA) Music Ed Univ of MD College Park (PHD) Scndry Music Ed 1980; Yale Univ *cr:* Ruxton Elem Tchr 1962-63; Deep Creek Jr Sr HS Tchr 1963-64; lle HS Dept Chair 1964-; Loyola Coll Adjunct Prof 1981-95; Essex Coll Choral Dir 1985-90Peabody Conservatory Of Music Adjunct 995-; *ai:* Music Dir, Musical Theatre Productions; Barbershop ; Founder Parkville Summer Choral Wkshp; Arnolia United Meth Music Dir; Alumni Choir Dir; Guest Conductor; NEA, MD St Tchrs Tchrs Assn Balto Co, Phi Mu Alpha Sinfonia 1962-; Music Ed Natl MD Music Educators Assn 1963-; MD Choral Ed Assn 1975-; Amer Dirs Assn 1980-; Kappa Delta Pi; Articles Printed by Baltimore urr Guides; Phi Kappa Phi; Univ MD College Park; Author Several s in MD Music Educator; Nom MD Music Educators Assn; Awd for 989; Founding Dir Greater Balto Youth CHorale; Dir Prgms ally Gifted, Talented Stdnts 1980-84; MD Choral Edu Assoc Pres 3; Pres Elect MD Mucis Ed Assoc 1995; Pikesville HS Alum Assoc Tchng Awd 1996; Pikesville Chamber of Commerce Exel in Tchng 995; *office:* Pikesville HS 7621 Labyrinth Rd Baltimore MD 21208*

AW, ERNEST JOHN,JR., Associate Professor; *b:* Niagara Falls, Bonnie L. Mac Kellar; *c:* Tammy L. Licastro, Tina Louise; *ed:* a Cty Comm coll (AAS) Liberal Arts Scis 1976; St Univ Coll at Buffalo (BS) Bio, Sec Ed 1979, (MS) Bio, Sec Ed 1989; *cr:* St Peters Schl Sci Instr 1981-83; DeSalles HS Bio, Chem Instr 1983-85; Niagara Falls HS Bio, Chem Instr 1985-92; Trocaire Coll Chem, Anatomy, physicology, Environmental Sci Instr 1992-; *ai:* Am Chem Sco 1993-; NEPETE 1994-; Mayoral Recycling Advy Comm 1993-; Niagara Fall Housing Authority 1994-, Commissioner, Sec; Oxy Cities Advy Panel; NFC Dev Corp 1994-, Bd Dirs; Pres Inst for Stud of Nature; Co-Author Nature, Sci Column for Niagara Gazette 15 Yrs; Research Project Ldr the Urban Ring-Necked Pheasant NY St Dep of Environmental Conservation; *home:* 626 70th St Niagara Falls NY 14304

DISIBIO, ROBERT A., Acting VP for Academic Affairs; *b:* Caronsburg, PA; *m:* Marie A. Thomas; *c:* Robert A. Jr.; *ed:* CA Univ of PA (BS) Elem Ed 1967; (MED) Eleme Ed 1969; IN Univ of PA (EDD) Ed, Curr Instr 1973; Attnd West VA Univ; *cr:* Caron-Millan Schl Dist Classroom Tchr 1967-69; Indiana Schl Flwshp 1970-71; Wilkes Schl Instr 1971; Edinboro Schl Asst prof 1972; King Schl Assoc Prof 1973-79; St Josephs UNIv Assoc Prof 1979-83; DYouville Coll Acting VP for Acad Affairs 1995-; *ai:* Chm Division of Ed 1983-94; King Coll Head Soccer Coch 1974-76; Soc of Edctrs, Schlars Exec Dir 1985-; Phi Delta Kappa 1968-; AAUP, Exec Cncl, Contract Admin; Outstdng NY Tchr 1991-, Edctr Awd; Buffalo Bison Bsbl Advy Bd 1994-; St John Maron 1992-, Lector; Mathewson Mc Carthy 1989-91, Bd Mem; Williamsville South PTA 1991-95; Nazareth Coll Swim Team, Parent Coord 1995-; Grants TX Instrument Calculator, Biling-ES Federal, NY St Tchr Trng, Buffalo City Summer Wellness Camp; Fisher Price Lecture Series; *office:* D'Youville Coll One D'Youville Sq Buffalo NY 14201*

DISMUKE, ROY EUGENE, Computer Science Teacher; *b:* Natrona Heights, PA; *m:* Deborah Ann; *c:* Drew, Reid, Eric; *ed:* Clarion Univ of PA (BS) Math, Sec Ed 1977; Shippensburg Univ of PA (MED) Sec Ed Admin 1983; Attnd Western MD Coll, Univ of MD; *cr:* Fox Chapel HS Cmptr Sci, Math Tchr 1977-79; Bermudian Springs HS Cmptr Sci, Math Tchr 1979-85; Prince Georges Cty Pub Schls Math Tchr 1985-91; Montgomery Cty Pub Schls Cmptr Sci, Math Tchr 1992-; *ai:* Boys Bsktbl, Track Coaches; Curr, Tech Comms; NEA, MD St Tchrs Assn 1985-; MD Pub Sec Schls Ath Assn 1987-; Fellowship to Univ of MD Inst for Engrg for Tchr of Math, Sci & Tech; Served Mid St Evaluation Team; *office:* Montgomery Blair HS 313 Wayne Ave Silver Spring MD 20910*

DISNEY, DONALD BRUCE,JR., Naval Science Instructor; *b:* Baltimore, MD; *m:* Linda Jean Lins; *c:* Shannon Jean, Sarah Lynn, Elizabeth Katherine; *ed:* US Naval Acad (BS) Foreign Affairs 1971; US Naval Post Grad Schl (MA) Natl Security Affairs 1980; US Naval War Coll (MA) Strategy & decisions 1985; SUNY Maritime Coll 6 Hrs Acctng & Fin; *cr:* US Navy Commander 1967-93; US Naval War Coll Prof of Strategy 1985-89; SUNY Maritime Coll Prof of Naval Sci 1989-93; US Naval War College Adj Prof NSDM 1993-; Suitland HS Naval Sci Instr 1993-; *ai:* NJROTC Drill, Ath & acad Team Coach; Schl Based Information Decision Mgmt Team; Schl Awds & Guid Dept Advy Comm; Dept Chprsn; US Naval Inst & USNA Alumni Assn 1971-; US Naval Reserve Assn & Surface Navy Assn 1990-; Comm UM Church 1993-, Trustee; Calvary UM Church 1986-89, Trustee VP; Articles Pub; Book Reviews; *office:* Suitland HS 5200 Silver Hill Rd Forestville MD 20747

DISPORTO, EMANUEL J., Middle School Teacher; *b:* Elizabeth, NJ; *m:* Marianne Heck; *ed:* Kean Coll (BA) Elem Ed 1973; *cr:* Franklin Schl Elem 5th Grd Tchr 1973-91; Burnett MS 6th-8th Grd Soc Stud Tchr 1991-; *ai:* Club Adv; Bsbl Trading Card Traders Club; NEA 1973-, UTEA 1973-; *office:* Burnet MS Caldwell Ave Union NJ 07083

DISTASI, JOANNA RUSSO, Mathematics Teacher; *b:* Brooklyn, NY; *m:* Daniel; *c:* Laura, Stephen, Christopher; *ed:* SUNY at Oneonta (BS) Ed & Math 1975; Rowan Coll (MA) Math 1979; Rowan Coll Supervision Cert 1989; *cr:* Overbrook Jr HS Tchr 1976-83; Camden Cty Comm Coll Adjunct Tchr 1979-85; Rowan Coll Adjunct Tchr 1979-85; Overbrook HS Tchr 1983-; *ai:* NJEA 1976-; *office:* Overbrook Regional Sr HS 1200 Turnerville Rd Pine Hill NJ 08021

DISTEFANO, ANTHONY ROBERT, Mathematics Teacher; *b:* Johnstown, PA; *m:* Barbara Lee Koerber; *c:* Lisa, Amy, Susan; *ed:* Univ of Pittsburgh (BS) Math 1972; 32 Addl Hrs; *cr:* Ridgely Jr HS Math Tchr 1975-77; Dumbarton Jr HS Math Tchr 1977-82; Pikesville MS Math Tchr 1982-83; Dumbarton MS Math Tchr 1983-; *ai:* Fac Cncl; Math Curr Ldr; Liason Office of Math; NEA, MSTA, TABCO 1975-; Loch Raven Recreation Cncl 1992-, Girls Sftbl Coach; *home:* 1213 Brook Hollow Rd Baltimore MD 21286

DISTEFANO, BRENDA, HS ESL Teacher; *b:* Lawrence, MA; *c:* Marisa, John; *ed:* Emmanuel Coll (BA) Eng 1964; Post Grad Stud Linguistics, Cooperative Ed Courses; *cr:* Newburyport HS Eng Tchr 1965-66; Tarbox Schl ESL Tchr 1967-70; Oliver Jr HS ESL Tchr 1970-82; Lawrence HS Transitional Eng, ESL Tchr 1982-; *ai:* Biling Pupil Stud Team Comm; AFT, MTA 1966-; *office:* Lawrence HS 233 Haverhill St Lawrence MA 01840

DISTRAVOLO, LOREDANA MARGARET, Spanish Teacher; *b:* Reading, PA; *ed:* Millersville Univ of PA (BS) Span Scndry Ed 1988; Bowling Green St Univ (MA) Span 1990; *cr:* Liberty HS Span Tchr 1990-; Alvernia Coll Span Instr 1991-; *ai:* Class Adv 1990-95; Intnl Stu Cncl; Bethlehem Ed Assn 1990-; NEA 1990-; PSEA 1990-; Italian Heritage Cncl 1995-, Dir; Span Hnr 1990; *office:* Liberty HS 1115 Linden St Bethlehem PA 18018*

DISTRAVOLO, PIETRO, Assoc Prof of Italian & Span; *b:* San Clemente, Caserta Italy; *m:* Elisabetta Zampella; *c:* Maria, Elliott, Loredana, Rossella; *ed:* Kutztown Univ (BS) Span 1975, (MA) Span 1980; Italy Acctng Degree; *cr:* Alvernia Coll Assoc Prof Italian, Span 1976-, Acting Chair Lang Dept 1996; *ai:* Hnrs & Awds, Rank & Tenure Comms; AATI; Italian Heritage Cncl 1976-, Pres, Wall of Hnr; Columbus Day Celebration, Co-Chprsn; Spartago Soc 1983-, Italian-Amer Citizenship Awd; Italian Amer Cultural Ctr, Bd Dir; Club of Yr Awd 1981-82 Frgn Lang Intercultural Club Adv; *office:* Alvernia Coll 400 St Bernardine St Reading PA 19607

DITCHCREEK, GLENNA M., First Grade Teacher; *b:* Johnstown, PA; *m:* Robert; *c:* Nathan, Nadine, Benjamin, Samuel; *ed:* Univ of Pittsburgh (BS) Elem Ed 1970; PA St Univ 36 Credit Hrs; Indiana Univ of PA Masters Equivalency; *cr:* Forest Hills Schl Dist 3rd Grd Tchr 1970-72; Cntrl Cambria Schl Dist K-1st, 3rd-4th Grd Tchr 1972-; *ai:* NEA, PSEA, CCEA 1970-, Bldg Rep; St Pauls Comm Nursery Schl Bd 1979-, Chprsn; *office:* Jackson Elem Schl Rd 6 Box 177 Johnstown PA 15909*

DITCHIK, DONNA R., Seventh Grade English Teacher; *b:* New York, NY; *ed:* C. W. Post Coll (BS) Speech, Theatre Arts Ed 1971, (MS) Educl Tech 1992; 34 Credit Hrs Post Grad Stud Hofstra Univ Hum, Drama; In-Svc Courses Levittown Tchrs Ctr; *cr:* Levittown Meml Jr Sr HS Eng Tchr 1971-79; Wisdom Lane Schl Eng Tchr 1980-81; MacArthur HS Eng Tchr 1981-87; Jonas E. Salk MS Eng Tchr 1989-; *ai:* Lang Arts Steering, TAWL, Cmptr Comms; Stu Tchr, GIT Adv; LUT, UFT 1972-; Tchr of Yr 1996; *office:* Jonas E. Salk MS Old Jerusalem Rd Levittown NY 11756

DITMAN, DAVID BRENT, Assistant Principal; *b:* Baltimore, MD; *m:* Denise Mary Valancius-Ditman; *c:* Benjamin E., Elliott J.; *ed:* Catonsville Comm Coll (AA) His, Ed 1975; Univ of MD at Baltimore (BA) His, Ed 1978; Loyola Coll in MD (MED) Educl Mngmt 1990; *cr:* Bishop John Neumann MS 7th-8th Grd Tchr 1981-84; Howard HS Soc Stud Tchr 1984-; *ai:* Class Adv 1987, 1990, 1992, 1994; Track Coach 1989-92; Howard Cty Ed Assoc, MD St Tchrs Assoc, NEA 1984-; Natl Assn of Schl Advs 1989-; Baltimore Street Car Museum 1977-, Trustee, VP; Catonsville United Meth Church 1967-, VP, United Meth Men; Tchng Excl Awd 1989; Outstanding Tchr, Historian US Capitol Historical Soc 1986; John Hanson Manuscript Awd, Baltimore Chapter, natl Railway Hist Soc 1984; *office:* Howard HS 8700 Old Annapolis Rd Rt 108 Ellicott City MD 21043

DITRI, ROBERT H., Social Studies Teacher; *b:* Providence, RI; *ed:* Univ MA at Boston (BA) His-Summa Cum Laude 1983; 16 Credit Hrs U MA at Boston; *cr:* Kennedy MS Soc Stud Tchr 1984-90; Waltham HS Soc Stud Tchr 1990-; *ai:* Intnl Relations Club, Peer Leadership Prgm Advs; Multi-Cultural Comm; Phi Alpha Theta 1982-; Waltham Educators Assn 1984-, Sec; NEA, MTA 1984-; Natl Cncl for Soc Stud; Horace Mann Grants Awded 3 Consecutive Yrs; Walthams Tchr Rcgntn Awd 1995; *office:* Waltham HS 617 Lexington St Waltham MA 02154

DITTELMAN, FAYE ALTSHULER, 7th Grd Eng & Lang Arts Tchr; *b:* Paterson, NJ; *w:* Stephen (dec); *c:* Jeffrey (dec), David, Michael; *ed:* Russell Sage Coll (BS) Elem Ed, Soc Stud 1964; Long Island Univ (MS) Spec Ed, LD 1987; 18 Grad Credits Rdng at Univ Hartford; 42 Credit Hrs General Ed Inservice; *cr:* South Windsor 1st Grd Tchr 1964-66; West Orchard Elem Schl Permanent Sub Tchr 1980-82; Chappaqua Childrens Wkshp Kndgtn Lead Tchr 1982-83; SAR Acad 1st, 2nd, 4th Grd General Stud Tchr 1983-87; Anne M. Dorner MS 6th-7th Grd ELA Tchr 1987-; *ai:* After Schl Bd Games Club Adv; Dist Comm on Rdng; PTA Tchr Rep; Fac Cncl; Westchester Cncl of Eng Educators 1987-; Hudson Valley Writing Project Fellow 1989-; Brandeis Womens Comm 1993-; Hadassah 1967-, Financial Sec; New Standards Lead Tchr; *office:* Anne M. Dorner MS Van Cortlandt Ave Ossining NY 10562*

DITTRICH, CHARLOTTE RYER, 7th-8th Grade English Teacher; *b:* Bayonne, NJ; *m:* Vincent; *c:* Stephen; *ed:* Jersey City St Coll (BA) Elem Ed 1969; *cr:* Lincoln Schl 6th Grd Tchr 1969-75; S. A. Roberson Schl 3rd, 6th-7th Grd Tchr 1977-87; J. M. Bailey Schl 5th-6th Grd, 7th-8th Grd Eng Tchr 1987-; *ai:* Peer Ldrshp, Yrbk Adv; Tech, Eng, Testing Comms; BTA, NJEA, NEA 1978-; *home:* 28 E 5th St Bayonne NJ 07002

DIVECCHIO, FRANCES, High School Computer Teacher; *ed:* Comm Coll of Beaver Cty (AS) Cmptr Sci 1984; Robert Morris Coll (BSBA) Bus Ed, Cmptr Sci 1989, (MS) Bus Ed 1992; *cr:* Medi Mart Ctr Data Entry Supvr 1985-88; Jefferson Cty Dubois Area Voc Tech Schl Cmptr Tchr 1989-91; Mt Pleasant Area HS Cmptr Tchr 1992-; *ai:* Delta Pi Epsilon, Tri St Bus Ed Assn, PA Bus Ed Assn 1989-; *office:* Mt Pleasant Area HS RR 4 Box 2222 Mount Pleasant PA 15666

DIVEKI, TIVADAR, Science Department Head; *b:* Jaszbereny, Hungary; *m:* Livija E. Klivecka; *ed:* Eotvos Lorand Univ at Budapest (MS) Math, Physics 1983; Attending NY Univ Math PHD Prgm; *cr:* Arpad HS Math, Physics Tchr 1983-85; Kando Kalman Tech Coll Asst Prof of Physics 1985-86; Anglo-Amer Int Schl Physics Tchr, Cmptr Coord 1986-88; Grace Church Schl Sci Dept Head 1988-; NY Univ Part-time Calculus Instr 1994; *ai:* Var Soccer, Boys Bsktbl Coach; Yrbk Adv; Educl Policy Comm; ATIS 1986-; Amer Math Soc 1994-; *office:* Grace Church Schl 86 4th Ave New York NY 10003*

DIVENUTO, MICHAEL JOSEPH, Italian Teacher; *b:* Springfield, MA; *m:* Dorothy Cocchi; *c:* Elena, Dominic; *ed:* Fairfield Univ (BA) Modern Langs 1973; Westfield St Coll Scndry Ed 1989; Universita Degli Studi Ital Lit, Art Cert 1972; Western New England Coll 15 Hrs; *cr:* Webb Jr HS Ital, Span Tchr 1973-77; Stan Home Intnl Intnl Prsnl Adm 1977-84; Springborne Labs VP Intnl Prsnl 1984-88; Springfield Cntrl HS Ital, Span Tchr 1988-; *ai:* MA Ital Tchrs Assn 1973-, MAFLA 1990-; SEA 1988-; Ital Cultural Ctr 1982-, Dir, Serviam Awd 1994I; *office:* Springfield Central HS 1840 Roosevelt Ave Springfield MA 01109

DIVIRGILIO, BARBARA ANN, Vice Principal & 6th Grd Tchr; *b:* Philadelphia, PA; *ed:* Gwynedd Mercy Coll (BS) Elem Ed 1977; *cr:* Most Blessed Sacrament Schl 3rd Grd Tchr 1961-62; Saint Callistus Schl Vice Prin, 6th Grd Tchr & CCD Dir 1962-; *ai:* Cofraternity Chrstn Doctrine Coord; NCEA, Elem Schls Admins 1983-; Distinguished Cath Educator 1987; Nom for Mirian Joseph Farrell Awd for Distinguished Tchrs 1991; *home:* 239 Bailey Rd Bryn Mawr PA 19010*

DIX, COLLEEN SCHROUDER, Spanish Teacher; *b:* Rochester, NY; *m:* Scott; *c:* Zachary; *ed:* SUNY at Cortland (BA) Ed 1987; Nazareth Coll (MS) Ed 1990; *cr:* Victor Jr HS Span Tchr 1987-.

DIX, DAVID J.,JR., Health Teacher; *b:* Albion, NY; *m:* Mary Jo Andalora; *ed:* Gannon Univ (BA) Hlth, PE 1988; St Univ of NY at Fredonia (MS) Elem Ed, Curr Dev 1995; *cr:* St Univ of NY at Brockport Grad Asst 1988; Jamestown Pub Schls Hlth, PE Tchr 1989-; *ai:* Var Boys Soccer, JV Girls Sftbl Coach 7 Yrs; NEA, Home Schl Comm Advy Bd 1989-; Natl Soccer Coaches Assn Amer 1994-; Jamestown Arsenal Soccer Club 1995-, Bd of Dirs, Head Coach; Jamestown Post Journal Soccer Coach of Yr 1995; *office:* Jefferson MS 195 Martin Rd Jamestown NY 14701

DIX, KATHLEEN M., Mathematics Teacher; *b:* Philadelphia, PA; *ed:* Univ Of NH (BA) Math 1969; *cr:* Portsmouth Jr HS Math Tchr 1969-72; Roosevelt Jr HS Math Tchr 1972-80; Westfield HS Math Tchr 1980-; *ai:* Cncl; NEA, NJEA 1972-; NCTM 1990-; Phi Beta Kappa 1969-; Nomination Shen Awd; *office:* Westfield HS 550 Dorian Rd Westfield NJ 07090

DIX, MARGUERITE ELIZABETH, Fifth Grade Teacher; *b:* Lewes, DE; *ed:* Salisbury St Coll (BS) Elem Ed 1984; Salisbury St Univ (MED) Math Ed 1989; *cr:* Selbyville MS Rdng, Eng, Math Tchr 1984-87; Georgetown Elem Schl Fifth Grd Tchr 1987-; *ai:* NEA 1984-; Natl Soc Daughters of Amer Revolution 1994-; Natl Soc Colonial Dames XVII Century 1995-; *office:* Georgetown Elem Schl 301A W Market St Georgetown DE 19947

DIX, ROBIN HARPER, 5th Grade Teacher; *b:* Dayton, OH; *m:* Anthony J.; *ed:* Univ of Dayton (BS) Elem Ed 1982; Wright St Univ (MS) Rdng Supervision 1985; 15 Hrs Gen Ed Antioch Univ 1994-95; *cr:* Hustead Elem Schl 5th Grd Tchr 1983-88; Indian Vly MS 5th Grd Tchr 1989-; *ai:* Soc Stud Course of Stu Comm; *office:* Indian Valley MS 510 Enon-Xenia Rd Enon OH 45323

DIXON, BETTY JO ZIMMERMAN, Third Grade Teacher; *b:* Steubenville, OH; *m:* Richard Nicholas; *c:* Devin Dylan, Dayson Drew; *ed:* West Liberty St (BA) Elem Ed 1971; West VA Univ (MA) Rdng 1978; 3 Hrs Soc Stud Cncl OH Univ; *cr:* Wintersville Elem Schl Second Grd Tchr 18 Yrs, Third Grd Tchr 7 Yrs; *ai:* Odyssey of the Mind Vol; ICEA, NEA 1971-; PTA 1971-; *home:* 108 Woodard Rd Weirton WV 26062

DIXON, BILLIE B., Business Teacher; *b:* Johnstown, PA; *m:* Lane; *c:* Lani, Deann, Eric; *ed:* Indiana Univ of PA (BA) Bus 1964; Univ of Pittsburgh 24 Credit Hrs; 12 Credit Hrs Co-Op Cert; *cr:* United HS Tchr 1964-, Co-Op Coord 1977-, Tech Prep Facilitator 1995-, Stu Tchr Co-Op; IUP Stu Tchr Co-Op; IN Vo-Tech Adult Ed; *ai:* FBLA; Bus Hnr Soc; UEA, PSEA, NEA 1964-; Tri-St 1990-; Lee Vol; Arin Grants; Edctr in Workplace; *office:* United HS PO Box 168 Armagh PA 15920

DIXON, CONSTANCE REBECCA (VALENTINE), Fifth Grade Teacher; *b:* Jersey City, NJ; *m:* Eric R.; *c:* Erica R.; *ed:* Jersey City St (BA) Psych 1979, (BA) Elem Ed 1979, (MS) Urban Ed, Sec Ed 1980; 3 Addl Hrs; *cr:* Hillside Schl GATE, Math, Sci Tchr 1979-80; Franklin Schl 3rd Grd Math, Sci Tchr 1981-82; J. F. Kennedy Schl 3rd Grd Math, Sci Tchr 1982-91, Head 5th Grd Tchr 1991-; *ai:* MEA 1979-80; NEA 1979-; SPEA 1981-; PDK 1980-; NAACP 1980-; YMCA 1992-, Trustee Bd; Phi Delta Kappa; Grant for Masters Prgm; *home:* 2 Sandra Ct Edison NJ 08820*

DIXON, DONALD T., English Teacher; *b:* Brooklyn, NY; *m:* Linda R. Sinsabaugh; *c:* Jennifer, Jeremiah, Jonathan; *ed:* St Univ of NY at New Paltz (BS) Eng Ed 1970; Masters Equivalency in Eng Ed at Coll of Saint Marys 1976; *cr:* Wappingers Falls Jr HS Eng Tchr 1970-72; Van Wyck Jr HS Eng Tchr 1972-; *ai:* Wappingers Congress of Tchrs 1970-; AFT, NYSUT 1970-; Drama Club Adv 1980-95; Stu Govt Adv 1973-83; *home:* 15 Reed Rd New Hamburg NY 12590

DIXON, JODY J., English Teacher; *b:* Hampton, VA; *m:* Michael A. Feldman; *ed:* St Lawrence Univ (BA) Eng Writing, Govt 1977; SUNY (MS) Ed 1981; *cr:* New York St Assembly Staff Writer 1982-89; Schoharie Cntrl Schl Eng Tchr 1989-; *ai:* Drama Dir; NYSUT 1989-; *office:* Schoharie Central Schl Main St Schoharie NY 12157

DIXON, KIMBERLY LAURENE, 3rd & 4th Grade Teacher; *b:* Spartanburg, SC; *ed:* Atlantic Union Coll (BS) Elem Ed 1993; *cr:* Kellogg Meml Elem 1-4 Grds Music Tchr 1992-93; Pine Tree Acad 3, 4 Grd Tchr 1994-; *ai:* Yth Comm Outreach Coord; Bd of Dir Wayside Evening Soup Kitchen; *office:* Pine Tree Acad 16 Pownal Rd Freeport ME 04032

DIXON, MARJORICE THOMAS, Business Education Teacher; *b:* Kinston, NC; *m:* Levy J.; *c:* Derrick; *ed:* Elizabeth City St Univ (BS) Bus Ed 1967; Trinity Coll (MAT) Concentrating in Schl Media Ctr 1974; 12 Credit Hrs Spcl Ed Courses; 12 Credit Hrs Comp Courses; 6 Credit Hrs Ubs Ed Courses; *cr:* Opportunities Industrialization Ctr Bus Tchr 1967-71, Supvr of Skills Trng 1971-72; LaReine HS Bus Tchr 1972-76; Martin Luther King Jr High Bus Tchr 1976-80; Crossland HS Bus Tchr 1980-; *ai:* PGCEA 1976-; NEA 1976-; Crosslands PTA 1980-; Camp Springs Civic Assn 1978-; Mt Calvary Bapt Church 1986-, Sunday Schl Tchr; *office:* Crossland HS 6901 Temple Hill Rd Temple Hills MD 20748*

DIXON, ROSWITHA B., Math Instructor; *b:* Ochtrup, Germany; *m:* Raymond; *c:* Rebecca; *ed:* Clarion Univ (BS) Math 1966; Univ of Pgh (MS) Math 1969; Attnd Univ of IN at Bloomington, Shippensburg Coll; *cr:* Oil City Schls Tchr 30 Yrs; *ai:* Stu Asst Core Team; Class, Peer Helper Adv; NEA, PSEA, OCEA 1966-; NSF & NDEA Grant to Shippensburg; Mentor Tchr; *office:* Oil City Area Sr HS 10 Lynch Blvd Oil City PA 16301*

DIXON, SHIRLEY ANN, Elementary School Principal; *b:* Cincinnati, OH; *ed:* Cabrini Coll (BS) ELC/EL 1984, (MA) ELC/EL 1989; Widener Univ Pursuing Doctor of Ed for Rdng & Lang; Addl 15 Credits in Ed; *cr:* The Philadelphia Housing Authority Re-Examination Analysis 1969-84; Girard Coll 5th Grd Classroom Tchr 1985-93, Prin/Instr Coord 1993-; Cabrini Coll Teaching in Dept of Ed; *ai:* Law-Related Curr-Tchng the Bill of Rights & Law; The Stock Market Game-Tchng Ec Mem of the PA Cncl of Ec ED; Mem of Opera Ebony Inc.; Mem of Toastmasters Intnl; Treasurer of the Haverford-Brown Coalition; Law-Related Curricular under the Philadelphia Schl Dist; NAACP 1960-; NAIS 1993-; ASCD 1986-; NASSP 1993-; AGB 1990-; Mem of Cabrini Coll Board Trustees 1990-; Cabrini Coll Bd of Trustee 1989-; Opera Ebony Inc 1980-; PA Stu Ed Assn 1984-; Middle St Assm of Colls & Schls; *office:* Girard Coll 2101 S College Ave Philadelphia PA 19121

DIXON, SUSAN GALE (WEBER), HS English & Lang Arts Tchr; *b:* Cleveland, OH; *m:* Lawrence; *c:* Gregory, Kathryn; *ed:* Heidelberg Coll (BA) Eng & Ed 1975; Ashland Univ (MA) Curr & Instr 1991; *cr:* Jefferson Jr HS 1975-79; Elyria HS 1979-; *ai:* Soph Class Adv; Site Based Mgmt Team; Amer Assn of Univ Women 1994-; NEA; OEA; EEA; *office:* Elyria HS 6th & Middle Ave Elyria OH 44035

DIZE, KAREN M., French & English Teacher; *b:* Baltimore, MD; *m:* Noah Benjamin III; *c:* Noah IV, Matthew Brennan; *ed:* Bridgewater Coll (BA) Fr 1969; Attnd Univ de Strasbourg, Univ of MD & WA Coll; *cr:* Chestertown HS Eng & Fr Tchr 1969-71; Kent Cty HS Eng & Fr Tchr 1971-; *ai:* Its Acad Coach; Fac Advy Comm; KCTA, MSTA & NEA 1969-; AATF 1970-; Delta Kappa Gamma 1975-, VP; Christ United Meth Church 1978-; Mid Shore Symphony Bd 1993-; *office:* Kent County HS Lambs Meadow Rd Worton MD 21678

DIZIGAN, DOROTHY SVAB, Fifth Grade Teacher; *b:* Bridgeport, CT; *m:* Robert A.; *c:* Matthew, Mark, Paula; *ed:* Southern CT St (BS) Early Chldhd Ed 1965; CT Coll (MAT) Ed 1988; *cr:* St Joseph Schl Fifth Grd Tchr 9 Yrs; *ai:* Stock Market Club Adv; NCTM 1992-; ADK 1989-, Treas; *office:* Saint Joseph Schl 25 Squire St New London CT 06320

DLOUHY, BARRY RICHARD, English Teacher & Dept Chair; *b:* Woodside, NY; *m:* Joan C.; *ed:* St Francis Coll at Loretto (BA) Eng 1972; SUNY at Stony Brook (MA) Tchng Lit 1984; Dowling Coll (PD) Cmptr Ed 1990, (PD) Educl Admin 1995; *cr:* Westhampton Beach HS Eng Tchr 1972-73; North Babylon HS Eng Tchr 1974-, Eng Dept Chair 1994-; *ai:* Schl Newspaper Adv; Effective Schls, Site-Based Mngmt Teams; Tech Assessment, Curr Dev & Implementation; NCTE 1975-; ASCD, NYASCD 1993-; *office:* North Babylon HS 1 Phelps Ln North Babylon NY 11703

DLOUHY, JOAN CECELIA, English Teacher; *b:* Bay Shore, NY; *m:* Barry R.; *ed:* Dowling Coll (BA) Eng 1984, (MS) Ed 1986; *cr:* East Islip HS Eng Tchr 1986-; *ai:* Newspaper Adv; Former NHS Adv; Dept Schl Improvement Team Rep; NCTE, Phi Delta Kappa 1986-; *office:* East Islip HS Redmen St Islip Terrace NY 11752

DLUGOS, JOANNA J., 6th Grade Teacher; *b:* Perth Amboy, NJ; *m:* Martin; *c:* Michele, Ann Marie, Allison; *ed:* Trenton St Coll (MA) Ed 1968, (BA) Elem Ed 1964; Supervisory Cert Georgian Ct Coll 1991; *cr:* Woodbridg Twp Schls Grds 1-2, 6th Grd Tchr 21 Yrs; Woodbridge MS 6th Grd Tchr 6 Yrs; *ai:* NEA, NJEA, MCEA, WTEA 1964-; Pt Pleasant Ath Boosters 1990-; Excl in Ed Awd Woodbridge Twp 1995; Nom Golden Apple Awd 1996.

DLUGOSZ, DAVID A., Health Teacher; *b:* Lorain, OH; *m:* Jennifer Jackson; *c:* Christian, Dennis, Andrew, Kerry; *ed:* Wilmington Coll (BS) Hlth & PE 1974; Kent St Univ (MA) Curr & Supervision 1977; *cr:* Troy Jr HS Hlth Tchr 1974-84; Avon Lake HS Hlth Tchr 1984-; *ai:* Hlth & PE Dept Chm; Ftbl Head Coach; Conditioning Coord; NEA, OEA, ALEA 1974-; AAHPERD; Various Coaching Orgs; City Recreation Commission 1988-, Chair; Avon Lake Schls Tchr of Yr; A P Dist Coach of Yr; Conf-Cty Coach of Yr; Coach of OH North-South Game 1995; *office:* Avon Lake HS 175 Avon Belden Rd Avon Lake OH 44012

DOAK, NANCY ANN, Mathematics Teacher; *b:* Philadelphia, PA; *c:* Michael C.; *ed:* Millersville Univ (BS) Math, Scndry Ed 1982; Beaver Coll 2 Programming Courses 6 Credit Hrs; Jersey City St Coll Adv Calc I, Fortran II 6 Credit Hrs; St Petersburg Coll Assertive Discipline 3 Credits Hrs; *cr:* Palisades Schl Sub Tchr 1982-83; Cntrl Bucks Schl Dist Long Term Sub Tchr 1982-83; Lakewood HS Math Tchr 1983-; Ingersol-Rand Mrktg 1994-95; *ai:* Homebound Tutor; Soc Club; Soc Comm; NEA, NJEA, LEA 1983-; Lenape Vly Soccer 1995-, Newspaper Correspondence; PTO Butler 1995-; PTA Lakewood 1993-; Key Club Awd for Tchng Excl by Stdnts; *office:* Lakewood HS 855 Somerset Ave Lakewood NJ 08701*

DOBECK, JOANN NAROLESKI, 4th Grade Teacher; *b:* Shamokin, PA; *w:* Edward W. Jr. (dec); *c:* Edward, Lindsey; *ed:* Bloomsburg Univ (BA) Elem Ed 1975, (MS) Elem Ed 1978; *cr:* Shamokin Area Elem Tchr 1975-; *ai:* NEA 1975-; PSEA 1975-; SEA 1975-; Our Lady of Hope Yth Group 1995-; *office:* Shamokin Area Elem Schl 3000 W State St Coal Township PA 17866

DOBINSKI, PATRICIA PETERS, Living Skills Teacher; *b:* Buffalo, NY; *m:* Thomas; *c:* Dana, Bradley; *ed:* St Univ of NY at Onconta (BS) Home Ec Ed, Clothing, Textiles 1985; St Univ of NY at Buffalo (MS) Scndry Ed 1989-; Continuing Ed; *cr:* Pembroke Cntrl Jr Sr HS Living Skills Tchr 1985-87; Cheetkowaga Cntrl Jr Sr HS Living Skills Tchr `987-; *ai:* SADD Adv; Stu Asst Prgm Steering Comm; Western NY United Against Drugs & Alcohol Consortium; Bsktbl, Vlybl, Soccer, Cross Cntry Cert Coach; Amer Home Ec Assn 1985-, Western NY VP; NYS Home Ec Tchrs Assn 1985-; Natl Fed Interscholastic Coaches Assn 1986-; Dean's List, Highest Hnrs for Undergrad, Grad Work; Frances K. ToddSchlrsp; NY St Challenger Flwshp; *office:* Cheektowaga Cntrl Jr Sr HS 3600 Union Rd Cheektowaga NY 14225

DOBRICK, DENNIS STEPHEN, Principal; *b:* West Mifflin, PA; *m:* Peggy Ann Dresel; *c:* Kristin, Matthew, Dennis; *ed:* Ft Hays Univ (BS) PE 1969; Univ of Dayton (MS) Elem Admin 1985; Attnd KS St Tchrs Coll Emporia, Kent St Univ, Franciscan Univ; *cr:* Edison Local Schl Dist 6th Grd Rdng Tchr 1970-93; S C dennis Elem Prin 1993-; *ai:* OEA 1970-93; ELEA 1970-93, Exec Branch 1 Yr; OAESA 1993-; Lions Club, 2 Yrs; Wintersville Cncl 1995-, Councilman; Nom for Jennings Scholar; Yrbk, Ftbl, Track, Golf, Girls Bsktbl Coach; *office:* S C Dennis Elem Schl 1305 Dennisway Toronto OH 43964*

DOBROWOLSKI, JOAN P., 11th-12th Grd English Teacher; *b:* Dickson City, PA; *m:* Alex; *c:* Carol Ann, Holly; *ed:* Montclair St (BA) Soc Stud, Eng 1963; 6 Credits Accounting; Civil War in Lit Symposium; *cr:* Holy Spirit Elem 6th-8th Grd Eng Tchr 1980-84; St Peter's HS Eng Tchr 1984-; *ai:* SADD; Diocese Metuchen Curr Comm; Stu Tchr Supvr; NCTA 1980-; NJ Comm for Hum Dickens Weekend; Nom Excl in Ed Awd New Brunswick Tomorrow; *office:* Saint Peters HS 175 Somerset St New Brunswick NJ 08901

DOCKERAY, KATHLEEN CROAKE, Fourth Grade Teacher; *b:* Washington, DC; *m:* William Floyd; *c:* Dawn Czahor, Jennifer Derrick; *ed:* Univ of MD (BS) Ed, Sociology 1969; Johns Hopkins (MS) GATE 1990; John F. Kennedy Ctr Tchr Ed Prgm Level 6 180 Hrs; Loyola Coll 24 Credit Hrs; *cr:* Howard Cty Schl Instrl Aide, Sub 1978-80; St Louis Schl 4th Grd Tchr 1980-; *ai:* Stu Cncl Co Moderator; Talent Show Dir; Mid Sts Accredidation Screening Comm; Soc Stud Curr; ASCD 1995-; NSTM; Elem Schl Tchrs Assn Balko Archdiocese 1985-; Columbia Figure Skating Club 1985-89, Sec; Washington Figure Skating Club 1989-; Washington Ice Club 1994-; *office:* St Louis Schl PO Box 155 Rt 108 Clarksville MD 21029*

DOCTOR, IVIN STUART, Chemistry Teacher; *b:* Brooklyn, NY; *m:* Miriam; *c:* Lenny, Robin, Adam; *ed:* Brooklyn Coll (BA) Chem 1966, (MA) Chem 1969; Advanced Cert in Admin & Supervision 1972; Natl Sci Fnd Summer Inst at City Coll & Brooklyn Polytech Material Sci Total 12 Credits; *cr:* F D Roosevelt HS Chem Tchr 1966-; *ai:* UFT & AFT 1966-; Outstanding Scndry Educator of Amer 1974, FDR HS Tchr of Yr 1995-; *home:* 741 Woolley Ave Staten Island NY 10314*

DODD, ALAN CHARLES, Art Teacher; *b:* Milford, CT; *m:* Dorothy Magee; *c:* Sara, Peter, Elizabeth; *ed:* Southern CT St (BS) Art Ed 1968, (MS) Art Ed 1979; 6th Yr Admin & Supervision 1991; *cr:* Milford Pub Schls Elem Art Specialist 1968-71; Milford HS Art Tchr 1972-73; Joseph A Foran HS Art Tchr 1974-; *ai:* Natural Helpers, Jr Class & Art Club Adv; NEA 1969-; Milford Fine Arts Cncl 1975-; Chrstn Svc Brigade 1984-, Ranger; Foran High Tchr of the Yr 1978; *office:* Joseph A Foran HS 80 Foran Rd Milford CT 06460*

DODD, BRIAN WILLARD, Music & Chorus Teacher; *b:* Wilmington, OH; *m:* Lori Lea Spicer; *c:* Devaney Danielle, Morgan Nicole; *ed:* OH St Univ (BMEd) 1985; *cr:* East Knox Local Schls Gen Music, Chorus & Instrumental Music Tchr 1985-; Mount Vernon Nazarene Coll Dir of Percussion Ensemble 1994-; *ai:* Class Adv 1985-; Bands: Marching, Jazz, Pep, Concert; Percussion Ensemble; OMEA 1981-; MENC 1981-; OEA 1985-; NEA 1985-; Amer Fed of Musicians 1985-; Mount Vernon Nazarene Coll Percussion Ensemble Dir 1993-; Bladensburg Fire Dept 1985-, Advance EMT, Firefighter, Squad Chief 3 Yrs, Fire Capt 1 Yr; East Knox Jr High Tchr of the Yr 1986-87; *office:* East Knox Local Schl Dist 23227 Coshocton Rd Box 128 Howard OH 43028*

DODDS, DEBORAH JOYCE, HS History Teacher; *b:* Youngstown, OH; *m:* William J. Jr.; *c:* Kerri, Tracy; *ed:* Bucknell Univ (BA) His 1970; Rutgers Univ (MS) Soc Stud Ed 1979; Applicant for Doctoral Prgm in Ed; *cr:* Orange Ave MS Tchr 1972-73; Summit MS Tchr 1973-77; W. Orange HS Tchr 1986-; *ai:* Jr St of Amer WOHS Chptr Tchr, Adv; NJ Selection Comm for US Senate Yth Schlsp Reader; NEA 1972-; WOEA 1986-; Kappa Delta Pi, Phi Alpha Theta 1970-; GS USA 1984-, Ldr, Registrar, Ldr Trainor Del, Outstdng Svc Ldr; The Pres Yth Svc Awd 1994, New Prov Branch Founder; New Providence Music Booster 1991-, VP; New Providence PTA 1982-; *office:* West Orange HS 51 Conforti Ave West Orange NJ 07052*

DODDS, RICHARD DELANO, English & AP English Teacher; *b:* Plattsburgh, NY; *m:* Margaret Sweet; *c:* Richard Delano Jr., Matthew Nesbit; *ed:* Williams Coll (BA) Eng-Cum Laude 1961; Harvard Univ (MAT) Eng 1962; Addl Stud Oxford Univ, Univ of VT; *cr:* Mt Greylock Regnl HS Eng Tchr 1962-; *ai:* Lit Magazine Adv; Supt Search, Prin Schedule, New England Assn of Schls Steering Comm; Coll Intern Prgm Mentor; Eng Curr Ldr; NEA, MTA, MGFTA, ASCD; Williamstown Schlsp Bd; Second Congregational Church, Mission Comm, Choir Mem; Williams Coll Gifford Comm; Williamstown Pub Libr Lecture on Hamlet; Williams Coll Panelist on ED; Darmouth Coll Tchr Recognition 1994-95; Tufts Univ Outstdng Tchr Awd 1995; Stdnts Outstdng Tchr Awd 1991, 1995; *office:* Mount Greylock Regnl HS 1781 Cold Spring Rd Williamstown MA 01267

DODGE, BETSEY CAROLINE, Former Teacher; *b:* Goffstown, NH; *ed:* Keene St Tchrs Coll (BED) Elem 1961; Antioch Grad Schl (MED) Elem Ed 1985; *cr:* Manchester Smyth Rd Elem 4th Grd Tchr 1962-63; Colt's Neck Elem 4th Grd Tchr 1963-64; Amherst Elem 2nd Grd Tchr 1965; New Boston Cntrl 3rd-6th Grd Classroom Tchr 1966-90; Headstart Organizing Tchr 1972; *ai:* Textbook Stud Curr; Statue of Liberty Restoration Fair Organizer; Involving Stu in Earth Day Prgmd & Hazardous Waste Day Annual Ed Prgms; New Boston Conservation Comm 1976-, Mem, Chm; Christa Mc Auliffe Sabbatical Runner-up; *home:* 40 Dodge Rd New Boston NH 03070

DODGE, BETTY WILCOX, Reading Teacher; *b:* Roslyn, NY; *m:* Henry C.; *c:* Matthew, Martha; *ed:* Keene St Univ (BED) Elem, Sp Ed 1968; Solve Trained; Brody Rdng Method Trng; GATE Extensive Trng; *cr:* Greenville Elem Schl 1st Grd Tchr 1968-70; New Ipswich Coop Kndgtn Schl Presch Tchr 1972-73; Con Val, Concord Schl Dists Sub, Staff Dev Comm 1974-81; James Mastricola MS 6th-8th Grd Rdng, Math, Eng, Lang Arts Tchr 1982-; *ai:* PTG Rep; Lang Arts Steering Comm; Bear Brook Environmental Ed Prgm Steering Comm; NEA, NHEA 1984-94; Pop Warner, Chrldng Dir; Project SALT Grand Awded; Project Safeguard; *office:* Mastricola MS 26 Baboosic Lk Rd Merrimack NH 03054*

DODGE, ELIZABETH LEYON, English Teacher; *b:* Wellesley, MA; *m:* David Sinclair; *c:* Jennifer Eldredge, John Sinclair, Andrew David; *ed:* Univ of NH (BA) Eng Lit 1958, (MED) Ed 1963; Grad Courses Ed Admin for Cert as Scndry Prin; *cr:* Somersworth HS Eng Tchr 1959-64; Winnacunnet HS Eng Tchr 1965-66; Oyster River HS Eng Tchr 1978-; *ai:* Stu Environmental Action League, Lit Magazine, Advy Cncl Adv; NEA 1985-; NCTE 1982-; NH Assn of Tchrs of Eng; Co-Author of Weaving In the Women Transforming the High School English Curriculum 1993; *office:* Oyster River HS 55 Coe Dr Durham NH 03824*

DODGE, MARGARET A., Foreign Language Dept Chair; *b:* Po VA; *c:* Rebecca, Andrea; *ed:* Colby Coll (BA) Fr 1964; St Univ Geneseo (MFEd) Fr & Ed 1982; *cr:* Georges Valley HS Fr Tchr Cordova HS Ger Tchr 1968; Honeoye Cntrl Schl 9th-12th Grd Foreign Lang Dept Chair 1979-; *ai:* Fr Club; Instructional Steeri Scndry Advy Cncl; Authentic Assessment Design Team; NYSAFLT, AATF, WAFFLE 1979-; Tchr of Yr; Multicultural & Co Ed Schlsp From Fr Cultural Svcs.

DODI, KAROL DEMKO, Seventh Grade Science Teacher; *b:* Ft GA; *m:* Alex; *ed:* Douglas Coll(BA) Span 1970; Rutgers Univ (1973; 75 Hrs Post Collegial Stud in Sci, Spec Ed, Cmptrs, Sandburg MS Span Tchr 1970-94, 7th Grd Sci Tchr 1994-; Innovation Comm; Stu of Month Comm; NEA, NJ Ed Assn, Midd Ed Assn 1970-; Old Bridge Ed Assn 1970-, Assn Rep 1972-73, 1978-81, 1990-93; United Daughters of The confederacy 1987-; Flwshp; Sandy Hook Marine Sci Consortium; *office:* Carl Sandbu 516 Old Bridge NJ 08859

DODRILL, DAVAN JAMES, English Teacher; *b:* Columbus, Rhonda Bogue; *c:* Andrew, Jennifer, James; *ed:* Univ of SC (BA) OH Univ (BSEd) Eng, Ed 1977; OH St Univ (MA) Ed Adm ABD-PHD Candidate; *cr:* Columbus Pub Schls Eng Tchr 1977-8 John F. Kennedy Schl Eng Tchr 1989-91; Columbus St Co Part-time Eng Tchr; *ai:* Kenyon Coll, HS Consortium Amer St OEA, CEA 1977-; Phi Delta Kappa 1995-; 23 Poems Pub; Natl En for Hum; 2 Germany Articles Pub; 6 Tchrs Writing Awds; 6 Publisher Awds; OH House of Rep for Stu Awd Winners; *office:* 1500 E Broad St Columbus OH 43205

DODRILL, JILL SUZANNE, K-12th Grade Music Tea Steubinville, OH; *ed:* IN Univ of PA (BSEd) Music Ed 1988; 24 II Perm Cert Duquesne Univ; *cr:* Adelphoi Village Group Hom 1989-90; Ferndale Area Schl Dist Grds K-12 Music Tchr 1 Marching Band Asst Dir; Schl Plays, Jackets Required Vocal Ja Annual Schl Talent Show, Talent Cross Keyshore Talent Show Di HS Drama Clubs Adv; Fernstock Dir, Founder; MENCI, PME Lights on Hill 1983-, Dir; Keystone Amer Red Cross Awd 1993; Awd Excl in Tchng, Meritorious Svc 1995; *office:* Ferndale Area 100 Dartmouth Ave Johnstown PA 15905*

DODSON, JAMES RICHARD, Soc Studies & History Tea Detroit, MI; *m:* Linda Ann Sturza; *c:* Sara Michelle, Joshua Ro Cntrl MI Univ (BS) His 1975; Ashland Univ, Baldwin-Wallace Credit Hrs Towards Masters; *cr:* Sacred Heart Acad His & Ge 1975-76; St Joseph Schl His, Rdng, Rel Tchr & Coach 1977-78; C HS Soc Stud, His & Pol Sci Tchr & Dept Chair & Coach 1978-95; HS His Tchr & Head Ftbl Coach 1995-; *ai:* Head Var Ftbl Coach Room Monitor; AFT 1995-; *office:* Buckeye HS 3084 Columbia Rd OH 44256

DODSON, LINDA MAE, Math Teacher; *b:* Roaring Spring, PA; Clayton; *c:* Clay, Ali; *ed:* Penn St Univ (BS) Scndry Ed 1983; St Coll (MS) Ed 1986; *cr:* Frederick HS Math Tchr 1983-84; Everett Tchr 1984-; Allegheny Comm Coll PartTime Math Tchr 19 Renaissance Treas; NHS Selection Comm; Schlrshp & Stu of th Comm; NEA 1983-; EAEA 1984-; Lower Claar Church of the 1979-, Bd.

DODSWORTH, ANNETTE MARIE, Junior High School Tea Dayton, OH; *m:* Charles R.; *c:* Christopher, Robin; *ed:* Univ of (BA) Eng 1965, (MA) Eng 1973; *cr:* St Mary-Margaret Schl Tchr Precious Blood Schl Tchr 1966-75; Sinclair Comm Coll Part-ti 1979-84; Precious Blood Schl Tchr 1984-; *ai:* Power of the Pen M Coach; Stu Vol, Safety Patrol Advs; OCTELA 1990-; WOCTELA NCTA 1984-; Tchr of Yr 1994; *office:* Precious Blood Cath Elem S Denlinger Rd Dayton OH 45426

DODSWORTH, JEAN, Math Dept Chair; *b:* Philadelphia, Caldwell Coll (BA) Ed, Math 1980; Cmptr Sci Cours Morristown-Beard Schl Math Tchr, Dept Chair 1980-; *ai:* Stu C Class Adv; Acad, Policy & Procedures, Benefits Comm; AMTNJ, MAA 1989-; *office:* Morristown-Beard Schl PO Box 591 Morrist 07962

DODSWORTH, MARJORIE VANSCOYOC, English Teac Altoona, PA; *c:* Gregory Kelly; *ed:* Edinboro Univ (BS) Scndry 1966; Syracuse Univ (MS) Eng Ed 1971; Edinboro Univ Rdng Ce Admin Cert 1980; *cr:* North Syracuse Schls Tchr 1966-71; Gira Tchr 1971-72; Erie Schl Dist Tchr 1972-; *ai:* Creative Writing Cl Magazines; Schl Newspaper; Dramatic Dir of Plays, Musicals, Dep N Syracuse; NYSTA, NEA 1966-; EEA, PSEA, NEA 1971-; NCTE IRA 1973-; *office:* Central HS 3325 Cherry St Erie PA 16508

DOE, WILLIAM J., Professor of Engineering; *b:* Ogdensburg, Carol M. Souce; *c:* Rebbecca Aiken, William, Steven, Christopher Univ of NY at Canton (AAS) Drafting & Design 1959; Rochester Tech (BSME) Mechanical Engrng 1962; Syracuse Univ Mechanical Engrng 1972; Univ of CA at Los Angeles 9 Credit Hr SUNY at Potsdam 3 Credit Hrs 1993; Attnd LeHeigh Univ, SUNY a Brook, CA Polytechnical Inst; *cr:* Eastman Kodak Co Dev Engr 1 Onondaga Comm Coll Asst Prof 1963-66; SUNY at Morrisville Ass 1966-67; Ford Fndtn Project Tech Consultant 1967-69; Jefferson Coll Engrng Prof 1969-; *ai:* Senate Nomng, Tech Advy & Long Planning for Tech Comms; Am Soc of Engrng Edctrs 1969-90; NEA Lions Club 1969-75; Adams Free Lib 1975-84, Dir; Adams NY P Bd 1988-; Chancellors Awd Recipient 1992; St Univ of NY Excl Svcs; *office:* Jefferson Comm Coll Outer Coffeen Street Waterto 13601

DOELFEL, EVELYN KATHERINE, Fourth Grade Teach Pittsburgh, PA; *ed:* PA St Univ (BS) Elem Ed 1964; 36 Credits Equivalency; *cr:* Highlands Schl Dist 4th Grd Tchr 1964-, 4th Gr Chprsn 1969-, K-6 Lang Arts Chprsn 1969-; Curr Cabinet 1991-; Cncl, Newspaper Spon; NEA, PSEA, HEA 1964-; ASCD 1991-; Family Inst Gift of Time Tribute 1991; *office:* Fawn Schl RD 1 B Natrona Heights PA 15065

DOELFEL, PAULA M., US History Teacher; *b:* Pittsburgh, PA; *ed.* Univ (BA) Sociology, (BS) EKED 1971; 24 Addl Hrs Post Grad C Scndry Soc Stud Cert; Masters Equivalency; *cr:* Highlands Schl D Grd Tchr 1972-79, 6th Grd Tchr World Cultures 1979-95, 8th Grd T His 1995-; *ai:* Stu Asst Team; NEA, PSEA 1972-; Highlands E 1972-, Alternate Rep; Carnegie Squirrel Hill Freinds of Lib Historical Soc of Western PA 1996-; Natl MS Conf Toronto Ont Pre 1989; Amer Family Inst Gift of Time Tribute 1991; *office:* Highlan Argonne Dr & Broadview Natrona Heights PA 15065

DOERR, VERONICA MAGDALENA, English Professor; *b:* Buc Hungary; *m:* Edgar R. III; *c:* Jonathan E. Bergholz, Damon M Carnegie Inst of Tech (BS) Eng 1961; Carnegie-Mellon Univ (MA 1967; Eng, Theater Arts Credits Univ of Pittsburgh; *cr:* Pittsburgh Planning Assn Rsrch sst, Ed Book 1961-63; Coll fo San Mateo Ass Eng 1969-70; Carnegie Mellon Univ Dept of Publications, Writ 1970-71; Comm Coll Allegheny Cty Inst Asst Prof Eng 1967-69, Prof, Eng Prof 1972-; *ai:* Adv Campus Newspaper, Lit Magazin Publications; Liaison Intnl Visitors; Established Jrnlsm Prgm; AFT Two Yr Coll Assn 1987-, Local Arrangements Chair, Treas, Exec C

Democratic Club; Woodrow Wilson Flwshp Honorable Mention; Flwshps; Frances Camp Parrington Meml Awd; Allegheny Cty b; Dir Plays; Pub, Ed in Chief Magazine, Newspaper; *office:* l Algny Co Algny Cmps 808 Ridge Ave Pittsburgh PA 15212

IATE, JUDITH EVERETT, Art Teacher; *b:* Lowell, MA; *m:* *ed:* Emmanuel Coll (BA) Fine Arts, Art His, Ed 1971; *cr:* Lowell Art Tchr 1971-; *ai:* Yrbk Adv; AFT 1985-; United Tchrs of 71-; *office:* Dr An Wang MS 365 W Meadow Rd Lowell MA

T, ALAN ROBERT, Social Studies Teacher; *b:* Newark, NJ; *m:* E. Heuberger; *c:* Pamela, Alison; *ed:* St Peter's Coll (BA) His ey City St Coll (MA) Urban Admin, Supervision 1986; Thirty it Hrs; *cr:* Harrison HS Basic Compensation Math Tchr 1977-81, Ftbl Coach 1981-85, Soc Stud Tchr 1985-, Contract Negoitator, Assn 1988-; *ai:* Soc Stud Facilitator; Chprsn Mid Sts Comm for ct Negotiator; NEA, NJEA 1977-; Kearny Youth Soccer 1990-, earney Thistle FC 1991-, Coach; Kearny Recreation 1990-, tle League Coach Bsbl, Sftbl, Bsktbl; *office:* Harrison HS 1 N 5th n NJ 07029

CK, RONALD G., 4th Grade Elementary Teacher; *b:* Yonkers, ancy Wright; *ed:* Jersey City St Tchrs Coll (BA) Elem Ed 1969; Egg Harbor Twp Schl Sixth Grd Tchr 1969-78; Elem Schl Fourth 1979-; *ai:* Elem Boys Bsktbl Coach; Earth Day, Christmas Tree EA, NJEA, LEHTT Assn 1969-; Jaycees 1973-, Charter Mem; g Harbor Twp Bd of Hlth 1975-77; Little Egg Harbor Twp n Club 1969; Ocean Cty NJ Realtors 1980-; Sarasota Cty FL 1995; Friends of LIbrary LEH; Golden Apple Achvmt Awd; ial Yrbk Dedication Recipient 1976; *office:* Little Egg Hrbr Twp Frog Pond Rd Little Egg Hbr NJ 08087

Y, JEFFREY DANIEL, Emerson House Dean; *b:* Malden, MA; a M. St Peter; *c:* Patrick, Bridget; *ed:* Merrimack Coll (BA) Eng ; Univ of MA at Lowell (MED) Scndry Admin 1993; *cr:* Parker Grd Eng Tchr 1976-79; Chelmsford HS 10th-12th Grd Eng Tchr Emerson House Dean 1995-; *ai:* ASCD 1994-; NASSP 1995-; b 1989-, Sec 3 Times, 100 Percent Sec Awd 3 Times; Chelmsford Dedication 1990; *office:* Chelmsford HS 200 Richardson Rd elmsford MA 01863

'Y, KATHRYN D'IMPERIO, Sixth Grade Teacher; *b:* Port Y; *m:* Stephen D.; *c:* Katy, Sean, Scott; *ed:* SUC at Cortland (BS) 1971, (MS) EE, Rdng 1974; *cr:* Whitney Point Cntrl Schl 6th Grd -; *ai:* Founded Elem Schl Store 1988; Dream Eagle Book Store 4-95; MS Store; Sixth Grd Dept Chprsn; WP Tchrs Assn 1971-, NYSUT 1971-; Town, Cnty Homemakers 1983-, Svc Org; CCD Grd 1989-, Natl Soc Tole, Decorative Painters; *home:* PO Box ney Point NY 13862

'Y, MARY GIBNEY, Sixth Grade Teacher; *b:* Jersey City, NJ; ew J.; *c:* Kathryn; *ed:* St Peter's Coll (BA) Eng 1986, (MS) Ed St Anthony HS 9th-11th Grd Eng Tchr 1986-90; Samuel E. Shull Grd Tchr 1991-93; Wm Mc Ginnis Schl 6th Grd Tchr 1993-95; hull Schl 6th Grd Tchr 1995-; *office:* Samuel E Shull MS 380 Hall Amboy NJ 08861*

AN, SHEILA, Fifth Grade Teacher; *b:* Brooklyn, NY; *m:* *c:* Scott, Cory; *ed:* Brooklyn Coll (BA) Elem Ed 1965; 19 Addl redit Hrs Brideport, Kean, Georgian Court; *cr:* P S 309 Third-Six 1965-70; Defino Cntrl 4-5 Grd Tchr 1985-; *ai:* PTO Liason 3 Yrs; ut Ldr 2 Yrs; Camp Indian Head Group Ldr; Tutoring; AFT NEA, NJEA 1985-; ORT 1965-, VP; Natl Cncl Jewish Women; HEV Shalom Bd; *office:* Defino Cntrl Schl 175 Hwy 79 Marlboro

, EILEEN MARIE, Fifth Grade Teacher; *b:* Bethlehem, PA; *ed:* Hill Coll (BA) Elem Ed 1983; Boston Coll (MA) Pastoral 1995; *ai:* Chrldng; Mission Club; Intervention Team for Tchrs,

, DEBORAH JO, English & Writing Teacher; *b:* Easton, PA; *m:* *c:* Joseph F. III, Brieana K., Kieren E.; *ed:* Allentown Coll of St le Soles (BA) Eng, ED 1975; East Stroudsburg Univ (MED) Ed ooperative Learning Wkshp Trng; Immigration Lit Course; *cr:* Cath Schl L A Tchr 1975-80; Bethlehern CAth HS Eng Tchr Lehigh Carbon C C Part-time Adj Fac 1989-91; Northampton C me Adj Fac 1990-91; Notre DAme HS Eng, Writing Tchr 1991-; TA 1980-, Bldg Rep; St Jane's Schl Bd 1994-; *office:* Notre Dame Church Rd Easton PA 18045

, GERALD JOHN,JR., Band Director; *b:* Marlboro, MA; *m:* ll; *ed:* St Michaels Coll (BA) Music 1978; Univ of MA at Amherst Music 1985; Conducting Stud at New England Conservatory of Electronic Music Stud at Berklee Coll of Music; *cr:* Northboro Pub usic Educator 1979-82; Ipswich Pub Schls Dir of Bands 1985-; *ai:* usic Educators 1979-, Dist Coord; Intnl Assn of Jazz Ed 1985-; nt Assn 1992-; Fullbright Scholar England 1992-93; Music Dir of hore Youth Symphony; *office:* Ipswich Pub Schls 130 High St MA 01938

, JAMES LAURENCE, Assoc Professor of Health Sci; *b:* gh, NY; *m:* Susan Friemarck; *c:* Dinh, Richard; *ed:* Univ of MI (BS) d, PE 1968; PA St Univ (MED) PE 1969; 64 Addl Credits ogy, Exercise Physiology Univ of TN, WV Univ, Penn St Univ; *cr:* aven Univ PE Tchr, Cross Cntry, Track Coach 1969-75, PE Tchr, ntry Coach 1975-86, Prof of Physiology, Exercise Physiology *i:* Univ Wide Promotions Comm; Distance Running, Road Racing e Person; ACSM 1988-; *office:* Lock Haven Univ 105 Himes Lock A 17745

, JEREMIAH J., Assoc Prof of Philosophy Dept; *b:* Worcester, Merina J. Healey; *c:* Jonathan J.; *ed:* Boston Coll (BA) Philosophy New Schl for Soc Rsrch (MA) Philosophy 1972; PHD Cand New Soc Rsrch Philosophy 1974; *cr:* New Schl for Soc Rsrch Mem of 5; Baruch Coll Adj Lecturer 1975-78; Rivier Coll Instr, Asst Prof, rf 1980-; *ai:* Fac Forum Prof Growth, Dev Comm Chair; Peace, Soc Series, Quality of Life Comm; Campus Ministry Cncl; Class Adv; Philosophical Assn 1980-; Northern New England Philosophical 981; Apple Hill Ctr for Chamber Music Inc 1986-, Sec, Bd of s, Advy Bd; Beaver Brook Assn 1995-, Ed Comm; Numerous Pub s, Local Lib Book Discussion Series; Grants New Hampshire Hum atl Endowment for Hum, Natl Sci Fnd; *office:* Rivier Coll 420 S Nashua NH 03060

N, JOHN J., Sr Guidance Counselor; *b:* New York City, NY; *m:* Anne Prosk; *c:* John, Christine, Colleen, MIchael; *ed:* Fordham BA) Pol Sci 1973, Criminal Justice (BA) 1974; Long Island Univ nslng Psych 1990; 6 Addl Hrs in Ed; *cr:* New York City Police Dept ant 1969-89; US Army & Army Natl Guard Field Grd Ofcr 1966-94; dy of Lourdes HS Guid Cnslr, Soc Stud Tchr 1994-; Marist Coll Adj Criminal Justice 1996-; *ai:* Var Bsbl, Cross Cntry Track Coach; Union Del; Amer Cnslng Assn 1991-; Disabled Amer Vets 1979-; Lay sn 1994-; Little League 1980-, Mgr; *office:* Our Lady-Lourdes HS amilton St Poughkeepsie NY 12601

N, JOHN WILLIAM, Social Studies Teacher; *b:* Jamaica, NY; *ed:* Univ (BA) His, Scndry Ed 1991; Adelphi Univ (MA) Soc Sci 1993; *cr:* Freeport HS Soc Stud Tchr 1991-; *ai:* Var Bsbl Coach; Jr Var Ftbl Coach; Cluster Prgm Mem; ASCO 1990-; NYSUT 1991-; Ath Against Drunk Driving 1990-; GCAA 1987-, Mgr.

DOLAN, KAREN DEIRDRE, English Teacher; *b:* Charleston, SC; *m:* John Clay; *c:* Zachary Clay, Cooper Clay; *ed:* Douglas Coll (BA) Eng 1986; 21 Addl Credit Hrs; *cr:* Princeton Packet Newpaper Journalist 1983-86; Globe Times Journalist 1986-89; Bethelehem Area Schl Dist Tchr 1989-; *ai:* Eng Lang Acquisition, Multicultural Ed Comms; Ed Lit Magazine; NEA, PSEA 1989-; Audoson Soc, Nature Conservary 1990-; Planned Parenthood 1985-; G Richard Dew Jrnlsm Awd; Keystone Press Awd; *office:* Nitschmann MS 909 W Union Blvd Bethlehem PA 18018*

DOLAN, KIM ELISE, Phys Ed & Health Teacher; *b:* New York, NY; *ed:* Cortland St Univ (BSE) PE 1983; Lehman Coll (MSE) PE 1990; *cr:* Bronx HS of Sci Hlth Tchr 1986-88; Walton HS PE Tchr 1988-89; Alfred E. Smith HS Hlth, PE Tchr 1989-; *ai:* Boys Cross Cntry, Indoor, Outdoor Track & Field, Golf Team Coach; Gender Equity, Local Equal Opportunity Coord; Interclass Competitions Dir; Condom Availability Comm; United Fed of Tchrs 1987-; Tchr of Yr Bronx Supt, Parents Assn 1995; *office:* Alfred E Smith HS 333 E 151st St Bronx NY 10451

DOLAN, KRISTINA LOUISE, Biology Teacher; *b:* Franklin Square, NY; *ed:* C. W. Post LIU (BS) Ed 1992; Adelphi Grad, Ed & Sci; *cr:* Sewanhaka HS Sci Tchr 1993-; *ai:* Var Bsktbl, Vlybl, Jr HS Girls Lacross Coach 1993-; NEA 1993-; NSTA 1994-; *office:* Sewanhaka HS 500 Tulip Ave Floral Park NY 11001

DOLAN, RITA B., Sixth Grade Teacher; *b:* Pittsburgh, PA; *m:* Patrick David; *c:* Patrick David, Anthony Joseph, Daniel Bernard; *ed:* Carlow Coll (BSEd) Elem Ed 1962; Attnd Shippensburg Univ of PA, Penn St Univ; *cr:* Gateway Schl Dist K-12 Grd Sub Tchr 1980-84; Woodland Hills Schl Dist K-12 Grd Sub Tchr 1980-84; St Irenaeus Schl Sixth Grd Tchr 1984-; *ai:* NCEA 1986-; Golden Apple Awd; Thanks to Tchrs Nom.

DOLBECK, KEITH ALLEN, 7th-12th Grd Science Teacher; *b:* Ticonderoga, NY; *m:* Mary Alice Snyder; *c:* Wendy, Sarah; *ed:* Syracuse Univ NYS Coll of Env Sci & Forestry (BS) Wildlife Mngmt 1972; Cornell Univ (MS) Outdoor Ed 1975; *cr:* Ticonderoga HS 7th-12th Grd Sci Tchr 12 Yrs; Fulton Montgomery Comm Coll Natural Resources Tchr 10 Yrs; Nassau BOCES Conservation Ed Tchr 2 Yrs; *ai:* Var Ftbl Coach 12 Yrs; Sftbl Coach 10 Yrs; Sci Tchr Assn of NY St; Masonic Lodge; Town Yth Commission, Chprsn; Slide Series, Book Pub; *office:* Ticonderoga Cntrl Schl Dist Calkins Pl Ticonderoga NY 12883

DOLBEER, CYNTHIA ABBE, Third Grade Teacher; *b:* Elyria, OH; *m:* Donald K.; *c:* Todd, Brett, Chad; *ed:* Wittenberg Univ (BA) Elem Ed 1963; 22 Post Grad Hrs Wright St Univ; Attnd Dayton Univ; *cr:* Fort Knox Dependent Schls 4th Grd Tchr 1963-64; Rockway Schl Sub Tchr 1975-79, 7-8 Grd Sci, Math Tchr 1979-81, 6-8 Grd Lang Arts, Eng, Rdng Tchr 1981-91, 3rd Grd Tchr 1991-; *ai:* Third Grd Writing Competency Comm; Book-It Spon; Environmental Promotions; Spon Tchr Wright St Stu Tchr; Third Grd Play; NEA 1963-64; WOCTELA 1979-90; Natl Wildlife 1986-; Sci Classes won Clark Cty Sci Fair 1981; Stu Attnd St Writing Competition 1991; Rate Tops in Cty Writing Competency 1993-95; *office:* Rockway MS 3500 W National Rd Springfield OH 45504

DOLCE, ANTHONY, AP Chemistry Teacher; *b:* Manhattan, NY; *m:* Ann Vanella; *c:* Joanne, Thomas A., Steven L., Paul J., Christopher M.; *ed:* Cortland St (BS) Chem, Ed 1964; Hofstra Univ (MS) Sci Ed 1968; City Coll of NY 9 Credit Hrs; Brooklyn Polytechnic Inst 12 Credit Hrs; Atlanta Univ 30 Credit Hrs; *cr:* Bayport Blue Point HS Chem Tchr 1964-; *ai:* Soccer Coach; NYS Sci Olympiad Adv; Natl Chem Olympiad; Amer Chem Soc Competition; NYSUT 1964-; Suffolk Cty Soccer Coaches 1964-, Sportsmanship Awd; NSF Study Grants; *office:* Bayport Blue Point HS 200 Snedecor Ave Bayport NY 11705*

DOLCE, KAREN MACK, 5th Grade Teacher; *b:* Buffalo, NY; *m:* Monte; *c:* Sonia, Nathan, Adam; *ed:* SUC at Fredonia (BS) Elem Ed 1973; SUC at Buffalo (MS) Elem Ed 1989; *cr:* SS Peter & Paul Schl Sci, Lang Arts Tchr 1987-90; Charles Drew Sci Magnet 5th Grd Tchr 1990-; *ai:* Tchr Mentor Comm Buffalo Pub Schls; NEA; *office:* Charles R. Drew Sci Magnet 1 Martin Luther King Buffalo NY 14211*

DOLCE, RICHARD G., Language Arts Instructor; *b:* Parsippany, NJ; *c:* Diane, Jennifer, Rebecca; *ed:* Montclair St Coll (BA) Eng & Tchng 1967, (MA) Rdng 1975; *cr:* High Point Regnl HS Eng Tchr 1967-, Rdng Specialist 1975-; *ai:* Stu Cncl Adv 1968-; Project Grad Coord 1987-; Lang Arts Overseas Travels Adv 1990-; NEA, NJEA, SCEA & HPEA 1967-, Pres & VP; Sussex Town Councilman 1972-76; NJ HSPT Dev Comm 1994-, Rdng Consultant; Schl Tchr of Yr 1980; Cty & Area Coach of Yr 1980; Governors Tchr Awd 1988; St Stu Cncl Adv of Yr 1989; *office:* High Point Regional HS 299 Pidgeon Hill Rd Sussex NJ 07461*

DOLESH, GLORIA DECKER, English Teacher; *b:* Kansas City, MO; *c:* Jennifer, Jonathan, Melanie, Joshua, Christopher; *ed:* NW MO Univ (BS) Sec Ed & Eng 1964; Attnd Univ of MO, Univ of MD & West MD Univ Towards Masters; Non-violent Intervention Technique & MD Stu Assessment Pgm Cert; *cr:* Abraham Lincoln HS Eng Tchr 1964-67; Garfield Elem 5th Grd Tchr 1967-68; Blessed Sacrament 5th Grd Tchr 1968-69; Friendly HS Eng Tchr 1983-; *ai:* Guid Dept Eng Consultant; Project Lead & SHOP Spon; SAT Prep Pgm Dir; NEA 1983-; MSTA 1983-; NTE 1983-; Book: The Gift of Grace; Text Tchr of Yr 1986, 1992 & 1995; McDonald Outstdng Tchr 1990; Pr Georges Co Outstdng Edctr Nom 1995-; *office:* Friendly HS 10000 Allentown Rd Fort Washington MD 20744

DOLGETTA, JOHN B., Criminal Justice Teacher; *b:* New York, NY; *m:* Patricia Raimo; *c:* Maria, Daniela; *ed:* Fordham Univ (BA) Italian Lit & Pol Sci 1977, (MA) Pol Sci 1986, (PHD) Ed & Admin 1988; Pace Univ 6 Credit Hrs; Westchester Comm Coll 12 Credit Hrs; *cr:* Fordham Prep Schl Italian & Pol Sci Tchr 1979-88; Gorton HS Pol Sci, Criminal Justice, Ethics & Human Relations Tchr 1988-; *ai:* Multicultural Group & Prom Comm Adv; Human Relations Coord; AFT 1988-; NEA 1988-; Brown Univ Rsrch Flwshp 1994; Brown Univ Pres Curr on Islamic Fundamentalism & US Frgn Policy 1995; *office:* Gorton HS 100 Shonnard Pl Yonkers NY 10703

DOLGOS, DAVID C., Social Studies Teacher; *b:* Braddock, PA; *m:* Paula Kay Brammer; *ed:* Slippery Rock Univ (BS) Sociology 1973; Duquessne Univ (MS) Ed Admin 1994; Post Bacl Ed 1974; Westminster Coll Psych 1989; CA St Coll Cert Motor Cycle Inst 1977; USVBA Coach I Certification; *cr:* Grove City HS Soc Stud & Driver Ed Instr 1974-75; Pittsburgh Job Corps Drivers Ed Instr 1975-77; Comm Coll of Allegheny Instr & Coord Motorcycle Safety 1979-86; Bd of Ed Pittsburgh Tchr on Spec Assn, Coord Drivers Ed Instr 1977-83, Soc Stud Tchr 1983-; *ai:* Vlybl Coach; Toastmaster Intnl Spon 1988-; Parent Tchr Stu Org; AFT & PA FT 1977-; Pittsburgh FT 1977-, Union Rep 1 Yr; ASCD 1993-; US Vlybl Assn 1974-, Player, Ofcl & Team Rep; Three Rivers Motorcycle Inst Assn 1980-85, Exec Sec; PA Vlybl Coaches Assn Dist 8 Rep 1989-; Parent Schl Comm Cncl 1994-; *office:* Oliver HS 2323 Brighton Rd Pittsburgh PA 15212*

DOLL, VIRGINIA LEE (ROWE), French & Latin Teacher; *b:* Salem, OH; *c:* Kristin, Shane; *ed:* OH Univ (BSEd) Fr, Latin 1966; Coll of Mount St Joseph (MSEd) Ed 1986; Hrs Toward Masters Degree Youngstown St Univ in Ed; *cr:* Salem HS Fr Tchr 1966-69; East Palestine HS Sub Tchr 1975-79; East Liverpool HS Fr, Latin Tchr 1980-; *ai:* Latin Club Adv; Attendance Comm; Mentor for Entry Yr Tchr; East Liverpool Ed Assn 1980-; OH Ed Assn, NEA 1966-; First United Presbyn Church, Chrstn Ed Comm, Nom Commk Chrstn Ed Tchr; Sigma Kappa 1963-, Panhellenic Pres; Tchr Cnslr ALSG, CHA, EF; *office:* East Liverpool HS 100 Maine Blvd East Liverpool OH 43920

DOLLARD, CATHERINE ANNE, Biology Teacher; *b:* Hartford, CT; *m:* Andrew Soles; *c:* Leah; *ed:* Univ of NH (BA) Span 1985, (BS) Biochemistry 1985; Northeastern Univ (MED) Ed 1991; *cr:* Harvard Med Schl Rsrch Asst 1985-90; Cambridge Rindge & Latin HS Bio Tchr 1990-; *ai:* Sci Team Coach; NSTA; NABT; *office:* Cambridge Rindge & Latin HS 459 Broadway Cambridge MA 02138

DOLLARD, WILLIAM E., Asst Principal for Stu Affairs; *b:* Spencerport, NY; *m:* Lynn Marie Garrett; *c:* Garrett, Moira; *ed:* St Univ at Oswego (BA) His, Pol Sci 1984; Univ at Albany (MS) Educl Admin 1994; *cr:* St Mary's Schl MS Soc Stud Tchr 1990-92; Christian Brothers Acad Ms Soc Stud Tchr 1992-95, Asst Prin 1995-; *ai:* Stu Cncl Moderator; LaSallian Yth Ministries; LaCrosse Team Head Coach; Acad Cncl; Ftbl Team Asst Coach; NHS Bd; NASSP 1995-; ASCD 1988-; Natl 1992-; NYS 1991-; Capital 1990-; Dist Cncl for Soc Stud; *office:* Christian Brothers Acad 1 De La Salle Rd Albany NY 12208*

DOLLE, PETER, Soc Stud & Woodworking Teacher; *b:* Brooklyn, NY; *m:* Donna Ackerman; *c:* Ethan, Judson, Adam; *ed:* NY Univ (BS) Ed 1966; Hunter Coll (MA) Fine Arts 1980; *cr:* Prof Cabinet, Woodworker 28 Yrs; PS 61 Manhattan 5th Grd Tchr 1966-67; Joan of Arc Jr HS Sci Tchr, Coach1967-70; Womacs Acad Dist 11 Math, Soc Stud Tchr 1971-8 8; MS 115 Bronx Woodworking, Soc Stud Tchr 1988-; Salvadori Educl Ctr Spec Project Dir 1993-; *ai:* Woodworking Wkshps; UFT 1975-; Project Dir The Bridge to Learning with SECBE 1993; Project Supvr SECBE Riverside Park Skateboard Summer Project 1996; *office:* MS 115 Elizabeth Browning 120 E 184th St Bronx NY 10468

DOLLINGER, MARILYN LONGO, Asst Professor of Nursing; *b:* Kitchener, Canada; *m:* Richard A.; *c:* Michael, Maureen, Timothy; *ed:* Univ of Toronto (BS) Nrsng 1974; Russell Sage Coll (MS) Med-Surg Nsg & Ed 1985; St John Fisher Coll (FNP) Primary Care Practice 1995; Post-Masters Cert; *cr:* Toronto Gen Hosp Staff Nurse 1974-75; MA Gen Hosp Staff Nurse & Team Ldr 1975-77; Albany Med Ctr Staff Nurse & ICU Instr 1977-80; Strong Memrl Hosp Staff Nurse 1980-87; St John Fisher Coll Asst Prof of Nrsng 1990-; *ai:* Natl Stu Nurses Assn Fac Spon; Sigma Theta Tau Fac Adv; Stu Well Being Comm Dept Chair; Various Dept & Coll Comms; Sigma Theata Tau 1980-, Pres & Fac Adv; NY St Nurses Assn 1990-; Natl League of Nrsng 1991-; Amer Acad of Nurse Practitioners 1995-; Jr League, Bd; Amer Heart Assn, Vol Awd; Assn for Blind & Visually Imp, Bd; *office:* Saint John Fisher Coll 3690 East Ave Rochester NY 14618

DOLOVACKY, KAREN, Science Dept Chair & Chem Tchr; *b:* Sewickley, PA; *ed:* Kent St Univ (MED) Scndry Ed 1989; Notre Dame Coll (BS) Chem 1975; 12 Grad Credits over Masters Degree in Environmental Sci & Tech; *cr:* Regina HS Chem Tchr 1977-79; Notre Dame Acad Chem & Math Tchr 1979-86; JFK HS Math & Rel Tchr 1986-90; Regina HS Chem Tchr & Environmental Sci Tchr 1990-; *ai:* Sci Dept Chprsn; Soph Class Adv; NCEA 1990-; NSTA 1990-; CRST 1990-; NDEA 1993-; Nature Conservancy 1995-; *office:* Regina HS 1857 S Green Rd South Euclid OH 44121*

DOLPHIN, MICHAEL DENNIS, Director of Counseling; *b:* Manchester, NH; *m:* Kathleen Anne Fleming; *c:* Tara, Thomas; *ed:* Keene St Coll (BS) Scndry Ed His 1974; Notre Dame Coll (MED) Guid, Cnslng 1983; Spec Ed 6 Grad Hrs; Fitchburg St Coll Spec Ed 18 Grad Hrs; *cr:* Cntrl HS Soc Stud Tchr 1974-81; Pembroke Schls K-12 Guid Cnslr 1983-89; Alvirne HS Dir of Cnslng 1989-; *ai:* Boys Cross Cntry Coach; Amer Cnslng Assoc, ASCA 1983-; NH Cnslng Assn 1983-, Pres 1985-87, Schl Cnslr of Yr; Ancient Order of Hibernians 1990-; AFSCME 1993-, Pres; NH Schl Cnslr Rookie of Yr 1983-84; *office:* Alvirne HS 200 Derry Rd Hudson NH 03051

DOLSAK, DONNA MILLIK, Math Teacher; *b:* Warren, OH; *m:* Edward J.; *c:* John, Tom, Mark, Melanie, Amy, Emily; *ed:* Youngstown St Univ (BSEd) Math 1972, (MSEd) Math, Sec Curr 1990; Attnd Kent St Univ; *cr:* Mc Donald HS Math Tchr, LD Tutor, Home Instr 1972-81; East HS Math Tchr 1981-83; Youngstown St Univ Math Instr 1981-84; Woodrow Wilson HS Math Tchr 1983-84; Mc Donald HS Math Tchr, Tutoring Coord 1984-; *ai:* Math Enrichment Prgm Coord; MEA, NEOTA, NEA, NCTM, OCTM 1972-; Mc Donald Comm Chest 1984-, VP; *home:* 511 Iowa Ave Mc Donald OH 44437

DOLWICK, DONALD M., Business Education Teacher; *b:* Wisnatches, WA; *m:* Barbara A. Keish; *c:* Kerri Shaffer, Donald S.; *ed:* Youngstown St (BA) Bus 1968, (BA) Ed 1970; *cr:* Sebring McKiney Bus Ed 1968-72; Champion Bus Ed 1972-74; Northridge Bus Ed 1974-77; Mt Vernon Bus Ed 1977-; *ai:* Involved With Coaching Until 1994; Restructering Prgm Capital Grant; *office:* Mt Vernon HS 302 Martinsburg Rd Mount Vernon OH 43050

DOMANICO, JERRY, Chemistry Teacher; *b:* Queens, NY; *m:* Susan Margret Cole; *c:* Robyn Angela; *ed:* Univ of DE (BA) chem Ed 1988; *cr:* Lansdowne HS Chem Tchr 1989-; *ai:* Ftbl, Track Coach; Class Adv; NSTA 1988-; ACS Chem Ed Div 1989-; ASCD 1994-; Natl Fed 1988-; *office:* Lansdowne HS 3800 Hollins Ferry Rd Baltimore MD 21227

DOMANSKI, RONALD RICHARD, Art Coordinator; *b:* Bay Shore, NY; *m:* Carol Mercurio; *c:* Kevin, Nicholas; *ed:* SUNY at New Paltz (BS) Art Ed 1978, (MA) Elem Ed; *cr:* Marlboro HS K-12 Grd Art Tchr 1978-80; Rondout Valley HS K-5 Grd Art Tchr 1981-85; Marlboro HS 9-12 Grd Art Tchr & Coord 1986-; *ai:* Jr Var Bsbl, Cross Cntry Winter Track Coach; Var Bsktbl Girls Coach, NYS Finalist 1979-80, St Tournament 1986, League, Section Champions; Girls Spring Track Coach 1986-, Div Champs 1995; NY St Art Tchrs Assn 1979-; Established Cmptr Graphics Prgm; *office:* Marlboro Central HS 50 Cross Rd Marlboro NY 12542*

DOMBROWSKI, FRANCES NOLETTE, First Grade Teacher; *b:* Central Falls, RI; *m:* John W.; *c:* Brian, Lynn; *ed:* RI Coll (BS) Elem Ed 1970, (MED) Elem Ed 1976; *cr:* Comm Schl 1st Grd Tchr 23 1/2 Yrs; *ai:* NEA 1970-, Exec Bd & Del for Cumberland; Co-Spon RISSI Grant Atten Curr Wkshp; *office:* Community Schl Arnold Mills Rd Cumberland RI 02864

DOMBROWSKI, JOHN WAYNE, History Teacher; *b:* Providence, RI; *m:* Frances Nolette; *c:* Brian, Lynn; *ed:* RI Coll (BA) His, Ed 1967, (MAT) His 1973; 30 Grad Hrs Completed 1987; *cr:* Pilgrim HS His Tchr 1967-72; Toll Gate HS His Tchr 1972-; *ai:* AFT, RIFT, RI Soc Stud Assn, Warwick Tchrs Union 1967-; Outstdng Tchr of the Yr 1982, 1995; *office:* Toll Gate HS 575 Centerville Rd Warwick RI 02886

DOMENICK, ANTHONY, Jr HS Rdng & Eng Teacher; *b:* Newark, NJ; *ed:* Emerson Coll at Boston (BS) Eng 1979; Jersey City St Coll (MA) Spec Ed 1986; Learning Disabilities Tchr Consultant (MA) Ed 1995; Addl Post Grad Hrs in Ed of the Hearing Impaired & Ed Admin; *cr:* NY City Pub Schls Scndry Eng 1984-84; Newark Pub Schls Jr HS Tchr 1985-; *ai:* Newark Pub Schls Debate Team Coach; Hearing Impaired Children & Adult Tutor; Adult Ed Prgm Eng as Second Lang Tchr; AFT 1985-; Eisenhower Grant for Curr Dev 1995; Kappa Delta Pi Educl Honor Soc 1994; Feature Articles Pub Local Boston Papers on Local, Feature & Educl Issues; *office:* Ridge Street Schl 2 Cedar St Newark NJ 07104*

DOMENICO, ORIN PHILIP, English Teacher; *b:* Syrcause, NY; *m:* Kim Christiana; *c:* Arwen, Nicholas, Molly, Edward; *ed:* SUNY Coll of Tchng (BA) Gen Stud Eng 1985; Colgate Univ (MAT) Eng 1995; *cr:* Mohawk Vly

Comm Coll Adj Instr 1988-94; Hamilton Coll Adj Instr 1988; SUNY Coll of Tchng Adj Instr 1989-92; Frankfort-Schuyler HS Eng Tchr 1988-89; Mohawk Cntrl Schl Eng Tchr 1989-; *ai:* Mohawk Tchrs Assn 1989-; NEH Summer Flwshp Ind Stud 1995; *home:* 17 Grant St Utica NY 13501*

DOMER, MITCHELL PARKER, Junior High Teacher; *b:* Canton, OH; *m:* Lisa; *ed:* Bapt Bible Coll (BS) Elem Ed 1983; *cr:* Brunswick Chrstn Elem Prin, 6th Grd Tchr 1983-87; First Bapt Chrstn Jr High Tchr 1987-93; *ai:* Jr High Girls Vlybl Coach; ACSI 1991-; *office:* First Baptist Christian Schl 3646 Medina Rd Medina OH 44256

DOMERASKI, VINCENT PAUL, Computer Education Teacher; *b:* Jersey City, NJ; *m:* Lynn Suzanne Hardy; *c:* Micahel, Elizabeth Anne Makarick; *ed:* Rutgers Univ (BA) Eng 1966, (MED) Educl Psych 1974 Lehigh Univ (MS) Educl Tech 1988; *cr:* Oxford Cntrl Schl Grd 5 Tchr 1966-68; Flocktown Rd Schl Grd 5 Tchr 1968-70; Long Vly MS Grd 5 Tchr 1970-74, 7, 8 Grd Math Tchr 1974-80, Cmptr Ed Tchr 1980-; *ai:* Lit Magazine; Tech Advy Comm; NEA 1966-; *office:* Long Valley MS 51 W Mill Rd Long Valley NJ 07853

DOMINELLO, CAROLE ANNE MC GEEHAN, AP Biology Teacher; *b:* Philadelphia, PA; *m:* Dominic D.; *ed:* Temple Univ (EDD) Hlth Bio; Penn St (MED) Psych; Chestnut Hill (BS) Sci; Attnd Temple Med Schl, Hahnemann Med Schl, Thomas Jefferson Med Schl; *cr:* Bishop Mc Devitt Schl Chm Sci Dept 20 Yrs; Bishop Conwell Schl Sci Tchr 6 Yrs; Queen of the Universe Schl First Grd Tchr 1 Yr; Our Lady of Mt Carmel Schl First Grd Tchr 6 Yrs; St Leo Schl First Grd Tchr 3 Yrs; *ai:* Chm Sci Curr Comm, SAP Team; Archdiocese of Philadelphia; NABT; Liberty League 1976-, VP; *office:* Bishop Mc Devitt HS 125 Royal Ave Wyncote PA 19095

DOMINIC, ANN, Teacher; *b:* Schenectady, NY; *ed:* Caldwell Coll (AD) Rel 1986; *cr:* Lady of the Lake Schl Tchr 2 Yrs; St John's Apostle Schl Tchr 2 Yrs; St Michael's Schl Tchr 28 Yrs; *ai:* Boys & Girls Club; Sr Olympics Camp; Fatima with Handicapped Children; Recreation Advy Comm; Link comm Schl Newark; Suffragettes Girls Coach.

DOMINIC, SHAWN MC CARY, Educational Consultant; *b:* Baldwyn, MS; *m:* Virgil Vincent; *ed:* LSU at Shreveport (BA) Elem Ed, Early Ch 1977; MS Univ for Women (MS) Elem Ed, Early Chldhd 1981; Mega Skills Ldrshp Trng 1994; *cr:* Mooretown Elem Schl Title I Kndgtn Tchr 1976-77; Bellaire Elem Schl Second Grd Tchr 1977-79; Warden Carden Elem Schl Kndgtn-Sixth Grd Fr Tchr 1979-81; Hillcrest Primary Schl Second Grd Academically Gifted Tchr 1981-94; Revere Local Schls Resource Tchr, Title I Coord 1994-95; A Comm Co Educl Consultant 1995; *ai:* Comm Ed Bus Advy Bd; Staff Dev Cncl; Supt Fac, Curr Advy Cncl; Tech Rdng Comm; Revere Ed Assn 1981-, Sec; OH Ed Assn, NEA 1981-; OH Assn Gifted Children 1990-; ASCD 1994-; Ronald Mc Donald House of Akron 1994-, Bd Trustees; Jr Womens Civic Club 1982-, Pres, 1st VP, Sec, Corresponding Sec, Historian; Hospice & Visiting Nurse Dev Bd 1995-, Svc Bd Mem; Friends Hospice & VNS 1995-, Founding Pres; Northeast OH Tchrs Assn 1987-88 Positivt Media Image Awd; Hillcrest Primary Schl PTA Outstdng Tchr Awd 1988.

DOMINIQUE, CHARLOTTE ROSE, English Teacher; *b:* Woonsocket, RI; *c:* Ross; *ed:* RI Coll (BA) Eng 1970; 20 Credit Hrs; *cr:* No Smithfield HS Rdng Tchr 1970-71; St Clare HS Eng Tchr 1971-73; Wood Cath Reg Schl Jr HS 8th-9th Grd Eng Tchr 1975-84; Mount St Charles Acad Eng Tchr 1985-; *ai:* Yrbk; RI Consortium of Writing Flwshp; *office:* Mount Saint Charles Acad 800 Logee St Woonsocket RI 02895

DOMINO, DEBORAH A., 9th Grade Math & Business Tchr; *b:* Buffalo, NY; *m:* Timothy M.; *c:* Danielle, Tim J., Michael; *ed:* SUNY at Buffalo (BS) Bus Ed 1977; Canisius (MS) Scndry Ed 1982; Post Grad Hrs Cmptr Courses, Scndry Math Ed, Tchng Styles, Learning Styles, Yth Empowerment Trng; *cr:* Lancaster HS Bus Tchr, Adult Ed 1978-82; Alden HS Bus, Math Tchr 1983-; *ai:* Soph Class Adv; Bldg Improvement Team; Hiring Prsnl Comm; Lancaster Boosters Club; Our Lady of Pompeii Church; *office:* Alden HS Park St Alden NY 14004

DOMOKOS, LARRY, 5th-6th Grade Teacher; *b:* Chardon, OH; *ed:* Faith Bapt Bible Coll (BS) Elem Ed 1980; Bob Jones Univ (MS) Admin, Supervision 1984; *cr:* Northfield Bapt Church Schl Tchr 1980-; *ai:* ACSI 1990-; *home:* 14765 Lakeview Dr # 1 Middlefield OH 44062

DONAGHY, CHRISTINE ANN, English Teacher; *b:* Allentown, PA; *ed:* Trenton St Coll (BA) Eng Ed 1989; Pursuing Masters in Eng Lit at William Paterson Coll; *cr:* Clinton Pub Schls Permanent Sub 1990-91; Parisppany Hills HS Eng Tchr 1992-95; Brooklawn MS Eng Tchr 1995-; *ai:* NEA, NCTE 1992-; *office:* Brooklawn MS 250 Beachwood Rd Parsippany NJ 07054

DONAHUE, BRIAN FRANK, Social Studies Tchr & Dept Chm; *b:* St Marys, PA; *m:* Sharon Murphy; *c:* Cory J., Kelly A., Kim M.; *ed:* Auburn Comm Coll (AA) Liberal Stud 1971; SUNY at Brockport (BS) His, Recreation 1973; Gannon Univ (BS) Soc Stud, Ed 1978; PA St Univ Post Grad Stud; PA Dept of Ed Permanent Cert 1980; *cr:* Queen of World Schl Tchr 1973-77; Elk Cty Chrstn HS Soc Stud Tchr 1978-; *ai:* St Marys Boys, Girls Club 1992-, Bd; St. Mary's Recreation Dept, Asst Dir; *office:* Elk Cty Chrstn HS 600 Maurus St Saint Marys PA 15857

DONAHUE, DENNIS J., English Supervisor; *b:* Summit, NJ; *m:* Judith Gerber; *c:* Tristan, Bevin; *ed:* Moravian Coll (BA) Eng 1972; Trenton St Coll (MAT) Ed 1974; 30 Addl Hrs; *cr:* Bound Brook HS Eng Tchr 1974-92, Supvr Eng 1992-; *ai:* Adv Newspaper, Lit Magazine; PSA 1992-; Phi Delta Kappa 1996; NCTE 1974-; *office:* Bound Brook Jr Sr HS 111 W Union Ave Bound Brook NJ 08805

DONAHUE, ELIZABETH C., HS Math Teacher & Dept Chprsn; *b:* Brooklyn, NY; *c:* Kerry, Sean, Gavin; *ed:* Hunter Coll (BA) Math 1973, (MA) Applied Math 1975; *cr:* Hunter Coll HS 7th-8th Grd Math Tchr 1973; Hunter Coll Adj Lecturer 1973-75 & 1985-86; SUNY Farmingdale Adj Lecturer 1985; Hofstra Univ Adj Lecturer 1985-86; Our Lady of Mercy Acad HS Math Tchr 1986-; *ai:* Channel One & Weighting Procedures for Hnr Roll Comm; NHS; Cummulative Grd & Ranking; NCAMS; NCMTA; AMNYS.

DONAHUE, JUDITH GERBER, English Teacher; *b:* Somerville, NJ; *m:* Dennis J.; *c:* Tristan, Bevin; *ed:* Tusculum Coll Univ of Bath (BA) Eng 1974; Trenton St Coll (MED) Rdng 1982; Post-Grad Stud Rdng Specialist Cert; *cr:* Bound Brook HS Tchr 1975-95; *ai:* Chrldng Adv; Educl Cncl; Mid States Evaluation, Curr Comms; NCTE, BBEA, NJEA, NEA 1975-; PTO 1988-; 7th-8th GATE Curr Formation; 9th-12th Dev Rsrch Consortium; 11th-12th Dev Verbal, Math Skills Prgm; *office:* Bound Brook Jr Sr HS 111 W Union Ave Bound Brook NJ 08805

DONAHUE, KATHERINE CURTIS, Anthropolgy Professor; *b:* Coral Gables, FL; *m:* William J.; *c:* Thomas J., Samuel C., James p.; *ed:* CT Coll (BA) Eng 1966; Boston Univ (MA) Anthropolgy 1976; Boston Univ (PHD) Anthropology 1981; *cr:* Johnson St Coll Mentor, Tchr 1980-87; Dartmouth Hitchcock Med Ctr Rsrch Assn 1986-; Comm Coll Adj Fac 1988-91; Schl for Lifelong Learning Adj Fac 1989-91; Plymouth St Coll Asst Prof Anthropology 1992-; *ai:* Acad Stan, Acad Dishonesty; Achvmt Schlsp; Interactive TV Etc Comms; Sec, Contributing Ed; Soc for Anthropolgy of Europe; Soc for Indstrl Arch Northern New England Clark 2nd VP; Amer Anthro Assn 1987-; Soc for Anthro of Europe 1988-, Sec; Soc for Indstrl Acd 1993-, 2nd VP; Hartland Historical Soc 1985 Pres; Natl Endowment for Hum Grant; Winner Gren Fnd; Phi Kappa Phi Elected Mem; Co-Ed of Article; *office:* Univ Of NH Plymouth St Coll Rounds Hall Plymouth NH 03264*

DONAHUE, M. ROBERT, Biology Teacher; *b:* Manchester, NH; *m:* Patricia Oconnor; *ed:* St Anselm Coll (BA) Bio 1966; Rivier Coll (MS) Bio 1971; Harvard Univ (ALM) His of Sci 1991; 12 Hrs Schl Admin Stu at NH Univ; 34 Hrs Post Masters Stud at Rivier Coll; *cr:* Manchester Pub Schls Bio Tchr 1967-68; Dracut Pub Schls Bio Tchr 1968-; *ai:* Palms Ldrshp Team & Doe Systemic Implementation Ldrshp team Mem; Sci Club Adv; NEA, MEA & DTA 1968-, DTA Sec; Amer Newspaper Guild 1976-, Manchester (NH) Ath Hall of Fame Selection Comm 1990-; *office:* Englesby Jr HS 1580 Lakeview Ave Dracut MA 01826

DONAHUE, NANCY WOLFF, Associate Professor of Nursing; *b:* Hudson, NY; *m:* Richard Michael; *c:* George, Deborah; *ed:* Russell Sage Coll (BSN) Nrsng 1966, (MSN) Nrsng 1969; SUNY at Albany (MS) Ed Admin 1983; Columbia Meml Schl of Nrsng Diploma 1957; *cr:* Columbia Meml Hosp Asst Head Nurse 1957-59, Nead Nurse 1959-60; Columbia Meml Hosp Schl of Nrsng Instr 1960-80, Acad Dean 1980-86; Columbia Greene Comm Coll Assoc Prof 1986-; *ai:* Phi Theta Kappa, Alpha Epsilon Xi, Nurses Club Adv; Pre-Nrsng Stdnts Part-time Adv; Stu Life, Curr, Chancelor's Awd, Fnd Assn Comms; Amer Nurses Assn, NY St Nurses Assn 1986-; NY St Nurses Assn Dist 9 1986-, Pres, Bd Mem; Elks Aux 1971-, VP, Pres, Trustee; Hudson Vly Girl Scouts 1983-, Trainer, Nominating Comm; BSA 1982-, Unit Commissioner; Visually Impaired Assn, Town of Claverack Lions 1995; Delta Pi; Who's Who in Amer Nrsng; *office:* Columbia Greene Comm Coll 4400 Rt 23 Hudson NY 12534

DONAHUE, SALLY R., Business Teacher; *b:* Elmira, NY; *m:* James A.; *c:* Kate O., Erin F.; *ed:* Cazenovia Coll (AA) Liberal Arts, Bus 1973; Nazareth Coll (BS) Bus, Ec 1975, (MS) Bus Ed 1980; *cr:* Elmira Bus Inst Instr 1 Yr; Rochester Bus Inst Instr 20 Yrs; *ai:* Golf Tournament Chprsn; MCBEA 1985-; *office:* Rochester Bus Inst 1850 Ridge Rd E Rochester NY 14622

DONAHUE, STEPHANIE QUINN, Secondary School History Tchr; *b:* Lowell, MA; *m:* Charles A.; *c:* Edward J., Brigid Q; *ed:* Marymount Coll at Tarrytown (BA) His 1972; Univ of WI at Madison 1 Semester 1972; Boston Coll MAT His 1974; 54 Post Grad Credits Univ of MA at Lowell & Boston Coll; *cr:* Butler Jr HS 7th Grd His Tchr 1974-77; St Patricks Grammar Sch 6th-8th Grd Title I Tchr 1977-78; Lowell HS His Tchr 1978-; *ai:* Mentor for Future Tchrs Univ of MA, Salem St; Fac Cncl; Accreditation Chair; Asst CHair; Dev In-Svc Prgms; AFT; Pi Lamda Theta; United Tchrs of Lowell; Lowell Historical Soc 1990-, Bd Mem; Cath Coll Club 1970-, Bd Mem, Publicity Chair, Nominating Comm; Steering Comm Natl Park Svc Mock Constitutional Convention 1987; Natl Endowment for Hum Flwshp 1987; Constitutional His Prgms; Tchrs Acad; *office:* Lowell HS 50 Fr Morrissette Blvd Lowell MA 01852

DONAHUE, STEPHEN JEFFREY, English Teacher; *b:* New York, NY; *ed:* Richmond Coll (BA) Eng 1970, (MS) Eng 1971; *cr:* US Army 1st Lieutenant 1970-72; Dreyfus Schl Tchr, Dean 1972-; *ai:* Bsktbl Coach; Advanced Writing; Arista Hnr Soc Adv; UFT, Natl Tchrs of Eng 1972-; USTA 1980-; NYC Marathon Comm 1983-; Best Documentary Awd 1989; NYC Tchr of Yr 1990-; Pub Poetry; *home:* 548 Ocean Blvd Long Branch NJ 07740*

DONAHUE, TIMOTHY S., Mathematics Instructor; *b:* Red Bank, NJ; *m:* Reta A. Cutler; *c:* Kathleen, Kelly, Renee; *ed:* SUNY at Potsdam (BA) Math 1970; Attnd Purdue Univ; 75 Credit Hrs Grad Work; *cr:* Potsdam HS Math Instr 26 Yrs; *ai:* Past Sr Adv 14 Yrs; Golf & Past Bsbl, Ftbl & Bowling Coach; Mentor Tchr; Assoc of Math Tchrs of NYS; NYSUT; Potsdam Tchrs Assoc, Past Pres; Worwood Vol Fire Dept 1967-, Ex-Chief; Amer Legion; *office:* Potsdam HS 29 Leroy St Potsdam NY 13676

DONALD, DAVID H., Chemistry Teacher; *b:* Oak Bluffs, MA; *ed:* Allegheny Coll (BS) Chem 1972; Cambridge Coll (MA) Ed 1992; *cr:* Cleveland Schl Dist Sci Tchr 1992-93; MVRHS Math, Sci, Chem Tchr 1993-; *ai:* Sci Dept Coord; NEA 1973-, Pres Local; Meth Church 1966-, Chm PPRC; Tchr of Yr 1989-90; *home:* PO Box 425 Vineyard Haven MA 02568

DONALDSON, LEONARD ROSS, Social Studies Dept Chprsn; *b:* Wilmerding, PA; *m:* Constance Ann Shenkel; *c:* Lisa E., Kenneth R.; *ed:* Duquesne Univ (BS) Scndry Ed 1967; Univ of Pittsburgh (MED) Curr & Supervision 1978; 30 Credit Hrs His Stud; *cr:* Peabody HS Soc Stud Tchr 1967-; Point Park Coll Soc Stud Methods Instr 1985-87; *ai:* Stu United Nations Club Spon; Soc Stud Dept Chprsn; Pittsburgh Fed of Tchrs 1968-; NCSS 1977-; ASCD 1993-; World Affairs Cncl of Pittsburgh 1975-, Educl Advy Comm Chm 1977-78 & 1993-, Donald E Farr Awd 1978; Western PA Historical Soc 1993-; Western PA Conservancy 1989-; Carnegie-Mellon Univ Making Thinking Visible Project Fellowship 1988-92; Article "Experiencing the Role of the Supporter for the First Time",NCTE 1994; *office:* Peabody HS 515 N Highland Ave Pittsburgh PA 15206*

DONAR, ROBERT ANTHONY, Bus Ed Tchr & Coach; *b:* Hazleton, PA; *m:* Susan Nancy Mitchell; *c:* Mitchell, Matthew; *ed:* Univ of ME at Machias (AS) Recreation Mngmt 1979, (BS) Bus Ed 1986; Univ of ME at Augusta (BS) Bus Admin 1980; *cr:* Dirigo Bank Loan Officer 1980-83; Erskine Acad Bus Ed Instr 1985-; *ai:* Girls Var Bsktbl Coach; Boys Var Soccer Coach; Boys JV Bsbl Coach; Soph Class Adv; Bus Club Adv; Recertification; Boys Var Bsktbl Coach; ME Tchrs Assn, NEA, Bus Ed Assn of ME 1985-, VP; St Mary's Parish Cncl 1993-, Chair, Family Life Commission; ME Bsktbl Coaches Assn, Knights of Columbus 1989-, First Degree Knight; Womens Bsktbl Coaches Assn 1994-; Coach of Yr Awd 1992-93; *office:* Erskine Acad RFD 6 Box 547 Augusta ME 04330*

DONAT, PATRICIA ANN, First Grade Teacher; *b:* Rockville Centre, NY; *ed:* Hofstra Univ (BS) Ed 1965; 30 Credit Hrs in Ed Admin; *cr:* Half Hollow Hills Dist #5 Tchr 1965-; *ai:* Monthly Parenting Class 1993-; AFT, NEA 1965-; PTA Life Mbrshp Awd 1972; *office:* Chestnut Hill Elem Schl 600 S Service Rd Melville NY 11746*

DONATH-GRAHAM, LESLIE C., Science Teacher; *b:* Scranton, PA; *m:* Michael J. Graham; *c:* Zachary; *ed:* Marywood Coll (BS) Bio 1986; Univ of Scranton 33 Grad Credits; *cr:* Bishop Hannan Sci Tchr 1986-; Lackawanna Jr Coll Bio Prof 1993-94; *ai:* Bio Club Moderator; Jr Class Adv; PSTA 1990-; *office:* Bishop Hannan HS 330 Wyoming Ave Scranton PA 18503

DONATI, DENNIS PETER, Earth Science & Astronomy Tchr; *b:* New Kensington, PA; *m:* Janet Elaine Magliocco; *c:* Matthew; *ed:* Indiana Univ of PA (BS) Earth Sci 1968; Penn St Univ (MED) Earth Sci 1969; 3 Credits Planetarium Operation; *cr:* US Army Signal Ofcr 1st Lt, Duty Ft Gordon GA, Ft Bliss TX, RVN 1969-71; New Ken Arnold Schl Dist Earth Sci, Astronomy Tchr 1971-; *ai:* Track Vol; PSEA, NEA 1971-; PAPA 1990-; Lower Borrell Parks Commission 1980-84, Chm; Eisenhower Grant 1990-91; *office:* Valley HS 703 Stevenson Blvd New Kensington PA 15068*

DONATI, JANET E., Business Teacher; *b:* New Kensington, PA; *m:* Dennis P.; *c:* Matthew; *ed:* Indiana Univ of PA (BS) Bus Ed 1968; Univ of Pittsburgh (MED) Ed 1972; *cr:* Burrell HS Bus Tchr 1968-72; Valley HS Bus Tchr 1981-; *ai:* Sr Class Adv; NEA, PSEA, Delta Pi Epsilon 1968-; *office:* Valley HS 703 Stevenson Blvd New Kensington PA 15068

DONATIO, DIANE MARIE, English Instructor; *b:* Medford, MA; *ed:* Univ of MA (BA) Eng, Art 1974; Boston Univ Coll of Comm (MS) Mass Comm 1979; *cr:* Northeastern Univ Eng Instr 1987-; Daniel Webster Coll Eng Instr 1992; Mt Ida Coll Eng Instr 1993-; Lasell Coll Eng Instr 1993-; *ai:* Fac Adv for Stu Newspaper; *office:* Lasell Coll Common
Newton MA 02166*

DONATO, DONNA VOLPE, World History Teacher; *b:* Philad
m: James; *c:* Rex, Brian; *ed:* Ursinus Coll (BA) His 1978; Univ
Ed & TESOL 1986; *cr:* Vineland Memrl Jr High Soc Stud Tch
Vineland HS Tchr 1984-85; Eastern HS US His Tchr 1986-9
Intermediate High World His Tchr 1991-; *ai:* World Affairs
Hoby Awd Selection Comm; NJEA 1979-; Cumberland Cty Cr
Stud 1983-85, Pres; EEA 1986-; Tchr of Yr Awd Memori
1984-85; *office:* Eastern Intermediate High Schl PO Box 2500 I
Rd Voorhees NJ 08043*

DONATO, GARY ROLAND, Adjunct Instructor of History;
NH; *m:* Marion Gulowsen; *ed:* St Univ of New York (BS) Ge
1979; FL Southern Coll (BA) Pol Sci 1982; Syracuse Univ (M
Politics 1989; Working Toward Doctorate at University of CT; *cr*
1972-94; Mitchell Coll Adjunct Instr of His 1990-; Th
Comm-Tech Coll Adjunct Instr of His & Pol Sci 1993-; *ai:* Algeb
Math Tutor; Dislocated Worker Retraining Prgms & Non-Traditi
Opportunities Coord; SHAFR, APSA 1994-; Historic Norwichto
Vice Chm; Founders of Norwich 1995-; Chelsea Heritage Fnd
Speaker to Various Local Civic Groups on Local & Amer Co
office: Three Rivers Comm-Tech Coll Mahan Dr Norwich CT 0

DONAWAY, FRANCES J., English Teacher; *b:* Seaford, DE;
M.; *ed:* Univ of DE (BA) Eng, Ed 1975; Salisbury St Univ (MA)
30 Addl Credit Hrs Salisbury St Univ, Univ of DE, DE
Instruction; *cr:* Sussex Cntrl Jr HS Eng Tchr 1975-80; Sussex Cn
Tchr 1980-; *ai:* SADD Adv; Prom Promise Coord; Field Hocky,
Scorer; NEA, DSEA 1975-; NCTE 1977-; Delta Kappa Gamma
of Chptr; Tchr of Yr 1989; Mid Sts Evaluation Comm 1995; Dis
Curr & Stans Comms; *office:* Sussex Central HS 301 W
Georgetown DE 19947

DONCHE, LOUIS, Physical Science Teacher; *b:* Brownsvill
Penn St (BS) Zoology 1969; Edinboro Univ (MS) Ecology 197
Scndry Ed 1971; *cr:* James Parker MS Sci Tchr 1971-; *ai:* NEA
GMEA 1971-; Presque Isle Audubon Soc 1972-; Natl Wildlife A
Natl Rose Soc 1991-; Erie Cty Rose Soc 1991-, VP; Nat
Environmental Sci Grant; *office:* James W Parker MS 11781 Ed
Edinboro PA 16412

DONEGAN, MARY GIBSON, English Teacher; *b:* Montclai
Bernard L.; *c:* Brendan, James, Meghan; *ed:* Caldwell Coll (BA)
William Paterson Coll Grad Prgm Eng 21 Credits; Manhattan C
Lit 3 Credits; *cr:* Middlesex HS Eng Tchr 1966-68; West Milf
Schl Eng Tchr, GED Prgm 1974-77; West Milford Twp HS Sup
Eng Tchr 1980-83, Eng Tchr 1983-; *ai:* Attendance Appea
WMEA, NEA, NJEA 1980-; NCTE 1984-; NJCTE 1993-; *off*
Milford Twp HS 67 Highlander Dr West Milford NJ 07480

DONEGAN, SUE A., ESOL Content & Soc Stud Tchr; *b:* Washin
m: Thomas F.; *c:* Kerry, Erin; *ed:* Univ of MS (BA) Scndry Ed 1
Courses Trinity Coll, Univ of MD at Baltimore, Bowie St;
Georgia Cty Soc Stud Tchr 1967-69; Skaneateles Cntrl Schl
Tchrs 1969-70; Liverpool MS Soc Stud Tchr 1970-711 Prince Ge
Soc Stud Tchr 1976-88; Northwestern HS Soc Stud Tchr 1988-
Coach; Mellow Comm; Multicultural Tchr Awd; *office:* Northw
7000 Adelphi Rd Hyattsville MD 20782*

DONELLY, BARRY, English Teacher; *b:* Paterson, NJ; *m:* Jan
c: Scott, Christopher; *ed:* Boston Coll (BA) Eng 1975; *cr:* St Jose
HS Eng Tchr 1977-; *ai:* Moderator Schl Newspaper; Chm Schl
Assn; NCTE 1980-; NJ Cncl Tchrs Eng 1994-; Tchr of Yr 1
Reviews, Articles; *office:* St Joseph Regnl HS 40 Chestnut
Montvale NJ 07645

DONFRIED, KARL PAUL, Minister & Theology Educator; *b:*
City, NY; *m:* Katharine E. Krayer; *c:* Paul Andrew, Karen Eri
Christopher; *ed:* Columbia Univ (AB) 1960; Harvard Univ (B
Union Theol Sem (STM) 1965; Univ Heidelberg, Fed Republic
(ThD); Ordained to Ministry Lutheran Church in Am 1963
Ecumenical Canon Christ Church Cathedral 1977; *cr:* NYC Chur
Pastor 1963-64; Columbia Univ Acting Luth Chaplain 1963-64; S
Faculty Mem 1968-, NT & Early Christianity Prof 1968-; Nat Lut
Cath Dialogue NT Panel Mem 1971-73, 1975-78; Columbia Se
Study of NT Chm 1976-77; Assumption Coll Vis Prof 1975; Amh
Vis Prof 1976, 1978, 1985; St Hyacinth Coll & Sem Vis Prof 197
Univ Vis Prof 1979; Mt Holyoke Coll Vis Prof 1983; Univ Ham
Prof 1985; *ai:* Editorial Bd Mem; Journal Bible Lit; Am Acad Reli
1972-73, Pres New Eng Region 1971-72; Studiorum Novi Te
Societas, Chm 1975-78, Exec Comm 1979-83; New Testament
Cultural Environmnet Seminar 1990-; Soc Bible Lit, Pres New En
1975-76; Cath Bible Assn, Participant Internat Congresses of Sc
Various Cities; Author & Editor for Various Books.

DONFRIO, ARCHIE JOSEPH, Jr Sr High Math Teacher; *b:* Wil
CT; *c:* Shannon, Andy, T.J.; *ed:* Thiel Coll (BA) Math 197
Westminster Coll, Youngstown St Univ; *cr:* Mohawk HS Tch
1974-; *ai:* Head Bsbl, Asst Var Ftbl Coach; MEA, PSEA, NEA 1
Right to Life 1990-; Pub 2 Articles in Gridiron Magazine, 1 A
Image; Gift of Time Tribute Awd; *office:* Mohawk Area Schl Dist
School Rd Bessemer PA 16112*

DONHAM, SUSAN VAUGHN, Title I HOTS Teacher; *b:* Holden,
James Boardman; *c:* Tracy Donham Smith, Scott Allan; *ed:* Wor
Coll (BSEd) Ed, Psych 1978; Lesley Coll (MSEd) Cmptr Curr
1988; 12 Credit Hrs Beyond Masters; *cr:* Blackstone Millville Re
Title Tchr 1978-80; Oxford Schls 5th Grd Tchr 1983-84; Athol r
Rgnl Schl Title I Tchr 1984-; *ai:* Riverbend Schl Cncl 3 Y
Mentoring Adv; Horace Mann Scholar 1987; *office:* Riverbend El
174 Riverbend St Athol MA 01331

DONIN, WARREN ELLIOT, History & Economics Teacher; *b:* B
NY; *m:* Mahnaz Nancy; *c:* Jason, Evan; *ed:* Elizabethtown Coll (
1969; NY Univ (MA) His 1973, (MED) Schl Admin & Supervisio
Post Grad Schl Admin & Supervision; *cr:* Whitelaw Reid Jr HS S
& Eng Tchr 1969-73; Washington Irving HS Soc Stud Tchr 19
Bound Brook, NJ Pub Schls & NK Brampton MS Prin Intern 1976-
& Girls HS Soc Stud Tchr 1977-81; The Styvesant HS & Gifted &
Sci & Math His & Ec Tchr 1981-; *ai:* Tchng Mentor; Trainer of Stu
AFT 1969-; *office:* Stuyvesant HS 345 Chambers St New York NY

DONKOCHIK, WINIFRED JANE, Economics & AP US Histo
b: Mt Carmel, PA; *w:* Barry G. (dec); *c:* Randy, Christy A. Sny
Bloomsburg St Univ (BS) His, (MED) Ed, Soc Stud; 30 Credits;
Snyder SD Tchr; Shikellamy SDTchr; *ai:* Shikellamy EA Rep;
NEA; *office:* Shikellamy HS 6th & Walnut Sts Sunbury PA 17801

DONLEY, LOREN D., Performing Arts Supervisor; *b:* Shadyside,
Lynn Appel; *c:* Mark, Kevin, Dana, Cheryl Warren; *ed:* Kent St U
Vocal Music 1956; OH St Univ (MA) Church & Choral Music 196
Jersey City St Coll, Rutgers Univ, Westminster Choir Coll; *cr*
Pleasant Borough Music Tchr & PA Sup 1959-; *ai:* Show Ch
Musical Productions Vocal Dir; NEA 1960-; NJEA 1960-; PPEA
Neg Chprsn; MENC 1970-; Pt Pl Presby Ch 1960-, Choir Dir 20 Yrs;
Point Pleasant Borough HS Laura Herbert Dr Point Pleasant NJ 08

BRENDON MICHAEL, English Teacher; *b:* Wilkes-Barre, PA; en Mahoney; *ed:* Kings Coll (BA) Eng 1968; Rutgers Univ, St Coll Grad Stud; *cr:* Camden Diosean Schl Eng Tchr 1968-80; ; Eng Tchr 1980-; *ai:* NEA, NJEA, NCTE, NJCTE 1968-; Rsrch r Schls Outstdng Tchr Awd 1978; Rutgers Univ Grant ısm Seminar 1988; *home:* 112 Heather Dr Mount Laurel NJ

L, DEBORAH SWANSON, Mathematics Teacher; *b:* , PA; *c:* Trevoa, Tara; *ed:* Edinboro Univ (BS) Math, Cmptr 1971; e Boeuf Math Tchr 1979-; *ai:* SADD Adv; NEA, PSEA 1979-; LeBoeuf HS 931 N High St Waterford PA 16441

LAN, DANIEL, Social Studies Teacher; *b:* Dover, NH; *ed:* St Coll (BS) Soc Sci Ed 1982; *cr:* Berlin HS Soc Stud Tchr Gilford HS Soc Stud Tchr 1984-86; Timberlane Rgnl HS Soc Stud -; *ai:* Var Girls Sftbl Coacl; Class Adv Class 1997; Fac NHS Comm; AFT 1991-, Bldg Rep; *office:* Timberlane Regional HS ugh Rd Plaistow NH 03865

LY, ANN MARIE DEGAETANO, Jr HS Language Arts : Cleveland, OH; *m:* John K. Jr.; *c:* Kevin, John Brian, Jessica; ne Coll (BA) Eng & Ed 1972; Working on MAT at Sacred Heart ıg & Ed; Spcl Topic in Lang & Lit Eng; *cr:* St Augustine Schl 5th 1973-76, Jr HS Lang Arts Tchr 1986-; *ai:* SAT; Crisis on Team; Moderator: Yrbk, Lit Magazine & Stu Cncl; Var Girls ch; NCEA 1986-; NCTE 1991-; CCTE 1993-; CAMLE 1995-; St Cathedral Singers 1980-; Arena Gymnastics Parent Club 1992-, ow CT Writing Project; Judge NCTE Promising Young Writers e: St Augustine Cathedral Schl 63 Pequonnock St Bridgeport CT

LY, DANIEL EDWARD, English Teacher; *b:* Philadelphia, PA; IcCarthy; *c:* Derek, Dylan, Corinne; *ed:* Kutztown St Coll (BS) l Commnctn 1982; Univ of the Arts (MS) Ed 1995; *cr:* St Marthas 8th Grd Eng Tchr 1982-89; Truman HS 11th-12th Grd Eng Tchr Roosevelt Jr HS 7th Grd Eng Tchr 1994-; *ai:* Truman HS 9th Grd Asst Var Girls Bsktbl Coach; NEA 1990-; PSEA 1990-; *office:* F elt Jr HS 1001 Rodgers Rd Bristol PA 19007

LY, HELEN-THOMAS RITCHIE, 8th Grade Social Studies Portsmouth, VA; *m:* Eugene Russell Jr.; *c:* Benjamin, Nicholas; burg St Coll (BS) His 1972; Mary Washington Coll 3 Yrs; *cr:* Brook MS 4th-7th Grd Rdng Part-Time Tchr 1985, 8th Grd Soc ng & Eng Tchr 1986-; *ai:* Schl Cncl 1992-95; Ldrshp Team NELMS 1994-; Friends of Lawrence Lib 1966-, Pres; Nashua tershed Assn 1970-, Citizen Vol Awd; *office:* Varnum Brook MS St Pepperell MA 01463*

LY, JAMES CHARLES,III, 9th & 10th Grade Biology Tchr; *b:* vn, PA; *m:* Aliceann Janssen; *ed:* Philadelphia Coll of Pharmacy S) Bio 1992; 6 Grad Credits Widener Univ; *cr:* Enfield MS 6th & Sci 1993; Chichester HS 9-12th Grd Sci 1993-; *ai:* Var Girls V Bsbl, Sci Olympiad Coach; NEA, PSEA 1993-; Pi Nu Phi 1988-, 1990-91; *office:* Chichester Sr HS 3333 Chichester Ave n PA 19061*

LY, JOSEPH FRANCIS, Assistant Principal; *b:* New k, NJ; *m:* JoAnn; *ed:* Univ of AL (BS) Ed 1973; Kean Coll (MA) min 1993; Tchr of Handicapped Cert 1988; *cr:* Hoffman HS PE 3-77; South Amboy MS PE Tchr 1977-88, Soc Ed Tchr 1988-93; nboy Elem Schl Asst Prin 1993-; *ai:* Inducted into Kappa Delta Kappa Phi Hnr socs; Govs Tchr Recognition Pgm Tchr of Yr 1991; outh Amboy Elem Schl 240 John St South Amboy NJ 08879

LY, JULIA ANN, Fourth Grade Teacher; *b:* Scranton, PA; *c:* Hugh, Robert McHugh; *ed:* Marywood Coll (BS) Elem Ed 1957; klin Schl 5th Grd Tchr 1957-62; Woodruff Schl 5th Grd Tchr Mt Park Schl 4th Grd Tchr 1968-; *ai:* 4th & 5th Grd Drama Club 4th Grd Family Math Facilitator; NEA 1968-; NJEA 1968-; rs Awd for Outstdng Tchng 1990; Union Cty Bd of Chosen ers Recognition for Outstdng Achvmnt 1992; *office:* Mountain m Schl 55 Fairfax Dr Berkeley Heights NJ 07922

LLY, KATHLEEN V., Assistant Prof of Advertising; *b:* h, PA; *ed:* Lycoming Coll (BA) Comm Arts 1972; Duquesne Univ Bus Admin 1983; Attnd Dublin City Univ, Fairfield Univ, Point ll; *cr:* Forbes Hlth System Publications Coord 1976-79; Tandem unt Exec 1985-87; K. Donnelly Comm Owner 1979-85; Point Park Prof 1987-; *ai:* Ad Club Adv; Ad Club 1987-, Comm Mbrshp; Pgh sic Ensemble 1977-, Bd, VITA Vol Arts; *office:* Point Park Coll d St Pittsburgh PA 15222*

LLY, KATHRYN R., Guidance Counselor; *b:* Auburn, NY; *ed:* Univ (BS) Home Ec Ed 1971; Syracuse Univ (MS) Guid 1989; swego St Coll, Bridgewater St, IN Univ of PA Post Grad Work; *cr:* eridian HS Home Ec & Hlth Ed 1971-88, Guid Cnslr 1989-; *ai:* Splits Adv; NUSUT 1973-, Pres & Bldg Rep; Delta Kappa Gamma res & VP; Tchr of Yr; *office:* Cato Meridian Cntrl Schls Rt 370 Box 100 Cato NY 13033*

LLY, LOUISE (FIUMARA), Guidance Director; *b:* Newark, NJ; Christopher; *ed:* Newark St Tchrs Coll (BA) Gen Elem Ed 1968; ll of NJ (MA) Stu Prsnl Svcs 1984; Supvrs Cert 1989; *cr:* Nathan l 3rd Grd Tchr 1968-72; Irvington Schls Supplemental, Sub Tchr ; Berkeley Terr Schl 6th Grd Tchr 1978; Union Ave Schl 5th Grd 978-79, 4th Grd Tchr 1979-85; Kean Coll Soc Worker 1984, g Disabilities Tchrs Consultant, Tchr of the Handicapped 1985; St ıbstance Awareness Coord 1993; Irvington HS Guid Dept Chprsn ; North Plainfield Schl System Guid Dir; *ai:* Instrl Cncl; Admin iasion Comm; Ministry Group; NJPSA, North Plainfield Prin, Sup omerset Cty Guid Dirs 1995-; NJ Prof Coun Assn 1986-; *office:* lainfield HS 34 Wilson Ave N Plainfield NJ 07060*

LLY, MARGARET WETHERBEE, Humanities Coord, English Charlottesville, VA; *m:* Glenn Minshall; *ed:* Coll of William & BA) Eng, Ed 1979; Middleburg Coll (MA) Eng 1988; *cr:* Stuarts S Eng Tchr 1980-82; Northfield Mt Hermon Schl Eng, Hum Tchr ai: Hum Coord; Admission Comm; Tennis Coach; NCTE 1986-; ı Cty Safety Network 1993-, Chair; Delta Koppa Gamma 1994-; Northfield Mt Hermon Schl 265 Main St Northfield MA 01360

ER, PATRICIA ANN (MARTIN), Health & Life 101 Teacher; *b:* gh, PA; *m:* George Russell; *ed:* PA St Univ (BS) Home Ec 1967, me Ec Ed 1969, (MED) Hlth Ed 1992; 48 Addl Hrs Cooperative g, Cmptr Skills, Teen Hlth, Child Dev, Genetics, Nutrition, Life 976-93; *cr:* Cumberland Vly Schl Dist Home Ec Tchr 1969-74; wn Area Schl Dist Home Ec, Hlth, Life 101 Tchr 1975-; *ai:* Hlth tions Club Adv; Shadowing Prgm Coord; NEA 1970-; PA Family, er Sci 1995-; PA Assn Hlth, PE, Recreation, Dance 1990-; Alpha Lambda; Eta Sigma Gamma; Pi Gamma Mu; Pi Lambda Theta; ta Epsilon; *office:* Jamestown Area Jr Sr HS 204 Shenango St own PA 16134*

FRIO, DOLORES DE SIMONE, French & Spanish Teacher; *b:* clano, Italy; *m:* Vincent E.; *c:* Adam, Kristin Mary, Elizabeth; *ed:* al Cushing Coll Fr, Sec Ed 1970; Univ of Paris-Sorbonne Fr 1972; air St Univ Span 1978; Tchr Effectiveness, Understanding Tchng, Langs Methods Courses Fitchburg St Univ 1987, 1991-93, 1995, Salem St Univ 1995-; *cr:* St Mary Elem Schl 6th Grd Tchr 1970-71; St Clement HS Fr, Span Curr Planner 1971-75; Lakeland Regnl Schls 8th-12th Grd All Subject Tchr 1975-79; Don Bosco Tech HS Fr, Span Tchr 1979-89; Salem HS Fr, Span Tchr 1990-; *ai:* Stu Trip Chaperone; MAFLA; AATSP; AATF; St Mary's Church, Eucharistic Minister; Girl Scouts, Asst Ldr Daisy Troop.

DONOFRIO, NANCY MERCIER, Junior High Teacher; *b:* Holyoke, MA; *c:* Anthony D.; *ed:* Our Lady of the Elms Coll (BA) His, Ed 1967; Cert in Religion Diocese Springfield; Young Adult Lit Course; *cr:* Litwin Schl 4th Grd Tchr 1967-68; Sacred Heart Schl 6th Grd Tchr 1968-70; St Stanislaus Schl Jr HS Tchr 1976-84; Mt Carmel Schl Jr HS Tchr 1985-; *ai:* Adv Stu Cncl; Cath Schls Accreditation Tm; Chicopee Cath Schls Identity Comm; NCEA 1984-; Nat Mid Schl Assn 1993-; *office:* Mt Carmel Schl 35 Mt Carmel Ave Chicopee MA 01013

DONOGHUE, RUTH ELLEN, Teacher; *b:* Chicopee, MA; *c:* Anna (dec); *ed:* Our Lady of the Elms Coll (BA) Chem & Math 1975; Cambridge Coll (MED) Integrated Stud 1992; *cr:* Saint Marys Schl Tchr 1975-78; James River Graphics Research Chemist 1978-83; Richardson Graphics Quality Control Mgr 1983-86; Immaculate Conception Schl Tchr 1986-88; Saint Marys Schl Tchr 1988-; *ai:* NCEA 1988-; *home:* 123 Applewood Dr Chicopee MA 01022*

DONOGHUE, TERRY L., Health Teacher & Coach; *b:* Silver Spring, MD; *ed:* Towson St Univ (BS) Hlth Ed 1994; *cr:* Barclay Elem-MS PE & Hlth Ed Tchr 1994; Thomas Stone HS Hlth Tchr & Coach 1994-; *ai:* Var Field Hockey & JV Sftbl Coach; Crisis Intervention Team; FRIENDS Spon; MAHPERD 1994-; NEA 1994; *office:* Thomas Stone HS 3785 Leonard Town Rd Waldorf MD 20601*

DONOHOE, FRANCIS XAVIER, Retired English Teacher; *b:* Philadelphia, PA; *m:* Mary Lou White; *c:* Katherine Truitt, Patrick, Michael, Eileen Hedrick, Theresa McDougall; *ed:* LaSalle Univ (BA) Eng, Ed 1955; St Josephs Univ (MA) Eng, Ed 1969; 35 Addl Grad Hrs; *cr:* Harding Jr HS Tchr, Dept Chm 1958-63; LaSalle Univ Evening Division Instr 1960-85; Frankford HS Tchr 1963-88; Mt St Joseph Academy Tchr 1988-96; *ai:* Yrbk Fac Adv; Asst Sftbl Coach; Stu Assistance Prgm Fac Mem; NCEA 1988-; AFT 1965-.

DONOHUE, ETHEL MAE, Fifth Grade Teacher; *b:* Cincinnati, OH; *c:* Heather, Kendra; *ed:* Eastern KY Univ (BS) Elem Ed 1969; Miami Univ (MED) Cnslng 1974; 18 Credit Post Grad Hrs; *cr:* Clermont Northeastern Intermediate Schl Tchr 1969-; *ai:* Bldg Advy Comm; New Tchr Mentor; Bus Partnership Comm; Schl Wide Heritage Day Chm; Clearmont Cty 5th Grd Soc Stud Consultant; Southwestern OH Soc Stud Acad; NEA, OEA, CNTA 1969-; Nazarene Church; Clermont Northeastern Schl Exemplary Svc Awd; *home:* 4485 State Route 133 Batavia OH 45103

DONOHUE, JAMES P., French & Spanish Teacher; *b:* Newark, NJ; *m:* Madelaine; *c:* Jessica, Ariel; *ed:* Rutgers Coll (BA) Fr 1973; SUNY New Paltz (MA) Fr, Ed 1986; *cr:* PRHS Fr, Sp Tchr 1978-; *ai:* NEA, NSEA, AATF 1978-; Little League 1994-, Coach; *office:* Park Ridge HS 2 Park Ave Park Ridge NJ 07656

DONOHUE, KATHLEEN A., English Teacher; *b:* Newark, NJ; *m:* John Thomas January; *c:* Thomas January; *ed:* Seton Hall Univ (BS) Eng 1973; 6 Credits Eng Rutgers Univ; 6 Credits Eng Ed Montclair St Univ; *cr:* West Kinney Jr HS 7-9 Grd Eng Tchr 1973-75; Cntrl HS 9-12 Grd Eng Tchr 1975-76; Sci HS 9-12 Grd Eng Tchr 1976-; Essex Co Coll Upward Bound Instr 1982-85; *ai:* Lit Magazine Adv; AFT, NTU 1973-; *office:* Science HS 40 Rector St Newark NJ 07102*

DONOHUE, KATHLEEN FRANCES, Science Specialist; *b:* Hoboken, NJ; *ed:* Jersey City St Coll (BA) Bio & Scndry Ed 1973; St Peters Coll Elem Ed 1982; *cr:* Our Lady of Mount Carmel Tchr 1974-94; Ezra L. Nolan School 1994-; *ai:* Vlybl; Moderator of Schl Sci Fair; Cadette Girl Scout Ldr; NCEA 1974-94; NEA; NJEA; JCEA 1994-; NJSTA 1995-; NSTA 1995.

DONOHUE, MARTHA CASSIDY, 8th Grade Social Studies Tchr; *b:* Albany, NY; *m:* Gavin J.; *ed:* Siena Coll (BA) His, Pol Sci 1990; SUNY at Albany (MA) His 1994; *cr:* Shaker Jr HS Soc Stud Tchr 1990-; *ai:* Yrbk, Stu Cncl Adv; Educl Assisstance Prgm Coord; Stud Skills, Soc Stud Steering Comms; AFT, NCTA 1990-; NYS Cncl Soc Studs Mini-Grant to Photograph Teddy Roosvelt's Home, Dev Mini-Unit; Pilot Prgm North Colonie Cntrl Schls on Assessment Lifes Not Fair Stud of Injustice in His, Lit; *office:* Shaker Jr HS 475 Watervliet Shaker Rd Latham NY 12110

DONOHUE, MAUREEN THERESE, Chemistry Teacher; *b:* Staten Island, NY; *ed:* Notre Dame Coll of Staten Island (BA) Chem 1956; NY Univ (MA) Sci Ed 1960; 30 Credit Hrs; *cr:* Tottenville HS Chem Tchr & Grd Adv 1957-; *ai:* NHS Adv; *office:* Tottenville HS 100 Luten Ave Staten Island NY 10312

DONOHUE, PATRICIA ANN, English Teacher; *b:* Valley Stream, NY; *ed:* Barry Coll (BA) Latin 1967; Adelphi Univ (MA) Ed 1971; *cr:* Baldwin Jr HS Eng Tchr 1967-; *ai:* Staff Advy Comm; NYSUT 1967-; South Nassau 1980-; Comm Hosp Vol.

DONOHUE, PATRICIA M., Voice Teacher; *b:* Kenmore, NY; *ed:* Oberlin Conservatory (BM) Voice 1983; New England Conservatory (MM) Voice 1985; *cr:* Pittsburgh HS for Creative & Performing Arts Voice Tchr 1990-93; Civic Light Acad Voice Tchr 1990-; Winchester-Thurston Schl Voice Tchr 1994-95; *ai:* CLO's Gene Kelly Awds Judge; Numerous Operatic Roles, Oratorio Perfs Opera Theater of Pittsburgh, Mendelssohn Choir, Pittsburgh Concert Chorale, Gateway to Music, Pittsburgh Opera; alto Soloist Trinity Cathedral, Rodef Shalom Temple; *office:* Civic Light Opera Acad 318 Oliver Ave Pittsburgh PA 15222*

DONOHUE, ROBERT THOMAS, English Teacher; *b:* Camden, NJ; *m:* Donnamarie; *c:* David Michael, Lisa Michael; *ed:* Dickinson Coll (BA) Eng 1963; Temple Univ (MED) Eng, Ed 1968; *cr:* Fairton Elem Schl 8th Grd Tchr 1963-65; Mechantville HS Eng Tchr 1965-70; Collingswood HS Eng Tchr 1970-82; Haddonfield Meml HS Eng Tchr 1982-84; Burlington City HS Eng Tchr 1986-; *ai:* Drama Club; NEA, NJEA 1963-; Contact 609 1991-; *office:* Burlington City HS 100 Dewey St Burlington NJ 08016

DONOHUE-BERTHIAUME, NANCY, Director of Vocational Ed; *b:* Worcester, MA; *m:* Blaise P.; *c:* Damien, Padgett; *ed:* Anna Maria Coll (BA) Sociology 1972, (MA) Cnslng Psych 1978; Addl Credits in Psych; Ed Credits Career Cnslng, School-to-Work, Voc Ed, Learning Styles, Curr Dev; *cr:* Quinsigamond Comm Coll Adj Fac 1979-94, Voc Ed Dir 1986-; *ai:* Staff Dev, Orientation, Hispanics Striving for Excl, ADA Compliance Stratgic Planning Comms; Women's Ctr Advy Bd; Amer Voc Assn; MA Women Pub Higher Ed; MA Consortium Post Scndry Learning DIsabilities; Natl Ski Patrol, Outdoor Emergency Care Instr, Outdoor Emergency Care Instr-Trainer; Wachusett Mountain Ski Patrol, Ski Patroller; *office:* Quinsigamond Comm Coll 670 W Boylston St Worcester MA 01606*

DONOVAN, BRIAN RICHARD, English Teacher; *b:* Glen Cove, NY; *ed:* Monmouth Coll (BA) Eng 1972; *cr:* Spaulding HS Eng Tchr 1977-87; Dover HS Eng Tchr 1987-90; *ai:* NEA 1990-; *office:* Dover HS Alumni Dr Dover NH 03820

DONOVAN, DONALD J.,JR., Science Teacher; *b:* Cleveland, OH; *m:* Lauren Beth; *c:* Brian, Mark; *ed:* Univ of MA at Amherst (BA) Chem 1988; Worcester Polytechnic Inst (MNS) Natural Scis 1996; *cr:* Scituate HS Sci Tchr 1989-90; Thayer Acad Sci Tchr 1990-; *ai:* Girls Var Soccer & Boys Var Golf Coach; NSTA 1991-; ASP 1992-; *office:* Thayer Acad 745 Washington St Braintree MA 02184

DONOVAN, EDMUND JOHN, Science Department Chairman; *b:* Bronx, NY; *m:* Florence Thompson; *c:* Edmund, Matthew, Katherine, Sean; *ed:* St John's Univ (BA) Eng 1968; Iona Coll (MSEd) Eng 1973; Addl 36 Credits Bio Air Command & Staff Coll; *cr:* St Mary Star Sea Schl Sci Tchr 1969-73; Salesian HS Sci Dept Chm 1973-; New Rochelle Coll Adj Prof 1994-; *ai:* Civil Air Patrol; Veterans Corps of Artillery; Blue & Grey Fife & Drums Corps; NYC Auxiliary Police 1973-, Lt Exec Ofcr Mounted Unit; New York Guard 1979-, Dept Operations Ofcr; NY City 20 Yrs Pub Svc Awd; NY St Military Commendation Awd; *home:* 1113 Quincy Ave Bronx NY 10465

DONOVAN, JOAN LAUER, Fourth Grade Teacher; *b:* Oil City, PA; *m:* James Campion; *c:* Tracy, Timothy; *ed:* Indiana Univ of PA (BS) Elem Ed 1969; Univ of MD (MED) Ed, Human Dev Psych 1973; Addl 48 Credit Hrs; *cr:* Laytonsville Elem Schl Fourth Grd Tchr 1969-; Montgomery Cty Pub Schls Sci Curr Writer, Rdng, Lang Arts, GATE, Criterioned Reference Tests Tchr 1973-90, New Tchrs Consultant 1987-91; *ai:* Yrbk Ed, Photographer; GATE Comm; Co-Chair Staff Soc Comm; Prof Review Achvmnt, Mngmt Team; NEA 1970-, Del 20 Natl Conventions; MD St Tchrs Assn 1970-, Elected Del 24 St Conventions, Chair Convention Soc Comm 9 Yrs; Montgomery Cty Ed Assn 1970-, Sec 2 Yrs, Bd of Dirs 8 Yrs, Bldg Rep 23 Yrs; Alpha Omicron Pi 1966-; Nom Tchr of Yr 1989; PTA Schl Bell Awd 1988; Who's Who Amer Coll, Univs 1969; Most Valuable Donor Awd NIH Platelet Ctr 11 Yrs; Wrote Schl Column Local Newspaper 3 Yrs; *office:* Laytonsville Elem Schl 21401 Laytonsville Rd Gaithersburg MD 20882

DONOVAN, MARIE ROCHE, 6th Grade Teacher; *b:* Taylor, PA; *m:* Joseph; *c:* Michele, Danielle; *ed:* Marywood Coll (AB) Elem 1969; Univ of Scranton (MS) Rdng Ed 1973; 64 Addl Credits; *cr:* Bridgewater-Raritan Schl Dist 1st Grd Tchr 1969-70; Riverside Schl Dist 1st, 2nd Grd Rdng Specialist, 4th-6th Grd Tchr 1970-; Luzerne Cty Comm Coll Adv 1990-; *ai:* NEA 1969-; PSEA 1970-; REA 1970-, Pres 1971-72; IRA; NPRA 1989-; PTA 1969-; *home:* 201 Moosic Rd Old Forge PA 18518*

DONOVAN, MICHAEL E., Fourth Grade Teacher; *b:* Harrisburg, PA; *ed:* Shippensburg St Coll (BS) Elem Ed 1973, (MS) Instructional Comm 1979; 51 Credits Towards Assoc Degree in Photography; *cr:* East Pennsboro 3rd Grd Tchr 1974-80, 4th Grd Tchr 1981-; *ai:* PTO Fac Rep 1985-95; NEA & PSEA 1975-; Ch 27 Harrisburg Class Act Tchr of the Week; Cert of Recognition from East Pennsboro Schl Dist; Recognized by the Gift of Time Prgm; *office:* East Pennsboro Area Elem Schl 840 Panther Pkwy Enola PA 17025

DONOVAN, NANCY ROMEOS, Fourth Grade Teacher; *b:* Salem, MA; *m:* Stephen Graham; *c:* Stephanie; *ed:* Salem St Coll (BS) Ed 1968, (MED) Elem Ed 1971; 66 Addl Hrs; *cr:* Crowell Schl 3rd Grd Tchr 1968-72; Nettle Schl 6-8th Grd Tchr 1972-92; Moody Schl 4th Grd Tchr 1992-; *ai:* Schl Newspaper; Cmptr Club; Cmptr, Tech Curr Commp Math Portfolio Assessment; NEA, MTA 1968-; *home:* 28 Eden Glen Ave Danvers MA 01923

DONOVAN, OLIVER MICHAEL, Associate Professor of Biology; *b:* Jersey City, NJ; *m:* Carolyn Theresa Ambrozia; *c:* Michael, Timothy, Oliver; *ed:* Jersey City St Coll (BA) Sci Ed 1966; Rutgers Univ (MS) Radiation Sci 1968, (PHD) Environmental Sci 1972; Post Doc Work Electron Microscopy 1983; *cr:* US Army Specialist 4-C 1958-62; Rutgers Univ Instr Radiation Sci 1968-69; Jersey City St Coll Bio Assoc Prof 1971-; US Environmental Protection Agency Part-time Consultant Environmental Scientist 1972-83; *ai:* AFT 1972-; Amer Hlth Physics Soc 1971-; VFW of US 1993-; Amer Legion 1987-; Vietnam Veterans of Amer 1988-; Articles Pub; Theodore Mitau Awd Pub Svc 1983; *office:* Jersey City State Coll 2039 Kennedy Blvd Jersey City NJ 07305

DONOVAN, STEPHEN, Social Studies Teacher; *b:* Providence, RI; *m:* Deirdre A.; *c:* Stephen; *ed:* Providence Coll (BA) Soc Work 1978, (BA) Scndry Ed 1990; *cr:* Johnston HS Soc Stud Tchr 1990-; *ai:* RI Skills Commission; Johnston Fed of Tchr 1990-, Treas; RI Fed of Tchr; AFT; *office:* Johnston Sr HS 345 Cherry Hill Rd Johnston RI 02919

DONOVAN, THOMAS C., Sixth Grade Teacher; *b:* Rockland, MA; *ed:* Bridgewater St Coll (BS) Elem Ed 1972; Boston St Coll (MS) Supervision 1974; 30 Credit Hrs Recertification Sci, Cmptrs, Math, Ed; *cr:* Humphrey Schl 6th Grd Tchr 1971-72; Ralph Talbot Schl 6th Grd Tchr 1972-87; Wessagussut Schl 6th Grd Tchr 1987-91; South Intermediate Schl 6th Grd Tchr 1991-; *ai:* Bsbl, Ftbl, Bsktbl Coach; Head Tchr; Team Ldr; Wheel A Bration Comm; Site Base Mngmt Team; NEA, MA Tchrs Assn, Norfolk Cty Tchrs Assn, Weymouth Tchrs Assn 1971-; *office:* South Intermediate Schl 280 Pleasant St Weymouth MA 02190

DONOVAN, THOMAS PAUL, Sixth Grade Teacher; *b:* Buffalo, NY; *c:* Timothy, Christina, Benjamin; *ed:* SUNY at Buffalo (MS) Elem Ed 1986; Medaille Coll (BA) Elem Ed 1972; *ai:* Jr Var Ftbl Coach 15 Yrs, Sftbl 5 Yrs; *office:* John T. Waugh Intrmdt Schl High St Angola NY 14006

DONOVAN, VICKI A., Fourth Grade Teacher; *b:* New Bedford, MA; *m:* John W.; *c:* Brett, Marissa; *ed:* Cape Cod Comm Coll (AA) Math, Sci 1979; Fitchburg St Coll (MS) Elem, Spec Ed 1982; Lesley Coll (MED) Creative Arts 1996; *cr:* Mashpee MS Grd 3 Tchr 1982-83; Ezra H. Baker Schl Chptr 1, Grd 1 Tchr 1983-86; Paul Smith Elem Schl Grd 2 Tchr 1986-87; Belmont Elem Schl Grd 5 Tchr 1987-95, Grd 4 Tchr 1995-; *ai:* Yrbk Adv 1987-; NEA 1986-; Belmont Civic Profile 1993-; Cntrl NH Educl Collaborative Awd 1993; *office:* Belmont Elem Schl Best St Belmont NH 03220

DOODY, LINDA MARIE (GOODRIDGE), Fifth Grade Teacher; *b:* Hartland, ME; *m:* Michael O.; *c:* M. Jason; *ed:* Univ of ME at Farmington (BS) Elem Ed 1980; *cr:* SAD #48 Tchr Assoc 1972-79; SAD #59 5th Grd Tchr 1980-; *ai:* Afterschool Spec Santa's Repair Wkshp; 5th Grd Team Ldr; MATA, NEA 1980-; Trout Fnd Grant; *office:* Madison Area Jr HS 199 Main St Madison ME 04950

DOOLEY, JEANNE MARIE (BRADLEY), 7th Grade Mathematics Teacher; *b:* Darby, PA; *m:* Gerald F.; *c:* Kevin, Jeannine; *ed:* Temple Univ (BS) Elem Ed 1968; Attnd Rowan Coll of NJ, St Joseph Univ; *cr:* Hattie Britt Schl Fifth Grd Tchr 1968-69; Hillside Schl Fifth Grd Tchr 1969-86; Thomas E. Harrington MS Seventh Grd Math Tchr 1986-; *ai:* Mt Laurel Twp Schl Dist Strategic Planning Comm; 7-8 Prgm Core Comm; MLEA 1968-, VP 1980, Negotiations Comm 1981-82; NJEA, NEA 1968-; ASCD 1994-; Mt Laurel Alliance 1990-, Treas 1992; MC Sipp Math Inst 1989-90; NJ Governors Tchr Recognition 1989-90; *home:* 729 Decatur Dr Mount Laurel NJ 08054*

DOOLING, WILLIAM PAUL, HS Social Studies Teacher; *b:* Boston, MA; *m:* Carol Scott; *c:* Shannon, Siobhan, Sarah; *ed:* Boston St Coll (BSEd) His, Ed 1965; Northeastern Univ (MA) Pol Sci 1971; Boston St Coll (MED) Guid, Cnslng 1978; Framingham St Coll (MA) Drug, Alcohol Cnslng 1984; *ai:* Driver Ed Instr; Class Adv; NEA 1973-; MA Tchrs Assn 1973-, VOTE Bd Mem; Millis Tchrs Assn 1973-, Vp, Norfolk Co Tchrs Awd; Holliston Democratic Town Comm 1980-, Chm; MA Democratic St Comm 1986-; Norfolk Cty Tchrs Assn Awd; Middlesex Daily News Recognized Tchr Awd; *office:* Millis HS 245 Plain St Millis MA 02054*

DOONER, VINCETTA DIROCCO, Second Grade Teacher; *b:* Cleveland, OH; *m:* Robert Richard; *c:* Robert Edward, Patrick Joseph, Genevieve Ann, Carole Suzanne; *ed:* Cleveland St Univ (BS) Elem Ed 1979, (MED) Curr, Instruction 1985; *cr:* Roxboro Elem Schl Fifth Grd Tchr 1979-80; Coventry

Elem Four, Five Grd Tchr 1980-82, Fifth Grd Tchr 1982-83, Second Grd Tchr 1983-; *ai:* Otudoor Classroom Coventry Playground PEACE Comm Adv; Larry Peacock Fnd Trustee; AFT 1979-; Phi Delta Kappa 1991-; Martha Holden Jennings Scholar 1993-94; Cleveland Museum of At, Resource Ctr Tchr; Book: Seasons of Life and Learning-An Educator's Handbook to Lakeview Cemetery 1990, 1995; OH Assn Historical Socs, Museums Outstdng Achvmt Awd 1994; Martha Holden Jennings Fnd, Cleveland Fnd Grants; *home:* 2563 Edgerton Rd University Ht OH 44118*

DOPKINS, SUZETTE FRATTI, Art Teacher; *b:* Queens, NY; *c:* Kaylee Jane; *ed:* Cntrl CT St Univ (BS) Art Ed 1988; St Univ of NY at Stony Brook (MA) Lbrl Stud 1993; *cr:* Lindenhurst Pub Schls K-5 Grd Art Tchr 1988-; *ai:* Art Club; Authors & Artists; Art Tutor; *office:* William Rall Elem Schl 761 N Wellwood Ave Lindenhurst NY 11757*

DORAN, ARLENE DESIMONE, Eighth Grade Teacher; *b:* New York City, NY; *m:* Maurice F.; *c:* Anthony, Thomas, Maura; *ed:* Queens Coll City U of NY (BA) His & Eng 1963, (MS) Ed 1973; Rutgers St Univ (MLS) Lib Sci 1994; *cr:* St Bartholomew Grd Schl 8th Grd Tchr 1979-; East Brunswick Pub Lib Youth Svcs Librn 1993-; *ai:* CA Achvmt Tests Coord; Confirmation Sacramental Preparation; Yrbk Adv; Eighth Grd Grad Liturgy; Grad Dance; NJ Ed Assn 1988-; NCTE 1992-; East Brunswick Ital Club 1995-; *office:* St Bartholomew Schl 470 Ryders Ln East Brunswick NJ 08816

DORAN, CARMEN BURT, English & Social Studies Tchr; *b:* Warren, OH; *m:* Regis P. Jr.; *ed:* Kent St Univ (BS) Comp, Soc Stud & Eng 1973; Youngstown St Univ (MS) Diagnostic Rdng 1985; *cr:* Warren City Schls Jr High Soc Stud & Eng Tchr 1977-93, Sr High Soc Stud & Eng Tchr 1993-95, Alternative Pgm Instr 1995-; *ai:* Great Books Club Adv; NEA & OEA 1979-; Phi Kappa Phi 1985-; *office:* Warren City Schls 261 Monroe St NW Warren OH 44483

DORAN, EDWARD G., Science Teacher; *b:* Queens, NY; *m:* Patricia M. Rhatigan; *c:* Julia, Cara; *ed:* St Univ Coll at Oneonta (BS) Bio 1984; City Univ of NY Coll at Staten Island (MS) Sci Ed 1986; *cr:* Moore Cath HS Sci Tchr 1984-86; Rondout Valley HS Sci Tchr 1986-; *ai:* Ulster Cty Math & Sci Schl & Industry Cncl Adv; NYSUT 1986-; Sci Tchrs Assn of New York St 1987-; Mid Hudson Astronomy Assn 1990-; Empire St Fellowship for Sci Tchrs; *office:* Rondout Valley HS PO Box 9 Accord NY 12404

DORAN, KERRY PARKER, History Teacher & Ath Director; *b:* Jackson Heights, NY; *m:* Christine A. Mule; *c:* Alison, Paul; *ed:* Simpson Coll (BS) His 1964; Hofstra Univ (MS) Ed 1969; Amer Univ Am Stud Fellow 1963; Univ of MT 40 Credits 1969-73; *cr:* Amityville Pub Schls MS Tchr 1964-69, HS His Tchr 1969-, Dept Chm & His Tchr 1974-76, Ath Dir 1984-; *ai:* Wrestling, Ftbl, Track, Sftbl, Soccer & IM Coach; ATA 1964-; Suffolk Cty Ath Dir 1986-; NY St Ath Dir Assn 1986-; Keep Encouraging Yth 1974-80, Trustee; Village of Amityville 1982-92, Trustee; Bd of Appeals Town of Babylon 1983-88, Mem & Chm; Deputy Mayor of Amityville 1986-88, Deputy Mayor; PTA Flwshp 1966; Suffolk Cty Mini Grant for Energy Pgm 1972; *home:* 66 Ocean Ave Amityville NY 11701

DORAN, LAURIE KIRKPATRICK, Art Instructor & Dept Head; *b:* Chester, PA; *m:* Edward; *ed:* Moore Coll of Art, Design (BFA) Painting 1985; 3 Credit Hrs Manhattan Coll 1993; Moore Coll of Art, Design Tchng Cert Ed 1992; *cr:* St Elizabeth HS Art Instr 1992-; Moore Coll of Art, Design Art Instr 1992-; *ai:* Acad Cncl; Art Club Spon; Yrbk Co Spon; Cath Schls Week Comm; Frosh Sftbl Coach; NAEA 1992-; AED 1992-, Rep to Diocese; Recipient of DuPont Mini Grant 1995; Exhibitions of Art; Art Work Displayed at DE Ctr, Fleisher Art Meml.

DORAN, NANCY FONTANA, Basic Skills Lang Arts Tchr; *b:* Paterson, NJ; *m:* James F.; *c:* Laura Doran Scherr, James H.; *ed:* Fairleigh Dickinson Univ (BS) Elem Ed 1965; *cr:* Walnut Ridge Schl 1st Grd Tchr 1973-79, 3rd Grd Tchr 1979-82; Glen Meadow Schl 3rd Grd Tchr 1982-89; Cedar Mountain Schl 4th Grd Tchr 1989-94, Basic Skills Lang Arts Tchr 1994-; *ai:* Partnership Comm; NJEA; NEA 1973-; VTEA Pres, Sec, VP, Fac Rep; Governor's Tchr Recognition 1987; Tchr Scholar Awd 1994; Express Creativity Writing; *home:* 30 Graphic Blvd Sparta NJ 07871

DORAN, RENATA THERESA, Spanish Teacher; *b:* London, England; *c:* Daniel John, Renata Lynne; *ed:* Temple Univ (BA) Span 1969; St Josephs Univ (MS) Span, Ed 1980; 45 Post Grad Credits Grd Stud in Ed Villanova Univ, Penn St Univ; *cr:* Chester Upland Schl Dist Span Instr 1969-; *ai:* Span Club; Tchr Mentor; Grad; NEA, Modern Lang Assn 1969-; *office:* Chester HS Acad 501 W 9th St Chester PA 19013

DORAN, ROSALIE SCHULER, 3rd Grade Teacher; *b:* Oxford, OH; *m:* Ronald Carl; *c:* Nicholas David, Michael Patrick; *ed:* Miami UNiv (BSEd) Elem Ed 1959, (MED) Rdng 1963; 15 Addl Hrs Miami Univ, Univ of Dayton; *cr:* Kinder Schl 3rd Grd Tchr 1959-60; Mc Guffey Lab Schl 3rd Grd Tchr 1960-65; Evanston Elem Schl 3rd Grd Tchr 1965-66; Hayes Elem Schl 3rd Grd Tchr 1966-67; Jefferson Schl 3rd Grd Tchr 1967-69; C R Coblentz Elem Schl 3rd Grd Tchr 1977-; *ai:* Delat Kappa Gamma 1985-, Tchr Honorary; OEA; NEA; *office:* C R Coblentz Elem Schl 115 N Spring St New Paris OH 45347

DORE, LYNNE MARIE, French Teacher; *b:* Pittsburgh, PA; *m:* Leonard; *c:* Daniel Nelson, Cara Veronica; *ed:* PA St Univ (BS) Scndry Ed, Fr 1987; Eng Cert; Currently in MED Prgm; *cr:* Methacton HS Fr Tchr 1987-89; Rgnl #8 HS Fr Tchr 1989-91; Phoenixville HS Fr Tchr 1992-; *ai:* Fr Club Adv; Schl Play Producer; NEA 1989-; Delta Kappa Gamma Soc Intnl 1995-; *office:* Phoenixville Area HS Gay St & City Line Ave Phoenixville PA 19460

DORF, LAWRENCE PETER, Mathematics Teacher; *b:* Queens, NY; *m:* Jennifer L.; *ed:* IN Univ of PA (BS) Math Ed 1983; Penn St Univ (MED) Tchng & Curr 1996; *cr:* Orange Cty HS Math Tchr 1983-85; Stonewall Jackson HS Math Tchr 1985-86; York Cty Vo-Tech Schl Math Facilitator 1990-91; Cntrl York HS Math Tchr 1991-; *ai:* PALS, Fr Class, Spin Class, IM Bowling Adv; NEA, PSEA 1990-; CYEA 1991-; Gift of Time Tribute Awd; *office:* Central York HS 300 E 7th Ave York PA 17404

DORIS, CECILIA SULPIZII, Spanish Teacher; *b:* Buenas Aires, Argentina; *m:* James; *c:* Peter, Christopher, Michael; *ed:* Hunter Coll (BA) Span 1967; Iona Coll (MS) Span 1974; Diploma en Cultura y Lengua Espanola Univ of Salamanca; Post Grad Stud in Cmptr Tech, The Frgn Lang Classroom; *cr:* St Gabriel HS Span Tchr 1967-74; St Dominic HS Span Tchr 1974-80; Northern Highlands HS Span Tchr 1985-; *ai:* AASTP, FLENJ 1986-; Ars Musica Chorale 1989-; Ldrshp Citation NY Frgn Lang Edctrs 1972; Elected to Delta Kappa Gamma Intnl 1994; *office:* Northern Highlands Reg HS 150 Hillside Ave Allendale NJ 07401

DORISH, BARBARA ANN, High School English Teacher; *b:* Wilkes-Barre, PA; *ed:* Wilkes Coll (BA) Eng 1968; PA St Univ (MA) Eng 1969; *cr:* Bridgewater-Raritan HS Eng Tchr 1970-; *ai:* HNS Adv; Bridgewater-Raritan Ed Assc 1971-; Somerset Cty Ed Assc 1972-; NEA Assc 1975-; NCTE 1985-; Natl Bd for Prof Tchng Stans Early Adolescent & Eng Lang Assessor; *office:* Bridgewater-Raritan HS Box 6569 Bridgewater NJ 08807

DORKA, CHARLES ANTHONY,JR., Sixth Grade Teacher; *b:* Akron, OH; *m:* Rebecca A. Griffeth; *c:* Abigail Eldridge, Amy Metzger; *ed:* Univ of Akron (BS) Comprehensive Spec Ed 1974; Ashland Univ (MED) Curr, Supervision 1987; Working on PHD Ed; *cr:* Akron Pub Schls Sub K-12 Tchr 1975; Shelby City Schls EMR, TMR K-6 Tchr 1975-79; Discovery MS 4-8 Grd Tchr 1979-80; Buckeye Cntrl Schls 1-6 Grd LD Resource Tchr1980-82; Shelby City Schls Sixth Grd Tchr 1983-86, LD Primary Tchr 1986-87, GATE Tchr 1987-95, Sixth Grd Tchr 1995-; *ai:* Dist Tech Comm; Bldg, Classroom Grant-Writing Proposals; Shelby Ed Assn 1974-, Past Pres, Past VP, Bldg Rep 3 times; OH Ed Assn, NEA 1974-; OAGC 1987-; Richland Cty Sexual Abuse Prevention Team 1987-; Martha Holden Jennings Scholar 1978; Commendation for Nom OH Tchr of Yr 1979; Jr Achvmt Bus Basics Awd 1985-86; MENSA 1986; North Cntrl OH Master Tchr Awd, Phi Delta Kappa 1988; Ashland Oil Golden Achiever Awd 1988, 1990; MENSA Master Tchr Awd East Cntrl OH 1991; Richland Cty YELL Literacy Grant 1995; Who's Who in Amer Ed 1990; *office:* Dowds Elem Schl 18 Seneca Dr Shelby OH 44875*

DORMAN, DALE L., 2nd Grade Teacher; *b:* Meadville, PA; *m:* Bonnie Sickler; *c:* Gretchen, Rachel, Laura, Joanna; *ed:* Kings Coll (BA) Music Ed 1970; Edinboro Univ (MS) Music 1975; Cert in Elem Ed at Edinboro Univ; *cr:* Spartansburg HS Band Dir 1970-73; Corry Schl Dist Elem Choral, Gen Music Instr 1974-88, Elem Tchr 1st-3rd Grds 1989-; *ai:* Asst Band Dir; Mentor; Lead Tchr; Comm of Reading, Writing; Comm of Alternative Assessment; Strategic Planning Ldr; PSEA, NEA 1970-; PTA 1992-, VP; Schlsp of Lucy Morris 1990-, Pres; Church Bd 1993-, Sec; *office:* Sparta Elem Schl 800 E South St Corry PA 16407

DORMAN, LINDA BUKOFF, Second Grade Teacher; *b:* Bridgeport, CT; *c:* Jamie Ellen; *ed:* Univ of CT (BA) Lbrl Arts, Eng 1965; Southern Ct St Univ (MS) Ed 1969; 6th Yr Cert in Ed St Josephs Coll at Hartford 1988; *cr:* Elias Howe Schl First Grd Tchr 1965-69; Stonybrook Schl First Grd Tchr 1969-70; Lordship Schl First Grd Tchr 1970-71; Wilcoxson Schl First Grd Tchr 1972-79; Second Hill Lane Schl Second Grd Tchr 1980-; *ai:* PTA Exec Bd Tchr Rep; SEA, CEA, NEA 1969-; *office:* Second Hill Lane Schl 65 2nd Hill Ln Stratford CT 06497

DORMAN, MARGARET A., Marketing Education Teacher; *b:* Chicago, IL; *ed:* Bowling Green Univ (BA) Fashion Merchandising 1976; OH St Univ (MA) Mrktg Ed 1982; Kent St Univ Post Grad Stud 6 Credit Hrs; *cr:* Paul Harris Sales Assoc 1972-75; M. O'Neil Co Asst Buyer 1976-78; Columbus Pub Schls Tchr 1978-; *ai:* DECA Chapter, Yrbk Adv; Tech Comm; Urban Concern Tutor; NEA, OEA, CEA 1970-; AVA, OVA, MEA 1978-; Urban Concern 1993-; *office:* Centennial HS 1441 Bethel Rd Columbus OH 43220

DORMAN, MARK R., Health Education Teacher; *b:* Newark, NY; *m:* Mary Bates; *c:* James Marcus; *ed:* St Univ of NY at Cortland (BS) Ed 1983; St Univ of NY at Brockport (MS) Ed 1990; *cr:* Pine Plains Cntrl Schl Hlth Ed 1989-90; Indian River Cntrl Schl Hlth Ed 1990-; *ai:* Hlth Advy Comm; NY St Fed of Prof Hlth Edctrs; NEA; Indian River Tchrs Assn; *office:* Indian River Cntrl Schl Rte 11 Philadelphia NY 13673

DORN, KATHLEEN MOORE, Second Grade Teacher; *b:* East Cleveland, OH; *c:* Debra Lynn (dec), Glenn Jeffrey, Gary James; *ed:* Wittenberg Univ (BS) Kndgtn, Elem Ed 1969; 20 Hrs Univ Of Dayton; Emergency Medical Technician Trng Clarl Tech; *cr:* Springfield Local Schls Kndgtn Tchr, Sub Tchr 1967-68; Mercy Med Ctr Ward Sec 1971-75; Springfield City Schls Second Grd Tchr 1975-; Parents and Children Together Child Supvr 1991-; *ai:* Bldg Leadership Team; Team Ldr; Sci, Math Bldg Coord; Enviromental Bldg Coord; Gifted & Talented Comm; Tchr Supvr For Stu Tchrs; NEA, OEA 1975-; SEA 1975-, Joint Communications Comm 1991; Highlands United Church Of Christ Choir 1973-, Music Chm, Flute Soloist; Springfield Animal Welfare League 1985-; EMT Vol Lawrenceville Fire Dept 1984-86; Foster Parent 1985; Natl Arbor Day Soc Awd of Merit, Cash Awd, Outstanding Class of OH 1987; Continuing Teaching Contract 1988; *home:* 3 Ninevah Bch Ashtabula OH 44004*

DORN, ROBERT ADAM, Physical Education Instructor; *b:* Albany, NY; *ed:* Hudson Vly Comm Coll (AA) PE 1981; St Univ Coll at Cortland (BS) PE 1984, (MSE) PE 1990; *cr:* St Univ Coll at Cortland Asst Cross Cntry, Track, Field Coach 1984-87; Albany City Pub Schl System PE Instr 1991-, Outdoor Track, Field Coach 1991-, Head Girls Cross Cntry Coach 1995-; *ai:* Head After Schl Bsktbl Prgm; NYSUT 1991-; Ind Project Pub; *home:* 259 Woodlawn Ave Albany NY 12208

DOROFEE, MARY ANNE, Mathematics Instructor; *b:* Vineland, TX; *ed:* Marywood Coll (BA) Math & Scndry Ed 1973; Rowan Coll of NJ (MA) Math 1995; Kellogg Inst 14 Week Intense Course; *cr:* John Carusi Schl Tchr 1973-77; Westside Floral Gardens Self-Employed 1977-90; Cumberland Cnty Coll Instr 1990-; *ai:* Basic Skills Math Coord; Chprsn; Curr Comm; NJEA, NEA 1990-, Mbrshp Chair; NCTM 1990-; AAUW 1990-; AMA 1991-; NADE 1992-; Grant Awded Writing in Math Class, Scheduling Lab Times into Stu Schedule; Geom Learning Packet & Algebra Lab Booklet Pub; *office:* Cumberland County Coll PO Box 517 Vineland NJ 08360

DORON, BARBARA KINGSLEY, 6th Grade Teacher; *b:* Salem, MA; *m:* Stanley; *c:* Melissa, Pamela; *ed:* Salem St Coll (BS) Ed 1972; Working Towards MS Cmptrs Ed Lesley Coll; *cr:* Sheridan Schl 2nd Grd Tchr 1972-73; Bentley Schl 3rd Grd Tchr 1973-81; Collins MS 6th Grd Tchr 1981-; *ai:* Fac Team Ldr; AFT 1972-; Bewitching Stitchers 1990-, Treas.

DOROSTI, MAHMOOD N., Math & Cmptr Science Teacher; *b:* Najafabad, Iran; *m:* Paula Sanderlin; *ed:* Univ of DC (BS) Electrical Engrng 1979; WV Inst of Tech Math 1976-77; George Washington Univ Engrng 1982; Georgetown Univ Math 1988-95; Univ of MD Univ Coll Math 1995; *cr:* Self-Employed Electrical Engrng 1979-83; DC Pub Schls Tchr 1983-; *ai:* Math Club; Tech Club; Cmptr Programming Club; Jr Engrng Tech Soc Club; NCTM, ASCD 1990-; Cert of Appreciation Outstdng & Dedicated Svc 1990-94; Cert of Excl Tchng of Algebra 1993; Cert of Awd Outstdng Performance by Tchr-Facilitator Saturday Acad Tutorial Prgm 1988; Cert of Appreciation Devoted & Invaluable Svcs Sci, Math Summer Enrichment Prgm 1988; *home:* 1371 Locust Rd NW Washington DC 20012

DORR, MARGARET GALLAGHER, Third Grade Teacher; *b:* Lowell, MA; *c:* Diane, Cynthia; *ed:* Framingham St Coll (BS) Elem Ed 1972; Fitchburg St Coll; *cr:* Joseph G Pyne 2nd Grd Tchr 1972-85; Riverside Schl 2nd Grd Tchr 1985-91; Cardinal O'Connell 3rd Grd Tchr 1991-; *ai:* United Tchrs Lowell 1972-; MA Fed Tchrs 1972-; *office:* Cardinal O'Connell Schl 21 Carter St Lowell MA 01852

DORSCH, JACQUELINE DICKEY, Health & Physical Ed Teacher; *b:* Cranston, RI; *m:* John L.; *c:* Thomas, Rachel, John R.; *ed:* Kent St Univ (BS) Hlth & PE 1968; *cr:* Fairview Park HS Hlth, PE & Swimming Tchr 1968-70; Nord Jr HS PE Tchr 1986-; *ai:* Vllybl Coach; Amherst Tchr Assn 1986-; NEOEA 1986-; NEA 1986-; Organized Local Yth Soccer Pgm 1978; *office:* Nord Jr HS 501 Lincoln St Amherst OH 44001

DORSEY, LOTTIE GISRIEL, Spanish Teacher; *b:* Baltimore, MD; *ed:* Hood Coll (BA) Span 1974; Millersburg Univ Span; Hood Coll Psych; *cr:* Clear Spring HS Span Tchr 1975-; *ai:* Acad Boosters Assn Tchr Rep Parent Organization; Exch Stu Adv, Coord ICEP; Span Club Adv; Essential Curr Comm; WA Cty Tchrs Assn, MSTA, NEA 1975-; Washington Co Humane Soc 1995-; Washington Cty Rep Tchng Oral Proficiency Trng of Experts MD Dept of Ed 1987-88; Facilitating In-Svc to Tchrs; ICEF Exchange Prgm Mexico 1990; *office:* Clear Spring HS 12630 Broadfording Rd Clear Spring MD 21722

DORSEY, SHIRL ELAINE, High School English Teacher; *b:* Brooklyn, NY; *ed:* George Mason Univ (BA) Eng 1991; Western MD Coll in Pursuit of a Masters Degree in Admin; *cr:* Carroll Cty Pub Schls Mem of Steering Comm 2 Yrs; Westminster HS Eng Tchr 3 Yrs; *ai:* We the People Founder; Track & Field Coach 4 Yrs; Trainer for Multicultural Ed for Carroll Cty Pub Schls; NEA 1993-; Proclamation by Carroll Cty Pub Schls in Celebrating Black His Month; 1st Tchr of the Yr for CCPS 19 Westminster HS 1225 Washington Rd Westminster MD 21157

D'ORSI, IRENE KARAJANIS, 5th Grade Teacher; *b:* New *m:* Nicholas Anthony; *c:* Robin M. Jex, Nicholas C., Paul B Catinazzo; *ed:* Southern CT St Univ (BS) K-8 Elem Ed 1952, Elem Ed 1958; 6th Yr Elem K-8 1976; *cr:* Walnut Beach 3rd 1952-53; Seabreeze Schl 4th Grd Tchr 1953-58; Devon Schl 5th Tchr 1958-62; Mathewson Schl 4th Grd Tchr 1966-68; Orange 5th-6th Grd Tchr 1968-76, 5th Grd Tchr 1994-; Cntrl Grar 4th-5th Grd Tchr 1976-91; Pumpkin Delight Schl 4th Grd Tch *ai:* CST; Soc Stud Comm; NEA 1952-; CEA 1952-; MEA 1 Olympics World Games Comm 1995; Phi Delta Kappa 1976; Nc Tchr of the Yr 1991; *office:* Orange Ave Elem Schl 260 Orange A CT 06460*

DORSO, THOMAS RAYMOND, School Social Worker; *b:* Eliz *m:* Anna Marie; *ed:* Olean Co Coll (AA) Lib Arts 1973; Williar (BA) Psych 1975; FL St Univ (MSW) Soc Worker 1977; Post- Cert in Parent Effectiveness & Substance Abuse; *cr:* Lacey Tw Soc Worker 1977-; Self Regulated Private Practice Licensed C Worker 1982-; *ai:* Wrestling Coach; IM Sftbl & Ftbl Adv; NJA Worker 1985-; Natl Assn of Soc Workers 1985-; Juvenile C Lacey Twp 1994-; Big Brother & Sister Pgm; Parent Effective Licensed St of NJ 1993; *office:* Lacey Township HS PO Box 2 Blvd Lanoka Harbor NJ 08734

DOSCH, GREGORY MARTIN, Soc Stud Tchr & Dept Zanesville, OH; *m:* Lisa A. Hatfield; *c:* Grant M., Drew T., Rac Muskingum Coll (BA) His & Pol Sci 1987; Univ of Dayton Admin 1994; OH Dominican Coll Tchr Cert Scndry, Comprehe Stud 1988; *cr:* Bloom Carrol HS Soc Stud Tchr 1989-; *ai:* Sr C Soc Stud Chair; Head Bsbl Coach; OH Citizen Bee Coord; OH BC Tchrs Assn 1992-; Lions Intnl 1993-; Knights of Columb Fairfield Cty Amer His Tchr of Yr 1993; Nom for Ashland Oil Awd 1994; *home:* 273 Washington St Canal Winchester OH 431

DOSH, DEBORAH ANN, Third Grade Teacher; *b:* Washington WV Univ (BS) Spec Ed, Elem Ed 1981; MD Univ, Trinity Co Equivalency Plus 9 Hrs; *cr:* Holy Redeemer Schl Learning 1981-85; Mc Lean Schl Third Grd LD 1985-; *ai:* Mentor to No Ind TutorialSvc; Orton Gillingham Soc 1988-; CEC 1986-; Chi for Lng Disabilities 1996; WV Alumnus 1981-; Tutorial Inte Article in Washington Post 1995; *office:* Mc Lean Schl Of Mary Lochinver Ln Potomac MD 20854

DOSKY, DOUGLAS ALLAN, High School Mathematics Columbus, OH; *m:* Shirley A. Bartlett; *ed:* Columbus St Comm Bus Mgmt 1988, (AS) Fin Mgmt 1989; OH Dominican Coll (1992; OH St Univ (MA) Math; Addl 30 Hrs; Ed Cert OH Domin *cr:* AMTI Consultant, Office Mgr 1988-92; Northland HS M 1992-; *ai:* Head Coach Boys Soccer, Cosmos Select Boys Soccer; Dept Chprsn; NEA, OEA, CEA 1992-; Delta Epsilon Sigma 1992 of Regents Flwshp; *office:* Northland HS 1919 Northcliff Dr Colu 43229

DOSSIANO, ANTIONETTE, Eighth Grade Science Tea Brooklyn, NY; *m:* Theodore Catena; *ed:* St Univ of NY at Sto (BS) Psych 1984; C W Post (MS) Bio & Ed 1985; Addl Post Inservice Credit Hrs Specializing in Specific Fields of Sci, Edu & Coaching Theory; *cr:* Hampton Bays Jr Sr HS Sci Tchr 1985- Jr HS & Intramural Girls Gymnastics Head Coach; NYSUT, AF NSTA 1986-; Suffolk Cty Girls Gymnastics Coaches Assn 199 Coach of Yr 1995; *office:* Hampton Bays Scndry Schl 88 Ar Hampton Bays NY 11946

DOSTER, DIANE LAFLEUR, Sixth Grade Teacher; *b:* Malone Potsdam St Coll (BA) Elem Ed 1965; Learning Styles; Co Learning; Portfolio Assessment; Introduction to MAC; Inclusion Handle Conflict & Manage Anger; *cr:* Waterford-Halfmoon 5th 4 Yrs; Hillview Elem 5th Grd Tchr 26 Yrs; Aurora MS 6th Grd T *ai:* Computerized Report Cards; 5th & 6th Grd Steering Comm; D Handbook; NYSTA, NEA 1965-; Lancaster Tchrs Assn 1986-, E Whole Lang Convention; *office:* Hillview Elem Schl 148 A Lancaster NY 14086

DOSTER, HARVEY M., Catalyst Theatre Director; *b:* Baltim *ed:* Western MD Coll (BS) Theatre, Music 1974; George Washing (MFA) Theatre, Directing 1982; *cr:* Towson St Sr Acting Ins Catalyst Theatre Dir 1991-; St Timothys Schl Theatre Dir 1 Splitting Image Threatre Co Co-Artistic Dir 1988-93; Theatre on Artistic Dir 1984-86; *office:* Towson St Univ Osler Dr Towson 21204*

DOTSON, PAMELA JANE, Sixth Grade Teacher; *b:* Columbus, OH Univ (BS) Elem Ed 1971, (MS) Curr, Instruction 1989; 22 P Hrs; 9 Semester Hrs Franciscan Univ of Steubenville; *cr:* Bloom Schls Tchr, Tutor 1972; Logan-Hocking Schls Tchr 1972-; *ai:* M Co-Adv; North Cntrl Accredidation Schl, Comm Co Venture-Capital Grant Comm; OH Univ Mid Schl Ed Consulta 1977-; OH Ed Assn 1972-; Logan Ed Assn 1972-, Sec; Jaycees 19 Delta Kappa, Delta Kappa Gamma 1989-; Hocking Vly Varietie Math Lead Tchr Project OH Univ; *office:* Logan-Hocking Sch Walnut St Logan OH 43138

DOTTERWEICH, PATRICIA LEE, Fourth Grade Teacher; *b:* Ba MD; *m:* Andrew Henry; *c:* Marybeth Buxton, Patrick, Andrew; *ed:* St Coll (BS) Ed 1958; Loyola Coll (MED) Ed 1988; 30 Addl Cre Villa Cresta Elem Schl 3rd Grd Tchr 1958-59; Riderwood Elem Grd Tchr 1969-; *ai:* Stu Cncl Co-Spon; Schl Store Spon; GAT Countywide, Local Schl; Phi Delta Kapap 1986-; CCD Tchr Cath Co-Chm Renew Comm; Outstdng Tchr Recognition Banquet Cha Commerce 3 Yrs; Natl Blue Ribbon Schl Outstndg Evaluation 26 Y Co; *home:* 1220 Molesworth Rd Parkton MD 21120

DOTTERWEICH, PATRICK TIMOTHY, 7th Grd Social Teacher; *b:* Baltimore, MD; *ed:* Univ of MD at Baltimore Cty (1983-; Loyola Coll (MS) Ed 1992; *cr:* Westminster West MS Tch *ai:* Team Ldr; Stu Assistance, Schl Improvement Teams; Sc Co-Adv; NEA, CCEA 1984-; *office:* Westminster West MS 60 M Westminster MD 21157

DOTY, SHARON M., Mathematics Teacher; *b:* Bellaire, OH; *m:* G.; *c:* Bonnie Moore, Jackie, Shari; *ed:* OH Univ (BS) Elem Ed 197 Math Ed 1980; Math Ed; WV Northern Comm Coll Cmptr Clas Union Local Schls 5th Grd Tchr 1969-71, 7th-8th Grd Math Tchr Math Tchr 1993-; *ai:* Mathcounts Team Coach 1986-93; OCTM OEA, NEA, ULACT 1969-; OH St Project Discovery Participan Martha Jennings Scholar 1985-86; OCTM Eastern Dist Outstandi 1991-92.*

DOTY, VINCENT ALLAN, Mathematics Teacher; *b:* Saranac La *m:* Christine E. Sforza; *c:* Kyle, Justin; *ed:* SUNY at Brockport (B Ed 1968; SUNY at Cortland (MS) Math Ed 1973; 30 Hrs Ed Adr Post 1989-90; *cr:* Canastota HS Math Tchr 1968-73; Hampton B Math Tchr 1973-; Dowline Coll Seminar Prof for Stu Tchrs of Math *ai:* Dir Schl Musical; Math Team & Cty Math All Star Team Coac

Acad Competition Club Adv; Supvr Mentathlon Team for Acad ion; NYSUT 1976-; SCMTA 1979-, Treas 1980, Bd Mem 1995-; 990-; AMTNYS 1990-; SUNY at Stoney Brook Summer Stud NSF 77; KY Pub TV Series Math the Basics Co-Creator & Screen 90; SUNY at Brockport NSF Grant Summer Stud 1991; SUNY at bury Eisenhower Grant Summer Problem Solving Wkshp; Chief nsultant & Co-Creator of Video & Worksheets; Human Relations easantville NY; *office:* Hampton Bays Jr Sr HS 88 Argonne Rd Bays NY 11946

E, BARBARA HARNEY, Learning Support, Spec Ed Tchr; *b:* e, PA; *m:* David J.; *c:* Christopher, Dean, Justin; *ed:* Edinboro St n Ed 1975; Edinboro Univ (ME) Spec Ed 1987; 6 Addl Hrs Carlow ectiveness Trng I, II 1992-93; 23 Addl Hrs Gannon Univ Prof Systems 1991-93; *cr:* Eric Infant's, Yth Home Severe & Profound Rice Avenue MS Learning Support 1988-; *ai:* Fairview HS Soccer 1987-95; Mc Dowell HS Wrestling Booster 1991-95; NEA, 84-; *office:* Rice Avenue MS 1100 Rice Ave Girard PA 16417

L, JOHN A., English Teacher; *b:* Ware, MA; *m:* Janet A. ; *c:* Sonya, Peter; *ed:* Amer Intnl Coll (BA) Eng 1962; Westfield MED) Rdng 1972; Attnd Univ of MA at Amherst; *cr:* Palmer HS 1962-; *ai:* Soph Class Adv; MA Tchrs Assn, NEA 1962-; *office:* IS 105 Main St Palmer MA 01079

ERTY, ELAINE, Seventh Grade Teacher; *b:* Youngstown, OH; gstown St Univ (BSE) Elem Ed 1974, (MED) Curr 1990; *cr:* St Schl Grd 7 Tchr 1974-; *ai:* Video Crew Moderator; Soc Stud Curr hm; Technology Team; NCEA, IRA 1974-; Delta Kappa Gamma, of Women Voters 1991-; Mahoning Valley Historical Soc, Cath e 1985-; OH Textbook Contributing Author 1992; *home:* 112 N Ave Youngstown OH 44515*

ERTY, ELIZABETH KIRN, Curr Coord, Art & Music Tchr; *b:* e, KY; *ed:* Syracuse Univ (BFA) Art Ed-Cum Laude 1979; SUNY altz (MS) Elem Ed 1984; Iona Coll Prof Diploma Admin 1990; Plus 60 Addl Credits; *cr:* South Orangetown Cntrl Schl Dist Art 81-; Curr Coord 1993-; *ai:* Yrbk & Photo Club Adv; Prof Dev Educl Assn Bldg Rep; NY St United Tchrs 1982-; NAEA 1993; l Art Edctrs Assn 1995-, VP; NY St Art Edctrs Assn; Arts Cncl of l 1989-, Exec Comm Arts in Ed; Hudson Vagabond Puppet Co & Sec; Rockland Tchr Ctr Bd of Dirs; Ldrshp Rockland 1993-; Vly Childrens Museum Steering Comm & Adv Comm; Impact II ing Grant; *office:* South Orangetown MS 160 Van Wyck Rd NY 10913

IERTY, JERELYN M. SKLENAR, Chemistry Teacher; *b:* Staten NY; *m:* Robert J.; *c:* Julia Crowley, Jennifer, Rachel, Daniel; *ed:* ame Coll (BA) Chem 1964; Attnd St Peters Coll & Kean Coll; *cr:* of NYC Tchr 3 Yrs; St Peters Girls HS Tchr 1 Yr; St John Vianney 19 Yrs; *ai:* NACST 1977-, VP; *office:* St John Vianney Reg HS Rd Holmdel NJ 07733

IERTY, JOHN MARTIN, Social Studies Teacher; *b:* Hoboken, Barbara Kuschman; *c:* Rebecca, Matthew, Martin; *ed:* Fordham s 1970; Attnd Univ of VA 30 Credit Hrs; *cr:* Canterbury Schl His orridor Master 1977-78; Baltimores Intnl Culinary Coll Chef Instr ; The Key Schl Soc Stud Tchr 1978-81, 1988-90; Kirov Acad of oc Stud Tchr 1993-; *ai:* Track, Field Coach; Drama Wilderness rticles Pub; *home:* 1603 Oriole Rd Edgewater MD 21037

IERTY, MARY ANN C., Director & French Teacher; *b:* phia, PA; *m:* Andrew F.; *c:* Andrew, Jeffrey, Carolyn, Colleen; *ed:* nt Coll (BA) Fr, Sec Ed 1964; Villanova Univ (MA) Fr 1968; *cr:* n Easttown Schl Dist Fr Tchr 1964-70; Cntry Day Schl of Sacred Tchr 1985-, Upper Schl Dir 1995-; *ai:* Lang Dept Chm; Stu Cncl or; Exch Prgm Moderator; AATF 1986-; *office:* Country Day Sch Heart 480 S Bryn Mawr Ave Bryn Mawr PA 19010

IERTY, SUSAN M., English Teacher; *b:* Buffalo, NY; *m:* James The Kings Coll (BA) Eng 1968; Trenton St Coll (MA) Eng 1982; Credit Hrs at Rutgers, Jersey City St Coll & NY Univ; *cr:* Arthur on Regnl HS Jrnlsm & Eng Tchr 1968-; *ai:* Lance Adv; Yrbk Adv, ious Natl Awds; Key Club Svc Org Adv; Prins Advy Bd; NEA, AFT NJCTE 1988-; Columbia Scholastic Press Advisers Assn 1992-; 1993-; Natl Assn of Stu Act 1994-; Union Countys Jr Miss Schlsp Exec Dir; Miss Middlesex County Schlsp 1984-, Exec Dir; Miss County Schlsp 1990-, Exec Dir; Fanwood Presbyn Church 1995-, Natl Endowment for the Hum Fellow on Nathaniel Hawthorne; Vol Yr Nom for Home News; *office:* Arthur L Johnson Regnl HS 365 ld Ave Clark NJ 07066

HTY, BEVERLY (INGERSOLL), Eighth Grade Lang Arts ; *b:* Salisbury, MD; *c:* Mark R.; *ed:* Towson St Univ (BS) Elem Ed 6 Credit Hrs Univ of DE at Newark; *cr:* Cecil Manor Elem Schl rd Tchr 1962-67, Fifth Grd Tchr 1969; Gauger MS Rdng Specialist 7th-8th Grd Lang Arts Tchr 1989-; *ai:* Christina Educ Assn DE St Educ Assn, NEA 1976-; *office:* Gauger-Cobbs MS 50 Gender ark DE 19713

HTY, SELBY M., Fine Arts Educator; *b:* Pittsburgh, PA; *m:* J. *ed:* Miami Univ (BFA) Fine Arts; *cr:* Wilson Jr HS Art Edctr; land Vly HS Fine Arts Edctr 1974-; *ai:* NEA; *office:* Cumberland HS 6746 Carlisle Pike Mechanicsburg PA 17055

LAS, KATHLEEN TRACIE, Social Studies Teacher; *b:* gh, PA; *m:* Steven Tauriello; *c:* Olivia; *ed:* SUNY Geneseo (BA) ndry Ed 1985, (MS) Scndry Ed 1991; *cr:* Weedsport HS Soc Stud 86-88; Gananda Cntrl Schl Soc Stud Tchr 1989-; *ai:* Model United s Adv; HS Improvement Team, Acceleration, Dist Cmptr Tech, ly, Master Schedule Comms; NEA 1986-; RACSS 1989-; Employee 992.

LAS, LINDA PELTON, Fifth Grade Teacher; *b:* Toledo, OH; *c:* alley; *ed:* Bowling Green St Univ (BS) Elem Ed 1967; Univ of (MS) Elem Ed 1995; *cr:* Washington Local Adult Basic Ed Coord, 977-85; Sylvania Schls Third Grd Tchr 1985-87, Fifth Grd Tchr *ai:* Curr Comms; NEA, SEA, OEA 1985-; AAUW 1995-; Westgate 1982-; *home:* 3145 Cheltenham Rd Toledo OH 43606

LAS, RONALD PAUL, Drafting Technology Instructor; *b:* own, PA; *m:* Paulette; *c:* Lara, Patrick; *ed:* CA Univ of PA (BS) Arts 1969; Kent St Univ (MED) Tech 1974; Post Grad Stud Univ of OH St Univ; *cr:* Woodster HS Ind Arts Tchr, Coach 1969-72; Wayne eer Ctr Drafting Instr 1974-; *ai:* Voc Indstrl Clubs of Amer Adv; Ed Assn 1974-, Past Pres; Wayne Co Ofcls Assn 1977-; Wooster odge 1973-, Various, 1991 Elk of Yr; OH Semi Finalist NASA Tchr e Prgm 1985; OH Voc Assn Drafting Tchr of Yr Awd 1986; *office:* Co Schools Career Center 518 W Prospect St Smithville OH 44677

LASS, BRUCE LINWOOD, Chemistry Tchr & Sci Dept Chm; *b:* d, ME; *m:* Cynthia M.; *c:* Allyson Lachowicz; *ed:* Univ of ME (BS) Ed 1972; Eastern CT St Univ (MS) Marine Environmental Sci 1978; Univ of CT; *cr:* Ledyard HS Chem & Earth Sci Tchr 1972-; *ai:* Girls Cntry Coach; Sci Dept Head; CT Sci Supvrs Assn 1995-; Natl Girls Coach of Yr 1993; Jury of Appeals US Olympic Track & Field Trials USA Track & Field Exec Comm; Natl Chm of Racewalking; *office:* d HS 24 Gallup Hill Rd Ledyard CT 06339

DOUGLASS, JACQUELINE STRATFORD, Third Grade Teacher; *b:* Cleveland, OH; *m:* Benjamin Terwood; *c:* Dara Ife, Kristen Allen; *ed:* Cntrl St Univ (BA) Elem Ed 1968; Baldwin Wallace univ (MA) Rdng 1977; Univ of Akron Gifted Ed Cert; Creative Problem Solving Inst Gifted Ed; Cleveland St Univ Cultural Linquistics; Ashland Theological Seminary Chrstn Cnslng; *cr:* Lafayette Elem Schl Tchr 1968-72; Compared to What Inc Arts Corrd 1972-74; Mercer Elem Schl Tchr 1975-78; Ludlow Elem Schl Primary Gifted Class 1979-87; Onaway Elem Schl Tchr, Tech 1987-; *ai:* Jesus Is Lord Ministries Church Co-Pastor; Tech Comm; Mentor, Future Tchrs of Amer Mentor, Tchr; Book of Month Adv; ASCD 1980-; CABSE 1985-; NCFTE 1983-; ISTE 1990-; AENON, Teen Mentors; ECCO Pres; Boston, London Fellow; Econ Awd, Young Gifted, Talented Stdnts; Proj Base Achieve; *office:* Onaway Elem Schl 3115 Woodbury Rd Cleveland OH 44120*

DOULAMIS, KATHERINE, Mathematics Dept Chairperson; *b:* Athens, Greece; *m:* Constantinos D.; *c:* Sonia; *ed:* Simmons Coll (BS) Math, Cmptr Sci 1986; U-Mass at Lowell Math Toward MS; *cr:* MA General Hospital Cmptr Programmer 1984-86; Data Resources Inc Tech Consultant 1986-87; Newton Cntry Day Schl Math Tchr 1987-89; Acad of Notre Dame Math Dept Head 1989-; Amer Microsystems Inc Database Wrk 1994; *ai:* Soph Class, Math Club Adv; NCTM 1987-; Assn of Women in Math 1984-; Women's Benevolent Soc Greek Orthodox Church 1984-; Andros Soc of MA 1984-, Treas 1989-91; Woodrow Wilson Fellowship for Tech in Classroom 1991-92; *office:* Acad Of Notre Dame 180 Middlesex Rd Tyngsboro MA 01879

DOUMANIDIS, CHARALABOS C., Professor of Mechanical Engrng; *b:* Thessaloniki, Greece; *ed:* Northwestern Univ (MS) Mechanical Engrng 1985; MA Inst of Tech (PHD) Mechanical Engrng 1988; Post Doctoral Stud Manufacturing 1988-89; Aristotelian Univ of Thessaloniki Diploma Mechanical Engrng 1983; *cr:* Greek Airforce Squadron Sgt, Rsrch Engr 1989-90;Aristotelian Univ Lecturer Mechanical Engrng 1990-91; Tufts Univ Prof Mechnical Engrng 1991-; *ai:* Fac Adv Hellenic Club, Orthodox Chrstn Flwshp, Chess Club, Pi Tau Sigma; Invited Lectures Boston Univ, Univ of Crete, Demokritos, Aristotelian Univ; ASME 1991-, Assoc Mem, Organizer & Chair Conf; IASTED 1992-, Organizer & Chair Conf; AWS 1995-; MITAA 1988-; IEEE, ASM, Organizer & Chair Conf; Hellenic Educ Ctr Socrates 1992-, Sec, Tchr; Inst Byzantine & Greek Stud 1995-; Hellenic Inst Biomedical Ethics 1994-; Hellenic Cardiac Fund for Children 1991-, Vol, Interpreter; Presidental Fac Fellow White House, NSF Young Investigator Awds; Grants DOE, SME, Fulbright Fnd, Bodosakis Fnd, IKY, TEE; Numerous Publications Journals, Conf Proceedings; Patent Scan Welding Process, Thermal Rapid Prototyping; *office:* Tufts Univ Anderson Hall Rm 221 Medford MA 02155*

DOUTHITT, PAMELA ANN, Phys Ed Tchr & Ath Director; *b:* Marietta, OH; *ed:* Rio Grande Coll (BA) Hlth, PE 1975; OH Univ (MS) Sport Sci 1988; *cr:* Eastern HS Tchr 1975-, Coach 1975-, Ath Dir 1987-; *ai:* Sftbl Coach; Ath Dir; NEA 1975-; *office:* Eastern HS 38900 SR 7 Reedsville OH 45772

DOVAL-OETTING, MARIE, Spanish Teacher; *b:* Malaga, Spain; *m:* Marshall C. Taylor III; *ed:* WA Univ (BA) His, Span Lit 1987; *cr:* Hotchkiss Schl Span Tchr 1987-89; Hopkins Schl Span Tchr 1989-; *ai:* Admissions Interviewer; Jr Schl Asst; Act Coord; Span Tutor; Career Review Comm; AATSP 1992-; AAUW 1994-; *office:* Hopkins Schl 986 Forest Rd New Haven CT 06515

DOVE, TIMOTHY MARK, 7th Grade Social Studies Tchr; *b:* Cincinnati, OH; *m:* Lisa M.; *c:* Kathryn Rochelle, Robert William; *ed:* Miami Univ (BSEd) Soc Stud Comprehension 1981; OH St Univ (MA) Curr & Instr Design 1988; Working Toward PHD in Global Ed, Curr & Tech; *cr:* Perry Mid Soc Stud Tchr 1981-86; Worthingway Mid Soc Stud Tchr 1986-88; McCord Mid Soc Stud Tchr 1988-; *ai:* Ski Club Adv; Curr Steering, Tech Comms; PDS Field Prof for OSU; Cooperating Tchr; NCSS, OCSS, ASCD, NEA, OEA, WEA; St Anthony Outreach; The Amer People, A History Co-Author; AACTB Publications, PoliEconomics Board Game, St Budget Simulation for OCLRE Author; Outstanding Young Educator Excl in Tchng Profession OSU; St Winner of Ec Curr Dev; Innovation Awd; *office:* Mc Cord MS 1500 Hard Rd Columbus OH 43235*

DOWD, JANICE LEE, ESL & Foreign Lang Tchr; *b:* New York, NY; *ed:* Marietta Coll (BA) Fr, Span 1969; Columbia Univ (MA) Span 1971, (EDM) Linguistics 1979, (EDD) Linguistics 1984; Attnd La Sorbonne 1972, La Universidad Ibero-Americana 1967-68; *cr:* Teaneck HS Fr, Span Tchr 1970-90, Foreign Lang, ESL Consulting Tchr 1990-; *ai:* Fr Club Adv; Global, Multicultural Mngmt Team Co-Chair; TESOL 1979-; AAAL 1985-; NEA, NJEA 1971-; AATF; Foreign Lang Educators of NJ; PEO 1966-; Bus & Prof Women 1974-78, Pres 1976-77; Rockefeller Fellowship 1988; Articles Pub; *office:* Teaneck HS 100 Elizabeth Ave Teaneck NJ 07666*

DOWD, JOAN BAKER, 2nd Grade Teacher; *b:* Pittston, PA; *m:* Michael; *c:* Kevin, Brian; *ed:* Marywood Coll (BS) Hlth & Phys Ed 1976 & Elem Ed 1977; *cr:* St Mary Assumption Schl 2nd Grd Tchr 1978-; *ai:* Forensics Adv.

DOWD, MARY ANN, 7th Grade Math Teacher; *b:* Bloomsburg, PA; *ed:* Bloomsburg St Coll (BSED) Scndry Math 1966; Villanova Univ (MA) Tchng of Math 1970; 54 Post Grad Credit in Cmptr Related Courses & Multicultural Stud; *cr:* Methacton Jr Sr HS 7th-8th Grd Math tachr 1966-69, 7th Grd Math Tchr 1969-74; Arcola Intermediate Schl 7th Grd Math 1974-; *ai:* Dist In-Svc, Staff Dev, Strategic Planning, Curr, Soc, Math Comms; Math Club; NHS; AFT; PAFT; Fed of Methacton Tchrs, Treas; NCTM; PCTM; ATMOPAV; PA Tchr of Yr Finalist 1989; *office:* Arcola Intermediate Schl Eagleville Rd Norristown PA 19403

DOWDELL, TIMOTHY MICHAEL, Math Department Chairman; *b:* Elyria, OH; *m:* Sheila; *c:* Erin, Daniel, Christopher, Bryan, Andrew; *ed:* OH Dominican Coll (BS) Math 1980; Cleveland St Univ (MS) Psych Soc Aspect of Sport in Soc 1986; *cr:* St Francis DeSales HS Math Tchr 1980-81; Benedictine HS Math Tchr 1981-; *ai:* Head Bsbl Coach Cuyahoga Comm Coll 1987-; Acad Challenge Moderator 1990-; Golf Coach 1984-90.

DOWER, DEBORAH A., Educational Therapist; *b:* Hackensack, NJ; *ed:* Cedarville Coll (BA) Elem Ed 1984; Columbia Intnl Univ 6 Qu Hrs; Pursuing Master's Degree in Spec Ed Rowan Coll; *cr:* Ringwood Chrstn Schl 2-3 Grd Tchr 1984-90; Black Forest Acad Educl Therapist 1991-; *ai:* Frosh Class Spon; Track Coach; Assn of Chrstn Schls Intnl 1984-; Pequannock Twp First Aid Squad 1986-91, Recording Sec; Seminar Ldr Addressing Spec Needs of Learning Disabled Stdnts at Home in Classroom; Article Pub; Asst Instr Natl Inst for Learning Disabilites Introductory Course; *office:* Black Forest Acad Postfach 1109 D-79396 Kandern Germany XX

DOWLER, KAREN LEWIS, Tchr of Deaf & Hard of Hearing; *b:* Oklahoma City, OK; *m:* Doug; *c:* Molly; *ed:* TX Chrstn Univ (MS) Deaf Ed 1989; *cr:* Skyline Elem Schl 4th Grd Tchr 1989-90; Eleanor Roosevelt HS Tchr of Deaf & Hard of Hearing 1990-; *ai:* Class of 95 Spon 4 Yrs; NEA 1989-; *office:* Eleanor Roosevelt HS 7601 Hanover Pky Greenbelt MD 20770*

DOWLING, AUDREY KAY, Teacher of Gifted & Talented; *b:* Jamestown, NY; *m:* Donald Douglas; *c:* Forrest Blake, Joseph Campbell; *ed:* SUNY at New Paltz (BS) Art Ed 1974; SUNY at Fredonia (MS) Ed 1990; *cr:* Warwick Vly Cntrl Schl Art Tchr 1974-79; Access to the Arts Ed Coord 1980; Bemus Point Cntrl Schl Art Tchr 1985-86; Erie II Chautauqua BOCES Tchr of Gifted & Talented 1986-; *ai:* Environmental Club Co-Adv; Church Teen Adv; Chautauqua Crafts Alliance 1984-, Co-Founder & Juror; AFT & NYSUT 1988-; AGATE 1988-; AAUW 1993-, Ed Chprsn 1994-; Mayville Schl Boosters Club 1995-; St & World Level Confs on Tchng Gifted Ed Presenter; Artist in Residence Grants 1977-80; Artist Re-Grant Projects Pool Chautauqua Assn for the Arts 1982, 1983 & 1987; Numerous One Woman Art Shows 1982-85; Whos Who in Amer Women 1995-96; *office:* Westfield Acad E Main St Westfield NY 14787*

DOWLING, DOROTHY WOODWARD, Social Studies Tchr & Team Ldr; *b:* Baltimore, MD; *m:* Howard S. Downing Jr.; *c:* Lisa; *ed:* Manhattanville Coll (BA) Pol Sci 1968, (MAT) Ed 1969; 30 Credit Hrs Toward Masters Loyola Coll; *cr:* Scarsdale Jr HS 7th Grd Soc Stud Tchr 1968-69; Stemmers Run MS 8 & 9th Grd Soc Stud Tchr 1969-86; Parkville MS 8th Grd Soc Stud Tchr 1986-; *ai:* 8th Grd Team Ldr; Stu Assistance Prgm Chprsn; Schl Site-based Comm; Peer Mediation Spon; Edctr of Yr Awd 1994; Fin Grant 1990; Part-time Editorial Writer on Ed; *office:* Parkville MS 8711 Avondale Rd Baltimore MD 21234*

DOWLING, MARK JOHN, Science Educator; *b:* Amityville, NY; *m:* Maura Keane; *c:* Joseph, Kathleen; *ed:* Boston Coll (BS) Bio 1987; Sacred Heart Univ (BS) Chem 1990; 80 Credits Hrs Pharmaceutical Organic Chemistry; 10 Credit Hrs Lab, Chemical Safety; 24 Credit Hrs Bus Admin; 20 Credit Hrs Physics, Radiopharmacy; *cr:* Amer Cyanamid Research Chemist 1987-91; MA Coll of Pharmacy Adjunct Prof 1992-94; Harvard Univ Head Tchng Fellow 1993-95; Cushing Acad Sci Educator 1994-; *ai:* Soccer, Bsbl Jr Var Coach; Jr Class Adv; Dormitory Resident Head; Amer Chem Soc 1988-; MA Sci Ed 1994-; Rho Pi Pharmacy Honors Soc 1993-.

DOWLING, WILLIAM C., Chemistry Teacher; *b:* Reading, PA; *m:* Dorothy Gantz; *ed:* Kutztown St Univ (BS) Chem 1955; Temple Univ (MED) Sci in Sec Ed 1961; Villanova Univ (MS) Chem 1963; Penn St Univ 30 Sem Hrs Sci; UCLA Grad Work; *cr:* North Wildwood Jr HS Sci Tchr 1954-55; West Reading Jr Sr HS Chem & Physics 1955-69; Wyomissing Jr Sr HS Chem 1969-; *ai:* Stu Cncl, Intnl Stu, European Trips & Schl Store Adv; High Adventure, Schl Banking & Schl Svc Clubs; WAEA, PSEA & NEA 1955-; Tchrs Assn Pres 3 Yrs & Treas 7 Yrs; PA Sci Tchrs Assn; Boy Scouts of Amer 1955-, Dist Trng Chm, Dist Camping Chm, Scout Master, Post Adv & Merit Badge Cnslr; 1977 PA Tchr of the Yr; 1974 Outsanding Scndry Educator Awd; 1978 Berks Cty Tchr of the Yr; *office:* Wyomissing Area Jr Sr HS Girard & Evans Aves Wyomissing PA 19610

DOWNARD, THOMAS, English Teacher; *b:* Chillicothe, OH; *ed:* Otterbein Coll (BA) Theatre 1978; Youngstown St (BS) Eng Ed 1988; Muskingum Coll (MA) Comm 1991; *cr:* Bardavon Theatre Exec Dir 1982-87; Youngstown Symphony Exec Dir 1987-89; Zanesville HS Tchr 1989-; *ai:* Drama Club Adv; OCTELA, NCTE, OEA, NEA 1988-; Outstdng Tchr Zanesville Daybreak Rotary Club; Grassman-Schultz Drama, Theta Alpha Phi Awds Otterbein Coll; Golden Key Youngstown St Univ; *office:* Zanesville HS 1701 Blue Ave Zanesville OH 43701*

DOWNES, JOHN F., Mathematics Teacher; *b:* Boston, MA; *m:* Patricia Anne Tanner; *c:* Christopher, Carolynne; *ed:* Boston Coll (AB) Math, Ed 1967; Worcester St Coll (MED) Admin 1972; Attnd Rensselaer Polytechnic Inst 1983; Algebra Curr Project EDC Inst 1992-95; *cr:* Marlborough HS Math Tchr 1967-; Adams & Smith Inc Cmptr Applications Engr 1980; Digital Equipt Corp Cmptr Educl Consultant 1983-86; *ai:* Marlboro Math Curr Project 1990-; NCTM, NEA 1967-; MEA 1967-, Recording Sec; Sterling Lions Club 1989-, VP; Appalacian Mountain Club 1967-, 25 Yr Pin; Tchrs Time & Transformation NSF Grant 1992-95; Article Pub; *office:* Marlborough HS 461 Bolton St Marlborough MA 01752

DOWNES, LILLI MATESIG, Assoc Professor of Sociology; *b:* Mc Keesport, PA; *ed:* Univ of S FL (BA) Sociology 1985, (MA) Sociology, Social Psych 1986; Univ of DE (ABD) Sociology, Social Psych1995; *cr:* Univ of S FL Tchng Asst 1985-86; Cntrl FL Comm Coll Instr Adj 1986-89; St Leo Coll Instr Adj 1986-89; Harford Comm Coll Asoc Prof 1989-; *ai:* Phi Theta Kappa Adv; Amer Sociological Assoc 1985; Harford Comm Coll Speakers Bureau 1990-; NISOD Awd for Tchng Excl 1996; Phi Kappa Phi Life-time Mem; Alpha Kappa Delta; Pi Gamma Mu; Sociology Sr Grad of Yr 1985 Univ of S FL; Grad 99th Percentile 1985 BA Degree; Innovation in Tchng Awd 1993; *office:* Harford Comm Coll 401 Thomas Run Rd Bel Air MD 21015

DOWNES, PATRICK HENRY, Social Studies Teacher; *b:* New York, NY; *m:* Deborah J.; *ed:* Hunter Coll (BA) Hist, Phys Sci 1960; Fordham Univ (MA) His 1963; NY Univ (ABD) Amer His; Columbia Univ 6 Rsrch Credits 1969; *cr:* Queensborough Comm Coll Instr 1967, 1969; Eron Prep Soc Stud Tchr 1979-72; Manhattan Schl Soc Stud Tchr 1973-74; Cardinal Spellman HS Soc Stud Tchr 1974-82; Columbia HS Soc Stud Tchr 1982-83; A. E. Smith HS Soc Stud Tchr 1984-; *ai:* AP Adv His; AFT, NEA 1984-; AAUP 1967-71; NY Pub Lib 1961-66, Trainee, Rsrch Grant Columbia Univ; Tchr Awd Queensborough Comm Coll, City Univ of NY; Best Tchr Soc Sci; NYC Bd of Ed Mentor; Tchr of Yr; *home:* 84 Quanopaug Trl Woodbury CT 06798*

DOWNEY, MARSHA LAMKE, High School English Teacher; *b:* Cleveland, OH; *c:* Heather, Jason; *ed:* OH St (BS) Eng Ed 1973; Certfd in Elem Ed 1988; OH Acad of Hypnotherapy Clinical Certfd Hypnotherapist 1995; *cr:* Bath MS 8th Grd Lang Arts Tchr 1973-76; Ridgemont HS 9th-10th Grd Eng Tchr 1988-89; Allen East HS 9th-10th Grd Eng Tchr 1989-; *ai:* Sr Class Adv; *office:* Allen East HS 1054 N Washington St Lafayette OH 45854

DOWNEY, MARY JO, English Instructor; *b:* Montpelier, VT; *ed:* Bryn Mawr Coll (AB) Eng 1982; Unification Theological Seminary (MRe) Rel Ed 1985; Univ of Buffalo (PHD) Eng 1996; Univ of VT 5th Yr Cert Scndry Eng 1987; *cr:* Univ of Buffalo Eng Tchng Asst 1990-; Villa Maria Coll Eng Adj Instr 1991-; *office:* Villa Maria Coll Of Buffalo 240 Pine Ridge Rd Buffalo NY 14225

DOWNEY, SUSAN MARIE WOLBERT, Career Development Secretary; *b:* Springfield, OH; *m:* Robert Harold Jr.; *c:* Jonathan Robert, Teresa Suzanne; *ed:* Wright St Univ (BSEd) Comprehensive Bus Ed 1971; 25 Credit Hrs Primarily in Tech; *cr:* Antioch Univ Payroll Asst 1967-70; North HS Bus Ed Instr 1970-72; Greene Cty Career Ctr HS, Adult Ed Bus Ed Instr 1972-75; Clark St Comm Coll Bus Ed Adj Instr 1974-79; Miami Vly Career Tech Ctr Adult Ed Bus Ed Instr 1984, Sub Bus Ed Instr 1988-93; Upper Vly Joint Voc Schl Sub Bus Ed Instr 1991-92; Springfield Clark Cty Joint Voc Schl Sub Bus Ed Instr 1992; Miami Vly Career Tech Ctr Sec, Career Dev Prgm 1994-; *ai:* OH Bus Tchrs Assn; NBEA; AFT; PTO St Christopher Schl, Treas, Sec, Consultant; *office:* Miami Vly Career Tech Ctr 6800 Hoke Rd Clayton OH 45315

DOWNEY, TIMOTHY JOSEPH, Mathematics Teacher; *b:* Napoleon, OH; *m:* Pamela A. Richardson; *c:* Michael, Benjamin, Sara, Andrew; *ed:* Univ of Toledo (BED) Math 1976; Completed Courses in Scndry Ed of Math; Masters Project in Progress; *cr:* Napoleon Cty Schls Math Tchr 1976-; *ai:* Men Var Track Head Coach; Def Coord Var Ftbl; OEA & NEA 1976-; NCTM 1985-; OH Cncl of Tchrs Math 1976-; BPOE 1992-.

DOWNEY, VALERIE, Mathematics Teacher; *b:* Birmingham, England; *c:* Stephen, Clare; *ed:* Aston Univ (HNC) Applied Physics 1964; Birmingham Univ (BS) Bio 1968; Southern CT St Coll (BS) Math 1979; 21 Addl Credit Hrs Math Ed; *cr:* Dunlop Rubber Co Physics Lab Tech, Microscopic Analyst 1957-65; Elem Schl 5TH Grd Tchr 1968-70; Hoadley Schl K-8TH Grd Math & Sci Tchr 1973-78; Marine Acad of Sci & Tech 9-12th Grd Math Tchr 1981-; *ai:* Math League Team Adv; Sr Class Moderator; Instructional Cncl Mem; Acad Team Co-Adv; NJEA 1993-; Middletown Reformed Church, Consistory Mem Deacon, Comm Outreach Group

Chprsn 1989-; *office:* Marine Acad Of Science & Tech Bldg 305 Gunnison Rd Sandy Hook NJ 07732*

DOWNIE, MARK, 7th & 8th Grade Math Teacher; *b:* Cleveland, OH; *m:* Joyce Alix; *c:* Jamie, Paul; *ed:* Shippensburg Univ (BS) Math 1971; PA Masters Equivalence Plus 30 Credits Penn St, York Coll, Western MD, Carlow Coll, Allentown Coll; *cr:* Spring Grove Schls Math Tchr 1971-; *ai:* Former Ath Dir, Coach 9th Grd Ftbl, Girls Bstkbl; NEA, PSEA 1975-; Honorary Math 1972-; Black Rock Church 1974-; *home:* RR 1 Box 1683 Brodbecks PA 17329*

DOWNIE, MARY JANE, English Teacher; *b:* Hamilton, OH; *ed:* Univ of Dayton (BS) Scndry Ed 1973, (MA) Eng 1982; Math Credits for Scnd Tchng Miami Univ; *cr:* St Anns Schl Eng & Math Tchr 1973-74; Carroll HS Eng & Math Tchr 1974-; Dayton & Montgomery Cty Pub Lib Sub Circulation & Reference Desks 1990-; *ai:* Dril Team 4 Yrs & Soph Class 6 Yrs Moderator; Vlybl Coach 7 Yrs; OCEA 1974-; WOCTELA 1992-93; NCEA 1974-; *office:* Carroll HS 4524 Linden Ave Dayton OH 45432

DOWNING, KEITH, OWA Head Football Coach; *b:* WA Court House, OH; *m:* Nancy L. Spears; *c:* Jayme, Joshua; *ed:* Southern St Comm Coll (AA) Bus 1980; Rio Grande Univ (BA) Bus Ed 1982; Univ OH at Dayton (MS) Guid & Schl Cnslng 1987; Cert in Occupational Work Adjustment; *cr:* Westfall HS Accntng 1982-91; Westfall HS OWA Head Ftbl Coach 1991-; *ai:* Head Ftbl Coach; OH Tchrs Assn 1982-; NEA 1991-; Pickaway Ross Tchrs Assn 1991-; Cntrl Dist Coaches Assn 1991-; OH Elks Lodge #77 1982-; OH HS Coaches Assn 1982-; South Cntrl Dist Coaches Assn 1995-, Treas; Big 33 OH HS All Star Game Coach 1995 & Coach of the Yr Awd 1985, 1987, 1990 & 1992-94; Cntrl Coach of Yr 1987; *office:* Westfall HS 19463 Pherson Pike Williamsport OH 43164*

DOWNING, M. GAIL FITZGERALD, Third Grade Teacher; *b:* Lowell, MA; *m:* J. Peter; *c:* Jeffrey; *ed:* Univ of MA Lowell (BS) Elem Ed 1963; Fitchburg St Coll (MED) Elem Ed 1982; Rivier Coll Cert Spec Needs 1983; 45 Addl Hrs Beyond Masters 1985; *cr:* Foster Schl 3rd Grd Tchr 1963-68; Shaker Ln 1st Grd Tchr 1977-82; Russell Street Schl 3-8th Grd Tchr 1982-; *ai:* Theatre Arts Club; NEA & MTA 1963-; Instr Grad Level How to Present Irish Culture to Children; *home:* 11 Magna Vista Cir Tewksbury MA 01876

DOWNS, DONNA LYNN, Art Teacher; *b:* Princeton, NJ; *m:* John W.; *c:* David, Jared; *cr:* Self-Employed Prof Puppeteer 1980-87; Stubbs Elem Schl Art Tchr 1987-94; St Edmonds Acad Art Tchr 1994-; *office:* St Edmond's Acad 2120 Veale Rd Wilmington DE 19810

DOWNS, LAWRENCE DOUGLAS, Assoc Prof of Mrktg & Chair; *b:* Rochester, NY; *m:* Sandra J. White; *c:* Nicole Y. Holland, Tamara L. Albert; *ed:* Rochester Inst of Tech (BS Bus Admin-High Hnrs 1963; MI St Univ (MBA) Mrktg, Mrktg Analysis 1964; Addl Hrs Babson Coll Small Bus, Entrepreneurship 1990-91; *cr:* Gen Foods Corp Sales Rep, Asst Prod Mgr 1964-78; Pfizer Inc Sr Prod Mrktg Mgr 1969-72; Warner Lambert Co Grp Mrktg Mgr, Div VP Mrktg; SNT Unlimited Consulting Owner, Prin 1978-; Nichols Coll MBA Adj Lecturer 1979-80, Asst Prof of Mrktg 1986-92, Assoc Prof of Mrktg 1992-; *ai:* Mu Kappa Tau Adv 1988-; Mrktg Club Adv 1988-; Fac Senate Chm 1989-90, Sec 1988-90; Numerous Acad, Stu Life Comms 1987-; RIT New Campus Fund Mgr 1963-65; Child Birth Ed Assn 1968-70; Marriage Encounter UCC MA 1974-77, Admin Trainer; United Way Comm 1989-91; Outstdng Young Men in Amer 1970; Grad Assistantship MI St Univ 1963-64; Beta Gamma Sigma Acad Hnr Soc 1964; Mngmt Fellow Babson Coll 1989-91; Outstdng Contribution & Svc Awd 1989; Who's Who in Fin & Industry 1992-92; Outstdng Tchng Awd Nichols Coll 1994; Who's Who in East 1995-; *office:* Nichols Coll Center Rd Dudley MA 01571

DOWNTON, MARY S., Admin, Math & History Teacher; *b:* San Francisco, CA; *c:* Robert, Stacy; *ed:* Zion Chrstn Coll (BA) Scndry Ed 1985; Kingsway Chrstn Coll (MEd) Chrstn Admin 1990, (PHD) Chrstn Admin 1995; *cr:* Zion Chrstn Coll Acad Dean 1995-; Zion Chrstn Acad Admin, Tchr; *ai:* US Dept of Ed Gifted, Talented Grant Prgm; Drama.

DOYLE, CAROLYN FLETCHER, Social Studies Teacher; *b:* Pittsburgh, PA; *ed:* Bloomsburg St Coll (BA) Eng, Soc Stud 1962; 60+ Credit Hrs Cntrl Ct St Coll; *cr:* Sage Park MS Jr HS Tchr 1962-; *ai:* Stu Cncl, 8th Grd Washington, 7th Grd Cape Cod Trip Adv; Yrbk Ed; NEA, CEA, WEA 1962-; Civitan 1990-; Jesters 1989-, Bd Mem; Windsor Histroical Soc 1989-, Greater Hartford 1985-, Bd Mem; Spec Olympics; DAR 1989 Outstdng Tchr of Amer His CT; *home:* 2 Kellogg St Windsor CT 06095

DOYLE, DEBORAH ZEMANICK, Spanish Teacher; *b:* Baltimore, MD; *m:* Daniel; *c:* Joseph, Elizabeth; *ed:* Univ of MD (BA) Span, Ed 1971; Georgetown Univ (MAT) Span Linguistics, Biling Ed, TESOL 1978; 26 Semester Hrs Cert Fr Univ of MD 1989; *cr:* Elizabeth Seton HS Span Tchr 1971-75; Mt Hebron HS Span Tchr 1975-88; Howard Cty Schl of Tech ESOL Tchr 1989-92; Mt Hebron HS Span Tchr 1992-; *ai:* United Way Campaighn Chprsn; Natl Span Hnr Soc Spon; NEA, AATSP 1975-; Natl, Local Confs Presenter; *office:* Mt Hebron HS 9440 State Route 99 Ellicott City MD 21042*

DOYLE, DENIS ALAN, Math & Earth Science Teacher; *b:* Rhinebeck, NY; *m:* Judith; *c:* Kimberly, Shawn; *ed:* SUNY at New Paltz (BS), (MS) Math & Sci 1975; *cr:* Germantown Cntrl Schl Math & Sci Tchr 1968-; *ai:* JV Bsktbl Coach; Math Tchr 1970-; Lions Club 1985-; NY St Section 2 Record 48 Wins 0 Losses; *office:* Germantown Central Schl 123 Main St Germantown NY 12526

DOYLE, DONNA MARIE, Amer His & Humanities Tchr; *b:* Manhattan, NY; *ed:* SUC at Brockport (BS) Therapeutic Recreation & His 1980; Hofstra Univ (MS) Scndry Ed 1985; *cr:* Bay Shore HS Soc Stud Tchr 1987-; *ai:* Sr Class Adv;Ethnic Sharing Comm; NYSUT 1987-; BSCTA 1987-, Tchr Rep 1992-; NYSCSS 1995-; *home:* 24 Willett Ave Sayville NY 11782

DOYLE, EILEEN M., Assoc Prof of Radiologic Tech; *b:* Rochester, NY; *ed:* Monroe Comm Coll (AAS) Radiologic Tech 1973; Rochester Inst of Tech (BS) Bus 1986; Currently in Masters of Pub Admin Prgm St Univ of NY Coll at Brockport; *cr:* Monroe Comm Coll Radiologic Tech Prof 1973-; *ai:* Mid Sts Accreditation Self Stud Steering Comm; Fac Senate; ASRT 1978-, Region X Ed Chapter Del; AERT 1976-, Past Pres, Bd Chm; RTSNYS 1990-, Ed Comm Chprsn; RSRT 1976-, Seminar Comm Chprsn 1994; Wayne-Finger Lakes BOCES Comm 1981-92, Occupational Ed Advy Chair 1989-91; Natl Inst for Leadership Dev Ldr 1992; *office:* Monroe Community Coll 1000 E Henrietta Rd Rochester NY 14623

DOYLE, ELAINE BEECKEN, Seventh Grade Teacher; *b:* New York City, NY; *c:* Susan P. Neel, Robin M.; *ed:* William Paterson Coll (BS) Elem Ed 1966; Univ of ME at Orono (MED) Mid Level Ed, Curr Dev 1993; *cr:* S Morrison Elem Schl Grd 5 Tchr 1966-67; Christ the King Intnl Schl Grd 8 Tchr 1967; US Armed Forces Inst Soldiers Tchr 1967-68; Holbrook MS Grd 7 Tchr 1977-; Bangor Adult Ed Schl GED Prep Tchr 1981-; *ai:* Schl Improvement Team; Schl Store Adv, Purchasing Agent; Acad Fair Dir, Founder; Schl Play Co-Dir; Odyssey of Mind Competitions Judge; MEA, NEA 1977-; ASCD 1990-; *office:* Holbrook MS RR 1 Box 22 E Holden ME 04429

DOYLE, ENID, Art Teacher; *b:* Jersey City, NJ; *m:* John; *c:* Robin Marc, Alyse Sara; *ed:* Jersey City St Coll (BA) Art Ed 1966, (MA) Prin & Supvr Urban Stud 1984; 30 Credits Beyond Masters; Prin & Supvr, Nursery Schl, Elem Ed & Schl Bus Admin Certs; *cr:* Bayonne Schl System Art Tchr 1966-; *ai:* Peer Mediation Adv; Pupil Assistance Comm; Yrbk; Tchr Recognition Comm; Annual Art Exhibit Chprsn; Stu Alumni Fac Art Exhibit Comm; Pride in NJ Schls Comm; Early Chldhd Chprsn; Bayonne Tchrs Assn 1966-, Bldg Rep; NAEA 1980-; AENJ 1985-; NJEA 1966-; Art Alliance 1990-; Bayonne Citizens for Clean Air 1986-; Bayonne Schl Systems Mini Grant 1984 & 1990; Bayonne Bailey Schl Tchr of Yr 1987; Early Chldhd Presenter Jersey City St Coll; *office:* John M Bailey Elem Schl 12 75 W 10th St Bayonne NJ 07002*

DOYLE, FRAN, Student Assistance Coord; *b:* Jersey City, NJ; *m:* Daniel; *c:* Erica Mercado, Todd Normane; *ed:* Fairleigh Dickinson Univ (BS) Elem Ed 1962; Jersey City St Coll (MA) Urban Ed 1988; Cert for Prin Supvr; Cert for Substance Awareness Coord; *cr:* Bayonne Pub Schls 2, 6-8 Grd Tchr 1970-83, K-8 Grd Cmptr Tchr 1983-89, Grant Coord 1989-91, Substance Awareness Coord 1991-; *ai:* Bayonne HS Peer Ldrshp Group Adv; Elem Peer Ldrshp Prgm Coord; Project Grad Coord; ASCD, NJ Peer Helping Assn 1990-; NEA, NJEA, BTA 1970-; Who's Who in Amer Ed 1988-; Bayonne Municipal Alliance 1990-, Coord; Bayonne Comm Day Nursery 1990-, Bd Pres; Kiwanis 1992-; Red Ribbon Campaign 1988-, Coord; Article Pub; Tchr St Cert Course Jersey City St Coll; *office:* Bayonne Bd of Ed 29th St & Ave A Bayonne NJ 07002*

DOYLE, JANE G., Assistant Professor of Nursing; *b:* Fitchburg, MS; *m:* Lawrence J.; *ed:* Skidmore Coll (BSN) Nrsng 1963; Boston Univ (MS) Nrsng 1976; Western New England Coll (MBA) Hlth Care Admin 1984; ANCC Cert Gerontology; Aids Train the Trainer cert; Alzheihers Train the Trainer Cert; IV cert; *cr:* Windham Hosp Unservice Edctr 1970-71; Leominster Hosp Schl Nursng Instr 1971-89; Fairlawn Nrsng Home Nurse Edctr Gerintology 1989-; Mount Wachusett Comm Coll Asst Prof Nrsng 1991-; *ai:* Fac Pres; Hnrs Prgm Adv; Outcomes Assessment Comm; Pres's Fdn Mem; NEA 1991-; Multiple Sclerosis Assn 1985-; Dialysis, Transplant Assn 1980-; Nancy Patch Retirement Home 1985-, Pres Bod; Lunenburg Rotary Club 1991 BOD Sgt At Arms; Lunenburg Cncl on Aging, Leominster HS Adv Hlth Profs 1992-; Created Third Thursday Series a Gerontology Lecture Prgm, Caregivers Fair at Leominster Hosp; Jane Doyle NCLEX_CAT RN Review Prgm; *home:* 160 Hemlock Dr Lunenburg MA 01462*

DOYLE, JUNE AUDREY, Art Teacher; *b:* Trenton, NJ; *ed:* Georgian Court Coll (BA) Ed; Cath Univ of Amer (MFA) Art; *ai:* Drama Scenery; Art Club; NCEA 1960-; *office:* Morris Catholic HS Morris Ave Denville NJ 07834

DOYLE, KATHERINE ANN, 4th Grade Teacher; *b:* Youngstown, OH; *c:* B. J., K. D., Molly; *ed:* Mount Union Coll (BA) El Ed, Span 1971; 20 Addl Hrs Elem Ed 1982; *cr:* Ridgeview Elem Schl 3rd-5th Grd Tchr 1971-; *ai:* Crisis Intervention Grief Cnslng Schl Dist; Peer Mediation Adv; Buckeye Ed Assn 1971-, Bldg Rep; NEA; OEA; Bethany Luth Church 1978-; *office:* Ridgeview Elem Schl 3456 Liberty Ashtabula OH 44004

DOYLE, KATHLEEN MARY, English Teacher; *b:* Stoneham, MA; *m:* John F.; *c:* Deirdre E.; *ed:* Tufts Univ (BA) Eng, Ed 1971; Suffolk Univ (MED) Counseling 1979; *cr:* Arlington High Eng Tchr 1971-; *ai:* Stu Assistance Team; NEA, MTA 1972-; AEA 1972-, Bldg Rep; Hlth Grant; *office:* Arlington HS 869 Massachusetts Ave Arlington MA 02174*

DOYLE, MARGARET G., Science Teacher; *b:* Pittsburgh, PA; *m:* William Ronald; *ed:* Duquesne Univ (BA) Elem Ed 1967; California Univ in PA (MA) Ed, Dev Cnslng 1971; 46 Credit Hrs Penn St Ext, Univ of Pittsburg; *cr:* Diocese of Pittsburgh Elem Tchr 1954-67; Pittsburgh Pub Schls Elem Tchr 1968-; *ai:* AFT, PFT 1968-; Distngd Ach in Sci Ed 1991; Outstdng Ach in Sci Ed 1994 Allegheny Hlth, Ed & Rsrch Fnd; *office:* Overbrook Elem Schl 2140 Saw Mill Run Blvd Pittsburgh PA 15210

DOYLE, MARGARET PATRICIA, English Teacher; *b:* Rochester, NY; *ed:* SUNY at Oswego (BA) Scndry Ed, Eng 1979; Nazareth Coll (MA) Rdng 1986; *ai:* WCS Tchrs Assn 1979-; *office:* James A. Beneway HS 6200 Ontario Center Rd S Ontario Center NY 14520

DOYLE, PHYLLIS LOUISE, Eng Dept Chair & Asst Prof; *b:* Portland, ME; *ed:* St Joseph's Coll (BA) Eng 1970; Univ of ME (MA) Eng 1974; Univ of RI (PHD) Eng 1980; *cr:* Cath Elem Schls Tchr 1951-67; St Patrick's Schl Prin 1968-69; John Bapt HS Eng Tchr 1971-74; St Joseph's Coll Asst Prof of Eng 1980-; *ai:* Eng Dept Chair; Delta Epsilon Sigma; Modern Lang Soc 1980-; Mercy Higher Ed Colloquium 1976-; F Scott Fitzgerald Soc 1992-; Regnl Comm Sponsorship 1994-, Comm; St Patrick's Parish 1993-, Lector; Poems Pub 1970-77, 1979, 1986-92; *office:* Saint Josephs Coll 278 White's Bridge Rd Standish ME 04084

DOYLE, SANDRA PRYOR, Kindergarten Teacher; *b:* Utica, NY; *c:* Brian, Timothy, Wendy; *ed:* St Univ Coll (BA) Ed 1966; Potsdam (MS) 1972; *cr:* Norwood Norfolk Schl 4th-5th Grd Tchr 1966-68; Colton-Pierrepont Cntrl Schl Kndgtn, 2nd, 4th Grd Tchr 1975-; *ai:* Class Adv; Dist, Inclusion Bldg Teams; Presch Organizer; BOCES Previewer; Mentor Tchr Handicapped Stdnts; CPT Assn 1975-; Friends of Lib 1986-, Pres, VP, Sec, Treas; *home:* 25 Foley Ln Colton NY 13625

DOYLE, WALTER, Science Dept Chairman; *b:* Newark, NJ; *ed:* Fordham (BS) Math 1954, (MS) Bio 1962; St John (PhD) Cytology 1969; St Michael (MA) Religion 1982; Attnd St Michaels VT, Corneil NY, Stanford CA; L.S.U. at LA; *cr:* McGill Inst Bio Instr 1955-60; Bishop Reilly HS Sci Chair 1962-72; Msgr McClancy HS Sci Chair 1972-; *ai:* McClancy Sci Club; Exec Bd NY Bio Tchrs Assn; ASCD; NSTA; NABT; NYBTA, Past Pres Outstanding Bio Tchr; Vertebrate Comm NAS; NYC Schl Sci Fairs; Natl Endowment Hum Grant; Natl Sci Fnd at Boulder, Stanford, Cornell, Cinncinatti; Can J Genet Cytology, Caryologia, Genet Res Pub; NASA, Westinghouse Talent Search, Future Scientist of Amer, Optimist Club Citations; Lumen Christi Awd 1996; *office:* Msgr McClancy HS 71-06 31st Ave East Elmhurst NY 11370

DRACHMAN, EDWARD RALPH, Assoc Prof of Political Sci; *b:* New York, NY; *m:* Barbara R.; *c:* Hayley Sherwood, Joy, Daniel Sherwood; *ed:* Harvard Coll (BA) Govt 1961; Univ of PA (MA) Pol Sci 1962, (PHD) Intnl Relations 1968; Harvard Grad Schl of Ed (MAT) Soc Stud 1963; *cr:* Boston Univ Instr 1960-68, Asst Prof of Pol Sci 1968-71, Prof of Intnl Relations 1988-91; Ipswich HS Soc Stud Dept Chair 1971-80; Univ of Hartford Assoc Prof of Pol Sci 1980-87; SUNY Coll at Geneseo Assoc Prof of Pol Sci 1991-; *ai:* Fac Adv; Model European Union; Options Pgm Dir; Schlsps & Flwshps Coll Comm Mem; Amer Pol Sci Assn; NY Pol Sci Assn; United Univ Professions; B'nai B'rith, VP Local Chptr; Books Pub: United States Policy Toward Vietnam 1940-1945, Challenging the Kremlin; Articles Pub; *office:* S U N Y Coll At Geneseo 1 College Cr Geneseo NY 14454*

DRACZ, SUSAN BUSOVSKY, Reading Specialist & Teacher; *b:* Kittanning, PA; *m:* Thomas; *c:* Ann; *ed:* Indian Univ of PA (BS) Elem Ed 1973; Shippensburg Univ (MED) Rdng Specialist 1990; Rdng Recovery; *cr:* Bethel Twp Elem Schl 6th Grd Tchr 1974-75; Troy Hill Elem Schl 4th Grd Tchr 1975-76; St Andrew's Elem Schl 4th Grd Tchr 1977-81, 1983-86; Greencastle Antrim MS Tells Math, Rdng Tchr 1986-94; Greencastle Antrim Elem Schl Rdng Specialist, Rdng Recovery Tchr 1994-; *ai:* G-A CARES; Parent to Parent Facilitator; Whole Lang Comm; PSEA, NEA 1986-; KSRA 1990-; GAEA 1986-, Rep; Greencastle Arts Cncl 1994-; BEST Grant; *office:* Greencastle-Antrim Elem Schl 500 E Leitersburg St Greencastle PA 17225*

DRAGHETTI, JANET A., English Teacher; *b:* Brattleboro, VT; *ed:* Emerson Coll (BA) Eng, Speech, Drama 1963; Bridgewater St Coll (MED) Instrl Media 1970; *cr:* Plymouth North HS Eng Tchr 1963-; *ai:* Lit Magazine Adv; NEA, MTA 1963-; MCTE 1995-; Delta Kappa Gamma; Presbyn Soc Duxbury Beach 1995-; *office:* Plymouth North HS St Plymouth MA 02360

DRAGO, MARY, 5th-6th Grd Teacher; *b:* Carbondale, PA; *ed:* S El Ed 1980, (MS) Ed 1985; *cr:* Delaware Acad 3rd-4th Grd Tch Center St Schl 5th-6th Grd Tchr 1986-; *ai:* NEA 1980-; You 1990-; *office:* Center Street Schl 31 Center St Oneonta NY 138

DRAGOVICH, MINDY STARK, High School Band Director; *b* NY; *m:* James; *c:* Charles, Jane; *ed:* Hofstra Univ (BS) Ed 1984; Schl of Music (MM) Clarinet 1986; Stud in Advanced Condu Heulett HS Orch Dir 1986-89; Woodmere MS Band Dir 1989-90 Elem Schl Band Dir 1990-94; Wantagh HS Band Dir 1994- Ensemble, Dixieland Band, Woodwind Quintet & Marching NMEA, MENC 1986-; WUT 1990-; *office:* Wantagh HS 3303 Be Wantagh NY 11793*

DRAHOUZAL, MARLIES, English Teacher; *b:* Ridgewood, NJ Mawr Coll (BA) Eng Lit 1988; Univ of ME at Orono (MA) Eng *cr:* Univ of ME Frosh Eng Instr 1990-92; Bergen Cath HS Eng T *ai:* Moderator Frosh Stud Hall; Chaperone to England-Irelar Bergen Cath HS 1040 Oradell Ave Oradell NJ 07649*

DRAHUS, SUZANNE CILIBERTO, Spanish Teacher; *b:* Pittst John W. Jr.; *c:* Tanya, Antoinette; *ed:* Mansfield Univ (BS) Sc 1972; MS Equivalency 36 Credit Hrs 1991, 6 Credit Hrs 1996; *c* Area Schl Dist Substitute Tchr 1972-86; Pocono Mtn Schl Dist 1986-87; Holy Child Schl 5th Grd Tchr 1987-88; Coughlin HS 1988-; *ai:* Span Club; Girls' Soccer Asst Coach; NEA 8 Yrs; *offi* M. Coughlin HS 80 N Washington St Wilkes Barre PA 18701

DRAJEM, LINDA, Supervisor of Student Teachers; *b:* Buffal Robert; *c:* Mark, Christopher; *ed:* D'Youville Coll (BA) Eng 196 Coll At Buffalo (MS) Eng Ed 1975; SUNY at Buffalo (MA Womens Stud 1993; Currently Working on PHD in Amer Stud; *c* Pub Schls HS Tchr 1975-95; SUNY at Buffalo Stu Tchrs Supvr Former Stu Cncl Adv; NCTE 1977-; WNY Writing Project 1 Buffalo Lit Ctr 1990-; Natl Endowment for the Hum Ind Stud NEH Grants; Poetry Pub.*

DRAKE, ANDREA NINA, English Teacher; *b:* Long Island Robert; *c:* Chris; *ed:* Marymount Coll (BA) Eng 1965; Stony B (MA) Eng 1971; 60 Credit Hrs Grad Art & Lit; *cr:* Marymoun Tchr 1965-66; Southside Jr High Eng Tchr 1966-70; James Wils Jr High Eng Tchr 1970-71; Patchogue MS Eng Tchr 1971-74; Bro High Eng Tchr 1976-78; West Babylon Jr High Eng Tchr 1980-; *a* Club; Lit Magazine & Schl Newspaper; Natl Jr Hnr Soc Comm 1966-; Excl in Tchng Awd 1993; *office:* West Babylon Jr HS Farmingdale Rd Babylon NY 11704

DRAKE, ANNE MELANIE, Language Arts Teacher; *b:* Cincin *m:* David C.; *c:* Clinton, Melanie; *ed:* Cumberland Coll (BS) 1972; Addl 13 Semester Hrs Grad Stud; *cr:* St Elizabeth Seton Grd Tchr 1967-75; St Andrew MS 5-8 Grd Tchr 1985-; *ai:* Spe Coord; Eng Dept Head; Formerly Acting Prin 1990, Rainbow Fa Intervention Team, Liaison Adm Fac; NCTE; Cinti Nature C Congressional Awd for Outstdng Svc to Comm; 1992 Tchr of Yr; Andrew Schl 555 Main St Milford OH 45150*

DRAKE, DIANE ELLEN, Sixth Grade Teacher; *b:* Passaic, NJ; C.; *c:* Jeffrey, Jaclyn; *ed:* Paterson St Coll (BA) K-8 Ed 1970; *cr* 4th-5th Grd Tchr 1970-75; Schl #15 5th Grd Tchr 1976-81; Schl # Tchr 1982; Schl #4 3rd Grd Tchr 1981-91; C. Columbus MS 6th 1991-; *ai:* Clifton Tchrs Assn 1970-, Sch, Local Rep; Passaic C Assns, NEA 1970-; Pequannock Twp HS Home, Schl Ass Pequannock Twp HS Band Parents Assn 1988-92, 1996-; First F Church 1988-, Sunday Schl Vol; Pequannock Piranhas Parents As Parent Rep; Governor's Tchr Recognition 1990; *office:* Ch Columbus MS 350 Piaget Ave Clifton NJ 07011

DRAKE, J. PAIGE, 1st Grade Teacher; *b:* Olean, NY; *w:* Donald Laura, John; *ed:* Mansfield St Coll (BSEd) Elem Ed 1961; St Bon Univ (MSEd) Guid 1965; *cr:* Olean Pub Schl System 3rd C 1961-63, 1st Grd Tchr 1963-; *ai:* TAB Rep; Educl Fair, Fitness & Comms; NEA 1961-; NEA of NY 1961-; Kappa Delta Pi; Alc Outstdng Tchr Awd; *office:* Washington West Elem Schl 1626 Wa St Olean NY 14760

DRAKE, JERRY FRANCIS, Band Director & Dept Chrmn; *b:* B MD; *m:* Louise Mary Morgan; *c:* Thomas, Patricia, Meli Montgomery Coll (AA) Music Ed 1965; Univ of MD (BM) Com 1968, (BED) Music Ed 1972, (MED) Music Ed 1977; 34 Credit Salb-Hanson Music Co Guitar, Trumpet & Flute Tchr 1963-78; B MS Band Dir & Dept Chm 1968-74; Montgomery Village MS Ba Dept Chm 1974-94; Watkins Mill HS Band Dir & Dept Co-Chm 1 Marching Band, Schl Musical Pit Orch Dir; Jazz Band Cond Arranger; Free-Lance Musician; Charles Cty Hnr Band 1972, Tri- Band 1973 & Montgomery Cty Hnr Band 1993 Conductor; Bras Montgomery Cty Hnr Band 1986; Amer Fed of Musicians 196 1968-; MCEA 1974-; Montgomery Village Trl Club 1982-92, S Cautious Skiing Awd 1982; Performed with Little Anthony Imperials & The Drifters 1966 & 1967; Conducted Highest Sco Band in St Finals 1992-94; Wrote Guitar Book; *home:* 190 Hampshire Ave Brinklow MD 20862*

DRAKE, JOSEPH ROBERT, 7th-12th Grd Art Teacher; *b:* Elm *m:* Amanda K.; *c:* Ryan MacKenzie, Morgan Ashleigh; *ed:* Buffalo (BA) Art Ed 1985, (MS) Prsnl Admin 1987; *cr:* Buffalo St Coll Pgr 1985-87; DeRuyter Cntrl Schl Tchr 1987-; *ai:* Stu Cncl, Drama C Assistance Team, NHS & Prom Adv; Peer Coaching Team, Arts in Comp Comm; NYSATA 1983-.

DRAKE, JOYCE WILLIAMS, Eighth Grade Reading Tchr; *b:* Pe NY; *m:* John William Sr.; *c:* Jennifer Drake Sweigart, John Syracuse Univ (BS) Comm 1958; Attnd Montclair St & NY Univ; Toward Grad Degree from Rutgers; *cr:* Natl Broadcasting Co Tonig Unit Mgrs Sec 1958-61; West Orange Pub Schl 7th Grd Lang A 1964-66; Bridgewater-Raritan Schls Basic Skills Tchr 1975-80, Rdng Tchr 1985-; *ai:* Lincoln Ctr Inst Tchr; Choral Groups Acco Groups; CNJIRA 1980-, Sec; NJRA, IRA 1980-; PTO, Parent Rep.

DRAKE, LINDA KERWIN, Sixth Grade Teacher; *b:* E Grand Rap *m:* F. Bradford; *ed:* Univ of VA Women's Coll (BA) Elem Ed, Chil 1973; St Joseph's Coll (MA) Elem Ed 1990; *cr:* Grafton Village Ele Second Grd Tchr 1973-75; St Andrews Episcopal Schl First G 1975-76; Skaneateles Schl Rdng Tchr 1977-79; Chester Elem Sch Grd Tchr 1987-; *ai:* Odyssey of Mind Coach; Tchr in Charge; NE 1987-; Florence Griswold Museum 1990-; Dist #4 Tchr of Yr 1 SNET Grant; *office:* Chester Elem Schl 23 Ridge Rd Chester CT 0

DRAKE, MARGARET ELIZABETH, Fourth Grade Teacher; *b:* OH; *m:* Paul Roderick; *c:* Craig Alan Roberts; *ed:* Bowling Green (BSED) Elem Ed 1972; Ashland Univ (MED) Supervision 19 Clinton Elem Schl Third Grd Tchr 1970-76; Berlin Elem Schl Fi Tchr 1978-79, Fourth Grd Tchr 1979-; *ai:* A Partnership for Educ Progress Report, Lang Arts & Math Courses of Stud Comms; BMTA Corresponding Sec & Bldg Rep; OEA, NEA 1978-; Delta Kappa 1986-; Phi Delta Kappa 1990-; *office:* Berlin Elem Schl 20 Center S Heights OH 44814*

MARY M., French & Spanish Teacher; b: Boston, MA; m: ; ed: Boston St Coll (BA) Sociology 1972, (MA) Ed, Foreign cr: Newman Jr HS Span Tchr 1979-80; St Clare HS Fr, Span 90, Foreign Lang Dept Chm 1986-90; Marian HS Fr, Span Tchr edham HS Fr, Span Tchr 1995-; ai: Stu Travel Coord 1982-85; v, Schl Nwsp Adv 1986-87, Stu Cncl Adv 1987-90; NEA, BATA, 80-, AATF, AATSP 1995-, MTA; home: 42R Massapoag St South MA 02190

WILLIAM R., Biology Teacher; ed: Millersville St (BED) Bio pensbrug St (MED) Bio 1974; 30 Credit Hrs Various Ed Courses; nsburg JHS Sci Tchr 1972-; ai: Asst Ath Dir; Asst HS Ftbl Stu Cncl Adv; Mentor Tchr; Cooperating Tchr; NEA 1972-; 2-; SAEA 1972-, Pres & Chief Negotiator; office: Shippensburg 101 Park Place Shippensburg PA 17257

EY, THOMAS EDWARD, Social Studies Teacher; b: Belmar, san Campbell; c: Scott Robert, Tim James, Matt Thomas; ed: n & Jefferson Coll (BA) Pol Sci, His 1977-; 30 Grad Credit Hrs : South Side Cath Schl Hlth, PE Tchr 1977-78; Peters Twp Schl ud Tchr 1978-82; Weber Natl Stores Sales Rep 1983-89; Trinity oc Stud Tchr 1989-; ai: Head Boys Var Bsktbl Coach 6 Yrs; MS n Mem; NEA, PSEA 1990-; Washington-Green Cty Coach of Yr Cty Coach of Yr Mens Bsktbl 1987, 1989; Gift of Time Awd e: Trinity MS Trinity MS Scenic Dr 50 Scenic Dr Washington

AMES A., English Teacher; b: Washington, PA; m: Kathleen ed: Univ of PA CA (BS) Ed 1992; Univ of Pittsburgh 6 Credits; Natl Writing Project; cr: Monaca Area HS Eng Tchr 1992-; ai: paper; Drama Club; Soph Class Spon; Writing Comm for Dist gm; Strategic Planning Comm; Monaca Area Ed Assn 1992-; naca Area Jr Sr HS 1500 Allen Ave Monaca PA 15061

ATHLEEN ANDERSON, English Teacher; b: Rochester, PA; m: rew; ed: Penn St Univ (BS) Scndry Ed 1990; cr: Homewell Area Lang Arts Instr 1993-; ai: Class of 1998, Forensic Club Spon; sessment Action Team Co-Chprsn; HASDEA 1994-; Gift of Time e: Hopewell Sr HS 1215 Longvue Ave Aliquippa PA 15001

, DANIEL A., Mathematics Curriculum Coord; b: Jamaica, NY; A. (dec); c: Matthew, Rene; ed: SUNY at Geneseo (BA) Math NY at Stony Brook (MS) Math 1975; 67 Credit Hrs Beyond r: Great Neck South Jr HS Tchr 1974-75; Babylon Jr-Sr HS Tchr th Curr Coord 1986-; ai: Jr Class Adv; Math Team Coach; Ftbl h; NCTM 1976-; AMTNYS 1986-; SCMTA 1984-, Tchr of Yr slip PTSA 1993-, Cncl Del; Pat Drance Meml Schlshp 1993-, nst Exemplary Tchrs of Math Hofstra Univ 1986-87; Presidential office: Babylon Jr Sr HS 50 RR Ave Babylon NY 11702*

ANTHONY JOSEPH, Guidance Department Supervisor; b: ; m: Judy Borovitz; c: Anthony Jr., Christopher, Stacy; ed: Kings Pol Sci & Ec 1965; Marywood Coll (MS) Scndry Guid 1972, ical Cnslng 1974; Univ of Scranton Guid Supvr Cert; cr: Pittston 1965-74, Guid Cnslr 1974-90, Guid Dept Supvr 1990-; ai: nunications Moderator; PA Cnslr Assoc 1988-; AFT 1972-; Cnslrs Assoc 1974-, Treas; Borough Cncl 1974-; Lions Club s; office: Pittston Area Schl Dist 5 Stout St Pittston PA 18640

, GERALD RICHARD, Social Studies Teacher; b: Brooklyn, elisa; c: Diana, Jennifer, Michael; ed: Brooklyn Coll (BA) His Univ (MA) His 1979; NY City Tech Coll (ASA) Opthamalic 1982; Hunter Coll Schl Soc Work; cr: Dr N Drayer Optician Cunningham Jr HS Tchr 1990-91; E R Murrow HS Tchr 1991-; Optician Soc; UFT 1990-; office: Edward R Murrow HS 1600 Brooklyn NY 11230

, JERRY K., Social Studies Teacher; b: Fairmont City, PA; w: . (dec); c: Steven, Kevin, Kristen; ed: Clarion St Univ (BS) ensive Soc Stud 1964; SUNY at Buffalo (MS) Ed 1971; 49 Hrs Past Masters Degree; cr: Schl #6 Buffalo Tchr 1964; Akron Cntrl ; ai: Var Wrestling Coach 1965-; Var Girls & Boys Track Coach y Scouts Merit Badge Cnslr 1975-; Var Boys & Girls Cross Cntry 88-; AFT Inception; Akron Fac Assn 1964-; NYSUT Inception; estling Coaches Assn; Cross Cntry Coach of Yr 1990; Wrestling ach of Yr 1981; Niagara Orleans League Fndtn Awd 1993 & Coach of Yr 1994; Top 10 Tchrs of Yr Awd 1995; office: Akron chl 47 Bloomingdale Ave Akron NY 14001

, DIANE RARUS, 6th Grade Teacher; b: Providence, RI; m: .; c: Joseph R.; ed: Bridgewater St Coll (BS) Elem Ed 1971; and Coll (MED) Elem 1975; Attnd Providence Coll, Univ MA at r: Bliss Schl 5th Grd Tchr 1971-76; Hill-Roberts Schl 4th-5th Grd 6-86; Robert J. Coelho Schl 5th-6th Grd Tchr 1986-; ai: Hlth ellness Comm Co-Chair; Sci Club Instr; Attleboro Hlth Advy Bd; 1-; ADK 1977-, Treas, Pres Elect; office: Robert J Coelho MS 75 Attleboro MA 02703

R, LOIS ANN, Art & Photography Teacher; b: Scranton, PA; ed: St Coll (BS) Art Ed 1969, (MED) Art Ed 1973; RI Schl of Design ainting, Drawing, Art Ed 1987; MAL Degree Candidate Wesyelan 8-80; cr: Univ of Scranton Continuing Ed Drawing & Painting Instr 1987-; Cntrl HS Art Tchr 1969-91; Scranton HS Art, Photo 1-; ai: Natl Art Hnr Soc Chptrs 101 Spon 1978-; NAEA, SFT Delta Kappa 1987-; Art Stdnts League 1990-, Life Mbrshp; PA of Parents & Tchrs 1989-, Honorary Life Mbrshp; Outstdng Svc Awd PAEA 1981; Awd of Excl in Tchng Photography Eastman 980; Natl Achvmt in Art Awd Scholastic Cert Awd 1977-80; of Monstein Castle in Pvt Collection of Baroness Hansi Von Outstdng Contribution to Comm Mayor Wenzel 1987; office: HS Adams Ave & Gibson St Scranton PA 18510

KO, JUDIANNE M., Social Studies Teacher; b: Albany, NY; ed: of NY at Albany (BA) Ed 1967; Post Grad Stud; cr: Lansingburgh 1968-; St Ed Dept Consultant 1988-; Lansingburgh HS Soc Stud 990-95; ai: Sr Class Adv; NY St Tchrs 1968-; Amer Psych Tchrs; Dist Cncl for Soc Stud, Bd Mem; NY Cncl Soc Stud; NCSS; PTA, nbership; office: Lansingburgh HS 320 7th Ave Troy NY 12182

SEL, JOANNE JEITNER, Professor of Lang & Lit; b: phia, PA; m: Alfred; c: Al J., Robert; ed: Holy Family Coll (BA) 2; Beaver Coll (MA) Eng 1984; Univ of PA PHD Candidate Prgm; cr: St Basil Acad Eng Tchr 1982-85; Holy Family Coll Eng 1985-88; Penn St Univ Eng Instr 1988-89; Bucks Cty Comm Coll Prof 1988-; ai: Institutional Assessment, Evaluation Comm; Pres Advy Group; NCTE, CCCC 1981-; MLA 1989-; AAUW 1995-; for Women 1989-; US Holocaust Meml Museum 1994-; office: ounty Comm Coll Swamp Road Newtown PA 18940

SLER, TERRY ANN, Mathematics Tchr; b: Columbus, GA; ed: y St (BA) Math 1977, (MED) Ed 1982; cr: Washington HS Math 7-; ai: Jr Class, Schl Improvement Team; Dept Chprsn; Sunshine Future Edctrs; NEA, NCTM 1977-; TASCO 1977-, Treas, Sec, VP; 1980-; Eastern Star 1980-, Worthy Matron; Mentor; office: ton H S 10902 Old Princess Anne Rd Princess Anne MD 21853*

DEDREE A., Art Prof & Cmptr Grphcs Coord; b: Utica, NY; m: ark Fisher; ed: Skidmore Coll (BS) Art 1967; PA St Univ (MFA) 1970; John Hopkins Univ (MLA) Art His 1979; Guild of Natl Sci Illus Cert; cr: CCC Prof Art, Coord Cmptr Graphics 1971-; ai: Coll Art Assn; Balto Print Mor Users Group; Fulbright Alum Assn; Guild of Natl Sch Illustrators; Fulbright to Netherlands, Belguim; Article Pub 1991; Natl Cncl of Art Admin Bd of Dir Awd 1988; NEH Grant; Integrate the Schlsp in Women; office: Catonsville Comm Coll 800 S Rolling Rd Catonsville MD 21228

DREHER, BEVERLY MARZULLO, Third Grade Teacher; *b:* New Kensington, PA; *m:* Robert A. Sr.; *c:* Robert A. Jr.; *ed:* Slippery Rock St Coll (BA) Elem Ed 1974; Addl Grad Credit Hrs; *cr:* New Kensington-Arnold Schl Dist Sub Tchr 1975-79, Second, Third, Fifth Grd Tchr 1980-; *ai:* Math Curr Comm; PSEA, NKAEA, NEA 1980-; *home:* 292 Elmtree Rd New Kensington PA 15068

DREHER, DENISE DEMPSEY, Fourth Grade Teacher; *b:* Hornell, NY; *m:* Max J. III; *c:* Hillary, Jay, Gracie; *ed:* SUNY at Cortland (BS) Elem Ed 1978; Elmira Coll Masters Ed 1982; *cr:* Jasper Cntrl Schl Fourth Grd Tchr 1978-87; Jasper-Troupsburg Cntrl Schl Fourth Grd Tchr 1987-; *ai:* United Meth Church 1970-; *home:* PO Box 26 Troupsburg NY 14885

DREHSEL, MARY BANISTER, Assistant Prof of German; *b:* Longview, TX; *m:* Karl; *c:* Susanne, Miriam, Karl, Markus; *ed:* Abilene Chrstn Univ (BS) Elem Ed 1971; Boston Univ (MS) Human Resource Ed 1987; *cr:* Arlington ISD 3rd & 4th Grd Tchr 1971-73; Heidelberg Gemeinde Christi Bible Tchr & Chldrns Act Ldr 1974-79; Pepperdine Univ Instr of Ger 1981-93; Asst Prof of Ger 1994-; Coord of Acad Adv 1989-; *ai:* AATG 1986-; *home:* Otto Han Platz 1 69126 Heidelberg Germany XX

DREIBELBIS, NEIL R., Art Teacher; *b:* West Reading, PA; *c:* Melissa A. Howerin, Kirsten L. Mey; *ed:* Kutztown Univ (BS) Art Ed 1962; Theater HB Studio; Western MI Univ, Skidmore Coll & St Univ of NY, PE St Univ Post Grad Stud; *cr:* Exeter Twp HS Art Tchr 1962-67; Muhlenberg Twp HS Art Tchr 1967-70; Conestoga Vly HS Art Tchr 1970-81; Manheim Twp HS Art Tchr 1987-; *ai:* Art Hnrs Club Adv; NAEA, PAEA 1970-; Outstdng Scndry Edctr of Amer Awd 1975; Related Arts Schlsp PA Dept of Ed 1976; Art Ed Flwshp in Painting Skidmore Coll 1988, 1991; Art Ed Flwshp Philadelphia Museum of Art 1990; Art Ed Flwshp Marie Walsh-Sharpe Fnd 1994; *office:* Manheim Twp HS PO Box 5134 School Rd Lancaster PA 17606

DRELICH, ROBERT JOSEPH,OSFS School Minister; *b:* Philadelphia, PA; *ed:* Lehigh Cty Comm Coll (ABM) Bus Mngmt 1976; Wilmington Coll (BS) Bus Admin 1980; Bethlehem Bus Schl Gen Bus Diploma 1972; Pastoral Ministry Cert Allentown Coll; Pastoral Music Cert Immaculata Coll; *cr:* Villa Maria Retreat Ctr Bus Dir 1980-83; St Francis de Sales Church Rel Ed Coord 1983-85; Nazareth Acad HS Schl Minister 1985-95; St Joachim Church Asst to Prof 1995-; *ai:* Comm Svc Corps; Liturgical Comm; Natl Assn Pastoral Musicians 1980-; Cath Fine Arts Assn, NCEA 1985-; Comm Svc Corps 1987-; For God & Yth Awd 1993; *home:* 1527 Church St Philadelphia PA 19124

DRENNEN, PAMELA SUSAN, French Teacher; *b:* Troy, NY; *m:* Russell W.; *c:* Genevieve, Christian, David; *ed:* St Univ of NY at Cortland (BA) Ed Fr 1972; Russell Sage Coll (MS) Elem Ed 1978; Attnd Univ of Neuchatel, Switzerland 1970-71; *cr:* Cohoes HS Fr Tchr 1974-; *ai:* Fr Club Adv; Bldg LoTrap Team Chairwoman 1994-95; Nom Employee of Yr 1989; *office:* Cohoes HS 1 Tiger Way Cohoes NY 12047

DRENNING, ALAN ROSS, Social Science Teacher; *b:* Huntingdon, PA; *m:* Rose Marie Steele; *c:* Jason, Erin; *ed:* Shippensburg Univ (BA) Soc Stud 1966; Penn St Univ (MED) Admin 1978; *cr:* Pa Dept of Labor & Ind Cnslr 1966-70; Bedford Gazette Sports Ed 1971-75; Northern Bedford SD Tchr 1976-; *ai:* Class Adv; Bsbl Coach; Bsktbl, Ftbl Statistician; AAA of Southern Pa, Bd Mem; *home:* PO Box 86 Woodbury PA 16695

DRENNING, CHARLES DAHL, Social Studies Teacher; *b:* Baltimore, MD; *m:* Peggy Jean Howser; *c:* Alexandra; *ed:* Univ of MD (BA) Soc Stud Ed 1969; Western KY Univ (MA) Soc Stud Ed 1972; Post Grad US His; *cr:* Westminster HS Soc St Tchr 1969-71; Walkersville HS Soc St Tchr 1972-86; Catoctin HS Soc St Tchr 1987-; Frederick Comm Coll Adj Prof 1987-; *ai:* UTP, NEA, MD St Teach Assn, Fred Co Teach Assn 1972-; Friends of Monocacy 1992-; Woodsboro Historical Soc Pres; MD Montadale Assn Pres; MD Cncl for Soc Stud Excl Awd 1992-93; Frederick Cty Tchr Historian 1987-88, 1992-93; Tchr Plus Awd Frederick Cty 1985; MD Hum Cncl Grant 1984; Innovative Tchng Awd 1984; *home:* PO Box 33 Woodsboro MD 21798

DRESCHER, ARTHUR J., Fourth Grade Teacher; *b:* Lebanon, PA; *m:* Bonnie; *c:* Adam, David, Heather, Jon, Sara; *ed:* Millersville St Coll (BSED) Elem 1964; Temple Univ (MED) Psych Rdng 1967; *cr:* Palmyra Area Schl Dist 6th Grd Tchr 1964-67; Abington Schl Dist 5th Grd Tchr 1967-83, 4th Grd Tchr 1983-; *ai:* PA St Ed Assn, NEA 1964-; Contributor to His Resource Book; Meritorious Awd Outstdng Educator, Innovative Audio Visual Prgm; Patriotic Order Sons Amer, Freedom, Fnd Excl Slide, Sound, Portrayol Amer Awds.

DRESHMAN-CHIODO, JANICE, Prevention Specialist; *b:* Pittsburgh, PA; *m:* Brian Chiono; *ed:* Chatham Coll (BA) Human Svcs Admin 1988; Univ of Pittsburgh (MSW) Soc Work 1990; Working on EDD Interdisciplinary Doctoral Prgm for Educl Ldrs DuQuesne Univ; *cr:* Adolescent & Family Treatment Fnd Therapist 1985-87; YMCA Child Care Dir 1988; Brighton Woods Treatment Ctr Therapist 1988-90; St Francis Med Ctr Ed Specialist 1990-92; Hopewell Area Schl Dist Prevention Specialist, Home & Schl Visitor 1992-; *ai:* HS Club Viking Influencing Peers Spon; Martial Arts Instr; LSW, CAC, NAADAC 1990-; AAGC 1995-; US Light House Soc, Marine Mammal Strandins Ctr, Zoological Soc of Pittsburgh, Marine Mammal Fund 1994-; Admin for Children, Yth & Families Trng Awd Univ of Pittsburgh 1990-91; Gift of Time Tribute Awd 1991-92; Cert of Appreciation Conservation Club 19 94; Beaver Cty Cncl Schlsp Hnr Roll by PTA 1995; St-Natl Level Healing Process & Trauma Speaker, Presenter; *office:* Hopewell Area Schl Dist 1215 Longvue Ave Aliquippa PA 15001*

DRESSLER, IRA, Orchestra Director; *b:* Bronx, NY; *m:* Rona Piotrokowski; *c:* Joseph; *ed:* Adelph Univ (BA) Music 1971; Queens Coll (MSEd) Music 1974; *cr:* Half Hollow Hills Schls Orch, Music Tchr 1971-; *ai:* Tchr Mentor; MENC 1971-; LISFA 1971-, Suffolk Cty VP; SCMEA 1971-, Orch Chprsn; Village Civic Assn 1980-, Bd of Dir; Guest Conductor for Three Village Schls Music Festival, Orange Cty Jr HS All Cty Orch & SCMEA Division II All Cty Orch; *home:* 25 Haskell Ln Stony Brook NY 11790*

DRESSMAN, JOAN ARENS, Fourth Grade Teacher; *b:* Covington, KY; *m:* John C.; *c:* Daniel, Timothy; *ed:* Thomas More (BA) Ed 1972; Xavier Univ (MS) 1978; *cr:* Fed Reserve Bank Acctng 1947-53; *ai:* ABWA 1991-, Ed; Happy Timers; *office:* St Lawrence Schl 1020 Carson Ave Cincinnati OH 45205

DRESSMAN, RITA,OSU, Religious Education Dir; *b:* Cumberland, MD; *ed:* Xavier Univ (MED) Ed 1969; Bellarmine Coll (BA) Soc Sci 1964; Frostburg St Univ 6 Credit Hrs Ed 1984, 1973; Baldwin-Wallace Coll 5 Credit Hrs Ed 1980; Spalding Coll 3 Credit Hrs Rel Ed 1972; Coll of St Joseph 2 Credit Hrs Rel Ed 1972; George Peabody Coll 12 Credit Hrs Ed 1970; 600+ Clock Hrs Eel Ed 1973-; *cr:* Our Lady of Lourdes Schl First Grd Tchr 1964-67; Ursuline Montessori Schl Montessori Tchr, Dir 1967-68, 1969-73; Xavier Univ Grad Stud 1968-69; SS Peter & Paul Schl Second Grd Tchr 1973-76, 1977-80, Admin Team, Tchr 1980-81, Rel Ed Dir 1989-; Sacred Heart Model Schl Kndgtn Tchr 1976-77; St John Neumann Schl Asst Prin 1981-82, Second Grd Tchr 1984-89; St Frances DeSales Schl Fourth Grd Tchr 1982-84; *ai:* Rel Curr Coord; Jr Yth Group, HS Yth Group Adv; Parish Staff, Cncl; Liturgy Comm; NCEA; Archdiocesan Medal of Hnr 1994; Advanced Prof Tchng Cert; Prof Catechist Cert MD, WV 1984, KY 1973; Montessori Primary Diploma 1969; *office:* SS Peter & Paul Parish 125 Fayette St Cumberland MD 21502

DREUCCI, WILLIAM M., Public Relations Coordinator; *b:* Stockdale, PA; *m:* Karen R. Moore; *c:* Karianne, Martin; *ed:* CA Univ of PA (BS) Ed 1961; Post Grad Stud in Scndry Music WV Univ, Duquesne Univ; *cr:* Oakmont Schl Dist Classroom Tchr 1961-63; Bethlehem Ctr Schl Dist Vocal Music Supvr, HS Choral Dir 1963-77, Elem Classroom Tchr 1977-79, Gifted Ed Coord 1979-86, Elem Classroom Tchr 1986-88, His, Lang Arts Tchr 1988-95; Pub Relations Coord 1995-; *ai:* NEA, PSEA 1961-; MENC, PMEA 1963-, Pres; Wash Cty Music Ed Assn; Amer Choral Dirs Assn 1963-; PENSPRA 1995-; Local Arts Cncl 1987-, Bd Mem; Bethlehem Ctr Ed Fnd 1995-, Trustee; St Theatre, Interim Mrktg Mgr 1991-; Great Ideas Grant; Selected to Conduct Goodwill Ambassador Tour of Europe; *office:* Bethlehem Ctr Schl Dist 194 Crawford Rd Fredericktown PA 15333

DREVNA, DAVID GENE, General Music & Band Teacher; *b:* Pittsburgh, PA; *m:* Nellie Lou Weingart; *c:* Alicia Marie, David Wayne; *ed:* Youngstown St Univ (BME) Music Ed 1972; 4 Addl Hrs Univ of Akron; 11 Addl Hrs Youngstown St Univ; *cr:* Jackson-Milton Local Schls General, Vocal, Instrument Music Tchr 22 Yrs; *ai:* Marching, Pep Band; Instrumental Solo, Ensemble Contest; On TASC Team; Inter Cty Music Chm; NEA, JMEA, MENC, OMEA 22 Yrs; AFM 24 Yrs; PAS 8 Yrs; Berlin-Ellsworth Ruritan 1978-; Ellsworth Zoning Bd 1987-; Ellsworth Presbyn Church Choir Dir 1972-; Martha Holden Jennings Grant; OH St Tchr Grant; Valley Forge Freedoms Fnd Awd; Outstanding Fine Arts Tchr Nomination 1991-92; *office:* Jackson-Milton Local Schl Dist 14110 Mahoning Ave P O Box 218 North Jackson OH 44451

DREVNA, DENNIS JOHN, Industrial Arts & Tech Ed Tchr; *b:* Sewickley, PA; *m:* Sheila M. Murphy; *c:* Richard A. Bennett Jr.; *ed:* CA St Univ (BS) Tech Ed 1979; 32 Credits Toward Masters; *cr:* Aliquippa Schl Dist Tchr 1979-; Thornberry Printing Owner 1990-; *ai:* Tech Stu Assn Adv; PSEA, NEA 1979-; Aliquippa Ed Assn 1979-, Pres Elect; PA Free, Accepted Mason 1993-, Sr Warden; Aliquippa Tchrs Credit Union 1980-, Bd Mem; Ancient Accepted Scottish Rite of Free Masonry 1993-; PA TSA Outstdng Adv 1986; *home:* 804 10th St Ambridge PA 15003

DREW, ANNE CREGAN, English Teacher; *b:* New York City, NY; *m:* Joseph W.; *c:* Kathryn; *ed:* St Johns Univ (BS) Ed 1967; Queens Coll (MS) Rdng Ed 1973; Manhattan Coll Cert in Admin; *cr:* St Andrew Avellino 3rd Grd Tchr 1964-68; Acad of St Joseph 6th Grd Tchr 1970-71; St Anthony 6th Grd Lang Arts Tchr 1970-71; Nativity Schl Self-Contained Jr HS Class Tchr 1971-74; New Bedford Stuyvesant Rdng Dept Chprsn 1974-77;St Agnes De Graw Street Prin 1977-82; Jr HS 258 Eng Tchr 1982-83; St Francis Coll Dir of Experiential Learning 1983-88; Bishop Loughlin HS Eng Tchr 1983-; *ai:* Schl Philosophy Comm; NCEA 1967-; NEA 1972-; Lay Fac Assn 1983-, Awd for Svc 1995; Natl Eng Tchrs Assoc 1985-; *office:* Bishop Loughlin HS 357 Clermont Ave Brooklyn NY 11238

DREW, BARBARA L., 9th & 10th Grade Eng Teacher; *b:* Erie, PA; *m:* John M.; *c:* Grove Blanchard, Dwayne Blanchard, Sheila Blanchard; *ed:* Gannon Coll (BA) ED 1977, (MS) Ed 1990; *cr:* Erie Schl Dist Adult Basic Ed Tchr 1977-87; Strong Vincent HS Classroom Tchr 1987-; Gannon Univ After Schl & Summers Tchr 1984-94; *ai:* Stu Assistance Prgm Chprsn; Alpha Teens Adv; EEA, PSEA, NEA 1987-, Bldg Rep; St Marks Church 1973-, Vestry; Alpha Kappa Alpha 1985-, Pres; Greater Erie Ec Dev Corp 1992-, Bd Mem; Tchr of Yr Erie Schl Dist; Edctr of Yr.

DREW, DIANE INSERRA, Fourth Grade Teacher; *b:* New York City, NY; *ed:* Hofstra Univ (BS) Ed 1966; Queens Coll (MS) Ed 1969; *cr:* Elmont Elem Schl Dist #16 Tchr 1966-; *ai:* Book & Grd Chm; PTA Tchr Rep 1992-93; NYSUT, NEA & AFT 1971-; Elmont Elem Tchrs Assn 1972-, Rep 1 1971-72 & Rep 2 1990-92; Stu Govt Rep; Soc Comm Chm; Stu Tchr Mentor; Sci Comm Rep; Report Card Comm Rep; Dist Math Comm; *office:* Covert Avenue Elem Schl 144 Covert Ave Elmont NY 11003

DREW, LAURA ALICE, English Teacher; *b:* New York, NY; *m:* Michael Kelly; *c:* Sarah Yuster, Elizabeth Yuster, Jared Yuster, Alexandra Yuster, Michaela Kelly; *ed:* Hunter Coll (BS) Eng Lit 1969; CUNY Grad Ctr ME Phys Anthropology 1969-71; 30 Addl Hrs at Cortland St SUNY, Fordham, Columbia; *cr:* Jewish Fnd Schl LA Coord, Lib Coord, 4-8 Eng, Sci, Math, SS Tchr 1969-75; New Dorp HS Eng Tchr, 1977-90, Dean 1992-86; Curtis HS Eng Tchr 1990-; *ai:* Curr Dev Comm; Fac Adv Poetry Club; SBM Del; AFT, UFT 1977-; NYCATE 1980-; Belles lettres 1989-, Sec, VP; Mud Ln 1976-; Writers Guild 1969-, Pres; Poetry, Short Stories, Articles Pub; Ed: Parachute; Grants from CCLM, S I Cncl on Arts; Taught Writing Wkshps; *office:* Curtis HS 105 Hamilton Ave Staten Island NY 10301*

DREWES, FRED W., Professor of Biology; *b:* Ridgewood, NY; *m:* Sandy Jones; *c:* Kristen Milligan, Brian; *ed:* Cornell Univ (BS) Sci Ed 1958, (MS) Bio 1962; Columbia Tchrs Coll; CO St Univ; *cr:* Herricks Jr HS General Sci Tchr 1958-60; Coll of Ag Bio Lab Asst Tchr 1961-62; St Francis Coll at Tanzania Sci Instr 1962-64; Suffolk Comm Coll Bio Prof 1965-; *ai:* Bio Curr Comm Principles; Bio Learning Ctr Coord; Del to NYS Tchrs Retirement System; Natl Sci Tchrs Assn; Empire St Assoc of 2 Yrs Coll Biologists; Amer Solar Energy Soc; Sierra Club; Audubon Soc; Environmental Defense Fund; LI Pine Barrens Assoc; Natural Resources Defense Cncl; Comm Svc Awd; *office:* Suffolk Comm Coll Ammerman Cmp 533 College Rd Selden NY 11784

DREWRY, WALTER J., Social Studies Teacher; *b:* Waterbury, CT; *m:* Andrea Perugini; *c:* Bud; *ed:* Southern CT St Univ (BS) His 1992; *cr:* Wilby HS Soc Stud Tchr 1993-; *ai:* Boys Bsbl & Girls Bsktbl Coach; CEA, NEA 1993-; *office:* Wilby HS 460 Bucks Hill Rd Waterbury CT 06704

DREXLER, JANET ELAINE (SAVAGE), 9th-12th Grade Math Teacher; *b:* Wauseon, OH; *m:* James H.; *c:* Deborah, Dana; *ed:* Defiance Coll (BS) Math 1975; Univ of Dayton (MS) Guid 1989; *cr:* Harrison Hills City Schls Math Tchr 1975-; *ai:* OEA 1975-.

DREYER, JEFF S., Math Teacher & Network Supvr; *b:* Ft Knox, KY; *m:* Elizabeth A. Wilson; *c:* Jamie Decker, Adam, Ethan; *ed:* TN Temple Univ (BA) Math, Scndry Ed 1981; *cr:* Centre Cty Chrstn Acad HS Math, Sci Tchr 1981-89; Lancaster Chrstn Schl HS Math Tchr 1989-, Coord 1992-; *office:* Lancaster Christian Schl 651 Lampeter Rd Lancaster PA 17602

DRIES, JAMES HENRY, Social Studies Teacher; *b:* Ashton, IA; *m:* Margaret Burton; *c:* Holly LaBarbera, Sean, Keri; *ed:* Univ of SD (BA) His, Govt 1963; Univ of HI (MA) His 1969; Working Towards EDD Tchrs Coll, Columbia Univ; *cr:* Philippines Pub Schls Co-Tchr 1963-65; Honolulu Jr Acad Soc Stud Tchr, Co-Team Ldr 1968-69; Tappan Zee HS Soc Stud Tchr, Co-Team Ldr 1969-; *ai:* Mock Trial Team, Stu Court Adv; Peer Mediation Prgm Co-Adv; 9th Grd Team Tchng; AFT, NYSUT 1969-, Bldg Rep; NCSS, NY Cncl Soc Stud 1970-; Cnslng Svc 1995-, Vol; Rise West Schl 1970-, Chm, Bd Mem; Rockland Cty Planning Bd 1980-; East West Ctr Grant; Natl Hum Grant Gandhi Wkshp; Rockland Cty Bar Assn Liberty Bell Awd Winner 1990; Peace Corps Vol Philippines 1963-65; *office:* Tappan Zee HS Dutch Hill Rd Orangeburg NY 10962*

DRINANE, JANICE DRUNSTADTER, ESL-BL Coordinator & Teacher; *b:* New York City, NY; *m:* Stephen M.; *c:* Jonathan Hopmayer, Aaron Hopmayer, Joan; *ed:* Hunter Coll (BA) Span, Eng 1967; Lehman Coll (MA)

Span 1973; Coll at New Paltz (CAS) Admin, Superv 1990; Grad Courses New Rochelle Coll, Long Island Univ, N R Tchrs Ctr; *cr:* Bethel HS Eng Tchr 1967-69; N Rockland HS ESL Tchr 1975-, Coord ESL, BL K-12th Grd 1994-; *ai:* Dist Task Force on Multicultural Issues; Coord Teen Issue Cnslr Prgm for Biling Stu; Improving Schl Morale Comm; Coord Hnrs Breakfast Prgm; TESOL, NYS Bil-ESL 1993-; Phi Beta Kappa; Sigma Delta Pi; *office:* North Rockland HS 65 Chapel St Garnerville NY 10923

DRIPPS, CRAIG R., Math Teacher; *b:* Bryn Mawr, PA; *m:* Betsy; *c:* Weston, Marion, Heidi, Perry; *ed:* Denison Univ (BA) Math 1969; Villanova Univ (MA) Math 1980; *cr:* The Haverford Schl 9th-12th Grd Math Tchr 1972-95, Math Dept Chair 1982-95; Martha's Vineyard Regnl HS 9th-12th Grd Math Tchr 1995-; *ai:* NCTM 1984-; Book: By Vineyard Light 1995; *home:* RR 1 Box 300D Chilmark MA 02535

DRISCHELL, DESMOND BRADY, Fourth Grade Teacher; *b:* Rockville Centre, NY; *ed:* Jamestown Comm Coll (AA) Hum 1981; Brockport St Coll (BS) Soc Work 1985; St Univ at Albany (MS) Educl Theory, Practice 1992; Attnd Buffalo St Coll; *cr:* S. Colonie Cntrl Schls Tchr 1987-; *ai:* NYSUT, S. Colonie Tchrs Assn 1987-; Luth Church of the Holy Spirit, Liturgical Deacon, Choir, Soloist, Yth Adv, Sunday Schl Tchr; *office:* S. Colonie Cntrl Schls 102 Loralee Dr Albany NY 12205

DRISCOLL, DAVID E.,JR., Math, Sci & Soc Stud Tchr; *b:* Boston, MA; *m:* Laura C.; *c:* Tamie M., Nellie G.; *ed:* Wentworth Inst (AD) Mech Eng 1966; Univ of AL at Birmingham (BS) Pathology 1972; Bridgewater St (MED) Elem Ed 1985; Post Grad Credit Hrs; *cr:* Litchfiel Schls 7th & 8th Grd Math & Sci Tchr 1985-86; Henry T Wing Schl 6th Grd Math, Sci & Soc Stud Tchr 1986-88, 1989-; Sandwich HS 8th Grd Algebra 1988-89; *ai:* NCTM 1989-; US Pony Club 1990-, CO Dist Commissioner; Cranberry Cty Pony Club; NCTS Grant for Integrating Art & Math into Classroom Curr; Peter Farley Tchr 1993-94; *office:* Henry T Wing Schl 33 Water St Sandwich MA 02563*

DRISCOLL, JOHN THOMAS, High School Science Instructor; *b:* Fall River, MA; *m:* Louisa Hall; *c:* Anna, Diantha, Johannah; *ed:* Univ of VT (BS) Wildlife Bio 1981, (MS) Scndry Ed 1991; Lyndon St Coll 5th Yr Cert Sci Ed 1986; *cr:* St Johnsbury Acad Sci Instr 1987-; *ai:* Girls Var Bsktbl Team; Ham Radio Club Adv; Univ of VT Outstdng VT Tchr Awd 1991; Distngd Tchr Awd 1995; *office:* St Johnsbury Acad 7 Main St Saint Johnsbury VT 05819

DRISCOLL, KAREN EILEEN, Kindergarten Teacher; *b:* Bridgeport, CT; *ed:* Southern CT St Univ (BS) Early Chldhd Ed 1974, (MS) Early Chldhd Ed 1978; *cr:* Ferry Schl Transitional Second Grd Tchr 1974-80; Mohegan Schl First Grd Tchr 1980-87, Kndgtn Tchr 1987-; *ai:* Tchr Liason Comm; Prof Dev Comm CEU Presenter; Effectiveness Comm; NEA 1974-; CT Ed Assn 1974-, RA Del 1993-95; Shelton Ed Assn 1974-, Pres, Negotiations Chair 1993-94; PTO 1980-; SCSC Alumni Assn 1975-; Natural Resources Defense Cncl 1996-; Lakewood-Trumbull YMCA 1966-, Camp Dir, Staff Ldrshp Awd 1995; Tchr of Yr Finalist 1992-93; *home:* 54 Ripton Rd Shelton CT 06484*

DRISCOLL, RODERICK MARTIN, US History & Govt Teacher; *b:* Jackson Heights, NY; *m:* Vicki; *c:* Kaitlin, Travis, Kiley; *ed:* SUNY at Plattsburgh (BS) Pol Sci 1975, (BA) Scndry Ed 1984, (MA) Ed & Admin 1990; *cr:* Willsboro Cntrl Schl Tchr 1986-87; Ausable Vly Cntrl Schl Tchr 1987-; *ai:* Cross Cntry, Tennis, Track & Bstkbl Coach; Model UN, Scholars for Dollars & Voice of Democracy Adv; Discipline, Scheduling, Staff Dev & Schl Improvement Comms; AFT & NYSUT 1986-, Bldg Rep & Liaison; North Cntry Ballet 1984-, Bd Mem; Peru Comm Church 1992-, Concert Coord & Fund Raising Comm; City of Plattsburgh NY Concert Coord 1978-82; *office:* Ausable Vly Cntrl Schl RR 1 Box 860 Clintonville NY 12924*

DRISCOLL, SUSANN R., Second Grade Teacher; *b:* New Haven, CT; *m:* Dr. Vincent R.; *c:* Colleen, Jennifer, Kathleen; *ed:* Coll of St Elizabeth (AB) Music 1964; Southern CT St Univ (MAT) Elem Ed 1975; 6th Yr Admin 1989; *cr:* Wintergreen Elem Schl First Grd Tchr 1967-68; Title I Waterbury Schl Rdng Tchr 1971-74; St Mary's Elem Schl First Grd Tchr 1974-86; Long Hill Elem Schl First-Second Grd Tchr 1986-; *ai:* Staff Dev; Curr Comm; Tchr Trainer Here's Looking at You 2000; Cooperating Tchr Mentor Best Prgm; SEA 1986-, Schl Rep; CEA; Celegration of Excl Awd; Nom Tchr of Yr; *office:* Long Hill Elem Schl 565 Long Hill Ave Shelton CT 06484

DROGAN, LISA MOKATELLO, Vocal Music Teacher; *b:* Woodbridge, NJ; *m:* Ronald; *ed:* Kean Coll (MA) Cnslr Ed 1996; *ai:* Chorus Dir; NJTEA 1988-; NJCA 1996-; *office:* Woodbridge MS 525 Barron Ave Woodbridge NJ 07095

DROMM, DANIEL PATRICK, Fourth Grade Teacher; *b:* Brooklyn, NY; *ed:* Marist Coll (BA) Comm Arts 1977; City Coll (MSEd) Elem Ed 1981; 24 Addl Credit Hrs Admin, Supervision, Methods, Curr; *cr:* Grant Day Care Ctr Ed Dir 1978-84; PS 199Q Tchr 1984-; *ai:* AAA Schl Safety Patrol Adv; Schl Assembly, Grad Coord; NYC Lesbian & Gay Teachers Assn 1992-; UFT 1984-, Former Del; Queens Lesbian & Gay Pride Comm 1992-, Founder, NYC Comptroller's Awd; Parents, Families & Friends of Lesbians & Gays 1993-, Founder, NYC Pub Advocate's Awd; Numerous Articles Pub; Chancellor's Ad-Hoc Comm 1993-94; *office:* PS 199Q Maurice Fitzgerald 39-20 48th Ave Long Island City NY 11104*

DROMS, PAUL ALAN, Teacher & Educl Tech Coord; *b:* Schenectady, NY; *ed:* Millersville Univ (BS) Scndry Ed, Math 1976; Johns Hopkins Univ (MS) Tech for Edctrs 1990; *cr:* Schl Dist of Lancaster Tchr 1977-83; Warwick Schl Dist Tchr, Educl Tech Coord 1983-; *ai:* Tech Coord; Equipment Mgr Ath Dept; Strategic Planning Comm; NEA, PSEA, WEA 1977-; ISTE 1995-; Lancaster Cty Jr Miss Schlsp Prgm 1982-, Co-Chm, Otstdng Local Prgm, Chm 1996; *office:* Warwick Schl Dist 301 W Orange St Lititz PA 17543

DRONEBURG, DONALD LEE, High School Mathematics Tchr; *b:* Frederick, MD; *m:* Linda Jane O'Bryon; *c:* Terri, Stacy, Casey; *ed:* Univ of MD (BS) Math Ed 1965; Univ of Dayton (MS) Math Ed 1971; Addl Courses at George Washington Univ & Bowie State Univ; *cr:* Bladensburg Sr HS Math Tchr 1965-78; Friendly HS Math Tchr 1978-86; Prince Georges Comm Coll Part-Time Math Tchr 1978-; Bowie HS Math Tchr 1986-; Anne Arundel Comm Coll Part-Time Math Tchr 1986-; *ai:* NEA 1965-; MSTA 1965-; PECEA 1965-; NSF Grant for Masters Degree Pgm; *office:* Bowie HS 15200 Annapolis Rd Bowie MD 20715

DROP, RONALD J., Biology & Earth Science Tchr; *b:* Pittsburgh, PA; *m:* Marjorie J.; *c:* David; *ed:* Edinboro Univ (BS) Bio 1969, (MED) Earth Sci 1971; *cr:* Pine Richland Schl Dist Tchr 27 Yrs; *ai:* Total Quality Mgmt Comm for Schl Discipline; PSEA 1969-; NEA 1969-; PREA 1969-; *office:* Pine-Richland HS 4300 Warrendale Rd Gibsonia PA 15044

DROSSMAN, JAMIE LYNN, Science Teacher; *b:* Chicago, IL; *c:* Lauren; *ed:* Bowling Green St Univ (BS) Sci Ed 1990; 12 Hrs Towards Masters Degee Scndry Ed; *cr:* Owens IL Inc Accounting Clerk 1985-88; Fremont City Schls Sci Tchr 1991-; *office:* Freemont City Schls 501 Croghan St Fremont OH 43420

DROSSOS, THERESA GRESALFI, Business Education Teacher; *b:* Amityville, NY; *m:* Theodore; *c:* Nicole, Amanda; *ed:* Nassau Comm Coll (AAS) Secretarial Stud 1973; Hofstra Univ (BS) Bus Ed 1975; SUNY at Stony Brook (MA) Liberal Stud 1978; Addl 75 Credits; Elem Ed Addl License; *cr:* East Islip HS Bus Ed Tchr 1975-; *ai:* Class, FBLA, DECA, Secretarial Club Adv; Schl Improvement Team; Exit Outcomes, Stdnts Rights & Responsibilities Comm; Co-Chair ACES Prgm; NYSUT, El Tchrs Assn, Suffolk Cty Bus Tchrs 1975-; *office:* East Islip HS Redmen St Islip Terrace NY 11752

DROTAR, CHERIE ABER, Mathematics Teacher; *b:* Pittsburgh, PA; *m:* John R.; *c:* Michael, Elliott; *ed:* Edinboro Univ (BS) Ed 1968; Univ of Pgh (MED) Math 1972; Univ of CT 6 Credits Summer Work 1973; Penn St Univ 3 Credits Staff Dev; *cr:* North Hills Sr HS Sec Math Ed Tchr 1968-; *ai:* NCTM, NEA, NHEA 1968-; Kinvara Civic Assn 1985; *office:* North Hills Sr HS 53 Rochester Rd Pittsburgh PA 15229

DROTLEFF, JOHN E., Retired Fine Arts Dept Chr; *b:* Youngstown, OH; *m:* Judy Slagle; *c:* Stefan; *ed:* Columbia Univ (MA) Music 1971; Youngstown St Univ Bachelor Music in Music Ed 1966; Attnd Westminster Choir Coll; *cr:* Boardman Local Schls Choral Dir 1967-76; Avon Lake HS Choral Dir 1976-87; Lakewood HS Fine Arts Dept Chm 1987-94; *ai:* Musical Dir; Schl Comm Mem; Chamber Choir & Vive L'Four Dir; OH Choral Dirs Assn 1968-, Pres 1981-85; OH Music Ed Assn & NEA 1968-94; West Shore Chorale 1984-, Conductor; Youngstown Symphony Chorus 1972-76, Conductor; Church Choir, Dir 1966-, Conductor; Performances at OCDA & OMEA Conventions; OH, PA & NY Guest Conductor; Guest Lecturer at Inservices & Coll Courses; *home:* 12700 Lake Ave Apt 2607 Lakewood OH 44107*

DROWNE, W. CHRISTOPHER, His Instr & Alumni Pblctns Dir; *b:* Suffern, NY; *ed:* Bucknell Univ (BA) His 1993; *cr:* Danville MS 7th Grd SS Stu Tchr 1992; Hill Schl His Instr, Alumni Pub Dir 1993-; *ai:* Asst Var Soccer, Bsbl Coach; Resident Mgr-Soph Dormitory; CASE 1993-; Birdsboro Amer Legion 1994-, Asst Sr Legion Coach; Lewisburg Daily Journal Coach of Yr 1992; *home:* 717 E High St Pottstown PA 19464

DROZD, STANLEY, Social Studies Teacher; *b:* Staten Island, NY; *ed:* Wagner Coll (BA) His 1972, (MSEd) Scndry Ed & Soc Stud 1974; *cr:* Saint Francis Schl Soc Stud Tchr 1974; Saint Rocco Schl Lang Arts & Soc Stud Tchr 1975-79; Robert R Lazar MS Soc Stud Tchr 1979-92; Montville Twp HS Soc Stud Tchr 1992-; *ai:* St & Tchr Mentoring Prgms; Montville Twp Ed Assn 1979-, Pres 1988-89, Negotiations Sec 1989-91; Saint Adalberts Church Cncl 1984-, VP 1984-90, Pres 1990-94; Nom for Governors Tchr Recognition Prgm-Robert R Lazar MS 1992; *office:* Montville Twp HS 100 Horse Neck Rd Montville NJ 07045

DRUBEL, AUGUST CHARLES, Assoc Professor of Business; *b:* Chicago, IL; *m:* Clara Elizabeth Kirkman; *c:* Charles Worth, John Lewis; *ed:* Duke Univ (AB) Psych, Sociology 1978; The Coll of William & Mary (MBA) Mngmt 1980; *cr:* WV Wesleyan Coll Bus Asst Prof 1980-85; Bell South Asst Staff Mgr 1985-86; Muskingum Coll Bus Asst Prof 1986-91, Assoc Bus Prof 1992-; *ai:* Bd of Trustees Dev Comm; Internship Fac Spon; Omicron Delta Kappa 1983-, WV Wesleyan Coll Outstdng Ldr of Yr 1984; Coll Drive Presbyn Church 1980-, Chm Trustee Comm; William Oxley Thompson Awd Excl in Tchng; Comm Cncl Outstdng Fac Awd WV Wesleyan Coll 1983; *office:* Muskingum Coll 163 Stormont New Concord OH 43762*

DRUCKENMILLER, RONALD LEE, Kindergarten Teacher; *b:* Phoenixville, PA; *m:* Georgette Marie Griffith; *c:* Andrew, W. Peter, James; *ed:* East Stroudsburg Univ (BS) Elem Ed 1971; Villanova Univ (MA) Elem Admin 1978; Attnd Kutztown Univ, Marywood Coll, Montgomery Cty Comm Coll; *cr:* Methacton Schl Dist Elem Tchr 1971-; *ai:* Kndgtn Grd Level Ldr; NEA, PSEA, Methacton Ed Assoc 1971-; *office:* Woodland Elem Schl 2700 Woodland Ave Norristown PA 19403*

DRUCKER, SUSAN, First Grade Teacher; *b:* Brooklyn, NY; *m:* Douglas; *c:* Gregory; *ed:* Brooklyn Coll Ed (BA) 1970, (MS) 1973; *cr:* P. S. 183 K-1st Grd Tchr 1970-74; Ethel McKnight Schl K-1st Grd Tchr 1978-; *ai:* NEA 1978-; E Windsor Regnl Schl Dist Action Grant 1985-87; Bd of Ed 1992, NJ Governors Tchr 1993 Recognition Awds; *office:* Ethel Mcknight Elem Schl 58 Twin Rivers Dr S Hightstown NJ 08520

DRUGAN, BARBARA, Retired Kindergarten Teacher; *b:* Columbus, OH; *ed:* OH St Univ (BS) Ed 1947; *cr:* Main Montrase Bexley Kndgtn Tchr 1947-49; Cassingham Bexley Kndgtn Tchr 1950-79; *ai:* Elem Sub.

DRULLINGER, DAVID WAYNE, Assoc Prof of Biblical Educ; *b:* Chadron, NE; *m:* Helen Mae Fischer; *c:* Randall, Carla; *ed:* Western Bapt Church (BS) Bible, Soc Stud 1967; San Francisco Bapt Seminary (BD) Bible, Theology 1971; Western Seminary (THM) Theology 1975; Western Seminary (DMIN) Pastoral Ministries 1980; *cr:* Western Bapt Coll Fac 1974-82, Part-time Fac 1986-88; Comm Bapt Church Pastor 1981-88; Cedarville Coll Fac 1989-; *ai:* Washington Hts Bapt Church Assoc Pastor; Evang Theol Soc 1989-; Adult Sunday Schl Curr; *office:* Cedarville Coll 251 N Main ST Box 601 Cedarville OH 45314

DRUMM, TIMOTHY S., Business Teacher; *b:* Toledo, OH; *m:* Ellen K.; *c:* Michael, John; *ed:* Miami Univ (BS) Ed 1977; Ashland Univ (MBA) Exec Admin 1993; *cr:* Roy C. Start HS Bus Tchr 1977-78; Univ of NV at Reno Rsrch Asst 1978-79; Toledo Pub Schls Sub Tchr 1979-80; Margaretta HS Bus Tchr 1980-; *ai:* Asst Var Ftbl Coach; New Tchr Mentor; Margaretta Tchrs Assn 1980-, VP; OEA, NEA 1980-; Phi Delta Kappa 1994-; Delta Mu Delta 1992-; *office:* Margaretta HS 209 Lowell St Castalia OH 44824*

DRURY, KAY P., Biology Teacher; *b:* Philadelphia, PA; *w:* Frederick H. (dec); *c:* Kathryn, Jonathan; *ed:* Univ of Rochester (BA) Gen Sci 1963, (MS) Bio 1965; Attnd Cornell Inst for Bio Tchrs; *cr:* Rush-Henrietta HS Bio Tchr 1965-72; Fairport HS Bio Tchr 1991-; *ai:* Class of 98 Adv; NEA, Fairport Edctrs Assn 1991-; Sci Tchrs Assn NYS 1995-; *office:* Fairport HS 1358 Ayrault Rd Fairport NY 14450

DRUSAK, LINDA C., Guidance Counselor; *b:* Johnstown, PA; *m:* John A.; *c:* Jason, Amy; *ed:* Univ of Pittsburgh at Johnstown (BA) Scndry Ed, Span 1973; IN Univ of PA (MED) Scndry Cnslng 1975; 12 Credit Hrs Post Grad Stud Univ of Pittsburgh at Johnstown; *cr:* Baltimore Cty Schls Span, Fr Tchr 1973; Conemaugh Twp Area HS Span Tchr 1973-86, Cnslr 1996; *ai:* Sr Class Adv; Stu Asst Team; PA Schl Cnslr 1986-; PSEA, NEA 1973-; Somerset Cty Cnslr 1986-, VP, Pres; *office:* Conemaugh Township Area HS West Campus Ave Davidsville PA 15928

DRUSBACKY, JANE ELLEN (BIRO), Sixth Grade Teacher; *b:* Port Clinton, OH; *m:* David A.; *c:* Jessica Ellen, Morgan Marie; *ed:* OH St Univ (BS) Elem Ed 1974; Addl 40 Hrs; *cr:* Cotati Rohnert Park City Schls Rdng Aid & 5th Grd Tchr 1974-76; Port Clinton City Schls K-8th Grd Substitute Tchr 1976-79; Immaculate Conception Schl 5th & 6th Grd Tchr 1979-; *ai:* Comptrs, Sci Fair, Medieval Fair & Red Cross Prgms; NCEA 1979-; Diosecan Math Leadership Council; *office:* Immaculate Conception Schl 109 W 4th St Port Clinton OH 43452*

DRUZEK, PATRICIA A., Second Grade Teacher; *b:* Elizabeth, NJ; *m:* Paul F. Healy; *ed:* Seton Hall Univ (BS) Elem Ed-Summa Cum Laude 1981; Minor Eng, Tchr 1981; Nursery Schl 1981; Addl Certs; *cr:* Garwood Pub Schls Second Grd Tchr 1983-; *ai:* Sacramental Preparation Class 2nd Grd Tchr; NJEA, GTA 1983-; St Annes Parish, CCD Coord 1992-94, Archdiocesan Parish Catechist Awd; NJ Governors Tchr Recognition Prgm 1987; *office:* Garwood Pub Schls Second Ave Garwood NJ 07027

DRYBURGH, SUSAN ALICE, Junior-Senior English Teacher; *b:* Cleveland, OH; *m:* Richard George; *c:* Virginia, Keith; *ed:* Muskingum Coll (BA) Eng 1969; IN Univ of PA (MA) Eng 1976; 30 Addl Hrs; *cr:* IN Area Jr HS Eighth Grd Eng Tchr 1969-71; Boardman HS Soph Eng Tchr 1971-75; Youngstown St Univ Composition Instr 1983-86; Boardman HS Jr, Sr Eng Tchr 1986-; *ai:* AAUW 1976-, EPF Chm; *office:* Boardman HS 7777 Glenwood Ave Youngstown OH 44512

DRYER, WILLIAM J., Teacher & Administrative Asst; *b:* J NJ; *m:* Beryl M.; *ed:* Jersey City St Coll (BA) Pol Sci 1971; NY Pol 1973; Univ of San Diego (MAT) Soc Stud Ed 1979; *cr:* Ridg HS Tchr, Admin Asst 1971-; *ai:* Stu Act Admin Asst; Sp Assessments Coord; NEA 1971-; NJ Cncl for Soc Stud 1980-; Cncl PTA Tchr Flwshp Awd; Elks Lodge Tchr Appreciation A Ridgefield Park Jr-Sr HS 1 Ozzie Nelson Dr Ridgefield Park N

DRYSDALE, DAVID VINCENT, 8th Grade Dean; *b:* Quee Aaron; *ed:* St Francis Coll (BS) Aviation Bus 1986; Hunter Col Hrs; *cr:* Asst Sales 1987-88; JHS 008 Sci, Math Tchr 1988-94, D *ai:* Restructuring Comm; AFT 1989-; UFT 1989-; NYSUT 1989 1990-; *office:* JHS 8 Richard Grossley 108-35 167th St Queens N

DUBAICH, MICHELE MEKIS, Biology Teacher; *b:* Johnstov John; *ed:* Univ of Pittsburgh (BS) Scndry Ed & Bio 1990; Pursuing MS at PA St Univ; *cr:* Greenwood HS Bio & Sci Tchr Soph Class Adv; Sci Fair Coord; Instructional Support Team; N NABT, NSTA, PBTA 1993-; Capital Area Math & Sci Alliance 1 Comm; ASCI HS Sci Tchr Fellowship Awd; *office:* Greenwoo 405 E Sunbury St Millerstown PA 17062

DUBE, JULIE LYNN, English Teacher; *b:* Bosier City, LA; *n* Lucien; *ed:* Univ of ME (BS) Ed 1993; Currently Pursuing Mast Cnslr of Ed Prgm; *cr:* Mattanawcook Jr HS Ed Tech III Tchr 1 III Voc Schl Adult Ed Tchr 1 Yr; Old Town HS Eng Tchr 2 Yrs Adv; Climate Comm Chprsn; Renaissance Coord.

DUBE, LORRAINE G., Math Teacher; *b:* Eagle Lake, ME; *e* ME Ed (BS) 1982, (MED) 1986; 6 Credit Hrs Beyond (ME Coursework; *cr:* Eastland Elem, Corinna Jr High Spec Ed Tc Glenburn Schl MS Tchr 1986-; *ai:* Pet Patrol Adv; NEA, MEA, TA 1987-, Former Local Pres, VP, Negotiator; NCTM 1995-; Ethical Treatment Animals 1989-; High Distinction Grad Univ o Yrbk Dedication 1989; Kappa Delta Pi 1980; 1995 Recognitic ME Coll of Ed; *home:* RR 2 Box 2170 East Holden ME 04429

DUBEAU, DOLORES MAGAZU, Fifth Grade Teacher; *b:* Woo *m:* Douglas; *ed:* Glassboro St Coll (BA) Elem Ed 1973; *cr:* Ce 1st Grd Tchr 1973-75; Lake Tract Schl 2nd Grd Tchr 1975-88, 3r 1988-94, 5th Grd Tchr 1994-; *ai:* DEA, GCEA 1973-, Bldg R NEA 1973-; *office:* Lake Tract Elem Schl 690 Iszard Rd Deptford

DU BOIS, EILEEN STAR, AP Calculus Teacher; *b:* Philadelph Raymond L.; *c:* Melissa P.; *ed:* Atlantic Comm Coll (AA) Tc Glassboro St Coll (BA) Scndry Schl Math 1971; Rowan Coll o Subject Matter Tchng, Math 1996; Post-Grad Courses; *cr:* Ple HS Math Tchr 1971-72; Atlantic City Friends Schl Math Tchr Woodstown HS Math Tchr 1977-; *ai:* Multicultural Renaissance Peer Ldrshp, NHS Fac, Human Relations Cncl Peer Mediation F Yth of Mnth, Wolverine of Month Comms; AMTNJ 1990-; NE 1977-; Human Relations Cncl 1990; Cultural Unity Day Co-Chp Drive Chprsn, Treas 1995-;Cultural Unity Day Planning Com Faith Treas 1969; Governor's Tchr Recognition; *office:* Woodstov East Ave Woodstown NJ 08098*

DUBOIS, LOUIS PETER,JR., Chemistry Teacher; *b:* Waterbu Mary Mulligan; *c:* Marnie Ciquera, Monica, Peter, Elizabeth, Mi St Michaels Coll (BA) Bio, Chem 1963; Central CT St Univ (MS UCLA Chem; Fairfield Univ Ed; Univ of Hartford Ed; *cr:* Sacred Chem Tchr 1963-66; Watertown HS Chem Tchr 1966-; *ai:* Chem Watertown Ed Assn 1966-, Exec Bd; CT Ed Assn, NEA 1966-; L 1993-; Wolcott Bd of Ed 1988-; Wolcott Town Cncl 1980-, Chm, Wolcott GOP Town Comm 1980-, Vice Chm; *office:* Watertow French St Watertown CT 06795*

DUBOIS, MARY MULLIGAN, Science & English Te Waterbury, CT; *m:* Louis P. Jr.; *c:* Marnie Ciquera, Moni Elizabeth, Michael; *ed:* Central CT St Univ (BA) Elem Ed 1982, *cr:* Town of Wolcot, Bd of Ed Tutor, Region 16 Bd of Ed 3 Yrs; L MS Tchr 10 Yrs; *ai:* NEA 1986-; CEA 1986-.

DUBOIS, PATRICIA A., Assistant Principal; *b:* Pawtucke Wilfred; *c:* Christopher, Danielle; *ed:* RI Coll (BA) Scndry Ed, M Providence Coll (MS) Sec Ed, Admin 1982-; 21 Credit Hrs Post G 96 Credit Hrs Electric Engrng; *cr:* Bellingham Jr Sr HS M 1976-78; Woonsocket Jr HS Math Tchr 1978-85; Woonsocket Tchr 1985-95, Asst Prin 1995-; *ai:* Math Team Adv; Attendance Comm Co-Chprsn; Schl Improvement Team Chprsn; Yrbk Awd; *office:* Woonsocket HS 777 Cass Ave Woonsocket RI 02895

DUBOIS, SUZANNE EVELYN, Theology Teacher; *b:* Woonso *ed:* Rivier Coll (BA) Ed 1974; *cr:* Good Shepherd Schl 1st 1962-63; Our Lady of Perpetual Help 4th-8th Grds Tchr 1964-74 of Arc Schl 7th-8th Grds Lang Arts Tchr 1974-75; Presentation Acad 9th-10th Grds Eng Tchr 1975-80; Notre Dame de Lourdes K-8th Grds 1980-87; Presentation of Mary Acad 9th-10th Grds Tc *ai:* NCEA 1980-; *office:* Presentation Of Mary Acad 209 Law Methuen MA 01844

DUBOIS, WILFRID, Asst Professor of Biology; *b:* Haiti, West I Josette Dupont; *c:* Dominique, Steven, Robert; *ed:* Columbia U Bio 1974; Boston Univ (PHD) Endocrinology; *cr:* Univ Post-Doctoral Assoc 1982-87; Boston Univ Rsrch Asst Prof D'Youville Coll Asst Prof of Bio 1990-; *ai:* Curr, Acad Policy, Ad Comms; NY Acad of Sci 1988-; Amer Soc Zoology 1992-; Re Prison Ministry 1996; NSF Grant; Lucille P. Markey Flwshp; Future Citation from Boston Mayor; 12 Original Rsrch Articles Pu D'Youville Coll 320 Porter Ave Buffalo NY 14201

DU BOSE, DAVID, Jr HS English Teacher; *b:* New York, NY; *m:* Samuel; *c:* David K., Lakisha Y.; *ed:* Herbert H. Lehman (BA) E Bernard M. Baruch (MS) Ed Admin, Supervision 1979; *cr:* JHS 1 Eng Tchr 1974-75; CJHS 145 Toscanini Eng Tchr 1975-; *ai:* A 1974-; *office:* CJHS Arturo Toscanini 1000 Teller Ave Bronx NY

DUBREUIL, GEORGE LEONARD, French Teacher; *b:* Manches *m:* Cathy Mayne; *c:* Sean, Michael; *ed:* Plymouth St Coll (BS) Fr Appalachian St Univ (MA) Fr Ed 1974; 30 Addl Hrs Observatio Techniques with Stu Tchrs; *cr:* Westside Cath Reg Jr HS Fr Tchr Hillsboro-Deering HS Fr Tchr 1980-; NH Tech Fr Tchr 1996; *ai:* Stu Cncl; NH Assn for Tchng of Frgn Langs 1980-; Outstdng Tch Co-Dedications in Yrbks; *office:* Hillsboro-Deering HS 12 Hi Hillsboro NH 03244

DUBREUIL, JED L., HS French Teacher; *b:* Manchester, NH; *n* S. Mayne; *c:* Sean, Michael; *ed:* Plymouth St Coll (BS) F Appalachian St Univ (MA) Fr 1974; *cr:* Westside Cath Reg F 1976-80; Hillsboro-Deering HS Fr Tchr 1980-; *ai:* Fr Club; N Tchrs of Foreign Lang On & Off 19 Yrs; Outstanding Tchr Awd Hillsboro-Deering HS 12 Hillcat Dr Hillsboro NH 03244

DUCCI, NANCY LYNN KRIEGER, Second Grade Teacher; *b:* OH; *m:* Chris Alexander; *ed:* OH Univ (BS) Elem Ed 1979; Add Hrs Tchng Cert, Advanced Cert Rel Ed; *cr:* G. C. Murphy Co Sale Cashier 1970-74; Imperial Glass Corp TOur Guide, Sales Clerk St John Cntrl Grd Schl 2-5 Grd Tchr 1979-; *ai:* Spelling Bee Coord Curr Comm; OH Cath Ed Assn 1979-; Parish Cncl 1980-; Bellaire Bd 1988-89; Italian Festival Bd 1993-; Madonna Crusaders Au

Employee 1995-; *home:* 89 Virginia Park Rd Wheeling WV

ME, CAROL ANN, English Teacher; *b:* Washington, DC; *ed:* D (BA) Eng 1970; 60 Credit Hrs at Loyola & Trinity Coll; *cr:* Seton HS His Tchr 1971-72; G Gardner Shugart Jr High Eng & Tchr 1972-77; M L King Jr High Eng Tchr 1977-78; Thomas High Tchr 1978-80; DuVal High Tchr 1980-; *ai:* Prince Georges ep; MSTA; NEA; Model Tchng Team 1980-82; Focus Group for abor Sec Commission on Achieving Necessary Skills 1991;); *office:* DuVal HS 9880 Good Luck Rd Lanham MD 20806

EDWARD B.,JR., Scndry English Education Tchr; *b:* r, CT; *ed:* Cntrl CT St Univ (BSEd) Eng 1990; *cr:* South Windsor chr 1991-; *ai:* Ftbl Asst Coach 1979-94; Boys Lacrosse Asst 39-91; Girls Lacrosse Coach 1991-; Drama Club Dir 1994-; Marion Gleason Awd Outstdng Promise as Tchr of Eng 1992; ath Windsor HS 161 Nevers Rd South Windsor CT 06074

ETTY ANN, Fourth Grade Teacher; *b:* Charleroi, PA; *ed:* CA St Elem Ed 1973, (MS) Elem Ed 1979; *cr:* Belle Vernon Area Schls 1973-; *ai:* NEA 1973-; *office:* Belle Vernon Area Schl Dist RD lle Vernon PA 15012

UDITH JAMITIS, Elementary Guidance Counselor; *b:* , PA; *m:* Frederick R.; *ed:* Univ of Pittsburgh (BA) Scndry His, , Comprehensive Soc Stud 1965, (MED) Scndry Soc Stud 1967; Univ (MSEd) Elem Counseling 1987; Univ of Pittsburgh Elem Duquesne Univ Scndry Counseling 1987; *cr:* Bishop McCort HS ud Tchr 1965-68; Allegheny Cty Schls Scndry Curr Specialist & tures 1968-72; Northgate Schl Dist HS Soc Stud Tchr, Jr High chr, MD Schl Soc Stud Tchr Elem 6th Grd Tchr & Elem Guidance 2-; *ai:* NEA, PSEA, NEA 1972-, Sec; ACA & PSCA 1987-; cal 1987-, VP & Pres; NHBPW 1990-; *office:* Avalon & Lincoln s 721 California Ave Pittsburgh PA 15202*

KAREN POLAHAR, Professor of Computer Science; *b:* , PA; *m:* Joseph M.; *c:* Emily, Quentin; *ed:* Indiana Univ of PA Ed 1971, (MSEd) Bus Ed, Mrktg 1975; Univ of Pittsburgh (PHD) Attnd Inst for Acad Tech, Kent St Univ, Inst for Interactive Tech; sburg Salem HS Bus Tchr 1971-79; Univ of Pittsburgh Asst Instr Monroeville Schl of Bus Asst Dir 1980-81; Youngstown St Univ nptr Sci, Information Systems Dept 1981-; *ai:* Dean's Advy Cncl; ngrng Tech Comm; Coll of Ed Search Comm; Delta Pi Epsilon a Chptr 1976-, Pres, VP; Phi Delta Kappa, NBEA 1981-; Office tes Assn 1987-; Assn of Applied Interactive Multimedia 1995-; EA; OEA; ISTE; ASCD; ASTD; Safe Kids Coalition 1995-; wn Diocese Mrktg Comm 1994-; Distngd Prof Tchng Awd wn St Univ 1992; Apple Tech Partnership Grant 1991; Pub Film, 1990, Article; *office:* Youngstown St Univ 410 Wick Ave wn OH 44555*

JOSEPH J., English & Language Arts Tchr; *b:* Monongahela, ssan Barnhart; *c:* Marc; *ed:* CA Univ of PA (BSED) Eng 1969; on & Jefferson Masters Equivalency 1975; Grad Work in Eng; of Banking Courses; Schenley Tchr Learning Ctr; *cr:* Avella Lang Arts, Eng Tchr 1969-; *ai:* Stu Newspaper Spon; Discipline c; Scndry Cncl Sec; Act 178 Staff Dev Comms Sec; Grad Project u Tchrs; Avella Ed Assn 1969-, Sec; PA St Ed Assn, NEA 1969-; estern PA Cncl Tchrs of Eng Assn; Assn for Supervision & Curr e: Avella Area Jr Sr HS 1000 Avella Rd Avella PA 15312

JULIE WANDER, MLT Program Director & Prof; *b:* Columbus, oseph; *c:* Amy Leigh, Amanda Daneille; *ed:* West Liberty Coll n 1969; OH Univ (MED) Higher Ed 1982; *cr:* Grant Medical Ctr ogy Lab Supvr 1972-80; Columbus St Comm Coll Prof, MLT r 1980-; *ai:* Prof Dev, Tenure Review, Promotion, MLT ns, Advy Comm; NACLS Site Visitor; NAACLS Paper Reviewer; tion for Licensure; SCACM 1972-, Wkshp Chm; ASCP 1969-, ent Comm; ASM 1974-; OSAHP 1980-; COSA, PTA, Ath, d Mem; Distinguished Tchr Nom; Prgm of Excl OH BOR, Tchng s; Master Tchr Recognition; *office:* Columbus St Comm Coll 550 St Columbus OH 43216

MARY JO PAWLIK, 7th-8th Grd Math Teacher; *b:* ana, NY; *m:* William R.; *ed:* St Univ Coll at Buffalo (BS) Scndry 1987, (MS) Scndry Soc Stud 1992; *cr:* Erie I Boces Summer Schl Ec Tchr 1987-95; Our Mother of Divine Grace 7-8 Math, Soc 1988; Queen of Heaven Elem Schl 6-8 Grd Math Tchr 1989-; *ai:* Adv; Annual Washington Trip Coord; Acad Adv; NCMT, NCSS ETA 1993-, Pres; ONC 1992-; *office:* Queen of Heaven Elem Schl Rd West Seneca NY 14224*

SANDRA LOU, English Teacher; *b:* Wauseon, OH; *m:* Frank L.; w, Joshua; *ed:* Kent St Univ (BS) Eng 1974; Coll of Mt St Joseph 1986; 1989 Wright St Univ Beginning Word Processing 1 Hr; vling Green St Univ Mentoring Tchrs 1 Hr; *cr:* Warren Cty Schls 1974-75; South Western City Schls Substitute Tchr 1975-76; erson Schls Permanent Substitute 1976-77; Vinton Cty Schls Eng 7-79; Upper Scioto Valley Schls Eng Tchr 1979-; *ai:* Frosh Class V New Tchrs Mentor; NEA, OEA, USVTA 1980-; Northwestern Ldr Network 1990-; Univ Club 1987-, VP 1990-91, Pres 1991-; oper Scioto Valley HS 510 S Courtright St Mc Guffey OH 45859

MAUREEN MALLON, Chemistry Teacher; *b:* Staten Island, onald J. Jr.; *c:* Samantha; *ed:* Wagner Coll (BS) Bacteriology, Pub 7; 4 Credit Hrs Physics; *cr:* Moore Cath HS Sci Tchr, Dept Chair Bishop George Ahr HS Chem Tchr 1993-; *ai:* Moore Cath-Sr ord; Bowling Team Moderator; NJSTA, ACS 1993-; PTA Exec Bd brshp Coord; North Edison Sftbl Rookies; *home:* 138 Sonora Ave 08830

Y, LAURA LOUISE, Second Grade Teacher; *b:* Wellsley, MA; *ed:* Messiah Coll (BA) Elem Ed 1993; *cr:* wn Chrstn Acad 2nd Grd Tchr 1993-; *ai:* Soccer Coach; PE Tchr; R 1 Box 326 Montgomery PA 17752

TED E., Science Teacher; *b:* Akron, OH; *c:* Natalie, Stephanie, Akron Univ (BAEd) Comprehensive Sci 1973, (MAEd) Scndry ; *cr:* Taft MS Sci Tchr 1973-; *ai:* Sci Team Ldr; Sci Olympiad Sci Fair; NEA, OEA 1973-; PLTA 1973-, Rep; Kiwanis 1994-; istorical Soc 1992-, Pres; Green Historical Commission 1993-; Civil Wa 1992-, 1st Sergent; Governor's Awd 4 Yrs; Sci Olympiad ; *office:* R A Taft MS 3829 Guilford Ave NW Canton OH 44718*

Y, JEFFREY B., K-12 Physical Education Tchr; *b:* Portsmouth, Kelly; *c:* Jeff Jr., Josh, Katie; *ed:* OH Univ at Athens (BSPE) PE btained 5th Yr Status; *cr:* Portsmouth City Schls Coach 1980-83; City Schls Sub Tchr, Coach 1983-85; Logan-Hocking Schls Tchr, 985-86; Green Local Schls K-12 PE Tchr, Coach 1989-; *ai:* Head oach; Muscular Dystrophie Coord; Coached Track 8 Yrs, Ftbl 10 tbl 14 Yrs, Bsbl 12 Yrs, Little League Bsbl & Bsktbl; NEA 1983-; 89-; Rubysville Comm Church 1987-, Teenagers Sunday Schl Tchr; oach of Yr 1991; *home:* 1498 Luther Rd Minford OH 45653

OVICH, DARLENE, Social Science Teacher; *b:* Johnstown, PA; Univ of PA (BS) Ed, Soc Scis 1969; Masters Equivalency PA St, Wm & Mary, Univ of Pittsburgh; NEH Fellowship Coll of William 1982; *cr:* Gr Johnstown Jr HS Soc Stud Tchr 1970-80; Gr Johnstown Sr HS Soc Stud Tchr 1981-; *ai:* Stu Schl Improvement Comm Adv; Bldg Rep; NHS Review Comm; NEA, PA St Ed Assn, Gr Johnstown Ed Assn 1970-; NCSS; Johnstown Area Heritage Assn 1988-; IN Univ of PA Alumni Assn 1987-; Supt Awd 1986; *office:* Greater Johnstown Sr HS 222 Central Ave Johnstown PA 15902

DUER, KATHY KLINE, Bus Ed Tchr & Dept Chair; *b:* Lodi, OH; *m:* G. Wesley; *c:* Matthew K., Brian; *ed:* Bowling Green St Univ (BS) Comprehensive Bus Ed 1975; Wright St Univ (MS) Bus Ed, Supvr 1988; 10 Sem Hrs Educl Tech, Bus; Univ of Dayton 10 Grad Hrs; *cr:* Tolles Tech Ctr Tchr 1975-78; OH Hi-Point Career Ctr Tchr 1078-80; Edison Comm Coll Adj Instr 1981-85; Graham HS Tchr Bus Dept Chair, Tchr 1981-; *ai:* Bus Profs of Amer Chptr Adv; Career Dev Comm; OH Bus Tchrs Assn 1975-, Convention Chair; Child Culture Club 1988-, Pres; Farm Bureau 1982-; 4-H Adv 1992-; *office:* Graham HS 7800 W St Rt 36 Saint Paris OH 43072

DUFALLA, ROSETTA VOLPE, English Teacher & Dept Chm; *b:* Pittsburgh, PA; *m:* Harry; *c:* Marie; *ed:* California Univ of PA (BA) Speech Comm 1979, (BS) Ed, Eng 1990; *ai:* Hi-Lites Newspaper Spon; Strategic Planning-Tech Comm; ESL Coord; West Hills Art League 1989-, Pres; *office:* Hopewell Sr HS 1215 Longvue Ave Aliquippa PA 15001

DUFAULT, ROSEANNA LEWIS, Associate Professor of French; *b:* Boulder, CO; *ed:* CO Womens Coll (BA) Fr 1975; Middlebury Coll (MA) Fr 1980; Univ of CO (PHD) Fr 1986; *cr:* Univ of CO Tchng Asst, Instr 1980-86; Colorado St Univ Asst Prof 1986-89; OH Northern Univ Assoc Prof 1989-; *ai:* Book Metaphors of Identity 1990, Women by Women 1996; Articles Pub; *office:* OH Northern Univ 525 S Main Ada OH 45810

DUFF, BARBARA R., 6th-8th Grade English Teacher; *b:* Baltimore, MD; *c:* Ryan; *ed:* Towson St Univ (BS) Ed 1972; *office:* Rising Sun MS 289 Pearl St Rising Sun MD 21911

DUFF, CATHERINE FLYNN, Chemistry Teacher; *b:* Washington, DC; *ed:* Univ of MD (BS) Sci Ed 1974, (MED) Sci Ed 1980; Attnd Cath Univ 8 Grad Credits Chem Ed 1992-93, Rsrch Grant 1994-95; *cr:* Northwestern HS Sci Tchr 1974-90; E Roosevelt HS Chem Tchr 1990-; *ai:* Sci Fair Coord; NEA 1974-; ACS 1994-; Amer Chem Soc Convention Presenter Summer 1995; *office:* Eleanor Roosevelt HS 7601 Hanover Pky Greenbelt MD 20770

DUFF, FRANCES FUSCO, Reading Specialist; *b:* Hoboken, NJ; *m:* Edward; *ed:* Montclair Univ (BA) Eng, Bio 1956; Rdng Specialist Post Grad Cert; *cr:* Leinkauf Schl Elem Tchr 1956-59; Hoboken HS Eng, Bio Tchr 1960-67, Rdng Specialist 1967-; *ai:* NHS Adv; Mid St Comm; Stu Review Assesment Coord; NCTE 1960-; NJEA, NEA 1956-; NASSP; OCEAn Reef Club 1987-; Belmar Fishing Club 1994-; Who's Who Among Amer Coll Stdnts; Coach of Yr Majorettes; *office:* Hoboken HS 9th & Clinton Sts Hoboken NJ 07030

DUFF, PAUL S., History Teacher; *b:* Quincy, MA; *m:* Elizabeth; *c:* Alexander, Carl; *ed:* North Adams St Coll (BA) His 1981; Bridgewater St Coll (MA) Phi Alpha Theta 1995; *cr:* Sharon HS His & Engl Tchr 1983-; *ai:* Class, Intnl Affairs & hockomock Senate Adv; Comm Svc Advy Bd; NEA 1983; MA Tchrs Assn 1983-; Assn Curr Dev 1990-; Friends of Carver Lib 1987-; *office:* Sharon HS 180 Pond St Sharon MA 02067

DUFFANY, RICHARD ARNOLD, Fifth Grade English Teacher; *b:* Philadelphia, PA; *m:* Gail D.; *c:* Elizabeth, Christopher; *ed:* Union Coll (BA) Ed 1966, (MA) Ed 1969; *cr:* London City Schls Eighth Grd Eng Tchr 1966-69; Upper Merion Area Sixth Grd Eng Tchr 1969-79; Haverford Schl Fifth Grd Eng Tchr 1985-; *office:* Haverford Schl 450 Lancaster Ave Haverford PA 19041*

DUFFIELD, JUDITH L., English Teacher; *b:* Buffalo, NY; *m:* William Kramer; *c:* Jacob Kramer, Michael Kramer; *ed:* Beaver Coll (BA) Eng 1968; Univ of NH (MAT) Tchng Eng 1970; George Washington Univ (MBA) Fin 1983; 96 Grad Credits; *cr:* Somersworth HS Eng Tchr; N Kingstown HS Eng Tchr; Pert, Marwick, Mitchell Ed; DC Dept of Recreation Ed, Writer; Sidney Kramer Books Chief Fin Ofcr; Seneca Vly HS Eng Tchr 1994-; *ai:* NCTE, NEA 1993-; Cabin John Citizen Assn, Sec; Clara Barton Ctr for Children, Pres, Bd of Dir; Pub Book: Washington DC The Complete Guide; *office:* Seneca Valley HS 12700 Middlebrook Rd Germantown MD 20874

DUFFY, ARTHUR JOSEPH, Social Studies Teacher; *b:* Boston, MA; *ed:* St John's Seminary (AB) Philosophy, His 1963; Boston Coll (MAT) His, Ed 1966; Northeastern Univ (MPA) Pub Admin 1977; Addl Grad Stu Boston St Coll, Fitchburg St Coll; *cr:* Cathedral HS His Tchr 1964-68; Comm of Mass Supervision in Ed 1969-72; Town of Canton His, Soc Stud Tchr 1973-; *ai:* NEA, MA Tchrs Assn, Canton Tchrs Assn 1973-; Town Meeting 1964-79, Elected Mem; Golden Apple Awd Quincy Patriot Ledger 1991, 1994; Excl in Tchng Awd 1994; Caring Tchng Awd Canton HS Wresting Team 1996; *office:* William Galvin MS 55 Pecunit St Canton MA 02021

DUFFY, BRIDGET M., Hlth, PE Chprsn & Science Tchr; *b:* Yonkers, NY; *ed:* SUNY at Cortland (BS) Hlth Sci 1987; CUNY Lehman Coll (MSEd) Hlth Ed 1990; Manhattan Coll Spec Ed Spec Ed; *cr:* Sacred Heart HS Tchr 1988-; *ai:* SADD Moderator.

DUFFY, CHRISTINE, Third Grade Teacher; *b:* MA; *m:* Bruce Whitmore; *cr:* Hanscom Primary Schl Classroom Tchr 25 Yrs; *ai:* Schl Advy Cncl; NEA 1971-.*

DUFFY, EILEEN M. (SAILER), Business Ed Instr & Chrpsn; *b:* NYC, NY; *m:* Francis Timothy; *c:* Timothy S., Katherine T.; *ed:* Orange Cty CC (AS) Hum 1972; SUNY at Albany (BS) Bus Ed 1974, (MS) Bus Ed 1975; Various Cmptr Courses; NYS Cert Work Stud Coord; *cr:* Pine Bush HS Bus Ed Tchr 1975-76; Monroe-Woodbury Sr HS Bus Ed Tchr 1976-81, 1985-, Bus Ed Dept Chair 1995-; *ai:* Peer Mediation, Anger Mngmt Team 1995-; FBLA Adv 1976-81, 1989-94; Bus Edctrs of Mid Hudson 1986-, Sec; NBEA, BTA of NYS 1974-; Prof Division FBLA-PBL 1989-; Amer Red Cross, Vol; Bike A Thon; Article Pub; *office:* Monroe Woodbury Sr HS 265 Dunderberg Rd Central Valley NY 10917*

DUFFY, HAROLD F., Assistant Principal; *b:* Johnsonburg, PA; *m:* Carol; *c:* Devon, Patrick; *ed:* Edinboro Univ of PA (BS) Soc Stud 1961, (MED) Soc Stud Ed 1964; Principals Cert Ed 1984; *cr:* Cambridge Springs HS Tchr, Coach 1961-65; Indiana HS Tchr, Coach, Asst Prin 1965-; *ai:* Responsible all Act in Bldg; NASSP 1994-; PSEA, NEA 1961-84; *office:* Indiana Area Sr HS 450 N 5th St Indiana PA 15701

DUFFY, JOSEPH BRADLEY, English Teacher; *b:* Manchester, NH; *m:* Claire Lillian Prince; *ed:* St. Anselm (BA) Eng 1969; Suffolk Univ (MED) Ed 1976; Univ of NH, Keene St Coll Post Grad Work; *cr:* Manchester West HS Eng Tchr 1969-; *ai:* Manchester Ed Assn, NH Ed Assn, NEA 1969-; Connendation Presented Bd of Schl Comm for Devotion Beyond The Call of Duty 1982; Outstdng Act of Heroism Medal of Hnr by Manchester Union Ldr 1983; *office:* Manchester HS West 9 Notre Dame Ave Manchester NH 03102

DUFFY, JOSEPH WILLIAM, History Instr & Guidance Cnslr; *b:* Hartford, CT; *m:* Donna Dombrosky; *c:* Kate-Lynn; *ed:* Fairfield Univ (BA) His, Philosophy 1965; St Joseph Coll (MA) European His 1967; Cntrl CT St Univ (MS) Guid; Trinity Coll (MA) Amer His 1981; *cr:* South Cath HS His Instr 1965-67; Archdioceson Dept of Urban Affairs 1973-75; East Cath HS His, Philosophy,, Guid Instr 1967-; *ai:* Oratory Coach; Ind His Ctr; Stud CT His Assn; CT Historical Soc 1970-93; NCEA 1967-; Assn for Cnslng, Dev 1981-; New England Assn of Coll Admissions Cnslrs, Cnslr of Yr 1991; Ko Kondo Karate 1995-; Natl Endowment for Hum Mentor Awd 1992; Tufts Univ Influential Tchr Awd; Bowdoin Coll Citation for Coll Admissions Letter; *office:* East Catholic H S 115 New State Rd Manchester CT 06040*

DUFFY, MARGARET KITZINGER, Third Grade Teacher; *b:* Altoona, PA; *m:* Kevin Charles; *c:* Chelsea Lynn; *ed:* Univ of MD (BS) Elem Ed 1980; Hood Coll Elem Math, Sci 30 Hrs; MCPS Inservice Credits 30 Hrs; *cr:* Wyngate Elem Schl Second, Third Grd Tchr 1981-84; Farmland Elem Schl Second, Third Grd Tchr 1984-85; Lake Seneca Elem Schl Third Grd Tchr 1985-88; S. Christa Mc Auliffe Elem Schl Third Grd Tchr 1988-; *ai:* Team Ldr, SERT & GATE Comm, Mngmt Team 1995-; Sci Comm 1988-; New Tchr Trainer Sci 1989-91, Trainer Classroom Mngmt 1994-95; Math, S Stud Connection Trainer 1994-95; MSPAP Trainer Sci; MCEA, MSTA, NEA 1981-; St John Newman Church 1992-; Articles Pub; *office:* S. Christa Mc Auliffe Elem 12500 Wisteria Dr Germantown MD 20874

DUFFY, MARY DRISCOLL, Math Teacher; *b:* New York City, NY; *m:* John Joseph; *c:* John Denis; *ed:* SUNY at Stonybrook (MA) Lbrl Stud 1992; 21 Grad Credits Hofstra Univ; 9 Grad Credits Brooklyn Coll; Grad Stud Coll of St Rose; *cr:* NY Archdiocese Tchr 1-8 Grd Tchr 1961-70; Elwood UFSD 7-9 Grd Math Tchr 1970-; *ai:* Discipline Comm 1993-94; Eligibility Comm 1993-95; Mathlethes 1970-73; NYSTMA; NSF Grants; *home:* 882 Lorenz Ave Baldwin NY 11510

DUFFY, MARY MARTIN,CSFN Principal; *b:* Bristol, PA; *ed:* Holy Family Coll at Philadelphia (BA) Math 1963; Villanova Univ at Philadelphia (MATM) Math 1974; *cr:* St Gregory Schl Prin 1972-78; Colegio Espiritu Santo Prin 1978-84; Nazareth Acad HS Asst Prin, Tchr 1984-94; Nazareth Acad Grd Schl Prin 1994-; *ai:* Mid Sts Self-Stud, Curr Coord; Mathletes, Alumnae Moderator; Dean of Stud; Math Chprsn; NCEA; NCTM; *office:* Nazareth Acad Grd Schl 4701 Grant Ave Philadelphia PA 19114

DUFFY, MAUREEN M., Family & Consumer Sci Tchr; *b:* Boston, MA; *m:* James; *c:* Jennifer, Robert, Erin, James; *ed:* Rivier Coll (BA) Home Ec 1970; Framingham St Cert Family & Consumer Tchng 1990; Bridgewater St Cert Prgm for Hlth; *cr:* Cohassett HS Tchr 1991-; *ai:* Club Adv for Comm Vol Svc; Stud Group Chm Block Schedule; Schl Cncl in Scituate MA Gates Schl; MTA, MAFCS 1990-; St Marys Guild 1990-; Dedication of Yrbk 1995; Patriot Ledger Golden Apple Awd 1992; *office:* Cohasset Jr Sr HS 143 Pond St Cohasset MA 02025*

DUFFY, PATRICK MICHAEL, High School Business Teacher; *b:* Scranton, PA; *m:* Magdalen Klos; *c:* Kathleen, Erin; *ed:* Kings Coll (BS) Accounting 1958; Elizabethtown Coll Tchr Cert 1970; 12 Grad Hrs Scranton Univ; 25 Addl Credit Hrs; Attnd Stroudsburg, Paterson St; *cr:* Hillcrest Schl 4th Grd Tchr 1958-60; Lancaster Cath HS Tchr 1960-64; St Augustine 6th Grd Tchr 1964-66; Lancaster Cath HS Accounting, Mrktg Tchr 1966-; *ai:* Debate Coach 1960-62; BsktblCoach 1960-81; Cross Ctnry Coach 1965-69; Natl Cath Tchr Org; Knights of Columbus 1979-; *office:* Lancaster Catholic HS 650 Juliette Ave Lancaster PA 17603

DUFFY, SUSANNE M., History & Government Teacher; *b:* New Haven, CT; *ed:* Southern CT St Univ (BS) Scndry Ed, Soc Stud 1968; Univ of CT (MA) Pol Sci 1970; Fairfield Univ (CAS) Pol Sci 1977; Southern CT St Univ Admin Cert; Yale Univ Post Grad; *cr:* Univ of CT Grad Asst 1968-69; Amity Regnl HS His, Govt Tchr 1969-, His Dept Chprsn 1982-92; *ai:* Block Schedule, Distngd Alumni Comm; Yth Govt Prgm Adv; PTSA Fac Liason; NEA 1969-; NCSS 1970-; League of Women Voters 1982; Amity Tchr of Yr Bd of Ed 1978; Yrbk Dedication 1978-; Amity PTSA Tchr of Yr 1986; Dartmouth Coll Tchr of Yr 1990; Yrbk Dedication 1995; Yale Univ Multi-Cultural Project Pub 1992; CT Celebration Excl Honrable Mention 1988, 1990; Northeast Regnl Soc Stud Conf Presenter 1988, 1990, 1992; Gale Publications Project Adv World Cultures; *office:* Amity Regnl Sr HS 25 Newton Rd Woodbridge CT 06525

DUFFY, THOMAS JOSEPH, English Professor; *b:* East Newark, NJ; *m:* Constance Ann Kern; *c:* T. J., Christopher; *ed:* Seton Hall Univ (BA) Eng 1959, (MA) Eng 1965; Post Grad Eng Comm Coll Tchrs KS St Univ; *cr:* Seton Hall Prep Schl Eng Tchr 1960-66; Seton Hall Univ Adj Prof Eng 1966-68; New Milford HS Eng Tchr 1966-68; Bergen Comm Coll Eng Prof 1968-; *ai:* Fac Senate; Dev Stud Comm; NEA, NJEA 1968-; NJADE 1982-; MACCRA 1995-; Lions Club 1988-, VP; Book: Looking Back on Palisades Park; *office:* Bergen Comm Coll 400 Paramus Rd Paramus NJ 07652

DUFORD, HARRIETTE GAVAZA, Chapter I Reading Teacher; *b:* Melrose, MA; *m:* Ronald L.; *c:* Amy Charpentier, Nathan, Emily; *ed:* Univ of ME at Farmington (BS) Elem Ed 1964; Univ of New England (MS) Ed 1996; 30 Credit Hrs 1967-93; *cr:* Wells-Oqunquit Schl Grd K-4 Tchr 1966-87; Tiny Pines Nursery Schl Owner, Operator 1978-87; Wells Elem Schl Chptr I Rdng Tchr 1988-; *ai:* Chptr I Rdng Advy Bd; Organizer Whole Schl Lit Act; Sftbl Team; MEA, NEA 1966-; New England Rdng Assn 1988-; Wells-Ogunquit Staff Dev; Wells-Ogunquit Sftbl; Girl Scout Ldr; Little League Coach, VP; PTA Recognition Awd; York Cty ME VIP; Chptr I Grd 1 Calendar Comm; Cert of Appreciation Wells-Ogunquit Schl; Book: Adopting School Hurricane Andrew; *home:* Hilton Ln Wells ME 04090

DUFOUR, CAROL TALLON, English, Typing & Math Teacher; *b:* Pontiac, MI; *m:* Roderick; *c:* Michael, Christopher, Andrea, Matthews; *ed:* Bob Jones Univ (BS) Elem Ed 1972; Credit Hrs Purdue Univ at Hammond; *cr:* Temple Chrstn Schl K-1, 3 Grd Tchr 1972-76; Georgetown Chrstn Schl Elem, HS Tchr 1976-83; Lewes Chrstn Acad 1-3 Grd Tchr 1983-86; Seaford Chrstn Acad Jr HS & HS Eng, Math, Typing Tchr 1994-; *ai:* Art Festival Annual Regnl Amer Assn Chrstn Schls Spon; Indian River Dist Migrant Prgm Art Specialist; *office:* Seaford Christian Acad 110 Holly St Seaford DE 19973

DUFOUR, LOUISE ELLA, Religion Dept Chairperson; *b:* Madawaska, ME; *ed:* Annhurst Coll (BA) Eng 1968; St Joseph Coll (MA) Sci Ed 1973; Boston Coll (MA) Rel Ed 1984; *cr:* Holy Cross HS Sci Chprsn, Tchr 1974-82; St Francis of Assisi Pastoral Assoc 1984-89; St Mary's HS Rel Chprsn, Tchr 1990-91; St Dominic Regnl HS Rel Chprsn, Tchr 1991-; *ai:* Campus Ministry; *office:* St Dominic Regnl HS 179 Blake St Lewiston ME 04240

DUFOUR, RICHARD EDWARD, Educational Consultant; *b:* Lyndonville, VT; *m:* Columbine Sonya Demars; *c:* Keith, Brent, Michele; *ed:* Univ of VT (BSED) Eng 1954, (MA) Eng 1963; 60 Hrs Eng, Hum, Ed; *cr:* Lyndon Inst Eng Tchr 1956-60; Roger Ludlowe HS Eng Tchr 1966-87; Fairfield HS Eng Tchr 1987-95; Consultant 1996; *ai:* Acad Bowl Coach; NEA, NCTE 1960-; ASCD 1980-; Fairfield Ed Assn, VP; Jr Chamber Commerce Educator of Yr; *home:* 284 Nonopoge Rd Fairfield CT 06432

DUFRESNE, ROGER, Accounting Professor; *b:* Lowell, MA; *m:* Marcia J.; *c:* Nicole, Angelina; *ed:* Lowell Tech Inst (BS) Bus 1973; Seton Hall Univ (MBA) Bus 1976; *cr:* Englehart Minerals & Chem Intern Auditor 1973-77; Moore Bus Forms Acctng, Budget Mgr 1977-78; Chelsea Industries Group Controller, Mgmt Consult 1978-80; Merrimack Coll Assist Prof 1980-82; Northern Essex CC Prof 1981-; *ai:* Veterans Club Adv; MA Comm Coll Cncl Prof St Univ Treas; NECCFA, MTA, NEA 1981-, Treas; MA Comm Coll Cncl 1981-, Treas, Bud; Who's Who Fin Industry 1990-; *office:* Northern Essex Comm Coll 100 Elliott St Haverhill MA 01830

DUGAI, DAVID JOHN, Business Education Teacher; *b:* Toledo, OH; *m:* Avis Ann French; *c:* Angela Sue, Wendy Lynn; *ed:* OH Univ (BS) Ed 1972; Bowling Green St Univ (MED) Ed 1976; *cr:* Maumee HS Bus Ed Tchr

1972-; *ai:* Head Bsbl, Boys Cross Cntry Coach; NEA, OH Ed Assn 1972-; Maumee Ed Assn 1972-, Bldg Rep, Elections Chprsn; Northwest OH Bsbl Coaches Assn, OH Bsbl Coaches Assn 1984-; *office:* Maumee HS 1147 Saco St Maumee OH 43537

DUGAN, ALICE BERNICE FARRIS, Math Chair; *b:* Darby, PA; *m:* William T.; *c:* Megan Anne, Sean Liam; *ed:* Immaculata Coll (BA) Math, Physics 1972; Villanova Univ (MA) Ed Admin 1981; Attnd West Chester Univ, Phila Coll of Textiles & Sci, LaSalle Univ, OH St Univ; *cr:* St Maria Goretti HS Stu Govt Mod Tchr 1972-75; Archbishop Carroll HS Tchr, Ath Dir 1975-77; Cardinal O'Hara HS Tchr, Stu Coun Mod 1978-, Cmptr Resource Person 1991-; *ai:* Stu Cncl; NCTM 1988-; ACT 1972-; Math Curr Comm 1985-; White House Presidential Tchr 1989; Tchr of Yr 1989.

DUGAN, CAROLYN JANE, Eng Tchr, Interactive TV Coord; *b:* Springfield, MA; *m:* Robert J. Leonard; *ed:* Notre Dame Coll (BA) Eng 1975; Univ of New Hampshire (MS) Bus, Comm 1984; *cr:* Cntrl HS Eng Tchr 1977-83; Meml HS Eng Tchr 1984-, ITV Coord 1989-; *ai:* Lit Magazine Adv; Phi Delta Kappa 1986-, Pub Relations 1987-88; NCTE 1980-; New England Women's Stud Assn 1989-; NEA 1977-; Friends of Manchester City Lib 1989-, Pres 1993-; Manch Jr Women's Club, Ticket Chair, Emcee for Fashion Show, Schlsp Fund 1988-89; WGOT-TV 60 Production Asst 1992-94; HS News Show Exec Producer; *office:* Meml HS 50 Porter St Manchester NH 03103

DUGAN, JAMES F., History Teacher; *b:* Bronx, NY; *m:* Katherine Finland; *c:* James Jr., Sean, Colin; *ed:* Iona Coll (BA) His 1964; Univ of Hartford (MED) Sped Ed 1972; *cr:* Cardinal Hayes HS Eng Tchr 1966-67; Dodd MS His Tchr 1967-; *ai:* Boys Track, Soccer Coach; Ed Assn Cheshire 1967-; CT Ed Assn, NEA 1972-; *office:* Dodd MS 100 Park Pl Cheshire CT 06410

DUGAN, JOAN M., Math Teacher; *b:* Philadelphia, PA; *c:* Hal, Liz; *ed:* West Chester Univ (BA) Math Ed 1971, (MS) Math Ed 1976; *cr:* Valley Forge Jr HS Math Tchr 1971-85; Conestoga HS Math Tchr 1985; Central Mont Co Area Voc Tech Schl Dept Head, Tchr 1985-88; Strawberry Mansion HS Math Tchr 1988-; *ai:* Class 1997 Spon; Sci Math Tech Tchr Resource Ldr; Cluster Stans Review; AFT, PFT 1988-; ATMOPAV, NCTM, PCTM1971-; *office:* Strawberry Mansion HS 32nd & Ridge Ave Philadelphia PA 19132*

DUGAN, NATALIE M., English & Computers Teacher; *b:* Philadelphia, PA; *m:* Dennis; *c:* Kelly; *ed:* (BS) Bus & Ed 1960; Attnd Penn St, Marywood, Kutztown Masters Equivalency 1988; *cr:* Perkiomen Vly HS Tchr & Coord of Gifted 1979-; *ai:* Schl Store Mgr; Strategic Planning, Intensive Scheduling & Bus & Schl Partnerships Comms; NEA; PSEA; AAUW; Grammar Workbooks Pub; Stu Handbook Dedication; *office:* Perkiomen Valley HS 509 Gravel Pike Rt 29 Collegeville PA 19426

DUGAN, PAUL EDWARD, Chem & Advanced Bio Tchr; *b:* Dayton, OH; *w:* Nancy A. Wagner (dec); *c:* Patrick, Stacey, Brian; *ed:* Univ of Dayton (BS) Bio Ed 1969, (MS) Ed 1988; 12 Hrs Chem Cert, 18 Hrs Asst Supt Cert at Wright St Univ; 3 Hrs Recombinant DNA, Microbiology, 3 Hrs Pharmaceutical Chem at Miami Univ; *cr:* Dayton Pub Schls Elem Tchr 1969-72; St Ritas Schl Jr HS Sci Tchr 1972-74; West Callolton Schls Jr HS Math 1985; Trotwood City Schls Chem, Bio Tchr 1985-; Sinclair Comm Coll Chem Instr 1991-; *ai:* NHS Adv 5 Yrs; Womans Var Soccer Coach 1 Yr; Sci Quiz Bowl Adv 3 Yrs; Amer Chem Soc, Miami Valley Chem 1995-; Tchrs Natl Assn of Sci Tchrs 1980-; Engrng Hall of Fame at Dayton Engrs Club for Excl in Sci Tchng 1993; *office:* Trotwood Madison HS 221 E Trotwood Blvd Trotwood OH 45426*

DUGAN, TIMOTHY PATRICK, World History Teacher; *b:* Hamilton, OH; *m:* Robin Ann Collien; *c:* Ashley, Corey; *ed:* Miami Univ (BS) Ed 1979; Xavier Univ (MED) Educl Admin 1982; 5 Hrs OH St Univ His; *cr:* Princeton HS Tchr 1979-, Intnl Baccalaureate Coord 1985-92; *ai:* Tech Comm CHm; Inservice Tchrs Cmptr Instruction Coord; NCSS, OH Cncl Soc Stud 1979-; Natl Cncl His Ed 1990-; PTA 1990-; Attnd OH His Acad NCHE Wkshp; *office:* Princeton HS 11080 Chester Rd Cincinnati OH 45246*

DUGDALE, JANE SWIFT, ESL Teacher; *b:* San Antonio, TX; *m:* Thomas Jan; *c:* Antony Lee, Anna Christina, Karen May; *ed:* Goucher Coll (BA) Eng, Amer Lit 1964; Marywood Coll (MA) Biling, Bicultural Stud 1992; 3 Grad Credits PA Writing Project; 3 Grad Credits Eastern Bapt Theological Seminary; 12 Grad Credits Univ of PA-Annenburg Schl of Comm; *cr:* Peace Corps Univ of Concepcion ESL Tchr 1964-66; Inst Deingles ESL Tchr 1971-72; DE Co Intermediate Unit ESL Tchr 1984-91; Radnor Twp Schl Dist ESL Tchr 1991-; *ai:* Schl Intl Exchange Prgm Adv; Tchrs of Eng to Speakers of Other Langs 1984-; PSEA 1991-; Phi Beta Kappa; Philadelphia Bapt Assn 1984-, Moderator; Cntrl Bapt Church 1992-, Chair, Outreach Bd; TX St PTA 1974-83, Life; *office:* Radnor HS King of Prussia Rd Wayne PA 19087

DUGGAN, BONNIE JUNE, 3rd Grade Teacher; *b:* Brooklyn, NY; *m:* Michael P.; *c:* Scott, Drew; *ed:* Univ of NY at Cortland (BS) Elem Ed 1971; Widener Univ (MS) Gifted & Talented 1986; 90 Plus Credits Various Schls; *cr:* Interboro Schl Dist K-8 Tchr 1972-; *ai:* Staff Dev, Dist Assessment Cores; Home Schl Ex Bd; Liason, Curr & Selection Comms; Mentor Tchr to New Staff; Cooperating Tchr to Stu Tchrs; Lead Tchr; Writing, Sci, Math Hlth, Rdng & Writing Curr; NEA, PSEA 1972-; PA Writing Project 1980- Liason Comm; Lead Tchr; Curr & Selection Comm; Mentor Tchr New Staff; Coop; Presbyn Church 1970-, Sunday Schl Tchr; PA Writing Fellow; Comm Cenntenial Service Awd; Articles on Childrens Writing Wrkshp Innovative Coop-Peer Editing Technique & a K-5 Curr Life Skills; *office:* Prospect Park Schl 9th & PA Aves Prospect Park PA 19076

DUGGAN, CHRISTINE, 5th Grade Teacher; *b:* Brooklyn, NY; *m:* David; *c:* Jennifer Troise, Jessica Troise, Jessica; *ed:* SCCC at Selden (AA) Lbrl Stud 1985; Dowling Coll (BA) Ed-Magna Cum Laude 1987, (MS) Ed 1991; *cr:* Cherry Ave Elem Schl 5th Grd Tchr 1987-; *ai:* Kappa Delta Pi 1986-; South Shore Coll Women's Club 1990-, Co-Pres 1993-95; John Astor, Acad Hnr Schlsp; *office:* Cherry Ave Elem Schl 155 Cherry Ave West Sayville NY 11796

DUGGAN, KENNETH J., Asst Prin & Supv of Math Dept; *b:* Brooklyn, NY; *m:* Laurene Farrell; *c:* Denise, Brian; *ed:* St Francis Coll (BS) Math 1965; Pace Univ (MS) Ed Admin 1978; Attnd Brooklyn Coll, Fordham Univ, Coll of St Rose; *cr:* Bishop Ford HS Math Tchr, Curr Coord 1965-78; Mamaroneck HS Asst Prin 1978-82; Edward R. Murrow HS Asst Prin Admin 1982-92; Dewitt Clinton HS Asst Prin Supv 1992-; *ai:* Prin Cabinet; Consultative Cncl; Tutoring Prgm; Tech Prep Curr; Ad Hoc Comms; AFSA; Cncl of Supvrs & Admin of NYC; Assn Math Asst Prin of NYS; St Francis Coll Alumni Assn 1965-, VP; Pace U Alumni Assn 1978-; Cath Tchrs Assn 1992-; Adj Asst Prof Ed Admin Pace Univ; Adj Instr Math Ramapo Coll; *office:* Dewitt Clinton HS 100 W Mosholu Pky S Bronx NY 10468

DUGRE, NANCY A. (CLOSSON), Mathematics Teacher; *b:* Manchester, NH; *m:* Marc S.; *c:* Jessica L., Neal T., Caitlin R.; *ed:* Westfield St Coll (BA) Math, Scndry Ed 1978; 15 Addl Credit Hrs; *cr:* Westfield Alternative Schl Math Tchr 1977; Enrico Fermi HS Math Tchr 1977-79; Granby MS Math Tchr 1983-84; Mater Dolorosa Schl Math, Sci Tchr 1989-93; Minnechaug Regnl HS Math Tchr 1993-; *ai:* Renaissance Co-Chprsn; Report Card Comm; Stu Act Chaperone; FBLA Fashion Show Model; Class of 1998 Adv; ASCD 1995-; NCTM, MATHWEST 1989-; MTA 1993-; Hampden, Wilbraham Tchrs Assn 1993-; Employer of Month; Frgn Stu Host Family; Rotary Vol Chicapee; Dedicated Tchr Awd; Excl in Math Tchng Presidental Awd Nom 1990-93, 1995; *home:* 71 Jefferson St Holyoke MA 01040

DUHAIME, SUSAN LILLIAN, 5th-6th Grade Science Teacher; *b:* Manchester, NH; *m:* Roger A.; *c:* Jocelyn, Alan; *ed:* Notre DAme Coll (BA) Bio & Ed 1972, (M Ed) 1996; NSF Wksbp SPICA Harvard Smithsonian Center for Astrophysics; NASA Workshop NEWEST JPL Pasadena CA; Purdue Univ APAST Summer Inst; *cr:* St Anthony Jr HS Sci Tchr 1973-74; St Anthony Schl Tchr 1974-, Asst Prin & Tchr 1987-; *ai:* Ski Club Adv; Soc Comm Chprsn; Sci Fair Coord; Pub Relations Comm; Sci Curr Team Chrpsn; NH Sci Tchrs Assn 1986-, VP 1991-, Sec 1990-91, Pres 1992-93; Natl Sci Tchrs CESI 1989-; NH Math, Sci & Tech Coalition, Governing Bd 1993; NH Sci Frmwrk 1994-; NH Sci Content Comm 1994-; Trinity HS Bd 1992-; NHSTA Bd Mem 1986-; Pres Awd for Excl in Sci & Math 1991; Sci Tchr of Yr-Diocese of Manchester 1991; Chprsn NHSTA Fall Confs 1990-91; SPICA Participant Harvard-Smithsonian Center of Astrophysics; NEWEST Participant JPL Pasadena CA; CIBA Mid Level Exempl Sci Tchr Awd 1995; *office:* St Anthony Schl 148 Belmont St Manchester NH 03103

DUHAMEL, PAUL G., Art Teacher; *b:* Providence, RI; *m:* Jacqueline Fromm; *c:* Nicole; *ed:* RI Coll (BS) Art Ed 1973; RI Coll (MA) Art Ed 1990; Providence Coll; RI Schl of Design; Cert in Cnslng; *cr:* Ponaganset HS Art Tchr 1973-; *ai:* Yrbk Adv 1975-; NEA 1973-, VP, Negotiation Chair, Bldg Rep; Lake Washington Assoc 1974-, VP, Pres; W Glocester Fire Dept 1980-87, Pres; *office:* Ponaganset HS 137 Anan Wade Rd North Scituate RI 02857

DUIN, PAMELA, English & Social Studies Tchr; *b:* Paterson, NJ; *m:* Donald; *c:* Edye, Curtis, Courtney; *ed:* William Paterson Coll (BA) Soc Stud 1963; Tchr of Handicapped Cert; *cr:* Lakeland Regnl HS Soc Stud Tchr 1973-70, Eng, Soc Stud Tchr 1984-; Indian Hills HS Supplemental, Spec Ed Tchr 1980-83; *ai:* Yrbk, Peer Mediation Adv; Tchrs Assn 1984-, VP; Passaic Ct Tchrs Assn, NJEA, NEA 1984-; NJ Governor's Tchr of Yr Awd 1992; Rutgers Tchr Recognition Day 1995; *office:* Lakeland Regional HS 205 Conklintown Rd Wanaque NJ 07465

DUKE, AMY LAWYER, 5th Grade Teacher; *b:* Syracuse, NY; *m:* Christopher J.; *ed:* Onondaga Comm Coll (AA) Hum 2 Yrs; Geneseo St (BS) Psych 4 Yrs; Oswego St (MS) Ed 5 Yrs; *cr:* Hillbrook Detention Facility Tchr 1986-89; Cato-Meridian MS GATE Tchr 1989-93, 5th Grd Tchr 1993-; *ai:* Odyssey of Mind Coach; Math Comm; JDA 1986-; GATE Advy Cnsl 1989-; Articles Pub; *office:* Cato-Meridian MS Rt 370 Box 100 Cato NY 13033

DUKE, DAVID ALLEN, 4th Grade Teacher; *b:* Danville, PA; *m:* Judith Truax; *c:* Brian D.; *ed:* Bloomsburg Coll (BS) Elem Ed 1969; 30 Credit Hrs; *cr:* Shikellamy Schl Dist 4th-5th Grd Tchr 1969-; *ai:* JV Bsktbl Coach 1981-93; Outdoor Ed Coord 1974-91; NEA, PSEA 1969-; Northumberland Cty Outstdng Conservation Tchr 1992; *home:* 980 Woodrow Ave Northumberland PA 17857

DUKES, DELORES SUITT, Kindergarten Teacher; *b:* Oxford, NC; *ed:* Winston Salem St Univ (BS) Elem Ed 1965; 42 Grad Hrs Early Chldhd Ed NC Cntrl Univ; 12 Grad Hrs Lehman Coll; *cr:* Leak St Schl Tchr 1965-66, 1966-67; Hillcrest for Children Cnslr 1967-68; Ossining Childrens Ctr Tchr 1968-82; PS 132 Tchr 1982-; *ai:* Missionary Messiah Bapt Church; Literacy Vol; United Fed of Tchrs, AFT, NY St United Tchrs 1982-; NY Chptr of WSSU Alumni Assn 1978-, Recording Sec 1980-; Eastern Atlantic Dist WSSU Alumni Assn 1978-, Recording Sec 1988-92, Corresponding Sec 1992-94; Natl Alumni Assn of WSSU 1978-; 1st Runner Up Miss Alumni Queen Winston Salem St Univ 1982.

DUKES, LINDA M., Medical Assisting Program Dir; *b:* Dayton, OH; *m:* Harold G.; *c:* Michael, Sarah; *ed:* Sinclair Comm Coll (ADN) Nursing 1977; Andrews Univ (BSN) Nursing, Comm 1994; *cr:* Miami Jacobs Instr, Dir 1994-; *ai:* Walk Amer Team Ldr, Annual Coach; AAMA; Dayton Able Prgm 1993-, Vol, Svc Awd; *office:* Miami Jacobs Jr Coll Of Bus 400 E 2nd St Dayton OH 45401*

DULAC, ELIZABETH ANN, 8th Grade Language Arts Tchr; *b:* Lewiston, ME; *m:* Wilfrid R.; *c:* David, John, Elizabeth; *ed:* Univ of ME (BS) Eng & His 1977; Univ of Southern ME (MS) Spec Ed 1985, (MS) Exceptionality & Gifted Ed 1993; *cr:* Lewiston Jr HS 7th-8th Grd Lang Arts Tchr & Tchr of Gifted Ed 1980-; *ai:* Intramural Coach; Staff Dev; Comm for Gifted & Talented; Liaison Comm; Schl Newspaper Adv; Lewiston Ed Assn 1980-, Bldg Rep 1993; John F Murphy Inc 1985-, VP 1993; *home:* 181 Whitney St Auburn ME 04210

DULAVITCH, EDWARD JOSEPH, Social Studies Teacher; *b:* Pittsburgh, PA; *m:* Lois J. Segerdahl; *c:* Katelynn, Jaye, Benjamin; *ed:* Allegheny Comm (AA) Pol Sci 1976; Univ of Pittsburgh (BA) Scndry Ed, Soc Stud 1986; Clarion Univ, Univ of IN Working Towards Masters; Art Inst of Pittsburgh Assoc in Applied Tech 1980; *cr:* Clarion-Limestone Area HS Soc Stud Tchr 1986-; *ai:* After Schl Act Supvr; NEA, PSEA, CLAEA 1986-; *office:* Clarion-Limestone Area HS RD 1 Box 205 Strattanville PA 16258

DULL, JACQUELINE ANN (MC GUIRE), Kindergarten Teacher; *b:* Pittsburgh, PA; *m:* Dennis; *c:* Kristen, Jaime; *ed:* Duquesne Univ (BS) Ed, Elem, Spec 1974; Completed Trng Univ of Pgh for Math 3 Prgm; *cr:* Gen Braddock Sub Tchr 1974-75; St Anselm Schl Kndgtn Tchr 1975-76; St Bernadette Schl Kndgtn Tchr 1977-; *ai:* Served on Mid St Core Comm of Diocesan Self Stud Prgm; ASCD 1994-; Pgh Fed Diocesan Tchrs 1989-; Implemented Progressive Math 3 Prgm at Kndgtn Level; Implemented Sensitive Instrl Course on Aids; *office:* St Bernadette Schl 245 Azalea Dr Monroeville PA 15146

DULL, JAMES JEFFREY, High School Band Director; *b:* Wheeling, WV; *c:* Jolene Renee, Danielle, JoAnna; *ed:* West Liberty St Coll (BA) Elem Music Ed 1975; Kent St Univ 6 Hrs; Vandencook Coll of Music 4 Hrs; Wright St Univ 1 Hr; Univ of Dayton 6 Hrs; Fresno Pacific Coll 3 Hrs; *cr:* Meadowbrook HS Asst Band Dir 1976-78; Buckeye Local Schls Band Dir 1978-93; *ai:* NEA, OMEA 1976-; OEA 1976-, Union Rep 1994-; OVAC All Star Band, Asst Band Dir; Copywright Original Manuscript Written for New HS Consilidation of Orignal Fight Song Bought by Bd of Ed 1993; *office:* Edison HS PO Box 308 Rt 152 Richmond OH 43944

DULL, STANLEY LYNN, HS English Teacher; *b:* Midland, MI; *m:* Carol J. Crewes; *c:* Michael, Joseph, Elizabeth Jackson, Jennifer, Joshua; *ed:* Cntrl MI Univ (BA) Ed, Eng & Psych 1969; Philadelphia Divinity Schl (MDiv) Theology 1975; Immaculate Coll (MA) Counseling Psych 1994; Completing (PsyD); *cr:* Hemlock Schl Dist Tchr & Rdng Specialist 1969-71; Octorara Area Schl Dist HS Eng 1975-; *ai:* Priest in Charge Church of the Ascension Parkersburg PA 1975-; ACA 1993-; *office:* Octorara Area HS PO Box 501 Atglen PA 19310

DUMAS, H. SCOTT, Mathematics Professor; *b:* Albuquerque, NM; *ed:* Rice Univ (BA) Fr & Physics 1979; Univ of CO (MA) Math 1981; Univ of NM (PHD) Applied Math 1988; Fulbright Fellow Ecole Normale Superieure in Paris 1986-87; *cr:* Univ of NY at Albany Visiting Asst Prof of Math, Physics 1988-89; IMA Univ of MN Postdoctoral Mem 1989-90; Univ of Cincinnati Assoc Math Prof 1990-94, Asst Math Prof 1994-; Universite d Amiens France Visiting Assoc Math Prof 1991-92; Ecole Normale Superieure Cachan France Visiting Math Prof 1994-; *ai:* Participant, Co-Organizer research Confs in Math; Principle Investigator Natl Sci Fnd DMS Geometric Analysis 1995-97, DMS Applied Math 1992-94; Pub Research Articles, Conf Proceedings, Books & Translations; *office:* Univ Of Cincinnati Math Dept Cincinnati OH 45221

DUMAS, ROBERT FRANK, Social Studies Teacher; *b:* Masse Theresa J.; *ed:* St John Fisher Coll (BA) His 1974; Brockport NY (MED) Scndry Ed 1979; *cr:* Albion Cntrl Schl 7th-8th Gr Tchr 1974-81; Hilton Cntrl Schl 7th-8th Grd Soc Stud Tch Brockport Cntrl Schls 7th-8th Grd Soc Stud Tchr 1982-; *ai:* Stu Yorkers Clubs Adv; Cty Curr Comms; Natl His Honor Soc in NYSUT 1974-; Grad from St John Fisher Magna Cum Laude; M for Highest Achvmt in His at Fisher; Jr Scholastic Comm Svc Tchr of Yr 1981; Grad Summa Cum Laude-Master from Brockport; *office:* Brockport Cntrl Schls 40 Allen St Brockport

DUMDUM, ULDARICO REX,JR., Associate Professor; *b:* Qu Philippines; *m:* Viola Yap; *c:* Cheryl Yvette; *ed:* Univ of Minc Civil Engrng 1973; SUNY at binghamton (MS) Cmptr Info Sys (PHD) Cmptr Info Systems 1993; Asian Inst of Tech Master En Grad Stud Dev Anthropology, Sociology 1977-80; *cr:* UNiv of Instr 1975-77; Cotabato-Agusan River Basin Dev Project Systems Planner 1975-77; SUNY Lecturer 1981-89; Marywood Cmptr Info, Telecomm Systems Prof 1989-; *ai:* Fulbright Schl Schlsp Comm Mem; Eastern Small Coll, Computing Conf, C 1996, Steering Comm; Assn for Information Systems; Intnl Assn Info Systems; Chrstn Life Ctr 1981-, Pastor; Canadian Govt Sch Inst Tech Bangkok Thailand Engrng Stud Master; Stu Grad Spea Inst Tech; Fulbright Scholar SUNY at Binghamton; Articles, b Pub; Multiple Intnl, Regnl Presentations; *office:* Marywood C Bus & Managerial Sci 2300 Adams Ave Scranton PA 18509

DUMM, JAMES F., Science Teacher; *b:* Pittsburgh, PA; Munson; *c:* Jeffrey, Jared, Lauren; *ed:* Waynesburg Coll (BA) Youngstown Univ Advertising; Chapman Coll; *cr:* Elizabeth F Tchr 1975-; *ai:* HS Ftbl 22 Yrs, Coll Ftbl 1 Yr Coaches; PS Charleroi Cougar Booster Club 1985-, Pres; Tenth St Athletic C Prebyn Church of Charleroi Elder; Former NFL Player with Colts 1973; *office:* Elizabeth Forward MS 401 Rock Run Rd Eli 15037

DUMONT, BARBARA A. BAILEY, Moderate Special Needs T Scranton, PA; *m:* John H.; *c:* Corinne, Thomas; *ed:* North Ada (BS) Ed 1970; Amer Intnl Coll (MS) Spec Ed 1976; *cr:* Town Schls 1-2nd Grd Tchr 1970-81; 7-8th Resource Rm Tchrs 1990- Schl Moderate Sp Need Tchr Elem 1993-; *ai:* Lang Arts Curr Co Schl Prgm Tchr; NEA, MTA 1990-; Lambert-Lavoie PTO 1986- Sec, Merit Awd for Svc; Chicopee Cncl PTO 1987-, VP, Sec, T Merit Awd; *office:* Litwin Schl 135 Litwin Ln Chicopee MA 01

DUMONT, MAUREEN MURPHY, English Teacher; *b:* Grinne Thomas J.; *c:* Georgette Du Mont Le Page, Aimee, Thomas Tyler, Bridget; *ed:* SUNY Potsdam (BA) Eng 1968; SUNY P (MA) Educl Stud 1984; Postive Self Concept; Co-operative Holocaust; Rubric Course; *cr:* Armory Street Schl 2nd Grd Tch Malone MS 7 Grd Fr Tchr 1987-89, 7 & 8 Grd Eng Tchr 1986- Acad 9th Grd Eng Tchr 1994-95; *ai:* Exit Standards Comm; A Malone Fed of Tchr 1984-, Sec 1994-; St Josephs Church 1 Parish Cncl 1994-, Chrstn Ed Tchr; *office:* Malone MS Francis NY 12953*

DUMOULIN, JULANN, Spanish Teacher; *b:* Boston, MA; *ed* MA (BA) Span 1969; Addl Courses; *cr:* E. Bridgewater Jr HS En Tchr 1969-70; Nashua Corp Intnl Sales Correspondant 1972-75 Notre Dame at Tyngsboro Span Tchr 1985-; *ai:* 9th Grd Adv 1985-; AATSP 1988-; Recognitions from Coll Stud as Tchr W Influened their Acad Careers; *office:* Acad of Notre Dame 180 Rd Tyngsboro MA 01879

DUMSER, PATRICIA MAHONEY, English & Soc Studies Buffalo, NY; *w:* Robert (dec); *c:* Joseph M., Robert J., Jame Fairfield Univ (MA) Eng 1987; St Bonaventure Univ His 1962; Oxford Univ; *cr:* South Park HS Tchr 1962-63; Danbury HS Tchr Wilton HS Eng, Soc St Tchr 1983-; *ai:* Educl Assn Del; PSTA Past NHS Moderator; Long Range Planning Comm-Town; NE 1983-, Local Del; Natl C tchr of Cy 1983-; Am Soc Den Curr; Chance 1996; Selected Phi Delta Kappa Nat Hnrs in Grad Ed; Cannondale; ASCD Publication Mini-Sabbaticals; *office:* Wilto Danbury Rd Wilton CT 06897*

DUNAWAY, KAREN ZANKE, Principal; *b:* Steubenville, William J.; *c:* Bria, Tessa, Krenna; *ed:* Univ of Dayton (MS) G Franciscan Univ (MS) Asst Supt Supervision 1995; Scndry Prin, Certs 1995; Grad Hrs Univ of MS, Youngstown Univ, OH Un Clairsville HS Eng, Speech Tchr 1972-78; Bellaire City Schls MS Tchr 1982-88, Guid Cnslr 1988-91, Prin 1991-; *ai:* Spec Ed Di Originator of Peer Mediation Prgm; OH Assn of Elem Prins 19 Cncl 1992-; Lifetime PTA Mem Status; *office:* First Ward Int 1731 Belmont St Bellaire OH 43906

DUNAWAY, MICHAEL EUGENE, 6th-12th Grd Vocal Music Dunbar, PA; *m:* Catherine Smailes; *c:* Shauna, Marisa; *ed:* Otter (BME) Music Ed 1981; Duquesne Univ 6 Credit Hrs; *cr:* Geibel Tchr 1989; Noble Local Schls Gen, Vocal Music Tchr 1990-93; City Schls Vocal Music 1993-; *ai:* All Schl Musical Plays; Sho Variety Show; NEA, OMEA 1990-; Outstdng Tchr 1995; Sh Declared City of Marietta's Ofcl Show Choir; *office:* Marietta C 208 Davis Ave Marietta OH 45750

DUNAWAY-HANEY, AMY, Spanish Teacher; *b:* Kettering, Timothy William; *ed:* Bowling Green St Univ (BS) Span Ed 1992 Dayton (MS) Cnslng Ed 1995; LPC Cnslng Degree 1996; *cr:* Fairmont HS Span Tchr 1992-; St Elizabeth Med Ctr Dir of ALS Support Group 1995-; *ai:* Span Club Adv; Tchr Support Group Fgn Lang Assn 1992-; Muscular Dystrophy Assn 1985-, Projec MDA 1992-, Personal Achvmt Awd; Passport Pgm Ed Grant; Sou Partial Hospitalization & Ctr for Drug & Alcohol Assn Vlntr Cns Kettering Fairmont HS 3301 Shroyer Rd Kettering OH 45429*

DUNBAR, CAROL L. (TESI), Earth Science Teacher; *b:* Buffalo Patrick R.; *c:* James C., Michael A., Mary E., Bryan P.; *ed:* Erie Co (AA) Tchr Preperation 1992; St Univ of NY at Buffalo (BA) Eler 1994; Educl Computing; *cr:* Frontier Cntrl Dist Sub Tchr; Hamb Dist Sub Tchr; Frontier Cntrl HS Earth Sci Tchr 1 Yr; *ai:* 5t Bernadetts Rel Ed Tchr; Hamburg Hockey Assn Booster Rep; Ma Laude; *home:* 4379 Kathaleen St Hamburg NY 14075

DUNBAR, DIANE, History, Eng & Rdng Teacher; *b:* Beverly, Erin, Colleen, Kara; *ed:* Boston Coll (BA) His 1967; 18 Addl Grad Peabody HS Tchr 1968-74; St John the Evangelist Schl Tchr 1 NEASC Chprsn Reacreditation; Beverly Girls Sftbl 1982-, VP, Coord; *office:* St John Evangelist Schl 111 New Balch St Bev 01915

DUNBAR, ELIZABETH S., English Teacher; *b:* Philadelphia Michael, Margaret, Douglas; *ed:* Hiram Coll (BA) Eng 196 Hopkins Univ (MS) Supervision, Curr 1975; Ind Stud Ed Univ of M Critical Thinking Hum Coppin St Coll 1984-86; MD Writing Towson St Univ 1983; *cr:* Northern HS Eng Tchr 1971-73; Wester Tchr 1974-77; Baltimore City Coll Eng, Latin, Instr Music Tchr Writing, Cmptr Tchr 1992-95, Eng Tchr 1996; *ai:* Yrbk, Lit Maga Virtual HS; Curr Comm; MD Writing Project 1983-; AF Greyhound Rescue 1994-; MD Eng Journal 2 Articles; Weekly

Collected Poems; Four Slim Poetry Volumes; Annual Painting Yrs; 2 Woman Show Gells Point; *office:* Baltimore City Coll HS Alameda Baltimore MD 21218*

., LYNNE SUMMER, ESL Teacher; *b:* Somers Point, NJ; *m:* aul; *c:* Megan, Bret; *ed:* Douglass Coll at Rutgers Univ (BA) Eng Kean Coll (MA) Instruction, Curr, Admin 1995; ESL Cert 1994; Brook HS Eng Tchr 1975-81; East Brunswick HS Home Tutor rth Amboy HS ESL Tchr 1991-; *ai:* Tchr Expectations for Stu acilitator; Schl Site Cncl; Rsrch Paper Comm; NJEA 1975-, Bldg ESOL-BE 1991-; Kappa Delta Pi, Phi Kappa Phi 1995-; *office:* boy HS Eagle Ave & Francis St Perth Amboy NJ 08861

, MARILYN NURSE, Teacher of Handicapped; *b:* Atlantic City, ia, Mark, Kerry, Saimee Saku; *ed:* Rowan St Coll (BA) Spec Ed red Hrs Rutgers; 6 Credit Hrs Univ of PA; Univ of MI Grad Stud, n; *cr:* Merchantville Schl Tchr of Handicapped Neurologically 1978-80; Pine Hill Bd of Ed NI, PI, Resource Room 1980-; *ai:* after Schl; NJEA, NEA, TPA 1978-; Notary Org 1976-, Notary; Cty Comm Women 1972-, Comm Woman; Who's Who in Amer 976; Who's Who in Ed 1988; Who's Who of the World 1990; Stoneshire Dr Glassboro NJ 08028*

, MARYLOU, 8th Grade Social Studies Tchr; *b:* New York, NY; Joseph Coll (BA) His 1966; SUNY at Stonybrook (MA) Liberal 1; 20 Addl Hrs in Anthropology, Sociology & Psych; *cr:* MS 7th-9th Grd Soc Stud Tchr 1966-, Alternative Ed Prgm 83, Dean of Stdnts 1986-88; *ai:* MAC Schl Coordinating Comm; aiaela Seminar Ldr; NEA 1966-, Del; ASCD; LICSS; Hicksville l 1980-85, Bd Mem & Pres; *office:* Hicksville MS Jerusalem Ave NY 11801

N, DAVID VINCENT, 8th Grd Phys Science Teacher; *b:* g, PA; *m:* Sharon Barnhart; *c:* Amanda, Seth; *ed:* Shippensburg S) Eart, Space Sci 1969; Millersville Univ Post Grad; *cr:* wn Area Schl Dist 8 Grd Phys Sci Tchr 1969-; *ai:* Club Adv; NEA, 69-; NSBA 1988-, Schl Bd Pres; Citizens Advy Comm, TMI *office:* G W Feaser MS 214 N Race St Middletown PA 17057

N, FRANCES MARIE,OSF, Chemistry & Physics Tchr; *b:* y, NJ; *ed:* Elms Coll (BA) Chem 1977; Lehigh Univ (MS) Educl 5; *cr:* St Francis Acad Sci Tchr 1978-86; St Mary's HS Physics d Cnslr 1986-87; Allentown Cntrl Cath Sci Tchr 1987-90; St ep Sci Tchr 1990-; *ai:* Sci Team, Peer Adv Moderators; Sci Rsrch EST 1983-; NCEA 1977-; JSEA 1990-; Hudson Cty Sci Fair egnl HS, Coord Cath Schls; Howard Hughes Rsrch Intrnshp; ICE m Instrumentation Grant; Lehigh Vly Tchr of Yr; Westinghouse t Search Tchr Awd; Yrbk Dedications 1994, St Mary's HS 1988; 0 Grand St Jersey City NJ 07302

N, JOANNA LOUISE, Sixth Grade Teacher; *b:* Pittsburgh, PA; rd B.; *c:* Julianne, Kerry Jayne; *ed:* Muskingum Coll (BA) Elem Ohio St (MA) Early, Mid Chldhd 1975; Attnd Univ of MD GATE, v Classroom Mngmt; *cr:* Wilson Schl 6th Grd Tchr 25 Yrs; *ai:* Ed Dir; Advy Cncl; Rdng Curr Dev; Writing Competency; NEA, A 1971-; Delta Kappa Gamma 1979-; SS Supt 1995-; Tchr of ants for Sci, Outdoor Ed, Rdng, Soc Stud, Zanesville TV Educl *ffice:* Wilson Elem Schl 1063 Superior St Zanesville OH 43701*

N, SUSAN MARIE (FLOOD), General Music Teacher; *b:* MI; *m:* Norman L. III; *c:* Catherine Lynn, Sean Patrick; *ed:* Univ of PA (BA) Music Ed K-12 1984; 24 Credits Conducting, l; *cr:* Sandhills HS Music Tchr 1984-85; Saegertown HS Theatre sic Tchr, Choral Conductor 1986-; *ai:* Barbershop Quartet Dir; h Grd Chorus, 9-12 Chamber Singers, Drama Club Adv; PMEA *fice:* Saegertown HS 18079 Mook Rd Saegertown PA 16433*

N, THOMAS MICHAEL, Assoc Prof of Chem Engrng; *b:* n, SC; *m:* Deborah Lynne; *c:* Maxwell; *ed:* Univ of Mi (BS) Chem 975; CA Inst of Tech (MS) Chem Engrng 1977, (PHD) Chem 980; *cr:* AT&T Bell Labs Distngd Mem of Tech Staff 1980-90; Jniv Assoc Dir 1990-; *ai:* Amer Inst Chem Engrng Stu Chptr Adv; t Chem Engrng 1980-; Amer Chem Soc 1977-; Amer Soc Engrng ; *office:* Cornell Univ Olin Hall Ithaca NY 14853

N, WILLIAM J., Challenge Coordinator; *b:* Bronx, NY; *m:* Jean; ce J., Catherine S.; *ed:* Cathedral Coll (BA) Philosophy 1960; U (STB) Theology 1964; New Schl for Soc Rsrch (MA) Sociology Kings Cty CC Adj Instr 1968-71; NYC CC Adj Instr 1969-71; CS Tchr 1972-; Sullivan Cty CC Adj Asst Prof 1980-; *ai:* Sullivan academic League Acad Coach; Adv: Comp Club, Future Problem Quiz Bowl & Debate Club; AFT 1972-; NYSUT 1972-, Fallsburg 1972-, Pres 1980-82; Dist Grants; *office:* Fallsburgh Jr Sr HS PO Fallsburg NY 12733

, STEPHEN CHARLES, Instrumental Music Teacher; *b:* ton, NY; *ed:* St Univ of NY at Potsdam (BM) Music Ed 1981; Univ M) Percussion Performance 1983; Univ of Calgary Diploma Wind ing 1994; 6 Grad Hrs George Mason Univ; *cr:* Univ of IL Grad sst 1981-83; Midland-Odessa Symphony Orch Prin Percussionst Millikin Univ Instr Percussion, Music Theory 1984-85; Van Wyck strumental Music Tchr, Band Dir 1985-; *ai:* Dir Jazz Ensemble; utchess Cty Music Edctrs Assn 1985-, Pres, VP, Trea, Band Chm, nsemble Chm; NY St Schl Music Assn 1985-, Certified All-St ator; NY St Band Dir Assn; Percussive Art Soc; Natl Band Assn; Jnited Tchr; AFT; Amer Fed of Musicians; Kappa Delta Pi; Phi hi; Woodstock Chamber Orch 1995, Prin Timpanist, Percussionist; aored: Curriculum Guide for Junior High Instrumental Music; Selection Comm for NY St Schl Music Assn; Presented Wkshps; ands Consistendly Scored Ratings of A+, Gold, Gold with Dist at st; *office:* Van Wyck Jr HS Hillside Lake Rd Wappingers Falls NY

S, LAUREN, Assistant Professor; *b:* Miami, FL; *m:* Michael B. *c:* Zachary, Madeline; *ed:* Stanford Univ (BA) Human Bio 1984; opkins Univ (MHS) Maternal, Child Hlth 1986, (SCD) Maternal, lth 1989; Post Doc Univ of FL Ctr for Criminology & Law Stud; oucher Coll Asst Prof 1992-; *ai:* Pre-Law Soc; gy-Anthropology Club Fac Adv; Pub Articles; *office:* Goucher Coll laney Valley Rd Baltimore MD 21204

AM, DARROW G., Professor of Mathematics; *b:* Geneva, NY; *m:* M. Clark; *c:* Matthew, Christopher, Laura; *ed:* St Univ at rt (BS) Math Ed 1963, (MS) Math Ed 1967; Syracuse Univ (MS) 68; *cr:* Middlesex Vly Cntrl Schl Math Tchr 1963-67; Finger Lakes Coll Math Prof 1968-; *ai:* Former Math Dept Coord; Math Stdnts aphing Calculator Resource Person; NY St Math Assn Two Yr IEA 1968-; NY St Schl Bd Assn, Marcus Whitman Bd of Ed ; NSF Grants Grad Stud Schlsp Syracuse Univ 1967-68, SUNY at nton 1973; *office:* Finger Lakes Comm Coll 4355 Lake Shore Dr aigua NY 14424

AM, KATHLEEN, 6th Grade Math & Science Tchr; *b:* Newark, NJ; of Notre Dame (BA) Elem Ed 1971; Boston Coll (MEd) Rel Ed ttnd Western IL Univ, Villanova Univ; *cr:* St Patrick Schl at Glen Grd Tchr 1962-65; St Francis Jr HS at New Britain 7th Grd Tchr ; St Leo at Irvington 7th-8th Grd Tchr 1969-75; St Mary at E Islip 75-80; Prince of Peace 5th & 6th Grd Tchr 1980-; *ai:* Intnl Day; Sci Fair; Math & Sci Coord; NCEA; MCTM 1993-; Natl Sci Fnd Grant; *home:* 200 Main St Sayville NY 11782

DUNHAM, KATHLEEN MARIE (REYNOLDS), Spanish Teacher; *b:* Kenmore, NY; *m:* Mark Angelo; *c:* Adam Jacob, Kaitlyn Marie; *ed:* SUNY Coll at Buffalo (BA) Ed & Span 1987; SUNY at Buffalo (MS) Ed & Span 1992; 20 Post Grad Credit Hrs of Ed; *cr:* North Park MS 8th Grd Span Tchr 1987-; *ai:* Intnl Club Adv 1987; Home Tutor; Interpreter for Cty Jail; LEA & NEA 1987-; WNYFLEC 1989-; NYSFLET 1990-; Kappa Delta Pi 1985-87; Sigma Delta Pi 1985-87; Whos Who HS & Coll Stdnts; *office:* North Park MS 160 Passaic Ave Lockport NY 14094*

DUNHAM, SUSAN SANDRA, Fifth Grade Teacher; *b:* Union, NJ; *c:* Stacey; *ed:* Tusculum Coll (BS) Elem Ed 1968; 4 Credits Children Tech; *cr:* Meml Schl 2nd Grd Tchr 1968-80, 1st Grd Tchr 1981-91, 5th Grd Tchr 1992-; *ai:* Schl Newspaper Adv; NEA 1968-.

DUNKER, ELEANOR VAUGHN (QUAY), Kindergarten Teacher; *b:* Mt Holly, NJ; *m:* Frank E.; *c:* Meredith, Rusty; *ed:* Glassboro St Coll (BA) Early Chldhd 1970; Trenton St Coll (MA) Elem Ed, Rdng; Rdng Specialist, Supervision, Curr Certs; *cr:* Woodbury Pub Schls 5th Grd Tchr 1970-71; Springfield Twp Schl 1st, 3rd Grd, Kndgtn Tchr 1971-; *ai:* Garden Club; Family Math Instr; Kappa Delta Pi 1995-, Corresponding Sec; NJ Kndgtn Assn 1980-; Kndgtn Support Group 1990-, Founder; NJEA 1970-; Springfield Twp Historical Soc; West Jersey Ski Club 1993-; Partners in Ed 1994-; Governor's Tchr Recognition Prgm Tchr of Yr 1987; *office:* Springfield Twp Elem Schl 2146 Jacksonville Rd Jobstown NJ 08041*

DUNKLEBERGER, LINDA STRAW, Secondary Mathematics Teacher; *b:* Wellsboro, PA; *m:* Thomas; *c:* Jason, Rebekah; *ed:* Mansfield St Coll (BS) Math Ed 1972, (MS) Math Ed 1975; *cr:* Sayre HS Math Tchr 1972-77; Mansfield St Coll Math Instr 1980-86; Mansfield HS Math Tchr 1986-; *ai:* Church Chr; NEA & PSEA 1972-; STEA 1986-; Roseville Meth Church 1978-, Treas; Eastern Star Lodge 1990-; *home:* RR 2 Box 2415 Mansfield PA 16933

DUNKLEY, PAULETTE SHIM, Spanish Teacher; *b:* Kingston, Jamaica; *m:* Desmond Anthony; *c:* Akene, Jenelle; *ed:* Lehman Coll (BA) Span 1989; 12 Credits Ed; *cr:* Manufacturers Hanover Teller 1985-87; Four Winds Travel Tour Coord 1987-89; Evander Childs HS Tchr 1989-90; St Rose HS Tchr 1992-; *ai:* Span NHS Moderator; ACTFL, ATSP, FLENJ 1992-; Mount Olivet 1994-, Youth Ldr; *office:* St Rose HS 607 7th Ave Belmar NJ 07719*

DUNKLEY, YVONNE BROWN, Personal & Career Counselor; *b:* Kingston, Jamaica; *c:* Keith, Leon; *ed:* Lesley Coll (BS) Child, Comm 1982; Univ of MA at Boston (MEd) Counseling, Guidance 1988; *cr:* Fernald St Schl MHA, Sup 1968-82; Dept of Soc Services Soc Worker 1982-88; Middlesex Comm Coll Personal, Career Cnslr 1988-; *ai:* Adv Black Unity Club, Adults Returning to Schl 25 Yrs, Gay & Lesbian Stdnts; Dept of MA Amer Legion Americanism Comm; Licensed Mental Hlth Cnslr 1993-; Contributions to Frosh Seminar Manual; Outstanding Foreign Born Citizen Annual Awd.*

DUNLAP, DWIGHT PATRICK, High School Science Teacher; *b:* Hersey, PA; *m:* Joy Barkley; *ed:* Geneva Coll (BS) Bio 1991, (BA) Philosophy 1991; Philadelphia Theological Seminary (MDiv) Theology 1993; *cr:* US Army Reserves Chaplain 1992-; City Center Acad Sci Tchr 1994-; *ai:* Asst Pastor Grace Chapel Rerform Episcopal; Chaplain 228th Avn Rgt; Sr League Street Hockey; Track Coach; US Army Grad Basic Trng; Chaplain Asst Schl, Honor Grad; Commissioned 1st Lev 1995; *office:* City Ctr Acad 1701 Delancey St Philadelphia PA 19103

DUNLAP, ELLYN ATCHISON, Fourth Grade Teacher; *b:* Canton, OH; *m:* David Lynn; *c:* Michael, Matthew, Marc, Mariellyn; *ed:* Malone Coll (BS) Elem Ed 1972; Attnd Akron U, Walsh & Ashland Univ; *cr:* Harlem Springs Elem 3rd Grd Tchr 1973-78; Willis Elem 4th Grd Tchr 1984-; *ai:* Lang Arts Curr Comm; NEA 1973-; First United Meth Church 1962-, Choir Accompanist, Ed & Worship Comms, Jr Church Ldr & Praise Ensemble Pianist; Band Boosters 1984-; Citizens for Excl in Ed Awd 1987; *home:* 5123 Bay Rd SE Carrollton OH 44615

DUNLEAVY, KEVIN M., Dean of Students & Sci Instr; *b:* New Haven, CT; *m:* Christine; *c:* Jack, Kyle; *ed:* Southern CT St Univ (BS) Bio, Sec Ed 1976, (MS) Bio 1989; *cr:* Immaculate HS Sci Dept 1976-, Dean of Stu 1986-; *ai:* Adv Environment Club; Assoc Aths; Ftbl, Sftbl Coach 1976-94; NCEA, DBEA 1976-; Audubon; Nature Conservancy; New Milford Lions 1992-, Exec Bd, Schlsp Chair, Golf Turn Chair; *office:* Immaculate HS 73 Southern Blvd Danbury CT 06810

DUNLEAVY, PATRICIA M., Third Grade Teacher; *b:* Coatesville, PA; *m:* Michael J.; *c:* Michael Jr., Timothy, Christopher; *ed:* West Chester Univ (BS) Elem Ed 1962; Attnd Saint Charles Seminary; *cr:* Friendship Elem 3rd Grd Tchr 1962-64; Coatesville Cath 3rd Grd Tchr 1976-; *ai:* Stu Cncl Adv; NCEA 1976-; *office:* Coatesville Area Cath Elem Sch 605 E Lincoln Hwy Coatesville PA 19320

DUNLEAVY, PAUL D., Life Science Teacher; *b:* Brooklyn, NY; *ed:* SUNY at Purchase (BA) Bio 1985; SUNY at Albany (MA) Ed 1987; *cr:* Rensselaer Polytechnic Inst Adj Prof Tchr Ed 1991-; Troy City Schl Dist Life Sci Tchr 1987-; *ai:* Natl Jr Hon Soc Adv; STANYS 1987-; NASSP, NASSA 1989-; NYS Regents Empire St Challanger Flwshp for Tchrs, Math & Sci Tchr Flwshp; Grad with Hnrs BA Bio; *office:* W. K. Doyle MS 1976 Burdett Ave Troy NY 12180*

DUNLOP, KAREN B., Howard Cty Ed Assn President; *b:* Minneapolis, MN; *m:* John; *c:* John, Andrew; *ed:* Univ of MN (BA) Fr 1962; Univ of MD (MA) Fr 1978; *cr:* Groves HS Tchr 1963-68; Centennial HS Tchr 1979-82; Hammond HS Tchr 1982-95; *ai:* NEA 1962-; Howard Cty Educ Assn 1978-, Pres; *office:* Hammond HS 5080 Dorsey Hall Dr Ellicott City MD 21042

DUNLOP, SANDRA LAHET, Retired High School Hlth Tchr; *b:* New Holland, PA; *m:* R. Graham; *c:* Stephanie Nicholas, Timothy Lahet; *ed:* West Chester Univ of PA (BS) Hlth, PE 1962; PA St of PA Perm Cert; *cr:* Lankenau Schl for Girls K-12th Grd PE Tchr 1962-63; Girl's Club Swimming Instr 1963-64; Bethel Park Schls 9th-12th Grd PE Tchr 1969-93, Hlth Tchr 1993-95; *ai:* Coached Tennis, Sftbl, Vlybl; Sponsored Chrldrs; AFT 1969-; Natl, Co, St AAHPERD, Demonstration Schl Team; Mt Lebanon Bd of Music 1977-; Keynotes 1977-, Bd Mem, Schlsp Co-Chm; Interfaith Care Team for HIV, Aids; Mt Lebanon Women's Golf Assn, Sec; *home:* 1012 Cochran Rd Pittsburgh PA 15243

DUNMYRE, KATHLEEN HALWA, Mathematics Teacher; *b:* New Kensington, PA; *m:* Bruce R.; *c:* Meghan, Brandon, Aaron; *ed:* PA St (BS) Math 1972; Univ of Pittsburgh & IN Univ Masters Equivalency 1981; In-House Cmptr Tech Trng 1994-; *cr:* Springdale HS Math Tchr 1972-; *ai:* PA St Eisenhower Project; Mid Sts Region of Coll Bd AP Calculus Placement; NEA 1972-, Assn for Supervision & Curr Dev; PSEA, AVEA 1972-; NCTM, Allegheny Cty Alliance for Pub Schls, Math Cncl of Western PA, PA Cncl of Tchrs of Math 1992-; All-Star Educator 1994 & 1995; SHS Internship Supvr 1990-; Ofcl Judge Math League 6th Annual Acad Triathalon; Numerous Pre-Stu Tchrs Supvr 1984-; Cooperating Tchr for Stu Tchrs 1976 & 1992; SHS Mentor Tchr 1994-95; Author of Calculus II, Calculus I, Algebra II & Basic Algebra Curr Guides.

DUNN, ANN STALFORD, English Teacher; *b:* Sayre, PA; *c:* Henry, Bryant; *ed:* Mansfield Univ (BS) Eng 1974; Elmira Coll (MS) Ed 1993; *cr:* Bradford Cty Action Instr 1988-90; Towanda HS Eng Tchr 1990-; Lackawanna Jr Coll Adj Prof; *ai:* Instrl Support Team; NCTE 1991-; PASCD 1995-; ACIS; AAUW; MADD; Presbyn Church; *office:* Towanda HS 1 High School Dr Towanda PA 18848*

DUNN, BILLY RAY, Associate Professor of Ed; *b:* Vago, WV; *m:* Cynthia Lynn Parsons; *c:* Laura Rutherford, Lisa, Nicholas Boyles; *ed:* WV Univ (BS) Ag Ed 1956, (MS) Ag Ed 1962; Ball St Univ (EDD) Educl Admin 1973; Marshall Univ (MS) Adult Ed 1988; CA St at Los Angeles Post Grad Stud Counseling; *cr:* Grant Cty Schls Tchr, Cnslr, Vice Prin 1956-67; Potomac St Coll Counseling Ctr Dir 1967-69; Shepherd Coll Dept of Ed Prof, Chm 1969-80; Marshall Univ Voc Ed Assoc Prof 1980-85; Randolph Cty Schls Supt 1985-91; Marietta Coll Ed Assoc Prof 1991-; *ai:* Masters Arts in Ed Adv; WVEA, NEA 1956-, Pres Cty Assn; Kiwanis 1956-, Pres; Doctoral Assistantship Ball St Univ; Grad Assistantship WV Univ; *home:* PO Box 1141 Marietta OH 45750

DUNN, CATHY MARTINE, Math Teacher; *b:* Erie, PA; *c:* Kimberly, Jennifer, Heather; *ed:* John Carroll U (BA) Math 1974; Masters Equivalent 42 Grad Hrs Math, Ed; *cr:* Greenview Jr HS Math 7th-8th Grd Tchr 1974-81; Beachwood HS Geometry Tchr 1981-82; Regina HS Math Specialist 1982-92; Brush HS Math Tchr 1992-; *ai:* Visions Comm 1994-95; Girls Sftbl Coach 1976-82; NEA 1974-; *office:* Charles F. Brush HS 4875 Glenlyn Rd Lyndhurst OH 44124

DUNN, CHARLES RAYMOND, English Instructor; *b:* Yonkers, NY; *m:* Carol; *c:* Carlene, Kevin; *ed:* Marist Coll (BA) Eng 1968; Post Grad Stud at NY Univ & SUNY at New Paltz; *cr:* Beacon HS Eng Instr 1968-; *ai:* Frosh, Soph, Jr, Sr & Ski Club Adv; NEA; *home:* 30 Deerfield Pl Beacon NY 12508

DUNN, DWIGHT ANTHONY, School Counselor; *b:* Paducah, KY; *m:* Pamela Jane Hicks; *c:* Lisa D. Stortz, Brandy S., Nicholas I.; *ed:* Northern KY Univ (BA) Elem Ed 1987; Xavier Univ (MED) Schl Cnslng 1992; Post Grad Hrs, Miami Univ Post; *cr:* Park Hills Elem Schl Tchr 1987-88; Woodland MS Tchr, Dean, Ath Dir 1988-92; Madeira Jr Sr HS Schl Cnslr 1992-; *ai:* Var Girls Vlybl Coach; OSCA 1993-.

DUNN, EDWIN JAMES, Biology & Chemistry Teacher; *b:* Cumberland, MD; *ed:* Frostburg St Univ (BS) Bio 1988, (MA) Ed 1995; Tchr Cert 1989; *cr:* Allegany Comm Coll Bio Lab Instr 1989-90; Flintstone Schl 7th-12th Grd Sci Tchr 1990-91; Allegany HS Bio & Chem Tchr 1991-, Sci Dept Chr 1994-; *ai:* Sci Fair Coord; NHS Adv; MD Assn of Sci Tchrs & NEA 1990-; Tchr of the Yr; *office:* Alleghany HS 616 Sedgewick St Cumberland MD 21502

DUNN, EMMARAE ENGLISH, Language Arts Teacher; *b:* Sharon, PA; *m:* Peter-Detlef; *ed:* Thiel Coll (BA) Eng 1967; Gannon Univ (MA) Eng 1971; Millerville 3 Post Grad Credits; Gannon 12 Post Grad Credits; *cr:* Shore Jr HS Eng, Rdng Tchr 1967-69; Westlake MS Eng, Lang Arts 1971-; *ai:* Fromewuik for Literacy 1991-; MEA, PSEA, NEA 1971-, Bldg Rep; Delta Hoppa Ganna 1987-, VP; NWPCTE 1971-, Bd Mem; Natl Writing Project 1987-; Thiel Womens Club 1980-; New Standards Project 1995-; PSEA-POE Outcome, Assessment Cadre I; Millcreek Twp Schl Dist Lead Tchr; Tchr Mentor; Dept Chprsn; Lang Arts Steering Comm; Portfolio Project; Writing Process Presenter.*

DUNN, GAIL PEDERZOLI, Professor of English; *b:* Springfield, MA; *m:* John H.; *ed:* Elmira Coll (BA) Eng 1969; Univ of WI (MA) Eng 1970; Springfield Coll (MED) Guidance, Psych Svcs 1976; *cr:* Springfield Tech Comm Coll Eng Prof 1970-; *ai:* NEA, MTA 1980-; NCTE 1978-; NISOD Award for Excellence in Tchng 1995; Co-Chair Ovations by STCC Honors Pgm 1995-; Dev and Tch Women in Lit I Class (1st Women's Stud at STCC) 1974- & Women in Lit II 1974-; *office:* Springfield Tech Comm Coll 1 Armory Sq Springfield MA 01105

DUNN, GEORGIA STILWELL, English Teacher; *b:* Columbus, OH; *m:* Wayne Lewis; *ed:* OH Univ (BS) Ed & Comprehensive Eng 1974; Xavier Univ (MED) Rdng 1985; *cr:* New Richmond HS Eng Tchr 1974-90; Wilmington HS Eng Tchr & Dept Chair 1990-; *ai:* Cooperative Learning Tchr Trainer; Venture Capital Grant Writer; Newspaper Adv; Eng Dept Chair; NEA & OEA 1974-; Wilmington Ed Assn 1990-, Sec & Ed of Newsletter; Jrnlsm Ed Assn 1993-; Jrnlism Assoc of OH Scls Bd of Dir; Bethany United Church of Christ 1980-, Treas, Choir & Sunday Schl Tchr; Amer Contract Bridge League 1987-; Wilmington Schls Fnd Grant; Amer Heart Assn & Cancer Soc Vol; *home:* 150 E Forest Ave South Lebanon OH 45065*

DUNN, JENNIFER S. (WEST), Fifth Grade Teacher; *b:* Prentress, WV; *m:* James Richard Jr.; *c:* Michael, Jason; *ed:* Lee Bible Coll (BS) Elem K-8th 1970; Univ of Dayton (MS) Rdng 1993; *cr:* Newark City Schls 6th Grd Tchr 1970-74; South Western City Schls 1st-5th Grd Tchr 1974-77; Columbus City Schls 2nd-5th Grd Tchr 1985-; *ai:* Safety Patrol Supv; Cafeteria Duty, Sci Club, 5th Grd Camp Organizer; Summer Schl Tchr, Tech Comm; NEA 1970-; COTA 1970-; CEA 1985-, Bldg Rep; Red Cross 1990-91, Vol; *office:* Clinton Elem Schl 10 Clinton Heights Ave Columbus OH 43202*

DUNN, JENNY BARRETT, Chemistry Teacher; *b:* Jamaica, West Indies; *c:* Kanika; *ed:* NY City Tech Coll (AAS) Chem 1981; St Francis Coll (BS) Chem 1984; Long Island Univ (MS) Ed 1992; 30 Credit Hrs; *cr:* Boys & Girls HS Chem Tchr 1985-87; Consolidated Edison Lab Tech 1987-88; Mass Transit Authority Lab Tech 1989; John Jay HS Chem Tchr 1989-; *ai:* Tchr of Yr by Arista 1994-95; Tandy Outstdng Tchr of Yr 1994-1995; *office:* John Jay HS 237 7th Ave Brooklyn NY 11215

DUNN, JOAN MARIE, Physical Education Teacher; *b:* Oneida, NY; *ed:* Brockport St (BS) PE 1979; Cortland St (Ma) PE 1988; *cr:* Village of Camden Lifeguard & Recreation Instr 1975-77, Summer Recreation Coord 1990-93; Camden Cntrl Schl PE Tchr 1983-; *ai:* Var Vlybl & Sftbl Coach; AAHPERD 1994-; NYSUT 1983-; Camden Cntrl Schl Female Ath of Yr 1976; Brockport St Deans List 1979; *office:* Camden Cntrl Schl 51 3rd St Camden NY 13316

DUNN, MARY M., Theology Teacher; *b:* Philadelphia, PA; *m:* Edward P. III; *ed:* Gwynedd Mercy Coll (BA) Hum, Ed 1970; 21 Credits West Chester Univ, PA St Univ, Carlow Coll; 9 Credits Towards MA Theology St Charles Borromeo Seminary; *cr:* St Anastasia's Schl 5th Grd Lang Arts, Sci Tchr 1970-75; St Francis De Sales Schl 2nd Gr, Sacramental Prgm Tchr 1977-83; Delcroft Elem Schl 1st Grd Tchr 1984-86; Archbishop Carroll HS Jr, Sr Theology Tchr 1992-93; St Maria Goretti HS Soph, Jr, Sr Theology Tchr 1993-; *ai:* Goretti Peace Ambassador Corps; Writing Club; NCEA 1970-, Outstdng Elem Tchr of Amer Awd 1975; *office:* St Maria Goretti HS 1736 S 10th St Philadelphia PA 19148*

DUNN, PATRICIA BROWN, Hlth & Physical Education Tchr; *b:* Summit, NJ; *m:* Thomas M.; *c:* Ryan P., Kevin P.; *ed:* Marymount Coll (AA) PE 1970; Bowling Green St Univ (BA) Hlth & PE 1972; *cr:* Brick Twp HS 9th-12th Grd Hlth & PE Tchr 1972-; *ai:* Swim Team Asst Coach; Sailing on Barnegat Bay Jr Coord; NJHPERD 1985-; CPR, Instr, Vol; Metedeconk River Yacht Club, Exec Bd; Peer Mediator, Affirmative Action 1991-.*

DUNN, PAULA FERNANDEZ, Spanish Teacher; *b:* Washington, DC; *m:* Paul Winston Sr.; *c:* Kristina, Paul Jr.; *ed:* Georgetown Coll (BA) Span 1974; Xavier Univ Post Grad Stud Cnslng, Ed; *cr:* Beavercreek Schls Span Tchr 1974-75; Northwest Local Schls Span Tchr 1975-; *ai:* Span Club, Span Hnr Soc, Span Elem Prgms Adv; Curr Comm for Span Dept; PTA Span for Fun Adv; OH Frgn Lang Assn, NEA, OEA 1974-; Amer Assn of Tchrs of Span, Portuguese 1989-; Sigma Delta Pi 1973-; Pisgah Heights Bapt Church 1990-, Sunday Schl Yth Tchr, Puppeteer Dir; Golden Apple

Achiever Awd 1994; Ashland Oil Tchr Achvmt Awrds Prgm 1994; Cincinnati Enquirer Tchr Recognition Awd 1994; *office:* Colerain Sr HS 8801 Cheviot Rd Cincinnati OH 45251

DUNN, ROBERT W., English Teacher; *b:* Peabody, MA; *m:* Cynthia Christine Driscoll; *c:* Jessica, Sean, Ryan; *ed:* Salem St Coll (BSEd) Ed 1970, (MED) Ed 1989, (CAGS) Ed 1995; Harvard Univ 3 Credits; *cr:* Saugus Pub Schls Eng Tchr 1975-81; Adams-Russel Cable Systems Pub Access Coord 1982-85; Beverly Pub Schls Eng Tchr 1985-; *ai:* Renaissance Fair Adv; Subcommittee for Instruction; Scheduling Comm; Stu Efficiancy Comm; NEA 1985-; Amer Red Cross 1975-, Blood Donor; *office:* Beverly HS 100 Sohier Rd Beverly MA 01915*

DUNN, ROGER C., Biology Teacher; *b:* Canton, PA; *m:* Tricia; *c:* Janine Miller, Ryan, Elizabeth, Rachele Kauffmann, Shelly Dosch, Jocelyn Hamsher; *ed:* Goshen Coll (BS) Bio 1963; MI St Univ (MS) Bio 1969; Notre Dame Univ AP Bio; *cr:* Millersburg HS Bio, Sci Tchr 1963-66; Hiland HS Bio Tchr 1966-; *ai:* Ath Dir; Coach Bsktbl, Bsbl, Soccer, Vlybl; Dir Sci Fairs; Class Spon; OEA, NEA 1963-; EHTA 1966-; Acad Booster Club 1980-; Ath Booster Club 1966-; Sci Fnd Grant; *office:* Hiland HS PO Box 275 Berlin OH 44610

DUNN, THOMAS J., Math Teacher & Dept Head; *b:* Jamestown, NY; *m:* Shelva Jean Cochran; *c:* Robin, Thomas; *ed:* PA St Univ (BS) Sec Ed Math, Sci 1962; 12 Post Grad Credit Hrs; *cr:* Youngsville HS Math Tchr 1962-73; Sheffield Jr Sr HS Math Tchr 1973-; *ai:* Asst Ftbl, Head Boys Track Coach; Schl Musicals Past Asst; NEA, PSEA 1963-; Beathany Luth Church, Treas; Ldrs of Scndry Ed 1972; *home:* 106 Church St Sheffield PA 16347

DUNN, WAYNE LEWIS, Eng, Jrnlsm & Photography Tchr; *b:* Middletown, OH; *m:* Georgia Anne Stilwell; *ed:* Wilmington Coll (BFA) Theatre, Hum 1974; Xavier Univ (MA) Eng 1983; Jrnlsm, Photojournalism Hrs OH Univ, Ball St Univ; *cr:* Lebanon HS Eng Tchr, Jrnlsm Tchr 1974-; *ai:* Newspaper Adv; Dir Stu Ldrshp Forum; Lang Arts Comm; OEA, NEA 1974-, Comm Sec, Treas, Sec; Jrnlsm Assn OH Schls 1987-, VP, Pres; Jrnlsm Ed Assn 1990-; Natl Press Photographers Assn 1994-; Bethany United Church of Christ 1962-, Trustee, Choir Dir; Amer Rose Soc; Dow Jones Flwshp; Project Excl Tchr of Excl; Pub Articles C-Jet Magazine; *office:* Lebanon HS 160 Miller Rd Lebanon OH 45036

DUNNAVAN, JAY C.,JR., Math Teacher; *b:* Lexington, KY; *m:* Carol Chamblin; *c:* Elizabeth Ann, David Alan; *ed:* Morehead St Univ (BA) Jrnlsm 1980; Minor Math 1986; *cr:* Whiteoak HS Math Tchr 1986-; *ai:* Stained Glass Hobbyist; NEA, BTEA 1986-; *home:* 463 S Shawnee Rd Maysville KY 41056

DUNNE, ANNE MARIE, Eighth Grade Teacher; *b:* Darby, PA; *ed:* Temple Univ (BBA) Mrktng 1987; St Josephs Univ 6 Hrs Elem Ed; *cr:* St Barnabas Tchr 1987-; *ai:* Math Coord; Yrbk Moderator; NCEA 1987-; *office:* St Barnabas Schl 6328 Buist Ave Philadelphia PA 19142

DUNNE, JOHN BENHAM, Fifth Grd Teacher & Asst Prin; *b:* Brooklyn, NY; *c:* Seth, Kristen; *ed:* Castleton St Coll (BS) Elem Ed 1973, (MAEd) Curr, Instruction 1982; 40 Addl Credit Hrs Math, Rdng, Testing Methods, MS Ed Techniques; *cr:* Orwell Village Schl Fifth Grd Tchr 1974-; *ai:* Addison-Rutland Supervisory Dist Relicensing Bd; 7th-8th Grd Spelling Team Coach, Adv; Soc Stud Curr Comm; Checker Tournament Adv; Advy Tchr; NEA Local, Addison-Rutland Ed Assn 1974-, Chief Negotiator, Grievance Comm Chm; Co Authored Article 1989; Addison-Rutland Sup Dist Spec Svc Awd 1988; A-RSU Tchr of Yr Awd 1992.

DUNNE, PATRICK FRANK, Social Studies Teacher; *b:* New York, NY; *m:* Linda Librizzi; *c:* Robert, Patrick, Danny; *ed:* Manhattan Coll (BA) His, Rel 1980; 9 Credits Ed Grad Courses Queens Coll; *cr:* Monsignor Scanlan HS Rel, His Tchr 1980-84; Nazareth Regnl HS Rel, His Tchr 1984-87; Holy Angels Acad Rel, His Tchr 1987-; *ai:* NHS Comm Mem; Moderator Tomorrow's Voices, Origins of Amer TV; Sci-Fi Club; Sr-Soph Picnic; NCEA 1980-; *home:* 133 Harcourt Ave Bergenfield NJ 07621

DUNNE, SHEILA A., Health & PE Teacher; *b:* Summit, NJ; *ed:* Kean Coll (BA) Hlth, PE 1983; Montclair St Univ (MS) Sports Admin 1993; *cr:* Mendham HS 9-12 Grd Tchr, Coach 1984-88; Summit HS 9-12 Grd Tchr, Coach 1988-; *ai:* Head Field Hockey, Vlybl Coach; NJEA 1983-; AAHPERD 1984-; Grad Symposium Speaker; *office:* Summit Sr HS 125 Kent Place Blvd Summit NJ 07901*

DUNNETT, CINDY JACOBS, Preschool Teacher; *b:* Dallas, TX; *m:* Craig; *c:* Melissa, Brian; *ed:* Cedarville Coll (BA) Elem Ed 1980; *cr:* Emmanuel Baptist 1st Grd Tchr 1980-85, Preschl Tchr 1993-; *ai:* Word of Life Club Ldr; Cherub Chair Dir; ACSI; CWA 1995-; *office:* Emmanuel Baptist Chrstn Schl 4207 Laskey Toledo OH 43623

DUNNETTE, J. KEVIN, HS Language Arts Teacher; *b:* Cincinnati, OH; *m:* Sharyn Lyn Dilley; *c:* Chase, Jordan; *ed:* Muskingum Coll (BA) Comm & Ed 1982; Post Grad Hrs Xavier Univ & Univ of Cincinnati; *cr:* Oak Hills HS Tchr 1983-86; New Miami HS Tchr 1986-; *ai:* Ath Dir; Yrbk & Newspaper adv; Vlybl, Boys & Girls Track Coach; NEA, OEA 1983-; Ath Coaching Awds in Bsktbl & Vlybl; *office:* New Miami HS 600 Seven Mile Ave Hamilton OH 45011

DUNNICK, MARGARET LEIGH, French & History Teacher; *b:* Superior, WI; *m:* John; *c:* John; *ed:* DePauw Univ (BA) Ec 1966; 30 Credit Hrs Ec, His Univ of MN; *cr:* Westlake HS Tchr, Soc Stud, Frgn Lang Dept Chair 1971-; *ai:* Citizen Bee, Cncl on World Affairs Advs; St Advy Comm Frgn Lang Model Curr; NEA; OH Frgn Lang Assn; OH Soc Stud Assn; Amer Tchrs of Fr; Co-Tchr of Yr; Outstdng Tchr Awd Univ of Chicago Nom Twice; *office:* Westlake HS 27830 Hilliard Blvd Westlake OH 44145

DUNNING, DONNA M., Psychology & Sociology Teacher; *b:* Chestnut Hill, PA; *ed:* Lycoming Coll (BA) His, Govt 1967; Kutztown St Coll (MED) Soc Sci 1973, (MA) Cnslng Psych 1985; *cr:* US Govt, Office of Ec Opp Vista Vol 1967-68; Pennridge HS Soc Stud Tchr 1969-; *ai:* Cultural Diversity Club Adv; Commencement Speakers Comm Adv, Facilitator; NEA, PSEA 1969-; PEA 1969-, Bldg Rep, Distngd Svc Awd; *office:* Pennridge HS 1228 N 5th St Perkasie PA 18944

DUNNING, VALERIE PIKE, English Teacher; *b:* Massena, NY; *m:* William L.; *c:* Keely, Joshua; *ed:* St Lawrence Univ (BA) Eng 1971; 30+ Post Grad Hrs; *cr:* Brushton-Moira Cntrl Scndry Eng Tchr 1971-; *ai:* Sr Class Play Dir; Jr Class Adv; Clarkson Univ Kraft & General Foods & Brushton-Moira Bus & Schl Partnership Comm; Brushton-Moira Tchrs Assoc 1971-, Past Sec; NY St United Tchrs 1975-; *office:* Brushton-Moira Schl Gale Rd Brushton NY 12916

DUNSMORE, CATHY COATS, Early Multiage Experience Tchr; *b:* Port Huron, MI; *m:* David Charles; *ed:* MI St Univ (BA) Tchr Ed 1986; St Clair Cty Comm Coll Transfer Ed; Enrolled Masters of Ed Univ of ME; *cr:* Head Start Tchr 1987; St Edwards on the Lake First Grd Tchr 1987-88; Ft Fairfield Elem SAD #20 First Grd Tchr 1989-91, Kndgtn Tchr 1991-94, Early Multi-Age Experience Tchr 1994-; *ai:* Family Math; Multi-Age Reflective Practice Group; Univ of ME Tchr Trng Prgm; MSAD #20 Svc Learning Project; MSU Alumni Assn 1988-; IRA, NAEYC, ME Tchrs Assn, Ft Fairfield Tchrs Assn 1989-; Natl Assn of Multiage Edctrs 1995-; Bldg Blocks of Rdng Grant; Dev Early Multi-Age Experience Prgm; *home:* RR 3 Box 24 Caribou ME 04736

DUNSON, CLENISTINE NORVELL, Bus & Industry Prep Teacher; *b:* Winnsboro, LA; *m:* Clyde G. Jr.; *c:* Shamaal N'ge Blaise; *ed:* Wiley Coll (BS) Bus Ed 1969; 27 Grad Work Credit Hrs; *cr:* Harrisburg HS Bus Tchr 1970; Harrisburg Intermediate Schl Bus Ed Tchr; Harrisburg Steelton-Highspire Vo Tech Bus Ed Tchr; Harrisburg HS Bus Tchr, Dir, Tchr Bus & Industry Prep 1991-; *ai:* Schl Store Dir Operated by Stdnts, Dir Operation of Stu owned & Operated Bus At Local Mall; NEA, HEA, PSEA 1970-; Shiloh Church of God in Christ 1971-, Pastor's Sec, Letter of Commendation Outstanding Mem; Greater Harrisburg Chapter NAACP Sec; Ec Summit Scholar, St Treas Catherine Baker Knoll Leadership Awds 1992; Rotary Club Tchr of Month, Supt's Natl Forum Black Admins Outstanding Svc to Youth in Comm Awds, Senate of PA Citation, Harrisburg City Cncl Resolution, Dauphin Cty Commissioners Congratulatory Letter, Channel 27's Class Act Tchr All 1993; *office:* Harrisburg HS John Harris Cam 2451 Market St Harrisburg PA 17103

DUNSTAN, DONALD LEE, English Department Chairman; *b:* Jamestown, NY; *m:* Patricia Marie Bird; *c:* Sandra Jean, William Bryant; *ed:* Cedarville Coll (BA) Eng, PE 1967; Central St Univ (MED) PE 1969; Univ of Dayton (MA) Eng 1975; Attnd Miami Univ at OH 1983; *cr:* Cedarville Coll PE Instr 1967-68; Goshen HS Eng Tchr 1968-69; Greenon HS Eng Tchr, Chm 1969-82, 1985-; Xenia Chrstn Day Schl Headmaster 1982-85; Athletic Director; *ai:* Track, Bsktbl, Bsbl Coach; Class & Newspaper Adv; Cedarville Coll Tchr Ed Comm; North Central Evaluation Chm 1990-91, 1994; NCTE, Eng Leadership 1975-; Modern Lang Assn 1985-; AFT 1980-; Emmanuel Bapt Church 1967-, Deacon 6 Yrs; Outstanding Cooperating Tchr Wittenberg Univ 1980; Excl in Tchng Springfield OH 1990-91; OH North Cntrl Comm Appreciation Awd 1991; Great Expectations Featured Tchr Channel 2 Dayton OH 1991; *office:* Greenon H S 3950 S Tecumseh Rd Springfield OH 45502*

DUNSTON, GREGORY ALAN, Mathematics Teacher; *b:* Connellsville, PA; *m:* Donna M. Chupella; *c:* Jill, Kelly, Shaun, Erin; *ed:* California St Univ at PA (BS) Math 1971; Western MD Coll (MED) Guidance, Counseling 1974; Montgomery Coll Math Instruction; *cr:* Woodward HS Math Tchr 1971-87; Walter Johnson HS 1987-; *ai:* Cross Cntry, Swimming, Diving, Track Field Coach; Ldr Recreation Club; Twinbrook Pool 1982-, Swim Team Rep; Richard Montgomery HS Booster's Club; Montgomery Cty Swim, Track Coach of Yr; Nom Agnes Myers Washington Post Tchr of Yr; *office:* Walter Johnson HS 6400 Rock Spring Dr Bethesda MD 20814

DUNTON, THOMAS JOSEPH, Biology Teacher; *b:* St Albans, NY; *m:* Frances; *c:* Michael, Andrew; *ed:* Hofstra Univ (BS) Bio 1971; SUNY at Albany 45 Credit Hrs; *cr:* Smithtown Schls 7th Grd Gen Sci Tchr 1974-75; South Cntry Schls Bio Tchr 1975-95; *ai:* Outing Club Adv 1980-85; Stdnts for Environmental Quality 1988-93; Sr Class Adv 1994-; HS Shared Decision Making Team 1994-.

DUNWORTH, DONNA COSTANZO, Eng, Sci & Cmptr Tchr; *b:* St Marys, PA; *m:* Francis E.; *c:* Brent A.; *ed:* Mercyhurst Coll (BA) Comprehensive Eng 1968; Attnd PA St Univ; *cr:* St Marys Area MS Lang Arts & Substitute Tchr 1968-85; Holy Rosary Parochial Schl Eng, Sci & Cmptr Sci Tchr 1986-; *ai:* 6th Grd Washington Trip Chprsn; Yrbk Adv; Schl Bd Tchr Rep; Curr Comm Accelerated Reader coord; Schl's Assistive Tech Rep; NEA 1968-77; PSEA 1968-77; Amer Heart Assn Vol 1968-78; Cub Scout Den Mother 1979-82; Knothole Youth Bsbl Vol 1979-90; PTO Comm Mem; *home:* 328 Mill St Johnsonburg PA 15845

DUPEE, SHARYN MARIE (DESANTY), 7th-8th Grade English Teacher; *b:* North Adams, MA; *m:* Richard F.; *c:* Nichole, Richard Jr., Jamieson; *ed:* North Adams St Coll (BS) MS Ed 1990; Currently Enrolled in MA Prgm; *cr:* St Stanislaus Kostka Schl 7th & 8th Grd Engl, SS Tchr 1990-94; Searls MS 7th-8th Grd Eng Tchr 1994-; *ai:* JV Sftbl Coach Mc Cann Tech Voc HS 1992-94; MA Tchrs Assn 1994-; Who's Who Among Amers Stdnts; *home:* 19 Forest St North Adams MA 01247*

DUPLISSEA, LYNDA A., English Teacher; *b:* Weymouth, MA; *m:* Herb V.; *ed:* Framingham St (BA) Eng 1978; Post Grad Stud in The Region & The Imagination at USM; 6 Credit Hrs Grad Courses at UMO; *cr:* Weymouth Pub Schls 7th-12th Grd Eng Tchr 1978-82; Dist 10 New Brunswick 9th-12th Grd Soc Stud Tchr 1982-83; Union 106 Calais 9th-12th Grd Eng Tchr 1983-; *ai:* US Acad Decathlon Coach; Journey for Change Steering Comm; NHS & JMG Fac Adv; NCTE 1978-; ME Tchrs Assn 1983-; Calais Ed Assn 1983-, Pres; ME Collaborative Assn 1995-; Trout Grant Recipient; Wabenaki Ed Cncl Presentor; *office:* Calais HS 22B River Rd Calais ME 04619

DUPNOCK, LORI ANNE, English Teacher; *b:* Johnstown, PA; *ed:* U of Pittsburgh at Johnstown (BA) Eng 1993; 3 Hrs MATE IN U of PA; *cr:* Bishop Mc Cort HS Eng Tchr 1993-; *ai:* Drama Club Adv; Ski Club Chaperone; NCSTA 1993-, Asst Bldg Rep; *home:* 215 Second St St Michael PA 15951*

DUPONT, CAROLE H., Professor of Biology; *b:* Brooklyn, NY; *c:* William, Kimberly Dupont Teevin, Necolle Peterson; *ed:* Amer Intnl Coll (BS) Bio 1961, (MA) Bio 1969; *cr:* Southwest Jr HS Sci Tchr, Grafton HS Sci Tchr, CHicopi HS Sci Tchr; Springfield Tech Comm Coll Bio Prof 1980-; *ai:* Kenpo Karate 4th Degree Black Belt; Vee Arnes Jetsu 7th Degree Black Belt; Rape Agression Defense Certfd Inst; Tchng Martial Arts, 2 Credit RAD Course; NEA 1980-; Fire Commissioner; St Staninslaw Home, Schl Asst Preschl, Treas; Heart Assn; League of Women Voters; March of Dimes; Writer Karate Intnl, Martial Arts Magazine; *office:* Springfield Tech Comm Coll Armory Square Springfield MA 01105

DUPPSTADT, MARGARET LOUISE, 4th Grade Teacher; *b:* New Kensington, PA; *ed:* Indiana Univ PA (BS) Elem Ed 1981, (MEd) Elem Ed 1982; *cr:* Kiski Area Schl Dist 1st & 3rd Grd Tchr 1982-83, 5th Grd Tchr 1983-84, Kindergarten & 3rd Grd Tchr 1984-85, 1st Grd Tchr 1985-86, Kindergarten 1986-87, 1st Grd Tchr 1987-89, Kindergarten Tchr 1989-92, 5th Grd Tchr 1992-93, 4th Grd Tchr 1993-; *ai:* NSEA, PSEA, KAEA 1982-; *office:* Kiski Area School District 200 Poplar St Vandergrift PA 15690

DUPRE, KAREN COTE, French & Spanish Teacher; *b:* Meriden, CT; *m:* Christopher James; *ed:* Nazareth Coll (BA) Fr, Scndry Ed 1988; Miami Univ of OH (MAT) Fr 1990; *cr:* Haddam-Killingworth HS Fr, Span Tchr 1990-; *ai:* Frgn Lang Dept Rep; Tchr Admin Liaison Comm; Healthy Comm Initiative Comm; NEA, CEA, HKEA 1990-; COLT 1991-; ACTFL 1994-; Tchr Grant 1994; *office:* Haddam-Killingworth HS Little City Rd Higganum CT 06441*

DUPUIS, CAROLYN WHITENETT, Business Teacher; *b:* Holyoke, MA; *m:* Richard J.; *ed:* Salem St Coll (BS) Bus Ed 1968; *cr:* Lawrence Jr HS Bus Tchr 1968-69; Holyoke HS Bus Tchr 1969-; *ai:* NEA, MTA, HTA 1970-; *office:* Holyoke HS 500 Beech St Holyoke MA 01040

DUQUE, GUILLERMO, Bilingual Social Studies Tchr; *b:* Colombia, South America; *m:* Maria Elena Henao; *c:* Angela M., Sara, Jorge A., Richard; *ed:* Santiago de Cali Univ (JD) Law & Pol Sci 1975; St John's Univ (MS) Scndry Ed 1994; 27 Credits Intensive Tchr Inst Biling Ed NY St Ed Dept 1992; *cr:* Colombian Ministry of Hlth Legal Cnsl 1978-83; San Buenaventura Univ Adj Prof Law Schl 1984-89; Jamaica HS Biling Soc Stud Tchr 1990-94; Long Beach HS Biling Soc Stud Tchr 1994-; *ai:* PAVE Prgm Career Edctr; Translator to Span Lang; AFT, NABE 1990-; Circulo dela Hispanidad 1994-; Cafh Fnd 1989-; Textbooks Pub Introduccion al Derecho 1987, Legislacion Administrativa 1988; Cert of Acad Excl MA Prgm St John's Univ 1994; *office:* Long Beach HS 322 Lagoon Dr W Long Beach NY 11561*

DURANT, ROSEMARY DERRY, Fifth Grade Teacher; *b:* Bellaire, OH; *m:* Jeff; *c:* Jeff; *ed:* OH Univ (BS) Elem Ed 1973, (MLS) Liberal Stud 1992; *cr:* St Joseph's Elem Third Grd Tchr 1973-76; Bellaire City Schls Third, Fifth, Sixth, Seventh Grd Tchr 1976-; *ai:* Rdng Comm; I[...] Mini-Course Dev; Bellaire Ed Assn 1976-, Pres 3 Times, S[...] Grievance Chair, Negotiations Team; OH Ed Assn, NEA 1976-[...] Intnl Rdng Assn 1985-; Bellaire Schls Advy Comm 1986-, Pres E[...] Ward PTA 1984-, Treas, Educator of Yr 1992; City Advy Comm[...] Field Outstanding Achvmt Alumni Awd 1992; *home:* 4524 H[...] Bellaire OH 43906*

DURANTE, JOANN SENNETTI, Assistant Principal; *b:* East[...] Richard; *c:* Louise, Christopher; *ed:* Bloomsburg Univ (BS) B[...] 1978, (BS) Bus Ed 1979; Lehigh Univ (MS) Ed Admin 1991;[...] Univ Cnslng Credits; *cr:* Bus Tchr 1979-93; Bus Dept Chprsn[...] Asst Prin 1994-; *ai:* NAASP; NEA; *office:* Liberty HS 1115 [...] Bethlehem PA 18018*

DURANTE, LEA R., Social Studies Teacher; *ed:* OH Univ (BS)[...] Comp 1980; Univ of Dayton (MS) Ed Admin 1992; *cr:* Goods [...] Mgmt 1980-82; Wilson Furniture Mgmt 1982-85; Shadyside [...] 1985-; *ai:* Stu Cncl; Debate Team Adv; Close up Govt Stud Pgm [...] & OEA 1985; Article Pub; *office:* Shadyside HS 3890 Lin[...] Shadyside OH 43947

DURBIN, JEFFREY ALLEN, Science Department Head; *b:* [...] WV; *m:* Charlene Marie Phillips; *ed:* Muskingum C (BS) Bio[...] Buckeye North Jr HS Sci Tchr 1982-84; Buckeye South HS[...] 1984-88; Buckeye Southwest HS Sci Tchr 1988-90; Buckeye Lo[...] Tchr 1990-; *ai:* Head Var Boys Bsktbl Coach; Sci & Var Club[...] Club; NEA, OEA, Local, NSTA 1982-; Audubon Soc; Nature Con[...] Natl Wildlife, Trout Unlimited; *office:* Buckeye Local HS Rd 2[...] Rayland OH 43943

DURCHIN, STEVEN ANDREW, Technology Education Te[...] Pottstown, PA; *m:* Elizabeth Ann Hoerner; *c:* Amy, Molly; *ed:* M[...] Univ (BA) Lbrl Arts, Art 1981; Cert Indstrl Arts 1987; MS Equin[...] *cr:* Red Lion Area Jr HS Tech Ed Tchr 1987-; *ai:* PSEA, NE[...] Article Pub; *office:* Red Lion Area Jr H S 200 Country Club Rd[...] PA 17356

DURFEE, SANDRA SUNDQUIST, English Dept Chai[...] Manchester, CT; *m:* David R.; *c:* David Jr., Susan; *ed:* Brown U[...] Eng Lit 1957; John Hopkins (MLA) Liberal Arts 1988; Attnd Yeat[...] Inst, Oxford Univer Summer Schl; *cr:* Norwich HS Tchr 1962-64;[...] HS Tchr 1964-80; St Pauls Schl for Girls Chair, Eng Tchr 1981-;[...] Tchr; BLack Awareness Club Adv; NCTE 1962-; *office:* St Paul's[...] Girls 11232 Falls Rd Brooklandville MD 21022

DURGIN, BELINDA TRACY, Fourth Grade Teacher; *b:* Lynn[...] Matthew Paul; *c:* Molly Ann; *ed:* Salem St Coll (BS) Elem Ed[...] City of Lynn Schl Dept Elem Tchr 1987-; *ai:* Summer Schl E[...] Prgm Co-Coord; Night Schl GED, One Way Phonics Tutori[...] Saturday Rdng & Writing Skills Prgm Tchr; AFT, MTRB, MTA[...] Mary's Jr HS Booster Club 1993-; *office:* Robert L Ford Elem Sch[...] St Lynn MA 01902

DURGIN, NANCY E.H., US His, Rdng & Eng Teacher; *b:* Ware[...] Ronald Edward; *c:* Ryan Edward; *ed:* Univ of ME at Orono (BS[...] Ed 1975; Credit Hrs Gifted & Talented Ed, Mid Level Ed, Drug &[...] Awareness Trng; *cr:* Tomwoomba St Schl in Australia 6th [...] 1975-76; Leichhardt State Schl in Australia 2nd Grd Tchr[...] Washburn Schl 2nd, 5th Grd Tchr 1978-80; A.D. Gray MS 7-8t[...] His, Rdng, Lang Arts Tchr 1980-; *ai:* Drama Dir; OM Coach[...] Awareness Prgm Coord; Spelling Bee Mistress; Gifted & Talen[...] Tchr; Medomak Valley Ed Assn, ME Tchrs Assn, NEA 1977-; He[...] Comm Drug & Alcohol Awareness Team 1989-, Mem; Studio T[...] Bath 1980-; Portland Lyric Theater 1990-; ME Governors Awd; N[...] for ME Tchr of Yr; *office:* A.D. Gray MS 56 School St Waldo[...] 04572

DURHAM, THOMAS A., Marketing Education Coord; *b:* Ashl[...] *m:* Debra G.; *ed:* Bowling Green St Univ (BA) Mrktg Ed 1982;[...] Univ (MS) Educl Admin 1990; *cr:* Swiss Hills JVS Mrktg E[...] 1983-84; Black Rivers HS Math Instr 1985; Lorain Cty JVS M[...] 1986; Norwalk HS Mrktg Ed Coord 1987-; *ai:* Frosh Bsktbl &[...] Track Coach; Natl Tchrs Assn 1982-; Natl & OH DECA 1986-[...] Norwalk HS 80 E Main St Norwalk OH 44857

DURHAM, THOMAS FISHER, English Teacher; *b:* Syracuse,[...] Patricia Ann Smolinski; *c:* Ian T., Maggie E.; *ed:* Univ of Roches[...] Eng 1966; Canisius Coll (MS) Eng, Ed 1970; Attnd Boston Univ[...] Theatre Inst 1981; *cr:* Iroquois Cntrl Schl Eng Tchr 1966-; *a[...]* Drama 1971-82; Class Adv 1970-74; Homecoming Float Adv[...] Iroquois Fac Assn, NYEA, NEA 1966-; NYSUT 1995-; NCT[...] Aurora Players 1967-, Treas, Lifetime Mem, 7 Acting Awds; Tchr[...] Assignment Curr 1984-86; Yrbk Dedication 1974; *office:* Iroqu[...] HS Box 32 Girdle Rd Elma NY 14059

DURKA, CHESTER S., Economics & Government Tchr; *b:* Buff[...] *m:* Linda Cioch; *c:* Erik, Jennifer; *ed:* Buffalo St Coll (BA) Soc St[...] St Univ Coll at Buffalo Soc Stud Ed 1975; Attnd Cheektowaga [...] Clarence Cntrl Schls; *cr:* Cardinal Dougherty HS Tchr [...] Cheektowaga Cntrl Tchr 1971-; US Army Reserves Instr 197[...] Mock Trial Team Adv; Curr Writing Comm; Dist Planning Team;[...] Comm; Cheektowaga Tchrs Assn 1971-; NYSUT & AFT 1971-[...] 1992-; NY St Cncl for the Soc Stud 1992-; Reserves Retirees Ass[...] Natl Issues Forum Interview Pub; Natl Fndtn for Ec Ed Field Pro[...] Cheektowaga Central H S 3600 Union Rd Cheektowaga NY 1422[...]

DURKAN, ANN A., Third Grade Teacher; *b:* Scranton, PA; *c:* [...] *ed:* Marywood Coll (BA) Elem Ed 1972; Univ of Scranton Rdng S[...] 1975; Coll Misericordia Eisenhower Grant Pgm for Ed Tech; *cr:* [...] Schl Dist 3rd Grd Tchr 1972-; *ai:* SFT 1972-; Northeast Math Tch[...] Girl Scouts 1987-, Asst Troop Ldr; Eisenhower Grant; *office:*[...] Willard Elem Schl 32 1100 Eynon St Scranton PA 18504

DURKEE, SHARON SEIDERS, Biology Teacher; *b:* Reading,[...] Aaron; *ed:* Elizabethtown Coll (BS) Bio 1971; Wilmington C[...] Human Resources 1991; 30 Addl Credits Univ of DE & Inservice[...] *cr:* William Penn HS Bio Tchr 1971-; *ai:* NEA 1974-; *office:* Willi[...] H S 713 E Basin Rd New Castle DE 19720

DURKIN, SHARON CROMIE, Third Grade Teacher; *b:* Troy,[...] Philip Steven; *c:* Laura Durkin LaMay, Michael P.,[...] Durkin-Markus; *ed:* SUNY at Plattsburgh (BS) Elem Ed 1967, (M[...] Ed 1973; Courses in Cooperative Learning, Cmptr sci, Mainstrea[...] Behavior Mgmt Drake Univ; *cr:* Camden Cntrl Schl 3rd & 4th C[...] 1967-70; Saranac Lake Cntrl Schl 3rd Grd Tchr 1971-; *ai:* Saran[...] Tchrs Assoc 1971-, Rep to Exec Comm; NYSUT 1971-; AFT 1971-[...] of the Elks 1984-, Historical Librn; *home:* HC 1 Box 140 Saranac L[...] 12983*

DUROCHER, JOAN TERESA, Science Teacher; *b:* Woonsocke[...] Elizabeth Brouillard, David Brouillard; *ed:* Rosemont Coll (BA[...] 1968; RI Coll (MED) 1993; *cr:* Bellingham Schl 3rd Grd Tchr 1[...] Millville Schl Dist 4th-6th Grd Tchr 1985-; Cultural Homestay I[...] Exch Tchr & Coord 1989-; *ai:* Sci Fair Coord; Elem Schl Newspap[...] Yr Book Comm; Blackstone-Millville Regnl Schl Dist Ed Assoc 198[...] MTA & NEA 1985-; YWCA of N RI Bd of Dir 1989-95, Sec;[...] Millville Elem Schl 122 Berthelette Way Millville MA 01529

IER, ROBERT JOSEPH, Biology & Health Teacher; *b:* Central *m:* Viola Wagoner; *c:* Michelle Marie, Julie Ann; *ed:* St Michaels Bio 1964; Providence Coll (MA) Sp Ed Learning Disabilities t Grad 3 Credits RI Coll, 3 Credits Univ of RI, 6 Credits RI Schl , 8 Credits Bryant C, 8 Credit Berkeley Schl of Music, 2 Credit :, 12 Credit Syracuse U, 3 Credit LaSalle U, 2 Credit Rochester it Ball St U, 3 Credit Union Coll, 3 Credits SUNY; *cr:* St Peters 7th Grd Tchr 1958-60; Notre Dame HS 10th & 12th Grd Bio, y Tchr 1960-65; Madawaska HS Bio Tchr 1966-70; Bellingham 10th Grd Gen Math & Sci Tchr 1970-72; Mt St Charles Acad Bio, y Tchr 1972-79; Norton HS Earth Sci, Geology Tchr 1979-81; others Acad Regents Hon Bio, Ap Bio Hlth Jr & Sr HS 1981-; *ai:* hrs 1993-94; NEA; NY St Tchrs Union 1981-96; Balsa 1991-96; 94-96; Outstanding Bio Tchr NABT 1974; Tchng of Yr 1990; rstn Brothers Acad 1 Delasalle Rd Albany NY 12208

ONNIE SAINE, 10th-12th Grd Biology Instr; *b:* Portsmouth, ary Thomas; *ed:* SUNY at Plattsburgh (BS) Ed, Bio 1970; SUNY (MS) Bio, Curr 1973; Addl 15 Hrs Soc Stud; 6 Hrs Genetics; 6 thical Issues; *cr:* Berne Knox Weterlo Bio Instr 1972-; *ai:* Tech Curr Comms; Sci Chm 19 Yrs; NABT, AFT, NYSUT, AIBS, ; Excl Ed Awd Twice; Tandy's Sci Awd; *office:* ox-Westerlo HS 1738 Helderberg Trl Berne NY 12023

T, SALLY HOFFMAN, Honors Political Sci Teacher; *b:* nd, MD; *m:* Robert Edwin; *ed:* Thiel Coll (BA) Pol Sci 1968; Coll (MA) 1971; Univ of Pittsburgh (JD) Law 1981; Duquesne g Specialist Admin; Harvard Univ Writing, Rdng, Civic Ed; *cr:* Pub Schls Tchr 1968-70; Pittsburgh Pub Schls Tchr 1972-78; S Sub Tchr 1 Yr; Hampton HS Tchr 1984-; *office:* Hampton HS ully Rd Allison Park PA 15101*

T, DORIS OAKCRUM, Language Arts Teacher; *b:* sville, VA; *c:* Michelle, Natalie; *ed:* Morgan St Univ (BA) Eng wie St Univ Rdng; Univ of MD Rdng; Johns Hopkins Univ Voc *r:* Anne Arundel Cty Pub Schls Tchr 1972-87; Santa Rita Pub r 1987-1988; Prince Georges Cty Pub Schls Tchr 1988-90; Anne Cty Pub Schls Tchr 1990-; *ai:* Human Relatins Comm Chprsn; rovement Team Mem; Homeroom Advy Comm Mem; NEA, AAAC 1972-; Delta Sigma Theta 1981-, Chapter Sec, Journalist; ill of Amer Inc 1990-, Chapter Pres; *office:* Mac Arthur MS ach Rd Fort Meade MD 20755

RENEE DAY, 2nd Grade Classroom Teacher; *b:* Clifton Springs, ephen Thomas Sr.; *c:* Stephen Jr., Kyla; *ed:* Cobleskill Coll (AS) dhd 1981-; Geneseo Coll (BS) Elem Ed 1983; Nazareth Coll (MS) 1989; Math Their Way Trng; Writing Process I & II; Talents l; Whole Lang I; *cr:* Midlakes Schl Dist 3rd Grd Tchr 1985-86, 'chr 1986-88, 2nd Grd Tchr 1988-90; Midlakes Schl 3rd Grd Tchr 2nd Grd Tchr 1991-; *ai:* JV & Var chrldng Coach 1985-92; Ftbl Coach; AFT; *office:* Midlakes Primary Schl Banta St Phelps NY

, THOMAS RALPH, Fifth Grade Teacher; *b:* Newark, NJ; *m:* . Miner; *c:* Tyler; *ed:* Glassboro St (BA) Elem Ed 1979; Lesley) Elem Ed, Circul 1992; *cr:* Buena Reg Cleary Schl 7th-8th Grd Tchr 1979-80, 4th Grd Tchr 1980-84; Grafton MS 5th Grd Tchr Hopedale-Meml Schl 5th Grd Tchr 1988-; *ai:* Jr HS Bsktbl, Cross ach 1988-; Odessy of the Mind 1990; Project Elect 1982; MTA ead Neg; MA Umpire Assn 1990-.*

DONNA WOJCIECHOWSKI, Algebra Teacher; *b:* Mc PA; *c:* Ryan, Erika, Adam; *ed:* CA Univ of PA (BS) Scndry Math vanced Prof Cert; *cr:* Southern HS Math Tchr 1974-76; Southern Sci Tchr 1987-90, Algebra Tchr 1990-; *ai:* Math Dept Chprsn; nces Spon; NEA, St, Local; MSTA; *office:* Southern MS 605 Winters Rd Oakland MD 21550

GAIL STASKO, 4th Grade Teacher; *b:* Windber, PA; *m:* Thomas nna Stopko, Steven Penrod; Jeremy; *ed:* Univ of Pittsburgh (BS) 1971; *cr:* Windber Area Schl Tchr 1971-; *ai:* Asst 7th Grd Girls oach; Windber Area EA 1971-, Sec, Pres; PSEA 1971-, Region omm Chair; NEA; Windber PTO 1971-; *office:* West End Elem Ave Windber PA 15963*

ENKO, THEODORE R., Mathematics Teacher; *b:* Bronx, NY; *m:* A. James; *c:* Debra Garvey, Roger James; *ed:* SUNY at Albany th & Physics 1964, (MS) Math & Ed 1967; 60 Grad Hrs; *cr:* wn HS North Wrestling Coach 1964-73, Math Tchr 1964-79, & 1988-; *ai:* Wrestling Coach; Adult Ed; HS Equivalency & Schl Tchr; Young Republican Club Adv; Clarkstown Tchrs Assn FT; BPOE Pearl River & Nannet Lodge 1993-; Former Jaycee; pvr 1980-85; Town Councilman 1992-95; Cty Legislator 1970-85 ; Instrumental in Acquiring & Developing Parks, Recreation s; Dir Drug & Yth Pgms, & Clarkstown Yth Court; Efficiencies to t Improved Intrestructure & Job Opportunities; *office:* Clarkstown Congers Rd New City NY 10956

U, MICHAEL JAMES, Science & Math Teacher; *b:* Barre, VT; of MA (BS) Astronomy, Physics 1983; 10 Credit Hrs Grad Level : Northampton HS Math Tchr 1984; Easthampton HS Sci Tchr , Amherst Regnl HS Physics Tchr 1987-88; Hopkins Acad Jr Sr HS h Tchr 1988-; *ai:* Sr Class Adv; Var Boys Soccer Coach; Bsktbl orekeeper; NEA, MTA 1984-; NSTA 1990-; *office:* Hopkins Acad Russell St Hadley MA 01035

EN, LAURIE, Computer & Math Teacher; *b:* New York City, NY; Ian; *c:* Stephanie, Michelle; *ed:* Queens Coll (BA) Math 1979; t Stony Brook (MALS) Cmptr Ed 1986; *cr:* Long Beach HS Math, chr 1979-82; Hicksville HS Cmptr Lab Mgr 1991-92; Hewlett Schl chr 1992-94; Glen Cove HS Math, Cmptr Tchr, Asst Cmptr Coord i: Exploratory Stud Prgm; Tech Plan Comm; NYSC & TE, NYSUT 'emple Beth El 1991-; *office:* Glen Cove Schls Dosoris LN Glen 11542

, GAIL MC MANIS, Elementary Teacher; *b:* Wellston, OH; *m:* Gary; *c:* Gina Sexton, Gary Scott; *ed:* Rio Grande Univ (BS) Elem ; Marshall Univ (MA) Elem Ed 1974; *cr:* South Point Elem Schl ond Grd Tchr 1963-65; Dawson-Bryant Elem Schl Kndgtn, Fourth Grd Tchr 1967-; *ai:* Dist Prof Staff Dev, Textbook n, Right to Read Week Comms; Vaughn Math Pilot; Family Support Johns Hopkins Model Schl Tchr; Dist Schlsp Fund, Yearly itor; Zoar Church Bible Schl, Vol; Pioneer Club, Refreshment Cancer Fund 1985-, Canvas Worker; March of Dimes 1985-, Vol.

, LORRAINE, Art Teacher; *b:* Philadelphia, PA; *c:* Gautam; *ed:* Coll (BA) Art Ed; *cr:* Kavesh & Basile Law Firm Sec 1977-80; d HS South Art Tchr 1980-; *ai:* SHAPE Adv; Review Comm; Head Mediation; Set Design for Play; Enter Stus Art in Arts & Final Art NJEA 1980-; NEA 1980-; AENJ; Love A Little One 1977-, Pres & n; Ananda Marga Universal Releif 1978-, Bd Mem; Dancezone d Mem; *office:* Vineland HS South 2880 E Chestnut Ave Vineland 0

, RAVI K., Professor of Business Admin; *b:* Bikaner, India; *c:* M.; *ed:* Univ of Scranton (MBA) Fin 1974; Rutgers Univ (EDD) 1992; NJ St Cert Pub Accountant; Dowling Coll at Long Island Cert Total Quality Mgmt 1994; *cr:* Stockton St Coll Instr 1974-77; Raritan Vly Comm Coll Prof 1978-84, Bus Dept Chm 1984-93, Prof 1993-; *ai:* Intnl Club; ASQC; Quality in Higher Ed Round Table; AFT 1978-, Auditor; AICPA 1984-; Vol Soc Svcs PA 1978-, Pres; Article Pub; Focus Group Mgmt; *office:* Raritan Valley Comm Coll PO Box 3300 Somerville NJ 08876

DUTTERER, MYRON A., Theater Instructor; *b:* Gettysburg, PA; *m:* Barbara A. Palmer; *c:* Lauren, Clark; *ed:* Univ of MD at College Park (BS) Music 1970, (MS) Cnslng, Coll Admin 1974, (MA) Theater 1977; *cr:* US Army Army Chorus-Bass Soloist 3 Yrs; Dunloggin MS Music, Drama, Guitar, Dance Tchr 4 Yrs; Centennial HS Theater, Stagecraft 19 Yrs; *ai:* Dir Ski Club; Thespian Troupe Spon; Golf Coach; NEA 1973-; AAEA 1991-; NTA 1976-; Howard Cty Summer Theater 1975-, Dir, Designer Actor; First Presbyn Church of Howard Cty 1981-; Howard Cty MD Edctr of Yr 1995; *office:* Centennial HS 4300 Centennial Ln Ellicott City MD 21042

DUTTON, CAROL TYMINSKI, Acctng & Bus Mgmt Assoc Prof; *b:* Port Chester, NY; *m:* Edmund L.; *c:* Vandy Elizabeth Paulk; *ed:* WA St (AAB) Acctng 1978; Marietta Coll (BA) Acctng 1985; WV Univ (MBA) Bus 1990; Univ of Akron 10 Semester Hrs; Nova Southeastern Univ 4 Semester Hrs; *cr:* E-Tek Office Mgr 1981-83; Accountant 1985-86; Girl Scouts of Amer Field Exec 1986; WA St Assoc Prof 1986-; Working Towards DBA; *ai:* AICPA, OH CPA Assn 1993-; Amer Assn of Accountants 1988-; Certfd Pub Accountant.

DUTTON, JENNIFER STEPTOE, 11th & 12th Grd English Tchr; *b:* Washington, DC; *m:* Robert James; *ed:* CA St Univ at Dominguez Hills (BA) Eng; Geo Mason Univ (MA) Linguistics 1984; Speech Pathology & Audiology Hampton Univ 1966-70; 3 Hrs Ctr for Renaissance Stud Univ of Md at Coll Pk 1993; 60 Hrs Theology Alpha Bible Inst 1991-; *cr:* David S. Dordan HS Eng Tchr; Chatsworth HS Eng Tchr 1978-85; Fairfax Cty Schl Eng Tchr 1980-85; Wicomico HS Eng Tchr 1987-; *ai:* Acad Assistance Coord; NEA 1981-, Uniserv Rep, Longwood Coll at Farmville; MSTA 1987-; WCEA 1987-, Minority Affairs Appreciation Awd 1993; Bethel Bible Inst, Alpha Bible Inst 1991-, Tchr, Stu, Assoc Degree Biblical Stud; Textbook Selection Comm 1989, 1994, Wicomico Cty Bd of Ed; MD Assn Elem Schl Admin Cert of Achvmt; Outstdng Achvmt in Poetry Eds Choice Awd Natl Lib of Poetry 1995; Spotlight on Chief Examiners 1994; CA St Univ at Dominguez Hills Cert of Completion Applied Linguistics 1980; Fleet Reserve Assoc Promoter Essay Contest for Stdnts 1993-94.*

DUTTON, NANCY C., English & Lang Arts Teacher; *b:* New York, NY; *m:* Bruce G.; *c:* Randall, Rebecca; *ed:* UVM (BA) Fr & Eng 1968; U Conn (MA) Eng 1975, (CAGS) Curr 1980; Sarbonne Advance Fr; *cr:* John Jay HS Tchr 1973-; Univ of CT Tchr Summers; Leicester HS Tchr & Dept Chair 1975-; *ai:* Schl Newspaper & Lit Magazine Adv; Theater Arts Dir & Adv; NEA 1978-; NCTE 1980-; ASCD 1980-; Arts Commission; Bd of Chrstn Ed; Hosp Vol; Portfoloio Grant; Curr Frameworks Team Mem; Master Tchr for 2 Apprentices; Eng & Lang Arts Team Ldr; *office:* Leicester HS 174 Paxton St Leicester MA 01524*

DUVALL, GARY EDGAR, Retired Teacher; *b:* Marietta, OH; *m:* Karen Alfred; *c:* Eric Clark Diehl; *ed:* OH Univ (BSED) His, Pol Sci 1965; 20 Semester Hrs His, Pol Sci; *cr:* Phillips Elem Schl OH His, World Geog Tchr 1965-66; Marietta Jr HS Amer His, Civics Tchr 1966-84; Marietta HS Amer His, Civics, Pol Sci Tchr 1984-95; *ai:* Class Adv; Stu Cncl; HS Golf Coach; NEA 1965-; Acad Excl Awd 1988, 1990, 1991; *home:* 112 Howard St Marietta OH 45750

DUWVE, LARRY R., Social Studies Teacher; *b:* Toledo, OH; *m:* Barbara Cutcher; *c:* Larry III, Jacob, Beth; *ed:* Toledo Univ (BE) Soc Stud 1973, (ME) Admin, Supervision 1978; Univ of Toledo Post Masters Work; *cr:* Cntrl Cath HS Soc Stud Tchr, Dean of Men 1973-76; St Joe Cntrl Cath HS Prin 1976-81; Roy C. Start HS Tchr 1986-; *ai:* Character Counts Instr; IM Sftbl Coach; AFT 1986-, Bldg Comm; ASSCA 1976-81; St Thomas Schl Bd of Ed 1982-86, Pres; *office:* Roy C. Start HS 2100 Tremainsville Rd Toledo OH 43613*

DUXBURY, JEAN M., Fifth Grade Teacher; *b:* Amsterdam, NY; *m:* Robert Barney; *c:* Erich Barney, Kurt Barney; *ed:* St Univ of NY at Potsdam (BA) Soc Sci 1973; Russell Sage Coll (MS) Ed 1978; Albany St, Coll of St Rose Post Grad Work; *cr:* Schalmont Cntrl Schls Elem Tchr 1973-; *ai:* Dist IDEA Comm Chprsn; Past Cheerleading Adv 1973-79, K-6th Grd Math Chrpsn 1980-92; AFT, NYSUT 1992-; Schalmont Tchrs Assn 1973-, VP, Negotiator, Newspaper Ed; NCTM 1980-; PBS WMHT 1985-; Proctor Theater Patron 1992-; *home:* 19 Munger Hill Rd Stillwater NY 12170

DWORAKOWSKI, KAREN COOPER, 3rd Grade Teacher; *b:* Erie, PA; *m:* Thomas E.; *ed:* Villa Coll (BS); 27 Grad Credits at Edinboro Univ, Gannon Univ; *cr:* Klein Elem Schl 5th Grd Tchr 8 Yrs, 6th Grd Tchr 11 Yrs, 3rd Grd Tchr 9 Yrs; *ai:* Strategic Planning, In-House, Text Book Adoption Comms; Lead Tchr; PTO Bd; NEA, PSEA 1968-; HCEA 1968-, Bldg Rep; Spirit of Tchng Awd Northwestern PA; *office:* Klein Elem Schl 5325 E Lake Rd Erie PA 16511

DWYER, CHRIS B., Fifth Grade Teacher; *m:* Sherry L.; *c:* Lauren, Meredith, Christian; *ed:* Lock Haven Univ (BS) Elem, Spec Ed, Early Childhood 1965; Attnd Penn St, IN Wesleyan; *cr:* Woodward Elem Schl 5th Grd & Head Tchr 1965-87, 5th Grd Tchr 1987-; *ai:* PSEA, NEA 1965-; Clinton Cty United Way 1985-, Asst Treas, VP; Bald Eagle Twp 1981-, Supvr, Bd Chm; Clinton Cty Republican Comm, Past Chm; PA Republican St Comm, St Committeeman; *home:* RR 2 Box 119 Mill Hall PA 17751

DWYER, GAIL GAVIGAN, High School Science Teacher; *b:* Rockville Centre, NY; *m:* Robert J.; *c:* Timothy, Erin Kate; *ed:* Molloy Coll (BS) Sci & 7th-12th Bio 1971; Course in Chem SUNY at Purchase 1990; Drew Univ Chem Com 1995; *cr:* Diocese of RVC Elem Schls 1st-3rd & 7th-8th Grd Tchr 1960-72; Notre Dame Elem Schl 1st-8th Grd Prin 1972-73; Multi Municipal Productivity Project Comm Coord 1973-75; St Agnes Cathedral HS 10th-12th Grd Bio Tchr 1975-76; St Thomas the Apostle 7th-8th Grd Sci Tchr 1976-77; St Fidelis Elem K-8th Grd PE Tchr 1984-85; Holy Name of Mary 5th-8th Grd Sci Prgm & Lab 1985-90; St Agnes Acad HS Phys Sci Bio & Chem Tchr 1990-, Sci Dept Chrpsn; *ai:* NY St Sci Honor Soc Coord; SADD; Bsktbl Moderator; Coached Sci Olympiad Team 1993-; Blue-White Sports Night Moderator; NCEA 1960-; Girl Scouts of Amer 1986-, Ldr of Brownies & Cadettes; *office:* St Agnes Acad HS 13-20 124th St College Point NY 11356*

DWYER, KEVIN FRANCIS, Assoc Prof of Religious Stud; *b:* Boston, MA; *ed:* Villanova Univ (BA) Philosophy 1958, (MA) His 1961; Augustinian Coll (MA) Rel Ed 1962; Post Grad Stud Cath Univ of Amer His, Washington Theological Union Theology; *cr:* Villanova Univ Instr 1962-63; Merrimack Coll Asst Prof 1963-91, Dept Chair 1973-78, Assoc Prof 1991-; *ai:* Archivist of the Coll; Fraternity Moderator; Fac Advy Comm for Continuing Ed; Honorary Degree Recipients' Comm; Coll Theology Soc; Amer Cath Historical Assn; Amer Cath Historical Soc, Bd of Mgrs 1962-64; New England Historical Assn; Order of St Augustine 1955-; Order of St Augustine Grant for Summer Stud in Europe 1976; Sabbatical Grant 1986, 1994; Who's Who in Religion; *home:* C/O Merrimack Coll Mail Stop 911 N Andover MA 01845

DWYER, MARIANNE JEAN, Special Needs Teacher; *b:* Melrose, MA; *ed:* Rivier Coll (BA) Elem, Spec Ed 1979; Boston Coll (MED) Severe Spec Ed 1982; 60 Addl Credit Hrs; *cr:* Landmark Schl Tchr, Residential 1979; Hoover Elem Schl 4-6 Grd Spec Ed Tchr 1979-89; Melrose Summer Enrichment Schl Cmptr Tchr 1984-; Melrose MS Moderate Spec Needs Tchr 1989-; *ai:* Tech Task Force; Evaluation, Lang Arts Comms; 7B Team; MEA, MTA 1979-; CEC 1982-; Phi Theta Xi 1990-, Bd of Governors; Challenge 1994-, Camera Person; Irish Georgan Soc 1993-; Horace Mann Grant; Horizons for Ed; *office:* Melrose MS 350 Lynn Fells Pky Melrose MA 02176

DWYER, PATRICIA A., Adj Prof of Curr & Instruction; *b:* New York, NY; *ed:* St Johns Univ (BS) Soc Stud Ed 1959, (MS) Ed 1961; C W Post (MA) Pol Sci 1983; Attnd Tamkang Univ, Jadaphur Univ, Oxford Univ Post Grad; *cr:* No Babylon Pub Schls Eng & Soc Stud Tchr 1961-64; Dept of Defense Schls at Germany & England Guid Cnslr & Tchr 1964-67; Oyster Bay HS Tchr Ctr Facilitator & Soc Stud Tchr 1967-90; Sewanhaka Cntrl HS Dist Soc Stud Coord 1990-95; C W Post Coll Adj Prof 1995-; *ai:* LI Soc Stud Cncl 1982-; NYS Soc Stud Cncl 1983-; NC Soc Stud 1985-; Schlsps: Fulbright at India 1976, Eng Speaking Union at Oxford 1979; Grants: Cncl for Hum 1987, NYS Cncl for Hum 1992; *home:* 20 Greenmeadow Ct Deer Park NY 11729

DWYER, VERONICA KELLY, Health Teacher; *b:* Peekskill, NY; *c:* Douglas, David, Doreen; *ed:* Long Island Univ (MS) Ed; Univ of Bridgeport (BS) Hlth & PE 1973; 30 Credit Hrs Beyond MS in Ed; *cr:* Yorktown HS & Mildred E. Strong MS PE Tchr 1974-83; Yorktown HS Hlth & Family Living Tchr 1983-; *ai:* Stu Senate Adv; AFT, YCT, NYSUT 1974-; NASSP 1993-; *office:* Yorktown HS 2727 Crompond Rd Yorktown Heights NY 10598

DYAS, NANNETTE, Mathematics Teacher; *b:* Atlanta, GA; *ed:* No Georgia Coll (BS) Math 1967; GA St Univ (MED) Math 1973; Attnd George Mason Univ, Univ of MD, American Univ; *cr:* Campbell of Smyrna HS Math Tchr 1967-75; Winston Churchill HS Math Tchr 1975-85; Montgomery Blair HS Math Tchr 1985-; *ai:* Rdng, Bkng, Wlkng on Bch; NEA, NCTM; *office:* Montgomery Blair HS 313 Wayne Ave Silver Spring MD 20910*

DYBACH, THERESA MARIA, English Teacher; *b:* Wilkes-Barre, PA; *ed:* Wilkes Univ (BA) Eng 1971; Penn St Univ M Equiv Ed 1989-90, K-12th Grd St Rdng Specialist 1992; 9 Credit Hrs St Rose Coll Ed 1995-; *cr:* Lewistown HS Eng Tchr 19 Yrs; *ai:* Lore-Yrbk Adv 8 Yrs; Career Club Adv 2 Yrs; Future Edctrs Club 2 Yrs; Assoc Mifflin Cty Ed 1977-; PSEA 1977-; NEA 1977-; Sacred Heart Schl Bd 3 Yrs, Bd Mem; Palmer Museum of Art, Penn St Mem; Wilkes Coll Grant; Deans List Wilkes Coll.

DYBOWSKI, JANE, Science Teacher; *b:* Fall River, MA; *m:* Harry Proudfoot; *ed:* Bridgewater St Coll (BS) Bio 1976; Tchng Grad Courses; Univ of MA at Dartmouth Chem, Physics Grad Courses; Brown Univ Scndry Inst Grad Work; *cr:* Morton Hosp Sr Lab Technician 1977-79; Bridgewater St Coll Lab Instr in Bio 1979-80; Westport HS Chem, Physics, Bio, Sci Tchr 1980-; *ai:* NEASC Fac, Staff Comm Co-Chair; NEASC Eng Comm; Co-Chaired Creation of Web Page; Scheduling Comm; Westport Tchrs Assn, AFT 1980-; MA Sci Supvrs 1991-; SE MA Physics Alliance 1985-; *office:* Westport HS 19 Main Rd Westport MA 02790

DYE, DEANA GAIL, HS Math Teacher; *b:* Marietta, OH; *m:* Douglas; *ed:* Mount Union Coll (BS) Math 1991; Marietta Coll (MA) Ed 1995; *cr:* Warren HS Math Tchr 1991-; *ai:* Teens Needing Teens Adv; NEA 1991-; Lowell United Meth Church 1981-, Sunday Schl Supt, Tchr; *home:* 199 Third St P.O. Box 437 Lowell OH 45744

DYE, DIANE STEVENS, Senior High Art Teacher; *b:* Cortland, NY; *m:* Quentin Lyle; *c:* Katie Christine Bohn, Amelia Rachel; *ed:* St Univ of NY at Fredonia (BA) Fine Arts Summa Cum Laude 1978; St Univ at Buffalo (MA) Art Ed 1986; Bowling Green St Univ Sociology 1964-67; *cr:* Salamanca City Schls Jr HS Art Tchr 1981-82; Gowanda Central Jr-Sr HS Sr High Art 1982-; *ai:* Sr Class Adv; Bldg Improvement Team; Pub Rel, Grants Comm; Gowanda Tchrs Assn 1982-; NY St United Tchrs 1982-; *office:* Gowanda Cntrl Schls Prospect St Gowanda NY 14070

DYE, IVAN D., Mathematics Teacher; *b:* Cleveland, OH; *m:* Cynthia D.; *c:* Cheyanne D.; *ed:* Mt Union Coll (BS) Cmptr Sci 1990; Univ of Toledo (BS) Scndry Ed, Cmptr Sci, Math 1992; Grad Schl 4 Credit Hrs; *cr:* Woodward HS Math Tchr 1992-; *ai:* Track Coach; Afro Club Adv.

DYE, PAMELA FRAMPTON, Elementary Classroom Teacher; *b:* E Liverpool, OH; *m:* Donald Robert; *c:* Katherine Nicole; *ed:* West Liberty St Coll (BA) Elem Ed 1971; Univ of Dayton (MA) Child, Yth Dev; Attnd Kent St Univ; 20 Addl Grad Hrs; *cr:* Edison Local Schls Elem Classroom Tchr 1971-76; Carrollton Ex village Schls Elem Classroom Tchr 1976-; *ai:* OEA, NEA 1971-; Carrollton Meth Church 1976-; Order of Eastern Stars 1986-; *home:* 106 N Star St NW Carrollton OH 44615

DYE, QUENTIN L., Language Arts Chairperson; *b:* Jamestown, NY; *m:* Diane Stevens; *c:* Katie C. Bohn, Amelia R.; *ed:* Bowling Green St Univ (BS) Jrnlsm 1967; Canisius Coll (MS) Eng Ed 1969; *cr:* Brochton Central Schl Eng Tchr 1969-71; Gowanda CS Eng Tchr 1971-; *ai:* Lang Arts Dept Chprsn; Gowanda TA 1971-, Negotiator; NY St United Tchrs 1969-; NCTE 1980-; *office:* Gowanda Cntrl Schl 24 Prospect St Gowanda NY 14070

DYE, TRACIE ANN, 6th Grade Teacher; *b:* Sandusky, OH; *m:* Gary C.; *c:* Hunter Garrett; *ed:* Univ of Toledo (BA) Elem Ed 1989; Bowling Green St U (ME) Ed 1994; Cmptr Trng Internet; *cr:* Otis Elem Schl 6th Grd Tchr 1989-; *ai:* 5-6th Grd Quiz Bowl, 6th Grd Safety Patrol Adv; Elem Stu Cncl Co-Adv; NEA, OEA 1989-; FEA 1989-, Union Rep 1992-95; Amer Heart Assn 1985-, Vol; Rsrch Article Pub; *office:* Otis Elem Schl 718 N Brush St Fremont OH 43420*

DYE, WILLIAM EDWARD, English Teacher; *b:* Westernport, MD; *m:* Sue Ann Lepley; *ed:* Frostburg St Univ (BA) His 1963, (MS) Ed 1967; *cr:* Fort Ashby HS Soc Stud Tchr 1963-73; Keyser HS Soc Stud Tchr 1973-80; Westman HS Eng Tchr 1980-; *ai:* Learning Svc Prgm Coord; Active Learning Svc Prgm Spon; Portfolio Comm Chm; Allegany Cty Tchrs Assn, MD St Tchrs Assn 1980-; NEA 1963-; Energy Conservation Curr Guide St Dept of Ed; Tchr of Yr Mineral Cty; *office:* Westmar HS Rt 36 Detmold St Lonaconing MD 21539*

DYER, ANN M., Secondary School French Tutor; *b:* E Orange, NJ; *ed:* Manhattan Coll of NY (BA) Eng 1954; Rivier Coll of NH (MA) Fr 1964; Fordham Univ Admin 18 Credit Hrs 1977; Plattsburg Univ Admin 3 Credit Hrs 1973; 7-12 Grd Fr Permanent NY St Cert 1965; Elem Schl Admin, Supvr 1977; *cr:* Mary Louis Acad Chrpsn 1965-69; Bishop Mc Donnell HS Chprsn 1970-73; St Thomas Aquinas Elem Prin 1973-79; St Joseph Acad Fr Tchr 1984-87; Sacred Heart 4-8 Grd Fr Tchr 1987-90; St Joseph Brentwood Ed Ctr Fr, Eng Tutor 1994-95; Sacred Heart Fr Tutor 1995-; *ai:* AATF 1965-; NCEA Grant 1963-; *office:* Sacred Heart Acad 47 Cathedral Ave Hempstead NY 11550

DYER, HILDE ROSE, English & History Teacher; *b:* Passaic, NJ; *m:* Wayne R.; *c:* Kristian; *ed:* Ramapo coll (BA) Soc Stud 1976; Rutgers Univ (MLS) Lib & Info Sci; Elem, Soc Stud Certs; Continuing Ed Credits; *cr:* Parsippany Chrstn Schl Sr HS Eng, Soc Stud Tchr 1987-91; Trinity Chrstn Schl Jr HS Eng, Soc Stud, Sci Tchr 1991-; *ai:* Lib, NHS Dir; Jr HS Speech Competition, Jr HS Creative Writing Coord; Govt Doc Assn; Amer Heart Assn, Neighborhood Campaign; HS Yrbk Dedication; *office:* Trinity Christian Schl Changebridge Rd Montville NJ 07045*

DYER, MARGO BUSQUE, Art & US History Teacher; *b:* Greenville, ME; *c:* Kristina, Lauree-Anne; *ed:* Univ of ME at Augusta (AA) Art 1973; Univ of ME at Orono (BA) Art 1975; *cr:* Mattanawcook Jr High 5th-8th Grd Art Tchr 1976-78; Greenville Schls K-12th Grd Art Tchr 1980-81; SAD Schls K-12th Grd Art Tchr 1988-; *ai:* Art Club; Prom, Hum Comms;

Art Dept Head; Ski Boosters Parents Group; NEA, MTA 1976-; Local Tchr Assn 1988-; *office:* Piscataquis Comm HS Blaine Ave Guilford ME 04443

DYHRBERG, GEOFFREY M., Social Studies Teacher; *b:* Omaha, NE; *m:* Stephenie L. Hill; *ed:* Boston Coll (BA) His & Scndry Ed 1992; *cr:* Nokomis Regnl HS Soc Stud Tchr 1993-; *ai:* Key Club & Recycling Club Adv; Rennaisance Mem; Hnrs Admissions Comm; Jobs for ME Grads Advy Bd; ME Educl Assn 1996; *office:* Nokomis Regional HS Williams Rd Newport ME 04953*

DYKE, WILLIAM FRANCIS, PE Tchr & Athletic Coach; *b:* Oneida, NY; *m:* Elizabeth Harrigan; *ed:* North Cntry Comm Coll (AS) PE 1975; Brockport St (BS) PE 1978; Univ of OK at Norman (MS) PE & Sociology of Sports 1980; *cr:* Norwood-Norfolk C Schl Permanent Sub Tchr 1980-83, Track & Field Coach 1980-; Trinity Cath Schl PE Tchr 1983-; *ai:* Northern NY Soccer Ofcls Assn 1992-, HS Boys & Girls Soccer Ofcl, Active Ofcl Awd; Boys Track & Field Coach Won Class C Section X Championship 12 Out of 14 Yrs; *home:* 27 Maple St Norfolk NY 13667*

DYKENS, MARYLIN CAROL, Eng Tchr & Dept Coord; *b:* Houston, TX; *c:* Marion, Brian, Jason; *ed:* SUNY at Oswego (bA) Eng 1970, MA) Eng Lit 1976; 90 Plus Hours Beyond (BA); *cr:* Rome Free Acad Eng Tchr 1970-; *ai:* 16 Yrs Newspaper & 10 Yrs Lit Magazine Advs; Elected Bldg Union Rep 10 Yrs; Curr Comm 6 Yrs; RTA 1970-, Ed Newsletter; NYSUT & AFT 1970-; NCTE 1980-; 1990 NY St Wide "Empire St Schl Press Assn- Adv of the Yr"; 1988-89 Sec of Empire St Schl Press Assn Bd of Dirs; Ed Rome Tchrs Assn Newsletter 1989-95; *office:* Rome Free Acad 500 Turin St Rome NY 13440*

DYKSHOORN, ELIZABETH JOYCE, 5th Grade Teacher; *b:* Goshen, NY; *m:* Albert; *ed:* Dordt Coll (BA) Ed 1985; 3 Credit Hrs Seton Hau; 3 Credit Hrs William Paterson Coll; 3 Credit Hrs St Peter's Coll; *cr:* Sussex Chrstn Schl 5th Grd Tchr 1985-, 6th Grd Homeroom Tchr 1992-, 5-8 Grd Art Tchr 1992-93, 4th Grd Sci Tchr 1992-, Gym Tchr 1995-; *ai:* Yrbk Coord; Goshen CRC 1993-95, Young Peoples Cnslr; Calvinettes 1995; *home:* RR 2 Box 105 Goshen NY 10924

DYKSTRA, JANET DZVRICSKO, Mathematics Teacher; *b:* Sharon, PA; *m:* John C.; *c:* James Bruce; *ed:* Westminster Coll (BS) Math 1988; Addl 24 Grad Credit Hrs; *cr:* Clairton City Math Tchr 1988-89; Baldwin-Whitehall Math Tchr 1990-91; Elizabeth Forward Math Tchr 1992-; *ai:* Girls Bsktbl Asst Coach; Girls Track Timer; Fac Advy Comm; PSEA, NEA 1988-; *office:* Elizabeth Forward Sr HS 1000 Weigle'S Hill Rd Elizabeth PA 15037

DYKSTRA, JASON A., Mathematics Department Chm; *b:* Buffalo, NY; *m:* Eleni Sopholles; *ed:* IN Univ (BS) Math Ed 1991; Governors Acad Math, Sci Tchrs 1993; Working Towards MS in Supervision & Admin Johns Hopkins Univ; *cr:* Lansdowne HS Math Tchr 1991-93, Math Dept Chair 1993-; *ai:* Var Vlybl Coach 1991-; Camp Airy Stu Ldrshp Retreat Adv; Grad Comm Chm; NCTM, Amer Vlbyl Coaches Assn 1991-; USA Vlby 1994-, Coach; Arbutus Optimist Club Tchr of Yr 1993; Coach of Yr 1994; Baltimore Sun All-Metro Coach of Yr 1994; *office:* Lansdowne HS 3800 Hollins Ferry Rd Baltimore MD 21227

DYLAG, CANDACE RAY, Second Grade Teacher; *b:* Lockport, NY; *m:* Charles P.; *c:* Sarah, Kathryn; *ed:* Kent St Univ (BS) Early Chldhd Ed 1971; 30 Addl Credit Hrs; *cr:* Gesu Elem Schl Third Grd Tchr 1971-76; St Ambrose Schl Fourth Grd Tchr 1976-77; Strongsville City Schls Fourth, Second Grd Tchr 1985-; *ai:* NEA 1985-; Outstdng Tchr Awd; Spec Ed Advy Cncl 1994; St Honorary Life Mem OH Congress of Parents, Tchrs 1995; *office:* Edna Surrarrer Elem Schl 9306 Priem Rd Strongsville OH 44136

DYMOND, KIMBERLY ANN, Chemistry & Physics Teacher; *b:* Tunkhannock, PA; *ed:* Kings Coll (BA) Eng Ed 1986, (BS) Sci Ed 1987; Wilkes Univ (MS) Ed 1992; Penn St Univ Post-Grad Stud in Curr & Comp Ed; *cr:* Mt View HS Scndry Eng 1987-88; Elk Lake HS Scndry Eng 1988-; *ai:* Supts Curr Advy Comm; New Fac Mentor; Yrbk Adv; NEA, PSEA & ELEA 1988-; *office:* Elk Lake HS PO Box 100 Dimock PA 18816*

DYNES, JAMES H., Soc Stud Team Leader & Tchr; *b:* North Adams, MA; *ed:* N Adams St (MED) Hist 1972; 28 Post Grad Credit Hrs; *cr:* C T Plunkett Jr HS Soc Stud Tchr 1965-70; Memorial & Hoosac MS Soc Stud Tchr 1970-93; Hoosac Valley HS Soc Stud Tchr 1993-; *ai:* Soc Stud Dept Team Ldr; NEA, MTA, ACTA 1965-; Lions Club 1971-, Pres, Numerous Other Offices; *office:* Hoosac Valley HS 125 Savoy Rd Adams MA 01220

DYRENFORTH, JOHN CHARLES, Fourth Grade Teacher; *b:* Cincinnati, OH; *m:* Katherine Johnson; *c:* David, Thomas; *ed:* WV Wesleyan (BA) Bus 1967; Western MD (MA) Ed 1977; Attnd Outward Bound Schl; *cr:* Cecil Co MD Tchr 1968-77; North Woodstock Tchr 1978-79; John Fuller Elem Schl Tchr 1980-; *ai:* Schl Radio Station; Cross Cntry Ski Prgm; NEA 1968-; NHEA 1978-; BSA 1985-; Little League Schlsp Comm 1987-; *home:* PO Box 14 Chocorua NH 03817

DYSON, ARNETHA LYNDELL, Third Grade Teacher; *b:* Amherst, VA; *m:* Francis T.; *c:* Teia M. Jordan; *ed:* St Paul's Coll (BS) Soc Sci, Elem Ed 1977; Univ of MD Tchng GATE 3 Hrs, Tchng Rdng in Content Area 3 Hrs, Systematic Trng for Effective Tchng 3 Hrs, Classroom Mngmt 1 Hr; Bowie St Univ Family Cnslng 3 Hrs, Group Cnslng 3 Hrs; Multi-Cultural Cnslng 3 Hrs, Adlerian Theory in Practice 3 Hrs; *cr:* Amherst Cty Pub Schls MS Hlth Ed Tchr 1977; Sandusky MS Lang Arts, Soc Stud Tchr 1977-79; Adult Ed Lang, Eng Tchr 1979; Benjamin Stoddert MS Lang Arts, Soc Stud Tchr 1979-83; Indian Head Elem Schl Soc Stud, Classroom Tchr 1983-; *ai:* NEA 1992-; Amer Red Cross 1975-, Chaplain's Asst, Certs; *office:* Indian Head Elem Schl Strauss Ave & Lackey Dr Indian Head MD 20640*

DZEDA, BRUCE, Social Studies Dept Chairman; *b:* Cleveland, OH; *m:* Christine Joanne Dedon; *c:* Gracie, Teddy, Abby; *ed:* Kent St Univ (BSEd) His, Soc Stud 1970, (MA) Eng 1979; *cr:* High Meadows Schl Tchr 1971-73; Beachwood HS Tchr 1973-77; Cleveland Hgts HS Tchr, Honors His 1977-80; Theodore Roosevelt HS Chm Soc Stud Dept 1980-; *ai:* Exec Tchrs Comm; Kent Ed Assn 1980-; OH Cncl for Soc Stud 1990-; Market St Railway 1994-; The Monarchist League 1968-; 1993 OH HS Soc Stud Tchr of Yr; Tchng Awd Kent St Univ 1991; *office:* Roosevelt HS 1400 N Mantua St Kent OH 44240

DZIRKALIS, ELGA GUTMANIS, Studio & Fine Arts Asst Prof; *b:* Esslingen, Germany; *m:* Andrew A.; *c:* Anna, Peter; *ed:* Univ of MN (BS) Fine Arts Ed; Columbia Univ (MA) Fine Arts Ed 1968; *cr:* Pub Schl Art Tchr 1968-70; Univ of Pittsburgh Asst Prof 1977-; *ai:* Lit, Art Pub Art Adv; Fine, Performing Arts Comm; Fac Dev Grant Travel, Pain Venice Italy; *office:* Univ Of Pittsburgh At Bradford 300 Campus Dr Bradford PA 16701

DZURICSKO, WILLIAM DAVID, Math Teacher; *b:* Sharon, PA; *m:* Barbara Ann Hartsky; *c:* William Thomas; *ed:* Westminster Coll (BS) Math 1981; Attnd Clarion Univ of PA, Youngstown St Univ, Gannon Univ, MidWestern Intermediate Unit IV; *cr:* Meadville Jr High 7th-8th Grd Math Tchr 1981-82; Grove City HS Math & Comp Tchr 1982-93; Hickory HS Math Tchr 1993-; *ai:* Head Boys Bsktbl & Asst Girls Track Coach; NEA 1981-; NCTM; St Michaels Byzantine Cath Church 1959-, CCD Tchr & Part-Time Cantor; GCU Lodge #258 1959-, Treas; *office:* Hickory HS Hermitage Schl Dist 640 N Hermitage Rd Hermitage PA 16148

DZURISIN, M. PHILIP,OSBM Religion Teacher; *b:* Pittston, PA; *ed:* Coll Misericordia (BA) Elem Ed 1963; De Paul Univ (MED) Ed 1972; *cr:* Elem Cath Schls Tchr PA 1950-63; Elem Cath Schls IN Prin 1963-73; Elem Cath Schls PA Prin 1973-85; Elem Cath Schls NJ Prin 1985-88; Elem Cath Schls PA Tchr 1988-; *ai:* Librn; *home:* 201 N Wyoming St Hazleton PA 18201

E

EADE, RONALD E., Administrator & Principal; *b:* Greensburg, PA; *m:* Pamela Lantz; *c:* Tamara, Ryan; *ed:* Fort Wayne Bible Coll (BS) Pastoral Ministries 1974; Attnd Bowling Green St Univ; *cr:* Parma Park Chrstn Life Acad PE, Sub Tchr 1985-87, 5th Grd Tchr 1987-91; New Castle Chrstn Acad Prin 1992-; *ai:* Greater New Castle Ministerial Flwshp 1991-; Mahoningtown Bus Assn 1995-; *office:* New Castle Chrstn Acad 1701 Albert St New Castle PA 16105

EADY, VIKKI LYNN, Jr HS Tchr & Math Dept Head; *b:* Akron, OH; *ed:* Ft Wayne Bible Coll (BS) Elem Ed 1973; Univ of Akron (MS) Elem Ed, Math 1983; 13 Post Grad Hrs Sci, Math Specialty; *cr:* Colonial Chrstn Schls Tchr, Dept Head 1973-77; Ravenna Chrstn Acad Prin 1977-85; Baltimore Chrstn Acad Jr HS Tchr 1985-88; Lake Ctr Chrstn Schl Jr HS Tchr 1988-; *ai:* Math Dept Head; Sci Fair Coord; Eisenhower Grant 1990; *office:* Lake Center Christian Schl 12893 Kaufman Ave NW Hartville OH 44632

EAGAN, MARY ANN, Sixth Grade Teacher; *b:* Johnson City, NY; *m:* Dennis J.; *c:* David J., Sara Ann; *ed:* Broome Comm Coll (AA) Liberal Arts 1972; St Univ of NY at Cortland (BA) Elem Ed 1974; 31 Grad Hrs; *cr:* Susquehanna Valley Cntrl Schl Dist Tchr 1974-; *ai:* Bldg Leadership Team; Schl-to-Work Mem; Character Ed Comm; Union Bldg Rep; NEA 1974-, Bldg Rep; *office:* Brookside Elem Schl 3849 Saddlemire Rd Binghamton NY 13903*

EAGER, KEVIN, Physics & Earth Science Tchr; *b:* Syracuse, NY; *m:* Lisa; *ed:* St Univ of NY at Oswego (BS) Scndry Ed 1991; St Univ of NY at Cortland (MS) Scndry Ed 1996; *cr:* North Syracuse Jr HS Physics & Earth Sci Tchr; *office:* North Syracuse Jr HS 5353 W Taft Rd North Syracuse NY 13212

EAKIN, RICHARD EUGENE,II, Instrumental Music Teacher; *b:* Findlay, OH; *m:* Jane A. Bailey; *c:* John R., Daniel J.; *ed:* OH St Univ (BME) Music Ed, Vocal 1978; Bowling Green St Univ (MME) Music, Instrumental 1982; Post Grad Stud Drake Univ, Seattle Pacific Univ; *cr:* Vanlue Local Schl K-12 Grd Vocal, Instrumental, Gen Music Tchr 1978-81; Bowling Green St Univ Grad Tchng Asst Music Ed 1981-82; Arcadia Local Schl Elem, Vocal Music Tchr 1982-85, Instrumental Music Tchr 1985-90; Van Buren Local Schl Instrumental Music Tchr, Fine Arts Chair 1990-; *ai:* North Cntrl Evaluation Team Ldr; Fine Arts Chm; MENC 1976-, Registered Music Edctr; OH Music Ed Assn 1976-; Natl Band Dir Assn 1984-; NEA, OEA, Van Buren Tchrs Assn 1990-; Article Pub 1982; *office:* Van Buren Local Schl 217 S Main St Van Buren OH 45889*

EAKINS, ROGER ALLEN, Math Teacher & Dept Co-Head; *b:* Warren, OH; *m:* Helen Reszegi; *ed:* Kent St (MA) Bio 1992; *cr:* Windham HS Math Tchr 1986-; Kent St Univ Upward Bound Sci Tchr 1989-92; *ai:* Ski Club; HS & Jr HS Yrbk; Jr HS Boys Track Coach 1 Yr; NEA & OEA 1986-; Windham Tchrs Assn 1986-, Pres 1991-; *office:* Windham Exempted Village Schl 9530 Bauer Ave Windham OH 44288

EARENFIGHT, RICHARD HUNTINGTON, 8th Grd English Teacher; *b:* Pipestone, MN; *m:* Ronda Ahearn; *c:* Olivia, Emily; *ed:* Seattle Univ (BA) Eng 1983; Trinity Coll (MA) Ed 1994; Dominican Schl of Philosophy Berkley CA Philosophy; *cr:* Univ Preparatory Acad 8th Grd Eng, His Tchr 1984-85; Tilden MS 8th Grd Eng Tchr 1985-; *ai:* Drama Dir; NEA, MCEA 1985-; *office:* Tilden MS 11211 Old Georgetown Rd Rockville MD 20852

EARICH, KRISTEN L., Fourth Grade Teacher; *b:* Circleville, OH; *m:* Mel A.; *c:* Mallory, Evan, Eli; *ed:* OH St Univ (BS) Elem Ed 1986; 20 Post Grad Hrs; *cr:* Frankfort Elem Schl Sixth Grd Tchr 1988-93; Adena Intermediate Schl Sixth Grd Tchr 1993-95, Fourth Grd Tchr 1995-; *ai:* Stu Cncl Adv Frankfort Elem Schl 1991-93; Farm Bureau 1987-, Cncl Pres, Mbrshp Pres; Ag in Classroom 1993-, Facilitator; *office:* Adena Intermediate Schl 10887 6th St Clarksburg OH 43115

EARL, PAUL F., Professor of Biology; *b:* Plattsburgh, NY; *m:* Carole Sabatini; *c:* Stephen, Brian, Laura; *ed:* Houghton Coll (BS) Botany 1957; Plattsburg St Univ (MS) Ed 1961; NY Univ (PHD) Bio Ed 1972; *cr:* Beekmantown Cntrl Schl Bio, Chem, Physics Tchr 1959-61; Elmont Meml Schl Bio, Physics Tchr 1963-67; Nassau Comm Coll Bio Prof 1967-; *ai:* Adv Inter Var Chrstn Flwshp 1968-; NCCFT 1967-; Levittown Bapt Ch 1985-, Elder, Trustee; NY St Univ Chancellor's Awd Excl in Tchng 1975.

EARL, SANDRA HALL, 7th Grade Life Science Teacher; *b:* Lockport, NY; *m:* Harry R.; *c:* Heather A., David R., Hannah M.; *ed:* Clarion Univ (BA) General, Earth & Space Sci 1976; Masters Equivalency Sci Ed 1995; *cr:* Wilmington Area Jr-Sr HS 7th Grd Sci Tchr 1985-91; Wilmington Area MS 7th Grd Sci Tchr 1991-; *ai:* Jr Acad of Sci Spon; 7th & 8th Grd Dance Chaperone; Courtyard Club Adv; Sci Fair Coord & Spon; Ski Trip Chaperone; WAEA, NEA 1985-, Rep; Girl Scouts 1961-, Ldr; Supporting Cesearean Mothers 1980-, Pres; First Presbyn Church 1980-, Sunday Schl Tchr, Deacon, Vlybl Team Capt; *office:* Wilmington Area MS 400 Wood St New Wilmington PA 16142

EARLE, J. MICHAEL, Biology Teacher; *b:* Lowell, MA; *m:* Eileen T. Moran; *c:* Michaeleen, Kathleen; *ed:* Univ of MA (BA) Bio & Philosophy 1969; *cr:* Lowell HS Bio Tchr 26 Yrs; *ai:* AFT & MFT 1989-; Family Svc Lowell 1970-, Pres, Distngd Svc; Democratic City Comm 1972-, Chair; Duquesne Univ Excl in Tchng Awd 1995; Voice of Democracy Distngd Svc Awd.*

EARLE, WILLIAM ROSS, Physical Education Teacher; *b:* Mt Vernon, NY; *m:* Sherry Sue Strohm; *c:* Alyssa Kelly, Christopher Gerald, David Matthew; *ed:* Springfield Coll (BS) PE 1970, (MED) Guid, Psych 1971; Kent St Univ 20 Hrs Adaptive PE; 55 Addl Hrs; *cr:* Fox Lane HS Scndry PE Tchr 1971-87; Bedford Hills Elem Schl PE Tchr 1987-; *ai:* Ftbl, Winter Spring Track Coach; African-Amer Studnts Adv; Weight Trng Club Adv; AFT, NEA 1971-; NY St Assoc of Hlth, PE, Recreation, Dance 1971-, Local Pres 1990-; Westchester Track Ofcl Assn 1976-, Pres; CT Western Dance Tchrs 1995-, Instr; Amer Red Cross 1976-, Instr, 500 Hrs Svc; Police Ath League 1982-, Coach; Adult Ed; St, Local Conf Presenter; *office:* Bedford Hills Elem Schl 123 Babbitt Rd Bedford Hills NY 10507*

EARLEY, CLARE LEPORE, Mathematics Teacher; *b:* Gardiner, ME; *m:* Stephen Myron; *ed:* Middlebury Coll (BA) Math 1972; St Michaels Coll (MED) Ed 1989; 30 Hrs Visual Math; *cr:* A. D. Lawton Intermediate Schl Math Tchr 1972-; *ai:* Essex Jct Ed Assn 1973-, Tchr of Yr 1985; VNEA, NEA 1973-; VT Assn for Mid Level Ed 1985-; NCTM 1985-, St Awardee Presidential Awd Tchr Math, Sci 1993; Teach Courses Tchrs Vis St Michaels Coll; *office:* Albert D. Lawton Inter School 104 Essex Junction VT 05452

EARLEY, DONNA, Foreign Language Teacher; *b:* Bay Shore Terry S.; *c:* Jon Peter, Steven; *ed:* SUNY at Stony Brook (BA) Ital Dowling (MS) Rdng 1985; SCOPE Courses; LILT Wkshps; Span Oakdale-Bohemia Rd JHS Frgn Lang Tchr 1981-83; Ronkonk Frgn Lang Tchr 1983-; *ai:* Frosh Chrldng Coach; Curr Writer; Sec; Frgn Lang Club, Natl Frgn Lang Honor Soc Adv; Long Isl Tchrs Assn; NY St Frgn Lang Tchrs Assn; Amer Assn Tchrs Ital 1995-, Den Ldr; NY St Stud Grant, Wkshp Presenter Annual Li Lang Tchr of Yr 1994.*

EARLY, JOYCE P., Third Grade Teacher; *b:* Syracuse, NY; *ed:* Oswego (BS) Elem Ed 1970; 40 Grad Hrs Beyond BS; Syracuse-Minoa Cntrl Schls Tchr 1974-; *ai:* Comm Comm; AF *office:* Woodland Elem Schl 6320 Fremont Rd East Syracuse NY

EARP, CAROLYN VELIER, Business Education Teacher; *b:* Sh WI; *w:* Thomas R. (dec); *c:* Laura Hughes, Steven; *ed:* Kent St U Bus 1961; 33 Hrs Grad Courses; *cr:* Highland Springs HS Tchr New Brunswick HS Tchr 1966-67; Shepherd Hill Regnl HS Tchr Adult Ed Night Schl; Majorette & Drill Team Adv; NEA, MTA, D Sec; *home:* 12 Mill Rd Dudley MA 01571

EASLEY, APRIL, Special Education Teacher; *b:* Philadelphia Cheyney Univ (BS) Spec Ed 1978, (MS) Elem Ed 1981; PA Doctorial Work Admin, Ed; *cr:* Wagner Jr HS Tchr 2 Yrs; Reserves Captain; *ai:* NHS Spon; Ninth Grd Coord; Governance C Proctor; Summer Schl Prgm Dir; Designed, Coord Project Jur Speaker for Various Orgs; Alpha Kappa Mu Overall Grd Achvm Delta Pi; Spec Ed; Phi Beta Kappan; PFT, NEA 1982-; Edctrs Rou Women in Ed 1991-; Tell Them We Are Rising 1989-, Mentor, Zion Bapt Church 1990-; DA's Office Yth Aid Panel 1989-, Panel *office:* George Washington HS Bustleton & Verree Rd Philade 19116

EASON, BRENDA A., 5th Grade Teacher, Chairperson; *b:* Hc NC; *ed:* Hofstra Univ (BA) Ed 1979; Adelphi Univ (MA) Ed 198 Admin Brooklyn Coll; *cr:* Hempstead Schl Dist Tchr 1979-81; Ur Schl Dist Tchr 1981-; *ai:* Performing Arts Club, Travel Club A Arts, Writing Comms; NYSUT, AFT 1980-; UTA 1982-; *office:* Parkway Elem Schl 440 Northern Pky Uniondale NY 11553

EASON, NORMA BERVINDA, Special Education Teacher; *b:* T *ed:* Univ of MA (BA) Ed-Cum Laude 1975, (MED) Urban Ed Bank of Boston Frgn Payments Clerk 1968-71; Boston Pub Schls Tchr 1976-; *ai:* Historical Black Coll Tour Dir, Cnslr; Double Du Rope Coach; AFT 1976-; BEAM 1990-; Boston Tchrs Union 1976 Bd Mem 1989-; Outstdng Young Women of Amer 1983; Action fo Comm Awd 1990; CCEBS Awd Scholastic Hnrs; NHS; *offic* Timilty MS 205 Roxbury St Roxbury MA 02119

EASSA, REBECCA BECHARD, Mathematics Teacher; *b:* Rous NY; *m:* Chad; *c:* Joshua; *ed:* SUNY at Oswego (BS) Scndry Ed, m SUNY at Cortland (MS) Elem Ed 1991; *cr:* Durgee Jr HS Math Tc *ai:* NEA 1987-; OCMTA 1989-; Kappa Delta Pi 1987-; *office:* HS E Oneida St Complex Baldwinsville NY 13027*

EAST, PHYLLIS ORR, Professor of Piano; *b:* Bloomingtor James; *c:* Alexander, Christopher; *ed:* Oberlin Coll Conservatory (BM) Music 1963; St Univ of NY at Fredonia (MM) Music 197 Western Reserve Univ, Franz Schubert Inst; *cr:* SUNY Coll Pia Prof, Keyboard Area Coord 1973-; *ai:* Piano Club Adv Chair; Prs Acad Bankruptcy, Environment Comms; VVP 1976-; Erie Mus Assn 1980-; Fredonia Prof Dev Grant 1982; Pres Excl in Tchng A Presser Schlsp at Marlboro; *office:* SUNY Univ at Fredonia S Music Mason Fredonia NY 14063

EASTERDAY, DANNIE DEAN, History & Geography Tea Chillicothe, OH; *m:* Lisa Colleen Shoemaker; *c:* Nicholas Morehead St Univ (BS) His 1975; Univ of Dayton (MA) Adm Scioto Valley Local Schls His, Geography Tchr 1975-; *ai:* Sou Jr-Sr HS Proficiency Tutoring Comm; Ross Co Tchrs Assn, NEA NCSS 1 Yr; Alpha Sigma Phi 21 Yrs; Southeastern Jr-Sr HS T 1990; Ross Co Curr Comm Mem; Jr HS Soc Stud Chm; Mem Sou PPO Comm; *home:* 56 Tanager Ct Chillicothe OH 45601

EASTIN, SUSAN BARD, High School English Teacher; *b:* Akron David; *c:* Aaron, Amy; *ed:* Muskingum Coll (BA) British Lit, Ed Grad Credits Univ of Akron, Kent St; *cr:* Cuyahoga Falls HS 1968-; *ai:* Cuyahoga Falls Ed Assn, NEA, OEA 1968-; Girl Scou Ldr; Boy Scouts of Am Cnslr; Sunday Schl Tchr; *office:* Cuyaho HS 2300 4th St Cuyahoga Falls OH 44236

EASTMAN, CHRISTOPHER J., Audio Visual Dir & Ftbl C Montclair, NJ; *ed:* William Paterson St Coll (BA) Acctng 1990; Credit Hrs His; *cr:* Jefferson Twp Bd of Ed Asst Ftbl Coach 1986- Law Enforcement Off 1990-91, Audiovisual Coord 1991-, Head Ft 1995-; *ai:* Asst Coach Indoor Track 1989-, Spring Track Weightroom Supvr 1988-; NJ Ftbl Coaches Assn, Morris Cty Ftbl Assn 1986-; *office:* Jefferson Township H S 1010 Weldon Rd Oa NJ 07438

EASTMAN, ELIZABETH CAMPBELL, Vocal Music Dire Camden, NJ; *m:* David Robert; *c:* Matthew C., Abigail E.; *ed:* G St Coll (BA) Music Ed 1979; Hortt Coll of Music Vocal Music E 1975-76; *cr:* Erial Elem Schl Gen Music Tchr 1980-81; Triton Vocal Music Dir 1983-; *ai:* Concert Choir; Chorale; Show Ch MENC 1983-; NJMEA & SJCDA 1983-; NEA & NJEA 1983-; 1st Church of Barrington, Organist; *office:* Triton Regional HS 250 Ave Runnemede NJ 08078

EASTMAN, J. EDWIN, Math Teacher; *b:* Towanda, PA; *m:* Humbert; *c:* James, Myron; *ed:* Mansfield St Coll (BS) Math F Cortland (MS) Math Ed 1965; *cr:* Newark Vly Cntrl Schl Ma 1962-67; Northeast Bradford Schl Math Tchr 1967-; *ai:* Juggli Local Tchrs Assn, PSEA, NEA 1968-; Orwell Cemetery Assn 1974 Sheep & Wool Growers 1969-, Sec; Orwell Grange 1955-.

EATON, LISA C., English & Theater Arts Teacher; *b:* West Che *m:* G. Wayne; *c:* Joshua Seth; *ed:* IN Univ of PA (BA) Hum, E West Chester Univ (MA) Eng, Lit 1982; 45 Addl Post Grad Telecommunications, Cmptr, Video Tech; *cr:* Great Vly HS Eng, Arts Tchr 1980-; *ai:* Theatre Dir; Great Vly Schl Dist Tech Com In-Svc Consultant, Tchr for Cmptr Literacy; NEA 1990-; WCTE 1 Arts Alliance Exemplary Site Theatre Arts Ed Awd Winner 1996 Great Valley HS 225 N Phoenixville Pike Malvern PA 19355

EATON, MARIELLEN LUCAS, English Teacher; *b:* Bangor, Jonathan Franklin; *c:* Matthew, Caitrin; *cr:* Garland St Jr HS E 1975078; Georges Vly HS Eng Tchr 1978-86, 1993-; *ai:* Yrbk Adv 1995-; GT Stud Comm 1995-; Strategic Planning Comm 1994- Georges Valley HS PO Box 192 Thomaston ME 04861

EATON, MILDRED HALL, Mathematics Teacher; *b:* Princes MD; *c:* Simone Eaton Jordan, Jacob Schiele; *ed:* UMES (BS) 1963; Attnd Georgetown Univ, UDC; Working Toward MS Na Univ; *cr:* Penns Grove Regnl HS PE, Hlth Tchr 1963-65; Mc K

:hr 1967-72; Washington & Lee HS Math Tchr 1985-86; Eastern :hr 1987-; *ai:* SCAC; Comm for Change; Union AFT; Math Club Tchrs Union 1970-, SCAC; DCCTM 1986-, Corresponding Sec; 6-; Pub in NTCM 1991 Yrbk.

ONALD A., English Teacher; *b:* Lockport, NY; *m:* Linda Kopf; Marc; *ed:* Roberts Wesleyan Coll (BA) Eng 1968; SUNY Coll MS) Ed 1972; *cr:* Panama Cntrl Schl Eng Tchr 1968-69; Hoover Tchr 1969-80; Kenmore East HS Eng Tchr 1980-; *ai:* Schl Adv; Schl CORE Team; Kenmore Tchrs Assn 1969-, Bldg Rep; 969-; NCTE 1982-; *office:* Kenmore East HS 350 Fries NY 14150

, DAWN MARIE, Mathematics Teacher; *b:* Baltimore, MD; *ed:* St Univ (BS) Math 1993; Wordperfect 6.0; CPR; Ath Trng; *cr:* ecatur HS Math Tchr 1994-; *ai:* Womens Bsktbl Coach 1993-; h 1993, 1996; Jr Class Adv 1995-; NEA, Worcester Cty Teach 4-; Berlin Rec Dept 1994-, Bsktbl Coach; *office:* Stephen S 9913 Seahawk Rd Berlin MD 21811

CK, BEN WRIGHT, Instructor & Research Assoc; *b:* Upper OH; *m:* Mary Jeanette; *ed:* Marietta Coll (BS) Petroleum g 1976; Univ of WY (MS) Petroleum Engineering 1984; *cr:* Corp Dist Operatins Engr 1976-79; Univ of WY Instr 1979-81; Corp Research Engr 1981-85, Div Head Formation Evaluation Cal Poly Pomona Instr 1985-87; Univ of Rochester Research ir 1987-; Soc of Hispanics Prof Engr Fac Adv; *ai:* Access to on Energy for African Dev Energy Corp Pres; Fac Spon Natl Soc ngrs; Deans Fellow; Project Dir Amers for Preparation in Tech; oleum Engrs 1972-, Tech Ed, Tech Info Comm, Judge Stu Paper JS Patent Awded 1987; World Bank Consulting Stud 1991; Various Confs, Seminars, Radio Prgms; Pub Several Articles; Non-Tech Guide to Energy Resources: Availability, Use & cyclopedia of Life Support Systems; *office:* Univ of Rochester Hall Rochester NY 14627*

CK, SARA V., Philosophy Professor; *b:* Leland, MI; *m:* Clyde; *d:* Aquinas Coll (BA) Eng 1960; Cath Univ (MA) Philosophy lham Univ (PHD) Philosophy 1976; *cr:* Aquinas Coll Instr on 1966-68; St Mary's Coll of MD Editorial Consultant 1977-87, g, Asst Prof of Philosophy 1987-; *ai:* Hnrs Coll Curr Review air; Margaret Brent Comm Co-Convener; Environmental Stud /; Philosophy-Rel Stud Stu Publication; Soc for Stud of Women rs, Bd Mem 1990-; Amer Philosophical Assn 1987-; Intnl Soc nmental Ethics 1990-; Articles Pub; Earth Ethics Co-Founder; ding Our Cities; a Reader in Urban Forestry; *office:* Saint Marys D St Marys Cy MD 20686

YAN ANDREW, Instrumental Music Director; *b:* Camden, NJ; th DeSantis; *c:* Elizabeth Ann, Sarah Kathryn; *ed:* Towson St) Music Ed 1996; *cr:* Mt Airy MS Instrumental Music Dir Liberty HS Instrumental Music Dir 1992-; *ai:* Marching Band; JBA 1988-; *office:* Liberty HS 5855 Bartholow Rd Eldersburg

RDT, NANCY M., 8th Grade US History Teacher; *b:* Hartford, ll of Our Lady of the Elms (BA) His 1965; Centeral CT St Univ His 1976; CEU Inst of Amer Indians Stud; *cr:* Memorial Schl 8th Arts Tchr 1965-67; Roosevelt MS 8th Grd US His & Rdng Tchr Soc Stud Curr Comm; Sr Cncl, Tchr Adv, Soc Stud Dept Chm; 7-; Plainville Historical Soc 1970-; Done Tchr Wkshps for Old : Village, CT Cncl for Soc Stud, Bicentenial Presidential ns for Museum of NY, Norman Rockwell Museum; Book: Men in the Civil War; *office:* Roosevelt MS 40 Goodwin St New 06051

CHARLES FRANCIS, Health & Phys Ed Instructor; *b:* d, MD; *m:* Linda Sue Spangler; *c:* Bridgitt Morrissey, Katie Jo; urg St Univ (BA) Hlth & PE 1976, (MA) Hlth & PE 1979; us 30 Credit Hrs; Certfd PE & K-12th Grd Supvr & Admin; *cr:* Tchr 1979-91; Beall High Tchr 1986-87; Braddock Mid Tchr e-Prin 1994-95; *ai:* Regnl Dir St Bsbl Comm; Asst Bsktbl & Bsbl A 1979-; MSTA 1979-; PAC 1982-; Church Cncl 1994-; Bel Air :l 1994-, Coach Swim Team; *office:* Braddock MS 909 Holland land MD 21502

LE, BARBARA JANE (BLAKE), AP Eng, Fr & Chorus Dir; *b:* H; *c:* Stephanie, Aaron; *ed:* OH Northern Univ (BA) Eng 1969; indlay Coll Music Cert; *cr:* Fostoria HS Eng Tchr 1969-70; ocal Schl Eng, Fr Tchr, Jr HS, HS Chorus Dir 1971-; *ai:* Jr Class EA; MENC; Univ of Toledo OH HS Outstdng Tchr 1994-95; cadia Local Schl 19033 State Route 12 Arcadia OH 44804

LE, CHARLES M., Band Director; *b:* Lancaster, PA; *m:* Linda chi; *c:* Judith, Rachel, Carmon, Seth, Candace; *ed:* IN Univ of Music Ed 1980; Temple Univ (MM) Music Performance 1990; *cr:* Altona & Johnstown Instrumental Music Tchr 1980-84; Area HS Instrumental Music Tchr 1985-; *ai:* Chamber , Marching, Concert & Pep Bands Dir; PMEA 1985-; MENC A 1988-; Grace Bible Flwshp Church 1993-, Choir Dir; *office:* Area HS 409 N Richmond St Fleetwood PA 19522*

LE, JACK MURRAY, Psychology & Sociology Teacher; *b:* n, MD; *m:* Deborah L. DiMaggio; *c:* Kyle, Rachel, Courtney, *l:* Frostburg St Univ (BS) Soc Sci Ed 1971; Western MD Coll rl Arts 1977; Hood Coll (MA) Psych 1996; *cr:* North Hagerstown 5 Yrs; *ai:* NEA 1971-; Amer Psych Assn 1990-; Habitat for Hum rture Comm; *office:* North Hagerstown HS 1200 Pennsylvania rstown MD 21742

LE, JANE M., 4th Grade Teacher; *b:* Martinsburg, PA; *ed:* oll (BA) Span 1968; Elem Cert Penn St Univ; *cr:* Concord HS : 1968-69; Spring Cove Schls 1st & 4th Grd Tchr 1969-; *ai:* rg Brethern in Christ Church 1957-, Sunday Schl Supt, Sunday , Church Bd Sec; *office:* Spring Cove Schls 415 E Spring St rg PA 16662

LE, JEAN ETTER, English Teacher; *b:* Waynesboro, PA; *c:* d, Brody; *ed:* Shippensburg Univ (BS) Eng & Speech 1970, (MS) Supervisory Cert 1976; 45 Credits Beyond Masters; *cr:* Central h-9th Grd Eng Tchr 1970-83; Faust Jr High 8th-9th Grd Eng Tchr PSEA, NEA & CAEA 1970-; *office:* Chambersburg Area Schl S 6th St Chambersburg PA 17201

JANET GILL, Business Education Teacher; *b:* Waterbury, CT; of ME (BS) Bus 1965; 30 Credit Hrs; *cr:* Erskine Acad Bus Ed 5-76; Lincoln Acad Bus Ed Tchr 1982-; *ai:* Governance, Tech, airs Comms; Sr Class Adv; BEAM 1980-; LAEA 1978-81, Schlsp IC Bus Champions 1986, 1988-89, 1991-95.

JEFFREY C., Sixth Grade Teacher; *b:* Allentown, PA; *m:* Terese : Lara, Jennifer, Bryan; *ed:* Kutztown St Coll (BA) Ec 1971; Univ (BA-TC) Elem Ed 1987; *cr:* City of Allentown Mgr, Fin -86; East Penn Schl Dist Elem Tchr 1987-; *ai:* Union Terrace AC; l Coach; NEA, PSEA, EPEA 1987-; East Penn Schoolmens Club *ice:* Shoemaker Schl 4068 N Fairview St Macungie PA 18062

STEVEN L., Frosh Social Studies Teacher; *b:* Fremont, OH; *m:* : Courtney Lynn; *ed:* BGSU (BA) Ed 1988; 28 Addl Hrs Toledo dry Ed; *cr:* Fremont Pub Schls His Tchr 1988-; *ai:* Head Bsbl Coach 2 Yrs; Jr HS Ftbl Coach; NEA 1988-; *office:* Fremont Jr HS 1100 Croghan St Fremont OH 43420

EBERTS, CAROL ANN (PETERS), Retired Elementary Principal; *b:* Dearborn Co, IN; *m:* Roger Everett; *c:* Jeffrey Alan, Roger Michael; *ed:* OH Univ (BS) Elem Ed 1967, (MS) Elem Admin 1983; Addl Work, Stud Early Childhood Ed Testing Training Gessel Org Readiness for Schl, Young Fives; *cr:* Zaleski Bd of Ed 2nd, 3rd Grd Elem Tchr 1964-65; Allensville Bd of Ed 6th Grd Elem Tchr 1965-66; Vinton Co Local Schls T1 Rdng, 1st Grd Elem Tchr 1966-84, PS 6 Elem Prin 1984-93; *ai:* OEA, NEA 1964-, Vinton Co Locat Tchrs Assoc Sec; Phi Delta Kappa 1986-, News Reporter; OH Elem Schl Adm 1984-, Hall of Fame Visitation Team; Delta Kappa Gamma 1970-, Second VP, Comm Chm; Mem of Curr, Instr Ed Assoc; Vinton Co MRDD Bd 1982-, Bd Mem; Cub Scout Ldr 1986-, Pack Ldr, Den Mother; FWB Sunday Schl TChr 1957-, Youth Ldr; FWB Church 1988-, Treas, 1956-, Mem; OH St Tchrs Grant; Tchr of Month; Martha Holden Jennings Scholar; Presenter Schl Readiness Prgms; Mem Regnl Tchr Training Corp Bd for Planning In-Service, St OH Team Working Inclusion; *home:* RR 1 Box 372 Hamden OH 45634*

EBERTS, HOWARD LOUIS, Mrktg Ed Coord & DECA Adv; *b:* Columbus, OH; *ed:* OH St Univ (BS) Mrktg Ed 1978; Wright St Univ 2 Grad Quarter Hrs; Dayton 2 Grad Quarter Hrs; Rio Grande 6 Quarter Hrs in Free Enterprise; *cr:* Licking Cty Jr HS Mrktg Ed Coord 1978-79; Hillsboro City Schls Mrktg Ed Coord 1980-; *ai:* OH DECA Summer Leadership Vol; AVA, OVA 1990-; Prof DECA 1978-; OH DECA Prof 1978-, Bd of Trustees 6 Yrs, Exec Cncl 3 Terms; OH & Natl AMVETS 1994-, Post 68 Adjunct General; 2 Rio Grande Free Enterprise Schlrsps; OH Retail Merchants 15 Yr Tchng Awd; *office:* Hillsboro HS 358 W Main St Hillsboro OH 45133*

EBIE, BRIAN D., Choral Music Teacher; *b:* Akron, OH; *m:* Melissa McDonald; *ed:* Univ of Akron (BA) Music Ed 1990, Music Performance-Organ 1990, (MA) Music Ed 1993; Kent St Univ Completing PHD in Music Ed; *cr:* Roberts MS Vocal & Gen Music Tchr 1990-; Univ of Akron Music Instr 1996; *ai:* 8th Grd Show Choir Dir; 6th-8th Grd Handbell Choir Dir; NEA & OEA 1990-; MENC & OMEA 1990-; Soc Rsrch in Music Ed 1992-; Am Choral Dir Assn 1995-; Mogadore Chrstn Church 1991-, Music Dir & Organist; Falls Ed Assn Grant; Article Pub; Presented Papers at Rsrch Forums; *office:* Roberts MS 3333 Charles St Cuyahoga Falls OH 44221

EBLE, ROBERT PAUL,II, Math & Science Teacher; *b:* Charleston, WV; *ed:* Bob Jones Univ (BS) Math Ed 1988, (MED) Bio Ed 1994; *cr:* Ebenezer Faith Chrstn Schl Math, Sci Tchr 1988-; *ai:* Head Girls Soccer, Asst Boys Bsktbl Coach; Ath Dir; PIAA Sports Ofcl 1989-; KCEA Outstdng Tchrs Awd 1995; *office:* Ebenezer Faith Christian Sch PO Box 99 Plymouth PA 18651

EBNER, DENNIS JOHN, English Teacher; *b:* Malvern, OH; *m:* Jeanne (Wexbrecht); *c:* Patrick, Katie, Julianne; *ed:* Walsh Univ (BA) Eng, Sec Ed 1981; Cleveland St Univ (MED) Curr, Instruction 1996; *cr:* St Peter's Schl 7-8 Grd Eng Tchr 1981-83; Trinity HS Eng Tchr, Yrbk Mod 1986-92; Lakewood HS Eng Tchr, Testing Facilitator, Yrbk Moderator 1992-; *ai:* Yrbk Moderator; Lakewood Tchrs Assn, OEA, NEA 1992-; *office:* Lakewood HS 14100 Franklin Blvd Lakewood OH 44107*

EBRIGHT, JACK CAIN, Social Studies Teacher; *b:* Columbus, OH; *m:* Teresa Finney; *c:* Nikki, Amy Smith, Nathan Smith; *ed:* Loretto Heights Coll (BA) Parapsychology 1976; Post Grad Stud at Univ of CO; *cr:* Romport HS Tchr 1984-89; I-Pass Tchr 1989-92; Briggs HS Tchr 1992-; *ai:* Mock Trial Team Spon; NEA 1984-, Local VP, Svc Awd; OEA 1989-; Phi Delta Kappa; Tchr of Month; Tchr of Grading Period; Educator of Yr; *office:* Briggs HS 2555 Briggs Rd Columbus OH 43223

EBY, G. NELSON, Professor of Earth Sciences; *b:* Bethlehem, PA; *m:* Susan James; *c:* Stephanie L., Jennifer A.; *ed:* LeHigh Univ (BA) Geology 1965, (MS) Geology 1967; Boston Univ (PHD) Geology 1971; *cr:* Univ of MA at Lowell Prof 1970-; *ai:* Adv: Soc Environmental Scis, Outing Club, Sigma Gamma Epsilon; Geological Soc of Amer 1969-; AAAS 1970-; Geochemical Soc 1970-; Journal of African Earth Scis Regnl Ed; Canadian Mineralogist Assoc Ed; Grants: NSF 3 Times, Geol Surv Canada 4 Times, EPA & NATO; Numerous Abstracts & Papers; *office:* Univ Of MA At Lowell Dept of Earth Scis 1 University Ln Lowell MA 01854

EBY, MARLENE J., Mathematics & Cmptr Sci Tchr; *b:* OH; *ed:* Bowling Green St Univ (BSEd) Math 1966, (MA) Math 1970; Attnd Miami Univ, Univ of Dayton & Univ of Cincinnati Post Grad Stud; *cr:* Wayne HS Tchr 1966-69; Great Valley HS Tchr 1970-71; Wayne HS Math & Cmptr Sci Tchr 1971-; Math Dept Head 1992-; *ai:* Acad Challenge Team Adv; Mentor Tchr; Instructional & Supt Adv Comms; NEA, WOEA & HHEA 1971-; WSUACTM 1990-; OCTM 1993-; NCTM 1993; Dayton-Montgomery Cty Math Collaborative Tchr Cncl; Tchr of Yr 1994-95; *office:* Wayne H S Huber Hghts City Schls 5400 Chambersburg Rd Huber Heights OH 45424

ECHEZABAL, MICHELLE MARIE, Third Grade Teacher; *b:* Bronx, NY; *c:* Amber Nowak; *ed:* Fordham Univ (BA) Eng 1981; St Univ at New Paltz (MS) Spcl Ed 1982; 33 Credit Hrs Above Masters; *cr:* PS 89 6th Grd Classroom Tchr 1983-84, 4th Grd Classroom Tchr 1984-87, 3rd-4th Bridge Classroom Tchr 1987-88, 3rd Grd Classroom Tchr 1988-90, 1992-95, Kndgtn Lang Cluster Tchr 1990-91; *ai:* AFT 1985-; UFT 1985-; *office:* PS 89 980 Mace Ave Bronx NY 10469

ECK, PHYLLIS, Instructor; *ed:* Bowling Green St Univ (BA) Eng 1981, (MA) Tech Writing 1982, (PHD) Rhetoric & Composition 1992; *office:* Columbus St Comm Coll 550 Spring St Columbus OH 43216*

ECK, TRACY J., Civics & World Cultures Tchr; *b:* Kittanning, PA; *cr:* Fox Chapel HS Stu Tchr 1991; North Allegheny Schl Dist Sub Tchr 1992-94; Highlands HS Tchr 1994-; *ai:* MS Chrldng Spon; Stud Skills Prgm Spokesperson; *office:* Highlands Sr HS Idaho at Pacific Ave Natrona Heights PA 15065*

ECKELBERGER, LINDA DE MARE, Fifth Grade Teacher; *b:* Warren, OH; *m:* Gary Allen; *ed:* Youngstown St Univ (BS) Elem Ed 1970, (MS) Elem Ed, Curr, Master Tchr 1981; Mentor Tchr, Consultant Tchr Prgm, Great Books Leadership Trng Courses; Addl Post Grad Stud KSU, Ashland Univ, Youngstown St Univ, Walsh Univ; *cr:* Jefferson Elem Schl Third & Fourth Grd Tchr 1971-80; Washington Elem Schl Fourth & Fifth Grd Tchr 1980-; *ai:* Dept Head, Lead Tchr Grds 4-6; Acad Prep Bowl Team Coach; Mentor Tchr; Spelling Bee Comm; Honors Assembly Coord; Family Math Dist Coord; Equations Math Competition Adv; Eastern OH Cncl Tchr of Math Contest; Niles Classroom Tchrs Assn, NEA, OEA, NEOEA, Parent Tchr Home & Schl 1971-; Kappa Delta Pi 1970-; Phi Kappa Phi 1982-; Delta Kappa Gamma 1982-, Music Comm Chprsn; Eastern OH Cncl of Tchrs of Math; Niles Bicentennial Chorus 1975-85, Accompanist; MADD 1990-; Amer Heart Assn 1990-, Vol; Amer Cancer Soc, 1991-, Vol; Outstanding Young Women of Amer 1985; Trumbull Cty A Plus Tchr Awd 1992; Golden Apple Achiever Awd 1992; Ashland Oil Tchr Achvmt Awd 1993; *home:* 667 Shadowood Ln SE Warren OH 44484*

ECKENRODE, KIMBERLY REDDING, Elementary School Counselor; *b:* Greensburg, PA; *m:* William David; *c:* Kerry Elizabeth, Jesse Christner; *ed:* Seton Hill Coll (BA) Psych 1977; Alfred Univ (MS) K-12th Cnslr Ed 1985; 9 Addl Grad Credits; Instructional Support Tchr Trng; Instructional Support Initiative of PA; SAP; Early Chldhd Ed Tchng Cert; *cr:* Northern Potter Schl Dist Kndgtn Tchr 1978-89; Wellsboro Schl Dist Elem Schl Cnslr 1989-91; Northern Potter Schl Dist Instructional Support Tchr 1991-93 & Schl Cnslr 1993-; *ai:* Instructional Support Team & Coord; HS Vol Prg; Prof Dev & Curr Comm; Outdoor Ed Prgm for 6th Graders; NEA, PSEA, Fac Rep; PA Schl Cnslr Assn 1989-; Amer Cnslng Assn 1994; Amer Schl Cnslr Assn 1994, Assoc for Supvr & Currclm Dev 1995-; PA Tchr of Yr Awd Nom 1980; *home:* RR 2 Box 96 Genesee PA 16923*

ECKENRODE, PAUL ANTHONY, Chemistry Teacher; *b:* Spangler, PA; *m:* Gina M. Korlinchak; *ed:* St Francis Coll (BS) Chem 1990; Cert Math 1993; *cr:* Cambria Hts Chem Tchr 1991-93; Northern Cambri Chem Tchr 1993-; *ai:* PSEA & NEA 1991-; Sportsman Assn 1983-; *office:* Northern Cambria HS 807 N 11th St Barnesboro PA 15714

ECKENRODE, ROBERT BRUCE, 9th-12th Grd Math Teacher; *b:* Pittsburgh, PA; *m:* Patricia Lee Lyden; *c:* Jill, Ryan; *ed:* CA St Coll (BS) Math 1966; Bowie St Coll (MS) 1989; *ai:* NEA; *office:* High Point HS 3601 Powder Mill Rd Beltsville MD 20705

ECKENROTH, PATTY YARNELL, First Grade Teacher; *b:* Bellefonte, PA; *c:* Jeremy, Joshua, Zachary, Joseph; *ed:* PA St Univ (BS) Elem Ed 1974; *cr:* Bellefonte Elem 5th Grd Tchr 1974-76, 2nd Grd Tchr 1976-78; Benner Elem 1st Grd Tchr 1989-; *ai:* Lang Arts Facilitator; NEA, PSEA 1989-; Pleasant Gap Elem PTO 1983-, Pres, VP, Sec; Most Outstanding Contribution Awd 1991-92.

ECKER, JOHN, 5th Grade Teacher; *b:* New York City, NY; *m:* Fanny Munoz; *c:* Joshua, Rochelle; *ed:* St Univ NY (BS) His 1968; Baylor Univ (MS) Elem Ed 1974, (EDD) Ed Psych 1978; Defense Lang Inst at Monterey CA; *cr:* Kings Park Dist 5th & 6th Grd Tchr 1972-73; Baylor Univ Tchng Fellow 1975-78; Howard Payne Univ Prof of Ed 1978-86; Plainedge Schl Dist 6th Grd Tchr 1986-87, Elem Sci Dir 1990-92; *ai:* Cmptr Wkshp Ldr; Sci Curr Writer; Apple Awd; Jenkins Awd; *office:* John West Elem 499 Boundary Ave Bethpage NY 11714

ECKERSON, JOHN DAVID, Social Studies Teacher; *b:* Buffalo, NY; *m:* Ethel Goldstein; *c:* Shoshana, Naomi, Jared Wright; *ed:* Univ of VT (BS) Human Dev 1977, (MED) Prof Ed, Curr 1985; Addl 30 Hrs Post Grad Work in His, Psych, Cmptr Applications; *cr:* Georgia Elem Grade 5 Tchr; BFA at Fairfax Soc Stud Tchr 1985-86; Milton Jr Sr HS Soc Stud Tchr 1986-; *ai:* NEA 1986-, Chief Negotitor of Milton Affiliate; ACLU 1988-, Amnesty Intnl 1989-; Tchr of Yr 1992-93; *office:* Milton Sr HS 17 Rebecca Lander Dr Milton VT 05468*

ECKERT, DANIEL A., Math & History Teacher; *ed:* (BSE) 1985; Assoc in Bus & Ed 1982; His Coursework; *cr:* Cincinnati Milacron Technician & Supvr 1965-80; Milford Schls Tchr 1986-; *ai:* MEA 1986-, Negotiator; OEA & NEA 1986-; *office:* Milfrod Exempted Village Schls 5735 Pleasant Hill Rd Milford OH 45150

ECKERT, NATALIE ALLENBAUGH, Mathematics & Chem Teacher; *b:* Ridgeway, PA; *m:* Jude Allen; *c:* Ashlee Nicolle; *ed:* Clarion Univ of PA (BS) Scndry Ed & Math 1992; Attnd Saint Bonaventure & Gannon Univ; *cr:* Johnsonburg HS Math & Chem Tchr 1993-; *ai:* Chem Lovers Club Spon; Frosh Class Adv; SAP Team Mem; PSEA 1992-; NCTM 1992-; Trinity United Meth Church 1986-; Clarion Univ Stu Tchr of Yr 1992; *office:* Johnsonburg Area HS 591 Elk Ave Johnsonburg PA 15845*

ECKERT, OLIVIA MORREALE, Kindergarten Teacher; *b:* Jersey City, NJ; *m:* Kerry; *c:* Francesca J., Alexis M.; *ed:* Jersey City St Coll (BA) Early Chldhd Ed 1975; Art Ed 40 Credits 1972-73; *cr:* Philip G. Vroom Schl Robinson Schl Kndgtn Tchr 1976-77; Vroom Learning Ctr Pre-Kndgtn, Kndgtn Tchr 1977-; *ai:* Civic Responsibility, Earth Day, Week of the Young Child Comms; Fall Act Coord; NEA, NJEA, Bayonne Tchrs Assn 1976-; NJAKE 1993-; NJ Governors Tchr of Yr Awd 1994; Hudson Cty Tchr of Yr Awd 1994; *office:* Vroom Learning Ctr 18 W 26th St Bayonne NJ 07002

ECKERT, WILLIAM JOHN, Business Instructor; *b:* Rensselaer, NY; *m:* Diane Barbara Butler; *c:* Lauren; *ed:* Hudson Vly Comm Coll (AAS) Electrical Tech 1961; Empire St Coll (BS) Indstrl Mngmt 1977; Coll of Saint Rose (MS) Mngmt 1980; 27 Credit Hrs SUNY at Albany MS Ec; *cr:* AT&T Tech Consultant 1961-89; Coll of Saint Rose Adj Instr 1986-93; Siena Coll Adj Instr 1989-93; Empire St Coll Adj Instr 1995-; Hudson Vly Comm Coll Adj Instr, Corporate Instruction 1991-; *ai:* Tchng Excl Awd Coll of St Rose 1993; *home:* 12 Huckleberry Dr Castleton NY 12033

ECKES, MARY KELLY, Retired Biology Teacher; *b:* New Brunswick, NJ; *m:* John Taylor; *ed:* Coll of St Elizabeth (BA) Math 1960; Univ of Notre Dame (MS) Bio 1968; 60 Credit Hrs Bio, Scndry Ed 1961-80; *cr:* De Paul HS Math, Bio Tchr 1957-68; East Orange Cath HS Bio I & II Tchr 1969-71; Northern Valley Regnl HS Accelerated Bio I, Advanced Placement Bio II Tchr 1971-; *ai:* NEA, NJ Sci Assn, NSTA, NABT 1971-; NVEA 1971-94, Sec 1970, 1980, Bldg Rep 1992-93; Cancer & Leukemia Socs Local Vol 1980-; Distinguished Scndry Schl Tchrs Princeton Prize Finalist 1987; Tchr of Yr 1986; Natl Sci Fnd Grants Recipient 1965-69; *home:* 254 Cedric Rd Centerville MA 02632

ECKHARDT, JOSEPH PAUL, Associate Professor of History; *b:* New Brighton, PA; *ed:* Clarion St Coll (BA) His 1966; Lehigh Univ (MA) His 1968; *cr:* Montgomery Cty Comm Coll Assoc Prof of His 1968-; *ai:* Betzwood Film Archive Founder; Betzwood Silent Film Festival Coord; AFT 1982-; DOMITOR 1989-; Natl Trust for His Preserv 1980-; NEH Summer Stipend Grant 1992; Numerous Articles Pub; Book Accepted for Publication; *office:* Montgomery County Comm Coll 340 Dekalb Pike Blue Bell PA 19422

ECKHARDT, PAUL, Mathematics Department Chm; *b:* Chattahoochee Cty, GA; *m:* Lucia; *c:* Paul J.; *ed:* Syracuse Univ (BS) Math 1964; Western CT Univ (MS) Math 1971; SUNY at New Paltz (CAS) Admin 1974; NSF Inst Colgate Univ AP Tchrs 1973; Advanced Grad Stud Syracuse Univ Math Sabbatical 1974-75; Discrete Math Statewide Inst Comm Coll of Finger Lakes 1989; *cr:* Lakeland HS 9-12 Grd Math Tchr 1964-65; Carmel Jr HS 7-8 Grd Math Tchr 1965-66; Carmel HS 9-12 Grd Math Tchr 1966-69; Carmel Cntrl Sch Dist Resource Tchr 1969-74, Dept Chm 1975-; *ai:* East Fishkill Town Soccer League Coach; NY St Assn of Math Supvr, Pres; Assn of Math Tchrs NYS, Corresp Sec; Ten-Cty Math Edctrs Assn, Exec Dir; NCTM; NCSM; NYS Cncl of Educl Assn Ldrshp 1984; AMS 1975; Pi Mu Epsilon 1964; Textbooks Pub; 30 Journal Articles Pub.

ECKHAUS, SHARON, Fifth Grade Teacher; *b:* Brooklyn, NY; *c:* Jennie, Joshua; *ed:* Hofstra Univ (BS) Ed 1965; Stony Brook Univ (Masters) Lbrl Stud 1984; 90 Credit Hrs Above Masters; *cr:* East Islip Schl Dist Elem Tchr 1965-; *ai:* Safety Patrol; Schl Newspaper & Play & Drama Club Spon; Amer Cancer Soc; *office:* John F Kennedy Elem Schl 94 Woodland Dr East Islip NY 11730*

ECKMAN, MARK A., Religion Teacher; *b:* Pittsburgh, PA; *ed:* Duquesne Univ (BA) Philosophy 1981; St Vincent Seminary (MDiv) Theology 1984; Cmptr Sci 100 Credits; *cr:* Resurrection Schl Rel, Cmptrs Tchr 1985-90; St Sebastian Schl Rel, Cmptrs Tchr 1990-91; St Valentine Schl Rel, Cmptrs Tchr 1991-92; Seton-LaSalle HS Rel Tchr 1992-; *ai:* Campus Ministry Dir; Stage Crew Moderator; NCEA 1992-; Article Pub 1987; Parish Information Prgm 1988; *office:* Seton-Lasalle HS 1000 Mcneilly Rd Pittsburgh PA 15226

ECKMAN, SANDRA NAGLE, Music Tchr & Choral Director; *b:* Lynn, MA; *m:* Art; *c:* Christopher, Melissa; *ed:* Univ of MA at Lowell (BS) Music Ed 1968; Cambridge Coll (MED) Ed 1994; *cr:* Wilmington Pub Schls Music Tchr 1968-73; Wakefield Pub Schls Music Tchr 1982-; *ai:* Show Choir Ex-Curr; Piano Tchr; MENC 1982-; NEA & MTA 1982-; ACDA.

ECONOMOPOULOS, ANDREW JAMES, Economics Professor; *b:* Westbury, NY; *m:* Deborah S.; *c:* Jennifer, Nicolas; *ed:* SUNC at Fredonia (BA) Ec 1976; VA Tech (MA) Ec 1982, (PHD) Ec 1985; *cr:* Millsaps Coll Asst Prof 1985-88; Ursinus Coll Assoc Prof 1988-; *ai:* Omicron Delta Epsilon Adv; Hobson Svc House; Chrstn Flwshp; Ec, Bus Clb; ACE, Cliometric Soc 1995-; Strategic Planning Comm for BASD 1993-; Trinity ECC Ministry Cncl 1994-, Pres; Numerous Publications; *office:* Ursinus Coll PO Box 1000 Collegeville PA 19426

ECONOMOU, CATHERINE FANOS, 4th Grade Classroom Teacher; *b:* Fitchburg, MA; *m:* Stephen; *ed:* (BS) Elem Ed 1974; Tufts Univ (MED) Ed 1978; 30 Addl Credits; Cert Rdng Specialist; Cert Rdng Supvr; *cr:* Reingold Elem Schl 2 Grd Tchr 1974-75, 4 Grd Tchr 1975-76; Initiated Gifted Prgm Pilot 1976-77; McKay Elem Chptr 1 Rdng Specalist 1977-85; Crocker Elem Schl 4 Grd Tchr 1985-; *ai:* Fitchburg Tchrs Assn, MA Tchr Assn 1974-; Friend of Tchr Libr 1995-; Natl Philoptochos 1980-, Local Chapter Sec; Amer Hellenic Educl Progressive Assn Daughters Penelope Div 1990-; Horace Mann Grant; Schl Improvement Cncl; *office:* Crocker Elem Schl Bigelow Rd Fitchburg MA 01420*

ECTON, JEANNE MARIE, Proj Challngr & TAG Teacher; *b:* Hagerstown, MD; *m:* Roger Eugene; *c:* Robert Eugene, Samantha Mae; *ed:* Shepherd Coll (BA) Bio, Gen Sci 1971; Shippensburg Univ (MS) Bio 1978; Tchng Spec Child in Regular Classroom; Cmptr Literacy; Chem, Bio Curr; Aquatic Bio; Critical Thinking; Lab Techniques; TAG Ed; Appleworks, Marine Sci; Biotechnology; Governors Acad of Sci & Math; MD Sci Initiative St Parks & Aquatics; Microsoft for Windows; *cr:* North Hagerstown HS Sci Tchr 1972-94; Shepherd Coll Bio Prof 1991-93; Boonsboro Elem Schl Resource Tchr 1994-; *ai:* Cmptr Advy, Social Comm; GLOBE Tchr; NEA, MD St Tchrs Assn, Wash Cty Tchrs Assn 1972-, Rep; NABT, MD Assn of Sci Tchrs, MD Assn of Bio Tchrs 1980-, Trustee, MD St Bio Tchr of Yr 1990; NSTA 1980-; One of 4 Outstddng Tchrs at North 1976; Jaycees Outstdng HS Tchr 1986; Potomac Edison Grant Winner 1986; Finalist Outstdng Bio Tchr in MD 1988; Nom Excl Tchng MD Assoc of Sci Tchrs 1988; MD Outstdng Bio Tchr 1990; Tandy Tech Schl 1992; Article Pub 1992; Presidential Finalist 1993; *office:* Boonsboro Elem Schl 5 Campus Dr Boonsboro MD 21713

ED, NORMAN, Art Teacher; *b:* Johnstown, PA; *m:* Michelle Frampton; *c:* Nelle, Wesley; *ed:* Tyler Schl of Art (BFA) Glass 1981; Grad Stud Sculpture Dr James Nestor 1993-; *cr:* WLC Co Consulting Engrs Field Svcs Dir 1983-87; WEstmont Hilltop Schl Dist Art Tchr 1989-; IN Univ of PA IUP Grad Asst 1993-94; Horizons Schl of Crafts Head Glass Dept 1995; *ai:* WECARE Club; Strategic Planning Facilitator; PSEA 1989-; Associated Artists of Pittsburgh 1994-, Saver Industries Awd; Allied Artists of Johnstown 1987-, Pres, Numerous Show Awds; Show Sculptpure Regularly PA, Natl Frequently Awded Various Shows; *office:* Westmont Hilltop Schl Dist 827 Diamond Blvd Johnstown PA 15905*

EDDINS, WILLIAM COLE, Fifth Grade Teacher; *b:* Canton, OH; *m:* Amy Carr; *c:* Meghan; *ed:* Mt Union Coll (BA) Elem Ed 1987; Ashland Univ (ME) Sports Sci 1994; *cr:* West Branch Local Schls 5th & 7th-8th Lang Arts Tchr 1987-91; Lake Local Schls 8th Grd Lang Arts Tchr 1991-93; Louisville City Schls 5th Grd Tchr 1993-; *ai:* Var Boys Bsktbl Head Coach; NEA & OEA 1987-; OHSBCA 1993-; Louisville Ath Cncl 1993-; W Branch Local Schls Adac Excl Awd; *home:* 5527 Oakridge St Louisville OH 44641

EDDOWES, WAYNE ARNOLD, Business Education Teacher; *b:* Philadelphia, PA; *m:* Jean Bidlack; *c:* Jeffrey, Jennifer; *ed:* Bloomsburg Univ of PA (BSEd) Acctng 1969, (MSEd) Acctng 1973; *cr:* Mifflinburg Area HS Bus Ed Tchr 30 Yrs; *ai:* Bus Dept Chprsn; NEA, PSEA, MAEA 1966-; NBEA, EB 1983-; PBEA 1970-; Mifflinburg Hose Co 1972-; Borough Cncl 1986-92; *home:* 249 Green St Mifflinburg PA 17844

EDDY, ROBERT J., Biology Teacher; *b:* Swansea, MA; *m:* Joyce McDonald; *ed:* Bridgewater St Coll (BA) Earth Scis 1973; Providence Coll (MA) Ed 1990; 70 Hrs Beyond Masters in Bio; *cr:* Case Jr HS 8th Grd Sci Tchr 1973-84; Case HS 10th-12th Grd Bio Tchr 1984-; *ai:* Schlsp Comm; Schl Comm; Church Comm; NSF Grants; Tchr of Yr Awd; Citizen of Yr Awd; Congressional Awds; Presidential Merit Awd; Gov Awd; *office:* Joseph Case HS 70 School St Swansea MA 02777*

EDELMANN, DORITA MARTINEZ, Spanish Teacher; *b:* Camaguey, Cuba; *m:* Diego F.; *c:* Kristina Nicole, Patricia Edelmann Mergler; *ed:* Montclair St Coll (BA) Span, Scndry Ed 1966; Loyola Coll, Univ of MD Grad Credits; Minor in Lib Sci; *cr:* Cresskill HS Span Tchr 1966-69; Martin Spalding HS Span Tchr, Dept Chair 1978-80; Anne Arundel Cty PS Part-time Tchr 3 Yrs, Span Tchr 1980-; *ai:* MD Stu Assistance Prgm; NEA, MSTA, TAAAC 1980-; *office:* South River Sr HS 201 E Central Ave Edgewater MD 21037

EDELSTEIN, DOROTHY ISENBERG, Fine Arts Teacher; *b:* Brooklyn, NY; *m:* Glen M.; *c:* Antonia Rose; *ed:* Schl of Visual Arts (BFA) Media Arts 1980; Hunter Coll (MS) Elem Ed & Early Chldhd 1995; NY Tchr Cert 1993; *cr:* St Angela Hall Acad K-8th Grd Fine Arts & Music Tchr & 5th-8th Grd Rdng, Lang Arts & ReligionTchr & Chorus Dir 1984-90, 5th-8th Grd Rdng, Lang Arts Tchr 1994-95; Sacred Heart-Mt Carmel Schl for the Arts Pre-K-8th Grd Fine Arts & Music Tchr 1990-93; ST Catherine of Genoa Schl K-8th Grd Fine Arts Tchr 1995-; *ai:* Entertainment Comm; Tchr Wkshp at Diocese of Brooklyn 1988-; Tchr Wkshp at NYCATA-UFT 1992; NAEA 1996-; ST Andrew the Apostle Parish 1995-, Parish Cncl; Sr Irene T Murphy & John J Duffy Awd for Creative Curr Materials at Archdiocese of NY 1992; *home:* 25 Oliver St Brooklyn NY 11209*

EDEN, ANN BISHOP, Resource Teacher; *b:* Utica, NY; *m:* John R.; *c:* Douglas, Scott; *ed:* Cortland St (BS) Elem Ed 1962; Hofstrea Univ (MS) K-Adult Spec Ed 1969; C. W. Post Rdng Cert; 59 Addl Credit Hrs; *cr:* N. Y. 5th Grd Tchr 1963; North Babylon 3rd, 5th Grd Spec Ed Tchr, Self Contained Classes 1964-69; Connetquot Elem-HS Spec Ed Tchr 1977-, Dist Consultant Tchr 3 Yrs; *ai:* Ad Hoc Site Mgmt Inclusion Team Chm; AFT, CTA 1977-; Consultant Tchr Svcs for K-12th Grd Spec Ed Prgm Co-Extablisher; Dev, Wrote Ed Plan Objectives; Stu Placement Wkshp Presenter.

EDER, JAMES MATTHEW, Social Studies Teacher; *b:* New York, NY; *c:* James A. Eder; *ed:* St John's Univ (BA) His, Philosophy 1961; CCNY (MA) Philosophy 1963; Ed Admin Hofstra Univ; *cr:* JHS NYC Tchr 1963-67; Northport HS Psych, Advanced Placement European His Tchr 1967-; *ai:* Amer Psych Assn 1977-; AFT 1963-; Pub Books Lessons in PsychJ. Weston Walch, AP European His; Author of IL Unpublished Novels; *office:* Northport H S Laurel Hill Rd Northport NY 11768*

EDGERLY, EUGENE C., History Teacher; *b:* Sault St Marie, MI; *m:* Gloria Milez Manansala; *c:* Alison Territo, Heather, Joshua; *ed:* Northern MI Univ (BA) Eng 1960; Boston Univ (MA) Intnl Relations 1969; MI St Univ (MA) Scndry Schl Admin 1973; *cr:* Lake Shore HS Eng & Soc Stud Tchr 1960-62; Dept of Defense Dependent Schls 1st-12th Grd Soc Stud, PE, Bus Eng & Speech Tchr 1962-; Cntrl TX Coll Adjunct Prof 10 Yrs; *ai:* NEA, Life Mem; Phi Delta Kappa; *office:* Yokota HS Dodds P/J Yhs Schl Unit 5072 APO AP 96328

EDGETTE, J. JOSEPH, Associate Professor of Ed; *b:* Philadelphia, PA; *ed:* West Chester St Coll (BS) Eng Ed 1966; Univ of PA (MS) Ed 1971, (MA) Folklore 1977, (PHD) Folklore, Folklife Stud 1982; *cr:* Ridley Schl Dist Jr HS Eng Tchr 1966-79; Villanova Univ Adj Fac 1979-89; Widener Univ Fac, Admin 1979-; *ai:* Stu Ed Assn Adv; Grad Ed Admissions Comm Chair; Promotion, Tenure, Acad Freedom Comm Chair; Amer Culture Assn 1986-, Chair-Elect; Children's Folklore Soc 1976-, Past Pres; Mid-Atlantic Folklife Assn 1990-, Treas; Phi Kappa Phi; Kappa Delta Pi; DE Co Hist Soc 1970-, Past VP; Assn for Gravestone Stud 1981-, Trustee; PA Inst of Tech 1994-, Bd of Acad Advs; PA Dept of Ed 1993-, Prgm Review Bd; Outstdng Tchr of Yr Awd Nom 1996; Numerous Articles, Several Chptrs Pub; *office:* Widener Univ 1 University Pl Chester PA 19013

EDHOLM, CARL E., Fourth Grade Teacher; *b:* Buffalo, NY; *m:* Mary Lovering; *c:* Carl Jr., Daniel, Christy; *ed:* St Univ Coll at Buffalo (BA) Elem Ed 1973; Cansius Coll (MS) Ed 1977; *cr:* 2nd Grd Tchr 1973-76; 3rd Grd Tchr 1976-93; Orchard Park Cntrl Schls 4th Grd Tchr 1993-; *ai:* Stu Cncl Adv 20 Yrs; Intramurals; Numerous Comms; OPTA, NYSUT, NEA 1973-; Youth Coaching 1975-95; *office:* Orchard Park Cntrl Schls Baker Rd Orchard Park NY 14127

EDINGFIELD, WAYNE ERIC, Secondary Education Teacher; *b:* Hillsboro, OH; *m:* Janice Gill; *c:* Chris, Kent; *ed:* Wilmington Coll (BA) Math 1984; Coll of Mt St Joseph (MS) Scndry Ed 1990; *cr:* OH Valley Local Math Tchr 1984-; *ai:* Var Track Coach; FCS Ldr; NEA, OEA, OVLEA 1984-; Nom Twice for Ashlands Tchr Achvmt Awd; Mem Venture Capital Grant TBHM; *office:* Peebles H S 1 Simmons Ave Peebles OH 45660*

EDISON, JOHN D., Math & Computer Teacher; *b:* Middletown, NY; *m:* Nancy Sharpe; *c:* Jane Margaret Stevenson; *ed:* Atlantic Union Coll (BS) Music Ed 1959; Ithaca Coll (MS) Music Ed 1963; Combs Coll of Music 3 Hrs; Westminster Choir Coll 8 Hrs; Kutztown Univ 6 Hrs; Penn St 12 Hrs; *cr:* Blue Mountain Acad Music Tchr, Band Dir 1959-90, Math, Cmptr Tchr 1990-; *ai:* Schl Newspaper Adv; NSTA 1994-; Tilden Township Planning Comm 1978-, Chrprsn; Blue Mt Acad Church 1970-, Elder; Elma Mc Kibbin Awd; *home:* RR 3 Box 3648 Hamburg PA 19526*

EDISON, NANCY SHARPE, Music Department Chairperson; *b:* North Tonawanda, NY; *m:* John Delma; *c:* Jane Margaret, Edison Stevenson; *ed:* Atlantic Un Coll (BS) Music Ed 1959; Coombs Coll of Music (MMus) Organ & Piano Performance 1972; Westminster Choir Coll Post Grad Work Choral, Organ, Piano & Handbell; *cr:* Blue Mountain Acad Music Tchr & Dept Chair 1959-; *ai:* Homeroom Tchr; Acad Standards & Curr Comms; Organ Recitalist; Amer Guild of Organist 1959-; Amer Choral Dir Assn 1983-; Amer Guild of Eng Handbell Ringers 1987-; MTNA, Rdng Music Tchrs Assn, Rdng Guild of Organists 1959-; Zapara Excl in Tchng Awd 1993; Alma Mc Kibben Sabbatical Awd 1992; Columbia Union Tchrs Comm Music Division Chprsn 1990; Mid Sts Evaluation Music Section Chprsn 1992; *office:* Blue Mountain Acad Rd 3 Box 3642 Hamburg PA 19526*

EDKIN, WAYNE SCOTT, English Department Chairperson; *b:* Oneida, NY; *c:* Scott, Trevor; *ed:* Springfield Coll (BS) Eng Ed 1970; Univ of NH (MST) Eng 1975; IN UNiv of PA (PHD) Rhetoric & Linguistics 1985; SUNY at Cortland (CAS) Ed Admin 1989; Post Grad Credits SUNY at Oswego; *cr:* New England Coll Head Resident & Asst Dean 1971-73; Mohawk Valley CC Eng Inst 1975-79; IN Univ of PA Grad Tchng Asst 1981; Camden HS Eng Tchr 1973, Eng Dept Head 1981-; *ai:* Var Wrestling Coach 1974-; League Wrestling Chm & Mem Regnl Wrestling Comm 11 Yrs; Dist & Building Level Schl Improvement Comm; Natl & Intnl Wrestling Offcial 1985-; Camden Tchrs Assn 1973-, Pres 1989-; AFT, NYSUT 1973-; NCTE 1975-; NYS Eng Cncl 1976-, Exec Cncl 1985; Camden Rotary Club 1981-, Pres 1985; NY Amer Legion Boys St, Cnslr 1976-82; Textbook Reviewer Eng Journal 1982-83; NYS Eng Cncl Tchr of Excl 1981; Outstanding Young Man of America 1983; Whos Who Amer Ed 1990; Kappa Delta Pi; *office:* Camden H S Oswego St Camden NY 13316*

EDLER, ALICE G., Work & Family Life Teacher; *b:* Columbus, OH; *m:* George; *ed:* OH Univ (BSHEC) Home Ec 1975; *ai:* FHA & Hero Key Adv; NEA & OEA 1975-; ACEA 1975-, Pres; Delta Kappa Gamma 1989-, Chprsn; Twig 6 Fairfield Med Ctr 1981-, VP, Hist & News Reporter Sec; Martha Holden Jennings Scholar 1982-83; *office:* Amanda-Clearcreek HS 414 N School St Amanda OH 43102

EDMISTON, ROBERT BEVERLY,JR., English Teacher; *b:* Harrisburg, PA; *m:* Dana Lee Johnson; *c:* Maxwell Curtis, Molly Ann; *ed:* Mansfield Univ (BA) Eng Lit 1983; Scndry Eng Cert 1987; Elem Ed Cert at East Stroudsburg Univ 1996; Trained Instr for Dr. John Collins Writing Prgm, Sandel Wrtng Prgm, Project Wild; *cr:* Hackettstown HS Eng Tchr 1987-90; East Side HS Eng, Math Instr 1990-91; Pleasant Vly HS Eng Tchr 1992-; *ai:* HS Portfolio Comm; Mock Trial, Media, Newspaper Adv; Asst Bsktbl, Softbl Coach; NEA 1987-; PVEA 1992-; *office:* Pleasant Valley HS Rt 209 Brodheadsville PA 18322

EDMISTON, ROSEMARY, Sixth Grade Teacher; *b:* Springfield, PA; *ed:* Saint Joseph Univ (BS) Bio 1986; Widener Univ (MS) Ed 1994; *cr:* Temple Univ Medical Schl Research Lab Tech 1986-89; Our Lady of Perpetual Help Schl 6th Grd Math & Sci Tchr 1989-; *ai:* Stu Govt Moderator; Sftbl Coach; Sci Fair Organizer; NCTM 1991-; Sci Coord; Tutoring; *office:* Our Lady-Perpetual Help Schl 2130 Franklin Ave Morton PA 19070*

EDMONDSON, ADAM RUSSEL,SR., AP Chemistry & Physics Teacher; *b:* Hazleton, PA; *m:* Margaret Delmonico; *c:* Adam; *ed:* PA St Univ (ASCH) Chem Engineering 1968, (BS) Chem 1970, (MS) Chem & Ed 1973; Addl 75 Credits in Electrical & Cmptr Engineering with System Interface Techniques; *cr:* Hazleton Area HS AP Chem & Physics Inst 1970-; *ai:* Jr Acad of Sci Adv; Amer Chem Soc Stu Adv; ACS 1970-, Outstanding Chem Tchr 1989; Phi Delta Kappa 1973-; NEA 1970-; Woodrow Wilson Master Tchr 1989; Outstanding Educator Wilkes Univ Awd 1991; Cmptr Interfacing Manual 1985; *office:* Hazelton Area HS 1601 W 23rd St Hazleton PA 18201*

EDMONDSON, DAVID LEN, English Instructor; *b:* Monroe, MI; *m:* Judith Kay Campbell; *c:* Guy Custer, Andrew; *ed:* Youngstown St Univ (BS) Ed 1974; Kent St Univ (MS) Ed Tech 1978; Univ of Akron, Ashland Coll Post-Grad Stud; *cr:* Newbury HS Eng Instr 1974-; *ai:* Ftbl Coach; Newbury Ed Assn 1974-, Pres; NEA, OH Ed Assn 1974-; NCTE, OH Cncl of Tchrs of Lang Arts; Phi Delta Kappa 1985-; Friends of Bainbridge Lib 1988-, VP; ATTEP Prgm Mentor Tchr Kent St Univ 1996; Outstdng Tchr Awd Univ of Chicago 1983; Martha Holden Jennings Scholar 1979; *office:* Newbury HS 14775 Auburn Rd Newbury OH 44065*

EDMONDSON, MICHAEL, History Instructor; *b:* Philadelphia, PA; *c:* Amanda Haley, Jonathan Victor; *ed:* Cabrini Coll (BA) His 1988; Villanova Univ (MA) His 1989; Temple Univ Working on PHD His; *cr:* Saint Anthony of Padua Elem Schl His Instr 1989-90; Bishop Eustace Preparatory Schl His Instr 1990-, Cabrini Coll His & Ed Instr 1992-; Peirce Tunion Coll His Instr 1993-; *ai:* His Club & Current Events Club Moderator; Bsbl Asst Coach; Womens Track Coach; Amer Historical Assn 1994; Soc for Historian of Amer Foreign Relations 1990-; Bus His Conf 1993-; Herbert Hoover Lib Presidential Grant 1993; Book Reviw Pub for Hispanic Amer Historical Review; Mentioned in Intnl Directory of Bus Historians & Intnl Directory of Bus & Mgmt Scholars & Research; *office:* Bishop Eustace Prep Schl Rt 70 Pennsauken NJ 08109*

EDMUNDS, MARGY, Guidance Counselor; *b:* Brooklyn, NY; *ed:* SUNY at Cortland (BS) PE 1965; CUNY at Lehman (MS) Hlth Ed 1974; Rollins Coll of FL (MA) Cnslng 1991; *cr:* Suffern HS 1970-; *ai:* Var Girls Bsktbl Coach; Hlth Players; Peer Ldrshp Adv; NYSTA; WPRCA; *office:* Suffern HS Viola Rd Suffern NY 10901

EDMUNDSON, LAWRENCE GEORGE, Social Studies Teacher; *b:* New Bedford, MA; *m:* Susan Benoit; *c:* Marc, Christopher; *ed:* Univ of MA at Amherst (BA) Pol Sci 1972; Addl Hrs RI Coll; *cr:* New Bedfo Stud Tchr 1973-; Newbury Coll Ec Tchr 1988-; *ai:* Former C Congress Adv; Organized SADD; MA Tchrs Assn & NEA 1973- Cncl for Soc Stud 1984-, Former Pres; Jr Achvt Greater Ne Applied Ec Tchr of Yr 1990 & 1993; Military Order of World W Tchr of Yr 1990; New Bedford Area Chamber of Commerce Co Awd Outstanding Svc Ec Tchr; *home:* 200 Beeden Rd Dart 02747

EDNER, ROBERT GRIFFITH, Biology Teacher; *b:* Dubois, Ben; *ed:* Clarion Univ (BS) Bio, His 1966, (MS) Speech Audiology 1976, Kent St Univ (PHD) Audiology, Psychoacou *cr:* Riverside Military Acad Tchr 1966; Falconer Jr HS Tch Iroudequioit HS Tchr 1967-68; Shaler Area HS Tchr 1968-; NEA; PA Speech & Hearing Assn; Amer Speech & Hearing As 1986-, Sec; Berkeley Hills Ath Assn 1985-, Sec; Presentation o Thesis, Rsrch; *office:* Shaler Area Sr HS 381 Wible Run Rd Pit 15209*

EDOBOR-OSULA, VALENTINE O., Science Teacher; Nigeria; *m:* Josephine S. Edobor-Oscula; *c:* Folly, Osat Valentine, Emmanuel; *ed:* Lincoln Univ (BA) Chem, G Sc 1976 CUNY (MA) Environ Sci Ed 1982; 29 Credits Tchrs Coll, Colu Post Grad Stud; *cr:* Brooklyn Tech HS Sci, Bio, Chem Tch Andrew Jackson HS Sci, Chem Tchr 1984-85; August Martin Tchr 1985-86; Grover Cleveland HS Sci, Chem Tchr 19 Rockaway HS Sci, Chem Tchr; *ai:* Tennis, Rdng, Bike Riding, Overseas, Africa; ALCHEM 1990-; Natl Inst of Hlth Awd; App York Coll CUNY; Fellowship Queens Coll Research Assoc; Rockaway HS 821 Bay 25th St Far Rockaway NY 11691

EDSON, LYNDA KAAKE, English Instr & Curr Developer; *b:* ME; *m:* Stephen; *ed:* Westfield St (BA) Eng & Span 1974; Cam (MED) Integrated Stud 1996; *cr:* Easton Jr HS Aide 1975-76; S Regnl Eng Instr 1976-; *ai:* Curr Developer; Implementor; AFT ASCD 1994-; Presented Amelthyst Apple by Supt for Outsta 1994; *office:* Southeastern Regnl Voc Tech 250 Foundry St So MA 02375

EDWARDS, BETHANN HECOX, Secondary Social Studies T Hartford, NY; *m:* Robert F.; *c:* Shane Chastain, James, Brigid; at Albany (BA) His, Psych 1983, (MA) Ed 1986; *cr:* Mohawk Coll Adj Soc Sci, Crim Justice 1988-90; Rome Cath HS Soc Dept Chprsn 1987-90; Oneida Cty BOCES Learning Coord, Alt 1990-93; Seuquoit Vly Cntrl Schls Scndry Soc Stud Tchr 199 Stu Cncl, SADD, Speech, DebateF Ldrshp Mentor, Close Up, S a Choice; NVSUT, AFT 1990-; SADD Tchr of Month 19 Sauquoit Valley Cntrl HS 2601 Oneida St Sauquoit NY 13456*

EDWARDS, CATHERINE FAIRLEY, Guidance Counselor Bend, IN; *m:* Wm. Keith; *ed:* Univ of Notre Dame (BA) Psych Univ of Amer (MA) Guid, Cnslng 1993; *cr:* Cath Univ Admiss 1990-92; Acad of Holy Cross Guid Cnslr 1993-; *office:* Acad O Cross 4920 Strathmore Ave Kensington MD 20895

EDWARDS, CATHY S., Basketball Coach; *b:* Gallipolis, OH *cr:* Meigs HS Sec 1989-; *ai:* Reserve Girls' Bsktbl Coach 1995 Adv; *office:* Meigs HS 42091 Pomeroy Pike Pomeroy OH 4576

EDWARDS, CHARLES DENNIS, Blackbelt Master Instruct York, NY; *ed:* Long Island Univ (BSN) Nrsng 1974; 30 Yrs M Stud; *cr:* Wassau Dev Ctr Registered Nurse 5 Yrs, Nrsng Adm Edwards Taekwondo Ctr Master Instr, Owner 20 Yrs; *ai:* PTO of Elem Childrens Self Defense Instr; Maplebrook Schl for Dev D Martial Arts Instr; Yth Empowerment Prgm Martial Arts Ins Nurses Assn; Pan Amer Taekwondo Fed 1984-, Bd of Trustees, 1992, Studio of Yr 1992; *home:* RR 2 Box 188A Pawling NY 1

EDWARDS, DANA JAMES, Health & Physical Ed Teacher; PA; *ed:* Lock Haven Univ (BS) Hlth, PE 1993, (BS) Hlth S Medicine 1995; *cr:* Pequea Vly HS Hlth, PE Tchr, Ath Trainer Dist Ath Trainer; NEA, PSEA, NATA 1993-; *office:* Pequea Valle E Newport Rd Kinzers PA 17535

EDWARDS, ELWOOD GENE, Math Dept Chairperson & Tc Bern, NC; *m:* Lucretia Walker; *c:* Ronnie, Glenn, Myrei Edwa *ed:* City Coll of NY (BA) Soc Sci-Statistics 1966; NY Univ (M Math Ed 1969; Columbia Pacific Univ (MS) (PHD) Math Ed 1 Stud at CUNY, Brooklyn Coll; NY Univ, Baruch Coll Admin & S Credits; Cmptr Credits During Sabbatical Stud Univ of Santo Attnd Ambassador Coll; *cr:* Metropolitan Life Insurance Co 1966-68; IS 201 M Math Tchr, Cnslr 1968-70; JHS 120M, Bro Math Tchr, Lecturer 1970-73; JHS 265K, Med Evers Coll Math Lecturer 1973-83; JHS-IS 285K Math Tchr, Dept Chprsn Specialized HS Test Tutorial Prgm, Sr Adv; Staff & Admin N Staff Developer; CCSP Chprsn 1988-89; Dist Wkshp Ldr & Notary Pub; AFT, UFT, ATMNYC 1972-; ASCD, NCTM, ATMN Cert of Recognition; SIAM, MAA, ASA, AAAS, AMS, AWM 1 of Memb Contribution; Planetary Soc, NYAS 1990-; 89th St A Assn 1986-, VP 1987-89, 69th Prec Recognition; Edwards-Payt Reunion Comm 1988-, Outstanding Achvmt; PTA 265 Outstanding Tchr of Yr; Dist Perfect Attendance Cert 1990-92 Theta Mem; Deans List 1990; NYU Alumni Awd; Natl TRS, E Stud, D D Honorary Degree Amer Bapt Fellowship; Research CPU Abstracts ERIC, UMI, AMN, NNA; Who's Who in Sci & Te Meyer Levin HS 285 5909 Beverly Rd Brooklyn NY 11203*

EDWARDS, HERBERT JOHN, 5th Grade Teacher; *b:* Canons *m:* Cheryl A. Sens; *c:* Timothy, Benjamin, Gabriel; *ed:* Westmi (BAEd) Elem Ed 1976, (MAEd) Elem Ed 1978; *cr:* Evans City 5 Grd Tchr 1976-; *ai:* NEA 1976-; PSEA 1976-, Del; EDCA 1993-, Sec; *office:* Evans City Elem 345 W Main St Evans City

EDWARDS, JAMES A., Social Studies Teacher; *b:* Sandusky Bowling Green St Univ (BEd) His & Pol Sci 1971, (MEd) G Cnslng 1978; Post Grad in Guidance & Cnslng; *cr:* Margaretta Dist HS Soc Stud Tchr 1971-; *ai:* Soc Stud Dept Chair; Sr C Dentention Supvr; NEA 1974-; OEA 1971-; NWOEA 1971-; M Pres 5 Yrs; Firelands Uni Svc Cncl 1983-, Chprsn; Phi Delta Ka 1976 Scott Paper Fellowship Awd; 1982-83 Jennings Scholar; Delta Kappa Ed Honorary; Nom in 1982-1983 OH Cncl for the Outstaning Tchr; Whos Who in Amer Ed 1987; NWOEA Outsta Aw 1984; Sandusky Reg Top Tchr Aw 3rd Pl 1994; *home:* 1504 Ave Sandusky OH 44870

EDWARDS, JANE OTTERMAN, 6th-8th Grd Span & Eng Youngstown, OH; *m:* John Rees; *c:* Charles Eduardo Munguia *ed:* Youngstown St Univ (BA) Span & Eng 1977, (MS) Schl Counseling 1988; 3 Hrs Alternatives to Violence Counseling C San Salvador El Salvador Craft Boutique Bus Woman 1970-75; Span & Eng Tchr 1979-83; Battered Persons Crisis Ctr Cnslr 1987; Youngstown St Univ Dept of Admin Grad Asst 1987 Edward Schl Span & Eng Tchr 1988-; *ai:* Jr Newman Club Mem; Chi Sigma Iota-ETA Chapter 1988-; Jr League of Youngsto Past Bd Mem; Various Counseling Wkshps; *home:* 542 Ma Youngstown OH 44504

S, JOANNE MORAVA, Elementary Art Teacher; *b:* Taylor, PA; wen; *c:* Lewis, Andrew; *ed:* Marywood Coll (BA) Art Ed 1974, Ed 1979; *cr:* Lakeland Schl Dist Elem Art Tchr 1974-; *ai:* Art d; NEA, Lakeland Ed Assn 1974-; *home:* 528 Deerfield Dr nmit PA 18411

S, JOHN ALISON, English, Science & Math Tchr; *b:* , PA; *m:* Janet Young; *c:* Matthew John, Elizabeth Young; *ed:* urg Univ (BS) Elem Ed 1964, (MS) Elem Ed 1968; 20 Hrs in rgm; Army Intelligence Schl 1970-71; *cr:* Harrisburg Pub Schls hr 1964-67; Cntrl Dauphin Schl Dist 6th Grd Tchr 1967-68; Univ ad Asst 1968-69; Army Svc in Vietnam 1969-72; Mifflinburg Dist 5th Grd Tchr 1972-74, 7th-8th Grd Tchr 1974-; *ai:* Dist e Planning Comm; MS Philosophy, Discipline & Grdng Comms; Comm chair 6 Yrs, Dev Model for Systematic Curr Mgmt & urr Coord & Schl Bd Liaison; *office:* Mifflinburg Area Schl Dist Mifflinburg PA 17844

S, JOYCE A., Second Grade Teacher; *m:* Scott; *c:* Jennifer, Bluffton Coll (BA) Elem Ed 1972; Bowling Green St Univ (MS) *r:* Lima City Schls Fourth Grd Tchr 1973-76; Columbus Grove Second Grd Tchr 1980-; *ai:* Putnam Co Insurance Consortium; Luth Church, Family 2000 Comm; Served on Third Grd Grant Comm Putnam Co; *office:* Columbus Grove Elem Schl ss St Columbus Grv OH 45830

S, KAMALA, English Professor; *b:* Hoshangabad, India; *m:* ldiyal; *c:* Jaya, Naomi, Ghildiyal; *ed:* Univ of Jabalpur (BA) Philosphy 1962, (MA) Eng 1965; Univ of South FL (PHD) Eng Doctoral: Harvard Univ, Edinburgh Univ, Cairo Univ, Delhi gai Inst, Nashville, Trinity Coll of Music at London; *cr:* Womens l Lecturer 1966-67; Houghton Coll Visiting Prof 1967-68; FL Coll Visiting Prof 1968-72; Univ of South FL Adj Prof 1972-74; ookman Coll Assoc Prof & Hnrs Prog Dir 1974-79; Isabella oll Pres, 1979-87; *ai:* Staff Dev Ldrshp Activities; MLA 1974-; ue of Amer Pen Women 1974-; NEA 1984-; AAUW 1994-; on the Hum 1990-, Vice Chair; NAACP Montgomery Cty 2-, Exec Sec 1995-; Office of New Amers 1996-, Governors l St of MD; Numerous Hnrs, Awds & Citations; Numerous & Paper Presentations; *office:* Montgomery Coll Rockville Mannakee St Rockville MD 20850

S, KEITH DAVID, Learning Support Teacher; *b:* McKeesport, mm Coll of Allegheny Cty (AA) Ed 1975; CA Univ of PA (BA) Duquesne Univ (MS) Ed 1981; Elem Cert 1984; *cr:* Bairdford ng Support Tchr 1978-81; Swissvale HS Learning Support Tchr Rankin Elem Schl Learning Support Tchr 1982-87; Swissvale HS Support Tchr 1987-88; West Mifflin Intermediate Bldg Learning hr 1987-88; West Mifflin Area HS Learning Support Tchr 1988-; Asst Dir; Asst Stage Mgr; Future Educators; AIUFT 1994-; 4 Grants From Mon Valley Consortium; Thanks to Tchr Nom os Who in Ed; 2 Articles Pub-PA Tchr Leadership & Leadership t; *office:* West Mifflin Area HS 91 Commonwealth Ave West 15122*

S, LARRY LEE, Business Teacher; *b:* Bloomsburg, PA; *m:* M. Lutz; *c:* Lisa M. Hebert, Carol Lea; *ed:* Bloomsburg Univ 966, (MS) Bus Ed 1971; *cr:* Middlesex Cntrl Bus Tchr 1966-68; hitman Bus Tchr 1968-; *ai:* Bookstore, Soph Class Adv; Budjest o-Work Comms; Bowling Coach; Tchrs Assn 1966-, Past Treas; ub 1982-, Past Treas; Masonic Lodge 1972-; Middlesex on Club 1970-, Past Pres, Treas, Conservationist of Yr; Helped fice Tech Course Tech Prep Used by Office Tech Tchrs s, Wayne BOCES Area Schls; *office:* Marcus Whitman Jr Sr H S d Rushville NY 14544

S, MANOLA LEE COLE, Retired Teacher; *b:* Americus, GA; L. Jr.; *c:* Bruce, Keith, Charles, Robert III, Douglas, Mark; *ed:* niv (BS) Elem Ed 1967; 27 Post Grad Hrs Wright St Univ & Univ *cr:* Pittsburgh Pub Schls Tchr 1965-68; Springfield City Schls -93; *ai:* Rdng is Fundamental Vol; Tutor; Clark Cty Chptr of OH Retired Tchrs Assn 1996; Urban League Guild 1986-; St John ch 1981-; Lethia Craig Missionary Circle 1989-, Sunshine artha Holden Jennings Scholar Awd; Clark Cty Excl in Ed Awd; ur Assn Awd; *home:* 2923 Cavins Dr Springfield OH 45503*

S, MARIE BYRNE, 4th Grade Teacher; *b:* Boston, MA; *m:* ; *c:* James L., Laura M.; *ed:* Boston Coll (MS) Elem Ed 1960; A (MS) Elem Ed 1970; 12 Addl Credit Hrs at St Joseph; 15 Addl at Anna Maria; 3 Credit Hrs Southern Ct St Univ; *cr:* Grafton 2 Grd Tchr 1960-61; Meadowbrook Elem Schl 2 Grd Tchr Riverdale Elem Schl 2 Grd Tchr 1964-71; St Emery Elem Schl 5 1984-87; Beardsley Elem Schl 4-5 Grd Tchr 1987-; *ai:* Schl ent, Action Plan, Curr Revision for Lang Arts Comms; Curr Dev Arts; Cmptr Club Chprsn; Adolpt A Schl Coord; 4 Grd Ldr; NEA, sn 1987-; Assn of Curr Supvr 1995-; Roscommon Club of Boston ner Assn of Univ Women; *office:* Beardsley Elem Schl 500 n Rd Bridgeport CT 06610

S, MARY LOU, English Teacher; *b:* South Bend, IN; *m:* Marcus Kent St Univ (BS) Ed 1968; SUNY at Fredonia (MA) Eng 1977; burg Cntrl Eng Tchr 1969-; *ai:* Yrbk, Quiz Bowl Adv; NCTE der of Eastern Star 1978, Dist Deputy; Meth Church 1956-; Eng Journal; Spoke at Grad 3 Times; *office:* Frewsburg Central stitute St Frewsburg NY 14738

S, MELINDA, HS Music Teacher; *b:* New York, NY; *ed:* oll (BM) Music Ed 1962; Northestern Univ (MM) Music 1966; Univ (EDD) Music Ed 1979; *cr:* Bay Shore Jr HS Gen Music ral Dir 1962-65; Baldwin Harbor Jr HS Gen Music Tchr, Choral 68; Baldwin Sr HS Choral Dir 1968-; *ai:* Boys, Girls Ensemble; 63-, Eastern Div Pres; MENC 1962-; NMEA 1965-, Third VP; Translations of Texts for Choral Music Publications; Co-Author of Sacred Son, Heritage of Amer Music; *office:* Baldwin Sr HS School Dr Baldwin NY 11510

S, MICHELLE LYNN, Chemistry Teacher; *b:* Dayton, OH; *m:* Cole A.; *ed:* Wrights St Univ (BS) Ed 1990; Miami Univ of OH ci Ed 1996; *cr:* Springfield Cath Cntrl HS Chem Tchr 1991; S Life Sci Tchr 1991-92; Butler HS Chem Tchr 1992-; *ai:* Tchng OYS Dist Ldr; NSTA 1991-; Presenter at NSTA Natl Convention; ng Chem Tchr in OH Awded by OH Univ; *office:* Butler HS 600 r Vandalia OH 45377*

S, MICHELLE STINVIL, Biology & Health Careers Tchr; *b:* NY; *m:* Glenford O.; *ed:* Oakwood Coll (BS) Bio 1987; NY Univ Ed 1996; *cr:* William H. Maxwell HS Bio, Hlth Careers Tchr : Hlth Occupations Stdnts of Amer Adv 1993-; Dwight D. er Flwshp; *office:* William H Maxwell Voc HS 145 Pennsylvania klyn NY 11207

S, NERISSA MICHELE, Career Counselor; *b:* Houston, TX; nder Cawley; *c:* Austin; *ed:* Lafayette Coll (BA) Psych & Ed nnson St Coll (MA) Cnslng; *cr:* Castle Schl Tchr 1988-90; er HS Cnslr 1990-; *ai:* Debate, Forensics; Civic Club; *office:* er HS 58 Barre St Montpelier VT 05602

EDWARDS, RICHARD L., Social Studies Teacher & Coach; *b:* Ashland, PA; *m:* Cathy A. Smith; *c:* Christopher, Matthew, Mark; *ed:* Susquehanna Univ (BA) Pol Sci 1974; Post Grad Work at Penn St Univ; *cr:* North Schuylkill HS Asst Wrestling Coach 1976-89, Scndry Soc Stud Tchr 1976-, Head Sftbl Coach 1978-89, Head Wrestling Coach 1989-, Asst Sftbl Coach 1996-; *ai:* Head Wrestling Coach 1989-; Asst Sftbl Coach 1996-; PSEA & NEA 1976-; Little League Coach; Pee Wee & Midget Ftbl Coach; Dist XI Wrestling Coach of the Yr 1995; PA St AA Coach of the Yr 1995; Team Won St Championship 1995; Team Finished 3rd in St 1996; *office:* North Schuylkill Jr Sr HS RD 2 Ashland PA 17921

EDWARDS, ROBERT A., Chemistry Teacher; *b:* Cleveland, OH; *m:* Jacklyn; *ed:* Kent St Univ (BSEd) Bio 1969, (MED) Bio 1973; 50 Addl Semester Hrs Post Grad; *cr:* Harding MS Sci Tchr 1969-83; Lakewood HS Chem Tchr 1983-; *ai:* Sci Seminar, Sci Fair Adv; Sci Dept Facilitator; NEA, OEA 1969-, Local Pres; *office:* Lakewood HS 14100 Franklin Blvd Lakewood OH 44107

EDWARDS, ROBERT K., Physics, Math & Computer Tchr; *b:* New Gloucester, ME; *m:* Donna; *c:* Michael, Cathy Coady, Jonathan; *ed:* Bowdoin Coll (BA) Physics, Math 1964; Univ of NH (MED) Sci 1968; Num Physics, Cmptr Courses; *cr:* Westbrook HS Physics Tchr 1964-70; Winthrop HS Physics, Cmptr Tchr 1970-; *ai:* NEA 1964-; *office:* Winthrop HS 11 Highland Ave Winthrop ME 04364

EDWARDS, RUTH SYKES, Elementary Teacher; *b:* Phiadelphia, PA; *c:* Kelli, Sabrina; *ed:* Comm Coll of Philadelphia (AA) Span 1971; Temple Univ (BS) Elem Ed 1973; Attnd Marywood Coll, Univ of the Arts, St Josephs; *cr:* Schl Dist of Philadelphia K-8th Grd Tchr 1973-; Philadelphia Pub Lib LEAP Instr 1992-95; *ai:* Self Image Extra-Curr Instr; Philadelphia Fire Dept Drama Contest Judge 1991-; PFT 1971-; AFT 1973-; Womens Way 1988-; Path Prism 1988-; Applewood Condo Assn 1996; Shalom Assembly of God; Letter of Appreciation Supt Phila Schls 1987; McCloskey Schls Anthology Ed 1989; Tchr of Yr Nom 1992; Rose Lindenbaum Tchr of Yr Finalist 1993; *office:* John F Mccloskey Elem Schl 8500 Pickering St Philadelphia PA 19150*

EDWARDS, SARAH MC DONALD, English & Government Teacher; *b:* Zanesville, OH; *m:* John Richard; *c:* Edward, John, Emily; *ed:* Bryan Coll (BS) Elem Ed 1965; Post Grad Work Scndry Ed Pensacola Chrstn Coll; *cr:* Newton Elem 8th Grd Sci Tchr 1965-66; Maysville Elem 8th Grd Sci Tchr 1967-68; Rhea HS 8th Grd Rdng Specialist 1968-72; Sandy Lane Schl 8th Grd Rdng Tchr 1972-74; Zanesville Chrstn 7th-12th Grd Tchr 1975-; *ai:* Drama, Speech Coach; OEA 1965-68, 1962-74, Local Chapter Sec; TEA 1968-72; Nom Outstanding Elem Tchr 1973; Nom Outstanding Amer Women 1980; *office:* Zanesville Christian Schl 2400 Chandlersville Rd Zanesville OH 43701

EDWARDS, TERI LYNNE, Mathematics Teacher; *b:* Pittsburgh, PA; *m:* Bruce Carl; *c:* Bryce, Scott; *ed:* West Chester St Coll (BS) Scndry Ed, Math 1981; Attnd Beaver Coll, Wilkes Univ, NEIU; *cr:* Centennial Schl Dist Math Tchr 1981-84; Cntrl Bucks Schl Dist Math Tchr 1984-85; Souderton Schl Dist Math Tchr 1985-86; Mountain View Schl Dist Math Tchr 1987-; *ai:* Asst Track Coach; Class Adv; Grad Project Comm; PSEA 1981-; NEA 1981-; MV Ed Assn 1987-, Treas; *home:* RR 1 Box 1310 Nicholson PA 18446

EDWARDS, TERRY LYNN, Director of Academic Affairs; *b:* Nashville, TN; *m:* Kimberly K.; *c:* Katie, Brandon, Jon, Chelsea; *ed:* Harding Univ (BA) Music Ed 1980; FL St Univ (MA) Hums 1991, (PHD) Hum 1993; Music His Butler Univ; *cr:* Indianapolis Chrstn Schls Music Dir; Harding Univ at Florence Field Dir 1984-93; FL St Univ Tchng Asst 1990-93; Harding Univ at Florence Dir Acad Affairs 1993-; *ai:* Yth Soccer Coach; Assn of Lit Scholars & Critics; Scandicci Calcio 1993-, Yth Soccer Coach; Cert of Recognition Admin Bd 1990; Outstdng Young Men of Amer 1992; Gamma Kappa Alpha Cert of Natl Italian Hnr Soc High Acad Merit; *home:* 1508 Hilltop Dr Tallahassee FL 32303*

EDWARDS, THOMAS BRODERICK, Computer Technology Teacher; *b:* Cohasset, MA; *m:* Lois Marie Greek; *c:* Thomas Michael, John Joseph, Lorie Marie Shea; *ed:* St Michael's Coll (BA) Eng 1965; Univ of MA at Boston St (MED) Admin, Supervision 1968; 45 Addl Hrs; *cr:* Boston Schl System Math, Eng Tchr 1965-67; USAF Grad Schl Asst Prof Cmptrs 1967-71; St Dept Of Ed Dir 1971-73; Self Employed Consultant 1973-79; Randolph Pub Schls Mgr, Dir Tchr 1979-; *ai:* Chair Philosophy; Adv Newspaper, Cmptr Club; Teen Forum Schlsp, Handbook, Tech, Occ Ed, Tech Prep, Schl to Work Comms; NEA, RTA 1979-; MTA 1979-, Tchr of Yr Entrant; N River Ath Club 1980-, Treas; HS Class Reviews 1961-, Treas; Two Summer Grants Servicing at Risk Stdnts 1994-95; USAF Liaison Ofcr Captain; Coffee Table Book: Good Stuff; 3 Bd Games; *office:* Randolph Jr Sr HS 70 Memorial Pky Randolph MA 02368*

EDWARDS, THOMAS STEVEN, Asst Prof of Eng & Amer Stud; *b:* Council Bluffs, IA; *m:* Barbara Bywaters; *c:* Emily Lynell; *ed:* Univ of NE at Omaha (BA) Ger 1981; Bowling Green St Univ (MA) Ger 1983, (PHD) Amer Culture 1989; *cr:* George Washington Univ Asst Professorial Lecturer in Eng 1990-91; Univ of MD European Div Lecturer in His, Eng 1990-91; Univ of WI at Parkside Lecturer in His 1991-92; Westbrook Coll Asst Prof of Eng, Amer Stud 1992-; *ai:* Salzburg Seminar Intnl Amer Stud & Lang Fac; Advanced Placement Exam for Eng Lit & Composition Fac Consultant; Amer Stud Assn, Amer Historical Assn, Org of Amer Historians 1992-; Amer Lit Translators Assn 1991-; Mary Rines Thompson Awd 1994; Charles Shanklin Awd 1988; 2 ME Hum Grants; Articles Pub; *office:* Westbrook Coll Stevens Ave Portland ME 04103*

EDWIN, EDWARD M., Bus, Mngmt & Mrktg Professor; *b:* Poland ; *m:* Evelyn; *c:* Gail Edwin Stein, Scott Edwin; *ed:* City Coll of NY (BBA) 1941; NYU (BME) 1946; Columbia (MS) 1974; St Johns (MBA) 1977; Heed Univ (PHD) 1981; Prof IE Columbia 1971; Certfd Pub Accountant NY St; Registered Prof Engr CA; Certfd Mngmt Consultant Inst of Mgt Const's; Bus Valuation & ME Ind'l Plant Appraisals Amer Soc of Appraisers; *cr:* Edward M. Edwin & Co Mngmt, Engrng Consultants 1973-; York Coll CUNT Prof, Bus, Acctg Dept Chm 1984-; *ai:* Amer Inst of CPAS 1970-; Natural Soc of PE's 1980-; Inst of Indstrl Engrs 1970-; Amer Soc of Mech Engrs 1960-.

EGAN, EILEEN WESOLOWSKI, Teacher & Assistant Principal; *b:* Manchester, NH; *m:* Philip J.; *c:* Amanda; *ed:* Plymouth St Coll (BS) Eng, Elem Ed 1970; Antioch (MED) Ed 1986; Post-Grad Stud Admin; *cr:* St Patrick Schl 3rd Grd Tchr 1970-71; Bakersville Schl 4th-6th Grd tchr 1971-85; Mc Donough Schl 5th Grd Tchr 1985-86; Jewett St Schl 6th Grd Tchr, Asst Prin 1986-; *ai:* Stadcom, Crisis Comms; Spelling Bee Adv; NEA 1971-; *office:* Jewett Street Schl 130 S Jewett St Manchester NH 03103*

EGAN, HUGH MC KEEVER, Dir & Assoc Prof of English; *b:* South Bend, IN; *m:* Deborah Homsher; *c:* Kevin, Michael; *ed:* Brown Univ (AB) Eng 1974; Univ of IA (MA) Eng 1979, (PHD) Eng 1983; *cr:* Loyola Univ Asst Eng Prof 1983-85; Ithaca Coll Asst Eng Prof 1985-90, Assoc Eng Prof 1990-; *ai:* Dir Hum Sci Hnrs Prgm; Amer Culture Assn 1990-; Natl Collegiate Hnrs Cncl 1995; Fulbright Lecturing, Rsrch Awd Amer Lit 1992; Dana Tchng Awd 1988; NEH Travel-to-Collections Grant 1987; Phi Beta Kappa, Magna Cum Laude Brown Univ 1974; *office:* Ithaca Coll Dept of Eng Ithaca NY 14850

EGAN, JACK, Math Teacher; *b:* Providence, RI; *m:* Anne Marie; *c:* John, Laurie, Heidi; *ed:* Merrimack Coll (BA) Math 1969; *cr:* Beckwith Schl Math Dept Head 1975-, Math Tchr 1969-; *ai:* Bsktbl, Sftbl, Math Team Head Coach; Schl Soc Dir; NEA 1969-; D-R Summer Pgrm 1971- Dir; Tchr of the Yr Awd; Coach of the Yr Awd; Citizen of the Yr Awd; *office:* Beckwith Schl Rt 44 Rehoboth MA 02769*

EGAN, JEROME P., Asst Uniserv Director; *b:* Providence, RI; *m:* Alma T. Lavallee; *c:* Stephanie, Susan, Sean; *ed:* Providence Coll (BA) Ed 1967, (MED) Guid Cnslng 1973; Univ MA at Amherst (MS) Labor Stud 1982; *cr:* Cumberland Schl Dept Tchr 1967-68; US Army 1st Lt 7th Inf Div 1968-70; Cumberland Schl Dist HS Tchr 1970-95; NEA RI Asst Uniserv Dir, Asst Exec Dir 1995-; *ai:* NEA, NEARI 1967; Cumberland Tchrs Assn 1967-, Pres 1975-79; RI St Legislature 1982-92, St Rep, Labor, Fin, Retirement Comms; Chair Joint Comm Retirement; *home:* 63 Glen Ave Cranston RI 02905

EGAN, JOAN MORROW, Math Tchr & Dept Chairperson; *b:* Pittston, PA; *m:* John J.; *c:* Alice Musto; *ed:* Coll Misericordia (BS) Math 1964; Temple Univ (MS); *ai:* Math Dept Chprsn; AFT, PAFT 1964-; LCCTM; *office:* Pittston Area Sr HS 5 Stout St Pittston PA 18640

EGAN, KAREN DONOVAN, Compensatory Education Teacher; *b:* Newark, NJ; *m:* Hugh J.; *c:* Trisha, Erin, Michael; *ed:* Kean Coll (BA) Elem Ed 1976; Fairleigh Dickinson Univ (MA) Hum 1980; 30 Post-Grad Credits Hum Caldwell Coll; 12 Credits Math Thomas Jefferson Univ; *cr:* Teen Inst of Garden St Cnslr 1994; Keansburg HS Tchr 1976-, At-Risk Cnslr 1993-, Conflict Resolution Cnslr 1994-; Keansburg Schl Dist Family Math Tchr 1991-; Rutgers Univ Family Math Trainer 1993-; *ai:* Discipline, Attendance, SRA, Basic Skills Parent Adv Comm; NEA, MCEA, KTA 1976-; PTA 1978-; PTA St Joseph's 1980-; PTA St John Vianney 1984-; Booster Club 1988-; Asbury Park Pres Article 1995; NJEA Review Article 1995; *office:* Keansburg HS 140 Port Monmouth Rd Keansburg NJ 07734

EGAN, KATHLEEN A. GROSSMAN, English Teacher; *b:* Pottsville, PA; *m:* Martin P.; *c:* Kaitlyn; *ed:* Shippensburg Univ (BS) Eng 1974; Lehigh Univ 12 Grad Hrs; Grad & Inservice Credits for PA Instrl II Cert, 24 Credits; *cr:* St Mary's Schl Lang Arts Tchr 1974-77; Immaculate Heart Schl Lang Arts Tchr 1977-80; Nativity B.V.M. HS Eng Tchr 1980-85; Bethlehem Cath HS Eng Tchr 1986-; *ai:* Adv Ski Club, Jr Sr Prom; Coord Yth Apprentice, STAR Acad Prgms; NCEA 1974-; ADLTA 1980-, Rep, Negotiator; Natl Seminars for Stu Act Adv 1980-; Haek Mtn Cncl 1980-85; Cath Yth Org 1974-77, Vol Coach; *office:* Bethlehem Catholic HS 2133 Madison Ave Bethlehem PA 18017*

EGAN, MARGARET M., History & Religion Teacher; *b:* Providence, RI; *ed:* RI Tchrs Coll (BS) Ed 1968; Wesleyan Univ (MALS) Lit 1975; North Eastern Univ Writing Courses; *cr:* NY, RI, CT Parochial Schls Elem Tchr 1960-68; Missionary Act Cntrl Amer 1968-70; Notre Dame Acad Eng Tchr 1971-89; St Thomas Aquinas His, Rel Tchr 1990-; Norwalk HS ESL Tchr; *ai:* Sister of Congregation of Notre Dame 1958-; Articles Pub; *office:* St Thomas Aquinas Schl 1719 Post Rd Fairfield CT 06430*

EGAN, MARILYN M., Assistant Prof of Eurhythmics; *b:* Midway, PA; *m:* Robert Joseph; *ed:* Duquesne Univ (BS) Music Ed 1972, (MM) Music Theory 1978; Kent St Univ (PhD) Music Ed 1995; Carnegie-Mellon Univ License & Elem Cert Dalcroze Eurhythmics 1989; Cert Orff-Schulwerk; Stud Alexander Technique; *cr:* South Side Area Elem Schl General Music Tchr 1973-83; Geneva Coll Adjunct Prof of Music 1977-91; Duquesne Univ Adjunct Prof of Eurhythmics & Music Ed 1986-94; Kent St Univ Doctoral Grad Asst 1991-93; Duquesne Univ Asst Prof of Eurhythmics & Music Ed 1994-; *ai:* Active Clinician & Wkshp Tchr; Univ Comms; Pittsburgh Symphony Orch; Edctrs Comm Mem; Music Educators Natl Conf 1970-; Dalcroze Soc of Amer 1974-; Soc Ethomusicology 1993-; Amer Orff-Schulwerk Assn 1976-, Local Chapter Sec, Children's Performance 1980 Natl Conf; Radio Information Svc 1983-, Vol Reader, Ten Yr Svc Awd; Several Articles Pub; *office:* Duquesne Univ Schl of Music 600 Forbes Ave Pittsburgh PA 15282*

EGAN, PATRICIA MARY, 6th & 7th Grd Soc Stud Tchr; *b:* Teaneck, NJ; *w:* James Stephan (dec); *c:* Kevin, Richard, Christen Mc Mahon, Michel Chojnacki; *ed:* Paterson St (BA) 1-8 Ed 1961; *ai:* Stokes St Forest Prog Coord 1976-89; PAC, Affirmative Action Comm; NEA, FHEA 1979-; FHEA 1984-, Exec Bd 1986-, Negotiating Team 1986-; Tchr of Yr; Governor Tchrs Recognition Awd 1991-92; *home:* 532 River Rd Fair Haven NJ 07704

EGAN, RICHARD A., Rel Studies Tchr & Dept Chm; *b:* Connellsville, PA; *m:* Leann Murphy; *c:* Robert; *ed:* Saint Vincent Coll (BA) His, Ed 1988; CA Univ of PA (MED) Rdng Specialist 1992; *cr:* Geibel Cath HS Tchr 1988-; *ai:* Stu Cncl Adv; Stu Assistance Core Team; NCEA, Stu Act Natl Assn Scndry Prin 1988-; ASCD 1991-; Knights of Columbus 1978-; *office:* Geibel Catholic HS 611 E Crawford Ave Connellsville PA 15425

EGER, JAMES LAWRENCE, Mathematics Teacher; *b:* Cincinnati, OH; *m:* Linda L. Vinson; *c:* Matthew, Christopher; *ed:* Univ of Cincinnati (BS) Math 1969, (MED) Scndry Ed 1971; *cr:* Bridgetown Jr HS Math Tchr 1969-83; Oak Hills HS Math Tchr 1983-; *ai:* Chess Coach; OH Math League Adv; NEA; Westwood-Cheviot Church of Christ 1963-, Elder; Translater Pan Amer Games 1987; AP Calculus Reader ETS 1995; *office:* Oak Hills HS 3200 Ebenezer Rd Cincinnati OH 45248

EGER, LINDA LOLOS, Latin Teacher; *b:* Fairmont, WV; *m:* Robert C.; *c:* Christen, Michael; *ed:* The OH St Univ (BSEd) Latin 1968; Attnd Univ of Dayton & Wright St Univ; *cr:* Columbus Pub Schls Latin & Eng Tchr 1968-70; Cedar Rapids Comm Schls Writing Tchr 1978-81; Bloomington Ind Schls Sub & Eng Tchr 1984-88; Lakota Local Schls Latin Tchr 1989-; *ai:* Jr Classical League Spon; Amer Classical League 1992-; *office:* Lakota HS 5050 Tylersville Rd West Chester OH 45069

EGGERS, CHARLES GARY, Mathematics Dept Chairperson; *b:* Oceanside, NY; *m:* Jeanne A.; *c:* Jeffrey T., Laura K.; *ed:* Hofstra Univ (BA) Math 1971, (MS) Scndry Ed 1974, (CAS) Educl Admin 1989; 3 Addl Educl Admin Dowling Coll; *cr:* Ward Melville HS Math Tchr 1973-87; Paul J. Gelinas Jr HS Dept Chair, Tchr 1987-; St Joseph's Coll Adj Prof 1993-; *ai:* Admin Mngmt Team; Math Fair Coord; Bldg Fundraiser Chair; Scndry Curr Cncl; NCTM 1988-; AMTNYS, ASCD 1990-; SCMTA 1987-; Outstdng Tchr Awd Ward Melville HS 1981, 1986; Yrbk Dedications Ward Melville HS 1981, Paul J. Gelinas Jr HS 1995; Girls Ath Assn Svc Awd 1976; West Islip HS Alumni Awd 1982; Univ of Chicago Outstdng Tchr Awd 1986; *home:* 9 Areskonk Ln Center Moriches NY 11934*

EGGERS, PHILIP, English Professor & Dept Chair; *b:* Ft Wayne, IN; *m:* Jane Young; *c:* David, Michael, Wendy, Victoria Young; *ed:* Columbia Coll (AB) Eng 1962; Columbia Univ (MA) Eng 1964, (PHD) Eng 1968; *cr:* Borough of Manhattan Comm Coll Prof 1965-; Hunter Adj; John Jay Adj; Pace U Adj; *ai:* Eng Dept Chair; Comms; Phi Beta Kappa; NCTE; PSC; Author 4 Books, 3 Textbooks; *office:* Borough Of Manhattan Comm Coll 199 Chambers St New York NY 10007*

EGGLESTON, CINDY L., Science Teacher & Drama Coach; *b:* Newport, NH; *ed:* Keene St Coll (BE) Elem Ed 1971; 15 Addl Hrs; *cr:* Paul Schl 6th-8th Grd Sci, K-8 Music Tchr 1974-85, 6th-8th Grd Sci Tchr 1985-87, 7th-8th Grd Sci Tchr 1987-; *ai:* Sci Club, Yrbk Advs; Drama Coach; MS Comm Chprsn; 8th Grd Chair of Advs; NHSTA 1975-; Cocheco Vly Humane Soc 1994-, Bd of Dirs; *office:* Paul Schl 60 Taylor Way Sanbornville NH 03872*

EGLER, SHARON K., Computer Programming Teacher; *b:* Zanesville, OH; *ed:* Kent St Univ (BS) Math 1979; Ashland Univ (ME) Curr, Instruction 1995; 6 Addl Credit Hrs CmptrWkshps; *cr:* New Philadelphia HS Math Tchr 1979-86, Math & Cmptr Programming Tchr 1986-93, Cmptr Programming, Applications Tchr 1993-; *ai:* Tech, Hardware Advy Comms;

office: New Philadelphia City Schls 303 Fourth St NW New Philadelphia OH 44663

EGLESTON, PATRICIA G., English Teacher; *b:* Orange, NJ; *m:* Donald C.; *c:* Stephanie Potts; *ed:* Lock Haven St Coll (BS) Scndry Ed, Eng 1969; *cr:* Lock Haven HS Eng Tchr 1969-; *ai:* ACCE, NEA 1969-; *office:* Lock Haven HS W Church St Lock Haven PA 17745

EGNER, KAREN I., Tchr & Frgn Lang Dept Chair; *b:* Latrobe, PA; *ed:* Seton Hill Coll (BA) Span & Soc Stud 1979; Universidad Ibero Americana 15 Credits 1976; Univ of Pittsburgh 6 Credits 1980; *cr:* Derry Area HS Tchr & Frgn Lang Chair 1979-80, 1989-; St John The Evangelist Tchr 1980-87; Ligonier Valley Sr HS Tchr 1980-81; Comm Coll 1981, 1988; Westmoreland Cty Instr 1994; *ai:* Yrbk Ad Staff Adv; PYEA Co-Spon; Frgn Lang Club & Sociedad Honoraria Hispanica Spon; Grad Project & Block Scheduling Comms; PSEA & NEA 1981-; PSMLA 1989-; AATSP 1995-; Wrote Curr for Exploratory Frgn Lang Classes at MS Level; New Tchrs Mentor; *office:* Derry Area HS RR 1 Box 169 Derry PA 15627

EGNOTOVICH, MARY ANN, Health, PE Tchr & Dept Chair; *b:* Carbondale, PA; *ed:* East Stroudsburg Univ (BS) Hlth, PE 1969; Cert Driver Ed; 30 Plus Post Grad Credits; *cr:* Carbondale Area HS Head Bsktbl Coach 1969-87, Head Field Hockey Coach 1971-78, Hlth, PE Tchr 1969-; Immaculate Coll Asst Bsktbl Coach; *ai:* IM Vlybl, Bsktbl Adv; NEA, PSEA 1969-; CATA 1969-, Sec 1980; Amer Red Cross 1988-, First Aid, AIDS, CPR Instr; Amer Heart Assn CPR Instr; Carbondale Area PTA, Carbondale Area Booster Club 1969-; Coach PIAA Class AA St Bsktbl Champions; PA Sports Hall of Fame NE Chptr; *office:* Carbondale Area HS Rt 6 Brooklyn St Carbondale PA 18407*

EGOLF, DEBRA SUE, Chemistry Professor; *b:* Abington, PA; *ed:* Lebanon Vly Coll (BS) Chem, Math 1983; PA St Univ (PHD) Phys Chem 1988; NSF Short Course Chemical Applications of Lasers; 3 ACS Short Courses Chemical Instrumentation; *cr:* Dickinson Coll Instr 1988, Asst Prof 1988-89; Marietta Coll Asst Prof 1989-; *ai:* Amer Chemical Soc Stu Affiliate Adv; Women in Sci Tchr Prgm for 5th-8th Grd; Chemometric Applications Researcher; Amer Chemical Soc 1984-, Sec 1995, Chair Elect 1996; Undergraduate Rsrch Cncl 1994-; 3 Articles Pub; NSF Instrumentation & Lab Improvement Grant 1991; Spectroscopy Soc of Pittsburgh Equipment Grants 1991, 1994; Coll Sponsored Prof ImprovementGr ants & Minigrants; *office:* Marietta Coll Dept of Chemistry Marietta OH 45750*

EGOLF, KENNETH LEE, Sci Teacher & Dept Chm; *b:* Carlisle, PA; *m:* June Louise Enck; *c:* Debra, Leanne, David; *ed:* Dickinson Coll (BS) Chem 1959; Purdue Univ (MS) Chem Ed 1966; Univ of MD (PHD) Sci Ed 1978; Shippensburg Univ Tchng Cert; Attnd Penn St; *cr:* US Army Officer, Instr, Ordnance 1959-60; Pennsalt Chem Corp Research Chemist 1960-61; Carlisle Area Schls Chem Tchr 1962-; Dickinson Coll Part Time Asst Chem Prof 1984-; *ai:* Var Golf, Acad Quiz Bowl Team Coach; NHS Adv; Carlisle Area Sci Advisory Comm 1962-, Pres 1985-86, Sec 1963-65; Carlisle HS Fac Comm 1965-, Treas 1968-; First Luth Church 1962-, Pres 1969, 1972-74; Little League Coach 1976-80; NSF Fellowship to Purdue Univ 1963-66, Research Grant to Muskingum Coll 1967; Jaycees Tchr of Yr 1969; Univ of MD HS Tchng Assoc 1972-73; REACTS Co-Ed 1973/ Partners in Sci Research Corp Grant 1991-92; CASD Mini Grants 1990-91; Tandy Tech Schlr Awd For Tchng Excl 1996; *office:* Carlisle Area Schl Dist 723 W Penn Carlisle PA 17013*

EGOLF, ROBERT H., English Teacher & Curr Coord; *b:* Allentown, PA; *m:* Brenda Petersen; *c:* Susan E. Burns, Robert S.; *ed:* Muhlenberg Coll (BA) Eng 1968; Lehigh Univ (MA) Eng 1971, (PHD) Eng 1978; Post Doctoral Curr, Admin; *cr:* William Allen HS Eng Tchr 1967-, Chair, Eng Dept 1975-; Allentown Schl Dist Curr Coord 1989-; Muhlenberg Coll Adjunct Prof of Eng 1987-; *ai:* Curr Comm; William Allen HS Schl Cncl, Mid St Steering Comm; Chief Rdr; PA Wrtng Assessment; PA Cncl of Tchrs of Eng 1967-, Past Pres; NCTE 1967-, Nominting Comm; MLA, PDK, PSEA, NEA, Altwn EdAssn, NASCD, PAASCD; Prof Articles Exec Educator InterRAM, Lrng '94; PA Cncl Humanities Conf Grant; Rider-Pool Ed Grants; B'nai B'rith, Allentown Ed Assn Outstanding Tchr; Curr & Supvr Awd; Eastern Rgn; PAASCD; *office:* Allentown Schl Dist 31 S Penn St Allentown PA 18105*

EHMANN, CLARE, Teacher; *b:* Rochester, NY; *ed:* Nazareth Coll (BA) His 1965; *ai:* Mid Sts Steering Comm; Soc Stud Coord; Theme Team Co-Coord; St Martin's, Bd Mem; *office:* Nazareth Schls 1001 Lake Ave Rochester NY 14613

EHRBAKER, RICHARD GEORGE, Science Teacher; *b:* Baltimore, MD; *m:* Bernadette Michalski; *c:* Michael, Toby; *ed:* Towson St (BS) Sci 1965; Univ of MD (MED) Ed 1967; 63 Addl Credit Hrs Sci, Ed; *cr:* Dundalk HS Sci Tchr 1967-, Essex Comm Coll Parttime Sci Tchr 1990; Loyola Coll Parttime Sci Tchr 1992; *ai:* Var Tennis Coach 1968-; Spon 3 Graduating Classes; Schl Improvement Comm; NEA, MSTA, TABEO 1967-; Baltimore Cty Outstdng Sci Tchr, Tchr of Yr, Outstdng Alternative Ed Awds; *office:* Dundalk HS 1901 Delvale Ave Baltimore MD 21222

EHRBAR, JOE VINCENT, Social Studies Teacher; *b:* Landstuhl, Germany; *m:* Joan; *c:* Amanda, Bill, Grace, John; *ed:* OH Dominican Coll (BA) Pol Sci 1977; Cleveland St Univ (MA) His 1984; John Carroll Rel Cert; Findlay Univ MS Math, Soc Stud 1996; *cr:* Holy Name HS World His Tchr 1977-; *ai:* Asst Ftbl Coach; Cleveland Plain Dealer Runner-up Apple Awd 1995; *office:* Holy Name HS 6000 Queens Hwy Parma OH 44130

EHRENKSANZ, ELEANOR MANGEL, English Teacher; *b:* New York, NY; *m:* Louis; *c:* Gil, Pam, David, Miles; *ed:* Brooklyn Coll (BA) Eng 1957, (MA) Eng Ed 1961; NYU (PHD) Eng Ed 1973; Columbia Univ (MSW) Psychotherapy 1988; Mercy Coll Prin License Ed 1976; *cr:* Thomas Jefferson HS Eng Tchr 1957-62; NYU Eng Instr 1967-70; Hunter Coll Adj Asst Prof Ed 1971-72; Mercy Coll Eng Asst Prof 1972; Rye Neck HS Eng Facilitator & Tchr 1975-; *ai:* Shakespeare Club Adv; Amer Mizarchi Women 1967-, Pres; AFT 1974-; Natl Endowment Grant; Arts Achvmt Awd SUNY Purchase; Numerous Articles Pub; *home:* 33 Baraud Rd Scarsdale NY 10583*

EHRET, KIRBY, Industrial Arts Teacher; *b:* Newark, NJ; *m:* Mary Catherine Thomas; *c:* Sandra, Karen; *ed:* Kean Coll (BA) Indstrl Arts Ed 1969, (MA) Admin & Supervision 1976; *cr:* Bloomfield HS Indstrl Arts Tchr 1969-; *ai:* JV Girls Soccer, Bsktbl, Var Boys Tennis Coach; NJEA, NEA 1969-; Crossbrook Civic Assn 1971-, VP 1974; Construction Techniques Grant 1980; *office:* Bloomfield HS 160 Broad St Bloomfield NJ 07003

EHRHARD, JOSEPH A., Science Dept Chair & Tchr; *b:* Danbury, CT; *m:* Beverly Marcia Baldwin; *c:* Joseph II, Christian P., Timothy R.; *ed:* Western CT U (BS) PE 1971, (MS) Sci Ed 1974; 6th Yr Southern Ct U Admin, Supervision 1980; Oxford U Physics; Fairfield U Psych; *cr:* Weston HS Physics Tchr, Dept Chair 1970-80; Peers Schl Fulbright Exch Oxford Physics 1980-81; Weston HS Physics Tchr, Dept Chair 1981-; *ai:* Coached Bsbl 15 Yrs, Soccer 3 Yrs, Ice Yockey 2 Yrs, JETS Teams 5 Yrs; NEA 1970-; WTA 1970-, HS Rep; Distngd Tchr Awd Presidential 1990; Nom CT St Tchrs Awd 1993; Fulbright Exch Tchr 1980; *office:* Weston HS 115 School Rd Weston CT 06883*

EHRHARDT, BARBARA A., Seventh & Eighth Grade Teacher; *b:* Flushing Hospital, NY; *ed:* St John's Univ (BS) Elem Ed 1988; Addl 9 Credits Rdng K-12; *cr:* St Kevin's Schl 7th-8th Grd Tchr 1988-; *ai:* Eight Grd Yrbk Moderator; Stu Cncl Asst Moderator; NEA 1988-.*

EHRHARDT, CATHLEEN HECHT, Science Teacher; *b:* St Louis, MO; *m:* Douglas A.; *c:* Stephanie Steigleman, Jennifer, Gregory; *ed:* Univ of MO (BS) Ed, PE, Hlth, Bio 1970; Univ of North FL Bio, Oceanography, Univ of RI Certs; Univ of MD Summer Bio Inst; Shenandoah Univ Classroom Mngmt; *cr:* Orange Park HS Sci Tchr 1987-89; Thompson MS Sci Tchr 1989-92; Portsmouth Abbey Summer Marine Bio Tchr 1989-94; Springbrook HS Sci Tchr 1992-; *ai:* Environmental Club Adv; NEA, MSTA, MBTA 1994-; Church Yth Group, Puppet Ministry; Chesapeake Bay Trust Grants; *office:* Springbrook HS 201 Valleybrook Dr Silver Spring MD 20904*

EHRHARDT, MARGARET FINN, Mathematics Teacher; *b:* Jersey City, NJ; *m:* Paul A. Jr.; *c:* Paul A. III, Megan, Karen; *ed:* Coll of St Elizabeth (AB) Math 1960; Univ of Notre Dame (MS) Math 1962; Catholic Univ (ABD) Math 1968; Completed PHD Stud; *cr:* Parochial HS Math Fac 1959-62; Coll of St Elizabeth Asst Prof 1962-65; Roosevelt HS Math Fac 1968-69; Univ of DC Asst Prof 1969-71; Simsbury HS Math Fac 1984-; *ai:* JETS Coach 8 Yrs; New England Assoc Schls & Colls HS Self-Study & Evaluation Co-Chair 1993-95; Stdnts at Risk Assistance Comm; MS to HS Transition Team; NEA, CEA & SEA 1984-; NCTM 1984-; ATOMIC 1988-; U Notre Dame Alumni Assn 1963-; U Chicago Parents 1987-; Georgetown Parents 1988-; Dartmouth Parents 1990-; NSF Fellow in Grad Stud Notre Dame; NIMH Fellow in Doctoral Stud Catholic Univ; Natl Awd JETS Coach; *office:* Simsbury HS 34 Farms Village Rd Simsbury CT 06070

EHRHART, DAVID S., Soc Stud Teacher & Dept Chm; *b:* Red Lion, PA; *m:* Melissa S.; *c:* Allison, Adam, Brittany; *ed:* Shippensburg Univ (BS) Ed, His 1972, (MED) Ed, His 1977; 45 Post Grad Credits; *cr:* Cntrl York Schl Dist Tchr 24 Yrs, Dept Chair 5 Yrs; *ai:* Boys Tennis Coach 13 Yrs; NEA, PSEA 1972-; NCSS; St & Mid St Cncls of Soc Stud.

EHRIG, DAVID ALAN, Sixth Grade Science Specialist; *b:* Allentown, PA; *m:* Bettina Fox; *c:* Elizabeth Ellen, Matthew David; *ed:* Kutztown Univ (BS) Elem 1968, (MED) Elem Sci 1973; *cr:* Whitehall-Coplay MS Sixth Grd Sci Tchr 1968-; *ai:* Environmental Ed Adv; En Ed, Oceanographer, Meteorology; WCEA, PSEA, NEA 1968-, Local Rep; PA Outdoor Writers Assn 1979-, Past Pres, Meritorious Svc Awd; PA Forestry Assn 1979-, 100th Conservation Awd; NSTA 1974-; Boy Scout Merit Badge Cnslr; Lehigh Vly Zoological Soc 1974-, Bd Mem; Photo Ecology Fnd 1976-; Author of 5 books; Correspondent 2 newspapers; Masthead Field Ed PA Sportsman Magazine; Host 6 Outdoor Videos; *office:* Whitehall Coplay MS 2930 Macarthur Rd Whitehall PA 18052*

EHRLICH, DEBBIE JACOBS, Fifth Grade Teacher; *b:* Brooklyn, NY; *m:* J.; *c:* Randi; *ed:* C. W. Post Univ (BS) Math 1965; Hofstra Univ (MA) Elem Ed 1968; Adlphi Univ, Hofstra Univ Doctorate Courses Ed; *cr:* PS 120 Q Schl 3rd Grd Tchr 1966-68, 5th Grd Tchr 1968-89, 6th Grd Tchr 1989-92, 5th Grd Tchr 1992-; *ai:* Tutoring; Career Cnslng; Suicide Hotline; Drug Intervention; AFT, NEA, NYSUT 1966-; NFT 1966-, Del; Soc Comm 1966-, Treas; Amer Jewish Acad PTA 1985-, Rec Sec; *office:* PS 120 58-01 136th St Flushing NY 11355

EHRLICH, ELIZABETH KORNECKI, Associate Professor; *b:* Bayrouth, Germany; *m:* Yigal H.; *ed:* Univ of IL (BS) Bio 1970, (MS) Bio 1973, (PHD) Pharmacology 1979; Postdoctoral Thrombosis Research Ctr Temple Univ; *cr:* Temple Univ Rsearch Assoc 1981-82; Univ of VT Asst Prof 1983-87; SUNY Hlth Sci Ctr Assoc Porf 1988-; *ai:* Peer Review Comm Amer Heart Assn; Natl Insts of Hlth; Amer Assn of Advanced Sci 1979-; Amer Heart Assn; Amer Soc for Neurochemistry; Amer Soc of Hematology; Grad Stud Comms 1991-; Amer Heart Assn Peer Review Comm; Research Awds Irwin Margulis Thormbosis Ctr Outstdng, Career Dev NIH; Pub Over 50 Articles in Sci; *office:* SUNY Health Sci Ctr - Brooklyn 450 Clarkson Ave Brooklyn NY 11304*

EHRLICH, SHIRLEY LEWINE, 3rd Grade Teacher; *b:* Philadelphia, PA; *m:* Robert; *c:* Melisse Boskovich, Sue Ann Lewine, Michael R. Lewine, Terri J. Lewine; *ed:* Univ of PA (BS) Ed 1953; Masters; *cr:* Local Preschools Tchr 1960-72; Inter-Cty Publishing Co Writer & Reporter 1972-74; J S Jenks Schl Tchr 1974-; *ai:* Environmental Pgm, Pol Elections, Thanksgiving Day Feast for Schl, Collection of Food for Homeless & Class Whale Watch Spon; Musical Performances Amer Music; Schl Newspaper & Yrbk Ed; PFT; FT; AFT; Republican Party 1982-, Comm Woman; Environmental & Animal Protection Orgs; *home:* 7907 Newbold Ln Glenside PA 19038

EHRLICH-JOHNSON, DORLEEN, Kindergarten Teacher; *b:* Troy, NY; *c:* Melissa Johnson, Mark Johnson; *ed:* Russell Sage Coll (BS) Elem, Spec Ed 1975; Coll of Saint Rose (MS) Learning Disabilities 1983; *cr:* Schl #2 Basic Skills Tchr 1975-76; Carroll HS Basic Skills Tchr 1976-87, Grd 1 Tchr 1988-93; Schl #18 Basic Skills Tchr 1993-94; Schl #12 Kndgtn Tchr 1994-; *ai:* Held Seminars to Teach Orton-Gillingham Methods; Discipline, Shared Decision Making Comms; NYSUT, AFT 1975-; Rensselaer Cty Historical Soc 1995-; *home:* 1559 Tibbits Ave Troy NY 12180

EHRMAN, ELIZABETH KEYES, English Teacher; *b:* Binghamton, NY; *m:* Charles; *c:* Clara; *ed:* Univ of Notre Dame (BA) Eng 1987; Villanova Univ (MA) Eng 1992; *cr:* Hancock Cntrl Schl Eng Tchr 1987-90; Our Lady of Mt Carmel Schl Eng Tchr 1991-; *ai:* Jr Class Christmas Skit; Sr Follies; *home:* 1407 Barrett Rd Baltimore MD 21207*

EHRMAN, NANCY WILSON, Retired Third Grade Teacher; *b:* Fremont, OH; *m:* Elden C.; *c:* James C., Stephanie Ehrman Kistler, Michael J.; *ed:* Heidelberg Coll (BA) Elem Ed 1960; *cr:* Hopewell-Louden Schl 4th Grd Tchr 1960-61; Clyde S Main St Schl 4th Grd Tchr 1961-62; Maumee-Wayne Trl Schl 2nd Grd Tchr 1962-64; Delta Elem Schl 2nd Grd Tchr 1965-69; Seneca East Schls 3rd Grd Tchr 1979-95; *ai:* NEA, OEA 1960-; *home:* 653 E Bayberry Ct Tiffin OH 44883

EHST, KENNETH M., Biology Teacher; *b:* Pottstown, PA; *m:* Anne Destine; *c:* K. Ryan, Kristin Joy, Melissa Dawn; *ed:* Kutztown Univ (BED) Bio 1971, (MED) 1976; Addl 30 Credit Hrs; *cr:* Pennridge South Jr HS Life Sci Tchr 1972-83; Pennridge HS Bio Tchr 1983-; *ai:* NEA 1972-; NAST 1990-; Zoning Hearing Bd 1993-; Ag Comm 1991-; *office:* Pennridge HS 1228 N 5th St Perkasie PA 18944*

EIBEL, ALBERT ANDREW, Biology Teacher; *b:* Canton, OH; *m:* Lucille Lynn Mc Gregor; *c:* Emily Lynn, Andrew Lee; *ed:* Univ of Akron (BA) Scndry Ed 1980; Grad Eng; *cr:* State Street MS Sci Tchr 1981-90; alliance HS Bio Tchr 1990-; *ai:* Wind River Sci Club Adv; Head Cross Cntry, Track, Knowledge Master Coach; NEA 1981-; OH Assn of Track, Cross Cntry Coaches 1990-; Jennings Scholar; Governor's Awd for Yth Sci Opportunities; Spec Recognition Awd OH Forestry Assn; Eisenhower Grant; Canton Garden Schlsp; Natl Sci Fnd Grant for Tchr Enhancement; Tchr of Yr Awd; OH Space Grant Consortium Grant; *office:* Alliance HS 400 Glamorgan St Alliance OH 44601*

EIBS, CHARLES EDWARD, Science Teacher; *ed:* William Paterson Coll (BA) Phys Sci 1972; *cr:* Dover HS Sci Tchr 1972-75; Long Branch MS Sci Tchr 1975-; *ai:* Long Branch Schl Employees Assn 1975-, VP 3 Terms; NJEA, NEA 1972-; *office:* Long Branch MS 364 Indiana Ave Long Branch NJ 07740

EICHE, BARBARA ANN V., Fifth Grade Teacher; *b:* Shenandoah Heights, PA; *m:* Edward J.; *c:* Kimberly Parry; *ed:* Alvernia Coll (BA) Elem Ed 1980; Penn St & Millersville Univ Instructional II; *cr:* St Francis Cadet Tchr, Third & Fifth Grd Tchr 1965-69; St Mauritius Fourth Grd Tchr 1969-72; Immaculate Heart Fourth & Fifth Grd Tchr 1972-; *ai:* Math Coord; Schl Bd Tchr Rep; Mid States Evaluation Steering Comm Chprsn; Pupil Svcs, Instructional Support Team; ADLTA 1990-; Church, Lector 1984-; *office:* Immaculate Heart Elem Schl Richard St Girardville PA 17935

EICHENSEHR-GORDON, DORIS ELLEN, Elementary Bimidji, MN; *m:* Ralph; *c:* Laura Eichensehr, Christine Eichens Pete Gordon; *ed:* OH St Univ (MS) Elem Ed 1964, MED Early 1981; Post Grad OSU Newspaper in Ed, Ec Ed, TRIBES Trng City Schls Math Their Way; *cr:* Columbus City Schls 2nd 1964-66, Rdng Tchr 1966-69, Kndgtn Tchr 1967-70, 1974-7 Tchr 1976-; *ai:* Intervention Assistance Team; ABC Bldg Parent Schl Partnership Comm; NEA, OEA, COTA 1964-; Church 1979-, Nursery, Jr Church; Bapt Assn 1989-94, Truste Kickin' Dance Troupe 1989-; *office:* East Linden Elem Schl 2 Ave Columbus OH 43211

EICHER, DONNA ALEXOVICH, Eighth Grd Social Studi New Kensington, PA; *c:* Richard C., Christopher J.; *ed:* CA (BSEd) Elem Ed 1974; MS Equivalency 58 Grad Credits; *cr:* Area Schl Dist Fourth Grd Tchr 1975-92, Eighth Grd Soc Stud *ai:* Comm Mass Media, Drama Club Adv; Dir Fall Talent Sh Play; NEA, PSEA 1975-; Hempfield Area Ed Assoc 1975-, Bl Writing Assessment Advy Comm 1990-; *office:* Harrold MS R Greensburg PA 15601

EICHLER, SUE LEUNG, Social Studies Teacher; *b:* Brookl Jeffrey; *c:* Nathaniel, Michael; *ed:* Hunter Coll of City Univ N 1971; NY Univ (MA) His 1973; *cr:* Hunter Coll HS Soc 1971-76; The Fieldston Schl His Tchr 1976-78; Hunter Coll H Tchr 1979-; Phi Beta Kappa; Phi Alpha Theta; *ai:* Asian Cultur AFT; NEA; AHA; Cornell Univ Spec Tchrs are Recognized Selected Participant in Korean Stud Wkshp Yonsei U Commentator & Moderator of Wkshps 1992; Article Pub 1991; Ldr, The Amer Forum on Global Ed 1995; Speaker-The Kor 1995; CLASS- Honored Designer in Dodge Foundation Curr D 1994; *office:* Hunter Coll HS 71 E 94th St New York NY 1012

EICHOLZER, ANDREW PAUL, Varsity Swim Coach; *b:* Syr *m:* Shelly J. Aylesworth; *c:* Amanda, Brendan; *ed:* 101 Credi Cortland Coll; *cr:* Fayetteville Manlius HS Var Swim Coach 19 Fayetteville-Manlius HS 8201 E Seneca Tnpk Manlius NY 131

EICHORN, ELENA MARIA DEROJAS, Spanish Teacher; Cuba; *c:* Maria Elena, Charles, Brian; *ed:* Wilkes Univ (BA) Ed 1973; Addl 37 Credit Hrs; Univ of Madrid 15 Credit Hrs Adv 1972; *cr:* Lower Dauphin Schl Dist 4th Grd Tchr 1973-75; Cres Dist 4-6th Grd Tchr 1975-79, 1987-88; Hazelton Area Schl Dist 1989-; *ai:* PA Assessment Testing Comm; Advy Cncl; Care Club Adv; PSEA; NEA; HAEA; Natl Assn of Span, Portugues Judes's Parents Guild; Bishop Hoban Parents Club; Hazelton St Jude's Parish Lector; Family Ministry Comm; Span Stdnts P Natl Span Contest Kings Coll; Stu Placed 2nd in Nation 1994 Won Various Awds; *office:* Hazleton Jr HS 700 N Wyoming St H 18201

EICHORN, HAROLD, Economics & Global Stud Tchr; *b:* Elm Patricia Kovic; *c:* Sarah; *ed:* Mansfield Univ (BS) Soc Stud 19 Coll (MS) Soc Stud 1978, (BS) Acctng 1985; *cr:* Waverly Cntr Tchr 1971, 1972-; Wassahickon Schl Dist Tchr 1971-72; *ai:* N & WTA 1972-; Athens Twp Planning Commission 1994-; *offic* Cntrl Schl Dist 1 Frederick St Waverly NY 14892

EICKELBERG, W. WARREN BARBOUR, Professor of Biolo York, NY; *m:* Marilyn Kellogg Banks; *c:* William, Margaret Luk Jane Beshlian; *ed:* Hope Coll (AB) Bio, Chem, Eng 1949; W (MA) Bio; Course work for Ph.D; *cr:* Adelphi Univ Prof 1956-69, Dir Pre-Med 1969-89; *ai:* AAUP 1952-; L. I. Pub Rel Pres, Dir, Pres Awd; Sigma Xi 1952-, Pres; Natl Ctr for Disa Consultant 1954-95; Dennis Fellow Weslyn Univ; Distingush Awd, Seno Teaching Awd Adelphi Univ; *office:* Adelphi Univ Garden City NY 11530

EIDENBERG, KAREN, Guidance Counselor; *b:* New York Ci CCNY (BS) Soc Stud 1965, (MS) Soc Stud 1969; Bark St Co Guid, Cnslng 1977; *cr:* Jr HS 15 Soc Stud Tchr 1965-69; Franklin HS Soc Stud Tchr 1970-73; John F. Kennedy HS Soc 1973-84; Grad Dodge HS Guid Cnslr 1984-; *ai:* UFT 1965-; *of* H Dodge Voc HS 2474 Crotona Ave Bronx NY 10458

EIDING, LYNN CANIGLIA, Clinical Instructor; *b:* Philadelph Bill; *c:* Gregory, Melissa, Daniel; *ed:* HAhnemann Univ (BSN) of PA (MSN) Adult Hlth 1987; 21 Credit Hts Widener Univ; H Schl of Nrsng Diploma in Nrsng 1982; *cr:* Hahnemann Hosp S 1982-85; Univ of PA Asst Head Nurse 1985-88; Meml Hosp S Float Pool 1988-; Helene Fuld Schl of Nrsng Clinical Instr, Edctr 1988-; *ai:* Supportive Intervention; Revenue Generation, Critical Care Nurses 1990-; Sigma Theta Tau 1987-; Alpha Eta *office:* Helene Fuld Schl Nursing PO Box 1669 Blackwood NJ

EIERMANN, LOUISA VERDE, Vocal Music Tchr & Dept Brooklyn, NY; *m:* Michael G.; *c:* Michael A., Alexander F.; *e* Coll, CUNY (BA) Music 1971; Hofstra Univ (MA) Scndry Ed 1 Island Univ (PHD) Educl Admin 1993; Elem Ed Cert; *cr:* Ba Point Schls 6-12 Grd Vocal Music Tchr 1971-, Dept Chprsn Site-based Mngmt Team; HS Musical, K-12 Music Persor Arts-in-Ed Chprsn; Peer Coach; BBP Tchrs Assn, AFT 19 Negotiator, Tchr of Yr 1994-95; MENC, NYSSMA, SCMEA, N Phi Delta Kappa, ASCD, ACDA 1971-; Comsewogue Alliance Hum, Founding Mem; Encouraging Arts Soc; NYS Tchr of Yr *home:* 39 Linda St Prt Jeff Sta NY 11776*

EIGEN, ELLIOT, HS English Teacher; *b:* Boston, MA; *ed:* R. I. Eng 1969; Boston Univ (MEA) Ed Admin 1975; *cr:* Halfhollow West Eng Tchr 1969-91; Burrs Lane JHS Eng Tchr 1991-; *ai:* L. Vol Prgm; AFT 1969-; *office:* Half Hollow Hills HS West 375 W Dix Hills NY 11746*

EILERMAN, CHRISTINA GILMORE, Fifth Grade Teach Wortk, TX; *m:* Robert Louis Jr.; *c:* Mark Daniel, Matthew J Wright St Univ (BS) Ed 1990; Project Discovery Grad 1994; Ma Wright St Univ; Resource Tchr Inst Grad 1995; *cr:* Shelby Co Tchr 1990-92; Sidney City Schls 5th Grd Tchr 1992-; *ai:* NEA, 1995-; SCIRCA 1990-; Band Parents 1991-; Copeland Gra Franklin B Walter Outstdng Educator Awd 1995; *office:* North 232 N Miami Ave 1152 St Marys Rd Sidney OH 45365

EILERS, ROBERT BRUCE, Cabinetmaking Instructor; *b:* D Rpblc; *m:* Dianne Burdette; *ed:* Univ of MD (BS) Indstrl Arts (MA) Indstrl Arts Ed 1977; *cr:* Robert Frost Jr HS Indstrl 1971-87; Damascus HS Cabinetmaking Tchr 1987-; *ai:* NEA MSTA; Montgomery Co Tech Ed Innovations Awds & Participati Damascus HS 25921 Ridge Rd Damascus MD 20872

EINHORN, SANDY MANES, Teacher of Gifted & Talented; *b:* NY; *m:* Richard D.; *c:* Beth C. Manes; *ed:* Queens Coll (BA) Elem (MS) Elem Ed; 15 Credit Hrs GATE Ed; *cr:* East Meadow Pub S Tchr 1959-66; Springfield Pub Schls Elem GATE Tchr 1978-; *ai:* Ec Prgm Liaison; Mental Marathon Coord; SEA, NJEA, NE NJEGT 1984-; LWV 1973-.*

N, MARK TENNYSON, History Teacher; *b:* Baltimore, MD; *m:* ard; *c:* Joshua, Benjamin, Matthew; *ed:* Glassboro St Coll (BA) 9 Grad Hrs Univ of PA; 6 Grad Hrs Lit Princeton; *cr:* St Margaret nl Soc Stud, Lit Tchr 1979-94; Gloucester Cty Alternative Schl 1994-; Highland Regnl HS His Tchr 1995-; *ai:* His Club Adv; ance, Pupil Assistance Comms; NEA Black Horse Pike Ed Assn ldn for Curr Dev 1993-; Riverton Yacht Club 1981-, Dir; Natl nt for Hum Summer Seminar 1992; Geraldine R. Dodge Flwshp Poet; *office:* Highland Regnl HS Erial Rd Blackwood NJ 08032*

, KATHLEEN FALCE, Mathematics Department Chprsn; *b:* a, PA; *m:* Ronald J.; *c:* Daniel, Ryan, Phillip; *ed:* PA St Univ (BS) 9; Univ of Pittsburgh (BS) Cmptr Sci 1986; *cr:* South Fayette HS , Dept Chprsn 1979-; *ai:* Math Dept Chprsn; Stu of Month, Schl ent, Tech Comms; AFT; NCTM; *office:* South Fayette HS 2254 ale Rd Mc Donald PA 15057*

KAREN S., Fr Tchr & Frgn Lang Dept Fac; *b:* McKeesport, PA; d E.; *ed:* CA St Coll (BS) Fr, Scndry Ed 1968; DuQuesne Univ cndry Ed 1974; *cr:* Binggold Schl Dist Span Tchr 1968-69; South Dist Fr Tchr 1969-; *ai:* Frgn Lang Dept Facilitator; NEA, PSEA MLA 1994-; *office:* South Park HS 2178 Ridge Rd Library PA

STANLEY PATTERSON, Guidance Counselor; *b:* Frostburg, Gloria Jean; *c:* Sarah; *ed:* Allegany Comm Coll (AA) Ed 1973; St Coll (BS) Ed 1974, (MS) Guid Cnslng & Admin 1985; Over Hrs Beyond Masters Degree Guid & Career Ed; *cr:* Alegany Co Ctr Soc Stud Tchr 1974-85; Oldtown Schl K-12th Grd Guid Cnslr in 1985-94; Beall Jr-Sr HS Guid Cnslr 1994-; *ai:* Ski Club Spon; ub; Stu Assistance Pgm Pres; NEA & MSTA 1974-; MD Cnslng 85-; First Bapt Church 1960-, Deacon; Western MD Photo Club ; Several Articles Pub; Co-Wrote Family Life Curr; *office:* Beall E Main St Frostburg MD 21532*

, CLAIRE HIRSCH, Teacher & Coord of Gifted Ed; *b:* , PA; *m:* Robert Malcolm; *c:* Karl Robert, Grant Kern; *ed:* Univ Intnl Relations 1964; SUNY at Brockport Ed 1967; Attnd Rochester; *cr:* Le Roy HS 9-12 Grd Soc Stud Tchr 1965-69; Cntrl Schls Tchr, Coord of Gifted 1979-; RIT U of R Prep Tchr, 1989-; *ai:* Bldg, Dist Gifted Comms Chair; Advanced Math Prgm m; AGATE Parent Advy Bd; Math Team Dir; Soc Stud, Sci Curr Kappa Delta Phi; NYS AGATE Advy Bd; NAGC; European Cncl l; World Cncl for Gifted; Natl Math Assn; Amer Assn Engrng ASCD; NEA Advy Bd; Pre-Engrng Prgm for Minority Stdnts Inst of Tech, Univ of Rochester; Susan B. Anthony Republican Yrs; PTSA; NY St AGATE Tchr of Yr Awd; Article Pub; PTSA shp Awd; Soc Stud Mini-Grant Awd; Amer Field Svc Tchr to , *office:* Brighton Cntrl Schls 488 French Rd Rochester NY

ERG, BEVERLY S., Interior Design Educator; *b:* Baltimore, Drexel Univ (BS) Interior Design 1974; Univ of OR (MARCH) 4; Prof Licensing NAAB Arch 1988, NCIDQ Interior Design Eisas Design Arch & Interior Design 1987-92; Drexel Univ PT r Studio, Grad Adv 1988-90; Univ of MD Eastern Short Interior oord 1990-; *ai:* Advy Cncl Pres; Judiciary Comm; Interior Design l; Human Ecology Club Adv; Schl of Ag & Nat Scis Fac Affairs uman Ecology Schlsp, Curr, Strategic Planning Comms; Amer rchitects 1989-; Interior Design Edctrs Cncl 1992-; Seton Ctr 1995-; Art Inst & Gallery Bd 1994-; Somerset Cty Homeless Bd ib Catalogue 1993; *office:* Univ Of MD Eastern Shore Richard A Ctr #2111 Princess Anne MD 21853

ERG, ESTHER, English Teacher; *b:* Norwalk, CT; *ed:* Univ of Eng 1965; Lehigh Univ (MA) Ed 1966; Credit Hrs Hofstra Univ, Univ, C. W. Post Coll, FL St Univ, Our Lady of Rose Coll; *cr:* Area HSD Eng Tchr 1965-66; Mid Island CHS Dist Eng Tchr Vly Stream CHS Dist Eng Tchr 1970-; *ai:* Stu Cncl Adv; Cultural d; Voluntary Compensatory Prgm, SAT Prep Class Instr; NYSUT *fice:* Valley Stream Memorial Jr HS 300 Fletcher Ave Valley Y 11582

ARD, BRUCE E., AP US History & Psych Tchr; *b:* Cincinnati, onda Greuninger; *c:* Brenton, Brianne; *ed:* Univ of OK (BS) Soc d 1972; Xavier Univ (MA) Guid & Cnslng 1980; *cr:* Ludlow Ind Stud Tchr & Coach 1974-79; Oak Hills Schls Soc Stud Tchr & 79-82; Forest Hills Schls Soc Stud Tchr & Coach 1982-; *ai:* Asst Coach; OEA & NEA 1978-; FHTA 1981-; SWOFCA 1981-; i Historical Soc 1990-; Amer Psychological Assoc 1995-; Jiffy r of Yr 1992; *office:* Turpin HS 2650 Bartels Rd Cincinnati OH

ARD, RONDA GRUENINGER, Guidance Counselor; *b:* i, OH; *m:* Bruce E.; *c:* Brenton, Brianne; *ed:* Eastern KY Univ iology, Eng 1973; Xavier Univ (MA) Guid, Cnslng 1979; Walsh ad Credit Hrs; *cr:* Reading Jr Sr HS Eng Tchr 1973-92, Guid Cnslr Boys, Girls Var Cross Cntry, Head Track Coach; Hnr Soc Adv; A 1973-; REA 1973-, Pres, VP, Head Negotiator; OACAC; *office:* Jr Sr HS 810 E Columbia Ave Cincinnati OH 45215

AUER, ELAINE CERUL, Russian Teacher; *b:* Boston, MA; *m:* ; *c:* Rebecca; *ed:* Brandeis Univ (BA) Russian Lang, Lit 1971; Coll (MAT) Russian Lang, Lit 1972; Bryn Mawr Ford Flwshp 990; *cr:* Newton South HS Russian Tchr 1973-; *ai:* Russian Club; L, ACTR 1972-; *office:* Newton South HS 140 Brandeis Rd MA 02159*

OUR, MICHAEL U., Math Department Chairman; *b:* Lebanon, Martha C. Pollio; *c:* Lyn, Beth; *ed:* Juniata Coll (BS) Math 1968; burg Univ (MED) Scndry Counseling 1973; Prins Cert Univ of DE Cntrl Islip HS Math Tchr 1968-78; Cape Henlopen HS Math Dept 8-; *ai:* Asst Girls Field Hockey Coach; Coord of Stu Acts; Video ; Asst Girls Bsktbl Coach; NEA; NCTM; NABC; ASA; Lewes ub; PAETM St Nom Dist Tchr of Yr 1990; *office:* Cape Henlopen s Hwy Lewes DE 19958

OWER, DOREEN MC CARTHY, Health Assistant Instructor; *b:* CT; *m:* Walter; *c:* Patrick, Ian; *ed:* Pace Univ (BS) Registered 985; Vocational Instr Cert PA St Univ; *cr:* Norwalk Hosp Staff RN Jersey Shore Hosp Staff RN 1985-95; Lycoming Coll Clinical Prgm 1990; Keystone Cntrl AVTS Instr Hlth Asst Prgm 1991-; *ai:* al Indstrl Clubs of Amer; Stu Assistance Prgm; NEA 1991-; Sigma u; *office:* Keystone Central Area Voc Tech 432 Railroad St Lock 17745

UTH, EDWARD GEORGE, Social Studies Teacher; *b:* , PA; *m:* Nanette Litwin; *c:* Kent; *ed:* Penn St Univ (BSS) Soc Sci tztown Univ (MA) Amer His 1977; *cr:* Minersville Area Schl Dist Tchr 1974-; *ai:* NEA, PA St EA 1974-; PA Cncl for Soc Stud ncl of Comm Ldrs 1993-; Time Warner Excl in Ed Awd; Gift of cipient; *office:* Minersville Area Schl Dist PO Box 787 Minersville 4

UTH, NANETTE LITWIN, Biology Teacher; *b:* Danville, PA; ard G.; *c:* Kent; *ed:* Mansfield Univ (BSED) Scndry Ed 1978; wealth of PA Masters Equivalency; *cr:* Minersville Area SD Sci 78-90; Hamburg Area SD Bio Tchr 1990-; *ai:* Soph Class Adv; NEA, PSEA 1978-; PA Sci Tchrs Assn 1990-; Outstdng Employee 1989; Pub Ed Fnd for Berks Cty Grant 1992-93; *home:* 250 Margaret Ave Orwigsburg PA 17961*

EISENMANN, FRANCINE COLANGELO, Fourth Grade Teacher; *b:* Camden, NJ; *m:* William J.; *c:* Marc, Kevin; *ed:* Immaculata Coll (BA) Psych, Elem Ed 1978; Working on Masters at Holy Family Coll Rdng Specialist Cert; Rowen Coll Mentorship Prgm Certfd 1993; 14 Grad Credits; *cr:* Cinnaminson Twp Schls Title 1 Tutor 1978; Pennsauken Twp Schls Tchr 1979-; *ai:* Ben Franklin Stu Resource, Schl Newspaper & Cmptr, Staff Dev, Soc Stud Comms; Handwriting Contest Judge; West Jersey Rdng Cncl 1980-, Bldg Rep, Prof Improvement Awd; Longfellow-Ben Franklin PTA, NEA, NJEA, PEA 1979-; Cinnaminson Home & Schl Assn 1988-; St Charles Borromeo Church 1960-, Altar, Rosary Soc, Tchr, Vacation Bible Schl, Carnival Worker; Immaculata Coll Alumnae Assn 1978-, Marian Chptr, Fund Raiser Coord, Class Rep; New Albany Schl Bldg Advy Comm; Cinnaminson Ed Assn Educl Achvmt Awd Honorable Mention 1992; Pennsauken Pub Schls Cert of Merit 1987-88; Governor's Tchr Recognition Awd 1988; NJ Assembly Resolution 1988; Jr Red Cross Coord; Cinnaminson PAL Supporter; Block Fund Raiser Amer Cancer Soc; *office:* Ben Franklin Elem Schl 7201 Irving Ave Pennsauken NJ 08109*

EISENSTADTER, PETER JULIAN, English & Communications Tchr; *b:* New York, NY; *m:* Susan T. Loman; *c:* David, Matthew; *ed:* City Coll of NY (BA) Langs, Lit 1967; Long Island Univ (MS) Eng, Ed 1969; *cr:* Franklin K. Lane HS Eng Tchr 1969-72; LaGuardia HS of Music & Arts Eng Tchr 1980-87; Thayer HS Eng Tchr 1988-; *ai:* Radio Show Producer; NEA; Marlow Planning Bd 1990-, Chm; *office:* Thayer Jr Sr HS 85 Parker St Winchester NH 03470

EISENSTAEDT, LYNNE ELLEN, Mathematics Teacher; *b:* New Rochelle, NY; *ed:* Penn St Univ (BA) Math 1963; West Chester Univ (MS) Instructional Media 1987; *cr:* Harriton HS Math Tchr 1963-; *ai:* Lower Merion Tchrs Assn, PSEA, NEA 1963-; *office:* Harriton HS 600 N Ithan Ave Rosemont PA 19010

EITEL, JOHN CHARLES,JR., Math Teacher; *b:* Ft Campbell, KY; *m:* Robin Thiel; *c:* Kara, Sean; *ed:* SUNY at New Paltz (BS) Soc Stud 1977, (MS) Soc Stud 1981; 96 Hrs Syracuse Univ, SUNY at New Paltz, MI St Univ, Mt St Mary Coll; *cr:* New Free Acad In-Schl Suspension Tchr 1979-82, Math Tchr 1982-; Mt St Mary Coll Grad Instr 1989-; AFT Natl Trainer 1993-; *ai:* AFT, NYSUT, Newburgh Tchrs Assn 1979-, ER&D Local Site Coord, Local, St, Natl Del, Profile Unionism Awd; AFT Ed Rsrch, Dissemination Revision Team 1993-; Union Ldrshp Grant project Coord 1995-; Wrote Rsrch Translation; *home:* 17 Old S Plank Rd Newburgh NY 12550

EJZAK, KRISTY FOLEY, Fifth Grade Teacher; *b:* Waterbury, CT; *m:* Bruce; *c:* Alexander, Kelsey; *ed:* Southern CT St (BS) Early Chldhd 1975, (MS) Eng 1982; *cr:* Waterbury Sub Tchr 1973-78; Pearson MS 6th Grd Tchr 1978-79; Hinsdale Elem 5th Grd Tchr 1979-; *ai:* Parent Involvement, Cheer, Potential Tchr Interviewing Comms; NEA, CEA 1978-; St Pauls Luth Church; *office:* Mary P Hinsdale Elem Schl 15 Hinsdale Ave Winsted CT 06098

EKLEBERRY, LEE EDWARD, Secondary Art Teacher; *b:* Tiffin, OH; *m:* Nancy Melvin; *c:* Andrew Lee, Sara Elizabeth; *ed:* Bowling Green St Univ (BS) Art Ed 1968; OH St Univ (PHD) Art Ed 1983; *cr:* Otsego Local Schls MS Art Tchr 1968-69; O. M. Scott & Sons Tech Instr 1970-75; OH St Univ Grad Tchng Asst 1976-79, Lecturer Art Ed 1979-81; Grandview Heights City Schls Scndry Art Tchr 1981-; *ai:* Art Club, Founded SADD Chapter Adv; Asst Wrestling Coach; Drug, Alcohol Intervention, Prevention Team; Natl Honorary Soc Selection; NEA, OEA, GHEA 1981-; Phi Delta Kappa 1983-; Cntrl OH Watercolor Assn 1989-, 2nd VP, 1st VP; OH Watercolor Soc 1993-; Upper Arlington Auxialary Police 1980-, Treas, Ten Yr Svc Awd; Exhibited Art Shows 1989-; Pub OH Art Ed Assn Journal Review Article 1987; Prof Dev Grant OH St Univ 1979; Tchr of Yr 1989; Who's Who in West 1993; *office:* Grandview Heights HS 1587 W Third Ave Columbus OH 43212*

EKSAA, GLENN T., Math & Science Teacher; *b:* Dumont, NJ; *ed:* Rutgers Univ (BS) Electrical Engrng 1979; LeHigh Univ (MS) Electrical Engrng 1992; *cr:* Phillipsburg Chrstn Acad 6th-8th Grd Math & Sci Tchr 1988-; *office:* Phillipsburg Christian Acad 300 Cromwell St Phillipsburg NJ 08865

EKSTEDT, PAULA YOUNG, Spanish Teacher; *b:* Chicago, IL; *m:* Terrance E.; *c:* Peter (dec); *ed:* Univ of Cincinnati (BA) Span Cum Laude 1979, (BS) Ed Summa Cum Laude 1979, (MA) Span Civilization 1981; Addl Hrs Foreign Lang Stud; 30 Semester Hrs Span, Fr; Phi Beta Kappa; *cr:* Clermont Coll Univ of Cinti Span Instr 1990-91; Western Brown HS Span Tchr 1981-; *ai:* Span Club Adv; NHS Selection; Voice of Democracy, Casting Judge; FHA Advy Bd; Track Ofcl; Class Spon; NEA, OEA, SWOEA, WBEA, OFLA 1981-; KY Colonel; *office:* Western Brown HS 3501 Tri-Cty Hwy Mt Orab OH 45154

EKSTRAND, SHARON KLEIN, High School Counselor; *b:* Bismarck, ND; *m:* Peter Carroll; *ed:* Mount Marty Coll (BA) Eng 1964; Bowie St Univ (MA) Scndry Ed 1974; 12 Addl Credit Hrs; Loyola Coll 20 Addl Credit Hrs; *cr:* Mount Mary HS Eng Tchr 1964-68; Laurel HS Eng Tchr 1968-90, Cnslr 1990-; *ai:* Renaissance Comm; MD Assn Cnslng & Dev, MD Schl Cnslrs Assn, PG Co Cnslng Assn 1992-; Smithsonian Assn 1995-; *office:* Laurel HS 8000 Cherry Ln Laurel MD 20707

EKSTROM, FRANCES HOVEY, Science Teacher; *b:* Greenport, NY; *m:* James V.; *c:* Susan; *ed:* Mt Holyoke Coll (BA) Physiology 1962; Harvard Univ (MAT) Sci Tchnr 1963; Univ of NH (CAGS) Admin, Supervision 1981; Post Grad Courses Univ of WY, Bowdoin Coll, Northeastern Univ, MIT; *cr:* Kaduna Govt Coll Eng, Sci Tchr 1963-65; Lincoln Sudbury Regnl HS Sci Tchr 1966-78; Winnauinett HS Sci Tchr 1978-79; Exeter Area HS Sci Tchr 1982-; *ai:* NH Sci Tchrs Assn 1982-, Bd; New England Assn Chem Tchrs 1985-; New Eng Sci Tchrs 1991-; Amateur Chamber Music Soc 1975-; Congregational Church Choir 1990-; NEST Awd 1991-; MIT Tchr Fellow; Grant Recipient; Wkshp Presenter; *office:* Exeter Area HS 30 Linden St Exeter NH 03833

ELACQUA, PETER JOSEPH, French & Spanish Teacher; *b:* Utica, NY; *m:* Karen Cichon; *c:* Joseph, Elizabeth; *ed:* SUNY at Oswego (BA) Fr, Span, Italian 1976; Colgate Univ (MAT) Romance Langs 1977; *cr:* Notre Dame HS Foreign Lang Tchr 1977-85; Mohawk Valley Comm Coll Adjunct Span Instr 1987-; *ai:* NHS Moderator; Coll Now Prgm Coord; NY St Assn for Lang Tchrs, Amer Assn Tchrs of Fr, NY St Tchrs Union 1985-; NASSP 1987-; Mt Carmel Church Music, Liturgy Dir; Colgate Univ Assistantship; Summa Cum Laude (BA), (MAT); Outstanding Educator Awd MVCC 1992; Optimist Tchr of Yr 1989; *office:* New York Mills Jr Sr HS 1 Marauder Blvd New York Mills NY 13417*

ELAM, ADA MARIA, Prof & Coordinator of Guidance; *b:* Saxe, VA; *ed:* VA St Univ (BA) His 1962, (MS) Guidance & Counseling 1964; PA St Univ (EDD) Cnslr Ed 1972; Attnd Univ of WI & George Washington Univ; *cr:* J E J Moore HS His Dept Chair 1962-64; Bowie St Univ Dean of Stdnts, Stu Affairs VP & Prof & Coord of Counseling Prgms 1964-; *ai:* Chi Sigma Iota Counseling Acad & Prof Honor Soc Intnl Adv; Grad Cncl Mem; Amer Counseling Assn 1970-; Natl Assn of Women Deans, Admin & Cnslrs 1967-, Exec Cncl; Amer Assn for Multicultural Counel & Dev 1967-; Bowie-Crofton Bus & Prof inc 1992-; Research & Stud Projects in Egypt, West Africa, India & Southeast Asia; Ford Fnd Advanced Stud Grant Recipient; Amer Cncl on Ed Fellows Prgm Recipient in Acad Admin 1972-73; Elam AM The Status of Blacks in Higher Ed Univ Press of Amer 1988; Elam AM Factbook on Blacks in HI ED NAFEO 1993; Elem AM Socio-Ec Pre-Requisites for Dev of East Oweinat Area Southwest Desert Egypt Cairo Univ Press 1992; *office:* Bowie St Univ Jericho Park Road Bowie MD 20715*

ELANJIAN, DOROTHY ELIZABETH, English Teacher; *b:* Nashua, NH; *m:* C. George; *c:* Janine, Loren, Rafael; *ed:* Plymouth St Coll (BED) Eng 1961; Salem St Coll, Middlesex Coll, Northeastern Univ Addl Hrs; *cr:* Winslow MS Lit, Eng Tchr 1962-64; Boston Ctr Blind Children Tchr, Child Care Supvr 1964-66; Joyce MS Sub Tchr 1980-91; Woburn Pub Schl ESL Tchr 1991-92; Woburn HS Eng Tchr 1992-; *ai:* Unofficial Adv; Supporter; Stu Act; Peer Mediation Adv; Statement of Purpose Comm Mem for New England Accreditation; 1994-95 Mem New England Project Portfolio Assessment; W-HS Eng Dept Curr Rev Comm 1995; Woburn Tchrs Assn; NEA; NCTE; Parent Tchr Advy, Prof Dev Comms; Coord Ninth Grd Values Curr.

ELBERTH, CONSTANCE H., High School English Teacher; *b:* Scranton, PA; *m:* Wayne T. Jr.; *c:* William, Laura Jean; *ed:* Penn St Univ (BS) Eng, Ed 1980; SUNY at New Paltz (MS) Eng, Ed 1985; *cr:* Tri-Vly Cntrl Schl Dist Eng Tchr 1981-; *ai:* Bldg Ldrshp Team; Staff Dev; CORE Team Mem; NYSUT 1981-, Chptr VP; Delta Kappa Gamma 1988-, Chptr Pres; Hudson Vly Portfolio Assessment Project 1994-; *office:* Tri-Vly Cntrl Schl Dist PO Box 420 Grahamsville NY 12740*

ELBERTY, SUSAN, English Teacher; *b:* Sharon, PA; *ed:* Penn St Univ (BA) Eng 1988; Westminster Coll (BA) Ed 1991; 24 Post Grad Credits Penn St Univ; *cr:* Hickory HS Eng Tchr 1993-; *ai:* Asst Forensics Coach; Ath Prgm, Newspaper, SADD Adv; NEA, PSEA 1991-; Phi Delta Kappa 1991-; *office:* Hermitage Schl Dist 640 N Hermitage Rd Hermitage PA 16148

ELBIN, GREGORY BLAIR, High School German Teacher; *b:* Lewistown, PA; *m:* Susan; *c:* Rachel; *ed:* Dickinson Coll (BA) Ger 1976; Penn St (MA) Ger 1979; Rutgers Cert Span 1994; *cr:* Hancock Cntrl Schl Dist Ger Tchr 1984-85; Morris Hills Regnl Schl Dist Ger & Span Tchr 1986-; *ai:* Ger Club; AFS; Tech Comm; Fulbright Stu Exch; AATG 1979-; NEA 1986-, Assn Rep; 1 Yr Study at Chrstn Albrechts Universitat Kiel Germany; Goethe Hans Fellowship For Study of Ger Culture Munich Germany; *office:* Morris Knolls HS 50 Knoll Dr Rockaway NJ 07866

ELBORNE, KATHY JEANNE (YOHE), Fifth Grade Teacher; *b:* Pittsburgh, PA; *m:* Robert F.; *c:* Karen J., Paul R.; *ed:* Indiana Univ of PA (BS) Scndry Ed 1971; Attnd Univ of MD; Trinity Coll; *cr:* Andrew Jackson Jr HS Eng Tchr 1972-77, Eng Dept Chm 1973-77; St Phillip the Apostle Schl Fifth Grd Tchr 1989-; *ai:* Lit Magazine Adv 1973-76; PTA Liaison; Advy Bd 1992-; Sci Fair, Journal Spelling Bee, Geog Bee Adv; *office:* St Philip The Apostle Schl 5414 Henderson Way Suitland MD 20746

ELCHERT, SCOTT THOMAS, Social Studies Teacher; *b:* Upper Sandusky, OH; *m:* Leisha Norris; *c:* Trey; *ed:* Univ of Findlay (BA) Comp Soc Stud 1989; Attending Univ of Dayton; *cr:* Jackson Ctr Soc Stud Tchr, Boys Var Bsktbl Coach 1989-; *office:* Jackson Ctr Local Schls 204 S Linden St Jackson Center OH 45334

ELDER, BEVERLY JILL, Choral Music Teacher; *b:* Harrisburg, PA; *ed:* Temple Univ (BA) Voice Performance 1991; Attnd York Coll of PA, Millersville Univ, Penn St, York; *cr:* Private Instr Voice, Piano, Guitar 1992-; Pine Grove U M Church Choir Dir 1993-; York Cath HS Choral Music Dir 1994-; *ai:* All-Schl Musical; Liturgical Singers, Players; Show, Concert Choirs; Sr Class Play Asst; PMEA, NCEA 1994-; York Music Matinee Club 1995-; Friends of Strand 1995-; *office:* York Catholic HS 601 E Springettsbury Ave York PA 17403*

ELDER, CAROL BREHM, Spanish Teacher; *b:* Darby, PA; *m:* E. Samuel Peters; *ed:* Towson St Univ (BA) Spanish 1970, (MED) Scndry Ed 1975; Cert in Fr 1989; *cr:* Mt Hebron HS Spanish Tchr 1970-88; Oakland Mills HS Fr, Spanish Tchr 1989-90; Howard HS Spanish Tchr 1990-; *ai:* Site-Based Mgmt Team; Ninth Grd Team; AATSP 1972-; NEA 1970-; Howard Cty Chamber of Commerce Educator of Yr 1994; Tchr of Yr 1996; King Juan Carlos I Fellowship to Study in Spain 1989; *office:* Howard HS 8700 Old Annapolis Rd Ellicott City MD 21043

ELDER, CAROLYN KAY, Elementary Teacher of Gifted; *b:* Natrona Hghts, PA; *c:* Adam Steighner, Amy Steighner; *ed:* Grove City Coll (BA) Elem Ed 1969; Slippery Rock Univ (MED) Elem Ed 1977; Grad Hrs Gifted Ed MS UNiv for Women at Columbus; *cr:* Butler Co Schl Dist Elem Tchr 3 Yrs; Columbus Pub Schls Gifted Coord 1 Yr; South Butler Co Schl Dist Elem Tchr of Gifted 11 Yrs; *ai:* Long-Range Planning Comm; PSEA; NEA; Grace U M Church; *office:* South Butler Co Schl Dist PO Box 627 Knoch Rd Saxonburg PA 16056*

ELDER, H. WILLIAM, Soc Stud & US Cultures Tchr; *b:* Tyrone, PA; *m:* Cara (Huffman); *c:* Ryan, Elisa; *ed:* Clarion St Coll (BA) Comp Soc Stud 1967; *cr:* Perry Central Soc Stud Tchr 1967; Brookville Area Soc Stud Tchr 1967-75; Williams Valley Soc Stud Tchr 1975-78; Mt Pleasant Area Soc Stud Tchr 1978-93; Penn Manor Soc Stud Tchr 1993-; *ai:* Citizen Bee Contest; Head Ftbl Coach; Asst Track Coach; Weight Room Supvr; NEA 1967-; PSEA 1967-; Penn Manor Jr Ftbl Comets, Bd of Dirs.

ELDER, JOAN WESTWOOD, Social Studies Teacher; *b:* Weehaken, NJ; *m:* Robert B.; *c:* Christopher, Gregory; *ed:* Jersey City St Coll (BA) Elem Ed 1969, (MA) Urban Ed 1986; *cr:* Grd 2 Tchr 1968-70; Grd 4 Tchr 1978; Grd 1 Tchr 1979; Grd 6 Tchr; Grd 7-8 Adv Soc Stud Tchr; Grd 7-8 Soc Stud Tchr; *ai:* Sussex-Wantage Ed Assn 1978-, Negotiations, Grievance Chair; Sussex Cty Ed Assn, NEA 1978-; NJ Excl in Tchg Awd; *office:* Sussex MS 10 Loomis Ave Sussex NJ 07461

ELDER, KATHERINE MCDOWELL, Home Economics Teacher; *b:* New Castle, PA; *m:* David C.; *c:* Loren, Darren; *ed:* Indiana Univ of PA (BS) Home Ec 1971; PA St Univ Grad Work; *cr:* Wilmington Area Home Ec Tchr 1971-; *ai:* Strategic Planning, Curr Comms; NEA, PSEA, Wilmington Area Ed Assn 1971-; VPAE 1980-, 5 cty-Midwestern Region Pres; Lawrence Cty Home Ec Assn 1971-, Pres 1974-76, VP 1972-74, Corresponding & Recording Sec, Prgm, Ed; *office:* Wilmington Area MS 350 Wood St New Wilmington PA 16142

ELDER, VINCENT K., Mathematics Teacher; *b:* Parkersburg, WV; *m:* Tamy Reane Ruble; *c:* Megan Renee, Ross Morgan; *ed:* WA St (MA) Electrical Engr 1982; OH Univ (BS) Math Ed 1986; 6 Addl Credit Hrs; *cr:* Frontier HS Math Tchr 1986-; *ai:* Sr Class Adv; Head Ftbl, Asst Sftbl Coach; NHS, Vo-Ag Comms; NEA, FLEA 8 Yrs; Boy Scouts of America 24 Yrs; *home:* 309 S Bradfield Dr Saint Marys WV 26170*

ELDERS, CHRISTOPHER A., Professor of Science; *b:* Portchester, NY; *m:* Theresa L. Hatin; *ed:* Dartmouth Coll (BA) Bio 1969; Post Grad Stud Toward PHD Univ of GA 1969-72; 6 Credit Hrs Gallaudet Coll 1974; Univ of VT 1977; 6 Credit Hrs NH Tech Coll 1985; *cr:* NH Tech Coll Sci Instr 1973-78, Sci Asst Prof 1978-81; Sci Assoc Prof 1981-85; Sci Prof 1985-; *ai:* Phi Theta Kappa Adv 1981-85; Stu Act Comm 1982-85; Stu Senate Adv 1984-92; Springfield Food Co-Op Bd of Dirs 1991-94, Bd Pres 1993-94; Town of Andover Emergency Mgmt Coord 1995-; Soc of Sigma Xi Grant-In-Aid of Rsrch 1971; Tch of Yr Awd 1986; *office:* NH Tech Coll At Claremont 1 College Dr Claremont NH 03743

ELDRIDGE, JOHN WILLIAM, Chemistry Teacher; *b:* Cooperstown, NY; *m:* Dianne C. Beaver; *ed:* WA Univ at St Louis (MS) Chemical Ed 1966; *cr:* SUNY at Oneonta Chem Instr 1962; Burnt Hills-Ballston Lake Sr HS Chem Instr 1962-; Tompkins Cty Comm Coll Chem Instr 1975; *ai:*

Sci Dept Chm; Burnt Hills-Ballston Lake Tchrs Assn 1962-, Pres, Negotiator; St Ed Dept Consultant; Tchr of Yr NHS 3 Times; *office:* Burnt Hills-Ballston Lake HS 88 Lakehill Rd Burnt Hills NY 12027

ELDRIDGE, STUART ALLYN, Anthropology & World His Tchr; *b:* New London, CT; *m:* Pamela Nelson; *c:* Abigail N., Rebecca C.; *ed:* Bates Coll (BA) Anthropology 1976; Univ of PA (MA) Anthropology 1980, (PHD) Anthropology 1990; *cr:* Northfield-Mt Hermon Schl Resident Fac 1980-; *ai:* Dir Archaeology Spain Prgm; Dormitory Staff Mem; Stu Adv; Coord World His, Soph Eng Interdisciplinary Prgm; Tech Advy Comm Mem; Bd of Trustees Acad & Residential Life Com; Soc for Amer Archaeology 1975-; Amer Anthropological Assn 1983-, Fellow; Northeastern Anthropological Assn 1983-; ME Archaeological Soc 1985-; Northfield MA Historical Commission 1991-; Bates Coll Alumni in Admissions Prgm 1980-; Regular Grants ME Historic Preservation Commission; *office:* Northfield Mount Hermon Schl PO Box 2616 Northfield MA 01360

ELDRIDGE, WILLIAM D., Assoc Position & Psych; *b:* Cincinnati, OH; *c:* Carrie; *ed:* Univ of AZ (BA) Sociology & Psych 1970; AZ St Univ (MSW) Soc Work 1972; Univ of Denver (PHD) Soc Work 1979; *cr:* US Army Mental Hlth Ofcr 1972-77; Pvt Psychotherapy Existential Psychotherapist 1972-; OH St Univ Assoc Prof 1977-; *ai:* The Ctr for Peace Stud & Comm Dev Founder & Dir; NASW 1972-; ACSW 1974-; AAVP 1979-; Acad of Certfd Soc Workers; Pub 30 Articles & 5 Books; *office:* Ohio State Coll Of Social Work 1947 College Rd Columbus OH 43210*

ELENKO, STUART S., Dir of Holocaust Studies Ctr; *b:* Brooklyn, NY; *m:* Carole; *c:* David Alan, Robin Andrea; *ed:* Hunter Coll (BA) His 1957; NY Univ (MA) His, Ed 1960; Metriculated for PHD NY Univ 1960-70; 76 Addl Credits Guid; Cert Guid Cnslr 1977; *cr:* Jr HS Soc Stud Tchr 1959-64; City Univ Asst Prof of His 1961-75; Bronx HS of Sci Dean 1964-65, 1988-91, Soc Stud Tchr 1964-91, Coll Adv 1965-88, Holocaust Stud Ctr Founder, Dir 1978-; City Univ Grad Ctr Guest Lecturer His 1987-89; *ai:* Author 2 Books; Holocaust Lib Editorial Bd 1982-90; Consultant Natl Holocaust Museum Washington DC 1983-88, NY City Holocaust Museum 1983-90; Afro-Amer His Curr Comm Chm; Org of Amer Historians 1960-91; Mensa 1982-; Cornell Univ Four Yr Schlsp in My Name for Outstdng Tchng 1990-94; Anti-Deformation League Torch of Liberty Awd 1985; Univ of Chicago Outstdng Tchr 1980, 1985; B'Nai Brith Edctr of Yr 1985; NY St Bd of Regents Yavner Awd; *office:* Bronx HS Of Science 75 W 205th St Bronx NY 10468

ELEY, ADELE WINTERS, Reading Teacher; *b:* Pittsburgh, PA; *m:* Robert H.; *c:* Craig; *ed:* Slippery Rock St Coll (MED) Elem Ed 1972; Univ of Pittsburgh (BS) Rdng Specialist 1976; *cr:* West Mifflin Area Schl Dist 3rd & 5th Grd, Remedial Rdng, 6th & 7th Grd Rdng Tchr 1972-; *ai:* Bldg Commnctn Team; Homework Hotline Coord; AFT 1976-; Mon Vly Ed Consortium Recipient of 5 Mini-Grants; *office:* West Mifflin MS 371 Camp Hollow Rd West Mifflin PA 15122

ELEY, ROBERT L., Mathematics Teacher; *b:* Norfolk, VA; *c:* Leigh Ann, Michele; *ed:* Vasinus Coll (BS) Math 1967; Cheyney Univ (MS) Educl Admin 1985; *cr:* Drexel Hill MS Math Tchr 1967-68; Springfield HS Math Tchr 1968-; *ai:* Golf Coach; Yrbk Editorial Adv; NEA, PSEA, SEA 1968-; *office:* Springfield HS 49 W Leamy Ave Springfield PA 19064*

ELIAS, BRIDGET GALLAGHER, English & Reading Teacher; *b:* Cleveland, OH; *m:* John Michael Elias; *c:* Shane; *ed:* Kent St Univ (BA) Telecommunications 1988; Baldwin Wallace (MA) Ed 1992; Attnd Cleveland St Ed, Kent St Ed; *cr:* Avon Lake HS Stu Tchr 1992; Maple Hghts HS Eng, Rdng Tchr 1992-; *ai:* Teens Needing Teens; 1998 Class Adv; NEA 1992-; *office:* Maple Heights HS 5500 Clement Ave Maple Heights OH 44137*

ELIAS, HARRY, Professor & Dir of Clinical Ed; *b:* Brooklyn, NY; *ed:* Columbia Univ Sph (MPH) Hlth Admin 1987; Columbia Univ Tchrs Coll (MS) Hlth Ed 1993, (EDD) Hlth Ed in Progress; Trng in Respiratory Care at NY Univ, Currently RRT; *cr:* UMONJ Shrp Prof 1987-91; Bergen Comm Coll Prof 1992-; *ai:* Grants, Safety, Continuing Fnd in Respiratory Care for HS Stdnts, Pediatric Pul Comms; AARC, APHA 1983-; NNJ Thoracic Soc, Ped Pul Comm; *office:* Bergen Comm Coll 400 Paramus Rd Paramus NJ 07652*

ELIAS, JANILYN, Tchr of Deaf & Hard of Hearing; *b:* Wilkes-Barre, PA; *ed:* Wilson Coll (BA) Eng 1990; Bloomsburg Univ (MS) Deaf Ed 1993; *cr:* Capital Area Intermediate Unit Edctr of the Deaf, Hard of Hearing 1993-; *ai:* Wilson Coll Pres of Class; Spec Ed Sftbl Asst Coach; NEA, CAEA, PSEA, Cncl on Ed of the Deaf 1993-; ASCD 1996; Poetry Pub; *office:* Capital Area Intermediate Unit 55 Miller St Summerdale PA 17093*

ELIAS, JUDITH BRICHFORD, Flute Instructor; *b:* Painesville, OH; *c:* Lori Anne, Kimberly Diane; *ed:* Youngstown St Univ (BME) Music Ed 1968; Attnd Kent St Univ; *cr:* Mentor Pub Schls K-6 Grd Gen Music Tchr 1968-69; Fine Arts Schl Flute Instr 1968-; Cuyahoga Comm Coll Music Prof 1991-; *ai:* Flute Ensemble Coach; Flwshp United Church of Christ Cncl 1989-; Cecilian Musical Club; Cleveland Fortnightly Musical Club; Lakeland Civic Orch 1968-; *office:* Schl Of Fine Arts 38660 Mentor Ave Willoughby OH 44094

ELIAS, MICHAEL DONALD,JR., Science Teacher; *b:* Wilkes-Barre, PA; *m:* Colleen Bergstrasser; *c:* Michael, Bradley, Joshua; *ed:* Wilkes Univ (BA) Bio, Ed 1987; Univ of Scranton (MS) Educl Admin 1992; *cr:* Wilkes Barre Area SD Sci Tchr 1987-; *ai:* Coach Jr HS Wrestling, Track & Field, Sci Olympiad; NEA 1987-; BSA 1994-, Asst Den Ldr; *office:* Elmer L Meyers Jr Sr HS 341 Carey Ave Wilkes Barre PA 18702*

ELIAS, MICHAEL JAMES, Music Department Chair; *b:* Youngstown, OH; *c:* Lori Anne, Kimberly Diane; *ed:* Cleveland St Univ (ME) Admin 1974; Attnd Indiana Univ of PA; *cr:* St Johns HS Music Dir 1966-68; W Geauga Jr HS Instrumental Music Dir 1968-72; Wickliffe City Schls Dept chm & Instrumental Music Dir 1972-; *ai:* Marching Band, Jazz Ensemble, Orch, Concert Band & Wind Ensemble Dir; NEA & OEA 1968-; OH Music Ed Assn 1968-, Dist 7 Pres 1989-91, NE Reg Sec Treas 1985-89; Lake Cty Music Ed Assn; Lakeland Civic Band 1978-, Steering Comm & Concert Master; Lake Cty Music Ed Assn Past Pres; *office:* Wickliffe City Schls 2255 Rockefeller Rd Wickliffe OH 44092

ELIAS, SUSAN S., English Teacher; *b:* Wilkes-Barre, PA; *m:* Samuel J.; *c:* Margaret; *ed:* Muhlenberg Coll (BA) Eng 1992; 21 Credit Hrs Univ of Scranton; *cr:* Montrose Area Jr Sr High Eng tchr 1992-; *ai:* NEA 1992-; NCTE 1992-.

ELINSKAS, AMY BARNEY, Nursing Instructor; *b:* Utica, NY; *m:* Robert J.; *c:* Robert S., Daniel, Richard, Suzanne; *ed:* St Elizabeth Hospital (RN) 1970; SUNY at Utica, Rome (BSN) Nursing 1979, (MS) Admin 1992; *cr:* St Elizabeth Hospital Staff & Charge Nurse 1970-79, Med-Surg Instr 1979-, Nursing Lab Coord 1990-; *ai:* NYSNA 1970-; Prof Nurses of Cntrl NY 1992-; Sigma Theta Tau 1991-, Nominating Chm; St Elizabeth Alumni Assn 1970-, Pres 1990-; Amer Diabetes Assn 19840, Bd; Amer Heart Assn Vol; Articles Pub 1993; *office:* St Elizabeth Hospital Schl of Nursing 2215 Genesee St Utica NY 13501

ELION, SANDRA (HAINLINE), 3rd-6th Grade Teacher; *b:* Chariton, IA; *m:* Carl Milofsky; *c:* Jude E., Nina J., Tessa S. Milofsky, Jake S. Milofsky; *ed:* CT Coll for Women (BA) Child Dev 1967; Univ of IA (MA) Ed 1970; 9 Credit Hrs Cntrl CT St Coll; Inservice, Conf Situations Credits; *cr:* Wapping Elem Schl 1st Grd Tchr 1967-68; Seaside Regnl Ctr Recreation Ldr 1967-68; Arthur Elem Schl K-1 Spec Ed Tchr 1968-69; Helen Lemme Elem Schl 1st-2nd Grd Tchr 1970-71; Williamsport Area HS Asst Swim Coach 1988-93; Bucknell Unv Asst Mens, Womens Swim Coach 1994-; West Branch Schl K-2 Tchr 1977-81, 3rd-6th Grd Tchr 1981-; *ai:* Admissions, Tchr Selection Comms; Asst Men's, Women's Swim Coach; Pi Lambda Theta 1970-; ASCD 1990-94, 1994-; Univ of IA Alumni Assn 1990-; YMCA 1977-; St Andrew's Episcopal Church 1944-, Vestry 1966, Altar Guild 1995-; Coll Swimming Coaches Amer 1994-; EDE; The Nature Conservancy; WWF; ARE; OUE 1993-; *office:* West Branch Schl 755 Moore Ave Williamsport PA 17701*

ELKO, DONALD J., Hlth & Physical Education Tchr; *m:* Karen A. Juricich; *c:* Nicole A., John A.; *ed:* Cntrl MO St Univ (BS) Hlth & PE 1968; 24 Hrs at Penn St Univ McKee & Monroeville Campus; *cr:* South Allegheny Schl Dist Hlth & PE Tchr 28 Yrs; *ai:* Ftbl Defensive Coord; NEA, PSEA 1968-, South Allegheny Ed Assn, Pres; BSA, Committeeman; Norwin Bsktbl Assn, Coach; *office:* South Allegheny Schl Dist 2743 Washington Blvd Mc Keesport PA 15133*

ELKO, WENDY SWANK, Instrumental Music Teacher; *b:* Johnstown, PA; *m:* Edmund L.; *ed:* Edinboro Univ of PA (BA) Music 1992; 6 Grad Credits Duquesne Univ; 5 Credits PA Univ of Arts at Philadelphia; *cr:* Northern Tioga Schl Dist K-6th Grd Music Tchr 1992-93; Penn Cambria Schl Dist Instrumental Music Tchr 1993-; Saint Francis Coll Music Adjunct Prof 1995-; *ai:* Marching, Pep & Jazz Bands Dir; PMEA, MENC 1991-; PSEA, NEA 1992; AF of M 1988-; Holy Name Choir 1993-; Johnstown Civic Band 1988-; *office:* Penn Cambria MS 401 Division St Gallitzin PA 16641

ELLENA-WYGONIK, MARY LOUISE, English Teacher; *b:* Natrona, PA; *m:* Robert J.; *ed:* IN Univ of PA (BS) Eng Ed 1973; IUP (MA) Eng 1976; Post Grad Stud: Jagiellonian Univ at Cracow Poland, Harvard Grad Schl of Ed, Penn St Univ & Univ of Pittsburgh Curr & Supv & Gifted Ed; *cr:* Hampton HS Eng Tchr 1973-; La Roche Coll Adj Eng 1977; Penn St Univ Adj Eng 1978; Comm Coll Adj Eng 1980; *ai:* Morning Announcments; After Schl Writers Group; Strategic Planning Team; NCTE 1972-; Western PA Cncl of Tchrs of Eng 1985-, Adv Bd Treas; Western PA Writing Project 1987-; Next Generation, Adv Bd; Amer Can Soc, Bd of Dir; Historical Soc of Western PA; Kosciuszko Fndtn; Articles Pub; PA Cncl for the Arts & Filene Fndtn Grants; *office:* Hampton HS 2929 Mccully Rd Allison Park PA 15101*

ELLENWOOD, DANIEL STEVEN, Bible & PE Teacher; *b:* Elmhurst, IL; *m:* Jeanette Ruth Willey; *c:* Andrew Daniel, Joel Daniel, Kayla Joy; *ed:* Bob Jones Univ (BA) Missions 1987; *cr:* Victory Chrstn Schl Bible, PE Tchr, Coach 1987-89; Parsippany Chrstn Schl Bible, PE Tchr, Ath Dir, Coach 1989-; *ai:* Boys Var Soccer, Bsktbl Coach; *office:* Parsippany Christian Schl 1179 Littleton Rd Parsippany NJ 07054

ELLING, BOB, Director of EMS Institute; *b:* New York, NY; *c:* Laura, Caitlin; *ed:* Nassau Comm Coll (AAS) Bio 1974; SUNY at Albany (BA) Psych 1982, (MPA) Mgmt 1992; NY St Paramedic; *cr:* NY City EMS Paramedic & Supvr 1977-80; Regnl Emergency Med Org Evaluation Coord 1980-83; NY St EMS Trng Coord & Assoc Dir 1983-93; Hudson Vly Comm Coll Dir EMS Inst & Pgm Coord Inst of Prehospital Emergency Medicine 1993-; *ai:* Physicians Asst Admissions Comm; Regnl EMS Cncl; Amer Motorcycle Assn; Natl Assn of EMTS 1979-; Natl Registry of EMTS 1982-; Colarie Fire Co 1984-, Rescue LT; Colarie EMS Dept 1990-, Flight Medic; EMS Ldrshp Awd; Numerous Commendations; Numerous Articles Pub; 3 Textbooks Pub; Contributing Author 5 Textbooks; Numerous Audio Visual Pgms; Educl Consultant to Monthly EMS Video Series 5 Yrs; *office:* Hudson Valley Comm Coll 80 Vandenburgh Ave Troy NY 12180

ELLINGSWORTH, REBECCA ANNE ROLAR, Second Grade Teacher; *b:* Chambersburg, PA; *m:* James R.; *ed:* Shippensburg Univ (BS) Elem Ed 1971, (MEd) Elem Ed 1974; *cr:* Big Spring Schl Dist 2nd Grd Tchr 1972-; *ai:* Big Spring Ed Assn 1972-; NEA; PSEA; Eastern Star 1989-; Mount Washington Observatory; Humane Soc of US; *office:* Mifflin Elem Schl 399 Roxbury Rd Newville PA 17241

ELLIOT, WAYNE I., Retired Teacher & Asst Prin; *b:* Portsmouth, NH; *m:* Betty Jean Mc Dade; *c:* Teresa Rezendes, Richard, David; *ed:* Univ of NH (BA) Eng 1964; Attnd UNH, Plymouth St, Keene St; 729 Addl Hrs Staff Dev; Duke Univ as Undergrad; *cr:* North Hampton Elem Schl Tchr of Eng 1963-89, Asst Prin, Admin Coord 1970-89, Acting Prin; NHEA Tchr of PE; *ai:* Oratorical Contest 25 Yrs; Spelling Bee 25 Yrs; Bsbl Coach 12 Yrs; Dramatics 13 Yrs; Audio-Visual Coord 22 Yrs; Numerous Lang Arts Comms; Photography Club; NH Ret Tchrs Assn 1989-; Seacoast Ed Assn; NH; NEA; N Hampton Yth Assn; BSA; Hampton United Meth Church; St James FAM #102 Masons; NH Consistory; Outstdng ELem Schl Tchr; US Jaycee Metropolitan Life Awrd; Outstdng Yng Men of Amer; Jay #21 Multi-Media Awds; Boosters Appreciation Awds; Various Awds; *home:* 106 Woodland Rd North Hampton NH 03862

ELLIOT-SMITH, T. P., Humanities Professor; *b:* New York City, NY; *c:* Gilbert P., Laura E. S. Ford; *ed:* Univ of VT (BA) Eng, Rhetoric 1961; Salem St Coll (MED) Eng 1966; Bridgewater St Coll Post Masters Stud Amer Lit; *cr:* Chelmsford HS Speech, Eng Tchr 1961-66; Lowell Tech Univ Adjunct Prof 1962-66; Massasoit Comm Coll Hum Prof 1966-; Dean Jr Coll Adjunct Prof 1996; *ai:* Reacreditation Self Stud Mem; Town Moderator 1973-; *office:* Massasoit Comm Coll 1 Massasoit Blvd Brockton MA 02402

ELLIOTT, ANN SHARPS, Second Grade Teacher; *b:* Laconia, NH; *c:* Andrea Soto, Jennifer Lamprey; *ed:* Brigham Young Univ (BA) His 1968; Plymouth St Coll Tchr Cert 1970; *cr:* Canterbury Elem Schl 1-6 Grd Tchr 1968-, Tchng Prin 1977-79, 2 Grd Tchr 1995-; *ai:* Drama, Christmas Fair Adv; Schl Newspaper; NEA, NEANH 1986-, Negotiation Team; *home:* 110 Stevens Rd Northfield NH 03276

ELLIOTT, CHRISTY L., Guidance Counselor; *b:* Reading, PA; *m:* Deborah J. Bachman; *c:* John D., Mark T., Katie A.; *ed:* Bloomsburg Univ (BS) Elem Ed 1973; Kutztown Univ (MED) Elem Ed 1979; 30 Credits Past (MS); *cr:* Conrad Weiser Area Schls 6th Grd Tchr 1973-89, Elem Guidance Cnslr 1989-; *ai:* NEA, PSEA 1973-; PSCA 1993-; *office:* Conrad Weiser W Elem Schl 102 S 3rd St Womelsdorf PA 19567

ELLIOTT, CLAUDIA JANE, Math Teacher; *b:* Amsterdam, NY; *c:* Beth Thurz, Jeffrey Schraver; *ed:* SUNY at Buffalo (BS) Math 1967; Univ of Rochester (MED) Math Ed 1983; SUNY at Brockport Math Ed; *cr:* Grass Lake Elem Schl 6th Grd Tchr 1967-68; Palm Beach Gardens HS Math, Scndry Tchr 1980-81; Pittsford Schls Math, Scndry Tchr 1982-; *ai:* Math Club Adv; Math Standards Steering Comm; NCTM 1994-; AFT, NYSUT 1981-; *office:* Pittsford Sutherland HS Sutherland St Pittsford NY 14534

ELLIOTT, DEBORAH SMITH, Assessment & Spec Ed Aide; *b:* Lebanon, PA; *m:* Barry L.; *c:* Jeremy L., Sheila E., Bruce D. Sando; *ed:* Natl Cert Cheer LTD; *cr:* Lebanon Cath HS Head Chrldng Coach 5 Yrs; Lancaster-Lebanon Schl Spec Ed Svcs 17 Yrs; Lebanan Cty Career & Tech Ctr Spec Ed, Applied Comm Aide 1 Yr; *ai:* Head Chrldng Coach Lebanon Cath HS; Lebanon Cty Spec Olympics 1987-, Advy Bd, Head of Lebanon Cty Delegation to St Level Events, Head Coach Bowling, Track & Field, 5 Yr Svc Awd; *office:* Lebanon Cty Career & Tech Ctr 833 Metro Dr Lebanon PA 17042

ELLIOTT, DEBRA JANE, Second Grade Teacher; *b:* Salisbury, MD; *ed:* Salisbury St Coll (BS) Ed 1975, (MS) Ed 1978 with Rdng Spec Cert; *cr:* North Salisbury Schl 2, 4-5 Grd Tchr 1974-85; *ai:* Teach Young Summer Enrichment Prgm; NEA, MSTA, WCEA 1976-, Fac Rep; Wicomico Jr & Minor Girls Sftbl, Fruitland Pee Wee & Minor Leagues, Mgr; 4 Yr Nom for Schl Rep Outstanding Tchr of Yr; *home:* 31995 Melson Rd De 21875

ELLIOTT, DIANE BEAULIEU, Special Education Tea Millinocket, ME; *m:* Peter G. Stratton; *c:* Richard D.; *ed:* Univ Orono (BS) Elem Ed 1973, (MA) Spec Ed 1990; *cr:* Earl C. Mc 2nd-3rd Grd Classroom, 1-2, 2-3 Combination, Spec Ed Tchr Bldg Level Response, Tchr Re-Evaluation Comm, Re-Cert Te MTA, NEA 1973-; Rural Spec Edctrs 1990-; *office:* Earl C. Mc Main Rd Hampden ME 04444

ELLIOTT, HELEN E., 7th Grade Social Studies Tchr; *b:* Seafo Elizabeth; *ed:* Salisbury St Univ (BA) Elem Ed 1990; Working Elem Ed; *cr:* DE Div for Visually Impaired Consultant 1990; La MS 7th Grd Soc Stud Tchr 1990-; *ai:* Stu Cncl Adv; Strategic Dist Discipline Comms; 7th Grd Mentor & Team Ldr; NEA 199 1990-; NCSS 1995-; DCSS 1995-; Amer Legion Auxiliary 1990- Sgt at Arms, Poppy Pgm; Outstdng Ldrshp Awd Jr Achvmt of DE; Kappa; *office:* Laurel Intermediate Schl 801 S Central Ave L 19956*

ELLIOTT, JANE RAUSCHER, Fifth Grade Teacher; *b:* Newa Louie C.; *c:* William, Thomas; *ed:* Mount Holyoke Coll (BA) 1956; Univ of MA (MED) Ed 1968; 15 Addl Hrs in Hum & Cmp *cr:* Mount Holyoke Coll Instr Dept Psych & Ed 1956-60; Town o Third Grd Tchr 1960-69; Town of Unity Tchr Grds 5-8 1983-; Writing; Newport Lib Arts Ctr 1974-, Treas; Gifted & Talented M Grants; *home:* 101 Chestnut Rd Newport NH 03773

ELLIOTT, MICHELE GASPICH, Biology Teacher; *b:* Oxford Michael; *c:* Meredith, Megan; *ed:* Marshall Univ (BA) Chem, S 1984; NSF Awd Univ of Dayton; Working Towards Masters in Ad St Univ; *cr:* Elida HS Tchr 1985-89; Ada HS Bio Tchr 1 Cheerleading & Prom Adv; *office:* Ada HS 500 Grand Ave Ada O

ELLIOTT, THERESA DARE, Fifth Grade Teacher; *b:* Wilming *m:* Randy; *ed:* Univ of Dayton (BS) Elem Ed 1987; Wo Supervision, Curr MS; *cr:* Little Miami Schl Dist Fifth Grd Tchr Stu Cncl Adv; Musical Asst Dir; Instrl Improvement, Speech Comms; Project Discovery; Southwestern OH Regnl Prof Dev OEA, LMTA 1988-; *office:* Morrow Elem Schl 10 Miranda St M 45152

ELLIOTT, THOMAS HENRY, Instrumental Music Dir Charleston, SC; *m:* Zenaida Gonzales; *c:* Joshua, Rachel; *ed:* T Inst of Music (BA) Trombone Performance 1976; West Chester U Music Ed 1989; PA Tchng Cert From Immaculata Coll; *cr* Shanahan HS Instrumental Music Tchr 1977-89; West Ches Trombone Instr 1981-82; Lower Merion HS Instrumental Music Univ of the Arts Instrumental Conducting & Chamber Music Tchr *ai:* Stu Assistance Prgm; Philadelphia Musical Soc 1972-; LMI Tenth Presbyn Church 1972-, Deacon, Bd of Elders; Philadel Regular Extra & Sub; Artistic Dir of Performance Orch of Phi Founder & Former Dir of Westminster Brass; *office:* Lower Meric E Montgomery Ave Ardmore PA 19003*

ELLIOTT, WILLIAM DITTO, Professor of Biology; *b:* Ha MD; *m:* Juanita Bittle; *c:* Beth, David Bittle, Beth Ann, Auld Bittle; *ed:* Shippensburg Univ (BS) Bio 1957; John Hopkins Un Ed 1963; William & Mary (MTS) Bio 1965; Amer Univ (ED 1972; *cr:* Towson HS Bio Tchr 1958-66; Hagerstown Jr Coll 1966-; *ai:* NEA; Co-Author Investigations in Biology; *office:* Ha Jr Coll 751 Robinwood Drive Hagerstown MD 21742*

ELLIS, ALFRED G., Assistant Principal; *b:* Jamaica, West In Queens Coll (BA) Span 1966; Pace Univ (MS) Educl Supervisio 1974; Univ of Seville Span Lit 1970-71; *cr:* Intermediate Schl 8 Tchr 1966-72; Hillcrest HS Tchr, Asst Prin 1972-; *ai:* Coord Mu Comm, Travel Abroad Prgm; Intnl Club Adv; AATSP; *office:* Hil 160-05 Highland Ave Jamaica NY 11432*

ELLIS, BONNIE BESCH, Special Education Teacher; *b:* Osweg James; *c:* Sierra Rose; *ed:* St Univ Coll at Buffalo (BS) Elem Nazareth Coll (MS) Spcl Ed 1988; *cr:* St Josephs Villa Spcl 1987-90; Wayne Finger Lakes BOCES Spcl Ed Tchr 1990-93; S Arts Spcl Edctr & Writing Resource Tchr 1993-; *ai:* 11th Grd A Tech Comm; Yrbk Staff; Outing Club; Cross Cntry & Track Coach Helper Pgm; ANYSEED 1987-; Project Adventure 1989-, F Wheatland Historical Assn 1991-; Residential Treatment Facili Presenter 1988 & 1989; *office:* Schl Of The Arts 45 Prince St NY 14607*

ELLIS, CAROL DOMINICK, English Teacher; *b:* Memphis, James M.; *c:* Laura L. Stanfield, William G. Stanfield; *ed:* Penn (BA) Jrnlsm 1960; 50 Post Grad Credits George WA U, Villanova of PA, Marywood Coll, Univ of VA; *cr:* Collingdale HS Fr, 1962-64; George WA HS Eng Tchr 1964-65; Nether Providence Tchr 1965-70; Strath Haven HS Eng Chrpsn 1977-; *ai:* Poetry C Facilities Comm; NEA, PSEA, WSEA 1977-; Amer Assoc of Uni 1970-; NCTE 1987-; Habitat for Humanity 1994-; Natl Endow Hum Grant; Phila Museum of Art Grant; Wallingford-Swarthm Awd; Distngd Newspaper Adv Temple Univ; *office:* Strath Have S Providence Rd Wallingford PA 19086

ELLIS, DEENA SCHWAMBERGER, Spanish & French Tea Hammond, IN; *m:* Richard S.; *c:* Richard, Robert, Michael; *ed* Univ (BA) Span & Fr 1975; Butler Univ (MS) Span, Fr & Ed Southern Hancock Schls Span & Fr Instr 1976-79; Rushville Con Schls Fr Instr 1980-81; Bloomfield Schl Corp Span & Fr Instr Elmwood Schl Corp Span & Fr Instr 1987-88; Anthony Wayne S & Fr Instr 1988-; *ai:* Frgn Lang Dept Chair; OEA 1987-; OFL Jennings Scholar; Bus Week Magazine Awd for Innovative Tch Schl Bd Assn Awd; Rockefeller Fndtn Recipient for Stud in Panam Anthony Wayne HS 5967 Finzel Rd Whitehouse OH 43571

ELLIS, DIANE DEANE, Asst Prof of Allied Dntl Prgm; *b:* G MA; *m:* Gordon E.; *c:* Ryan, Lyndsey; *ed:* West Liberty St Coll (A Hygiene 1971; Univ of Bridgeport (BS) Dental Hygiene Ed 1977; St Univ (MS) Admin 1993; Cont Ed in Pharmacology 18 Hrs Implants, Nutrition, Collabortive Learning 20 Hrs; *cr:* Felix L General Practive Dental Hygienist 1981-88; Steven Peiser DI Dental Hygienist 1986-88; Comm Coll of RI Instr 1988-90; Tunx Tech Coll Asst Prof 1990-; *ai:* Exec Bd Prof Staff Org; Regnl Chprsn of Campus Wellness Comm; Amer Dental Hygienist Ass Human Anatomy & Physiol 1993-; United Church of Christ, Tch Tunxis Comm-Tech Coll 271 Scottswamp Rd Farmington CT 06

ELLIS, HOWARD CHARLES, Associate Professor of His Washington, DC; *m:* Clara Jean Wilkins; *ed:* Univ of MD (BA) (MA) Amer His 1967; Kent St Univ Further Ed; Akron Univ PH Univ AZ Univ Scholar; *cr:* Univ MD Grad Tchng Asst 1966-67; L Comm Coll Instr, Asst Prof, Assoc Prof 1967-; Lorain Cty Co Tutoring Ctr Coord 1993-; *ai:* Black River Stamp Club 1970-, NEH Summer Seminar Grant Univ NM 1979, Univ IL at Chica Chicago IL Newberry Lib Treaty Grant 1991, Newberry Lib M 1993; Cncl for Advancement, Support of Ed Washington DC OH F 1992; *office:* Lorain County Comm Coll 1005 N Abbe Rd Elyria O

NET DECORTE, Mathematics & Tchr of Gifted; *b:* E Brady, /id C.; *c:* Brian D., Michael A.; *ed:* Slippery Rock Univ (BS) 963, (MED) Rdng Specialist 1972; IN Univ of PA Doctoral rk; Northeast Regnl Ctr Stu Assistance Prgm Trng; *cr:* Ctr Twp hr 1963-64; Butler Jr HS Rdng Specialist 1975-77; Slippery dng Specialist 1977-90, Math, Tchr of Gifted 1990-; *ai:* Math :ad Team Coach; Holiday Charity Raffle Spon; Math Curr Delta Kappa; SRAEA, Past Pres; Amer Assn of Univ Women; A; NCTM; PCTM; Keystone St Rdng Assn; North Pittsburgh rs; Cubs Auxilary Assn; SRU Alumni Assn; Ducks Unlimited; Butler Co Assoc Artists; Brenson & Assoc Consultant; Thanks om; Gift of Time Awds; *office:* Slippery Rock Area Schl Dist Slippery Rock PA 16057*

NET LANGDON, Fourth Grade Teacher; *b:* Endicott, NY; *m:* ; *c:* Kelly L., Matthew L.; *ed:* Cortland St Univ (BA) Elem Ed Elem Ed, Rdng 1976; *cr:* Apalachin Elem Schl Permanent Sub 2nd Grd Tchr 3 Yrs, 4th Grd Tchr 18 Yrs, 4th Grd Team Tchr th Grd Level Chprsn 1985-; Dimensions of Learning Dist Team; Cmptr Ed, Hlth & Wellness, Integrated Lang Arts Comms; FT 1974-; Oweog-Apalachin Tchrs Assn 1974-, Bldg Rep; ; *office:* Apalachin Elem Schl 405 Pennsylvania Ave Apalachin

HN MICHAEL, High School Chemistry Teacher; *b:* Charleroi, Univ of PA (BS) Ed & Chem 1971, (BS) Industrial Mgt & Comp Duquesne Univ at Pittsburgh (MS) Admin & Supervision 1992; 1-Whitehall Schl Dist Tchr 1971-; *ai:* NEA, PSEA & BWEA sburgh Energy & Tech Ctr Summer Flwshp; Testing & Rsrch lidation Coal Corp Project Acid Mine Drainage 1991; US Dept Energy Project Flue Gas Emmissions 1993; *office:* Baldwin HS on Blvd Pittsburgh PA 15236

HN SIDNEY, Veterinary Technology Prof; *b:* Abington, PA; *m:* nrach; *c:* Sarah, Carrie; *ed:* PA St Univ (BS) Animal Sci 1975; ferson Univ (PHD) biochem 1983; Inst for Lab Animal Mngmt Med Univ of SC Post-Doctoral Fellow 1981; Trident Tech Coll 82; Manor Jr Coll Adj Fac 1993-; Univ of Med & Dent of NJ rof 1994-; *ai:* Amer Assn for Lab Animal Sci, Lab Animal n 1992-; Cheltenham Aux Police 1974-, Sr Asst Dir; US Coast liary 1982-, Division Captain, Operational Merit; Cheltenham dvy Comm 1994-; Foerder Flwshp Grad Stud; 2 Posters m Assn Lab Animal Sci Meetings; 2 Papers Pub; *office:* Manor Fox Chase Rd Jenkintown PA 19046

ARTHA ALDEN, Math Teacher; *b:* Belfast, ME; *m:* David H.; Maggie, Ame; *ed:* Colby Coll (BA) Math 1970; Univ of MA d, Cnslng 1974; Attnd AP Calculus Inst, Woodrow Wilson Inst odeling, GATE Inst, Math Solutions Inst; *cr:* Amherst Regnl Jr chr 1971-75; Maranacook Comm Schl Math Tchr 1976-; *ai:* Jr NCTM 1991-; Grant Awded 1994 to do Wkshps on Alternative t; *office:* Maranacook Comm Schl Rt 17 Readfield ME 04355

AUREEN MALONEY, Math Teacher & Dept Chr; *b:* PA; *m:* William Robert; *c:* William, Scott, Ryan, Timothy; *ed:* oll (BA) Ed, Scndry Math 1969; Attnd Niagara Comm Coll, Canisius Coll; *cr:* Myrtle Beach Jr HS Tchr 1969-70; St Peter Tchr 1972-73; Mt St Mary Acad Tchr, Chr 1988-; *ai:* Coach Team; Coach SAT Prep 20 Yrs; Schl Bd; St Albert the Great Cub Scout Ldr; AMTNYS 1992-; *office:* Mt St Mary Acad 3756 ve Kenmore NY 14217

EPHEN CHARLES, Social Studies Dept Chair; *b:* Altoona, et Kay Fries; *ed:* IN Univ of PA (BS) Soc Scis 1969, (MED) Soc *cr:* Hollidaysburg Area Schls Tchr 1969-; *ai:* K-12 Scope & Comm; NEA 1969-; PSEA 1969-, Treas, VP, Negotiator; ASCD opa Delta Pi; PA Acad for Tchgn Salute to Tchng Awd; Taft Univ of PA: Westminster Coll Intnl Stud Inst; *home:* 505 50th PA 16602

, KITTY L., English Instructor; *b:* Beaufort, NC; *c:* Beverly *:* Fordham Univ (MS) Ed, Writing 1983; Shaw Univ (BA) Eng; tud George Mason Univ; Jrnlsm Ford Fnd Fellow; Dev Skills iv; *cr:* Ford Fnd Consultant 1969-70; Natl Schlsp Svc Asst Dir s 1970-73; NYC Human Resources Admin Pub Affairs Staff 3-74; Malcolm-King Coll Dir Learning Ctr, Eng Chprsn, Instr City Univ of NY Eng Instr 1973-89; NY Urban Coalition Ed, 4-76; NY City Bd of Ed Ed, Writer 1976-79; Univ of Dist of nst 1992-95; Howard Univ Instr 1992-; *ai:* Eng Club Adv; Exec, Dept; Readmissions CommE; NCTE 1994-; Publicity Club of Friends of Lib 1996; Outstdng Svc Awd Malcolm King Coll munications to Black Comms Awd Seagrams Co 1986; Phi Delta 3; Summa Cum Laude 1984; Natl Assn of Black Accountants *office:* Howard Univ 2400 6th St NW Washington DC 20059

, WILLIAM CHARLES, Mathematics Teacher & Coach; *b:* ; *m:* Diana L.; *c:* Rennique, Rianan, Lori; *ed:* Indiana Univ of ath Ed 1978; Attnd Univ of Pittsburgh; *cr:* Plum Borough Schl 1978-; *ai:* Ftbl Coach 1978-; Bsktbl Coach 1980-85, 1990-92; oach 1987-89; NEA & PSEA 1978-; PTA 1986-.

, CAROLYN (WAGNER), Middle School Mathematics Tchr; *b:* , NC; *m:* Kenneth Lloyd; *c:* Richard Rohrberg Jr., Barb Debbie Stein; *ed:* St Univ of NY at Brockport (BS) Ed 1963, 973; Post Grad Stud in Math, Ed & Cmptrs; *cr:* Gates Chili Cntrl 1963-68; Greece Cntrl Part-Time Adult Math Tchr 1968-79; MS Math Tchr 1979-; *ai:* Present Wkshps at Confs, Local Colls Groups; Mentor Tchr to Other Math Tchrs Specializing in Phys, t It Out, Reality Math; NYSUT 1963-; ACE 1979-; AMTRA, Greece Recreation Comm, Commissioner, Lifetime Achvmt ce Girls Soccer, VP; BSA, Den Mother; Alternative Schl Greece y Bd; Pub NAPSS Journal; Nom Natl Tchr of Yr Awd; Merit Nom Ch I Math Lab for Pres Initiative for Ed of Disadvantaged fice: Gates-Chili MS 910 Wegman Rd Rochester NY 14624*

RTH, DELBERT WARREN, Professor of Psychology; *b:* A; *m:* Mary Lou Holbrook; *c:* Kevin, Kristen, Carolyn Durant, Lynne Ann, Sharon; *ed:* Univ of CA at Davis (BA) Psych 1962; sco St Coll (MA) Psych 1964; Univ of CA at Berkeley (PHD) 7; *cr:* Univ of CA Post Grd Rsrch Psych 1963-67, USPHS Fellow Elizabethtown Coll Prof of Psych 1970-; *ai:* Councilman; orough; PA Soc of Biofeedback, Behav Medicine 1976-, Pres; Restoration Assn 1990-; Lebonon VA Med Ctr Consultant; PA Drug, Alcohol Ed; Tallaot Pl; Private Clinical Practice; *office:* own Coll One Alpha Dr Elizabethtown PA 17022

RTH, PENELOPE SUSAN, Teacher of Gifted & Talented; *b:* OH; *c:* Ashley, Anna; *ed:* Muskingum Coll (BA) Elem, Scndry 1973; Ashland Univ (MED) Curr, Gifted 1985; *cr:* Big Walnut 6 Grds Tchr 1073-85; Gahanna-Jefferson Schls GATE Prgm Tchr Math Counts Team Coach; NEA; OEA; OCTM, NCTM 1986-; andbell Choirs 1973-, Dir; *office:* Gahanna-Jefferson Pub Schls e Dr Gahanna OH 43230

D, MARK W., His Tchr & Soc Stud Chprsn; *b:* Dover, OH; *m:* Smith; *c:* Joshua, Benjamin, Daniel; *ed:* OH Univ (BSEd) Soc o 1971, (MS) His 1972; Ashland Univ 24 Hrs Completed on Curr & Instruction & Cert in Scndry Admin; *cr:* Lancaster HS His Tchr 1971; Mt Vernon MS His Tchr 1971-72; Gahanna Lincoln HS Tchr & Coach 1972-78; Worthington HS Tchr & Coach 1978-; *ai:* Adv FCA; WEA 1978-, Treas, Bldg Rep; OEA, NEA 1978-; Worthington Chrstn Church 1991-, Deacon 1992-; TWHS Tchr of Yr 1987, Inductee Hall of Fame 1992; Outstanding Tchr Recognition 1989, 1991; Other Coll Recognitions Since 1985; *office:* Thomas Worthington HS 300 W Dublin Granville Rd Worthington OH 43085

ELLYSON, STEVE L., Professor of Psychology; *b:* Baltimore, MD; *m:* Carol A. Olson; *ed:* Washington Coll MD (BA) Psych 1970; Univ of DE (MA) Psych 1973, (PHD) Psych 1974; *cr:* Beaver Coll Asst Prof 1974-78; Linfield Coll Assoc Prof 1978-81; Univ of CA at Davis Assoc Prof 1981-86; Youngstown St Univ Prof 1986-; *ai:* Human Subjects Research Comm Chr 1994-; Amer Psychological Assn 1974-; Amer Psychological Soc 1986-; Soc for Experimental Soc Psych 1987-; Greater Akron Bsktbl Ofcls 1986-, Pres 1996-97, Exec Bd 1990-96; Distinguished Prof Awd YSU 1988-91; 3 Books & Over 150 Articles & Presentations; *office:* Youngstown St Univ 410 Wick Ave Youngstown OH 44555

ELMES, CELIA M. HAFLETT, English Teacher; *b:* Troy, PA; *m:* Jonathan C.; *c:* Faith, Abigail; *ed:* PA St Univ (BS) Scndry Eng Ed 1988; Shippensburg Univ (MS) Scndry Eng Ed 1992; Univ of AK 3 Credits; *cr:* West Perr High Eng Tchr 1988-; *ai:* Var Vlybl Coach; *office:* West Perry HS Rd 1 Box 7 Elliottsburg PA 17024*

ELMO, LIN J., Art Teacher; *b:* Stamford, CT; *m:* Joseph J.; *c:* Jennifer, Stephanie; *ed:* Southern CT St Univ (BS) Art Ed 1969, (MS) Elem Ed 1976; 6th Yr Art 1989; CT Dept of Ed BEST Pgm; Attnd Fairfield Univ; *cr:* Milford Pub Schls Art Tchr 1969-; *ai:* Curr Comm; CEA & NEA 1976-; CAEA 1978-95; Milford Ed Assoc Exec Bd; Milford Fine Arts Cncl 1970-, Various Comms; Milford Historical Soc 1987-; Lions Clubs Intnl 1996, VP; CT St Dept of Ed Celebration of Excl Honorable Mention 1989; Amer Mothers Inc St Winner 1990; Milford Bd of Ed Mini-Grant Recipient 1995; *home:* 31 Green St Milford CT 06460

ELMONT, MAXINE, Professor of Social Sciences; *b:* Brooklyn, NY; *c:* Stephen; *ed:* Suffolk Univ (AB) Psych, Sociology 1966; Boston Univ (MED) Rehabilitation Cnslng 1968; Univ of MA at Amherst (EDD) Higher Ed, Staff Dev 1986; Continuing Ed; *cr:* Jewish Comm Ctr Prgm Supvr 1953-63; Margaret Fuller House Prgm Dir 1963-65; Neighborhood Yth Corps Dir Out of Schl Prgm 1967-68; MA Bay Comm Coll Prof Soc Sci 1968-; *ai:* Psi Beta Adv, Silver Key, MACER; Learn Asst Assoc of NE 1983-, Pres, Ex Bd; Natl Assn Dev Ed 1983-, Com Chair, Outstdng Dissertation; MA Teach Assn 1970-; Grievance, Ex Bd; Natl Rehabilitation Assn 1968-; Natl Rehabilitation Cnslng Assn; Brookline Visit Nurse 1990-, Pres, Ex Bd; Brookline Friendly Sco 1993-, Trustee; Aids Action Comm 1980-, Vol; Consum, All for Sup Ed 1993-, Ex Bd; Phi Theta Kappa Honorary Mem; Whos Who Among Hum Svc Pro 1986; Whos Who in East; Worlds Who Who of Women; Intnl Women of Yr 1992-93; Numerous Articles Pub; Numerous Workshops; *office:* MA Bay Community Coll 19 Flagg Dr Framingham MA 01701*

ELMS, MICHAEL THOMAS, Biology Instructor; *b:* Portland, OR; *m:* Carol J. Mundorff-Elms; *ed:* OR St Univ (BS) Wilflife Bio 1967; Boise St Univ Tchng Cert Ed 1986; Cmptrs in Sci Classroom 9 Hrs; The Stud of Tchng 4 Hrs; Advanced Placement Wkshps 9 Hrs; Environmental Sci in Classroom 3 Hrs; *cr:* ID Fish, Game Dept Conservation Ofcr 1967-85; Dept of Defense Dependent Schl Sci Instr 1987-; *ai:* Sci Dept Chrprsn; Schl Mngmt Cncl; Stu Act Fund Cncl Sec; NEA, OES 1987-; Widelife Soc 1967-; NABT 1988-; Natl Wildlife Fed 1967; *home:* Cmr 475 Box 259 APO AE 09036

EL-NAGGAR, LETICIA JIMENEZ, Chemistry Prof & Area Coord; *b:* Mexico DF, Mexico; *m:* Shaaban F.; *c:* Fouad, Mariam, Omar, Leticia; *ed:* Natl Univ of Mexico (BSC) Pharmacy, Chem, Bio 1973, (MSC) Natural Products Chem 1975; The OH St Univ (PHD) Natural Products Chem 1980; *cr:* Natl Polytechnic Inst Research Assoc 1972-73; Natl Univ of Mexico Instr 1973-75; The OH St Univ Research Asst 1975-80; Bucks Cty Comm Coll Prof 1984-; *ai:* Curricular Revision, Dev Ed, Evaluation of Instruction Comms; Key Resource Fac Cmptr Augmented Instruction; Amer Chem Soc 1980-; AFT 1984-; Bucks Cty Sci Tchr Assn 1993-; J Natural Products 1980-, Referee for Scientific Papers; PTO Chancellor St Goodnoe Elem 1980-; Research Assistanship OSU, Schlsp UNAM Grants; Publications Phytochemistry, J. Natural Products, Syllabus Pharmaceutical Congress Mexico, Intnl ACS Meeting, Intnl Congress Natural Products, Easter Small Coll Computing Conf; *office:* Bucks County Community Coll Swamp Rd Newtown PA 18940

ELPREN, CARI SILVERMAN, Former Teacher; *b:* NYC, NY; *m:* Jay David; *c:* Alex Silverman, Ross; *ed:* Queens Coll at CUNY (BA) Elem Ed 1981, (MS) Rdng Tchr K-12 1984; Prof Diploma Schl Admin, Supervision 1995; *cr:* PS 89 Q Elem Ed Tchr 1981-85, Rdng Tchr 1990-95.*

ELTON, GAIL ANN, Voc Computer & Acctng Tchr; *b:* Wauseon, OH; *m:* Edward; *c:* Michael Edward, Kristy Lyn; *ed:* Univ of Toledo (BS) Bus Ed 1973, (MS) Bus Ed 1984; *cr:* Four Cty Voc Schl Cmptr, Acctng Instr 1973-; *ai:* Chapter Adv Bus Profs Amer; NBEA 1987-; OH Voc Assn, Five Star Tchr; Delta Dolphins Swim Team 1987-, Treas; Delta Meth Church Bell Choir 1994-; Tchrs in Amer Enterprise Second Pl 1983; Northwest Regnl Outstdng Consumer Ec Ed Edctr Awd First Runner-up 1984; Author of Free Enterprise Abstract 1983; *office:* Four County Vocational Schl 22-900 SR 32 Archbold OH 43502

ELWELL, DOROTHY MARIE, Third Grade Teacher; *b:* Vineland, NJ; *c:* Christopher Bunker, Alyson Bunker, Ella Krajewski, Deborah Bunker; *ed:* Glassboro St Coll (BA) Elem Ed; *cr:* Morris Goodwin Schl 3rd-4th Grd Tchr 1969-73; Main Road Schl Sub, Basic Skills, 5th, 3rd Grd Tchr 1976-; *ai:* NJEA 1979-; GCEA 1979-, TFEA Cty Rep; TFEA 1979-, VP, Mbrshp Chm; Newfield Womens Club; Newfield Democratic Comm Woman 1986-88; Gloucester Cty Outstdng Tchr 1994.

ELWOOD, CRAIG R., Music Teacher & Band Director; *b:* Syracuse, NY; *m:* Jeawette M. Carr; *c:* Heather, Alyssa; *ed:* SUNY at Potsdam (BMEd) Music Ed 1985; Syracuse Univ (MM) Trumpet Performance 1989; *cr:* Cntrl Square Elem Band Tchr 1985-88, HS Band Tchr 1989-; *ai:* Marching, Parade, Jazz Bands; Brass Quintet; Schl Musical; Winter Guard; Audio Visual Club; Peruissin Ensemble; NY Fed of Contest Judges 1985-, Audjicator; Intnl Trumpet Guild 1985-; Mid York Color Guard Circuit 1990-, Pres; Cntrl Square Comm Tech 1994-; Schlsp Syracuse Univ; *office:* Cntrl Square Cntrl Schls Main St Central Square NY 13036*

ELY, DAVID S., Science Teacher; *b:* Concord, VT; *m:* Diane Louise Fricke; *c:* Marion, Julia, Kristin; *ed:* Univ of VT (BA) Zoology 1967, (MAT) Zoology 1974; 149 Addl Credits; *cr:* Univ of VT Research Asst 1966-73; Champlain Valley Union Sci Tchr 1973-; *ai:* NEA 1973-; NSTA, NABT 1975-; APAST 1985-; Shelburne Meth Church 1974-, Chprsn; Allenbrook Homes for Youth 1992-, VP; VT Sci Tchrs 1980-, Pres 1986-89; Outstanding Bio Tchr Awd; Presidential Sci Awd; Distinguished Tchr Awd; VT Tchr of Yr; New England Sci Tchr Awd; Tandy Scholar Awd; Shell Outstanding Tchr Awd; CVU Tchr Awd; Star Awd; Burger King Tchr Recognition; Sabbatical; *office:* Champlain Valley Union HS RR 2 Box 160 Hinesburg VT 05461*

ELY, JO ANN, First Grade Teacher; *b:* Dover, OH; *ed:* Kent St Univ (BS) Elem Ed 1981; Univ of Akron (MS) Elem Ed 1993; *cr:* Garaway Local Schls Elem Tchr 1983-; *ai:* Dundee Elem Head Tchr; PTO Rep; NEA, OEA 1983-; Garaway Tchrs Assn 1983-, Bldg Rep, Grievance Comm; Sugarcreek Arts Cncl 1996, Trustee; *home:* 6456 Old Route 39 NW Dover OH 44622

ELY, LYNETTE FRIEDLINE, Art Teacher; *b:* Boswell, PA; *m:* Richard C.; *ed:* IN St Coll of PA (BS) Art Ed 1961; Post Grad Credits Univ of Pittsburgh at Johnstown, PA St Univ & WV Univ; *cr:* North Star Schl Dist Art Tchr 1961-; *ai:* Past 9th Grd Adv; Yrbk Adv; PAEA 1961-; NAEA 1961-; Hoffman Luth Church 1939-; 4-H Ldr 1960-; Boswell Area Jaycees Comm Svc Awd 1993; *office:* North Star HS 400 Ohio St Boswell PA 15531

ELY, TED C., High School Principal; *b:* Chillicothe, OH; *c:* Seth, Shawn; *ed:* OH Univ (BSEd) Math 1979, (MED) Educl Admin 1981, (EDS) Educl Admin 1984, (PHD) Educl Admin 1993; Attnd KS St Univ; *cr:* Chillicothe City Math Tchr, Coord 1979-94; Zane Trace Local HD Prin 1994-; *ai:* Bsktbl, Track, Ftbl Coach; Chess Club; Quiz Bowl Adv; NEA, OEA 1979-94; Phi Delta Kappa 1982-, Local Pres 1982-83; Kappa Delta Pi 1984-; Chillicothe Educl Assn 1970-, Pres 1993-94; Great Seal Fiber Optics Network 1991-; Phi Delta Kappa Pres 1982-83; Dissertation on Tchr Job Satifaction 1993; *office:* Zane Trace Local Schl Dist 946 St Rt 180 Chillicothe OH 45601*

ELZEER, WANDA, First Grade Teacher; *b:* Connellsville, PA; *m:* Bradley; *c:* Bradley II, Jeffrey, Kimrey; *ed:* Waynesburg Coll (BA) Ed 1960; 30 Hrs Ashland Coll, Kent Coll, Bowling Greene, LaVerne Coll; *cr:* Forest Elem Schl Tchr 14 Yrs;Birch Schl Chptr 1, 1st Grd Tchr 10 Yrs; Garfield Schl Tchr 3 Yrs; *ai:* Lang Arts Comm; Delta Kappa Gamma; West Shore Rdng Assn 15 Yrs; Jennings, Educl Fnd Grants; Houghton Mifflin Honoree.*

EMANUEL, LINDA J., Assistant Professor of French; *b:* Pittsburgh, PA; *m:* Dennis A.; *c:* Timothy; *ed:* Clarion Univ (BA) Fr 1969; Penn St Univ (MA) Fr 1971, (PHD) Fr 1978; *cr:* Univ of HI Visiting Asst Prof Fr; Onslow Cty Schls Tchr; Amer Univ Lecturer Fr; Lock HAven Univ Asst Prof Fr 1990-; *ai:* Various Comms; Foreign Lang Dept Sec; Foreign Lang Honor Soc Adv; AATF 1980-, Sec, Treas, Cntrl PA Chapter; Phi Delta Kappa 1991-, Sec Lock Haven Chapter; PA Assoc of Tchng Scholars 1992-; Northeast MLA; Clinton Cty Historical Soc; 2 Fellowships at Penn St Univ; AAUW Schlsp Awd; Small Campus Grant for Seminar in Canada; Presentations Dealing with Foreign Lang Tchng; *office:* Lock Haven University Lock Haven PA 17745*

EMBORSKY, EUGENE F., Science Teacher; *b:* Salamanca, NY; *m:* Jane Adair Kendall; *c:* Andrew, Peter; *ed:* St Univ Coll at Geneseo (BS) Bio & Scndry Ed 1977, (MA) Cellular & Molecular Bio 1982; St Univ Coll at Brockport (CAS) Educl Admin 1989; *cr:* St Univ Coll at Geneseo Tchng Asst 1977; Letchworth Cntrl Schl Jr HS Sci Tchr 1977-80; Alexander Cntrl Schl Sci & Chem Tchr 1980-, Sci Dept Chprsn 1986-92; *ai:* Sr HS Sci Club; NYSUT & STANYS 1980-; Alexander United Tchrs 1980-, Pres 1989-; Cub Scouts of America 1985-91, Cubmaster 1988-91; Vince Lomardi Ftbl Coach 1990-92; Excl in Scndry Tchng Awd 1990; Howard Hughes Med Inst Summer Research Fellowship 1993; Amer Soc for Clin Invstgtn Summer Rsrch Fellowship 1994; *office:* Alexander Central Schl 3314 Buffalo St Alexander NY 14005

EMEH, MICHELLE APPLEWHAITE, Math & Religion Teacher; *b:* Brooklyn, NY; *m:* Emmanuel N.; *c:* Christina, Angelica; *ed:* Long Island Univ at Brooklyn (BS) Elem Ed-Cum Laude 1977, (MS) Ed 1979; *cr:* Our Lady of Loretto Schl Sci, Rdng, Lang Arts, Religion Jr HS Tchr 1978-86; Holy Cross Schl Math, Religion, Soc Stud Jr HS Tchr 1986-; *ai:* NEA; Attnd Undergraduate Schl on Full Acad Schlsp; Who's Who in Amer Colls & Univs 1977; *office:* Holy Cross Schl 2520 Church Ave Brooklyn NY 11226

EMELY-ROACH, JANE KATHRYN, English Chairperson; *b:* Philadelphia, PA; *m:* Kevin A. Roach; *ed:* PA St Univ (BS) Eng Ed 1969; Temple Univ (MED) Eng Ed 1973; Supervisory Cert Bloomsburg Univ Comm Arts 1981; Cert Elem & Scndry Prin Beaver Coll 1994; Grad Level Courses in Drama, Eng, Etc; *cr:* Huntingdon Jr HS Eng Tchr 1969-83; Abington Jr HS Eng Dept Chprsn 1983-; *ai:* Dir of Schl Musical 1983-; Co-Chair Assessment Comm for Dist Strategic Action Plan; NEA, PSEA, NCTE 1969-; ASCD 1983-; St Pauls Presbyn Church 1988-, Music Dir; Simpson Meth Church 1980-, Music Dir; Montgomery Cty Intermediate Unit 1983-, Cmptr Instr; *office:* Abington Jr HS 2056 Susquehanna Rd Abington PA 19001*

EMERICK, KAREN SUE (CRAWFORD), Gifted & English Teacher; *b:* E Liverpool, OH; *m:* Jonathan Scott; *ed:* Kent St Univ (BS) Elem Ed 1979; Ashland Univ (MA) 1992; Gifted Cert 1986; *cr:* Carrollton Southern Local Substitute Tchr 1979-80; Carrollton Exempted Village Schl 1st Grd Tchr 1981, 5th Grd Tchr 1981-86, 5-8 Grd Tchr of Gifted 1986-, 7th-8th Grd Eng Tchr 1986-; *ai:* Future Problem Solving Coach; Inservice Comms; Odyssey of Mind Coach; CEA, NEA 1980-; OAGC 1987-; Martha Holden Jennings Scholar; Ashland Nom for Tchr Achvmt Awd; *office:* Carrollton Exempted Vlg Schl 252 Third St NE Carrollton OH 44615

EMERICK, LINDA COWGILL, English Language Arts Teacher; *b:* Camden, NJ; *c:* Kristen Armstrong, Megan, Amy, Brett; *ed:* Beaver Coll (BS) Elem Ed 1969; Univ of DE (MAEd) Human Dev 1979; 45 Addl Credits Univ of DE, DE Dept of Pub Instruction, DE Tchr Ctr; *cr:* DE Tech & Comm Coll Instr 1978-; Wilmington Montessori Schl Rdng, Eng Tchr 1980-86; Skyline MS Rdng Tchr 1986-93; Cab Calloway Schl of Arts Eng Lang Arts Tchr 1993-; *ai:* Musicals Producer; Coord New Castle Cty Shakespeare Festival; Stu Govt Assn Spon; NCTE 1993-; IRA 1969-; NEA 1986-; DE Inst for Arts in Ed, Wilmington Drama League, Bd Mem; West Wilmington Kiwanis Red Clay Tchr of Yr 1995; *office:* Cab Calloway Schl of the Arts 100 N duPont Rd Wilmington DE 19807

EMERICK, ROBERT WILLIAM, Adj Psychology Prof & Director; *b:* Cumberland, MD; *c:* Elaina; *ed:* Albright Coll (BA) Philosophy 1971; Union Theological Seminary (MDiv) Theology 1974; Yeshiva Univ (MSW) Clinical Casework 1987; Doctoral Candidate; *cr:* United Meth Church Pastor 1974-88; Bayonne Mental Hlth Ctr Therapist 1988-91; Jersey City St Coll Adj Psych Prof 1989-; Bayonne Mental Hlth Ctr Dir 1991-; *ai:* NASW, NJNASW 1987-; Licensed NJ Clinical Soc Worker; *office:* Jersey City St Coll 601 Broadway Bayonne NJ 07002

EMERSON, JOHN G., 7th Grade Mathematics Teacher; *b:* Winchester, MA; *m:* Patti D.; *c:* Jennifer, Ryan; *ed:* Dartmouth (BA) Eng & Ed 1971; NH Coll (MBA) Bus 1983; *cr:* Berlin Elem Schl 2nd Grd Tchr & Prin 1971-78; Phoenix Mutual Life Insurance Sales & Trainer 1979-82; Jaffrey-Rindge Schl Dist HS Math Tchr 1983-85, 7th Grd Math Tchr 1985-; *ai:* Math & Debate Clubs Adv; Schl Improvement Team; NCTM 1989-; NEA 1971-; Dollars for Scholars 1994-, Sec; *office:* Jaffrey-Rindge MS 1 Conant Way Jaffrey NH 03452

EMERT, JOYCE DIANE, English Teacher; *b:* Somerset, PA; *m:* Richard W. Jr.; *ed:* CA St Univ (BA) Comprehensive Eng 1969; Masters Rdng 1972; Cert of Recognition Commonwealth PA Dept of Ed 1989; Pres, Bd of Dirs Assn for Supervision, Curr Dev 1989; Madeline Hunter Inst 1989; *cr:* Rockwood Area HS Scndry Eng, Rdng 1969-; *ai:* Trained Peer Coaching, Cooperative Learning; Coord Power Writing Prgm 7-12; Vol Apointee; Grammatic Ed for ATS, ASCD Network Newsletter; Lead Tchr 3 Yrs; Mentor Inductee Prgm 8 Yrs; Class Adv 10th; Schlsp Comm; PSEA, NEA, NCTE 1969-; Rockwood Ed Assn 1969-, Treas 15 Yrs; Somerset Church 1958; Mid St Evaluation Comm 1984; Project 81 Curr Improvement Comm; Dev SAT Verbal Curr 11th Grd; Lead Tchr 3 Yrs; Conducted Wrksps Cooperative Learning, Motivation K-12; Presenter Somerset Cty In-Service; RAHS Discipline Comm 3 Yrs; Cooperating Tchr for St

Vincent, Wilson Univs; Presenter Sr Citizens; *office:* Rockwood Area HS Somerset Ave Rockwood PA 15557

EMERY, CHRISTOPHER, Physics & Electronics Teacher; *b:* Northampton, MA; *m:* Carol Lemke; *c:* Brian, Jennifer; *ed:* Univ of MA at Amherst (BS) Physics 1972, (MEd) Ed 1977, (CAGS) Ed 1987; Attnd Univ of RI & CO Schl of Mines; *cr:* Ralph C. Mahar Regnl HS Sci Tchr 1972-74; Amherst Regnl HS Physics & Electronics Tchr 1974-; *ai:* NSTA 1972-; AAPT 1972-; MA Assn of Sci Tchrs 1974-, Sec, Bd of Dir; Robert Frost Tchng Chair 1979-80; Tchng Merit Awd 1984; MA Assn of Sci Tchrs Sci Ed of Yr Awd 1995; Numerous Articles Pub; *office:* Amherst Regnl HS 21 Mattoon St Amherst MA 01002*

EMERY, DAVID R., Mathematics Teacher; *b:* New York, NY; *m:* Margaret Irene Sensenic; *c:* Robert David, James Christopher; *ed:* Ursinus Coll (BS) Math 1961; Univ of PA (MA) Math 1963; PA St Univ 24 Credits; Univ of PA 8 Credits; *cr:* Methacton Schl Dist Tchr 1960-; Ursinus Coll Lecturer in Math 1962-66; Montgomery Cty Comm Coll Evening Instr 1970-83; *ai:* NHS, Methacton Math Team & Comp Club Spon; Sr HS Instructional Software Support Specialist; NEA, MEA & PSEA 1963-; ATMOPAU & PCTM 1968-; Chief Negotiator MEA 1968-73; Cntrl Schwenkfelder Church 1972-, Audit Chm 1985-; PA Acad Decathlon 1985-, Exec Dir; Montgomery Cty Acad Decathlon 1985-, Exec Dir; Who's Who in Amer Ed 1992; NFS Summer Inst of Univ of PA 1965-; US Acad Decathlon Dev Grant 1990; Article Pub; *office:* Methacton Sr HS 1001 Kriebel Mill Rd Norristown PA 19403

EMERY, EVELYN PECK, Adult Education Teacher; *b:* Attleboro, MA; *w:* Ralph Edmund (dec); *c:* David, Raymond, Bruce, Norma Emery Woodcock, Alan; *ed:* Ricker Coll (BA) Lbrl Arts 1978; Providence Bible Inst Music 1946; Univ of ME Elem Ed Courses; *cr:* Wytopitlock Elem Tchr 1975-87; Temple Chrstn Acad Tchr 1988-90; Life Chrstn Acad Tchr 1990-92; Voc Schl Region III Tchr 1993-; *ai:* NEA 1987-; ME Tchrs Assn 1987-; *home:* RR 2 Box 141 Lincoln ME 04457

EMERY, PATRICIA FURLONG, Fifth Grade Teacher; *b:* Sandusky, OH; *m:* Gregory R.; *c:* Hayden, Alec; *ed:* Mt St Joseph Coll (BA) Ed 1974; Xavier Univ (MA) Ed 1991; Master +30 Credit Hrs from Univ of Cincinnati, Miami Univ, Drake Univ; *cr:* St Francis DeSales Kndgtn Tchr 1974-75; Santa Barbara Cty Shcls Kndgtn Tchr 1976-78; West Clearmont Schl Kndgtn & 5th-6th Grd Tchr 1978-; *ai:* Parenting Class Tchr 3 Yrs; Intervention Assistance Team 3 Yrs; Comp Coord 1995-; OH Horsemans Cncl 1991-, Fam Mem; *office:* Summerside Elem Schl 4639 Vermona Dr Cincinnati OH 45245

EMERY, ROBERT, Health & Phys Ed Teacher; *b:* Philadelphia, PA; *m:* Sallie; *c:* Renee, Bryan; *ed:* West Chester St (BS) Hlth, PE 1967; Univ of Pittsburgh (MED) Hlth, PE 1968; 10 Credits at Trenton St Coll; 30 Credits at Temple Univ; *cr:* Monroeville Elem Schl Elem PE 1967-68; Neshaminy MS Hlth, PE 1968-; *ai:* Curr Dev Comm Dept Chm; Coach Girls, Boys Bsktbl, Bsbl, Former Ftbl, Soccer Coach; 6th Grd IM Dir; Spec Act Days Coord; AFT; AAHPERD; PA St Assn Hlth PE Rm, Dist Comm, St Tchr of Yr; Doylestown Ath Assn, Coach Soccer, Bookathon, Bsbl; Schl Dist Mini Grants; PA St PE Convention Speaker 1990, 1992; Cty PE Wkshps Speaker; Articles Pub; Dev Hnred PE Prgms Recognized by St; *office:* Neshaminy MS 1200 Langhorne Newtown Rd Langhorne PA 19047*

EMHOFF, JANET A., Latin Tchr & Frgn Lang Chprsn; *b:* Benton Harbor, MI; *ed:* Valparaiso Univ (BA) Classics & Eng 1964; Rutgers Univ (MA) Classics 1977; Attnd Amer Acad at Rome, Tufts Univ, Dartmouth CANE Insts, Salve Regina Greek Inst, Bowdoin Coll; *cr:* Bound Brook HS Head Latin & Eng Tchr 1964-, Frgn Lang Chprsn 1979-; Rutgers Univ Classic Tchng Assistantship 1975; *ai:* Latin Club & PUSH Adv; Sr Hnrs Dinner Chprsn; Prin Advy, Sr Grad Awds & Stu of the Month Awd Comms; NEA 1965-; NJEA 1965-; BBEA 1965-; NJ Classical Assn 1970-; Amer Classical Assn 1973-; CANE 1985-; All St Luth Church 1966-, Hospitality Pgm for Homeless Participant; Fulbright for Amer Acad at Rome & Cumae 1975; Amer Classical League Schlsp 1980; Bound Brook HS Tchr of the Yr 1984; Bowdoin Coll NEH Grant 1986-87; Princeton U Distngd Tchng Awd 1988; *office:* Bound Brook Jr Sr HS 111 W Union Ave Bound Brook NJ 08805

EMIG, JAMES MATTHEW, Associate Prof of Accounting; *b:* Willow Street, PA; *m:* Julie Williams; *c:* Kelsey, Matthew, Jessica; *ed:* Catawba Coll (BA) Accounting & Bus Admin 1975; Univ of NC at Greensboro (MBA) Accounting & Finance 1977; TX A&M Univ (PHD) Accounting 1987; *cr:* Univ of NC at Greensboro Lecturer of Accounting 1977-79; TX A&M Univ Lecturer of Accounting 1982-83; Villanova Univ Assoc Prof of Accountancy 1983-; *ai:* 2nd & 3rd Grd Girls Bsktbl Coach; Amer Accounting Assn 1980-; Church, Sftbl League Coach; Lindback Fnd Tchng Awd 1988; Amer Accounting Assn Doctoral Consortium Fellow 1982; *office:* Villanova Univ Villanova PA 19085*

EMIGH, JAMES MICHAEL, Science Teacher; *b:* Pittsburgh, PA; *m:* Barbara Stefanski; *c:* Michael James, Matthew Justin; *ed:* Allegheny Coll (BS) Bio 1971, (MA) Ed 1972; Credit Hrs Ashland Coll; *cr:* Olmsted Falls HS Bio, Advanced Lab Sci Tchr 1971-; *ai:* Ftbl, Wrestling, Bsbl Coach 24 Yrs; OFTA 1972-; OF Environmental Bd 1973-75; OF Parks & Rec Bd 1980-85; OF Bsbl League 1976-81, Commissioner; SWC Conf Wrestling Coach of Yr; Cleveland Area Wrestling Coach of Yr; *office:* Olmsted Falls HS 26939 Bagley Rd Olmsted Falls OH 44138

EMILSON, PAULINE R., Instrumental Music Teacher; *b:* Dansville, NY; *m:* C. Rudolph; *c:* Jeffrey; *ed:* SUNY Coll at Fredonia NY (MM) Music Performance 1987, (BM) Music Ed 1977; 33 Addl Hrs; *cr:* St Elizabeth Ann Seton Schl Vocal Music Tchr K-8th Grds 1984-85; Panama Central Schl Vocal Music Tchr K-3rd Grds 1982-85; Westfield Acad Inst Music 5th-12th Grds 1986-; *ai:* Dixie Ensemble Dir; Olympic Torch Comm; NYS Zone 1 Area All-State Music Coord; NEA-NY, MENC-NYSSMA 1986-; NYSBDA 1989-, Exec Bd; CCMTA 1983-; WTA 1986-; YMCA 1993-; *office:* Westfield Acad & Central Schl E Main St Westfield NY 14787

EMMANUEL, ERNEST, Science Teacher; *b:* Martin Pur, Pakistan; *m:* Khubseerat Shah Din; *c:* Shahdin, Jaan; *ed:* Panjab Univ (MS) Chem 1966; *ai:* Physics Club Adv; Amer Chem Soc 1976-; SCTO 1980-; NSTA 1985-; Assn of Retarded Citizens 1989-; *office:* Holy Spirit HS California & New Rd Absecon NJ 08201

EMMERLING, KEITH, Soc Stud Coord & His Teacher; *b:* Waynesburg, PA; *c:* Jeffery, Elissa; *ed:* Waynesburg Coll (BA) His 1970; Duqueshe Univ (MA) European His 1974; *cr:* Thomas Jefferson HS Soc Stud Coord 1970-; *ai:* AFT 1970-; *office:* Thomas Jefferson HS Box 18019 Old Clairton Rd Pittsburgh PA 15236

EMMERSON, ANNE MASSIMO, Asst Prof & Office Tech Chrpsn; *b:* New York, NY; *ed:* Nassau Comm Coll (AAS) Bus 1981; SUNY at Empire St (BS) Bus 1984; SUNY at Stoney Brook (MALS) Tech 1987; 3 Credits Hofstra Univ; 6 Credits C. W. Post; *cr:* Nassau Comm Coll Chair 1995-, Asst Prof 1993-, Instr 1988-93, Tech Asst 1984-88, Consulting 1981-; *ai:* Amer Assn Med Transcriptionists 1993-, Corresponding Secc; Assoc Adults, Children Learning Disabilities 1980-, Parent Advocate; Island Trees Bd Ed 1979-94, Pres 3 Terms; NYS Chancellor's Awd Excl in Tchng 1995; *office:* Nassau Comm Coll Office Tech Dept Garden City NY 11530

EMMERT, JORIE (KEYSER), English Teacher; *b:* Schnectady, NY; *m:* JOhn Martin; *c:* Covey; *ed:* Univ of KY (BA) Eng Ed 1987; Wright St Univ (MED) Gen Classroom Tchr 1992; *cr:* Tates Creek Jr HS 7th Grd Eng Tchr 1987-89; Layton HS 10th-11th Grd Eng Tchr 1990-92; Wayne HS 10th-12th Grd Eng Tchr 1992-; *ai:* Tolerance Comm, Sub-Comm; NEA 1987-; HHEA 1992-; NCTE 1990-; Al Crabb Awd KCTE 1988; Golden Apple Achvmt Awd Ashland Oil 1995; *home:* 4583 Irelan St Kettering OH 45440

EMMET, BRIAN MILES, Headmaster; *b:* Detroit, MI; *m:* Katharine Bell; *c:* Katie, Amy, Peter; *ed:* Harvard (BA) Eng, Amer Lit 1974; *cr:* Logos Bookstores Mgr 1976-86; Covenant Schl Headmaster 1985-; Covenant Church Assoc Pastor 1985-, Sr Pastor; *ai:* Worship Choir Ldr; Fund Raising, Educl Philosophy Comm; Arlington Soccer Club 1993-, Asst Coach; Chrstns in Arts Networking 1985-, Chm; *home:* 26 Udine St Arlington MA 02174*

EMMETT, CAMILLE A., 9th-12th Grd Soc Stud Teacher; *b:* New York, NY; *m:* Joseph F.; *ed:* St Johns Univ (BA) Govt & Politics 1983, (MA) Govt & Politics 1984; 18 Post Grad Credits Ed; *cr:* Marys Nativity Schl Soc Stud & Rdng Tchr 1984-86; St Michaels Schl Soc Stud & Rdng Tchr 1986-87; The Mary Louis Acad Soc Stud Tchr 1987-; *ai:* Expand Tchr; TMLA & Rel Act Comm; NCEA 1987-; NCSS 1987-; NY St Cncl for Soc Stud 1987-; Our Lady of Peace Parish in Lynbrook; Magazine Staff Mem & Lector 1995-; *office:* Mary Louis Acad 17621 Wexford Ter Jamaica NY 11432

EMMETT, KAREN CAMPMAN, Vocal Music Educator; *b:* Sharon, PA; *m:* Paul V. Emmett III; *ed:* Westminster Coll (BM) Music Ed, Voice 1975; Slippery Rock Univ of PA (MA) Stu Personnel, Counseling Svcs 1982; PA Cert in Admin; Slippery Rock Univ of PA Elem Ed Cert 1984; *cr:* Lakeview Schl Dist Vocal Music Educator 1975-83; West Middlesex Schl Dist Vocal Music Educator 1985-; *ai:* Dir of Choral Act; Adv of Show Choir; WMEA 1985-, Past Pres; MENC, PA Music Educators, NEA 1975-; ACDA 1994; Coll Womens Assn 1987-, Past Pres; Active Soloist; Pvt Voice Tchr; *office:* West MIddlesex Jr Sr HS Rt 18 West Middlesex PA 16159

EMMICH, LINDA L., Mathematics & Literature Tchr; *b:* Cincinnati, OH; *ed:* Univ of Cincinnati (BS) Scndry Ed Math & Eng 1971, (MA) Mental Hlth Cnslng 1986; *cr:* Guardian Angels Schl Jr High Math Tchr 1971-80; St Thomas More Schl Jr High Math & Lang Arts Tchr 1980-86; Purcell Marian HS Summer Schl Math Tchr 1991-95; Nativity Schl Tchr & Cnslr 1986-; *ai:* E-Case Hlth Team Rep; NCEA 1971-; OCEA 1971-; NCTM 1995-; SEM 1992-94, Rep of Legislative Bd; Fed Grant to Attend UC 1978-79; Archdiocese Curr Comm 1983; Guest Speaker at OCEA Convention 1987; Cnslr at Friars Club 1986-89; Consultant with Creative Therapy Assocs 1989 & 1990; Intnl Whos Who of Contemporary Achvmt; Whos Who in Amer Ed.*

EMMITH, WILLIAM H., Math & Science Teacher; *b:* Beverly, MA; *m:* Barbara L. Turner; *c:* David, Mark, Christine, Diane; *ed:* Cath Univ of Amer (AB) European His 1961; Salem St Coll (MED) Ed 1967; *cr:* Currier Jr HS Tchr 1962-69; Horace Mann Lab Schl Cooperating Tchr 1969-81; Collins MS Tchr 1981-; *ai:* AFT 1970-, Past Treas; Natl Rifle Assn, Life Mem; Essex Cty Sheriff's Dept, Deputy Sheriff; US Coast Guard Auxiliary 1971-, Division Ed Ofcr Retired; NSF Grant Cmptrs Star Schls Project 1989; *office:* Collins MS 29 Highland Ave Salem MA 01970

EMMONS, CHARLOTTE M.,RSM, Assistant Principal; *b:* Atlantic City ; *ed:* Georgian Court Coll (BA) Elem Ed 1963; *cr:* St Marys Fourth Grd Tchr 1950-53; Sacred Heart Fourth Grd Tchr 1953-57; St John First, Fourth Grd 1957-67; Holy Spirit Prin 1967-74; St Catherine First Grd Tchr 1974-94; St Dominic Asst Prin Pre K-Fourth Grd 1994-; *ai:* Blessed Mother Sodality; Religion Club; NCEA 1967-; MEEN; *office:* St Dominic School 250 Old Squan Rd Brick NJ 08724

EMRICH, ROBERT KEITH, Soc Stud Teacher & Dept Chair; *b:* Portland, OR; *m:* Deborah Ann Wilcox; *c:* James, Cari, David; *ed:* Clatsap Comm Coll (AS) Forest Mgmt 1973; Univ of ME (BS) Scndry Ed 1993; New Brunswick Bible Inst 1976; *cr:* Grace Bible Church Minister 1984-90; Piscataquis Comm HS Tchr 1992-, Chair of Soc Stud 1994-; *ai:* Cross Cntry, Track & Ski Coach; Mem Hum Comm; *office:* Piscataquis Cmty HS Blaine Ave Guilford ME 04443*

ENCARNACION, NANCY BONILLA, Pre-Kndgtn & Bilingual Teacher; *b:* New York, NY; *c:* Tamara Nieves-Garay; *ed:* Hunter Coll (BA) Eng Lang Arts 1974; Herbert H. Lehman Coll (MS) Early Chldhd Ed 1980; 30 Credit Hrs; *cr:* PS 98 Shorackappock 1st Grd Biling Tchr 1976-78, Kndgtn Biling Tchr 1978-83; Little Apple Schl Kndgtn Biling Tchr 1983-91; PS 98 Shorackappock Staff Dev 1991-92, Kndgtn, Biling Tchr 1992-93, Resource Tchr 1993-94, Pre-Kndgtn Tchr 1994-; *ai:* Schl Based Mngmt Sub-Comms; Parental Involvement Comm 1991-93; Early Chldhd Comm Chprsn 1989-94; Early Intervention Comm 1993-94; AFT 1976-; Candidate for Natl Bd Prof Tchng Stan Early Chldhd 1995.

ENCK, KURT E., American Cultures Teacher; *b:* Lancaster, PA; *m:* Patricia Singer; *ed:* Millersville Univ of PA (BS) Bus Admin 1984; PENN St Tchng Cert; *cr:* USMC Artillery Officer 1984-91; Donegal Schl Dist Tchr 1991-; *ai:* Asst Jr High Wrestling Coach; Fly Tying Club Adv, Instr; NEA 1991-; VFW 1991-; Trout Unlimited 1992-; Ruffed Grouse Soc 1995-; Sosquehanna Small Mouth Alliance 1993-.

END, ALBERT W., 8th Grade Social Studies Tchr; *b:* Pittsburgh, PA; *m:* Christine; *c:* Natalie, Sidney; *ed:* IN Univ of PA (BA) Soc Stud 1968, (MSEQ) Psych 1974; 30 Addl Credits; *cr:* Montour MS Tchr 27 Yrs; *ai:* Stu Cncl Rep Adv; NEA 1968-; Birmingham United Church of Christ 1946-, Church Cncl; YMCA Tennis; *office:* Montour MS Porters Hollow Rd Coraopolis PA 15108

ENDERS, MARK EUGENE, High School Spanish Teacher; *b:* Harrisburg, PA; *ed:* Shippensburg Univ of PA (BSEd) Span 1985; Attnd Univ of Northern IA Summer in Spain, East TN St Univ Summer in Ecuador; *cr:* Line Mountain HS Span Tchr 1986; FMSO Cmptr Programmer Analyst Intern 1986-89; NSPCC Cmptr Programmer analyst Intern 1986-89; Annville-Cleona HS Span Tchr 1989-; *ai:* Class of 1997, Span Club Adv; AATSP 1989-, VP; ACEA 1989-, Sec; PSEA, NEA 1989-; *office:* Annville Cleona Jr Sr HS 500 S White Oak St Annville PA 17003

ENDERS, PATRICIA LOGAN, Retired Elementary Teacher; *b:* Wyandot, OH; *m:* Edwin E.; *c:* Thomas Burwell, Mark Burwell, Ann Kasch, Michael Burwell; *ed:* Bowling Green St Univ (BS) Elem Ed 1964, (MED) Elem Ed 1976; Miami Univ of OH Won Field Trip to Stud Geology of Wind River Range in WY 1990; Tiffin Univ His of Wyandot Cty 1993; *cr:* Willard Elem Schl Fifth Grd Tchr 1960-70; Seneca East Elem Schl Fourth-Sixth Grd Tchr 1971-93; Willard Migrant Schl First, Sixth Grd Summer Tchr 1973-85; Tiffin Univ Bus Math Tchr 1980-83; *ai:* Sub Tchng; OEA, NEA 1960-93; SEEA 1993-, Pres 1988-89; STRS 1993-; Attica Recreational Org 1970-80; Attica Park Bd 1985-90, Pres 1 Yr; Lib Bd 1996; Martha Jennings Awd; *home:* 106 E High St Attica OH 44807*

ENDERS, RONALD RUSSELL, Anthropology & Sociology Instr; *b:* Hartford, CT; *m:* Nancy Ann Messenger; *ed:* Univ of Hartford (BA) His-Cum Laude 1974; Syracuse Univ (MA) His 1978; Univ of CT (MA) Anthropology 1992; Working Toward PHD Anthropology; 30 Grad Credits Andover Newton Theological Schl; 9 Grad Credits Univ of CA at Los Angeles; 12 Grad Credits Wesleyan Univ; *cr:* Automobile Club of Hartford Branch Supvr 1985-90; Univ of CT Tchng Asst 1992-93; Tunxis Comm Tech Coll Part-time Instr 1993-; *ai:* Univ of CT Rsrch Fnd Doctoral Dissertation Flwshp, Extraordinary Expense Awd, Dept of Anthropology Pre-Doctoral Flwshp 1992-93; *home:* 121 Tremont St New Britain CT 06051*

ENDERS, RUTH RATHGEBER, Fifth Grade Teacher; *b:* Baltimore, MD; *m:* Martin Kirk; *c:* Kristen; *ed:* Univ of MD (BS) Elem Ed 1964; Post Grad Stud Towson St Univ; *cr:* Baltimore City Pub Schl 4th-5th 1964-70; St Peter's Chrstn Day Schl 5th Grd Tchr 1985-; *ai:* Sc Prgm Coord; Cadet Safety Patrol Adv; Schl Store Supvr; Evang Ed Assn 1985-; St Peter's Schl Bd 1977-, Pres, VP; Church Grc Yth, Flwshp, Evangelism, Sunday Schl; *office:* St Peter's Ch Sch 7910 Belair Rd Baltimore MD 21236

ENDLER, SUSAN, Middle School Math Teacher; *b:* Elizabe Kean (BA) Elem Ed 1982; *ai:* NCEA 1983-; Outstdng Edctr 19 St John Vianney Schl 420 Inman Ave Colonia NJ 07067

ENDRIS, ANNE BEESON, Religious Studies Teacher; *b:* Be IN; *m:* Ned P.; *c:* Nathaniel M.; *ed:* Marian Coll (BA) Theolog Cath Yth Org Teen Cnslr 1992, Food Svc Supvr 1993-94; Se Stud Tchr 1993-95; *ai:* Schlars, ProLife Adv; Co-Campus Minis Cath Yth Org 1989-, Advy Bd, Camps; Archdiocese of Indp 1989-; *office:* Seton HS 3901 Glenway Ave Cincinnati OH 452

ENDY-O'KANE, GENEVIEVE ELIZABETH, First Grade T Philadelphia, PA; *m:* Charles Edward O'Kane; *c:* Charles O'K O'Kane, Helen O'Kane; *ed:* Holy Family Coll (BA) Elem & Ea Ed 1985; Beaver Coll (MED) Rdng 1994; *cr:* Our Lady of Help Schl 2nd Grd Tchr 1985-86; Mary Knoll Schl 2nd Grd Tchr 1 Martin Schl 1st Grd Tchr 1987; Bethune Schl 3rd Grd Tch Webster Schl 1st Grd Tchr 1989-; *ai:* Prof Dev Sessions E Process Approach to Tchng of Writing Ldr; Cheerleading C Climate Comm; PFT 1987-; *office:* John H Webster Elem Frankford Ave Philadelphia PA 19134*

ENDZULL, SUSAN, Mathematics Teacher; *b:* Queens, NY; *ed* Coll (BA) Math 1963; Hunter Coll (MA) Math 1967; 30 Addl Hr Univ, Queens Coll, Post Coll, Drew Univ; *cr:* Forest Hills HS 1963-64; John Adams HS Math Tchr 1964-; *ai:* NCTM, UFT,

ENG, ANNA WONG, Health Teacher; *b:* Brooklyn, NY; *m:* C Jennifer, Elizabeth; *ed:* Brooklyn Coll (BA) Hlth Ed 1973, (M 1975; *cr:* Cornell Univ Med Coll Rsrch Assoc 1979-83; Dist 25 1984-89; Manhasset HS Hlth Tchr 1989-; *ai:* Peer AIDS E Substance Abuse Task Force Mem; Numerous Pub; Tchr Exemplors 1992, 1995; *office:* Manhassett HS 200 Memorial P NY 11030

ENGEL, JONATHAN P., Teacher & Athletic Trainer; *b:* Def *m:* Rebecca J. Banta; *c:* Jennifer, Jacob, Kelly; *ed:* Defiance Natural Systems, Bio 1981; OH Univ (MS) Ath Trng 1982; *cr:* C HS Tchr, Ath Trainer 1982-86; APRN Phys Therapy Co Ath Trn 1986-90; Sylvania Northview HS Tchr, Ath Trainer 1990-; *ai:* Chess Club, Stu Ath Trainers Coach; Natl Ath Trainers Assn 198 Church Yr Group Ldr 1988-; Nom Edctr of Yr Sylvania Schl Dis

ENGEL, JUDITH S., Mathematics Teacher; *b:* Bronx, NY; Coll (BA) Math 1952, (MA) Math, Ed 1956; Attnd NY Univ, Columbia Univ, The New Schl for Soc Research; *cr:* Bronx Vo Tchr 1952-53; David G. Farragut Jr HS Acting Chprsn, Math Tch Bronx HS of Sci Math Tchr 1955-; *ai:* Arranged Stu Trips; Math Prgm Class Won Top Honors in Sing; Organized Stu Dances; Social Dance for Stu Fac Adv; Coaching Classes, Proctoring fo Exam for Bronx HS of Sci;Planned Bulletin Boards; Dev Inno Centered Tchng Strategy; SQS Presented at Natl & Intnl Meetir Math Instr After Schl; Math Assembly Pgm; Lehman Coll W 1994; Staff Dev Day Presentation of SQS; Invited Guest Presentations of Socratic Questionin; NCTM 1976-; Intnl A Invitational Ed 1982-, Members Spotlights; Assn of Math Tch Yrs; ASCD; AFT; United Fed of Tchrs NYC; Amer Ed Rsrch Invitational Ed Spcl Interest Group Mem 1996; NY St United Soc for Experimental Stud of Ed, Math Section, VP 1957-58; Tchng Bus Week Grant 1990 & Impact II Grant 1992; Semi-Fin for NYC Pub Ed Math Video Project 1993; Natl Thirteen Texac for Math, Sci, Tech 1992; Natl Sci Fnd Inst to Study Math Syra 1966 & Drew Univ 1967; Stdnts Questioning Stdnts Artic Television Appearance 1986; AFT Video Series; Ctr fo Linguistics Video Natl Meetings 1989; Potsdam Coll Stu as Made Significant Contribution to Personal & Ed Dev 1992; Le NY Wrtng Project "Wrtng Across the Curr" Inst Awd 1983; SQ Ed Life Supplement, NY Times 1994; Question & Answer SQS Article, Chicago 1994; Personality Plus Article, "Helping Her St Lead," NCTM News Bulletin 1995; NSF Pres Awd Nom; Bri Awds, Distngd Tchng of Math & Sci Fnls; *office:* The Bronx HS 75 W 205th St Bronx NY 10468*

ENGEL, KATE QUEALLY, Math Dept Teacher & Chairman; *b* NY; *m:* Jay; *c:* Margaret, James, Timothy, Christine McNam Davies; *ed:* St Marys Coll at South Bend (BS) Math 1957; *c* 1957-60; Sacred Heart High Math Tchr 1978-; Chm of Math De *ai:* PSAT & SAT Tchr 15 Yrs; *home:* 342 Park Ave Yonkers NY

ENGEL, KIMBERLY S., Spanish Teacher; *b:* Zanesville, OH; A.; *ed:* OH St Univ (BS) Span Ed 1989; Attnd Univ of Cinc Eurocentres-Institutos Mangold at Madrid Eng Tchr 1989-90 An Span Tchr & Dept Chm 1990-; *ai:* Co-Adv Span Club; Inservice Frgn Lang Dept Chm; OFLA; ACTFL; *office:* Anderson HS 7560 Cincinnati OH 45255*

ENGELS, EILEEN O'BRIEN, Fifth Grade Teacher; *b:* New B *m:* Peter Joel; *c:* Colin; *ed:* St Joseph Coll (BA) Child Stud 19 Univ (MS) Math 1970; 30 Addl Hrs Soc His, Sci; *cr:* West W Fifth Grd Tchr 1966-82; South Side Schl Fifth Grd Tchr 1982- 1970-; *office:* South Side Schl Tuttle Rd Bristol CT 06010

ENGLAND, EILEEN M., Assoc Professor of Psychology Kensington, PA; *m:* Boyd A.; *c:* Jennifer E. Belden-; *ed:* FL St Eng 1966; Villanova Univ (MS) Experimental Psych 1983; Le (PHD) Experimental Psych 1987; *cr:* Colby Coll Visiting 1987-88, Univ of Scranton Visiting Asst Prof 1988-89; Ursinus Prof 1989-; *ai:* Psych Club, Prison Literacy Prgm Adv; Soph Stud Group Convener; Governonce, Tchr Ed, Undergrad Rs Search Comms; SRCD, APS 1992-; APA, EPA 1987; CUR 19 Paperweight Collectors 1993-, Pres; Lindback Awd Tchng Excl Dev Grant 1995; Sex Roles 1989, 1992; *office:* Ursinus Coll PO Collegeville PA 19426*

ENGLANDER, CAROL MARCUS, 7th-8th Grade Science T Mineola, NY; *m:* Larry; *c:* Beth, Jefford, Benjamin; *ed:* Cornell Bio, Chem 1967; OR St Univ (MS) Plant Pathology 1970; 30 Hrs Stud Univ of RI; *cr:* South Kingstown Jr HS 7th-8th Grd Sci T *ai:* Dir RI SMILE; NEA, NSTA 1975-; RI Commission Women Civil Rights Equity,Access 1993-; RI Fnd, Amer Power Conv Kingstown Lions Club, Gender, Ethnic Expectations, Stu Achvm *office:* South Kingstown Jr HS 301 Curtis Corner Rd Wakefield

ENGLANDER-KRAUT, DENISE L., European History T Annapolis, MD; *m:* William D. Kraut; *c:* Adam Jeremy Kraut, Da *ed:* Fairleigh Dickinson Univ (BA) European His 1970; Villan (MA) European His 1485-Present 1976; Addl 21 Credit Hrs Masters in Math; *cr:* DE Cty Comm Coll Part-time Tchr; Int European His Tchr 1971-; *ai:* Interboro Chptr of NHS, Key Club Policy Comms; Stu Assistance Team for Substance Abuse, Me NEA, PSEA, IEA 1971-; NASAA 1995-; Philadelphia Muse

Guides 1971-, Treas; Womens Republican Club of Chester Cty *e:* Interboro HS 16th & Amosland Rd Prospect Park PA 19076*

ELIZABETH DEVORE, Lang Arts Dept Chpsn, Eng Tchr; *b:* , PA; *m:* Jesse S.; *c:* Guwain; *ed:* CA Univ of PA (BS) Speech, Attnd PA St Univ, Univ of IN, Univ of IL; *cr:* Everett Area Schls Lang Arts Dept Chprsn 1960-; PA St univ Speech Comm Tchr Tennis, Drama, FFA Pub Speaking Coach; Tennis League; St scopal Church Organist; Comm Variety Shows; Halloween Fun anizer; Bicentennial Week Creator 1995; Trashy Woman Contest lass Adv 1960-94; Jr Miss Pageants Dir; Lang Arts Dept Chprsn; naissance Prgm 1993-, Bd of Trustees; Tennis League Coord; ecreation Tennis Instr; Author, Dir 1976, 1995; Newspaper Renaissance Prgm Employee of Quarter; Everett Citizen of Yr orary Keystone Farmer Degree; Everett Comm Xmas Lighting n Awd; *home:* RR 4 Box 302 Everett PA 15537*

EUGENIE HAMILTON, History Teacher & Tutor; *b:* New York, ward Francis; *c:* David, John; *ed:* Smith Coll (BA) Psych & Art New Schl for Soc Rsrch 6 Credit Hrs; NY Univ Inst of Fine Arts Hrs; Hunter Coll 6 Credit Hrs; *cr:* PS 40 Vol Tchng 1972-79; hl 7th & 8th Grd His Tchr 1985-93, 9th & 10th Grd His Tchr, & Tutoring for Exceptional Stdnts 1994-; *ai:* NY Cornell Hosp lsp Comm 1965-67, Treas; St James Church 1983-89, Chrstn Ed *ice:* Dwight Jr Sr HS 291 Central Park W New York NY 10024

KAREN ELAINE, Sixth Grade Teacher; *b:* Lewistown, PA; *ed:* urg Univ (BS) Elem Ed 1971, (MS) Elem Ed 1975; *cr:* Paxtonia 4th, 6th Grd Tchr 1971-; *ai:* NEA, PSEA, CDEA 1971-, Fac Yr, Negotiations Comm; Keystone St Rdng Assn 1990-; Capital 1990-91, VP, Pres; IRA 1990-91; Distinguished Svc Awd 1995; onia Elem Schl 6135 Jonestown Rd Harrisburg PA 17112

KATHERINE LESHER, High School English Teacher; *b:* A; *m:* Stephen S.; *c:* Marc D., Johanna M.; *ed:* St Lawrence Univ 1972; Univ of VT Ed 15 Credit Hrs; Catleton St Coll Ed 6 Credit omm Coll of VT Instr 1985-86; Mt Anthony Union HS Eng Tchr Sr Class Adv 1989-94; Schl Dev Inititaive; NEA 1986-; NCTE *ce:* Mt Anthony Union HS 301 Park St Bennington VT 05201*

RONALD JOHN, English Teacher; *b:* Baltimore, MD; *m:* Edna *c:* John F., Susan E. Parks; *ed:* Towson St Univ (BS) Ed 1962; l (MED) Admin 1966; Johns Hopkins Univ (MA) Eng Lit 1968; iv (CASE) Rdng 1969; PA Univ (PHD) Linguistics 1994; *cr:* Jr HS Eng Tchr 1962-69; Perry Hall HS Eng Tchr, Coach Dundalk MS Eng Chprsn 1982-86; Parkville MS Eng Chprsn, ; *ai:* Stu Cncl Adv; Chm Fac Cncl; NEA, MSTA 1962-; TABCO as 6 Yrs, Edctrs Awd; Outstdng MS Tchr Balto Chamber of e; PTSA Best Edctrs Awd; Fulbright Tchng Flwshp; *office:* MS 8711 Avondale Rd Baltimore MD 21234

A, V. LYNNE, Cosmetology Teacher; *b:* Johnstown, PA; *c:* Krall; *ed:* Univ of Pittsburgh (BS) Voc Indstrl 1975, (ME) olicy 1991; *cr:* Admiral Peary AVTS Tchr 1972-80; Greater AVTS Tchr 1980-, Svc Cluster Chprsn 1986-; Univ of Pittsburgh 90; *ai:* Jr Class, Cosmetology VICA Adv; Stu Assistance Prgm Johnstown AVTSEA 1980-, Pres 1992-; NEA 1980-; AVTEC stern VP; VICA 1972-, Adv; Order of Eastern Star 1977-, WM; Amaranth 1984-, Treas, RM, Sec; White Shrine 1979-, WHP, ticle Pub; *office:* Greater Johnstown Voc Tech Sch 445 se Rd Johnstown PA 15904

AN, JULIE ANN, Social Studies Teacher; *b:* Washington, DC; ce M.; *c:* Kathryn; *ed:* Towson St Univ (BS) His 1970; 14 Grad Ed; *cr:* Wilde Lake MS Soc Stud Tchr & Dept Head 1970-77; adel Cty 6th-12th Grd Home Tchr 1981-82; St Piux X Schl Soc & Dept Head 1984-91; Holy Trinity Episcopal Day Schl Soc 1993-; *ai:* NCSS; Stephen Minister 1993-; Phi Alpha Theta; ta Pi; *office:* Holy Trinity Day Schl 13106 Annapolis Rd Bowie

GARY ROBERT, Fifth Grade Teacher; *b:* Port Clinton, OH; *m:* Paul; *ed:* Adrian Coll (BA) Bus 1968; Case-Western Reserve Ed 1970; *cr:* Cleveland Pub Schls 4th Grd Tchr 1968-70; Dept Schls 6th Grd Tchr 1970-77; Port Clinton Pub Schls 5th Grd -; *ai:* Bsktbl Coach; AFT 1977-; Lions Club; Martha Holden nd Sci, Math & Rdng Grants.

T, THOMAS G., Fifth Grade Teacher; *b:* Lancaster, PA; *ed:* Coll (BA) Elem Ed, His 1976; Webster Univ (MAT) Lang Arts Grad Stud Villanova Univ, Rutgers Univ, IN Univ, Millersville Lancaster Cntry Day Schl Second-Third Grd Tchr 1976-78; Cntry Day Schl Fifth Grd Tchr 1978-82; Rossman Schl Fifth Grd -87; Cocalico Schl Dist Fifth Grd Tchr 1987-; *ai:* Cocatico Ed -, Pres, VP; PA St Ed Assn, NEA 1987-; Historic Lancaster our 1989-, Bd Mem; Wheatland Decent Guild 1995-, Founding s; St Grant for Ed NJ St Govt; *office:* Reamstown Elem Schl 44 wn Rd Reamstown PA 17567

CHRISTINA SUE, Social Studies Teacher; *b:* Toledo, OH; *m:* ott; *c:* Kelsey Leann; *ed:* Clarion Univ of PA (BA) Soc Stud & 8; Post Grad Classes toward Scndry Guid & Cnslng at Slippery of PA; *cr:* Rocky Grove HS Soc Stud Tchr 1989-; *ai:* Jr Class, NHS & Stu Govt Adv; Var Vllybl Coach; NEA 1989-; Amer ical Assn 1995-.

DEBORAH SPINELLI, Learning Support Teacher; *b:* New n, PA; *m:* Jeffrey A.; *c:* Dana, Dylan; *ed:* CA Univ (BS) Spec Ed v of Pittsburgh (MED) Spec Ed 1986; Schl Consultation Cert Homerville Elem Schl Learning Support Tchr 1978-79; Morton Schl Learning Support Tchr 1979-81; Allegheny Intermediate ning Support Tchr 1981-82; Acmetonia Elem Schl Learning chr 1982-87; Colfax Elem Schl Learning Support Tchr 1987-89; Jr Sr HS Learning Support Tchr 1989-; *ai:* NEA, PSEA 1982-;

BE, MARILYN MARSTON, Classroom Teacher; *b:* Des A; *m:* William; *c:* Janice, Michael; *ed:* MI St (BA) Speech d 1963; Attnd Rowan Coll & St Peters Coll; *cr:* San Diego City Speech Therapy 1963-67; Barrington NJ Speech Therapist Voorhees NJ 1st Grd Tchr 1983-; *ai:* NEA; NJEA; Natl Rdng 1959-, Pres & VP; *office:* Edward T Hamilton Elem Schl 23 Dr Voorhees NJ 08043

H, JOHN N., HS Spanish Teacher; *b:* St Louis, MO; *m:* Erin D.; ristin; *ed:* Miami Univ at OH (BA) Bio & Span 1981; Northern (MA) Ed 1996; *cr:* Peace Corps Tchr-Honduras 1982-84; Boys Amer Cnslr 1985-89; McNicolas HS Span & Bio Tchr 1989-90; S Span Tchr 1990-; *ai:* Sr Class Adv; NEA, OFLA 1993-; Youth Soccer 1992-, Coach; *office:* Turpin HS 2650 Bartels Rd OH 45244

H, MARIE ANTOINETTE, Psychology Professor; *b:* Abingdon, regory B.; *c:* Monica, Alexis; *ed:* VA St Univ (BS) Psych 1974; St Univ (MED) Ed 1977; Temple Univ (PHD) Psycho Educl 1991; *cr:* Schl for Exec Secs Dir 1983-85; Temple Univ Assoc ec Recruitment & Admissions Prgm 1985-90; Camden Cty Coll of Psych 1990-; *ai:* Psi Beta NHS Spon; NJEA 1990-; Alpha Beta *office:* Camden County Coll PO Box 200 Blackwood NJ 08012

ENGLISH, PATRICIA SUPPA, Teacher; *b:* Warren, PA; *m:* Robert George Jr.; *c:* Robert, Cassie, Callie; *ed:* Edinboro St Univ (BA) El Ed 1972, (MS) Sp Ed 1974; 36 Credit Hrs; *cr:* Northwest Tri-Cty Intermediate Unit 5 Tchr 1972-73; Schl Dist City of Erie Tchr 1973-; *ai:* NEA, PSEA, EEA 1972-; PTSA 1972-, Bd Mem; Tchr of Yr 1991; Math Manipulatives Grant; Writing Ctr Grant; Creative Art Pertaining to Stories Read Grant; Classroom Lib Grant; *office:* Diehl Elem Schl 2327 Fairmount Pky Erie PA 16510

ENGLISH, RANDY STEVEN, Fifth Grade Teacher; *b:* Bryan, OH; *m:* Julie Feindel; *ed:* Defiance Coll (BS) Elem Ed 1977; Univ of Toledo (ME) Educl Tech 1986; Attnd Bowling Green St Univ, IN Univ; *cr:* Edon Schl 4th Grd Tchr 1977-87; Northwest Schl 4th Grd Tchr 1977-87; Defiance City Schls 5th Grd Tchr 1987-; *ai:* NEA, OEA 1977-; OHSAA Ofcl 1982-; Edon Masonic Lodge; Co-Creator, Co-Presenter Sci Wkshps Elem Edctrs; *office:* Defiance MS 801 S Clinton St Defiance OH 43512

ENGLUND, GAIL BUTTLER, Social Studies Teacher; *b:* Paterson, NJ; *c:* Laura Quinter, Tracey; *ed:* Denison Univ (BA) Soc Stud & His 1956; Amer Univ (MA) US His 1959; *cr:* Stratford Jr HS Tchr 1956-58; Port Lyautey Tchr 1959-60; Trexter Jr HS Tchr 1968-83; William Allen HS Tchr 1983-; *ai:* Odyssey of Mind Coach; NEA, PSEA, & AEA 1968-, Rep; Smithsonian Inst 1985-; Presbyn Church 1968-; *office:* William Allen HS 106 N 17th St Allentown PA 18104

ENGRAM, PAMELA SUE, Psych Visiting Asst Professor; *b:* St Louis, MO; *m:* Daniel A. Briotta Jr.; *c:* Robert Daniel Briotta; *ed:* Alfred Univ (BA) Psych 1975; SUNY at Buffalo (MA) Psych 1978, (PHD) Psych 1981; Post-Grad Stud Penn St Univ 1979; *cr:* SUNY at Buffalo Instr Dept Psych 1977-78; Penn St Univ Temporary Asst Prof Psych 1980-81; Ithaca Coll Asst Prof Psych 1981-89; Engram Consulting Svc Pres, Owner 1989-; Wells Coll Asst Prof Psych, Visiting 1994-; *office:* Wells Coll Psych Dept Aurora NY 13026

ENGSTROM, JEFFREY DUWAINE, Eighth Grade Reading Teacher; *b:* Grove City, PA; *m:* Pamela Frances Mattocks; *c:* Douglas DuWaine, Daniel William; *ed:* Clarion St Coll (BS) Elem Ed 1976; Slippery Rock St Coll (ME) Elem Ed 1982; *cr:* Lakeview Oakview Elem Schl 3rd Grd Tchr 1976-82; Lakeview MS 5th Grd Tchr 1982-83, 8th Grd Rdng Tchr 1983-; *ai:* 9th Grd Boys Bsktbl Coach; MS Yrbk Adv; LEA, PSEA, NEA 1976-; *office:* Lakeview Schl Dist 2482 Mercer St Stoneboro PA 16153

ENNIS, KATHLEEN MACRIDIS, Humanities Teacher; *ed:* Brandeis Univ (BA) His 1972; Bread Loaf Schl of Eng at Middlebury Coll (MA) Eng 1977; *cr:* Needham HS Eng Tchr 1991-93; MA Acad of Math & Sci Hum Tchr 1993-; *ai:* Literary Magazine Adv; NATE 1992-; Needham HS Supts Distngd Achvmt Awd; Peter Farrelly Tchng Awd; *office:* Mass Acad-Math & Science 100 Institute Rd Worcester MA 01609*

ENNIS, ROGER D., Social Studies Teacher; *b:* Burlington, VT; *m:* Barbara Ann Graham; *c:* Erin; *ed:* Plymouth St Coll (BED) Soc Stud 1968; Coll of St Joseph (MED) Gen Ed 1994; Addl 50 Hrs Various Univs; *cr:* Randolph Union HS Tchr 1969-; *ai:* Soc Stud Standing Comm on Curr Dev; Soc Stud Dept Head; Ameteur Radio Club Adv; Curr, Assessment & Rprtng Steering Comm Mem; NEA 1969-; ASCD 1994-; Bethany Church 1987-, Chrstn Ed, Diaconate; JC Outstanding Young Educator 1976; Tchr of Yr 1986; *office:* Randolph Union HS 13 Forest St Randolph VT 05060

ENNIS, ROSEMARY KOLKS, History Teacher; *b:* Cincinnati, OH; *m:* Chris H.; *ed:* Univ of Cincinnati (BA) His 1975, (BSEd) Soc Stud Ed 1975, (MA) Amer His 1976; Natl Endowment for Humanities Summer Seminar at Yale, Reformation; NEH Summer Seminar for Scndry Tchrs Univ of KS at Lawrence, Civil War; *cr:* Natl Park Svc Summer Interpreter 1977-84; Lima Sr HS Ec, Govt & His Tchr 1977-84; Sycamore HS His Tchr 1984-; *ai:* Jr Cncl on World Affairs Adv; Mentoring Prgm; Sycamore His Fair Co-Chprsn; NEA 1977-; Org of Amer Historians 1977-; Lakeview United Church of Christ 1984-, Moderator of Church Cncl, Financial Sec; Reader of Amer His Advanced Placement Exams for Coll Bd; Consultant for Coll Bd; *office:* Sycamore HS 7400 Cornell Rd Cincinnati OH 45242

ENOS, THEODORA SEDER, Third Grade Teacher; *b:* Pittsburgh, PA; *m:* Andrew; *c:* Damon; *ed:* Univ of Pittsburgh (BS) Elem Ed 1955; *cr:* PittsburghPub Schls 2nd Grd Tchr 1955-60; Burgettstown Area SD 1st Grd Tchr 1960-67; Burgettstown Area SD Kndgtn-First, Third Grd Tchr 1974-; *ai:* Burgettstown Area Ed Assn; PSEA; NEA.

ENRIGHT, MARY ANN MALONE, Second Grade Teacher; *b:* Ozone Park, NY; *m:* Bernard R.; *c:* Michael E., John R.; *ed:* St Joseph Coll (BA) Early Chldhd Ed 1960; Eastern CT St Univ (MA) Gen Ed 1971; *cr:* John B. Stanton Schl Second Grd Tchr 1960-65; William Budkingham Schl Fifth Grd Tchr 1979-80, Third Grd Tchr 1980-81; Samuel Huntington Schl Kndgtn Tchr 1983-84; John B. Stanton Schl Second Grd Tchr 1984-; *ai:* Delta Gamma 1990-; Norwich Tchrs League, CT Ed Assn, NEA 1979-; Sacred Heart Parish Rosary Altar Soc 1966-; William W. Backus Hosp Auxiliary 1970-; *home:* 373 Scotland Rd Norwich CT 06360

ENRIGHT, MARY ROSE, English & Reading Teacher; *b:* New York City, NY; *ed:* Fordham Univ (BS) Elem Ed 1962; Scranton Univ (MS) Rdng 1969; 30 Credits Rel Stud; 18 Credits Supervision & Admin; *cr:* Elem Schls Tchr 1957-68; St Francis of Rome 1st-6th Grd Prin 1968-75; St Jude Schl K-8th Grd Prin 1975-78; St Michael Acad Rdng & Eng Tchr 1978-; *ai:* Tutoring Pgm; *office:* Saint Michael Acad 425 W 33rd St New York NY 10001

ENRIQUEZ, ANASTACIO LAZARO, Latin, Religion, Soc Stud Tchr; *b:* Obando, Bulacan, Philippines; *m:* Norma Torres; *c:* Sir Amante, Sir Richard, Sir Richmond; *ed:* Maryhurst Seminary (BA) Eng Lit 1974; 12 Hrs Lit Criticism Univ of Philippines; 3 Hrs Rdng Fordham Univ; *cr:* Colegio de San Pascual Baylon Classroom Tchr 1976-86; Meycauayan Coll Instr 1982-86; St Angela Merici Schl Tchr 1987-; Catechetical Instruction Cert Level 1 & 2 Archidiocese of NY; *ai:* Rel Ed Dir; Comm Svc Coord; Fed of Cath Tchrs 1988-; Assn of Filipino Tchrs in Amer 1988-94, Bd, Appreciation Awd.*

ENRIQUEZ, LEON LAZARO, Science Teacher; *b:* Obando Bulacan, Philippines; *m:* Marivic Jover; *ed:* Philippine Normal (BS) General Sci 1980; St Peters Coll (MS) Sci & Tech; Kobe Univ in Wapan Chem Ed & Research Trainee 1986; *cr:* Colegio De San Pascual Baylon Chem Tchr 1980-84; St Augustine Schl Sci Tchr 1987-; *ai:* Sci Fair, Vlybl Coord; Mid St Accreditation Sci Chm; AFTA 1988-, Founder; NSTA 1989-, Mem; St Augustine Church 1989-, Lector; Leadership Awd; Best Tchr 1982; Japanese Govt Schlsp Grants; Retrospect & Prospect of Tchng Chem in HS 1986; *office:* St Augustine Schl 3920 New York Ave Union City NJ 07087*

ENRIQUEZ, SERGIO AGUSTO, Spanish Teacher; *b:* Guatemala, guatemala; *m:* Vilma Perez-Enriquez; *c:* Airis Haydee, Reyna; *ed:* Brooklyn Coll (BS) Psych, Ed 1984; Completing Biling Ed Stud; *cr:* Shell Bank Intermediate Schl #14 Span Tchr 1987-; *ai:* UFT, AFT 1987-; *home:* 782 E 32nd St Brooklyn NY 11210

ENSERRO, ETHEL G., High School Math Teacher; *b:* Jamestown, NY; *c:* Stephanie, Robert; *ed:* Univ of Buffalo (BA) Math 1963; SUNY at Fredonia (MS) Math Ed 1973; *cr:* Southwestern Cntrl HS Math Tchr 1963-67, 1974-; Jamestown Comm Coll Algebra Tchr 1981-; *ai:* Var Golf Coach; Co-curricular Act Coord; Ski Club Adv; NEA, NYEA, STA, NYSMTA 1967-; *office:* Southwestern HS 600 Hunt Rd WE Jamestown NY 14701*

ENSINGER, LARRY RAY, 9th Grade Algebra Teacher; *b:* E Liverpool, OH; *m:* Linda Ferguson; *c:* Sean, Pamela Ensinger-Antos; *ed:* Bowling Green St Univ (BS) Math 1969, (MA) Math 1970; 6 Hrs Drake Univ; 36 Hrs Univ of Pacific; 3 Hrs Bowling Green St Univ; *cr:* Niles Comm Schls Math Tchr 1970-82; Bowling Green HS Algebra Tchr 1982-; *ai:* 9th Grd Head Ftbl, Asst Var Track Coach; NEA 1970-; OEA, BGEA 1982-; Jennings Scholar 1994-95; *office:* Bowling Green Sr HS 530 W Poe Rd Bowling Green OH 43402*

ENSINGER, RONALD H., Retired Health & PE Teacher; *b:* East Liverpool, OH; *m:* Cassandra L. Thrasher; *c:* Jeff, Doug; *ed:* Bowling Green (BS) Hlth, PE 1965; *cr:* Wellsville HS Tchr 1965; Southern Local HS Tchr 1966; Beaver Local HS Tchr 1967-95; *ai:* Girls Sftbl Coach; *home:* 49153 Maple Ln East Liverpool OH 43920

ENSMINGER, KAREN MARIE, Mathematics Teacher; *b:* Dearborn, MI; *ed:* Frostburg St Univ (BS) Math, Ed 1990; *cr:* Chopticon HS Math Tchr 1990-; *ai:* Class of 99 Co-Spon; Schls Tutoring Prgm Coord; Functional Testing Comm; Schl Improvement Team; NEA, Educl Assn St Mary's Cty 1990-; SMECO'S Outstdng Math Tchr Awd 1994; Grad of Governor's Acad for Math, Sci, Tech 1993; 2 Governatorial Citations for Excl 1993-94; Math, Sci Integration Grant 1994; *office:* Chopticon HS Rt 242 Morganza MD 20660*

ENTERLINE, SUSAN PICTON, Fourth Grade Teacher; *b:* Sunbury, PA; *m:* William; *c:* Christy S., Lori A.; *ed:* Lock Haven Univ (BS) Elem, Early Chldhd; Commonwealth of PA MA Equivalency Cert 1989; PA St Univ, IN Wesleyan, Bloomsburg Univ 41 Addl Hrs; Inst of Childrens Lit Cert; *cr:* Milton Schl Dist Third Grd Tchr; Ward Myers Elem Schl First, Third, Fourth Grd Tchr 1983-; *ai:* Rdng, Tchr Selection, Sci, Assessment Comms; NEA, PSEA 1983-; St Andrew Luth Church 1977-; Humane Soc US 1992-; Smithsonian Soc 1986-; PTO 1978-, Pres; Pub Articles; *office:* Ward L Myers Elem Schl Mew St Muncy PA 17756

ENYEDY, ZOE ZACHLIN, Chemistry Teacher; *b:* South Euclid, OH; *c:* Louise Enyedy Bergin, Roseann Enyedy Cyngier, Arthur, Lillian Enyedy Lothamer, Edward; *ed:* Mt St Joseph Coll (BS) Chem 1954; Cleveland St Univ (MED) Ed 1981; 45 Addl Grad Hrs; *cr:* Standard Oil Co Chemist 1954-57, 1981-85; Univ of Pacific Curr Designer 1993; Cleveland St Univ Adj Instr as Needed; Mentor Pub Schls Chem Tchr 1976-; *ai:* Sr Project Spon 3 Yrs; Amer Chemical Soc 1982-, 2nd VP; NEOEA, MAT, OEA 1989-; Western Reserve Photographic Soc, 2nd VP; St Justin Church 1988-, Eucharistic Minister; Sci Fair Judge; St Justin Over 50 Club, Pres; Ashland Tchr Achvmt 10 Top Tchrs in OH; Amer Inst Chemists Gold Medal; Article Pub 1981; Paper to Amer Chemical Soc 1989; Nom Outstdng Sci Tchr 1992; Numerous Photographic, Art Awds; *home:* 152 W Overlook Dr Eastlake OH 44095

EPHRAIM, ELIZEBETH, Language Arts Teacher; *b:* Dayton, OH; *ed:* Bowling Green St Univ (BFA) Creative Writing 1983; Univ of Akron (MAEd) Scndry Ed 1990; 56 Credit Hrs Univ of Cincinnati; *cr:* Cleveland Bd of Ed Preserve Tchr 1989-93; Dayton Bd of Ed Lang Arts Tchr 1993-; *ai:* MS Creative Writing Contest for Jr Achievers Coord; NEA; Flwshp Univ of Akron Grad Schlsp; Dayton Pub Schls Creative Writing Awd; *home:* PO Box 804 Dayton OH 45402

EPPOLITE, ANNETTE VARSACI, Latin & English Teacher; *b:* Riverside, NJ; *m:* Robert R.; *c:* Brett, Robb; *ed:* Montclair St Univ (BA) Scndry Ed 1968; Glassboro St Coll (MA) Educl Supervision 1975; *cr:* Meml Jr HS Latin Tchr 1968-84; Twin Hills Schl Latin, Eng Tchr 1984-89; John F. Kennedy Jr HS Latin Tchr 1989-91; Meml Jr HS Latin, Eng Tchr 1991-; *ai:* NEA; Amer Classical League; *office:* Meml Jr HS Van Sciver Pkwy Willingboro NJ 08046

EPPS, JANICE SHERMAN, Elementary Art Teacher; *b:* Lawrence, MA; *m:* Jimmy D.; *c:* Jody, Jared; *ed:* Lesley Coll (BSEd) Ed 1971; Notre Dame Coll Art Cert 1991; *cr:* Salem Schl Dist Elem Tchr 1971-91, Elem Art Tchr 1991-; *ai:* Wellness Comm; SEA, NHEA, NEA 1971-; Alpha Delta Kappa 1995-; Big Brothers Big Sister 1995-; *office:* Lancaster Haigh & Barron Schls Main St Salem NH 03079

EPPS, KURT E., English Teacher; *b:* Perth Amboy, NJ; *m:* Donna Barreto; *c:* Brett L., Kacy A., Cody J.; *ed:* Montclair St Coll (BA) Eng 1969; Kean Coll (MA) Stu Prsnl 1975; *cr:* Passaic HS Tchr 1969-71; Arthur L Johnson Regnl HS Tchr 1971-; *ai:* Stu Cncl & Newspaper Adv; Pageant Dir; AFT 1981-; NJSBA 1989-; Perth Amboy Port Authority 1988-, Chm; Perth Amboy Schl Bd 1989-; NRA; Royal Governors Mansion-Proprietary House Trustee; *office:* Arthur L Johnson Regnl HS 365 Westfield Ave Clark NJ 07066

EPSTEIN, DAVIE JEAN (ASNIS), 7th-8th Grd Lang Arts Teacher; *b:* Brooklyn, NY; *m:* Joel P.; *c:* Tricia, Michael, Brian; *ed:* Univ of Toledo (BED) Elem Ed 1969, (MED) Elem Ed 1986; 12 Credit Hrs in Post Grad Ed Courses; *cr:* Wernert Schl 6th Grd Tchr 1969-70; Arbor Hills Jr HS Tchr Aide 1977-78; Stewart Elem Rdng Lab Tchr 1978-79; Stewart & Gunckel Elem Math Lab Tchr 1979-80; Riverside Elem Math Lab Tchr 1980-81; DeVeaux Jr HS Math Tchr 1981-88; Robinson Jr HS Lang Arts & Rdng Tchr 1990-; *ai:* Bldg Comm; Asst Girls Bsktbl Coach; AFT 1978-; Womens Amer Ort 1969-, Natl & Local Bd, Pres; *office:* Robinson Jr HS 1007 Grand Ave Toledo OH 43606*

EPSTEIN, DIANE ENGELBERG, English Teacher; *b:* Memphis, TN; *m:* Nathan H.; *c:* Yitzchak, Yisroel, Zev, Zipporah Boylan, Yosef David; *ed:* Stern Coll for Women (BA) Eng 1964; Tchrs Coll Columbia Univ (MA) Tchng Eng 1965; Addl Credits in ESL & Linquistics Univ of PA; *cr:* Maimonides Schl Scndry Eng Tchr 1965-67; Beth Rochel Schl Scndry Eng Tchr 1979-81; Bergen Comm Coll Adj ESL Tchr 1980-86; Rockland Comm Coll Adj Eng Instr 1981-; Bais Yaakov HS Scndry Eng Tchr 1981-; *ai:* Yrbk Adv; Head Eng Dept; NCTE; Rdng Curr Dev; *office:* Bais Yaakov HS 11 Smolley Dr Monsey NY 10952

EPSTEIN, ELLEN DAVIS, English Teacher; *b:* New York City, NY; *m:* Leonard; *c:* Laura, Andrew; *ed:* Brandeis Univ (BA) Eng; Harvard Univ (MAT) Eng; NY Univ (MPA) Pub Admin; *cr:* J P Stevens HS Eng Tchr 1985-; *ai:* NCTE & NEA.

EPSTEIN, HARRIET M., Guidance Cnslr & Health Tchr; *b:* Brooklyn, NY; *m:* Morton; *c:* Robert Grossman, Deborah Grossman, Suzanne Sokolov, Terry Barbee, Mitchell, Judith Pepper, Joanne; *ed:* Long Island Univ (BS) PE 1965; City Coll of NY (MS) Hlth Ed 1970; Hunter Coll (MS) Guid, Cnslng 1994; St Univ at Stonybrook Grad Work; *cr:* Sarah J. Hale HS Hlth Tchr 1981, Hlth Cnslr, Tchr 1981-93, Grd Adv, Tchr 1993-; *ai:* Hlth, PE Ind Stud Tchr; UFT 1965-; Port Jefferson Sta Civic Assn 1994-.*

EPSTEIN, MARCIA GOLDSCHLAGER, Psych Assoc Prof & Ed Coord; *b:* New York City, NY; *m:* Paul Elliott; *c:* Amy Epstein Feldman, Robin Kaye; *ed:* Cornell Univ (AB) Psych 1964; Harvard Univ (EDM) Guidance, Counseling 1965, (CAS) Guidance, Counseling 1966; Univ of Chicago (ABD) Ed Psych; *cr:* Comm Coll of Philadelphia Psych Assoc Prof 1970-; *ai:* Ed Coord; Club Fac Adv; Cornell Univ 1964-, Class VP, Scndry Schls Chm 1984, Rebmann Svc Awd; Comm Coll of Philadelphia 1990-, Dev Ed Awd; Lower Merion Twp Schlsp Comm 1987-; *office:* Comm Coll of Philadelphia 1700 Spring Garden St Philadelphia PA 19130

EPSTEIN, MARK STEVEN, Social Studies Teacher; *b:* Brooklyn, NY; *m:* Lynne Anne Freiberger-Epstein; *c:* Ethan, Stephanie, Benjamin; *ed:* Montclair St Coll (BA) His 1987; Southern CT St Univ (MA) His 1993; Attnd Cty Coll of Morris; Oxford Univ, Exeter Coll; Enrolled Sacred heart Univ 6th Yr Degree; *cr:* Franklin Mint Freelance Writer 1980-84; Franklin Lib Freelance Writer 1980-84; Scholastic Magazine Freelance Writer 1980-84; Greenwich HS soc Stud Tchr 1985-; *ai:* Ind Stud; Bd of Dir

Greenwich Ed Assn; Prgm Team; NEA, CT Ed Assn 1984-; Greenwich Ed Assn 1984-, Bd of Dir; Pub Reader Guides, Articles; *office:* Greenwich HS 10 Hillside Ave Greenwich CT 06830*

EPSTEIN, RACHELLE JANET, 6th Grade Teacher; *b:* Portsmouth, NH; *ed:* Penn St Univ (BS) Ed 1963; Hunter Coll (MS) Ed 1971; Bank St Coll of Ed (MS) Guid & Cnslng 1975; lincoln Ctr Inst 6 Credits; *cr:* William Woodruff Schl 3rd Grd Tchr 1963-66; Grimes Elem Schl 3rd Grd Tchr 1966-67; Floral Park-Bellerose Schl 5th & 6th Grd Tchr 1967-; *ai:* Grd Chprsn 1976-90; Spelling Curr Comm Chprsn 1992; Curr for Rdng in the Content Areas Mem 1985; AFT 1966-; NYSUT 1966-; FPBDTA 1967-, Pub Relations Chprsn 1978-80, Legislative Chprsn 1982-84, Corresponding Sec 1984-88, Ed Policies Comm 1990-92; Lincoln Ctr Theater 1986-; Bank St Coll Alumni Assoc 1990-; Long Island Cncl for Soc Stud 1994-; *office:* Hs Floral Park Bellerose Schl 6100 Larch Ave Floral Park NY 11001*

EPSTEIN, RENEE, Adjunct Lecturer; *b:* Brooklyn, NY; *ed:* Univ of WI at Madison (BA) Comparative Lit 1971; Grad Ctr City Univ of NY (MA) His & Eng 1995; 30 Credit Hrs; *cr:* Borough of Manhattan Comm Coll City Univ of NY Adj Lecturer 1989-; *ai:* Prof Staff Congress 1989-; AFT; Amer Civil Liberties Union 1972-; Ford Fndtn Grant; NEH Awd; Summer Seminar for Coll Tchrs; Pub in MA Review; *office:* Borough Of Manhattan Comm Coll 199 Chambers St New York NY 10007*

EPSTEIN, RICHARD GARY, Professor; *b:* Newark, NJ; *ed:* George Washington Univ (BA) Math 1070, (BA) Physics 1970; Univ of PA (MSE) Math Ed Rsrch 1972; Temple Univ (PHD) Cmptr, Inf Sci 1988; *cr:* Temple Univ Instr 1977-83; West Chester Univ Asst, Assoc Prof 1983-88; George Washington Univ Asst Prof 1988-91; West Chester Univ Prof 1991-; *ai:* Cmptr CLub Adv; Basic Hebrew Vol Tchr; ACM, Curr Task Force; IEEE Comp Soc, Curr Task Force, Meritorious Svc; Kesher Israel Cong 1994-, Adult Ed Chair; Danforth, NSF Grad Fellow; Pub Papers on Data Bases, Tchng Cmptr Ethics; Book: The Case of the Killer Robot 1996, Co-Author Fundamentals of Computing 1995, Volume II; *office:* West Chester Univ Dept of Computer Sci College Ave & S High St West Chester PA 19383*

EPSTEIN, SANFORD MARK, 5th Grade Math & Science Tchr; *b:* Newark, NJ; *m:* Gail Ann Fogel; *ed:* Newark St Coll (BA) General Elem Ed 1970; Kean Coll (MA) Math Ed 1976; 6th Yr Level; Admin-Supervision Cert; *cr:* Arbo Schl 5th Grd Tchr 1970; South Mountain Schl 5th-6th Grd Tchr 1970-89; South Orange MS 5th-6th Grd Tchr 1989-; *ai:* Authentic Assessment Comm; SOMEA, ECEA, NJEA, NEA 1970-, Local Rep; *office:* South Orange MS 70 N Ridgewood Rd South Orange NJ 07079

ERAMO, PETER W., Computer Teacher; *b:* Herkimer, NY; *m:* Anne; *c:* Lisa, Julie, Michael; *ed:* Mohawk Vly Comm Coll (AAS) Electrical Tech 1973; SUNY Coll at Oswego (BS) Tech Ed 1977; SUNY Coll of Tech (BT) Micro Processors 1985; *cr:* Intnl Comps Test Engr 1978-82; Mohawk Data Sci Software Engr 1983-87; Poland Cntrl Schl Comp Tchr 1987-; *ai:* Comp Club; AFT & NYSUT 1987-; APT 1987-; Mohawk Vly PC Users Group 1984-; *office:* Poland Central Schl Rt 2 Box 8 Poland NY 13431

ERATH, MARY REGINA, 8th Grade Teacher; *b:* New Brunswick, NJ; *ed:* Walsh Coll (AA) 1969; Trenton St Coll (BA) Soc Stud 1973; *cr:* St Nicholas Schl 6th Grd Tchr 1964-65; Our Lady of Mercy Schl 7th Grd Tchr 1965-66; Holy Trinity Schl 7th Grd Tchr 1966-76; Our Lady of Pompei Schl 7th Grd Tchr 1967-70; St Peter Elem Schl 8th Grd Tchr 1070-; *ai:* Soc Stud Chair; Testing Coord; NCEA 1970-; NPM 1982-; Villa Victoria Acad 1989-, Bd of Dirs, Vice Chair, Chair; St Peter Liturgy Comm 1982-; St Peter Parish Dir of Music 1981-; Regina Coeli Medal; *office:* St Peter Elem Schl 165 Somerset St New Brunswick NJ 08901

ERB, LISA M., HS English Department Chair; *b:* Pittsburgh, PA; *m:* Nelson L.; *c:* Michael, Lindsay; *ed:* Edinboro Univ (BS) Sec Ed Eng 1972; *cr:* Pine-Richland HS Eng Tchr 1985-; *ai:* Eng Dept Chprsn; Soph Class, Jr Class, Newspaper Spon; Delta Kappa Gamma 1994-; One Pub Childrens Play; *office:* Pine-Richland HS 4300 Warrendale Rd Gibsonia PA 15044

ERB, MELANIE CHAPMAN, Mathematics Teacher; *b:* Lock Haven, PA; *m:* Harold E.; *c:* John, Susan; *ed:* Lock Haven St Coll (BS) Math 1970; *cr:* Bald Eagle Area Math Tchr 1970-; *ai:* NEA, PSEA, BEAEA 1971-; *office:* Bald Eagle Area Jr Sr HS 751 S Eagle Vly Rd Wingate PA 16823

ERB, SUSAL PATCHES, Fourth Grade Teacher; *b:* Lebanon, PA; *m:* Donald E.; *ed:* Millersville St Coll (BS) Elem Ed 1975, (MED) Elem Ed 1982; 30 Credits Lancaster-Lebanon IU 13 Millersville Univ; *cr:* Cornwall-Lebanon Schl Dist Elem Tchr Grd 2-5 1975-; *ai:* PSEA, NEA 1975-; Lebanon Vly Coll, PA St Univ Cooperating Tchr; Co-Author Article Pub; *office:* South Lebanon Elem Schl 1825 S 5th Ave Lebanon PA 17042

ERBACHER, HERMAN H., HS Instrumental Music Teacher; *b:* Cincinnati, OH; *m:* Michele R. North; *c:* Monica, Megan; *ed:* SUC at Fredonia (BMED) Music, Math 1979; SUNY at Buffalo (MMED) Music 1985; *cr:* West Seneca Cntrl Schls Permanent Sub Elem Band, Orch Park Tchr 1979-80; SUNY at Buffalo Sports Band Dir 1982-85; Newfane Cntrl Schls Sr HS Band Dir 1980-; Comp Instr Orleans-Niagara Tchr Cntr 1985-; *ai:* Adv NHS, Schl Musical, Sr Class Night; Gifted, Talented, Prgm Facilities Comms; Educators Support Team Co-Founder; Newfane Tchrs Assn 1980-, VP; Niagara Cty Music Ed Assn 1980-, VP; NYSUT, AFT, NYSSMA, MENC 1980-; Newfane Tchrs Assn Grievance Chm; Co-founder Newfane Initiative for Tchr Excellence; St Bridget's Church 1980-, Bldg, Grounds Comm; BSA 1964-, Merit Badge Cnslr; Lockport Concert Assn; Tchr Ctr Grant Recipient; NY St Tchr of Yr Finalist; Guest Conductor Orleans All-Cty Band, Niagara All-Cty Band; Conductor Buffalo Silver Band; Trombonist Don Keller Big Band; Co-Publisher The Nest; *office:* Newfane Sr HS 2649 Transit Newfane NY 14108*

ERBE, J. MICHAEL, Associate Prof of Biology; *b:* Cincinnati, OH; *m:* Barbara Whitney; *c:* Austin Call; *ed:* Marietta Coll (BS) Bio 1986; RI Coll (MAT) Bio 1988; *cr:* Martinsville HS Tchr 1988-90; Sinclair Comm Coll Assoc Prof 1990-; *ai:* Sinclair Fnd, Prsnl & Bio Assessment Comms; Divisional Merit for Tchng Awd at Sinclair Comm Coll; *office:* Sinclair Comm Coll 444 W 3rd St Dayton OH 45402

ERCOLANO, PHYLLIS MARIA, French Teacher; *b:* Baltimore, MD; *m:* Ernesto; *c:* Angela, Joseph, Anthony; *ed:* Towson St Univ (BA) Fr 1971; Johns Hopkins (MED) Ed 1975; 18 Credit Hrs; *cr:* North Pt Jr HS Fr Tchr 1971-80; Parkville SR Fr Tchr 1980-81; Ridgley MS Fr Tchr 1981-82; Perry Hall MS Fr Tchr 1982-; *ai:* Fr Club; Discovery & Awds Comm; NEA; Fallston Booster Club 1992-; Class Act Awd 1992; *office:* Perry Hall MS 4300 Ebenezer Rd Baltimore MD 21236

ERDMANN, TIM ALAN, Bio & Environmental Sci Tchr; *b:* Toledo, OH; *m:* Diana Lynn; *c:* Shelly, Christopher; *ed:* Univ of Cincinnati (BS) Scndry Ed, Bio & General Scis 1987; *cr:* Archbishop Moeller HS Sci Tchr 9 Yrs; *ai:* Cross Cntry & Track Coach; *office:* Archbishop Moeller HS 9001 Montgomery Rd Cincinnati OH 45242

EREDITARIO, REBECCA KOTH, 3rd Grade Teacher; *b:* Detroit Lakes, MN; *m:* Patrick A.; *c:* Aaron, Daniel; *ed:* Univ of ND (BS) Elem, Spec Ed 1974; Kent St Univ (MS) Gifted Ed 1993; *cr:* Lorain City Schls LD Tchr 1974-79; Open Door Chrstn Schl 3rd Grd Tchr 1979-80, 4th Grd Tchr 1980-81, 2nd Grd Tchr 1982-87, Gifted Prgm 1987-93, 3rd Grd Tchr 1993-; *office:* Open Door Christian Schl 8287 W Ridge Rd Elyria OH 44035

ERHARDT, WENDY CHARLES, English Teacher; *b:* West Chester, PA; *m:* Joseph; *ed:* West Chester Univ (BS) Eng 1994; Kutztown Univ 3 Credits Eng Ed; *cr:* Easton Area HS Eng Tchr 1994-; *ai:* Adv Lit Magazine; NCTE 1994-; Binney & Smith Mini-Grant; *office:* Easton Area HS 2601 William Penn Hwy Easton PA 18045

ERHARTIC, GERALDINE MC GLINCHEY, Sixth Grade Teacher; *b:* Brooklyn, NY; *m:* Richard S.; *c:* Scott Richard, Andrew Patrick; *ed:* Molloy Coll (BA) Soc Stud, Elem Ed 1969; Adelphi Univ (MA) Elem Ed 1973; Grad Credits SUNY at Stony Brook Oceonography, Bio 1994-95; *cr:* Fifth Avenue Schl Fifth Grd Tchr 1969-71; Gardiner Manor Schl 5th Grd Tchr 1071-73, 4th Grd Tchr 1975-78, 6th Grd Tchr 1980-86; Bayshore MS 6th Grd Tchr 1986-; *ai:* Environmental Club Adv; Chptr I Summer Schl Tchr; Sci & Soc Stud Curr Comms; Sci Teach Assn NYC 1994-; AFT, NYSUT, BSCTA 1969-; Natl MS Assn Conf in Cincinnati Presenter 1994; *office:* Bay Shore MS 393 Brook Ave Bay Shore NY 11706

ERICKSON, ANN MARIE, 6th Grade Teacher; *b:* Brockton, MA; *c:* Kristin, Gary; *ed:* Framingham St Coll (BS) Elem Ed 1965; Cambridge Coll (MED) Ed 1992; 15 Addl Hrs; *cr:* West Elem Schl 4th Grd Tchr 1965-71, 6th Grd Tchr 1971-; *ai:* Working with HS Jrs, Srs in SAT; Review Course Tchng Wrkshps Tchrs Assn; Writing Curr; STA 1965-, VP, Sec, Negotiating Team; MTA, NEA, NCTA 1965-; Holy Cross Church 1965-; Stoughton Tchr of Yr; Norfolk Cty Tchr of Yr; Laura Warcup Awd; *office:* West Elem Schl 1322 Central St Stoughton MA 02072*

ERICKSON, CARRIE SHUMAN, Spanish Teacher; *b:* Flemington, NJ; *m:* Eric George; *ed:* Dickinson Coll (BA) Span 1988; Univ of PA (MA) Ed 1991; Classes Completed Towards Doctors in Ed; Working on Dissertation; *cr:* Centennial Schl Dist Span Tchr 1988-89; Lower Merion Schl Dist Span Tchr 1989-90; Quakertown Schl Dist Span Tchr 1990-92; Lower Merion Schl Dist Span Tchr 1992-; *ai:* Span Club Spon; Coord, Spon & Ldr of Foreign Exch to Costa Rica; AATSP 1990-; *office:* Lower Merion HS 245 E Montgomery Ave Ardmore PA 19003

ERICKSON, JANE MARGARET (SAKAL), HS Vocal Music & Theatre Tchr; *b:* Port Chester, NY; *m:* Glenn E.; *c:* Julianne, Thomas; *ed:* Westminster Choir Coll (BME) Music 1970; Attnd Boston Univ Theatre Institute; Fairleigh Dickenson Univ Working Toward a Masters Degree; *cr:* Douglas HS at Ellsworth AFB SD Music Tchr 1970-73; Manville HS Vocal Music Tchr 1989-; Installed Music Theatre/Drama Dept 1991; *ai:* Drama Club Coach; MENC 1989-; STANJ 1991-; NJEA MEA, 1989; Strollers Local Drama Group 1983-, VP 2 Yrs; *office:* Manville H S 1100 Brooks Blvd Manville NJ 08835

ERICKSON, KAREN L., Professor of Chemistry; *b:* Covington, MI; *ed:* Siena Hghts Coll (BS) Chem 1960; Purdue Univ (PHD) Organic Chem 1964; Cornell Univ Post Doctoral Study 1964-65; *cr:* Clark Univ Asst Prof 1965-69, Assoc Prof 1969-79, Prof 1979-; *ai:* Amer Chemical Soc, Cncl; Sigma Xi; Amer Assn of Women in Sci; NIH Post Doctoral Flwshp 1964-65 & Spcl Flwshp 1972-73; Roche Rsrch Inst in Australia Sr Visiting Rsrch Flw 1979-80; Numerous Articles Pub; *office:* Clark Univ 950 Main St Worcester MA 01610

ERICKSON, NANCY NYE, 9th-12th Grade English Teacher; *b:* Newark, NJ; *m:* Richard; *c:* Richie, Pam Llewellyn, Wendy Johnson; *ed:* Upsala Coll (BA) Eng 1959; *cr:* Fairview Park HS Eng Tchr 1959-61; Olmsted Falls HS Eng Tchr 1971-72; Manasquan HS Eng Tchr 1973-; *ai:* Stu Cncl Adv; Co-Chair of Mid Sts; Detention Tchr; Comm on Disaffected Stdnts; Mentor Class Tchr; In-class Support Tchr; NEA 1973-; NTEA; MEA Choral Union 1973-, Sec; NJEA; Jersey Shore Medical Ctr 1973-, Vol, 1500 Hr Pin Awd; Sunday Schl Tchr; Tchr of Yr 1991; Runner Up Tchr of Yr 1987; *home:* 26 Squan Ct Manasquan NJ 08736*

ERICKSON, RICHARD E., HS Social Studies Teacher; *b:* Philadelphia, PA; *m:* Renee Sarchet; *c:* Ned, Lee; *ed:* Westminster Coll (BA) His 1964; Temple Univ (MA) His 1967, (PhD) His 1979; MI St NSF Geography Grant; *cr:* Marple Newton Schls Tchr 1964-; *ai:* Speech, Debate, World Affairs cncl; His Day; NEA, PSEA, & MNEA 1964-, Local Treas, Tchr of Yr; NCSS, DCCSS, PCSS 1966-, St Sec; Middletown Land Conservancy 1986-; Media Presbyterian Church 1988-, Elder; Fulbright Scholar, Stud & Traveled India, & China; Danforth Fellow; William Penn Scholar; St His Day Tchr of Yr; DE Cty Hum Tchr of Yr; Cty Historical Preservation Awd; Pub Artciles & Lessons; *office:* Marple Newtown Sr HS 120 Media Line Rd Newtown Square PA 19073*

ERICKSON, ROGER CRAIG, 8th Grade Reading Teacher; *b:* New Haven, CT; *m:* Karen Weeks; *c:* Camellia; *ed:* Southern CT St Univ (BS) Spec Ed 1986, (MS) Ed 1995; Working Towards Post Grad Master's Degree Educl Ldrshp; *cr:* Boy's Village Schl Spec Ed Tchr 1986-87; Bailey MS Spec Ed Tchr 1987-90, 8th Grd Rdng Tchr 1994-; Alma Pagels Elem Schl 6th Grd Tchr 1990-94; *ai:* AFT 1987-, Steward; ASCD 1995-; Amer Cancer Soc 1985-, Cnslr; Camp Rising Sun 1994-, Camp Comm, Jr Cnslr Prgm Dir 1995; *home:* 10 S Forest Cir New Haven CT 06515*

ERICSON, MELANIE A., High School Social Worker; *b:* Worcester, MA; *ed:* Russell Sage Coll (BA) Psych 1983; Univ of CT (MSW) Soc Work 1988; *cr:* Planfield Meml Schl 4-6 Grd Soc Worker 1984-85; Plainfield Cntrl Schl 7-8 Grd Soc Worker 1984-86; Plainfield HS 9-12 Grd Soc Worker 1984-; *ai:* Peer Helper Adv 1987-; Stu Assistance Model Coord 1988-; Comm for Drug Free Yth 1989; Crisis Team Coord 1990-; CT Assn of Schl Soc Workers, NEA, Natl Assn of Soc Workers 1984-; *office:* Plainfield HS 87 Putnam Rd Central Village CT 06332

ERICSON, ROGER JOHN, Music Instructor; *b:* Dover, NJ; *m:* Shirley Cerar; *c:* Roger (dec), Kendra, Richard; *ed:* Wilkes Coll (BS) Music 1969; Marywood Coll 24 Grad Credits; East Stroudsburg Univ 6 Grad Credits; *cr:* Delaware Valley HS Music Instr 1969-; *ai:* Ftbl, Jazz Band; Brass, Flute Ensemble; NEA, PSEA 1969-; MENC, PMEA 1973-; Intnl Assn of Jazz Educators 1994-; Trout Unlimited 1980-, Pres, Pike Wayne Chapter, Silver Trout Awd; Fontinalis Fly Fishermen 1975-, Pres; Audubon Soc 1980-; *office:* Delaware Valley HS HC 77 Box 379c Milford PA 18337

ERIKSEN, JANE REYNOLDS, English Department Chairperson; *b:* New York, NY; *m:* Richard G.; *c:* Meredith E., Rick G.; *ed:* Univ of CT (BA) Eng 1965, (MA) Eng Ed 1989; Southern CT St Univ 18 Hrs Educl Leadership; *cr:* Morgan HS 9-12th Grd Eng Tchr 1987-; *ai:* Lang Art Curr Comm Co-Chair; Curr Advy Cncl; Pi Lambda Theta, NCTE, CCTE 1988-; NEATE 1994-; CASCD 1995-; Durham Lib 1978- Chm; Friends of Lib 1982-, Outstanding Friend of Small Libs Awd; Clinton Tchr of Yr 1993; *office:* Morgan HS Rt 81 Clinton CT 06413

ERIKSEN, TED D.,II, English Department Chairman; *b:* Detroit, MI; *m:* Kimberlee A.; *c:* Zack, Katherine; *ed:* MI St Univ (BA) Eng 1976; Edinboro Univ (MA) Cnslng 1981; *cr:* Susquehanna Vly Schls Eng Instr 1976-77; Maplewood HS Eng Instr 1977-83, Dir of Guid 1983-85, Eng Dept Chair 1985-; *ai:* Boys Soccer Coach; Ice Hockey Coach; *office:* Maplewood HS RD 1 Guys Mills PA 16327

ERINAKES, JAMES H.,II, High School Mathematics Tchr; *b:* Warwick, RI; *ed:* Univ of RI (BA) Scndry Ed, Math 1990; Providence Coll (MS) Math 1994; *cr:* Coventry MS Math Tchr 1990-94; Coventry HS Math Tchr 1994-; Comm Coll of RI Math Instr 1994-; *ai:* Boys Bsbl Team Head Coach; Soph Class Adv; AFT, NCTM 1990-; RIMTA 1990-, West Bay Rep; Babe Ruth League 1994-, VP; Rimta Dept Awd 1992-93; Outstdng Edctr Awd Nom; *office:* Coventry HS 40 Reservoir Rd Coventry RI 02816

ERKERD, IVORY DANSBY, History Teacher; *b:* Little Rock, AR; *m:* James; *c:* Allyna Erkerd Heath, Jahmari; *ed:* TX Chrstn Univ (BA) His 1970; Southern CT St Univ (MS) Ed 1980; Yale Univ, Yale New Haven Inst 9 Post Grad Hrs; *cr:* Lee HS Eng Tchr 1970-83; Hillhouse HS His Tchr 1984-; *ai:* Adv Young Womens Ldrshp Group; Fac Senate Rep; AFT 1970-; CCSS 1980-; Lib Media 1995-; TAPS, Prin Awd; *office:* James Hillhouse HS 480 Sherman Pky New Haven CT 06511

ERLENMEYER, EDITH C., Retired French Teacher; *b:* Germany; *ed:* Smith Coll (BA) Fr, His 1936; Radcliffe Coll (MA 3 Summer Sessions Middleberry Coll Fr, Span; Sorbonne Paris *cr:* Colby Jr Coll Ger, Fr Tchr 1940-42; Foxcroft Schl Span 1942-44; Wheeler Schl Frgn Lang Chm 1944-78; Providence C 1984; *ai:* Providence Jr Alliance Franchise Past Adv; TIAA Franchise de Providence 1946-96, Pres 1964-78; Providence Ladys Bd 1970-96, Pres 1982-84; Cty Garden Club 1972-96, P 1992-96; Shakespeare Soc 1956-96, Reader; *home:* 355 Blacks Providence RI 02906

ERMISH, GLORIA MAZZITTI, Fourth Grade Teacher; *b:* Be *w:* H. Carleton (dec); *c:* Susan D.; *ed:* Bloomsburg Univ (BS 1952; *cr:* Berwick Area Schl Dist Elem Tchr 1952-95; *ai:* NE Berwick Area Ed Assn 1952-; Kathleen Jones Meml Awd for Di Articles Pub.

ERNST, BEVERLY KAY (REPSHER), Principal & HS Sup Easton, PA; *m:* David M.; *c:* Cami Sweeney, David; *ed:* Schl of Admin 1995; Essential Learning Inst Trng for Learning Disable Prevention for Teens I & II; *cr:* Easton Chrstn Schl Monitor, S 1992-; *ai:* Chapel Tchr; Supvr of HS Lrng Ctr; Tutor; Easton As God 1965-, Sunday Schl Tchr; *office:* Easton Christian Freemansburg Ave Easton PA 18045

ERNST, JOANNE, Reading Consultant; *b:* Manhasset, NY; *m:* John; *ed:* Kutztown Univ (BS) Elem Ed 1984; Univ of Cntrl Rdng Specialist 1990; 12 Credit Hrs Kutztown Univ; *cr:* Allen Dist Elem Tchr 1984-88, Rdng Consultant 1991-; Lee Adult GED Instr 1988-89; Lake Sumter Comm Coll Rdng, Eng Instr 19 St Univ Acad Support 1990-91; *ai:* Schl Cncl; PSEA, NEA 198 Delta Pi 1984-, Sec; Eng Acad Awds; *home:* 7776 Coral Ct Sla 18080*

ERNST, MARC WILLIAM, Physical Education Teacher; *b:* C OH; *m:* Mary Hadley Smith; *ed:* Univ of Cincinnati (BS) Post-Grad Hrs in Sports Nutrition; *cr:* Southwest Local Schls H Suspension Monitor 1988-91; Whitewater Vly Elem Schl PE Tch Wm. H. Harrison HS PE Tchr 1993-; *ai:* Asst Wrestling Coach.

ERNSTEDT, BARBARA JEAN, Sixth Grade Mathematics Tch River, NJ; *m:* James E.; *c:* Jeffrey, Karin; *ed:* Univ of MD (BS 1970; Attnd Amer Univ & Frostburg St Univ; *cr:* Southgate Ele Sci, Soc Stud & Math Tchr 1971-75; Bayview MS 8th Grd 1976-77; West Frederick MS 6th & 7th Grd Tchr 1985-91; Baller MS 6th Grd Tchr 1991-; *ai:* Schl Improvement Team; PTSA, Sch Rep, Life Membership Awd 1995; NEA, MD St Tchrs Assn 1971 Club Achvmt Awd 1993; Frederick Cty Outstanding Tchr No Ballenger Creek MS 5525 Ballenger Creek Pike Frederick MD

ERRIERA, LUISA, English Professor; *b:* Lisbon, Portugal; *ed:* (BA) Eng & Philosophy 1989, (MA) Eng 1993; *cr:* Iona Coll 1989-93; Berkeley Coll Eng Prof 1993-; *ai:* Intnl Club Adv; Quality Tchng & Stu Svcs Comms; In Charge of Acad Resource 78 7th St New Rochelle NY 10801

ERTLE, DEIDRE A., High School Guidance Counselor; *b:* Je NJ; *ed:* Providence Coll (BA) Ed, Soc Stud 1976; Jersey City St Admin, Supervision 1987; Stu Prsnl Services Cert; *cr:* Ir Conception Schl 8th Grd Tchr 1977-79; Secaucus Mid Sc 7th-12th Grd Soc Stud Tchr 1980-88; Secaucus MS 7th-8th Gr Tchr 1988-89; Secaucus HS Guidance Cnslr 1989-; *ai:* PE Intram Instr; *office:* Secaucus H S Milridge Rd Secaucus NJ 07094

ERTLE, KARL JOSEPH, Theology Teacher; *b:* Cleveland, OH Klein; *c:* Timothy, Katherine, Mary, Anne; *ed:* Borromeo Coll Philosophy 1983; John Carroll Univ (MA) Rel Stud 1986; Post Fordham Univ Schl of Ed; *cr:* St Ignatius HS Theology Tchr 19 Comm Svc 1985-89, Dir Admissions, Fin Aid 1989-95, Theo 1995-; *ai:* Multicultural Club, Frosh Class, Head Schlsp Drive M ACAD 1990-, Founding Chair; JSEA 1983-, Midwest Chair; CA Newcomer's Schlsp Awd; Lkwd Rec Dept 1982-, Certfd Ofcl, Ro *office:* Saint Ignatius H S 1911 W 30th St Cleveland OH 44113

ERTMAN, EARL LESLIE, Professor of Art; *b:* Parma, OH; Ann Williamson; *c:* Elliot, Kreg; *ed:* Univ of South MS (BS) Case Western Reserve Univ (MA) 1967; Univ of MA Extension Univ of Akron Classics 1967-69; *cr:* Cleveland Museum of 1966-67; Univ of Akron Instr to Prof of Art 1967-; *ai:* Intn Egyptologists; Archeological Soc of Amer; Amer Rsrch Ctr Egypt Exploration Soc; Soc for the Stud of Egyptian A Smithsonian Rsrch & Dev Awd 1971; Amer Cncl Learned Societ Grant 1976; Univ of Akron 2 Rsrch Flwshps & 3 Rsrch Grants; *of* Of Akron Schl of Art Folk Hall Akron OH 44325

ESCANDEL, ROSE ANN, Family & Consumer Sci Tchr; *b:* PA; *m:* Thomas Raymond; *c:* Keith, Lindsey; *ed:* Mansfield U (BS) Home Ec 1973; Marywood Coll Grad Work Early Chldhd *cr:* Northeast #19 Intermediate Unit Day Care Dir 1973-82; Su Comm HS Family, Consumer Sci Tchr 1982-; *ai:* Stu Cncl Adv High NHS Adv 1 Yr; NEA, PSEA 1982-; Delton Kappa Gamma VP; PASC Dist IX Stu Cncl Adv 1995, Exec Bd Adv 3 Susquehanna Comm HS Rd 3 Box 5-A Susquehanna PA 18847

ESCANDEL, THOMAS RAYMOND, 6th Grade Teacher; *b:* B PA; *m:* Rose Ann Stengele; *c:* Keith, Lindsey; *ed:* Keystone Co 1970; Mansfield Univ (BS) Ed 1972; *cr:* Susq Elem Schl 4th-6th 24 Yrs; *ai:* Elem Stu Cncl; Chess Club Adv; PSEA, NEA, SC *home:* PO Box 64 Brooklyn PA 18813

ESDON, LYNETTE GRACE, Retired Teacher; *b:* Greensboro *ed:* Johnson St Coll (BS) Elem Ed 1950; *ai:* Day Spring Pregnanc Primary Sunday Schl Tchr; Childrens' Church Ldr; Schl Lib He of Yr.

ESHBACH, VALETTA PAINTER, Mathematics Teacher; *b:* Re *ed:* Alvrenia Coll (BED) Math 1968; Kutztown Univ (MED) M *cr:* Reading-Muhlenber Area Vo-Tech Schl Math Tchr 1968-69; Math Tchr 1969-70; Muhlenberg HS Math Tchr 1970-; *a* Yth-to-Yth Adv 1984-94; NEA, PSEA 1968-; NCTM, PCTM 198 Muhlenberg HS Sharp Ave & Frances St Laureldale PA 19605*

ESHLEMAN, RONALD EUGENE, Chem Teacher & Sci Dep Waynesboro, PA; *m:* Jo Ann Berry Eshleman; *c:* Ronald Jr., Sha Millersville St Coll (BS) Phys Sci 1961; Penn St Univ (MED) 1966; Post Grad Stud MT St Univ 1971, Hope Coll 1973 & U 1971-76; *cr:* Highstown HS Chem Tchr & Sci Dept Head Claymont HS Chem Tchr & Sci Dept Head 1970-89; Brandywine Tchr & Sci Dept Head 1989-; *ai:* Sci Dept Head; Bsbl Coach; Jr Olympiad & Sci Club Adv; NEA 1961-; DE Sci Tchrs 1970-, C of Yr 1987; Bible Bapt Church 1975-, Bd Pres; Natl Sci Fnd *office:* Brandywine HS 1400 Foulk Rd Wilmington DE 19803

ESKELUND, ERIK DAVID, School Chaplain; *b:* Miami, FL; Browne; *c:* Luke, Tehillah; *ed:* Missions Coll Elyon Woord 1988-89; *cr:* Hosannah Chrstn Acad K-12 Gym Tchr, Chaplain, 1993-95; Greenville Chrstn Life Ctr Yth Pastor 1993-; *ai:* Yth Debut Album Released, Distributed Throughout Europe, Southe 1996; *office:* Hosanna Chrstn Acad Rt 32 PO Box 456 Gree 12083*

MARCELLA HART, Coord of Developmental Math; *b:* d, OH; *m:* J. Grant; *c:* Dan, Emily, Stephen, Gregory, Bridget; *ed:* 'niv (BSME) Music Ed 1976; SUNY at Brockport (BA) Math Bishop Borgess HS Vocal Music Dir 1976-77; Saint Charles Schl rd Gen Music Tchr 1977-78; SUNY at Brockport Grad Asst Developmental Math Coord 1993-; *ai:* Fac Senate Gen Ed nittee; Frosh Advy Bd; Assessment Advy Cncl; NYCLSA, C, AMA, ASCD, AMS; NCTM 1990-; Sacred Heart Cathedral Bd 36-91; Childbirth Ed Assn of Rochester 1983-88; Webster Theatre 38-91, VP; Educl Tech Initiative Awd 1994; *office:* S U N Y Coll port Brockport NY 14420

MICHAEL VAUGHN, Political Science Professor; *b:* Fort N; *m:* Marie Frances Mika; *c:* Mary Isabella, Ava Marie; *ed:* AZ BS) Pol Sci 1978, (MA) Pol Sci 1981; OH St Univ (PHD) Pol Sci OH Wesleyan Univ Instr 1985-89; Southern IL Univ Asst Prof OH Wesleyan Univ Asst Prof 1995-; *ai:* Moot Court Team Coach; Adv; Amer Pol Sci Assn 1978-; Midwest Pol Sci Assn; Ed of Due of Journal Articles, Prof Books Author; *office:* OH Wesleyan Univ Govt Dept Delaware OH 43015

A, BARBARA ANGELA, Phys Ed Tchr & Coach; *b:* Brooklyn, CUNY Staten Island Comm Coll (AA) Lbrl Arts 1974; CUNY oll (BA) PE 1977, (MS) PE 1983; CUNY Coll of Staten Island 6th Cert Admin; *cr:* Murry Bergtraum HS PE Tchr 1978-, Sr Adv Dean of Houses, Attendance, External Prgms 1994-; Pub Schl Ath d of Ed Commissioner Boys Vlybl 1987-; *ai:* Vlybl 1977-, Tennis Gymnastics 1981-84 Girls Var Coach; Bd of Dir Alumni Assn; 8-; USTA 1988-; AAHPERD 1990-; Hunter Coll MVP Tennis '6; *office:* Murry Bergtraum HS 411 Pearl St New York NY 10038

A, RAFAEL,JR., Spanish Teacher; *b:* Eatontown, NJ; *ed:* Jniv (BA) Pol Sci, Span 1983; *cr:* Asbury Park HS Permanent Sub 5-88; Jackson Meml HS Span Tchr 1988-; *ai:* Class of 96 Adv; 38-; NJEA 1988-; Jackson Ed Assn 1988-, Rep Prof Rights & bilities Comm; *office:* Jackson Memorial HS 101 Don Connor kson NJ 08527

TO, ALYCE, Fifth Grade Teacher; *b:* Elizabeth, NJ; *ed:* Rutgers glass Coll (BA) Psych 1988; Georgian Ct Coll (MA) Educl Admin pvrs, Prins, Bus Admin, Criminal Justice Certs; *cr:* Veterans Elem Schl Third Grd Tchr 1987-88, Fifth Grd Tchr 1988-; *ai:* ized Testing, Presenter Parent Univ Family Life, Hlth Curr Ocean Cty Rdng Cncl 1988-; NJ Assn for Educl Tech 1994-; NEA eorgian Ct Alumnoe Org 1995-; Pub Project Multicultural Curr; Malibu Rd Lavallette NJ 08735*

TO, BARBARA PATRIZI, Spanish & English Teacher; *b:* hia, PA; *m:* John V. D.D.S.; *c:* John, Mark, Dean; *ed:* Holy Family) Span 1961; 9 Credit Hrs Rutgers Univ; *cr:* Camden Cath HS g Tchr 1980-, Span NHS Moderator 1989-, Drama Club Moderator Drama Club, Span NHS Moderator; AATSP, NCTE 1980-; *office:* Catholic HS Chrry Hill Rt 38 & Cuthbert Rd Cherry Hill NJ 08002

TO, DONNA MARIE, High School Math Teacher; *b:* Vineland, Glassboro St (BA) Scndry, K-12 Math, Earth Sci 1980; Master d Pyschoanalysis 1985; Post Grad Stud Math 1981; *cr:* Glassbor ate Phy Sci Tchr 1978-79; Rieck Ave Elem Math, Earth Sci Tchr mberland Regnl 9-12 Grd Math Tchr 1980-; *ai:* Home Bound me Instr; Math Tutor GED Adult Schl Prgm; Cheerleading Coach NEA, NJEA, CREA Ed Assn 1980-; Norma Alliance Amb, Fire , Pres, Treas, Sec, VP; Rescue Squad 1980-, Lt; Emergency Tech 1976-; Mayslanding Rescue Squad, EMT-D; Product Dev C Southern NJ Consortium on Ed; *office:* Cumberland Regional ox 5115 Silver Lake Rd Seabrook NJ 08302*

TO, IRENE M., 7th Grade Teacher; *b:* Jersey City, NJ; *ed:* St oll (BA) Elem Ed 1974; Jersey City St Coll 15 Grad Credits; *cr:* 8 Grd Tchr 1974-; *ai:* NEA, NJEA 1974-; *office:* PS 27 201 North City NJ 07307

TO, JEAN KILIMAN, English Teacher & Dept Chair; *b:* Salem, William Michael; *ed:* Kent St Univ (BA) Eng 1974, (MA) Eng st Grad Hrs in Eng, Ed; *cr:* Salem HS Eng Tchr 1975-, Dept Chm : Writing, Cmptr, Curr Dev Comms; NEA, OEA, SEA 1975-; 985-92; Jennings Scholar; Salem HS Tchr of the Yr 1993; *office:* 1200 E 6th St Salem OH 44460

TO, LUCILLE RICCILLI, English & Drama Teacher; *b:* Akron, alph Jr.; *c:* Doreen Osmun, Gina Marie; *ed:* Univ of Akron (BA) ; Ashland Univ (MAEd) Curr 1994; Attnd Hofstra Univ, NY Univ ; *cr:* Saint Joseph Schl 5th Grd Tchr 1965-66; IHM Schl 5th Grd 7-69; Holy Family 5th & 8th Grd Tchr 1970-84; STV-M HS Eng Tchr 1984-90; Maple Heights HS Eng & Drama Tchr 1990-; M Drama Tchr 1994-; *ai:* Drama; NEA, Intnl Thespian 1990-; Kappa 1988-; NCTE 1984-; Cuyahoga Falls General Hospital ec Olympics 1987-; Hunger Ctr 1990-; Stow Arts Cncl 1992-; ing Tchr in Amer 1975; Wrote A Booklet on Writing 1994; Scholar 1994; OH Arts Cncl 1995; Fellowship & Grants for ng; Maple Heights Tchr of Yr 1994; Ashland Oil Golden Apple 2 90-91; Master Tchr Nomination 1991-94.

TO, ROBERT L., High School Chemistry Teacher; *b:* Jamica NY; *m:* Patrice Himmellman; *c:* Patrice Krompier, Amy Krompier, ebecca, Mike Krompier, Tim Krompier; *ed:* Nassau Comm Coll 1975; Southampton Coll (BS) Marine Bio 1977; C. W. Post LIU c Ed 1982; First Aid, CPR, Coaching Cert 45 Post Grad Credits; nt Smith Schl 7th-12th Grd Tchr 1978-81; Uniondale HS Chem, 1981-; Hofstra Upward Bound Sci Tchr 1985-; *ai:* JHS Cross ack & Field Coach; St Martin of Tours of Amityville Schl Bd 6 ssapequa Cultural Arts Prgm Marine Sci Instr; AFT, NYST, e Tchrs Assn 1981-; Amityville St Martin of Tours 1989-, VP; niondale HS 933 Goodrich St Uniondale NY 11553*

TO, STEPHANIE (HORINEK), Biology Teacher; *b:* Atwood, ndrew John; *c:* Andrew J. Jr., AnnMarie; *ed:* Univ of NE (BS) Bio, 1970, (MS) Guid, Cnslr 1973; *cr:* Omaha Pub Schls Bio Tchr Bishop Clarkson Meml Hosp Cnslr, Lab, Eng Instr 1976-79; IS Bio Tchr 1979-; *ai:* Yrbk Co-Adv; CEA, NEA, TEA 1979-; NEME 1986-; Historical Soc 1995-; Tolland Ftbl Rec League Ofcr Achvmts Awd.*

TO, WILLIAM M., English Teacher; *b:* New York, NY; *m:* Jean *ed:* Mt Union Coll (BA) Eng 1969; Westminster Coll (Med) Eng st Grad Credits in Eng & Ed; *cr:* Delehanty HS Sci Tchr 1970; Eng Tchr 1970-; *ai:* NEA & OEA 1970-; Salem Ed Assn 1970-, Salem HS Tchr of Yr 1991; Jennings Schlr; *office:* Salem HS h St Salem OH 44460

BARBARA MCCLOSKEY, English & Speech Teacher; *b:* g, PA; *m:* J. Paul; *c:* Jamie Maureen (Espy) McGlaughlin, John P. rove City Coll (AB) Eng 1963; Attnd Shippensburg Univ, PA St Post Grad Hrs; *cr:* Tyrone Area HS Eng Tchr 1963-68; Juniata Eng Tchr 1976-; *ai:* Speech League Adv; Mentor Tchr; PA CTE, 81-; Juniata Valley Ed Assn, PA St Ed Assn, NEA 1977-; Western 992-; Lower Spruce Creek Presbyn Chrch 1967-; Tchr of Yr 1966, holars Recognition Awd 1994; Yrbk Dedication 1995; *office:* alley HS RD 1 box 318 Alexandria PA 16611

ESQUER, PATRICIA ANN, Second Grade Teacher; *b:* Waynesboro, PA; *m:* Eugene L.; *ed:* Elizabethtown Coll (BS) Elem Ed 1970; Shipensburg Univ (MED) Elem Ed 1972; *cr:* Greencastle-Antrim Schl Dist 2nd Grd Tchr 1970-; *ai:* Second Grd Chprsn; Prof Assessment, Strategic Planning Comms; NEA, PSEA 1970-; Greencastle-Antrim Ed Assn 1970-, Sec; IRA 1995-; Greencastle-Antrim Women's Club, Pres, VP, Sec; Tayamenta Sachta Advy Comm; Dists Excl in Ed Awd; *home:* 115 N Allison St Greencastle PA 17225

ESRICK, JO ANN GIANFAGNA, French & Spanish Teacher; *b:* Deer Park, NY; *m:* Edward Ephram; *c:* Michael, Karen, Matthew; *ed:* SUNY at Albany (BA) Fr & Ed 1971, (MA) Fr 1972; Mac Acad Comps 1994; *cr:* Pierson HS Fr & Span Tchr 1972-74; East Northport Jr HS Fr & Span Tchr 1974-78; Poquoson HS Fr & Span Tchr 1978-81; Magic City HS Fr & Span Tchr 1984-85; Sewanhaka Cntrl Schl Dist HS Fr & Span Tchr 1990-; *ai:* Frgn Lang Hnr Soc Adv; RAVE Comm; New Frgn Lang Curr Guide Lines Wkshp Coord; NYSAFLT 1972-; AATSP 1990-; AATF 1990-; NEA 1990-; City of Poquoson Outstdng Young Edctrs Awd 1978-79; Long Island Incentive Awd 1990; Tchr of the Month 1991-92; Sewanhaken Cntrl HS Grants 1991-; Hofstra Univ Poetry Competition 1st Pl Awd Best HS; Tech Frgn Lang Dev Grant 1991-95; *office:* Elmont Memorial HS 555 Ridge Rd Elmont NY 11003

ESSELSTEIN, MARK J., PE, Driver Ed Tchr & Coach; *b:* Dayton, OH; *m:* Ann Elizabeth Sutton; *ed:* Wright St Univ (BS) Bus Ed 1980; Univ of Dayton (MS) Educl Admin 1995; *cr:* Springfield Cath Cntrl HS Bus & PE Tchr 1981-86; Parkway Local Schls Bus, PE & Driver Ed Tchr 1986-; *ai:* Head Var Fastpitch Sftbl Coach; Parkway Ed Assoc 1986-, Pres 1993-95; OEA & NEA 1986-; OH HS Fastpitch Sftbl Coaches Assn 1989-; Parkway Ath Boosters 1986-; 131-41 Record in Sftbl; 4 Dist Championships; 2 Regnl Finalists; *office:* Parkway Local Schls 401 S Franklin St Rockford OH 45882*

ESSIG, CARL E., Associate Professor of Bus; *b:* Philadelphia, PA; *m:* Judith Ann Freed; *c:* Stephen; *ed:* Peirce Jr Coll (AS) Bus 1967-; Northern MI Univ (BS) Bus & Ed 1969; Temple Univ (MBA) Bus 1974; 15 Credits in Post Grad Courses; *cr:* Peirce Jr Coll Instr 1969-76; Montgomery Cty Comm Coll Assoc Prof 1976-; *ai:* Various Comms; AFT 1980-; Outstdng Tchr & Svc Awd 1992; *office:* Montgomery County Comm Coll 340 Dekalb Pike Blue Bell PA 19422*

ESSIG-MARKSZ, MARY JO, 2nd Grade Teacher; *b:* Akron, OH; *m:* Daniel Carl; *ed:* Kent St Univ (MED) Math Clinician 1978; Doctoral Stud Curr Instruction; *cr:* Akron Pub Schls Kndgtn, 1st, 3rd-5th Grd & ESEA Math Tchr 1975-93; Kent St Univ Tchng Fellow 1993-95, Coord Akron Pub Schls & Kent St Univ Intern Pgm 1993-; Akron Pub Schls 2nd Grd Tchr 1995-; *ai:* NCTM 1978-; PDS Partnership 1992-; AERA 1994-; Parent Anonymous 1990-93, Bd Mem; Fairlawn Schl PTA Tchr of the Yr Awd 1991-92; Kent St Univ Tchng Flwshp 1993-95; Book: Reflective Teaching; *office:* King School 805 Memorial Pkwy Akron OH 44303*

ESTABROOK, KAREN JUNE, English Teacher; *b:* Warsaw, NY; *ed:* Houghton Coll (BA) Eng Lit 1979; Alfred Univ (MS) Tchng Eng 1984; *cr:* Scio Cntrl Schl Eng Tchr 1979-; *office:* Scio Central Schl Washington St Scio NY 14880*

ESTERBURG, ARLENE CATHERINE, 5th Grade Teacher; *b:* Pittsburgh, PA; *ed:* Duquesne Univ (BS) Elem Ed 1973; *cr:* Court Schl 5th Grd Tchr 1974-75, 4th Grd Tchr 1975-79, 6th Grd Tchr 1979-80; Carnegie Elem Schl 6th Grd Tchr 1980-81, 5th Grd Tchr 1981-86, 2nd Grd Tchr 1986-87, 5th Grd Tchr 1987-; *ai:* Safety Patrol Spon 1992-; Summer Rdng Prgm Music, Art Tchr 1994-95; AFT, CFT 1974-; Holy Trinity Choir 1975-; *office:* Carnegie Elem Schl Franklin Ave Carnegie PA 15106

ESTES, GISELA BEHRENDT, Instructor of German; *b:* Allenstein, Germany; *m:* Paul Livingston; *c:* Heide Ruth, Christopher Paul; *ed:* Inst for Teachers (Slaatsexamen) Child Psych & Ed 1959; *cr:* Childrens Ctr Tchr 1959-61; Amer Military Schl Ger Tchr 1961-64; Plymouth St Coll Ger Lecturer 1978-84, Ger Instr 1989-; *ai:* Annual Summer Seminar Dir Ger Tchrs; AATG 1978-; NHATFL 1980-; Ger Amer Union 1986-; Plymouth Conservation Commission 1987-, Sec; Ger Math Ed Article Co-Author; *office:* Plymouth St Coll Dept of Foreign Lang Plymouth NH 03264

ESTES, PAUL L., Professor of Mathematics; *b:* Lewiston, ME; *m:* Gisela Behrendt; *c:* Heide, Christopher; *ed:* Bowdoin Coll (BA) Math 1959; Brown Univ (MAT) Math 1967; Univ of NH (MS) Math 1969, (PHD) Math 1972; *cr:* Plymouth St Coll Prof 1971-; *ai:* MAA 1984-, PSC Rep; Articles Pub in Math Journals; *office:* Univ Of NH Plymouth St Coll Dept Of Math Plymouth NH 03264

ESTIS, DOROTHY MONTAGNOLO, Retired First Grade Teacher; *b:* Philadelphia, PA; *m:* Arnold; *c:* Monty; *ed:* West Chester St U (BS) Math & Eng 1949; Penn St & U of P (MS) Elem Ed 1973; 41 Addl Credit Hrs Penn St, Cabrini Coll; *cr:* Alice Grim Elem Schl First Grd Tchr 1949-53; Oakdale & Sabold Schls First Grd Tchr 1953-57; Sabold Schl Sub Tchr All Grds to 6 1957-59; Charles H. Russell Schl First Grd Tchr 1959-92; *ai:* NEA, PSEA 1949-; PSERS 1992-; Kazangian Awd for Ec; Vly Forge Tchrs Medal Freedoms Fnd Vly Forge PA; Kodak Cameras in Schl Curr Photography; Grd Tchr Mag Article on Ec in First Grd; *home:* 18 Llangollen Ln Newtown Square PA 19073

ESTRADA, ANN BELAND, Theology Teacher; *b:* Waterbury, CT; *m:* Pastor; *c:* Tiana, Ramon; *ed:* St Joseph Coll (BA) Rel Stud 1982; Sacred Heart Univ (MA) Rel Stud 1989; *cr:* Holy Cross HS Theology Dept Tchr 1982-; Sacred Heart Univ Adjunct Tchr 1990-; St Joseph Coll Adjunct Tchr 1994; *ai:* Yrbk Adv; Asst Moderator Outdoors Club; Girl Scouts 1989-, Troop Ldr; *office:* Holy Cross HS 587 Oronoke Rd Waterbury CT 06708

ESTREICHER, ALETA GLASEROFF, Law Professor; *b:* New York City, NY; *m:* Samuel; *c:* Michael S., Hannah R.; *ed:* Bryn Mawr Coll (AB) Classical, Near Eastern Archaeology 1970; Columbia Law Schl (JD) Law 1981; *cr:* Hon Eugene H. Nicherson USDJ Law Clerk 1981-82; Cleary Gottlieb Steen & Hamilton Assoc 1982-84; NY Law Schl Asst Prof 1984-85, Assoc Prof 1985-92, Prof of Law 1992-; *ai:* Law Review Articles Pub; *office:* NY Law School 57 Worth St New York NY 10013

ETCHISON, CRAIG, Associate Prof of English; *b:* Baltimore, MD; *ed:* Lynchburg Coll (BA) Philosophy 1967; Shippensburg Univ (MA) Eng 1972; IN Univ of PA (PHD) Rhetoric, Linguistics 1985; *cr:* Glenville St Coll Assoc Prof Eng, Chair 1985-93; ALlegany Coll Assoc Prof Eng 1993-; *ai:* NCTE 1985-; The World Weaver 1995; Articles 1989, 1991, 1995, Short Stories Pub; *office:* Allegany Coll 12401 Willowbrook Rd SE Cumberland MD 21502*

ETERNO, JAMES NICHOLAS, Social Studies Teacher; *b:* Port Jefferson, NY; *ed:* Queens Coll at CUNY (BA) His 1982, (MS) Soc Stud Ed 1993; 18 Credit Hrs Brooklyn Coll at CUNY, After Schl Prof Dev Prgm; *cr:* NYC Bd of Ed Sub Tchr 1985-90; Jamaica HS Soc Stud Tchr 1990-; *ai:* PM Schl; Tutor Advanced Placement US His; UFT 1985-, Del; UFT New Action Caucus 1995-; AFT, NYSUT 1985-; REM Club 1987-; Queens Coll Schl of Ed Grad Merit Awd; *office:* Jamaica HS 167-01 Gothic Dr Jamaica NY 11432

ETHIER, GERARD WILFRED, High School Math Teacher; *b:* Woonsocket, RI; *m:* Nancy Helen; *c:* Christopher, Jeffrey, Kerri; *ed:* Providence Coll (BA) Math 1968; RI Coll (MAT) Math 1973; RI Cert Ed 9 Credits; *cr:* Blackstone HS Math Tchr 1968-69; Moses Brown Schl Math Tchr 1969-70; Blackstone-Millville Reg Math Tchr 1970-81; RI Coll Math Instr 1975-; Cumberland HS Math Tchr 1990-; *ai:* Girls Frosh Bsktbl Coach; Talent Show Dir; NEA 1990-; North Smithfield Little League 1975-, Coach 8 Yrs, Bd Mem; *home:* 17 Cynthia Dr North Smithfield RI 02896

ETHINGTON, MARIROSE TORCELLO, Biology Instructor; *b:* Batavia, NY; *m:* Gordon Lawrence; *c:* Marcella Lee, Jared Ralph; *ed:* St Univ of NY at Geneseo (BS) Bio 1986, (MA) Bio 1990; 6 Grad Hrs in Environmental Impact From St Univ of NY at Brockport; *cr:* Camden Cntrl Schl Tchr 1987-89; Monroe Comm Coll Adjunct Instr 1990-91; Genesee Comm Coll Instr 1991-; *ai:* 3 New Fac Search Comms Chprsn; Fac Senate; Math & Sci Self Stud Comm; AAWCC 1995-; ESTYCB 1996; GEA, NEA 1991-; GCNH Day Care-Parent Group 1992-; *office:* Genesee Comm Coll 1 College Rd Batavia NY 14020*

ETRE, THOMAS ANTHONY, 4th Grade Teacher; *b:* Worcester, MA; *m:* Barbara Ann Ranieri; *c:* Kelli Ann, Suzanne, Neal; *ed:* Boston Univ (BA) His, Gov 1963; Framingham St (MA) ELem Ed 1971; Attnd Harvard Univ Ctr for Astrophysics; BU, Framingham, Norchester 30 Credit Hrs ELem ed 1974; *cr:* Franklin Schl Grd III Tchr 1970-91; City of Newton Primary Coord 1971-, Title I Prin 1972-77, Media Specialists 1980-95, Grd IV, Sci Specialist 1992-; *ai:* Theater Groups Vol; Camera Club Vol; Fund Raising with Parents; AFT 1970-71; MTA 1971-; NTA 1971-, Fac Rep; Yth Scocer Coach 1980-84 VP; Yth Soccer Pres 1985-88 Civic Awd; Sci Tchr 1995-; Co-Author for New Sci Prgm; *home:* 36 Dove Rd Marlborough MA 01752*

ETTER, CHARLES R., 10th Grade World Cultures Tchr; *b:* Harrisburg, PA; *m:* Dodie J. L.; *c:* Nathan; *ed:* Lebanon Valley Coll (BA) His 1972; 24 Grad Credits Beyond Degree; *cr:* Lower Dauphin HS Soc Stud Tchr 1973-; *ai:* Former Bsktbl Coach All Levels; Drug Alcohol Team SAS; Outstanding Classroom Tchng Awd Mid 70s; *home:* 5010 Bossler Rd Elizabethtown PA 17022

ETTER, LOUISA SLAYBAUGH, Art Teacher; *b:* Chambersburg, PA; *m:* David S.; *ed:* Kutztown Univ (BS) Art Ed 1970; Attnd Shippensburg Univ & Penn St; *cr:* Cntrl Jr HS Art Tchr 1970-71; Chambersburg Area Sr HS Art Tchr 1971-; *ai:* Art Svc Club & Natl Art Hnr Soc Adv; Girls Tennis Coach; PSEA & NEA 1970-; CAEA 1970-; NAEA 1983-; *office:* Chambersburg Area Sr HS 511 S 6th St Chambersburg PA 17201

ETTINGER, MARCIA MILLER, Special Education Teacher; *b:* Brooklyn, NY; *m:* Howard; *c:* Jason, David; *ed:* Hofstra Univ (BS) Psych, Elem Ed 1969, (MS) Spec Ed 1970; Grad, Inservice Stud; *cr:* Commack HS Spec Ed Tchr 1970-; *ai:* Schl Based Mgmt Team; Dists Comm Spec Ed; Flwshp Hofstra Univ; *office:* Commack HS Scholar Ln Commack NY 11725

ETTINGER, RICHARD S., High School Biology Teacher; *b:* Cleveland, OH; *m:* Carole Leisek; *c:* Aaron; *ed:* Kent St Univ (BS) PE 1981, (BS) Ed 1984, (MA) Bio 1991; 6 Credit Hrs Post Grad Stud; *cr:* West Geauga HS Sci Tchr 1985-86; Ravenna HS Sci Tchr 1986-; *ai:* Project Green Schl Contact; NABT 1986-; NSTA 1986-; SECO 1986-; REA 1986-, Treas; Metro League Soccer Coach of the Yr 1988; Northeastern OH Univ Coll of Medicine Rsrch in Biochem 1993; Eisonhower Grant 1994-96.*

ETTL, PAUL, US History Teacher; *b:* Grand Forks, ND; *ed:* Univ of ND (BS) Ed Soc Sci 1980; Wichita St Univ (MA) Ed US His 1987; 15 Plus Grad Hrs Spec Ed; *cr:* Greeley Cty HS Sociology, Drivers Ed, Govt, US His Tchr, Head Girls Vlybl, BB Coach, Stu Cncl Supvr 1984-85; Louisburg HS Scndry Soc Sci Tchr, Jr Class Spon 1986-89; US Peace Corps ESL, PE Tchr 1989-91; Nile C. Kinnick HS Jr Class Spon, His, Soc Stud Instr 1992-; *ai:* Head Boys Var Bsktbl Coach; NEA 1992-.

EUELL, THOMAS EDWIN,III, Fifth Grade Teacher; *b:* New York City, NY; *m:* Linda McLane; *c:* Kelly, Megan; *ed:* Univ of Miami (BE) Ed 1969; IN Univ at Bloomington (MA) Instructional Systems Tech 1974; *cr:* Riley Ave Elem Schl 6th Grd Tchr 1969-73; Pulaski St Elem Schl 6th Grd Tchr 1973-79, 5th Grd Tchr 1979-; *ai:* RCFA Bldg Rep; NYSTA, RCFA 1969-; NYS Marine Sci Assn 1981-; Stimulation of Natural Aptitude Through Photography NYS Prgm Grant; Photography In-Svc, Parent Wkshps; Chisanbop Math; Drug, Alcohol Abuse Trng; *office:* Pulaski Street Elem Schl 300 Pulaski St Riverhead NY 11901

EUGANEO, KATHLEEN DORAN, Allied Health Instructor; *b:* Darby, PA; *m:* Anthony; *c:* Bethany, Anthony, Kathryn; *ed:* Mercy Cath Med Ctr (RT) Radiologic Tech 1975; Widener Univ (BS) Radiologic Tech, Ed 1982; St Joseph's Univ (MS) Hlth Care Admin 1988; *cr:* Presbyn Univ of PA Med Ctr Radiographer 1975-79; Med Ctr of DE Schl of Rad Tech Clinical Instr 1979-80, Prgm Dir 1980-93; DE Tech & Comm Coll Allied Hlth Instr 1993-; *ai:* Grad Continuing Ed; Philadelphia Soc of Rad Tech 1979-, Pres 1986-87, Bd Chm 1989-90; Assn of Edctrs in Rad Sci 1980-; Amer Soc of Rad Tech 1979-; St George Church 1955-, Organist; Authored Workbook, Videodisc; *office:* DE Tech & Comm Coll/Wilmington 333 N Shipley St Wilmington DE 19801

EULBERG, LYN, Math Teacher; *b:* Toledo, OH; *m:* Roy W.; *c:* Liana, Jeremy; *ed:* Capital Univ (BA) Math 1968; 13 Quarter Hrs Grad Courses; *cr:* Yorktown Jr HS Tchr 1968-69; Mctigue Jr HS Tchr 1969-73; Emerson Jr HS Tchr 1973-76; Toledo Chrstn Schl 1987-; *ai:* Sr Class Adv; Natl Honor Soc Faculty Adv.

EUSTACE, THOMAS JOSEPH, Biology Teacher; *b:* Stamford, CT; *m:* Susan Fabian; *c:* Michael, Eric; *ed:* St Michaels Coll (BA) Bio 1969; Southern Ct St Univ (MS) Sci Ed 1978; 12 Post Grad Credits; *cr:* Middletown MS 7th-8th Grd Sci Tchr 1969-71; Orange Ave Schl 7th-8th Grd Sci Tchr 1971-73; Pumpkin Delight Schl 7th-8th Grd Sci Tchr 1973-91; Foran HS P lanetarium & Observatory Dir 1991-; *ai:* Town-Wide Space Sci Enrichment Prgm; Publ Telescope Observing Sessions; Ault Ed Class; Pub Mgmnt Team Mem; NEA 1969-; CEA 1971-; MEA 1971-, Negotiating Comm; Project to Increase Mastery in Math, Sci 1989-, Flwshp; BSA 1957, Cubmaster, Asst Scoutmaster; Bsbl Summer League Coach 1980; Bsktbl League Coach 1980; *office:* Joseph A Foran HS 80 Foran Rd Milford CT 06460*

EUSTICE, MICHELLE, Math Teacher; *b:* Grand Rapids, MI; *ed:* Univ of Northern CO (BA) Math Ed 1983, (MA) SPED, Accous, HNCP 1987; Post Grad Summer Prgms Haskel Jr Coll & CO Schl of Mines; Math & Sci Summer Enrichment Prgm 3 Yrs; Cooperative Learning & Discovery Learning Trng; *cr:* Mc Intosh HS Math Tchr 1984-86; Wingate HS Math Tchr 1986-; *ai:* Amer Indian Sci & Engineering Soc Chapter Spon; Mentor of Gifted & Talented; EEO Cnslr; NEA 1988-89; AFT 1989-; ALSES 1988-; *office:* Wingate HS Box 2 Ft Wingate NY 87316*

EUSTIS, SARAH R., Mathematics Teacher; *b:* Washington, PA; *ed:* Indiana Univ of PA (BSEd) Math 1971; PA St Univ (MED) 1976; 36 Hrs Post-Grad Stud Wilkes Coll, Marywood Coll; *cr:* Holicong Jr HS Math Tchr, Team Ldr, Math Coord, Coach 1971-81; Central Bucks West HS Math Coord, Coach, Math Tchr, AP Calculus Tchr 1981-; *ai:* NEA, PA St Tchr Org 1971-; NCTM 1994-; *office:* Central Bucks-West HS 375 W Court St Doylestown PA 18901*

EUTSEY, JAMES EDWARD, Secondary Math Teacher; *b:* Mount Pleasant, PA; *m:* Deneen T. Cole; *c:* Nicole Ashley, Jorden Leigh; *ed:* Cedarville Coll (BA) Math 1989; 21 Educl Grad Credits; *cr:* Portsmouth Chrstn Schls Math & Physics Tchr 1989-91; Berlin Brothers Valley Scndry Math & Principles of Tech Tchr 1991-; *ai:* Jr HS Boys Bsktbl & Boys Var Bsbl Coach; Crusaders Club Adv; NEA & PSEA 1991-; Heritage Bapt Church 1993-, Young Adult Sunday Schl Tchr; Berlin Brothers Valley Outstdng Tchr of Yr 1994-95; *office:* Berlin Brothers Valley Schl 1025 E Main St Berlin PA 15530*

EVAN, ANDREW J., Technology Education Teacher; *b:* Norristown, PA; *m:* Lynn L. Cameron; *c:* Jacob; *ed:* MIllersville Univ (BS) Indstrl Arts 1984; Addl 36 Credits Towards Masters Prgm Allentown Coll Cmptrs in Ed; *cr:* Sun Rise Concessions l984-87; Spring-Ford Schl Dist Tech Ed Tchr 1987-; *ai:* Tech Ed Assn of PA 1987-, VP Region 3E; Nea 1987-; Presented Information at TEAP Conf 1994; *office:* Spring-Ford Area Schl Dist 199 Bechtel Rd Collegeville PA 19426

EVANGELISTA, BARBARA POPPENDICK, English Teacher; *b:* New Haven, CT; *m:* Chet P.; *c:* Michael, Alicia; *ed:* Univ of CT (BA) Eng 1973; Southern CT St Univ (MS) Rdng 1976; 6th Yr Educl Fnds 1991; *cr:* West Haven HS Drama & Eng Tchr 1973-76; Carrigan MS Eng Tchr 1976-78; West Haven HS Eng Tchr 1978-; *ai:* Honors Comm Chm; Teen Assistance Group Facilitator; AFT 1973-, Steward; BSA 1988-, Den Mother; BEST Cooperating Tchrs 1978-, Mem; Adv to Classes of 1985 & 1995; Excl in Ed Awd; *office:* West Haven HS 1 Circle St West Haven CT 06516*

EVANICH, KATHERINE POULOS, Spanish & German Teacher; *b:* Cleveland, OH; *m:* Norman Michael; *c:* Christopher, Michael; *ed:* Cleveland St Univ (BA) Span & Ger Ed 1977; Baldwin Wallace Coll (MA) Rdng; Univ of Akron Grad Stud Ed; Baldwin Wallace Coll Working Towards Master of Arts in Ed; *cr:* Parma City Schls Ger Tchr 1977-78; North Royalton HS Span & Ger Tchr 1978-; *ai:* Span Club Adv; Latin Club Asst; Hope Youth Group Adv; Amer Assn of Tchrs of Span & Portuguese 1992-; North Royalton Ed Assn 1977-; St Paul Bd of Ed; Span Honor Sigma Delta Pi; *office:* North Royalton HS 14713 Ridge Rd North Royalton OH 44133

EVANOFF, MARK L., Visual Communications Teacher; *b:* Erie, PA; *m:* Elizabeth M.; *c:* Mark J., Kathleen M. Horvath, Daniel R., Karen M., Patricia M.; *ed:* Penn St Univ (BS) Industrial Arts 1969; Masters Equivalency Tech Ed 1975 St Univ of NY at Buffalo; *cr:* Northwestern Sr HS Tech Ed, Industrial Materials Tchr 1969-; *ai:* NWEA, PSEA & NEA 1969-; TEAP & TEANP 1969-; *office:* Northwestern Sr HS 200 Harthan Way Albion PA 16401

EVANOFF, MIRIAM ANNE,SC, 8th Grd Tchr & Vice Principal; *b:* Jersey City, NJ; *ed:* Coll of St Elizabeth (BS) Elem Ed 1959; Math, Cmptr, Span; *cr:* St Cecilia Schl Fourth Grd Tchr 1950-61; Sacred Heart Schl Sixth-Eighth Grd Tchr 1961-64; St Peter Schl Eighth Grd Tchr, Vice Prin 1964-; *ai:* Moderator Chrldrs; Coord Altar Servers; Liturgy Comm; NCEA; Outstdng Educator 1993; Plaque, Banner 15 Yrs Participation in Crop Walk; Comm Prepared Math Syllabus; Math, Rel Coord; *office:* St Peter's Elem Schl 153 York St Jersey City NJ 07302

EVANOSKY, REBECCA MILLIGAN, Kindergarten Teacher; *b:* Steubenville, OH; *m:* William Edward; *c:* Michael; *ed:* Coll of Steubenville (BS) Elem Ed 1971; Addl Hrs Towards Masters Univ of Dayton; *cr:* John Gregg Elem Schl 2nd Grd Tchr 1970-76, Adult Basic Ed Tchr 1978-81; East Springfield Elem Title I Rdng Tchr 1979-82; Richmond Elem Schl Kndgtn Tchr 1982-; *ai:* Odyssey of the Mind Building Coord, Team Spon; NEA, OEA 1970-; Edison Local EA 1970-, Sec; OEA Convention Del; Delta Kappa Gamma 1977-, Pres; Jennings Scholar 1987-88; Ashland Tchr Achvmnt Awd 1989; *home:* PO Box 234 Bergholz OH 43908

EVANS, BETTY R., Sixth Grade Teacher; *b:* Detroit, MI; *m:* James William; *c:* Marja, Carlton; *ed:* Wayne St Univ (BA) Elem Ed 1971; Univ of MI (MS) Admin 1978; 13 Credit Hrs Towards Educl Specialist Degree in Admin; *cr:* Ferris MS Tchr 1971-84; Southside MS Tchr 1985-90; Navarre Elem Tchr 1990-; *ai:* Schl Newsletter; Partners in Ed; Black His Month Celebration; Women in His Celebration; Phi Delta Kappa 1993-.

EVANS, CONNIE K., Spanish Teacher; *b:* Summit, NJ; *m:* Gary A.; *c:* Jessica, Cassie; *ed:* Green Mountain Coll (AA) Art 1968; Univ of NH (BA) Span 1970, (MA) Span 1976; Franklin Pierce Coll Tchng Cert; *cr:* John Stark HS Span Tchr 1987-; *ai:* Blood Drive Chprsn; NHATFL, JS Tchrs Assn 1987-; Henniker & San Ramon Sister Project 1995-; *office:* John Stark Regional HS 618 N Stark Hwy Weare NH 03281*

EVANS, DAVID CHARLES, 8th Grade Lang Arts Teacher; *b:* Cleveland, OH; *m:* Nancy Ellen Smith; *c:* Charles Ray, James Neal; *ed:* Otterbein Coll (BSEd) Elem Ed 1967; Kent St Univ (MED) Educl Admin 1970; Attnd OH St Univ & Kent St Univ Supervision Tchrs, Cmptr Tech, Drug & Alcohol Awareness Trng, Career Ed, At Risk Stu; *cr:* Salem Elem Sixth Grd Tchr 1967; John Glenn Elem Sixth Grd Tchr 1967-70, Team Ldr Differentiated Staffing 1970-75; Ridgebrook Elem Sixth Grd Tchr 1975-77; Pleasantview MS Sci, Math Tchr 1978; Burbank Elem Sixth Grd Tchr 1978-80; Barrington Elem Sixth Grd Tchr 1980-83; Jones MS Sixth Grd Team Ldr, Math & Sci 1983-90, Eighth Grd Eng Tchr 1990-93, Seventh Grd Soc Stud Tchr 1993-94; 8th Grd Eng Tchr 1994-; *ai:* Saturday Schl Supvr; Dist WA DC Trip Coord; Upper Arlington Ed Assn 1978-, Pres; OH Ed Assn 1966-; NEA 1967-; Natl MS Assn 1988-; Martha Holdings Jennings Scholar 1972-73; Outstanding Young Men of Amer 1974; Career Ed Leadership Awds 1987-89; Upper Arlington Civic Assn Golden Apple Awd 1989; Tchr of Yr 1992; Ashland Oil Tchr Achvmt Awd Nom 1994-96; Ashlnd Oil Gldn Apple Achvr Awd 1995; Tchr of Yr 1995; OH Tchr of Yr Nom; Amer Tchr Awd Nom; *home:* 4323 Stratton Rd Columbus OH 43220

EVANS, DAVID F., Professor of Music; *b:* Pittsburgh, PA; *m:* Dorlene Custer; *c:* Lydia, Jeremy; *ed:* Oberlin Coll (BM) Voice Performance 1965; WV Univ (MM) Voice Performance 1974, (DMA) Voice Performance 1979; Akademie Fur Music Und Darsfelleude Kunst, Mozarteum, Salzburg Austraia Diploma Song, Opera 1968; *cr:* St Andrews Coll Instr 1973-76; SUNY at Fredonia Prof 1979-; *ai:* Ger Prgm Chaperone; NATS 1973-; Chancellor's Awd 1985; *office:* S U N Y Coll At Fredonia Fredonia NY 14063

EVANS, DAVID R., Science Teacher; *b:* Tarrytown, NY; *m:* Amy Parelman; *ed:* CT Coll (BA) Zoology 1980; Brown Univ (MAT) Bio Tchng 1990; *cr:* Mt Pleasant HS Sci Tchr 1990-; *ai:* Chess Team Coach; Adv Greenhouse Club, Tchr Acad; Schl Improvement Team Vol; AFT, NSTA, RI Sci Tchrs Assn 1990-; *office:* Mt Pleasant HS 434 Mount Pleasant Ave Providence RI 02908

EVANS, DIANE J., Mathematics Teacher; *b:* Troy, NY; *m:* Francis; *c:* Sean; *ed:* SUNY at Albany (BS) Math 1970, (MS) Advanced Classroom Tchng 1971; *cr:* Guilderland HS Math Tchr 1970-80; Schalmont HS Math Dept Chair 1990-94; *ai:* Adv Class of 1995; HS Bldg Planning Comm 1992-93, 1994-; Colonial Cncl Math Contest Adv; AFT, NYSUT 1993-; NCTM, AMTNYS 1971-; Capital Dist Assn of Math Supvrs 1990-92; Schalmont Tchrs Assn 1990-; Nom Tchr of Yr 1992-95; Capital Rgn Schlr-Tchr Recognition Awd 1995; *office:* Schalmont HS 1 Sabre Dr Schenectady NY 12306

EVANS, DONALD G., Spanish Teacher; *b:* Fulton, NY; *m:* Shirley Jean; *c:* Jeremy, Jonathan, Johanna, Jennifer; *ed:* Mansfield St (BA) Span 1966; Plattsburgh St (MS) Hlth Ed 1975, (MS) Admin 1983; 67 Hrs Beyond Masters; Cert in Span, Soc Stud, Hlth Ed & Admin; *cr:* Peru Cntrl Schl Span & Hlth Tchr 1970-; *ai:* Jr Var Sftbl & Soccer Coach; NEA, NYSAFLT 1970-; NYSFPHE; *home:* PO Box 655 Peru NY 12972

EVANS, ELLEN DEAN CRAWFORD, 2nd Grade Teacher; *b:* Lancaster, SC; *m:* Meredith Milton Jr.; *c:* Christopher; *ed:* Johnson C Smith Univ (BA) Elem Ed 1964; Master Equivalent Plus 45 Grad Hrs Morgan St, Coppin st; *cr:* Spartanburg SC Bd of Ed 4th Grd Tchr 1964-65; Baltimore Cty Bd of Ed 1st-5th Grd Tchr 1965-; Bowie St Coll (dir Summer Comp Camp 1990-91; *ai:* Baltimore Harbor City Links Org Fin Sec; BCAC Delta Sigma Theta 2nd VP; Epworth United Meth Chapel Mem: Staff Parish, Altar Guild & Fin Team; TABCO 1964-; NEA 1964-; MSTA 1964; US Yth Game 1985-, Vol, Plaque; Baltimore Cty Chamber of Commerce Awd for Excellency in Tchng 1993; *home:* 4775 Bonnie Brae Rd Pikesville MD 21208*

EVANS, GERALD J., Paralegal Professor; *b:* Rochester, NY; *ed:* Hartwick Coll (BS) Bus Admin 1968; NY Law Schl (JD) Law 1978; Grad Stud ED SUNY; *cr:* SUNY Adj Prof 1968-84; Schenectady Cty Comm Coll Prof 1984-; *ai:* Internship Supvr; NEA 1984-; ABA, NYSBA 1978-; St Univ NY Excl Tchng Awd; *office:* Schenectady County Comm Coll 78 Washington Ave Schenectady NY 12305

EVANS, HARRY DAGER,III, English Teacher; *b:* Philadelphia, PA; *m:* Philly Abbatiello; *c:* Courtney P., Brooke M.; *ed:* Castleton St Coll (BS) Eng, Scndry Ed 1970; Grad Stud Bridgewater St Coll, Suffolk Univ; *cr:* Barnstable HS Var Soccer, Lacrosse Coach 1988-94, Asst Girls Lacrosse Coach 1995; Sandwich HS Eng Tchr 1971-; *ai:* Var Soccer Coach 1973-87; Fac Schedule Comm; Asst Boys Lacrosse Coach; NEA, MTA 1971-; Sandwich Ed Assn 1971-, Prof Rights & Responsibilities Comm Chair; NCT Eng; N Soccer Coaches Assn; Cape Cod Soccer Coach of Yr; *office:* Sandwich HS 365 Quaker Meeting House Rd East Sandwich MA 02537

EVANS, JERRY, Social Studies Teacher; *b:* Heber Springs, AR; *c:* Nick; *ed:* Harding Univ (BS) Soc Sci 1971; Attnd Harding Univ, Ashland Univ 83-; *cr:* Searcy Pub Schls Tchr, Coach 1971-72; England Acad Tchr, Coach 1972-73; Chapel Acad Tchr, Coach 1973-74; Altheimer-Sherrill Schl Tchr, Coach 1977-82; Clyde HS Tchr 1983-; *ai:* Mock Trail; NEA; Clyde Fair Bd 1985-; Exch Club 1990-92.

EVANS, JOAN PAULINE, Third Grade Teacher; *b:* Charleroi, PA; *c:* Robert G., Timothy G., Eric G., Susan M., Kathleen M.; *ed:* Mercyhurst Coll (BS) Elem Ed 1960; Edinboro Univ, Duquesne Univ Addl Grad Credits Credits; *cr:* Pittsburgh Pub Schls 1st Grd Tchr 1960-61; Elizabeth-Forward Schls 2nd Grd Tchr 1961-62; LaPlata Schls Kndgtn & 6th Grd Tchr 1962-63; Our Lady of Peace Schl Kndgtn Tchr 1985-86; Blessed Sacrament Schl 3rd Grd Tchr 1986-; *ai:* Rdng, Religion, Soc Stud Curr Comms; Yrbk; NCEA 1986-; Mercyhurst Coll Alumni Bd, Mem, Past Sec, Alumni Awd 1991; Golden Apple Awd 1995; Grants Erie Comm Fnd; *office:* Blessed Sacrament Schl 2510 Greengarden Rd Erie PA 16502

EVANS, JULIE SMITH, Chemistry & Physics Teacher; *b:* Portsmouth, OH; *m:* Brad D.; *c:* Taylor Renee; *ed:* Morehead St Univ (BS) Biological & General Sci 1989; *cr:* Piketon HS Chem, Physics Tchr 1991-; *ai:* JETS, Envrionmental Team & FCS Adv; NEA 1991-; *office:* Piketon HS West St Piketon OH 45661

EVANS, KATHRYN FARRELL, Fifth Grade Teacher; *b:* Long Island, NY; *m:* Alfred Thomas; *c:* Matthew, Julianne, Katie; *ed:* Marywood Coll (BA) Elem, Spec Ed 1976; 24 Post-Grad Credits Instrucational II Cert PA; *cr:* St Stanislaus Schl Second Grd Tchr 1979-80; St Rose Schl Jr HS Tchr 1987-93, Fifth Grd Tchr 1993-; *ai:* St Rose Action Plan Mid Sts Accredtitation Chprsn; St Rose Lib Acquisition Comm; 4-H Club Adv; NCEA 1987-; Lakcawanna Cty 4-H 1989-, Bd of Dirs 1991-92; PA for Human Life 1986-; *home:* 69 N Church St Carbondale PA 18407

EVANS, L'TANYA C., Eng Tchr & Coll Counseling Dir; *b:* Tachiakawa AFB, Japan; *ed:* Chatham Coll (BA) Eng, Comm 1984; Bucknell Univ Eng, Ed Grad Work; *cr:* Bucknell Univ Admission Assoc Dir 1984-90; The Wellington Schl Coll Counseling Dir, Eng Tchr 1990-; *ai:* Career Explorers Club Adv; Spirit Boosters; Black His Club; Theater Tech Dir; NACAC 1984-; PACAC 1984-, Human Relations Chair; OACAC 1990-; NCTE; OCTELA; YWCA 1992-, Vol; *office:* The Wellington Schl 3650 Reed Rd Columbus OH 43220*

EVANS, LYNNAE RICHTER, History Department Chair; *b:* Oakland, CA; *m:* David Andreoff Evans; *c:* Brynn, Erinn; *ed:* Univ of CA at Berkeley (BA) His 1967; Stanford Univ (MA) East Asia Stud 1970, (MA) His 1971; Attnd Hamburg Univ Germany; *cr:* Japan Soc of San Francisco Exec Dir 1974-80; Winchester Thurston Schl His Tchr & Dept Chair 1984-; *ai:* World Affairs Club, Teen Expressions & Class Adv; Grant to Stud Soc His at Carnegie Mellon Univ.

EVANS, MARGARET A., Chemistry Teacher; *b:* Troy, NY; *m:* Michael Matthysse; *c:* Evan Matthysse, Lynn Matthysse; *ed:* Niagara Univ (BS) Bio Ed 1970; Cornell Univ (MNS) Nutrition 1974; Chem II, Organic Chem, Vitamins & Minerals Courses; *cr:* Crozer-Chester Meml Hosp Nutritionist 1976-80; Penn St Coll Nutrition Tchr 1981-89; La Roche Coll Nutrition Tchr 1989-93; Carlow Coll Nutrition Tchr 1989-93; Oakland Cath HS Chem Tchr 1993-; *ai:* MAPS Moderator; Amer Dietetic Assn, PDA 1974-; NCEA 1993-; *office:* Oakland Catholic HS 144 N Craig St Pittsburgh PA 15213

EVANS, MARY K., Med & Biological Thematic Tchr; *b:* Cincinnati, OH; *ed:* Notre Dame of OH (BS) Biological Sci 1965; John Carroll Univ (MA) Sci Ed 1975; Attnd CWRU, CSU, UWM, JCU, URI, Baldwin-Wallace Coll; *cr:* Glenville HS Bio Tchr 1965-81; JFK HS Bio Tchr 1981-84; John Hay HS Bio Tchr Med Thematic Prgm 1984-; *ai:* Sci Fair; Sci Olympiad; Edison Biotechnology Symposium; AFT 1976-; Sci Ed Cncl of OH 1978-, Treas, Fin Svc Awd Chprsn, Mbrshp Chprsn; NSTA; Cleveland Regnl Assn of Biologists 1967-, Treas, Newsletter Comm; Articles & Sci Puzzles Pub; Writing Med, Biological Theratic Prgm Cleveland Clinic Fnd; CCF Mini Grant; *office:* John Hay HS 2075 Stokes Blvd Cleveland OH 44106

EVANS, NATALIE ANN, English Teacher; *b:* Washington, DC; *m:* David W.; *c:* Ian, Christian; *ed:* Hood Coll (BA) Eng 1985, (MA) Rdng 1989; *cr:* Linganore HS Eng, Jrnlsm Tchr 1985-; *ai:* Jrnlsm, Newspaper Advs; PTA Sec 1994-; *office:* Linganore HS 12013 Old Annapolis Rd Frederick MD 21701*

EVANS, NED JOHN, 6th Grade Teacher; *b:* Wilkes-Barre, PA; *m:* Rose Ann Moosic; *c:* John, Kyle, Caitlin; *ed:* Wilks Univ (BA) Elem Ed 1977; Scranton Univ (MS) Elem Admin 1982, Scndry Admin 1992; *cr:* Wilkes-Barre Area Schl Dist 6th Grd Head Tchr 1993-; *ai:* Safety Patrols Supvr; WBEA 1978-.

EVANS, PATRICIA ANN FURGAL, Soc Stud Dept Chair & Tchr; *b:* Miami, FL; *ed:* Onondaga Comm Coll (AAS) Data Processing 1983; LeMoyne Coll (BA) His, Scndry Ed 1989, (MS) Scndry Ed 1996; *cr:* Mutual of NY Sec to Dir of SQC 1973-79; Dey Brothers Prsnl Mgr 1980-81; Skaneateles HS Amer His, Govt Tchr 1989-91; West Genesee HS 10th, 12th Grd Soc Stud Tchr 1991-; *ai:* Advy to Model United Nations Club; Jr Class Co-Adv; Sr Class Adv 1992-94; Ski Club Chaperone; HS Curr Cncl; CNYCSS 1989-, Bd of Dirs; AFT 1991-; Grants: West Genesee Enrichment Fnd, Holocuast Museum Snow Fnd, Participated in Seminar at Williamsburg VA; *office:* West Genesee HS 5201 W Genesee St Camillus NY 13031*

EVANS, PETER M., Fine & Applied Arts Teacher; *b:* Montgomery, AL; *m:* Debra Maloney; *c:* Jackson, Ross, Erin; *ed:* Univ of VT (BS) Ed 1977, (MED) Ed 1987; Rochester Inst of Tech Fine Arts; Norwich Univ Ed; *cr:* Northfield HS Industrial Arts Tchr 1977-87, Fine & Applied Arts Tchr 1992-; Roxbury Village Schl Prin & Tchr 1987-91; Northfield Elem 4th Grd Tchr 1991-92; *ai:* Stu Cncl; Sr Class Adv; NEASC Chair; Yrbk; NEA 1978-; Phi Delta Kappa 1987-; United Church 1988-, Deacon; VT Clay Studio 1995-, Bd Mem; Advy Cncl VOTC 1995-; VT Industrial Arts Tchr of the Yr; Schl Shop Magazine; Natl Industrial Arts Curr Validation; *home:* RR 1 Box 1710 Northfield VT 05663

EVANS, RICHARD MARK, High School English Teacher; *b:* Lawrence, MA; *m:* Carol Hoag; *c:* Justin; *ed:* Merrimack Coll (BA) Eng 1966; Lesley Coll (MS) Ed 1996; Attnd Boston Coll, Harvard Univ; *cr:* Cushing Acad Eng & Span Tchr 1966-68; Andover HS Eng Tch

EVANS, ROBIN STEVENS, Spanish Teacher; *b:* Meshoppe, Mark Evans; *c:* Mark Jr, Tyler; *ed:* East Stroudsburg Univ (BS) 1978; Middlebury Coll (MA) Span 1987; Johnson St Coll Ec Valencia Spain Span; Wilkes Univ Ed 6 Addl Credits; *cr:* Willia HS Span Tchr 1979-81; Fed Govt Interpreter for Cuban Refug Montrose HS Long Term Substitute Span Tchr 1982-83; Wyo Courthouse Interpreter; Tunkhannock HS Span Tchr 1983-; *ai:* Border Mexico Trip Club; Aerobics Instr; TAEA, NEA 1983-; PS *office:* Tunkhannock H S 200 Franklin St Tunkhannock PA 186

EVANS, ROGER J., Mathematics Teacher; *b:* Scranton, PA; *n* J.; *c:* Cynthia Boaman, Sandra Lyon, Carla Kaznitz, Sharon Faus Stroudsburg St Univ Math 1960; Tulane Univ Math 1973; Rut Yeshiva Univ; New Paltz St Univ NY; *cr:* Oakcrest HS at May NJ 1960-61; Statsburg Schl Dist in NY 1961-62; F. D. Roose Hyde Park, NY 1962-68; Wyomissing Area HS in PA 1968-; *ai:* F (Weights) Coach; Contract Neg; NEA 1960-; PSEA 1968-; WA Pres; *office:* Wyomissing Area Jr Sr HS 630 Evans Ave Wyom 19610

EVANS, ROGER L., Guidance Counselor; *b:* Waterbury, CT; *m:* *c:* Lindsay, Ashleigh; *ed:* Muhlenberg Coll (BA) Soc Sci 197 Hartford (MS) Counseling 1976; Southern CT St Univ 6th Yr Supervision 1988; Certified Coord for Personal Dynamics Inst; Street Schl 5th Grd Tchr 1972-73; Shelter Rock Schl 5th 1973-77; Mill Ridge Int Schl Cnslr 1977-86; Rogers Park MS C *ai:* Mountain Biking Club Adv; Peer Mediation, Multicultural R & Anti-Harassment Prgm Co-adv; Adv-Advisee Prgm NEA-Danbury 1972-; Pomperaug Valley Jaycees 1978-, Pres Dept of Justice Cert of Achvmt for Multicultural Roundtable Prg Rogers Park MS 21 Memorial Dr Danbury CT 06810*

EVANS, SHARON MERTZ, Spanish Teacher; *b:* Pottstown, PA A.; *ed:* Lock Haven Univ (BS) Ed, Span 1983; Penn St Univ (1985; *cr:* Penn St Univ at State College Tchng Asst 1983-85; Pe at Altoona Span Instr 1985-86; The Calverton Schl Span Tchr Northern HS Span Tchr 1989-; *ai:* New & Beginning Tchrs Sup MD St Tchrs Assn 1989-; *office:* Northern HS 2950 Chane Owings MD 20736

EVANS, SHEILA JEAN, High School Counselor; *b:* Warsaw, N Polcyn; *c:* Jordan Polcyn-Evans; *ed:* Brockport St Coll (MSE) 1990, (CAS) Cnslng 1992; *cr:* United Cerebral Palsy Assn T Recreation Specialist 1985-87; Rochester Rehabilitation Ctr T Recreation Specialist 1987-90; Greece Arcadia HS Chslr Amnesty Intnl, Human Diversity Club Advs; Care Team Drug Coord; NEA 1990-; MCSCA 1991-, Steering Comm; Neighborhood Coalition 1994-; Natl Coalition Bldg Inst 199 Greece Arcadia HS 120 Island Cottage Rd Rochester NY 14612

EVANS, SUE ANN, Twelfth Grade English Teacher; *b:* OH; S.; *c:* Jill C. Henson, Kathleen S. Pitts; *ed:* OH Wesleyan Univ 1971; Coll of Mount St Joseph (MA) Ed 1988; Admin, Appplications Seven Habits of Highly Effective People Ashla Hrs; *cr:* Seventh Grd Eng Tchr 1971-79; Tenth Grd Eng Tch Eleventh Grd Eng Tchr 1992-93; Twelfth Grd Eng Tchr 1993- Arts Comm; Sr Class Adv; Poetry Pub; *office:* Marion Hardin Presidential Dr Marion OH 43302

EVANS, TIMOTHY E., Sociology Professor; *b:* Pittsburgh, PA; A.; *ed:* Pt Park Coll (BA) Psych 1980; St Vincent Coll (MA) 1986; Unv of Pgh (MA) Sociology 1988, (PHD) Sociolo Interdepartmental Grad Cert Latin American Stud; *cr:* St Vi Lecturer, Instr 1985-86; Univ of Pgh Lecturer 1987; St Vincent Assist Prof 1988-92; Commun Coll Alleg Co Assist, Assoc Prof Club Adv; 2 Comms; AFT 1992-; Guatemalan Scholars Netwo Tinker Grant; Book Pub Understanding Chemical Dependenc Comm Coll Algny Co Algny Cmps 808 Ridge Ave Pittsburgh PA

EVANS, VAUGHN DALE,SR., Reading & Lang Arts Teacher; DE; *m:* Zara Johnson; *c:* Vaughn Jr., Renita; *ed:* Bowie St Univ Ed 1982, (MS) Admin & Supervision 1992; 3 Addl Credits in Part 1 & 2; 3 Addl Credits Tchng Stdnts Spec Needs; *cr:* Rawls 1st Grd Tchr 1982-83; Southern Mid Hils Lab Tchr 1983-84; C 6th-8th Grd Rdng & Lang Arts Tchr 1984-; *ai:* Boys Head Bsk Coach; Sports Club & Stu Month Spon; Black His Co Improvement Team; STARS Coord; NEA & MD St Tchrs As Calvert Ed Assn 1983-, PAC Chm & Schl Rep; Victoria Lodge 1987-, Sr Deacon; Schl Bd Comm; Big Brothers & Big Sist NAACP 1984-; MD St Democratic Cntrl Comm 1990-; Calvert Black Men Inc; Bowie St Univ Natl Alumni Assn, Pres, Fndtn Today Idea Exchange; 1st Black Democratic Elected Ofcl in C Tchr of Yr 3 Consecutive Yrs; Outstanding Mem; *office:* C Armory Rd Prince Frederick MD 20678*

EVANS, WAYNE CURTIS, 5th Grade Teacher; *b:* Burlingtor Betty; *c:* Wayne Jr.; *ed:* Trinity Coll (MS) Early Childhood 19 Pub Schl Math Tchr; Montgomery Cty Schl 5th Grd Tchr 1996; Stu Cncl; NEA 1974-; Mason 1969-; *office:* Lucy V Barnsley 14516 Nadine Dr Rockville MD 20853

EVANSON, CLIFFORD GEORGE, Air Force Junior ROTC Cleveland, OH; *m:* Diana Delavaux; *c:* Lia K.; *cr:* USAF Airc Supvr 1959-85; Plainfield HS AFJROTS Instr 1985-87, Kaiserl AFJROTC Instr 1987-; *ai:* AFJROTC Drill Team; Little Le OEA, NEA 1987-; Amer Legion 1985-, JROTC Chprsn, Bronse, Medal; Outstdng AFJROTC Instr 1994-95; *office:* Kaiserslautern HS Unit 3240 Box 440 APO AE 09094

EVARTS, RHODES H., 4th Grade Teacher; *b:* Brockport Charlotte; *c:* Michael, Daryl, Holly; *ed:* Columbia I Univ (BA Elmira Coll (MS) Ed 1973; St Univ of Brockport Schl Dist Adm 1985; *cr:* Taylor Instuements Utility Person 1960-62; US Army A Svc 1963-65; Savona Cntrl Schl Tchr 1968-92; Campbell-Sav Schl Tchr 1992-; *ai:* Elem Sci Fair Dir 1971-; 4th Grds Chprsn 1 1974-; Campbell-Savona Assn 1992-, VP; *home:* 5395 Bauter NY 14809

EVEGAN, ELIZABETH PEPE, Retired First Grade Te Plainfield, NJ; *m:* Harold L.; *c:* Harold, Judith Ranno, Robert Thomas; *ed:* Newark St Tchrs Coll (BS) Elem Ed 1951; *cr:* Em Fourth Grd Tchr 1951-56; Sacred Heart Schl Title I Tchr 1971-7 Riley Schl Title I Tchr 1973-79, Kndgtn Tchr 1979-81, Third 1981-83, First Grd Tchr 1983-95; *ai:* NEA, NJEA, Local Assns

EVEREST WOJTKOWSKI, ANNE, Professor of Engine Pittsfield, MA; *m:* Thomas C.; *c:* Thomas C. Jr., Marcella W Bradway; *ed:* Boston Univ (BSAE) Aeronautical Engrng 1956; Tech 1960-61; Union Coll Grad Schl 1979-87; Wentworth Ins 1987; *cr:* Arthur D. Little Inc Applied Thermodynamicist Berkshire Comm Coll Prof of Engrng 1969087; City of Pittsfie 1988-92; Berkshire Comm Coll Prof of Engrng 1992-; *ai:* Engr Comm Founder, Fac Adv; Everest Awd for Acad Excl in Engrng, Contributor, Admin; Bus & Prof Women 1986, Comm Chair; M of Yr; MTA, MCCC 1977-, Local Union Grievance Ofcr, Initiate

Lack of Pay Equity all MA Comm Colls 1992; Berkshire Cty Bank 1973-, Trustee; Berkshire Cty Historical Soc 1994-, VP, erkshire Med Ctr 1966-, Corporator, Dir, Bldg Comm; Pittsfield ms 1968-76; Pittsfield Schl Bldg Needs Comm 1970-78, Chm; 11 Energy Grants; Author Computer Programming in BASIC Text tudy in Contrasts 1972; Boston Univ Alumni Awd for Distngd Svc stdng Women in Engrng Awd 1988; *office:* Berkshire Comm Coll t St Pittsfield MA 01201

'T, CHERYL GILBERT, Biology Teacher; *b:* West Chester, PA; nce A. III; *c:* Larry, Ashley; *ed:* Millersville St Univ (BS) Bio st chester St Univ (MED) Scndry Ed 1979; 15 Post Grad Credit Ed; *cr:* Phoenixville Area Jr HS Sci Tchr 1974-93; Phoenixville HS Bio Tchr 1993-; *ai:* Acad Competition Team Coach; NSTA, 84-; ABT 1993-; Delta Kappa Gamma 1994-; NSTA, PSTA ons Presenter; *office:* Phoenixville Area Sr HS Gay St & City Line nixville PA 19460

'T, DAVID J., Social Studies Teacher; *b:* Buffalo, NY; *m:* Endres; *c:* Kristen, Gregory, Timothy; *ed:* Univ of Buffalo (BA) 967, (MED) Ed, Soc Stud 1972; Amer Univ at WA Cert Psych, His iv of buffalo at Camisius Coll Cert Guidance & Counseling 1974; my G2 Security & Intelligence Trainer 1967-69; Lake Shore Cntrl & 11th Grd Soc Stud Tchr 1969-70; West Seneca Cntrl Schls Grd Soc Stud Tchr 1970-; Bryant & Stratton Bus Coll Tchr West Seneca Continuing Ed Cnslr 1983-; *ai:* Comprehensive Schl nent Comm 1991-92, Chprsn; West Seneca Comm Ed Cnslr; ction Learning Internship Prgm; NYSUT, AFT, West Seneca TA uilding Rep; Natl Cncl Soc Stud, NY St Cncl Soc Stud 1970-; Ctr, Fire Cty Comm Coll North 1975-, Chm, Bishops Comm for *office:* West Seneca West Sr HS 3330 Seneca St West Seneca NY

'T, MARGARET, Physics Teacher; *b:* Port Chester, NY; *m:* *c:* William, Eileen; *ed:* St Univ of NY at Binghamton (BA) uma Cum Laude 1968; CA Inst of Tech (MS) Engineering Sci Westridge Schl Physics, Chem Tchr 1969-70; Mount St Mary sics, Math Tchr 1989-; *ai:* Moderator NHS; Adv Physics Club; ess Corps; Amer Assn of Univ Women 1990-; Natl Defense Ed w 1968-69 at CA Inst of Tech; Councilwoman Borough of N 1979-87; Somerset Cty Lib Comm 1978-88; NJ St Noise Control 3-89; Somerset Cty Bd of Soc Services 1986-89; *office:* Mount y Acad 1645 US Rt 22 W Watchung NJ 07060

'T, MINNIE BOBBITT, Special Education Tchr & Coord; *b:* o, KY; *c:* Yolanda Barnes, Sondra Williams; *ed:* KY St Coll (BS) Eng 1963; Knoxville Coll Eng, Soc Sci; Univ of Cincinnati Sp pec Ed 1965, 30 Plus Hrs Spec Ed 1972; *cr:* Lincoln Heights HS nlsm Tchr 1963-64; Cincinnati Pub Schls Sub Tchr 1964-65; ech HS Spec Ed Tchr 1965-72; Withrow HS Tchr & tchr Coord Work Stud; OASWSC 1979-, Coord of Yr; CEC 1975-; Tchrs 3-; OEA; Delta Sigma Theata 1988-, Schlsp Chair; Natl Cancer RP Bd; Teac; OASWSC Regnl, St; Comm Cncl; Work Stud Chprsn.*

T, PATRICIA ANNE, 7th Grade Language Arts Tchr; *b:* on, DC; *ed:* Frostburg St Univ (BA) Elem Ed 1973; 38 Addl Credit ters Equivalency & Advanced Prof Cert MD Ed; *cr:* Burlington l 2nd Grd Tchr 1973-76; Ridgely Primary MS 4th, 7th & 8th Grd s Tchr 1976-80; E Russell Hicks MS 6th-8th Grd Title I Rdng Tchr 1980-81; Boonsboro MS 6th-8th Grd Lang Arts Tchr Smithsburg MS 6th-8th Grd Lang Arts Tchr 1982-; *ai:* Schl nent Team Mem; Morning Announcements Adv; Math Tchr 991-1992; Various Comms; Olympics of the Mind Judge 1994 & scipline Comm Mem; Professional Vol at Poplar Forest; NEA STA & WCTA 1980-, Rep 2 Yrs; WVTA & MCTA 1973-80; NCTE TA Burlington Elem Schl 1973-76, Treas 1 Yr; PTA Ridgely MS 1976-80; Natl Trust for Historic Preservation 1990-; gical Soc of Maryland, Inc 1993-; Smithsburg Middle PTA 1993-; xcl in Ed 1993; *office:* Smithsburg M S 68 N Main St Smithsburg 3*

TS, RUSSELL L., Sixth Grd Mathematics Teacher; *b:* urg, PA; *m:* Jane Fox; *c:* Douglas, Adnrew; *ed:* Shippensburg) Sci, Math 1962; Attnd Shippensburg St Coll, Penn St Univ; *cr:* Schl Dist Scndry Math Tchr 1962-71; Fox Buick Owner, Mgr Greencastle Antrim MS Sixth Grd Math Tchr 1989-; *ai:* Soccer, eld Coach; Class Adv; PAL, Long Range Planning Comms; le Ed Assn 1962-, Treas; NEA, PA St Ed Assn 1962-; Church 55-, Pres; Mercersburg Sportsmen Assn 1970-, Fin Sec; le Sportsmen Assn; Old Home Week Assn 1995-, VP; *office:* le Antrim MS 370 S Ridge Ave Greencastle PA 17225

ART, AARON GREGORY, PE Tchr, Coach & Ath Dir; *b:* NY; *m:* Lisa Hoover; *ed:* Bapt Bible Coll (BS) Bible & PE 1993; Tiers Bapt HS Bible & PE Tchr, Coach 1993-94; Heritage Acad Coach, Ath Dir 1994-; *ai:* Ath Dir; Var Soccer, Jr High Bsktbl, Coach; ACSI 1993-; *office:* Heritage Acad 12215 Walnut Pt W wn MD 21740

ART, JOHN MARK, Fine Arts Teacher; *b:* Philadelphia, PA; *m:* Miller; *c:* Rebecca, Christina, Jeffrey; *ed:* Millersville Univ (BS) 977; Attnd Weidner Univ; West Chester Univ Grad, Cert Credits Lancaster Cty Dists Sub Tchr 2 Yrs; East Bradford Elem Schl s; Penn Wood Elem Schl Tchr 4 Yrs; LEEP, PROBE Gifted Prgms 13 Yrs; *ai:* Enrichment Prgm Tchr; Curr Cncl; NEA; PSEA; 994-; PA Coalition for Arts; BSA, Merit Badge Cnslr; Great Vly Church, Session, Chancel Choir, Coventry Singers 1980-; *office:* ster Area Schl Dist 829 Paoli Pike West Chester PA 19380*

GE, NANCY MULROONEY, 5th Grade Special Educator; *b:* , MA; *m:* Jack; *ed:* RI Coll (BS) Spcl Ed 1981; Fitchburg St (MS) 1992; *cr:* Crystal Springs Schl Spcl Edctr 1981-84; Joseph H rd 5 Spcl Edctr 1984-; *ai:* Taunton Ed Assn 1984-, Bldg Rep, hair; NEA; Cncl Exceptional Children 1988-; Amer Fitness Assn 1994-, Cert Instr; *office:* Joseph Martin Schl 131 Caswell St nton MA 02718

T, MARY ELLEN KRAUS, Kindergarten Teacher; *b:* Trenton, omas F. (dec); *ed:* Trenton St Coll (BA) Kndgt-Primary Ed 1969; Children; Ctrs the Whole Spectrum UNCG; Whole Langs SUNY, *cr:* Lore Elem Schl 4 Grd Tchr 1972-74; Fisk Elem Schl K Tchr Antheil Elem Schl K Tchr 1979-; *ai:* 1st Yr Tchr Mentor; Stu Prgm, 2 Sr Stu Tchrs from England; Previewed Workbook from ishers; Co-operating Tchr for Sr Stdnts TSC, Rider Univ; NEA, CEA 1972-; ETEA 1972-, Pres 1979; Assn of Kdgn Edctrs 1992-; Realtors 1985-; *office:* William Antheil Elem Schl 339 Ewingville on NJ 08638*

GLORIA POCHEKAILO, Elementary Guidance Counselor; *b:* PA; *m:* Brian Keith; *c:* Benjamin; *ed:* Lebanon Vly Coll (BS) 1985; Bucknell Univ (MSEd) Elem Cnslng 1991; *cr:* Schuylkill ea Schl Dist MS Music Tchr 1985-91, Elem Guid Cnslr 1991-; *ai:* hl Store, Superstudents Job Prgm Adv, Created, Initiated; e Helper Big Brother, Big Sister Prgm Co-Adv, Created, Initiated; EA 1985-; Divine Redeemer Church Choir, Anthracite Citizen's 994-; Dalpiaz Schl of Dance 1994-, Dance Instr; Time Warner Cable Excl in Ed Grant Elem Career Prgm; Presenter Mid-Atlantic Networking for Career Dev; *office:* Schuylkill Haven Area Elem Ctr 120 Haven St Schuylkill Haven PA 17972*

EVITTS, ERIC ALLEN, High School Mathematics Tchr; *b:* Pottsville, PA; *ed:* Kutztown Univ (BS) Scndry Ed 1994; *cr:* Liberty HS Math Tchr 1995; Freedom HS Math Tchr 1995-; *ai:* Var Bsbl Asst Coach; PSEA 1994-, Mem; NCTM, NEA 1995-, Mem.*

EWAN, CHRISTINA ANNE, HS Spanish Teacher & Coach; *b:* Plant City, FL; *ed:* John Brown Univ (BA) PE & Hlth 1992; Univ of Southern MS (MS) Tchng Frgn Lang 1996; Wilson NC K-12 Span Cert; *cr:* NC Pub Schls K-5th Span Tchr 1992-93; Stony Brook HS Span, Dorm Mom & Coach 1993-; *ai:* Span Trip & Outdoor Ed Club; Bible Stud; Track, Soccer & Bstkbl Coach; Leading Guitar Music; Tchr of Yr 1993 Nom; *office:* The Stony Brook Schl Chapman Pkwy Stony Brook NY 11790*

EWART, FRANCES LEVENSTEIN, Fourth Grade Teacher; *m:* Shad; *c:* Max; *ed:* Univ of MD Coll Park (BS) Elem Ed 1986; 20 Credit Hrs Ed Trinity Coll; 10 Credit Hrs Ed George WA Univ; *cr:* Thomas Elem Schl 4th Grd Tchr 1987-; *ai:* WTU, AFT 1990-; EDS Tech, Eisenhower St Grants; *home:* 408 Kentucky Ave SE Washington DC 20003

EWART, PATRICIA ANN (CONNOLLY), Spanish Teacher; *b:* Jersey City, NJ; *m:* Richard Thomas; *c:* Adam, Jared; *ed:* Univ of Valencia Spain, Glassboro St Coll NJ (BA) Span, Scndry Ed 1975; 37 Post Grad Credit Hrs Summer Inst at Southern Regnl; *cr:* Martin J. Gauger MS Span Tchr 1976-77; Southern Regnl MS Span Tchr 1978-83, 1990-; *ai:* Span Club; Frgn Lang Club; Restructuring Cncl Co-Chprsn; NEA, NJEA 1978-; FLENJ 1995-; MSA 1994-; BSA cub Scouts 1987-92, Den Ldr, Awds Chprsn; Improving Tchng, Learning Environment of Schl; *office:* Southern Regional HS 75 Cedar Bridge Rd Manahawkin NJ 08050*

EWART, SUSAN B., Science Teacher; *b:* Rouses Point, NY; *ed:* Springfield Coll (BS) PE & Hlth Ed 1982; CCSU (MS) Admin & Supervision 1991; Western New England Schl of Law 32 Grad Credit Hrs; *cr:* Alburg Elem Schl Sci, Hlth & PE Tchr 1982-84; Torrington MS Sci Tchr 1984-; *ai:* Torrington HS Var Girls Soccer & Sftbl Coach; NEA 1982-; CEA 1984-; TEA 1984-; *office:* Torrington MS 100 Middle School Dr Torrington CT 06790

EWELL, JAMES FLOYD,JR., 7th Grade Social Studies Tchr; *b:* Norfolk, VA; *m:* Sheila Moher; *c:* Jessica, Journey; *ed:* Sam Houston St Univ (BS) His 1968; Rivier Coll (MA) Soc Sci 1974; Univ of NH (MA) Cnslng, Ed; Addl 30 Hrs; Military Police Ofcrs Basic, Advanced Course; Command, Gen Staff Coll; Counter Terrorism Schl, Installation Provost Marshal Course; *cr:* Hillside Jr HS World His Tchr 1970-82; Memorial HS Civics, European His Tchr 1982-83; Southside Jr HS World, Amer His Tchr 1983-84; Hillside Jr HS China, Far East Tchr 1984-; *ai:* Schl Newspaper; NEA, Manchester Ed Assn, NH Ed Assn 1970-; St Hedwig Men's Soc 1985-; US Army Reserves: Awds Achvmnt Desert Shield Stud, Soldier Survivability Battlefield, Commendation Logistics Work Field Exercise Stud; USAF Achvmnt Letter Joint Military Exercises; Army Commendation Letter Far East Assessment Stud; *office:* Hillside Jr HS 112 Reservoir Ave Manchester NH 03104*

EWING, BETTE SHELTON, School Counselor; *b:* Union, SC; *m:* Frederick; *c:* Kristen Spuck, Dawn Mosher, Gregory; *ed:* Roger Williams Hosp (RN) Nrsng 1963; Russell Sage Coll (BS) Hlth Ed 1986; SUNY at Oswego (MS) Cnslng 1990; *cr:* Middleburgh Cntrl Elem Schl RN 1980-86; Jordan-Elbridge Jr-Sr HS Family Life Educ Prgm Coord, Hlth Edctr 1986-90; Schenectady HS Schl Cnslr 1990-; *ai:* Shared Decision-Making Team; Fac Mod Cncl Facilitator; Bldg Dir; Comprehensive Dev Guid Comm; NY Cnslng Assn 1991-; Capital Dist Couns Assn 1991-, Senator; SFT, AFT 1986-, Bldg Dir; Phi Kappa Phi 1986-; Natl Coalition Bldg Inst 1995-; Tchr Ctr Grant 1988; Golden Apple Awd 1995; *office:* Schenectady HS 1401 The Plaza Schenectady NY 12308

EWING, DIANE BRAZAWSKIS, Math Teacher & Dept Head; *b:* Hartford, CT; *m:* James A.; *c:* Wade, Heather, Wendy; *ed:* Fitchburg St Coll (BSEd) Math, Ed 1964; Diversified 45 Credits Beyond BS; Attnd Holy Cross, WPI, Worcestor St & Fitchburg St; *cr:* Narragansett Regnl HS Math Tchr 31 Yrs; *ai:* Future Tchr Club Adv 7 Yrs; Math Honor Soc Adv 3 yrs; High Schl Yrbk Adv 15 Yrs; Exam Comm Chm 6 Yrs; Mu Alpha Theta 2 Yrs; NEA, MTA 1964-; NDEA 1964- Sec 5 Yrs, Pres 2 Yrs; NCTM; ATMIM; Girl Scouts of Amer 5 Yrs, Asst Troop Ldr 2 Yrs; BSA Den Ldr 3 yrs; Math Cncl for Tchrs; Recipient of 2 Natl Sci Fnd Grants in Sci & Math at Holy Cross Coll & WPI; *office:* Narragansett Regional H S S Main St Baldwinville MA 01436

EWING, JANICE KRYSKI, Child Development Professor; *b:* Trail BC, Canada; *m:* Clayton Randolph Shedd; *ed:* Univ of Bristish Columbia (BA) Soc 1973; WA St Univ (MA) Speech Pathology 1977; Univ of SC (PHD) Elem Ed, Early Chldhd 1990; *cr:* Kern Co Supt of Schls Speech Pathologist 1978-87; Univ of SC Instr 1987-90; Univ of AL Asst Prof 1991-95; Colby-Sawyer Coll Asst Prof 1995-; *ai:* Advy Bd NH Preservice Ed Review Project; NAEYC 1986-; ACEI 1990-; ASHA 1977-; Fac Exchange; Articles Pub; *office:* Colby-Sawyer Coll 100 Main St New London NH 03257*

EWING, ROBERT E.,JR., Social Studies Chairman; *b:* Johnstown, PA; *m:* Sharon A.; *c:* Robert, Jessica; *ed:* Univ of Pittsburgh (BA) Soc Sci & Ed 1975; St Francis (MA) Industrial Relations 1983; *cr:* N Star HS Tchr & Soc Stud Chm 1979-; *ai:* Faculty & Stu Advisory Comm; Lead & Mentor Tchr; NEA & PSEA 1979-; SW PA Lead Tchr Consortium; *home:* PO Box 117 Jerome PA 15937*

EWING, SHARON WILT, Secondary Math Teacher; *b:* Johnstown, PA; *m:* Robert E. Jr.; *c:* Robert, Jessica; *ed:* Univ of Pittsburgh at Johnstown (BS) Scndry Math Ed 1975; IN Univ of PA (BS) Elem Ed 1983; *cr:* Richland Sch Dist Math Tchr 1975-; *ai:* NEA & PSEA 1975-; *home:* PO Box 117 Jerome PA 15937

EWINGS TRAVIS, WILLIE MAE, Science Teacher; *b:* Evergreen, AL; *c:* Camille, Ingrid; *ed:* Wilberforce Univ (BS) Bio 1964; John Carroll Univ 30 Hrs Supervision, Admin; *cr:* Glenville HS Bio Tchr 1964-67; Nathan Hale Schl Bio, Phy, Gen Sci Tchr, Sci Chprsn 1970-92; James Ford Rhodes HS Bio Tchr 1993-; *ai:* Grant Writing, Residential Provision Comms; Tutor; Cleveland Tchrs Union 1964-, Past Bldg Co-Chair; AFT; Alpha Kappa Alpha 1962-, Housing Chair; Aldersgate UM Church, Ministries Cncl Chair; United Meth Women, Past Pres, Outstdng Svc; Plaques & Certs for Excl in Tchng, Outstdng Svc, Outstdng Contributions, Perfect Attendance Awd from Prins, Supvr, Tchrs, Parents, Stdnts, Martha Holden Jennings Fnd; Phy Sci Tchr of Yr 1992; Sci Ed Presenter; Authored Booklet, Pamphlets; *office:* James Ford Rhodes HS 5100 Biddulph Rd Cleveland OH 44144*

EXLINE, LOIS A., HS Art Teacher; *b:* Marysville, OH; *ed:* OH St Univ (BA) Art Ed 1986; 35 Grad Hrs Family, Marriage Cnslng Univ of Akron; *cr:* Maple Heights HS Art Tchr 1987-89; Barberton HS Art Tchr 1989-92; Woodridge HS Art Tchr 1992-; *ai:* OH Art Ed Assn 1987-; *office:* Woodridge HS 4440 Quick Rd Peninsula OH 44264

EXUM, MARCIA MOTEN, Biology Teacher; *b:* Washington, DC; *m:* Waddell; *c:* Carolyn D., Sherrill E.; *ed:* Howard Univ (BS) Bio 1969; Cath Univ (MA) Scndry Ed 1970; Post Grad Stud Trinity Coll; *cr:* Roosevelt HS Bio Tchr 1969-70; Dunbar HS Bio Tchr 1970-; *ai:* Amenities Chm; Sci Exchange Prgm Spon; NSTA; NABT; DC Sci Edctrs Assoc; Zeta Phi Beta; WA Post Mini Grant; Supt Vol Svc Awd; DCPS Bio Curr Writer; DC Rdng Cncl Lit Awd; *office:* Dunbar HS 1301 New Jersey Ave NW Washington DC 20001

EYCKE, DIANA E. (BUSH), Title I Reading & Math Tchr; *b:* Columbus, OH; *m:* Phillip Patrick; *c:* Danielle Eycke Dixon, Kristi Renee; *ed:* OH Univ (BS) K-8 Elem 1969; Mount St Joseph (MA) K-12 Rdng 1985; Ashland Univ 31 Hrs; *cr:* Richmond Dale Elem First Grd 4 Yrs; Londonderry Elem First Grade Tchr 7 Yrs; Richmond Dale Elem Kndgtn, Title I, Rdng, Math 8 Yrs; *ai:* OEA, NEA, RCEA 1969-; Phi Delta Kappa 1980-, Sec 2 Yrs; 4-H 1976-89, Adv; *home:* 364 US Highway 35 Ray OH 45672

EYINK, NANCY J. MANGER, Math Teacher; *b:* Lima, OH; *m:* Gerald B.; *c:* Monty R., Lucinda C., Kelli L.; *ed:* OH Northern Univ (BA) Math Ed 1972; Wright St Univ (MA) Classroom Tchr 1991; Elem Cert 1983; *cr:* Third Grd Tchr 1969-70; Botkins HS Math Tchr 1972-73; Botkins 2nd Grd Tchr 1982-84, 4th Grd Tchr 1984-93; Botkins jr High HS Math Tchr 1993-; *ai:* Math Schlsp & Prof Math Adv All Grds; Mentor 1994-; *home:* 502 W State St Botkins OH 45306*

EYLER, SUZY RITA, Theology Teacher & Dept Coord; *b:* New Orleans, LA; *ed:* Univ of Dayton (MA) Theology 1985; *cr:* Epiphany of Our Lord Schl 2nd Grd Tchr 1972-73; St Timothy Schl 1st Grd Tchr 1973-78; St Peter Celestine Schl 1st Grd Tchr 1978-87; Bishop Eustace Prep 9th-12th Grd Tchr 1988-; *ai:* Amnesty Intnl Chapter Fac Adv; Pax Christi 1988-; Amnesty Intnl 1989-; NCEA 1988-; *office:* Bishop Eustace Prep Schl 5552 Rt 70 E Pennsauken NJ 08109

EYNON, WILLIAM L., Health & Physical Ed Teacher; *b:* Scranton, PA; *m:* Anne Linda Egan; *c:* Jennifer, Michael, Elizabeth; *ed:* East Stroudsburg So Coll (BS) Hlth, PE 1970; 26 Hrs Penn St Univ, Marywood Coll, East Stroudsburg Univ; *cr:* Abington Hghts SD Tchr, Coach 26 Yrs; *ai:* Frosh Class Adv; Coached Ftbl 20 Yrs; NEA; PSEA; *office:* Abington Hghts Schl Dist Grove St Clarks Summit PA 18411

EYRE, HOWARD L., Landscape Contracting Prof; *b:* Doylestown, PA; *m:* Joan Kathleen Hutchinson; *c:* David F., Michael B.; *ed:* Penn St Univ (ASF) Forest Technician 1967; Stephen F. Austin St Univ (BSF) Forestry 1970, (MSF) Forestry 1973; *cr:* Simpson Landscape Ctr Garden Ctr Sales 1973-77; R. A. Nursery Mgr 1977-85; H.L.E. Landscaping Owner 1985-90; *ai:* Stu Govt Bd Adv; Landscape Nursery Club Adv; Var Coll Comms; PA Landscape Nursery Assn 1991-, PA Accredited Nurseryman; *office:* Delaware Valley Coll 700 E Butler Ave Doylestown PA 18901

EZDINLI, SUZAN, Italian & Latin Teacher; *b:* New York, NY; *ed:* Univ of WI at Madison (BA) Italian Stud, Anthropology 1981; Post Qualifying Doctoral Candidate Italian Stud (PHD) Rutgers Univ 1997; *cr:* Rutgers Univ Italian Lecturer 1982-86; Princeton Univ Italian Lecturer 1986-93; Linwood MS Italian, Latin Tchr 1993-; North Brunswick Twp HS Italian, Latin Tchr 1993-; *ai:* NBTHS Natl Jr Classical League, NJ Jr Classical League Spon; Class of 99 Adv; Diversity Training Comm Co-Chair; NEA, NJEA 1993-; NJ Classical Assn, Amer Classical league 1995-; Fulbright-Hays Flwshp Rsrch Bosphorchs Univ; Rutgers Univ Rsrch Schlsp; *office:* Linwood MS NBTHS Raider Rd North Brunswick NJ 08902

EZEKA, HYACINTH A., Assistant Prof of Accounting; *b:* Oawu-Ikele Via, Nigeria; *m:* Rose Nwobi; *c:* Chinelo, Christine, Geraldine, Uchenna; *ed:* AL A&M Univ (BS) Accounting 1985, (MBA) Accounting 1987; *cr:* South Eastern Accountancy Financial Analyst 1987-88; Edward Waters Coll Asst Prof Accounting & Acting Chair 1988-89; Coppin St Coll Asst Prof Accounting 1989-; *ai:* Accounting Club & Stdnts in Free Enterprise Fac Adv; Amer Inst of CPAs 1989-; MD Assn of CPAs 1989-; Amer Accounting Assn 1996-; Natl Assn of Black Accountants 1995-; African Chrstn Fellowship 1990-, VP; Outstanding Educator Awd 1990; Comm Svc Awd 1989; Certified Pub Accountant in FL & MD.*

EZMAN, JEAN MARIE, Kindergarten Teacher; *b:* Carbondale, PA; *ed:* Marywood Coll (BS) Bus Ed 1969, (MS) Elem Ed 1975; 7 Inservice Credits NEIU-19; 12 Post Grad Credits; *cr:* PA St Oral Schl Elem Tchr for Children with Mulitple Handicaps 1969-70; Various Schls Sub Tchr 1970-72; Carbondale Area Schl Dist Elem Tchr 1972-; *ai:* PSEA, NEA 1972-; Marywood Coll Alumnae Assn 1969-; *office:* Carbondale Schl Dist Rt 6 Brooklyn St Carbondale PA 18407*

EZZO, MICHELLE ERACLIO, Hlth Chprsn & PE Teacher; *b:* Queens, NY; *m:* Joseph; *c:* Matthew, David; *ed:* York Coll (BA) PE 1974; Adelphi Univ (MS) Hlth Ed 1977; *cr:* Rhodes Schl Swimming Tchr 1974-75; Mary Louis Acad PE & Hlth Tchr 1975-90, Chprsn 1990-; *ai:* NCEA 1975-; AAHPERD, NYSAHPERD, NYSFPHE 1990-; PTA 1988-; Stu Cncl Fac Awd; *office:* The Mary Louis Acad 176-21 Wexford Terr Jamaica NY 11432

F

FABIAN, CAROL FLORY, First Grade Teacher; *b:* Defiance, OH; *m:* Jonathan W.; *c:* Natalie J.; *ed:* Manchester Coll (BS) Elem Ed 1972; St Francis Coll (MS) Ed 1986; Attnd Bowling Green St Univ & Coll of Mt St Joseph; *cr:* Hicksville Schls Tchr 1972-; *ai:* Staff Dev Prgms; Arts Unlimited; Defiance Cty Lang Arts Comm; Early Chldhd Ed Occupations Prgm; Hicksville Ed Assn 1972-, Sec; OEA & NEA 1974-; Delta Kappa Gamma Soc Intnl 1987-.

FABIAN, GERRY, English Teacher; *b:* Doylestown, PA; *m:* Jane Mras; *c:* Jesse, Jennifer; *ed:* Mansfield Univ (BA) Eng 1971; Trenton St Coll (MA) Eng; Addl 20 Credits Beyond Masters East Stroudsburg, 10 Credits Wilkes; *cr:* Central Bucks HS West Eng Tchr 1972-; *ai:* PIAA Sftbl Ofcl; Lit Magazine Adv; NEA, PSEA 1972-; CBEA 1972-, Rep; ICFY 1973-, Grand Master; Pub Poetry; *office:* Central Bucks-West HS 375 W Court St Doylestown PA 18901*

FABIAN, LORRAINE L. (LIGHTHALL), Second Grade Teacher; *b:* Orange, CA; *m:* George W.; *c:* George Wesley S., Miles Russell L.; *ed:* CA St Univ at Fullerton (BA) Eng 1970; 5th Yr Tchng Credential; Post Grad Courses Bowling Green St Univ Gifted Ed, Elem Ed; *cr:* Graytown Elem Schl First Grd Tchr 1972-75; Rocky Ridge Elem Schl First Grd Tchr 1975-76; Graytown Elem Schl Second Grd Tchr 1976-; *ai:* Head Tchr; Young Author Adv 1980-95; Olympics of Mind Coach 1986-91; NEA 1976-; OEA 1972-; NWOEA 1972-, Svc Awd; OHEA 1972-, Pres, VP, Sec; IRA 1986-; OCIRA 1978-, Svc Awd; Vacationland Cncl IRA 1978-, Pres, VP, Sec; Tchng Ideas Pub; Martha Holden Jennings Scholar; *office:* Graytown Elem Schl 1661 N Walker St Graytown OH 43432

FABIANO, MARIA STILLITANO, English & Journalism Teacher; *b:* Elizabeth, NJ; *m:* Felix; *c:* Giovanna, Gianpaolo, Felice, Enza Maria; *ed:*

Rutgers Univ (BA) Eng, Ed 1976; 12 Credit Hrs; *cr:* Edison Voc, Tech HS Eng Tchr 1976-77; Lafayette MS Eng Tchr 1977-82; Battin Gifted, Talented MS Eng Tchr 1982-84; Elizabeth HS Eng, Jrnlsm Tchr 1985-; *ai:* Newspaper Adv; Alternate Route for Tchrs Prgm Mentor; NEA, EEA 1976-; NJ Press Women Assn; Columbia Press Assn; Museum of Natural His 1995-; Liberty Sci Ctr 1993-; *office:* Elizabeth HS 600 Pearl St Elizabeth NJ 07202

FABICH, PENELOPE SWINGLE, Latin & World History Teacher; *b:* Medina, OH; *m:* Ronald W.; *c:* Nathaniel, Emmaline, Abigail; *ed:* Univ of Akron (BA) His, Latin 1975; (MA) Mltcltrl Ed; Attnd Kent St Univ 1971-72; Post Grad Eng Cert Univ of Akron; *cr:* Polaris Voc Center Soc Stud Tchr 1982-83; Our Lady of Elms HS Soc Stud Tchr 1983-84; Brunswick HS His, Latin Tchr 1977-81, 1985-; *ai:* Latin Club Adv; Curr, Soc Stud, Foreign Lan Comms; Amer Classical League 1977-; *office:* Brunswick H S 3581 Center Rd Brunswick OH 44212

FABICH, RONALD WILLIAM, Earth Sci & Field Stud Tchr; *b:* Cleveland, OH; *m:* Penelope Swingle; *c:* Nathaniel, Emmaline, Abigail; *ed:* Kent St Univ (BS) Geology 1971; Akron Univ (MS) Earth Sci Ed 1992; Cleveland St Univ Scndry Cert 1972; 30 Hrs Past Masters in Ed; *cr:* Bay Village HS 9th Grd Earth Sci Tchr 1972-73; Brunswick HS 9th-11th Grd Earth Sci & Field Stud Tchr 1973-; *ai:* Geology Soc Adv 1974-; Field Stud Coord 1986-; NAGT 1970-; NESTA, OESTA 1985-; Saint Martins Church, Altar Server 1994-; Martha Holden Jennings Grant 1985; Nom OH Tchr of Yr 1977; OH Outstanding Earth Sci Tchr 1982; *office:* Brunswick HS 3581 Center Rd Brunswick OH 44212

FABIETTI, LOUISE CAPUTO, High School Mathematics Tchr; *b:* Brooklyn, NY; *m:* Richard Anthony; *c:* Anthony, Jonathan; *ed:* St Joseph's Coll (BA) Math, Scndry Ed 1981; Brooklyn Coll (MA) Math, Scndry Ed 1985; *cr:* Bishop Kearney HS Math Tchr 1981-; *ai:* Bowling Club Moderator; NCTM 1981-.

FABISZAK, ROSE E. MONACO, Spanish Teacher; *b:* Caracas, Venezuela; *m:* Richard A.; *c:* Jacqueline, Victoria; *ed:* SUNY Empire St (BS) Inter-educl Stud 1990; Working Toward MED at Fordham; *cr:* Donaldson Lufkin Jenrette Reg Stock Trader 1978-81; Hamershlag Kempner & Co VP Stock Underwriter-New Issues 1981-85; St Thomas Aquinos Elem Schl 6-8 Grd Math, Rdng Tchr 1985-90; St Saviour HS Span Lang Tchr 1990-; *ai:* Teen Rap Facilitator Cnslng Teen Group; Coll Level Exam Prgm Admin; Natl Assn of Cath Tchr 1985-; Caribean Comm Chamber, 1994 Civic Yth Ldrshp; Bklyn Boro Pres Office, 1994 Civic Comm Ldrshp; Young Amer Pres Pres 1992-95; Media Arts Yth Fd Pres 1992-95; *office:* St Saviour HS 588 6th St Brooklyn NY 11215

FABRICATORE, ANNMARIE, English Teacher; *b:* Mineola, NY; *ed:* C W Post Coll (BA) Eng 1984, (MA) Eng 1986; *cr:* C W Post Coll Instr 1984-86; Saint Anthonys HS Eng Tchr 1986-; Polytechnic Univ Instr 1990-91; *ai:* Theatre Co Dir, Producer, Choreographer; Girls Var Lacrosse Moderator; ACIS Cnslr; C W Post Coll Grad Fellowship; *office:* St Anthony's HS 275 Wolf Hill Rd South Huntington NY 11747

FABRICIUS, DANIEL, Director of Bands; *b:* Allentown, PA; *m:* Thesha M. Crocker; *ed:* Mansfield Univ (BS) Music Ed 1979; Ithaca Coll (MM) Music Ed 1983; *cr:* Port Byron HS Band Dir 1979-81; Chenango Vly HS Band Dir 1981-86; Haverling HS Band Dir 1986-88; Owego Free Acad Band Dir 1988-; *ai:* Marching, Concert & Jazz Bands; Percussive Arts Soc 1975-; NYS Schl Music Assoc 1979-; NYS Band Dirs Assoc 1985-, Past Pres; Natl Band Assoc 1988-; Intnl Assoc of Jazz Ed 1988-; 2 NY Southern Tier Tech Ed Grants; Binghamton Univ Adj Instr of Percussion & Conductor of Percussion Ensemble; *office:* Owego Free Acad George St Owego NY 13827

FABRIS, LEO, Retired Teacher; *b:* Rochester, NY; *m:* Audrey; *c:* Deborah Fabris-Coon, David; *ed:* St John Fisher (BS) His 1958; Univ Rochester (MS) Soc Stud Curr 1967; *cr:* Manchester-Shortsville Cntrl Schl Soc Stud Tchr 1958-91; *ai:* US Coast Guard Auxiliary Pub Ed Ofcr; NYSVT 1958-, Del; NYSUT Ret Tchrs Assn; Excl in Ed Awd 1991; Awd of Gratitude; Amer Legion Awd for Coaching Speaking Contests; *home:* 8 W High St Shortsville NY 14548*

FABRIZIO, BEATRICE GRACE, Sixth Grade Teacher; *b:* Vineland, NJ; *ed:* Trevecca Nazarene Coll (BS) Elem Ed 1973; *cr:* Main Road Schl 4th Grd Tchr 1973-78; South Hall Jr HS 8th Grd Sci Tchr 1979; Main Road Schl 5th Grd Tchr 1979-88, 6th Grd Tchr 1988-; *ai:* EWT Comm; NEA, TFEA, GCEA & NJEA 1973-; *office:* Main Road Elem Schl Main Rd Newfield NJ 08344

FABRIZIO, PATRICIA A., 8th Grade Humanities Teacher; *b:* Glen Cove, NY; *m:* Dominick; *c:* Laura S. Cubbs, Nancy A. Arvan; *ed:* GA Court Coll (BA) Eng, Ed 1981; St Lawrence Univ (MA) Ed 1986; *cr:* St Mary Acad Tchr, Coach 1980-85, Coord Gifted & Talented 1983-85; Indian River MS Tchr 1986-; *ai:* Bldg Compact Team; Prins Advy Comm; Bd of Dir of NY St MS Dir Region X; NYSRA, ASCD, NYSMSA; Curr Dev; Tech Grant; *office:* Indian River MS Plank Rd Philadelphia NY 13673*

FACAROS, SOPHIA CALABOYIAS, Health, PE Tchr & Dept Chprsn; *b:* Johnstown, PA; *m:* John; *c:* Theologos, Zacharia, Dimitri, Sideris; *ed:* Slippery Rock Univ (BS) Hlth, PE 1974; Univ of Pittsburgh (MEd) Hlth, PE 1977; Real Estate License; Biling in Greek; *cr:* Comm Coll of Allegheny Cty Adult Ed Tchr 1974-75; Reizenstein MS Hlth, PE Tchr Ldr, Dept Head 1975-; *ai:* Swimming Club Spon; Teen Pregnancy, Core Team Coord; Girls Vlybl Coach; AFT 1975-; Greek Orthodox Church 1974-, Sunday Schl Supvr; Mother of Yr 1995; 1995 Thanks to Tchrs Outstdng Prgms Awd Univ of Pittsburgh, KDKA-TV Partnership; *office:* Reizenstein MS 129 Denniston Ave Pittsburgh PA 15206

FACTOR, ELLEN LESTER, Choral Director; *b:* Brooklyn, NY; *m:* Harvey A.; *ed:* St Univ Coll at Potsdam (BS) Music Ed 1969, (MS) Music Ed 1970; *cr:* Arrowhead Schl K-6th Grd Vocal & General Music Tchr 1970-72; St Univ Coll at Potsdam Campus Learning Ctr Pre-K-8th Grd & Coll Stu Vocal & General Music Tchr 1973-81; Davis Schl 1st-6th Grd Vocal & General Music Tchr 1984-89; Franklin Acad 6th-12th Grd Choral & General Music Tchr 1989-; *ai:* Co-Advisor Allegro Club; Swinging Sounds Dir; MENC 1969-; NYSSMA 1969-; NYSUT, AFT 1969-; ACDA 1989-; Served as Turnkey Trainer NY St Music Curr for Music in Our Lives; BOCES District-Franklin, Essex & Clinton Ctys; *office:* Franklin Acad State St Malone NY 12953*

FADALE, CARL, Sixth Grade Teacher; *b:* Elmira, NY; *m:* Mary Ann Colasurdo; *c:* Gabe; *ed:* SUNY at Cortland (BS) Ed 1971, (MS) Ed 1975; 20 Addl Hrs; *cr:* Virgil Elem Schl 4-6 Grd Tchr 1971-75; F. S. Barry Schl 4-6 Grd Sci Tchr 1975-76; Pomeroy Elem Schl 5th Grd Tchr 1978-79; Smith Elem Schl 4th Grd Tchr 1979-80; F. S. Barry Elem Schl 4th, 6th Grd Tchr 1981-; *ai:* 6th, 7th Grd Articulation Comm; NYSUT, CUT 1971-; St Anthonys Church 1971-, Parish Cncl; NSF Grant 1988; *office:* Franklyn S Barry Elem Schl 20 Raymond Ave Cortland NY 13045

FADLEY, DAVID ALLEN, Fifth Grade Teacher; *b:* Bucyrus, OH; *m:* Virginia M. Gottfried; *c:* Brent, Todd, Melissa; *ed:* OH Northern Univ (BS) Elem Ed 1967; Post-Grad Hrs from Bowling Green St Univ; *cr:* Upper Sandusky Schls 5th Grd & Head Tchr 1967-88, 5th Grd Tchr 1989-; *ai:* Coach 8 to 11 Yr Old Girls Sftbl; NEA, OEA 1967-; Upper Sandusky Ed Assn 1967-, Treas; United Meth Church 1945-, Dist Bd; Gideons Intnl 1994-, VP- Local; *home:* 15512 TH 44 Wharton OH 43359

FADULE, ALIDA ESCALONA, Spanish & Italian Teacher; *b:* Havana, Cuba; *m:* Joseph G. Jr.; *c:* Aubrey, Joseph III; *ed:* Rowan Univ (BA) Span 1989; 30 Credit Hrs Italian Lang & Lit West Chester Univ PA; *cr:* Cherokee HS Frgn Lang Tchr 1989-; *ai:* Span Club, Italian Club, Italian Hnr Soc, Asst Chrldr Adv; NEA 1989-; *office:* Cherokee HS Willow Bend Rd Marlton NJ 08053

FAGAN, GENEVIEVE TAYLOR, 2nd Grd Tchr & Tech Instrl Ldr; *b:* Middletown, NY; *m:* James Cleary; *c:* Kathleen Fagan Ronning, Michael, John, Thomas, Daniel; *ed:* St Univ of NY at Plattsburgh (BSED) Early Chldhd 1953; Univ of Bridgeport (MS) Rdng 1980; Prof Diploma Advanced Stud Tech 1984; IBM Trainer & Educl Consultant; Univ of Chicago Schl Math Project Tchr Trainer; St of CT Tchr Mentor & Cooperating Tchr; *cr:* White Plains Pub Schls Kndgtn Tchr 1953-59; Comstock Pub Schl K-2 Grd Tchr 1978-79; Miller Pub Schl 2nd Grd Tchr 1979-80, 1st Grd Tchr 1980-90, 2nd Grd Tchr 1990-; *ai:* Rdng, Report Card, Math Text Selection, Prin Search Comms; Tchr Recruitment, Comm Planning, Tech Advy Teams; Tri St Standards Consortium Evaluator; Mentor Tchr; Tech Instructional Ldr; NEA, CEA, CT ED Assn 1978-; Wilton Ed Assn 1978-, Pres 1995-, VP, Tchr Rights, Responsibilities Chair; ASCD 1993-; Grants Awded Wilton Pub Schls, Wilton Ed Fnd; Tchr of Yr 1986; *office:* Tilford W. Miller Schl 217 Wolfpit Rd Wilton CT 06897

FAGAN, LISA KEIM, 11th & 12th Grade Science Tchr; *b:* Lebanon, PA; *m:* Brian P.; *c:* Jason, Justin; *ed:* Cumberland Cty Coll (A) Math & Sci 1980; Lebanon Valley Coll (BS) Chem 1982; Rowan Coll Phys Sci Tchrs Cert 1992; *cr:* Buena Regnl HS Sci Tchr 1993-94; Vineland HS Sci Tchr 1994-; *office:* Vineland HS South 2880 E Chestnut Ave Vineland NJ 08360

FAGAN, MARGARET M., Eighth Grade Teacher; *b:* Delaware Cty, PA; *ed:* Immaculata Coll (BA) Ed 1985; Masters Moral Theology St Charles Seminary; *cr:* Annumciation BVM 7th & 8th Grd Tchr 1977-81; St Laurence 7th Grd Tchr 1984-87; Sacred Heart 8th Grd Tchr 1987-91; St Agnes 8th Grd Tchr 1991-; *ai:* Stu Cncl, Yrbk Moderator; NEA 1984-; Mid St Assn 1989-; *office:* St Agnes Schl 205 W Gay St West Chester PA 19380*

FAGAN, TRUDY BROWN, Family & Consumer Science Tchr; *b:* Saxton, PA; *m:* Wayne M.; *c:* Tara, Chelsea, Lauren; *ed:* Indiana Univ of PA (BS) Home Ec Ed 1978; Pvt Nursery Schl Cert 1978; Post Grad Credits Millersville Univ, Penn St Univ; *cr:* Chestnut Ridge Schl Dist Scndry Home Ec Tchr 1978-80; Saxton Day Care Ctr Head Tchr 1980-81; Huntingdon Day Care Ctr Head Tchr 1984-85; Tussey Mountain Schl Dist Family, Consumer Sci Tchr 1989-; *ai:* FHA Adv; HS Liaison Comm; PA St Ed Assn 1989-; *office:* Tussey Mountain Schl Dist Rd 1 Box 178a Saxton PA 16678

FAGNANT, JOSEPH ALBERT, Instrumental Teacher; *b:* Woonsocket, RI; *ed:* Univ of ME (BM) Music Ed 1993; *cr:* Univ of ME Summer Yth Music Instrumental Tchr, Cnslr 1990-; Houlton HS 9-12 Grd Instrumental Tchr 1993-; *ai:* Jazz Band, Jazz Combo Dir; Musical Asst Dir; HS Show Choir Tech Dir; Asst to Jr, Sr HS Choirs; ME Tchrs Assn 1995-; Kappa Kappa Psi; Phi Kappa Phi; Pi Kappa Lambda; Houlton Comm Chorus 1993-, Dir; Mc Gill's Comm Band 1993-; *office:* Houlton HS 5 Bird St Houlton ME 04730

FAGON, ADELE C., Enrichment Teacher; *b:* New York City, NY; *ed:* Marymount Coll (BA) Art & Ed 1960; Coll of New Rochelle (MS) Spec Ed 1981; Natl Acad of Design; Art Stdnts League Schl of Visual Arts; Sonoma St Univ Expressive Therapy Trng; Learning to Read Through the Arts Trng at East Stroudsburg Univ; *cr:* Charles Campagne Schl Second Grd Tchr 1960-61, First Grd Tchr 1962; Schl Five First Grd Tchr 1963-66, 3rd Grd Tchr 1967-86, 2-6 Grd Enrichment Tchr 1987-; *ai:* Organize & Manage CIMS Lending Lib for Tchrs; Yonkers Fed of Tchrs, NYSUT, AFT; Westchester Rdng Cncl 1990-; Art Stdnts League; Pelham Art Ctr 1990-; *home:* 1440 Midland Ave Bronxville NY 10708*

FAHEY, EILEEN KENNEDY, High School English Teacher; *b:* New York City, NY; *ed:* Saint Johns Univ NY (BA) Eng 1964; Addl 30 Hrs at Cntrl Ct Univ; *cr:* Lawrence Jr HS Eng Tchr 3 yrs; Vogel Jr HS Eng Tchr 14 Yrs; Torrington HS Eng Tchr 13 Yrs; *ai:* Leadership & PAC Comm; NEA, CEA 1969-; *office:* Torrington HS Major Besse Dr Torrington CT 06790

FAHEY, MARIA FRANZISKER, Instr of Eng & Anthropology; *b:* New York, NY; *ed:* Columbia Univ (BA) Anthropology 1985, (MA) Eng 1995; *cr:* Dir of Stud; *ai:* Klingerstein Fellow 1992-93: NEH Fellow 1991, 1995; Cncl for Basic Ed Flwshp 1994; *office:* Friends Seminary Schl 222 E 16th St New York NY 10003

FAHEY, ROSEMARY, Kindergarten Teacher; *b:* Staten Island, NY; *m:* John; *c:* Kristin, Susan; *ed:* St John's Univ (BS) Elem Ed 1970; Coll of SI (MS) Early Chldhd 1975; 30 Credit Hrs at Brookdale Coll 1988-94; *cr:* PS 18 R Tchr Cluster 1970-71; PS 40 R Tchr 1971-74; PS 36 R Tchr 1974-84; PS 50 R Tchr 1984-; *ai:* Former Corresponding Sec of SI Chptr of the Early Chldhd Assn; UFT 1973-; AFT 1973-.

FAHNCKE, RONALD EUGENE, Junior High Language Arts Tchr; *b:* Celina, OH; *m:* Therese Marie Limbert; *c:* Adam Michael, Seth Andrew; *ed:* OH Northern Univ (BA) Music Ed 1975; Wright St Univ (BS) Elem Ed 1982; Production Materials Whole Lang; Course Work Cath Catechist Cert; *cr:* Wapakoneta City Schls Instrumental Musci Tchr 1977-82; St Joseph Elem Schl 4th Grd Self-Contained Class Tchr 1982-91, Jr HS 5th-8th Grd Lang Arts Tchr 1991-; *ai:* Coord Schl, Dist Spelling Bees, Speech Writing Contest, 6th Grd 1995 News Prgm; Coach, Tchr Judge Writing Tournament; Evaluator Competency Based Writing Assessment Prgm; PTO 1995-, VP, Svc; St Joseph's Schl Bd Ed 1984-, Tchr, Rep; *home:* 1206 Indian Hill Dr Wapakoneta OH 45895

FAHNESTOCK, CHARLES R., Mathematics Professor; *b:* Hershey, PA; *m:* Dianne K.; *ed:* Hershey Jr Coll (AA) Engr 1969; Elizabethtown Coll (BS) Math, Physics 1966; Shippensburg Univ (MED) Cnslng 1969; UT St Psych 1963-64; *cr:* HACC Adm Asst to VP Educl Svc 1973-75, Voc Ed Coord 1975-78, Asst to Dean, Acad Affairs 1978-79, Math Prof, Cnslng 1979-; *ai:* Fac Prsnl Policies Comm; Peer Review Mentor; Math Anxiety Coach; Amer Cnslng Assn, PA St Math Assn 1969-; Humanistic Ed Assn 1990-; PA Assn of Dev Ed 1980-; Network of Bus Opportunity Entrepeneurs 1988-; Brethren Vol Svc 1963-, Spokesman Project Navajo Indian; Cert of Appreciation 25 Yrs of Svc HACC; Natl Certfd Cnslr; Sabbatical For Rsrch on Math Anxiety 1988; Designed Course Bldg Self Confidence in Math; *office:* Harrisburg Area Comm Coll 1 HACC Dr Harrisburg PA 17110

FAHRENBACH, MELINDA WOOD, Third Grade Teacher; *b:* MA; *m:* Paul Thomas; *c:* Nathan; *ed:* Lock Haven Univ (BS) Elem Ed 1973; Masters Equiv; *cr:* Sonestown Elem Schl 1st Grd Tchr 1973-74; Sullivan Cty Elem Schl 3rd Grd Tchr 1974-75, 1st Grd Tchr 1975-77, Chptr I Math Tchr 1977-78, 3rd Grd Tchr 1978-81, 1st Grd Tchr 1981-82, 3rd Grd Tchr 1982-; *ai:* Staff Dev Comm 1986-87; PSEA, NEA 1973-; East Lycoming Soccer Assn 1993-, Sec; *office:* Sullivan Co Elem Schl Beech St Laporte PA 18626

FAHRER, FRANKLIN JAMES, 7th-12th Vocal Music Instr; *b:* New Rockford, ND; *m:* Karen Sue Harrold; *c:* Nicole Marie, Amanda Louise; *ed:* North Eastern Univ at Chicago (BA) Music Ed 1971; North Western Univ at Evanston (MA) Music Ed 1973; *ai:* OEA, SEA, MENC 1973-; Lions 1982-, Lion Tamer; *office:* Sidney HS 1215 Campbell Rd Sidney OH 45365*

FAHRER, LINDA M., Social Studies & Spanish Tchr; *b:* Flushing, NY; *m:* Donald B.; *c:* Dina Ditrano, Alissa, Donald Jr.; *ed:* St Johns Univ (BA) Fr & Ed 1969; Queens Coll; *cr:* Our Lady of the Blessed Sacrament Tchr 1985-; *ai:* Schl Newspaper Moderator; AAA Safety Patrol Adv; Soc Stud Coord; Mid Sts Steering Comm; NCEA 1985-; LICSS 1995-; *of* Lady-Blessed Sacrament Sch 3445 202nd St Bayside NY 11361

FAHRINGER, JAMES NOLAN, 4th Grade Teacher; *b:* York, York Jr Coll (AS) Elem Ed 1967; Millersville Univ (BS) Elem Grad Work Penn St at York; *cr:* North Hills Elem Schl 6th 1969-70, 4th Grd Tchr 1989-; Pleasureville Elem Schl 4th 1971-81; Hayshire Elem Schl 4th Grd Tchr 1982-88; *ai:* Elem Comm & Assn of Retarded Citizens Bike Hike Chms; Envirotho NEA 1969-; Faith & Prayer Mission 1977-; Grant for Shortwave Ctr; Grant for Shortwave Pgm Production; *office:* North Hills El 1330 N Hills Rd York PA 17402

FAHS, BERIT MARGARETA, Adjunct Professor of Psych; *b:* Finland; *m:* Gerald Richard; *c:* Pio M., Chad G.; *ed:* Nrsng Inst (R 1954; Lancaster Bible Coll (BS) Bible 1983; Millersville Univ Cnslr Ed 1985; 12 Credit Hrs Doctoral Stud Temple Univ; *cr:* Hosp I Nrsng & Head Nurse 1959-72; Lancaster Bible Coll Adj Pr *ai:* ACA; ASCA; AACC; Westminster Presbyn Church, Deacone & Soloist; *office:* Lancaster Bible Coll 901 Eden Rd Lancaster P

FAHY, MARIETTA R., Lang Arts & Literature Tchr; *b:* Trentor William F. Jr.; *c:* Theresa Cooper, William R., Susan Gabori Trenton St Coll (BS) K-8th Grd Elem Ed 1980; *cr:* Melvin Kreps 1977-80; Winthrop Schl Resource Aide 1980-82; St John The Ba 7th-8th Grd Sci & Math Tchr 1982-86; St Pius V Jr HS 7th-8th Arts Tchr 1987-; *ai:* Dama Club Adv & Dir; Ski Trip Coord; NCE Awd; St Mary Star of Sea 1980-, CCD Tchr, Eucharistic Minister; Cove Civic Assn; Former BSA & Camp Fire Girls Ldr; Intro Implemented Acad Olympics, Vivid Lang Writing Wkshp Introduced to Debating; Dir Childrens TV Pgm on Local TV *office:* St Pius V Schl 28 Bowler St Lynn MA 01904*

FAIG, CAROL MAYBRIAR, Third Grade Teacher; *b:* Cincinnati John A.; *c:* Dan, Holli, Julie; *ed:* Univ of Cincinnati (BA) Elem Xavier Univ (MS) Rdng 1991; Post-Grad Hrs From Wright St Univ OH; *cr:* Colerain Elem Schl 4th Grd Tchr 1978-79; Hous Schl 1st & 3rd Grd Tchr 1979-92; Bevis Elem Schl 3rd Grd Tc *office:* Bevis Elem Schl 10133 Pottinger Rd Cincinnati OH 4525

FAIGLEY, JOSEPH R., Social Studies Dept Chairman; *b:* Can *m:* Mary E. Simpson; *ed:* Walsh Univ (BA) His 1972, (MA) Ashland Univ Supt Cert 1991; *cr:* St Thomas Aquinas HS Soc S 1974-; Walsh Univ Adj Lecturer His 1992-; *ai:* Mrktg, Comm Dir; Phi Delta Kappa 1991-; ASCD, NCHE 1990-; NCSS 1992- 1996; WHBC Stark Cty Tchr of Week 1992; *office:* Saint Thomas HS 2121 Reno Dr NE Louisville OH 44641

FAIIA, MARJORIE MARCOUX, Assoc Professor of Soci Manchester, NH; *m:* James; *c:* Anthony, James; *ed:* Boston Col Psych Soc Work 1974; Northeastern Univ (PHD) Sociology, Ant *cr:* Rivier Coll Assoc Prof Sociology 16 Yrs; *ai:* Comms; Class A Soc Assn; Eastern Soc Soc; NAWCNP; AUW; NASW; *office:* Ri 420 S Main St Nashua NH 03060

FAIMAN, BONNIE MARGOLIN, Language Arts Teacher; *b:* KS; *ed:* Boston Univ (BS) Ed 1967; Masters Plus 30 Hrs; *cr:* Framingham Lang Arts Tchr 1976-; *ai:* Former Odyssey of Min Mentor Prgm Adv; Safe Schls Comm MS Liaison; NEA 1976-; Su Comm 1996-; Free-Lance Writer Pub Prof Articles; Framingham to Integrate a Major Boston Newspaper with MS Lang Arts Cur Several Curricula for Gifted & Talented Prgm; *office:* Walsh MS 3 St Framingham MA 01701

FAIR, DOROTHY R., Title I Coord & Ed Consultant; *b:* Cambri *m:* Robert C.; *ed:* Cntrl Ct St Coll (BS) Ed 1970; Lesley Coll (M Chldhd 1978; Admin Stud Wheelock Coll; *cr:* Wakefield Pub S 1970-86; NH Dept Ed Ed Consultant 1986-; *office:* NH Dept o Pleasant St Concord NH 03301*

FAIR, TIMOTHY ALLEN, Industrial Tech Instructor; *b:* Wooste Amy Steingraber; *c:* Christopher, Staci; *ed:* Kent St Univ (BS) I Tech Ed 1974; 27 Post Grad Hrs at Ashland Univ; *cr:* Map Industrial Tech Instr 2 Yrs; Hillsdale MS Industrial Tech Instr 20 Stu Cncl Adv; OH Ed Assn, NEA 1974-, Pres, VP, Tchr of Yr A Elks 1979-; 1978 Ed Grant in Photography; *home:* 879 N Elyria Rd OH 44691

FAIRALL, MARY LOU NICHOLS, Retired Tchr of GATE; *b:* C OH; *w:* Robert (dec); *c:* Melissa Bailey, Melinda; *ed:* OH St Univ 1957, (MS) Family Relations, Human Dev 1979; Attnd Bank S NYC, Lindenwood Coll at St Charles; *cr:* Swing Set Child Co-Owner, Co-Dir 1972-76; Licking Heights Schl Kndgtn Tchr Southwest Licking Schls Kndgtn Tchr 1974-82, Tchr of Gifted *ai:* NEA, OEA 1974-, Life Mem; SLEA 1974-, Life Mem, Pres CEC; OAGC; NAGC; Mortor Bd 1956-; Southwest Licking Com & Sewer Dist 1992-, Treas, Sec, Trustee; West Licking Pub Com Author; United Way 1993-, Allocations Comm; Church Organis Par Excl Schl 1995-, Vol Music Tchr; Bicentennial Book Writin Phi Kappa Phi 1979-; *home:* 4242 York Rd SW Pataskala OH 43

FAIRBAIRN, JANET ALISON, Professor of Art; *b:* Augusta, Univ of ME (AA) Art 1979; ME Coll of Art (BFA) Graphic Desi Yale Univ Schl of Art (MFA) Graphic Design 1991; Attnd Schl Art Advertising 1979-81; Summer Prgm Graphic Design Switzerland 1988; Ctr for Creative Imaging 1993; *cr:* Freelance Designer 1982-; SUNY Art Prof 1992-; *ai:* Women's His Mon Chair; Fac Cncl; Chancellor's Awd for Distngd Svc Prof; Cncl for Concerns; Amer Inst for Graphic Designers 1992-; NYS-UUP Quality Working Life, Inst Implementation Screening Grants; N Term Fac Dev, Scholarly Incentive Awds; *office:* State Univ Coll/Fredonia Art Dept Rockefeller Arts Ctr Fredonia NY 14063

FAIRBANKS, DAVID JOEL, AP Amer History & Ec Teacher; *b:* NY; *m:* Marsha Runge; *c:* Vonda Woodfield, Tamara Marchi Roberts Wesleyan Coll (BA) Soc Stud 1963; St Univ Coll at Buff Ed & Soc Stud 1969; St Bonaventure Univ Schl Admin; *cr:* James Soc Stud Tchr 1963-; *ai:* Jamestown Tchrs Assn 1963-, Legisl C NEA 1963-; Zion Covenant Church 1964-, Church Cncl, Tchr Sun Bd of Ch Ed; NYS Certified Ftbl Assn 1964-, Pres Membershi *home:* 4800 Westman Rd Bemus Point NY 14712

FAIRBANKS, DONNA JEAN, Social Studies Teacher; *b:* Flin Barbara; *ed:* Univ of MI (BA) His, Soc Stud 1963; 66 Post Grad Santa Clara Cty Soc Worker 1965-67; Waltham Cntrl Jr HS Tchr Waltham HS Tchr 1978-; *ai:* NEA, MTA 1968-; Waltham Edc 1968-, Rep Cncl; Trinity Church Boston 1985-, Usher, Flower, Ne Guilds; Eleanor Nelson Curr Dev Awd 1988; NEH Seminar Gra 1990; *office:* Waltham HS 617 Lexington St Waltham MA 02154

FAIRBANKS, STEPHEN, 7th Grade Language Arts Tchr; *b:* Far ME; *m:* Donna D'onofrio; *c:* Alicia, Lorne; *ed:* Southern CT St Elem Ed 1966; Univ of ME at Gorham (MS) Elem Admin 1974; *ai* Team Asst Coach; *office:* Tripp MS Box 1251B Turner ME 0428

FAIRCHILD, ANN DOWE, Third Grade Teacher; *b:* Lewiston, William; *c:* Tip, Samantha; *ed:* Univ of ME at Orono (BS) Elem *cr:* Wales Cntrl Schl 2nd Grd Tchr 1979-86; Henry L Cottrell Sc Tchr 1987-90, 3rd Grd Tchr 1991-; *ai:* Tech Coord; Cumston stee & Sec; Monmouth Comm Players Stage Crew & Costumes; ıry Cottrell Elem Sch 169 Academy Rd Monmouth ME 04259

LD, DANIEL JON, English Teacher; *b:* East Greenbush, NY; *m:* llanan; *c:* Whitney; *ed:* St Univ of NY at Plattsburgh (BA) ı 1985; St Univ of NY at Albany (MA) Eng 1992; Syracuse Univ Toward MA in Philosophy; Siena Coll NYS Cert in Scndry Ed verill Park HS Eng Tchr 1987-; *ai:* NHS Adv; Stu Newspaper; Vlybl Coach; Ski Club; Intramural Bsktbl; NYSUT & APTA eenbush Reformed Church 1978-, Youth Group Dir, Deacon; rill Park HS 16 Gettle Rd Averill Park NY 12018

BARBARA TRADER, Professor of Mathematics; *b:* n, DC; *m:* John Douglas; *c:* Erika; *ed:* East Carolina Univ (BS) ıs 1965; Univ of SC (MS) Math 1967; Kent St Univ (PHD) Math Carnegie Mellon Univ Asst Prof 1974-76; Westminster Coll Asst ›c Prof & Prof 1976-; Westminster Coll VP for Acad Affairs *ai:* Fac Dev Comm; Acad Adv; Math Assn of Amer, Fin Comm, m Chair, Budget Comm Chair, Meritorious Svc Awd 1994; Amer Soc Industrial & Applied Mathematicians; Butler Museum of ish Step Dancers Boosters; Outstdng Fac Nom to CASE by er; Co-Author Book: Calculus; Numerous Articles Pub; NSF Support & Fac Rsrch Funds; *office:* Westminster Coll New n PA 16142

D, DONALD E., Health Teacher; *b:* New York, NY; *c:* David J., ; *ed:* Slippery Rock Univ (BS) PE & Hlth 1970; Adelphi Univ Ed 1974; Hofstra Univ 15 Grad Credits; *cr:* Salk MS 6th & 8th chr 26 Yrs; *ai:* MS Soccer & Track Coach; Git Pgm; AFT 1970-; he Yr 1970-73; Salk MS Tchr of the Yr 1989; *office:* Salk MS lem Rd Levittown NY 11756

, ROBERT C., Sixth Grade Teacher; *b:* Indiana, PA; *m:* Emma sbit; *c:* Bradley, Chad, John; *ed:* Indiana Univ of PA (BS) Elem (MS) Elem Ed 1978; *cr:* US Army Field Artillery Officer N Area Schl Dist 6th Grd Elem Tchr 1971-; *ai:* PSEA, NEA, 72-; Creekside Borough Cncl 1983-, Past VP, Current Pres; U Meth Church 1971-, Trustee & Bd Chair; *office:* Benjamin lem Schl 95 Ben Franklin Rd N Indiana PA 15701

ILLIAM R., Math Teacher; *b:* Pittsfield, MA; *m:* Darlene A. Kerry A., James W.; *ed:* N Adams St Coll (BA) Math 1970, ıl Admin 1975; *cr:* Berlin HS Math Tchr 1970-77, Prin 1977-83, 1983-; *ai:* NEA; NYSUT; *office:* Berlin Jr & Sr HS Berlin Rt NY 12022

RS, HEATHER M., Sequential Math I & II Teacher; *b:* St ON, Caanada; *m:* Robert L. Sears; *c:* Matthew Robert; *ed:* oll (BA) Psych 1971; St Rose Coll (MS) Ed & Rdng 1981; NY Albany for PhD; Grad Courses in Cmptr Sci at Union Coll, RPI, ge & SUNY; *cr:* Schuylerville Central Rdng Specialist 1982-85; ashing BOCES Math & Rdng Coord 1986-87; St Univ Ed Dept 1987-89; Lake George HS Comp Coord & Math Tchr 1987-; *ai:* dv 5 Yrs; 7th Grd Class Adv; Restructuring Comms; Effective CD 1993-; NY Math Tchrs 1990-; Stu Assist Pgrm; 1st Presbyn 60-; Scholars Recognition Recipient 1989; Mem St Ed Dept upational Related Math & Sci Curr; Empire St Stu Cncl Advr of 991; *office:* Lake George HS 425 Canada St Lake George NY

ETHEL SPEIGHT, 5th Grade Teacher; *b:* Snow Hill, NC; *m:* : James III, Franklin V; *ed:* D. C. Tchrs Coll (BS) Elem Ed 1969; at Home Inst-Trinity Coll, Univ of DC, Southeastern Univ; *cr:* Govt Schl Admin Asst 1954-65; DC Pub Schls Tchr 1969-; *ai:* Georg Club Spon; Safety Patrol & Sci Comm; Intern Mentor rs Choral Group 15 Yrs; DC Geog Alliance 1994-; Natl Geog Soc ce: Harriet Tubman Elem Schl 13th Kenyon St NW Washington

LLIAM LANCE, Mathematics Teacher; *b:* Greensburg, PA; *m:* n Mc Gill; *c:* Jacob Ian, Sarah Min; *ed:* Slippery Rock Univ ndry Math 1974; Edinboro Univ (MED) Scndry Guid, Cnslng ion Univ Cmptr Sci Credits; *cr:* Meadville Jr HS Math Tchr IM Tennis; Mid Sts Steering Comm; CCEA 1974-, Bldg Rep; 4-, Region Del; NEA 1974-; Grace United Meth Church 1982-, ission, Trustee Pres, Admin Bd, Endowment Comm, Tchr, Church; Cub Scouts, Webelos Den Ldr; USRSA 10 Yrs; *office:* Jr HS N Main St Meadville PA 16335

TI, JUDITH AUTHIER, World Languages Dept Chair; *b:* MA; *m:* Michael; *c:* Louis, Daniel; *ed:* Univ MA (BA) Span field St (MEd) Scndry Schl Admin 1982; *cr:* Peck MS Span Tchr Magnet MS Span Tchr 1991-92; Holyoke HS Span Tchr, Dept 2-; *ai:* Span Club Adv; MTA, NEA, HTA, MAFLA 1973-; AA; outh Soccer Bd 1992-, Bd; *office:* Holyoke HS 500 Beech St IA 01040

OHN JOSEPH, Sixth Grade Teacher; *b:* New York City, NY; *m:* dwards; *c:* Jakob; *ed:* Alfred St Coll (AAS) Accounting 1965; Coll (BS) Ed 1968; Elmira Coll (MS) Ed 1976; SUNY at Excl in Tchng Prgm; *cr:* Hornell City Schl Dist Tchr 1968-; *ai:* Tennis Var Coach 1972-80; Summer Recreation Dir 1970-88; n Ski Ctr Ski Club 1980-, Stu Govt 1972-; NEA, Hornell Tchrs -; Hornell Red Cross 1992-, Recreation Bd 1985-; Hillside Bapt 85-, Deacon, Sunday Schl Supt; School Staff Dev Mentor; Who's ; *office:* Hornell Intermediate School 21 Park St Maple City Dr Y 14843*

E, ARNOLD M., History Teacher; *b:* Boston, MA; *ed:* Univ of His 1967, (MA) His 1972; *cr:* Dover HS His Tchr 1967-; *ai:* Asst ct; NEA 1967-; Dover ABC Schlsp Comm 1978-; Bentley Coll g Awd 1988; *office:* Dover HS Alumni Dr Dover NH 03820

OSEPH JAMES, Social Studies Teacher; *b:* Passaic, NJ; *ed:* aterson Coll (BA) His 1984; *cr:* Mount Vernon Ave Schl Soc Stud rs; *ai:* His, Poetry Club, Stu Cncl Adv; NJEA 1985-; Bergen Cty Dept 1980-, Vol; Books: Sacred Ground 1992, A Man of My 93, Chasing Sunsets 1994; Senator Bradley's Geography Contest Awd of Excl 1988; *office:* Mt Vernon Ave Schl 36 non Ave Irvington NJ 07111

KAREN MCGAHERAN, Math Teacher; *b:* Red Bank, NJ; *m:* elissa, Venessa, Paul Joseph; *ed:* St Francis Coll (BS) Ed 1978; rs; *cr:* St Catherines Schl 7th-8th Grd Math, Sci Tchr 1978-80; Cath Schl Math Tchr, Stu Cncl Moderaton 1980-; *ai:* Stu Cncl ; Steering Comm for MS Evaluation; NMTA 1980-; NASSP TA; Kiwanis; *office:* Red Bank Catholic H S 10 Peters Pl Red 7734

E, FRANK E., Adj Assoc Prof of Engineering; *b:* Camden, NJ; Altadonna; *c:* Jessica M., Wendy M.; *ed:* Villanova Univ (BE) ng 1970, (MS) Civil Engrng 1973; Devry Inst of Tech Digital s; *cr:* US Naval Reserve Ensign to Capt 1970-; O'Brien & Gere : Prog Engrng, Man Engrng, Mrktg Dir 1973-91; Chzm Hill Inc Dir; Villanova Univ Engrng Fac 1974-; *ai:* Amer Soc of Civil lerator; Fundamentals of Engrng Exam Fac; Tau Beta Pi 1973-; ner Military Engrs 1977-, Bd of Dir, Fellow Selectee; PA Bus Bus Assn, DE Bus Assn 1980-, Envir Comm, Ports & Docks John Neumann Choir 1995-; St Charles Kiddie Summer Fair 1979-, Chm; Meritorious Svc; 2 Navy Commendation Medals; Navy Achvmt Medal; Navy Seabee Battalion, Navy Seabee Regiment Commanding Ofcr; Pub Eng Peace 1993; *office:* Villanova Univ 800 Lancaster Ave Villanova PA 19085*

FALCONE, SUSAN HULL, Family Studies Teacher; *b:* Johnson City, NY; *m:* J. Thomas; *c:* Christina Marie Callahan, Kathryn E.; *ed:* SUNY at Oneonta (BS) Ed & Home Ec 1964; SUNY at Potsdam 18 Credits; Western MD Coll 6 Credtis; Northern MI Univ 12 Credits; Towson St Univ 18 Credits; Loyola Coll 18 Credits; *cr:* Whitney Point Cntrl Schl Tchr 1 Yr; Clifton-Fine Cntrl Schl Tchr 4 Yrs; Loch Raven HS Tchr 23 Yrs, Dept Chair 15 Yrs; *ai:* Future Edctrs of Amer Spon; Assessment Dev Comm Chair Cty Level; Svc Learning Coord; NEA 1978-; ASCD 1994-; Flwshps: MD St Dept of Ed Curr Dev & MD Svc Learning Alliance; Tchng Excl Awd 1986 & 1989; Tchr of the Yr in Family Stud 1987; Book: Spinning A Service-Learning Web 1995; *office:* Loch Raven HS 1212 Cowpens Ave Baltimore MD 21286

FALCONELLO, PATRICIA L., Business Education Teacher; *b:* Trenton, NJ; *m:* Samuel; *c:* Samuel Jr., Robert; *ed:* River Coll (BS) Bus Ed-Cum Laude 1969, (MA) Bus Ed-Summa Cum Laude 1973; 30 Post Grad Hrs Bloomsburg, Villanova & Mercer Co Comm Coll; *cr:* Pennsbury HS Bus Ed Tchr 1969-; Edgewood Schl Keyboarding Tchr, Elem Summer Schl 1972-93; *ai:* Chprsn Guid Svcs, Mid Sts Re-Evaluation Comm; Implemented Bus Stu of Month Awd; Coord Stu Svcs for Main Office & Guid Office; Prof Comm Revision of Attendance Policy; PEA, NEA, PSEA, Bucks Co Bus Ed Assn 1969-; Alpha Chi Chapter of Delta Pi Epsilon 1972-, Rider Coll Key; Our Lady of Sorrows Church 1965-; Bus Tchr of Yr from Cittone Inst 1992; Gift of Time Awd 1992; Most Outstdng & Dedicated Tchr Plaque from Shorthand Class 1993; Cert Temple Univ 1994, Proficiency in Word Processing Mercer Co Comm Coll; Schlsp Rider Coll; Dean's List; *office:* Pennsbury HS 705 Hood Blvd Fairless Hills PA 19030

FALCONER, RAYMOND GEOFFREY, English Teacher & Choral Dir; *b:* Chelsea, MA; *m:* Corinne Cather; *ed:* Hamilton Coll (BA) Eng, Music 1990; Westminster Choir Coll Music; *cr:* The Hun Schl of Princeton Eng Tchr, Choral Dir 1990-; *ai:* MS Boys Bsktbl, Girls Sftbl Coach; Comm Svc Dir; Musical Dir for Winter Musical; Meritorius Svc Awd 1994-95; *home:* 176 Edgerstoune Rd Princeton NJ 08540

FALCONETT, BARBARA JOAN, Librarian; *b:* Melrose, MA; *ed:* Saint Johns Univ (BS) Elem Ed 1965, (MS) Elem Ed & Lib Sci; Advanced Math; Cmptr Sci; *cr:* Pub Schl 45 2nd Grd Tchr 1965-66, EC Librn & Tchr 1966-67, 3rd Grd Tchr 1967-68, 2nd Grd Tchr 1968-95, 1st-5th Grd tchr & lbrn 1995-; *ai:* Schl Based Mgmt; After Schl Ctr-Tchr-In-Charge; UFT 1965-, Chapter Ldr, Unity Caucus Mem 1995-, Trachenburg awd; Staten Island Rdng Assn, IRA 1985-; AFT 1965-; Polish Tchrs Assn 1975-; Democratic Assn 1965-; Grant-Project Oasis for Pub Schl 45; *office:* PS 45 John Tyler 58 Lawrence Ave Staten Island NY 10310

FALDETI, KATHRYN T., Social Studies Dept Chprsn; *b:* Ridley Park, PA; *m:* Joseph J.; *c:* Cameron, Estelle; *ed:* Immaculata Coll (AB) His & Soc Scis 1969; West Chester Univ (MED) Behavior, Soc Scis & Scndry Ed 1976; Attnd Intnl Stud Inst; *cr:* Chester HS Soc Stud Tchr 1969-, Soc Stud Dept Chprsn 1991-; *ai:* Curr Comm; Dev Ec Ed Prgms; Jr Achvmt Ec; Stu Support Team; NCSS, PCSS; NEA, PSEA 1969-; Girl Scouts of Amer 1984-, Vol; NSCSS Grant for Sociology Stud at Univ of PA; Scott Paper Fellowship Awd; *office:* Chester HS 200 W 9th St Chester PA 19013

FALER, KAY D., Kindergarten Teacher; *b:* Hillsdale, MI; *m:* Raymond Eugene; *c:* Dawn Follis, Douglas; *ed:* Bowling Green St Univ (BS) Elem Ed 1969; Univ of Toledo (MS) Early Chldhd 1989; *ai:* Jennings Scholar; *office:* Storrer Elem Schl 320 S Platt St Montpelier OH 43543

FALINI, DOMINICK JOSEPH, HS Social Studies Teacher; *b:* West Chester, PA; *m:* Marguerite C.; *c:* Leslie Dominic; *ed:* Villanova Univ (BS) Soc Stud, Eng Ed 1960; 20 Credits West Chester St, Cheynoy St 1960-68; *cr:* Holy Cross HS Soc Stud, Eng Tchr 1960-61; West Chester Jr HS Spec Ed, Eng Tchr 1961-68; Roman Cath HS Soc Stud, Eng Tchr 1968-83; Archbishop John Carroll HS Soc Stud Tchr 1983-; *ai:* Annual Fund Drive; Schlsp Selection Comm; NCEA 1969-; Assn of Cath Tchr 1971-, Union Del; Planning Comm 1968-, Chm, Mem; Newlin Township 1985-, Bldg Inspector, Zoning Offices; *office:* Archbishop John Carroll HS 211 Matsonford Rd Radnor PA 19087

FALK, MADELINE VARON, Peer Helper Pgm Facilitator; *b:* New York, NY; *m:* David M.; *c:* Jonathan, Alexander; *ed:* City Coll of NY (BA) Sociology & Psych 1964; Smith Coll Schl of Soc Work 1966-67; Columbia Univ Schl of Soc Work 1967; CCNY Grad Course 1995; *cr:* Bird S Coler Hosp Soc Work Asst 1966-68; St Vincents Roster Care Agency Soc Work Asst 1968-69; Dunlap & Manhattan St Hosp Outpatient Division Soc Work Asst 1969-73; HS of Art & Design SPARK Pgm Peer Helper Facilitator 1981-; Coll of Staten Island Prof of Personal Commnctn 1996; *ai:* HIV & AIDS Team; FAD; Amer Cnslng Assn 1993-; NYS Cert Substance Abuse Cnslr 1994-; Amer Ortho Psychiatric Assn 1996; Yorkville Civic Cncl 1996, Child Abuse Ed Network; HIV & AIDS Base Grant 1993, 1995, 1996; HS of Art & Design Citation of Excl 1987; *home:* 792 Columbus Ave New York NY 10025*

FALK, STEPHEN, English Teacher; *b:* Jersey City, NJ; *m:* Marcia Felix; *c:* Christine Falk Dalessio, Stephen C., Kathleen, Thomas; *ed:* Jersey City St Coll (BA) Eng, Scndry Educ 1971; Post Grad Stud Eng Lit, Cmptrs; Prof Stud Ed, Spec Ed; *cr:* Northern Vly Regnl HS Eng Tchr 1971-; *ai:* Northern Vly Educ Assn, NJ Educ Assn, NEA 1973-; VFW 1969-; Northvale Vol Ambulance Corps 1975-; Awd Winning Yrbk Adv CSPA; Pub Articles Natl Fire Svc Journal; *office:* Northern Valley Regional HS Central Ave Old Tappan NJ 07675

FALK, VIRGINIA KNOX, Fifth Grade Teacher; *b:* Azores, Portugal; *m:* Arnold R.; *c:* Jennifer Ledell, Jebediah Ledell, Johanna, Emily; *ed:* Univ of Louisville (BS) Elem Ed 1975; Keene St Coll (MED) Spec Ed 1981; *cr:* Munsonville Schl Prin 1983-89; Jonathan Daniels Elem Schl 5 Grd Tchr 1989-; *ai:* Mentor Prgm; K-12 Math Rep; Summer Math, Spec Ed Curr Projects; NEA, KEA 1989-; *office:* Jonathan M Daniels Elem Schl 179 Maple Ave Keene NH 03431

FALKENBERG, KIM STEVEN, Tchng Prin & Eng, His Teacher; *b:* Oceanside, NY; *m:* Diana Hilton; *c:* Kelly Lindh, Jody Lorenzo, Leah; *ed:* SUNY at Oswego (BS) Ed 1973; Hofstra Univ (MS) Ed 1974; *cr:* Northside Blodgett MS EMR Class Tchr 1974-81; Elmira Chrstn Acad 2nd Grd Resource Room Tchr 1981-83; BOCES Jr HS Emotionally Disturbed Tchr 1983-84; Hope Chrstn Acad Tchng Prin, Jr, Sr HS Tchr 1987-; *ai:* Soccer Coach; Yrbk Adv, Ed, Act Dir; *office:* Hope Christian Acad 22 John St Painted Post NY 14870

FALKENHEIM, RHEA, English Teacher; *b:* Newark, NJ; *ed:* Upsala Coll (BA) Eng 1959; 30 Grd Hrs Comm William Paterson Coll; *cr:* Fair Lawn News Reporter 1959-60; West Orange Pub Schls Eng Tchr 1969-68; Intnl Schl Eng Tchr 1968-69; East Patterson HS Eng Tchr 1969-70; Midland Park HS Eng Tchr 1970-; *ai:* Prin Tchr Cncl; NEA, NJEA 1960-; Bergen Cty Ed Assn, Midland Park Ed Assn 1970-; *office:* Midland Park HS 250 Prospect St Midland Park NJ 07432

FALKENSTEIN, JACQUELINE WELCH, Art Teacher; *b:* Rochester, NY; *m:* Richard; *c:* Eva; *ed:* SUNY Coll at Buffalo (BFA) Fine Art, Painting 1987; Cert Tchng Art 1995; *cr:* Albright-Knox Art Gallery Freelance Tchng Artist 1989-95; Mt Mercy Acad Art Tchr 1992-; *ai:* Fac Moderator Art Club, Art, Lit Magazine, Co-Chair Art Dept; Buffalo Soc Artists 1990-, Active Exhibiting Mem; NY St Art Tchrs Assn 1994-; Akron Historical Soc 1996; Arts, Hum Stu Awd Grant 1986; Illustrations Pub; Juror Erie Cty Botanical Gardens Art Show 1995; Gold Medal Awd 1995 Edition Art, Lit Magazine; *home:* 107 East Ave Akron NY 14001

FALKMAN, ERIC, Math Teacher; *b:* Brooklyn, NY; *m:* Susan Kojick; *c:* Kein, Stacy; *ed:* SUNY at Geneseo (BA) Math 1973; SUNY at Brockport (MS) Admin 1978, (CAS) Admin 1980; *cr:* Victor Cntrl Schl Dist 7-8 Grd Math Tchr 1973-; *ai:* Referee Lacrosse, Soccer; NYSUT, AFT 1973-; Victor Tchrs Assn 1973-, Pres, Prof Ed Chair, Grievance Chair; BSA 1986-; Cubmaster, Scoutmaster, Dist Comm, George Meany Awd, Dist Awd of Merit; Natl Eagle Scout Assn 1990-; Scout Master's Awd of Merit; *office:* Victor Cntrl Schl dist 953 High St Victor NY 14564

FALKMAN, FRANK MARTIN,JR., Reading Instructor; *b:* Cleveland, OH; *m:* Dee; *c:* Mary Elizabeth, Amy Louise; *ed:* Kent St Univ (BS) Elem Ed 1-8 1969; Cleveland St Univ (MS) Elem Admin 1975; *cr:* Forrest Elem 6th Grd Tchr 1969-77; Thoreau Park Elem 6th Grd Tchr 1977-78; John Muir Elem 6th Grd Tchr 1978-84; Hillside Jr HS Rdng Tchr 1984-; *ai:* Jr HS Bsktbl, Wrestling & Vlybl Ofcl Scorer & Timekeeper; NEA, OEA 1969-; PEA 1969-, Bldg Rep 24 Yrs, Exec Bd Mem 6 Yrs; *office:* Hillside Jr HS 1320 Educational Park Dr Seven Hills OH 44131

FALKOWSKI, EDWARD ALBERT, School Psychologist; *b:* Scranton, PA; *m:* Patricia Mrykalo; *c:* Andrew, Maura; *ed:* Univ of Scranton (BS) Psych 1975; Marywood Coll (MA) Psych 1977; PA St Cert Schl Psych 1977; PA St Cert Elem & Scndry Prin; *cr:* NEIU #19 Schl Psychologist 1978-92; Luzerne Cty Comm Coll Adjunt Prof 1988-95; Elk Lake Schl Dist Schl Psychologist 1992-; *ai:* NEA, PSEA, ELEA 1994-; Abington Youth Soccer League 1996-, U 10 Commissioner; *office:* Elk Lake Schl Dist PO Box 100 Dimock PA 18816

FALL, MARCELLA MCNALLY, 4th Grade Teacher; *b:* Englewood, NJ; *w:* Richard (dec); *c:* Joan Fall-Hoffman, Richard, Theresa; *ed:* SUNY at New Paltz (BS) Elem Ed 1965; Addl 30 Grad Hrs; *cr:* Ostrander Elem Schl 1st Grd Tchr 1965-66; Highland Elem Schl 1st Grd Tchr 1969-70; Duzine Elem 3rd Grd Tchr 1979-80, Open Classroom Tchr 1980-81; New Paltz MS 5th Grd Tchr 1981-82; Puzine Elem Schl 4th Grd Tchr 1983-92; Lenape Elem Schl 4th Grd Tchr 1992-; *ai:* NY St United Tchrs, AFT 1980-; *office:* Lenape Elementary Schl 196 Main St New Paltz NY 12561

FALLEN, JAMES CRAIG, Fifth Grade Teacher; *b:* Newton, NJ; *m:* Nancy Ellen Chodaczok; *c:* Kerry Leigh, Keith Owen, Kristen Nicole; *ed:* Trenton St Coll (BA) Elem Ed 1970, (MED) Elem Ed 1979; 18 Credits Beyond MED; Nursery Schl Cert 1978; Supvr, Prin Cert 1981; *cr:* Memorial Schl Third, Fifth Grd Tchr, Tchr in Charge 1970-; *ai:* Math Curr Comm Mem; WCEA, NJEA, NEA 1970-; WEA 1970-, VP, Treas, Negotiations Chair; NCTM 1995-; Kappa Delta Pi; Presbyn Church, Life Mem, Church, Schl Supt, Deacon; BSA 1985-95; Tiger Club Coord, Asst Cub Master, Webelas Ldr Comm Chm; Warren Cty Tchr of Yr 1983-84; Governors Outstanding Tchng Awd 1991; Washington Borough Tchr of Yr 1995; Dist Inservice Presenter 1994-95; *office:* Washington Memorial Elem Sch 300 W Stewart St Washington NJ 07882

FALLER, ELAINE CELIA, Sixth Grade Teacher; *b:* Jersey City, NJ; *m:* Richard Robert; *c:* Jenna; *ed:* Jersey City St Coll (BA) Elem Ed 1969; *cr:* Pub Schl #5 2nd Grd ESL Tchr 1969-72, Pub Schl #2, 2nd-3rd Grd ESL, 4th-5th Grd Tchr 1972-79; Bloomfield Writing Tchr 1985; Brookdale Schl 6th Grd Tchr 1985-; *ai:* Liason & Affirmative Action Officers; Self-Esteem, Language Arts, Multi-Cultural Ed Comms & Faculty Adv Schlsp Comms; Native Amer Day Coord; Sci Equipment Mgr; NEA & NJEA 1969-; ECEA & BEA 1985-; 1992 Governors Tchr Recognition Awd Recipient; *home:* 63 Hillside Ave Glen Ridge NJ 07028

FALLIS, NANCY KUHNE, Social Studies Curr Coord; *b:* Gloversville, NY; *w:* John D. (dec); *c:* Erin J., Evan J.; *ed:* SUNY at Oneonta (BA) Scndry Soc Stud 1971, (MA) Amer His 1973; *cr:* Canajoharie HS 10th-12th Grd Soc Stud Tchr 1972-75; Gloversville HS 9th-11th Grd Soc Stud Tchr 1978-81; Broadalbin-Perth HS 11th-12th Grd Soc Stud Tchr 1982-; Johnstown Continuing Ed Adult Ed Soc Stud Tchr 1992-93; *ai:* Soc Stud Curr Coord; Past Class & Yrbk Adv; AFT 1972-; NYSUT 1972-; Grad Assistantship SUNY Oneonta; Tchr of the Month; Yrbk Dedication Class of 1991; *office:* Broadalbin-Perth HS Bridge St Ext Broadalbin NY 12025

FALLON, DANIEL J., History Teacher; *b:* Flushing, NY; *ed:* Hobart Coll 90 (BA) Span & Pol Sci 1990; Tchrs Coll Columbia U (MA) Soc Stud Tchr 1992; *cr:* Farmingdale HS Global Stud 1992-93; Rumson-Fair Haven Reg HS Global Events, World His & US His 1 1993-; *ai:* Pep Club Adv & Ski Club Co-Adv; Golf Coach; NJEA & NEA 1993-; Kappa Delta Pi 1992-; *office:* Rumson Fairhaven Reg HS 74 Ridge Rd Rumson NJ 07760*

FALLON, RAE M., Asst Prof of Psychology; *b:* New York City, NY; *m:* John J.; *c:* Sean, Christopher; *ed:* Hunter Coll CUNY (BA) Early Chldhd Ed 1968; Lehman Coll CUNY (MA) Ed 1971; *cr:* O-U Boces Early Chldhd Specialist 1982-89; Mt St Mary Coll Part-time Tchr 1985-90, Instr 1990-93, Asst Prof of Ed 1993-; *ai:* Fac Affairs Comm; Admission Comm; Delta Kappa Gamma 1993-; Phi Delta Kappa 1989-; AEYC 1989-, Regnl Coord; *office:* Mount Saint Mary College 330 Powell Ave Newburgh NY 12550

FALLON, THOMAS TRACEY, 6th Grade Teacher; *b:* St Louis, MO; *m:* Kathleen Ward; *c:* Meghan, Jonathan; *ed:* Glassboro St Coll (BA) Elem Ed 1968, (MA) 1976; *cr:* Gloucester Twp Schls 6th Grd Tchr 1968-; *ai:* NEA, NJEA 1968-; Kappa Delta Pi 1994-; Second PA 43rd Regiment of Foot 1981-, Reenactor; NJ Tchr of Yr 1995; Outstdng Soc Stud NJ Tchr 1993; Governors Awd Outstdng Tchr; *office:* Glen Landing MS 85 Little Gloucester Rd Blackwood NJ 08012*

FALLONE, SILVANA, Vocal Music & Drama Director; *b:* Hoboken, NJ; *ed:* Hartt Schl of Music (BM) Music Ed 1987; NY Univ (MA) Voice Performance 1993; Attnd Amer Inst of Musical Stud in Austria; *cr:* Parish Hill HS Dir Vocal Music & Drama 1987-90; Indian Hills HS Dir Vocal Music & Drama 1990-; *ai:* Artistic & Musical Dir of Dramatic Productions; ACDA 1987-; MENC 1987-; NETC 1987-; Recitalist; Stage Performer; Guest Choral Conductor.

FALLORETTA, CHARLES A., Fourth Grade Teacher; *b:* Sewickly, PA; *m:* Karen Lewis; *c:* Kate Elizabeth; *ed:* Edinboro Univ of PA (BS) Elem Ed 1970; PA St Univ (ME) Elem Ed 1976; *cr:* Hopewell Area Schl Dist 2, 4-6 Grd Tchr 1970-; *ai:* Hopewell Ed Assn 1970-, VP 1974; PSEA, NEA 1970-; *office:* Hopewell Area Schl Dist 1955 Maratta Rd Aliquippa PA 15001

FALVEY, DANIEL J., Math Teacher; *b:* York, PA; *m:* Claudia Fillippo; *ed:* Shippensburg Univ (BSE) Math 1982; OH St Univ (MA) Math 1987; *cr:* Colalico HS Math Tchr 1982-86; Garden Spot HS Math Tchr 1987-; *ai:* Quiz Bowl Adv; PCTM, NCTM, NEA, PSEA 1982-.

FALVO, CONSTANCE DIFEDELE, Teacher of Gifted & Talented; *b:* South Amboy, NJ; *m:* Joseph J. Jr.; *c:* Mary Ann; *ed:* Brookdale Comm Coll (AA) Elem Ed K-8 1971; Monmouth Coll (BS) Elem Ed K-8-Summa Cum Laude 1974; Katharine Gibbs Secretarial Schl Graduated 1962; *cr:* St Agnes Elem Schl 5th Grd Tchr 1971-72; Wolf Hill Schl 5th Grd Tchr 1974-75; Maple Place Schl 5-8 Grd Gifted & Talented, 7 & 8 Grd Lit, 8th Grd Math Tchr 1975-; *ai:* NEA, NJEA 1974-; OEA 1974-, Treas; Tchr of Yr 1994; *office:* Maple Place Schl Maple Pl Oceanport NJ 07757

FALVO, JAMES LOUIS, Head Music Teacher; *b:* Oklahoma City, OK; *m:* Donna Sue Kinnan; *c:* Jamie, Mark; *ed:* WV Univ (BM) Music Ed 1967,

(MM) Music Ed 1968; *cr:* Canon-McMillan Jr HS Band Dir 1968-69; Canon-McMillan HS Band Dir 1969-; Canon-McMillan Schl Dist Head Music Tchr 1989-; *ai:* Marching Band, Stage Band & Musical; NEA 1968-; PA Music Educators Assn 1968-, St Bd 2 Yrs, Past Pres of Dist 1 Yr, Citation of Excl 1990; Amer Schl Band Dirs Assn 1974-; Phi Beta Mu 1988-; Canon-McMillan Tchr of Yr; PA Tchr of Yr Nom; *office:* Canon-McMillan Schl Dist 1 N Jefferson Ave Canonsburg PA 15317

FAMA, DONALD F., Prof of Math & Computer Sci; *b:* Ilion, NY; *m:* Barbara Murphy; *c:* Christopher, Jeffrey; *ed:* UtIca Coll (BA) Math 1961; Syracruse Univ (MS) Math 1965; Univ of IL (MWT) Engrng Tech 1969; Attnd Madison Univ, Univ of Cntrl OK, Univ of MI; *cr:* Sperry Rand Univ Design, Layout 1961-62; Chittenange Cntrl Schl Math Tchr 1960-61; Manlius Schl Math Tchr 1962-64; Cayuga Comm Coll Math, Cmptr Sci Prof 1965-; *ai:* Phi Theta Kappa Adv; NEA, NYSARYC, NAA 1980-; SUNY Chancellors, CCCC Awd of Excl; Outstdng Edctr of Amer; Natl Sci Fnd Awds; *office:* Cayuga Comm Coll 197 Franklin St Auburn NY 13021

FAMA, KATHERINE CAHILL, English & Journalism Teacher; *b:* New Brunswick, NJ; *m:* Peter; *ed:* Coll Misericordia (BA) Eng, Jrnlsm 1968; Trenton St Coll (MA) Prsnl Svcs Guid Ed 1973; *cr:* Franklin HS Tchr 1968-; *ai:* Schl Newspaper the Beacon Adv; Globelink Mem; NCTE, JEA 1980-, NEA, NJEA 1968-; *office:* Franklin HS 415 Francis St Somerset NJ 08873*

FAMY, E. ARLENE, Senior Guidance Counselor; *b:* Paterson, NJ; *ed:* Wm Paterson Coll (BS) Ed 1955; Seton Hall Univ (MA) Guid, Stu Personnel Admin 1959; Columbia Univ (MA) Stu Pers Adm 1962; *cr:* Franklin HS Tchr 1959-62; Paramus HS Cnslr 1962-; *ai:* Commentator on Telephone Hotline; Guid Rep to Parent Ed Cncl; NEA 1959; Ed Assn of Paramus, Bergen Guid Assn 1962-; *office:* Paramus HS East 99 Century Rd Paramus NJ 07652

FANCHER, WILLIAM W., Instrumental Music Teacher; *b:* Olean, NY; *ed:* Potsdam St Univ (BM) Music 1988; St Bonaventure Univ (BS) Ed 1994; *cr:* Allegany Cntrl Schl Grds 5-12 Instrumental Music Tchr 1989-95; Allegany-Limestone Cntrl Schl Instrumental Music Tchr 1995-; *ai:* Stu Cncl Adv; Jazz, Marching Band Dir; Girls Track Coach; Music Edctrs Natl Conf 1989-.*

FANCY, BRENDA LEE, Housemaster; *b:* Worcester, MA; *ed:* Worcester St Coll (BSEd) Elem Ed, Math 1981; Lesley Coll (MED) Curr, Instruction 1989; Bridgewater St Coll 30 Addl Credits CAGS Prgm in Educl Ldrshp; *cr:* Worcester East MS 8th Grd Math Tchr 1981; Coolidge Schl 2nd Grd Tchr 1982; Nathaniel Morton Schl 7th Grd Math Tchr 1982-87; Plymouth Comm Intermediate Schl 7th Grd Math Tchr 1987-95, Housemaster 1995-; *ai:* EAPC Prof Rights & Responsibilities Comm 1985-88; Schl Cncl 1993-95; Tech Coord Cncl 1995-; NEA, Plymouth Cty Ed Assn 1982-, Honor Awd 1994; Camp Fire Girls, Bd of Dirs 1981-82; Horace Mann Grant Position Math Team Coach; Dropout Prevention Grant Position Group Ldr, Liaison; Reach for Stars Grant Participant; CESAME Grant; NSF St Finalist; Excl in Sci, Math Tchng Presidential Awd 1994-95; *office:* Plymouth Cmty Intermediate Sch 117 Long Pond Rd Plymouth MA 02360*

FANELLI, MARY SANDERLIN, Seventh Grade Math Teacher; *b:* Camp Le Jeune, NC; *m:* James Patrick; *ed:* Glassboro St Coll (BA) Elem Ed 1973; *cr:* Glen Landing MS 6th Grd Tchr 8 Yrs, 7th Grd Self-Contained Tchr 5 Yrs, 7th Grd Math Tchr 10 Yrs; *ai:* Stu Assistance Cncl; Peer Group Ldr; Positive Action Comm; Math Career Day Co-Chm; NEA & NJEA 1973-; *office:* Glen Landing MS 85 Little Gloucester Rd Blackwood NJ 08012*

FANELLI, MICHAEL, Band Director & Music Teacher; *b:* Orange, NJ; *m:* Laura Ann Kazar; *c:* Devon Anne, Erin Marie; *ed:* Jersey City St Coll (BA) Music Ed 1978; Glassboro St Coll (MA) Scndry Schl Admin 1985; *cr:* Immaculata HS Band Dir, Music Tchr 1978-79; Immaculate Conception Schl Band Dir, Music Tchr 1978-79; South Brunswick HS Band Dir, Music Tchr 1979-81; Absegami HS Band Dir, Music Tchr 1981-; *ai:* Marching, Concert, Pit Bands; NJEA, NJMEA 1979-; Natl Judges Assn 1983-.

FANNICK, ANTHONY JOSEPH, Sixth Grade Teacher; *b:* Wilkes-Barre, PA; *m:* Anne Marts; *c:* Alyssa Jane, Anthony Michael; *ed:* York Coll (BA) Elem Ed 1976; 30 Post Grad Hrs at Bloomsburg Univ; *cr:* Milton Area Schl Dist 6th Grd Tchr 1976-; *ai:* Boys Var Bsktbl Coach 1977-; NEA 1977-; CSC Coach of Yr 1986-87, 1988 & 1993; *office:* Milton Area Schl Dist Mahoning St Milton PA 17847

FANNIN, ELIZABETH, Resource Teacher; *b:* Portsmouth, OH; *m:* Alan E.; *c:* Chad Alan, Cara Renee; *ed:* OH Univ (BA) Elem 1978; Univ of Dayton (MS) Admin 1989; Post Grad Work at Univ of Dayton, Miami OH Univ; *cr:* Shawnee St Univ Tchr, Adj Prof 2 Yrs; Bloom-Vernon Local Schls Tchr, Resource Tchr 17 Yrs; *ai:* Yrbk Adv; OH Proficiency Tutor; Sci Fair, Writing Comms; Spelling Bee Judge Pronouncer; Phi Delta Kappa, Newsletter; OH Assn Intnl Rdng Assn 1990-, Chprsn Parent Comm; Amer Assn of Univ Women 1994-, Newsletter; Wheelersburg Meth Church 1985-; Women of Wheelersburg 1990-, Yrbk; Porter Twp Ladies Auxiliary 1990-, Sec; Ashland Oil Tchr Achvmt Awd 1994; Ashland Oil Golden Apple Achvmt Awd 1993; AB Catalin Awd 1993; OH Cncl Intnl Rdng Assn Grant 1992.*

FANNING, JOSEPH PATRICK, 8th Grd Social Studies Teacher; *b:* Philadelphia, PA; *m:* Lucy Vierck; *c:* Erin, Michael, Julie; *ed:* Penn St (BS) Scndry Ed 1971; Prins Cert Temple; 60 Addl Credits; *cr:* Cecelia Snyder MS Tchr 1968-69; Neil Armstrong MS Tchr 1969-79; Robert K Shafer MS Tchr 1980-; *ai:* Bensalem HS Var Field Hockey, Ninth GrdBoys Bsktbl Coach; Track Coach; NEA 1973-; *office:* Robert K Shafer MS 3333 Hulmeville Rd Bensalem PA 19020

FANONE, PAMELA VELLENTE, French Teacher; *b:* Sharon, PA; *m:* Donald; *c:* Marissa; *ed:* Slippery Rock Univ (BA) Fr 1970; Attnd PA St Univ, Youngstown St Univ, Univ of MA, Westminster Coll; *cr:* Farrell Area Schl Dist Fr Tchr 1970-; *ai:* Fr Club Adv; Sr Breakfast Comm; Pupil Support Team; NEA, PSEA, PSMLA 1970-; *office:* Farrell Area HS 1600 Roemer Blvd Farrell PA 16121

FANOS, CHRISTINE, Fourth Grade Teacher; *b:* Fitchburg, MA; *ed:* Fitchburg St Coll (BS) Elem Ed, Music Ed 1979; (MS) Elem Ed 1997; 6 Credit Hrs Rdng Ed Boxton Univ; 3 Credit Hrs Orff UMass at Lowell; *cr:* Mc Kovy Campus Schl K-6 Grd Music Specialist Tchr 1979-80; Lawrence Pub Schls K-6 Grd Music Specialist Tchr 1980-82; N Middlesex Regnl Schl 5 Grd Tchr 1983-84; Gardner Pub Schls 1-6 Grd Music Specialist, Chorus Tchr 1984-90, 4, 6 Grd Tchr 1990-; *ai:* MTA, GEA 1985-; AFM Local #173 1990-; *office:* Elm Street Elem Schl 160 Elm St Gardner MA 01440

FANTO, ELIZABETH CUPPETT, English Teacher; *b:* Thomas, WV; *m:* Robert F.; *c:* Mark Stephen; *ed:* Potomac St Coll (AA) Bus 1957; Towson St Univ Ed Eng (BS) 1973, (MA) 1981; Masters plus 60 Hrs; *cr:* Golden Ring Jr HS Eng Tchr 10 Yrs; Overlea HS Eng Tchr 2 yrs; Dulaney HS Eng, Creative Writing, Research in Sci Tchr 11 Yrs; *ai:* Sequel Literary Art Magazine and NHS Adv; NCTE 1975-; MCTELA 1973-, Newsletter Ed: MWP 1984-, Tchr & Consultant Chair; ASCD 1995-; *office:* Dulaney HS 255 Padonia Rd Timonium MD 21093

FANTONE, JAMES JOSEPH, Biology Teacher; *b:* East Liverpool, OH; *m:* Kathleen Louise Grist; *c:* Kevin, Adam; *ed:* Clarion Univ of PA (BS) Scndry Ed 1971; Slippery Rock Univ of PA (MED) Hlth, PE & Recreation 1976; Westminster Coll 15 Grad Hrs in Cnslng; *cr:* Union Area Schls Jr High Sci Tchr 1971-74; Edison Local Schls Bio & 8th Grd Sci Tchr 1976-79; South Range Local Schls MS Sci, PE & Soc Stud Tchr 1979-82; Wellsville Local Schls Bio, Chem, Physics & Earth Sci Tchr 1982-; *ai:* Columbiana Cty Soil & Water Conservation Enviorthon Coach; OEA 1976-; WCTA 1976-; Youngstown St U Hnrs Earth Sci Wkshp 1984; Tech Prep Pgm 1995; *home:* 47831 Lincoln St East Liverpool OH 43920

FAPPIANO, VIRGINIA GREATOREX, Art Teacher; *b:* Waterbury, CT; *m:* Gene; *c:* Robert, Gene Michael, Dan Manning, James; *ed:* Mattatuck Comm Coll (AA) Liberal Arts 1974; Central CT St Univ (BS) Art Ed 1976; Wesleyan Univ (MALS) Liberal Stud 1981; 30 Credits Post Grad Stud; *cr:* Regnl Schl Dist 15 Art Tchr 19 Yrs; *ai:* Admin Team Mem; Chaperone Stu Trip to Spain; NEA, CEA 1977-; Pomperaug Tchrs Assn 1977, Schl Rep; Middlebury Historic Club 1990-; EHL Golf Assn 1985-, Bd of Dirs; Celebration of Excl Awd; Presenter at ASCD Consortium 1995; *office:* Pomperaug Regional HS 234 Judd Rd Southbury CT 06488

FARABAUGH, SALLY ANN (PARRISH), Math Teacher; *b:* Spangler, PA; *m:* Eugene B.; *c:* Jason, Jeffrey, Gregory, Chad; *ed:* St Francis Coll (BA) Math 1972; Elem Cert 1984; *cr:* Harrisburg Area Schl Dist Math Tchr 1972-73; Northern Cambria Cath Schl Math Tchr 1986-; *ai:* Ath Dir; PA Jr Acad of Sci & Diversity Pgm Spon; NCTA 1986-; Altar Rosary Soc 1973-, Sec & Treas; Bishop Carroll Band Parents 1989-, Sec; Bishop Carroll HS Advy Bd 1996; *office:* Northern Cambria Catholic Sch PO Box 249 Rt 271-S Nicktown PA 15762

FARABEE, DARLENE F. H., Fifth Grade Teacher; *b:* Aliquippa, PA; *m:* Matthew R.; *c:* Kaly Frances-Elyse, Hadley Jo; *ed:* PA St Univ (BA) Elem Ed 1979; California Univ of PA (MS) Elem Ed 1983; 30 Credit Hrs in Elem Ed; *cr:* McGuffey Schl Dist 4th Grd Tchr 1979-82, 5th Grd Tchr 1982-; *ai:* NEA, PSEA 1979-; Soc of Immaculate Conception Church 1989-, Lector, Commentator; *office:* McGuffey Schl Dist Inter Schl 119 Main St PO Box 421 Claysville PA 15323*

FARACE, DENNIS ALLEN, Global Studies & Ec Tchr; *b:* Lackawanna, NY; *m:* Sally Jean Pratt; *c:* Scott, Todd; *ed:* SUNY at Brockport (BS) Elem Ed 1964; SUNY at Buffalo (MS) Scndry Ed Soc Stud 1970; 9 Addl Hrs; *cr:* Candor Cntrl Schl 5th Grd Tchr 1964; Eden Cntrl Schl 6th Grd Tchr 1964-68; Eden Jr HS 8th-10th, 12th Grd Tchr 1968-; *ai:* Var Golf, Var Sftbl Coach; NYSUT 1964-; Eden Tchrs Assn 1964-, Chief Negotiator 1993-; Natl Fed HS Coaches, ECIC Coaches Assn 1965-; Eden Bsbl Assn 1975-85; Buffalo Dist Jr Golf 1965-, Lake Shore Div Chm; Wrote All Unit Tests for Global Stud 9, Pub 1988.

FARAGLIA, KATHLEEN A., English Teacher & Librarian; *b:* Trenton, NJ; *ed:* Caldwell Coll (BA) Eng 1971; Trenton St Coll (MA) Eng 1984; Pub Librn & Assoc Media Specialist Certs; *cr:* St Philomena Schl Tchr & Librn 1971-72; McCorristin Cath HS Tchr & Librn 1972-; *ai:* NHS Moderator; Friend of Trenton Pub Lib 1992-; *office:* McCorristin Cath HS 175 Leonard Ave Trenton NJ 08610

FARAGO, MARTHA WILLEY, English Teacher; *b:* Fremont, OH; *m:* Tony; *c:* Lisa, David, Michael, Andrew, Christopher; *ed:* Bowling Green St Univ (BS) Eng 1965; Ashland Univ (MS) Gifted Ed 1994; *cr:* Oberlin HS Eng Tchr 1965-68; Mc Cormick MS Eng Tchr 1986-87; Wellington HS, MMS Gifted, Hnrs, AP Coord 1987-91; Wellington HS Eng Tchr 1991-; *ai:* NHS; Odyssey of the Mind; Scholastic Challenge; Wellington Ed Assn, OH Ed Assn 1986-; *office:* Wellington HS 629 N Main St Wellington OH 44090

FARALLO, LIVIO, Assistant Professor of Biology; *b:* Niagara Falls, NY; *m:* Lori Biggins; *c:* Andrew; *ed:* Niagara Univ (BA) Bio 1978, (MS) Ed 1988; Cert Grad Tchr Trng Prgm in Prof Ed; *cr:* Wrotniak Pharmacy Pharmacy Mgr 1976-85; Niagara Cty Comm Coll Part-Time Bio Instr 1988-91, Instr 1991-; *ai:* Tech Prep Allied Hlth Prgm Chrm; Fac Senate; General Ed Comm; Promotion & Tenure Comm; NEA 1991-; Slipstream Magazine 1981-, Co-Ed; Lifelong Learning Advy Cncl 1991-; *office:* Niagara County Comm Coll 3111 Saunders Settlement Rd Sanborn NY 14132

FARAONE, NICHOLAS FRANK, Social Studies Teacher; *b:* Brooklyn, NY; *m:* Carol Infantolino; *c:* Nicholas J., John M.; *ed:* C. W. Post Coll (BA) Pol Sci 1966, (MS) His 1972; *cr:* North Babylon Schls Soc Stud Tchr 1969-; *ai:* Sr Class Adv; AFT, NEA, NYSTA, North Babylon Tchrs Org 1969-; Knights of Columbus 1995-, 3rd Degree; NY St Regents Schlsp Scholar Incentive Awd 1962; *office:* North Babylon HS 1 Phelps Ln North Babylon NY 11703*

FARBER-SOULE, CYNTHIA L., Latin Teacher; *b:* New York City, NY; *m:* Donald Soule; *c:* Byron, Dorothea, Amanda; *ed:* Earlham Coll (BA) Classics 1973; Univ of WA (MA) Classics 1974; *cr:* Allendale Columbia Schl Latin Tchr, Lang Dept Chm 1974-; *ai:* Sr Stud Comm Adv; Amer Classical League 1975-; CAES 1980-, Nominating Chair; *office:* Allendale Columbia School 519 Allens Creek Rd Rochester NY 14618*

FARBMAN, PAULA GREENBAUM, Choral Director; *b:* New York, NY; *m:* Lawrence; *c:* Richard, Ethan, Michael; *ed:* SUNY at Buffalo (BA) Music 1971, (MED) Music Ed 1972; Cornell Univ Credit Hrs Toward PHD Musicology; Julliard Schl of Music Voice; *cr:* Plainview Pub Schls Music Tchr 1974-77; Hicksville Pub Schls Music Tchr 1986-88; Bethpage Pub Schls Choral Dir 1988-; Midway Jewish Ctr Choir Dir 1990-; *ai:* Choral Adv; MENC 1974-; NMEA 1974-; ACDA 1986-; Long Island Philharmonic Chorus 1993-; Berkshire Choral Festival 1993-; *home:* 37 Netto Ln Plainview NY 11803

FARDEN, DEBRA CIPRA, Instrumental Music Teacher; *b:* Endicott, NY; *m:* Dennis J.; *c:* Matthew J., Michael L.; *ed:* Ithaca Coll (BM) Music Ed 1980, (MM) Music Ed 1985; *cr:* Desantis Music Tchr, Store Employee 1980-81; Phoenix MS Band Dir 1981-87; Fulton Jr HS Band Dir 1987-; *ai:* Pvt Clarinet, Flute Instr; Past Marching Band Woodwinds Instr; Schl Comms; Solo Festival Adjudicator; AFT, Phoenix-Fulton Tchrs Assn 1980-; MENC, NYSSMA 1980-, Past Cty Pres; Oswego Cty MEA 1980-, Past Pres, Sec, Comm Mem; NYSBDA 1980-, Past Sec; *office:* Fulton Jr HS 129 Curtis St Fulton NY 13069

FARE, THOMAS PAUL, Technology Teacher; *b:* Rockville Centre, NY; *m:* Kathleen E.; *c:* Bridget M., Barbara L., Thomas J.; *ed:* St Univ of NY at Buffalo (BS) Ed 1970, (MS) Ed 1971; 35 Addl Hrs; *cr:* Wilson Cntrl Schl Industrial Arts Tchr 1972-81; Newfane Cntrl Schl Tech Tchr 1981-; *ai:* Niagara Cty Tech Prep Consortium, Schl to Work Transition Comms; Video, Photography Clubs, Peer Leadership Advs; Newfane Tchrs Assn; NY St United Tchrs; AFT; Wilson Free Lib Bd 1978-, Bldg Chm, VP, Pres; Our Lady of Rosary Parish, Cncl Mem; Niagara Cty Underwater Explorers Club VP; BSA Merit Badge Cnslr; Outstanding Tchr, Stu Team Nom 1995; *office:* Newfane Cntrl Schl 1 Panther Dr Newfane NY 14108*

FARIAS, TERRY DE FRANCESCO, Third Grade Teacher; *b:* Wilkes-Barre, PA; *m:* George M.; *c:* Rebecca Bene, Ronald Bienkowski, Terri D'Allandro, Audrey Matteo; *ed:* Wilkes Coll (BS) Elem Ed 1965; Rhode Island Coll (ME) Ed 1972; *cr:* Melville Elem Schl Third Grd Tchr 17 Yrs; Coggeshall Elem Schl Third Grd Tchr 11 Yrs; *ai:* Lang Arts Curr Comm; NEA 1968-; NEA Portsmouth 1968-, Exec Cncl Bd; *office:* Melville Elem Schl 1351 W Main Rd Portsmouth RI 02871

FARINA, ANNE BRESLIN, Second Grade Teacher; *b:* Shenandoah, PA; *m:* Michael A.; *c:* Lynn Amato; *ed:* Bloomsburg Univ (BS) Elem Ed 1959; *cr:* Pemberton Boro Elem Schl Kndgtn, Art Tchr 1959-62; C. R. Weeks Elem Schl Kndgtn Tchr 1962-65; F. L. Bell Elem Schl Art Tchr 1967-80, Second Grd Tchr 1980-; *ai:* NJEA 1959-62; NEA 1959-; AFT, NYEA, WTA 1962-; *home:* 76 Trim St Kirkwood NY 13795

FARINA, MARY DOLORES-SUSINKA, Mathematics Teacher; *b:* Youngstown, OH; *m:* James A.; *c:* Anthony, James II; *ed:* Youngstown St Univ (BA) Math 1971, (MS) Math 1975; Post Grad Hrs in ... Application; *cr:* Poland Seminary High Math Tchr 1971-; Youn... Univ Limited Svc Math Tchr 1976; *ai:* NHS Selection Comm; N... PEA 1971-, Chief Negotiator, Sec; NCTM 1990-; *office:* Poland ... HS 3199 Dobbins Rd Youngstown OH 44514*

FARIS, KAY E., Elementary Principal; *b:* Columbia City, IN; *m* ... *c:* Terylle Austin, Leigh Austin-Cain, Caroline Austin, Aaron; ... Univ at Oxford (BS) Elem Ed 1981, Elem Ed & Sci 1984; Workin... PHD Educl Admin; *cr:* Clovernook Elem Tchr 1981-92, Prin 199... Univ Stu Tchr Supvr 1992-93; *ai:* Phi Kappa Phi 1980-; Kapp... 1980-; ASCD 1993-; OAEP 1995-; *office:* Clovernook Elem Sch... Galbraith Rd Cincinnati OH 45231

FARKAS, RICHARD DAVID, Sixth Grade Teacher; *b:* Northam... *m:* Debra J. Remaly; *c:* Eric, Ross; *ed:* E Stroudsburg Univ (BA ... 1972; Wilkes Coll (MSE) Elem Ed 1989; *cr:* Upper Perkiomen M... Tchr 1972-73; Hereford Elem Schl 4th Grd Tchr 1973-8... Perkiomen MS 5th Grd Tchr 1982-91, 6th Grd Tchr 1... Audio-Visual Coord 1982; Kutztown Univ Stdnts Prof Field ... Cooperating Tchr 1982; Peer Coaching & 1st Yr Tchr Mentor ... Recognition Comm 1990-92; NEA, PSEA & Upper Perkiomen ... 1973-; Little League Bsbl 1985-89, Coach; Religious Ed Inster... Young Outstanding Educator Nom 1983; Creative Motivation for ... Presentations at PA MS Conf 1989 & PA St Conf at Carlisle 19... Eng Odyssey Interdisciplinary Unit Cmn 1993-; Presentation for ... Journal of Ed 1994; *office:* Upper Perkiomen MS Jefferso... Greenville PA 18041

FARKAS, ROBERT ERNEST, 7th-8th Grd Lang Arts Teacher; ... OH; *ed:* Kent St (BAEd) Eng 1968, (MA) Master Tchr 1976; R... *cr:* Manchester MS 7th-8th Grd Lang Arts, Rdng Tchr 1968-; *ai* ... Bee, Asst Girls Vlybl Coach; NEA, OEA, Manchester Ed As... Manchester Church of Christ 1958-, Sunday Schl Supt, Tch... Holden Jennings Scholar; Mentor Tchr.

FARLEY, ANNJULIE BOGATCH, Math & Soc Stud Teacher; ... City, NJ; *m:* Jeffrey; *c:* Heidi, Kristen; *ed:* Jersey City St Coll ... Ed 1975; NTE Cert in Elem Ed; *cr:* Bayonne PAL Day Care Ctr T... St Henry Schl Tchr 1983-84; Our Lady of Mt Carmel Tchr & ... 1984-; *ai:* Bayonne HS Choir Parents Assn Pres; NCE 1984-; Bay... 1982-; *office:* Our Lady of Mt Carmel Schl 23 E 22nd St Bayonne ...

FARLEY, JACK F.,JR., US History & Government Instr; *b:* W... MA; *m:* Joellen Martin; *c:* Jamie, Allison; *ed:* Assumption Coll ... 1972; Worchester Coll (BA) His 1969; 30 Addnl Hrs (Candida... Univ of MA; *cr:* Deverelux Schl for Emotional Disturbed Soc S... N Attleboro Jr HS Math Instr 1972-73; Assabet Reg Voc HS Soc ... Bskbtl Coach 1973-86; Wachusett Reg HS Soc Stud Instr ... Wachusett Reg HS Asst Prin 1995-; *ai:* Frosh Girls Bsktbl Coach; ... Day Adv; Class Adv; Close Up Club Adv; NEA 1972-; MA Tc... Wacausett Reg Tchrs Assn 1986-; Eastern Assn of Intercolleg... Officials 1986-; US Lifesaving Assn 1980-; Cape Cod Chapter T... Central MA Ftbl Officials; Close Up Fellowship 1988, 1991-; V... MA Soccer Officials; *office:* Wachusett Regional H S 1401 Main ... MA 01520

FARLEY, JOELLEN, High School English Teacher; *b:* Worce... *m:* Jack; *c:* Jamie, Allison; *ed:* Worcester St Coll (BS) Eng 19... Rdng 1990; 30 Credits Beyond Masters; *cr:* Grafton Memrl M... Rdng Tchr 1970-75; Auburn HS Eng & Rdng Tchr 1984-; *ai:* S... Mgmt & Schlrshp Comm; ATA 1984; MTA 1984; NEA 1984; ... Windsor Cir Jefferson MA 01522

FARLEY, JOHN E., 11th & 12th Grd Soc Stud Tchr; *b:* Danvers... St Anselm Coll (BA) Span & His 1972; Salem St Grad Schl (M... Stud 1975; Suffolk Law Schl (JD) Law 1980; *cr:* Bishop Fenwick... & Coach 1972-; *ai:* Cross Cntry, Indoor Track & Spring Track Boy... Coach; NCEA 1972-; Boston Archiocese Tchrs Assn 1972-; *offic*... Fenwick HS 99 Margin St Peabody MA 01960

FARLEY, JOHN GILBERT, Science Teacher; *b:* Latrobe... Josephine; *c:* Matthew, David, William; *ed:* So CT St Coll (BS)... Ed 1975; SoCT St Univ (MS) Environmental Ed 1986; 6th Yr S... 1988; *cr:* HillHouse HS 1974-75; St Louis Schl 1975-79; Norwa... Tchr 1978-79; Stratfrd Ct Sci Tchr 1979-81; Sleeping Giant Jr H... 1981-83; Hamden HS Sci, Bio Tchr 1986-91,AP Bio 1993-; Ha... Sci Tchr 1983-86, 1991-93; *ai:* Class Spon 5 Yrs; NEA 1981-; CT ... Assn 1980-; BSA 1971-, Scout Master, Silver Beaver 1991; BEST... for CT D Ed 1989-91; *office:* Hamden HS 2040 Dixwell Avenue... CT 06517*

FARLEY, MARY R., Fourth Grade Teacher; *b:* Saratoga Spring... St Bonaventure Univ (BA) Mass Comm 1987; Coll of Saint R... Elem Ed 1989; *cr:* Albany Schl of Hum Sixth Grd Tchr 1985-9... Grd Tchr; *ai:* Shared Decision Making Team Tchr Rep; Child S... Co-Chair; Mentoring Prmg Coord; AFT, NYSUT 1989-; R... Donald House 1996, Vol; Albany City Cncl PTA Founders Day Aw... Albany Schl Of Humanities 108 Whitehall Rd Albany NY 12209

FARLEY, MARYANN CLAUDIO, Elementary Teacher; *b:* Je... NJ; *m:* William J.; *c:* Renee; *ed:* Jersey City St Coll (BA) Elem ... 15 Post Grad Credits Montclair St, Jersey City St; *cr:* Secaucus ... Sub Tchr 1972-73; Clarendon Schl 5th, 6th Grd Tchr 1973-76; ... Schl 6th Grd Tchr 1976-78, 1981-, 4th Grd Tchr 1980-81; *ai:* Saf... Coord; Bldg Rep Secaucus Ed Assn; NEA 1973-; NJEA; Hudso... Assn; PTA; *office:* Huber Street Schl Paterson Plank Rd Sec... 07094

FARLEY, SEAN MICHAEL, Social Studies & Govt Teacher; *b* ... NY; *m:* Jenifer Munson; *c:* Ethan; *ed:* Daemen Coll (BA) His, G... Castleton St Coll (MS) Rdng 1994; *cr:* St Mary's Acad of G... Scndry Soc Stud Tchr 1987-89; Hartford Cntrl Schl Mid, Scndry ... Tchr 1989-; *ai:* Modified Soccer Coach; 6th Grd Team Ldr; MS ... Univ Facilitator; Staff Dev Comm; NYSUT 1989-; *office:* Hartfo... Schl PO Box 79 Hartford NY 12838

FARLEY, WILLIAM HENRY, Mathematics Teacher; *b:* State... NY; *m:* Peggy Ann Christy; *c:* Jared, Jessica, Jody; *ed:* Merrin... (BA) Ed 1967; SUNY at Stoneybrook (MS) Ed 1973; 15 Credit H... Cmptr Literacy; *cr:* West Islip Jr HS 7-9 Grd Math Tchr 1967-91, ... Math Tchr 1991-; *ai:* Mathletes Club Adv; SAT Review; AFT, NE... 1967-; Cntrl Suffolk Golf Assn 1986-, Sec; *office:* West Islip HS 1... West Islip NY 11795

FARMER, DAVID L., Language Arts Teacher; *b:* Lancaster, PA; ... E. Crownover; *c:* Cherise Harper, Danielle Malik; *ed:* Elizabeth... (BS) Eng 1964; Penn State Univ (MED) Eng 1970; Grad Stud M... Univ, Penn St Univ at Harrisburg; *cr:* Warwick Union Schl Dist ... 1964-66; Middletown Area Schl Dist Lang Arts Tchr 1966-, D... 1970-77; *ai:* MAEA 1966-; PSEA, NEA 1964-, Life Mem; Maso... 682 1974-; Publications Fiction, Non-Fiction & Poetry... Middletown Area HS 1155 N Union St Middletown PA 17057

FARMER, MARK E., Social Studies Teacher; *b:* Saranac Lak... Sharon L. LaBrake; *c:* Erin, Ryan; *ed:* SUNY Cortland (BA) ... 1983; SUNY Plattsburgh (MA) Ed 1994; *cr:* Saranac Lake P... Patrolman 1983-86; Saranac Lake HS Tchr 1989-; *ai:* Var Ftbl, V... & Jr Var Sftbl Coach; Co-Adv Stu Cncl; Speech Contest Club ...

YSUT 1989-; *office:* Saranac Lake HS 99 La Pan Hwy Saranac 12983

, **SARAH STAPLES,** High School English Teacher; *b:* tic, Canada; *m:* Randall W.; *ed:* Univ of NE (BA) Eng 1989, (MA) Attnd Oxford Univ in England Summer 1988; *cr:* Univ of NE at utor & Athletic Dept 1989-92; Milton Hershey Schl Eng Tchr Girls Fastpitch Sftbl Coach; Amer Cncl of Exercise 1994-, Aerobics Instr; *office:* Milton Hershey Schl PO Box 830 Hershey

L, ALFRED WILLIAM, Technology Teacher; *b:* Ilion, NY; *m:* nne; *c:* Kimberly Anne Coyne, Amy Lynne; *ed:* Auburn Comm) Liberal Arts 1966; St Univ Coll at Oswego (BS) Industrial Arts l 36 Hrs Post Grad Stud & 60 Hrs of Trng to Tch Tech Ed; *cr:* n Cntrl Schl Driver Ed Tchr 1970; East MS Industrial Arts & Tech 1971-; *ai:* Master Tchr for Stu Tchrs 5 Yrs; NYUST 1971-; 1996; *office:* Auburn Enlarged City Schl Dist Thornton Ave Y 13021*

, JAMES JOSEPH, Social Studies Teacher; *b:* Millford, CT; *m:* Central CT St Univ (BA) His, Pol Sci 1991; Sacred Heart Univ 1993; *cr:* Trumbull High Soc Stud Tchr 1993-; *ai:* Jr Class, Mock Trial Adv; Ftbl, Sftbl Coach; CT Ed Assn, NEA 1993-; Rotary, CT HS Coaches Assn 1993-; Trumbull Key Club Cert of on; *office:* Trumbull HS 72 Strobel Rd Trumbull CT 06611*

E, ROSANNA, Spanish Teacher; *b:* Caracas, Venezuela; *m:* Michele, Micheal, Salvatore; *ed:* Saint Peter's Coll (BA) Span Jr, Sr Prom, Span Club, Modeling Club, Schl Missions ; *office:* Acad Of Sacred Heart HS 713 Washington St Hoboken

LZ, KIMBERLY KAISER, Mathematics Teacher; *b:* Rochester, mes R.; *ed:* Brockport St (BS) Math 1990; Nazareth Coll (MS) *cr:* LeRoy Cntrl Schl Jr HS Math Tchr 1990-92; Livonia Cntrl Math Tchr 1992-93; Brockport Cntrl Schl HS Math Tchr 1993-; 1990-; Assn Math Tchr of Rochester Area 1993-; *home:* 9363 Rd Le Roy NY 14482

ORTH, GERALD M., Senior High Math Teacher; *b:* Coaldale, usan Lukman; *c:* Morgan, Taylor; *ed:* Susquchanna Univ (BA) ; Kutztown Univ Math 1972; 24 Credit Hrs Moravian Coll; 6 Penn St; 3 Credit Hrs Muhlenburg Coll; 1 Credit Hr Allentown Panther Valley Math Tchr 1966-70; Parkloma HS Math Tchr PSEA 1966-; NCTM 1981-; COMAP 1992-; *office:* Parkland HS efield PA 18069

ORTH, JEFFREY SCOTT, HS Social Studies Teacher; *b:* NY; *m:* Donna Lynn; *c:* Bethany, Christopher, Kara; *ed:* Roberts Coll (BA) His, Ed 1980; Brockport St Univ (MS) Ed 1985; Natl rom Natl Soccer Coaches Assn of Amer 1985; *cr:* Spencerport al Behavior Problem Children Tchr 1981-85, Soccer Coach Genesee Comm Coll Men's Soccer Coach, Ath 1995-; rt Cntrl Schl HS Soc Stud Tchr 1985-; *ai:* Boys Under 10 Soccer str Intnl Soccer Skills Acad; Section V Boys Soccer Chm; NY St mm Sec; Chm of NY St Soccer Championship Tournament for NY St Tchrs Assn 1981-; Natl Soccer Coaches Assn 1981-, Nat ; Ogden Presbyn Church 1968-; Spencerport Soccer Club 1977-, , VP; Spencerport European Club 1985-, Pres, VP; Ed of NY St ers Soccer Poll; Convention Comm for Natl Soccer Coaches mer; Gatorade HS All Amer Selection Comm; *office:* Spencerport 2707 Spencerport Rd Spencerport NY 14559*

, AUDREY KEEFE, Instructor of English; *b:* Hartford, CT; *m:* *c:* Philip T., Claire, Gregory, Edward, Anne; *ed:* Russell Sage Eng 1956; Cntrl CT St (MS) Elem Ed 1964; 15 Credits Scndry sboro St Coll; *cr:* Bleck Jr Schl Supplemental Tchr of Eng Cherry Hill Pub Schls Bedside Tutor 1981-84; Camden Cty Coll ting Tchr 1985-90; Gloucester Cty Coll Eng Instr 1990-; *ai:* n Learning 1994-; Crisis Worker Contact Comm Svcs 1985-; Recording foir Blind & Dyslexic 1995; *home:* 3407 Church Rd ll NJ 08002

, BILL, 6th Grade Teacher; *b:* Jamaica, NY; *m:* Diane; *c:* *ed:* Adelphi Suffolk (BA) Eng 1967; Adelphi (MA) Ed 1972; 60 ver MA; *cr:* Sachem Schls Tchr 1968-; *ai:* SCTA 1968-, Bldg

MARY-ELLEN SIMKO, Spanish Teacher; *b:* Derby, CT; *m:* Sr.; *c:* Russell Jr., Michael; *ed:* St Joseph Coll (BA) Home Ec Ed thern CT St Univ (MS) Environmental Ed 1978; Cert Span 1985; HS Home Ec & Span Tchr 1975-; *ai:* FHA Adv 1975-79; Span 1984-; Disciplinary Action Comm 1994-; NEA 1975-; CT Ed -; Derby Ed Assn 1975-, Treas 1980-82; AATSP 1987-; Bethany -, Treas 1989-91, VP 1991-93; Tchr of Rel Ed Our Lady of the n Church 1993-; Amity Yth Ftbl 1993-, Comm; Amity Regnl Jr 1995-; Cub Scouts, Asst Ldr; *office:* Derby HS 8 Nutmeg Ave 06418

AR, ROBERT A., Chemistry & Psychology Teacher; *b:* nela, PA; *m:* Peggy; *c:* Rob, Heath; *ed:* CA Univ of PA (BS) Chem S) Psych 1972; 6 Hrs Psych Westminister Coll; 3 Hrs Chem oll; PHD Commisioner Sci Penn St Univ; PA Act 235 Cert; *cr:* non Area Sr HS Chem, Psych Tchr 1966-; *ai:* Career Prep Rep; ge Plan Comm; Chem Contest Liason; Belle Vernon Area E A as, Pres; PSEA, NEA 1966-, Del; BSA 1978-, Dist Scoutmaster, s Keys, R t Commissioner Cncl, Woodbadge; Scout Ldr Trng st Awd of Merit; Soc Antiquaries of Scotland 1995-; Clain on 1973-, PA St Commissioner; NSF Flwshp Psych, Chem; lle Vernon Area Schl Dist Rd 2 Crest Ave Belle Vernon PA 15012

RUCE, Agricultural Science Instr; *b:* Lebanon, NH; *ed:* St Coll (BS) Soc Sci Ed 1973; Univ of NH (AS) Horticultural, i 1975, (MA) Educl Admin 1985; *cr:* Canaan Schl Dist Soc Sci -74; Smyrna Schl Dist Ag Ed Instr 1975-78; Coe-Brown Acad Ag Voc Dir 1978-88; Epsom Schl Dist Schl Prin 1988-94; Governor h Schl Dist Ag Ed Instr 1994-; *ai:* FFA Advisorship; Instrl Task Force;Staff Senate; Scheduling Comm; Phi Delta Kappa H Voc Ag Assn, Pres; NH Prin Assn 1988; NASSP, ASCD, NAESP 1988-; NEA 1994-; AVA 1993-; Farm Bureau 1990-; d Bd Adj 1989-, Chm; NW Conservation Comm 1983-, Chm; NW Comm 1994-; Outstdng NH Vo-Ag Tchr 1985; Outstdng NH Ag 995; Article Ag Ed Magazine 1984; *home:* Rt 107 Northwood NH

UDITH BANZER, Professor of English; *b:* New York City, NY; orge F. Jr; *c:* Alec Winfield; *ed:* Marymount Manhattan Coll (BA) Yale Univ (MA) Eng 1959, (PHD) Eng 1965; Marymount n Coll (LHD) 1992; *cr:* Vassar Coll Eng Instr 1961-63; St Marys A Asst Prof 1964-68; SUNY at New Platz Assoc Prof 1968-77; wn Univ Assoc Prof 1977-89, Eng Prof 1990-; *ai:* Cosmos Club Books The Passion of Emily Dickinson, The Life & Art of Elinor h Century Interpretations of Sons & Lovers, New Century Views ckinson, Critical Stud & Novel I Never Came To You In White; search Grants; Amer Philosophical Soc Grant; Georgetown Ctr tud Fellowship; Morgan Porter Fellowship of Yale Univ; *office:* wn Univ 37th & O St N W Washington DC 20057

FARR, ROSE ANNE DURKIN, Third Grade Teacher; *b:* Brooklyn, NY; *m:* Robert G.; *c:* Mary Beth, Brian Scott; *ed:* Adirondack Comm (AA) Psych & His 1976; Skidmore Coll (BS) Elem Ed 1978; Russell Sage (MS) Elem Ed 1983; 55 Credit Hrs SUNY at Plattsburgh; *cr:* St Peter's Elem Schl 7th &8th Grd Math, Sci & 5th Grd Tchr 1978-84; Corinth Cntrl Schl 2nd, 3rd & 5th Grd Tchr 1984-; *office:* Corinth Cntrl Schl 105 Oak St Corinth NY 12822

FARRAH, PAUL GREG, Math Teacher; *b:* Alliance, OH; *m:* Debra Donofrio; *c:* Angela, Allyson; *ed:* Baldwin Wallace Coll (BS) Elem Ed 1988; Ashland Coll (MS) Elem Admin 1996; *cr:* Louisville City Schls His Tchr 1988-94; Tuslaw Schls Math Tchr 1994-; *ai:* Head Ftbl Coach; NEA 1988-.

FARRAR, MIRIAM OMAN, 5th Grade Teacher; *b:* Clay Center, KS; *w:* J. Craig (dec); *c:* Eric, Anne; *ed:* Bethany Coll (BS) Music 1961; OH Univ 150 Hrs Elem Ed; *cr:* Gardner Pub Schls 1st-12th Grd Music Tchr 1961-63; Overland Pk 1st-6th Grd Music Tchr 1963-65; Urbana Pub Schls 1st-6th Grd Music Tchr 1966-68; Athens Pub Schls 5th Grd Tchr 1984-; *ai:* Stu Cncl & Safety Patrol Adv; OH Tchrs Assn 1983-; NEA 1983-; Christ Luth Church 1971-, Cncl Chair; *office:* East Elem Schl 3 Wallace Dr Athens OH 45701

FARRAR, RICK, Lead Science Teacher; *b:* Penn Yan, NY; *ed:* Houghton Coll (BS) Bio; Frostburg Univ (MS) Bio; *cr:* Northern HS Lead Sci Tchr 1987-; *office:* Northern HS 86 Pride Pkwy Accident MD 21520

FARRELL, CHARLES, Social Studies Teacher; *b:* Philadelphia, PA; *m:* Carolyn; *ed:* Holy Family Coll (BA) His 1990; Cert Scndry Soc Stud 1995; *cr:* Saint Katherine of Siena Soc Stud Tchr 1992-; *ai:* PE Coord; Var Ftbl & Bsbl Coach; NCEA 1992-; Torresdale Boys Club 1992-, Ftbl Dir; *office:* St Katherine Of Siena Schl 9738 Frankford Ave Philadelphia PA 19114

FARRELL, DENNIS ALAN, Sixth Grade Teacher; *b:* Akron, OH; *c:* Daniel, David, Dawn, Dustin; *ed:* Univ of Akron (BS) Elem Ed 1975; 40 Grad Credit Hrs; *cr:* Lincoln Elem Schl 3rd, 5th Grd Tchr 1975-88; Rimer Elem Schl 6th Grd Tchr 1988-; *ai:* Chess Club Supvr; Track Coach; Environmental Ed Cncl of OH 1988-; OH Cncl Intnl Rdng Assn, Akron Area Intnl Rdng Assn 1996-; *office:* Akron Pub Schl 70 N Broadway Akron OH 44308

FARRELL, EMILY C., English Teacher; *b:* New York City, NY; *m:* Dr. Jay P.; *c:* Christopher, Steven; *ed:* Beaver Coll (BA) Eng 1969; Univ of MI (MA) Eng 1970; 30 Credits Beyond Masters at Wilke, Widener Univ, Villanova Univ; *cr:* Hartland HS Eng Tchr 1970-71; Sterling HS Eng Tchr 1971-72; Nether Providence Eng Tchr 1972-84; Strath Haven HS Eng Tchr 1984-; *ai:* Japperwocky Schl Lit Magazine; Hadassah 1980-; Helen Furness Book Selection Comm 1985-; Impact Grants Tchng Awds 2; Wesleyan Coll Inspirational Tchr Recognition; Schl Dist Achvmt Awd for Tchng & Writing 2; Various Tchng Awds; Writing Contest Winners, Cash, Cmptr Etc; *office:* Strath Haven HS 205 S Providence Rd Wallingford PA 19086*

FARRELL, GAIL A., Teacher of Gifted & Talented; *b:* Jackson Hghts, NY; *ed:* William Paterson Coll (BA) Ed 1967; Fairleigh Dickinson Univ (MA) Ed 1980 -; 30 Addl Credits; *cr:* Hillside Schl Second Grd Tchr 1967-80, Third Grd Tchr 1980-92, Basic Skills Tchr 1992-93, GATE, Enrichment Tchr 1993-; Brookside Schl GATE, Enrichment Tchr 1993-; *ai:* Stu Invention Through Ed Coord, Judge; Dev GATE Prgm Third-Sixth Grds; Odyssey of Mind Competition Judge; Recycling Contests Judge; NEA, NJEA, AEA 1967-; Gifted Ed Network 1993-; Girl Scout Ldr; *office:* Brookside Schl Brookside Ave Allendale NJ 07401*

FARRELL, JAMES J., Senior High Art Teacher; *b:* Boston, MA; *m:* Marnie H.; *c:* Brandon, Niki; *ed:* Westmar Coll at LaMare (BA) Art & Ed 1973; Assumption Coll (MFA) Art Ed; MA Art at Boston & Salem St Post Grad Credits; Bates Coll AP Trng; *cr:* Marblehead Jr & Sr High Tchr 1973-; *ai:* Soph Class Adv; Ski Club; MTA 1973-; Natl Art Ed Assn 1994-; Boston Globe Scholastic Art Awd Advy Bd; Horace Mann Grant; Nom Tchr of the Yr MA; Christy Tchr 1996; *office:* Marblehead HS Duncan Sleigh Sq Marblehead MA 01945

FARRELL, MARK O., Chemistry Professor & Chprsn; *b:* California, PA; *m:* Louise Marie; *c:* Christopher; *ed:* CA St Coll (BS) Chem & Ed 1969; Carnegie-Mellon Univ (MS) Chem 1974, (PHD) Chem 1978; *cr:* West Jefferson Schl Dist HS Chem Tchr 1969-79; LaRoche Coll Assoc Chem Prof & Natl Sci Chair 1979-89; Point Park Coll Chem Prof & Natl Sci & Eng Tech Chair 1989-; *ai:* PA Governors Schl for the Scis Fac Mem 13 Yrs; Amer Chemical Soc, Amer Soc for Eng Ed; Amer Assn of Univ Prof; Aircraft Owners & Pilots Assn 1985-; *office:* Point Park Coll 201 Wood St Pittsburgh PA 15222

FARRELL, MICHAEL R., 7th Grade Life Science Teacher; *b:* Pittsburgh, PA; *ed:* Slippery Rock Univ (BS) Elem Ed 1990; Univ of DE Instruction Candidate; *cr:* Selbyville MS Seventh Grd Life Sci Tchr 1991-; *ai:* 7th, 8th Grd Head Ftbl, Asst Wrstlng Coaches; NEA, IREA 1991-; DE Tchrs of Sci 1993-; PTA at Selbyville Mid 1991-; *office:* Selbyville MS PO Box 230 Selbyville DE 19975

FARRELL, SEAN MICHAEL, Assistant Dean of Students; *b:* Middlebury, VT; *m:* Michelle; *c:* Paige; *ed:* Plymouth St Coll (BS) PE 1992; *cr:* Vermont Acad Intern Sci Dept 1992, Asst Dean of Stdnts 1992-; *ai:* Stu Govt Fac Rep; Asst Ftbl, Asst Ski, Head Track Coach; *office:* Vermont Acad PO Box 500 Saxtons River VT 05154

FARRELL, SUSAN ANNE, Sociology Professor; *b:* Jamaica Queens, NY; *m:* Edward J. Jr.; *c:* Jessica, Edward III; *ed:* Queens Coll CUNY (BA) Eng Lit 1974; St Johns Univ (MA) Theology 1982; City Univ of NY Grad Schl (PHD) Sociology, Womens Stud 1992; *cr:* Queens Coll Adj Asst Prof 1987-92; Kingsborough Comm Coll Adj Lecturer 1986-92, Asst Prof 1992-; *ai:* Womens Stud Advy, Curr Comms; Amer Sociological Assn 1986-; Sociologists for Women in Soc 1986-, Chair, Publications Comm; Assn for Scientific Stud of Rel 1987-; Amer Assn of Univ of Women 1994-; Articles Pub; New Visions Grant Dev of Womens Stud City Univ of NY; *office:* Kingsborough Comm Coll 2001 Oriental Blvd Brooklyn NY 11235*

FARRELL, SUSAN JANET, 7th Grade Social Studies Tchr; *b:* Norristown, PA; *ed:* Lafayette Coll (BA) Anthropology, Sociology 1992; Cabrini Coll (MED) Ed 1996; Ursinus Coll Ed Cert 1992; *cr:* Perkiomen Vly MS 7th Grd Soc Stud Tchr 1993-; *ai:* Head 7-9 Grd Lacrosse, Asst HS Field Hockey Coach; Stu Assist Team; NEA, PVEA, US Field Hockey Assn 1993-; US Womens Lacrosse Assn 1996; *office:* Perkiomen Valley MS 29 E 1st Ave Collegeville PA 19426

FARRELL, WILLIAM ROBERT, Ret Latin & History Teacher; *b:* Syracuse, NY; *m:* Judith Barrett Chapman; *c:* Christina Newton, Diana F. Urbine; *ed:* Cath Univ of Amer (BA) Philosphy, Latin 1960; Syracuse Univ (MS) Ed 1970; *cr:* Fayetteville-Manlius Latin, His Tchr 1961-95; *ai:* Boys, Girls Bowling Coach, NY St HS Champions Girls 1995; HS Golf Coach; Assn of Tchrs of Latin Around Syracuse 1988-95, Pres; Classical Assn Empire St 1975-; Amer Classical League 1975-; NY St Latin Tchrs Assn Bd of Dirs 1995-; Articles Pub; *home:* 128 Cashin Dr Fayetteville NY 13066

FARRELLY, DELPHINE JOHNS, Guid Cnslr & Career Ed Coord; *b:* Bristol, CT; *m:* Francis J.; *c:* Sean, Meeghan; *ed:* St Joseph Coll (BA) Span 1965; Cntrl CT St Univ (MS) Ed 1969, (MS) Cnslng 1990; 30 Addl Credit Hrs Voc Assessment; Cert Translation Planning; Career St Advy Comm; *cr:* Wethersfield's Mitchell Schl 1st-2nd Grd Tchr 1966-72; Wethersfield HS Cnslr 1992-; Wethersfield Pub Schls Career Ed Coord 1979-; *ai:* Coord Shadow Prgm 1986-; Jr Achvmnt 1979-82; NEA, CEA 1994-; WEA; CCEA 1979-, Pres, Cert Merit; CCA 1989-, Sec; Chamber Commerce 1980-, Shadow Co-Chair; Yth Adv Bd 1983-, Chprsn; *office:* Wethersfield HS 411 Wolcott Hill Rd Wethersfield CT 06109*

FARRINGTON, RONALD J., Prof of Business; *b:* Norristown, PA; *m:* Ruth Eileen Teany; *ed:* Temple Univ (BS) Acctng 1965; Certfd Pub Accountant Commonwealth of PA; *cr:* Big 8 Accounting Staff 1965-69; Private Acctng Assoc Controller 1969-70; Private Practice Owner of CPA Firm 1970-; Montgomery Cty Comm Coll Prof of Bus 1970-; *ai:* Amer Inst of CPA's, PA Inst of CPA's 1969-; AFT; Kiwanis Club 1972-, Pres, VP, Treas; Zoning Hearing Bd, Previous Chair; *office:* Montgomery County Comm Coll 340 Dekalb Pike Blue Bell PA 19422

FARROW, ROSEMARIE TAYLOR, US History Teacher; *b:* Philadelphia, PA; *m:* Wayne T. Sr.; *c:* Wayne Jr., Timothy, Kevin; *ed:* Glassboro St Coll (BA) Sec Ed, Soc St 1975, (MA) Pub Schl Adm 1986; *cr:* St Charles Borromeo 6th-8th Grd Tchr 1969-78; St Mary's Schl 7th-8th Grd Tchr 1979-81; Sacred Heart HS His Tchr, Dean of Stdnts 1981-86; Camden Cath HS His Tchr, Dept Chair 1986-; *ai:* Mock Trial Team Moderator; South Jersey Cath Tchrs 1985-, Past Pres, VP; NACST 1985-; Coalition for Educl Choice 1994-, Pres; SCTO 1995-, Legislative Liaison; *office:* Camden Catholic HS Rt 38 & Cuthbert Blvd Cherry Hill NJ 08002

FARRY, MARY E., English Teacher; *b:* Walpole, MA; *c:* Ellen Hamilton; *ed:* Regis Coll at Weston (BA) Eng; Framingham Coll (MED) Spec Ed 1981; Grad Work Northeastern Univ, Southern ME Coll, Fitchburg St Coll; 60 Addl Grad Credits; *cr:* Holbrook HS Eng Tchr 1963-65; Ashland HS Eng Tchr 1966-; *ai:* Schl Cncl; Staff Dev Project; Curr Dev Comm; NEA, MTA 1963-; AEA 1963-, Bldg Rep; NCTE 1990-; MA Cncl Tchrs of Eng 1989-; Ed Alliance for Eng Tchrs 1993-; Excl in Ed Awd; St Paul's Schl Scientist as Humanist Grant 1993; Dept of Ed Portfolio Assessment Project Lead Tchr; New Standards Project MA Rep at UT, CA; MA Assessment Prgm Lead Tchr; Worcester St Coll Portfolio Presentations; MA Dept of Ed Portfolio Assessment Grant.*

FARSTER, JAMES RAY, Mathematics Teacher; *b:* Kittaning, PA; *c:* Amy, Renee, Brandon; *ed:* Indiana Univ of PA (BS) Math 1969; Univ of Pittsburgh (MA) Math 1972; 20 Addl Credit Hrs Educl; *cr:* Shaler Schl Dist Math Tchr 1969-71; Deer Lakes Schl Dist Math Tchr 1971-; *ai:* Head Boys Bsktbl Coach; Part-Time Tchr Allegheny Comm Coll; PSEA, NEA 1969-; OLEA 1971-, Pres, Treas; *office:* Deer Lakes Schl Dist RD 2 Cheswick PA 15024*

FARTHING, CAROL ELLEN, English Teacher & Dept Chprsn; *b:* Amelia, OH; *m:* Leslie A.; *ed:* Trevecca Nazarene Coll at Nashville (BA) Eng & Scndry Ed 1962; Attnd OH Univ & Kent St Univ; *cr:* Central HS Eng Tchr 1962-66; J A Garfield HS Eng Tchr 1966-, Eng Dept Chprsn 1971-; *ai:* Y-Teen Club Adv 1964-77; NHS Club Adv 1968-; Sr Class Adv 1970-78; Faculty Advisory Cncl 1971-; Cntry Lang Arts Cur & Cty Lang Arts Festival Cncls; NEA & NCTE 1962-; Garfield Ed Assn 1967-; OH Ed Assn 1966-; Martha Holden Jennings Scholar 1975-76; J.A. Garfield Tchr of Yr 1991; *office:* James A Garfield H S James A Garfield Dist 10233 SR 88 Garrettsville OH 44231

FARVER, BARBARA MAY, Second Grade Teacher; *b:* Harrisburg, PA; *ed:* Houghton Coll (BA) Elem Ed 1971; Shippensburg St Univ (ME) Ed 1974; *cr:* Harrisburg Chrstn Schl 1st Grd Tchr 1971-81, 2nd Grd Tchr 1981-; *ai:* Elem Dept Head 1984-; Educl Policies Comm 1975-; Church 1980-, Yth Ldr, Sunday Schl Tchr, Choir; *office:* Harrisburg Christian Schl 2000 Blue Mountain Pky Harrisburg PA 17112

FASHANO, GRACEANN D'ANGELO, Fourth Grade Teacher; *b:* Jamestown, NY; *c:* Amy; *ed:* Jamestown Comm Coll (AA) Arts 1975; St Univ of NY at Fredonia (BS) Early Chldhd Ed-Magna Cum Laude 1978, (MS) Rdng 1981; SUC at Fredonia Clinical Field Supvr Term 1993-95, Educl Stud 2 Year Term; Advanced Cert Schl Admin, Supvr 1995; *cr:* Panama Cntrl Schl Head Star Tchr 1978-79; Jamestown Pub Schls Head Start Tchr 1979-83, Fourth Grd Tchr 1983-; *ai:* NEA 1978-; Sertoma Club 1992-, Sec.

FASNACHT, JUDY ANN, Science Teacher; *b:* Harrisburg, PA; *m:* Donald A.; *c:* Joelle Alayne; *ed:* Bloomsburg Univ (BSEd) Earth, Space Sci, Gen Sci 1975; Temple Univ (MSEd) Gen Prgm in Gen Ed 1980; *cr:* Halifax Area Schl Dist Sci Tchr 1975-; *ai:* Sci Task Group; NEA, PA St Ed Assn 1975-; Halifax Ed Assn 1975-, Treas; NSTA; PA Sci Tchrs Assn; Amer Bus Women's Assn 1979-, Pres, VP, Rec Sec, Woman of Yr 1987; Team Parent Girls Sftbl Millersburg; Band Aids Org Millersburg; David's Church Choir; Dept of Energy Grant PA 1990; Dir of Sci Fair 1983-94; *office:* Halifax Area Schl Dist 3940 Peters Mountain Rd Halifax PA 17032*

FASNACHT, LLOYD J.,JR., Economics & Government Teacher; *b:* Lebanon, PA; *m:* Elizabeth Ann Dissinger; *c:* Matthew Jon, Chad ANdrew; *ed:* Temple Univ (MS) Ed 1978; Western MD Admin Cert 1977; 60 Credit Hrs Penn St, Millersville Univ; *cr:* Lebanon Cath HS Soc Stud Tchr 1972-73; Middletown HS Soc Stud Tchr 1973-; *ai:* Negotiation, In-Svc, NHS, Schl Improvement Comms; NEA 1973-; Local Blood Bank, Chm; *office:* Middletown Area HS 1155 N Union St Middletown PA 17057

FASSETT, BERT ARNOLD, 4th Grade Teacher; *b:* Cleveland, OH; *m:* Deborah Lynn Stuart; *c:* Michael, Scott; *ed:* Cleveland St (BA) Comm 1973; Tchng Cert 1986; *cr:* Complexicable Dir, Audio, Visual 1973-76; Top Svcs Branch Mgr 1976-85; Lakewood City Schls Tchr 1985-; *ai:* Safety Patrol Dir; Cmptr Lab Head; 4th, 5th Grd Bsktbl Prgm Organizer, Referee; BSA 1992-; PTA Edctr of Yr Schl & Lakwood 1994; Sallie Mae First Yr Tchr Awd; Nom Ashland Oil Tchr Awd; *office:* Mc Kinley Elem Schl 1351 W Clifton Blvd Lakewood OH 44107

FASSETT, LORRAINE HILMA, Medical Careers Teacher; *b:* New York City, NY; *c:* JoAnne Vernon, Michael Vernon; *ed:* Mountainside Hospital Schl of Nursing (RN) Nursing 1952; Jersey City St Coll (BA) Hlth Ed 1971; Hood Coll (MA) Psych 1981, (MA) Comm Counseling 1985; *cr:* Various Private Hospitals Staff Nurse 1952-61; Boonton Pub Schls Nurse 1961-66; Planned Parenthood Clinic Supvr 1971-74; Montgomery Cty Pub Schls Hlth Ed Tchr 1974-80, Medical Careers Tchr 1980-; *ai:* Medical Career Club; Wellness Coord Fac; In Svc Tchr of Family Life & Human Sexuality; NEA, MD St Tchrs Assn 1979-; Montgomery Cty Tchrs Assn, Staff Rep 1981-85; Heritage Green Condominium Assn 1977-, Comm Mem, Pres 3 Terms, VP 2 Terms, Outstanding Svc Awd 2 Yrs; Amer Heart Assn Save-a-Sweet Heart Prgm 6 Yrs; Amer Red Cross Youth Act; Feed the Homeless with Medical Careers Club; *home:* 13215 Dairymaid Dr Apt T-1 Germantown MD 20874

FASSETT, MARILYN CAROL, Social Studies Teacher; *b:* Manhatten, NY; *ed:* Morgan St Univ (BA) Pol Sci 1970; St Univ at Stony Brook (MLA) Liberal Stud 1978; 45 Credit Hrs in Post Grad Stud; *cr:* Longwood Jr HS Dist Tchr 1970-; *ai:* Tutoring; AFT 1970-; NYST 1970-; Natl Cncl for Soc Stud 1990-; Mid Island Tchrs Assn 1970-, Bldg Rep; Longwood Jr HS Excl in Tchng Awd 1988; Outstanding Contribution Awd to Amityville, Copiague, & E Farmingdale Ctr 1987; *office:* Longwood Jr HS 198 Longwood Rd Middle Island NY 11953*

FASTIGGI, JOANN MAIELLO, Resource Room Teacher; *b:* Bronx, NY; *m:* John H.; *c:* Jennifer, Christine; *ed:* Dominican Coll (BA) Psych 1981; NY Univ (MA) Spcl Ed Tchr of Emotionally Challenged 1982; 9 Credit Hrs in Comp Tech; 9 Credit Hrs in Rdng; *cr:* Margaret Chapman Schl Tchr of Physically & Mentally Challenged 1982-83; A MacArthur Barr MS Resource Room Tchr 1983-; *ai:* NYSUT 1983-; AFT 1983-; Nanuet Tchrs

Assn Local Union 1983-, Treas 1988-; *office:* Nanuet MS 143 Church St Nanuet NY 10954

FASULO, RINA CRESPO, Bilingual Teacher; *b:* Havana, Cuba; *m:* Andrew; *c:* Teresa Maria Fogel; *ed:* Univ of Havana (PHD) Dr in Pedagogy 1970; Hunter Coll at NY City (MS) Arts 1971; Long Island Univ (MS) Ed 1980; Guid Stud Lehman Coll of NY City; *cr:* Pub Schl 21 Biling Tchr 3 Yrs; Pub Schl 9 Biling Tchr 8 Yrs; Pub Schl 22 Biling Tchr 1 Yr; Pub Schl 19 Biling Tchr 7 Yrs; Pub Schl 3 Biling Tchr 1 Yr; Pub Schl 12 Tchr 2 Yrs; Ctr for Continuing Ed GED Tchr, Guid Cnslr 10 Yrs; Instituto Felix Varela Tchr 5 Yrs; Monsignor Scanlon HS Lang Tchr 5 Yrs; *ai:* Span Club; Puertorican Day Parade; NABT 1980-; SABE 1980-, Biling Tchr of Yr; Assn of Hispanic Prof, One of the Founders; *home:* 31 Yonkers Ter Yonkers NY 10704

FATICA, JAMES FRANKLIN, High School Vocal Teacher; *b:* Cleveland, OH; *m:* Amy Mottice; *c:* Zachary; *ed:* Coll Conservatory of Music (BA) Music Ed 1990; Mary Sowul & Communicate Inst at Walsh Univ; *cr:* Trinity Luth Church Vocal Music Dir 1991-; Wickliffe HS Vocal Music Dir 1990-; *ai:* Womens Chorus; Music Asst Rockefeller Road Review; Marching Band Asst Dir; WEA 1990-; OMEA 1990-; KIDS Comm; Cleveland Orch Chorus 1995; *office:* Wickliffe City Schls 2255 Rockefeller Rd Wickliffe OH 44092

FATOUROS, VASILIKI, Professor of Business Mgmt; *b:* Sparta, Greece; *m:* Christos; *c:* Diane, Maria; *ed:* Northeastern Univ (BS) Bus Admin 1974; Babson Coll (MBA) Fin 1976; Schl of Indstrl Stud at Athens; *cr:* Mass Bay Comm Coll Lecturer 1978-81; Hellenic coll Assoc Prof 1979-87; Curry Coll Prof of Bus Mngmt 1987-; *ai:* Comm on Comm, Lib, Keighton Fund Comms; AAUP 1987-, Treas; Philoptohos Soc 1975-, Bd; Hellenic Wooman Assn 1981-; Babson Women In Bus Assn 1979-; Honorary Letter Awd; Field Experience Awd; *office:* Curry Coll 1071 Blue Hill Ave Milton MA 02186

FATTORUSSO, JULIE-ANN, High School Mathematics Tchr; *b:* Brooklyn, NY; *ed:* Saint John Univ (BA) Math 1977, (MA) Math 1979; Addl 30 Credits Beyond Masters Degree; *cr:* Saint Peters Girls HS Math Tchr 1979-84; Edward R Murrow HS Math Tchr 1984-; *ai:* Math Dept Programming Comm; Cooperating Tchr for Stu Tchrs; Asst to Dept Supvr During Regents; Math Dept Curr Comm; NCTM, ATMNYC 1976-; UFT 1984-; *office:* Edward R Murrow HS 1600 Avenue L Brooklyn NY 11230*

FATULA, CAROL ANN, Art Teacher; *b:* Johnstown, PA; *ed:* IN Univ of PA (BS) Art Ed 1990; 18 Credit Hrs; *cr:* Forest Hills HS Art Tchr 1990-; *ai:* Girls Var Bsktbl Coach; Yrbk & Newspaper Adv; NEA 1990-; PSEA 1990-; Cambria Cty Comm Arts Ctr 1995-; *office:* Forest Hills Sr HS 489 Locust St PO Box 325 Sidman PA 15955

FATUZZO, JOHN JUSTIN, Life Science Teacher; *b:* Jersey City, NJ; *m:* Josephine; *c:* John Justin II, Anthony Michael; *ed:* Rutgers St Univ (BA) Sci & His 1966; Jersey City St Coll (MAT) Sci 1970; 45 Credit Hrs Montclair St Coll Admin Supvr Pgm; Prin Supvr Cert 1982; Post Grad Stud Trenton St Coll, Bridgewater St Coll; *cr:* Good Counsel HS Algebra & Gen Sci Tchr 1966-69; Tenafly MS Life & Earth Sci Photography Tchr 1969-80; Eric S Smith MS Life Sci, Earth & Phys Sci Tchr 1981-; Ramsey HS Fndtns in Sci Tchr 1982-87; *ai:* Stu Cncl, Photography, Ecology & Radio Control Club Former Adv; Sci Fiction, Video Classics Adv; Local Hockey, Ftbl & Bsbl Coach & Mgr; NEA 1969-; NSTA 1993-; Jaycees Former Mem; COSMOS; Garden St Ski Club 1989-, Ski VP; Summer Trng Inst Outstdng MS Tchr Grant Awd 1994; Natl Sci Tchrs Convention Presenter 1996; Designed, Implemented & Chaired Dist Wide Sci Symposium Day; Sci Grants Tenafly & Ramsey; *office:* Eric S Smith MS 2 Monroe St Ramsey NJ 07446*

FAUB, PATRICIA A., English Teacher; *b:* Pittsburgh, PA; *ed:* LaRoche Coll (BA) Sociology 1973; Marywood Coll (MS) Elem Ed 1984; *cr:* Our Lady Queen of Peace 3rd-6th Grd Tchr 1971-74, 1976-81; St Joseph 4th & 5th Grd Tchr 1974-75; Sts Peter & Paul 4th-7th Grd Tchr 1975-76; St Marys 3rd, 6th-7th Grd Tchr 1981-82; Sacred Heart Elem 5th-8th Grd Tchr 1982-; *ai:* Schl Newspaper; Safety Patrol; NCEA 1971-; WPTE 1993-; *office:* Sacred Heart Elem Schl 325 Emerson St Pittsburgh PA 15206

FAUB, ROBERT ALAN, Assistant Professor of Music; *b:* Pittsburgh, PA; *m:* Cathryn; *ed:* SUNY at Potsdam (BM) Music Ed 1986; Univ of NC at Greensboro (MM) Music Performance 1988; *cr:* SUNY Potsdam Asst Prof of Music 1990-; *ai:* UUP 1990-; NASA 1984-; *office:* S U N Y Coll At Potsdam Pierrepont Avenue Potsdam NY 13676

FAUCEGLIA, MARION LYNN, Teacher; *b:* Sharon, PA; *m:* Ted; *ed:* Youngstown St Univ (BS) Eng & Theatre 1971; Westminister Coll 1982; *cr:* Sharpsville Area Schl Dist Eng, Speech Tchr 1973-; *ai:* Audiovisual Dir; Prof Dev, Steering, Fac Advy, Strategic Planning Comm; Field Trip Coord; Dist Writing Resource Person; Tchr Mentor; Coach; NEA 1973-; PSEA 1973-, Bldg Rep; Delta Kappa Gamma 1983-, Alpha Alpha St DKG Intnl Schlsp; NCTE; Humane Soc of Mercer Cty 1984-, Treas, VP, Outstanding Achvmt Awd; Alpha Alpha St DKG Intnl, Phi Delta Kappa Schlsp.

FAUGHNAN, LORRAINE DESIANO, Mathematics Tchr; *b:* Brooklyn, NY; *c:* Stephen, Brian; *ed:* St Joseph's Coll (BA) Math 1972; Richmond Coll (MS) Math Ed 1975; *cr:* Our Lady of Angels Schl 7th-8th Grd Math, Sci Tchr 1972-76; Fontbonne Hall Acad Math Tchr 1976-79; Tottenville HS Math Tchr 1986-; *ai:* Fac Adv; Math Olympics Team; NCTM 1994-; *office:* Tottenville HS 100 Luten Ave Staten Island NY 10312*

FAULK, PAMELA COLE, 7th-8th Grade English Teacher; *b:* Columbus, OH; *m:* Larry D.; *c:* Jeffrey A., Erin M.; *ed:* Bluffton Coll (BA) Eng 1969; *cr:* Lakewood Jr HS 7-9 Grd Eng Tchr 1969-70; Jonathan Alder Schls 7-8 Grd Eng Tchr 1970-; *ai:* Delta Kappa Gamma 1973-, VP, Pres; NCTE 1992-; Dublin Music Boosters 1988-; Girl Scouts of Amer 1984-, Ldrshp; *office:* Canaan MS Rt 42 Plain City OH 43064

FAULKNER, KYLE L., Social Studies Teacher; *b:* Oswego, NY; *m:* Deborah LaSalle; *c:* Kaitlin Renee; *ed:* LeMoyne Coll (BA) His 1991; 15 Grad Hrs St Bonaventure Univ; *cr:* Fillmore Central Schl Scndry Soc Stud Tchr 1993-; *ai:* JV Bsbl Coach; Jr HS Girls Bsktbl; Class Adv; *home:* 105 Bernard St Fillmore NY 14735*

FAULKNER, SANDRA, Title I Coordinator; *ed:* Slippery Rock Univ (MS) Rdng Specialist 1972; Univ of Pittsburgh (MS) Supervision 1978; *cr:* Hopewell Area-Raccoon Elem Schl 3rd Grd Tchr 1968-70; Hopewell Area ISD Title I Rdng Specialist 1971-74; Hopewell Area Schl Title I Coord 1975-; *ai:* Parent Involvement Project; Strategic Planning Action Team Ldr; Leotta C. Hawthorne Rdng Cncl 1970-, Pres, Literacy Awd; KSRA 1970-, Bd; IRA 1970-; PAFPC 1973-; PTA 1968-, Kid Care Gift of Time Tribute, PA Congress of Parents & Tchrs.

FAULKNER, SHAWN ALAN, Teacher; *b:* Tiffin, OH; *ed:* TN Temple Univ (BS) Elem Ed 1988; Wright St Univ (MED) Educl Admin 1991; OH Real Estate Sales Liscense 1990; *cr:* Temple Chrstn Schl Tchr 1988-, Supvr 1993-; *ai:* Sr Play-Musical Dir; OH Music Ed Assn 1989-; Lima Bapt Temple 1967-; *office:* Temple Christian Schl 982 Brower Rd Lima OH 45801*

FAULKNER, SYLVIA JANE (SANFORD), Music Teacher; *b:* Galesburg, IL; *m:* William L.; *c:* Julia Faulkner Pechlivanos, David E.; *ed:* 70 Hrs Post Grad Stud; *cr:* Lexington Pub Schls K-12th Grd Music Tchr 1963-64; Brookfield K-8th Grd Music Tchr 1964-65; Winnebago Cty Schls K-8th Grd Music Tchr 1968-69; Rockford Pub Schls K-6th Music Tchr, 4th & 6th Grd Classroom Tchr 1969-68; Tchng Act for Lang Knowledge Facilitator 1978-80; Toledo Pub Schls K-8th Grd Music Tchr & Choir Dir 1987-; *ai:* Toledo Pub Schls Fine Arts Chm; Toledo Fed of Tchrs, Music Tchrs Rep; Alpha Delta Kappa, Chptr Pres; Delta Kappa Gamma, VP; Music Edctrs Natl Conf; OH Music Edctrs Assn; Visiting Nurse Extra Care Vol; Amer Cancer Soc Vol; Amer Heart Assn Vol; Woodward HS Hockey Boosters Vol; Series of Childrens Songs Pub 1984; *home:* 3615 Christie Blvd Toledo OH 43606*

FAUNCE, RUSSELL J., Lead Music Teacher; *b:* Watertown, NY; *ed:* Potsdam Coll (BM) Music Ed 1982, (MM) Music Ed 1987; Attnd St Lawrence Univ; *cr:* Watertown City Schls Music Dir 1982-; *office:* Watertown City Schl Dist 1335 Washington St Watertown NY 13601

FAUST, CARL H., Biological Science Teacher; *b:* New York City, NY; *c:* Carl Eric, Christopher, Christian; *ed:* C. W. Post (BS) Bio 1962, (MS) Bio 1966; Hofstra Univ 15 Hrs; SUNY at Stony Brook 25 Hrs; Suffolk Comm Coll 15 Hrs; *cr:* Hicksville HS Sci Tchr 1962-67; Smithtown HS Biological Scis Tchr 1967-; *ai:* NSTA 1980-; AFT 1970-; STA 1967-; Mason Dungan Patent Lodge #1134 1961-; Shriner Kismet Tmpl 1964-; *office:* Smithtown HS 100 Central Rd Smithtown NY 11787

FAUVELL, THOMAS CARMINE, Social Studies Teacher; *b:* Brooklyn, NY; *m:* Patrica Ann; *c:* Thomas John, Meghan Leigh; *ed:* Nassau Comm Jr Coll (AA) Liberal Arts 1975; LI Univ C. W. Post Ctr (BA) Scndry Soc Stud 7-12 1977, (MS) Admin, Supervision 1981; Coaching Cert Ftbl, Wrestling, Track, LaCrosse; NYS First Aid, CPR Certs; Anti Drug, Violence Trainer; *cr:* Brentwood Sonderling HS 10th Grd Soc Stud Tchr, Ftbl, Wrestling, Lacrosse Coach 1977-79; Long Island Luth HS 9th-12th Grd Soc Stud Tchr, Ftbl, Wrestling, Track Coach 1979-86; Herricks MS 8th Grd Soc Stud Tchr, Ftbl, Lacrosse Coach 1986-; *ai:* Head Ftbl, Lacrosse Coach; Herricks Comm Yth Cncl Adv; Nassau Cty Wrestling Ofcl; Herricks Mentoring for 1st Yr Tchrs; AFT, NYSTA, HTA, Long Island Cncl for Soc Stud, Nassau Cty Lacrosse Coaches Assn 1986-; Natl Fed of Coaches, Ofcls Assn 1979-; PTA, West Islip PTA 1986-; NYSPTA 1995-, Life Mem, Jenkins Awd; Coach of Yr Suffolk Cty Wrestling League One JV 1977-78, Atlantic Coast Luth HS Track 1981-82, NYS Private Schls Wrestling 1982-84, Island Ftbl 1985, Vince Lombardi 1985; Nassau Cty Lacrosse Coaches Assn Most Improved Team 1991, 1995, Conf A Coach of Yr 1995; *office:* Herricks MS 7 Hilldale Rd Albertson NY 11507*

FAVA, STEVEN RAYMOND, Asst Hdmstr, Eng & Math Tchr; *b:* Weehawken, NJ; *ed:* Fordham (BA) Eng, Philosphy 1975; Notre Dame (MA) Eng, Theology 1990; Oxford Univ 1977, Summer Grad; *cr:* Regis HS Eng Tchr 1975-78; St Peters Prep Eng & His Tchr 1978-80; Oratory Prep Eng & Latin Tchr 1980-; *ai:* Coll Placement Guidance Dir; Teen Arts Dir; NHS Moderator; NEA, NCTE 1975-; Poetry Pub 1974, 1977-80; *office:* Oratory Prep Schl 1 Beverly Rd Summit NJ 07901

FAVALI, DALEN NAWROCKI, Music Dept Chair; *b:* Woonsocket, RI; *m:* Joseph Downey Jr.; *ed:* Harvard Univ (AB) Music 1980; Attending RI Coll MAT Music; *cr:* Burrillville HS Music Dept Chair, Band Dir 1986-; *ai:* NEA, MENC 1986-; RI Music Edctrs Assn 1986-, Pres; Natl Band Assn 1989-, VP; Harvard Club of RI 1986-, Schls Comm; *office:* Burrillville H S 425 East Ave Harrisville RI 02830*

FAVAZZO, DOMINIC MICHAEL, Chemistry Teacher; *b:* Cleveland, OH; *ed:* Miami Univ (BS) Chem Ed 1992; John Carroll Univ (MED) Guid, Cnslng 1996; 6 Hrs Toward Admin, Supervision Cert; Working Toward LPC; *cr:* Charles F. Brush HS Chem Tchr 1992-; *ai:* Head Var Bsbl Coach; Asst Bsktbl Coach; Vision Comm; Attendance Comm Chm; Teen Inst Adv; Core Team; Holiday Family Drive for Poor Chm; NEA 1992-; OHSAA 1995-; Brush Booster Club 1992-; Alumni Assn 1995-; *office:* Charles F. Brush HS 4875 Glenlyn Rd Lyndhst-Mayfld OH 44124

FAVINGER, ANTHONY WILLIAM, 8th Grd Earth & Space Sci Tchr; *b:* Allentown, PA; *m:* Karen Louse Lechler; *c:* Sarah, Rachel, Christy; *ed:* East Stroudsburg St (BS) Geography & Sci 1966; Lehigh Univ (MS) Ed Tech 1990; Wilkes Coll Post Grad Hrs ISCS Sci Curr 1969-71; *cr:* Williams Valley Schl Dist Sci Tchr 1966-67; Bethlehem Area Schl Dist Sci Tchr 1967-; *ai:* PA Jr Acad of Sci; Bethlehem Area Church League & Girls Hurricane Youth Team Bsktbl Coach; Materials Sci Camp 1990-93; BEA, PSEA & NEA 1967-; NSTA 1988-; Pocono Environmental Ed Ctr 1988-; NSTA, Local Ldr 1995-; Burnside Plantation 1989-, Bd of Dir; Musikfest 1988-93, Vol; North Cntrl Bsbl Assn, Sect; Otustanding Svc 1984 & 1991; Howard Hughes Grant 1989; NASA Lunar Sampling Prgm 1991; Co-Chair Sci Mid Sts 1993-; *office:* East Hills MS 2005 Chester Ave Bethlehem PA 18018*

FAVORITO, LEE ANN MARTINDALE, Science & History Teacher; *b:* Lima, OH; *m:* Benedict; *c:* Andrew; *ed:* Eastern KY Univ (BS) Ed 1979; Wright St Univ Bio; *cr:* St Marys City Schls 7th Grd Sci, Elem PE Tchr 1979-84; Black River Local 7th-8th Grd Sci Tchr 1984-88; STS Joseph & John Schl 7th Grd Sci, His Tchr 1990-; *ai:* Right-To-Read Week Co-Chair; 7th-8th Grd Stdnts Career Day Organizer; Neighborhood Watch Eaton Twp 1995-, Organizer; Black River 8th Grd Sci Stdnts Took 1st Place in Natl Sci Olympiad 1985; *office:* SS Joseph & John Schl 12580 Pearl Rd Strongsville OH 44136

FAWCETT, CHERYL LYNN, Asst Prof of Chrstn Ed; *b:* Bethesa, MD; *ed:* Bapt Bible Coll (AA) Bible 1973, (BRE) Bible 1975; Wheaton Grad Schl (MA) Chrstn Ministries 1977; Trinity Evangelical Divinity (EdD) Chrstn Ed 1991; *cr:* Faith Bapt Church Chrstn Ed Dir 1976-80; Tabernacle Bapt Church Chrstn Ed Dir 1980-82; Bapt Coll Stu Activities Dir 1982-91; Cedarville Coll Asst Prof 1991-; *ai:* Chi Delta Nu Adv; Chaplain Womens Vllybl; North Amer Prof CE 1991-; Prof Assoc CE 1991-; Several Articles Pub; *office:* Cedarville Coll PO Box 601 Cedarville OH 45314*

FAWCETT, GAY, Curr & Instr Director; *b:* Akron, OH; *m:* John; *c:* Jonathan, Christopher; *ed:* Univ of Akron (BS) Elem Ed 1970, (MS) Lang Arts Ed 1985; Kent St Univ (PHD) Curr & Instr 1994; *cr:* Guernsey Cty Schls Tchr 1975-78; Stow City Schls Tchr 1980-90; Summit Cty Ed Svc Ctr Lang Arts Consultant 1990-94, C&I Dir 1994-; *ai:* IRA 1980-, Assoc Ed of Rdng Tchr; North East OH ASCD 1985-, Pres; Phi Delta Kappa 1987-; Federal Tech Learning Challenge Grant Co-Dir; Outstdng Dissertation Awd Assn of Supvision & Curr Dev; Numerous Articles Pub; *office:* Summit Cty Educl Svc Ctr 420 Washington Ave Cuyahoga Falls OH 44221

FAX, JESSE STEWART, English & Speech Teacher; *b:* Rochester, NY; *m:* JoAnn Haynes; *c:* Allison Haynes; *ed:* Howard Univ (BFA) 1968; NY Univ (MED) 1971; Trinity Coll 29 Credit Hrs; *cr:* NY City Pub Schls Tchr 1968-71; DC Pub Schls Tchr 1971-73; WHUR-FM Music & Pgm Dir 1973-87; *ai:* Radio Trng Pgm Coord; Stu Trainer for Careers in Radio Broadcasting; Amer Film Inst 1981-; NCTE 1996; WHUR-FM Pgm Dir Led Station to #1 Arbitron Rating in 1985 1st Time Ever; Univ Owned & Operated Radio Station Reached #1 in Major Market; *office:* Suitland HS 5200 Silver Hill Rd District Heights MD 20747

FAY, BRIAN G., English Instr; *b:* Syracuse, NY; *m:* Stephanie Fay; *ed:* Onondaga Comm Coll (AA) Arts, Sci 1988; Oswego SUNY (BA) Scndry Ed, Eng 1992; Radford Univ (MA) Eng 1994; *cr:* Fayetteville Manius HS Eng Instr 1995-; *office:* Fayetteville-Manlius HS 8201 E Seneca Tnpke Manlius NY 13104

FAY, MARY HERLIHY, Director & Professor; *b:* Teaneck, NJ; *m:* Thomas Patrick; *c:* Christopher, Kerrianne, Erin; *ed:* West Chester Univ (BS) Comm 1979; Temple Univ Schl of Law (JD) Law 1987; Post Grad Stud West Chester Univ; *cr:* Widener Univ Adjunct Prof 1981-90; Cumberland Cty Coll Asst Prof 1989-94, Pres 1995-; *ai:* Mock Tr Adv; Curr Comm; Clearview Regnl HS Bd of Ed; NJ Bar Fndtn;M Comm 1993-; Amer Bar Assn, NJ Bar Assn 1988-; NJ Consc Paralegal Educators 1992-, Founder & Chair; Amer Assn of Educators 1989-; NJ Supreme Court Comm on Paralegal E Clearview Regnl HS Schlsp Comm Pres 1992-; Widener Univ Prof 1988; *office:* Cumberland County Coll PO Box 517 Cc Vineland NJ 08360

FAY, THOMAS WILLIAM, Mathematics & Religion Teacher; *b:* NY; *m:* Mary LaLonde; *c:* Thomas R., Peter M., Matthew J.; *ed* Dayton (BA) Philosophy 1968; 74 Post Grad Hrs St John Seininitry, East Aurora, Canisius Coll at Buffalo, Niagara Univ a Falls; *cr:* Holy Redeemer Schl Eighth Grd Tchr 1971-73; Cardina HS Rel, Math Tchr 1973-78; NYS Office of Drug Abuse Remed GED Tchr 1975-76; Canisius HS Math Tchr 1978-79; St Mary's Rel Tchr 1979-; *ai:* Math Chm; Tecruitment Team; Curr Comm Lay Tchrs 1974-, Pres; Diocesan Tchr Awd 1982, Tchr of Yr 19 Tchr of Yr 1994; *home:* 196 Hamilton Dr Amherst NY 14226*

FAY, WILLIAM JOSEPH, Music Teacher; *b:* Waterloo, NY; *ed* Coll at Fredonia (BM) Music Ed 1975; St Univ Coll at Buff Multidisciplinary Stud 1989; Cert of Advanced Stud SUNY at Attnd Saratoga Potsdam Choral Inst; Addl Stud Ithaca Coll, Univ, Westminster Choir Coll; *cr:* Sweet Home Schls Music Tchr St Thomas Aquinas Schl & Church Music Dir 1979-81; Niagara F Music Tchr 1981-; *ai:* Vocal Coach; LaSalle Players Drama Clu Educators Natl Con, NY St Schl Music Assn, Phi Delta Kap Choral Dirs Assn; Schlsp Saratoga Potsdam Choral Inst; S Granted By Niagara Falls Schl Dist; *office:* La Salle Sr HS 1500 Rd Niagara Falls NY 14217

FAYAD, SALIM H., Math & Physics Instructor; *b:* Beirut, Leb Diane Gemo; *c:* Mark, Laura; *ed:* Purdue Univ (MS) Math 1973 Montpellier (BS) Math; *cr:* Brookdale Comm Coll Physics Instr Ocean Cty Coll Math Instr 1987-95; Red Bank Cath HS Math & Tchr 1987-; *ai:* Calculus & Physics Publications; *office:* R Catholic H S 10 Peters Pl Red Bank NJ 07701

FAYAN, ANNE MARIE M., Mathematics Teacher; *b:* Fall Rive Marisa Barnaby; *ed:* Salve Regin Univ (BA) Math 1977; V Polytechnic Inst (MS) Math 1996; *cr:* St Xavier Acad Math Instr Bishop Connolly HS Math Tchr 1981-; *office:* Bishop Connolly Elsbree St Fall River MA 02720*

FAZENBAKER, CHARLES ROBERT, Social Studies Dept C Keyser, WV; *m:* Patricia Wolf; *c:* Brian, Alex; *ed:* Frostburg St Pol Sci 1969; Western MD Coll (ME) Spec Ed 1976; 30 Hrs Ps Coll; *cr:* South Carroll HS Work Stud Tchr 1972-74, Work St 1974-75, Learning Disabilities Specialist 1975-81, Psych Tchr SS Dept Chprsn 1994-; *ai:* Var Men's Soccer, Jr Var Woman's Sft Discipline Comm Chprsn; Amer Psychological Assn; NCSS; Li YMCA 1990-, Comm, Mbrshp & Means; *office:* South Carroll HS Old Liberty Rd Sykesville MD 21784

FAZENBAKER, R. ALLEN, Science Educator; *b:* Langley AF Deborah Lynn Staudt-Roediger; *c:* Paula Roediger, Amy Roedig Kay Prusnick, Rachel (dec); *ed:* OH St Univ (BS) Ag 19 Agronomy 1977; John Carroll Univ Cert Ed 1985; Kent St Univ Boromeo Coll Philosophy, Theology; *cr:* ISOLAB Corp Pr Chemist 1978-80; Union Carbide Research Biologist 1980-82; Shamrock Research Biologist 1982-84; Buckeye Local Schls Sci 1986-; *ai:* Asst Wrestling Coach; Exploring Post High Advent Host Family for AFS;Bcyclng; NEA, OEA, BEA 1986-, Local Pr 1991-; Asntabula Cty Conservation Tchr of Yr 1993; *office:* Edg HS 2428 Blake Rd Ashtabula OH 44004

FAZIO, DOLORES ANN (DANKO), Eighth Grade English Te McKeesport, PA; *c:* Scott A., Mark W.; *ed:* Penn St Univ (BS) E MS Eq Eng 1982; *cr:* Ft Couch MS 7th Grd Lang Arts Tchr 196 & 8th Grd Lang Arts Tchr 1973-; *ai:* Comp Comm; Girls Bsktbl Coach; AFT 1976-, Treas; *office:* Ft Couch MS 515 Fort C Pittsburgh PA 15241

FAZIO, GREGORY GRANT, Soc Stud Tchr & Dept Head; Brighton, PA; *m:* Phyllis Malagise; *c:* Bryan, Shelley; *ed:* Edinb of PA (BS) Scndry Soc Stud 1970; 24 Post Grad Hrs; *cr:* New High Soc Stud Tchr 1970-, Soc Stud Tchr & Dept Head 1993-; Ge Instr & Tchng of Soc Stud 1987-; *ai:* Fresh Class Spon 1973-; H Coach 1971-; Head Girls Tennis Coach 1987-; NEA 1970-; *h* Klein Rd New Brighton PA 15066*

FAZIO, RONALD WALTER, Art Teacher; *b:* Oneonta, NY; *m* Ann; *c:* Brett, Erich; *ed:* SUCO at Oneonta (BA) Art Studio 1972 Hrs Pro-Ed; Defense Lang Inst Presidio Stud Vietnamese; *cr* Valley-Springfield Cntrl Schl 24 Yrs; *ai:* APART; NYSUT 197 Legion Post 259 20 Yrs, Bd Mem; US Marines 1966-68, Sv Presidential Unit Citation, 3 Purple Hearts, Disabled Vet; *office* Valley-Springfield Ctr Nielsen Rd Cherry Valley NY 13320

FAZIO, THOMAS MICHAEL, Student Assistance Coun Huntington, NY; *m:* Jean Anne Hutton; *c:* Thomas, Caitlin; *ed:* Brockport (BS) Psych 1975, (MS) Special Needs 1977; C. W. P Schl Cnslng 1984; 45 Credit Hrs Cnslng; *cr:* SUNY Instr 1975-78 Therapist 1978-80; Concepts for Narcotics Prevent Comm Cnslr Northport Schl Dist Stu Assistance Cnslr 1985-; *ai:* Drug, Alc Force, Schl Store, Peer Facilitator Adv; Boys Soccer, Weight Coach; 8th Grd Trip Coord; WSCA 1990-; UTN 1985-; UTN 19 Dirs; NYSUT 1994-95, Del; Coord Parent Ctr USFD #4; *home:* 1 Ct Northport NY 11768*

FAZZIO, GERARD JOSEPH, Social Studies Teacher; *b:* Kearn Ali Marie, Kristen Leigh; *ed:* Montelair St (BA) Geography, Urb Attnd Catawba Coll 1977-78; William Paterson Admin, Supvr St Mary's Schl PE, Hlth Tchr 1979-80; DePaul HS Soc Stud Tc *ai:* Frosh Ftbl, Var Wrestling, Var Girls Track Head Coach 198 Class Adv 1987-; Bsktbl Site Supvr; NEA, NCEA, PCCA 198 Natl 1976-; Wrestling Coach of Yr 1987; Merit Stipend Awd 199 Tchng Awd 1988; PCCA Wrestling Victories 1995; PCCA Merit A *home:* 199 Lafayette Ave Lyndhurst NJ 07071*

FEAR, DON W., Photography Teacher; *b:* McKeesport, PA; McClellan; *c:* Alan; *ed:* Corcoran Schl of Art (BFA) Photograp Univ of DE (MFA) Photography 1986; *cr:* E Systems Photographic Technician 1975-79; McGraw Hill Photographic T 1979-81; US Govt Tech & Scientific Photographer 1981-83; Su for the Arts Photography Instr 1986-; Corcoran Schl of Art Ph Instr 1996-; *ai:* Photography Club; Kathleen Ewing Gallery E Artist; Soc For Photographic Ed 1986-; NEA 1986-; PGCEA 19 Endowment for the Arts 1993-, Panel Mem; Cncl for Basic Ed; A Comm; Natl Endowment for the Arts Flwshp; Lois E Vinnette Ph Tchr of the Yr; Design & Implemented Facilities & Curr for Ph Pgm Suitland Ctr For the Arts; *office:* Suitland HS 5200 Silve Forestville MD 20747

FEATHERSTONE, JOSEPH, Physical Education Teacher; *b:* NY; *ed:* Univ of CA at Davis (MA) Exercise Sci 1992; *cr:* Univ Davis Cardiac Rehabilitation Coord 1983-85; Beech Channel HS efferson HS PE Tchr 1988-91; Cardozo HS PE Tchr 1991-; *ai:* Track Team, Coed Marine Corps Yth Phys Fitness Team, Jr Var ach; Spec Olympics 1994-, Vol Coach; St Camillus Sports 1993-, l Coach; Rockaway Gliders Running Club 1991-, Pres; Article of CA Rsrch Grant; *office:* Benjamin N Cardozo HS 57-00 223rd e NY 11364

ALPH JOHN, High School Math Teacher; *b:* Perth Amboy, NJ; ne Kavka; *c:* Wendy, Timothy; *ed:* St Francis Coll at PA (BS) 8; Newark St Coll (MA) Math, Ed 1973; *cr:* South Plainfield HS r 1959-; Instructivision Inc Author, Math Consultant 1988-; *ai:* ls Var Bowling Coach 1975-; Boys Var Tennis Coach 1970-80; EA, SPEA, AMTNJ 1959-; NCTM 1991-; Middlesex Cty Coaches)-, Pres 1982-83; Knights of Columbus 1959-; South Plainfield and 1972-, Civic Chm, Educl Division; Author of SAT I Test ator, ACT Mathematics, HSPT Success, EWT Succes Math ks; Co-Author of SRA for NJ HSPT Math Workbook; ing Author of SAT Edge Math Workbook; *home:* 110 Dorset Dr infield NJ 07080*

ERRY LEE, Dir of Communication Media; *b:* Morgantown, WV; Jean Tasker; *c:* Cassandra; *ed:* Fairmont St Coll (BA) Ed 1971; Jniv (MS) Commnctn 1975; *cr:* Allegany Comm Coll Dir 1975-; & Stu Adv; Various Comm Assignments; Outstdng Citizen of the Article Pub; *office:* Allegany Comm Coll 12401 Willowbrook Rd nd MD 21502

JOHN GEORGE, Science Teacher; *b:* Wilkes-Barre, PA; *ed:* PA AS) Wildlife Bio 1982; Lock Haven Univ (BS) Scndry Ed, Bio rion Univ (ME) Sci Ed 1989; *cr:* Redbank Valley Schl Dist Sci 5-; *ai:* Vlybl, Sftbl, Wrestling Coach; Ski Club, Stdnts Against Earth Adv; NEA, PSEA, RVEA 1986-; Seneca Rocks Audubon , Pres, Newsletter Ed; Conservation Educator of Yr Clarion Co o's Who Among Amer Ed 1996-; Pub Ldr-Vindicator Amer Bio *ne:* 221 Washington St New Bethlehem PA 16242

MADELINE STAMATO, Teacher; *b:* Long Branch, NJ; *c:* Ray; of Rochester (AB) General Sci 1961; Trenton St (MA) Phys Sci +; *cr:* Thompson Jr HS Tchr 1961-70; Memorial Tchr 1983; MS Tchr 1985-; *ai:* Math-Sci Club Adv; ROGATE Adv; NEA, CTM, NSTA, AMTNJ, NJSTA, Assn for Gifted Children; Amer v Women, Past Pres; Bd of Ed, Past Pres; NJ Local Tchr of Yr *ce:* Memorial MS Laura Herbert Dr Point Pleasant NJ 08742

, TAMARA A., Mathematics Teacher; *b:* Canton, OH; *ed:* Kent (BS) Mathematical Sci 1990; Akron Univ Masters Degree Scndry Admin; Ashland Univ Post Grad Stud; Malone Coll Post ; *cr:* Timken Sr HS Math Tchr 1991-; OH St Univ Young Scholars n Tutor 1992-95; Canton City Schls Summer Math Instr 1992-; Tech Prep Consortium Auto Engrng, Math Instr & Consultant Frosh, Soph, & Jr Class Co-Adv 1992-; Timken Adult Booster 2-; A to the Third Power Incentive Pgm Comm 1994-; Venture omm 1994-; Chrldng Adv 1995-; NCTM 1988-; NEA & OEA appa Delta Pi 1989-; Canton Prof Ed Assn 1991-; Intnl Order of ghters 1979-, OH Miss Jobs Daughter 1985, Honored Queen 1986, 2-; *office:* Timken Sr HS 521 Tuscarawas St W Canton OH 44702

N, MATTHEW SEAN, Physics Teacher; *b:* Huntington, NY; *ed:* E (BAAS) Physics Ed 1991; 27 Credit Hrs SUNY Stony Brook; rt HS Physics Tchr 5 Yrs; *ai:* MS Bsktbl & JV LaCrosse Coach; 93-; *office:* Bellport HS Beaver Dam Rd Brookhaven NY 11719

AN, DEANNA, Eighth Grade Teacher; *b:* Philadelphia, PA; *c:* oldstein, Rick Goldstein; *ed:* Temple Univ (BA) Elem Ed 1960, Psych 1979, (PHD) Ed Psych 1984; *cr:* Philadelphia Pub Schl chr 1962-64, 1974-78, 1988-; Temple Univ Tchng Grad Asst St Univ of NY Asst Prof 1985-88; *ai:* NMSA 1992-; NCTE EH CBE Flwshp; NEH Summer Seminar; RJR Next Century Schl ths, Prism Grant; *home:* 1052 N 67th St Philadelphia PA 19151*

ENNIFER ELMER, English Teacher; *b:* Johnson City, NY; *m:* ; *ed:* St Univ of NY at Binghamton (BA) Eng, Gen Lit 1989; Univ (MS) Eng Ed 1990; *cr:* Norwich HS 10th Grd Eng Tchr Weedsport Jr, Sr HS Eng Tchr 1992-; Cayuga Comm Coll Adj ng, 11th Grd Eng, Remedial Writing Tchr 1994-; *ai:* Weedsport NHS Adv; NCTE 1991-; NYSUT 1992-; NASAA 1993-; *office:* t Jr Sr HS East Brutus St Weedsport NY 13166*

, MARY JUSTINE, 4th Grade Teacher; *b:* Shamokin, PA; *ed:* rg Univ (BS) Elem Ed 1975; 24 Addl Credits; *cr:* St Mary's Schl chr 1977-80; Holy Spirit Schl 4th Grd Tchr 1982-; *office:* Holy l 250 West Ave Mount Carmel PA 17851

CELIA MAJKA, Fourth Grade Teacher; *b:* Utica, NY; *c:* Faith ssell, Christiana M. Fedor Rivet; *ed:* St Univ of NY at Oswego n Ed 1960; Attnd St Univ of NY at Cortland, St Univ of NY at Long Island Univ; Sci Undergraduate at MVCC, Utica Coll; *cr:* ro Cntrl 3rd-4th Grd Tchr 1960-63; WestMoreland Cntrl 3rd, 4th d Tchr 1964-; *office:* Westmoreland Cntrl Elem Schl Rt 233 land NY 13490

SKA, RICHARD PAUL, History, Psych, Sociology Tchr; *b:* , PA; *m:* Georgene Wilson; *c:* Erin Bridgid, Colin Michael; *ed:* Univ (BS) Ed 1982; 9 Credits Univ of IN at Bloomington; 7 vernia Coll at Reading; 4 Credits Marywood Coll at Scranton; 4 chuylkill Intermediate; *cr:* Holy Redeemer Soc Stud Tchr Nativity BVM HS Soc Stud Tchr 1988-; *ai:* Bsktbl 1983-94; r, Acad Competition Team Moderator; Audio-Visual, Locker cket Seller Ftbl; NCEA 1982-; Schuylkill Cty Historical Sco;)rder of Hibernians; Taft Inst for Two Party System; Essay's on & Politics, HS Sports; *office:* Nativity BVM HS 1 Lawtons Hl PA 17901*

O, JOHN CHARLES, Mathematics Department Chm; *b:* rg, PA; *ed:* Clarion Univ of PA (BSEd) Math 1964; Rutgers Univ ath 1971; Attnd Penn St Univ 18 Grad Credits Math, Univ of me 3 Grad Credits Math; *cr:* St Marys Area HS Math Tchr Math Tchr & Dept Chm 1988-; *ai:* NEA, PA St Ed Assn, & St ea Ed Assn 1964-; PA Cncl Tchrs of Math 1966-; Math Assn of 1987-; Natl Sci Fnd Grants from Rutgers Univ 1968-71 & Univ of ne 1979; Penn St Univ Distinguished Tchr of Honor Stdnts 1987; Area Schl Dist Tchr of Yr 1990-91; *office:* St Marys Area HS 977 s Rd Saint Marys PA 15857

O, MARY WEIS, Fifth Grade Teacher; *b:* St Marys, PA; *m:* .; *c:* David, Jeanne Fedorko Nierle, Donald, Mary Fedorko Paul; *ed:* Bloomsburg Univ (BS) El Ed 1980; PA St, Bloomsburg) El Ed 1993; Attnd UTEP at El Paso El Ed 1976; *cr:* St Bomface l Third Grd Tchr 8 Yrs; Wmspt Area Schl Dist Sub Tchr 1 Yr; e Schl Fifth Grd Tchr 6 Yrs; *ai:* Fac Fund Treas; Crossing Guard h, Schl Wide Project Comms; Peer Mediator Co-Chprsn; NEA, 0-; Church Lector, Commentator 1979-; *office:* Lose Elem Schl norial Ave Williamsport PA 17701*

O, ROBERT J., Social Studies Teacher; *b:* Shamokin, PA; *m:* cher; *c:* Brent, Christy; *ed:* Univ of Tulsa (BA) Soc Stud, Ed 1965; Credits; *cr:* Geibel Cath HS Tchr 1966-; *ai:* Asst Var Bsktbl, JV oc Stud Chprsn; NACST; Greensburg Cath Tchrs Assn, Treas; rs Cath Ed, Treas; Honoree PA Gift of Time, Greensburg Diocese 25 Yrs; *office:* Geibel Catholic HS 611 E Crawford Ave Connellsville PA 15425

FEE, ELLEN MARIE, Art Department Chairperson; *b:* New York, NY; *ed:* Marymount Manhattan Coll (BA) Art 1964; Hunter Coll (MA) Studio Art 1974; *cr:* St Benedicts Schl Art Tchr 1964-67; St Catharine Acad Art Tchr 1967-70; St Joseph's Acad Art Tchr 1971-75; Cathedral HS Art Tchr 1975-76; The Loyola Schl Art Tchr 1976-86; Mount St Michael Acad Art Tchr 1986-87; The Mary Louis Acad Chprsn, Tchr 1988-; *ai:* Steering, Open House Comms; Grant Writing Comm Co-Chair 1995-; NCEA 1976-; NAEA 1989-; ASCD 1993-; *office:* The Mary Louis Acad 176-21 Wexford Terr Jamaica NY 11432

FEELEY, RUTH ENGEL, English Teacher; *b:* Quito, Ecuador; *m:* Leo T. Jr.; *c:* Michael, Matthew, Dan, Catherine; *ed:* SUNY at Fredonia (BA) Eng 1967; Coll of St Rose Eng Ed; *cr:* Livonia Elem Schl Librn 1967-68; Van Antwerp Jr HS Eng Tchr 1968-71; Brainerd Jr HS Eng Tchr 1971-85; Beck MS Rdng, Eng Tchr 1987-; *ai:* Peer Mediation; Conflict Resolution; Curr; CHEA, NJEA 1971-; NEA 1967-; *office:* Henry C Beck Jr HS Cropwell Rd Cherry Hill NJ 08002*

FEELEY, WILLIAM A., English Chairperson & Teacher; *b:* Philadelphia, PA; *m:* Maria A. Savvas; *c:* Maria Ann, William A. IV; *ed:* La Salle Univ (BA) Pol Sci 1967; Widner (MED) Scndry Ed 1981; 6 Credit Hrs Temple Univ; *cr:* St John Neumann HS Tchr 1967-; *ai:* Pirates Quill Moderator; Cnslr; NCTE 1967-; NCTA 1967-; ACT 1967-; Elmwood Park Boy & Girls Club 1973-, Pres AOH Svc Awd 1995; Elmwood Park Bob Myers Memrl Awd 1978; St John Neumann Tchr of Yr 1986; *office:* Saint John Neumann HS 2600 Moore St Philadelphia PA 19145

FEENEY, JANE MCGARRY, Business & Soc Studies Teacher; *b:* Taylor, PA; *m:* Robert P.; *c:* Patrick, Eugene; *ed:* Coll Misericordia (BS) Bus 1957; U of Scranton, Marywood, Masters Equivalency 33 Credit Hrs; *cr:* Avoca HS Bus Tchr 1957-60; Scranton Schl Dist Adult Ed & Bus Tchr 1961-75; Lackawanna Jr Coll Acctng Tchr 1975-77; Pittston Area HS Bus & Soc Stud Tchr 1978-; *ai:* FBLA Moderator; AFT 1978-; PA Bus Ed Assn 1985-; *home:* 227 Gedding St Avoca PA 18641

FEENEY, ROBERTA, English Teacher; *b:* New York City, NY; *m:* Robert; *c:* Katie, Christopher; *ed:* Nassau Comm Coll (AA) Liberal Arts 1967; Hofstra Univ (BA) Eng & Scndry Ed 1969; SUNY at Stony Brook (MA) Liberal Stud 1972; *cr:* St Mary Help of Chrstns 6th Grd Eng Tchr 1969-70; S. S. Cyril & Methodious 7th-8th Grd Rdng Tchr 1970-71; Longwood Schl Dist 9th-12th Grd Eng Tchr 1973-; *ai:* Mid Island Tchrs Assn 1973-; NY St Tchrs Assn 1973-; Holbrook Rd PTA 1983-, Membership & Schlsp Chprsn; Centereach PTSA 1992-; LJHS PTA 1980-; Centereach Civic 1990-; Compact for Learning 1993-; Dawnwood MS SITE BASE 1994-; Longwood Jr HS Natl Honor Soc Fac Cncl 1995-; *office:* Longwood Jr HS 198 Longwood Rd Middle Island NY 11953*

FEGELY, KATHY MULLER, German Tchr & Frgn Lang Chprsn; *b:* Reading, PA; *m:* Roger C. Jr.; *c:* Robert Wickstrom; *ed:* Clarion St Coll (BS) Scndry Ed Ger 1979; Kutztown Univ (MA) Eng 1990; Univ Of Stuttgart Summer Study Prgm; PA St Univ; Goethe Inst Seminars; *cr:* Northeastern HS Ger Permanent Substitute 1980; Schuylkill Haven HS Ger & Eng Tchr 1980-81; Antietam HS Ger & Eng Tchr 1986-, Foreign Lang Chprsn; *ai:* Modern Lang Club Adv; GAPP Spon; Cheerleading Coach 1991-92; CLass Adv 1992-; NEA 1986-; AATG 1979-; Kappa Delta Pi 1978-; MLA 1991-; PSMLA 1994-; *office:* Antietam HS 100 Antietam Rd Story Creek Mills PA 19606

FEGGINS, ERIC R., Eng & Creative Writing Tchr; *b:* Newport News, VA; *m:* Bernette Bowman; *c:* Fanya, Brian, Kyle; *ed:* Seton Hall Univ (BA) Eng 1977; City Univ of NY (MA) Eng Ed 1995; 30 Credits Toward PHD; *cr:* South Bronx HS Eng Tchr 1985-90; HS of Graphic Comm Arts Eng, Creative Writing Tchr 1990-; *ai:* NYC Mentoring Prgm Schl Coord; AFL, CIO 1990-; UFT 1987-; *office:* HS of Graphic Comm Arts 439 W 49th St New York NY 10019

FEGHALI, ELIAS, Architecture & Math Instructor; *b:* Beirut, Lebanon; *m:* Renee; *c:* Mirna, Josiane, Anthony; *ed:* Inst of Fine Arts of Lebanese Univ (BS) Arch 1978; Math, Physics; *cr:* Ajaltoun Tech Coll Prof 1979-85; Cincinnati St Coll Instr Part-time 1986-91, Instr Full Time 1991-; *ai:* Sabbatical Comm, Tchng Excl Comm Co-Chair; Eng Facilities; Coll Wide Arch, Eng Selection, Coll Wide Assessment Comms; Amer Inst of Arch 1987-; Amer Inst of Constr 1991-; House Bruckman Fac Excl Awd; *office:* Cincinnati St Tech & Comm Coll 3520 Central Pky Cincinnati OH 45223

FEGLEY, DENISE KISSEL, Business Teacher; *b:* Shamokin, PA; *m:* Kenneth A.; *c:* Denika M., Kenneth A. Jr.; *ed:* Bloomsburg St Coll (BS) Bus Ed 1976, (MED) Bus Ed 1981; *cr:* Shamokin Area HS Bus Tchr 1977-; *ai:* NEA, PSEA, SAEA 1977-; Ralpho Area Women's Club 1992-; *office:* Shamokin Area HS 2000 W State St Coal Township PA 17866

FEGLEY, STEPHEN ROBERT, Associate Prof of Marine Sci; *b:* Harrisburg, PA; *m:* Jill Diane Coldren; *c:* Bryan, Erin; *ed:* Lebanon Vly Coll (BS) Bio 1978; Univ of NC at Chapel Hill (PHD) Bio 1985; *cr:* Stockton St Coll Asst Prof 1985-87; Rutgers Univ Asst Rsrch Prof 1987-91; Maine Maritime Acad Assoc Prof 1991-; *ai:* 3 PHD & Masters Comms; Ocean Sci Club Adv; Ecological Soc of Amer 1979-; Sigma Xi 1980-; Soc for Stud of Evolution 1980-; Maine Aquaculture Innovation Ctr 1992-95, Bd of Governors; Principle Investigator for Rsrch Grants; Numerous Articles Pub; Wilson Flwshp for Marine Rsrch; Lerner Gray Mar Res Flwshp; Sigma Xi Grant in Aid; *office:* Maine Maritime Acad Castine ME 04421

FEGREUS-REYNOLDS, MARY ELIZABETH, Instr of Anatomy & Physiology; *b:* Worcester, MA; *m:* Richard R.; *c:* Katherine E., Richard C., Edward A.; *ed:* Clark Univ (BA) Bio 1975; Boston Univ Schl of Medicine & Schl of Pub Hlth (MPH) Epidemiology & Pub Hlth 1984; Univ of MA at Amherst Doctoral Candidate Epidemiology & Pub Hlth 1991-; *cr:* Wachusett Regnl Schl Dist Comm Hlth Liaison 1992-94; Quinsigamond Comm Coll Instr Anatomy & Physiology 1993-; *ai:* MTA 1993-; *office:* Quinsigamond Comm Coll 670 W Boylston St Worcester MA 01606

FEHM, MARGARET QUINN, 4th Grade Teacher; *b:* Bridgeport, CT; *w:* Noel F. (dec); *c:* David, Thomas, Susan, Mary, Michael, Matthew; *ed:* St Joseph Coll (BA) Child Psych; Fairfield Univ (MA) Elem Ed; *cr:* Thomas Hooker 2nd-3rd Grd Tchr 4 Yrs; St Peter 3rd-4th Grd Tchr 1978-95; Sacred Heart St Peter 4th Grd Tchr 1995-; *ai:* CEA 1978-; *office:* Sacred Heart St Peter Schl 208 Columbus Ave New Haven CT 06519

FEHNEL, BARRY JAMES, Business Ed & Computer Teacher; *b:* Reading, PA; *c:* Eileen Jennings, Kevin; *ed:* Temple Univ (BS) Bus Ed, Cmptr Tech 1976; IBM Schl Cmptr Courses; *cr:* Reading Muhlenberg Voc Tech Schl Cmptr Tchr 1971-84; Reading HS Bus Ed Tchr 1984-; *ai:* Schl Show Bus Mgr; FBLA Adv; NBEA; PA, Berks Cty Bus Ed Assns; Reading, PA St Ed Assns; Red Cross Water Safety Instr 25 Yrs; Jaycees 10 Yrs; Reading Area Comm Coll Adult Ed Dept First Annual Instr of Yr Awd 1993; *home:* 1149 Perry St Reading PA 19604

FEHNEL, LOUISE KEPPEL, 1st Grade Teacher; *b:* Allentown, PA; *m:* Lowell K.; *c:* Raechel, Ross; *ed:* Kutztown Univ (BS) Elem Ed 1978; *cr:* Northampton Area Schl Dist Pre-first, First, Second Grd Tchr 1978-; *ai:* Fundraiser Comm; PSEA, NEA, NAEA 1978-; Chrstn Ed 1994-; Sunday Schl Tchr 1984-; *office:* Lehigh Elem Schl 800 Blue Mountain Dr Walnutport PA 18088*

FEIBEL, ANN E., Asst Prof & Academic Coord; *b:* Brooklyn, NY; *ed:* Kingsborough Comm Coll (AAS) Librl Arts & Sci 1973; Hunter Coll (BS) Phys Therapy 1975; Long Island Univ (MS) Comm Hlth 1986; *cr:* LaGuardia CC Asst Prof & ACCE 3 Yrs; St Marys Hosp for Children Consultant Phys Therapist 4 Yrs; NYC Bd of Ed Consultant Phys Therapist 2 Yrs; Malmonides Med Ctr Rehad Coord 2 Yrs; Metropolitan Jewish Geri Ctr Rehab Dir 5 Yrs; Cabrini Med Ctr Staff PT 6 Yrs; *ai:* Amer Phys Therapy Assn 1986-; Amer Legion Auxillary 1960-; Wrote PTA Core Course Curr; EDIT Grant for Audio Visual Aids; *office:* La Guardia Comm Coll Rm E 300-0 31-10 Thomson Ave Long Island City NY 11101

FEIG, WERNER M., AP American History Teacher; *b:* Germany; *c:* Jonathon, Rebecca; *ed:* Univ of Pittsburg (BA) Govt 1955; Harvard (MAT) Ed 1959; Univ of Chicago (MA) Govt 1965; NYU Post Grad; *cr:* Tappun Lee HS Chair 1965-67; Scarsdale HS Tchr 1968-91; Nightingale-Bamford Schl Chair, Tchr 1991-; *ai:* Diversity Club Adv; Multi-Cultural, Prof Dev Comms Chair; OAH 1972-; AHA 1970-; AFT, Chief Negotiator; UJA, Urban League 1970-; ACLU 1967-; NAACP 1965-; Grant NEH 1983; 3 Yrbk Dedications; Books Written: 1987 A Simulation Came, A History & US Text, AP US Review Book, NY Times Microfilm; *office:* Nightingale-Bamford Schl 20 E 92nd St New York NY 10128*

FEIGENBAUM, RUTH, Assoc Professor of Mathematics; *b:* Paterson, NJ; *c:* Adam, Tobie, Heidi, Ellen; *ed:* Douglass Coll at Rutgers Univ (BA) Math 1966; Tchrs Coll at Columbia Univ (MA) Math Ed 1967; Univ of SC (PHD) Math 1975; Fairleigh Dickinson Univ (MS) Comp Sci 1986; *ai:* Co-Adv for Hillel; *office:* Bergen Comm Coll 400 Paramus Rd Paramus NJ 07652*

FEIGHAN, REGINA ANN, Seventh Grade Teacher; *b:* Philadelphia, PA; *ed:* Cabrini Coll (BA) Fine Art 1983; Immaculata Coll Cert in Art Ed & Elem Ed; *cr:* Holy Innocents Schl 8th Grd Tchr 1985-86; St Hugh Schl 8th Grd Tchr 1986-88; St Donato Schl 8th Grd Tchr 1988-93; Abigail Vare Schl 7th Grd Tchr 1993-; *ai:* Comms: Assembly, & Schl Play; Stu Cncl Adv; Yrbk Adv; PFT 1993-.

FEIGHT, CAROLYN CONLEY, Second Grade Teacher; *b:* Jersey City, NJ; *m:* Dennis Dean; *c:* Yvonne Feight Giffin; *ed:* Shippensburg St Coll (BS) Elem Ed 1968; Level II Cert 1977; Rdng Specialist Prgm 12 Credit Hrs; PA St Univ Continuing Ed Prgm 6 Credit Hrs; Intermediate Units 8-11-PDE Approved Courses for Cert 8 Credit Hrs; *cr:* Tussey Mountain Schl Dist Elem Tchr 1969-70, 1972-; *ai:* IST Child Stud Team; PTA; NEA, PSEA, TMEA 1969-; Shermans Vly Church 1975-, Sunday Schl Tchr; Amer Family Inst Gift of Time Tribute.

FEILD, BEVERLEY SEWARD, Fifth Grade Teacher; *b:* Philadelphia, PA; *ed:* Mary Baldwin Coll (BA) His 1975; His, Elem Ed Tchng Cert; Credit Hrs Cmptr Sci Within Schls, Dev of Effective Instrument for Tchr Evaluation, Peer Coaching; *cr:* Woodbury Heights Elem Schl 4th Grd Sub Tchr 1976; Wash Twp MS 7th, 8th Grd St Compens Ed 1976-78; Wedgwood Elem Schl 3rd Grd Tchr 6 Yrs, 4th Grd Tchr 6 Yrs, 5th Grd Tchr 6 Yrs; *ai:* Co-Chair London Brass Rubbing Wkshp Org, Acrylics Artistic Talent Dev; NEA, WTEA, GCEA 1977-; NJEA 1977-, Sec, Bldg Rep, Sr Bldg Rep-WTEA; Church 1993-, Vestry Mem, Schl 4-6 Grds Tchr, Eucharistic Minister, Lay Reader; W T Parks & Rec 1993-, Summer Theatre; Governor's Tchr Recognition Awd; *office:* Wedgwood Elem Schl 236 Hurffville Rd Sewell NJ 08080*

FEIN, DENISE BURNE, Sociology & Criminology Instr; *b:* Scranton, PA; *m:* Robert A.; *ed:* Univ of MD (BA) Criminology 1981; Univ of Baltimore (MS) Criminal Justice 1986; Pursuing Second Masters at Univ of Scranton in Elem Ed with Tchr Cert; *cr:* Temple Univ Grad Tchng, Rsrch Asst 1981-82; Univ of Baltimore Grad Rsrch Asst 1983, Adj Instr 1987; Lackawanna Jr Coll Adj Instr 1989 & 1994; Marywood Coll Instr 1994-; Keystone Jr Coll Adj Instr 1996; *ai:* 1999 Class Adv; Pre-Law Awd Selection Comm; Distance Ed Prgm Fac Mem; Criminal Justice Planners' Assn 1986-; Criminal Justice Baltimore MD 1986-88, Fiscal Ofcr, Grants Admin, Mayor's Coordinating Cncl CJ Planner; *office:* Marywood Coll 2300 Adams Ave Scranton PA 18509*

FEINBERG, CHARLES, Fifth Grade Teacher & Dean; *b:* Brooklyn, NY; *m:* Julie; *ed:* St Univ of NY at Oswego (BA) Ed 1966; *cr:* PS 257K 5th Grd Tchr & Dean 1966-; *ai:* Head of Upper Grd Lunchroom; UFT 1968-; Prof Wine Educators of Amer 1982-; *office:* PS 257 John F Hyland 60 Cook St Brooklyn NY 11206*

FEINBERG, ROBERT CHARLES, American History Teacher; *b:* Providence, RI; *m:* Janice F. Flanagan; *c:* Laura K., Kurt L., Benjamin J. J.; *ed:* Univ of RI (BA) His, Ger 1982; Providence Coll (MA) His 1993; Attnd Univ Passau 1985-86, Univ Salzburg 1980-81; *cr:* Coventry MS His, Cultural Geog Tchr 1987-94; Comm Coll of RI His Instr 1994-; Coventy HS Amer His Tchr 1994-; *ai:* Work Comm; RI Skills Commission; AFT 1987-; Phi Alpha Theta 1993-; RI Soc Stud Assn 1987-; Coventry PTA 1987-; North Kingstown PTO 1989-; Numerous Articles Pub; *office:* Coventry HS 40 Reservoir Rd Coventry RI 02816*

FEINBERG, SUSAN ELCONIN, English Teacher; *b:* Milwaukee, WI; *m:* Harvey; *c:* Victor, Paul; *ed:* Univ of MI (BA) Eng 1962; Boston Coll (MA) Eng 1968; Wesleyan Univ Hum Stud 1986; Southern CT St Univ Tatnials Bible as Lit & Mythology; *cr:* Yorktown HS Eng Tchr 1962-63; Scituate HS Eng Tchr 1963-65; Wesley Girls HS Cape Coast Ghana Eng Tchr 1967-68; Albertus Magnus Coll Eng Tchr 1972-73; Hopkins Eng Tchr & Dept Head 1974-; *ai:* Newspaper Adv; Fac Agenda Comm; Assn of Tchrs of Bible 1994-; NEH Summer Seminars Transformations of Etecha 1993, Bible as Lit 1987; Classical Assn of New England Periclean Athens 1992; NEH Summer Inst Songs of the Muses 1990; *office:* Hopkins Schl 986 Forest Rd New Haven CT 06515*

FEINSTEIN, JUDITH S., 9th Grd World His & Geog Tchr; *b:* Munich, Germany; *m:* Bernard; *c:* David Eric, Robert Jordan; *ed:* Temple Univ (BA) Soc Stud, His, Ec 1969; *cr:* Collingswood HS Tchr 1970-72; Vineland HS Tchr 1990-; *ai:* Bd of Ed Sixth Grd, K-12 Grd Soc Stud Curr Review Comms; Planning Comm for Holocaust Mandate Conf; NEA, NJ Educl Assn, VEA 1990-; Hadassah 1976-, Meetings Sec; Beth Israel Congregation 1976-, Bd of Dirs; Kerem Torah Presch Comm, Chairwomen 3 Yrs; *office:* Vineland HS North 3010 E Chestnut Ave Vineland NJ 08360

FEIT, MARILYN RUTH, Art Dept Chprsn & Teacher; *b:* Baltimore, MD; *m:* Andrew; *c:* Seth, Douglas; *ed:* American Univ (BA) Fine Arts & Ed 1967; Towson St Univ (MED) Art Ed 1980; Attnd MD Inst Coll of Art; *cr:* JFK HS Art Tchr & Dept Chair 1967-70; Dulaney HS Art Tchr 1971-73; Owings Mills HS Art Tchr 1980-84; Parkville HS Art Dept Chair & Tchr 1985-89; Catonsville HS Art Dept Chair & Tchr 1989-; *ai:* Art Club Spon; Baltimore Cty Comm for Gifted & Talented; Aesthetics-Beautifaction Comm Chprsn; Spon of Catonsville's Chapt of Natl Art Honor Society; G/T Resource Tchr; MAEA; NAEA; NEA; Amer Craft Cncl; Dev Studio Fair Day at MD Inst Coll of Art for Gifted & Talented Cty Stdnts; *office:* Catonsville HS 421 Bloomsbury Ave Catonsville MD 21228

FELD, RITA, ESL & Russian Teacher; *b:* Odessa, The Ukraine; *m:* Edward; *c:* Tanya; *ed:* Odessa St Univ (BA) Ger Land 1961, (MA) Eng Lang, Lit 1964; Georgetown Univ (PHD) RUssian Area Stud 1987; Cert Biling Scndry Ed; *cr:* Howard Univ Prof 1979-84; Amer Univ Prof 1984-90; A. Deal Jr HS Tchr 1990-; *ai:* Russian Dance Class Spon; Biling Dept Chprsn 1993-94; Frgn Lang Dept Chprsn 1994-95; Amer Assn Tchrs of East European Langs 1979-; PHD Dissertation Pub; *home:* 10607 Edgewood Ave Silver Spring MD 20901*

FELD, STEVE, Computer Graphics Instructor; *b:* Brooklyn, NY; *ed:* Hunter Coll (BA) Art 1969; Brooklyn Coll Tchr Educa Prgm 1971; NY

Univ Comm 1972; Pace Univ Early Chldhd Educa 1973; *cr:* Internation Ctr of Photography Dialogue Ldr 1979; Math Applications Group Inc Assoc Producer 1980; John F. Kennedy HS Cmptr Graphics Instr 1981, Data Coord 1995-; *ai:* Dev Attendance Taker, Mediator; NAEA, Educator of Yr; Media Arts Tchrs Assn, Pres, Bd Mem; Author Computers In The Art Classroom; Learning Fnd Intnl Grand Prize; William T. Grant Fnd-Media House; Learning Techs Fair St Champion; Software Designer for Disk Care US Constitution & Telecommunications in Classroom; *office:* John F Kennedy HS 99 Terrace View Ave Bronx NY 10468

FELDBERG, PHILIP L., 6th Grade Teacher; *b:* Boston, MA; *m:* Claudia Friedman; *c:* Susan, Michael, Brian; *ed:* Salem St Coll (EdM) Guidance, Eng 1966; Boston Univ (BA) Psych, Eng 1964; 40 Credits Beyond Masters; 8 Credit Hr Course Anatomy, Physiology; *cr:* Wolcott Schl Eng Tchr 1964-78; Garfield Schl Eng Tchr 1978-87; Beachmont Schl Eng Tchr 1987-91; Garfield Schl 6th Grd Tchr 1991-; *ai:* Childrens Market Facilitator; Revere Tchrs Assn, NEA 1964-; Horace Mann Tchng Fellow; Horace Mann Tchng Fellow; *office:* James Garfield Cmty Magnet Sch 140 Garfield Ave Revere MA 02151

FELDER, CHERYL MCGEE, Math Teacher; *b:* Hartford, CT; *c:* Dawn; *ed:* Univ of Hartford (BA) Math 1969, (MA) Scndry Ed 1973-; 12 Credit Hrs Admin & Supervision; *cr:* Hartford Pub HS Math Tchr 26 Yrs; *ai:* Jr Class Adv; AFT 1969-; *office:* Hartford Public HS 55 Forest St Hartford CT 06105

FELDMAN, BETH MASON, Teacher of Gifted & Talented; *b:* New York, NY; *ed:* St Univ of NY at Buffalo (BA) Eng, Ed 1967, (MED) Urban Ed 1973; Univ of CT Ed of GATE; Working 6th Yr Post Grad Degree; *cr:* John Adams HS Eng Tchr 1967-68; Woodlawn Jr HS Eng Tchr 1968-72; PS 46 Rdng Ctr Resource Rdng Tchr Trainee 1972-73; West Hertel MS Resource Rdng Tchr 1973-75; Brussels Amer Schl Rdng, Eng, GATE Tchr 1975-; *ai:* Sr Class Adv; Odyssey of the Mind; Acad Games Coach; NEA, FEA 1975-; Phi Delta Kappa 1980-; NCTE 1991-; Amer Horticultural Soc 1993-; Noetic Sci 1991-; Integral Yoga Belgium 1986-; NY Metropolitan Museum of Art 1988-; *office:* Brussels Amer Schl Bas/Nsa PSC Box 79 Box 3 APO AE 09724

FELDMAN, IRMA ARLENE, Science Teacher; *b:* Brooklyn, NY; *m:* David; *c:* Deborah, Leslie; *ed:* Brooklyn Coll (MA) Ed 1965; 60 Credits Beyond Masters Ed & Soc Scis; *cr:* Coll of New Rochelle Adjunct Prof 1987-88; Queens Coll Adjunct Prof 1988-90; NYC Tchrs Consortium Human Relations Tchr 29 Yrs; *ai:* Schl Chorus Ldr; Dist 24 PDAC Comm; UFT 1963-, Chapter Chm 1990-; Bnai Brith, Sr Citizen Bd of Dirs, Asst Dir Youth Org of NYC 1973-95; Received Impact Grants Several Times for Sci & Soc Sci; *office:* PS 153 60-02 60th Ln Maspeth NY 11378*

FELDMAN, JUDITH L., English & Journalism Teacher; *b:* Grove City, PA; *c:* Mark J., Scott D.; *ed:* Clarion Univ (BS) Eng 1983; Trng & Credit Hrs in Instructional Strategies, Tech Curr, Stdnts-at-Risk, Assessment Alternatives, Cooperative Learning, Poetry & Lit, St Assessment Trng, Pub & Adult Learner Facilitator Trng; *cr:* Brookville Area Schls Eng Tchr 1983-84; Clarion-Limestone Area Schls Eng Tchr 1984-; *ai:* Stu Assistance Dist Coord; Clarion Univ Upward Bound Prgm Learning Coach; Assessment Trainer; Lead Tchr; Clarion-Limestone Area Ed Assn 1983-, Bldg Rep; PSEA, NEA 1983-; Clarion-Limestone Tchr of Yr 1993-94; Gettysburg Family Inst Gift of Time Recipient 1994; *office:* Clarion-Limestone Area Schls RD 1 Box 205 Strattanville PA 16258

FELDMAN, MARILYN W., Language Arts Teacher; *b:* Canton, OH; *m:* Paul J.; *c:* Steffy Goldberg, Lisa Goldberg; *ed:* OH St Univ (BS) Eng 1969; Walsh Univ Hrs Toward Masters; *cr:* Lake Local Schls Tchr 1986-; *ai:* Drama Club; NCTE 1993-; NEA 1986-; Canton Jewish Ctr 1972-, Pres; Canton Jewish Fed 1972-, Bd Mem; Temple Israel 1972-, Bd Mem; Hadaisah 1972-, Pres; *office:* Lake MS 12001 N Market St Hartville OH 44632

FELDMAN, MARK JEFFREY, Mathematics Teacher; *b:* Clarion, PA; *m:* Susan; *ed:* Mercyhurst Coll (BA) Math 1990; *cr:* Bellefonte Area HS Math Tchr 1990-; *ai:* Cross Cntry Head Coach; Asst Track Coach; Asst Acad Decathlon Adv; NEA 1990-; PSEA 1990; Bellefonte Jaycees Outstndg Young Edctr 1992-93; *home:* 1275 Fairview Dr Bellefonte PA 16823

FELDMAN, MARTIN ROBERT, Chemistry Professor; *b:* New York, NY; *m:* Janet Steinfeld; *c:* Jonathan, Lisa Ginns; *ed:* Columbia Univ (BA) Chem 1958; UCLA (PHD) Chem 1963; Post Doctoral Rsrch Assoc U Cal Berkley 1962-63; *cr:* Howard Univ Asst Prof Chem 1963-68, Assoc Prof 1968-71; Prof 1971-; U CS at San Diego Visiting Prof 1994; *ai:* Amer Chem Soc 1959-; His of Sci Soc 1987-; Soc for His of Tech 1987-; Hands-On Science Outreach 1985-, VP; NSF Grad Flwshp 1958-62, Fac Flwshp 1969-70; Smithsonian Fac Flwshp 1987; *office:* Howard Univ 2400 6th St NW Washington DC 20059

FELDMAN, ROBERT STEPHEN, Psychology Professor; *b:* Newark, NJ; *m:* Katherine Vorwerk; *ed:* Wesleyan Univ (BA) Psych 1970; Univ of WI at Madison (MS) Psych 1972, (PHD) Psych 1974; *cr:* VA Commonwealth Univ Prof of Psych 1974-77; Univ of MA at Amherst Prof of Psych 1977-; *ai:* Undergraduate Studies Dir; Amer Psychological Assn 1974-, Fellow; Amer Psychological Soc 1989-, Fellow; Fulbright Rsrch Scholar; Author 12 Books, Understanding Psychology; *office:* Univ Of MA At Amherst Dept of Psychology Amherst MA 01003

FELDMAN, SALLIE ALLMAN, Frgn Lang Tchr & Dept Chprsn; *b:* Charleston, WV; *m:* Noel; *c:* Lisa, David; *ed:* PA St Univ (BA) Span, Fr 1968; Univ of DE (MED) Ed, Span 1973; Addl 30 Credit Hrs; *cr:* Old Court Jr HS Fr, Ger Tchr 1969-70; Valley Forge Jr HS Fr, Span Tchr 1970-78; East HS Span, Fr Tchr 1981-; *ai:* Span Hnr Soc; Annual Trips to Europe Chaperone; NEA, PSEA 1981-; AATSP 1990-; Stu Workbook Viday Voces Level I, II; Pasos a Ingles; Medline Hunter Prgm Mentor; Peer Partnership Prgm; *office:* W C East High School 450 Ellis Ln West Chester PA 19380

FELDMAN, STEVEN JAY, 5th Grade Teacher; *b:* Princeton, NJ; *m:* Nancy Vanden Berg Green; *c:* Aaron, Eliot; *ed:* Princeton (BA) Eng 1968; Rutgers (MED) Elem Ed 1974; Trenton St Univ (MED) Hlth Ed 1988; *cr:* Roosevelt Pub Schl 4th-8th Grd, PE Tchr 1971-74; Woodland Schl 5th-6th Grd Tchr 1974-; *ai:* Environmental Ctr Dir 1980-; Monroe Twp Sci Curr Comm 1975-; Family Living, Human Sexuality Ed for Boys Dir 1979-; NEA, NJ Ed Assn 1971-; East Windsor PAL 1988-93, Soccer, Bsbl, Bsktbl Coach, Numerous Championships; Recipient NJ Governors Tchr Recognition Awd 1992; Winner Youth Garden Grant Natl Gardening Assn 1995; Recipient Environmental Protection Agency Youth Awds for Schl Envrionmental Projects 1979-; *office:* Woodland Elem Schl 42 Harrison Ave Spotswood NJ 08884*

FELDMAN, TAMI ZEFERS, Former Music Teacher; *b:* Gowanda, NY; *m:* David L.; *c:* Emily K., Nathaniel Z. D.; *ed:* Oral Roberts Univ (BME) Music Ed 1985; SUNY Coll at Fredonia (MM) Music Ed 1990; *cr:* Cincinnatus Cntrl Schl Instrumental, Vocal Music Tchr 1985-88; North Collins Cntrl Schl Instrumental, Vocal Music Tchr 1988-92; *ai:* Wesleyan Church of Orchard Park 1992-, Adult Choir Dir; *home:* 3871 N Freeman Rd Orchard Park NY 14127

FELDMESSER, LINDA BORKAN, Resource Teacher of G&T; *b:* East Orange, NJ; *m:* Howard; *c:* Michelle, Joshua; *ed:* Johns Hopkins Univ (MS) Tech 1992; Attnd Univ MD at Loyola; *cr:* Oaklands Elem Schl 3rd Grd Tchr 1968-71; Hammond MS Asst Tchr 1982-85; Hammond Elem Schl Tchr of GATE, 4th Grd Tchr 1985-94; Manor Woods Elem Schl Tchr of GATE 1994-; *ai:* Stu Cncl, Schl Store, Mini Bank Adv; Cmptr Rep; Schl Improvement Team; Math Comm Chair; NCTM; MCTM; MICCA; *office:* Manor Woods Elem Schl 11575 Frederick Rd Ellicott City MD 21042

FELDSHUH, MURIEL, Library Media Specialist; *b:* New York, NY; *ed:* Brooklyn Coll (BA) Ed 1962, (MS) Ed 1967; NYS Cert 1968; Pratt Inst Lib Sci Courses; OW Post Storytelling; Mac Cmptr Course; Fr Ancillary License 1965; Stu Tchr Trainer 1963-68; *cr:* PS 16 Schl Classroom Tchr 1962-68, Lib Media Specialist 1962-; *ai:* Multicultural, Book It, RIF, Spec Projects, Safety Contest, Women's His Contest, Big Book Writing & Illustrating Club, Brooklyn Anti-Graffiti Campaign, Creative Writing Coord 1980-92; Coach Citywide Contest 1978-; UFT; ALA; NYSSLA; Kappa Delta Pi; ASCD; Brooklyn Rdng Cncl; NYSRA 1992-, Outstdng Elem Schl Lib Media Specialist Awd; NYLA; AASL; SCBWI; NEA; Midwood Civic Assn; PTA 1988, 1992, Outstdng Schl Svc Awd; Grants: Dist Lib 1973-93, Impact II 1987, 1989, NYC Fund for Pub Ed 1989, NYS Rdng Assn 1990-, Producing Big Books, Ezra Jack Keats Fnd 1995; Making Big Books; Awds Cool Schl Lib Prgm 1995, Excl Awd PTA Presentation 1990, 1994; Brooklyn Citation Team Up to Clean Up 1993; Excl in Ed Citation, Howard Golden 1992, NY St Assn Outstdng Elem Schl Lib Media Specialist 1991, Fire Safety Contest Tchr 1989, Storytelling Coaching 1987, OETA 1974-75; Co-Pub Dist 14 Lib Manual 1975; Instr Magazine 1991, 1994; Whats Working Parent Magazine 1993-94; Yearly Children's Calendars Lib World Newspaper 1979-.

FELDSTEIN, BERNARD, Prof of Marketing & Management; *b:* New York, NY; *m:* Mary; *c:* Donald, Robert; *ed:* St Univ of NY at Albany (BS) Bus Admin 1968, (MBA) Mrktg 1969; 30 Credit Hrs Toward EDD; *cr:* Barclay Clover Inc Sales Rep 1946-54; Royal Accessory Co Owner & Mgr 1954-68; Siena Coll Asst & Assoc Prof of Mrktg & Mgmt 1970-83, Prof 1984-; *ai:* Asst Dean of Bus Division; Internship Coord; Small Bus Inst Dir; Amer Banking Inst Coord; Surrey Hill Homeowners Assn 1992-, Bd of Trustees.

FELHUHN, SUSAN BAYLIN, Biology Teacher; *b:* New York, NY; *m:* Robert; *c:* Andrew, Richard; *ed:* Russell Sage Coll (BA) Bio 1963; NY Univ (MS) Sci Ed 1964; U of Rochester Med & Dental Schl 3 Credits; Cold Spring Harbor Genetics; Trinity Coll 3 Credits; *cr:* New Brunswick HS Bio Tchr 1964-65; Jewish Day Schl Sci Tchr 1972-74; Springbrook HS Bio & AP Bio Tchr 1974-; *ai:* AIDS Awareness Spon; Stu Awds Comm; NABT 1980-; AIBS 1993-; Tchr Recognition Awds Comm 1989-; AP Bio Consultant 1992-; NSF; Governors Acad; Westinghouse Sci Talent Search Hnr; Tech Writers Recognition Awd; Article Pub; *office:* Springbrook HS 201 Valleybrook Dr Silver Spring MD 20904

FELICETTA, MARY ELENA, General Music & Choral Teacher; *b:* Sayville, NY; *ed:* Suffolk Comm Coll (AA) Theatre Arts 1982; Stony Brook Univ (BA) Music 1985; Long Island Univ C.W. Post (MS) Music Ed 1991; *cr:* Tangier Smith Elem Schl Grds 1-5 Gen, Local Music Tchr, Grds 3-5 Chorus Dir 1985-; *ai:* Cultural Arts Comm Mem; Long Island Amer Schl Week Assn Mbrshp Chprsn 1992-95; Suffolk Cty Music Edctrs Assn Chprsn; Chorus Chprsn William Floyd; AOSA 1985-; LIAOSA 1985-; SCMEA 1985-; MENC 1985-; GIML 1990-; ACDA 1992-; *office:* Tangier Smith Elem Schl Blanco Dr Mastic Beach NY 11951

FELICETTI, LINDA ROSCOE, Professor of Marketing; *b:* Muncie, IN; *m:* Carmen S.; *c:* Laura A., David A.; *ed:* Western Coll for Women (BA) Ec 1964; IN Univ (MBA) Mngmt, Mrktg 1966; Univ of Pittsburgh (PHD) Higher Ed 1985; *cr:* Clarion Univ of PA Mrktg Prof 1971-; *ai:* Womens Stud Advy Bd; Writing Across the Curr Steering Comm; Lib, Evaluation Comms; Editorial Reviewer for Journal of Bus Ethics; Amer Mrktg Assn 1985-; Lib Bd 1993-; Outstdng Tchr 1988; Rsrch Grant; Articles Pub; *office:* Clarion Univ Of PA Still Hall Clarion PA 16214

FELIX, CAROL W., Business Education Teacher; *b:* Sunbury, PA; *m:* Jack; *c:* Brian, Swatara; *ed:* Susquehanna Univ (BS) Bus Ed 1966; IBM Cmptr Schl; Attnd Bloomsburg, Penn St, Indiana of PA & Millersville Grad Stud Ed, Cmptr Tech; *cr:* Midwest Schl Dist Bus Ed Tchr 1966-69; Skikellamy Schl Dist Bus Ed Tchr 1973-; *ai:* Adv to Skikellamy FBLA; Skikellamy Ed Assn 1973-, Recording Sec; PA Bus Ed Assn 1995-; Beta Sigma Phi 1965-, Lifetime Mem, Order Of Rose Silver Cr; *office:* Shikellamy HS 6th & Walnut Sts Sunbury PA 17801

FELIX, JOHN WILLIAM, English, Drama & Speech Tchr; *b:* Flushing, NY; *ed:* Franklin & Marshall Coll (AB) Eng Lit 1968; Long Island Univ (MA) Eng Lit 1970, (PD) Ed Admin 1980; Univ of CT Medieval Stud; *cr:* Quinnipiac Coll Instr of Eng 1970-73; Half Hollow Hills Pub Schls Eng Tchr 1978-90; Suffolk Comm Coll Assoc Prof of Eng 1980-; St John the Bapt HS Eng, Drama, Speech Tchr 1993-; *ai:* AAUP 1970-; AFT 1980-; NYSUT 1968-; Aquaduct Irrigation Sys Inc 1986-, Pres; OR Shakespearean Festival Assn Federal Schlsp Grant; Former Production Coord Actor's Showcase Ltd; NY St Cncl of Arts Bicentennial Productions Former Mem, Actor; *office:* St John the Bapt HS 1170 Montauk Hwy West Islip NY 11795*

FELIX-FOURNIER, CARMEN, Spanish Teacher; *b:* Guayama, PR; *m:* Thomas J. Fournier; *c:* Maurice; *ed:* Univ of PR (BA) Bus Ed 1972; Inter Amer Univ (MED) Admin, Sup 1979; Univ of MA (EDD) Curr, Span, Biling Ed 1985; Univ of PR Hispanic Stud Credit Hrs; *cr:* Inst Tec Com Jr Coll Bus, Sp Prof 1975-79; Sumner Av Schl Biling Tchr 1979-81; Univ of MA Stu Tchr Supvr 1981-82; HS of Commerce Span Tchr 1982-; *ai:* Span Club Adv; TQM Steering Comm; NEA, SEA, MTA 1979-; NABE; *office:* HS Of Commerce 415 State St Springfield MA 01105*

FELL, GILBERT SAMUEL, Professor of Philosophy; *b:* Trenton, NJ; *m:* Janet Elizabeth; *c:* Karen Powers, Linda Mertz, Nancy Hill; *ed:* Drew Univ (BA) Soc Sci 1953; Temple Univ (MDiv) Theology 1958, (MA) Philosophy 1960, (PHD) Philosophy 1969; *ai:* Assoc Ed Journal of Contemporary Philosophy; Chm Prgm; Inst for Advanced Philosophic Research; Realia; Soc of Chrstn Philosophy; NJ Regnl Philosophic Assn; Grant NJ Comm on Humanities, Tech, Values; *office:* Monmouth Univ West Long Branch NJ 07764

FELL, MICHAEL J., HS Math Teacher & Dept Chair; *b:* Baltimore, MD; *m:* Judith M. Kwaitkowski; *c:* Stephen M.; *ed:* Towson St Univ (BA) Math 1985; Loyola Univ (MA) Ed 1995; *cr:* Archbishop Curley HS Math, Ger Tchr 1985-95, Math Dept Chprsn 1991-; Kent Co HS Math 1995-; *ai:* Var Tennis Coach; Intramural Ath Dir; Acad Cncl Mem; NCTM 1985-; MCTM 1990-; ASCD 1991-; Archbishop Curley HS Tchr of Yr 1992; MD Cncl of Tchrs of Math Outstanding HS Tchr 1992, Outstanding HS Tchr Finalist 1993-94; Fac Rep to Schl Bd 1989-91; *office:* Kent County HS 25301 Lambs Meadow Rd Worton MD 21213*

FELLENCER, DAVID EUGENE, Education Professor; *b:* East Stroudsburg, PA; *m:* Laura Lou; *c:* Timothy, Mary E. Elmahdi, Elizabeth, Abigail; *ed:* KS City Coll & Bible Sch (BA) Elem Ed 1988; Grace Coll (MA) Chrstn Schl Administ 1991; *cr:* Hallmark Cards Inc Cmptr Operator, Accounts Payable Auditor1969-86; Kirksville Bible Schl Prin, Bus Mgr 1988-89; KS City Coll, Bible Schl 5th-6th Grd Tchr, Ass t Prin 1989-93; Penn View Bible Inst Ed Prof 1993-; *ai:* Coll Class Spon Soph 1993-94, Jr 1994-95, Sr 1995-96; *home:* PO Box 118 Penns Creek PA 17862

FELLENGER, JANET DANIELS, Third Grade Teacher; *b:* Warren, OH; *m:* Dennis L.; *c:* Steven D., Denise L.; *ed:* Spring Arbor Coll (BS) Ed 1972; *cr:* Edison Local Schls Sub Tchr 1981-83, 1985; E Liverpool Chrstn 3rd Grd Tchr 1983-84; Minerva Local Schls Sub Tchr 1986-88; Real Live Chrstn Acad 3rd Grd & span Tchr 1988-; *ai:* Church of the Nazarene 1972-; *home:* 509 N Market St Lisbon OH 44432

FELLER, JOHN ALLEN, Math & Algebra 1 Teacher; *b:* Dove Myra Ann Wolfe; *c:* Brian, Amy; *ed:* Kent St Univ (BS) Elem (MS) Math Clinician 1985; *cr:* Claymont City Schls Math Tchr Newcomerstown Schls Math Tchr 1974-; *ai:* Newcomerstown T 1974-; NEA, OEA 1967-; *home:* 5397 Oldtown Valley Rd Philadelphia OH 44663

FELLONA, CHRISTINE MARIE, HS Physical & Health Ed Silver Spring, MD; *ed:* Univ of MD (BS) PE 1992; Cert in Hlth Fed Interscholastic Coaches Ed Prgm; *cr:* Arundel HS PE, Hlth 1993-, Home, Hosp Tchr 1996; *ai:* Girls Lacrosse Head Coa Soccer Asst Coach; Acad Adv; Curr Writing Hlth Ed; NEA 19 Alliance Hlth, PE Recreation, Dance 1990-, Outstdng PE Ma Coaching Fed 1996; Tchrs Assn of Anne Arundel Cty 1992-; Suns Girls Lacrosse Coach of Yr AA Cty; Speaker at MAHPERD Convention; *office:* Arundel Sr HS 1001 Annapolis Rd Gamb 21054*

FELLONA, EDWARD JAMES, Technology Education Te Philadelphia, PA; *m:* Mary Maguire; *c:* Liza, Liam; *ed:* Frederick Bio 1968; Millersville Univ (MED) Industrial Arts 1980; Comp Desktop Pubng & Psych Courses; *cr:* Norwell HS Ind Arts Tchr Minnechaugh HS Ind Arts Tchr 1981-82; Laconia HS Ind Arts T *ai:* Music Club 1978; Soccer Coach 1979; IA Intnl Hnr 1975-; NE Laconia Ed Assn 1982-, Bldg Rep; Grad Assistantship 198 Laconia HS 345 Union Ave Laconia NH 03246

FELLOWS, FELICIA P., Social Studies Teacher; *b:* Montclai Drew Univ (BA) His 1985; Coll of Saint Elizabeth NJ Cert, Tc Stud K-12th, Scndry Ed 1985 & 15 Credits Towards Masters Saint George 6th Grd Tchr 1986; Madison Jr Schl 7th & 8th Grd Tchr 1987-; *office:* Madison Jr HS 160 Main St Madison NJ 079

FELSON, RICHARD BARNET, Professor of Sociology; *b:* C OH; *m:* Sharon Weber; *c:* Jacob, Benjamin; *ed:* U of Cincin Sociology 1972; IN U (PHD) Sociology 1977; *cr:* SUNY 1977-83, Assoc Prof 1983-88, Full Prof 1988-; *ai:* Amer Sociolog 1976-; Amer Criminological Assn 1993-; Parents Excl MS Com Chair; NSF, NIMH Grants; 2 Books, Numerous Articles Pub; *offic* at Albany 1400 Washington Ave Albany NY 12222

FELTON, ROBERT ONEIL,II, OWA Coord; *b:* Akron, OH; *c:* O., Skylar K. O., Neill R., Kalan M.; *ed:* Malone Coll (BA) His 1 of Akron Post Grad Stud His, Ed; *cr:* Warrensville Hts City Schls Geog Tchr 1978-80; Univ of Akron Grad Tchng Asst 1980-82; City Schls PE, His, OWA Tchr 1982-; *ai:* REA 1983-, VP; NEO NEA 1983-; NAACP 1991-, VP; Democratic Cntrl Comm 1992-; Councilman 1996; Ldrshp Portage Cty 1994; Kent City Cncl C *office:* Ravenna HS 345 E Main Ravenna OH 44266

FELTT, GARY WILLIAM, Sixth Grade Teacher; *b:* Plattsburg Barbara Tatro; *c:* Amy, Christopher, Katherine; *ed:* Central CT (MS) Guidance 1975; *cr:* Toffolon Elem Schl 4th & 6th Grd Tchr MS of Plainville 6th Grd Tchr 1991-; *ai:* 6th Grd Sci Coord & T Tech Liaison for Schl with Town of Plainville; CEA 1970-; Co Safe Sr Grad 1993-; Nom Tchr of Yr 1984; *home:* 160 Pinnacle CT 06010

FELTZ, CATHERINE MARINO, Asst Professor of Special Ed; City, NJ; *c:* Carl Robert, David Charles; *ed:* GA Ct Coll (BA) 1976; Montclair St Coll (MA) Cnslng 1979; GA Ct Coll (MA) 1985; 32 Addl Credit Hrs; Cert Learning Disablity; Elem Ed, Supervision, Pre Schl, Guid, LDTC Certs; *cr:* Pt Plesant E Disigner, Impl First Rsrch Room 1979-80; Georgian Ct Coll Asst Ed, Supervision Tchr 1980-; *ai:* Cncl of Exceptions Child 1979-; Learning Consulant 1985-; Assn Retarded Citizen Ocean Cty VP, Pres, Bd of Dirs; Bd of Trustees 1993-; Private Leaning Admin Bd of Learning Disablity; Edctr of Yr St of NJ Assoc; Hemispheicity & Impheation; Spec Ed Chm 1990-94; *office:* Court Coll Hamilton Hall 7th St Lakewood NJ 08701

FENELON, LEONARD G., Program Director; *b:* Southampton Jacqueline A.; *c:* Reneck Weiss, Jeffrey A., Mark J.; *ed:* Cntrl C (BA) His & Soc Stud 1969, (MA) His & Soc Stud 1974; Univ of Ed Admin, Curr & Supervision 1982; *cr:* Avon Pub Schls His & Tchr 1969-80, His Dept Chair 1980-82, Dept Supvr 1982-95, Dis 1995-; *office:* Avon Pub Schls 34 Simsbury Rd Avon CT 06001

FENILI, SUSAN PORTER, Third Grade Teacher; *b:* Dover David; *c:* Elizabeth Lichtenstein, Scott; *ed:* Glassboro St (BA) 1988; *cr:* Cleary MS Instr & Ed Classroom Tchr 1977-83; Sacred Foods & Nutrition Tchr 1983-87; Silver Run Schl 3rd Grd Tchr Math Lab for Stus after Schl; NEA 1988-; NJEA 1988-; MTA 19 Rep; Vineland Environmental Comm 1973-, Chm; Mayors Sh Comm 1985-; Recipient of 4 Dwight D Eisenhower Grants for Sci *office:* Silver Run Schl Silver Run Rd Millville NJ 08332*

FENIMORE, PATRICIA ANN FLANNERY, Kindergarten Te Portsmouth, OH; *m:* Carl David; *c:* Jeffrey Scot, Jamie Leigh E OH Univ (BAEd) Ed; 27 Addl Hrs; *cr:* Vly Elem Schl Knd 1964-65; Wheelersburg Elem Schl Kndgtn Tchr 1965-; *ai:* OH 1963-; OH Kndgtn Ed Assn 1970-; *home:* 1113 Norwood St Whe OH 45694

FENNELLY, JANE KOZURA, Math & Physics Teacher; *b:* F PA; *m:* David J.; *ed:* Shippensburg Univ (BS) Math & Sec Bloomsburg Univ (MS) Physics 1978; PSU, Millersville Univ, Bo 54 Credits Past Masters; *cr:* Pine Grove Area HS Math & Phy 1974-; *ai:* HS Vol & Class Adv; PSEA 1974-, Innovative Tchr A 1974-; PCTM 1990-; Pine Grove Historical Soc 1985-; Tulpehoc & Pistol Club 1980-; Article Pub on Math Modeling for a PSU Wkshp in 1987; *office:* Pine Grove Area HS 101 School St Pine 17963

FENNESSEY, BETTYANNE A., Second Grade Teacher; *b:* You OH; *m:* Thomas Edward; *c:* Breona, Alison; *ed:* Youngstown St U Early Chldhd 1980; *cr:* Warren Richey Schl 2nd-3rd Grd Tchr John White Schl 2nd-4th Grd Tchr 1979-; *ai:* Stu Cncl, Kid Carnation Benefit Ball Adv; Fellowship, Soc Comms; NEA 1968 1974-77; OEA 1977-; PTA 1969-; Colonial Manor Nursing H Appreciation Spon 1994-; Annual Benefit Ball, Organizer; Awded Dev Appreciation of Shakespears Era Acting, Costume Making Theatre in the Round; Wrote Kids Court Prgm & Manual; *off* White Elem Schl 1061 Lyden Ave Youngstown OH 44505*

FENNIMORE, BEATRICE SCHNELLER, Professor; *b:* Plain *c:* Sharon Ellen; Maryann; *ed:* Brooklyn Coll CUNY (MS) Spec Tchrs Coll Columbia Univ (MED) Curr, Tchng 1982, (EDD) Cu 1986; *cr:* Tchrs Coll Columbia Univ Adj Fac 1987-; IN Univ of Prof 1987-92, Assoc Prof 1992-95, Prof 1995-; *ai:* Chair Mul Ethics Comm; Multicultural Comm Amer Assn Coll for Tchr Ed Relations Cncl Pittsburgh Pub Schls; Amer Educl Rsrch Assn ACEI 1987-; Books Pub: Student Centered Classroom Managem Child Advocacy for Early Childhood Educators 1989; Outstdng 1991; Articles Pub; *office:* Indiana Univ Of PA 203 Stouffer Hal PA 15705

FENSLER, AMY BETH, Social Studies Teacher; *b:* Defiance, Post Grad Stud at Bowling Green St Univ, Defiance Coll in Pol

; Soc Stud Tchr 1992-; *ai:* Jr Class Adv; Strategic Planning EA, OEA, BEA 1992-; *office:* Bryan HS 150 S Portland St Bryan)

R, ROBERT MICHAEL, Social Studies Teacher; *b:* n, NJ; *ed:* Rutgers Coll (BA) His & Pol Sci 1991; Rutgers Grad d (EDM) Soc Stud Ed 1993; *cr:* Hilsborough HS Soc Stud Ed 3 ock Trial, Model Congress & Model UN Club & Team Adv; Open tbl Spon; NEA 1993-; Friends of Hillborough Pub Lib 1994-; llsborough HS 463 Raider Blvd Belle Mead NJ 08502*

RMACHER, ROWENA SUMMERS, Latin Teacher; *b:* ı, CT; *m:* Barry W.; *ed:* Trinity Coll (BA) Classics 1980; City Y, Grad Ctr (MA) Classical Stud 1991; *cr:* Masters Schl Latin -86; Hastings HS Latin Tchr 1986-87; Tuxedo Park Schl Eng 3-90; Hackley Schl Latin Tchr, Fencing Coach 1990-; *ai:* Latin er Classical League 1982-; Classical Assoc of Empire St 1990-; -Millerton Lib 1994-, Vol; *office:* Hackley Schl 293 Benedict Ave NY 10591

, DAVID CHRISTIAN, Technology Teacher; *b:* Brooklyn, NY; que Pluviose-Fenton; *ed:* City Coll (BE) Civil Engrng 1990; Univ S) Applied Mechanics 1993, (ME) Biomedical Engrng 1994; *ai:* Coach; *office:* Oxon Hill HS 6701 Leyte Dr Oxon Hill MD 20745

, TERESA B., First Grade Teacher; *b:* Rutland, VT; *m:* D. *c:* Elizabeth, John; *ed:* Castleton St Coll (BS) Elem Ed 1972; 39 Credits; *cr:* Granville Cntrl Schl 1st Grd Tchr 1972-73, 3rd Grd 3-81, 1st Grd Tchr 1981-; *ai:* NEA 1972-; Cub Scouts, Den *ffice:* Granville Cntrl Schl Quaker St Granville NY 12832

MARTHA LAMKIN, Assoc Prof of Humanities; *b:* Atlantic *m:* David Allen; *c:* Scott, Maria; *ed:* Fisk Univ (BA) Eng 1960; Binghamton (MST) Eng 1977; Grad Courses for Cert, Prof Dev Cornell, Harpur Coll, Ithaca Coll 1961-65, Binghamton Univ Atlantic City Bd of Ed 7-8th Grd Eng Tchr 1960-61; Union Cntrl Schls 9th Grd Eng Tchr 1961-65; Victor Vly Cntrl Schls Rdng Tchr 1979-80; Broome Comm Coll Adj Inst of Speech Asst Prof of Hum 1991-94, Assoc Prof of Hum1995-; *ai:* Extra can Amer His Month Planning Comms; Poetry Rdng Prgm; NEA A 1995-; SCA 1994-; YWCA Bd 1994-95; BCCC Jail Ministry; opa Alpha 1957-; Woman of Achvmt Awd 1990; NEH Inst for Arts 1993; *office:* Broome Comm Coll PO Box 1017 Binghamton NY

K, BONNIE JEAN, High School Mathematics Tchr; *b:* wn, MD; *ed:* Frostburg St Coll (BA) Recreation, Math 1984; St Univ (MS) Ed 1987; *cr:* Linganore HS Math Tchr 1987-; *ai:* d Hockey, Head Sftbl Coach; Frederick Cty Tchrs Assn, MSTA, 4-; Field Hockey Coach of Yr 1993, 1994; *office:* Linganore HS Annapolis Rd Frederick MD 21701

A, LEE, Religion Department Chprsn; *b:* Brooklyn, NY; *ed:* ıs Univ (BSEd) Elem Ed 1969; Fordham Univ (MSEd) Elem Ed Saint Jerome Schl Soc Stud Chprsn 1969-81; Saint Saviour HS Dept Chprsn 1981-; *ai:* Drama Club Dir; NCEA 1981-; *office:* St S 588 6th St Brooklyn NY 11215

ER, J. PETER, Economics Professor; *b:* Saint Paul, MN; *m:* Allan Ales; *c:* Kip; *ed:* Univ of Saint Thomas (BA) Ec 1983; WA) Ec 1985, (PHD) Ec 1989; *cr:* Clark Univ Asst Prof of Ec The Jerome Levy Ecs Inst Visiting Schlr 1993-94; Clark Univ 1994-; *ai:* Honors Prgm Coord; Acad Advising; Research Bd er Ec Assn 1988-; Midwestern Ec Assn 1989-; Jerome Levy Ec lent Research Fellowship; Clark Univ Fac Dev Grants; Articles urnal of Money, Credit & Banking; Journal of Ec His, Journal of nomics & Journal of Post Keynesian Ec; *office:* Clark Univ 950 Vorcester MA 01610

, GERARD ALPHONSE, Prof of Fr, Span & Linquistics; *b:* en, Haiti; *m:* Nancy; *c:* Magali, Rachel; *ed:* Naval Acad of (BA) Navigation 1953; Villanova Univ (MA) Fr & Span 1967; PA (PHD) Linguistics 1974; US Fleet Sonar Schl Diploma marine War 1956; IAGS Cartographic Schl Diploma nmetry 1959; *cr:* Haitian Navy Lt J G & Ship Captain 1953-58; sts in Haiti Lang Prof 1958-63; St Josephs Univ in Philadelphia , Span & Linguistics 1964-; *ai:* AATF; DE Vly Translators Assn Court, Roster of Multilingual Interpreters; Coalition for Haitian 1980-, Pres & Founder; Natl Coalition for Haitian Refugees d Mem; PA Ethnic Heritage 1990-, Commissioner; Outstdng Coll Tchr Awd St Joseph Univ; Humanitarian Awd US Cath ce; Bene Merenti Medal St Josephs Univ; Three Decades of Svc seph Univ; *office:* Saint Josephs Univ 5600 City Ave Philadelphia

, KATHY SCHRENK, Science Teacher; *b:* Buffalo, NY; *m:* Jenelle, Marc, Jessica; *ed:* St Univ Coll At Buffalo (BS) Bio, 1976; St Bonaventure Univ (MS) Advanced Tchr Ed 1988; *cr:* s Med Technologist 1977-88; Portville Cntrl Schl GATE Coord Allegany Cntrl Schl Sci Tchr 1990-92; Gates-Chili HS Sci Tchr Awds Assembly Presenter; Svc Club Spon; Rochester Acad of ; Challenger Flwshp Awd; NYS Regents Earth Sci Exam Writer; ates Chili HS 910 Wegman Rd Rochester NY 14624

ON, DELPHINE DAVID, Sixth Grade Teacher; *b:* Hamlet, NC; e Nathaniel; *c:* Michelle D. Ferguson-Allen; *ed:* St Augustine's Elem Ed 1964; George Washington Univ (MA) Ed 1977; Further ty Coll, Univ of DC, CA St Polytechnic Univ; *cr:* Wake Cty Schls ghth Grd Tchr 1964-65; D C Pub Schls One-Six Grd Tchr 1965-; riends mentor Prgm; Tutorial Prgms; Church, Schl Act; BSA; lub; Amer Cancer Soc; Kiwanis Intnl; Yth Act Adv; Schl g Comm; AFT 1967-; AARP 1994-; Anacostia Civic Assn 1990-; ntal Hlth 1992-, Asst Treas; D C congress of PTA 1989-, Bd of mfortable Approach Tchng Sci Flwshp; Vol Svc Awds Tutoring; nidon Elem Schl 4th & Eye Sts SW Washington DC 20024

ON, DUANE FRANCIS, Guidance Dir & Amer His Tchr; *b:* VA; *m:* A. Elaine Miller; *c:* Lowell, David, Karyl Lynne Kramer; ws Univ (BA) His 1964; Kutztown Univ (MED) Scndry Cnslng IN Acad Rel Tchr 1973-77; Ozark Acad Rel Tchr 1977-79; Blue Acad Guid, Rel, His Tchr 1979-; *ai:* Class, Outdoor Club, Frgn ub Spon; ASCA 1986-; ASPA 1989-; *office:* Blue Mountain Acad 3642 Hamburg PA 19526

ON, F. ALLAN, History & Social Sciences Tchr; *b:* N d, CA; *m:* Jeanneatte L. Erbacher; *c:* Ian Colin Michael, Tristan er; *ed:* St Univ of NY at Buffalo (BA) His 1989; Canisius Coll dry Ed 1996; *cr:* S. S. Peter & Paul Grammar Schl K-8 Grd Sci, Tchr 1989-90; Orchard Park HS His, Soc Scis Tchr 1992-; *ai:* HS he Comm Adv; Orchard Park Tchrs Assn 1992-; NEH Schlsp for e Stalinist Experience; *office:* Orchard Park HS 4040 Baker Rd Park NY 14127

ON, JAMES JOSEPH, Sixth Grade Teacher; *b:* Dunmore, PA; ne Lucas; *c:* Kariann, Michael, John, Mary Kate; *ed:* Univ of (BS) Elem Ed 1964, (MS) Elem Ed 1967; 31 Post Grad Hrs; *cr:* Elem 5th Grd Tchr 1964-68; Washington Annex Elem 5th Grd 3-71; Dunmore Elem Ctr 5th Grd Tchr 1971-91; Dunmore MS 6th Tchr 1991-; *ai:* 6th Grd Team Ldr, Dept Head 1971-; Dunmore Fed of Tchrs 1965-, Treas; PA Fed of Tchrs, AFT 1965-; Dunmore Lions Club 1967-, Pres; *office:* Dunmore MS 300 W Warren St Dunmore PA 18512

FERGUSON, JAY W., Math Teacher; *b:* Lorain, OH; *ed:* Denicon Univ (BA) Econ, Comm 1977; Baldwin Wallace Coll (MA) Supervision 1988; *cr:* Hawthorne Jr HS Math Tchr 1986-87; Loraine HS Math Tchr 1987-95; Loraine Admiral King HS Math Tchr 1995-; *ai:* Asst Boys Bsktbl Coach; OEA, NEA 1985-; OCTM 1995-; ASCD 1987-; Lorain Intnl 1984-, Past Pres; *office:* Loraine Admiral King HS 2600 Ashland Ave Lorain OH 44053

FERGUSON, LISA CORBISELLO, Elementary Principal; *b:* East Liverpool, OH; *m:* Kevin L.; *ed:* Morehead St Univ (BS) Voc Home Ec 1979; Youngstown St Univ (MS) Educl Admin 1985-; Univ of Akron Post Grad Stud; *cr:* Wellsville Local Schls Tchr 14 Yrs, Admin 2 Yrs; *ai:* Stu Govt; Ath; CCFCS; OEA; NEA; OAESA; Grad Schl Schlsp; *home:* 1215 Willow Ln Wellsville OH 43968

FERGUSON, LORETTA MENSCH, Social Studies Teacher; *b:* Greensburg, PA; *m:* Richmond H. III; *c:* Michael David, Terrance Clark; *ed:* Seton Hill Coll (BA) His, Soc Stud 1971; Carnegio-Mellon Univ (MA) His, Soc Stud 1975; Comparative Educl Tour Soviet Union 1988; In Svc Prgms; *cr:* Greater Latrobe Schl Dist Tchr 1972-; *ai:* Co-Chair Career Day Prgm; GLEA 1972-, Bldg Rep, Negotiations Mem 1993, Red Rose; PSEA, NEA 1972-; Hospital Aid 1991-; *home:* 207 Apple Hill Dr Latrobe PA 15650

FERGUSON, MICHAEL WILLIAM, 5th & 6th Grade Science Tchr; *b:* Portsmouth, NH; *c:* Cody, Jake, Luke; *ed:* Univ of NH (BS) PE 1981; *cr:* Spring St MS PE Tchr, JV Ftbl Coach 1982-83; Rochester MS Sci Tchr 1983-84; Greenland Cntrl Schl Sci Tchr, Bsktbl, Track Coach 1984-87; Marshwood HS PE, Hlth Tchr, Track Coach 1987-95; Berwick Acad Sci Tchr 1995-; *ai:* Lower Schl Soccer; MS Bsktbl; Ski Club Adv; ME HS Track, Field St Championship 1995; Marshwood HS Yrbk Dedication 1995; *office:* Berwick Acad 31 Academy St South Berwick ME 03908*

FERGUSON, PAMELA LAMONE, Spanish & French Teacher; *b:* Wellsburg, WV; *m:* Richard D.; *c:* Todd, Chad, Cory; *ed:* WV Univ (BA) Fr, Span 1969; 34 Grad Hrs; *cr:* Brooke HS Span Tchr 1969-74; Buckeye Local HS Span, Fr Tchr 1989-; *ai:* Frgn Lang Club Spon; Traveled Abroad with Stdnts to Europe, Carribbean Islands; NEA 1989-; OFTA; *office:* Buckeye Local HS Rd 2 Box 475 Rayland OH 43943

FERGUSON, PATRICIA HAMEL, 5th Grade Language Teacher; *b:* Lawrence, MA; *m:* William A. Jr.; *c:* Kristen, William H.; *ed:* Westfield St Coll (BA) Eng, Ed 1974; Merrimack Coll 3 Credit Hrs; Holyoke Comm Coll 3 Credit Hrs; *cr:* Westfield Pub Schls Tchrs Aid 1986-87, 2nd Grd Tchr 1987-88; Blessed Sacrament Schl 5th Grd, 7th Grd Enrichment Tchr 1988-; *ai:* Church, Yth Ath Vol; Ath Fundraising COmm; NCEA; *office:* Blessed Sacrament Schl 21 Westfield Rd Holyoke MA 01040

FERGUSON, PATRICIA RAUCH, 6th Grd Language Arts Teacher; *b:* Dayton, OH; *m:* Neil David; *c:* Chad, Kristel; *ed:* Wright St Univ (BS) Elem Ed 1971; Univ of Dayton (MS) Elem Ed 1995; Learning Disability, Behavior Disorder Cert 1981; Kndgtn Cert Wright St Univ 1975; *cr:* Fairbrook Elem Schl Kndgtn Tchr 1981-82; E.G. Shaw Elem Schl 6th Grd Lang Arts Tchr 1982-; *ai:* Team Ldr; WOCTELA 1985-, Past Pres; NEA, BEA 1981-; Phi Delta Kappa 1983-; PTO 1982-, Corresponding Sec; SHINE 1980-, Pres; Martha Holden Jennings Scholar 1989-90; *office:* E G Shaw Elem Schl 3560 Kemp Rd Beavercreek OH 45431*

FERGUSON, PAUL WARREN, Counselor; *b:* Springdale, PA; *m:* Alice Renee Weber; *c:* Matthew, Kelly; *ed:* Brown Univ (BA) Classics 1963; IN Univ of PA (MED) Guid Cnslng 1964; Univ of MD (EDD) Cnslng 1971; *cr:* Univ of MD Fac Resident 1964-66, Resident Dir 1966-67; Montclair St Coll Asst Registrar 1967-69, Vice Provost Admin Svcs 1969-72; Prince George Comm Coll Cnslr 1971-; *ai:* Indian, Pakistan Stu Assn Adv; Gen Ed Task Force; Stu Transfer Adv Comm; MS Higher Ed Commission; Transfer Coords Inter-Segmental Working Group; MD Assn Higher Ed; *office:* Prince Georges Comm Coll 301 Largo Rd Uppr Marlboro MD 20774

FERGUSON, PAULINE DINGEY, Fourth Grade Teacher; *b:* Zanesville, OH; *m:* James; *c:* Amanda; *ed:* OH Univ (BS) Elem Ed 1973; Post Grad Stud Ashland Univ, Muskingum Coll, Rio Grande Coll; *cr:* Franklin Local Schl Dist 4th Grd Tchr 1968-; *ai:* Martha Holden Jennings Scholar 1988-89; Dist Mentor; Ashland Oil Tchr Achvmt Awd Nom 1991; Zo Show 1992; Cooperating Tchr of Stu Tchrs; Phi Delta Kappa Outstdng Edctr Awd 1995; *office:* Philo Intermediate Schl 225 Market St Philo OH 43771

FERGUSON, ROBERT W.,JR., Sixth Grade Teacher; *b:* Wilkes-Barre, PA; *m:* Carol M. Smith; *c:* Jared B., Erin J.; *ed:* Mansfield Univ (BS) Scndry Ed 1968; 36 Credit Hrs; *cr:* Elk Lake Schl Dist 6th Grd Tchr 1968-; *ai:* Geog Bee Coord; NEA 1968-; PA St Ed Assn 1968-; Elk Lake Ed Assn 1968-; *home:* RR 4 Box 199 Tunkhannock PA 18657

FERGUSON, THADDEUS JULIUS, Latin & French Teacher; *b:* Harrisburg, PA; *ed:* The PA St Univ (BA) Scndry Ed 1962; Columbia Univ (MA) Romance Linguistics 1965, (PHD) Romance Linguistics 1970; Columbia Univ Tchrs Coll Addl Post Grad Stud; *cr:* Columbia Univ Tchr 1967-84; Newtown HS Tchr 1984-87; Townsend Harris HS Tchr 1987-; *office:* Townsend Harris HS 149-11 Melbourne Ave Flushing NY 11367

FERGUSON, VICTORIA RUNAC, 9th Grade Business Teacher; *b:* Pittsburgh, PA; *m:* Robert Alan; *c:* Michael Vincent; *ed:* Robert Morris Coll (BS) Bus, Ed 1975; Univ of Pittsburgh (MS) Bus, Ed 1982; *cr:* Comm Coll of Allegheny Cty Part-time Evening Adult Ed Instr 1976-85; North Hills Schl Dist Tchr 1976-; *ai:* NEA 1976-; NBEA 1992-; *office:* North Hills Schl Dist 55 Rochester Rd Pittsburgh PA 15229

FERGUSON, WILLIAM G., Math Teacher & Asst Principal; *b:* New York, NY; *m:* Frances Cirolli; *c:* Bill Jr., Maria; *ed:* St John's Univ (BS) Admin, Math 1968; City Univ of NY Grad Schl 18 Credit Hrs Math; *cr:* St Elizabeth Schl Tchr 1970-75, Asst Prin, Tchr 1976-; *ai:* Math Dept Chm; Math League Coord; NCEA 1970-; St John's Univ Coaches Clipboard Awd of Coach Lou Carneseca; *office:* St Elizabeth Schl 94-01 85th St Ozone Park NY 11416

FERKO, THOMAS J., Sixth Grade Teacher; *b:* Punxsutawney, PA; *m:* Patricia Skarbek; *c:* Michelene, Marquetta; *ed:* Clarion Univ of PA (MS) Elem Ed Sci 1978; IN Univ of PA (BS) Elem Ed; Penn St Principalship Cert 1987; 30 Addl Credits Various Local Colls, Univs Western PA Area; *cr:* Hickory Grove Elem Schl 4th Grd Tchr 1972-74; Northside Elem Schl 3rd Grd Tchr, Bldg Prin 1974-86; Hickory Grove Elem Schl 6th Grd, Head Tchr 1986-; *ai:* Writing, Assessment Comm; BAEA, PSEA, NEA 1972-, Exec Cncl; Secure Credit Union 1980-, Pres, CEO; Lib Bd 1987-90, Bd Mem; Du Bois Schl Bd 1991-95, Bd Mem; Knights of Columbus 1985-, Various Offices; Brookville Area Tchr of Yr 1978; *office:* Hickory Grove Elem Schl Jenks St Ext Brookville PA 15825*

FERLITO, ALISSA MARIE, Earth Science Teacher; *b:* New Orleans, LA; *m:* Jeffrey A. Johnson; *ed:* Mt Holyoke Coll (BA) Geology 1986; SUNY at Albany (MS) Earth Sci Ed 1988; *cr:* Ichabod Crane HS Earth Sci Tchr 1988-; *ai:* Girls Bsktbl Coach 1989-91; Var Girls Swim Coach 1990-94; Stu Against Violating the Earth 1991-; NSTA 1988-; STANYS 1988-; TIME Grant; *office:* Ichabod Crane HS Rt 9 Valatie NY 12184

FERN, TAMI LYNNE, Teacher of the Gifted; *b:* Brooklyn, NY; *ed:* Russell Sage Coll (BS) Elem Ed 1966; Queens Coll (MS) Elem Ed 1970; Tchrs Coll, Columbia Univ (EDD) Gifted Ed 1989; *cr:* Franklin Sq Schls 4th-6th Grd Tchr 1966-82, Tchr of the Gifted 1983-; Columbia Univ Adjunct Prof 1990-; *ai:* NAGC 1983-; CEC 1986-; AGATE 1983-; AAUW 1990-; ASCD 1990-; PTA Outstanding Tchr Awds; Project Funny Bone Book Pub 1990; *office:* Washington Street Schl 760 Washington St Franklin Square NY 11010

FERNAN, MATTHEW F., 11th-12th Grade Religion Tchr; *ed:* Hofstra Univ (BBA) Prsnl Mngmt 1984; St Joseph's Seminary at Dunwoodie (MDiv) Theology 1988; The Angelicum (STB) Theology 1989; *cr:* Parish of Saint Benedict Diocesan Priest 1989-92; Cardinal Hayes HS Rel Stud Tchr 1992-; *ai:* Var Soccer Asst Coach; Yrbk Moderator; Respect Life Club Moderator; Jr Var Bsbl Asst Coach, Moderator; *office:* Cardinal Hayes HS 650 Grand Concourse Bronx NY 10451

FERNANDES, ANTHONY R., Social Studies Teacher; *b:* Holyoke, MA; *m:* Katherine M. Hogan; *c:* Anthony B., Matthew, Katherine; *ed:* Holyoke Comm Coll (AA) 1969; Amer Intnl Coll (BA) Soc Stud, His 1971; *cr:* H. B. Lawrence Schl Soc Stud, Eng Tchr 1971-73; Peck Jr. HS Eng Tchr 1973-83; Peck MS Soc Stud Tchr 1983-; *ai:* After-Schl Tutoring Coord; Adv Schl Dance, Drama Club, PAC Parent-Tchr; MS Alliance Rep; Holyoke Tchrs Assn 1971-, Exec Bd 1984; NEA 1971-, Rep Assembly 1985-95; Holyoke Yth Soccer; BSA; Portuguese-Amer Club Amer; *office:* Peck MS 1916 Northampton St Holyoke MA 01040

FERNANDES, CYNTHIA DIXON, Evaluation Staff Mediator; *b:* Bridgeport, CT; *m:* Keith; *c:* Faith; *ed:* Western CT St Univ (BS) Ed 1976; Univ of Bpt (MS) Rdng 1980; Sacred Heart Univ 6th Yr Admin 1993; *cr:* Cntrl HS Eng, Rdng Tchr 1976-91, Dept Chair, Tchr 1991-94, Evaluation Mediator, Tchr 1994-; Norwalk Comm Tech Coll Adj Prof 1996; *ai:* NEA, CEA, BEA 1976-; CT Ed Assn 1996, Instr Ldrs Comm; United Way 1994-, Advy Comm; Greater Bpt Cncl of Churches 1994-, Dir; Bpt Rotary Club Tchr of Yr 1994-95; Bridgeport Pub Schls Tchr of Yr Nom 1994-95; *office:* Bridgeport Pub Schls 1 Lincoln Blvd Bridgeport CT 06606

FERNANDES, ELISE M., Law Professor; *b:* New Bedford, MA; *ed:* Lehigh Univ (BA) Psych & Law 1987; New England Schl of Law (JD) Law 1990; *cr:* Law Offices of Fernandes & Finnerty Paralegal 1985-90; Fisher Coll Paralegal & Criminal Justice Prof 1990-; Salve Regina Univ Part-Time Politics Prof 1991-; *ai:* Paralegal Internship Prgm Fac Supvr; Big Brothers-Big Sisters of Greater New Bedford 1991-; New Bedford YWCA 1992-93, Bd of Dirs; *home:* 233 England St New Bedford MA 02745

FERNANDES, ROSEANNA MARIE, Music Teacher; *b:* Philadelphia, PA; *m:* Julin; *c:* Gregory, Tyisha, Deanna; *ed:* Boston Univ (BA) Music Ed 1973; Bridgewater St Coll (MS) Admin 1991; *ai:* Show Choir 60 Stdnts 10-12 Grd; Gospel Choir 125 Stdnts 10-12 Grd; Golden Apple Awd 1995; Terrific Tchrs Making ADifference 1992; Saluted in Red Book 1994; *office:* Boston Latin Schl 78 Avenue Louis Pasteur Boston MA 02115*

FERNANDEZ, DAMARIS, English Teacher; *b:* PR; *m:* Richard; *c:* Tricia; *ed:* City Coll (BS) Ed & Eng 1982; Lehman Coll (MA) Ed & Amer Lit 1987; Coll of New Rochelle 30 Credit Hrs; Prof Diploma in Admin & Supervision; *cr:* PS 138 2nd Grd Tchr 1983-84; PS 69 1st-4th Grd Tchr 1984-87; Harry S Truman HS Eng Tchr 1987-89; Bronx HS of Sci Eng Tchr 1989-; *ai:* Coll Mentor; UFT 1983-; AFT 1983-; Tchr of Yr 1991-92; *office:* Bronx HS Of Sci 75 W 205th St Bronx NY 10468

FERNANDEZ, KATHY MILLER, 7th & 8th Grd Lang Arts Tchr; *b:* Toledo, OH; *m:* J. Ramon; *c:* Nicole, Jason, Carmen; *ed:* Univ of Toledo (BE) Elem & Spec Ed 1981, (ME) Admin & Supvr 1984; *ai:* OCTELA 1990-; Natl Cncl of Tchrs of Eng 1991-; *office:* St Charles Schl 1850 Airport Hwy Toledo OH 43609

FERNANDEZ, LORI GREENE, Business Education Teacher; *b:* Geneva, NY; *m:* Victor P.; *c:* Nicole; *ed:* Bryant, Stratton Bus Inst (AOS) Secretarial Sci 1981; Nazareth Coll of Rochester (BS) Bus Ed 1989; Alfred Univ (MS) Bus Ed 1993; *cr:* Assemblyman Frank Talanie Sr Exec Sec; Geneva, Phelps, Clifton Springs K-12 Sub Tchr Half a Yr; Alfred-Almond Cntrl Schl Bus Tchr 7 Yrs; *ai:* Bus Club Adv; Bus Tchrs Assn of NYS 1995-; *office:* Alfred-Almond Cntrl Schl 6795 State Route 21 Almond NY 14804*

FERNANDEZ, MAGALI, Spanish Teacher; *b:* Havana, Cuba; *m:* Raimundo; *ed:* NY Univ Schl of Ed (BS) Ed 1968; NY Univ GSAS (MA) Span Lit 1970, (PHD) Span & Latin Am Lit 1984; *cr:* Newtown HS Span Tchr 1970-74; Eastern Dist HS Span Tchr 1974-; *ai:* AFT 1970-; AFSFL 1970-; Circulo Panamerican 1988-; *office:* Eastern District HS 850 Grand St Brooklyn NY 11211

FERNANDEZ, RONALD JOSEPH, Social Studies Teacher; *b:* Elizabeth, NJ; *m:* Arlene Ambrose; *ed:* Jersey City St Coll (BA) Soc Stud, Eng 1966; Kean Coll (MA) Contemporary Amer Issues 1970; Addl 30 Hrs Admin, Supervisory Cert; *cr:* Dunellen HS Soc Stud Tchr 1966-70; Union Cty Regnl HS Dist #1 Soc Stud Tchr 1970-, Soc Stud Dept Tchr Ldr 1981-85, Soc Stud Supv 1985-92, Eng, Soc Stud Supv 1990-92; *ai:* Prin Advy Cncl; Stu of Month Comm; NEA 1966-85; NJ Edctrs Assn 1966-85; AFT 1985-; Prin & Supervisory Assn 1985-92; *office:* Gov Livingston Reg HS 175 Watchung Blvd Berkeley Heights NJ 07922

FERNANDEZ, YOLANDA DE LA PENA, Spanish Teacher; *b:* Cienfuegos, Cuba; *m:* Abilio; *c:* Marilys, Gilbert; *ed:* Havana Univ (DR) Pedagogy 1959; Cath Univ of Amer (MS) Span Lang, Lit 1969; 56 Credits Frgn Lang Ed, Span; *cr:* LaJaula Schl Tchr 1960-61; Holy Redeemer Schll 7th-8th Grd Tchr 1963-72; Broome Jr HS Span Tchr 1972-90; Richard Montgomery HS Span Tchr, Resource Tchr, Chprsn 1980-; *ai:* Mid Sts Comm; Instr FL 16, FL 18 Span Schl Prsnl; MFLA 1972-, Bd 1986 GWTFL Outstdng Frgn Lang Tchr; GWTFL 1972; MCES, MSTA, NEA 1972-, Del St, NEA Convention; Articles Pub; *office:* Richard Montgomery HS 250 Richard Montgomery Dr Rockville MD 20850

FERNANDO, CHANDRA COORAY, Academic Dean; *b:* Sri Lanka; *c:* Sudarshan, Siromi Fernando-Santana, Sarath; *ed:* Good Shepherd Tchr Trng Coll (AMI) Early Chldhd 1959; Antioch Coll (BA) Early Chldhd, Elem 1976; St Nicholas Coll Tchrs Cert Elem 1974; Attnd Loyola Coll, Oxford Univ; *cr:* Lilliput Schoolhouse Tchr 3 Yrs; Montessori Schl Tchr 25 Yrs, Acad Dean 19 Yrs; *ai:* Pgrm Dir MD Ctr for Montessori Stud; Comm Diversity Assn of Independent MD Schl; Sci of Peace Comm Montessori Accreditation Cncl Teach Ed; Assn of Supervision & Curr Dev 1991-; North Amer Tchrs Assn 1987-; Amer Montessori Soc 1977-, Sci to Children 1983, Sci to Peers 1988; Baltimore Cncl on Frgn Affairs 1994-; Amer Assn of Univ Women 1995-; MD St Dept of Ed 1993-95, Mem Panels to Select, Christa Mc Auliffe Flwshp Awd; Numerous Articles Pub; *office:* Montessori Society Cntrl MD 10807 Tony Dr Lutherville MD 21093*

FERO, MARY JO TRESSLER, High School Art Teacher; *b:* Tecumseh, MI; *m:* Patrick; *c:* Michael, Michelle Orwig; *ed:* Millersville Univ (BS) Art Ed 1978, (MED) Art Ed 1987; Attnd York Coll of PA 1974-76, Siena Heights Coll 1958-60; *cr:* Temple Univ Adult Learning Ctr Tchr 1980-81; Alexander M. Patch Amer HS Art Tchr 1981-83; York Suburban HS Art Tchr 1985-; *ai:* Art Dept Chm; Natl Art Hon Soc Adv; Calligraphy Club Co-Adv; NEA 1989-; NAEA 1990-; St John the Bapt Cath Church 1973-, Tchr, Eucharistic Minister; Laurel Art Guild 1967-70, Pres; Superior Work Performance Awd 1982; Exceptional Performance Awd 1983; *office:* York Suburban Sr HS Hollywood Dr And Southern Rd York PA 17403

FERRALL, ALAN SCOTT, Tech Director & Auditorium Mgr; *b:* Columbiana, OH; *ed:* Tech Theatre OSU at Columbus; Tisch Schl of the Arts NYU at New york Scenic Design; *cr:* Cuyahoga Falls HS Auditorium Mgr 1989-95; *ai:* Stage Crw Adv; Play Dir; USITT 1991-, Excl in Design for Carousel 1995; Weathervane Comm Playhouse 1990-, Backstage Vol, top 10 Col 1990-92, Stage Mgr Bes Production Awd Fences 1993; *home:* 1426 Meriline St Cuyahoga Falls OH 44221*

FERRANTE, JEANNE W., Retired Elementary Teacher; *b:* Newton, MA; *m:* Victor A.; *c:* James V., Laura Ferrante Snyder; *ed:* SUNY at Oswego (BS) Elem Ed 1953; Addl 32 Credit Hrs; *cr:* Cazenovia Cntrl Schl 3rd Grd Tchr 1953-54; Burnt Hills Schl Elem Grd Tchr 1954-62, 1969-92; Ballston Lake Cent Schl Elem Grds Tchr 1954-62, 1969-92; *ai:* NY St Ret Tchrs 1992-; *home:* PO Box 222 Burnt Hills NY 12027

FERRARA, ANN KILCOYNE, English Teacher; *b:* Lawrence, MA; *m:* Maurice S.; *c:* Frank, Marylou, Marisa, Julie; *ed:* Emmanuel Coll (BA) Eng, Ed 1963; Boston Coll (MA) Eng 1969; *cr:* Bishop Fenwick HS Eng Tchr 1965-70; Bishop Stang HS Eng Tchr 1970-72; Winnacunnet HS Eng Tchr 1972-90; Presentation of Mary Acad Eng Tchr 1992-; *ai:* Earth Awareness; *office:* Presentation Of Mary Acad 209 Lawrence St Methuen MA 01844*

FERRARA, ANNE QUATTRONE, English Teacher; *b:* Salamanca, NY; *m:* Michael L.; *c:* Ted, Jennifer; *ed:* Fredonia SUNY Coll (BA) Eng 1964; Grad Work for Permanent Cert at St Bonaventure Univ, Fredonia Coll & Oxford Univ; *cr:* Little Vly Cntrl Schl Eng Tchr 1965-69, 9th-12th Grd Eng Tchr 1977-; 3rd & 6th Grd Tchr of Gifted & Talented 1979-92; 7th-12th Grd Eng Tchr 1992-; *ai:* Class, Lit Magazine & Drama Club Adv; Play & Musical Dir; Shared Decision Making Team; AFT & NYSUT 1965-; NCTE 1965-; Little Vly Memrl Lib Bd 1973-76; Village Players Comm Theater 1975-, Founder & Dir; NYS Grant to Dev GT Pgm; *office:* Little Valley Central Schl 207 Rock City St Little Valley NY 14755*

FERRARA, EMILE JOSEPH, Art Instructor; *b:* Bristol, RI; *m:* Dianne Lavallee; *c:* Jessica, Marcie, Jana; *ed:* Univ of MA (BFA) Fine Arts Painting 1966; RI Schl of Design (MAE) Sculpture 1980; RI Coll 36 Credit Hrs Ed; Roger Williams Univ 12 Credit Hrs Ed; Providence Coll; *cr:* Mt Hope HS Instr of Art 1967-; *ai:* Yrbk Adv 1987-92; BWEA 1967-; RIEA 1967-; NEA 1967-; Gertrude Vanderbilt Whitney Awd; Tchng Assistantship RISD; *home:* 13 Kingswood Rd Bristol RI 02809

FERRARA, KATHLEEN LINDSAY, Sixth Grade Science Teacher; *b:* Camden, NJ; *m:* Nicholas; *c:* Jill, Nicholas, Daniel; *ed:* Trenton St Coll (BS) Ed & Psych 1972; *cr:* Seaside Park Schl 5th Grd Tchr 1974-78; North Dover Schl 6th Grd Sci Tchr 1990-; *ai:* Environmental Club & Sci Fair Moderator; Basic Math Skills Tchr; Sports IM; Sci Comm Mem; NEA 1974-; Toms River Dist Tchr of Yr; *office:* North Dover Elem Schl 1759 New Hampshire Ave Toms River NJ 08755*

FERRARA, LEONARD, High School Science Teacher; *b:* Newark, NJ; *m:* Elizabeth Ann Gallis; *c:* Christopher, Steven, Michelle; *ed:* Rutgers Univ (BA) Geology 1965; Montclair St Univ (MAT) Sci Tchng 1969; Attnd Lehigh Univ Marine Sci Dept, Upsala Coll Tchng Methods Courses; *cr:* Park Ridge Bd of Ed Earth Sci Tchr 1966-67; Union Cty Regnl HS Dist #1 Sci Tchr 1967-; *ai:* Boys Soccer Asst Coach; Earth Sci Team Coach; AFT 1982-, Local 3417 Treas; Scotch Plains-Fanwood Soccer Assn 1981-93, Exec VP; St of NJ Systemic Initiative for Sci Tchrs; *office:* Jonathan Dayton Reg HS 139 Mountain Ave Springfield NJ 07081

FERRARA, LINA ANDREE, French Teacher; *b:* Trivieres, Belgium; *m:* Harold; *c:* Michele, Daniele Seikunas, Noelle Novack; *ed:* Montclair St Univ (BA) Fr 1980, (MA) 1983; *cr:* Grammar Schl Tchr in Belgium 1954-60; Sabena Airline Air Hostess 1960-62; Pope John HS Fr Tchr 1983-; *ai:* Fr Club; Fr Honor Soc; Fgn Lang Dept Chprsn; AATF 1983-; Amer Legion Womens Auxiliary 1990-; Numerous Articles Pub; *office:* Pope John HS 28 Andover Rd Sparta NJ 07871

FERRARA, MICHAEL L., Advanced Placement Eng Tchr; *b:* Jamestown, NY; *m:* Anne Marie Quattrone; *c:* Ted; *ed:* St Bonaventure Univ (BA) Eng 1960; SUNY at Fredonia (MA) Eng, Theatre 1965; *cr:* Salamanca HS Scndry, Eng, Theatre 1960-; *ai:* Drama Club Adv; Boys, Girls Tennis Coach; IATSE; Past Lt Gov Kiwanis Lt Gov; *office:* Salamanca HS 50 Iroquois Dr Salamanca NY 14779

FERRARA, ROBERT GERARD, US His, Latin Tchr & Dept Head; *b:* Montclair, NJ; *m:* Jacquelyn Vogl; *ed:* Don Bosco Coll (BA) Philosophy 1976; Pontifical Coll Josephinum 86 Credits Philosophy & Theology; *cr:* Salesian HS Tchr 1976-78; Don Bosco Tech HS Tchr 1980-82; Don Bosco Preparatory HS Tchr, Dean 1982-, Soc Stud Dept Head; *ai:* Ftbl, Track Asst Coach; Mock Trail Team Coach; NCEA 1982-; *office:* Don Bosco Prep HS 492 N Franklin Tpk Ramsey NJ 07446

FERRARA, SUSAN, High School ESL Teacher; *b:* Newark, NJ; *ed:* Caldwell Coll (BA) Elem Ed 1975; Jersey City St Coll (MA) Urban Ed 1986; Montclair St Univ (MA) Eng; Caldwell Coll Eng Cert 1994, Soc Stud Cert 1996; Jersey City St Prin, Supvr 1986; *cr:* Washington Schl 6th Grd ESL Tchr 1979-82; Lyndhurst HS ESL Tchr 1983-; Kean Coll Adj Prof 1987-93; Bergen Comm Adj Prof 1987-90; Jersey City St Adj Prof 1987-88; *ai:* Yrbk Adv 1985-90; Multicultural Awareness Club 1995-; NJEA, Lyndhurst Ed Assn 1983-; Kappa Delta Epsilon; *office:* Lyndhurst HS Weart Ave Lyndhurst NJ 07071*

FERRARI, INEZ IOLANDA, Asst Prin & Science Teacher; *b:* North Adams, MA; *ed:* Anna Maria Coll (BA) Ed 1958; Boston Coll (MED) Admin 1964; 18 Credit Hrs Sci Holy Cross; *cr:* Instantaneous Translator Mem Intnl Gen Chptr Rome Italy 1987, 1990, 1995; Cath Charities Interim Project Dir Sr Employment Prgm 1995; St Anthony Schl Prin; Venerini Acad Prin; *ai:* Rel Venerini Sister's Provincial Cncl Fac Adv; NCEA 1982-; Crime Watch 1996; Edward Calesa Natl Fnd Terrific Tchrs Making A Difference Awd; *office:* Venerini Acad 23 Edward St Worcester MA 01605*

FERRARI, KENDRA CHORDAS, Sixth Grade Teacher; *b:* Perth Amboy, NJ; *m:* David; *c:* Daniel; *ed:* Trenton St Coll (BS) Elem Ed 1988; *cr:* James J. Flynn Schl BSIP Tchr 1988-89; Hillcrest Elem Schl 6th Grd Tchr 1989-91; Conerly Rd Schl 6th Grd Tchr 1991-92; Franklin Park Schl 6th Grd Tchr 1992-93; Sampson G. Smith Schl 6th Grd Tchr 1993-; *ai:* NJEA, NEA 1989-; *office:* Sampson G Smith Interm Sch 1649 Amwell Rd Somerset NJ 08873

FERRARI, ROSALIE, Spanish Teacher; *b:* Philadelphia, PA; *ed:* Villanova Univ (BA) Hum 1967; Millersville Univ (MA) Span 1993; Bryn Mawr Coll Post Grad Stud; *cr:* Our Lady of Mt carmel Elem Schl 2nd Grd Tchr 1959-61; St Denis Elem Schl 7th Grd Tchr 1961-64; Allentown Cntrl HS Span, Latin Tchr 1964-67; Archbishop Carrol HS Span Tchr 1967-78; Gwynedd Mercy Acad Span Tchr 1978-80; Merion Mercy Acad Span Tchr 1980-; *ai:* Span Club Adv; Span NHS Moderator; Svc Org Moderator; Steering Comm Mid Sts Evaluation; AATSP 1970-, Natl Pres Span NHS; NCEA 1980-; Greater Phila Area Chapter AATSP 1990-, VP; Grant for Stud Bryn Mawr Coll Post Grad; Honorary Inductee Sigma Delta Pi; PA Area Span Edtrs Tchr of the Yr 1995-; *office:* Merion Mercy Acad 511 Montgomery Ave Merion Station PA 19066*

FERRARIO, EDWARD JOHN, Fourth Grade Teacher; *b:* Providence, RI; *m:* Patricia; *c:* Kerri, Kevin; *ed:* Comm Coll of RI (AA) Lbrl Arts 1978; RI Coll (BS) Spec Ed, Elem Ed 1981; Providence Coll (MED) Ed, Admin 1993; Attnd RI Southern Collabrative, Thames Sci Ctr; *cr:* Forest Park Schl Tchr 10 Yrs, Prin 1 Yr; *ai:* Drug Free Schl, Math, Sci, Prof Dev Comms; NEA 1987-; Tapestry Toyota Grant; Sci Tchr of Yr Awd 1991; *office:* Forest Park Elem Schl 50 Woodlawn Dr North Kingstown RI 02852

FERRARO, BARBARA FOLTS, 5th Grade Teacher; *c:* Donald V.; *cr:* Nativity of Our Lord Fac Coord 1960-65; Sci Mentor K-6th Grd 1965-; Track & Girls Sftbl Coach & Asst Prin 1984-86; *ai:* Schl Learning Garden Chrprsn; NCEA; Elizabeth Ann Seton Awd 1980; Natl Home Schl Assn Awd 1980.

FERRARO, CAMILLE MARIA, Second Grade Teacher; *b:* Jamaica, NY; *ed:* St John's Univ (BS) Elem Ed 1975, (MS) Elem Ed 1979; *cr:* St Mary Gate of Heaven Schl 5th, 2nd Grd Tchr 1976-77; Blessed Sacrament 2nd Grd Tchr 1977-78; St Mary Gate of Heaven Schl 1st, 7th, 8th, 2nd Grd Tchr 1978-; *ai:* Mission, Rel Coord; Mid Sts Evaluation Steering Comm; NCEA 1976-; Ferrini Welfare League 1977-; Catechetical Awd; *office:* St Mary Gate Of Heaven Schl 104-06 101st Ave Ozone Park NY 11416

FERRARO, JOSEPH PETER, PE & Math Teacher; *b:* Newark, NJ; *m:* Ellen Marie Adam; *c:* Lisa Marie, Kelly Lynn; *ed:* Seton Hall Univ (BS) PE 1972; Kean Coll K-12 Math Tchr Cert 1989; PE 6 Credit Hrs; Math 33 Credits; Cmptr Tech 6 Credits; *cr:* Barringer HS Hlth, PE Tchr 1972-74; Lavallette Elem Schl PE, Math Tchr 1974-; *ai:* Coach Boys Soccer, Girls Bsktbl, Sftbl; Safety Patrol, Math Club, Ath Adv; NJEA 1974-; Cntrl Jersey MS Ath League 1995-, Pres; St Justins Church 1972-, Yth Minister; NJ St Governor's Outstdng Tchng Awd 1993; Phi Theta Kappa 1987.*

FERRARO, THERESA LUCCHI, Chapter I Math Specialist; *b:* Bronx, NY; *m:* Stephen A.; *ed:* Herbert H. Lehman Coll CUNY (BA) Sociology, Elem Ed 1975, (MS) Rdng, Audio-VisualMedia 1977; 28 Addl Credits Spec Ed, Math, Math Ed; *cr:* PS 21 Tchr K-6 Grds 8 Yrs; MS 113 Math, Sci Tchr 1 Yr, PS 83 Math, Sci Tchr 1 Yr, MS 135 Math, Sci, Study Skills Tchr 3 Yrs; *ai:* Dist 11 Math Working Group; NYC Real World Math Group; UFT, AFT 1983; NCTM 1994-; ASCD 1996-.*

FERREIRA, ANNA MUNTZENBERGER, English Teacher; *b:* Brooklyn, NY; *ed:* St John's Univ (BA) Eng 1966, (MA) Eng 1973; *cr:* Newtown HS Eng Tchr 1966-; *ai:* UFT 1966-; *office:* Newtown HS 4801 90th St Elmhurst NY 11372

FERREIRA, BONNIE M., Secondary Sciene Teacher; *b:* New Bedford, MA; *ed:* Stonehill Coll (BS) Bio 1984; Bowling Green St Univ (MED) Cnslng 1986; Northeastern Univ CAGS Cnslng; *cr:* Merrimack Coll Resident Dir 1986-87; New Bedford HS Scndry Sci Tchr; *ai:* Whaling City Tennis; NABT 1990-; Natl Org of Almes; Polaroid Project Bridge Internship 1991-92; *office:* New Bedford HS 230 Hathaway Blvd New Bedford MA 02740*

FERREIRA, STEVE, Ec, Law & Finance Teacher; *b:* New Bedford, MA; *m:* Corinne; *c:* Steve, Jason; *ed:* Univ of MA at Dartmouth (BS) Bus Admin 1967; Univ of VT (MEd) Ed 1982; 45 Addl Grad Hrs above Masters; *cr:* Essex HS Tchr, Coach, & Dept Chair 1967-; *ai:* Head Var Bsbl Coach & Head Frosh Ftbl Coach; NEA & VEA 1967-; AVA 1990-; ABCA 1985-; VT Bsbl Coaches 1982-, Pres; VT Realtors 1982-; VT Life Insurance Agents 1981-; IAABO & Bd 105 1975-; Essex HS Yrbk Dedication 1969, 1981, & 1985; VT Coach of Yr in 1977; *office:* Essex HS 2 Educational Dr Essex Junction VT 05452

FERRELL, JAMES FREDERICK, Spanish Teacher; *b:* Zanesville, OH; *ed:* OH St Univ (BSEd) Span Ed 1982; Attnd Univ of Dayton; *cr:* Tippecanoe HS Span, Fr Tchr 1982-; *office:* Tippecanoe HS 555 N Hyatt St Tipp City OH 45371

FERRENCE, GARY M., Professor of Biology; *b:* Pottsville, PA; *m:* Carol Ann Nawrot; *c:* Gregory, Jeanine, Matthew; *ed:* Kutztown Univ (BS) Ed & Comprehensive Sci 1962; IN Univ at Bloomington (MAT) Earth Sci 1966, (EDD) Sci Ed 1968; Attnd Temple Univ & Millersville Univ; *cr:* Penns Manor Jr Sr HS Bio & Gen Sci Tchr 1962-65; IN Univ Stu Tchr Consultant 1966-68; Seton Hill Coll Instr 1972-74; IN Univ of PA Prof of Bio 1968-; *ai:* Bio Club Adv; Internship Coord; NSTA 1967-; Phi Delta Kappa 1968-; Assn of PA St Coll & Univ Facs 1968-, Sec; Commonwealth of PA Univ Biologists 1969-, Sci Ed Comm Chair; Friends of the Parks 1988-, Chm Bd of Dirs; IUP Tchng Excl Awd 1994-95; Conservation Awd Rocky Mountain Elk Fndtn; Books: Fundamentals of Environmental Biology 1994 & Conservation of Plant and Animal Resources 1996 & A Study Guide for Marine Science for Middle School Students 1994; *office:* Indiana Univ Of PA Indiana PA 15705*

FERRENCE, JOHN JOSEPH,OSA, Chemistry Teacher; *b:* Philadelphia, PA; *ed:* Villanova Univ (BA) Philosophy 1949, (BS) Bio, Chem 1952, (MS) Bio, Chem 1960; 12 Addl Credits 1965; Beaver Coll 12 Credits Chem 1966; *cr:* Carroll HS Chem, Math Tchr 1953-56; Augustinian Acad Prin, Tchr 1956-62; St Nicholas Tolentine Chem, Math Tchr 1962-64; Msr. Bonner HS Sci Chair 1964-75, Chem Tchr 1964-; *ai:* Retreat Team; Father's Club Moderator; NEA; Parish Priest 1964-; Knights of Columbus 1966-; NFS Grants; *office:* Msr. Bonner HS 403 N Lansdowne Ave Drexel Hill PA 19026

FERRENCE, SUZANNE LOUISE (SNYDER), Secondary English Teacher; *b:* Nazareth, PA; *m:* Brian C.; *c:* Christopher, Carrie, Annie; *ed:* Millersville St Coll (BS) Scndry Eng 1972; 24 Addl Hrs; *cr:* Hempfield Schl Dist Scndry Eng Tchr 1972-76; Schuylkill Haven Area Schl Dist Scndry Eng Tchr 1982-84; Minersville Area Schl Dist Scndry Eng Tchr 1984-; *ai:* SADD Adv; Fac Discipline Comm; *office:* Minersville Area HS PO Box 787 Minersville PA 17954

FERRER, EFRAIN JOSE, Assistant Professor; *b:* Havana, Cuba; *c:* Efrain Jr.; *ed:* Havana Univ at Cuba (BS) Physics 1974; PN Lebedev Physical Inst at Moscow (PHD) Math, Physics 1988; *cr:* Pedagogical Univ Assoc Prof 1974-79; Inst of Cybernetics, Math, Physics Research Assoc 1979-84; P N Lebedev Physical Inst Research Assoc 1984-90; FL Intern Univ Adjunct Prof 1991-93; SUNY at Fredonia Asst Prof 1993-; *ai:* Cooperative Engrng, Intnl Ed Comm; Amer Physical Soc 1995-; Over 18 Yrs Scientific Research; Over 30 Publications; Undergraduate and Grad Tchng; Research Grant Awd 1995; *office:* S U N Y Coll At Fredonia Fredonia NY 14063

FERRERA, VICTORIA, English Teacher; *b:* Newark, NJ; *w:* Donato V. (dec); *c:* Dana; *ed:* Kean Coll (BA) Eng 1965; New Schl for Soc Rsrch Broadcasting, Comm MA; *cr:* West Kinney Jr HS Eng Tchr 1965-79; Chestnut St Schl Eng Tchr 1979-92; Univ HS Eng Tchr 1992-; *ai:* Schl Improvement Team; SAT Tutoring; NTU, NCTE 1965-; GOPAE 1994-; LUSO Fraternal Assn 1965-; Pub Poetry; *office:* University HS 55 Clinton Pl Newark NJ 07108

FERRETRI, NANCY, Choral Director; *b:* Keene, NH; *w:* August J. (dec); *c:* Lisa A., Michael A.; *ed:* Boston Univ (BA) Music, Voice 1959; Long Island Univ (MS) Music, Ed 1972; 36 Post Grad Credits Fitchburg St, Tafts Univ, Emmanuel, Simmons; *cr:* Kings Pk Jr Sr HS Music Tchr 7-12 Grds 1960-62; Friends Acad 1-8 Grd Music Tchr 1968-71; Burlington Von Schl Music, Spec Needs Tchr 1072-90; Pine Glen Schl Music, Spec Needs Tchr 1972-1990; Burlington HS Choral Dir 1990-; *ai:* Drama Club Adv; Church Choir Soloist; Nerburyport Choral Soc; MENC 1959-; MMEA Northeast Dist 1972-, Jr, Sr Dist; Bea, Chorus Mgr; Lib Bd 1978-, Vice Chm; Arts Cncl 1980-, Chm; Murphy Schl Bldg Comm 1976-; New England Classical Singers, Pres; N Reading Comm Chorale Music Dir; Union Congregational Church Choir Dir; Comm Theater Groups Music Dir.*

FERRETTI, CAROL N., School Nurse; *b:* Leechburg, PA; *m:* Ralph D.; *c:* Joseph, Robert, Daniel; *ed:* Shadyside Hospital Schl of Nursing (RN) 1960; Indiana Univ (BAEd) Nursing 1980; Indiana Univ, Arin IU (MS) Nursing 1994; *cr:* Allegheny Valley Hospital Registered Obsterical Nurse 1960-80; Apollo Ridge Schl Dist Nurse 1980-81; Leechburg Area Schl Dist Nurse 1982-; *ai:* Stu Cncl; Bloodmobile Chm; Caring Prgm Underprivileged Children; Stu Assistance Prgm; NEA, PSEA, LEA 1982-; WCSNA 1991-; St Catherines Ladies Guild 1989-, Pres & Trustee; CDA 1989-, Sec; *office:* Leechburg Area Schls Dist 200 Siberian Ave L
PA 15656

FERRETTI, JEAN, Elementary Science Teacher; *b:* Passaic, N
Renee, Bryan, Rachel Lynn; *ed:* WM Paterson Coll of NJ (BS)
Dowling Coll 30 Credit Hrs Elem Ed; *cr:* Clifton Sr HS Bio Tchr
Lakota Jr Schl Jr HS Sci Tchr 1974-76; St John the Evangelist
5-8 Sci Tchr, Dept Head 1989-95; Southold USFD Elem Sci Tc
ai: Mattituck HS Girls Jr HS Sftbl Coach 1988-91, Girls Jr
Coach 1991; Lakota Jr Schl Yrbk Adv 1975-76, Judo Club
1974-75; NEA, NJEA 1971-; NCEA 1989-; Mattituck Cutch
1981-, VP, Pres; North Fork Soccer League 1986-, Sec; Cub Sco
Den Mother; Ecumenical Nursery Schl Bd 1980-, Purchasing Rep
Mini-Grant Co-Recipient; Spec Curr Wkshp Presenter; Parents
Focusing on Identification of Eating Disorders Wkshp Presenter

FERRETTI, NANCY ANN, Choral Director & Music Tchr;
NH; *w:* Chet (dec); *c:* Lisa A., Michael A.; *ed:* Boston Univ (B
Ed, Voice 1959; Long Island Univ (MS) Music Ed, Voice 197
Univ, Berklee Coll of Music, Tafts Univ, Fitchburg St In Svc,
Music Ed, Law in Ed 36 Credits; *cr:* Kings Park Jr Sr HS Gene
Choral Tchr 1959-60; Friends Acad 1st-8th Grd Vocal Tchr
Burlington Pub Schls Music Elem Classroom, Spec Ed Tchr 197
Choral Dir 1990-; *ai:* Drama Club Adv; Madrigal Singers Adv,
Schl Chorus Dir; Music, Schl Climate, 9th Grd Interdis Comm
1959-; MMEA 1972-, Jr Sr Dist Chorus Mgr 5 Yrs; NEA, MTA
Bd 1978-, Sec, Vice Chm; Arts Cncl 1980-, Pres, Vice Chm; Mu
Selectman, Appointee; North Parish Choral Soc, Pres, Sing
Congregational Church Jr Sr Choir Dir; North Rdng Comm Chor
Dir; Colonial Chorus, Lynnfield Players, Comm Theatre D
Burlington Pub Schls 123 Cambridge St Burlington MA 01803*

FERRI, ELEANOR HARDY, Math Teacher; *b:* Boston, MA;
Hrny Sr.; *c:* Bruce Jr., Debra Dugan; *ed:* Boston St Coll (BA) Ma
1972; Bridgewater St Coll (MED) Counseling 1975; (MBA) Mn
cr: Westport MS Math Tchr 1972-77; Fisher Jr Coll Psych Instr
Portsmouth MS Math Tchr 1977-81; Portsmouth HS Math Tchr
Ski Club Adv 1980-93; Honor Soc Selection Comm; Crisis Mng
Math Cncl; RIMTA, NEA 1978-; NCTM 1972-; RI Math Tc
Recognition Awd 1992; NCTM Cert of Commendation; RI Senat
for Excl as an Educator; *office:* Portsmouth HS Education Ln P
RI 02871

FERRI, LISA M., Elementary Principal; *b:* White Plains,
Manhattan Coll (BS) Math, Spec Ed 1988; Fordham Univ (MS
1991; Inst of Rel Stud (MA) Yth Ministry 1994; Fordham Un
Ldrshp Doctoral Stu; *cr:* Harrison Recreation Dept Day Camp
1982-; St Gregory the Great Schl Tchr 1988-95; Holy Family
1995-; *ai:* Yrbk Moderator; Parish Cncl Sec; Lector; Eucharistic
Tutor; Chrldng Coach; NEEA 1988-; AERA 1995-; *office:* Ho
Schl 100 Mt Joy Pl New Rochelle NY 10801*

FERRI, LOUIS J., Mathematics Teacher; *b:* Stamford, CT;
Frances; *c:* Mickey, Benjamin, Kevin; *ed:* Fairfield Univ (BA)
(MA) Ed 1968; Univ of Bridgeport 6th Yr Cert in Ed 1990; *cr*
Schl Math Tchr 1966-78; Stamford HS Math Tchr 1978-; *ai:* N

FERRICK, PATRICIA S., Mathematics Teacher; *b:* Bellaire, O
Univ (BSEd) Math 1966, (MED) Ed 1972; Post-Grad Work
Garaway Schls Math Tchr 1966-70; Logan City Schls Math Tchr
Bellaire City Schls Math Tchr 1974-; *ai:* NEA, OEA 1966-; B
NCTM 1970-; Kazanjian Awd; Featured in Article; Numreous Art
office: Bellaire HS 35th & Guernsey St Bellaire OH 43906

FERRIGNO, NICOLE, Mathematics Teacher; *b:* Hackensack
Providence Coll (BA) Math, Scndry Ed 1993; Jersey City St
Urban Ed, Admin 1996; *cr:* James J. Ferris HS Math Tchr 199
City Pub Schls Math Tchr 1993-; *ai:* Girls St Adv; SAT Tchr; HSF
JCEA 1993-; Sallie Mae First Class Tchr Awd; *office:* James J.
35 Colgate St Jersey City NJ 07302*

FERRIGNO, ROBERT STEVEN, English Teacher; *b:* Brooklyn
Hofstra Univ (BA) Eng 1986, (MA) Scndry Ed 1988, Queen C
Eng, Crtv Wrtng; Long Island Writing Project; *cr:* West Hempste
Grd Eng Tchr 1986-93; West Hempstead HS 10-11 Grd Eng Tc
ai: MS Newspaper Adv 1990-; Seventh Grd Curr Revision 1
Hempstead Ed Assn 1986-, MS Bldg Rep 1991-92; NY St Tc
1986-; Pub Short Story 1989; *office:* West Hempstead Mid-S
Nassau Blvd West Hempstead NY 11552

FERRIS, CAROLYN MARIE, Bus & Cmptr Ed Dept Chair; *b:* U
ed: Utica Coll of Syracuse Univ (BS) Bus, Ec 1980; SUC at Cort
Ed Rdng 1986; *cr:* St Joe-St Pats Schl 3rd Grd Rdng Tchr 1985-
Dame HS Bus, Cmptr Ed Dept Chprsn 1986-; *ai:* Sr Class, SA
Store Entreprenuership Advs; Stu Travel Group; Acad Cncl;
Assn 1988-; *office:* Notre Dame Jr Sr HS 2 Notre Dame Ln
13502*

FERRIS, JANET CARPENTER, English & Public Speaking
Buffalo, NY; *c:* Kelli, Kevin; *ed:* Ithaca Coll (BS) Speech Cor
Syracuse Univ (MED) Eng 1982; Attnd Univ of GA 30 Hrs; *cr:*
HS Speech, Drama, Eng Tchr, Golf Coach 1973-82; Bishop Gr
Speech, Drama, Eng Tchr, Golf Coach 1982-87; Onondaga
Speech, Eng Tchr, Golf Coach 1987-; *ai:* Yrbk, Sr Class, Acad I
Adv; Acad Advy Comm; NYSUT 1987-; Amer Cancer Soc
Championship Comm, Chm; Most Spirited Tchr Awd; *office:* On
Sr HS 4479 S Onondaga Rd Nedrow NY 13120

FERRIS, KENNETH JAMES, English Teacher; *b:* Cincinnati,
Miami Univ (BA) Eng Ed 1973, (MED) Curr & Supervision
Princeton HS Tchr & Coord 1973-; *ai:* NEA 1994-; Prince
Classroom Ed 1994-.

FERRIS, LINDA T., French Teacher; *b:* Buffalo, NY; *m:* G
Christine; *ed:* St Univ of Buffalo (BS) Scndry Ed 1965; Elmira
Eng 1970; *cr:* Cohocton Central Schl Scndry Fr & Eng Tchr
Wayland Cohocton Cntrl Scndry Fr Tchr 1993-; *ai:* NEA 196
8788 State Route 53 Bath NY 14810

FERRIS, LORRAINE CATHERINE, Language Arts Tea
Woodside-Queens, NY; *ed:* Ladycliffe Coll (BA) His 1964; C
Modern European His 1970; *cr:* Saint James Schl Tchr 1957-
Matthews Schl Tchr 1964-66; Lieutenant Joseph P Kennedy Jr H
Dir 1967-68, 1969-70; Saint Anthony Schl Tchr 1970-; *ai:*
Moderator; Mid Atlantic Sts 3rd Yr Report Chprsn; NCE
Archdiocesan of WA; Certs for Years Svc; *office:* St Anthony G
12th & Lawrence St NE Washington DC 20017*

FERRIS, PATRICIA ANNE, Sixth Grade Teacher; *b:* Bronx,
SUNY Coll at Brockport (BS) Elem Ed 1970; Hofstra Univ (MA)
1975; Long Island Univ 39 Credit Hrs Schl Cnslr; *cr:* G. N. Gallo
& 6 Grd Tchr 1970-77; J. F. Sparke Schl 2 & 5 Grd Tchr 1978,
M. F. Stokes Schl 6th Grd Tchr 1978-79, 1981-91; Island Trees
Grd Tchr 1991-; *ai:* Sportsnight Adv; UTIT 1979-, Treas; AFT
1970-; ACA, NYCA 1995-; Jenkins Awd Presented by PTA Ou
Svc to Children; *home:* 400 Fulton St Apt 4E Farmingdale NY 1

FERRIS-FEARNSIDE, KAREN F., Social Studies Teacher; *b*
NY; *m:* Richard; *c:* Matthew, Jeffrey, Brittany; *ed:* SUNY at Alb
Soc St Educ 1972, (MA) Soc Stud Educ 1976; 40 Addl Cred

r: Niskayuna HS Soc Stud Tchr 1972-74; Voorheesville HS Soc r 1975-76; Burnt Hills MS Soc Stud Tchr 1979-81; Burnt Hills Sr tud Tchr 1974-75, 1976-79, 1981-; ai: Bill of Rights Competition apital Dist Cncl Soc Stuc 1972-, Bd of Dirs 1991-; NYS Cncl Soc ; Burnt Hills Tchrs Assn 1974-; PEACE; Holocaust & Jewish :e Fellowship 1993; Advanced Placement Testing Comm Amer s; Write NYS Regents Exam 8 Yrs; Golub Awd Outstanding Tchr General Electric Star Awd Outstanding Tchr 1990, 1992, 1993, hr of Yr 1990;Coe Flwshp 1994; Mltcltrl Comp Edctnl Schlrshp y 1995; *office:* Burnt Hills-Balston Lake HS Lakehill Rd Burnt 12027*

O, ORESTA MARY, Science Teacher; *b:* Paterson, NJ; *ed:* Seton v (BS) Scndry Ed, Sci, Psych 1979; Montclair St Coll (MA) Ed Supervision 1993; *cr:* Mary Help of Christn Acad Sci Dept Chm DePaul HS Sci Tchr 1989-; *ai:* Dir Paterson Diocesan Forensic Forensic Coach; Astronomy Club; Chrpsn Discipline Task Force IS; NCEA 1979-; ASCD 1989-; NJESTA 1985-; Phi Delta Kappa hr of Yr Awd Felician Coll 1991; Nom Presidential Awd for Excl Math 1991; *office:* DePaul HS 1512 Alps Rd Wayne NJ 07470*

TO, JOHN EDMUND, Associate Professor; *b:* East Cleveland, Marcia Leigh; *ed:* Cleveland Inst of Music (BM) Piano, Music le Schl of Music (MM) Composition 1965; *cr:* Music Ctr of North tec Asst 1965-67; Univ of Chicago Lecturer in Music 1966-67; en Symphony Assoc Conductor 1967-70; Hiron Coll Asst Prof of 70-71; Univ of TX Guest Lecturer 1970; Intnl Congress of Strings ir 1981-85; Kent-Blossom Festival Schl Dir 1986-89; Sprgfield h Music Dir, Conductor; Kent St Schl of Music Assoc Prof of 983-; Cleveland Hts Orch, Music Dir, Conductor 1991-; *ai:* 's Awd 1991; 30 Works Pub Amer Composers Alliance; Various Pub; *office:* Kent St Univ Hugh Glauser Schl of Music Kent OH

N, GALE HODOROWSKI, Social Studies Teacher; *b:* Madison, Timothy J.; *c:* Tim, Mark; *ed:* St Univ Oswego (BS) Ed 1979, (MS) 1985; Attnd Williamsburg Tchr Inst 1996; *cr:* Liverpool HS Soc ner His, Law Elective, Sociology Elective Tchr 1988-; *ai:* Mock m Adv 1988-; Better Schl Comm 1990-94; Pupil Svcs Team 1994-; iverpool Fac Assn, NY Cncl Soc Stud, NY Tchrs Assn, Cntrl NY Stud 1988-; *office:* Liverpool HS 4338 Wetzel Rd Liverpool NY

ZZI, DONALD ROCCO, Professor of Biology; *b:* Weehawken, Diane Apostol; *c:* Chris, Alex; *ed:* Rochester Inst of Tech (AAS) h 1966; NY Univ (BA) Bio 1968; St Johns Univ (MS) Physiology Credits Post Masters in PHD Prgm SUNY at Stony Brook; *cr:* est Schl Bio Prof 1974-; *ai:* Chair, Tech Dev & Utilization mittee of Mid States Self-Stud; Computing, Coll Wide Multimedia AAAS 1987-; NSTA, Empire St Assn of Two Yr Coll Biologists NYU Alumni Assn 1969-; SUNY at Stony Brook Assn 1975-; Grant; SUNY Rsrch Fnd Fac Grant; NSF Grad Flwshp; A ry Manual of Human Anatomy & Physiology Pub; *office:* Suffolk ity Coll Crooked Hill Rd Brentwood NY 11717

, JANE ANN, First Grade Teacher; *b:* Marion, OH; *ed:* OH St Univ rly Ed, Supervision 1980, 1987; Univ of Dayton (MA) Admin Cert : Prairie Lincoln Elem Schl 1st Grd, K-1 Grd, 2nd Grd Tchr Darby Woods Elem Schl 1st Grd Tchr 1995-; OH St Univ Coll ourse Tchr; *ai:* Prof Assistance Ldr; Transition Team; Phi Delta 980-; OEA, NEA; PTSA 1975-, SWEA; Delta Gamma Alum 1975-; s Scholar; TRIBES Trainer; Ashland Golden Apple Achiever; Capital Grant; PTA Edctr Nom; *office:* Darby Woods Elem Schl woods Blvd Galloway OH 43119

, KEVIN, English Teacher; *b:* Yonkers, NY; *m:* Beatrice Costa; *c:* e, Brendan; *ed:* SUNY at Stony Brook (BA) Eng, Lib Arts 1973, ng, Lib Arts 1977; 80 Addl Credits; *cr:* Centereach HS Eng Tchr *ai:* Cmptr Club Adv; AFT, NYSUT 1974-; Ancient Order of ns 1989-; *office:* Centereach HS 14 43rd St Centereach NY 11720

., CAROL COOKE, Fifth Grade Teacher; *b:* Bethlehem, PA; *m:* G.; *c:* Bridget (dec) Melissa; *ed:* Gwynedd Mercy Coll (BS) El Ed : Sts Simon & Jude Schl 2nd Grd Tchr 5 Yrs; Holy Infancy Schl Tchr 6 Yrs, 4th Grd Tchr 5 Yrs, 5th Grd Tchr 1 Yr; *ai:* Instrl Team; Rdng Corrd; NCA 1966-; Grant to Attend New Frontiers m at Dayton OH Univ, to Stud Math Manipulatives, Sci in Elem *office:* Holy Infancy School E 4th & Webster Sts Bethlehem PA

, SUSAN SHABUS, Global Studies Teacher; *b:* Greene, NY; *m:* .; *c:* Rebecca, Benjamin; *ed:* Cedar Crest Coll (BA) His 1972; NY (MS) Scndry Soc Stud 1994; Coll of Cortland; *cr:* St Anns Schl 4th r 1974-76; Norwich HS 10th Grd Global Stud Tchr 1991-; *ai:* ated & Continue to Work on Semestering our HS Have Successfully ed; Create Wellness Day for Stu, Create an Interest I Block Stu, tdnts for Honor Soc & HOBY Ldrshp Conf; Chaperone Stdnts to - London & Paris; NEA 1991-; YMCA Camp Bd 1990-; Hosp y Bd 1989-92, Chm TV Svcs; Planned Parenthood of Broome & go 1986-92, Bd of Dirs, VP; *office:* Norwich HS Midland Dr NY 13815

LO, STEVAN M., Physical Education Teacher; *b:* Newark, NJ; *m:* e L. Herseg; *c:* Stacey, Stefanie, Aimee, Stevan Jr.; *ed:* Univ of on (BA) Hlth & PE 1974; *cr:* Pt Pleas Memorial MS Hlth & PE Yrs; *ai:* Wrestling Coach 20 Yrs; Pt Pleasant HS Soccer Coach 15 A 1976-; NJEA 1976-; *home:* 2319 Oak Tree Rd Pt Pleasant NJ

E, MELANIE BUTSCHERE, Guidance Director; *b:* Brooklyn, Michael D.; *c:* Michael Hayden, Peter Butschere; *ed:* Long Island S) Guidance & Counseling 1973; Sacred Heart Coll (BS) Ed 1971; Edmunds Elem Schl Tchr 1971-73; Elem Schl Tchr 1977-83; Holy f Jesus Guidance Cnslr 1983-92; Saint Saviour HS Guidance Dir *i:* Amer Guidance Cnslrs; *home:* 7414 Colonial Rd Brooklyn NY

YER, CYNTHIA FITZSIMMONS, Primary Physical Ed ; *b:* Ravenna, OH; *m:* David; *ed:* Kent St Univ (BA) PE 1982; *cr:* st Local Schls Hlth, PE Tchr 1985-; *ai:* Head Girls Var Cross Cntry, Girls Track Coach; Wayland Comm Church 1994-; *home:* 6506 l Rd Ravenna OH 44266

MYER, DIANA KALAMAJKA, 7th Grade Teacher; *b:* Oil City, William C.; *c:* William J., Kerri D., Danielle E.; *ed:* Clarion Univ ath 1973, (MS) Math 1982; Attnd Slippery Rock Univ, Fredonia NY Edinboro Univ; *cr:* Oil City Area HS Substitute 1973-74; ga Valley HS 7th-8th Grd Math 1974-76; Cranberry Area HS Math 76-; *ai:* Jr Class Adv; Prom Adv; Jr HS Stu Cncl; Dist 1 Bd Mem; ounts Coach; Twenty-Four Coach; Sr HS Stu Cncl Adv; PCTM A Math League Coach; PA Tchrs Ed Assn 1976-, Treas 6 Yrs; 1989-; NEA 1974-; Bus & Prof Women 1978-, Pres 2 Yrs, Treas 2 men of Rosary 1976-, Band Ldr 10 Yrs; PASC Asst Dir 1995-; BPW -; St of PA Stu Cncl Adv of Yr 1991-92; *office:* Cranberry Jr-Sr H 09 Seneca PA 16346*

MYER, GRETTA M., English Teacher; *b:* Clarion, PA; *ed:* St Coll (BA) Eng, Sec Ed 1994; *cr:* Bedford HS Eng Tchr 1994-; *ai:* NEA, PSEA, BAEA 1994-; *office:* Bedford HS 330 E John St Bedford PA 15522*

FESOLOVICH, DEBORAH WILDE, Second Grade Teacher; *b:* Wilkes-Barre, PA; *m:* Joseph John; *c:* Brad, Megan; *ed:* Mansfield St Coll (BS) Elem Ed 1976; East Stroudsburg St Coll (MS) Elem Ed 1989; Attnd Univ of Scranton; *cr:* North Pocono Schl Dist Second Grd Tchr 1976-; *ai:* PTA, NEA, PSEA 1976-; Moscow Cty Fair 1990-, Chm Artist & Patron Reception; Ed First 1994-; *office:* North Pocono Schl Dist Church St Moscow PA 18444*

FETCHEN, LINDA J. (JAMES), Tchr of Gifted Support Stdnts; *b:* New Eagle, PA; *m:* John H.; *ed:* Univ of Pittsburgh (BA) Scndy Ed 1970; California Univ of PA (MA) Eng 1974; Art Inst of Pittsburgh Photographic Tech; *cr:* Ringgold Schl Dist Tchr 26 Yrs; Comm Coll of Allegheny Cty Continuing Ed Tchr 1 Yr; *ai:* Acad, Mock Trial, Health Quest Team Coach; Acad Competitions, Newsletter Spon; Distance Learning Prgm; PAGE 1980-; PSEA 1970-; Riverview Bapt Church 1964-, Clerk; Amateur Radio Club 1990-; Local His Books Author; *office:* Ringgold HS 3645 Dry Run Rd Monongahela PA 15063

FETCHICK, CAROL ANNE, Former MS Math Teacher; *b:* Yonkers, NY; *ed:* SUNY at New Paltz (BA) Math Ed 1970; Attnd Manhattanville Coll, SUNY at Purchase; *cr:* Pierre Van Cortlandt MS Math Tchr 1970-77; Croton Harmon HS Math Tchr 1977-83; Pierre Van Cortlandt MS Math Tchr 1983-94; *ai:* NYSUT, AFT 1970-; Croton Tchrs Assn 1970-, Exec Bd.

FETCHKO, JOHN D., Physics Instructor; *b:* Windber, PA; *m:* Shirley Ann Molnar; *ed:* Carnegie-Mellon Univ (BS) Physics 1970; Indiana Univ of PA (MED) Physics 1975; *cr:* Greater Johnstown Career & Tech Ctr Physics Instr 1970-; *ai:* ROTC Model Rocket Club; SAT Math Review; NEA, PSEA & GJVTEA 1970-; *office:* Greater Johnstown Career Ctr 445 Schoolhouse Rd Johnstown PA 15904

FETCKO, BEVERLY LARSON, 2nd Grade Teacher; *b:* Bellefonte, PA; *m:* August R.; *c:* Heather, Christopher; *ed:* PA St Univ (BS) Ele Ed 1967; Post Grad Credits, Cert; *cr:* Braddock Hills Elem Schl 1st Grd Tchr 1967-68; Hartford Heights Elem Schl 1st, 4th Grd Tchr 1968-76; North East Schls K-6th Grd Sub Tchr 1980-82; E C Davis Elem Schl 2nd Grd Tchr 1983-; *ai:* Lang Arts Comm; PSEA, NEA 1967-; Jr Women's Club 1980-85; Pi Beta Phi 1964-; *office:* E. C. Davis Elem Schl 50 E Division St North East PA 16428

FETKO, SALLY DUCKWALL, History Teacher; *b:* Fort Sill, OK; *m:* G. Carl; *c:* Nicholas, Christopher; *ed:* OH St Univ (BS) Soc Stud Ed 1970; Coll of Mt St Joseph (MA) Ed 1987; 40 Semester Hrs Baldwin-Wallace Coll, John Carroll Univ; *cr:* Lee Burneson MS His Tchr 1987-; *ai:* 8th Grd Team Ldr; Stu Cncl Adv; Bldg Ldrshp Team; Soc Stud Curr, North Cntrl Steering Comms; Natl Cncl for His Ed 1995-; OH Cncl for Soc Stud, Westlake Tchrs Assn 1987-; Phi Delta Kappa 1986-; Pi Beta Phi Alum Club, Amer Assn of Univ Women 1970-; Westlake Tchr of Yr 1991-92; PTA St Honorary Lifetime Mbrshp Awd 1996; Subject of WVIZ TV Documentary Cooperative Learning 1992; Nom OH Soc Stud Tchr of Yr; *office:* Lee Burneson MS 2240 Dover Center Rd Westlake OH 44145

FETSKO, MICHAEL RICHARD, Physics Teacher; *b:* Manitowoc, WI; *ed:* LeMoyne Coll (BS) Multiple Sci 1990; St Univ of NY at Plattsburgh (MST) Physics 1991; *cr:* Museum of Sci at Boston Ed Assoc 1992-94; Braintree HS Physics Tchr 1994-; *ai:* Stu Cncl Adv; AAPT 1994-; *office:* Braintree HS 128 Town St Braintree MA 02184

FETT, BASIL RAY, Choir Director; *b:* Springfield, OH; *m:* Claudia Lee Goodyear; *ed:* Miami Univ (BA) Music Ed 1976; Bowling Green St U (MM) Choral Conducting 1987; *cr:* Kitty Hawk Elem Music Specialist 1978-81; Wayne HS Choral, Music Dir 1981-; Wittenberg Univ Adjunct Prof of Voice 1989-; *ai:* OEA, NEA 1980-, VP, Treas; ACDA 1986-; OMEA, MENC 1976-, Pres; NATS 1988-; South Fountain Pres 1978-, Dir, Bd; Springfield Redevelopment Corp 1992-, Bd; Recordings by Prof Choral Group; Grad Assistantship 1992; *office:* Wayne HS 5400 Chambersburg Rd Huber Heights OH 45424*

FETTER, DIAN E., Professor of Arts & Humanities; *ed:* Syracuse Univ (BFA) Fine Arts 1955; Kutztown Univ (MED) Arts Ed 1966; PA St Univ (PHD) Coll Arts, Arch 1983; Syracuse Univ 5th Yr Prgm NY St Cert 1957; Millersville Univ PA ST Cert 1960; Temple Univ Interdisciplinary Hum Prgm Cert Stud 1967; *cr:* PA St Art Supvr 1960-68; PA St Univ Coll Arts, Arch Asst Prof 1968-73; Catonsville Comm Coll Prof Arts, Hum 1974-; *ai:* Pres Aids Task Force Chair; MD, China Sister St Ed Comm Coll Rep; Art His Stud Tours Abroad; Natl Gallery Stu Tours Lecturer; Scholars Bank MD Hum Cncl 1995-; Soc Stud Early Modern Women Univ of MD 1994-; Lib Congress Assoc 1993-, Founding Mem; Natl Museum Womens Art 1986-, Founding Mem; KRB Rsrch Symposium 1989-, Intnl Rsrch Consortium Bd of Dirs; Smithsonian Inst 1973-, Resident Assoc; Natl Trust 1995-; Fullbright-Hays Schlsp; Natl Endowment for Hum Greek Stud Schlsp, Prgm Grant Inter-Disciplinary Stud; Phi Kappa Phi; Phi Theta Kappa; *home:* 1732 Hobart St NW Washington DC 20009

FETTERMAN, CATHERINE OBREZA, French Teacher; *b:* Little Falls, NY; *m:* Michael Charles; *ed:* Middleburg Coll (MS) 1996; *cr:* Mercersburg Acad Fr Tchr 1991-; *ai:* Fr Club & Yrbk Adv; Tennis & Bsktbl Coach; Dorm Dean; Learning Strategies, Admissions & Comp Comms; AATF 1995-; *office:* Mercersburg Acad 300 E Seminary St Mercersburg PA 17236*

FETTEROLF, SCOTT J., Guid Counselor & Bible Tchr; *b:* Ashland, PA; *m:* Brenda Snyder; *c:* Jacob, Seth, Caleb; *ed:* Lancaster Bible Coll (BS) Bible, Ed 1995; Attnd Wheaton Coll, La Salle Univ; *cr:* Sunbury Chrstn Acad Guid Cnslr, Bible Tchr 1992-; *ai:* Susquehanna Vly Bible Church 1992-, Pastor; Outstdng Young Man of Amer 1985-87; *home:* 15 Fisher Rd Selinsgrove PA 17870

FETTNER, ELLEN RUTH, Former Ethnic Studies Tchr; *b:* Chicago, IL; *m:* Saul; *c:* Shelli Belillti, Brian; *ed:* IN Univ (BS) Ed 1963; Univ of Cincinnati 18 Credit Hrs; Coll of Mt. St. Joseph 15 Credit Hrs; Haifa Univ 4 Credit Hrs; *cr:* Cincinnati Pub Schls Tchr 1963-80, Content Rdng Facilitator 1980-88, Comm Facilitator 1988-90, Tchr 1990-94; Consultant, Lecturer, Wkshp Facil 1994-; *ai:* Cultural Diversity Trng Adv; AFT; Children's Museum of Cincinnati 1993-, Advy Bd; City of Hope 1976-, Pres; Intnl Visitors Bureau 1990-, Consultant; Interfaith Holocaust Fnd 1977-, VP; Ed Advy Bd 1986-87; Distinguished Tchr; First Honors Recognition as Outstanding Tchr; OH Cncl Holocaust Ed 1986-; Holocaust & Resistance 1987; Amer Gathering of Holocaust Survivors; Curr Adv Holocaust & Resistance Fellowship 1989-; Pub Lessons; Natl Conf Chrstn & Jews Comm Svc Awd, Multicltrl Educl Yth 1995; *home:* 11251 Ironwood Ct Cincinnati OH 45249*

FETZER, RICHARD E., Sixth Grade Teacher; *b:* Bellefonte, PA; *m:* Sharon C.; *c:* Becky, Rick, Robin; *ed:* Shippensburg Univ (BS) Elem 1967; West Chester Univ (MED) Geog; *cr:* Oxford Schl Dist 5th-6th Grd Tchr 1967-70; Keystone Cntrl 6th Grd Tchr 1970-; *ai:* NEA; PSEA; Natl Soc Stud 1990-; *home:* PO Box 151 Burris Rd Bellefonte PA 16823

FETZNER, KATHERINE COLETTA, 8th Grade Physical Sci Teacher; *b:* Erie, PA; *m:* Richard F.; *c:* Angela Marie, Richard Paul; *ed:* Maryhurst Coll (BS) Bio 1973; Gannon Univ (MED) Environmental Sci 1981; Addl 6 Credit Hrs; *cr:* Veteran's Admin Hosp Lab Aid 1972-73; Edinboro Univ Lab Technician 1973-74; Welch Foods Inc Quality Control 1974-75; East HS Bio, Chem Tchr 1975-82; Roosevelt MS Phys, Life Sci Tchr 1985-; *ai:* Bldg, 8th Grd Acts, Stu Cncl Comm; Sci Dept Chprsn; PA Jr Acad of Sci; Co-Adv Annual Awds Assembly; NEA, PSEA, EEA, NSTA 1975-; PTA 1985-; St Mark's Cath Church 1981-, Catechism Tchr 1989-; Gospel Hill Garden Club 1987-90, VP 1990-; Edinboro Univ Cnslr Nuclear Energy Summer Camp 1977; Tchr of Yr 1993; Past Mem Mid Sts Steering Comm, Adv PA Inventors Assn Earth Kids Club, Teams; Girls Gymnastics Coach East HS 1976-81; *office:* Roosevelt MS 2300 Cranberry St Erie PA 16502

FEUDO, PETER, Professor & Chair; *b:* Revere, MA; *m:* Julia; *c:* Elizabeth; *ed:* Boston Coll (AB) Psych; MI St Univ (MA) Audiology & Speech Sci; Boston Univ (ScD) Comm Sci & Disorders; *cr:* AZ St Univ Clinical Prof 1989-81; Marywood Coll Prof 1991-; *ai:* Class of 1996 Adv; Acad Computing Advy Comm; Commencement Speaker & Honorary Doctorate Comm; NAPP 1991-, Pres; AAA; ASHA; AAS; St Josephs Ctr 1991-, Chair, Prof Svcs; Amer Cancer Soc; *office:* Marywood Coll Dept Commnctn Sci-Disorder 2300 Adams Ave Scranton PA 18509*

FEULMER, JUDITH A. (DOTTS), First Grade Teacher; *b:* Greensburg, PA; *m:* Thomas C.; *c:* Sam Dotts, Charles Dotts, Thomas Jr.; *ed:* IN Univ of PA (BA) Elem Ed 1965; Grad Stud; *cr:* IN Area Schl Dist First Grd Tchr 29 Yrs; *ai:* Prof Dev Comm Co-Chair; Peer Coaching Trainer; NEA 1965-, St Del; PSEA 1965-, CW Region Sec, Pub Relations Awd; IAEA 1965-, Pres, Sec, Cty Pres, Sec; Red Cross Bd of Dirs 1989-, Support Group Ldr; IASD Grants 3 Yrs; *office:* Benjamin Franklin Elem Schl 95 Ben Franklin Rd Indiana PA 15701

FEURTADO, MARGARET BOYD, Math Department Chairman; *b:* New York, NY; *c:* Ann, Rachael; *ed:* St Univ Coll at Fredonia (AB) Elem Ed 1970, (MS) General Ed 1973; Youngstown St Univ Math & Ed Courses; Kent St Gftd Ed Courses; *cr:* Dunkirk City Schls 3-5th Grd Tchr 1970-80; Youngstown Pub Schl 5-6th Grd Tchr 1983-84, Jr HS Math Tchr 1984-; *ai:* Math Counts Coach 1988-; Stu Cncl Co-Adv 1988-90; AFT 1973-; NCTM, OCTM 1987-; EOCTM Vice Pres 1995-.*

FEW, GARY W., Retired Jr & Sr HS Music Tchr; *b:* Lockport, NY; *m:* Patricia Meiklejohn; *c:* Kevin, James, Melissa; *ed:* SUNY Coll at Fredonia (BS) Music Ed 1961; SUNY at Buffalo (MED) Music 1975; *cr:* Lockport City Bd of Ed Vocal Music Tchr 1961-62; Niagara Wheatfield CSD Vocal Music Tchr 1963-79; Royalton Hartland CSD Vocal Music Tchr 1979-94; *ai:* Musicals; All Cty Music Festivals; All St Music Festivals; United Meth Church Chr; Lock Cty Glee Clb Dir; Lions Club 1991-; Masonic Orgs 1965-; Lockport YMCA, Youth Bd 1975-91.*

FEYL, ANDREW WESLEY, Ninth Grade Math Teacher; *b:* Buffalo, NY; *ed:* SUNY Coll at Buffalo (BS) Math 1969; Canisius Coll at Buffalo (MS) Ed 1973; *cr:* Hamburg Jr High Math Tchr 1968-; *office:* Hamburg Jr HS 360 Division St Hamburg NY 14075

FIALKOFF, IRIS F., Speech & Theater Teacher; *b:* New York City, NY; *m:* Allan; *c:* Lisa Ellen Wolf, Jeffrey Scott; *ed:* Queens Coll (BA) Speech & Ed 1957, (MS) Ed & Theater Minor 1959; 61 Credit Hrs; *cr:* Jamaica HS Eng Tchr 1957-58, Eng Tchr 1958-59; NYC Bd of Ed Visiting Speech Therapist 1958; Taft HS Eng Tchr 1959-60; HS of Music & Art Eng & Speech Tchr 1960-66; Spring Vly HS Eng, Speech & Theater Tchr 1971-; *ai:* Thespian, Forensic League, Spots N Flats & Cap N Bells Adv; Stu & Fac Cncl Chprsn; NEA 1971-; Educl Theater Assn 1971-; NYSTEA 1994-; ITT; Temple Beth El 1973-, Fin Sec; Rockland Theater Arts Dev Group 1988-, Trustee; Tchr of Yr Nom 1994.

FIANO, PILAR MARIA, Elementary School Counselor; *b:* La Coruna, Spain; *ed:* Kean Coll of NJ (MA) Ed 1994; Addl 24 Credits Cnslng; *cr:* George Washington Schl 1 Biling Ed Tchr 1972-78; William F. Halloran Schl #22 Rdng, Lang Arts Tchr 1978-93; Peterstown Schl #3 Elem Cnslr 1993-; *ai:* Schl Ldrshp Team; Pub Relations, Pride Comm; NEA, NJEA 1972-; UCEA 1972-, Rep; EEA 1972-, Exec Bd; Alpha Delta Kappa 1978-; HAPPA 1990-; Governor's Tchrs Recognition Awd; Project Teach Grants; *office:* Peterstown Schl #3 700 2nd Ave Elizabeth NJ 07202

FIBIGER, JOANNE ROBINSON, 1st Grade Teacher; *b:* Albany, NY; *m:* Frederick; *c:* Gregory; *ed:* St Univ at Cortland (BS) Elem Ed 1971; Russell Sage Coll (MS) Elem Ed 1974; *cr:* Glens Falls City Schls 1st-2nd Grd Tchr 1971-; *ai:* Site Team; Iroquois Rdng Cncl; AFT, NEA 1971-; Iroquois Rdng Cncl 1971-, Bd; *office:* Glens Falls City Schls 10 Sanford St Glens Falls NY 12801

FICARA, EILEEN P., English & Keyboarding Teacher; *b:* Staten Island, NY; *ed:* Hunter Coll (BA) Bus Ed 1963; *cr:* New Dorp HS Bus Tchr 1963-65; Drake Bus Schl Bus Tchr 1981-82; St Peter's Girls HS Bus, Eng Tchr 1982-; *ai:* Yrbk Fins.

FICCA, TAMMY KNERR, English Teacher; *b:* Pottsville, PA; *m:* Christopher John; *ed:* Lebanon Vly Coll (BA) Eng 1991; Millersville Univ (MA) Eng 1994; 15 Addl Credit Hrs; *cr:* Elizabethtown HS Eng Tchr 1991-; *ai:* Lit Magazine Club Adv; NEA, NCTE 1991-; *office:* Elizabethtown HS 600 E High St Elizabethtown PA 17022

FICCO, MICHELLE ANNETTE, Athletic Trainer; *b:* Johnstown, PA; *ed:* Slippery Rock Univ (BS) Hlth Ed, Ath Trng 1989; CA Univ of PA (MS) Sportsmedicine 1992; Emergency Med Technician; *cr:* Westmoreland Cty Comm Coll Hlth, Fitness Instr; Gym Supvr, Ath Trainer 1989-90; Carlow Coll Prof, Ath Trainer, Wellness Dir 1990-91; Assoc Rehabilitation Svcs Ath Trainer 1991-94; Keystone Rehabilitation Systems Ath Trainer 1994-; *ai:* Stu Ath Trainer Club Adv; NATA 1986-; NEA, PSEA 1989-; PATS 1991-; Kappa Delta Pi 1987-; Eta Sigma Gamma 1986-, Sec; Red Cross 1989-, Recruitment Ofcr; Girls Scouts 1991-; Ldr, Asst Svc UNit Mgr; Acad All-Amer Collegiate Awd; Cert Merit Amer Red Cross Flight 427, 1000 Hrs Vol Svc.*

FICETO, GERALD J., Instrumental Music Teacher; *b:* Newark, NJ; *m:* Denise Dodson; *c:* Alyssa, Ashley; *ed:* Montclair St Coll (BA) Music Ed 1975; 10 Post Grad Credits Towards MA; *cr:* Prof Musician 1975-93; Kearny HS Instrumental Music Tchr, Asst Band Dir 1993-; *ai:* Asst Marching Band, Instrumental Music, Sax & Clarient Ensemble, Stage Band Dir; Musical Conductor; Phi Mu Alpha 1971-; MENC; NJMEA; KEA; NJ Jazz Soc; Amer Fed of Musicians; Prof Percussionist, Recording Artist Jazz, Rock Group, Universal & Nickelodean Studios, Symphony Orchs, TV, Films; Composer, Arranger Films, Stage, Commercials, Jingles; Musical Dir, Conductor Numerouse Theatre Groups; Prod Recordings, Jazz, Rock, Musical Theatre, Classical; *home:* 507 Chestnut St Kearny NJ 07032*

FICK, BRENDA STEVENS, English Instructor; *b:* Loch Haven, PA; *c:* Devon, Elaine; *ed:* Univ of MD (BA) Eng 1970; Coll Notre Dame (MA) Lbrl Stud 1990; *cr:* Howard Comm Coll Eng Instr 1990-; Essex Comm Coll Eng Instr 1990-; Dundalk Comm Coll Eng Instr 1991-; *ai:* Fac Adv Lit Magazine 1993-94; NCTE 1995-; MD Lit & Poetry Soc 1992-, VP; Co-Authored Play Baltimore Playwrights Festival 1989; Pub Poetry; First Prize Poetry Contest 1994; *home:* 40 Glenwood Ave Catonsville MD 21228*

FICKEL, R. EDWARD, Biology Teacher; *b:* Logan, OH; *m:* Cynthia Ricketts; *c:* Emily, Benjamin, Matt; *ed:* OH Univ (BS) Bio 1970; Grad Work; *cr:* Logan HS Bio Tchr 1972-; *ai:* Acad Coach; LEA, SEOEA, OEA, NEA 1972-; Boy Scout Troop 236 1991-, Asst Scout Master; *home:* 220 Wilson Ave Logan OH 43138

FICKES, CARRIE ANN ENICKS, Fine Arts Chairperson & Tchr; *b:* Charleston, WV; *m:* Victor M.; *c:* Kelly A., Ryan L.; *ed:* Kutztown Univ (BS) Art Ed 1975; Univ of MD (MED) Human Dev 1985; Renaissance Stud; Attnd PA St; *cr:* Margaret Brent MS Art Tchr 1976-81; Greenview Knolls Elem Schl Art Tchr 1981-82; Leonardtown HS Art Tchr 1983-84;

Chopticon HS Art Tchr 1984-; *ai:* Fine Arts Chprsn; Schl Improvement Team; Discipline Comm; St Mary's Tchrs Assn 1976-, Schl Rep; MSTA, NEA 1976-; Women in His in St Marys 1986-; Carnegie Grant; *office:* Chopticon HS Rt 242 Morganza MD 20660*

FICKES, ELIZABETH JAMES, Elementary Art Teacher; *b:* Reading, PA; *m:* John Charles; *ed:* Kutztown Univ (BS) Art Ed 1974; 24 Post Grad Credits PA Permanent Cert 1978; 36 Post Grad Credits Masters Equivalency 1986; Addl 9 Post Grad Credits Beyond MA Equivalency; *cr:* Mifflinburg Area Schl Dist Elem Art Tchr 1974-; Millersville Univ Adj Instr 1987-; *ai:* 1994 Chm Fine Arts, Stess Mngmt Comm; Mifflinburg Area Ed Assn, PA St Ed Assn, NEA 1974-; Heritage, Revitalization Bd 1989-91; Promotion Comm 1989-92; Jaycees Outstdng Young Educator Awd 1989; *office:* Mifflinburg Elem Schl 115 Shipton St Mifflinburg PA 17844*

FIDANZA, RICHARD JOSEPH, Physics Teacher; *b:* New York City, NY; *ed:* Bloomfield Coll (BS) Bio 1963; Long Island Univ (MS) Marine Sci 1982; *cr:* East Side HS Physics Lab Asst 1964-65; Broadway Jr HS Sci Tchr 1965-69; Middleton HS Physics, Math Tchr 1970-76; Middletown HS South Physics, Math Tchr 1976-; *ai:* Sci League Adv Physics; NEA, NJEA 1970-; NSF Grant Grad Stud 1967-68.

FIDDES, BLANCHE NADEAU, Fifth Grade Teacher; *b:* Webster, MA; *m:* Donald A.; *c:* Julie Hewey, Gregg; *ed:* State Coll (BS) Ed 1969, (MED) Rdng 1972; Addl 36 Hrs; *cr:* Webster Schl System Grade 5 Tchr 1969-71, Rdng Dept, Remedial, Enrichment 1971-89, Grd 5 Tchr 1989-96; *ai:* NEA; *office:* Anthony J. Sitkowski Schl 27 Negus St Webster MA 01570

FIDEMI, STEPHEN, English Teacher; *b:* East Orange, NJ; *ed:* Fordham Univ (BA) Eng 1971, (MA) Eng 1973; 30 Addl Credits; *cr:* Paramus Cath HS Eng Tchr, Dept Chprsn 1975-; *office:* Paramus Cath HS 425 Paramus Rd Paramus NJ 07652

FIEBELKORN, LENORE CATALANO, Second Grade Teacher; *b:* Dunkirk, NY; *m:* Michael; *c:* Todd, Chad; *ed:* Jamestown Comm Coll (AA) Liberal Arts 1970; St Univ of NY at Fredonia (BA) Ed 1972, (MS) Early Chldhd 1976; *cr:* Dunkirk Pub Schls 3rd Grd Tchr 1973-80, 4th Grd Tchr 1981-82, 6th Grd Tchr 1982-83, 2nd Grd Tchr 1983-; *ai:* AFT, Dunkirk Tchrs Assn 1973-; AAUW 1985-; Friends of Dunkirk Lib 1993-; Schl #7 PTO, Fac Adv; Schl #7 Cub Scouts, Den Mother; *home:* 21 Finch St Dunkirk NY 14048

FIEDLER, JOSEPH CONRAD, Health & PE Coordinator; *b:* Greenport, NY; *m:* Perla Asmundson; *c:* Joseph Thor, Holly Inga; *ed:* IN St Univ (BS) PE 1967; IN St Univ at Terre Haute (MA) PE 1968; 30 Addl Hrs PE Danish St Inst of PE 1970; Minors Hlth Ed, Recreation, Life Sci; *cr:* A. T. Mahan HS PE, Hlth Tchr, Coach 1973-75; Dubois HS PE, HLth Tchr, Coach, Ath Dir 1975-77; Argentia-Newfoundland Schls K-12 PE, Hlth Tchr, Coach 1977-79; Brussels Amer Schl HS PE, Hlth, 9th Grd Sci Tchr, Coach 1979-; *ai:* HS Head Ftbl, Wrestling, Soccer Coach; Var Club Spon; NEA, OEA 1977-; Division III Wrestling Coach of Yr 1993.*

FIEDLER, WILLIAM G.,JR., 7th-9th Grade Teacher; *b:* Bayshore, NY; *m:* Delia Funari; *c:* Lucas, Season, Billy III; *ed:* Salem Coll of WV (BA) Soc Stud, Ed 1974; 30 Hrs Adelphia Univ; *cr:* Margaretville Cntrl Schl 7-9 Grd Soc Stud Tchr 21 Yrs; *ai:* Peer Mediation; Sftbl Coach; Remedial Rdng Prgm; NEA 1980-; Twp of Hardenburgh, Councilman 1988, Supvr 1990; Tchr of Yr 1990-91; *office:* Margaretville Central Schl PO Box 319 Main St Margaretville NY 12455*

FIEGER, BARBARA A., Instrumental Music Teacher; *b:* Youngstown, OH; *ed:* Bowling Green St Univ (BA) Music 1984, (MA) Music 1996; *cr:* South Range Schls MS Band Tchr 1984; Howland Local Schl Elem Music Tchr 1985; Grand Vly Local Schl Instrumental Music Tchr 1985-89; Wellsville Local Schl Instrumental Music Schl 1991-; *ai:* NEA, OMEA, MENC 1984-; Potter Players C. Theatre Bd 1993-, Bd Pres 1994-; Sigma Alpha Iota 1983-, Pres Alumni Chptr 1995-, Sword of Hnr 1994.

FIEGER, KATHRYN MARIE (KRUER), 7th & 9th Grade Health Teacher; *b:* Woodhaven, NY; *ed:* Dean Jr Coll (Assoc) Gen 1968; Capital Univ BS Hlth & PE 1971; Grad Hrs: Kent St Univ & Akron Univ; *cr:* Field Local Schls Hlth & PE Tchr 1972-; *ai:* Ski Club Adv; 9th Grd Boys Bsktbl & Jr HS Track Timer; OEA 1972-; FLTA 1972-; Akron Zoo 1995-, Vol; *office:* Field Local Schls 1379 Saxe Rd Mogadore OH 44260

FIELD, CYNTHIA CYRKIEWICZ, Eighth Grade English Teacher; *b:* Rockville, CT; *ed:* Univ of CT (BA) Eng 1966; Central CT St Univ (MS) Ed K-8 1969; Attnd Eastern CT St Univ, Elem Sci Survey Insts, St Joseph Coll, Elem Energy Ed Inst, Univ of CT; *cr:* Pleasant Valley Schl 6th Grd Tchr 1966-68; Ellsworth Schl 6 Grd Tchr 1968-73; Pleasant Valley Schl 6 Grd Sci, Lang Arts Tchr 1973-84; Timothy Edwards MS 6 Grd Sci, Lang Arts Tchr 1984-87, 8 Grd Eng Tchr 1987-; *ai:* Consultant for CT Writing Project, Co-Dir; CRISS Presenter; Hartford Hum Cncl Presenter, Writing Consultant; Arts for Champion Intl Consultant; Team Ldr; NEA, CEA 1966-; SWEA 1966-, VP 1960; CT Cncl of Tchrs of Eng 1984-, Presenter at Conf; Natl Writing Project 1984-; New England League MS 1992-; CT Assn of Middle Level Eductrs 1994-, Bd of Dir; Natl MS Assn 1995-, St Joseph Schl 1994-, Mem of Schl Bd; Timothy Edwards Schl Parent Advy Comm 1993-; Article Pub Stu Assistance Jrnl 1994; Milken Family Fnd Natl Educator Awd 1993; Tchr of Yr South Windsor 1992; CT Tchr of Yr Runner-up 1992; South Windsor Bd of Ed Excl Tchng Awd 1982; *office:* Timothy Edwards MS 100 Arnold Way South Windsor CT 06074*

FIELD, JEFFREY E., Technology Education Teacher; *b:* Camden, NJ; *m:* Sandra Hagelstein-Field; *c:* Jeffrey, Jeanna; *ed:* Glassboro St Coll (BA) Indstrl Arts Ed 1982; *cr:* YALE Acad Indstrl Arts Tchr 1982-83; Clayton MS HS Indstrl Arts Tchr 1983-; *ai:* Asst Ftbl Coach; Yrbk Adv; Tech Coord; Tech Dir Musicals; Tech Comm; Odessy of the Mind Judge; NEA, NJEA, CEA 1983-; Clayton Historical Presentation 1993-, Chm; *home:* 211 S Broad St Clayton NJ 08312

FIELD, KEVIN LLOYD,SR., English Teacher; *b:* Medford, MA; *m:* Gayle Sherwood; *c:* Heidi Field Ellsworht, Kevin Jr.; *ed:* Northeastern Univ (BS) Eng 1967; Regis Coll (MA) Ed 1978; *cr:* Francis Wyman MS Eng Tchr 1967-81; Burlington HS Eng Tchr 1981-; *ai:* Burlington Ed Assn, MA Tchrs Assn, NEA 1967-; Wilmington Fire Dept 1962-, Firefighter; Concord Recreation 1980-, After Schl Prgm Dir; New England Sports Agents 1989-, Asst Dir; Wilmington Cncl of Churches 1990-; 25 Yr Awd; *office:* Burlington HS 123 Cambridge St Burlington MA 01803

FIELD, ROBERT, Secondary Soc Science Tchr; *b:* Salem, OH; *m:* Stephanie Zimmerman; *c:* Ben; *ed:* Miami Univ (BA) Soc Sci Ed 1974; Ashland Univ (MS) Curr, INstruction 1995; *cr:* Western Australia Ed Dept Tchr, Dir Aboriginal Ed 1974-76; Frost Vly YMCA Outdoor Ed Instr 1977; Youngstown YMCA Outdoor Ed Instr 1978; United Local Schls Tchr, World His, Psych, Soc 1979-; *ai:* Ftbl Asst Coach; Track Head Coach; Sr Class Adv; NEA, OEA 1979-, Pres 1980-84; Mount Union Coll 1992-, Advy Bd; Kent St Branch Campus 1987-, Advy Bd; *office:* United Local Schls 8143 St Rt 9 Hanoverton OH 44423*

FIELDER, JANICE LARAINE, Mathematics Teacher; *b:* Milford, MA; *c:* Cheryl Power; *ed:* Worcester St Coll (BS) Ed 1965; Wentworth Inst of Tech (BS) Cmptr Sci 1985; Attnd Worcester St Coll, Framingham St Coll, Fitchburg St Coll, Boston Coll; *cr:* Northbridge Schl Dept Grd 6 Tchr 1965-66; Hopedale Schl Dept Grd 4-6 Tchr 1967-80, Grd 7-12 Math Tchr 1980-; *ai:* Math Frameworks Comm; Local Contact Person Portfolio Assessment Adv 1990, 1996; NEA, MTA 1967-; Hopedale Tchrs Assn 1967, Pres 3 Terms, Treas 2 Terms; NCTM; ASCD 1994-; MA Portfolio Assessment Project 2nd Yr Grant; NSF Prgm Boston Coll on Discrete Math Participant; *office:* Hopedale Jr-Sr HS 25 Adin St Hopedale MA 01747

FIELDHOUSE, SALLY STEFFEL, 5th Grade Teacher; *b:* Salem, OH; *c:* John, Julie, Jeff; *ed:* Youngstown St Univ (BS) Elem Ed 1962; *cr:* St Paul Elem Tchr 5 Yrs; Washingtonville Schl 5th Grd Tchr 2 Yrs; Fourth St Schl 6th Grd Tchr 1 Yr; Leetonia HS Eng, Math, 9th Grd Tchr 1 Yr; Southeast Schl Title I Rdng Tchr 2 Yrs; St Paul 5th Grd Tchr 14 Yrs; *ai:* Mini Course Coord; NCEA 1981-; Awded Outstanding Alumni 1993.

FIELDING, PATRICIA M., Kindergarten Teacher; *b:* Bethlehem, PA; *ed:* Chestnut Hill Coll (BA) Ger 1972; St Charles Seminary (MA) Rel Stud 1985; Marywood Coll Admin I Elem Prin Cert 1993; Chestnut Hill Coll Instrl II Ger & Elem Cert 1976; *cr:* St Calistus Schl Second Grd Tchr 1965-66; St Timothy Schl Second Grd Tchr 1966-70; St Isidore Schl Second Grd Tchr 1971-75; St Therese Schl 2-6 Grd Tchr 1975-82; Sacred Heart Schl Kndgtn-First Grd Tchr 1983-; *ai:* NCEA 1983-; St Lukes Hosp 1982-, Vol, 1500 Hrs Svc; Sacred Heart Hosp Auxilary 1990-, Nom Comm; Musikfest Assn 1984-, Vol, 10 Yrs Svc; Rose Garden Children's Fest 1992-, Vol; Election Bd 1985-, Judge of Election; Eisenhower Grants; *office:* Sacred Heart Schl 1814 2nd St Bethlehem PA 18017

FIELDING, PATRICIA MARGARET, Fourth Grade Teacher; *b:* Niskayuna, NY; *m:* William Raymond; *c:* Carly Ann; *ed:* SUNY at Plattsburgh (BS) Elem Ed 1987; SUNY at Albany (MS) Dev Rdng 1990; In-Svc Courses & Confs Assertive Discipline, Cooperative Discipline, Whole Lang Conf, Bldg an Outstdng 4th Grade Prgm, AGATE Conf; *cr:* Shenendehowa-Chango Elem Schl Sixth Grd Tchr 1989-93, 4th Grd Tchr 1993-; *ai:* Drama Club; Talent Show; Shared Decision Making; Wrote Goals for Regents Excl in Accountability Projects; Stu-Staff, Lang Arts, Cultural Arts Advy, Hiring Comms; Ski Club Adv; NYSUT 1989-; *office:* Shenendehowa Cntrl Schl-Chango Chango Dr Ballston Lake NY 12019

FIELDS, DENNIS ALLEN, Mathematics Teacher; *b:* Monongahela, PA; *m:* Nancy Cherok; *c:* Scott Allen; *ed:* CA Univ of PA (BS) Math Ed 1971; PA St Univ Post Grad Stud; *cr:* Hempfield Area HS Math Tchr 1972-; *ai:* Stu Govt Adv; Act Dir; Stu Act Treas; NEA, PSEA, HAEA 1972-; *office:* Hempfield Area Sr HS Rd 6 Box 77 Greensburg PA 15601

FIELDS, GERALDINE, History Teacher; *b:* Hackensack, NJ; *ed:* Rutgers Univ (BA) His 1985; 12 Addl Credit Hrs Lib Sci; *cr:* Blessed Sacrament Schl Elem Ed Tchr 1985-87; Frank H. Morrell HS His Tchr 1987-; *ai:* Schl Based Planning Comm Chprsn; NEA, IEA 1989-; Young Adult Missionaries 1995-, Sec.

FIELDS, HOWARD RUSSELL, Math & Computer Sci Teacher; *b:* Chaleroi, PA; *m:* Pamela Bombalek; *c:* Heather Marie, Renae Alane; *ed:* CA Univ of PA (BS) Ed, Math 1964; Post Grad Stud Univ of Pittsburgh, CA Univ of PA; *cr:* Franklin Area HS Math Tchr 1964-68; Hempfield Area HS Math Tchr 1968-72; Bemtworth HS Math, Cmptr Sci Tchr 1972-; *ai:* Sr Class Adv; Mentor Tchr; Adult Ed Cmptr Trng Classes; Dist Tech Comm; NEA, PSWA, Bentworth EA 1972-, Pres, Adv; PCTM 1980-; NEA, PSEA 1964-; Bentleyville United Meth Church 1956-, Lay Pastor, Admin Bd Chm;, PPR Comm Chmf Church Schl Tchr, Choir Dir; PA Acad Prof of Tchng Tchr of Yr; Math Curr Work PA Assn Curr Dir Conf 1995; *office:* Bentworth Sr HS 500 Lincoln Ave Bentleyville PA 15314*

FIELDS, O. EUGENE, Biology Teacher; *b:* Jonesville, VA; *m:* Elizabeth Shelton; *c:* Michael, Pamela, Jennifer; *ed:* Union Coll (BS) Bio 1965, (MA) Ed 1966; 30 Post Grad Credits Holy Cross Coll, Worcester St Coll, Framingham St Coll; *cr:* US Army Team, Platoon Ldr 1966-69; Westborough HS Scndry Bio Tchr 1969-; *ai:* Class Adv; Tennis Coach; Dev Current Hlth Curr; NEA, MA Tchrs Assn, Westborough Tchrs Assn 1969-; SHARE 1994-; United Meth Outreach 1986-, Chm; Natl Sci Fnd Grant Holy Cross Coll; *office:* Westborough HS 70 W Main St Westborough MA 01581*

FIELDS, TODD LESTER, Drafting Instructor; *b:* Sanford, ME; *m:* Ellen Chenard; *c:* Jordan, Jonathan; *ed:* Univ of Southern ME (BS) Industrial Arts 1985, (BS) Tech Ed 1991; *cr:* Livermore Falls HS Industrial Arts Instr 1985-87; Westbrook Regnl Voc Instr 1988-; *ai:* Natl Voc Tech Honor Soc Adv; WEA, MTA, NEA, 1988-, Bldg Rep; ME Voc Assn MVA, 1988-; *office:* Westbrook Regional Voc Center 125 Stroudwater St Westbrook ME 04092

FIELDS, WILLIAM A., Eng Tchr & 9th Grd Prgm Coord; *b:* Rocky Mount, NC; *m:* Caroline C.; *c:* Charlotte, William; *ed:* Univ of NC (BA) Eng 1979; Brown Univ (MAT) Eng, Ed 1981; *cr:* Worcester Acad Eng Tchr 1981-84; The Wheeler Schl Eng Tchr 1984-, Head of Dept 1994-95, Coord of Ninth Grd Prgm 1993-; *home:* 12 Burlington St Providence RI 02906

FIERRO, DIANE MC LAUGHLIN, Sixth Grade Teacher; *b:* Queens, NY; *m:* Christopher; *ed:* Molloy Coll (BA) Psych, Ed N-6 1986; Hofstra Univ (MS) Spec Ed K-12 1990; 3 Credits Museum Educator; *cr:* St Peter of Alcantara Schl 5th-6th Grd Rdng Tchr 1986-87; Caroline G. Atkinson Schl 6th Grd Tchr 1987-; *ai:* Lincoln Ctr Inst Participating Tchr; Newspaper in Ed Prgm; Soc Stud Comm, Curr Dev; Tchrs Assn Election Supervision Comm; NYSUT, AFT, Freeport Tchrs Assn 1987-; Grad Schlsp; Educl Incentive Grant Awd; *office:* Caroline G Atkinson MS Seaman Ave Freeport NY 11520*

FIFAREK, MARY ANNE (SANOICA), 8th Grade Language Arts Tchr; *b:* Chicago, IL; *m:* Fred W.; *c:* Aaron, Jeremy; *ed:* Northeastern IL Univ (BA) Eng 1973; Northern IL Univ (MAEd) Admin 1978; Miami Univ 22 Sem Hrs Ed; Univ of Cincinnati 7 Qtr Hrs Ec; Univ of Dayton 4 Qtr Hrs Mentoring; Coll of Mt St Joseph 9 Sem Hrs Rdng; Xavier Univ 3 Sem Hrs Pol Sci; *cr:* Good Counsel HS Eng Tchr 1973-74; Queen Bee Schl Dist #16 Lang Arts Tchr 1974-81; Lakota Local Schl Dist Sub Tchr 1983-87; Hopewell Jr Schl Lang Arts Tchr 1987-; *ai:* Yrbk Ed, Adv; Mentor Tchr; Newspaper Ed, Adv; NEA, OEA, LEA 1988-; PTSO 1985-; Church Choir 1981-; Newspaper Articles Pub; Yrbk Production Achvmt; Lakota Goals 2000 Comm; *home:* 7731 Jonathon Ct West Chester OH 45069

FIFE, D. MARK, Science Teacher; *b:* Xenia, OH; *m:* Patricia Zelinskas; *c:* Lauren; *ed:* Miami Univ (BS) Bio 1979; Univ of Dayton (MS) Bio Ed 1986; 35 Post-Grad Hrs Wright St Univ; *cr:* Springboro HS Phys Sci Tchr 1979-80; Centerville HS Bio, Phys Sci, Field Stud Tchr 1980-; *office:* Centerville HS 500 E Franklin St Centerville OH 45459

FIGUEREDO, SOPHIA PANTAGES, Sixth Grade English Teacher; *b:* Milwaukee, WI; *m:* Juan; *c:* Maria; *ed:* Mt Mary Coll (BA) Eng, Drama; Manhattan Coll (MA) Eng 1980; Hunter Coll Eng 1987-88; Attnd Marquette Univ; *cr:* David A. Stein Riverdale MS 6th Grd Eng Tchr; *ai:* United Fed of Tchrs; Riverdale Contemporary Theater 1984-, Pres, Treas, Actress; *home:* 630 W 246th St Apt 233 Bronx NY 10471

FILAS, GAIL ANN, Resource Room & Spec Ed Tchr; *b:* Syracuse, NY; *ed:* St Univ of NY at Geneseo (BS) Elem & Spec Ed 1991, (MS) N-12th Grd Rdng 1992; *cr:* Sackets Harbor Cntrl Resource Room & Spec Ed Tchr 1992-; Thompson Park Conservency Asst Zookeeper 1995-; World Class Taekwondo Asst Instr 1995-; *ai:* NCC Cup Participant; Class of 1999 Adv; Yrbk Ed & Adv; Modified Sftbl Coach; Bldg Ambassador; Curr Dev & Math Curr Dev Comms; NEA-NY 1992-; Mohawk Valley Learning Disability Assn 1992-; World Class Taekwondo 1993-, Intermediate Red Belt; World Taekwondo Fed; BSA 1984-94, Bus Mgr, Prgm Dir & Vol; *office:* Sackets Harbor Central Schl Broad St Sackets Harbor NY 13685

FILIACI, CAMILLO, Track Coach; *b:* Rochester, NY; *m:* Mary Dorety; *c:* Christopher, Lawrence, Paul, Peter, Mark; *ed:* Rider U (BS) Fin 1945; *cr:* Tredyffrin-Easttown Sch Dist Treas 1975-80; *ai:* Coach Track, X-Cntry; *office:* Saints Philip & James Schl 701 E Lincoln Hwy 19341

FILIPEK, DOROTHY STEFFENS, Business Education Te Passaic, NJ; *m:* Richard E.; *c:* Erik Jason; *ed:* Montclair St Coll Ed 1969; 15 Credit Hrs Cooperative Bus Ed Coord; Voc Ed Tc Cert; *cr:* Saddle Brook HS Bus Ed Tchr 1969-, CBE Coord 19 Interact Club Co-Adv; Tech Ed Comm; NEA, NJEA, NJBE NJCBECA 1978-; Saddle Brook PTSA 1969-; Woodrow Wilso Garfield HSA 1994-; St Valentine Schl Bd of Ed 1987-88; O Amer Scndry Educators 1975; Governor's Tchr Recognition Recipient 1986; *office:* Saddle Brook HS 355 Mayhill St Saddle 07663*

FILIPOWSKI, MICHAEL J., English Dept Chair & Teacher; *b* NJ; *ed:* Wilkes Univ (BA) Eng 1973; Attnd East Stroudsburg Univ Paterson Coll; Centenary Coll; *cr:* Halsted St Schl 7th Grd Lang 1973-77; Newton HS Eng Tchr 1977-; *ai:* Class Adv; Drama; Y NJEA 1973-; Bus & Ed Together, Advy Comm; *office:* Newt Ryerson Ave Newton NJ 07860

FILIPPELLI, JAMES ANTHONY, English Teacher; *b:* New NY; *m:* Carolyn T. Crecelius; *c:* James, Amanda; *ed:* St Leo Theatre, Eng, Speech, Ed 1975; Brooklyn Coll of CUN Performing Arts Adm 1978; Long Island Univ Grad Stud; *cr:* Cntrl Schl Dist Eng Tchr 1979-; Dominican Coll Adj Instr of Con City Schl Dist GED Instr, Summer Schl Tchr 1983-; Gifted & Tal Ctr Afternoon Dir 1995-; *ai:* 9th-12th Class Adv 1992-95; Dr 1979-; 9th Grd Team WISE Mentor 1995-; Dominican Coll Aqu Adv 1979-; AFT 1979-; Knights of Columbus 1975-, 3rd Degree Editorial Advy Bd; BSA Eagle Scout, St George Awd; Edctr of E State Eng Cncl 1996; *office:* Walter Panas HS Rt 132 Main St S NY 10588

FILIPPELLO, LARA L., Bio & Human Physiology Tchr; *b:* NJ; *ed:* Marist Coll (BS) Bio 1994; Montclair St Univ MAT Marylawn of Oranges Bio, Phys Sci & Human Physiology Tchr Track Coach; Sci & Dance Club; CCAT 1994-; *office:* Marylaw Oranges Schl 445 Scotland Rd South Orange NJ 07079

FILIPPETTI, MIA RAE, Dance Instructor; *b:* Elmira, NY; *e* Coll (BA) Commnctns 1992; SUNY at Brockport Grad Degree D Filippettis Acad of Dance Arts Dance Instr 1984-; Elmira Coll D 1992-; *ai:* Orchesis Club Adv; Elmira Little Theatres Play Comm; Local Musicals Choreography; Southside Festival Playe Players; Dance Caravan 1986-; Prof Dance Tchrs Assn 1992- Attendance; Chamber of Commerce 1990-, Vol Worker; Arts of Finger Lakes Grant; *home:* 141 Marian Ave Elmira NY 14903*

FILLEY, CHERYL ANN, Family & Consumer Sci Educator; *b:* *m:* Karl L.; *c:* Emily Susanne, David Karl; *ed:* Gannon Univ (B Ec Ed 1992; Addl 18 Credit Hrs Towards MED in Curr & Instru East HS Family, Consumer Sci Edctr 1993-; *ai:* Sr Class Adv; P & Consumes Sci Assoc 1992-, Chair-Elect 1995; Elk Vly Ele PTO 2 Term Pres; *office:* East HS 1151 Atkins St Erie PA 16503

FILLIPON, ELAINE M. (VALLANTE), English Teacher; *b:* L MA; *m:* Ralph G.; *c:* Nicholas, Ryan; *ed:* Master Tchr Prgm Re 145 Credit Hrs; *cr:* Holy Rosary Schl 2-3 Grd Tchr 1970-71; Ho Schl 3-4 Grd Tchr 1971-74, Grd 2 Tchr 1978-81, 5-8 Grd Tchr Yrbk Adv 1988, 1995; Sec Boys Bsktbl League 1986-88; Pre 1978-95; NCEA 1986-; MRA 1995-; Merrimack Coll Alumni As Phillips Acad Merrimack Vly Parent Assn 1995-; *office:* Holy Tri 31 Trinity St Lawrence MA 01844

FILLMAN, G. ALLAN, Religion Teacher; *b:* Defiance, OH; *ed:* Coll of Josephinum (BA) Amer Stud 1973, (MA) Theology 1977 Toledo (MA) Eng 1989; *cr:* St Wendeline Church Assoc Pastor Blessed Sacrament Church Assoc Pastor 1982-89; Galvert HS Ir Chm 1989-; *ai:* Schola Cantorum Conductor; St Francis Moth Chaplain; NCEA; KAC 1977-; Family Cnslng Bd, Tiflin 1990-, V Tiffin Calvert HS 152 Madison St Tiffin OH 44883

FILOON, RAYMOND GEORGE, 8th Grade Teacher; *b:* Phil PA; *m:* Maryanne (Kutelmack); *c:* Christopher, Kevin, R. J.; *ed* Univ (BS) Ed 1971; Phila Coll of Textile & Sci; *cr:* Maternity B Tchr 1980-; *ai:* Dept of Recreation for Outstanding Svc Boys S 1988-; *office:* Maternity BVM Schl 9322 Bustleton Ave Philade 19115

FILORAMO, J. ROBERT, English Teacher; *b:* Jersey City, NJ; Stenger; *c:* Robert, Thomas, Nancy O Brien, Mark, Katherine, E Margaret, Joseph, Mary Ruth, Anna-Marie; *ed:* Montclair St Coll 1964, (MA) Eng 1967; 48 Credits Beyond Masters; Supvrs Cert in Northern Valley Regnl HS Eng Tchr 1963-69, Ftbl & Bsktbl Coach Supvr of Eng Dept 1969-88; Montclair St Coll Adjunct Fac Koinomia Acad Eng Tchr 1992-; *ai:* Koinomia Acad Trustee Work Alumni Assn; NCTE & NJ Scndry Schls Prin & Supvrs Assn; Hope 1977-, Coord; Tchr of Yr 1968; Outstanding Young Man 1975; Dev the Northern Valley Lang Arts Guide & Writing Prgr Writer & Ed of Raising Children For Heaven; Poems Pub; *office:* Acad 114 Stirling Rd Warren NJ 07059

FILOUS, AUDREY CINCALA, Sci Dept Coord & Bio Springdale, PA; *m:* Thomas J.; *c:* Brett D., Brian T.; *ed:* Kent St U Bio Sci 1971; Cleveland St Univ Ed Cert; Kent St Univ & Akron U Grad; *cr:* Cloverleaf Local Schls Sci & AP Bio Instr 1974-; *ai:* Coord; NSTA 1974-; NEA 1974-; OEA 1974-; Equity in Tech Gran CloverLeaf Sr HS 8525 Friendsville Rd Lodi OH 44254

FILTEAU, ARDATH MILLS, Science Teacher; *b:* Norwalk, Heather Susan Tilteau, Holly Ann, Heau-Grant; *ed:* Univ of CT (Psych 1967; Fitchburg St Coll (MS) Sci Ed 1986; 75 Addl Cre Gardner Jr HS Sci Tchr 1982-, Dept Head 1993-; *ai:* NEA, MT NSTA 1983-; MASS 1993-; Boy Scout Merit Badge 1993-; NIH Summer Flwshp 1993; PALMS Grant 1993-95; PALMS Summ 1994; NSF 4 Yr Grant; PALMS Summer Prgm NESC Worcest *office:* Gardner Jr HS 62 Waterford St Gardner MA 01440

FIMOGNARI, CHERYL L., Amer Lit & Eng Comp Tchr; *b:* Sha *c:* Michael, Therese; *ed:* Youngstown St Univ (BS) Eng 1984, (1991; Rdng Cert K-12; *cr:* Brookfield Jr HS Grd 9 Tchr 1984-8 Tchr 1985-89; Brookfield HS Grd 11 Tchr 1989-; *ai:* Jr Class Adv Tchrs Club Adv; YSU Eng Festival Coord; *office:* Brookfield HS 209 7000 Grove St Brookfield OH 44403

FINACEY, CAROL JEAN, French & Spanish Teacher; *b:* Spr PA; *ed:* Boston Coll (BA) Ed, Fr, Span 1977; Cambridge Coll (1993; Sorbonne Univ 9 Credit Hrs; Boston Coll Grad Schl Fr 45 Cr 30 Credit Hrs Psych, Guidance Cnsler Cert; Univ of Hartford Credits Span; *cr:* Chelmsford Pub Schls Fr, Span Tchr 9-12 Grd Lunenburg Pub Schls Fr, Span, Eng Tchr 8-12 Grd Chathumborough Pub Schls Fr, Span, Eng Tchr 8-12 Grd 198 John's Prep Summer Schl Fr, Span, Eng 1987-89; Gloucester Pub Adult Ed, Fr, Span, Eng Tchr 1987-; *ai:* Sr Class, Fr, Span Club, It Spain Trip Adv; Schl Cncl Mem; Gloucester Tchrs Assn, MA Forei Assn, MA Assn Scndry Guidance Cnslrs 1987-; MA Realtor's Ass Salesperson Licence; *office:* Gloucester HS 32 Leslie Ojohr Gloucester MA 01930*

)O, DONNA JUNE, Oriental Medicine Teacher; *b:* New York, NY; n J.; *c:* Mark; *ed:* Queens Coll of City Univ of NY (BA) Ed 1969; ssage Therapy; 92 Credit Hrs Acupuncture Cert; *cr:* New Ctr for e Hlth, Ed, Rsrch Tchr, Dean of Oriental Stud 1982-88; Tri St Inst ional Chinese Acupuncture Tchr 1991-; *ai:* Consultant NYS Dept ffice of Prof Regulation; Co-Author AMMA The Ancient Art of Medicine; *office:* Tri-St Inst Trad Chinese Accupuncture 80 8th Flr New York NY 10020

:G, PAULINE ESTHER, 9th-12th Grd Art Teacher; *b:* Lubbock, Stephens Coll (AA) 1963; Univ of Houston (BFA) Fine Arts 1965; Univ (EdM) Admin, Policy, Soc Policy 1981; Northeastern Univ uid 1988; *cr:* Mc Reynolds Jr HS Art Tchr 1966-68; Arlington HS 1968-; *ai:* Var Chrldng Coach; Stu Govt, Teen Depression Wkshp A 1966-; MTA, Arlington Ed Assn 1968-; MA Peer Helpers Assn P; Town Employee of Yr 1991; Golden Apple Awd 1989; *office:* n HS 869 Massachusetts Ave Arlington MA 02174*

:, BARBARA, Dance Teacher & Counselor; *b:* Oceanside, NY; *m:* irschtritt; *c:* Matthew, Zachary, Deirdre; *ed:* SUC at Brockport nce 1976; Univ of MI (MFA) Dance 1978; Coll of New Rochelle ; *cr:* Westchester Comm Coll Tchr, Asst Prof Dance 1978-82; Lehman HS Tchr, Cnslr of Conflict Resolution 1984-; Marymount rtist-in-Residence 1989; *ai:* Coach Dance Club, Dance ances; PTA Bd Ward Elem Schl, Beth El Synagog; Choreographer ., Shows Beth El Synagog; NYSDA 1982-; ADG 1978-82; ERD 1988-, Prgm Planner, Presenter; Amer Red Cross 1991-, Vol rtfd Lifeguard & Water Safety Instr; *office:* Herbert H Lehman HS Tremont Ave Bronx NY 10461*

ATHRYN J., Vice Principal; *b:* Irvington, NJ; *ed:* Brookdale Coll 1976; Georgian Court Coll (BA) Ed 1978, (MA) Ed 1988; NJ Cert ecialist 1988 & Supvr 1989; *cr:* Holy Family Schl 6th Grd Tchr St Veronica Schl 5th Grd Tchr 1979-88, Vice Prin 1988-; *ai:* Coach; Forensic Team Moderator; NCEA 1978-; ASCD 1988-; n Court Chorale 1992-; Monmouth Cty Historical Soc & gy Club 1993- Monmouth Univ Chorus 1995-; 1990 Cert of dation US Senator Bill Bradley for Geography Awareness Prgm; Cncl for the Soc Stud Outstanding Educator of the Yr; *office:* Saint Schl 4219 Hwy 9 N Howell NJ 07731

HELDON J., Math & Science Acad Director; *b:* Bronx, NY; *m:* Samson, Joshua; *ed:* City Coll of NY (BS) Ed 1970, (MA) Math ; Hunter Coll (MS) Spcl Ed 1979; Adv Cert Ed Admin & ion 1979; Tchrs Coll Columbia Univ Doctoral Stud; *cr:* Comm liate Schl #148 Tchr 1970-78, Spcl Ed Unit Coord 1978-85, Asst 85-94, Prin 1991-92; Comm Schl Dist 9 Dir of Math 1995; Dr R Drew Acads Dir of Math & Sci Acad 1995-; *ai:* Sci Prep Pgm Mathline MS Math Project Facilitor; Real World Math Insts Advy 92-; NCTM; Assn of Supervision & Curr Dev; Natl MS Assn; W for Sr Housing 1977-, Sec; Area Policy Bd #7 1980-, Chm; Comm #3 1986-89, Chm; Golden Apple Awd PBS-WNET NY 1995; 84 W End Ave Apt 103 New York NY 10025*

), BARBARA HAWKINS, Second Grade Teacher; *b:* Middletown, Thomas John; *c:* Scott Thomas, Shera Fineco Moulton; *ed:* NYS Cortland (BS) Elem Ed 1961; NYS Univ at Oswego Post Grad Stud; nibal Cntrl Schl Bio Tchr 1961-64; St Patrick Schl Rdng Tchr ; Seneca Falls Cntrl Schl Second Grd Tchr 1972-; *ai:* Frank Knight , Dist Steering Comms; Tchr Resource Ctr Bd of Dir; SF Tchrs ake Ctys Rdng Assn, NEA 1966-; United Meth Church; Seneca storical Soc; Amer Diabetes Assn 3 Different Groups; Wanaksink sn; NEX; *home:* 63 Cayuga St Seneca Falls NY 13148

R, JANICE M., 3rd-4th Grade Teacher; *b:* Hudson, NY; *ed:* SUNY am (BA) Soc Stud, Sec Ed 1968; North Adams St (MED) Ed, Guid oll of St Rose Grad Hrs; *cr:* Ichabod Crane MS 6th Grd Tchr ; Martin H. Glynn Schl 4th Grd Tchr 1983-86; Ichabod Crane Schl 2nd Grd Tchr 1986-87; Martin Van Buren Schl 3rd-4th Grd 87-; *ai:* Vol Advy Bd; Odyssey of Mind Coach; Educationally Able Elem Act Account Adv; Arts in Ed Coord; NYSUT 1980-; NEA Columbia Cty Cooperative Extension 1976-, 4H Prgm Comm Chair, omm, Bd of Dirs, Partner in 4H Awd, 4H Alumni Awd; Ichabod mployee of Distinction; Arch Chptr Co Author; *office:* Martin Van lem Schl 25 Broad St Kinderhook NY 12106

R, MARILYN ENGSTROM, Spanish Teacher; *b:* Harvey, IL; *m:* E.; *c:* Rachel, Bethany; *ed:* Marshall Univ (BA) Span, Eng 1968; Univ (MS) Scndry Ed 1988; *cr:* St Marys Area HS Eng Tchr , Span Tchr 1985-; *ai:* Foreign Lang Dept Chprsn; NEA 1968-; Saint Marys Area HS 977 S St Marys St Saint Marys PA 15857

I, MARGUERITE MARTIN, English Teacher; *b:* Allentown, PA; oh Anthony; *ed:* Kutztown Univ (BS) Scndry Ed 1956; Lehigh Univ ng 1973; *cr:* Harrison-Morton Jr HS Eng Tchr 1956-64; Louis E. HS Eng Tchr 1964-76; William Allen HS Eng Tchr, Publications 76-; *ai:* Newspaper, Lit Magazine Adv; AEA, PSEA, NEA 1956-, , Sec, Soc Chprsn, PIN Awd; NCTE 1956-, Natl Post Chprsn, Cert; 1992-, Regnl Chprsn; Mountainville Bowling League 1995-; Ladies Bowling League 1980-, VP, Treas; Dow Jones Newspaper, nwealth Partnership Flwshps; Dorothy Rider Pool Classroom Excl utztown Univ Hum Project; *home:* 3025 Pearl Ave Allentown PA

LINDA TURNER, Reading Teacher; *b:* Wheeling, WV; *m:* Charles Brett Allen, Steven Richard, Betsy Ann; *ed:* West Liberty St Coll -8 Elem Ed 1972; *cr:* West Liberty Elem Schl Early Chldhd ; Wellston City Schl Sub Tchr 1986-88; Wellston Jr HS 8 Grd Rdng 88-95; *ai:* Chrldng Vol 2 Yrs; Spelling Bee Coord 5 Yrs; Yrbk Coord Wellston HS Chrldr Coach Vol 1 Yr, Coach 2 Yrs; NHS Adv 2 Yrs; /TA 1988-; Jackson Church of Christ Tchr, Organist, Pianist, Yth 5-; *office:* Wellston Jr HS 118 S New York Ave Wellston OH 45692

EINER, ROBIN LEE, Second Grade Teacher; *b:* Lansdale, PA; *ed:* ble Coll (BRE) Elem Ed 1979; *cr:* Calvary Bapt Schl Kndgtn , Second Grd Tchr 1980-; *office:* Calvary Baptist School 1380 S Forge Rd Lansdale PA 19446

, JUANITA A., Biology Teacher; *b:* Cox's Mill, WV; *m:* Ben R.; *c:* , Resa Finke Tobin; *ed:* Glenville St Coll (BA) Bio, Home Ec 1951; v (MS) Ed, Home Ec 1969; *cr:* WV Univ Extension Dept Home 951-52; Hanover Toboso HS Home Ec Tchr 1955-56; Rushville HS Home Ec Tchr 1956-57; Millersport HS Bio Tchr 1966-95; *ai:* Twp Tchrs Assn; OH Ed Assn; NEA; *home:* 4240 Logan Thornville Rushville OH 43150

L, NATALIE HOROWITZ, HS Mathematics Teacher; *b:* New Y; *m:* Seymour; *c:* Suzanne, Stephen; *ed:* Hunter Coll (BA) Math chrs Coll Columbia Univ (MS) Ed 1960; 30 Credit Hrs; *cr:* Evander HS Math Tchr 1958-63; HS Art & Design Math Tchr 1972-; *ai:* g, Math; AFT, UFT 1972-; Woodrow Wilson Flwshp; *office:* Art & HS 1075 2nd Ave New York NY 10022

LSTEIN, DAVID MARK, Judaic Teacher; *b:* Memphis, TN; *m:* h T.; *c:* Avi, Elisheva, Chaim, Yonaton; *ed:* Johns Hopkins (MS) us 1985; NIRC (MS) Talmudic Law, Rabbinics 1986; *cr:* Shoresh Yth Dir 1981-; Beth Tfiloh 5th-8th Grd Judaic Tchr 1989-; *ai:* Troubled Yth; Cncl Organ Donors; Teen Torah Ctr Dir; Adult Ed Dir; Shoresh Dir & Fin Dir; NCSY 1984, Adv, Adv of the Yr 1986-87, 1992, 1994; Various Svc Awds from Shoresh, The Teen Torah Ctr, NCSY; *office:* Beth Tfiloh Comm Day Schl 3300 Old Court Rd Pikesville MD 21208

FINLAN, AUTUMN PATRICIA, Retired English Teacher; *b:* Bradford, PA; *ed:* St Bonaventure (BA) Eng 1959; Syracuse Univ & Univ of Rochester 60 Credit Hrs Beyond Masters; *cr:* Falconer Cntrl Schl Eng Tchr 1959-61; Greece Olympia HS Eng Tchr 1963-71; Greece Athena HS Eng Tchr 1971-78; Greece Arcadia HS Eng Tchr 1978-95; *ai:* Drama Club, Lit Magazine & NHS Adv; NeEA, NYEA & Greece Tchrs Assn 1963-95; NEA Life 1995-; Tchr of Yr 1985, 1994, Univ of Rochester Awd for Excl in Scndry Tchng; Who's Who in Amer Edctrs 1989-90.*

FINLEY, EARLENE E., K-12th Grd Gifted Support Tchr; *b:* Waynesboro, PA; *m:* Earl R. Jr.; *c:* Grant D., Drew D.; *ed:* Robert Morris Coll (Assoc) Secretarial Sci 1966; CA Univ (BS) Elem Ed 1968; *cr:* Beth Ctr Schl 2nd Grd Tchr 1968-78, K-12th Grd Gifted Support Tchr 1988-; *ai:* Acad League Coach; BCTA 1988-; PSTA 1988-; NEA 1988-; Daisytown UP Church 1954-, Sunday Schl Supt 1985-86; Great Ideas Grant Robotics; *home:* 396 Ridgewood Dr Fredericktown PA 15333

FINLEY, JAMES BOGARD, 7th & 8th Grd English Teacher; *b:* Zanesville, OH; *m:* Mary E.; *c:* Kathy E.; *ed:* Univ of Cincinnati (BA) Eng 1973; Marietta Coll (MS) His 1990; 20 Addl Hrs, Permanent Cert; Bowling Green St Univ Tchrs Cert; Univ of Toledo Linguistics Stud; *cr:* Toledo Pub Schl Tchr 1973-75; Belpre City Schls Tchr 1976-77; Warren Local Schls Tchr 1979-; *ai:* WLEA Bldg Rep; NEA, OEA 1976-; *home:* 314 Fair View Ln Marietta OH 45750*

FINLEY, KELLY ANN, English & Art Teacher; *b:* Cleveland, OH; *ed:* Bowling Green St Univ (BA) Ed 1990; 5 Credit Hrs Kent St Univ; *cr:* Lake Cath HS Eng, Art Tchr 1993-; *ai:* Teen Inst, SADD Adv; Chalta 1993-; Sigma Tau Delta; *office:* Lake Catholic HS 6733 Reynolds Rd Mentor OH 44060

FINLEY, MARY D., English & Business Professor; *b:* Rochester, NY; *c:* John, Sarah; *ed:* St Univ of NY at Albany (BS) Bus 1955; Nazareth Coll of Rochester (MS) Ed 1985; *cr:* Webster Cntrl Schls Instr & Dir of Work Coop 1955-63; Veigel Bus Inst Instr & Dir of Secretarial Sci Schl 1963-65; Empire St Coll Assessment Evaluator 1996; Rochester Bus Inst Instr & Liaison to Dean for Lang Arts 1996; *ai:* Review Text Ed; Coll Credits Assessor; MCBEA 1990-, Sec 1992-94; Rochester Bus Inst Instr of Yr 1994-95; *office:* Rochester Bus Inst 1850 Ridge Rd E Rochester NY 14622

FINLEY, PATRICK DANIEL, Vocal Music & Music His Tchr; *b:* Akron, OH; *m:* Christine Shortell Nash; *c:* Morgan, Leslie; *ed:* Akron Univ (BM) Piano, Theory, Composition 1980; Penn St Univ (MM) Composition 1982; City Univ of NY (PHD) Composition 1993; Baromeo Seminary at Wickliffe OH Philos Major 1975-76; WV Univ at Morgantown DMA Stu 1982-83; *cr:* US Navy Hosp Corpsman 1970-74; Penn St Adj Prof 1980-82; WV Univ Adj Prof 1982-83; Self-Employed Piano Tchr 1983-90; Park Ridge HS Music His, Vocal Music Tchr 1990-; *ai:* Talent Show, Jr HS Madrigals Singers Dir; NJ Composer's Guild 1988-; Music Edctrs of Bergen Cty, MENC 1993-; NJ Cncl on Arts Grant 1985, 1990; Piano Music Pub; A Catalogue of the Works of Ralph Shapey Book Pub 1996; *office:* Park Ridge HS 2 Park Ave Park Ridge NJ 07656

FINLEY, PATRICK L., Hlth Scis Division Assoc Prof; *b:* Baton Rouge, LA; *ed:* Univ of MD (BGS) Kinesiology, Philosophy 1983; George Washington Univ (MA) Exercise Sci 1986; Univ of MD PHD in Progress; *cr:* George Washington Univ Adj Lecturer 1985-86; Amer Univ Adj Lecturer 1985-87; Walter Reed Army Inst Rsrch Asst 1986; League of the Handicapped Dir, Hlth, Fitness 1987; Howard Comm Coll Prof Hlth, PE 1987-; *ai:* Adv, Instr Martial Arts Club; Amer Coll of Sports Med 1983; Natl Strength, Conditioning Assn 1984; *office:* Howard Comm Coll 10901 Little Patuxent Pkwy Columbia MD 21044

FINLON, JANE HIRSCH, 8th Grd Language Arts Teacher; *b:* New York City, NY; *m:* LeRoy; *c:* Jason; *ed:* Penn St Univ (BS) Elem Ed 1971; Univ of Scranton (MS) Elem Ed 1976; 14 Post Grad Credit Hrs; *cr:* Western Wayne Schl Dist 4th Grd Tchr 1971-82, 8th Grd Tchr 1982-; *ai:* SAP; Spirit Club Adv; Discipline Comm; NEA 1971-; PSEA 1971-; WWEA 1971-; PMSA 1991-; PTA 1971-; *home:* RR 2 Box 315 Waymart PA 18472*

FINN, ELEANOR, Instructor; *b:* N Andover, MA; *ed:* BridgeWater St Coll (BS) Ed 1950; Univ of MS at Amherst (MED) Ed 1957; Attnd Univ of NH, River Coll; *cr:* Amherst MA Pub Schls Math Tchr 1950-54; Andover MA Pub Schls Math Tchr 1954-56; St Thomas Aquinas 7th Grade Teacher 1957-58; Mt St Mary HS Math Tchr 1959-92; Bishop Gourtis HS Math Tchr 1992-94; Chester Coll Math Instr 1992-; *ai:* Sr Class Adv; Non Pub Schl Advy Cncl; Diocesan Schl Bd, Diocese of Manchester; Prof Stans Bd of NH; Delta Kappa Gamma 1991-; Sisters of Mercy 1956-; *office:* Castle Coll Searles Rd Windham NH 03087

FINN, JOHN FRANCIS, Visual Arts Instr; *b:* Providence, RI; *m:* Colette Roberts; *ed:* RIJC (AFA) Painting 1986; Schl of Art Inst of Chicago (BFA) Painting, Ceramics 1989; *cr:* Hartford HS Visual Arts Instr 1991-92; Thetford Acad Visual Arts Instr 1992-; *ai:* 9th Grd Adv; Instrl Support Team; NH League of Arts 1993-; Illustration for Chicago Tribune; Best of Show N Haverhill Art Show; 1st Place Watercolor Art Show; *office:* Thetford Acad PO Box 190 Thetford VT 05074

FINN, JOHN JOSEPH, English & Latin Teacher; *b:* Mt Vernon, NY; *m:* Judith Ventura; *c:* Elizabeth, John; *ed:* Fordham Univ (BA) Eng 1971; Univ of Rochester (MA) Eng 1973; 30 Addl Credits; *cr:* Bishop Kearney HS Eng Tchr, Guid Cnslr 1974-81; Mc Quaid Jesuit Schl Eng, Latin, Rel Tchr 1981-; Nazareth Coll of Rochester Shakespeare Instr 1989-; *ai:* Yrbk Moderator; NCEA 1981-; St Margaret Mary Schl Advy Bd 1991-, Chm; Cub Scouts 1994-, Den Ldr; Irondequoit Little League 1992-, Coach; Tchr of Yr Awd 1990; *office:* Mc Quaid Jesuit HS 1800 S Clinton Ave Rochester NY 14618

FINNEGAN, DAWN TURNEY, Sixth Grade Teacher; *b:* Sewickley, PA; *m:* Daniel; *c:* Daniel Jr.; *ed:* PA St Univ (BS) Elem Ed 1971; *cr:* Highland Schl 3-6 Grd Tchr 1971-; *ai:* Stu Cncl Adv; Yrbk Spon; NEA, PSEA, AAEA 1971-; PTO 1971-, Pres; PSU Alumni 1989-, Life Mem; Alpha Delta Pi 1969-; Pi Lambda Theta 1971-; Good Samaritan Parish; Ambridge Jaycees Outstdng Young Edctr; *office:* Highland Elem Schl 740 Park Rd Ambridge PA 15003

FINNEGAN, DIANE DEFILIPPO, English Teacher & Dept Chm; *b:* Pittsburgh, PA; *m:* Robert M.; *c:* Patrick A., Robert J.; *ed:* Duquesne Univ (BA) Speech & Comm 1976; Post Grad Stud; *cr:* St Mary of the Mount HS Eng Tchr 1976-82; Canevin Cath HS Eng Tchr 1982-; *ai:* Newspaper Moderator 1987-1995; Pittsburgh Fed of Diocesan Tchrs 1976-; NCTE 1990-; *home:* 3037 Churchview Ave Pittsburgh PA 15227

FINNEGAN, ROBERT EUGENE, Third Grade Teacher; *b:* Brooklyn, NY; *m:* Joan; *c:* Jennifer, Keri Ann, Kristen; *ed:* St Univ Coll at Oneonta (BSE) Ed 1971, (MSE) Ed 1976; Attained 51 Hrs of Credit Beyond BS; *cr:* Sidney Elem Schl 6th Grd Tchr 1971-73, Multi Age Class Tchr 1973-92, 3rd Grd Tchr 1992-96; *ai:* Boys & Girls Var Cross Cntry, Var Golf, Jr Var Boys Bsktbl Coach; Stamp Club Adv; Tchrs Assn Retirement, Budget Comm; Tchrs Assn Exec Bd; NYS PHSAA Section 4 Class C Golf Championship Site Chm; Sidney Tchrs Assn 1971-, Treas 1974-; NY St United Tchrs, AFT 1973-; Tri-Town Nursery Schl Bd of Dirs 1974-, Sec; Tri-Cty Stamp Club 1973-, Treas; Sidney Elem Schl PTO 1977-, Treas; Tchr of Yr 1980 Sidney Tchrs Assn; Voc Svc Awd 1990 By Rotary Club of Sidney; *home:* 27 Pearl St E Sidney NY 13838*

FINNERAN, MARILYN HARRISON, Fifth Grade Teacher; *b:* Minneapolis, MN; *m:* Patrick; *c:* Kelly Ann Parks, Darlene O'Malley; *ed:* Suffolk Comm Coll (AS) Gen Stud 1971; Dowling Coll (BA) Ed 1973, (MS) Ed 1976; 75 Addl Credits; *cr:* Sachem Schl Dist Kndgtn Tchr 1973-77, 2nd Grd Tchr 1978-81, 3rd Grd Tchr 1982-83, 5th Grd Tchr 1984-; *ai:* AFT, NEA, CTA 1973-; Brownie Ldr; Girl Scout, Ldr; *home:* 94 Ackerly Ln Lake Ronkonkoma NY 11779

FINNESSEY, THOMAS JOHN,SR., Retired Sixth Grade Teacher; *b:* Mineville, NY; *m:* Natalie DePaoli; *c:* Thomas Jr., Timothy; *ed:* St Univ Coll at Pittsburgh (BS) K-8 1957, (MS) Elem Admin, Supvr 1962; 32 Addl Grad Hrs SUC, St Lawrence Univ, Univ of VT; *cr:* Moriah Cntrl Schl Sixth Grd Tchr 1957-92; *ai:* NY St United Tchrs 1957-; NY St Ret Tchrs Assn 1993-; *home:* 9 Long Pl Port Henry NY 12974

FINNESSEY, TIMOTHY J., French Teacher; *b:* Ticonderosa, NY; *m:* Gail Fisher; *c:* Christi, Aaron, Nicholas; *ed:* Potsdam Coll (BA) Fr 1983; SUNY at Binghamton (MA) Translation Stud 1985; *cr:* R. C. S. Jr HS Fr Tchr 1984-85; New Lebanon Jr Sr HS Fr Tchr 1986-88; Owego-Apalachin Mid Fr Tchr 1988-; *ai:* Fr Club; Dept Chprsn; NY Assn of Frgn Lang Tchrs; Tchr Recognition Awd 1990, 1993; Tchr Exch Istanbul Turkey; *office:* Owego-Apalachin MS Elm St Owego NY 13827

FINNEY, DANIELA BUCCILLI, 9th Grade English Teacher; *b:* Sora, Italy; *m:* Edward; *ed:* PA St Univ (BS) Scndry Eng Ed 1992; Attnd Duquesne Univ, Pittsburgh Univ. Western PA; *cr:* Ellwood City Schl Dist Acad Eng Tchr 1993-; *ai:* Ellwoodian Yrbk Spon; NEA 1993-; Western PA Jostens Rookie of the Yr Awd; *office:* Ellwood City Schl 501 Crescent Ave Ellwood City PA 16117

FINNEY, PAMELA LYNNE, Art Teacher & Dept Head; *b:* Sharon, PA; *m:* David Roy; *ed:* Edinboro Univ of PA (BS) Art 1968; 24 Post Grad Credits at Penn St Univ; *cr:* S Butler Cty Schl Dist Art Tchr 1968-; *ai:* PSEA, NEA 1968-; NAEA, PAEA 1994-; Ducks Unlimited 1988-, Chprsn & Pres; One Man Show 1994; *office:* Knox HS Box 628 Saxonburg PA 16056

FINOTTI, ROGER C., Fifth Grade Teacher; *b:* Indiana, PA; *m:* Charlene Harvey; *c:* Matthew, Michele; *ed:* IN Univ of PA (BSED) Soc Stud 1968; Univ of Pittsburgh (MS) Math 1975; 15 Hrs Post MS; *cr:* Homer Ctr Elem 6th Grd Tchr 1968-80, 5th Grd Tchr 1980-; *ai:* Childrens Hosp Fund Raising comm; TAPS; HCEA VP; PSEA 1968-; NEA 1968-; HCEA 1968-, Treas & VP; PTA 1978-; Knight of Columbus 1993-; PTA Founder; *office:* Homer Ctr Schl Dist 20 Wildcat Ln Homer City PA 15748

FINSEL, SANDRA L., High School Math Teacher; *b:* Philadelphia, PA; *ed:* 24 Credit Hrs Post-Grad; *cr:* Glasgow HS Math Tchr 1976-80; Wilmington Friends Schl HS & MS Math Tchr 1980-82; East HS Math Tchr 1982-; *office:* East HS 450 Ellis Ln West Chester PA 19380*

FINSTEIN, MARILYN LAIACONA, Associate Professor of Biology; *b:* Medford, MA; *ed:* Fordham Univ (MS) Bio 1966; Rutgers Univ, New Brunswick Microbiology; *cr:* Pearl River Scndry Schl Tchr 1960-64; Jersey City St Coll Assoc Prof, Biology 1967-; *ai:* ASM, AAAS, NYAS, NABT, NEA, AIBS, AFT 1967-; Article Pub; Richland Cty Grant Tchr Indstrl Rsrch Reward 1963; NY St Grant Summer Stud 1961; *office:* Jersey City St Coll 2039 Kennedy Boulevard Jersey City NJ 07305

FINZEL, CHERYL HARRISON, 8th Grade Science Teacher; *b:* Sharon, PA; *c:* Kristen, Erica; *ed:* Univ of Pitt at Bradford (BS) Bio 1986; Edinboro Univ Masters Equivalency; *cr:* Warren Cty Schls Sub Tchr 1987-90, Spcl Ed Tchr 1990-93; Beaty MS 8th Grd Sci Tchr 1993-; *ai:* Yrbk Ed & Adv; Advisee & Adv Steering Comm Mem; NEA 1990-; PSEA 1990-; *office:* Beaty Warren MS 2 E 3rd Ave Warren PA 16365

FIOCCA, PAUL JOHN, Language Arts Teacher; *b:* Akron, OH; *m:* Alice M.; *c:* Lisa; *ed:* Univ of Akron (BA) Scndry Engl 1971; *cr:* Woodbridge Local Schl Tchr 1971-; *ai:* Ftbl, Bsktbl & Track Coach; NEA, OEA 1971-; WEA 1971-, Pres; *home:* 4725 Emerald Woods Dr Stow OH 44224

FIORE, CAROL ANN DRURY, Second Grade Teacher; *b:* Jersey City, NJ; *m:* Ronald M.; *c:* Christine, Jamie Michael, Jeanine, Brian Christopher, Lauren Marie; *ed:* King's Coll (BA) Elem Ed 1980; *cr:* St Anthony Grammar Schl 1 Grd Tchr 1980-81; Our Lady of Victories Schl 2, 4 Grd Tchr 1981-85; Ukrainian Assumption Schl 2 Grd Tchr 1985-; *ai:* Schl Newspaper Advr; Mid Sts Assn of Colls & Schls Steering Comm Co-Chair; NCEA 1980-; Old Bridge Ath Assn 1992-, Sec 1994, Chrldng Commissioner 1995-; Tchr of the Yr 1994; *office:* Ukrainian Assumption Schl 300 Meredith St Perth Amboy NJ 08861*

FIORE, CAROLYN LEE KRAUSE, Elementary Music Teacher; *b:* Rockville Centre, NY; *m:* Salvatore G.; *c:* Barbara, Rosemarie; *ed:* LIU CW Post (BA) Music Ed 1984; SUNY at Stonybrook (MA) Arts Ed 1986; Seminary of the Immaculate Conception Working Towards MA in Theology; *cr:* Diocese of Rockville Ctr Music Tchr 1982-86; Amityville Schls Music Tchr 1987-89; Middle Cntry Schls Music Tchr 1989-; *ai:* Selden Jazz Singers Dir 1989-94; Southbay Chamber Singers Bd Mem 1986-; AFT, NYSUT, SCMEA, NYSSMA 1986-; MCTA 1989-; C W Post Acad, Music Schlsps 1980-84, Deans List 1980-84; *office:* New Lane Elem Schl Centereach NY 11784*

FIORE, CHRISTINE RICHTER, Spanish Teacher; *b:* Mineola, NY; *m:* Louis John; *c:* Alexandra, Jacqueline; *ed:* Albertus Magnus Coll, C. W. Post Coll (BA) Ed, Span 1971, (MA) Guid 1976; 10 Inservice Credits AIDS Awareness; *cr:* Lawrence Rd Jr HS Piloted GATE Prgm 1977, Piloted ESL Prgm 1980, Span Tchr 1971-; *ai:* Span Club Adv; Mentor 12 Stu Tchrs; TESA Coord; Adopt A Stu Prgm; AFT, UTA, NYSUT 1971-; GC Historical Soc 1993-, Tour Guide, Comm Hostess; GC Comm Fund 1988-, Canvasser; GC PTA 1985-; Uniondale PTA 1971-; Grad Summa Cum Laude; Outstdng Frgn Lang Stu 1971; Article Pub; Adv Curr GATE 1977, ESL Prgm 1980; *office:* Lawrence Road Jr HS 50 Lawrence Rd Hempstead NY 11550

FIORE, JOHN JAMES, English & Literature Teacher; *b:* Jamaica, NY; *ed:* Hofstra Univ (BA) Comm, Eng 1990; *cr:* St Anthony of Padua Eng Tchr 1990-; *ai:* Advanced Regents Seq Course for 8th Grdrs; *office:* St Anthony Of Padua Schl 125-18 Rockaway Blvd So Ozone Park NY 11420

FIORE, SUSAN E., 4th Grade Teacher; *b:* Troy, NY; *m:* James P.; *c:* David, Matthew, Megan, James; *ed:* Maria Coll (AA) Lbrl Arts 1969; Oneonta St Coll (BS) Math Ed 1971; Rensselaer Polytechnic Inst 3 Grad Credit Hrs; *cr:* Vincentian Inst 9-10 Grd Math Tchr 1971-72; Clayton A. Bouton Jr Sr HS 6-8 Grd Math Tchr 1972-74; Our Lady of Victory Schl 4 Grd Tchr 1985-; *ai:* Kidsummer Recreation, Enrichment Summer Camp Dir; After Schl Challenge Prgm Moderator; Bazaar Comm Co-Chair; Math Tutor; Mentor Tchr for Stu Tchrs; NEA, NASTA 1992-; Cath Schl Tchrs of Amer 1985-; Ola Church, Svc Projects; Amer Cancer Soc, Svc Projects; Amer Heart Assn, Svc Projects; *office:* Our Lady Of Victory Schl 451 Marshland Ct Troy NY 12180*

FIORELLA, JON LAURENCE, Science Teacher; *b:* Staten Island, NY; *m:* Millie Pepe; *c:* Lori, Carrie; *ed:* Richmond Coll CUNY (BS) Bio 1969, (MS) Scndry Schl Sci 1971; 77 Credits Attnd Manhattanville Coll Univ, Long Island Univ, Univ of ME, Univ of Rochester, Fordham Univ & Western CT St Univ; *cr:* Alexander Hamilton Jr HS Sci Tchr 1969-71; Fox Lane HS Sci Tchr 1971-; *ai:* Boys Cross Cntry Coach; Girls Spring Track Coach; Aeroallergen Research Club Adv; AFT, NYSUT 1971; NSTA 1987-; NABT 1987-, Outstanding Bio Tchr Awd 1991; Cert of Creative Excellence US Industrial Film Festival 1986; Outstandingf Sci Tchr Recognition Awd 1991; NBC Natl Tchrs Awd 1991; NY St Century Club

Awd Cross Cntry 1992; Alumni Hall of Fame Richmond Coll CUNY 1994; *office:* Fox Lane HS PO Box 390 Bedford NY 10506

FIORESI, VERONICA MONFARDINI, Kindergarten Teacher; *b:* Woodbury, NJ; *m:* Ronald; *c:* Mark, Rhonda; *ed:* Rowan-Glassboro St Coll (BA) Elem Ed 1968; Cath Rel Cert; *cr:* Solve D'Eppolito Pub Schl Kndgtn Tchr 1968-76; Our Lady of Victories Schl Kndgtn Tchr 1982-91; Notre Dame Regnl Schl Kndgtn Tchr 1992-; *ai:* Kndgtn Play Dir; CNEA 1982-; Our Lady of Victories Parish Cncl 1994-; *office:* Notre Dame Reg Schl 105 Church St Newfield NJ 08344

FIORI, CAROLANN, Early Childhood Science Tchr; *b:* Queens, NY; *ed:* St Univ of NY Coll at Oswego (BS) Elem Ed 1983; Coll of Staten Island (MS) Elem Ed 1987; 40 Addl Post Grad Credit Hrs; Eisenhower Educl Grant Sci Prgm for Elem Tchrs Hunter Coll CUNY; *cr:* St Christopher Schl 6th-8th Grd Tchr 1983-84; PS 200 1st Grd Tchr 1984-95, Early Chldhd Sci Tchr 1995-; *ai:* AFT, UFT, Cath Tchrs Assn 1984-; Elem Schl Sci Assn 1995-; Staten Island Children's Museum Assn 1994-; *office:* Public Schl 200 1940 Benson Ave Brooklyn NY 11214

FIORI, SANDRA TURLIK, Language Arts Teacher; *b:* Pittsburgh, PA; *m:* Joseph F.; *c:* Frank Stephen, Clayton J.; *ed:* Univ of Pittsburgh (BS) Elem Ed 1963; Attnd California Univ of PA; *cr:* West Mifflin Area Schls 4th Grd Tchr 1963-68; Brentwood Presbyn Church Presch Tchr 1976-87; Alternative Employment Agency Cnslr 1977-78; Our Lady of Grace Schl Tchr 1978-; *ai:* Readers' Club Spon; Spirit Show Dir; Pittsburgh Fed Cath Schl Tchrs 1990-, Bldg Rep; NCEA 1978-; Western PA Cncl Eng Schl Tchrs 1992-; Diocese Pittsburgh's Acad Excl Comm; *home:* 230 Cherokee Rd Pittsburgh PA 15241

FIORILLO, JOHN ANTHONY, Prof of Electrical Eng Tech; *b:* New York City, NY; *m:* Linda L. Hansen; *c:* Steven; *ed:* Acad of Aeronautics (AAS) Electrical Engrng Tech 1968; NY Inst of Tech (BS) Electrical Engrng Tech 1970; Long Island Univ (MS) Mngmt Engrng 1974; New York Univ (PHD) Tech, Ed 1980; *cr:* Metaval Division of Optics Tech Electronics Eng 1969-73; Acad of Aeronautics Asst Prof of Electrical Engrng Tech 1973-75; St Univ of NY Prof of Electrical Engrng Tech 1975-; *ai:* Electrical Engrng Tech StdntsAcad Adv; Amer Soc Engrng Ed 1980-; United Univ Professors 1975-; Tau Alpha Pi; St Univ of NY Chancellor's Awd for Excl Tchng 1994; Articles Pub Cmptrs Ed Journal of Amer Soc Engrng Ed; *office:* St Univ of NY at Farmingdale Farmingdale NY 11735*

FIOROT, ROSE MARY VALLETTA, Spanish Teacher; *b:* Bethlehem, PA; *m:* Michael; *c:* Lisa, Gregory; *ed:* East Stroudsburg Univ (BS) Scndry Ed, Eng 1965; Lehigh Univ Cert Span 1976; 15 Grad Credit Hrs Beyond Masters Equivalency; *cr:* Pen Argyl Area HS Eng Tchr 1965-67, Eng & Span Tchr 1976-80, Span Tchr 1980-; *ai:* Frosh Class Co-Adv; Jr Miss Scholarship Pgm Adv; NEA 1965-67, 1976-; PSEA 1965-67, 1976-; *office:* Pen Argyl Area HS 501 W Laurel Ave Pen Argyl PA 18072

FIRENZE, WEGA SCONZO, Spanish Teacher; *b:* Venice, Italy; *m:* Angelo R.; *c:* Marc, Angelo, Peter; *ed:* Boston Univ (BA) Romance Lang 1966; Harvard (MED) Educl Admin 1990-; Various Courses; *cr:* Belmont HS Span Tchr 1966-68, Fr, Ger Tchr 1977-78, 1982-; *ai:* Chair Sexual Harassment Comm; Organizer, chaperone Stu Exchanges to Spain; Mentor Tchr to Stu Tchrs; BEA, NEA, MTA, AATSP 1966-; St Joseph's Church 1967-, Euchristic Minister; Nom Tchr of Yr; *office:* Belmont HS 221 Concord Ave Belmont MA 02178*

FIRESTONE, DAVID ALLEN, Mathematics Teacher; *b:* York, PA; *m:* Joanne; *c:* Daniel; *ed:* Lock Haven (BA) Math, Ed 1977; PA St York 25 Post Grad Credits; *cr:* St Joseph Acad Math Tchr 1977-80; Northeastern Math Tchr 1980-; *ai:* NEA 1980-, Bldg Rep, Negotiating Team; *office:* Northeastern Sr HS 300 High St Manchester PA 17345

FIRESTONE, DAVID FREDERIC, AP Studio Art Teacher; *b:* Pottstown, PA; *c:* Erin; *ed:* Kutztown Univ (BA) Art 1969, (MS) Art 1972; Nature Photography; Painting en Plein Air; *cr:* Freelance Photog, Advertising 1964-80; Allentown SchlDist Adult Evening Schl Studio Art, Painting, Printmaking Tchr 1983-86; Northampton Comm Coll Commercial Photog Tchr 1977-80; Allentown Schl Dist HS Studio Art Tchr 1969-; *ai:* Life Drawing Classes; Art Adv Lit Art Magazine; Curr Dev Comm; AEA, NEA, PSEA 1969-; Article Pub; Judge Comm, Schl Art Exhibits; *office:* Schl Dist City of Allentown 31 S Penn St Allentown PA 18105

FIRESTONE, RUSSELL GEORGE, Social Studies Teacher; *b:* Pittsburgh, PA; *m:* Cynthia L. Wilcox; *c:* Dennis; *ed:* CA Univ of PA (BS) Scndry Ed Soc Sci 1983; 24 Credits Toward Masters; *cr:* St Therese Schl Soc Stud Tchr 1983-; *ai:* Var Ftbl Coach; Stu Assistance Pgm Coord; Mid Sts Comm Chm; NCEA 1984-; Lions Club 1990-94; St Therese Parish Cncl 1994-, VP; Diocese of Pittsburgh Golden Apple Awd Winner 1993; Thanks to Tchrs Nom 1996; *office:* St Therese School-Munhall 3 Saint Therese Ct Homestead PA 15120*

FIRETTO, MEL VIOLA, Fourth Grade Teacher; *b:* Newark, NJ; *m:* Barbara Miller; *c:* Mel, Anthony; *ed:* Daemen Coll (BS) Elem Ed, Early Chldhd 1984; Georgian Court Coll (MS) Supvr, Prin, Curr 1990; *cr:* Ridgeway Elem Schl 3rd Grd Tchr 1984-92; Manchester Twp Elem Schl 4th Grd Tchr 1992-; *ai:* Fac Advy Comm; Core Team; PTA; NJEA 1984-, Assoc Mem; Tchr of Yr Govenor's Recognition Awd 1990-91; *home:* 297 Grand Central Pkwy Bayville NJ 08721

FIRKEY, ANN CLEMINSON, Retired 6th Grade Teacher; *b:* Woodford, VT; *m:* Stanley C.; *c:* Deborah F. Conway, Stephen A.; *ed:* Castleton St Coll (BS) Elem Ed 1953; *cr:* Hartland Elem Schl 3 Grd Tchr 1953-54; Carendish Elem Schl 3 Grd Tchr 1955-58, 3 Grd & 4-8 Rdng Tchr 1961-70; Ludlow Elem Schl 6 Grd Tchr 1970-92, 6 Grd Tchr & Acting Prin 1984-85; *ai:* Delta Kappa Gamma 1973-, Initiation Chm; Tchr of Yr 1980.

FIRMIN, MICHAEL, Assoc Prof & Psych Dept Chrmn; *b:* New Orleans, LA; *m:* Karen Tuttle; *c:* Ruth, Sarah; *ed:* Calvary Bible Coll (BA) Pastoral Stud 1983, (MA) Biblical Stud 1985; Bob Jones Univ (MS) Prsnl Svcs 1987, (PHD) Church Admin 1988; Marywood Coll (MA) Clinical Psych 1992; Syracuse Univ Working on PHD Cnslr Ed; *cr:* Bapt Bible Coll of PA Psych Dept Assoc Prof & Chair, Counseling Svcs Dir 1988-, Grad Studies Dir 1995-; *ai:* Psi Chi 1991-; Natl Certified Cnslr 1992-; Faith Fellowship Bapt Church 1991-94, Pastor; Pub in Theological Research Exch Network, Fac Dialogue, Jrnl of Adult and Training AABC Newsletter; Syracuse Univ Tchng Asst, Clinical Supervisor; *office:* Baptist Bible Coll 538 Venard Rd Clarks Summit PA 18411

FIRST, LESLIE SUZANNE, HS Home Economics Teacher; *b:* Berea, OH; *m:* Dana; *c:* Kendal, Deanna; *ed:* Kent St Univ (BS) Consumer Homemaking & Voc Home Ec 1979; Attnd Ashland Univ, Akron; *cr:* Berea Bd of Ed Home Ec Tchr 1980-81; North Royalton Bd of Ed Home Ec Tchr 1981-; *ai:* NEA, OEA; *office:* North Royalton HS 14713 Ridge Rd North Royalton OH 44133

FISCELLA, EDWARD PHILLIP,JR., Language Arts Teacher; *b:* Philadelphia, PA; *m:* Nancy Lewis; *c:* Aimee, Kaitlin, Christina; *ed:* LaSalle Univ (BA) Eng, Ed 1975; Temple Univ (MS) Ed 1981; *cr:* Gloucester Twp Pub Schls Lang Art, Rdng Tchr 1976-; *ai:* Drama Club Adv, Awded Best Prgm in Schl System; NEA, NJEA 1976-; GTEA 1976-, Sr Rep; Gloucester Twp Ctr for the Arts 1989-, Founder, Pres; Intnl Ballet Theatre 1996, Bd of Dir; NJ Governor's Tchr of Yr1994; *office:* Glen Landing MS 85 Little Gloucester Rd Blackwood NJ 08012*

FISCH, THOMAS MICHAEL, Social Studies Teacher; *b:* Northport, NY; *m:* Kathleen E. Cowell; *c:* Linda, Lauri, Shane; *ed:* St Michaels Coll Ut (BA) Pol Sci 1968; 30 Grad Hrs Plattsburgh St Univ; *cr:* St Pius X Cntrl Schl 7th & 8th Grd Soc Stud, Math & Rdng Tchr 1968-71; Saranac Lake MS 8th Grd Soc Stud 1971-; *ai:* Jr Var Bsbl Coach; Teaming Comm Chm; AFT, NYSUT 1971-; St Bernards Schl Bd of Ed 1972-75; St Johns Church Parish Cncl 1985-86; Town Councilman Town of Santa Clara 1981-86; 1991 Tchr of Yr Prgm Cmptr Use in Classroom; *office:* Saranac Lake MS Petrova Ave Saranac Lake NY 12983

FISCH, WALTER H., Social Studies Teacher; *b:* Philadelphia, PA; *m:* Carol Kunkele; *c:* Melissa; *ed:* Bloomsburg St Univ (BS) Comp Soc Stud & Scndry Ed 1975, (MS) European His 1980; 45 Grad Credits; *cr:* Selinsgrove Area HS Soc Stud Team Ldr 1981-, Soc Stud Tchr 1976-; Susquehanna Univ Instr 1994-; *ai:* Curr, Meet & Discuss & NHS Comms; NEA & PSEA 1976-; NCSS & PCSS 1993-; *home:* 712 Picnic Ln Selinsgrove PA 17870

FISCHER, BARBARA ANN (BROWN), Resource Room Teacher; *b:* Harrisburg, PA; *m:* Walt; *c:* Heather, Travis; *ed:* Millersville Univ (BS) Elem, Spec Ed 1972, (MED) Ed Rdng Specialist 1974; Spec Ed Cert 1972; Rdng Specialist Cert 1981; 3 Credit Hrs Criminal Justice Univ of AK at Fairbanks; 3 Credit Hrs Art Ed for Spec Needs Penn St Univ Schuylkill Campus; *cr:* Lancaster Schl Dist Spec Ed Tchr 1972-74; Eielson AFB Spec Needs Tchr 1974-75; Northern Lebanon HS Adult Ed Ctr Tchr 1983-84, HS Res Rm Tchr 1984-94; Northern Lebanon Schl Dist HS Resource Rm 1994-; *ai:* Gardening, Plant Club 1992-94; Film Club 1991-92; NEA, PSEA 1994-; LLIUEA 1994-, Bd 2 Yrs; NLEA 1994-; St Pauls United Church of Christ 1962-, Vol Work; *office:* Northern Lebanon Schl Dist PO Box 100 Fredericksburg PA 17026

FISCHER, BRIAN J., Music Educator; *b:* Wilkes-Barre, PA; *m:* Darlene Anderscavage; *c:* Tiffany, Jyllian; *ed:* Attnd Coll of St Rose, Luzerne Int Univ; IN Wesleyan Masters Equivalency 1996; *cr:* Couglin HS Band Dir 1984-85; Meyers HS Music Edctr 1984-85, 1993-94; Gar HS Music Edctr, Band Dir 1985-93; Plains Jr HS Music Edctr, Band Dir 1993-; *ai:* Assist Stu Act; NEA, PA St Ed Assn 1984-; Local 140 Music 1977-; Keystone St Games 1985-; Coord St Music Festival 1993; Mid Sts Assn Schl Accreditation; *office:* Plains Jr HS 33 W Carey St Wilkes Barre PA 18705*

FISCHER, CLAUDIE DESCHASEAUX, Lang Dept Head & French Tchr; *b:* Neufchateau, France; *ed:* Univ of Nancy (BA) Eng Lang 1970; Cntrl CT Univ (MA) Fr 1972; Sorbonne (ABD) Applied Linguistics 1974; Attnd Columbia Univ Schl Admin, Ed, Law; *cr:* Cntrl Ct Univ Fr TA 1970-72; Yale Univ TA Corrective Phonetics, Asst to Dir of Lang Lab 1970-72; Univ of Paris XI Instr 1972-74; Tuddlebury Coll Lecturer in Fr 1974-76; George Schl Head of Lang Dept, Tchr of Fr 1976-; Univ of MI Lecturer in Romance Lang Summer Prgm in France 1990-; *ai:* Coord of Exch Prgms; AATF Phil Chptr; Buck Cty Tchrs Assn; Klingenstein Flwshp 1970; *office:* George Schl Rt 413 Box 4244 Newtown PA 18940

FISCHER, JOHN EDWARD, Art, Drafting & Business Tchr; *b:* Philadelphia, PA; *c:* John F., Paul D., Donald C.; *ed:* Temple Univ (BSEd) Art Ed, (MEd) Art Ed; *cr:* Get Set Day Care Soc Work 1970-76; Schl Dist Phila Art Edctr 1979-83; Emlen Arms Schl Art Edctr, Geriatriac 1983-; Yale Schl Art Edctr, Spec Ed Tchr 1984-; Martin Luther Schl Art Edctr, Spec Ed Tchr 1985-; Allen's La Art Ctr Art Edctr Pre K-8th Grd Tchr 1984; Father Judge HS Art Edctr 9-12th Grd Tchr 1986-; Coll Gifted Prgm Art Edctr 4-11th Grd Tchr 1994-, Adm Dir 4-11th Grd Tchr 1994-; Bucks Cty Comm Coll Art Edctr 1-9th Grd Tchr 1994-95, Art Edctr, Adult 1994-95; *ai:* Coach Archery Team; Moderator Chapel Act, Art Club; NAEA; Valley Forge Highland Band 1976-, Pres; Mac Gregor Pipe Band 1996; Temple Univ Tyler Schl of Fine Art; Lib Master Thesis; Hlth Hazards Art Materials; *office:* Father Judge HS 3301 Solly Ave Philadelphia PA 19136*

FISCHER, JUDITH RAMP, Physics Teacher; *b:* Randolph, VT; *c:* Jane; *ed:* Ursinus Coll (BS) Physics 1971; Grad Courses from Penn St, Bloomsburg, Boston Univ, Temple Univ; *cr:* Neshaminy Schl Dist Tchr 1971-; *ai:* AFT 1971-; NSTA 1991-; AAPT 1992-; TRAC Tchr at Princeton Plasma Physics Lab; *office:* Neshaminy H S 2001 Old Lincoln Hwy Langhorne PA 19047

FISCHER, JUDITH (WEBER), Health & Religious Stud Tchr; *b:* Ottoville, OH; *m:* Vernon L.; *c:* Craig, Sheila, Keith, Curt; *ed:* Bowling Green St Univ (BS) Hlth, PE 1972; Univ of Dayton (MA) Theological Stud 1993; OH St Univ Ed; Univ of UT Correspondence Stud; Attnd Vantage Voc Schl; *cr:* Ottoville Local Schl Hlth, PE, Bio Tchr 1972-77; Delphos City Schls Sub Tchr 1977-84; St John HS Rel Stud, Hlth Tchr 1985-; *ai:* Liturgy Team Co-Adv; NHS Adv; Rel Dept Vice-Chprsn; St John Parish 1985-, Eucharistic Minister; *office:* St Johns HS 515 E 2nd St Delphos OH 45833

FISCHER, MARY ALBERT,OP, Learning Center Director; *b:* New York, NY; *ed:* St John's Univ (BA) Rel 1955; Albany St Adv Genetics, Animal Taxonomy 6 Credits; Boston Coll Physics 24 Credits; RCA Inst Electronics 6 Credits; Manhattan Coll Physics 24 Credits; *cr:* St Pancras Schl Elem Ed Tchr 1946-57; St Barbara Schl Elem Ed Tchr 1946-57; St Mary's Schl Elem Ed Tchr 1946-57; Bishop Mc Donnell HS Sci Tchr 1957-65; St Joseph's HS Sci Tchr 1957-65; St Joseph's Coll Sci Tchr 1957-65; Saint Joseph Sanatorium Admin 1965-73; Notre Dame Schl Learning Ctr Dir 1973-; *ai:* Math Cmptr Lab; NCEA; *office:* Notre Dame Schl 25 Mayfair Rd New Hyde Park NY 11040

FISCHER, RAE-ANN, ESL Tchr & Foreign Stu Coord; *b:* Brooklyn, NY; *ed:* Brooklyn Coll (BA) Fr 1972; NY Univ (MA) Tchng ESL 1975; *cr:* Chapter 1 Non-Pub Schl Prgm ESL Tchr 1972-86; F. D. R. HS ESL Tchr & Foreign Stu Coord 1986-; *ai:* Acad Olympics Team Adv; Limited Eng Proficient Stdnts Comm; TESOL & NY St TESOL 1975-; AFT & UFT 1972-; Brooklyn HS Staff Recognition Day Honoree; *office:* Franklin Delano Roosevelt HS 5800 20th Ave Brooklyn NY 11204

FISCHETTE, CAROL M., Health & PE Instr; *b:* Washington, DC; *m:* Raymond C.; *c:* Lisa, Krista, Raymond; *ed:* Onondaga Comm Coll (AAS) Dental Hygiene 1966; Empire St Coll (BS) Exercise, Phys Fitness 1987; BUNY at Brockport (MS) Hlth Ed 1992; *cr:* Clyde-Savannah Central Schl Dental Hygiene Tchr 1967; Dr R T Sweeney DDS Dental Hygienist 1975-; Finger Lakes Comm Coll Hlth, PE Instr 1992-; *ai:* Wellness Consultant Palmyra-Macedon Central Schl; Wellness Dir; Comprehensive Schl Hlth, Wellness Comm Palmyra-Macedon Central Schl; Eta Sigma Gamma 1992-; NYS Fed of Prof Hlth Edctrs 1994-; Intnl Dance & Exercise Assn 1984-; Amer Cancer Soc, Amer Heart Assn 1994-, Bd Mem; Specialty Recognition Mind-Body Integration 1994; Spec Recognition Awd Bd of Ed Palmyra-Macedon Central Schl 1994; *home:* 439 W Main St Palmyra NY 14522*

FISCHMAN, BRUCE, Fourth Grade Teacher; *b:* Wilkes-Barre, PA; *m:* Fredda Schneer; *ed:* West Chester Univ (BS) Elem Ed 1973; Wilkes Coll (MS) Elem Ed 1980; Lehigh Univ (EDD) Rdng 1988; Whole Lang Consultant, Trainer 1989-95; Learning Styles Bernice Mc Carthy Trainer 1989-94; Natl Writing Project Fellow West Chester Univ 1984; Multiple Ingelligences Presenter 1995-; *cr:* Upper Perkiomen Schl Dist 1st Grd, Third Grd, 4th Grd Tchr, Staff Dev Dir Writing, Rdng Supvr, Rdng Specialist 1973-; *ai:* Staff Dev Performance Assessment Wkshps 1993-; Art as Way of Learning trainer Pilot Prgm Binney & Smith Northampton Comm Coll 1995-; PDK Lehigh Univ 1987-, Pres 1990-91, VP; ASCD 1986-; NEA, PSEA 1973-; Lehigh Univ Alumni Cncl Outstdng Tchr Awd 1992; *office:* Hereford Elem Schl 1043 Gravel Pike Hereford PA 18056*

FISCHMAN, JUDY GOLDSCHMIDT, Basic Skills Teacher; *b:* New York, NY; *m:* Marc Robert; *c:* Aron, Jill, Amy, Lisa; *ed:* Mills Coll of Ed (BS) Ed 1969; *cr:* Prof Childrens Schl 3rd Grd Tchr 1968-69; Mc Kinley St 2nd & 3rd Grd Basic Skills Tchr 1969-94; Barringer HS G Tchr 1994-; *ai:* AFT, NTU 1969-; Temple Nertamid VP Prgm M

FISCO, MARY SUSAN, Biology & Chemistry Teacher; *b:* Ne *m:* Ricardo A.; *c:* Richard, Danielle, Erick; *ed:* Montclair St Co 1977; Attnd Rutgers Univ; *cr:* Colonia HS Tchr 1978-81; John F HS Tchr 1983-89; Woodbridge HS Tchr, Stu Dir 1990-; *ai:* Ad Stu Cncl; Stu Dir; AFT, Sci Supvr 1978-; NJEA 1984-; G,T P Sec; Elem Schl PTO 1986-, Sec; Woodbridge HS PTO; *home:* Dr Edison NJ 08820

FISH, DIANA STAAB, English Second Lang Tchr; *b:* Oil Ci Harry M.; *c:* Ben; *ed:* VILLA Maria Coll (BS) Elem Ed 1969; Univ (MA) Child Drama 1979; RI Coll Eng as a Second Lang En 1989; *cr:* Erie Parochial Schls Elem Tchr 1965-69; Cranston Elem Tchr 1969-80; NM Arts Div Artists in Schls Coord 1980- Brown Ind Private Schl Elem Tchr 1983-87; Providence Coll A Drama-in-Ed 1990-93; Robert F. Kennedy Schl 3-6 Grd ESL T *ai:* Drama Coach; Chorale Dir; Safety Patrol Adv; Cultural A After-Schl Clubs, LIFT Team Head Tchr; Schl Improveme Remedial Rdng Tchr; Providence Tchrs Union, AFT 1988-; Edu Assn 1984-; Artists-in-Schls 1984-, Advy Cncl; Arts-in-Ed Treas, Sec; Greater Camp Neighborhood Assn 1990-, Sec; Mu Arts Grant; Providence First-Night Vol Cert of Recognition 5 Y Robert F. Kennedy Elem Schl 195 Nelson St Providence RI 029

FISH, JAMES E., Mathematics Teacher; *b:* Buffalo, NY; *m:* Forrest; *c:* Lauren, Katherine, Kristen, James Jr.; *ed:* SUNY Coll (BS) Scndry Math Ed 1984, (MS) Scndry Math Ed 1995; *cr:* Wil Cntrl Schls Math Tchr 1987-93; John F. Kennedy HS Math Tchr Natl Jr Honor Soc Adv; Acad Eligibility, Tech, Values Com NYSUT 1987-; TAC Tchrs Assn 1993-; Church Parish Cncl 1994- Umpire 1987-; *office:* John F Kennedy HS 305 Cayuga Cheektowaga NY 14227

FISH, JAMES LEON, Retired Voc Power Equip Tchr; *b:* Ashlan Judith Mc Farland; *c:* James Grant, Jennifer Natalie; *ed:* OH St Ag 1961; 84 Qtr Hrs Indstrl Arts Ed; 14 Qtr Hrs Voc Ag Ed; Driver Ed; Numerous CEU's; *cr:* Ashland City Schls Woodwor 1964-68, Metals & Machine Shop Instr 1968-74; Ashland Co We JVS Power Equipment Instr 1974-95; *ai:* FFA Adv; OH Ed As Ashland Voc Tchrs 1974-, Pres; Ashland Co Yesteryear Machi 1991-, Sec; *home:* 1557 County Road 995 Ashland OH 44805

FISH, JAN S., English Teacher; *b:* Akron, OH; *c:* Matt, Laure *ed:* OH Univ (BED) Eng 1969; Antioch (MED) Ed 1973; 30 Ad St Univ; *cr:* Mt Holly Elem Schl 5th Grd Tchr 1969-70; Melr 7th-9th Grd Rdng Tchr 1970-73; Phoenix-Carl Hayden HS 9th- Rdng Tchr 1974-70; Franklin Univ Instr 1980-89; Columbus St C Instr 1980-90; TWHS 9th-12th Grd Eng Tchr 1990-; *ai:* SADD Yrbk Adv; NEA 1990-.

FISH, PETER JAMES, Technology Education Teacher; *b:* Alb *m:* Donna Vache; *c:* Scott, Suzanne, Megan; *ed:* Hudson Vly C (AS) Construction 1963; Murray St Univ (BS) Ind Arts & Tech SUNY Coll of Tech (MS) Voc & Tech Ed 1980; SUNY at Alban Hrs Ed; Russel Sage Coll 30 Credit Hrs Ed; *cr:* Catskill Jr Industrial Arts Tchr 1967-74; Guilderland HS Industrial A 1974-81; Schoharie Jr Sr High Industrial Arts Tchr 1981-85; B MS Tech Ed Tchr 1985-; *ai:* Restructuring Task Force; NEA 1967 Dist Ind Arts Assn 1970-, Pres & Treas, 3 Svc Awds; NYS Ind 1973-, Del & Chair Curr Comm, Regnl Tchr of the Yr; Bethleh League 1980-, Coach; Bethlehem Babe Ruth 1983-, Coach; Po Ftbl 1983-, Coach; Dir Yth Conservation Corp Albany Cty; Work for NYS Div for Yth; *office:* Bethlehem Central MS 332 Kenw Delmar NY 12054

FISH, RUTH SIEDLE, Music Instructor; *b:* Pittsburgh, PA; *c:* D., Jessica R., Zachary W.; *ed:* Duquesne Univ (BSME) Voice 1976; Carnegie Mellon Univ (MFA) Conducting & Voice 1989 Credits; *cr:* St Francis of Assisi Parish Minister of Music & Cho Carnegie Mellon Dept of Music Concert Mgr & Asst Conductor Ensembles 1989-91; Oakland Cath HS Music Fac, Vocal & Ins Tchr 1991-; *ai:* Campus Ministry Dir; MENC 1991-; PMEA 199 Oakland Catholic HS 144 N Craig St Pittsburgh PA 15213

FISHBAUGH, JOYCE A., High School Mathematics Tchr; *b:* Sid *m:* David W.; *c:* Brian D.; *ed:* Miami Univ (BS) Math Ed 1979; Univ (MED) Math Ed 1984; *cr:* Piqua City Schls Math Tchr 1 NEA, OEA, OCTM 1979-; Kent St Univ Chptr of Sigma Xi Out Tchr of Math 1992; *office:* Piqua HS Indian Trl Piqua OH 45356

FISHER, BETTE L. HINMAN, English Teacher; *b:* Muscatin Fred C.; *c:* Elizabeth Saxby, Katherine, Derick; *ed:* OH Univ (BS Ed 1986; Marshall Univ (MA) Eng 1992; K-12 Gifted; *cr:* St Jos HS Tchr 1986-88; Rock Hill HS Eng Tchr 1988-; *ai:* Yrbk Adv NEA, OEA & OCTELA 1988-; Democracy for Ed 1989-; Friends 1985-; IA Alumni Assn 1970-; OH Univ Alumni Assn 1986-; Mars Alumni Assn 1992-; Blake Confederate Schlsp; *office:* Rock Hill Cty Rd 26 Ironton OH 45638*

FISHER, BONNIE BOYLE, Art Department Head; *b:* Chelsea Joseph W., Patrick K.; *ed:* Kutztown Univ (BS) Art Ed 1967, (M Ed 1971; Attnd East Stroudsburg Univ, IN Univ; *cr:* Pocono Mt Art Tchr 1967-73; Pocono Mt Sr HS Art Tchr 1973-95, Art D 1995-; *ai:* PMEA; PSEA; NEA; NAEA; Mid Sts Evaluating Tea Hazleton Art League Sherwin Williams Awd; *office:* Pocono Mo HS PO Box 200 School Rd Swiftwater PA 18703

FISHER, CAROL BEST, Retired Second Grade Teacher; *b:* Willi PA; *m:* Orlan J.; *c:* Orlan J. II; *ed:* Edinboro St Coll (BS) Art Lycoming Coll & Penn St Elem Ed Cert 1968; *cr:* Montoursville Elem Art Instr 1962-66; Loyalsock Vly Elem Schl Second C 1966-93; *ai:* Art Ed Consultant 3 Yrs; 10 Stu Tchrs Art & Elem Ed New Tchrs; Elem Ed Consultant; MAEA 1962-; NEA, PSEA 19 Life Time Mem; Bald Eagle Art League 1962-64; Nom Tchr of *home:* HC 31 Box 185 Williamsport PA 17701

FISHER, DANIEL CRAIG, English Teacher; *b:* Binghamton, Kristin Bradshaw; *ed:* Univ of MD at Coll Park (BA) Eng 1990; T Univ (MA) Tchng 1993; *cr:* Calvert HS Eng Tchr 1993-; *ai:* Writing Group Spon; NHS Selection Comm; SAT Preparatio *office:* Calvert HS 600 Dares Beach Rd Prince Frederick MD 206

FISHER, DENNIS JOSEPH, Theology Teacher; *b:* Philadelphia Maryanne Shannon; *c:* Maureen, Megan, Daniel; *ed:* St Charles S (BA) Philosophy, Theology 1971, (MA) Philosophy, Theolog Villanova Univ (MA) Ed Admin 1980; Temple Univ (ABD) Urban Boston Coll Post Grad Stud Rel Ed 1996; *cr:* Msgr Bonner HS 1973-79; Roman Cath HS Dept Chair, Rel Tchr 1979-85; Arch C Dept Chair, Asst Prin, Tchr 1985-; St Josephs Univ Adj Prof, Tchr 1982-; *ai:* Lasallian Yth Svc Club; Boys Bsktbl Team M NCEA, NACST 1973-; St Denis Church 1987-, Parish Fin Coord, Ed; St Josephs Univ Tchr Excl Awd 1992; Connelley Fnd Grant Coll Univ 1996; *office:* Archbishop Carroll HS 211 Matsonford R PA 19087*

FISHER, DIANE SCHAEFFER, Spanish Teacher; *b:* Dayton, O Hart Fisher Jr.; *c:* T. Hart III, Robert; *ed:* Univ od Dayton (BA) Sp

Univ (MED) Spec Ed 1984; Addl 8 Hrs Univ of Cincinnati, 12 of MN, 4 Hrs Calvin Coll; *cr:* Jefferson HS Spec Ed Tutor Montgomery Cty Joint Voc Schl Spec Ed Tutor, Tchr 1981-84; rg HS Span Tchr 1986-; *ai:* AFS Intercultural Exch Prgm AA Adv an Club Jr Achvmt Adv 1986-; Earth Club, Sr Class Adv 1994-; Lang Assn; Portuguese, Span Tchrs Assn; Outstdng Tchr Awd 2 hvmt Awd; *office:* Miamisburg Sr HS 1860 Belvo Rd Miamisburg 2*

DONNA LYNN, Scndry Eng Tchr & Yrbk Adv; *b:* Towson, MI St Univ (BA) Eng 1987; Oakland Univ (MA) Eng 1989; 27 eyond MA; *cr:* Towson Cath HS Eng Tchr & Newspaper Adv Cath HS of Baltimore Eng Tchr 1991-, Yrbk Adv 1992-; *ai:* Yrbk Class Adv; Ctr Stage Coord; Mentor Tchr 1995-96; Frosh Retreat :; NCTE 1989-; CSPA Yrbk Adv 1992-; Yrbk Awds 1993-95; Scholastic Press Assn.

GORDON HARL,II, Instrumental Music Director; *b:* San A; *m:* Penny R. Leonard; *c:* William Harl, Elisabeth Claire; *ed:* o Univ (BME) Music Ed 1984; 6 Credits Towards Masters on, Prin Cert; *cr:* Ocean Cty Windjammers Jr Drum, Bugle Corps n Coord 1978-80; Pompton Lakes Schl Dist Co-Band Dir 1985; Meml HS Asst Band Dir 1985-86; Fair Lawn HS Instrumental r 1986-; *ai:* Marching, Jazz Bands, Wind Ensemble, Schl Musical Dir; Prins, Vice Prins Advy; Former Jr Prom Adv, Discipline Code Comm; MENC 1980-; NEA, NJEA, NJ Music Edctrs Assn, Music Bergen Cty Inc 1985-; Prince of Peace Luth Church 1994-, Cncl ce: Fair Lawn HS 14-00 Berdan Ave Fair Lawn NJ 07410*

HERSHA S., Retired History Teacher; *b:* Oklahoma City, OK; A. Moren; *ed:* Univ of Chicago (AB) Ancient Near Eastern Stud rvard Grad Schl of Ed (MAT) Soc Stud 1967, (CAS) Soc Stud DD) His of Ed 1980; *cr:* Beverly HS Soc Stud Tchr 1961-66; ade Schl Soc Stud Tchr 1961-66; Ottoson Jr HS Soc Stud Tchr Bigelow Jr HS Eng, Soc Stud Tchr 1970-84; Newton South HS Stud Tchr 1984-; *ai:* Debate Team; MA Tchrs Assn 1965-; NEA ambridge Political Work; Boston Edison Fellowship; Sabbatical Newton 1990-91; *home:* 2130 Massachusetts Ave Apt 3C ge MA 02140

HOWARD B., AP Bio, Anatomy, Physio Tchr; *b:* Oceanside, Caren Benstock; *c:* Justin, Jessica; *ed:* Univ of Bridgeport (BA) d, Bio 1970, (MS) Scndry Ed, Bio 1973; SUNY at Binghamton l Courses, Cmptr Ed; *cr:* Woodland Jr HS Life & Phys Sci Tchr West Jr HS Bio & Phys Sci Tchr 1974085; Binghamton HS Bio 5-; *ai:* Odyssey of the Mind Coach; NHS Adv, Knowledge Master NY St Sci Olympiad Coach; Marine Bio Enrichment Instr; ton Univ Adjunct Fac; Cooperating Tchr; HS Challenge Coach; Intervention Team; NEA 1974-; Co-Ed Binghamton Tchrs Assn er 1987; Tchr the Yr Binghamton City Schl Dist 1987; Mensa Awd ice 1983; Binghamton Univ Inst Biosafety Comm Mem; Kopernik Regnl Sci Center Planning Grant Advisory Comm; Tech Tchr of Yr Sel Comm; *office:* Binghamton HS 31 Main St ton NY 13905

JACK, Teacher & Coach; *b:* Rockville Center, NY; *m:* Kathleen : Jack, Lance; *ed:* St Univ at Cortland (BS) PE 1971, (MS) PE st Grad Hrs Admin; *cr:* Newark HS Var Ftbl Coach 1971-95, Head tling Coach 1971-; Newark Cntrl Schl PE Tchr 1971-; Newark Ath -86; *ai:* Coaching; FL East Coaches Assn 1971-, League Chm, V Coach of the Yr 1981, 1993 & 1994; NYSTA 1971-; Section V Yr 1980-81, 1992-94; NY St Awd; 20 Yrs Head Wrestling Coach al Meet Victories, 30 Team Championships, 31 Sectional ns; *office:* Newark HS 625 Pierson Ave Newark NY 14513

JAMES CLYDE, Math Teacher; *b:* Lima, OH; *m:* Karol A. *c:* Debra Finn, Barbara Mc Crina, Teresa Howell, James Jr.; *ed:* ll (AA) Lbrl Arts 1973; OH St Univ (BS) Elem Ed 1980; Post-Grad yles Bowling Green St Univ, Math in the Minds Eye Portland St he Inland Sea; *cr:* Shawnee Elmwood Elem Schl 4th Grd Tchr Shawnee Maplewood Elem Schl 5th Grd Tchr 1981-93; Shawnee Grd Math, Soc Stud Tchr 1993-94, 7th-8th Grd Math Tchr 1994-; h MS Girls Sftbl 1993-, 5th Grd Quiz Bowl 1988-93; SEA 1980-, p; OEA, NEA 1980-; WSU Cncl Tchrs Math 1990-; *office:* MS 3235 Zurmehly Rd Lima OH 45806

JAMES T., Biology Teacher; *b:* Greenville, NC; *m:* Janet *c:* Jethro, Jadyn; *ed:* Univ of Redlands (BA) Pol Sci 1966; Univ MA) Intnl Relations 1971; Boise St Univ (BS) Bio 1983; *cr:* Peace ng Tchr 1966-67; US Army Infantry Vientam 1967-69; US Coast adio USCGC Buttonwood 1976-80; Dodds England, Germany Bio 85-; *ai:* Expedition Ldr Spon; Duke of Edinburgh Prgm; NEA oyal Yachting Assn 1987-, Coastal Skipper Awd; *office:* Mannheim S Unit 29939 APO AE 09086

JEFFERY K., Fifth Grade Teacher; *b:* Bedford, PA; *m:* ; *c:* Suzanna, Brian, Rebecca, Jeannette; *ed:* IN Univ of PA Hlth, PE 1976, (BSEd) Hlth, PE 1976; *cr:* Chestnut Ridge MS 5th r 1983-94, Hlth, PE Tchr 1994-95, 5th Grd Tchr; *ai:* CEAI 1993-; hestnut Ridge MS Rd 1 Fishertown PA 15539

JUDITH WRIGHT, First Grade Teacher; *b:* Bowling Green, Thomas E.; *c:* Thomas J., Katherine, Meredith, Timothy; *ed:* Green St Univ (BSEd) Elem Ed 1972; Addl Credit Hrs Ashland oledo Univ; *cr:* Hilfiker Elem Schl Lib Coord 1972-85, 1-6 Grd 72-; *ai:* NEA, OEA 1972-; GTA 1972-, Sec; Delta Kappa Gamma Gibsonburg HS Music Boosters 1991-, Sec; Zion Luth Church Martha Holden Jennings Scholar 1985; *office:* James J Hilfinker hl Harrison St Gibsonburg OH 43431

KATHERINE A., Eng, History & Theater Teacher; *b:* Massillon, Kent St Univ (BS) Ed, Eng, His, Govt 1971; Univ of Akron (MFA) Arts Mngmt 1991; *cr:* Alliance Comm Hosp Dir Vol Svc, Risk Pub Rel 1973-76; KATFISH Productions of Northeast OH Inc , Exec Artistic Dir 1995-; Highland HS Tchr 1976-; *ai:* Sr Class, n, Close-up Adv; Theater Dir; OH Theater Assn, OH Comm 1995-; Stark Cty Women's Hall of Fame; OTA Encore Awd; OH ges Awd; *office:* Highland HS 3880 Ridge Rd Medina OH 44256*

KIMBERLY A., Business Teacher; *b:* Amsterdam, NY; *m:* Tocci; *ed:* SUNY at Oswego (BS) Voc Tech Ed 1990, (MS) Voc 1991; 6 Hrs Diversified Work Stud Coord 1995; *cr:* Northville hl Bus Tchr 4 Yrs; *ai:* Sr Play Adv 1993; Bus Club Adv 1993-94; Club Adv 1995-; TPIS Comm 1992-; Tech Prep, Work Stud Comm Adult Ed Cmptr Trng 1995-; In House Cmptr Trng 1994-; VTEA *office:* Northville Central Schl Third St Northville NY 12134*

KIMBERLY ANN, Mathematics Teacher; *b:* Frederick, MD; *ed:* oll (BA) Math 1992; Shippensburg Univ Math; *cr:* Lingamore HS chr 1993-; *ai:* Pom Pon Coach; NEA 1992-; Pi Mu Epsilon; *office:* re HS 12013 Old Annapolis Rd Frederick MD 21701

LINDA DIANE, English Teacher; *b:* Pittsburgh, PA; *c:* Jason, *ed:* CA Univ of PA (BS) Eng, Ed 1972, (MS) Rdng Specialist; BA Prgm Univ of Pittsburgh; *cr:* Bethel Park Schl Dist Eng Tchr, ecialist 1979-89; Allegheny Comm Coll Instr Part-Time 1982-94; Park Schl Dist Pub Relations Dir 1989-92, Eng Tchr 1992-; *ai:* aper Spon; AFT 1979-; St Benedict Cath Church 1977-, Pub Relations Consultant; PA Schl Bd Assn Publication Awds; *office:* Bethel Park Sr HS 309 Church Rd Bethel Park PA 15102

FISHER, MARY LOU POLLICK, Sixth Grade Teacher; *b:* Philadelphia, PA; *m:* Keith F.; *ed:* St Joseph Coll (BS) Elem Ed 1971; Villanova Univ (MA) Elem Ed 1974; *cr:* St Ladislaus Schl Second Grd Tchr 1968-72, 1975-78, Fourth Grd Tchr 1972-75; St Dominic Schl First Grd Tchr 1978-84, Third Grd Tchr 1984-90, Sixth Grd Tchr 1990-; *ai:* 6th-8th Grd Math Coord; NCEA; *office:* St Dominic Schl 8510 Frankford Ave Philadelphia PA 19136

FISHER, MICHAEL L., Spanish Teacher; *b:* Mexico City, Mexico; *ed:* Escuela Normal Querelana (BA) Ed 1970; Universidad De Mexico (MS) Ed 1975; Boston Schl of Modern Lang; *cr:* Inst Hidelguense Eng Tchr & Prin 1968-84; St Marys HS Span Tchr 1984-90; Archbishop Molloy HS Span Tchr 1990-; *ai:* Soccer Moderator; Parents & Stu Activity Comm; Best Stu in Mexico 1975; Fellowship Govt of Japan 1976; *office:* Archbishop Molloy HS 83-53 Manton St Briarwood NY 11435*

FISHER, NATALIE ANN, 8th Grade Mathematics Teacher; *b:* West Reading, PA; *ed:* Alvernia Coll (BS) Math, Scndry Ed 1987; Immaculata Coll (MA) Educl Ldrshp 1995; Pursuing Prin Cert; *cr:* Conrad Weiser Area Schl Dist Math Tchr 1988-; *ai:* Jr HS Stu Cncl Adv; MATHCOUNTS Coach; Marching Band Staff; CWEA, PSEA, NEA 1988-; Ringgold Band 1986-, Trombonist, Trustee; AF of M 1986-, Musician; PTO Jr HS Tchr of Yr Awd 1991-92, 1994-95; *office:* Conrad Weiser Area Schl Dist 347 E Penn Ave Robesonia PA 19551*

FISHER, NELLIE R., Sixth Grade Teacher; *b:* Jacksonville, FL; *m:* Charles E.; *c:* Anthony O.; *ed:* Onondaga Comm (AA) Hum 1980; Syracuse Univ (BA) Early Chldhd Dev 1982, (MS) Elem Ed 1984; *cr:* Roosevelt Jr HS Tchr Asst 1967-79; Gilfed Ctr Logic 1981-83; Danforth Elem Schl 6th Grd Tchr 1983-; *ai:* Danforth Extended Day Prgm Dance Tchr 10 Yrs; *office:* Danforth Elem Schl 309 W Brighton Ave Syracuse NY 13205

FISHER, PATRICIA JAYNE (NORTON), Fourth Grade Teacher; *b:* Findlay, OH; *m:* Scott Lee; *c:* Gregory Scott, Christopher David, Jonathan Paul; *ed:* Kent St Univ (BS) Spec, Elem Ed 1972; Tchng Certs: K-12 Spec Ed Dev Handicapped, Prof K-12 Spec Ed Multiple Dev Handicapped, Provisional 1-8 Elem Ed, K-12 Validated TESOL, Temporary Sp Ed LDIBD; *cr:* Letchworth Village Recreation Therapist Residential Inst 1971; Nueva Granada Escuela Schl Sub Tchr 1972; LaBrae Local SchlsSp Ed Primary, Intermediate DH, Home Inst 1973-76; Louisville City Schls Spec Ed Primary 1976-79; Northeastern Local Schls LD Tutor 1979-80; Defiance City Schls Spec Ed, Elem Ed Tchr 1980-; *ai:* Cmptr, Soc Stud, Sci, Math Curr Comms; NEA, OEA, DCEA 1985-; ARC 1983-, Pres; NW Nine Mentorship 1991-, Mentor, Mentor Trainer; Avenues 1980-; Muscular Dystrophy 1983-; Down Syndrome Congress 1980-; Chrstn Home Ed Org 1985-; Span Schlsp Team 1964; Tchr Grant PROP Dev Prescribed Rdng Operative Prgm 1978; Nom Valley Forge Freedom Fnd 1975; Outstdng Tchr of Exceptional Children 1978-87; Nom for Pres Awd Sci, Math Tchng 1991-; Nom Ashland Achvmt Awd 1996; *office:* Spencer Elem Schl 140 E Broadway Ave Defiance OH 43512*

FISHER, RAYMOND ROBERT, Remedial Mathematics Teacher; *b:* Wooster, OH; *ed:* Kent St Univ (BSEd) Math 1970, (MAEd) Scndry Ed, Math 1975; Addl 16 Hrs Elem Math, Lead To Math Diagnostic Cert 1975-76; 16 Addl Univ of Akron Cmptr Ed, Learning Styles; *cr:* Lehman HS Math Tchr 1970-76; Somers Jr HS Math Tchr 1976-89; Mc Kinley HS Math, Prescriptive Math Tchr 1989-95; Hartford MS Math Prescriptive Tchr 1995; Mc Kinley HS Math Prescriptive Tchr 1996; *ai:* NEA, OEA 1970-; Canton Prof Tchrs Assn 1970-, Former Treas 3 Yrs; Cmptr Ed Grant; *office:* Mc Kinley Sr HS 2323 17th St NW Canton OH 44708

FISHER, ROBERT R., Fourth Grade Teacher; *b:* Binghamton, NY; *ed:* Cedarville Coll (BME) Music Ed 1976; Elem Cert Ed Marywood Coll 1979; 3 Hrs Univ of Scranton; 31 Hrs Marywood Coll; 9 Hrs Wilkes Univ; 3 Hrs Penn St; 10 In-Svc Credits; *cr:* Elk Lake Schl Dist Grds 7-12 Spell Tchr, Jr, Sr Chorus Dir 1976-77; Summit Bapt Acad Grds 5-8 Math & Sci Tchr, Grds K-8 Music Tchr 1979-81; Harford Elem Schl Grds 4-6 Rdng Tchr, 4th Grd Sci Tchr 1983-91; Mt View Elem Schl 4th Grd Math, Sci, Rdng Tchr 1991-; *ai:* Pianist, Directing Church Music; Cooperating Tchr; PSEA, NEA 1988-; Harford Historical Soc; *office:* Mountain View Elem Schl RR 1 Box 339 Kingsley PA 18826*

FISHER, ROBERT W., Mathematics Teacher; *b:* Philadelphia, PA; *m:* Bridget DelBuono; *c:* Christine M., Katherine P., Michael R.; *ed:* LaSalle Coll (BA) His 1974; Temple Univ (MA) Therapeutic Recreation 1983; Math Recertification Prgm 1986-89; *cr:* Philadelphia Dept of Recreation Part-time Asst Rec Ldr 1977-; Girard Coll Houseparent 1978-85, Tchr 1984-; *ai:* Stu Cncl Adv; AFT 1985-, Local Unit VP; NCTM 1988-; Jeopardy Champion 1995; *office:* Girard Coll HS 2101 S College Ave Philadelphia PA 19121

FISHER, ROBIN DUBOSQUE, Third & Fourth Grade Teacher; *b:* Woodbury, NJ; *m:* Timothy Hyland; *c:* Jason, Michael; *ed:* Columbia Union Coll (BS) Elem Ed 1976; East Stroudsburg Univ (MED) Rdng, Ed 1994; Post-Grad Stud Early Chldhd Ed; *cr:* John Nevins Andrews Schl Tchr 1976-78; Sussex Cty Day Care Ctr Tchr, Aide 1980-82; Hackettstown Comm Hosp Dir Day Care Ctr 1982-87; Tranquility Adventist Schl Tchr 1987-; *ai:* Yrbk Spon, Adv; Chamber Commerce 1984-87; Zappara Excl Tchr Awd 1990; *home:* PO Box 125 Greendell NJ 07839

FISHER, ROBIN (FRY), Physics & Mathematics Teacher; *b:* Greenville, PA; *m:* Thomas A.; *ed:* Grove City Coll (BS) Industrial Eng 1987, (BS) Scndy Ed Physics, Math 1989; *cr:* Greenville Area HS Tchr 6 Yrs; *ai:* Var HS Girls Bsktball Coach, Prin Advy Comm; Mentor Tchr; NEA, PSEA 1990-; 1992 Greenville Yrbk Dedication Awd; *office:* Greenville Area HS 9 Donation Rd Greenville PA 16125*

FISHER, SCOTT J., Sixth Grade Teacher; *b:* Lewisburg, PA; *m:* Elizabeth Anderson; *c:* Benjamin, William; *ed:* PA St Univ (BS) Elem Ed 1982; *cr:* Mt Morris First Bapt Church Chrstn Ed & Yth Dir 1982-87; Mountain View Elem Schl 6th Grd Tchr 1988-; *ai:* Lang Arts, Sci Curr Comms; Sci Fair Coord; Inservice Cncl; CESTA 1991-.

FISHER, SHEILA BRENNAN, Life Science Instructor; *b:* Attleboro, MA; *m:* Mark C.; *c:* Sean, Rebecca, Catherine, Margaret, Carolyn; *ed:* Emmanuel Coll (BA) Math, Ed 1970; Bridgewater St Coll (MAT) Phys Scis 1993; Pre-Doctoral Prgm Physics Ed Clark Univ; Physics Grad Work NSF Univ of MA at Dartmouth; 21 Credits Scis, Admin RIC; *cr:* South Attleboro Jr HS Math, Sci Tchr 1970-73; Cranston Schl Dept Itinerant Sci Tchrn, Consultant 1973-75; Norton HS Adult Ed Schl Tchr, Dir 1987-89; Bishop Feehan HS Chm, Tchr 1989-93; Newbury Coll Anatomy, Physiology Tchr, North Attleburg Tchr; Fischer Coll Instr; *ai:* Sr Class Adv; Sci Fair Coord; NSTA; MAST; NACT; N. A. Jr HS Prin Advy Bd, Schlsp Fnd; Girl Scouts of Amer; St Mark's Church Bd; Tapestry Winner, Tandy Tchr of Yr 1991; NSF Grants 1991-93; Wright Ctr Conf for Space Engineering 1993; Nom Tchr of Yr 1992-94; Girl Scouts of Amer Woman of Distinction 1992; Tchr of Yr 1994; Eductr of Yr 1994; *office:* North Attleburg Jr HS 43 S Wash Str North Attleburg MA 02763*

FISHER, SHERRI WILLIAMS, Educational Specialist; *b:* Mt Holly, NJ; *m:* Isaac A. Jr.; *c:* Meg L., Iain A.; *ed:* Amer Intnl Coll (BA) His, Eng 1980, (MED) Scndry 1982; Kildonan Schl Orton Gillingham Trained; *cr:* Jemicy Schl Tchr 1986-92; Hebron Acad Prgm Dir 1992-93; Ruxton Cntry Schl Prgm Dir 1993-94; Jemicy Schl Camp Dir 1994-; S. Fisher & Assocs Educl Consultant, Owner, Operator 1994-; *ai:* Church Choir; Child, Family IEP Advocate; Orton Dyslexia Soc 1984-; Learning Disability Assn 1992-; 9th Grd Transition Stud Jemicy Schl Grads 1991.*

FISHER, THOMAS JAY, Amer His & Behavioral Sci Tchr; *b:* Philadelphia, PA; *ed:* Temple Univ (BA) His 1967, (MA) Amer His 1968; 42 Addl Credits; Scndry Prin Cert; *cr:* Cheltenham HS Tchr 1968-; *ai:* Yrbk, Stu Ticket Spon; Mock Trial Adv; Pub Address Announcer Supvr; Cheltenham Ed Assn, PSEA, NEA, 1968-; Phi Delta Kappa 1978-; Phi Alpha Theta 1966-; PA Historical Soc 1990-; CO Historical Soc 1974-; Friends of Laurel Hill Cem 1988-; Gravestone Stud Assn 1993-; Friends of Mt Auburn Cem 1995-; Natl Trust for Historic Preservation 1996-; *office:* Cheltenham HS Rices Mill Rd Carlton Ave Wyncote PA 19095

FISHER, TIMOTHY HYLAND, 5th-8th Grade Teacher; *b:* Dover, NJ; *m:* Robin Du Bosque; *c:* Jason, Michael; *ed:* Columbia Union Coll (BS) Elem Ed 1978; East Stroudsburg Univ (MA) His 1994; *cr:* Tranquility Adventist Schl Tchr, Vice Prin 1978-; *ai:* Ski Spon; Model A Ford Club 1986-, Pres, VP; Antique Truck Club of Amer 1980-, VP, Sec; *home:* PO Box 125 Greendell NJ 07839

FISHER, UMBRENDA HERRINGTON, Mathematics Teacher; *b:* Philadelphia, PA; *m:* Jerral Andrew; *ed:* OH Wesleyan Univ (BA) Elem Ed 1974; Prof Cert Post Grad Work Bowie St Univ; 1989 Grad of MD Governors Acad for Math, Sci, Tech; *cr:* laurel Elem Schl 3-6 Grd Tchr 1974-81; Bond Mill Elem Schl 4-5 Grd Math Tchr 1981-; Governor's Acad PPrgm Coord 1990-; *ai:* St Jude's Childrens Hosp Math-A-Thon Coord; Stu Tchng Supvr; Contact Person Math Coord; 24 Challenge Math Prgm Coord; NEA, PGCEA 1974-; NCTM, MCTM 1989-; Homeowner Assn 1990-, VP, Sec, Treas; Tutor of Stdnts in Comm; St Marks UMC; Presidential Awd Finalists for Math 1992; Outstdng Edctrs Awd 1993; Tchr of Yr Finalist; PTA Tchr of Yr; *office:* Bond Mill Elem Schl 16001 Sherwood Ave Laurel MD 20707*

FISHER, VIVIAN M. VILORIA, Spanish Teacher; *b:* Santo Domingo, Dominican Repub; *m:* Stuart; *c:* Donna DiStefano, Christian DiStefano, Marc DiStefano, Daniel, Stefanie; *ed:* Hunter Coll (BA) Eng 1969; SUNY at Stony Brook (MALS) Eng 1973; Enrolled Long Island Univ Schl Admin; Natl Endowment Hum Flwshp; Span Lit; *cr:* Selden Jr HS Eng Tchr 1969-73; Dawnwood Jr HS Eng, Span Tchr 1980-83; Centereach HS Span Tchr 1983-90; Ward Melville HS Span Tchr 1990-; Suffolk Comm Coll Span Tchr, Adj 1995-; *ai:* Adv Span Club, Span Honor Soc; Amer Assn Span, Portuguese 1993-; Forsythe Meadow Homeowners 1987-, Pres; Walk for Beauty Fund 1993-, Exec Bd; *office:* Ward Melville High School 380 Old Town Rd East Setauket NY 11733*

FISHMAN, BONNIE CORRINE, English Teacher; *b:* Brooklyn, NY; *m:* Stuart M.; *c:* Matthew S., Robert H.; *ed:* St Univ of NY at Buffalo (BA) Scndry Ed, Eng 1968; Hofstra Univ (MA) Scndry Ed, Eng 1972; 45 Addl Post Grad Credits; *cr:* Herricks MS Eng Tchr 1968-72; Jericho HS Writing Tchr 1986-89, Eng Tchr 1989-; *ai:* 1998 Class Adv; NCTE 1968-; NY St United Tchrs, AFT 1989-; Jericho Parent Stu Tchr Org 1986-; Young Mens, Womens Hebrew Org 1975-; Holocaust Mem Museum Mem 1994-; Spec Ed PTA 1978-; *office:* Jericho Sr HS 99 Cedar Swamp Rd Jericho NY 11753

FISHWICK, JOHN JOSEPH, Advanced Life Science Teacher; *b:* Brooklyn, NY; *m:* Susan Morley; *c:* John Jr., Ann Marie; *ed:* Saint Johns Univ (BS) Scndry Ed & Sci 1969, (MS) Ed & Sci 1973; Brooklyn Coll Natl Sci Fnd Cert 1975; Post Grad Stud in Anatomy, Physiology, Botany & Oceanography at Farmingdale Univ; *cr:* Jr HS #44 Bronx Sci Tchr 1969-70; Mount Arlington Schl Sci Tchr 1970-71; Jr HS 294 Brooklyn Sci Tchr 1971-87; Jr HS 226 Queens Advanced Life Sci Tchr 1987-; *ai:* Track Coach & Adv; Sci Fair Coord; Sci Curr Adv to Schl; Sci Coord; Mentor Tchr Intern Advy; Nassau Cty Track & Field Ofcl; Natl Sci Tchrs 1972-; Knights of Columbus 1981-, Recorder, Youth Act Dir, Family of Yr Awd, Track Meets Dir, Knight of Month Awd; Natl Sci Fed Grant for Physics at Brooklyn Coll; *office:* JHS 226 Virgil I Grissom 121-10 Rockaway Blvd South Ozone Par NY 11420*

FISK, FRANK EDWARD, Retired Teacher; *b:* Danville, PA; *m:* Mary Elizabeth Moyer; *c:* Douglas; *ed:* Bloomsburg SC (BS) Sci; Bloomsburg Univ Masters Equivalent; Attnd Bucknell Univ, Mansfield Univ, Thiel Coll; *cr:* Millville HS Tchr 1960-93; *ai:* PSEA; NEA; PSER.

FISK, STEPHANIE LAUREN, Var Girls Bsktbl & Sftbl Coach; *b:* Westfield, MA; *ed:* Bay Path Jr Coll (AS) Exec Sec 1984; *cr:* Savage Industries Inc Sales Admin 1984-87; Gateway Regnl Schl Dist Admin Asst to Supt, Var Girls Bsktbl & Sftbl Coach 1988-; *ai:* Var Girls Bsktbl & Sftbl Coach; MA Bsktbl Coaches Assn 1994-; *office:* Gateway Regional HS 12 Littleville Rd Huntington MA 01050

FISK, WALTER C.,JR., 7th Grade Life Science Teacher; *b:* Sayre, PA; *m:* Kathy E. Brennan; *c:* Joshua, Matthew; *ed:* Lycoming Coll (BA) Bio 1981; Elmira Coll (BS) Ed 1983; *cr:* Wyalusing Vly Jr-Sr HS Sci Tchr 1983-; *ai:* Head Wrestling Coach 10 Yrs; Elem Soccer Coach WAYS 2 Yrs; Little League Coach 6 Yrs; PSEA & NEA 1983-; Dist IV Wrestling Coaches Assn 1986-, Pres, Coach of Yr 1993; PA Wrestling Coaches Assn 1986-, Exec Comm; Wyalusing PTO Playground Project, Bldg Mgr; Marine Corps; Boston Marathon; *home:* RR 2 Box 27A Wyalusing PA 18853*

FISKE, MARTHA C., English Teacher; *b:* Albany, NY; *m:* John A.; *c:* Addie, Hal, Jeff; *ed:* Smith Coll (BA) Eng-Cum Laude 1957; Univ of MI (MA) Lit 1960; 30 Grad Credits Northeastern Univ, Framingham St Coll, Regis Coll in MA; *cr:* Hillsdale Schl Tchr 1958-59; The Spence Schl Tchr 1963-64; Wellesley HS Tchr 1970-; *ai:* Many HS Working Groups on Curr, Attendance; MTA, NEA 1971-; Conf Dir 1987; White House Distinguished Tchr 1985; NEH Grant; Eng Journal.

FISLER, MICHELE BEAUREGARD, English Teacher; *b:* Penfield, NY; *m:* Craig H.; *ed:* SUNY at Geneseo (BA) Eng 1989, (MS) Ed 1993; *cr:* Bolivar Cntrl Schl Eng Tchr 1989-93; Williamson Cntrl Schl Eng Tchr 1993-; *ai:* Boys, Girls Modified, JV, Var Cross Cntry; Yrbk Adv; WFA, NYSUT, NCTE 1993-; Rochester Track Club 1992-; Univ of Rochester Excl in HS Tchng Awd; Rosalind Fisher Awd; *office:* Williamson HS PO Box 900 Williamson NY 14589

FISTEK, MICHELLE ANNE, Assoc Prof of Political Sci; *b:* Euclid, OH; *ed:* Juniata Coll (BA) Pol Sci 1978; Miami Univ of OH (MA) Pol Sci 1979, (PHD) Pol Sci 1985; *cr:* Plymouth St Coll Instr Pol Sci 1983-86, Asst Prof Pol Sci 1986-90, Assoc Prof Pol Sci 1990-; *ai:* Acad Advising Comm Chair; Task Force Against Homophobia; Fraternity Adv; Writing Across the Curr Task Force; Acad Orientation Cncl; Amer Pol Sci Assn 1987-; Northeastern Pol Sci Assn 1990; NH Civil Liberties Union 1990-, Chair of Bd; NH Citizen Bee Sterring Comm 1991-; Chptr for Interst Groups in the Northeastern Sts, Political Parties in NH; Dean's Dev Grant 1991; *office:* Plymouth St Coll Social Science Dept Plymouth NH 03264*

FITCH, DIANE PILGRIM, High School English Teacher; *b:* Brooklyn, NY; *ed:* Univ of VA (BA) Eng 1971; SUNY at Birmingham, Elmira Coll 100 Addl Credit Hrs; *cr:* T. Benton Gayle Jr HS Scndry Eng Tchr 1970-71; Jennie F. Snapp Jr HS Scndry Eng Tchr 1971-77; Union-Endicott HS Scndry Eng Tchr 1977-; *ai:* Mock Trial Adv; *office:* Union Endicott HS 1200 E Main St Endicott NY 13760*

FITCHETT, SHARMAN ORAM, Art Teacher; *b:* Syracuse, NY; *m:* William A.; *c:* Shallyn, Ryan; *ed:* SUNY at Oswego (BA) Studio Art 1972, (MA) Ceramics & Drawing 1974; *cr:* CW Baker HS Art Tchr 1972-73; FD Roosevelt HS Art & Tech Tchr 1974-77, Art Tchr 1986-; Bulkeley MS Art

Tchr 1984-85; Haviland MS Art Tchr 1985-86; *ai:* NYSATA; *office:* F D Roosevelt HS S Cross Rd Hyde Park NY 12538

FITLER-SATTAN, SUSAN, English Teacher; *b:* Toms River, NJ; *m:* Scott G. Sattan; *ed:* Trenton St Coll (BA) Eng Ed 1992; 3 Credit Hrs Assertive Discipline; *cr:* Pierce Jr HS 8th-9th Grd Eng Tchr 1993-94; Southern Regnl HS 10th-11th Grd Eng Tchr 1994-; *ai:* Soph Class Adv; NCTE 1994-; NJEA 1994-; *office:* Southern Regional HS 75 Cedar Bridge Rd Manahawkin NJ 08050*

FITTS, JANICE HARVEY, Retired Counselor; *b:* Lawrence, MA; *m:* Duane O.; *c:* Bryan, Lori Raines, Holly Davidson; *ed:* Emerson Coll (BA) Eng 1949; Kent St Univ (MED) Guid, Cnslng 1970; Scndry Admin; Elem Admin; 50 Hrs; *cr:* Attleboro HS Eng Tchr 1949-51; Wise Schl 6th-7th Grd Tchr 1962-65; Davey MS Dean of Girls, Eng Tchr 1965-77, Cnslr 1977-94; *ai:* Stu Cncl Adv; MS Stud, Substance Abuse Comms; K-8 Cnslng Chprsn; Delta Kappa Gamma 1970-, Pres, St Bd; KEA 1968-, Rep; ASCA, OASCA; OH Assn of Women Deans Admin, Cnslrs 1970-, Pres, VP; NAWDAC 1970-, Natl Bd; Alpha XI Alpha Housing Corp, Pres 1965-75; A. Margaret Boyd Flwshp 1978; Jennings Scholar 1984-85; *home:* 1740 Walnut Rd PO Box 131 Kent OH 44240*

FITZ, SHIRLEY COOPER, English Teacher; *b:* Ithaca, NY; *m:* H. Rodney; *ed:* Catonsville Jr Coll (AA) Liberal Arts 1965; Shepherd Coll (BA) Eng 1967; Shippensburg Univ (MA) Eng 1970; *cr:* East Jr HS Eng Tchr 1967-89; Waynesboro Sr HS Eng Tchr 1989-; *ai:* NEA, PSEA, WAEA 1967-; *office:* Waynesboro Area Sr HS 550 E 2nd St Waynesboro PA 17268

FITZGERALD, BETSY FORRESTER, History Dept Head; *b:* Blue Hill, ME; *c:* Bruce; *ed:* Univ of ME at Machias (BS) Ed 1970; Univ of So Miami (MA) Pub Policy 1990; St of ME Certfd Plumbing Inspector; Certfd Scuba Diver; *cr:* Land Hall Schl Alternative Ed Guid Cnslr 1970-71; Washington Acad Eng Tchr 1971-72; Erksine Acad His Tchr 1972-81, Dept Chair 1981-; *ai:* Var Swim Coach; YMCA Yth & Govt Pgm; Citizen Bee Adv; Grad Coord; Staff Dev, Gifted & Talented, NHS Advy & Tchr Evaluation Comm; NEA 1986-; MEA 1986-; NISCA 1992-; China Four Seasons Club 1977-, Treas; Amer Red Cross 1988-, Bd Sec & Hlth & Safety Comm Chair; China Historical Soc 1990-; Town of China Selectman; China Lake Regnl Alliance & Vol Monitors Pgm Bd of Dirs; Informed Notaries of ME Bd of Dirs; Curr Materials Pub for Trng of Notary Pubs in ME; *office:* Erskine Acad RR 2 Box 547 South China ME 04358

FITZGERALD, DORIS B., Accounting Professor; *ed:* Montclair Univ (BA) Acctng; NY Univ (MBA) Acctng, (PHD) Acctng; *cr:* BMCC Acctng Prof 1972-95, Fac Dean 1976-85, Dept Chair 1989-95; *office:* Borough Of Manhattan Comm Coll 199 Chambers St New York NY 10007

FITZGERALD, ELIZABETH LANGLE, Second Grade Teacher; *b:* White Plains, NY; *c:* Kari, Heidi; *ed:* Bates Coll (BA) Psych 1960; Columbia U Tchrs Coll (MA) Elem Ed 1961; *cr:* Pacontico Hills Schl Elem Tchr 1976-; *ai:* PTA Tchr VP; Westchester Horse Cncl 1986-, Exec Bd; *office:* Pocantico Hills Central Schl 599 Bedford Rd N Tarrytown NY 10591

FITZGERALD, GARY M., Geometry Teacher; *b:* Scranton, PA; *m:* Diane Zawistoski; *c:* Mark, Michele; *ed:* Univ of Scranton (BS) Ed 1971; Post Grad Stud Math; *cr:* Mid Vly Schl Dist Geometry, Algebra Tchr 1974-; *ai:* Var Sftbl Coach Scranton Prep; NEA 1974-; *office:* Mid Vly Schl Dist Underwood Rd Throop PA 18512

FITZGERALD, KATHLEEN E., Fourth Grade Teacher; *b:* NY; *ed:* Mt St Vincent (BA) His 1965; Western CT St Coll (MS) Ed, Psych 1971; *cr:* St Anthony Schl 3rd Grd Tchr 1958-59; St Bernard Schl 2nd Grd Tchr 1959-64; St Patrick's Schl 1st, 6th-8th, 4th Grd Tchr 1964-; *ai:* CCD Tchr; Soccer, Floor Hockey Coach; Remedial Work; NCEA 1995-; *office:* St Patrick's Schl State Rd Bedford NY 10506*

FITZGERALD, KELLY ANNE, Fifth Grade Teacher; *b:* Abington, PA; *ed:* Immaculata Coll (BA) Eng 1987; *cr:* JET Pgm Eng Tchr 1987-89; West Chester Eng Tchr 1989-90; Holy Redeemer Schl Tchr 1990-; *office:* Holy Redeemer Schl 915 Vine St Philadelphia PA 19107

FITZGERALD, RICHARD DANIEL, Social Studies Teacher; *b:* Utica, NY; *m:* Kathleen Brady; *c:* Michael, Christine; *ed:* Niagara Univ (BA) His, Philosophy 1971, (MAT) His 1973; Post-Grad Credit Hrs St Univ of NY At Cortland, Syracuse Univ; *cr:* Lyncourt Cntrl Schl Soc Stud Tchr 1974-78; Liverpool Cntrl Schl Soc Stud Tchr 1978-; *ai:* Lib Advy, Tenth Grd Soc Stud Curr Comms; NYS United Tchrs 1974-; Soc for Hist Ed 1983-; NYS Historical Assn 1980-; Natl His Judge; Day Contest NYS Historical Assn; House III Tchr of Yr 1990; Soc Stud, Lang Grant NYS Assn of Foreign Lang Tchrs 1993; Review of Book 1986; Reviewed World His Textbook 1984; *office:* Liverpool HS 4338 Wetzel Rd Liverpool NY 13090*

FITZGERALD, ROBERT PATRICK,SR., Mathematics Teacher; *b:* New York City, NY; *m:* Elaine B. Hodgkins; *c:* Jillian M., Robert P. Jr.; *ed:* Univ of ME At Farmington (BS) Math 1975; Univ of Southern ME (MS) Psych 1980; Prin Cert 1985; *cr:* Jay HS Math Tchr 1975-; *ai:* Var Boys Bsktbl Coach; ME ASSN of Bsktbl Coaches Treas 4 Yrs, Coach of Yr 1980-; ME Math Tchrs 1976-; Natl Bsktbl Coaches New England Rep tp Natl Comm 1982-; Who's Who in Ed; Who's Who in Coaching; *office:* Jay HS 4 School St Jay ME 04239

FITZGERALD, ROBERT PATRICK, Performing Arts Coordinator; *b:* Jersey City, NJ; *m:* Jill; *ed:* St Peters Coll (BA) Eng 1967; Attnd Montclair St; *cr:* Hasbrouck Hghts HS Tchr 28 Yrs; *ai:* Performing Arts Coord; Forensic Adv; HHEA 1967-1995, Pres; NJEA & BCEA 1967-; Artist in Residence Prgm Grant; PTA Fellowship & Governors Tchr Recognition Awds.

FITZGERALD, RONALD J., English Teacher; *b:* New York, NY; *m:* Rita Ann Barglowsky; *ed:* Manhattan Coll (BS) Eng 1955; Fordham Univ (MSE) Eng 1961; Queens Coll Eng 1963; St Johns Univ Law 1965; Empire St Coll Eng 1992; *cr:* NYC Bd of Ed Tchr & Union Organzier 1958-75; Freelance Writing Scndry Text Writer 1975-85; Exec Search Recruiter 1980-85; NYC Bd of Ed Eng Tchr 1985-86; Moriah Cntrl Schl Eng Tchr 1987-; Clinton Comm Coll Eng Instr 1987-; Upward Bound Prg Eng Inst 1987-; *ai:* NYSUT 1987-; ECHO 1987-, Dir; NY St Mentor & Intern Pgm; *office:* Moriah Central Schl HC 1 Box 7a Port Henry NY 12974*

FITZGERALD, SUZANNE DELUCA, Second Grade Teacher; *b:* Jersey City, NJ; *m:* Art; *c:* Matthew, John, Patricia; *ed:* Seton Hall Univ (BS) Elem Ed 1971; *cr:* Silver Bay Elem 2nd Grd Tchr 1983-; *ai:* NEA 1983-; NJEA 1983-; TREA 1983-; *office:* Silver Bay Elem Schl 100 Silver Bay Rd Toms River NJ 08753

FITZGERALD, T. KERN, Bio Tchr, PE & Athletic Trnr; *b:* Newton, MA; *m:* Brenda Elsie Simmons; *c:* Kaitlin; *ed:* Springfiedl Coll (BS) Athetic Trng 1983; Masters Work in Ed Specialization of Sports Medicine; *cr:* Saint Sebastians Athletic Trainer, Bio & PE Tchr 1985-; Northeastern Univ Lab Instr Gross Anatomy Part-Time 1989-; *ai:* Natl Athletic Trainers Assn 1982-; Vol Boston Marathon Medical Team 1988-; *office:* St Sebastians Schl 1191 Greendale Ave Needham MA 02192*

FITZGERALD-HOYT, MARY, Professor of English; *b:* Albany, NY; *m:* Donald C. Hoyt; *ed:* Siena Coll (BA) Eng 1977; Univ of CT (MA) Eng 1979, (PHD) Eng 1985; *cr:* SUNY Eng Instr 1984; Siena Coll Eng Asst Prof 1984-90, Eng Assoc Prof 1991-93, Eng Prof 1994-; *ai:* Amer Conf Irish Stud 1989-, Mid-Atlantic Rep; Intnl Assn Stud Anglo-Irish Lit 1993-; Numerous Articles Pub; *office:* Siena Coll 515 Loudon Rd Loudonville NY 12211

FITZGIBBONS, JANICE MAZZOTTA, French & Spanish Teacher; *b:* Lawrence, MA; *m:* Joseph; *ed:* Boston Coll (BS) Fr, Ed 1966; NDEA Inst Univ of ME, Univ of Rennes; Span Cert Tufts Univ, Merrimack Coll; *cr:* Salem HS Fr, Eng Tchr 1966-68; Elmhurst Acad Fr Tchr 1968-69; West MS Fr, Span Tchr 1969-91; Andover HS Frgn Lang Dept Head 1987-88, Fr & Span Tchr 1991-; *ai:* Project Teamwork Adv; Stu Govt Fac Mem; Andover Ed Assn, MA Tchrs Assn, NEA 1969-; A Better Chance Outstdng Tchr Awd 1993, 1995; Project Teamwork Awd Ctr for Stud of Sport in Soc Northeastern Univ 1993; *office:* Andover HS Shawsheen Rd Andover MA 01810

FITZHUGH, SHARI RONDO, Home Economics Teacher; *b:* Standish, MI; *m:* Frederick E. Jr.; *c:* Kristen, Chelsea; *ed:* Cntrl MI Univ (BSEd) Home Ec 1971; Attnd Capital Univ, OH Domincan Univ; *cr:* Milan MS Home Ec Tchr 1972-73; Westerville MS Home Ed Tchr 1981-83; Westerville North HS Home Ed Tchr 1983-87; Rocky River HS Home Ec Tchr 1988-; *office:* Rocky River HS 20951 Detroit Rd Rocky River OH 44116

FITZKEE, CARLA WAELDE, Elementary School Librarian; *b:* York, PA; *c:* Nicholas; *ed:* Millersville Univ (BS) Lib Sci, Soc Stud 1968; Shippensburg Univ (MS) Comm 1972; 45 Grad Credits Lib Sci, Elem Ed, Soc Stud; *cr:* York Hosp Lib Asst 1967-68; Red Lion Jr HS Librn 1968-78; Mazie Gable Elem Schl, Edgar Moore Elem Schl Locust, Grove Elem Schl, Winterstown Elem Schl Librn 1978-; *ai:* Continuing Prof Dev, Tech, Parent-Tchr Liason Comms; NEA, PSEA, RLAEA, PSLA, ALA 1968-; Amer Heart Assn, Amer Cancer Soc, York Literacy Cncl Vol; Parents of Gifted Children York Cty Chptr 1988-; Mini Grant First Capital Assn Explore Rdng Motivational Act; *home:* 25 S Ogontz St York PA 17403

FITZMAIER, GAYLE GUTHEIL, HS Guidance Counselor; *b:* Los Angeles, CA; *m:* George Eugene; *c:* Michael, Thomas, Stephen; *ed:* Jersey City St Coll (BA) Elem Ed 1974; Monmouth Univ (MSEd) Pupil Prsnl Svcs 1988; *cr:* Holmdel Bd of Ed Tchr 1974-79; EAI Human Resources Rep 1979-83; Concurrent Comp Corp Human Resources Rep 1989-91; Long Branch HS Guid Cnslr 1991-; *ai:* Adj Prof Brookdale Comm Coll; Sunday Schl Tchr; NHS, Schl Bd Planning Comm; NEA, NJEA, MCSCA 1991-; NJSCA 1995-; *office:* Long Branch HS 6 West End Ct Long Branch NJ 07740

FITZMAURICE, JEANNE M., Mathematics Teacher; *b:* New York, NY; *ed:* Saint Johns Univ (BA) Ec 1988, (MS) Math Ed 1991; *cr:* Saint Johns Preparatory Schl Math Tchr 1988-; *ai:* Amer Mathematical Assn 1992-; Saint Vincent DePaul Soc; LaGuardia Comm Coll Adjunct Lecturer; *office:* Saint Johns Preparatory HS 2121 Crescent St Astoria NY 11105

FITZMIER, C. DIANNE, Physics Teacher; *b:* Upper Darby, PA; *m:* H. James; *c:* James, Nancy Barkley, Stephen; *ed:* Ursinus Coll (BS) Bio 1963; West Chester Univ (MED) Sci 1969; 48 Post Grad Hrs; *ai:* Chi Alpha Spon; NEA 1979-; PSEA 1979-; WCAEA 1979-; *office:* Henderson HS Lincoln & Montgomery Aves West Chester PA 19380

FITZPATRICK, BRIAN PAUL, Social Studies Teacher; *b:* Houlton, ME; *m:* Gretchen Prince; *c:* Colleen Elizabeth, Samuel Prince; *ed:* Univ of ME at Presque Isle (BS) Soc Scis 1984; *cr:* Hodgdon High Tchr 1985-; *ai:* Var Girls Soccer; Interactive Theater Adv; Gifted & Talented, Accreditation, Drug & Alcohol Comm; Soc Stud Dept Chair; Schl Plays; NEA 1985-; ME Soccer; Coaches Assn 1988-; Yrbk Dedication 1987, 1994; *office:* Hodgdon HS RR 4 Box 1870 Houlton ME 04730

FITZPATRICK, CATHY EILEEN CONDON, High School Counselor; *b:* Dayton, OH; *m:* Robert R. Jr.; *c:* Brad, Mark; *ed:* Bowling Green St Univ (BS) His, Eng 1974; Univ of Dayton (MS) Ed Admin 1992, (MS) Schl Cnslr 1994; One Grad Quarter Hr 1995; *cr:* Clermont Northeastern HS Eng Tchr, Cnslr 1976-95; Batavia HS Cnslr 1995-; *ai:* Individual Career Plan Coord; Mem of Core Team; NEA, OEA 1983-; Clermont Co Cnslrs Assn 1994-; CNE Kids II 1994-, Chprsn; United Wesleyan Church 1992-, Tchr; Stan Setting Comm for OH Ninth Grd Proficiency Test in Writing; *office:* Batavia HS 800 Bauer Ave Batavia OH 45103*

FITZPATRICK, DAVID JOSEPH, Adjunct Instructor; *b:* Lynwood, CA; *m:* Patricia Ann White; *c:* Sean, Hope; *ed:* St Tech Inst at Memphis (AE) Environ Eng Tech 1976; Natl Univ (BBA) Bus, Hlth Svc 1981; Johnson & Wales Univ (MS) Cmptr Ed 1991; *cr:* Fishe Coll Adj Fac, Former Dir Med Red Prgm 1991-; Katherine Gibbs Adj Fac 1994-95; Jonson & Wales Univ Adj Fac 1994; *ai:* Amer Hlth Info Mngmt Assn 1994-; IOOF 1991-; *office:* Fisher Coll 777 Church St New Bedford MA 02745*

FITZPATRICK, JAMES DONALD,JR., Social Studies Teacher; *b:* Baltimore, MD; *m:* Kathleen Elizabeth; *c:* Timothy Ryan, James Donald III; *ed:* Univ of MD Baltimore Cty (BA) His 1981; Loyola Coll Grad Schl Cmptr Applications, Counseling; Towson St Univ Grad Schl Dev Psych; Univ of MD Baltimore Cty Instructional Systems Dev; *cr:* Thomas Johnson HS Soc Stud Tchr, Soccer Coach 1981-85; Linganore HS Soc Stud Tchr, Soccer Coach 1985-; *ai:* Jr Var Soccer 1981-84, Var Soccer 1985-92, Asst Drama 1982-87 Coach, Girls Var Soccer 1994-; NEA 1990-; APA Division 2 1992-; NSCAA, MACS 1985-; FCCA Soccer Coach of Yr 1987; Chamber of Commerce Tchr Excl Awd 1993; Phi Alpha Theta; Fred Cty Girls Coach of Yr 1995; *office:* Linganore HS 12013 Old Annapolis Rd Frederick MD 21701

FITZPATRICK, JOHN EDWARD, Physical Education Teacher; *b:* Troy, NY; *m:* Virginia A. Moreton; *ed:* Hudson Vly Comm Coll (Assoc) Recreation Supervision 1968; Springfield Coll (BS) Recreation Supervision, PE 1970, (MS) PE 1976; Schl Admin NYS 1984; *cr:* Catholic Cntrl HS PE Tchr, Ftbl, Track Coach 1970-75; Troy HS PE Tchr, Var Swim Coach 1975-; *ai:* Var Men, Women Swimming Coach; Aquatic Dir; AAHPERD; NISCA: NYSAHPERD; Amer Red Cross 1968-, LIfeguarding, Water Safety Instr Trainer, Natl Aquatic Schl CPR, First Aid Instr; *office:* Troy HS 1950 Burdett Ave Troy NY 12180

FITZPATRICK, KAREN A. (BOUDREAU), Kindergarten Teacher; *b:* Fitchburg, MA; *m:* Richard O. Jr.; *c:* Kelly A., Ryan M.; *ed:* Fitchburg St Coll (BS) Elem Ed 1974, (MED) Early Chldhd 1996; 15 Addl Grad Credit Hrs Early Chldhd Ed; Catechist Cert Rel Ed; Drug Ed Cert; *cr:* St Joseph Schl Kndgtn Tchr Half Day 1974-80, 1-8 Grd Various Subjects Tchr 1974-84, Pvt Tutoring 1975-78, First Grd Tchr 1981-82, Kndgtn Tchr Half Day 1983-84, Kndgtn Tchr Full Day 1984-; *ai:* PTA 1974; Schl Bd 1977-79, Sec; Primary Dept Chprsn 1991-; Pre-K Dir 1995-; NCEA 1974-; NAEYC 1994-; St Joseph Bazaar Comm Booth Chprsn 1975-93; *office:* St Joseph Schl 35 Columbus St Fitchburg MA 01420

FITZPATRICK, KATHRYN ANN (MANLOVE), Social Studies Teacher; *b:* Ft Campbell, KY; *m:* James E.; *c:* Erin, Carly, Shawn, Kelsey; *ed:* Widener Univ (BA) Behavioral Scis 1976; *cr:* Career Educl Inst Eng Tchr 1976-78; Delsea Regnl HS Soc Stud Tchr 1978-79; Burlington Cty Coll Eng as Second Lang Tchr 1980-81; Pemberton & Palmyra HSs Night Schl Tchr 1981-84; Ocean Cty Coll Eng as Second Lang Tchr 1982-83; Pemberton Twp HS Soc Stud Tchr 1984-; *ai:* Interactive Television Sociology Tchr; Schl Television Station Announcer for Sports & Spec Events; NJEA, NEA 1978-79, 1984-; Tenby Chase Bd of Trustees 1990-, VP; Selected by Pemberton Twp HS Stdnts as 1995 funniest Tchr & Best All-Around Tchr; *office:* Pemberton Township HS Arneys Mt Rd Pemberton NJ 08068*

FITZPATRICK, KEVIN PETER, Second Grade Teacher; *b:* New York, NY; *c:* Kathy; *ed:* Hunter (BA) Ed 1974; AZ St (MS) Ed; *cr:* Valley of Sun Tchr 1975-78; White River Tchr 1978-84; Saint Lukes Schl Tchr NEA 1975-; *home:* 1314 Gillespie Ave Bronx NY 10461*

FITZPATRICK, MARY MORALES, Kindergarten Teacher; *b:* City, NY; *m:* Howard; *c:* Catherine Christina; *ed:* Herbert H. Leh (BA) Sociology 1978, (MS) Ed 1987; *cr:* Pub Schl 47 Parapro 1969-75; Various Schls Sub Tchr 1979-83; Pub Schl 69 Kndgtn Tchr 1984-; *ai:* UFT, AFT 1985-; Kappa Delta Pi 1977-; Tchr Re Soiree Cert 1993.

FITZPATRICK, SUZANNE L., Kindergarten Teacher; *b:* Colum *m:* George; *c:* Erin; *ed:* Univ of Dayton (BS) El Ed 1970; Clevelan (MA) Curr, Instruction El Ed 1982; *cr:* Westwood El Schl 1st 1969-72; Moreland El Schl 1st Grd Tchr 1972-76; Onaway El 1978-; Fenway El Schl Kdg Tchr 1978-; Shaker Hts City Schls Grd Tchr Summer Literacy Parent Outreach Prgm 1990-93; Liaison Comm Shaker Family Ctr; NEA 1972-; NAEYC 1980-; S Comm Rose Garden 1993-; Martha Holden Jennings Grant 1989-9 Fernway Elem Schl 17420 Fernway Rd Shaker Hts OH 44120*

FITZSIMMONS, BARBARA SMITH, Assoc Prof of Early Chld Mt Vernon, IN; *m:* Robert T.; *c:* Van Robert; *ed:* Old Dominion U His 1972; Univ of Southern CA (MSEd) Early Chldhd Ed 198 Early Chldhd Ed 1985; *cr:* Univ of Southern CA Instr 1984-86; for Federal Tchrs Dir 1986-87; Lasell Coll Assoc Prof 1989-; Quilt Project; His, Math, Quilt Project for 5th Graders; OME NAEYC 1985-, Local Bd; ACEI 1985-; Wayside Quilters Guild Mem; Mbrshp Action Grant; Article Pub; Dev Non-Violent Resolution Curr; *office:* Lasell Coll 1844 Commonwealth Ave Ne 02166

FITZSIMMONS, BEVERLY A., Rdng Specialist & Title I T Amboy, NJ; *m:* John J.; *c:* Kerry Ann, Kristen Marie; *ed:* Rutg (BS) Elem & Early Chldhd Ed 1982; Kean Coll (MA) Rdng S 1988; *cr:* Oak Tree Village Nursery Schl Tchr 1982-83; St S Kostka Schl 1st-2nd Grd Tchr 1983-85; Dwight D Eisenhower Sc Grd Tchr 1985-95; Emma Arleth Schl Title I Tchr & Rdng Special *ai:* NEA 1985-; NJ Ed Assoc 1985-; Sayerville Ed Assoc 1985-; NJ Rdng Assoc 1996; Governors Tchr Recognition Awd 199 Emma Arleth Elem Schl 3198 Washington Rd Parlin NJ 08859*

FITZSIMMONS, DIANA, Science & Mathematics Teacher; *b:* B NY; *m:* James; *c:* James, Diana Dreher, Kathleen, John; *ed:* St Un at Albany (BS) Math & Sci 1955; NY Univ (MA) Tchng of Jr 1957; Colgate Univ 12 Hrs 1960-61, Boston Coll 30 Credit Hrs Acad of Natl Sci Fnd; *cr:* Clarkstown Jr-Sr HS 7th-12th Grd M 1955-65; Saint Thomas of Canterbury Math & Sci Tchr 1979-; Thomas Canterbury Schl 336 Hudson St Cornwall On Hudson N

FITZSIMMONS, SUZANNE N., Science Dept Chair & Te Carbondale, PA; *m:* Joseph; *c:* Katherine, Connor; *ed:* Maryw (BS) Bio & Chem 1974; Boston Univ (MED) Bio & Scndry Ed Post Grad Credits Univ of S; 6 Post Grad Credits Penn St; *cr* O'Hara HS Bio & Chem Tchr 1975-80; Scranton Preparatory Schl & Sci Chair 1980-; *ai:* Scranton Preparatory Drama Players Prod Jr Acad Sci Moderator; PA Jr Acad of Sci 1976-, Sec; NSTA, Natl Assn 1980-; Waverly Comm House 1985-; Women Educators 199 Gamma Nu 1993-; Outstanding Tchr Awd Univ of Chicago N Women; *office:* Scranton Prep Schl 1000 Wyoming Ave Scra 18509*

FITZSIMMONS, VERNA M., Research Assistant; *b:* Cincinnati James N.; *c:* Gail Lynn, Joan; *ed:* Univ of Cincinnati (BSE) Inds 1985, (MSE) Indstrl Engr 1992; Work Towards PHD System Engrng; *cr:* Wright St Univ Lake Campus Instr 1988-89; G. Systems Safety & Regulatory Engr 1990-91; Ohmeda Product Saf 1991-92; Milwaukee Schl of Engrng Asst Prof 1992-95; *ai:* IE WG2 Comm Mem; Safety of Cmptrs Med Electrical Equipme Indstrl Engrs; Alpha Pi Mu; Soc System Safety; ASQC; NIDSH Pub; *office:* Univ of Cincinnati PO Box D116 304 Old Servi Cincinnati OH 45221*

FITZWATER, DIANA C. (SINES), Art Teacher; *b:* Uniontown Ken E.; *c:* Amy E.; *ed:* MD Inst Coll of Art (BFA) Art Ed 1966, (M Ed 1973; *cr:* Beltsville Jr HS Art Tchr 1966-70; Dundalk Co Part-time Art Tchr 1974-80; Laurel HS Art Tchr 1970-; *ai:* Dept 4.5 Mem Dept; Natl Art Hnr Soc Spon; Tchr of Advanced Placemen Art; Schl-Based Instrl Decision-making Team; NEA, NAEA, PGCEA 1966-; Balto Watercolor Soc 1975-; Poolesville Bapt 1983-, Sunday Schl, VBS Tchr; Nominated for Tchr of Yr; Master 6 Stu Tchrs; Prestigious Art Exhibitions; Numerous Contests Stdnts; *home:* PO Box 331 Poolesville MD 20837

FIUMARELLO, SHEILA NANCY, Vocal Music Teach Poughkeepsie, NY; *ed:* SUNY at Fredonia (BM) Music Ed, Vocal P Boston Conservatory (MM) Vocal Performance 1988; SUNY at N (CAS) Educl Admin 1990; Master Classes Iride Pilla Arico Polo Zambarro; *cr:* Canesteo Cntrl Schls Vocal Music Tchr 1976-77; Cntrl Schls Vocal Music Tchr 1977-79; Poughkeepsie City Schl Choral Tchr 1979-; Boston Conservatory Voice Prof 1995-; *ai:* Voice Tchr; NYSSMA 1976-, Zone 10 Rep, Voice Clinician; NATS Adjunct Prof SUNY at Purchase, Curtis Inst of Music; *home:* 4 Wor Poughkeepsie NY 12603

FIUTAK, ERIKA ANNE, Art Teacher & Dept Chairman; *b:* Buff *m:* Paul; *c:* Geoffrey, Jon, Joel; *ed:* St Univ Coll at Buffalo (BS) 1965; Grad Stud Art His Syracuse Univ; *cr:* Genesee Humboldt Jr Tchr 1965-67; Liverpool Cntrl Schls Art Tchr 1976-86; Christian Acad Art Tchr, Dept Chair 1986-; *ai:* Moderator Art Club Intervention Team; AFT, NEA, NYSUT 1984-; NAEA 1990-; Roo of Yr Bflo Pub Schls; *office:* Christian Brothers Acad 6245 Ra Syracuse NY 13214

FIVE, CORA LEE, Fifth Grade Teacher; *ed:* Bucknell Univ (Harvard Univ (MED) Ed; Northeastern Univ (MA) Writing; *cr:* S Pub Schls Elem Schl Tchr; *ai:* New Tchr Mentor; Curr Comm; St Wkshp Conducter & Presenter; Natl Bd for Prof Tchng Standar Chldhd Eng Lang Arts Stand; NCTE Comm to Review Editorship to Eval Curr Guide, Elem Section Nominating Comm, Wlem Steering Comm, Natl Conf & Convention Presenter; IC; WLU ASCD; AERA; Achilles Track Club Vol; Prof Best Leadersh Learning Mag 1990; Pub Chapters in Many Books & Articles; A Bks; *home:* 400 E 85th St Apt 5C New York NY 10028*

FLAGG, WILLIAM R.,JR., Math & Science Teacher; *b:* Eastp *m:* Janice Carol Bailey; *c:* Dawn, Scott; *ed:* Univ of ME at Orono 1958; Reanselaer Polytechnicle Inst (MS) Natural Scis 1974; V Ed, Cmptr Courses; *cr:* Boothbay Harbor HS Sci Tchr 1958-59; Sh Math Tchr 1959-61; Bus 1961-68; Deer Isle-Stonington Jr, Sr H Sci Tchr 1968-; *ai:* NHS Adv; NEA, ME Educl Assn 1968-; ME 1974-; DI-S TA Local 1968-, Pred 1975-76; Recognized by Local as Outstdng Tchr.

FLAHERTY, FRANCES BACHAND, Eighth Grade US History Southbridge, MA; *m:* John F.; *c:* Shawn, Timothy; *ed:* North Adams (BS) Elem Ed 1969, (MED) Educ 1978; Addlt 40 Hrs Grad W Greylock Elem Schl 4-5 Grd Tchr 1970-86; Conti MS 6-8 Grd Tch *ai:* Yrbk Adv; Stu Act Comm; 8th Grd Dance Adv; NEA, MTA 197 ild Sturbridge Village; North Adams Historical Soc Awd; *office:* 'onte MS Church St North Adams MA 01247

TY, LINDA CONSTANCE, Spanish & Portuguese Teacher; *b:* r, MA; *m:* William A. Jr.; *c:* William A. III, Roslyn; *ed:* ern MA Univ (BA) Fr 1980; Eng & Span Cert; *cr:* Fall River Pub Tchr 1980-85; Wareham Pub Schls Tchr 1985-; *ai:* AATSP NELL 1982-; Recipient of Horace Mann Grant; *home:* 96 Clapp ster MA 02770

TY, PATRICIA CHUDECKI, Fourth Grade Teacher; *b:* New T; *m:* Robert L.; *c:* Sarah, Ryan; *ed:* CCSU (BS) Elem Ed Rdng 970, (MS) Elem Ed Rdng 1971; *cr:* Squadron Line Elem 5th 1971-74; Tootin Hills Elem Schl 5th Grd Tchr 1974-77, 3rd Grd -89, 6th Grd Tchr 1989-95, 4th Grd Tchr 1995-; *ai:* NEA, SEA *ce:* Tootin Hills Elem Schl 25 Nimrod Rd West Simsbury CT

ERNARD VINCENT, Math Teacher; *b:* Bronx, NY; *c:* Rachel lliot Martin; *ed:* City Coll NY (BS) Psych 1969; Yeshiva Univ d Credits; CUNY Math Credits; Webster Coll Ed Credits; *cr:* IS Tchr 1969-75; IS 192x Math Tchr 1975-; *ai:* UFT, AFT 1969-, n 3 Yrs; Salvation Army 1993-, Flood Relief Vol, Cert; Who's mer Ed 1996-; Inspirational Tchr Fordham Prep Schl 1995; *home:* River Rd Bronxville NY 10708

, JUDY ONYSYK, Vocational Commercial Art Tchr; *b:* , OH; *m:* George John; *c:* George Gary, Glenn Carl; *ed:* Lake Erie); Attnd Cleveland Inst of Art, Kent St Univ, Baldwin Wallace St Univ, Ashland Univ; *cr:* OH Bell Draftsperson 1968-69; Shop st 1970-74; ATC Lakewood Artist 1974-; Pitt Studio Artist Nutron Namplate Art Dir 1977-78; AM Greeting Artist 1978-79; Schls 1979-80; Willoughby Eastlake Schls 1980-; *ai:* SADD, omm Art Club Advs; NEA, OEA, OAEO, NAEA, AVA, OVA raphic Arts Cncl 1994-, Stu Seminars; Cleve Ballet 1989-, Ed ast OH Gas Co 1984-, Ed Comm, Classroom Awds; Lakewood HS , Advy Cncl; Rocky River Comm Theater 1991-, Artist; Sammuel Awd Harvard Bus Schl Club 1993; Excl in Econ Ed 1984, 1990; Scholar 1993-94; Designed 1995 Easter Seal; Illustrator EPIC Amer 1994-; *office:* Willoughby-Eastlake Tech Ctr 25 Public Sq by OH 44094*

IA, LOUGENIA T., 5th Grade Teacher; *b:* White Plains, NY; *m:* .; *c:* Anthony, Justin; *ed:* Lesley Coll at Cambridge (BS) Elem, 1980; Coll of New Rochelle (MSEd) Spec Ed 1988; Working on egree, Cert Curr, Staff Dev; *cr:* White Plains HS 9-12th Grd Spec Amer His Tchr 1982-85; John Burroughs Jr HS 7-9th Grd Spec Ed 7-89; Hawthorne PEARLS Prgm 5th Grd Tchr 1989-; NY Med rning Styles, Stud Skills Consultant 1989-; *ai:* North Yonkers ls Club Chrldng Coach; Phi Delta Kappa 1989-, Sec, Historian; awthorne PEARLS Schl 350 Hawthorne Ave Yonkers NY 10705*

AN, BERNARD A., Director of Spiritual Act; *b:* Allentown, PA; of Scranton (BS) Human Svcs 1978; Mary Immaculate Seminary Theology 1982; Post Grad Ed Credits Wilkes Univ; *cr:* Parishes or 1982-84; Reading Cntrl Cath HS Theology Tchr, Spiritual Dir Nativity BVM HS Theology Tchr, Spiritual Act Dir 1989-; *ai:* of Allentown Diocesan Yth Ministry Advy Bd; NCEA 1985-; of Allentown God & Yth Awd 1995; *office:* Nativity of the BVM wtons Hill Pottsville PA 17901

AN, CHARLES M., English & History Dept Chm; *b:* Fall River, Jane Riedy; *c:* Charles; *ed:* Assumption Coll (BA) Eng & His Johns Coll (MA) Lbrl Arts 1988; PHD in Amer Stud 1993-; *cr:* duct Svcs Tchr 1981-82; Blue Ridge Schl Tchr 1982-87; The Key r 1987-; *ai:* Stu Newspaper Adv; Amer Stud Assn 1995-; DAR Tchr of Amer His for St of MD 1995; *office:* The Key Schl 534 e Dr Annapolis MD 21403

AN, JOYCE BIPPES, Piano Teacher & Pianist; *b:* Tekoa, WA; Benjamin; *c:* Christopher, Jennifer Tanau, Jonathan; *ed:* Eastern (BA) Music Ed 1953; Univ of WA 23 Credits 1953-55; Columbia Credits; *cr:* Oswego Pub Schls 5th Grd, Music Tchr 1953-54; ub Schls 5th Grd, Music Tchr 1954-55; Succasunna Pub Schls 6th isic Tchr 1956; Brookhaven Pub Schls 5th Grd, Music Tchr Pvt Piano Teacher 1975-; *ai:* Burlington Friends of Music, Piano 90-; MTNA Prof Cert 1991-, Composition Chm, Auditions Chm, MTA 1988-; Amer Natl Guild of Piano Tchrs 1978-; First Night n 1991-, Bd Mem; Burlington Friends of Music 1972-84; *home:* St Burlington VT 05401

AN, PATRICIA ANN, Social Studies Teacher; *b:* Elmhurst, NY; ington Coll (BA) Sociology, US His 1973; Univ of MD, George ton Univ MEQ Scndry Ed 1975; *cr:* Albert Einstein HS Soc Stud 73-; *ai:* Golf, Var Sftbl Coach; Discipline Comm Chprsn; AFT eorge Washington Univ NSF Grant; *home:* 608 Wayne Ave Silver MD 20910

AN, ROBERT WILLIAM, Science Teacher; *b:* Boston, MA; *m:* tricia Kane; *c:* Robert Jr., Kathryn Anne, Joan Marie Lowrie; *ed:* ary Acad (BS) Engineering 1951; Univ of NH (MBA) Bus 1981; of Notre Dame Mil Sci Asst Prof 1961-65; St Joseph Regnl Schl Grd Sci Tchr 1986-, Lead Tchr 1994-95; *ai:* Sci Fair, Grad Act Yrbk, Class Officer, Graduating Class Adv; Parent Tchr Cncl Comm; NCEA, NHSTA 1992-.

AN, ELLEN FONNER, Math Teacher & Facilitator; *b:* burg, PA; *m:* James R.; *ed:* Waynesburg Coll (BS) Math 1969; Post edits WV Univ Ger, PA St Univ Ed, Duquesne Univ Physics; *cr:* Highlands Schl Dist Math, Ger Tchr 1971-75; Bentworth Schl Dist chr 1977-78; Chartiers-Houston Schl Dist Math Tchr 1978-80; wp Schl Dist Math Tchr, Math Team Facilitator 1980-; *ai:* Lead mm; AFT, PTFT 1980-, Pres, VP; PCTM 1985-; United Presbyn of Claysville; Claysville Chptr OES #187, Past Matron; Church Elder; Amer Family Inst Gift of Time Tribute; Local Svc Awds; eters Township HS 264 E Mcmurray Rd Mc Murray PA 15317*

AN, JAMES ROBERT, English Teacher; *b:* Charleroi, PA; *m:* nner; *ed:* Waynesburg Coll (BA) Eng 1964; Attnd CA Univ of PA St Univ; *cr:* Waynesburg Cntrl HS Tchr 1965; West Greene Schl hr 1967-68; McCouffey Schl Dist Tchr 1968-; *ai:* NEA; PSEA; horeau Soc 1983-; United Presbyn Church of Claysville; Claysville 47 F&AM 1979-, Past Master; WA Chptr 150 1993-; WA Cncl 1 Recorder; Jacqua De Molay Commandry 3 1993-; Natl Endowment Concord Authors Seminar; Gift of Time Tribute Amer Family Inst; Parks Pgm 300 Hr Awd Natl Park Svc; Univ of Pittsburgh & gh Press All-St Edctr 1992; *office:* Mc Guffey H S 86 McGuffey Dr le PA 15323

GAN, VICTORIA LYNN, Special Education Teacher; *b:* Canton, David Allen; *c:* Ashley Lynn, Tricia Ann; *ed:* Kent St Univ (BA) , Elem Ed 1989; *cr:* Lake Shore MS EMH Tchr 1990-92; East HS LD, DH Tchr 1993-; *ai:* MS Vlybl Coach; Yrbk Adv; NEA OEA 1993-; *office:* East Canton HS Browning St East Canton OH

IERY, JUDITH WHITE, 7th-8th Grd Soc Studies Tchr; *b:* n, NY; *m:* Kyran J. Jr.; *c:* Susan, Kristin Flannery Barnes, Erin; *ed:* Saint Rose (BA) Elem Ed 1986; NY St Univ at Albany (MS) Rdng 1991; *cr:* Acad of the Holy Names 7th-8th Grd Soc Stud Tchr 1986-; *ai:* Stu Adv Prgm Coord & Adv; NCEA 1990-; Ladies of Charity 1990-; Tchr of Yr 1991; *office:* Acad Of The Holy Names HS 1065 New Scotland Ave Albany NY 12208*

FLASCO, ANITA SALLOUM, Spanish Teacher & Dept Chprsn; *b:* McKeesport, PA; *m:* John Curtis; *c:* Brandon, Zachary, Jenna; *ed:* California Univ at PA (BS) Span 1974; Elem Ed at Geneva Coll 1981; *cr:* Hopewell HS Span Tchr 1 Yr; Center HS Span Tchr 17 Yrs; *ai:* Span Club, Ski Club Spon; Stdnts Asstnc Pgm Mem; Young Womens Ldrshp Cncl Rep; PSMLA 1990-; Center Area Schl Dist Tchr of Yr Awd 1990; PTA Schlsp Hnrb Mntn Awd 1996; *office:* Center HS Baker Rd Extension Monaca PA 15061

FLASS, BARBARA ULINE, English Teacher; *b:* Ballston Spa, NY; *m:* Peter; *c:* Cindi, Rebecca; *ed:* Marietta Coll (BA) Eng 1967; St Univ of NY at Albany (MA) Eng 1979; *cr:* Amherst Cntrl Jr HS Eng Tchr 1967-69; Adirondack Comm Coll Adjunct Instr in Writing 1984-88; Saint Paul-Assumption Schl Eng Tchr 1987-89; Catholic Cntrl HS Eng Tchr 1989-; *ai:* Jr HS SADD; NCTE 1996; Phi Beta Kappa 1967-; Intnl Womens Writing Guild 1994-; *office:* Catholic Central Jr HS 116th St & 7th Ave Troy NY 12182

FLAVIN, JACK, Intermediate Grade Teacher; *b:* Pittsburgh, PA; *m:* Carolyn Arrigan; *c:* Jennifer; *ed:* IN Univ of PA (BS) Criminology & Ed 1969; *cr:* St John of God Tchr 1969-82; Resurrection Schl Tchr 1982-; *ai:* Resurrection JV girls Bsktbl Coach 1992-94; Resurrection Var Girls Bsktbl Coach 1994-; PFDT 1988-; Resurrection Schl Bd 1984-88; *office:* Resurrection Schl 1100 Creedmore Ave Pittsburgh PA 15226

FLAVIN, PAUL STEPHEN, Alternative Education Teacher; *b:* Worcester, MA; *m:* Laura; *c:* Kyle, Lucas; *ed:* Massasoit Comm Coll (AS) Human Resources 1973; RI Coll (BS) Spec Ed 1976; Univ of MA Cooperative Ed Stud; *cr:* Bradley Hospital Cognitive Therapist 1976-83; Attleboro HS Alternative Ed Tchr 1983-; *ai:* Youth Soccer Coach; Big Brothers of Amer; MTA 1983-; Challenge Through Choice Ropes Course; JEPTA Prgm Summer Youth Employment; Nom Tchr of Yr 1994 & 1995; *home:* 88 LeRoy Dr Riverside RI 02915*

FLECK, GEORGE MORRISON, Professor of Chemistry; *b:* Warren, IN; *m:* Margaret Dyer Reynolds; *c:* Margaret Morrison, Louise Elizabeth; *ed:* Yale Univ (BS) Chem 1956; Univ of WI (PHD) Physical Chem 1961; *cr:* Smith Coll Asst Prof 1961-67, Assoc Prof 1967-76, Prof 1976-; *ai:* Sigma Xi 1961-; Amer Chemical Soc; New England Assn of Chem Tchrs; MA Assn of Sci Tchrs; Hampshire Regnl Schl Comm; Williamsburg Schl Cncl; Bd of Meekihs Lib Trustees; Whitley Cty Historical Soc; Pioneer Valley Regnl Ed Alliance; Barge Prize; Griffin Scholar; Danforth Fellow; du Pont Fellow; Author Equilibria in Solution; Chemical Reaction Mechanisms; Carbozxlic Acid Equilibria; Chem Molecules that Matter; Patterns of Symmetry; Shaping Space a Polyhedral Approach; *office:* Smith Coll Clark Sci Ctr Northampton MA 01063

FLECK, NICK, English Teacher; *ed:* Bowdoin Coll (AB) Eng 1962; *ai:* Ski Coach 25 Yrs; Lit Magazine; Ornothology; *office:* Northfield Mount Hermon Schl Main St Northfield MA 01360*

FLECK, ROBERT K., Social Studies Teacher; *b:* Waynesboro, PA; *m:* Peggy Lorraine Jones; *ed:* Kutztown St Coll (BS) Comprehensive Soc Stud 1973, (MA) Amer His 1983; 77.3 Addl Credits; *cr:* Exeter Twp Sr HS Soc Stud Tchr 1973-; *ai:* NHS Adv; Schl Dist Strategic Planning Comm; Sports Ofcl Wrestling, Track, Girls Bsktbl, Field Hockey; NEA, NCSS 1973-; Phi Alpha Theta 1972-; Exeter Twp EA 1973-, Bldg Rep, PRR Chm; Phi Delta Kappa, Pres, Ed Fnd Rep, Svc Key; PCSS; United Meth Church 1979-; Allentown Diocese Speaker Directory, PA Museum of Art, Tchrs Advy Comm 1993-; Finalist PA Tchr of Yr 1989; NCSS Exch prgm with West Germany 1990; Natl Endowment for Hum Grant 1996; Schls, Comm Orgs Motivational Speaker;NEH Grant 1994; *office:* Exeter Twp Sr HS 201 E 37th St Reading PA 19606*

FLECK, WILLIAM JOSEPH, Middle School English Teacher; *b:* Middletown, NY; *m:* Jessica N. Perrenod; *c:* Michael, James; *ed:* Ulster Cty Comm Coll (AA) Liberal Arts, Comm 1985; SUNY at New Paltz (BA) Comm 1986, (MA) Ed 1994; *cr:* Liberty MS Eng Tchr 1989-; *ai:* Core Subject Team Ldr; NYSUT 1989-; Jehovah's Witnesses 1991-; Co-Authoring Adolescent Lit Textbook; *office:* Liberty MS 145 Buckley St Liberty NY 12754

FLEEGER, CONNIE L., English Teacher; *b:* Butler, PA; *c:* Jared; *ed:* Slippery Rock Univ (BS) Scndry Ed 1989, (MA) Eng 1993; Working on Rdng Specialist Degree; *cr:* Karns City HS Eng Tchr 1993-; *ai:* NHS Co-Adv; NCTE 1990-; PSEA 1993-; NEA 1993-; *office:* Karns City Jr Sr HS 1446 Kittanning Pike Karns City PA 16041

FLEET, DIANE MARIE (SMITH), Fourth-Fifth Grade Teacher; *b:* Manhattan, NY; *m:* Thomas Scott; *c:* Kristen; *ed:* Indiana Univ of PA (BA) Sec Ed Soc Stud 1973; Working on MS Carlow Coll Ed Ldrshp Prin Cert; 27 Credit Hrs Penn St, Allegheny Intermediate; 9 Hrs Towards MA; 2 Yr Completion Prospective Prin Prgm Diocese of Pittsburgh; *cr:* St Clare of Assisi Tchr 1980-; *ai:* Cath War Veterans Spelling Moderator; Mid Sts Evaluation Team; Natl Geographic Bee, Pgh Press, Post Gazette Spelling Bee, Stu Cncl, Mission Awareness Moderator; Stu Assistance Prgm Core Team Mem Fac Rep; Sftbl Mgr; NCEA 1980-; PTA 1981-94, Phone Comm Chprsn; PLG, PTG 1980-, PAGE 1996; Block Parent; Girl Scouts 1964-, Ldr, Asst Ldr, Troop Consultant, Neighborhood Ldr Awd; Ladies of Charity; Band Parents 1990-93; Election Bd, Majority Inspector; Chrstn Mothers, Day Camp Cnslr; Track, Bsktbl, Vlybl Parent; 15 Yr Vol Girl Scouts; Cathecist Awd; Tip Top Troop Girl Scouts Awd; *office:* St Clare Of Assisi Schl 336 Wilson Ave Clairton PA 15025*

FLEISCHER, JON HENRI, Chemistry Teacher; *b:* New Castle, PA; *m:* Sherry L. Emig; *c:* Jeffery, Jon Jr.; *ed:* PA St Univ (BS) Sci 1971; Edinboro Univ of PA (BS) Comp Sci 1988; Attnd Slippery Rock Univ; *cr:* Prince Georges Cty MD Sci Tchr 1972-75; Crawford Cntrl Schl Dist Chem Tchr 1973-; *ai:* Golf Coach; NEA 1972-; CCEA 1973-; PSEA 1973-; *office:* Meadville Area Sr HS North St Ext Meadville PA 16335

FLEMING, LARRY D., Professor of Accounting; *b:* Grafton, ND; *m:* Peggy Sue; *c:* Scott, Stephanie; *ed:* Univ of ND (BS) Bus Admin 1963, (MS) Accounting 1965; *cr:* City of Grand Forks ND Data Processing Supvr 1964-69; MO Valley Coll Accounting Instr 1969-74; Grove City Coll Assoc Prof Accounting 1974-; *ai:* Deacon Presbyn Church; Adv to Stu Missions Fellowship Intervarsity Chrstn Fellowship; Acctg Soc Adv; AICPA 1972-; Chrstn Camping Assn 1993-, Vol of the Yr Awd; Certified Pub Accountant 1971; *home:* 511 Oak Hill Dr Grove City PA 16127

FLEMING, LEANORA ILARDO, Spanish Teacher; *b:* Newark, NJ; *m:* Thomas; *c:* Kara, Kerry, Bret; *ed:* Fairleigh Dickinson Univ (BA) Span 1973; Kean Coll of NJ (MA) Instruction, Curr & Admin 1988; Prin & Supvr Cert; Working Toward Plus 30 & Spcl Ed Cert; *cr:* Union Cty Regnl HS Dist Span Tchr 1973-; *ai:* Peer Ldrshp & Peer Mediation Adv; AFT 1980-; *office:* Arthur L Johnson Regnl HS 365 Westfield Ave Clark NJ 07066

FLEMING, LEROY DUKE, Social Studies Teacher; *b:* Enfield, NC; *m:* Kathryn Blanchard; *c:* Kathryn Fleming Budzik, Barry LeRoy; *ed:* High Point Univ (BA) Soc Stud & His 1960; Hood Coll (MA) Admin & Supervision 1990; AP 30 Plus Hrs; Attnd Univ of MD, Univ of WV, Western MD Coll, Shepherd Coll, Univ of NC; *cr:* Frederick Cty Bd of Ed Tchr 1960-; *ai:* NHS, Stu Govt, Sr Class & Eligibility Comm Past Adv; NEA & MD St Tchrs Assn 1960-; Fred Cty Assn of Tchrs Natl Soc Stud 1960-; Jaycees 1970-, Dir, VP; Sertoma Intnl 1972-, Pres, VP, Dirs Gold Coat Awd; Outstdng Young Man; Gold Coat Pres; *office:* New Market MS PO Box 58 New Market MD 21774

FLEMING, LINDA TEETS, Principal; *b:* Cumberland, MD; *m:* Albert John; *c:* Lucinda Davis, Lawre Virts, Lissa, Albert John II; *ed:* Garrett Comm Coll (AA) Elem Ed 1974; Frostburg St Univ (BS) Elem Ed 1975, (MEd) Admin, Supervision 1979; *cr:* Rt 40 Schl 6-8th Grd Tchr 1975-77; Dennett Rd Elem Schl 5th Grd Tchr 1977-89, Chapter I Tchr 1989-92; Swan Meadow Schl Prin 1992-; *ai:* NAESP, MAESP 1992-; Otterbein United Meth Church 1961-, Admin Bd Chprsn, Lay Ldr, Church Schl Tchr, Conf Del; Romney Dist United Meth Church 1961-, Childrens Coord; *office:* Swan Meadow School 6709 Garrett Hwy Oakland MD 21550

FLEMING, MARY MARGARET DAY, Math, Computer & Sci Teacher; *b:* Pittsburgh, PA; *m:* Robert W.; *c:* Bernis, Mary, Sara; *ed:* CA Coll (BA) Spec Ed, Elem Ed 1967; 24 Post Grad Hrs; *cr:* Pittsburgh Pub Schls Spec Ed Tchr 1967-68; Montour Schls 6th Grd Lang Arts Tchr 1968-71; Holy Child Cath Schl Intermediate Tchr 1980-; *ai:* Cmptr Rm Supvr; Stu Assistant Prgm; Tutor; NCEA 1980-; *office:* Holy Child Cath Schl 220 Station St Bridgeville PA 15017

FLEMING, MICHAEL, European & World His Tchr; *b:* Worcester, MA; *ed:* Assumption Coll (BA) His 1966, (MA) His 1971; Attnd Clark Univ, MA Coll of Art; Havard Coll Prof Dev; *cr:* Quinsigamond C. Coll Instr 1974-76; Town of Hopkinton Dept Chair 1978-92, Tchr 1966-; *ai:* Sr Class, Stu Cncl Adv; NEA, MA Tchrs 1966-; Hopkinton Tchr Assn 1966-, Pres 1976-88; Schl Cncl 1994-; Presidential Tchr Awd 1993; Jiffylube Corp Tchr Excl Awd; *office:* Hopkinton Middle HS 88 Hayden Rowe St Hopkinton MA 01748

FLEMING, PAIGE, Middle School Math Teacher; *b:* Marietta, OH; *m:* Harry Edward; *c:* Donald Andrew; *ed:* Muskingum Coll (BA) Elem Ed 1984; 12 Addl Hrs Ed; *cr:* Marietta City Schls Tchr 1984-87, Tchr & Team Leader 1994-; Warren Local Schls SLD Tchr 1987-88, Tchr 1988-89; Frontier Local Schls Tchr & Math Dept Chair 1989-94; *ai:* 8th Grd Class Adv; Tutor; Spelling Bee Coord; Mentor Tchr; Builder's Club Adv; Chrldng Coach; NEA 1985-; Nom Presidential Awd of Excl Sci & Math Tchng.

FLEMING, SANDRA LEE, Mathematics Teacher; *b:* Buffalo, NY; *m:* Guy R.; *c:* Jeff, John, Jim, Joyce; *ed:* St Univ Coll at Buffalo (BSEd) Scndry Math Ed 1970, (MSEd) Scndry Math Ed 1973; Post Grad Stud Connecting Math & Sci, Transit T4, Calculus, Calculators & Cmptrs AC3, Tchng Through Learning Channels, Pride & Teach; *cr:* Reszel Jr HS 7th-9th Grd Math Tchr 1970-87; North Tonawanda Sr HS 9th-12th Grd Math Tchr 1988-; *ai:* Math Stans Support Group; Tchrs Tchng Tchrs Tech; 5 Yr Plan of Math Curr Changes Comm; New Tchrs Mentor; *office:* North Tonawanda Sr HS 405 Meadow Dr North Tonawanda NY 14120

FLEMING, SUSAN J., English Teacher; *b:* Pittsburgh, PA; *ed:* Duquesne Univ (BA) Eng 1968; Univ of Pittsburgh (MED) Eng 1971; Comp Courses; Stu Asst Trng; *cr:* Penn Hills Schl Dist Tchr 28 Yrs; *ai:* NEA & PSEA 1968-; NCTE; *office:* Penn Hills Schl Dist 12200 Garland Dr Pittsburgh PA 15235

FLEMMING, JAMES E., Assoc Professor of Education; *b:* Philadelphia, PA; *c:* Nova, Jalal, Adrienne, Mustafa; *ed:* Cheyney Univ (BS) Indstrl Ed 1978, (MED) Indstrl Ed 1980, (MED) Ed Admin 1991; Addl 9 Comp Concepts West Chester Univ; *cr:* SE Delco Schl Dist Ind Ed Tchr 1978-81; Cheyney Univ Indstrl Tech Tchr 1981-91, Assoc Prof of Ed, Prof Svcs 1991-; *ai:* Omega PSI Phi, Stu Govt Adv; Univ Sabatical Comm Chair; Cheyney Karate Club Coach; APSCUF 1981-, Tenure; ASCD 1992-; Coord for Distance Learning; *office:* Cheyney Univ Of PA PO Box 119 Cheyney PA 19312*

FLESCH, FRANCES, Social Studies Teacher; *b:* Newark, NJ; *ed:* Caldwell Coll (BA) Sociology 1973; Montclair Univ (MA) US His 1978; 15 Addl Credits St Peter's Coll, Kean Coll; *cr:* St Mary Schl Soc Stud Tchr 1973-78; Lafayette Schl Soc Stud Tchr 1978-80; Summit HS Soc Stud Tchr 1980-; *ai:* Curr Cncl; NCSS, NJEA, Union Cty Ed Assn 1980-; Summit Ed Assn 1980-, Pres 1989-93; *office:* Summit HS 125 Kent Place Blvd Summit NJ 07901*

FLETCHER, BARBARA (ARTERS), 2nd Grade Teacher; *b:* Reading, PA; *m:* Michael D.; *c:* Lauren M.; *ed:* Shippensburg Univ (BA) Elem Ed 1974; 36 Credits Master's Equiv Penn St Univ, Millersville Univ; *cr:* Jacksonwald Elem Schl 2nd Grd Tchr 1974-; *ai:* NEA, PSEA, ETEA 1974-; St Mark's Luth Church 1985-, 1st Grd Tchr Sunday Schl; *home:* 371 E Baumstown Rd Birdsboro PA 19508

FLETCHER, DEBORAH A., Agriculture Teacher; *b:* Plattsburg, NY; *m:* Mark S.; *c:* Matt, Nick; *ed:* St Univ of NY at Cobleskill (AAS) Animal Sci 1985; PA St Univ (BS) Agricultural Ed 1987; Univ at Albany (MS) Instructional Tech 1994; *cr:* Cobleskill-Richmondville Cntrl Schl Ag Tchr 1987-; *ai:* FFA & Class of 1999 Adv; Assn Tchrs of Ag NY 1987-, Regnl Rep; NVATA, CRTA 1987-; Carlisle Fire Auxiliary 1988-, Pres 1992-94; Scho Cty 4-H Comm 1994-, Sec 1995-; *office:* Cobleskill-Richmondville HS Washington Hts Cobleskill NY 12043*

FLETCHER, EUGENE HOWARD, Mathematics Teacher; *b:* Saranac Lake, NY; *ed:* Paul Smith's Coll (AA) Lbrl Arts 1966; Parsons Coll (BA) Ed 1968; Grad Stud Plattsburg St Univ, Potsdam St Univ; *cr:* Syracuse Schl System 5th Grd Tchr 1968-69; Saranac Lake Elem Schl 5th Grd Tchr 1969-88; Adirondack Correctional Facility GED Eve Prgm Tchr 1982-92; Saranac Lake MS 7th-8th Grd Math Tchr 1988-; *ai:* NYSt United Tchr, AFT, Saranac Lake Tchrs Assn 1969-; *home:* PO Box 535 Saranac Lake NY 12983

FLETCHER, INA C., Physical Education Teacher; *b:* New York, NY; *ed:* Boston Univ (BS) PE 1964; St Johns Univ Guidance Cert 1970; *cr:* Baldwin Sr HS PE Tchr 1964-; *ai:* Var Girls Tennis, Badminton; NYSAHPER 1964-, Pres 1970; *office:* Baldwin HS 841 High School Dr BALDWIN NY 11572

FLETCHER, JANICE WHITEHEAD, Fourth Grade Teacher; *b:* Minneapolis, MN; *m:* Gilbert Alan; *c:* Emily, Molly; *ed:* Univ of RI (BA) Soc Stud 1968, (MA) Ed 1972; *cr:* North Kingstown Schls Elem Tchr 1969-70; Killeen Schls Elem Tchr 1970; Jamestown Schls Elem Tchr 1970-; *ai:* Jamestown Chance to Dance Prgm Coord 10 Yrs; NEA 1970-; Women's Alliance 1st Bapt Church 1988-, Pres; *office:* Jamestown Schl 76 Melrose Ave Jamestown RI 02835

FLETCHER, JUDITH METZ, English Teacher; *b:* Lyons, NY; *m:* Donald E.; *c:* Kenneth; *ed:* SUNY at Brockport (MA) Eng 1977; Attnd Univ of Rochester; *cr:* Wayne MS Lang Arts Tchr 1972-87; Wayne HS Eng Tchr 1988-; *ai:* NHS Adv; Olympics of the Mind Coord; Delta Kappa Gamma 1984-; United Church of Marion, Sunday Schl Tchr; St Johns Luth Church, Liturgical & Preaching Deacon for ELCA; *office:* Wayne HS 6200 Ontario Center Dr Ontario Center NY 14520

FLETCHER, JULIA ALMEIDA, English Teacher; *b:* Middletown, NY; *m:* Michael; *c:* Kevin Baird, Eric Baird; *ed:* St Univ of NY at Oneonta (BS) Ed 1969; St Univ at New Paltz (MS) Rdng 1981; *cr:* LaGrange Jr High Eng Tchr 1969-73; Dutchess Comm Coll Eng Tutor 1988-90; Titusville MS Eng Tchr 1981-; *ai:* Drama Club Adv; AFT & NYSUT 1969-; Arlington Tchrs Assn 1969-, Sec 1973; ASCD 1993-; *home:* 13 Julia Dr Hyde Park NY 12538*

FLETCHER, KATHI L. HARRIS, Bus Tchr & Occupations Coord; *b:* Easton, MD; *c:* Kenya, Garon; *ed:* Univ of MD (BS) Bus Ed Tchng 1973; *cr:* Seaford MS Tchr 1973-89; The Caroline Ctr Part-time Support Cnslr 1989-95; Seaford HS Tchr, Diversified Occupations Coord 1989-; Benedictine Schl Part-time Comm Cnslr 1995-; *ai:* Schl-to-Work Transition Comm; NEA, DSEA, SEA 1973-; Bell's Chapel AME Church 1965-; Seaford Finalist Tchr of Yr Prgm 1980-81; *office:* Seaford HS 399 N Market St Ext Seaford DE 19973

FLETCHER, MARCIA ANN, Title I Coordinator; *b:* Mansfield, OH; *m:* John Lee; *c:* Scott, Rusty Jodi; *ed:* Ashland Univ El Ed 1963; Post Grad Hrs Rdng, Rdng Recovery Trng; *cr:* Lexington Schl 4th Grd Tchr 1963-65; Butler Elem Schl 1-3 Grd, Title Tchr 1967-; *ai:* AFT; Clearfork Vly Tchrs Assn; *home:* 1601 State Route 97 Butler OH 44822

FLEURY, MARGUERITE DESIMONE, First Grade Teacher; *b:* Winthrop, MA; *m:* Gerald Edward; *c:* Michelle; *ed:* Northeastern Univ (BS) Elem Ed, Hum 1971; *cr:* A. C. Whelan Schl Grd I Tchr 1972-; *ai:* Piloted 1st Grd Rdng Prgm for Rdng Curr, Eng & Lang Arts Prgm; Supervising, Mentor Tchr HS Coll; RTA, MTA, NEA 1972-; Saugus Founders Day 1992-, Comm; Theatre Co of Saugus 1991-, Corr Sec, Bd of Dir; Our Lady of Nazareth 1995-, Comm Co-Chair; Guild Acad.*

FLEWELLING, KAREN A., HS Physical Education Teacher; *b:* Hudson, NY; *ed:* SUNY at Cortland (BS) PE 1964; Russell Sage Coll (MS) Hlth Sci, Ed 1976; *cr:* Shaker HS PE Tchr 1967-, FAM Girls Sports 1980-; *ai:* Var Field Hockey Coach; Suburban Cncl FH Rep; Sect 11 FH All-Star Dinner Chm; St FH Tourn Comm; NHS Comm; M. Fitzgerald Scholar Comm; NYSAHPER 1970-; AFT, NYSUT, North Colonial T Assn 1964-; FH Asst Timer, Scorer Olympics 1996; *office:* Shaker HS 445 Watervliet Shaker Rd Latham NY 12110*

FLIBBERT, JOSEPH THOMAS, English Professor; *b:* Worcester, MA; *m:* Marilyn Sallack; *c:* Michael, Andrew, John; *ed:* Assumption Coll (AB) Eng 1960; Boston Coll (MA) Eng 1963; Univ of IL (PHD) Amer Lit 1970; *cr:* al-Hikma Univ at Baghdad Inst, Eng Tchr 1961-62; Merrimack Coll Asst Prof, Eng Tchr 1963-67; Universite du Mans in France Visiting Prof 1979; Salem St Coll Prof, Dept of Eng 1970-; *ai:* Grad Cncl; Eng Grad Comm Chair; Editorial Bd; Modern Lang Assn 1969-; Nathaniel Hawthorne Soc 1974-, Pred, Bd Mem; Melville Soc 1970-; Phi Kappa Phi 1977; Salem Sthenaeum 1986-, Bd of Trustees, Pres; House of Seven Gables 1976-, Hawthorne Awd; Essex Inst 1981-83, Lib Bd; Book: Melville and the Art of Burlesque; Book Chptr; Articles Pub; Distngd Svc Awd 3 Times; Salem Conf Coord 1992, 1985, 1981, 1977; *office:* Salem St Coll 352 Lafayette St Salem MA 01970

FLICK, DOUGLAS YARNALL, Communication Arts Teacher; *b:* Lancaster, PA; *m:* Sandra Celeste Hake; *c:* Alison C., Matthew D.; *ed:* Bucknell Univ (BA) Eng 1973; Widener Schl of Law (JD) 1989; 9 Credit Hrs Prin Cert Penn St; *cr:* John Piersol Mc Caskey HS Comm Arts Tchr 1973-; *ai:* IM Weight Room Coach; NEA 1985-; Keystone Awd Lit Magazine Adv 1982-85; *office:* J P Mc Caskey HS 445 N Reservoir St Lancaster PA 17601*

FLICK, LESLEY SUSAN, Mathematics Teacher; *b:* Rochester, NY; *ed:* Roberts Weslyan Coll (BS) Math, Ed 1987; St Univ of NY at Brockport (MS) Math, Ed 1992; SUNY Brockport (CAS) Admin 1996; *cr:* Byron Bergen CSD Math Tchr 1987-89; York Cntrl Schl Dist MathTchr 1989-92; East Irondequoit CSD Math Tchr 1992-; *ai:* Stu Task Force; New Standards Project; HYS HS Math Pilot Classroom; NCTM 1990-; ASCD 1994-; Margaret Warner Grad Schl Ed, Human Dev Awd Excl Scndry Schl Tchng 1995; *office:* E Irondequoit Cntrl Schl Dist 2350 E Ridge Rd Rochester NY 14622*

FLICKER, MARK A., 7th Grade Social Studies Tchr; *b:* Philadelphia, PA; *m:* H. Paulette Grinch; *c:* Jennifer, Jill, Jack; *ed:* PA St Univ (BA) His 1972; 24 Grad Credits in Amer Stud Prgm at Penn St Capitol Campus Harrisburg PA; *cr:* Cntrl Dauphin East Jr HS 7th Grd Soc Stud Tchr 1973-; *ai:* HS Soccer Coach; NEA 1973-; Natl Soccer Coaches Assn of Amer 1990-; *office:* Central Dauphin East Jr HS 628 Rutherford Rd Harrisburg PA 17109

FLICKSTEIN, DAN, English, Speech Tchr & Dean; *b:* Jersey City, NJ; *m:* Sandra; *c:* Amy Schulman, Nancy; *ed:* Brooklyn Coll (BA) Speech, Drama 1966, (MA) Rhetoric, Pub Address; Prof Diploma Educl Supervision, Admin; 30 Grad Credits Eng, Speech, Philosophy; *cr:* Abraham Lincoln HS Tchr, Dir Drama 1966-67; Sheepshead Bay HS Tchr 1967-68; Abraham Lincoln HS Drug Ed Specialist, Dean of Discipline 1968-; Brooklyn Coll Adjunct Lecturer 1970-; *ai:* Sing, Dept Coord; Lit Adv; Handball Team Coach; Parents Assn Dedication Awd 1992; Numerous Magazine Articles, Poem, Lit Tchng Guide Pub; *office:* Abraham Lincoln HS 2800 Ocean Parkway Brooklyn NY 11235*

FLIEDER, KAREN W., English Teacher & Dept Chprsn; *b:* Philadelphia, PA; *m:* Saul; *c:* Carlye, Jeremy; *ed:* Temple Univ (BA) Scndry Eng, Speech & Theatre 1968, (MA) Speech Commnctn 1974; East Stroudsburg +30 Ed 1989; *cr:* Plymouth Whitemarsh HS Eng Tchr 1972-76; Hatboro-Horsham HS Lang Arts Tchr 1976-, Dept Chair 1992-; *ai:* Sr Class Adv; Staff Mems Mentor; Sr Advy Bd; Schl Wide Red & Black Night Co-Chair; SCA; NEA; PSEA; Speech Tchr; H-H Tchr of Yr Nom; H-H Champion of Learning Nom.*

FLIESSER, STUART, Biology Teacher; *b:* Bronx, NY; *m:* Robin Karchawer; *c:* Jill, Brett, Scott; *ed:* Lehman Coll (BA) Bio 1977, (MA) Biological Sci 1980; *cr:* Clarkstown Cntrl Schls Sci Tchr 1978-; *ai:* CTA 1978-, Union Rep; MY Zoological Soc 1990-; Rsrch Article Pub; *office:* Clarkstown HS North 151 Congers Rd New City NY 10956

FLIGGE, HERMAN R., High School Math Dept Chair; *b:* Pottsville, PA; *m:* Beth Ann Davenport; *c:* Patrick; *ed:* Kutztown (BA) Sec Ed, Math 1973, (MED) Sec Ed 1978; Cmptr Sci; *cr:* Blue Mountain HS Tchr 1973-; *ai:* Dept Chair; *office:* Blue Mountain H S Rd 1 Schuylkill Haven PA 17972

FLIGIER, LISA ANN, Secondary English Teacher; *b:* Camden, NJ; *ed:* Rutgers Univ (BA) Eng 1990; 12 Credit Hrs Toward Masters in Eng; Completed Enrichment Courses in Learning Styles & Cmptr Literacy for Scndry Schl Tchrs; *cr:* Pennsauken & Cinnaminson MSs Sub Tchr 1990-91; Pennsauken HS Sub Tchr 1991, Eng Tchr 1991-; *ai:* Pennsauken Chapter of NHS Fac Cncl Mem; Rowan Stu Tchr Cooperating Tchr; Grad Speeches Fac Adv; NEA, NJEA, CCCEA, PEA 1991-; Kappa Delta Pi 1989-; NCTE, Northeast Modern Lang Assn 1995-; PTA 1991-; Inservice Wkshps Co-Chprsn; Prin Schlsp & Awds Comm; Century III Schlsp Comm; Stu Plays Fac Adv; Nom for Grad Paper Awd; Rutgers Undergraduate Ralph Bergen Writing Awd; *office:* Pennsauken HS 800 Hylton Rd Pennsauken NJ 08110*

FLINN, ROBERT PETER, Social Studies Chairperson; *b:* Flushing, NY; *m:* Judith McLafferty; *c:* Andrew, Brenna, Daniel; *ed:* Univ of Dayton (BS) Ed 1969; Queens Coll (MS) His 1972; St Univ of NY at Stony brook (MS) Ed 1975; Hofstra Univ Prof Diploma Ed Admin 1987; *cr:* US Army Co Commander 1969-72; Sachem South HS Soc Stud Tchr 1972-90, Soc Stud Chprsn 1990-; *ai:* Zenith Honor Soc Co-Adv; Long Island Cncl on Soc Stud 1980-; LICSS-Supvrs Group 1990-; AFT 1972-; Sachem Cntrl Tchrs Assn 1972-; St Anthonys Parish Outreach Adv Bd 1993-, Chprsn; Cath Youth Org 1990; Northport Youth Ctr Soccer League 1977-87, VP Operations; East Northport Little League 1983-87; Presenter at AFT Natl Convention in Washington DC-Pgrms That Succeed 1995; Presenter at LICSS Annual Convention Huntington NY-The Sachem Challenge Problem 1995; Co-author of NY St Variance Project for Global Studs 1994; *office:* Sachem HS South 51 School St Ronkonkoma NY 11779

FLINT, MARK FRANCIS, Jr HS Coord & Eighth Grd Tchr; *b:* Boston, MA; *ed:* Boston Coll (BA) Elem Ed 1982; Univ of MA at Boston (MED) Educl Admin 1989; *cr:* St Patrick Schl 7-9 Grd Tchr 1982-85; Bunker Hill Comm Coll Part-time Math Instr 1991-; St Mary's Schl 7-8 Grd Tchr, Jr HS Coord 1985-; *ai:* Stu Cncl Adv; Grad Coord; NCEA 1982-; NEA, MTA 1992-; St Mary's Choir 1974-; Boston Coll Schl of Ed John J. Cardinal Wright Awd 1982; *office:* Saint Marys Schl 4 Myrtle St Melrose MA 02176*

FLITTERMAN-LEWIS, SANDY, Assoc Prof Eng & Cinema; *b:* Los Angeles, CA; *m:* Joel Lewis; *ed:* Univ CA Berkeley (BA) Fr & Comp Lit 1968, (MA) Comp Lit 1971, (PHD) Comparative Lit 1982; Cert Pratique de Langue Francaise; *cr:* Brown Univ Visiting Asst Prof 1982-83; Rutgers Univ Asst Prof 1983-89, Assoc Prof 1989-; *ai:* Editorial Bd; Cinema Journal; Soc for Cinema Stud 1975-, Dissertation Awd; Modern Lang Assoc 1980-; AAUP 1983-; Books: To Desire Differently, Feminism & the French Cinema, New Vocabularies in Film Semiotics; Numerous Articles in Journals; *office:* Rutgers Univ Murray Hall C.A.C. English Dept New Brunswick NJ 08903*

FLOCCO, ANGELA FARINA, 5th Grade Teacher; *b:* Queens, NY; *c:* William, Thomas, David; *ed:* St Joseph's Coll (BA) Child Stud 1960; Fairfield Univ (MA) Elem Ed 1989, (CAS) Prof Dev 1994; *cr:* West End Schl Kndgtn Tchr 1960-61; Rhame Ave Schl Kndgtn Tchr 1963-66; Strong Comstock Schl 1st Grd Tchr 1973-74, 3rd Grd Tchr 1974-81; Cider Mill Schl 4th Grd Tchr 1981-88, 5th Grd Tchr 1988-; *ai:* NEA, Wilton PTA 1973-; Delta Kappa Gamma 1989-.

FLOCK, GILBERT C., Instrumental Music Teacher; *b:* Utica, NY; *m:* Candace L.; *c:* Geoffrey, Adam; *ed:* Ithaca Coll (BA) Music Ed 1988, (MS) Music Ed 1994; *cr:* Hamilton Cntrl Schls Instrumental Music Tchr 1988-89; East Syracuse-Minoa Cntrl Schls Instrumental Music Tchr 1989-; *ai:* Marching Band, Winter Guard, Jazz Band Dir; Mid-York Color Guard Circuit Pres 1995-; NY Fild Band Conf Class Rep 1991-; AFT, NYSSMA, ESMUT 1989-; *office:* East Syracuse-Minoa Cntrl Schl 6320 Fremont Rd East Syracuse NY 13057

FLOHR, PATRICIA MILES, Administration & Geog Teacher; *b:* Desdemona, TX; *m:* Donald Myers; *c:* Nancy Graves, Donna Koerber; *ed:* Univ of MO (MS) Ed 1966; Towson St Univ; *cr:* Cecil Cty 6th Grd Tchr 1956-57; Baltimore Cty MS Tchr 1958-68; Loch Raven Pre Kndgtn Tchr 1971-81; Calvery Luth 3rd Grd Tchr 1981-82; Open Bible Day Schl MS Tchr 1982-; *ai:* Drama Productions; *office:* Open Bible Day Schl 5814 Harford Rd Baltimore MD 21214

FLOM, DAVID SIMMONS, English & Theater Teacher; *b:* Crookston, MN; *c:* Amanda, Eric; *ed:* Concordia Coll (BA) Eng 1971; Goddard Coll (MA) Theatre Arts 1991; *cr:* Park Sr HS Eng, Jrnlsm Tchr 1971-73; Crookston Cntrl HS Eng, Drama, Jrnlsm Tchr 1974-76; George Dewey HS Eng, Drama Tchr 1976-78; Estes Park HS Eng, Drama Tchr 1978-80; Wuerzburg Amer HS Eng, Drama Tchr 1980-; *ai:* Drama Dir; Federal Ed Assn 1980-; *office:* Wurzburg American HS Cmr 475 Box 264 APO AE 09036

FLOMMERSFELD, JODY L., Guidance Counselor; *b:* Greenville, OH; *ed:* Wright St Univ (BS) Bus Ed, PE 1982; Univ of Dayton (MS) Cnslng 1993; *cr:* Natl Trail HS Tchr 1985-93, Cnslr 1993-; *ai:* Var Boys Bsktbl Asst; Adv NHS, Sr Class; FCA; *office:* National Trail HS 6940 Oxford Gettysburg Rd New Paris OH 45347

FLOOD, JOYCE A., English Teacher of Disabled; *b:* N Tonawanda, NY; *m:* John; *c:* John III, Jeffrey; *ed:* Dearnan Coll (BA) Eng 1971; *cr:* Williamsville HS Eng Tchr; *ai:* Jr Class Adv; PA NEA; *office:* Wyalusing Vly Jr Sr HS RR 2 Box 7 Wyalusing PA 18853

FLOOD, MARILYN R., Kindergarten Teacher; *b:* Brooklyn, NY; *m:* James; *c:* Jeremy; *ed:* SUNY at New Paltz (BA) Elem Ed 1971; Montessori Ed Cert; *cr:* St Patricks Schl 3rd Grd Tchr 1971-75; Our Lady of Mt Carmel Kndgtn Tchr 1981-; *ai:* FCT 1983-; Six Tchng Grants from Area Fund of Dutchess Cty; *office:* Our Lady-Mt Carmel Schl 15 Mount Carmel Pl Poughkeepsie NY 12601

FLOOD, PAMELA SUE, Math, Reading & Lang Arts Tchr; *b:* Columbus, OH; *m:* Dana Wayne; *c:* Beverly, Tasha; *ed:* Bevard Comm Coll (AA) Lbrl Arts 1978; Univ of ME (BS) Elem Ed 1985; 27 Addl Post Grad Credit Hrs Ldrshp; ME Geographic Alliance Tchr Consultant trng; *cr:* North Orrington 2 Grd Tchr 1985-87; Bangor Schl Dept 1 Grd Tchr 1987-90; Ctr Drive Schl MS So Stud, Hlth, Stud Skills Tchr 1992-; *ai:* Cross Country Coach; Recerfication Comm; Emergency Response Team; Fund Raising Acts; ME Geographic Alliance Schlsp; Article Pub; High Hnrs Grad; Hnr Fraternity; *office:* Center Drive Schl RR 3 Box 100 Orrington ME 04474*

FLOOR, FRANK RICHARD, Human Development Teacher; *b:* Taunton, MA; *m:* Maureen Katherine Galleshaw; *c:* Frank, Kristen, Matthew; *ed:* RI Coll (MAT) Bio 1968, (CAGS) Scndry Admin 1972, (MED) Instructional Tech 1977; *cr:* Bellingham Jr-Sr HS General Sci & Bio Tchr 1969-70; East Providence Sr HS Bio Tchr 1970-92, Sci Dept Head & Human Dev Tchr 1992-; *ai:* RI Statewide Sci Framework Dev Team; East Bay Sci Framework Dev Plan; Curr Coordination Comm; East Providence Ed Assn 1970-, VP; NABT 1968-, Membership Chprsn, OBTA Outstanding Bio Tchr Awd; East Smithfield Lib 1970-, Asst Dir, Champlin Grants; Leadership Inst in Human & Molecular Genetics at Cold Spring Harbor; Natl Leadership Inst for Tchrs of Bio at Rutgers Univ; US Dept of Ed Project in Biotechnology LabLink 2000 at Boston Univ Schl of Medicine; 13120 Dollars ECIA Grant to Set up Biotechnology Prgm at East Providence HS; Encouragement Grant East Providences 1st Acad Decathlon Team; East Providence Tchr of Month; Write Newsletter & Newspaper Articles for East Smithfiled Pub Lib; *office:* East Providence Sr HS 2000 Pawtucket Ave East Providence RI 02914*

FLORENTINE, MARGARET TOOMEY, Social Studies Dept Head; *b:* Boston, MA; *m:* George Jr.; *ed:* Boston Coll (BA) His, Ec 1974; Univ of MA-Boston St (MED) Scndry Admin 1980; Boston Coll (MA) His; JSEA Symposium Ignation Paradigon; *cr:* Misson HS His Tchr 1974-80; Boston Coll HS Soc Stud Dept Head, Amer, World His Tchr 1980-; *ai:* Stu Cncl Moderator; Fac Prof Dev Comm Chair; JSEA Ldrshp Seminars; NCSS, ASCD 1980-; JFK Pres Lib Advy 1984-; MA St Senate Ldrshp Awd for Tchng; *office:* Boston College HS 150 William T Morrissey Blvd Dorchester MA 02125

FLORENTINO-JAMES, GINA, Social Studies Teacher; *b:* Rockville Centre, NY; *m:* Robert E. James; *c:* Gregory; *ed:* Boston Coll (BA) Sociology-Cum Laude 1978; SUNY at Stony Brook (MALS) Soc Stud 1984; Certfd to Teach Eng, N-6th; 45 Addl Hrs Eng; Working Towards an Admin Degree; *cr:* St Hugh of Lincoln Elem Schl Jr HS Soc Stud Tchr 1980-86; Amityville Meml HS Soc Stud Tchr 1986-91; C. W. Post Univ Adj Prof of Ed 1985-; Riverhead HS Soc Stud, Eng Tchr 1991-; *ai:* Admin Intern; Cooperating Tchr; NYSUT, Long Island Cncl for SS 1986-; Ed Reporter 1986-88; *office:* Riverhead HS 700 Harrison Ave Riverhead NY 11901*

FLORES, LORENA ALEXI, Bilingual HS History Teacher; *b:* Bronx, NY; *c:* Adriana; *ed:* Jersey City St Coll (BA) His 1992; Seton Hall Univ (MA) Ed 1995; *cr:* Mngmt Technologies Cmptr Libr 1985-90; James J. Ferris HS Biling His Tchr 1992-; Hudson Cty Comm Coll Adj Prof Latin Amer His 1994-; *ai:* Span Club, TIGS Ldrshp Camp Conf Adv; N *office:* James J Ferris HS 35 Colgate St Jersey City NJ 07302*

FLORI, KATHERINE A., Business Education Teacher; *b:* New *m:* Jerry; *c:* Monica G., Paige K., Guy N., Gennaro M.; *ed:* Quee Comm Coll (AA) Secretarial Sci 1988; Bernard Baruch Coll (B 1992; 18 Credits MS Instrl Tech NY Inst of Tech; Coord L Cooperative Work Stud Prgms; *cr:* Grover Cleveland HS Bus 1992-; Dist 25 Adult Ed World Perfect Instr 1995; *ai:* Career E Internship Prgm Coord, Tchr; Kappa Delta Pi 1993-, Sec 1993-94 Ed Assn 1992-; NBEA 1992-, Awd of Merit; Golden Key Hon S Peat Marwick Scholar Awd, Outstdng Sr.

FLORI, MONICA G., 6th Grade Reading Teacher; *b:* New York Queens Coll (BA) His 1991, (MS) Rdng Ed 1995; *cr:* Grover Cle Soc Stud Tchr 1992-93; IS 73 Rdng Tchr 1993-; *ai:* Kappa Delta Phi Alpha Theta 1991-, Pres.*

FLORIG, NANCY MAC DONALD, Sixth Grade Teacher; *b* MA; *m:* David Scott; *c:* Dylan; *ed:* Fitchburg St Coll (BS) Spec 1974; *cr:* Greenhalge Schl Sp Ed tchr 1974-82, 1st Grd Tchr Edison Schl 6th Grd Tchr 1988-; *ai:* Safety Patrol Adv; Yrbk, Selection Comms; Talent Sho Coord; Spec Olympics Coach; Ma Facilitator; Peer Mediation Coach; NEA 1988-; AFT 1974-87; GATE Design, Instruction; Supvr Stu Tchrs; *office:* Thomas Ec 205 Melrose Ave Westmont NJ 08108*

FLORIO, MICHAEL LEONARD, Seventh Grade Teacher; *b:* Canada; *m:* Carolyn Arthurs; *c:* Michael Jr.; *ed:* Mc Master Univ His 1979; Brock Univ (BED) Jr, Intermediate Stud 1980; Add Master Univ Eng; *cr:* Stelco Pub Relations 1975-80; Dufferin-Pe Cath Schl Tchr 1981-; *ai:* Bsbl, Vlybl, Bsktbl, Track & Field Rep 1981-; Brampton, Orangeville Ath Assn Sec, Treas 1982-85 Eng Cath Tchrs Assn 1981-; *home:* 17 Barr Crescent Brampton 3C3 Canada CN *

FLORKOWSKI, CAROLANNE FISHER, Teacher; *b:* Yonker Mark; *ed:* SUNY at Cortland (BA) Ed 1988, (MSE) Scndry Ed, M *cr:* Maplewood MS Tchr 1990-91; JHS 142 Tchr 1991-92; W. H Tchr 1992-95; LMK MS Tchr 1995-; *ai:* Math Club Adv; NCT MAA 1994-; UFT, AFT 1990-; *home:* 24 Overlook Rd Ardsley N

FLOWER, TERRY, Humanities Teacher; *b:* Cooperstown, NY; *m* *c:* Nathan, Katherine; *ed:* SUNY at Oswego (BS) Eng Ed 1965, Ed 1986; 12 Grad Gredit Hrs Syracuse Univ; *cr:* Roxboro Jr HS Tchr 1965-67; Cicero HS Grd 10 Eng Tchr 1968-71; North Syra 8-9 Grd Eng, Hum Tchr, Gifted Prgm 1982-, Eng Dept Chprsn Lit Magazine; Announcement Team; Peer Coaching; Stu Supp NYSUT, AFT, NEA, NCTE 1965-; NYSEC 1965-, Tchr of Excl; Intnl 1993-, Bd Mem; *office:* North Syracuse Jr HS 5353 W Taft Syracuse NY 13212*

FLOWERS, MARGARET M., Business Teacher; *b:* Philadelphi Jerry C.; *c:* Cheryl, Jerry Jr.; *ed:* DE St Univ (BS) Bus Ed 1968; Univ (ME) Educl Admin 1978; *cr:* Shoemaker Jr HS Typing Tchr Howard HS Bus Dept Tchr 1970-73; Bayard MS Typing Tchr 19 S. DuPont HS Bus Dept Tchr 1975-79; Henry Conrad Jr HS 1979-80; Wilmington HS Acad of Fin, Bus Tchr 1980-; *ai:* Bu Amer Comm; Phoenix Prgm Stu Adv; Sr Class Spon; Red Clay 1970-; Jack & Jill of Amer 1983-, Group Adv; Kappa Delta F Wilmington HS 100 N Dupont Rd Wilmington DE 19807

FLOWERS, PEARL WILSON, Mathematics Dept Chairpe Suffolk, VA; *m:* Delbert L.; *c:* David, Duane, Delisa Flowers Edc Cntrl St Univ (BS) Math 1961; Attnd Western MD, Trinity Coll MD; *cr:* Ann Arbor HS Math Tchr 1962-63; Union Endicott HS M 1968-71; Mont Co Pub Schls Math Tchr 1973-; *ai:* Math, Cmptr Chprsn; NEA 1970-; NCTM 1973-; Delta Sigma Theta 1960-, Trea Quince Orchard HS 15800 Quince Orchard Rd Gaithersburg MD

FLOYD, MURIEL HEFFLIN, Main Stream Teacher; *b:* Pittsbu *c:* Robbin Jones, Autumn L., Jude E., Monica L. Fowler, Ralph C.; *ed:* Univ of Pittsburgh (BS) Elem Ed 1973, (MED) Spec Credit Hrs Comm Coll of Allegheny Cty; Credit Hrs Post Grad Halls Grove Spec Ed Ctr Spec Ed Tchr 5 Yrs; Lemington Elem Ed Tchr 5 Yrs; Miliones MS Spec Ed Tchr 6 Months; Madison E Mainstream Tchr 11 Yrs; *ai:* Instrl Cabinet Comm; Comprehensi Improvement Plan; Safety Patrol Supvr; AFT 1974-; GPABS Corresponding Sec, Cert; NANBPW 1989-, Historian, Cert; Mad Fac 1985-, Soc Comm, Cert; Comprehension Ed Plan 1983-, A Urban League 1980-; Proficiency in Tchng Profession; Humanitar Going the Extra Mile Tutorial Prgm; Excl in Work Attendence Madison Elem Schl Milwaukee & Orion Sts Pittsburgh PA 15219

FLOYD, SHARON ELIZABETH, Dept Chair of Special Baltimore, MD; *m:* Charles Michael; *c:* Ellis Alexander, F Matthew; *ed:* High Point Coll (BS) Spcl Ed 1980; The Johns Hopk (MS) Ec Ed 1987; Anticipated EDD in Spcl Ed 1997; *cr:* Pikes Tchr of Spcl Ed 1980-93, Dept Chm 1993-; *ai:* Comms: Schl Perfc Minority Achvmt Participation & Success; Black Awareness; B Month Chm; Disruptive Yth Project; Project STAY; Human Rel Values Ed; Fac Cncl; MD Orton Soc 1988-90, Exec Adv Bd; Recognition 1980-, Awd Selection Comm; *office:* Pikesville Seven Mile Ln Baltimore MD 21208*

FLUENT, PAMELA J., Second Grade Teacher; *b:* Salamanca, SUNY Geneseo (BA) Elem Ed N-6 1966; Elmire Coll; Numerous I Courses; *cr:* Olean Bd of Ed 2nd Grd Tchr 1966-67; Horseheads 1st-3rd Grd Tchr 1967-; *ai:* Nature Ctr Founder, Stocking & Mair Horseheads Tchrs Assn 1967-, Sec, Chm, Bldg Rep; NEA 1967 Delta Kappa 1970-, VP; *office:* Gardner Road Elem Schl 541 Ga Horseheads NY 14845

FLUHARTY, CHARLES ROBERT, Chemistry Teacher; *b:* Steu OH; *m:* Stacey Lynn Rauenzahn; *ed:* W VA Univ (BS) Scndry (BA) Bio 1993; 9 Post Grad Credit Hrs Toward Bachelors; *cr:* Cntrl Cath HS Chem Tchr 1994-; *ai:* Stu Assistance Prgm; Allentown Diocese Lay Tchrs Assn 1994-, Fac Rep; *office:* Cntrl 1400 Hill Rd Reading PA 19602

FLUHARTY, KAY A., Latin Teacher; *b:* Canton, OH; *m:* Willia Meghan, Lyndsay; *ed:* OH Univ (BA) Eng 1970; Xavier Univ (ME Latin 1991; Attnd Miami Univ, Univ of FL; *cr:* West Hartford Pu Eng Tchr 1970-71; Northwest Local Schls Eng Tchr 1972-78; Made Schls Latin Tchr 1990-; *ai:* Latin Club Spon; Natl & OH Jr C Leagues Spon; Eng & Frgn Lang Curr Comms; Amer Classical 1989-; OH Classical League 1989-; Cincinnati Assn of Tchrs 1990-, Pres; Pub Classical World; OH Classical Conf Schlsp; Lo Dist PTA Tchr of Yr; Ashland Tchr Awd Nom; *office:* Madeira Jr School 7465 Loannes Dr Cincinnati OH 45243*

FLYNN, CHRISTOPHER ALBERT, Special Education Tchr & C Georgetown, DC; *ed:* Indiana Univ of PA (BS) Exceptional Child E Working Toward Masters; *cr:* Mark Twain Schl Emotionally I Adolescents Tchr, Cnslr 1989-93; Walt Whitman HS Emotionally I Adolescents Tchr, Cnslr 1993-; *ai:* Track 1990-, Indoor Track Coach; Gonzaga HS Cross Cntry 1994, Indoor Track 1994 Coach Tchr Assn, NEA 1989-; Individual, Relay St Champions Track ıry St Champs, Montgomery Cty Coach of Yr 1995; *office:* Walt HS 7100 Whittier Blvd Bethesda MD 20817

ELAINE SAMONA, Language Arts Teacher; *b:* Passaic, NJ; *m:* *c:* John, Daniel; *ed:* William Paterson Coll of NJ (MA) Eng 1975; irad Credits; *cr:* Park Ridge HS Amer Lit Tchr 1971-78; Garfield s Compensatory Ed, PT Tchr 1979-85; Woodrow Wilson MS 8th Arts Tchr 1985-; *ai:* Natl Jr Hnr Soc Adv; Curr Cncl; Acad Team ır; Clifton Tchrs Assn, Passaic Cty Tchrs Assn, NJEA, NEA ıtl Assn of Stu Act Advs 1986-; *office:* Woodrow Wilson MS 1400 en Ave Clifton NJ 07013

HELENE RAINIS, Guidance Counselor; *b:* New York, NY; *m:* ı. Jr.; *c:* Bernard, Helene, Julia; *ed:* Dowling Coll (BS) Spcl Ed U CW Post (MS) Schl Cnslng 1985; Prof Diploma Pgm in & Family Cnslng; *cr:* Newfield HS Spcl Ed Tchr 1983-86, Guid 86-; *ai:* SADD Adv; Dist Coll Night Consortium & Dist 11th Grd Pgm Standing Comm Mem; Mem of Stu & Fac Compass; AFT SCA 1987-; Setacket Civic Assn 1970-, Bd Mem; Three Village ıl Soc 1973-; SEPTA Jenkins Awd; *office:* Newfield HS 145 Dr Selden NY 11784*

IDA MORETTI, Information Science Professor; *b:* Torino, Italy; R.; *c:* Anthony M., Christopher G.; *ed:* Adelphi Univ (BA) Math Inst of Tech (MST) Cmptr Sci 1973; Univ of Pittsburgh (MBA) ain 1980, (PHD) Lib Sci 1994; *cr:* Forest View HS Math Tchr Point Park Coll Assoc Prof 1975-80; Univ of Pittsburgh Info Sci t Prof 1980-;, Bachelor of Sci Info Svc Dir 1991-; *ai:* PA Jr Acad dge; Intnl Stdnts & Undergrad Info Sci Stdnts Fac Spon; ACM; ,A; Book Pub 1991; Articles Pub 1990, 1992; *office:* University of h SLIS Bldg Room 712 Pittsburgh PA 15260

JAMES R.,OSA, Mathematics & Theology Teacher; *b:* phia, PA; *ed:* Villanova Univ (BA) Philosophy 1969; WA cal Union (MA) Theology 1973; Villanova Univ (MAT) Math Ed iquesne Univ (MA) Formative Spirituality 1992; Post Grad Stud e Univ Math Ed 1990 & Drexel Univ Math Ed 1993; *cr:* Malvern ory Schl Math & Theology Tchr 1972-80; Our Mother of Good Novitiate Prior 1980-82; Austin Preparatory Schl Tchr, Math Dept Trustee 1982-88; Villanova Univ Adjunct Prof of Math 1988-92; Preparatory Schl Math & Theology Tchr 1988-; Math Dept Chair 'rustee for Malvern Prep & St Augustine's Prep; Counselor for of St Thomas fo Villanova, 1994-; *ai:* Ftbl, Sr Retreat Prgm & Sr oderator; Campus Ministry Staff; Acad Affairs & Marketing NCTM & Assn of Tchrs of Math of Philadelphia & Vicinity; reparatory Rdng Awd 1988; *office:* Malvern Prep Schl For Boys Ave Malvern PA 19355

JAMES WALTER, Sixth Grade Teacher; *b:* Wilkes-Barre, PA; h Haytmanek; *c:* Kevin, Tracy; *ed:* Bloomsburg Univ (BS) Elem ; West Chester Univ Counselor Ed; *cr:* Colonial Schl Dist 6th Grd '1-; *ai:* 8th Grd Girls Bsktbl Coach; Sftbl Coach; Bldg Equipment ı Grd Team Ldr; PSEA & NEA 1971-; Colonial Ed Assn 1971-, p; *office:* Colonial MS 716 Belvoir Rd Norristown PA 19440

JOSEPH M., MS Social Studies Teacher; *b:* Philadelphia, PA; *m:* Lyons; *c:* Melanie; *ed:* Temple Univ (BA) Scndry Soc Stus 1988; Univ (MA) Elem Ed 1994; *cr:* Glenolden Schl MS Soc Stud *i:* Environmental Group; Safety Patrol; MS Dance Coord; NEA EA 1988-; *office:* Glenolden Schl 150 Mac Dade Blvd Prospect 19076

KATHLEEN T., Prof & Surgical Tech Dept Chm; *b:* Chicopee, Boston Coll Schl of Nrsng (BS) Nrsng 1970, (MS) Nrsng 1972; Rochester Primary Care 1977; *cr:* Mercy Providence Hosp ıg Room Nurse 1957-68; Northwestern Univ Nrsng Instr Part-time ; Univ of MA Asst Prof Nrsng 1972-77; Yale Univ Assoc Prof ; Springfield Tech Comm Coll Prof Surgical Tech 1988-; *ai:* Sigma au 1970-, NHS in Nrsng; Amer Assn of Operating Room Nurses; umerous Articles Pub; Rsrch on Delivery of Nrsng Care & Women east Cancer; Distngd Tchr Yale Univ; *office:* Springfield Tech Coll 1 Armory Sq Springfield MA 01105*

KATHY L., Mathematics Teacher; *b:* Webster, MA; *m:* Kevin J.; ıfield St Coll (BA) Math 1982; Anna Maria Coll (MA) Counseling, 995; *cr:* David Prouty Regnl HS Math Tchr 1983-; Guidance or Intern 1995-; *ai:* MTA, NEA, SEBTA 1983-; Kappa Delta Pi The Emerald Club 1994-; Worcester Cty Deputy Sheriffs Assn David Prouty Yrbk Dedication 1987; *office:* David Prouty Regnl HS n St Spencer MA 01562

LUCILLE GRAHAM, Physical Education Teacher; *b:* er, PA; *m:* David J.; *c:* Kelley Ann, Alayna Leigh; *ed:* Slippery niv (BA) Hlth, PE 1975; Penn St Univ (MS) Hlth Ed 1995; *cr:* Schl Dist Hlth, PE Tchr 1984-; *ai:* Pep Club Adv; AAHPERD, ERD 1991-; Slippery Rock Alumni Assn 1975-; Amer Red Cross r 1996-; *office:* Beaver Area Middle-HS Gypsy Glen Rd Beaver PA

MARGARET HENNESSEY, Spelling Teacher; *b:* Oswego, NY; aret Ellen; *ed:* St Univ of NY at Oswego (BS) Elem Ed 1950, (MS) 953; 24 Addl Hrs; 3 Cmptr Courses; *cr:* Kingsford Park 1st Grd 52-57; Cherry Road 2nd, 4th Grd Tchr 1957-63; St Charles Kndgtn 69-94, 4th-5th Grd Spelling Tchr 1994-; *ai:* After Schl Prgm 7 Yrs; ssn Cath Tchrs; Awded NY St Amer Revolution Bicentennial ssion Cert; *office:* St Charles Borromeo Schl 200 W High Ter se NY 13219

MARY SETOW, Teacher; *b:* Jersey City, NJ; *ed:* (BS) Elem Ed, 60; *cr:* Sacred Heart Schl 2nd Grd Tchr 1949-50; Our Lady of Schl 4th, 5th Grd Tchr 1950-59; St Catherine Schl 7th Grd Tchr 9; Epiphany Schl 8th Grd Tchr 1969-79; St Thomas The Apostle d Grd Tchr 1979-94, 3rd Grd Part-Timr Rel, Math Tchr 1993-95; *ai:* Worker, Part-Time Tchr; NCEA 1958-94; Tchr Of Yr 1993.

MICHAEL JAMES, Social Studies Teacher; *b:* Kingston, NY; ıca Coll (BA) His 1992; Binghamton Univ (MAT) Soc Stud Ed 1994; enango Forks HS Soc Stud Tchr 1994-; *ai:* Modified Ftbl, Wrestling osse Coach; *office:* Chenango Forks HS 1 Gordon Dr Binghamton 901*

PATRICK MICHAEL, Math & Computer Science Tchr; *b:* mton, NY; *m:* Carol Fitzsimmons; *c:* Sean; *ed:* E Stroudsburg Univ cndry Math 1969; Marywood Coll (MS) Mgmt Info Sys 1978; Grad at Univ of Scranton; *cr:* Elk Lake HS Scndry Math Tchr 1969-75; City Regnl HS Scndry Math & Cmptr Sci Tchr 1975-; *ai:* NHS Adv; ic Planning Comm; Schl Improvement Comm Co-Chprsn; stu ling; Stdnts Group Facilitator; NEA 1969-; PSEA, NCTM 1969-; easant Twp 1976-, Auditor; *office:* Forest City Regnl HS 100 hanna St Forest City PA 18421

PATTY JUREWICZ, 1st Grade Teacher; *b:* Batavia, NY; *m:* L.; *c:* Maura, Mallory; *ed:* Mercyhurst Coll (BA) Elem Ed 1973; St oll at Buffalo (MS) Spec Ed 1976; *cr:* Pioneer Cntrl Schl 1st Grd 973-76; St Joseph's Elem Schl Kndgtn Tchr 1976-77; Pembroke Schl K-2nd Grd Tchr 1977-82; Batavia City Schls Resource Room 982-83; Pembroke Cntrl Schl 1st-2nd Grd Tchr 1984-; *ai:* NY St Tchrs, AFT 1973-; Pembroke Tchrs Fed 1977-, Bldg Rep; Genesee Region Whole Lang Group; *office:* Pembroke Primary Schl Main Rd-West Ave PO Box 190 East Pembroke NY 14056

FLYNN, SHEILA ALDRICH, Second Grade Teacher; *b:* Addison, NY; *m:* George; *c:* Tammy Marzo; *ed:* Mansfield St Coll (BS) Elem Ed 1973; 59 Credit Hrs Post Grad Stud Mansfield St Coll, Penn St Univ, Elmira Coll; *cr:* Addison Cntrl Schl Rdng Tutor 1973-74, Elem Tchr 1974-; *ai:* NEA, Addison TA 1975-; *office:* Tuscarora Elem Schl 7 Cleveland Dr Addison NY 14801

FLYNN LOW, BERNADETTE, Professor of English; *b:* El Paso, TX; *m:* John R. Low III; *c:* Raissa Snyder, Jack, Maggie; *ed:* Univ of Tx at El Paso (BA) Eng 1966, (MA) Eng 1969; Univ of NM (PHD) Eng 1982; *cr:* Univ of Texas Tchng Asst 1966-69; Univ of NM Tchng Asst 1969-71; El Paso Comm Coll Prof of Eng 1971-72; Dundalk Comm Coll Prof of Eng 1972-; *ai:* Dir of Hnrs Pgm; Adv of Phi Theta Kappa; Natl Collegiate Hnrs Cncl 1982-, Exec Comm; Northeast NCHC 1982-, VP; Maryland Collegiate Hnrs 1982-, VP; AAUW 1995-; Grace Episcopal Church 1972-, Vestry; PTA 1984-, Pres, VP, Sect; Maryland Assn Higher Ed Rsrch Awd; Numerous Articles Pub; *office:* Dundalk Comm Coll 7200 Sollers Point Rd Baltimore MD 21222*

FLYTHE, NANCY PARKER, Fifth Grade Teacher; *b:* SAlisbury, NC; *c:* Mario Damon, Brian Lamar; *ed:* Livingston Coll (BA) Early Chldhd 1973; 15 Hrs Univ of MD at College Park; *ai:* Founder, Coord Uniting for Cause; Legislative Contact Team; Lou Rawls Telethon Chm; NEA 1973-, Del; MD St Tchrs Assn 1973-, Apprentice Prgm, Minority Affairs Comm; A A C Tchr Assn 1973-, Bd of Dir; Banneker-Douglass 1995-, Bd of Dir; TAAAC 1973-, Bd of Dir; WA Post Agnes Meyer Outstdng Tchr Awd; US Coast Guard Black His Spkr Awd; MD St Tchrs Assns Minority Recognition Comm Svc; *office:* Sunset Elem Schl 8572 Fort Smallwood Rd Pasadena MD 21122*

FOG, SUSAN FAIRBANKS, History & Psychology Teacher; *b:* Springfield, VT; *m:* Robert R.; *c:* James Williamson; *ed:* Wilson Coll (BA) His 1969; Keene St Coll (MED) Admin 1989; 30 Addl Credit Hrs in Admin, Curr, Dev, Supervision; Reality Therapy, Control Theory Cert; *cr:* Deray Twp Pub Schls His Tchr 1969-72; Springfield HS His, Eng, Latin Tchr 1973-79, His, Psych Tchr 1985-; *ai:* Sr Class, Latin Club Adv; Instructional Support Team; Steering Comm; New Amer Schls Grant; Standards & Assessment, Curr, Instruction Chair; Dist Wide Comm of NAS Grant; STA, VT NEA, NEA, Treas, Bldg Rep; ASCD, Inst for Reality Therapy 1989-; VT Standards Bd for Prof Educators, Charter Mem 1989-94; Local Budget Advy Comm 1991-93; Delta Kappa Gamma 1993-; *office:* Springfield HS 303 South St Springfield VT 05156

FOGARTY, ROBIN A., AP History Teacher; *b:* Rochester, NY; *m:* Judy; *c:* Scott, Christopher, Leslie Ann Boslough; *ed:* SUNY at Brockport (BS) His 1961; Univ of Rochester (MA) His 1964; Attnd Wm Howard Taft Inst, Russian Lang & Cult Inst; *cr:* Dake Jr HS 7th & 8th Grd Soc Stud Tchr 1961-64; SUNY at Brockport Asst His Prof 1965-66; Irondequoit HS AP His Tchr 1966-; *ai:* Chess Club; Bsbl Coach; Value Ed Wkshp Instr; Various Curr Writing Projects; Select Mem Supt; Prin Fac & Stu Advy Cncl Chm; IHS Planning Team Mentor & Co-Chair; WITA 1961-, VP & Contract Negot; Amer His Soc 1961-; AFT 1964-; Sr Class Outstdng Tchr Awd 1982-83; His Tchr of Yr 1984; Dist Tchr of Yr 1984; Duke Univ Tchr of Yr 1988; Univ of Chicago Tchr of Yr 1989; Excl in Scndry Schl Tchng Awd 1990; Univ of Roch Outstdng Sr Tchr Recog 1994; Grants: ESEA Title IV-C, Fed Russian Lang Inst; Dist Merit Tchng Awds; Univ of Rochester Grad Schl Ed & Human Dev Awd; *office:* Irondequoit HS 260 Cooper Rd Rochester NY 14617*

FOGARTY, ROSEMARY A., Math & Computer Science Tchr; *b:* W Hazelton, PA; *ed:* Bloomsburg Univ (BA) Sec Ed, Math 1966; Temple Univ (MS) GEPT 1972; Rider Univ Cert Sec Prin, Supvr Math 1981; Attnd Bloomsburg U, Millersville U, Ball St, Univ of UT, Trenton St; *cr:* Hammondsport Cntrl Schl Math Tchr 1966; Bristol Borough Schl Dist 6th Grd Tchr 1966; Pennsbury Schl Dist Math, Cnptr Sci Tchr 1967-; *ai:* Stu Govt; NCTM 1965-; PCTM; BCCTM 1968-, Pres; NEA; PSEA; PEA; ATMOPAV; Morrisville Schl Dist Authority Chm; Morrisville Lib Bd.*

FOGELL, HEATHER E., Biology Teacher; *b:* York, PA; *m:* Paul B.; *ed:* Millersville Univ (BSED) Bio 1993; Rutgers Univ 13 Credit Hrs Grad Work; *cr:* Coatesville Area Schl Dist Bio Tchr 1993-; *ai:* Nature Trail Coord; Curr Dev Team; Peer Mediation Adv; GLOBE Lead Tchr; NEA, PSEA, CATA 1993-; Phi Kappa Phi Honor Soc 1993-; NE Shoemaker Bio Tchng Awd; Isaak Walton League Schlsps; Nemyer-Hodgekins Research Grant; CASD Instructional Improvement Grants; NASA-GLOBE Grant; Huston Fnd Grant to Dev Nature Trail; *office:* Coatesville Area School Dist 1425 E Lincoln Hwy Coatesville PA 19320

FOGELSON, NANCY J., History Teacher; *b:* Paterson, NJ; *m:* M. Harold; *c:* Daniel, Alex, Stephen; *ed:* Univ of CT (BS) Child Dev 1954; Western Reserve (MS) Ed 1959; Univ of Cincinnati (MA) His 1975, (PHD) His 1983; *cr:* Various Nursery Schls thru Grad Schls 1954-87; Cincinnati Cntry Day Schl Tchr 1987-; *ai:* Model United Nations & Model Congress, Tufts Univ Inquiry Project & Class Adv; Org Amer Historians 1980-; Numerous Articles on Artic Exploration; Pub Arctic Exploration & Intnl Relations Pub 1992; *office:* Cincinnati Country Day Schl 6905 Given Rd Cincinnati OH 45243

FOGLE, JUDY LANCASTER, Kindergarten Teacher; *b:* Frostburg, MD; *m:* John Louis; *c:* Amanda Conn, Laura, John B., Kirk; *ed:* Frostburg St Coll (BS) Elem Ed 1965, (ME) 1975; Early Chldhd Degree 1970; *cr:* Midland Elem Schl First-Second Grd Tchr 1965-66; Private Kndgtn Tchr 1966-70; Westernport Elem Schl Kndgtn Tchr 1970-; *ai:* NEA 1965-; Presbyn Church 1950-, Deacon; Cooperating Tchr 1970-; *home:* 16608 Blubaugh Rd SW Lonaconing MD 21539

FOGLEMAN, ROBERT TYSON, Instrumental Music Teacher; *b:* Durham, NC; *m:* Dawn Patricia Trainor; *c:* Evelyn, Derek; *ed:* Lenoir Rhyne Coll (BS) Pol Sci 1974; Univ of MA at Boston (BA) Music Ed 1990; Berklee Coll of Music at Boston Credit Hrs; *cr:* Boston Schl of Music Woodwin Instr 1987-89; Robert Fogleman Woodwin Studio Pvt Instr 1989-; Oxon Hill MS Band Dir 1991-92; Montgomery Cty Pub Schls Elem Instrumental Music Tchr 1995-; *ai:* WA Area Archdiocese Hnrs Bnds Adjudicator; Amer Fed of Musicians 1995-; Halpine Bapt Church 1992-; Berklee Coll of Music Prof Performance Schlsp; Outstdng Soloist Chaffee Jazz Festival; Performed for Natl Pub TV, Mayor Tom Bradley, Stevie Wonder; Pvt Stud; *home:* 4515 Sigsbee Rd Silver Spring MD 20906

FOISY, ARTHUR JOSEPH, English Teacher; *b:* Dorchester, MA; *m:* Elaine L. Ludwinowicz; *c:* Suzanne, Jennifer; *ed:* BA Eng Merrimack College 1970; M ED Univ of Mass, Lowell, 1980 Educl Admin; *cr:* Arlington HS Eng Tchr 1971-; *ai:* Founder & Club Adv Schl Lit Magazine; Part-Time Admin in Addition Tchng Full Schedule Engl Classes; Univ of MA ESL Testng Ctr Mem 1987-; Curr Bd Mem Eng Dept Arlington HS 1995-; Arlington Ed Assn; MA Tchrs Assn; NEA; *office:* Arlington H S 869 Massachusetts Ave Arlington MA 02174

FOLAN, MARY TERESA, Associate Professor of Nursing; *b:* Cambridge, MA; *ed:* Boston Coll (BS) Nrsng 1973; Univ of FL (MSN) Pediatric Nrsg 1974; Harvard Univ (CAGS) Admin Planning, Soc Policy 1989; Continuing Ed in Nrsng; *cr:* Boston Univ Nrsng Fac, Asst Prof 1974-83; Cntrl Hosp Nrsng Supvr 1984-94; Univ MA Nrsng Fac, Lecturer 1985-87; Bunker Hill Comm Coll Nrsng Fac, Assoc Prof 1988-; *ai:* Chprsn Nrsng Ed Dept Curr Comm; Fac Preceptor for Grad Stdnts in Nrsng Ed; Natl League for Nrsng, Amer Nurses Assn 1985-; Sigma Theta Tau, Phi Kappa Phi 1974-; Pub Author; Prgm Evaluator; Excl in Tchng Awd; Amer Nurses Assn Cert as Clinical Specialist in Med-Surgical Nrsng, Nurse Admin, Psychiatric Mental Hlth Nurse; Who's Who in Amer Nrsng; Item Writer; *office:* Bunker Hill Comm Coll New Rutherford Ave Charlestown MA 02129*

FOLEY, DEANA SCHOCH, Chemistry Teacher; *b:* Altoona, PA; *m:* John; *c:* Julia, Elaine, Rita; *ed:* Univ of Pittsburg (BS) Chem 1981, (MS) Chem 1985, (MAT) Sci Ed 1989; *cr:* Naval Research Lab Research Chemist 1979-83; Montefiore Hospital Research Chemist 1986-88; CCAC-S Campus Chem Instr 1991-; Penn Hills HS Chem Tchr 1993-; *ai:* St Andrews Episcopal Church Schl Coord; PSEA 1993-; Pub in Journal of Solid St Chem; *office:* Penn Hills Sr HS 309 Collins Dr Pittsburgh PA 15235*

FOLEY, DOUGLAS EDWARD, Guidance Counselor; *b:* Lima, OH; *m:* Patricia Mary Lockemeyer; *c:* Jacob, Adam; *ed:* OH St Univ (BS) Elem Ed 1983; Univ of Dayton (MS) Schl Counseling 1989; *cr:* Columbus Grove Jr HS 5th Grd Tchr & Jr HS Sci Tchr 1983-86; Elida MS 8th Grd Amer His Tchr 1986-95; *ai:* Var Ftbl Asst Coach; Frosh Boys Bsktbl Coach, 8th Grd Boys Bsktbl Coach; NEA 1983-; Elida Ed Assn 1986-95; Lima Ed Assn 1996-; *office:* St Charles Schl 2175 W Elm St Lima OH 45805*

FOLEY, FRANCIS TIMOTHY, Eng Lit & Jrnlsm Teacher; *b:* Boston, MA; *m:* Audrey J. Lewandowska; *c:* Francis III, Dominick T.; *ed:* Univ of MA at Boston (BSEd) Eng 1965; Kean Coll (MA) Supervision, Admin 1985; 36 Post Masters Credits; *cr:* Linden HS Eng Tchr 1965-, Head Ath Trainer 1969-; *ai:* NJ St Licensed Ath All Sports Trainer; Stu Newspaper Adv; Dist Acad Philosophy Comm Chair; NEA, NJ Ed Assn 1970-; Linden Fed of Tchrs, Pres; Amer Kennel Club 1969-, Del; R E Lee Civil War Round Table 1994-; Guest Lecturer Ath Medicine Rutgers Univ & Kean Coll; *home:* 20 Sandalwood Ln Colonia NJ 07067

FOLEY, JACK J., Fifth Grade Teacher; *b:* Amesbury, MA; *m:* Mary Gardiner; *c:* Erin, Kyla, Jillian, Michael, Ryan; *ed:* Salem St Coll (BS) Elem Ed 1972; Attnd UNH, Merrimack Coll; *cr:* Dr. Lewis F. Soule Schl 5th Grd Tchr 1977-; *ai:* Boys Little League Bsbl Coach; Girls, Boys Yth Bsktbl Coach; Yth Leagues Umpire; NEA 1977-; Knights of Columbus 1988-; Boosters Club; *office:* Dr. Lewis F. Soule Schl 173 S Policy St Salem NH 03079

FOLEY, JOAN ROBBINS, Social Studies Teacher; *b:* Brooklyn, NY; *m:* George J.; *ed:* SUNY at Buffalo (BA) His 1970; Boston Univ (MED) Ed 1971; Bridgewater St (CAGS) Schl Admin 1983; Addl 36 Credit Hrs Ed, Soc Sci; *cr:* Cohasset Jr Sr HS Soc Stud Tchr 1971-87; S Kingstown HS Soc Stud Tchr 1987-; *ai:* NHS; RI Soc Stud Assn 1991-, Pres, VP Stu Prgms; Vol of Warwick Schls Bd of Dirs 1993-, Vice-Chm; *office:* South Kingstown HS 215 Columbia St Wakefield RI 02879*

FOLEY, KATHLEEN NEILSON, Chemistry Teacher; *b:* New York, NY; *m:* George P. Sr.; *c:* Kathleen, George Jr., Beth, Joseph; *ed:* Molloy Coll (BS) Chem 1963; William Paterson (EDM) Adm, Supervision 1989; Rutgers Univ (EdD) Sci Ed 1995; Boston Coll Chem Assistantship 1963-64; Queens Coll Ed 1965-68; *cr:* Middletown Twp HS Chem Tchr 1968-71; Wroxeter on Severn Chem Tchr 1977-79; Immaculate Heart Acad Chem Tchr 1982-86; Northern Valley HS Chem Tchr 1986-; *ai:* Competitive Sci League Chem Team; Chem Olympics; Sci Career Club; Women's Issues Discussion; NSTA 1990-; NJEA 1986-; AAUW 1991-; NJSTA 1995; Amer Chemical Soc Northern NJ Tchr of Yr; Assistantship Boston Coll 1963-64; *office:* Northern Valley Regional H S Central Ave Old Tappan NJ 07675*

FOLEY, KEVIN THOMAS, HS Social Studies Teacher; *b:* Cleveland, OH; *m:* Diana Kolp; *c:* Chris, Kelly, Lauren; *ed:* Edinboro Univ (BS) Soc Stud Ed 1977; OH St Univ (MA) Educl Admin 1992; *cr:* Holy Name HS Tchr 1979-80; Mentor Lake Cath HS Tchr 1980-87; Dublin Coffman HS Tchr 1987-95; Dublin Scioto HS Tchr 1995-; *ai:* Head Cross Cntry, Track Coach; NEA 1987-; Cntrl OH Track, Cross Cntry Coaches Assn 1988-; Phi Delta Kappa 1991-; United Way Comm Hero; *office:* Dublin Scioto HS 4000 Hard Rd Dublin OH 43016*

FOLEY, MARY ANNE A., Asst Professor of Theology; *b:* Brooklyn, NY; *ed:* Sacred Heart Univ (BA) Eng 1969; Weston Jesuit Schl of Theology (MTS) Theology 1983; Yale Univ (PHD) Historical Theology 1991; *cr:* Waterbury CT Cath HS & Holy Cross HS Eng & Religion Tchr 1969-76; St Joseph Coll Tchr of Theology & Spirituality 1983-86; Univ of Scranton Asst Prof of Theology & Rel Stud 1991-; *ai:* Theta Alpha Kappa Moderator; Status of Women Comm Chair; Coll Theology Soc 1992-; Theta Alpha Kappa 1993-; Congregation de Notre Dame 1969-; Numerous Articles Pub; *office:* Univ Of Scranton Scranton PA 18510

FOLEY, MICHAEL P., Science Teacher; *b:* Oceanside, NY; *m:* Lisa Gribbin; *c:* Thomas; *ed:* SUNY at Stony Brook (BS) Bio 1985, (MA) Lbrl Stud 1990; Chem Inst Purchase Coll 1992; Woodrow Wilson Flwshp Genetics Princetion Univ 1994; Cornell Inst for Bio Mentors Cornell Univ 1995; *cr:* Hauppauge MS Sci Tchr 1985-86; Grumman Aerospace Configuration Eng 1986-89; Wyandanch HS Sci Tchr 1989-93; Miller Pl HS Sci Tchr 1993-; *ai:* Sci Rsrch Adv; STANYS 1994-, Bio Area Rep; Woodrow Wilson Grant for 4 Wkshps on Genetics; Dev & Taught Environmental Pgm Sponsored by Brookhaven Natl Lab 3 Yrs; *office:* Miller Place HS 15 Memorial Dr Miller Place NY 11764*

FOLEY, PATRICIA AULT, First Grade Teacher; *b:* Oakland, MD; *m:* Larry W.; *c:* Todd, Amy Beth; *ed:* Frostburg St Univ (BS) Elem Ed 1976, (MS) Elem Ed 1981; *cr:* Dennett Rd Elem Schl 1st Grd Tchr 1976-; *ai:* GCTA; NEA; Mountaintop Soccer Assoc, Treas; Luth Church, Organist; *office:* Dennett Road Elem Schl 770 Dennett Rd Oakland MD 21550

FOLEY, PATRICIA MARY LOCKEMEYER, Kindergarten Teacher; *b:* Clifton Springs, NY; *m:* Douglas Edward; *c:* Jacob, Adam; *ed:* Heidelberg Coll (BA) Elem Ed 1981; Univ of Dayton (MS) Schl Cnslng 1986; *cr:* Perry Elem Schl Kndgtn Tchr 1981-; *ai:* JV Girls Bsktbl Coach 1981-86; Var Girls Vllybl Coach 1981-90; JV Girls Vllybl Coach 1996; NEA 1981-; OEA 1981-; PEA 1981-; *office:* Perry Elem Schl 2770 E Breese Rd Lima OH 45806

FOLEY, PAUL PATRICK, Guidance Counselor; *b:* Woburn, MA; *m:* Betty Lureny Negus; *c:* John, Paul, Ann, Beth; *ed:* Univ of MA (BA) PE 1962; Indiana Univ of PA (MED) Ed Guidance 1968; Saint Michaels Coll (MA) Admin 1986; *cr:* US Army Officer 1962-88; City of Barre Cty Mgr 1988-89; Blue Mountain Union Schl Dist Guidance Cnslr & K-12th Grd Schl Dir 1989-; *ai:* VT Guidance Assn 1989-; Barre Amer Legion 1989-; Barre Veterans of Foreign Wars 1989-; Woburn Elks Club 1958-; Wells River-Woodsville Rotary 1995-.

FOLEY, PAULA CHRISTINE, Fifth Grade Teacher; *b:* Everett, MA; *ed:* Salem St Coll (BS) Ed, Art 1972; Working of Masters Degree Fine Arts Boston Univ; Stud in Cmptr Sci, Hum, His, Managing Trends, Curr; *ai:* Schl Cncl; Fac Rep to Local Union Arlington Ed Assn; NEA; MTA; AEA; Whole Lang Tchrs Assn Participant; Parish Pastoral Cncl; Led Sub-Comm to Write Mission Statement; Devl Welcoming Handbook for New Parishioners; Rep Concerns of Parishioners; Pub Svc Awds; Prof Achvmts.

FOLEY, PETER PAUL, Social Studies Teacher; *b:* Brooklyn, NY; *m:* Catherine R. Herbrecht; *c:* Peter, Matthew, Christine, Thomas; *ed:* Fordham Univ (BA) His 1968; St Univ at Stoney Brook (MA) Sociology 1976; 42 Insvc Credits; *cr:* Elwood Jr HS Soc Stud Tchr 1969-87; John H. Glenn HS Soc Stud Tchr 1987-; *ai:* Stu Cncl Class Adv 1987-90; Govt Club Adv 1987-; Sited Based Mngmt, Shard Decision Making Comm 1994-;

AFT 1969-; NYSUT 1975-; C F Cncl SS Tchrs 1980-; YMCA 1995-, Yth, Adult Bd Mem; *office:* John H. Glenn HS 478 Elwood Rd Elwood NY 11731*

FOLEY, STEPHANIE JEPSON, First Grade Teacher; *b:* Boston, MA; *m:* Kenan R.; *ed:* Bridgewater St Coll (BS) Elem Ed 1972; 30 Plus Grad Hrs; *cr:* Americacn Schl of Bilboa Vizcaya, Spain 1st Grd Tchr 1972-73; Archie T. Morrison Schl 3rd Grd Tchr 1973-76, 1st Grd Tchr 1976-; *ai:* Early Chldhd, Handwriting, Schl Pride Comms; NEA, MA Tchr Assn, Braintree Ed Assn, Norfolk Cty Tchrs Assn 1973-; Horace Mann Grant; *office:* Archie Morrison Elem Sch 15 Mayflower Rd Braintree MA 02184*

FOLEY, TRACY AUMANN, 9th & 11th English Teacher; *b:* Baltimore, MD; *m:* William P.; *c:* Daniel; *ed:* St Marys Coll of Md (BA) Eng 1978; George Washington Univ (MED) Adult Ed 1983; *cr:* Lundeberg Schl Adult Ed Dir 1977-88; St Marys Coll of MD Writing Instr 1979-81; Charles Cty Comm Coll Engr Tchr 1981-86; St Marys Rykmen HS Eng Tchr 1989-; *ai:* Sr Class, Photography Club, Literary Magazine Adv; NCTE 1980-; MD Stu Assistance Assn 1994-; Pub Poet; *office:* Saint Marys Ryken HS Camp Calvert Rd Leonardtown MD 20650

FOLINO, LYNN ANNE, Mathematics Teacher; *b:* Staten Island, NY; *ed:* Seton Hall Univ (BS) Math Ed 1986; Rider Univ (MA) Ed Admin 1991; *cr:* Allentown HS Math Tchr 1986-; *ai:* Class & Ski Club Adv; Support Tchr; Mentor; Detention Monitor; Stu of the Month Comm; NCTM 1986-; AMTNJ 1986-; NJEA & UFREA 1986-; AHS Tchr of the Yr Nom (Twice); CIESE Basic Comp Software Grant; *office:* Allentown HS 27 High St Allentown NJ 08501

FOLKMAN, BARBARA BACHNER, Calculus Teacher; *b:* New York City, NY; *m:* Theodore J.; *c:* Margaret Robertson, Andrea, Theodore; *ed:* Hofstra Univ (BA) Math 1966, (MS) Math Ed 1967; Addl 170 Credits Beyond Masters; Advanced Cert Tchng Gifted; 45 Credits Toward the 60 Credits Needed for MBA; *cr:* Grand Avenue Jr HS Tchr 1966-87; Mepham HS Advanced Placement Calculus Tchr 1987-; *ai:* 9th Grd Math Club; Stu of Month Comm; Budget Advy Comm; SAT Tchr Adult Ed; NCTM 1966-; Nassau Cty Math 1966-, Pres 1994-; Tchrs Assn MAA; Goudreaux Math Museum 1980-, Educl Advy Comm; Grand Avenue Jr HS Tchr of Yr; Grand Avenue PTA Life Membership; Nassau Cty Math Tchr of Yr; Tandy Tech Awd for 100 Outstanding Math & Sci Tchrs; Mepham HS Outstanding Prof; 4 Natl Sci Fnd Grants; *office:* Mepham HS 2401 Camp Ave North Bellmore NY 11710*

FOLLETT, PHYLLIS V., French Teacher; *b:* Rochester, NY; *m:* Richard; *c:* Nicholas; *ed:* Amer Univ (BA) Fr 1968; Boston Univ (MA) Fr Lit 1970; *cr:* East HS Fr, Linguistics Tchr 1970-77; Pittsford Sutherland HS Fr Tchr 1978-87; Suffolk Univ Fr Lecturer 1988; Sandwich HS Fr Tchr 1988-; *ai:* Sandwich-Lyon Exch Adv, Organizer; NEA 1972-; MTA, MFLA 1988-; AATF 1970-; South SHore 1989-, Trustee; Conservatory 1995-; Tchr of Yr 1994; Terrific Tchrs Making a Difference Awd 1993; Nom MA Tchr of YR 1993, 1995; *office:* Sandwich HS 365 Quaker Meeting House Rd East Sandwich MA 02537

FOLLMER, LAURA, 4th Grd Teacher & Asst Prin; *b:* Medford, NY; *ed:* Manhattan Coll (BA) Ed 1960; Audit Coll Courses; Attnd Fordham Univ; *cr:* New York Diocese Tchr; Brooklyn Diocese 1952-; *ai:* Rel Ed Coord Grd K-4; Mid Sts On-Going Coord; Testing Coord; NCEA 1980-; *home:* 15724 84th St Howard Beach NY 11414

FOLMAR, JOHN KENT,JR., 11th Grd Amer Cultures Tchr; *b:* Birmingham, AL; *m:* Joy E.; *c:* Jennifer M., Johnny K. III, Jared G.; *ed:* Univ of PA at California (BA) Soc Stud 1976; Nova Univ (MA) Admin & Supervision 1987; LaSalle Univ (PHD) Ed Admin & Supervision 1995; Asst Mine Foreman Cert; Emergency Medical Tech; Scndry Prin Cert 8th-12th Grd; *cr:* Republic Steel Corp Asst Mine Foreman 1977-82; Bethlehem Steel Corp Asst Mine Foreman 1982-83; Broward Co Schl Dist Soc Stud Tchr 1984-87; Belle Vernon Area Schl Dist Soc Stud Tchr 1992-; *ai:* Strategic Planning & Steering Comms; Spon Leo Club; NEA, PSEA 1992-; Brazwell CMH Church 1988-, Elder, Sunday Schl Tchr, AYF Youth Ldr; Lions Club Intl 1995-; Veterans of Foreign Wars 1974-; Dist Service Awd Univ of PA at California 1976; Broward Co Sportsman Bsktbl Awd 1987; Air Traffic Control Tech US Navy in Vietnam 1971-73; *office:* Belle Vernon Area HS RR 2 Crest Ave Belle Vernon PA 15012

FOLSY, ARTHUR JOSEPH, English Teacher; *b:* Dorchester, MA; *m:* Elaine Ludwinowicz; *c:* Suzanne, Jennifer; *ed:* Merrimack Coll (BA) Eng 1970; Univ MA at Lowell (MED) Educl Admin 1979; Attnd Tufts Univ; *cr:* Arlington HS Eng Tchr 1970-; *ai:* Arlington Ed Assn-, MA Tchrs Assn, NEA 1970-; *office:* Arlington HS 869 Massachusetts Ave Arlington MA 02174*

FOLTZ, ANNE MOEGLING, 4th Grade Teacher; *b:* Canton, OH; *m:* Stanley Charles; *c:* Renee, Amy Lynn; *ed:* Univ of Akron (BS) Elem Ed 1976; Ashland Univ (MA) Curr, Instruction 1993; *cr:* T. C. Knapp Elem Schl Kndgtn Tchr 1977-78, 1st Grd Tchr 1978-85, 3rd Grd Tchr 1985-94, 4th Grd Tchr 1994-; *ai:* NEA 1977-; SECO 1996; Co-Author 3rd Grd Soc Stud Curr, Citizenship Resource Kit for 4th Grd Proficiency Stud; Sci Ldrshp Team for Stark Cty OH; *office:* T C Knapp Elem Schl 5151 Oakcliff St SW Canton OH 44706*

FOLTZ, CARRIE MELISSA, English & Journalism Teacher; *b:* Dover, OH; *ed:* Bowling Green St Univ (BS) Comp Comm 1989; Enrolled Master's Prgm Univ of Dayton Schl Cnslng; *cr:* Elmwood MS Eng, Lit Tchr 1989-90; Bannister & Assoc Inc Account Exec 1990-91; Northwestern HS Eng, Jrnlsm Tchr 1991-; *ai:* Yrbk Adv 1991-; Jr Class Adv; Odyssey of Mind Coach; NCTE 1988-; *office:* Northwestern HS 5650 Troy Rd Springfield OH 45502*

FOLTZ, PETER CHRISTIAN, Professor of Mathematics; *b:* Ft Mills, Phillippine I; *m:* Patricia Reese; *c:* Michael Steven, David Reese, Susan Foltz Afflebach; *ed:* Dartmouth Coll (AB) Engrng Sci 1959; Rutgers St Univ (AM) Math 1966; Cert with Distinction Operations Research Amer Univ 1975; *cr:* US Navy Damage Control Officer 1959-62; Blair Jr HS at Norfolk Math Tchr 1962-63; Oscar Smith HS at Chesapeake Physics & Math 1963-64; Hershey Jr Coll Engrng & Math 1964-65; Harrisburg Area Comm Coll Engrng & Math 1965-; *ai:* Curr Instruction; Lib Comm; MAA 1966-; PSMATYC 1966-, Pres, Svc Awd; Natl Sci Fnd Fellowship Rutgers; Tchng Fellowship Amer Univ; Capt US Naval Reserve; *office:* Harrisburg Area Comm Coll 1 HACC Dr Harrisburg PA 17110*

FONG, JERRY DAVID, Chemistry Professor; *b:* Berkeley, CA; *m:* Day-Lin Tung; *c:* LuAnn, LiAnn; *ed:* Univ of CA at Berkeley (BS) Chem 1973; Univ of MI (MS) Phys Chem 1975, (PHD) Phys Chem 1978; Elmira Coll 19 Credit Hrs Scndry Ed; *cr:* Univ of MI Chem Prof 1976-79; Purdue Univ Chem Prof 1979-81; Corning Incorporated Sr Rsrch Scientist 1981-92; Alfred St Coll Asst Prof of Chem 1992-; *ai:* Chem Curr Adv; Amer Chem Soc 1986-, Ed Exec Comm, Local Section Corning; Several US Patents; Natl Rsrch Cncl, Jet Propulsion Lab Flwshp 1978; Post Doctoral Flwshp; *office:* SUNY Alfred St Coll Allied Health Room 312 Alfred NY 14802

FONSECA, DONALD R., Director of Counseling; *b:* New Bedford, MA; *m:* Ruth Thompson; *c:* Cynthia Masters, Sandra Duncan, Diane Brandt; *ed:* Barrington Coll (BA) Bible Psych 1953, 1968; Univ of VA (MED) Educl Psych 1973; 90 Hrs Beyond Masters; *cr:* Rift Valley Acad Tchr 1963-75; Univ of VA Grad Instr 1972-73; Stony Brook Schl Dir of Counseling 1975-; *ai:* Coaching; Acad Comm; Counseling & Stu Affairs Staff Chair; Phi Delta Kappa 1973-; ACA 1982-; NBCC 1984-; NACAC 1983; NY Mets 1981-, Chaplain; NY Yankees 1982-, Chaplain; NY Jets Ftbl Team 1975-84, Chaplain; Book Pub Coll Getting & Staying in 1990; Many Articles Pub; *office:* Stony Brook Schl Chapman Pkwy Stony Brook NY 11790

FONTAINE, CAROLYN EDDY, Second Grade Teacher; *b:* Ludlow, MA; *m:* Robert Dennis; *ed:* Westfield St Coll (BSE) Elem Ed 1968; Summer Math for Tchrs Mount Holyoke Coll 1990; Literacy Learning in Classroom Richard Owen Publishers, Early Literacy Trng Hampshire Educl Collaborative 1994; *cr:* Woodland Schl Second Grd Tchr 1968-94, Fourth Grd Tchr 1994-95, Second Grd Tchr 1995-; *ai:* Audio-Visual, Soc Stud Coord; Southwick Ed Assn 1968-, Bldg Rep; MA Tchrs Assn, NEA 1968-; East Forest Park Civic Assn 1989-; *office:* Woodland Elem Schl 80 Powder Mill Rd Southwick MA 01077*

FONTAINE, PAMELA E., 10th-11th Grade Chemistry Tchr; *b:* Newark, NJ; *m:* Russell E.; *c:* Eric N.; *ed:* Roger Williams Univ (BA) Bio 1975; Worcester Polytechnic Inst (MNS) Bio, Chem, Physics & Calculus 1986; 24 Addl Credit Hrs in Bio, Chem & Ed at RI Coll, Providence Coll; *cr:* St Patrick HS Sci Tchr & Dept Head 1975-80; Mt St Charles Acad Sci Tchr 1980-81, Sci Dept Head 1981-95; LaSalle Acad Sci Tchr 1995-; *ai:* Pegasus Comm Mem, Sci Olympiad Moderator; St Sci Fair Judge; NSTA 1982-; ASCD 1985-; RISTA 1985-; Delta Kappa Gamma 1994-; Natl Catholic Ed Assn 1983-; RI Hum Forum 1990-; RI Math & Sci Curr Frameworks Team 1993-; RI Cape Math Frameworks Team 1993-, RI Global Change Ed Team 1995-, Bd Mem; RI Environmental Ed Exec Bd 1995-; NSF Grant Recipient for Master's Prgm at WPI; Tandy Scholar 1992; Presdntl Edctr Nominee 1988; *office:* LaSalle Acad Academy Ave Providence RI 02895*

FONTANA, JANET MARIE, Spanish Teacher; *b:* Norristown, PA; *m:* Conrad; *c:* Carolyn, Christine, Lauren; *ed:* West Chester Univ (BS) Ed 1970; Villanova Univ (MA) Ed 1976; *cr:* Downingtown HS Span Tchr 1970-80; Wissakickon MS Span Tchr 1987-89; Gwynedd Mercy Acad Span Tchr 1990-; *ai:* Natl Span Hnr Soc Adv; Head JV Sftbl Coach; Parish Schl Bd 1985-, Pres; *office:* Gwynedd Mercy Acad HS Sumneytown Pk Evans Gwynedd Valley PA 19437

FONTANA, MAXINE ATTEA, Instructor; *b:* Cleveland, OH; *m:* Dr. Joseph A.; *c:* James; *ed:* Siena Hghts Coll (BS) Chem 1964; Johns Hopkins Univ (MS) Biochemistry 1967; WV Univ (MS) Comp Sci 1984; *cr:* WV Univ Instr 1980-82; PC Tech Journal Tech Ed 1985-87; Northern Virginia Comm Coll Instr 1988-90; Univ of MD at Coll Park Instr 1990-; *office:* Univ of MD at Coll Park AV Williams Bldg College Park MD 20742

FONTECCHIO, THOMAS A., Gymnastics Teacher & Coach; *b:* Newton, MA; *c:* Christopher, Patricia; *ed:* Springfield Coll (BS) PE 1969; Bridgewater St (MS) Hlth Ed 1975; *cr:* Norwood Pub Schl PE Tchr 1969; Milton Pub Schl PE Tchr 1970-91; Somersault Ctr Owner, Coach 1991-; *ai:* New England Chm USA Gymnastics; NGJA 1980-, Natl Ofcr; USA Gymnastics 1975-, Chm, Svc; *office:* Somersault Ctr Inc 471 Page St Stoughton MA 02072*

FOOS, LISA MICHAEL, English & Reading Teacher; *b:* Fremont, OH; *m:* Mark Alan; *c:* Adam, Ellen; *ed:* Bowling Green St Univ (BA) Eng & His 1983, (MA) Eng 1989; *cr:* Norwalk HS Eng & Rdng Tchr 1983-85; Gibsonburg HS Eng & Rdng Tchr 1985-; *ai:* Stu Newspaper & Sr Class Adv; NHS & Schlsp Comms; Gibsonburg Tchrs Assn 1985-, Bldg Rep; Chprsn for Coats for Kids & Canned Food Dr; Eng Dept Head & Mentor; Mem of Diagogue with Bd of Ed; *office:* Gibsonburg Jr Sr HS S Harrison St Gibsonburg OH 43431

FOOTE, ELIZABETH, Third Grade Teacher; *b:* East Orange, NJ; *ed:* Kean Coll of NJ Elem Ed (BA) 1978, (MA) 1990; 30 Credits Beyond MA in Ed; *cr:* Washington Schl 2nd Grd Tchr 1978-79, 3rd Grd Tchr 1979-; *ai:* NEA 1979-; Phi Kappa Phi Honor Soc 1990-; *office:* Washington Schl 155 Washington Ave Nutley NJ 07110

FOOTE, GARY E., Science Teacher; *b:* Natrina Heights, PA; *m:* Maria Joan Mincis; *c:* Elizabeth, Nathaniel; *ed:* Wittenberg Univ (BA) Chem 1982; Tchrs Coll Colmbia (MA) Sci Ed 1988; City Coll (MA) chem 1990; *cr:* Peace Corpes Schl Sci Tchr 1982-86; Herbert Ulman HS Sci Tchr 1986-91; South Carroll HS Sci Tchr 1991-; *ai:* SADD Fac Schl Improvement Team; Stu Assistance Team Mem; WEA, NSTA, MAST 1991-; AAPT 1989-; Peace Corps Fellows Schlsp Colombia Univ 1986-88; Summer, Rsrch, Prgm for Scndry Schl Sci 1990-91; *office:* South Carroll HS 1300 W Old Liberty Rd Sykesville MD 21784*

FOOTE, SUSAN MC CLAY, Math Teacher; *b:* Seattle, WA; *m:* George Arthur; *ed:* Univ of MD (BS) Ed 1969; UMCP, Towson Univ Masters Equivalency; *cr:* Brock Bridge Elem Schl 6th Grd Tchr 1969; Benfield Elem Schl 6th Grd Tchr 1969-92; Severna Park MS Math Tchr 1992-; *ai:* Interdepartmental Team Ldr; TAAAC, MSTA, NEA 1969-; NCTM 1992-; *office:* Severna Park MS 450 Jumpers Hole Rd Severna Park MD 21146

FORAND, ROGER KENNETH, Global Studies Teacher; *b:* Brooklyn, NY; *m:* Joan Mary Brown; *ed:* Iona Coll (BA) His, Pol Sci, Ed 1963; 30 Credit Hrs NY Univ 1964; *cr:* Charles E. Gorton Jr HS 7-8th Grd Tchr 1965-69; The Roosevelt HS Amer His, Global Stud Tchr 1969-; *ai:* Schl Redesign Curr Comm; Ed 2000 Schl Restructuring Steering Comm; Yonkers Fed of Tchrs 1965-; Westchester Cncl for Soc Stud 1993-; Yonkers Tchr of Yr Nom; Westchester Cty Soc Stud Tchr of Yr 1993; *office:* Roosevelt HS 631 Tuckahoe Rd Yonkers NY 10710

FORBES, EDWARD JOHN,III, Associate Professor of Psych; *b:* Syracuse, NY; *m:* Eileen Paula Kuehnel; *c:* Kirsten Heather Forbes Puskar, Kip Pieter, Michael Ian, Courtney Anne; *ed:* Syracuse Univ (BS) Microbiology 1963; West VA Univ (MA) Dev Psych 1973; 27 Undergraduate Credits Psych Wayne St Univ 1963-69; 48 Cr Toward PHD WV Univ 1972-74; 15 Cr Doctoral Level Adult, Contin Ed PA St Univ 1993-94; *cr:* Parke Davis & Co Pharmaceutical Microbiologist 1963-69; WV Univ Grad Stu, Tchng Asst 1969-74; Mansfield St Coll Asst Prof 1974-80; Lock Haven Univ Asst Prof 19 80-84, Dept Chair 1985-89, Assoc Prof 1985-; *ai:* Distance Ed Advy Cncl; VP Exec Cncl Meet & Discuss Team; Grad Cncl Arts & Sci Curr, Tech, Enrollment Mngmt Comm; Amer Psych Assn 1974, 1979-; Soc for Res Child Dev 1973-; Soc for Res Adolescence 1986-; Jean Piaget Soc 1978-; Assn of PA St Coll & Univ Fac 1974-, VP; Psi Chi Psych 1984-, Adv 1990; Phi Kappa Phi; Fac Dev Comm Grant for Rsrch on Distance Ed; *office:* Lock Haven Univ N Fairview St Lock Haven PA 17745*

FORBES, LIESL LUX, English & Psychology Teacher; *b:* Canton, OH; *m:* Thomas; *c:* Stephen, Jeffrey; *ed:* Muskingum Coll (BA) Eng & Psych 1981; Ashland Univ (MEd) Curr & Instruction 1990; 32 Post-Grad Hrs; *cr:* McKinley HS Psych, Advanced Placement Psych, Eng III, Sociology & Creative Writing Tchr & Eng III Adv 14 Yrs, C.P., Eng Dept Chm 1995-; *ai:* Stdnts Against a Violent Environment Club & Peer Mediation Adv 1992-; the Scribe (Stu Lit Magazine) Adv 1983-86; The Phoenix (Yrbk) Adv 1982-84; NEA, OEA & CPEA 1982-; NCTE 1995-; *office:* Mc Kinley Sr HS 2323 17th St NW Canton OH 44708

FORBES, PATRICIA FABRITIIS, English Dept Chair; *b:* Philadelphia, PA; *m:* William Ross; *c:* Kristen, Ross, Philip; *ed:* KS Wesleyan Univ (BA) Eng 1968; Trenton St Coll (MED) Eng Ed 1977; Middlebury Coll (MA) Eng 1994; Post Grad Stud Drew Univ; *cr:* Princeton HS Tchr 1974-75; Westminster Schls MS Tchr 1975-80; Awty Int Schls Eng Dept Chair 1980-83; St John's Schl Tchr 1984-89; Montclair Kimberly Acad Eng Dept Chair 1989-; *ai:* HS Yrbk Adv; Acad Prgms Comm; NCTE, NJ Assn of Independent Schls 1990-; Presbyn Church of Westfield 1989-, Sunday Schl Supt; Natl Endowment Hum 1990, 1995; Margins Conf Present[...]; Montclair Kimberley Acad 201 Valley Rd Montclair NJ 07042

FORCELLESE, CESARE AUGUSTO, Biology Teacher; *b:* Italy; *m:* Carolyn Lambert; *c:* Terri Powers, Fred Aliff; *ed:* Tows[...] (BA) Sci 1974; Morgan St Univ (MS) Ed 1984; *cr:* Baltimore Schls Tchr 1974-; *ai:* Womens Track & Field Coach; Chess [...] NAST 1983-; Track & Field Coach of Yr 1995; *office:* Paul L. D[...] 1400 Orleans St Baltimore MD 21231

FORD, GENE ALLEN, 9th Grd World Studies Teacher; *b:* Denn[...] *m:* Karen Faye DiGenova; *c:* Gene Jr., Dustin, Ryan; *ed:* Muskin[...] (BA) His 1974; OH Univ (MS) Hlth, Human Svcs 1988; *cr:* N[...] Govt Tchr 1974-75; Tuscarawas Valley US His Tchr 1975-80; [...] City World Stud Tchr 1980-; *ai:* Boys Head Bsktbl, Golf, B[...] Cntry, Track Coach; Jr, Sr Class Adv; OEA, NEA 1974-; Dist 1[...] 1974-, Pres; ASCD 1989-; *office:* Cambridge City Schls 1201 [...] Ave Cambridge OH 43725*

FORD, GRABLE MEDINA, English Teacher & Dept Chair; *b:* OK; *m:* Albert C.; *ed:* Purdue Univ (BA) Eng 1966, (MA) Eng 1[...] Coll Prsnl 1973; Post Grad Stud Ball St Univ at Muncie, Xavie[...] Cincinnati, Miami Univ; Attnd Mt St Joseph Coll at Cincinnati[...] Coll at Richmond; *cr:* Purdue Univ Instr 1966-69; Cntrl Cath[...] Dean of Women 1970-75; Colerain HS Tchr 1975-; *ai:* Yrbk; Jr-Sr Class Spon; Acad Team; Eng Dept Chair; North Cn[...] Evaluating Comm; Northwest Assoc Selection of Prin; [...] Negotiations, Bargaining Team; Interviewing Team; NEA, NC[...] NW Assn Edctrs 1975-; ASCD 1988-; Phi Delta Kappa 1985-; C[...] Exams, NTE Core Battery Test Comm Skills, SAT II Writing Test[...] Prof Assessments Beginning Tchrs Grader; *office:* Colerain [...] Cheviot Rd Cincinnati OH 45251*

FORD, JIM, Junior High History Teacher; *b:* Oneida, NY; *m:* Jo[...] *c:* Geoff, Michael; *ed:* Oneonta St (BS) His Ed 1969; Colgate U[...] Tchng 1974; *cr:* Stockbridge Valley CS Jr Sr HS His Tchr [...] Madison Cntrl Schl Jr HS His Tchr 1970-; *ai:* Class Adv; Jr [...] Bsktbl Coach; Tchrs Assn 1969-, Pres; NYSUT, NEA 1969 [...] Coaches Assn 1976-; Yrbk Dedication 1976; *office:* Madison Ce[...] Rt 20 PO Box 155 Madison NY 13402

FORD, JOHN W., 7th Grd Soc Stud Tchr & Coach; *b:* Lancaste[...] Sandy McMurtrie; *c:* Taylor Leigh; *ed:* Elizabethtown Coll (BS) [...] 1974; Penn St 8 Grad Credits; Millersville Univ 18 Grad Cr[...] Coatesville Area Schl Dist Soc Stud Tchr 1978-; *ai:* Girls Var Bs[...] Coach; 9th-12th Grd Girls Bsktbl & 6th Grd Boys Bsktbl Intram[...] Honors Group Trip to Williamsburg Coord; CATA, PSEA, NE[...] Mens Coaches Bsktbl Assn 1992-; Lancaster First Presbyn Chur[...] Ches-Mont Champion, Dist 1 Champion, PA St AAAA Champ[...] Asst Coach; Ches-Mont Championship, Dist 1 Championship 1[...] Coach Girls Bsktbl; *office:* South Brandywine MS 1445 E Lin[...] Coatesville PA 19320

FORD, MARY PAT, Art Teacher; *b:* Philadelphia, PA; *m:* Samue[...] Mario; *ed:* PA St Univ (BS) Art Ed 1983; Temple Univ Tyler Sch[...] Credits; Univ of Arts 21 Credits; Beaver Coll 6 Credits; *cr:* Inte[...] Art Tchr 1983-85; Therapeutic Ctr Art, Spec Ed Tchr 1986-87; Weldon Schl Art Tchr 1988-89; Pennsauken HS Art Tchr 1994-[...] Musical Stage Crew 1988-; NJEA, NEA 1994-; PAEA 1983-; S[...] PA Odyssey of Mind 1988-, Merchandise Dir; PA Odyssey of Mi[...] Merchandise Dir; Awd of Excl, Svc Project Grad 1995; *office:* Pe[...] HS 800 Hylton Rd Pennsauken NJ 08110*

FORD, RICHARD J., Math Teacher; *b:* Wilkes-Barre, PA; *m:* [...] Bossuot; *c:* Jennifer, Richard, Sara; *ed:* Luzerne Cty Comm (AS) [...] 1969; Millersville Univ (BSE) Math, Scndry Ed 1971; 36 A[...] Credits Math, Ed Masters Equivalency; *cr:* Northern Chester Cty [...] Math Tchr 1971-90; Chester Cty Intermediate Unit Math Tchr [...] Wrestling Coach 1971-75; Sr Class Adv; NEA 1971-; CCIUEA 1[...] 1974-76; NCTM 1972-; Golden Apple Awd 1992; *home:* 210 Br[...] Church Rd Spring City PA 19475*

FORD, RONALD HARRISON, Learning Support Teac[...] Philadelphia, PA; *m:* Cristal Watkins; *c:* Derrick, Laurin, Sheri, [...] Cheyney Univ (BS) Elem Ed 1964; Antioch Univ (MS) Elem, Se[...] 1979; Cert Spec Ed Cheyney Univ; Cert Urban Affairs LaSalle U[...] PERT, CPM Spring Garden Coll; *cr:* R. S. Walton Elem Schl Tchr [...] Temple Univ Instrl Specialist 1970-71; Philadelphia O.I.C. Relations Dir 1971-74; Pepsi-Cola Co Natl Dir of Yth Com[...] 1974-79; Overbrook HS Math, Soc Living Skills Tchr, Desci[...] 1979-; *ai:* Jr Var Bsktbl, Mens Var Tennis Coach; Spon Stu [...] Relations Comm; Crisis Mngmt Team Comm; NAACP 1980-; Phi[...] League 1970-; AFT, PFT 1979-; Phila Coaches Assn 1989-, M[...] Achvmt; Kappa Alpha Psi 1975-; Natl Soc of Fund Raisers 1[...] Carmel Bapt Church 1993; Men Making a Difference Achvmt Aw[...] W. Hayre Schlsp Svc Awd; Pepsi Cola Co Outstdng Svc Awd [...] Overbrook HS 59th & Lancaster Philadelphia PA 19131*

FORD, SCOTT CLINTON, Eighth Grade English Tea[...] Steubenville, OH; *ed:* OH St Univ (BS) Comp Soc Sci, Elem E[...] Ashland Univ (ME) Elem Admin 1985; *cr:* Peace Corps HS E[...] Thailand 1970-74; Bronson Schl Elem Tchr 1976-81; Peters Colo[...] Schl Elem Tchr 1981-82; Norwalk MS Eng Tchr 1982-; *ai:* Acad C[...] Team Adv; Schl Play Production Dir; Newspaper Adv; Norwalk Te[...] 1976-, Treas 1977-79, VP 1982-86, Pres 1987-88, 1990-91; Left[...] Bsbl League 1977-, Sec 1984-87, Commissioner 1987-91; 1994-[...] Yr Norwalk Tchrs Assn 1981; Distinguished Citizen of Yr Norwa[...] Chamber of Commerce 1986; Dedicated Service Awd 1994; Norwa[...] Commerce Service Awd 1995, 1996; Norwalk VFM Post #2743; *h*[...] Baker St Apt 25 Norwalk OH 44857

FORD, TERRY MICHAEL, High School History Teacher; *b:* [...] Germany; *ed:* Western New England Coll (BA) His 1981; Weste[...] England Schl of Law 32 Hrs Completed; *cr:* Kiley Jr HS Long T[...] Tchr 1981-82; Duggan Jr HS Long Term Sub Tchr 1983; Cathedral[...] Tchr 1983-; *ai:* Lighting & Sound Dir; NCEA 1983-; ASCD 1994-[...] Civil War Re-Enactment 1981-, Officer; *office:* Cathedral HS 260[...] Rd Springfield MA 01118*

FORD, WALLY, Social Studies Teacher; *b:* Youngstown, OH; *m:* [...] Nicole, Sara Jo; *ed:* Grad Stu Youngstown St Univ; *cr:* Austintow[...] Tchr 8 Yrs; *ai:* Asst Var Ftbl & Bsbl Coach; AEA, NEA & Cncl [...] Stud 1987-; *office:* Fitch HS 4560 Fallon Dr Austintown OH 4451[...]

FORDE, MARY FRANCIS, Comm & Inclusion Teacher; *b:* Evans[...] *m:* Francis Anthony; *c:* Jennifer Mary, Michael Ryan; *ed:* St Lou[...] (BA) Psych, Ed 1974; *cr:* Stanley Field Jr HS 6-8 Grd Sped Resour[...] 1984-87; St Joan of Arc Schl 4, 8 Grd Tchr 1987-89; Blessed Sa[...] Schl 4, 8 Grd Comm Tchr 1990-95; Brennan MS 7 Grd Comm, In[...] Tchr 1995; *ai:* Yrbk, Newspaper Adv; Drama Club; Tutoring; La[...] Review Comms; Sftbl Coach; NEA 1982-; Walpole Little League[...] Bd Sec; Walpole Pop Warner 1991-; Cleveland 1st Young Autho[...] Dir; *office:* Brennan MS 135 County St Attleboro MA 02703*

FORDE, PATRICIA ANN (JOYCE), College Instructor; *b:* Bost[...] *m:* Patrick C.; *c:* Tara J., Ashley B., Ryan P.; *ed:* Boston St Coll ([...] 1975; Lesley Coll (MS) Mgmt 1983; Cert in Perceptually Handi[...] Boston St 1975-76; Grad Course in Mgmt, Dev of Human Re[...]

Jniv 1981; *cr:* Saint Mary's Schl Tchr 1975-79; Intercontinental nl Asst 1972-80; Marshalls Inc Regnl Mgr of Trng, Dev, g 1980-88; Fisher Coll Adj instr 1985-89; Becker Coll Adj Instr entworth Inst of Tech Adj Instr 1988-90; Mount Ida Coll Adj Instr in in Own Co Human Resource Consultant 1995-; PIne Manor Instr 1996; *ai:* Michell Schl Media Vol; Room Parent; ASTD NSPI 1983-88; Needham Women's Club 1988-; Who's Who in Awd 1984; Outstdng Contributor to Trng Future Retailers Awd Prof in Human Resources Distinction 1995; *office:* Mount Ida Coll am St Newton Center MA 02159

SEON JAMES, Math Dept Chairperson & Tchr; *b:* Calcutta #2 rinidad WI; *m:* Wilma David; *c:* Jenice, Sean, Andre, Michael; of WI at Trinidad (BA) Ec 1974; Brooklyn Coll (MS) Math 1991, nin 1993; NY Stock Exch Cert of Achvmt for Tchng Prgm; Teach t for Excl in Trng & Assessment of Tchrs; Thirteen/WNET & ert as Master Tchr in ITV & Tech; *cr:* Alpha Coll Vice Prin, Tchr Forde's Educl Inst Prin, Tchr 1970-87; Prof Tutoring Dir 1987-; Leod Bethune IS 394 Math Chprsn Staff Trrainer, Tchr 1988-; *ai:* Stdnts for Stock Market Same & Math Competitions; Sunday Trng Yths in Knowledge of God; Tutoring Yth in Comm for to Top HSs; AMTNYC 1993-, Exec Bd Mem; NCTM 1990-; ner 1994-, Review Bd Mem, Cert of Excl; St Michael Spiritual 987-, Minister; PTA 1988-, Adv; Block Assn 1990-, Yth Ofcr; Pres Awd for Excl in Sci & Math Tchng; Papers Pub; *home:* 693 Brooklyn NY 11203*

, CARIE L., Professor of Psychology; *b:* San Jose, CA; *ed:* Univ Santa Cruz (BA) Psych 1978; St Univ of NY at Stony Brook (MA) HD) Psych; *cr:* St Univ of NY at Old Westbury Adjunct Prof La Guardia Coll Adjunct Asst Prof 1987-92; Queens Coll Adjunct 1991-92; Clarion Univ of PA Asst Prof of Psych 1992-; *ai:* Campus Psych Club Adv; Presidential Comm-Affirmative Action versity Comm Chair-Spons Entertainment, Lectures & Aquistion als Related to Increasing Soc & Cultural Diversity; San Venango Schlsp Comm; Fac Forum Sec; PA Sts System Womens um, Soc for the Psychological Stud of Soc Issues 1992-; ing Adjunct Fac Awd at La Guardia Coll 1990; Article Pub in Sex 81; Research Presented at Natl Conf of Amer Psychological Assn 1995; *office:* Clarion Univ Of PA Venango 1801 W 1st St Oil City *

AM, WAYNE ROBINSON, Biology Teacher; *b:* Rumford, ME; a W. Halleman; *c:* Kimberly, Ryan; *ed:* Univ of Southern ME (BA) 1972; 30 Addl Hrs; *cr:* Greely Jr HS Bio, Math Tchr 1973-86; S Bio Tchr 1986-; *ai:* Cross Cntry Coach; NEA, ME Ed Assn *fice:* Greely HS 303 Main Cumberland Center ME 04021

ITOLLO, ELLEN JAYNE, 2nd Grade Teacher; *b:* Staten Island, ohn Michael; *c:* Michael Vincent Vitollo; *ed:* Coll of Staten Is 1974, (MS) Elem Ed 1978, (MS) Spec Ed 1986; *cr:* IS 34 Math 8-80; IS 7 Eng Tchr 1980-82; PS 55 Spec Ed Tchr 1982-84; Pub -3 Grd Tchr 1984-; *ai:* Coach Little League; AFT, UFT 1983-; 1 Tottenville 58 Summit St Staten Island NY 10307*

CE, ROBERT ALLEN, Science Dept Head & Ath Dir; *b:* Dover, Cynthia; *c:* Henry, Raymond; *ed:* Univ of Bridgeport (BA) Bio ontclair St Coll Ed Cert 1978; *cr:* Rockaway Valley Schl Sci Tchr, Ath Dir 1978-; *ai:* Yrbk Adv; Vlybl, Girls Bsktbl & Sftbl Coach; 985-; Morris Cty Coaches Assn 1981-, Treas 1985-; Coached Girls Championships 1985, 1986, 1992, 1996 & Girls Sftbl onships 1988-92; *office:* Rockaway Valley Schl 11 Valley Rd NJ 07005

AN, JOHNNIE L., Asst Ath Dir & PE Dept Head; *b:* Baltimore, Eileen G.; *c:* Johnnie III, James C.; *ed:* Morgan St Coll (BS) PE organ St Univ (MS) PE 1982; *cr:* Herring Run Jr HS Sci, PE Tchr ; Northern Sr HS PE Tchr, Assit FB Coach, Head Track Co Severn Schl Hlth, PE, Coach 1983-84; Gilman Schl Assit AD, PE ad, Assit V FB, Head Track Coach 1984-; *ai:* Head Track Coach; Ftbl Coach; Black Awareness MS Spon; Dir Mentoring Prgm; 1987-; Track Coaches Assn 1990-, Coach of Yr 1995; NAACP hi Beta Sigma 1973-, Dean of Pledges.*

AN, ROBERT B., Chemistry Teacher; *b:* Chicago, IL; *m:* Patricia Kim, Jodi, Sarah; *ed:* Univ of NC (BA) Chem 1968, (MAT) Ed, 75; 4 Credit Hrs; *cr:* Guy B. Phillips HS Sci Tchr 1968-69; Taft Tchr 1979-80; Walnut Hills HS Chem Tchr 1980-; *ai:* Tchrs Bldg, mm; Var Golf Coach; Rowing Club Fac Adv; Amer Chem Soc FT 1979-; Natl Sci Fnd Grant 1981; *office:* Walnut Hills HS 3201 Pkwy Cincinnati OH 45207

IAN, ROBERT GEORGE,IV, Instrumental Music Instructor; *b:* NY; *m:* Elizabeth Ann Palimter; *c:* Jenny, Christopher, Marisa; *ed:* chl of Music SUNY at Potsdam (BS) Music 1968; Ithaca Coll (MS) str 1973; *cr:* Kenmore West Sr HS 9-12th Grd Instrumental Music 68-72; Cato-Meridian CS 4-12th Grd Instrumental Music Tchr ; Port Byron CS 5-12th Grd Instrumental Music Tchr 1973-; Dept Arts Dept 1993-; *ai:* HS Marching, Jazz Ensembles; HS Musical Dir; Cato-Meridian TA 1973-83, Negotiation Chm; Port Byron TA P, Neg Chm; Cayug-Onondaga Tchr Ctr 1985-, Policy Bd Chm; t, 1981-, Town Justice; Magistrate of Yr Cayuga Cty 1990; *office:* on Cntrl Schls Maple Ave Port Byron NY 13140*

Z, JOHN, Automotive Technology Instr; *b:* White Plains, NY; *m:* h A. Dates; *c:* Sarah E.; *ed:* Alfred St Coll (AOS) Automotive Svc AOS Diesel Mechanics 1981; SUNY at Oswego Tchng License ent Cert 1986; *cr:* Monro Muffler & Brake Automotive Mechanic Shop Mgr 1982-84; Steuben Allegany BOCES Wildwood Ctr tive Tech Instr 1984-89; Steuben Allegany BOCES Coopers Ctr tive Tech Instr 1989-; *ai:* Voc Indstrl Clubs of Amer Adv 1985-, Contest Coord 1990-; NEA 1984-; Buena Vista Weslyan Church *office:* Wildwood Ed Ctr 1126 Bald Hill Rd Hornell NY 14843

O, RONALD FRANCIS, Social Studies Teacher; *b:* Orange, NJ; leen Marie Winters; *c:* Kate Elizabeth; *ed:* Seton Hall Univ (BA) d 1974; 40 Addl Grad Credits NJ Cert Tchr of Handicapped; *cr:* any HS Soc Stud Tchr 1974-; *ai:* Pep Club, Var Club, Interact Club, Co-Adv; His Club Adv; Ftbl Play-By-PLay Announcer; Scorer, irls, Boys Bsktbl; Pol, Legal Ed Inst Co-Coord; PTHEA, MCCEA, NEA 1974-; Assoc of US Army 1981-; PTSA 1974-; Amer Legion ietnam Veterans of Amer 1993-; Natl Rifle Assn 1976-; ASMIC, C, OMRS, OMSA 1989-; Co of Military Historians 1988-; Awded y Mbrshp Par-Troy Rotary Club; Honorary Life Mem NJ PTA; Life Mem Assoc of Grads USMA; NJ Governors Tchr Recog Awd 1994; Fnd Grant 1987; PTH Distngd Fac Awd 1985; US Army Achvmt 1984; PTH Twp Outstdng Achvmt Awd 1993; NTN Golden Acorn 90; *office:* Parsippany HS 309 Baldwin Rd Parsippany NJ 07054

OTCH, BERNARD M., Social Studies Tchr & Dept Chm; *b:* y City, PA; *m:* Kathleen; *c:* Brendan; *ed:* Allentown Coll (BA) 1972; Ed Cert, Credits; Penn St Univ; Alvernia Coll; Marywood Mahonoy City Cath Schl Sci, Soc Stud Tchr 1972-81; Marian S Tchr, Dept Chair 1981-; *ai:* Future Lawners, Stockmarket Club; rial Team, Sr Class Adv; Sr Disciplinarian; Sr Play Asst; Tennis nent Coord; Eucharistil Minister; Lector Acad Cncl Mem; Soc Stud hm; NCEA 1972-, Pottsville Republican, Newspaper in Ed Advy Comm 1985-; Allentown Diocese Lay Tchrs Assn 1972-, PIAA Track, Field Official 1982-; Assumption Bvm Parish 1950-, Lector, Collector; Mahanoy City Little League 1985-, Umpire; Mahonoy City Biddy Bstkbl 1990-, Referee; Outstdng Tchr Golden Apple Awd 1995; Rotary Club Yth Merit Awd 1988; *office:* Marian Catholic HS Rd 4 Box 446 Tamaqua PA 18252

FORGRAVE, SUSAN MONROE, Intl Baccalaureate Eng Teacher; *b:* Pittsburgh, PA; *m:* Tom; *c:* Reid, Julia; *ed:* OH Univ (BA) Eng 1970; Duquesne Univ (MATE) Eng 1973; *cr:* Various Elem Schls Elem Tchr 1967-71; Pittsburgh Pub Schls MS Tchr 1974-79; Penn St-Ogontz Campus Lecturer in Eng 1986-88; Pgh Pub Schls Eng Tchr 1988-; *ai:* Poetry Club; Coaching Grad Speakers; Mentor to Intl Baccalaureate Diploma Candidates; AFT 1974-; NCTE 1988-; *office:* Schenley HS 4101 Bigelow Blvd Pittsburgh PA 15213*

FORHAN, JEANNA KATHLEEN, Administrator; *b:* Cleveland, OH; *ed:* (BA) Ed 1974; Bowling Green St Univ (ME) Rdng Specialist, Ed 1981; 20 Addl Post Grad Hrs Eng, Educl Theory, Cnslng, Rel Stud; *cr:* St Francis Schl Jr HS Tchr 1974-81; Ursuline Coll Part-time Instr, Ed Dept Asst 1983-86; Lake Cath HS Rdng Specialist 1984-87; Christ the King Schl Jr HS Tchr 1987-95; Metro Cath Parish Schl Admin 1995-; *ai:* Teen Yth Group; Jr Great Books Club; Teens Stud Skills Improvement; Rainbows Support Prgm Facilitator; Yth Ldrshp Trng; IRA 1986-; ASCD 1993-; Dirs of Rel Ed 1989-; Tchrs Urban Yth Grant; Pastoral Minister Candidate Cleveland Cath Diocese; *home:* 16021 Helmsdale Rd East Cleveland OH 44112*

FORMAINI, GUIDO, Sociology, World Cultures Tchr; *b:* Yatesboro, PA; *m:* Jolene Maffei; *c:* Damon, Adele, Nathan; *ed:* IN Univ of PA (BS) Comp Soc Stud 1970, (ME Equiv) Comp Soc Stud 1990, (MA) Sociology 1995; *cr:* Kittanning Sr HS Soc Stud Tchr & Chprsn 1970-95; *ai:* Stu & Instrl Support Teams; Asst Ftbl Coach; Former Stu Cncl Class Adv; NEA 1970-; PSEA 1970-; Alpha Kappa Delta 1991-; Knights of Columbus 1979-; Armstrong-IN Drug & Alcohol Comm 1994-, Bd Mem; *office:* Kittanning Sr HS 1200 Orr Ave Kittanning PA 16201

FORMAN, CAROL J., Mathematics Teacher; *b:* Allentown, PA; *m:* Harry W.; *c:* Christopher, Jennifer; *ed:* Gettysburg Coll (BA) Math, Physics 1974; Western MD Coll (MS) Scndry Ed 1984; *cr:* South Carroll HS Math Tchr 1974-80; Catoctin HS Math Tchr 1981-, Dept Chm 1985-94; *ai:* MSTA, NEA 1974-; MCTM, NCTM; Local Recycling Comm 1990-94; First Presbyn Church 1978-, Deacon 1987-91, Elder 1994-; *office:* Catoctin H S 14745 Sabillasville Rd Thurmont MD 21788*

FORMAN, HONEY DAVIDSON, Instructional Teacher Leader; *b:* Pittsburgh, PA; *m:* Harold S.; *c:* David; *ed:* Univ of Pittsburgh (BA) Sociology 1974, (MAT) Tchng 1975; Rdng Spec Cert 1978; 30 Addl Post Grad Hrs Rdng Ed Rsrch & Dissemb; *cr:* Pittsburgh Pub Schls Sub Tchr 1975-77, Rdng Specialist 1978-85; John Minadeo Elem Schl Lang Arts Tchr, Instrl Tchr Ldr 1985-; *ai:* 5th Grd Adv; PTO Tchr Rep, Bd; Rdng Comm; Mentor for New Tchrs; PFT 1978-; Pi Lambda Theta 1976-; ASCD 1980-; CArnegie Lib 1987-, Summer Vol; Synagogue, Rel Schl Chprsn; Tchr Excl Awd; Thanks to Tchr Nom; *office:* John Minadeo Elem Schl 6502 Lilac St Pittsburgh PA 15217*

FORMAN, LINDA RODMAN, HS Foreign Lang Tchr; *b:* New Rochelle, NY; *m:* Robert William; *c:* Michael; *ed:* Boston Univ (BS) Span, Scndry Ed 1976; Iona Coll (MS) Span with Biling Ed Concen 1980; Attnd Inst de Cultura Hispanica 1974-75, Univ de Salamanca 1972, Westchester Comm Coll, Fordham Univ 1981; *cr:* Albert Leonard Jr High Span Tchr 1976-77; Oakdale Schl Span Tchr 1977-78; Carmel HS Foreign Lang Tchr 1978-; *ai:* NYSAFLT 1977-; West Assn for Lang Tchrs; West Comm Coll 1979-; AATSP 1995-; Country Children's Ctr 1988-, Past Pres Parents Group, Bd of Dir, Cubby Awd; KES-PTO 1990-; CHS Rainbow Connection; *office:* Carmel HS 30 Fair St Carmel NY 10512*

FORMAN, REYNOLD S., Honors English Teacher; *b:* Brooklyn, NY; *ed:* Montclair Univ (BA) Eng 1987; Georgian Court Coll, La Salle Univ 3 Post Grad Hrs; *cr:* Brookside Schl Elem Tchr 1988-92; Freehold Twp Hnrs Eng Tchr 1992-; *ai:* Drama Club, Stu Govt Adv; Co-Curr Supervisory Comm; NEA, FRHSEA 1992-; NJCTE 1995-; *office:* Freehold Township HS 281 Elton Adelphia Rd Freehold NJ 07728*

FORQUER, RAY WARREN, Art Teacher; *b:* Washington, PA; *c:* Susanne; *ed:* Clarion Univ of PA (BS) Comprehensive Soc Stud 1966; Univ of Pittsburgh (MED) Art Ed 1973; *cr:* Chartiers-Houston MS His Tchr 1967-68; Chartiers-Houston HS Art Tchr 1969-; *ai:* AFT 1970-; Chartiers-Houston Fed Tchrs 1970-, Pres; Washington Cty Historical Soc; Illustrations for Historical Books & Pub Television; Owner Countryside Prints Inc, Dir Gallery 200; *home:* 35 W Prospect Ave Washington PA 15301

FORREST, BONITA JEAN, English & Spanish Teacher; *b:* Olean, NY; *m:* Daniel E. Sr.; *c:* Daniel Jr., Jacob; *ed:* Mansfield Univ (BS) Scndry Eng 1972; Elmira Coll (MS) Scndry Eng 1977; *cr:* Thomas A. Edison Eng Tchr 1972-73; Horseheads Chrstn Schl Eng Tchr 1973-77; Twin Tiers Bapt High Eng Tchr 1982-; *ai:* 8th Grd Homeroom; Lang Arts Festival; Campbells Soup Label Prgm Chm; Publicity for Schl Play; *office:* Twin Tiers Baptist HS Box K Breesport NY 14816

FORREST, CAMILLE WALTON, Principal; *b:* Richmond, VA; *m:* Christopher; *c:* Brady, Beth, Matthew; *ed:* Radford Univ (BS) Fr, Ed 1968, (MS) Guid, Cnslng 1969; Georgian Court Coll (MA) Admin 1995; *cr:* Duquesne Univ Asst Dean of Women 1969-70; NW MO St Dir of Stu Act 1970-72; Corpus Christi Schl Second Grd Tchr 1980-86; St Joan of Arc Schl Seventh Grd Tchr 1980-92; *ai:* NCEA 1980-; NAESP Elem Schls Prins Assn 1992-; AAUW, ASCD, NJASCD 1992-, Sec, Treas; *office:* St Peter Celestine Cath Schl 402 N Kings Hwy Cherry Hill NJ 08034

FORRESTER, WILLIAM J., Band Director; *b:* Warren, OH; *m:* Jenna Julian; *c:* Jessica; *ed:* Youngstown St Univ (BM) Music Ed 1975; 36 Hrs Credit Towards MA; *cr:* Mathews HS Band Dir 1975-76; Hubbard HS Asst Band Dir 1976- 83, Band Dir 1983-; *ai:* Marching & Jazz Band; NEA, MENC & OMEA 1975-; AFM 1970-; W D Packard Band 1978-; *office:* Hubbard H S 350 Hall Ave Hubbard OH 44425

FORRESTER-FRYE, LOIS G., English, Soc Stud & Sci Tchr; *b:* Camden, NJ; *m:* Harold Russell; *c:* Leslee; *ed:* Morgan St Univ (BS) Elem Ed 1970; Villanova Univ (MA) Elem Ed 1977; Attnd Temple Univ Coll of Performing Arts; *cr:* Moore Elem Schl Ed Tchr 1970-74; Baldi MS Sci, Soc Stud, Eng Tchr 1974-; *ai:* Beta Hnr Soc Spon; Stans Comm; World Affairs Liaison; Stu Assistance Prgm; Phi Delta Kappa 1983-; NCTE 1987-; BWEA 1982-; AKA 1979-; Silhouettes 1981-, Corresp Sec; Tchr Entrepeneur Awd; Stdnts at Risk, Implementing ESL Prmg, World Affairs on Japan Grants; Women in Ed Awd; *office:* C. C. A. Baldi MS Verree & Alburger St Philadelphia PA 19115*

FORSEY, BARBARA FINEGAN, Third Grade Teacher; *b:* Everett, MA; *m:* Clyde G.; *c:* Steven, Michael; *ed:* Salem St Coll (BSEd) Elem Ed 1959, (MED) Elem Ed 1981; 6 Credit Hrs; 45 Credit Hrs Peabody Schl Dept In-Svc; *cr:* Everett Pub Schls 3rd Grd Tchr 1959-61; Peabody Pub Schls 3rd Grd Tchr 1966-; *ai:* Schl Improvement Cncl; PFT, MFT 1966-; LWV of Greater Peabody 1993-; *office:* Ctr Elem Schl 18 Irving St Peabody MA 01960

FORSHEE, SHARON, French & Spanish Teacher; *b:* Sidney, NY; *m:* Jerome Bellnier; *c:* Claire; *ed:* Cayuga Cty Comm Coll (AA) Lbrl Arts 1971; St Univ at Geneseo (BA) Fr & Ed 1974; St Univ at Cortland (MA); *cr:* Jordan Elbridge HS Fr & Span Tchr 1976-; *ai:* Lang Club; Encampment Project Club; NYSAFLT 1986-; Natl Soc Stud Awd for Encampment Project 1995; *office:* Jordan Elbridge JR/SR HS 5721 Hamilton Rd Jordan NY 13080

FORST, RONALD HARRISON, Math Dept Chprsn & Teacher; *b:* Haddonfield, NJ; *m:* Judith Mead; *c:* Andrew J., Douglas A.; *ed:* Glassboro St Coll (BA) Math 1968, (MA) Supervision, Curr Dev 1972; *cr:* Burlington City HS Math Tchr 1968-, Math Dept Chprsn 1972-; Burlington Cty Coll Adj Math Prof 1980-; *ai:* Class Spon 9-12; Trip Coord 12; Fire Squad Adv; NEA, NJ Ed Assn, City of Burlingotn Ed Assn 1968-; NCTM 1972-; Delran Twp Bd of Ed, NJ Schl Bd Assn 1992-; Prins #1 Club; Yrbk Dedications; *office:* Burlington City HS 1001 Dewey St Burlington NJ 08016*

FORSTATER, MATHEW BRAM, Asst Professor of Economics; *b:* Philadelphia, PA; *m:* Gail Jane Rothstein; *c:* Harris; *ed:* Temple Univ (BA) African Amer Stud 1987; New Schl for Soc Rsrch (MA) 1993, (PHD) Ec 1996; *cr:* Gettysburg Coll Ec Instr 1992-95, Asst Prof of Ec 1996-; *ai:* African Amer Stud Pgm Advy Cncl; Environmental Stud & Area Stud Comms; Amer Ec Assn 1992-; PA Ec Assn 1993-; Eastern Ec Assn 1993-; Soka Gakkai Intnl 1983-; Articles Pub; Shirley Graham DuBois Awd for Acad Excl in African Amer Stud; *office:* Gettysburg Coll Dept of Ec Gettysburg PA 17325

FORSTER, ANNA KATHRYN, Science Teacher; *b:* Kingston, NY; *ed:* Keaka Coll (BA) Bio 1964; Union Univ (BS) Med Tech 1966; SUNY at New Paltz (MS) Bio 1982; MT, BB ASCP; NYS Bio, Chem, Eng 7-12 Cert Credit Hrs; On Site Natural His Stud Thailand, Myanmar, E Australia, N India, New Guinea, New Br, Kenya, Tanzania, Sao Tome, Principe, Trinidad, Tobago, W. China, Peru, Equador, HI; *cr:* Diakonessen Luis Lab Tech 1963; St Peters Hosp Lab Tech 1964-66; City of Kingston Lab Immunohoematologist 1966-86; Hurley Veterinary Hosp Lab Tech 1986-1987; Daniel Smiley Rsrch Ctr Naturalist, Rsrch Asst 1987-91; Marlboro Cntrl HS Hnrs Bio, 10th-11th Grd Sci, Regents Chem Tchr 1993-; *ai:* Fac Adv Class of 98; ASCP, AABB, NYSMT 1967-; AFT 1993-; Numerous Rsrch Articles Natural His Shawangank Mts; *office:* Marlboro Central HS 50 Cross Rd Marlboro NY 12542

FORSTER, DIETER, Professor of Physics; *b:* Gaildorf, Germany; *m:* Sara Wheeler; *ed:* Harvard Univ (PHD) Physics 1969; Univ Of Stullgart Diploma Physics 1964; *cr:* Columbia Univ Postdoctoral Assoc 1969-70; Univ of Chicago Asst Prof of Physics 1970-74; Temple Univ Prof of Physics 1974-; *ai:* Benjamin Franklin Inst Sci & Arts Comm; APS 1970-; ACLU 1980-; Union of Concerned Scientists 1978-; Pub Book: Hydrodynamic Fluctuations, Broken Symmetry, and Correlation Function; Great Tchr Awd 1994; Hnrs Prof of Yr 1992; Distngd Tchng Awd 1988; *office:* Temple Univ Dept of Physics Philadelphia PA 19122

FORSYTH, LOUISE J., History Teacher; *b:* Brooklyn, NY; *m:* Howard Stein; *c:* Leonora stein, Micaela Stein; *ed:* Univ of Rochester (BA) European His 1968; City Coll of NY (MA) European His 1979; Completed Coursework for PHD CUNY Grad Ctr; *cr:* Borough of Manhattan Comm Coll Adj Instr 1980-87; Poly Prep Tchr 1987-, Head of Dept 1987-88; *ai:* Mid East Caucus Adv; Curr Task Force; Curr, Diversity & Comm All-Schl Comm; NCSS 1995-; Tchr Recognition Awd Coll Bd 1996; Articles Pub 1992-; Endowel Chairs 1992-93, 1995; NEH Summer Seminars at Insts 1988, 1990, 1994-95; *office:* Poly Prep Cntry Day Schl 9216 7th Ave Brooklyn NY 11218*

FORSYTHE, RALPH THOMAS, Fifth Grade Teacher; *b:* Providence, RI; *m:* Toni Elm Hosser; *c:* Scott, Kate Lynn; *ed:* St Univ of NY at New Paltz (BA) Elem Ed, Eng 1976, (MS) Elem Ed 1984; *cr:* NY St Prison Life Skills Instr 1978-79; Arlington Cntrl Schls Fifth Grade Teacher 1980-; *ai:* Fifth Grd Chm; After Schl Sports Prgm; Arlington Schl Dist Drug Liaison; Arlington Dist Sci Curr Comm; NY St DARE Officers Assn, Natl DARE Officers Assn 1990-; Parent Partnership DARE 1995-, Treas; Arlington Educl Alternatives 1991-, Chm; Organized & Implemented Arlington Schls Eye Exams, Eyeglasses Prgm; *office:* Arlington Elem Schl 25 Raymond Ave Poughkeepsie NY 12603*

FORTE, FRANCIS CARMINE, Physics Teacher; *b:* Bridgeport, CT; *m:* Rina Giovanna Viselli; *c:* Francis; *ed:* Rensselaer Polytechnic Inst (BS) Engrng 1968; Univ of Bridgeport (MS) Scndry Schl Ed 1974; 6th Yr Admin Univ of New Haven 1975; *cr:* Pratt & Whitney Aircraft Mechanical Engr 1968-70; Bassick HS Sci Tchr 1970-86; Cntrl HS Physics Tchr 1986-; *ai:* Class Adv 1974-76; Fac Cabinet 1976-80; Curr Comm 1970-80; Prof Dev Comm 1985-93; BEA, CEA, NEA 1970-; Tandy Tech Scholars Outstdng Tchr Awd 1989-90; *home:* 24 Tahmore Pl Shelton CT 06484

FORTE, STEPHEN J., English Teacher & Dept Chm; *b:* Lancaster, PA; *ed:* Millersville Univ (BS) Comprenhensive Eng; Temple Univ (MS) Ed 1972; Millersville Univ Supervisory Cert; *cr:* Donegal Jr HS Spec Ed Tchr 1965-66; Conestoga Vly Jr HS Eng Tchr 1966-93; Conestoga Vly Sr HS Eng Tchr 1994-; *ai:* Gifted Coord 1978-86; Portfolio, Assessment Comm Chm; Effective Tchng Team; Mentorship Prgm; Strategic Planning Curr Comm; Goals 2000 Assessment Consortium; NCTE, ASCD 1987-; PSFA, NEA 1965-87; St Mary's 1940-, Bldg Comm 1988-; *office:* Conestoga Valley Sr HS 2110 Horseshoe Rd Lancaster PA 17601

FORTE, WENDY L., Spanish Teacher; *b:* Brooklyn, NY; *m:* Jeffrey B. Nackenson; *c:* Joshua Elliot, Chase Gabriel; *ed:* SUNY at Albany (BA) Span 1977, (MS) Biling Ed 1981; El Inst Intnl 1975-76 27 Credits; L'Universite d'Avignon France 9 Credits; *cr:* Pub Schl Span Tchr 1981-86; Mineola HS Span, Fr Tchr 1986-; *ai:* Jr, Sr Class Adv 1987-89; NYSAFLT 1977-; AFT 1981; AATSP 1992-; Temple Beth Torah 1992-; *office:* Mineola HS 10 Armstrong Rd New Hyde Park NY 11040

FORTIER, GREGORY K., Social Studies Teacher; *b:* Dover-Foxcroft, ME; *m:* Kathleen Mc Namara; *c:* Elizabeth; *ed:* Univ of Southern ME (BA) His 1971; Tchng Cert Univ of ME; *cr:* Etna-Dixmont Schl Mid Level Tchr 1976-; *ai:* Boys Bsktbl, Bsbl Coach; 8th Grd Adv; Nature Trail Coord; Outing Club Adv; Kids Trailside Movie Making, Patent Invention Convention Coord; SS Curr Comm; Class Trip Organizer; NEA, MEA 1977-; EDTA 1977-, Pres; ME Island Trail Assn 1990-; Nature Conservancy, Nordic Ski Patrol 1987-; Archetectural Comm for Homeowners Assn 1993-; Pub Newsletter; Stu Vols Salvation Army; Dev Offshore Islands Stu Exch Prgm; Coordination Outdoor Experiences Chewonki Fnd; Led Stdnts Five Week Trip; Organized Woodcock Radio Tracking Moosehorn Natl Wildlife Refuge; Liason Aspirations Proj; *office:* Etna Dixmont Schl Box 1800 Etna ME 04434*

FORTIER, JOANNE MENDES, High School English Teacher; *b:* New Bedford, MA; *m:* Ronald; *c:* Christopher, Meaghan; *ed:* Univ of MA at Dartmouth (BA) Pol Sci 1970; Post Grad Stud RI Coll; *cr:* Bishop Stang HS Eng Tchr 1982-, Eng, Fine Arts Dept Chprsn 3 Yrs; St Frnacis Xavier Schl Jr HS Lang Arts Tchr 1975-82, Vice Prin 2 Yrs, 5th Grd Tchr 1970-75; *ai:* Sr Class Adv; Field Hockey Clinic Coord; Initiated Stu Ldrshp Prgm & SADD; Cheering, Natl Jr Hnr Soc Adv; Natl Cath Tchrs of Eng 1990-; NCEA 1985-; Who's Who Among Elem Tchr 1977; *office:* Bishop Stang HS 500 Slocum Rd North Dartmouth MA 02747*

FORTIN-NOSSAVAGE, ANDREA S., Social Studies Teacher; *b:* Lewiston, NY; *m:* Kenneth F. Nossavage; *ed:* SUNY at Buffalo (BS) Soc Stud Ed 1991; Niagara Univ (MS) Fnds in Tchng 1995; *cr:* Niagara Falls HS Soc Stud Tchr 1992-93; LaSalle Sr HS Soc Stud Tchr 1992-; *ai:* Adv Clas of 1997, 1992; Inclusion Steering Comm; NYSCSS, AFT, NYSUT 1992-; ASCD 1995-; *office:* La Salle Sr HS 1500 Military Rd Niagara Falls NY 14304

FORTINO, JOSEPH G., Soc Stud, Rdng & Rel Tchr; *b:* New Haven, CT; *m:* Marcia Glynne; *c:* Elizabeth; *ed:* Fairfield Univ (BA) His 1971; Geog 100; Tchng Exceptional Stu in Regular Classroom; *cr:* Our Lady of Victory Schl Tchr 1971-; *ai:* Soccer Coach; Schl Accredidation Team; NCEA 1972-; West Haven Lib Bd 1974-, Pres & Prsnl Chprsn; Deans List Fairfield Univ; *office:* Our Lady Of Victory Schl 620 Jones Hill Rd West Haven CT 06516

FORTKIEWICZ, DIANA BRZEZINSKI, Biology Teacher; *b:* Glen Ridge, NJ; *m:* Victor A.; *c:* Kevin, Susan; *ed:* Rutgers NCAS (BA) Botany, Bio Ed 1974; Cornell Univ (MS) Ornamental Floriculture 1976; Attnd Montclair St, Rutgers Univ; *cr:* Paul VI HS Bio Tchr 1976-79; Bloomfield HS Bio Tchr 1979-; *ai:* Club Adv Tech Bio I Sci Team; NJ Sci Tchr Assn, NJEA 1979-; NJSTA 1994-; Pub Article Hort Sci; *office:* Bloomfield HS 160 Broad St Bloomfield NJ 07003

FORTMANN, NANCY MERRION, 11th Grade English Teacher; *b:* Danville, PA; *ed:* West Chester St Univ (BS) Comp Eng 1971; Art Ed 36 Credit Hrs; Cmptr Sci 9 Credit Hrs; *cr:* Perkiomen Vly HS 11th Grd Tchr 1973-; *ai:* NEA, PSEA, NCTE 1973-; *office:* Perkiomen Valley HS Rt 29 Graterford PA 19426

FORTSON, MARY WILLIAMS, English Teacher; *b:* Lewistown, PA; *c:* Nina, Damien, Christian; *ed:* Juniata coll (BA) Scndry Ed, Eng 1990; Addl Hrs Frostburg Univi Rdng; Credit Hrs Stu Svc Learning Project; *cr:* South Hagerstown HS Tchr 1990-; Hagerstown Jr Coll Part-Time Fac 1991-; *ai:* Class of 97, 92 Adv; Play Dir 1991-93, 1995; Multicultural Comm; Equity Cncl; Future Tchrs Assn Adv; SAT Verbal Instr; WCTA 1990-, Bldg Rep; NEA, MSTA, NCTE 1990-; Co-Wrote Proposal Penn St Univ Regnl Upward Bound Math, Sci Ctr, Asst Dir 1991-95; *home:* 138 E Washington St Hagerstown MD 21740*

FORTUN, DAVID R., English Teacher; *b:* Pittsburgh, PA; *m:* Charlene A.; *c:* Justin, Ben; *ed:* IN Univ of PA (BS) Eng 1970; *cr:* Shaler Area Schl Dist Eng Tchr 1970-; *ai:* Fox Chapel HS Asst Soccer Coach; Mid Sts Evaluation Steering Comm; SAEA 1970-; PSEA 1970-; NEA 1970-; Vol St Margarets Memrl Hosp; *home:* 528 Saxonburg Rd Pittsburgh PA 15238*

FORTUNA, MYRNA ZAYAS, Eighth Grade Teacher; *b:* Santurce, PR; *m:* Edwin; *c:* Giselle, Lizbeth; *ed:* Jersey City St Coll (BA) Elem Ed 1972; 16 Credits Grad Stud; *cr:* Pub Schl #22 Elem Tchr 1972-; *ai:* Taught Bible Stud to Teenagers; NEA, NJEA, JCEA 1972-; *office:* Public Schl 22 264 Van Horne St Jersey City NJ 07304

FORTUNOFF, DAVID, English Teacher; *b:* Bronx, NY; *m:* Sandra A. Willis-Fortunoff; *c:* Dawn Okst, Rachel, Laura; *ed:* SUNY at Stony Brook (BA) Eng 1968, (MA) Eng 1974, (PHD) Philosophy 1987; *cr:* SUNY at Stony Brook Residence Life Asst Dir 196.-76; Smithtown HS Eng Tchr 1977-84; Dowling Coll Adjunct Asst Philosophy Prof 1992-; Longwood HS Eng Tchr 1984-; *ai:* AFT 1977-; APA, SAGP, IAGP, NANS 1986-; SAAP 1986-, Writing Awd 1986; Articles Pub; *office:* Longwood HS 100 Longwood Rd Middle Island NY 11953*

FORWARD, JUDITH B., School Nurse; *b:* Hanover, NH; *m:* Allan J.; *c:* Seth, A. J.; *ed:* Norwich Univ (AS) Nursing 1993; Hanover Schl of Pract Nursing LPN 1963; *cr:* Lebanon Schl Dist Hlth, Nursing Tchr 1980-; *ai:* Team One; Visions Comm; NEA 1986-; NHSNA 1994-; *office:* Lebanon Jr HS 75 Bank St Lebanon NH 03766*

FORWARD, TERRY BOLING, Eng as a Second Lang Tchr; *b:* E Chicago, IN; *m:* Timothy J.; *c:* Linda, Janet; *ed:* Murray St Univ (BS) Eng 1968; Univ of IL (MA) Tchng of Eng 1975; Univ of Rochester, Nazareth Coll, D'Youville Coll 18 Credit Hrs Leading to Cert to Tch Eng as a Second Lang; *cr:* Lamphier HS Eng Tchr 1973-74; Southeast HS Eng TChr 1968-71, 1974-75; Rochester City Schls Eng Tchr 1988-89; Greece Athena HS Eng as a Second Lang Tchr 1991-; *ai:* ESL Newsletter Adv; NEA 1968-; *office:* Greece Athena HS 800 Long Pond Rd Rochester NY 14612

FORZANO, ROBERT JOHN, History Teacher; *b:* E Liverpool, OH; *m:* Donna Jean Bolton; *c:* Stephanie Anne Grey; *ed:* Kent St Univ (BS) Comprehensive Soc Stud 1974; Coll of Mount St Joseph (MS) Ed 1987; *cr:* Vietnam War Veterans; US Army Comm Ctr Specialist 1966-69; East Palestine HS Tchr 1975-79; Beaver Local HS Tchr 1979-; *ai:* North Cntrl Accreditation Comm; NEA 1979-; OEA 1975-; BLEA 1979-, Pres, Exec Cncl; *office:* Beaver Local HS 13187 State Rt 7 Lisbon OH 44432

FOSBENNER, KENNETH LEE, Mathematics Teacher; *b:* Sellersville, PA; *ed:* Bapt Bible Coll (BRE) Ed 1973; Math Courses at West Chester Univ; *cr:* High Point Comp & Conf Ctr Food Svc Dir 1971-89; High Point Bapt Acad Tchr 1973-; *ai:* Chess Club Adv; Chapel Pianist; Music Planning Comm; PBX Programming; High Point Bapt Chapel 1973-, Organist; *home:* PO Box 132 Geigertown PA 19523

FOSCOLO, MARY M., Third Grade Teacher; *b:* Mineola, NY; *ed:* SUNY at Farmingdale (AS) Early Chldhd Ed 1981; C. W. Post LIU (BS) Elem Ed 1983, (MS) Cmptrs, Ed 1987; 3 Hrs Cmptr Graphics; 30 In-Svc Hrs; *cr:* Hicksville UFSD First Grd Tchr 1984-86, Third Grd Tchr 1986-; *ai:* NEA NY 1984-; Hicks Congress of Tchrs 1984-, Union Del; Nassau TRACT, Policy Bd 1989-90, Asst Chprsn 1990-91; Hicksville TRACT 1991-93, Satellite Ctr Dir; PTA Founders Day Honoree 1993; *office:* Lee Avenue Schl 1 7th St Hicksville NY 11801

FOSDICK, WILLIAM CHARLES, 4th Grade Teacher; *b:* Brooklyn, NY; *c:* Brian, Kristin, Elizabeth; *ed:* Adelphi Univ (BA) Ed 1970, (MA) Ed & Psych 1973; *cr:* Patchogue-Medford Schls Tchr 1970-; Adelphi Univ Adj Assoc Prof 1971-; *ai:* Canaan Elem Site Based Mgmt Team; AFT 1970-; Assn of Univ Profs; Book Pub 1977.

FOSHER, MARY JANE, English Curriculum Director; *b:* Shakopee, MN; *c:* Cassandra McKiernan, Jonathan; *ed:* Notre Dame Coll (BA) Eng 1969; Univ of NH (MST) Eng 1987; *cr:* Raymond HS Eng Tchr 1980-; Raymond Schl Dist 5th-12th Grd Eng Curr Dir 1987-; *ai:* Appledore Proj; Sex Harrassment Awarement Comm; NCTE & NHATE 1987-; AAUW; NOW; NARAL; Amnesty Intnl; Natl Museum of Women in the Arts; NEH Summer Seminars for Tchrs 1987 & 1991; Natl Hum Ctr Summer Inst 1987; NH Summer Tchrs Acad 1990; NEH Summer Inst 1989; MMLA Conf 1988; *office:* Raymond H S 45 Harriman Hill Rd Raymond NH 03077

FOSNIGHT, JENNIFER TREXLER, 5th Grade Teacher; *b:* Ravenna, OH; *m:* Alan; *c:* Andrew; *ed:* (MED) (BS) Schl Cnclng 1994; Grad Work; *cr:* Dodge MS Tchr 1990-; *ai:* Coached Cheerleading 2 Yrs & Track 3 Yrs; Stu Cncl; PANDA; Odyssey of the Mind; Spelling Bee; Multi-Cultural Comm Spon; 5th Grd Lang Art s & Soc Stud; NEA 1990-; Worked on Grant For Gifted Ed in Dist; Received Grant for Svcng Gifted Stdnts in Regular Classroom; *office:* Dodge MS 10225 Ravenna Rd Twinsburg OH 44087*

FOSS, ALEXANDRA, Guidance Counselor; *b:* Ridgewood, NJ; *ed:* Northeastern Univ (MEd) Curr Dev 1993; Saint Michaels Coll (BA) Psych 1985; Emergency Medical Technician Certification; *cr:* Saint Clement HS Guidance Director 1993-; Dept of Youth Services Clinical Coord 1986-93; Univ of MA at Boston Womens Vlybl Coach 1995-; *ai:* NHS Adv; Charlestown Dist Court Comm Recognition Awd; *office:* St Clement HS 579 Boston Ave Somerville MA 02144*

FOSS, ROBIN H., Reading Specialist; *b:* Pittsfield, MA; *m:* Michael J.; *ed:* Syracuse Univ (BA) Eng, Psych 1974; Boston Univ (E&M) Scndry Rdng Ed 1975; *cr:* Wakefield Jr HS Rdng Tchr 1975-77; Kennett Sr HS Eng, Rdng Tchr 1978-79; Masconomet sr HS Eng, Rdng Tchr 1979-80; Pentucket Sr HS Rdng Specialist Tchr 1985-; *ai:* Schl Newspaper Club Adv 7 Yrs; SADD Club Adv 8 Yrs; NEA, MTA, NCTE, IRA 1975-; *office:* Pentucket Regional HS 22 Main St West Newbury MA 01985

FOSSELMAN, LINDA EILEEN, French Teacher; *b:* Camp Breckinridge, KY; *ed:* Shippensburg St Coll (BS) Scndry Ed 1973; Middlebury Coll (MA) Fr 1976; *cr:* Linglestown Jr HS Fr Tchr 1974-81; East Pennsboro HS Fr Tchr 1976-77; Central Daughin HS Fr Tchr 1978-80; Central Dauphin East Sr HS Fr Tchr 1979-; *ai:* Scndry Enrollment Stud, Mid Sts Evaluation, Fac Advy, Commencement Comm; NEA, PSEA, CDEA 1974-; Fr Phonetics Cert of Proficiency; *office:* Central Dauphin East Sr HS 626 Rutherford Rd Harrisburg PA 17109

FOSTER, BARBARA R., ESL Professor; *b:* Hackensack, NJ; *m:* Jack D.; *c:* David, Ronald, Diane Rock; *ed:* Broome Comm Coll (AS) Med Lab Tech 1980; Calvin Coll (BA) Elem Ed, Eng 1962; *cr:* Broome Comm Coll ESL Tchr 5 Yrs, CASS Prgm Asst 5 Yrs; Church World Svc Local Refugee Office Admin 3 Yrs; *office:* Broome Comm Coll PO Box 1017 Binghamton NY 13902

FOSTER, BETTE CAROL, Sixth Grade Teacher; *b:* Gallipolis, OH; *m:* James; *c:* Lori, Andy; *ed:* Rio Grande Univ (BS) Elem Ed 1973; Dayton Univ (MS) Educl Admin 1995; *cr:* Comm Action of Vinton Cty Head Start Dir 1972-73; Waverly City Schls First Grd Tchr 1973-74; Gallipolis City Schls First Grd Tchr 1974-79; Vinton Cty Local Schls Sixth Grd Tchr 1989-; *ai:* Governing, Grant Writing Comm; Safety Patrol Supvr; NEA, OEA 1973-; VCLTA 1989-; Delta Kappa Gamma 1986-88; Fed of Women's Club; Golden Apple Achvmt Awd Asland Oil 1994; Southern OH Coal Grants 1994, 1995; Conflict Resolution Grant, Mem of Comm; *office:* Allensville Elem Schl RR 1 Box 668 Mc Arthur OH 45651*

FOSTER, BETTY J. (FULTON), Second Grade Teacher; *b:* Butler, PA; *m:* Larry W.; *c:* Gretel E., Everett L.; *ed:* Univ of Pittsburgh (BS) Elem Ed 1982; 36 Post Grad Credits; *cr:* Portersville Chrstn Schl 3rd-6th Grd Tchr 1982-85, Kndgtn Tchr 1985-90; Middlesex Presbyn Church Presch Tchr 1990-91; Portersville Chr Schl 6th Grd Tchr 1991-92, 2nd Grd Tchr 1992-; *ai:* Ed Comm; ACSI 1986-; Girl Scout USA 1992-, Troop Ldr; Church Choir 1995-, Deacon 1996-, Sec, Sunday Schl Sec 1995-; *home:* 421 N Jackson St Evans City PA 16033*

FOSTER, BRUCE MICHAEL, Global Studies Teacher; *b:* Little Falls, NY; *m:* Debra DeLucco; *c:* Nicole, Megan; *ed:* Utica Coll of Syracuse U (BA) Pol Sci 1977; SUNY at Cortland (MED) His Ed 1985; Post Grad Hrs CAS Admin; Grad Hrs Rdng; *cr:* New Hartford Cntrl Schl Soc Stud Tchr 1980-85; Dolgeville Cntrl Schl Soc Stud Tchr 1985-; *ai:* 9th Grd Class Adv; Bsktbl Coach 1982-82; Variety of Comms; Dolgeville Tchrs Assn 1985-; NYS Tchrs Union 1980-; F&A Masons 1976-, Sr Warden, Outstdng Ofcr of Yr; Boy Scouts 1970-, Troop Ldr; Salisbury Town Bd 1976-80, Councilman; Salisbury Town Justice 1976-92, Judge; Dibble-Tuttle Cemetary Assn 1986-, Pres; *home:* PO Box 126 Dolgeville NY 13329*

FOSTER, CATHERINE KEATING, 5th Grade Math & Science Tchr; *b:* Elizabeth, NJ; *m:* Edward; *c:* William, Ann Marie, Michael, Susan; *ed:* Benedectine Coll (BA) Ec & Ed 1952; Seton Hall U 6 Credit Hrs 1953; *cr:* Vail-Deane Pvt Schl Tchr Math, Soc S 1952-55; Woodbridge Pub Schl Sub 1960-66; St John Vianney Schl Tchr Math, Sci 1966-; *ai:* Steering Comm for Schl Evaluation; Facilator in Evaluation of Schl Prins; NCEA 1966-; Edctr of Yr; *office:* St John Vianney Schl 420 Inman Ave Colonia NJ 07067

FOSTER, DAVID EUGENE, Biology & Physical Sci Tchr; *b:* Orbisonia, PA; *m:* Lorraine L.; *c:* David J., Kate E.; *ed:* Davis & Elkins Coll (BA) Art 1969; Penn St Univ (MED) Art Ed 1974; Cert in Gen Sci at Univ of MD 1987; 60 Addl Credits; *cr:* Huntingdon Area MS Art Tchr 1974-77; Old Mill South MS Art Tchr 1978-81; Old Mill North MS Art, Sci Tchr 1981-94; Glen Burnie HS bio, Phys Sci Tchr 1994-; *ai:* Local Drama Troup Design Work; NEA 1974-; MSTA, TAACO 1978-; Glen Burnie Recreation Assn 1985-, Exec Bd; *office:* Glen Burnie HS 7550 Balto Annapolis Blvd SE Glen Burnie MD 21061

FOSTER, DWAYNE EDWARD, English Teacher; *b:* Washington, DC; *ed:* DE St Univ (BA) Eng Ed 1993; *cr:* Bishop Mc Namara HS Eng Tchr 1993-94; Archbishop Carroll HS Eng Tchr 1994-; *ai:* Head Frosh Ftbl, Strength & Conditioning Coach; NCEA 1993-; NCTE 1996; *office:* Archbishop Carroll HS 4300 Harewood Rd NE Washington DC 20017*

FOSTER, ELAINE P., Retired French Teacher; *b:* Boston, MA; *m:* Bradford; *c:* Eric, Karen; *ed:* Univ of MA at Amherst (BA) Fr 1970; *cr:* Behnart HS Fr Tchr 1970-73; Inter-Lakes HS Fr Tchr 1981-95; *ai:* NEA 1981-, Negotiator, Bldg Rep; AATF, Phi Beta Kappa 1970-.

FOSTER, GITA HAKEREN, Science Teacher; *b:* New York City, NY; *m:* David; *ed:* Univ of Rochester (BS) Physics 1986; Univ of MA (MED) Ed 1987; Boston Univ (EDD) Curr & Instrucional Sci & Ed 1996; *cr:* Framingham HS Sci Tchr 1987-; *ai:* AAPT 1987-; NSTA 1987-; FTA & NEA 1987-; MAST 1988-; NARST 1991-; Hadssah 1991-, Group Pres 1995-; Paper Presented NARST Annual Meeting 1993; Poster Presented AERA Annual Meeting 1993; *office:* Framingham HS 115 A St Framingham MA 01701*

FOSTER, JAMES H., Religion Teacher; *b:* Valdosta, GA; *ed:* Morris Brown Coll (BA) Philosophy, Rel 1960; Union Bapt Coll (PHD) Honorary 1971; United Theological Seminary (MDiv) Theology 1973; Vanderbilt Univ (PHD) Rel 1984; Attnd Tuland Univ, Chicago Grad Schl of Theology, Boston Univ; *cr:* Albany St Coll Chaplain, Instr 1962-66; Alcon St Univ Chaplain, Asst Prof 1967-68; Wilberforce Univ Chaplain, Asst Prof 1972-80; Payne Theological Seminary Asst Prof 1976-80; DArtmouth Coll Assoc Chaplain, Lecturer 1980-84; Mercy Coll Adj Prof of Rel; *ai:* NCEA 1987-; Optmists Club 1975-; *office:* St John Vianney HS 94 Line Rd Holmdel NJ 07733

FOSTER, JAN STRICKLAND, Business Teacher; *b:* columbus, MS; *ed:* MS Univ for Women (BS) Bus Ed 1960; 45 Grad hrs Frostburg St Coll, Univ of MD, Bowie St, No VA Comm; *cr:* Gen Motors Accept Corp Stenographer, Discount Clerk 1960-65; Real Estate Broker, Sales Salesperson, Part-time Broker 1974-81; PG Cty Pub Schls Bus Tchr 1966-; *ai:* NEA 1967-; *home:* 735 S Alfred St Alexandria VA 22314

FOSTER, JANE WALLIS, First Grade Teacher; *b:* Pittsburgh, PA; *ed:* Westminster Coll (BA) Elem Ed 1966; Univ of Pittsburgh (MED) Ed 1970; 9 Post Grad Credits Wilkes Coll; 1 Post Grad Credit Penn St Univ; 1 Post Grad Credit Fairfield Univ; 3 Post-Grad Credits; 6 Credits Allegheny Co Intermediate Unit; *cr:* Shaler Area Schl Dist First Grd Tchr 1966-; *ai:* St Barnabas Charitable Fnd Presents for Patients Chprsn; Whole Schl Project Chprsn; Amer Cancer Soc Daffodil Days; Annual Staff Project; NEA, PSEA, Shaler Area Ed Assn 1966-; Westminster Coll Women's Club 1966-, Past Pres, Sec, Treas; Schlsp Comm Oakmont Woman's Club 1985-, Sec; Thomas House of Oakmont 1994-, House Advy Bd Chm; PA Tchr of Yr Nom 1969-70, 1972, 1974, 1989; Amer Family Inst Tribute of Time Awd 1990-92; Thanks to Tchrs Nom 1990, 1996; *office:* Marzolf Road Elem Schl 101 Marzolf Road Ext Pittsburgh PA 15209*

FOSTER, JEAN ZENKE, Mathematics Teacher; *b:* Scranton, PA; *m:* John; *c:* Susan, Ken; *ed:* Bloomsburg Univ (BS) Scndry Ed Math 1966, Mstrs Equivlncy Degree PA Dept of Ed; 72 Addl Credit Hrs Univ NH, PA St Univ, Univ Scranton; *cr:* Abington Hgts HS Math Tchr 1966-71, 1980-; *ai:* Stu Cncl; Stu Month Comm; Stu Recognition Comm; Cheerleading Advisor; Majorette Advisor; Class Advisor; AHEA, PSEA, NEA 1966-; PCTM, NPCTM 1989-; Past Mem Abington Hgts Civic League; Clarks Summit Presbyn Church 1966-; Natl Sci Fnd Grant; *home:* 626 Sunset St Clarks Summit PA 18411

FOSTER, LINDA PORTER, Vocal Music Teacher; *b:* Warre John C.; *c:* Nicole, Jennifer, Renee, Jessica, Julia, Erin; *ed:* Da Music of Youngstown St Univ (BM) Music Ed, Piano 1978; Jers Coll (MA) Music Ed, Voice 1991; Jersey City St Coll 30 H Supervision; *cr:* Fort Lee Schls Elem Gen Music Tchr 1986-89, Music Tchr 1989-; *ai:* Tri-M Intnl Hnr Soc for Music Spon; The Music Dir; MENC 1986-, Registered Music Educator; Music Ed Co 1989-, Conductor Selection Comm; NEA 1986-, Governor's T WOR A+ For Kids Tchr Awd, Grant 1988; WOR A+ ForKids Dis Grant 1989; MENC Registered Music Educator; NJ Governor's T *office:* Fort Lee HS 3000 Lemoine Ave Fort Lee NJ 07024*

FOSTER, LOUISE HEATON, Retired Elementary Teacher; *b:* GA; *m:* Robert H.; *c:* Robert Douglas, Risa Louise; *ed:* GA S Women (BA) Span, Eng, Ed 1953; Russell Sage Coll (MA) Elem 6 Post Grad Hrs Cnslng Univ of GA 1956; *cr:* GA St Schls I 1953-57; Glatewater City Schl Elem Tchr 1957-58; Greenhill S Tchr 1961-63; Saratoga Sprgs City Schls Elem Tchr 1966-89; *a* Plays Drama Act, Six Grd Tutors Dir; NY St United Tchrs 196 Chief Negotiator, Negotiating Team; NY St United Tchrs Retire AARP; Written Book Reviews; Several Articles Pub; *home:* 145 Saratoga Springs NY 12866*

FOSTER, MARGARET CAREY, English Teacher; *b:* Portland Univ of ME (BA) Sociology & Eng 1969; Univ of MA (MED) 4 Hrs Beyond Masters at Univ of Southern ME; *cr:* South Portlar Tchr 1970-; *ai:* Foreign Exch Adv 13 Yrs; NHS Comm Mem 5 Portland Tchrs Assn 1970, RA 2 Yrs; ME Ed Assn, NEA 197 Squares 1992-, Bd of Dirs; South Portland Bd of Ed Educl Gra HS Bus Eng & Word Processing Prgm; *office:* South Portlan Highland Ave South Portland ME 04106

FOSTER, MARY K., English Teacher; *b:* Jersey City, NJ; Richard; *c:* Rider Rocco, Ford Reilly; *ed:* Bloomsburg St Coll (B Ed & Eng 1975; *cr:* Lancaster Cath HS Eng Tchr 1978-80; C BHS Remedial Tchr 1980-82; Montville HS Eng GED Tchr Lady of Mt Carmel Schl Eng Tchr 1983-95; The Wilson Schl 1995-; *ai:* Rdng Incentive Coord; 8th Grd Adv; NCTE 1983-; Morris Choral Soc 1987-; *office:* The Wilson School 271 Mountain Lakes NJ 07046

FOSTER, PAMELA GAIL, 5th Grade Teacher; *b:* Queens, N A&M Univ (BS) Elem Ed 1987; Western MD Coll Working Tow in Lib Sci; *cr:* Jones Ln Elem 5th Grd Tchr 1987-90; Gen Comm Schl Eng & Bus Comm Instr 1991-94; Sequoyah Elem 5th Grd T *ai:* Stu Cncl Spon & Adv; MSTA 1987-; NEA 1987-; MEMO 1 1996; Alpha Kappa Alpha 1993-, Philactor; *office:* Sequoyah E 17301 Bowie Mill Rd Derwood MD 20855

FOSTER, VERDA ELAINE, Assistant Professor of Nrsng; *b:* West Indies; *ed:* Atlantic Union Coll (BS) Nrsng 1959; Loma Li of CA (MA) Cnslng, Guid 1969; St Univ of NY at Stony Broo Nrsng 1991; Obstetrics Cert Post Grad; 20 Post Grad Credit Hrs *cr:* Worcester St Hosp Staff Nurse, Psych 1959-60; Logan Mem H Nurse, Med, Surgical Nrsng 1960-61; New England Mem Hsp N 1961-64; Mt Sinau Hosp Chage Nurse, Obstenis 1964-67; Lo Univ Nrsng Instr 1967-69; Bronx Comm Coll Asst Prof of Nrsng Clinical Agency Coord; Materal Child Hlth Nrsng, Pharmacolog Curr, Prsnl & Budget, Admin & Promotion, Continuing Ed, Coll B Comms; Amer Nurse Assn, NY St Nuse Assn 1976-; PSC, A Organization at Obstetics 1970-; Neonatal Nurses 1989 Temperance Soc 1975-, Local Church Sec; Bronx Westchester E Sec; Dev Curr Parent Child Nrsng Hlth, Human Svcs Title III Gran Bronx Comm Coll 181st St & Univ Ave Bronx NY 10453

FOSTER, VICKI STALEY, First Grade Teacher; *b:* Frederick, Jeffrey Allen; *c:* Nathan; *ed:* Frostburg St (BA) Early Chldhd Rdng Specialist Hood Coll; NSF Sci Course; Western MD Coll Myersville Elem Schl Kndgtn Tchr 1975-76; Urbana Elem Sch Tchr 1976-79, First Grd Tchr 1979-; *ai:* First Grd Team, M Co-Author CARE Package; NEA 1976-; MSTA 1976-, Del; FCT Schl Rep; IRA, SOMIRAC, FCRC 1990-; PTSA 1976-; Nom Agn Outstdng Tchr Awd 1989; Tchr Plus; Who's Who Among Young An 1988; *office:* Urbana Elem Schl 3554 Urbana Pike Frederick MD

FOSTER, WILLIAM CHET, Health & Physical Ed Teacher; *b:* Heights, PA; *m:* Lavella L. Holman; *c:* Michael; *ed:* Southern C Hlth Ed & Phys Ed 1966; Slippery Rock Coll (MS) Curr Dev 19 Penn St at New Kensington; *cr:* St Marys HS Bio, Hlth & PE Tchr Highlands Schl Dist Hlth & PE Tchr 1968-; *ai:* Boys & Girls Head Coach; Core Team Mem, Crisis Intervention Mem; 24-H Comm Chair; Highlands Ed Assn 1966-, Bldg Rep; NEA & PSE Tri-St Track Coaches Assn 1991-; Tar-Brack Rotary 1972-, Pres Rotarian of the Yr 1989-90, Paul Harris Flwshp; Mason-Naze 1991-, Sec SW; *office:* Highlands Sr HS Idaho At Pacific Natrona PA 15065*

FOSTVEIT, TAMARA S., First Grade Teacher; *b:* DeRuyter, Edgar H.; *c:* Edgar M.; *ed:* SUNY at Cortland (BS) K-6 Elem Addl Hrs; *cr:* DeRuyter Cntrl Scl Elem Tchr 1961-; *ai:* NEA; Del Gamma; DeRuyter Fac Assoc; Order of the Eastern Star; Childre Written; *home:* 728 Railroad St De Ruyter NY 13052

FOUCHE, SHARON LEAHY, Language Arts Teacher; *b:* Hartf *m:* Gerald T.; *c:* Heather Keaveny, Carrie; *ed:* Framingham St C Eng 1967; Amer Intnl Coll (MED) Mid Level Ed 1993; Univ of NH Prgm 6 Hrs 1992; Bard Col Inst for Writing, Thinking 1991; *cr:* HS 8th Grd LA Tchr 1967-70; St Mary's Elem Schl 3rd Grd Tchr Westfield MS 8th Grd LA Tchr 1985-91; Powder Mill MS 7th-8th Tchr 1991-; *ai:* Crisis Response Team; Team Ldr; Peer Mediati Scheduling, Advy, Stud Skills, Lang Arts Curr Comms; NCTE, NE MTA, Southwick Tchr Assn 1985-91; MA Rdng Assn, IRA 1994-; Vly Rdng Assn 1992-; *office:* Powder Mill MS 94 Powder Southwick MA 01085

FOURNIER, KAREN K., Science Teacher; *b:* New Britain, CT; F.; *c:* Bryan, Leanne; *ed:* Cntrl CT St Univ (BS) Bio 1975; St Jose (MS) Bio 1986; 3-6 Credit Hrs Univ of CT, Wesleyan Univ, Mid CT, Southern CT St Univ; *cr:* St Paul Cath HS Sci, Math Tchr 1983-85; Bristol Cntrl HS Sci Tchr 1985-87; Bristol Eastern HS 1987-; *ai:* Sci Natl Honor Sco Adv; NSTA, CT Sci Tchrs Assn NABT 1987-; Barnes Nature Ctr 1991-, Trustee; *office:* Bristol Eas 632 King St Bristol CT 06010*

FOURNIER, LISA M., 8th Grade Science Teacher; *b:* Newport, Univ of NH (BS) Plant Bio 1989, (MED) Ed 1990; *cr:* Dover Jr Tchr 1990-; *ai:* Girls Soccer Coach; Schl to Work Ldrshp Comm; NH Sci Tchrs Assn 1990-; Distngd Fac Awd 1995; NASA, NSTA Tchr Awd; *office:* Dover Jr HS 30 Saint Thomas St Dover NH 038

FOURNIER, STEVEN W., Computer Coordinator; *b:* Berlin, NH Gail; *c:* Nannette G., Loreen P. C., B. Dannielle; *ed:* PSC (BS) Mat (MS) Math 1988; *cr:* Groveton HS Math 1976-79; Belmont HS Cmptr 1979-; *ai:* Cmptr Coord; Budget Comm 1986-, Sec; Mo 1991-.*

FOUSE, GAIL DICKERSON, Fourth Grade Teacher; *b:* Dover, Terry E.; *c:* Deborah Fouse Stec, David S.; *ed:* Juniata Coll (BS) E

East Windsor Schl Dist 2nd Grd Tchr 1960-62; Cedarville Elem ›rd Tchr 1962-65; Sunnybrae Schl Supplemental Tchr 1974-80; 4th Grd Tchr 1980-82; Yardville Schl 4th Grd Tchr 1982-; *ai:* ncl Adv; Cooperating Tchr Stdnts Rider, Trenton; Family Math ., NJEA-; HTEA 1980-, AR; Yardville Tchr of Yr 1988-89; Pres Church 1967-, Elder, Deacon, Sunday Schl Tchr, Choir, Soc Comm; *office:* Yardville Elem Schl 450 Allentown Rd Yardville

USAN E., Business Teacher; *b:* Homestead, PA; *m:* Gary L.; *c:* : Indiana Univ of PA (BS) Bus Ed 1971; Attnd PA St Univ, ock Univ; *cr:* Armstrong Schl Dist Bus Tchr 24 Yrs; *ai:* FBLA , PSEA 1972-; AEA 1972-, Sec; *office:* Elderton Jr Sr HS 428 lderton PA 15736

WILLIAM D., Global Studies Teacher; *b:* Kansas City, MO; *m:* glin; *c:* Gretchen E., W. Bradley; *ed:* Edinboro Univ (BS) Scndry 30 Credit Hrs Permanent Cert Soc Stud, Driver Ed NY St; *cr:* HS Driver Ed 1971-92, Global Stud 1992-; *ai:* Bsbl Coach; EA 1971-; Jamestown Coll Stadium Tenants Comm 1979-; *home:* town St Sugar Grove PA 16350

, STEPHEN TROY, Eighth Grade Science Teacher; *b:* Marietta, ara Lee Jackson; *ed:* Belmont Tech Coll (BA) Industrial Eng Univ (BAED) Elem Ed 1990; Marietta Coll (MAEd) Ed 1995; eeling Coll; *cr:* Marietta MS 7th-8th Grd Tchr 1990-; *ai:* Career ; Bsbl & Golf Coach; NEA 1990-; MEA 1990-, Bldg Rep; Schlep Awd; Outstanding Ed Nom; *home:* 200 Ingleside Ave OH 45750*

, LEAH RUTH, Home Economics Teacher; *b:* Plainview, MN; of WI at Stout (BS) Home Ec, Jrnlsm 1971; Post Grad Stud Trinity Madison Jr JS Home Ec Tchr 1974-80; Suitland HS Home Ec Tchr F. Douglass HS Home Ec Tchr 1990-; *ai:* Dept Chprsn; Schl mgmt Team; Awds Night Comm; NEA, MSTA, PGCEA 1975-; h Church 1994-, Church Cncl; Carrington HOA 1993-, Bd of Dir; Major Portions of Foods & Nutrition Curr; *office:* Frederick HS 8000 Croom Rd Upper Marlboro MD 20772*

, WILLIAM JAMES,JR., Biology Teacher; *b:* North Charleroi, l Hanrahan; *c:* Shannon, Andrew; *ed:* CA Univ of PA (BS) Bio hng Cert Frostburg St Univ 1986; 30 Grad Credit Hrs; *cr:* g HS Bio Tchr 1988-; *ai:* JV, Var Bsktbl Coach 1986-95; Bsbl sst 1987-91; *office:* Smithsburg HS 66 N Main St Smithsburg MD

R, DEBORAH LOUISE, Physical Ed & Health Teacher; *b:* H; *ed:* OH Univ (BS) Hlth, PE, Biological 1970; Ashland Univ orts, Sci 1994; *cr:* Plain Local Schls PE, Hlth Tchr 1970-; *ai:* sktbl, Sftbl Coach; NEA, OEA, PLTA 1970-; OHSFPA 1983-; A Taft MS 3829 Guilford Ave NW Canton OH 44718

R, DIANE MARIE, Language Arts Teacher; *b:* Trenton, NJ; *m:* Joseph; *c:* Jennifer Nicole Pratt; *ed:* Douglass Coll (BA) Eng Melvin H Kreps MS Lang Arts Tchr 1982-88, Gifted & Talented Lang Arts 1995-; *ai:* Stu Cncl; Schl Store; Lit Magazine; NJEA; AMLE; Rider Coll Deans Awd 1990; NJ Gov Tchrs Recognition 2-93, 1995-96; Melvin H Kreps MS Hall of Fame 1994; *office:* . Kreps MS 5 Kent Ln East Windsor NJ 08520

R, MEREDITH ANDERSON, French & Spanish Teacher; *b:* e, MA; *m:* Robert T. III; *ed:* Univ of ME (BA) Fr 1973; Univ of D) Scndry Ed 1980; *cr:* Billerica Meml HS Fr, Span Tchr 1973-; lub Co-Adv; MAFLA 1973-; GBWLC 1994-; *office:* Billerica l HS 35 River St Billerica MA 01821

R, WILLIAM ARTHUR, 6th Grade Teacher; *b:* Star Lake, NY; e L. Nelson; *c:* Katelyn E., Koby D.; *ed:* St Univ of NY at Oswego n Ed 1990, (MS) Elem Curr 1996; *cr:* Cntrl Square Jr HS 8th Grd r 1991; Cleveland Elem 6th Grd Tchr 1991-93; Cntrl Square MS Math & Hlth Tchr 1993-; *ai:* Asst Var Ftbl, JV Bsktbl & JV Bsbl NYSUT 1991-; *office:* Cntrl Square MS 1150 US Rt 11 S Central Y 13036

ETTY LOU (CORBIN), Second Grade Teacher; *b:* Erie, PA; *m:* lan; *c:* Chelsea Laurin; *ed:* Nyack Coll (BS) Elem Ed 1985; Univ (MS) Rdng 1988; Attnd Alliance Theological Seminary; *cr:* ne Chrstn Acad Fifth Grd Tchr 1986-88; Alliance Day Care, Ctr Dir, Admin 1988-91; Greater Erie Comm Action Comm Yth g, Job Training Instr 1993-95; First Assembly Chrstn Acad Second r 1995-; *ai:* HS Chrldng Adv; *home:* 62 Franklin St Albion PA

AROL HAMPSTON, Instrumental Teacher; *b:* Utica, NY; *m:* D.; *c:* Kathryn, Gabrielle; *ed:* Crane Schl of Music SUC at (BS) Music Ed 1964; IN Univ (MM) Oboe Performance 1966; *cr:* d St Univ Instr of Music 1966-68; Obwego City Schls Instr Tchr, r 1968-70; G Schirmer Performance Dept 1970-71, Instrumental and Dir 1971-; Fulton City Schls Facilitator of Music 1992-; *ai:* Music Assn; Band Dir; AFT 1968-, Negotiating Team 1983-; MENC NY St Schl Music Assn; Oswego Opera Theater 1976-; Oswego rchestra; Performances; *office:* Fulton City Schl Dist S 4th St NY 13069*

CAROL KIMBALL, 7th Grd Communications Teacher; *b:* ry, NJ; *c:* Amy, Andy; *ed:* Kutztown St Coll (BS) Elem Ed 1971; an Schls 4th Grd Tchr 1971-73, 4th-5th Grd Remedial Math, Gifted ted Tchr & 7th Grd Tchr 1975-; Highland Falls NY 4th Grd Tchr ; *ai:* HS Chrldng Coach; Stu Cncl Adv; 7th Grd Team Ldr; Pupil ce, Block Scheduling & Staff Dev Comms; Mentor; NEA; NJEA; es & VP; Meth Church 1996-, Bd of Trustees, United Meth Women; Pitman MS 138 E Holly Ave Pitman NJ 08071

HARLES JOSEPH, Science Teacher; *b:* Newark, NJ; *m:* Deborah e; *c:* Michael, James; *ed:* Wm Paterson Coll (BA) Elem Ed 1972; its Beyond BA; *cr:* Lyndhurst Bd of Ed Tchr 1972-; *ai:* Bsktbl, Soccer Coach; Comp Club Adv; NEA 1972-; NJEA; LEA; Jaycees , Most Outstdng Jaycee; Governors Awd for Outstdng Tchng 1990; Lincoln MS 281 Ridge Rd Lyndhurst NJ 07071

AVID LEWIS, Physics Teacher; *b:* Boston, MA; *ed:* Rochester Inst (BS) Physics 1980; Univ of VT Post Bac Tchr Cert 1992; *cr:* Coll hysics Tchr 1993-95; Dighton-Rehoboth Regnl HS Physics Tchr *ai:* Sci Club Adv; AAPT 1993-; NSTA 1992-; Amer MENSA Ltd Pub Relations, Proctor, Gifted Children Coord; Article Pub in Sci 96; *office:* Dighton-Rehoboth Regnl HS 155 R New St Rehoboth 769

DONNA STARK, Orchestra Teacher; *ed:* Carnegie-Mellon Univ Music 1973, (BFA) Music 1974; *cr:* Pittsburgh Pub Schls Ctrs for lly Talented Instr 1973-74; Carnegie-Mellon Prep Division Violin 73-84; Churchill Area Schls Music Tchr 1974; Peters Twp Schls Specialist, Orch Tchr 1975-; *ai:* Asst Marching Band, Musical Dir; Music Hnr Soc Chptr Spon; MENC 1970-, Tri-M Distngd Svc Awd; sic Edctrs Assn 1970-, Ex-Officio Tri-M Chair; Amer String Tchrs 970-, PA Pres, Distngd Svc Awd; Pittsburgh Chamber Music Soc Natl Chair of Tri-M Music Hnr Soc; PA String Tchrs Newsletter Ed; Eastern Div Festival Orch Mgr 1991, 1993, 1995.

FOX, ELIZABETH ANN, Music Director; *b:* Oberlin, OH; *ed:* Capital Univ (BM) Music Ed 1993; *cr:* Crooksville HS Music Dir 1993-; *ai:* Marching Band, Pep Band Dir; Drama Dir; OH Music Edctrs Assn 1993; *office:* Crooksville HS 4075 Ceramic Way Crooksville OH 43731*

FOX, ELIZABETH ANNE, First Grade Teacher; *b:* Buffalo, NY; *m:* Bruce J.; *c:* Jennifer Fox Fee; *ed:* Buffalo St (BS) Elem Ed 1964; Inservice Hrs System Operator, Courseware Insruction, Access, Word Microsoft Works; *cr:* Hamburg Cntrl Schl 4th Grd Tchr 1964-68, 1970-72; Bethlehem Schl 4th Grd Tchr 1968-69; Iroqouis Cntrl Schl Sub, 1st-2nd Grd Tchr 1979-; *ai:* Parent Resource Prgm Chair-Comm; Tech, Courseware Selection, Lang Arts, Report Card Comms; Wales Bldg Team; NYSUT 1995-; NEA; St Matthias Episcopal Church Life Mem; Dev Parent Resource Prgm; Presented Collabration Theme; *office:* Wales Primary Schl Woodchuck Rd East Aurora NY 14052*

FOX, FRANCINE TRANI, 1st Grade Teacher; *b:* New York, NY; *m:* Walter J.; *c:* Christopher, Brian, Peter, Daniel; *ed:* Rosemont Coll (BA) Elem Ed 1958; *cr:* Good Shepherd Schl 3rd Grd Tchr 1958-59; Project Learn Schl Primary Grd Tchr 1970-, Admin 1975-89; *ai:* Alumni Assn Co-Chair; DE Vly Tchrs Inst 1995-, Coord; Founding Tchr Project Learn Schl; *office:* Project Learn Schl 6525 Germantown Ave Philadelphia PA 19119*

FOX, JAMES A., History & Government Teacher; *b:* Philadelphia, PA; *m:* Teresa E. Schmid; *c:* Anne Pellicano, James, Thomas, Benadette, Megan Zandi; *ed:* Villanova Univ (BA) Ed, His 1958, (MA) His 1962; Temple Univ His 10 Addl Credits; Penn St Ed 10 Addl Credits; Univ of San Francisco Ed 12 Addl Credits; *cr:* Upper Merion Schl Dist Tchr 1958-; Penn St Extension Campus His Tchr 1965-73; Philadelphia Coll Textile, Sci His Tchr 1967-74; *ai:* NHS Spon; NEA, PSEA 1958-; Natl Cncl His Tchrs 1989-; Org Amer His 1988-; Villanova Univ Alumni 1958-, Local Dist Chm; Philadelphia Area Lector, Speaker Assn 1961-; PA St Stu Tchrs Coll Preparation Stans Recommendations Comm 1972; *office:* Upper Merion Area HS 435 Crossfield Rd King Of Prussia PA 19406

FOX, JAMES M., Asst Prof of Criminal Justice; *b:* Brooklyn, NY; *m:* Jean Honig; *c:* James, Jeff, Jennifer; *ed:* St Francis Coll (BA) Sociology 1973; CUNY- John Jay coll (MA) Criminal Justice 1977; *cr:* US Probation& Parole Dept Chief Deputy 1975-; *ai:* St Bernards Yth Bsktbl Pres; Ruggiero, Chem Bank Super League Commissioner; Long Island Lightning AAA Bsktbl Exec Dir; APPA 1993-; *office:* Saint Johns Univ Grand Cen & Utopia Pkwys Jamaica NY 11439

FOX, JENNIFER L., Ninth & Tenth Grd English Tchr; *b:* Pittsburgh, PA; *m:* Richard Matthew; *ed:* Rdng Specialist Cert 1995; *cr:* West Allegheny HS Eng Tchr 1992-; *ai:* Sign Lang Originator & Spon; Mentor Tchr; NCTE 1993-; PSEA 1992-, Fac Rep 1 Yr; *office:* West Allegheny HS 205 W Allegheny Rd Imperial PA 15126*

FOX, JOANNE MARY, Fourth Grade Teacher; *b:* Syracuse, NY; *m:* Robert Danier; *c:* Joseph D., Karen A.; *ed:* LeMoyne Coll (BS) Sociology 1967; Cortland St Coll (MS) Elem Ed 1973; *cr:* Fairmount Elem 2nd Grd Tchr 1967-78, 3rd Grd Tchr 1978-80, 5th Grd Tchr 1980-81; Onondaga Rd Elem Schl 4th Grd Tchr 1981-85, 4th Grd Tchr 1985-86, 3rd Grd Tchr 1986-; *ai:* Elem Curr Cncl; Union Rep; WGTA 1967-, Bldg Pres; NYSUT, NEA 1967-; *office:* Onondaga Road Elem Schl 703 Onondaga Rd S Syracuse NY 13219

FOX, LINDA E., Eng Tchr & Humanities Team Ldr; *b:* Methuen, MA; *m:* Duane E.; *c:* Aaron D.; *ed:* Merrimack Coll (BA) Eng 1969; Rivier Coll (MA) Eng 1976; Univ of NH (CAGS) Ed Admin 1986; Univ of MA Doctoral Stu in Ldrshp in Schooling; *cr:* Pelham Meml Schl Eng Tchr 1969-72; Alvirne HS Eng Tchr 1972-74; Pelham HS Eng Tchr, Dept Head 1974-; *ai:* Schl Cncl; Hum Team Ldr; Young Writers Club Adv; Mentoring; Coaching Tchrs; Frameworks for Quality, Grd Weighting Stud Comms; NCTE, NHATE, NEATE 1970's; ASCD, Phi Delta Kappa, NHASCO 1980's; Northeast Regnl Mentoring Lab 1995-; Sabbatical for Doctoral Stu; Cmptr, Innovatice Curr Grants; *office:* Pelham HS 85 Marsh Rd Pelham NH 03076*

FOX, LYNN DENISE, Social Studies & Lit Teacher; *b:* Brooklyn, NJ; *m:* Joseph M.; *c:* Daniel, Jonathan; *ed:* Seton Hall Univ (BS) Elem Ed 1969; *cr:* Ringwood Schl Dist 3rd Grd Tchr 1969-73; St Francis Schl 6th Grd Tchr 1979-81; St Marys Schl 8th Grd Tchr 1984-; *ai:* Mid Sts Steering Comm; Drama Club, Yrbk Adv; NCEA; Cert Heres Looking at You 2000, Great Books; *office:* St Mary Schl 25 Pompton Ave Pompton Lakes NJ 07442

FOX, MARY CONSUELA,RSM, French Teacher; *b:* Brooklyn, NY; *ed:* St Johns Univ (BS) Ed 1962; Seton Hall Univ (MA) Fr 1968; Attnd Adelphi Univ, Cambridge, Sorbonne, Edgewood, Rennes, Nice, LaRochelle, Salamanca; *cr:* Convent of Mercy, St Marys & St Pius X K-1st Grd Tchr 1950-61; Holy Rosary K-8th Grd Prin 1961-68; Holy Trinity HS Fr Tchr & Dept Chprsn 1968-; *ai:* Trip Organizer France; Canada Societe Honoraire de Francais Club; Fr Chprsn 1980-93; St Johns U Fr Adj; Local Prison Vol Tchr; Annual Soiree; AATF; LILT; NYSAFLT 1968-; Srs of Mercy 1944-.

FOX, MITCHELL, Geosciences Teacher; *b:* Brooklyn, NY; *m:* Sandra Carole Weinstein; *ed:* CCNY (BS) Geology, Geophysics & Oceanography 1971; Queens Coll (MS) Sci Ed 1976; Hofstra Univ (MA) Comp Sci & Natural Sci 1983; *cr:* Forest Hills HS Sci Tchr 1971-74; Beach Channel HS Sci Tchr 1975-82; BN Cardozo HS Sci Tchr 1982-90; Bronx HS of Sci Phys Sci Rsrch Coord 1990-; *ai:* NY Bio Tchrs Assn 1985-91; NSTA 1985-; Assn of Supvrs & Curr Developers 1990-91; AAPT 1990-92; STANYS 1990-; Work with NASA GISS Inst on Climate & Planets; MIT Letter of Recognition For Motivational Tchng 1995; NASA GISS Sci Tchr Rsrch Awd & Grant 1995; Letter of Recognition from Dan Goldin NASA Head & Chief Admin 1995; Tufts Letter & Cert of recognition for Motivational Tchng 1994; Cert of Hnr from Sci Svc Westinghouse 1985 & 1995; Cert of Appreciation fron NYS Engergy Rsrch & Dev Corp 1985 & 1992; Outstdng HS Tchr Achvmt Awd from Manhattan Coll 1992; Cert of Appreciation from Space Shuttle Stu Involvement Pgm 1985, 1988, 1990 & 1992; Spcl Commendation for 10 Yrs of Support & Inspiration to the NYS Energy Rsrch & Dev Authority 1991; *office:* Bronx Sci Schl 75 Bronx Science Blvd Bronx NY 10468

FOX, RAYMOND PETER, High School Mathematics Instr; *b:* Newark, NJ; *m:* Carol E. Karg; *c:* Lisa Meelheir, Michael, Robert; *ed:* Bloomfield Coll (BS) Math, Ed 1963; Trenton St Coll (MA) Stu Prsnl Svcs 1972; 30 Addl Grad Credits Montclair St Coll, Trenton St Coll, Jersey City St Coll; *cr:* Keansborg Pub Schl Math Instr 1963-64; Toms River Reg Schls Math Instr 1964-; *ai:* Coach Wrestling, Ftbl, Girls Track; Math Club, NHS, Peer Ldrshp Adv; NEA, NJEA 1963-; Toms River Ed Assn, AMTNJ 1964-; BPO Elks; *home:* 1115 Ruby Dr Toms River NJ 08753*

FOX, ROBERT HARRY,JR., Mathematics Teacher; *b:* Williamsport, PA; *m:* Marie E. Leidigh; *ed:* Penn St Univ (BS) Ed, Math 1990; Working Towards MED in Admin; Principals Cert; *cr:* Lackey HS Math Tchr 1990-93; Jersey Shore Jr HS Math Tchr 1993-; *ai:* Jr High 9th Grd Ftbl Head Coach; HS Track & Field Asst Coach; Stu Assistance Prgm; NEA, Jersey Shore Tchrs Assn 1993-; Antes Fort United Meth Church 1982-, Auditor; Paul Douglas Tchng Schlsp; *office:* Jersey Shore Area Jr HS 601 Thompson St Jersey Shore PA 17740*

FOX-CARDAMONE, LEE, Asst Professor of Psychology; *b:* Homestead, PA; *m:* Caesar T. Cardamone; *ed:* PA St Univ (BS) Psych 1983; Univ of Pittsburgh (MS) Soc Psych 1987; Miami Univ (PHD) Soc Psych 1990; *cr:* Miami Univ Post-Doctoral Fellow 1990-93; Case Western Reserve Univ Psych Adj Asst Prof 1993-94; Kent St Univ Psych Temporary Asst Prof 1994-95; Kent St Univ-Stark Psych Asst Prof; *ai:* Psych Club Founder, Adv; Acad Planning Comm; Assoc of Univ Regnl Campuses of OH-Fac Rep; Women's Stud Comm; Midwestern Psych Assn 1987-; Sigma Xi 1989; Amer Psychological Soc, Charter Mem; Conf Presentations Nationally, Internationally; Publications in Journal of Appled Psych, British Journal of Soc Psych; Several Small Research Grants Miami U, KSU; *office:* Kent St Univ Stark Campus 6000 Frank Ave NW Canton OH 44720*

FOY, JOE ANTHONY,II, Guid Cnslr & Dir of Diversity; *b:* Bronx, NY; *ed:* The Coll of the Holy Cross (BA) Psych 1991; Fordham Univ (MA) Cnslng 1994; 18 Credit Hrs Admin & Supervision Prgm; *cr:* The Shield Inst Tchrs Asst 1991; Fordham Prep Schl Guid Cnslr 1991-; My Brothers Keeper BMCC Dir & Prgm Coord 1996; *ai:* Kawaida Club Fac Moderator; African Amer Org Dir of Diversity, Ldrshp Moderator; Minority Consortion Speaker; ACA 1991-; *office:* Fordham Prep Schl 441 E Fordham Rd Bronx NY 10458*

FOYE, JANE LIBBY, Kindergarten Teacher; *b:* Lewiston, ME; *m:* Michael A.; *c:* Kimbery Anne, Todd Michael; *ed:* Gorham St Tchrs (BA) Elem Ed 1967; 44 Addl Credits Not in Masters Pgm; *cr:* Lincoln Elem Schl 1st Grd Tchr 1967-68; Pittston Elem Schl 1st Grd Tchr 1968-69; Woolwich Elem Schl 1st Grd Tchr 1969-71; SAD 61 Naples Elem & Songo Locks Elem Kndgtn Tchr 1976-; *ai:* Tech Comm; Kndgtn & Negotiation Teams; Lake Region Tchrs Assn Sec; NEA 1976-; MEA 1976-; Lake Region Tchrs Assn 1976-, Sec; Friends of Lib 1989-, Treas; PTA 1989-; Lib Trustee 1995-, Treas; *office:* Songo Locks Schl RR 1 Box 51AA Naples ME 04055

FOYS, JUDITH CAFFREY, English Teacher; *b:* Sugar Notch, PA; *c:* Martin Foys; *ed:* Glassboro St Coll (BA) Eng 1964; Bowling Green Univ (MA) 1969; Supvrs Cert St of NJ; *cr:* Edgewood Regnl HS Eng Tchr 1964-65; Penta-Cty Voc-Tech Schls Eng Tchr 1966-68; Bowling Green Univ Part-time Eng Instr 1968-71; Camden Co Voc-Tech Schls Eng Tchr 1972-; *ai:* VICA Coach Prepared Speech; NEA, NJEA, CCEA 1972-; Cam-Voc Assn 1972-, Sec, Fac Rep; Contact Crisis Line 1980-87, Telephone Worker; *office:* Camden Cty Voc & Tech Schls 6008 Browning Rd Pennsauken NJ 08109

FRACALOSSI, JOSEPH R., Biology Teacher; *ed:* SUNY at Plattsburgh (BS) Hlth Ed 1979; SUNY at New Platz (MS) Bio 1985; *cr:* Our Lady of Mt Carmel Schl 7th-8th Grd Sci Tchr 1979-84; Valley Cntrl Schl Dist 9-10th Grd Sci Tchr 1984-; *ai:* NYSUT, AFT 1984-; *office:* Valley Central HS 1175 State Route 17K Montgomery NY 12549

FRADKIN, AMY LYNN, Chemistry Teacher; *b:* Waterbury, CT; *m:* Gregg; *c:* D. J.; *ed:* Univ of ME (BA) Bio 1988; Cntrl St Univ Cert Chem, Bio, Gen Sci 1990; *cr:* Naugatuck HS Sci Tchr 1991-93; King Phillip Regnl HS Sci Tchr 1993-; *ai:* 1996 Class Adv; Sci Fair Coord 1995; CSTA, NEA 1991-; MAST 1993-; NSTA, NEACT 1992-; Hadassah 1979-, Lifetime Mem; Plan Now Grant #111 Sci Data Base Rsrch Support Awded, Recognized Commonwealth of MA, Senate; Adv Awd Stu Regnl Finalist NSTA Space Sci Prgm; Lab, Act Writer Scientific Amer Frontiers Ed Guide; *office:* King Philip Reg HS PO Box 49 Wrentham MA 02093

FRAGA, STEPHEN, English Teacher; *b:* New Bedford, MA; *m:* Cheryl Walder; *c:* Jennifer; *ed:* Univ of MA at Dartmouth (BA) Eng 1970; Cambridge Coll (MS) Ed 1993; 80 Hrs Univ of Haifa 1987; Summer Study Prgm Holocaust, Jewish Resistence GheltoFisher's House; *cr:* Keith Jr HS Eng Tchr 1970-73; Normandian Jr HS Eng Tchr 1973-74; New Bedford HS Eng Tchr 1974-; *ai:* NEA, MA Tchrs Assn, New Bedford Ed Assn 1970-; Jewish Fed of Greater New Bedford 1980-92, Educl Liaison; Philip Bronspiegel Meml Awd 1987; Flwshp Awded Jewish Labor Comm, Amer Gathering Jewish Holocaust Survivors 1987; Chm Eng Dept Self-Evaluation Accreditation Co mm; *home:* 8 Village Dr North Dartmouth MA 02747

FRAHME, NINA HOVELL, Art Teacher; *b:* Jersey City, NJ; *ed:* Newark St (BA) Elem Ed 1962; Kane (BA) Fine Arts 1967; *cr:* Elizabeth Bd of Ed 1st Grd Tchr 1963-67; Winfield Bd of Ed Art Tchr 1968-69; Edison Bd of Ed Art Tchr 1969-; *ai:* NJEA, NEA 1962-; ETEA 1969-; Woman of Week.

FRAIL, ROBERT JOHN, Assoc Prof of Eng & Intl Stud; *b:* New York City, NY; *m:* Irene Mc Cormick; *ed:* Manhattan Coll (BS) Tchr Preparation 1971; Columbia Univ (MA) Fr 1978, (PHD) Fr, Romance Philology 1985; *cr:* Polytechnic Univ Instr of Hum 1985-86; Centenary Coll Asst Prof of Eng, Intnl Stud 1986-; Obirin Univ Visiting Prof 1988; *ai:* Fulbright, Stud Abroad Adv; Speaker's Bureau Engagements; MLA 1983-, Regnl Del; AATF 1980-; ASECS 1985-; FLENJ 1986-; Knights of Columbus 1991-; Numerous Scholarly Articles, Poetry, Prose Pub; Many Conf Papers Presented; Translation for Bus, Private Orgs; Several Grant Proposals Funded; *office:* Centenary Coll 400 Jefferson St Hackettstown NJ 07840

FRAKER, MAX T., Mathematics Teacher; *b:* Chambersburg, PA; *ed:* Shippensburg Univ (BS) Math 1969; Grad Stud at Millersville Univ, West Chester Univ & PA St Univ; *cr:* Octorara Schl Dist Math Tchr 27 Yrs; *ai:* Bus Route, Math Curr, Standardized Testing & Tchr Evaluation Comms; PSEA 1969-, Bldg Rep, Rep of Yr Awd; Jaycees 1970-72; USGA 1975-; 25 Yrs Distinguished Svc Cert; *home:* 303 High St Atglen PA 19310

FRALEY, MARIAN SCARAZZO, Employability Instructor; *b:* New Castle, PA; *m:* Bryan T.; *c:* Michael; *ed:* Ashland Univ (BS) Ed, Job Trng 1977; Wright St Univ (MED) Curr, Supervision 1987; Miami Univ Post Grad Classes; *cr:* Miami Valley Career Ctr Restaurant, Hospitality Mgmt Instr 1977-92; Miami Valley CTC Employability Instr 1992-; *ai:* Employability Team Chair; Consultant St Dept Dev of Performance Assessments; Amer Culinary Fed 1988-, Ed Chair, Chef of Yr; Own Your Own Grant; Honorary Mem OH FHA, HERO; *office:* Miami Vly Career Tchntgy Ctr 6800 Hoke Rd Clayton OH 45315*

FRALEY, MARILYN PRICE, Bible & Science Teacher; *b:* San Antonio, TX; *m:* Christian; *c:* Jason Murray, Amanda Murray, Heather, Chris, Jonathon; *ed:* Univ of Toledo (BED) Elem Ed 1974; *cr:* Toledo Pub Schls Sub Tchr 1978-81; Owens IL Sec 1979-81; Sylvania Chrstn Schl Tchr 1981-83; Calvary Chrstn Schl Tchr 1989-; *ai:* Yth Group Adv Calvary Assembly of God; WGTE Grants; *office:* Calvary Christian Schl 5025 Glendale Ave Toledo OH 43614

FRANCE, PATRICIA A. (MALLANEY), Math Teacher; *b:* New York City, NY; *m:* Nicholas; *c:* Nicholas Jr., Emma Louise, Barbara Jean, Tricia; *ed:* Coll of Mt St Vincent (BA) Math & Scndry Ed 1968; Yeshura Univ Belfour Grad Schl of Sci (MS) Math Ed 1974; Attnd SUNY at Albany; *cr:* Walton HS Tchr & Prgm Chair 1969-; *ai:* Girl Scouts USA Troop Ldr, Product Chair, Svc Merit Rep; Orangetown Mighty Midgets Bd Mem & Forum Coord; NCTM 1993 Convention; *office:* Walton HS 196th St & Reservoir Ave Bronx NY 10468*

FRANCELLO, ERMA JEANNE, Fourth Grade Teacher; *b:* Kingston, NY; *ed:* Dutchess Comm Coll (AA) Lbrl Arts 1964; SUNY at New Paltz (BA) Ed 1976, (MS) Rdng 1982; 60 Addl Credit Hrs; *cr:* Onteora Cntrl Schl Second Grd Tchr 1977-78, Title I Rdn, Math Tchr 1978-79, Third Grd Tchr 1979-80, Title I Rdng Tchr 1980-81, Fifth Grd Tchr 1981-82, Third Grd Tchr 1982, Third Grd Tchr 1982-83, First Grd Tchr 1983, Kndgtn Tchr, Remedial Math 1983-84, First Grd Tchr 1984-85, Third Grd Tchr 1986-89, Fourth Grd Tchr 1989-; *ai:* A-V Coord 1991-; OTA Assn 1977-, Sec 1985-91; OTA Benefit Trust 1991-, Treas 1991-; *office:* Onteora Central Schl Rt 28 Boiceville NY 12412

FRANCESCHINA, MONA JEAN, Math & Science Teacher; *b:* Holyoke, MA; *ed:* Elms Coll (BA) Math 1972; *cr:* St Patrick Schl 4-5- Grd Tchr 1968-69; Holy Name Schl 5-6 Grd Tchr 1969-72; St Matthew Math & Sci Tchr 1972-78; Cathedral HS Math Tchr 1978-80; St Matthew Math & Sci Tchr 1980-85, Prin 1985-87; Blesses Sacrament Sci Tchr 1987-90; Notre Dame-Immaculate Conception Math & Sci Tchr 1990-; *ai:* Drama Coach; NCEA 1968-; NSF Grant 1984; *office:* Notre Dame Immaculate Schl 35 Pleasant St Easthampton MA 01027*

FRANCESCHINI, VANESSA FRANGIOSA, First Grade Teacher; *b:* Teaneck, NJ; *m:* William V.; *c:* Kyle, Karina; *ed:* William Paterson Coll (BA) Elem Ed 1987; *cr:* Anna C Scott Schl 3rd Grd Tchr 1987-93, 4th Grd Tchr 1993-94, 1st Grd Tchr 1994-; *ai:* NEA 1987-; *office:* Anna C Scott Elem Schl 250 Highland St Leonia NJ 07605

FRANCHAK, MARYANN BILICH, Algebra Teacher; *b:* Aliquippa, PA; *m:* Michael R.; *c:* Michael Anthony, Mark Andrew; *ed:* Mt Union Coll (BS) Bio 1963; Attnd Duquesne Univ & Carlow Coll Natl Sci Grants; *cr:* N Allegheny HS Bio & Chem Tchr 1963-68; Comm Coll of Allegheny Coll Algebra & Geometry Tchr Summers 1985-93; Pine Richland HS Algebra Tchr 1987-; *ai:* Inclusion Team; Coaching for Algebra Contest; NEA & PSEA 1963-; MTCM 1993-; All Star Ed Univ of Pittsburgh in Collabaration with the Pittsburgh Press 1991; *office:* Pine-Richland HS 4300 Warrendale Rd Gibsonia PA 15044

FRANCIN, ROBERT DOMINICK, Mathematics Teacher; *b:* Jersey City, NJ; *ed:* Saint Peter's Coll (BS) Math, Cmptr Sci 1992; *cr:* Ridgefield Park Jr Sr HS Sub Tchr 1992-93; St Dominic Acad Math Tchr 1993-; *ai:* Cmptr Club Moderator; Pi Mu Epsilon 1989-, Pres; Kappa Alpha Alpha 1987-; Mc Mackin Outstdng Math Proficiency, Math Ed Promise Awd; *office:* Saint Dominic Acad 2572 Kennedy Blvd Jersey City NJ 07304

FRANCIONE, MARY FAITH, Bus Ed & Cmptr Tech Teacher; *b:* Rochester, NY; *ed:* Nazareth Coll (BS) Ed 1966; Aquinas Coll (MS) Theology 1980; Permanent Cert Nazareth Coll Tchr 1966; *cr:* Diocesan Schls Tchr 1948-58; St Joseph's Schl Prin 1958-65; Our Lady of Mercy HS Bus Admin 1965-68; Holy Family Schl Prin 1968-73; Our Lady of Mercy HS Tchr 1973-; *ai:* NHS Cncl Mem; Goals, Philosophy Comm Mid Sts Evaluation; Schlsp Bd Mem; NCEA; NEA; NBTA; Jail Ministry 1968-75, Tchr; Hosp Ministry 1975-, Chaplain; *home:* 1437 Blossom Rd Rochester NY 14610

FRANCIOSI, PETER MICHAEL, Chemistry Teacher; *b:* Leominster, MA; *c:* Jill, Julie; *ed:* Fitchburg St Coll (BA) Bio 1974, (MA) Ed 1978; Chem Cert Boston Coll 1987 Inservice Inst Chem Tchrs; *cr:* North Middlesex Regnl HS Chem, Bio Tchr 1974-; *ai:* Driver Ed Dir; NEA, MTA 1974-; *office:* North Middlesex Regional HS 19 Main St Townsend MA 01469

FRANCIS, CATHERINE, Math Teacher & Guidance Cnslr; *b:* Manville, NJ; *m:* Geoffrey; *ed:* Montclair St Univ (BA) Math 1975, (MA) Stu Prsnl Svcs 1990; 12 Credit Hrs Jersey City St Coll; 3 Credit Hrs Caldwell Coll; *cr:* Rosbury HS Math Tchr 1980-82; Hillside HS Math Tchr, Guid Cnslr 1982-; *ai:* Schl Lunch Prgm Coord; Pub Schl Calendar; NEA; Union Cty Schl Cnslr Assn; Newark Classic Run Vol 1985-; *office:* Hillside HS 1085 Liberty Ave Hillside NJ 07205

FRANCIS, DANN, History Teacher; *b:* Burlington, VT; *m:* Jacky Laba; *c:* Ethan, Lindsay; *ed:* Univ of VT (BS) Scndry Ed 1980; *cr:* Lamoille Union HS His Tchr 1980-85; Delsea Regnl HS Tchr 1985-86; Cumberland Regnl HS His Tchr 1986-; *ai:* Vlybl Club Adv; TV Studio Supvr; NEA 1980-; NJEA 1985-; CREA 1986-; *office:* Cumberland Regional HS Silver Lake Rd PO Box 5115 Seabrook NJ 08302

FRANCIS, DAVID FRANKLIN, Electronics Instructor; *b:* Charleroi, PA; *m:* Patricia Bargerstock; *c:* William, Melisssa Brownback; *ed:* Penna MDTA (AS) Electronics 1963; 48 Hrs Towardd Voc Cert Temple Univ; *cr:* Burroughs Corp Tech, Supvr 1966-86; CAT-Brandywine Electronics Instr 1988-95; CAT-Pickering Electronics Instr 1991-; *ai:* PSEA, NEA 1988-; F&AM 1983-, Past-Master; Lions Club 1994-; Rotary Dist 7450 Voc Tchng Excl Awd; *office:* Ctr For Art/Tech-Pickering 1580 Charlestown Rd Phoenixville PA 19460

FRANCIS, GERALD PETER, Mechanical Engineering Prof; *b:* Seattle, WA; *m:* Ann Virginia Stewart; *c:* Timothy, Michael, Peter; *ed:* Univ of Dayton (BME) Mechanical Engineering 1958; Cornell Univ (MME) Mechanical Engineering 1960, (PHD) Mechanical Engineering 1965; *cr:* Cornell Univ Instr 1961-64; GA Inst of Tech Asst Prof 1964-66; SUNY at Buffalo Fac & Chair of Dept 1966-77; US Merchant Marine Acad Head of Engineering 1977-80; Univ of VT Prof, Dean, VP, Provost 1980-; *ai:* Engineering Hnr Soc Adv; Tau Beta Pi; ASEE 1964-, Excl in Inst Awd; ASME 1964-; Inst Marine Engrs 1977-, Fellow Awd; NSPE 1980-; Western Electric Fund Awd for Excl in Instruction 1970; US Dept of Commerce Silver Medal 1979; VT Engr of Yr 1989; *office:* Univ Of VT & St Agri Coll 209-C Votey Hall Burlington VT 05405

FRANCIS, GWEN (STURGEON), English Teacher & Dept Chm; *b:* Salem, OH; *m:* Frank Jeffrey; *c:* Scott, Sarah; *ed:* Bowling Green St Univ (BS) Ed, Eng 1971; Youngstown St Univ (MS) Eng 1988; *cr:* Souther Local HS Eng Tchr 1971-78; Columbiana Cty JVS Eng Tchr, Attendance Officer 1981-85; Southern Local Jr Sr HS Eng Tchr 1985-; *ai:* Yrbk, Var Club, Sr Class Adv; Vlybl Asst Coach; Southern Local Tchrs Assn 1985-, Pres 2 Yrs; ECOEA, OEA, NEA 1985-; Bethel Presbyn Church 1987-; *office:* Southern Local Jr Sr HS 38095 St Rt 39 Salineville OH 43945

FRANCIS, JOAN ANNETTE, Professor of History; *b:* Barbados, West Indies; *ed:* Atlantic Union Coll (BA) His 1973; Andrews Univ (MA) His 1974; Carnegie Mellon Univ (DA) Soc His 1990; *cr:* Barbados Scndry Schl His, Eng & Math Tchr 1965-68 & 1970-71; West Indies Coll Jamaica Division of Hum Chair, His Dept Chair & His Prof 1980-87; Atlantic Union Coll His Prof & Division of Theology, Hum & Fine Arts Chair 1989-; *ai:* Scndry Curr in Soc Stud Consultant; Churches Womens & Youth Issues Speaker; Phi Alpha Theta 1973-; World His Assn 1991-; Amer Historical Assn 1989-; Black Scholar of New England 1992; Zapara Excl in Tchng Awd 1991; Roothbert Fellowship 1988-89; Black Chrstn Stu Union Spon 1991-95; *office:* Atlantic Union Coll PO Box 1000 338 Main St South Lancaster MA 01561*

FRANCIS, JOHN E., English Teacher; *b:* Syracuse, NY; *m:* Camille J. Tucci; *c:* Lynelle M., Michael J.; *ed:* SUNY at Oswego (BS) Scndry Eng 1964, (MA) Eng Ed 1970; 18 Hrs Schl Admin; *cr:* Syracuse City Schls Eng Tchr 1964-65; Weedsport Cntrl Schl Eng Tchr 1965-68; Solvay Schls Eng Tchr 1970-; *ai:* Schl Newspaper Adv; Var Bsktbl Coach; AFT 1980-; NYSUT, NEA 1965-; NYS Eng Cncl 1972-; *home:* 300 Fern Rd Syracuse NY 13219*

FRANCIS, JOHN EDWARD, Chemistry Teacher; *b:* Shenandoah, PA; *m:* Ira A. Bebaut; *c:* Suzanne Dowling, David Francis; *ed:* PA St Univ (BS) Sci Ed 1961, (MED) Biological 1968; 20 Credit Hrs Advanced Chem Rochester Inst of Tech & 20 Credit Hrs Advanced Chem Univ of Rochester; *cr:* USAF Electronics & Communication Officer 1961-66; Brighton Cntrl Schls Sci Tchr 1966-; Rochester Inst of Tech Adjunct Fac 1974-76; *ai:* Ski Club Adv; Tchrs Assn Rep; Equity Comm; Sci Olympiad; Amer Chemical Soc 1967-, Tchr of Yr 1981; NY St Sci Tchrs 1967-; Merrell Scientific 1970-88, Bd of Dirs; BSA 1967-93, Scoutmaster, Ed Chm; Victor Hiking Club 1995-; Victor Meth Church 1995-; Fulbright Exch Tchr England Advanced Chem; Woodrow Wilson Fellowship Environmental Chem; Copyrights Plastic Embedments in Chem; Textbooks Publisher Ginsberg Scientific Inc; *office:* Brighton HS 1150 Winton Rd S Rochester NY 14618*

FRANCIS, MARGARET (KIRKBRIDE), Third Grade Teacher; *b:* Camden, NJ; *m:* Robert E.; *c:* Carolyn, Amy; *ed:* Rowan Coll (BA) Elem Ed 1964; Addl 15 Credits Speech, Rdng 1964-66; *cr:* Sewell Elem Schl 2nd Grd Tchr 1964-68; Washington Twp Bd of Ed Sub Tchr 1974-78; Hurffville Schl Second, Third Grd Tchr 1978-; Camp Matollionequay Prgm Dir 1972-78; *ai:* WA Twp Affirmative Action Comm 1983-95; WA Twp Soc Stud Comm 1995-; Tutoring; Peer Coaching 1994-95; Cooperating Tchr for Practicum, Stu Tchrs; NJ Ed Assn 1964-; South Jersey Rdng Cncl 1990-; Kappa Delta Gamma 1989-, VP, Corresponding Sec; Amer Red Cross 1964-86; Amer Cancer Soc 1980-86, Sec 1983-84; YMCA Camp Ockanickon 1986-, Dir; *home:* 49 Wildwood Ave Pitman NJ 08071*

FRANCIS, NANCY D., Fifth Grade Teacher; *b:* Oceanside, NY; *m:* Michael T.; *ed:* Wagner Coll (BSEd) Ed 1971; SUNY at Stony Brook (MS) Ed 1975; Post Grad Stud Ed C. W. Post Coll, Rollins Coll, Univ of HI; *cr:* William Sidney Mount Elem Schl 1971-86; Setauket Elem Schl 1986-; *ai:* Three Village Tchrs Assn, NYSUT 1971-; Alpha Omicron Pi 1990-, Newsletter, Corresponding Sec; Port Jefferson Historical Soc 1986-, Trustee; Tchr of Yr 1988-89; *office:* Setauket Elem Schl 134 Main St East Setauket NY 11733

FRANCIS, ROBERT C., House & Mill Carpentry Instr; *b:* Fairhaven, MA; *m:* Barbara St Jean; *c:* Aimee Lee, Jessica B.; *ed:* 1 Yr Cert in Carpentry from Fitchburg St 1978; *cr:* Pechham Kitchen Cabinet Maker 1965-76; Old Colony House & Mill Carpentry Instr 1976-; *ai:* Job Site Safety Comm; Teamsters Union 1977-; Southeastern MA Bldg Ofcls 1981-; MA Bldg Ofcls 1982-; BOCA Intnl 1983-; Certified Bldg Inspector MA; *office:* Old Colony Reg Voc Tech Schl 476 North Ave Rochester MA 02770

FRANCISCO, ANNA MARIE, Vocal Music Teacher; *b:* Mingo Jct, OH; *m:* Gery W.; *ed:* Youngstown St Univ (BA) Music Ed & Voice 1980; *cr:* Leetonia Exempted Village Schls Elem Vocal Music Tchr 1980-.

FRANCO, JOSEPH RICHARD, Adj Assoc Prof of Sociology; *b:* Bronx, NY; *ed:* Mercy Coll (BS) Psych 1982; Long Island Univ (MS) Cnslng, Dev 1983, (MS) Soc Sci 1985; *cr:* Mercy Coll Coord Frosh Advising 1982-86, Adj Prof 1984-91; Iona Coll Asst Dir Admissions 1986-87; Pace Univ Assoc Dir, Career Svcs 1987-, Adj Assoc Prof SOciology 1988-; *ai:* Fac Adv Assn Men of Color 1995, Delta Phi Epsilon 1994-95; Vol in Action Hunger Stu Task Froce Comm, Contributor; Amer Cnslng Assn, Amer Sociological Assn 1990-; Soc Stu Soc Problems 1992-; Pace Univ Project 1992-, Presenter; Advy Group Pace Univ Newly Enrolled 1993-; Pace Univ Std, Fac DIversity Forumsss 1995-, Presenter; Alva Cooper Awd Outstdng Career Svcs; Rep, Researcher; Metropolitan NY Coll Placement Ofcrs Assn Ed, Writer; Pace Univ Stu Govt Fac Recognition Awd; *office:* Pace Univ 861 Bedford Rd Pleasantville NY 10570*

FRANCO, MARY ANN CIARDI, Nursery School Teacher; *b:* Jersey City, NJ; *m:* Anthony S.; *c:* Stephen; *ed:* Jersey City St Coll (BA) Early Chldhd, Elem Ed 1978; *cr:* St Augustine's Schl First Grd Tchr 1978-86, Second Grd Tchr 1986-91, Kndgtn Tchr 1991-93, Nursery Schl Tchr 1995-; *ai:* NCEA 1978-; *office:* St Augustine Schl 3920 New York Ave Union City NJ 07087

FRANEK, MARTHA LOUISE, Engineering Technology Instr; *b:* Blanchester, OH; *c:* Wayne Kiphart, Bradley Kiphart, Keith Kiphart, Kevin Kiphart, Jeanette Kiphart; *ed:* univ of Cincinnati (BSMET) Design Engrng 1988; Wright St Univ Voc Ed Tchng Cert 1994; AutoCad CAD, A-E Micro System; Attnd Future Tech, Gen Electric; *cr:* Graphel Inc Design Engr 1988-91; Pvt Consulting, Hamilton Fixture, Hyper-Tech Applied Solutions, K-West; Butler Cty Joint Voc Schl Engrng Tech Instr 1991-; *ai:* VICA Advy 1991-, Instr, 1st Pl St Arch Contest; Soc of Manufacturing Engrs, Treas; Greater Cincinnati Tech Prep Consortium; Manage, Maintain Personal Cmptrs; Tchng Seminars for CAD CAM, DOS, Windows; Design Proposal Preprations; *office:* D. Russel Lee Butler Co Schl 3603 Hamilton Middletown Rd Indian Springs OH 45011

FRANEK, SHARON ALDERSON, Teacher of Gifted & Talented; *b:* San Diego, CA; *m:* John; *c:* John Jahu, Craig Richard; *ed:* Miami Univ (MED) Supervision & Curr 1988; Univ of Dayton Admin Cert Prin; *cr:* Blanchester Local Tchr 1966-73; Little Miami Local Tchr 1974-; *ai:* 4-H Adv; NEA & OEA 1966-; OAGC, COCG & NAGC 1985-; Grants: Title IV 1979, Consumer Ec Ed 1980, IVC 1980 & 1981, Consumer Ed 1983 & 1991, OH Dept of Ed Bldg Incentive 1990, D D Eisenhower Math & Sci Ed Improvement Grant 1991; Project Excl Nom 1988-92; Ashland Oil Nom 1988, 1990 & 1994-95; Whos Who in Am Ed 1988-90 & 1995; St of OH Pilot Pgm for Females in the Area of Math 1991; Warren Cty Area Progress Cncl Excl Tchr Awd 1992; *office:* Little Miami Local Schl Dist 10 Miranda Ave Morrow OH 45152

FRANEY, SHAUN, Asst Professor of History; *b:* Trenton, NJ; *ed:* Georgian Court Coll (AB) Soc Stud 1957; Villanova Univ (MA) US His 1960; *cr:* Notre Dame HS His Tchr 1957-66; Georgian Court Coll Registrar, Tchr 1966-72; Mt St Mary Acad His Tchr, Asst Prin 1972-76; Camden Cath HS His Tchr 1976-80; Holy Spirit HS Asst Prin 1980-81; Georgian Court Coll Tchr 1981-; *ai:* James Madison Schlsp Prgm Adv; Amer Stud Minor Prgm Dir; Fin Aid, Schlsp, 7th Anniversary Woman Suffrage Comms; Mercy Higher Ed Col 1987-; Ocean Co Hist Soc 1985-; Phi Alpha Theta, US Capitol Hist Soc 1989-; Amnesty Intnl 1991-; Alliance Women in His 1989-; Christopher Spon 1985-; Who's Who in Amer Coll, Univ Admins; Outstdng Edctr of Amer; NDEA His Inst IN St Univ; NSF Admin, His Tchr Inst at Albany NY; *home:* 900 Lakewood Ave Lakewood NJ 08701

FRANGAS, HARRIET, Social Studies Teacher; *b:* New York, NY; *m:* Emmanuel; *c:* Andrew, Harry, Nick, Alex; *ed:* Queens Coll (BA) His 1969, (MS) Scndry Ed & His 1972; 6 Credit Hrs Biling Ed Courses at LaGuardia Coll; *cr:* Jamaica Day Schl Soc Stud Tchr 1969-71; Archbishop Iakovos HS Soc Stud Tchr & Asst Prin 1983-94; Bd of Ed of NYC Tchrs 1994-; *ai:* Yrbk Adv; Sr Adv; *office:* Archbishop Iakovos HS 84-35 152nd St Jamaica NY 11432

FRANGELLA, LOUISE CANCRO, Dean of Students; *b:* New York, NY; *m:* Angelo; *c:* Richard Digilio; *ed:* Coll of White Plains (BA) Soc Stud 1972; St Joseph's Seminary (MA) Rel Stud 1986; SAS, SDA Cert NY St 1996; *cr:* Good Counsel Acad 9th, 11th Grd SS Tchr 1971-73; St Dominic Schl 5th-7th Grd SS Tchr 1974-77, 1979-81; St Frances de Chantal 3rd, 7th Grd SS Tchr 1981-84; Preston HS 9th-12th Grd Rel Tchr 1984-89; St Catharine Acad Dean, 9th-12th Rel Tchr 1989-; *ai:* NSEA 1984-; ASCD 1994-.*

FRANGICETTO, THOMAS JOSEPH, Professor of Psychology; *b:* Philadelphia, PA; *m:* Carol Lyons; *c:* Colin, Chris, Alison; *ed:* LaSalle Univ (BS) Mrktg, Psych 1971; Trenton St Coll (MED) Counseling, Psych 1973; 9 Credits Glassboro St Coll; 6 Credits Temple Univ; 3 Credits Hannemann Univ; Private Supervision for Licensure 2 Yrs; *cr:* Bristol-Bensalem Human Svcs Outpatient Coord 1974-79; Catch Comm Mental Hlth Ctr Assoc Dir Elderly Svcs 1979-85; Northampton Comm Coll Prg Coord, Prof 1985-; *ai:* Comms Amer Disabilities Act, Mid Sts Accreditation; Little Leaue Bsbl Coach; Awd for Excl in Tchng 1993; Pub Instruction Manuals, Articles; *office:* Northampton Community College 3835 Green Pond Rd Bethlehem PA 18017

FRANGIOSA, JESSE V., Middle School Reading Teacher; *b:* Norristown, PA; *ed:* Univ of Tampa (BS) Elem Ed 1968; Univ of MS Non-Degree Grad 1969; West Chester Univ Masters Equivalency 1983; *cr:* Metch[...] Dist Tchr 1968-; *ai:* Woodland Elem Schl Head Tchr; Head of S[...] Grd Ldr; Yrbk Spon; NEA 1968-; AFT 1985-; Methacton Ed Ass[...] Theta Chi 1965-; Mount Carmel Sportsman Club 1970-; *offic[...]* Intermediate Schl Arcola Rd Norristown PA 19403*

FRANK, ANN LOUISE (ZEZNICK), Program Director of B[...] Salamanca, NY; *m:* Gregory B.; *c:* Jessica, Bryan, Megan; *ed:* [...] Coll (BS) Bus Ed 1989; *cr:* Bryant & Stratton Bus Inst Accoun[...] Stu Svcs Adv 1990-95, Program Dir Bus Division 1996-; Accounting Chprsn, Advy Bd, Curr Framework Team; NYSB[...] NBEA 1993-; ASCD 1994-; Pittsford PTSA 1986-; 2 Tchr of Qua[...] Employee of Quarter; *office:* Bryant & Stratton Bus Inst 82 S[...] Rochester NY 14604

FRANK, ANN PATRICIA, English & Math Instructor; *b:* East[...] Bruce; *ed:* IN Univ of PA (BS) Ed 1978; Attnd Moravian Col[...] Univ; *ai:* Cheering Coach; NHS Adv Stu Govt Adv; Mentor Tc[...] St Evaluation Comm, AMTNJ Speaker; NCTM & ATMNJ 198[...] Tchr of Yr; *office:* Warren County Vo-Tech Schl 1500 Rt 57 Wash[...] 07882

FRANK, CAROLYN MC KIMM, Third Grade Teacher; *b:* Alli[...] *m:* Lawrence P.; *c:* John, Geoffrey, Amy; *ed:* Mount Union Coll [...] Ed 1975; Univ of Akron (MA) Schl Cnslng 1990; Post Grad [...] Ashland Univ, Univ of Dayton; *cr:* West Branch Local Schls 6th [...] 1975-77; Marlington Local Schls 5th Grd Tchr 1977-92, 3rd [...] 1992-; *ai:* After Schl Bunch Comm; N E Regnl Lang Arts Re[...] Ldrshp Team; NEA, OEA 1975-; GCCTM 1990-; Phi Delta Kap[...] St Joseph Church 1960-, Lector, Confirmation Ldr; *office:* W[...] Elem Schl 5786 Beechwood Ave Alliance OH 44601*

FRANK, EUGENE MARTIN, Retired English Teacher; *b:* New [...] *m:* Ojela Mc Mahon; *ed:* Iona Coll (BA) Eng 1962; 33 Grad Cred[...] at St John's Univ; *cr:* Clark Jr HS Eng Tchr 1962-95; *ai:* Lib; Cm[...] Mentor; UFT 1963-; *home:* 8 Windmill Ln New City NY 10956*

FRANK, HARA SIMMONS, Computer Coordinator; *b:* Harris[...] *m:* Harry E. Jr.; *c:* Alison, Harrison; *ed:* Harrisburg Area Comm [...] Ed 1971; Shippensburg Univ (BS) Bus Ed, Date Processing 19[...] Bus Ed, Data Processing 1976; Elizabethtown Coll 3 Credit Hrs; Valleye Coll; Hillersville Univ 12 Credit Hrs; *cr:* Millersburg [...] Dist Cmptr Coord 11 Yrs; Millersburg Area HS Bus Ed Tchr 1[...] Class Adv; Chrldng Adv 1978-82; Millersville Univ Lasion [...] Wrkshp Offerings at Campus 1992-; NEA, PA St Ed Assn, M[...] Area Ed Assn 1973-; Valley's United Church of Christ 1983-, Co-Writer of ITEC Grant Place Cmptrs in Dist; MA Inst of T[...] Recognition 3 Yrbk Dedications; *office:* Millersburg Area HS 7[...] St Millersburg PA 17061*

FRANK, JEFFREY, Social Studies Teacher; *b:* Astoria Queens[...] Madeline Ann Halpern; *c:* Sara Isidora, Suzanne Clara; *ed:* Schl [...] Arts (BFA) Graphics & Illustration 1983; Hunter Coll (MA) [...] 1994; 30 Addl Grad & Undergraduate Credits; Spcl Course C[...] Adlai E Stevenson HS Soc Stud Tchr 1986-89; Murry Bergtraun[...] Stud & Spcl Ed Tchr 1989-91; Julia Richmond HS Soc Stud Tchr [...] Washington Irving HS Soc Stud Tchr 1992-; *ai:* NYC Bd of [...] Mentor; Mentee Pgm; *home:* 1774 Forest Hill Rd Staten Island N[...]

FRANK, PATRICIA A. JAROMIN, High School Math Tea[...] Lackawanna, NY; *m:* Peter S.; *ed:* (BS) Elem Ed 1974; (MS) E[...] Math 1978; *cr:* St James 6, 7, 8 Grds Math Tchr 1974-77; St Pete[...] 7-8 Grd Math Tchr 1977-80; Springville MS 7-8 Grd Math Tchr [...] Springville HS 9-11 Grd Math Tchr 1984-; *ai:* GAC Adv; Chrldr[...] AVT, NYSUT 1980-; GIFA Local Union, Treas 1992-; Credit Uni[...] 1991-, Credit Comm.

FRANK, PENNY, Senior Modern Dance Teacher; *b:* New York [...] Michael Mandel; *c:* David Mandel, Joshua Mandel, Matthew Ma[...] Sarah Lawrence Coll (BA) Dance & Lit 1960; City Univ of NY [...] Grad Credits in Ed; *cr:* June Taylor Schl Ballet & Mod Dar[...] 1958-61; Martha Graham Schl of Contemporary Dance Tchr & [...] Adv 1958-68; HS of Performing Arts Sr Modern Dance Tchr 1968 [...] Chm 1984-85; New Dance Group Mod Dance Tchr 1969-74; Dance[...] of Harlem Ballet Mod Dance Tchr 1970-73; Alvin Ailey Amer D[...] Tchr, Dir of Trng Pgms & Co Choreographer 1972-88; Bat Dor [...] Guest Tchr 1973-78, 1983 & 1992; Interlochen Arts Acad 1986, [...] *ai:* Whitehouse Commission Presidential Scholars Distngd Tch[...] Arts 1985-87; Natl Fndtn in Advancement Arts Tchr of Yr 1992; Arts Parents Assn Tchr of Yr Awd 1995; *office:* HS of Performing [...] Amsterdam Ave New York NY 10023

FRANK, RONALD JAMES, Biology, Health & PE Teacher; *b:* L[...] NY; *c:* Stephen, Michael, Timothy; *ed:* SUNY at Cortland (MS) [...] Post Grad Hrs at SUNY at Potsdam, Oswego & Utica C[...] LaFargeville Cntrl Tchr 1963-64; Oriskany Cntrl Tchr 1[...] Clifton-Fine Cntrl Bio, Hlth, PE, Gen Sci, & Drivers Ed Tchr 196[...] Yrs of Coaching Includes Ftbl, Soccer, Var & JV Boys Bsktbl, [...] Bsktbl, Bsbl & Sftbl; AFT 1963-; NYSTA 1963-; Clifton-Fine [...] 1968-, Pres; Town of Fine 1982-, Supvr; *home:* PO Box 95 Star L[...] 13690

FRANK, RONALD PATRICK, Art Teacher; *b:* St Louis, [...] Maureen Keneavy; *c:* Patrick, Michael, Timothy; *ed:* CCAC (A[...] Arts 1973; IN Univ of PA (BS) Art Ed 1974, (MA) Metal Arts 197[...] of Pittsburgh Elem Ed 1985; *cr:* Fox Chapel HS Art Tchr 22 Y[...] Chapel Ed Assn Pres & Chief Negotiator 12 Yrs; *ai:* Head Wrestli[...] Bsbl & Asst Ftbl Coach; NEA 1974-; PSEA 1974-; FCEA 1974-, Chief Negotiator; PSEA Western Region 1986-, Bargaining Task[...] WPIAL Hall of Fame 1988-, Selection Comm; IN Twp Bsbl Assn[...] Founder; Whos Who in Rising Young Amers; Whos Who in W[...] *home:* 754 Heathergate Pittsburgh PA 15238

FRANK, STEPHEN EUGENE, Mathematics Teacher; *b:* Altoona [...] Janice Stofka; *c:* Kristin, Scott; *ed:* IN Univ of PA (BS) Math E[...] Penn St Univ (ME) Ed Adm 1979; Working Prin Cert Penn St U[...] Active Army Officer Training & Operations Officer 1983-86, O[...] Desert Shield 1991-; Roosevelt Jr HS Math Tchr 1970-83, Ma[...] 1986-; *ai:* NEA, PSEA & AAEA 1970-, Reserve Officers Assn[...] Various Military Awds; *office:* Altoona Area Schl Dist 5th Ave & [...] Altoona PA 16602*

FRANK, TIMOTHY JAMES, Science Teacher; *b:* N Tonawanda, [...] Judith Ann; *c:* Kathleen Scalise Shoemaker, Anthony Scalise, Raed[...] Niagara Cty Comm Coll (AAS) Liberal Arts & Soc Sci 1972; St [...] Buffalo (BS) Scndry Ed & Soc Stud 1974, (MS) Scndry Ed & S[...] 1976; Attnd Numerous Insts Various Stud Courses; *cr:* Tw[...] Ambulance EMT Paramedic 1972-; Niagara Cty Soc Services Cas[...] 1975-76; Niagara Cty Hlth Dept Environmental Tech 1976-80; Bak[...] Soc Stud Tchr 1978-79; Wilson Schls Soc Stud Tchr 1979-80; Emergency Medical Services Rep 1980-83; Erie Cty Emergency [...] Services Dir 1983-88; Royalton Hartland Schls Sci Tchr 1985-86 Tonawanda Schls Sci Tchr 1986-; Western NY Emergency Med S[...] Training Inst Intsr 1986-; *ai:* Stu Mentor Tutor; AFT & NYSUT 1[...] Tonawanda United Tchrs 1986-, Labor Cncl Rep; Regnl NYS-EMS [...] 1987-; N Tonawanda Fire Dept #7 Sweeney Hose 1971-, Captain [...] Pres 8 Yrs, 2nd Lt 1 Yr; Red Cross Vol 1975-, Chm 3 Yrs; Red Cro[...] 1977-89; N Tonawanda Disaster Preparedness Asst Dir 1983-94; An[...]

ns Advanced Trauma Life Support Course Asst Faculty; tal Trauma Life Support Course Instr; Intnl PHTLS; Basic fe Support Instr; *office:* North Tonawanda Sr HS 405 Meadow Tonawanda NY 14120*

VALERIE CERCIELLO, Business Teacher; *b:* Dover, NJ; *m:* hristopher, Kevin, Jennifer; *ed:* Montclair St Univ (BA) Bus Ed Randolph HS Bus Tchr 1962-67; Centenary Coll Adjunct Bus -85; Lenape Valley Regnl HS Bus Tchr 1985-; *ai:* FBLA Adv; v Jersey Ed Assn 1985-; New Jersey Business Ed Assn 1978-; lley Ed Assn 1985-, Sec; *office:* Lenape Valley Reg HS PO Box ope NJ 07874

RT, CAROL SUE, English Teacher; *b:* Willard, OH; *m:* Eugene anda B.; *ed:* Bowling Green St Univ (BS) Eng 1971; *cr:* Seneca s Tchr Jr High 1971-74, Tchr HS 1977-; *ai:* Soph Class Adv; A; SEEA; *office:* Seneca East HS Seneca St Attica OH 44807

, KAREN SIMS, Science Teacher; *b:* Pittsburgh, PA; *m:* William egan R., Michelle K.; *ed:* Univ of NH (BA) Zoology 1974; St Coll (MED) Scndry Sci 1988; Operation Physics Instr Cert; t HS Sci Tchr 1984-; *ai:* Class of 1996 Adv; Fac Cncl; Conway ion Commission 1993-; Kennett Boosters 1994-; *office:* Kennett ain St Conway NH 03818*

L, EILEEN D., Spanish Teacher; *b:* Norwalk, CT; *ed:* Fairfield) Mod Lang 1975; Univ of Bpt (MS) Ed 1980; *cr:* Fairfield HS -; *ai:* Stu Forum, Schl Store, Total Comm Club Adv; FEA, COLT, 977-; Music & Arts Ctr for Handicapped 1988-, VP, Dinner Dance rls Scouts Woman of Distinction 1994; *office:* Fairfield HS 755 Ave Fairfield CT 06432

L, YITZCHOK DAVID, Teacher; *b:* New York, NY; *m:* Renee *c:* Batya Weinberg, Moshe Y., Esther, Shoshana, Avi, Shimon, Mordechai, S. Aryeh, Ashira, Akiva Y.; *ed:* Brooklyn Coll (BA) 1969; Queens Coll (BA) Ec, Math 1969; Mesivtha Tifereth Rabbinical Seminary Conferral of Smicha Yorah Yorah 1970; lah Schl Grad Mohel 1973; Mesivtha Tifereth Jerusalem l Seminray Conferral of Advanced Smicha Yadin Yadin 1974; *cr:* ad of Greater Philadelphia 1974-77; Yeshiva Univ HS 1977-78; ad for Girls 1978-79; Yeshiva Dvar Yerushalayim 1979-80; cad of the Five Towns & Rockaway 1980-85; Hebrew Acad of ty 1985-; *ai:* Bible Club Adv; South Shore VAAD, Founding; ch Fire Dept, Chaplain; Gruss Awd for Excl in Tchng; *home:* 256 St Long Beach NY 11561

NBACH, CHARLES HENRY, English Teacher; *b:* Plainfield, auren Badenhausen; *c:* Carla Louise; *ed:* Gettysburg Coll (BA) ; IN Univ (MA) Eng 1989; *cr:* Loomis Chaffee Schl Eng Tchr IN Univ Eng Grad Instr 1988-89; Hotchkiss Schl Eng Tchr 1989-; Coach; Disciplinary Comm.

NFIELD, JEANETTE, Second Grade Teacher; *b:* Sellersville, West Chester St Coll (BS) Elem Ed 1969; Lehigh Univ (MED) 4; 24 Addl Credit Hrs Course Work Penn St, West Chester St; *cr:* lford Schl Transitional First Grd Tchr 1969-71, Second Grd Tchr Third Grd Tchr 1979-83, Second Grd Tchr 1983-; *ai:* NEA 1969-; wer Salford Elem Schl 250 Maple Ave Harleysville PA 19438*

NFIELD, NEIL A., Assistant Principal; *b:* Easton, PA; *m:* Jayne ; *c:* Anne E., Jill A.; *ed:* Rutgers Coll (BS) Elem Ed 1976; East rg Univ (MED) Elem, Sec Admin 1993; *cr:* Stewartsville Schl 76-94; Phillipsburg Bd of Ed HS Cross Cntry, Track Coach Pohatcong Twp Bd of Ed K-8th Grd Asst Prin 1994-; Shimer Schl d Prin 1994-; *ai:* NAESP, NJPSA 1994-; ASCD 1992-; NEA 1976; nor's Tchr Recognition Prgm Tchr of Yr Awd 1988; Phillipsburg Girls Cross Cntry, Track Coach, Conf Championship; *home:* 117 Bloomsbury NJ 08804

FORD, STEPHANIE ANN RAGOZINE, Health & Physical Ed *b:* Youngstown, OH; *c:* Nichol Rosace, Jennifer; *ed:* Kent St Univ & PE 1968; Coll of Mt St Joseph (MS) Master Tchr 1980; 30 d Hrs Ashland, Drake Univ, Youngstown St; *cr:* Austintown Local r 1971-; *ai:* ONTASC Team; Teens Who Can Adv; Coord Drug & Prevention Pgms; OEA 1971-; NEA 1971-; AEA 1971-; Girard 1990-; Girard Ath Cncl 1990-; Drug Free Schls Grant; 4-M nt Grant; *office:* Austintown Local Schls 4560 Falcon Dr wn OH 44515*

HOUSER, RICHARD EDWARD, Physical Education Teacher; ng, PA; *m:* Carol Perkins; *c:* Ryan; *ed:* West VA Univ (BS) PE yola Coll (ME) Ed 1978; Bowie St Univ, Univ of Md Grad Credits; O Pub Schls Tchr, Coach 1970-; *ai:* IM Dir; HS Var Ftbl, Bsktbl Stu Tchr Mentor Univ of MD, Townsend St Univ; TAAC, NEA, 970-; *office:* Old Mill MS North Patriot Ln Millersville MD 21108

LIN, BARBARA A. (BLACKMON), Choral Director; *b:* Detroit, onald James; *ed:* Univ of MI (BM) Music 1970; Univ of ME (MM) Directing 1991; Post Grad Stud at Univ of VA, Univ of Southern Redford Union Schls K-6th Grd Music Tchr 1970-71; Chesapeake 8th Grd Music Tchr 1972-77; Brunswick Schls 6th-8th Grd Music 77-82; Mount Ararat HS 9th-12th Grd Choral Dir 1982-; *ai:* Mt horal Prgm; Stage Co; Amer Choral Dirs Assn 1980-, ME Choral 1995; Music Educators Natl Conf 1978-; ME Music Educators 78-, St VP 1985-88; Most Environmental, Animal Rights Orgs; ub in Natl Choral Journal; Honorary Music Soc Mem; Pi Kappa Honor Soc Mem Phi Kappa Phi; *office:* Mt Ararat HS RR 201 ME 04086

LIN, JANE K., Earth Science Teacher; *b:* NY; *m:* John; *c:* Daniel, e, Margaret; *ed:* SUNY at New Paltz (BS) Sci Ed 1988, (MS) nental Sci 1990; *cr:* Wappingers Cntrl Schl Sci Tchr 1988-92; n City Schls Sci Tchr 1992-; *ai:* Coach Sci Olympiad Team; S 1987-; NYSUT 1988-; NYS Regents Challenger Flwshp; *office:* rd Miller Mid Schl 65 Fording Place Rd Lake Katrine NY 12449

LIN, KATHERINE COURTNEY, 8th Grade Social Studies Tchr; o, TX; *ed:* Wellesley Coll (BA) Pol Sci & Sociology 1987; Sacred niv (MAT) Scndry Ed 1991; *cr:* Hamden HS Stu Tchr & Intern ; Sage Park MS 8th Grd Soc Stud Tchr 1992-; Naugatuck Adult Ed r 1992; Windsor HS Summer Schl 9th & 10th Grd Eng Tchr 1993; Adult Ed Creative Writing Course Tchr 1995; *ai:* NEA, Windsor 1992-; Soc for Prof Journalist 1989-; *home:* 40 Hillside St Apt B-9 rtford CT 06108

LIN, PAULA HORNREICH, 1st Grd Tchr & Math Consultant; *b:* NJ; *m:* Arthur J.; *c:* Richard Kalhofer, Jill Tricarico, Rick, Andrea *ed:* Hunter Coll (BA) Early Chldhd Ed, Sociology 1959; Brooklyn S) Corrective, Remedial Rdng 1971; 19 Credits Early Chldhd Ed, 50 Credits Math, Learning Disabilities, Elem Ed; *cr:* Hunter Coll chl First Grd Tchr 1960-62; PS 212 Second Grd Tchr 1963-64; Road Schl First Grd Tchr 1970-77; Clearstream Ave Schl First Grd Math Consultant 1977-; *ai:* Univ of Chicago Schl Math Project ant, Tchr, Trainer; Created Univ of Chicago Schl Math Project First ath Assessment for UFSD #30; Supts Confs Lecturer, Facilitator; sultation, Math, GATE Comms Rep; AFT 1959-; VSTA 1971-, Unit CD 1994-; Big Books Grant; Articles Pub; *office:* Clearstream Ave Clearstream Ave Valley Stream NY 11582*

FRANKLIN, VIVIAN NATBONY, Spanish Teacher; *b:* Brooklyn, NY; *c:* Matthew, Andrew; *ed:* Queens Coll (BA) Span 1970; 30 Credit Hrs After Schl Prof Dev Courses; *cr:* IS 59 Span Tchr 1970-75; MS 67 Span Tchr 1987-90; MS 158 Span Tchr 1990-; *ai:* Schl Cncl; 40th Anniversary Comm; Staff Planning Team; Career Day Comm Fundraiser Chprsn; Sr Adv Liaison; UFT 1970-; NYSAFLT 1990-; *office:* MS 158 Marie Curie 46-35 Oceania St Bayside NY 11361

FRANKO, MARILYN, Elementary Teacher; *b:* Niles, OH; *m:* Joseph J.; *c:* Natalie, Joseph, Elizabeth; *ed:* Youngstown St Univ (AB) Psych 1978; Certfd Elem Ed; Currently Enrolled in Masters Pgm for Elem Ed; *cr:* Word of Life Chrstn Acad Tchr 1989-; *office:* Word Of Life Christian Acad 2577 Schenley Ave NE Warren OH 44483

FRANKO, SUSAN MARIE, Seventh & Eighth Grade Teacher; *b:* Youngstown, OH; *ed:* Youngstown St Univ (BSEd) Elem Ed 1972, (MSEd) Curr 1977; *cr:* St Brendan Sixth Grd Tchr 1972-76; Roosevelt Elem Sixth Grd Tchr 1976-89; McDonald Jr HS Seventh & Eighth Grd Tchr 1989-; *ai:* McDonald Ed Assn 1976-; Martha Holden Jennings Scholar 1990-91; *office:* McDonald Jr HS 600 Iowa Ave Mc Donald OH 44437

FRANKO, WILMA A., Latin, French & English Tchr; *b:* Brownsville, PA; *ed:* Waynesburg Coll (BA) Fr 1959; Seton Hill Latin Cert 1965; *cr:* John A. Brashear HS Latin, Fr Tchr 1959-63; Redstone HS Latin Tchr 1963-66; Brownsville Area HS Latn, Fr, Math, Eng Tchr 1966-; *ai:* Latin & Fr Club Spon; France Trip Spon 1980; Italy & Greece Trip Spon 1992; PSEA, NEA, Brownsville Area Ed Assn 1969-; Pittsburgh Post Gazette & the Univ of Pittsburgh Schl of Ed; All-Star Educator 1993; *office:* Brownsville Area HS Brashear Ave Brownsville PA 15417

FRANKS, DOUGLAS CRAIG, Physics Instructor; *b:* New York, NY; *m:* Kathleen; *c:* Hannah, Joshua, Dolores, Caleb, Ariel, Isaac, Nathaniel, Daniel; *ed:* Eastern Coll (BA) Ed 1976; Bucks Cty Comm (AS) Ed 1977; Lehigh Univ (MA) Physics Ed 1986; Addl 6 Hrs Penn St Nuclear Specialist, 12 Hrs Aurora Univ Argonne Rsrch Assoc; *cr:* New Life Yth & Family Svcs Tchr 1976-86; Plumstead Chrstn Schl Chem, Physics Tchr 1989-93; Montgomery Cty Math, Physics Tchr 1992-; Temple Univ Math Tchr 1992-94; Christopher Dock Mennonite HS Physics, Cmptrs Tchr 1994-; *ai:* AAPT 1986-; Int Solar Energy, ASEA, NE Sustainable Energy Assn 1993-; *office:* Christopher Dock Mennonite HS 1000 Forty Foot Rd Lansdale PA 19446

FRANTZ, CHERYL DETTENMAYER, Sixth Grade Teacher; *b:* Philadelphia, PA; *m:* James; *ed:* East Stroudsburg Univ (BS) Elem Ed 1969; Univ of Scranton (MS) Elem Ed 1974; *cr:* Andrew Jackson Schl First Grd Tchr 1969-77; Lincoln-Jackson Schl First & Third Grd Tchr 1977-90; West Scranton Inter Schl Sixth Grd Tchr 1990-; *ai:* Mentor Stu Asst Prgm; Scranton Schl Dist In-Svc Comm; Educl Research & Dissemination Prgm Tchr, Research Linker; AFT 1969-; Scranton Fed of Tchrs 1969-, Trustee, Exec Bd; Phi Delta Kappa 1981-; Auxiliary of St Joseph Childrens Ctr 1976-, Historian; Women Tchrs of Scranton 1970-; Humane Soc 1992-; People for Ethreal Treatment of Animals 1991-; In-Svc Presentor from ER & D Prgm, Self-Esteem Trng Prgm; Negotiating Team Mem for SFT 1977-; Peer Coaching-Inductee Pgm 1995-; *home:* 131 Storrs St Taylor PA 18517

FRANTZ, JAMES ALBERT, Mathematics Teacher; *b:* Springfield, OH; *m:* Elizabeth J. Wells; *c:* Mark, J. Paul, David; *ed:* Wittenberg Univ (BS) Scndry Math, Sci 1964; Miami Univ (MED) Admin 1968; Wright St Univ, Univ of Dayton Post Grad Stud; *cr:* Springfield City Schls Math Tchr 1964-69, Prin 1970-86, Supt 1987-94; Southeastern Local Schls Math Tchr 1995-; *ai:* Instructional Improvement Comm; BASA 1987-; Outstanding Young Educator Awd Springfield Clark Cty 1968; OH Reg Supts Awd; *home:* 3018 Malibu St Springfield OH 45503

FRANTZ, RICHARD EARL, English Teacher; *b:* Washington, DC; *m:* Beatrice L. Ulrich; *c:* Richard Jr., Kevin, Michael, Steven, Timothy; *ed:* Elizabethtown Coll (BA) Bible, Philosophy, Eng 1964; Kutztown Univ (MA) Eng 1995; PA St Univ Cooperative Ed; *cr:* Tulpehocken Area Schls Eng Tchr 1964-79; Weis Markets Dept Mgr 1979-80; Lebanon Cty Voc Tech Schl Coop Coord 1980-82; Tulpehocken Area Schls Eng Tchr 1982-; *ai:* NEA, PSEA 1964-; Tulpehocken Ed Assn 1964-, VP, Tchr of Quarter; Little Swatara Church of Brethren 1951-, Moderator; Cub Scouts 1964-81, Cub Master; Jaycees 1970-75, Sec; Tulpehocken Sports Boosters Club 1978-88, Pres; Sports Boosters Club Presents 2 Coll Schlsps in Honor of my Wife's & My Svc to Schl Ath Prgm; *home:* 35 Wintersville Rd Richland PA 17087*

FRANTZEN, JULIE HAVERTY, Second Grade Teacher; *b:* Leominster, MA; *m:* Henry A.; *c:* J. Blair, Jill, Eric; *ed:* Monmouth Univ (BS) Elem Ed-Summa Cum Laude 1983; *cr:* Eatontown Bd of Ed Second Grd Tchr 1983-; *ai:* PTO Exec Comm Mem; Grd Chprsn; Ed Advy Comm Mem; NEA, Kappa Delta 1983-; *office:* Vetter Schl Grant Ave Eatontown NJ 07724*

FRANZER, PATRICIA ROSE (SEVERT), Algebra & General Math Tchr; *b:* Coldwater, OH; *m:* Michael; *c:* Neal, Greg, Mark; *ed:* Wright St Univ (BS) Scndry Math Ed 1974, (MS) Curr, Supervision 1986; Project Discovery Summer 1996; *cr:* Celina City Schls Jr High Math, Cmptr Ed 1974-; *ai:* Scholastic & Math Counts Team Coaches; Team Ldr Supvr; NCTM, OCTM, NEA 1974-; OEA, WOEA; CEA, VP 1982-84; Coldwater Acad Promoters 1985-, Sec 1987-90; Alpha Delta Kappa 1078-94, VP 1987-89, Pres 1990-92; Martha Holden Jennings Scholar 1989; *office:* Celina Jr HS 615 Holly St Celina OH 45822

FRANZOSA, SAMUEL C., Resource Room Science Teacher; *b:* Hazleton, PA; *m:* Maureen Aita; *c:* Samuel, Alyssa, Adrianne, Christina; *ed:* Lock Haven Univ (BS) Elem & Spec Ed 1973; Univ of Scranton (MS) Rdng 1980; Extensive Post Grad Spec Ed Research at Long Island Univ, East Stroudsburg Univ, Wilkes Univ; *cr:* Hazleton Area Tchr 1973-; *ai:* Soccer Adv; NEA 1973-; Hazleton Easter Seal 1973-, Adv, Brace for an Ace Awd; *office:* Hazleton Area Schl Dist 1601 W 23rd St Hazleton PA 18201*

FRASCA, GRACE BALLENGER, First Grade Teacher; *b:* Trafford, PA; *w:* E. Elmer (dec); *ed:* CA St Univ (BS) Elem Ed 1960; Attnd Univ of Rhode Island, Penn St Univ Ext; *cr:* Gateway Schl Dist Second Grd Tchr 1960-62; Willingboro Schl Dist Second-Third Grd Tchr 1962-65; Norwin Schl Dist First-Third Grd Tchr 1965-95; *ai:* NEA 1960-; PSEA 1965-; NEA 1965-, Bldg Rep; Norwin Jr Women, Ed Chprsn; First Meth Church 1965-, Chair Altar Area Worship Comm; *home:* 1219 9th St Irwin PA 15642

FRASCHE, RAYMOND M., Music Teacher; *b:* Hackensack, NJ; *m:* Tracy; *ed:* William Paterson (BS) Music Ed 1984; *cr:* Holy Angles Church Music Dir 1983-93; Passaic Valley HS Musi Instr 1985-; Queen of Peace Church Music Dir 1993-; *ai:* Vocal Ensemble & Pit Orchestra Adv; MENC 1984-, Active Mem; *office:* Passaic Valley HS East Main St Little Falls NJ 07424*

FRASENE, STEPHEN JAMES, Business Teacher; *b:* White Plains, NY; *ed:* Lehman Coll (MS) Scndry Ed 1993; *cr:* Jane Adams HS Bus House Coord, Retail Acad Coord 199-3; *ai:* Natl Fnd Tchng Entrepreneurship Tchr of Yr 1996; *office:* Jane Addams Voc HS 900 Tinton Ave Bronx NY 10456

FRASER, DAVID MICHAEL, Science Teacher & Coach; *b:* Glendale, AZ; *c:* Alec; *ed:* Hope Coll (BA) Sci Composite 1983; Post Grad Stud OH St Univ & Ashland Univ; *cr:* Houston ISD Sci Tchr 1983-84; Lamar Consd ISD Sci Tchr & Coach 1984-88; Southwestern City Schls Sci & His Tchr & Coach 1988-; *ai:* Basketland Coach; Track Coach; NEA 1983-; OH Ed Assn 1988-; PTA & PTSA 1988-; Various Awds of Recognition; PTSA Edctr of the Yr 1996; Norton MS Edctr of Yr; *office:* Norton MS 215 Norton Rd Columbus OH 43228*

FRASER, GRACE MORTH, Assoc Professor & Asst Chrmn; *b:* Fargo, ND; *m:* Thomas M. Jr.; *ed:* Univ UT (BA) Anthropology 1969; Univ MA Amherst (MA) Anthropology 1971, (PHD) Anthropology 1979; *cr:* PSC Adj 1986-89, Asst Prof 1990-94, Assoc Prof 1994-; *ai:* Dept Soc Sci Asst Chair; Coll Admin Selection, Acad Advising, Planning Comm; Coord Anthropology & Soc; NEAA 1970-, Treas; Amer Anthropology Assn 1985-, Fellow; Local His Soc Church 1975-, Pres, Clerk, Organist; Alpha Lambda Delta; Sigma Alpha Iota; Delta Kappa Gamma; Phi Kappa Phi; NIMH, PSC Deans Career Dev Grant; Univ MA Amherst Rsrch Fellow; Grange Citizenship Awd; 2 Articles Conflict Mgmt, Disaster Rsrch; *office:* Univ Of NH Plymouth St Coll 17 Highland St Plymouth NH 03264*

FRASER, MARILYN, Mathematics Teacher; *ed:* Bucknell (BA) Soc Stud 1956; *ai:* Renaissance Comm Chprsn; 10th Grd Class Adv; NEA; NJEA; AMTNJ; FTEA; NJ Tchr of Yr Governors Awd; *office:* Franklin HS 15 Francis St Somerset NJ 08873

FRASSENEI, JOSEPH ROGERS, Health & Physical Ed Teacher; *b:* Lewisburg, PA; *m:* Christine Rodgers; *c:* Carolyn, Lauren; *ed:* West Chester Univ (BS) Hlth, PE 1982; Rowan Coll Ath Admin; Glassboro St Coll Driver Ed Cert; *cr:* Coatesville HS Hlth, PE Tchr 1982-84; Lower Merion HS Hlth, PE Tchr 1984-85; Haddonfield HS Hlth, PE Tchr 1985-91; Woodstown Schl Hlth, PE Tchr 1991-; *ai:* Head Wrestling, Girls Track, Asst Boys Soccer Coach; Curr Coordinating Cncl; NEA 1985-; *home:* 15 Woodduck Dr Mullica Hill NJ 08062

FRATTEROLO, JOANNE FERIOLI, 8th Grade Mathematics Teacher; *b:* Perth Amboy, NJ; *m:* Matthew Joseph; *c:* Joseph, Jennifer Nemeth, Jessica; *ed:* Georgian Ct Coll (BA) Math 1963; *cr:* Colonia MS Math Tchr 1963-67; JFK HS Math Tchr 1982-91; Avenel MS Math Tchr 1991-; *ai:* 8th Grd Team Ldr 1991-95; Stu Cncl Adv; NEA.

FRATZ, CARL E., English Teacher; *b:* Camden, NJ; *m:* Amy Golembiewski; *c:* Kristen, Karli; *ed:* Gloucester Cty Coll (AAS) Cmptr Information Processing, (AA) Liberal Arts 1972; Glassboro St Coll (BA) Scndry Ed Soc Stud 1974, (MA) Rdng Ed; NJ Tchr Cert; *cr:* St Joan of Arc Schl 6-8 Grd Soc Stud Tchr 1975-77; Camden Cty Vo-Tech Schl 9-12 Grd Eng Tchr 1977-79; Penns Grove HS 9-12 Grd Eng Tchr 1979-; *ai:* Future Tchrs Club Adv; Stu Affairs Coord; Stu Assistance Team; Schl, Dist Planning, Scheduling Comms; NEA 1977-, Del; NJ Ed Assn 1977-, Del, Cert, Evaluation, Tenure Comm, Tchr Ed Subcom Chprsn; Salem Cty Cncl of Ed 1979-, VP; Penns Grove, Carneys Pt Schl Emp Assn, AR Newsletter Ed; IRA 1988-; Rdng Cncl of South NJ 1988-, Bd of Dirs, Corresponding Sec, Philanthropic Comm Chair; Gloucester Co Children's Shelter 1976-79, Bd of Trustees; Juvenile Conf Comm 1984-, Chm; Clearview Comm Schlsp Comm 1994-, Exec Bd; Sketch Club Players 1981-92, Exec Bd; Salem Cty 2,000 1995-, Tchr Advy Bd; Governor's Tchr Recognition Awd 1994-95; Wkshp Presenter 1989-; *office:* Penns Grove HS 334 Harding Hwy Carneys Point NJ 08069

FRAWLEY, TIMOTHY J., Mathematics Chair; *b:* Elmira, NY; *ed:* SUNY at Albany (BS) Math 1973; Elmira Coll (MS) Math Ed 1977; *cr:* Sodus Cntrl Schl Math Tchr 1973-74; C-PP West HS Math Tchr, Chair 1974-; *ai:* AFT 1973-; NCTM 1972-; NCSM 1976-; *office:* Corning Painted Post West HS Victory Hwy Painted Post NY 14870*

FRAYER, CHARLES ALBERT,JR., Swim Coach; *b:* Norwich, NY; *ed:* Morrisville Coll (AAS) Bus 1989; Hartwick Coll 9 Credit Hrs Bus Mgmt; *cr:* Norwich YMCA Asst Aquatic Dir 1981-89; Whitney Point Cntrl Schls Swim Coach, Instr 1989-; Jewish Comm Ctr Asst Aquatic Dir 1990-; *ai:* Girls, Boys Var Swim Team Coach; Whitney Point Swim Club; Chenango Cty Red Cross 1985-, Bd of Dir, Sec, Vol Recognition Awd; *office:* Whitney Point Cntrl Schls PO Box 249 Keibel Rd Whitney Point NY 13862

FRAZIER, MARK LEWIS, Band & Asst Director; *b:* Zanesville, OH; *ed:* Otterbein Coll (BA) Music Ed 1986; OH St Univ, Ashland Univ Post Grad Credit Hrs; *cr:* Hamilton Local Schls Band Dir MS, Asst Dir HS 1986-; *ai:* Winter Guard, Color Guard, Dist Dram & Musical Dir; Prom Adv; IM Coach; NEA, Hamilton Local Tchrs Assn, OH Music Ed Assn, OH MS Assn 1986-; *office:* Hamilton Local Schls 4999 Lockbourne Rd Columbus OH 43207

FRAZIER, ROBERT E., Social Studies Teacher; *b:* Weymouth, MA; *ed:* Stonehill Coll (BA) Eng; Working Toward MAT in His; *cr:* East MS Soc Stud Tchr 1982-; *ai:* Cinematography; Animation; NEA, MA Tchrs Assn 1981-; Appalachian Mountain Club 1985-; MA Arts Lottery Grant.*

FRAZIER, RODERICK JOHN, Electrical Instructor; *b:* Meadville, PA; *m:* Carol; *c:* Michael, Karen; *ed:* Attnd Edinboro Univ Electrical, IUP Univ Electrical; *cr:* Electrical Maintenance Labor to Foreman 1967-90; *ai:* NEA 1990-; Elks 1975-; *office:* Crawford Co Voc Tech Schl 860 Thurston Rd Meadville PA 16335*

FRAZIER, WILLIAM J., Guidance Counselor; *b:* Randolpy Cty, NC; *c:* Bryant; *ed:* Louisburg Coll (AA) 1963; Univ of NC (BA) Soc Stud Ed 1965; Montclair St Coll (MED) Amer His 1969; Post Grad 22 Credit Hrs Continuing Ed; North Adams St Coll Cert Guid 1971; *cr:* Millburn Jr HS Soc Stud Tchr 1967-69; Pittsfield HS Soc Stud Tchr 1969-74, Guid Cnslr 1974-; *ai:* Berkshire Cty Guid Assn 1974-, Treas, Pres; St Stephen's Parish 1987-, Jr, Sr Warden Choir; Oratorio Comm Coir 1980-; *office:* Pittsfield HS 300 East St Pittsfield MA 01201

FRECHETTE, GARTH JOSEPH, Chemistry Teacher; *b:* Plattsburgh, NY; *m:* Michelle Lynn; *c:* Taren, Carter, Mikaela; *ed:* SUNY at Plattsburgh (BS) Sci Ed 1985, (MS) Admin 1993; *cr:* St Johns Acad Chem & Physics Tchr 1986-88; Beekmantown Cntrl Schl Regents Chem Tchr 1988-; *ai:* Ftbl, Bsktbl & Girls Track Coach; Frosh Class & Ski & Hiking Club Adv; NYSUT & AFT 1988-; STANYS 1989-; Cath Church 1962-, Eucharistic Ministry; *office:* Beekmantown Mid Sr High PO Box 829 Plattsburgh NY 12901*

FRECK, HARRISON JAMES, Social Studies Teacher; *b:* Niles, OH; *ed:* Bowling Green St Univ (BSEd) Soc Stud 1969; Youngstown St Univ (MA) Amer His 1991; Studying in PHD Prgm in Amer His at Bowling Green St Univ; *cr:* Pymatuning Vly Schl Tchr 1972-73; Parkway Schls Soc Stud Tchr 1973-; *ai:* NEA 1972-; OH Historical Soc 1990-; OHSEA 1996; Assoc of Soc on Early Amer His &Cultures; Mercer Cty High Soc 1995-, Bd of Dirs.

FREDA, AUGUST ROBERT, Prof of Engineering & Dept Dir; *b:* Pittsburgh, PA; *m:* Victoria Bonosky; *c:* August R. Jr., Anthony B.; *ed:* Univ of Notre Dame (BS) Metallurgy 1953, (MS) Metallurgy 1955, (PHD) 1957; *cr:* Univ of Pittsburgh Asst Prof in Met Engr 1957-67; Univ of Pittsburg at Bradford Prof & Dir of Engrng 1967-; *ai:* Engrng Stdnts, Engrng Club Acad Advs; Sigma Lambda Xi Adv; Major Time Devoted Recruiting Stdnts, Administering the Dept, Serving on Campus Comms; *office:* Univ Of Pittsburgh At Bradford Campus Dr Bradford PA 16701

FREDA, ELLEN SCHWARTZ, Eighth Grade Teacher; *b:* Bronx, NY; *m:* Roger; *ed:* Univ of Bridgeport (BS) Ed 1970; Fairfield Univ (MED) Ed 1973; 63+ Credit Hrs beyond MED; *cr:* Haverstraw MS Tchr 1973-; *ai:* Yrbk Adv; Schl Improvement Planning Team; Comp Club Co-Adv; AFT & NCTM 1973-; Impact II Grant Winner 3 Times; *office:* Haverstraw MS Grant St Haverstraw NY 10927*

FREDA, JOHN MICHAEL, Third Grade Teacher; *b:* Buffalo, NY; *m:* Renee L. Gademske; *c:* Maria Rose; *ed:* Buffalo St Coll (BS) Elem Ed 1989, (MS) Elem Ed Instruction 1993; 18 Hrs Credit Profession Growth; *cr:* Herbert Hoover Elem Schl Fifth Grd Tchr 1989-95, Third Grd Tchr 1995-; *ai:* Comms Facilitator Schl Planning, Monitoring Ldr, Cmptr; Coach Girl's Soccer, Vlybl, Boy's Wrestling; AFT 1989-; Grant Writing Team to Improve Prof Dev Site Prgm; *office:* Herbert Hoover Elem Schl 199 Thorncliff Rd Buffalo NY 14223*

FREDA, ROGER LOUIS, Secondary School Administrator; *b:* Bronx, NY; *m:* Ellen Schwartz; *ed:* Manhattan Coll (BA) Lbrl Arts 1967; City Univ of City of NY (MA) Ed 1972; Coll of New Rochelle (SDS) Schl Admin 1993; *cr:* Intermediate Schl 155 8th Grd Eng Tchr 1967-70; Clarkstown Sr HS 12th Grd Eng Tchr 1970-71; Haverstraw MS Lang Arts Tchr 1971-94; James A Farley MS Asst Prin 1994-; *ai:* Mensa Club Adv; NCTE 1970-; ASCD 1984-; SANNYS 1994-; Congressman Ben Gilmans Educl Advy Comm 1987-; IS 155 tchr of Yr 1969; *home:* 6 Colonel Conklin Dr Stony Point NY 10980

FREDERICK, AUDRIENNE MERCURE, Fifth Grade Teacher; *b:* Leetonia, OH; *m:* Richard; *ed:* Kent St Univ (BS) Elem Ed 1964; Univ of TN (MS) Spec Ed 1979; Attnd Miami Univ, Xavier Univ, Univ of Cincinnati, Drake Univ; *cr:* Streetsboro 5th-7th 1958-60; Field Local 5th-7th 1960-64; Stow City 5th-7th 1969-73; Lakota 5th-6th 1973-76; LaRue 7th-8th Math 1976; Pleasant 5th-6th 1976; Michael Dunn Rehab Center Tchr Supvr 1975; Harriman El Read Center Adult Ed 1975-79; Occupational HS 11th Grd Eng, Math 1975-79; Kingston HS 9th-10th LD Math 1979-80; Lakota 3rd-5th 1980-; *ai:* OEA, NEA 1958-; LEA 1980-; *office:* Adena Elem Schl 9316 Minuteman Way West Chester OH 45069

FREDERICK, BARBARA JO, 7th-8th Grade Special Educator; *b:* Dayton, OH; *ed:* Wright St Univ (BSEd) Soc Stud Comprehension 1970; Xavier Univ (MED) Spec Ed LD, BD 1974; Soc Stud, Supervision, Admin K-12, Spec Ed LD-BD, Asst Supt Certs; *cr:* Dayton Pub Schls K-12 Grd Sub Tchr 1969-70; Stebbins HS 11-12 Grd Psych, Sociology Tchr 1970-75; Nicholas Liberty Schl 3-12 Grd Spec Edctr 1979-88; Fairview Elem Schl 4th Grd Tchr 1988-89; Liberty Jr Schl 7-8 Grd Spec Edctr 1989-; *ai:* Curr Review; Dist-Wide Curr Counsel; Stu Tutoring; Acad Awds & Teaming; Amer Bus Women's Assn 1968-; LEA, OEA, NEA 1989-; US Humane Soc; Amer Red Cross, Vol Instr; Nom Outstdng Tchr of Yr; Chartering Nicholas Liberty Schl OH Dept of Ed; Mont Co Presecutor's Office Vol Advocate; *office:* Liberty Jr Schl 7055 Dutchland Blvd Middletown OH 45044*

FREDERICK, BERTRAM FRANK, History Teacher; *b:* Buffalo, NY; *m:* Brigitte; *c:* Paul, Kathryn; *ed:* Canisius Coll (BS) His 1958; Christ the King (AA) Moral Theology 1963; Canisius Coll (MA) His 1966; Addl 100 Grad Hrs at St Univ of NY & John Carroll; *cr:* SUCB Part-Time Pol Sci & Survey of Western Civilization Tchr; Canisius Coll Part-Time Pol Sci & Survey of Western Civilization; Nativity-Williamsville 7th Grd Tchr 1963-64; Baker HS His Instr 1964-66; Orchard Park HS His Instr 1966-; *ai:* Mentor Tchr; Saint James Schl Rel Ed Tchr; AFT 1966-, Local Rep; NAACP 1969-75; NFC for Soc Stud; Congress of Racial Equality; ACLU; Smithsonia Assn; OLV Infant Home 1966-69, Bd; Choirs Etc; Nation Democratic Comm; OP Cncl on World Affairs & Yorkers-Young NY St Historian Past Adv; Mid Sts Schl Evaluation Team Mem; NHS Honors Seminars at Canisius Coll; Pres Cncl Mem at Canisius Coll 1982-91; *home:* 8300 Old Post Rd E East Amherst NY 14051*

FREDERICK, DONALD A., Fifth Grade Teacher; *b:* New Kensington, PA; *m:* Kathy Girdano; *ed:* CA St Univ (BS) Elem Ed 1969, Scndry Soc Stud 1971, (MS) 1992; *cr:* Riverview Schl Dist Tchr 1969-; *ai:* Ftbl Coach; Var Club; Negotiation Comm Chprsn; NEA, PSEA 1969-; REA 1969-, Pres; Vol Fireman 1972-; Chamber of Commerce 1983-; *office:* Riverview Schl Dist 701 10th St Oakmont PA 15139

FREDERICK, ELIZABETH BILDERBACK, English Teacher; *b:* New Orleans, LA; *w:* Harold (dec); *c:* Ren, Alex, Ervin, Elizabeth A.; *ed:* Chatham Coll (BA) Eng 1949; PA St (MS) Hum 1988; *cr:* Harrisburg Acad Eng Tchr 1969-, Dept Ch; *ai:* Drama Coach; Award Winner Scholastic Wrtng; *office:* The Harrisburg Acad 10 Erford Rd Wormleysburg PA 17043

FREDERICK, ERLA MAE (KREIDER), Math Dept Chm & Tchr; *b:* Hershey, PA; *m:* Frank William Frederick, Sr.; *c:* Douglas Andrew, David Russel; *ed:* Lock Haven St Coll (BS) Scndry Math 1973; Millersville St Coll 12 Grad Credits Rdng, Elem Math; Wilkes Coll 9 Credits Pride, Teach; Lock Haven Univ 6 Credits Aviation; *cr:* Edward Hard Jr HS 7th Grd Tchr 1973-76; Paper Amcroft Corp Market Analyst, Cmptr Statiscal Analysis 1976-84; East Lycoming HS 8-10th Grd Math Tchr 1985; Bald Eagle Area Schl Calculus, Cmptrs, 7th Grd Tchr 1985-87; Lock Haven HS, Buckail HS Scndry Math Tchr 1987-; *ai:* Adv Sr High Stu Cncl, Soph Class; Act, Coord Fund Raisers; Math Dept Chair; SAP Team Mem; NCPCTM 1990-, Sec, Bd; Penn Cncl of Tchrs of Math 1991-; East Main St United Meth Church 1976-, Bd, Sec, Cncl of Ministries, Lay Ldr; Yth Group 1978-, Adv; Boy Scouts 1990-, Comm Chm; *office:* Lock Haven HS 301 W Church St Lock Haven PA 17745*

FREDERICK, L. SCOTT, American Cultures Teacher; *b:* Pittsburgh, PA; *m:* Virginia Ferguson; *c:* Aimee L., Kerri A., Erin Kathleen; *ed:* CA Univ of PA (BS) Soc Sci 1976, (ME) Soc Sci 1983; Allegheny Intermediate Unit,His Consortium Prins Cert Prgm; *cr:* Ringgold Sr HS Soc Stud Instr 1976-; WA, Jefferson Coll Adj Instr, Geography 1990-; *ai:* Head Coach Boys, Girls Cross Cntry, Boys Track Teams; Class Spon; Natl Ed Assn PA St Ed Assn 1976-; WA Cty Authority 1990-, Chm, Sec; Mid-Mon Vly Transit Authority, Chm Personnel Comm; Monongahela City Cncl 1984-88; Monogahela Area Lib, Bd of Dirs, Citizens of Yr; Whiskey Rebellion 200th Anniversary Schlsp; *office:* Ringgold Sr HS 3645 Dry Run Rd Monongahela PA 15063

FREDERICK, RICHARD D., Amer His & Government Tchr; *b:* Brooklyn, NY; *ed:* Rider Univ (BA) His Ed 1969; *cr:* Iselin MS Tchr 1969-90; Avenel MS Dept Head 1990-91; Iselin MS Team Ldr 1991-; *ai:* NEA, NJEA 1982-; Woodbridge Tchrs Ed Assn 1992-, Assoc Rep 1982-90; NJ Governors Tchr Recognition Prgm Awd 1993; *office:* Iselin MS Woodruff St Iselin NJ 08830*

FREDERICKS, DOUGLAS L., Calculus Teacher; *b:* Niagara Falls, NY; *m:* Gail Wompierski; *c:* Lynn, Sue Selbe; *ed:* St Univ of NY at Geneseo (BS) Math 1964; Rutgers (MS) Math 1970; *cr:* North Tona Pub Schls Tchr 1964-70; Woodbridge HS Advanced Placement Calculus Tchr 1970-; *ai:* NHS Adv; Stu Cncl Asst Adv; Math Club Adv; NJEA, NEA 1964-; BPO Elks 1983-; Natl Sci Fnd Schlsp for Grad Stud.

FREDERICKS, JOHN ROBERT, Chemistry Teacher; *b:* Pottsville, PA; *m:* Sharon Yee; *ed:* Kings Coll (BA) Chem 1991; Univ of Pittsburgh (MS) Chem 1993; *cr:* Elderton Jr-Sr HS Chem, Sci Tchr 1993-; Quaker Vly HS Chem Tchr 1994-; *ai:* Yrbk, Carnegie Sci Fair Adv; Amer Chem Soc, Spectroscopy Soc of Pittsburgh 1993-; NSTA 1992-; Dept of Ed Flwshp; Safford Awd for Excl in Undergraduate Tchng; *office:* Quaker Valley Sr HS 625 Beaver St Leetsdale PA 15056

FREDERICKS, RICHARD JAMES, High School Mathematics Tchr; *b:* Boston, MA; *m:* Janet Palli; *c:* Melissa, Rebecca; *ed:* Univ of MA (BS) Ecs 1969; Attnd Bridgewater St, Northeastern, Fisher Jr Coll, Hartford Univ, Massasoit Comm Coll; *cr:* Rockland HS Math Tchr 1972-; *ai:* Acad Cncl; Coach Bsbl 1980-, Girls Bsktbl 1983-; MTA, NEA, REA 1975-; N Comm Church, Usher; *office:* Rockland HS 52 Goddard Ave Rockland MA 02370

FREDERICKSON, ELLEN DECKER, 5th Grade Teacher; *b:* Newark, NJ; *m:* Mathias Jr.; *ed:* Trenton St Coll (BS) Elem Ed 1984; *cr:* Roosevelt Schl 5th Grd Tchr 1984-89, 1990-, 4th Grd Tchr 1989-90; *ai:* Chrldng Head Coach; Stokes Schl of Conservation Coord; NJEA 1984-; SPEA 1984-, Bldg Rep; NEA 1984-; SP Lib Bd 1985-88; Governors Tchr Recognition Pgm 1993; *office:* Roosevelt Elem Schl 110 Jackson Ave South Plainfield NJ 07080*

FREDERICKSON, KATHY ANN, English Professor; *b:* Leominster, MA; *m:* Ronald; *c:* Joshua, Rachel; *ed:* Fitchburg St Coll (BS) Eng 1974; Univ of MA (MA) Eng 1991; 24 Credit Hrs Doctoral Prgm Eng; *cr:* MA Xorrectional Inst Tchr 2 Yrs; Adult Ed Prgm Tchr 8 Yrs; Mt Wachusett Comm Coll Writing Ctr Dir 10 Yrs; Quinsigamond Comm Coll Assoc Prof 4 Yrs; *ai:* Women's Ctr Advy Bd; Phi Theta Kappa, Co-Chair; NCTE 1982-; NEA, MA Women in Pub Higher Ed 1990-; Pub Dreiser Stud; Essay Forthcoming Theodore Dreiser, New Readings; Presenter at Amer Lit Assn Conf, New England Regnl Conf Tchng Eng; *office:* Quinsigamond Comm Coll 670 W Boylston St Worcester MA 01606

FREDRICK, MARK, English Dept Chprsn & Tchr; *b:* Cleveland, OH; *m:* MaryAnn Flaviani; *c:* Laura; *ed:* John Carroll Univ (BA) Eng 1975, (MED) Ed 1980; Kent St Univ Writing Curr & Process; *cr:* St Augustine Acad Eng Tchr 1975-78; Collinwood HS Tchr 1978-81; East HS Tchr 1982-89; Max Hayes HS Dept Head & Tchr 1989-; *ai:* 4-H; FFA; OH Fed Tchrs 1975-; Cty Ag Extension 1989-, Master Gardener; Inspriational Tchr of the Yr B P Amer 1994; *office:* Max S Hayes Vocational High 4600 Detroit Ave Cleveland OH 44102*

FREDRICKS, KAREN CHAPMAN, Third Grade Teacher; *b:* Manchester, NH; *m:* Harry Edward; *c:* Katie, Joel; *ed:* Univ of DE (BS) Elem Ed 1975; *cr:* Alexis I DuPont MS 5-8th Grd Tchr 1977-78; Gunning Bedford Jr HS 7-8th Grd Tchr 1978-79; Richradson Park Elem Schl 2nd, 5th Grd Tchr 1979-81; Downes Elem Schl 1st Grd Tchr 1981-82; Cobbs Elem Schl 1-2nd Grd Tchr 1982-93; Thurgood Marshall Elem Schl 3rd Grd Tchr 1993-; *ai:* Tiger Marching Bank Front, Dance Club Coach; Grd Level Chprsn; Tech, Behavior Mngmt, Portfolio Comms; Rstructuring, Stu Asst Team; Lang Arts Comm; Drug Ed Coord; NEA 1979-; Natl Sci Tchrs Alliance Convention Presenter 1995; Christina Schl Dist Drug Curr Trnr.*

FREDSELL, ROCHELLE MARY, English Teacher; *b:* Utica, NY; *m:* Michael Erik; *c:* Erik, Justin; *ed:* Alfred Univ (BA) Eng 1973; Addl 48 Credit Hrs; *cr:* John F. Kennedy MS Eng Tchr 1973-; *ai:* Newspaper Adv; RESPECT Club; Young Scholars Prgm; CARE Prgm at John F. Kennedy MS; Key Club Adv; NYSUT 1973-; *office:* John F Kennedy MS 500 Deerfield Dr E Utica NY 13502

FREE, ANNE REBECCA, Instructor in Theatre; *b:* Bloomington, IN; *m:* Rory P. B.; *ed:* Miami Univ (BA) His 1984, (MA) Theatre 1987; Doctoral Work at IN Univ; *cr:* Goucher Coll Instr 1992-; *ai:* Dir of Theatre; *office:* Goucher College 1021 Dulaney Valley Rd Baltimore MD 21204

FREEBERG, PRISCILLA MARIE, Music Teacher; *b:* Galesburg, IL; *m:* Darrel Myron; *c:* Karin, Eric, Karl; *ed:* Univ of MN (BS) Elem Ed 1967; *cr:* Minneapolis Pub Schl Elem Tchr 1967-70; Home Music Studio All Age Children 1966-; Minnehaha Acad Minneapolis Music Tchr 1984-90; First Assembly Christian Acad Worchester Music Tchr 1991-; *ai:* MTNA 1970-, Vol Svc Awd; MA Music Tchr 1990-; Music Educators Assn 1991-; MN Music Teachers Assn 1970-, Theory Judge; Charisters Guild 1995-; 100th Town Chorus 1990-, Accompanist; Salem Covenant Church 1990-, Pianist & Choir Accompanist; *office:* First Assembly Christian Acad 30 Tyler Prentice Rd Worcester MA 01605

FREECE, ERIC W., Fifth Grade Teacher; *b:* Findlay, OH; *m:* Debbie Cannon; *c:* Ian C., Katelyn A.; *ed:* OH St Univ (BA) Elem Ed 1972, (MA) Elem Ed & Early Chldhd Ed 1976; *cr:* Worthington City Schls Elem Tchr 1972-; *ai:* Sci Curr Revision Comm; Supt Advy Cncl; Comp Comm; Mentor Pgm Adv; Peer Mediation Comm; NEA, OEA, WEA 1975-; OH Cncl of Elem Schl Tchrs 1975-; Biofeedback Soc of Amer & OH 1976-90; OCESS & SECO 1990-, Bd of Dir, Pres; N Columbus IM League Coach 1987-; Amer Heart Assn, Vol; US Dept Ed Excl in Ed Awd 1985-86; Keep Franklin Cty Beautiful Grant 1994-95; Articles Pub; *office:* Worthington Hills Elem Schl 1221 Candlewood Dr Worthington OH 43235

FREED, VIRGINIA KELLY, Asst Prof & Academic Dev Dir; *b:* Springfield, MA; *m:* Larry A.; *c:* Meghan; *ed:* Amer Intnl Coll (BA) Eng 1968; Westfield St Coll (MED) Ed 1978; 25 Addl Hrs Eng Trinity Coll; *cr:* E Longmeadow HS Eng Tchr 1968-75; Bay Path Coll Asst Prof, Acad Cnslr 1984-; *ai:* Frosh Class, Fac Adv; Reaccreditation Subcomm Chair; Fac Club Co-Chair; Intnl Stu Mentor; NCTE 1970-; NACADA 1992-; CHLA 1993-; Carew Hill Girls Club 1995-, Bd; Mile Tree Schl Cncl 1995-, Comm Liaison; Wilbraham Republican Town Comm 1980-; Wilbraham Schl Comm 1981-84, Vice Chair 3 Yrs, Chair 1 Yr; *office:* Bay Path Coll 588 Longmeadow St Longmeadow MA 01106*

FREED-FAGAN, ELISE, Assistant Professor; *b:* Philadelphia, PA; *m:* Stan Fagan; *c:* Joshua Fagan, Alana Fagan; *ed:* OH St Univ (BS) Psych 1972; Temple Univ (MED) Group & Organizational Process 1977, (PHD) Group & Organizational Process 1984; *cr:* Freed-Fagan Assoc Dir 1985-; Family Planning Cncl Trainer, Consultant 1987-89; Comm Coll Philadelp0hia Asst Prof 1989-; *ai:* Organizational Consultant to Soc Svc Agencies; Dept of Mental Hlth & Soc Sci; Wrote Stages of Change Manual for CDC; *office:* Community Coll of Philadelphia 1700 Spring Garden St Philadelphia PA 19130

FREEDMAN, DAVID BRIAN, Sixth Grade Teacher; *b:* Cleveland, OH; *ed:* Univ of CO (BS) Elem Ed 1981; Bates Coll Psych; 18 Addl Hrs; *cr:* Conway Elem Schl Chapter I Instr 1982-84, 5-6 Grd Tchr 1984-85, 6 Grd Tchr 1985-; *ai:* Peer Leadership Adv; Northeast Regnl Ctr of Drug Free Schls, Comm Trainer; Substance Abuse Prevention Prgm; Jr Ski Pgm; Crss Cntry Coord; Rotary Spon Visitation to Finland; *office:* Conway Elem Schl Main St Conway NH 03818*

FREEDMAN, MARTIN, Professor of Accounting; *b:* New York, NY; *m:* Ora Levin; *c:* Danna, Gili; *ed:* SUNY at Buffalo (BS) Acctng 1969; Univ of PA (MS) Acctng 1970; Univ of IL (PHD) Acctng 1975; *cr:* Branch Coll Asst Prof 1978; Binghampton Univ Asst Assoc Full Prof 1978-; Hebrew Univ Fulbright Lecturer 1985-86; Technion in Israel Lady Davis Pvt 1992-93; *ai:* Amer Acctng Assoc 1974-; UUP 1978-; HYPKG 1988-; Co-Authored Book; Numerous Articles Pub; Received 3 Grants; 2 Flwshps; 2 Outstdng Tchng Awds; *office:* S U N Y At Binghamton Schl of Mgmt Binghamton NY 13902

FREEDMAN, MATTHEW R., Tech Arts Dept Chair & Tchr; *b:* Cleveland, OH; *ed:* Miami Univ (BS) Scndry Math Ed 1988; Univ of Pittsburg (MED) Math Ed 1996; *cr:* Steubenville City Schls Tchr 1988-, Tech Arts Dept Chair 1993-, Adult Ed 1991-94; Carnegie Science Ctr Sci Prgrms Presenter 1994-; *ai:* NCTM, NEA 1988-; *home:* 3266 Ward St Apt 6 Pittsburgh PA 15213

FREEDMAN, MICHAEL PAUL, Science Department Head; *b:* Philadelphia, PA; *m:* Marsha J.; *c:* Deena, Juliet; *ed:* Penn St Univ (BS) Sci 1965; Temple Univ (MED) Sci Ed 1972, (DED) Sci Ed 1995; *cr:* Northeast HS Tchr 1965-80; University City HS Dept Head 1980-82; Olney HS Dept Head 1982-92; GWCHSES Dept Head 1992-94; South Philadelphia HS Dept Head 1994-; *ai:* Phi Delta Kappa; NSELA; *home:* 92 Misty Meadow Dr Richboro PA 18954

FREEH, JOHN, Secondary Computer Specialist; *b:* Phillipsburg, NJ; *m:* Diane; *c:* Anthony, Matthew; *ed:* Trenton St Coll (BA) Sci Ed 1970; LeHigh Univ (MS) Educl Tech 1989; Math Courses Muhlenber Math Work Churchmans Bus Coll; Post Grad Work in Sci Ed *cr:* Hillsboro Schl Dist Math, Sci Tchr 1970-73; Franklin Tw Math Tchr 1973-85; Bethlehem Area Schl Dist Math, Sci Tc Cmptr Specialist 1994-; Allentown Coll Math, Cmptr Sci Le 1994-; *ai:* NEA 1970-; PSEA, Bethlehem Ed Assn 1985-; Chu & Acts 1992-, Team Ldr; Tech Ed Grant Natl Assn for Advance & Bell Atlantic Co; *office:* Bethlehem Area Schl Dist 104 E El Bethlehem PA 18017*

FREELING, ANNE D., English Teacher; *b:* Waterville, ME; E.; *c:* Scott Pasco, Andrea Marcoux, Jennifer Wilson, Matthew Univ of Southern ME (BS) Ed 1972; Univ of ME (MA) E Waterville HS Eng Tchr 1976-; *ai:* Screening & Curr Comms; & WTA 1976-; *office:* Waterville Sr HS 1 Brooklyn Ave Wa 04901*

FREELING, THOMAS ELTON, English Teacher; *b:* Chica Anne Delia Doucette; *c:* Kristin, Elisa; *ed:* Lawrence Coll (BA Univ of IL (MA) Linguistics 1968; Univ of ME (CAS) Ed 1993; Grove Schls Lang Arts Tchr 1963-68; Amer Comm Schl Eng I Head 1968-73; Waterville Schls Eng Instr & Dept Head 1973- 1973-; NCTE 1973-; MCELA 1973-; *office:* Waterville Sr HS Ave Waterville ME 04901

FREEMAN, CAROL L., Math Dept Chair; *b:* Connersville, James; *ed:* St Louis Univ (MS) Math 1968, (PHD) Statistica Math Ed 1982; Inst for Retraining Cmptr Sci 1987-89; *cr:* Font Prof, Chair 1968-89; NE Wesleyan Prof, Chair 1989-93; Fi Comm Coll Assoc Prof 1993-; *ai:* MAA 1986-; NCTM 19 Epsilon, Sigma Xi 1964-; Math Reform Curr Grants; Endov Numerous Math Ed, Tchng Math Presentations, Wkshps; off Lakes Comm Coll 4355 Lake Shore Dr Canandaigua NY 1442

FREEMAN, CYNTHIA ANN, Fifth Grade Teacher; *b:* Nelso *m:* Bret D.; *c:* Jacob; *ed:* Wilmington Coll (BS) Elem Ed, Spe OH Univ (MS) Elem Ed 1990; *cr:* Bloom-Carroll Jr HS SLD Tc Carroll Elem Schl Fifth Grd Tchr 1987-; Bloom Carroll Schls Su Dir 1986; *ai:* Outdoor Ed Coord; Spelling Bee Coord 1987 Chrldng Adv 1986-88; Lancaster Montessori Schl 1992-93, *office:* Carroll Elem 69 S Beaver St Carroll OH 43112*

FREEMAN, DORIS PATRICIA, Middle School Mathemati Baltimore, MD; *m:* Calvin; *c:* Dena, Quinton; *ed:* Morgan St Un 1969; John Hopkins Univ (MAS) Admin 1984; 15 Credit Hr Math Coppins St Coll; *cr:* Leith Walk Elem Tchr 1969-74; Intermediate Schl Tchr 1986-92; Hamilton MS Tchr 1992- Improvement Team; Natl Acad League Coach; Attendance C Poster Comm Spon; AFT, Baltimore Tchrs Union 1969-.*

FREEMAN, EVE, Speech Language Pathologist; *b:* Metuche David; *ed:* Douglas Coll (BA) Speech Pathology 1980; Kean Speech Pathology 1981; NJ Licensure; Cert of Clinical Comp South Amboy Bd of Ed Speech Lang Pathologist 1980-; *ai:* NJ & NJSHLA 1980-.*

FREEMAN, JEAN PERROTT, Global Stud & Psycholog Brooklyn, NY; *m:* Peter James; *ed:* St Univ of NY Coll at Os Scndry Ed, Soc Stud 1967 Hofstra Univ (MA) Scndry Ed 197 Grad Credits; *cr:* Sachem Schl Dist 6th Grd Tchr 1967-68; Wes Dist Scndry Soc Stud Tchr 1968-; *ai:* AFT, NYSUT 1967-; W Old South Islip Civil Assn 1978-; Historical Soc of Islip Ha House Tour Comm; Seatuck Fnd 1992-; Islip Arts Cncl; *office:* Sr HS 1 Lions Path West Islip NY 11795

FREEMAN, ROSALEE CALEMINE, Reading & English T Keyser, WV; *m:* Ronald Allan; *c:* Melanie Raye; *ed:* Potomac St Pre-Ed 1966; WV Univ (BS) Elem Ed 1968, (MA) Rdng 1969; Hrs; *cr:* Washington MS 7th & 8th Grd Rdng Tchr 1970-74; C K-3rd Grd Resource Room Tchr 1974-77; Broad Ford Elem 3rd Resource Room Tchr 1977-80; 6th Grd Tchr 1980-81; Bruce Mi 7th & 8th Grd Rdng & Eng Tchr 1981-87; Westmor MS 7th G Eng Tchr 1987-; *ai:* Project Basic Rdng Consultant; Stu Svc Ad & Gift Comm; ACTA 1970-; NEA 1970-; MSTA 1970-; TOPS Pres.

FREEMAN, SUSAN NICOLE, Fourth Grade Teacher; *b:* Newa 18 Credits Thistle Critical Thinking at Montclair St Coll; *cr:* Schl Fourth Grd Elem Tchr 1985-; *ai:* Trinity United Meth Chu Pastor Parish Relations, Chprsn; Leslie St 300 Block Assn 199 Mount Vernon Elem Schl 142 Mount Vernon Pl Newark NJ 071

FREER, KATHIE J., French Teacher; *b:* Columbus, OH; *m:* Emma, Christian; *ed:* OH St Univ (BA) Fr, Inter Bus 1987, (MA Cleveland St Univ Tchr Cert 1991; 30 Hrs Span; 2 Sem Hrs Intern Works; *cr:* OH St Univ Fr Tchng Asst 1987-89; Spokane Com Tchr 1990; Aurora HS Fr Tchr 1991-; *ai:* Soph Class Adv; D OFLA, NEO 1991-; ACTFL 1994-; *office:* Aurora HS W Pioneer OH 44202*

FREER, RONI JO, Professional Office Technology; *b:* Harris *ed:* Central MI Univ (BSEd) Bus Ed 1961; Western MI Univ (M 1966; Post Grad Work Univ of WI at Eau Claire, univ of CO, U SUNY at Albany, SUNY at New Paltz; *cr:* HS Tchr 1961-65; Coll of Bus Instr 1965-66; Kellogg Comm Coll Instr 1966-68; O Comm Coll Prof 1968-; Orange Cty Comm Coll Asst to VP Ac 1995-; *ai:* Asst to VP of Acad Affairs; NYEA, NEA 1968-; OCCC 1968-95 Pres, VP, Sec; ARMA, Inc, Mid-Hudson Chapter 1989-, Treas; OCCC Staff & Chm Assn 1995-; Bus Ed Assoc of Mi 1968-, Pres; OT, SE SUNY, CUNY Univ Women 1975-, VP; Counsel SARA 1991-, Vice Chair; ARMA Mem of Yr 198 Governance System, Pres 1990-95; *office:* Orange County Comm 115 South St Middletown NY 10940

FREESE, MATHIAS BALOGH, Retired English Teacher; *b:* NY; *m:* Rochelle; *c:* Caryn, Brett, Jordan; *ed:* Queens Coll (BA) (MSEd) Ed 1966; SUNY at Stony Brook (MSW) Soc Work 19 Island Inst-Mental Hlth-Psychoanalytic Inst; Hofstra Univ 20 Credits; *cr:* Edgar D. Shimer JHS Soc Stud Tchr 1962-63; Elm HS Soc Stud Tchr 1963-69; Bd of Cooperative Educl Curricul 1969-72; Hauppauge HS Eng Tchr 1972-74; Half Hollow Hills Tchr 1974-; Book Rvwr; *ai:* NASW 1978-; AFT 1977-; The Auth 1994-; Listed: Intnl Authors, Writers Who's Who 1993, Director Poets, Fiction Writers 1994, Distinctive Short Stories 1974, B Short Stories 1975; Short Story Writer; John Warkentin Awar Spiritual Jrnl.*

FREESE, MICHAEL EDWARD, Math & Computer Tea Brooklyn, NY; *ed:* Manhattan Coll (BS) Acctng 1989; *cr:* C Lybrand Auditor 1989-90; Tchrs Insurance Accountant 1990- Peters Boys HS Tchr 1994-; *ai:* Forensics & Pub Speaking Mode

FREGOSI, MARY HELEN, History Teacher; *b:* Proctor, VT; *ed.* VT (BS) His 1966, (MA) Renaissance His 1969; Castleton St C Educl Admin 1978, (CAGS) Curr & Supervision 1984; Fulbrig Univ of Florence in Italy; Univ of ME at Orono 6 Addl Credits; Joseph the Provider 3 Addl Credits; *cr:* Proctor HS Tchr 1969; R HS Tchr & Admin 1969-; *ai:* Schl Newspaper Adv; Fulbright Schl r 1986; Pub NASSP Bulletin; *office:* Rutland Sr HS 65 Library nd VT 05701

RGER, STEVEN Z., Social Studies Supervisor; *b:* Brooklyn, eronica George; *c:* Ashley, Joshua; *ed:* Pace Univ (BA) Soc Sci 71; WV Univ (MA) His 1974; Rutgers Univ (PHD) His 1990; Hebrew Univ 18 Credits in Psych & Scndry Admin; *cr:* WV Univ 2-74; Woodbridge Sr HS Soc Stud Tchr 1974-80; Columiba HS Tchr 1980-81; Chatham HS Soc Stud Tchr 1981-91; Coll of St Assoc His Prof 1983-; Franklin Pierce Coll Assoc His Prof Chatham HS Soc Stud Supvr 1992-; *ai:* Model United Nations, Club; Soc of Amer Diplomatic Historians 1990-; Amer Historical 3-; Org of Amer Historians 1990-; Natl Cncl for Soc Stud 1980-; Fellowship 1984; NJ St Govenors Tchng Awd 1992; Outstanding ince William Cty 1979; Books: Dawn Over Suez & Money Mgmt; atham HS 255 Lafayette Ave Chatham NJ 07928*

Y, MARK S., Telecommunications Teacher; *b:* Darby, PA; *ed:* (BSC) Comm 1983; *cr:* Newark HS Telecommunications Tchr *i:* Fine Arts Dept Chm; Audio-Visual Dir; Restructuring, ative Discipline, Bldg Utilization, Renovation Comms; unications Club Adv; Brookside Lions Club 1996; Natl Video Judge NSPRA 1989-92; *office:* Newark HS E Delaware Ave DE 19711

, AUDREY WERNER, Dental Hygiene Professor; *b:* Brooklyn, tto A.; *c:* David, Scott; *ed:* Columbia Univ Schl of Dental & Oral (BS) Dental Hygiene 1962; Columbia Univ Tchrs Coll (MS) Ed 1964; Montclair St Univ (MA) Hlth Ed 1994; *cr:* Columbia l of Dental & Oral Surgery Instr 1962-66; Bergen Cty Coll Adj 5; Middlesex Cty Coll Asst Prof 1986-; *ai:* Middlesex Cty Coll Divisional Cncl Treas; NJ Hlth Ed Cncl; Amer Dental Hygienists 52-; Columbia Univ Dental Hygienists Assn 1962-, Exec Bd Treas 1962-65; Assn of Dental Alumni Columbia Univ; AFT; Soc Hlth Prof 1994-; Phi Kappa Phi Life Mem; Acad Achvmt Awd ma Phi Alpha; F. J. Swanson Gold Medal.

LD, HOWARD GEORGE, Chemistry Teacher; *b:* New York, NY; ly Brenda Scher; *ed:* Queens Coll (BA) Chem 1968; Hunter Coll em 1971; *cr:* Andrew Jackson HS Chem Tchr 1968-95; New Dorp -; *ai:* NHS Adv; NY City Sci Fairs Judge; Selection Comm Sci ersn; New Tchr Mentor; CSIP Comm; Writing, Critical Thinking orough Inst; Phys Sci Prgm Specialist; NY Chem Tchrs Club c, Treas, VP; AFT, UFT, Amer Chemical Soc 1968-; Past Phys Sci ord; York Coll Recognition Cert; Conducted Sci Tchr Colleagues Sci Software Project Liaison; Dev Chem Advanced Placement urse; York Coll Project Leadership Distinction Cert; Woodrow ellowship; Wrote Chem Exam Questions NY St Ed Dept; *office:* p HS 465 New Dorp Ln Staten Island NY 10306*

UER, JACQUELINE LINDA, English Teacher; *b:* New York *m:* Richard; *c:* Stacey, Scott; *ed:* Seton Hall Univ (MA) Ed 1995; Paterson, Fairleigh Dickinson, Univ of MA Credits; *cr:* Rockland Tchr 1968-69; Savannah HS Eng Tchr 1969-71; Copeland MS Eng 1-72; Dover HS Eng Tchr 1978-79; Roxbury HS Eng Tchr 1979-; spaper, Class Adv; Tennis Coach; NJEA 1978-; NCTE 1985-; d Assn, ASCD 1993-; Pub 2 Texts Oceana Publication; Tchr of Yr *ice:* Roxbury HS 1 Bryant Dr Succasunna NJ 07876*

LLER, JANE, Asst Professor of Philosophy; *b:* Philadelphia, PA; C. Connolly; *ed:* Boston Coll (PHD) Philosophy 1993; *cr:* Boston ow Tchng 1988-93; Univ of MA Asst Prof 1993-; *ai:* General Ed Cncl on Diversity, Pluralism; Asian Stud Project; NEA 1993-; Pub; Boston Coll Excl in Tchng Awd 1990, 1992; *office:* Univ Of owell Dept of Philosophy 1 University Ave Lowell MA 01854

HLAG, JOHN MICHAEL, Military Science Instructor; *b:* Falls, NY; *m:* Nancy Parker; *c:* Kurt M., Grant R.; *ed:* Central TX) General Stud 1992; Niagara Univ (BS) Commerce Mgmt 1996; ns, Intel, Light Ldrs Course; Grad Northern Warfare, ANCOC; PLDC; Jungle Warfare Grad Road Test Examiner, Master Driver; ewart Ranger Tow, Sec Leader 1978-81; Berlin Brigade Scout gt 1981-86; Fort Drum Plt, Opns Sgt 1986-93; Niagara Univ Sr str, Army ROTC 1993-; *ai:* Scabbard & Blade Honor Soc, ng Club Adv; Continuing Ed Counseling; Niagara Cty 4-H 1970-, r; Wilson Youth Bsbl 1994-, Coach Asst; Church Eumc 1994-, Officer; Continuing Ed Svc Awd Ft Drum; Airborne & Ranger Tabs ultinational Forces & Observers Egypt; *office:* Niagara Univ PO 4 Niagara University NY 14109

ALD, JOSEPH A., Professor of Mathematics; *b:* Mc Keesport, PA; Clark; *c:* Amy, Christopher; *ed:* Millersville Univ (BS) Ed 1966, Math 1970; Villanova Univ 24 Grad Credits Applied Sci; Beaver rad Credits; *cr:* Columbia Borough Schl Dist 7th Grd Math Tchr , Lancaster City Schl Dist Sr HS Math Tchr 1967-70; Montgomery m Coll Math Prof 1970-; *ai:* Dev Stud Comm; AFT 1982-, Pres A St Math Assn of Two Yr Colls 1973-; Spec Olympics 1985-, oach 1995-.*

H, BARBARA JEAN, ESOL Teacher; *b:* Houston, TX; *m:* Russell *ed:* Southwest TX St Univ (BS) Eng 1972; San Francisco St Univ g as Second Lang 1983; Univ of MD Spec Ed, Rdng Classes; Cty Testing, Evaluation, Progressive Writing; Western MD Coll tive Learning, Verbal Skills; *cr:* La Sara Schl Tchr 1972-73; Peace chr 1973-75; Danville HS Eng Tchr 1975-81; Prince George Cty OL Tchr 1985-; *ai:* Dept Chair; Soc Comm; Prof Needs Task Force; 1985-; WATESOL 1986-; Univ Lit Journal, P. G. Cty Lit Journal Multicultural Lit Jornal Connections Story; *office:* Kenmoor MS nmoor Dr Hyattsville MD 20785*

H, DAVID A., Guidance Counselor; *b:* Greenfield, MA; *m:* Wendy Sarah, Caleb, Todd Seaman, Jessica Seaman; *ed:* Bridgewater St SEd) Earth Sci 1966; Univ of MA at Amherst (MED) Guidance & ing 1973; Facilitator Trng for Northeast Regnl Ctr for Drug Free Communities; *cr:* Dag Hammarsfjold Jr HS Sci Tchr 1966-67; nsett Regnl HS Sci Tchr 1967-69; Turners Falls Jr HS Sci Tchr ; Barnstable MS Sci Tchr 1973-85; Barnstable HS Guidance Cnslr Leadership Adv 1985-93; Nauset Regnl HS Guidance Cnslr 1993-; r Leadership Adv; Peer Leadership Transition Wkshp Dir; Stu ace Team Mem; Cape & Islands Guidance Assn 1985-, VP 1995, 95-, Guidance Cnslr Of Yr 1992-93; MA Schl Cnslrs Assn; Cape ch, Advy Cncl 1993-95; Words Not Weapons Grant 1995; Peer hip Consultant Wellesley & Hudson MA; Participant on Television eer Prgms with Paraclete Television; *office:* Nauset Regional HS d North Eastham MA 02651*

H, DEBORAH ANN (DU PHILY), Fourth Grade Teacher; *b:* rg, MA; *m:* Stephen; *c:* Amber, Michael; *ed:* Fitchburg St Coll (BA) d 1977; *cr:* St Joseph Schl Tchr 19 Yrs; *ai:* NCEA 1978-; St Joseph 4 Yrs; *home:* 18 Carter Rd Westminster MA 01473

H, GILEEN WIDMER, Fifth Grade Teacher; *b:* Buffalo, NY; *m:* n J.; *ed:* SUC at Fredonia 1963; SUC at Oswego (BS) Sci 1965; L St Univ, Long Island Univ, SUC at Buffalo; *cr:* Wilson Cntrl Schl Grd Tchr 1965-68; Huth Road Elem Schl 1st-5th Grd Tchr 1968-; g Arts, NYS Sci, Soc Stud Curr; Enrichment Chm; Grand Is Tchrs, 1968-; PTA 1968-, Sec, VP, Cncl Del, NYS Life Mem; *office:* Huth lem Schl 1773 Huth Rd Grand Island NY 14072

FRENCH, LENNY SUE MAYNE, Jr-Sr HS Music Teacher; *b:* Norwich, NY; *m:* Matthew S.; *c:* Lane Matthew; *ed:* Crane Schl of Music (BM) Piano, Voice Ed 1989; SUNY at Potsdam (MS) Elem Ed 1993; *cr:* Salmon-River Cntrl Schl Scndry Vocal Music Tchr 1989-; *ai:* Select Choir; Drama Club; Private Lessons; NYSSMA, MENC, NYSUT 1989-; SAI 1988-; Cantus Singers 1993-, Dir; *office:* Salmon River Central Schl Bombay Rd Fort Covington NY 12937

FRENCH, MARY PENKETH, English Department Chair; *b:* Chicago, IL; *c:* Ross, Claudia, John, David, Andrew; *ed:* Jacksonville Univ (BA); Villanova Univ (MA); 75 Addl Credit Hrs; *cr:* Inglewood HS Tchr 1960-63; Downingtown HS Tchr 1963-, Dept Chair 1982-; *ai:* NEA & ASCD 1980-; Theatre Arts Assn of PA 1993-; Peoples Light & Theatre Co Project Discovery Bd 1991-.*

FRENCH, ROBIN JON, Fourth Grade Teacher; *b:* Lewistown, PA; *ed:* Eastern Mennonite Coll (BS) Early Chldhd Ed 1984; Attnd Tuscarora Intermediate Unit 11, Shippensburg Univ, Penn St Univ, Wilkes Univ, Allentown Coll 28 Credit Hrs; Working on Masters Equivalency; *cr:* Lewis Cty Head Start Spec Ed Asst 1984-85; Belleville Mennonite Schl 2nd Grd Tchr 1985-92, 4th Grd Tchr 1992-; *ai:* Drama Dir; Sci Fair & Talent Show Comm; IRA 1995-; *office:* Belleville Mennonite Schl 4105 Front Mountain Rd Belleville PA 17004

FRENZILLI, ROCCO JOSEPH,III, Physical Education Teacher; *b:* Portland, ME; *m:* Katherine Marie Mercier; *ed:* Niagara Univ (BA) His 1970; Univ of So ME (BS) Sci 1973; US Sports Acad (MSS) Fitness Ed 1985; *cr:* St Mary's Schl Tchr 1973-75; King MS Sci Tchr 1975-92; Portland HS PE Tchr 1992-; *ai:* Co-Adv Project Grad; Var Girls Soccer, Frosh Girls Sftbl Coach; NEA 1975-; Italian Heritage 1996; Russell Chair Awd 1995; Article Pub; Coord ME Spec Olympics Fundraisers; *office:* Portland HS 284 Cumberland Ave Portland ME 04101

FRESCURA, F. DANIEL, English, German & Video Tchr; *b:* Pittsburgh, PA; *m:* Deborah A. Rebitch; *c:* Christina, Daniel P.; *ed:* Indiana Univ of PA (BS) Ed 1971; Attnd Karl-Ruprecht Univ Heidelberg Germany 1 Yr, Seton Hall Coll Theology; *cr:* Penn Trafford Schl Dist Eng, Ger, Video Tchr, Past GATE Coord 1971-; *ai:* Video Coach; NEA, PSEA, PTEA 1971-; SWPASCD 1986-; Cursillo Movement 1979-, Lay Dir; Articles Pub Ultreyo Magazine; Past Nom PA St Tchr of Yr; *office:* Penn Trafford HS PO Box 530 Harrison City PA 15636*

FRESE, AMERICO PETER, US History Teacher; *b:* Albany, NY; *m:* Beth Ann Tierney; *c:* Christian; *ed:* Hudson Vly Comm Coll (AA) Lbrl Arts 1990; Univ at Albany (BA) His 1993; 16 Credit Hrs Towards Masters; *cr:* Shaker HS Permanent Sub Tchr 1993; Maple Hill HS Scndry Soc Stud Tchr 1993-; *ai:* Jr Class Adv; Var Bsbl Coach; Dist Planning Team Mem; Stu of the Month Comm; Capital Dist Cncl of Soc Stud 1993-, Bd Mem; *office:* Maple Hill HS 1216 Maple Hill Rd Castleton On Hudso NY 12033*

FRESE, DONALD L., Health Teacher; *b:* Boston, MA; *c:* Lisa, Brian, Jeffrey, Laura; *ed:* Springfield Coll (BS) PE & Hlth 1961; OH Univ (MS) PE & Hlth 1967; Attnd Lehman Coll; *cr:* Hackley Schl Sci Tchr & Asst AD 1961-65; OH Univ PE Tchr 1966-67; Valhalla HS Sci Tchr 1967-70; Mahopac HS Hlth Tchr 1970-; *ai:* Discipline Comm; Blood Drive; AFT 1967-; MTA 1970-, Rep; NYSHPCA 1970-; Town of Carmel Environment Bd 1970-, Chm; Westchester-Putnam Hlth Tchr of the Yr 1975; *home:* 21 Cheryl Ct Mahopac NY 10541*

FREY, CECILE PARRIS, Supvr of Gifted Support Prgm; *b:* Philadelphia, PA; *m:* Frederick Ward; *c:* Bradley Remick, Lauren Remick Martone; *ed:* Univ of PA (AB) Pol Sci 1959, (MS) Cnclng 1962,(EDD) His of Ed 1975; Supervisory Cert Soc Stud K-12 1990; *cr:* PA Schl Dist HS Eng Tchr 1959-62; Rosemont Coll Lecturer in Ed 1973,Lower Merion Schl Dist Tcr of Gifted 1976-87, Coord of Gifted 1987-90, Supv of Gifted 1990-; *ai:* Acad Decathlon Spon; Natl Assn of Gifted; CEC; PA Assn for Gifted Ed, Tchr of Yr 1991; Articles Pub; Book Reviews; Presentations; *office:* Lower Merion Schl Dist 301 Montgomery Ave Ardmore PA 19003*

FREY, FRANCES ANNE, Earth Science Teacher; *b:* Buffalo, NY; *m:* John Walter II; *c:* Elizabeth, Lisa; *ed:* St Bonaventure Univ (BS) El Ed 1974; St Univ Coll at Buff (MSEd) Ed 1978; 40 Hrs Sci, Hlth; *cr:* St Bernadette's Schl Mid Grds Sci Tchr 1976-78; Mount Mercy Acad Sci, Hlth Tchr 1984-89; SS Peter & Paul Schl 4th Grd Tchr 1989-91; Southwestern HS Earth Sci Tchr 1991-; *ai:* 1997 Class, Envirothon Competition Adv; Help Sftbl Girls Team; NEA 1991-; STANYS 1992-; Natl Women in Sci 1986-; Canisius Coll Grant Natl Sci Fnd 2 Yrs; Called Bio Instr Guild, Partners Ed; *office:* Southwestern HS 600 Hunt Rd Jamestown NY 14701

FREY, GARY MICHAEL, Chemistry Teacher; *b:* Canton, OH; *ed:* OH St Univ (BS) Forestry 1974; Bowling Green St Univ (MS) Botany 1977; 45 Credit Hrs Beyond MS; *cr:* St of OH Div of Parks Naturalist 1975-77; Zanesville HS Chem & Bio Tchr 1977-; Muskingum Tech Coll Bio Instr 1988-95; *ai:* Zanesville Ed Assn Pres; Jennings Scholar 1985-, Honorarium; Phi Delta Kappa 1986-, Honorary Mem; Rotary Intnl Outstdng Tchr Awd 1995; *office:* Zanesville HS 1701 Blue Ave Zanesville OH 43701

FREY, JOAN ACKERMAN, Kindergarten Teacher; *b:* Bucyrus, OH; *m:* Wallace Frederick; *c:* Kip, Dan, Shelley Drobnick, Sue Johnson; *ed:* OH St Univ (BS) Elem Ed 1974; *cr:* Prairie Norton 5th Grd Tchr 1968-69, Kndgtn Tchr 1969-73; Prairie Lincoln Kndgtn Tchr 1974-92; Harmon Elem Extended Day Kndgtn Tchr 1992-95; Darby Woods Elem Tchr 1995-; *ai:* Bldg Curr, Kndgtn Entrance Comms; NEA; OEA; SWEA; PTSA; Phi Delta Kappa; Alpha Delta Kappa; Darby Woods Core Team 1995; Nom OH Otstndng Edctr 1991; Selected Intrn OSO 1990; SWCS Tchr of Yr Finalist 1991, Ambassador Awd, Numerous Bell Awds; Selected to Receive Intern for OSU 1990; *home:* 6666 Spicewood Ct Columbus OH 43228

FREY, KAREN TRIMMER, Learning Support Teacher; *b:* Easton, PA; *m:* Jack; *c:* Kristen, Lauren; *ed:* Trenton St Coll (BS) Spec Ed 1976; Grad Stud Humanistic Ed, Comm Intervention-Drug & Alcohol; *cr:* Colonial Northampton Intermediate Unit #20 Tchr 1976-; *ai:* Nazareth Schl Dist GATEWAYS Team; Shafer Schl Lang Arts Team; PSEA, NEA 1976-; Tchr of Yr 1992-93; *office:* Colonial Nrthmptn IU #20 Schl 49 N Liberty St Nazareth PA 18064*

FREY, KIMBERLY HAU, 5th Grade Teacher; *b:* Parma, OH; *m:* Thomas; *ed:* Cleveland St Univ (BA) Elem Ed 1989; Baldwin Wallace (MED) Spec Ed 1994; *cr:* Thoreau Park Elem Schl 5th Grd Tchr 1989-; *ai:* Stu Cncl; NEA, PEA 1989-; *office:* Thoreau Park Elem Schl 5401 W 54th St Parma OH 44129*

FREY, LEE E., Psychology & Amer His Teacher; *b:* Pittsburgh, PA; *m:* Laura Farmer; *c:* Julie, Laura, Louise; *ed:* Heidelberg Coll (BA) Soc Stud 1971; St John's 30 Hrs; Youngstown St 9 Hrs; Walsh Coll 9 Hrs; *cr:* Franklin Jr HS Tchr, Coach 1971-74; Canfield HS Tchr, Coach 1974-; *ai:* Head Coach Boys Soccer, Girls Sftbl; Canfield City Cncl 1990-, Councilman, Pres 1992-; Canfield Ed Assn 1974-, Pres 1996; NEA, OH EA 1971-; Montivational Speaker 1980-; Canfield Historical Soc 1985-; Bethel Luth Church 1976-, Cncl 1982-88; Soccer Coach of Yr Akron; Soccer Coach of Yr Div I Youngstown 1995; *office:* Canfield HS 100 Cardinal Dr Canfield OH 44406*

FREY, RO MC GOVERN, Instructional Support Teacher; *b:* Philadelphia, PA; *c:* Shawn, Michael; *ed:* Temple Univ (BS) Elem Ed 1972; Wilkes Univ (MS) Ed Dev, Strategies 1992; East Stroudsburg Univ (MS) Elem Ed 1995; Prins Cert; *cr:* Phila Pub Schl Dist 5th Grd Tchr 1972-73; St Joan of Arc Schl 4-8th Grd Tchr 1973-78; Pleasant Vly Sch Dist 4th Grd Tchr 1985-92, Instrl Support Tchr 1992-; *ai:* Dist Strategic Planning Exec Comm; ASCD; PSEA, Pleasant Vly Ed Assn 1984-; *home:* PO Box 262 Blakeslee PA 18610*

FREY, RUTH LAZETTA, History Teacher; *b:* Baltimore, MD; *ed:* Goucher Coll (AB) Amer Stud 1966; Columbia Univ (MA) His 1968; Tchrs Coll His, Soc Stud Prof Diploma 1968; Johns Hopkins Univ MLA Prgm; *cr:* Overlea HS His Tchr 1968-83; Pikesville HS His Tchr 1983-; *ai:* Natl His Day; Fac Cncl Chair; NEA, MD St Tchrs Assn, Tchrs Assn of Baltimore Cty, Amer Historical Assn 1968-; Soc for His Ed 1986-; Org of Amer Historians 1968-75, 1996-; Phi Beta Kappa; Kappa Delta Pi; US Combined Trng Assn 1972-; MD Combined Trng Assn 1972-, Sec, Newsletter Ed, Novice Champion 1983; US Dressage Fed; Amer Horse Shows Assn; Baltimore Cty Curr Wkshps 1971, 1977, 1991; *office:* Pikesville HS 7621 Labyrinth Rd Baltimore MD 21208

FREY, SHIRLEY N., Chemistry Teacher; *b:* Cincinnati, OH; *m:* Joseph V. Jr.; *c:* Kelley Kluener, Kimberly Anglin, J. Christopher; *ed:* Edgecliff Coll (BA) Chem & Math 1965; Coll of Mt St Joseph (MA) Ed 1985; Various Wkshps & Classes; *cr:* US Govt Chemist 1965-68; McAuley HS Tchr 1985-95; *ai:* NHS Adv; Sci Olympiad Coach; Retreat Team; ACS 1986-; NSTA 1988-; SECO 1988-; *office:* Mc Auley HS 6000 Oakwood Ave Cincinnati OH 45224

FREY, TIMOTHY CHARLES, US History & Government Tchr; *b:* Tupper Lake, NY; *ed:* St Univ of NY at Plattsburgh (BS) 7th-12th Grd Soc Sci 1987, (MS) Ed Admin 1990; *cr:* Moriah Cntrl Schl US His, Govt Tchr 1988-91; Onondaga Jr-Sr High US His, Govt Tchr 1991-; *ai:* Stu Cncl, Class of 1998 Fac Adv; Close Up Fnd Coord; AFT, Kappa Delta Pi 1988-; NCSS 1991-; Acad Advy Cncl, New Compact for Learning Dist Comm 1991-; *office:* Onondaga Jr-Sr HS 4479 S Onondaga Rd Nedrow NY 13120

FREYER, RICHARD ALBERT, Physics & Chemistry Teacher; *b:* Callicoon, NY; *m:* Robin Lee Fuchs; *c:* Jeffrey, Jill; *ed:* SUC at Cortland (BS) Secondary Chem 1970; Syracuse Univ (MSEd) Sci Ed 1971; 18 Post Grad Hrs; Physics Cert; *cr:* Voorheesville HS Sci Tchr 1971-; *ai:* Fac Consul Honor Soc; Evaluation Comm; NYSUT, AFT 1971-, Bldg Rep; Meth Church 1971-, Layleader; Vol Ambulance 1973-91, Bd; St Ed Dept Physics Consultant; *office:* Voorheesville Ctr Schl Dist Rt 85A Voorheesville NY 12186

FREYMAN, WILLIAM DAVID, Vocational Drafting Teacher; *b:* Baltimore, MD; *m:* Linda Oursler; *c:* Michael, Kara; *ed:* Univ of MD (BS) Industrial Art 1969, (MED) Ed 1973; *cr:* Belt Jr HS Ind Arts Tchr 1969-73; Southern Garrett HS Voc Drafting Tchr 1973-; *ai:* Asst Track Coach; Ski Activity Adv; NEA,MSTA 1969-; GCTA 1973-; Natl Ski Patrol 1969-, Ldr, Eastern Division Staff Mem 1985; Cert Patroller 1986, Yellow Merit Star 1985; BSA, Ass Scout Master; Miniphil Prgm Summer Camp; *office:* Southern Garrett HS 345 Oakland Dr Oakland MD 21550

FREY-MASON, PATRICIA, Math Dept Chairperson & Tchr; *b:* New York, NY; *ed:* D'Youville Coll (BA) Math 1970; SUNY at Buffalo (MED) Math Ed 1975, (SDA) Admin 1989; Post Grad Studies in Math Ed; *cr:* PS #43 Math Tchr 1970-77; Buffalo Acad for Visual & Performing Arts Math Dept Chprsn & Tchr 1977-; *ai:* Jr Class & Comp Club Adv; AP Coord; Makeup Designer Schl Productions; NEA 1973-; NCTM 1973-; AMTNYS 1985-, Dist Rep & ARC; Allentown Assn 1989-, Mem Bd of Dir; Woodrow Wilson Master Tchr; Book: Mathematics Applications and Connection courses 1, 2, 3; Numerous Articles Pub; Buffalo Tchr Ctr Conf Grant; *office:* Buffalo Acad Vsl/Perf Arts 333 Clinton St Buffalo NY 14204*

FRIANT, G. DAVID, English Teacher; *b:* Muncy, PA; *m:* Linda Pletcher; *ed:* Lock Haven Univ (BA) Hum, Eng 1972; Duquesne Univ (MA) Eng 1973; Wilkes Univ Cmptr Stud 6 Hrs; *cr:* Montoursville HS Eng Tchr 1973-; *ai:* Millbrook Playhouse Bd of Dirs 1978-, Sec; *office:* Montoursville Area Sr HS 100 N Arch St Montoursville PA 17754

FRICK, GARY WAYNE, Mathematics Teacher; *b:* Hagerstown, MD; *m:* Catherine Brion; *ed:* Univ of MD (MD) Math Ed; Frostburg St Univ (BS) Math 1973; *cr:* Charles Cty Comm Coll Part-Time Math Instr 1983-; *ai:* NHS Selection Comm; NEA 1973-; Ed Assoc of Charles Cty 1973-; MD Cncl Tchrs of Math 1973-; Southern MD Tennis Assn 1994-; Tennis Coach of Yr 1976, 1977 & 1983; Exemplary Tchr from Charles Cty Bd of Ed 1989.

FRICK, ROBERT GEORGE, 5th Grade Teacher; *b:* Philadelphia, PA; *m:* Kristina W.; *ed:* Shippensburg Univ (BS) Elem Ed 1971; Villanova Univ (MA) Cnslng 1974, (MA) Admin 1976; *cr:* Garrettford Elem Schl 4-6 Grd Tchr, Acting Prin 1971-; *office:* Garrettford Elem Schl Garrett & Burmont Rds Drexel Hill PA 19026

FRICKE, DAVID JOHN, Inst Music Teacher; *b:* Trenton, NJ; *m:* Rosanna Litchfield; *c:* David, Jessica, Christopher, Tarah-Marie; *ed:* Glassboro St Coll (BA) Music 1969; Attnd NYU Summer Ex, Rutger Jazz Extension Grad Courses, Rosanna Summer Jazz Music Cr; *cr:* Newark Bd of Ed Music Tchr 1965-, After Schl Yth Dev Prgm Tchr 1990-; City of Newark Drum & Bugel Corps Tchr 1990-; *ai:* Bsbl Little League Coach 1990-93; City of Newark Marching 100; Newark Tchrs Union 1969-; Amer Fed of Musicians Local #336, #802.

FRIDAY, MARJORIE ANGELA, Mathematics Teacher; *b:* Jamaica, West Indies; *m:* Brian Lester; *c:* Ikinlabi A., Ola J.M.; *ed:* Univ of West Indies (BS) Zoology 1973; Univ of Ibana (MS) Human Nutrition 1984; 30 Prof Ed Credits; 12 Credits Tchng Math Grds 5-10; 6 Credits Tchng of Rdng; *cr:* St Rose of Lima Schl Math, Sci Tchr 1987-88; Holy Rosary Schl Math, Rdng Tchr 1988-; *ai:* Educl Specialist Police Ath League; Eighth Grd Adv; Math Fair, Math Curr Coord; NCTM 1992-; Friends of Crofts; Hill & Kellits Assn 1991-, Asst Sec, Svc Awd; *office:* Holy Rosary Schl 180 Bainbridge St Brooklyn NY 11233

FRIDAY, SUSAN G., English Teacher; *b:* Cleveland, OH; *m:* Bernard J.; *c:* Keith Robert; *ed:* SUNY at Albany (BA) Eng 1968; Addl 15 Hrs Ed 1969-71; Russell Sage 17 Hrs Eng, Ed 1971-73; St Rose 6 Hrs Rdng 1993; *cr:* Saratoga Springs Jr HS Eng Tchr 1968-71; Local Schls Sub Tchr 1971-82; Hartford Cntrl Schl Eng Tchr 1983-; *ai:* Teach Equestrian Skills Handicapped Individuals; NYSTA 1968-; AHSA 1970-; AMHA 1968-; NYSSHA 1962-, Pres, Svc; NYSMHS 1968-, Yth Ldr; Certfd Equine Spec Olympics Coach; *home:* 22 Scout Rd Gansevoort NY 12831

FRIDY, JERE WAYNE, Director of Music; *b:* Lancaster, PA; *m:* Myrna P.; *c:* Donna F. Westlake, Scott W.; *ed:* Penn St Univ (BS) Music Ed 1958; West Chestern Univ (MM) Music Ed 1974; *cr:* Octorara Area Schl Dist Dir of Music 1963-; *ai:* PA St Ed Assn 1963-; MENC 1963-, St Band Chm; Phi Beta Mu 1965-, VP; Phi Mu Alpha 1955-; Natl Band Assn 1991- Penn; PA St Ed Assn 1963-; MENC 1963-, St Band Chm; Phi Beta Mu 1965-, VP; Phi Mu Alpha 1955-; Natl Band Assn 1991-; New Holland Band 1977-, Asst Musical Dir; Grand VA Military Band 1993-; Air Force Assn 1978-; Natl Guard Assn of US; Distngd Bandmaster of Amer 1976 First Chair of Amer; Outstdng Bandmaster Awd 1986 Phi Beta Mu; Retired Air Force Bandmaster Col 31 Yrs; *home:* 203 Winding Ln Kennett Square PA 19348

FRIED, ANDREW, Secondary English Teacher; *b:* Suffern, NY; *m:* Gigi Ragone-Fried; *c:* Jordan; *ed:* SUNY at Onconta (BA) Eng 1987; SUNY at New Paltz (MS) Eng 1992; *cr:* Eldred Cntrl Schl 7, 8, 10 Grd Tchr 1988-89; Chester Union Free Schl 7-8 Grd Writing, Eng Tchr 1989-91; Cornwall Cntrl HS 9, 11, 12 Grd Eng Tchr 1991-; *ai:* NCTE 1987-; AFT 1988-; *office:* Cornwall Central HS 122 Main St Cornwall NY 12518

FRIED, HARVEY S., English Teacher; *b:* Brooklyn, NY; *c:* Gregory; *ed:* Fairleigh Dickinson Univ (BA) Scndry Ed, Eng 1969, (MA) Eng Lit 197; Post-Grad Doctoral Stud Eng Linguistics NY Univ, New Schl Soc Rsrch;

H. B. StudiosDrama Stud; *cr:* Thomas Jefferson MS Eng Tchr 1987-91; Teaneck HS Eng, Jrnlsm Tchr 1969-86, Eng Tchr 1992-; *ai:* HS Tennis Coach; Yrbk Adv; Liason Jrnlsm Class, Comm Newspaper; Lighting DIr Play Productions; Mem Waiting for Godot Acting Ensemble; Instr Adult Ed Prgm SAT Preparation; ITEA, NEA, BCEA, NJEA 1969-; *office:* Teaneck HS 100 Elizabeth Ave Teaneck NJ 07666*

FRIED, LINDA JOYCE, Third Grade Teacher; *b:* Cleveland, OH; *ed:* OH St Univ (BA) Elem Ed 1968; Cleveland St Univ 32 Credit Hrs; *cr:* Eastwood Elem Schl Third Grd Tchr 1968-; *ai:* Stu Cncl Adv; Bldg Ldrshp Team; Soc Stud Curr Comm; NEA, OEA, WEA 1968-; Marth Holden Jennings Scholar; *office:* Eastwood Elem Schl 4050 Eastwood Ln Warrensville Heigh OH 44122

FRIED, PATRICIA HELEN (SMITH), Science Teacher; *b:* Ashland, PA; *m:* Mark A.; *c:* David S. Shoup, Elizabeth D. Shoup; *ed:* PA St Univ (BS) Scndry Ed 1973; Master's Equivalency 1976; Project-16 Biotechnology Cedar Crest Coll 1992-; Human Genetics, Bioethical Decision Making Ball St Univ 1991; *cr:* Whitehall HS Sci Tchr 1973-; *ai:* Tech Prep Comm; NEA, PSEA 1973-; PA Sci Tchrs Assn 1980-; *office:* Whitehall HS 3800 Mechanicsville Rd Whitehall PA 18052*

FRIEDBERG, ARTHUR LINCOLN, Professor of Economics; *b:* Kingston, NY; *m:* Jean Edwards; *c:* Melissa, Lisa; *ed:* Ulster Cty Comm coll (AA) Hum & Soc Sci 1965; St Univ of NY at Oneonta (BS) Scndry Soc Stud 1968, (MA) Ec 1970; St Univ of NY Coll of Tech; *cr:* Mohawk Valley Comm Coll Instr to Prof 1970-; *ai:* Promotions, Acad Advisement, Coll Competencies, Continuing Appointments, Coll Facilities & Acad Appeals Comms; Export Assistance; Fac Liaison; NYSUT, AFT 1970-; NY St Ec Assn 1975-; Mohawk Valley World Trade Cncl 1983-, Pres, VP, Exec Bd Mem; Mohawk Valley Comm Coll Excl in Tchng 1994; St Univ of NY Chancellors Awd for Tchng 1995; Manuscript & Textbook Reviewer in Coll Ec Texts 1972-; *office:* Mohawk Valley Comm Coll 1101 Sherman Dr Utica NY 13501

FRIEDER, WENDY SCHMIDT, HS Multi-Handicapped Teacher; *b:* Mansfield, OH; *c:* Jessica, Lauren; *ed:* OH Univ (BSEd) Elem Ed 1971, (MSEd) Lrng Disabilities 1975; Attnd LaMar Univ, OH Univ; *cr:* Meigs Local Schls 4-6 Grd EMR 1972-73; Pasadena City Schls Elem Learning Disabilities Tchr 1973-74; Meigs Local Schls Elem Learning Disabilities Tchr 1974-79; Wood Cty Schls Severe Behavior Tchr 1979-85; Willoughby Eastlake Schls Multi-Handicapped Tchr 1985-; *ai:* Frosh, Jr Class Adv; Spec Ed Dept Chm; Core Team; Newspaper Adv; Willoughby Eastlake Tchrs Assn 1985-; NEA 1972-; Christ Presbyn Church 1987-, Sunday Schl Tchr; *office:* Willoughby South HS 5000 Shankland Rd Willoughby OH 44094*

FRIEDLAND, NEIL M., Coordinator of Writing; *b:* New York City, NY; *ed:* City Coll (BA) Eng Lit 1966; Hunter Coll CUNY (MA) Eng Lit 1973; *cr:* LaGuardia Coll Lecturer 1976-79; Schl of Visual Arts Coord Writing 1979-; *ai:* NEA 1994-; Articles Pub; Regents Schlsp; *office:* Schl Of Visual Arts 209 E 23rd St New York NY 10010*

FRIEDLINE, KAREN ANN, First Grade Teacher; *b:* Somerset, PA; *m:* George Edward; *c:* Benjamin, Laura; *ed:* Univ of Pittsburgh (BS) Ed 1974, (ME) Ed 1979; Slingerland Inst I, II, III; ITEC I, II; *cr:* North Star Schl Dist 3rd Grd Tchr 1974-75; Sault Ste Marie Schls 3rd-6th Grd Tchr 1975-76; Berlin Brothersvalley Schl Dist 1st Grd Tchr 1976-; *ai:* NEA 1974-, Pub Relations; AYSO 1992-, Treas; Sunday Schl Ex Bd 1991-, Sec; *office:* Berlin Brothersvalley Schl Dis 1025 E Main St Berlin PA 15530

FRIEDMAN, AUDREY VALADE, Adj Assoc Prof of Education; *b:* Attleboro, MA; *m:* John E.; *c:* Michael, Adam; *ed:* U of MA at Amherst (BS) Zoology, Scndry Ed 1972; U of PA (MS) Rdng, Lang Arts 1975; U MASS at Boston (MA) Critcial, Creative 1990; Boston Coll (PHD) Curr, Instruction 1995; *cr:* Philadelphia Pub Schls HS Tchr 1972-76; Attleboro Pub Schls HS Tchr 1978-82; Boston Coll Grad Asst 1990-95, City of Attleboro Coordinate Alternative Assessment 1994-; Boston Coll Adj Prof 1995-; *ai:* Adv MAT's in His; ASCD 1988-; IRA, NCTE, AAUW 1985-; CCD, Tchr; Parent Advy Cncl 1993-95; Outstdng Tchr Awd; Pub Case Studies in Reflective Giftedness in Book Remarkable Women; *home:* 815 West St Attleboro MA 02703*

FRIEDMAN, EDWARD, Music Teacher; *b:* New York, NY; *m:* Sarah Barrett; *c:* Alison, Jessica; *ed:* Univ of Miami (MM) Music Ed 1975; Univ of CT (PHD) Music His 1987; *cr:* East Hampton Ctr Schl 4th-6th Grd Music Tchr 1976-80; East Hampton MS 6th-8th Grd Music Tchr 1981-; *ai:* NEA, MENC 1976-; Amer Musicological Soc 1979-; Phi Kappa Phi; Book Review Pub 1985; Univ of CT Doctoral Dissertation Flwshp 1986; *office:* East Hampton MS 19 Childs Rd East Hampton CT 06424*

FRIEDMAN, HOWARD, Physics Teacher; *b:* Brooklyn, NY; *ed:* Brooklyn Coll (BS) Chem 1969; Rutgers Univ (MS) Analytical Chem 1972; Kean Coll (MA) Guidance & Counseling 1982; *cr:* Windsor Schl Sci, Math Tchr 1973-77; Elizabeth HS Chem, Physics Tchr 1977-82; Fair Lawn HS Physics Tchr 1982-; *ai:* Boptones Charity Rock Band, Chess Club, Sftbl Marathon Charity Adv; NEA 1977-; NSTA, Natl Assn Physics Tchrs 1982-; Tchr of Yr 1992; Bergen Cty Tchr of Yr 1993; *office:* Fair Lawn HS 14-00 Berdan Ave Fair Lawn NJ 07410

FRIEDMAN, IRA ALVIN, Mathematics Teacher; *b:* Brooklyn, NY; *m:* Ellen Ruth; *c:* Robert, Perry, Mindy; *ed:* Brooklyn Coll (BS) Math 1964, (MA) Math 1969; Columbia Tchrs Coll Doctoral Pgm 1989-94; *cr:* Peter Rouget Jr HS Math Tchr 1964-69; Longwood HS Math Tchr 1969-70; East Islip HS Math Tchr 1970-; *ai:* HS Math Team Adv; NCTM 1991-; AMTNYS 1991-; SCMTA 1988-; Dept of Energy Tchr Rsrch Assoc at Fermi Lab; Nom: Tandy Schl, Presidential Awd for Excl Math Tchng; NSF Lead Tchr Precalculus & Calculus; NCTM & AMTNS Confs Wkshps; *office:* East Islip HS Redmen St Islip Terrace NY 11752*

FRIEDMAN, M. DOUGLAS, Social Science Teacher; *b:* Willamantiz, CT; *m:* Arline; *c:* Jennifer, Jenny, Janneth; *ed:* Syracuse Univ (BA) Pol Sci 1956; William Paterson Coll (BA) Ed 1985; *cr:* Bus Admin Mgmt 1957-82; *ai:* Stu Cncl, His & Chess Clubs Adv; March of Dimes Coord; UCSS, NJCSS & Will Paterson Alumni 1986-; Union Cty Div March of Dimes Parochial Div 1985-, Coord, 1st Pl 1986-1993; Fairleigh Dickinson Univ Fellow; Strengthening HS Hum; *office:* Saint Patricks HS 221 Court St Elizabeth NJ 07206

FRIEDMAN, MARCIA KRAMER, Choral Music Teacher; *b:* Brooklyn, NY; *w:* Joseph (dec); *c:* Naomi, Daniel; *ed:* Hunter Coll (BA) Music & Theatre 1966; Grad Stud NYU, Western CT Coll & Mercy Coll; *cr:* NY City Pub Schls Music & 6th Grd Tchr 1966-71; Yorktown Cntrl Schls Vocal Music Tchr & Musical Theatre Dir 1971-; *ai:* Music Theatre Group Coach & Dir; Hendrick HS Speech & Debate Coach; AFT 1971-; NY Schl Music Tchrs Org 1971-; Music Edctrs Natl Conf 1971-; Hudson Players Comm Theatre, Dir & Co-Founder; *home:* 107 Coachlight Sq Montrose NY 10548

FRIEDMAN, MURIEL SCARABINO, ESL & Spanish Teacher; *b:* Queens, NY; *m:* Alan C.; *c:* Lawrence, Karen; *ed:* Fordham UNIv (BS) Ed 1962; Brooklyn Coll (MA) Fr 1967; C W Post LIU (MA) TESOL 1984; Brooklyn Coll Cert Admin 1992; *cr:* Uniondale HS ESL, Span, Fr Tchr 1962-; *ai:* ESL Stdnts Adv; Fac Relations Comm Chprsn; Phi Delta Kappa 1990-; Tchrs of Eng to Speakers of Other Lang 1984-, NYS Foreign Lang Tchrs 1962-; Long Island Lang Tchrs 1984-; Tchr of Month 1992-94; *office:* Uniondale HS 933 Goodrich St Uniondale NY 11553*

FRIEDMAN, SUSAN BARBARA (ROSS), 6th Grade Teacher; *b:* Philadelphia, PA; *m:* Paul L.; *c:* Mark Alexander; Lauren Rebecca; *ed:* Univ of Pittsburgh (BS) Psych 1969, (MAT) Elem Ed 1970; Temple Univ (MED) Cnslng Psych 1972; Villanova Univ (MA) Ed Admin 1979; Numerous Enrichment Courses; *cr:* Franklin Elem Schl Cnslr 1972-75; Christopher Columbus Schl Cnslr, Supvr of Grad Stdnts 1975-79; Soloman Schechter Day Schl Sixth Grd Tchr, Stu Cncl Adv 1987-; *ai:* Head Sixth Grd Tchr; Architects Comm; Negotiating Team Tchrs Rep; Phi Kappa Phi, Kappa Delta Pi 1979-; AFT 1987-; Temple Sholom of Broomall 1979-; CHADD of Montgomery Co 1994-; PA Auxiliary of Edna Glodney Ctr 1979-, Pres; Amer Heart Assn 1976-, Vol; *office:* Solomon Schechter Day Schl Old Lancaster Rd Highland Ave Bala Cynwyd PA 19004

FRIEDNER, EVA MARIE, Former Teacher; *b:* Prague, Czechoslovakia; *m:* Amos; *c:* Sharon, Tamar; *ed:* Hunter Coll (BA) Anthropology, Ed 1968, (MA) ESL 1973; *cr:* PS 139 Tchr 1969-74; Morris Nirenberg Rel Schl Tchr 1979-95; Milford Pub Schls Sub Tchr 1980-95; Mt Ida Coll ESL Tchr 1990-91; MA Bay Comm Coll ESL Tchr 1992, 1994-95; Digital Equipment Corp ESL Tchr 1993-94; *ai:* Temple Music Comm; AFT 1969-85; NSSHLA 1995-; Congregation Brai Shalom Choir 1990-.

FRIEDRICH, BARBARA KOHLER, Sixth Grd Soc Studies Teacher; *b:* Pearl River, NY; *m:* William A.; *c:* Terri Lyn, Pearlstein, Stephen Wayne; *ed:* Wagner Coll (BS) Elem Ed 1970; SUNY at New Paltz (MS) Ed 1974; 60 Addl Grad Credits; *cr:* N Garnerville Elem Schl 4th Grd Tchr 1970-71; W Haverstraw Elem Schl 4th-5th Grd Tchr 1971-83; J. A. Farley MS 6th Grd Soc Stud Tchr 1983-; *ai:* Yrbk Co-Adv; Team Ldr; Living His Coord; Dist Planning Team; Schl Improvement Planning Team; AFT, NYSUT 1970-; N Rockland Tchrs Assn 1970-, Corr Sec 1976-83; ASCD 1993-; NYS Soc St Assn 1985-; Summer Educl Grant; Co-Dev of Nature Ctr Curr; Writer Soc Stud Curr K-6; Co-Creator of Living His Events; Colonial Encampment & Medieval Fair; *office:* James A Farley MS 140 Route 210 Stony Point NY 10980*

FRIEDRICHS, VIRGINIA ANN, First Grade Teacher; *b:* Cincinnati, OH; *ed:* Univ of Cincinnati (BS) Primary Ed 1964; Credits from Miami Univ, Xavier Univ, Univ of Dayton, Wright St Univ; *cr:* John F. Dumont Elem Schl First Grd Tchr 1964-69; C. H. Holliday Elem Schl First Grd Tchr 1969-; *ai:* Rdng, Phonics, Math, Sci, Soc Stud Comms; Stu Tchrs Grd 10-12 from Miami Univ, Univ of Dayton, Wright St; MADEIRA Educ Assn 1964-69, Sec; West Carrollton Educ Assn 1969-, Bldg Rep 1994-; OEA, NEA 1969-; Martha Holden Jennings Scholar; Hands-On Sci Grant; Guest Presenter for Grad Classes; *office:* C F Holliday Elem Schl 4100 S Dixie Dr Dayton OH 45439*

FRIEL, JAMES P., Professor; *b:* Bronx, NY; *m:* Katherine Kelly; *ed:* Marist Coll (BA) Eng & Ed 1956; Fordham Univ (MA) Philosophy 1965; 45 Credit Hrs Grad Fac New Schl 1969; *cr:* Marist Coll Instr 1961 & 1963; City Univ of NY Part-Time Prof 1979 & 1981; St Univ of NY at Farmingdale Prof 1970-; *ai:* Philosophy Club Moderator; Hum Magazine Ed; Ctr for Philosophy Law Dir; AFT 1963-, Del; NYSUT 1963-, Del, Chair & Task Force Acad Freedom; UUP 1974-, Del; Amer Philosophy Assn 1970-, Chair & Tchng Philosophy Comm; Pub Justin Books; St Univ Chancellors Awd Excl in Tchng; Grants: Matchette Fndtn, Marguerite Eyer Wilbur Fndtn, Rsrch Fndtn St Univ NY & SUNY Farmingdale Stu Govt; *office:* S U N Y Coll Of Tech At Frmgdl 20 Vail St Northport NY 11768*

FRIEL, MARTIN JOSEPH, Fifth Grade Teacher; *b:* Philadelphia, PA; *m:* Linda R. Stewart; *c:* Jason; *ed:* Kutztown Univ (BS) Elem, Early Chldhd Ed 1980; Wilkes Coll (MS) Educl Dev, Strategies 1989; 30 Addl Credits Allentown Coll, East Stroudsburg Univ, Millersville Univ, Beaver Coll; In-Service Credits; *cr:* Richland Elem Schl 5th Grd Tchr 1985-; *ai:* Lang Arts Curr Comm; Quakerstown Comm Ed Assn, PA St Ed Assn, NEA 1985-; *office:* Richland Elem Schl 500 Fairview Ave Quakertown PA 18951

FRIEMAN, LAUREN JILL, 9th-12th Grd Soc Stud Teacher; *b:* Cincinnati, OH; *ed:* Tulane Univ (BA) Intnl Relations 1988; Xavier Univ (MED) Ed 1996; *cr:* Ursuline Acad Soc Stud Tchr 1993-; *ai:* Mock Trial Team & Young Democrats Moderator; Mother Club of Ursuline Acad Grant; *office:* Ursuline Acad 5535 Pfeiffer Rd Cincinnati OH 45242

FRIEND, SCOTT LESLIE, Instrumental Music Director; *b:* Manchester, CT; *m:* Kim Janssen; *c:* Derek K., Anneliese N.; *ed:* Univ of CT (BS) Music Ed 1980; Western CT St Univ (MS) Music Ed 1989; US Navy Schl of Music Diploma 1971, 2nd in Class; *cr:* Laurel Music Camp Jazz Band Dir 1975-95; Univ of CT Marching Band Lecturer 1978-80; Bolton Schl System Choral Instrumental Dir 1980-82; Naugatuek HS Instrumental Music Dir 1982-; *ai:* Colorguard Adv; Stu Cncl Co-Adv; Fac Advy acomm; NEA, CT Educators Assn 1980-; Music Ed Natl Conf 1979-; CT Music Educators 1980-, Allstate Comm, Distinguished Svc Awd 1991; Naugatuck Jaycees 1985-, Outstanding Citizen Awd 1989; Article Pub in CT Music Educator Magazine 1991; Guest Conductor CMEA Regnl MS Festival March 1996, Music Camp Laurel Jaz Band 1992-95; *office:* Naugatuck HS 543 Rubber Ave Naugatuck CT 06770*

FRIEND, TIM ALLEN, English & Journalism Teacher; *b:* Toledo, OH; *m:* Lora Conger; *c:* Devon; *ed:* Univ of Toledo (BA) Eng 1983; Bowling Green St Univ (MA) Eng 1992; *cr:* Stryker HS Eng, Jrnlsm Tchr 1984-; *ai:* Newspaper, Yrbk Adv; NCTE 1988-; 180th Wing Security Police Squadron 1979-, Squad Ldr; *office:* Stryker HS PO Box 624 Stryker OH 43557

FRIERMOOD, PAMELA A., 7th Grade Language Arts Tchr; *b:* Logansport, IN; *m:* Thomas A.; *c:* Amanda, Michael; *ed:* Purdue Univ (BS) Elem Ed 1974; Continuing Ed Units Numerous Classes; *cr:* Ludlow Pub Schls 2nd Grd Tchr 1975-78; Harrison Elem 5th Grd Tchr 1985-91; Whitewater Valley Elem 5th Grd Tchr 1991-94; Harrison Jr HS 7th Grd Lang Arts Tchr 1994-; *ai:* Pep Club Co-Spon; 9th Grd Proficiency Test Tutor; NEA, OEA, SLCTA 1985-; OH Cncl Tchrs of Eng Lang Arts 1995-; PTA Educator of Yr 1992-93; Harrison Elem Tchr of Yr 1990-91; Grant Recipient 1992; Martha Holden Jennings Scholar 1994; Mentor Tchr 1991-92; *office:* Harrison Jr HS 9860 West Rd Harrison OH 45030

FRIES, DANIEL THOMAS, American Cultures Teacher; *b:* Reading, PA; *ed:* Kutztown Univ of PA (BS) Sec Ed, His 1993; 9 Credits Toward Masters in Soc Stud; *cr:* Boyertown Area Sr HS 11th Grd Amer Cultures, Sociology Tchr 1993-; *ai:* Jr HS Girls Var Bsktbl, HS Asst, Jr HS Girls Sftbl Coach; PSEA, NEA 1993-; Interdisciplinary Unit Grant Kutztown Univ; *office:* Boyertown Area Sr HS 500 E 4th St Boyertown PA 19512*

FRIES, DAVID MARK, Elem Physical Education Tchr; *b:* Syracuse, NY; *ed:* Ithaca Coll (BS) PE 1986; Syracuse Univ (MS) PE 1988; *cr:* Central Square Cntrl Schls Elem PE Tchr 1989-; Town of Constantia Parks, Recreation Dir 1989-; *ai:* Boys Var Asst Track, Girls Jr Var Bsktbl Coach 1989-; NYSUT, AAHPERD, NYSAHPERD 1989-; *office:* Central Square Central Schls Main St Central Square NY 13036

FRIES, DONALD O., Professor of History; *b:* Fort Dodge, IA; *m:* Deborah Weisbern; *c:* Ingrid Bowers, Kiersten Zweibuum, Charley Wested, Jubilea Westol; *ed:* Univ of MI (BA) His 1961, (MA) European His 1961; MI St Univ (PHD) Eng His 1969; *cr:* Coll Misericordia His Prof 1969-; *ai:* His Dept Chair 1986-; AHA 1990-; *office:* Coll Misericordia Lake Street Dallas PA 18612

FRIES, DOUG W., High School Counselor & Coach; *b:* Findlay, OH; *m:* Kristina K. Richardson; *c:* Whitney, Taylor, Kela; *ed:* Bluffton Coll (BA) HPER 1983; Bowling Green St Univ (MA) Guid, Cnslng 1985; Univ of Dayton (MA) Ed Admin 1991; 23 Addl Hrs; *cr:* Ada Exempted Village Schls K-6 Grd Cnslr, PE Tchr, Head BsktblCoach 1984-85, K-8 Grd Cnslr, Head Bsktbl, Bsbl Coach 1985-86; Greenville City Schls Jr HS Hlth, Quest Tchr, Head Bsktbl Asst Bsbl Coach 1986-88, HS Cnslr, Head Bsbktl Coach 1988-, Asst Bsbl Coach 1988-94, Bsbl Coach 1994-; *ai:* NHS, Advy Comms; NEA, OH HS Bsktbl Coach Assn 1984-; Dist 8 Coach Assn 1984-, Dist 9 All Star Coach 1987, 1991; Miam Coach Assn 1994-; OH HS Bsbl Coach Assn 1995-; St John L 1987-, Parish Ed, Cncl; Girls Sftbl Assn 1994-95, T-Ball Coach; Fairfax Ct Greenville OH 45331

FRIES, GREGORY THOMAS, History Teacher; *b:* Readin Kutztown Univ (BSEd) Soc Stud 1988, (MED) Soc Stud Instruc *cr:* Wayne Highlands Schl Dist Soc Stud Tchr 1988-93; Muhle Dist Soc Stud Tchr 1993-; *ai:* Curr Cncl; Prin Advy, Act 17 Alternative Ed; PSEA 1988-; *office:* Muhlenberg Sr HS Sha Francis St Laureldale PA 19605

FRIES, JANET E. CLOSE, 6th Grade Teacher; *b:* Bellefontai Gary; *c:* Tonya, Tony, Tyler; *ed:* Bowling Green St Univ (BS 1974, (MA) Elem Ed 1980; Post Grad Courses in Lang Unlimited, Gen Ed; *cr:* Bowling Green City Schls 4th Grd Tch Eastwood Schls 1st, 3rd-4th Grd Tchr 1978-84; Bowling Green S Tchr Supvr 1984-94; Eastwood Schls 6th Grd Tchr 1994-; *ai:* 6t Bowl Coach; GATE Strategic Planning Comm; Fac Advy Bd; Team Sec; Stu Cncl Adv; Presch Co-op Pres; NEA; Conneaut F Landscaping Chm, Mem at Large, Svc Awd 1994; BGHS PTO 1 Mbrshp, Former Pres, VP; Sunday Schl Tchr; St Jude's Fundrai

FRIES, MARIKA H. PROSAK, Fourth Grade Teacher; *b:* Alle *m:* Douglas W.; *c:* Marika T. Chronister, Justin T.; *ed:* Kutztown Elem Ed 1965; Addl 24 Credits; 18 Credits at Carbon-Lehigh In Unit; *cr:* Souderton Schl Dist 3rd Grd Tchr 1965-66; New Yor Grd Tchr 1966-68; Whitehall-Coplay Schl Dist 2nd-4th Grd T *ai:* Koininia; Ladies Circle; PSEA, NEA 1965-; WCEA 1968 Schl; *home:* 1321 Gaspar Ave Bethlehem PA 18017

FRIES, RICHARD DONALD, Band Director; *b:* Altoona Michele; *c:* Michael, Gwen; *ed:* Penn St Univ (BS) Music Ed 19 Music Ed 1980; *cr:* DHH Lengel MS Band Dir 1974-77; Potts HS Band Dir 1977-; *ai:* Marching & Jazz Band; Lead Tchr; NE 1974-; MENC 1974-; Intnl Horn Soc 1974-; NBA 1992-; PME Outstdng Music Edctr 1994; *office:* Pottsville Area HS 16th & Pottsville PA 17901

FRIESEN, RONALD LEE, Professor of Economics; *b:* Inma Phyllis Ruth Sawatzky; *c:* Janine Renee Paul, Jon, Julie; *ed:* B (BA) Soc Sci 1961; Univ of KS (MA) Ec 1962; Columbia Univ 1973; Attnd Univ of AZ, Univ of KS; *cr:* Alliance Scndry 1962-65; Bluffton Coll Prof of Ec 1969-; *ai:* Curr Sub, Tenure Review Comms; Amer Ec Assn, African Studies Assn 1969-; E Allied for Arms Reduction 1990-; Univ of KS, Columbia Un Albert Schwitzer Travel Schlsp for Rsrch East Africa; Articles F

FRIIA, L. JOHN, English Instructor; *b:* Jackson Heights, NY; *m* A. Ciaccio; *c:* L. John III, L. Victoria, L. Brianna; *ed:* Queens Eng 1967, (MS) Eng Ed 1972; Suny at Stony Brook 40 Post Gra in Eng; NYU Drivers Ed Cert; Suffulic Cty Police Acad Cert Poli 1981; *cr:* Commack HS Eng, Math, Drivers Ed Instr 1967-; NYS Ir Adjunct Eng Prof 1973-; Suny at Stony Brook Adjunct Eng P Ward Melville HS Drivers Ed Instr 1992-; *ai:* Yrbk; Drama, Ch Playwrights; Mock Trial; NEA, AFT, NCTE 1967-; *office:* Com Townline Rd & Scholar Ln Commack NY 11725*

FRINK, MADELYN B., English Teacher; *b:* Norwich, CT; *m:* II; *c:* Janice L.; *ed:* Eastern CT St Univ (BA) Eng 1979; Wesle (MALS) Lit 1984; Sacred Heart Univ Prof Admin 1991; *cr:* Cutl Lang Arts Tchr 1979-80; Groton Board of Ed Eng Tchr 1980-83 High Lang Arts Tchr 1983-84; Robert E. Fitch Sr High Eng Tch West Side MS Reading Tchr 1989-90; Robert E. Fitch Sr High 1990-; *ai:* Cutler Jr HS Lang Arts Tchr 1979-80, 1983-84; Wes Rdng Tchr 1989-90; Robert E. Fitch Sr HS 1980-88, 1990-; Standards, NHS, Scheduling Comms; *office:* Robert E Fitch S Groton Long Point Rd Groton CT 06340*

FRISBEY, ROBERT EUGENE, Retired Principal; *b:* Columbu Avanell Patricia Smith; *c:* Steven, Susan Hartter, Sheryl Mc M OH Univ (BSEd) Sci 1954; Xavier (MEd) Schl Admin 1970; N Oceanography, Physics; *cr:* St of OH Dir Trng 1974-78; Hilliard Winsdsor Schl Prin; Wharton MS Sci Tchr 1989-90; *home:* 553 C Ave Columbus OH 43228

FRISBIE, LINDA BURGERHOFF, English Teacher; *b:* Yonker H. Benjamin Jr.; *c:* Shannon; *ed:* Oneonta St (BA) Ed, Eng 197 Coll (MS) Ed 1976; *cr:* Owego Free Acad Eng Tchr 1972-; *ai:* Instructional Strategies, Prins Advy Comms; Dimensions of Team; AFT, NYSUT 1972-; Delta Kappa Gamma 1985-, 1st VP NYSEC 1980-, Tchr of Excl Awd; OA Tchrs Assn 1972-, Bldg R 1975-; *office:* Owego Free Acad George St Owego NY 13827

FRISENDA, ATTILIO ARTHUR, Social Studies Teacher; *b:* NY; *m:* Andrea Anne Aievoli; *c:* Jennifer, Lauren; *ed:* St Johns U Scndry Ed, Soc Sci 1968; C. W. Post, Long Island Univ (MS) S His 1971; Prof Diploma Educl Admin 1983; 60+ Credit Hrs Ove North Shore Sr HS Stu Tchr 1968; Lawrence Road Jr HS 7-9 Grd Tchr 1968-; *ai:* 9th Grd Graduating Class Adv 1970-; Fac Relatior School Based Mngmt Team Rep; Union Rep 9 Yrs; NYSUT, Un Assn; NYS Cncl Soc Stud, Long Island Cncl Soc Stud 1968 Huntington Knights of Columbus 1990-, Grand Knight, Achvmt Elizabeth's RC Church 1978-,Eucharistic Mem; Yrbk Dedicate PTA Jenkins Meml Awd; Spon Extracurric Acts; *office:* Lawrence 50 Lawrence Rd Hempstead NY 11550*

FRISKNEY, THOMAS E., Prof of Greek & New Testament; *b:* E *m:* Ruth Margaret Miller; *c:* Elizabeth Love, Stephen, Ester Fi Santel, Paul, Sara Jones; *ed:* Concinnati Bible Coll (BA) Gre Cincinnati Bible Coll & Seminary (MA) Greek & New Testame (MDIV) Greek, New Testament 1955; Attnd Trinity Evangelica Schl; *cr:* Cincinnati Bible Coll & Seminary Prof of Greek Testament, Head of Biblical Stud 1954-; *ai:* Acad Cabinet; Ldrs Br Cty Bd of Ed, Pres 1 Yr; Delta Alpha Tau Tchr of Yr 199 Strength for Victory; Book: Solving Church Problems; Book: Stu to I, II Thessalonians; Contributor & Bd of Review for The C Biblical Lib: The NT Greek-Eng Dictionary; *office:* Cincinnati B & Sem 2700 Glenway Ave Cincinnati OH 45204*

FRISONI, ROBERTA DIANE, Business Education Teacher; *b:* Falls, NY; *ed:* NCCC (AAS) Secretarial Sci 1971; Daemen Coll Ecs 1973; Niagara Univ (MS) Ed 1977; Buffalo St Coll Di Cooperative Work-Stud Cert 1995; *cr:* Grand Island HS Bus 1973-; *ai:* Yrbk Adv 1989-; Internship, Shadow Day, Taste of Grar Expo Coord; NYSUT 1973, Bus Tchr Assn NYS 1973-; Pi Gam Celebration of Inspiration Awd; NHS Honorary Mem 1993; Ch Commerce Expo Awd, Most Informative Booth; *office:* Grand Is 1100 Ransom Rd Grand Island NY 14072

FRISTICK, SUSIE J., Latin & Social Studies Tchr; *b:* Waynesb *m:* Vincent; *ed:* Geneva Coll (BS) Latin, His 1973; Univ of Dayton Admin 1982; Attnd Slippery Rock Univ, WV Univ; *cr:* Shenang Tchr 1973-74; Cadiz HS Tchr 1974-; *ai:* Jr Classical Leagu Classical League 1974-; *office:* Cadiz HS 440 E Market St Cadiz O

SON, KENNETH HERBERT, HS Science Teacher; *b:* NY; *m:* Claudia N.; *c:* Erika, Kenneth; *ed:* ME Maritime Acad ical Sci 1977; Johnson St Coll (MA) Ed 1993; *cr:* Websterville HS Sci Tchr, Chem, Physics, Gen Sci 1994-; *ai:* Soccer Coach; dv; Lt USNR; 2nd Mate Any Oceans Gross Tons, Upon Oceans; ·ds Rd Orange VT 05641*

, JOSEPH EDWARD,III, Math Teacher; *b:* Pottstown, PA; *m:* arie Day; *ed:* Millersville St Coll (BS) Ed 1975, (ME) Math 1979; d Area Schl Dist HS Math Tchr 1976-; *ai:* Girls Track & Field h 1982-; NEA, PSEA 1980-, Pres; NCTM 1985-; *office:* Oxford 01 5th Street Rd Oxford PA 19363

ARBARA JEZIORO, Fourth Grade Teacher; *b:* Buffalo, NY; *m:* *ed:* Medaille Coll (BS) N-12th, SS Ed 1975; St Univ Coll at AS) Ed 1979; 90 Hrs Past Masters; *cr:* Orchard Park Cntrl Schls rd Tchr 1976-; *ai:* Odyssey of Mind Turn Key Judge; Schl Ticket Chprsn; Wellness Aerobics for Staff; NYSUT, AFT 1976-; 3-; Sheilas Aerobic Jazz Instr 1986-; *office:* Ellicott Road Elem Ellicott Rd Orchard Park NY 14127

CAROLYN RODAK, Mathematics Tchr & Dept Chprsn; *b:* H; *m:* John L.; *c:* Todd, Kevin, Laura; *ed:* OH St Univ (BS) Ed Brooklyn HS Tchr 1970-72; Keystone HS Tchr 1972-75; Lorain oll Part-Time Tchr 1976-; Elyria Cath HS Tchr 1981-; *ai:* ; Math Dept Chprsn; NCTM 1981-; ASCD 1985-; Eucharistic 992-.

NANCY JANE, French Teacher; *b:* East Stroudsburg, PA; *ed:* udsburg Univ (BS) Scndry Educ, Fr 1968; L'Universite Laval, ite de la Sorbonne, Kutztown St Univ, Towson St Univ Masters cy, 6 Credits; *cr:* Nazareth Area Jr HS Fr Tchr 1968-69; East urg Area HS Fr Tchr 1969-; *ai:* NEA 1968-; AATF 1990-; Animal Protection Orgs 1980-; *office:* E Stroudsburg HS North St East Stroudsburg PA 18301

L, MARK EDWARD, Technology Education Teacher; *b:* MA; *m:* Sandra Adele Rehm; *c:* Tyler, Connor; *ed:* Fitchburg St Ed 1980, (MED) Indstrl Ed 1981; Univ of CT ((PHD Ed 1986; Admin 1988; Grad US Marine Corps Basic Warrant Ofcr Schl; *cr:* Regnl Ed Svc Ctr Prgm Coord 1988-89; Natchaug Hosp Dir of nt PHP 1989-91; Three Rivers Comm Tech Coll Adj Fac 1989-; Jr Sr HS Tchr 1992-; *ai:* Griswold Ed Assn Bldg Rep; NHS Fac ; Jostens, Renaissance Adv; NEA, CT Ed Assn 1992-; Assn for Curr Dev 1995-; Phi Delta Kappa; Pi Lambda Theta; Epsilon Pi Marine Corps Reserve 1974-, Ofcr, CWO-2; Hampton tional Church 1990-; *home:* 90 Estabrooks Rd Hampton CT

L-JOERG, MELISSA SUSAN, Chemistry Teacher; *b:* Toledo, . Jeff Joerg; *ed:* Bowling Green St Univ (BS) Bio 1987, (BED) 987, (MED) Guidance, Counseling 1992; *cr:* Fremont Jr HS Sci -92; Fremont Ross HS Chem Tchr 1992-; *ai:* Jr Class Adv; Var erleading Coach; Stu Assistance Team; NEA, OH Ed Assn, Ed Assn, Sci Educators Cncl OH 1987-; OH Schl Cnslrs Assn TA 1992-; Delta Zeta 1983-, Chapter Adv; Bowling Green Club Adult Precision Team 1991; *office:* Fremont Ross HS 1100 Fremont OH 43420

R, JANICE DECKER, Ger Tchr & Frgn Lang Dept Chr; *b:* nia, PA; *m:* Arthur; *c:* Cynthia Babcock, Sally Babcock; *ed:* ter Coll (BA) Ger 1964; Master's Equivalency; *cr:* Springfield HS 1964-67; Summit Jr HS Ger Tchr 1967-72; Marpel Newtown MS Long Term Sub 1979-80; Upper Dublin HS Ger Tchr, Frgn Lang ir 1980-; *ai:* Ger Exch Prgm Coord; Curr Task Force; Hnr Soc Comm; AATG 1980-; Outstdng Tchr; *office:* Upper Dublin HS Alsh Ave Fort Washington PA 19034

NI, DOMINICK,JR., Chemistry Teacher; *b:* Pittsburgh, PA; *m:* Mooney; *c:* Nick, Sarah; *ed:* Clarion Univ of PA (BS) Chem Sec Univ of Pittsburgh (PHD) Analytical Chem 1980; *cr:* Fisher : Schl Instrument Product Mgr 1980-90; Antech Ltd Mgr Chem 1990-93; Steel Valley Schl Dist Chem Tchr 1993-; *ai:* Sci Chem Stud Group Adv; Ast Wrestling Coach; PSEA 1993-; Amer : 1980-; Trafford Lions 1989-, VP; Penn Trafford Schl Bd 1989-, ctroscopy Soc of Pittsburgh Instrument, Project MIME Grant; 5 Duquesne Ave Trafford PA 15085*

, JOANNE CLAIRE, History & English Teacher; *b:* Rahway, ctor J.; *c:* Jonathan; *ed:* Univ of VA (BA) His, Eng 1980, (MED) Ed 1981; *cr:* Oak Knoll Schl of Holy Child His Tchr 1981-84; cad of Sci & Tech His & Eng Tchr 1984-; *ai:* Mock Trial Team & m Adv; NJEA 1993-; NJ His Assn 1990-; *office:* Marine Acad Of ch Bldg 305 Gunnison Rd Highlands NJ 07732*

DAVID, Associate Professor of Music; *b:* Santa Rosa, CA; *m:* rth; *ed:* Univ of CA at Berkeley (BA) Music 1976; Univ of CA (MM) Music Composition 1978; Columbia Univ (DMA) omposition 1984; Attnd Cambridge Univ Fulbright 1983-84 & ood Fromm Fellowship Summer 1981; *cr:* Garland Publishing Asst 1982-85; Baruch Coll Adjunct Asst Prof 1985; Univ of UT Asst 5-89; Saint Marys Coll of MD Assoc Prof 1989-; *ai:* Amer Music ; Broadcast Music Inc 1980-; Fulbright Grant Cambridge England Charles Ives Fellowship 1983-84; Kennedy Ctr Friedheim Awd; nd at Harvard Commission; Music is Recorded on Centaur & Pub Inc; *office:* Saint Marys Coll Of MD Div Of Arts & Letters St MD 20686*

BETTY ANN MILLER, Biology Instructor; *b:* New Haven, CT; ael Paul; *c:* Elaine Judith, Joan Amity; *ed:* CT Coll (BA) Bio & 983; Sacred Heart Univ (MAT) Ed & Bio; *cr:* Notre Dame HS Bio Tchr 1983-92; Gateway Comm Tech Coll Bil Instr 1992-.

CARLTON P., 8th Grade English Teacher; *b:* Englewood, NJ; *m:* alph; *c:* Sarah, Carlton; *ed:* Dartmouth Coll (BA) Eng, Ed 1974; Paterson (MA) Schl Admin 1990; *cr:* Cavallini MS 8th Grd Eng 75-; Michael Acad Dir of Eng 1993-; *ai:* Tennis, Comedy & d Test Taking Mini Course; Dartmouth Alumni Club 1975-, Cty Schlsp Chm; Governors Tchr Recognition Awd Recipient; mil A Cavallini MS 395 W Saddle River Rd Upper Saddle River

FRED N., Anatomy & Physiology Chem Tchr; *b:* Braddock, PA; a L. Caruso; *c:* Fred W.; *ed:* IN Univ of PA (BS) Bio 1972; Univ gh Chem 1994; PA St Univ 20 Credit Hrs; US Army Warfare Schl Grad; *cr:* East Alleyhamy Schls Sci Tchr 1972-; *ai:* Long Distance ; Regnl Math Sci Collaburetive Liasen; Sci Mentor for New Tchrs; SEA, NEA, PTA 1972-; PSTA, NSTA 1992-; Spec Soc 1995-; Mt Christ Church 1980-, Chm of Cog; US Army 1971-86, Capt; Univ urgh 4 Time Dist Tchr Awd; St Vincent Coll Outstdng Tchr Awd *fice:* East Allegheny HS 1150 Jacks Run Rd North Versailles PA

ROBERT ALAN, Social Studies Teacher; *b:* Newark, NJ; *m:* eckstein; *c:* Joshua, Andrew; *ed:* Rutgers Coll (BA) Amer His A Prgm Monmouth Univ Completed 1999; *cr:* Long Branch MS Tchr 1972-; *ai:* Stu Cncl Adv; Schl Store Coord; NEA 1972-; oring Vols 1993-; *office:* Long Branch MS 364 Indiana Ave Long NJ 07740

FROST, SANDRA RENAYE, Fourth Grade Teacher; *b:* Franklin, VA; *m:* David; *c:* David, Yasmin, Tawana; *ed:* Brooklyn Coll (BS) Acctng 1986, (MS) Rdng 1992; Attnd Writing Inst at Columbia, Cmptr NY Inst of Tech 1995; *cr:* NY City Bd of Ed Tchr 1987-; Chemical Bank Ofcr 1987-91; *ai:* UFT, AFT 1988-; *office:* Public Schl 161 330 Crown St Brooklyn NY 11225

FROST, WILLIAM J., Athletic Dir & Schl Counselor; *b:* Belpre, OH; *m:* Marilyn Brady; *c:* Emily, Melissa; *ed:* Glenville St (BA) PE 1969; Univ of Dayton (MS) Schl Cnslng 1985; Frostburg St & WV Saftey & Drivers Ed; *cr:* Southern Garrett Driver Ed & Head Ftbl Coach 1969-74; Logan Elem PE Tchr 1974-94, Schl Cnslng 1995-; *ai:* Past Ftbl & Sftbl Coach; Lecta, NEA & OEA 1969-; OH Ftbl Coaches 1969-; OEA, NEA 1974-; OH HS Ftbl Coaches 1974-; OH Hunter r Safety Instr 1980-; OH HS Sftbl Coaches 1984-; Wrote & Received Grant for PE; Hunting & Fishing Safety; PE Dept Head; St Awd for Excl; *office:* Logan Elm HS 9575 Tarlton Rd Circleville OH 43113

FRUCI, DAVID JOSEPH, Eighth Grd Social Studies Tchr; *b:* Paterson, NJ; *m:* Barbara Joan; *ed:* Tombrock Coll (AA) Ed 1972; Ramapo Coll of NJ (BA) Amer Stud 1976; Manhattanville Coll (MAT) Ed, Soc Stud 1990; *cr:* Immaculate Conception Schl Eighth Grd Soc Stud Tchr 1988-; *ai:* Schl Yrbk; Natl Geographic Geog Bee; Intnl Ethnic Food Fair; Amer Govt Prgm; Geog Club; *office:* Immaculate Conception Schl 16 N Broadway Irvington NY 10533

FRUMIN, PAOLA JUDITH, Spanish Teacher; *b:* Buenos Aires, Argentina; *ed:* Salisburty St Univ (BA) Span Scndry Ed 1991; Working Towards MED in Guid & Cnslng Univ of MD at Eastern Shore; *cr:* Salisbury St Univ Institutional Advancement Sec 1989-91, Campus Police Comm Supvr 1989-94; Univ of MD Span Instr 1992; James M. Bennett Sr HS Span Tchr 1994-; *ai:* Span Hnr Soc, Span Club Spon, Adv; Schl Dances Chaperon; NEA, Wicomico Cty Ed Assn 1994-; AATSP 1994-; Phi Eta Sigma 1989-; Taught Coll, Univ Level Span; *office:* James M. Bennett Sr HS 300 E College Ave Salisbury MD 21804

FRUSCIONE, ALBERT A., Biology Teacher; *b:* Waterbury, CT; *m:* Edith E. Joy; *c:* Brenda, Brian, Douglas; *ed:* Univ of CT (BS) Bio 1949, (MA) Ed 1963; *cr:* Lexington HS Tchr 1963-; *ai:* Club Adv Gay, Lesbian Support Group; NEA 1963-; Minute Man Assn Retarded Citizens 1969-, Bd 1988-94; Certfd Sex Educator; *home:* 40 Upland Rd Concord MA 01742*

FRUTCHEY, JAMES A., Soc Stud Coord Tchr; *b:* Scranton, PA; *m:* Barbara M.; *c:* James, Matthew; *ed:* Union Coll (BS) Soc Stud 1964; PA St Univ (MA) His 1968; 27 Post Grad Credits; *cr:* Scotch Plains-Fanwood NJ HS Tchr 1965-70; Abington Hghts HS Soc Stud Coord, Tchr 1970-, Russian Stud; *ai:* Var Sftbl Coach 1975-95; Contemporary Issues Clb Adv 1995-; NCSS 1972-; SSSA 1982-; ASCD 1993-; NEPA Soc Stud Cncl; Fellowship for Travel to Soviet Union; Sftbl Coach of Yr 1990, 1993; Co-Founder of NEPA 1994; *office:* Abington Heights HS 222 Noble Rd Clarks Summit PA 18411

FRUTKIN, LARRY, Social Studies Teacher; *b:* Bronx, NY; *m:* Adele Luttinger; *c:* Carlye, Beth; *ed:* Univ of WI at Eau Claire (BA) His 1971; Iona Coll (MSC) Scndry Ed, Soc Stud 1975; *cr:* Hawthorne MS Soc Stud Tchr 1972-86; Burroughs JHS Soc Stud Tchr 1986-; *ai:* Counseling Stdnts with Difficulties in Class, Assisting in Solving Problems Between Each Other Team Adv; Yonkers Fed of Tchrs 1972-; Cncl Soc Stud 1980-; *office:* Burroughs Jr HS 150 Rockland Ave Yonkers NY 10705*

FRY, CLARENCE ARTHUR, Lecturer of Ind Engineering; *b:* Shamokin, PA; *m:* Eunice Charlotte Long; *c:* David, Thomas; *ed:* Penn St Univ (BS) Aero Engrng 1957; George Washington Univ (MS) Engrng Mngmt 1972; Grad Stud Aero Eng Drexel Univ, Psych Univ of DE; *cr:* Martin Co Flight Test, Power Plants 1957-60; Russell Assocs Engrng Sales 1960-72; Army Human Engrng Lab Researcher, Division Chief 1972-91; Morgan St Univ Lecturer 1991-95; *ai:* Habitat for Humanity Bd; APG Fed Credit Union Bd Consultant; Advent Luth Church Pres; Amer Helo Soc 1960-, Comm Chair; Amer Soc Engrng Ed 1991-; Inst Indstrl Engr 1992-; Amer Legion; NASA Grant Multidiscipline Analysis; Beaver Cty PA Grant Mobility Mgr; *office:* Morgan St Univ Cold Spring Ln & Hillen Ave Baltimore MD 21239

FRY, JILL BAUMGARDNER, Reading Recovery Teacher; *b:* Coshocton, OH; *m:* Charles; *ed:* OH St Univ (BA) Early, Mid Chldhd Ed 1977; Cu Ashland Univ (MS) Curr, Instruction 1985; Supervisory Cert; *cr:* Pleasant Vly Elem Schl Kndgtn Tchr 1977-78; Conesville Elem Schl 1st, 6th Grd Tchr 1978-84, 3rd Grd Tchr 1984-95; Union Elem Schl Rdng Recovery Tchr 1995-; River View Schl Dist Curr Coord 1995-; *ai:* Staff Dev.*

FRY, KAREN ANN (SWINSICK), Acad Learning Support Teacher; *b:* Blossburg, PA; *m:* Dwight David; *c:* Nathaniel, Nicholas, Tina; *ed:* Mansfield St Coll (BSEd) Mentally & Physically Handicapped 1979; 46 Grad Hrs; *cr:* Lycoming Cty Crippled Childrens Soc Tchr 1979-82; Hope Enterprises Tchr & Cnslr 1979-81; Blast IU 17 & Southern Tioga Schl Dist Tchr & Acad Learning Support 1982-; *ai:* Scndry Instrl Support Chprsn; Scndry Transition Coord; Make a Difference Org Adv; Frgn Lang Club Co-Adv; PSEA & NEA 1982-; ASCD 1995-; Rel Ed Instr 1986-; *office:* North Penn Jr Sr HS 300 Morris St Blossburg PA 16912*

FRY, MARYBETH B., English Tchr & College Cnslr; *b:* Johnstown, PA; *ed:* Manhattanville Coll (BA) Eng & Amer Lit 1984; Chatham Coll Scndry Ed Cert 1992; *cr:* Harper & Row Publishers Asst Ed 1986-89; Freelance Ed 1989-92; Shadyside Acad Eng Tchr 1993-95, Eng Tchr & Coll Cnslr 1995-; *ai:* Girls Sftbl Coach; All Schl Book Comm; Prize Comm; 5th Form Adv; NCTE 1994-; NACAC 1995-; *office:* Shady Side Acad Sr Schl 423 Fox Chapel Rd Pittsburgh PA 15238

FRY, MELANIE ANN (WORLEY), Kindergarten Teacher; *b:* Bellefontaine, OH; *m:* Dennis H.; *c:* Andrew, Zane, Joel; *ed:* Bowling Green St Univ (BS) Elem Ed 1978; 150 Addl Hrs; *cr:* Indian Lake Schls Kndgtn Tchr 1978-; *ai:* Delta Kappa Gamma 1993-; ILEA 1978-; Belle Ctr United Meth Church, Pastor Parrish Comm, Women; Hamma Chptr #312 Eastern Stars; Logan Cty Ed Fnd Grant; *office:* Indian Lake Local Schls 4601 Napoleon St Huntsville OH 43324*

FRY, RALMA CHRISTINE, Chemistry Teacher; *b:* Chambersburg, PA; *m:* Donald Andrew; *c:* Colby A. R., Timothy D., Abigail K., Katherine Y.; *ed:* Millersville Univ (BS) Chem Ed 1971; Shippensburg Univ (MED) Chem 1978; *cr:* West York Schl Dist Sci Tchr 1971-73; Cumberland Valley HS Chem Tchr 1973-79; Carlisle Tire & Rubber Asst Research Chemist 1974; Shippensburg Univ Chem Instr 1977; Carlisle Schl Dist Chem Tchr 1981-; *ai:* HS Sci Projects Adv; Sci Projects Club Adv; Carlisle Sci Advy 1981-; Capitol Area Sci Eng Fair, Selection Comm Co-Chair; Shippensburg Pub Lib Assn, Pres; Denna Chem Industrial Cncl, Ed Comm for TIE Conf; Southeastern PA Amer Chem Soc Whalen Awd Winner 1993; Assisted in Writing Awd Winning Energy Ed Curr for PA Power & Light; Served on Comm That Wrote Grant for ITEC Monies of Cmptrs at Our HS; *home:* 49 W King St Shippensburg PA 17257

FRY, VICTORIA TOMCHO, Assoc Dean of Spec Acad Prgms; *b:* Goshen, NY; *m:* Gerald R.; *ed:* Utica Coll of Syracuse Univ (BA) Eng Ed 1975; Univ of TX at El Paso (MED) Rdng-Curr, Instruction 1979; Syracuse Univ (PHD) Ed 1990; GA Southern Edcl Psych; *cr:* El Paso Pub Schls Eng, Rdng Tchr 6 Yrs; El Paso Comm Coll Adj ESL Prof 2 Yrs; SUNY at Morrisville Coll Skills Ctr Dir 11 Yrs, Tchng Excl Ctr Dir 2 Yrs; *ai:* Dir Frosh Experience Courses, Individual Stud Prgm Planning Comms for Intnl Day, Women's Hist Month, Acad Review, Cncl, Mid Sts Cmte on Stu Learning Resources; Pi Lambda Theta 1989-; Intnl Rdng Assn 1986-, NCTE 1975-; LVA-Mid-York Inc 1989-, Charter Pres; Literacy Vols Advy Bd 1988-; Mid-St Tchr Ctr Bd 1993-; Awds St Univ of NY Chancellor's for Prof Svc 1991, Svc 1993, Unted Univ Profs Recognition 1986, LVA Cnty Contact Person, 200 Hr Tutoring Pin 1992; *home:* PO Box 30 Hamilton NY 13346*

FRY, WOODROW WARREN, Sixth Grade Teacher; *b:* Muncy, PA; *m:* Ruth Ann VanBuskirk; *c:* Jacob; *ed:* Bloomsburg Univ (BS) Elem Ed 1983, (MS) Rdng 1991; 24 Post Grad Hrs Ed; *cr:* Muncy Schl Dist 6th Grd Tchr 1984-; *ai:* Wrestling Coach; Munch Ed Assn, PSEA, NEA 1984-; *office:* Ward L. Myers Elem Schl 125 New St Muncy PA 17756

FRYCZYNSKI, STAN, 4th-6th Grd Basic Skills Tchr; *b:* Bayonne, NJ; *m:* Claire McAndrew; *c:* Amy; *ed:* St Peters Coll (BA) Elem & Presch Ed 1975, (MA) Admin Supervision 1991; 12 Post Grad Credits in Philosophy & Thinking in Mid Grds at Montclair St; *cr:* Bayonne Bd of Ed Title I Rdng 1975-78; Secaucus Bd of Ed 5th Grd Tchr 1978-89, Rdng Elem Tchr & Hs Ath Dir 1989-; *ai:* Head Cross Cntry Coach for Male & Female; Head Indoor & Outdoor Track & fields for Male & Female; NEA 1975-, Bldg Rep 1976, 1986-88; NJSIAA St Ofcls Assoc 1975-, St Exec Bd; Hudson Cty Track Coaches Assoc 1971-, Pres; Inducted Into Hudson Cty Track & Field Hall of Fame 1989 & NJ Coaches Hall of Fame 1991; NJ Track & Field Official of Yr 1995; Natl Fed of Coaches Service Award for Track & Field 1995; Selected Mem of NJ SIAA Outdoor Track & Field Exec Comm; *office:* Secaucus HS Mill Ridge Rd Secaucus NJ 07094

FRYE, HARRY ALFRED, Science Teacher; *b:* Nashua, NH; *ed:* Plymouth St Coll (BED) Sci Ed 1967; Worcester Polytechnical INst (MNS) Sci 1974; 6 Credit Hrs Chemical Instrumentation, Microscale Chem; *cr:* Milford Jr Sr HS Sci Tchr 1967; Pembroke Acad Sci, Math Tchr, Dept Chair 1967-; *ai:* Sci Club Adv 1967-; NH Sci Tchrs Assn 1967-, VP, Pres, Bd Dir; B&M RRH Soc 1970-, Historian; Hooksett Historical Soc 1990-; Presidential Awd Excl in Sci Tchng St Level 1986-87; Who's Who Among Amer Coll Stdnts 1966-67; *office:* Pembroke Acad 209 Academy Rd Pembroke NH 03275*

FRYE, RANDY LYNN, Chairman of Business Dept; *b:* Johnstown, PA; *m:* Barbara Caroff; *c:* Nathan, Cullen, Randall; *ed:* Univ of Pittsburgh at Johnstown (BA) Soc Scis 1978; Indiana Univ of PA (MBA) 1980; Saint Francis Coll (MA) Human Resource Mngmt, Indstrl Relations 1990; Univ of Pittsburgh Working Towards ABD Admin & Policy Stud; Inst of Mngmt Accountants Mngmt Acctng Cert 1986; *cr:* Retail Store Mgr, Asst Mgr; Mount Aloysius Coll Bus Division Chair, Prof 1980-84; Saint Francis Coll Mngmt Asst Prof 1984-, Bus Dept Chair 1988-; MBA Prgm Dir 1990-; *ai:* AYSO Soccer Coach; Club Adv; Beta Delta Sigma Chptr; Inst for Mngmt Acctng 1986-, Higher Ed Relations Dir 1989-90; Alternative Comm Resources Inc 1992-, Bd Mem; Numerous Presentations & Wkshps to Bus Comm; Grad Assistantship IUP Schl of Bus 1979; *office:* Saint Francis Coll 225A Scotus Hall Loretto PA 15940*

FRYE, WINI HOFFMAN, Spanish & French Teacher; *b:* Brooklyn, NY; *m:* Roger; *c:* Karin, Emily; *ed:* St Univ of NY at Buffalo (BA) Span 1968; 46 Grad Hrs; *cr:* Mill MS Span Tchr 1969-70; Saint Marys Jr HS Span Tchr 1970-71; Sweet Home Jr-Sr HS Span Tchr 1971-72; Travel Agents Intnl Travel Consultant 1983-; Baltimore Cty Bd of Ed Span & Fr Tchr 1990-; *ai:* Dept Chm; Stu Cncl Adv; MSTA, NEA, TABCO, MFLA 1990-; *office:* Pine Grove MS 9200 Old Harford Rd Baltimore MD 21234*

FRYLING, GEORGE E., Art Teacher; *b:* Philadelphia, PA; *m:* Gayle A. Spohn; *c:* Grant D.; *ed:* Temple Univ Tyler Schl of Art (BFA) Graphic Design & Illus 1969, (MED) Art Ed 1973; 12 Credit Hrs; *cr:* Whitemarsh Elem Schl Art Tchr 1969-87; Colonial MS Art Tchr 1987-; *ai:* 8th Grd Art Show Act Spon; Jr Hnr Soc Fac Comm; NAEA 1970-; PSEA & NEA 1970-; Pottstown Elks 1990-; *office:* Colonial MS 716 Belvoir Rd Norristown PA 19401

FRYSCINSKI, STAN, Athletic Director & Coach; *b:* Bayonne, NJ; *m:* Claire McAndrew; *c:* Amy; *ed:* St Peters Coll (BA) Elem Ed & Nursery Schl 1975, (MA) Admin 1991; *cr:* Bayonne Bd of Ed Elem Ed Tchr 1975-78; Secaucus Bd of Ed Elem Ed Tchr 1978-89, Dir of Ath 1989-; *ai:* Cross Cntry, Indoor & Outdoor Track & Field Head Coach; Hudson Cty Track Coaches Assn 1976-, Pres 1976-; NJSIAA Certfd T&F Ofcl 1978-, St Bd Trustee; USATF Natl & Intnl Certfd Track & Field Ofcl 1986-; 5 Time Hudson Cty Track Coach of the Yr; 4 Time BCSC Cross Cntry & Track Coach of the Yr; Inducted into Hudson Cty Hall of Fame 1989 & NJ St Coaches Hall of Fame 1991; Coaches Care & Scholastic Coach Awd 1993; Natl Fed of Coaches Svc Awd for Track & Field 1994.

FUCCI, RICHARD M., English Dept Chairman; *b:* Providence, RI; *m:* Mary E. Greyard; *c:* Judith, Tricia, Peter; *ed:* Univ of RI (BA) Eng 1967; Univ of RI (MA) Eng 1975; Providence Coll (MED) Scndry Admin 1979; *cr:* Warwick Veterans Meml HS Eng Tchr 1967-72; Toll Gate HS Eng Tchr 1972-86; RI Coll Adj Fac 1980-; Toll Gate HS Eng Dept Chm 1986-; Comm Coll of RI Part-time Fac 1995-; Warwick Summer Schl Prin; *ai:* Acad Decathlon Coach; Eng Steering Comm Chm; RI Cncl of Tchrs of Eng Exec Bd; AFT 1967-; Tchr of Yr; NHS; Outstdng Mentor Amer Assn of Univ Women; Articles Pub; *office:* Toll Gate HS 575 Centerville Rd Warwick RI 02886

FUCCILLO, CHERYL-ANN, Third Grade Teacher; *b:* Boston, MA; *ed:* Boston College (BA) Elem Ed 1969; Fitchburg St (MS) Elem Ed 1988; 60 Addl Credit Hrs Enrichment, GATE Courses; *cr:* Ditson Schl 4-5 Grd GATE, 3 Grd Tchr 1969-; *ai:* GATE Prgm Enrichment Adv; Schlsp, Cultural Arts, Sci & Math, Sci St Stans Comms; AFT 1969-, BFT Assn, Former VP; Yankee Doodle Parade Comm; BATV; Horace Mann, Billerica Partnership Grants; *office:* Thomas Ditson Elem Sch 793 Boston Rd Billerica MA 01821*

FUCHS, ASENATH J., Science Teacher; *b:* Brooklyn, NY; *m:* Roy; *ed:* Wells Coll (BA) Pre-Med 1955; Hofstra Univ (MA) Bio 1958; 75 Credits in Sci, Ed; *cr:* Nassau Cty Medical Lab Cytologist 1955-58; Hofstra Univ Full Time Bio Instr 1958-64; South Huntington Schls Title I Prgm 1975-77; Syosset Pub Schls 9th-12th Grd Sci Tchr 1985-; *ai:* Establishment of Weather Station; NYSSTA 1984-; South Huntington Schl PTA, Treas; Old Firsts Presbyn Church 1970-, Moderator, Deacon, VP UPW; Writing Curr Nature Prgm at Sagamore Hall; *office:* Syosset HS South Woods Rd Syosset NY 11791*

FUCHS, HILDEGARD MARY, English Teacher; *b:* Cleveland, OH; *ed:* Western Reserve Un (BA) Eng, Soc Stud, Gifted 1965; Half Way to Masters Degree, Numerous Inservice Hrs; *cr:* Cleveland Bd of Ed Eng Tchr 1965-; *ai:* Stu Congress, Founder Eng Honorary, 10th Grd Bridges to Success Adv; Lead Tchr Broker-Career Beginners; GCTE 1965-, VP; NCTE 1965-; Sweet Adelines 1977-, Regent, Pres; Numerous Grants; PTA Lifetime Mbrshp Awd; Master Tchr-Martha Holden Jennings Fnd; Cleveland's Nomination OH Tchr of Yr; Outstdng Stu Cncl Adv Awd; 3 Outstdng Tchr Awds Jennings Fnd; *office:* Lincoln-West HS 3202 W 30th St Cleveland OH 44109

FUCHS, RICHARD WALTER, Art Teacher; *b:* Quito Ecuador, South America; *m:* Patricia Starjak; *ed:* Montclair St Coll (BA) Art Ed 1971; 15 Addl Hrs Supvr, Admin; *cr:* Washington Elem Schl Art Tchr 1972-93; Smith Long Meml Schl Art Tchr 1972-; Frank Elem Schl Art Tchr 1972-; *ai:* Safety Patrol Dir; Co-Founder, Dir Safety Town; Founder, Dir Safety Town Plus; Saddlebrook Ed Assn 1972-, VP 1976; NJ Ed Assn, NEA 1972-; Juvenile Conf Comm 1992-, Chm; Tchr of Yr PTA 1984; Outstdng Citizen Awd Saddlebrook Bd of Ed 1986; St NJ Governor's Tchr Recognition Prgm

1988; Amer Legion Citation Meritorious Svc, Outstdng Edctr 1989; *home:* 444 N Midland Ave Apt Q2 Saddle Brook NJ 07663

FUCHS, ROBERT ALAN, Math Teacher; *b:* New York City, NY; *ed:* Lehman Coll (BA) Math 1974; (MS) Math Jr HS 1977; *cr:* Yeshiva Turah Vemuvah Math Tchr 1974-76; JHS 125 Math Tchr 1977; Evander Childs HS Math Tchr 1977-; *ai:* Asst to AP & Math Supervision; AFT 1977-; VFT 1977-.*

FUGATE, ELIZA COMBS, Sixth Grade Teacher; *b:* Crockettsville, KY; *m:* Robert Jr.; *ed:* Morehead St Univ (BA) Elem Ed 1971; Attnd Ashland Univ, Lees Jr Coll; *cr:* Pioneer Joint Voc Schl Rdng Lab Asst 1971-72; Plymouth Local Schls Tchr 1972-; *ai:* NEA, OEA, PEA 1973-; *home:* 5316 State Route 39 W Shelby OH 44875

FUHRMAN, ELISABETH P., Fine Arts & Art History Tchr; *b:* Delaware County, PA; *m:* Garry W.; *c:* Matthew, Brandon, Kaitlin; *ed:* Millersburg Univ (BS) Art 1978; Working Towards Masters Art Ed, His Millersville Univ, Univ of DE; *cr:* Bridgeton Pub Schls K-6th Grd Art Tchr 1979-82; Warwick Schl Dist Grd 9-12 Art Tchr 1984-; *ai:* Stage Art Dir; NEA, PSEA, WEA 1984-; AENJ 1979-82; PAEA 1986-; Natl Preservation Trust 1994-.

FULCINITI, NICOLE C., Biology Teacher; *b:* Long Island, NY; *m:* Thomas; *ed:* Wagner Coll (BS) Bio 1992; Working on MS Sci Ed-Bio Coll of Staten Island; *cr:* St John Villa Acad Bio Tchr 1994-; *ai:* VIP Moderator; NABT 1994-; Ladies of Charity 1996-; *office:* St John Villa Acad HS 26 Landis Ave Staten Island NY 10305*

FULCOMER, WILLIAM E., Psychology & History Teacher; *b:* Latrobe, PA; *m:* Kathleen M.; *c:* William, Thomas, Michael; *ed:* Villanova Univ (BS) Ed SS, Eng 1960; St Joseph Univ 12 Credits; *cr:* Roman Cath HS Tchr 1960-75; Cardinal O'Hara HS Tchr 1975-; *ai:* Lacrosse Head Coach; Korate Instr; Natl Cath Ed Assn; *office:* Cardinal O Hara HS 1701 S Sproul Rd Springfield PA 19064

FULENA, STEPHANIE LEE, Coordinator of Gifted; *b:* New Castle, PA; *m:* Charles J.; *c:* LeeAnn A., RoseAnn M.; *ed:* Slippery Rock Univ (BS) Elem Ed 1978, (MS) Rdng Spec Ed 1986; 24 Credit Hrs Cmptr Instruction; 34 Credit Hrs Gifted Ed; *cr:* Union Area Schl Dist MS Tchr 1981-84, Coord of Gifted 1985-, Pub Relations Chprsn 1989-, Chapter I Self Coord 1993-; *ai:* Forensics Coach; Acad Games Coach; Brashear Problem Solving Coach; SERC Comm; Tchr Mentor; Pub Relations Comm; Union Focus Ed; PSEA, NEA & UAEA 1979-, Exec Cncl; PAGE & NAGE 1988-; Lawrence Co Rdng Cncl & Keystone St Rdng Assn 1993-; Lawrence Cty Historical Soc; Hoyt Inst of Fine Arts; Saint Vitus R C Church, Marriage Spon Couple; Southwest Instructional Video Cncl, Bd Mem; Slippery Rock Univ Outstanding Grad Stu; Curr & Instruction Prgm 1987; *office:* Union Area Mid & HS 2106 Camden Ave New Castle PA 16101

FULGINITI, JAMES KEVIN, Assistant Principal; *b:* Ridley Park, PA; *ed:* Albright Coll (BA) Sociology 1978; Widener Univ (MS) Ed 1986; Currently Enrolled in Doctoral Prgm at Widener Univ; *cr:* USAF Guardsmen Reservist 1985-87; PA Air Natl Guard Fighter Pilot 1980-; Unionville HS Soc Stud Tchr 1978-85; C. F. Patton MS Soc Stud Tchr 1987-92; Unionville HS Asst Prin 1993-; *ai:* Asst Yth Indoor Soccer Coach; Little League Asst Coach, Umpire; Windsor Baptist Church 1987-, Deacon, Advy Cncl, Sunday Schl Tchr for Adults; *office:* Unionville HS 750 Unionville Rd Kennett Square PA 19348

FULLAM, BONNIE BURNS, Mathematics Supervisor; *b:* Rockville Ctr, NY; *m:* Harland G.; *c:* Lori, Brett; *ed:* Hartwick Coll (BA) Math 1966; Univ of HI (Prof Dlp) Ed 1970; East Stroudsburg Univ (MED) Ed 1988; *cr:* Weber Jr High Schl Algebra Tchr 1966-68; Roxbury HS 9-12th Grd Math Tchr 1980-84; Centenary Coll Math Instr 1984-86; Hackettstown HS 5-12th Grd Tchr & Supvr 1986-; *ai:* NHS Fac Comm; NCTM 1983-; ASCD 1992-; PSA 1992-; WNET & Texaco Master Tchr; Channel 13 Golden Apple Awd; Clarkson Univ Exceptional Tchr Awd; 1990 Hackettstown Tchr of Yr Awd; *office:* Hackettstown HS 701 Warren St Hackettstown NJ 07840

FULLARD, BARBARA LOIS, English Teacher; *b:* New York, NY; *c:* Julien; *ed:* Howard Univ (BA) Eng 1970; Trinity Coll (MAT) Eng 1980; Univ of Dist of Columbia ODYSSEY PROJECT 1987; Multicultural Ed at UDC 1995; *cr:* J. Hayden Johnson Jr HS 7-9 Grd Eng, Jrnlsm, Pub Speaking, Dramatics, Creative Writing Tchr 1970-; *ai:* Schl Newspaper Adv, Ed; Remedial, Enrichment for Eng, Creative Writing, Jrnlsm Tutorial Instr; Johnson PTA Sec; WA Tchrs Union 1973-; Supts Acad for Humanities, Arts Tchng; Grant to Implement an Original Curr Dev for Humanities; Tchng Lit Classics to Academically Challenged Stdnts Curr Writer 1995; Writing Eng Stan for Office of Ed for Systematic Change; *office:* J Hayden Johnson Jr HS Bruce & Robinson Sts SE Washington DC 20020

FULLEM, LINDA DECARLUCCI, Eighth Grade English Teacher; *b:* Uniontown, PA; *m:* Robert A. Jr.; *c:* Marc Eric; *ed:* California Univ (BS) Eng 1970; WV Univ (ME) Rdng Specialist 1976; *cr:* Laurel Highlands Schl Dist Rdng & Eng Tchr 25 Yrs; *ai:* Wellness Comm Co-Chprsn; Strategic Planning Comm; NEA 1970-; YMCA Bd Mem 1979-81; Amer Heart Assn, Heart Safe Rep; *home:* 200 Brown Blvd Uniontown PA 15401

FULLER, ABIGAIL M., Elementary Art Teacher; *b:* West Springfield, MA; *c:* Gordon R. Dillard Jr., Aidan J. Dillard, Selene Dillard Sevigny, Stephen K. Dillard; *ed:* MA Coll of Art (BFA) Painting & Illustration 1960; Univ of MA at Amherst (MFA) Painting 1984; Art New England at Bennington Coll with 8 Grad Credits 1992 & 1993; 30 Plus Credits From North Adams St Coll, Syracuse Univ, Harvard Univ, Berkshire Comm Coll 1960-90; *cr:* Pittsfield Pub Schls Jr HS Art Tchr 1960-64; Stockbridge Pub Schl HS Art Tchr & 1st-12th Grd Art Supvr 1964-65; Art Tchr & Design & Drawing Instr 1965-84; Adams-Cheshire Regnl Schls Art Tchr 1985-; *ai:* NEA 1987-; AFT 1961-64; NAACP Berkshire Cty, Housing Chair, Brotherhood Awd; Urban Coalition Housing Task Force, Pittsfield Youth Resources Bd; Pittsfield Cultural Cncl Grant 1995-; Paintings Represented in Jurried Exhibitions Throughout the Northeast 1960-90; *office:* C T Plunckett Elem Schl 14 Commercial St Adams MA 01220*

FULLER, CHARLES LINCOLN, Science Teacher; *b:* Binghamton, NY; *m:* Kathryn Ann Dean; *c:* Gregory, Scott, Daniel; *ed:* Univ of PA (BA) Bio 1975; Univ of Scranton Instrl I Cert 1978; 28 Credit Hrs Post-Grad; *cr:* Elk Lake Schl Dist Sci Tchr 1977-85; Susquehanna Schl Dist Sci Tchr 1985-; *ai:* Video Productions Act Adv; Natl Jr Hnr Soc Fac Cncl; Dist Sci Exposition Comm; Track Booster Sec, Treas; PSEA, NEA 1977-; PIAA 1987, Track Ofcl; BSA 1995-, Troop Comm; PFT 89 1995-, Charter Mem; Northeast Ath Conf Track Coach of Yr 1988, 1990-91; *office:* Susquehanna Comm Schl Dist RD 3 Box 5A Susquehanna PA 18847*

FULLER, DARCY M., Spanish & German Teacher; *b:* Brockport, NY; *m:* Michael; *c:* Kurt, Kera; *ed:* Houghton Coll (BA) Ger 1975; Alfred Univ (MS) Rdng 1988; Attnd Univ of Mannheim Germany; *cr:* Alfred-Almond Cntrl Schl Ger, Span, Rem Rdng Tchr 1986-91; Scio Cntrl Schl Ger, Span Tchr 1991-; *ai:* Class of 96, Span Club Adv; Prom 96 Co-Advisor; AATG 1988-93; NEA 1986-; *office:* Scio Central Schl Washington St Scio NY 14880

FULLER, DRUSILLA OVERWYK, Art Teacher; *b:* Colorado Springs, CO; *c:* Lauren Elizabeth, Gwendolyn Ann; *ed:* Findlay Coll (BS) Art Ed 1973; SUNY at Stony Brook (MA) Lbrl Stud 1981; Attnd Parsons Schl of Design, Southampton Coll, SUNY at Farmingdale, Pratt; *cr:* Oakdale-Bohemia Rd Jr HS Grds 7-9 Art Tchr 1973-82; Connetquot HS Grds 10-12 Art Tchr 1983-; *ai:* Yrbk Adv; Art Club Adv; Jr Prom, Sr Prom, Sr Trip Chaperone; Mind Mapping Instr; Connetquot Tchrs Assn 1973-; Buzan Centre 1994-, Radiant Thinking Instr; PTSO 1973-; Tri-M Music Honor Soc Honorary Mem; Illustrator for The Vision, Superselff, Sunlight on Water, The Hendricks Holiday in NYC Activity Book; *office:* Connetquot HS 7th St Bohemia NY 11716*

FULLER, GARY DAVID, Social Studies Teacher; *b:* Abington, PA; *m:* Joyce Susan Wittmer; *c:* Zachary, Anna; *ed:* Penn St (BS) Educ-Soc Stud 1969; Beaver Coll (MED) Ed 1980; Trenton St Coll Prin Cert 1995; Admin Cert; *cr:* Haverford Sch Dist Soc Stud Tchr 1969-71; Cntrl Bucks Sch Dist Soc Stud Tchr 1971-; Phila Coll Sci, Textiles Soc Stud Prof 1995-; *ai:* Dean of Stdnts; Dept Chprsn; AD Admin Ath Dept; Supvr Club Acts; Mentor Tchr; Co-Chair 9th Grd Assessment Eng Exchange Prgm-Svc Learning; NEA, PSEA, CBEA 1969-; NCSS 1990-; Asst BSA Scout Master, Eagle Scout; Plumstead Twp Park, Rec 1988-, Chm; C B Schl Dist Tchry of Yr 1974-75; *home:* PO Box 235 Point Pleasant PA 18950*

FULLER, HOPE TOLIVER, Mathematics Teacher; *b:* Aliquippa, PA; *m:* Reuben J.; *c:* Reuben J. II, Debbie Rainey, Deanne; *ed:* Indiana Univ of PA (BS) Math 1968; Penn St 30 Credits; Duquesne Univ 8 Credits; Comm Coll of Beaver Cty 8 Credits; *cr:* Aliquippa Jr HS 7th-8th Grd Math Tchr 1968-71; Aliquippa Sr HS 9-12 Grd Acad Math Tchr 1973-; Yth Guid Inc Elem Club Coord 1988-; *ai:* Sr Class Spon; Detention Cnslr; Yth Guid Elem Club Cnslr, Summer Camp Recruiter; NEA 1968-, PSEA 1968-, Retirement & Welfare Comm; Aliquippa Ed Assn 1968-, Exec Bd; Modern Club 1985-, Pres 1991-95, VP 1987-91; Church Choir, Dir 1987-, Organist 1969-83; *home:* 307 4th Ave Aliquippa PA 15001*

FULLER, JULIAN RODNEY, Math Teacher; *b:* Baltimore, MD; *m:* Teresa Stevenson; *ed:* Howard Univ (BA) Math 1992; *cr:* Univ DC Math Instr 1993-94; Bowie Sr HS Math Tchr 1993-; *ai:* Chess Team Coach; NEA, PGCEA 1993-; *office:* Bowie Sr HS 15200 Annapolis Rd Bowie MD 20715

FULLER, KATHLEEN WILE, French Teacher; *b:* Gloucester, MA; *m:* Darryl William; *c:* Fitz William, Jenna Rose, Sarah Jane; *ed:* Univ of MA at Amherst (BA) Fr 1985; MA Prgm Simmons Coll Fr; *cr:* Gloucester HS Fr, Span Tchr 1986-; *ai:* Fr Club Adv; MaFla 1986-; Phi Betta Kappa, Phi Kappa Phi 1985-; *office:* Gloucester HS 32 Leslie O Johnson Rd Gloucester MA 01930

FULLER, KATHRYN DEAN, Fourth Grade Teacher; *b:* Binghamton, NY; *m:* Charles L.; *c:* Gregory D., Scott M., Daniel C.; *ed:* Kutztown Univ (BS) Elem Ed 1976; Masters Equivalency 36 Credit Hrs; *cr:* Susquehanna Comm 4th Grd Tchr 1976-; *ai:* NEA, PSEA, SCEA 1976-; BSA 1989-, Ldr 4 Yrs; Peals of Joy Comm Handbell Choir 1988-, Pres 2 Yrs; Delta Kappa Gamma 1988-; Kutztown Univ Alumni Band 1976-; *office:* Susquehanna Comm Schl Dist RD 3 Box 5A Susquehanna PA 18847

FULLER, KAY ANN (MARKEL), Second Grade Teacher; *b:* Windsor, PA; *m:* Ray F. Jr.; *ed:* Millersville St Coll (BS) Elem Ed 1970, (MED) Elem Ed 1973; 45 Addl Hrs Wilkes, Millersville; *cr:* Lower Chanceford Elem Schl Second Grd Tchr 1970-83; Clearview Elem Schl Second Grd Tchr 1983-; *ai:* Second Grd Tchrs Team Ldr; RLAEA, PSEA, NEA 1970-; Emanuel Luth Church 1950-, Adult Sunday Schl Tchr, WELCA Sec; Magazine Article Pub; *office:* Clearview Elem Schl RR 1 Box 340 Brogue PA 17309

FULLER, LOUIS JOSEPH, A P History & Economics Tchr; *b:* Philadelphia, PA; *ed:* Lebanon Vly Coll (BA) Soc 1976; Glassboro Univ (MA) Educl Admin 1980; 12 Credit Hrs Post-Masters Amer His, Cmptr Applications; *cr:* Eastern HS Soc Stud Tchr 1976-, Soc Stud Supvr 1981-86, Pub Information Offcr 1984-87, GATE Coord 1985-87; *ai:* AP Exam Facilitator; NEA, NJEA 1976-; EEA 1976-, Treas 1 Yr; Phi Delta Kappa, NCSS 1980-; ASCD 1982-; OAH 1987-; Jubilate Deo Chorale & Orchestra 1992-, Govt of Personnel 1994-; Tchr of Yr 1987-88; *office:* Easterm Camden Co Reg Schl Dst PO Box 2500 1306 Argyle Ave Voorhees NJ 08043

FULLER, MARY BAKER, Chemistry Instructor; *b:* Baltimore, MD; *m:* William H. Jr.; *c:* Kathleen, Rebecca; *ed:* Frostburg St Univ (BA) Bio, His 1972; Joshua Hopkins Univ (MLA) Sci 1974; Attnd Manhattan Coll, East Washington Univ, Univ of ME, Univ of AL at Huntsville; *cr:* Notre Dame Preparatory Schl Bio, Chem Instr 1972-74; Vo-Tech Ctr Sci Instr 1974-82; Fort Hill HS Chem Instr 1982-; *ai:* Soph Class Adv; NHS Review Bd; Sci Bowl, Chemathon Team Coach; Acting Sci Dept Head; NEA, MSTA 1983-; People to People Sci Ambassador to Soviet Union 1990; Edctrs in Space Prgm; *office:* Fort Hill HS 500 Greenway Ave Cumberland MD 21502

FULLER, PAMELA ANN, High School English Teacher; *b:* Queens, NY; *ed:* Cobleskill A&T (AAS) Animal Husbandry Horse 1980; Boston Univ (BA) Eng Lit 1983; Queens Coll (MSEd) Scndry Ed Eng 1991; Attnd Coll of Staten Island; *cr:* Samuel J. Tilden HS Tchr 1986-87; Paul Robeson HS Tchr 1987-88; August Martin HS Tchr 1988-89; Franklin D. Roosevelt HS Tchr 1989-; *ai:* NCTE 1986-; ASCD 1988-; Phi Delta Kappa 1995-; *office:* Franklin D Roosevelt HS 5800 20th Ave Brooklyn NY 11434

FULLERTON, ILA R., Fourth Grade Teacher; *b:* Pawtucket, RI; *m:* Kenneth N.; *ed:* Univ of RI (BA) Elem Ed 1962; 36 Addl Hrs; *cr:* Howard W. Hathaway Schl 4th Grd Tchr 1962-95; *ai:* NEA, NEA Portsmouth 1962-; Order of Eastern Star 1964-; *office:* Howard W. Hathaway Schl Tallman Ave Portsmouth RI 02871

FULTON, CURT SVEN, 6th Grd Math, Hlth & Dare Tchr; *b:* Gallitzin, PA; *m:* Linda DuBois; *c:* Grant, Gregory; *ed:* SUNY At New Paltz (BA) K-9 Elem, Fr Ed 1973, (MS) K-6 Ed 1976; *cr:* Wallkill Cntrl Schls 5th-6th Grd Math, Hlth Tchr 1973-; St Lukes Hosp Respiratory Technician 1984-92; Marlboro Police Dept Comm Officer 1993-; *ai:* Drug Abuse Resistance Ed Tchr; Instr, Presenter Tchr Center St Univ NY at New Paltz; AFT, NEA, NYSUT 1973-; Wallkill Tchrs Assn 1973-, Sec, Corresponding Sec; Marlboro Police Benevolent Assn 1993-; Marlboro Ambulance 1976-, Capt, Trng Dir, Pres, Vassar Hosp EMS Excl Awd; United Meth Church 1965-, Lay Speaker; Marlboro Yth Bsbl, Coach, Med Adv; NYS Schl Bds Assn Presenter 1989; NYS Certfd Emergency Med Technician Defibrillation Certfd 1976-; *home:* 137 Western Ave Marlboro NY 12542*

FULTON, GARY ROY, 6th Grade Teacher; *b:* Johnstown, PA; *c:* Michael, Kimberly Wolfe, Stacy; *ed:* IN Univ of PA (BS) Elem Ed 1966; Univ of Pittsburgh (MED) Elem Ed 1971; Elem Ed Prin Cert 1971; *cr:* Richland Schl Dist Tchr 1966-72; Conemaugh Twp Schl Dist Tchr 1972-; *ai:* PSEA 1966-; NEA 1966-; Conemaugh Twp Ed Assn 1977-, Treas; *office:* Conemaugh Twp Intermediate Sch RD 4 Box 49 Johnstown PA 15905

FULTON, LAURA LITTNER, Chemistry Teacher; *b:* Mittenwald, Germany; *m:* Martin Zemel; *c:* Jennifer Carroll; *ed:* Vassar Coll (BA) Chem 1969; Columbia Univ (MAT) Sci Ed 1973; *cr:* Commack Sawmill Jr HS 8th Grd Sci Tchr 1973-74; Commack HS North Chem Tchr 1974-83; Greece Cntrl Schl Dist 7th-8th Grd Sci, HS Chem Tchr 1983-; *office:* Greece Arcadia HS 120 Island Cottage Rd Rochester NY 14612

FULTON, RHONDA BEVERLY, Fifth Grade Teacher; *b:* Philadelphia, PA; *ed:* Temple Univ (MED) 1986; West Chester Univ (BA) Elem Ed; *cr:* Edward Gideon Elem Schl 4th Grd Tchr 1986-87, 5th Grd Tchr 1987-; *ai:* Bldg Comm; Schl & Schl Improvement Cncls; Commencement Coord; Ruth Hayre Schlsp Fund Chprsn; Phila Fed of Tchrs 1978-; AFT 1978-; Rose Lindebaum Awd Nom; Celebration of Excl in Tchng Semifinalist; *office:* Edward Gideon Elem Schl 2801 W Glenwood Ave Philadelphia PA 19121*

FULTZ, CARLA SIKORA, AP Chemistry Teacher; *b:* Tarentu Daniel G.; *c:* Charles, Alex; *ed:* Capital Univ (BA) Chem, Ed Stud at OH St Univ, Ashland Coll; *cr:* Owens Corning Fiberglass Analyst 1981-83; Rockwell Intnl quality Assurance Analys Bishop Watterson HS Chem Tchr 1985-91; Pickerington HS C 1992-; *ai:* Var Chrldng Coach; NHS Adv; PEA, OEA, NEA 19 Bldg Rep; ACS 1982-; SECO; TWIG SW5 1995-; *office:* Picker 300 Opportunity Way Pickerington OH 43147*

FULWILER, ARLEN L., Professor & Chair of Rdng, ESL; *b:* F TN; *m:* Karen L.; *c:* Ginger, Mary Beth; *ed:* Lincoln Meml Uni Bio 1959; East TN St Univ (MA) Rdng, Cnslng 1962; Univ of M Hrs; *cr:* Turkey Creek Elem Schl 4th Grd Tchr 1959-60; East T Grad Asst 1961-62; Sligo Jr HS 7-9th Grd Tchr 1962-63; Montg Schls Educl Diagnostician 1963-66; Montgomery Coll Prof, Cr *ai:* Rdng Amer Eng Lang Prgm Chair; Chrstn Flwshp C Assessment, ESOL Placement, Coll Rdng Comms; MD Comm Assn 1970-, Pres 1981-82; New Life Chrstn Schl Bd 1985-, C *office:* Montgomery Coll At Germantown 20200 Observ Germantown MD 20876*

FUNARO, MICHAEL JOSEPH, 5th-8th Grade Math Te Brooklyn, NY; *m:* Margaret Martello; *ed:* Queens Coll (BA) M 11 Grad Credits Long Island Univ; 4 Grad Credits Brooklyn Col Rosary Schl 7th-8th Grd Math Tchr 1970-72; Holy Spirit Schl 6 Math Tchr 1972-82; St Mary's Schl 5th-8th Grd Math Tchr 19 Frances Cabrini Schl 5th-8th Grd Math Tchr 1983-; *ai:* Math D Cath Schls Week Organizer of Christmas, Spring Show; NEA Prgm 1996; IM Bsktbl Prgm; Handball Tournaments; NEA 1970

FUNCHION, PEGGY JO, Learning Disabilities Teacher; *b:* OH; *ed:* Bowling Green St Univ (BSEd) Learning Disabilitie Behavior Handicap, Elem Ed 1973, (MSEd) Guid, Cnslng 198 Semester Hrs; *cr:* Napoleon Area Schls Tchr, Coach 1973-; *ai:* H Asst Girls Bsktbl Coach; NEA, OEA, NEA 1973-; Dist 7 Vlyb Assn, Pres; NW OH SERRC Outstdng Spec Edctr Awd 1991-92 Yr 1978, 1982; OH HS Vlybl Assn 1994-; 200 Vlybl, 253 JV Bsk Victories; *home:* 1353 Richmar Ln Napoleon OH 43545

FUNDERBURK, JANE MC BAIN, Chemistry Teacher; *b:* Bo *m:* John Rex; *c:* Anne, Kathryn; *ed:* Rosemont Coll (AB) Chem Marshfield HS Chem Tchr 1972-78; Barnstable HS Chem Tchr Archbishop williams HS Chem Tchr 1992-; *ai:* Curr, Schedulir BATA 1993-; NEACT 1996; NSF Grant Microscale Lab 19 Archbishop Williams HS 80 Independence Ave Braintree MA 0

FUNDERBURK, JOAN TEPOORTEN, Mathematics Teacher; *b* CO; *m:* Jeffrey M.; *c:* Keegan, Logan; *ed:* Univ of CO (BA) M *cr:* Overland HS Math Tchr 1989-91; St Rose HS Math Tchr Costume Design; NJMT, NCEA 1992-; NCTM 1988-.

FUNK, CONSTANCE ANN, 8th Grade Amer History Teacher Mawr, PA; *m:* Carl E.; *c:* Carl Joseph, Julia Marie; *ed:* Cedar (BA) His & Ger 1974; West Chester Univ (MA) His 1977; *cr:* Ce HS His Tchr 1974; Marple Newtown HS His Tchr 1974-76; Ellis Stud & Ger Tchr 1976-77; Springfield HS Soc Stud Tchr 197 Richardson MS Soc Stud Tchr 1981-; *ai:* Girls Track Coach; I Comm; NEA, PSEA 1974-; SEA 1977-; CYO 1991-, Coach; G 1989-95, Ldr; Camp Fire Girls 1995-, Ldr; Home & Schl Assn Comm Chm; Cub Scouts 1985-89, Ldr; DE Cty Chamber of Com Tchr Awd; PA Cncl of Soc Stud Tchr Excl; *office:* E T Richards W Woodland Ave Springfield PA 19064

FUNK, DANA SHEARER, Secondary Health & PE Te McConnellsburg, PA; *m:* Bill; *ed:* Frostburg St Univ (BS) Hlth & Working on Masters at Shippensburg St Univ in Spec Ed 12 Northern Lebanon Schl Dist Scndry Hlth & PE Tchr 1988-89; Mo Area Schl Dist Hlth & PE Tchr 1989-; *ai:* Sftbl Asst Coach; Girls Assn Adv; Schl Musical Vol; NEA, PSEA 1989-; Tri-Valley Sftb VP; *home:* 311 Cooper Ln Mc Connellsburg PA 17233

FUNK, JANICE ALTEMOSE, Math Tchr & Gifted Adv; *b:* P PA; *c:* Valerie Louise, Victoria Mae Funk Miller; *ed:* Shippensbu Math, Eng, Ed 1963; PA St (ME) Math, Ed 1986; Attnd Beaver C St, West Chester Univ, Marymount Coll; *cr:* West Chester Jr HS Math Tchr 1963-66; Pennridge Cntrl Jr HS 9th Grd Math, Gi 1966-70; North Penn Jr HS 9th Grd Math, Gifted Tchr 1973-82; N Sr HS Math, Gifted Tchr, Adv 1982-; *ai:* Intercounty Hnrs Sympo Coord; Math Coach; Acad Decathlon Team; NPAGE; Gifted Monitor; Auxillary Coach Math Team; NEA, PSEA, NPEA 1964- PCTM 1974-; ASA 1985-; PAGE, NPAGE 1988-; Lib Vol 199 Church, Vol Math Tutor 1977-; Delaware Vly Day Lily Soc, Oratorio Soc, September Opera Troupe 1989-; Chamber Arts Gui NPAGE Svc Awd; Recognition Outstdng Tchr Finalist Wilkes Uni Coll; EPCTM Speaker; Tchr Who Made A Difference Awd 199 North Penn HS 1340 S Valley Forge Rd Lansdale PA 19446*

FUNK, PATRICK EUGENE, Chemistry Instructor; *b:* Somerset Judith Ellen Case; *c:* Mike, Meghan; *ed:* OH St Univ Comprehensive Scis 1968; Temple Univ (MSEd) Biological S 1972; Doctoral Stud in Ed 1990-91; Summer Schl 1988-91; Cmpt Chem & Plant Physiology; *cr:* Reemlin HS General Sci Tchr Crookesville HS General Sci Bio Instr 1969-71; Sheridan HS B & Physics Instr 1972-88; Watkins Meml HS Chem Instr 1988-; *ai:* & JETS Team Adv; Sci Fair Dir; Ftbl Team Acad Adv; Bsktbl & V Teams Pub Address Announcer; COMU Tourney Adv; NEA, OEA, 1968- Dist Rep, Negotiator; OH Acad of Scis 1969-, Krecker A 1979 & 1991; Amer Chemical Soc 1981-, Sec 1991, Natl Test Co 1993; Lions Club 1980-, Sight Comm Chm; Somerset Emergenc 1977-89, Asst Chief, Ed Officer, CPR Instr; NSF Acad Yr I 1971-72; AZ Univ Inst of Chemical Ed Chemical Instrumentation 1993; Article Pub "Better Tchng " 1993; *office:* Watkins Meml Watkins Rd Pataskala OH 43062*

FUNKA, SERENA HECHT, 2nd Grade Teacher; *b:* Washington James L.; *c:* Kristy Lynn, Kelly Elizabeth; *ed:* CA Univ (BS) El Spcl Ed 1968; *cr:* Avalon Elem Primary Spcl Ed 1968-70, 3rd 1970-71, 2nd Grd Tchr 1971-; *ai:* Effective Schl Team & Prima Dept Chprsn; NEA 1968-; MSTA 1968-; Prince Georges Cty Ed 1968-; South Run Swim Team 1985-, Timer & Parent Vol; Lake B Booster Club; Nom Tchr of the Yr from Avalon Elem Schl; *office* Elem Schl 7302 Webster Ln Fort Washington MD 20744

FUNTEK, KAREN ANN, Sixth Grade Teacher; *b:* Cleveland, Saint John Coll of Cleveland (BS) Ed 1965; Case Western Reser (MA) Rdng 1969; *cr:* St Ignatius Elem Schl Sixth Grd Tchr Arlington Elem Schl Fifth, Sixth Grd Tchr 1967-69; W. J. Stroud E Sixth Grd Tchr 1969-81; Arlington Elem Schl Sixth Grd Tchr Pleasant Vly Elem Schl Sixth Grd Tchr 1993-95; *ai:* Stu Cncl Ad NEOEA, PEA 1967-; Alpha Delta Kappa 1969-, Historian, Treas Gamma Pi 1965-, Treas; Martha Holden Jennings Fnd 1975 Named Scholar, 1979 Received $2,000 Grant; *office:* Pleasant Valley El 9906 W Pleasant Valley Rd Parma OH 44130

FUQUA, LENIESE MARIE, 4th Grd Self-Contained Teacher; *b:* OH; *ed:* Univ of Cincinnati (BA) Elem Ed 1985, (MS) Educl Adm *cr:* Midway Elem Schl Tchr 1985-; *ai:* Racquetball Player; Under n Mentor; AFT 1995-; Young Democratic Party; Nom Afro-Amer Yr 1992; *home:* 2671 W North Bend Rd Cincinnati OH 45239

, MARIA A., Biology Teacher & Curr Leader; *b:* Bronx, NY; *ed:* tenville Coll (BA) Bio & Eng 1981; Columbia Univ (MA) Sci Ed ordham Univ EDD Anticipated 1997, Curr, Supervision & Admin; oll Scndry; *cr:* Msgr Scanlan HS Sci Tchr 1985-88; Ardsley HS Bio chr, 9th-12th Grd Curr Ldr 1988-; *ai:* Ind Sci Rsrch & Model UN dv; NABT 1985-; STANYS 1985-; Empire St Flwshp for Math & ipient 1985; Westchester Tchr Ctr Grant for Curr Dev Recipient Manhattan Coll Centennial Awd for Outstdng HS Tchrs 1992; ester Tchr Ctr Grant for Telecommunication & Tchng Curr Dev nt 1996; *office:* Ardsley HS 300 Farm Rd Ardsley NY 10502*

, FLORENCE L., Govt Ec & Humanitites Teacher; *b:* Canton, Tom; *c:* Jennifer, Christopher; *ed:* OH St Univ (BS) His 1972; Univ (BA) Ed & Latin 1974; Dayton Univ (MS) Cnslng 1985; +20 Credit Hrs Kent St Univ Ashlandand; *cr:* Carrollton HS Latin, ist, Govt, Ec & Ec Hum Tchr 22 Yrs; *ai:* Chrldr Adv 1976 & 1979; Jp WA Trip 1990; Chprsn for Soc Stud Dept 1990-; Delta Kappa 1985-; *office:* Carrollton HS 252 3rd St Carrollton OH 44615*

UELE, JANIS, Spanish & English Teacher; *b:* Rochester, PA; *ed:* of PA (BS) Span 1967; Attnd Univ of Valladolid Spain, Univ of , Millersville St Univ, Geneva Coll; *cr:* Rochester Areas Jr-Sr HS Eng Tchr 1967-; *ai:* Card Club Co-Spon; Ticket Sales Schl ; Steering Comm, Mid Sts Schl Evaluation; Dept Honors Adv; SEA, Rochester Area Ed Assn, PA St Foreign Lang Assn 1967-; Cty For Lang Teach 1990-; Delta Kappa Gamma Soc Intern 1980, 8-90; Gift of Time Tribute; *office:* Rochester Jr-Sr H S 540 Reno ester PA 15074

, ROBERT, Guidance Counselor; *b:* Brooklyn, NY; *m:* Sarah L. ; *c:* Matthew, Jennifer, Dennis, Robby, Douglas, Annie; *ed:* Univ of (BS) Eng & PE 1971; Xavier Univ (MED) Ed & Guidance 1973; l Credit Hrs; Inst for Reality Therapy Intensive Stud Cert; *cr:* Univ Ftbl Asst Coach 1971-73; Greenhills HS 9th-12th Grd Eng 973-91; Winton Woods HS Eng Tchr 1991-93; Princeton HS e Cnslr 1993-95; Mason HS Guidance Cnslr 1995-; *office:* William HS 770 S Mason-Montgomery Rd Mason OH 45040

LO, MARY BEARD, English & Reading Instructor; *b:* Cleveland, Michael J.; *c:* Michael O., Robert, Kerry Bauer, Kim; *ed:* Hiram A) Eng 1960; Akron Univ (MA) Scndry Ed 1985; Attnd Kent St shland Univ, Walsh Coll; *cr:* James A. Garfield 7-12 Grd Eng Tchr ; Crestwood HS 7-12 Eng, Rdng Tchr 1077-; *ai:* CEA 1977-; NEA, 1960-; Jr Women 1960-, Pres; 20th Century 1986-, Pres; *office:* od HS 10919 N Main St Mantua OH 44255

NG, CATHLEEN ANNE, K-2nd Grade Multi-Age Teacher; *b:* epsie, NY; *m:* Allan Herschlag; *ed:* New England Coll (BA) Elem ; Univ of NH (MED) Early Chldhd Ed 1985; 30 Credit Hrs Educl Cmptr Tech, Rdng Recovery, Tchng Writing; *cr:* Hillsboro Elem dgtn, Readiness Tchr 1977-83; Pembroke Hill Schl Readiness, econd Grd Tchr 1982-88; Rumford Schl First, 1st-2nd Grd ge Tchr 1988-91; Beaver Meadow Schl 1st, 1st-2nd, K-1-2 Grd ge Tchr 1991-; *ai:* Notre Dame Coll Adj Fac 1994-95; NH Tech Fac 1995; NH Readiness Assn 1977-; NEA 1982-; Granite St Rdng 86-; Concord Chamber of Commerce Ed Grants 1994-95; Japanese Mc Auliffe Grant 1995; Concord Innovative Projects 1991, 1993; ame Coll Wkshp Presenter 1994-95; Granite St Rdng Assn Spring kshp Presenter 1994-; *office:* Beaver Meadow Schl 40 Sewalls Falls cord NH 03301*

AN, ANN MARIE, Third Grade Teacher; *b:* Johnstown, PA; *ed:* Pittsburgh (BS) Elem Ed 1970; IN Univ of Pennsylvania (MED) d 1975; *cr:* Conemaugh Vly Schls Elem Tchr 1970-; *ai:* NEA, 970-; Keystone St Rdng Cncl, Greater Johnstown Rdng Cncl 1985-; Pgh Alumni Assn 1994-; *home:* 177 Strayer St Johnstown PA 15906

AN, MINDY, Sci Dept Chair & Biology Tchr; *b:* Passaic, NJ; *m:* : Joshua, Andrew, Benjamin; *ed:* Univ of MS (BS) Microbiology ontclair St Univ (MAT) Sci Tchng 1984; NY Medical Coll (PHD) ology 1989; *cr:* NY Medical Coll Post Doctoral Fellow 1989-91; ch Schl Bio Tchr 1991-93, Sci Dept Chair 1993-; *ai:* AAAS, NY Scis 1989-; NJ Sci Tchrs Assn 1991-; *office:* The Frisch Schl 243 t Paramus NJ 07652

ATO, TARYN JAYNE, High School Biology Teacher; *b:* Summit, Matthew J. Jr.; *c:* Christopher; *ed:* Cook Coll & Rutgers Univ (BS) 981; Attnd Coll of Atlantic at Bar Harbor; *cr:* Hopewell Vly HS Life Sci Tchr 1982; Hillsborough HS Bio Tchr 1982-; *ai:* Bicycle v 1982-88; Sr Class Adv 1985-94; Plant-A-Thon Adv 1989; Jr-Sr dv; NJEA 1982-; NEA 1982-; NJSEA; NJ Bio Tchrs Assn; *office:* ough HS Raider Blvd Belle Mead NJ 08502

RI, KIMBERLY A., 7th-8th Grade Science Teacher; *b:* wn, PA; *c:* Alissa, Kristen; *ed:* Univ of Pittsburgh at Johnstown Scndry Sci 1991; Masters Degree in Cnslr Ed 1996; *cr:* Cntrl MS Sci Tchr 1991-; *ai:* Stu Cncl Adv; Stu Assistance Prgm; Group or; PA St Educ Assn 1991-; PA Schl Cnslrs Assn 1994-; PA Assn 1995-; Cntrl Cambria Educ Assn 1991-, Treas; Scholars in Ed Awd lsp; Beta Beta Beta; *office:* Central Cambria MS 205 W Highland nsburg PA 15931*

SHEILA FROST, First Grade Teacher; *b:* Batavia, NY; *m:* Laney lizabeth, Thomas; *ed:* SUNY at Brockport (BS) Ed 1968; 30 Hr d Remedial Rdng 1975; *cr:* Caledonia-Mumford 4th Grd Tchr ; LeRoy Cntrl Schl 1st Grd Tchr 1979-; *ai:* Wellness Comm; Comm tion Drug & Alcohol Awareness; Parents as Rdng Partners; Grd NYSUT 1979-; LeRoy Comm Intervention 1984-; *home:* 8281 E Le Roy NY 14482

VIG, KAREN MCGRATH, Business & Computer Ed Tchr; *b:* k City, NY; *m:* Mark J.; *c:* Jeanette; *ed:* Glassboro St Coll (BA) Ed : Hank Forsberg Advertising Inc Media Buyer & Accounting Asst ; Ramapo Ridge Jr HS Tchr 1977-80; Holy Family Acad Tchr *i:* Jr Class Coord; NHS Selection Comm; NCEA 1983-; NJAET *ffice:* Holy Family Acad 239 Avenue A Bayonne NJ 07002

, DEBORAH NORQUIST, Second Grade Teacher; *b:* Columbus, Chris Wendell; *c:* Kristen Annelle, Nathan Charles, Alison Nicole; kingum Coll (BA) Elem Ed, Psyc 1975; *cr:* Noble Local Remedial chr 1975-78, 2nd Grd Tchr 1978-; *ai:* NEA 1975-; *office:* oah Elem Schl 20977 State ROute 146 Sarahsville OH 43779

K, BARBARA ANN, English Teacher; *b:* Holyoke, MA; *ed:* Our Elms Coll (BA) Eng 1972; Masters Degree Candidate; Attnd Univ stfield St Coll, Holyoke Comm Coll; *cr:* Frontier Regnl Schl Eng 2-; *ai:* Globelink; Eng Dept; FTA Comm; NCTE; NEA, MTA, FTA Elms Coll Alumnae Assoc 1972-; Twenty Yr Svc Awd Frontier chl Dist; *office:* Frontier Regnl Schl 311 N Main St South Deerfie 73

K, HOWARD LEON, Physical Education Teacher; *b:* Bridgeton, Hope, Amy; *ed:* Glassboro St Coll (BA) Hlth, PE 1975; *cr:* n Pub Schls Hlth, PE Tchr 21 Yrs; *ai:* Winter Track Head Coach 8 St Championships; Spring Track Asst Coach 14 Yrs, 5 St onships; NEA, NJEA, Bridgeton Ed Assn 1975-; South Jersey Track Coaches Assn Winter Track Coach of Yr 1991, 1993-94; *home:* 40 Sycamore Rd Millville NJ 08332

FUSCO, ANDY ANTHONY, 10th Grade Mathematics Tchr; *b:* Amsterdam, NY; *m:* Ellen; *c:* Lynette, Adam; *ed:* SUNY at Potsdam (BA) Math Ed 1972; 60 Credit Hrs Permanent Cert SUNY at Geneseo; *cr:* York Cntrl HS Math Tchr 1972-95; *ai:* JV Wrestling 1972-81; JV Ftbl 1984-87; Jr HS Ftbl 1987-94; NYSUT; *office:* York Cntrl HS PO Box 102 Rt 3 Retsof NY 14539

FUSCO, FRANK L., Community Service Director; *b:* Brooklyn, NY; *ed:* ICCOP-Siena Coll (BA) Philisophy 1973; St John's Univ 15 Credits Ed; *cr:* Bishop Ford Cntrl Cath HS Tchr 1973-; *ai:* IM Dir; Founder PIC, PY, HS Stdnts Image Prgms; NCEA 1973-; Make-A-Wish Fnd; *office:* Bishop Ford Cntrl Cath HS 500 19th St Brooklyn NY 11215*

FUSCO, JANET, English Teacher; *b:* Newark, NJ; *ed:* Bloomfield Coll (BA) Eng, Fr 1973; Fairleigh Dickenson Univ (MAT) Ed 1980; Penn St Univ Addl Grad Credits; *cr:* Blue Cross of NJ Contract Writer 1973-78; St Vincent Acad 9th Grd Tchr 1978-79; Queen of Peace HS Eng Tchr 1979-; *ai:* Sr Class Adv; Coord Pre HS Summer Prgm; After Schl Stud Prgm Moderator; Soc Adventures Club Moderator; NCTE 1979-; ASCD 1987-; NJCTE 1991-; Archdiocese of Newark Tchr Recognition Awd 1992; *office:* Queen Of Peace HS 191 Rutherford Pl North Arlington NJ 07031

FUSCO, LEONA JEAN, Mathematics Teacher; *b:* Bridgeport, CT; *ed:* Western CT (BS) Ed 1964; Univ of Bpt (MS) Ed 1967; 6th Yr Lang Arts 1978; Assorted Credits Ed; *cr:* Franklin Schl 3-5 Grd Elem Tchr 1964-70; East Side MS 6-8 Grd ESOL Tchr 1970-77, 6-8 Grd Lang Dev Tchr 1977-81; Blackham MS 6-8 Grd Lang Arts Tchr 1981-90, 7-8 Grd Math Tchr 1990-; *ai:* yrbk Adv, Co-Adv; BEA, CEA, NEA 1964-; How Help Stdnts Increase Scores Various Stud Techniques, Bringing Lang Arts Alive, Yrbk Memories Grant; *office:* Blackham MS 425 Thorme St Bridgeport CT 06606*

FUSCO, PAULA G., Social Studies Teacher; *b:* Westerly, RI; *ed:* Providence Coll (BS) Hlth Svcs Admin 1986, (MA) Scndry Admin 1995; *cr:* Westerly HS Soc Stud Tchr 1990-; *ai:* Soph Class Adv; NEA, NEARI 1990-; *office:* Westerly HS 23 Ward Ave Westerly RI 02891

FUSELIER, CYNTHIA MARANICH, English Teacher; *b:* Pittsburgh, PA; *m:* Peter A.; *ed:* Duquesne Univ (BS) Comm 1978, (MS) Schl Psych 1981; Psychologist Cert 1991; Courses Penn St Univ, Univ of UT, Robert Morris Coll, Univ of Pittsburgh; *cr:* Finley Jr HS Eng Tchr 1979-82; Trinity HS Eng Tchr 1982-; Washington Coll Adj Prof 1992-; Jefferson Coll Adj Prof 1992-; *ai:* Classes of 1989, 1996, Key Club, FTA Adv; PSEA, NEA 1979-; South Hills Power Squadron 1988-, Sec, Newsletter Ed, Journalistic Excl Awd 1995; Pristine Fields 1995-, Bd of Dir; Holy Rosary Church 1995-, Eucharistic Minister, Altar Soc; *office:* Trinity HS Park Ave Washington PA 15301*

FUSS, CHRISTOPHER C., Mathematics & Science Teacher; *b:* Barberton, OH; *m:* Julie Anne; *c:* Alexander; *ed:* The Univ of Akron (BA) Ed, Math 1990, (MA) Ed, Bus Admin 1994; 21 Addl Semester Hrs Ec; *cr:* Southeast Local Schls Math, Sci Tchr 1990-; Coll of Wooster Math Prof 1991; *ai:* NEA, NCTM 1990-; Eagle Scout 1986; *office:* Waynedale HS 9050 Dover Rd Apple Creek OH 44606

FUTRELL, MICHELLE TOBIN, Nutrition Professor; *b:* New York, NY; *m:* Ronald Sr.; *c:* Tiffany Flanagan, John Eric Smith, Ronald Jr., Shawndell; *ed:* Brooklyn Coll CUNY (BA) Nutrition 1980; Hunter Coll CUNY (MS) Nutrition 1986; *cr:* Hunter Coll Lecturer 1986-; Hostos Comm Coll Lecturer 1988-; NY Univ Lecturer 1991-; Brooklyn Coll Lecturer 1994-; Goldstar Consultants Pres; *ai:* Abyssinian Bapt Church Mem; CBNP 1985-, Chprsn; GNYDA 1990-; ADA 1980-; Comm to Promote Breast Feeding 1990-; Registered Dietitian; Cert Dietitian, Nutritionist; Michael Hisch Awd; NYSDOH-AIDS Inst Awd; *office:* Hostos Comm Coll 475 Grand Concourse Bronx NY 10451

FYE, JERRY E., 5th Grade Teacher; *b:* DuBois, PA; *m:* Bonnie Joyce Anderson; *c:* Chad, Ryan; *ed:* Southwestern Coll (BA) Elem Ed, PE 1972; Addl 24 Credits for PA St Cert Clarion Univ, Slippery Rock & Wilkes Coll; *cr:* Halstead Elem Schl 6th-7th Grd Math Tchr 4 Yrs; Charles G. Johnson Elem Schl DuBois Area Schl Dist 5th Grd Tchr 10 Yrs; Sykesville Elem Schl DuBois Area Schl Dist 5th Grd Tchr 5 Yrs; *ai:* Stu Cncl Adv; Ecomeet Ldr; Coached Bsktbl 1982-89; PSEA, NEA 1982-; *home:* 232 Main St Falls Creek PA 15840

FYHR, GORDON PHILIP,JR., English Teacher; *b:* Brockton, MA; *c:* Joseph, Richard; *ed:* Boston Univ (BS) Eng 1962; Attnd OH St Univ, St Univ of NY at Albany, St Univ of NY at New Paltz; *cr:* Saugerties HS Eng Tchr 1963-; *ai:* Schl Newspaper 1963-71; Sr Class Play 1964-78; Quiz Team 1965-; Yrbk 1975-79; Cornell Model Congress 1989-; Saugerties TA 1963-, Rep Assembly & Negotiations Team; NYSUT 1963-; NCTE 1963-; Boston Univ Alumni Rep 1980-; Eng Dept Chprsn 1970-81; *office:* Saugerties HS Washington Ave Saugerties NY 12477

FYNN, CAROL WITWER, English & Psychology Teacher; *b:* Findlay, OH; *m:* David C.; *c:* Nicola, Luke; *ed:* Wittenberg Univ (BA) Psych, Eng 1971; Kent St Univ (MED) Guid & Cnslng 1979; *cr:* Kirtland MS Lang Arts Tchr 1971-73; Kirtland HS Eng, Psych Tchr 1975-; *ai:* AFS Club Adv; Lead Stu Tours Abroad Annually; NEOTA 1976-; Ashland Oil Tchr Achvmt Awd 1991; *office:* Kirtland HS 9150 Chillicothe Rd Willoughby OH 44094

FYSZ, JOSEPH JOHN, Mathematics Teacher; *b:* Trenton, NJ; *ed:* Rider Coll (BA) Scndry Ed 1978; Univ of NH (MST) Math 1991; Geometer's Sketchpad Inst, Discovery Geometry Inst Key Curr Press; *cr:* Trenton Cntrl HS Biling, Bicultural Math Tchr 1978-83; Steinert HS Math Tchr 1983-; *ai:* NEA, NJEA 1978-; NCTM 1985-; *office:* Steinert HS 2900 Klockner Rd Trenton NJ 08690

G

GAAB, JEFFREY S., Assistant Professor of History; *b:* Bethpage, NY; *ed:* Hofstra Univ (BA) European His 1985; SUNY Stony Brook (MA) Modern European His 1987, (PHD) Modern Ger His 1992; *cr:* SUNY Stoney Brook Schl Grad Asst Tchr 1986-89; Nassau Comm Coll Adj Asst Prof 1990-91; SUNY Farmingdale His Instr 1991-93, His Asst Prof 1993-; *ai:* Fac Adv; His Club; Stu Affairs Comm; Amer Historical Assn 1985-; Max Kade 1995-; United Univ Profession 1991-; US Aid Grant 1993-94; United Univ Professions Grant 1995; Articles Pub; Paper Pub 1996; *office:* S U N Y Coll Of Tech At Frmgdl Rt 110 Melville Rd Farmingdale NY 11735

GABB, PHILIP LAWRENCE, Sixth Grade Teacher; *b:* Nanticoke, PA; *m:* Mary Kathryn Hospador; *c:* Jonathan, Sarah; *ed:* Attnd Penn St Univ, Clarion Univ, Mansfield Univ; *cr:* Athens Area Schls Tchr 1969-; *ai:* NEA, PSEA; AAEA 1969-, Treas; PIAA Ofcl 1975-, Ofcl; Credit Union 1980-, Pres; Elks Drug, Alcohol Chm Lodge #1148; *office:* Harlan Rowe MS 0 Pennsylvania Ave Athens PA 18810

GABBARD, PAULA D., Fourth Grade Teacher; *b:* Dayton, OH; *ed:* OH Univ (BS) Elem Ed 1968; *cr:* Fairborn City Schl Fourth Grd Tchr 1968-72; Valley View Local Schls Fourth Grd Tchr 1972-; *ai:* OEA, NEA, 1968-; VVCTA 1972-.

GABEL, NANCY J., Frgn Lang Chair & Fr Teacher; *b:* Newark, NJ; *m:* Richard; *c:* Ellen, Jane; *ed:* Wheaton Coll (BA) Fr 1961; Mid Grad Schl of Fr in France (MA) Fr Culture & Civ 1962; *cr:* Wallingford-Swarthmore Schl Dist Fr Tchr & Frgn Lang Chair 1962-; *ai:* Exch Pgm Spon & Organizer Lycees in Paris; PSMLA 1980-; ACTF 1980-; MLAPV; AATF 1980-, Sec-Treas, VP & Pres 1985-93; Fr Intnl Schl of Philadelphia 1990-, Chm of the Bd 1995; Commonwealth Partnership Frence Inst in PA & France Asst Dir 1987-89; Williams Coll Olmsted Awd Excl in Tchng 1990; Journal Francais d'Amerique Connaissance de l'Actualite Prize 1995; *office:* Strath Haven HS 205 S Providence Rd Wallingford PA 19086

GABEL, PATRICIA RIELINGER, 6th-8th Grade Teacher; *b:* Cleveland, OH; *m:* Terrel L.; *c:* Brian, Bradley, Bridget, Brittany; *ed:* Cleveland St Univ (BA) His 1972; *cr:* St Mark Schl Tchr Grd 6-8 Soc Stud & Rel 1988-; *ai:* His Day Chprsn.

GABELE, SUSAN ELAINE, English Teacher; *b:* Perth Amboy, NJ; *m:* Jay Allen Gabele; *ed:* Columbia Union Coll (BA) Eng Ed 1990; Western MD Coll, Trinity Coll Post Grad Work; *cr:* John Nevins Andrews Elem Jr High Eng Tchr 1990; Takoma Acad Eng Tchr 1990-; *ai:* Class Spon Frosh 1992-93, Soph 1991-92; Stu Govt, Pep Club Spon 1993-; Admin Discipline Comm 1992-; Stdnt govt Spon 1993-; Bkstore Mngr 1995-; NCTE 1992-; NASSP 1994-; *office:* Takoma Acad 8120 Carroll Ave Takoma Park MD 20912

GABLE, DAVID JOSEPH, Biology Teacher; *b:* York, PA; *m:* Amy McFarland; *c:* Clay, Allyson; *ed:* Franklin & Marshall Coll (BA) Anthropology 1986; Millersville Univ Tchr Cert Bio 1988; Masters Equivalency 1996; *cr:* Dallastown Area Schl Dist HS Bio Tchr 1988-; *ai:* Var Wrestling Coach; Intramural Weight Training; Bio Summer Field Stud Coord; Career Integration Comm; NEA, PSEA 1988-; *office:* Dallastown Area Sr HS 700 New School Ln Dallastown PA 17313

GABLE, KENT ERIC, Math Teacher; *b:* York, PA; *m:* Heather Sue Mihm; *ed:* Millersville Univ (BS) Ed, Math 1990, (MS) Ed, Math 1995; *cr:* York City HS Math Tchr 1990-93; York Suburban HS Math Tchr 1993-; *ai:* NHS Adv; Asst Girls Sftbl Coach; Math Curr Comm; NEA, PSEA 1990-; *office:* York Suburban HS 1800 Hollywood Dr York PA 17403

GABLE, MARIAN E., Laboratory Facilitator; *b:* Coatesville, PA; *ed:* Kutztown Univ (BS) Scndry Ed & Eng 1966, (MED) Scndry Ed & Eng 1971; Attnd Rosemont Coll Ed Tech Stud; *cr:* Exeter Jr HS Eng Tchr 1966-95, Cmptr Lab Facilitator 1995-; *ai:* ETEA, PSEA, NEA 1966-; ISTE 1995-; Fellowship PA Writing Project; *office:* Exeter Jr H S 151 E 39th St Reading PA 19606

GABLE, MICHAEL FRANCIS, Professor of Biology; *b:* Lancaster, PA; *ed:* Univ of FL (BS) Zoology 1967; Univ of NH (MS) Zoology 1969, (PHD) Zoology 1972; *cr:* Eastern CT St Univ Asst Prof 1972-77, Assoc Prof 1977-82, Prof 1982-; Peabody Museum Yale Univ Curatorial Affiliate 1987-; *ai:* Departmental & Univ Comms Club Adv; New England Estuarine Rsrch Soc 1970-; Soc for Comparative & Integrative Bio 1972-; AAUP 1977-; Crustacean Soc 1981-; Biological Soc of WA 1985-; CT Acad of Arts & Scis 1988-; Amer Soc of Parasitologists 1991-; Pub; 8 CT St Univ Rsrch Grants; Yale Visiting Fac Prgm; Pres Awd Distngd Tchng ECSU 1975; Distngd Fac Mem of Yr Awd ESCU 1994; *office:* Eastern CT St Univ 83 Windham St Willimantic CT 06226

GABRIEL, ANN LOUISE, Library-Media Specialist; *b:* Hazleton, PA; *ed:* Southern CT St Univ (BS) Lib, Media Ed 1969, (MS) Cnslng 1975; 6th Yr Marriage, Family Therapy 1985; *cr:* West Haven HS Lib-Media Specialist 1969-; West Haven Yth Svc Bureau Family Therapist 1990-; *ai:* NHS, Schl Newspaper Adv; Theater Wkshp Asst Dir; Stu Asst Team Case Coord; WH Fed of Tchrs, AFT 1969-, Steward Asst; AAMFT 1985-; ACA 1987-; CT Drama Assn 1972-, Sec; West Haven Drug, Alcohol Task Force 1983-, Sec; Article Pub; Co-Writer, Svc Provider Project SAINT Grant; *office:* West Haven HS 1 Circle St West Haven CT 06516

GABRIEL, CAROL A., Home Economics Teacher; *b:* Husbey, PA; *m:* George; *c:* Michael, Holly Thomee, Dawn Desmond, Nicole; *ed:* IN Univ of PA (BS) Home Ec 1963; Montclair St Univ (MSEd) Home Ec, Family 1972; Cooperative Ed, Supervision, Prin, Spec Ed Cert; Post Grad Stud; *cr:* Raritan Twp HS Home Ec Tchr 1963-64, 1966-67; Henry Hudson Regnl HS Home Ec Tchr 1965-66; Freehold Regnl HS Home Ec Tchr 1967-69; Monmouth Regnl HS Home Ec Tchr 1971-; *ai:* FHA Club Adv; Curr Comm; Dept Chair Backup; Minority Mentor Acad Achvmt Prgm; NEA, NJEA 1963-; MREA 1972-, Legislative Acton Team; Amer Assn Family & Consumer Sci, Mon Ocean Family & Consumer Sci 1963-, Mbrshp Chair; NJ Assn Family & Consumer Sci; AAUW 1995-; UHEEA 1980-, Networking Chprsn; NY Lyme Disease Support Group 1988-, Pres; NJ Lyme Coalition 1990-, Sec, Bd; Lyme Disease Assn NJ; Cath Daughters of Amer 1980-; Educl Grants; Certfd Family & Consumer Sci Home Economist; 1992 Karen Opyoke Outstdng FHA-HERO Adv; 1983 Voc Ed Tchr Excl Home Ec Ed; Field Tested Child Dev Curr, H Econ Competency Based Curr; *office:* Monmouth Regional HS 1 Norman J Field Way Tinton Falls NJ 07724*

GABRIEL, CYNTHIA JEAN, English Tchr & Professor; *b:* Little Falls, NY; *ed:* Herkimer Cty Comm Coll (AA) Hum 1987; Oneonta St Coll (BS) Scndry Eng Ed 1989, (MA) Eng Amer Lit Romanticism 1993; Sign Lang ASL; Daedalus & Distance Learning Instr; *cr:* Richfield Springs Cntrl Schl 8th-12th Grd Eng Tchr 1989-; Mohawk Cntrl Schl Summer Schl Eng Instr 1993-; Herkimer Cty Comm Coll Eng Instr & Prof 1994-; *ai:* Class Adv; Prom Chairwoman; Schl Play Dir; Kids on the Block Adv; Bloodmobile Coord; Co-Chairwoman for Pop Warner Season & Home Base Cooperating Tchr & Mentor; AFT 1989-; *home:* 249 E Steele St Herkimer NY 13350*

GABRIEL, JANET FLORENDO, High School Math Teacher; *b:* Manila, Philippines; *m:* George; *ed:* Philippine Normal Coll (BS) Math-Cum Laude 1982; Jersey City St Coll 24 Credit Hrs Urban Ed Masters; *cr:* St Elizabeth Schl Elem Tchr 1987-93; William Dickinson HS HS Math Tchr 1993-; *ai:* NCTM, NEA 1193-, Mem; *office:* William L Dickinson HS 2 Palisade Ave Jersey City NJ 07306

GABRIEL, JOHN DAVID, Teacher, Priest & Yth Minister; *b:* Paterson, NJ; *ed:* Seton Hall Univ (BA) Psych, Philosophy 1982; Immaculate Conception Seminary & Grad Schl of Theology (MDiv) Theology, Pastoral Ministry 1986; *cr:* Eastern Chrstn Childrens Retreat Spec Ed Tchr 1979-83; Fair Lawn Opportunity Ctr Spec Ed Tchr 1984-86; Roselle Cath HS Campus Ministry Dir, Guid Tchr 1987-91; St Thomas the Apostle Church & Schl Parochial Vicar, Tchr 1991-; *ai:* HS Yth Ministry Moderator; Liturgy Comm; Chaplain; Bloomfield Police Benevolent Assn 1992-, Chaplain; Bloomfield Emergency Squad 1991-, Chaplain; Cath League for Rel & Civil Liberty 1995-; *office:* St Thomas The Apostle Schl 60 Byrd Ave Bloomfield NJ 07003

GABRIEL, JUDITH A. (TOBIAS), English Teacher; *b:* Reading, PA; *ed:* Kutztown Univ (BS) Eng Ed 1971, (MED) Eng Ed 1977; 15 Addl Hrs Eng Ed; Advanced Placement Carnegie Mellon; Massage Therapy Degree Avocation; *cr:* Hamburg Area Jr Sr HS Tchr 25 Yrs; *ai:* AP Eng Tchr, Drama Tchr, Chrldng & Club Adv, Honor Soc Comm; *home:* 319 Grant St Leesport PA 19533

GABRIEL, PETER JAMES, Social Studies Teacher; *b:* Sharon, PA; *m:* Julia Roberts; *c:* Peter, Joseph; *ed:* Slippery Rock Univ (BS) Scndry His 1969; YSU Masters Scndry Admin 1973; Post Grad Kent, Akron, Walsh, Drake; *cr:* Hubbard Schls 6th Grd Tchr 1969-71; Girard Schls Scndry Soc Stud, Jr, Sr World, US, Vietnam His Tchr 1971-; Trumbull Cty Joint Voc Schl Summer Schl, His Tchr 1987-95; *ai:* Head Girls Vlybl, Fastpitch Sftbl Coach; OEA, NEA 1969-; GEA 1971-, Pres, VP 1981-85; OH Cncl Soc Stud 1971-; *office:* Girard HS 31 N Ward Ave Girard OH 44420

GABRIEL, ROBERT F., Theology Chm & Teacher; *b:* Brooklyn, NY; *ed:* St Francis Coll (BA) His 1969; Wagner Coll (MS) Ed 1976; 6 Credit Hrs Fordham Univ; *cr:* Our Lady of Angels Schl 6th Grd Tchr 1968-69, 8th Grd Tchr 1969-76, Prin 1976-92; *ai:* Campus Ministry; Liturgical Preparation; Help Our Planet Earth Moderator; NCEA 1968-; ASAP 1976-92; *office:* St Anthony's HS 275 Wolf Hill Rd Melville NY 11747

GACCIONE, ANNE MARIE CALISE, Social Studies Teacher; *b:* Passaic, NJ; *m:* Peter J.; *c:* Joseph, Victoria; *ed:* Montclair St Coll (BA) Soc Stud 1976; William Paterson St Coll Tchng Cert 1978; *cr:* Clifton Bd of Ed Soc Stud Tchr 1979-80, 1986-; *ai:* HS Graduation Honor Guard 1993-; Mid Sts Evaluation Comm Chprsn Visual Arts 1995-; Grading Comm 1989-91, Fac Advy Comm 1988-90; NEA, NJEA, PCEA 1986-; Clifton Tchrs Ass 1986-, Del; Clifton Safety Town Dir 1985-87, Dir; Passaic Cty Juvenile Conf Comm 1982-, Vol; Safety Town 1995-, Vol; St Philip Rel Ed 1988-91, Vol; *home:* 60 Lockwood Pl Clifton NJ 07012

GACIOCH, FRANCIS JOSEPH, High School Mathematics Tchr; *b:* Binghamton, NY; *m:* Patricia Amberg; *c:* Mary Beth, Joseph, Jonathan; *ed:* Brooke Comm Coll (AA) Math 1973; Cortland St Univ (BA) Scndry Ed & Math 1975; Nazareth Coll of Rochester (MA) Scndry Ed & Spec Ed 1980; *cr:* Victor Cntrl Schls PSEN Dir & HS Math Tchr 1975-; Saint John Fisher Coll Ed Dept Adjunct Prof 1988-; Finger Lakes Comm Coll Summer Instr; Math Dept Chair, Victor HS 1995-; *ai:* Alternative Ed Formation & Implementation Comm; Schl Reform Team; Key Club Advsr 1995-; NYSUT & AFT 1975-; Pac Mac Youth Bsbl 1990-; Macedon Recreation 1995; *office:* Victor Central Schl 953 High St Victor NY 14564*

GADEK, BARBARA ANN, English Teacher; *b:* Perth Amboy, NJ; *m:* Edwin J.; *c:* Craig, Nicole, Matthew; *ed:* Newark St Coll (BA) Elem Ed 1962; Kean Coll Eng Cert 1980; *cr:* Edison Twp Bd of Ed Elem Tchr 1962-66, 1979, Eng Tchr 1979-; *ai:* Stu Cncl, Bookstore, Play Adv; First Yr Tchrs Mentor; Adult ESL Tchr; NEA, NJEA, MCEA, ETEA 1979-; Amer Diabetic Assn 1988-; NJ Governor's Awd; *office:* Woodrow Wilson MS 50 Woodrow Wilson Dr Edison NJ 08820

GAERTNER, STEPHEN ANDREW, Service Representative; *b:* Washington, DC; *ed:* Shepherd Coll (BS) Bus Admin 1987; Loyola Coll at Baltimore Ed Admin; *cr:* Charles Cty Bd of Ed Full Time Sub Tchr 1989-91; Grace Brethren Chrstn Schl Jr Sr High Bus Tchr 1994-95; Man Power Svc Rep; *ai:* Boys Var Bsktbl Asst Coach 7 Yrs; Conf & Touraments Championship 5 Yrs; Soph Boys Bskbl Head Coach 1 Yr; Tourament Asst Dir; Spec Olympics Vol; Yth Bsktbl Coach Vol; *home:* 9167 Preference Dr La Plata MD 20646

GAETANO, RICHARD FRANCIS, HS Teacher; *b:* Utica, NY; *m:* Linda Anne Jones; *c:* Aaron, Evan; *ed:* SUNY at Brockport (BS) Ed, Scndry Soc Stud 1973; Syracuse Univ (MS) Spec Ed 1978; SUNY at Cortland (CAS) Pub Schl Admin 1992; *cr:* House of Good Shepherd Tchr 1973-75; Whitesboro MS Spec Ed Tchr 1978-91, Soc Stud Tchr 1992; Whitesboro HS Resource Room Tchr 1993-; *ai:* Stu Tutoring Prgm Co-Spon; AFT, NEA 1978-; BSA 1993-, Unit Chm; Fellowship in Spec Ed Syracuse Univ; *home:* 5060 Jenkins Rd Vernon NY 13476

GAFFNEY, CARMELLA SUE, Business Education Teacher; *b:* Ravenna, OH; *c:* Erin, Daniel; *ed:* OH St Univ (BS) Comprehensive Bus Ed 1974; Kent St Univ (MA) Educl Admin 1993; *cr:* Father Wehrel HS Bus Ed Tchr 1974-75; Eisenhower HS Tchr 1975-82; Kenston HS IOE Voc Tchr 1985-88; Nordonia HS Bus Ed Tchr 1989-; *ai:* Bus Dept Chair; NEA 1970-; CABTA 1989-; *office:* Nordonia HS 8006 S Bedford Rd Macedonia OH 44056

GAGE, DONALD R.,II, Science Teacher; *b:* Goffstown, NH; *m:* Kathleen Marie; *c:* Donald III, Parker; *ed:* Hesser Coll (AB) Bus Admin 1980; Notre Dame Coll (BA) Sci, Bio 1983; LaSalle Univ (PHD) 1992; *cr:* Trinity HS Sci Tchr 1983-87; John Stark Regnl HS Sci Tchr 1987-; *ai:* McClintock Biotechnology Lab for Stdnts Dir; NH Sci Tchrs Assn, NSTA, NEA; 21st Century Tchr of Yr 1995; Pub in Natl Sci Tchrs 1989; *office:* John Stark Regional HS 618 N Stark Hwy Weare NH 03281

GAGE, PAUL LARKIN, US His, US Govt & Ec Teacher; *b:* Syracuse, NY; *c:* Shannon, Melissa; *ed:* Syracuse Univ (BA) Soc Stud Ed 1966, (MS) Soc Stud Ed 1967; 15 Addl Grad Hrs; *cr:* Attica HS Soc Stud Tchr 1967-69; Bermuda Dept of Defense Schl Soc Stud Tchr 1969-71; Subic Bay Dept of Defense Schl Soc Stud Tchr 1971-73; Ramstein Dept of Defense Schl Soc Stud Tchr 1973-75; Afcent HS Soc Stud Tchr 1975-; *ai:* Sr Class Adv; Soc Stud Dept Chm; NEA 1980-, Pres, Local VP; Schl Advy Comm 3 Yrs; *home:* Usae Cmr 460 Box 195 APO AE 09703

GAGE, RICHARD CHARLES, High School English Teacher; *b:* Youngstown, OH; *m:* Eleni N.; *c:* Alyssa; *ed:* Youngstown St Univ (BS) Ed 1989, (MS) Ed 1996; *cr:* Struthers City Schls Eng Tchr 1991-; *ai:* Jr Class Spon; Adult Basic & Literacy Ed Recruiter; NEA 1991-; NCTE 1989-; Article Pub in Eng Journal; *office:* Struthers HS 111 Euclid Ave Struthers OH 44471

GAGE, STEPHEN LAWRENCE, Asst Prof of Music & Band Dir; *b:* Warsaw, NY; *m:* Stephanie Samford; *c:* Matthew, Claudia; *ed:* SUNY at Fredonia (BM) Music Ed 1978; Eastman Schl of Music (MM) 1983; Univ of IL (EdD) Music Ed 1994; *cr:* Warsaw Sr HS Band Dir 1978-80; Auburn HS Band Dir 1980-89; Emporia ST Univ Asst Prof, Band Dir 1989-93; Youngstown ST Univ Asst Prof, Band Dir 1993-; *ai:* Recruitment Comm Chair; Music Ed Comm; Kappa Kappa Psi Chapter Spon; NEA, OMEA, MENC 1978-; CBDNA, NBA 1989-; Pub in KS Music Review Journal; Guest Conductor All-st Dist, Regnl Festivals; Pres IAJE NY St 1986-89; *office:* Youngstown St Univ 410 Wick Ave Youngstown OH 44555*

GAGGINI, NORMAN WAYNE, Physics Professor; *b:* Cadogan, PA; *m:* Dawn Rose Millemann; *c:* Cathy Rose Bosnic, Sherri Marie; *ed:* IN Univ of PA (BS) Chem Ed 1961, (MED) Physics Ed 1968; 39 Credit Hrs in Sci Ed at Univ of PA 1972-75; 6 Credit Hrs in ISCS at FL St Univ 1975; NSF Inst Operation Physics San Diego St Univ 1988; NSF Inst PIMCES at Syracuse Univ 1991; *cr:* Ferndale Area Schls Physics & Chem Tchr 1964-67; Hanover Area Schls Physics & Chem Tchr 1968-71; IN Univ Asst Prof Physics 1971-75, Assoc Prof Physics 1975-94, Prof of Physics 1994-; *ai:* Recruiter for Hnrs Coll; Pre-Prof Adv; Univ Task Force on Stu Retention Co-Chair; Annual Spon of Physics Problem for 7th & 8th Grd Sci Competition; APSCUF 1985-; Rsrch & Scholarly Act Grant; ESEA Title 1 & 2 Grant; Grad Schl Recruiting Grant 6 Yrs; Tchng Ctr Awd for Excl in Innovative Practices; Coll of Natural Sci & Math Outstdng Tchr Awd; Stu PSEA Outstdng Tchr Awd; 7 Articles Pub; *office:* Indiana Univ Of PA 334A Weyandt Hall Indiana PA 15705

GAGLIANO, REBECCA ANN, Biology Teacher; *b:* Evanston, IL; *ed:* Univ of Dayton (BS) Ed 1994; 4 Credit Hrs Post Grad; *cr:* Fairmont HS Sci Tchr 1994-; *ai:* Frosh Class Cncl; Amer Field Stud; Yth Ending Hunger; Staff Dev Comm; OEA 1994-; KEA 1994-; NSTA 1994-; *office:* Kettering Fairmont HS 3301 Shroyer Rd Kettering OH 45429*

GAGLIARDI, CYNTHIA COSTER, English Teacher; *b:* Summit, NJ; *ed:* Muhlenberg Coll (BA) Eng with Scndry Cert 1992; *cr:* Kittatinny Regnl HS Eng Tchr 1992-94; Chatham Middle School Eng Tchr 1994-; *ai:* Var Asst Cheerleading; Debate Club Adv; NEA, NJEA, Assoc of Chatham Tchrs; NCTE; Nom Sallie-Mae 1st Yr Tchr of Yr Awd 1993; Published NCTE Jrnl 1996; *home:* 64 Tudor Ct Springfield NJ 07081*

GAGLIARDI, JOSEPH LAWRENCE, History Dept Chairman; *b:* Brooklyn, NY; *ed:* Brooklyn Coll (BA) His 1972, (MA) His & Ed 1976; Drug Prevention Ed Cert & Drug Cnslr; Amer Red Cross Advanced First Aid & Emergency Care Cert; *cr:* St Angela Hall HS His Tchr 1976-80; Christ the King HS His Tchr 1980-81; Jr HS 126 His Tchr 1981-82; St Michael Acad His Dept Chm 1982-; *ai:* His Tutor; Schl Recruiter; In Charge of Schl Emergency Med Care; Lay Fac Assn 1983-; Ridgewood Vol Ambulance Corps 1976-, Chief Instr; *office:* Saint Michael Acad 425 W 33rd St New York NY 10016*

GAGLIARDI, JOSEPHA, Social Studies Teacher; *b:* Philadelphia, PA; *ed:* Holy Family Coll (BA) Soc Stud; Univ of Scranton (MA) Amer His; *cr:* Our Lady of Calvary Schl Tchr; Archbishop Ryan HS Tchr, Act Dir; Nazareth AcadTchr, Prin; Cardinal Dougherty HS Tchr; *ai:* NHS Moderator; NCEA; Pastorial Musicians; *office:* Cardinal Dougherty HS 6301 N 2nd St Philadelphia PA 19120

GAGLIARDI, RICHARD A., Athletic Dir & Math Teacher; *b:* Hamden, CT; *m:* Manon Begue; *c:* Joseph A., Richard A. Jr.; *ed:* Boston Coll (BSEd) Ed 1956; *cr:* SVS Hockey Schl Dir 20 Yrs; Yale Univ Var Ice Hockey Coach 17 Yrs; Hamden HS 10-11th Math Tchr 35 Years; *office:* Sacred Heart Acad 265 Benham St Hamden CT 06518

GAGLIONE, ROSEMARY S., Social Studies Teacher; *b:* NJ; *ed:* Glassboro St Coll (BA) Elem Ed 1976; *cr:* St Edward's Schl 7th, 8th Grd Teacher 1976-77; Greenwich Twp Schls Remedial Math Tchr 1978-79; Logan Twp Elem Schl 1979-; *ai:* Soc Stud, AVA, EWT Dist Coord; Regnl Soc Stud Articulation & Geog Skills Comm; 8th Grd Class, Yrbk, Stu Cncl Adv; NEA, NJEA 1978-; LTEA 1979-; LAT 1991-; Logan Twp Home & Schl League 1979-; *office:* Logan Township Elem Schl 110 School Ln Swedesboro NJ 08085*

GAGNE, KATHLEEN DUNNE, Humanities Communications Tchr; *b:* Springfield, MA; *c:* Timothy, Jeffrey; *ed:* Westfield St Coll (BSE) Ed 1970; Univ of MA at Amherst (MED) Ed 1983, (EDD) Childrens Lit Media 1992; *cr:* Springfield Pub Schls 1st-3rd Grd Tchr 1970-73 & 1976-77; Holy Cross Diocese Lang Arts & Rdng Tchr 1983-92; Chestnut MS Video/TV Resource Tchr 1992-; *ai:* Drama & TV Production Group; Pioneer Valley Rdng Cncl 1983-, VP 1988-89, Pres 1989-90 & Bd of Dirs 1985-88, Celebrate Lit Awd 1987; MA Tchrs Assn & NEA; Kids & Books Inc 1983-, Bd of Dirs; Co-Author; Action for Childrens Television Awd 1988; Producer & Host Television Series; ACE Nominations; *office:* Chestnut MS 495 Chestnut St Springfield MA 01107*

GAGNE, ROBERT LEONARD, English Teacher; *b:* Pawtucket, RI; *c:* Kristen Lynn, William Walter; *ed:* Providence Coll (AB) Ed, Eng & Soc Stud 1970, (MED) Elem Admin 1972; 90 Credit Hrs Past Masters at RI Coll, Univ of RI & Brown Univ; *cr:* Lincoln MS Eng Tchr 1970-83; Lincoln Sr High Eng Tchr 1983-, Soccer Coach 1990-; *ai:* Soccer Head Coach; MS IM & AV Dir; Hnr Soc, Stud Cncl & LHS Classes Adv OF 1977-78 & 1992; NETE 1970-; AFT 1970-, Bd of Dirs; NCTE 1970-; Rotary Intnl 1987-, Sgt at Arms; Blackstone Vly Chamber of Commerce; Narragannsett Cncl BSA; Over 30 Articles Pub; *office:* Lincoln Jr Sr HS 135 Old River Rd Lincoln RI 02865*

GAGNON, JACQUELINE ANNE, English Teacher; *b:* Salem, MA; *ed:* Salem St Coll (BS) Scndry Eng, Soc Stud 1969; *cr:* St Mary's Schl Eng Tchr 1969-71; Chelsea HS Eng Tchr 1971-; *ai:* Curr Eng Comm; Tchr of Yr; A Different Sept Fnd; Nom for WBZ Tchr of Yr; Letter of Commendation Tufts Univ; *office:* Chelsea HS 8 Clark Ave Chelsea MA 02150*

GAGNON, JANE MARIE, Business Education Teacher; *b:* Nashua, NH; *m:* Louis; *c:* Pamela J., Peter A.; *ed:* Plymouth St Coll (BED) Bus Ed 1964; Attnd Univ of VT, Univ of MA; *cr:* Alvirne HS Bus Ed Tchr 1964-66; Amherst Reg HS Bus Ed Tchr 1966-70; Nashua Sr HS Bus Ed Tchr 1972-79; Pennichuck Jr HS Bus Ed Tchr 1980-; *ai:* Core Mem of NYNEX Pennichuck Partnership; Tchr, Adv of Raiders Corner; Schl to Work Comm; *office:* Pennichuck Jr HS 207 Manchester St Nashua NH 03060

GAHAGAN, PATRICIA HILL, Mathematics Teacher; *b:* Phoenixville, PA; *m:* Harry Ellsworth III; *c:* Daniel Ellsworth; *ed:* Juniata Coll (BS) Math, Biological Sci 1963; 12 Credit Hrs Penn St Univ; *cr:* Derry Twp Jr HS Math, Sci Tchr 1963-64; Tyrone Area HS Jr HS Math Tchr 1964-66; Gov Thomas Johnson HS Jr HS Math Tchr 1966-68; St Louis Scndry Schl Jr & Sr HS Math, Sewing, Sci Tchr 1968-70; Cntrl HS Sr HS Math Tchr 1986-; *ai:* SCEA 1986-; PSEA, NEA 1963-68, 1986-; Martinsburg Comm Lib Bd 1982-88, Nom Comm, VP; CCCOB Church Bd 1982-88, Sec Stewards Commission; *office:* Central HS Rd 2 Martinsburg PA 16662

GAHAGEN, AMY LINN, French Teacher; *b:* Uniontown, PA; *ed:* Lenoir-Rhyne Coll (BA) Fr & Intnl Relations 1986; Kent St Univ (MA) Fr 1993; Slippery Rock Univ Ed Cert 1989; Attnd Inst for Amer Univs in Aix-en-Provenu France; *cr:* Wicomico MS Fr Tchr 1989-91; Kent St Univ Grad Asst & Fr Instr 1991-93; Frederick Douglass HS Fr & Span Tchr 1993-; *ai:* Class Adv 1993-; Fr NHS Adv; NEA 1993-; AATF 1993-; GWATFL 1993-; Amer Univ Post Scndry Schlsp 1986-87; *office:* Frederick Douglass HS 8000 Croom Rd Upper Marlboro MD 20772*

GAHM, CONNIE S. (JACKSON), Kindergarten Teacher; *b:* Columbus, OH; *m:* Mike E.; *c:* Corey Michael, Cody Austin; *ed:* OH Univ (BA) Ed 1976; Coll of Mt St Joseph (MS) Ed 1988; Attnd Ashland Coll, Univ of Rio Grande; *cr:* Zane Trace MS Art & Eng Tchr 1976-78; Zane Trace Elem Kndgtn Tchr 1978-; *ai:* Curr & Soc Comms; NEA 1978-, Bldg Rep; OEA 1978-; ZTEA 1978-; RCEA; Chillicothe Child Guid Librn; Zane Trace Edctr of Yr 1990; *office:* Zane Trace Schl 946 St Rt 180 Chillicothe OH 45601*

GAHR, CRAIG JOSEPH, Drafting Teacher; *b:* St Marys, PA; *m:* Joanne Fustine; *c:* Brant, Hayden, Kent; *ed:* CA St Coll (BS) Indstrl Arts 1972; 12 Credit Hrs Cmptr Sci PA St; 9 Credit Hrs Comm Clarion St; 3 Credit Hrs Behavior Modifications Lycoming Coll; *cr:* St Marys Area HS Indstrl Arts Metal Maching Tchr 20 Yrs, Drafting Tchr 4 Yrs; *ai:* PSEA, NEA 1972-; SMAEA 1972-, Pres, Treas; Fox Twp Recreation 1995-; Fox Twp Little League 1981-, Pres; St Marys Bsktbl Booster 1993-; *home:* 574 Brandy Camp Rd Kersey PA 15846*

GAIARDO, ALBERT JOHN, Social Studies Teacher; *b:* Passaic, NJ; *m:* Barbara A. Gibson; *ed:* Univ of Pittsburgh (BA) His 1986; Univ of Pittsburgh Cert Soc Stud 1993; Defense Lang Inst Diploma Russian 1989; *cr:* Dept of Defense Russian Instr 1989-91; Schenley HS Cmptr Lab 1991-93; Hempfield Area HS Soc Stud Tchr, Ftbl Coach 1993-; *ai:* Asst Ftbl, Strength & Conditioning Coach; NEA 1993-; Univ of Pittsburgh 1994-, Fac Mem; J. C. Sparkman Ctr Educl Tech Schlsp; *office:* Hempfield Area HS Rd 6 Box 77 Greensburg PA 15601

GAINER, JERE ALLEN, Aerospace Science Instructor; *b:* Nev PA; *m:* Suzanne Begley; *c:* Wayne, Anne Marie, Tammy, David St Univ (BS) Chem 1962; Golden Gate Univ (MS) Bus 1970, (F Relations 1981; Attnd Squadron Ofcr Schl, Air Command & Sta War Coll; *cr:* USAF C-S Navigator 1979-84, Contracting Ofc Cherry Hill HS Aerospace Sci Instr 1989-93; WA Twp HS Aer Instr 1993-; *ai:* Drill Team; Color, Honor Guard; Model Rock Aircraft Club; NEA 1988-; Air Force Assn 1962-; Amer Legion Twp Yth Svcs 1993-; Outstdng Aerospace Sci Instr 1991, 19 *office:* Washington Township HS 529 Hurffville Crosskeys Rd 08080

GAINER, LARRY, Physical Education Teacher; *b:* Newar Marsha Bennett; *c:* Nichelle, Tuwana; *ed:* Glassboro St (BA) 1971; 21 Credits; *cr:* Pennsauken Elem Tchr 1971-73; Pennsau Tchr 1973-90; Pennsauken HS Tchr 1990-; *ai:* Cross Cntry He Girls Track Asst Coach; *office:* Pennsauken HS 800 Hylton Rd P NJ 08110

GAINER-CECCHINI, GAIL L., Social Studies Teacher; *b:* Ca *m:* Peter W.; *c:* Peter W., Matthew D.; *ed:* Glassboro St (BA) 1971; *cr:* Audubon HS Tchr 1971-; *ai:* Field Hocky Asst 18 Yr Tennis 1 Yr; Frosh Girls Bsktbl 3 Yrs; Asst Girls Track 3 Yrs; 8th 10 Yrs, 12th Grd Class 3 Yrs, 9th Grd Class 1 Yr Adv; Audubo 1971-, VP 1 Yr, Rep Cncl; Camden Cty Ed Assn, NJEA, N Church of Good Shepherd 1980-, Dir of Chrstn Ed 1993-, Mi 1995; *home:* 3 Princeton Ct Berlin NJ 08009

GAINEY, LINDA PERRY, Science & English Teacher; *b:* NY; *m:* Carlyle C.; *c:* Nicholl Lynn, Nicholas; *ed:* Coll of Wes Elem Ed 1981; C. W. Post Long Island Univ (MS) Spec Ed, R Devereux Fnd Cert Spec Ed 1967; 15 Credits Ed Coll of Saint Suffolk Dev Ctr Therapy Asst 1967-77; Wyandanch Schl Dist K- Aide 1970, 2nd-6th Grd Tchr 1983-86; Wyandanch Day Care 1981-83; *ai:* Shared Decision Making Team; Amityville Tchrs A Wyandanch PTA 1980-, Cncl VP 1980, Pre-K Pres 1981-; Eas Electra #22 1975-; Wyandanch Schl Bd 1990-, VP; *office:* E Miller Jr HS 501 Broadway Amityville NY 11701

GAINOR, BARRY, Amer His & Legal System Tchr; *b:* Mech PA; *m:* Carol Diebert; *c:* Jonathan, Matthew; *ed:* PA St-Capit (BA) Soc Sci 1969; Shippensburg Univ (MS) Ed 1972; Harris Comm Coll Assoc Soc Stud 1967; *cr:* E Pennsboro Schl Dist T *ai:* Chess Club Adv; NEA, PSEA 1969-;E Pennsboro Ed Assn Local; BSA 1960-, Asst Scout Master, Comm Man; *office:* East Area HS 425 W Shady Ln Enola PA 17025

GAINOR, JOHN WESLEY,III, Naval Science Instructor; *b:* W DE; *m:* Shirley Mae; *c:* Christina Mae Clinedinst, Karen Marie of DE (BA) His 1962; *cr:* US Navy Naval Ofcr 1962-83; Gaithe Sr Naval Sci Instr 1983-; *ai:* NJROTC Rifle Teacm Coach; Ins Cncl; NEA, Montgomery Cty Ed Assn1983-; VFW, Military orde Ward 1984-; Fleet Reserve Assn 1992-; Af, AM of VA 1975 Gaithersburg 1991-, Patriotic Observance Comm; 2 Bronz Star Navy Commendation Medals; Vietnamese Gallantry Cross; NJR Designated Honor Unit Schlsps, Top Area Awds 1983 Gaithersburg HS 314 S Frederick Ave Gaithersburg MD 20877

GAIO, LAUREL LOUISE (DUNCAN), First Grade Teacher; *b:* *m:* Edward; *c:* Edward J., Margaret Pedersen; *ed:* Edinboro St Elem, Sp Ed 1968, (MA) Elem 1973; Post Grad Hrs John Car Ashland Coll, East Stroudsburg Univ, Mount St Joseph Coll; *cr.* Local Schls Tchr of Dev Handicapped 1968-73, 1st-2nd Grd Tchr 4th-5th Grd Tchr 1981-84, 1st Grd Tchr 1985-; *ai:* Youngstow Cooperating Tchr; BEA 1968-, Sec, Bldg Rep; OEA, NEA 19 Kappa Gamma Mem; *home:* 8181 Munson Hill Rd Ashtabula O

GAITHER, HELENA THERESA, Retired First Grade Te Cooksville, MD; *ed:* Bowie St Tchrs Coll (BS) Elem Ed 1955; Prof Cert Elem Ed, Mid 1974; Masters Equivaliency Western M CO, Univ of Md, George Washington Univ, Johns Hopkins; *ai:* Tchrs Assn; Black Stu Achvmt Prgm, Elder; Natl Cncl of Sr Howard Edctrs Assn of Retired Tchrs 1990-, Comm Adv, H Honoree; Mt Gregory UM Church, Sunday Schl Tchr, Supt, Dedicated Svc; Natl Parent Tchr Stu Assn Life Mbrshp; Wm T. I Fund Inc Honoree; *home:* 2375 Duvall Rd Woodbine MD 21797

GAJDEROWICZ, DEE MOONEY, Spanish Teacher; *b:* Alexan *m:* Frank J.; *c:* Michele, Shari G. Cassel; *ed:* Rowan St Coll (1978; Attnd Roanoke Coll; Tchr Cert; Addl Tchr Cert Rutgers; 1983-; *office:* Washington Township HS 529 Hurffville Cros Sewell NJ 08080

GAL, JULIE B., Mathematics Teacher; *b:* Union, NY; *m:* Jo Kathryn, Steven; *ed:* Buffalo St Coll (BA) Lang & Lit 1973; Bi Univ (MAT) Math; Cortland Coll (CAS) Admin 1995; *cr:* Ow Acad Math Tchr 1984-85; Johnson City HS Math Tchr 1985-; *ai.* Math Tchrs of NY St 1985-; Southern Tier Math Tchrs As Southern Tier Assn for Gifted Ed; Honorable Mention New Y Exch Call to Educators-a Test For Bus 1985; Most Outstanding Cert Binghamton Univ 1984; More Math for More Females An Past Presenter at Bing Binghampton Univ; Full Tuition Waver Math Dept at Binghampton Univ 1983-84; *office:* Johnson City Reynolds Rd Johnson City NY 13790

GALA, JOHN, High School Technology Teacher; *b:* Olyphant Rose Ann Karpowich; *c:* Rebecca, Christina, John; *ed:* Mohaw Comm Coll (AAS) Mechanical Tech 1966; SUNY at Osw Industrial Arts 1968; Bowling Green St Univ (MED) Industrial *ai:* NY St United Tchrs, Assn Poland Tchrs 1970-; PTA Tc 1992-93; *home:* RR 2 Ilion NY 13357

GALANTE, JOSEPH JAMES, Asst Professor of Business; *b:* Br *m:* Rosanne Bisconte; *c:* Ferdinand; *ed:* Iona Coll (BBA) Acc (MBA) Taxation 1981; Rutgers Univ (MA) Labor Relations 1988 M Cooley Law Schl (JD) Law 1992; Post Masters Cert Iona Coll Iona Coll Instr of Acctng 1981-85, Asst Prof of Acctng 1985-89 Univ Visiting Lecturer 1987-89; Davenport Coll Lead Instr i 1990-92; Marywood Coll Asst Prof of Bus 1992-; *ai:* Fac Fellow Bus Internship Pgm Dir; Bd of Governors for the Inst of Internal Mem; Industrial Relations 1987-; Amer Bar Assn 1993-; PA & NJ 1993-; Acad of Legal Stud 1993-; Vol Income Tax Asst 1994-, Coord; PA Bar Assn Comm on Legal Ed 1995-, Comm Mem; Art *office:* Marywood Coll Dept of Business 2300 Adams Ave Scr 18509*

GALANTE, MARYANNE O'CONNELL, Jr HS Mathematics Te Boston, MA; *m:* Alfred M. Jr.; *c:* Michelle M., Kristen M.; Stephe Boston St Coll (BSEd) Math 1966; Northeastern Univ 3 Grad 1967-68; Eastern Nazarene 2 Cmptr Couses 1984; Newbury J Classes 1980-81; Sinnott Schl Inc 41 Hrs; *cr:* Braintree Pub Schl 7 Math Tchr 1966-71, Part-time Adult EdInstr 1976-79; Newburg Part-time Math Instr 1983-86; Massasuit Comm Coll Part-time M 1987-89; Sacred Heart Schl Part-time 7th-8th Grd Math Tchr 1 New England Math League Contest Adv for 7-8th Grd; Stu C NCTM; Assoc of Tchrs of Math in New England; Assoc of Tchrs in MA 1989-; Girl Scouts of Amer 1978-83, Asst Troop Ldr; Natl Life 1980-; Excl in Tchng Awd 1994.

E, ROBERT FREDERICK, Social Studies Instructor; *b:* ia, PA; *ed:* Franklin & Marshall Coll (BA) Govt & Fr 1985; Dickinson Univ (MAT) Soc Stud Curr & Methods 1988; *cr:* e MS Soc Stud Instr 1988-94; Monmouth Regnl HS Soc Sci & 1994-95; Forrestdale MS Soc Stud Tchr 1995-; *ai:* Fac Comm ilosophy Coord; NCSS, Ctr for Civic Ed Calabassas CA 1990-; hilosophy of the US Constitution Natl Endowment for the Hum eld at Univ of CA at Los Angeles 1990; Editorial Op Ed ns in the Newark Star Ledger & Asbury Park Press 1988, 1990 *ffice:* Forrestdale MS Forrest Ave Rumson NJ 07760*

INI, MAUREEN L., Cmptr Ed Tchr & Coord; *b:* Pittsburgh, PA; d F.; *c:* Michael, Kristen, David; *ed:* Slippery Rock Univ (BS) 971; Univ of Pittsburgh (MED) Ed 1975; Cmptr Ed; St Francis RE Team Trng; *cr:* South Fayette Jr Sr HS 7 Grd Sci, 7-12 Grd chr 1971-76; Comm Coll of Allegheny Cty Adults Aerobics Tchr South Park MS 508 Grd Hlth, PE Tchr 1986-87; San Joan of Arc rd Lang Arts, Hlth Tchr 1987-94; St Louise de Marillac Schl 1-8 Tchr 1994-; *ai:* Drama Club; Adult Ed; Mentor Tchr; Forensics RE Team; NCEA, NCTE 1987-; NACST 1994-; Recreation Bd prsn, Sec; Natl Neighborhood Panel 1990-; Hockey Team 1989-, s Mgr; *office:* St Louise De Marillac Schl 310 Mcmurray Rd PA 15241

MARY MICHAELANE,CSSF 6th-8th Grd Soc Studies Tchr; *b:* na, NY; *ed:* Villa Maria Coll at Buffalo (AAS) Elem Ed 1969; e Coll (BS) Elem Ed 1974; SUNY Coll at Buffalo (MS) Elem Ed Grad Elem Rdng; *cr:* Various Elem Schls Grd 2 Tchr 1967-77; ia Montessori 2-4 Yr Old Prgm Tchr 1977-80; St James Grd 2 -82; Villa Maria Learning Ctr 1-5 Grd Tchr 1982-89; North a Cath 6-8 Grd Soc Stud Tchr 1989-; *ai:* Cath Hnr Soc; NCEA ffalo Soc Stud Cncl 1995-.

O, NANCY HANKINS, Jr High Art Tchr & Dept Chprsn; *b:* ille, PA; *m:* James H. Sr.; *c:* James Jr.; *ed:* Indiana Univ of PA Ed 1964; California Univ of PA (BS) Elem Ed 1966; Addl Credit fied SAP; *cr:* Connellsville Area Schls Elem Art Tchr 1964-66; d Schl Dist Elem & Jr High Art Tchr 1966-76; Beaver Schl Dist Tchr 1968; Hopewell Area Schls Jr High Art Tchr, Dept Chair Jr High Art Club; SAP Team; Art Dept Chprsn; PSEA, NEA, -, Scndry VP 5 Yrs, PAEA, NAEA; Alpha Delta Kappa 1989-, rs, VP 2 Yrs; Nom PAEA Outstanding Art Ed 1984; Nom PTA pperson Hearst Outstanding Educator Awd; Nom KDKA Alliance Awd; *office:* Hopewell Area Schls 2121 Brodhead Rd Aliquippa

JOSEPH A., Biology Teacher; *b:* Carbondale, PA; *ed:* rg Univ (BS) Bio 1975; Marywood Coll (MS) Cnslng 1996; Attnd niv, Univ of Scranton, IN Univ of P; *cr:* Cncl Rock HS Bio Tchr MASP Bio Tchr 1976-; *ai:* NEA 1974-, Local Pres; ACA 1996; Iota Cnslrs Hnr Soc; *home:* PO Box 262 Carbondale PA 18407*

ITH, PHYLLIS LASKEY, Retired English Teacher; *b:* Duluth, Melanie, Currie; *ed:* Trenton St (BS) Bus Ed 1950; 8 Credit Hrs 16 Credit Hrs Trenton St; *cr:* Sayreville War Meml HS Tchr 1954-78; *ai:* NEA 1950-; *home:* 1304 Blueberry Ct Edison NJ

ATH, CYCREL C., Retired Fifth Grade Teacher; *b:* le, NC; *m:* Elnora Harris; *c:* Brenda Nunn, Michael Todd; *ed:* le St Univ (BA) Elem Ed 1948; 6 Post Grad Hrs NC Cntrl Univ; rad Hrs Morgan St Univ; 10 Post Grad Hrs Towson St Univ; 10 Hrs Johns Hopkins Univ; *cr:* NC Pub Schls 6th Grd Tchr Baltimore City Pub Schls 5th-6th Grd Tchr 1967-94; *ai:* NCTA, -, Robeson Cty Chptr Pres; AFT 1969-; BTU 1969-, Bldg Rep; Sigma 1950-; Co-Wrote Vandalism Curr, Afro-Amer Stud; *home:* lwood Pkwy Baltimore MD 21229

WEISSMAN, NATALIE ANN, Teacher; *b:* New York, NY; *m:* en; *c:* Adam Justin; *ed:* Adelphi (BA) His 1970, (MA) His 1971; D) His 1978; *cr:* JHS 101 Tchr 1971-80; Mercy Coll Adj Prof Evander Child HS Tchr 1980-82; South Bronx HS Tchr 1982-; *ai:* Tutor; UFT 1971-; Irish Water Spaniel Club 1993-; 1st Dog Trng J 1995-.

MARY ETHEL, 2nd Grade Teacher; *b:* Berkeley, CA; *m:* Walter rding Univ (BA) Music Ed 1965; Boston Univ (MA) Early Chldhd *cr:* W Babylon Pub Schl Music Tchr 1965-67; Islip Pub Schls chr 1968-79, 2 Grd Tchr 1980-; *ai:* Sci Comm; NYSUT 1965-; L ionic Chorus 1980; W I Day Care Ctr 1972-, Bd VP; *office:* Maud od Elem Schl 301 Smith Ave Islip NY 11751*

ICHARD G., English Teacher; *b:* Pittsburgh, PA; *m:* Maxine F.; r, Tiffany; *ed:* St Univ of NY at Oswego (BA) Eng Ed 1969; St Y at Stony Brook (MA) Lbrl Stud 1975; 52 Addl Hrs; *cr:* A. G. HS Eng Tchr 1969-87; Massapequa HS Eng Tchr 1987-; *ai:* Sr Adv; Renaissance, Sr Awds Selection Comms; Scale Coll Credit ssau Cty Acad League Coords; AFT 1969-; Three Village Swim -91, Sec, Bd of Drs; Articles Pub; *office:* Massapequa HS 4925 Rd Massapequa NY 11758

PAUL WAYNE, Schl Minister & Rel Dept Head; *b:* Waterbury, arcia Merrick; *c:* Michael, Bethany; *ed:* Westfield St Coll (BA) 1975; Gordon-Conwell Theological Seminary (MTS) Bible Stud Theological Seminary Inst for Schl Ministry Grad 1992; *cr:* hl of Knoxville Chaplain 1985-90; Mercersburg Acad Schl 1990-; *ai:* Cnslng Staff Mem; JV Bsbl Coach; Lighthouse, Vestry dv; United Church of Christ 1993-, Ordained Clergy; Most al Tchr By 1987 Class Webb Schl of Knoxville; *office:* The urg Acad 300 E Seminary St Mercersburg PA 17236

NO, LOUIS JOHN, Fifth Grade Teacher; *b:* Coaldale, PA; *m:* aldini; *c:* Thomas, John, Michael; *ed:* Fordham Univ (BA) Ec dham Grad Schl of Ed (MS) Edctr 1968; Masters 60 Credit Hrs; nder Hamilton HS Soc Stud 1965-70; Columbus Ave Elem Fifth 1970-; *ai:* Eighth Grd CYO Bsktbl & Bsbl Coach; NYSUT 1965-; olumbus Avenue Elem Schl 70 Columbus Ave Valhalla NY 10595

O, MARYANN MELCER, Language Arts Teacher; *b:* New A; *m:* Richard J.; *ed:* Indiana Univ of PA (BS) Fr Ed 1973; ster Coll (MA) Eng 1979, (MA) Rdng Specialist 1980; *cr:* HS Fr & Eng Tchr 1977-78; Union Area Schl Dist Rdng & Eng -95; *ai:* NEA 1977-; PSEA 1977-, Fac Rep; Lawrence Cty Rdng -; Keystone St Rdng Cncl; Lawrence Cty Historical Soc 1993-; ncis Hosp 1990-, Vol; Intermediate Unit In-Svc Courses-Tchng Process 1990; Whole Lang & Whole Lang Assessment 1991; ng Good Behavior & Macintosh 1993; *office:* Union Area Mid & Camden Ave New Castle PA 16101

, MICHAEL JOHN, Physical Education Teacher; *b:* Pottsville, aula Popadiuk; *c:* Wendy; *ed:* Montclair St Coll (BA) Hlth & PE *r:* Bridgewater-Raritan Schls Elem PE Tchr 1970-; *ai:* ter-Raritan HS Strength & Conditioning Coach; NJSIAA Track & l; NEA, BREA 1970-; NSCA 1988-; NJSIAA Track & Field Ofcl Golden Apple Awds; *office:* John F Kennedy Elem Schl Woodmere NJ 08869

DOREEN J., Theology & Pub Speaking Tchr; *b:* New on, PA; *ed:* Allentown Coll of St Francis Desalles (BA) Eng, Comm 1987; 14 Post Grad Hrs; 6 Hrs Theology La Salle Univ; 6 Hrs Rdng E Stroudsburg Univ; *cr:* Easton Hosp Phys Therapy Asst 1981-84; Lansdale Cath HS Longterm Sub Tchr 1987-88; Cathedral of St Catharine Adult Rel Ed Dir 1988-92; Notre Dame HS Tchr 1992-; *ai:* Moderator NHS; Asst JV Sftbl Coach; Cooperating Tchr; *office:* Notre Dame HS 3417 Church Rd Easton PA 18045

GALIPAULT, PAMELA HECKER, Soc Stud Tchr & Schlsp Cnslr; *b:* Columbus, OH; *w:* John B. Sr. (dec); *c:* Abigail, John Jr.; *ed:* Coll of William & Mary (AB) His 1968; OH St Univ (MED) Guid & Cnslng 1974; 68 Quarter Hrs Soc Stud, Drug, Alcohol Ed, Educl Admin; *cr:* Thomas Worthington HS Tchr 28 Yrs; *ai:* Boys & Girls Teams Schl Adv; CARD's Inc Bd of Trustees; Sr Act Comm; WEA, OEA, NEA 1968-, Bldg Rep; OH Assn of Scndry Schl Cnslrs 1992-; Worthington Educl Fnd 1995-, Trustee; Worthington Alumni Assn 1991-, Charter Mem, Bd of Dirs; Kappa Alpha Theta Alumni 1968-, St Ch, Rec Bd Ch, Theta of Yr 1989; DAR Tchng Awd 1982; OH St Univ Coll of Ed Cooperating Tchr Awd 1987; Hall of Fame 1993; *office:* Thomas Worthington HS 300 W Dublin Granville Rd Worthington OH 43085

GALITSKIY, EMMANUIL, Physics Teacher; *b:* Odessa, USSR; *m:* Bella Galant; *c:* Aleksandr; *ed:* Odessa St Univ (MS) Theoretical Physics-Hnrs 1971; Post-Grad Aerosol Physics; *cr:* Odessa HS #38 Physics, Math Instr 1971-75; Odessa St Univ Researcher, Lecturer 1975-91; Odesssa Spec Schl for Gifted Physics Instr 1985-91; Acad for Advancement of Sci & Tech Physics Instr 1991-; *ai:* Chess Club Adv; NJEA 1991-; 18 Scientific Pubs Aerosol Sci; *office:* Acad Advancement Sci & Tech 200 Hackensack Ave Hackensack NJ 07601

GALITSKY, DARLEEN YEAGER, Family & Consumer Science Tchr; *b:* Chicago, IL; *m:* Ronald J.; *c:* R. Joseph, Lisa Galitsky McCarthy; *ed:* Kent St Univ (BS) Home Ec Ed 1963; West Chester Univ (ME) Rdng Ed 1993; *cr:* Chartiers Valley Schl Dist Home Ec Tchr 1963-64; Hinsdale HS Home Ec Tchr 1964-65; East HS Family & Consumer Sci Tchr 1988-; *ai:* Mentor Tchr; Act 178 Comm Mem; After Schl Cooking Class Tchr for Elem Schl Stdnts; Amer Assn of Family & Consumers Scis, PA Assn of Family & Consumer Scis 1994-; Chester Cty Assn of Family & Consumer Scis 1995-; Westminster Presbyn Church 1978-, Elder, Active Mem; Originated Little Viking Presch an Intregal Part of the Curr for Child Dev Courses; *office:* East H S 450 Ellis Ln West Chester PA 19380*

GALIYAS, MITCHELL EDWIN, History Teacher; *b:* Mc Keesport, PA; *m:* Mary Jo Conley; *c:* Juliana, Nathan, Zachary, Moira; *ed:* AR (BA) His 1972; Pitt Tchrs Cert 1973; Penn St 36 Hrs Masters Equivalency; *cr:* Montour HS Dept Head 1979-86, Tchr 1975-, Fac Mgr 1994-; *ai:* Act Dir; MEA, PSEA, NEA 1975-; Kennedy Twp Parks & Recreation Bd, VP; Kennedy Zoning Bd, Vice-Chm; Allegheny Cty Democratic Party, Committeeman; US Senator Rick Santorum's Comm Advy Bd; Article Pub; *office:* Montour HS 90 Clever Rd Mc Kees Rocks PA 15136

GALL, ANN M., Business Education Teacher; *b:* Warren, OH; *m:* Lawrence R. II; *c:* Korey; *ed:* Kent St Univ (BS) Bus Ed 1991; Working on MS Educl Admin Youngstown St Univ; *cr:* Mathews HS Bus Ed Tchr 1992-; *ai:* Chrldng Coach 1992-; Class of 1996 Adv 1992-96; NEA, OEA, Mathews Ed Assn 1992-; Trumbull Cty ASA Umpires Assn 1993-; *office:* Mathews HS 4429 Warren Sharon Rd Vienna OH 44473*

GALLA, NELIDA M., Spanish Teacher; *b:* Buenos Aires, Argentina; *c:* Georgeanna Lila Murgatroyd, Gabriela Maria Murgatroyd; *ed:* Coll of Notre Dame (BA) Intnl Bus; Towson St Univ (BA) Span, (MA) Span Lit 1993; Facultad De Economia Ec; *cr:* Consulado De La Republica Argentina Cultural Adv, Gen Consul Private Asst 1985-90; St Paul HS Tchr; Morgan St Univ Tchr, Frgn Lang Lab Dir 1988-95; Loyola Blakefield Schl Tchr 1991-; Towson St Univ Tchr 1995-; *ai:* Boletin Espanol, Espanol Club, Recitation Contests Adv; Folk Dancing Instr; Museum of Art 1985-; Walters Gallery 1990-; *home:* 32 Alanbrooke Ct Baltimore MD 21204

GALLAGHER, ALISON WATSON, Fifth Grade Teacher; *b:* Long Branch, NJ; *m:* Thomas Francis III; *c:* Michelle, Kristin; *ed:* Glassboro St Coll (BA) General Elem 1972; Rutgers Grad Schl of Ed (MED) Creative Arts in Ed 1988; *cr:* Elison Elem 1st-6th Grd Math, Sci Tchr 1972-73; Cheesequake Schl 5th Grd Tchr 1973-75; Cooper Schl 3rd Grd Kndgtn Tchr 1976-79; Voorhees Math Basic Skills Improvement Prgm Tchr 1980-84; Memorial 3rd, 5th Grd Tchr 1985-; *ai:* Dist Soc Stud Comm; Schl Paper Adv; Stu of Month Chrldrs Coach; NEA, NJEA, OBTA 1973-; Kappa Delta Pi 1989-; Woman's Club 1974-, Pres, VP, Music, Drama, Ed Chm; Original Play 1st Place St; Governor's Tchr Recognition Grant 1989; Trenton St Coll Commissioner's Outstanding Tchrs Symposium; At For Kids Dssmntr Grant Winner Pub 1995.*

GALLAGHER, BARBARA MUZIO, Physical Education Dept Chm; *b:* West Chester, PA; *m:* John D.; *c:* Lauren, Caroline; *ed:* West Chester St Coll (BS) PE 1974; West Chester Univ (MED) PE 1979; *cr:* Lansdowne Aldan HS Instr 1974-81; Dance Ctr Instr, Aerobics Coord 1981-88; Immaculata Coll PE Dept Chm 1988-; *ai:* Asst Field Hockey Coach; Spirit Club Adv; Stu Life & Dev, Acad Policy Comms; AAAI 1982-; Natl Fed of Sports 1974-; Brandywine Ballet Co Bd of Dirs 1982-, Pres, Treas; Tri-Cty Chapter of Bsktbl Ofcls 1975-, Pres, Sec, Treas, Rules Interpreter; Philadelphia Women's Lacrosse Assn 1982-, Sec; *office:* Immaculata College Alumnae Hall Immaculata PA 19345*

GALLAGHER, BARRY LEE, Eco, World & European His Tchr; *b:* Lansdale, PA; *m:* Debra Ann Kulbatsky; *c:* Gwen, Lara, Katie, Marlee; *ed:* PA St Univ (BA) His 1976; Masters in Ed (Equivilancy); *cr:* St Thomas Schl 4th-8th Grd Tchr 1977; Parkview HS 9th Grd World His & 11th Grd US His Tchr 1978-84; Du Bois Area HS 9th Grd His & Civics & 10th Grd World His Tchr 1984-, Eco & AP European His Tchr; *ai:* 11th Grd Adv; Prom Comm Adv 1987-93; Var Golf Coach 1993-, Pres; NEA 1984-; Natl Geography Alliance 1989-; Franklin Life 1980-, Sales Rep; *home:* 72 Treasure Lk Du Bois PA 15801*

GALLAGHER, CATHERINE BERARDINI, Advanced Placement Bio Tchr; *b:* Staten Island, NY; *m:* Kevin; *ed:* Trenton St Coll (BS) Hlth & PE 1981; 28 Credit Hrs Toward Cert as Tchr of Biological Sci 1985; *cr:* Immaculate Conception Grammar Schl HPE-Sci Tchr 1981-83; McCorristin HS Bio Tchr 1983-85; Wall HS Bio Tchr 1985-; *ai:* Frosh Field Hockey Coach; NEA, NJEA, NJ Sci Tchrs Assn, WTEA 1985-; Tandy Outstanding Sci Tchr Awd 1988; *office:* Wall HS 18th Ave & New Bedford Rd Wall NJ 07719

GALLAGHER, DAVID, Mathematics Teacher; *b:* Sheffield, England; *m:* Virginia Miceli; *ed:* Open Univ (BA) Math, Ed 1978; City Univ of New York (MSE) Math, Ed 1994; Totley Thornbridge Coll of Ed Math, Ed Cert 1973; *cr:* St Joseph's Schl Jr 2 Tchr 1973-75; St Catherines Jr 4 Tchr 1975-80; Monsignor Farrell Schl Math Tchr 1981-, Acting Chair 1995; *ai:* Amnesty Intnl Fac Adv; Math Club Moderator; NCTM 1992-; Lay Fac Assn 1989-, Del; Amnesty Intnl, Green Peace 1988-; Southern Poverty Law Ctr 1995-; *office:* Monsignor Farrell HS 2900 Amboy Rd Staten Island NY 10306*

GALLAGHER, DENISE O'BRIEN, Math, Lang Arts & Reading Tchr; *b:* New Rochelle, NY; *m:* James; *c:* Martin, Patty Ann; *ed:* Mercy Coll (BS) Eng, Psych 1974; Working Towards (MS) Rdng Long Island Univ; *cr:* Parkway Schl 4th Grd Tchr 1978-79; St Barnabas 5th Grd Tchr 1984-88; Sacred Heart 6th, 3rd, 7th, 8th Grd Tchr 1989-; *ai:* Lang Dept Chprsn; Yrbk Adv; ACLD; New Rochelle IBS 1989-; Pres, VP.*

GALLAGHER, JAMES RODGERS, Art Teacher; *b:* Allentown, PA; *m:* Kelly Lehr; *c:* Shawn, Shannon; *ed:* Kutztown Univ (BS) Art Ed 1967; Tyler Schl of Art (MED) Art Ed 1974; Millersville Univ (Supervision) Art Ed 1984; *cr:* Harrisburg HS Art Tchr 1967-72; Manheim Twp HS Art Supvr 1972-; Lebanon Valley Coll Ceramic Instr 1996; *ai:* Yrbk; Stu Assistance; NEA; NAEA; Scholastic Art Comm; Lanc Arts Cncl; Flwshp Skidmore Coll; Nom Art Edctr of Yr St 1980; Art Edctr of the Yr Lancaster Cty 1993; Numerous Art Exhibits & Awds; *office:* Manheim Twp HS Box 5134 Lancaster PA 17601

GALLAGHER, JOAN NAGY, Bus Admin Chair & Professor; *b:* Bridgeport, CT; *m:* William H.; *ed:* Univ of Bridgeport (AA) Bus 1963, (BS) Bus 1966, (MS) Rdng Consultant 1968; 6th Prof Supervision & Curr Cert; Attnd Wellesley Coll, World Trade Inst, Comp USA; *cr:* Dresser Industries Confidential Sec 1955-66; Trumbull HS 11th-12th Grd Bus Tchr 1968-78; Bus Admin HCTC Asst, Assoc & Full Prof 1978-86, Bus Admin Chair 1989-; *ai:* Adm Careers Alumni Office; NBEA 1967-; CBEA 1967-, Ed; AAUP 18 Yrs; CT Bus Edctrs 1967-, Ed; Milford Yacht Club 1977-, Ed; Awds: CT Acad Excl Tchng, Merit, Acad Deans; Various Whos Who; *office:* Housatonic Comm-Tech College 510 Barnum Ave Bridgeport CT 06608

GALLAGHER, JOANNE KITTELL, Sixth Grade Science Teacher; *b:* Jamaica, NY; *c:* Peter, Roger, Christopher, Lynn; *ed:* Middlebury Coll (BA) Bio 1955; Attnd Columbia Univ Tchrs Coll, North Adams St, St Univ of NY at Albany, St Univ Coll at Oneonta, Cornell Univ, Rensselaer Polytechnic Inst; *cr:* Northfield Jr HS 7th & 8th Grd Sci Tchr 1955-57; Tamarac MS Sci Tchr 1972-; *ai:* Sixth Grd Team Ldr; Tchrs Assn Pres; Sci Cycle, Aths, Evaluation Comms Chm; Sci Tchrs Assn of NY St 1972-, Pres 1994-95, Fellow 1990; Natl Mid Level Sci Tchrs Assn 1990-, Pres 1995-; NYSUT, AFT, NYSCEA; Rensselaer 1993-94, Bd Mem; Cty Jr Museum; Pittstown Planning Bd 1993-90, Sec; Pres Awd Excl in Sci Tchng NY St 1989; Amer Optical Soc Outstndng Tchr; Delta Kappa Gamma Frederika Hollister Awd; *home:* 14 Whetstone Dr Brattleboro VT 05301*

GALLAGHER, JOHN PATRICK, Retired Elementary Teacher; *b:* New York City, NY; *m:* Ann M. Mc Donnell; *c:* John E., Roseann, Brian J.; *ed:* Iona Coll (BS) Physics 1954; Fordham Univ (MS) Elem Ed 1957; 24-30 Undergraduate Credit Hrs Fordham 1955-57; 12 Post Grad Hrs Fordham 1962; 3 Post Grad Hrs St John's Univ 1965; 3 Post Grad Hrs Hofstra Univ 1969; *cr:* Meadowlawn Elem Schl Floating Sub Tchr 1957; US Army 1957-59; Bowling Green Elem Schl 4th & 5th Grd Tchr 1959-93; *ai:* East Meadow Tchrs Assn 1957-, Bldg Rep, VP, Treas; NEA 1957-70; NY St Tchrs Assn, AFT 1970-; NYS Ret Tchrs Assn 1993-; Amer Legion 1990-; *home:* 1 Geoffrey Ln Kings Park NY 11754

GALLAGHER, JOSEPH JAMES, Physical Education & Hlth Tchr; *b:* Chester, PA; *m:* Karen DeAngelis; *c:* Kristin; *ed:* Univ of TN (BS) Hlth Ed 1979; PE Cert Eastern Coll 1994; Currently Enrolled in Multi-Cultural Master of Ed Prgm; *cr:* RETS Cnslr 1980-81; DE Cty Juvenile Detention Ctr Prgm Dir 1981-93; Haverford HS PE, Hlth Tchr 1993-; *ai:* Head Var Ftbl Coach; Frosh Lacrosse Coach; NEA 1993-; *office:* Haverford HS 200 Mill Rd Havertown PA 19083

GALLAGHER, JUDITH LEONA (FRANKS), Fourth Grade Teacher; *b:* Amherst, OH; *m:* Larry; *ed:* Malone Coll (BS) Elem Ed 1970; 147 Addl Hrs Ashland Univ, Coll of Mount St Joseph, Akron Univ, Kent St Univ; *cr:* Plain Ctr Elem Stu Tchng, 3 Grd Tchr 1970-73; Edgefield Elem Schl 5 Grd Tchr 1973-81; Avondale Elem Schl 3-5 Grd Tchr 1981-; *ai:* Annual Talent Show Chprsn, Coord, Judge, MC 1990-; Intervention Team Mentor, Trainer 1990-; Sci Ed in Elem Dev Skills 30 Hrs of Trng 1995-; Stark Cty Ldrshp Conf Host Tchr 1996; Tchr Exch Host Tchr; Odyssey of Mind Dir, Organizer 2 Yrs; Schl Historian 2 Yrs; Sci Judge; Stu Cncl Adv 2 Yrs; Soc Stud Textbook Adoption Comm; Math Olympic Chprsn; Soc Comm; Arts & Sci Night Lang Arts Chprsn; NEA, PTA 1970-; Plain Local Tchrs Assn 1970-, Bdlg Rep 2 Yrs; Fourth Grd Proficiency Test Comm 1993-, Presenter; Plain Local Tchrs Assn 1988-, Harry Tempe Schlsp Comm; Church Choir, Women's Flwshp Comm 1995-; Church Worship Song Ldr, VBS Music Ldr 1996-; Domestic Violence Awareness 1989-91; Sweet Adelines Inc Chorus 1976-88, Dir, Recording Sec; Sweet Adelines Inc Quartet 1982-88, Section Ldr, Choreographer; Presenter at Area Colls 1989-95; Plain Local's Tchr of Yr 1985; Ashland Oil Golden Apple Achiever Awd 1990; Featured in Akron-Beacon Journal, Plain's Pride Newsletter; Edctr of Yr & Most Creative; Stu Tchrs; Nom Can Chamber of Commerce Tchr of Yr; Nom OH St Tchr of Yr 1996; Initiated Humane Soc Love-A-Pet, Salvation Army Hunger Task Force Hands Across Avondale; *home:* 3445 Capricio St NE Canton OH 44721

GALLAGHER, LINDA MARIE, 6th Grd Language Arts Teacher; *b:* Philadelphia, PA; *m:* Michael; *c:* Brian, Shannon, Daniel; *ed:* Holy Family Coll (BA) Elem Ed; *cr:* Christ The King Schl Second Grd Tchr 1968-76; Macalester Nursery Schl Dir 1980-90; St Christopher Schl Sixth Grd Tchr 1990-; *ai:* Mid Sts Evaluation Comm Chprsn; *office:* St Christopher Schl 13305 Proctor Rd Philadelphia PA 19116

GALLAGHER, LOUISE GARDECKI, English Teacher; *b:* Kingston, NY; *m:* William J.; *c:* Sean; *ed:* SUNY at New Paltz (BA) Eng, Scndry Ed 1982, (MS) Humanistic Ed 1987; *cr:* Saugerties HS Eng Tchr 1984-; *ai:* Staff Dev Comm Co Chr; Lip Sync Co Adv, Key Club Adv; AFT 1983-; Saugerties Tchrs Assn 1983-, Sr Bldg Rep; *office:* Saugerties HS Washington Ave Saugerties NY 12477

GALLAGHER, LYNNE ANDERSON, Tchr of Perceptually Impaired; *b:* Kearny, NJ; *m:* Mark Gallagher; *c:* Julie; *ed:* Kean Coll (BA) Spec Ed 1984; *cr:* Jersey City Pub Schls Tchr of Handicapped NI 1984-87; Clifton Pub Schls Tchr of Handicapped PI 1987-; *ai:* After Schl Enrichment Prgm; NEA, NJEA 1984-; Clifton Tchrs Assn 1987-; Christopher Columbus Fac Org, Clifton Home, Schl Assn 1987-; *office:* Christopher Columbus MS 350 Piaget Ave Clifton NJ 07011

GALLAGHER, MARILYN FLANAGAN, Regents Earth Science Teacher; *b:* New York City, NY; *m:* Denis F.; *c:* Michael; *ed:* Marymount Coll at Tarrytown (BS) 1973; Westers CT St Univ (MS) Bio, Tchr Ed 1977-78; So CT St Univ at New Haven 6th Yr Prof Diploma Admin, Supervision 1990-91; Human Relations Facilitator Trng 6 Credit Hrs; Interret Cmptr Trng; *cr:* Commerce MS General Sci, Auto Mechanics Tchr 3 Yrs; Commerce HS General Sci, Auto Mechanics Tchr 3 Yrs; Hawthorne MS Earth Sci Tchr 10 Yrs; John Rurroughs JHS Earth Sci Tchr 3 Yrs; Gorton HS Earth Sci, Chem, Bio Tchr 5 Yrs; *ai:* Sign Club Tutor, Moderator; JV Acad Bowl Coach; Steering Comm Cycle 1; Schl Improvement Team; AFT 1973-, Pres; NEA; Phi Lambda Theta; Cub Scouts 2 Yrs; PTSA; Jenkins Awd 1990; Readers Digest 1992-93, Innovations 1991-92, NASSP 1993 Mini Grants; *office:* Saunder HS 145 Palmer Yonkers NY 10701*

GALLAGHER, MARJORIE RUTH-TAYLOR, 4th Grade Teacher; *b:* Wooster, OH; *m:* Michael Joseph; *ed:* Otterbein Coll (BSME) Flute 1977; Ashland Univ Cleveland St Univ (BED) Elem 1989; Cleveland St Spec Ed Temp Cert; *cr:* South Amherst Schls Music 5-12th Grd Vocal Tchr 1977-82; Sheffield Lake Schls Sub Tchr 1983-84, Chapter 1 Rdng Tchr 1984, 2nd Grd Tchr 1984-85, 3rd Grd Tchr 1985-86, Tutor Spec Ed Tchr 1986-87, 4th Grd Tchr 1987-; *ai:* Schl System Tech Comm; Former IAT; Cty Leadership Group Mentor Prgm; Arts Advy Group; NEA, Delta Omicron, OEA 1977-; Tau Epsilon Mu Sorority 1975-; Art Advy Group 1995-, Elections; Levy Comm 1990-; Comm Relations Comm 1995-; Lorain Cty Beautiful Grant Awded Twice; Schl Lib Grant Awded Twice; Comm Environmental

Clean-Up Project Twice; Cleveland Beck Cntr Arts Project Grant; *home:* 4353 E Lake Rd Sheffield Lake OH 44054*

GALLAGHER, MARY LOU WALSH, 2nd Grade Teacher; *b:* Rutherford, NJ; *m:* Robert J.; *c:* Thomas A., Timothy M., Theresa A. Moran; *ed:* Misericordia Coll (BS) Elem Ed 1956; 25 Addl Hrs; Lincoln Ctr Inst 6 Credits; *cr:* Catherine E. Doyle Schl 3rd-4th Grd Tchr 1956-61; Mary A. Hubbard Schl 2nd-3rd Grd Tchr 1973-84; Wesley D. Tisdale Elem Schl 2nd Grd Tchr 1984-; *ai:* Adv 2nd Grd Musical Production; Talent Show Dir 12 Yrs; Ramsey Tchrs Assoc 1973-, Rep 12 Yrs; NEA 1973-; PTO 1990- Tchr Rep; *home:* 285 Woodland Ave Ramsey NJ 07446

GALLAGHER, MICHAEL, AP Biology Teacher & Coach; *b:* Philadelphia, PA; *ed:* Bucknell Univ (BS) Bio 1987; Villanova Univ 30 Credits Bio; *cr:* Perkomen Schl Sci Tchr, Doormparent, Coach 1987-; *ai:* Var Boys Bsktbl, Golf Coach; Sci Dept Chair; Asst Head of Dorm; *office:* Perkiomen Schl PO Box 130 Pennsburg PA 18073*

GALLAGHER, RICHARD JAMES, Eng Dept Chm & Cmptr Lab Coord; *b:* Johnstown, PA; *m:* Josephine A. Ketner; *ed:* Mount St Marys Coll (BS) Eng Ed 1971; Morgan St Univ (MS) Rdng 1975; Post Grad Work at Towson St Univ & Howard Comm Coll; Univ of MD, Univ of Notre Dame & Univ of TN Fellowships; Georgetown Univ Fellowship; *cr:* Edgewood HS Eng Tchr, Rdng Specialist, Eng Dept Chm & Cmptr Lab Coord 1971-; *ai:* Former Bsktbl & Bsbl Coach; Former Mid Sts Evaluation Steering Comm; Sr Class Adv; Cty Lang Arts Dept Chm Comm; Dept Chairs Comm; Supts Advisory Comm 1989; Schl Impvmt Comm; NEA, MSTA & HCEA 1971-; NCTE & MCTELA 1976-; NEH Fellowship 1987 & 1991; MD Hum Fellowship 1988, 1992, 1993; McDonalds Local Tchr Awd 1990, 1994; *office:* Edgewood HS 2415 Willoughby Beach Rd Edgewood MD 21040

GALLAGHER, RITA DAVIS, Retired 5th Grade Teacher; *b:* Columbus, OH; *m:* Nicholas D. Jr.; *c:* Joseph S., Julia M. Galbreath, Theresa A. Thompson, Margaret M. White, Michael V., Nora E. Fisher, Nicholas D. IV; *ed:* Wright St Univ (BS) Ed 1973; *cr:* St Patrick Schl Fifth Grd Tchr, Plus Math 4-6 15 Yrs; *home:* 701 Gateshead Rd Troy OH 45373

GALLAGHER, ROBERT J., College Instructor; *b:* Phila, PA; *m:* Susan Busch; *c:* Robert, Ryan; *ed:* LaSalle Coll (BS) Acctng 1989; Grad Stud Cmptr Sci Temple Univ; Continuing ED Cmptr Cos-Compag, Novell, Microsoft; *cr:* Comm Coll of Phila Instr 1981-; Self Employed Cmptr Consultant 1983-; *ai:* AFT 1988-; Certfd Computing Prof-ICCP, Network Admin-Novell.

GALLAGHER, ROSEMARY MURPHY, Support Services Director; *b:* Portchester, NY; *m:* Lawrence W.; *c:* Lawrence, Paul, Peter, Carolyn; *ed:* Fordham Univ at NYC (BS) K-8 Elem Ed 1963; Manhattanville Coll at Purchase (MPS) Spec Ed 1987; Springfield Coll in IL (AA) Music 1990; Post Grad Stud Manhattanville Coll; CACLD, Orton Gillingham Soc, Landmark Coll Confs; *cr:* St Patricks Schl Pre K-8 Grd Music Tchr 1978-82; Bedford Hills Elem Schl Spec Ed Contained Class Tchr 1982-86; King & Low Heywood Thomas Schl 3 Grd Tchr 1987-89, Lower Schl Support Svcs Dir 1989-; *ai:* Ed Comm Bd of Trustees; Fac Evaluation Comm; CT Assn Children LD 1990-; NY Orton Dyslexia Soc 1989-; IRA 1993-; St Patricks Church 1963-, Choir Dir, Soloist, Founder Parents Assn of St Patricks Schl, Pres of St Patricks Schl Bd; Village Singers 1978-, Bd of Dirs, Soloist; Prof Dev Grant 1995; Fac Svc Awd 1992; Author Copyrighted Addition Math Prgm for Elem Stdnts, Learning Disabled Children; *office:* King & Low-Heywood Thomas Sch 1450 Newfield Ave Stamford CT 06905

GALLAGHER, THOMAS F., Elementary Education Teacher; *b:* Kingston, PA; *m:* Paula Ann Dorish; *c:* Erin Ann, Thomas John; *ed:* Mansfield St Univ (BS) Elem Ed 1972; Scranton Univ (MS) Schl Admin 1976; Attnd Bloomsburg Univ; *cr:* Crestwood Schl Dist Elem Edctr 1972-; *ai:* Jr High & Asst Var Soccer Coach; NEA 1972-; PSEA 1972-; CEA 1972-, VP; Luzerne Cty Coordinating Cncl; Jaycees, VP; Kirby Lib Bd, Ed Chair; St Judes Mens Club, Pres; Wright Twp Recreation Bd, Rep; Fairview Tchr of the Yr.

GALLAHER, LAURA ESSEX, English Teacher; *b:* Toledo, OH; *m:* Christopher G.; *c:* Seth, Paige; *ed:* Univ of Toledo (BED) Eng 1981; *cr:* Notre Dame Acad Eng Tchr 1981-; *ai:* NCTE 1981-; OCEA 1982-; *office:* Notre Dame Acad 3535 Sylvania Ave Toledo OH 43623*

GALLAHER, MELISSA ANNE, Language Arts Teacher; *b:* Dayton, OH; *m:* Brian Scott; *c:* Tyler Dalton; *ed:* Wright St Univ (BS) Elem Ed 1989; Univ of Dayton Career Tchng Credit Hrs; *cr:* Tri-Cty North MS 7th, 8th Grd Lang Arts Tchr 1990-; *ai:* Class, Newsletter Adv; Lang Arts Dept, Career Chair; Var Vlybl Coach; Advy, Effective Schls Comms; OEA, NEA 1990-, Sec 1994-95; Zeta Tau Alpha Alumnae 1989-; *office:* Tri-County North MS 530 Panther Way Lewisburg OH 45338

GALLEY, LISA ANN, Secondary History Teacher; *b:* Trenton, NJ; *ed:* East Stroudsburg Univ (MA) Amer His 1991-; *cr:* Mt Olive HS His Tchr 1985-; *ai:* Girls' Tennis 1985-, Track 1986-, Boys' Tennis 1987-, Coach; Interact Club Adv 1989-; Ed Assn of Mt Olive 1985-, Newsletter Ed 1990-, Legislative Chprsn 1996-; *office:* Mount Olive HS Corey Rd Flanders NJ 07836

GALLICHOTTE, PAUL A., Technology Education Teacher; *b:* Palo Alto, CA; *m:* Christine E.; *ed:* Cntrl CT St Coll (BS) Indstrl Arts Ed 1978; Cntrl CT St Univ (MS) Tech Ed 1988; Tech Tchr Enhancement Ctr; *cr:* Johnson Jr HS Indstrl Arts Tchr 1980-81; Bunnell HS Tech Ed Tchr 1981-; *ai:* Telecommunication Club Adv; Ski Club Adv; Tech Comm; SEA, CEA, NEA 1980-; CTEA 1985-; ITEA 1993-; *office:* Bunnell HS 1 Bulldog Blvd Stratford CT 06497*

GALLIGAN, JOHN SHEILA, Theology Professor; *b:* Olean, NY; *ed:* Immaculata Coll (BA) Theology 1972; St Charles Seminary (MA) Rel Stud 1980; Angelicum Romr (STD) Theology 1985; *cr:* St John of the Cross Schl First Grd Tchr 1968-69; St Thomas More First Grd Tchr 1969-71; St Katherine 1-3 Grd Tchr 1971-72; St Aloysius Acad 1, 4-5 Grd Tchr 1972-80; St Cyprian 8 Grd Tchr; Hallahan Hight Schl Frosh, Soph 1985-87; Archbishop Presndergast Frosh, Soph 1987-90; Immaculata Coll All Levels Theology 1990-; *ai:* Campus Ministry Team; Honors Comm; Spkrs Bureau; Articles Pub in Review for Rel, Spirituality Today, Emmanuel, Carmelite Digest, Pastoral Life, Momentum; Book Reviews Op-Editorials; Pub Svc Teens, Chastity Prgms; *office:* Immaculata College King Rd Immaculata PA 19345

GALLIGAN, MARY J., Fourth Grade Teacher; *b:* New Haven, CT; *ed:* Coll of St Joseph (BS) Elem Ed 1972; Sacred Heart Univ (MA) Ed 1989; Fairfield Univ Spec Ed 30 Credits 1976; *cr:* Mathewson Schl Primary Spec Ed Tchr 1974-86; Meadowside Schl Third Grd Tchr 1986-91; Harborside MS Resource Room Tchr 1991-92; Mathewson Schl Fourth Grd Tchr 1992-; *ai:* Sci Curr Comm; Milford Ed Assn, CEA, NEA 1974-; Book Writing Mini-Grant; *office:* Mathewson Elem Schl 466 W River St Milford CT 06460

GALLIHER, KELLY MARIE, Speech Therapist; *b:* New Hartford, NY; *ed:* Elmira Coll (BS) Tchr of Speech & Hearing Handicapped 1992; SUNY at Oswego (MSEd) Rdng 1995; *cr:* Pulaski Cntrl Schl Speech Therapist 1992-; *ai:* Girls Var Track Asst Coach; GAC & VC Adv; Figure Skating Instr; Amer Speech & Hearing Assn 1992-; *home:* 6 McHarrie St Baldwinsville NY 13027

GALLINO, JOHN FRANK, History Teacher; *b:* New Brunswick, NJ; *m:* Zoe Ann Moritz; *c:* Jennifer, Stacey; *ed:* Seton Hall Univ (BA) Lbrl Arts 1963, (MA) His 1970; 15 Credit Hrs Rutgers Univ; 10 Credit Hrs Trenton St Coll; 20 Credit Hrs Kean Coll; *cr:* Washington Schl Tchr 1964-65; Irving Schl Tchr 1965-67; Middle Schl Tchr 1967-85; Highland Park HS Tchr 1985-; *ai:* Stu Congress Adv; Adult Schl Vlybl Instr; NEA, NJEA, MCEA 1964-; Emergency Mngmt 1990-; *home:* 104 S 3rd Ave Highland Park NJ 08904

GALLIS, DIMITRIOS P., Social Studies Teacher; *b:* Athens, Greece; *m:* Katerina Sirakoulis; *c:* Pantelis; *ed:* Long Island Univ (BA) His, Scndry Ed 1984; NYU (MA) His 1989; 30 Addl Credits at Brooklyn Coll; *cr:* F. D. Roosevelt HS Soc Stud Tchr 1984-; *ai:* Media & Resource Ctr Coord; Articulation Comm; AFT 1984-; Rockefeller Fnd Grant to NYU Summer Seminary 1986; Earthwatch Tchr Flwshp in Archeological Expedition to Yugoslavia 1987; Returned Peace Corps Vols Sent on Trip to Kenya & Botswana to Chaperone Essay Contest Winners 1989; *office:* Franklin D Roosevelt HS 5800 20th Ave Brooklyn NY 11204

GALLIVAN, STEPHEN JOSEPH, German Teacher; *b:* Boston, MA; *m:* Erica Landgraf; *c:* Stephen, Catherine, Kristina Gallivan Belvin; *ed:* Northeastern Univ (BA) Modern Langs 1968; Boston Univ (MA) Ger 1970; *cr:* Boston Latin Ger Tchr 1974-; *ai:* Ger Club Adv; GAAP; AATG 1974-; *office:* Boston Latin Schl 78 Avenue Louis Pasteur Boston MA 02115

GALLO, ANGELO FRED, Seventh Grd Lang Arts Tchr; *b:* Philadelphia, PA; *m:* Jacqueline F. Knecht; *c:* Mark, Susan Fago, Matthew; *ed:* Glassboro St Coll (BA) Elem Ed 1964; *cr:* Ethel Burke Schl 5th Grd Tchr 1964-70; Bell Oaks Upper Elem Schl 7th Grd Lang Arts Tchr 1970-; *ai:* Peer Tutoring Comm; VFW Yth Essay Coord; NEA, NJEA, CCEA, Bellmawr Ed Assn 1964-; Knights of Columbus 1960-; *home:* 14 Gray Birch Rd Turnersville NJ 08012

GALLO, ANN M., Guidance Director; *b:* New York, NY; *m:* Paul; *c:* Cristina, Jeanne, Michael, Tricia, Kate; *ed:* Pace Univ (BA) His; Long Island Univ (MS) Cnslng; Fordham Univ PD Pgm Cnslng; *cr:* St Raymond Acad Schl Cnslr 1982-83; St Catharine Acad Schl Cnslr 1983-90, Guid Dir 1990-; *ai:* ACA 1984-; NYSACD 1984-; WPRACD 1993; *office:* St Catharine Acad 2250 Williamsbridge Rd Bronx NY 10469

GALLO, JACQUELINE KNECHT, Third Grade Teacher; *b:* Woodbury, NJ; *m:* Angelo F.; *c:* Marc, Susan Gallo Fago, Matthew; *ed:* Rowen Coll Glassboro (BA) Elem Ed 1964; *cr:* Ethel Burke Schl Tchr 1964-65; Bellmawr Park Schl Tchr 1972-; *ai:* NEA 1972-; NJEA 1972-; BEA 1972-; *office:* Bellmawr Park School 29 Peach Rd Bellmawr NJ 08031*

GALLO, JOHN WILLIAM, Fifth Grade Teacher; *b:* Yonkers, NY; *m:* Lynn; *c:* Mikala Renee, Christopher Niebuhr; *ed:* St Univ of NY at Oneonta (BS) Bio 1971, (MS) Ed 1976; Post Grad Stud in Archaeology, Early Amer His & Culture; *cr:* Unatego Cntrl Schl 4th Grd Tchr 1971-74, 5th Grd Tchr 1975-; *ai:* Math & Sci Comm; AFT 1971-; Unatego Tchrs Assn 1971-, Exec Comm, Bldg Rep; Unadilla Assn 1971-, Treas, Pres; World Wildlife Fed 1988-; Green Peace 1985-; Little League, Coach; Art Pub on Pottery; Authored, Photographed & Pub Book 19th & 20th Century Yellowware; Research in US, Canada & England; *home:* 75 Main St Otego NY 13825

GALLO, KIMBERLY H., Assistant Principal; *b:* Waterbury, CT; *m:* Thomas J.; *c:* Sarah, Adam, Michael; *ed:* Southern CT St Coll (BS) Elem Ed 1980, (MS) Schl Cnslng 1987; Sacred Heart Univ 6 Yr Cert Admin 1994; *cr:* City Hall MS Sci Tchr 1980-87, Cnslr 1987-93; Naugatuck HS Cnslr 1992-94, Asst Prin.1994-; *ai:* ASCD, NASSP 1994-; Delinquency Prevention Bd Mem 1995-; *office:* Naugatuck HS 543 Rubber Ave Naugatuck CT 06770*

GALLO, LEONARD J., Spanish Teacher; *b:* Cienfuegos, Cuba; *m:* Jeanne Marie Bachand; *c:* John, Christopher; *ed:* Marist Coll (BA) Span 1969; Rutgers Univ (MA) Span Lit 1974; *cr:* St Peters HS Span Tchr 1969-70; Dunellen HS Span Tchr, Dept Chprsn 1970-; Middlesex Cty Coll Adjunct Span Prof 1980-; *ai:* Audio Visual Coord; World Lang Dept Chprsn; NEA, NJEA 1970-; Foreign Lang Ed of NJ; Cedar Hill Swim Club 1980-, VP, Treas; NJ St Governors Tchr Recognition Awd 1990; *office:* Dunellen HS 411 Dunellen Ave Dunellen NJ 08812*

GALLO, LOUIS JOHN, Social Studies Teacher; *b:* New York, NY; *m:* Linda J. Della Villa; *c:* Sharette L., Damon P., Janelle M.; *ed:* Nassau Comm Coll (AA) Liberal Arts; SUNY at Albany (BA) Soc Stud 1967, (MA) Soc Stud 1968; *cr:* Longwood HS Soc Stud Tchr 1968-; Suffolk Comm Coll Adjunct Instr 1989-; *ai:* Local Govt Internship Prgm; Mid Island Tchrs Assn, NYS United Tchrs, AFT 1968-; Brookhaven TN Republican Comm 1990-, Committeeman, Area Coord; Miller Place Civic Assn 1989-, Spec Projects Chm; St Italo-Amer Pol Action Comm 1988-, Dir; Brookhaven TN Accessory Dept Review Bd Chm 1996-; Admin Classroom Awd 1978; Admin Tchr Dedication Awd HS of Yr 1984; *office:* Longwood HS 100 Longwood Rd Middle Island NY 11953

GALLO, MICHAEL ANTHONY, Health & PE Teacher; *ed:* Montclair St Coll (BS) Hlth, PE 1990; Jersey City Coll Driver Ed 1992; BCS Natl Safety Cncl Instr; *cr:* Immaculate Conception HS Hlth, PE Tchr, 9-12 Grd Ath Dir 4 Yrs; *ai:* Coach Head Cross Cntry 3 Yrs, JV Bsktbl, JV Sftbl; Essex Coach JV Boys Bsktbl; NJAHPRD 1989-; NJSOPHE 1990-; *home:* 43 Rosedale Ave Saddle Brook NJ 07663*

GALLO, PATRICK JOSEPH, 11th-12th Grd Amer His Tchr; *b:* Bronx, NY; *m:* Grace Marie Bruno; *c:* Laura Ann, Andrew, Daniela; *ed:* Montclair St Univ (BA) Soc Stud 1959; Seton Hall Univ (MA) Amer His 1962; NY Univ (PHD) Pol Sci 1971; *cr:* Teaneck HS Amer His Tchr 1959-; *ai:* APSA, AHA, NJEA, NEA 1959-; GR Youth Guidance Cncl 1983-86; Amer Acad in Rome Scholar in Residence; NEH Fellow; Fulbright Scholar; NJ Soc Stud Tchr of Yr; Univ of Chicago Tchng Awd; Books Old Bread New Wine, Ethnic Alienation, Swords & Plowshares, Indias Imabe of Intnl System, An Amer Paradox-Politics & Justice; *home:* 29 Roxbury Pl Glen Rock NJ 07452*

GALLON, WILLIAM J., TV Teacher & Production Coord; *b:* Syracuse, NY; *m:* Grace D. Jones; *c:* Kristy R., Danielle J., Jasmine; *ed:* Gloucester Cty Coll (AA) Mrktg, Mngmt 1975; Glassboro St Coll (BA) Scndry Ed, Mrktg, Mngmt 1979; RCA Tech Inst Diploma Cmptr, Television, Radio Tech 1967; *cr:* Glassboro HS TV Tchr, Production Coord 1979-82, 1989-; *ai:* Stage Crew, Explorer's Post # 2309, Career Shadowing, FYI Radio Show, Morning Announcement Adv; Discipline Review, Climate Curr & Stans, Grad Schl Profile, Stu of Month, Tech & Facilities Comms; Glassboro Ed Assn 1979-, Rep, Golden Apple Tchr of Yr Awd 3 Times; NJ Ed Assn, NEA 1979-; Glassboro Ed Fnd 1989-; US Army 1968-70, Specialist 5th Class, Good Conduct Army Svc; *office:* Glassboro HS Joseph Bowe Blvd Glassboro NJ 08028*

GALLOWAY, LEIRDRE CLEMENTS, Social Studies Teacher; *b:* St Petersburg, FL; *m:* Antoine; *c:* Taeyler, Kyndal; *ed:* Univ of MD at Coll Park (BS) Criminology, LENF 1984; Trinity Coll (MAT) Scndry Ed 1993; *cr:* Martin Luther King Acad Ctr Tchr 1987-91; Laurel HS Soc Stud Educator 1991-; *ai:* Fac Advy Cncl; Pom-Pon Spon; Co-Coord Stdnts Against Fearful Environment; Pilot Drug Awareness Prgm, DARE Educator; Sr Class Spon; Human Relations Liason Withuin Schl; NEA 1987-; *office:* Laurel HS 8000 Cherry Ln Laurel MD 20707

GALLOWAY, LEROY MICHAEL, Eighth Grade English Teacher; *b:* Harrisburg, PA; *m:* Shirl Denise; *c:* Michael, Tania; *ed:* Shippensburg Univ (BS) Elem Ed 1975; *cr:* Milton Hershey Schl 8th Grd Eng Tchr 1975-; *ai:* Var Boys & Girls Head Track & Field Coach; Variety Show Coord; MHEA 1995-, Bldg Rep; PIAA Ofcl 1979-; PTFCA 1985-, Hall of Fame Selection Comm, Coach of Yr 1990; Harrisburg Optimist Club 1980-, Yth Coord, Friend of Youth; Penna Track & Field Coaches Assn Girls Track Coach of Yr 1989; Boys Track Coach of Yr 1990; Natl Interscholastic A[illegible] Coach of Yr in PA 1993; *office:* Milton Hershey Schl Cath[illegible] Hershey PA 17033

GALLUCCI, DALE JOSEPH, Fifth Grade Science Teacher; [illegible] OH; *m:* Debra Ann Lucas; *c:* Jennifer, Anthony, Matthew; *ed:* Ke[illegible] (BS) Elem Ed 1977; Akron Univ (MS) Elem Admin 1984; [illegible] Physics; Law Related Ed; Project WILD, Learning Tree; *cr:* [illegible] Youngstown 7th-8th Grd Sci Tchr 1977-78; Jackson Local Sch[illegible] Sci Tchr 1978-; *ai:* Jackson HS Girls Tennis Head Coach; Pee[illegible] Vol; PANDA Camp Co-Facilitator; NEA 1978-; Phi Delta Kap[illegible] DARE Assn of OH 1993-; Comm Drug Bd 1994, Vol; SEEDS Ld[illegible] 1993 OH Dare Educator of Yr; Federal League Girls Tennis C[illegible] 1994 & 1995; *office:* Jackson Mem MS 7355 Mudbrook NW Mas[illegible] 44646*

GALLUZZO, CAROLYN MARCOTTE, English Dept Chair & [illegible] *b:* Ft Worth, TX; *m:* Joseph A.; *c:* Taffany; *ed:* Suffolk Univ [illegible] 1975; Boston St Coll 30 Credit Hrs Eng; Salem St Coll 9 C[illegible] Watertown Schls Eng Tchr 4 Yrs; Higgins MS Eng Tchr 2 Yrs; [illegible] Schl Eng Tchr, Chair 5 Yrs; *ai:* Drama Club Dir; Schl Musi[illegible] Choreographer; SAT Instr for Mc Nff Consultants 10 Yrs; NCTE [illegible] 1987-; *office:* St John The Baptist Schl 19 Chestnut St Pea[illegible] 01960*

GALOUGH, JAMIE PEREAU, Family & Consumer Science[illegible] Crown Point, NY; *m:* Mark B.; *c:* Jacob M., Kathryn E.; *ed:* [illegible] Plattsburgh (BS) Home Ec Ed 1979, (MS) Home Ec Ed 1983; 20 [illegible] Hrs Family & Consumer Sci; *cr:* Argyle Cntrl Schl Human Reso[illegible] Chprsn 1979-; *ai:* Natural Helpers Coord; Dist Planning, Fami[illegible] & Natl Jr Hnr Soc Comm; Class Adv; NYSAFCSE 1979-; Arg[illegible] Assn 1979-, Tchr of the Yr 1992-93; PTSO 1989-; Article Pub; C[illegible] for NY St Ed Dept; *office:* Argyle Central Schl Sheridan St A[illegible] 12809*

GALUSKA, MARYANNE ARONSON, High School Guidance [illegible] Springfield, VT; *m:* Peter; *ed:* Univ of RI (BA) Eng 1963; Univ o[illegible] (MED) Counseling 1967, (CAGS) Schl Psych 1972; *cr:* Canto[illegible] Tchr 1963-64; Boston HS Eng Tchr 1964-68; Gideon Wells Jr HS [illegible] Cnslr 1968-72; Glastonbury HS Guidance Cnslr 1972-; *ai:* HO[illegible] Adv; NHS & Schlsp Comms; NEA, CT Ed Assn 1964-; Glast[illegible] Assn, CT Schl Cnslrs Assn 1968-; *office:* Glastonbury HS 320 H[illegible] Glastonbury CT 06033

GALUSKA, MICHAEL R., 6th-8th Grade Teacher; *b:* Pittsbur[illegible] Duquesne Univ (BS) Scndry Ed 1969, (MSEd) Elem Admin [illegible] Sacred Heart Elem Schl Tchr, Dept Chprsn 1970-78; St Mich[illegible] Tchr, Vice Prin 1978-79; Resurrection Schl Tchr 1979-; *ai:* [illegible] Pittsburg Diocesan Tchrs 1987-, VP, Exec Bd; *office:* Resurre[illegible] 1100 Creedmore Ave Pittsburgh PA 15226*

GALVANEK, JOY B., Second Grade Teacher; *b:* Mt Pleasan[illegible] James W. Sr.; *c:* James W. Jr., Janel B.; *ed:* CA St Univ (BSEd[illegible] 1960, (MSEd) Elem Ed 1973; *cr:* Hempfield Area Schl Dist [illegible] 1969-; *ai:* Grd Level Chprsn; Book Adoption Comm; PSEA, NE[illegible] Local 1969-; Calvary Bapt Church 1979-, Choir, Former Tchr; [illegible] Williamsburg Pl Irwin PA 15642*

GALVANEK, SHARON BRECHKA, Family & Consumer Sci T[illegible] Elizabeth, NJ; *m:* Richard G.; *c:* Sarah Irene; *ed:* Univ of DE ([illegible] Ec, Child Dev, Elem Ed 1975; *cr:* Carteret Pub Schl System [illegible] 1975-76; Columbus Schl Spec Ed Aide 1976-77; Washington Sc[illegible] Grd Tchr 1977-87; Columbus Schl First Grd Tchr 1988-93; Lin[illegible] Home Ec Tchr 1993-; Nathan Hale Schl Home Ec Tchr 1993-; [illegible] CEA 1976-; NJHEA, HEEA 1993-; PTA-PTO 1976-; HSA 1991-[illegible] Recognition Awd 1990, 1993; Dist Tchr of Yr Finalist 1992-[illegible] Discovery Phonics Prgm Companion Pub 1993; *home:* 45 Fre[illegible] Carteret NJ 07008*

GALVANO, DAVID MARK, Chef Instructor; *b:* Niagara Falls [illegible] Niagara Cty Comm Coll (AA) Lbrl Arts, Scis 1986; Univ at Buf[illegible] Psych 1989; Niagara Univ (MS) Schl Admin 1991; The Culina[illegible] Amer (AOS) Culinary Arts 1993; St Univ Coll at Buffalo Post [illegible] Voc Ed; Niagara Falls Bd of Ed Staff Dev; *cr:* The Goos[illegible] Restaurant Chef Grillardin 1977-79; Niagara Hilton Hotel Che[illegible] 1980-83; Various Area Hotels Kitchen Positions 1991-93; Niagar[illegible] of Ed Chef Instr 1994-; *office:* LaSalle Sr HS 1500 Military R[illegible] Falls NY 14304

GALVIN, ALOYSIUS C.,SJ, Math Teacher; *b:* Baltimore, [illegible] Loyola Coll (AB) Classics 1948; Woodstock Coll (MA) Tchng 19[illegible] Philosophy 1953, (STL) Theology 1958; *cr:* Loyola Coll Dea[illegible] 1959-65, Acad VP 1960-65; Univ of Scranton Pres 1965-70; Ge[illegible] Prep Schl Math Tchr 1970-, Coll Cnslr 1971-95; *ai:* Corp Sec; A[illegible] Comm; Cnslr; Ftbl Team Chaplain; *office:* Georgetown Prep Sc[illegible] Rockville Pike N Bethesda MD 20852

GALVIN, JOHN BRETT, Mathematics Teacher; *b:* Waterbury[illegible] Alberta Campoli; *c:* Laura Ann, Peggy Nelson, Jennifer; *ed:* Fair[illegible] (BA) Math Ed 1966, (MA) Math Ed 1967; Addl 33 Grad Credi[illegible] Advanced Stud Prgm; *cr:* Watertown HS Math Tchr 1967-; W[illegible] Tuition Summer Schl Tchr 1970-85; *ai:* Cross Cntry Coach [illegible] Naugatuck Valley League Cross Cntry Chm; Watertown Ed Assn [illegible] NEA 1967-; USA Track & Field 1979-; Libra AA 1985-; Nat[illegible] Grant 1970 & 1972; *home:* 113 Newton Ter Waterbury CT 0670[illegible]

GALYA, BETTY JAKUBOVICS, English & Theme Writing [illegible] Duquesne, PA; *m:* Donald Paul; *ed:* Slippery Rock St Tchrs (BS) [illegible] Sci 1957; Duquesne Univ Permanent Cert; *cr:* Hopewell Ind Ra[illegible] Eng Tchr 1957-58; Duquesne Jr HS Eng, Sci Tchr 1958-60; We[illegible] HS Eng, Theme Writing Tchr 1960-; *ai:* PSEA 1957-; NCT[illegible] Outstdng Tchr; Master Tchr; *office:* West Mifflin Area [illegible] Commonwealth Ave West Mifflin PA 15122

GAMBA, MARIA NEGRON, Third Grade Bilingual Teacher; *b* [illegible] PR; *m:* Rafael Gamba; *c:* Rafael Andres; *ed:* City Coll NY (BA) [illegible] 1982; (MS) Adult Ed 1984; *cr:* PS 169 Tchr 1982-; *ai:* AFT; ASC[illegible] *office:* PS 169 Sunset Park 4305 7th Ave Brooklyn NY 11232

GAMBER, DONNA LEE, Learning Support Tchr; *b:* Philadelphi[illegible] Jeffrey Lee; *c:* Dean; *ed:* Millersville St Univ (BS) Spec Ed 1971 [illegible] MD Coll (MS) Spec Ed 1991; *cr:* Penn Manor HS Spec Ed Tchr [illegible] Red Lion Area Sr HS Learning Support Tchr 1979-; York C[illegible] Adjunct Fac, Ed Tchr 1991; *ai:* NHS Adv; Spec Ed Dept Coo[illegible] PSEA, RL Tchrs Assn 1979-; *office:* Red Lion Area Sr HS 20[illegible] Mann Ave Red Lion PA 17356*

GAMBINO, SALVATORE VINCENT, Mathematics Teacher; *b:* [illegible] Sicily; *ed:* Hudson Vly Comm Coll (AAS) Chemical Tech 1963; [illegible] Albany (BS) Math 1965, (MS) Math 1966; 66 Post Grad Credits [illegible] Univ 1969, Hope Coll 1970, FL St Univ 1972-73, Univ of M[illegible] Oswego C 1976, Univ of MA 1977, Univ of CT 1978, Univ of [illegible] *cr:* SUNY at Albany Resident Asst 1964-66; Arlington HS M[illegible] 1966-; Dutchess Comm Coll Math Tchr 1977-94; *ai:* AFT, NEA, [illegible] Arlington TA 1966-; AARP 1994-; Omega Tau 1963-; Kappa M[illegible] 1966-; Colgate Univ AP Calculus Grant 1969; Hope C NSF Gr[illegible] FSU NFS Flwshp 1972-73; SUNY Most Influential Tchr 1983; [illegible] Tchr Awds MIT 1985 & 1988, Nazareth C 1986, Cornell Univ 19[illegible] PO Box 234 Lagrangeville NY 12540

, HAL WALTER, English Teacher; *b:* Sewickley, PA; *m:* ae; *c:* Shane, Megan; *ed:* Univ of AZ (BA Elem Ed 1968, (MED) 973; Univ of MD (EdD) Curr Instruction 1984; US Naval Lang orth Vietnamese; *cr:* MO Schl for Deaf Eng Tchr 1973-79; MD eaf Eng Tchr 1979-; Frederick Comm Coll Eng Tchr 1985-; *ai:* 'rof; Convention of Amer Instrs of Deaf 1981-; Cncl on Ed for -; Frederick Cty Spcl Ed Tchr of Yr 1989; Numerous Articles : 206 Challedon Dr Walkersville MD 21793

, NANCY STROHSCHER, High School English Teacher; *b:* H; *m:* Bruce Alexander; *c:* Joy Elizabeth, Allison Suzanne; *ed:* Green St Univ (BS) Eng, His, Pol Sci 1967, (MA) Amer Stud Fremont Ross HS Soc Stud Dept Head, Eng & His Tchr 1967-77; HS Eng Tchr 1978-79; Owens Technical Coll Eng Composition 1979-88; Oak Harbor HS Honors Eng, Creative Writing Tchr Lit Magazine Adv; NCTE, OH Cncl Tchrs Eng 1988-; OH Ed -; The Delta Kappa Gamma Soc; *office:* Oak Harbor HS 11661 163 Oak Harbor OH 43449

, ROBERT JOHN, Dir Tchr Cert & Asst Prof; *b:* Buffalo, NY; Vilkins; *ed:* SUNY at Fredonia (BS) Elem Ed 1971, (MS) Elem SUNY at Buffalo (PHD) Early Chldhd 1985; *cr:* Univ at Buffalo t 1981-86; Cntrl CT St Asst Prof 1987-88; Castleton St Asst Prof D'Youville Coll Asst Prof & Dir Tchr Cert 1990-; *ai:* Cert Tennis 89; Tennis Dir 1990-; AAUP 1989-, Prsnl Coord; NEA; Books: vities for Young Children 1995 & Noncompetitive Games for the Teacher 1996; Numerous Articles Pub; *office:* D'Youville Coll Ave Buffalo NY 14201*

, ROBERT MARTIN, Carpentry & Psychology Prof; *b:* Centre, NY; *m:* Diane Bannwarth; *c:* Philip R., Lori L.; *ed:* Oneonta (BA) Psych 1969; Nassau Comm Coll (AA) Lib Arts dl 15 Hrs SUNY at Farmingdale Pre-Med; *cr:* Wonderworld wner, Dir 1971-79; Long Island Railroad Carpenter 1979-86; Gamble Contractor 1986-91; Delhi Coll of Tech Asst Prof Psych 1991-; *ai:* Dacum Facilitator; Zoning, Bldg Code nt Ofcr; Rotary Intnl 1988-; Bd of Dir; Amer Legion 1987-; hi Coll of Tech SUNY Coll of Technology Delhi NY 13753

R, RAE ANN RICHMAN, Sixth Grade Teacher; *b:* Defiance, obert F.; *c:* Wendy, B. J.; *ed:* Defiance Coll (BS) Elem Ed 1981; v of Toledo, Bowling Green St Univ; *cr:* Defiance Jr HS 7th Grd Tchr 1981; Brickell Elem 2nd Grd Tchr 1981-82; Spencer Elem chr 1982-84; Defiance MS 5th Grd Tchr 6 Yrs, 6th Grd Tchr 6 dv Stu Cncl; Adv & Coach 5th-6th, Jr HS, HS Quiz Teams; OEA, -; NWOEA 1981-, Dist Rep; DCEA 1981-, Pres 1983-87, VP ta Kappa Gamma Beta Zeta Ch 1995-; Jenning Scholar; 1993 Sci Wkshp, Mentor 1992-93; 2 Time Nom Presidential Sci Awrd; r & Prsntr of Sci Wrkshp; *office:* Defiance MS 801 S Clinton OH 43512*

DARREN MATTHEW, English Teacher; *b:* Cherry Hill, NJ; *m:* Fleisher; *ed:* St Joseph's Univ (BA) Eng 1993; Working on Tchr apped Cert; *cr:* Rancocas Vly Regnl HS Eng Tchr 1993-; *ai:* cer, Strength Coach; Home Instruction Tchr; NEA, NJEA 1993-; 1-; Natl Soccer Coaches Assn 1994-; Intnl Eng Hnrs Soc; *office:* Valley Reg HS 572 Jacksonville Rd Mount Holly NJ 08060*

, PATRICIA A. (MURLEY), First Grade Teacher; *b:* Montague, ames H.; *c:* Mary E. Haskins, Brenda J., Suzanne T., Maureen C., *ed:* North Adams St (BS) Elem Ed 1956; Univ MA (MED) Rdng Mc Kinley Schl 5th Grd Tchr 1956-57; Old Deerfield Schl 5th 1961-63, Kndgtn Tchr 1965-67, Remedial Rdng Tchr 1967-75; erfield 1st Grd Tchr 1975-83, 4th Grd Tchr 1983-86; Deerfield Grd Tchr 1986-; *ai:* Natures Classroom; Dist Math Curr; Math NCTM Wkshps in Svcs 1993; Portfolio, Assessment Comm; n Tm 5 Times; Union 38 Tchrs Assn 1968-, Sec 2 yrs, Treas 5 Yr, Pres 1 Yr; MTA, NEA; Holy Trinity Schl Guild 1962-82, Sec, ?, Pres 1 Yr Each; Blessed Sacrament Parish Cncl 1973-79; Club #43 1985-, Sec, VP, Pres 1 Yr Each; *office:* Deerfield Elem nt St South Deerfield MA 01373

MICHAEL LEE, Junior Accounting Instructor; *b:* Portsmouth, haron Hawkins; *c:* Michael II, Melissa Beth; *ed:* Morehead St Accounting & Math 1969, (MBE) Bus Ed 1973; *cr:* Shawnee St a Processing Asst Prof 1981-87, Univ Information Asst Dir Scioto Cty Joint Voc Schl Accounting & Computing Instr 1990-; dvisory & Evaluation Comms; Bus Profs of America Adv; Scioto Voc Schl Tchrs Assn, Exec Comm; OH Ed Assn; Scioto Cty Fair Scioto Cty Joint Voc Schl PO Box 766 Lucasville OH 45648

PAMELA SUE, Social Studies Teacher; *b:* Portsmouth, OH; *ed:* (BS) Soc Stud 1972; *cr:* Bloom Local Schl 7th-8th Grd Soc Stud 2-73; Wheelersburg Local Schl 7th-8th Soc Stud Tchr 1973-74; ocal Schl 9th-10th Soc Stud Tchr 1974-; *ai:* Adv Jr Class, NHS; A, MEA 1974-; Nom Ashland Oil Tchr Awd 1991; *office:* Minford ox 204 Minford OH 45653

N, GLORIANE KLEIN, Mathematics Teacher; *b:* Mount Y; *m:* Stanley F.; *c:* Scott, Michael; *ed:* Hunter Coll (AB) Math S) Ed 1967; 60 Credit Hrs Above Masters; *cr:* PS 73 Tchr Woodland HS Tchr 1976-77; Fox Lane MS Tchr 1977-79; HS 1981-; *ai:* Math Team Co-Adv; Bldg Leadership Cncl; Del Stu Mentor; NCTM, AMTNYS, Ten Cty Math Assn 1985-; gh Fed of Tchrs, NYSUT 1976-; Hadassah 1969-; Nom Tandy holar; *office:* Woodlands HS 475 W Hartsdale Ave Hartsdale NY

RZ, VALERIE JANE, Business Education Teacher; *b:* ck, NY; *ed:* William Paterson Coll (BA) Elem Ed 1974; Attnd St Univ; Tchr of Bus Ed; *cr:* Holy Angels Grammar Schl Soc 1974-77; Sawyer Schl Sec Stud Tchr 1978-89; Manchester Regnl d Tchr 1989-90; West Essex Regnl Jr HS Bus Ed Tchr 1990-92; ck HS Bus Ed Tchr 1992-; *ai:* Future Bus Ldrs of Amer, Frosh rbk Advs; NEA, NJEA 1989-; NJBEA 1978-; Adult Schl of 1978-92, Instr, 15 Yrs Svc; *office:* Hackensack HS First & Beech ackensack NJ 07601

DEBRA RUBERTI, Senior Learning Center Supvr; *b:* Vineland, ank Jay; *c:* Danielle Lee, Frank Joseph; *ed:* Cumberland Cty Coll s Ed, Hlth 1978; US Army (AS) Pharmacy 1980; Salem Coll 40 s Phys Ed, Hlth; Cumberland Cty Coll 8 Hrs Math, Statistics; *cr:* hrstn Ctr Acad Supvr, Math, Sci Tchr 1991-; *ai:* Var Girls Vlybl, ftbl Coach; ACE Convention Spon; Jump Rope for Heart Amer sn; Schl Chprsn; Ranch Hope Citizen of Yr 1991; *office:* Fairton Ctr Acad PO Box 96 Fairton Rd Fairton NJ 08320

LFI, M'LENA, Phys Ed & Health Teacher; *b:* Lynn, MA; *c:* *ed:* Univ of MA at Amherst (BA) PE, Hlth 1972; Cambridge Coll 1995; 15 Addl Hrs; *cr:* Frontier Regnl Schl PE, Hlth Tchr Manchester HS PE, Hlth Tchr 1985-; *ai:* Var Field Hockey Coach; 1998 Adv; Hlth, PE Dept Chprsn; US Field Hockey Assn 1985-; ch's Assn 1990-; NEA, MTA 1972-; Coach of Yr Boston Globe 5, Cape Ann League 1986, 1990, 1992, 1995; *office:* Manchester n St Manchester MA 01944*

LFO, JAMES M., Instructor in Theatre & Speech; *b:* Brooklyn, Tammy Roche; *c:* Christian, Stephanie; *ed:* Gannon Univ (BA) Comm Arts 1980; *cr:* Mercyhurst College Theatre Instr 1992-; Mercyhurst Preparatory 1992-; *ai:* Dir of Theatre; ITS Adv; Jr Var Girls Soccer Coach, Announcer; Educl Theatre Assn 1992-; Intl Thesbian Soc 1992-, Spon; St Peters Cathedral 1988-, Lector Choir; Founder Comedy Troupe in All Seriousness Inc;Professional Natl Touring Troupe Colls, Clubs & Corps Since 1983; Dir & Performer Erie Playhouse Since 1978; Best Actor Awd St of PA 1983; Eastern Sts Regnl, Natl Runner Up 1983; Instr ITS St Conf 1993-; *office:* Mercyhurst Prep HS 538 East Grandview Blvd Erie PA 16504*

GANEY, DENNIS BARTHOLOMEW, Religious Studies Tchr & Coach; *b:* Bronx, NY; *m:* Barbara Jean Hite; *ed:* Manhattan Coll (BS) Ed 1967; New York Univ (BS) PE 1969; 30 Hrs Admin 1972; Rel Stud St Joseph's; World Religions Iona Coll; *cr:* Poughkeepsie Pub Schls PE Tchr 1969-72; Pelham Meml HS PE Tchr 1972-81; Mater Dei HS Rel Stud Tchr 1981-84; St Rose HS Rel Stud Tchr 1984-; *ai:* Ftbl, Girls Bsktbl, Boys Track Coach Red Bank Cath HS; NCEA 1982-; NEA 1971-; Red Bank YMCA 1982-, Vol Asst Cardiovascular Room; Pelham Womans League Grant 1971; *office:* St Rose HS 7th Ave Belmar NJ 07719

GANG, CAROLYN FRANCES, Mathematics Teacher; *b:* Lorain, OH; *m:* William J.; *ed:* Bowling Green St Univ (BS) LD, Elem Ed, Math 1982; Baldwin-Wallace Coll (MA) Admin & Supervision 1985; 24 Plus Post Masters Hrs; *cr:* Brookside HS LD Tchr 1982-85; Learwood Jr HS & Avon Lake HS LD Tchr 1985-86; Brookside HS Math Tchr 1986-; *ai:* Sr Class Adv; Team Cardinal Mem; Chaperone to United Kingdom; NEA 1982-; LEMMA 1990-; Article Pub in B W Lit Journal Decade; Nom for Tchr of Yr Sheffield & Sheffield Lake; *office:* Brookside HS 1812 Harris Rd Sheffield Lake OH 44054

GANGE, RICHARD EDWARD, Science Teacher; *b:* Woburn, MA; *ed:* Merrimack Coll (BA) Bio 1972; Rutgers Univ (MS) Zoology 1974; 30 Addl Hrs; *cr:* Westfield HS Sci Tchr 1974-; *ai:* Environmental Awareness Club Adv; Schl Bldg, Conf Approval Comm Dist Chair, Supervision, Evaluation, Future Directions, Bd, Staff Relations Comms; NEA 1974-; NJ Sci Tchrs Assn 1988-; NJ Bio Tchrs Assn 1995-; Coalition for Hunger Awareness 1995-; Outstdng Tchr Foose Awd 1990; 1 of 4 Tchrs to Design, First Teach in Project 79; *office:* Westfield HS 550 Dorian Rd Westfield NJ 07090*

GANGEMI, CHRISTINE LAIACONA, English Teacher; *b:* Troy, NY; *m:* Richard; *c:* Ryan; *ed:* Kean Coll of NJ (BA) Eng Ed 1974; William Paterson Coll of NJ (MA) Comm, Theatre 1980; Rdng Cert prgm Kean Coll of NJ 1975; *cr:* Byram Intermediate Schl Lang Arts, Rdng Tchr 1976-80; Shenendehowa HS Eng Tchr 1980-84; Burnt Hills-Ballston Lake HS Eng Tchr 1988-; *ai:* Dir of Drama Productions 1990-95, Dev Writing Curr Comm 1991-93; NYSUT 1980-; NCTE 1991-, NCTE Writing Awd Judge 1994, 1995, 1996; *office:* Burnt Hills-Balston Lake HS Lakehill Rd Burnt Hills NY 12027

GANGI, ROBYN JOSEPH, Choral Activities Director; *b:* New York, NY; *m:* Jane Mc Brayer; *c:* Devin, Caryn, Peter; *ed:* Temple Univ (BM) Music Ed 1977; Wesleyan Univ (MA) Lit, Art 1980; Doctoral Candidate Columbia Univ; Yale Univ Norfolk Summer Music; *cr:* Lyme-Old Lyme MS Choral Act Dir 1977-84; Lyme-Old Lyme HS Choral Act Dir 1977-84; New York City Prof Tenor Soloist 1984-91; Masuk HS Choral Act Dir 1991-; *ai:* Producer, Dir Spring Musical; Chamber Choir, Camarata Choral Dir; MENC, CMEA, NEA 1991-; St Thomas Episcopal Church 2 Yrs, Choir Master, Organist; Attnd Aspen Music Festival; Tchrs Coll Columbia Univ Schlsp; PA Music Edctr Assn St Conf Rsrch Presentation; Intnl Symposium of Intnl Soc Phenomenology, Aesthetics, Fine Arts Rsrch Presentation, Publication; *office:* Masuk HS 1014 Monroe Tpke Monroe CT 06468

GANGI, VINCENT JOHN, Jr HS Social Studies Tchr; *b:* Brooklyn, NY; *c:* Rosanne; *ed:* NY Univ (BS) Soc Stud Ed 1966, (MA) Soc Stud Ed 1968; 30 Hrs Asian Stud Post Grad, Inservice Stud; *cr:* IS 49K Tchr 30 Yrs; *ai:* UFT 1966-, Chapter Chm 1970-80, 10 Yr Awd; *office:* IS 49K 223 Graham Ave Brooklyn NY 11206

GANGLOFF, GAIL MARGARET, HS Mathematics Teacher; *b:* Allentown, PA; *m:* Joseph M.; *c:* Benjamin, Scott; *ed:* Millersville Univ (BS) Scndry Ed, Math 1969; Millersville Univ 12 Credit Hrs; Penn St Univ 6 Credit Hrs; Wilkes Coll 3 Credit Hrs; Shippensburg Univ 3 Credit Hrs; Lincoln Intermediate Univ 3 Credit Hrs; *cr:* Dallastown HS Math Tchr 1969-70; Penn St Univ Lib Clerk 1981-86; St Joseph Elem Schl Math Tchr 1986-89; York Cath HS Math Tchr 1989-; *ai:* Math Dept Chm; NHS, Quiz Bowl Team Adv; NCTM 1994-; NCEA 1986-; *office:* York Catholic HS 601 E Springettsbury Ave York PA 17403

GANLEY, THERESA MC DONNELL, Fourth Grade Teacher; *b:* Queens, NY; *c:* Jennifer Elizabeth; *ed:* Molloy Coll (BA) Eng, Ed 1980; Adelphi Univ (MA) Early Child Ed 1990; Educl Leadership, Admin Prof Diploma Candidate C. W. Post Univ 30 Credits; *cr:* Davison Ave Elem Schl Stu Tchr 1979; St Raymond's Tchr 1980-82; Davison Ave Elem Schl Tchr 1984-; *ai:* More Effective Schls Bldg Level Team; Stu Cncl Moderator; Soc Comm Chprsn; Sci Coord; Literacy Stans Comm Liason; PTA, Rep; ASCD; Malverne Tchrs Assn; Fulton Ave Schl PTA, Rep; NYC Transit Police Assn, Officers Benevolent Schlsp Co-Chprsn; *office:* Davison Ave Elem Schl Davison Ave Lynbrook NY 11563

GANN, DEBORAH MILLER, Second Grade Teacher; *b:* Canton, OH; *m:* Dan L.; *ed:* Univ of Akron (BS) K-8th Grd Elem Ed 1979; *cr:* Canton City Schls 1st Grd Tchr 1979-81, 2nd Grd Tchr 1981-93, 1st Grd Tchr 1993-95, 2nd Grd Tchr 1995-; *ai:* Drama Club; Career Ed Bldg Liaison; Math, Bldg Lead team, Multi-Cultural Comms; Schl Pictures for Birthday & Stu of Month; OEA, NEA 1979-; USTA 1986-; Washington Schl PTO 1979-; Worked with Schl Comm for 2 Grants, Awded Effective Schls & Venture Capital Grant; Attnd Whole Lang, Math Manipulatives, Interdisciplinary Curr, SEEDS Sci & Multiage Grouping Wkshp; *office:* Washington Elem Schl 1220 9th St NE Canton OH 44705

GANNON, BARBARA BENDLER, Second Grade Teacher; *b:* Cleveland, OH; *m:* Timothy R.; *c:* Bradley; *ed:* Bowling Green St Univ (BA) Elem Ed 1977; Credit Hrs Akron Univ, Ashland Univ; *cr:* Parma City Schls 1-4, 6 Grds Tchr 1978-95; *ai:* OH Classroom Mngmt Team; Noontime Structure Comm; PTA Tchr Rep, Yrbk Comm; NEA, OH Ed Assn, Parma Ed Assn, NEOEA 1978-; Pama Chapter #552 Order of Eastern Star 1974-, Worthy Matron 1985, 1994, Grand Page to Deputy Grand Matron 1996; Cub Scouts 1995-96, Den Ldr; Ridgewood United Meth Church 1968-, Sunday Schl Supt 1992-95; Ladies Oriental Shrine of N Amer Kheedowee Ct #6 1987-, Kourt Klowns, Sec; *office:* John Muir Elem Schl 5531 W 24th St Cleveland OH 44134*

GANNON, DAVID STEPHEN, English, Drama Tchr & Dir; *b:* Cleveland, OH; *m:* Jane Marie Mc Millen; *c:* Kellie Marie, Jonathon David, Bryn William; *ed:* Bowling Green St Univ (BS) Ed Eng, Drama, Speech, Broadcasting, Jrnlsm, Rdng; Cleveland St Univ Comm Theory, Methodology; Kent St Univ; *cr:* Warrensville Hts Jr HS Seventh Grd Eng Tchr 1979-80; Richmond Hts HS Eng, Speech, Drama, 7th Grd Rdng, HS Drama Dir 1980-82; Newbury HS Eng, Speech, Drama Tchr, Drama Dir 1982-85; Lakewood HS Eng, Speech, Drama Tchr, Drama Dir 1985-; *ai:* Barnstormer Drama Club Adv; Dir HS Plays One of Comedy, Drama, Musical; Educl Theater Assn; NEA 1979-, Guid Chprsn 1984-85; *office:* Lakewood HS 14100 Franklin Blvd Lakewood OH 44107*

GANNON, DONALD FRANCIS, 2nd Grade Teacher; *b:* Worcester, MA; *m:* Marguerite L. Smith; *c:* Robert M., Katelyn R.; *ed:* Worcester St Coll (BSEd) His 1970; Lesley Coll (MAEd) Arts Integration & Curr 1995; Addl 29 Hrs; *cr:* City of Worcester Tchr 26 Yrs; *ai:* EAW 1970-, Del, Bd of Dir; MTA, NEA 1970-, Del; Alliance for Ed Mini-Grant 1982; Hands on Sci 1987, Sci Coord, Tchr Trainer, Curr Dev 1988 Horace Mann Grant; Earthwatch Research Team Grant 1988; *office:* Clark Street Cmty Elem Schl 280 Clark St Worcester MA 01606

GANNON, TIMOTHY MICHAEL, Dean of Students & Math Tchr; *b:* New York City, NY; *m:* Carolyn Geraghty; *ed:* Iona Coll (BA) Math 1980; SUNY at Albany (MS) Math Ed 1985; Coll of Staten Island 6th Yr Schl Admin Cert 1987; *cr:* Power Memrl Acad Math Tchr & Comp Chm 1980-83; Msgr Farrell HS Math Tchr 1983-86; Xaverian HS Math Tchr 1986-87; Curtis HS Math Tchr & Dean 1987-; *ai:* Boys Var Bsktbl & Var Vllybl Coach; NHS Adv; IM dir; NCTM 1986-; UFT 1987-; Natl Fed of Aths 1993-; Bsktbl Coaches Assn of NY St 1993-; Staten Is Bsktbl Coach of Yr 1993 & 1995; *office:* Curtis HS 105 Hamilton Ave Staten Island NY 10301

GANSLE, MARBRY PULVER, Secondary PE Teacher & Coach; *b:* Hudson, NY; *m:* Stephen L.; *c:* Ashley E.; *ed:* Russell Sage Coll (BS) PE, Psych 1977, (MS) Hlth 1983; 21 Hrs Toward Masters in Guidance, Counseling; *cr:* Shaker HS PE Instr 1977-; *ai:* Sr Class, Ski Club Advs; Cross Cntry, Gymnastics, Track, Field Var Coach; Womens Gymnastics NYS St Chprsn; Section 2 Chprsn Cross Cntry, Gymnastics; Cross Cntry NYS St Chprsn; Open Womens Empire St Games T & F Coach; AAPERD, NYSAHPERD, CN AHPERD 1973-; NHSGCA, AFT, NEA, NYSCA 1977-; USGF 1974-; NYSSCOGS 1989-; CDCAD 1987-; HMRCC 1969-; Crescent Estates Women Club 1989-; Russell Sage Coll Class Agent 1985-; All Amer Gymnastic Team, Individuals Coach; NY St Gymnastics Coach of Yr 1992;; NYSAHPERD Amazing Tchr of Yr, Coached Cross Cntry Kinney Finalist 1991; *office:* Shaker HS 445 Watervliet Shaker Rd Latham NY 12110*

GANSLE, PAUL B., PE Teacher & Coach; *b:* Albany, NY; *m:* Sandra Jean Bedinotti; *c:* Paul, Rachel, Eric, Megan, Samantha; *ed:* SUNY at Cortland (BS) PE 1964; 36 Addl Hrs; *cr:* Berkshire Farm for Boys PE Tchr 1964-66; Colonie Cntrl HS PE Tchr 1966-, Head Cross Cntry Coach 1966-, Head Indoor Track Coach 1966-; *ai:* AFT, NEA 1964-; Colonie Tchrs Assn 1966-; Reserve Ofcrs Assn 1978-; Ret US Coast Guard Reserve 1967-, 3 Commanding Ofcrs Billets; Ret LCDR; *home:* 18 Peter Dr Albany NY 12205

GANSON, LEO ELWIN, High School Mathematics Tchr; *b:* Lacombe, Alberta; *m:* Gloria Anne Eklund; *c:* Gerald Wayne, Janice Lorraine Clark, Julie Anne Shipowick, Glenda June, Jonathan Joel; *ed:* Loma Linda Univ (BA) Math 1967, (MA) Elem Ed 1989; *cr:* Newfoundland Seventh-day Adventist Conf Tchr 1964-71; Alberta Conf of Seventh-day Adventist Jr HS Tchr 1971-89; Canadian Union Coll & Parkview Adventist Acad Math Tchr 1989-; *ai:* Sr Class Fac Spon; Campus Life Comm; HS Hockey Asst Coach; Woodlands Adventist Schl Bd 1994-; Woodlands Adventist Acad Band Tchr; Parkland Adventist Acad Discipline Comm; Thomas & Violet Zapara Excl in Tchng Awd 1994; *home:* Box 14 Site 1 RR 3 Ponoka AB T4J 1R3 Canada CN

GANT, PAUL J., English Teacher; *b:* Point Pleasant, NJ; *m:* Lucy Phillips; *c:* Esther, Ansley, Ruth; *ed:* The King's Coll (BA) Eng 1977; Morgan St Univ (MA) Eng 1985; *cr:* Edgewood HS Eng Tchr 1977-89; Hanz Long Tchrs Coll Eng Tchr in China 1989-90; North Harford HS Eng Tchr 1990-; *ai:* Forensics Coach; Schoolwide Enrichment Comm Chprsn; Mt Zion United Meth Church 1988-, Worship Ldr; MD Emmaus 1988-, Lay Dir; *office:* North Harford HS 211 Pylesville Rd Pylesville MD 21132

GANTTER, CAROL STRICKER, Fifth Grade Teacher; *b:* Maywood, NJ; *m:* Wallace F.; *c:* Gail Mc Gurgan, Gwyn Rogan, Gigi Jarboe, Gregory; *ed:* Glassboro St Coll (BS) Primary Ed 1957; Pepperdine Univ (MA) Ed 1974; 18 Grad Credit Hrs; Trng Holistic Approach, Lit Based Prgms; *cr:* Meml Schl 3rd Grd Tchr 1957-60; Dept of Defense Schl 2nd Grd Tchr 1964-65; Loda Elem Schl 5th Grd, 5-8 Grd Math Tchr 1978-86; Goshen Intermediate 4th-5th Grd Tchr 1987-; *ai:* Bldg Rep; Supt Search, Soc Stud Comms; NEA, NY Tchrs Assn 1987-; Hospice of Orange Cty 1988-, Vol; *home:* 20 Gregory Dr Goshen NY 10924*

GANTZ, ANN HARDING, Science Teacher; *b:* Patterson, NJ; *m:* Albert J.; *c:* Heather; *ed:* William Patterson Coll (BA) Tchng Sci 1976; *cr:* West Milford HS Sci Tchr 1976-81; Vernon HS Sci Tchr 1988-95; *ai:* Ski Team Coach; NEA 1976-; *office:* Vernon HS Rt 565 Vernon NJ 07418

GANTZ, SCOTT M., 4th & 5th Grade Teacher; *b:* Clearfield, PA; *m:* Candace Lee Plank; *c:* Megan Kay; *ed:* Lock Haven Univ (BS) Elem Ed 1985; Post Grad Stud Penn St Univ, Shippensburg Univ, Wilson Coll; *cr:* Fermanagh-Mifflintown Elem Schl 4th & 5th Grd Tchr 1985-; *ai:* Asst Var Ftbl Coach E Juanita HS 1985-; Head Track & Field Coach E Juanita HS 1985-; JCEA, NEA, PSEA 1988-; *office:* Fermanagh Mifflintown Elem Sch PO Box 227 Mifflintown PA 17059

GANZ, ALBERT HARDING, History Professor; *b:* New York City, NY; *m:* Diane Sue Frobose; *c:* Erik Albert, Victoria Jean; *ed:* Wittenberg Univ (BA) His 1961; Columbia Univ (MA) European His 1963; OH St Univ (PHD) Ger, His 1972; Attnd Pingry Preparatory Schl 1957; *cr:* US Army Lieutenant, Armor 1963-66; Oh St Univ Instr, Asst, Assoc Prof 1971-; *ai:* Univ Comms; Speaker for Comm Events; OH Acad of His, OH Arms Control Seminar, Soc of Military Historians 1971-; Articles Pub; *office:* Ohio State Univ At Newark Country Club Dr Newark OH 43076

GAPPER, KARIN FREAS, Assistant Professor of Nursing; *b:* Newton, NJ; *m:* Joseph T.; *c:* Jason, Jessica; *ed:* St Luke's Hosp Sch of Nrsg (RN) Nrsng 1965; Hunter Coll CUNY (BSN) Nrsng 1970; Cath Univ of Amer (MSN) Nrsng 1972; *cr:* St Luke's Hosp Schl of Nrsng Instr 1966-68; Columbia Univ Schl of Nrsng Instr 1972-75; Adelphi Univ Schl of Nrsng Asst Clinical Prof 1977-90; Queensborough Comm Coll Dept of Nrsng Asst Prof 1990-; *ai:* P S 188 Parent Liason Dist 26 Schl Bd, Prin Selection Comm; PSC-CUNY, AFT 1991-; Nurses Assn of Cty L I Dist 14; NYSNA; Sigma Theta Tau 1971-; Hollis Hills Civic Assn 1994-; Chapel of Redeemer Luth 1978, Pres; *office:* Queensborough Comm Coll 222-05 56th Ave Bayside NY 11364

GARANT, JOSEPH A., United States History Teacher; *b:* Philadelphia, PA; *m:* Katherine V.; *c:* Joseph W., Daniel C.; *ed:* La Salle Univ (BA) His, Pol Sci 1967; Attnd Trenton St Coll, Glassboro St Coll; *cr:* Medill Bair Jr HS Soc Stud Tchr 1967-68; J.F.K. HS US His Tchr 1969-75; Willingboro HS US His Tchr 1975-; *ai:* Var Golf Head Coach 1973-; NEA, NJEA, WEA 1969-, Pres; PSEA, PEA 1967-68; *office:* Willingboro HS JFK Way Willingboro NJ 08046

GARAY, STEPHEN RICHARD, Music Teacher & Band Director; *b:* Sewickley, PA; *m:* Suzanne Meeder; *c:* Andrew Stephen, Jason Carl; *ed:* Westminster Coll (BM) Music Ed 1985, (MED) Scndry Admin 1992; Educl Supervision; *cr:* Mercer Area Schls Choir & Band Music Tchr 1985-87; Hermitage Schl Dist Choir & Band Music Tchr 1987-; *ai:* Marching, Concert, Pep, Jazz & MS Bands; Sr Class Adv; Mentor Tchr; Music Dept Liason; All Schl Musical Music Dir; HEA, NEA, & PSEA 1987-, Schlsp Chm; PMEA & MENC 1985-; ASCD 1990-; *office:* Hermitage Schl Dist 640 N Hermitage Rd Hermitage PA 16148*

GARBART, MARILYN J., Teacher of Gifted; *b:* Hopwood, PA; *m:* Robert L.; *c:* Donna, William; *ed:* CA Univ of PA (BS) Elem Ed 1967, (MA) Elem Ed 1968; *cr:* Laurel Highlands Schl Dist Tchr 1967-; *ai:* Stu Cncl, Quiz Team Spon; Yrbk Adv; NEA, PSEA, LHEA 1967-; *office:* Laurel Highlands Jr HS 18-20 Hookton Ave Uniontown PA 15401*

GARBER, GEORGE ANDREW,JR., Director of Bands; *b:* Boston, MA; *m:* Suzanne; *c:* Grace; *ed:* Berklee Coll of Music (BA) Music Ed 1977; 16 Hrs; *cr:* Chicopee Pub Schls Jr High Gen Music Tchr 1977-79, HS Choral Tchr 1979-81; David Prouty Schls Dir of Bands 1981-; *ai:* Marching Band & Jazz Rock Band Dir; NEA 1979-; MA Tchrs Assn 1979-; Musicians Local 172 1980-; Town Bd Dir 1983-; Golden Apple Awd Winner; Article Pub; *office:* David Prouty HS 302 Main St Spencer MA 01562*

GARBER, GEORGIA I., English Teacher; *b:* Coudersport, PA; *m:* James F.; *c:* Abbe, Matthew, Jodie, Andrew; *ed:* St Univ Coll of NY at Geneseo (BA) Eng 1971; ST Univ Coll of NY at Buffalo (MS) Scndry Ed 1978; 30 Addl Hrs Eng, Cmptr, Ed; *cr:* Pavilion Schl 7th Grd Eng Tchr 1971; Alden Cntrl HS 9-12 Grds Eng Tchr 1971-; *ai:* Bldng Improvement Team 1990-91, 1995-; Dist Planning Team 1990-95; Yrbk 1989-92; Soph Class Adv; NYSUT, NCTE 1971-; Alden Tchrs Assn 1971-, Grievance Chair, Bldg Rep; Girl Scouts of Amer 1956-, Ldr; *office:* Alden Cntrl HS 13190 Park St Alden NY 14004*

GARBUS, CHERYL SALERNO, 6th Grade Teacher; *b:* Warren, OH; *m:* Richard W.; *c:* Brian; *ed:* Youngstown St (BS) Elem Ed 1984; 23 Addl Hrs; *cr:* Niles City Schls Tchr 1984-; *ai:* Sci Fair Chprsn; 6th Grd Math Team Coach; OEA, NEA 1984-; OH Math League 1987-; NE OH Tchrs of Math 1989-; Trumbull Area Rdng Cncl 1989-; Lake to River Sci 1994-; Mothers March of Dimes, Amer Cancer Soc 1990-; *office:* Washington Elem Schl 805 Hartzell Ave Niles OH 44446

GARBUTT, ROBERT, Cmptr Assisted Drafting Tchr; *b:* Atlantic City, NJ; *m:* Judith Pelker; *c:* Robert, Jeffrey, Matthew, Daniel; *ed:* Fairmont St Univ (BS) PE, Ind Arts 1964; 27 Grad Credits at Trenton St Coll, Montclair St Coll, East Stroudsburg St Univ; *cr:* Pleasantville HS Tchr, Wrestling Coach 1964-66; Holy Spirit HS Tchr, Ftbl, Wresting, Rowing Coach 1968-73; Atlantic City HS Tchr, Rowing Coach 1973-; *ai:* NJEA, NEA 1973-; NLA 1958-; Dollars for Scholars 1995-; Coached Rowing Team to Natl Championship, 2nd in World 1994; *office:* Atlantic City HS Albany Ave Atlantic City NJ 08401*

GARCEAU, MARK C., Director of Instrumental Music; *b:* Providence, RI; *m:* Robin; *c:* Marcus, Miles; *ed:* Berklee Coll of Music (BA) Music Ed, Performance 1987; RI Coll (MA) Tchng 1996; *cr:* Providence Pub Schls Music Instr 1987-89; Cranston Pub Schls Instrumental Music Dir 1989-; The Music Schl Interim Dir RI Yth Yazz Ensemble 1995; *ai:* AFT, RI Music Edctrs Assn, MENC 1987-; Providence Fed of Musicians 1985-; *office:* Western Hills MS 400 Phenix Ave Cranston RI 02920

GARCIA, ANA E. PEREZ, Spanish Teacher; *b:* Las Villas, Cuba; *m:* Luis T.; *c:* Luis Jose, Juan Carlos; *ed:* KS Newman Coll (BA) Span; KS St Univ (MA) Span; *cr:* Manhattan HS Tchr 1 Yr; Woodrow Wilson HS Tchr 16 Yrs, Foreign Lang Dept Chprsn 8 Yrs; *ai:* Hispanic Amer Club; Prof Dev Schl; Interdistrict Out-Reach Prgm; Schlsp Comm; FLNENJ 1988-; NJEA 1980-; *office:* Woodrow Wilson HS 3100 Federal St Camden NJ 08105

GARCIA, GABRIEL, Vocational Instructor; *b:* Bronx, NY; *m:* Theresa; *c:* Andrew; *ed:* Delhi Coll Electrical Installation 1992; *cr:* Alfred E Smith HS Electrical Instr 1994-; *ai:* Schl Construction Authority Project Pathways Liaison; Graduating Class 1995 Thank You Plaque; *office:* Alfred E Smith HS 333 E 151st St Bronx NY 10451

GARCIA, JUDITH GANN, Choral & General Music Teacher; *b:* Philadelphia, PA; *m:* Arthur F. Jr.; *c:* Juliana, Michael; *ed:* Temple UNiv (BME) Voice 1966; Univ of MD (MED) Music Ed 1972; Music K-12, Math 5-12 Advanced Prof Cert; 9 Credit Hrs Cmptr Sci; *cr:* Seabook Elem Schl Choral, Gen Music Tchr 1966-68; Rockledhe Elem Schl Choral, Gen Music Tchr 1968-73; William Wirt Jr HS Choral, Gen Music Tchr 1973-74; Thomas Pullen Jr HS Choral, Gen Music Tchr 1974-78; Martin Luther King Jr HS Choral, Gen Music Tchr 1981-83; DuFief Elem Schl Choral, Gen Music Tchr 1983-85; Montgomery Coll Cmptr Programming Instr 1985-86; Watkins Mill Elem Schl Choral, Gen Music Tchr 1985-94; Cabin John MS Choral, Gen Music Tchr 1994-; *ai:* MCPS Math Content Connections Project Instr 1992-; Choral Dir; Recorder Club Spon; Minority Achvmt Comm; NEA, MSTA 1966-, Agnes Meyer Awd Nom 1988, 1990, 1993; NENC 1966-, Excl in Performance Cert 1990; MMEA 1966-, Excl in Performance Cert 1996, Svc Awd 1990; ACDA 1995-; Jewish Women Intnl 1991-, VP of Comm; Choirs Performed St 1996, Natl 1990 Conf; Natl Literacy Hnrs White House 1990, 1992; Performed with Many Celebrities; Kennedy Ctr Hnrs 1989, 1992; 52nd Presidential Inagaugural Gala.*

GARCIA, OBDULIA LAPIS, First Grade Teacher; *b:* Los Banos Laguna, Philippines; *m:* Ernesto V.; *c:* Leonisa, Geronimo, Michael, Harris; *ed:* Philippine Normal Coll (BS) Elem Ed 1965; Natl Tchrs Coll (MS) Elem Ed 1973; Bloomfield Coll Early Chldhd Cert 1978; *cr:* Los Barios Cntrl Schl Demonstration Tchr 1965-75; Newark Pre-Schl Tchr 1975-78; Newark Headstart Prgm Tchr 1979-; Mt Vernon Schl Tchr 1985-; *ai:* Mentoring Prgm for Adopt A Child Prgm; NJ Tchrs Assn, NEA, Tchrs Union 1985-; Educl Improvement Plan 1995-; Comm Svc Awd for Gifted Children; *home:* 22 Cherry Tree Cir Howell NJ 07731

GARCIA, ODILE, Science Teacher; *b:* Toulouse, France; *m:* Narciso; *c:* Letitia, Andres; *ed:* Queens Coll (BA) Bio 1985, (MA) Bio 1990; Research Asst; *cr:* Upper Volta Mission to United Nations Sec to Ambassador 1967-72; Townsed Harris HS Tchr 1985-; *ai:* Adv Archon Svc Honor Soc; Puffles Anti-Drug Prgm; Stu for Preservation of the Earths Save the Children; Amnesty Intnl; NY Bio Assn 1985-; Sigma XI 1985-; Torrey Botanical Club 1985-; Queens Cty Farm Museum 1990-, Bd; Dean Margaret Kelly Awd; Tchr of Yr; Marcelle Shair Silman Incentive Awd; Howard Hughes Fellowship; Variation in Canopy Composition of the Forest of Alley Park; Book Reviews; *office:* Townsend Harris HS at Queens College 149-11 Melbourne Ave Flushing NY 11367

GARCIA-ESTEBAN, FERNANDO, Spanish Teacher; *b:* La Horra, Spain; *m:* Mary Jo Miles; *c:* Sara, Alex; *ed:* Ursinus Coll (BA) Span 1989; Villanova Univ (BA) Span, Lit 1991; Ursinus Coll Span Cert 1989; Chestnut Hill Coll Fr Cert 1993; *cr:* Mangold Schl of Langs Eng Instr 1978-82; DE Vly Mental Hlth Fnd Cnslr 1982-86; Prudential Insurance Co Biling Rep 1986-91; Abington Schl Dist Span Tchr 1991-; *ai:* Soccer Coach; NEA 1992-; Mentor Tchr; Wkshp on Span Adolescent Jargon; *office:* Abington Jr HS 2056 Susquehanna Rd Abington PA 19001*

GARCIA-VAZQUEZ, NELLY RAFAELA, Eighth Grade Teacher; *b:* New York City, NY; *m:* Manuel Vazquez; *c:* Victor Gabriel, Daniel Elijah; *ed:* Rutgers Univ (BA) Zoology 1978, (BA) Span 1978; NJ Elem Schl Cert 1980; *cr:* Jersey City Bd of Ed K-8 Grd Sub Tchr 1978-79; St James Schl 5th Grd Tchr 1981; St Casimir's Schl 8th Grd Tchr 1981-85; St Lucy Filippini Acad 8th Grd Tchr 1985-; *ai:* Testing, Sci Fair Coord; Detention Proctor; Blue Ribbon Awd Comm Ed; Accreditation Steering Comm (Phil Author); NCEA 1985-; St James Parish, Lector; Rutgers Elem Ed Awd 1981; Filippini Acad Tchr of the Yr 1995-96; *office:* Saint Lucy Filippini Acad 142 Jefferson St Newark NJ 07105

GARCZYNSKI, M. ROBERTA,CSFN Science Teacher; *b:* Clifton Hghts, PA; *ed:* Holy Family Coll (BA) Ed 1961; Villanova Univ (MSS) Scndry Sci 1973; 73 Credit Hrs Coll of the Holy Cross; *cr:* St Mary's HS Sci Tchr 1961-73; St Stanislaus Kostka Sci Tchr 1973-76; Bishop Ford CC HS Sci Tchr 1976-89; St Mary's HS Sci Tchr 1989-; *ai:* Natl Young Ldrs Conf Educl Adv; Natl Sci Fnd Grants; Quo Vadis Awd; Diocese of Brooklyn Sci Cncl Awd; Intnl Sci Fair Commendation; Future Scientists of Amer Tchr Awd; Tomorrow's Scientists & Engrs Tchr Awd; *office:* St Mary's HS 50 Richland St Worcester MA 01610

GARD, CLAUDIA TROUT, High School Guidance Cnslr; *b:* Woodbury, NJ; *m:* Paul E.; *c:* Julie, Peter, Lauren; *ed:* Meth Hosp Schl of Nrsng (RN) Nrsng 1968; Glassboro St Coll (BA) Hlth Ed 1971, (MA) Guid & Cnslng 1979; *cr:* Washington Memrl Hosp Nrsng Supvr, Staff Dev Instr 1972-83; Meth Hosp Nrsng Supvr, Staff Dev Instr 1979-83; James Martin Schl Nrsng Instr 1983-85; Franklin Learning Ctr Hlth Sci Tchr 1985-89, Cnslr 1989-; *ai:* Chrldng Coach; Hlth Occupations Stdnts of Amer Adv; PFT Cnslrs Steering Comm; AFT 1983-; PFT 1983-; CAGP 1990-; PASSCAC 1991-; Girl Scouts of Amer 1972-91, Ldr; United Meth Women 1979-, Pres; IHN 1992-; Meth Hosp Alumni Assn Schlsp; *home:* 432 Witley Rd Wynnewood PA 19096

GARD, DARLEEN DUFFY, Fifth Grade Teacher; *b:* Coshocton, OH; *m:* Paul Nelson; *c:* Eve Belak, Fonda Morgan, Ginneen Parry; *ed:* West KY Univ (BS) Elem Ed 1966; Mt St Joseph Coll (MS) Master Ed 1985; *cr:* Newcomerstown Schl Tchr 1966-68; Sandy Valley Schl Tchr 1968-69; New Philadelphia Schl Tchr 1969-71; St Clemens Schl Tchr 1971-72; Claymont Schl Tchr 1973-79; Perry Local Schl Tchr 1979-; *ai:* Spelling, Math Teams Coach; Delta Upsilon 10 Yrs; Phi Delta Kappa 5 Yrs; Kappa Delta Pi 12 Yrs; Massillon Womens Club 10 Yrs; New Neighbors 2 Yrs; Stark Co Bicycle Club 5 Yrs; Hilltop Hikers 2 Yrs; Supervised Stu Tchrs; *office:* Genoa Elem Schl 519 Genoa Rd SW Massillon OH 44646

GARDENHIRE, MARILYN ATLEE, Nursing Professor; *b:* New Orleans, LA; *w:* Joseph (dec); *c:* Barbara, Cheryle, Joseph jr., Tracy; *ed:* Cumberland Cty Coll (AAS) Nrsng 1982; Stockton St Coll (BSN) Nrsng 1987; Univ of DE (MS) Nrsng 1988; *cr:* Newcomb Med Ctr Staff Nurse 1982-; US Army Reserver Capt 1987-; Cumberland Cty Coll Asst Prof I 1988-; Holy Redeemer Home Hlth 1993-94; *ai:* Admission, Stans & Academic Calender Comms; Sci Fair Judge; Amer Nurses Assoc 1982-; NJ St Nurses Assoc 1982-, Bernadine Hefferd Awd; NEA 1990-; NJEA 1990-; YMCA 1976-; Amer Red Cross 1979-; Sigma Theta Tau 1987-; US Army Reserve 1987-, Capt; Amer Heart Assoc 1989-; Univ Flwshp at Univ of DE; YMCA Svc to Yth Awd; Amer Red Cross Vol Svc Awd; *office:* Cumberland County Coll Orchard Rd & College Dr Vineland NJ 08360

GARDENHOUR, RICHARD EARL, Instrumental Music Tchr; *b:* Waynesboro, PA; *m:* Margaret; *c:* Chris, Dana; *ed:* Indiana Univ of PA (BS) Music 1969; Penn St Univ 29 Grad Credit Hrs; *cr:* Cochran Jr HS Instrumental Music 1969-80; Johnstown Sr High Instrumental Music 1981-95; 1 Johnstown MS Intrumental Music 1995; *ai:* Marching, Concert & Stage Band; Indoor Guard; Musical; PMEA & MENC 1970-, Cambria Cty Pres; PSEA, GJEA & NEA 1969-; AFM-Local 41 1980-; Tchr of Yr 1992, 1994; *office* Johnstown Sr HS 222 Central Ave Johnstown PA 15902

GARDETTO, MARY-SUE WITHINGTON, English Tchr & Dept Chair; *b:* Boston, MA; *c:* Stephen, Michael, Paula (dec), Diane Lux; *ed:* U Mass at Amherst (BA) Eng 1959; Wright St Univ (MED) Eng 1982; Cert in Latin; *cr:* Menchville HS Eng Tchr 1976; Ankeney JHS Eng Tchr 1977-; *ai:* OTSA Team Coach; Curr Improvement Cncl; NCTE 1976-, Sec, JHMS Assembly; OCTELA 1977-, Sec, Outstdng JH-MS Tchr; WOCTELA 1977-, Pres; Victoria Theatre 1995-, Vol, Svc Awd; Memorial Hall 1996, Vol; Valedictorians Awd; 3 Beavercreek Grants; JC Outstdng Edctr; Articles Pub; *office:* Arkeney Jr HS 4085 Shakertown Rd Beavercreek OH 45430

GARDINER, RUTHANN AUDREY, English Teacher; *b:* Pomptain Plains, NJ; *m:* Marc; *c:* Christian; *ed:* East Stroudsburg Univ (BSEd) Eng 1986, (MEd) Rdng Specialist 1988; *cr:* Bangor Jr HS 8th Grd Eng Tchr 1986-87; Leighton Area HS 10th-11th Grd Eng Tchr 1989-; *ai:* First Presbyn Church of Panther Vly Sunday Schl Supt & Tchr; Drama Club & Class Play Adv 6 Yrs; PSEA, NEA, LAEA 1989-; Order of Eastern Star 1985-, Matron; *office:* Lehighton Area Sr HS 1275 Mahoning St Lehighton PA 18235

GARDLER, BUD, English Teacher & Bsktbl Coach; *b:* Philadelphia, PA; *m:* Mary Joan Lake; *c:* Chris, Meghan, Mariketa; *ed:* St Joseph's Univ (BS) Bus 1968; 15 Hrs Ed; *cr:* Bishop Kenrisk Tchr 1968-75; Amer Univ Tchr 1975-76; Cardinal O'Hara Tchr 1976-; *ai:* Bsktbl Coach 27 Yrs; ACT 1968-; Coach of Yr 6 Times; *office:* Cardinal O'Hara HS Eagle & Springfield Rd Springfield PA 19064

GARDNER, ALAN M., Biology Instructor; *b:* Buffalo, NY; *ed:* Grove City Coll (BS) Bio 1995; SUNY at Buffalo MS Ed 1997; Georgetown Univ Biotechnology Inst 1986; UVA at Charlottesville 1989; *cr:* Sacred Heart Acad Bio Tchr 1987-88; Las Vegas HS Bio Tchr 1988-89; Salzburg Intnl Prep Schl Bio Tchr 1989-91; Harrison HS Bio Tchr 1991-; *ai:* Renaissance Festival & Austria Exch Pgm Coord; NABT 1986-; NSTA 1986-; Pub American Biology Teacher 1988; Texaco Excl in Tchng Grant 1992; Tenure Harrison Cntrl Schl Dist 1994; *office:* Harrison HS Union Ave Harrison NY 10528*

GARDNER, ALICE RUNDELL, Fourth Grade Teacher; *b:* Curwensville, PA; *m:* Herbert Koller Sr.; *c:* Herb Jr., Michael, Suzanne Wilson; *ed:* Bob Jones Univ (BS) Elem Ed 1954; PA St Univ 6 Grad Credits; Elizabeth Town Coll 6 Grad Credits; *cr:* Blythe Elem Third Grd Tchr 1955-58; East Pennsboro Elem Fourth Grd Tchr 1958-; *ai:* PSEA, NEEA 1958-; EPEA 1958-, Treas, Bldg Rep; East Pennsboro PTO 1958-, Bd 7 Yrs; Amer Family Ins of Valley Forge Gift of Time Tribute 1991; Conducted Math Wkshps; Peer Ldr with Sci Ed Prtnrshp & Lebanon Vly Coll; *office:* East Pennsboro Elem Schl 840 Panther Pkwy Enola PA 17025

GARDNER, DEIRDRE RYAN, Retired English Teacher; *b:* New York City, NY; *m:* Bruce; *ed:* Univ of CT (BA) Eng; Attnd Fairfield Univ, Southern CT, Univ of Bridgeport; *cr:* Madison Jr HS Eng Tchr 1973-77, His Tchr 1976-77; Trumbull HS Eng Tchr 1977-94; *ai:* NEA, CEA, TEA, NCYE 1973-; *home:* 13 Stonewall Ridge Rd Newtown CT 06470

GARDNER, EILEEN KAUFMAN, Dept of Nursing Chairperson; *b:* New York, NY; *m:* David; *c:* Eric Neal, Jeffrey Brian, Amy Beth; *ed:* Mt Sinai Hosp Schl of Nrsng 1956; Hunter Coll CUNY (BSE) Nrsng 1960; NY Univ (MA) Comm Hlth Nrsng 1963; Rutgers Univ (EDD) Soc & Philosophical Fndtns 1993; Registered Prof Nurse NJ & NY; Cert Schl Nurse Tchr NJ; *cr:* NY City Pub Hlth Dept; Kean Coll Fac Hlth & Recreation; William Paterson Coll Asst Prof 1973-76; West Orange Hlth Dept Supvr 1977-78; Jersey City St Coll Asst Prof 1978-; *ai:* Jersey City St Coll All Coll Senate Senator-at-Large; Jersey City St Coll COOP Pgm Advy Comm; All Coll Senate Grad Curr Comm; Dept of Nrsng Curr Comm & Rsrch Comm; Amer Nurses Assn 1956-; Mt Sinai Alumni Assn 1956-; NY Univ Alumni Assn 1960-; NJ St Nurses Assn 1960-, Pgm Comm, Nominating Comm; NJ Pub Hlth Assn 1973-; AFT 1973-; Amer Pub Hlth Assn 1980-, Pgm Planning Comm PH Nrsng Section, Resolutions Comm, Annual Meeting Planning Comm Co-Chair; Livingston Advy Hlth Cncl 1973-, Chprsn & NICL Chair; Temple Bnai Jeshurun, Soc Action Comm, Youth Group Adv; West Essex Comm Hlth Svc 1991-, Prsnl Comm Chair, Rsrch Comm; West Essex Prof Advy Cncl 1991-; North Essex Bd of Trustees Drug & Alcohol Cncl; Federal Traineeship Grad Stud Selantic Fund Schlsp Hunter Coll; Career Dev Grant JCSC Doctoral Work John Hernan Bildner Schlsp; Mt Sinai Hosp Schl of Nrsng for Doctoral Rsrch; Kappa Eta Chptr Sigma Theta Tau Nrsng Hnr Soc; Delta Xi Chptr Ed Hnr Soc.

GARDNER, ELAINE HANCLICH, Seventh Grade Math Teacher; *b:* Paterson, NJ; *m:* Alan; *c:* Paul, Caryn, James; *ed:* William Paterson Coll (BA) Elem Ed 1964; Seton Hall Univ (MA) Elem Ed 1967; 30 Insvc Credits; *cr:* Thomas Jefferson Elem Schl Fifth-Sixth Grd Tchr 1964-67; Sicomac Schl Sixth Grd Tchr 1967-69, 1971-93; Rohr Schl Fifth-Sixth Grd Tchr 1969-70; Eisenhower MS Seventh Grd Math Tchr 1993-; *ai:* NCTM 1994-; NEA 1964-; BCEA, WEA 1967-; Honored for 25 Yrs of S Dwight D Eisenhower MS 344 Calvin Ct Wyckoff NJ 07481*

GARDNER, JOAN MARGUERITE, Social Studies & Englis Columbus, OH; *m:* Daniel Clay Igo; *c:* Brian David Risi Kathleen Risinger; *ed:* OH St Univ (BS) Ed 1966, (MA) Ed 1983 Hrs Beyond Masters many Hrs in Cmptr Ed; *cr:* Columbus Paroc 6th Grd All Subject 1965-67; Southwestern City Schls 5th-6th Tchr 1967-68, Learning Disabilities Tutor 1973-76; Gahanna Lir Learning Disabilities Tutor 1976-78; Gahanna MS E 6th Grd A Tchr 1978-92, 7th Grd Soc Stud, Eng Tchr 1992-; *ai:* Tchr Classes to Tchr for Coll Credit; Tchr Coord for Dist Back to S Gahanna Jefferson Ed Asson Schlsp Comm; Gahanna Jefferso 1981-, Past Treas; NEA, OH Ed Assn, Cntrl OH Tchrs Assn Jefferson Vision Awd 1994; Jennings Scholar 1992-93; Honori Ed OH St Univ 1992; *office:* Gahanna MS South 349 Shady Gahanna OH 43230

GARDNER, JOHN THOMAS, Percussion Instructor; *b:* Elyri Beverly Dawn Addrews; *c:* Matthew, Sarah; *ed:* Kent St Un Math, Sci 1970; Oberlin Conservatory (BM) Percussion Pe 1978; Coll Conservatory UC (MM) Percussion Performance 198 Percussion Inst 1989, 1992; *cr:* Cinti Sch Cr Perf Arts Perc Chair 1980-; DAyton Philharmonic Orch Percussionist, Outreac Interlochen Arts Camp Percussion Instr 1990-91; Xavier Ur Northern Ky Univ 1983-; Coll of Mt St Joseph 1983-; *ai:* M Outreach Comm Chm; Percussive Arts Soc 1975-, OH Ch Pre Recruiting Contest 1986; Menc 1983-, Perf OMEA Con 1987; N Vis & Perf Arts Schl, Perf Natl Convention 1987; Superior RAtin Solo, Ens Contest 1980-; Grants Days of Percussion Perc 1990-95; *office:* Creative Performing Arts Sch 1310 Syc Cincinnati OH 45210

GARDNER, JUDITH RODDA, High School English Te Wilkes-Barre, PA; *m:* Robert S.; *c:* Joseph J. Rasimas, Nicc Wilkes Univ (BA) Eng 1971, (MS) Sec Eng 1975; Univ of PA Ldrshp 1993; Bloomsburg Univ Grad Level Rdng 12 Credit Hrs Germany 6 Credits Stud Summer 1973; *cr:* Luz Cty Comm Col of Eng 1977-84, 1994-; Northwest Area Schl Eng Tchr 1984-; W Adj Prof of Ed 1996; *ai:* Lit Magazine; Knowledge Master Oper Bee; NEA, PSEA, NAEA 1984-; Phi Delta Kappa, ASCD 1 Article; *office:* Northwest Area Jr Sr HS RR 2 Box 2271 Shick 18655*

GARDNER, LYNN ELLEN, Special Education Teacher; *b:* C OH; *ed:* Rio Grande (BS) PE 1986; *cr:* St Martins Schl PE Tch Greenhills MS Hlth Tchr 1988-89; Colerain HS Spec Ed Tchr Var Girls Bsktbl, Vlybl Coach; NEA, OEA 1989-; Vlybl Coa *office:* Colerain HS 8801 Cheviot Rd Cincinnati OH 45251

GARDNER, MARGARET HAMMER, Fourth Grade Te Harrisville, NY; *w:* Henry P (dec); *c:* Peggy Eisenhart, Patricia E.; *ed:* St Univ of NY at Potsdam (BS) Soc Stud, Eng 1952; 30 Hr Course; *cr:* Wappingers Cntrl Schl Tchr 1952-54; Traver Rd 1954-55; Arlington Cntrl Schls Sub Tchr 1978-84; Regina Coe Grd Soc Stud Tchr 1984-; *ai:* NCEA 1995-; Area Grant; *offic* Coeli Schl Rt 9 Albany Post Rd Hyde Park NY 12538

GARDNER, PHYLLIS JEAN, High School Mathematics Dayton, OH; *m:* Paul Douglas; *c:* Erica, Elizabeth; *ed:* Alderson Coll (BA) Scndry Ed 1975; Univ of Dayton (MS) Ed 1987; 30 H Counseling Masters Degree; *cr:* Belmont HS Math Tchr 3 Yrs; G Math Tchr 7 Yrs; Eastern HS Math Tchr 10 Yrs; *ai:* Acad Cc Comm; Summer PE; OEA, NEA, ELEA 1975-, Pres-Elect, Pres OCTM 1985-; Mowrystown Sftbl 1994-, League Dir; Hillsboro Nazarine 1995-, Missionary Pres; Esenhower Grant Winner 2 Y 971 Harvey Rd Sardinia OH 45171

GARDNER, RICHARD ALLEN, Chemistry & Math Te Middletown, OH; *m:* Dona Garret; *c:* Carrie, Chris; *ed:* Mi (BSEd) Math & Chem 1973, (MED) Ed Ldrshp, Curr & Supvr Middletown HS Chem & Math Tchr 1973-; *ai:* Bldg Led Team & Comm Mem; Middletown Tchrs Assn 1973-; DEA & NEA 197 1993-; Martha Holden Jennings Schlr 1995-; Crystal Apple 1995; *office:* Middletown HS 601 N Breiel Blvd Middletown O

GARDNER, RICK ALAN, HS Art Instructor; *b:* Baltimore, Glenda Morris; *c:* Melanie; *ed:* MD Inst Coll of Art (BFA) Art (MFA) Art Ed K-12 1978; Grad Course Supervision, Admin i Howard Cty Elem Schl System K-5 Grd Art Instr 1974-90; Mayfi MS 6-8 Grd Art Instr 1990-95; MD Inst Coll of Art 8-12 Grd Satu Courses 1993-; Howard HS 9-12 Grd Art Instr 1995-; *ai:* 9th Advy Group, 11th Grd Advy, Spon; Visual Art GATE Prgm Com Curr Mem; NEA 1978-; NAEA 1993-; MD Art Ed Assn 1993-, MS Dir, Outstdng Art Ed 1994; MD St Tchrs Assn 1976-; MD Inst C Alumni Assn 1978-, Alumni Mem; Career Svc Awd Howard Cty System; Articles MAEA Gazette Newsletter; Video Cable Pr Columbia Visual Art Ctr; Various Exhibits MD, DC 1979-; *

GARDNER, ROBERT S., Social Studies Teacher; *b:* Kingsto Judith A.; *c:* Nicole L., Joseph Rasimas; *ed:* Wilkes Univ (BA) (MS) His, Ed 1973; PA St Univ, Wilkes, Others 48 Post Hrs; *c* Univ Ed Prof 8 Yrs; Northwest Area Schl Dist Soc Stud Tchr 2 Head Track, Field, Head Cross Cty Coach; NCSS 1985-; PSE Local Pres; NEA; Article Presenter Natl Convention 199 Northwest Area Jr Sr HS RR 2 Box 2271 Shickshinny PA 18655

GARDNER, SETH F., Music Teacher; *b:* Messhoppen, PA; *m:* N Bowman; *ed:* Ithaca Coll (BSME) Music 1975; 40 Hrs West Che *cr:* Lackawanna Trl Grd 7-12 Vocal, Gen, Instrumental Tchr Haverford Twp MS Grds 6-8 Vocal, Gen Music Tchr 1979-; *ai:* Se Seventh Heaven Dir; NEA 1979-; MENC 1974-; ACD Performances MENC Eastern Conf 1991, PMEA St Conf 1986, 1 1996, Concert in Pk 1st Pl 1989, 1991, 1993, 1995; Outstdng Y in Amer 1982; PA Choir Rep We the People 200 1987; *office:* Township Schl Dist 1801 Darby Rd Havertown PA 19083

GARDNER, STEWART CHARLES,JR., English & Speech Ins Amityville, NY; *ed:* OH St Univ (BA) Comm 1975, (BS) Eng Post-Grad Hrs Eng; *cr:* North Union HS Eng, Speech Instr 1979 Coach 2 Yrs; Bsbl Coach 9 Yrs; Yrbk Adv 12 Yrs; Voice of D Speech Contest Organizer; NEA, OEA, NUEA 1979-; Outstdng Denison Univ 1995; Sports Broadcaster WCHO-FM bsktbl, Ftb *office:* North Union HS 401 N Franklin St Richwood OH 43344

GAREAU, CHARLOTTE ANN, English Teacher; *b:* Worcester, Worcester St Coll (BA) Eng 1974; Assumption Coll (MA) Rel S *cr:* Divine Redeemer Schl 5th Grd Tchr 1974-78; St Marys Sch Eng Tchr 1978-83; Holy Name HS 9th-12th Grd Eng Tchr 1983- Adv 1983-85; Class Adv 1990-94; Faculty Cncl 1987-89; 1983-87; Curr Dev Comms; Asst Prin 1975-78; AFT 1986-; DE Local 4445 1986-, Bldg Rep 3 Yrs; NCTE 1988-; *office:* Hc Central Catholic HS 144 Granite St Worcester MA 01604*

GARELY, ELINOR, Travel Tourism Bus Mngmt Prof; *b:* Jersey *ed:* Lesley Coll (BS) Art & Ed 1962; NYY (MBA) Intnl Bus 1975 Prompter Cable Television Co-host & Prgm Dir 1968-70; Helms Inc Mgr, Mrktg, Pub Relations 1970-72; Sydney Greene Assoc Ins ‹tg, Pub Relations 1972-74; Garely, Franck & Marshall Inc Mngmt Consultants 1974-79; Dolron Inc Mgr, Sales, Pub Mrktg 1979-81; Playboy Clubs & Hotels Intnl Mgr, Mrktg & 1981-83; City Univ of NY Prof 1983-; Hospitality, Travel & onsultant 1983-; RUS Hotels, Moscow Dir, Intnl Operations, Org perations First Soviet-Amer Joint Venture Hotel in Moscow; *ai:* inistry of Tourism Guest Speaker, Crises Planning; Women in Intnl Conf Travel & Tourism Shanghai; First Intnl Conf Hotel obean; NY St Task Force Travel & Tourism Mem; Assoc Republic Rep; Intnl Inst for Peace Through Tourism, Grant; Ctr drshp, Schlshp Ldrshp Dev Prgm; Intnl Assn Hotel Reservation st Speaker; Amer Hotel & Motel Assn Speaker; Ec Dev Plan , Chair, Svc Comm; Intnl Assn Hospitality Accountants; CHRIE spitality Edctrs; Princeton Club of NY Prgm Comm, Wine Cr, r, Dev Spec Events; Beta Gamma Sigma; South African Amer Comm, Mem; Natl Writers Union Mem; One Hundred Club, air, Prgm Comm Mem; Princeton Class of NY 1990-, Prgm exington Democratic Club 1970-, Dist Ldr; Comm Bd 1980-, Comm; Numerous Articles Pub; Outstdng Businesswoman of Yr ll; Who's Who in Travel & Tourism; Who's Who in Hospitality Who's Who Amer Businesswomen USA; *office:* Borough Of Comm Coll 199 Chambers St New York NY 10007

AY ALLEN, Bands Dir & Fine Arts Dpt Head; *b:* Denison, OH; e S. Yaden; *ed:* Mount Union Coll (BME) Trumpet 1984; Attnd St Univ, Univ WI at Whitewater; *cr:* Manchester HS 5th-12th mental Music Tchr 1984-91; Hillsboro HS 5th-12th Grd Bands *ai:* Fine Arts Dept Head; NCA Comm; All Music Act; OMEA , Treas; MENC 1984-; NEA 1985-; Lion's Club 1993-; BSA Cncl gle Scout; *office:* Hillsboro HS 358 W Main St Hillsboro OH

D, JOHN M., Dir of Stud & His Teacher; *b:* Concord, MA; *m:* Andrew, James; *ed:* Williams Coll (BA) His 1956; Wesleyan LS) Soc Sci 1969; Attnd Yale Law Schl, Univ of Edinburgh; *cr:* Schl His, Fr Tchr 1960-61; Wilbraham Acad His Dept Head Hamden Hall His Dept Head, Stud Dir 1971-; *ai:* Master Chess Club; Curr Dir; Asst Squash Coach; Curr Comm; Amer Assn 1989-; Childbirth Ed Assn of Greater Springfield 1964-71, Haven Prevention Trust 1989-; North Haven Historical Soc yflower Soc of North Haven 1980-, Pres; *office:* Hamden Hall ay Schl 1108 Whitney Ave Hamden CT 06517

KEL, SUSAN HEYMAN, Second Grade Teacher; *b:* Brooklyn, elly; *c:* Lori E., Jill M.; *ed:* SUNY at Buffao (BSEd) El Ed 1968; Oswego (MS) El Ed 1996; *cr:* Liverpool Cntrl Schls El Ed Tchr Bldg Advy Cncl; Family Math Night Prgms; Portfolio Dev NYSUT, AFT 1968-; Assoc Compensatory Edctrs Prof, NYS Prof Grants; *home:* 320 Garfield Ave Liverpool NY 13088*

I, MARY ANN (WINJERSON), Mathematics Teacher; *b:* , PA; *m:* Roland J.; *c:* Anne Krieger, John, Roland, James; *ed:* Univ (BEd) Math 195, (MEd) Scndry Ed 1961; 12 Post Grad niv of PA; *cr:* Taylor Alderdice HS Math Tchr 1957-60; Peabody Tchr 1960-61; Our Lady of Loretto Schl Math, Sci, Religion Tchr Seton La Salle HS Math Tchr 1980-; *ai:* Math Team, Stock Mrkt n; Math Cncl West PA 1973-, Exec Bd, Co-Chair Sr Hi Math ICWP Svc Awd & Mini Grant; PA Cncl Tchrs of Math 1973-; 985-; Resurrection Church 1961-, Lector; NSF Fellowship Article Pub in PCTM Newsletter; Speaker at Various Meetings; Chair; 5 Mid Sts Visiting Teams & Mem Seton La Salles Mid St Comm; *office:* Seton-La Salle Regnl HS 1000 Mcneilly Rd PA 15226

, KELLY REED, Spanish Teacher; *b:* Toledo, OH; *m:* Robert J.; of Toledo (BBA) 1987, (MED) Sndry Ed 1991; *cr:* Notre Dame Tchr 1988-; *ai:* Span Club Moderator 1990-; AATSP, OFLA mni Delta Delta Delta 1982-; Span Wkbk Level I Univ of Toledo : Notre Dame Acad 3535 W Sylvania Ave Toledo OH 43623

LA, JUDE-ANN ESPOSITO, Music Teacher; *b:* Bronx, NY; *m:* *d:* Coll of St Rose (BA) Music Ed & Vocal 1992; 30 Credit Hrs; ondville Cntrl Schl Elem Music & Vocal Tchr 1992; Middleburgh Jr & Sr Vocal Tchr 1992-93; Schoharie Cntrl Schl Elem Jr & Sr r 1993-; *ai:* MENC & NYSSMA 1988-; ORFF 1990-; Church p 1988-, Dir; Schoharie Cty Music Edctrs Assn, Sec; JH Select ; HS Swing Choir, Dir; Rel Heritage of Amer Natl Yth Ldr 1991; Miller Ave Albany NY 12203

LO, MARIA THERESA, Social Studies Dept Chair; *b:* New *ed:* St Thomas Aquinas Coll (BS) Soc Sci 1970; St Univ at (MS) Ed 1976; *cr:* Sacred Heart Schl 2, 3, 5-8 Grd Tchr Monsignor Scanlan HS Tchr, Chprsn 1985-; *ai:* Moderator NHS; 67-; NASAA 1990-; NCSS 1995-; Schlsp to Plattsburgh St for d; *office:* Monsignor Scanlan H S 915 Hutchinson River Pky 10465

, JOHN J., Social Studies Teacher & Coach; *b:* Scranton, PA; ., Aileen; *ed:* Univ of Scranton (BS) Scndry Ed 1966, (MS) 1971; Addl Svc Credits; Coaching Cert; *cr:* Delaware Acad Soc , Coach 1966-; *ai:* Var Boys, Girls Cross Cntry, Var Golf Coach; 970-; Bsktbl Ofcl; Summer Recreation Dir; Chm of Golf nts; *office:* Delaware Acad 2 Sheldon Dr Delhi NY 13753*

D, JACQUELINE D., Sixth Grade Teacher; *b:* Butler, PA; *m:* ade; *c:* Wendy Garland, David Wade; *ed:* Clarion St Coll (BS) 5; Masters Equiv 1990; *cr:* Richburg Cntrl Schl 6th Grd Tchr Salamanca Cntrl Schl 6th Grd Tchr 1970-71; Shinglehouse Elem 3rd Tchr 1973-; *ai:* Mid Sts Comm; NEA, PSEA 1973-; *office:* alley Elem Schl Oswayo St PO Box 610 Shinglehouse PA 16748*

D, KENNETH WARREN, Pgm Dir, Aviation Maint Tech; *b:* lle, NH; *m:* Mildred Louise; *c:* Steve Bridgett, Darlene Rhodes, idgett, Yvonne Cooper; *ed:* Univ of DC (BS) Voc Ed 1986; *cr:* ways Maintenance Mgr 1963-71; Univ of DC Asst Prof Airways 1971-; *office:* Univ Of The Dist Of Columbia 4200 Connecticut Washington DC 20008

D, WINSOME W., Orchestra & Music Dept Dir; *b:* Pottsville, Univ of PA (BSE) Music 1969, (MED) Music 1972; Post Grad of MI at Interlochen, George Mason Univ, Cntrl Ct St Univ & Univ; *cr:* Curwensville Area Schls Band Dir 1969-71; Cntrl Schls Instrumental Inst 1971-73; Richland Schls Orch Dir 1974-; Elem Orchs; Sr High String Ensemble; Grading Assessment, visory Comms; Strategic Planning Comm-Richland Schl Dist; Sr m; NEA, PMEA 1969-, Ex Comm 4 Yrs, Dist Orch Coord 1986-; atl Conf 1972-, Natl Registry Awd 1990; Natl Cert 1991; PMEA c-Treas 8 Yrs, Cit of Excel Awd 1988-89; NSOA-ASTA 1987-; Kennedy Ctr 1984-; Amer Fed of Musicians 1964-, Jud Bd 2 Yrs; SD Curr Dev Grant 1986; Instr in Paul Rollands Pedagogy at Geo 1989-90; PMEA Coord of W Reg St Orch 1988-; Former Prin Johnstown Pa Sym 1974-82; Dist 6 PMEA Exec Sec, Treas; Inst Distinguished Ldrshp in String Ed; *office:* Richland Schl Highfield Ave Johnstown PA 15904

GTON-CARRIER, BARBARA MC ALLISTER, Early l Teacher; *b:* Atlanta, GA; *m:* Charles H. Carrier; *c:* William C. n, Laurie Ann Garlington; *ed:* Spelman Coll (BA) Soc Stud 1959; Lesley Coll (MED) Early Chldhd 1992; Addl 15 Credit Hrs Beyond Masters; *cr:* Boston Pub Lib Librn 1959-61; Brookline Pub LIb Librn 1961-62; Boston Pub Schl Systems Early Chldhd Edctr 1962-; *ai:* Lesley Alumni Comm for Homeless Women; AFT, NEA 1963-; Natl Black Child Dev Inst 1995-; Compassion Intnl 1994-; Lesley Coll Alumni 1992-; Spelman Coll Alumni 1959-; Impact II Grant; IDS Svc to Yth Awd 1994; Peer Mentoring Prgm; Golden Apple Awd; Cert of Recognition; Article Pub 1990; *office:* Early Learning Ctr East 370 Columbia Rd Dorchester MA 02125*

GARM, FRED GERARD, High School English Teacher; *b:* Carbondale, PA; *m:* Mary O'Pecko; *c:* Zachary F.; *ed:* Wilkes Univ (BA) Eng & Scndry Ed 1990; *cr:* Wayne Highlands HS Eng Tchr 1990-91; Mountain View Jr Sr HS Eng Tchr 1992-; *ai:* Acad Team Coach; Scholastic Bowl & Sci Exposition Adv; NEA, PSEA 1990-; NCTE 1989-91; MVEA 1992-, HS Rep, Exec Cncl; *office:* Mountain View Jr Sr HS RR 1 Box 339 Kingsley PA 18826

GARMAN, THOMAS LAMAR, History & Science Teacher; *b:* PA; *m:* Judith Louise Good; *c:* Thomas Lamar Jr.; *ed:* Millersville Univ (BS) Soc Stud 1968, (MS) Cnslng 1970; Addl Stud His; 4 Credit Hrs at Lancaster Bible Coll; *cr:* Schl Dist of Lancaster Jr HS Remedial Tchr 1968-71; Manheim Chrstn Day Schl Jr HS Tchr 1971-85; Living Word Acad Jr HS Tchr 1985-; *ai:* Ath Comm.

GARNER, EMILY MCNICKLE, 12th Grade English Teacher; *b:* New Castle, PA; *m:* Jesse Kit; *ed:* Westminster Coll (BA) Eng & Ed 1992; *cr:* Moniteau HS 12th Grd Eng Tchr 1993-; *ai:* Yrbk Adv; NTE 1993-; *office:* Moniteau HS 1810 W Sunbury Rd West Sunbury PA 16061*

GARNER, ERNEST, Secondary Mathematics Teacher; *b:* Washington, DC; *ed:* VA St Univ (BS) Soc Stud Ed 1970; Univ of DC (MST) Math Ed 1992; 12 Hrs Math Cath Univ; 5 Hrs South AL Univ; 21 Hrs Natl-Louis Univ; *cr:* D. C. Skills Ctr Adult Ed Tchr 1979-81; Univ of DC Summer Math Tchr 1988-89; Stuart-Hobson MS Math Chprsn 1986-; *ai:* Math Counts Prgm Spon; Oratorial Contest Ofcl; Track, Field Coach; SECME Team; NCTM 1986-; Awd Excl Tchng Math 1988; Outstdng Achvmt Awd 1994; Outstdng Svc Awd 1994; *office:* Stuart Hobson MS 410 E St NE Washington DC 20002*

GARNER, JUDITH LYNN, English & Computer Teacher; *b:* Mc Keesport, PA; *m:* Dennis Lee; *ed:* Mansfield Univ of PA (BSEd) Scndry Ed Eng 1973, (MSEd) Cmptrs 1995; Grad Credits PA St Univ; *cr:* Northern Potter Jr-Sr HS Eng Tchr 1974-, Eng, Cmptr Tchr 1990-; *ai:* NEA, PSEA 1974-; NPEA 1974-, Pub Relations Chprsn; Editorial Adv to Lit Publications; Tchr Assoc for PA St Univ Regnl Cmptr Resource Ctr; *office:* Northern Potter Jr Sr HS RR 1 Box 400 Ulysses PA 16948*

GARNER, LEAH LORRAINE, Sci & Math Ldrshp Tchr; *b:* Baltimore, MD; *m:* Stewart; *c:* Yvette Hurt; *ed:* Coppin St Coll (BS) Elem Ed 1969; Morgan St Univ (MS) Elem Ed 1971; 55 Credit Hrs Post Grad Admin & Supervision, Sci, Math, Lang Arts; Hold on Advance Prof Cert; *cr:* Eutaw Marshburn Elem Schl Sixth Grd Tchr 1969-74, Fifth Grd Tchr 1974-91, Intermediate Sci Lead Tchr 1991-, Intermediate Math Lead Tchr 1994-; *ai:* Drug-Free Schls Contact; Just Say No to Drugs Club Spon; SIT, Staff Dev Team Mem; HIV Adv; STARS, MARS Lead Tchr; MD Assn Sci Tchr 1990-; Benjamin Banneker Assn 1992-; NSTA 1991-; NCTM 1993-; Natl Cncl Self Esteem 1994-; Red Cross Youth 1874-, Nellie Hines, Youth Adv of Yr 1987; Zeta Phi Beta 1994-, Mayor's Citation; Focus 39 Tchr of Yr 1989; PTA Salute Governor's Citation 1989; Governor's Citation 1993; Chemical Industries Cncl Tchr of Yr 1994-95; Class Act Tchr 1995; Champion of Courage 1996.*

GARNER, WANDA GRACE, Science & PE Teacher; *b:* Hagerstown, MD; *m:* James Gregory; *c:* Gayla; *ed:* Lee Coll (BS) Hlth, PE 1992; *cr:* Washington Cty Bd of Ed Sub Tchr 1992-93; Grace Acad Sci, PE Tchr 1993-; *ai:* Var Vlybl Coach; Chrstn Svc Club Chaperone; Sr Class Adv, Chaperone; *office:* Grace Acad 530 N Locust St Hagerstown MD 21740

GARNETT, WILLIAM B., Professor of Biology; *b:* Cleveland, OH; *m:* Gina; *ed:* Denison Univ (BA) Bio, Geology 1963; Kent St Univ (MA) Zoology 1965; WA St Univ (PHD) Entomology 1974; *cr:* Natl Park Svc Seasonal Ranger, Naturalist 1962-63; Kent St Univ Instr 1965-68; WA St Univ Rsrch, Tchng 1969-75; Raymond Walters Coll, Univ of Cincinnati Asst to Full Prof 1975-; *ai:* Stu Govt Fac Adv; Entomological Soc Amer 1964-, Book Rev Comm Chair; Sigma Xi 1973-; AAUP 1975-; OH Cncl Against Hlth Fraud 1989-, Trustee, Sec; Numerous Articles Pub; Rsrch Entomologist WA St Univ; *office:* Raymond Walters Coll 9555 Plainfield Rd Cincinnati OH 45236

GARNHAM, KENNETH JOSEPH, 11th Grade US History Teacher; *b:* Nashua, NH; *c:* Jason, Rebecca; *ed:* Plymouth St Coll (BA) Soc Sci 1975; Long Island Univ Ed Permanent Cert 1980; Georgetown Univ Lbrl Stud 15 Hrs; *cr:* Hampton Bays HS Soc Stud Tchr 9 Yrs; Milford HS Soc Stud Tchr 12 Yrs; *ai:* Var Cross Cntry Coach; NEA 1975-; Milford Tchrs Assn 1984-, VP; Lion's Club 1982-83; Milford Comm Ath Assn 5 Yrs; James Madison Flwshp Awd 1994; Yrbk Dedication 1991; Yth Involvement Awd 1981; Suffolk Cty Long Island Cross Cntry Coach of Yr 1981; *office:* Milford HS 100 West St Milford NH 03055*

GAROFALO, DONNA D'AMICO, Fifth Grade Teacher; *b:* Paterson, NJ; *m:* Michael Jr.; *c:* Marcia Anne, Michael Dante, Daniel Paul; *ed:* Paterson St Coll (BA) Ed 1968; *cr:* Sayreville Jr HS Math Tchr 1968-69; St Gerard Majella Fifth Grd Tchr 1978-; *ai:* Coord Standardized Testing; CTBS, ACRE; MS Accreditation Review Comm; Lay Collaborator Salesian Provincial Chptr; Eucharistic Minister; NCEA 1980-; Haledon Zoning Bd Adjustment 1972-79, Sec; *office:* St Gerard Majella Schl 10 Carrelton Dr Paterson NJ 07522

GAROFOLO, NANCY GOMBAS, First Grade Teacher; *b:* Bridgeport, CT; *c:* Paul, Andrea; *ed:* Univ of CT (BS) Psych Ed 1961; Univ of Bridgeport (MA) Early Chldhd Ed 1964; 6th Yr; Continuing Ed Units; *cr:* Honey Hill Elem Schl K Tchr 1961-64; Fawn Hollow Elem Schl 1 Grd Tchr 1967-69, 1976-; *ai:* Multi-Cultural & Diversity Comm; Assessment & Report Card Comms; Mentor; MEA 1961-; NEA, CEA 1967-; Delta Kappa Gamma 1990-; Celebration of Excl Awd; Crystal Apple Colleague Recognition Awds; *office:* Fawn Hollow Elem Schl 345 Fan Hill Rd Monroe CT 06468

GARR, DONNA FARNETI, Guidance Director; *b:* Binghamton, NY; *m:* Dino; *c:* Chrystie, Laura; *ed:* Hartwick Coll (BA) Eng, Psych 1973; Coll of New Rochelle (MS) Spec Ed 1977; Lehman Coll (MS) Guid, Cnslng 1985; Long Island Univ Prof Diploma Admin; *cr:* Rye HS Eng Tchr 1974-85; Westlake HS Guid Dir 1985-; *ai:* Svc Club Adv; Schlshp, Rotary Stu of Month Comm; Mount Pleasant Tchrs Assn Del; US Armed Forces Liaison; WRPGA, NYCAC 1985-; AFT, NEA 1974-; NYS Congress PTA 1974-, Jenkins Awd, Edctr of Yr 1994; Pres Svc Cncl 1994-, Pres Clinton Svc Awd 1995; J C Penney Svc Cncl 1994-, Golden Rule Awd 1995; Kappa Delta PI 1985-, Distngd Prof Awd 1994; Long Island Univ Presidential Schlrshp 1996; Schl, Comm Svc Guide HS Advs 1986; USAF Recruiting Awd 1992; *office:* Westlake HS Westlake Dr Thornwood NY 10594*

GARRAFFO, STEVEN JOSEPH, Global Stud & Economics Tchr; *b:* Ephrata, PA; *m:* Carol A. DeFazio; *ed:* St Bonaventure Univ (BA) His 1986, (MS) Advanced Tchr Ed 1990; *cr:* Fillmoe Cntrl Schl 9th & 10th Grd Soc Stud Tchr 1986-88; Liverpool Cntrl Schl 10th & 12th Grd Soc Stud Tchr 1988-; *ai:* CNYCSS 1988-; United Liverpool Fac Assoc 1996, VP for Mbrshp; Tchr of the Yr 1989-90; *office:* Liverpool HS 4338 Wetzel Rd Liverpool NY 13090

GARRAMONE, MARIO, Social Studies Teacher; *b:* Potenza, Italy; *m:* JoAnn Haynes; *c:* Joseph, Nicole, Rocco, Candace; *ed:* Queens Coll (BA) Pol Sci 1982; 25 Addl Credits Math, Sci, Religion; Queens Coll; *cr:* Metro North Foreman Track Maintenance 1976-81; Brooklyn Union Gas Appliance Mechanic 1982-86; Our Lady Mt Carmel Math, Sci, Religion, Sports Dir, Foreign Lang, Guidance Cnslr 1987-95; Bd of Ed City of NY; Soc Stu Tchr; *ai:* Dir After Schl Prgm; CYO Dir; Bsktbl, Bsbl, Sftbl, Vlybl Coach; ICYP Youth Org Treas; ASCD 1989-; ICYP 1984-, Treas; Italian Amer Better Govt, VP; Diocesan Math Awd Outstanding Tchng; Fed Parents Club Awd Merit; Cert Merit Outstanding Merit Awded by Mem St Assembly; *office:* I.S. 10 Schl 46th St & 31st Ave Long Is City NY 11103

GARRAMONE, ROSEMARIE JANINE, English Teacher; *b:* Hazleton, PA; *ed:* Penn St univ (BS) Elem Ed 1975; Bloomsburg St Coll (MED) Elem Ed 1980; Wilkes Univ Cmptr Lit; Luzerne Intermediate Univ Cmptr Course; *cr:* Msgr Molino Elem Schl Tchr 1975-91; Holy Spirit Acad Tchr 1991-; *ai:* Schl Newspaper Adv; Union Negotiator; Tchr Mentor; Book Orders Coord; Schl Handbook Comm; NCEA 1975-; ASCD 1989-; SDACT 1993-; ITEC Grant for Wilkes Univ Coursework.

GARRAN, CHRISTOPHER S., Social Studies Teacher; *b:* Hanover, NH; *ed:* The Amer Univ (BA) Intnl Stud & Ec 1990, (MAT) Soc Sci & Tchng 1992; *cr:* Walter Johnson HS Soc Stud Tchr 1992-; *ai:* Jr Var Field Hockey Coach; NHS Spon; STAGE Producer; Stu Govt Adv; Montgomery Cty Ed Assn & NEA 1992-; Sallie Mae Natl 1st Yr Tchr Awd Winner, 1 of 100 Selected; *office:* Walter Johnson HS 6400 Rock Spring Dr Bethesda MD 20814*

GARRATT, MARY KATHLEEN, Kindergarten Teacher; *b:* Washington, DC; *m:* David G.; *c:* Jessica, Amanda; *ed:* Univ of MD (BS) Early Chldhd Ed 1970; Masters Equivalence Plus 30 Hrs Grad Credits; *cr:* Adak Elem 1st & 4th Grd Combination Tchr 1970; Wyngate Elem Kndgtn & 2nd Grd Tchr 1971-74; Ashburton Elem Kndgtn & 1st Grd Tchr 1975-77; Rollingwood Elem Kndgtn Tchr 1978-79; Olney Elem Kndgtn Tchr 1979-80; Bel Pre Elem Kndgtn Tchr 1981; Olney Elem Kndgtn Tchr 1982; Burtonsville Elem Kndgtn Tchr 1983-; *ai:* Staff Dev Comm; Kndgtn Team Ldr; NEA, MSTA, MCEA 1971-; Demonstration Math Tchr on Television Course for Tchrs Tchng Children with Spec Needs; Washington Post Agnes Meyer Tchr of Yr Awd Nom.

GARREN, CORINNE BROWN, Fifth Grade Teacher; *b:* Heidleberg, Germany; *m:* Stanley; *c:* Anna Christa, Gabriello; *ed:* SUCO at Oneonta (BS) ElemEd 1979; LI Univ at CW Post (MS) Spec Ed 1983; Dowling Coll at Oakdale SDA 12 Credit Hrs; *cr:* Oysterponds Elem Schl 4-6 Grd Tchr 1982-; Greenport HS Drama Club, Dir, Choreographer 1995-; *ai:* Created, Dev Multi Generational Rdng Prgm; *office:* Oysterponds Elem Schl PO Box 98 Orient NY 11957*

GARRETT, ISABEL T.,OSF, Teacher & Asst Dean of Stdnts; *b:* Elkton, MD; *ed:* Villanova (MA) Span Lit, Ling 1976; Marywood Immaculata (MA) Bilin, Cultural Ed 1982; Cert Gestalt Inst of Psychotherapy Gostalt Theory, Practice 1993; *cr:* Elem Schls 3-8 Grd Tchr; Prin 1965-86; St May's Hosp Soc, Mental Hlth Worker 1986-88; Card Dougherty HS Tchr, Asst Dean 1988-; *ai:* Stu Assistance Prgm Coord; Sr Prom, Soph Hop Moderator; Stu Talent Show; Prop Crew Moderator; Rel Comm Chptr Rsrch Comm Coord 1995-, Pastoral Svc Comm Contact Cnslr 1994-, Soc Justice Fund Comm; PMLA 1972-; NCEA 1965-; Environment Group NGO Mem of UN; Who's Who in Ed in the East 1981; Marywood Immaculata Federal Schlsp; Citation from MSEA for Admin Phila Schl Dist; *office:* Cardinal Dougherty HS 6301 N 2nd St Philadelphia PA 19120

GARRETT, JANE NIENBERG, Third Grade Teacher; *b:* Lima, OH; *m:* Thomas James; *c:* Jodi Marie, Lindsay Kay; *ed:* Western Carolina Univ (BS) Ed 1975, (MA) Early Chldhd Ed 1980; 6 Hrs Ashland Univ; *cr:* Landeck Elem Schl 1-4 Grd Tchr 1970-73; St John's Elem Schl 1st Grd Tchr 1973-74; Edncyville Primary Schl 1-2 Grd Tchr 1976-80; St Joseph Elem Schl 1-2 Grd Tchr 1980-86, Prin 1986-89; Holy Trinity Schl 3 Grd Tchr 1989-; *ai:* OH Cath Ed Assn, Crawford Cty Intl Rdng Assn 1980-; St Joseph Folk Group 1990-; Crestline Swim Team Boosters 1992-, Tiny Tots Invitational Dir, 1995 Treas; St Joseph Parish 1986-89, Dir Rel Ed Prgm Presch-12 Grd; *home:* 301 Saint James St Crestline OH 44827

GARRETT, NINA ADRIENNE (RIHARD), 7th Grade Math Teacher; *b:* San Antonio, TX; *ed:* Towson St Univ (BA) Elem Ed 1974; Post Grad Stud Univ of WV; Hood Coll Masters Degree Work Admin, Mngmt; *cr:* Plesant Vly Elem Schl 6th Grd Tchr 1974-77; Boonsboro MS 6-8 Grd Soc Stud Tchr 1977-83; Smithsburg MS 6-8 Grd Soc Stud Tchr 1983-91; Washington Cty Tchrs Assn Release-time Pres 1991-93; E. Russell Hicks MS 7th Grd Math Tchr 1993-; *ai:* Newspaper Adv; Peer Mediation Coord; NEA 1974-; Wash Co Tchrs Assn 1974-, Past Pres, Treas; MD Tchrs Assn 1974-, Past Del to St Convention; AAUW 1981-, Newsletter Ed; NCTM 1994-; *home:* PO Box 525 4 Maple Ave Smithsburg MD 21783*

GARRETT, ROBERT L., Third Grade Teacher; *b:* Mechanisburg, PA; *c:* Lindsay W.; *ed:* West Chester St (BS) Elem Ed 1972; Masters Equivalency Elem Ed; Grad Credits in Ed, Psych; *cr:* Lincoln Elem Schl Fifth Grd Tchr 1970-73; E. N. Pierce Elem Schl Fifth Grd Tchr 1973-77; Hillsdale Elem Schl Third Grd Tchr 1977-85; Exton Elem Schl Third-Fourth Grd Tchr 1985-; *ai:* NEA, PSEA 1972-; Salvation Army 1992-, Vol; YMCA 1991-, Vol; Perkiomen Vly Watershed Nature Photo Best of Show 1981; Creative Eye Photo Best of Show 1982; *home:* 525 W 2nd St Birdsboro PA 19508

GARRETT, VERNON C., Resource Tchr & Pgm Manager; *b:* Akron, OH; *m:* Marlene M.; *c:* Todd, Gregory, Brian, Michelle Pribonic; *ed:* Univ of Akron (BS) Elem Ed, Math 1973, (MS) Ed Admin 1977; Assoc Degree Electronics; Math U of A, Kent St Univ; Marietta Coll Ldrshp; *cr:* Akron Pub Schls Math, Sci Tchr 1974-94, Dean of Stdnts 1994-95, Resource Tchr, Prgm Mgr 1995-; *ai:* Wrestling, Bsktbl, Soccer Coach; Math Dept, Fac Cncl Chm; Peer Mediation Adv; Akron Ed Assn, NCTM 1974-; Knights of Columbus 1977-, GK, DD, 5 Times Outstdng Dist Deputy; Math, Sci Tchr of Yr 1985; Project Bus Hall of Fame Tchr; *office:* Riedinger MS 77 W Thornton St Akron OH 44311*

GARRICK, BARBARA GEORGIA, 3rd Grade Teacher; *b:* Bridgeport, CT; *ed:* Western CT St (BS) Elem Ed 1971; Fairfield Univ (MA) Prof Dev 1976; Addl 6th Yr Admin; *cr:* Diocese of Bpt Tchr, Admin-Prin 1971-85; Diocese of Hartford Admin-Prin 1985-87; Westport Pub Schls Tchr 1987-; *ai:* Lions Pride Adv; Grade Level Coord; NEA, CEA 1987-; Aims 1994-; *office:* Long Lots Elem 13 Hyde Ln Westport CT 06880

GARRIGAN, THOMAS EDWARD, Social Studies Teacher; *b:* Sunburg, PA; *m:* Donna Marie Butz; *c:* Robert; *ed:* Univ of MD (BA) US His 1970; Towson St Univ (MSecEd) His, Soc, Ed 1972; John Hopkins Univ (MLA) His 1974; *cr:* Andover SR HS Soc Stud Tchr 1972-83; Amerde SR HS Soc Stud Tchr 1983-; Stevens Park HS Summer Schl Soc Stud Tchr 1983-92; Bel Air Summer Schl Soc Stud, Eng Tchr 1993-; *ai:* NEA, MSTA 1972-; Am Karati Assn 1989-, Black Belt; Civil War Re-enactor 1994-; Pol Organizer 1977-, Campaign Mgr; *office:* Meade Sr HS Clark Rd Fort Meade MD 20755*

GARRINATO, FRANK, Mathematics Teacher; *b:* Stratford, NJ; *m:* Christine Mumma; *ed:* Holy Family Coll (BA) Math 1989; Temple Univ (MEd) Ed Admin 1995; Working on Prin Cert; *cr:* Bensalem YDC Math Tchr 1989-93; Simon Gratz HS Math Tchr 1993-; *ai:* Bldg Comm; AFT 1993-; NCTM 1989-; *home:* 15031 Liberty Ln Philadelphia PA 19116*

GARRIS, ALANDER WILSON,III, Eighth Grade Teacher; *b:* Philadelphia, PA; *m:* Valentina Lisa Zamichieli; *ed:* Univ of Pittsburgh (BA) Pol Sci 1989; Towards MA Ed St Josephs Univ; *cr:* Luthern HS of Philadelphia Eighth Grd Tchr 1991-92, Interum Mid Div Prin 1992-93, 5th Grd Tchr 1992-93; Eight Grd Tchr 1992-, Dir Dev Ctr 1993-; *ai:* JV Bskbl Coach; Asst Var Bskbl Coach; ASCD, NCTE, NSTA 1993-; NAACP 1988-; Most Valued Tchr Prin Awd 1991-92; Black His Tchr of Yr Recip 1994; *office:* Lutheran HS of Philadelphia 6101 Oxford Philadelphia PA 19111*

GARRISON, CHARLES JOSEPH, Drama & Media Comm Tchr; *b:* Sacramento, CA; *m:* Lois Ann Gaskell; *ed:* West Chester Univ (BS) Comm, Theatre & Eng 1988; *cr:* Absegami HS Drama, Media Comm Tchr 1990-; *ai:* Drama Club; Stagecraft Adv; Dramatic Productions Dir; Media Club Co-Adv; NEA, NJEA 1990-; ITS 1983-, Spon; Natl Pub Speaking Awds, Nom Tchr of Yr; Disney's Excl in Tchng Awds; *office:* Absegami HS 201 Wrangleboro Rd Absecon NJ 08201

GARRISON, DEBORAH GARDNER, Spanish Teacher; *b:* Butler, PA; *m:* James E.; *c:* Gregory, Kaitlyn; *ed:* Univ of Akron-Schl of Law (JD) Law 1984; *cr:* Stow City Schls Span Tchr 1975-; *ai:* Stow Tchrs Assn 1975-, Pres; OEA, NEA 1975-, Del; OH Bar Assn 1985-; Cub Scouts of Amer 1993-, Den Ldr; *office:* Stow-Munroe Falls HS 3227 E Graham Rd Stow OH 44224*

GARRISON, PHYLLIS SUSAN, Career Education Coordinator; *b:* Bronx, NY; *ed:* Southern Ct St Univ (BS) Ed 1965; Univ of Bridgeport (MS) Ed 1970, (MS) Cnslng 1977; Sixth Yr Admin, Supervision 1980; Ldrshp Trng Omega Inst, Lifespring, Ctr of Humanistic Ed, Sacred Heart Univ; *cr:* Blackham Maplewood Schls Art Tchr 1965-67; Harding HS Art Tchr 1967-77, Art Dept Coord 1969-77, Career Cnslr 1977-78; Cntrl HS Career Cnslr 1977-78; Bassick HS Career Cnslr 1977-78, Career Ed Coord 1979-; *ai:* Adopt-A-Schl Advy Bd; PACE Proj Coord; Contract Coord; Schl Improvement Comm; Bassick HS Planning, Support Comm; Strategic Planning Team; Chprsn Frosh Orientation; Incentive Awds Prgm Dir; CT Career Cnslrs Assn, CT Schl Cnslrs Assn 1980-; CT Assn Cnslr Ed & Supervision 1985-; Phi Delta Kappa 1975-, Prgm Chprsn, VP, Svc Awd; Bassick HS Sr Schlsp Fund Co-Chprsn; Bpt Pub Ed Fund MAACS Advy Bd; Univ Bpt Talent Search Advy Bd; Co-Author 1990; Bridgeport Pub Ed Mini-Grant 1980-; Carl Perkins Federal Grants; CT Career Ed Grants 1977-; Tchr of Yr 1995; Bridgeport Pub Ed Fund Outstdng Edctr 1994-95; Svc Above Self Awd 1995; *office:* Bassick HS 1181 Fairfield Ave Bridgeport CT 06605*

GARRISON, ROBERT,JR., Sixth Grade Teacher; *b:* New Bedford, MA; *c:* Melissa Culyon; *ed:* Northeast Inst of Indstrl Tech (AS) Indstrl Electronics 1967; Univ of MA at Dartmouth (BS) His, Ed 1974; 15 Credit Hrs Post Grad Stud Mngmt; *cr:* Donaghy Schl Chptr I Rdng Expert 1975-81; Gomes Schl Chptr I Rdng Expert 1975-81; Normandin Jr HS 7 Grd Eng Tchr 1981-86; Alfred J Gomes Schl 5 Grd Enrichment Class Tchr 1987-91; John Hannigan Schl 6 Grd Tchr 1992-; *ai:* Hannigan Schl Counsel, Cmptr Club; MA Tchrs Assn, New Bedford Edctrs Assn 1975-; *office:* John Hannigan Schl 33 Emery St New Bedford MA 02744

GARRITY, DEBBE ANNE, Language Arts & Math Teacher; *b:* Akron, OH; *ed:* Malone Coll (BS) Elem Ed 1973; Kent St Univ (MS) Curr, Instruction 1983; Youngstown St Univ 1990-; *cr:* B. L. Miller Elem Schl 3, 6 Grd Tchr 1973-; Sebring Mc Kinley 7, 8 Grd Tchr; *ai:* Sr Class Co-Adv; Jr HS Stu Senate Adv; OEA, NEA 1973-; NEOTA 1973-, Exec Comm; NCTM, OCTM, EOCTM 1983-; *office:* Sebring Mc Kinley HS 225 E Indiana Ave Sebring OH 44672

GARROW, J. BRENT, 4th Grade Teacher; *b:* St Albans, VT; *m:* Glenda Robinson; *c:* Kristopher, Peter, Curtis, Jocelyn; *ed:* Castleton St Coll (BS) Elem Ed 1979; 30 Addl Credits Ed Courses; *cr:* Enosburg Elem Schl 2nd Grd, 5th-6th Grd, 4th Grd Tchr 1979-; *ai:* Local Relicensing Bd 1994-, Chm; Pub Lib 1992-, Trustee; HS Alumni Assn 1991-, Pres; Jaycee Outstdng Tchr; *office:* Enosburg Elem Schl Dickenson Ave Enosburg Falls VT 05450

GARRUBBA-CASTELLI, MARY ROSE, English Professor; *b:* Pittsburgh, PA; *m:* Gregory A.; *c:* Angelina Nicole; *ed:* Duquesne Univ (BA) Eng, Span 1990; Carnegie Mellon Univ (MA) Eng, Rhetoric 1991; Paralegal Cert at Georgetown Univ; JD in Law at Duquesne Univ 1997; *cr:* Duquesne Univ Frosh Eng Prof 1994-; *ai:* Editor in Chief of Juris Schl Law Newsmagazine; Italian Heritage Soc 1996-; Italian Heritage Soc Schlsp; Lawyers Auxilary Schlsp; Whos Who Among Amer Law Stdnts; *office:* Duquesne Univ 600 Forbes Ave Pittsburgh PA 15282

GARRY, KATHLEEN ANNE, Kindergarten Teacher; *b:* Buffalo, NY; *ed:* SUNY at Cobleskill (AAS) Early Chldhd Ed 1981; SUNY at Oswego (BS) Elem Ed 1983; SUNY at Cortland (MS) Math Ed 1993; 18 Hrs Schl Psych at SUNY at Oswego; *cr:* Stepping Stones Nursery Schl Tchr 1983-84; St Marys Schl Second Grd Tchr 1984-86; Cntrl Square Schls Kndgtn, First Grd Tchr 1986-; *ai:* Prof Dev Dist Comms; Tchr Ctr Rep; Chrldng Coach; Tutor; Bldg Act Comms; Strategic Planning Comm; AFT, NYS Tchrs Assn 1986-; Goals 2000 Grant; *office:* Cntrl Square Schl Dist Hillcrest Dr Central Square NY 13036*

GARSHELIS, JUDITH MAGGARD, 6th Grd Lang Arts & Rdng Tchr; *b:* Hamilton, OH; *m:* Jerry; *c:* Benjamin; *ed:* Miami Univ of OH (BSEd) Elem Ed 1972; Mount St Joseph (MAEd) Ed 1988; Attnd Lang Arts Acad Univ of Cincinnati 1994-95, Cmptr Sci Univ of Dayton 1989, Drake & Andrews Univs; Addl 18 Hrs; *cr:* Lakota Schl Dist 4th, 6th Grd Tchr 1966-74; Dohahran Acad 5th Grd Tchr 1974-76; Lakota Schl Dist 6th Grd Tchr 1976-82; Fairfield City Schls 6th Grd Tchr 1984-; *ai:* Wellness Comm; Aerobic Instr; Line Dancing Tchr; Needy Kids Fund Founder, Financial Contributer; Venture Capitol Grant Writing Comm; NEA, OEA 1967-; FCTA 1984-; Natl MS Assn 1985-, Soc Chm Convention 1994; Classroom Archaelogy Unit Author, Presenter Butler Co Educl Growth Opportunities Seminars 1995-96; Presenter Staff Dev Seminars Lakota Schls, Middletown City Schls 1995; Golden Apple Awd Ashland Oil 1988; Fairfield City Schls Ambassador Awd 1995; *home:* 4328 Millikin Rd Hamilton OH 45011*

GARTH, AL M., 6th Grade Teacher; *b:* Passaic, NJ; *m:* Carol Ann Carr; *c:* Allen, Janet, Andrew, Jean, Joyce; *ed:* William Paterson Coll (BS) Ed 1959, (MA) Ed 1965; 30 Credits beyond Masters Degree; *cr:* USMC Infantry Officer 1959-62; Upper Saddle River Schl Elem Tchr 1962-63; Bloomfield Schl Elem Tchr 1963-; *ai:* Safety Patrol Adv; Tchr in Charge; Spelling Bee Coord; Boys Bsktbl Coach; Bloomfield Ed Assn 1963-; Essex Cty EA 1963-; NJEA 1963-; NEA 1963-; BSA 1982-, Advancement Chm; NJ Governors Tchr Recognition Recipiant 1988; *office:* Brookdale Elem Schl 1230 Broad St Bloomfield NJ 07003

GARTNER, GAD, Guidance Counselor; *b:* Naharya, Israel; *m:* Sallie Veghte; *c:* Jared, Jordan; *ed:* Rider Univ (BA) Sociology 1973; Trenton St Coll (MED) Spec Ed 1978; Rowan Coll (MA) Stu Prsnl Svcs 1988; Real Estate License 1981; *cr:* Vineland Bd of Ed Tchr of Migrant Ed 1973-89; Vineland HS Guid Cnslr 1989-; *ai:* Schl Improvement Team Chprsn 1992-95; Co-Chprsn Mid Sts Evaluation 1994-95; NEA 1973-; CCCEA, VEA 1975-; Cumberland Cty Cnslr of Yr 1994; Exch Club Edctr of Yr 1992-93; African Amer Cultural League Awd; *office:* Vineland HS 3010 E Chestnut Ave Vineland NJ 08360

GARTNER, LESLIE PAUL, Anatomy Professor; *b:* Szolnok, Hungary; *m:* Roseann Kollar; *c:* Jennifer; *ed:* Rutgers Univ (BA) Zoology 1965; Rutgers Univ (MS) Radiation Hlth Physics 1968, (PHD) Radiation Bio 1970; *cr:* Dental Schl-Univ MD Instr 1970-71, Asst Prof 1971-74, Assoc Prof 1974-; *ai:* Yrbk Fac Adv; Admissions Comm; Amer Assn Anatomists 1971-; Sigma Xi 1973-; Baltimore Writers Alliance 1991-, Treas; Several Books Pub; *office:* Dental Schl-Univ of MD 666 W Baltimore St Baltimore MD 21201

GARTNER, LINDA F., Vocal Music Director; *b:* Pasadena, CA; *m:* Neil; *c:* Mark, Matthew; *ed:* Cottey Coll (AA) Liberal Arts 1977; Bowling Green St Univ (BSME) Music Ed 1979; Masters Music Choral Conducting 1980; Lee Canter's Video Courses with Drake Univ 15 Grad Hrs; *cr:* Sycamore Jr High Vocal Music Dir 1982-; *ai:* Variety Show & Musical Dir; Fac Adv Comm; Mentor Tchr Panel; OMEA 1982-, Certified Music Educator; ACDA 1982-; OH Arts Cncl Grant; Rotary Distinguished Comm Svc Awd; Sycamore Tchng Excl Prgm Recipient; OH Tchr Schlr Pgm; *office:* Sycamore Jr High 5757 Cooper Rd Cincinnati OH 45242*

GARTNER, MARK GORHAM, Math, Physics & Comp Sci Tchr; *b:* Trenton, NJ; *m:* Ann Louise Lanman; *c:* Nathaniel, Halley; *ed:* Coll of William & Mary (BS) Physics 1988; *cr:* Trinity-Pawling Schl Physics Tchr, Track Coach & Dorm Spon 1988-90; Peddie Schl Physics, Track Coach & Dorm Spon 1990-; *ai:* Boys & Girls Winter & Spring Head Track Coach; Head of Disciplinary Comm; Dorm Supvr for 26 Girls; NAAPT 1990-; NCTM 1994-; Peddies Nom for the Princeton Prize for Distngd Scndry Schl Tchng 1995; Coach of the Yr Trenton Times 1993; *office:* The Peddie Schl S Main & E Ward Sts Hightstown NJ 08520

GARTNER, ROCHELLE PRESSER, Third Grade Teacher; *b:* New York City, NY; *m:* Marvin J.; *c:* David, Jeffrey, Alan; *ed:* City Coll of NY (BS) Ed 1956; Salem St Coll (MED) Ed 1970; MED with Distinction Elem Cert in NJ, NY, MA & PA; *cr:* Swampscott Pub Schl Art Sub Tchr 1969-70; Antietam & Exeter Schls Sub Tchr 1970-75; Poughkeepsie JCC Nursery Schl Tchr 1977-79; Trocki Hebrew Acad 3rd Grd Tchr 1979-; *home:* 26 N Austin Ave Ventnor City NJ 08406

GARTUNG, MARY J., Fourth Grade Teacher; *b:* Peoria, IL; *ed:* Univ of IL (BS) Elem Ed 1968; Cambridge Coll (MED) Ed 1996; *cr:* Denver Pub Schl 4th Grd Elem Tchr 1968-69; Braintree Pub Schls 3rd-6th Grd Elem Tchr 1969-; *ai:* Soc Comm Treas; Schlsp, Recycle Comm; NEA 1968-; Braintree Ed Assn 1969-, Bd of Dirs, Prof Rights, Responsibilites Comm, Negotiating Comm, VP.

GARULLI, KATHLEEN ANN, Language Arts & Homeroom Tchr; *b:* Weehawken, NJ; *m:* Edward J.; *c:* Corin Lane, Ed, Colleen; *ed:* Edward Williams Coll (AA) Bus 1967; Caldwell Coll (BA) Ed 1972; Certfd Rel Ed Seton Hall Univ; *cr:* Sacred Heart 5th-8th Grd Eng Tchr 1975-81; St Nicholas Schl 5th-8th Grd Eng Tchr 1981-82; ST Elizabeth Seton Inter 5th-8th Grd Eng Tchr 1982-; *ai:* Yrbk & Safety Patrol Adv; Home & Schl Rep; NJCEA 1975-; Parish Cncl 1981-, Sec; Home & Schl 1982-, Pres; *office:* St Elizabeth Seton Schl 4th & Walker Sts Fairview NJ 07022

GARVER, NED ALAN, Art Teacher; *b:* Bryan, OH; *m:* Cynthia Lee Kissel; *c:* Brianna, Chase; *ed:* Univ of Toledo (BA) Art Ed 1982, (MS) Art Ed 1991; Post Grad Stud Drkae Univ, Bowling Green St Univ; *cr:* Bryan MS Art Tchr 1983-; *office:* Bryan MS 120 S Beech St Bryan OH 43506

GARVEY, SHARON WALTZ, Mathematics Teacher; *b:* Scranton, PA; *c:* Dana, Mary, Karen, David; *ed:* Marywood Coll (BA) Math 1965; OH Univ (MS) Math 1971; Boston Univ Schl of Theology 16 Cr Hrs; Marywood Coll 6 Cr Hrs Ed; Oswego SUNY 3 Credits; *cr:* Jefferson Twp Math Tchr 1966; Scranton Cntrl HS Math Tchr 1966-68; Wyoming Seminary Math Tchr 1968-70; Onondaga Cntrl Schls Math Tchr 1970-; *ai:* AFT, NYSUT 1970-; Onondaga Tchrs Assn 1970-, VP 3 Yrs, Building Rep 2 Yrs; NY St Math Tchrs Assn; Onondaga Cty Tchrs of Math; Marcellus Food Cooperative 1979-, Treas 10 Yrs; St Johns Church 1970-94, Jr Warden 2 Yrs, Altar Guild Pres 8 Yrs; St JAmes Church Choir 1994-; Natl Sci Fnd Awd to OH Univ; Service Awd Little Learners & Syracuse Chapter of Girl Scouts of America; Volunteer IRS VITA Prgm 4 Yrs; *home:* 101 Barnstable Ct Camillus NY 13031*

GARVIN, JOYCE LORAYNE, Full-Time Consultant; *b:* Brooklyn, NY; *m:* Aaron; *c:* David, Vicki; *ed:* Vassar Coll (BA) Earth Scis & Ger 1948; Masters Equivalent & All Course Work for PHD Columbia Univ Fac of Philosophy; Scndry Schl Cert at Montclair Coll; Lang Stu Fr & Ger at Middlebury Lang Schls; *cr:* Gifted Child Soc Dir of Saturday Wkshps, Curr Coord, Summer Schl Dir & Tchr 1960-70; Fairview Elem Schl Enrichment & Resource Tchr 1962; Westbrook Jr HS Fr Tchr 1963; Maywood Jr HS 9th Grd Fr Tchr 1964-68; River Dell HS Fr Tchr 1969; Farleigh Dickinson Univ Eng Composition & Lit Tchr 1970; Lehigh Univ Tchr in the Grad Schl of Ed 1980; River Dell Regnl Schls Eng & Advanced Placement Eng Tchr 1971-82, Coord G&T Pgm & AP Eng Tchr 1982-90, Interdisciplinary Consultant 1990-; *ai:* Creative Writing Honors Spon; Initiating New Courses; Coaching Mock Trial Team & Acad Decathlon Team; All Acad Disciplines Consultant & Lang Expert; Preparing New Curricular; NEA, NJA, & Phi Beta Kappa; Hnrs & Awds: Phi Beta Kappa, River Dell Tchr of the Yr, Outstdng Tchr of the Hum Lehigh Univ; NJ Tchr of the Yr 1978; gifted Child Soc Tchr of the Yr; Commendation Resolution 1979; Distngd Scndry Schl Tchng 1990; Numerous Articles Pub; *office:* River Dell Regnl Sr HS Pyle St Oradell NJ 07649

GARVIN, MEGAN ELIZABETH, Seventh Grade Teacher; *b:* Wilmington, DE; *ed:* Univ of DE (BS) Elem & Spec Ed 1992; 1 Addl Credit Hrs; *cr:* Avon Grove MS 7th Grd Tchr 1993-; *ai:* Chrldr Coach; *office:* Avon Grove MS 107 Schoolhouse Rd West Grove PA 19390

GARVIN, NANCY E., Science Teacher; *ed:* UMASS Amherst (BS) Zoology; Framingham St (MED) Scndry Ed, Bio; *cr:* Ayer Sr HS Sci Tchr 1977-; *ai:* NHS Adv; Sci League Coach; MA Assn of Sci Tchrs; NEA; MTA; ATA; Tchr of Yr 1993 Paul Harris Fellow Rotary Club; *office:* Ayer Sr HS 141 Washington St Ayer MA 01432

GARWOOD, JAMES A., English Teacher; *b:* Camden, NJ; *m:* Lynne Nogle; *ed:* Saint Francis Coll (BA) Eng & Scndry Ed 1972; 18 Credit Hrs Cmptr Sci; *cr:* Samuel M Ridgway MS Eng Tchr 1973-85; Eastern Sr HS Eng Tchr 1987-; *ai:* NEA, NJEA, EEA 1973-85, Bldg Rep; NEA, JNEA, EEA 1987-; NCTE 1988-; *home:* 57 Oakwood Dr Medford NJ 08055

GASDASKA, WILLIAM GEORGE, Biology Teacher; *b:* Bethlehem, PA; *m:* Mary Alyce Polenchar; *c:* Matthew, Mark; *ed:* Seaton Hall Univ (BA) Bio Ed 1968; Kutztown Univ (MED) Bio Ed 1972; *cr:* Trexler Jr HS Bio Tchr 1968-81; Wm Allen HS Bio Tchr 1981-; *ai:* NEA, PSEA 1970-; *office:* William Allen HS 106 N 17th St Allentown PA 18104

GASIOR, FLORENCE E., 1st Grade Teacher; *b:* Wilkes Barre, PA; *m:* Edward F.; *ed:* Seton Hall Univ (BS) Elem Ed 1971, (MA) Rdng Specialist 1977; *cr:* Hopeland Schl #10 1st Grd Tchr 10 Yrs; Woodbridge Twp Schl #19 1st Grd Tchr 15 Yrs; *ai:* NJEA 1971-; ADK 1990-; NJ Governors Excl in Tchng Awd 1982 & 1995; *home:* 67 Jefferson Ave Edison NJ 08837

GASIOR, FLORENCE THERESE, Mathematics Teacher; *b:* Acushnet, MA; *m:* Walter; *ed:* Univ of MA at Dartmouth (BS) Math 1967, (MS) Math 1972; 30 Addl Credits in Cmptr Sci, Geology, Bio, Rdng; *cr:* Albuquerque Pub Schls Math Tchr 1967-70; Pvt Bus Ceramic, Art Tchr 1974-78; Stoughton Pub Schls Math Tchr 1978-; *ai:* Schl Improvement Cncl 1995-; NCTM 1989-; NEA, MTA 1978-; PTSA 1995-; St Josephs Church Food Cellar 1995-; Golden Apple Awds; *office:* R. G. O'Donnell MS 211 Cushing St Stoughton MA 02072*

GASKIN, PAUL SCOTT, High School Math Teacher; *b:* Somerset, KY; *m:* Linda K.; *c:* Michael G., Robert N.; *ed:* Univ of Cincinnati (MED) Ed 1974, (BS) Schl Admin 1981; 15 Addl Semester Hrs; *cr:* Kenton Cty Schls Sci Tchr 1974-75; Mason City Schls Math, Sci Tchr 1976-; *ai:* NEA 1976-; OEA 1976-, VP; Boy Scouts 1996, Comm Mem; *office:* William M 770 S Mason Montgomery Rd Mason OH 45040

GASPAR, CHARLES E., Math Teacher & Dept Head; *b:* York Carolyn Elizabeth Lochance; *c:* Kenneth C., Thomas J., Andrew M.; *ed:* Gorham St Tchrs C (BSEd) Math 1964, (MSEd) Math 1 Great Theorams in Math OH St U 1992; *cr:* Montello JHS M 1964-73; Lewiston JHS Math Tchr 1973-76; Marshwood HS M 1976-; *ai:* Track Ofcl-Starter; Support Team; NEA, ME Teach As Quamphegan TA 1976-; Our Lady of Peace Church Chm-Stewardship; Cable Advy Comm 1980-; Boy Scouts Com Chm-Comm; Nat Sci Fnd Western MI Univ 1965, Univ Southern NEH Great Theormas in Math OH S U 1992; *office:* Marshwoo Dow Hwy Eliot ME 03903*

GASPAR, JOHN, HS Mathematics Teacher; *b:* Perth Amboy, N Ann Brostow; *c:* Awn, Joseph, Brian, Justin; *ed:* Montclair St Math Ed 1968, (MA) Math Ed 1972; *cr:* Colonia HS Math Tc Middlesex Cty Coll Adj Prof Math 1991-; *ai:* Schlsp Comm; N Adv; NEA; Mystic Seaport 1990-; Tchr of Yr 1987; *office:* Coloni St Colonia NJ 07067

GASPARD, CATHERINE, Home Economics Teacher; *b:* Newb *ed:* James Madison Univ (BS) Home Ec Ed 1976; SUNY at New P Early Chldhd 1982; 46 Addl Hrs; *cr:* Mt St Mary HS Home 1976-77; Newburgh Schl Dist 1977-78; Washington Schl Dist Tchr 1978-, Vlybl Coach, Stu Govt Adv, Schl-to-Work Coor Coalition Adv; NYSHTA 1976-; NYSPHSAA 1978-; NYSUT 197 1986-; Acad Tenants Assn 1995-, Pres; Accomplishment WA Bd 1994; Above Beyond Call of Duty Awd Tchrs & Stdnt Washingtonville HS 54 W Main St Washingtonville NY 10992

GASSER, JANICE LANGHALS, English Teacher; *b:* Lima Robert J.; *c:* Andrew, Bradley, Ryan; *ed:* Bowling Green St (BS 1979; Wright St Univ (ME) Ed; *cr:* Kalida Jr HS Eng Tchr 1979-8 HS Eng Tchr 1989-; *ai:* NEA, OEA 1979-; Kalida Ed Assn 1 1986; Sunday Schl Tchr; Parish Cncl; Lib Bd; Martha Holden Grant 1985; *office:* Kalida H S 301 N Third St Kalida OH 4585

GASSER, ROBERT J., Social Studies Teacher; *b:* Lima, OH; K. Langhals; *c:* Andy, Bradley, Ryan; *ed:* Bowling Green Univ Stud 1979; Dayton Univ (MS) Admin 1983; OCSS Conf, Seminars; *cr:* Kalida HS Soc Stud Tchr 1980-; *ai:* Little Intramural Soccer Coach; Acad Club Adv; NEA, OEA, OCAA 19 Bd at Ottoville 1990-, VP 3 Yrs; *home:* PO Box 353 Ottoville O

GAST, RICHARD H., Mathematics Teacher; *b:* New York, NY; Cook; *c:* Patricia, Richard; *ed:* St Johns Univ (BS) Math 1957, (1959; Columbia Univ (EDD) Math Ed 1978; *cr:* St Johns Prep M 1957-58; H Frank Carey Jr-Sr HS Math Tchr 1958-62; Edgemont Math Tchr 1962-; *ai:* Mathletes Adv; Edgemont Stu Fund Treas AFT 1958-; NCTM 1958-; NYSMT 1960-; ETA 1962-, Treas, Pre Manor Assn 1966-, Treas, Pres; NSF Grant; Experienced Tch Co-Author Integrated Geometry; Author The High School Controversy; Referee NCTM Mathematics Tchr; *office:* Edgemon 199 White Oak Ln Scarsdale NY 10583

GASTADELLO, STEFANIE, Guidance Counselor; *b:* Englew *ed:* Slippery Rock Univ (BS) PE 1977; CO St Univ (MED) William Paterson Coll Guid Cert; Jersey City St Coll Supervisory Wayne Hills HS PE Tchr 1979-80; Vernon Twp HS PE Tchr 1980 Cnslr 1994-; *ai:* Head Field Hockey & Asst Bsktbl Coach; CO Peer Ldr Asst Adv; NJEA 1980-; NEA 1980-; VTEA 1980-; *offic* Township HS PO Box 1832 Cty Rt 565 Vernon NJ 07462*

GASTEIER, CHRIS JAMES, Agriculture & Soc Studies Sandusky, OH; *m:* Linda Fritz; *c:* Gretchen, Jefferson; *ed* Washington Univ (BA) His 1982; Bowling Green St Univ (MED) 1995; Prin Cert 1996; Ag Ed Cert OH St Univ 1984; *cr:* Perk Schls Tchr 1982-; *ai:* Acad Team, FFA, Yth in Govt Adv; NEA, C 1986-, VP; OVA, NVATA 1982-, Legislative Liason; OH Cncl for 1990-; IAB 1991-; Precinct Committman 1992-; Tchr of Yr 1992; Vermilion Ed Symposium 1993; *office:* Perkins HS 3714 Car Sandusky OH 44870

GASTON, GAIL HAYDON, Latin Teacher; *b:* Cincinnati, OH; *c* J., Lisa G.; *ed:* OH Wesleyan Univ (BA) Eng, Ed 1969; West Ch of PA (MED) Instructional Media Ed 1975; West Chester Univ 15 Credit Hrs 1989; St Joseph's Univ Ed 6 Credit Hrs 1992; Dr Ed 6 Credit Hrs 1992; *cr:* North Jr HS Eng Tchr 1969-70; Ardm Eng Tchr 1970-76; Miss Annette's Nursery & Kndgtn Presch Tchr Interboro HS Latin Tchr 1986-; *ai:* Spon Jr Classical League European Tour Ldr; NEA, PSEA 1970-; IEA 1987-; Natl Classic 1988-; *office:* Interboro HS 16th & Amosland Rd Prospect Park

GATCHELL, LYNETTE TITUS, Third Grade Teacher; *b:* Lewi *m:* William; *c:* Christopher, David; *ed:* Univ of Southern ME (Ed 1977; Univ of ME (MS) Ed 1991; *cr:* Waterford Meml Schl Tchr 1978-84; Guy E. Rowe Schl First Grd Tchr 1984-86, Third 1986-; *ai:* Schl Improvement Team; NEA, MEA 1978-; Del Gamma 1993-, Chprsn Rsrch Comm.*

GATCHELL, SUSAN COOK, Business Teacher; *b:* Philadelphi Richard; *ed:* Bloomsburg St Coll (BS) Bus Ed 1971; Temple Uni Masters Equiv 1974; West Chester Univ Ed Masters Equiv 197 Widener Univ; *cr:* Morrisville HS Bus Tchr 1971-72; Ridley HS 1972-83; Garnet Vly HS Bus Tchr 1983-; *ai:* FBLA Adv; NE 1971-; GVEA 1983-; DE Cty Chamber of Commerce Awd of Excl Tchr of Yr Nom; *office:* Garnet Vly HS 552 Smithbridge Rd Glen 19342

GATELY, DANIEL EDWARD, High School Biology Teacher; *b:* NY; *m:* Shawna Doody; *ed:* Potsdam Coll (MS) Bio & Scndry Ed Tri-Valley Schls Bio Tchr 1978-79; Massena HS 9th Grd Sci Tchr Saratoga Springs HS Bio & Chem Tchr 1980-; *ai:* Var Hockey Yrs; AFT, NYSUT 1978-; STANYS 1980-; BALSA 1988-; *office:* Spgs Sr HS 186 West Ave Saratoga Springs NY 12866

GATELY, JAMES M., Social Studies Dept Chairman; *b:* Lock *m:* Diane Gifford; *c:* Tammi Leavitt, Kevin; *ed:* St Univ of NY a (BA) His 1967, (MED) Tchng Soc Stud 1968; Num Addl Credi Starpoint Central Schl Soc Stud Tchr 1968-; *ai:* Scndry Schl B Chm; Dist Sharded Decision Making Comm; NYNEX Competiti Travel & Culture Club Co-Adv; NYSUT, Leadership; Starpoint T 1968-, Negotiating Team; AFT; Starpoint Parent Tchrs Assn Lifet Niagara Frontier Wrestling Ofcl Assn Outstanding Sportsman C NY St United Tchrs Leadership Awd; Natl Sci Fnd NY St Cncl Natl Endowment for Hum His Acad Fellowships; Tanks to Tchrs Nom Twice; *office:* Starpoint Central Schl 4363 Mapleton Rd Loc 14094

GATELY, LORRAINE M., Biology & Health Teacher; *b:* Lynr Michael; *ed:* Goddard Coll (BA) Bioagriculture Botany 1978; Tc Chem Courses at Salem St Coll; *cr:* Malden HS 9th Grd Earth 1985-86; Chelsea-Williams Jr HS 7th Grd Earth Sci Tchr 1986- Breed Jr HS 8th Grd Earth Sci Tchr 1988-94; Lynn Classical HS Phys Sci Tchr 1994-; *ai:* JV Girls Bsktbl Coach 1985-94, Starte Club 1986; Jr HS Golf Team 1993-94; Bd of Dirs Adult Sftbl As

PATRICIA POST, Art Teacher; *b:* Somerville, NJ; *m:* Richard; wn Univ (BS) Art Ed 1976; *cr:* Bridgewater-Raritan HS Art Tchr Hillsborough HS Art Tchr 1980-82; Watchung Hills Regnl HS Art -; *ai:* Jr, Sr Class, Prom, Stu Cncl Co-Adv, Lit Magazine Adv; Coach; Somerset Cty Teen Arts Festival Coord; NEA, NJEA, AEA 1977-; Former NJ & PA Watercolor Socs; Instituted One of tudio Art Prgms; Best Tchr Somerset Cty 1995; Instituted Prgm Parents on Portfolio Preparation, Career Exploration, Coll s; *office:* Watchung Hills Regional HS 108 Stirling Rd Watchung

EAN SZYMBORSKI, Teacher; *b:* Panama, Republic of Pan; *w:* lec); *c:* Scott, Lance; *ed:* Trento St Coll (BS) Elem Ed 1959; *cr:* d Schl 3rd-4th Grd Tchr 1959-61; Benjamin Franklin Schl 3rd 961-63; Klockner Schl 1st Grd Tchr 1965-66; Langtree Schl 3rd 966-72; Kuser Schl 3rd Grd Tchr 1974-; *ai:* NEA, NJEA 1959-; ser Elem Schl 70 Newkirk Ave Trenton NJ 08629

MILY ANN (MANGAS), Business Teacher; *b:* Union City, IN; John; *c:* Rick Alan, Lori Ann Cox, Lynn Ann Doppler, Lea Ann ; *ed:* Ball St Univ (BS) Comprehensive Bus Ed 1965; Wright St) Scndry Classroom Bus Tchr 1987; *cr:* Mississinawa Vly HS Tchr 1965-; *ai:* Bus Prof of Amer, Sr Class Adv; NEA, OEA, VCTA 1978-, Treas of Local; AVA, OVA, OBTA 1989-; BPA ice: Mississinawa Valley HS 1469 State Road 47 E Union City

VANGELINE SENIOR, Eng Dept Head & Tchr; *b:* Utica, NY; Covell; *c:* Holly Manners, Julie Cunningham; *ed:* Mount Holyoke 1958; Attnd SUNY at Cortland, Univ of WI at Madison; *cr:* and Cntrl Schl 7-12 Grd Eng Tchr 1970-; *ai:* Soph Class Adv; ls Comm; NCTE; Westmoreland Tchrs Assn; Oneida Cty 4-H , Judge, Friend of 4-H Awd; Clinton Chamber of Comm; Amer Soc; Carriage Assn of Amer; St & Natl Pub Speaking, ations Judge 4-H Projects; *office:* Westmoreland Cntrl Schl 5176 Westmoreland Rd Westmoreland NY 13490

REIDA FRANCES, 4th Grade Teacher; *b:* New York City, NY; narles; *c:* Rosemarie Cramer; *ed:* LeMoyne Coll (BS) His 1965; rad Hrs Elem Ed Syracuse Univ; 18 Post Grad Hrs Elem Ed r: Chittenango Cntrl Schl 1st Grd Tchr 1965-73, 3rd Grd Tchr 4th Grd Tchr 1981-; *home:* 5085 Audrey Dr North Syracuse NY

GRACE RUTH, Kindergarten Teacher; *b:* Buffalo, NY; *ed:* St Y at Buffalo (EDB) Early Chldhd Ed 1965; *cr:* Allendale Elem -90; Ed Ctr Tchr 1990-; *ai:* Bldg Child Stud Team Tchr Rep; West hrs Assn 1965-, Exec Cncl Rep; Erie Cty Ed Assn, NY St United T 1965-; City Mission Soc 1991-; Soc for Prevention of Cruelty ; Humane Ed Soc of US; World Wild Life Fed; WHED, WNEQ p; Nom West Seneca Chamber of Commerce 1973; Edctr of Yr covery Toys Bldg Self Esteem Awd Nom 1992; Outstdng Elem Amer Selected for Inclusion in 1974; *office:* Education Center ard Park Rd West Seneca NY 14224

JAMES STEARNS, Drafting Instructor; *b:* Waltham, MA; *ed:* Coll (AS) Architectural, Bldg Tech 1973; Univ of Southern ME Ed 1977; *cr:* Lawrence HS Drafting Instr 1977-; *ai:* Yrbk her; Co-Chair Facility Advy Comm; Stu Assistance Team; Stu of lection Comm; Class Adv 1978-87; Tech Edctrs Assn of ME scover Mid ME 1992-, 1st Place Design Contest Winner; *office:* HS Sad 49 School St Fairfield ME 04937

KATHRYN BURGESON, Sixth Grade Math Teacher; *b:* , PA; *m:* James A.; *c:* Andrew, Emily; *ed:* Clarioin St (BS) Elem Shippensburg St (MED) Elem Ed 1974; Addl 27 Credit Hrs; *cr:* Schl Dist Tchr 1971-73; Big Spring Schl Dist Tchr 1977; nd Vly Schl Dist Tchr 1977-; *ai:* Stu Asst Team; NEA, PSEA EA 1977-; Salute to Tchng Awd 1990; WHTM Class Act Tchr e: Eagle View MS 6746 Carlisle Pike Mechanicsburg PA 17055*

LESLI FERRARA, 3rd Grade Teacher; *b:* Cincinnati, OH; *m:* h; *c:* Nicholas, Lauryn, Michael; *ed:* Univ of Cincinnati (BS) Ed ier Univ (ME) Ed 1991; *cr:* Forest Hills Schls HS Swim Coach 4th Grd Tchr 1985-87, 3rd Grd Tchr 1987-; *ai:* Enrichment fice: Wilson Elem Schl 2465 Little Dry Run Rd Cincinnati OH

LYNDA, High School English Teacher; *b:* Pittsburgh, PA; *ed:* er Coll (BA) Eng 1973; SUNY at Buffalo (MS) Ed 1977; *cr:* chls HS Eng Tchr 1974-; *ai:* Phi Delta Kappa 1993-; Zeta Tau m 1988-; Tandy Cmptr Grant; *office:* Frontier Sr HS Bay View rg NY 14075

NANCY LEE, Intermediate English Teacher; *b:* Baltimore, MD; Lewis, Terri Lewis; *ed:* Notre Dame of MD (BA) Ed 1976; 15 MD Writing Project; *cr:* St Anthonys Tchr 33 Yrs; *ai:* In Charge Contests; NEA 1980-; MD Writing Project; *office:* St Anthony Schl 4410 Frankford Ave Baltimore MD 21206

S, BARBARA BROWN, Fifth Grade Teacher; *b:* Brooklyn, NY; ; *ed:* Long Island Univ (BA) Elem Ed 1978; Brooklyn Coll (MS) 991; *cr:* PS 235 Tchr 1985-; *ai:* Conduct Africa Tours for Stdnts, ites of Passage Consultant; Genealogist; UFT, AFT 1985; Pub fice: P S 235 Annex 779 E 49th St Brooklyn NY 11203

S, LILLIAN J., Business & English Teacher; *b:* Cleveland, OH; ; *ed:* OH St Univ (BS) Ed 1972; 15 Addl Hrs; Post-Grad Stud at oll, Kent St, Ashland; *cr:* Padua Franciscan HS Bus, Eng Tchr CABTA 1975-; NCTE 1989-; *office:* Padua Franciscan H S 6740 Parma OH 44134*

DURENBERGER, JANET, HS Art Education Teacher; *b:* e, OH; *m:* Gregory Keith; *c:* Megan, Tiffany; *ed:* Bowling Green BFA) Graphic Design, Art Ed 1983; Attnd OH St Univ-Lima niv of Dayton, Walsh Univ; *cr:* Riverdale Jr HS tchr 1986-89; HS Tchr 1986-; *ai:* Riverdale Art Club-Haunted Barn Candy Class, Prom Adv; Mini-Arts Prgm; NWNEA 1986-; REA 1986-, ions, Legislation; Northwest OH Archery Assn 1995-, 2nd Place ment; *office:* Riverdale HS 20613 State Route 37 Mt Blanchard

MARGARET VAUGHAN, Health Academy Teacher; *b:* Suffern, aul P. Jr.; *c:* David, Lori, Michael, Katie, Brian; *ed:* Empire St Hlth 1992; St Marys Schl RN Nrsg 1967; Inservice Change into Learning, Listening; Working on MS Ed Admin SUNY at ; *cr:* Crouse Meml Pediatrics, OR-RR Staff Charge 1967-69; aimonedes OR, RR ER, Med-Surg Staff Charge 1969-712; Pub Perdiem Nutritional Ed 1981-86; Childbirgh Ed Ind Instr 1975-; S Schl Nurse 1986-93; Sullivan Co BOCES Hlth Acad Tchr Ath Against Substance Abuse 1987-; Kids Group Support Group -95; AFT, NEA 1986-; Liberty Booster 1992-; Cares Coalition on Awd 1993.

S, GARY HUGH, Technology Education Teacher; *b:* Keyser, Marguerite Elizabeth Determan; *c:* Erin Elizabeth, David Hugh, llison; *ed:* California St Coll at PA (BS) Indstrl Arts 1979; Univ of PA (MED) Indstrl Arts 1985; Post-Grad Stud Penn St Hrs, Millersville Univ of PA 15 Hrs; *cr:* US Navy Aviation th 1972-76; Allegany HS Indstrl Arts Tchr 1979-85; Dept of Navy Electronic Equipment Spec 1985-88; USAF Reserve, PA Air Natl Guard 1977-; Elizabethtown Area HS Tech Ed Tchr 1988-; *ai:* PSEA, NEA, Tech Ed Assn of PA, Lancaster-Lebanon Tech Ed Assn 1988-; Amer Legion Post 189 1973-; VFW Post 5280 1991-; US Coast Guard Aux, Flotilla 14-03 1992-; *office:* Elizabethtown Area HS 600 E High St Elizabethtown PA 17022

GATTI, PATRICIA FITZSIMMONS, Religious Teacher; *b:* New York, NY; *c:* Edward, Regina; *ed:* Mercy Coll (BA) His 1972; Archdiocesan Catechetical Inst (MA) Rel Stud 1986; Addl Stud at Schl of Reg Stud, Marymount Coll & Iona Coll; *cr:* St Barnabas Schl 6th-8th Grd Tchr 1979-86; Our Lady of Victory Acad Religion & Soc Stud Tchr 1986-, Rel Dept Chrprsn 1994-; "Relig" Staff Dev Coord 1994-; *ai:* Victory in Svc & Action & Ath Assn Adv; Clothing & Food Drive Spon; Westchester Charity Prjct Coord; NCEA 1979-; *office:* Our Lady Of Victory Acad 565 Broadway Dobbs Ferry NY 10522*

GATTO, WILLIAM JOSEPH, Band & General Music Teacher; *b:* Rockville Center, NY; *m:* Hallie Duval; *ed:* Hofstra Univ (BSME) 1972; SUNY at Stony Brook (MAEd) 1977; *cr:* Seneca Jr HS Band Tchr & Gen Music Tchr 1972-; *ai:* Seneca Jazz Ensemble; *office:* Seneca Jr HS 850 Main St Holbrook NY 11741*

GATTON, SUSAN RYAN, First Grade Teacher; *b:* Stuttgart, Germany; *m:* Mark; *c:* Adam, Andrew; *ed:* OH Univ (BS) Elem Ed 1978, (MS) Elem Ed 1983; Post Grad Stud; *cr:* Franklin Local Schls First Grd Tchr 1978-; *ai:* Delta Kappa Gamma 1993-; Nashport Pack 174 Cub Scouts 1989-, Den Ldr, Asst Cubmaster; Immanuel United Church of Christ Comm; *office:* Duncan Falls Primary Schl 397 Oak St Duncan Falls OH 43734*

GATTONE, LYNN, English Teacher; *b:* Somerville, NJ; *m:* Joseph Kopka; *c:* Keith Kopka; *ed:* Simmons Coll (MA) Eng 1972; Boston Univ (BS) Eng 1969; 15 Hrs Post Grad Stud; *cr:* Sharon HS Eng Tchr 1970-86 1988-; *ai:* NHS Fac Comm; Fac Cncl; NEA, MTA 1970-; Southeastern MA HS Alliance 1995-; Partners in Learning, Oral His Project Sharon Historical Soc Comm Svc; *office:* Sharon HS 180 Pond St Sharon MA 02067

GAUCHER, PETER STANLEY, English Teacher; *b:* Exeter, NH; *ed:* Dartmouth Coll (BA) Eng 1974; Univ of NH (MST) Eng Ed 1979; *cr:* Pinkerton Acad Eng Tchr 1974-; *ai:* NHS & Asst Drama Adv; NCTE; NEATE; NHATE; NEH Summer Seimar for Tchrs Faulkner 1987; NEH Flwshp for Ind Stud in Hum 1988; *home:* 12 Hope Hill Rd Derry NH 03038

GAUDET, JOSEPH EDWARD, Mathematics Instructor; *b:* Leominster, MA; *m:* Barbara; *c:* Justin, Kellie; *ed:* Fitchburg St (BS) Math 1969, (MS) Guid 1973; Attnd Math Sci Inst, Worcester Polytechnic Inst Cmptr Sci, Framingham St Coll; *cr:* Laura White Schl Math Tchr 1969-70; Narragansett Regnl Schl Math Tchr 1970-71; Marian HS Math Tchr 1971-78; Norwood HS Math Tchr 1978-79; Canton HS Math Tchr 1979-; Framingham St Coll Cont Ed Instr 1988-; *ai:* Cmptr Club Adv; Cmptr Programming, Girls Tennis Coach; Bsktbl, Soccer Referee; NEA, MTA 1969-; NCTM 1995-; EMSOA 1979-; NISOA 1994-; Framingham Yth Soccer 1985-; NSF Grant Worcester Polytech; Math Sci Inst Awarded Associateship withUS Army HS Sci & Math Fac Prgm 1990-; *office:* Canton HS 900 Washington St Canton MA 02021*

GAUDET, MARY I., Sixth Grade Teacher; *b:* Malden, MA; *ed:* Regis Coll (BA) Ed, Psych 1960; Suffolk U at Boston 16 Cr Hr; Coll of Santa Fe 30 Cr Hr; *cr:* St John Schl Tchr 1955-62; St Gabriel Schl Tchr 1962-66; Cristo Rey Schl Tchr 1966-70; Malden Pub Schls Tchr 1970-83, 1988-90; Immaculate Conception Schl Tchr 1990-; *ai:* NCEA 1990-; NEA, MTA 1970-90; Malden Tchrs Assn 1970-90, Exec Treas; CYP Bsktbl 1970-72, Coach; Santa Fe Yth Recreation 1968-70, Asst Dir, Coach; *office:* Immaculate Conception Schl 127 Winthrop Ave Revere MA 02151

GAUDIO, CHRISTINE L., 6th Grade Teacher; *b:* Rochester, NY; *m:* Richard; *c:* Michael, David; *ed:* Univ of Rochester (BA) Sociology, Psych 1974; Nazareth Coll (MS) Elem Ed 1982; 12 Post Grad Hrs Rdng; 6 Hrs Post Scndry Credit Hrs; *cr:* St Michaels Schl 7th-8th Grd Tchr 1974-76; Rush Hennetta Cntrl Schl 7th-8th Grd Math, Rdng Tchr, Skills Ctr 1986-88; Fairport Cntrl Schl Dist 6th Grd Tchr 1988-; *ai:* 6th Grd Jr Great Books Discussion Group, 7th-8th Grd Jr Great Books Discussion Group Adv; Dist Shared Decision Making Sub Comm; Schl Hlth Team Comm; NYSUT 1986-; Brighton Meml Lib, Vol; BSA, Ldr, Comm Mem; *office:* Johanna Perrin MS 85 Potter Pl Fairport NY 14450

GAUER, KATHRYN M., 8th Grd Earth Science Teacher; *b:* Barberton, OH; *m:* John P.; *c:* James, Kristina; *ed:* Univ of Akron (MSEd) Ed 1992; 18 Hrs Post Grad Stud; *cr:* Erie Island Elem 4th Grd Tchr 1985-93; Innes MS 8th Grd Earth Sci Tchr 1993-; *ai:* Previously Comp & Audio Visual Coord; Stu Assistance Team Mem; Current Sci Activity Person; AEA 1985-; *home:* 510 Vaughn Trl Akron OH 44319

GAUGHENBAUGH, KATHLEEN WILLIAMS, Fifth Grade Teacher; *b:* Lancaster, PA; *ed:* Bloomsburg Univ (BS) Elem Ed 1979; 28 Credit Hrs, Instrl II Cert; *cr:* St Mary's Kulpmont 2, 8 Grd Tchr 1979-80; ST Michael's Schl 7th Grd Tchr 1980-81; St Columba's Schl 5th Grd Tchr 1981-; *ai:* Mentor; Math Curr, Sci Fair Coord; Schl Planning Cycle; Safety Patrols Adv; NCEA 1979-; *office:* St Columba Schl 40 E 3rd St Bloomsburg PA 17815

GAUGLER, FRANKLIN NORWOOD, Business Data Processing Tchr; *b:* Selinsgrove, PA; *m:* Faye Marie Helman; *c:* Steven, Matthew, Cherie Ann Stiffler; *ed:* Shippensburg Univ (BS) Bus Ed 1983, (MED) Bus Ed 1989, (MED) Scndry Schl Admin 1995; 12 Grad Hrs Cmptr Tech PA St Univ; Scndry Prin Cert; *cr:* Chambersburg Area Schl Dist Asst Bus Mgr, Treas 1969-83; Franklin Cty Area Vo-Tech Schl Bus Data Processing Tchr 1984-; *ai:* FBLA Adv; Bus Data Processing Prof Advy Comm Chprsn; Voc Indstrl Clubs of Amer; Pub, Prnsl Relations Comm; Tech Ctr Task Force; PA Bus Ed Assn 1987-, Conf Prgm Co-Chprsn 1995, Mbrshp Chprsn 1996; NBEA, EBEA 1989-; NEA, PSEA, FCTEA 1993-; Phi Delta Kappa 1995-, Kapstone Columnist 1995-; Delta Pi Epsilon 1987-; South Cntrl Chptr PA Sports Hall of Fame 1987-; Back the Lions 1979-; Salem United Brethren Church 1969-, Bd Mem, Tchr, Vocalist; YMCA 1975-; PA FBLA Outstdng Adv, Newspaper Recognition Outstdng Edctr Franklin Cty 1993; Tchr of Yr Finalist 1995-; PBEA Conf Presenter 1987-89, 1993-94; *office:* Franklin Cty Area Voc Tech Sch 2463 Loop Rd Chambersburg PA 17201*

GAUGLER, PENNY L., Seventh Grade Reading Teacher; *b:* Sunbury, PA; *m:* Marvin; *c:* Kathryn Elizabeth, Kyle Gregory; *ed:* Bloomsburg Univ (BS) Span 1979; Rdng Cert at Bloomsburg Univ 1980; *cr:* Danville Area Schls 7th Grd Rdng Tchr 1980-; *ai:* Prof Dev comm Chprsn; MS Peer Mediation Team Tchr, Mediator; Seventh Grd Dolphin Team Ldr; Tchr Ldrshp Ctr Governing Bd Mem; NEA, PSEA 1980-; Trinity Luth Church 1995-, Church Cncl Sec; *office:* Danville MS Northumberland Rd Danville PA 17821*

GAUL, GERALD MARTIN, 7th-8th Grd Sci & Math Teacher; *b:* Philadelphia, PA; *m:* Janet Francis; *c:* Gerald Jr.; *ed:* Temple Univ (BA) Elem Ed 1985; *cr:* Most Blessed Sacrament Tchr 1985-; *ai:* WHHS Haverford HS Radio Station Supvr; Local CYO Coach; HS Bsbl Umpire; HS Soccer Referee; NEA 1990-; *home:* 2612 S 66th St Philadelphia PA 19142

GAULT, G. GARY, World Cultures Teacher; *b:* Annapolis, MD; *m:* Barbara Ann Carl; *c:* Michael, Susan; *ed:* Elizabethtown Coll (BS) Scndry Ed, Soc Stud 1967; Master's Equivalency Scndry Ed; *cr:* Spring Grove Area Schl Dist Soc Stud Tchr 1967-; *ai:* Girls Var Bsktbl Coach; Stu Assistance Prgm; NEA, PSEA 1967-; Coach's Corner Articles; Wharton Bus Schl Tchr Awd; *office:* Spring Grove Area Sr HS Hanover & Jackson Sts Spring Grove PA 17362

GAUSE, JULIA M., 2nd Grade Teacher; *b:* Dowagiac, MI; *m:* Joseph L.; *c:* Sonji, Alecia, Aaron, Crystal; *ed:* Murray St Univ (MS) Elem Ed 1981; Indiana Univ (BS) Elem Ed 1978; 40 Hrs Past Masters; *cr:* North Jr High 7th-8th Grd Rdng Tchr; Windsor Elem 4th Grd Classroom Tchr 3 Yrs; Windsor Elem, South Side Elem 2nd Grd Classroom Tchr 12 Yrs; *ai:* IAT; Recycle Coord; Sci Pilot Prgm, Contact Person New Sci Adoption; NEA 1978-; Church Childrens Ministry Coord 1993-; *office:* Windsor Elem Schl 264 Windsor Dr Elyria OH 44035*

GAUVIN, ANN MARIE, English Teacher; *b:* Woonsocket, RI; *m:* Charles G.; *c:* Paula Gauvin Goss; *ed:* RI Coll (EDB) Ed 1961; Providence Coll Post Grad Work; *cr:* Woonsocket Jr HS Eng Tchr 1961-67; Mt St Charles Acad Eng Tchr 1969-73; Woonsocket MS Eng Tchr 1973-; *ai:* St Patricks Church 1969-, Food Pantry Coord & Lector; *office:* Woonsocket MS Park Pl Woonsocket RI 02895

GAUVIN-THARNEY, DENISE ANN, Mathematics Dept Chair & Tchr; *b:* Camden, NJ; *m:* Leonard J.; *c:* Karen L. Verrecchia, Linda L.; *ed:* Trenton St Coll (BS) Elem Ed, Psych 1977, (MED) Math Ed 1994; 30 Credits Math Cert 1984, 12 Credits Supervisory Cert; *cr:* Freehold Borough Schls St Compensatory Ed Rdng Tchr 1978; St Ann's Schl 7th-8th Grd Math, Soc Stud Tchr 1978-80; Notre Dame HS Math Tchr 1980-, Math Chair 1992-; Mercer Cty Comm Coll Adj Math Tchr 1991-; *ai:* Curr Cncl; Long-Term Strategic Planning, Accreditation Comms; Mid Sts Assn; NCTM 1993-; Kappa Delta Pi 1995-; PTA Svc Awd 1995; Adult Appreciation Awd 1979; *home:* 20 Lawrenceville Penning Rd Lawrenceville NJ 08648

GAVAGHAN, MARGARET, Teacher & Counselor; *b:* Philadelphia, PA; *ed:* Chestnut Hill Coll (BS) Elem Ed 1969; La Salle Univ (MA) Theology 1984; (MA) Counseling Psych; Admin 6 Credits; *cr:* St Isidore Grd Schl Prin & Eighth Grd Tchr 1972-78; St Geneieve Grd Schl Prin 1978-81; St Peter Grd Schl Jr High Tchr 1981-84; St Rose HS Tchr, Cnslr, Chair 1984-; *ai:* Mid Sts Teams; Acad Cncl; Soph Class & Peer Cnslrs Moderator; Rel Dept Chair; Diocese of Trenton Moral Issues Comm; Key Club Mod; NCEA 1959-; ASCD 1991-; NJPHA 1987-; Svc Moderator 12 Yrs; Schl Svc Awd 1992; Diocesan Pro Life Awd 1993.

GAVAZZI, KAREN HISIRO, 7th Grade Reading Specialist; *b:* Charleroi, PA; *m:* Oswald V.; *c:* Brian, Justin; *ed:* California Univ of PA (BS) Ed 1974, (MEd) Rdng 1977; Guid 6 Credits; Rdng Supvr 6 Credits; *cr:* Tyler Co Schls 1st Grd Tchr 1974-76; Ringgold Schl Dist Rdng Intern 1976-77; Canon-Mc Millan Schl Dist Rdng Specialist 1977-; *ai:* Spelling Bee Spon; Lang Arts Curr Comm; CMEA, PSEA 1977-; Flag of Learning; *office:* Cecil MS 676 Millers Run Rd Mc Donald PA 15057

GAVETT, JAMES W., Science Teacher; *b:* Ithaca, NY; *m:* Susan A. Mennecke; *c:* Jennifer, Carolyn, Trisha; *ed:* Colgate Univ (BA) Bio 1976, (MAT) 1981; *ai:* Girls Var Soccer Coach; *office:* Waterville Central Schl 381 Madison St Waterville NY 13480

GAVIN, CAROLE O'CONNOR, Prof of Language & Literature; *b:* Camden, NJ; *m:* James Gerald; *c:* Claudine, Jocelyne, Brigitte; *ed:* Marygrove (BA) Fr 1966; Middlebury (MA) Fr 1971; Rutgers New Brunswick (EDD) Second Lang Ed 1989; Univ of Grenoble Cert d'Etudes 2e Degree, Cert d'Etudes 1e Degree; *cr:* Burlington Cty Coll Lang, Lit Division Prof 1971-; *ai:* Phi Theta Kappa, Chi Iota Chapter Adv; Fnd Schlsp Comm; Fac Senate Exec Bd; Intnl Stu Adv; NEA 1971-; *office:* Burlington County College County Rt 530 Pemberton NJ 08068

GAVIN, MAURICE DANIEL,JR., Math Instructor; *b:* Buffalo, NY; *m:* Tracy Ann Tierney; *c:* Brett, Casey, Jack; *ed:* Buffalo St Coll (MA) Spcl Ed 1986; *cr:* Orchard Pk MS Math Instr 1983-; *ai:* 9th Grd Boys Modified Ftbl Coach; Girls Var HS Track Coach; NYSUT 1983-; AFT 1983-; NYSMT 1990-; E Aurora Lions 1994-; *office:* Orchard Park MS 60 S Lincoln Ave Orchard Park NY 14127

GAVIN, SUZANNE, Fine & Prfrmng Arts Dept Chair; *b:* Brighton, MA; *ed:* Kean Coll (BA) Math, Sec Ed 1971; Montclair St Coll (MA) Theatre 1976; *cr:* St Vincent Acad Math Tchr 1971-74; DePaul HS Fine, Performing Arts Dept Chprsn 1976-; *ai:* Dir, Designer Theatre Prgm; Retreat Dir Asst; Tech Dir, Designer Paris Theatre Prgm; NCEA 1976-; Theatre Comm Group 1991-; Outstanding Tchr Dawn De Stefano Awd 1995; *office:* DePaul HS 1512 Alps Rd Wayne NJ 07470

GAW, MARTIN JOSEPH, Social Studies Teacher; *b:* Poughkeepsie, NY; *c:* Hannah; *ed:* Marist Coll (BA) His, Ed 1975; Addl Credits SUNY at New Paltz, Coll of St Rose, Emerson Coll, Azusa Pacific; *cr:* LaGrange Jr HS 7, 8, 9 Grds Soc Stud Tchr 1975-79; Arlington HS South Campus 9 Grd Soc Stud Tchr 1979-84; Titusville MS 6, 8 Grds Soc Stud Tchr 1984-; *ai:* Var Boy's Bsktbl, Golf; Bsktbl Coaches Assn of NY, Dutchess Cty Bsktbl Coachess Assn 1975-; Dutchess Cty Golf Coaches Assn 1984-; Assn for Retarded Citizens of Dutchess Cty, 1990 Vol of Yr Awd.

GAWLE, FRANK EDWARD, Dean of Students; *b:* Springfield, MA; *m:* Patricia Conway; *c:* Benjamin, Sarah; *ed:* Univ of Ct (BS) Music Ed 1981; Western Ct St Univ (MS) Music Ed 1989; Fairfield Univ (CAS) Ed Admin 1993; *cr:* Wilton HS Band Dir 1981-95, Dean of Stdnts 1995-; *ai:* Club, Act Supvr; NASSP 1995-; MENC 1981-; *office:* Wilton HS 395 Danbury Rd Wilton CT 06897

GAWNE, BRIAN JOHN, Health Educator; *b:* Buffalo, NY; *m:* Patricia M. Furdyn; *c:* Jenna M., Adam B., Matthew A.; *ed:* SUNY at Brockport (BS) Hlth Ed 1983, (MS) Hlth Ed 1990; *cr:* Watkin Glen Schl Dist Sr HS Hlth Educator 1983-85; Lyndonville Schl Dist Elem & Scndry Hlth Educator 1985-; SUNY Coll at Brockport Adjuct Instr; *ai:* Jr Var Vlybl Coach; Dance Chaperone; Former Wrestling & Track Coach; Peer Leadership Coord; Twn of Yates Yth CMSSN; AFT 1983-93; PTA 1990-93; *office:* Lyndonville Schl Dist Housel Ave Lyndonville NY 14098*

GAY, JAMES M., Vocal Music Director; *b:* Baltimore, MD; *m:* Joyce A. Byrd; *c:* Lisa; *ed:* Morgan St Univ (BS) Music Ed 1964; Seton Hall Univ Post Grad Stud; *cr:* Eastern-Stockton Elem Schl Vocal Music Tchr 1964-68; Vernon L Davey Jr HS Vocal Music Tchr 1968-75; Upsala Coll Tchr Corp Supvr 1974-76; Seton Hall Univ Adj Instr 1976-77; Clifford J Scott HS Dir Vocal Music 1975-; *ai:* Asst Band Dir; Choral & Glee Club Adv; NEA 1964-; EOEA 1964-; NACD 1975-; NATS 1995-; NJ St Bd of Ed 1995-; Mid St Assn of Colls & Schls 1995-; Outstdng Contribution in Music Ed 1987; Outstdng Svc Awd 1989; EO Tchr of the Yr 1991; Governors Tchr Recognition Pgm 1991; EO Dist Awd for Excl in Tchng 1991; *home:* 137 Forest Glen Dr Highland Park NJ 08904*

GAY, KENNETH PAUL, 6th Grade Teacher; *b:* Brockton, MA; *m:* Jeannette M. Doyle; *ed:* Bridgewater St Coll (BS) Elem Ed 1976, (MED) Schl Admin 1987; *cr:* Edwin A Jones Elem Schl 5th & 6th Grd Tchr 1976-; *ai:* Schl Cncl; Awd & Incentive Comm; Schl Awd Ceremonies Coord; Schl Field Days Coord; NEA 1976-; Norfolk Cty Tchr Assn 1976-; Stoughton Tchr Assn 1976-, Bldg Rep; Brockton YMCA 1979-82, Camp Dir, Svc to Youth Awd; Outstanding Young Men of Amer 1982; BSA Eagle Scout Awd 1971; *office:* Edwin A Jones Elem Schl 137 Walnut St Stoughton MA 02072*

GAY, LIELA MARIE (ENGELHAUPT), Eng & Sci Tchr, Dept Chm; *b:* Cleveland, OH; *w:* Edward Bernard (dec); *c:* Mary Katherine Janis, M. Therese Whaley, Steven E., Julie M., Kevin T.; *ed:* John Carroll Univ Ed & Ec Courses 30 Grad Credits; Nicholls St Univ European Stud 6 Grad Credits; Ursuline Coll Peaceful Response Conflicts 3 Grad Credits; *cr:* St

Roberts Tchr 1959-60; St Bede Schl Tchr 1961-62; Immaculate Conception Schl Tchr 1977-; *ai:* Sci Dept Head; Religious Ed Dir; Stu European Tours Conductor; WWF 1977-; Natl Arbor Day Fnd 1985-; NCEA, OCEA 1977-; Natl Right to Life 1975-; *office:* Immaculate Conception Schl 37940 Euclid Ave Willoughby OH 44094

GAY, THOMAS SCOTT, Science Teacher; *b:* Philadelphia, PA; *m:* Catherine E. Honeywell; *c:* Christina Ricketts, Michael, Amanda, Scott; *ed:* Penn St Univ (BS) Ag Ed, Forest Sci 1976; *cr:* US Army Medical Evacuation Pilot 1968-71; Reynolds HS Ag Instr 1976-91, Sci Tchr 1991-95; *ai:* Bible, Environment Club; Boys Bsktbl Coach 17 Yrs; FFA Adv 15 Yrs; REA, PSEA, NEA 1976-.

GAYDA, JACQUELINE ELIZABETH, 7th-12th Grd Eng & Lit Teacher; *b:* Kettering, OH; *m:* Anthony E.; *ed:* Wheaton Coll (BA) Lit 1993; *cr:* Xenia Chrstn HS Eng, Lit Tchr 1993-; *ai:* Jr Class, Yrbk Adv.

GAYDEN, CAROL J. HICKMAN, Hlth, PE & Drivers Ed Teacher; *b:* Bishopville, SC; *m:* Tony; *ed:* Alcorn St Univ (BS) Hlth, PE 1976; William Paterson Coll Admin, Super 1982-83; Kean Coll Driver Ed 1987; Jersey City St Coll Substance Awareness 1992-93; Troy St Univ Schl Cnslng 1995-; *cr:* PS #10 Schl Tchr 1981-84; PS 30, 16 Schl Tchr 1984-85; Eastside HS Tchr, Coach 1985-; *ai:* Track, Field Coach; Bedside Instr; NEA, NJEA 1981-, Rep; Faith Chapel 1964-, Sunday Schl Supt, Numerous Awds; Delta Sigma Theta 1977-, Pres, VP, Woman of Yr; We Think The Same Thoughts 1996.*

GAYDOS, CAROL WYSOKINSKI, 8th Grade Teacher; *b:* Jersey City, NJ; *m:* Eugene M.; *c:* Alexa; *ed:* St Peter's Coll (BS) Math 1973; Steven's Inst of Tech (MS) Math 1981; St Peter's Coll K-12 Math Specialist, Cert 1986; *cr:* St Nicholas Schl 8th Grd Tchr 1973-74, Math Tchr 1981-; *ai:* Stu Cncl Adv; Math, Mid Grd Coord; NCTM 1987-; NASAA 1994-; Schl Bd 1992-, Sec; Eucharistic Minister 1986-; Neward Archdiocese Outstdng Tchr 1995.

GAYDOS, RICHARD C., Trigonometry & Geometry Tchr; *b:* Braddock, PA; *m:* Mary Margaret Sholtis; *c:* Rachelle Sestina, Renee Bittner; *ed:* Duquesne Univ (BED) Ed Math 1960, (MED) Scndry Admin 1962; 60 Credits Beyond Masters; *cr:* Park Terrace Jr High Algebra Tchr 1960-68; East McKeesport 9th Grd Algebra Tchr 1968-69; East Allegheny Algebra I, II, Geometry, Trigonometry, Analysis Tchr 1969-; *ai:* Bsktbl, Swimming Coach; Stu Cncl Adv; NEA, PSEA, EAEA; *office:* East Allegheny HS 1150 Jacks Run Rd North Versailles PA 15137

GAYFORD, NORMAN RODNEY, Assistant Professor of English; *b:* Cuba, NY; *m:* Mary H. Conable; *c:* Ian; *ed:* St Lawrence Univ (BA) Eng 1980; Brown Univ (MAT) Eng, Tchng 1981; SUNY at Brockport (MA) Eng 1986; *cr:* Salem HS Tchr 1981-82; Caledonia-Manford HS Eng Tchr 1982-88; Genesee Comm Coll Asst Prof 1988-; *ai:* Information Literacy, Mid Sts Accreditation Comms; Lib Task Force; Cty Campus at Warsaw Advy Bd; SUNY Cncl on Writing; NCTE 1991-; AATW, CCCC 1990-; Literacy Vol 1990-, Tutor 1992, Newsletter Ed; Planned Parenthood 1984-94, Vol; 8 Articles Pub; *office:* Genesee Comm Coll 1 College Rd Batavia NY 14020

GAYHART, DAVID KEITH, Math Teacher, Basketball Coach; *b:* Beaver Falls, PA; *m:* Dianne Lee Staley; *c:* Chad Aaron, Alexis Renae; *ed:* Geneva Coll (BS) Math 1972; 24 Post-Grad Hrs Penn St Beaver Campus; *cr:* South Side Area Schl Dist Math Tchr 24 Yrs; *ai:* Coach Head Bsktbl, Asst Ftbl; Mentor Tchr; SAP Team; NEA, PSEA 1972-; MAC Coaches Assn 1981-, Sec; *home:* 1915 13th St Beaver Falls PA 15010

GAYLE, GEORGE WILLIAM, Health & PE Dept Chair; *b:* Mathews, VA; *m:* Susan E.; *ed:* Univ of WI at LaCrosse (MS) Adapted PE 1977; OH St Univ (PHD) Adapted PE 1988; *cr:* LaEscuela Bella Vista Tchr 1974-76; Wright St Univ Dir of Adapted Ath 1977-82, Asst Prof 1982-88, Assoc Prof 1988-95, HPR Dept Chair 1995-; *ai:* Univ Budget Review & Adapted PE Natl Standards Comms; Acad Council; AAHPERD, OHHPZRD 1983-; NCPERID, CEC 1990-; Grafton Hill Comm Dev Corp 1990-, VP; HPR Dept Apple Awd for Tchng; Dayton Pub Schls Peach Awd; OH Wheelchair Sports Hall of Fame; Adapted Aquatics Book "In Press"; *office:* Wright St Univ Nutter Ctr Rm 316 Dayton OH 45435*

GAYLETS, RAYMOND T., Social Studies Teacher; *b:* Scranton, PA; *m:* Susan Stock; *c:* Tyler David, Ryan Patrick, Stephen Vincent; *ed:* Kings Coll (BA) His & Ed 1978; *ai:* Var Ftbl, Bsktbl & Bsbl Coach; Teddy Roosevelt Club; Strength Trng Adv; Flwshp of Chrstn Aths 1990-; *home:* 526 Kitchen Ln West Pittston PA 18643

GAYLORD, CAROL ANN, 4th Grade Teacher; *b:* Pittston, PA; *m:* William F.; *c:* Marcy, Michael; *ed:* Wilkes Univ (BA) Elem Ed 1974; MS Equivalency +40 Credit Hrs; *cr:* Tunkhannock Area K-4th Grd Tchr 20 Yrs; *ai:* Bsbl & Sftbl Team Mom; PSEA & NEA 1975-; *office:* Tunkhannock Area Schl Franklin Ave Tunkhannock PA 18657

GAYNOR, BONNIE MC KINNEY, Seventh Grade Math Teacher; *b:* Buffalo, NY; *m:* James; *c:* Meghan, James, Scott; *ed:* SUNY at Potsdam (BA) Math 1969; SUNY at Buffalo (MS) Math 1969; *cr:* Depew Schls Scndry Tchr 1969-89, 7th Grd Math Tchr 1989-; *ai:* AMTNYS 1995-.

GAZZILLO, IRMA ANN, Music Teacher; *b:* Philadelphia, PA; *ed:* Chestnut Hill Coll (MB) Music Ed 1967; Cath Univ of Amer DC (MM) Ed, Voice 1974; 3 Hrs Voice Marywood; 6 Hrs String, Orch Tech; Addl 6 Hrs; *cr:* Holy Angels Tchr 1954-65; St Ann Tchr 1965-72; Bishop Mc Guinness HS Tchr 1972-80, 1989-92; Holy Family Acad Music, Drama Tchr 1980-89, 1992-; *ai:* Forensics, Instrumental Ensembles Moderator; Chorus Dir; One Act Plays, Christmas Play Dir; Co-Dir, Musical Dir String Musical; MENC 1972-; NJMEA, NCEA 1980-; Outstdng Tchr of Yr 1995; *office:* Holy Family Acad 239 Avenue A Bayonne NJ 07002

GEACINTOV, LYDIA B., Director of Studies; *b:* Sofia, Bulgaria; *m:* Nicholas E.; *c:* J. Glenn, Derek N., Pew; *ed:* Univ of Rochester (BA) Fr Lit 1964; Villanova Univ (MA) Fr Lit 1979; Attn NY Univ at New York City, Sorbonne at Paris, Domine at Madrid; *cr:* Pittsford HS F L Tchr 1963-64; Slipperty Rock HS F L Tchr 1964-66; Shipley Schl Dept Head 1973-81; Pingry Schl Dept Head, Dir of Stud 1982-; *ai:* Drama; Dev, Dept Heads, Admin, Diversity, Interdisciplinary Comms; NAIS, ASCD, NJAIS, NEA 1981-; Petrushka 1987-, Staff, Publicity; NORR 1973-, Bd of Dirs, Ldrshp; Woodrow Wilson; Cum Laude Soc; Phi Sigma Iota; Dedication Drama 1991; Yrbk Dedication 1977; Tomlinson Chair Hum; *office:* The Pingry Schl PO Box 366 Martinsville NJ 08836*

GEAN, ANNE DUGGAN, Spanish & French Teacher; *b:* Boston, MA; *m:* William; *c:* Shaun, Christian; *ed:* Emmanuel Coll (BA) Fr 1967; Univ of Paris (MA) Fr 1968; Addl 30 Hrs Span; *cr:* Hingham Schl FLES Tchr 1968-69; Westwood Sr HS Fr, Scndry Tchr 1969-76; Notre Dame Acad Span, Fr Tchr 1983-; *ai:* Soph Class Adv; Fr NHS Moderator; AATF, MAFLA 1968-; *home:* 6 Burr Rd Hingham MA 02043*

GEARAN, JANICE WALENDZIAK, Instructor of Psychology; *b:* Gardner, MA; *m:* John Jr.; *c:* Jack, Michael; *ed:* Anna Maria Coll (BA) Soc Work 1974, (MA) Cnslng Psych 1982; 20 Continuing Ed Units Every 2 Yrs for Relicense as Soc Worker; *cr:* Head Start Prgm Soc Worker 1974; Montachusett Home Care Corp Intake Supvr, Dir of Adult Foster Care 1975-87; Mt Wachusett Comm Coll Adj Fac, Grant Coord 1987-93, Instr 1993-; *ai:* Human Svcs Club Adv; Outcomes Comm; MA Bd of Registration 1981-, Licensed Cert Soc Worker; MTA, NEA 1993-; Amer Psychological Assn Division II 1992-; Gardner VNA 1990-, Bd of Dir; Gardner Coll Club 1976-, Sec; Comprehensive Comm Support System 1994-, Sec; Outstdng Staff Awd 1993-; *office:* Mount Wachusett Comm Coll 444 Green St Gardner MA 01440

GEARHART, JANET (RUMBAUGH), Fourth Grade Teacher; *b:* Akron, OH; *m:* Dennis W.; *c:* Gregory, Timothy, Jeffery; *ed:* Univ of Akron (BS) Elem Ed 1975; *cr:* Mogadore Local Schls Tchr 1981-; *ai:* NEA; OEA; PTA Outstdng Edctrs, Summit Cty 1993; *office:* O H Somers Elem Schl 3600 Herbert St Mogadore OH 44260

GEARHART, KIM RUSSELL, College Field Advisor & Instr; *b:* Buffalo, NY; *m:* Mary; *c:* Jonathan, Joseph, Jessica, Carrie; *ed:* Ithaca Coll (BA) Sociology 1979; Marywood Coll (MSW) Soc Work 1988; *cr:* Elmira Glove House Aftercare Caseworker 1980-86; St Josephs Hosp Psychiatric Soc Worker 1986-88; Elmira Glove House Foster Home Supvr 1988-93; Corning Comm Coll Field Adv, Instr 1993-; *ai:* NASW 1992-; *office:* Corning Comm Coll 1 Academic Dr Corning NY 14830

GEARHART, OLIVER C., Retired English Teacher; *b:* Harrisburg, PA; *m:* Jacquelyn Jean Osman; *c:* Elaine I. Hykes, Thomas C. (dec), Timothy M.; *ed:* Shippensburg St Tchrs (BS) Scndry Ed 1954; Temple U (MED) 1975; *cr:* Cntrl Dauphin HS Eng Tchr 1959-63; West Shore Sch Dist Eng Tchr 1963-93; *ai:* NEA 1959-93; PSEA Life Mem 1959-93; WSEA 1963-93; VFW 1987-, Life Mem; Amer Legion 1987-; *home:* 23 Ridgeway Dr Carlisle PA 17013

GEARHART, PAMELA OSBURN, Child Development Teacher; *b:* Louisville, KY; *m:* Robert Bruce; *c:* Eric, Kirstin; *ed:* Marshall Univ (BA) Comprehensive Voc Home Ec Ed 1971; Univ of MD (MS) Home Ec Ed 1978; 12 Yrs Studying Native Amer Culture; *cr:* WV Univ 4-H Camp Cnslr 1962-71, Cooperative Extension 4-H Agent 1971; Howard Cty MD Sec Ed Family & Consumer Scis Tchr 1971-78; Interior Design Cos Interior Designer 1978-83; Frederick HS Child Dev Tchr in Family & Consumer Scis Dept 1983-; *ai:* Future Tchrs of Amer Co-Spon; BOE Comm for Multiculture Ed; Native Amer Culture Pub Speaker & Tchr; AHEA, MHEA & FCHEA 1968-; NEA, MSTA & FCTA 1971-, Bldg Rep; Delta Kappa 1975-; 4-H 1960-, Agent, Ldr & Cnslr; BSA & Girl Scouts 1990-, Ldr & Asst Vol; United Meth Church Life Mem, Tchr; MD Home Ec Tchr of Yr 1978; Washington DC Designer Showcase of the Yr Awd 1980; Chamber of Commerce Tchr of Excl 1989; *office:* Frederick HS 650 Carroll Pky Frederick MD 21701*

GEARHART, RITA ANN (VARGO), 7th Grade Math Teacher; *b:* Akron, OH; *m:* Otto A.; *c:* Stephanie, Emilie; *ed:* Univ of Akron (BS) Elem Ed 1969; Master Tchng Prgm 1976; Univ of MT STEM Trng; *cr:* Leggett Elem Schl 4th, 6th Grd Tchr 1969-76; Mc Bright Elem Schl 5th-6th Grd Tchr 1977-80; Barrett Elem Schl 5th Grd Tchr 1980-81; Lincoln Elem Schl ESEA Rdng Specialist 1981-84; Voris Elem Schl 5th-6th Grd Tchr 1984-88; Kent MS Traditional, Integrated 6th-8th Grd Math Tchr 1988-; *ai:* Natl Jr Hnr Soc Adv Team; Fac Adv Cncl; Spelling Bee Coach, Cooard; Math Dept Chprsn; BUG Coord, Iniator; STEM Pilot Tchr, Trainer; NCTM 1993-; Greater Akron Math Edctrs Soc 1990-; Pi Lambda Theta 1988-; Akron Ed Assn 1969-; Assn for Supervision, Curr Dev; Trinity United Church of Christ, Cncl, Elder, Lay Reader; Alpha Delta Pi Alumnae; Division A Scndry Tchr of Yr 1994; Bldng Tchr of Yr 1994; Nom Outstdng Educator Awd 1995, 1987; Ashland Oil Golden Apple Achiever Awd; Nom Presidential Awd Excl in Math, Sci Tchng; Jennings Scholar; *office:* Roswell Kent MS 1445 Hammel St Akron OH 44306

GEARIN, DAWN DUCHARME, Science Teacher; *b:* Lowell, MA; *m:* Sean; *ed:* Univ of NH (BS) Plant Bio 1990; Fitchburg St Coll (MAT) Bio 1995; *cr:* Lunenburg HS Sci, Bio & Horticulture Tchr 1994-; *ai:* Billerica HS Var Gymnastics Coach; Frosh Class of 1999 Adv; NABT 1994-; *office:* Lunenburg HS 1079 Massachusetts Ave Lunenburg MA 01462

GEARINGER, MARY ANN BRUSH, Third Grade Teacher; *b:* Huntington, NY; *m:* Charles Edward; *c:* David Scott, Autumn Beth Stitely; *ed:* Hood Coll (BA) Early Chldhd Ed 1960; Queens Coll Temple Univ (MS) Elem Ed; Hofstra Univ (MS) Elem Ed; 40 Credit Hrs; *cr:* Lewistown Elem Schl Second Grd Tchr 1960-61; North Frederick Elem Schl Third Grd Tchr 1961-62; Maywood Elem Schl Third Grd Tchr 1962-64; Southdown Elem Schl 6th Grd Tcr 1967-72; Waverley Elem Schl 3rd & 4th Grd Tchr 1972-; *ai:* Rdng Incentive Comm; MD St Tchrs Assn, Frederick Cty Tchrs Assn, NEA 1972-; Centennial Meml United Meth Church 1972-, Sunday Schl Supt, Staff Parish Relations Comm; Writing Curr MD St Testing; Mentor Tchr; Stu Tchrs Supvr; Schl Improvement Team; Team Ldr; *home:* PO Box 292 Frederick MD 21705

GEARON, ESTELLE KATHLEEN, Prof of Chem & Dept Chair; *b:* New York, NY; *ed:* St John's Univ (BS) Chem 1954; Cath Univ (MS) Chem 1968, (PHD) Chem 1973; *cr:* St Joseph's Coll Instr 1965-74; Montgomery Coll Prof 1974-;, Acting Dean 1994, Prof of Chem, Dept Chair 1990-; *ai:* NSTA 1985-, Ohaus Awd; Fac Advy Cncl 1994-, Rep; NASA Flwshp Grad Schl; NSF Tchrs Awd 2 Yrs; Svc Awd; Full Tuition Acad Schlsps; NY City Chem Club Awd Outstdng Tchr of Sci; *office:* Montgomery Coll Takoma Park 7600 Takoma Ave Takoma Park MD 20912*

GEARY, K. MICHAEL, Accounting Professor; *b:* Kokomo, IN; *m:* Jacqueline Marie Link; *c:* Beth, Ben; *ed:* IN Univ (BS) Scndry Ed 1969; Miami Univ (MBA) Acctng 1974; Univ of Cincinnati (PHD) Acctng 1982; *cr:* Peat, Marwick, Mitchell & Co Staff Auditor 1974-76; Univ of Dayton Assoc Prof 1976-; *ai:* Beta Alpha Psi, Acctng Hnrs Stdnts, Acctng Cooperative Ed Stdnts Adv; AICPA 1975-; OSCPA 1976-, Dayton Chptr Bd; AAA 1976-; IL CPA 1975, OH CPA 1976; Ernst & Young Fac Scholar 1989; Tchng Innovation Awd 1991; Several Articles Pub; *office:* Univ Of Dayton 300 College Park Ave Dayton OH 45469

GEASON, MARIAN CASTER, Vocal Music Teacher; *b:* Kilmarnock, VA; *c:* Sean L.; *ed:* Hampton Univ (BA) Music 1962; Grad Courses Radford Coll, Univ of MD; *cr:* Brookvale HS Vocal Music Tchr 1962-69; Forestville Elem Schl Vocal Music Tchr 1969-74; Malcolm Elem Schl Vocal Music Tchr 1976-; *ai:* Chorus; Grant Comm Charles Cty Bd of Ed; Charles Cty Arts Alliance 1985-; MSTA, NEA 1969-; EACC 1974-; East Heights Bapt Church 1969-, Church; NAACP 1969-; Charles Cty Exemplary Tchr; Presented Stdnts for Performance MD St Dept for Staff; *home:* 6205 Terence Dr Clinton MD 20735*

GEBEY, JANE WILSON, 6th Grade Teacher; *b:* New York, NY; *m:* Charles L.; *c:* Clare, Brian, Maria; *ed:* Anna Maria Coll (AB) Eng 1968; Attnd Work Boston Coll, Worcester St Coll, PA St Univ; *cr:* Notre Dame Acad 9-10 Grd Eng Tchr 1968-70; Anna Maria Coll Pub Relations Dir 1970-72; St Thomas More Schl 6 Grd Tchr 1983-; *office:* St Thomas More Schl 1040 Flexer Ave Allentown PA 18103

GEBHARDT, PAUL LOUIS, Theology Instr & Rel Dept Chm; *b:* Dayton, OH; *ed:* Pontifical Col Josephinum (BA) Theology, Philosophy 1986; Athenaeum of OH (M Div) Theology 1991; Univ of Dayton Educl Ldrshp Masters Prgm; *cr:* Philmont Scout Ranch Cath Chaplain 1990; Bishop Fenwick HS Instr, Chaplain 1991-; St Albert the Great Parish Resident Assoc Pastor 1991-; *ai:* Golf Coach; NCEA 1992-; Ordained to Roman Cath Priesthood for Archdiocese of Cincinnati 1991; *office:* Bishop Fenwick HS 3800 Manchester Rd Middletown OH 45042*

GEBLEIN, JEFFREY P., Instrumental Music Teacher; *b:* Buffalo, NY; *m:* Karen Kimbrough; *c:* Megan R., Jennifer M., Rebecca K., Rachel L., Benjamin J.; *ed:* SUNY at Fredonia (BM) Music Ed 1977, (MM) Music Ed 1983; *cr:* Forestville Cntrl Schl 4th-12th Grd Instrumental Music Tchr 1977-; *ai:* Marching Band, Jazz Ensemble & Schl Musical Dir; IMPACT Team; Schl Improvement Bldg Team Chm; Chautauqu Co Music Tchr Assn 1977-, VP & Pres 1982-84; NYSSMA, MENC & AFT 1977-; Fredonia Clinical Field Supvr Cert; Implementing a Compreh Assistance Prgm Youth Empowering Systems Cert; *office:* Central Schl Water St Forestville NY 14062

GECAWICH, MICHAEL, Business & Computer Teacher; *b:* P RI; *m:* Kathleen Cooney; *c:* Halle; *ed:* Widener Univ (BS) Bus Johnson & Wales Univ (MED) Cmptr Ed 1996; *cr:* Tiverton HS 1990-91; Nasson Int Bus, Cmptr Instr 1992-95; Westerly HS 1992-; Comm Coll of RI Cmptr Instr 1995; *ai:* Asst Ftbl Co RIBEA 1990-; Outstdng Stu Tchr of Yr; Johnson & Wales Te Schlsp Awd; *office:* Westerly HS 23 Ward Ave Westerly RI 028

GECI, GERALD G., Language Art Dept Chairman; *b:* Hartfo Bette Mosher; *c:* Benjamin, John; *ed:* Univ of CT (BA) Math I Eng Ed 1969; Univ of Hartford 15 Credit Hrs; Univ of Bridgepor Hrs; South CT St Univ 30 Credit Hrs; *cr:* Litchfield HS Eng T *ai:* X-C Coach 1970-92, Track Coach 1971-74, Quiz Bowl Te Newspaper Adv; Litchfield Ed Assn 1986-, Treas; NEA; CE 1993-; *office:* Litchfield HS 14 Plumb Hill Rd Litchfield CT 06

GECKELER, DOUGLAS LEE, Mathematics Teacher; *b:* Dayt Marilyn Ann; *c:* Mark, Brian; *ed:* OH St Univ (MS) Ed Admin Upper Arlington Schls Math Tchr 1975-; *ai:* Asst Golf Coach; Prep HS Asst Bsktbl Coach; NCTM 1990-; St of OH Bsktbl Coac Intnl Tchng Fellow Australia 1988; Coaching Awds 1984-86, *home:* 2684 Andover Rd Columbus OH 43221*

GEDDES, SUZANNE DEVINS, Family & Consumer Sci Ossining, NY; *m:* Robert; *ed:* Cornell Univ (BS) Food, Nutri (MS) Food Sci 1970; 90 Addl Grad Credits Drake Univ, F Southampton Coll, Univ of Bridgeport, College of St Rose, Brockport; *cr:* Cornell Univ Tchng Asst 1969-70; Alexander Ha Home Ec Tchr 1970-71; Pleasantville Schls Home Ec Tchr Carmel HS FCS Tchr 1988-; Dutchess Comm Coll Adj Lecture 1989-; *ai:* Sr Class, Yrbk Adv; Bowling Coach; Dept Chprsn; United Tchrs, NYSHETA 1970-; AAFCS 1969-; Putnam Com Prgm 1990-; *office:* Dutchess Comm Coll 53 Pendell Rd Poughk 12601

GEDDIS, MARILYN CROWE, 4th Grade Teacher; *b:* Canto Ronald; *c:* Lindsay, Matthew, Lauren; *ed:* SUNY at Plattsburg 1976; SUNY at Potsdam (MS) Ed 1980; *cr:* Heuvelton Cntrl Tchr 1976-; SUNY at Potsdam Stu & Spon Tchr 1992 & 1994-, Supvr of Stu Tchrs 1996; *ai:* Potsdam Field Experience in Sci Ma Hiring & Comp Tech Comms; Alpha Unit Writing Team Mem; A Heuvelton PTSO 1990-, Treas; NY St Sci Tchrs Ass Shared-Decision Comm 1995-, Parent Rep; SUNY at Potsdam M Tech Flwshp 1995-; *home:* 168 Union St Heuvelton NY 13654*

GEDRICH, KATHLEEN HOLMES, Art & Photography T Washington, DC; *m:* Joseph Raymond; *c:* Daniel, Colleen, Kath Marywood Coll (BA) Fine Arts 1976, (MA) Illustration 1994; Neighborhood Svcs Art Ed Coord 1977-79; WNEP-TV C Courtroom Artist 1979-90; Bishop O'Hara HS Art, Photogr 1990-; *ai:* Art Svc, Photography Clubs; Stu Assistance Prgm 19 Mem; Interboro Lib 1990-92, Lib Bd; IHM Grad Level Sc 1990-91; Sister M. Cuthbert Grad Schlsp 1995; Scranton Dioc Grant 1994; *office:* Bishop Ohara HS 501 E Drinker St Du 18512*

GEE, JOHN HOWARD, 5th Grd History & Reading Tchr; *b:* E *m:* Magdalena M.; *c:* Jennifer, Katherine; *ed:* Univ of Akron (BS (MS) Sci 1987; *cr:* Highland MS Eighth Grd His Tchr 1979- River MS Fifth Grd His, Rdng Tchr 1981-; *ai:* Dist Recycling Co Coord Soc Stud & Rdng; Lib Bd 1990-; *home:* 9830 Daniels Rd 44273

GEE, TODD D., Chemistry Teacher; *b:* Cincinnati, OH; *ed:* O (BS) Ed 1986; Norther KY Univ (MA) Ed 1988; 32 Sem Hrs Pa Degree; *cr:* Glen Este HS Chem Tchr 1986-; *ai:* Var Tennis Co Team Reader; NEA, OEA 1986-; WCEA 1986-, Assn Rep; *of* Este HS 4342 Glen Este Withamsville Rd Cincinnati OH 45245

GEER, BRUCE M., Principal; *b:* Nashua, NH; *m:* Patricia Clar Shannon; *ed:* Plymouth St Coll (BS) Elem Ed 1974; Rivier C Educl Admin 1977; *cr:* E. G. Sherburne Schl Grd 4 Tchr 1974- Hill Schl Grd 5-6 Tchr 1977-81; Bicentennial Schl Grd 5 Tchr Main Dunstable Schl Grd 4-5 Tchr, Asst Prin 1982-94; Mt Ple Prin 1994-; *ai:* GATE Tchr; Curr, Character Ed Comm; Sft NAESP, NHASP 1990-; *office:* Mt Pleasant Schl 10 Monchester NH 03060

GEER, KIMBERLY DIRKX, Secondary English Teacher; *b:* NY; *c:* Kenneth C.; *ed:* Monroe Comm Coll (AS) Lblr Arts, Sc Univ of NY at Brookport (BS) Eng-Cum Laude 1993; 6 Grad C *cr:* Eastridge HS Scndry Eng Tchr 1995-; *ai:* Frosh Class Adv; P Magazine Adv; NYSUT, AFT 1996; PTSA 1996; Phi Theta Ka *office:* Eastridge HS 2250 E Ridge Rd Rochester NY 14622

GEER, TARI SCHOLLER, 7th & 8th Grade Health Teacher; *b:* OH; *m:* Norman J.; *c:* Elizabeth Apt, Erin Scholler, N. Mi Bowling Green St Univ (BS) Hlth, PE, Recreation 1968, (M Admin, Supervision 1980; 30 Hrs Coll Stu Prsnl, Schl Law, EDAS *cr:* Bowling Green Jr HS 9th Grd Hlth, PE Tchr 1973-90, 7-8 Gr 1990-95, 7-8th Grd Hlth Tchr 1995-; *ai:* 9th Grd Vlybl Coach; NE 1973-; BGSU Schl of HPER Alumni Bd 1995-; City Park & Rec 1984-94; City Traffic Commission 1977-; BGSU Recreatio 1989-.*

GEESEY, KATHY LOUISE (ZIMMERMAN), Math Teacher PA; *m:* Ray E.; *ed:* Millersburg St Coll (MS) Math Ed 1975, (MS 1983; 41 Credit Hrs Ed, Math; *cr:* Dover Area Intermediate Sc Grd Math Tchr 1975-86; Dallastown Area HS 9th-12th Grd M 1986-; *ai:* Dist Steering Comm; NEA 1975-; Alpha Delta Kap Chptr Pres; *office:* Dallastown Area HS 700 New School Ln Dalla 17313

GEESEY, L. KATHLEEN, Language Arts Teacher; *b:* Coatesvil James E.; *c:* Pamela Scott, Amy; *ed:* West Chester Univ (BS) Fellow PA Writing Project 1988; 24 Credit Hrs Lit & Wr Coatesville Area HS Eng Tchr 1983-84; Oxford Area HS 1984-89; Penns Grove Schl Lang Arts Tchr 1989-; West Chester with Yth Writing Project 1984-; *ai:* Steering Comm; OAEA, PS 1985-; Sigma Tau Delta 1983-, Hnr Soc; PA Writing Project 1 Chamber PA Renaissance Faire 1989-; Written Several Plays, Musical; Directing & Costuming Local Theatre & Schls 8 Y Penns Grove HS 602 Garfield St Oxford PA 19363*

GEFFEN, PETER A., Founder; *b:* New York City, NY; *m:* K Kessler; *c:* Jonah, Daniel, Nessa; *ed:* Queens Coll (BA) His 1968; (MA) Rel Ed 1972; Alfred Adler Inst psychotherapy, Cnslng Cert Park Avenue Synagogue HS Prin 1967-85; Abraham Joshua Hes Assoc Dir 1985-92; The CRB Fnd Israel Experience Prgm Dir I Amer Jewish World Svc, Bd, Founding Mem; Southern Chrstn Ld 1965-66, Vol.

GEFRORER, CHARLES A., German Teacher; *b:* Chester, PA; Coll (BA) German 1964; Attn Westchester Univ, Penn St; *cr:* Pe India Vol Ed 1965-66; Interboro HS Ger Tchr 1967-; *ai:* Ger C

St Evaluation Comm Chm Various Areas 1970-; IEA, PSEA, NEA ATG 1970-; Okehocking Heritage Soc, Pres, Silver Turtle; Tchr of 1977-78; *office:* Interboro HS 16th Ave & Amosland Rd Prospect 9076

VILLIAM ARTHUR, Substance Abuse Coordinator; *b:* Toledo, Elizabeth Bailey; *c:* Nicole, Matthew, Mark, Andrea; *ed:* Mary oll (BA) Ed 1975; Univ of Toledo 27 Credit Hrs; OH Certfd n Consultant; Chemical Abuse Trng; *cr:* St Clement Elem Schl Jr Tchr 1968-73; St Francis De Sales HS Amer His Tchr 1974; on Local Schls Jr HS Sci Tchr 1975-89, Substance Abuse Coord *ai:* Co-Dir Amer Pride Prevention Team; Yth to Yth Drug Free, Pride Drug Free Group Dir; NEA, OEA 1975-; YMCA, Legion of IDE 1988-, Advy Bd, Parent to Parent; City of Toledo, Spirit of wd; Northeast Region Dept of Ed Innovative Programming; ed Article; Prevention Prgm Blast off Pride; *office:* Washington als 5530 Whitmer Dr Toledo OH 43613

ACH, GRETCHEN D., English Teacher; *b:* Cincinnati, OH; *c:* Renner; *ed:* Ctr Coll of KY (BA) Eng 1962; Univ of Cincinnati sych 1963; Attnd OH St Univ; *cr:* Princeton Local Schls Eng Tchr Springfield Local Schls Eng Tchr 1965-67; Canal Winchester ls Eng Tchr 1973-; *ai:* NEA, OEA, CWEA 1973-; Fiction Writers 993-; Schl Yrbk Dedication 1979; Milton Will Svc Awd 1984; anal Winchester HS 300 Washington St Canal Winchester OH

, ANN CHRISTINA, 8th Grade Science Teacher; *b:* Columbus, tanford Paul; *ed:* (BA) Biological Scis Comp 1969; 40 Grad Hrs H St Univ; *cr:* Wedgewood MS 8th Grd Sci Tchr 1969-; *ai:* Classroom Outdoor Ed Camp; Stu Cncl, 8th Grd Musical Co-Adv; e Sci Fair Chm; NEA, NSTA 1969-; Governor's Excl in Yth Sci ities Awd 1994-95; Natl Endowment of Arts Costume Design ice: Wedgewood MS 3771 Eakin Rd Columbus OH 43228

, STANFORD PAUL, Computer Awareness Teacher; *b:* OH; *m:* Tina Ann Christina Miles; *ed:* Kent St Univ (BS) Indstrl ; OH St Univ (MA) Educl Comm 1977; *cr:* Mc Guffey Jr HS rts, Metal Shop Tchr 1978-79; Westmoor MS Pupil Support Tchr 1979-82, Media Specialist 1982-87; Wedgewood MS Cmptr s 1987-; *ai:* Friday Friendly Photo Fantasy, Take Home-A-Little od Pride Photo Prgms; Ski Club; Soccer Team Coach; 8th Grd Production; Yrbk Adv; ABC, Tech Comms; NEA, OEA 1968-; est Civic Assn 1971-, Pres, Trustee; Westside Curb Recycling vuli Prof Dance Co 1973-87; Edctr of Yr 2 Times; Martha Holder Scholar; 2 Grants LEGO Tech Ingram, Martha Holden Jennings e: 230 Greenwood Dr Galloway OH 43119*

, JANE HENRY, Elementary Life Skills Teacher; *b:* Reading, Villiam M.; *c:* Thane C.; *ed:* Kutztown St Coll (BS) Spcl Ed & 1978; Masters Equivalency 1985; *cr:* Berks Cty Intermediate Unit Disabilities & EMR Tchr 1979-93; Twin Vly Schl Dist Life Skills 3-; *ai:* PSEA 1979-; NEA 1979-; TVEA 1993-; *office:* Twin Vly RD 3 Box 54 Elverson PA 19520

, MELISSA DOLCHIN, Science Instructor; *b:* Philadelphia, ichael John; *ed:* Temple Univ (BA) Bio 1991, (MA) Bio 1993; *cr:* g Area Comm Coll Sci Instr 1993-; *ai:* Sci, Nursing, Allied Hlth pts Division Facilitator; *office:* Harrisburg Area Comm Coll 735 nd St Lebanon PA 17042

G, CHRISTINE JOHNSON, Geometry Teacher; *b:* Salisbury, Timothy P.; *c:* Alyssa, Kaili; *ed:* Salisbury St Univ (BS) Math Ed ungstown St Univ Scndry Admin; *cr:* Reed MS Algebra, Cmptr 5-87; Hubbard HS Geometry Tchr 1987-; *ai:* Mentor Tchr; Stu ; OEA, NEA, HEA 1975-, Treas; OCTM 1987-; Tchr of Yr 1984; Tchr 1991-; Pres Exc Awd Nom; Ashland Golden Apple Wnnr; ubbard HS 350 Hall Ave Hubbard OH 44425*

EIN, WILLIAM JOSEPH, Reading Specialist; *b:* Erie, PA; *m:* rie Lastowski; *c:* William Jr.; *ed:* Edinboro Univ (BS) Scnry Ed, s 1974, (MED) Rdng Specialist 1980; *cr:* J. S. Wilson Schl Grd 7 s Tchr 1974-75; Wattsburg MS Rdng, Lang Arts Tchr 1975-; *ai:* cer Coach; NEA, PSEA, WEA 1974-; *home:* 2550 E 44th St Erie *

OHN DAVID, Instructor in Biblical Studies; *b:* Uniontown, PA; een M. Flaherty; *ed:* Malone Coll (BA) Pre-Seiminary, Bible 977; Talbot Theological Seminary (MA) Biblical Stud 1984; ible Inst; D Phil Prgm Oxford Grad Schl, D Phil Candidate; *cr:* Churches Pastoral Ministry, Ed 1977-85; Malone Coll Instr 1985-; enate; Vol Stu Bible Fellowship Group; Crisis Pregnancy Support Cty 1986-89, Exec Dir, Bd 1989-; Ezra Enterprises 1985-, Exec cator; 12 Articles Pub; 200 Educl Presentations Local Churches fice: Malone Coll 515 25th St NW Canton OH 44709

, JOHN RAYMOND, Retired Second Grade Teacher; *b:* Cty, PA; *m:* Mildred S. Conley; *c:* Sharon K., Bruce W., Christine ; *ed:* Kent St Univ (BS) Elem Ed 1970; Univ of Akron (MS) Elem 975; Univ of Ashland 15 Hrs; *cr:* Heritage Chrstn Schl 6th Grd ach 1969-71; East Canton Elem Schl 4th, 6th Grd Tchr 1971-75; chnical coll Coord Safety, Bus Math Tchr 1975-77; Lexington l 2nd, 4th Grd Tchr 1977-93; *ai:* Coord Sports Act; Schl Patrol; Local Schl Bd; East Canton Schl PTA, Pres; Strk Co PTA, VP.

, MARGE VITKO, Assoc Prof of English; *b:* Buffalo, NY; *m:* Jr.; *c:* Kevin, Gary, Matt; *ed:* D'Youville Coll (BA) Eng 1962; rroll Univ (MA) Eng 1964; Finishing PHD Dissertation ABD ern Reserve Univ 1993; *cr:* John Carroll Univ Lecturer 1964-89; s HS Eng Tchr 1889-90; Cuyahoga Comm Coll Assoc Prof Eng : Vice Chair of Joint Fac Senate; Governance Comm for Curr Requirement, Calendar; Adv Intnl Multicultural Club; Ed of Lib er Mentor; AAUP, NCTE 1990-; Choral Arts Soc of Cleve 1991-, , Treas 1995-; Sang with Blossom Festival Chorus, Cleveland a Chorus 1980-89; *office:* Cuyahoga Comm Coll 4250 Richmond and Hills OH 44122*

, PEGGY CHEVALIER, 4th Grade Language Arts Tchr; *b:* s, OH; *m:* R. Thomas; *c:* Matthew, Mallory; *ed:* OH Univ (BA) 1981; Cert Spec Rdgn, Coll Courses; *cr:* Bundy Elem Schl 2nd 1981-94; Coalton Elem Schl 4th Grade Tchr 1994-; *ai:* Wellston ssn 1981-; Jennings Scholar 1988-89; *home:* 1188 Mt Zion Rd OH 45640

, ROBIN S., High School English Teacher; *b:* NYC, NY; *m:* L.; *c:* Alexandra, Jacqueline; *ed:* SUNY at New Paltz (BA) Eng S) Scndry Ed 1982; *cr:* Middletown HS Eng Tchr 1978-; *ai:* Schl er Adv; MTA 1978-; NYSET 1978-; NYSEC 1992-, Tchr of Excl ice: Middletown HS Gardner Avenue Ext Middletown NY 10940

, ROMA RAE, Teacher & Science Coord; *b:* Auburn, NY; *ed:* St (BS) Elem Ed 1977, (MS) Elem Ed 1982; *cr:* Groton Elem Schl rd Tchr 1977-, K-6 Grd Sci Coord 1990-; *ai:* K-6 Grd Sci Comm STA; STANYS; NEA 1977-; SEPA 1992-, Presidential Awardee; mane Soc; ASPCA; Presidential Awds 1991-92; Natl Presidential 1992; Presenter Wkshps Sci Ed Integration 1987-; Rural Schls ner Speaker 1992; Presenter AAAS Conf 1993; *office:* Groton l 516 Elm St Groton NY 13073*

GEILING-YELLE, SONDRA SUE G., Associate Professor; *b:* NY; *m:* Raymond P. Yelle; *c:* Ryan; *ed:* SUNY at Alfred (AA) Office, Reporting 1973; Nazareth Coll (BS) Bus, Ec 1977; SUNY at Buffalo (MS) Bus 1980; *cr:* SUNY at Alfred Assoc Prof 1977-; *ai:* Curr Coord for Exec Office Admin, Word Processing-Med Office Admin; EBEA 1980-; NYSBFA 1977-; Comm Schl Org 1990-; Odyssey of Mind, Coach 1994-95; *office:* S U N Y Coll Of Tech At Alfred Alfred NY 14802

GEIS, GEORGE EDWARD, French Teacher; *b:* Pittsburgh, PA; *m:* Gwendolyn Jones; *c:* Gregg, Geoff; *ed:* Grove City Coll (BA) Fr & Soc Stud 1966; Attnd Duquesne Univ & Penn St Univ; *cr:* West Mifflin Area Schl Tchr 1965-; *ai:* Modern Lang Dept Chm; Planned Course Comm Co-Chm; Bsbl Asst Coach; PSEA & NEA 1966-; Elks 1970-; Amer Legion 1991-; West Mifflin Area HS Tchr of Month; Declaration of Achvmt Presented by PA St Senator Albert V Belan; Cert of Honor St Vincent Coll Great Tchr Recgntion Prgrm; Univ of Pitsbgh Schl of Edctn & Pitsbgh Post Gazette; *office:* West Mifflin Area HS 91 Commonwealth Ave West Mifflin PA 15122*

GEISE, LUCILLE MARIE NUNCIA,SND, Adult Rel Ed Tchr & Principal; *b:* Youngstown, OH; *ed:* St John Coll (BSE) Elem Ed 1945; Cath Univ of Amer (MA) Admin, Guid 1968; Diocese of Youngstown (MA) Rel Ed, Coord 1977; Notre Dame Coll 12 Credit Hrs CH Spirituality 1972; Comtemporary Rel Problems 1970; *cr:* St Boniface Schl Tchr 1936-38, 1953-54; St Michael Schl Tchr 1938-39, 1944-47; St Mary Schl Tchr 1939-40, 1941-; St Peter Schl Tchr 1940-43, 1955-56; St Mary Schl Tchr 1948-49; St Joseph Schl Tchr 1949-52, 1956-61; St Aloysius Schl Tchr 1954-55; Immaculate Heart of Mary Schl Tchr 1961-67; St James Schl Tchr 1968-70; *ai:* Chprsn St Mary Liturgy Comm; Team for Rite of Chrstn Initiation Adults; Massillon Adult Rel Ed Comm; Parish Cncl; Dept of Rel Ed 1936-; NCEA; Helped Writing Series; Master Thesis; Sister of Yr; Trng, Guiding New Tchrs in Classroom; *office:* St Mary Schl 726 1st St NE Massillon OH 44646

GEISELMAN, KATE BRADLEY, English Teacher; *b:* Cincinnati, OH; *m:* Eric; *c:* Ellen; *ed:* IN Univ (BA) Eng 1988, (MAT) Eng 1990; *cr:* WY HS Eng Tchr 1990-91; WY MS Eng Tchr 1990-91; YWCA Clermont Cty Teen Choices Coord 1991-92; WY HS Eng Tchr 1992-; *ai:* Magazine Adv; NEA 1992-; *office:* Wyoming HS 106 Pendery Ave Cincinnati OH 45215*

GEISER, LINDA WISE, Fourth Grade Teacher; *b:* Johnstown, PA; *m:* Michael Paul; *c:* Lindsay; *ed:* Univ of Pittsburgh at Johnstown (BS) Elem Ed 1988; Indiana Univ of PA (MED) Early Chldhd Ed 1995; *cr:* Cntrl Cath Schl 4th Grd Tchr 1988-; *ai:* New Tchrs Mentor; Keystone St Rdng Assn 1989-; Established & Publish Monthly Classroom Newspaper; Wrote & Produced Earth Day Spec on Pub Access Channel; Produced & Directed Several Plays.*

GEKOSKIE, ANDREW R., Director of Bands; *b:* Shamokin, PA; *m:* Katrina Betts; *c:* Nicholas; *ed:* Susquehanna Univ (BSME) Music Ed 1986; Grad Work at Hartt Schl of Music, Juilliard Schl of Music, Duquesne Univ, Butler Univ; *cr:* South Williamsport HS Dir of Bands 1986-89; Northwestern Lehigh HS Dir of Bands 1989-; Lehigh Vly Yth Wind Symphony Founder, Conductor & Music Dir 1990-; Campus Music Festivals Artistic Dir & Resident Conductor 1994-; *ai:* CoCurricular: Marching, Jazz & Concert Bands; Small Instrumental Ensembles; AV Dir; MENC 1986-; CBDNA 1989-; Conductors Guild 1989-; NW Music Task Force 1989-; CMBL Advy Bd 1989-94; NW Lehigh Restructing Comm 1995-; NW Comm Ed Bd 1995-; Consistently Rated Superior & Recognized Throughout Eastern Seaboard in Ensembles I Have Dir; *office:* Northwestern Lehigh HS 6493 Route 309 New Tripoli PA 18066*

GELBAUGH, DENISE LYNNE MARTIN, Fifth Grade Teacher; *b:* Carlisle, PA; *c:* Corey, Colin; *ed:* IN Univ of PA (BE) Elem Ed 1983; Shippensburg Univ (ME) Elem Ed 1988; *cr:* Mount Holly Elem Schl 5th Grd Tchr 1983-85; LeTort Elem Schl 5th Grd Tchr 1985-; *ai:* 5th Grd Play Dir; *office:* LeTort Elem Schl 623 W Penn St Carlisle PA 17013

GELBERG, DENISE SUSAN, 1st Grade Teacher; *b:* Brooklyn, NY; *m:* Charles Wilson; *c:* Elsa Gelberg Wilson; *ed:* Cornell Univ (BS) Labor Relations 1972; SUNY at Cortland (MS) Ed 1975; Cornell Univ (PHD) Labor Relations 1993; *cr:* Cornell Univ Tchng Assoc 1972-74; Trumansburg Cntrl Schl Tchr 1974-75; South Ctr Cntrl Schl Tchr 1975-76; Ithaca City Schl Dist Tchr 1976-; *ai:* Ithaca Tchrs Assn, 1st VP 1994-; NEA 1976-; Presidents Cncl of Cornell Women Grant 1992-93; Sage Fellowship Cornell Univ 1988-89; *office:* South Hill Elem Schl 520 Hudson St Ithaca NY 14850

GELDART, LETICIA CARA, English Teacher; *b:* Rockville Centre, NY; *ed:* Hofstra Univ at New College (BA) Soc Stud 1987; Hofstra Univ Schl of Ed (MS) Scndry Ed, Eng 1991; *cr:* Uniondale HS Eng Tchr 1993-94; Hempstead HS Eng Tchr 1994-; Uniondale Alternative HS Eng Tchr 1994-; *ai:* NCTE 1991-; Phi Beta Kappa 1987-; MENSA 1994-; *office:* Hempstead HS President St Hempstead NY 11550*

GELINEAU, CATHERINE ROSE (CERSOSIMO), English Teacher; *b:* Hartford, CT; *c:* Abbey E.; *ed:* St Joseph Coll (BA) Eng, Ed 1971; Cntrl CT St Univ 30 Hrs Eng; *cr:* Henry James Meml Jr HS Eng, Rdng Tchr 1971-83; Simsbury HS Eng Tchr 1983-; Simsbury Continuing Ed Eng Tchr 1975-; *ai:* Class Adv 1995; Jr Sr HS Transition Team; NEA, CEA, SEA 1971-; Terpsichore Dance, Theater Co 1993-; *office:* Simsbury HS 34 Farms Village Rd Simsbury CT 06070

GELTING, KAREN A., Spanish Teacher; *b:* Pottsville, PA; *m:* Jeffrey; *c:* Garrett; *ed:* Kutztown Univ (NS) Scndry Ed, Span 1972; PA Dept of Ed Instrl II 1984; 18 Credits Univ of Valencia Spain; 36 Post Grad Stud Credits; *cr:* Nativity BVM Schl Span Tchr 1981-87; Blue Mountain Area Schls Span Tchr 1975-76, 1987-; *ai:* Span Hnr Soc; Interational Club Adv; PSEA, NEA, AATSP, PMLA 1987-; Excl in Ed Innovative & Effective Learning Methods Awd; *office:* Blue Mountain HS RR 1 Box 1215 Schuylkill Haven PA 17972

GEMEREK, GAIL MARIE, Business & Home Economics Tchr; *b:* Buffalo, NY; *ed:* SUNY Coll at Buffalo (MSEd) Home Ec Ed 1980; Bus Cert 1991; 24 Credit Hrs in Elem Ed; *cr:* Ellicottville Cntrl Schl Bus, Home Ec Tchr 1983-; *ai:* MS Newsletter; 10th Grd Class Adv; AFT, Ellicottville Tchrs Assn 1983-; NYS Bus Tchrs Assn 1991-; Literacy Vols of Amer 1995; Amer Red Cross Instr; *office:* Ellicottville Cntrl Schl 5873 Route 219 S Ellicottville NY 14731

GENA, DAVID C., History Teacher; *b:* Olean, NY; *m:* Marsha Faye Balcom; *c:* Nathaniel, Andrew, Lindsay; *ed:* Houghton Coll (BA) His 1972; St Bonaventure Univ; *cr:* FRanklinville Cntrl Schl His Tchr 1974-; *ai:* Cty Govt Liaison 1974-91; Curr Contact Person 1989-; Discipline Comm Chm 1990-91; AFT 1974-; NYSUT 1974-, Pres; Franklinville Tchrs Assn 1980-, FTA Local Union; Educator of Yr 1991; *office:* Franklinville Central Schl 32 N Main Franklinville NY 14737

GENAKOS, MAUREEN E. DANAHY, 9th-12th Grade Math Teacher; *b:* Methuen, MA; *m:* John Theodore; *c:* John, Shane; *ed:* Univ of Lowell (BS) Scndry Ed & Math 1976; Univ of MA at Lovell; *cr:* Methuen HS Math Tchr 1976-80, 1984-86; Dover HS Math Tchr 1986-; *ai:* Class Adv; NEA; NCTM; NHATME; *office:* Dover HS 25 Alumni Dr Dover NH 03820

GENARO, TERESA A., HS English Teacher; *b:* Yonkers, NY; *ed:* Skidmore Coll (BA) Eng 1987; Coll of William & Mary (MA) Eng 1993; *cr:* Phillips Acad Summer Session Tchr, Coord Writing Ctr, Expository Writing 1989-; Oldfields Schl HS Eng Tchr 1990-95; Amer Schl HS Eng Tchr 1995-; *ai:* NCTE, Natl Writing Ctr Assn, Natl Writing Project 1990-; Papers Given Natl Peer-Tutoring Conf 1989, 1993, Mid-Atlantic Writing Ctr Assn 1994; Article Pub 1993; *office:* American Schl in London 2-8 Loudoun Rd London NW8 0NP England XX*

GENAWAY, MARY-LOU TOURTELLOTTE, Agriculture Teacher; *b:* Providence, RI; *m:* Barry John; *ed:* Cornell Univ (BS) Animal Sci, Ag Ed 1985, (MAT) Ag Ed 1991; *cr:* Rushford Cntrl Schl Ag Tchr 1985-90; Pioneer HS Ag Tchr 1990-; *ai:* Co-Adv Pioneer Chptr FFA; NHS Comm; NY Ag Tchrs ssn 1985-, Treas 1995; NVATA 1993-; NYS Ag Ed Governing Bd, Dist Trustee.

GENDREAU, MARIANNE, Business Dept Chprsn & Tchr; *b:* Cambridge, MA; *m:* Frank A. Jr.; *c:* Michelle Elyse; *ed:* Aquinas Jr Coll (AA) Medical Secretarial 1974; Suffolk Univ (BS) Bus Ed 1976; *cr:* Arlington HS Bus Tchr 1976-77; Matignon HS Bus Dept Chprsn & Tchr 1977-; *ai:* Leukemia Type A Thon Spon; Bus Club & Future Bus Ldrs of America Moderator; Dress Code & Schlsp Selection Comms; NEA, MTA & NBEA 1976-; BATA 1977-; *office:* Matignon H S 1 Matignon Rd Cambridge MA 02140*

GENDRON, REBEKAH JOHN, Technology Education Teacher; *b:* Providence, RI; *m:* John B.; *c:* John H., Sarah R.; *ed:* RI Coll (BS) Indstrl Arts 1982, (MED) Indstrl Ed 1990; *cr:* The Sawyer Schl Drafting Instr 1982-84; Warwick Schl Dept Long Term Math Sub Tchr 1985-86; Riverside Jr HS Tech Ed Tchr 1986-; *ai:* Drama Club Dir, Stu Cncl Advs; NEA, EPEA 1986-; RITEA 1982-; Concerned Women for Amer 1994-; *office:* Riverside Jr HS 179 Forbes St E Providence RI 02915

GENELLO, DENISE MARIA ANN, Instructional Support Teacher; *b:* Scranton, PA; *m:* Stephen Hollis; *ed:* Marywood Coll (BS) Spec Ed, Elem Ed 1979; Marywood Grad Schl (MS) Rdng Ed 1987; Penn St Grad Schl Educl Courses 36 Credit Hrs Beyond Masters; *cr:* Wallenpaupack Primary Ctr Instrl Support Tchr 1 Yr; WallenpaupackMS 7-8 Grd Lit Tchr 2 Yrs; Mid Vly Elem Ctr Instrl Support Tchr 2 Yrs, 6th Grd Tchr 1 Yr; Clearview Elem Schl 4th Grd Tchr 5 Yrs; Mid Vly Schls 1st Grd Tchr 1 Yr; *ai:* Mid Sts Chair Several Comms; NEA, NRA 1980-; Keystone Rdng Assoc 1990-; 1st Place Statewide Amer Yth Citizenship Competition 1994; *home:* 1809 E Gibson St Scranton PA 18510*

GENERALLI, GENEVIEVE TAMBURR, Third Grade Teacher; *b:* Newark, NJ; *m:* Ernest; *c:* Roseanna Burlingham, Janet, Julie Dominic, Ernest Jr., Victoria Loxton, Robert; *ed:* Montclair St Univ (BA) Bus Ed, Elem Ed 1949; 12 Addl Hrs; *cr:* Bogota Schl 5th Grd Tchr 1949-52; Clifton Schl 3-5th Grd Tchr 1974-; *ai:* Affirmative Action Rep; Stu Inventions Through Ed Coord; Lang Arts Curr, Schl Goals Comm; NEA, NJEA, PCTA 1974-; CTA, IRA 1974-, Del; UNICO 1970-, Pres, VP, Schlsp Comm; Montclair St Univ Alumni Assn 1949-; Tech for Children St Grant; A+ For Kids Grant; Edctr of Yr; Governor's Tchr Recognition Grant; *office:* School No 14 99 St Andrews Blvd Clifton NJ 07012*

GENERAZZO, ARLENE DIAMOND, Fourth Grade Educator; *b:* Malden, MA; *m:* Ronald A.; *ed:* Long Island Univ (BS) Psych Ed 1969; Boston St Coll (MED) Ed 1974; Addl Hrs Tufts Univ; *cr:* Stratten Schl Edctr 1969; Parmenter Schl Edctr 1969-70; Swan Schl Edctr 1971-86; Dame Schl Edctr 1986-87; Roberts MS Edctr 1986-87; Roberts MS Librn & Edctr 1993-94; Osgood Schl Edctr 1987-; *ai:* Lang Arts Framework Comm; Medford Tchrs Assn 1971-, Rep; MA Tchrs Assn, NEA 1971-; Medford Historical Soc 1986-, VP; Royall House Assn 1993-; Book: Looking at Olde Medford And It's Past'; 5 Certs; *office:* Osgood Elem Schl 101 4th St Medford MA 02155

GENERELLI, DENISE, Third Grade Teacher; *b:* Germany ; *m:* Frank J.; *c:* Alexandra; *ed:* Monmouth Coll (BS) Elem Ed 1984; 30 Credit Hrs Brookdale Comm Coll & Middletown Twp; *cr:* Bayview Schl 1st-3rd Grd Tchr 1985-; *ai:* PAC Comm Asst 1994-; MTEA 1985-; NJ Tchr of the Yr Awd 1988; *office:* Bayview Elem Schl 300 Leonardville Rd Belford NJ 07718

GENESE, EUGENE J., Business & Soc Stud Teacher; *b:* Worcester, MA; *m:* Nancy; *c:* Danny, Robert, Matthew; *ed:* Worcester Jr Coll (AA) Bus 1973; Worcester St (BS) Soc Stud 1977, (MA) Soc Stud 1983; 45 Credit Hrs; *cr:* Mechanics Natl Bank Ofcr 1965-73; Millbury Pub Schl Tchr 1981-; Worc Pub Schls Tchr 1981-; *ai:* Yrbk & Class Adv 1996; NEA 1981-; MA Tchr Assn 1981-.

GENITO, DEBORAH JOHNSON, Art Teacher; *b:* Natrona Heights, PA; *m:* Joseph R.; *c:* Kristen B., Shelley G.; *ed:* Edinboro St Coll (BS) Art Ed 1972; Slippery Rock St Coll Cert Elem Ed; *cr:* Hancock Cty Schls Elem Art Tchr 1972-76; Chester Intermediate Schl 6th Grd Tchr 1976-77; Kiski Area Schl Dist Elem Art Tchr 1987-88; Weinels Elem Schl 2nd Grd Tchr 1988-89; Huston MS Art Tchr 1991-; *ai:* MS Drama Club Dir; Stu Assistance Prgm Team; NEA, PSEA 1991-, Bldg Rep; *office:* Huston MS Puckety Church Rd Lower Burrell PA 15068

GENIUSZ, JEAN ANN, Biology Teacher; *b:* Cleveland, OH; *c:* Terri Bish, Carolyn, Tammi Wilson; *ed:* Bowling Green St Univ (BS) Hlth, PE, Bio 1964; Wright St Univ (MS) Stu Lrng & Behavior 1982, (MS) Sci 1993, (EdS) Curr, Supervision 1995; *cr:* Sheffield-Sheffield Lake Local Hlth, PE Tchr 1964-65; Northmont Local Schls Hlth, PE Tchr 1965-66; Fairborn Local Schl Hlth, PE Tchr 1967-69; Huber Heights, Fairborn, Mad River Locals Sub Tchr 1970-79; Huber Heights City Schls Hlth, Bio Tchr 1979-; *ai:* Mentor Tchr; NEA, OEA 1980-; NSTA 1990-; SECO 1994-; Beavercreek Wetlands Assn 1994-; Team Presentor Sci Ed Conf, Smart, Alliance for Ed, Univ of Dayton Natl Sci Fnd, Miami Univ OH Bd of Regents Grants; *office:* Wayne HS 5400 Chambersburg Rd Dayton OH 45424*

GENIVIVA, FRANK J., Biology Teacher; *b:* Ellwood City, PA; *m:* Betty Kay; *c:* Channa Rae, Patty Jean; *ed:* Baldwin Wallace (BS) Bio 1964; Attnd Slippery Rock Univ, Univ of IN, Penn St; *cr:* Beaver Area Schls Tchr 1965-1971; Ellwood City Area Schls Tchr 1971-; *ai:* Photo Club; Cross Cntry Coach; AFT 1989-; Wolves Clum 1965-; PA Commonwealth Parnter; *office:* Ellwood City Area Schls 501 Crescent Ave Ellwood City PA 16117*

GENOVESI, JOSEPH PHILIP, Teacher; *b:* Greenville, PA; *m:* Eleanor; *c:* Mark Andrew, Donald Joseph, Jacqueline; *ed:* Thiel Coll (BA) Ger 1961; Westminster Coll (MED) Guid 1970; Univ of Akron 26 Hrs Elem Prin; *cr:* US Army Reg 1989; Norwalk HS Guid Cnslr 3 Yrs; St Pauls HS Tchr 6 Yrs; *ai:* Wrestling; Arts Cncl; NEA 1972-; Montessori Schl 1975-, VP Bd; NHS; Delta Phi Alpha; Natl Ger Honorary Soc; *home:* 28 Valley Park Dr Norwalk OH 44857

GENT, PAMELA JOYCE, Asst Professor of Special Ed; *b:* Youngstown, OH; *m:* Richard W.; *c:* Stephanie R., Ethan R.; *ed:* Youngstown St Univ (BSEd) Spec & Elem Ed 1980; Kent St Univ (MED) Spec Ed 1983; Working on PHD Spec Ed; *cr:* Boardman Local Schls Spec Ed Tchr 1980-83; Kent St Univ Demonstration Classroom Tchr 1983-84; Family Child Learning Ctr Coord of Tchrs 1984-85; Kent St Univ Grad Asst 1985-88; Clarion Univ Asst Prof of Sped 1988-; *ai:* Chair Presidential Commission on Disabilities; Co-Coord Summer SMILES; Courses & Prgms of Stud Comm; Presidential Affirmative Action Comm; APSCUF 1988-; CEC 1985-; TASH 1984-; AAMR 1986-; Boardman Local Schls PTA, Ballet Western Reserve Parents Group 1994-; Montessori Schl Parents Group 1989-; PA Campus Compact, OH Dept of MR-DD Grants; Articles Pub; Handbook Pub, Won Honorable Mention; *office:* Clarion Univ Of PA 110-B Sped Clarion PA 16214*

GENTHNER, FREDERIC, Fifth Grade Teacher; *b:* Rochester, NY; *ed:* SUNY at Geneseo (BA) Ed 1965; 30 Addl Hrs; *cr:* Allen Creek Schl

5th-6th Grd Tchr 1965-85; Pittsford Cntrl Schls Prgms for Academically Talented Stdnts Coord 1985-87; Thornell Road Schl 5th Grd Tchr 1987-; *ai:* Bldg Ldrshp Team; Grd Level Chm; Safety Patrol Adv; Mentor Tchr; AFT, NY St Tchrs Assn 1965-; Phi Delta Kappa 1990-; Pittsford PTO, Lifetime Mbrshp; Local, St Schl Dists, Belgrade Yugoslavia Wkshp Presenter; *office:* Thornell Road Schl 431 Thornell Rd Pittsford NY 14534

GENTILE, CHRISTOPHER D., Earth & Space Sci Hnrs Tchr; *b:* Newark, NJ; *ed:* Kean Coll of NJ (BA) Earth, Space Sci 1990; K-12 Earth, Space Sci Cert 1990; *cr:* Franklin HS Earth, Space Sci Tchr 5 Yrs; *ai:* Stokes St Forest Cnslr; Sci League Adv; NJEA, NEA Franklin Tchrs Assn 1991-; Nom Disney's Outstdng Tchr Awd 1994-95; *office:* Franklin HS 415 Francis St Somerset NJ 08873

GENTILE, DONALD LOUIS, Mathematics Teacher; *b:* Westerly, RI; *ed:* Univ of RI (BA) Math Ed 1973; URI (MA) Math Ed 1976; *cr:* South Kingstown Jr HS Math Tchr 1974; South Kingstown HS Math Tchr 1975-; *ai:* Pez Club Coord; Math Team, Surfing Club Adv; NEA 1975-.

GENTILE, JACQUE ANDERSON, Third Grade Teacher; *b:* Portsmouth, OH; *m:* Pat; *c:* Betsy, Sarah; *ed:* OH Univ (BS) Ed 1972; Attnd Xavier Univ, Miami Univ, Bowling Green & Wright St Univ; *cr:* Greenhills-Forest Park City Schls 3rd Grd Tchr 1972-77; John F Dumont, Madeira City Schls 3rd Grd Tchr 1984-; *ai:* K-3rd Grd Soc Stud Curr Coord; IRA 1990-.

GENTILE, PATRICIA, Junior High Teacher; *b:* Cleveland, OH; *ed:* Baldwin-Wallace Coll (BSEd) Elem Ed 1982; Catechist Cert; *cr:* St Paschal Baylon Sixth Grd Tchr 1982-86; Notre Dame Elem Schl Jr HS Tchr 1986-88; St Mary Schl Jr HS Tchr 1989-95; Metro Cath Parish Schl Jr HS Tchr 1995-; *ai:* Notre Dame Ed Assn 1991-; *office:* Metro Cath Parish Schl 1910 W 54th St Cleveland OH 44102

GENTILE, RICHARD B., French & Spanish Teacher; *b:* New York, NY; *m:* Antoinette Zasa; *ed:* SUNY at Stony Brook (BA) Fr 1965; St Johns Univ (MA) Fr; Univ de Neuchatel Switzerland Cert Fr 1966; Grad Work in Span at Inst de Cultura Hispanica at Madrid; Grad Work in Fr, Eng at Univ De Neuchatel Switzerland; *cr:* Hicksville HS Fr, Span, Eng 1966-; *ai:* Fr Club Adv; NEANY Bldg Del & Negotiator; Prins Site-Based Mngmt Comm; Fr Honor Soc Adv; Long Island Lang Tchrs 1980-, Pres, Treas, Founding Mem; NY St Assn of F L Tchrs 1965-, Various Comm; AATF, AATSP 1965-; Co-Author Story of My Life, Suibez-Moi, Authentic Assessment for the Intermediate Level in French; *office:* Hicksville HS 180 Division Ave Hicksville NY 11801

GENTILI, RITA KLIMASEWSKI, Elementary Counselor; *b:* Waterbury, CT; *m:* Dennis R.; *c:* Jill A., Jodi M.; *ed:* Cntrl CT St Univ (BA) Elem Ed 1970; Providence Coll (MS) Guid Cnslr 1975; RI Coll 20 Addl Credits; *cr:* Andrew St Schl 2nd Grd Tchr 1970-71; Pothier Elem Schl 3rd Grd Tchr 1971-87; George St Schl 3rd Grd Tchr 1987-91; Citizen's Meml Elem Schl Cnslr 1991-; *ai:* Schl Improvement, Crisis Intervention Teams 1995-; AFT Woonsocket 1971-; RI Mental Hlth Cnslng Assn, Amer Cnslng Assn 1992-; PTO 1991-; *office:* Citizens Meml Elem Schl 250 Winthrop St Woonsocket RI 02895

GENTILUCCI, THEODORE C., Physical Education Teacher; *b:* Paterson, NJ; *m:* Mary Ann Stastny; *c:* Duane, Todd, Gary, Steven, Mary Beth; *ed:* Montclair St Coll (BA) PE, Hlth 1964; Azuza Pacific Coll 10 Credit Hrs; Somerset Cty Tchrs 7 Credit Hrs; *cr:* Ridgefield Pub Schls PE K-8 Tchr 1964-66; US Army Lt Charge Prsnl Office 1966-69; Bridgewater Raritan Schls PE 6-8th Grd Tchr 1969-95, PE 3-6th Grd Tchr 1995-; *ai:* 6th Grd Girls Sftbl, Bsktbl, Floor Hockey, Boys & Girls Track & Field Coach; Ike Comm Chm; 2 Indermediate Schls After Schl Sports Prgm Coord; NEA, NJEA 1964-; Somerset Cty TA, BREA 1969-; Parish St Matthias, Marriage Prep Prgm Coord 1984; *office:* Eisenhower Intermediate Schl Eisenhower Ave Bridgewater NJ 08807

GENTZEL, MARK JOSEPH, Fifth Grade Teacher; *b:* Huntingdon, PA; *m:* Sandra Kay Orndorf-Gentzel; *ed:* Lock Haven Univ (BSEd) Elem Ed 1988; 33 Post-Grad Credit Hrs Penn St Univ; *cr:* Bellefonte Area SChol Dist 5th Grd Tchr 8 Years; *ai:* Homework Club; Union Rep at Large; IM Ldr; Steering Comm; Lead Tchr; Steering Comm; Sunshine Club Caretaker; PSEA, NEA, BAEA 1988-, Rep At Large; ASCD 1993-; Kappa Delta Pi 1987-; Grace United Meth Church 1970-; Tchr, Var Comms; Sundy Schl Supt; *home:* 1232 Daruss Dr Bellefonte PA 16823

GEORGE, DANIELLE RUTH (BARONE), Spanish Teacher; *b:* Pittsburgh, PA; *m:* Rodney Vernon; *c:* Joseph Thomas; *ed:* IN Univ of PA (BSED) Scndry Ed, Span 1990; Undergraduate Univ of Pittsburgh 1984-87; 24 Post-Grad Credits Millersville Univ, Wilkes Univ, Carlow Coll; *cr:* Dover Area HS Span Tchr 1990-; *ai:* Chrldng Coach 1990-95; Class Adv 1991-95; Spon, Cnslr Frgn Travel Coasta Rica 1995, Mexico 1997; NEA 1990-.

GEORGE, DAVID F., Professor of English; *b:* Brierfield, England; *m:* Rita Lagace; *c:* Paul, Alison; *ed:* Univ of Manchester (BA) Eng 1961, (MA) Eng 1962; Univ of London (PHD) Eng 1966; Theology Diploma 1967; *cr:* Pomona Coll Asst Prof 1966-69; Univ of Western Ontario Asst Prof 1969-72; Howard Univ Asst Prof 1974-76; Univ of MN Asst Prof 1978-79; Fisk Univ Asst Prof 1979-80; Urbana Univ Prof 1981-; *ai:* Midwest Modern Lang Assn; Recors of Early Eng Drama; Shakespeare Assn of Amer; Folger, NEH, Andrew W. Mellon Fund Flwshps; Fulbright Travel Grant; 30 Articles, 2 Books Pub; *office:* Urbana Univ College Way Urbana OH 43078

GEORGE, DEBORAH DEE, Cosmetology Teacher; *b:* Johnstown, PA; *ed:* IN Univ of Pa (BS) Ed 1993; Tri-Cty Sch of Cosmetology PA Cosmetologist License; Altoona Beauty Schl PA Cosme Tchr License; *cr:* Empire Beauty Schls Tchr 1971-72; Franco Beauty Schls Supvr, Tchr 1974-77; Altoona Beauty Schl Supvr, Tchr 1977-80; Admiral Peary AVTS Supvr, Tchr 1980-; *ai:* NEA 1981-; PSEA 1981-, Local Treas; NCA, PCA 1990-, Local Pres; Women's Help Ctr 1990-, Annual Fundraising #1 3 Yrs; PA St Bd of Cosmetology 1985-90; 1st Voc Tchr Represent Pub Ed PA; Sec to Bd 1988-90; Ed Comm, PA St Cosmetology Newsletter Chprsn; *office:* Admiral Peary Area Voc Tech 948 Ben Franklin Hwy 422 N West St Ebensburg PA 15931*

GEORGE, DONALD P., Mathematics Chprsn & Tchr; *b:* Youngstown, OH; *m:* Karen K. Jacob; *c:* Carrie L., Donald P. Jr., Jacob M., Cassie L.; *ed:* Youngstown St Univ (BSEd) Math 1975, (MSEd) Curr & Supervision 1986; Attnd OH Univ, Akron, Kent St; T3-CMS Participant; *cr:* Pt Clinton City Schls HS Math Tchr 1976-78; Canfield HS Math & Comp Sci Tchr 1978-82; ITT Tech Inst Chief Instr & Data Processing 1982-87; Canfield HS Math Tchr & Dept Head 1987-; *ai:* Stu Cncl Adv; HS Blood Drive Coord; Curr Cncl; Area Tech Rep; Math Rep; OH Cncl Tchrs of Math 1980-; Canfield Ed Assn 1987-, VP & Pres; OEA, NEA & EOCTM 1987-; Holy Name Soc; IFSMACSE 2 Yr Ed Pgm at Kent St; Educl Resource Ctr Workshops; *office:* Canfield HS 100 Cardinal Dr Canfield OH 44406*

GEORGE, DOREEN ELEONORA (RAYMOND), Teacher; *b:* New Bedford, MA; *m:* Robert B.; *c:* Edward, Robert; *ed:* Our Lady of Elms (BA) Bio, Sec Ed 1983; *cr:* Portsmouth HS Bio I, Hnrs Bio I, Bio II, Botany, Oceans Tchr 1984-; *ai:* NEA, NHEA 1984-; *office:* Portsmouth HS 50 Andrew Jarvis Dr Portsmouth NH 03801

GEORGE, JEFFREY CRAIG, 8th Grade Science Teacher; *b:* Mount Vernon, OH; *m:* Helen M. Delbauve; *c:* Lisa George-Clipse; *ed:* Kent St Univ (BS) Ed, Bio, Hlth 1969, (MS) Bio 1975; *cr:* Euclid City Schls 7-8 Grd Sci Tchr 1970-74; Mt Vernon City Schls 8th Grd Sci Tchr 1975-; *ai:* NEA, OEA, NCOEA, MVEA 1979-; *office:* Mt Vernon MS 301 N Mulberry St Mount Vernon OH 43050

GEORGE, JOHN JOSEPH, Athletic Dir & Spec Ed Teacher; *b:* Monogahela, PA; *m:* Doreen Smith-George; *c:* John David; *ed:* St Vincent Coll (BS) Sociology, Bus 1985; CA Univ of PA (MED) Spec Ed 1988; 36 Grad Credits Cnslng; 12 Credits Toward Admin Prin Cert; *cr:* Cntrl Greene Schl Dist Spec Ed Tchr 1988-95, Ath Dir 1995-; *ai:* Head Var Bsbl 1988-, Head Var Soccer 1990-93, Asst Var Ftbl 1993-94, Head, Asst Jr HS, Var Bsktbl 1989-93 Coach; SADD Dir 1988-90; Stu Assisted Prgms 1989-95; NEA, PSEA 1989-; Washington Presbyn Church 1989-; *home:* 272 Preston Rd Washington PA 15301

GEORGE, JOHN KEITH, Biology Teacher; *b:* Indiana, PA; *m:* Mary; *c:* Rebecca, John, Sarah, Justine, Megan; *ed:* Millsaps Coll (BS) Bio 1969; IN Univ of PA (MED) Bio 1975; Southwestern Univ (PHD) Environmental Stud 1982; *cr:* Hempfield HS Bio Tchr 26 Yrs; *office:* Hempfield Area Sr HS Rd 6 Box 77 Greensburg PA 15601

GEORGE, JOHN W., Fifth Grade Teacher; *b:* Warsaw, NY; *m:* Paulette Narkiewicz; *c:* Erica, Jonathan; *ed:* SUNY at Geneseo (BS) Ed, Bio 1972; Coll of St Rose (MS) Philosophy of Ed 1975; *cr:* Glen Worden Schl 6th Grd Tchr 1972-75; Mohawk Schl 5th Grd Tchr 1976-80; Glendaal Elem Schl 5th Grd Tchr 1980-; *ai:* Italian Exch Prgm; NYSUT 1972-; Knights of Columbus 1993-; *home:* 509 Swaggertown Rd Schenectady NY 12302*

GEORGE, JUDITH ANN, Second Grade Teacher; *b:* Warren, OH; *ed:* Kent St Univ (BE) Elem Ed 1968, (MS) Guidance & Counseling 1972; *cr:* Niles City Schls Bonham Elem 2nd Grd Tchr 1968-; *ai:* Drug Free OH Week Coord; Festival of Trees Co-Chm; NEA, OEA 1968-; Niles Classroom Tchr Assn 1968-, Negotiations Team, Building Rep; Jennings Scholar 1975-76; A Plus Tchr Awd Trumbull Cty, OH 1995; *office:* S. J. Bonham Elem Schl 120 E Margaret St Niles OH 44446

GEORGE, PATRICIA KARLOVETZ, English Teacher; *b:* Fremont, OH; *m:* David; *c:* L. Kelly; *ed:* Bowling Green Univ (BA) Eng 1968, (MA) Rdng 1988; 15 Addl Hrs Guid, Cnslng; *cr:* Bataan Elem 3rd-4th Grd Tchr 1986-88; Port Clinton HS Eng Tchr 1988-89, 1995-; *ai:* 4 Yr Class of 1996 Adv; NHS Bd; IAT; Natl Tchr of Eng Assn 5 Yrs; OH Cncl Tchrs of Eng Lang Assn 7 Yrs; Cty Wide Top Ten Tchr; *office:* Port Clinton HS 821 S Jefferson St Port Clinton OH 43452

GEORGE, ROBERT MEREDITH, PE Teacher & Head Coach; *b:* Imperial, PA; *m:* Kathleen Spearman; *c:* Caitlin Meredith, Laura Ruth, Kelly Marie; *ed:* Frostburg St Univ (BA) Hlth & PE 1981; Masters Equivalency Montgomery Cty Inservice Pgm 1994; *cr:* Montgomery Cty Pub Schls PE Tchr 1981-; Rockville HS Bsktbl & Ftbl Coach 1982-; Richard Montgomery HS Bsbl Coach 1987-; *ai:* Head Var Bsktbl & JV Ftbl Coach; Richard Montgomery HS Head Var Bsbl Coach; NEA 1982-; MSTA 1982-; Richard Montgomery HS Div 3A Champions Var Bsbl 1987 & 1991; *home:* 17008 Olde Mill Run Derwood MD 20855

GEORGE, RONALD A., Art Teacher; *b:* Vineland, NJ; *m:* Jane Pompilio; *c:* Michele, Michael; *ed:* Glassboro St Coll (BA) Art Ed 1969; *cr:* Washington Twp HS Art Tchr 1992-; *ai:* Natl Art Hnr Soc Adv; NEA, NJEA, GCEA 1992-; *home:* 43 Union St Mount Holly NJ 08060

GEORGE, STANLEY EMERSON, 5th-12th Grade Music Educator; *b:* Wauseon, OH; *m:* Konnie Diane Nicholson-George; *ed:* Bowling Green St Univ (BA) Music Performance 1989; Music Ed Cert 1991, 10 Hrs Music Performance; 3 Hrs Ed Drake Univ; *cr:* Elmwood Local Schls Bands Dir 1992-95; St John's Jesuit HS Asst Band Dir 1995-; *ai:* Jazz Band, Men's Chorus, Asst Marching Band Dir; Bible Stud Adv; OH Music Edctrs Assn, NEA 1992-; OH Natl Guard Enlisted Assn 1996-; OH Air Natl Guard 555th Band 1994-, Sr Airman, Distngd Awd; OH Arts Cncl Grant; Toledo Concerto Competition Winner; Semi-Finalist of Natl Fischoff Chamber Music Competition; The President's Own Marine Corps Band Finalist; *office:* St John's Jesuit HS 5901 Airport Hwy Toledo OH 43615

GEORGE, TED DAIB, US History & Law Teacher; *b:* Beckley, WV; *m:* Sue Ann Collins; *c:* Ryan, Ashley; *ed:* Beckley Coll (BA) His1964; Marshall Univ (BA) His 1967; Washington Coll (MA) His 1973; Law Classes LaSalle Coll; Extra Ed Class Univ of DE; *cr:* Dover HS Tchr 1967-; *ai:* Phi Delta Kappa 1980-; Governor's Comm to Reform DE Courts; *office:* Dover HS 625 Walker Rd Dover DE 19901

GEORGE, THOMAS C., Geography Teacher; *b:* Wilkes Barre, PA; *m:* Claudette M.; *c:* Sarah J., Jessica E.; *ed:* Mansfield St Univ (BS) Scndry Soc Stud 1973; 34 Addl Hrs PA St Univ, Wilkes Univ, Mansfield St Univ; *cr:* Montrose Jr Sr HS Soc Stud Tchr 1974-; *ai:* Sr Class Adv; Instruction Scndry Support Team; Discipline Comm; Mentor Tchr; Natl Cncl Geo Ed 1986-; NEA, PA SEA 1974-; Triton Vol Fire Co, Lighthouse Chrstn Singers, Republican Committeeman 1991-; Tunkhannock Presbyn Ch 1984-, Elder Prsnl Comm; PA Game Comm Coop, Game Birds 1979-; *office:* Montrose Area Jr/Sr HS RR 3 Box 28 Montrose PA 18801

GEORGIADIS-LIBECCI, GEORGETTE, Fourth Grade Teacher; *b:* New York, NY; *ed:* Montclair St Univ (BA) Eng 1985; William Paterson Coll (MAT) Ed 1993; *cr:* Mother Cabrini Schl 8th Grd Tchr 1991-94; Schl 6 4th Grd Tchr 1994-; *office:* Schl 6 Oakdene Ave Cliffside Park NJ 07010*

GEORGIANA, SAM, Chemistry Instructor; *b:* Pittsburgh, PA; *ed:* CA Univ (BS) Chem, Ed 1973, (MS) Chem, Ed 1982; *cr:* Kent Cty HS Sci Tchr 1973-74; US Steel Chemist 1975-76; Bethel Park HS Chem Instr 1978-; *ai:* AFT, PAFT 1978-; BPFT 1978-, Treas; PSTA; NSTA; *office:* Bethel Park HS 309 Church Rd Bethel Park PA 15102

GEPHART, RAYMOND G., 9th Grd Team English Teacher; *b:* Williamsport, PA; *m:* Susan Jane Nicholes; *c:* Nicholas, Jamie, Kaitlyn; *ed:* Lock Haven St Coll (BS) Comm 1973; 65 Credit Hrs; *cr:* Bellefonte Area Schls Eng, Scndry 1974-; *ai:* NEA, PSEA 1974-; Round Table Presentations 1992, 1994, 1995; *home:* 351 E Bishop St Bellefonte PA 16823

GERAGHTY, JAMES JOSEPH, Social Studies Teacher; *b:* Newport, RI; *m:* Nancy Elizabeth Jones; *c:* Patrick, Amy, Christopher; *ed:* Providence Coll (BA) His 1965, (MA) His 1966; *cr:* Barrington HS Soc Stud Tchr 1966-; *ai:* NEA 1966-; *office:* Barrington HS Lincoln Ave Barrington RI 02806

GERAN, JOHN JAMES, Mathematics Teacher; *b:* South Amboy, NJ; *m:* Patricia Vicari; *c:* Gregory, Geran; *ed:* Kean Coll (BA) Math 1982; *cr:* Matawan Regnl HS Math Tchr 1982-; *ai:* Frosh Ftbl & Sftbl Head Coach; NJEA 1982-; NEA 1982-; MRTA 1982-; *office:* Matawan Regional HS 450 Atlantic Ave Matawan NJ 07747*

GERAN, PATRICIA VICARI, Math Department Chairperson; *b:* Newark, NJ; *m:* John James; *c:* Gregory; *ed:* Seton Hall Univ (BS) Math 1978; *cr:* Red Bank Cath HS Math Tchr 1978-89, Math Chprsn 1989-; *ai:* Tchr, Fr Class Adv; Curr Comm; AMTNJ, NCTM 1992-; *home:* 479 Alexander Rd Brick NJ 08724

GERARDI, JOSEPHINE A., Family & Consumer Science Tchr; *b:* Warren, PA; *ed:* Mansfield Uni (BS) Home Ecs Ed 1969; IN Uni of PA (MED) Home Ecs Ed 1979; *cr:* Warren Cty Schl Dist Tchr 1969-; *ai:* Internal Coord Acrrediation for Growth Mid Sts Assn; WCEA, PSEA, NEA 1969-; APESA; PFCSA; Natl Ski Patrol 1986-, Ambassador Awd; Amer Quilters Sco; Assn of Coll Women, Mentorship Comm; Loranger Tchr of Yr Awd 1994; *office:* Warren Cty Schl Dist 227 College St Youngsville PA 16371

GERBER, TRACEY LYNN, French Teacher; *b:* Bridgeton, NJ; P.; *ed:* Montclair St Coll (BA) Fr 1989; Addl Stud in Fr Towards *cr:* Schuylere-Colfax Jr HS Fr Tchr 1990-92; Wayne-Hills Hig Tchr 1992-; *ai:* Fr Club, Hnr Soc Adv 1992-; Natl Assn of T 1990-; *office:* Wayne Hills HS 272 Berdan Ave Wayne NJ 07470

GERBERRY, KATHRYN SCHRUM, Biology I & Chemistry T Youngstown, OH; *m:* Ronald V.; *c:* Deanna Lynn, Ronald V. J Schrum; *ed:* Youngstown St Univ (BS) Biological Sci 19 Youngstown St Univ; *cr:* Villa Maria HS Sci, Math Tchr 1974- Mc Kinley HS Bio, Chem Tchr 1975-88; Boardman HS Bio, C 1988-; *ai:* NEA; OEA; BEA; *office:* Boardman HS 7777 Glen Boardman OH 44512

GERBES, ANGELIKA RENATE, Dance History Professor; *b* Germany; *c:* Arnika R. Brown; *ed:* CT Coll (BA) Fr 1964; Mills C Dance 1966; OH St Univ (PHD) Theatre, Dance 1972; Labanotat Cert 1968; *cr:* Univ of IA Dance Technique, Labanotation Instr Denison Univ Labanotation Instr 1973-74; OH St Univ Dance 1973-; *ai:* ASECS 1985-; Congress on Rsrch in Dance 1974-, E 1980-83; Soc of Dance His Scholars 1979-, Bd of Dirs 1982-84, Articles, Translation Pub; Many Reconstructed Renaissance, Dance Material Pub Performances; *office:* OH St Univ Dept of D N High St Columbus OH 43210

GERCHMAN, MARK ROBERT, Mathematics Teacher; *b:* Scra *m:* Elizabeth Wehrle; *c:* Alexa Corrine, Griffin Charles; *ed:* Pen (BS) Bus Mngmt 1985; East Stroudsburg Univ (MED) Admin 19 Cert 1993; *cr:* Macy's Sales Mgr, Asst Buyer 1986-89; IDS, Am Fin Planner 1989-90; Filrae's Basement Asst Store Mgr 1990-; M Operations Mgr 1990-91; East Stroudsburg Univ Grad Asst 1991 Var Bsbl Coach; Mat SAT Prep; SADD Adv; Liason Comm; PCT Susquehanna Comm HS RR 3 Box 5a Susquehanna PA 18847

GERDEMAN, CAROL NIEMEYER, Second Grade Teacher; OH; *m:* James E.; *c:* Vicki, Kristopher; *ed:* Univ of Toledo Gr Credit Hrs; *cr:* SS Cyril & Methodius Schl 2nd Grd Tchr 1971-7 Tchr 1972-73; St Joseph Schl 3rd Grd Tchr 1983, 1st Grd Tchr 2nd Grd Tchr 1988-; *ai:* Eucharist & Reconciliation Planning T & Parish Eucharistic Minister; NEA 1983-; TACIRA Bldg Multiple Sclerosis Org 1990-; Cert from Bishop of Toledo & Dio in Recognition for 10+ Yrs of Svc to Cath Ed; *office:* St Josephs S Main St Sylvania OH 43560*

GERHART, ROSE WOLF, English & German Teacher; Tulpehocken, PA; *m:* Michael P.; *c:* Elizabeth, Jonathan; *ed:* M Univ (BS) Ger 1969; Philipps Univ Jr Yr Abroad Marburg Ger 1967-68; Albright Coll Eng Cert 1989; Kutztown Univ 24 Grad C 1970-74; *cr:* Conrad Weiser HS Ger Tchr 1969-74, Ger Tch Wyomissing HS Ger Sub Tchr 1986; Rdng Schl Dist Ger Sub Tch Conrad Weiser HS Eng, Ger Tchr 1991-; *ai:* Ger Club; CWEA, PS 1969-74, 1991-; AATG 1969-; GFWC Woman's Club of Robeso 1st VP; PTO 1980-, Treas; Amer-Ger Union 1985-; Tax Collecto of Robesonia PA 1986-; *home:* 130 S Robeson St Robesonia PA

GERIC, JAMES W., Sr High School Guidance Cnslr; *b:* Brad *m:* Carol Shalkowski; *ed:* Youngstown St Univ (BS) Elem Duquesne Univ (MS) Elem Guid & Cnslng & Sec Cn Carnegie-Mellon Univ (M) Pub Mgmt, Prsnl Mgmt & Labor 1987; PA St Univ Cert Credits 1971-72; Comm Coll & Allegheny Paramedic Cert 1980; *cr:* Warren City Schls 6th Grd Elem Tchr East Pittsburgh Schl Dist 6th-8th Grd Tchr 1969-70; Duquesne 4th-6th Grd Elem Tchr 1970-93, Sr Guid Cnslr 1993-; *ai:* NE PSEA 1970-; DEA 1970-, Grievance Chm; East Pittsburgh 1970-, Treas 2 Yrs; East Pittsburgh Boro Cncl 1986-95, Pre Duquesne City Schls 28 S 3rd St Duquesne PA 15110

GERK, CAROLYN CRAIG, First Grade Teacher; *b:* Clevelanc Theodore L.; *c:* Kyle Matthew, Courtney Denise; *ed:* Calvin Elem Ed 1976; Cornerstone Chrstn Coll (BA) Eng 1977; *cr:* Hinc Schl Kndgtn Tchr 1979-84, First Grd Tchr 1985-; *ai:* Transiti 1992-; Right-to-Read, Sunshine Soc Comms; NEA 1979.

GERKEN, ANNE, 5th Grade Teacher; *b:* Bronx, NY; *m:* Willia *ed:* Hofstra Univ (BA) Ed-Hnrs 1972; Adelphi Univ (MA) Ed Credit Hrs Beyond MS Degree; *cr:* Bay Shore Pub Schls 5th 1972-; *ai:* Schl Improvement Team; Prin Selection Comm; AFT & 1972-; Bay Shore Classroom TA 1972-; *office:* Gardiner Manor S Wohseepee Dr Bay Shore NY 11706

GERKEN, BRUCE VICTOR, Percussion Studies Director; *b:* OH; *m:* Denise Lynn Sawatzky; *ed:* OH Univ (BM) Music Ed 19 Applied Percussion 1978; *cr:* Lancaster City Schls Percussion Music Dept Chair 1978-; *ai:* Percussion Ensemble Conductor; Percussion Dir; NEA, MENC, Percussive Arts SOC 1978-; MTN Amer Fed of Musicians 1970-; Amer Schl Band Dirs Assn Stan 1988; OH Univ Schl of Music Soc Achvmt in Music Awd 1993; Tchr of Month 1995; *office:* Lancaster City Schls 1312 Granv Lancaster OH 43130

GERKEN, JOAN NICELY, Third Grade Teacher; *b:* Defiance Henry D.; *ed:* St Francis Coll (BS) Elem Ed 1963; 152 Credit H Post Grad Stud; Defiance Coll Cadet Elem Ed 1957; *cr:* Hicksv Third Grd Tchr 1957-58; Wauseon Elem Kndgtn Tchr 1985-61; E Cty Fifth Grd Tchr 1963-68; Continental Elem Fifth Grd Tchr Northeastern Local Schl Third, Fifth Grd Tchr 1969-; *ai:* NE Relations Comm; Music, Ath, Acad Boosters; Northeastern Lo Assn 1969-; OH Ed Assn 1968-; NEA 1957-; Young Peoples The 1984-, Pres 1989-92, 94-, VP 1990-91, 93-94; Alpah Delta Kappa Comm Chprsn; St John Luth Church 1940-, Past Choir, Sunday S Lib Friends 1984-; *home:* 21319 Whisler Rd Defiance OH 43512

GERLACH, BETTY KROLICK, English Teacher; *b:* Sulphur TX; *m:* Richard; *c:* Jennifer; *ed:* St Univ Coll at Buffalo (BS) Sc Ed 1968, (MS) Scndry Eng Ed 1972; *cr:* Niagara Wheatfield HS Tchr 1968-; *ai:* AFT, NYSUT 1968-; NW Tchrs Assn 1968-, E Sanborn-Pekin Free Lib 1985-, Sec; Alpha Delta Kappa 1987-, of Yr Nom; *office:* Niagara Wheatfield Sr HS 2292 Saunders Settl Sanborn NY 14132

GERLACH, JOANNE ELIZABETH, Eight Grade Teacher; *b* Ferry, OH; *m:* Daniel Charles; *c:* Joel, Heidi, Jared; *ed:* Colum Inst (AS) Respiratory Therapy 1976; OH Univ Zoology; *cr:* C Acad Fr Tchr 1982-87, Bio Tchr 1986-87, 3rd Grd Tchr 1987-88 Grd Tchr 1988-91, 8th Grd Tchr 1991-; *ai:* Amer Jr HS Math Exa Challenge, Natl Geographic Geog Bee, PA Math League Spor Hills Chrstn Ctr 1974-, Catechism Class Tchr; WA Chrstn Outrea Vol; *office:* Ctr Christian Acad 3831 Washington Pike Bridg 15017

GERLACH, PAUL CHARLES, 7th & 8th Grade Teacher & Cleveland, OH; *m:* Linda Luke; *c:* Lisa, Jonathan, Julie; *ed:* C Coll at River Forest (BS) Elem Ed 1962; City Coll of NY (MS) 1970; *cr:* Grace Luth Schl 5th-6th Grd Tchr 1962-65; St Matthew 6th-8th Grd Tchr & Prin 1965-74; Our Saviour Luth Schl 5th 1974-77; St Paul Luth Schl 7th-8th Grd Tchr & Prin 1977-; *ai:* of Luth Schls Treas; W NY Luth Schls Sci Fair Chr; WNY Luth 1977-, Treas; Natl Sci Tchrs Assn 1962-; Cmptr Educators Leag

38-; *office:* Saint Paul Lutheran Schl 453 Old Falls Blvd North a NY 14120

N, EDWARD BARNARD, English Instructor; *b:* Saginaw, MI; 'eeks; *c:* Valerie; *ed:* Univ of MI (BA) 1961, (MA) 1964, (PHD) & Lit 1969; *cr:* Pomona Coll Asst Prof 1969-75; Wayne St Univ 1976; Nathaniel Hawthorne Coll Assoc Prof 1976-79; Phillips Instr 1979-; Schl Yr Abroad Eng Instr 1982-83; *ai:* Search & r; Whitewater Kayaking Coach; Amnesty Intnl 1970-; Fidonet sop; Ed of Numerous Books; Numerous Essays on Poets, Poetry ; *office:* Phillips Acad S. Main St Andover MA 01810

N, STUART H., 8th Grd Dean & Behavior Cnslr; *b:* Brooklyn, lenys Cynthia Hammond; *c:* Aubrey Neil, Bryce Devlin, Fiona *l:* Hunter Coll (BA) His 1970; Brooklyn Coll (MA) His 1975; ugh Comm Coll 30 Credits 1987; NY Univ 5 Credits 1971; *cr:* ermediate Schl World, Global Stud, Amer His, Geography Tchr, n Coord, 8th Grd Behavior Cnslr 1970-; *ai:* Dean of 8th Grd; Sci Comm; AFT, UFT, ATSS 1970-.*

, GEORGE A., English & Latin Teacher; *b:* Edwardsville, PA; Coll (BA) Philosophy 1958; Scranton Univ (MA) Eng & Ed ld NY Schl of Interior Design, St Bonaventure Univ, PA St Univ Univ; *cr:* Pemberton Schl Dist Tchr 1958-59; Woodbridge Schl 1959-63; Kingston Schl Dist Tchr 1963-66; WY Vly West Schl 1966-; *ai:* Natl Jr Hrn Soc & Yrbk adv; NEA 1958-; NCTE 1958-; VVWEA 1963-; NASSP 1982-; Slovak Cath Sokol 1935-, Treas; v NDEA Linguistics Grant 1968; 1 of 20 Tchrs Selected to Stud ve Ed at Oxford Univ 1989; Visited Slovakia & Spoke in Pub d & Amer Yth; Organized 1st Natl Hnr Soc Chptr & 1st Yrbk in *e:* 1506 Wyoming Ave Forty Fort PA 18704

IN, MICHAEL, High School Math Teacher; *b:* Passaic, NJ; *m:* simone; *c:* Matthew; *ed:* William Peterson Coll (BA) Math 1979; y St Coll (MA) Admin 1991; *cr:* Westwood HS Math Tchr Secaucus HS Math Tchr 1985-; *ai:* HOPE Club; NEA 1979-; 3d of Ed 1987-, VP 1990 & Pres 1991; Secaucas HS Tchr of the 8; *office:* Secaucus HS Mill Ridge Rd Secaucus NJ 07094

IN, WANDA FAULKNER, Social Studies Teacher; *b:* le, OH; *m:* William Jr.; *c:* Matthew, Amanda; *ed:* Marietta Coll & Soc Stud 1971; Univ of Dayton (MS) Ed 1988; *cr:* Eastern Hs 'chr 1971-; Southern St Comm Coll His & Sociology Adjunct Fac Acad Team Coach; Mentor Tchr; NEA, OEA, ELEA 1971-; Saint hurch 1975-; Martha Holden Jennings Scholar Tchr.*

Y, WILMA FLAKES, Science & Social Studies Tchr; *b:* AL; *m:* John H.; *c:* Derri K. Eugene; *ed:* Miles Coll (BA) Soc ; Atlantic Union Coll Elem Cert; Univ of MA 3 Credit Hrs; *cr:* 'ty Trng Schl 7th & 9th Grd Sci & Math Tchr 1955-65; H P Hood tatistical Clerk 1965-67; Head Start SNAP Head Start Tchr 3erea SDA Acad Asst Prin, Sci, Soc Stud & Bible Tchr 1970-; *ai:* Mem; Womens Ministry; Active with Natl Ctr Afro Amer Artists; nion Ed Assn 1970-; ASCD 1993-; Berea SDA Church 1970-, Ed e Outstdng Svc; Mattapan Neighborhood Block Assn 1975-; MA ral Soc Cert of Merit; Tutored Stdnts Privately; Worked with Specializing in Helping Stdnts to Prepare for GED Examination; ltasca St Mattapan MA 02126*

T, LEE HENRY, World Cultures Teacher; *b:* Lebanon, PA; *m:* 'aye Krall; *c:* Sherry L. Stoltzfus, Suzanne M. Morrison, Stacie *d:* Mansfield Univ (BS) Geography 1965; Penn St Univ (MED) y 1968; *cr:* Conestoga Valley Jr High Geography Tchr 1965-85; Valley HS World Cultures Tchr 1985-; *ai:* Boys, Girls Head ach; Soccer Club Adv; NEA, PSEA 1965-; Conestoga Valley EA es 2 Times; Leola United Meth Church 1968-, Lay Speaker; Recepient; *office:* Conestoga Valley HS 2110 Horseshoe Rd PA 17601

NTHONY FRANCIS, HS Social Studies Teacher; *b:* Oswego, inda Crye; *c:* Theresa, Katherine; *ed:* SUC at Oswego (BS) d, Soc Stud 1970; SUC at Cortland (MA) His 1991; NYS 7-12 Scndry Ed Cert; *cr:* Auburn HS Soc Stud Tchr 1970-; *ai:* r; His Club; Behavioral Modification, Mid-States Evaluation SIO; Essential Elements Trng & Discipline with Dignity Trng t; Auburn Tchrs Assn 1970-, Exec Comm Mem; AFT, NYSUT trl NYS Cncl of Soc Stud 1980-; Seymour Lib 1989-, Bd Mem, AHS Great Books Prgm Tchr 1980-; Military Historians Co ellow; Military Uniforms in Amer Ed; Author of 90 Military His Books, Journals, Magazines; Cooperstown NY St Historical Soc 'henung Cty His Soc, Onondaga Cty His Soc; *office:* Auburn HS Auburn NY 13021

CLAUDIA, Social Studies Teacher; *b:* Sharon, PA; *ed:* wn St Univ (BS) Elem Ed 1974; Westminster Coll (MA) Counseling 1983; Attnd Slipper Rock Univ; *cr:* Notre Dame 1971-74; West Middlesex Schl Elem Tchr 1978-89, Scndry Tchr NEA, PA Ed Assn, West Middlesex Ed Assn 1978-, Treas; Kappa *office:* West Middlesex HS Sharon-New Castle Rd West PA 16159*

D, RUTH, English Teacher & Gifted Coord; *b:* Alliance, OH; of Wooster (BA) Sociology, Eng 1962, (MAT) Eng 1967; 1 Yr n Cert Youngstown St Univ; 24 Semester Hrs Gifted Cert, Prof St Univ; *cr:* Orrville City Schls Grd 9 Eng Instr 1962-64; Local Schls Grd 11 Engl Instr 1964-66; Wooster City Schls Grd tr 1967-69; Youngstown St Univ Eng Instr 1969-71; Austintown ls Grds 11-12 Eng Instr 1971-; *ai:* RDE Coord; AEA, OEA, NEA, 52-; Delta Kappa Gamma 1968-; Phi Delta Kappa 1992-; AAUW m Woman of Yr in Ed; Presbyn Church 1950-, Elder; Martha ennings Scholar; Invited Contributor to Teaching Shakespeare Book Reviews Written; Numerous Articles Pub; *home:* PO Box eld OH 44406

SE, KATHLEEN MARIE,CR, Math Coord & Teacher; *b:* , NJ; *ed:* St Rose Coll (BS) Elem Ed, Soc Sci 1983; St Charles (MA) Rel Stud, Moral Theology 1992; Attnd Maria Coll Early Yr; *cr:* Rel Edctrs Tchr 1975-90; St Veronica Schl 5th-6th Grd Tchr 1982-84; St Francis of Assisi Schl 7th-8th Grd Tchr St Veronica Schl 7th-8th Grd Rel, Math Tchr 1987-; *ai:* Grad, ; Peer Tutoring, Math, Family Math, Maria Museum, Math Day, Coord; NCEA 1982-, NCTM, AMTNJ 1988-; Sr of the on 1973-; Bishop John C. Reiss Respect Life Edctrs Awd 1996; Cath Edctrs Awd 1994; *office:* St Veronica Schl 4219 Rt 9 N J 07731

NSKY, LIBBY T., English as a Second Lang Tchr; *b:* Brooklyn, a Gershansky; *c:* Sarah Jessica; *ed:* Brooklyn Coll CUNY (BA) ; Adelphi Univ (MA) Tchng Eng; Span Lang & Lit CUNY Grad rooklyn Coll CUNY Asst Dir Lang Labs 1975-89; Lafayette HS 1989-, ESL Coord 1993-; *ai:* Temple Israel 1990-, Schl Bd; UFT Tchrs Ctrs Consortium Mini Grant 1996; Articles Pub; *office:* HS 2630 Benson Ave Brooklyn NY 11214

IAN, ANDREA CLAYMAN, Resource Teacher; *b:* Baltimore ; *m:* Ira; *c:* Blake Henry, Samantha Morgan; *ed:* Johns Hopkins) Cnslng 1980; Univ of CT Trng Gifted & Talented Educ; *cr:* Ridge Elem Schl 4th-5th Grd Tchr 1976-83; Worthington Elem Schl 4th-5th Grd Tchr 1983-86, Gifted-Talented Resource Tchr 1986-; *ai:* Coordinate Field TRips Math, Disability Awareness Days; Memory Book Ed; Dir Schoolwide Theatrical Productions; NEA, HCEA, MSTA 1976-; Comm Theatre; Beth Shalom Sisterhood; *office:* Worthington Elem Schl 4570 Roundhill Rd Ellicott City MD 21043

GERSON, KATHLEEN, Sociology Professor; *b:* Montgomery, AL; *m:* Prof. John Mollenkopf; *c:* Emily Mollenkopf; *ed:* Stanford Univ (BA) Sociology 1969; Univ of CA at Berkeley (MA) Sociology 1974, (PHD) Sociology 1981; *cr:* NY Univ Asst Prof 1980-87; Russell Sage Fnd Visiting Scholar 1987-88; NY Univ Assoc Prof 1988-95, Prof 1995-; *ai:* Dir of Undergraduate Stud; Princeton Univ Dept of Sociology Advy Cncl; Sloan Fnd Research Network on Work Redesign, Work & Family; Amer Sociological Assn 1980-; Eastern Sociological Soc 1980-, Exec Comm; Sociologists for Women in Soc 1980-; Author No Mans Land Mens Changing Commitments to Family & Work Basic Books 1993; Author Hard Choices How Women Decide About Work, Career & Motherhood Univ of CA Press 1985; *office:* NY Univ 269 Mercer St Dept of Sociology New York NY 10003

GERSON, ROSALIND, Business Education Teacher; *b:* Woodbury, NJ; *ed:* Rider Coll (AA) Secretarial 1957, (BS) Bus Ed 1982; Goldey Beacom Coll Word Processing 1982; 3 Grad Credits Rowan Coll Instrl Application of Cmptrs 1995; *cr:* RCA Sec 1957-58; Interstate Commerce Commission Sec 1958-59; Goldey Beacom Coll Tchr 1961-63; Bridgeton HS Tchr 1965-; *ai:* Mid Sts Steering Comm; Monitoring Comm Chprsn; Appeals Hearing Comm; NJEA, BEA, CCEA, NEA 1965-; *office:* Bridgeton HS 111 N West Ave Bridgeton NJ 08302

GERSONY, SUSAN MIRSKY, Mathematics Teacher; *b:* Brooklyn, NY; *m:* Welton M.; *c:* Janice Dittelman, Laura Baer; *ed:* Brooklyn Coll (BA) Math, Ed 1965; Montclair St Univ (MS) Math, Ed 1974; *cr:* Flushing Jr HS 189 Math Tchr 1965-66; Felix Festa Jr HSMath Tchr 1972-84; Clarkstown HS North Math Tchr 1985-; *ai:* Bridge Club Adv; AFT 1975-; Amer Contract Bridge League 1974-, Life Master.*

GERSPACH, VIRGINIA A., Second Grade Teacher; *b:* Easton, PA; *m:* David E.; *ed:* PA St Univ (BS) Elem Ed 1965; Temple Univ (MED) Educl Admin 1972; 45 Addl Post Grad Credit Hrs; Elem Prin Cert 1974; *cr:* Interboro Schl Dist 2nd Grd Tchr 31 Yrs; *ai:* Home, Schl Assn Prgm Chprsn; NEA 1988-; PA St Ed Assn 1988-; Interboro Ed Assn 1988-, Recording Sec; Young Republican Club 1995-; PA Congress PTA 1965-, Pres, Life Mem 1974-; PA St Univ Coll of Ed, Nom Alumni Awd 1983; Delta Kappa Gamma, Pres; Jr League of the Lehigh Valley 1978-; Outstdng Elem Tchr of Amer 1972-; Grant Impact Partners for Ed 1989; *office:* Interboro Schl Dist 9th & Washington Ave Prospect Park PA 19076

GERST, LINDA WALLACE, First Grade Teacher; *b:* Shamokin, PA; *m:* Joseph M.; *c:* Kristi L.; *ed:* Mansfield St Coll (BS) Elem & Spcl Ed 1968, (Masters Equiv) Elem Ed 1985; *cr:* Mifflinburg Area Schl Dist 3rd Grd Tchr 1968-76, 1st Grd Tchr 1982-; *ai:* PSEA 1968-; NEA 1968-; MAEA Local 1968-, Bldg Rep; *office:* Mifflinburg Area Schl Dist 115 Shipton St Mifflinburg PA 17844

GERSTENBERG, ROBERT W., Vocal Music Teacher; *b:* New York City, NY; *m:* Evangeline; *c:* Mari, Christine; *ed:* NYU (BM) Piano 1962; C. W. Post Coll (MA) Music Ed 1972; NY ST Univ Piano Performance; *cr:* Tetard Jr HS Music Tchr 1963-77; Sachem Schl Vocal Music Tchr 1977-; *ai:* Church Organist; Choir Dir; SCMEA 1967-; Warner Hawkins Performance Schlsp; *office:* Sachem HS South 51 School St Ronkonkoma NY 11779

GERVER, ROBERT K., Math Teacher; *b:* NYC, NY; *m:* Linda Spooner; *c:* Julianne, Michael; *ed:* Queens Coll (BA) Math 1976, (MS) Math Ed 1980; NY Univ (PHD) Math Ed 1990; *cr:* North Shore HS Math Tchr 1977-; Adelphi Univ Adjunct Lecturer 1981-85; CW Post Coll Adjunct Lecturer 1981-85; Dowling Coll Adjunct Prof 1984-88; *ai:* Math Team Coach; Toy Drive Dir; Exit Assessment Comm; NCTM 1980-; CPAM 1988-; Goudreau Math Museum 1980-; Text Author South-Western Pub Co; Key Curr Press Author; Articles Pub; Presidential Awd for Math 1988; *office:* North Shore HS 450 Glen Cove Ave Glen Head NY 11545

GERVOLINO, COLLEEN SULLIVAN, High School Chemistry Teacher; *b:* Passaic, NJ; *m:* Ronald; *ed:* Seton Hall Univ (BS) Physics 1991; *cr:* Pompton Lakes HS Chem Tchr 1993-; *ai:* Mentor New Tchrs; Chem League Adv; NEA, NJEA, PLEA, NJSTA 1993-; Soc of Physics Stu 1989-; *home:* 563 Laurel Rd Ridgewood NJ 07450*

GERY, KAREN ANN, Math Teacher; *b:* Cleveland, OH; *ed:* Lakeland Comm Coll (AS) Cmptr 1971; Cleveland St Univ (BS) Ed 1973; Grad Stud at Ursuline Coll, Drake Univ, Andrew Univ, Baldwin-Wallace Univ; *cr:* Bellflower Elem Schl Asst Tchr Primary 1973-74; St Mary of Mentor Tchr 1974-84; St William Schl Math Tchr 1984-; *ai:* Jr HS Dept Chprsn 1980-84, 1990-94; Testing Coord 1975-; Stu Cncl Adv 1974-80; Schl Yrbk Adv 1975-83; Schl Newspaper Adv 1995-; NCEA, OCEA, NCTM 1975-; Lakeland Civic Assn 1974-; Jr Achvmt Project Bus Tchrs Awd 1978-84; *office:* St William Schl 351 E 260th St Euclid OH 44132*

GESSLER, CHRISTOPHER L., Accounting Teacher; *b:* Hazleton, PA; *m:* Marianne E. Puchyr; *c:* John C.; *ed:* Bloomsburg Univ (BS) Accounting 1970; Kutztown Univ (MS) Scndry Guidance 1976; Lehigh Univ 9 Credits in Finance; *cr:* Trexler Jr HS Bus Ed Tchr 1970-81; Allen HS Accounting Tchr 1981-; *ai:* Jr HS Bsktbl Coach 5 Yrs; Schl Store Spon; Various Schl Comm; NEA 1970-; Knights of Columbus 1965-; Allentown Schl Mens Club 1970-; *office:* William Allen HS 17th & Turner Sts Allentown PA 18104

GESTRI, JACK, Language Arts Teacher; *b:* Brooklyn, NY; *m:* Donna Lillian Giarratano; *c:* Brandi D.; *ed:* Queens Coll (BA) Comm 1971; Long Island Univ (MS) Comm 1975; Addl 78 Credits Post Masters; *cr:* Candlewood MS Lang Arts Tchr 1971-; *ai:* Prin Advy Comm; Adv-Advisee Comm; AFT,NEA, Half Hollow Hills TA 1971-; Long Island Theatre of Deaf 1982-, Dir; Dir of Schl Plays 1972-81; Started Human Relations Club 1986-88; Dir of TEEN Canteen 1988-91; Mentor Prgm Dir 1990-92; Hackett Awd for Oration 1967; Bowling Club Adv 1980-89; *office:* Candlewood MS 1200 Carlls Straight Path Huntingtn Sta NY 11746

GESTWICKI, RALPH ALLEN, Social Stud Tchr & Dept Chair; *b:* Corning, NY; *m:* Bonnie Jo Richards; *ed:* Corning Comm Coll (AA) 1969; SUNY at Brockport (BS) Pol Sci 1971; Northern IL Univ (MA) SE Asian Stud 1974; Attnd Elmira Coll Scndry Ed 27 hrs, Mansfield Univ Scndry Ed 15 Hrs, Drake Univ Scndry Ed 3 Hrs, Penn St Univ Scndry Ed 3hrs; *cr:* Horseheads Schl Dist Home Instruction Tchr 1976-80; Corning Corning Comm Coll Soc Sci Adjunct Prof 1976-83; Troy HS Soc Stud Tchr 1980-83; SRU HS Soc Stud Tchr 1983-85; Troy HS Soc Stud Tchr & Dept Chm 1985-; *ai:* Peer Helper Prgm; Schlsp Channenge; Power of Positive Stdnts; Sr Class Trip; Renaissance Prgm; SADD; Soc Studies Instruction Support Team 1992-; Stamp Club, Photography Club, Fly Tying Club; NEA 1980-, Cncl Rep 3 Yrs; NCSS 1980-; Assn for Asian Stud 1971-; Phi Delta Kappa 1994; PA CSS 1994-; Troy Prof Dev Comm 1989-; Chemung Historical Soc 1978-; Corning Painted Post Historical Soc 1980-; Amer Philatic Soc 1976-; Troy Strategic Action Plan 1994-; Arndt Art Museum 1976-; Amer Museum Fly Fishing 1990-; Catskill Fly Fishing Ctr 1990-; Catskill Fly Tyers Guild 1995-; Trout Unlimited 1990-; Mansfield Univ Tchr Ed Advy Comm 1992-; Troy HS Tchr of Yr 1983 & 1989; Natl Endowment for Hum Fellowship 1985; Sigma Alpha 1972; Pi Sigma Alpha 1972; *office:* Troy H S 250 High St Troy PA 16947*

GESUALDI, SUSAN ANNE, Social Studies Teacher; *b:* Hartford, CT; *m:* Mark Sinnott; *ed:* Univ of CT (BA) His, Scndry Ed 1977; (MA) Ed 1983, (MA) His 1993-; *cr:* Granby Mem HS Soc Stud Tchr 1978-88; Simsbury HS Soc Stud Tchr 1988-; Univ of Hartford Adj Prof 1990-94; *ai:* Club Adv, Coach for Mock Trial Competition Team; Club Adv for Close up Prgm; NEA, CT Ed Assn 1978-; Simsbury Ed Assn 1988-; Phi Alpha Theta 1991-; Awded Flwshp Univ of Ct 1989; Accepted as Participant in His Component Inst of Univ of CT 1992, 1993; Presenter Northeast Regnl Soc Stud Conf 1983, 1988; Presenter CT Cncl Soc Stud Conf 1992; *office:* Simsbury HS 34 Farms Village Rd Simsbury CT 06070*

GETCHELL, DONNA GIORDANO, Mathematics Teacher; *b:* Queens, NY; *m:* William P.; *ed:* St John's Univ (BA) Math 1987, (MS) Scndry Ed 1989; Post Grad Ldrshp Prgm Probability Theory Rutgers Univ 1994-95; *cr:* St John's Prep HS Math Tchr 1987-92; The Mary Louis Acad Math Tchr 1993-; *ai:* Ath Dir; Ath Assn Moderator; ATMNYC 1993-; Goudreau Museum Math Art Sci 1989-, Chprsn Pi Day Contest; *office:* The Mary Louis Acad 176-21 Wexford Terr Jamaica NY 11432*

GETGEN, TERESA CISNEY, Health & PE Teacher; *b:* Huntingdon, PA; *m:* Michael Lee; *ed:* Lock Haven Univ (BA) Hlth & PE 1992; *cr:* LaPlata HS Tchr 1992-; *ai:* Class of 1997 Spon; Field Hockey Coach; NEA 1992-; NDIETA 1996; *home:* 29110 Linda Way Mechanicsville MD 20659

GETMAN, HAROLD JOSEPH, Mathematics Teacher; *b:* Buffalo, NY; *m:* Diane M. Neumeister; *c:* Lisa M., Kate E.; *ed:* St Univ Coll of NY at Buffalo (BS) Math 1971, (MS) Ed 1974; *cr:* West Seneca East Jr HS Math Tchr 1971-73; West Seneca Allendate Jr HS Math Tchr 1973-86; West Seneca West Jr HS Math Tchr 1986-90; West Seneca East Sr HS Math Tchr 1990-; *ai:* AFT, NYSUT & West Seneca Tchr Assn 1971-.

GETMAN, JANET M., PE Teacher & Coach; *b:* Saratoga Springs, NY; *m:* James Edward; *c:* Amy, James Jr., Jered James; *ed:* Herkimer Comm Coll (AS) PE 1975; Brockport St Univ (BA) PE 1977; Upper Division Utica Elem Degree & PE 1988; *ai:* Var Field Hockey & Var Bsktbl Coach; WBCA; YMCA, Bd; *office:* Herkimer Cntrl Schl Church St Herkimer NY 13350

GETMAN, JOHN DOUGLAS, Chemistry Teacher; *b:* Rochester, NY; *m:* Linda Gardner Lukaszewski; *c:* Lisa Lukaszewski, Taryn Lukaszewski, Kristi Lorden, Missy; *ed:* SUNY at Cortland (BS) Chem 1966; SUNY at New Paltz (MS) Chem 1973; 30 Addl Hrs Ed Admin; *cr:* Rome Free Acad Chem Tchr 1966-67; Kingston HS Chem Tchr 1967-; *ai:* Sci Dept Liason; Sci Olympics Team Coach; Frosh Ftbl Coach 1969-79; STANYS 1985-; AFT 1966-; Outstanding Sci Tchr Awd Sci Tchrs Assn 1989; *office:* Kingston HS 403 Broadway Kingston NY 12401

GETSKO, ANTHONY J., Biology Teacher; *b:* Shenandoah, PA; *m:* Madeline S.; *c:* Anthony D., Kristen S., Kara Lyn; *ed:* Kutztown Univ (BSE) Sci 1965, (MS) Bio 1978; Attnd Syracuse U, Univ of Scranton; *cr:* Coll Gifted Prgm Inc at Blair Acad Astronomy Tchr 1989; Northampton Cty Comm Coll Bio Tchr 1990; Phillipsburg HS Bio, Gen Sci Tchr 1965-; *ai:* Tutor; Interpretor for Czech Stdnts; NEA, NJEA, PEA 1965-; Lehigh Vly Rose Soc 1969-, Pres; PA Earth Sci Assn 1994-; Kappa Delta Phi; Articles Pub; *office:* Phillipsburg HS Hillcrest Blvd Phillipsburg NJ 08865*

GETSY, JENNIFER L., Learning Support Teacher; *b:* Pittsburgh, PA; *ed:* Slippery Rock Univ (BS) Spec, Elem Ed 1993; Working Towards Masters Degree in Ed, Rdng; *cr:* Queens Annes Cty Learning Support Tchr 1993-94; Quaker Vly Schl Dist Learning Support Tchr 1994-; *ai:* Asst Var Girls Vlybl Coach; PSEA 1994-; NEA 1993-; PMSA 1995-; *office:* Quaker Valley Jr HS 618 Harbaugh St Sewickley PA 15143

GETTY, CAROLYNN MAE, Eng, Law & Geog Tchr of Deaf; *b:* Moncton NB, Canada; *c:* Caryn Anne Piorkowski; *ed:* Queen's Univ (BA) PSych 1989; Attnd North Bay Tchrs Coll 1969-70; Tchr Trng in Deaf Ed 1970-71; *cr:* Alberta Schl for Deaf Elem Tchr 1971-73; Sir James Whitney Ontario Schl of Deaf Elem, Scndry Tchr 1973-; *ai:* Past Staff Assn Pres, Hockey Team Mgr, Canvasser for United Way; Grad Class Staff Adv; Dist 57, PSAT; OSSTF; *office:* Sir James Whitney Schl 350 Dundas St W Belleville ON K8P 1B2 Canada CN*

GETTYS, DARRELL LEE, Fine Arts Teacher; *b:* Pittsburgh, PA; *c:* Leslie Anona; *ed:* Edinboro St Univ of PA (BS) Art Ed 1975; 24 Post Grad Hrs for PA Cert; *cr:* Meadville Jr HS Art Tchr, Drawing, Painting 1975-90; Meadville Sr HS Fine Art, Photography Inst 1990-; *ai:* NEA, PSEA, CSEA 1975-; IPRA 1988-, Photographer of Yr 1987-88; Over 200 Photos Pub; Artwork Article 1989; 1st Place Alleheny West Art Show 1993-94, Cody WY Art League Annual Show 1994-95, Red Lodge Artists Show 1995; *office:* Meadville Area Sr HS North St Ext Meadville PA 16335

GETZ, BRIAN DAVID, Health & Life Skills Teacher; *b:* East Stroudsburg, PA; *m:* Janet Patricia Buckheit; *ed:* Penn St Univ (BS) Hlth Ed 1992; Post Grad Work at Bloomsburg Univ; *cr:* Smithsburg HS Hlth & Life Skills Tchr 1994-; *ai:* Girls Jr Var Bsktbl & Sftbl Coach; SADD Adv; Fire Safety Chm; MD Stu Assisstance Prgm Mem; Athletic Game Mgr; Cmptr Comm; NEA 1994-; PA Dept of Hlth 1993-, Emergency Medical Technician; VA Dept of Hlth 1994-, Emergency Medical Technician; Amer Heart Assn 1994-, Certified Pulminary Resuscitation Instr; *home:* 1415 Kensington Dr Apt 301 Hagerstown MD 21742*

GETZKE, THOMAS, English & Literature Teacher; *b:* Philadelphia, PA; *m:* Eleanor Jane Graham; *c:* Sarah Jane, Marc Thomas; *ed:* Richard Stockton Coll (BA); NJ St Tchng Cert; Attnd Rowan Coll, Jersey City St Coll & Saint Peters Coll; *cr:* Mill Road MS 6th Grd Eng Tchr 1974-83; Egg Harbor Twp HS Eng Dept, 9th-12th Grd Coll Prep, Hspt & Jrnslm Tchr 1986-90; Eugene A Tighe Schl Eng & Lit Tchr 1990-; *ai:* Great Books Club Adv; Margate Ed Assn 1990-, Bldg Rep; NEA, NJEA 1974-; NCTE 1986-; Pleasantville City 1990-, Councilman; Christ Espicopal Church 1995-, Vestry; Kiwanis Club Local & Natl 1995-; Eastern Svc Workers 1990-; Radio & Local Television Sports Broadcaster 1983-; Sports Journalist 1987-90; NJ Sportswriter of Yr 1989; *home:* 38 Montclair Dr Pleasantville NJ 08232

GEUTHER, RONALD CHARLES, Chemistry & Biology Teacher; *b:* Huntington Long Is, NY; *ed:* SUNY Coll at Cortland (BA) Scndry Bio 1974; SUNY at Albany (MA) Advanced Classroom Tchng 1979; 4 Credit Hrs Biochemistry; *cr:* Tamarac HS Sci Tchr 1974-; *ai:* Class 1998 Adv; AFT, NY St United Tchr 1974-; NSTA 1978-; Sci Tchrs Assn of NY St 1984-, Eastern Section Treas; Amer Chemical Soc Ed Division; 1st Bapt Church of Troy 1976-; Troy Musical Arts Chorus 1979-; Saratoga Performing Arts Ctr, Vol 1982; Dow, NSTA Summer Wkshp Participant; *office:* Tamarac HS 3992 NY 2 Troy NY 12180*

GEWIRTZ, JOSEPH M., 3rd & 8th Grade Teacher; *b:* New York, NY; *m:* Varda Lapa; *c:* Layah, Miriam, Devorah, Rachel, Yael, Auraham, Sarah; *ed:* Queens Coll (BA) Psych 1976; Rabbinicol Seminary of Amer (Semicha) Talmud 1983; Torah Umesorah Tchr Ed Prgm; *cr:* WI Inst for Torah Study Tchr 1983-85; Rabbi David L Silver Yeshiva Acad 3rd Grd MS Tchr 1985-; *ai:* After Schl Enrichment Tchr; Parent Ed Tchr; HS Hebrew Tchr; Natl Assn of Hebrew Day Schls 1985-; *office:* Rabbi D L Silver Yeshiva Acad 100 Vaughn St Harrisburg PA 17110*

GEYER, ELAINE T., Advanced Placement Bio Teacher; *b:* Morristown, NJ; *ed:* Montclair St Univ (BS) Bio 1971; East Stroudsburg Univ (MS) Bio 1986; 36 Grad Credits Ed; *cr:* Roxbury HS Sci Instr 1971-; Sussex Cty Comm Coll Adj Sci Tchr 1989-90; *ai:* Acad Decathalon Tutor; Humane Ed Club Adv; Honors Criteria Comm; NEA; NJ St Sci Tchr Assn 1990-;

Frelinghysen Twsp Environmental Commission 1992-, Vice-Chprsn; NSF 1973, Dodge Fnd 1986, Bus & Ed Together 1993 Grants; Presentation Commendation NJ Sci Tchrs Convention 1988; Dist Nom Princeton Tchng Awd 1991; Stu Nom Bd of Ed Awds Acad Inspiration 1990-95; Tchr Mentor 1993; *home:* 11 Pippin Hill Rd Blairstown NJ 07825*

GEYER, TOM F., Art Education Coord & Instr; *b:* St Marys, PA; *m:* Nancy A. Bootier; *ed:* Edinboro St Coll (BS) Art Ed 1970; Penn St Univ (MED) Art Ed 1971; *cr:* Glens Falls City Schls Art Ed 1971-; *ai:* NHS Adv; Dept Chair Grds K-12; NYSATA; NYSUT; Bd of Realtors; Care for Terminally of Chronically Ill; Tchr of Yr 1992; PTSA Founders Day Awd; 3 Articles Pub; Nom NY St Tchr of Yr 1993; *office:* Glens Falls HS 10 Quade St Glens Falls NY 12801*

GEYER, VIRGINIA E., Physical Ed & Health Teacher; *b:* Marenna, NY; *ed:* Univ of ME at Orono (BS) PE & Hlth 1972; *office:* Winthrop HS 11 Highland Ave Winthrop ME 04364

GEYSEN, THOMAS FRANCIS, English Teacher & Coach; *b:* Boston, MA; *m:* Margaret Anne Leonard; *c:* Marybeth Marchand, Laurie Anne, Thomas Joseph; *ed:* Boston St Coll (BA) Eng 1967; 42 Post Grad Credit Hrs Scndry Admin, Spec Ed, Rdng, Gen Ed; *cr:* Davis Thayer Schl Eng, Soc Stud Tchr, Coach 1968-71; Horace Mann Schl Eng Tchr, Coach 1971-86, 1987-92; Franklin HS Asst Prin, Coach 1986-87, 1992--87; *ai:* Schl, Fac Cncl; Peer Ldrshp, Peer Mediation Adv; Girls Var Soccer, Indoor & Outdoor Track Coach; Franklin Ed Assn 1968-, Pres 1970; NEA, MTA 1968-; *office:* Franklin HS 218 Oak St Franklin MA 02038

GFELLER, MARC ANDRE, Mathematics Teacher; *b:* Allentown, PA; *m:* Cherie Christian; *c:* Tyler; *ed:* Westminster Coll (BS) Math 1991; In-Svc Credit LIU; 3 Credit Hrs at IN Wesleyan; *cr:* Bishop Hoban HS Part-Time Math Tchr 1992; Regis Acad MS Math Tchr 1992-93; WY Area SD HS Math Tchr 1993-; *ai:* Head Swimming & Diving Coach 1991-; PSEA, NEA & WAEA 1993-; *office:* Wyoming Area Schl 20 Memorial St Exeter PA 18643

GFELLER, NICOLE LOUISE, Swim Coach; *b:* St Imier, Switzerland; *m:* Klaus; *c:* Marc, Paul, Miriam; *cr:* Elmer L. Meyers HS Swim Coach.

GHAFOOR, IMRAN, Associate Professor; *b:* Lyaccpur, Pakistan; *m:* Iram Imran; *c:* Ali Imran, Omar Imran; *ed:* Columbia Univ (MS) Chemical Engrng 1981; CUNY Grad Ctr (PHD) Comp Sc; *cr:* Bronx Comm Coll Assoc Prof 1984-; *ai:* Indian Club, Muslim Stu Club & Data Processing Club Adv; 12 Publications 1985-; Various Awds; *office:* City Univ Of NY Bronx Comm Col W 181 St & University Ave Bronx NY 10453

GHANAVATI, KATHLEEN, Chemistry Teacher; *b:* Clairton, PA; *m:* Ali; *c:* Kayla, Kameron; *ed:* IN Univ of PA; CA Univ of PA (BS) Scndry Ed Chem 1983; *cr:* Ocean City HS Chem Tchr 1983-; *ai:* NEA 1983-; NJEA 1983-; NSTA 1989-; Mother Club of Upper Twp 1989-; *office:* Ocean City HS 6th & Atlantic Ave Ocean City NJ 08226

GHANER, PHILIP WILSON, Eighth Grade Mathematics Tchr; *b:* Bellefonte, PA; *m:* Cathy Myers; *c:* Brad, Heather, Hilary, Ben; *ed:* West Chester Univ (BS) Math Ed 1973; Addl 15 Credits; 9 Credits Chester Cty IU; *cr:* North Chester Cty Tech Schl Tchr 1973-83; OJ Roberts 8th Grd Math Tchr 1986-; *ai:* PSEA; NEA; *office:* Owen J. Roberts Schl Dist Rd 1 Pottstown PA 19465

GHERIDIAN, MARIA, Spanish & Bilingual Teacher; *b:* Buenos Aires, South america; *ed:* Univ of MA (BA) Bachelor of Arts 1977; Boston Univ (MS) Intnl PR 1985; Bridgewater St (CAGS) Schl Admin 1989; St Univ in South America Lang Specialist 1962; *cr:* St Univ of S America Span Lang Instr 1963-72; MA Coll of Pharmacy Span Lang Instr 1977-; YMCA GED Instr 1978-80; Adult Ed Evening Schl ESL Instr 1983-94; Brighton High Biling Span & ESL Tchr 1989-; *ai:* Wrote Biling Curr; Master Tchr for Stdnts Tchrs Fraction; Span, Eng Lang Tutor; MATSOL & MABE 1977-; Schl Set Cncl; Lead Tchr Boston Pub Schls; Visiting Comm New England Assn of Schls & Colls; *home:* 60 Hobbs Brook Rd Waltham MA 02154*

GHEZZI, BERNARD, Chemistry Teacher; *b:* Kingston, NY; *m:* Judy; *c:* Lea, Andrew; *ed:* SUNY at New Paltz (BS) Chem Ed 1963, (MS) Chem 1968; 90 Addl Hrs; *cr:* Kingston Consolidated Schls Chem Tchr 1963-64; Wappingers Cntrl Schls Chem Tchr 1964-; *ai:* Cross Cntry Coach; AFT, NEA, NYSUT 1963-; 3 NSF Tchr Grants; BOCES Vision Awd 1994; NASA Awd 1972; *office:* Roy C Ketcham H S 99 Myers Corners Rd Wappingers Falls NY 12590

GHEZZI, JUDY CLARKE, Fifth Grade Teacher; *b:* Poughkeepsie, NY; *m:* Bernard; *c:* Lea, Andrew; *ed:* St Univ at New Paltz (BS) Elem Ed 1964; 30 Credit Hrs; *cr:* Evans Schl Tchr 1964-66; Kenry Rd Schl Tchr 1966-69, 1979-84; Fishkill Plains Schl Tchr 1984-; *ai:* PTA, Sci Fair Liasons; Grd Level Rep; NEA; AFT; WCT, NYSUT 1964-; Sabattical 1984; Pub Problem Solving Manual 1983.

GHOSN, C. JOSEF, Business Professor; *b:* Beirut, Lebanon; *m:* Fiona E.; *c:* Josef C.; *ed:* Mid East Coll (BA) Bus Dmin 1981; Andrews Univ (MBA) Mgmt 1986; 39 Post Grad Credits; *cr:* Atlantic Union Coll Asst Prof 1989-; *ai:* Bus Club Spon; Amer Mktg Assn 1990-; Town of Lancaster Industrial Dev Comm 1996-; Direct Mktg assn Fellow; Sam Walton Fellow; Stus in Free Enterprise; Chemical Bank Diploma in Documentary Letters of Credit; Harvard Univ Diploma in Tchng by the core Method; *office:* Atlantic Union Coll PO Box 1000 338 Main St South Lancaster MA 01561

GIACALONE, PETER JOSEPH, Spanish Teacher; *b:* West Islip, NY; *ed:* Dowling Coll (BA) Romance Lang 1990, (MS) Reading 1996; *cr:* Beach St Jr HS Span Stu Tchr 1989-90; Holy Trinity HS Span Tchr 1990-; Holy Trinity HS Span Tchr 1990-95; Bellmore-Merrick CHSD Span Tchr 1995-; *ai:* Sr Stu Cncl Class Adv; Philosophy Comm; Captain We Care Prgm; Frosh Class Adv; NYSAFLT, LILT 1990-; AATSP 1995-; Wrote Children's Book; *office:* Mepham HS Camp Ave Bellmore NY 11710

GIACALONE, SARAH A., High School Counselor; *b:* Gloucester, MA; *ed:* Regis Coll (BA) Psych 1962; Boston Coll (MSED) Counseling 1964; 45 Credits Beyond Masters; *cr:* Waltham HS Guidance Cnslr; *ai:* Waltham Ed Assn, Mass Tchrs Assn, Mass Schl Cnslrs Assn, Greater Boston Schl Cnslrs Assn.*

GIACOIA, ANN MARIE VOLPE, Home Economics Teacher; *b:* Bloomfield, NJ; *m:* Michael; *c:* Brianna, Michael R., Christopher; *ed:* SUNY at Oneonta (BS) Home Ec Ed 1982; SUNY at New Paltz (MS) Elem Ed 1993; *cr:* Land & Sea Fashions Garment Cost Any 1983-85; T. A. Enterprise Dessert Chef 1986-89; Marlboro HS Home Ec Tchr 1992-; *ai:* FHA Adv; Jr Girl Scouts Asst Ldr; NYSAFCSE 1992-, Pres, Sec; NYSUT, NYSFHA 1992-; *office:* Marlboro Central HS 50 Cross Rd Marlboro NY 12542

GIACOLONE, STEVEN RICHARD, Business Chairman; *b:* Brooklyn, NY; *m:* Theresa Buscemi; *ed:* Hofstra Univ (BA) Bus, Acctng 1984; Stony Brook Univ (MA) Lib Stud 1994; *cr:* Brentwood HS Sub, Var Coach 1987-89; Eastport HS Tchr, Var Coach 1989-; *ai:* Var Coach Boys Soccer, Girls Bsktbl, Sftbl; *office:* Eastport Schl 390 Montauk Hwy Eastport NY 11941

GIACOMELLI, MARION WOOD, Social Studies Department Head; *b:* Worcester, MA; *c:* Lauren; *ed:* Elms Coll (BA) His 1968; Assumption Coll (MA) His 1972; Boston Univ CAGS Soc Stud Curr 1976; *cr:* Forest-Grove MS Tchr 1968-79; Worcester East Mid Soc Stud Dept Head 1980-87; North HS Soc Stud Dept Head 1987-92; Doherty Meml HS Soc Stud Dept Head 1992-; *ai:* Model Congress Adv; NEA, MTA, EAW 1968-; *office:* Doherty Memorial HS 299 Highland St Worcester MA 01602

GIACOMINI, PATRICIA BERNARDI, Second Grade Teacher; *b:* Pittston, PA; *m:* Nino J.; *c:* Janine, Carina; *ed:* Bloomsburg St Univ (BS) Elem Ed 1961; NEIU #19 25 Addl Credits in Elem Ed; REI 18 Addl Credits in Religious Ed; *cr:* South Plainsfield JFK Schl Elem Tchr 1961-69; Riverside Roosevelt Schl Elem Tchr 1969-70; Old Forge Elem Schl Permanent Sub 1979-85; Saint Marys Schl Elem Tchr 1985-; *ai:* NCEA 1985-; *home:* 556 Milwaukee Ave Old Forge PA 18518

GIACOMINI, TONI, Fifth Grade Teacher; *b:* Hartford, CT; *c:* John Michael; *ed:* SUNY at Geneseo (BS) Elem Ed 1968; SUNY at New Paltz (MS) Elem Ed 1976; 13 Post Grad Credit Hrs; *cr:* Myers Corners Elem Schl 3rd Grd Tchr 1968-70; Violet Ave Elem Schl 4th Grd Tchr 1970-74; Mt Marion Elem Schl 4th Grd Tchr 1974-82; Grant D. Morse Elem Schl 5th Grd Tchr 1982-; *ai:* Bldg Compact Site Team Mem; Articulation Comm; Banana Splits; NYSUT 1968-; Saugerties Tchrs Assn 1974-, Head Bldg Rep; Hospice of Kingston 1994-, Vol; Ulster Co Crimes Victims Asst 1995-, Vol; *home:* PO Box 2212 Kingston NY 12401*

GIACONIA, JULEANNA CROWLEY, Business Teacher; *b:* Passaic, NJ; *m:* William Jr.; *c:* Thaddea; *ed:* Montclair St Coll (BA) Secretarial Stud 1962; *cr:* Clifton Adult Schl Tchr; Nutley Adult Schl Tchr; Clifton Summer Schl Tchr; *ai:* FBLA, DECA Stu Preparation for Competion; Curr Revision Comm; Facilities Comm for Mid Sts Evaluation; NEA, NJEA, PCEA; Clifton Tchrs Assn, Recording Sec; Clifton Coll Women's Club; *office:* Clifton HS 333 Colfax Ave Clifton NJ 07013*

GIACOPELLI, DEBORAH ROSE, English Teacher; *b:* Mt Vernon, NY; *m:* Paul; *c:* Mark, Dana; *ed:* Herbert H Lehman Coll (BA) Eng 1973; Iona Coll (MS) Ed 1978; Attnd Syracuse Univ Project Advance Writing Instruction 3 Credits; *cr:* Incarnation Schl 7th & 8th Grd Tchr 1974-78; Hallen Schl Eng Tchr 1978-79; Port Chester HS Eng Tchr 1984-; *ai:* Jr Class Adv; *office:* Port Chester HS Tamarack Rd Port Chester NY 10573

GIAMATTI, TONI SMITH, English Teacher; *b:* Orange, NJ; *w:* A. Bartlett (dec); *c:* Marcus, Elena, Paul; *ed:* Columbia Univ (BS) Eng, Comparative Lit 1960; Attnd Yale Schl of Drama 1960; *cr:* Hopkins Grammar Schl Drama Tchr 1969-70; Day Prospect Hill Schl Drama Tchr 1970-71; Creative Wkshp Drama Coach 1970-72; Hopkins Schl Eng Tchr 1974-; *ai:* Eng Writing Lab Tutor; Fin Aid Comm; Grd 9 Adv; Long Wharf Theatre Assocs 1971-, Chm; Yale Univ Wilbur Cross Medalist 1990; MIT Tchng Awds 1995; Univ of Chicago Tchr of Yr 1983; *office:* Hopkins Schl 986 Forest Rd New Haven CT 06515

GIAMBATTISTA, LISA A., Sixth Grade Teacher; *b:* Perth Amboy, NJ; *m:* Nicholas; *ed:* Seton Hall Univ (BA) Pol Sci Ed 1979; 27 Addl Credits; *cr:* Christ the King Schl Tchr 1981-82; Blue Cross Blue Shield of NJ Trainer, Recruiter 1982-86; Perth Amboy Bd of Ed Tchr 1987-; Bankers Savings Part-time Customer Svc Rep 1987-; *ai:* Safety Patrol, Band Front, After Schl Homework Club Adv; Schl Site Cncl; Pupil Assistance Comm; NJEA 1989-; NJ Governor's Tchr Awd 1993-94; *office:* Samuel E Shull MS 380 Hall Ave Perth Amboy NJ 08861

GIAMBRONE, MARCIA A., Music Teacher; *b:* Buffalo, NY; *ed:* SUNY at Buffalo (BFA) Music Ed 1967, (MFA) Vocal Pedogogy 1975; Attnd SUC at Fredonia, Westminster Choir Coll & Canisius Coll; *cr:* Potters Rd Elem Schl Music Tchr 1967-70; West Seneca West Sr HS Music Tchr 1970-; *ai:* Musical Producer & Dir 25 Yrs; Dept Ldrs Comm; Cadre Trainer Dist Collaborative Decision Making; JV Bsbl Coach; Music Dept Act Dir; MENC, NYSSMA 1967-; WSTA 1967-, Tchr of Yr 1981; ECMEA 1967-, Bd of Dir; NYACDA 1967-, Sec; NYSCDG 1980-, VP & Sec; Shared Desicion Making Teams; Orchard Pk Chorale 1981-86, Conductor & Music Dir; Buffalo Choral Arts Soc 1986-, Conductor & Music Dir; BPO Music Ed of the Yr 1995; NYACDA Choral Dir of the Yr 1995; *home:* 96 Danielle Dr Cheektowaga NY 14227*

GIAMBRUNO, NEIL G., Social Studies Teacher; *b:* Granville, NY; *m:* Cynthia R.; *c:* Todd, Victoria; *ed:* Colgate Univ (BA) Eng 1965; Univ of Bridgeport (MS) Scndry Ed 1970; 33 Addl Grad Hrs Psych; *cr:* Taught Every Grd Level From 7th-12th Grd; Taught Eng, Rdng Soc, 10th-12th Grd Ec, Govt Psych I & II & Child Psych.

GIAMMATTEI, JAMES L., Math Teacher; *m:* Jill; *ed:* Univ at Albany (BS) Math 1986; Univ of London (BS) Math 1986; Univ at Albany (MA) Math 1988, (MA) Math Ed 1988; *cr:* Scotia-Glenville HS Math Tchr 1988-; *ai:* Boys Var Bsktbl Coach; NHS; Hall of Fame Ath Comm; AAU Ath; NCTM, AMTNYS 1988-; *office:* Scotia Glenville HS 1 Tartan Way Scotia NY 12302*

GIAMPETRO, THERESA, Social Studies Teacher; *b:* Philadelphia, PA; *ed:* Rider Coll (BA) His 1972; Rutgers Univ, Trenton St Coll 24 Post Grad Credits; *cr:* Naval Air Tech Svcs Facility Procurement Analyst 1972-73; Notre Dame HS Tchr 1973-; *ai:* Advanced Placement His Stdnts Coach; NEA, NJEA 1973-; *office:* Notre Dame HS 601 Lawrence Rd Lawrenceville NJ 08648

GIANFORTE, CARL JOSEPH, English Teacher; *b:* Rochester, NY; *ed:* St Univ of NY (BA) Eng 1973, (MS) Ed 1976, (CAS) Admin 1985; Univ of Pisa Hum 1972; *cr:* Greece Cntrl Schl Dist Eng Tchr 1973-78; Greece Athena HS Vice Prin 1977-90, Eng Tchr 1978-; *ai:* Yrbk Adv; NEA, GTA 1973-; Outstdng Tchr Awd 1995; *office:* Greece Athena HS 800 Long Pond Rd Rochester NY 14612

GIANNETTE, HELEN, Retired Elementary Ed Teacher; *b:* Conway, PA; *w:* William (dec); *c:* Patricia Lematte; *ed:* Geneva Coll (BS) Elem Ed 1965; Slippery Rock (MA) Elem Ed 1969; 21 Post Grad Hrs Early Chldhd Ed, Rdng; *cr:* Vanport Schl 1st-3rd Grd Tchr 1965-76; FT Mc Intosh Schl 1st Grd Tchr 1976-81; Coll Square Schl 1st Grd Tchr 1981-93; *ai:* NEA, PSEA 1965-; PASR 1993-; BAEA 1965-93, Bldg Rep 1988; Crimson Line Auxiliary of the Beaver Vly Geriatric Ctr 1967-, 1000 Svc Hrs; Century Club of Beaver 1967-, Treas 1979-80, Pres 1991-92; *home:* 1309 2nd Ave Conway PA 15027

GIANNETTO, MARY GREZZO, Math Department Chairperson; *b:* Brooklyn, NY; *m:* Michael J.; *c:* Michael Jr., William; *ed:* Wagner Coll (BS) Math 1973; Western CT St Univ (MS) Curr 1990; Portland St Univ 3 Grad Credits; *cr:* Pawling HS Math Tchr, Dept Chprsn 1983-; *ai:* Sr Class Adv; Peer Leadership Co-Adv; Bldg Level Team; Tech Comm; Tech Prep Comm; NEA, MAA 1990-; AMTNYS 1983-, Cty Chair; NCTM 1983-; NYSAMS 1994-; Willow Lake Estates Homeowners 1978-, Past Pres; WLEPO Water Commissioner 1985-; Hewlett-Packard Graphing Calculator Grant; Wrote Curr for MST; *office:* Pawling HS Reservoir Rd Pawling NY 12564*

GIANNINI, VITO STEPHEN, Mathematics Teacher; *b:* Turi, Italy; *m:* Jane Salvio; *c:* Kristin, Michael; *ed:* CCSU (BA) Math 1969, (MS) Curr, Supervision 1978; *cr:* Income Tax Preparer Enrolled Agent 25 Yrs; Hillside MS Math Tchr 27 Yrs; *ai:* 7th Grd Class, Field Trip Adv; Naugatuck HS Girls Jr Var Soccer Coach; Coord Math Counts Competition; Store Co-Chm; NEA, CEA, Naugatuck Tchr League 1969-; Natl Assn Enrolled Agents 1992-; Kiwanis Club 1985-, Pres, Distinguished Pres Awd 1992; *office:* Hillside MS 51 Hillside Ave Naugatuck CT 06770

GIANNONE, MARIE M., European His & Psych Tchr; *b:* Middle Village, NY; *ed:* Masters Pending Queens Coll in Scndry Ed & St Johns Univ in Pol Sci; Schl of Modern Psychanalysis; *cr:* St Demetrios Schl Tchr 1981-85; Christ The King RHS Tchr & Coord of Global Stud 1985-; *ai:* Young Peoples Flwshp Moderator; Global Stud Pgm & Hugh OBrien Yth Fndtn Coord; *office:* Christ The King Regional HS 68-02 Metrop Flushing NY 11379*

GIANOULIS, GLORIA (MASSA), Jr High English Teacher; *b:* NY; *m:* John; *c:* Tara, Ashley; *ed:* Coll of SI (BA) Eng 1990, 1992; Credits in Eng, Ed; *cr:* New Dorp Chrstn Acad Jr HS T Coll of SI Lecturer, Eng Dept 1991-; Eng Lang Inst Instr 1995; Fac Stud Group; Paired Linked Courses; Frosh Wrkshp; Writing Assessment Comm; PSC 1991-; New Dorp Bapt Church 1987- Numerous Articles Pub; CUNY Assn of Writing Supvr Conf 19 New Dorp Christian Acad Willowbrook Campus 25-218 259 Staten Island NY 10314

GIANSANTI, RITA MURPHY, Psychology Teacher; *b:* Mt Ho Michael; *c:* Mychal Anne, Dana Marie; *ed:* Trenton St Coll (1987; Rowen St Coll, SAC Cert 1995; *cr:* St Mary of the Lakes Tchr 1987-89; Overbrook Sr HS Psych Tchr 1989-90, 1993-; Team Mem; nEA, NJEA 1989-; TSAA 1987-; *office:* Overbr Turnersville Rd Pine Hill NJ 08021

GIANSIRACUSA, MICHAEL, Theology Teacher; *b:* Philade *ed:* La Salle Univ (BA) Commnctn Arts 1990; Villanova U Theology 1993; *cr:* Archdiocese of Portland Yth Minister 1 Marks HS Theology Tchr 1994-; *ai:* SADD Co-Adv; NCEA 199 St Mark's HS Pike Creek Rd Wilmington DE 19808

GIAVEDONI, BARBARA CUBA, Math Teacher & Yearboo DuBois, PA; *m:* Anthony; *c:* Lauren; *ed:* Penn St Univ (BS) 1990; *cr:* Punxsutawney Sr HS Math Tchr 1993-; *ai:* Yrbk A PSEA, NCTM 1993-; *office:* Punxsutawney Area Sr HS N Punxsutawney PA 15767

GIBB, REEN DOROTHEE, Science Curriculum Coord Wuppertal, Germany; *m:* Thomas R. P.; *ed:* Tufts Univ (BS) Che 1977; Worcester Polytechnic Inst Masters Natural Sci 1988 Credits Physics, Biotechnology, Chem Courses Boston Univ Sc MIT, Univ of MA; *cr:* Tufts Univ Instr 1977-78; North Andove 1978-79; Brookline HS Tchr 1980-, Sci Curr Coord 1994-; *ai:* Ldr; WGBH NOVA Educl Consultant 1985-; Conduct, Attend C Session Sci Staff; Amer Chemical Soc 1988-, Northeast Regn Chem Tchng; NEACT, Aula Laudis Soc; NEACS; AAAS; Presb 1983-, Deacon; Brookline Fnd Grant Learn Digital Image Proces CESAME Grant Dev Interdisciplinary Unit Between Bio, M Amer Assoc Rsrch Grant Clinical Investigation 1991.*

GIBB, WILLIAM MARTIN, Mathematics Teacher; *b:* Ellwoo *m:* Ellen June Hain; *c:* Abegale J., Jason W.; *ed:* Lock Haven Sec Ed Math 1976; Millersville Univ (MED) Math 1989; *cr:* A Dist Math Tchr 1976-77; St Francis Prep Schl Math Dept Chprs Northeastern Schl Dist Math Tchr 1985-; *ai:* NHS Adv; NEA 19 1985-; Kappa Delta Pi Ed Honor Soc; *office:* Northeastern Sr HS St Manchester PA 17345*

GIBBON, SHERRY SMITH, Soc Stud Dept Chair & Te Binghamton, NY; *m:* John W. II; *c:* Michelle Verstringhe, Verstringhe; *ed:* SUNY Coll at Geneseo (BS) Ed 1970; Elmira Ed 1976; Trng in Interlearn, Integrative Learning, Tchng of S Across the Curr; Advanced Trng in Outcome Based Ed; Mode Lrng Styles & AP Lrng Styles; *cr:* Penn Yan Acad Soc Stud T Gifted & Talented Prgm Coord 1985-93, Soc Stud Dept Chair 1 Imprvmnt Fcltr; *ai:* HS Variety Show Dir; Excl & Accountabil Acad Clb Adv; NEA, NYNEA; Penn Yan Tchrs Assn 1970-; Wa Lakes Soc Stud Cncl, Sec; Delta Kappa Gamma Soc Intnl 1993 NYS Soc Stud Cncl; ASCD; Tchrs of Psych Scndry Schls; F Theater Co, Bd of Dirs; Phelps-Clifton Springs Comm Theater; Cross Vol, Organized Schl Blood Drives; *office:* Penn Yan Acad St Penn Yan NY 14527*

GIBBONS, DENNIS DAVE, Assistant Professor; *b:* New York NY Hosp Cornell Med Ctr (RT) Radiography 1974; NY Univ (RDMS) Diagnostic Med Sonography 1984; City Univ of NY B (BA) Bio 1985; NY Univ (MPH) Comm Hlth Ed 1989; T Columbia Univ (ABD) (EdM) Higher & Adult Ed 1992; Cert NY Ctr Ultrasound Physics, Adv OB-GYN Sonography 1988; Cert I Med Imaging CT 1983; *cr:* NY Hosp Cornell Med Clinical Ins NY Univ Med Ctr Adj Instr 1982-8; CUNY Rsrch Fnd Adj 1988-9; City Univ of NY Hostos Comm Coll Asst Prof 1984-; Stdnts Club Adv; Chair Curr Review Comm; Hostos AIDS T Minority Access to the Licensed Professions Prgm; ARDMS 19 ARRT 1974-; *office:* City Univ Of NY Hostos Coll 475 Grand Bronx NY 10451

GIBBONS, EILEEN ANN, Math Teacher; *b:* Danvers, MA; (dec); *c:* Laurie, John M.; *ed:* Salem St Coll (BSEd) Math, Sci Danvers Jr HS Math Tchr 1959-61, Sub Tchr 1968-73; St Ma Math Tchr 1974-76; Peabody Jr HS Math Tchr 1976-82; Bisho HS Math Tchr 1982-; *ai:* NEA 1980-; *office:* Bishop Fenwi Margin St Peabody MA 01960

GIBBONS, MARGARET ANN O'MALLEY, Second Grade T Cleveland, OH; *m:* Michael J.; *c:* Daniel F., Mary Michelle, Dav St John Coll of Cleveland (BSE) Ed 1974; *cr:* Our Lady of A 1st-2nd, 4th Grd Tchr 1963-66, 1975-; *ai:* First Communion Coo NCEA 1995-; Diocese of Cleveland Tchng Excl Awd 1992; Lady Of Angels Schl 3644 Rocky River Dr Cleveland OH 4411

GIBBONS, RICHARD PAUL, Psychology Teacher; *b:* New H *m:* Estelle Garbatini; *c:* Jonathan, Bethany; *ed:* Quinnipiac Liberal Arts 1961; Fairfield Univ (BSS) Soc Stud 1963, (MA) Ps *cr:* Cntrl Cath HS World His Tchr 1963-68; Amity Regnl HS Ps His Tchr 1968-; *ai:* SADD & Youth & Govt Adv; NEA 1971-; Assn 1971-, Pres; Amer Psych Assn 1988-; Bethany Bd Of Ed Bicentennial Commission 1976-; Bethany One Room Schoolho 1986-, Treas; CT St Tchr of Yr Finalist 1990; Amity Br of E Distinction 1990; Sigma Xi Co of Quinnipiac Coll Outstanding South CT Awd 1986; Frendian Psych Lessons Plans Pub in Butlers Book Tchng With Style; *office:* Amity RSD #5 Schl 25 N Woodbridge CT 06525*

GIBBONS, VICENTA CALZADILLA, Spanish Teacher; Oriente, Cuba; *m:* John A.; *c:* Elena, John; *ed:* Albertus Magnus Span, Scndry Ed 1976; Southern CT St Univ (MA) Span, Latin 1983; 6th Yr Admin 1991; *cr:* Coleytown Jr HS Span Tchr 1976- Regnl Sr HS Span Tchr 1978-, Co-Coord Intnl Ctr 1992-; *ai:* Bldg Staff Dev, Stu Assistance Prgm Comms; Fr Exch Prgm; A Tchrs of Span, Portuguese, CT Org Lang Tchrs 1980-; New Chapter Latin Amer Stud 1985-; Phi Delta Kappa 1994-; R Fellowship Finalist 1989; Articles Pub 1989; PTA Tchr of Yr 1 Pen Awd 1992; *office:* Amity Regional Sr HS 25 Newton Rd W CT 06525*

GIBBS, CYNTHIA WALLACE, First Grade Teacher; *b:* Scrant Roy H.; *c:* Stacy, Kari, Ryan; *ed:* Evangel Coll (BS) Elem Ed 1 of Scranton (MA) Ed 1977; Yearly Conf Attendance to Update Changes in Curr Especially Society Dev Ed; *cr:* Robert D. Wi SchlTchr Grd 1 1972-; *ai:* Lang Arts, Report, Assessment C Western Wayne Dist; NEA, PSEA 1972-; *office:* Robert D Wi Schl PO Box 316 Waymart PA 18472

INDA L., 6th Grade Teacher; *b:* Coshocton, OH; *m:* Russell; *c:* ; *ed:* OH St Univ (BS) PE, Hlth 1968; Retraining Akron Univ 980; *cr:* Riverview Schl PE, Hlth, Elem Ed Tchr 1968-; *ai:* 8-, Bldg Rep; NEA, OEA 1968-; Renners United Church of :l, Sunday Schl Tchr, Choir; *office:* Riverview Schls 199 State lle OH 43811

, TOM LLOYD, Social Studies Teacher; *b:* Columbus, OH; *ed:* 3A) Mrktg 1987; OH St Univ (MA) Soc Stud Ed 1989; Cleveland Working Towards Masters; *cr:* Olmsted Falls HS Soc Stud Tchr Var Girls Bsktbl Coach; Stu Cncl Adv; Ath Pub Address ; *office:* Olmsted Falls HS 26939 Bagley Rd Olmsted Falls OH

N, M. LINDA MORSE, Business Teacher; *b:* Mt Holly, NJ; *c:* Western KY Univ (BM) Music 1968; Trenton St (BA) Bus 1980; rses; *cr:* Pemberton Twp Music tchr 1968-70; Rancocas Vly Tchr 1975-81; Eastern High Bus Tchr 1984; McCorristin High 1985-; *ai:* Tutoring; Assist Layout Spring Play Ad Book & Office; NJBEA 1985-; Delta Omicron 1965-, Historian; Kappa 79-; *office:* Mc Corristin HS 175 Leonard Ave Trenton NJ 08610

KEVIN RAYMOND, Algebra & Religion Teacher; *b:* n, NY; *m:* Karen Lynn; *c:* Liam Jude, Colin Patrick; *ed:* n Coll (BA) Amer Stud 1985; Trinity Coll (MAT) Math Ed 1994; own Univ Asst La Crosse Coach 1986; Mater Dei Schl Algebra ; St Albans Schl La Crosse Coach 1987; Georgetown Prep Schl Coach 1988-; *ai:* Math Club Adv; 8th Grd Unlimited Ftbl, 6th , 8th Grd La Crosse, Var La Crosse Coach; Serra Club Bd Mem; 3-; AIMS 1987-; Serra Club 1995-, Bd Mem; *office:* Mater Dei Seven Locks Rd Bethesda MD 20817

ELLEN M., English Dept Chairperson; *b:* Hoboken, NJ; *ed:* ll (BA) Eng 1966; Columbia Univ Tchrs Coll (MA) Tchng of Attnd Rutgers Univ, Kean Coll, New Schl Soc Work; *cr:* Snyder chr 1966-76; Acad HS Eng Tchr 1976-78, Eng Dept Chprsn Theatre Club; Shakespeare Festival; NEA, NCTE, NJEA, 76-; Featured in NY Times Ad 1990-93; Jersey City Tchr of Yr rnors Tchr Awd 1986; 1990-91 Grant Shakespeare Festival; MA h Letter of Recognition 1990; Univ of Chicago Outstdng Tchr *office:* Acad HS 16 Bentley Ave Jersey City NJ 07304*

AMY J., English Teacher; *b:* Zanesville, OH; *ed:* OH Univ ng 1993; *cr:* Muskingman Area Tech Coll Adj Writing Instr; HS Eng Tchr, Publications Adv 1993-; *ai:* Adv Yrbk, ; Dir Stu-Written Variety Show; Ninth Grd Intervention Comm; E, OCTELA 1993-; Bd YWCA 1995-; Taught Swaziland; *office:* HS 1701 Blue Ave Zanesville OH 43701

BEN, Professor of Art; *b:* Grand Rapids, MI; *m:* Jane E. Struyk; Jeff Morin, Dan Morin, Jill Morin; *ed:* Aquinas Coll (BA) 970; Univ of NE (MFA) Painting 1973; Kendall Schl of Design f Grad Fine Arts Illustration 1967; *cr:* Damaen Coll Asst Prof Attica Correctional Facility Asst Prof 1975-76; Edinboro Univ rt 1976-; *ai:* APSCUF 1976-; NW PA Artists Assn 1979-; Artists Assn 1980-; Edinboro Univ Rsrch Grants; NW PA Artists d 1995; Jurors Awd 59th Midyear Exhibition Butler Inst of Amer *office:* Edinboro Univ Of PA Meadville & Normal Edinboro PA

BRIAN SCOTT, Secondary Math & Science Tchr; *b:* Teaneck, Univ of PA (BS) Physics, Math Ed 1989, (MED) Scndry Guid Richland HS Long Term Sub Tchr 1989-90; Blacklick Vly Jr, Sr Sci, Math Tchr 1990-; *ai:* Vols In-Svc, PA Jr Acad of Sci, Math v; Planned Course Comm; PSEA, NEA 1989-; *office:* Blacklick r HS 555 Birch St Nanty Glo PA 15943

CHERYLE L., Diagnostic Reading Specialist; *b:* Cleveland, ayne A.; *ed:* Kent St Univ (BS) Elem Ed 1969, (MA) Rdng 1971; allace Supervision, Rdg Cert 1985; Stud Groups Remediation in ole Lang Instruction, Dyslexia, Storytelling; *cr:* Parma City sroom Tchr Grad-86; Parma Schls Team Tchr 1973-80, Rdng ; *ai:* Right-To-Read Bldg Coord; Oasis Vol Trainer; Alpha Delta 3-, VP; Kappa Delta Pi, NEA, OEA, Parma Ed Assn 1969-; IRA y Summit Rdng Assn 1986-, Pres; Ballet Cncl-Cleveland; holar; Parma Jaycee Tchr of Yr; OH Jaycee Tchr of Yr; *office:* Schls-Ridge Brook 7915 Manhatten Ave Parma OH 44129

DIANE KNOX, Family & Consumer Science Tchr; *b:* Newport *m:* Harald-snoh; *ed:* KY St Univ (BS) Voc Home Ec Ed 1979; incinnati (MED) Educl Fnds 1988; *cr:* Withrow HS Family, Sci Tchr 1979-; *ai:* FHA Club Adv; CFT 1994-.

DONALD BERNARD, English Professor; *b:* Kansas City, MO; e Ivory; *c:* David, Douglas; *ed:* Univ of Kansas City (BA) Eng) Eng 1957; Brown Univ (PHD) Eng 1961; *cr:* Wayne St Univ Prof 1961-67; Univ of CT Assoc Prof, Prof 1967-74; Rutgers II 1974-; *ai:* Modern Lang Assn 1962-; Coll Lang Assn 1968-; Assn 1988-; NCTE; Natl Endowment for Hum 1970, 1992-93; l of Learned Soc 1970; Politics of Lit Expression Essays on ck Writers 1981; Five Black Writers 1968; *office:* Rutgers St ew Brnswck New Brunswick NJ 08903

DONNA MCNEILL, English Teacher; *b:* Hartford, CT; *m:* *c:* Matthew, Kathy; *ed:* Albertus Magnus Coll (BA) Eng; CT St Univ (MS) Eng; *office:* Lauralton Hall Schl 200 High St CT 06460

EILEEN MYRA, Fourth Grade Teacher; *b:* Hazleton, PA; *ed:* (BS) Scndry, Soc Stud 1972; Bloomsburg Univ (MS) Elem Ed redit Hrs in Elem Ed; *cr:* Hazleton Area Schl Dist 4th Grd Tchr AFT, NEA 1972-; *office:* Heights Terrace Elem Schl 275 Mill n PA 18201

GERALDINE D., 6th Grd Tchr & Asst Principal; *b:* Chester, ester M.; *c:* Carol Jane, David Chester; *ed:* Temple Univ (BA) 1950; Immaculata Coll (MS) Admin 1988; 35 Credit Hrs; *cr:* El e Nemors Chemist 1950-60; West Chester Friends Schl Tchr & 5-; *ai:* Yrbk & Geog Team Adv; Curr & Testing Comm; PA Geog , Distngd Tchr Awd; NCSS; Scottish Historical Soc 1992-; Soc 1992-; *office:* West Chester Friends Schl 415 N High St West A 19380

JAMES C., 8th Grade Science Teacher; *b:* Anchorage, AK; *m:* : Leslie, David, Daniel; *ed:* Colby Coll (BA) Bio 1975; Univ of Crosse (MA) Chem Ed 1995; Woodrow Wilson Chem & Physics 5-92; ICE Chemical Instrumentation 1992; Tchng Concepted 93; *cr:* Fryebrug Acad Sci Tchr 1980-90; Piscataquis Comm HS r 1990-92; Molly Ockett MS Phys Sci Tchr 1992-; *ai:* Biking Fair Adv; Tin Mt. Liason; Tech Comm; NSTA 1988-; ME Sci n 1982-; Natl Mid Level Sci Tchrs Assn 1991-; Fryeburg ional Church 1985-, Bd of Trustees Deacon; 1989 Woodrow atl Fellowship Fnd Dreyfuss Master Tchr; 1990 & 1995 al Tchr Nom; Contributed to WWNFF Publication In the Mid of Publication Cooperative Learning; *home:* 20 Oxford St Fryeburg *

JANET C. STEVENS, Teacher of GATE; *b:* Rahway, NJ; *m:* .; *c:* Jeffrey S., Mark R.; *ed:* Muhlenberg Coll (BA) Eng, Ed t Chester St Coll (MED) Ed 1967; Webster Coll; Inservice Trng & Courses; *cr:* Ithan Elem Schl 4th Grd Tchr 1964-67; Broad St Schl 4th Grd Tchr, 4th & 5th Grd Enrichment Tchr1968-71; Cure of Ars 7th-8th Grd Eng Tchr 1981-82; Pembroke Cntr y Day Schl 6th Grd Eng Tchr 1982-83; Flemington Raritan Schl Dist 4th Grd Tchr 1984-85, 3rd-8th Grd Tchr of GATE 1985-91, 3rd-5th Grd Tchr of GATE 1991-; *ai:* Hunterdon Cty Tech Ed Steering, Schoolwide Enrichment Comms; Cncl on Instruction; NEA 1984-; Conducted Tchr Wkshps on Problem Solving & Inventions; *office:* Barley Sheaf Elem Schl 80 Barley Sheaf Rd Flemington NJ 08822*

GIBSON, JANET MAHANEY, First Grade Teacher; *b:* Pittsburgh, PA; *m:* Les C.; *c:* Deborah; *ed:* Edinboro St Univ (BS) Elem Ed 1968; Penn St Univ Master Eq Elem Ed 1972; *cr:* Adlai E. Stevenson Elem Schl 1st Grd Tchr 1968-; *ai:* NEA & PSEA 1968-; PTA 1968-; *office:* Adlai E Stevenson Elem Schl 313 Holiday Park Dr Pittsburgh PA 15239

GIBSON, JOHN, HS Bible & Math Teacher; *b:* Pikeville, KY; *m:* Tara Lynne Blunc; *ed:* Morehead St Univ (BA) Ed 1992; *cr:* World Harvest Chrstn Acad Instr 1992-; *ai:* HS Chapel; *office:* World Harvest Chrstn Acad 4595 Gender Rd Canal Winchester OH 43110

GIBSON, JOSEPH THOMAS,JR., Business Education Teacher; *b:* Philadelphia, PA; *m:* Katherine A.; *c:* Katherine, Joseph, Susan; *ed:* LaSalle Univ (BS) Acctng 1968; *cr:* Roman Cath HS Bus Ed, Soc Stud Tchr 1968-86; St John Newmann HS Bus Ed Tchr, Disciplinarian 1986-; *ai:* ACT, NEA 1968-; NCEA; *office:* Saint John Neumann HS 2600 Moore St Philadelphia PA 19145

GIBSON, LESSIE (WALTON), Business Teacher; *b:* Norfolk, VA; *m:* William Edward; *c:* Sonja Wilson Carr, Sheri Wilson Jackson, Lesley Wilson, Synthia Wilson; *ed:* VA St Univ (BS) Bus Ed 1957; George Washington (MS) Ed 1979; Miami Univ Ed Cert 1963; *cr:* Georgie Tyler Schl Tchr 1957-58; Waldorf Elem Tchr 1968-69; Maurice J McDonough Tchr 1981-; *ai:* McDonough Chptr of FBLA Spon; Ed Assn of Charles Cty Bldg Rep; AKA 1956-, 3rd VP, Charter Mem; EACC, MSTA & NEA 1980-; *office:* Maurice Mcdonough HS 7165 Marshall Corner Rd Pomfret MD 20675

GIBSON, LOVIE HENRY, Reading Lab Teacher; *b:* Houston, TX; *m:* Louis M. Sr.; *c:* Marie Gibson-Price, Louis Jr., Van D.; *ed:* TX Southern Univ (BA) Sociology 1960; Herbert H. Lehman Coll (MS) Elem Ed 1978; *cr:* Cntrl Islip St Hosp Psychiatric Soc Worker 1960-61; Bd of Ed Tchr 1967-; *ai:* AFT 1968-; UFT 1967-.*

GIBSON, PAMELA H., 5th Grade Teacher; *b:* Sewickley, PA; *m:* Robert G.; *c:* Brian, Brad, Brett; *ed:* Attnd Penn St; CCAC Towards Scndry Math Degree; *cr:* Cornell Schl Dist 1st, 6th Grd Tchr 1974-75, 6th Grd Tchr 1975-76, 7th-11th Grd Math Tchr 1976-81, 5th, 6th Grd Tchr 1981-; *ai:* Pres, Math Dev Comm; Boosters Pres; PTC Yrbk; CEA, NEA, PSEA 1975-; PTC 1975-, Yrbk Ed 8 Yrs; Meth Church 1952-, Supt Sunday Schl; *office:* Cornell Schl Dist 1099 Maple Street Ext Coraopolis PA 15108

GIBSON, ROBERT ALFRED, History Teacher; *b:* New Rochelle, NY; *m:* Sandra Good; *ed:* Trinity Coll (BA) His 1976; Southern CT St Univ (MA) His 1992; Lib & Media Specialist Cert 1995; *cr:* Hillhouse HS His Tchr 1976-; *ai:* Stu Cncl Adv; NHS Facilitator; Hillhouse Fac Senate; AFT 1976-; NAACP 1995-; Yale-New Haven Tchrs Inst Fellow; Natl Endowment for Hum Fellow; Article Pub 1991; *office:* Hillhouse HS 480 Sherman Pky New Haven CT 06511

GIBSON, WAUNETA MARCEIL (HORINE), Retired Teacher; *b:* Darke Cty, OH; *m:* Kritson N.; *c:* David E., Susan E., John C.; *ed:* Ball St Univ (BS) Elem Ed 1969, (MS) Elem Ed 1971; *cr:* West Side MS 4th Grd Self-Contained Tchr 1969-71, 5th Grd Self-Contained Tchr 1972-82, 6th Grd Math, Sci Tchr 1983-94; *ai:* 5th, 6th Grd Girls IM Coach 1973-80; Grd Level Chprsn 1984-88; RE Classroom Assn 1969-, Sec; ISTA, NEA 1969-; RCRTA, ISTA-R 1994-; Sigma Phi Gamma 1951-, Treas, Sec, Historian, 25 Yr Life Mbrshp; Wesley United Meth Ch 1958-, SS Tchr; Rand Co Art Assn 1994-; *home:* 613 Beatrice Dr Union City OH 45390

GIBSON BUROZSKI, BILLIE ELIZA RUTH, 5th Grade Teacher; *b:* Eldorado, AR; *c:* Mark Patrick; *ed:* Univ of Cntrl AK (BSE); Seton Hall Univ (MA) Tchng Handicapped 1987; AZ St Univ Home Ec; Kean Coll; Elem Cert; *cr:* AZ HS Home Ec Tchr 1952-56; Phoenix Elem Schl Home Ec Tchr 1957-62; Tulsa Elem Schl Home Ec Tchr 1963; Pub Schls of Edison Township 5 Grd Tchr; *ai:* Church Org; Edison Woodbrook Schl Org; Middletown Comm Committees; NEA 1952-; NJEA 1963-; PTA; Early Chdhd Ed Natl Candidate to Pres 1967-; Natl Assn for Female Exec Writers Clubs; Franklin Mint Classics; Amer Freedoms Fnd Awd; Intnl Who's Who of Intellectuals; Two Thousand Notable Amer Women; *office:* Pub Schls of Edison Township 100 Municipal Blvd Edison NJ 08817*

GIBSON-GALLAGHER, KATHLEEN, 1st Grade Teacher; *b:* Hazleton, PA; *m:* Thomas M. Jr.; *c:* Tommy III; *ed:* Penn St Univ (BS) El Ed, Sec Ed, Soc Stds 1971; Bloomsburg Univ (ME) El Ed 1974; Post Grad 60 Credits; *cr:* T. L. Hinkle El Schl 1st-6th Grd Transitional Class Tchr 1973-75; Poplar Street Elem Schl 1st Grd Tchr 1971-73, 3rd-6th Rdng Tchr 1975-77; Heights Terrace Schl 1st Grd Tchr 1977-; *ai:* AFT 1975-; PTA Bd 1977-, Tchr Rep; Lahm Ave Playground Assn 1991-; Diabetes Campaign Coord 1993-; *office:* Heights Terrace Elem Schl 275 Mill St Hazleton PA 18201

GIEGENGACK, EDWARD, Math Teacher; *b:* Iowa City, IA; *m:* Teresa Marie Flynn; *c:* Philip, Paul, Daniel; *ed:* Villanova Univ (BS) Ed 1966; Fairfield Univ (MA) Ed 1967; 3 Credits Fairfield Univ; 9 Credits Natl Sci Fnd Flwshp 1994-95; *cr:* Al Hikma Univ Math, Statistics Tchr 1967-69; Deerfield Acad Math Tchr 1970; Greenwich Cntry Day Schl Math, Sci Tchr 1971-72; Staten Island Acad Math Tchr 1973-75; Fairfield Prep Math Tchr 1976-; *ai:* Rifle Team Moderator; Natl Sci Fnd Flwshp Chronological Dev of Math for Scndry Schl Tchrs Fairfield Univ; *office:* Fairfield Coll Preparatory Sch N Benson Rd Fairfield CT 06430

GIEL, CORRINE,VSC, Elementary School Principal; *b:* Pittsburgh, PA; *ed:* LaRoche Coll (BA) His 1968; Duquesne Univ (MSEd) Elem Admin 1973; *cr:* St Sebastian Schl Tchr 1963-68; St Andrew Schl Tchr 1968-79; St Agnes Schl Tchr 1979-83; Holy Rosary Schl Prin 1983-; *ai:* Diocese of Greensburg Supts Cabinet; NCEA 1963-; Literacy Tutor 1987-; *office:* Holy Rosary Schl PO Box 797 Abigale St Republic PA 15475

GIENAPP, WILLIAM E., Professor of History; *b:* Denton, TX; *m:* Erica L. Kilian; *c:* William K., Jonathan E.; *ed:* Univ of CA at Berkeley (BA) His 1967; Yale Univ (MA) His 1969; Univof CA at Berkeley (PHD) His 1980; *cr:* Univ of CA at Berkeley Acting Instr 1979-80; Univ of Wyoming Asst Prof to Prof 1980-89; Harvard Univ Prof 1989-; *ai:* Org of Am Historians 1978-, Craven Prize; Southern Historical Assn 1978; Soc for Historian of Early Repbulic 1980-; Books: The Origins of the Republican Party 1852-1856, 1987, Co-Author, Nation of Nations 1990, Co-Author Essays on American Antebellum Politics 1982; Co-Author Abraham Lincoln and the American Political Tradition 1986, Co-Author We Cannot Escape History 1995, Co-Author Why the War Came 1995; Contributor Encyclopedia of Amer Soc His 1993; Walter Prescott Webb Prize 1981; Siebold Prof 1988-89; *office:* Harvard Univ Robinson Hall Cambridge MA 02138

GIESE, MARYELLEN ZIMMERMANN, Chorus Teacher; *b:* Hudson, NY; *m:* Jay L.; *c:* Andrew King, Jay Adam; *ed:* Nazareth Coll (BS) Music Ed 1971; SUNY Brockport Eastman Schl of Music Perm Cert 1975; *cr:* Brockport Cntrl Schl Elem, MS, HS Vocal Music Tchr 1971-; *ai:* Select Vocal Ensembles Triple Trio, Swing Choir; Music Dept Chm; Church, Childrens, Handbell Choirs; NYSUT, AFT 1971-; MENC, NYSSMA 1968-, Monroe Cty Music Assn Pres; NYSCAME, RACAME 1984-, Pres Roch Area Cncl of Admins of Music Ed; First Presbyn Church, Various Comms; Conducts Various All Cty Choruses NY St; Tours with HS Choir; Choral Groups & Ensembles Perform for Schl & Comm Functions; *office:* Brockport HS 40 Allen St Brockport NY 14420

GIESIGE, THOMAS EDWARD, Spanish Teacher; *b:* Celina, OH; *m:* Ann Maribeth; *c:* Danielle, Brett; *ed:* Wright St Univ (BS) Elem Ed 1985; *cr:* Spinning Hills MS 7th Grd Math & 8th Grd Sci Tchr 1985-86; Mad River MS 6th Grd Core Curr 1986-87; US Peace Corps Vol 1987-89; Lima Cntrl Cath 9th-12th Grd Span Tchr 1991-; *ai:* Environmental & Span Club Adv; Asst Track Coach; *office:* Lima Central Catholic HS 720 S Cable Rd Lima OH 45805

GIESKE, FRANK H., 8th Grd Earth Science Teacher; *b:* Beckly, WV; *m:* Helen Ehrlich; *c:* Maria, Ehren; *ed:* Concord Coll (BS) Ed, Sci 1967; Univ of DE (MS) Sci Ed 1972; 75 Addl Hrs; *cr:* Woodrow Wilson HS His, Sci Tchr 1967; Cntrl MS Earth Sci Tchr 1967-; *ai:* Sci Olympiad Adv; Schl Technological Coord; Sci Advy Comm; Sci Curr Comm Capital Schl Dist; NEA, DSEA, CEA 1967-; Delmarua Sportsmen 1970-, Sec; Amer Motorcyclist 1971-; Natl Rifle Assn 1995-; DE St News Good Neighbor Awd; Nom Presidential Awd Excl Sci & Math Tchng; *office:* Cntrl MS 1 Delaware Ave Dover DE 19901

GIFFORD, BARBARA HANDSCHUH, 5th Grade Teacher; *b:* Salamanca, NY; *m:* Albert F.; *c:* Thomas Scott, William Albert; *ed:* Newark St Tchrs Coll (BS) Elem Ed 1959; Math Course Brookdale Comm Coll; *cr:* Colonia Schl 5th Grd Tchr 1959-61; Shark River Hills Schl 3rd-5th Grd Tchr 1961-68; Old Mill Wall Schl Sub Tchr 1976-81; St Rose Schl 2nd-5th Grd Tchr 1981-; *ai:* Soc Stud Dept Chm; Past Testing Coord; NJ Cncl for Soc Stud 1993-; Cath Ed Assn 1981-; Allaire Women's Club 1972-, Publicity Sec; *home:* 1628 Bailey Rd Wall NJ 07719

GIFFORD, GARA L., English Teacher; *b:* Kittanning, PA; *m:* Gary G.; *ed:* IN Univ of PA (BSEd) Eng 1972; 24 Post Grad Credits; *cr:* Ford City HS 9th-12th Grd Eng Tchr 1972-80; Ambridge HS 9th-12th Grd Eng Tchr 1980-81; South Side HS 9th & 11th Grd Eng Tchr 1981-82; South Side MS 7th Grd Eng Tchr 1982-; *ai:* Eng Dept Chair; Transitional Benchmark Outcomes for Outcomes-Based Ed Comm Chair; Writing Assessment & Block Scheduling Comms; Spelling Bee Spon; MS Newspaper; PMSA 1995-; W PA Quarter Horse Assn 1980-, Recording Sec, Most Valuable Mem Awd 1984; *office:* South Side MS 4949 St Rt 168 Hookstown PA 15050

GIFT, GERALD BRENTON, Biology Teacher; *b:* Chambersburg, PA; *m:* Barbara A.; *ed:* Shippensburg St Univ (BS) Bio 1971; Univ of ME (MS) Zoology 1989; *cr:* Mercersburg Acad Bio Tchr 1971-; *ai:* Head Var Vllybl & Asst Var Bsbl Coach; Asst Dean of Stdnts; NABT; Amer Soc of Mammalogists; Soc for Conservation Bio; Amer Inst of Biological Sci; Tuscarora Wildlife Ed Project 1989-, Pres of Bd; *office:* Mercersburg Acad 300 E Seminary St Mercersburg PA 17236

GIGGEY, DIANE, Spanish & French Teacher; *b:* Fall River, MA; *m:* Richard E.; *c:* Dana, Joanne; *ed:* Emmanuel Coll at Boston (BA) Fr 1967; Merrimack Coll at N Andover 1963-65; Span Cert Eastern CT St Univ; Post-Grad Rivier Coll at Nashua & Univ CT at Storrs; 3 Credit Hrs Providence Coll; *cr:* St Anselms Schl 4th-8th Grd Fr Tchr 1968-69; South Windsor Schls 4th-6th Grd Fr Tchr 1969-70; Timothy Edwards Mid 7th-8th Grd Fr Tchr 1970-72; Horace Porter Schls 7th-8th Grd Fr & Span Tchr 1984-; *ai:* Enrichment Comm 10 Yrs; Colt CT Org of Lang Tchrs 1986-; Eastern CT Alliance of Frgn Lang Tchrs 1992-, Steering Comm; CCD 1978-80, Tchr; US Girls Scouts 1980-84, Troop Ldr; Comm Mem for Writing Current CT St; Frgn Lang Curr Guide; *office:* Horace W Porter Elem Schl PO Box 166 Schoolhouse Rd Columbia CT 06237

GIGGEY, MARYANNE SHAPAZIAN, Third Grade Teacher; *b:* Portland, ME; *m:* Timothy James; *c:* Timothy James Jr.; *ed:* Univ of Southern ME (BS) Ed 1973; Addl 30 Post Grad Credit Hrs; *cr:* Westbrook Schl Dept Third Grd Tchr 1973-; *ai:* Stu Cncl; Past Pres PTO; Sunshine Fund; Past Admin Aide; Assessment Comm; Past Bldg Rep; NEA, MEA 1973-; WEA 1973-, VP; *office:* Congin Elem Schl 341 Cumberland St Westbrook ME 04092

GIGL, RONALD WILLIAM, Industrial Technology Teacher; *b:* Lancaster, PA; *m:* Janet Barron; *c:* Todd Sargent, Craig Sargent; *ed:* Millersville Univ (BS) Indstrl Arts 1968; 24 Post Grad Hrs; *cr:* Conestoga Vly MS 7th-8th Grd Tchr 1968-; *ai:* NEA, PSEA, CVEA 1968-; Trained Tchrs in Field; *office:* Conestoga Valley MS 11 School Dr Leola PA 17540

GIGLIO, LOUIS W., Math & Computer Science Tchr; *b:* Brooklyn, NY; *m:* Honore M. O'Neill; *c:* Jamie Lee, Jessica Ann, Joseph Paterno; *ed:* Fairleigh Dickinson Univ (BA) His Minor Math 1964-; Montclair St Univ (MA) Personnel Svcs 1973; Cert Learning Disabilities; Stevens Inst of Tech Cert Prgm Math & Cmptr Sci; Rutgers Univ Grad Schl of Ed 12 Credit Math Ed; *cr:* East Paterson Meml HS Math Tchr 1965-69; River Dell Regnl HS Math, Cmptr Sci Tchr 1969-; *ai:* NHS Co-Adv; NCTM 1987-; NEA, NJEA 1965-; RDEA 1969-; NCSM 1995-; Tandy Tech Tchr Awd 1994; Grants Awded Amer Math Project 2 Yr Funding, PRIMES 4 Yr NJ DNE Eisenhower Funds, Montclair St SSI Site 2 Yr Funding; PTO Mini-Grant 1996; *office:* River Dell Regnl HS Pyle St Oradell NJ 07649*

GIGLIO, WILLIAM VITO, Business Education Teacher; *b:* Elizabeth, NJ; *m:* Carol; *c:* Scott, Robert; *ed:* Seton Hall Univ (BS) Bus Admin 1968, (MA) Scndry Bus Ed 1970; Montclair St Coll 30 Grad Credits; Prin, Supvr Certs; *cr:* Middlesex HS Bus Ed Tchr 1968-72; Mt Olive HS Bus Ed Tchr 1972-74; Ridge HS Bus Ed Tchr 1974-; *ai:* Var Bsbl Coach; NHS Selection Comm; NEA, NJEA 1968-; BTEA, SCEA 1974-; NJ Ctr Law Focused Ed 1985-; Amer Legion Bsbl, Babe Ruth Bsbl 1990-; Somerset Cty Bsbl Coach of Yr 1995; Newark Star Ledger Awd; Tchr of Month PTO Awd; *office:* Ridge HS S Finley Ave Basking Ridge NJ 07920

GIGLIORRI, LINDA I., Accounting Professor; *b:* Utica, NY; *ed:* Syracuse Univ (BS) Acctng 1969, (MBA) Prsnl & Indstrl Relations 1977, (EDD) Higher Ed 1987; Control Data Inst Data Processing & Systems Analysis, Design Cert; *cr:* Mohawk Vly Comm Coll Prof 1976-, Coord New Fac, Staff Orientation 1992-, Coord Adj Fac Staff Dev 1989-; *ai:* Search, Curr Review Comms; Assessment Task Force; NYS Assn of 2 Yr Colls 1976-, Pres, VP, Sec Coord of Insts, Pres Awd; NYSUT 1976-; Excl in Tchng Awd 1995; Inst for CC Rsrch Dissertation Awd 1987; Assn Systems Mngmt Div III Awd; Achvmt Awd; NYS Assn of 2 Yr Coll Past Pres Awd 1992; Campus Rep Awd; *office:* Mohawk Valley Comm Coll 1101 Sherman Dr Utica NY 13501

GIHORSKI, THOMAS PATRICK, Health, Drivers Ed & PE Tchr; *b:* Cape May Ct House, NJ; *ed:* Montclair Univ (BS) Hlt, PE 1987; Columbia Univ (MA) Admin, Supervision 1992; Montclair Univ 15 Hrs Hlth Ed 1987; Chelsea Univ Observed Hlth, PE Dept 1987; Jersey City St Driver's Ed Cert 1994; Natl Safety Cncl Defensive Driving Instr 1994; *cr:* Glenview Acad Hlth, PE Tchr 1989-90; Orange Elem Schl Hlth, PE Tchr 1990-91; Harrington Park Schl Dist Hlth, PE Tchr 1991-94; Parsippany HS Hlth, Driver's Ed, PE Tchr 1994-; *ai:* Head Bsbl Coach; Asst Ftbl, Bsktbl; Pupil Assistance, Tech, Hlth, PE Dist, Driver's Ed Comms; NEA 1989-; AAHPERD, NASPE, AAALF 1995-; NJSIAA Coaches 1993-; *office:* Parsippany HS Baldwin & Vail Rds Parsippany NJ 07054*

GILBERG, MARGOT DERUVO, Chair Foreign Language Dept; *b:* New York, NY; *ed:* Hunter Coll (AB) Span 1964; Lehman Coll (MA) Span Lit 1974; *cr:* St Nicholas of Tolentine HS Span Tchr 1971-84; St Catharine

Acad Span Tchr & Forgein Lang Chair 1984-; *ai:* Chprsn Curr Comm; AATSP, MLA & NYSTFL 1984-; ACTFL; ASCD.

GILBERT, CHARLES L., Aerospace Science Instructor; *b:* Bostwick, GA; *m:* Diane S.; *c:* Elisabeth, Julie, Stephan; *ed:* Southern IL Univ (MS) Govt 1974; *cr:* USAF Col 1961-89; Northern Vance HS Aerospace Sci Instr 1990-93; Lackey HS Aerospace Sci Instr 1993-; *ai:* Drill Team & Color Guard Spon; Site Based Team Mem; NEA 1993-; *office:* Lackey HS 3000 Chicamuxen Rd Indian Head MD 20640

GILBERT, DAVID WAYNE, Science Teacher; *b:* Lancaster, NH; *m:* Brenda; *c:* Lance, Silas, Isaac, Caleb, Brody, Dylan, Ruben; *ed:* Plymouth St (BE) PE 1963; Univ of VT (MED) Admin 1994; 30 Post Grad Hrs in Ed; *cr:* Whitefield HS Sci Tchr 1963-64; St Albans City Elem PE Tchr 1964-71; Trinity Coll Farm Migrant Ed 1978-83; Milton High Sci Tchr 1983-; *ai:* Var Girls Soccer, AHAUS Olympic Dev Coach; Var Boys Ice Hockey; Soph Class Adv; Var Boys Bsbl; New England Schl Approval Comm; Var Girls Bsktbl; NEA 1963-; Natl Soccer Coaches Assn 1991, Vt Coach of Yr 1992; VT Hockey League 1985, VT Coach of Yr 1991; Outstanding Young Men of Amer 1970; Med Tech Stipend UVM 1993; *office:* Milton HS Becky Lander Dr Milton VT 05468*

GILBERT, DEBORAH LYNN, High School Math Teacher; *b:* Columbia, PA; *ed:* Millersville St Univ (BSEd) Math 1971; 29 Grad Credits; *cr:* Elizabethtown Jr HS Math Tchr 1971-72; Western HS Math Tchr 1974-; *ai:* Asst Schl Treas; NCTM 1970-; *office:* Western H S 4600 Falls Rd Baltimore MD 21209

GILBERT, ELIZABETH REES, 6th-8th Grd Classroom Teacher; *b:* Washington, DC; *m:* Jeffrey William; *c:* Suzanne; *ed:* Univ of MD (BS) 1977; The George Washington Univ (MAT) Museum Ed 1980; Courses Toward Cert in Tchng at Frostburg St Univ; *cr:* Smithsonian Inst Contractual Author 1980-81; Calvert Marine Museum Edctr 1981-82; Garrett Cty Hlth Dept Hlth Ed 1983-88; Swan Meadow Schl 6th-8th Grd Tchr 1992-; *ai:* Wellness Cncl Chprsn Garrett Cty Bd of Ed; MSTA 1991-, Schl Rep; St Mark's Luth Church 1984-, Church Cncl, Choir; Garrett Choral Soc 1988-; Museum Ed Roundtable 1980-; Author Fair & Festivals, A Smithsonian Guide to Annual Events in Md, VA & Washington DC 1982; Articles Pub; *office:* Swan Meadow Schl 6709 Garrett Hwy Oakland MD 21550

GILBERT, HARRY JAMES, High School Math Teacher; *b:* Philadelpha, PA; *m:* Linda Marie Andreacchio; *c:* Brian, Gina; *ed:* Temple (BS) Math Ed 1972; Rutgers (MS) Math Ed 1980; 3 Credits Metric Ed Penn St; 3 Credits Affective Ed Marywood; 6 Credits Natl Sci Fnd Drexel; *cr:* Camden HS Math Tchr 1972-73; South Phila HS Math Tchr 1973-90; Academics Plus Schl Math Instr, Tutor 1986-90; Northeast HS Math Tchr 1990-; *ai:* Disciplinary Transfer Stdnts Mentor; AFT, NEA 1973-; Phila Fed Tchrs 1973-, Bldg Comm 1988-89; Croydon United Soccer Club 1991-; Dir, Asst Coach; Knights of Columbus Dart League 1978-; Croydon Little League Bsbl 1984-, Asst Coach; Truman Ice Hockey Club 1993-; *office:* Northeast HS Cottman & Algon Aves Philadelphia PA 19111

GILBERT, HELEN C., Guidance Director; *b:* Toledo, OH; *c:* Jay; *ed:* Univ of Toledo (BED) Elem Ed 1961; Univ of NE (MS) Guidance & Counseling 1971; *cr:* Lompoc Unified Schls Tchr 1962-64; Ojai Unified Schls Tchr 1965-66; East Side Cntrl Tchr 1966-76; East Toledo Jr High Cnslr 1976-79; Waite HS Guidance Dir, Cnslr 1979-; *ai:* Teen Pep Adv; Intern Cnslrs Mentor; OSCA 1971-, VP Dist I; NWOCA 1971-, Exec Bd; TAAP 1976-, Trustee; PAK 1976-; OCA, ASCA 1971-; Teen Line 1990-, Adv; St Pauls Luth Church Chrstn Ed Dir 10 Yrs Plus; Natl Certified Cnslr; *office:* Morrison R. Waite HS 301 Morrison Dr Toledo OH 43605

GILBERT, JEAN H., Retired Elementary Teacher; *b:* Covington, KY; *m:* Douglas C.; *c:* Jeffrey, Jayne Chamberlin, Jennifer Collins, Janine; *ed:* Wright St Univ (BS) Elem Ed 1969; Post Grad Hrs Univ of Dayton, Univ of WI at Whitewater; *cr:* C. E. Holliday Schl 1st, Multiage 2nd & 3rd, 4th, 6th Grd Tchr 1969-92; *ai:* Odyssey of the Mind Adv; NEA 1969-, Lifetime Mem; OEA, WCEA 1969-; OH Ret Tchrs 1992-, Life Mem; West Carrollton Ed Fnd 1992-, Grants Comm; Excl Tchng Nom 1986, 1988; Ed Recognition Assn Significant Tchr Awd 1987-95; Ashland Oil Tchr Achvmt Awd Nom 1988, 1990; Western OH Ed Assn Tchr of Yr Nom 1989, 1990.

GILBERT, JUDITH MACBETH, French & Lang Arts Teacher; *b:* NY, NY; *m:* Thomas D.; *c:* Thomas Jr., Michael; *ed:* Annhurst Coll (BA) Elem Ed 1966; South Eastern CT Univ 5th Yr Rdng 1973; Attnd CT Coll, Univ Laval-Quebec; *cr:* Holy Family Parochial Schl 5th Grd Tchr 1965-66; Ste Anne Schl 7th-8th Grd Tchr 1966-67; Griswold Elem Schl 6th Grd Tchr 1967-69; Preston Plains Schl 6th Grd, 7th-8th Grd Tchr 1971-; *ai:* Frgn Lang Curr; Pub Relations Fundraising; NEA, CEA 1967-; FAP 1971-, Pres 2 Yrs; Alpha Delta Kappa 1990-, Pres; Schlsp for Summer Stud Laval Univ Quebec; *office:* Preston Plains MS Rt 164 Preston CT 06365

GILBERT, KATHLEEN ERICKSON, Math, Civics & Economics Tchr; *b:* Trenton, NJ; *m:* Bret M.; *ed:* Burlington Cty Coll (AA) Ed 1973; Trenton St Coll (BS) 1975; Attnd North Adams St Coll; *cr:* Fieldsboro Schl Basic Skills Rdng, Math Kndgtn Tchr 1976-82; Columbia Schl 1st, 2nd, 6th Grd Tchr 1982-90; Atlantis Schl 6th Grd Self Contained Classroom Tchr 1990-91; Challenger Schl 6th Grd Self Contained Classroom Tchr 1991-94; Clarence B. Lamb Schl 5th-6th Grd Math, Civics, Ec Tchr 1994-; *ai:* NEA, NJEA 1976-; Tchr of Yr 1990-91; *office:* C B Lamb Schl 46 Schoolhouse Rd Wrightstown NJ 08562

GILBERT, LAINEY, High School English Teacher; *b:* Brooklyn, NY; *c:* Alison, Adam; *ed:* Long Island Univ (BA) Eng 1970; CUNY at Staten Island (MA) Eng 1974; 36 Addl Hrs; *cr:* Grady Voc Tech HS Eng Tchr 1970-91; Home Grown Poems Prin 1990-; Airborn Flightware Co Pres 1992-; Kingsborough Comm Coll Adj Prof 1986-91; *ai:* Yrbk 1974-79; Dean of Women 1989-91; AFT, NEA 1970-; Title IX Grant; Poetry Pub.

GILBERT, LORI SHEA, Prevention Specialist; *b:* Butler, PA; *m:* Harold D.; *c:* Robert L., Joshua D.; *ed:* Waynesburg Coll (BA) Psych, Sociology 1989; Soc Stud Cert 1989; Certfd Prevention Specialist; *cr:* Waynesburg Coll Upward Bound Soc Stud Tchr 1992-; VISION Comprehensive Prevention Svcs Prevention Specialist 1990-.

GILBERT, MICHAEL JON, 8th Grade American His Teacher; *b:* West Carrollton, OH; *m:* Linda Cook; *c:* Erin, Abby; *ed:* Bowling Green St Univ (BS) Comp Soc Stud 1975, (MS) Comp Soc Stud 1980, (MS) Scndry Soc Stud; 30 Addl Hrs 1984; *cr:* Fremont Jr HS Tchr 7th Grd Geography Tchr 1975-80, 8th Grd His Tchr 1980-, 8th Grd Amer His Citizenship Tchr 1991-, Insight Tchr 1984-95; *ai:* 8th Grd Ftbl Coach; 7th Grd Girls Bsktbl Coach; Vol Coach 1993-, Moose Lodge #1286 Mem 1992; Asst Var Sftbl Coach; Volunteer Girls Sftbl Coach Summers 1989-; NEA 1975-; OH Cncl Soc Stud 1991-; Usher Grace Luth 1975-; Vol Girls Sftbl Coach 1989-; 7th Grd Tchr of Yr Fremont 1980; Excl Action Awd 1985; *office:* Fremont Jr H S 501 Croghan St Fremont OH 43420*

GILBERT, NEIL ROBERT, Biology & Marine Biology Tchr; *b:* Levittown, PA; *m:* Barbara Ellen Kucinski-Gilbert; *ed:* Trenton St Coll (BA) Elem Ed 1979, (MED) Sci Ed 1984; *cr:* Nottingham MS Sci Tchr 1979-82; Nottinham HS Bio, Marine Bio Tchr 1983-; *ai:* Var Tennis Coach; Ftbl Announcer; Multicultural Club Adv; NEA 1979-, Bldg Rep; NJ Sci Tchrs Assn 1983-; Natl Marine Educators Assn 1995-; US Tennis Assn 1982-; NJ Coaches Assn 1994-, Conf Rep; Mercer Cty Tennis Coach of Yr; *home:* 25 Hedgerow Dr Fairless Hills PA 19030

GILBERT, ROBERT CRAIG, Fourth Grade Teacher; *b:* Milford, MA; *ed:* Penn State Univ (BS) Elem Ed 1984; *cr:* The Basics Schl Fourth Grd Tchr 1986-95; *ai:* Schl Newspaper Ed; Chorus, Afterschool IM Dirs; NEA, PSEA 1986-; *office:* The Basics Schl 401 Emerson Ave Lansdowne PA 19050

GILBERT, RODNEY, Asst Prof of Animal Science; *b:* Hartford, CT; *m:* Barbara Smith; *c:* Katherine, Seth, Hannah; *ed:* Univ of CT (BS) Animal Sci 1971, (MS) Ag 1973; *cr:* DE Vly Coll Asst Prof of Animal Sci 1973-; *ai:* Adv to Collegiate 4-H Club; Co-Adv Block & Bridle Club; Coach of Intercollegiate Livestock Judging Team; AAUP 1996; Soil Conservation Soc of Amer Awd; PA St FFA Awd for Svc; *office:* Delaware Valley Coll 700 E Butler Ave Doylestown PA 18901

GILBERT, STEVEN EDWARD, HS Social Studies Teacher; *b:* Mansfield, OH; *m:* Nancy Ann Kosinski; *c:* Aaron, Kyle; *ed:* Toledo Univ (BE) Comp Soc Stud 1973; BGSU (MA) Scndry Ed 1979; Attnd Kent State Vo-Ed OWE 1990; *cr:* Bowling Green HS Soc Stud Tchr, Asst Ftbl, Wrestling Tchr 1976-81; Norwalk HS Soc Stud Tchr, Asst Ftbl, Wrestling Coach 1981-85; Ashland Crestview HS Soc Stud Tchr, Head Ftbl Coach 1985-87; Mansfield Sr HS OWE Tchr, Head Ftbl Coach 1987-92; Columbian HS Soc Stud Tchr, Head Ftbl Coach 1993-; *ai:* Head Ftbl Coach; NWOFCA 1985-, 2nd VP; Numerous Coach of Yr Honors; Martha Haldon Jennings Awd 1981; *office:* Tiffin Columbian HS 300 S Monroe St Tiffin OH 44883*

GILBERT, STUART MARC, Physical Ed Teacher & Coach; *b:* Cleveland, OH; *m:* Carolyn; *ed:* Miami Univ (BS) PE 1981; Cleveland St Univ (MED) Exercise Sci 1988; *cr:* Shaker Hghts City Schl Dist HS PE Tchr 1983-; *ai:* MS Girls Tennis, Asst Var Boys Track Coach; OH Assn Track, Cross Cntry Coaches; Shaker Hghts Tchrs Assn; *office:* Shaker Hghts City Schl Dist 15600 Parkland Dr Shaker Hts OH 44120

GILBERT, TIMOTHY PAUL, Senior Army Instructor; *b:* Phoenix, AZ; *m:* Carolyn Brock; *c:* Jennifer L., Timothy D.; *ed:* USMA at West Point NY (BS) General Sci 1967; Indiana Univ of PA at Indiana (MA) His 1973; CGSC at Leavenworth Intnl Politics 1981; Infantry Officers Basic Course 1967, Airborne Schl & Ranger Schl 1967; Armor Officers Advanced Course 1970-71; Jungle Schl 1976; Sr Officers Legal Course 1987; *cr:* Indiana Univ of PA Asst Prof 1971-74; St Univ of NY Assoc Prof 1978-80; Indiana Univ of PA Prof & Dept Chair 1989-93; United Jr-Sr HS Sr Army Instr & Jr Reserve Officer Training Corps 1993-; *ai:* Indiana Univ of PA Orienteering Club Founder & Adv 1989-; Rifle Team, Drill Team, Color Guard & Cannon Crew Adv; PSEA 1989-; US Orienteering Fed 1971-; North Eastern OH Orienteering Club 1993-; 196th Light Infantry Brigade Assn 1989-; IN Borough Police Civil Svc Commission 1995-; Cty World War II Commemorative Comm 1992-; Veterans of Foreign Wars Chapter 1989 1991-; United HS Ski Club, Elk Lodge 1993-; Founded JROTC Prgm at United HS 1993; Brought Vietnam Wall to IN Cty 1992; Excl Fnd Nom Educator of Yr 1995; US Orienteering Fed Ranking 25th in US of Amer; IN Cty Veteran of Yr 1993; *office:* United Jr Sr HS PO Box 168 Armagh PA 15920*

GILBERT, TRACY, Mathematics Teacher; *b:* Kearny, NJ; *ed:* Seton Hall Univ (BS) Math 1989, (MS) Math 1991; Montclair Trng Ctr for Tchr Trng Alternate Rt for NJ Cert; *cr:* Seton Hall Univ Grad Tchng Asst Math 1989-91, Part Time Math Instr 1991-92; St Marys HS Math Tchr 1992-; *ai:* Math Chprsn; Yrbk Adv; Kappa Delta Pi 1988-; Pi Mu Epsilon 1989-; Seton Hall Univ Math Honors Citation 1989; *office:* Saint Mary HS 64 Chestnut St Rutherford NJ 07070

GILBO, JOHN ROBERT, Health Education Teacher; *b:* Port Henry, NY; *m:* Anna Carolyn Stirewalt; *c:* Lisa Catherine Yost Kirkpatrick, Theodore Martin Yost; *ed:* Wittenberg Univ (BA) Hlth & PE 1974; Bowling Green St Univ (MEd) Admin & Supervision 1975; Adolescent Psych Grad Course 2 Hrs Univ of Northern IA; *cr:* W.D. Sugg MS PE Tchr 1975-77; Culberth Jr High Hlth, PE Tchr, Ftbl, Bsbl Coach 1977-79; Ravenscroft Schl PE Tchr, Ftbl, Bsbl Coach 1979-81; Orange HS PE Tchr, Head Ftbl Coach 1981-88; Zama Amer HS Hlth Ed Tchr, Head Ftbl Coach 1990-; *ai:* Var Head Ftbl Coach; Sr Class Co-Spon; Natl Jr Honor Soc, Renaissance Prgm, Guidance, Grad Comms; Mark Twain Stud Guest Lecturer & Performer; NEA 1977-; Phi Delta Kappa 1976-, Guest Speaker Awd 1992; OEA 1990-; Grad Assistantship Bowling Green St Univ 1974-75; Articles Pub JOHPER 1976; Midstate Conf Ftbl Coach of Yr 1984; Natl HS Ftbl Coaches Awd 1989; Sustained Superior Tchng Awd 1995; *home:* Unit 45013 APO AP 96338

GILBO, MARY MC NULTY, Second Grade Teacher; *b:* Port Henry, NY; *m:* Joseph H.; *c:* Kathleen O'Rourke, Stacey de Avila, Peter, Lisa Pelkey, Amy, Beth, Jennifer, Megan; *ed:* SUNY at Plattsburgh (BS) Early Chldhd Ed 1959; *cr:* Head Start Tchr 1968-69; Moriah Cntrl Schl Second Grd Tchr 1969-; *ai:* MCTA, NYSUT, AFT 1969-; *office:* Moriah Central Schl HC 1 Box 7a Port Henry NY 12974

GILCHREST, PRISCILLA (TRIPP), Fifth Grade Teacher; *b:* New Bedford, MA; *m:* Edwin B. Jr.; *c:* Lucy Mendes, Glenna Mansfield, Berk, Cynthia, Pamela Mello, Linda Almeida; *ed:* Bridgewater St Coll (BA) Elem Ed 1956; *cr:* Shoshone Indian Reservation Pub Schl Tchr 1956-58; Crow Indian Reservation Pub Schl Tchr 1958-59; New Bedford Pub Schl Tchr 1959-; *ai:* Club Adv; Schl Cncl; NEA, NBEA 1964-; *office:* Jireh Swift Elem Schl 2203 Acushnet Ave New Bedford MA 02745

GILCHRIST, KATHLEEN, Social Studies Teacher; *b:* Richmond Hill, NY; *ed:* Adelphi Univ (BA) His 1983, (MA) Ed 1989; 30 Credits Inservice & Grad Above Masters; *cr:* William Floyd HS 9th-10th & 12th Grd SS Tchr 11 Yrs; Holy Trinity 7th-8th Grd SS Tchr 2 Yrs; *ai:* Var Chrldng Coach 8 Yrs; JH Chrldng Coach 2 Yrs; Class Adv 1990-92; Fac Mediator; AFT 1986-; *office:* William Floyd HS 230 Mastic Beach Rd Mastic NY 11950

GILDE, HANS-GEORG, Retired Professor; *b:* Ragnit, Germany; *m:* Helen C. Schoeuer; *c:* Emily C., Ellen L. Schwendeman; *ed:* Albright Coll (BS) Chem, Math 1957; OH Univ (PHD) Organic Chem 1961; Case Western Reserve Univ Post Doctoral Work; Univ of Loudon Sabbaticals 1968-69, MIT, Harvard 1976, Univ of Erlangen 1984; 43 Hrs; *cr:* OH Univ Instr 1960; Marietta Coll Asst, EB Andrews Prof of Chem, Prof Elm 1961-92; *ai:* Amer Chem Soc 1957-, Chm of Local Section; Chem Soc London 1960-; Rsrch Flwshp at OH Univ; Harness Flwshp at Marietta Coll; Outstdng Alumni Awd at OH Univ, Albright Coll; E. B. Andrews Prof of Chem Multiple NSF Awd; Rsrch Corp Grants.

GILDEA, JUDY A., Health & Physical Ed Tchr; *b:* Allentown, NJ; *m:* Barry; *c:* Jonathan, Jason; *ed:* Bethel Coll (BS) Hlth & PE 1970; Penn St (ME) 1996; Attnd Wilkes-Coll, Kings Coll & IN Wesleyan; *cr:* Plains HS Hlth Tchr, PE Tchr & Coach 1970-72; Couglin HS Hlth & PE Tchr 1973-, Coach 1973-93; *ai:* NEA & PSEA 1970-; Bsktbl Booster Club 1990-; *office:* Coughlin HS 720 S Main St Wilkes Barre PA 18701

GILE, MARY STUART SINCLAIR, Prof of Early Childhood Ed; *b:* Montreal, Canada; *m:* Robert H.; *c:* Christopher Tridek, Julia Casey, Robertson; *ed:* Mc Gill Univ (BS) PE 1957; Univ of NH (MED) Early Chldhd Ed 1971; Vanderbilt Univ (EDS) Ed, Prgm, Staff Dev 1982; Attnd Harvard Grad Schl of Ed, Tufts Univ, Harvard Grad Schl of Design; *cr:* Protestant Schl PE, Hlth Tchr 1957-63, Kndgtn Tchr 1963-65; White Mtn Reg Schl Bd Kndgtn, Head Start Tchr 1965-69; St Dept of Ed Consultant in EC, Title I, ECEA 1969-85; Acad of Applied Sci VP Ed & Dev 1985-90; *ai:* Pres Fac Forum, Senate; Adv Stud Early Chldhd Assn; NH Child Care Advy Bd; St Ldshp Team of Prevention of Child Abuse; Success by Six; Concord Children's Initiative Inc; Phi Delta Kappa 1980-, 10 Yrs Awd; NAEYC; ACEI 1990-; Greater Concord Chamber Commerce 1986-, Ed, Bus Task Force, Ldrshp Concord; United Way of Mess Cty 1980-, Chair, Admissions, Leo J. Rubin Awd; South Congregational Churc Deacon, Choir; 1969 Awded EC Flwshp; 1992 NH Young Invent *office:* NH Tech Inst 11 Institute Dr Concord NH 03301*

GILES, BILLIE MOORE, Art Teacher; *b:* Euclid, OH; *m:* R Katie, Michael; *ed:* Kent St Univ (BS) Art Ed 1975; 7 Hrs Grad C Greensburg Elem Art Tchr 1976; Windham Elem Schl Art Tchr Tallmadge HS Art Tchr, Yrbk Adv 1978-82; Aurora HS Art Tchr Hudson HS Art Tchr, Yrbk Adv 1983-; *ai:* Yrbk Adv; NE Distinguished Tchr Awd 1993; *office:* Hudson HS 2500 Hudson A Hudson OH 44236

GILES, CAROL SPADORA, Science Teacher; *b:* Brooklyn, NY F. Jr.; *ed:* Bloomsburg Univ (BS) Ed in Bio 1989; Rhode Island C Tchng in Bio 1992; Wilkes Univ Tchng AP in Bio 3 Credits; *cr* Island Schl Sci Supvr 1989-; *ai:* Jr High Bsktbl Coach; Hug Ldrshp Selection Comm; Hnr Soc Selection Comm; Ed Adv Magnet Stu Selection Comm; Homework Hall Monitor; Schls NYSUT 1989-; Fishers Island Civic Assn 1991-, Bd Mem 1995 Fishers Island Schl Greenwood Rd Fishers Island NY 06390

GILES, MARGARET ELLEN, English Teacher; *b:* Monticell Arnold (dec); *c:* Lynn, Leigh Giles-Brown; *ed:* IL St Univ (BS) E Iona Coll (MS) Eng 1981; 60 Credits Beyond Masters Coll Rochelle, Long Island Univ; *cr:* Pomona Jr HS Eng Tchr 1 Supervise Homework Ctr; Mem Sick Bank Comm, Awds Site-Based Decision Making Team; Rockland Negro Schlsp Fu Sec; Tchr of Yr East Ramapo Schl Dist; *office:* Pomona Jr H S P Suffern NY 10901*

GILES, PHILIP LAURENCE, History Department Chai Kingsport, TN; *m:* Candace Morgan; *c:* Andrew, Daniel; *ed:* Bo (MDIV) New Testament 1976; Univ of Rochester (PHD) Amer Colgate Divinity Schl Stud Greek, Hebrew; *cr:* Aquinas Inst 1981-84; Daewon Coll Adj Tchr 1990; SUNY Adj Tchr 1991- Finnely HS His Tchr 1994-; *ai:* Bible Tchr; Music Ministry; *office* Finney HS 2070 5 Mile Line Rd Penfield NY 14526*

GILFILLEN, RITA E., Science Teacher; *b:* Oak Park, IL; *m:* V Rex, Ginger Davidson, Mindy, Molly; *ed:* Wright St Univ (BS) E Cum Laude 1971, (MS) Ed 1978; *cr:* Miami East Schl 1st Grd T Fairlaw Local Schl 6th-8th Grd Tchr 1972-; *ai:* Sci Fair Coord Class Trip Adv; OH Sci Acad Dist 10, Cty Rep; First United Met Sunday Schl Tchr; Kappa Delta Pi, Phi Eta Tau Honor Socs; Governers Awd; Martha Holden Jennings Scholar 1986 Outstanding Tchr Awd 1993; *office:* Fairlawn Local Schl 18000 Rd Sidney OH 45365

GILFUS, JONNA KERST, English Teacher; *b:* Providence Joseph; *c:* Zachary, Georgia; *ed:* Syracuse Univ (BA), (BS) Eng Univ of NY (MS) Ed 1992; *cr:* Syracuse City Schls Tc Cato-Meridian Cntrl Schl Eng Tchr 1986-; *ai:* Ski Club, Sr Cl Adv; AFT, NCTE, NYSUT; *office:* Cato Meridian Elem Schl PO Cato NY 13033

GILL, BONNIE S., Teacher; *b:* Williamsburg, KY; *c:* Mark Be Cumberland Coll (BS) Scndry Ed 1969; George Washington U Rdng; *cr:* Suitland HS Bus Tchr 1969-73; Friendly HS Bus Tchr NEA, MSTA, PGCEA 1969-; *office:* Friendly HS 10000 Allentow Washington MD 20744

GILL, CYNTHIA HOLDER, Lecturer of Physical Therapy; *b:* NJ; *m:* Henry William III; *ed:* Univ of VA (BA) Math 1984; Me VA (BS) Phys Therapy 1986; Univ of VA (MED) Exercise P 1990; PHD Candidate in Sports Med Univ of VA; *cr:* Shelter Rehab Hosp Staff Phys Therapist 1986-88; Martha Jefferson H Phys Therapist 1988-93; Univ of VA Tchng Asst, Lecturer 1990 of MD Eastern Shore Visiting Lecturer Phys Therapy 1993-; *ai:* F Comm Chair; Motion Analysis Lab Dir; Phy Therapy Dept A Comm; Dev of Multimedia Cmptr Lab for PT Stdnts; Amer Ph Assn 1984-; Amer Coll of Sports Med 1988-; Rsrch Publication; with Title III Grant; *office:* Univ Of MD Eastern Shore Kiah H Princess Anne MD 21853

GILL, FRANK J., English Teacher; *b:* Mineola IV, NY; *m:* Fairbairn; *c:* David R., Mary Kate, Laile J.; *ed:* Dowling (BA) E C.W. Post (MS) Admin 1988; 75 Addl Hrs; *cr:* Bellport MS 1963-86; Bellport HS Eng Tchr 1987-; *ai:* AFT, NYSUT, BT *office:* Bellport HS Beaver Dam Rd Brookhaven NY 11719

GILL, JAMES EDWARD, American History Teacher; *b:* Cheste Kelly; *c:* Martina, Jonathan; *ed:* Brandywine JC (AA) Lbrl A Cheyney Univ (BS) Scndry Ed His 1979; Addl 12 Credit Hrs; O 12 Credit Hrs; *cr:* Archdiocese of Phila Tchr & Coac DE-Brandywine Tchr Tchr 2 Yrs; Chichester Schl Dist Tchr & Co *ai:* Head Boys Bsktbl Coach.

GILL, JOHN JOSEPH,JR., High School Science Tea Binghamton, NY; *m:* Diane Marie Danzer; *c:* Colleen, Shanno Maureen; *ed:* Univ of Scranton (BS) Bio, Scndry Ed 1978, (MS Sci 1980; 60 Addl Credits Ed & Sci; *cr:* Kittatinny Regnl HS Head Wrestling Coach 1978-; *ai:* Head Wrestling Coach; Kitt Assn 1978-, Pres 1988-; NJ Ed Assn, NEA 1978-; NJ Field Hoc Assn 1987-, Cadet Instr 1989-; NJ Track & Field Ofcls Assn Beekeepers Assn 1982-; *office:* Rittatinny Regional H S 77 Hals 10 Box 10255 Newton NJ 07860

GILL, PATRICIA DERSTINE, Third Grade Teacher; *b:* Sellers *m:* James G. III; *c:* Clinton; *ed:* Bloomsburg Univ (BS) Elem Gwynedd Mercy Coll (MS) Rdng 1993; *cr:* West Broad St Elem Tchr 1974-84, 3rd Grd Tchr 1985-; *ai:* NEA 1974-; Natl Rdng As Bd of Chrstn Ed 1993-, Pres; *office:* West Broad St Elem Sch 342 St Souderton PA 18964

GILLAN, KAY DORWARD, Social Studies Teacher; *b:* DeRuyt Eugene; *c:* Nathaniel; *ed:* SUNY at New Paltz (BA) Sociolo Nazareth Coll (MS) Ed 1978; *cr:* Eastridge Jr Sr HS Sub Tchr Eastridge Sr HS Soc Stud Tchr 1985-; *ai:* Curr, Scheduling, Re Discipline Comms; NYSUT, AFT 1982-; ASCO 1992-; NCS ASCD Conf on Assessment & NYS MS Conf Wkshps Presented.

GILLAN, SALLY WHEATON, Retired Nursery School T Corning, NY; *m:* Howard J.; *c:* Susan Henninger, Judie Mraz; *e* Univ (BS) Early Chldhd 1959; *cr:* Falk Schl Nursery Schl Tchr Pittsford Schls First Grd Tchr 1961-62; Twelve Corners Nursery 3, 4 Yrs Olds 1972-80; *ai:* Rochester Museum, Sci Ctr 19 Relations; Women's Cncl Mem Art Gallery 1994-; Women's C Gamma Natl Ga.

GILLAND, MARY MATSKO, Third Grade Teacher; *b:* Hazleto William; *c:* Jonathan; *ed:* West Chester Univ (BS) Elem Ed 196 Grad Credits; *cr:* East Bradford Elem Schl Tchr 1968-; *ai* Relations Comm; NEA, PSEA, WCAEA 1968-; ASCD 1995- Women Voters 1983-.

GILLARD, GREGORY ALBERT, Former Teacher; *b:* Rocheste Peggy Goodrich; *c:* Maureen, Keenan, Piper, Cassidy; *ed:* C Cnslng; *cr:* Nativity of Our Lord Schl 4th Grd Tchr 1977-82; Col HS 6th Grd Tchr 1982-83; Westford Elem Schl 1983-84; H. O h Grd Tchr 1984-90; *ai:* Tutor, Writing, Sub Tchng; Numerous ²ub; *home:* 8 Sunderland Woods Colchester VT 05446

D, MARTIN P., Biology Teacher; *b:* Fulton, NY; *m:* Peggy L. :: Scott, Timothy, Lindsay; *ed:* SUNY at Cortland (BS) Bio Ed NY at Oswego (MS) Scndry Ed Bio 1983, (CAS) Educl Admin Mexico Acad Perm Tchng Asst 1977-78; G Ray Bodley HS Sec ɔ 1978-, Admin Intern 1994-95; *ai:* Bsktbl Coach 1977-86; Ftbl 77-92; Lacrosse Coach 1987-; Ath Dist Site Based & Dist Safety ci Olympiad; Fulton Tchrs Assn, NYSUT & AFT; ASCD; Sci sn of NYS; Lions Clubs Intnl Fulton Chptr; Natl Fed of St HS Coaches; The Lacrosse Fndtn; Brine Upstate Lacrosse League VP; II Class A-1 Ftbl Coach of Yr 1990; Numerous Articles Pub; Ray Bodley HS 6 William Gillard Dr Fulton NY 13069

GH, MELANIE ROBERTA (SMITH), Spanish Teacher; *b:* ı, PA; *m:* Michael E.; *c:* Sarah, Matthew, Ashleigh, Corey; *ed:* niv (BA) Span 1976, (BSEd) Span & Fr 1976; Univ of Dayton Schl Cnslng 1980; Attnd Inst for Amer Univs, Univ of Valencia; rville HS Span & Fr Tchr 1976-77; Tower Hghts MS Fr Tchr Span Tchr 1979-; *ai:* NEA 1976-; OEA 1976-; *office:* Tower ⁴IS 195 N Johanna Dr Dayton OH 45459

UDEAU, MARINA, Biology & Russian Teacher; *b:* Kishinev USSR; *m:* John Adam; *ed:* Univ of AL (BS) Bio, Chem 1981; RI (MS) Animal, Virology 1984; Hunter Coll 18 Credits Psych *cr:* Univ of RI Research, Teaching Asst 1981-84; Mt Sinai Schl es Asst, Instr 1985-88; Dominican Acad Sci, Russian Instr 1989-; Chr; *ai:* Moderator of Sci Club; Organizer of Intl Stu Travel; Glee derator of After Schl Sci Tutoring; NY Zoological Soc 1993-; ıldlife Fund 1991-; Smithsonian Inst 1993-; Articles Pub 1986, *ice:* Dominican Academy 44 East 68th St New York NY 10021

, JOHN MICHAEL, Professor of English; *b:* Rochester, NY; *m:* therine Quinn; *c:* Katherine Anne, Michael John; *ed:* LeMoyne Eng 1964; Univ of MA (MA) Eng 1967; *cr:* Castleton St Coll 1970-; *ai:* Tchng & Schlsp Comm Mem; AFT 1974-, Pres of VT Fac Fed 1979-83; Stu Assn Tchr of Yr 1994; VT St Colls Fac 994; Fac Mem of Colls Awded by AAHE 1994; Outstanding Frosh Awded by John Gardners Frosh Yr Experience Ctr at the Univ of *office:* Castleton St Coll Seminary St Castleton VT 05735

, MICHAEL EUGENE, Mathematics Teacher; *b:* Jersey City, ıne Butler; *c:* Maureen, Michael, Mark; *ed:* Fordham Univ (BA) 59; Columbia Univ (MA) PE 1975; 12 Hrs in Cnslng NYU; *cr:* San Ignacio Math Tchr, Coach 1969-72; St Agnes HS Math Tchr, 73-77; Montville HS Math Tchr, Coach 1977-82; Mendham HS ır, Coach 1982-89; Whipple Russ & Hirsch Law Office Admin Irvington HS Math Tchr 1992-93; Watchung Hills HS Math Tchr, 993-; *ai:* Field Hockey, Bsktbl, Track Coach; Assn of Legal Track Ofcls Assn; Field Hockey Coaches Assn; *office:* Watching ional HS 108 Stirling Rd Warren NJ 07059

, VINCE J., 4th Grade Self Contained Tchr; *b:* Charleroi, PA; *m:* Bellan-Gillen; *ed:* CA Univ of PA (BA) Elem 1970; CA Univ of onmental Teach Cert 1974; *ai:* Ski Club Chaperone; People to u Ambassador Prgm Ldr 1992-; Burg Area Ed Assn 1970-, Bldg -; NEA 1970-; Assoc Artist of PA 1982-; PA Grants for Arts 1988; anover Elem Schl 10 Grey Ln Burgettstown PA 15021*

TINE, LINDA EMERSON, Sixth Grade Teacher; *b:* Pitt Gas, Lee; *c:* Jennifer Schwenk; *ed:* Asbury Coll (BA) Elem Ed 1965; Univ (MA) Curr & Instr 1988; Martha Holden Jennings Scholar Fairview Schl System 5th & 6th Grd Tchr 1965-67; Fairfax Cty Tchr 1968-69; Cambridge MD 6th Grd Tchr 1969-71; North OH 6th Grd Tchr 1977-79; Wooster City 3rd, 5th & 6th Grd Tchr : NEA 1965-; Numerous Curr Act Pub; Mentor Tchr; Wooster s Tchr of the Yr 1990; *office:* Layton Elem Schl 1859 Burbank Rd OH 44691

PIE, ANGUS KRESS, Assoc Prof of American Studies; *b:* Bryn ı; *m:* Rowena Cosico; *c:* Neil Craig, Tristan Wade; *ed:* Yale Univ er Stud 1964; Univ of PA (PHD) Amer Civilization 1975; *cr:* Univ Instr 1973-75, Asst Prof 1975-81, Assoc Prof 1981-; *ai:* Mid Folklife Assn 1978-, Pres 1984-85; NJ Forklore Soc 1978-, Exec 980-85; PA Folklore Soc 1978-, Pres 1979-80; NJ Folk Festival, 1975-; New Netherlands Museum 1992-, Treas 1992-; Millstone re Dept 1977-, Pres 1987; Rutgers Presidential Awd for Pub Svc rtners of Amers Travel Grants to Haiti 1990, 1993; Univ of es Fulbright Scholar 1985-86; NJ Historical Commission Awd for ion 1980; *office:* Rutgers St Univ of NJ Amer Studies PO Box 270 nswick NJ 08903

PIE, BARBARA J. LONG, French Teacher & Stu Act Coord; *b:* , MA; *m:* James W.; *ed:* Stonehill Coll (BA) Fr & Ed 1976; Boston ı) Fr Lit 1980; LUniv de Nice des Etudes Francaises Cert; LUniv ɔonne Post Grad Stud; Bridgewater St Coll 15 Credit Hrs; Harvard ı Univ 3 Credit Hrs; *cr:* Weymouth Pub Schls Fr & Span Tchr East Bridgewater Pub Schls Fr & Span Tchr & St Act Coord : Stu Senate & AFS Adv; France Exch Pgm Liaison; MTA & NEA ATF 1977-; MAFLA 1977-; MLA 1980-; PCEA Achvmt Awd; ast Bridgewater HS 11 Plymouth St East Bridgewater MA 02333

PIE, JUDY B., English Teacher; *b:* Syracuse, NY; *m:* David B.; ıan Gonenne, Alexander Gonenne, Joshua; *ed:* Univ of WI at (BS) Eng, His 1965; 46 Credit Grad Work Eng Ed, His; *cr:* Young Ed Dev Prgm Title I Prgm Tchr 1966-72; Montessori Presch at CA 7-79, at PA 1985-87; PWHS Tchr 1989-; *ai:* Orientation Prgm for Other Stu Adv; Multi-Cultural Awareness, Curr Dev Comm; Stu ce Team Mem; PSEA, NEA; *office:* Plymouth Whitemarsh HS E. ɔwn Pk Plymouth Meeting PA 19462

PIE, LINDA, English Teacher; *b:* Brooklyn, NY; *ed:* St John's ı) Eng 1968; C. W. Post, LIU (MA) Eng 1975; *cr:* Sheepshead Bay Tchr 1968-73; St Martin of Tours Eng Tchr 1977-79; Maria Regina Tchr 1979-84; St Anthony's HS Eng Tchr 1985-; *ai:* Molloy Coll ın Team Asst Coach; 7th Grd Parish Religion Tchr; NCTE 1986-; of Rockville Ctr Pius XII Awd; *office:* St Anthonys HS 275 Wolf Melville NY 11747*

PIE, MARY M., Asst Prof of Human Svcs Dept; *b:* Catskill, NY; iv of NY at Albany (BA) Music 1974; Springfield Coll (MED) PE ntioch New England Grad Schl (MA) Psych 1986; Doctorial e; 118 Addl Credits Psy D Degree Clinical Psych; *cr:* Union Coll Coach 1981-83; Berkshire Cncl Addictions Cnslr 1983-86; AL dictions Therapist 1986-88; Hudson Valley Comm Coll Human t Prof 1988-; *ai:* Amer Psych Assn 1991-; Nat Assn Alcoholism, slrs 1990-; Completed Doctoral Internship Psy D Berkshire Ctr Family Ctr of Berkshires; *office:* Hudson Valley Community Vandenburgh Ave Troy NY 12180

PIE, MICHAEL C., Assoc Prof & Dir of Tchr Ed; *b:* Mt Vernon, Brown Univ (AB-MAT) Eng Lit 1972; Columbia Tchrs Coll (MA) Ed Admin 1980, (EDD) Ed 1983; *cr:* Phillips Acad Lit Tchr Classical HS Eng Tchr 1972-78; Columbia Tchrs Coll Adj Asst 1983-84; City Coll of NY Dir, Prins Ctr, Adj Assoc Prof 1987-92; omm Coll Assoc Prof, Dir Tchr Ed Prgm 1992-; *ai:* Co-Adv Ed l Soc Ed Admin 1994-, Charter Mem; NYC Assoc Supvr, Curr Dev 1990-, Adv Bd; Intnl Network Prins Ctrs 1989-, Adv Bd; Ackerman Inst Family Therapy 1991-, Bd Trustees; Boys Choir Harlem Acad 1990-, Adv Bd Chm; Grants Danforth FndSchl Lders, Prins Prep Prgm, Ford Fnd Natl Urban Partnership Prgm; City Univ of NY Chancellor's Honoree Grantmanship; Who's Who in Ed; Westchester Cty Distngd Comm Svc Awd; Outstdng Young Men Amer; Phi Delta Kappa; Created Schlsp Minority Stdnts; *office:* City Univ Of NY Bronx Comm Col W 181 St & University Ave Bronx NY 10453

GILLETT, DANIEL WILLIAM, 5th Grade Teacher; *b:* Central Square, NY; *m:* Jeannette Gabriel; *c:* Kelsey, Danielle; *ed:* SUNY ar Oswego (BS) Elem Ed 1979, (MS) Elem Ed 1984; Cntrl Square Cntrl Schls Tchr 1979-; *cr:* Cntrl Square Schl Tchr 1979-96; *ai:* AFT 1879-, Bldg Rep.

GILLETTE, SUSAN LYNN, Chemistry Teacher; *b:* Pittsburgh, PA; *ed:* Washington & Jefferson Coll (BA) Chem & Ed 1994; *cr:* West Muskingum HS Chem Tchr 1994-; *ai:* Head Sftbl Coach; Asst Vllybl Coach; Kappa Delta Epsilon 1994-; Zanesville Comm Theater 1994-.

GILLIAM, EDRA L., Math Teacher; *b:* Washington, DC; *m:* Stephen S.; *c:* Kelli Renee, Sean Stephen; *ed:* Univ of Cincinnati (BS) Math Scndry 1979; Attnd Marshall Univ, Miami Univ, Coll of Mt St Joseph; *cr:* Norwood Jr HS 7th Grd Math Tchr 1979-83; Norwood HS Algebra & Geometry Tchr 1985-95; *ai:* Soph Class Adv; Chrldng Coach; Norwood Tchrs Assn 1979-; OEA 1979-; NEA 1979-; Natl Multiple Sclerosis Soc, Outstdng Vol 1995; 1st Place Awd in OSBA Stay in Schl Contest; Gen Electric Fndtn Math Tchr Recognition Pgm Grant Recipient; Co-Authored Graded Course of Stud Judged to be Excl by OH Dept of Ed.

GILLILAND, JUDY WITHEROW, 8th Grade Science Teacher; *b:* New Millport, PA; *c:* John W., Jamison K.; *ed:* Lock Haven Univ (BS) Elem K-8 1964; 35 Post Grad Courses Psych, Comms Penn St Univ; *cr:* Tyrone Area Schls 2nd Grade Teacher 1964-65; Clearfield Area Schls 3rd Grd Tchr 1965-66, 4th Grd TChr 1969-70, 8th Grd Sci 1973-; *ai:* Gymnastics Coach 1973-77; Track Coach 1980-84; Homebound Tutoring; PSEA, NEA 1973-; CEA 1973-, Past Sec; Childrens Aid Soc; *home:* 1010 S 2nd St Clearfield PA 16830*

GILLILAND, LINDA FRACE, German Teacher & Dept Head; *b:* East Stroudsburg, PA; *m:* Scott Thomas; *c:* Joseph, Randall; *ed:* Millersville Univ (BS) Frgn Lang & Eng 1978; East Stroudsburg Univ (MED) Ed 1992; Prin Cert Marywood Univ 1996; Supervisory Cert Widener Univ 1992; *cr:* East Stroudsburg HS Ger Tchr, Frgn Lang, Dept Chair, Stu Assistance Cnslr 1979-; *ai:* Drug & Alcohol Awareness in Comm Act 211 Mem; Stdnts Against Substance Abuse, Ski Club Adv; Mt Pocono United Meth Church Yth Flwshp Adv; NEA, PSEA 1979-; East Stroudsburg Univ Tchr Advy Bd 1992-; Carbon, Monroe, Pike Drug & Alcohol Grant 4 Yrs; PA Attorney Gens Drug & Alcohol Awareness Grant 1995; *office:* East Stroudsburg Sr HS 279 N Courtland St East Stroudsburg PA 18301*

GILLIO, GERALDINE, Social Studies Teacher; *b:* Jersey City, NJ; *ed:* Notre Dame Coll (BA) His 1961; Seton Hall Univ (MA) European His 1964; NY Univ (MA) Near East Langs & Lit 1974; *cr:* Henry Snyder HS Soc Stud Thcr 1961-1966, 1969-1987, 1989-; *ai:* NHS Moderator; NJ Cncl of Soc Stud 1987-; Mid East Stud Assoc 1974-; League of Women Voters 1980-, Voter Svc Chair; Intnl Inst of NJ 1979-, Sec, Treas; Returned Peace Corps Vol of NJ 1979-, Pres; *office:* Henry Snyder HS 239 Bergen Ave Jersey City NJ 07305

GILLIVAN, SHARON L., 2nd Grade Teacher; *b:* Columbus, OH; *ed:* OH Dominican Coll (BS) Elem Ed 1971; *cr:* St Agnes Schl 5th Grd Tchr 1971-72; St Paul Schl 2nd Grd Tchr 1972-; *ai:* Columbus Diocesan Ed Assn 1972-; TWIG #196 1976-, Pres; *home:* 2942 Hollyhead Dr Dublin OH 43017

GILLON, ROSELLEN E., Chapter I Teacher; *b:* Holyoke, MA; *m:* Francis Rosellen; *c:* Kara, Timothy, Maura; *ed:* Elms Coll (BA) His 1969; 2 Grad Courses Summer Math Prgm Mt Holyoke Coll; *cr:* Kirtland Schl Grd 4 Tchr 1969-71; Lawrence Schl Grd 5, 6 Tchr 1073-74; E. N. White Schl Grd 3 Tchr 1975-80; Highland Schl Grd 3 Tchr 1980-87; Sullivan Schl Chptr I Tchr 1987-; *ai:* Chptr I Liaison; Holyoke, MA Tchrs Assn 1969-; NEA 1974-.*

GILLOTT, MARIANNE J., Physics & Mathematics Teacher; *b:* Mt Pleasant, PA; *ed:* St Vincent Coll (BS) Physics 1991; Addl 27 Credits Math, Physics; *cr:* Greensburg Cntrl Cath HS Physics, Math Tchr 1993-; *ai:* Jr Class Moderator; Prom Spon; *office:* Greensburg Cntrl Catholic HS 901 Armory Dr Greensburg PA 15601

GILMAN, BRUCE ALAN, Conservation Professor; *b:* Rochester, NY; *m:* C. Margo; *c:* Kelly, Kara; *ed:* St John Fisher Coll (BS) Bio 1973; SUNY Coll of Environmental Sci & Foerestry (PHD) Comm Ecology 1975, (MS) Aquatic Ecology 1976; *cr:* SUNY Coll of Environmental Sci & Forestry Tchng Asst 1974; SEAGRANT Rsrch Asst 1974-75; Oneida Cty Planning Dept Enviromnental Intrn 75; Finger Lakes Comm Coll Tchng 1976-; *ai:* Herbarium Curator Ontario Cty Botanist; Envirothon Scientific Adv Bd NY Fed Lake Assns; Ontario Cty Water Resources Cncl; Sci Olympics; Intnl Alvar Conservation Initative; Nature Conservancy 1973-, Chptr Trustee, Friend of the Land 1995; Ecological Soc of Amer 1986-; Rochester Acad of Sci 1975-, Vice Chm, Fellow; Honeoye Vly Assn 1995-; Canandaigua Lake Pur Waters 1980-, Comm Chm, Friend of the Lake 1984; Finger Lakes Assn 1984-, Adv Bd; Rsrch Flwshps; Outstdng Svc Ontario Cty Awd 1985-86; Author Cty Flora; Articles Pub; Co-Author, Project Dir Rsrch & Equipment Grants; *office:* Finger Lakes Comm Coll 4355 Lake Shore Dr Canandaigua NY 14424

GILMARTIN, HELEN PENCZAK, Substitute Teacher; *b:* New York City, NY; *m:* James J.; *c:* Erin, Jimmy; *ed:* Molloy Coll (BA) Elem Ed 1971; St Michaels Coll (MA) Rel Ed 1976; *cr:* St Catherine of Sienna 1st Grd Tchr 1968-70, 7th-8th Grd Sci & Eng Tchr 1979-84; Notre Dame 5th & 7th Grd Tchr 1970-74; St Edwards 7th-8th Grd Tchr 1974-79; Notre Dame Elem Grds Sub Tchr 1995-; *ai:* NHP & GCP Spcl Ed Founder; Schl Decision Making Dist Comm; Schl Advy Comm; NYSSBA 1995-; Schl Bd Trustee; PTA, Past Pres, Current Historian & Pgm Chprsn; Nassau Cty Coordng Cncl of SEPTA's, Recording Sec; *home:* 110 Maple Cir New Hyde Park NY 11040

GILMARTIN, JOYCE ELEANOR, Social Studies Teacher; *b:* Fitchburg, MA; *ed:* North Adams St Coll (BA) Sociology 1976; Eastern Nazarene Coll (MED) Scndry Ed 1987; *cr:* Conanat HS Soc Stud Tchr 1986-; *ai:* NEA 1987-; Reserve Officer Assn 1985-; *office:* Conant HS 109 Stratton Rd Jaffrey NH 03452

GILMARTIN, MARY ELLEN GERNER, Fashion Technology Instructor; *b:* Milford, CT; *m:* W. Kerry; *c:* Kyla Ellen; *ed:* Housatonic Comm Coll (AS) Studio Art 1975; Southern CT St Univ (BA) Theater1982; Enrolled Masters Ed; Cntrl CT St Univ Voc Ed; *cr:* Betsy Ross Arts Magnet Schl Creative Dramatics Instr 1985-86; Bustles & Breeches Costume Shoppe Costumer, Asst to Designer 1978-; E. C. Goodwin RVTS Fashion Tech Tchr 1992-; *ai:* Drama, Gardening, Class 96 Adv; St Voc Fed Tchrs 1992-; Crescent Players Theatrical Production Co 1979-, Sr Mgr Costumes; *home:* 49 Osborn Ave New Haven CT 06511

GILMORE, LOLA KISER, Second Grade Teacher; *b:* Concord, NC; *m:* Fredrick D. Sr.; *c:* Fredrick Jr., Melanie; *ed:* Livingston Coll (BA) Elem Ed 1954; St Johns Univ (MA) Early Chldhd Ed 1971; Teachers Coll at Columbia Univ NY Cert 1956; 30 Credits Above Masters; *ai:* Allen A. M. E. Church Act Club; Queens Cty Borough Pres Claire Shulman Issued Proclamation Celebrating My 25 Yrs Svc to NYC Pub Schl System 1992; *office:* P. S. 54Q Schl 8602 127th St Richmond Hill NY 11418

GILMORE, ROBERT H., HS American History Teacher; *b:* Beaver Falls, PA; *m:* Saundra; *c:* Robb, Adam, Meghan; *ed:* PA St Univ (BS) Scndry Ed 1970; PA Dept of Ed Masters Equivalency Scndry Ed 1991, Addl 48 Credit Hrs Post Baccalareate; *cr:* Ambridge Area HS World Cultures Tchr 1971-84; Ambridge Area Jr HS World Cultures Tchr 1984-86; Ambridge Area HS Amer Cultures Tchr 1986-, Gifted Amer Cultures Tchr 1995-; *ai:* DECA Adv, Local Co-Spon; NEA, PSEA 1971-, Past Recording Sec; Mellon, Scaife Schlsp for Grad Stud 1974; Gift of Time Tribute 1994, 1996; *office:* Ambridge Area HS 909 Duss Ave Ambridge PA 15003

GILMORE, SANDRA BUCHANAN, Latin & Spanish Teacher; *b:* Poteau, OK; *m:* Stephen R.; *c:* Scott W.; *ed:* Millersville Univ (BS) Latin, Span 1975; *cr:* Lewisburg HS Latin Tchr 1976-77; Danville HS Latin, Span Tchr 1978-; *ai:* NEA, PSEA, Pompeiiana Inc 1978-; Amer Classical League 1985-; PA Classical Assn 1979-; Classical Assn of Atlantic Sts 1994-; *office:* Danville Sr HS 600 Walnut St Danville PA 17821

GILMORE, VIRGINIA CULVER, 2nd Grd Tchr & Prin Aide; *b:* Westhampton, NY; *c:* Glen Alden II; *ed:* SUNY at Oswego (BS) Elem Ed 1963; LIU at Southampton (MS) Elem Ed 1980; 81 Addl Credits; Natl Sci Fnd Honors Inst K-6 Tchrs, Admin Hofstra Univ; Kean Coll 6 Credits Geology Hawaiian Islands; *cr:* Waverly 2nd Grd Tchr 1963-64; Hill Co Schl 1st-2nd Grd Tchr 1964-65; Waverly 2nd Grd Tchr 1965-; *ai:* Prin's Aide; Policy Bd Tchr Ctr; Elem Sci Mentor, Facilitator El Sci Prgm Evaluation Test; Meet Author Comm; Community Cupboard; PTA, SCTA, NYSUT, NEA, AFT 1963-; Sci, Children 1979; *office:* Waverly Ave Schl 1111 Waverly Ave Holtsville NY 11742

GILOTTI, BARBARA ELIZABETH, Spanish Teacher & Librarian; *b:* Scranton, PA; *ed:* Wilkes Coll (BA) Span 1973; Kutztown Univ (MS) Lib Sci 1991; Summer Stud Grad Courses in Span at Millersville Univ 1974, 1984; Summer Stud Through Univ of AZ in Guadalajara Mexico 1980; *cr:* Old Forge HS Span Tchr & Librn 1973-; *ai:* Span Club Adv; AATSP 1990-; MENSA 1985-, Scranton Local Coord; Sierra Club 1991-; HS Valedictorian.

GILSON, MICHELLE A., Third Grade Teacher; *b:* Middletown, NY; *m:* Glenn R.; *c:* Glenn II, Samantha; *ed:* Oneonta St Univ (BS) Elem Early Scndry, Eng 1984; Coll of New Rochelle (MA) GATE 1989; *cr:* Norwich MS 8th Grd Tchr 1983; All Saints Schl 6th Grd Tchr 1983; Mechanicstown Elem 3rd Grd Tchr 1984-; *ai:* Video Club; AFT 1985-; *office:* Mechanicstown Elem Schl 425 E Main St Middletown NY 10940*

GILTINAN, DAVID A., Prof & Physics Dept Chprsn; *b:* Jamestown, NY; *m:* Janice M. Peterson; *c:* Brian, Kevin; *ed:* Case Inst of Tech (BS) Electrical Engrng 1959, (MS) Physics 1963, (PHD) Physics 1968; *cr:* Edinboro Univ of PA Prof 1968-; *ai:* Univ Sabbatical Comm Chair; Ski Club Adv; Fac Assn Exec Bd; Amer Assn Physics Tchrs 1968-; Amer Soc Engrng Ed 1988-; Natl Ski Patrol 1976-; Articles Pub 1994-; *office:* Edinboro Univ Of PA Hendricks Hall G-34 Edinboro PA 16444

GILVARY, MARGARET LAGGAN, Second Grade Teacher; *b:* Scranton, PA; *m:* Martin J.; *c:* Katie Gilvary Haugerud; Marty, Kevin, Colleen; *ed:* Marywood Coll (BA) Elem Ed 1957; Bloomsburg Univ (MED) Rdng 1987; Exemplary Ctr for Rdng Instruction at Salt Lake City UT Mastery Learning Instr; *cr:* Jefferson Schl 4th Grd Tchr 1957-58; Montoursville Elem Schls 1st & 2nd Grd Sub Tchr 1959-; *ai:* Tutoring; Rdng Theme Days Coord; Org of Montoursville Educators 1985-; North Cntrl Rdng Cncl 1993-, Historian; Applied for Tchr in Space Prgm; *office:* Lyter Elem Schl 900 Spruce St Montoursville PA 17754

GINDER-DELVENTHAL, TRACY L., Teacher of Acting; *b:* Oakland, CA; *m:* Thom Delventhal; *c:* Zachariah Clay, Elijah Linwood, Willem Dwight Danial; *ed:* Carnegie Mellon Univ (BFA) Acting 1983, (MFA) Directing 1990; *cr:* Pittsburgh Playhouse Conservatory Tchr of Acting, Dir 1989-94; Cntrl Coll of Allegheny Cty Tchr of Acting; Cranegie Mellon Univ Precollege Tchr of Acting 1994-; Act One Theatre Schl Coord of Teen Prgm 1993-; Creative & Performing Arts HS Tchr of Acting, Dir 1991-; *ai:* GREX 1988-, Artistic Dir; *home:* 437 Elmer St Pittsburgh PA 15218

GINDI, ELAINE, Resource Room Teacher; *b:* Brooklyn, NY; *c:* Lisa, Cheryl; *ed:* Brooklyn Coll (BA) Sociology; Adelphi Univ (MS) Spec Ed 1983; *cr:* Abraham Lincoln HS Resource Room Tchr 1980-; *ai:* Dist Advy Comm for St Incentive Grant Chprsn; UFT 1980-; AFT 1981-; *office:* Abraham Lincoln HS 2800 Ocean Pkwy Brooklyn NY 11235

GINETTO, CHARLES, Foreign Language Teacher; *b:* New York, NY; *m:* Maria Fernanda Alcivar; *c:* Steve; *ed:* Long Island Univ (BA) Frgn Langs 1967; MIddlebury Coll (MA) Italian 1968; Fairleigh Dickenson (MBA) Acctng, Taxation 1976; CPA 1987; NYS Cert Court Interpreter Span 1994, Italian 1995; *cr:* Long IL Univ Italian, Span Instr 1968-70; Montclair St Italian Instr 1970-71; New Cath HS Span Tchr 1971-73; Clarkstown Sr HS Frgn Lang Tchr 1973-; *ai:* Italian Club Adv; AFT 1973-; AICPA 1987-; APLIT 1990-; Dante Alighieri Cultural Soc 1980-, Founder, Satisfaction; NEH Flwshp Span-Amer Cacuto Vanderbilt Univ 1984; MCES Schlsp Siena Italy for Italian Update 1989, Salamanca Spain Span Philology 1991; *office:* Clarkstown South HS 31 Demarest Mill Rd West Nyack NY 10994

GINGERICH, JOHN EDWIN, Bible & English Teacher; *b:* Hartville, OH; *m:* Grace Miller; *c:* Philip, Rhoda Sommers, Erika Smith; *ed:* Eastern Menn Coll (BA) Bible, Philosphy 1963; Kent St Univ at Stark Branch His; Malone Coll Child Psych, His; *cr:* Mennonite Cntrl Comm Refugee Resettmemts 15 Yrs; Church Pastoring Sr Pastor 23 Yrs; Lake Ctr Chrstn Schl Prin 3 Yrs; Hartville Chrstn Schl Soc Stud Dept 20 Yrs; *home:* PO Box 472 Hartville OH 44632

GINGO, STEPHEN PAUL, Computer Coordinator & Coach; *b:* Mc Keesport, PA; *m:* Lorraine Frances Rozycki; *c:* Ryan; *ed:* St Vincent Coll (BA) Bio 1971; 12 Hrs Toward MED Univ of Pittsburgh; *cr:* St Xavier Acad Advanced Bio Tchr 1970-71; Transfiguration Schl Sci, PE Tchr 1971-74; Chapin Schl Sci, Cmptr, Photography Tchr 1974-; *ai:* Cross Cntry, Sftbl Coach; Ham Radio; Photography; Newspaper; Runathon; NJAIS 1974-; DE Vly Umpire Assn 1991-; DE Vly Radio Assn 1995-; Hamilton Crime Watch, Perpetual Adoration 1991-; Yrbk Dedication 1982; *office:* Chapin Schl 4101 Princeton Pike Princeton NJ 08540

GINGRICH, CINDY LANE, Mathematics Teacher; *b:* Lewisburg, PA; *m:* Theodore L.; *ed:* Bloomsburg Univ (BS) Scndry Ed Math 1978; Stan-Scndry Tchng Cert for Assn Chrstn Schls Intnl; Cert for Old Testament Series, External Stud Moody Bible Inst; *cr:* Susquenita HS 7th-8th Grd Math Tchr, 7th-9th Grd Federal Govt Title I Tchr for Remedial Math 1978-85; Meadowbrook Chrstn Schl 7th-12th Grd Math Tchr 1990-; *ai:* Soph Class Adv; Assn of Chrstn Schls Intnl 1993-; *home:* RR 1 Box 325-3 Milton PA 17847

GINNETTI, ANTONIA M., Latin & Business Ed Teacher; *b:* New Haven, CT; *m:* Ronald D. Arena; *ed:* Clark Univ (BA) Latin 1969; Univ of New Haven (MBA) Bus 1980; Trinity Coll Latin; St Joseph Coll Paleography; *cr:* Guilford HS Tchr 1969-71; East Haven HS Tchr 1976-; *ai:* Latin Club Adv; Class CT; Pompeiana; Classical Assn of New England; *office:* East Haven HS 200 Tyler St East Haven CT 06512

GINSBERG, ILSE MEER, Fine Arts Teacher; *b:* Vienna, Austria; *m:* Melvin; *c:* Ilona, Adam; *ed:* Hunter Coll (BFA) Painting & Illustration 1958, (MA) Art 1963; 60 Addl Hrs; *cr:* Henry Brackner Jr HS #101 Art Tchr 1958-73; NY Schls 26, 32, 17, 19, 28 Art Tchr 1973-76; Schl 21 & 22 Art Tchr 1973-76; King Schl Art Tchr 1973-76; Mark Twain Elem Schl Art

Tchr 1973-76; Roosevelt HS Art Tchr 1976-; *ai:* Tchr Expectation-Stu Achvmt Trainer; Museum Club Spon; AFT, YFT 1973-; *office:* Roosevelt HS 631 Tuckahoe Rd Yonkers NY 10710

GINSBERG, KARI M., Science Teacher; *b:* Nyack, NY; *ed:* Cornell Univ (BS) Animal Sci 1991; Tchrs Coll at Columbia Univ (MA) Scndry Sci Ed 1992; *cr:* Louis D. Brandeis HS Sci Tchr 1992-, Asst Coll Adv 1993; Mt Siani Hosp SETH Instr 1994-; *ai:* SBM, SDM Team; Hlth Careers SETH Coord; UFT, AFT 1992-; *office:* Louis D. Brandeis HS 145 W 84th St New York NY 10024

GINSBERG, ROBERT, 6th Grade Social Studies Tchr; *b:* Newark, NJ; *m:* Lee Goldberg; *c:* Allen LuLu, Jon LuLu, Michael; *ed:* Newark St Coll (BA) Gen Elem Ed 1966, (MA) Admin 1968; Rutgers Univ (EDS) Admin 1977; Elebron Southern Univ (EDD) Admin 1993; Admin Internship 1975-76; Morris Cty Math Consortium 1978; *cr:* Boylan St Schl Home Bound Instruction Tchr 1965-66; South 8th St Schl Self Contained 7th Grd Tchr 1966-70; Mt View Schl Self Contained 6th Grd Tchr 1970-75; 6th-7th Grd Math Tchr 1975-81, 6th Grd Soc Stud Tchr 1981-91; CMS Mt Olive MS 6th Grd Soc Stud Tchr 1991-; *ai:* Stud Club, Bsktbl Supervision; Mentor Prgm; Safety Patrol Supvr; Mt Olive Ed Assn 1970-, Pres 1974-75, Chief Negotiator 1974-75, Negotiations Team 1972-74, Fac Rep 1975-77; Supts Advy Comm 1977-79; Supt 3-3 Comm 1979-83; JCC Fin Assistance Dir 1986-; Temple Hatikvah; MENSA 1986-; Morris Cty Math Consortium 1978; *home:* 4 Apollo Way Flanders NJ 07836

GINTER, RONALD M., Social Studies Teacher; *b:* Intnl Falls, MN; *m:* Jill M. Hinz; *c:* Jaya E., Shannon L.; *ed:* Concorida Coll (BS) Hlth & PE 1974; Mankato ST Univ (BS) Soc Stud 1978; MI St Univ (MA) Ed 1984; Post Grad Courses From Boston Univ, Fresno Pacific Coll & Univ of MD; *cr:* Echo Pub Schl Tchr 1975-77; St Clair Pub Schl Tchr 1977-81; Subic Bay Tchr 1981-85; Baumholder HS Tchr 1985-; *ai:* MUN Spon; Adv Acad Bowl, Stu Cncl; Staff Dev Mem; Dept Chair; Schl Improvement Comm Chair; Tennis, Track & Field, Wrestling, Hockey, Bsktbl, Bsbl, Sftbl, Ftbl coach; NEA 1975-; NCSS 1985-; FEA 1981-; Federal Grant in 1981 From IPLE; *office:* Baumholder Amer HS Bhr Cmr 405 Box 1298 APO AE 09034*

GINTERT, CONNIE JEAN, English Teacher; *b:* Columbus, OH; *m:* Timothy B. Cassidy; *ed:* Kent St Univ (BS) Eng 1979, (MED) Rdng 1983; *cr:* Howland HS Eng Tchr 1979-81; Newton Falls Jr HS Eng, Rdng Tchr 1981-; *ai:* Career Planning Coord; Youngstown Eng Festival Adv; AFT 1993-; Tchr of Yr 1991; *office:* Newton Falls Jr HS 907 Milton Blvd Newton Falls OH 44444

GINTOWT, CECILIA S., Office Systems Teacher; *ed:* Springfield Tech Comm Coll (AS) Exec Secretarial 1981; Amer Intnl Coll (BS) Bus 1983; *cr:* HS of Commerce Office Systems Dept Tchr 1986-; *ai:* Class Adv; NEA; MTA; *office:* HS Of Commerce 415 State St Springfield MA 01105

GINTY, JAMES PATRICK, English Teacher; *b:* Bridgeport, CT; *c:* Molly, Bridget, Maura; *ed:* Huntington Coll (BA) Lang Art 1963; St Francis Coll (MS) Eng 1966; Doctoral Work; *cr:* St Mary's Elem Schl Tchr 1963-64; Tchr 1964-70; Ball St Univ Tchr 1970-78; Ridgefield HS Tchr 1978-; *ai:* NEA, NCTE 1978-; *home:* 64 Locust Ave New Canaan CT 06840

GINTY, KAREN LADZINSKI, Kindergarten Teacher; *b:* Perth Amboy, NJ; *m:* Thomas; *c:* Matthew, Allison; *ed:* Lynchburg Coll (BA) Elem Ed 1972; Kean Coll of NJ (MA) Early Chldhd Ed 1978; *cr:* Monmouth Beach Elem Schl Kndgtn Tchr 1972-80, Kndgtn & Learning Ctr Tchr 1979-82, Kndgtn Tchr 1981-84 & 1985-; *ai:* NJEA, NEA, MCEA 1972-; MBTA 1972-, VP, Sec; NJAKE, Mon Cty AKE, Planning Comm, Hospitality; MBPTA 1972-; WLBPTA 1986-; Block Parent Prgm 1987-; Strategic Planning Cncl for WLB Pub Schls 1995; Parents Planning & Advy Cncl-Shore Regnl HS Dist 1995; Monmouth Beach Tchr of Yr 1988; *office:* Monmouth Beach Elem Schl Hastings Pl Monmouth Beach NJ 07750*

GIOIA, DONNA J. (PRINGLE), 3rd Grade Teacher; *b:* Coudersport, PA; *m:* Anthony; *c:* Louis A., William J., Laura J.; *ed:* Union Coll (BA) Ed 1961; 60 Grad Hrs St Univ of NY at Buffalo, Univ of WI at Madison, Univ of Buffalo, Niagara Univ; *cr:* Richester Cty Schl Dist #40 3rd-5th Grd Tchr 1961-66; Anna Merritt Elem Schl 5th Grd Tchr 1966-71; John Pound Elem Schl 2nd Grd Tchr 1976; Anna Merritt Elem Schl 3rd Grd Tchr 1976-; *ai:* Schl Improvement, Schl Wide Planning Comms; Odyssey of Mind Team Coach 1992-; Summer Schl Space Camp Instr; NY St Tchrs Assn 1961-; AFT 1961-; Lockport Schls Employees Assn 1966-, Life Mbrshp; Lockport Coll Women's Club 1966-; PTA 1966-, Lifetime Mbrshp; Eisenhower Grant 1966; Cmptr Tech Innovative Grant 1992; *office:* Anna Merritt Elem Schl 389 Green St Lockport NY 14094*

GIORDANO, DENISE MARIE, K-5th Grd Language Arts Tchr; *b:* Brooklyn, NY; *m:* John B.; *c:* Jeanine M., John C.; *ed:* St Johns Univ (BS) Elem Ed 1958; Brooklyn Coll Grad Schl & Post-Grad Work; Univ of VT Grad Schl & Post-Grad Work; *cr:* St Emerics Schl Kndgtn Tchr 1957-58; PS 145 1st-3rd Grd Tchr 1958-67; NY City Bd of Ed Title I Rdng Tchr 1968-77; PS 86 Sub Tchr 1968-77; PS 200 4th Grd Gifted & Lang Arts Tchr 1977-; *ai:* Cath Tchrs Assn 1958-, Educator of the Yr 1995; UFT 1977-; Emerald Socy NYC Bd of Ed 1980-; *office:* Public Schl 200 1940 Benson Ave Brooklyn NY 11214*

GIORDANO, JAMES V., Social Studies Teacher; *b:* Suffern, NY; *m:* Karen E. Ford; *c:* J.J., Kevin; *ed:* Saint Thomas Aquinas Coll (BA) Soc Sci 1990, (MS) Ed 1996; *cr:* Pub Schls of the Tarrytowns Tchr 1990-; *ai:* Mock Trail Team & Bsbl Coach; South Nyack Village Bd 1990-, Trustee; Nyack Fire Dept 1984-, Captain; Nyack Little League 1980-, VP; *office:* Sleepy Hollow HS 210 N Broadway Tarrytown NY 10591

GIORDANO, MARK, Band Director & Music Educator; *b:* Albany, NY; *ed:* Coll of St Rose (BS) Music Ed 1989, (MS) Music Ed 1991; Army-Navy-Marine Schl of Music Compl Music Performance 1982; *cr:* Chatham HS HS Band Dir 1991-; *ai:* Jazz & Marching Bands; Ski Club; Brass & Woodwind Ensembles; NYS Music Assn 1985-; TUBA & Intnl Trombonist Assn 1991-; US Army 1981-85, Specialist; ROTC 1985-89, 2nd LT; Tchr of Yr 1992-93.*

GIORDANO, MARY D., Principal; *b:* Providence, RI; *m:* Antonio L.; *c:* Antonio, Mary, Madonna, Marlena; *ed:* Annhurst Coll (BA) Psych 1968; Providence Coll (MA) Ed; Nova Univ Ed 1980; Walden Univ Psych 1979; Salve Regina Univ Nrsng & Spec Ed; *cr:* Hope HS Dean of Stdnts 1983-90; Prov Schl Dept Asst Prin 1976-80, Guid Dept 1970-76, Dir of Gifted Prgm 1991-92, Dir of Chptr I 1990-93; *ai:* Bd of Governors, Futures Comm at La Salle Acad; Modeling Club; Confirmation Class; Natl Chap I Comm; Amer Psychological Assn 1992-; Forensic Psych Assn 1996; Amer Guid Assn 1985; Delta Kappa Gamma Pres; Who's Who in Amer Colls & Universities 1968; Joseph Cordoza Comm Svc Awd; Authored The Walking Wounded, You Shouldn't Have to Quit School Trying-Recovery Thinking; *home:* 229 Potter Rd North Kingstown RI 02852

GIORDANO, STEPHEN A., Spanish & French Teacher; *b:* New York, NY; *ed:* St Univ of NY at Albany (BA) Span & Fr 1963; Working Toward Masters at Hunter Coll; *cr:* Massapequa HS Tchr 1963-; *ai:* NHS Adv 1985-; *office:* Massapequa HS 4925 Merrick Rd Massapequa NY 11758

GIORGI, ANDREA C., Social Studies Teacher; *b:* Framingham, MA; *ed:* Wellesley Coll (BA) His 1988; Worcester St Coll (MED) Scndry Ed 1991; *cr:* Marlborough MS Educl Asst 1988-92; Marlborough HS Soc Stud Tchr 1992-; *ai:* Dram Club Adv; Soc Club Chprsn; Marlborough Eductrs Assn 1992-, Bldg Rep; MA Tchrs Assn 1992-; *office:* Marlborough HS Poirier Dr Marlborough MA 01752

GIORGI, MARY A., English Teacher; *b:* Marlborough, MA; *m:* Anthony D.; *c:* Andrea, Francisca Scott, Marisa, David, Peter; *ed:* Anna Maria Coll (BA) Eng Lit 1964; Harvard Univ Summer Inst Amer His The Female Experience 1988; *cr:* Milford HS Eng Tchr 1964-66; Marlborough MS Soc Stud Tchr 1984-86, Marlborough HS Soc Stud, Eng Tchr 1986-; *ai:* NEASC Accreditation Philosophy, Library, Policy Drafting Comms; NEA 1984-; MEA 1984-, Rep HS; Grant Awded Digital Equipment Corp 1996; *office:* Marlboro HS Bolton St Marlborough MA 01752

GIORGINI, FLORENCE LOSCALZO, Art & Music Coordinator; *b:* Philadelphia, PA; *m:* Renato; *c:* Tara, Tanya; *ed:* Dowling Coll (MS) Ed 1981; Long Island Univ (SDS), (SDA) Admin 1986; *cr:* Lindenhurst Pub Schls Music Tchr 1971-88; Dowling Coll Field Supvr, Adj Prof of Ed 1988-92; Lindenhurst Pub Schls Music, Fine Arts Coord 1992-; *ai:* Jazz Quartet; Ray White Co Jazz; NYSCAME 1992-; MENC, NYSSMA, SCMEA 1971-; ASCAP 1972-; Jenkins Meml Awd Outstdng Tchr 1988; 2 Songs Pub 1972; *office:* Lindenhurst Pub Schls 350 Daniel St Lindenhurst NY 11757*

GIORSOS, LOUIS, Earth Science Teacher; *b:* New York, NY; *m:* Joyce Lichtenheld; *c:* Jeanette, Cristie; *ed:* Queens Coll (BA) PE, Earth Sci, Bio 1975; Brooklyn Coll (MS) Ed 1988; Post Grad Courses Astronomy, Oceanography, Meteorology; *cr:* The Windsor Schl Sci, PE, Hlth Ed Tchr 1974-90; H. Frank Carey HS Earth Sci Tchr 1990-; *ai:* Jr HS Boys Soccer, Jr HS Girls Sftbl, Bsktbl Coach; NEA 1990-; *office:* H Frank Carey HS 230 Poppy Ave Franklin Square NY 11010

GIOUINAZZO, MARYANNE CISTARO, Eng & Creative Writing Tchr; *b:* Bayonne, NJ; *m:* Frank; *c:* John Cistaro, Marcus Cistaro; *ed:* Jersey City St Coll (BA) Eng 1974; *cr:* Our Lady of Mt Carmel 2nd, 7-8th Grd Tchr 1982-88; Bayonne HS Eng Tchr 1990-; *ai:* SRA Coord; After Schl Comuterized Remedial Instruction Prgm Instr; NJEA, BTA 1990-; *office:* Bayonne HS Ave A & 28th St Bayonne NJ 07002

GIOVANNANGELI, ARTHUR JOSEPH,JR., Chemistry Teacher; *b:* Portland, ME; *m:* Judith; *c:* Kelley, Jo Jo, Roger; *ed:* KSC (BED) Sci 1966; Keene St Coll (MED) Sci 1970; UNH; *cr:* Conval Chem Tchr 30 Yrs; *ai:* Var Bsktbl Coach; NEA 1968-; ACBL 1960-; Elks 1963-; NHSTA 1968-; NHCA 1970-; *office:* Conval HS RR 202 N Peterborough NH 03458

GIOVIA, DONNA ANN (HIGGINS), Substance Awareness Coord; *b:* Saddle Brook, NJ; *m:* Samuel Jr.; *c:* Jaime, Jimmy, Megan; *ed:* Trenton St Coll (BS) K-12 PE & Hlth; Jersey City St Coll Cert Substance Awareness Coord & Cnslng, 100 Credit Hrs in Alcohol & Drug Cnslng; Montclair St Coll Cert Driver Ed & Family Life Ed; *cr:* Northern Highland Regnl HS PE, Hlth & Drivers Ed Tchr 1975-78; Saddle Brook HS PE, Hlth & Drivers Ed Tchr 1978-87; Queen of Peace HS PE & Hlth Tchr 1987-94; Queen of Peace HS & Elem Substance Awareness Coord 1994-; *ai:* Bergen Cty Cncl of Alcoholism & Drug Abuse Inc; North Arlington Comm Alliance Pgm; 9th-12th Grd PEARLS, 7th-8th Grd PEP & K-8th Grd Rainbows Pgm Coord; Var Vllybl Coach; BC Women Coaches Assn 1977-; NCEA 1988-; ASAP NJ 1994-; NALSAP 1994-; Saddle Brook Soccer Assn 1987-, Sec; Saddle Brook Ladies Aux of Saddle Brook Fire Dept 1992-, Sec; *office:* Queen Of Peace HS 191 Rutherford Pl North Arlington NJ 07031*

GIPSON, JOAN ANNETTEBOYD, English Teacher; *b:* New York City, NY; *m:* Richard R.; *ed:* Cheyney Univ (BS) Scndry Ed Eng 1966; Attnd Kean Coll, Thousand Oaks Univ, LaVerne Univ; *cr:* LA USD Eng Tchr 1973-80; Millburn Schl Dist Eng Tchr 1981-82; Montclair Schl Dist Eng Tchr 1983-; *ai:* Svc Awds Comm; Grad Comm; NHS; NEA, NJEA 1980-; *office:* Montclair HS 100 Chestnut St Montclair NJ 07042

GIRARD-COUTURE, GLENN R., Physics Teacher; *b:* Norwich, CT; *m:* Christine L.; *ed:* Goddard Coll (BA) Ed 1989, (MA) Sci, Ed; Attnd Thames Vly St Tech Coll; *cr:* Plainfield HS Tchng Asst, Performing Arts 1987-90; H. H. Ellis Regnl Voc Tech Schl Sci Tchr 1990-91, Spec Ed 1991-92; Norwalk HS Physics Tchr 1993-; *ai:* Schl Newspaper, Drama Club, His Club Adv; Stu Acts Chair; Fac Cncl; CT Sci Tchrs Assn 1995-; AFT 1993-; Brigade of Amer Revolution 1994-; Fund for Excl Awd 1994; 2 Fund for Excl Awds 1996; Educating High Performance Awd CT Cncl Voc-Tech Ed; Goddard Review; *office:* Norwalk HS 23 Calvin Murphy Dr Norwalk CT 06851*

GIRARDI, THERESA A., Second Grade Teacher; *b:* Jamaica Queens, NY; *m:* Anthony; *c:* Nicole Cox, Theresa Yunger, Toni; *ed:* Dowling Coll (BS) Elem Ed 1979; C. W. Post Coll (MS) GATE 1983; 75 Addl Credits; *cr:* Charles E. Walters Elem Schl K-1st, 3rd-5th AGP Tchr 1979-93; Coram Elem Schl 2nd-3rd Grd Tchr 1993-; *ai:* Schl Bldg Team Sec; Nutrition, Bldg Integrated,Thematic, Decorating Comms; Drama Club Adv; AFT, NYSUT 1979-; MITA 1979-, Union Rep, Sec Del; NYSPTA 1979-, Life; *office:* Coram Elem Schl Coram-Mt Sinai Rd Coram NY 11727*

GIRO, ALICIA GODOY, Spanish Teacher; *b:* Havana, Cuba; *m:* Jorge A.; *c:* Alicia Giro Martinez, Christine Giro Goode; *ed:* Towson St Univ (BA) Scndry Ed, Span 1972, (MA) Scndry Ed, Span 1974; 60 Addl Credits Psych 1978; *cr:* Balto Cty Pub Schls Span Tchr 1972-; Goucher Coll Part-time Span Tchr 1979; Towson St Univ Part-time Span Tchr 1980; *ai:* Span Club, Soph Class Adv; Staff Dev Comm; Frgn Lang book, Media Order Comm Baltimore Cty Schls; Spain Tour Guide 23 Yrs; *office:* Towson HS 69 Cedar Ave Towson MD 21286

GIROD, ALLISON BEINERT, Professor of Mathematics; *b:* Buffalo, NY; *m:* Donald; *c:* Lewis, Carolyn; *ed:* Middlebury Coll (BA) Math 1967; Univ of Rochester (MA) Math 1969; St Univ of NY at Buffalo (MS) Cmptr Sci 1986; *cr:* Erie Comm Coll Math & Cmptr Sci Prof 1970-; *ai:* Cmptr Sci Comm Chair; Cmptr Sci Lab Supvr; Asst Dept Chair; North Campus Instructional Tech Comm Chair; MAA 1967-; Chancellors Awd for Excl in Tchng; *office:* Erie Comm Coll North Cmps 6205 Main St Williamsville NY 14221

GIROLMO, STEPHEN D., High School Physical Ed Tchr; *b:* Canandaigua, NY; *m:* Sharon R.; *c:* Scott, Matt; *ed:* SUNY Coll at Cortland (BS) PE 1979; SUNY Coll at Brockport (MS) PE 1989; 36 Hrs Toward Admin Cert; *cr:* East HS PE Tchr, Asst Ftbl Coach 1980-85; Livonia Jr Sr HS PE Tchr, Head Ftbl Coach 1985-; *ai:* Head Ftbl Coach; Past Co-Chair, Current Core Team Mem; Weight Room Supvr Dir; Ftbl Skills Camp; IM Ftbl Coord; NYSUT, LTA 1985-; NYSHSFCA 1994-; YMCA 1995-, Vol; GATES Chili Little League Bsbl Inc 1992-, Bd of Dirs; Livingston Conf Coach of Yr 1990, 1992-93; Section V Class B Coach of Yr 1991, 1993-94; Author of Manual; Book of Spec Plays Author, Contributor; Section V Class B Finals Coaches Awd 1989-93; *office:* Livonia Cntrl Schl Dist PO Box E Livonia NY 14487

GIRONDA, JOSEPH A., Social Studies Dept Chairman; *b:* Bayonne, NJ; *m:* Stephanie Gregory; *ed:* St Peters Coll (BA) His 1973; Jersey City St (MA) Urban Ed 1981; Pacific Western Univ (MA) Philosophy 1994; *cr:* Holy Family Acad Soc Stud Dept Chm 1985-, World & Amer His Sociology & Philosophy Tchr 1975-; Psych Tchr; *ai:* NJ Cncl for Soc Stud 1985-; Natl Cath Ed Assn 1978-; *office:* Holy Family Acad 239 Avenue A Bayonne NJ 07002

GIRONDA, MARIE MISITA, English & Latin Teacher; *b:* Bayonne, NJ; *m:* Michael; *c:* Matt, Megan; *ed:* Rutgers Univ at Newark (BA) Eng 1972; 6 Post Grad Hrs; *cr:* Weequahic HS Eng Tchr 1972-78; Shabazz HS Eng Tchr 1980-82; Univ HS Eng, Latin Tchr 1982-; *ai:* Head Debate Coach; Soc Comm; Assist Coord of AP Tests; AFT 1972-; NCTE 1994-; Natl Debate Coaches Assn 1992-; NJ Forensic League 1990-, F Columbiettes 1996; Governor's Awd for Tchng Excl; Commenda Mayor for Svc to Stdnts; *home:* 108 Isabelle St Metuchen NJ 088

GIRONDI, ALFRED JOSEPH, Chemistry Teacher; *b:* Harrist *ed:* Shippensburg Univ (BS) Chem 1967, (MED) Chem 1971; OH (PHD) Environmental Ed 1980; Attnd Milersville Inst, Bowdoi Univ of CA at Berkeley Summer Insts; *cr:* Cumberland Valley Tchr 1967-79; West Shore Schl Dist Tchr 1980-; *ai:* Amer Chen 1991-, Whalen Awd 1985; NEA, PA St Ed Assn 1967-; West Shore 1985-; GPU Nuclear Educl Advy Panel 1990-; Capital Area Sci Fa Pres 1975; The OH St Univ Thomas C. Holy Schlsp Awd; Publi Journal of Environmental Ed 1983; *office:* Cedar Cliff HS C Warwick Rds Camp Hill PA 17011

GIROUX, JUDITH MAXWELL, English Teacher; *b:* Putnam Francis J.; *c:* Christopher, Eric; *ed:* Univ of MA at Amherst (1967; Springfield Coll (MED) Rehabilitation Cnslng 1970; Fitc Coll (MED) Media Literacy 1995; *cr:* Hawley Jr HS Eng, Fr Tchr Locke MS Eng, Fr Tchr 1970-72; Billerica Meml HS Eng Tchr 1 Class 1996, Newspaper 1985-95 Adv; BFT, MFT, AFT 1970-; R Donald House 1979-, Vol; Bone Marrow Drive 1992-, Coord; Bd o Pub Lib 1979-, Sec; NBC Tchr of Yr 1988; Horace Mann Grant; P Newsletter; *office:* Billerica Memorial HS 35 River St Billerica M

GIRTON, DENNIS, Choral Activities Director; *b:* New London Carol Anne; *c:* Matthew D.; *ed:* Bowling Green St Univ (BME) 1969; Youngstown St Univ Music Ed 1978; *cr:* Jackson Milton Sc Dir 1969-71; Warren G. Harding HS Choral Act Dir 1971-; *ai:* Fut of Amer, NHS Adv; Warren Ed Assn 1971-, Tchr of Yr 1985; O Educ Assn 1971-, Pres Dist V; NEA, Music Ed Natl 1971-; AM Dir 1977-; Old Frie #3 Masonic Lodge 1980-, Dir, Masonic Chorus First United Meth Church 1976-, Dir of Music; Warren City Schl Yr 1985; 440; *office:* Warren G Harding Sr HS 860 Elm Rd NE W 44483*

GISE, NANCY JEANNETTE (REED), Retired 4th Grade Te Hagerstown, MD; *m:* Homer Lewis Jr.; *c:* Jeffrey L., Laura J. Du J. Weir; *ed:* Millersville Univ (BS) Elem Ed 1964, (ME) 199 Albright Coll 1949-52, Penn St at York & York Coll; *cr:* Pleasurev 4th Grd Tchr 1961-63; A H Martin 3rd Grd Stu Tchr 1964; Wei Elem Spec Ed Tchr 1964-69; Dover Elem 4th Grd Tchr 1970-93 Orgs of NEA & PSEA 1961-; Ret Org of DAEA 1964-, Sec 1 Yr; Grove Comm Church, Sunday Schl, Choir, HGCC Quiltng Grp.

GISMONDE, PASQUALE F.,JR., English Teacher; *b:* Philadel *m:* Karen Ann McMenamin; *c:* Martin, Pasquale III, Timoth Shaun; *ed:* Seton Hall Univ (BS) Eng Ed & His 1971; Glassbor (BA) Law & Justice 1981; Certified Breathalyzer Operator for *cr:* Camden Cty Voc-Tech Tchr & Bsktbl Coach 1971-72; Burlin HS Tchr & Ftbl Coach 1972-73; Township of Cherry Hill Polic 1973-86; Triton Reg HS Tchr 1986-; Woodbury HS Girls Bsktb Coach 1995-; *ai:* Var Ftbl Running Backs, Girls Jr Var Bsktbl C Sftbl Asst Coach; Bsbl Coach; Discipline Comm; NEA, BHPE Fraternal Order of Police 1973-; Policemans Benevolent Assn 19 Cherry Hill Pop Warner Ftbl 1976-, Pres; Cherry Hill Eastern Littl 1989-, Pres; Heroism Awd from Mayor Greenwald of CA T Commendations from the Mayor, Chief & St Police for Kidnappin Cars, Drugs & Burglary Arrests Made 1974-86; *office:* Triton Reg 250 Schubert Ave Runnemede NJ 08078*

GISOLDI, ANNE MARIE, 5th Grade Teacher; *b:* Summit, Trenton St Coll (BS) Elem Ed, Early Chldhd 1978; *cr:* St Vince Schl 4th Grd Tchr 1978-81, 7th Grd Tchr 1981-93, 6th Grd Tchr 5th Grd Tchr 1987-; *ai:* Rel, Sci Coords; Christmas Musical Dir; Cncl, Drama Club Adv, Talentow Co-Dir, Coord Cath Schl Diocesan Fac Area Rep, CTBS Coord; NCEA 1975-; Outstdng V Madison NJ 1990; *office:* St Vincent Martyr Schl 26 Green V Madison NJ 07940

GIST, DONNA SABATINO, Business Teacher; *b:* Jamaica, NY Earl III; *c:* Francesca, John-Joseph; *ed:* Univ of ND (BS) Bus 197 at Stony Brook (MA) Lib Stud 1975; Attnd Univ of HI; *cr:* Sayvi Bus Tchr 1972-85; Sayville HS Bus Tchr 1985-; *ai:* Hnr Soc A Store; Mentor Prgm Head; NYSTA, SCBA 1972-; Mentor to N *office:* Sayville HS 20 Brook St West Sayville NY 11796*

GIST, KAREN WINGFIELD, High School English Tea Harrisburg, PA; *c:* Maya Jemelle; *ed:* Clarion Univ (BS) Scndry 1972; Univ of Pittsburgh (MEd) Ed 1974; Post Grad Stud CA U & Old Dominion Univ; *cr:* Comm Coll of Allegheny Cty 1974-84; Pittsburgh Bd of Pub Ed Eng Tchr 1974-; Carlon Coll Part Time 1990-; *ai:* Discussion Club & Black His Month Prgm Sp Adv; PFT 1983-; NCTE & PSEA 1980-; NEH Fellowsip; We Writing Project Fellow; Recipient of the Leonard Kubiak Gold Awd 1989 & 1992; Carnegie Mellow Univ Making Thinking Fellow; Article Pub in Making Thinking Visible; *home:* 1737 Gra Pittsburgh PA 15235*

GITTERS, SUSAN, 4th Grade Teacher; *b:* Brooklyn, NY; *m:* Dean, Scott; *ed:* Long Island Univ (BS) Ed 1965; Stony Brook U Lbrl Stud 1991; MA plus 75 Hrs Rdng & Sci; *cr:* PS 307 5th & Tchr 1965-69; Coram Elem 1st-4th Grd Tchr 1977-; *ai:* PTA Ex Yrs; Mid Island Tchrs Assn 1977-; NEA; WLIB Tchr of the Lifetime Mbrshp Awd PTA 1989; *office:* Coram Elem Schl 6 Mount Sinai Rd Coram NY 11727

GITTINGS, JULIE ANNE, Enrichment Teacher; *b:* York, PA; *m:* *c:* Hilary, Leslie; *ed:* PA St (BA) Eng 1974, (MED) Eng 1984; 1 Grad Eng at Northwestern; *cr:* St Coll HS Eng Tchr 1975-87, En Tchr 1987-; *ai:* Acad Quiz; Acad Decathlon; Shakespeare Com Ski Club; Phi Delta Kappa 1979-; Jaycees, Young Educato Co-Writer of Bell Grant Futures Schl 60000 Dollars; Co-Write Ribbon Schls; *office:* State College Area HS 650 Westerly Pk College PA 16801*

GITTINGS, PATRICIA YVONNE, Fifth Grade Teacher; *b:* Wa DC; *m:* James Robinson; *c:* D'Nai Monique; *ed:* Morgan St Univ (Ed 1970; Loyola Coll (MS) Elem Ed 1978; Post Grad Stud Johns Univ; Coppin St Coll; *cr:* Frankford Elem Schl Edctr 1970- Springs Elem Schl Edctr 1975-76; Harford Heights Schl Edctr 1 MSPAP Comm Chm; Dance Instr; Reach Out, Touch Prgm; Readi Project Lift; BTU, AFT 1970-; Delta Sigma Theta 1968-; *office* Heights Elem Schl 1919 N Broadway Baltimore MD 21213

GIUGGIO, SANDRA, Biology Teacher; *b:* Ludlow, MA; *m:* Joseph; *c:* Michael, Caitlin, Anthony; *ed:* Westfield St Coll (B 1978, (BS) Bio 1978, (MED) Scndry Ed 1980, (CAGS) Educl Ldr *cr:* Cathedral HS Physics, Cmptr Sci Tchr 1982-85; Granville Vi Sci, Cmptr Tchr 1986-87; Thornton W. Burgess Intermediate Schl 1987-92; Northampton HS Bio Tchr 1993-; *ai:* Adv, Advise Westfield Boys & Girls Club 1993-, Bd of Dirs; Westfield Pub Sc Range Bldg, Facilities Comm; *office:* Northampton HS 38 Northampton MA 01060*

GIULIANO, GERARD, Graphic Comm Instructor; *b:* Rochester Monroe Comm Coll (AAS) Graphic Arts, Printing 1988; SUNY a (BS) Voc Tech Ed 1992; *cr:* Monroe Graphics Print Consultant

ndstrl Clubs of Amer Adv; Soccer Coach Marcellus Jr HS; Tech NAPL, IGAEA 1993-; GATF 1995-; *office:* OCM BOCES 6820 n Rd Syracuse NY 13211

NO, MARK M., 6th Grade Teacher; *b:* Brooklyn, NY; *m:* Anna; lle, Diana; *ed:* SUNY at Stony Brook (BA) Elem Ed 1976, (MA) 1979; 30 Credit Hrs Post-Grad Stud; *cr:* Atkinson Schl Tchr : NYSUT, AFT 1976-; *office:* Caroline G Atkinson MS 58 W Ave Freeport NY 11520*

, MAUREEN PRENDA, English Teacher & Dept Chair; *b:* ce, RI; *m:* Anthony Joseph; *ed:* Univ of RI (BA) Eng 1969; Univ MA) Lit 1985; *cr:* Coventry HS Eng Tchr 1969-70; Lawton Schl ng Arts LD Prgm 1971; Ayer HS Sub Tchr 1973-74; Ellsworth HS 1975-; *ai:* NHS, New Voices Magazine Adv; Schl Atmosphere, ng Comms; Dept Chair Eng; Coord Dev Young Writers um at Haystack; NCTEA; NEATE; MCELA; NEA; Grant to Oral His; Outstdng Achvmt Awd 1992; *office:* Ellsworth HS 275 ate St Ellsworth ME 04605

MAC FADDEN, Associate Professor of Biology; *b:* Abington, arbara E. Scott; *ed:* Brown Univ (BA) Bio 1977; Univ of CT at HD) Zoology 1987; *cr:* Friends Cntrl Schl Chem Tchr 1977-81; ce Coll Adj Asst Prof 1987-89; Neumann Coll Assoc Prof 1990-; P 1994-, VP; AAAS 1983-; Sigma Xi 1977-; Pendle Hill Conf Ctr d Mem; Excl in Tchng & Campus Ldrshp Awd 1995; Growth wd 1991; Pub Rsrch; *office:* Neumann Coll Concord Rd Aston PA

MADELYN KENNISTON, First Grade Teacher; *b:* Waterville, dward P.; *c:* Michael E., Heather G. Bell; *ed:* Aroostook St Tchrs) Elem Ed 1966; Univ of ME at Gorham (MS) Elem Ed 1981; chr Cert; *cr:* Waterville Schl System Fourth Grd Tchr 3 Yrs; Schl System Home Tutoring 1969-70, Sub Tchr 1976-77, 1 Grd Yrs; Auburn Schl System Home Tutoring 1969-70; *ai:* Lewiston sn 1976-; ME Tchrs Assn, NEA 1966-; DKG 1986-; Girl Scouts Patricks Church Euchristic Minister.*

SCOTT W., Reading Teacher; *b:* Lansadale, PA; *m:* Patricia M.; vell, Kathryn; *ed:* PA St Univ (BS) Elem, Kndgtn Ed 1985; urg Univ (MED) Rdng Ed 1986; Penn St 20 Credits Hrs; *cr:* h MS 8-9 Yr Olds Tchr 1985; Bloomsburg Univ Rdng Clinician St Coll Area Schls Fourth-Sixth Grd Tchr 1986-91, Rdng t, HOTS Tchr 1991-; *ai:* St Coll Area MS Steering Comm; Instrl Core Team; Elem IM Coach; NEA, PA St Ed Assn 1986-; St Coll 1986-, Exec Cncl; Pi Lambda Theta 1985-; Back The Lions 1986-, tany Lion Club 1986-; Penn St Alumni Assn 1985-; *home:* 1331 State College PA 16803

:, FLOYD C.,JR., US History & Sociology Teacher; *b:* n, PA; *c:* David C., Brenda L.; *ed:* Kutztown St Univ (BS) Ed, Soc 51; Lehigh Univ (MA) Schl Admin 1968; Amer Stud East urg Univ; *cr:* Belvidere HS Soc Stud Tchr 1961-; The Times Sportswriter, Columnist 1977-; *ai:* Girls Var Bsktbl Coach; 54-; Belvidere Ed Assn 1961-, Pres, Negotiator; Warren Cty Ed 4-, Pres; NJ Ed Assn 1961-, Del Assembly; Elon Coll Local Hero 4; Orange Cty Speedway Writer of Yr Fleming Speedway; Easter orts Press Assn 1st Pl Writing Awds; *home:* 1 Lexington Ct Easton)*

, JEANNE M., Chemistry Professor; *b:* New York, NY; *m:* A.; *c:* Thomas W., Randy J.; *ed:* Alfred Univ (BA) Sci Ed 1968;) Sci Ed 1975; Univ of Albany (PHD) Curr & Instruction 1989; ne Cntrl Schl Chem Tchr 1968-69; Mercy HS Chem Tchr 1969-73; a Greene Comm Coll Chem Prof 1977-; *ai:* Prof Comms; NEA YS 2 Yr Coll Chem Tchrs Assn 1979-; Article Pub; Flwshps & r Summer Wkshps; *office:* Columbia Greene Comm Coll 4400 Rt on NY 12534

SKI, PATRICIA ANN, Biology Teacher; *b:* Ilion, NY; *m:* Carl; *c:* : Syracuse Univ (BA) Bio, (BS) Med Tech; 30 Grad Hrs; *cr:* -Schuyler HS 7, 8th Grds Bio Tchr 1975-86, 10, 12 Grds Bio Tchr : Jr Class Adv; NEA; AFT; NABT; *office:* Frankfurt-Schuyler 608 Palmer St Frankfort NY 13340

JOANNE KONKLE, Second Grade Teacher; *b:* Williamsport, ichard S.; *c:* Michael, Jennifer; *ed:* Lock Haven Univ (BA) Elem Penn St Univ (MS) Elem Ed 1975; *cr:* Penn Center Schl Kndgtn 72-74; Woolrich Elem Schl Kndgtn Tchr 1974-77; Dickey Elem ond Grd Tchr 1977-; *ai:* Instructional Support Team Tchr; Sci ech Comm; Curr Comm; Strat Planng Comm; PSEA, NEA 1973-; ickey Elem Schl S Farview St Lock Haven PA 17745

Y, MARY GIBBONS, Vice Principal; *b:* Wilkes-Barre, PA; *m:* : Mary Jo E. Gladey Lyke; *ed:* Coll Misericordia (BA) Soc Stud Nazareth Acad World, Amer His Tchr 1962-63; St Edmunds HS s 1963-66; St Charles Borromeo Schl Soc Stud Tchr 1984-; *ai:* ı; MS Coord; 8th Grd Adv; NCEA 1962-; Hope Hall Schl Bd of 4-; *home:* 119 Briarcliff Rd Rochester NY 14616

NG, SCOTT B., HS English Tchr & Theatre Dir; *b:* Camden, NJ; a Glasscock Glading; *c:* Amanda Leigh, Ashlea Victoria; *ed:* St Coll (BA) Speech Comms, Theatre Arts 1977; WV Univ Acting, , Tech & Design; *cr:* Haddon Heights Jr, Sr HS Eng Tchr, Theatre -95; *ai:* Dir Musical Theatre Productions; Jr, Sr Class Adv; Peer r; Jr Miss Adv; Dir Haddon Summer Music Theatre Semi onal Musical Theatre Co; NEA, NJEA, HHEA 1977-; Haddon Music Theatre 1988-, Artistic Dir; Tchr of Yr 1994-95; Comm st Practices & Star Schls for NJ St Dept of Ed; *office:* Haddon HS 2nd & Garden Haddon Hts NJ 08035

TONE, JOHN JOSEPH, Science Teacher; *b:* Philadelphia, PA; e M. Dolezal; *c:* Christopher, Elizabeth; *ed:* Penn St (BA) Elem ; Beaver Coll (MED) Educl Ldrshp 1981; *cr:* Schl Dist of phia Sci Tchr 1972-; *ai:* AFT 1972-; *home:* 415 Valley Rd vn PA 19083

TONE, JOSEPH PAUL, Math Teacher; *b:* New York City, NY; *m:* anne Alterman; *c:* Melanie; *ed:* Queens Coll (BA) Comm Arts, Scis onybrook Univ (MA) Liberal Stud 1974; 75 Hrs Past Masters; *cr:* HS Math Tchr 1969-; *ai:* Sr Musical Dir 1971-80; AFT 1969-; The g, Hofstra Univ Alumni Theater Org 1984-, Bd Mem; *office:* HS South Woods Rd Syosset NY 11791

, AL THOMAS, Associate Professor of Art; *b:* Toledo, OH; *m:* avarise; *c:* Kim; *ed:* Columbus Coll of Art & Design (BFA) on 1973; Art Otterbein Coll; 3 Credit Hrs Welding Technologies; Hrs Cmptr Graphics; *cr:* Columbus Coll of Art & Design Asst Prof : EDP Inc Art Dir, Consultant; Stu Exhibition Chm; Columbus Art 1984-; Fac Cncl 1991-94, Pres, Found Rep; Columbus Pub Lib Awd; Art Reach Show Best Sculpture Awd 1985-86; *home:* 244 Dr Gahanna OH 43230

ILLE, SUSAN KIME, Health Occupations Teacher; *b:* Waterloo, Robert Edward; *ed:* Comm Coll of the Finger Lakes (AAS) Nrsng UNY at Buffalo (BSN) Nrsng 1983; Buffalo St Coll (MED) Voc Ed eneva Schl of Practical Nrsng LPN 1970; *cr:* Erie #1 Boces Adult ctical Nrsng Tchr 1983-91; Erie #1 Boces Harkness Ctr ional Ed, LPN, CNA Tchr 1991-; *ai:* Mentor Intern Prgms Mentor; Hlth Occupations Stdnts of Amer 5 Yrs, Club Adv, Co-Lt NYS Competitions 1992-94; AFT 1991-; NYSHOEA 1995-; ANA.*

GLAROS, GEORGE RAYMOND, Professor of Chemistry; *b:* Minneapolis, MN; *m:* Roberta Nicole Baldwin; *c:* Steven Paul, Michael John; *ed:* Univ of MN (BCHEM) Chem 1965; Univ of NE (PHD) Organic Chem 1971; *cr:* Univ of CT Postdoctoral Instr 1971-72; Russell Sage Coll Prof 1972-; *ai:* Amer Chem Soc 1972-; NSF Traineeship; Avery Flwshp; Articles Pub; PRF Type G Grant; *office:* Russell Sage Coll Troy NY 12180

GLAS, J. ROBERT, Art Teacher; *b:* Manhattan, NY; *m:* Dorothy D.; *c:* Dylan, Robin; *ed:* Southampton Coll (BA) Art 1971, (BA) Elem Ed 1971; 30 Post Grad Credits; *cr:* Otsego Northern Catskills Boces Itinerant Art Tchr 1973-77; South Kortright Cntrl Schl Art Tchr 1977-; Stamford Home Video Owner 1984-; *ai:* Yrbk Adv; NEA 1973-; Natl Publication of Integrated Tech Lesson Plans Cmptr Learning Fnd; *office:* South Kortright Central Schl PO Box 113 South Kortright NY 13842

GLASBERG, RUTH, 6th Grd Tchr & MS Coordinator; *b:* Bronx, NY; *m:* Murray; *c:* Lori Siedman, Michele Weiss; *ed:* Herbert Lehman, Hunter Coll (BA) Ed, Eng, Acctng, Bus Practice 1959; City Coll 20 Credits; *cr:* Hauppauge Schls 6th Grd Tchr 1971-84; HASC 6th Grd Tchr 1984-89; Solomon Schechter MS 6th Grd Eng, SS Tchr, Coord 1989-; *ai:* Schl Bd Head Advy Prgm; Comm Svc Adv; NEA 1989-; PTA, VP, Jenkins Meml Awd; Hauppauge Tchrs Assn; Temple Bd 1975-; PTA Bd Mem; Alpha Kai Alpha; *office:* Solomon Schechter MS East St Hicksville NY 11801

GLASER, MICHAEL S., Professor of English; *b:* Chicago, IL; *m:* Kathleen W.; *c:* Brian, Joshua, Daniel, Amira, Eva; *ed:* Denison Univ (BA) Eng 1965; Kent St Univ (MA) eng 1967, (PHD) Eng 1971; Attnd Univ of CA at San Diego, Univ of CA at Santa Barbara; *cr:* Kent St Univ Tchng Fellow 1966-70; St Mary's Coll Asst Prof 1970-73, Assoc Prof 1974-80, Prof 1980-; *ai:* Oxford Prgm, Lit Rdng Series, Lit Festival, Writing Wkshps Dir; Inst of Humanistic Ed 1972-80, Pres; Charlie Logan Seafarers Intnl Schlsp Comm, Poetry Comm Greater Washington DC Area 1984-; St Mary's Cty Housing Authority 1975-89, Chair 1982-89; St Mary's Cty A-ts Cncl 1976-91, Bd Mem; MD Assn of Tchr Edctrs 1977-79, Steering Comm; MD St Arts Cncl Advy Panel for Lit 1988-91; Danforth Assoc 1980-86; Fac, Stu Life Awd 1992; Book: the Cooke Book: A Seasoning of Poets 1987; Book: A Lover's Eye 1989; Book: In The Men's Room and Other Poems, Painted Bride Quarterly Chapbook 1996; *office:* Saint Marys Coll Of MD Montgomery Hall St Marys Cy MD 20686*

GLASER, SUSAN ABORN, Vocal Music Director; *b:* Boston, MA; *m:* Donald Edward; *ed:* Curry Coll (MED) Ed 1992; Westfield St Coll (BA) Music Ed 1996; *cr:* Cntrl MS Vocal Dir 1987-95; Bernazzani Elem Schl Vocal Music Tchr 1995-; Beechwood Knoll Elem Schl Vocal Music Tchr 1995-; *ai:* St Agatha Folk Choir 1978-; MMEA, MEA, MTA, NEA 1987-; Multicultural Music Ed Grants; 6 Golden Apple Awds; *office:* Central MS 1012 Hancock St Quincy MA 02169*

GLASGOW, BRENNAN, Fourth Grade Teacher; *b:* Boulder, CO; *m:* Janice Elizabeth Kitching; *c:* Meghan E., Katy-Rose, Michael P.; *ed:* CT Coll (BS) Psych & Elem Ed 1985; Working Toward Masters in Rdng & Math at Cntrl CT St Univ; *cr:* Canton Intermediate 4th Grd Tchr 1985-; *ai:* Boys Var Bsktl Coach; NEA, CEA, FCAC 1985-, VP Local Chapter; Park & Recreation Little Warriors 1985-93, Organizer & Coach; Farmington Park & Recreation Soccer 1996, Coach; *office:* Canton Intermediate Schl 39 Dyer Ave Collinsville CT 06022*

GLASGOW, HARRY KIRK, Technology Education Teacher; *b:* Martins Ferry, OH; *m:* Marcia Ann Mays; *c:* Amber Lodge, Dean; *ed:* Eastern KY Univ (BS) Scndry Arts Ed 1976; Univ of Dayton (MS) Ed Admin 1990; Cmptr Aided Drafting 8 Hrs; *cr:* St Clairsville HS Tchr 1976-; *ai:* Prom Chm, Dept Chm, Tech Drawing & Design Club Chm; Tech Ed Curr Dev; OEA, NEA, OTEA 1976-; ITEA 1989-; Masonic Lodge 1987-; Scottish Rite 1988-; Psiris Shrine 1990-; Saints Club 1993-, Bldg Project Chm, Man of Yr Awd; Successful Implementation of New Tech Ed Lab; Ashland Oil Golden Apple Awd; *office:* Saint Clairsville HS 102 Woodrow Ave Saint Clairsville OH 43950

GLASS, JENNIFER MCCONKEY, Biology & Anatomy Teacher; *b:* Akron, OH; *m:* Todd Andrew; *ed:* Miami Univ (BA) Ed & Bio 1993; *cr:* Mt Notre Dame HS Bio & Anatomy Tchr 1994-; *ai:* Ecology Club Adv; Hamilton Cty Youth Conf Coord; *office:* Mount Notre Dame H S 711 E Columbia Ave Cincinnati OH 45215

GLASS, MARJORIE GATES, Kindergarten Teacher; *b:* Johnstown, PA; *m:* Charles Alex; *c:* Melissa, Jennifer, Laura; *ed:* IN Univ of PA (BS) Elem Ed Minor Sci 1966; Univ of Pittsburgh (MED) Ed 1969; Attnd Shippensburg Univ, Univ of Pitts at Johnstown Cooperativing Tchr; *cr:* Forest HIlls Sch Dist Second Grd Tchr 2 Yrs; Peters Township Schl Second Grd Tchr 4 Yrs; Forest Hills Schl Dist Second, First, Kndgtn Tchr 22 Yrs; *ai:* Stu Tchrs Supvr; Proj Kids Home Tchr; NEA, PSEA, FHEA 1966-, Bldg Rep; Delta Kappa Gamma 1984-, Prof Affairs Chm; Women's Club 1976-, Ed Chm; Jaycee-ettes 1972-, Sec; Wrote, Pub Articles in PDE Newsletters; Project Kids Wkshp Presenter.*

GLASS, TERRENCE L., Professor of English & Chair; *b:* Dayton, OH; *m:* Barbara Combs; *c:* Grace, John, Sarah; *ed:* Cntrl St Univ (BA) Eng 1968; OH St Univ (MA) Eng 1970, (PHD) Eng 1973; *cr:* OH St Univ Tchng Assoc 1971-73; Eastern KY Univ Adj Instr 1973-74; Univ of KY Lecturer 1974-75; Cntrl St Univ Eng Prof & Dept Chair 1975-; Union Inst Grad Schl Adj Grad Prof 1994-; *ai:* Alpha Kappa Mu Hnr Soc Fac Adv; Steering, Hrns Pgm Advy & Tchr Ed Pgm Advy Comm; Toward Independence Inc 1994-, Bd of Dirs; St Brigid Church 1986-, Lector; OH St Univ Amer Poets Competion 1st Pl Awd 2 Times; Cntrl St Univ Alumni Achvmt Hall of Fame; Poems Pub; *office:* Central St Univ Wilberforce OH 45384

GLASSCOCK, RUTH KNEPFLE, Sixth Grade Teacher; *b:* Cincinnati, OH; *c:* Gary, Alicia (dec), Sandra (dec); *ed:* Mt St Joseph (BA) Elem Ed 1972; Grad Stud Miami Univ, Xavier Univ; *cr:* Harrison Elem Schl Sixth Grd Tchr 1971-; *ai:* NEA, OEA 1971-; SLCTA 1971-, Neg Team 3 Yrs, Bldg Rep 18 Yrs; Harrison Cty Cncl 1984-87, 1990-, Elected Mem; Fernald Environmental Mngmt Project Grant Set Up Yth for Environmental Awareness Prgm; CGE Grants.

GLASSER, ELAINE JUNASZ, Professor of Art; *b:* Youngstown, OH; *m:* Robert P.; *ed:* Youngstown Univ (BSEd) Art Ed 1960; Kent St Univ (MSEd) Art Ed 1965; Cmptr Tech; Pottery; Theater Props; Puppetry; *cr:* Youngstown Pub Schls Art Tchr 1960-66; Youngstown Univ Art Instr 1961-66; Trumbull Branch Kent St Univ Summer Instr 1966; Youngstown Mahoning Coll Television Art Tchr 1966-70; Youngstown St Univ Prof 1966-; *ai:* Art Curr Chair Comm; Stu Field Exp Campus Supvr; Mentoring Prgm, Art Dept, Little Sisters Alpha Phi Delta Adv; OEA, YSU, NEA 1960-; OAEA 1960-70; Natl Puppetry Assn; United Church of Christ 1980-, Deacon; Altrusa Club; Steel Valley Art Tchrs Assn, Corres, Sec, Mem; Univ Women Club, Pres, VP Corres, Sec 1977-79; YMCA Women of Yr Cultural Arts 1990; NEO Regnl Scholastic Art Coord; NCATE Evaluation of Schls 1966-88; *office:* Youngstown St Univ 410 Wick Ave Youngstown OH 44555*

GLATT, HOWARD, English Teacher; *b:* Jersey City, NJ; *m:* Sandy; *c:* Carra, Josh; *ed:* Rutgers Coll (BA) Eng Lit 1973; Rutgers Coll-New Brunswick (MA) Eng Lit 1979; Credits for PHD Eng Lit; *cr:* Elizabeth HS Eng Tchr 1974-76; Rutgers Coll Tchng Asst 1976-81; Columbia HS Eng Tchr 1981-; *ai:* NEA, NJEA, SOMEA 1981-; *home:* 15 Rossmore Ter Livingston NJ 07039

GLAUDE, MIMI WARDWELL, Fifth Grade Educator; *b:* Methuen, MA; *m:* Roland Joseph; *ed:* New England Coll (BA) Elem Ed 1958; 30 Credit Hrs Toward Masters in Ed at Suffolk Univ; *cr:* West Medway Elem Schl 5th Grd Tchr 1959-64; Barron Schl 5th Grd Tchr 1964-; *ai:* Tchr Cncl; SEA 1964-, Fac Rep, Annual Banuet Organizer, Annual Retirement Tea Organizer; NHEA, NEA 1964-; MEA 1959-64; *home:* 54 Hampshire St Methuen MA 01844

GLAVAN, JAMES DAVID, Vocational Agriculture Instr; *b:* Alliance, OH; *ed:* OH St Univ (BS) Ag Ed, Mechanization 1983; *cr:* Niuman Meats Butcher, Meat Cutter 1982-91; Southern Local HS Vo-Ag Instr 1988-; Kiko Meats Butcher 1991-94; *ai:* FFA Adv; NOVATA 8 Yrs; Ruritans 1983-, Pres 2 Yrs, Pres Club 1987; *office:* Southern Local H S 38095 State Rt 39 Salineville OH 43945

GLAWATZ, MARION MOELLER, French Teacher; *b:* Buffalo, NY; *m:* Kurt J.; *c:* James K., Pamela S. Rowley, Jeffrey R.; *ed:* Univ of Buffalo (BA) Latin & Fr 1956; Canisius Coll (MS) Ed 1975; *cr:* North Collins Cntrl Tchr 1956-58; Lockport-Emmett Belknap Jr HS Tchr 1973-75; Williamsville North HS Tchr 1975-76; Amsdell Jr HS- Frontier MS Tchr 1976-; *ai:* Classical Assn of Western NY, Sec; Classical Assn of Empire St, NY St Foreign Lang Tchrs, Western NY Foreign Lang Ed Comm; Latin Club Adv 1976-94; Musical & Drama Productions Asst Dir 1985-95; *office:* Frontier MS Amsdell Rd Hamburg NY 14075

GLAZE, VICKI L., Sixth Grade Teacher; *b:* Wauseon, OH; *m:* Max D.; *c:* Shannon Armstrong; *ed:* BGSU (BS) Elem, Scndry Ed, Soc Stud 1969; Univ of Toledo (MSED) Elem 1983; Attnd Univ of HI; *cr:* Wauseon Schls 6th Grd Tchr 1969-70; Wahiwa Elem Schl 6th Grd Tchr 1970-71; Pike Delta York Schl 5th Grd Tchr 1971-72; Findlay City Schls 6th Grd Tchr 1972-74; Lake Local Schls 3rd, 5th-6th Grd Tchr 1979-; *ai:* Red Ribbon; Right to Read; St Fair Project; NEA 1969-; LEA 1974-; *office:* Lake Elem Schl 28025 Main St PO Box 151 Millbury OH 43447

GLAZIER, RHODA RAAB, English Teacher; *b:* New York City, NY; *m:* Leonard; *c:* Beth Mc Donald, Jeffrey, Ellen Schwartz; *ed:* Cedar Crest Coll (BA) Eng 1964; Temple Univ (MS) Ed 1974; Addl Credits In-Svc Courses; *cr:* Allen HS Eng Tchr 1974-; *ai:* In Charge of Writing Contests & Contestants; NEA, AEA 1975-; NCTE 1980-; PCTE 1976-; Hadassah 1952-, Pres 1964-65; Keneseth Israel 1951-, Bd Mem; *office:* William Allen HS 106 N 17th St Allentown PA 18104

GLEASON, BARBARA J. BIELEFELD, Dept Chairwomen & Teacher; *b:* Brooklyn, NY; *m:* Michael; *c:* Michael, Mary, Kathleen, Timothy; *ed:* Good Counsel Coll (BA) His 1961; St John's Univ (MA) 20th Century His 1962; Columbia Univ 3 Credits Driver Ed 1964; *cr:* St Peter's HS 10-11 Grd Tchr 1984-87; St Peter's Elem Schl 5-7 Grd Tchr 1987-89; Mt St Mary Acad Tchr, Chairwomen 1989-; *ai:* Jr Class Moderator; Advy Bd 1990-; NEA 1990-; Grad Assistanship St John's Univ; *office:* Mount St Mary Acad 1645 US Hwy 22 Plainfield Watchung NJ 07060*

GLEASON, BEVERLY ANDERSON, Sixth Grade Teacher; *b:* Boston, MA; *m:* Russell C.; *c:* Russell S., Catherine S.; *ed:* Univ of MA (BA) Elem Ed 1959; *cr:* Osborn Hill Schl 3rd Grd Tchr 1959-60; Faulkner Kndgtn Tchr 1970-73; Atwell-Galvin Schl 6th Grd Tchr 1979-; *ai:* Lang Arts Curr Comm; NEA, MTA, Wakefield Tchrs Assoc 1979-; *office:* Atwell-Galvin Schl 485 Main St Wakefield MA 01880

GLEASON, ELAINE CHAMPLIN, Third Grade Teacher; *b:* Penn Yan, NY; *m:* P. Earle; *c:* Aaron; *ed:* Corning Comm (AS) Lbrl Arts 1969; SUC at Brockport (BS) Elem Ed 1971; Nazareth Coll (MS) Elem Ed 1976; *cr:* Seneca Falls Elem 2nd Grd Tchr 1971-73; Penn Yan Elem 2nd Grd Tchr 1973-76, 3rd Grd Tchr 1976-81, 1985-, 1st Grd Tchr 1982-85; *ai:* Rdng & Lang Arts Comm K-12th Grd 1993-; NEA 1971-; Amer Legion Auxiliary 1980-, Americanism Chm 1986-88, Mary Smack Americanism Awd 1987; St Pauls Luth Church 1949-, Asst Minister 1989-; Amer Lawyers Auxiliary 3rd Pl 1990-91; Amer Lawyers Auxiliary Law Related Ed 1st Pl 1991-92; Wayne Finger Lakes Cncl for the Soc Stud Elem Tchr of the Yr 1993-94, Convention Speaker 1994; *home:* 1383 Milo Center Rd Penn Yan NY 14527

GLEASON, LISA FRANCHI, Learning Support Teacher; *b:* Holbrook, NY; *m:* William; *c:* Keaton, Brodie, Logan; *ed:* St Bonaventure Univ (BA) Psych, Scndry Soc Stud 1982; Long Island Univ (MED) Sped Ed 1983; *cr:* William Floyd HS Soc Stud, Spec Ed Tchr 1984-87; Palmyra MS IV #13 Spec Ed Tchr 1988; Solanco HS 9-10 Grd Spec Ed Tchr 1989-; *ai:* Yth in Ed Assn, Class of 1999 Adv; PSEA 1988-, Bldg Rep; *office:* Solanco HS 585 Solanco Rd Quarryville PA 17566*

GLEASON, PHYLLIS SUZANNE, Associate Prof of Humanities; *b:* Cambridge, MA; *m:* Mark R.; *c:* Mark R. II, Keri-Lynn; *ed:* Middlesex Comm Coll (AS) Lbrl Arts & Sci 1982; Framingham St Coll (BA) Eng 1986; Boston Coll (MA) Eng 1989; *cr:* Middlesex Comm Coll Assoc Prof 1992-; *office:* Middlesex Comm Coll Springs Road Bedford MA 01730

GLEASON, ROSALIE GRAMMAR, Retired 3rd Grade Teacher; *b:* Buffalo, NY; *w:* Charles (dec); *c:* Cynthia Sielski, Kathy Jachter; *ed:* Univ of Buffalo (BA) Ed 1960, (MS) Ed-Magna Cum Laude 1975; *cr:* Eggert Rd Elem Schl 4th Grd Tchr 1960-75, Curr Coord 1975-80; Winderemere Blvd Elem Schl 3rd Grd Tchr 1980-87; *ai:* AFT, NEA, Amherst Tchr Assn 1960-; *home:* 507 W Delavan Ave Buffalo NY 14222*

GLEIM, CAROL JANE (HILL), Reading & English Teacher; *b:* Ironton, OH; *m:* Galen H.; *c:* Julie Anne; *ed:* OH Univ (BS) Ed 1966; Marshall Univ (MA) Ed 1976; Post-Grad Work OH Univ, Univ of Dayton; *cr:* Wheelersburg Elem Schl 7-8 Grds Rdng, Eng Tchr 1966-; *ai:* Scioto Cty Writing Comm; CBE Grd Level Ldr Writing; NEA 1980-, OH Ed Assoc 1966-; Delta Kappa Gamma 1976-, 1st VP, 2nd VP, St Rsrch Comm; Delta Kappa Gamma 1976-; OCTELA 1992-; *home:* 8652 Green St Wheelersburg OH 45694

GLEMMING, PATRICIA REYNOLDS, Reading & Language Arts Tchr; *b:* Montclair, NJ; *m:* James H. Jr.; *ed:* Fairleigh Dickinson Univ (BA) Elem Ed 1974; *cr:* St Catherines 6th-8th Grd Eng Tchr 1974-76; Atlantic Elem & Cedar Dr Schl Tchr 1976-; *ai:* Yrbk Co-Adv; MS Comm; NEA 1976-; NJEA 1976-; PETA 1988-; HSUS 1988-; Governors Tchr Recognition Pgm Recipient 1991; *office:* Cedar Drive Schl 73 Cedar Dr Colts Neck NJ 07722

GLENCER, SUZANNE THOMSON, Science Teacher; *b:* Monongahela, PA; *ed:* Penn St Univ (BS) Zoology 1964; CA St Univ (MED) Bio 1968; Over 60 Credits Univ of Pittsburgh, Penn St Univ 1968-; *cr:* Northgate Schl Dist Sci Tchr 1967-; Penn St Univ New Kensington Bio Instr 1978-84; Allegheny Comm Coll Bio Instr 1969-85; *ai:* Just Say No Club; Sci Club; Drug & Alcohol Coord; PSEA Intergroup Relations 1987-, Chprsn, Fac Rep 1995-; Sci, Math Collaborative 1995-; Animal Friends 1974-84, VP; Amer Cancer Soc 1979-83, Chprsn, Pub Ed Awd; Teen Recreation Fed 1989-, Pres, Obtained Grants; Citizens Against Substance Abuse 19 90-93, Grant; North Hills Jaycees 1979 Outstdng Young Edctr; 1979 PA St Jaycees Outstdng Young Edctr; 1982 PA St Tchr of Yr; 1982 Citizen of Yr Pittsburgh, PA Police Assn; Received Numerous Grants; Recipient Natl Drug Free Schl Awd 1989; Citation PA House of Rep 1993; 4th Place Natl Humane Edctr of Yr; Who's Who in the East & Sci & Engrng; *office:* Northgate Jr Sr HS 589 Union Ave Pittsburgh PA 15202*

GLENN, DAVID SAMUEL, Counselor & Guidance Dept Chm; *b:* Roswell, NM; *ed:* Loyola Coll in MD (BA) Psych 1984, (MS) Cnslng Psych 1986; *cr:* Mt St Joseph HS Guid Cnslr 1986-89; Howard HS Guid Cnslr 1989-; *ai:* Jr Var, Var Ftbl, Track Coach; Stu Govt Adv; Accountability Coord; Peer Mediation Coord; Site Based Mngmt, Attendance Teams; Stu Support Team Co-Chair; Crisis Intervention Team

Cty Wide; NEA, HCEA 1989-; ACA 1986-; Loyola Coll Acct Advy Bd 1995-; *office:* Howard HS # 108 8700 Old Annapolis Rd Ellicott City MD 21043*

GLENN, DORIS SWIGGETT, Math Teacher; *b:* Chester, PA; *m:* Clark L.; *c:* Clark, David, Mary, Michael, Patrick, Anna, Christopher; *ed:* DE St Coll (BS) Bio 1954; Bowie St Coll 12 Credit Hrs Post Grad; *cr:* Parkerman HS Math Tchr 1954-57; Henry H Schl Math Tchr 1957-58; Sukian Ed Ctr Test Dir & Tchng Gls 1958-59; Kubasaki HS Math Tchr 1959-60; *ai:* Math Chprsn; NCTM 1986-; Team of Our Lady 1970-.*

GLENN, JANE BENCHOFF, 2nd Grade Teacher; *b:* Waynesboro, PA; *m:* Edwin Joseph Jr.; *c:* Zachary, Alex; *ed:* Shippensburg Univ (BS) Elem, Early Chldhd 1979; Models of Tchng In-Service; Whole Lang Process Penn St; *cr:* New Baltimore Elem Schl 1st Grd Tchr 1979-81; Mowrey Elem Schl 2nd Grd Tchr 1981-83, Transition 2nd Grd Tchr 1985-95; Mont Alton Elem Schl 1st, Transition Grd Tchr 1983-85; Hooverville Elem Schl 2nd Grd Tchr 1995-; *ai:* Prof Dev Comm; NEA 1979-92; Children's Lit Cncl 1981-83; Coll Club, Children's Club 1994-; *home:* 10278 Candura Dr Waynesboro PA 17268

GLENN, MARSHALL DARWIN, Industrial Arts & PE Teacher; *b:* Mansfield, OH; *m:* Linda Jean Fisher; *ed:* Fairmont St Coll (AB) Ed, Indstrl Arts, PE 1967; Xavier Univ (MA) PE 1971; 30 Plus Quarter Hrs Post Grad Stud OH St Univ Towards Cert Elem Ed; *cr:* Highland HS Indstrl Arts Tchr, Coach 1965-66; Van Wert HS Indstrl Arts Tchr 1967; Highland HS Indstrl Arts Tchr, Coach 1967-69; Hahanna Lincoln HS Indstrl Arts, PE Tchr, Coach 1969-; *ai:* Golf Coach; Ski Club Adv; NEA, OH Ed Assn, Gahanna Jefferson Ed Assn 1969-; OH HS Golf Coaches Assn 1970-; Pataskala Presbyn Church 1973, Deacon, Elder; OH HS Golf Coaches Assn Hall of Fame 1986; *home:* 12114 Mill St Pataskala OH 43062

GLENN, SALLY ANN PIAZZA, 7th Grade Language Arts Tchr; *b:* Avon, OH; *m:* Robert J.; *c:* Cheryl A. Cramer, Judith A. Gauntner; *ed:* Lorain Co Comm (AA) Elem Ed 1972; Univ of Akron (BSEd) Elem Ed 1974; Baldwin Wallace Coll (MAEd) 1990; Post Grad Ashland Univ; *cr:* Cntrl Schl 5 & 6 Grd LD Tchr 1974-80; Nord Schl 7 & 8 Grd LD Tchr 1980-84, Lang Arts Tchr 1984-; *ai:* TV News & Newspaper; Power of Pen Past; Spelling Bee Past; NEA, OEA 1974-; ATA 1974-, Grievance, Bldg Rep; Cable TV Advy Bd 1994-; Church PSR Prgm 1990-, Dir; Vacation Bible Schl 1993-, Dir; Parish Cncl, Exec Bd 1991-; *office:* Walter G Nord Jr HS 501 Lincoln St Amherst OH 44001*

GLENNON, BEVERLY ANN SABBATINI, Art Instructor & Dept Chprsn; *b:* Pittston, PA; *c:* Christina; *ed:* Wilkes Coll (BA) Fine Arts 1971; 28 Post Grad Credits Art, Cmptr Lir, Graphics; *cr:* Seton Cath HS Art Instr, Dept Chair 1971-; Penn St W-B Yth Prgm Art Instr 1989-94; *ai:* Yrbk, Newspaper, Drama Club Adv; Stu Assistance Prgm; Seton Disciplinary Bd; NHS Fac Cncl; NCEA 1971-; NAEA, PAEA 1992-; Scholastic Arts Regnl Advy Bd 1982-94; Seton Cath, St John's, PCC Alumni Assn 1990-; *office:* Seton Catholic HS 37 William St Pittston PA 18640

GLESER, MARILYN BETH (ZOLOTOR), Developmental Studies Instr; *b:* Brooklyn, NY; *m:* Leon Jay; *c:* Kimberly; *ed:* Brooklyn Coll (BA) Eng Lit 1966; NY Univ (MA) Educl Psych 1969; Post Grad Stud Purdue Univ; *cr:* AMIC Day Schl Tchr 1979-80; Lafayette Adult Rdng Acad Tchr 1980-85; IN Voc Tech Coll Skills Advancement Instr 1983-89; Comm Coll Allegheny Co Dev Stud Instr 1989-; *ai:* NADE 1985-; PADE 1989-; Bibliophiles 1991-; Friends of the Lib 1993-; IN Adult Literacy Coalition Gov Letter of Recognition 1985; IN Dept of Ed Div Adult & Continuing Ed Cert of Mert 1983; NADE Conf Prgm Book Ed 1993; CCAC Curr Grant Rdng in Content Areas 1993; Pittsburgh Partnership Curr Grant; *office:* Comm Coll Algny Co Algny Cmps 808 Ridge Ave Pittsburgh PA 15212

GLICK, DEBBIE HILLEGASS, Instrumental Music Teacher; *b:* Quakertown, PA; *m:* James; *c:* Andrew, Caitlin, Brittany; *ed:* West Chester St Coll (BA) Music Ed 1981; Continuing Post Grad Ed Villanova Univ; *cr:* Milford Pub Schl Instrumental Music Tchr 1986-89; Frenchtown Elem Schl Instrumental Music Tchr 1986-; *ai:* Chrldng Coach; Pep Club Adv; Dist Band Coord; NEA, NJEA, NJMEA 1986-; North Penn Symphony Orch 1984-, Prin Flute; Quakertown Band 1974-; Tchr of Yr 1992; *home:* 606 Lonely Cottage Rd Upper Black Eddy PA 18972*

GLICK, SYLVIA PERLO, Reading Teacher; *b:* New York, NY; *m:* Harold; *c:* Michael H., Nan G. Klein; *ed:* New York Univ (BA) Retailing & Fine Arts 1954; Lehman Coll (MS) Rdng 1975; Saint Thomas Aquences Ed Credits Rdng & Soc Stud 1972; *cr:* Summit Park Elem Intensive Tchr 1972-75; Eldorado Elem Intensive Tchr 1975-76; Elmwood Elem Classroom Tchr 1976-77; Kakiat Jr HS Rdng Tchr 1977-78; Spring Valley NS Rdng Tchr 1978-; *ai:* Natl Rdng Assn 1977-; NEA 1973-; *home:* 17 Carlisle Rd Chestnut Ridge NY 10977

GLICKMAN, ANDI, Social Studies Teacher; *b:* Cleveland, OH; *ed:* Miami Univ (BA) Ec 1985; Univ of CO at Boulder (MA) Ec 1988; John Carroll Univ (MED) Ed 1994; *cr:* Univ of CO at Boulder Instr, Rsrch Asst 1986-88; RCG Hagler-Bailly Inc Econometrician 1989-91; Steve Jones Guide & Outfitter Wrangler, Stable Mgr 1990-92; Brush HS Soc Stud Tchr, Intern 1993-94; Beachwood HS Soc Stud Tchr 1994-; *ai:* Yrbk, Stu Cncl Soph Class Adv; JCWA Asst Adv; *office:* Beachwood HS 25100 Fairmount Blvd Beachwood OH 44122*

GLICKMAN, JEFFREY LOREN, Rabbi; *b:* Los Angeles, CA; *m:* Shauna Treza Levine; *c:* Seth, Evan, Hanna, Naomi; *ed:* Wesleyan Univ (BA) Math, Ec 1982; Hebrew Union Coll at Cincinnati Rabbi Prayer, Hlth 1987; Math, Art Tchng Cert 1982; Hebrew Union Coll at Los Angeles MAHL Hebrew Letters; Bezalel Israeli Arts Acad Painting; *cr:* Temple De Hirsch Sinai Rabbi 1987-89; Univ of WA Fac 1988; Temple Adath Joseph Rabbi 1989-95; MO Western St Coll Fac 1990-94; Temple Beth Hillel Rabbi 1995-; *ai:* Nrsng Home Chaplancy; Camping Dir; CCAR 1987-; AAPC, SWCA 1995-; The Window 1990-, Pres, Outstdng Svc; Jewish Voc Svc 1990-, Pres, Outstdng Commitment; Open Door Food Kitchen 1989-, Bd, Honoree; Mayor's Thanksgiving Dinner 1989-, Bd, Honoree; Numerous Articles Pub.

GLICKSMAN, JANET LIFSCHITZ, Second Grade Teacher; *b:* Brooklyn, NY; *m:* Ronald; *ed:* St Univ at Brockport (BS) Ed 1966; *cr:* Pub Schl 316 Second Grd Tchr 1966-67; Jefferson Ave Schl Second Grd Tchr 1967-; *ai:* Fairport Educ Assn, NYSUT 1967-; Griffin Alley Clowns, Clowns of Amer Intnl 1994-; Amer Red Cross vol 1993-; Crystal Apple Awd 1994; *home:* 8 Demere Blvd Fairport NY 14450

GLICKSTEIN, BARRY NEAL, High School Science Teacher; *b:* Bronx, NY; *m:* Angela Mays; *c:* Gilbert, Arthur; *ed:* MI St Univ (BS) Bio 1970; Hofstra Univ (MA) Bio 1972; St Univ of NY Coll of Environmental Sci & Forestry (PHD) Silviculture & Forest Influences 1983; *cr:* Franklin Schl Sci Tchr 1973-74; Rye Neck MS Sci Tchr 1974-76; Comm Coll of Finger Lakes Tchr 1983; Altmar-Parish-Williamstown HS Sci Tchr 1983-; *ai:* Dist Shared Decision Making Comm; NHS Comm; Altmar-Parish-Williamstown Fac Assn 1983-, Pres, 1st VP; NYSUT, AFT 1974-; *office:* Altmar Parish Williamstown HS PO Box 97 Parish NY 13131

GLIKES, GLADYS GRAHAM, English Teacher; *b:* Brilliant, OH; *m:* George; *c:* Dr. G. Jeffrey, Kimberly L.; *ed:* WV Northern (AA) Eng 1974; Highest Honors West Liberty St Coll (BA) Eng, Comp Soc Stud 1975; Highest Honors Univ of Dayton (MS) Tchng 1980; Steubenville Bus Coll 36 Hrs; *cr:* Buckeye North Eng Tchr 1976-89; Buckeye Local HS Eng Tchr 1990-; *ai:* Class Adv; N Girls Bsktbl Coach, Stud Cncl Adv; Drama Dir; Chrldr Adv; NEA 10 Yrs; Jr HS Tchr of Yr; *home:* 99 Bryden Rd Steubenville OH 43952

GLIONNA, JOSEPH MICHAEL, Eighth Grade Reading Teacher; *b:* Malden, MA; *m:* Joyce F. Hopkinson; *ed:* Gordon Coll (BA) His 1966; Boston Univ (MED) Rdng 1976; *cr:* Malden Schls 8th Grd Tchr 1966-; *ai:* Malden Tchrs Assn, MA Tchrs Assn, NEA 1966-; Maplewood Bapt Church 1958-; *office:* Malden MS 77 Salem St Malden MA 02148

GLISERMAN, MARTIN JOEL, Associate Professor of English; *b:* Winthrop, MA; *m:* Marilyn Rye; *c:* Nicholas; *ed:* Colby Coll (BA) Eng 1967; IN Univ (PHD) Eng Lit & Lang 1973; Certified as Psychoanalyst at Ctr for Modern Psychoanalytic Stud 1995; *cr:* Rutgers Univ Assoc Prof 1971-; *ai:* Amer Imago Stud in Psychoanalysis & Culture Ed; Livingston Coll Exec Cncl of Fellows Chprsn; AAUP 1971-; NAAP 1984-; SMP 1990-; Pub Psychoanalysis, Lang & The Body of the Text U Press of FL 1996; Amer Inayo Index 1939-89 Johns Hopkins Univ Press 1990; *office:* Rutgers St Univ At New Brnswck Dept of English New Brunswick NJ 08903*

GLISPIN, PATRICIA J., Athletic Administrator & Coach; *b:* Miford, MA; *ed:* Univ of MA at Amherst (BS) Hlth & PE 1975, (MED) Ed 1987; *cr:* Grafton HS Hlth & PE Tchr, Coach 1975-82; Univ of MA at Amherst Asst Bsktbl Coach 1982-83; Clark Univ Primary Women's Admin, Women's Bsktbl Coach 1984-90, Women's Bsktbl Coach, M & W Asst Cross Cntry Coach 1990-; *ai:* WBCA 1982-; *office:* Clark Univ 950 Main St Worcester MA 01610*

GLOCK, CAROL THOMAS, Foreign Language Instructor; *b:* Pittsburgh, PA; *m:* Carl C. III; *c:* Taylor Kathryn; *ed:* Clarion (BS) Fr 1965; Univ of Pittsburgh (MED) 1970; Slippery Rock Univ Guidance Stud; *cr:* Millvale HS Fr Instr 1965-66; E Deer HS Fr Instr 1966-67; Valley HS Foreign Lang Dept Chprsn & Instr; *ai:* Fr Club Adv; SERC Facilitator (Japanese & Russian); NEA & PSEA; *office:* Valley HS 703 Stevenson Blvd New Kensington PA 15068

GLOD, ANDREA ANNE, English & Speech Teacher; *b:* Wilkes Barre, PA; *ed:* Coll Misericordia (BA) Eng 1966; MED Addl 54 Credits Cath Univ, Bloomsburg Univ, PA St Univ, Wilkes Univ; IU 19 In-Svc; *cr:* J. M. Coughlin HS Tchr 1966-; *ai:* Speech Coach FBLA; NEA, PSEA 1966-; W-BAEA 1966-, Pres, VP; Amer Red Cross 1960-, Pheresis Donations 1975.*

GLODEK, JAMES FRANCIS, Physics Teacher; *b:* Philadelphia, PA; *ed:* Temple Univ (BS) Physics 1986; *cr:* North Penn HS Physics Tchr 1986-; *ai:* Astornomy Physics, Simulation Gaming Soc Adv; NEA, PSEA, NPEA 1986-; Tchr of Yr 1989; *office:* North Penn HS 1340 S Valley Forge Rd Lansdale PA 19446*

GLOER, MARY S., English Teacher; *b:* Lima, OH; *m:* Gary L.; *cr:* Fremont Ross HS Eng Tchr 1972-74; Cntrl Cath Schl Eng Tchr 1974-; *home:* 23850 W Star Rt 5A Curtice OH 43412

GLORE, BEVERLEY ANNE, Second Grade Teacher; *b:* Bryan, OH; *m:* William; *c:* Daniel, Mark (dec), Brenda (dec); *ed:* Bowling Green St Univ (BS) Elem 1973; Northwest St Comm Coll Cmptr Sci; Curr Dev; *cr:* Bryan Comm Presch Tchr 1974-78; Edgerton Local Schls Kndgtn Tchr 9 Yrs, Second Grd Tchr 9 Yrs, Jr HS Vlybl Coach 1989-; *ai:* OEA 1978-; NEA, EEA 1978-, Bldg Rep; Alpha Mu of Alpha Delta Kappa 1995-, Bylaws Comm; OH Cmptr Consortium 1994-; Friends of Lib 1995-; Comm Ed Cncl 1992-95, Trustee; Ashland Oil Golden Apple Awd; Grant for Learning Ctrs in Kndgtn; *home:* 7962 County Road F Bryan OH 43506

GLOSKIN, ELLIOTT RICHARD, Mathematics Teacher; *b:* Brooklyn, NY; *m:* Yvonne Susan Lorenzo; *ed:* Lehman Coll (BA) Math 1973, (MA) Math, Ed 1976; 30 Credits; *cr:* Dewitt Clinton HS Tchr 1973-74; Jane Addams V HS Tchr 1974-; *ai:* Asst Prgm Chm; AFT 1973-; *office:* Jane Adams Vocational HS 900 Tinton Ave Bronx NY 10456*

GLOSKIN, YVONNE LORENZO, Science Teacher; *b:* New York, NY; *m:* Elliott Richard; *c:* Michelle, Jessica, Lauren; *ed:* Borough of Manhattan CC (AA) Fine Arts 1979; NY Univ (BS) Art Ed 1982; City Coll of NY City (MS) Sci Ed 1986; *cr:* J. F. Kennedy HS Art Tchr 1981-82; JHS 127 Sci Tchr 1982-87; Jane Addams Voc HS Sci Tchr 1989-; *ai:* Asst to Math, Sci Dept; United Fed of Tchrs, AFT 1981-; City Coll of NYC Masters Flwshp; *home:* 675 N Terrace Ave # 6H Mount Vernon NY 10552

GLOSSNER, RICHARD AUGUSTINE, Professor of Psychology; *b:* Rochester, NY; *c:* Thomas A., Samuel E., Ann R Eckrich, James S., Rita M. Rajca; *ed:* St John Fisher Coll (BA) Philosophy 1965; Univ of Ottawa (MA) Philosophy 1967; Duquesne Univ (MA) Clinical Psych 1974; Susan Grace Branch & Assoc Ctr for Neuro-Linguistic Programming, Cert Practitioner of NLP 1992; Cert Master Practitioner of NLP 1993; *cr:* Holy Apostle's Coll Instr of Philosophy 1967-70; Convalescent Hosp for Children Dir of Group Work 1969-72; Monroe Comm Coll Prof of Psych 1974-; *ai:* AFT 1974-; *office:* Monroe Comm Coll 1000 E Henrietta Rd Rochester NY 14623

GLOTFELTY, MELVIN ROSS, 5th Grade Teacher; *b:* Oakland, MD; *ed:* Frostburg St Univ (BS) Elem Ed 1984, (MS) K-8th Elem Ed Admin & Supvr 1989; Zion Schl of Christ Ed (Bachelor of Rel Ed) 1984; Master Tchr Acad Course IV Awd Cert 1988; Directions in MD Ed Completion Cert 1989; Reviewing the Principalship Accomplishment Cert 1992; 30 Grad Credit Hrs Beyond Masters 1996; *cr:* Garrett Comm Coll Basic Adult Ed Instr 1984-87; Friendsville Elem 5th Grd Position Tchr 1984-; Self-Employed Pvt Rdng Tutor 1985-; Mountaineer Challenge Acad Chaplain 1994-; *ai:* Elem Schl Yrbk Adv; CEAI 1988-; Aldersgate Inc 1990-, Bd Mem; Garrett Cty Chrstn Coalition 1994-, Chm; Potomac Edison Hardward Grant Pgm Awded Apple IIGS Comp & Printer; *office:* Friendsville Elem Schl 1st Ave PO Box 59 Friendsville MD 21531*

GLOTFELTY, THOMAS AUSTIN, ABE & GED Instructor; *b:* Crellin, MD; *m:* Barbara Ann Smith; *c:* Thomas Jr., Rebecca Lynn; *ed:* Univ of MD (BS) Agricultural Ed 1962; WV Univ (MS) Agricultural Ed 1975; Cert in Educl Admin 1980 & 1995; Medium Duty Diesels & Diesel Injection at OH Diesel Tech Inst Cleveland; Spec Ed at Marshall Univ, Huntington & COGS Montgomery; *cr:* Mason Cty Voc Ctr Ag Mechanic 5 Yrs; James Rumsey Voc-Tech Ctr Ag Mechanic 2 Yrs; Preston Cty Voc-Tech Ctr Ag Mechanic & Tchr of Spec Ed 18 Yrs; Southern Garrett Cty HS Earth Sci & Bio Tchr 1 Yr; *ai:* AVA, AVATA, WVVA 1968-; WVATA 1968-, Pres North Dist, Tchr of Tchrs Awd; Preston Cty ARC 1978-, Pres; Mt Crisis Pregnancy Ctr 1987-, Founders & Bd of Dirs; Preston Cty Buckwheat Festival 1976-, Farmers Day Chm; NEA, WVEA 1968-90; United Meth Church 1970-, Lay Ldr, Lay Speaker; United Brethren in Christ 1983-, Lay Ldr, Conf Del; garrett Cty Historical Soc 1985-; Governors Citation Historical Video of Crellin MD; Whos Who in US; Nomination of Whos Who in World; *home:* 2667 Hutton Rd Oakland MD 21550

GLOVER, ROBERT S., American History Teacher; *b:* Chicago, IL; *m:* Catherine; *c:* Smith; *ed:* Williams Coll (BA) Pol Sci 1963; NY Univ (MBA) Corp Fin 1969; Rutgers U (MED) Soc Stud 1993; *cr:* Bus Career 1963-93; West Windsor Schl Tchr 1993-; *ai:* Model UN Adv; NJEA, NCSS, NJSS 1993-; DE Lrarjaw 1991-, Treas; Canal Watch; James Madison Flwshp.

GLOVER, SHIRLEY ROBINSON, Guidance Counselor; *b:* Paulsboro, NJ; *c:* Adell; *ed:* Cheyney St Coll (BS) Ed 1972; Antioch Coll (MS) Ed 1976; *cr:* Chester-Upland Schl Dist Guidance Cnslr, 1979-; Classroom Tchr 1972-79; Dir of TELLS Prgm 1987; Lead Tchr STEP Prgm 1990-91; *ai:* Adv of Class; PSEA, NEA, CUEA 1972-; ASCD, PSCA 1977-; AKA Sorority Inc 1977-; Calvary Bapt Church 1955-, Chm Schlsp Comm, Bd of Chrstn Ed; Calvary Bapt Flwshp Choir; *office:* Chester HS 200 Chester PA 19013*

GLOVKA, MARY CLAIRE BAUER, Third Grade Teacher; *b:* OR; *m:* Robert M.; *c:* Thad, Todd; *ed:* Marylhurst Coll (BSEd) 1964; Wright St Univ (MED) Intnl LIt for Children, Young Ad Attnd Univ of CA; *cr:* Immaculate Conception Elem Schl Fourth 1964-65; St Luke Elem Third Grd Tchr 1984-; *ai:* Primary De NCEA 1984-; NCTE 1987-; Archdiocese of Cincinnati Tchr of E 1994; *office:* St Luke Cath Elem Schl 1442 N Fairfield Rd Da 45432

GLOWACKI, DORIS HENTRICH, German Teacher; *b:* Eliza *m:* Michael; *c:* Christopher; *ed:* New England Coll (BA) Ger & S 1975; Rutgers Grad Schl (MA) Ger 1980; Collegium Palatin Diploma in Germany 1973; *cr:* Bridgewater Raritan HS East 1976-77; Bridgewater Raritan HS West Ger Tchr 1977-78; Ham Ger Tchr 1978-80; Union Twp HS Ger Tchr 1980-; *ai:* Ger Cl Epsilon Phi; Report Card & NHS Comm; AATG 1978-; FLENJ 19 of 8 Trips for Ger Stdnts Travel to Germany, Austria & Switzerla

GLUBERMAN, FRANK MARTIN, Business Education Teache York, NY; *m:* Karen Lynn; *c:* Allison, Laura; *ed:* Baruch Coll (B Mrktg 1972, (MS) Supervision & Admin 1976; Hunter Coll (MS) 1974; *cr:* Cntrl Commercial HS Distributive Ed Tchr 1972-7 Liaison Coord & Multi Occupational Sub Tchr 1975-76; Mt Vern Pgm Tchr 1976-80; N Rockland HS Bus Ed Tchr 1980-82; Ollin Math Tchr 1982-85; Woodlands HS Bus Ed, Bus Admin & M 1985-; *ai:* DECA & FBLA Advs; EBCA Club; Westchester Bus T 1985-.*

GLUECK, RICHARD D., Sixth Grd Mathematics Teacher; *b:* NY; *ed:* St Univ of NY (BA) Child Psych 1973-; Univ of M Marine Ed 1978; NASA Newest 1995; *cr:* Orrington Schl Dept 6t Tchr 1979-85; Bangor Schl Dept 7th Grd Life Sci Tchr 1985-87; C 6th Grd Math Tchr 1988-; *ai:* NSTA 1991-; Town of Hampden Harbor Commission; Presidential Awd Elem Math Tchng 1993 Cncl for Basic Ed 1994; *office:* Orono MS 14 Goodridge Rd O 04473*

GLYDA, BONNIE RAE, Foreign Lang Tchr & Dept Chair; *b:* Wa DC; *m:* Dewaine Joseph; *ed:* Univ of MD (BA) Foreign Lang, Ed Credit Hrs Bowie St Univ in Ed; Attnd Towson St Univ; *cr:* PR. Bd of Ed Foreign Lang Tchr, Dept Chair 1967-; *ai:* Outstandin Geos Co MD 1978-79; Counseling Advocate Awd 1989; *office* Burroughs M S 14400 Livingston Rd Accokeek MD 20607

GLYNN, ED, Dean of Academic Affairs; *b:* Cleveland, OH; *ed:* C Coll of Art, Design (BFA) Painting 1970; Southern IL Uni Painting 1973; Cooper Schl of Art Diploma Fine Arts 1968; *cr* Schl of Art Instr, Gallery Dir 1973-77; Cleveland St Univ Instr, Ga 1977-79; Lake Erie Coll Asst Art Prof 1979-85; Western Reserve Arts Exec Dir 1985-89; MD Coll of Art & Design Dean 1989-; *ai:* Cncl Montgomery Cty; Architectural Planning Review Bd; Bd of Strathmon Hall Arts Fnd; Natl Cncl Art Admin 1993-; Mor Chamber of Comm 1990-; 17 One Man Exhibits; Regnl, Natl *office:* MD Coll Of Art & Design 10500 Georgia Ave Silver Sp 20902*

GLYNN, JOSEPH GRAHAM, Associate Professor of Mngmt River, MA; *ed:* Univ of RI (BA) Ec 1967, (MBA) Mngmt Sci 197 Univ (PHD) Mngmt Sci 1979; *cr:* Canisius Coll Dept Mngmt, Mrk *ai:* Project to Enhance Stu Retention; Decision Sci Inst 197 Application Paper Awd Decision Sci Inst; Outstdng Prof MBA P 1995; *office:* Canisius Coll Wehle Schl of Bus 2001 Main St Bu 14208

GLYNN, PATRICIA HOLWEGER, Third Grade Teacher; *b:* OH; *w:* Joseph X. (dec); *c:* Katie Butler, Rory; *ed:* Miami Univ 1960; 21 Grad Hrs Sci, Math, Geog, Ed; 1 Grad Hr San Jose St U Grad Hrs Santa Clara Univ Art Ed; *cr:* Anthony Wayne Schl 4th 1960-61; Landing Schl 4th Grd Tchr 1961-63; Campbell Union S Grd Tchr 1972-78; John XXIII Elem Schl 3rd Grd Tchr 1 Campbell Tchrs Assn Elem Rep, Bd of Dir 1975-76; Schl Bd Rep NCEA 1982-; CA Tchrs Assn, NEA 1972-78; Holy Family Pari 1984-; *office:* John XXIII Elem Schl 3907 Central Ave Middle 45044

GNEZDA-SMITH, NICOLE, Art Teacher & Dept Chairpe Columbus, OH; *m:* Gary A. Smith; *c:* Yvonne, Anthony, Katharine Wesleyan Univ (BFA) Fine Art & Ed 1973; OH St Univ (MA) Art PHD Stu; *cr:* Worthington City Schls Art Tchr, Dept Chair 1973-8 OH St Univ Coll of Dentistry Part-time Ancillary Instr 1981-8 Arlington City Schls HS, Elem Art Tchr 1987-89; Westerville C HS, Elem Art Tchr 1989-93; *ai:* Dept Chprsn; NEA 1973-; NAE Dept; Phi Kappa Phi 1994-; OH Assn Gifted Children 1992-94; Pub 1994; *office:* Worthington Kilbourne HS 1499 Hard Rd Colur 43235

GNIRREP, GARY RICHARD, English Teacher; *b:* Englewood Sandra Clark; *c:* Amanda; *ed:* SUNY at Albany (BA) Eng Ed 19 at Chapel Hill (MA) Eng 1990; *cr:* St Vincent Acad Eng Tchr Guilderland HS Eng Tchr 1990-; *ai:* Guilderpirg & Yth Ending Hu & Founder; NEA 1990-; NCTE 1990-; NYSEC 1993-; C Carro Prize U NC Outstdng MA Thesis 1991; NYSEC Edctrs of Exc 1994.

GOBER, STEVEN, Fourth Grade Teacher; *b:* Northampton, Adrianna; *ed:* Bloomsburg Univ (BS) Elem Ed 1971; Penn St Uni 1977; Need Assessment, Curr Dev Credits; *cr:* Whitehall, Coplay 4th Grd Tchr 1971-; *ai:* Grd Level Master Tchr, Mentor; Inst Support Team; NEA, PSEA, WCEA 1971-; St John the Bapt 196 of Mo Nom 1995; *office:* Whitehall Coplay MS 2928 Mac A Whitehall PA 18052*

GOBLE, KENNETH C., Professor of Counseling; *b:* Jenkins, Ramona P. Randall; *c:* Stacey A. Goble-Wilkin; *ed:* Univ of Psych; Cincinnatti Bible Sem (MA) Rel Stud 1969, (MDiv) Old T 1974; Eden Theological Sem (DMin) Pastoral Care 1979; Xavier Hrs Grad Psych; *cr:* Cincinnati Bible Coll & Sem Prof of Cnsln Grassy Creek Chrstn Church Minister 1966-72; Metamora C Christ Minister 1973-79; Cincinnati Therapy Ctr Therapist 1987- Cincinnati Bible Coll & Sem 2700 Glenway Ave Cincinnati OH 4

GOCKE, TIMOTHY NEFF, Assoc Prof of Bus Managen Clarksburg, WV; *m:* Mary Aldridge; *c:* Molly, Tim Jr.; *ed:* WV U Bus Admin 1972, (MS) Labor Relation 1979; *cr:* Marshall U Mngmt Instr 1982-84; Eastern KY Univ Bus Mngmt Instr 1985-8 St Comm Coll Bus Mngmt Assoc Prof 1987-; *ai:* Bus Club 1989 Senate 1993- Fac Adv; Presidential Search Comm 1993; Terra F AFT 1987-, VP; Tchr of Yr 1994; *office:* Terra State Comm C Napoleon Rd Fremont OH 43420*

GOCKLEY, ANEGELA GREEN, Science Teacher; *b:* Harrisburg Brian D.; *c:* Alyssa M., David A.; *ed:* Lebanon Vly Coll (BS) Che Univ of Bridgeport (MS) Scndry Ed 1990; *cr:* Central HS Sci Tch *ai:* CT Chem Tchrs Assn, ACS 1996; Bridgeport West Side Cor 1995-; *office:* Central HS 1 Lincoln Blvd Bridgeport CT 06606

S, CATHY ANN, Instructor of Mathematics; *b:* Shirley, MA; *c:* ıcqueline, Catherine; *ed:* Univ TX at Arlington (MS) Math 1992, h 1985; Mountain View Coll (AAS) Electronics 1982; 60 Addl ;; *cr:* Lancaster Campus HACC Instr of Math 1993-95; *ai:* AWM; ; PSMATYC; MAA; NCTM; AMS; ASA; Sonia Kovalevsky HS ncaster Campus Strategic Planning Grant; Manipulatives in Math Planning Grant; Summer Instrl Dev Grants; UTA Awd for Achvmt in Math; *office:* Harrisburg Area Community Coll 1008 and Ave Lancaster PA 17601*

RD, FRANCES EVELYN, Sci, Health & Spelling Teacher; *b:* H; *m:* Russell Blair; *c:* Brad Russell; *ed:* OH Univ (AS) 1987, ı Ed 1988; *cr:* Matamoras Elem 6th-8th Grd Sci, Spelling & Hlth -; *ai:* 8th Grd Adv; Sci Fair Coord; NEA 1992-; Governors Awd 3-95; *office:* New Matamoras Elem Schl PO Box 338 Grandview Matamoras OH 45767

RD, JEFFREY K., Sixth Grade Teacher; *b:* Washington, PA; *m:* ›erthy; *c:* Jodie, Jeffrey; *ed:* 26 Addl Hrs; Degree Spec Ed, Elem Cherry Elem 3rd Grd Tchr 1974-75, 4th Grd Tchr 1976-78, 6th 1979-93, Special Ed 1993-; *ai:* Boys Youth Bsbl Coach; PSEA, EA 1974-; *office:* Fort Cherry Elem Schl R D 4 Mc Donald PA

RD, KATHY SAUNDERS, English Department Chair; *b:* ence, MO; *m:* Dan; *c:* Thomas, Elizabeth, James; *ed:* Andrews) Eng, Elem Ed 1970; Johns Hopkins Univ (MA) Writing 1996; Hrs; *cr:* Mile High Acad Classroom Tchr 1971-72; Beltsville Schl Kndgtn, 7th-8th Grd Classroom Tchr 1981-86; Shenandoah ad Sr Classroom Tchr 1987-89; Shenandoah Adventist Elem Schl rd Classroom Tchr 1989-91; Highland View Acad 9th-12th Grd ı Tchr 1991-; *ai:* Schl Newspaper Spon 1991-; Puppet Ministry 4-; Class of 1998 Spon 1995-; NCTE 1991-; Journal of Adventist , Bd, Adv; Frederick Adventist Church 1995-, Childrens s Coord; Book Pub-God is the Victor 1990; Edited Journal of Ed 1993-94; Zapara Awd 1993; *office:* Highland View Acad ademy Dr Hagerstown MD 21740

RD, PAULA C., Junior High Teacher; *b:* Oceanside, NY; *ed:* Coll (BA) Fr 1968; St Univ Coll at Brockport (MST) Tchng Rochester Chrstn Schl Third Grd Tchr 1968-70; Martin B. Schl #1 Fourth Grd Intern Tchr 1970-71; Westminster Acad Sixth 1971-73; Office of Tchr Ed & Prof Standards Rsrch Asst 1973-74; Chrstn Schl Jr HS Tchr 1974-75; Nashua Chrstn HS Fifth, Sixth 1975-77; Chrstn Schl of Greater Fall River Fourth, Fifth, Sixth 1977-86; Coastal Chrstn Schl Jr HS Tchr 1986-; *ai:* Drama, Bible n Coach; Fine Arts Fair Coord; New England Assn Chrstn Schl 86-; Amer Assn Chrstn Schls 1995-, 25 Yr Svc Awd; *office:* hristian Schl 574 N Nobleboro Rd Waldoboro ME 04572

RD, SANDRA KAY, Sixth Grade Teacher; *b:* Steubenville, OH; i Univ of OH (BSEd) Soc Stud 1969, (MED) Elem Ed 1973; *cr:* regg Elem Schl Sixth Grd Tchr 1969-; *ai:* Tchrs Adult Amer Red Sixth Grds Who Receive Red Cross Card Comm CPR, First Aid lyssey of the Mind Judge, Problem Captain, Regnl Dir, St Judge, Comm; Spelling Bee Comm; Edison Local Curr Improvement erson Cty Schls Hlth Curr Comm; Presenter Inservice Meetings; 59-, Pres, VP, Exec Comm; EOEA 1969-, Pres, Elect Pres, Exec DE 1969-, St Exec Comm, Appeals Bd; NEA 1969-, OH Rep latl Conventions, Regnl Confs; OH Vly Uniserv Cncl 1969-90, ner Red Cross 1988-92, Comm First Aid & Safety Inst, Instr isaster Comm; Martha Holden Jennings Scholar 1973; Jefferson Mini Grant 1991, 1995; Delta Kappa Gamma; *office:* John E em Schl RR 1 Bergholz OH 43908

DIANE MARIE (PEPIN), Eighth Grade Math Teacher; *b:* MA; *m:* Edward J. Jr.; *c:* Edward J. III; *ed:* Elms Coll (BA) Math v of MA (MED) Ed 1994; Post Grad Course Comm Svc Learning Lynch Schl Math Tchr 1975-; *ai:* Svc Club, Hnr Soc, Stu Cncl, ; Cluster Coord; MS Wkshp Presenter; PBS Mathline Participant; Tchrs Assn, Holyoke Tchrs Assn 1975-; ASCD 1995-; NCTM ms Coll Alumnae Assn 1992-, Distinguished Alumnae Awd Comm Chair; *office:* Lynch MS 1575 Northampton St Holyoke 0

I, JOAN, Youth Minister; *b:* Perth Amboy, NJ; *ed:* Felician Coll BA) Elem Ed 1978; La Salle Univ (MA) Rel Ed 1989; *cr:* St f Assisi Parish Kndgtn Tchr 1978-79; St Philip Schl Kndgtn-5th Tchr 1980-81; St Joan of Arc Schl 2nd Grd Tchr 1981-82, Kndgtn 2-84; St Philip 2nd Grd Tchr 1984-85; St Mary's Schl 2nd Grd 5-88; St Joseph Schl 2nd Grd Tchr 1988-89; St Joan of Arc Schl Tchr 1989-92; St Francis of Assisi Parish Dir of Rel Ed 1992-95; illa Acad Yth Minister, Rel Tchr 1995-; *ai:* Lector, Angel Clubs Dir Spiritual Retreat Team, Vocation Club; NCEA 1978-.

, HEATHER LYNN, High School Mathematics Tchr; *b:* PA; *m:* Gary Michael; *ed:* PA St Univ (BS) Math 1992; 24 Grad oward Masters in Ed; *cr:* Central York HS Math Tchr 1992-; *ai:* Class Adv; NEA 1992-; *office:* Central York HS 300 E 7th Ave 17404

L-MYERS, JEAN E., Assistant Professor of German; *b:* Bryn ; *m:* Stephen Elliott Myers; *c:* Robert, Timothy; *ed:* Smith Coll 1973; Univ of MI (MA) Ger 1976; Bryn Mawr Coll (PHD) Ger s 1981; Univ of MI Tchr Cert 1976; *cr:* The Baldwin Schl Ger -77; Berlitz Eng, Ger Tchr 1981-82; Widener Univ Asst Ger Prof, Coll of Arts & Sci 1982-; *ai:* Intl Stdnts Co-Adv; Advy Bd Mem repare Prgm; Acad Dir NCN Japanese Stdnts, Art Undecided; s Comms; AATG 1976-, Var Comm; MLA 1982-; NEMLA 1990-; GSA; AAUP; ICLA; Anna Seghers Gesellschaft; WELCA 1982-, air; Co-Author Book: Why Study German?, Book Reviews; Landeskunde Awd 1983; A. S. Fac Awd Exl in Tchng; *office:* Univ 1 University Pl Chester PA 19013*

, MELISSA ANN, Spanish Teacher; *b:* Dayton, OH; *ed:* Wright BSEd) Span, Eng Ed 1987; 8 Credit Hrs Ed; *cr:* Urbana HS Span, 1987-90; Stebbins HS Span Tchr 1990-; *ai:* Muse Machine, Fr ; Jr Class Adv; MREA 1990-; *office:* Walter E Stebbins HS 1900 Rd Dayton OH 45424*

ALK, PAMELA M., History & English Teacher; *b:* Akron, OH; St Univ (BS) Scndry Ed 1971, (MLS) Lib Sci 1984; F D Roosevelt Coll 1984; Summit Cty Tech Acad 1995-; *cr:* St Vincent-St Mary 1971-, Librn 1995-; *ai:* NHS & Sr Class Adv; N Cntrl Steering hair; Beta Phi Mu 1984-; NCSS 1988-; Natl Endowment of Hum; o F D Roosevelt Inst Bard Coll Summer 1994; *office:* Saint Saint Mary Schl 15 N Maple St Akron OH 44303

ALL, GAIL ELYSE, 5th Grade Teacher; *b:* Jersey City, NJ; *ed:* udsburg Univ (BS) Elem 1967; Lehigh Univ (MED) Ed 1971; Inst en's Lit Grad; *cr:* Pleasant Vly Schl Dist 5th Grd Tchr 1967-; *ai:* 967-, Pres, VP; PSEA, NEA 1967-; Jaycees Outstdng Young Edctr; hn C Mills Schl John C Mills Intermediate Schl Brodheadsville

, MATTHEW BURTON, Art Teacher; *b:* Columbus, OH; *m:* nn Boulton; *c:* J. Michael, Luaren Ann, Andrea Lynn; *ed:* Bowling Unvi (BFA) Fine Art, Ed 1983; OH St Univ; *cr:* Madison South Jr HS Art Tchr 1983-85; Madison Comprehensive HS Art Tchr 1985-, Var Ftbl Coach 1986-; Mansfield Art Ctr Art Tchr 1989-; Richland Acad of Arts Tchr 1994-; *ai:* Var Ftbl, Wrestling, Spring Fitness Coach; Adv Art Club, Class, Natural Helper; NEA, OEA, MLEA 1983-; Mansfield Art Ctr 1985-; Tandem Intnl Art Show Awd 1985, 1986; Madison Acad Booster Club Tchr Honoree 1990-91, 1995; *home:* 641 Highland Ave Mansfield OH 44903*

GODSOE, GERALD BENSON, 4th Grade Teacher; *b:* Plainfield, NJ; *m:* Marilyn Lena Christiansen; *c:* Rachel, John; *ed:* Middlebury Coll (BA) Eng 1959; Western CT Univ (MS) Elem Ed 1970; Numerous In Svc Courses; *cr:* USAF 1st Lt 1959-63; CA Casualty Insurance & Branch Mgr 1963-69; Pawling Elem Schl 4th Grd Tchr 1970-; *ai:* NEA 1970-; Pawling United Meth Church Trustee; *office:* Pawling Elem Schl 7 Haight St Pawling NY 12564

GOECKE, LYNDA, 4th Grade Teacher; *b:* Middletown, OH; *m:* Gene; *c:* Emily, Jonathan; *ed:* OH Univ (BA) Spec Ed 1971; Wright St Univ (MED) Supervision & Curr 1985; Attnd Miami Univ, Univ of Dayton, Mt St Joseph Coll; OH St Univ; *cr:* Freshman Schl Spec Ed Tchr 1972-73; Mc Kinley MS Spec Ed Tchr 1973-77; Wilson Elem Schl Spec Ed Tchr 1977-87, 4th Grd Tchr 1987-; *ai:* Middletown Musical Arts Assn; Venture Capital Grant Comm; NEA, OEA 1972-; Ed Commission 1995-; *office:* Wilson Elem Schl 106 S Highview Rd Middletown OH 45044

GOEHNER, CAROL J., Social Studies Teacher; *b:* Syracuse, NY; *m:* Gerald J. Testa; *c:* Elizabeth Goehner-Testa; *ed:* Coll of William & Mary (BA) Psych & Sociology 1979; Syracuse Univ (MS) Soc Stud Ed 1989; *cr:* Cicero North Syracuse High Soc Stud Tchr 1988-; *ai:* Stdnts Against Driving Drunk Adv; stu Support Team; Interdiscplinary Schl Team; Process Consultation; Staff Dev Comm; N Syracuse Ed Assn 1989-, Bldg Rep; *office:* Cicero North Syracuse Schl Rt 31 Cicero NY 13039

GOEHRINGER, FREDERICK,III, Business Professor; *b:* Camden, NJ; *m:* Gladys Irene Heiken; *c:* Frederick IV, Charles H., Glady A., Michael A.; *ed:* Univ of PA (BA) Eng Lit 1955; Univ of PA at Wharton (MBA) Indstrl Mngmt 1957; Attnd Univ of PA Applied Ec; Univ of HI, Pacific Asian Mngmt Inst Cert in Intnl Bus; *cr:* Univ of PA Instr, Admin 1958-63; Rutgers Univ Asst Prof 1963-72; Milsan Assoc Sr Consultant 1972-74; Drexel Univ Adj Assoc Prof 1974-; Salem Comm Coll Assoc Prof of Bus 1974-; *ai:* Retention, Distance Learning, Safety Comm; NEA 1978-; NJ Collegiate Bus Admin Assn 1980-; Parksdie Comm Assn 1980-, Dir; Wallenpaupack Comm Assn 1989-; Freedoms Fnd Fac Dev Seminary Flwshp; Unsung Hero Awd Salem Comm Coll Veterans Club; *office:* Salem Comm Coll 460 Hollywood Ave Carneys Point NJ 08069

GOELLER, JUDITH ANN, Third Grade Teacher; *b:* Mc Cutchenville, OH; *m:* James M.; *c:* Sara Wise, Carrie Smith, Mary Davis, Todd; *ed:* Bowling Green St Univ (BS) Elem Ed 1969; 155 Grad Hrs Ashland Coll, Loyola Marymount Coll; *cr:* Mc Cutchenville El Schl First Grd Tchr 1966-85, Third Grd Tchr 1985-; *ai:* Wenner-Galbraith Presch Schlsp Spon; Sci, Math Stud Comm; PTO; Mohawk Ed Assn; OH Ed Assn; NEA; Antique Club 1976-, V Pres, Pres; Our Lady of Consolation Church; Co-Writer Home Instruction of Neurologically Handicapped Children & Parent Handbook for Math Instruction; Nom Who's Who Among Amer Outstdng Tchrs 1972, 1974, 1992, 1996; *office:* Mc Cutchenville Elem Sch 8850 S State Route 53 Mc Cutchenville OH 44844

GOELLER, PATRICIA WOLF, Assistant Principal; *b:* Queens, NY; *m:* Robert; *c:* Marybeth; *ed:* St John's Univ (BS) Elem Ed 1961, (MS) Early Chldhd Ed 1963, (PD) Rdng Specialist 1994; St John's Univ Admin, Supervision; Columbia Univ Writing Process; Bank St Coll Literacy Inst; *cr:* PS 102 Queens Tchr 1962-64; PS 171 Queens Tchr 1964-86, Interim Asst Prin 1964-86, Staff Dev, Tchr Trainer 1989-; PS 229 Asst Prin 1995-; *ai:* Schl Based Mngmt, Primary Book, Mainstreaming, Schl Consultation Comms; NY Early Chldhd Assn 1964-, Treas; Phi Delta Kappa 1986-; ACSD 1990-; AAUW, IRA 1986-, Cncl Supvrs & Admins; AFT, NEA, UFT 1964-; Assn Chldhd Ed Intnl; St Johns Univ Alumnae Assn 1961-, Pres, Treas, Exec Bd; Outstdng Tchr of Yr; Readers Digest DeWitt Wallace Grant; *office:* PS 229 6725 51 Rd Woodside NY 11377*

GOELLER, STEPHEN BRYAN, Social Studies Teacher & Chair; *b:* Baltimore, MD; *m:* Irene Catherine Lucas; *c:* Stacy Smith; *ed:* Univ of MD at Baltimore (BA) Sociology 1976; Loyola Coll (MED) Admin 1992; LaSalle Univ (EDD) Admin 1993; *cr:* Our Lady of Pompei HS Soc STud Tchr, Chair 1988-; *ai:* Mid Sts Evaluation Steering Comm; Soph Moderator; Cath Schls 2000 Team Mem; Phi Delta Kappa 1992-; Self Pub Text World Constitutions-A Comparative View; *home:* 411 Crisfield Rd Middle River MD 21220*

GOELTZ, HEATHER WERTLEY, Spanish Teacher; *b:* Reading, PA; *m:* Douglas A.; *c:* Stephen; *ed:* Duquesne Univ (BA) Span, Soc 1983; Kutztown Univ Cert Scndry Ed, Span, Eng 1991; Working on Masters Ed Degree Prgm Penn St; *cr:* Peace Corps Vol 1987-89; Reading Area Comm Coll Span Adj Prof 1991-93; Muhlenberg Schl Dist Span Tchr 1991-; *ai:* Class of 96 Adv; NEA 1991-; *office:* Muhlenberg Schl Dist 801 Bellvue Ave Laureldale PA 19605

GOEPFERT, SANDRA, Guidance Counselor; *b:* Mt Vernon, NY; *c:* Rick, Jim; *ed:* Russell Sage Coll (BS) PE 1963; C W Post Coll (MS) Guid, Cnslng 1968; 30 Credits Spec Ed Univ of MS 1984; Certfd Instr, Phys Restraint, Aggressive Replacement & Crisis Prevention Intervention 1992; *cr:* Garden City HS PE Resource Tchr 1966070; Mark Twain Schl Crisis Support Tchr 1988-92; Gaithersburg Elem Schl Guid Cnslr 1991-92; Martin Luther King Jr MS Guid Cnslr, Chair 1990-93; Paint Branch HS Guid Cnslr 1993-; *ai:* Peer Mediation, Peer Group Cnslng, Peer Mentor Spon; Montgomery Cty Pub Schl 1988-, Supt ABCD Awd; Potomac Almanac Newspaper 1987-, Coach, Almanac Coach of Yr; Mark Twain Schl Tchr of Yr 1990; *home:* 107 Manette Ct Gaithersburg MD 20878

GOETHALS, SUSAN CLAIRE, Schl Admin & Science Teacher; *b:* Buffalo, NY; *m:* James C.; *c:* Jeff, Andrew, Mary Megan; *ed:* Univ of Dayton (BS) Bio Ed 1969; Western CT St Univ (MS) Earth Sci Ed 1990; Southern CT St Univ 6th Yr Scndry Sci, Gen 1996; *cr:* North HS Bio Tchr 1969-71; Orono MS Life Sci Tchr 1981-83; St Joseph Schl Life, Earth Sci Tchr 1984-, Prin 1988-; *ai:* Saturday Sci Club; Sci Horizons Inc; Sci Curr Comm Chair; Diocese of Bridgeport; NCEA 1984-; CTSTA 1990-; NSTA 1989-.*

GOETTLER, CHRISTINE YOUNG, Science Teacher; *b:* Pittsburgh, PA; *c:* Rachel, Andrew; *ed:* Slippery Rock Univ (BS) Scndry Ed 1991; Grad Credits LaRoche Coll; *cr:* Karns City HS Bio Instr 1991; Butler Intermediate HS Bio Instr 1992; Butler Sr HS Gen Sci, Anatomy, Physiology, AP Bio Instr 1992-; *ai:* Stdnt Cncl Adv; 7th-8th Grd Girls Jr Track Team Coach; NEA, PA Ed Assn, Butler Ed Assn 1991-; NSTA 1992-; *office:* Butler Sr HS 165 New Castle Rd Butler PA 16001

GOETZ, ARLETTA WEST, Seventh Grade English Teacher; *b:* Forest Hill, MD; *m:* Edward; *ed:* Salisbury St Coll (BA) Eng 1964; Master's Equivalency Plus; *cr:* Pointer Jr HS 7th Grd Eng Tchr 1964-66; North Harford Jr-Sr HS 7-8 Grd Eng Tchr 1968-76; North Harford MS 7th Grd Eng Tchr 1976-; *ai:* Deer Creek Earth Day Comm; NEA, MSTA, HCEA 1968-; Aberdeen Proving Ground Vol 1992-; *office:* North Harford MS 112 Pylesville Rd Pylesville MD 21132

GOETZ, C. JON, Physics Teacher; *b:* Huntington, NY; *ed:* MA Inst of Tech (BSE) Aeronautical Engrng 1992; Univ of PA (MSE) Mechanical Engrng 1993; Harvard Univ (MED) HS Ed 1994; *cr:* Richard Montgomery HS Physics, Math Tchr 1994-; *ai:* Lacrosse Coach; Chess, Sci Bowl Spon; Conflict Resolution Comm; NEA, MCEA 1994-; Phi Sigma Kappa 1989-, Alumni Pres; Montgomery Cty Sallie Mae First Yr Tchr Awd Finalist; *office:* Richard Montgomery HS 250 Richard Montgomery Dr Rockville MD 20852

GOETZ, GARY R., Language Arts Teacher & Coach; *b:* Chambersburg, PA; *m:* Nora G. Gittings; *c:* Gary R. Jr.; *ed:* Catawba Coll (BA) Eng & His 1967; Attnd Univ of Pittsburg & Univ of NH; *cr:* BSA East Boros Cncl Field Sports Dir 1965-68; Churchill Schl Dist Lang Arts Tchr, Coach 1969-81; Woodland Hills Schl Dist Lang Arts Tchr, Coach 1981-; *ai:* Rifle Team Coach; Vlybl Coach; NEA 1967-; WPIAL Rifle Comm 1978-, Chm; Woodland Hills Tchrs Assn 1981-; BSA 1967-, Merit Badge Adv; Woodland Hills Ed Assn 1981-; Jr Olympic's Shooters at Olympic Trng Ctr Coach 1981; Woodland Hills Coach of Yr 1988; Western PA Sports Hall of Fame Coach of Yr 1975, 1992; Nalt Bd Presbyn Marriage Encounter 1993-95; *home:* 137 Gardenia Dr Turtle Creek PA 15145

GOETZ, GERALD GERARD, Physical Education Teacher; *b:* Trail BC, Canada; *m:* Stasia Mary Flisinski; *c:* Jason; *ed:* Univ of Calgary (BPE PE 1970; Dip Ed Admin 1978; *ai:* IM Prgm Dir; Invitational B'Ball, Browns Initational Bsktbl Tournament Chprsn; Alberta Tchrs Assn, Hlth & PE Cncl 1971-; Canadian IM & Recreation Assn 1977-; Silver Springs Comm Bsktbl Assn 1989-, Coach; *office:* St Francis HS 877 Northmouth Dr NW Calgary AB T2L 0A3 Canada CN*

GOETZ, SARAH LUBKA, Second Grade Teacher; *b:* Stuttgart, Germany; *m:* Michael E.; *c:* David, Rachel; *ed:* Adelphi Univ at Garden City (BSEd) Ed & Math 1968; Univ of MA at Amherst (MSEd) Ed & Elem Guid Cnslr 1969; 60 Credit Hrs; Coll of New Rochelle; Univ CT; Univ of Hartford; *cr:* Fred D Wish Schl 1st-2nd Grd Tchr 1969-75; Various Rockland NY Schls Tchr 1975-76; Monroe Woodbury Schls Kndgtn Tchr 1976-78, 1st Grd Tchr 1978-94, 2nd Grd Tchr 1994-; *ai:* Long Range Curr Mapping Comm to Asst Supt; Dist & Size Comms; Mentor Tchr for Stu Tchrs; Dist Math Consultant for New Chicago Math Pgm; Dist Child Stud Team; Bldg Ldrshp Team; Bldg Level Class; AFT 1975-; MWTA 1975-, Bldg Del; Pine Tree PTA 1979-; New City Jewish Ctr 1981-, Bd of Ed Mem 4 Yrs; Rockland YM-YWHA 1988-, Admin Asst for North Amer Yth Games 8 Yrs; Clarkstown South PTSA 1990-, Corresponding Sec 3 Yrs; Multicultural Curr & Festivities Including Parents; United Nations Stud & Projects Culminating in a Spring Trip; Unicef Collections Evolved into Bank Trip Etc; *office:* Pine Tree Elem Schl Pine Tree Rd Monroe NY 10950*

GOETZ, SHARON FORTNA, Chem, Physics & Phys Sci Tchr; *b:* Chambersburg, PA; *m:* James C.; *c:* Sarah L., Susan E.; *ed:* Shippensburg Univ (BSEd) Physics & Math 1970, (MED) Physics 1973; San Diego St Univ 4 Credits 1972; *cr:* Waynesboro Area Sr HS Sci & Math Tchr 1970-71; Chambersburg Area Sr HS Physics & Advanced Physics Tchr 1971-78, Physics Tchr 1979 & 1982-83 Shalom Chrstn Acad Physics, Chem, 9th Grd Phys Sci, Algebra, Yrbk, Photography & Girls Hlth Tchr 1984-; *ai:* King St United Brethren Church; NSF Grant; *office:* Shalom Christian Acad 126 Social Island Rd Chambersburg PA 17201

GOETZMANN, KATHERINE WALLIS, Elementary Challenge Teacher; *b:* Spokane, WA; *m:* Donald C.; *c:* Gordon J., Evan M.; *ed:* Syracuse Univ (BS) Elem Ed, Psych 1960; Nazareth coll of Rochester (MS) Gen Ed 1982; Attnd Tchrs Coll Columbia Univ, Cortland SUNY, Southern Methodist Univ, Brockport SUNY, Buffalo Ctr for Stud of Creativity, Lamar Univ; *cr:* Suffern Cntrl Schls Fourth Grd Tchr 1960-62; Dallas City Schl Dist 5-6 Grd Math Tchr 1962-63; Elmira City Schl Dist Second Grd Tchr 1970-71; Palmyra-Macedorf K-8 Long Term Sub Tchr 1973-81; Wayne Cntrl Schl Dist Prefirst-First Grd Tchr of GATE 1981-; *ai:* Continental Math League Facilitator; Odyssey of the Mind Facilitator; Kids as Problem Solvers; Star Gazing Adv; Supporting Emotional Needs of Gifted Facilitator; PTA 1960-; Advocated for GATE Ed NY St 1985-; NEA, NEANY, WTA 1981-; Macedon Pub Lib Bd 1987-; Church Choir 1974-; One Child's Book Pub; Grant for Friendship; WCSD Tchr of Significance 1992; *home:* 2753 Quaker Rd Palmyra NY 14522*

GOFF, CINDY KOERBER, Third Grade Teacher; *b:* Barnesville, OH; *m:* David; *ed:* OH Univ (BS) Elem Ed 1978; Addl 14 Quarter Hrs; Extra Hrs for Prof Cert; *cr:* Morristown Elem Schl Third Grd Tchr 1978-, Head Tchr 1989-; *ai:* Numerous Textbooks, Curr Comms; OEA, NEA 1978-; ULACT 1978-, Bldg Rep; Martha Holden Jennings Scholar 1985-86; *office:* Morristown Elem Schl West Cross St PO Box 1 Morristown OH 43759

GOFFREDO, SSJ, DAMIAN, Sci & Jr HS Homeroom Tchr; *b:* Carbondale, PA; *ed:* Nazareth Coll of Rochester (BS) Ed 1964, (BA) His 1968, (MSEd) Learning Disabilities 1976; *cr:* Diocesan Elem Schls 4th-7th Grd Classroom Tchr 1959-64; Schl of Holy Chldhd Spec Ed Tchr 1964-65; Diocesan Elem Schl Hr HS Tchr 1965-70; Saint Josephs Villa Dir of Ed, Bldg Prin & Tchr 1970-83; Nazareth Acad Sci, Eng, Rdng & Mastery Learning Tchr 1983-93; The Nazareth Schls Sci Tchr 1993-; *ai:* MS Sci Curr Coord; MS Fndrsng Comm; Sci Educators 1991-; Rep Body of Sisters of Saint Joseph 1988-; Univ of Rochester Excl in Scndry Schl Tchng 1991; Stdnts Spec Tchr Awd 1993; *office:* The Nazareth Schls 1001 Lake Ave Rochester NY 14613

GOFORTH, MARY DAVEY, Retired English Teacher; *b:* Barnesville, OH; *m:* Richard Eugene; *c:* Diane L. Goforth Ohning; *ed:* Oberlin Coll (BMED) Music Ed 1944; Coll of Mt St Joseph (MA) Ed 1987; *cr:* Leipsic Music Tchr 1944-46; Stone Creek Tusacarawas New Philadelphia Eng Tchr 1946-68; Indian Valley HS Eng Tchr 1972-93; *ai:* Lang Arts Graded Stud Course Comm; Indian Valley Tchrs Assn 1972-; NCTE 1985-87; New Philadelphia Ed Assn 1986-, Pres 1987; OH Ed Assn, NEA 1944-; Nom OH Tchr of Yr 1985; Indian Valley Tchr of Yr 1985; Martha Holden Jennings Schlsp Awd 1985-86; *home:* 2123 E High Ave New Philadelphia OH 44663*

GOGAS, CAROL A., 5th & 6th Grd Homeroom Teacher; *b:* Scranton, PA; *c:* Richard Jr., Lucinda Teague, Lynda, Christine, Donna Yearing, Michelle, Christopher, Paul; *ed:* Marywood Coll (BS) Elem Ed 1985; Post Grad 10 Credit Hrs; *ai:* Holy Chldhd Assn Coord; NCEA 1986-; *office:* St Mary's Greenwood Schl 3557 Greenwood Ave Moosic PA 18507*

GOGGINS, DEBORAH STRINGFELLOW, Teacher; *b:* Washington, DC; *m:* James Davis; *c:* James II, Joy Alyssa, Janeen Alexis; *ed:* Freedmen's Hosp Schl of Nrsng (RN) Nrsng 1967; West VA St Coll (BA) Sociology 1978; 12 Hrs Cnslng Univ of DC; *cr:* Hadley Hosp RN Surgical 1967-69; DC Hlth Dept Comm Hlth Nrsng 1969-74; Kanawha Cty Schl Bd Schl Nurse 1974-78; Montgomery Cty Hlth Dept Schl Nurse 1979-86; Holy Temple Chrstn Acad Elem Tchr 1987-; *ai:* Fine Arts Adv; PTA 1990-; Morning Star Church 1959-, Pres Jr Missionaries, Adult Ed Tchr, VBS Tchr, Gospel Choir Dir, Adv Yth Action; *office:* Holy Temple Christian Acad 739 12th St SE Washington DC 20003

GOING, DENISE (BIANCULLI), English Teacher; *b:* Bayside, NY; *m:* Raymond; *ed:* St John's Univ (BS) Elem Ed, Eng 7-12 1992; Adelphi Univ (MS) Rdng K-12 1995; *cr:* Elmont Meml HS Eng Tchr 1993-; *ai:* Class of 99 Adv; Jr HS Sftbl Coach 1993-95; JV Sftbl Coach; NEA 1993-; *office:* Elmont Meml Jr Sr HS 555 Ridge Rd Elmont NY 11003

GOINS, LAURIE LEEANN, Spanish Teacher; *b:* Marion, OH; *m:* Don; *ed:* Bowling Green St Univ (BA) Span 1986; OH St Univ 25 Credit Hrs; Univ of Dayton 6 Credit Hrs; *cr:* West Jefferson Local Schls Span Tchr 1989-94; Pleasant Local Schls Span Tchr 1994-; *ai:* Span Club Adv; NEA, OH Tchrs Assn 1989-; Pleasant Tchrs Assn 1994-; *office:* Pleasant Local Schools 1101 Owens Rd W Marion OH 43302

GOLA, HOWARD R., Third Grade Teacher; *b:* Wilkes-Barre, PA; *m:* Lillian G. Price; *c:* Michelle Dotzel, Paul; *ed:* Wilkes Univ (BS) Elem Ed 1967; Bloomsburg Univ (MS) Elem Ed 1971; 50 Addl Hrs; *cr:* Crestwood Schl Dist Tchr 1967-; *ai:* Crestwood Ed Assn 1967-, Chprsn 1988-90; PSEA, NEA 1967-; PTA 1967-; PA 76ers 1991-, Wagonmaster.

GOLABEK, JANET, Secondary Art Teacher; *b:* Hackensack, NJ; *ed:* Philadelphia Coll of Art (BFA) Illustration 1969; Ed Cert Montclair St Art Tchr K-12 1971; Attnd Joe Kubert Schl of Cartoon & Graphic Art, Montclair Art Museum Schl, Du Cret Schl of Art & Design; *cr:* Ginsberg's Clothing Store Salesgirl & Model 1968; Art Dept of INA Part-time in House Artist 1969-70; American Girl Magazine Free Lance Illustrator 1970-71; Parsippany HS Scndry Art Tchr 1972-; *ai:* Art Club Spon 1974-; NJAE, NJEA; Recognition for Animal Rescue & Adoption Work 1988-, Photograph & Article in Newspaper; Forgotten Pets 1988-89, VP; Cliffton Animal Shelter 1992-, Comm Svc Awd; Illustrations Pub in American Girl Magazine, Scholastic Scope; Cover Illustration & Inside Cartoons in Booklet for Givenche Co 1984; *office:* Parispanny HS 309 Baldwin Rds Parsippany NJ 07054

GOLANKA, CHRISTINE STEFFENS, Secondary Math Teacher; *b:* New York City, NY; *m:* Mathew E.; *c:* Tiffany, Brittany; *ed:* Niagara Cty Comm Coll (AS) Lib Arts, Math 1986; SUNY at Buffalo (BS) Math Ed 1993; Niagara-Orleans Boces Clerk, Typist 1982; *cr:* Mount St Mary Acad Scndry Math Tchr 1994-; *ai:* Schl Play Props Coord; NCTM 1992-; Girl Scouts 1985-, Ldr; *office:* Mt St Mary Acad 3756 Delaware Ave Kenmore NY 14217

GOLD, DEBRA LYNN, Physical Education & Hlth Tchr; *b:* New York, NY; *m:* Dr. Avram; *c:* Jason A. Kersch, Dara M., Ilan P.; *ed:* Queens Coll (BA) PE 1980, (MS) Exercise Physiology 1986; *cr:* Cardozo HS PE Tchr 1980-83, Girls Track & Vlybl Coach 1981-82; Saint Johns Univ Co-organizer Spec Olympics 1982; Jamaica HS PE Tchr 1983-84; Benjamin N Cardozo HS Girls Track & Vlybl Coach 1983-84; BQE Racquetball & Hlth Club Asst Dir 1984-86; Martin Van Buren HS PE & Hlth Tchr 1986-; Bay Terrace YMHA & YWHA After Schl Sports Prgm Coord 1987-88; *ai:* Ldrs Org Adv; *office:* Martin Van Buren HS 23017 Hillside Ave Queens Village NY 11427*

GOLD, JILL A., Guidance Counselor; *b:* New York City, NY; *m:* Fredric C.; *c:* Lauren; *ed:* MI St Univ (BA) Soc Sci, Scndry Ed 1973; Hofstra Univ (MS) Cnslr Ed 1976, (PHD) Cnslr Ed 1993; Attnd Long Island Univ Post PHD Ed Admin; *cr:* Bear, Stearns & Co Personnel Mgr 1973-76; Shearson, Lehman Human Resources VP 1979-81; Long Island Jewish Medical Ctr Employment Mgr 1987-88; Valley Stream North HS Guidance Cnslr 1990-; *ai:* Peer Mediation, Stdnts Helping Others Advs; Recognition Night Coord; NYSUT 1990-; Phi Kappa Phi 1973-; Chi Sigma Iota 1995-; Phi Delta Kappa 1996-; Women's Amer ORT 1981-, Co-Pres, Woman of Yr; Sisterhood Comm Synagogue 1986-, Trustee; Roslyn Trinity Nursery Schl 1983-, VP; *office:* Valley Stream North HS 750 Herman Ave Franklin Square NY 11010*

GOLD, MARGARET M., Social Studies Teacher; *b:* Rockeville Centre, NY; *ed:* Stonehill Coll (BA) Eng 1984; Long Island Univ (MS) Ed 1992; Attnd Columbia Univ, Rutgers Univ; *cr:* Chirst the King HS Soc Stud Tchr 1991-92; Paramus HS Soc Stud Tchr 1992-; *ai:* Amnesty Intnl Club, Soph Class Adv; Winter Track Asst Coach; Spring Track Head Coach; NCSS, NJCSS 1992-; Woodrow Wilson Flwshp Awd; Lincoln Ctr Fellow; *office:* Paramus HS 99 E Century Rd Paramus NJ 07652*

GOLD, VICTORIA J., Art & Pottery Teacher; *b:* Pittsburg, PA; *m:* Larry S.; *c:* Elizabeth; *ed:* Phila Coll of Art (BA) Pottery, Sculpture 1967; *cr:* Germantown YWCA Pottery Tchr 1968-80; Univ City Arts League Pottery Tchr 1970-77; The Baldwin Schl MS Art & US Pottery Tchr 1980-; *ai:* Yrbk Adv; MS Search, Curr, Governance Comms; Head of Sr Externships; Fac Senate; Acting Dept Head 1992; Admin of 2 Yr Prgm Called Women Creatings; Sabbatical Using Time to Work at Project Home, a Homeless Shelter in Phila; Working with Residents to Create a Mosiac Wall Relief in Entrance Hall of Bldg; Numerous Person Shows at Galleries; *office:* The Baldwin Schl 701 Montgomery Ave Bryn Mawr PA 19010*

GOLDAMMER, BARBARA HARFORD, Secondary Mathematics Teacher; *b:* Jamestown, NY; *m:* James Jr.; *c:* Dylan, Alec; *ed:* St Univ of NY at Geneseo (BA) Math 1987; Nazareth of Rochester (MS) Cmptr Lit 1992; *ai:* Masterminds Coach; LTA 1988-; *office:* Lyons Jr Sr HS 10 Clyde Rd Lyons NY 14489

GOLDBERG, ALECK, Physics Professor; *b:* Philadelphia, PA; *c:* Mark F.; *ed:* Temple Univ (BA) Physics 1946, (MA) Physics 1948; Attnd Univ of Southern CA Advanced Stud Physics; Addl 40 Credit Hrs; *cr:* PA St Univ Assoc Prof, Physics 1964-66; La Salle Univ Adjunct Prof, Physcis 1964-86; Montgomery Cty Comm Coll Prof of Physics, Math 1966-; Beaver Coll Adjunct Prof, Physics 1980-85; *ai:* Assn of CAth Tchrs 1965-; Univ of Southern CA Flwshp 1949-50; Temple Univ Flwshp 1946-48; Contributing Author, Guided Missle Handbook; Authored 2 Articles, 8 Reports; *office:* Montgomery County Comm Coll 340 Dekalb Pike Blue Bell PA 19422

GOLDBERG, ANITA, English Teacher; *b:* Malden, MA; *ed:* Univ of MA at Boston (BA) Pol Sci 1973, (MED) Scndry Ed 1981; *cr:* Pope John XXIII HS Eng Tchr 1981-; *ai:* NHS Adv 10 Yrs; Jr Class Adv; MEH Summer Seminar Grant Stud at Western WA Univ at Bellingham 1995, Gettysburg Coll 1992; *office:* Pope John XXIII Cntl HS 888 Broadway Everett MA 02149

GOLDBERG, EDWARD MICHAEL, Language Arts Teacher; *b:* New London, CT; *m:* Carol Cowan; *ed:* Univ of CT (BA) Eng 1982, (MA) Ed 1989; *cr:* Mystic MS Eng & Fr Tchr 1986-; *ai:* Drama Coach; Fellowship Awd for Stud in Senegal West Africa; CT Celebration of Excl Awd; Fellowship CT Acad of Eng His & Geo; CT Writing Project; Pub Fiction & Lit Essays; *office:* Mystic MS 204 Mistuxet Ave Mystic CT 06355*

GOLDBERG, EILEEN, Biology Teacher; *b:* Brooklyn, NY; *ed:* Brooklyn Coll (BS) Bio 1966; City Univ (MS) Bio 1971; NY Univ (BS) Cmptr Prgmng Tech 1982; *cr:* Albert Research Ctr Lab Technologist 1 Yr; New Utrecht HS Bio Tchr 16 Yrs; Royale Insurance Cmptr Programmer 2 Yrs; Deliotte Haskinssils Cmptr Programmer 1 Yr; Brooklyn Tech HS Bio Tchr 11 Yrs; *ai:* Sci Fair Adv; UFT, Bio Tchrs Assn 1966-; Natl Sci Fnd Grants in Stellar Physics San Diego St Coll & Nuclear Physics KA St Univ; *office:* Brooklyn Technical HS 29 Fort Greene Pl Brooklyn NY 11217

GOLDBERG, EUNICE MEIER, English Teacher; *b:* Cleveland, OH; *c:* Tiffany, David; *ed:* Eastern Nazarene Coll (BA) Eng 1967; St Univ Coll of NY at Buffalo (MS) Ed 1970; Fitchburg St Coll 30 Grad Hrs; *cr:* West Seneca Cntrl Schls Eng Tchr 1967-71; Silver Lake Regnl HS Eng Tchr 1987-; *ai:* Yrbk Adv; SLEA 1987-, Treas; MTA, NEA 1987-; Delta Kappa Gamma 1990-, Mbrshp Chm; NEH Summer Seminars 1989; *office:* Silver Lake Reg HS-Kingston 132 Pembroke St Kingston MA 02364

GOLDBERG, GARY M., Math Teacher; *b:* Brooklyn, NY; *m:* Ellen; *c:* David; *ed:* SUNY at Buffalo (BA) His 1967; Long Island Univ (MS) Guid 1973; 24 Credit Hrs Math Ed Hofstra Univ; *cr:* PS 40 Sci Tchr 1969-76; Philippa Schuyler Math Tchr 1977-; *ai:* Pgm Chm; UFT 1969-; NYS Soc of CPAs 1986-; Amer Ins of CPAs 1986-; Bellmore Jewish Ctr 1974-, Pres, Treas & Sec; Bellmore-Merrick Cntrl Schl Dist Citizens Budget Comm; *home:* 2517 Army Pl Bellmore NY 11710*

GOLDBERG, IRA ALLEN, Music Coordinator; *b:* New York City, NY; *m:* Carmen Amoros; *ed:* NY Univ (BS) Music Ed 1972, (MA) Supervision, Admin in Music Ed 1974; 30 Credits Beyond MA at Juilliard Schl of Music; *cr:* Sheepshead Bay HS Music Tchr 1972-75; Erasumus HS Music Tchr 1975; Adelphi Acad Music Tchr 1976-78; Boys & Girls HS Music Tchr 1978-82; Forest Hills HS Music Coord 1982-; *ai:* Jazz Band Dir; Music Dir of Play Productions; Queens Cty Annual Music Festival Comm; MENC, NYS Schl Music Assn 1970-; United Fed of Tchr 1972-; Music Edctrs Assn of NY 1990-; *office:* Forest Hills HS 67-01 110th St Forest Hills NY 11375*

GOLDBERG, IRWIN S., Music Teacher; *b:* New York, NY; *m:* Beth Hillman; *c:* Cara, Andrew; *ed:* Ithaca Coll (BM) Music Ed 1971; Syracuse Univ (MS) Music Ed 1976; Addl Credits SUNY & IN Univ; *cr:* Fayetteville-Manlius Schls Music Tchr 1971-85; East Syracuse Minoa Music Tchr 1986-; *ai:* Musical Theater Dir; Tech Comm; Tech Stage Crew Adv; ACDA 1971-, Zone Rep; NYSSMA & MENC 1971-, Chprsn; NYSUT 1971-; Manlius Fire Dept 1990-; *office:* E Syracuse Minoa Ctl HS 6400 Fremont Rd East Syracuse NY 13057

GOLDBERG, JACQUELINE FREDRICKA, Second Grade Teacher; *b:* Uniontown, PA; *ed:* CA St Coll (BS) Elem Ed 1973, (MS) Elem Guid 1977; *cr:* Laurel Highlands Schl Dist K-8 Grd Sub Tchr 1973-74; Uniontown Schl Dist K-8 Grd Sub Tchr 1973-74; Wharton Elem Schl Second-Third Grd Tchr 1974-82; Boyle Elem Schl Second Grd Tchr 1982-86; Ben Franklin Schl Second Grd Tchr 1986-; *ai:* NEA 1974-, Delta Kappa Gamma 1983-, 1st VP, Pres; Uniontown Coll Club 1974-; KDKA TV Thanks to Tchrs Nom; *office:* Ben Franklin Schl 351 Morgantown St Uniontown PA 15401

GOLDBERG, JOAN CROSBY, Third Grade Teacher; *b:* Cambridge, MA; *m:* Herbert; *c:* Jennifer Weinreich, Allison Russo, Elizabeth; *ed:* Boston Univ (AB) His of Art 1960; 15 Hrs Ed Courses Beyond AB; *cr:* Brockton Schl Dept 4th Grd Tchr 1960-65, Sub Tchr 1978-84, 3rd Grd Tchr 1984-; *ai:* Quilt Shop Owner Summer Bus; BEA, NEA 1984-; Creative Arts Assn 1980-85, Treas; Sharon Arts Lottery Comm 1980-82; Basic Skills Advy Comm 1980-84; Patriot Ledger Golden Apple Awd 1989; Most Inspiring Tchr 1995; *office:* Huntington Elem Schl 1121 Warren Ave Brockton MA 02401*

GOLDBERG, JONATHAN B., Teacher & Prof Growth Coord; *b:* Boston, MA; *m:* Ursula Marrello; *c:* Alexandra, Jamison; *ed:* Vassar Coll (AB) His 1977; Tchrs Coll at Columbia (MA) Philosophy 1982; Attnd Fordham Univ; *cr:* George Fischer MS Faculty 1977-88; Carmel HS Faculty 1988-; *ai:* Dist Staff Dev Prof Growth Coord; ASCD 1984-; NCSS 1966-; Phi Delta Kappa 1988-; Kappa Delta Pi 1982-; Natl Staff Dev Cncl 1988-; *office:* Carmel HS 30 Fair St Carmel NY 10512*

GOLDBERG, MARK B., Soc Stud Tchr & Project Coord; *b:* Bronx, NY; *m:* Jean E.; *c:* Andrew, Barry; *ed:* Queens Coll (MS) Ed 1970; C W Post (PD) Ed Admin & Sup 1977; Credentialed Substance Abuse Cnslr; *cr:* Springfield Gardens HS Tchr 1967-70; Far Rockaway HS Drug Ed Specialist 1972-93, Tchr & Coord 1996; Suffolk Comm Coll Adj 1990-; *ai:* Boys Var Bowling Coach; AFT; UFT; Little League 1978-, VP; *office:* Far Rockaway HS 821 Bay 25th St Far Rockaway NY 11691

GOLDBERG, P. DAVID, Fourth Grade Teacher; *b:* Pittsburgh, PA; *m:* Cheryl Schmidt; *c:* Elliot; *ed:* Univ of Pittsburgh (BA) Elem Ed 1976, (MA) Elem Ed 1978; *cr:* North Allegheny Schl Dist Tchr 1978-87, Lead Tchr 1987-88, Tchr 1989-; *ai:* Co-Chair Elem Time Comm; North Allegheny Fed of Tchrs 1978-, Elem VP, Negotiating Team; Natl Geographic Soc 1988-; *office:* North Allegheny Schl Dist 500 Cumberland Rd Pittsburgh PA 15237

GOLDBERG, STEVEN A., Guidance Counselor; *b:* Queens, NY; *m:* Stephanie; *c:* Halle; *ed:* SUNY at Albany (BS) Psych 1989; LIU-C W Post (MS) Cnslng 1990; 27 Credits Admin; *cr:* H F Carey HS Guid Cnslr 1990-; *ai:* Soccer, Bsktbl & LaCrosse Coach; NCA 1989-; *office:* H Frank Carey HS 230 Poppy Ave Franklin Square NY 11010

GOLDBERG, STEVEN DAVID, Asst Professor of Management; *b:* Hartford, CT; *m:* Cynthia Jean Platt; *c:* Lee Hersh, Richard Ashley, James Michael; *ed:* Yale Univ & NH COll (BS) HRA 1968; Univ of New Haven (MBA) Bus 1986; Univ of MA (EdD) Org Dev 1991; Kensington Univ (PhD) Bus Admin 1994; Babson Coll Post Grad Stud 1992; *cr:* Shoprite Supermarkets Exec VP & COO 1979-86; Expressive Svcs Pres & CEO 1986-88; Univ of MA Tchng Assoc 1988-91; Univ of New Haven Asst Prof of Mngmt 1991-; *ai:* Schl Newspaper & Chi Kappa Rho Adv; Small Bus Inst Dir; Entrepeneurship Prgm Coord; Acad of Mngmt, Family Firm Inst, US Assn for Sm Bus & Entrepreneurship 1991-; World Spec Olympics 1993-, Vol Recognition Chm; ECaP 1993-, Sec; Outstanding Contribution to Field Awd for Research 1992; Research Fac Fellowship 1992; *office:* Univeristy of New Haven 300 Orange Ave West Haven CT 06516

GOLDEN, CATHERINE HARRIET, 2nd Grade Teacher; *b:* Barton, NY; *m:* Michael; *c:* Alexandra Grant; *ed:* Buffalo St Coll (BS) Elem Ed 1967, (MS) Ed 1969; City of Tonawanda Pub Schls 2nd Grd Tchr 1967-; *cr:* Report Card Comm 11995; Mentor New Tchrs 1992-93; *ai:* NYSUT, AFT 1967-; Finalist Tchr of Yr 1993; *home:* 5696 Kippen Dr East Amherst NY 14051

GOLDEN, DARCY SENDER, Spanish & French Teacher; *b:* Philadelphia, PA; *m:* Robert J.; *c:* Rickie Joanna; *ed:* Temple Univ (BSEd) Foreign Lang, Sec Ed 1971, (EDM) Foreign Lang Educ 1973; Attnd Univ of Salamanca 1992, Univ of Madrid 1972; *cr:* Cntrl Bucks-East HS Span & Fr Tchr 1971-74; Hillcrest Jr HS Fr Tchr 1974-76; Penn Valley Schl ESL Tchr 1988-90; Pennsbury HS ESL Tchr 1990-91; Medill-Bair HS Span Tchr 1991-; *ai:* Pennsbury Summer Schl Abroad Prgm Facilitator 1992-; Asst Bsktbl Coach; Pub Relations Dir; Stu Cncl & Lit Magazine Adv 1974-76; Sr Class Adv 1971-74; NEA, PSEA, PEA 1991-; Freelance Feature Writer; *office:* Medill Bair HS 608 S Olds Blvd Fairless Hills PA 19030*

GOLDEN, DAVID MICHAEL, Social Studies Teacher; *b:* Mechanicville, NY; *m:* Janice Crabbis Jaskorka; *c:* Llesel, Tim, Paul; *ed:* SUNY at Oneonta (BS) Ed 1960, (MS); Attnd Cornell, SUNY at Albany; *cr:* Ft Plain CS Tchr 1961-65; Norwich City Schl Tchr 1965-68; Shenendehowa CS Tchr & AV Coor 1968-; *ai:* Mock Trial & Partnership Teams; European Travel Pgm; Facilities, Fin & Budget Comms; AFL-CIO 1996-, Del; AFT 25 Yrs, Del; NYSAT 25 Yrs, Del; NYSCSS 15 Yrs, Sec, Distngd Svc Awd; NCSS 16 Yrs; NY St Local Gov Records Advy Comm, 1986-, Vice Chair; Neiderberger Outstldng Svc; 2 Distngd Svc Awds; *home:* 4 Royal Oak Dr Clifton Park NY 12065

GOLDEN, JOYCE A., Math Dept Chairperson; *b:* Johnson City, NY; *ed:* St Univ of NY at Geneseo (BA) Math 1968; St Univ of NY at Cortland (MS) Ed 1972; Attnd Univ of Scranton, St Univ of NY at Binghamton; *cr:* Susquehanna Vly Schls Dept Chair & Tchr 1968-; *ai:* Tennis Coach; Section Chprsn; Dist Schl-to-Work Comm Co-Chair; Tech Prep Ldrshp Comm; Scndry Curr Cncl; NYSMTA; Triple Cities Math Tchr; USTA; NEA & SV Tchrs Assn; NYS Compact Schl Quality Review; *office:* Susquehanna Vly Schls 1040 Conklin Rd Conklin NY 13748

GOLDEN, MICHAEL S., 6th Grade Teacher; *b:* New York City, NY; *m:* Joan Brough; *c:* Andrew, Lauren; *ed:* SUNY at Binghamton (BA) Psych 1970; Brooklyn Coll, CUNY (MS) Urban Ed 1973; The New Schl for Soc Rsrch (MA) Media Stud 1983; Working on EDD Columbia Univ Tchrs Coll 1993-; *cr:* PS 229 Q 4-5 Grd Classroom Tchr 1971-74; PS 335 K 4-5 Grd Classroom Tchr 1975-85; PS 243K 4-5 Grd Classroom Tchr 1975-85; Lakeville Schl 5 Grd Tchr 1985-89; Great Neck South MS 6 Grd Tchr 1989-; *ai:* After Schl Math Enrichment Prgm; IM Prgm Coach; Bldg Rep Comm; Union Del; NYSUT, AFT 1971-; Great Neck Tchr Assn 1 Assn Gate Children, NCTM 1995-; Articles, Essays Pub; Author Guides, Curr Units; *office:* Great Neck South MS 349 Lakeville Neck NY 11020*

GOLDEN, TERRANCE, Science Teacher; *b:* Pittsburg, PA Lindsey; *ed:* IN Univ (BS) Rehabilitation Ed 1981; Duque (MSEd) Sci Ed 1988; *cr:* Harmarville Rehab Ctr Cnslr 1981-88; Ed Sci Tchr 1988-; Duquesne Univ Lecturer 1990-; *ai:* Sci Cl Acad of Sci; Cross Cntry Coach; Ski Club Moderator; PSTA 198 PAFT 1988-; Aquatic Ecosystem Grant; Project SEPIA; *ho* Chislett St Pittsburgh PA 15206

GOLDENBERG, ELIOT, Guidance Counselor; *b:* Brooklyr Sahfi; *ed:* Brooklyn Coll (BS) Ed 1964; Ithaca Coll (MS) Syracuse Univ (MS) Guid & Cnslng 1969; Nova Univ Adm & St *cr:* ME Endwell Elem Schl Tchr 1966-68; Elmcrest Childrens (Parent & Admin 1969-73; Ithaca Schl Dist Tchr 1973-78; Palm I Schls Cnslr 1979-85; Copiague Jr HS Cnslr 1986-; *ai:* Liberty P & Step Pgm Adv; LIAC 1986-; NEA 1986-; NYSUT 1986 Copiague Jr HS 2650 Great Neck Rd Copiague NY 11726

GOLDENTYER, PATRICIA YOUNG, Visiting Lecturer of Philadelphia, PA; *c:* Joshua, Philip; *ed:* Temple Univ (BA) & (BF 1958, (MS) Cnslng & Guid 1970, (PHD) Psycho Ed Processes 19 Boston U, Penn St, Gratz Coll; *cr:* Shaw Jr HS Art Tchr Overbrook HS Art Tchr 1962-70, Cnslr 1970-93; Comm Philadelphia Adj Prof of Psych 1978-95, Visiting Lecturer 1995- Advng; Amer Psychological Assn 1985-; Cnslrs Assn Greater F Humanitarian Awd; DE Vly Group Psychotherapy Assn 1985-89 Phi Soc of Clinical Hypnosis 1995-; AFT; MENSA 1984-, Mem (Comm; Gen Electric Careers Flwshp; Temple Univ Flwshp 1 Rational Emotive Therapy; PA License Psychologist NCC 198 Comm Coll Of Philadelphia 17 & Spring Garden Sts Philad 19130

GOLDFADEN, DAVID LOUIS, English & Philosophy Pro Baltimore, MD; *m:* Gloria Antoinette; *c:* Shawn, Shana, Stefan, S Univ of MD (AB) Eng & Phil 1965; Trinity Coll (MA) Eng & Doctoral Candidate; Post Grad Studs Cath Univ; *cr:* US Dept Ed Admin Asst Dir 1965-66; Natl Tchr Corps Instr 1966-67; US Comm Instr 1968; Prince Georges Coll Prof 1968-; *ai:* Coll Coord; Curr Adv & Registration Cnslr; Modern Lang Assn 1979-; 1990-; People Against Child Abuse 1984-, Co-Founder & Bd M Comm Rights of Child; JC Penny Golden Rule Awd 1st Pl 199 Prince Georges Comm Coll 301 Largo Rd Largo MD 20772

GOLDFARB, RONALD C., Acctng & Legal Stud Dept Chm; *b:* NY; *m:* Marianne Kelleher; *c:* Rachel; *ed:* Richmond Coll (BA) NY Law Schl (JD) Law 1975; *cr:* Middlesex Cnty Coll Adj Instr Fordham Univ Grad Schl of Bus Adj Asst Prof 1991-93; *ai:* Cn Fac Dev; Chair By-Laws Task Force; Defining Excl in Classroo Curr Task Force; Acad of Legal Stud in Bus 1988-; NE Acad of L in Bus 1988-, Pres; Amer Assn for Paralegal Ed 1995-; Articles P Middlesex County Coll 155 Mill Rd Edison NJ 08837*

GOLDFARB, VICKI KRASNER, Health & Physical Ed Te Bronx, NY; *m:* Ivan; *c:* David, Beth, Rebecca; *ed:* Itha Coll (BS) SUNY at Stony Brook (MLS) Lbrl Stud; *cr:* Hicksville HS 1966-67; North Cty Elem Schl PE Instr 1967-70; Ward Melville PE Instr 1980-; *ai:* Coach Var Girls, Boys Tennis; TVTA 1967- Asst Bldg Rep; Suffolk Cty Tennis Coaches Assn 1989-, Bd of (1992; Woman of Yr in Sports 1989; Outstdng Prof Achvmt 19 Ward Melville HS 380 Old Town Rd Setauket NY 11733

GOLDING, PETER, HS Soc Stud & His Lead Teacher; *b:* Se *m:* Tracey Jane Burdick; *ed:* Bowdoin Coll (BA) His 1985; Wesl GLSP 1992-93; *cr:* Woodberry Forest Schl His Tchr 1985 Cambridge Schl His Tchr 1988-89; Sewickley Acad His Tchr Amer Embassy Schl HS Soc Stud Lead Tchr, His Dept 1994-; Soccer Coach; 30 Humanitarian & Enviromental Groups; Distr Awd White House Commission on Presidential Scholars 1995; Tchng Awd Univ of Chicago 1994; *office:* Amer Embassy Schl N Chanakyapuri New Delhi India XX 00000*

GOLDMAN, CINDY (SAFER), Third Grade Teacher; *b:* Denve Michael Gary; *c:* Matthew, Brian; *ed:* Univ of CO (BS) Elem Ed St Univ (MS) Ed 1991; *cr:* Dept of Defense Schls 3rd Grd Tchr 3rd & 4th Grd Tchr 1987-90, Compensatory Ed Tchr 1990-95; 3rd 1995-; *ai:* NEA, OEA 1986-; PDK 1990-.

GOLDMAN, JOHN PATRICK, English Teacher; *b:* Silver Sp *m:* Theresa Bass; *ed:* Towson St Univ (BA) Eng 1989; Working Masters in 18th Century British; John Hopkins in Baltimor Springbrook HS Eng Tchr 1990; Paint Branch HS Eng Tchr 1990- Adv Felidae 1993-95; Outdoor Track Coach 1994-95; Environmental, Saftey Comm 1993-95; MSTA, MCEA 1990-; Place Recognition for Ed of Felidae Columbia Scholastic Press A Statewide First Place Recognition Ed of Felidae 1994; *office:* Pai HS 14121 Old Columbia Pike Burtonsville MD 20866

GOLDMAN, LYNN CLEARE, Art Instructor; *b:* Rochester Richard Goldman; *ed:* Pratt Inst (BFA) Design 1974; Rochest Tech (MST) Art ed 1976; Attnd C. W. Post Univ, Horizons Craft Mahar Regnl Schl 9-12th Grd Art Tchr 1976-77; Hawley Jr HS Art Tchr 1977-85; Northampton HS 9-12th Grd Art Tchr Scheduling Comm; MA Tchrs Assoc; Amer Craft Cncl; NEMSH of Dir; Assn de Criadores de Caballos Falabella 1988-, Regnl Shown at Glassmasters Gallery 1987; Breeder of Miniature Hor the Yr 1989-90; *office:* Northampton HS 380 Elm St Northam 01060

GOLDMAN, MICHAEL C., Mathematics Teacher; *b:* Chicag Faye M.; *c:* Melissa; *ed:* MIT (BS) Math 1971; Boston St Coll (Admin 1974, (CAGS) Ed Admin 1976; *cr:* Broadmeadows Jr HS 1971-73; Braintree HS Math Tchr 1973-; *ai:* Var Sftbl Coach; Stu Treas; CTM, NEA, MA Tchrs Assn 1971-; Local Sports Ofcls As Ftbl, Bsbl Rules Interpreter; *office:* Braintree HS 128 Town St MA 02184

GOLDMAN, MYRON W., Math Teacher; *b:* Boston, MA; *m:* L *c:* David, Richard, Bethanne; *ed:* Boston Univ (AB) His 1964, (M of Ed 1966; Elem Math Cert St Josephs Univ 1992; Scndry M Temple Univ 1967; *cr:* Masterman Demonstration Schl Math Tc Studdart-Fleisher Schl Math Tchr 14 Yrs; Frank Nicholas Schl Tchr 1 Yr; *ai:* AFT 1976-, Bldg Rep; NEA 1966-77, VP of Loca 1976-; Schl Bd Mem 1985-89, VP; Friends of Elkins Park Lib 19 1994-; A Neglected Minority Math Tchr 1980; Geometry Cours *home:* 8102 High School Rd Elkins Park PA 19027

GOLDMAN, WENDY SINGER, 9th-12th Grade Art Instr Washington, DC; *m:* Benjamin Z.; *ed:* Univ of MD at College F Art Ed K-12 1984; Bowie St Univ (MED) Spec Ed 1994; 6 Addl C Guid, Cnslng; *cr:* Meridian Corp Graphic Artist 1983-86; St Eliza Art Instr Grds 1-8 1985-86; Frederick Douglass HS Art Instr Gr 1986-; *ai:* Art Club Adv, Spon; Crisis Intervention Team; NE *office:* Frederick Douglass HS 8000 Croom Rd Upper Marl 20772*

AN-BRODIE, ERICA SIMONE, Third Grade Teacher; *b:* England; *m:* Rabbi Joseph A.; *c:* Rachel, Hayim Daniel; *ed:* Univ (BA) Ed, Psych 1968; Hunter Coll (MS) Elem Ed 1972; *cr:* 2nd & 5th Grd Tchr 1968-73; Schl #4 3rd Grd Tchr 1973-; *ai:* 73-; Hadassah 1976-, VP Chapter Lenox Hill; UJA-Fed 1979-, l Chprsn, Leadership Winner 1983; Jewish Braille Inst 1985-, & Taper, Magazine Issue Dedicated to Me; Pub Speaker to Civic Australian Jewry; Lead Jewish Identity Wkshps; *office:* School #4 St West New York NJ 07093

ANN, BRENDA R., First Grade Teacher; *b:* Hackensack, NJ; *m:* M.; *ed:* William Paterson Coll (BA) Elem Ed 1961; *cr:* Memorial Grd Tchr 1961-; *ai:* NEA 1961-; NJEA 1961-; EAP 1961-, Past ship Chm; Bergen Cty Assn 1961-; NJ Spec Olympics 1981-, Vol ol of Yr; *home:* 491 Spring Valley Rd Paramus NJ 07652

EER, SUSAN ANN, HS Spanish & Italian Teacher; *b:* New York ; *m:* Samuel; *c:* Guy, Sara Moore, Cara Damer, William; *ed:* Univ (BA) Span, Ed 1970; Univ of Valencia Span; Queens Coll d; *cr:* Locust Vly Schl HS Tchr 1971-; *ai:* Italian Hnr Soc; Class lubs; AATSP, AATI 1971-.

CHMIDT, ROBERT H., Assistant Principal; *b:* Camden, NJ; *m:* cCartney; *c:* Caitlyn, Robert Jr., Jennifer; *ed:* Rowan Coll (MA) in 1994; EDD Pgm Rutgers Univ; *cr:* Pennsauken HS Tchr Oakcrest HS Tchr 1990-94; Hammonton Pub Schls Supv Pitman MS Asst Prin 1995-; *ai:* NASSP 1994-; NJPSA 1994-, l; Phi Delta Kappa 1993-, Treas; *office:* Pitman MS 138 E. Holly an NJ 08071*

MITH, FRANCES PURYEAR, Mathematics Teacher; *b:* on, DC; *m:* David E.; *c:* Donna Tkach, Guy; *ed:* Towson Univ 1965; 30 Hrs Math; *cr:* Glenridge Jr HS Math Tchr 1981-83; Heights HS Math Tchr 1984; Bowie HS Math Tchr 1985-; *ai:* IT'S on; AP Calculus Tchr; NEA, PGCES 1981-; *office:* Bowie HS nnapolis Rd Bowie MD 20715

MITH, KATHRYN KORET, Latin & English Teacher; *b:* d, OH; *m:* Martin; *ed:* OH St Univ (BA) Eng Lit; Post Degree Cert Eng, Hebrew & Latin; *cr:* Columbus Pub Schls Latin, Eng Tchr : NEA 1984-; Tchr of Yr Awd 1993; *office:* Eastmoor HS 417 S Ave Columbus OH 43213

MITH, MARILYN MC NEAR, Special Education Teacher; *b:* dale, MO; *m:* Milton; *c:* Marlisa, Matthew; *ed:* AR St Univ (BSE) Elem Ed 1979; Univ of the Dist of Columbia (MA) Adult Ed, Supervision 1986; Working Toward Sign Lang Cert; 30 Post Grad *cr:* Wynne Intermediate Schl Tchr 1979-81; Leonardtown HS Tchr DC Dept of Corrections Tchr 1984-86; Gwynn Park HS Tchr Kettering MS Admin 1995-; *ai:* Chrldr Coach; Tutor; Sign Lang oung Marine Pgm, Vol Mentor; NEA, MSTA, CEC 1986-; ASCD; omens Chrstn Cncl 1994-; Womens Dept Wkshp Comm; Womens ering Comm Mem; *home:* 3171 Chester Grove Rd Upper Marlboro 74*

MITH, PAULA LEVENDORF, English Teacher; *b:* Steubenville, arry S.; *ed:* OH St Univ (BS) Eng Ed 1985; MS Equival Work Eng lantation HS Eng Tchr 1985-89; Santa Fe Comm Coll Eng Tchr Bethesda Chevy Chase HS Eng Tchr 1993-95; Thomas S. Wootton Tchr 1995-; *ai:* Forensic Team Coach; Tech Prep Eng Consultant; ontgomery Cty Educ Assoc 1995-; *office:* Thomas S Wootton HS otton Pkwy Rockville MD 20850*

TEIN, CAROL ROBERTA, English Teacher; *b:* Brooklyn, NY; y City St Coll (MA) Ed 1963; NY Univ (MA) Human Relations Rahway Elem Schl 6th Grd Tchr 1960-61; Rahway HS Eng & Soc r 1962-63; Thomas Jefferson Jr HS Rdng Tchr 1963-82; Teaneck Tchr 1982-; *ai:* Multicultural Comm; Possibilities; NEA 1960-, rs; NJEA, BCEA 1960-; TTEA 1963-, Pres, Grievance Chprsn; 982-; *office:* Teaneck HS 100 Elizabeth Ave Teaneck NJ 07666

TEIN, DONALD ROBERT, Mathematics Teacher & Coord; *b:* , NY; *m:* Diane Rochelle Klosner; *c:* Andrew, Marissa; *ed:* St NY at Oswego (BA) Scndry Ed 1973, (MS) Scndry Ed 1977; *cr:* le-De Witt MS Math Tchr 1974-77; Bellmore-Merrick Cntrl Schl h Tchr 1977-82; Westhampton Beach HS Math Tchr 1982-; *ai:* entathlon, Mathletes Teams Coach; NYSUT 1973-; SCMTA ICTM 1982-; Island Estates Civic Assn 1987-, Treas; *office:* pton Beach HS Lilac Rd Westhampton Beach NY 11978*

TEIN, JACK LEON, High School Art Teacher; *b:* Brooklyn, NY; e M.; *c:* Richard, Bonnie; *ed:* Adelphi Univ (MS) Art Ed 1965; Credit Hrs; *cr:* Elmont Memorial HS 30 Yrs; *ai:* Class of 1997; Art Club; NEA 1965-; *office:* Elmont Memorial HS 555 Ridge Rd NY 11366

TEIN, JAN J., Director of Guidance; *b:* Bronx, NY; *m:* Robert; *c:* , Lisa; *ed:* St Univ of NY at Buffalo (BS) Home Ec Ed 1970; C W (MSPD) Guidance & Counseling 1976, (PD) Ed Admin 1986; *cr:* mpstead HS Home Ec Tchr 1970-74; Half Hollow Hills HS Cnslr Herricks Schls Dir of Guidance 1988-; *ai:* NYSCA Summer Inst NACAC, NYCA, ACA 1988-; NCA 1988-, Sec, 2 Honorable Exemplary Guidance Prgms; Roslyn Estates Civic Assn 1982-, Selected for WSCA Schlpsp Awd By Julie Pulerurtz for How My elped Me Essay; *office:* Herricks HS 100 Shelter Rock Rd New k NY 11040

TEIN, JANE LOVI, English Teacher; *b:* Manhattan, NY; *m:* *ed:* Fairleigh Dickinson Univ (BA) Eng Ed 1972; Rutgers Univ ng Ed 1977; *cr:* Franklin Twp HS Eng Tchr 1973-86; Freehold Reg m Eng Tchr 1986-; *ai:* NEA, NJEA 1973-; NCTE 1992-; NJCTE *ffice:* Marlboro HS 95 N Main St Marlboro NJ 07746

TEIN, LARRY M., Language Arts Dept Chprsn; *b:* Trenton, NJ; Salkin; *c:* Jay; *ed:* Syracuse Univ (BA) Eng 1970, (MS) Eng Ed tgers Univ (EDD) Creative Arts Ed 1985; *cr:* Matawan Regnl HS r 1974-, Lang Arts Dept Chprsn 1989-; *ai:* Tennis, Track Coach; JEA 1974-; Kappa Delta Pi 1985-; ACBL; *office:* Matawan HS Atlantic Ave Matawan NJ 07747*

TEIN, SHOSHANA, Adjunct Assistant Professor; *b:* Tel Aviv, NY Univ (BS) Ed & Hebrew Culture 1970, (MA) Phil, Sociology hn Jay Coll of Crim Just (MA) Criminal Justice 1989; Grad Univ sm in Los Angeles Tchrs Diploma; *cr:* John Jay Coll of Crim srch Asst 1971-76; Hudson Cty Comm Coll Adj Asst Prof 1981-; ept of Probation Branch Chief 1983-; *ai:* Annual Winner of e Suggestion Awd for 1988-89 NYC Dept of Probation; *office:* County Community Coll 25 Journal Sq Jersey City NJ 07306*

TEIN, STEPHEN CRAIG, Eighth Grade Math Teacher; *b:* , NY; *m:* Beth; *ed:* Brooklyn Coll (BA) Ec 1986; Adelphi Univ ec Ed 1994; *cr:* Lever Bros Co Accountant 1980-83; Metropolitan Salesman 1983-86; JHS 217 Math Tchr 1986-; *ai:* Math Team ports; Bowling; Bsktbl; UFT 1986-, Tchr; *office:* JHS 217 Q 85-05 Briarwood NY 11435*

TEIN, VICKI LYN, Classroom Teacher; *b:* Columbus, OH; *ed:* Cincinnati (BS) Elem Ed 1982; *cr:* Roosevelt Elem Schl 4th-6th h Tchr 1985-90; Eastwood Paideia Schl 4th-6th Grd Math Tchr : OH Cncl of Tchrs of Math, Greater Cincinnati Cncl of Tchrs of Math 1991-; Outstanding Tchr of Yr Cincinnati Pub Schls 1988; Inclusion Wkshp; *office:* Eastwood Paideia Schl 5030 Duck Creek Rd Cincinnati OH 45227

GOLDSTONE, BETTE PERILSTEIN, Professor; *b:* Philadelphia, PA; *m:* Peter Jay; *c:* Avra Sharon, Rebecca Hannah; *ed:* Univ of PA (BA) Art His 1969; Boston Univ (MED) Elem Ed 1972; Temple Univ (EDD) Elem Eng 1982; *cr:* Phila Get Set Ctrs Tchr 1969-70; Solomon Schechter Day Schl 3rd Grd Tchr 1971-73; Temple Univ Instr 1977; Beaver Coll Prof 1979-; *ai:* Coord Lang Arts, Art Ed, Schl Lib Cert Prgms; Adv Undergraduate, Grad Stdnts; Spon Children's Lit Tchng Awd; Lecture Series Childrens Book Authors, Illustrators; NCTE 1985-; IRA 1986-; PCRRT 1987-; Articles Prof Journals; Books Pub: Lessons to be Learned, Word Wizards, Image Makers; St, Local Grants; Presenter Natl, Regnl Conf; Lindbach Awd Excl Tchng; *office:* Beaver Coll 450 S Easton Rd Glenside PA 19038

GOLD-TOULSON, DIANE WEHNER, Music Teacher; *b:* Rochester, NY; *m:* Smith Catlin Toulson III; *c:* Barbara, Julia, Daniel; *ed:* Univ of Rochester Eastmar Schl of Music (BMus) Flute, Music Ed 1962; Columbia Univ Tchrs Coll (MA) Music 1965; *cr:* Music Acad Flute Instr, Prof 1965-; Juniata Coll Flute Instr, Prof 1970-; Buehnell Univ Flute Instr, Prof 1978-; Lehigh Univ Flute Instr, Prof 1991-93; York Coll Flute Instr, Prof 1990-; *ai:* Orange Arts Festival Concerts; Coord Sr Recital; Natl Flute Assn 1970-, Comm Coord; League of Women Composer 1980-; Sigma Alpha Iota 1962-; Prin Flute of Symphony in PA; Altoona, York, Nittany Vly Symphony; Artistic Dir of Easterly Chamber Players; Recordings with Huntingdon Trio, Alard String Quartet; Flute Talk Magazine New Music Reviewer; *office:* The Music Acad 519 W College Ave State College PA 16801

GOLIA, MICHAEL ANTHONY, English Teacher; *b:* McKees Rocks, PA; *m:* Shawn Marie Cotter; *c:* Elizabeth, Kristen, Carissa; *ed:* Davis & Elkins Coll (BA) Comphrensive Eng 1970; Bowling Green Univ (MA) Eng 1972; Attnd PA St Univ, Allegheny Intermediate Unit; *cr:* Altoona Area HS Eng Tchr 1971-83; PA St Univ Part-Time Eng Tchr 1980-83; South Park HS Eng Tchr 1983-; *ai:* Dist Advy & Portfolio Comms; NEA, PSEA & SPEA Collective Bargaining Team; Grad Assistantship Bowling Green Univ; *office:* South Park HS 2178 Ridge Rd Library PA 15129

GOLISH, LARRY G., Mathematics Teacher; *b:* Windber, PA; *m:* Donna T.; *c:* Brad, Cara, Krista; *ed:* Univ of Pittsburgh (BS) Scndry Ed, Math 1974; Attnd Univ of Pittsburgh, Penn St Univ; *cr:* Richland Schl Dist Math Instr 1974-; *ai:* NEA, PSEA 1974-; Richland Ed Assn 1974-, Former Pres, Bldg Rep; Grad Magna Cum Laude Univ of Pittsburgh; *office:* Richland Schl Dist 1740 Highfield St Johnstown PA 15904

GOLLA, WILLIAM J., Biology Teacher; *b:* Pittsburgh, PA; *m:* Pamela Santelli; *c:* Scott, Mark, Bill; *ed:* Edinboro Univ (BS) Bio & Ed 1964; Univ of Pittsburgh (MED) Bio & Ed 1965; Attnd Brandeis Univ, Univ of CA at Berkley, Univ of NY at Potsdam, OH St, Rio Grande Coll; *cr:* Baldwin-Whitehall Schls Sci Tchr 1965; Penn Hills Schl Dist Bio Tchr 1965-; *ai:* Wrestling Coach; NEA, PSEA, PHEA 1965-, Bldg Rep; BSA, Scout Master; Rails to Trails Assn 1994-; West PA Conservancy 1980-; *office:* Penn Hills HS 12200 Garland Dr Pittsburgh PA 15235

GOLLUSCIO, GENE, 6th Grd Eng & Lit Tchr; *b:* Bronx, NY; *m:* Eileen Dalton; *c:* Jennifer, Scott; *ed:* St John's Univ (BS) Elem Ed 1969, (MS) Elem Ed 1974; *cr:* Washington St Schl 5th Grd Tchr 1969-73; California Ave Schl 6th Grd Tchr 1973-81; Mt Laurel Schls 6th Grd Tchr 1981-; *ai:* Drama Club 17 Yrs; Green Thumb Club 8 Yrs; NY St Ed Assn, NEA 1969-; NJEA, BCEA 1981-; Medford Lakes Colony Club 1982-; St John Neumann Choir 1988-; Tanglewood Singers, Metropolitan Opera Guild 1974-; Dutton Voice, Amato Opera Voice Schlsps; NJ Governors Tchr of Yr Awd 1986; *office:* Mt Laurel Hartford Schl Hartford Rd Mount Laurel NJ 08054*

GOLOGORSKY, EDYTHE E., Second Grade Teacher; *b:* Jersey City, NJ; *m:* Gary; *c:* Justin, Keith; *ed:* Kent St Univ (BA) Early Chldhd 1972; *cr:* WNY Schl System 1st Grd Tchr 1972-78, Kndgtn Tchr 1983-84, Title Tchr 1984-85, 2nd Grd Tchr 1985-; *ai:* Schl Improvement Team; After Schl Tutorial Prgm; NJEA 1972-; *office:* Pub Schl #1 62nd & Polk St West New York NJ 07093*

GOLOSKI, PETER GREGORY, Instrumental Music Teacher; *b:* Syracuse, NY; *m:* Linda A. Gural; *c:* Amy, Julie, William; *ed:* SUNY at Potsdam (BME) Music Ed 1972; *cr:* St Lawrence Cntrl Schl Instrumental Music Tchr 1972-85; Romulus Cntrl Schl Instrumental Music 1985-; *ai:* Jazz Ensemble; Marching Band; Romulus Fac Assn 1985-, Pres 1995-; *office:* Romulus Central Schl Main St Romulus NY 14541

GOLOWENSKI, LIZ, Science Teacher; *b:* Lubbock, TX; *m:* David J.; *c:* Matthew, Alan; *ed:* OH Univ (BS) Ed 1977; Ashland Univ (MS) Supervision 1991; OH St Univ Bus, Fin; *cr:* Lorain Cath HS Chem, Physics 1977-79; Lorain City Schls Bio, Anatomy 1979-89; Olentangy HS Adv Phys Sci 1989-; *ai:* Class Adv 4 Yrs; NEA, OEA 1979-, Treas; NSTA 1977-; Martha Holden Jennings Scholar 1979; *office:* Olentangy HS 675 Lewis Center Rd Lewis Center OH 43035*

GOLUBIESKI, MARY WILLARD, Art Teacher; *b:* Bridgeport, CT; *m:* John; *c:* John C., Christopher S.; *ed:* Caldwell Coll (BA) Fine Art 1971, (BFA) Graphic Arts 1984; Miami Univ (MA) Art Ed 1988; 60 Addl Semester Hrs Post Grad Stud OH Univ, Univ of Cincinnati, Xavier Univ; Getty Inst for Advancement of Arts; OH Arts Cncl Media Inst; Evening for Edctrs at Cincinnati Art Museum, Tchr Tuesdays at Contemporary Arts Ctr; *cr:* Archdiocese of Newark Art Tchr 1971-72; Kinnelon Pub Schls Art Tchr 1983-86; Miami Univ Schl of Fine Arts Grad Tchng Asst 1987-88; Rdng Comm Schls Hilltop Schl Art Tchr 1988-89; Indian Hill Exempted Village Schls Art Tchr 1989-; *ai:* Instrl Ldr Dept of Fine Arts; Arts Dept Chprsn; Regnl Dir OH Govenors Art Exhibition; Photography Club Adv; Regnl Dir Southwest OH Art Ed Assn; OH Art Ed Assn 1988-, Regnl Dir 1996-98, Outstdng Art Tchr 1993, Governmental Relations Liason, OAEA Exec Bd; Natl Art Ed Assn 1988-; OH Ed Assn, NEA 1988-; Cincinnati Art Museum, Contemporary Arts Ctr 1988-; Outstdng Art Tchr Awd Southwest OH Art Ed Assn; Photography, Art Awds Regnl & Local Shows Montgomery Photo Show, Middletown Art Show 1988-90, 1992-95; Solo Art Shows Caldwell Coll 1984, Kinnelon Pub Lib 1985, Miami Univ, Hiestand Gallery 1988-, Sycamore Pub Lib 1988; *office:* Indian Hill HS 6845 Drake Rd Cincinnati OH 45243

GOLUBJATNIKOV, LISA SALERNO, English Teacher; *b:* Jacksonville, FL; *m:* Ken; *ed:* St John Fisher Coll (BA) Eng 1991; 18 Credits Gen Scndry Ed Nazareth Coll of Rochester; *cr:* Wayne Cntrl Schl Dist 9-12 Grd Eng Tchr 1992-; *ai:* Frosh Class Adv; Bldg Planning, Schl Crisis Response Teams; NEA, Wayne Tchrs Assn 1992-; NCTE 1990-; *office:* Wayne Central H S 6200 Ontario Center Rd Ontario Center NY 14520*

GOMBERT, BARBARA, ESL Teacher; *b:* Rockville Center, NY; *ed:* Adelphi Univ (BA) Educ, Eng, Ger 1980; Stony Brook Univ (BA) TESOL, Ger 1981; 100 Credits Toward Doctorate in TESOL; *cr:* Stony Brook Univ ESL TChr 1981; Three Village Schl Dist Night Schl ESL Tchr 1981; Stony Brook Univ Summer EOP, ESL Tchr 1982-84, EOP-Rdng Tchr 1982; Elmont HS ESL Tchr 1986-; *ai:* Foreign Lang Club, Intnl Stu Org Adv; Agenda Comm; NEA 1986-; Intnl TESOL 1980-82, 1995-; NYS TESOL 1980-82, 1986-87, 1995-; NCSS 1995-; *office:* Elmont Meml HS 555 Ridge Rd Elmont NY 11003*

GOMES, JOEL J., Earth Science Teacher; *b:* Danbury, CT; *ed:* Western CT St Univ (BA) Earth Sci, Ed 1989; Central CT St Univ 12 Credit Hrs Towards MS; *cr:* Talcott Mt Sci Ctr Astronomer 1992; Avon HS Tchr 1992-; *ai:* Astronomy Club, JETS Adv; Boys Tennis Team Asst Coach; CESTA 1992-, Ed; NEA, CSTA 1992-; *office:* Avon HS 510 W Avon Rd Avon CT 06001*

GOMES, LUIS AUGUSTO, Portuguese Teacher; *b:* Horta Fayal Azores, Portugal; *m:* Almeirinda Pereira daSilva; *c:* Almerinda P. DaSilva, Isabel M.; *ed:* Escola Magisterio Da Horta (BA) Elem Ed 1952; Boston St Coll (BA) Biling; *cr:* Lowell Pub Schls Biling Tchr 1972-75; Lowell HS Biling, Portuguese Tchr 1975-; *ai:* Portuguese Chptr Club Adv; *office:* Lowell HS 50 Fr Morrissette Blvd Lowell MA 01852

GOMEZ, SUSAN L., Computer Education Teacher; *b:* Philadelphia, PA; *m:* George L.; *ed:* Boston St Coll (MS) Career Ed 1980; 15 Credit Hrs Lesley Coll Cmptr Ed 1993; 15 Credit Hrs Lowell Inst Schl Cmptr Tech 1994-95; *cr:* Jeremiah Burke HS Bus Ed Tchr 1969-76; Boston Bus Schl Bus Ed Tchr 1977-82; Mario Umana Tech HS Bus Ed Tchr 1982-89; Boston HS Cmptr Ed Tchr 1989-; *ai:* Boston Tchrs Union 1969-; MA Fed of Tchrs 1969-; Habitat for Humanity 1995-; Boston Bus Alumni Assn 1977-90; Temple Univ of Alumni Assn, Riber Coll Alumni Assn 1980-; *office:* Boston HS 152 Arlington St Boston MA 02116

GOMEZ-CORTES VILLALO, MARIA ELENA, High School Spanish Teacher; *b:* Havana, Cuba; *m:* Jose M.; *c:* Alicia, Sofia, Felipe, Andres, Lucia; *ed:* Pontificia Univ Catolica (BAEd) Span & Lit 1970; Univ of Cincinnati (MA) Romance Langs 1976; Attnd Chestnut Hill Coll, Univ de Villanueva; Coll of Mt St Joseph Other Credit Hrs in Ed; *cr:* Colegio de Las Visulinas Rel Tchr 1967-68; Cath Missions Missionary & Catechist 1969-70; Mt Campus Schl Span Tchr 1986-87; McAuley HS Span & Fr Tchr 1986-; Xavier Univ Span Tchr 1989-91, Xavier HS Span Tchr 1990; *ai:* Span Club Helper; Land Lab Comm; Sigma Delta Pi 1975-, Span Scholars; Chestnut Hill Coll Deans List 1962; Univ of Cincinnati Tchng Assistantship While Studying for MS 1972-76.

GONDAL, CAROLE ANN DEE, Fifth Grade Teacher; *b:* Pottstown, PA; *ed:* Bloomsburg Univ (BS) Spec Ed 1974; West Chester Univ (MED) Elem Ed 1978; Millersville Univ Spec Ed; Penn St, St. Joseph's Univs Supervisory Cert, Credits; *cr:* Summerville Schl Dist Educatable M R 1974-75; Pottstown Schl Dist Educatable Mentally Retarded 1975-77, Basic Skills 1977-79, Learning Disabilities 1979-81, Second Grd Tchr 1981-82, Scndry Socially, Emotionally Disturbed 1982-87, Second Grd Tchr 1986-87, Fourth Grd Tchr 1987-88, Third Grd Tchr 1988-92, Fifth Grd Tchr 1992-; *ai:* West Chester, Kutztown Univs, Cabrini Coll Cooperating Tchr of Stu Tchrs; Track Official; Mentor for New Tchrs; Elem, Spec Ed Tutor Homebound Stdnts; Head Tchr Alternative Ed Prgm; AFT 1996-; *home:* 722 Center St Stowe PA 19464

GONDEK, BARBARA ANN (SMITH), Lang Arts Curr Coord & Teacher; *b:* Dallas, TX; *m:* Ronald James; *ed:* Mary Hardin-Baylor Coll (BA) Eng, His 1970; Rivier Coll (MED) Learning Disabilities 1983, (MED) Schl Admin 1985; *cr:* Mc Kelvie MS Classroom Tchr 1971-83, Lang Arts Curr Coord 1983-; *ai:* Stu Tchrs Coord; News Reporters Adv; Boys Bsktbl, Bsbl Scorekeeper; Annual Spelling Bee, Prize Speaking Contest Coord; Bedford Ed Assn, NH-Nea 1972-, Sec, Treas, VP; ASCD 1981-; NATE, NELMS 1980-; IRA 1993-; Souhegan Vly Chorus 1986-, Pub Relations Chair, Featured Soloist; Plymouth St Coll 1992-, Team Facilitator, Masters Ed Prgm Planning Commm; New England Assn Schls & Colls Eval Team Mem 4 Times; Numerous Articles Pub; New England MS League Wkshp, Conf Presenter 3 Times; *office:* Mc Kelvie MS 108 Liberty Hill Rd Bedford NH 03110

GONDREE, LILLIAN LEWANDOWSKI, Science Teacher & Chairperson; *b:* Buffalo, NY; *m:* Howard F.; *c:* Kathryn Rand, Eric D., Mark A.; *ed:* SUNY Coll at Buffalo (BS) Sci Ed 1967, (MS) Sci Ed 1970; Post Grad Work Hlth Ed Cert 1981; *cr:* Hoover Jr HS Tchr 1967-75; Franklin MS Tchr 1977-84; Kenmore West HS Tchr 1984-86; Hoover MS Tchr, Sci Chprsn 1986-; SUNY Coll Adjunct Prof Sci Ed 1990; *ai:* Schl Contact WNY Sci Congress; Schl Paper Recycling Prgm, Hoover Elem Schl Read to Me Partnership Coord; Acquired Clear Thinking Prgm Design Team; Gifted, Talented Prgm Comm; NSTA, NEA, NYSUTA, KTA 1967-; BSA, Merit Badge Cnslr 1986-; PTA Tchr of Yr 1993; Presenter Cornell Univ NYS Inst for Mid Level Ed 1990; Lawrence Hall of Sci SEPUP Field Test Participant 1994-95; Cooperating Tchr Canisus Coll, SUNY; Author for Magazine 1988, 1996; *office:* Herbert Hoover MS 249 Thorncliff Rd Kenmore NY 14223

GONNERMAN, MADELYN JONES, Latin & French Teacher; *b:* Savannah, GA; *c:* Michael, Laura, Christopher (dec), Kathryn; *ed:* Univ of MO at Columbia (BA) Fr, Eng 1965, (MA) Fr 1968, (PHD) Romance Lang, Lit 1985; Boston Univ Latin Tchng Cert; Classical Summer Schl Amer Acad of Rome; *cr:* Univ of MO at Columbia Asst Eng Instr 1965-67; Moberly HS Fr, Eng Tchr 1968-70; Univ of MO at Columbia Fr Grad Fellow 1970-72; Northern HS Eng Tchr 1973-75; Bellingham Meml Jr Sr HS Lat, Fr Tchr 1976-79; Boston Univ Fr Lecturer 1977-79; Brookline HS Latin, Fr Tchr 1979-; *ai:* Latin Club Adv; St Ofcr MA Jr Classical LeagueSpon; Frgn Lang Dept Proficiency Testing Co-Chair; Frgn Lang, Spec Ed Collaboration on Inclusion; Classical Assn of New England 1979-, NECTFL Del; Northeast Conf Tchng of FL 1987-, Advy Cncl; Modern Lang Assn, NEA 1970-; Phi Beta Kappa 1965-; United Parish of Auburndale 1987-; Newton Historical Soc 1986-, Dir 1987-90; Natl Endowment for Hum Summer Seminar Participant; Cncl Basic Ed Ind Stud Flwshp; Tchr as Curr Dev Awd; Articles Pub; *office:* Brookline HS 115 Greenough St Brookline MA 02146*

GONNEVILLE, MICHAEL ANDRE, PE Tchr & Girls Soccer Coach; *b:* New Bedford, MA; *m:* Nancy Pash; *c:* Whitney, Nicholas; *ed:* Norwich Univ (BS) PE 1977, (MED) PE 1978; Natl Soccer Coaches Assn Diploma 1988; *cr:* Northfield Elem & HS Tchr & Coach 1978-; *ai:* Girls HS Soccer Coach; Phys Fitness Club; Jump Rope Team; Outing Club; IM; AAHPERD 1978-, VT PE Tchr of the Yr 1986; NSCAA 1978-, VT COY (4 Times), NE COY (3 Times), Natl COY 1995; Northfield Yth Soccer Assoc 1980-, Dir; Northfield Recreation Bd 1991-; *office:* Northfield Comiskey Schl Garvey Hill Northfield VT 05663*

GONOT, CATHY LYNN (FRANKE), 4th Grade Teacher; *b:* Martins Ferry, OH; *m:* George W.; *c:* Meredith, Adam; *ed:* Ohio Univ (BA)Elem Ed 1972; Post Grad Hrs Univ of Dayton; *cr:* Martins Ferry City Schls MS Tchr 10 Yrs, Elem Schl Tchr 12 Yrs; *ai:* VP Band Parents; Cath Doctrine Tchr; MFEA, OEA, NEA 1972-; Cath Womens Club 1968-; Ftbl Moms, Bsktbl Moms 1995-; Hilltop PTO 1972-; *home:* RR 1 Adena OH 43901

GONSON, DOROTHY ROSE, English Teacher; *b:* Chicago, IL; *m:* S. Donald; *c:* Julia, Claudia; *ed:* Bannard Coll (BA) Eng 1960; Harvard Univ (AMT) Eng 1962; 30 Credit Hrs; *cr:* Newton South HS Eng Tchr 1963-; *ai:* Lit Magazine; Grader of ETS & SAT II; Table Ldr of ETS Eng AP Exam; NEA; Cambridge Ctr for Adult Ed 30 Yrs; *office:* Newton South HS 140 Brandeis Rd Newton Center MA 02159

GONTARUK, RITA PAPA, Jr High Teacher; *b:* Hubbard, OH; *c:* William F., Barbara, Anthony, Stacie, David; *ed:* Youngstown St Univ (BSEd) Elem Ed 1982; *cr:* St Patrick Schl 4th Grd Tchr 1959-61, 3rd Grd Tchr 1972-74, 3rd Grd & Jr High Tchr 1979-; *ai:* Bldrs Club & Chrldr Advs; Consultative Bd Mem; Parish Cncl Comm Chprsn; AIB Tchr-Adult Ed; Girl Scout Ldr; Sftbl Coach; Support Tchr 1992-93; Stu Cncl Adv 1995-96;

NEOTA 1979-; YDCT 1990; Kiwanis 1987-,Youth Chprsn; Tchr of the Yr 1990 & 1993; *home:* 28 Sciota Ave Boardman OH 44512

GONZALES, BARBARA DEAR, HS Social Studies Teacher; *b:* San Antonio, TX; *m:* Rex; *c:* Jennifer; *ed:* Univ of TX at Austin (BSEd) His, Govt 1970; Mid Schl & HS Trng Acad; *cr:* Pat M. Neff Jr HS Soc Stud Tchr 1970-71; William P. Hobby MS Soc Stud Tchr 1971-75; Ramstein Elem Schl 6th Grd Tchr 1981-82; Ramstein Jr HS Soc Stud Tchr 1982-95; Ramstein HS Soc Stud Tchr 1995-; *ai:* Soc Stud Dept Chprsn 1982-95; Frosh Class Co-Spon 1993-94; Advy 1993-94, Natl Geog Bee Schl 1988-95, Stu Recognition Prgm 1990-95, Stu Honor Card 1990-95 Coords; Natl Cncl for Geographic Ed 1988-; NCSS 1996; *office:* Ramstein HS 86 SPTG/CCSH-R Unit 3240 Box 445 APO AE 09094

GONZALEZ, APRIL LEE, English Teacher; *b:* Somerville, NJ; *m:* Joe I.; *c:* Christian, Justin, Cody; *ed:* Montclair St Univ (BA) Eng, Psych 1987; AP Eng Course; HSPT Rdng, Regnl Curr Svcs Unit 2 Credits; Microsoftworks II Class 1 Inservice Credit; *cr:* South Brunswick Comm Ed SAT Tutor 1988-89, SAT Tchr 1990; South Brunswick HS Eng Tchr 1987-88, 1990-; *ai:* Lit Magazine Adv 1991-95; Soph Assessment Comm 1992; Frosh Class Co-Adv 1987-88; NJEA 1987-; NCTE 1987-88; Hamilton Sq Presbyn Church 1993; Geraldine R. Dodge Fnd Writing, Discussion Group; Article Pub; *office:* S Brunswick HS PO Box 183 Major Rd Monmouth Junction NJ 08852

GONZALEZ, JOHANNA PUMA, English Teacher; *b:* Newark, NJ; *m:* James; *c:* Jason, Jessica; *ed:* Wm Paterson Coll (BA) Eng & Soc Stud 1963; Attnd Seton Hall Univ at South Orange, InterAmerican Univ at San German; *cr:* Edison HS Eng Tchr & Yrbk Adv 1963-68, 1969-71; IAU Campus Schl Eng & Soc Stud Tchr & Yrbk Adv 1968-69; Toms River HS East Eng Tchr & Yrbk Adv 1979-; *ai:* Yrbk Adv; Culture Club Adv; NEA; NJEA; NCTE; Toms River East Tchr of the Yr 1988-89; *office:* Toms River HS East Raider Way Toms River NJ 08753*

GONZALEZ, LYDIA LIZZETTE, Spanish Teacher; *b:* Newark, NJ; *m:* Daniel; *ed:* Lehigh Comm Coll (AA) Ed 1989; Kutztown Univ (BS) Sec Ed 1992; LaSalle Univ MA Biling, Bicultural Stud Grad Schl; *cr:* Biling Mid Magnet ESOL Tchr 1993; Strawberry Mansion HS Span Tchr 1993-; *ai:* Chrldng Coach; Family Group Adv; AFT 1993-; MLAP 1994-; *office:* Strawberry Mansion HS 32nd & Ridge Ave Philadelphia PA 19132

GONZALEZ, VIRGINIA TANIS, Spanish Teacher; *b:* Paterson, NJ; *m:* Jose L.; *c:* Joseph L.; *ed:* Douglass Coll (BA) Span 1966; Rutgers Univ (MA) Span 1973; Wm Paterson Coll Cert; *cr:* Wm. Paterson Coll Span Adj Prof 1988-89; Hawthorne HS Span Tchr 1989-; *ai:* Span Hnr Soc, Span Club Adv; NEA, NJEA, PCEA, HTA, AATSP 1989-; FLENJ 1990-; BSA Mothers Aux 1987-, Pres; Gealdine Dodge Flwshp; Diploma de Espanol Como Lengua Extranjera Superior from Span Govt; *office:* Hawthorne HS Parmelee Ave Hawthorne NJ 07506

GONZALEZ, ZOE M., English Teacher; *b:* Habana, Cuba; *ed:* Saint Peters Coll (BA) Eng 1980; Ruters Univ Grad Schl of Ed (EDM) 1985; *cr:* Vroom Learning Ctr Eng Tchr 1985-; *ai:* NEA, NJEA, HCEA, BTA 1985-; Governors Awd for Excl in Tchng 1996; Hudson Cty Tchr Recognition Awd 1995-96; Book Publication A Story from Widg 1990; *office:* Vroom Learning Ctr 18 W 26th St Bayonne NJ 07002

GONZALEZ-HABES, DOLORES, English & Biling Ed Teacher; *b:* Santurce, PR; *m:* John D. Habes; *c:* Juan Daniel III; *ed:* Univ of PR (BA) Eng, Ed 1975; Nazareth Coll (MS) Ed 1990; *cr:* Monroe HS Biling Ed, Eng Tchr 1985-88; East HS Biling Ed, Eng Tchr 1988-; *ai:* Jr Class Adv; Org of Latin Amer Stdnts Dance Co-Adv; Rochester's Tchrs Assn 1988-; NY St Assn of Biling Edctrs 1991-; Rochester Civil Svc Commission 1993-, Commissioner; Rochester Biling Ed Cncl 1995-, VP; NY Cncl for the Hum, Colgate Univ Grant to Participate Tchrs Inst 1992; Cert of Recogntion Rochester City Schl Dist NESH Prgm Mentor; *office:* East HS 1801 Main St E Rochester NY 14605*

GONZI, BARBARA MC CURDY, Tchr of Learning Disabilities; *b:* Akron, OH; *m:* Richard S.; *c:* Stephanie, Julieann, Jacqueline, Nicholas, Patricia; *ed:* Kent St Univ (BS) Elem Ed 1967, (MED) Spec Ed, Learning & Behavior Disorders 1976; *cr:* Immaculate Heart of Mary Schl Fourth Grd Tchr 1967-68; Nordonia Local Schls First Grd Tchr 1968-69; Immaculate Heart of Mary Schl Fourth Grd Tchr 1969-71; Cuyahoga Falls Schls Learning Disability Tutor 1971-74; Magadore Local Schls Learning Disability Teacher 1974-; *ai:* Lang Arts Comm; Mogadore Ed Assn 1974-, Treas 1991-93; St Vincent St Mary Parent Club 1994-, Treas 1995-; CEC Dr. Ruth B. Clayton Outstdng Edctr Awd 1987; *office:* O. H. Somers Schl 3600 Herbert St Mogadore OH 44260*

GOOCH, CHERYL RENEE, Asst Prof of Communication; *b:* Waterbury, CT; *ed:* Howard Univ (BA) Pol Sci 1984; Northwestern Univ (MS) Jrnlsm 1986; FL St Univ (PHD) Mass Comm 1993; *cr:* AL St Univ Chprsn, Asst Prof Comm Media 1987-89, 1992-95; Univ of ND Assoc Prof of Comm 1995-96; Rutgers Univ Asst Prof of Comm 1996-; *ai:* Assn for Ed in Jrnlsm & Mass Comm; Intnl Comm Assoc; AAUP; Natl Pol Congress of Black Women; Freedom Forum Jrnlsm Profs Publishing Grant; Articles Pub; *office:* Rutgers Univ 4 Huntington St New Brunswick NJ 08901

GOOD, C. EDWARD, Math Department Head; *b:* Presque Isle, ME; *m:* Rosemary; *c:* Andrew, Michael, Sally Ann Neal, Robert; *ed:* Brandeis Univ (BA) Ec 1960; Univ of New Brunswick (MED) Ed 1964; Univ of NH (MST) Math 1970; *cr:* Saint John Pub HS His & Math 1960-65; Lexington Pub Schls Math 1965-; *ai:* Comp Club Adv; Schedule & HS Comm; Curr Cabinet; NCTM 1965-; Lex Ed Assn 1965-; Bd of Dirs of Credit Union 1975-; 1989-, Sec; Multimedia Ed & Sabbatical Design Team; Shell Fellow; NSF Grant for Grad Stud; Paper Presented at SALT; *office:* Lexington HS 251 Waltham St Lexington MA 02173*

GOOD, PETER J.,JR., Math Teacher; *b:* Orange, NJ; *c:* Jennifer, Rebecca, Peter; *ed:* Univ of DE (BS) PE 1978; Wilimington Coll (MS) Human Resource Mngmt 1988; *cr:* Red Clay Schl Dist PE, Hlth Tchr 1979-82; St Marks HS Math Tchr, Coach 1982-; *ai:* Asst Var Ftbl Coach; Frosh Bsbl Coach; DIFCA 1982-; NCEA 1990-; *office:* St Marks School Pike Creek Rd Wilmington DE 19808

GOOD, VIVIAN D.(YE), English & Theater Teacher; *b:* Somerset, PA; *c:* Mark, Beth; *ed:* IN Univ of PA (BS) Eng, Speech 1960; Villanova Univ (MA) Theater 1983; Syracuse Univ 3 Credit Hrs; West Chester Univ 15 Credit Hrs; PA St Univ, Chestnut Hill Coll Post Grad Hrs; *cr:* Phoenixville Schl Dist Tchr 1960-63; Coatsville Area Schl Dist Tchr 1971; Phoenixville Area Schl Dist Tchr 1971-; Fox & Lazo Real Estate Sales Assoc 1986; Deleware Comm Coll Adjunct Instr 1990; *ai:* Thespian Club Adv; NEA, PSEA 1971-; Delta Kappa Gamma 1990-.*

GOODALE, ELIZABETH HORIGAN, Social Studies Teacher; *b:* Utica, NY; *m:* John G.; *c:* John Cooper, Kellie Cooper; *ed:* Utica Coll (BA) His 1964; Syracuse Univ (MS) Soc Stud 1973; *cr:* Frankfort-Schuyler 2nd-8th Grd Tchr 1964-72, 9th-12th Grd Tchr 1973-; *ai:* Co-Edvisor Yrbk, Schl Newspaper, Class of 1995; Chprsn Natl Honor Fac Comm; Greenpeace, World Wildlife Fund 1980-; Amnesty Intnl 1990-; Worked for NYS Ed Dept Preparation of Soc Stud Regents Cooperating Tchr Utica Coll Stu Tchr Prgm; *office:* Frankfort-Schuyler Cntrl Schl Palmer St Frankfort NY 13340

GOODALL, WILLIAM ROBERT, History & Government Teacher; *b:* Ironton, OH; *m:* Connie Clithero; *c:* Joshua; *ed:* Rio Grande Coll (BA) His 1971; OH St Univ (mED) Educl Admin 1980; Meth Theological Schl of OH (MDiv) Parish Ministry 1989; *cr:* Symmes Vly HS Tchr 1971-; *ai:* Sr Adv; OEA 1971-; NEA; SVEA; Jennings Scholar; *office:* Symmes Valley HS 14778 State Route 141 Willow Wood OH 45696

GOODE, BOBBY CLAUDE, Advanced Physics Teacher; *b:* Celestes, TX; *m:* Jean Ames; *c:* James, Joel, John; *ed:* MA Inst of Tech (SB) Hum & Sci 1963; Andover Newton Theological Schl (MA) Religion 1968; Rensselaer Polytechnic Inst (MS) Natural Sci 1972; *cr:* L.D. Bell HS Math Tchr 1966-67; Grapevine HS Physics, Chem Tchr 1967-70; South Plainfield HS Advanced Physics, Chem, Bio Tchr 1970-; *ai:* Sci Club Adv; AAPT 1980-; NSTA 1980-, Exemplary Scndry Sci Tchr Awd; NJ Ed Assn, NEA 1970-; Scientific Research Soc Sigma Xi, Outstanding Sci Tchr Awd; First Bapt Church of New Market 1973-, Church Schl Tchr; Princeton Univ Prize Distinguished Scndry Schl Tchng Finalist Taugh One Term of Sci 1983; *office:* South Plainfield HS 200 Lake St South Plainfield NJ 07080

GOODE, LAMONT EDWARD, Social Studies Department Chm; *b:* Baltimore, MD; *m:* Sylvia C.; *c:* Aaron, Danyale; *ed:* Towson St Univ (BS) His 1972, (MS) Scndry Ed 1980; Addl 12 Credits in Scndry Admin; *cr:* Mount Hebron HS Soc Stud Tchr 1972-74; Oakland Mills HS Dept Chm 1983-; *ai:* Jr Var & Var Bsktbl Coach 1972-; Staff Advy Comm 1980-; Capitol Historical Soc 1980-, Mem, Stu Spon Awd; HCEA 1972-, Tchr Rep, Comm Chprsn; NCSS 1972-; Howard Cty Youth Assn 1980-, Bsbl Coach, 3 Titles; Oakland Mills HS PTA 1974-, Bd of Dirs 2 Yrs; Mount Saint Joseph Fathers Club 1995-; Phi Delta Kappa, Towson Chapter; MAT Advy comm 1981-; Acknowledgments for Publication of Handicapped People in Soc By Ruth-Ellen Ross; hapter; *home:* 4709 Salterforth Pl Ellicott City MD 21043*

GOODELL, DIANNE LEE, Human Svcs & Social Sci Prof; *b:* Exeter, NH; *m:* Andrew D. Zimmerman; *c:* Moriah Rose, Jacob Alexander, Ariana Mae; *ed:* Univ of DE (BA) Pol Sci 1973, (MA) Pol Theory 1977; *cr:* Lester Custom Designer, Builder Interior Designer 1973-76; Univ of DE Grad Asst 1976-77; YWCA Tchr 1977; St of DE Pub Schls Sub Tchr 1977-78; DE Tech, Comm Coll Prof 1978-; *ai:* Human Svcs Club Adv; Cultural Diversity Comm; Coming of Age Outreach Prgm Fac Rep; Adjunct Fac Mentor; Natl Org of Human Svcs Educators 1990-; Birth Ctr of DE Bd 1985-, VP; Womens' Correctional Inst Mentoring Prgm Bd 1993-; Univ of DE Grad Fellowship; DE Tech Stu Govt Assn Svc Awd; Coll Educl Newspaper Pub; *office:* Delaware Tech & Comm Coll 333 Shipley St Wilmington DE 19801*

GOODEMOTE, BARBARA HOLMBERG, Retired 6th Grade Teacher; *b:* Orange, NJ; *m:* Richard Arthur; *c:* David, Terry, Kevin; *ed:* St Tchrs Coll at Brockport (BA) Math; St Tchrs Coll at Oneonta (BA) Math; Cmptr Courses 1990-91; *cr:* Rock City Falls 3-4 Grd Tchr 1960-62; Broadalbin Cntrl Schl 2 Grd Tchr 1963-67; Galway Cntrl Schl 6 Grd Tchr 1971-94; *ai:* Drug Awareness Prgm ASAPP 1978-94; 6th Grd Sci Fair 1976-94; 6th Grd Grad 1976-94; GTA Negotions, Bd of Dirs; 4-6 Grd Dept Head 1971-92; 6th Grd Level Ldr 1993-94; Joseph Wilkinson Meml Lib Worker 1995; Career Connection BOCES 1989-94; Women of Moose 1977-; *home:* 436 State Highway 29 Broadalbin NY 12025

GOODGE, JOYCE B., Sixth Grade Teacher; *b:* Garner, KY; *m:* Nigel Dereck; *c:* Bonita, Kristie, Mark; *ed:* OH St Univ (BA) Elem Ed 1990; *cr:* Highland West Elem Schl 6th Grd Tchr 1990-; *ai:* OH NEED Energy Prgm; Kids Tchng Kids Adv; OEA, NEA, IRA 1990-; *home:* 2467 County Road 170 Marengo OH 43334

GOODHART, THOMAS SCOTT, Health Educator; *b:* Philadelphia, PA; *m:* Paula DeLallo; *c:* Brenton, Lexie; *ed:* SUNY at Brockport (BA); Life Cert Cortland; *ai:* Bsktbl, Soccer Coaches.

GOODHEART, KATHLEEN FRANCES, English Teacher; *b:* Jametown, NY; *ed:* Medaille Coll (BS) Ed 1965; Canisius Coll (MS) Ed 1974; *cr:* Elem Ed Tchr 1955-72; DeSales HS Tchr 1972-83; Turner Carroll HS Tchr 1983-; *ai:* Eng Dept Chprsn, Fr Club; NCEA 1955-; *office:* Turner-Carroll HS 185 Lang Ave Buffalo NY 14215*

GOODING, MARIANNE BALL, Fr, Span Teacher & Dept Chair; *b:* Canton, OH; *m:* Robert L.; *ed:* Kent St Univ (BSEd) Scndry Ed Fr, Span 1975, (MA) Fr 1978; St Univ of NY 1 Yr Grad Stud 1976-77; *cr:* Godwin MS Fr, Span Tchr 1979-80; Kent St Univ Fr, Span Instr 1980-88; Alliance HS Fr, Span Tchr 1981-83; Lake HS Fr, Span Tchr 1983-; *ai:* Fr Club Ecology Club; Curr, Grading Comms; Dept Chprsn; Led Stu Groups to France; NEA, OEA, LLEA, AATF, OFLA 1980-; Adult Fr Club 1990-, Pres; Stark Cty Bicycle Club 1981-, Sec, Trustee, Road Captain Svc Awd; SCBC Safety Team 1981-.

GOODLETT, ROXIE WRIGHT, Business & COE Teacher; *b:* East Liverpool, OH; *c:* Anthony Thornton, Tasmin, Sabrina, Darrin Green; *ed:* Kent St Univ (BS) Bus Ed 1972; OH St Univ (MA) Bus Ed 1974; *cr:* Mohawk Jr-Sr HS Bus Voc Tchr 1972-74; Yorktown Jr HS Bus Ed Tchr 1974-78; Whetstone HS COE Tchr, Coord 1978-85; South HS COE Tchr, Coord 1986-; *ai:* Bus Ldrs of Tomorrow Club Adv; Scout Schl Cabinet; Coord Tech Prep Bus Acad Comm; NEA 1972-; PSI 1987-, Bd Mem, CPS Rating; Project Bus Tchr Awd; Edctr of Yr Awd; *home:* 2395 Somersworth Dr Columbus OH 43219*

GOODLING, ROB W., Vocal Music Director; *b:* Colorado Springs, CO; *ed:* Lebanon Valley Coll (BS) Music Ed;1967; Eastman Schl of Music (MA) Musicology 1972; *cr:* 553 Air Force Reserve Band Tuba, Piano 1964-70; Corning Philharmonic Youth Orch Conductor 1967-69; Corning Philharmonic Orch Violinist 1967-76; Elmira Symphony Violinist 1967-70; Hochstein Schl of Music Instr Music His 1973-75; Salem Church of Christ Music Dir 1976-82; Churchville-Chili Sr HS Vocal Music Dir 1973-; *ai:* Singing Saints Show Choir Dir; Morning Show, Choral Cncl, Grad Comm Adv; Past Pres of Prin Staff Advy Comm; Select Men's & Women's Choruses; Musical Theater Dir; Principal's Staff Advy Chprsn; NOA; Fac Club; Music Educators Natl Conf; NY St Schl of Music Assn Solo Adjudicator; NEA; Amer Choral Dir Assoc; Cornhill Neighbors DAC-TAC Assn; Cornhill Arts Festival Chprsn; Who's Who Among Stdnts in Amer Coll & Univ 1966; Affiliate Prof Awd 1981; Outstanding Music Educator 1988; Outstanding Educator by MIT; Outstanding Influence on HS Stdnts; Prof Expertise 440; *office:* Churchville-Chili Sr HS 5786 Buffalo Rd Churchville NY 14428

GOODLOE, YVETTE CECELIA, Science & Zoology Teacher; *b:* New York, NY; *m:* Samuel Jr.; *c:* Samuel III; *ed:* Howard Univ (BS) Zoology 1971, (MED) Ed 1976; *cr:* DC Sci Tchr 1971-78; Buffalo Bd of Ed Coord of Sci, Zoo 1978-; *ai:* Western NY Sci Congress Judge; Schl Sci Olympiad; NEA 1978-; Natl Sci Assn 1979-; NY St Sci Assn 1985-; ASCD 1989-; Allyway Theatre 1986-, VP; Alpha Kappa Alpha 1985-; Recipient of Sci Tchrs Prgm in Kanazawa Japan 1989; NSTA Search for Excl in Sci Ed 1983; Natl Awd Sec Schl Recognition Prgm US Dept of Ed 1985; US Ed Del To Vietnam 1995; *office:* Charles Drew Sci Magnet Schl 1 N Meadow Dr Buffalo NY 14214*

GOODMAN, BONNIE WORTHMAN, Art Teacher; *b:* Brooklyn, NY; *m:* Daniel; *c:* Gregory; *ed:* SUNY at Binghamton (BA) Studio Art 1968; Pratt Inst (MFA) Printmaking, Painting 1974; Art Stdnts League; Brooklyn Museum; Attnd Brooklyn Coll; *cr:* Erasmus Hall HS Art Tchr 1970-75; Boys & Girls HS Art Tchr 1975-79; Washington Irving HS Art Tchr 1986-; *ai:* Art House Store Adv; Yrbk, Art & Lit Magazine Art Adv; Prof Dev Comm; New York City Art Tchrs Assn 1986-, HS Art Edctr of Yr 1992; NY St Art Tchrs Assn; Roosevelt Island Jewish Congregation 1985-, Bd of Dirs; Co-Author Global Art Curr; *office:* Washington Irving HS 40 Irving Pl New York NY 10003

GOODMAN, ELISE, Art History Professor; *b:* Towanda, PA; *ed* Bridgeport (BA) Eng 1969; OH St Univ Art His (MA) 1975, (PH *cr:* Univ of Cincinnati RWC Art His Prof 1979-; *ai:* Coll Art As Amer Soc for Eighteenth Century Stud 1987-; NEH Fellowshi Tchrs, NEH Summer Stipends, CASVA, Natl Gallery of Art Fel Amer Philosophical Soc Grants; Pub Book Rubens the Garden o Conversatie a la Mode 1992; Pub 15 Articles in Scholarly Art His *office:* Univ Of Cin R Walters Coll 9555 Plainfield Rd Cinci 45236

GOODMAN, JOAN GOODWIN, Teacher; *b:* White Plains, NY J.; *c:* Drew David; *ed:* 60 Grad Credits Hunter Coll, Bank Street Coll of NY; *cr:* St Ann's Ave Schl Tchr 1963-65; The Willis Av Tchr 1965-; *ai:* Child Abuse Comm Chprsn; Citywide Responsibi 1963-, Exec Bd, Smallheiser Awd; UFT 1988; Delta Sigma Th Dist Rep Dist 7; Bronx UFT 1970; *office:* The Willis Avenue S 383 E 139th St Bronx NY 10454*

GOODMAN, KAREN SIDEHAMER, 6th Grade Teacher; *b:* Mt PA; *m:* Louis; *ed:* PA St Univ (BS) Elem Ed 1980; Working o Degree Instrl Ldrshp at Robert Morris Coll; *cr:* Swissvale Schl 3rd Grd Tchr 1980-82; Comm Day Schl K-8 Sci Specialist 1982-8 MS 6th Grd Math Tchr 1988-; *ai:* AFT 1988-; PA MS Assn 199 Time Honoree 1991; Robert E. Wolf Tchr Excl Awd Nominee 1 Ribbon Nationally Recognized Schl of Excl 1994; Don Eichor Awd 1995; Regular Ed Tchrs Are Spec Too Awd 1995; *office:* C 200 Hillvue Ln Pittsburgh PA 15237*

GOODMAN, LES H., 4th Grade Teacher; *b:* Glens Falls, NY; *m* Moore; *c:* Alisa, Erica, Jessica; *ed:* Castleotn St Coll (BS) Elem St Univ of NY at Plattsburgh (MS) Sci Ed 1976; *cr:* Quaker St 4th, 6th Grd Tchr 1973-; *ai:* Ftbl Coach 1974-76; Var Bskt 1978-81; NYSUT; *office:* Granville Cntrl Schl Quaker St Gra 12832

GOODMAN, MARILYN, Theatre & Communications Prof; *b:* NY; *ed:* SUNY at Cortland (BA) Speech & Theatre 1966; Univ o Theatre 1967; 36 Grad Credit Hrs SUNY at Stony Brook; *cr:* Comm Coll Instr 1967-68; Suffolk Comm Coll Selden Ca 1968-88, Brentwood Campus Prof 1988-; *ai:* Campus Hnrs Pg Exec Comm Acad Assembly; Directing Campus Theatrical Pro AFT & NYSUT 1968-; *office:* Suffolk Community Coll Crooke Brentwood NY 11717

GOODMAN, MARILYN, Kindergarten Teacher; *b:* Brooklyn Harvey B.; *c:* Marc, Michelle; *ed:* Brooklyn Coll (BA) Ed 196 Grad Credit Hrs; *cr:* PS 65 Schl Early Childhood Tchr 1968-; 1968-; UFT 1968-, Delegate Chptr Ldr; Schl Wide Project Grant Grants Awarded to Schl; *office:* PS 65 Annex Schl 288 W Brooklyn NY 11207

GOODMAN, MICHAEL, American History & Psych Tchr; *b* Springs, NY; *m:* Barbara Ann Powanda; *c:* Michael David; *ed* Coll (BS) Pol Sci 1964; Elmira Coll (MS) Ed 1990; Attnd Geneseo, Nazareth Coll & Univ of Rochester; *cr:* Notre Dame HS Tchr 1964-67; Victor Cntrl Schl Soc Stud Tchr 1967-, Dept Chm *ai:* SADD, Jr Class & Sr Class Advs; Victor Tchrs Assn 19 1990-94; NYSUT 1967-; AFT 1967-; Knights of Columbus 196 Knight, Church & Civic Awd; Natl Cncl on Alcoholism Intervention 1985-; *office:* Victor Central HS 953 High St Victor

GOODMAN, MICHELLE CAROL, Physical Education Te Brooklyn, NY; *ed:* Brooklyn Coll (BS) PE 1979; Coll of Staten Isl Spec Ed 1988; Long Island Univ 12 Grad Credits Admin; *cr:* IS Ed Tchr 1982-83; IS 391 Spec Ed Tchr 1983-84; IS 390 Spec 1984-92; Canarsie HS PE Tchr 1992-; *ai:* Girls Bsktbl Coach; 1982-.

GOODMAN, ROBERT S., Assistant Principal; *b:* Bronx, NY; *e* Coll of CUNY (BA) Ger, Hebrew 1967, (MA) Hebrew Lit 1972; Long Island Univ Prof Diploma Educl Admin 1986; *cr:* Bayside Hebrew Tchr 1970-85; Townsend Harris HS Ger Tchr 1985-91; N. Cardozo HS Asst Prin, Supv For Lang, ESL 1991-; *ai:* Mode Club Adv; Phi Beta Kappa 1967-; AATG 1971-; Modern Lang As Amer Cncl Tchng of For Lang 1980-; Univ of Chicago Outstdng T Hellenic Amer Edctrs Assn Awd; *office:* Benjamin N Cardozo 223rd St Flushing NY 11364

GOODNIGHT, EDITH HOWE, Earth Science Teacher; *b:* G CT; *m:* Edward R.; *c:* Adam; *ed:* Briarcliff Coll (AA) Liberal A Clark Univ (BA) Geog 1967; SUNY at Buffalo (BA) Ec Geog Credit Hrs in Ed, Sci & Comp Sci; *cr:* Wilson Cntrl Jr Sr HS 9 Grd Earth Sci Tchr 1970-1988, 8th Grd Phys Sci Tchr 1989-91, Earth Sci, 8th Grd Accelerated Earth Sci & Gen Sci Tchr Odyssey of the Mind; Intnl GLOBE Pgm; Local & Natl Automated System Pgm; NEA 1970-; WTA 1970-; NYSUT 1970-; REST 199 Wilson Central Schl 412 Lake St Wilson NY 14172

GOODREMOTE, CECIL J.,JR., Jr HS Science Teacher; *b:* Buf *ed:* Trocaire Coll (AAS) Ed 1973; Diocese of Buffalo Perman Cert 1968; *cr:* S. S. Peter & Paul Schl 5th Grd Tchr 1960-66, 6th 1961-62, 7-8th Grd Sci Tchr 1966-83, 6-8th Grd Sci Tchr 1983-9 Grd Sci Tchr 1995-; *ai:* Quiz Bowl Moderator; Sci Book Selectio Region 7 Sci Mentor 1987; Elem Schl Tchr Dev Grant Herbarium Nature Articles Pub Springville Journal; St Elizabeth Ann Seton *office:* S. S. Peter & Paul Schl 68 E Main St Hamburg NY 1407

GOODWIN, ALAN S., English Department Chairman; *b:* Wa DC; *m:* Eleanor Christmas; *c:* Michael, Christopher; *ed:* Univ of Eng Ed 1975, (MA) Eng Ed 1980, (PHD) Curr & Instr 1989; *cr:* HS Eng Tchr 1975-79; Kennedy HS Eng Tchr 1979-84; Banneke Dept Chm 1984-86; Rockville HS Eng Dept Chm 1986-; *ai:* M Comm Chm; NEA 1975-; Montgomery Cty Ed Assn 1975-, Rep; Eng in Montgomery Cty, Pres 1982-83, VP 1983-84; PTSA 1994; NEH Rdng Grant 1993; Nom for Agnes Meyer Outstanding 1986; *office:* Rockville HS 2100 Baltimore Rd Rockville MD 20

GOODWIN, ANNA DUNLAP, Mathematics Teacher; *b:* Elmira Harry S.; *c:* Casie M., Patrick J.; *ed:* SUNY at Cortland (BS Scndry Math Ed 1982; SUNY at Oswego (MS) Curr & Instructio Math 1987; *cr:* Caledonia-Mumford Cntrl Schls 7th Grd Remedia Tchr 1982-83; Phoenix Cntrl Schls HS Math Tchr 1983-; *ai:* 1982-; PCSTA 1993-, Treas; NCTM 1993-; NYSTMA 1989 Phoenix Cntrl Schls 470 Main St Phoenix NY 13135

GOODWIN, CHARLES HUGH, Tech & Mngmt Sciences Cortland, NY; *m:* Barbara Louetta Milan; *c:* Chad; *ed:* Osweg Indstrl Arts 1967, (MS) Indstrl Arts 1973; 90 Hrs Practicum Tech Trainer 1986; Principles of Engrng Pilot Tchr Trng 1992; Cert Applied Physics 1993; *cr:* Worcester Cntrl Schl 7-12 Grd Indstrl 1967-69; Henry B. Endicott 7-9 Grd Indstrl Arts Tchr; Union-En 9-12 Grd Tech Ed Tchr 1974-; Broome Comm Coll Applied Physi *ai:* Tech CLub, Tech Club, Solar Tiger, Adv; Cmptr Bulletin Bd Car Project; UECS Dist Planning, Bldg Planning Team; NYS Tech 1971-, Pres, Pres Awd; Soc of Plastics Engrs 1980-, Pres, Mem of Intl Tech Ed Assn 1975-, Membership Comm; Endicott Tech C Tech Prep Consortium 1992-, Ldrshp Team; NYS Strategic Initiative 1993-; NYS Ed Dept 1980-, Schl Quality Reviewer; E

; Tech Ed Tchr of Yr 1986; Distngd Alumnus of Oswego St 1986; Life Mem NYS Congress of Parents & Tchrs; Who's Who in n Education 1996-97; Numerous Articles Pub; *office:* Union HS 1200 Main St Endicott NY 13760*

'IN, MARYANN, 9th-12th Grd PE Teacher; *b:* Paterson, NJ; *m:* : Seton Hall Univ (BS) Hlth, PE 1986; Montclair St Univ (MA) 1992; 6th Yr Level Hlth, PE 1994; *cr:* Paramus Cath HS PE, Hlth ach 1986-88; Clifton HS PE, Hlth Tchr 1988-; *ai:* HS Coach Girls er, Asst Sftbl 1989-, Var Boys & Girls Swim 1990-; NEA 1988-; ifton HS 333 Colfax Ave Clifton NJ 07013

'IN, PATRICIA V., English Teacher; *b:* Brooklyn, NY; *ed:* St l at Oswego (BA) Scndry Eng 1968; St Univ Coll at Brockport 42 .ng; Permanent Cert 7-12th Grd Eng 1973; Peer Mediator, Mentor, nt Drug & Alcohol & Prejudice Reduction Trng; *cr:* Britton Rd Jr & Eng Tchr 1968-69; Greece Arcadia HS Eng Tchr 1969-, Bldg ng 1977-; *ai:* Human Diversity & Ski Club; Peer Mediation; Care an Exch Prgm with Barcelona; Tech Prep Team; Diversity Trainer Dist; Greece Tchrs Assn 1968-, Election Comm; NYEA, NEA erto Rican Youth Dev & Resource Ctr 1995-, VP; Natl Coalition ı 1993-; 1st Universalist Church 1992-, Chair of Fund Raising; an Comm Woman 1974-; Park Ridge Auxiliary 1988-; Natl ent for Hum Prgm Summer 1986; *office:* Greece Arcadia HS 120 ottage Rd Rochester NY 14612*

IN, PETER H., Sci Dept Chm & Physics Tchr; *b:* Hartford, CT; ; *c:* Hunt, John; *ed:* Middlebury Coll (AB) Physics 1973; Trinity ı) Ed 1977; *cr:* Kent Schl Sci Tchr 1973-, Chm 1991-; *ai:* Soccer ering Coach; Peer Cnslng Adv; AAPT 1973-; CVISSTA 1974-, 7-80; Lions 1983-, Pres 1986-87; Books Pub: Physics Can be Fun, Physics Labs, How Things Work, Physics With Computers, ing Projects for Young Scientists, More Engineering Projects for ientists & Physics Projects for Young Scientists; *office:* Kent Schl 2006 Kent CT 06757*

'IN, ROSEMARIE LEVESQUE, Retired 8th Grd Lang Arts Lewiston, ME; *m:* Thomas L.; *c:* Debra M. Crocker, David J. Hall; of ME at Gordham (BS) K-8 Lang Arts 1965; 42 Addl Credit Hrs; berlain Schl Grd 4 Tchr 1965-67; Auburn Sherwood Heights Elem 5 Tchr 1968-78; MSAD 70 Schl 5-8 Grd Lang Arts Tchr 1978-81; Jr HS Grd 8 Lang Arts Tchr 1982-93; Lewiston HS Team Ldr Adult Ed Bridge Tchr 1994-; *ai:* Auburn Tchrs Assn 1965-78; Tchrs Assn 1982-93, MS Rep; ME Tchrs Assn 1965-; NEA 1965-; ntract Bridge League 1975-, Life Master 1984; NE Bride Assn ournment Coord, Bd Mem; New England Bridge Conf 1982-, Sec *ome:* 94 Hogan Rd Lewiston ME 04240

'IN, TIM J., Math Teacher; *b:* Lima, OH; *m:* Dawn R. VanAtta; *ed:* Univ of Findlay (BA) Math 1994; *cr:* Bluffton HS Math Tchr : Asst Ftbl, Head Bsbl Coach; *office:* Bluffton HS 106 W College fton OH 45817

EAR, MICHAEL JOHN, Business Education Teacher; *b:* OLean, ndiana Univ of PA (BSEd) Mrktg & Bus 1992; Bloomsburg Univ nrolled in the MS Prgm for Instructional Technologies; *cr:* Comm Corp Mrktg Asst 1990-91; Liberty HS Bus Ed Tchr 1993-; of 1996 Adv; FBLA Adv; Girls Var Vlybl Coach; Track & Field 'urr Planning Comm; PBEA 1990-; NEA, PSEA 1992-; Strategic for Southern Tioga Schl Dist 1995-; *office:* Liberty Jr Sr HS PO Liberty PA 16930*

SH, STEVEN JAMES, English Teacher; *b:* Dover, OH; *c:* Jason; niv (BS) Eng 1970; Miami Univ (MED) 1974; *cr:* New Lexington s Eng Tchr 1970-72; Kettering Sch Eng Tchr 1972-; Moraine Schl · 1972-; *ai:* Writing Team; Jr Class Adv; NEA, OEA 1970-; KEA arious Offices; NCTE 1970-; *office:* Kettering-Moraine City Schls oyer Rd Kettering OH 45429

HIAN, HELEN WADE, Professor of Psychology; *b:* Holyoke, Gregory A. Sr.; *c:* Wade T., Gregory A. Jr.; *ed:* Mount Holyoke) Psych 1971; Univ of MA (MED) Cnslng Psych 1973, (EDD) Ed 981; *cr:* Greenfield Pub Schls Psychologist 1973-74; Cape Cod oll Psychology Prof 1974-; *ai:* Women in Transition Fac Adv; oc, AAUW 1980-; UNA-USA of Cape Cod 1990-, VP; Mt Holyoke Club of Cape Cod 1972-, Pres; Fulbright Scholar China 1990; elegation Russia 1992, England 1995; Intnl Piaget Symposium and 1979; *home:* 1216 Main St East Dennis MA 02641

N, CONSTANCE SGROI, French Teacher; *b:* Syracuse, NY; *m:* .; *c:* Erin, Sean; *ed:* Nazareth Coll of Rochester (BA) Fr 1970; Brockport (MS) Scndry Ed 1975; Universite de Poitiers France t Grad Stud Nazareth Coll; *cr:* West Genesee HS Fr Tchr 1970-71; lle-Chili HS Fr, Span Tchr 1972-78; Diocese of Rochester Tchr Gifted Ed 1979-83; Greece Cntrl Schl Dist Fr Tchr 1983-; *ai:* thena Bldg Mngmt Comm Chprsn; Class Adv; Prof Dev Comm; Adv; Fr Lang Dept Team Ldr; Overseas Exch Dir; NEA 1970-; 'chrs Assn 1983-, Sr HS Rep; NY St Frgn Lang Tchrs Assn 1970-, .egnl Conf Svc Awds; Greece NY Vitre' France Sister City Comm IS Liaison; St John the Evangelist Church Folk Group 1994-, anist; Greece Cntrl Mentor Tchr; Staff Dev Wkshp Presenter For Cntrl, Nazareth Coll of Rochester; *office:* Greece Arcadia HS 120 ottage Rd Rochester NY 14612*

N, MARY FATIMA, Math & Religion Teacher; *b:* Holyoke, MA; Lady of the Elms (BA) Latin & Ed 1956, (MAT) Yth Ministry; 'estfield St, The Elms, Worcester Plytech, Springfield Tech, eld Coll; *cr:* St Mary HS Span, Eng Tchr 1961-64; Cathedral HS ath Tchr 1964-89; St Catherine Indian Schl Math, Rel Tchr 1989; of the Sacred Heart 7th-8th Grd Math, 7th Grd Rel Tchr 1990-; Schl Vol Tutoring; NCEA 1959-; Sisters of St Joseph 1956-; NSF

AN, CHARLES WILLIAM, Diesel & Auto Teacher; *b:* East d, OH; *m:* Marquerite; *c:* Kelli Cerne, Kristine; *cr:* Max S. Hayes 77-; *ai:* Iota Lambda Sigma 1988-; *home:* 1604 Clarius Cir oro OH 44241

YNSKI, CAROLYN A., Math & Computer Sci Teacher; *b:* NY; *m:* Ron; *c:* Kristen, Kaitlyn; *ed:* D'Youville Coll (BA) Math Univ Coll at Buff (MS) Math Ed 1977; St Univ at Buffalo (BA) ci 1987; *cr:* Depew HS Math Tchr 1974-; *ai:* Yrbk Adv; AFT, DTO 1974-; Kappa Gamma Pi 1973-; *office:* Depew HS 5201 S d Depew NY 14043

T, JOAN LESLIE, Math Tchr & Specialist; *b:* Manhattan, NY; ns Coll (BA) Math, (MS) Scndry Eng, Math; *cr:* Dalton Schl HS ır, Math Dept Head Admin Asst; Convent of Sacred Heart HS Math c Avd to Math Club; Day Schl Jr HS Math Tchr; Ethical Culture Math Tchr; Dwight Schl HS Math Tchr, HS Math Specialist in : NCTM; *office:* Dwight Schl 291 Central Park W New York NY

LLO, HILDA, English Teacher; *b:* Vineland, NJ; *m:* Luis A. Sr.; ., Derek; *ed:* Rowan, Glassboro St Coll (BA) Eng Ed 1977; *cr:* HS North Eng Tchr 1977-; *ai:* HAACC 1991-, Co-Adv; *office:* HS N 3010 E Chestnut Ave Vineland NJ 08360*

N, BARBARA, French Teacher; *b:* Canton, IL; *m:* Barry; *c:* G., Erica G.; *ed:* W Chester Univ (BS) Fr Ed 1965; Syracuse Univ (MA) Fr Lit 1971; 9 Addl Grad Hrs; *cr:* Goshen Acad Fr Tchr 1965-67; Roger B. Taney Jr High Fr Tchr 1967-69; Syracuse Univ TA 1969-71; Cicero HS Fr Tchr 1975-76; Liverpool HS Fr Tchr 1976-; *ai:* Fr Club Adv; AFT, AATF, NYSAFLT 1976-; FLACNY 1979-; NSAFLT Grant; Pub Articles; *office:* Liverpool HS Wetzel Rd Liverpool NY 13090*

GORDON, BARBARA JUNE, Former Social Studies Teacher; *b:* New York City, NY; *m:* Charles P. Cavas; *c:* Samuel Gordon Cavas, Maxwell Gordon Cavas; *ed:* Brown Univ (A) His 1986, (MAT) Scndry Soc Stud 1987; *cr:* Whitman-Hanson Regnl HS Soc Stud Tchr 1987-; *ai:* Recycling Club; Stu Environmental Awareness Club; MA Tchrs Assn, NEA, Southshore Cncl Soc Stud, MA Cncl Soc Stud 1987-; Natl Endowment for the Hum Grants 1990, 1992.

GORDON, BRUCE LEE, Social Studies Teacher; *b:* Oxford, PA; *m:* Jennie Garretson; *c:* Jacob Brandt; *ed:* Millersville Univ of Pa (BSEd) Soc Stud 1988; Attnd Carlow Coll, IN Wesleyan Univ; *cr:* West Shore Schl Dist 11th Grd Soc Stud Tchr1991-; *ai:* Asst Ath Traner; Aduio-Visual Coord; Mentor Tchr; PA Army Natl Guard 1988-, Sergeant, Distinguished Honor Grad US Army Infantry Schl; WHTM Channel 27 News-Class Act Tchr of Week; *office:* Red Land HS 560 Fishing Creek Rd Lewisberry PA 17339

GORDON, ERIC TYLER, 6th & 7th Grade Science Tchr; *b:* Cape May, NJ; *m:* Debra Louise; *c:* Amber, Ashley; *ed:* Bucks Cty Comm (Assoc) Bio 1985; Kutztown Univ (BS) Scndry Sci Ed 1988; Holy Family Coll (MS) Scndry Ed 1995; *cr:* Shafer MS Sci Tchr 1988-; *ai:* Head Track Coach; Animal Club Supvr; NEA 1988-; PSEA 1988-; *office:* Robert K Shafer MS 3333 Hulmeville Rd Bensalem PA 19020

GORDON, HAZEL KISER, First Grade Teacher; *b:* Warren, OH; *m:* Philip Alan; *c:* Annette Gordon-Howell, Roger, Ryan; *ed:* OH St Univ (BS) El Ed 1979; Univ of Dayton (MS) Schl Guid Cnslng 1986; 30 Addl Semester Hrs; *cr:* Allen East Local Schls 5th Grd, Jr HS Home Ec Tchr 1980-81; Elida Local Schls 1st Grd Tchr 1982-; *ai:* Evaluate Redistricting, North Cntrl, Venture Capital Comms; Elida Ed Assn 1984-, Bldg Rep; OH Ed Assn, NEA 1984-; NW OH Ed Assn 1984-, Elected Del; Martha Holden Jennings Scholar; *office:* Gomer Elem Schl 4040 W Lincoln Hwy Gomer OH 45809*

GORDON, JOAN GRILLO, Social Studies Chair & Teacher; *b:* Jamaica, NY; *m:* Ronald Lee; *c:* Ronald, Debra, Joseph; *ed:* Queens Coll (BS) His 1960, (MA) Soc Stud Tchng 1963; Brooklyn Coll Admin; Manhattan Coll Admin; Stony Brook Univ Eng; 45 Credits Post Masters; *cr:* Van Wyck Jr HS Soc Stud Tchr 1960-61, 1963-65; Our Lady of Mercy Acad Soc Stud Tchr & Chair 1974-; *ai:* Clubs: Mock Trial, Businessworks, Run a Balloon, Bus, Justice Simulation; Ad HOC Comms; LICSS 1974-; NCEA 1974-; NYSCSS 1980-; NYSTA 1985-; Church Group 1960-; Channel 13 & Newsday Grants; Elizabeth Seton Awd CCD Svc; *office:* Our Lady Of Mercy Acad 815 Convent Rd Syosset NY 11791

GORDON, JUNE SACAVAGE, HS Art Teacher; *b:* Ringtown, PA; *m:* Peter Curry; *ed:* Mansfield Univ (BSEd) Art Ed 1983; Elmira Coll (MSEd) Ed 1987; Addl 15 Credit Hrs; Prof Dev Prgm; *cr:* Elmira City Schl Dist K-12 Art Tchr 1983-; *ai:* Environmentally Aware & Ready to Help, Art Club Adv; Bldg Planning Team 1992-; TALC 1991; AFT; NEA 1983-; NAEA 1993-; Amer Assn of Univ Women 1993-; United Way Sub Allocations Comm 1990-1993; Juror of Local Art Shows; Pub Poem 1990; 1st Pl Bl, Wh Photography Wonder of NY Regnl Show; 3rd Pl Colored Pencil Drawing 1st Citizens Natl Bank Juried Show 1988; *office:* Elmira Free Acad 933 Hoffman St Elmira NY 14905*

GORDON, LAUREN SUE, 4th Grade Teacher; *b:* Philadelphia, PA; *m:* Jay; *c:* Eli, Benjamin, Rachel; *ed:* Univ of PA (BA) Elem Ed 1988; *cr:* Lindenwold Schl Five 4th, 5th Grd Tchr 1988-; *ai:* Hebrew Enrichment Congregation Rel Instr; NEA 1988-; *home:* 118 Sherwood Ln Toms River NJ 08753

GORDON, MARILYN BAUMANN, Retired Teacher; *b:* Lisbon Falls, ME; *w:* William Reginald (dec); *c:* William R. Jr., Martha A.; *ed:* Univ of Southern ME at Gorham (BS) Ed 1975; *cr:* Levant Schl Multi-age, 4th-8th Grd Tchr 1956-63; West Levant Schl Multi-age, 4th-8th Grd Tchr 1956-63; Hampden Elem Schl Self Contained 2nd Grd Tchr 1963-66; West Paris Elem Schl 4th-5th Grd Tchr 1966-67; Woolwich Cntrl Schl Self Contained 2nd Grd Tchr 1969-91; *ai:* 4th-8th Grd Sftbl Coach 1980-81; Woolwich Tchr's Assn 1973-91; ME Tchr's Assn, NEA 1956-91; Ret MTA, NEA 1991-.

GORDON, MURIELENE ELIZABETH, Art Teacher; *b:* Washington, DC; *w:* Alvin M. (dec); *c:* Michelle Gordon Rennie, Andrea, Marcus; *ed:* Washington Tech Inst (AAS) Advertising-Suma Cum Laude 1975; Univ of DC (BA) Art Ed-Sum Cum Laude 1979; Trinity Coll Credit Hrs; *cr:* Natl Labor Relations Bd Legal Stenographer 1969-73; DC Commission on Arts Admin 1979-82; DC Pub Schls Art Tchr 1980-; *ai:* Art Club, Discover Art Wkshp Spon; Duke Ellington Project; BAAD Task Force; NEA, WTU 1979-; Art Alliance 1990-; Beta Zeta Chapter 1980-, Zeta Phi Beta Finer Womanhood Awd; Vol Svcs Appreciation, Project Impact Achvmt Certs; Marc Jenkins, Omega Phi, Martin Luther King Jr Keeping Dream Alive Svc Awds; Hubert Horatio Humphrey Art Schlsp Awd; Whos Who in Amer Univs & Colls; *office:* Ballou Sr HS 3401 4th St SE Washington DC 20032*

GORDON, PAMELA C., Sixth Grade Teacher; *b:* Pittsburgh, PA; *ed:* Edinboro Univ (BS) Elem Ed 1992; *cr:* Shady Lane Schl Older Fours Tchr 1992-93; McKeesport Area Schl Dist Tchr 1993-; *ai:* Multicultural Comm; I-Team; PSEA, MEA 1993-; *office:* Cornell MS 1600 Cornell St Mc Keesport PA 15132*

GORDON, PATRICIA KUHLTHAU, 7th-8th Grade English Teacher; *b:* New Brunswick, NJ; *m:* Samuel; *c:* Jill Gordon Szabo, Mark Barrett; *ed:* Fairleigh Dickinson Univ (BA) 2nd Ed Eng 1968; 15 Credits Elem Ed Cert; 30 Grad Credits Rdng Specialization Cert K-12; *cr:* NK Brampton Schl 7-8 Grd Eng Tchr 1984-; Rutgers Preparatory Schl SAT Verbal Tchr 1992-; St Matthews Schl 7-8 Grd Eng Tchr 1975-84; East Brunswick Pub Schl 5-6 Grd Tchr 1967-69; *ai:* NEA, NJEA 1984-; Cedar Wood Womens Club 1975-, VP, Sec, News Ed; Who's Who Among Women; *home:* 114 Dayton Ave Somerset NJ 08873

GORDON, ROBERT QUINLAND, Fifth Grade Teacher; *b:* Greenwich, CT; *m:* Sharon Coram; *c:* Derrick, Sean, Dwayne, Bradley, Lance; *ed:* Fairfield Univ (MA) Guidance & Counseling 1972; 60 Credit Hrs Post Grad Stud; *cr:* Wiltwyck Schl For Boys Elem Tchr 1960-61; Highland St Trng Schl Elem Tchr 1962-63; North Salem Cntrl Schl Dist #1 Elem Tchr 1963-; *ai:* Rocketry Club; Sci Curr Comm; Adjunct Prof Manhattanville Coll; AFT 1963-, Del; NYSUT 1963-, Local Pres, Del; North Salem Tchrs Assn 1963-, Pres; Omega Psi Phi 1960-, Coll Bagelius; Westchester Cty Bsktbl Assn 1963-83; Westchester Bsbl Coaches Assn 1968-84, Pres 1983-84; Tchrs Ed & Practices Bd; NY St Tchr Cert Examination Written Response Scorer; Supervising Tchr Course Co-Writer; Tchr Evalutation Select Seminar Report Co-Writer 1993; *office:* Pequenakonck Elem Schl 173 June Rd North Salem NY 10560*

GORDON-LAND, CARRIE W., Counselor; *b:* New York, NY; *m:* David M.; *c:* Jessica L. Gordon; *ed:* NY Univ (BA) Eng Lit 1963; City Coll of NY (MA) Eng 1965; Univ of Bridgeport (MA) Cnslr Ed 1975; *cr:* PS 137 Lang Arts Tchr 1963-69; Hommocks MS Eng Tchr 1969-70; Ridgefield HS Cnslr 1975-; *ai:* Grief & Loss Group; Peer Mediators; Gay & Straight Alliance; NEA 1975-; CEA 1975-; REA 1975-; *office:* Ridgefield HS 700 N Salem Rd Ridgefield CT 06877*

GORE, RICHARD Z., Assoc Prof of Earth Science; *b:* New York, NY; *m:* Kathleen A.; *c:* Zandra A.; *ed:* City Coll of NY (BS) Geology 1963; Boston Coll (MS) Geophysics 1967; Boston Univ (PHD) Geology 1973; *cr:* US Geological Survey 1963-64; North Shore Comm Coll Instr 1966-69;l U MA at Lowell Assoc Prof 1971-; *ai:* Geological Soc Amer; Town Geologist 1988-; *office:* Univ Of MA At Lowell 1 University Ave Lowell MA 01854

GORE, SUSAN SITTERLY, Second Grade Teacher; *b:* Norwalk, OH; *m:* Ernest; *c:* Christopher, Keran; *ed:* Bowling Green St Univ (BS) Elem Ed 1970; *cr:* Lorain City Schl Fourth Grd Tchr 1970-72; New London Local Schl Second-Fourth Grd Tchr 1982-; *ai:* Labor Mngmt Comm; OH Conf of Tchr of Eng & Lang Arts 1992-; NLEA, OEA, NEA 1970-; Delta Kappa Gamma; Jennings Scholar 1995; *office:* New London Elem Schl 17 Park Ave New London OH 44851

GOREY, ROBERT, Upper School Science Educator; *b:* Lexington, KY; *ed:* Univ of Dayton (BS) Sci 1965; Xavier Univ (MED) Admin 1970; *cr:* Our Lady of Angels HS Sci Edctr, Asst Prin 1968-73; Regina HS Sci Edctr 1973-74; Summit Cntry Day Schl Sci Edctr 1974-; *ai:* Adventure Club, Soph Moderator; NSTA 1983-92; NABT 1988-; NSSA 1983-94; Evans Grant 1994-95; *office:* Summit Country Day Schl 2161 Grandin Rd Cincinnati OH 45208*

GORHAM, FRANK, 6th Grade Teacher; *b:* Houlton, ME; *m:* Kathleen; *c:* Heather, Heath; *ed:* Univ of Southern ME (BS) Ed 1971, (MS) Admin 1983; *cr:* SAD 51 Cumberland Schl 4-6 Grds Tchr 12 Yrs, Prin 1 Yr; ME Dept of Ed Ed Consultant 1 Yr; Jordan-Small Schl Tchr 11 Yrs; *ai:* Curr Cncl Chprsn; IM Bsktbl; NEA 1971-; MTA 1971-, Negotiator; SAD 15 Schl Bd 1977-82, Policy Comm Chair; *office:* Jordan Small Schl Rt 85 Raymond ME 04071*

GORIN, ROBERT MURRAY,JR., Social Studies Teacher; *b:* Mineola, NY; *ed:* Xavier Univ (AB) (MA) His 1970; Hofstra Univ (MS) Ed 1974; Fordham Univ (MA) Philosophy 1978; Saint Louis Univ (PHD) His 1980; Johns Hopkins Univ (MS) Ed 1993; Attnd Adelphi U, Baruch Coll, CUNY, Bridgewater St Coll, U of CA at Berkeley, Gettysburg Coll, Harvard U, Saint Joseph's U, Saint Louis U Schl of Law, Worcester Coll, Oxford Univ, Yale U; *cr:* Bellmore-Merrick Cntrl HS Dist Soc Stud Tchr 1974-83; South Side HS Soc Stud Tchr 1977-78; Manhasset HS Soc Stud Tchr 1983-; Hofstra Univ His Adj Asst Prof 1986-; *ai:* Fac Cncl NHS Chptr; Judge Long Island Natl His Day Contest 1986-94; Amer Historical Assn, Org of Amer Historians 1968-; Southern Historical Assn 1970-; NCSS 1973-, Prof Ethics Comm 1982-92, Chair 1986; Long Island Cncl for Soc St, NY St Cncl for Soc St 1973-; ASCD 1983-; AAUP 1986-; NY SUT AFT 1974-; Ctr for Stud of Pres 1982-; Soc for His Ed 1990-; Worcester Coll, Oxford U Assocs; Civil War Soc; Civil War Round Table of NY; Amer Friends of Renley House, Oxford; Plimoth Plantation; Amer Museum of Natural His; Abraham Lincoln Assn, Theodore Roosevelt Assn; Metropolitan Opera Guild; NY Pub Lib; Friends for Long Island's Heritages; Garden City Historical Study; South Street Seaport; Metropolitan Museum of Art; Assn for Preservation of Civil War Sites; Paper Presented Dist, Nat Confs; Taft, Robert A. Taft Inst of Govt Fewllows, Soc for Values in Higher Ed; Phi Alpha Theta; Who's Who in East, Amer Ed; Yrbk Dedication 1988; Tchr of Yr 1988; Hon Men NHS; *office:* Manhasset Sr HS 200 Memorial Pl Manhasset NY 11030

GORLINE, GARY GENE, PE Teacher & Dist Coordinator; *b:* Highland, IL; *m:* Lynda Ruth; *c:* Timothy, Jeremy, Rebekah; *ed:* Concordia Univ (BA) Ed 1968; SUNY at Buffalo (MED) PE 1975, (EDD) Exercise Sci 1988; *cr:* Hamburg Elem Schls PE Tchr 1970-86; Hamburg Cntrl Schls Track, Cross Cntry Coach 1970-90; Hamburg HS PE Tchr 1987-; *ai:* Shared Decision Making Team; Phi Delta Kappa 1985-, Exec Bd; AAHPERD 1975-; People to People 1992-, Del to Russia 1992; USA Track Ofcl 1992-, Nation Cert; *office:* Hamburg Sr HS 4111 Legion Dr Hamburg NY 14075

GORMAN, BARBARA JO AMATO, Spanish & French Teacher; *b:* Easton, PA; *c:* Sean Joseph, Corinne Marie; *ed:* Seton Hill Coll (BA) Fr Ed 1971; Le High Univ (MA) Ed, Span 1973; *cr:* Allentown Cntrl Cath HS Span, Fr Tchr 1971-76; Bethlehem Cath HS Lang Dept Chprsn 1976-, Public Relations Dir, Summer Schl Dir; *ai:* Natl Honor Soc Adv; Homecoming Coord; Exch Stu; Schl Regnl Liason; Majorette & Bandfront Coach; Allentown Diocese Log Tchr Assn 10 Yrs; Natl Cath Tchr Assn 23 Yrs; AATF 25 Yrs; Amer Assn of Tchrs of Span & Portuguese 25 Yrs; St Jane's Schl PTA Bd 1991-, Sec 1995-; HS Advy Bd 1992-; HS Endowment Bd of Trustees 1993-; HS Band Parents Exec Bd 1976-92; *home:* 4600 Henry St Easton PA 18045*

GORMAN, ROSE M., History & English Teacher; *b:* Gloucester, NJ; *ed:* Rowan Coll (BA) Sociology 1987; *cr:* St Edward Schl 7th Grd Tchr 1987-94; Gloucester Cath HS 1994-; *ai:* Yrbk Adv; Project TEAMS; AKD 1985-; *office:* Gloucester Catholic HS 333 Ridgeway St Gloucester City NJ 08030

GORMAN, TERESA PLUNTINO, First Grade Teacher; *b:* Bronx, NY; *m:* Christopher; *c:* Angela, Christina; *ed:* Iona Coll (BA) Psych, Ed 1979; Coll of New Rochelle (MS) Therapeutic Ed 1982; Level 1, 2 Cert Cath Schl Catechist; *cr:* St ann Schl Second Grd Tchr 1979-83; St Eugene Schl Kndgtn-Second Grd Tchr 1983-; *ai:* Field Trip Coord; Standardized Testing Coord; NCEA 1984-; Psi Chi 1979-; *office:* St Eugene Schl 707 Tuckahoe Rd Yonkers NY 10710*

GORMAN, THOMAS JOSEPH, Mathematics Teacher; *b:* Pittston, PA; *ed:* Univ of Scranton (MS) Scndry Schl Admin 1985; *cr:* St Paul Schl 7th-8th Grd Math Tchr 1970-75; Mary Wood Coll Admissions Cnslr 1975-76; Scranton Prep Schl 10th-11th Grd Math Tchr 1976-; *ai:* Scoreboard Operator for Bsktbl & Wrestling 19 Yrs; SAT Course; NCEA 1976-; NPCTM 1980-; *office:* Scranton Prep Schl 1000 Wyoming Ave Scranton PA 18509

GORMLEY, JANET SUSAN, Second Grade Teacher; *b:* Westerly, RI; *m:* James; *c:* Jimmy; *ed:* Suffolk Univ (BA) Psych 1965; 48 Credit Hrs Ed; *cr:* Children's Hosp Boston Rsrch Asst 1966; Floyd Bell Elem Grd 2 & 4 Tchr 1966-79; C. R. Weeks Elem Grd 2 Tchr 1979-; *ai:* K-2 Curr, Report Card Comms; AFT, NY St Tchrs, Windsor Tchrs 1966-; Delta Kappa Gamma 1995-; Suffolk Univ Alumni Assn 1966-; *office:* C R Weeks Elem Schl 440 Foley Rd Windsor NY 13865

GORNEY, JAMES A., Jr High Math Teacher; *b:* Weirton, WV; *m:* Joanne; *ed:* West Liberty St Coll (BA) Ele Ed 1971; WV Univ Masters Ele Ed 1973; Univ Pittsburgh 16 Credit Hrs; *cr:* Indian Creek Schl Dist Teacher 27 Yrs; *ai:* NEA, OEA 1968-; *home:* 207 Summit Ave Mingo Junction OH 43938

GORNICKI, HENRY A., HS History & Law Teacher; *b:* Fargniers, France; *m:* Lucyna A.; *c:* Lisa A. Bolender; *ed:* Niagara Cty Comm Coll (AA) Liberal Arts 1966; St Univ Coll at Buffalo (BS) Sec Ed Soc Stud 1968, (MS) His 1971; Niagara Cty Comm Coll (AAS) Criminal Justice 1983; St Univ Coll at Buffalo (MS) Criminal Justice 1986; Univ of Richmond Law 1983; St Univ at Buffalo His Toward PHD; *cr:* US Marine Corps Flight Clearance 1960-64; Niagaro Cty Comm Coll Criminal Justice Instr 1986-87; Niagara Wheatfield Cntrl Schl HS Tchr 1969-; *ai:* Soc Stud Hiring, Tchr of Yr Comms; NWTA, NYSUT 1969-; Lions Club 1984-; Amer Legion 1985-; Elks 1988-; Tchr of Yr 1994; *office:* Niagara Wheatfield Sr HS 2292 Saunders Steelement Rd Sanborn NY 14132

GORSE, LYNN GAIL, Physical Education Teacher; *b:* Brooklyn, NY; *c:* Jeffrey; *ed:* Hunter Coll (BA) Hlth, PE 1968; Brooklyn Coll (MS) PE 1975; 30 Addl Credits Kingsborough Coll; *cr:* PS 251 Sub Tchr 1972; Various HS Sub Tchr 1972-73; Wingate HS PE Tchr 1973-; Prospect Hghts HS PE Tchr

1975-76; *ai:* Girls Bowling, Gymnastics Club, Sftbl, Vlybl, Boys Vlybl Coach; UFT 1973-; *office:* George W Wingate HS 600 Kingston Ave Brooklyn NY 11203

GORTON, RHONWEN N., French Teacher; *b:* Batavia, NY; *c:* Ashley; *ed:* Lebanon Vly Coll (BA) Fr 1965; SUNY at Cortland (MS) Secd Ed, Fr 1971; Post Grad Stud Laval Univ, SUNY at Binghamton, Univ de Paris VIII; *cr:* Mac Arther Jr HS Fr, Eng Tchr 1965-67; North HS Fr Tchr 1967-71; Binghamton HS Fr Tchr 1971-; *ai:* Fr Club, Peer Mentoring, Tutoring Fr Adv; Intnl Baccalauriate Comm; NEA, AATF 1965-; PTSA 1971-; Jr League 1972-, Chm of Publicity, Show House Comm; Natl Endowment for Hum Grant 1984; Awded AATF Stage at Universile de Paris; NEH Grant 1993; *office:* Binghamton HS 31 Main St Binghamton NY 13905*

GOSBEE, JUDITH ANN (GAUTHIER), English & Journalism Teacher; *b:* Manchester, NH; *m:* Gary B.; *c:* Beth Lauren, Mark J.; *ed:* Univ of Lowell (BA) Eng 1969; Univ of NH (MS) Am Lit 1973, (MS) Writing 1992; *cr:* Haverhill HS Eng, Jrnlsm Tchr 1969-; *ai:* Schl Newspaper Adv Pres 1980; Wkshp Presenter; Merrimack Vly MA Cncl Tchrs of Eng Chair; NCTE 1970-, Exhibit Chair Spring Conf 1996; MCTE 1970-, Merrimack Vly Chair; NEA, HEA 1969-; Bd of Trustees Topsfield Cong Church 1980-, Sec; Chapter Pub; *office:* Haverhill HS 137 Monument St Haverhill MA 01832*

GOSCH, PEGGY (LIPPMANN), First Grade Teacher; *b:* Buffalo, NY; *m:* D. Jeffrey; *c:* Lindsay, Sean; *ed:* Geneseo St Univ (BS) Elem Ed 1968; Cortland St Univ (MS) Elem Ed 1973; *cr:* Kenmore Schls 1st Grd Tchr 1968-69; Copperas Cove Schl Dist 1st Grd Tchr 1969-70; Fayetteville-Manlius Schls 1st-3rd Grd Tchr 1970-73; Niskayuna Schls 1st, 3rd Grd Tchr 1973-76; Liverpool Schl Dist K-2nd, 4th Grd Tchr 1977-; *ai:* Bldg Improvement Team; STARS, Elem Dist Planning Comm; AFT; NYSUT; ULFA; Various Church, Charity Orgs; *home:* 4307 Cinnamon Path Liverpool NY 13090*

GOSEWISCH, STEVEN A., Choral Music Teacher; *b:* New York City, NY; *ed:* Susquehanna Univ (BME) Music Ed 1976; Northwestern Univ (MME) Music Ed 1985; Addl Credits at Dartmouth Univ, Westminster Choir Coll, Western MI Univ; *cr:* Howell HS Choral & Band Tchr 1976-85; Freelance Musician 1976-; Howell HS Choral Tchr 1985-; Monmouth Symphony Orch Assoc Conductor 1994-; *ai:* Annual Musical Vocal Dir; NJEA, NEA, NJMEA, MENC, Phi Mu Alpha Sinfonia 1976-; All Shore Chorus Dirs Past Pres, Conductor & Sec; Region II Jr HS Chorus Past Conductor; Region II HS Symphonic Band Past Conductor; NJ All St Chorus Comm 1985-93; Howell HS Tchr of Yr 1991, Tchr of Month 1995; *office:* Howell HS Squankum-Yellowbrook Rd Farmingdale NJ 07727*

GOSS, GERALDINE CHARLES, Third Grade Teacher; *b:* Jersey City, NJ; *m:* Loney; *c:* Brianne; *ed:* Jersey City St Coll (BA)Early Chldhd Ed 1971; Zoology 3 Credits 1994; Tchng the Holocaust 3 Credits 1995; Tchng Tolerance 6 Credits 1995; *cr:* James F. Murray Schl #38 Tchr First Grd 1971-86, Tchr Third Grd 1987-88, Tchr Second Grd 1988-91, Tchr Third Grd GATE 1991-; *ai:* Organized & Remained Cnslr for Yth Group That Attends the Black Presbyn Caucus Yearly; Cnslr, Adv Yth Group of Jersey City Chptr of NAACP;Comm Mem Who Selected Rdng Prgm for Jersey City Dist 1995; NEA, NJEA, Jersey City EA 1971-; Natl Alliance of Black Schl Edctrs 1993-; Provided Ldrshp in Planning, Dev of a Teen Pregnancy Prevention Prgm Rahway NJ; Jersey City Tchr Recognition Prgm for Outstdng Svc to Children Merrill Lynch, Macmillan, Mc Graw-Hill; *office:* James F. Murray Schl #38 339 Stegman Pky Jersey City NJ 07305

GOSS, STACYANN, Mathematics Teacher; *b:* Trenton, NJ; *m:* John Joseph; *c:* Carly Elizabeth; *ed:* Trenton St Coll (BA) Math Ed 1991; *cr:* Toms River HS South Math Tchr 1991-; *ai:* Choreographer Adv Dance Team, Schl Musicals; Sr Class Adv; NJEA 1991-; *office:* Toms River HS South Hyers St Toms River NJ 08753*

GOSSE, DAVID RONOLD, Mathematics & Computer Tchr; *b:* Lynn, MA; *m:* Janice Kennedy; *c:* Sarah Gosse Dresser, Bryan; *ed:* Wesleyon Univ (MALS) Math 1966; Bowdoin Coll (AB) Math 1958; Boston Univ 70 Hrs Math Ed; Univ of MI 40 Hrs Math; *cr:* Hamilton Wheman Regnl High Tchr 1961-65; Governor Dummer Acad Math Dept Chair 1966-70, Math Tchr 1990-95; Trtiton Regnl Schl Math Dept Chair 1971-90; *ai:* Comp Coord; Comm Svc Dir; Ftbl & Track Coach 1966-71 & 1961-65; NCTM 1961-; NEA & MTA 1971-90; MAA 1990, Departmental Mbrshp; MA Track & Field Ofcls Assn 1985-; Comm Svc Pgm 1990-, Dir; YWCA Vol, Awd 1996; NSF Grants: Salem St, Wesleyan U, U of MI & Penn St; Article Pub; Independent Schl Press; Programming The TI81 Calculator; *office:* Govenor Dummer Acad 1 Elm St Byfield MA 01922

GOSSELIN, CHRISTOPHER MARTYN, Biology Teacher; *b:* Winchester, MA; *m:* Cynthia L.; *ed:* Univ of ME (BS) Wildlife Bio, Sec Sci Ed 1986; Post Grad Curr Dev Sci Ed; *cr:* Londonderry HS Sci Tchr 1989-; *ai:* Sci Club Adv; Recycling Comm; NEA, Londonderry Ed Assn 1989-; Hudson Conservation Commission 1994-; Tchr of Yr 1994-95; St of NH Wildlife Mngmt Curr Comm Mem; *office:* Londonderry HS 295 Mammoth Rd Londonderry NH 03053

GOSSER, RICHARD ALLEN, Mathematics Professor; *b:* St Marys, PA; *m:* E. Danneen Hoover; *ed:* Carnegie-Mellon Univ (MS) Math 1972, (DA) Math 1975; MA Stud Theology at Franciscan Univ of Steubenville OH; Intensive Lang Stud; *cr:* St Vincent Coll Assoc Prof Math 1975-; Wheeling Jesuit Coll Asst Prof Math 1976-77; Franciscan Univ of Steubenville Adjunct Prof Math, Theology 1989-90; *ai:* Hnr Soc Moderator; Coll Tchr Ed Comm; Math Assn of Amer, Sigma Xi 1971-; Haitian Stud Assn 1994-; Washington Ofc on Haiti BOD 1995-, Sec; Greensburg Human Life, Justice Commission 1991-; Alumnus of Distinction St Vincents Coll 1994; Prof of Yr Nom St Vincent Coll 1989; Articles Pub; Haiti Oral His Project; *office:* Saint Vincents Coll & Sem 300 Fraser Purchase Rd Latrobe PA 15650*

GOTCHALL, GLENN JOSEPH, Marketing Ed Coordinator; *b:* Canton, OH; *m:* JoAnn Marie Cinson; *c:* Jessica, Isaac; *ed:* Kent St Univ (BS) Bus Admin 1980; Walsh Univ Ed Cert 1988; Kent St Univ Voc Ed Cert; Ashland Univ Post-Grad Schl Admin & Asst Supts Cert; *cr:* Sandy Valley HS Mrktg Coord 1988-; *ai:* DECA Adv; Var Boys Bstkbl Head Coach; NEA, OEA 1988-; *office:* Sandy Valley HS 5362 St Rt 183 NE Magnolia OH 44643*

GOTSHALL, JONELL, Retired Language Arts Teacher; *b:* Indiana, PA; *m:* Chris C. Gotshall; *ed:* Adrian Coll (BA) Eng 1967; *cr:* Bryan HS Lang Arts Tchr 1967-95; *ai:* Aca Booster Club Exec Bd Schlsp Comm; Acad league Moderator; Strategic Action Comm; Former Lang Arts Dept Chair; NCTE, OH Ed Assn, NEA 1967-95; Bryan Ed Assn 1967-95, Schlsp Comm; Delta Kappa Gamma Soc 1972-, Prgm Comm, Auditing Comm, Initiation Comm; First Church of Christ 1968-, Bd Sec, Deaconess; YWCA 1990-, Nom Comm, Membership Comm, Board of Trustees; Friends of Bryan Lib 1991-.

GOTTLICH, HENRY, Zoology, Chem & Bio Tchr; *b:* Dallas, TX; *m:* Merel; *c:* Kendra, Travis; *ed:* Univ of MD (AA) Paralegal Stud; Lafayette Coll (BA) Bio; George Washington Univ (MED) Admin & Supervision; Gallaudet Univ (MS) Cmptr Tech & Instruction; *cr:* Annapolis Jr HS Sci Tchr 1969-72; Northeast HS Sci Tchr 1972-73; Anne Arundel Cty Sci Resource Tchr 1973-76; Chesapeake HS Sci Dept Chm 1976-86, Zoology, Chem, Advanced Placement Bio Tchr & Cmptr Lab Coord 1986-; *ai:* Var Wrestling Asst Coach; MSTA, TAAAC, NEA; *office:* Chesapeake SR HS 4798 Mountain Rd Pasadena MD 21122

GOTTLIEB, ELIMELECH, Principal; *b:* New York, NY; *m:* Evelyn G.; *c:* Meir, Moile, David, Deena; *ed:* Rabbinical Seminary of Amboy (BS) Pastoral, Cnslng 1976; Long Island Univ (MS) Ed 1981; Yeshia Univ PHD Candidate; *cr:* Hebrew Acad of Nassau Cty Tchr 1987-92, Prin 1992-; *ai:* ASCD, Prin Conf, Regnl Cncl of Queens 1992-; *office:* Hebrew Acad of Nassau Cty 609 Hempstead Ave West Hempstead NY 11552*

GOTTSCH, BREWSTER C., Biology Teacher; *b:* Bayshore, NY; *m:* Jean Ann Quigley; *c:* Katie, Adam; *ed:* Dowling Coll (BA) Bio 1971; Adelphi Univ (MS) Marine Sci 1975; Post Grad 45 Hrs Bio & Ed; 30 Hrs Ed Related; *cr:* Sachem Jr HS Bio Tchr 1971-80; Sachem South HS Bio Tchr 1980-; Suffolk Comm Coll Asst Prof of Bio 1976-; Licensed Marine Capt 1995-; *ai:* Class Govt Adv 1982-; Chaperone Sr Trip 1982-; Curr Writing for Adv Bio Courses, Basic Bio Courses; SCTA 1971-; Babylon Yacht Club 1982-, Bd of Governors; VFW 1988-; Selected as Top Bio Tchr at South; Honorary Mem NHS by Stdnts Twice; Tchr of Week 5 Yrs in Arow; *office:* Sachem South HS 51 School St Lake Ronkonkoma NY 11779

GOTTSCHALK, ELAINE MOYER, Mathematics Teacher; *b:* Baltimore, MD; *m:* John Clark; *c:* Jeffrey C., Kevin A.; *ed:* Coll of Notre Dame MD (BA) Math 1968; Towson St Univ (MED) Scndry Ed 1987; *cr:* Maryvale Prep Schl Math Tchr 1968-70; Notre Dame Prep Schl Math Tchr 1980-; *ai:* Cum Laude Soc Moderator; Run the Schl Textbook Sale; Bus Mgr Schl Play; In Charge Grad Ceremony; Bookkeeper for Sr Class Account; Homeroom Tchr; MCTM, NCTM, AIMS 1980-; Awded Annual Hunt Awd as Outstdng Tchr of Yr; *office:* Notre Dame Prep Schl 815 Hampton Ln Baltimore MD 21286

GOTTSMAN, EARL EUGENE, Vice Pres of Acadamic Affairs; *b:* Carrollton, OH; *m:* Janice Marie Howard; *c:* Kevin Lee, Kendra Louise, Kelly Lynn; *ed:* OH St Univ (BS) Chem 1968; IA St Univ (MS) Chem 1972; *cr:* Capitol Coll Prof 1972-77, Acad Dean 1977-85, Acting Pres 1994, VP Acad Affairs 1985-; *ai:* Yth Bsbl, Bsktbl, Coll Bsktbl, Sftbl Coach; ASEE Past Chprsn; EWC Bd of Dir; James H. Mc Graw Awd Comm; Frederick J. Berger Awd Comm; James H. Mc Graw Awd Recipient Macmillan, Mc Graw, Hill Pub Co 1991; *office:* Capitol Coll 11301 Springfield Rd Laurel MD 20708

GOUDIE, KATHLEEN DONOVAN, English Teacher; *b:* Boston, MA; *c:* Robert Eugene Jr., Kathryn Goudie Tropeano, Colleen Patricia, Michael I., Sean X., Brian N., Douglas P., Kara T., Steven A. (dec); *ed:* Boston Coll (AB) Eng 1956; Smith Coll PG Japan Spec Grant Prgm; Clark Univ Global Stud Fellowship; Amherst Coll NEH Grant; Univ of MA at Amherst Taft Pol Sci Fellow; *cr:* Wareham HS Eng, Civics Tchr 1956-57; Dedham HS His, Civics Tchr 1957-58; Norwell Jr HS His Tchr 1965-67; Athol MS His, Eng Tchr, Gifted & Talented Coord 1970-; *ai:* Team Ldr; MA Tchrs Assn 1960-; NEA; Athol Tchrs Assn, Pres 1989-93, Exec Bd; Delta Kappa Gamma Alpha Mu Chapter, Outstanding Tchrs Intnl Org 1980-; Petersham Meml Lib 1980-, Elected Trustee; Worcester, Franklin, Hampdent, Hampshire Senatorial Dist 1980-95, Democratic St Committeewoman; Petersham Democratic Town Comm 1980-, Chprsn; Bus, Prof Women Mt Grace Chapter, Pres 1993-95; *office:* Athol MS 494 School St Athol MA 01331*

GOUDREAU, MARIANNE, Assistant Headmaster; *b:* Bayshore, NY; *c:* Kristoffer Kegan; *ed:* Suny at Stony Brook (BA) Elem Ed 1971; 60 Credit Hrs; *cr:* Bodreau Museum of Math Dir 1980-83; Buckley Cntry Day Schl Math Dept Coord 1983-90, Asst Headmaster 1991-; *ai:* Goudreau Museum of Math Advy Bd; ASCD 1982-; NCTM, NCAMS 1981-; NCMTA 1981-, Newsletter Ed 1982-85; *office:* Buckley Country Day Schl I U Willets Rd Roslyn NY 11576

GOUGH, MIRIAM, Director of Travel & Tourism; *b:* Portland, ME; *m:* Timothy Reardon; *ed:* Univ of ME at Orono (BA) His 1981; McConnell Schl Cert in Travel 1986; *cr:* Quest Travel Travel Consultant 1986-89; Hewins Travel Travel Consultant 1989-91; Casco Bay Coll dir of Travel & Tourism 1991-; *ai:* Portland Symphony Orch Golf Tournament Vol; Travel & Tourism Adv & Trip Coord; STTE 1991-; ASTA 1991-; State Street Church 1974-, Bd of Deacons, Choir; *office:* Casco Bay Coll 477 Congress St Portland ME 04101

GOUGOUTAS, LINDA HATTMAN, Fourth Grade Teacher; *b:* Mansfield, OH; *m:* Jack Z.; *c:* Christina Areti, Anne Katharine, Alexander Jacob; *ed:* Boston Univ (BA) Ed 1963; Tufts Univ (MS) Ed 1966; 16 Credit Hrs; *cr:* Maria Hastings Schl 1st Grd Tchr 1963-66; Minneapolis Pub Schls 1st-6th Grd Tchr of Gifted & Talented 1980-83; Comm Park Schl 4th Grd Tchr 1985-; *ai:* Sci & Math Comm 1992-; SLP Comm 1994-; Geog Bee Comm 1994-; Gifted & Talented Comm; PTO & PTA 1963-; NEA & NJEA 1985-; Grants: Princeton Regnl Schls Geog & Geology, Indentification of Gifted & Talented, Gifted & Talented Pgm in Minneapolis, McKnight Fndtn for Continuation of Gifted Pgm; Numerous Poems Pub; *office:* Community Park Elem Schl 372 Witherspoon St Princeton Township NJ 08540

GOULART, AMY E., Art Instructor; *b:* Providence, RI; *m:* Edmond Jr.; *ed:* U Mass at Dartmouth (BFA) Painting 1969; Continuing Ed, Jewelry of Metals Course; South Coast Educl Collaborative Cmptr Tech Ctr Cmptr Courses; *cr:* Klitzner Industries Emblematic Jewelry Designer 1969-70; Somerset HS Art Instr 1970-; *ai:* Fac Advy Cncl 1992-93; Restructuring Task Force 1995-; Crisis Intervention Team 1993-; NEA, MTA Somerset Tchrs Assn 1970-; Designed & Had Limited Edition Numbered Prints Produced to Present as Gifts to Retiring Schl Prsnl; *home:* 64 Tucker Ln North Dartmouth MA 02747

GOULD, BARBARA WOODRUFF, Professor of Education; *b:* Saranac Lake, NY; *m:* William D.; *c:* Elizabeth, Will, Warriner; *ed:* Cornell Univ (BA) Sociology 1957; Tchrs Coll at Columbia (MAT) Elem Ed 1958; The Johns Hopkins Univ (EDD) Rdng, Learning Disabilities 1982; *cr:* Goucher Coll Prof, Chair Ed Dept, Lecturer, Asst Prof, Assoc Prof 1983-; *office:* Goucher Coll 1021 Dulaney Valley Rd Baltimore MD 21204

GOULD, BRUCE ALLAN, Electronics & Drafting Teacher; *b:* Passaic, NJ; *m:* Eugenia Mary Mikola; *c:* Jonathan, Rebecca, Aaron; *ed:* Montclair St Coll (BA) Industrial Ed 1968; Montclair St Coll 36 Credit Hrs Post BA; Natl Ed Ctr Electronics Tech 12 Credit Hrs; Apple Comp Svc Comp Tech 24 Credit Hrs; *cr:* Augusta St Schl K-6th Grd Tchr 1968-75; Union Ave Schl K-8th Grd Tchr 1968-75; Berkeley Terr Schl Industrial Arts Tchr 1975-77; Frank Morrell HS Electronics Tchr 1977-; *ai:* Radio Club; Audio Visual Stage Sound & Lighting; Affirmative Action Chm HS & Dist; Monitor Tchr 1994-95; ECEA, NJEA, NEA 1968-; IEA 1968-, Bldg Rep 1968-80, Corresponding Sec 1970-; BSA 1956-, Scout Master 1967-1972; Montville Twp FAS 1972-80, Engr; USAF Aux Civil Air Patrol 1994-, Commnctn Ofcr; HS Tchr of the Yr 1984; BSA Life Saving Awd 1972; MTFSA Gold Piper Awd 1974; *office:* Frank H Morrell HS 1253 Clinton Ave Irvington NJ 07111*

GOULD, CAROLINE ADAMS, Professor of Psychology; *b:* New York City, NY; *m:* Alfred Della Penna; *c:* Laurie Gould Kappe, Cathy Gould Rath, Amy; *ed:* Queens Coll of City Univ of NY (BA) Psych 1964, (MA) Psych 1969; NY Univ (PHD) Psych 1984; *cr:* Suffolk Comm Coll Prof of Psych 1967-; Nassau Comm Coll Adjunct Prof 1970-75; *ai:* Work with Returning Adult Stdnts 1972-; Curr, Schlsp, Prof Dev & Accreditation Comms; Psych Club Adv; Amer Psych Assn 1985-; AFT, NYS United Tchrs 1975-; NY St Ed Dept Psychologist License; Co-Edited Book The Psych of Behavior & Personality 1972; Dissertation Personality Deterimants of Distressed Ident Toward Disabled Pub 1984; SCCC Who Made a Difference Awd 1988; St Univ of NY Chancellors Tchng Excl Awd 1995; Originated Test-Anxiety Prgm 1980, Give Seminars, Made Classroom Video; *office:* Suffolk Community Coll Crooked Hill Rd Brent 11717*

GOULD, DONNA CHICK, Reading Rcvry & Title I Tchr; *b:* NY; *m:* James; *c:* Laura Grant, Jennifer Cushman; *ed:* Colby Coll Lit 1968; 36 Credit Hrs Ed, Elem Rdng & Lang Arts; 6 Credit ME Rdng Recovery Trng; *cr:* Waterville HS Eng Tchr 1968-70; Pub Elem Schls Title I 1978-79; Cushing Schl Title I 1982- Recovery, Title I 1993-; *ai:* Curr Coordinating Cncl Comm;, 1968-; RRCNA 1993-; *office:* Cushing Schl PO Box 548 Wilton

GOULD, DOROTHY LUNKEN, Assoc Prof of Speech & E Niagara Falls, NY; *m:* Lester M.; *c:* Laurie Blinder, Jeffrey Coh Cohen, Wendy Kohlenberg; *ed:* Ithaca Coll (BS) Speech Ed 1951 Univ (MS) Ed 1966; SUNY at Buffalo (MA) Speech Comm 197 Grad Hrs Niagara Univ; *cr:* Niagara Falls Schl System Eng Tchr Niagara Univ Part-time Instr of Eng 1964-66, Inst of Eng 1966-6 Assoc Prof of Eng 1969-; *ai:* Niagara Share Schlsp, Gen Ed Ove Appeals Comms; Friends of Niagara Univ Theatre VP 1989; AA AAUW 1994-; Niagara Hospice 1990-, Bd Mem; Temple Beth Isr Pres; Facilitator for Occidental Chemical Corps Comm Advy B Niagara Univ Niagara University NY 14109*

GOULD, LINDA HARKCOM, Sixth Grade Teacher; *b:* Bridget Cara; *ed:* IN Univ of PA (BS) Elem Ed 1969, (MED) Elem Ed 19 Hrs Univ of Pittsburgh, Univ of PA, Duquesne Univ IN; *cr:* Ap Joint Schl Dist Jr First Grd Tchr 1968-69; Somerset Area Schl Grd Tchr 1969-70, Jr First Grd Tchr 1970-72, Sixth Grd Tchr Kndgtn Tchr 1976-83, Sixth Grd Tchr 1983-; *ai:* Spelling Bee, Club Adv; Publicity Comm & Usher Comm Advs for Musicals; C Grd Camping Trip; SAEA, PSEA, NEA 1969-, Prof Dev Chm Trinity Evangelical Luth Church 1971-; Bell Choir 1992-; Auxiliary Pres; Yth Group Adv 1992-94; Math Tchng Suggestion in Math: Applications & Connections 1994; Holiday Inn Nom O HS Tcdhr 1995.

GOULD, ROBERT ANDREW, Science Dept Head & Te Hackensack, NJ; *m:* Joyce Audrey Cole; *c:* Christopher, Kim Houghton Coll (BS) Zoology 1971; TX A&M Univ (MS) Marine 1973; Montclair St Coll NJ Tchng Cert 1974; *cr:* Wardlaw-Hart Sci Tchr 1974-; *ai:* Grd 9 Head Adv; Boys Var Tennis, Girls Jr Te Coach; Grace Bapt Church 1980-; Pub Article 1973; *home:* 106 Hill Rd Hopatcong NJ 07843

GOULD-LEIGHTON, SUSAN, Math Teacher; *b:* Bethesda, Stephen; *c:* Josiah, Matthew; *ed:* Univ of FL (BA) Speech Pathol FL St (MS) Audiology 1973; Univ of ME at Presque Isle Addl Math; Attnd Univ of Miami & univ of Chicago; *cr:* Univ of M Schl Audiologist 1971-72; Alford, Snider & Assocs Clinical A 1973-74; Aroostook Mental Hlth Ctr Clinical Audiologist 1974 20 Hearing Impaired Pgm Ed Audiologist to Aroostook Cty Schls Aural Rehabilitation Svcs Audiologist 1977-88; Easton Schl Dept Grd Math & Comp Tchr 1988-; *ai:* Odyssey of Mind Coach; Jr Peer Helper Fac Adv; NCTM 1988-; Atomim Assn Tchr of Ma 1989-; ME Ed Assn; NEA; Brainstorming & Grant Writing Group Math, Sci & Tech; Easton Tchrs Assn 1993-, Negotiation Tea Alliance for Math & Sci Reform 1993-, Statewide Action Tea Northern ME Ed Partnership 1994, Reflective Practice Group Mem; Aurora Tchrs Acad at UMPI 1994, Planning Comm; Ct Math & Sci Ldrshp 1994-; ME Schl of Sci & Math 1994-,Bd of Odyssey of Mind Coach 1988-93, 1995; Math Team Coach 19 Conf of MSTA & Atomim Presenter 1992; MMSA Ldrshp Sch Person for Easton 1992-; ME Rsrch Internship for Tchrs & Stdnts Summit ME Coalition for Excl Participant 1993; Techprep Tr Odyssey of Mind Judge 1994; Atomim Fall Conf Presenter 1994; Framework for Math & Sci Reader 1994; Aurora Sci & Math T Participant & Presenter 1994; *office:* ME Schl of Sci & Math 7 Limestone ME 04750*

GOULET, KAREN MC AFEE, 5th Grade Teacher; *b:* Nashua Gary G.; *c:* Megan, Kate; *ed:* Keene St Coll (BA) Elem Ed 197 Coll Post Grad Courses Psych, Art; *cr:* Birch Hill Elem Schl 5t Tchr 1973-76; Bicentennial Elem Schl 5th Grd Tchr 1976- Dunstable Elem Schl 2nd, 5th Grd Tchr 1981-; *ai:* Adopt-A-Sc PTO Bd Tchr Rep; AFT 1973-.*

GOULET, MADELEINE J., Hlth, Phys Educator & Coach; *b:* B ME; *ed:* Plymouth St Coll (BS) PE & Hlth 1983; Continuing Ed *cr:* Biddeford MS Hlth & PE Tchr 1983-85, Sftbl Coach 1983-; B HS Var Field Hockey Coach 1983-, Hlth & PE Tchr 1985-; *ai:* Hockey & 8th Grd Sftbl Coach; NEA 1983-; MTA 1983-; ME Fiel Assn 1983-, Southern Rep; SMAA Coach of Yr 1993, 1988 & 19 Hockey Titles St Champions 1990, Western ME Champions 1990 SMAA League Champions 1991, 1993 & 1995; *office:* Bidde Maplewood Ave Biddeford ME 04005

GOULEY, RAYMOND F., Math Teacher; *b:* Ware, MA; *c:* Ray Christine, Jeffrey; *ed:* Worcester St Coll (BSEd) Math 1962 Scndry Ed 1965; 15 Grad Hrs Holly Cross Coll; 24 Grad Hrs Un *cr:* Holliston HS Tchr, Dept Head 1962-; Cntrl New England 1986-90; *ai:* Tech Comm Chm; Stu Cncl Adv 1965-93; Hollist Assn, MA Fed Tchrs, AFT 1962-; CCD Tchr; Little League Co Grants UVM 1968-72, HC 1967-71; MA St Legislature, Worce Cncl Christmas Party for Underprivileged Children.*

GOURHAN, MARIA MOLINARI, English & World Teacher; City, NJ; *m:* Paul; *ed:* NY Univ (BA) Eng Lit 1987; 16 Credits Inte Italian Lang Course, Intermediate Ger Lang Course of Stu Richmond Coll at London; *cr:* Mc Graw-Hill Inc Mrktg Asst 198 St Dominic Acad Eng Tchr 1989-91; The Blair Acad Summer G Prgm 1991; St Dominic Acad AP Eng, World, Dramatic Lit Tchr 1 Wkshp Inc Pres 1995-; *ai:* Dance Club Moderator; Former Schl N Adv; Frosh Team; NCTE 1989-.

GOURLEY, ROY JAMES, 8th Grd Physical Science Tchr; *b:* S *m:* Mary Lee Porter; *c:* Larry, David, John; *ed:* Clarion Univ (BS) Attnd Allegheny Coll, Penn St at Behrend, Gannon Univ; *cr:* W Schl Dist Sci Tchr1960-; *ai:* Former Wrestling Coach; Aviation C Class Advs, Many Comms; Mid Sts; Wattsburg Ed Assn 1960-, A Offices Held, Tchr of Yr; PA St Ed Assn, NEA 1960-; Local Commission Past Sec; PSEA Retirement Comm 1984-; Church A Several Offices Held; Local Newspaper Articles; Search for Tchng Notes; *home:* 9955 Jamestown Rd Wattsburg PA 16442

GOUTHRO, BARBARA NORTON, Vocal & Drama Teacher; *b.* Kenneth Robert; *c:* Scott David, Amanda Lori; *ed:* Western Ct St U Music Ed 1971; Cntrl CT St Univ (MS) Music Ed 1984; New Engla Trng Ctr Grad; Accelerated Chrstn Ed Trng Cert; *cr:* Pvt Piano Tc Harwinton Con Schl Music, Drama Tchr 1971-78; Torrington C Music Tchr 1985-86; Joy Chr Acad Supvr, Music Tchr 1987-91; Vly Chrstn Schl Music, Drama Tchr 1991-; *ai:* Drama Coach; Song, Play Writers; Music Curr Comm; Dev, Planning Comm Svcs; CEA 1971-, Rep; ACEI 1986-, Admin, Sup; ACSI 1991 Coord Music; MENC 1971-; Chrstn Writers Flwshp 1992-; His 1993-, Pres; Numerous Songs, Plays, Poems Pub 1994-; NE Reg ACSI Conf Speaker 1992-; *office:* Pioneer Valley Christian Plumtree Rd Springfield MA 01119*

, WENDY BYRNE, Language Arts Teacher; *b:* Springfield, MA; V.; *c:* Aaron B., Lauren C.; *ed:* Castleton St Coll (BS) Span 1971; Jniv Elem Ed Cert; *cr:* Woodstock Union HS 9th-12th Grd Span -72; Linwood Pub Schls 6th Grd Tchr 1976-88; Holderness Cntrl 8th Grd Lang Arts Tchr 1988-; *ai:* Yrbk, 8th Grd Adv; Lang Arts nm; NEA 1977-; New England League Mid Schls 1987-, Mid r Recognition Awd 1995; Parenting Conf Planning Comm 1995-; olderness Central Elem Schl RR 3 Box 95 Rt 175 Plymouth NH

, LISA CHASE, Foreign Language Teacher; *b:* Midland, MI; *m:* ; *ed:* MI St Univ (BA) Ger, Fr Ed 1989; Enrolled Ger Ed SUNY 'altz; 9 Credits Span Dutchess Comm Coll; *cr:* Arlington MS Fr Tchr 1990-91; Haviland Jr HS Part-time Fr Tchr 1991; Jr Sr HS Ger, Fr, Span Tchr 1991-; *ai:* Organized, Chaperoned dg Excl Team 1994-95; Dev Sexual Haressment Policy Comm; Tchrs Assn 1991-; NY St Assn Frgn Lang Tchrs 1992-; Our ith Church 1990-, Usher, Lay Reader; Dutchess Cty Area Fund itiated Ger Prgm; Distance Learning Network Tchr; *office:* Jr Sr HS PO Box N Haight Rd Amenia NY 12501*

, RICHARD EDWARD, Elem Instructor; *b:* Chillicothe, OH; *m:* ay; *c:* Matthew, Melissa, Melanie; *ed:* BGSU (BS) Ed 1973; egree Ed; *cr:* Tiffin City Schls Elem Instr 1973-; *ai:* Jr HS Track, oach Early Career; OEA, NEA 1995-; OH MS Assn 1993-; le Lions Club; BSA Den Ldr; Noble Schl PTO, Treas, Sec, VP 3 *e:* Tiffin MS 59 W Market St Tiffin OH 44883

A, STEVE R., History Teacher; *b:* Perth Amboy, NJ; *m:* Irene Stefanie; *ed:* Millersville St (BS) His & Scndry Ed 1967; *cr:* HS Tchr 1969-; *ai:* Var Bsbl Head Coach; NEA, NJEA, MCEA ayreville Ed Assn 1969-, Bldg Rep; South Amboy Lions Club Pres; Amer Legion 1994-; *office:* Sayreville War Memorial HS ington Rd Parlin NJ 08859*

WILMA C., Freelance Artist in Residence; *b:* Rochester, NY; *ed:* Coll (BA) Art 1952; Attnd Syracuse Univ, Boston Univ, RIT; *cr:* Coll Tchr 1954-64; Our Lady of Lourdes 5th-6th Grd Tchr Sacred Heart Prin 1964-69; St Mary's Prin 1970-74; St Ambrose Grd Tchr 1975-85.

NSTATTER, DAVID, 9th-12th Grade Math Teacher; *b:* Buffalo, Nancy Ostempowski; *c:* Eric; *ed:* Univ of Buffalo (MS) Ed 1976; Credits & Math Tech 3 Credits; *cr:* West Seneca Cntrl Schls Math d Tchr 1971-; *ai:* AFT 1971-; NYSUT & WSTA 1971-; *office:* eca Central Schls 4760 Seneca St West Seneca NY 14224

NSTEIN, CAROLE M., Elementary Teacher; *b:* Milwaukee, WI; as; *c:* Lynn; *ed:* Alverno Coll (BED) Ed 1972; Towson St Univ 1975; *cr:* Charles Carroll Elem Schl Tchr 1973-76; Arlington l Tchr 1977-82; Hamilton Elem MS Tchr 1983-; *ai:* Cultural nt Comm; Sci Coord; MIST 1988-; NEA 1975-; St Josephs Parish chr of Yr 1980, 1985; Keystone Inst 1995, Aubudon Ecology 996 Schlsps; *office:* Hamilton Elem Sch 236 2500 E Northern Pky MD 21214*

R, ELISE J., English Teacher; *b:* Hartford, CT; *c:* Caleb; *ed:* eabody Coll Tchrs (BS) Eng 1977; Eastern CT St U (BA) Ed, Eng; Hrs; *cr:* Parish Hill HS Eng Tchr, MS Coord 1986-; *ai:* Peer n Advy Comm; MS Lit Magazine; NEA 1986-93; NELMS; chl Synagogue 1993-, Tchr, Dir; Big Sister, Big Brother 1983-, r; Tchr of Yr 1994; Article Pub; Perkins Grant; *office:* Parish Hill 304 Parish Hill Rd Chaplin CT 06235*

ER, MARY JOAN (TRAYNOR), English Teacher; *b:* Pittsburgh, ric; *ed:* Queens Coll (BA) Eng 1984, (MS) Scndry Ed 1988; 30 ng, Ed, Specializing Writing Lehman Coll; *cr:* Grover Cleveland 1984; Bayside HS Eng Tchr 1984-85; Newtown HS Eng Tchr hman Coll Writing Project Wkshp Ldr 1990; *ai:* Writing Project v 1994-; Schl Play Asst Dir 1988-94; AFT, UFT 1984-; Natl Project 1986-; New York City Writing Project 1986-; NEH Grant Coll 1993; NEH Grant SUNY at Old Westbury 1995; *office:* HS 48-01 90th St Elmhurst NY 11373*

ER, ROBERTA KAPLAN, 6th Grade Teacher; *b:* Brooklyn, NY; Gary; *c:* Samantha Irene; *ed:* Long Island Univ (BS) Ed 1969; v (MS) Admin, Supervision 1993; *cr:* PS 397 Math Coord, 4th h Tchr 1970-78, PS 92 Math Coord, 4th Grd, Math Tchr 1970-78; Math Coord, 4th Grd, Math Tchr 1970-78; PS 1 6th Grd, 5-6 Grd, ldren, Art, ESL Tchr 1984-; *ai:* UFT Chprsn; Schl Based Mngmt, ide Projects Team Mem; Sr Citizens, Stdnts Intergenerational Chess Club Coord; Yrbk, Handbook Co-Coord; Phi Beta Kappa ce Univ Mentor for Stu Tchrs & Schlshp Stdnts 1991-; 2 Articles -95; Chosen Outstdng Educl Stu of Yr 1993; *office:* PS 1 Alfred 8 Henry St New York NY 10038

AN, PAMELA GARVIN, Sixth Grade Teacher; *b:* Beaver Falls, ric B.; *c:* Erick B., Brett; *ed:* Geneva Coll (BSEd) Elem Ed 1976; wn St Univ (MS) Rdng Specialist 1980; Post Grad Work; Grad rs Kent St Univ; Post Grad Work Walsh Univ; *cr:* Boardman Ctr rd Tchr 1976-80; Market Street Elem Schl 2nd Grd Tchr 1982-86, chr 1986-87; Pvt Tutor 1987-89; Market Street Elem Schl 1st Grd 9-93; Boardman Ctr MS 6th Grd Tchr 1993-; Pvt Tutor 1994-; *ai:* dv 1978-80; IRA, NEA, OEA 1976-; Phi Delta Kappa 1985-; Acad es Educl Club 1982-, Treas, Trustee; Cub Scout Pack 25 1995-, stn Ed 1990-, Comm; Eastvale Reformed Church, Comm; PTA ep; Market Street Elem PTA Tchr Edctr of Yr 1992; Martha Holden Grant Purchasing Math Manipulatives 1993; Eng Festival Judge wn St Univ 1996; *office:* Boardman Center MS 7410 Market St n OH 44512

ER-SINCLAIR, EVONNE, 2nd Grade Teacher; *b:* Rochester, Edinboro Univ (BS) Elem Ed 1971; Slippery Rock Univ Masters 1974; *cr:* Rochester Elem Schl 1st & 2nd Grd Tchr 1972-; *ai:* Registration Coord; NEA, PSEA, RAEA 1972-, Sec RAEA; Delta Gamma Soc Intnl 1990-; Conway Area Jaycees Outstdng Young 81; Communique Magazine Beaver Cty Edctr of the Month 1991; ochester Area Schl District 540 Reno St Rochester PA 15074

N, KATHLEEN ANN, English Teacher; *b:* White Plains, NY; *m:* Corey, Bryan, Tom; *ed:* Univ of Albany (BA) Eng Ed 1973; Univ lo (EDM) Eng Ed 1992; In-Svc Courses IBM Working with , Cooperative Learning Principles; *cr:* Holland MS 5th-8th Grd Gifted & Talented 1992-93; Orchard Park MS 8th Grd Eng Tchr *:* Staff Dev Comm; 8th Friendship Fringe Day Chprsn; Sleepout Homeless Fundraising; NCTE, NEA 1990-; East Aurora Boys & b 1995-, Exec Bd Mem; East Aurora HS PTO 1991-; Orchard Park 3-; Platelet Donor for Amer Red Cross 1990-; *office:* Orchard Park Lincoln Ave Orchard Park NY 14127

WSKI, CAROLE FRANTZ, 2nd Grade Teacher; *b:* Long Branch, homas; *c:* Thomas, Carlee, Katelyn; *ed:* Kean Coll (BA) Ed 1970; Dickenson (MS) Human Dev 1990; *cr:* UB Memrl Schl Kndgtn 2-86, 2nd Grd Tchr 1986-; *ai:* Keyport HS Hall of Fame Comm; 70-; NJEA; UBEA; Keyport Historical Soc; Mini Grant 1973; emorial Schl Morningside Ave Union Beach NJ 07735

WSKI, SUSAN MCDERMOTT, Secondary Math Teacher; *b:* ty, NJ; *m:* Thomas H.; *c:* Matthew, Phillip, Jaime; *ed:* Jersey City St (BA) Math 1985, (MA) Math Ed 1990; *cr:* Jonathalogan Finc Collection 1969-74; Telaction Phone Full Charge Bookkeeper 1974-77; Nanos Simsarian Agency Insurance Bookkeeper 1977-79; Memrl HS Math Tchr 1985-; *ai:* Math Club & Acad Team Adv; NEA 19885-; NJEA 1985-; WNYEA 1985-; *office:* Memorial HS 5501 Park Ave West New York NJ 07093*

GRACE, BETTY MC KOY, Second Grade Teacher; *b:* Broadway, NC; *c:* Valerie Harris, Ramona, Cassandra Alleyne, Arlesia Mc Gowan, Vanessa; *ed:* Rutgers Coll at Newark (BA) Urban Stud, Elem Ed 1976; Working Towards Masters at Kean Coll, Jersey City St; *cr:* George Wash Schl 5th Grd Tchr 1976; Walter O. Krumbiegel Schl 2nd Grd Tchr 1977-87; Hurden Looker Schl 2nd Grd Tchr 1988-; *ai:* In House, Textbook, Vreeland Awd Comms; NJEA, NEA, HEA 1976-; Tchr of Yr 1992; *home:* 820 Summer St Elizabeth NJ 07202

GRACE, C. DWANE, Curriculum Director; *b:* Lima, OH; *ed:* Bluffton Coll (BS) Bio 1967; Saint Francis Coll (MSEd) Bio 1979; Wright St Univ (EDS) Curr & Supervision 1986; *cr:* Lima Perry Local Schls Tchr 1967-72; Celina City Schls Tchr 1973-94, Curr Dir 1994-; *ai:* NABT, SECO, NCSE, ASCO; Optimist Club 1994-; Univ of Dayton-WOEA Tchr of Yr 1986; Natl Assn of Bio Tchrs Outstanding Bio Tchr Ohio 1991; *office:* Celina City Schls 585 E Livingston Celina OH 45822

GRACE, KAY WILLIAMSON, First Grade Teacher; *b:* Ft Lewis, WA; *m:* Geoffrey Leon; *c:* Erich W., Bryan E.; *ed:* SUNY at Fredonia (MS) Elem Ed 1979; St Bonaventure Univ (BS) Elem Ed 1972; Jefferson Comm Coll (AA) Liberal Arts 1970; Post-Grad Stud Admin 30 Hrs; *cr:* Wellsville Cntrl Schls Remedial Rdng Tchr 1972-74; Hamburg Cntrl Schls Level 5, Level 2 Tchr 1975-; Union Pleasant Schl Level K, Readiness Tchr 1977; Armor Schl Level 6 Tchr 1980-93; Charlotte Ave Schl Level 1 Tchr 1993-; *ai:* Ath Intramural Coach; Builders Adv; Compact for Learning Dist Level Mem; IST, Bldg Level, Staff Dev, Tech, Pub Relations, PTA Comms; Reflections Chprsn 1990-; AFT, NEA 1972-; NYSUT 1972-, Legislative Rep, Svc Awd; PDK 1985-; Kiwanis Org 1992-, L6-Adv; PTA 1978-, VP, Membership Chprsn, Reflections Chprsn, Corr-Rec Sec; Jane Skrypek Ed of Yr Awd 1990; Excl in Tchng Awd 1987-93; Distinguished Svc Awd 1993; Lifetime Membership Awd PTA 1990; *office:* Hamburg Cntrl Schls 301 Charlotte Ave Hamburg NY 14075

GRACE, LYNNE R., English Teacher; *b:* Pittsburgh, PA; *m:* Thomas A.; *c:* Stephanie, Cindy; *ed:* Penn St Univ (BA) Eng 1970; Montclair St Univ (MA) Eng 1976; *cr:* Moon Jr High 7th Grd Eng Tchr 1970-71; Irvington HS Remedial Eng 1971; Carteret HS Eng Tchr 1971-; *ai:* Anne Scott News, Loudspeaker Yrbk & Natl Hnr Soc Adv; CEA, NJEA & NEA 1971-; NCTE 1990-; GSSPA 1990-; NEH Ind Stud Flwshp; *office:* Carteret HS 199 Washington Ave Carteret NJ 07008

GRACE, SALLY ANN (LEFOER), Kindergarten Teacher; *b:* Youngstown, OH; *m:* Dominic Joseph; *c:* Celeste Conrad, Denise Lindheim, Carol Mullen; *ed:* Youngstown St Univ (BS) Elem Ed 1972, (MA) Elem Ed, Rdng Specialist, Supervision 1976; Attnd Univ of Akron, Kent St Univ, Ashland Coll; *cr:* Strouss Hirshberg Co IBM Keypunch Operator 1956-57; Attorney Countryman Sec 1957-61; Youngstown Parochial Schls Tchr 1968-70; Youngstown St Univ Tchr, Limited Fac 1990; Youngstown City Schls Tchr 1970-; *ai:* Kndgtn Report Card, Early Chldhd Dev, Curr Prospectus Comm; NEA, Youngstown Ed Assn, OH Ed Assn, Intl Rdng Assn 1970-; Children's Intl Summer Village 1970-, Sec; *office:* West Elem Schl 134 N Hazelwood Ave Youngstown OH 44509

GRADILONE, EDWARD ANTHONY, Guidance Counselor; *b:* Westerly, RI; *m:* Joan Mac Donald; *c:* Jonathan Ferraro, Joshua Ferraro; *ed:* Univ of RI (BA) Italian, Span 1970, (MA) Ed Cnslng 1976; *cr:* Stamford HS Tchr 1971-73; Westerly HS Italian, Span, ESL Tchr 1973-84, Cnslr 1984-; *ai:* Peer Mediation Adv; NEA, RIAT 1971-; NEAT 1971-, Treas; Dante Soc of Westerly 1970-, Pres, Treas; *office:* Westerly HS 23 Ward Ave Westerly RI 02891*

GRADONE, JEANNE MARINARO, Math Teacher & Administrator; *b:* Springfield, MA; *m:* Richard Anthony; *c:* Richard II, Jeffrey; *ed:* Montclair St Coll (BA) Math 1967; Seton Hall Univ (MA) Educl Admin 1983; Fordham Univ PHD Cand Educl Admin 1996-; *cr:* Parsippany HS Math Tchr 1967-69; Potomac Sr HS Math Tchr 1969-70; Bayley-Ellard HS Math & Rel Tchr, Assoc Prin, Alumni Relations & Dev Prin Dir 1978-; *ai:* Stu Cncl; Alumni & Dev Dir; Mid Sts Steering & Curr Comms; NCEA 1978-; ASCD 1984-; NASSP 1988-; Phi Delta Kappa 1994-; St Vincents Schl Bd 1992-, Pres; Diocesan Tchr of Yr Nom; Bayley Ellard HS Outstdng Svc Awd & Prins Awd; *office:* Bayley Ellard HS 205 Madison Ave Madison NJ 07940*

GRADONE, RICHARD ANTHONY, Professor of Music; *b:* Newark, NJ; *m:* Jeanne Marinaro; *c:* Richard, Jeffrey, Christine O'Toole; *ed:* Manhattan Schl of Music (BM) Trumpet Performance 1968; Cath Univ of Amer (MA) Musicology 1972; NY Univ (PHD) Music His 1980; *cr:* USAF Band Trumpeter & Tech Sgt 1968-72; Chatham Boro Bd of Ed Instrumental Music Instr 1972-80; Fairleigh Dickinson Univ Adj Music Prof 1974-80; Cty Coll of Morris Music Prof 1980-; *ai:* Concerts, Recitals & Performances Throughout US & Europe; Amer Fed of Musicians 1964-; NEA & NJEA 1972-; Cty Coll of Morris VP Awd for Acad Excl 1993-94; Univ of TX at Austin Natl Inst for Salt & Orgnl Dev Tchr Excl Awd Recipient 1996; *office:* County Coll Of Morris Rt 10 & Center Grove Road Randolph NJ 07869

GRADSIHAR, SUSAN CLOR, Mathematics Teacher; *b:* Harbor Beach, MI; *m:* Frederick J.; *c:* Daniel F., Matthew J., Michael J.; *ed:* Univ of DE (BS) Elem Ed 1970, (MED) Math Ed 1982; *cr:* Dowell Elem Schl 4th, 6th Grd Math Tchr 1971-72; Shue MS 6th-8th Grd Resource Tchr 1972-1973; Medill Elem Sch 5th Grd Tchr 1973-76; Magnolia MS Math Tchr 7th & 8th Grd Math Tchr 1979-81; John Carroll Schl 9th-12th Grd Tchr 1981-; *ai:* Moderator, Adv Schl Lit Magazine; Mem Tech Comm; Mem Admissions Comm; NCEA; NCTM 1981-; Forest Hill Rec Cncl 1983-, Tennis Chprsn; Presbyterian Church Sunday Schl Tchr; VAST at Univ of DE; Tchr of Yr 1993; *office:* John Carroll Schl 703 E Churchville Rd Bel Air MD 21014

GRADY, JACQUELINE J. STUCKEY, Social Worker; *b:* Brooklyn, NY; *m:* Charles E.; *c:* Yvette Hodge, Charles, Todd E.; *ed:* NH Coll (BS) Human Svcs, Drug, Alcohol 1983; Springfield Coll (MSW) Genotology 1988; Credits Spec Ed Law 1994, Legislative Process 1995; Scndry Schl New SAT Mbrshp Trng 1995; *cr:* CT Comm Care Inc Case Mgr Soc Worker 1984-94; Douglas House Dir; West Haven HS Tchr, Asst, Soc Worker 1993-.

GRADY, KATHY CERDA, 5th Grade Teacher; *b:* Bronx, NY; *m:* Richard C.; *c:* Richard Jr., Patricia, Regina; *ed:* Adelphi Univ (BA) Ed 1965; Continued Ed Past BA with Inservice & Grad Courses; *cr:* Marion St Schl 5th Grd Classroom Tchr 1965-66; Ctr Ave Schl 4th Grd Classroom Tchr 1966-70; Woodland Schl 3rd, 5th-6th Grd Classroom Tchr 1981-; *ai:* Schl Site Base, Dist Curr Comms; NEA 1981-; Hicksville Congress of Tchrs 1980-, Del; Scholars Awd 1991-93, 1995; PTA Founders Day Honoree 1990; *office:* Woodland Avenue Elem Schl 85 Ketcham Rd Hicksville NY 11801

GRADY, MARY LOU MAGEE, Teacher of Gifted & Talented; *b:* Brooklyn, NY; *m:* Alan; *c:* Kevin, Beth Ann Grady-Acker; *ed:* St Johns (BA); Attnd Columbia Tchr Coll, Tchrs Inst of Tech, St Laurence Univ Canadian Stud; *cr:* St Peters Schl 2nd Grd Tchr 1966-68; St Aidans Schl 4th-8th Grd Tchr 1968-76; St Peter Alcantara Schl 4th-5th Grd Sci, Gifted Prgm Tchr 1976-; *ai:* Young Astronauts of Amer Club 1979-89; Odyssey of Mind Coach 1989-; Tech Chair on Line Across Cntry, World; NCEA 1976-; St Aidans Mothers Club 1965-, Pres 1971-72; Rosary Altar Soc 1970-, Pres 1981-82, 1991-93; Bishops Advy Bd 1991-; Cath Tchr Forum 1982-; Comm Citizen Patrol 1987-, Chm; St Anne's Awd Girl Scouts 1978; Grants: Canada Stud St Lawrence Univ 1987, Create Weather Station 1979, Create Astronomy Wkshp 1989; Woman of Yr 1978; St Aidans Time Capsule Burial 1976; Natl Durg Awareness Winners 1986; NY St Invention Convention Winners 1990; Odyssey of Mind Regnl Winners Every Year, 5 1st Place Awds 1996; *office:* St Peter of Alcantara Schl 1321 Port Washington Blvd Port Washington NY 11050*

GRADY, NANCY DIMARIA, Fifth Grade Teacher; *b:* Waterbury, CT; *m:* David; *c:* Jonathan, Jason; *ed:* St Josephs Coll (BA) Eng 1968; Cntrl CT St Univ (MS) Ed; Southern CSU; *cr:* Naugatuck Bd of Ed Tchr 28 Yrs; *ai:* Hnr Soc Moderator; Fac Stu Advy Comm; Yrbk Adv; NEA 1968-; CT Ed Assoc 1968-; Suzuki Parents Assoc 1980-, Comm Mem; BSA 1985-, Comm Mem; Holy Cross Mothers Club 1990-, Corresp Sec; Basset Breeders of CT 1995-, Mem; *office:* Central Ave Elem Schl 28 Central Ave Naugatuck CT 06770

GRADY, RACHAEL EMMONS, History Dept Chairperson; *m:* D. Benet; *ed:* Bowdon Coll (AB) His, Ed 1990; *cr:* Kathahdin HS His Dept Chprsn 1991-; *ai:* Outstdng Club Adv; Frosh Class Co-Adv; NEA, MEA 1991-; *office:* Katahdin HS PO Box 60 Sherman Station ME 04777*

GRADY, RAYMOND F., AP American History Teacher; *b:* Boston, MA; *m:* Vicki Apostolu; *c:* Raymond, Kara; *ed:* Plymouth St Coll (BA) Amer His, Ed 1969; Salem St Coll (MA) Amer His, Ed 1973; Post Grad Univ of NH 1970-72, Fitchburg St Coll 1980-83; Harvard Univ 1995-; *cr:* Exeter Area Jr HS Tchr 1969-71; North Andover HS Tchr 1971-; *ai:* NEA 1969-; MTA, NATA 1971-; Lowell Lawrence Scholars Prgm Harvard Univ; *office:* North Andover HS 675 Chickering Rd North Andover MA 01845*

GRADY, VERONA MARJORIE, 4th Grade Teacher; *b:* Ventnor City, NJ; *m:* Dominic J.; *c:* Pamela Grady Rozelsky, James D.; *ed:* Trenton St Coll (BA) Elem Ed 1961; West Chester Univ (MA) Elem Ed 1992; *cr:* Carl O. Benner Schl Tchr 1961-62; King's Hwy Schl Tchr 1978-; *ai:* Grd Level Chprsn; Mentor Tchr; NEA, PSEA, CA Tchrs Assn, Phi Delta Kappa; Olivet United Meth Church; Coatesville Book Club; Coatesville United Charities, Past Chprsn; Bannon Schlsp Grad Schl WCU; Outstanding Tchr of Yr; Writer D. C. Heath Soc Stud 1993 Ed; *home:* 100 Morris Rd Coatesville PA 19320

GRAESER, BARBARA PARK, Teacher of Gifted; *b:* Warren, OH; *m:* Joseph H. Jr.; *c:* Cynthia, Jonathan; *ed:* Westminster Coll (MED) Rdng 1990; Ashland Univ 20 Hrs Gifted; *cr:* Bascom Elem 3rd Grd Tchr 1974-77; Hillyer Primary Tchr 1985-86; Lakeview MS Tchr of Gifted 1990-; *ai:* Power of the Pen Writing Coach; Sunday Schl Tchr; Alliance Women, Pres; Power of the Pen Awd; *office:* Lakeview MS 640 Wakefield Dr Cortland OH 44410

GRAF, CAROL COLES, English & Journalism Teacher; *b:* Woodbury, NJ; *m:* Philip V.; *ed:* Moravian Coll (BA) Eng 1966; Trenton St Coll Addl Credits; *cr:* Rancocas Valley Regnl HS Eng Tchr 1966-; *ai:* Yrbk Adv; Sr Trip Coord; Mid Sts Co-Coord; Schlsp & Recognition Comm; Class Adv; NEA, NJEA, BCEA 1966-; RVRHSEA 1966-, VP, Sec; Tchr of Yr, Local Schl Awd Recognized by Governor; *office:* Rancocas Valley Reg HS 572 Jacksonville Rd Mount Holly NJ 08060

GRAF, MONIQUE, Criminal Justice Professor; *b:* Beverly, MA; *m:* Lawrence J. McKenna Jr.; *c:* Rachel Emily McKenna; *ed:* Univ of MA (BS) 1992, (MA) Criminal Justice 1993; Pursuing Assocs in Alcohol & Drug Abuse Counseling; *cr:* Univ of MA at Lowell Tchng Asst 1992-93, Adjunct Fac 1993-; Hesser Coll Adjunct Fac 1993-94; NH Tech Inst Instr 1993-; *ai:* Criminal Justice Club Adv; Mem of Judicial Comm II & Customer Svc Comm at NH Tech Inst; Amer Correctional Assn 1994-; Acad Criminal Justice Sci 1994-; New England Cncl on Crime & delinquency 1993-; Outstanding Grad Stu Awd; *office:* NH Tech Inst 11 Institute Dr Concord NH 03301

GRAFF, CARLEEN A., Professor of Music; *b:* Bloomington, IL; *ed:* IL Wesleyan Univ (BME) Piano 1968; Univ of Denver (MA) Piano Performance 1970; Univ of Nothern CO (DA) Piano Performance & Pedagogy 1984; Attnd Columbia Tchrs Coll; *cr:* IN St Univ Class Piano Instr 1972-73; Plymouth St Coll Music Prof 1973-; *ai:* Fac Adv; MTNA Stu Chapter; MTNA 1973-, Collegiate Coord Competitions, Natl Competitions Chair, Master Tchr Cert; NHMTA Tchr of Yr 1993; *office:* Univ Of NH Plymouth St Coll Dept Of Music Theatre Plymouth NH 03264

GRAFF, DAVID P., Health & PE Teacher; *b:* New York, NY; *m:* Marsha Goldman; *c:* Michael; *ed:* Adelphi Univ (BS) PE 1976, (MA) Hlth Ed 1978; *cr:* JCC on the Palisades Ath Dir 1980-83; Riverdale YM-YWHA Hlth & Recreation Svcs Dir 1983-87; Westbury HS Hlth, PE Tchr 1987-; *ai:* Boys Var Bsktbl Asst Coach; JV Boys Bsktbl Head Coach; Peer Aids Edctrs Group Adv; Westbury Tchrs Assn, AAPHERD 1988-; Bsktbl Var 3 Time Nassau Cty B Champions 1993-96; Jr Var86 and 5 over Last 6 Seasons; Drug Ed Shows for Grd Schls in Dist; *office:* Westbury HS 1 Post Rd Old Westbury NY 11568

GRAFF, G. ARCHIE, 8th Grd Social Studies Teacher; *b:* Kittanning, PA; *ed:* Shepherd Coll (BASC) Soc Stud 1984; 15 Grad Credit Hrs His; 15 Grd Credit Hrs Ed; *cr:* Boonsboro High His Tchr 1985; Northern Mid Soc Stud Tchr 1985-; *ai:* Var Sftbl Coach; United Way Rep; IM Coord; NEA 1985-; WCTA 1985-; Natl Wildlife Fed; Nature Concervency; *office:* Northern MS 701 Northern Ave Hagerstown MD 21742*

GRAFF, HAL, English Teacher; *b:* Pittsburgh, PA; *ed:* Geneva Coll (BA) Eng 1965; Duquesne Univ (MA) Eng 1976; Attnd Carnegie-Mellon Univ; *cr:* Keystone Oaks HS Eng Tchr 1965-; *ai:* NHS; NEA, PSEA 1965-; NCTE 1964-; *office:* Keystone Oaks HS 1000 Kelton Ave Pittsburgh PA 15216

GRAFFAM, ALLEN CLINTON, Band Director; *b:* Portland, ME; *m:* Laura Waite; *c:* Kyra, Brooke; *ed:* Univ of ME (BS) Music Ed 1975; 9 Credit Hrs; 9 Credit Hrs Univ of Southern ME; *cr:* Brunswick Jr HS Band Dir 1975-81; Brunswick HS Band Dir 1981-83; Mt Ararat HS Band Dir & Dept Chair 1983-; *ai:* Mem Goals 2000 Comm-MSAD 75; Brunswick Yth Soccer League Coach; Amer Fed of Musicians 1971-; Music Edctrs Natl Conf 1975-, Band VP, Dist Pres, Dist Band Mgr; NEA 1975-; Natl Band Assn 1991-; Frequent Guest Conductor Band & Orch Festivals & Camps; Music Dir & Conductor Chandlers Band ME; Active Free Lance Musician at Various Orch, Chorales, Symphony & Big Band Productions in the ME Area; *office:* Mount Ararat Schl Rt 201 Topsham ME 04086

GRAFFEO, GUSSIE VICTORIA, Business Teacher & Treasurer; *b:* Brooklyn, NY; *ed:* Queens Coll (BA) Ec 1974; St Johns Univ (MBA) Acctng 1977, (MA) Cnslng 1996; PD Admin 1993; *cr:* Deloitte Haskins & Sells Accountant 1977-80; Forest Hills HS Bus Tchr 1983-86, 1988-89; NYC BOE Bus Occupational Specialist 1986-87; Grafco Fin Svcs CPA, CFP, Owner 1981-; LaGuardia Comm Coll Asst Prof 1986-; Long Island City HS Bus Tchr & Treas 1989-; *ai:* Coopers & Lybrand NYC Mentoring Pgm; NYNEX Mentor Coord & Recruitment Adv; NYS Peace Pgm Coord; Schls Telecomm Station Founder; GETN Linkage; Bus Ed Assn 1983-, Exec Bd; NYSSCPAS 1986-, Pub Speaker; AICPA 1986-; Intnl Assn Fin Planning 1994-; TASCA 1986-; Phi Delta Kappa 1993-; Appalachian Mountain Club 1993-; Sierra Club 1993-; Long Island City HS Tchr of Yr Nom; Grant Writer: Coopers & Lybrand Bus Awareness, NYC BOE Bus Cluster Curr; Queens Women Ctr Pub Speaker; Numerous Articles Pub; *office:* Long Island City HS 1430 Broadway Long Island City NY 11106

GRAFTON, DIRK S., Asst Prof of Criminology; *b:* Kittanning, PA; *m:* Beth P. Reifsteck; *c:* Christopher, Diana; *ed:* Indiana Univ of PA (BA) Criminology 1977, (MA) Criminology 1986; PA St Police Municipal Police Officers Trng Acad; *cr:* Kittanning Police Dept Police Officer 1978-81; IN Police Dept Police Officer 1981-87; Mt Aloysius Coll Asst Prof 1987-; *ai:* Ben Franklin Lodge of Free & Accepted Masons 1986-; Ancient Accepted Scottish Rite, JAffa Temple AAONMS 1993-; Contributing Authorship; *office:* Mount Aolysius College 1 College Dr Cresson PA 16630

GRAHAM, BEVERLY NICOLIS, Science Teacher; *b:* Long Island City, NY; *m:* John Edward; *c:* Gavin A., Kyle M.; *ed:* SUNY at Plattsburgh (MS) Sec Ed, Bio 1975; SUNY at STonybrook (MA) Lbrl Stud 1980; 66 Credit Hrs Grad, Inservice Courses; *cr:* Lindenhurst Schl Dist Sci Tchr 1976-78; Brentwood Schl Dist Sci Tchr 1978-82; Longwood Schl Dist Sci Tchr 1982-; *ai:* Natl Schl of Excl Fac; NYS Blue Ribbon Schl Fac; *office:* Longwood Jr HS 198 Longwood Rd Middle Island NY 11953*

GRAHAM, DONNA MC CARVER, High School Business Ed Instr; *b:* Poplar Bluff, MO; *ed:* Kent St Univ (BA) Bus Ed 1971; Marietta Coll (MA) Ed 1995; Addl Hrs OH Univ, Ashland Coll, Kent St Univ; *cr:* Ft Frue HS Bus Instr 1971-; *ai:* Newspaper, Class Adv; St Dept Career Focus Group; Career Ed Coord; OH Bus Tchrs Assn 1968-; SE OH Bus Tchrs Assn 1971-; Human Soc of OH Vly 1971-, Treas, Bd of Dirs; Amer Trakehoner Assn 1982-, Bd of Dir; Jennings Scholar; Outstdng Young Edctr; Honorary Degree Quill & Scroll, FFA; Book: The Equine Record; Outstdng Young Women of Amer; *office:* Fort Frye HS PO Box 68 Beverly OH 45715

GRAHAM, DOROTHY Y., Global Studies Teacher; *b:* Rochester, NY; *m:* David R.; *c:* Rebecca, Jeffrey; *ed:* St Univ Coll at Oswego (BS) Sec Ed Soc Stud 1967; Elmira Coll (MS) Sec Ed Soc Stud 1990; *cr:* Pittsford Cntrl Schls Sec Ed Soc Stud Tchr 1967-68; Horseheads Cntrl Schl Dist Global Stud Tchr 1991-; *ai:* Acad Challenge Competition Team Adv; AFT, NYSCSS 1991-; Kappa Delta Pi 1990-; Chemung Co League of Women Voters 1980-, Pres; *office:* Horseheads HS 401 Fletcher St Horseheads NY 14845

GRAHAM, FRAN E., First Grade Teacher; *b:* Lockport, NY; *m:* Daniel Thomas; *c:* Sara Elizabeth, Kelli Jessica; *ed:* Rosary Hill Coll at Buffalo (BS) Elem Ed 1975; Buffalo St Coll (MS) Early Chldhd Ed 1979; Univ of Buffalo Ed Courses; In-Svc Courses; *cr:* Heim Elem Schl K-3rd Grd Tchr 1975-; *ai:* WTA, NYSUT 1975-; NY Rdng Assn 1980-; *office:* Heim Elem Schl 155 Heim Rd Williamsville NY 14221

GRAHAM, GAIL PETRAS, Kindergarten Teacher; *b:* Plattsburg, NY; *m:* Robert D.; *c:* Jennifer H. Douris, Marla A. Del Giudice; *ed:* Cornell Univ (BS) Child Dev, Family Relationships 1961; 15 Grad Credits; *cr:* Atlantic City Day Nursery Dir 1972-82; Upper Twp Schl Kndgtn Tchr 1974-; *ai:* NEA, NJEA 1974-; UTEA 1974-, Corresponding Sec; Charity League Atlantic Cty 1962-, Sec, VP; Girl Scouts Cape Cumberland Cty 1970-, Bd of Dirs; Historical Preservation Soc Upper Twp 1994-; Elem Schl Tchr of Yr 1990-91; Hands Across the Water Soviet-Amer Tchr Exch 1991-92; Cape Educl Fund Grant Winner 1993-95; Harrah's Casino Mini Grant 1995; *home:* 4 Gardners Ln Marmora NJ 08223*

GRAHAM, H. GLEN,JR., Biology Teacher; *b:* Buffalo, NY; *m:* Stephanie R. Lewis; *c:* Kendra; *ed:* SUC at Buffalo (BSEd) Bio 1990; Canisius Coll (MS) Ed 1995; 4 Yrs of Stud in PE; *cr:* Cleveland Hill HS Sci Tchr 1990-; *ai:* Var Ftbl Asst Coach; Var Co-Coach Girls Bsktbl; Sr Class Adv; NYSUT 1990-; Black Coaches Assn 1990-; Roswell Park Cancer Rsrch Inst Minority Stu Sci Rsrch Pgm 3 Yr Flwshp; *office:* Cleveland Hill HS 105 Mapleview Rd Cheektowaga NY 14225

GRAHAM, JUDITH ANNE, 2nd Grade Teacher; *b:* Lorain, OH; *m:* Michael D.; *c:* Stephanie Graham Zmuda, Kristi; *ed:* Southeast Mo St U (BS) Elem Ed 1969; Post Grad Courses: OH St Univ, Bowling Green St Univ, Ashland Univ; *cr:* Cardington-Lincoln 2nd Grd Tchr 1969-70; Mt Gilead Ex Village 3rd Grd Tchr 1970-71; Highland Local Schls 2nd Grd Tchr 1979-82; Mt Gilead Ex Village 1st & 2nd Grd Tchr 1982-83 & 1995-; *ai:* Comms: Schl Net Plus Grant Writing, Right-to-Read Steering, Math Competency, Rdng Competency & Levy Campaign 1985, 1994 & 1996; Supt & Prin Advy; Lang Arts, Rdng & Math Currs; NEA 1979-80, 1982-83; OEA 1979-80, 1982-83; Morrow Cty Rdng Assoc 1988-, Bldg Rep 1994-; Vacation Bible Schl, Dir & Tchr 10 Yrs; Sunday Schl Tchr 2 Yrs; Amer Lutheran Church Women 1969-; Cub Scout Den Mother 1970-71; Living Stones Luth Svc Group 1974-79, Co-Founder; 4-H Adv 1986-88; Little Prides & Joys Mothers Club 1991-, Historian, VP, Project Chm; Bd of Ed Innovation Grant 1983 & 1984; NHS Honored Tchr 1994; Martha Holden Jennings Scholar; *office:* Cherry Street Elem Sch 145 N Cherry St Mount Gilead OH 43338

GRAHAM, LINDA MARIE, Second Grade Teacher; *b:* Toledo, OH; *ed:* Bowling Green St Univ (BS) Elem, Early Chldhd 1980; *cr:* St Jude Cath Elem Third Grd Tchr 1981-90, Second Grd Tchr 1990-; *ai:* Amer Heart Assn Jump Rope for Heart Coord; Sacramental Prgm Instr; Extended Day Care Supvr; Amer Legion Auxialiary 1967-; *office:* St Jude Cath Elem Schl 3648 Victory Ave Toledo OH 43607

GRAHAM, MARGARET MARY, Consumer & Life Stud Teacher; *b:* Winchester, MA; *m:* Charles A.; *c:* Meghan, Ryan; *ed:* Univ of MA at Amherst (BA) Home Ec Ed 1974; Admin Ed in Process; *cr:* Billerica Pub Schls Home Ec Instr 1974-79; Lexington Pub Schls Home Ec Instr 1983-86; Arlington Pub Schls Consumer & Life Stud Tchr 1986-; *ai:* Cancer Support & More Group Co-Chair; Breast Cancer Wkshp Chair; Co-Author Video; Curr Dev Consumer & Life Stud; NEA 1974-; MTA 1974-; Early Chldhd Cncl 1995-; Horace Mann Grant 1988; Runner-Up for Lucretia Crocker Grant; Author of Sexual Harassment & Domestic Violence Curriculum; *office:* Arlington Pub Schls 869 Massachusetts Ave Arlington MA 02174*

GRAHAM, MICHAEL PATRICK, Social Studies Teacher; *b:* St Louis, MO; *m:* Rita Ann Anderson; *c:* Maggie May, Ian Michael; *ed:* OH St Univ (BS) Ed 1977; Attnd OH Dominican; Working Toward MS; *cr:* Grove City HS Soc Stud Tchr 7 Yrs; Amer Comm Schl Amman Jordan 7-12 Grd Soc Stud Tchr 2 Yrs; Union Schl Tchr 1 Yr; US Peace Corps Tchr, Trainer 2 Yrs; *ai:* Soccer, Sftbl, Bsktbl Coach; Schl Newspaper; OEA, NEA 1982-; PTSA Star Awd; *office:* Grove City HS 4665 Hoover Rd Grove City OH 43123*

GRAHAM, NANCY ALDEN, Reading Teacher; *b:* Syracuse, NY; *m:* Robert J.; *ed:* SUNY at Geneseo (BA) His, Elem Ed 1975; Syracuse Univ (MS) Rdng 1978; 25 Addl Grad Credit Hrs; *cr:* Lyncourt Union Free Schls PSEN Rdng, Math Tchr 1977-80; Liverpool Cntrl Schls PSEN Rdng MS Tchr 1980-83, PSEN Rdng Elem Tchr 1983-; *ai:* Church Yth Group; Church Deacon; AFT, NYSUT 1975-; *office:* Wetzel Rd Elem Schl 4246 Wetzel Rd Liverpool NY 13090

GRAHAM, PATRICIA JOAN HOELTZEL, Middle School Teacher; *b:* Brooklyn, NY; *m:* Thomas Joseph; *c:* Lenora; *ed:* St Bonaventure Univ (BA) Scndry Ed 1972; City Univ of NY (MA) Sci Ed; Attnd NY St Docent Pgm at Bear Mountain St Park; *cr:* St Joseph Regnl HS Tchr 1982-86; St Peters Schl Tchr 1987-; City Coll of NY Environmental Ed Dept Adj Fac 1994-; *ai:* St Peters Sci Club Adv; *office:* St Peter's Schl 21 Ridge St Haverstraw NY 10927*

GRAHAM, PATRICIA SADLER, Social Studies Teacher; *b:* Raul, WV; *c:* Lee, Sabrina, Samantha; *ed:* Marshall Univ (BA) Soc Stud, PE 1968; Attnd Marshall Univ & OH Univ; *cr:* Logan Cty Schls Tchr 1965-68; Ashland City Schls Elem PE Pol Prog Tchr 1970-72; Gallia Co Local Schls Jr HS Soc Stud Tchr 1975-; *ai:* Stu Cncl, Jr HS Chrldr Spons; PTO, Soc Comm; NEA, OEA, GCLEA; Church of Chris of Kenova 1974-; *home:* PO Box 135 Chesapeake OH 45619*

GRAHAM, ROBERT THOMAS, Math Teacher; *b:* Norristown, PA; *m:* Susan Marie Moore; *c:* Kevin, Kelly; *ed:* Beaver Coll (MA) Admin 1990; Bloomsburg Univ Elem Ed 1980; *cr:* Souderton Schl Dist 6th Grd Tchr 1981-84; Cedarbrook MS Math Tchr, Nature Ctr 1986-; *ai:* Ftbl, Bsktbl, Bsbl Coach; PSEA, NEA, Cheltenham Ed Assn 1986-; Enhancement Nature Center Grant 1993-94; *office:* Cedarbrook MS 300 Longfellow Rd Wyncote PA 19095

GRAHAM, ROY P., 6th Grade Teacher; *b:* Barberton, OH; *m:* Monica P. Vinay; *ed:* Univ of Akron (BSEd) Elem Ed 1983, (MSEd) Elem Ed 1990; Addl Hrs Elem Ed; *cr:* Protage Elem Schl 4, 5 Grds Tchr 1983-89; Highland MS 6 Grd Tchr 1989-; *ai:* Sci Curr Comm; Boy's Bsktbl Coach 1989-92; Outdoor Ed Prgm Staff; NEA, BEA 1983-; *office:* Highland MS 1152 Belleview Ave Barberton OH 44203*

GRAHAM, SANDRA KENDRA, Kindergarten Teacher; *b:* New Castle, PA; *m:* Richard B. Sr.; *c:* Richard Jr.; *ed:* Youngstown St Univ (BS) Ed 1968; Westminister (ME) 1970; Rdng Specialist Cert 1970; Cert in Early Chldhd; 6 Addl Hrs Ed; Cmptr, Sign Lang Classes; *cr:* New Castle Area Schl Dist Kndgtn Tchr 28 Yrs; *ai:* TESA Trng; FADAC Drug & Alcohol Task Force; AFT 1990-; NEA 1970-; Delta Kappa Gamma, Pres, VP, Sec; ABWA, Pres, VP, Sec, Treas, Woman of Yr; City Cncl PTA, Pres; Outstanding Elem Tchr of Amer; Outstanding Product of Thaddues Steven Elem Schl; Spec Proclamation by Senate for Contributions Ed & Comm 1985; KDKA Television & Giant Eagle & Apple Cmptr Awd for Thanks to Tchr Awd 1990; Gift of Time Trib Awd 1994; *home:* 424 Smith Ln New Castle PA 16105*

GRAHAM, SHARON L., English Teacher & Dept Chprsn; *b:* Washington, DC; *ed:* Amer Univ (BA) Lit 1973; Univ of DC (MS) Lib Sci 1983; *cr:* Frederick Douglass Jr HS Tchr 1973-80; J. Hayden Johnson Jr HS Tchr 1980-87; Charles W. Eliot Jr HS Tchr 1987-; *ai:* Amer Red Cross, Creative Writing Clubs Spon; Sr Class Comm; AFT, WA Tchrs Union 1973-; DCPS Hum Collaborative 1995-; Holy Comforter-St Cyprian Federal Credit Union 1970-, Asst Treas, Vol; Listed in US Congressional Record for Sponsoring Stdnts of Winning Essays 1988-89; *office:* Charles W. Eliot Jr HS 1830 Constitution Ave NE Washington DC 20002*

GRAHAM, SUSAN ANN (HENNING), Enrichment Teacher; *b:* Cleveland, OH; *m:* Gary L.; *c:* G. Michael, Andrew R., Stacey C., Kelly M.; *ed:* OH Univ (BSEd) Math 1972; IN Univ (MS) Math, Ed 1990; Currently Earning Gifted Validation at Ashland Univ; *cr:* Mendon-Union Local Schls Math Tchr 1985-90; Crestview Local Schl Math Tchr 1991-92; Parkway Local Schls Jr HS Math Tchr 1992-95; Huron Cty Educl Svc Ctr Tchr of Gifted 1995-; *ai:* Math Counts, Quiz Bowl Coach; OH Cncl Tchrs Math, NCTM 1989-; Tchr of Yr 1991-92 Crestview Local Schls; Nom for OH Tchr of Yr; *office:* Huron Cty Educl Svc Ctr 180 Milan Ave Norwalk OH 44857

GRAHAM, TERRI, Art Teacher; *b:* Jersey City, NJ; *ed:* Jersey City St Coll (BA) Art Ed 1977; *cr:* St Josephs Home Art & Activity Dir 1977-82; Bayonne HS Art Instr 1982-; *ai:* Key Club Co-Adv; Supts Excl Comm; Annual Bayonne Dist Art Show Co-Chprsn; NEA & BTA 1982-; Bayonne Comm Mental Hlth Bd 1994-; *office:* Bayonne HS House I 29th St & Ave A Bayonne NJ 07002*

GRAHAM, VERA GIBSON, Business Education Teacher; *b:* Pisgah, WV; *w:* Marvin G. (dec); *c:* Heather Gale Graham Cuppert; *ed:* WV Univ (BS) Sec Ed Bus, Eng 1960, (MA) Sec Ed Eng, Sp Ed 1974; Attnd Frostburg St Univ; *cr:* Bruceton HS Bus Ed Tchr 1960-69; Green Street Schl Sp Ed Tchr 1969-77; Southern Garrett HS Sp Ed Tchr 1977-83; Northern Garrett HS Bus Ed Tchr 1983-89; Southern Garrett HS Bus Ed Tchr 1989-; *ai:* NEA 1960-; MD St TA 1969-; Garrett Cty Tchrs Assn 1969-, Fac Rep; Delta Kappa Gamma 1969-, Recording Secy, Comm Chprsn; United Meth Church 1980-, Sunday & Bible Schl Tchr; *office:* Southern Garrett HS 1100 Oak St Oakland MD 21550*

GRAHAM, W. JOSEPH, Professor of Biology; *b:* Cle Elum, WA; *m:* Margaret Chase Orbison; *c:* James S. Lungu; *ed:* Whitman Coll (BA) Bio 1954; Univ of MI (MS) Zoology 1962, (PHD) Zoology 1968; *cr:* Univ of MI Zoology Instr 1966-67; City Coll of NY Instr, Asst Bio Prof 1967-71; SUNY Coll Asst Bio Prof 1971-75; Monroe Comm Coll Assoc Bio Prof 1975-; *ai:* Classsroom Comm; Coll Wide Dept Budget, Cmptr, Personnael; Ecological Soc Amer 1968-; Am Soc Mammalogists 1962-; AAAS 1975-; Cty, Town Planning Bd 1987-; Environment Speaker 1st Earth Day Celebration 1971; Fellow AAAS; *office:* Monroe Comm Coll 1000 E Henrietta Rd Rochester NY 14623

GRAHAM, WANDA D., Tchng, Lrng Network Faciliator; *b:* Philadelphia, PA; *m:* Burley W.; *c:* Katrice; *ed:* Wilmington Coll (BS) Eng & Commnctn 1974; Chestnut Hill Coll (MED) Elem Ed 1984; Trenton St Coll Pursuing Prins Cert; Univ of PA Penn Literacy; *cr:* Shaw MS 6th Grd Classroom Tchr 1988-89; John L Kinsey Elem Various Grds Tchr 1989-95; Schoolwide Projects NW Region Instrl Support Tchr 1994-95; Strawberry Mansion Cluster Tchng & Learning Network Facilitator 1995-; *ai:* Tchr Ldrs of Math, Work Sampling Pgm & Urban Systemic Intitiative Facilitator; Philadelphia Writing Project 1990-, Fellow; Black Women in Ed Assoc 1995-; NCTM 1996; Salem Bapt Church 1989-, Presentations & Summer Festival Camp; Elkins Park Lib 1990-, Presentations & African Cultural; Selected Semi-Finalist Tchr of Excl 1989; Tchr of Excl Nom 1990-93; Awded Dwight Evans Office Grant; *office:* Strawberry Mansion Cluster 32nd & Ridge Ave Philadelphia PA 19121*

GRAHNERT, LISA ANN, German & Spanish Teacher; *b:* Buffalo, NY; *m:* Knut H.; *c:* Luke, Mitchell; *ed:* Canisius Coll (BA) Ger, Span Ed 1990; Univ of Buffalo (MED) Elem Ed 1993; Attnd Taebingen Universitaet Germany 1989; *cr:* Lancaster Cntrl Schls Ger, Span Tchr 1990-; Akron Cntrl Schls Span Tchr 1991-92; *ai:* Ger Hnr Soc & Union of Frgn Friends Adv; Sftbl Coach; AATG 1993-; ACTFL 1992-; *office:* Lancaster Cntrl HS 1 Forton Dr Lancaster NY 14086*

GRAISER, KENNETH SAUL, Language Arts Teacher; *b:* Brooklyn, NY; *m:* Grace Schulberg; *c:* Audrey Beth, Marcy Lynne; *ed:* Queens Coll of CUNY (BA) Eng 1966; Univ of NC at Chapel Hill (MAT) Eng 1968; SUNY at Stony Brook (MALS) Liberal Stud 1975; Title VI Fed Grant Rutgers Univ; Supervision & Admin St John's Univ, NY Univ; *cr:* E. E. Smith HS Eng Tchr, Yrbk Adv 1966-68; Hicksville HS Eng Tchr 1968-, AP Tchr 1990-; *ai:* NYSEC 1992-, Nom Excl in Ed 1994; NCTE 1970-; Hicksville Congress of Tchrs 1988-; Commack Jewish Ctr 1974-, Bd of Trustees, Fundraising Chm, Sunshine Comm Chm; Solomon Schechter DS of Suffolk Cty 1982-, Co-Founder, Bd of Trustees& Educ; Tchr of Yr 1991; NY St Eng Cncl Edctr of Excl 1994; *home:* 93 Morewood Dr Smithtown NY 11787*

GRAJKO, CHRISTINE ROSCOE, Second Grade Teacher; *b:* Brooklyn, NY; *m:* Philip F.; *c:* Carolyn Danaher, Jennifer; *ed:* SUNY at Oswego (BS) Elem Ed 1965; *cr:* West Genesee Schls Grd 1 & 2 Tchr 1965-68, 1976-77; Skaneateles Schls K-2 Grd Tchr 1977-; *ai:* Pupil Personnel Team in Bldg; AFT, NYSTA 1976-; Skaneateles Tchrs Assn 1976-, Bldg Rep, Negotiator; NY St Grant; *office:* Waterman Elem Schl 55 East St Skaneateles NY 13152

GRALTON, MARY (REGAN), Mathematics Teacher; *b:* Portsmouth, NH; *m:* James M.; *c:* Robert, Maureen Durgin, Kathryn, Karen; *ed:* Univ of NH (BA) Bio 1961; Boston St COll (MED) Ed, Sci 1968; 30 Ad Boston St Coll, UMass at Boston; *cr:* Winnacunnet HS Sci Tch Beverly Schl Sys Sci Tchr 1964-66; North Quincy HS Math T *ai:* Sr Class Adv; NEA 1961-; MTA 1964-; QTA 1984-; Quincy St Ann's Church, CCD Tchr, Eucharistic Minister; Sigma Xi; F Golden Apple Awd; *office:* North Quincy HS 316 Hancock St Q 02171

GRAMAGLIA, JO-ANNE VITUCCI, High School English T Mount Vernon, NY; *m:* William Michael; *c:* Nina, Michele; *e* New Rochelle (BA) Eng, Ed 1961; Coll of New Rochelle Grad Ed, Rdng 1975; 20 Credits PHD Ed Prgm Fordham Univ 1983-; *c* Elem Schl 4th Grd Acad Tchr 1961-64; Immaculate Heart of His, Eng Tchr 1971-82; Ursuline Schl HS Eng Tchr 1982-; Co Rochelle Grad Schl Rdng, Writing Prof 1982-; *ai:* Open Hou Moderator; SAT, Coll Application Tutorial Svc; NY St Eng Ed C Wkshp Presenter, St Presentation 1994-95; Westchester Cnc 1989-, Wkshp; Intnl Rdng Assn 1988-, Article Pub Pending; BE Consortium 1994-, Educl Presenter, In-Svc Course Presenter; N of Yr Finalist 1996; Outstdng Scndry Tchrs of Amer 1986; Outs Tchr of Amer 1976; Writing Strategy Pub Phi Beta Kappa; *office* School 1354 North Ave New Rochelle NY 10804

GRAMLEY, HAROLD DEAN, Professor; *b:* Sunbury, PA; *m:* Dickerson; *c:* Kurtis D., Kevin E., Nathan T., Steven E.; *ed:* P (BS) Eng 1960, (MED) Scndry Ed, Eng 1963; Kent St Univ (A Lit 1969; *cr:* York Suburban HS Eng, Drama Tchr 1960-65; Ke Tchng Fellow 1966-69; Edinboro St Coll Eng Prof 1969-80; A Amer Lit Prof 1980-81; Edinboro Univ of PA Eng Prof 1981-; *a* for Chinese Profs & Stdnts; Dept Comm, Chprsn; Adv, Spon, Individual Stdnts; Assn of PA St Coll & Univ Fac 1975-; PSEA Band Boosters 1989-; WJET-TV Outstdng Tchr Awd; Article P Edinboro Univ Of PA Dept of Eng & Theater Arts Edenboro S C

GRAMLICH, ELAINE MARIE, High School Biology Teacher; City, NJ; *c:* Lynn; *ed:* Masters Equivalency Sci Ed; Cold Spri Lab NSF Pgm; Numerous Continuing Ed Courses; *cr:* Bensale Tchr 1973-; *ai:* Distr Peer Mediation Pgm Tchr Adv; NEA 19 1992-; NSTA 1994-; *home:* 93 Junewood Dr Levittown PA 1905

GRAMLING, DAVID KARL, Social Studies Dept Chm & Williamsport, PA; *m:* Jean Elaine Daylor; *c:* Michael Donov Donovan, Patricia Donovan; *ed:* Villanova Univ (BA) Philoso Boston Coll (CAGS) His 1970; Univ of IL (MA) Ec 1973; Rad Women's Stud 12 Hrs; Merrimack Coll Cmptr Sci 12 Hrs; *cr:* A Schl Tchr, Dept Chm 1967-; Daniel Webster Coll Ec Part-t 1975-78; *ai:* Class 1982, 1990, 1994 Moderator, Adv; Asst AD Sftbl Coach; Acad Decathlon Team Coach 1989-; AFT, NCSS 1 HS Coaches Assn 1991-; Natl Sci Fnd Grants 1970-73 Ec, 1978- Sci; Outstanding Young Men Amer Jaycees 1975; *office:* Austin 101 Willow St Reading MA 01867*

GRAMLING, DONNA GALLARDY, Former Spanish Te Johnstown, PA; *m:* Gary; *c:* Garrett, Gerrica, Greanne, Genae; *ed* of PA (BS) Scndry Ed & Span 1971; Ind Research in Ecuador; at Univ of Mexico; Post Grad Courses at Shippensburg Univ Pittsburgh Pursuing Educl Subattical; *cr:* Bedford Area HS S 1971-75; Forest Hills Sr HS Span Tchr 1975-; *ai:* Natl Span Hnr Adv; PSEA & AATSP 1971-.*

GRAMMATICO, MICHAEL P., Music Teacher; *b:* Rochester Mary Jane Fuller; *c:* Matthew, Melanie; *ed:* St Univ Coll at Fred Music Ed 1966, (MM) Music 1972; Credit Hrs from Eastma Music, St Univ Coll at Brookport; *cr:* Lyndonville Cntrl Schl Ins Music Tchr 1966-77; Albion Cntrl Schl Instrumental Music Tchr AFT, Albion TA 1977-; MENC, NY St Schl Music Assn 1965- Cty Music Edctrs 1966-; Barker Comm Band 1984-, Asst Conduct Four Vocal Quartet 1983-; Ashwood Wesleyan Church 1973-, Tr Mem, Choir Dir; *home:* 9523 Somerset Dr Barker NY 14012

GRAMMATICO, REGINA BOWLER, French Teacher; *b:* V CT; *m:* Stephen A.; *c:* Kathleen; *ed:* Albertus Magnus Coll (AB Addl 30 Credits Southern CT St Univ; Continuing Ed Credits; Regnl Sr HS Fr Tchr 1972-93, Amity Regnl Jr HS Fr Tchr 196 Regnl Sr HS Fr Tchr 1969-, Dept Chr Frgn Lang 1972-93; *ai:* Co- Fr Hnr Soc, Fr Club; NEA, CT Ed Assn 1966-; AATF 1966-, Amity Ed Assn 1966-, Chair Negotiating Team; COLT 1966-; A Frgn Lang Scholastic Press 1987-92; Advy Chair Tchr Eval Cooperating Tchr; *office:* Amity Regnl Sr HS 25 Newton Rd W CT 06525

GRANATA, WILLIAM EDWARD, Spanish Teacher; *b:* Norwa Kathleen Ann Errico; *c:* William C., Nicholas, Anne Marie; *ed:* Univ (BA) Ec 1969, (MA) Ed 1978; *cr:* Rogers Park Jr HS S 1969-91; Danbury HS Span Tchr 1991-; *ai:* Boys Bsktbl Co Milford Chptr Jaycees 1982-87, Bd of Dir & Mbrshp VP; *home:* 8 Ridge Ln New Milford CT 06776

GRANCHE, WILLIAM J., 9th-12th Grade English Tea Greensburg, PA; *m:* Karen Marie Marley; *c:* Dawn, Daniel, Jac Edinboro St Coll (BS) Eng Scndry Ed Comp 1971, (MA) Amer *cr:* St Marys Area Schls Eng Tchr Grd 9-12th 1972-; *ai:* Weig Ecology Club Supvr; Asst Wrestling, Track, Tchr Dev Coach; Li Adv; PSEA, NEA 1972-; Written Media, Environmental Ed Gran St Marys Area HS 977 S Saint Marys Rd Saint Marys PA 15857*

GRANDAZZO, ALINE M., High School Art Teacher; *b:* Middle *m:* Anthony; *c:* Paul; *ed:* Cntrl CT St Univ (BS) Art Ed, Eng 19 Art Ed 1981; *cr:* Macdonough Schl K-6 Grd Art Tchr 1974-77; Sr K-6 Grd Art Tchr 1974-77; Keigwin MS 7-8 Grd Art Tchr 1977-8 St John Schl 6-11 Grd Art Tchr, Spec Ed Componant 1981-86; HS 9-12 Grd Art Tchr 1986-; *ai:* Art Club Adv; Charter Oak Conf Historian; Phi Delta Kappa 1992-; CT Art Ed Assn 198 Commendation 1995; Cromwell Ed Fnd 1993-, Bd of Dirs; T 1994-95; Univ of CT Excl in HS Tchng Awd 1994; *office:* Cromw Evergreen Rd Cromwell CT 06416

GRANDE, NICOLAS, Social Studies Teacher; *b:* Bronx, Ann-Marie; *ed:* C W Post (BA) His & Ed 1988, (MS) Spec Ed Deer Park HS Soc Stud Tchr 1988-92; Island Trees HS Soc S 1992-; *ai:* Schl Improvement Team Mem; Var Bsbl Coach; *offic* Trees HS 59 Straight Ln Levittown NY 11756

GRANDFIELD, MARIA L., Language Arts Teacher; *b:* New H *m:* William R.; *c:* Kristen, Kelli; *ed:* Univ of New Haven (BA) E *cr:* St Brendan Schl Lang Arts Tchr 1976-; *ai:* Civic Oration Cont & Adv; Peer Tutoring Prgm Adv; Lang Arts Coord; NEA 1992 Tchrs Assn; Nom Tchr of Yr 1990; *home:* 10 Stanford Ln North H 06473

GRANDINETTI, FRANCIS, Superintendent; *b:* Johnstown, Carolyn Caribardi; *c:* Kristin; *ed:* St Francis (BA) Phil & Eng Univ at PA (MA) & (EDD) Cnslr Ed & Admin 1972-81; St Bo Univ at Alleshany NY Prin Cert & Supt Letter; Harvard Univ at C Post Doctoral Stu; *ai:* PA Assn of Schl Admin 1993; United Fu Chamber of Commerce 1993-; Rotary 1994-, Treas; Stackdale H Planning Comm 1995-; Womens Rebel Corps 1994-, Dir; 2 Pub

000 Curr & Distance Learning; *office:* Ridgway Area Schl District idgway PA 15853

ONE, ROBERTA MAKI, World Language Dept Head; *b:* r, MA; *m:* Roy F.; *c:* Joseph O.; *ed:* Clark Univ (BA) Latin 1958; iv (MA) Ed, Eng 1962; Post Grad Stud Tufts Univ, Worcester St nmons Coll, Anna Maria Coll; *cr:* Barre HS Latin, Eng Tchr Wauchusett Regnl HS Latin Tchr 1960-62; Quabbin Regnl Jr Sr Eng Tchr 1967-73, Frgn Lang Dept Head 1973-94; Quabbin World Lang Dept Head 1994-; *ai:* Latin Club Adv; Cabinet Mem; g Exhibits Parents Nights Spon; MTA, NEA 1967-; CANE, Amer League 1960-; MA FLA 1980-; Barre Womans Club; Delta Kappa Womens Natl Hon Soc; Eng Grant Simmons Coll 1969; Elect Serve NEASC Accreditation Teams; *office:* Quabbin Regnl HS South St A 01005

Y, JOHN RICHARD, Eighth Grade History Teacher; *b:* lle, PA; *m:* Paula (Stanley); *c:* Jaclyn, Patrick, Courtney; *ed:* St Coll (BS) Elem Ed 1975; Attnd Penn St Shenaugo Campus, ., NCO Acad Indiantown, Westminister Coll; *cr:* Joseph Badger Grd Tchr 1975-79; West Middlesex Schls 6th Grd Tchr 1979-82, City Schls 8th Grd TChr 1983-; *ai:* FCA Dir; NEA, OEA, SEA ffice: Struthers MS 800 5th St Struthers OH 44471*

Y, COLLEEN H., American History Teacher; *b:* Englewood, NJ; of PA (BA) Amer Civilization 1992, (MSEd) Scndry Ed 1993; St Univ 9 Credits; East Stroudesburg Univ 3 Credit Units; *cr:* e HS Amer His Tchr 1993-; *ai:* Class of 1997 Adv; Dist Strategic Comm Mem; NCSS 1992-; Pi Lambda Theta 1993-; NEA 1993-; 994-; Bucks Cty Historical Soc 1995-; *office:* Pennridge HS 1228 Perkasie PA 18944*

, ADRIENNE WILSON, Elem Theatre Arts Option Tchr; *b:* MA; *ed:* Bridgewater St Coll (BS) Ed 1958; Harvard Univ (MED) Addl Hrs St Univ of NY at Stony Brook; *cr:* Needham Pub Schls 58-60; Marple-Newtown Schls Tchr 1960-61; North Merrick Schls 61-64; Three Village Schls Tchr 1964-; *ai:* Performance, Drawing, g Clubs; PTA Rep; C. W. Post Coll Adj Fac; NYSUT 1967-; AFT; llage T Assn 1965-, VP, Bd of Dirs; Brookhaven Theatre Dance 70-, Advy Bd; Greater Port Jefferson Arts Cncl 1988-, Bd of Dirs, Chair; 3 Theatre Productions Pub 1981; Outstdng Young Edctr chr of Yr 1993; Woman of Yr in Arts 1995; *office:* Setauket Schl n St East Setauket NY 11733*

, ANDREW MORTON, Life Science Teacher; *b:* Chicago, IL; *m:* Pounds; *c:* Andrew D., Margaret K.; *ed:* Univ of Toronto (BA) hy 1961; Cleveland St Univ (MED) Admin 1979; Univ of Windsor l Stud 1983; Doctoral Candidate at Kent St Univ; *cr:* Cath Cntrl Tchr 1961-64, 1968-70; Pontiac Cath HS Sci Tchr 1970-72; *ai:* Curr CRCST 1976-; SECO 1978-; OH Acad of Sci 1982-; ASCD 1990-; d Flwshp; Martha Holden Jennings Grant; *office:* Richmond HS 447 Richmond Rd Cleveland OH 44143*

, GARY SAMUEL, Band Director; *b:* Woodstock, IL; *m:* Ann s; *c:* Laurie, Mark, Elisa; *ed:* Univ of IL (BS) Music Ed 1985; Univ MM) Conducting 1990, (PLD) Music Ed 1993; *cr:* Univ of MO of Bands 1990-93; Edinboro Univ of PA Dir of Bands 1993-; *ai:* nic Wind Ensemble, Marching Band, Jazz Ensemble, Pep Band, Drums, Winterguard, Campus Competion Comm, Institutinal ement Comm Advs; NBA, CBDNA, MENC, IASE; Articles Pub in l Music Magazine, Natl Fed Interscholastic Music Assn Journal; o Univ of PA Research Grant; Research Grant at Univ of MO; Edinboro Univ Of PA 118 Heather Hall Edinboro PA 16444

, GLENN, History Teacher; *b:* Camden, NJ; *m:* Virginia Kidd; *c:* Matthew; *ed:* Univ of MD (BA) His 1971; Rowan Coll 29 ad Hrs; *cr:* Williamstown HS His Tchr 1972-; *ai:* NHS Adv; Soc r Comm; AFT 1976-; Clan Grant Soc 1992-; *office:* Williamstown Clayton Rd Williamstown NJ 08094

, JOANNE O'NEILL, Third Grade Teacher; *b:* Woburn, MA; *m:* : Shannon; *ed:* Lowell St Coll (BSEd) Elem Ed 1965; *cr:* Reeves Grd Tchr 31 Yrs; *ai:* WT, MTA, NEA 1965-; Horace Mann Grant; Clyde Francis Reeves Schl Lexington St Woburn MA 01801

, KAREN WECKERLE, Sr HS Resource Room Teacher; *b:* Bay NY; *c:* Tyler, Aaron; *ed:* SUNY at Geneseo (BS) Spec Ed 1977, pec Ed 1980; 18 Addl Grad Hrs in Rdng, Substance Abuse ation; *cr:* Letchworth Cntrl Schl Elem Spec Ed Tchr 1978-87; York hl Sr High Spec Ed Tchr 1987-; *ai:* Outdoor Ed Prgm Adv; NYSUT Kappa Delta Pi 1982-; *office:* York Central Schl PO Box 102 Retsof 39

, MARY TARO, 3rd-4th Grd Team Teacher; *b:* Malone, NY; *m:* S.; *c:* Nicole, MIchael; *ed:* Plattsburgh St Coll (BS) Elem Ed 1967; n St Coll (MS) Elem Ed 1976; 9 Addl Credit Hrs in Ed; *cr:* wn Cntrl Schl 3, 6 Grd Tchr 1967-69; NY Mills Schl 6 Grd Tchr ; Chateaugay Cntrl Schl 2 Grd Tchr 1972; Norwood-Norfolk Cntrl 5 Grd Tchr 1973-; *ai:* Dist Curr Dev Stans Comm; Revisions Comm Sick Leave Pool Rep; Spon Tchr SUNY at Potsdam Supvr of Stu Math Comm Rep; Norwood-Norfolk Tchrs Assn 1986-, Sec; , NEA 1967-; Norwood Lake Assn 1986-, Sec; St Andrews Parish office: Norwood-Norfolk Cntrl Schl Po Box 202 Rt 56 Norwood NY

T, NONA TURNER, 5th Grade Teacher; *b:* Bridgeport, CT; *m:* lo; *c:* Brianna, Taylor; *ed:* Atlantic Union Coll (BA) Elem Ed 1977; edit Hrs Ldrshp; 20+ Grad Credit Hrs Math; 12+ Grad Credit Hrs in Loyola Univ Cnslng; *cr:* RF Kennedy Ctr Math & Rdng Specialist 4; Lowell SDA Elem 5th-8th Grd Tchr & Prin 1984-86; Elm St Elem Tchr 1986-90; Montpelier Elem 5th-6th Grd Tchr 1990-; *ai:* Hlth Math Chprsn; Stu Cncl Adv; NCTM 1991-; Worcester Telegram Motivational Speaker; Stories Pub; *office:* Montpelier Elem Schl uirkirk Rd Laurel MD 20708*

T, PAUL Q., Mathematics Teacher; *b:* Caribou, ME; *m:* Annette r; *c:* Leah; *ed:* Univ of ME at Orono (BSEd) Math Ed 1968; Rutgers (MSEd) Math Ed 1975; 23 Credit Hrs Beyond MS; *cr:* Comm HS Tchr 28 Yrs; Univ of ME Adj Fac 3 Yrs; *ai:* Tchr Recertification ; Future Ed Planning Compact; Northern Acoostook Tchrs Assn Treas; ME Ed Assn 1968-; NEA 1968-; ATOMIM 1990-, St Bd; Ft ross Cntry Ski Club 1975-, Pres, VP & Treas; Town Cncl 2nd nent; *office:* Fort Kent Community HS 51 Pleasant St Fort Kent ME

T, REGINALD T., HS Guidance Counselor; *b:* Houlton, ME; *m:* lele Lynds; *c:* Cale Thaddeus; *ed:* Gorham St Coll (BS) Ed 1971; Southern ME (MS) Admin 1975, (MS) Cnslr Ed 1986; *cr:* SAD #70 on Tchr 1971-72; Westbrook Schl System Tchr, Coach 1972-88; d Pub Schl Guid Cnslr 1988-; *ai:* Frosh Class Adv; Sr Tutorial Stu Assistance Tem; Career Beginnings Mem; NEA, MTA 1971-; #21 1977-, Exec Bd, Ethics Comm; ME Cnslrs Assn 1986-; Write Column for Area Bus, Trade Paper; *office:* Portland HS 284 rland Ave Portland ME 04101

T, ROBERT MAYNARD, Retired Principal; *b:* Malden, MA; *m:* hyllis Nahum; *c:* Joyce Hamlyn, James, Ellen Walker, Miriam; *ed:* Univ (BA) eng 1957, (MA) Ed 1958; Univ of MA at Boston) 1962; Univ of Southern CA 1948-50; *cr:* Stoneham Pub Schls Eng Tchr 1957-68, Asst Jr HS Prin 1968-69, 4 & 5 Grd Tchr 1069-71, Prin 1971-93; *ai:* Stoneham Tchrs Assn 1957-; MA Tchrs Assn 1957-, Life Mem; NEA 1957-, Life Mem; MA Elem Prins, NAESP 1971-; Natl Assn of Supervision, Curr Dev; MA Assn of Children with Learning Disabilities; Stoneham Pub Lib 1980-86, Chm, Outstdng Svc; Lynnfield Pub Lib 1983-93; Dept of Interior Visitors Ctr vol; Chosen 9 Times as Fellow by Kettering Fnd; *home:* 11 Church St Apt 301 Salem MA 01970*

GRANT, ROSE GUINDON, Science & Health Teacher; *b:* Pawtucket, RI; *m:* John P. Jr.; *c:* Kevin, Heather; *ed:* Univ of MA at Dartmouth (BS) Bio, Pre-Med 1971, (MS) Bio 1979; 4 Credits Coastal Ecology Univ of RI; Tchr Mentor Prgm U Mass Dartmouth; *cr:* Bishop Stang HS Tch r1971-75; Bristol Comm Coll Adjunct Instr 1979-85; Fisher Coll Adjunct Instr 1979-85; Bishop Stang HS Tchr 1985-; *ai:* Sr Class Adv; Sharing the Faith Comm; Drama Club Costumes; Region III Sci Fair Judge; Fac Rep 1994-; NCEA, MA Assn Sci Tchrs 1985-; MA Audubon Soc 1982-; Appalachian Mountain Club 1973-; Tandy Scholar 1993-94; Yrbk Dedication 1993; *office:* Bishop Stang HS 500 Slocum Rd North Dartmouth MA 02747

GRANT, SHERRY COLBY, Spanish Teacher; *b:* Westbrok, MO; *m:* Terrence; *c:* Jonathon, Kristen; *ed:* Univ of ME (BA) Fr & Span 1983; Loyola Coll (MED) Curr & Instruction 1988; Biling Ed Tchr Trng Prgm; *cr:* Edgewood HS Tchr 1983- & Dept Chair 1984-; *ai:* Sociedad Honoraria Hispanica; NHS; Elem Schl Foreign Lang Prgm; NEA, MSTA & HCEA 1993-; Phi Sigma Iota 1982-; Mexico Stud Awd; *office:* Edgewood HS Willoughby Beach Rd Edgewood MD 21040

GRANT, WARREN HERBERT, Professor of Chemistry; *b:* New Orleans, LA; *m:* Theresa E. Hannon; *c:* Carliss, Warren III, Kevin; *ed:* Talladego Coll (AB) Bio & Chem 1955; Howard Univ (MS) Chem 1963, (PHD) Chem 1968; *ai:* Amer Chem Soc Stu Club Adv; Amer Chem Soc 1980-; *office:* Montgomery Coll 51 Mannakee St Rockville MD 20850

GRANTEED, DONNA DEANGELO, English & Applied Comm Teacher; *b:* Pittston, PA; *m:* David D.; *c:* Marin, Kelsey; *ed:* Bloomsburg Univ (BS) Scndry Ed, Eng 1973; Addl Theatre, Comm Prgm; Univ of Scranton Lang Arts Prgm; *cr:* Pittston Area Jr HS Pub Speaking, Eng Tchr 1973-82; Pittston Area Sr HS Eng, Applied Comms Tchr 1982-; *ai:* AFT 1973-; Pittston Area Parent-Tchr Org 1992-; *office:* Pittston Area Sr HS 5 Stout St Pittston PA 18640

GRANT-NELSON, ANA LORAINE, 6th Grade Teacher; *b:* Puerto Limon, Costa Rica; *m:* Yves; *c:* Andre, Chrstopher; *ed:* Bronx Comm Coll (AA) Lbrl Arts 1974; Hunter Coll (BA) Span, Ed 1976; *cr:* The Children's Aid Soc Remedial Tchr, Para Prof Soc Work 1976-79; St Rose of Lima Schl Elem Tchr 1980-; *ai:* Afterschool Homework Prgm Tchr, Supvr; NCEA 1980-; *office:* Saint Rose Of Lima Schl 517 W 164th St New York NY 10032

GRANVILLE, ROBERT T., 6th Grade Math Teacher; *b:* Rochester, NY; *m:* Sandra Lee Armstrong; *c:* Timothy, Jacqueline; *ed:* Brockport SUNY (BS) Ed 1972; Spcl Ed (MS) Learning Disabilities 1976; *cr:* Greece Cntrl Tchr 1972-; *ai:* Bldg Mgmt Team; Greece Tchrs 1972-, Sr Rep; *home:* 88 Creighton Ln Rochester NY 14612

GRANVILLE-MC KEOWN, MARION (ADELAAR), MS Mathematics Teacher; *b:* New York, NY; *m:* John J.; *c:* Diane Granville-Perelle, Austyn W. Granville Jr.; *ed:* Hunter Coll (BA) Math, Statistics 1953; Manhahanville Coll (MAT) Ed 1972; 23 Post-Grad Credits Biomedical Issues, Cmptr, Cooperative Learning, Madeline Hunter, Learning Disabilities; *cr:* North Amer Reassurance Co Statistician 1953-57; Greenburgh Cntrl Schl Dist Intermediate Tchr 1972-78; Blind Brook-Rye UFSD Math Tchr 1978-; *ai:* MS Yrbk Adv; Site-Based Compact Comm; NYSUT 1984-; NCTM 1974-; *office:* Blind Brook MS HS 840 King St Rye Brook NY 10573*

GRAPPONE, KAREN FOSTER, 7th Grade Lang Arts Teacher; *b:* Norwich, CT; *m:* Michael; *c:* Michael Anthony, Nicholas John II; *ed:* SCSU (BA) Ed 1973, (MA) Ed 1985; Law Related Ed CUES; Holocaust Stud CUES; *cr:* St Phillips Parochial Pre-School 1973-74; Beecher Schl South 4th Grd Tchr 1974-77; Great Oak MS 6th-8th Grd Lang Arts Tchr 1977-; *ai:* Stu of the Month Adv; Lang Arts Curr Comm; Dancing Through the Decades Club Adv; Debate Coach; Newspaper Supvr; OEA 1977-; NEA 1977-; CEA 1977-; Cub Scout Ldr 1988-89; CCD Rel Classes 1990-91; Stu Cncl Dev Grant-LRE; *office:* Great Oak MS 50 Great Oak Rd Oxford CT 06478

GRASHA, PHILIP JOHN, Chemistry & Physics Teacher; *b:* Pittsburgh, PA; *ed:* Univ of Pittsburgh (BS) Chem & Ed 1988; 19 Credits Grad Physics Indiana Univ of PA; *cr:* West Forest Sr High Chem & Physics Tchr 1988-91; Freeport Sr High Chem & Physics Tchr 1991-; *ai:* Var Vlybl Coach; Yrbk Adv; PSEA & PSTA 1988-; *office:* Freeport Sr HS Drawer H Freeport PA 16229

GRASSANO, CHARLES A., Language Arts Teacher; *b:* Chester, PA; *m:* Mary Ann Kryka; *c:* Jesse, Kendra, Christopher; *ed:* (BA) Eng 1968; W Chester Univ (MED) Ed 1978; Attnd Penn St, Villanova & LaSalle Self-Improvement in Ed & Eng 1991; *ai:* Wrestling Coach; Class of 1996 & SADD Spon; NEA, PSEA, PDEA 1978-; PA Coaches Assn; TKE Bd of Control 1972-, Sec, Treas; St Josephs Church 1978-; Several Articles; Nom for PA Tchr of Yr 1988; Coach of Yr 1973-75, 1978, 1980, 1983, 1985, 1991 & 1993; *office:* Sun Valley HS Duttons Mill Rd Aston PA 19014*

GRASSELL, DUANE V., Mathematics Teacher; *b:* Bethesda, MD; *ed:* Univ of Akron (BS) Math, Ed 1980, (MS) Applied Math 1981, (MS) Ed Admin 1993; Doctorate Prgm 1994-; Air Traffic Control Acad 1986; *cr:* Brookside HS Math, Cmptr Tchr 1984-85; Cardinal HS Math, Cmptr Tchr 1985-86; Fed Aviation Admin Air Traffic Control Specialist 1986-87; East HS Math Tchr 1988-; *ai:* Children-at-Risk Asst Team; Chess Club; NEA 1979-; OEA 1985-; YES 1988-; Chapel of Akron 1991-; MENSA 1982-; Pub: Reader's Digest, Twilight Zone, Alfred Hitchcock Mystery, Swimming World, Bird Talk; *office:* East HS 1544 E High Ave Youngstown OH 44505*

GRASSO, FLORENCE, HS Reading & English Teacher; *b:* W Hudson Weehawken, NJ; *m:* Christopher; *c:* Christopher, Mark; *ed:* Montclair St Coll (BA) Eng 1973; Addl 30 Credits Rdng Concentration; *cr:* Henry P. Becton Reg HS 10th Grd Eng, Rdng Tchr 23 Yrs; *ai:* Quill & Scroll; *office:* Henry P Becton Reg HS Paterson Ave Cornelius E Rutherford NJ 07073

GRASSO, FRANK JAMES, Sixth Grade Teacher; *b:* Kingston, PA; *m:* Antoinette M. Champi; *c:* Michael, David; *ed:* 60 Addl Hrs; Chenango Forks Cntrl Schl Tchr 1964-68; Wyoming Vly West Schl Academically Gifted Prgm 1975-91, Head Tchr 1971-75, Tchr 1968-; *cr:* Site-Based Mngmt Comm; His Day Judge; *ai:* PSEA, NEA, WVWEA 1968-; *office:* Wyoming Valley West MS 201 Chester St Kingston PA 18704

GRASSO, LETIZIA, Italian Teacher; *b:* Rome, Italy; *m:* Nicola Berardi; *c:* Andre Berardi, Alexey Berardi; *ed:* Hunter Coll (BA) Psych 1975; SUNY Inst of Tech (BS) Cmptr Sci 1984; Middlebury Coll (MS) Italian 1989; *cr:* St Joseph Patron Schl First Grd Tchr 1969-71; Cath Migration Office Immigration Cnslr 1973-75; Rome Free Acad Italian Tchr 1985-; *ai:* Italian Club Adv; Amer Assn Tchrs of Italian 1987-; NYS Assn Frgn Lang Tchrs, Italian Tchrs Assn of Cntrl NY 1988-; Italian Govt Grant; *office:* Rome Free Acad 500 Turin St Rome NY 13440

GRASSO, MICHAEL, Emeritus Professor of Physics; *b:* Lackawanna, NY; *m:* Irene LaChauce; *c:* June Marie, Michael, Richard; *ed:* SUNY at Buffalo (BA) Physics 1953, (MA) Physics 1968; Over 90 Credit Hrs in Physics, Math; *cr:* SUNY Coll Assoc Prof of Physics 1959-79, Engrng Prgms Coord 1975-93, Prof of Physics 1979-93, Chprsn Dept of Physics 1984-93; *ai:* Dev, Implemented, Coord Cooperative Legendary Prgm; Adv for Stdnts; Fac Adv Fredonia Soc, Physics Soc Engrng Soc, Physics Soc; Amer Phys Soc-; Amer Assn of Physics Tchr; Sigma Pi Sigma; Sigma Xi; Fredonia Farm Festival 1975-, Dir; Chautauqua Cnty Soc fo Artch; Art Cncl for Chautqua Ctyp Fredonia Presewatin Soc; 3 Articles Pub; Received Meritorious Svc Awd 1990; Honored Amer Assn of Higher Ed; Received Awd From Reusselaea Polytechnic Inst 1988; Ed 1975-93; *home:* 15 Birchwood Dr Fredonia NY 14063

GRASSO, NORMA ARNESEN, Physical Education Teacher; *b:* Staten Island, NY; *m:* John Gerard; *c:* Jonathan, Justin, Jason; *ed:* Trenton St Coll (BS) Hlth, PE 1980, (MED) Hlth, PE, Adaptive PE; *cr:* Woodbridge HS PE Tchr 1980-, Track, Cross Cntry Coach 1980-84; *ai:* Chrstn Club Adv; Head Spring Track 1980-87, Winter Track 1982-87, Head Cross Cntry 1980-94, Coach; NEA 1980-; NJHPERD; Shore Ath Club 1980-, Hall of Fame 1993; Woodbridge Alumni Ath Assn, Hall of Fame 1996; NJ St Tchr Recognition Prgm Tchr of Yr 1993; Greater Middlesex Cty Conference 1993, Home News & News Tribune 1994 Coach of Yr; 2 Time Natl Track & Field Team Mem Racewalker 1981, 1983; NYC Marathon Winner Racewalk Division 1983; *office:* Woodbridge HS Freeman & Kelly St Woodbridge NJ 07095

GRASSO, VIRGINIA M., Reading & Lang Arts Consultant; *b:* Middletown, CT; *ed:* Southern CT St Univ (BS) Elem Ed 1974; Cntrl Ct St Univ (MS) Early Chldhd 1977; 6th Yr Rdng 1991; Rdng, Lang Arts Consultant K-12 Cert 1990; Trained in Higher Order Thinking Skills; *cr:* Snow Schl 3 Gr Tchr 1974-75; Woodrow Wilson MS 7 Gr Soc Stud Tchr 1975-76; Wesley Schl 3-4 Gr Tchr 1976-77; Snow Schl 2 Gr Tchr 1977-78, 3 Gr Tchr 1978-87; Macdonough Schl Instructional, Rdng Consultant 1987-93; Lawrence Schl Rdng, Lang Arts Consultant 1993-; *ai:* Middletown Fed of Tchrs 1974-; 2 CAUSE Mini-Grants Rdng Incentive Prgms; *office:* Lawrence Schl Kaplan Dr 675 Newfield St Middletown CT 06457

GRASTORF, PENNY A., Ninth Grade Math Teacher; *b:* Angelica, NY; *ed:* SUNY at Albany (BA) Math 1964, (MA) Tchr Ed 1969; *ai:* Shenendehowa Tchrs Assn, NYSUT, AMINYS, AFT 1964-; NSF Insts ME, OR & NY; *office:* Gowana Jr HS 970 Route 146 Clifton Park NY 12065

GRATALE, ROCCO JOSEPH, High School English Teacher; *b:* Jersey City, NJ; *m:* Judy C. Martinelli; *c:* Daniella, Stefanie; *ed:* Fairleigh Dickinson Univ (BA) Scndry Ed, Eng 1974, (MA) Eng, Comparative Lit 1980; 55 Credit Hrs Post Grad Certs Prin, Asst to Supt Curr Dev, Supvr, Speech & Drama, Rdng; *cr:* Annin Jr HS 8th Grd Eng Tchr 1974-75; Basking Ridge Jr & Sr HS Compeniatory Ed 1976-77; Lakeland Regnl HS Eng Tchr 1977-, GATE Coord 1988-; *ai:* Boys & Girls Track Coach; NHS Comm; NEA, NJEA 1974-; Honor Soc Phi Kappa Phi; NJ Passaic Cty Coaches Assn Honor Awd 1994; *office:* Lakeland Regional HS 205 Conklintown Rd Wanaque NJ 07465

GRATE, DAIVD ROBERT, Jrnlsm Adv & English Teacher; *b:* New York, NY; *m:* Mary Ann M. Galati-Grate; *c:* David Michael, Justine Renee; *ed:* Hebert H. Lehman Coll (BA) Eng 1992; *cr:* Alfred E. Smith Record Fac Adv 1993-; Alfred E. Smith HS Eng Tchr 1993-; *ai:* WHLC Radio Herbert H. Lehman Coll; AFT, NYC Scholatic Press, UFT 1993-.*

GRATTAN, JOYCE OSBORNE, College Counselor & Eng Tchr; *b:* Southampton, NY; *c:* Leslie, Lisa, George; *ed:* Wells Coll (BA) Ec, Govt 1959; Hofstra Univ (MS) Ed, Eng 1962; Addl 33 Credits; *cr:* Plainedge HS Eng Tchr 1961-63; Mattituck HS AP Eng Tchr, Coll Cnslr 1973-; *ai:* NACAC 1986-; AFT, MCTA 1973-; Suffolk Cty Tchr of Yr 1993; Summer Inst Coll Admissions Harvard Univ 1984, 1986; *office:* Mattituck HS Main Rd Mattituck NY 11952

GRAU, JOANN (MOLINARO), English Teacher; *b:* Kenosha, WI; *m:* George Michael; *c:* Jeremy, Jeffrey; *ed:* OH St Univ (BS) Eng 1965; Lib Sci Cert 1965; *cr:* Xenia HS Eng Tchr 1965-67; Glenville HS Eng Tchr 1968-69; Elyria HS Eng Tchr 1985-; *ai:* Ecology Club Adv; OEA, NEA 1985-; Secular Franciscian Order 1985-, Tchr, Formation Dir; St Thomas Church 1970-, Eucharistic Minister; CCD Classes 1972-85, Tchr, Dir, Rel Ed Awd 1977; *office:* Elyria HS 6th & Middle Ave Elyria OH 44035

GRAUER, MARIE CHARLES,SSND HS English Teacher; *b:* Baltimore, MD; *ed:* Seton Hall Univ (BS) Ed1952; Loyola (MED) Ed 1969; Notre of MD Theology; *cr:* St Leo Schl Grd One Tchr 1946-51, Grd Six Tchr 1951-54; St Anne Grd Seven Tchr 1954-57; Mt Calvary Grd Eight Tchr 1957-59; St Mark Grd Eight Tchr 1959-67; Inst of Notre Dame 9-12 Grd Tchr 1967-; *ai:* NCTE 1970-.

GRAUSSO, KATHLEEN GRAY, English Teacher; *b:* Newark, NJ; *m:* Frank J.; *c:* Vance, Shannon; *ed:* Northern MI Univ (BA) Eng 1970; *ai:* NCTE 1976-; *office:* St Rose HS 601 7th Ave Belmar NJ 07719

GRAVEL, CLAUDE J., Religion & Math Teacher; *b:* Montreal, Quebec Canada; *ed:* Ahuntsic Coll (BA) Bus Admin 1974; Oblate Coll (BA) Philosophy 1990-, (MDIV) Theology 1990; 20 Credit Hrs Math Prince Georges Comm Coll 1987; *cr:* Holy Trinity Librn, Dorm dir 1974-75; Univ of Montreal Theology Tchr 1976-78; Angelicum Theology Tchr 1978-79; Hockey Prgm Dir 1987-; *ai:* Bsbl, Soccer, Golf Moderators; NCEA 1979-; *home:* 4310 Madison St Hyattsville MD 20781

GRAVEL, LEO RAYMOND, Mathematics Dept Chprsn; *b:* Worcester, MA; *m:* Joyce Henry; *c:* Karyn Lee Stacy, Gayle Denise Donato, Leanne Marie Lacasse, Kristine Elaine; *ed:* Worcester St Coll (BSE) Ed 1962; Holy Cross Coll 2 Summer Inst; Clark Univ 4 Summer Inst; Assumption Coll 9 Credit Hrs; Worcester St Coll 6 Credit Hrs; Fitchburg St Coll 15 Credit Hrs; *cr:* Chandler St Jr HS Math Tchr 1962-66; Marian CC HS Math Tchr 1966-76; St Peter Marian CC Jr Sr HS Math Tchr 1976-; *ai:* Acad Cncl; AFT, MFT 1986-; Delta 1984-95, VP 7 Yrs; NCEA; NACST; Democratic Town Comm 1980-; St Marys Church 1969-; Lay Building Rep 23 Yrs; *home:* 30 Suzanne Ter North Grafton MA 01536*

GRAVELIN, GEORGE DAVID, French Teacher & Dept Chprsn; *b:* Providence, RI; *m:* Carol Costa; *c:* David, Eric; *ed:* Univ of RI (MA) Fr, Ed 1975; *cr:* East Greenwich HS Dept Chair, Fr Tchr 1969-; *ai:* Intnl Club, Fr Exch Prgm, Schl Partnerships Intnl Adv; RI Frgn Lang Assn 1989-, Bd Mem; AATF 1985-; NEA 1969-; St Mary's Church of Warwick 1977-, Vestry; *office:* East Greenwich HS 300 Avenger Dr East Greenwich RI 02818

GRAVELLE, STEVEN JOHN, Asst Professor of Chemistry; *b:* Minneapolis, MN; *m:* Ann Ruth Mc Leod; *c:* Sean Steven, Brian Joseph; *ed:* St John's Univ (BA) Chem 1984; Northwestern Univ (MS) Phys Chem 1989, (PHD) Phys Chem 1989; Post Doctoral Flwshp Univ of TX at Austin 1989-91; *cr:* Saint Vincent Coll Asst Prof 1991-; *ai:* Ski Club Adv; Amer Chem Soc 1989-; Spectroscopy Soc of Pittsburgh 1992-; Articles Pub; NSF Rsrch Prgm 1995; *office:* Saint Vincent Coll 300 Fraser Purchase Rd Latrobe PA 15650*

GRAVER, JAMES BRIAN, Elementary Teacher; *b:* Allentown, PA; *m:* Kathleen Ann Simons; *c:* Kathleen, James, Angelica; *ed:* Kutztown St Coll (BS) Elem Ed 1975; Masters Equivalency Plus 30 Credits; *cr:* Perkasie Elem 4th Grd Tchr 1975-76; Sellersville Elem 4th Grd Tchr 1976-78; Elem Gifted Support 1978-; *ai:* NEA, PSEA 1975-; *office:* Robert B Deibler Elem Schl 1506 N 5th St Perkasie PA 18944

GRAVES, BEVERLY J., English Teacher; *b:* Columbus, OH; *m:* Ron; *c:* Amanda, Matthew; *ed:* Taylor Univ (BS) Speech, Eng 1973; OH St Univ (MS) Eng 1982; 45 Hrs beyond Masters; *cr:* Worthington Kilbourne Schl Tchr 1973-74; Thomas Worthington Schl Tchr 1974-90; Milton Union HS

Tchr 1990-; *ai:* SADD, 4 Pointers Adv; NEA 1973-; OEA, WEA 1974-; Liberty Presbyn Church 1990-; Numerous Articles Pub; Worthington Fnd Grant; Tchr of Yr 1993; *office:* Worthington Kilbourne HS 1499 Hard Rd Columbus OH 43235*

GRAVES, BONNIE LAURA READ, French & Latin Teacher; *b:* Quantico, VA; *m:* Ronald Dean; *ed:* Kent St Univ (BSEd) Fr 1968; Univ of Akron (MA) Fr 1973; 30 Semester Hrs in Latin; 24 Quarter Hrs in Biblical Stud; 24 Semester Hrs in Eng; *cr:* Bolich Jr HS Fr Tchr 1968-70; Univ of Akron Grad Asst 1971-73; Cuyahoga Vly Chrstn Acad Fr, Latin Tchr 1973-82, 1984-; *ai:* Jr Classical League Spon; Frgn Lang Dept Chprsn; 2000 Planning Comm; AATF 1991-; ACL 1990-; OH Classical League 1993-; Pi Delta Phi; Eta Sigma Phi; Stow Alliance Flwshp 1980-, WMPF Pres; Ashland Theological Seminary Advy Comm 1996; OJCL Pres Spon 1994-95; 20 Yr Svc Awd; *office:* Cuyahoga Valley Chrstn Acad 4687 Wyoga Lake Rd Cuyahoga Falls OH 44224*

GRAVES, JUNE MERRIWEATHER, Technology Teacher; *b:* Brooklyn, NY; *c:* Justin Merriweather; *ed:* Jersey City St Coll (BA) Elem Ed 1971; Attnd NJ Inst of Tech at Newark, Tchrs Coll at Columbia Univ NYC; *cr:* Springfield Ave Comm Schl K-4 Grd Tchr 1971-80; Harriet Tubman Schl 4-6 Grd GATE Tchr 1980-94, K-6 Grd Tech Tchr 1994-; *ai:* Educl Improvement Plan, Tech Comms; Testing Coord; Dev Curr for Schl & Dist; NEA, AFT, NTU 1971-; 1993 Governor's Awd Excl in Tchng; 1992 Tchr of Yr Newark by Municipal Cncl; *office:* Harriet Tubman Schl 504 S 10th St Newark NJ 07104

GRAVES, LISA DENTON, Third Grade Teacher; *b:* Rockville Centre, NY; *c:* Michael; *ed:* Hofstra Univ (BA) ELem Ed, Psych, Min Fine Arts 1987, (MA) Rdng 1991; *cr:* Smith Street School Elem Tchr 1987-; *ai:* Cmptr Club, Peer Medition, Conflict Resolution Adv; Lang Arts & Math Textbook Selection Comms; Kappa Delta Pi 1987-; Sunday Schl Tchr 1978-; Co-Author of Eng Lang Arts Stans; Curr & Literacy Profile 1995; *office:* Smith Street Elem Schl 780 Smith St Uniondale NY 11553*

GRAVES, RANDY L., Adj Prof of Cmptr Info System; *b:* Manhattan, NY; *m:* Petra Idelsi; *c:* Gabriella Martina; *ed:* WV St Coll (BS) Math 1974; 30 Credits Towards Master's Cmptr Sci WV Univ; *cr:* NCR Systems Analyst 1977; Computhrift Corp Assembler Programmer 1984; LaGuardia Comm Coll Systems Programmer 1984-; *ai:* Sexual Harassment, Coll 25th Anniversary Comms; NYSUR, PSC, CUNY 1984-; *office:* LaGuardia Comm Coll 31-10 Thomson Ave Long Island City NY 11101

GRAVES, RICHARD DAVID, K-12th Grd Soc Stud Supvr; *b:* Newark, NJ; *m:* Shirley Ann Nixon; *c:* Stephen, Ronald; *ed:* Sioux Falls Univ (BA) His & Art; Montclair St Univ (MA) Ed; Over 42 Post Grad Hrs; *cr:* Belleville HS Tchr Supvr 1957-; *ai:* Prins & Supvrs Assn, ASCD; BSA, Cub Master, Silver Beaver, Session Watchung, Scout Master, Eagle Scout; Presbyn Church, Cncl Commissioner, Choir.*

GRAVINO, BEATRICE IRMIERE, Secondary English Teacher; *b:* Paterson, NJ; *m:* Michael; *c:* Amy Louise; *ed:* William Paterson Coll (BA) Eng 1972; SUNY at Stony Brook (MA) Lbrl Stud 1975, (MA) TESOL 1990; Myth & Masterpiece Rome 1994; *cr:* Mid Cntry Cntrl Schl Dist Scndry Eng Tchr 1972-; *ai:* Hnr Soc Bd; NCTE 1973-; NYSUT 1972-; NYSEC 1994-; ASA, LISE 1995-; MCCSD Mini-Grants; *office:* Newfield HS 145 Marshall Dr Selden NY 11784

GRAY, ANITA GAMBONE, Principal; *b:* Phila, PA; *m:* William G.; *c:* Wm Jr., Daniel; *ed:* St Joseph's Univ (BS) Elem Ed 1969; Penn St Univ Tchng Cert; *cr:* St Kevin's Elem Schl 5th Grd Tchr 1966-69; Linwood Elem Schl 5-6 Grd Tchr 1969-71; Chrstn Acad at Media 7th-8th Grd Math Tchr 1979-84; Chrstn Acad at Brookhaven 6-8 Grd Math Tchr 1984-86, Curr Supvr 1986-91, Vice Prin 1991-93, Prin 1994-.*

GRAY, BONNIE LEE (MILLS), Foreign Language Teacher; *b:* Rutland, VT; *m:* Richard F. Jr.; *c:* Richard III, T. Tel; *ed:* Castleton St Coll)BA) Fr, Span, (MAEd) Rdng, Lang Arts 1983; Addl 27 Credit Hrs, also from Univ of VT, Middlebury Coll Lang Schls; *cr:* Vermont Adult Basic Ed Diploma Assessor, Adv, Tutor 1980-85; Currier Memorial Schl Rdng Spec 1984-85; Orwell Vlg Schl Rdng, Fr, Span Tchr 1985-90; Granville Jr, Sr HS Fr, Span Tchr 1990-; *ai:* Class of 1996 Adv, Shared Decision Making; Drama Dir 1993-95; Travel Cnslr; AFT, NYSUT 1990-; NYSFL 1994-; Addison Rutland Tchr of Yr 1987; Title XX Grant Recipient Writing Children's Books; *office:* Granville HS Quaker St Granville NY 12832

GRAY, CHERYL CHRISTINE, Fifth Grade Teacher; *b:* Washington, DC; *ed:* Bowie St Univ (BA) Elem Ed 1969; Standard Prof Cert; *cr:* Capitol Hghts Elem Schl Second Grd Tchr 1969-72; Templeton Elem Schl Fourth-Fifth Grd Tchr 1972-; *ai:* Chrldr Spon; Cmptr Writing Wkshp; NEA, MSTA, PGCEA 1969-; Grd Level Chprsn 1971-1990; Outstdng Edctrs Nom 1985-86; Outstdng Math Tchr Nom; Unsung Heroine 1990; *office:* Templeton Elem Schl 6001 Carters Ln Riverdale MD 20737

GRAY, FRANCES THOMAS, Retired Second Grade Teacher; *b:* Baltimore, MD; *m:* Charles Edward; *c:* Charles T., Edward, Michael; *ed:* Towson St Tchrs Coll (BSEE) Elem Ed 1953; Masters Equivalency Plus 30 Credit Hrs for Advanced Prof Degree thru Baltimore Cty Bd of Ed in Assn with Johns Hopkins Univ & Loyola Coll; *cr:* Edgemere Elem Schl Tchr 1953-90; *ai:* MD Retired Tchrs Assn 1990-; MD Congress of Parents & Tchrs Inc 1991-, Honorary Life Mbrshp; AARP Natl Assn 1989-; AARP Dundalk Chptr 1991-, Pub Relations Chprsn; Lioness Dundalk Chptr 1984-85; *home:* 3110 Dunglow Rd Baltimore MD 21222

GRAY, GLENN WILLIAM, Science Teacher; *b:* Columbus, OH; *ed:* OH St Univ (BS) Ag 1970, (MA) Ed 1973; Univ of Toledo Post Grad Ed Stud; *cr:* Clyde HS Sci Tchr 1973-; *ai:* North Cntrl Stud Comm Co-Chm; CGSEA, OEA, NEA 1973-; Jennings Scholar; Clyde Green Springs Bd of Ed Appreciation, Stu Cncl Honorary Svc Awds; *office:* Clyde Sr HS 1015 Race St Clyde OH 43410

GRAY, JACK F., Director of Bands; *b:* Bucyrus, OH; *m:* Christina Lyon; *c:* Jeffrey, Jon; *ed:* Bowling Green Univ (BM) Music Ed 1970, (MM) Music Ed 1974; Attnd Ashland Univ; *cr:* Shelby City Schls Instrumental Music 1970-; *ai:* Dept Chair; MENC, OMEA 1970-, Adjudicated Events, 25 Yr Awd; Phi Beta Mu 1989-; ASBDA 1987-; Phi Mu Alpha 1966-, Chptr Pres; Kappa Kappa Psi 1967-; First Presbyn Church 1970-, Choir Dir; Boy Scout Troop 406, Scoutmaster; Golden Apple Awd, Ashland Oil Co; OMEA Adjudicated Events Comm 15 Yrs, Adjudicator 21 Yrs; *office:* Shelby Sr HS 109 W Smiley Ave Shelby OH 44875

GRAY, M. KATHLEEN, Second Grade Teacher; *b:* Butler, PA; *m:* Eugene T. Danko; *c:* Jeremy; *ed:* Butler Cty Comm Coll (AA) 1979; Slippery Rock Univ (BS) Elem Ed 1981; Butler Cty Comm Coll (MED) Early Chldhd 1982; Duquesne Univ Prins Cert 1988; *cr:* Quaker Vly Schl Dist Rdng Specialist 1 Yr, 6th Grd Tchr 1 Yr, 3rd Grd Tchr 10 Yrs, 2nd Grd Tchr 2 Yrs; *ai:* PSEA 1982-; *office:* Quaker Vly Schl Dist 200 Meadow Ln Sewickley PA 15143*

GRAY, MARY REGINA, English & Language Arts Tchr; *b:* Queens, NY; *m:* Thomas Lamont; *ed:* Fisk Univ (BA) Eng Lit 1971; Bowie St Univ (MED) Guid Cnslng 1990; Averett Coll 30 Credit Hrs Rdng 1979-80; *cr:* Rogers HS Eng Tchr 1971-74; Suitland Jr HS Eng, Lang Arts Tchr 1975-82; Forestville HS Eng, Lang Arts Tchr 1982-; *ai:* Female mentoring Outstdng Women of Future; Mid Sts Assn of Colls, Schls Visiting Comm; Scheduling Transition Comm Chprsn; Human Relations Comm; PGCEA, MSTA, NEA 1975-; Evangel Church 1981-, Usher Ldr; Outstdng Svc to Schl, Comm PTSA Awd; Outstdng Ninth Grd Tchr; Tchr of Yr 1982.*

GRAY, PATRICIA HOOKS, 6th Grd Rdng & Soc Stud Tchr; *b:* Chicago, IL; *c:* Carlos, Carlton; *ed:* Fiak Univ (BA) Frgn Lang 1968; Xavier Univ (MA) Rdng Specialist 1985; *cr:* Princeton Schl Sub Tchr 1968-69, 5th, 3rd Grd Tchr 1969-72; Sharonville Schl 6th Grd Tchr 1972-; Xavier Univ Adj Lecturer 1985-; *ai:* Intermediate Facilitator; Stu Cncl Asst Adv; 6th Grd Level Ldr; NEA.*

GRAY, STEVEN ALLAN, Spanish Teacher; *b:* Littleton, NH; *ed:* Plymouth St Coll (MA) Span 1990; Middlebury Coll (MA) Span Lit 1991; Attnd Sorbonne 1995 Fr, Universite Laval 1989 Fr; DML in Progress; *cr:* Plymouth St Coll Span AT Tchr 1989; Bertie Cty Schls Span Tchr 1991-93; Portledge Schl Span Tchr 1994-; *ai:* 9th Grd Adv; Bertie Arts Cncl 1992-, Pres; *office:* Portledge School 355 Duck Pond Rd Locust Valley NY 11560*

GRAY, SUSAN TELLOR, First Grade Teacher; *b:* Cedar Rapids, IA; *m:* Stephen Edward; *c:* Elise, Kelsey, Kailyn; *ed:* Baldwin Wallace Coll (BS) Elem Ed 1981; Ashland Univ (MA) Curr, Instruction 1991; *cr:* Strongsville City Schls Kndgtn Tchr 1981-82, 2nd Grd Tchr 1982-83; Buckeye Cntrl Local Schls Kndgtn Tchr 1983-85, 1st Grd Tchr 1985-; *ai:* Dist Tech Comm Co-Chprsn; NEA 1983-; NAEYC 1992-; Ashland AEYC 1992-94, Pres; *home:* 23 Kimberwick Rd Lexington OH 44904*

GRAY, VICKI GERHARD, Science Dept Teacher; *b:* Reading, PA; *m:* Samuel V.; *ed:* E Stroudsburg St Coll (BS) Scndry Ed, Chem 1968; 30 Credits Post-Grad Stud; *cr:* Northern HS Tchr 1968-79; Chambersburg Area Sr HS Tchr 1981-1990; Carlisle HS Tchr 1990-; *ai:* Sci Dept Head Tchr; Staff Dev Cncl; CAEA, CASD Back to Schl Prgm; CASD Dickinson Coll Liason Comm; NEA, PSEA 1968-; CAEA 1990-; NSTA, ACS 1993-; *office:* Carlisle HS 623 W Penn St Carlisle PA 17013*

GRAY, WILLIAM J., High School Biology Teacher; *b:* Columbus, OH; *m:* Delecia Lou Cox; *c:* James R., John E., Jeremy W.; *ed:* Adrian Coll (BS) Bio 1965; 73 Post Grad Hrs Bio & Earth Sci Courses; *cr:* Pike-Delta-York Schls Bio, Anatomy & Earth Sci Tchr 1967-; *ai:* 7th Grd Bsktbl Coach 25 Yrs; Frosh Class Adv 15 Yrs; Future Tchrs of Amer Adv 16 Yrs; PDYEA 1967-, Bldg Rep, Numerous Comms; OEA, NEA 1967-; *office:* Pike-Delta-York Local Schls 605 Taylor St Delta OH 43515

GRAY, WILLIAM SUTTIE, Dir of Hospitality; *b:* Forfar, Scotland; *m:* Diane Alice Davies; *ed:* Concordia Univ Comm Accounting 1961; Completed Canadian Equivalent of CPA; *cr:* Sheraton Intnl Controller 1966-71; Loews Hotels Treas 1971-79; Whiteco Hospitality Corp Controller 1979-87; Equinox Resorte Spa Controller 1987-92; Southern VT Coll Dir of Hospitality & Resort Mgmt 1993-; *ai:* Assn of Chartered Accountants in Amer Vt Rep; Canadian Inst of Chartered Accountants 1957-, C A AWDF; Assn of Chartered Accountants in US 1990-; Intnl Assn of Hotel Accountants 1981-; Author of Hospitality Accounting 1995; Co-Author Hotel & Motel Mgmt & Operation 1980; *office:* Southern VT Coll Monument Ave Bennington VT 05201

GRAY, WINSTON ROBERT, Vocal Music Teacher; *b:* Baltimore, MD; *c:* Simone Marie; *ed:* Coppin St Coll (BS) Psych, Music 1986; Grad Hrs Towson St Coll; *cr:* Woodstock Job Corp Instr, Test Coord 1986-88; Fellowship of Lights Cnslr 1987-88; Lemmel MS Vocal Music Tchr 1988-93; Walbrook HS Vocal Music Tchr 1993-; *ai:* Soph Class Adv; Cntrl Bapt Church & Minister of Music; MD St Choir, Hampton Choir Dir; Phi Beta Sigma 1985-; Hampton Univ Choir Dir Guild 1983-; Phi Mu Alpha Sinfonia 1982-; Who's Who in Music 1990.*

GRAYBILL, DONNA MARILU (ROBB), Music Teacher & Choral Dir; *b:* Washington, DC; *m:* Dale; *c:* Jody; *ed:* Susquehanna Univ (BS) Music Ed 1963; Penn St, Wilkes Col Psych, Ed Stud; *cr:* East Juniata PE Tchr 1963-64, Instrumental Music Tchr 1967-68, ESEA Prgm, Elem Instrumental Music Tchr 1972-74; Greenwood Schl Dist Part Time Elem Vocal Music Tchr 1974, Elem, HS Vocal Music Tchr 1980-; *ai:* Xmas, Spring, May Day Elem Schl Musical Prgm Dir; Swing Choir Musical Dir; Dist, Regnl, Cty Chorus & Honors Choir Adv; NEA, PSEA, MENC, PMEA, Greenwood Tchrs Assn 1980-; Church 1960-80, Choir Dir, Pianist.

GRAYDON, ELIZABETH GANNON, 6th-8th Grade Social Stud Tchr; *b:* Kew Gardens, NY; *m:* Rob; *ed:* Fordham Law Schl 2 Yrs; *cr:* St Benedict Joseph Labre Schl 6th & 8th Grd Soc Stud Tchr 1987-94; St Francis of Assisi Schl 6th-8th Grd Soc Stud Tchr 1995-; *ai:* Drama Club & After-Schl Pgm Adv; Stu-Fac Bsktbl Team Mem; Soc Stud Comm; Amnesty Intnl 1990-, Caribbean Action Coord & Death Penalty Comm Mem; Northern Lights 1994-; Womens Intnl League for Peace & Freedom 1995-; Designed & Taught Prof Enrichment Wkshps on Tchng Soc Stud for Diocese of Brooklyn Last 6 Yrs; *office:* St Francis of Assisi Schl 21-18 46th St Long Island Cty NY 11105*

GRAYSON, CAROLE HAMMER, Principal; *b:* Jersey City, NJ; *m:* Mark; *c:* Jeremy, Rebecca, Ariel; *ed:* Jersey City St Coll Math (BA) 1965, (MA) 1968; Rutgers Univ (MBA) Accounting 1980; Rider Univ 21 Credits in Ed Admin; 3 Credits in Ed Admin, 6 Credits in Math Ed; *cr:* Rahway Sr HS Math Tchr 1966-69; Wayne Valley Sr HS Math Tchr 1969-72; Ewing HS Math Tchr 1983-84; Abraham Clark HS Math Tchr 1986-94, Math Tchr, Math Supvr 1994-95; Raritan Valley Comm Coll Asst Prop 1990-95; Leonard V. Moore MS Prin 1995-; *ai:* NCTM 1990-; NJ Math Cncl 1993-; PSA 1995-; *office:* Leonard V Moore Middle School 720 Locust St Roselle NJ 07203*

GRAZADO, ROBERT WILLIAM, Guidance Counselor; *b:* Norwood, MA; *m:* Jean M.; *c:* Elizabeth, Julianne, Mark; *ed:* Boston Coll (BA) Pre-Medicine 1963, (MST) bio & Ed 1968; 30 Plus Beyond Guidance Cert; *cr:* Xavierian Brothers HS Bio Tchr & Guidance Cnslr 1964-69; Norwood HS Guidance Cnslr 1969-; *ai:* Norwood Tchrs Assn 1969-, Treas; MA Tchrs Assn, NEA 1969-; King Philip Music Assn 1989-, Pres, Treas; Knights of Columbus 1965-; Islington Businessmens Bowling League 1976-, Sec; Saint Marthas Parish 1972-, Lector, Minister; Excl in Counseling Awd from Bentley Coll 1992; Golden Apple Awd from Norwood HS 1989; *office:* Norwood HS Nichols St Norwood MA 02062

GRAZIANO, BARBARA LYNNE (JOHNSTON), 3rd & 4th Grade Teacher; *b:* Pittsburgh, PA; *m:* Thomas R.; *c:* Gregory, Lynn; *ed:* Waynesburg Coll (BA) Elem Ed 1967; Clarion Univ (MA) Elem Ed 1970; *cr:* Warren Co Schl Dist Elem Tchr 1967-72, 1987-; *ai:* Am Heart Assoc Jump for Heart Coord 8 Yrs; NEA; WCEA 1972-; Comm Chorus; Am Cancer Soc Great Am Smokeout 1st Place Class Play; *home:* 104 Pleasant Dr Warren PA 16365

GRAZIANO, NICOLETTE, English Teacher; *b:* Hoboken, NJ; *m:* Armand; *c:* Lawrence, Andrew, Lisa Marie Vallo; *ed:* Montclair St Univ (BA) Eng Tchr 1979; William Paterson Coll (MA) Eng Lit Tchr 1989; Jersey City St Supervisory Cert; Credit Hrs 30 Above Masters; *cr:* Nutley Bd of Ed Eng Tchr 1979-; Nutley Adult Schl Hum Tchr 1980; Kean Coll Writing Course Tchr 1992; *ai:* Yrbk Adv; NEA 1979; *office:* Nutley HS 300 Franklin Ave Nutley NJ 07110

GREACEN, KATHLEEN KARLE, English Teacher; *b:* Rochester, NY; *m:* Matthew; *ed:* Houghton Coll (BA) Eng 1986; Alfred Univ (MS) Eng, Ed 1987; *cr:* Marcus Whitman Eng Tchr 1987-88; Faith Temple Schl Eng Tchr 1988-92; C. G. Finney HS Eng Tchr 1992-; Honeoye Cntrl 1995-; *ai:* Brainstormers, Cheerleading Coach; Class Adv; Master Tchr Stu Tchrs; Faith Bible Church 1984-; Honeoye Tchr Assoc; WXXI Grant; Tchr Excl Awd 1993; Tchr of Yr 1994-95; *office:* Honeoye Central PO Box 170 Honeoye NY 14471

GREANEY, DEBRA S., Math Teacher; *b:* New York, NY; *m:* Edward; *c:* Keith Wolfson; *ed:* Boston Univ (BA) Math 1971; Rider Univ (MA) Educl Admin 1989; *cr:* Park Ridge HS Math Tchr 1971-74; Hunter Regnl HS Math Tchr 1978-; *ai:* NCTM 1980-; AMTNJ 199 Huntedon Central Regional HS 84 State Route 31 Flemington N

GREATHOUSE, SUSAN E., Reading Teacher; *b:* Akron, OH; *m* G. Melecki; *ed:* Univ of Akron (BS) Elem Ed 1970, (MSEd) R Addl 29 Grad Hrs Lit, Lang Dev, Tchng of Writing, His; Natl E for Hum Fellow 1986; *cr:* Annunciation Schl Elem Tchr 1970-7 Akron Grad Asst 1973-74; Cuyahoga Falls Pub Schls Title I, Cha 1974-83; Bolich MS Rdng, Lang Arts Tchr 1983-; *ai:* Readin Festival Summit Cty, Day of Peace Coord; Textbook Selectic Trainer of Trainers; IRA, NCTE, Phi Delta Kappa 1983-; Grea Tchrs of Eng 1989-, Sec; OCIRA; AKRON; ARCA; IRA; Comm 1981-, Chprsn; Bread for the World 1978-; Amnesty Intnl 198 Cncl 1993-; Jennings Scholar 1991; MENSA Awd Tchr 1990 Month 1993; CFEA Profession Svc Awd 1983; Cuyahoga Falls S of Yr 1995; OH Tchr of Yr Nom 1995; *office:* Bolich MS 263 Cuyahoga Falls OH 44223

GREB, E. BARRY B., Mathematics Teacher; *b:* Scranton, PA; A. Miller; *c:* Chuck, Jeff, Christopher, Meredith; *ed:* Bloomsbu (BS) Math 1972; Rutgers Univ 9 Hrs Ed Stud; *cr:* Maple Shade Tchr 1972-87; Hamilton HS East Math Tchr 1987-; *ai:* NCTM 1972-; Knights of Columbus 1973-; Queen of Universe Home & 1984-, Pres 1984-85, Treas 1992-94; Queen of the Univ Socce Middletown Ath Assoc Sftbl Coach; *office:* Hamilton HS E Klockner Rd Trenton NJ 08690*

GREB, LINDA S., Mathematics Teacher; *b:* Louisville, KY; *m* G.; *c:* Molly S.; *ed:* Clarion Univ of PA (BS) Math, Comp Sci Univ of PA (MED) Math Ed 1988; Addl Post-Grad Hrs Ldrshp Portland St Univ, Western OR St Coll; *cr:* Cranberry HS Math Tchr 1983-87; Mars Area HS Math, Cmptrs, Ldrshp Tchr 1987 Cncl Adv; Mars Area Ed Assn 1987-, VP 1994-95; PA St Ed A 1983-; PA Assn of Stu Cncls 1984-, Dist 2 Dir 1989-; Natl As Cncls 1984-; Prudential Spirit Comm Awd St Chprsn 1995-; C Ldrs Schlsp St Chprsn 1993-95; *home:* 1877 Concord Dr Alliso 15101

GRECCO, DAVID A., Social Studies Teacher; *b:* Scranton, PA; E Murphy; *c:* Scott, Stephen, Rebecca, David; *ed:* Univ of Scra Scndry Ed 1970, (MS) Elem Admin 1975; Elem Prin Cert 1977; Courses at East Stroudsburg St Univ, Marywood Coll; *cr:* Dunr Dist Elem Tchr 1970-87, HS Tchr 1987-; *ai:* Swim Team Coach; Comm Long Range Plan; Curr Comm; AFT, PAFT 1970-; Dunm Tchrs 1970-, Exec Comm 1975-85; Boy Scout Comm 1981-, Tr 1981-; Natl Fed of Interscholastic Coaches & Officials Assn 198 Assn for Supervision & Curr, Middle States Assn & Schl Evaluat PIAA Track & Field Official 1979-; PIAA Swim & Diving Offic *office:* Dunmore H S Quincy Ave & Warren St Dunmore PA 185

GRECO, ANITA (CAMPANIOLO), Fourth Grade Teacher; Haven, CT; *m:* Michael R.; *c:* Michael N., Cynthia, Sherri I Southern Ct St Coll (BS) Elem Ed 1969; Southern CT St Univ 1988; 6th Yr Degree Educl Fnds, 18 Credits Post Grad; *cr:* Union Grd Tchr 1969-70; Price St Schl 2nd Grd Tchr 1972-75; Ridge R Schl 3-4, 6th Grd Tchr 1985-; *ai:* Unit Ldr 3-5 Grds; K-5 Sci, Curr Comm; NEA, CEA 1985-; Boy Scouts of Amer 1979-81, Der Girl Scouts of Amer 1981-84, Ldr; St Barnabas Rel Ed 1988-89, C Cert of Appreciation North Haven Fire Fighter Assn Food Drive North Haven Pub Schls Outstdng Achvmt 1995; *office:* Ridge R Schl 1341 Ridge Rd North Haven CT 06473*

GRECO, DANIEL THOMAS, Math & Soc Stud Teacher; *b:* Ja NY; *m:* Carol Post; *c:* Daniel, Michelle; *ed:* SUNY at Fredonia 1975; 30 Credit Hrs Elem Ed; *cr:* Persell Schl Elem Ed Tchr 1975 Club, Chess Club & Weight Club Adv; Ftbl Coach; Soc Stud, Math Arts Curr Selection Comms; Prin Selection Comm; Jamestow Union 1975-; NEA 1975-; Midget Ftbl Bd of Dir; Babe Ruth B Dir; *office:* Persell MS 375 Baker St Jamestown NY 14701

GRECO, RUTH ANNE, Math, Science Instr & Coord; *b:* New Y NY; *m:* John; *c:* Jason, Wendy, Tracey; *ed:* Lehman Coll (BS) (MS) Ed 1974; 30 Credit Hrs Columbia Univ; *cr:* PS 75 Schl Tchr JHS 142 Schl Tchr 1977-90; John Adas HS Tchr MSI Coord 1 Math, Sci Inst Grd Adv; AFT, UFT 1972-; NSTA 1990-; *office:* Joh HS Rockaway Blvd & 102nd St Queens NY 11417

GRECO, VITA GALLICCHIO, Business Ed Dept Chairpe Newark, NJ; *m:* Anthony; *c:* Anthony, Barbara, Michael; *ed:* Dickinson Univ (BS) Bus Ed 1964; *cr:* Linden HS Tchr 1964-68; Cath HS Tchr & Dept Chair 1979-; *ai:* Performing Arts club & Fu Ldrs of Amer Moderator; Schl Liaison; NJBEA 1963-; Mysti Players 1990-, Treas, Sec & Prod Coord; Linden Cultural & hertiag 1994-, Prod Coord; Act Awds, Nominator; *office:* Roselle Catho Raritan Rd Roselle NJ 07203*

GREEBE, CATHERINE KAUFMAN, Fifth Grade Teacher; *b:* NJ; *m:* Neil; *ed:* Univ of Buffalo (BS) Sociology, Elem Ed 1964; P Stud Elem Ed William Paterson Coll; *cr:* Schl #10 Paterson 1 1964-65; Waldwick Schl 1 Grd Tchr 1965-66; Mc Guffey Schl 1 1966-69; Mc Kinley Schl 5 Grd Tchr 1969-; *office:* Mc Kinley E 1901 W Central Ave Toledo OH 43606*

GREELEY, DORIS, German Teacher & Dept Coord; *b:* Philadel *ed:* East Stroudsburg (BS) Ger 1972; St Josephs (ME) ESL; Univ & Univ Breyhen Ger; *cr:* Pennridge HS Ger Tchr 24 Yrs; *ai:* Class Club Adv; Fac Comm; AATG 1972-; PSEA 1972-; Commo Partnership Fellow; *office:* Pennridge H S 1228 N 5th St Perk 18944*

GREEN, ALBERT THOMAS, Seventh Grade Art Teac Schenectady, NY; *m:* Heather Stuckey; *c:* Laurel Elizabeth; *ed:* J Albany (AS) Fine Arts, Photography 1985; SUNY at New Paltz Ed 1989; SUNY at Albany (MS) Spec Ed 1995; *cr:* Ramapo Ar Comp Prgm Dir 1986-; Shenendehowa Schl 7th Grd Art Tchr 1989- Club, Peer Mediation Adv; Soccer Coach; Set Designer HS; Jr H Schl Environment Comm; NEA, NY St Art Tchrs 1989-; W Emotional Distrubed Children in Camp Environment; Shenendehowa HS 970 Route 146 Clifton Park NY 12065*

GREEN, BARBARA LAYENETTE, Associate Professor of His Edna, TX; *ed:* Presbyterian Coll (BA) His 1973; North TX St Un His 1975; Univ of MO at Columbia (PHD) His 1980; *cr:* Univ Visiting Prof His 1981-82; Williamette Univ Adj Prof His 1983; Univ Prof His 1983-87; Wright St Univ Prof His 1987-; *ai:* African Amer Stud Prgm Dir; NEH Evaluator; Reader Princeton Testing Svc; AP Tests His 1988; Assn for Stud Afro-Amer Life, Hi OH Acad His 1987-; Phi Alpha Theta 1974-; Articles, Book R *office:* Wright St Univ 3640 Col Glenn Hwy Dept of His Day 45435*

GREEN, CONSTANCE ROGERS, First Grade Teacher; *b:* Utica, John D. Sr.; *ed:* Ulster Cty Comm (AAS) Recreation Supervisio SUNY at Brockport (BS) PE K-12 1975; SUNY at Cortland (MS) 1987; 30 Addl Credit Hrs; 6 Inservice Hrs; *cr:* Brookfield Cntrl Sch 1978-83, Tchrs Asst 1/2 Time 1978-84, PE K-12 1/2 Time 1978- Grd Tchr 1984-; *ai:* Postal Svc, World Wide Web Project, g, Playground Bldg, Inservice Comms; Flag Day Prgm Coord; ?9-, Pres 1992-94, Sec 1989-91; ASCD; Brookfield Optimist 1996, ır; Brookfield PTSA 1995-; Amer Legion Auxilary 1991-, Treas; ɛld Historical Soc; Coaching Accomplishments League Titles, ybl, Sectional Title Sftbl; *office:* Brookfield Central Schl PO Box ound Rd Brookfield NY 13314

, **DEIRDRE MONIQUE,** Counselor & Acad Instructor; *b:* NY; *ed:* Russell Sage Coll (BS) Criminal Sci 1985; Southern IL Credit Hrs Grad Prgm Correctional Admin; *cr:* Southern IL Univ ısst Criminal Justice Dept 1985-86, Stud Skills Instr 1987-88; le Coll HEOP Cnslr, A S Instr 1989-; *ai:* Mastiff Club of Amer; n Mastiff Club; Amer Bullmastiff Assn; Canadian Bullmastiff ; Three Rivers Mastiff Club; Pacific Northwest Mastiff Fanciers; Mastiff Fanciers; Northeast Mastiff Fanciers; HEOP-PO 1989-, 5 NYCLSA 1990-; Erie Cty Pub Lib Friends of Lib 1992-; *office:* le Coll 320 Porter Ave Buffalo NY 14201

, **DONNA MARINE,** French Teacher; *b:* Passaic, NJ; *m:* Daniel ebecca, Rachel; *ed:* Montclair Univ (BA) Fr, Latin 1972; NJ Acad tive Learning; *cr:* Freehold HS Fr, Latin Tchr 1972-78; Howell HS chr 1983-85; Manaladan & Freehold Twp HS Fr, Latin Tchr Howell HS Fr Tchr 1987-; *ai:* Fr Hnr Soc Club, Fr Club Adv; JEA 1972-; AATF, NJ Classical League 1990-; FLENJ 1985-; atic Club 1985-; *office:* Howell HS Squankum-Yellowbrook Rd dale NJ 07727*

, **DORIS JEAN,** Academic Chemistry Teacher; *b:* Philipsburg, arrell; *c:* Christian; *ed:* Indiana Univ of PA (MED) Chem Ed 1967; ɔrk Penn St Univ, Juniata Coll & Wilkes Coll; *cr:* Keith Jr High Dept Chm 1967-96; Altoona Area HS Thcr 1971-; *ai:* AAEA, NEA, NSTA 1971-; Delta Kappa Gamma 1980-; Oustanding r, St Francis Coll; Outstanding Sci Tchr Nom with Head Tchr ead Tchr; Mentor Prgm, Young Tchrs; *office:* Altoona Area HS ı Ave Altoona PA 16602*

, **GARY M.,** Retired Teacher; *b:* Batavia, NY; *m:* Justine Elaine n; *c:* Jonathan David; *ed:* SUNY at Fredonia (BA) Elem Ed 1970, em Ed, Rdng 1974; *cr:* Westfield Acad Third Grd Tchr 1970-83; Schl Third Grd Tchr 1970-83; Westfield Acad Kndgtn Tchr ; Central Schl Kndgtn Tchr 1983-93; *ai:* Westfield Tchrs Assn /P; NEA, NYSTA 1970-; Westfield United Fund 1993-, Campaign 'estfield Comm Kitchen 1993-, Cooking, Serving Vol; *home:* 46 ı St Westfield NY 14787

, **GWENDOLYN GRAY,** Family & Consumer Sci Teacher; *b:* le, AL; *m:* Calvin Levester Jr.; *c:* Cavetta G., Calvin L. III; *ed:* e Univ (BS) Family, Consumer Scis 1975, (MSEd) Family, er Scis 1976; 30 Hrs Beyond MS at FL St, Wright St, Univ of ati; *cr:* Barbour Cty Bd of Ed Tchr, Cnslr 1979-80; Wake Cty nities Inc Ed Coord, Heat Start 1980-86; Taylor Cty Bd of Ed 1st ır 1986-88; Cincinnati Bd of Ed 9th Grd Tchr 1989-; *ai:* Frosh 'een Inst, Amer Yth Fdn Ldrshp Adv; African-Amer His Month AFT, OH Voc Assn, Amer Home Ec Assoc 1990-; Human Relations 1995-; Urban League of Greater Cin 1993-; Schlsp Comm for 1992-; Amer Cancer Soc 1991-, Capt; Lead Tchr Family, Consumer a; Tchr of Yr; Friendship Awd for Human Relations Commission Cincinnati; *home:* 11528 Lincolnshire Rd Cincinnati OH 45240

, **HARVEY,** Professor of History; *b:* Buffalo, NY; *m:* Susan ls Williams; *ed:* Univ of Rochester (BA) His 1968; Rutgers Univ is 1970, (PHD) His 1976; Cooperstown Grad Prgms, Coursework; v of Rochester Adjunet Assoc Prof 1983-89; Strong Museum VP ; Northeastern Univ Assoc Prof 1989-93, Prof 1993-; *ai:* Grad Dir t Coord; Pub His Prgms; AHA, AASLH, OAH 1977-; ASA; Lib Bd Conservation Comm 1992-; Falbright Lecturing Awd 1995; 3 Books *ice:* Northeastern Univ 249 Meserve Hall Boston MA 02115

, **JANET KADOWAKI,** First Grade Teacher; *b:* Los Angeles, CA; ıeth A.; *c:* Douglass, Brian, Amy; *ed:* Kent St Univ (BS) Ed 1963; Cleveland St Univ, Kent St Univ, Univ of Akron, Univ of Toledo, ame Coll; *cr:* Garfield Heights City Schls Third Grd Tchr 1963-64; d City Schls First Grd Tchr 1964-67, LD Tchr 1972-77; Anthony Local Schls First Grd Tchr 1977-; *ai:* Head Tchr; Author Comm appa Delta Pi 1991-; Anthony Wayne Ed Assn 1977-; ON Ed Assn 7, 1972-; NEA 1963-67, 1972-; Phi Delta Kappa 1982-, Grant ; Sylvan United Church of Christ 1977-, Numerous Comms; l 30 Aution 1986-, Comm; Ashland Oil Tchr Achvmt Awd 1990; Yr 1995; I Make a Difference Awd Lucas Cty Schls 1990, 1995; rt Brace Jovanovich Prgm Reviewer; *home:* 4333 Vicksburg Dr a OH 43560

, **JEAN M.,** Chemistry Teacher; *b:* Hornell, NY; *m:* Victor B.; *c:* *ed:* Carlow Coll (BS) Bio & Chem 1988; Alfred Univ (MS) Sci Ed *r:* Greenwood Cntrl Schl Sci Tchr 1989; Addison Cntrl Schl Jr High ernative Sci Tchr & Chem Tchr 1989-; *ai:* Discipline Comm Mem; Y 1989-; ATA 1989-, Pub Relations 1994-; St Catherines Church CCD Instr; Masters Thesis Paper; *office:* Addison Central Schl 1 St Addison NY 14801

, **KATHLEEN ANN (HAYWARD),** Former Elementary Teacher; ıut Creek, CA; *m:* Theodore Allan; *c:* Katherine Michelle, Michael *ed:* UC Davis (BA) Pol Sci 1981; USF (MA) Ed Admin 1993; UC Clear Ryan Multiple Sub Ed 1982; *cr:* Jefferson Elem Schl 5th Grd 982-85; Crittentenden MS 5th Grd Tchr 1985-86; St Bartholemew d Grd Tchr 1986-88; Eisenhut Elem Schl 6th Grd, 5th Grd Tchr 2; *ai:* Welcome Wagon 1994-, VP, Pres 1996-97; *home:* 8 Bordeaux ıirport NY 14450

, **LEIGH,** Drama & English Teacher; *b:* Delaware Wilming, DE; əhen Michael Catterton; *ed:* Univ of MD (BS) Eng Drama & Scndry 2; Exeter Univ at Oxford (CC) Eng Lit 1995; Cert of Completion in ; *cr:* High Point HS Drama & Eng Tchr 1992-; *ai:* Eng Speaking Shakespearan Speech Competition & Drama Clb Spon; Schl ıg & Mgmt Team; Drama Dept & Intl Thespian Dir; Co-Chair Black ınth Pgm; Minorities in Engrng Comm; Ed Theatre Assn 1993-; NEA Eng Tchrs of Amer 1995-; St Hughs Church 1990-, Vol Toys for Josephs Church 1994-, Yth Cnslr; ATLAS Grant Proposal 1994-95; Speaker New Tchrs Seminar of Prince Georges Cty 1994; Tchr of the High Point HS 1995; Recognized by Washington Post Feb 1995; Vinner of Shakespearean Schlsp to Study Eng In Oxford Eng; *office:* oint High School 3601 Powder Mill Rd Beltsville MD 20705*

, **LOREN R.,** Fourth Grade Teacher; *b:* Akron, OH; *m:* Kay; *c:* Scott, Tyler; *ed:* Xavier Univ (BA) Ed; 41 Hrs Above Masters; *cr:* vood Elem 1965-67; Pleasant St Elem 1969-; *ai:* Girls Sftbl & Var Golf Coach; ACTA; NEA; *office:* Pleasant St Schl 317 Pleasant St d OH 44805

, **LORRAINE EILEEN,** Eng as a Second Lang Teacher; *b:* White NY; *c:* Thomas, Jennifer; *ed:* Kingsborough Comm Coll (Assoc) Ed City Univ of NY (BA) Applied Linguistics 1993; 16 Credits Eng Lit, c City Univ of NY (MA) ESL, 16 Credits Eng Lit, c City Univ of NY of Staten Island; *cr:* F.D. Roosevelt HS Assoc 8 Yrs, ESL Tchr 2 Yrs; *ai:* Peer Tutoring Prgm Adv; AFT, UFT Bay Ridge Comm Cncl 1993-, Rep; *office:* F D Roosevelt HS 5800 ve Brooklyn NY 11204

GREEN, MARGARET MILDRED, English Teacher; *b:* Kansas City, MO; *m:* Michael Kent; *c:* Megan; *ed:* Univ of KS (BS) Eng Ed 1973; SUNY at Oneonta (MS) Eng Ed 1986; *cr:* Univ of Chicago Editorial Asst ACTA CYTOLOGICA 1973-77; Holmes Jr HS Eng Tchr 1977-79; Zion Benton Twp Sr HS Eng Tchr 1979-81; Schenevus Cntrl Schl Sr HS Eng Tchr 1981-; *ai:* Yrbk; Drama Club, Lit Magazine Adv; Stu Recognition, Grad Requirements, Shared Decision Making, Acad Excl Comms; NCTE 1986-; NYSUT Schenevus Tchrs Assn 1981-; CATE 1993-; Tchr of Yr 1986; Tchr Ctr Dev Rdng, Writing Wkshp; RSEC TV Artie Awd Best TV Documentary 1990, Production Team 1991; *office:* Schenevus Central Schl 100 Main St Schenevus NY 12155

GREEN, MARTRICE, 6th Grade Math Teacher; *b:* Washington, DC; *ed:* Amer Univ (BA) Elem Ed 1973; Howard Univ (MED) Admin & Supervision 1978; Grad Courses UMD at Coll Park, Trinity Coll DC, Western MD Coll; *cr:* Langley Park-Mc Cormick Elem Schl 1-2, 4 Grd Tchr 1973-86; Paint Branch Elem Schl 6 Grd Tchr, Math, Testing Coord 1986-; *ai:* Schl Based Mngmt Comm; NEA, PGCEA, MSTA 1973-; NCTM 1985-; Wesleyan Choir Asbury UMC 1976-, Librn, Appreciation; Unsung Heroine Awd P G Co Commission on Women; *office:* Paint Branch Elem Schl 5101 Pierce Ave College Park MD 20740

GREEN, MARY CARROLL, Third Grade Teacher; *b:* Johnstown, PA; *m:* John N.; *c:* Rebecca Lee Wasson; *ed:* Lock Haven St Univ (BS) Elem Ed 1963; 28 Grad Hrs IN Univ of PA; *cr:* Richland Schl Dist 1st Grd Tchr 1964; Bald Eagle Area Schls 1st & 6th Grd Tchr 1964-76; Our Mother of Sorrows 3rd Grd Tchr 1986-; *home:* 137 Dahlia St Johnstown PA 15905

GREEN, PHYLLIS GOLDSTEIN, Resource Room Teacher; *b:* New York, NY; *m:* Theodore; *c:* Charles, Janice Green Falk; *ed:* NY Univ (BA) Psych 1959, (MA) Elem Ed 1964; Coll of New Rochelle (MS) Spec Ed 1981; *cr:* NY City Bd of Ed Tchr.

GREEN, ROBERT BRUCE, Orchestra Director; *b:* Massillon, OH; *c:* Robert F.; *ed:* Univ of AK (BM) Music 1975, (BSED) Music Ed 1976; Univ of MT (MM) Music Performance 1992; *cr:* Univ of MT Music Ed Tchng Asst 1991-92; Steubenville City Schls 4th-8th Grd Orch, Kndgtn-6th Grd Vocal Music Tchr 1978-83, MS Gen Music 1983-91, 4th-12th Grd Orch Dir 1992-; *ai:* Conductor HS Chamber Orch, Pops Orch; NEA, OEA, SEA 1978-, Sea Human Relations Chair 1994-95; Music Edctrs Natl Conf 1970-, Omea Dist Conf Chair 1992-93, 1995-; Natl Schl Orch Assn 1993-; Amer Fed Musicians 1974-; BSA 1981-, Troop Comm Chair, Dist Trng Chair, Cncl Exec Bd, Dist Awd Merit; Prin Horn Tuscarawas Philharmonic 1976; Founder, Performer Chamber Music Ensembles; *home:* 400 Anna Maria Dr Apt 9 Wintersville OH 43952*

GREEN, RONALD MICHAEL, Director & Ethics Institute; *b:* New York, NY; *m:* Mary Jean Matthews; *c:* Julie, Matthew; *ed:* Brown Univ (AB) Rel Stud 1964; Harvard Univ (PHD) Rel Ethics 1973; *cr:* Harvard Univ Tchng 1968-69; Dartmouth Coll Asst, Assoc Prof 1969-79; Stanford Univ Visiting Prof 1984-85; Dartmouth Coll John Phillips Prof of Rel 1981-; *ai:* Consultant for Natl Inst of Hlth, Natl Ctr for Human Genome Rsrch; Amer Acad of Rel 1975-, Sec; Soc of Chrstn Ethics 1971-, Bd; Natl Inst of Hlth Human Embryo Rsrch Panel 1994, Mem; Author of Five Books in Rel, Ethics; Distngd Tchr Awd 1980; *office:* Dartmouth Coll 6031 Parker House Hanover NH 03755

GREEN, SANDRA A., Acad Talented Class Teacher; *b:* Lakewood, NJ; *m:* George E.; *c:* Samantha Leo, Kristyn, Michael, John; *ed:* Monmouth Coll NJ (BS) Elem Ed 1969; *cr:* Brick Twp Schl 6th Grd Tchr 1969-71; Bell Oaks Upper Elem 6th Grd Tchr 1971-75; Crescent Park Schl 4th Grd Tchr 1976-80; Bell Oaks Upper Elem 6th Grd Tchr 1980-84; Bellmawr Park and Burke Schl Acad Talented Class 1984-96; *ai:* Brick Twp Schls 6th Grd Tchr 1969-71; Bell Oaks Upper Elem 6th Grd Tchr 1971-75, 1980-84; Crescent Park Schl 4th Grd Tchr 1976-80; Bellmawr Park & Burke Schl Academically Talented Class Tchr 1984-; Text Selection, Curr Dev Comm; Tech Comm Co-Chair; NEA, NJ Ed Assn 1970-; Bellmawr Ed Assn 1971-, VP; *office:* Bellmawr Park Elem Schl 112 Black Horse Pike Bellmawr NJ 08031

GREEN, SHARON, Sixth Grade Teacher; *b:* Batesville, IN; *m:* Michael; *c:* Christopher, Jeffrey; *ed:* Ball St Univ (BA) Elem Ed Tchr 1980; Xavier Univ (MS) LD-BD 1984; *cr:* Franklin Cty Schl Corp 3rd Grd Tchr 1980-81; St Michael Schl 5th Grd Tchr 1981-84; St John The Baptist Schl 6th Grd Tchr 1984-; *ai:* Cath Schls Week, Environmental Comm; Natl Cath Ed Assn 1984-; *office:* Saint John The Baptist Schl 5375 Dry Ridge Rd Cincinnati OH 45252

GREEN, SHEREE SLIFMAN, Business Teacher; *b:* Queen, NY; *m:* Joel; *c:* Todd, Walter; *ed:* Adelphi Univ (BBA) Acctng 1978; Montclair St Coll (MS) Bus Ed 1982; 32 Hrs Post Grad Fairleigh Dickinson Univ, Iona Coll, Montclair St Univ; *cr:* Seffern HS Bus Tchr 1978-87; Manhattan Career Inst Evening Bus Instr 1982-86; Teaneck HS Bus Tchr 1987-; *ai:* Yrbk 1988-, Class 1979-82, 1984-85 Adv; NJEA 1987-; NBEA; Stillman Schl HSA 1992-; *office:* Teaneck HS 100 Elizabeth Ave Teaneck NJ 07666

GREEN, SUSAN A., Second Grade Teacher; *b:* Malden, MA; *m:* Michael; *c:* Scott, Joshua, William; *ed:* Univ of MA (BSEd) Elem Ed 1972; *cr:* Osgood Schl Elem Tchr1972-; *ai:* NEA, MA Tchrs Assn 1972-.

GREEN, SUSAN BELL, English Teacher; *b:* Alliance, OH; *m:* David G.; *c:* Johanna R. Lynn; *ed:* Grove City Coll (BS) Eng 1974; Credit Hrs Clarion Univ; *cr:* Rocky Grove Jr, Sr HS Eng Tchr 1974-; *ai:* NEA, PSEA 1974-; VGEA Tchrs Assn 1974-, VP, Various Comms Chprsn; *office:* Rocky Grove Jr, Sr HS 403 Rocky Grove Ave Franklin PA 16323

GREEN, THOMAS FRANK, Physics Teacher; *b:* Mauston, WI; *m:* Mary A. Wallace; *ed:* Univ of WI (BS) Math, Physics 1964; 36 Addl Post Grad Credits; *cr:* Platteville Pub Schls Math Tchr 1964-68; Roncalli HS Physics, Math Tchr, Dean of Stdnts 1968-75; Queen Anne Schl Math Chair, Asst Head Master 1977-82; Good Counsel HS Physics Tchr 1988-.

GREEN, WANDA RIZPAH, Retired Title 1 Reading Coord; *b:* Delaware County, OH; *ed:* Bowling Green St Univ (BS) Elem Ed 1964, (MS) Rdng 1974; Otterbein Coll Admin; *cr:* Hartford Elem Schl 3rd Grd Tchr 1957-59; Southwest Licking Schl 1-2nd Grd Tchr 1959-68; Northridge Local Elem Schl 1-4 Grd Tchr 1968-85, Prin 1985-95, Title I Rdng Coord 1985-95; *ai:* Alexandria Lib Bd of Trustees; OEA, NEA 1957-85; OH Elem Admin 1985-; Lib Bd 1995-, Trustee; Geneological Soc 1986-; Dist Testing, Title I Coord; Family Genological Book Pub; *home:* 374 Hillview Dr Johnstown OH 43031

GREENAGEL, HEATHER ARLING, English Dept Chairman & Tchr; *b:* Minneapolis, MN; *c:* Jill Heather, Frank Louis Jr.; *ed:* Univ of MN (BS) Eng, Comm 1961, (MA) Comm, Eng 1969; Tchrs Coll of Columbia (EdM) Ed Admin 1994; Cornell Univ, UCLA, Doctoral Candidate 1996, Ed Admin Tchrs Coll, Colubia Univ, Ed Leadership & Restructury; *cr:* Denver Schls Tchr, Librn 1961-62, 1964-66; Bryant Jr HS Eng, Speech Tchr 1962-64; San Marino HS Eng Tchr 1966-69; Suffield HS 9-12 Grd Eng, Speech Tchr1969-71; Metuchen HS 9-12 Grd Eng Tchr 1973-76; Elizabeth HS Eng Chair, Tchr 1987-; *ai:* Natl Cncl Admin Women in Ed; ASCD; Natl Cncl Tchrs of Eng; NJ Natl Cncl Tchrs of Eng 1991; Tchrs Coll Admin Women in Ed 1993-; Northeast Coalition Educl Ldrs 1992-, Bd Dirs, Co-Chair St Meet, Writing Group; Phi Delta Kappa; AAUW; Redlands Admissions Assistance Prgm; Project Teach Grants 1990-91, 1992-93; Inservice Educator Writing Wkshp1991, Writing Across the Curr 1990; Middle States Evaluation C0-Chair; Panel Member for Groups Addressing New Educators; Panel Member from tchrs Coll Columbia Selecting Finalists for Redbook Magazine Best Elem Schls Project 1994-95, Best HS Project 1995-96; Dept Scholarship Ed Admin TC Columbia Univ; *home:* 4 Hunters Cir Lebanon NJ 08833*

GREENAN, JAMES PATRICK, Mathematics Chairman; *b:* Brooklyn, NY; *m:* Mary Mc Hugh; *c:* Maureen, Bernadette, Colleen; *ed:* Manhattan Coll (BS) Math 1966; Brooklyn Coll (MA) Math 1971; St John's Univ (PHD) Admin 1976; NSF Math Inst Hofstra Univ; *cr:* Gorton HS Math Tchr 1966-69; Lawrence HS Math Tchr 1969-86; St Francis Coll Adj Prof 1983-86; Elmont Meml HS Math Chm 1986-; *ai:* NCTM 1970-; St Vincent DePaul 1978-, Pres; Supt Grant Family Math; Mid Sts Vistation Comm; *office:* Elmont Memorial HS 555 Ridge Rd Elmont NY 11003*

GREENAWAY, FREDERICK THOMAS, Chem Prof & Dean of Grad Stud; *b:* Rakaia, New Zealand; *ed:* Univ of Canterbury New Zealand (BS) Chem 1969, (PHD) Chem 1973; *cr:* MI St Univ Research Assoc 1974-74; Syracuse Univ Research Assoc 1974-80; Clark Univ Asst Prof 1980-86, Assoc Prof 1986-93, Prof 1993-; *ai:* Rugby Club Coach; Author of Over 50 Scientific Articles; Recipient of Many Grants for Scientific Research, Advancing Research Opportunities for Women & Minorities; *office:* Clark Univ Dept of Chemistry Worcester MA 01610*

GREENBERG, ALEX, Prof of Criminal Justice & Law; *b:* Bardisal, Austria; *m:* Randee Lee Winer; *c:* Julee, Sara; *ed:* Northeastern Univ (BS) Criminal Justice 1970; WA St Univ (MA) Criminal Justice 1974; NY Univ Law Schl (DLS) Law 1990; Soc Work St Univ of NY at Buffalo; *cr:* White Plains Police Dept Police Ofcr 1970-72; US Dept of Justice Crime Analyst 1972-73; WA St Univ Tchng Asst 1973-74; Niagara Cty Comm Coll Prof 1974-; *ai:* Chair Affirmative Action Comm; Cross Ctry Team Coach; Academy Criminal Justice Scis 1974-, Comm Coll Cncl 1975, 1981; Big Bro Big Sisters 1977-, Bd of Dir 1977; Pres Awd Excl Coll Advisement 1995; Pres Awd Excl Coll Tchng 1985; Coll Text Reviewer West Publishing Co, Glencoe Publishing Co; *office:* Niagara County Comm Coll 3111 Saunders Settlement Rd Sanborn NY 14132

GREENBERG, GERALDINE GERVER, Educl Enrichment Specialist; *b:* Brooklyn, NY; *m:* Charles; *c:* Marc Jay, Caren Lazarus, Tricia Ellen, Jordyn Lazarus; *ed:* Brooklyn Coll (BS) Elem Ed 1960, (MA) Elem Ed 1970; Art Ed 15 Credit Hrs 1994-95; Future Prob Solving 35 Credit Hrs 1983-90; Real Estate Brokers License Courses 1969-72; Certified Paralegal 1970; *cr:* PS 282 K 2nd, 4th Grd, After Schl Folk Dancing Tchr 1960-63; Cmptr Search Realty RE Broker, Salesperson, Staff Trainer 1972-; PS 81 3rd-4th, 6th Grd Tchr 1983-88, World Geog Cluster Tchr 1988-91, Educl Enrichment Specialist 1991-; *ai:* Storytelling, Future Problem Solving Coach; One-to-One Staff Dev; Contest Coord; Theater Guild 1972-, Choreographer; NY St Future Problem Solving Championships 1992-94; Comm Awarded Grants Artists in Residence; Pub Lesson Plans; *office:* Pub Schl 81 Q 559 Cypress Ave Ridgewood NY 11385

GREENBERG, JULIE ELIZABETH, Mathematics Teacher; *b:* Brooklyn, NY; *ed:* Union Coll (BS) Math 1993; Manhattanville Coll Working Toward Masters in Scndry Math Ed; *cr:* White Plains HS Tchr 1993-; *ai:* Stage Crew; Midnight Run; NCTM 1993-, Mem; New Standards Project 1994-, Mem, Benchmarker; *office:* White Plains HS 550 North St White Plains NY 10605*

GREENBERG, ROBIN S., Social Studies & Reading Tchr; *b:* Jersey City, NJ; *ed:* Rider Coll (BA) Elem Ed 1980; *cr:* Mt Carmel Schl Grd 4-5 Tchr 1980-82; PS #25 Grd 4 Tchr 1982-83; PS #39 Grd 6-7 Tchr 1984-; *ai:* NEA 1982-; Big Brother, Sister Prgm 1990-; *office:* Dr Charles Defuccio Schl PS 39 214 Plainfield Ave Jersey City NJ 07306

GREENBERG, SHEILA I., Sixth Grade Teacher; *b:* Bronx, NY; *c:* Gregory, Lance; *ed:* Queens Coll CUNY (BA), (MS); 60 Addl Grad Credits; *cr:* Hempstead UFSD Tchr 1967-72; Levittown UFSD Tchr 1986-; *ai:* Vice Chprsn Tchrs Ctr; Dist Prof Affairs Comm; Adv Natl Jr Hon Soc, Sci Club; Curr Comm for Sci, Lang Arts, Cmptrs; Levittown United Tchrs, NEA, NYSUT 1986-; Natl Assn of Scndry Schl Admin 1994-; Outstdng Elem Schl Tchrs; *office:* Jonas E. Salk MS Old Jerusalem Rd Levittown NY 11756

GREENBERG, SUSAN BAIM, Social Studies Teacher; *b:* Chicago, IL; *m:* Robert; *c:* Karen, Randi; *ed:* Univ of Wi at Madison (BS) His 1970; Case Western Reserve Univ 6 Credits His; *cr:* Beck MS 7th Grade Soc Stud Tchr 1972-77; Camden Cty Coll Adj Fac 1986-87; Carusi Jr Schl 7th Grd Soc Stud Tchr 1988-; *ai:* Yrbk Adv; Staff Dev & Discipline Comms; Bldg Liaison; NEA & NJEA 1988-; CHEA 1988-; Womens Amer Ort 1977-, Pres; Congregation M'Kor Shalom 1988-; *office:* Carusi Jr Schl Roosevelt & Jackson Rds Cherry Hill NJ 08002

GREENE, BENJAMIN THOMAS, Music Teacher; *b:* Providence, RI; *m:* Faith Williams; *c:* Andrew, Sarah, Joshua, Benjamin; *ed:* RI Coll (BS) Music Ed 1982; *cr:* Providence Pub Schl 5th-8th Grd Music Tchr 1982-83; Winnisquam Reg MS 5th-8th Grd Music Tchr 1983-86; Concord HS Orch Dir 1986-; *ai:* Dir Greater Manchester Yth Symphony; NEA, MENC 1983-; ASTA 1986-, St Pres; *home:* 127 South St Concord NH 03301*

GREENE, EARLINE EVANS, First & Second Grade Teacher; *b:* Marion, SC; *m:* John W.; *c:* Nyoka Iline; *ed:* Columbia Union Coll (BS) Elem Ed 1967; Temple Univ (MA) Elem Ed 1978; 3 Hrs Cmptrs, Applied Ed, 3 Hrs Hlth Ed Trenton St Coll; 3 Credit Hrs La Sierra Univ, 3 Credit Hrs Andrews Univ Workbook Pubs; *cr:* Thornbury SBA Schl Grds 4-6 Tchr 1967-68; Jr HS #1 Grd 6 Tchr 1968-69; Grant Elem Schl Grd 4 Tchr 1969-70, Grd 3 Tchr 1970-76; Mt Sinai Elem Schl 1-2 Grds Tchr 1970-, Prin 1980-85; *ai:* Exec Bd Mt Sinai Day Care; Schl Evaluation Team Allegheny East Conference; Proclamations for Local Churches, SDA Schls, Govt Ofcls; Pathfinders Sign Lang Adv; Bo-Rietta Inc 1985-, Historian, Svc; Thomas & Violet Zapara Excl in Tchng Awd; Dr. Martin Luther King Jr. Recognition Awd Presented by His Son; AEC Ministry of Tchng Awd; Mt Sinai Day Care Dedicated Svc Awd; Article Pub; *home:* 35 Bruce Park Dr Trenton NJ 08618*

GREENE, GREGORY IAN, Mathematics Teacher; *b:* San Diego, CA; *ed:* Queens Coll (BA) Physics 1967; Univ of MI (MS) Physics 1968; 30 Credits Beyond Masters; *cr:* Stuyvesant HS Math Tchr 1968-69; Bronx HS of Sci Math Tchr 1969-; *ai:* Boys Var, Girls Var Vlybl Coach; UFT 1970-; *office:* The Bronx HS Of Science 75 W Main St Bronx NY 10468

GREENE, JAMES AUGUSTUS,JR., 8th Grade US History Teacher; *b:* Baltimore, MD; *m:* Sharon Frances Dickerson; *c:* James Augustus III; *ed:* Morgan St Univ (BA) His Ed 1973; 15 Hrs Johns Hopkings Univ Admin, Supervision; 15 Hrs Admin, Supervision Loyola Coll; *cr:* Greenspring MS 8th Grd US His Tchr 1973-; *ai:* Natl Jr Honor Soc Co-Spon; Chm Father, Son Conf; Tchr Ldrshp Acad; Mentor Tchr; Baltimore Tchrs Union, AFT 1973-; *office:* Greenspring MS 82 4701 Greenspring Ave Baltimore MD 21209*

GREENE, JEAN HILL, Elementary Guidance Counselor; *b:* Raleigh, NC; *c:* Janettarose L.; *ed:* St Augustine Coll (BS) Sociology 1957; Antioch Coll (MS) 1974; Certs Cnslng K-12, Soc Stud; 60 Addl Hrs; *cr:* NC Bd of Ed Soc Stud Tchr 1957-59; Inter-Church Child Care Soc Caseworker 1959-62; Women's Chrstn Alliance Caseworker 1962-65; Philadelphia Bd of Ed Suprv Home & Schl Coords 1965-67; Lincoln Day Nursery Casework 1967-75; Philadelphia Bd of Ed Elem Cnslr 1975-; *ai:* Philadelphia Fed of Tchrs; Alpha Kappa Alpha; Semi-Finalist Tchr of Excl 1995.

GREENE, JEFFREY DEL, Band Director; *b:* Oceanside, CA; *m:* Cheryl; *c:* Kevin, Allison; *ed:* Ithaca Coll (BA) Music Ed 1976; Brockport Coll

(MS) Ed 1979; *cr:* Hilton Schls Music Tchr 1976; Warsaw Schls HS Band Dir 1977-78; Greece Olympia HS Bands Dir 1979-; *ai:* Musicals Orch Dir 1979-; Stu Cncl Adv 1986-92; Fac Cncl 1995-; NEA, MENC 1976-; NYS BDA 1977-; Tchr of Yr 1987, 1995; *office:* Greece Olympia HS 1139 Maiden Ln Rochester NY 14615*

GREENE, JOHN ROBERT, History & Comm Professor; *b:* Syracuse, NY; *m:* Patty N. Messer; *c:* Thomas, Christopher, Mary Rose; *ed:* St Bonaventure Univ (BA) His 1977, (MA) His 1978; Syracuse Univ (PHD) Amer His 1983; *cr:* t Bonaventure Univ Grad Instr 1977-78; Cazenovia Coll His, Comm Prof 1979-; Univ Coll Syracuse coll Adjunct Instr 1981-; *ai:* Phi Theta Kappa Adv; Cncl on Acad Affairs Chair; Amer Historical Assn; Org of Amer Historians; Cntr for the Stud of the Presidency; Distinguished Fac Achvmt Awd 1993; Books; Received Fellowships, Grants & Awds; *office:* Cazenovia College Box F Cazenovia NY 13035*

GREENE, JOSEPH ANDREW, Govt, Ec & AP US His Tchr; *b:* Erie, PA; *m:* Theresa Gecewicz; *c:* Matthew, Kathryn; *ed:* Edinboro St Univ (BS) Ed 1976; John CArroll Univ (MED) 1988; *cr:* Kori Day Schl 7th, 8th Grd Tchr 1979-81; Regina HS Soc Stud Instr 1983-; *ai:* Sr Class Modertor; Schl Scheduling Ofcr; *office:* Regina HS 1857 S Green Rd South Euclid OH 44121

GREENE, JUDY, English Teacher; *b:* Pikeville, KY; *m:* David Keith; *c:* Keith; *ed:* Pikeville Coll (BS) Eng, Pol Sci 1968; Morehead St Univ (MA) Scndry Ed 1978; *cr:* Zane Trace HS Tchr 1968-69; Huntington HS Eng Tchr 1969-; *ai:* Cntrl OEA, NEA Instruction & Prof Dev, OEA Awds Comm Chair; Planning, Curr Comm; OH Cncl Tchr Eng; NEA 1968-, Bd of Dirs; OH Ed Assn 1968-, Exec Comm; Central OEA, NEA 1968-, Exec Comm, 2 Accolade Awds for Svc to Mems; Hazen Flwshp; *home:* 1256 Mingo Rd Chillicothe OH 45601*

GREENE, LINDA M., Adjunct & Flute Instructor; *b:* Syracuse, NY; *ed:* Syracuse Univ (BM) Music Performance 1979; *cr:* Hamilton Coll Adj, Flute Instr 1986-; St Univ of NY at Oswego Adj, Flute Instr 1993-; *office:* Hamilton Coll Dept of Music 198 College Hill Rd Clinton NY 13323

GREENE, LORI E., First Grade Teacher; *b:* Ridgway, PA; *ed:* Clarion Univ of PA (BS) Music Ed 1982; CA Univ of PA (BS) Elem Ed 1986, (BS) Early Chldhd Ed 1989; *cr:* Cntrl Greene Schl Dist Elem Gen Music, MS Chorus Tchr 1982-86, MS Chorus Tchr 1987-91, MS Band Tchr 1991-92, MS Band, Chorus Tchr 1992-93, First Grd Tchr 1993-; *ai:* PSEA, NEA, PMEA, MENC 1982-; Greene Theater Co 1989-; Trinity Luth Church 1990-, Church Cncl; *home:* 205 Hague Ln Uniontown PA 15401

GREENE, LUCIA ANN, Vocational Special Ed Coord; *b:* Berea, OH; *m:* David Michael; *c:* Christopher, Katie, Karli; *ed:* Ashland Coll (BS) Ed 1980; Baldwin Wallace Coll (MA) Ed 1989; *cr:* St Francis Xavier Chapter I Remedial Math Tchr 1980-81; Berea City Schls Remedial Rdng, Elem Tchr 1980-84; Medina Cty Career Ctr Adult Basic Ed Instr 1982-87, Voc Spec Ed Coord 1984-; *ai:* OH Voc Assn of Spec Needs Prsnl; CEC; Medina Cty Voc Ctr Ed Assn; Brownie Troop #730, 1994-, Co-Ldr; St Martin's Cath Church 1995-, Mission Coord; *office:* Medina County Career Ctr 1101 W Liberty St Medina OH 44256*

GREENE, MARC ELLIOT, Vocal Music Teacher; *b:* Englewood, NJ; *m:* Suzanne Winter; *c:* Cassandra; *ed:* Ithaca Coll (BS) Comm Mngmt 1980; Coll of Saint Rose (MS) Music Ed 1986; *cr:* Bethlehem Cntrl MS Vocal Music Tchr 1981-88; Scotia Glenville Jr & Sr HS Vocal Music Tchr 1988-90; Solvay HS Choral Dir 1991-93; Newfield HS Choral Dir 1993-; *ai:* Choral Dir Select Vocal Ensemble, A Cappella Singers, Advanced Chorus; Dir Choreographer, Piano Accompont, Drama & Murial Productions; Drama Club, Thespian Soc, Schl Newspaper, Talent Variety Show Advs; AFT, NYSUT 1988-; MENC, NYSSMA 1981-; Phi Mu Alpha Sintoria 1976-, Chapter Treas; Performed with Empire St Youth Theatre Inst Saratoga-Potsdam; Chorus Syracuse Vocal Ensemble Albany Pro Musical; Hour Mgr, Staff Saratoga Performing Art Ctr 1981-90; *home:* 40 Pine St Ardsley NY 10502*

GREENE, NORMA HERMAN, 6th Grade Math Teacher; *b:* Brooklyn, NY; *m:* Leonard; *c:* Jennifer Greene Shaw, Peter Daniel; *ed:* Univ of MI (BA) Ed Psych 1959; Montclair St Univ Grad Courses Towards Masters; *cr:* PS 279 3, 4th Grd Tchr 1959-61; Livingston Supplemental Inst 1965-77; West Orange Dist Coord, Elem St Compensatory Ed 1977-80; Gregory Elem Schl 6th Grd Tchr 1980-88; Roosevelt MS Schl 6th Grd Math Tchr 1988-; *ai:* Math Contest Coord 1980-87; Curr Revision, Textbook Selection Math; WOEA 1977-; NEA; NCTM; NCJW Rec Sec; PT Cncl Rec Sec; JESPY House Bd Mem; Math Wkshp Presenter; *office:* Roosevelt MS 36 Gilbert Pl West Orange NJ 07052

GREENE, ROBERT DEWARD, Tech Teacher & Dept Chair; *b:* Syracuse, NY; *m:* Janice Linda; *c:* Cary Robert, Heather Julia; *ed:* SUNY at Oswego (BA) Industrial Arts 1962, (MS) Industrial Arts 1969; Various Elective Courses from Broome Comm Coll & Cornell; *cr:* Newark Valley HS Tech Tchr & Dept Head 1962-; *ai:* Track Coach; Ski Club Adv; Cross Cntry Coach; NY St Tech Assoc 1958-; NYSUT 1962-; Southern Tier Tech Assoc 1962-, Pres, Tchr of the Yr 1983; NJ Historical Soc 1970-; Various Comm Based Org; Thesis on Image of Ind Arts in Southern Tier 1969.

GREENE, ROBERT STICKNEY, Professor of Biology; *b:* Daton, OH; *m:* Carol Ann Gibbens; *c:* Christoperh, Michael; *ed:* Niagara Univ (BS) Bio 1975, (MS) Bio 1977; SUNY at Buffalo (PHD) Physiology 1982; Post Doctoral Stud US Army Med Rsrch Inst Infectious Diseases, Roswell Park Cancer Inst; *cr:* Niagara Univ Prof Bio 1991-; Roswell Park Cancer Inst Asst Rsrch Prof 1993-; *ai:* AAAS, AAUP 1981-; ASM 1983-; US Army Reserve 1971-, Major Med Svc; *office:* Niagara Univ Dept of Biology Niagara Univ NY 14109

GREENE, WILLIAM JOSEPH, Asst Prof; *b:* New York City, NY; *m:* Alice Dallmann; *c:* Rosemary; *ed:* Fordham Univ (BA) Modern Lang, Fr 1961, (JD) Law Schl 1965, (MBA) Mngmt Systems 1987; *cr:* Chemical Bank Asst Treas 1961-72; Private Law Practice Attorney 1972-76; NY Cty Lawyers Assn Exec Dir, Coo 1976-90; Fordham Univ Asst Prof 1990-; *ai:* Enviromental Law, Related Issues Rsrch Guest Speaker, Listing Stu Act; NY Cty Lawyers Assn 1966-, Fgn, Intl Law Comm 1991-, Bus Bankruptcy Comm 1972-76; HEART Corp 1995-, Contr Writer; Hudson river Fishermens Assn 1994-, Speaker; Antique Automobile Club of Amer 1968-, Pres 2 Terms, Ray Keeler Awd; HEART Beat Article 1995; Featured Comments Weekly Newsmagazine 1994; *office:* Fordham Univ 441 E Fordham Rd Bronx NY 10458*

GREENE-DANSBY, SHARON, Vocal Music Teacher; *b:* New York City, NY; *m:* Earnest; *ed:* MI St Univ (BME) Music Ed 1964; Tchrs Coll Columbia (MA) Music, Interdisciplinary Areas 1974; 30 Hrs Ethnomusicology Hunter Coll; *cr:* Gage Jr HS Vocal, Gen Music Tchr 1964-65; Otto Jr HS Vocal, Gen Music Tchr 1965-66; White Plains Elem Schl Gen Music Tchr 1966-74; WHite Plains HS Vocal Music Tchr, Dir Musical Productions 1974-; *ai:* Dir Musical Productions, Select Ensembles; Tennis Coach 1977-89; MENC, WCSMA 1974-; Outstdng Svc Awd Delta Sigma Theta; Comm Svc Awd Westchester Black His Month Comm; *office:* White Plains HS 550 North St White Plains NY 10605*

GREENFIELD, MARSHA DIANE, 1st Grade Teacher; *b:* Balto, MD; *m:* Louis; *c:* Charles; *ed:* Univ of MD Coll Park (BS) Elem Ed1970; Johns Hopkins Loyola Coll, Towson St Univ Master Equivalency Elem Ed 1988; MD Writing Project Tchr Consultant; STARS Sci Ldrshp Trng; *cr:* Balto City #59, #38, #64 4th, 6th Grd Tchr 1970-72; Pub Schls #52, #5 1st, 2nd, 2nd & 3rd, 4th Grd Tchr 1974-85; Thomas Johnson Pub Schl #84 1st Grd Tchr 1985-; *ai:* Schl Improvement Team; STARS Ldrshp Tchr; Read Your Way Through Winter Project Dir; Grant, Pub Relations Dirs; Led 4 Sci Fairs; Standards Comm Eng, Lang Arts; MD Writing Project 1988-, TC Cncl Chm, Co-Coord 2 Summer Insts, Conf Comm, Prof Offerings Port Folios, Stud Writers, Transitions & Transformation; Admin Asst for Cty Councilmen 1988-94, Renew, Chai, Neighborhood Ldrshp Group; Tchr of Yr 1994-95; Awded, Directed 13 Grants for Educl Excl, MD Writing Project; Made Presentations: Partnering Learning by Tchng, Writing Wkshp, Portfolios for Sci Extensions; *office:* Thomas Johnson Elem Schl 84 100 E Heath St Baltimore MD 21230*

GREENLEE, KIMBERLY BEIGHLEY, Business Teacher; *b:* Greenville, PA; *m:* Todd A.; *c:* Allison; *ed:* IN Univ of PA (BSEd) Bus Ed 1990; Attnd Slippery Rock Univ of PA, Gannon Univ; *cr:* Cranberry Jr, Sr HS Bus Tchr 1991-; *ai:* FBLA Club Adv; NBEA, PBEA 1990-; NEA 1991-.

GREENSPAN, WENDY JILL, Elementary Resource Cntr Tchr; *b:* Newark, NJ; *ed:* East Stroudsburg St Coll (BS) Ed, Certfd Tchr of Handicapped 1982; Kean Coll (MA) Educl Admin 1991; *cr:* Franklin Schl Spec Ed Tchr; *ai:* Family Math Instr; PTA 1984-, Life Mbrshp Awd 1990; Governor's Tchr Recognition Prgm 1987; *office:* Franklin Elem Schl 1550 Lindy Ter Union NJ 07083

GREENSPAN, WILLIAM EDWARD, Professor of Business Law; *b:* Bridgeport, CT; *ed:* Babson Coll (BS) Accounting 1964; Suffolk Univ Law Schl (JD) Law 1967, (LLM) Law 1970; *cr:* Univ of Bridgeport Bus Law Prof 1970-; *office:* Univ Of Bridgeport Park Ave Bridgeport CT 06601

GREENSTREET, MICHAEL BRADLEY,SR., Fifth Grade Teacher; *b:* Baltimore, MD; *m:* Helen Rae Cordner; *c:* Michael Timothy, Kenneth Mitchell, Christine Michele, Steven Eldred, Michael Bradley Jr.; *ed:* Charleston Southern (BS) Elem Ed 1986; 42 Addl Hrs Var Colls; Post Grad 32 Credit Hrs; *cr:* US Navy Master Chief Petty Ofcr 1960-83; Roye-Williams Elem Schl 5th Grd Tchr 1986-88; Hickory ELem Schl 5th Grd Tchr 1988-; *ai:* Grd Level Chprsn Soc Stud Comm; NEA 1986-; BSA 1988-, Merit Badge Cnslr; Natl Wildlife Fed 1977-; Save Our Streams 1987-; *office:* Hickory Elem Schl 2100 Conowingo Rd Bel Air MD 21014*

GREENWALD, JOSEPH GILSTON, Eng, His & Greek Teacher; *b:* New Orleans, LA; *m:* Barbara Koerber; *c:* Jessica; *ed:* Univ of VT (BS) Scndry Ed, Eng, His 1983; Over 100 Hrs Eng, Ed; Tufts, Dartmouth Greek, Classical Stud; *cr:* Shelburne Museum Ed Dir 1979-84; Champlain Valley Union Eng, His 1984-; *ai:* Yrbk Adv Regnl, Natl Awds; Scholars Bowl St Awds; NCTE, NEA 1985-; NE Classicl Assn 1987-; Assn for Retarded Citizens 1978-, Pres, K. S. Meml Awd; Local Schl Bd 1982-85; NEH Fellowship Greek Stud; Article Pub; Intern's Publishing Yrbk Awd; VT Stud VCH Scholar; NEA Grant; Chmn Vt Intrgnrtnl Conf; *office:* Champlain Valley Union HS Box 160 Hinesburg VT 05461*

GREENWALD, NEIL, Health, PE Teacher & Coach; *b:* Worcester, MA; *m:* Lisa; *c:* Dyian; *ed:* Bridgewater St Coll (BS) Hlth, PE 1982; *cr:* Al Regnl HS Tchr 1983-85; Avon HS Tchr 1985-87; Tahanto Regnl HS Tchr 1989-; *ai:* SAPD, Sr Class Adv; Golf, Bsktbl, Bsbl Coach; MA Bsbl Coaches, MA Tchr Assn, MA Assn of Dance 1982-; St Marks Golf Assn, Northboro Umpire Assn 1990-; Centray MA Coach of Yr 1993; *office:* Tahanto Regional Jr Sr HS 1001 Main St Boylston MA 01505*

GREENWALT, MARY CAROL, Mathematics Teacher; *b:* Baltimore, MD; *m:* Robert B.; *c:* Brett C., Julie C.; *ed:* Univ of MD at Balto Co (BA) Psych, Math Ed 1975; Geometry, Discrete Math, Algebra, Functions Woodrow Wilson; *cr:* Macon MS Math Tchr 1976; Soc Cir MS Math Tchr 1976-77; Milford Mill HS Math Tchr 1977-87; Lansdowne HS Math Tchr 1987-94; Catonsville HS Math Tchr 1994-; *ai:* JV Sftbl Coach; Math Club Adv; Fac Cncl; Fac Soc Comm; NCTM 1988-; MCTM, NEA, TABCO, MSTA 1980-; Yth Soccer 1984-, Dir Girls League; UMBC Ath Hall of Fame; NSA Inst for Math Tchrs 1994-95; *office:* Catonsville HS 421 Bloomsbury Ave Baltimore MD 21228*

GREENWOOD, SUSAN JEAN, Third Grade Teacher; *b:* Buffalo, NY; *ed:* Damen Coll (BS) Elem Ed 1970; St Univ of NY at Buffalo (MS) Early Chldhd 1972; Over 70 Hrs Post Grad Stud in Ed, Cmptrs & Admin; *cr:* Frontier Cntrl Schls Tchr 1971-; *ai:* Delta Kappa Gamma Beta Zeta Chapter 1980-, Corresponding Sec 6 Yrs, Pres 194-; AFT, NYSUT 1971-; *office:* Big Tree Elem Schl 4460 Bay View Rd Hamburg NY 14075

GREER, EDITH LEVERNE, Fourth Grade Teacher; *b:* Greenwood, MS; *ed:* Oakwood Coll (BS) Elem Ed 1977; OH St Univ (MS) Elem Ed, Rdng 1978; *cr:* MS Vly St Univ Rdng Instr 1978-83; Emmanuel Temple SDA Church Schl 1st-4th Grd Tchr 1983-85, Prin 1985-90; West Hertel Acad 4th Grd Tchr 1991-; *ai:* Asst Dir Yth Gospel Group; Richmond Speaking Contest Stdnts Coach; Fourth Grd Tchrs' Team Captain; NEA, ASCD 1978-; Buffalo Pub Schls Sci Comm 1995-; Minority Stu Flwshp OH St Univ 1 Yr; Outstdng Young Women of Amer 3 Yrs; *home:* 201 Cambridge Ave Buffalo NY 14215

GREER, VICKY LEE (SWOPE), Vice President; *b:* Bethesda, MD; *m:* John M.; *c:* Christina, Tyler; *ed:* Prince Georges Comm Coll (AA) Ed 1977; Univ of MD (BS) Ed 1978; George Washington Univ (MA) Admin 1990; *cr:* General Smallwood MS Math Tchr 1978-81, Sci Tchr 1978-94; Benjamin Stoddert MS VP 1994-; *ai:* Stdnts At Risk Mentor; EACC, NEA 1978-; NASSP, Alpha Beta Kappa 1995-; Nom Tchr of Yr 1981; Tchr Asst Team Co-Ed; Sci Dept Chair; Naval Ord Station-Liasson Schl; *office:* Benjamin Stoddert MS 2040 St Thomas Dr Waldorf MD 20602*

GREER, VICTORIA LEE (BURR), 8th Grade Life Science Teacher; *b:* Port Clinton, OH; *m:* James Patrick; *c:* Ryan, Tiffany; *ed:* Bowling Green St Univ (BS) Bio 1974; Post Grad Work at Univ of Toledo; *cr:* Port Clinton Jr HS 8th Grd Sci Tchr 1974-; *ai:* Sci Dept Chprsn; Port Clinton Fed of Tchrs, OH Fed of Tchrs & AFT 1974-; Port Clinton Ath Boosters 1975-; Port Clinton Music Boosters 1989-; Consulting Tchr to Intern Tchrs; Creative Tchr & Eisenhower Grants; *office:* Port Clinton Jr HS 110 E 4th St Port Clinton OH 43452

GREFE, BRUCE PAUL, Art Teacher; *b:* Longbranch, NJ; *m:* Victoria Valdes-Dapena; *c:* Julian-Alexander, Christiana Morgan; *ed:* Tayler Schl of Art (BA) Painting 1968; Tyler, Rutgers 30 Addl Credit Hrs; *cr:* Camden HS Art Tchr 1968-74; Veterans Mem MS Art Tchr 1974-80; Woodrow Wilson HS Art Tchr 1980-94; Henry L. Bonsall Family Schl Art Tchr 1994-; *ai:* All City Schl for Fine, Performing Arts Instr; NEA, NJEA, CCCEA 1968-; CEA 1968-, MS Rep; Title One Advy Comm 1978-, Exec Sec; Ed Rsrch Ctr 1979-, Bd of Dirs; Pub Article 1978; *home:* 304 3rd Ave Hammonton NJ 08037

GREFF, CAROL BYRNES, Language & Reading Teacher; *b:* Akron, OH; *m:* Ronald M.; *c:* Kari Marie, Kati Maureen; *ed:* OH St Univ (BA) Pol Sci, Ec 1969; Masters Early, Mid Chldhd Ed 1993; *cr:* Indian Lake MS 7 Grd Eng Tchr 1970-71; Miramar HS Psych, Jrnlsm, Eng Tchr 1971-73; Seminole MS 8 Grd Eng Tchr 1973-75, Tchr of GATE 1976-78; Evangel Chrstn Acad 4 Yr Olds Tchr 1980; Licking Heights HS, MS 7-8, 10 Grd, Jrnlsm, Fr, Soc Stud 1980-; *ai:* Spelling Bee Coach; NEA, OEA 1980-; LHEA 1980-, Sec, Tchr of Yr 1994-95; *office:* Licking Heights MS 6539 Summit Rd SW Summit Station OH 43073*

GREFFER, CHANTEL MARIE, Biology Teacher; *b:* Perth Amboy, NJ; *ed:* Camden Cty Comm Coll (AAS) Animal Hlth Tech 1977; Penn St Univ (BS) Ag 1981; Kean Coll Tchng Cert Scndry Sci 1988; *cr:* Sayreville War Memorial Sci Tchr 1988; Colonia HS Sci Tchr 1988-; *ai:* Ecology Club Adv; Schlsp Comm; Woodbridge Twp Environmental Commission 1995-; Eco-Lab Grant; *office:* Colonia HS East St Colonia NJ 07067*

GREGG, DAVID P., Biology Teacher; *b:* Marion, OH; *m:* Karin *c:* Austin B.; *ed:* Findlay Coll (BS) Hlth, PE 1977; Credit Hrs OI Grad Course Cmptrs Ashland Univ, Mount Vernon Nazerene Col Knox HS Bio Tchr 1983-; *ai:* Sr Class Adv; Sci Fair Co-Coord; N 1991-; *office:* East Knox HS 23227 Coshocton Rd Howard OH 4

GREGG, GARY LEE,II, Professor of Political Science; *b:* Co PA; *m:* Krysten Welke; *c:* Jacob Robert, Thomas; *ed:* Davis & El (BA) Pol Sci, His 1990; Miami Univ (MA) Pol Sci 1991, (PHD 1994; Univ of Notre Dame Post Grad Stud; *cr:* Clarion Univ 1994-; *ai:* Phi Delta Theta, Pol Sci Assn Advs; Amer Pol Sci As Essays & Book Reviews Pub; *office:* Clarion Univ Of PA PSSP C 16214

GREGG, GLORIA BZDULA, Third Grade Teacher; *b:* Provic *m:* John W.; *ed:* Northeastern Univ (BSEd) Elem Ed, Rdng Hearing 1975; Bridgewater St Coll (MED) Instrucional Media Addl Hrs; *cr:* North Pub Schls Tchr 1975-; *ai:* 2nd-3rd Grd Unit I Kappa Gamma 1984-; Norton Tchrs Assn 1975-; Norton Histo 1989-; Taunton Historical Soc 1990-; Horace Mann Grant Dev 1 1991 Kennedy Lib Tchng Awd; Nom 1991 Presidential Awds Ex Math Tchng; Participate 1985-86 NASA Tchr in Spac Interdiciplinary Curr Mini Grant 1995-; *office:* L G Nourse Eler Plain St Norton MA 02766

GREGG, JAYNE RODERICK, Support Rdng Teacher of C Wilkes Barre, PA; *m:* John M.; *c:* Joshua Todd, Jenna Nicole; *e* Univ (BA) El Ed 1975, (MS) El Ed 1977; Spec Ed, Gifted Shippensburg 1980, Penn St 1982; *cr:* Wilkes Barre Schls 6th 1975-77, GS Sci Tchr 1977-78, 6th Grd Math, Sci Tchr 1979-86, Arts Tchr 1986-; *ai:* NEA 1975-; Coord of the Learn & Serve Gra Dr David W Kistler Elem Schl 301 Old River Rd Wilkes Barre P

GREGG, KATIE O'CONNELL, Language Arts & Religion Cincinnati, OH; *m:* John William; *ed:* Coll of Mt St Joseph (BA) 1968; Xavier Univ 20 Hrs Ed; *cr:* Cure of Ars Schl 3, 7 Grd Tchr Immaculate Heart of Mary 6-8 Grd Tchr 1973-79; St Mary Sch Tchr 1979-; *ai:* Talents Unlimited Consultant; Stu Govt Moderato of Pen Coach; Eighth Grd Comm Svc Moderator; NCEA, OCE OCTELA 1989-92; Coll of Mt St Joseph Alumni Bd 1980-90; Acad Alumni Bd 1980-92; Natl Certfd Trainer Talents Unlimited Unlimited to the Scndry Power; *office:* St Mary Schl 2845 Cincinnati OH 45208

GREGG, LORI HARTMAN, HS Mathematics Teacher; *b:* C OH; *m:* Mike; *c:* Jessica, Kelly; *ed:* SUNY Coll at Cortland (BA) Wright St Univ (MA) Educl Ldrshp 1994; 15 Addl Hrs; *cr:* Frank Math Tchr 1973-82; Franklin HS Math Tchr 1985-; *ai:* NEA, F 1973-, Bldg Rep; NCTM 1985-; *office:* Franklin Sr HS 750 Franklin OH 45005*

GREGG, LUANN M., German Teacher; *b:* Pittsburgh, PA; *c:* F IN Univ of PA (BA) Ger 1979; Tchng Cert Ger Univ of Pittsbur *cr:* St NJ Payroll Clerk 1983-86; Nash & Co Office Admin Montour HS Ger Tchr 1992-; *ai:* Ger Club, Bi-Annual Trip Europ Annual Schl Musical; Amer Assn Tchrs Ger, NEA, PSEA 1992-; 1992-, Asst Den Ldr, Sec; *office:* Montour HS 90 Clever Rd Mc Ke PA 15136

GREGGO, THERSA S., First Grade Teacher; *b:* East Stroudsburg John W.; *ed:* Mansfield Univ (BSE) Elem Ed 1984; 24 Addl C Marywood Coll, East Stroudsburg Univ, Wilkes Univ, Antioch U Pleasant Valley Schl Dist First Grd Tchr 1984-; *ai:* 7th-9th G Bsktbl Coach 1991-; Soc Stud Curr Cord 1989-94; Mentoring N Tchrs 3 Yrs; Planning Comm 1994-; NEA 1984-; *office:* Pleasar Schl Dist RD 3 Box 505 Kunkletown PA 18058*

GREGO, NICHOLAS V., Sixth Grade Teacher; *b:* Sayre, PA; *m:* *c:* Paul, Jon Martin, Tom Martin, Wendy Burt; *ed:* Mansfield U Elem Ed 1970; Elmira Coll (MS) Ed 1972; Scranton Univ (MS) E 1975; Grad Courses Penn St Univ; *cr:* Athens Area Schls 6th 1970-, Wrestling Head Coach 1970-86, Ftbl Coach 1970-81; *ai:* Adv; AAEA, PSEA, NEA 1970-; Phi Delta Kappa 1973-.

GREGOIRE, MARY JULIE (CONNOR), High School English *b:* Methuen, MA; *m:* Paul Joseph; *c:* Jonathan, Kathleen, Air Merrimack Coll (BA) Eng 1977; Salem St Coll (MA) En introduction to MacIntosh Comp Course; *cr:* Salem HS Eng Tchr North Andover HS Eng Tchr 1978-; *ai:* Schl Support Accredicatior NEA, MTA & NATA 1978-; St Monicas PTO 1992-.*

GREGORIOUS, CAROL ANN, English Teacher & Dept C Manchester, NH; *ed:* Univ of New Hampshire (BA) Eng Lit 1967 Rdng Specialization 1975; Cert Advanced Grad Stud Admin, Sup 1991; 30 Addl Credits Curr, Writing 1983; *cr:* Memorial HS E 1967-, Rdng Specialist 1975-, Eng Dept Coord 1986-; *ai:* Res Organizing Selection Process Regnl, Local Schlrsps Awded la Block Scheduling Dist-Wide Curr Comm Chair; Phi Delta Kapp NEA, NH Ed Assn 1967-; Amer Cancer Soc 1986-90, Bd of Dir; C Ctr Assoc 1991-; Cath Med Ctr, Hospice Vol 1992-94; Church Bl Comm, 1987-89, Chprsn; Awded Authored Title IV-C Federal Rdn Authored Tests Accompany Hnrs Level Eng Anthology; Cmpt Grant; *office:* Memorial HS South Porter St Manchester NH 0310

GREGORY, CHRISTINE MARIA (PETAK), Sixth Grade Tea Warren, OH; *c:* Melissa, Gregory; *ed:* Youngstown St Univ (BS) 1977, (MS) Curr 1984; *cr:* Niles City Schls Tchr 1979-; *ai:* Equatio Team Chprsn; Math Team Competitions Coord; Safety Patrol Su Fair Chprsn 1979-94; OEA, NEA 1979-; Easter Seals 1984-; A+ Tc Outstanding Young Women of Amer; East OH Gas Educator Awd Bonham Elem Schl 120 E Margaret St Niles OH 44446

GREGORY, FRANK R., History Teacher; *b:* Jersey City, Catherine; *c:* Denise, Nicole; *ed:* Northeast MO St Univ (BS) H (MA) His 1968; Univ of CO 21 Credit Hrs; Univ of MN 6 Credit H of DE 30 Credit Hrs; *cr:* Dover HS Tchr of His 1968-70; Hibbing S His Instr 1971-72; Dover HS Tchr of His, Chm of Soc Stud Dept 19 Girls, Boys St Coord; AP Dir; Curr Comm Dist-Wide; NCSS Presidential Scholars Distngd Tchr 1993; Tchr of Yr 1995; Distn 1990; *office:* Dover HS One Pat Lynn Dr Dover DE 19904

GREGORY, GARY J., Professor of Church Music; *b:* E Saint Lo *m:* Sherry Marie Andrew; *c:* Benjamin, Hannah; *ed:* Murray St Univ Music Ed 1970; Eastman Schl of Music (MM) Performance & L Attnd Milligan Coll & Cincinnati Bible Seminary; *cr:* NY Chrstn I of Music 1971-80; Great Lakes Bible Coll Prof & Chair of P Ministries 1981-87; Cincinnati Bible Coll & Seminary Prof of Music & Chair of Music Dept 1988-; *ai:* Come Alive Singers Di Cabinet; Assn of Chrstn Coll Music Educators 1980-, Treas, Pres; 1995-; *office:* Cincinnati Bible Coll & Sem 2700 Glenway Ave Cir OH 45204

GREGORY, JAMES RICHARD, Sixth Grade Teacher; *b:* Detro *ed:* Univ of Toledo (BED) Elem Ed 1973, (MED) Curr 1990; *cr:* Timbers MS Tchr 1973-; *ai:* Var Bsktbl Asst; Soc Stud Dept Chair NEA 1973-; AWEA; Article Pub in OH Cncl for the Soc Stud Revie *office:* Fallen Timbers MS 6119 Finzel Rd Whitehouse OH 43571

GREGORY, JAMES RONALD, HS Social Studies Teacher; *b:* OH; *m:* Jayne Brantingham; *c:* Rebecca, Sarah, Christopher; *ed:*

BS) Comp Soc Stud 1981; Addl Hrs Sci, Eng; *cr:* Warren Chrstn Schl HS Soc Stud, Sci Tchr 1983-85, HS Soc Stud, Sci Tchr 1986-; bus Chrstn Schl Jr-Sr HS Soc Stud, Sci Tchr 1985-86; *ai:* Amer Red 1984-, Blood Donor; Grace United Meth Church 1980-, Missions , Prsnl Nominating Comm, Bsktbl, Sftbl Teams; Western REserve cycle Club; Bsktbl Coach; Co Ath Dir; Stu Cncl Adv; Missions Mem; Homecoming Adv; *office:* Warren Christian Schl 2640 an Rd Warren OH 44485

ORY, JAMES THOMAS, Math Tchr & Building Liaison; *b:* Port NY; *m:* Sandra Mattison; *c:* James Jr., Jennifer; *ed:* SUNY at New BA) Scndry Math 1970, (MA) Scndry Ed 1975; *cr:* Kingston City Math Instr 1970-; Ulster Cty Comm Coll Adjunct Math Fac 1982-; Cty BOCES Summer Schl Scndry Math Tchr 1985-; *ai:* Supvr of portation; Kingston Tchrs Fed, NY St United Tchrs, AFT 1971-, Past ial Sec; Hurley Heritage Soc, Past Financial Sec; Reformed Church ley, Past Deacon; Outstanding Scndry Educator of Amer Nom 1975; PO Box 195 Hurley NY 12443

ORY, JOHN EDWARD, English Teacher; *b:* Camden, NJ; *m:* *c:* John Jr., Shannon, Sean; *ed:* 31 Post Grad Hrs; *cr:* Riverside HS 1969-; *ai:* NHS Adv; Core Team Help Disfunctional Families; rly Forensics Coach, Class Adv; NEA, NJEA, BCEA 1969-; REA Past Treas; Gibbsburg Councilman; Gibbsboro Fire Co, Gibbsboro Bd, Pres; Gibbsboro Men's Sftbl, Commissioner; Certfd NJ HSPT , SRA Evaluator; Most Popular Tchr Awd; *office:* Riverside HS ngton St Riverside NJ 08075

ORY, LAWRENCE, English Teacher; *b:* Passaic, NJ; *ed:* Fordham BA) Pol Sci, Philosophy 1973; NY Univ (MA) Ed, Rdng 1974; m Univ (MS) Spec Ed, Learning Dis, Emot Dist 1976; Brooklyn MBA) Supervision, Admin 1991; 10 Credits Cmptrs 1996; *cr:* USAF Yrs; Bd of Ed Tchr 18 Yrs; *ai:* Yrbk, African Amer Culture Club Adv; Group Adv, Mentor; UFT 1973-; Fund Raiser for Natl Charities, Post Office, GPO; Jr Achvmt Rep; AFB Comm Laison; Pub Articles; ultural Cord Tchr Handbook.

ORY, STEPHANIE R. SASSO, Dept Chprsn & Spanish Teacher; nx, NY; *m:* Daniel M.; *ed:* C. W. Post (BS) Span, ESL 1978, (MA) 983; 6 Addl Credit Hrs Span Theatre of Golden Age; Italian 1978; Matriculated 1979; *cr:* Eng Now Prgm ESL Tchr 1977; BOCES Prgm n Charge ESL Prgm 1986-89; Farmingdale Schl Dist Eng as Second Tchr 1979-80; *ai:* Foreign Lang Dept Chprsn Holy Trinity HS; Stu Adv 1984-92; La Sociedad Honoraria Hispanica 1995-; NYSFLTA LILT 1978-94; AATSP 1995-; Partial Schlsp C.W. Post 1974; Eta Phi Grad Phi Beta Kappa 1978; *office:* Holy Trinity HS 98 Cherry Ln ville NY 11801

F, MARION, 5th Grade Teacher; *b:* New York, NY; *m:* Alan R. ; *ed:* Brandeis Univ (AB) Sociology of Art 1963; Harvard Univ Elem Ed 1964; Oriental Art Course Work Towards PHD 1964-65, Univ at Tokyo 1970; *cr:* Concord PS 6th Grd Tchr 1964; Lexington Grd Tchr 1965; Belmont PS 6th Grd Tchr 1966-67; Great Neck PS rd, 5/6 Interage, Gifted Prgm, 5th Grd Tchr 1967-; *ai:* Bldg entation Comm; Negotiating Team 1970-71; AFT, NYSUT 1967-; Neck Tchrs Assn 1967-, Del Assembly Rep; NSF Filmed Class Elem d Inquiry Unit for Tchr, Parent Ed; Vasser, Brandeis, C. W. Post Ed es to Grad Stdnts; Parent Wkshps; Harvard, Brandeis Joint Flwshp 4; *office:* E M Baker Schl 69 Baker Hill Rd Great Neck NY 11023*

G, JEFFREY C., 6th Grd Social Studies Tchr; *b:* Cleveland, OH; *m:* : Colin; *ed:* Bowling Green St Univ (BS) Scndry Soc Stud Ed 1985; and St, Kent St Addl 30 Credit Hrs; *cr:* Perry MS 6th Grd Soc Stud 985-; *ai:* Stu Cncl, Yrbk Adv; Cross Cntry, Track Coach; Camp Dir r Ed; NEA, OH Ed Assn 1985-; Perry Classroom Tchrs Assn 1985-, Rep, VP; Bowling Green St Univ, Mem of Dean's Cncl Coll of Ed, f President's Club; *office:* Perry MS 4221 Manchester Ave Perry OH

G, TINA KUSCH, Dir of Secondary Vocal Music; *b:* Somerset, PA; chard Tad; *c:* David, Devin; *ed:* Grove City Coll (BME) Music mma Cum Laude 1982; Working Toward Scndry Guid ME inster Coll; Post Grad Stud SUNY at Fredonia, Youngstown St Univ, niv, Wilkes Coll, Stroudsburg Univ; *cr:* Marshall Cty Schls K-6 Grd Music Dir 1982-84; Kane Schl Dist 1-12 Grd Vocal Music Dir 7; Mercer HS 7-12 Grd Vocal Music Dir 1987-; *ai:* All Schl Musical peech, Drama Coach; Show Choir Dir; NEA, MENC 1982-; St John's hurch 1994-, Cncl Mem; Jaycee's Edctr of Yr 1989; PMEA St Conf mer 1995; Presidential Ed Excl Awd 1987; *office:* Mercer Area Jr Sr 5 W Butler St Mercer PA 16137

N, MARILYN LOUISE (YOUND), Kindergarten Teacher; *b:* ster, OH; *m:* Jack Raymond; *c:* Mary, Adam; *ed:* OH Univ (BSEd) Ed 1975; Ashland Univ (MSEd) Early Chldhd Ed, Curr 1993; *cr:* ster Cty Schl First Grd Tchr 1975-87, Kndgtn Tchr 1987-; OH Univ 994-; *ai:* NEA, OEA 1975-; NAEYC 1994-, Phi Delta Kappa 1986-; C 1994-, Delta Kappa Gamma 1983-; Outstdng Cooperationg Tchr OH 1983; *home:* 1116 Ridgewood Way NE Lancaster OH 43130

DA, GAIL FULTON, Associate Professor; *b:* Clarion, PA; *m:* d S.; *c:* Richard E., Steven D.; *ed:* Clarion Univ (BS) Elem & Spec 6, (MED) Elem Ed 1968; PA St Univ (PhD) Curr & Instruction 1988; ookville Area Schl Dist Elem Tchr 3 Yrs; Clarion Area Schl Dist Tchr & Dir Gifted Prgm 18 Yrs; Beijing Intnl Embassy Schl Elem Yr; Clarion Univ 8 Yrs; *ai:* Presentations, Book Reviews, Comms, g Grants, Wkshps & Publishing; Phi Delta Kappa 1985-, VP; Natl Computing Consortium 1988-, Conf Presenter, Facilitator & ations; Intnl Soc for Tech in Ed 1988-, Presenter, Presider & ations; Pub 15 Articles & 1 Book Chapter; 14 Grants; 2 Fellowships; Clarion Univ Of PA 110 Stevens Hall Clarion PA 16214

A, CATHERINE, Social Studies Teacher; *b:* Waterloo, NY; *ed:* at Cortland (BS) SS Ed 1983, (MS) SS Ed 1990; *cr:* Waterloo Cntrl oc Stud Tchr 1986-; *ai:* Dist Wellness Team; Co-Adv Yrbk; Co-Adv of 1999; Waterloo Ed Assn & NEA 1986-, Sec 1989-; *home:* PO Box terloo NY 13165

ILI, JACK L., Performing Arts Dir & Teacher; *b:* Nyack, NY; *m:* Lynne Rosenhagen; *c:* Jordan Donal; *ed:* Ithaca Coll Schl of Music Music Ed 1972; Columbia Univ Tchrs Coll (MA) Arts in Ed 1989; ng Toward EDD Instrl Ldrshp St John's Univ; Attnd H. B. Studios, Handman Studios; *cr:* Pearl RIver Pub Schls Music Tchr 1972-74; k Vly Regnl Schls Music Tchr 1974-77; Free Lance Actor, Dir 88; Nanuet Pub Schls Music Tchr, Performing Arts Dir 1989-; *ai:* Fall Spring Musical Dir; MS Drama Club, Performing Arts Cncl Adv; MENC, NYSSMA, Rockland Cty Music Ed Assn 1989-; Rotar Pub wd; Nanuet Prof, Hudson Vagabond Puppets Grants; Nom Rockland ec Arts Awd; Publications: Arts in the Classroom Handbook, Arts in oin Curriculum, MENC Journal; *office:* Nanuet Pub Schls 103 n St Nanuet NY 10954*

CI, JOHN LOUIS, Mathematics Instructor; *b:* Butler, PA; *ed:* ry Rock Univ (BS) Math Ed 1985; IN Univ of PA (MS) Math 1988; tler Cty Comm Coll Instr 1985-92; Carlow Coll Instr 1989-94; Coll Instr 1989-95; Clarion Univ Instr 1990-; *ai:* Ski Club Adv; Freedom of Choice in cancer Therapy 1994-; Passed Two Actuarial ; Letters Pub; *home:* 614 Center Ave Butler PA 16001

GRENIER, KATHLEEN, Math Teacher; *b:* Berkyll, Netherlands; *m:* Michael; *c:* Taylor, Morgan; *ed:* Temple Univ (BSE) Math 1991; Millersville Univ 24 Post Grad Credits; *cr:* Penn Manor Math Tchr 1992-; *ai:* Chrldng Coach 2 Yrs; Class Adv; NCTM 1991-; PMEA 1992-; NEA 1992-; *office:* Penn Manor HS Cottage Ave Millersville PA 17551

GRENIER, ROBERT L., Latin & French Teacher; *b:* Bronxville, NY; *m:* Kerry Dunne; *c:* Marc, Steven; *ed:* Laval Univ (BA) 1966; Attnd Central CT & Keene St; *cr:* Brookfield HS Latin & Fr Tchr 1968-70; Fall Mountain Regnl HS Latin & Fr Tchr 1970-; *ai:* Latin Club Adv; Ice Hockey Coach; Staff Dev Chm; NHATFL, CANE & NHCA; NEH Summer Inst in Paris 1986; *office:* Fall Mountain Regional H S RR 1 Alstead NH 03602

GRENINGER, RICHARD D., Math Teacher; *b:* Tylersville, PA; *m:* Cynthia J. Leiby; *c:* Wade D.; *ed:* Lock Haven Univ (BS) Chem, Physics, Math 1962; *cr:* Lock Haven HS Math Tchr 1962-; *ai:* Ftbl, Bsktbl, Track Timer 32 Yrs; PSEA, NEA 1962-; Schl Org 1962-; Who's Who; *office:* Lock Haven HS W Church St Lock Haven PA 17745

GREPPIN, MARY HANNAN, 4th-5th Grade Directress; *b:* Sayre, PA; *m:* John A.C.; *c:* Sara de Korne, Carl; *ed:* Univ of Rochester (BA) Eng 1961; AMI Montessori Cert; *cr:* First Presbyn Nursery Schl Tchr 1965-67; South Woodstock Cty Schl Eng Tchr 1967-72; Fairmount Co-op Nurses Schl Tchr, Dir 1975-83; Ruffing Montessori Schl 4th, 5th Grd Tchr 1983-; *ai:* Rehabilitating North East OH Abandoned or Orphaned Birds, Small Mammals Tchng Stdnts to Do This; British Ornithologists Union 1975-; Northeast OH Wildlife Rehabilitation Assn 1989-; Article Pub; *home:* 3349 Fairmount Blvd Cleveland OH 44118*

GRESKO, JOHN JAMES, 6th Grade Teacher; *b:* Akron, OH; *c:* Christine, John; *ed:* Univ of Akron (BS) Elem Ed 1974, (MS) Elem Admin 1976; Kent St Univ Educl Specialist Stud; *cr:* US Navy Musician 1965-69; Thom McAnn Shoes Sales & Mgmt 1969-74; Louisville City Schls Tchr 1974-; *ai:* Var Vllybl & Var Girls Bsktbl Coach; Drama Dir; LEA 1974-, VP; OEA 1974-; NEA 1974-; OHSCA 1983-; Grange 1986-; *office:* Louisville MS 300 E Gorgas St Louisville OH 44641*

GRESKO, MICHAEL A., Chemistry Teacher; *b:* NYC, NY; *m:* Barbara Ann; *c:* Kirsten Gittle, Janine Marie; *ed:* Amherst Coll (BSE) Philosophy of Rel 1968; Long Is Univ (MS) Ed Cnslng 1972; Fordham Univ 60 Post Grad Credit Hrs; *cr:* Walton HS Chem Tchr 1968-74; Truman HS Chem Tchr 1974-84; Stevenson HS Chem Tchr & Pgm Chm 1984-; *ai:* UFT 1968-; NY Acad of Scis 1975-; ASCD 1975-; Columbia Presbyn Med Schl Rsrch Fellow 1993; Bristol Meyers Fellow at Lamont Dougherty 1994; *office:* Adlai E Stevenson HS 1980 Lafayette Ave Bronx NY 10473*

GRESSOCK, JOSEPH E., Theology Teacher; *b:* Cleveland, OH; *m:* Eileen; *c:* Erica, J. Neal; *ed:* Bowling Green Univ (BS) Ed 1970; Lake Erie Coll (MA) Bus 1983; Univ of Notre Dame 9 Grad Hrs; *cr:* Cleveland Cntrl Cath HS Tchr, Coach 1984-88; Holy Name HS Tchr, Coach 1988-94; Cleveland Cntrl Cath HS Tchr, Coach 1994-95; Padua Franciscan HS Tchr, Coach 1995-; *ai:* Asst Ftbl, Asst Bsbl Coach; City fo Willowick 1958-87, Councilman; Jaycees 1975-77; *home:* 4596 N Miami Dr Parma OH 44134*

GRETZ, LINDA SUE (HOUGHTON), Biology Teacher; *b:* Buffalo, NY; *m:* Walter Jacob; *c:* Melissa Ann, Stacy Lynn; *ed:* Broome Comm (LA) Lbrl Arts, Sci 1975; Binghamton Univ (BS) Bio, Zoology 1978, (MAT) Bio, Ed 1981; 6 Credit Hrs Cornell Univ, 4 Credit Hrs Syracuse Univ, Inservice Elmira Coll, 3 Credit Hrs Cortland Coll; *cr:* Fred Johnson MS 8th Grd Sci Tchr 1982; Owego Free Acad Phys Sci Tchr 1983-88; Owego Apalachin Cntrl Schls Bio, Advanced Bio, Environmental Sci Tchr 1988-; *ai:* Sftbl Coach 1984-; Bsktbl Coach 1994; Class Adv 1984-92; Sci Club Adv; Acad Design Model Comm; Instrl Strategies Comm; NYSUT 1983-; NABT; STANYS; Jason Project Stu Argonaut Coord 1991; Dist Tchr Recognition Awd 1992; Goals 2000 Grant 1996; Howard Hughes Molecular Bio Grant; Natl Sci Fnd Grant; *office:* Owego Free Acad George St Owego NY 13827

GREVE, PHILLIP THOMAS, Band Director; *b:* Milwaukee, WI; *ed:* West Chester Univ (BS) Music Ed 1992; Peabody Conservatory of the Johns Hopkins Univ Toward MS in Bands of Amer Dir Symposium IL St Univ Music Ed; *cr:* North Harford HS Band Dir 1993-; *ai:* NHS Adv; Marching Band Dir; Asst Var Tennis, Vlybl Coach; Awds, Schl-Based Decision Making Comms; MMEA 1993-; MENC 1991-; CEAI 1995-; St Matthew Luth Church 1993-, Worship, Music Chair; Natl Judges Assn 1994-.

GRGAS, ALICE LOUISE, Math Teacher; *b:* Queens Village, NY; *m:* Billy; *c:* Justin; *ed:* FL St Univ (BS) Math Ed 1976; Queens Coll (MS) Math Ed 1980; 30 Credits Above Masters; *cr:* Halsey JHS 157 Math Tchr 1978-; *ai:* UFT Chptr Ldr; UFT Ely Trachtenberg Awd 1994; *office:* JHS 157 Stephen Halsey 6400 102nd St Rego Park NY 11374

GRIB, EVELYN SPOSATO, Substitute Teacher; *b:* Brooklyn, NY; *m:* Marion Joseph; *c:* John Marion; *ed:* Oswego St Tchrs (BS) Ed, Common Branches Kdg-8th 1952; 60 Addl Credits Queens Coll; *cr:* Fork Lane Schl 1st-3rd Grd Tchr 1952-92, Sub Tchr 1993-; *ai:* Good, Welfare Comm Sr Citizens; NEA, Lifetime Mem; Hicksville Classroom Tchrs; Assn Ret Hicksville Schl Employees 1993-, Helped Form Group, Sec; PTA Life Time Mbrshp, Plaque 25, 40 Yrs Svc; Nassau Cty Police Dept 10 Yr Svc Pin for Tchng Safety Lesson in Classroom; *home:* 27 Heights Rd Northport NY 11768*

GRIBKO, RICHARD JOSEPH, Social Studies Teacher; *b:* Bridgeport, CT; *c:* Richard J. Jr., Robert C., Joy C.; *ed:* Univ of CT (BA) His & Govt; Univ of Bridgeport (MA) Guid; Amer Stud Fairfield Univ; Ec & Fin Wesleyan; *cr:* Fairfield Woods Jr HS Tchr; Roger Ludlawe HS Tchr, Evaluation Adv; Fairfield HS Tchr; *ai:* Habitat for Hum; Amnesty Intnl Club; Fairfield Ed Assn Salary Chair, VP, Tchr of Yr 1968-69; CT Ed Assn; NEA; Amer Civil Liberties Union; Democratic Natl Comm; NAACP; Natl Audubon Soc; People for Amer Way; Smithsonian Assocs; Democratic Town Comm; Southern Poverty Law Ctr; Tchng Tolerance; Democratic Senatorial Campaign Comm; Natl Org of Women; Sierra Club; Wesleyan Flwshp; Fairfield Historical Calendar 1989; Fairfield Flwshp; *office:* Fairfield HS 755 Melville Ave Fairfield CT 06430

GRIBLER, LOIS ANN (KRUSE), Math Teacher; *b:* Cincinnati, OH; *m:* David J.; *c:* Joanne; *ed:* Univ of Cincinnati (BSEd) Scndry Sci & Hlth 1972, (MED) Scndry Sci & Hlth 1975; Attnd Univ of Dayton, La Verne Coll; *cr:* Cincinnati Pub Schls Sci, Bio, Hlth Tchr 1972-77; Elkhart Pub Schls Sci Tchr 1977-78; Math Tchr 1978-; *ai:* 7-8th Grd Track, 7-9th Grd Vlybl Head Coach 1978-; Phi Delta Kappa 1976-; Wright St Univ Cncl of Math Tchrs; Englewood Civic Band 1978-, Bd; Sinclair Comm Coll Concert Band 1980-; M.G. Car Club 1981-, Bd; North Amer M.G.A. Register; OH Buck Ayes; Beavercreek Outstanding Tchr 1992-93; Cincinnati Recreation Employee of Month June 1992; *office:* Ankney Jr HS 4085 Shakertown Rd Beavercreek OH 45430

GRIDA, RENA E., Health & Physical Ed Teacher; *b:* Willoughby, OH; *m:* Salvatore; *c:* Devin; *ed:* Mount Union Coll (BA) Hlth, PE 1987; Cleveland St Univ (MA) PE 1993; *cr:* North Royalton City Schls HS Hlth, PE Tchr 1988-; *ai:* Sftbl Coach; NEA 1988-.

GRIDLEY, GAYLE M., English Teacher; *b:* Bayshore, NY; *m:* Richard Courtland; *c:* Barbara, Richard; *ed:* SUNY at New Paltz (BS) Eng 1981, (MS) Eng 1985; attnd Rider Coll Undergraduate Work; *cr:* Nelco Accountant 1976-79; Valley Cntrl MS 8th Grd Eng Tchr 1981-86; Valley Cntrl HS Eng Tchr 1986-; *ai:* Gradus Honoris Adv; NHS; Schl of Liberal Arts at SUNY at New Paltz Highest Grd Point Average Awd; *home:* 72 N Montgomery St Walden NY 12586

GRIDLEY, PATTI LYNN (HUTCHESON), English Teacher; *b:* Wellsboro, PA; *m:* Steven J.; *c:* Jonathon; *ed:* IN Univ of PA (BS) Eng, Scndry Ed 1980; Post Grad Stud 24 Credit Hrs; *cr:* Chapel Chrstn Schl Eng Tchr 1980-85; Bishop Mc Cort HS Eng Tchr 1985-; *ai:* Club Adv of Schl Newspaper; NCTE, Kappa Delta Pi 1980-; *office:* Bishop Mc Cort HS 25 Osborne St Johnstown PA 15905*

GRIEBEL, BRIAN R., Instrumental Music Teacher; *b:* Lakewood, OH; *m:* Pamela S. Olm; *c:* Mallory, Brian; *ed:* OH St Univ (BMEd) Music Ed 1980; Akron Univ (MA) Music Ed 1994; Attnd Kent St Univ, Ashland-Baldwin Wallace Coll for Addl Credit Hrs; *cr:* Warrensville Hghts Schl Instrumental Music Tchr 1980-83; Lakewood City Schls Instrumental Music Tchr 1983-; *ai:* Marching Band Asst Dir; Harding MS Jazz Band Dir; Lakewood Tchrs Assn 1983-; NEA 1980-; Music Educators Natl Conf 1980-; NE OH Jass Soc 1985-; St Raphael Church 1984, Counter; Lakewood Schls MS Tchr of Yr 1989; *office:* Harding MS-Lakewood City Schl 1470 Warren rd Lakewood OH 44107

GRIECO, LEONARD,JR., 7th-12th Grd Hlth & Sci Tchr; *b:* Buffalo, NY; *m:* Marie Allette; *c:* Stephen, Rana; *ed:* Jamestown Comm Coll (AS) Sci 1969; SUNY at Fredonia (BS) Sci 1971; 50+ Grad Hrs; *cr:* Holland Cntrl Schl Hlth & Sci Tchr 1973-; Genesee Comm Coll Part-Time Adult Ed Vlybl Instr 1993-; *ai:* Var Girls Vlybl Coach; Boys Modified Wrestling Coach; Jr Var Girls Sftbl Coach; NEA 1976-, Bldg Rep; BIG & PIE 1989-; AIDS Advy Comm 1988-, Cncl Mem; Erie-Catt Tchr Ctr Grants "Introducing Scientific Notation Through Cell Counting" 1990 & "Simulations in Bio" 1991; *office:* Holland Cntrl Schl 103 Canada St Holland NY 14080*

GRIEK, LYNDA GALOARDI, Special Education Teacher; *b:* Jersey City, NJ; *m:* Paul M.; *ed:* Trenton St Coll (BA) Spec Ed, Speech Therapy 1968; 45 Grad Courses Montclair, Jersey City St, William Paterson Coll; Holocaust, Genocide Stud Ramapo Coll; *cr:* Garfield Pub Schls Speech Therapist 1968-69; River Edge Pub Schl Spec Ed Tchr 1969-; *ai:* Dist Art & Lit Magazine Co-Ed, Asst Ed Newsletter; Homework, Soc Stud, Plan for Learning, In-Class Support Units Curr Comm; River Edge Ed Assn 1968-, Treas, Assn Rep; NJ Ed Assn, NEA 1968-; First Dog Trng Club of Northern NJ 1983-, Sec 1985-89, Pres 1989-; Article Pub; 6th Grd Holocaust, 4th, 5th Grd Predjudice Reduction Curr Co-Author; Pioneer of Rdng, Writing Connection Curr; Recognition from Center for Holocoust Stud; *office:* Roosevelt Elem Schl 711 Summit Ave River Edge NJ 07661

GRIER, MARGARET MAYNARD, 6th Grade Teacher; *b:* Fitchburg, MA; *c:* Keith, Margaret, Shaun; *ed:* Fitchburg St Coll (BSE) Ed 1965, (MSE) Ed, Rdng 1973; 33 Addl Hrs Grad & In-Service Course Work; *cr:* J. R. Briggs Elem Schl 1st Grd Tchr 1969-74; McKay Elem Schl Kndgtn Tchr 1983-84; Spaulding Meml Chptr 1, Kndgtn Tchr 1984-86; Meml MS 6th Grd Tchr 1986-; *ai:* Stu Cncl, WA Trip Advs; Schl Improvement Cncl; Eng Curr Planning Comm; Co-Operating Tchr for Stu Tchrs Fitchburg ST Coll; NEA, MTA, FTA 1986-; St Camillus CCD Tchng Staff 1984; Warren Litsky Distngd Tchr Awd 1993; *office:* Memorial MS 615 Rollstone St Fitchburg MA 01420

GRIESBACH, DANIEL PETER, 9th-12th Grd Science Teacher; *b:* Brooklyn, NY; *m:* Mary Ann Currie; *c:* Danielle, Joseph; *ed:* St Francis Coll (BA) Sociology 1968; Rutgers Univ (MA) Sci Ed 1991; Brooklyn Coll Grad Stud 33 Cred Sociology, 14 Cred Physics; *cr:* St Francis Xavier Inst, Staff Sci Tchr 1968-73; Holmdel HS Sci Tchr 1973-; Rutgers Univ New Tchr Inst, Staff Sci Tchr 1987-95; *ai:* 8th Grd Field Hockey 1990-95, Boys Bsbl 1990-94, Boys Bsktbl 1995 Coach; Frosh Field Hockey 1984-86, Boys Bsktbl 1974 Coach; JV Bsbl 1974-76, Field Hockey 1987-90, Boys Bsktbl 1975-76 Coach; Var Bsbl 1977-84, Girls Bsktbl 1977-84 Coach; NJ Sci Tchrs Assn 1987-; Kappa Delta Chi; Cath Charities Advy Bd MO Cty 1 Yr; Citizens Advy Comm For Coastal Conservation 1995-; Gov Awd for Tchng Excl 1987; Contributor to Facts on File; Diocese of Trenton Sci Tchr Convention Keynote Speaker 1991; Participant in Natl Ldrshp Insts for Physics Tchrs 1988, Bio Tchrs 1990; *office:* Holmdel HS 36 Crawfords Corner Rd Holmdel NJ 07733*

GRIESHEIMER, CINDY LORRAINE, Pre-Kndgtn & 8th Grd Span Tchr; *b:* Toledo, OH; *m:* Joseph Richard; *c:* Matthew J., Jodi C.; *ed:* OH Univ (BA) Span 1969; Bowling Green St Univ (MA) Span 1974; St of OH 7-12 Grd Span Tchr Re-Cert 1994; *cr:* Bowling Green HS 4th Grd Span Tchr 1969-71; St James, St Charles, Our Lady of Perpetual Help Schls 7th-8th Grd Span Tchr 1988-90; Queen of Apostles Schl Pre-Kndgtn-8th Grd Span Tchr 1990-; *ai:* Mem Queen of Apostles Tech Comm; Co-Adv Safety Patrol; Mem Intervention Assistance Team; Phi Beta Kappa 1968-; Phi Sigma Iota 1967-; Mission Svc in Guatemala 1995; Presenter Global Awareness in Ed Seminar 1996; *office:* Queen Of Apostles Schl 235 Courtland Ave Toledo OH 43609

GRIEST, JO ANN LOUISE, 6th Grade Teacher; *b:* Sidney, OH; *m:* Terry A.; *c:* Michael, Jennifer; *ed:* Bowling Green St Univ (BS) Scndry Ed, Eng, Jrnlsm 1971; Wright St Univ (MS) Tchr Ldr 1991; Recertification Elem Ed Urbana Univ, Post Grad Hrs Univ of Dayton; *cr:* Graham Jr HS 8th Grd Lang Arts Tchr 1971-79; Graham South Elem Schl 5th Grd Tchr 1985-87, 6th Grd Tchr 1987-; *ai:* Drama Coach Schl Choir Plays; Sftbl Coach Summer Girls League; Graham Ed Assn 1971-, Bldg Rep; OH Ed Assn, NEA 1971-; OH Cncl Int Rdg Assn, Intnl Rdg Assn 1991-; Kappa Delta Pi 1991-, Ed Honorary; 4-H 1985-, Adv; *office:* Graham South Elem Schl 2955 Saint Paris Jackson Rd Saint Paris OH 43072

GRIEVE, JOHANNA MARIE, Science Teacher; *b:* Annapolis, MD; *m:* Douglas; *c:* Audrey; *ed:* Anne Arundel Comm Coll (AA) Environmental Stud 1979; NC St Univ (BS) Forestry 1981; Univ of NH (MAT) Scndry Sci Ed 1991; Courses on Various Sci Topics & Tchng Methods; *cr:* Kingswood Regional HS Step II Pgm, Spcl Ed Aide & Sci Tchr 1986-87, Full Time UNH Intern & Bio Tchr 1987-88; Brewster Acad Learning Skills Instr 1989-92; Plymouth Regional HS Sci Tchr 1992-; *ai:* Recycling Pgm Adv; Envirothon Team Adv; Class of 99 Adv; NEA & NEANH 1992-; NABT 1993-, NH OBTA 1994 Awd; NSTA 1993-; ASCD 1993-; SPNHF Environmental Tchr of the Yr 1994; Comm Svc Learning Grants 1994 & 1995; Excl in Ed Scndry Sci 1995; 1995 Yrbk Dedication; 1995 NH Charitable Fndtn Grant; Grafton Co Conservation Tchr of the Yr 1996; *office:* Plymouth Regional HS 1 Old Wardbridge Rd Plymouth NH 03264*

GRIFFIN, CAROL M. (CARLUCCIO), Mathematics Teacher; *b:* Hoboken, NJ; *m:* John W.; *c:* Michelle, Sean, Casey; *ed:* St Joseph Coll (BA) Math 1968; Attnd Salem St Coll Admin; *cr:* Pickering Jr HS Math Tchr 3 Yrs; Lynn Voc Tech Inst Algebra, Geometry Tchr 2 Yrs; Eastern Jr HS Algebra, Math Tchr 15 Yrs; Marshall MS Algebra, Cluster Ldr 3 Yrs; *ai:* Stu Cncl, Comm Svc Learning Adv; Yrbk Comm; Grade 8-9 Transition Team; NCTM 1980-; New England League MS Presenter; Democratic City Comm; Comm Dev Citizens Advy Bd; *office:* Thurgood Marshall MS 19 Porter St Lynn MA 01902*

GRIFFIN, CHRISTINE ARCAROLA, Eng Tchr & Guidance Counselor; *b:* Kingston, NY; *m:* Kirk; *c:* Mac Kenzie Leigh; *ed:* Hobart & William Smith (BA) Eng & Pol Sci 1989; St Univ of NY at New Paltz (MA) Eng 1995; *cr:* John A Coleman HS Eng Tchr & Guidance Cnslr 1990-; *ai:* Yrbk Adv; Paper Pub in St Univ of NY at New Paltz Grad Review 1993; *office:* John A Coleman HS 430 Hurley Ave Hurley NY 12443

GRIFFIN, CHRISTOPHER GERALD, Teacher; *b:* Galway, Ireland; *m:* Janet Alexander; *c:* Deirdre; *ed:* Univ Coll at Dublin (BA) Eng, Philosophy 1973, (MA) Anglo-Irish Lit 1976; Trinity Coll Dublin Higher Diploma Anglo-Irish Lit 1975, Ed 1976; Attnd Univ of WI at Milwaukee, Univ of MD at Coll Park; *cr:* Univ of WI Tchng Asst 1977-80; WA Schl for Sec

Tchr 1981-83; George Washington Univ Adj Instr 1982-83; Strayer Coll Tchr 1983-; *ai:* Drama Club, Intnl Stdnts, Cnslng for Registration Adv; Modern Lang Assn; Amer Conf for Soc Stud; Pub Articles, Reviews on Lit; Reviewing Washington Area Theatre; Conf, Bookstore, Theatre Lecturer; *office:* Strayer Coll 1025 15th St NW Washington DC 20005

GRIFFIN, DONNA DEWITT, English Teacher; *b:* Wheeling, WV; *m:* Robert L.; *c:* Nicholas, Lisa, Laura; *ed:* West Liberty St Coll (BA) Lang Arts 1979; OH Univ (MA) Higher Ed 1993; *cr:* Steubenville Cath HS Eng Tchr 1979-82; Union Local HS Eng Tchr 1984-; *ai:* Sr Class Adv; NHS Adv, FEA Adv; NEA 1979-; OCTELLA 1984-; Union Local Boosters 200 Club 1989-; Flushing Parent Tchr Org 1987-, Sec 1990-; Citizens Advisory Comm 1991-; Union Local Dist PTO; *office:* Union Local H S 66859 Belmont-Morristown Rd Belmont OH 43718

GRIFFIN, ELIZABETH MARKER, Third Grade Teacher; *b:* Camden, NJ; *m:* Joseph V.; *c:* Joseph James, Elizabeth Kelly; *ed:* Glassboro St (BA) Elem Ed 1977; Whole Lang; Math A New Way of Thinking; *cr:* Hainesport Elem Schl 1-8th Grd Tchr 1977-; *ai:* Battle of Books Adv 1992; NEA, NJEA 1977-; Riverside Wrestling 1991-, Treas; St Casimir Bd of Ed 1989-91; Turners Assn 1993-; St Casimir's CCD Tchrs; *office:* Hainesport Township Elem Sch 211 Broad St Hainesport NJ 08036*

GRIFFIN, GEOFFREY WILLIAM, Instructional Technology Tchr; *b:* Boston, MA; *c:* William; *ed:* Dickinson Coll (BS) Cmptr Sci 1985-; Shippensburg Univ (MS) Cmptr Sci 1992; 9 Credit Hrs Ed; *cr:* Cumberland Vly Schl Dist Instrl Tech Tchr 1986-; *ai:* Cumberland Vly Prof Dev Cncl; Adult Ed Tech Instr; Instrl Support Team; Tech Based Prof Dev Prgms Instr Cumberland Vly; NEA, PSEA 1986-; CVEA 1986-, Bldg Rep; Caveman Cmptr Users Group 1993-, Pres; *office:* Eagle View MS 6746 Carlisle Pike Mechanicsburg PA 17055

GRIFFIN, JENNIFER S., Psychology Professor; *b:* Warren, OH; *m:* Peter A. Beckett; *c:* Caitlin G. Beckett; *ed:* Youngstown St Univ (BS) Psych 1988; Kent St Univ (MA) Psych Experimental 1991, (PHD) Psych Experimental 1995; *cr:* Kent St Univ Tchng Asst 1989-93; Thiel Coll Prof 1993-; *ai:* Lamda Sigma, Media Bd Comm, Thiel Women's Forum Adv; Sigma Xi 1991-; Amnesty Intnl, NOW 1988-; Numerous Articles Pub; *office:* Thiel Coll 75 College Ave Greenville PA 16125*

GRIFFIN, JENNIFER SMITH, Earth Science Teacher; *b:* Syracuse, NY; *m:* Peter; *c:* Daniel, Caitlin; *ed:* Mt Vernon Coll (BS) Bio 1982; SUNY Hlth Sci Ctr (BS) Cytotechnology 1983; SUNY at Oswego Tchr Cert 1992; 6 Hrs Post-Grad SUNY at Cortland; Syracuse Univ Regents Bio Inst 1993; *cr:* Marcellus Cntrl Schl Vlybl, Soccer Coach 1988-, Homebound Tutor 1994; West Genesee Cntrl Schl Homebound Tutor 1994-95; Skaneateles Cntrl Schl Earth Sci Tchr 1995-; *ai:* Modified Vlybl Coach 1988-90; JV Vlybl Coach 1991-93; Var Vlybl Coach 1994-; Var Soccer Coach 194-; STANYS 1992-; NSTA 1993-; NSCAA 1995-; Marcellus Yth Soccer 1994-, Bd Mem; Amer Soc of Clinical Pathologists Pub, Co-Authored; *office:* Skaneateles Cntrl Schl 49 E Elizabeth St Skaneateles NY 13152

GRIFFIN, JOHN L., Administrative Principal; *b:* Norwood, MA; *m:* Lorraine; *c:* Donna Doliner, James M., John, Diane Finn; *ed:* St Francis Xavier Univ (BA) Elem Ed 1962; Boston St Coll (MED) Elem Ed 1968; Attnd Bridgewater St Coll 1968-71; 12 Cr Cmptr Tech 1994-95; MESPA Ed Ctr, 8 Cr Consensrs Decision Making 1993; *cr:* Stoughton South Schl 5-6 Grd Tchr 1964-71, Asst Prin 1968-71; J. H. Gibbons Schl Admin Prin 1971-; *ai:* Gibbons Schl Improvement Cncl Co-Chair; Mngmt Team; Hlth Grant Comm 10 Yrs; MA Assn Elem Schl Prin, NAESP, South Shore Elem Schl Prin Assn 1980-; Norwood K of C 1962-; Norwood Lodge of Elks 1982-; Gibbons Schl PTA 1971-, Exec Dir; *office:* Joseph H. Gibbons Schl 235 Morton St Stoughton MA 02072*

GRIFFIN, JOHN WILLIAM, 6th Grade Teacher; *b:* Cleveland, OH; *m:* Sharon Cerra; *c:* Matthew; *ed:* Clarion Univ (BA) ELem Ed 1974; Attnd Univ of Pittsburgh, Duquesne Univ; *cr:* Seneca Vly Schls Tchr 1974-; *ai:* NEA, PSEA 1974-; Founder, Dir Discovery Chess.

GRIFFIN, KEITH DOUGLAS, Physical Education Teacher; *b:* New York City, NY; *ed:* Long Island Univ (BS) PE 1978; Jersey City St Coll (MA) Urban Ed 1995; Attnd St Rose Coll of Ed; *cr:* Norman Thomas HS PE Tchr 1992-; *ai:* All City HS Marching Band Drill Master; AFT, United Fed of Tchrs 1988-; *office:* Norman Thomas HS 111 E 33rd St New York NY 10016*

GRIFFIN, KENNETH GARRY, Business Educator; *b:* Oshawa, CN; *m:* Judy A. Calabrese; *c:* Keith; *ed:* SUNY at Buffalo (BS) Bus Ed 1974; Nazareth Coll of Rochester (MS) Bus Ed 1977; *cr:* Canandaigua HS Bus Edctr 1974-77; West Seneca East Sr HS Bus Edctr 1977-; *ai:* DECA Chptr Adv; WS Tchrs Assn 1977-; Stu Chcl Tchr of Yr; NYDECA Outstdng Svc Awd, Honerary Life Mem; *office:* West Seneca East Sr HS 4760 Seneca St West Seneca NY 14224

GRIFFIN, LARRY, Director of Choral Music; *b:* Harrodsburg, KY; *m:* Jane Evelyn Terry; *c:* Calvin Thomas, Emma Leigh; *ed:* Eastern KY Univ (BME) Music Ed 1983; Wright St Univ 9 Credit Hrs; The OH St Univ 9 Credit Hrs; *ai:* Livingston United Meth Church Choir Dir; OH Music Ed Assn 1983-, Dist XVI Pres; Am Choral Dirs Assn 1991-; *home:* 1218 Amol Ln Columbus OH 43235*

GRIFFIN, MARYALICE (FINNERTY), English Teacher; *b:* Brooklyn, NY; *m:* Raymond L. Jr.; *c:* Raymond III, Kerry Griffin Vann, Michael, Sean; *ed:* Molloy Coll (BA) Eng-Magna Cum Laude 1966; SUNY at Stony Brook (MLS) Liberal Arts 1985; Masters Plus 45; *cr:* Sachem Schl Dist Eng Tchr 1982-92; Southold HS Eng Tchr 1992-93; Hampton Bays HS Eng Tchr 1993-; *ai:* Yrbk Adv; NHS Selection Comm; HBTA Schlrsp Comm; NYSUT 1982-; HBTA 1993-; Kappa Gamma Pi, NHS 1966-; Wrote Curr for AP Eng Lit & Composition for Hampton Bays HS; *office:* Hampton Bays Jr Sr HS 88 Argonne Rd Hampton Bays NY 11946

GRIFFIN, ROSALIE M., Mathematics Department Chprsn; *b:* Waterbury, CT; *m:* Michael; *c:* Maria, Michael, Maureen, Matthew, Meghan; *ed:* Albertus Magnus Coll (BA) Math 1964; Wesleyan Univ (MALS) Math 1973; Saint Joseph Coll (MA) Counseling 1986; *cr:* Crosby HS Math Tchr 1964-; *ai:* Curr Revision Comm; Wkshp Coord; NEA, CEA, WTA, NCTM 1965-; ATOMIC 1975-; *office:* Crosby HS 300 Pierpont Rd Waterbury CT 06705

GRIFFIN, SANDRA ANITA, Mathematics Teacher; *b:* Washington, DC; *ed:* DC Tchrs Coll (BS) Hlth, PE 1974; Univ of DC (MST) Math 1984; 3 Credits Univ MD College Park; 6 Credits Trinity Coll; 1 Credit George Washington Univ; 3 Credits Georgetown Univ; *cr:* DC Dept of Recreation Specialist 1971-79; DC Pub Schls Tchr 1979-; *ai:* Ath Dir 1994, 1995; Vlybl Coach; Sr Class Spon; WA Tchrs Union, NCTM 1983-; DCCTM 1989-; Delta Sigma Theta 1976-, Ed Dev Chprsn; *office:* Calvin Coolidge Sr HS 5th & Tuckerman Sts NW Washington DC 20011

GRIFFING, DORIS BEMAN, Kindergarten Teacher; *b:* North Hornell, NY; *m:* Darryl W.; *c:* Donald, Deborah Moyer; *ed:* St Univ of NY at Geneseo (BA) Elem Ed 1961; *cr:* Spencerport Cntrl Schl 1st Grd Tchr 1961-62; Corning City Schl Winfield St 1st Grd Tchr 1962-63; Bryant Schl 3rd Grd Tchr 1963-64; Wayland Cntrl Schl Kndgtn Tchr 1964-66; Wayland Cohocton Cntrl Schl Kndgtn & 2nd Grd Tchr 1970-; *ai:* Lang Arts Comm; Dept Chm; Wayland Tchrs Assoc 1970-, Sec; NEA 1970-; NYEA 1970-; St Pauls UCC Church 1968-, Church Cncl Sec; Wayland Chptr Order of Eastern Star 1976-, Matron & St Grand Ofcr; Kate Jackson Court of Amaranth 1979-, Matron & St Grand Ofcr; Lowell Club Wayland, Pres; *office:* Wayland-Cohocton Cntrl Schl 2350 State Route 63 Wayland NY 14572

GRIFFITH, BRIAN KEITH, Mathematics Teacher; *b:* Broad Top, PA; *ed:* Penn St Univ (BA) Math Ed 1990; 27 Addl Credits in Ed Admin, Prin Cert; *cr:* West Snyder HS Math Tchr 1992-; *ai:* Class of 1999, Ski Club Adv; Discipline, Tech, Schl & Comm Comms; NEA, PSEA, MWEA 1991-; *office:* West Snyder HS RR 1 Box 292 Beaver Springs PA 17812*

GRIFFITH, CAROL, Science Teacher; *b:* Brooklyn, NY; *m:* William P.; *c:* Robert, Jeanne Marie, Michael, Kathleen; *ed:* Brooklyn Coll (BS) Sci 1968; Addl 21 Credit Hrs; SUNY at Stoneybrook 10 Credit Hrs; *cr:* Bishop McDowell HS Hlth & PE Chprsn 1968-71; Bishop Loughlin HS Hlth & PE Chprsn 1971-75; Holy Family Sci Tchr 1986-; *ai:* 7th-8th Grd Sci Coord; Schl Play Moderator; Assembly Comm; Rainbows Coord; *office:* Holy Family Schl 25 Fordham Ave Hicksville NY 11801

GRIFFITH, DONNA MARGARET, American History Teacher; *b:* Washington, DC; *ed:* OH Univ (BSE) Soc Studs Comprehensive 1985; Xavier Univ Working Towards Masters Degree; *cr:* New Richmond HS Eng & World Georgraphy Tchr 1986-89; Cincinnati Hills Chrstn Acad Soc Studs & Eng Tchr 1990-92; John W. Reiley MS Eng Tchr 1992-94; Wm. Mason HS Soc Studs Amer His 1994-; *ai:* Coach MS Girls Track Team; Adv Soph Class; NEA 1994-; Coach of Yr OH HS Gymnastics Coaches Assn 1993; *office:* William Mason HS 770 S Mason Montgomery Rd Mason OH 45040

GRIFFITH, JAMES RICHARD, Mathematics Teacher; *b:* Glendive, MT; *m:* Carol Phelan; *ed:* Univ MT (BS) Ed Math 1967, (ME) Ed 1974; Addl 60 Credits; *cr:* Amityville Jr HS Math Tchr 1967-68; Udall Road Jr HS Math Tchr 1968-91; West Islip HS Math Tchr 1991-; *ai:* Bsktbl Coach; NY St United Tchrs, AFT 1967-; NCTM 1989-; West Islip Boosters 1973-; *office:* West Islip HS Lions Path West Islip NY 11795

GRIFFITH, JEAN MILNER, Reading Specialist; *b:* Jefferson, OH; *m:* Michael B.; *c:* Jennifer Griffith Beer, Betsy Griffith Grimm; *ed:* OH St Univ (BS) Elem Ed 1960, (MA) Elem Ed 1964; 30 Semester Hrs Beyong MA Ashland Univ, OH St Univ; *cr:* Upper Arlington Schls Elem Tchr 1961-65; OH St Univ Fac, Supvr of Stu Tchrs 1968-74; Dublin Schls Elem Tchr 1981-87, Rdng Specialist 1987-; *ai:* PTO Tchr Rep; Deer Run Tech, Authentic Alternative Assessment Comms; Dublin Edctrs Assn 1984-, Rep; Pi Lambda Theta 1960-, Prgm Comm; Phi Delta Kappa 1991-; Mortar Bd Alumni 1960-, Past Pres; Dublin Plus 1982-, Founder, 1st Pres; Chldhd League 1974-; Columbus Museum of Art 1971-, Docent; *office:* Deer Run Elem Schl 8815 Manley Rd Dublin OH 43017

GRIFFITH, JEWEL ANN, K-8th-12th Grd Voc Music Tchr; *b:* Bloomsburg, PA; *m:* Kenneth C.; *c:* Amy, Lori, Mindy; *ed:* Mansfield Univ (BA) Music Ed 1964; 45 Grad Hrs Bloomsburg Univ, Mansfield Univ, Potsdam Crane Schl of Music; *cr:* Newark Vly Elem Schl Music Tchr 1964-70, HS 1973, Elem Schl 1979-82, HS 1983-; *ai:* All Cty, Area All-State Chorus; Vocal Ensemble; NYSUT, AFT, NY St Schl Music Assn, Music Edctrs Natl Conf 1964-; Amer Choral Dirs Assn 1994-; Cty Music Tchrs Assn 1964-, Pres, Sec; PEO 1970-, Musician, Soloist St Convention; Eastern Star 1974-, Musician Conductress, Soloist St Convention; Delta Kappa Gamma 1975-, Musician; Amer Music Abroad Dir European Tours HS Stdnts 1991-; Church Organist, Choir Dir 1967-; Guest Conductor Music Festivals; *office:* Newark Valley HS Wilson Creek Rd Newark Valley NY 13811*

GRIFFITH, JOHN L., Adj Prof of Human Resources; *b:* Pittsburgh, PA; *m:* Myrna Davis; *c:* John, Mona, Mark, Mary, Gemma, William; *ed:* Salem Coll in WV (BS) Chem, Bio 1952; Attnd Baltimore Coll of Dental Surgery; *cr:* Montgomery Ward Jr Indstrl Engr 1951-53; Bendix-Radio Sr Indstrl Engr 1953-55; Pittsburgh Plate Glass Co Brush Div Chief Indstrl Engr 1955-56, Glass Div Chief Indstrl Engr 1956-63; Continental Can Co Chief Indstrl Engr 1963-65; MA Bay Transp Authority Chief Indstrl Engr 1965-70; *ai:* Town of Braintree MA Supt Thermal Waste Reduction Incinerator; Commonwealth of MA Section Chief Rsrch Environmental Stud; Clean Harbors Co Bd of Dirs; MA Org of Scientists, Engrs 1975-, Bd Mem; Amer Inst of Indstrl Engrs 1955-; Tchng Excl Awd in Bus Admin 1993 Northeastern Univ; 25 Yrs Svc Tchng Awd Univ Coll 1992; Article Pub; Co-Author of Report on St Generation of Hazardous Waste 1990; *office:* Northeastern Univ 360 Huntington Ave Boston MA 02115*

GRIFFITH, KAREN C., HS Business Education Tchr; *b:* Boston, MA; *ed:* Salem St Coll (BS) Bus Ed-Magna Cum Laude 1975; Univ of MA (MED) Career Ed 1982; Addl Extensive Work Toward Cert of Advanced Grad Stud in Admin; *cr:* Cambridge Rindge & Latin HS Tchr 1975-; *ai:* Contract, Grievance, Supts Advy, Pol Action, Schlsp Comm Rep; Bd of Trustees for Dental Fund; Camb Tchrs Assn, MTA, NEA 1975-; Natl Bus Ed Assn 1975-; St Bartholomews Episcopal Church, Choir Mem, Hughes Meml Comm, Licensed Lay Reader, Area IV Teen Ctr, Vol Asst; Schl Improvement Grant to Dev Newsletter The Fundamental Correspondent; INROADS/Cntrl New England Inc Educator of Yr; City of Cambridge Wigfall Awd for Comm Service Recipient 1996; *office:* Cambridge Rindge & Latin HS 459 Broadway St Cambridge MA 02138

GRIFFITH, RICHARD R., 9th-12th Grd Soc Stud Teacher; *b:* Wallington, NJ; *m:* Ann E. Croteau; *c:* Julie Snider, Michael, Elizabeth; *ed:* Univ of VT (BA) Pol Sci 1955; Univ of Guam (MA) Asian, Pacific His 1970; Univ of Denver (PHD) Asian His 1978; *cr:* Univ of Denver His Instr 1970-73; Enosburg HS His Instr 1973-79; Intnl Schl His Instr 1979-85; Whitcomb Jr Sr HS His Tchr 1985-; *ai:* Stu Cncl Adv; Amer Historical Assn; Org Amer Historians; Org Asian Scholars; Ed Book Received Hnrs Govt Thailand; Two Books About Asia; Misc Articles; *office:* Whitcomb Jr Sr HS PO Box 62 Bethel VT 05032*

GRIFFITH, THOMAS CALVIN, Social Studies Teacher; *b:* Hagerstown, MD; *m:* Nancy Jo Hart; *c:* Shane, Geoffrey, Christi Jo; *ed:* MD Univ (BA) Soc Stud 1970; (MA) Soc Stud 1976; 30 Addl Post Grad Hrs; *cr:* Colonel Joseph Belt Jr HS Soc Stud Tchr; Kensington Jr HS Soc Stud Tchr; E Brooke Lee MS Soc Stud Tchr 1977-80; John F Kennedy HS Soc Stud Tchr 1980-; *ai:* Stu Govt Assn Spon; Future Lawyers of Amer; Key Club; Class Adv; Stu Discipline Comm; Liason Comm; NEA, MED 1975-; MCEA 1970-; *office:* John F Kennedy HS 1901 Randolph Rd Whiteoak MD 20906*

GRIFFITH, THOMAS ROBERT, English Teacher; *b:* Wilkes-Barre, PA; *ed:* Wilkes Univ (BA) Eng, Comms 1990 & (MS) Eng Ed 1994; *cr:* WY Valley West HS Eng Tchr 1990-; *ai:* Coach Cross Cntry, Winter, Spring Track; Class Stu Assistance Pgm Mem; Sr Class Adv; PSEA, NEA 1990-; Luzerne Cty Rdng Cncl, Keystone St Rdng Assn 1993-; Cross Cntry Coach of Yr 1992 & 1995; Fellow of Northeastern PA Writing Project 1992; Track Coach of Yr 1995; *office:* Wyoming Valley W HS 150 Wadham St Plymouth PA 18651

GRIFFITH, WILLIAM GRADY, 8th Grade Math Teacher; *b:* Bakersfield, CA; *m:* Jeanne Marie; *c:* Timothy William; *ed:* CA St Univ at Bakersfield (BS) Music, Math 1980; *cr:* Belridge Schl Dist Elem Music Tchr 1981-85; Greenfield Union Schl Dist Math Tchr, Band Dir 1985-89; Rochester Area Schl Dist Math Tchr, HS Band Dir 1989-90; Montour Schl Dist Math Tchr 1990-; *ai:* NEA 1981-; Taught Eng Peoples Republic of China 1987, 1991; *office:* David Williams MS Porters Hollow Rd Coraopolis PA 15108

GRIFFITHS, DIANE ARLENE, Spanish Teacher; *b:* Taylor, PA; *ed:* Bloomsburg St Coll (BA) 1969; Millersville Univ (MA) Span 1977; Penn St Univ PA Cert 24 Credit Hrs; Univ of Scranton 12 Credit Hrs; M Coll Supervision of Stu Tchrs; Attnd Univ Iberoamericana MX Madrid; *cr:* Scranton Schl Dist Eng & Span Tchr 1969-77; CET Labor Field Monitor & Investigator 1977-80; Elizabethtown Coll Instr 1980-82; Solanco Schl Dist HS Span Tchr 1980-; *ai:* B Comm; Spring Musical Ticket Sales Coord; Frgn Langs Dept Ch 1969-; PSEA 1969-, Exec Bd 2 Yrs; Bethany Presbyn Choir 198 Masters Thesis; 12 Grd Biling Eng & Span Textbook Sp Trans.

GRIFFITHS, FREDERICK JOHN, Chemistry Teacher; *b:* Abin *m:* Misty Dawn Cysyk; *cr:* Solanco HS Chem Tchr 1993-.

GRIFFITHS, KIT, Business Education Teacher; *b:* Wilkes-Barre Bloomsburg St Coll (BS) Ed, Bus 1976, (MS) Ed, Bus 1979; 60 *cr:* Williams Vly Schl Dist Bus Ed Tchr 1976-77; Pine Grove Schl Ed Tchr 1977-78; Wilkes-Barre Area Schl Dist Sub Tchr Keystone Job Corps Ctr Clerical Instr 1979-80; Wilkes-Barre Dist Bus Ed Tchr 1980-; *ai:* FBLA Adv; Delta Pi Epsilon, Wilk Area EA, PSEA, NEA 1980-; *office:* Elmer L Meyers Jr Sr HS 3 Ave Wilkes Barre PA 18702

GRIFFITHS, LINDA LIEDKE, School Counselor; *b:* Pittsburg Stephen R.; *ed:* Seton Hill Coll (BA) Psych, Ed 1974; Temple U Ed 1980; Trenton St Coll (MA) Cnslng 1990; *cr:* Pennsbury Schl 1974-90, Schl Cnslr 1990-; *ai:* Lower Bucks Cty Fair-Coll Fair C Stu Life Co-Spon; Group Facilitator; SAP Team; PSEA, NE PSCA, BCSCA 1990-; Elk Mt Ski Group Prgm 1994-; *office:* P HS 705 Hood Blvd Fairless Hills PA 19030

GRIFFITHS, ROBERT MICHAEL, History Teacher; *b:* Wilk PA; *m:* Sharon Lee Wakowiak; *c:* Melissa Teter, Robert, Michae *ed:* Bloomsburg Univ (BS) Scndry Ed, His 1971; *cr:* Tor Intermediate Schl Soc Stud Tchr 1971-87; Toms River HS East 1987-; US Merchant Marine Acad Admissions Rep 1995-; Wrestling Coach; Bowling Club; NEA, NJ EA 1971-; Toms River 1971-, Rep; Coach of Yr 1993; *office:* Toms River H S East Ra Toms River NJ 08753

GRIFFO, JOSEPH J., Social Studies Teacher; *b:* Buffalo, Rosemary F. Notaro; *ed:* St Univ Coll at Buffalo (BS) Soc Stud (MS) Soc Stud Ed 1968; Cert of Advanced Stud in Supervision Sweet Home MS Tchr 1965-94, Dept Chair 1970-94, Attendanc 1979-; Sweet Home HS Soc Stud Tchr 1994-; *ai:* Chess Club & Bo Advs; Boys Soccer Coach; Sweet Home Assn 1966-, Rep; NYST Del; NCSS 1970-; *office:* Sweet Home Cntrl Schl 4150 Maple Rd NY 14226

GRIGALUNAS, ANN, English Teacher; *b:* Peckville, PA; *ed:* M Coll (BA) Eng Ed 1975, (MS) Ed 1978; *cr:* Valley View Elem Sch Tchr 1974-75; Valley View Jr-Sr HS 7th-11th Grd Tchr 1975-8 View MS 8th Grd Tchr 1988-; *ai:* Strategic Planning Comm; NE NCTE 1975-; St James Church 1970-, CCD Coord; Young De 1973-; Assn for Blind 1975-; Aux St Josephs Ctr 1972-; *office:* Val MS 1 Columbus Dr Archbald PA 18403

GRIGAS, DEBORAH ANN (DURAN), Science Teacher; *b:* Bost *m:* Paul F.; *c:* Dane, Dacia; *ed:* Massasoit Comm Coll (AA) G Bridgewater St Coll (BS) Ed 1971; Curry Coll (MED) Ed 1 Highland Schl 6th Grd Sci Tchr 1971-72; South MS 6th Grd 1972-79; Morrison Schl 6th Grd Tchr 1979-81; Braintree Pub Sch MS 6th Grd Sci Tchr 1981-; *ai:* MA Assn for Supervision & C NEA, MTA, BEA; ASCD Peter Faralley Tchr Ldrshp Awd 1994 Higham Area 1995 Recognition Awd; *office:* South MS 232 Braintree MA 02184

GRIGGS, ARLENE, 8th Grade English Teacher; *b:* NYC, NY; *m:* *c:* Jason, Brian; *ed:* Rockland C C (AA) 1972; Cortland (BS) 1974; New Paltz (MS) Ed 1976; 75 Credits Beyond MS Degree; *cr:* Cntrl Schl 1st Grd & 6th Grd Eng Tchr 1974-81; Jerusalem Ave Tchr & Gifted Coord 1982-85; Grand Ave JHS Eng Hnrs Tchr 1 Chrldng & Hnr Soc Adv; Tennis & Soccer Coach; Tchr Recogniti *office:* Bellmore-Merrick Cntrl HS Meadowbrook Rd Merrick NY

GRIGGS, HOWARD G.,JR., Business Education Dept Chm; *b:* S PA; *m:* Judith A.; *c:* Jeffrey S., Janice L.; *ed:* Bloomsburg St (BS) 1964, (MED) Bus Ed 1969; *cr:* Tunkhannock HS Bus Ed Tch Wyoming Cty Schl Employees Federal Credit Union Sec-Treas 1966-; Tunhannock HS Bus Ed dept Chm 1983-; *ai:* Tunkhannock Assn 1964-; PSEA, NEA; Glenburn Twp 1985-94, Supvr; BSA Tr Asst Scoutmaster 1995-, Cub Scout Den Ldr 1993-94; *office:* Tunk Area HS 120 W Tioga St Tunkhannock PA 18657

GRIGGS, SHIRLEY KELLY, Associate Professor of Nurs Peekskill, NY; *c:* Thomas, David Kim, Daniel Kim, Peter, Kimo, K Univ of Rochester (BS) Nursing 1950; Russell Sage Coll (MS) 1982; *cr:* Strong Meml Hospital Pediatrics Staff Nurse 1950-52; VA Hospital Neurology Staff Nurse 1952-54; Laupahoshoe Su Hospital Operating Room Staff Nurse 1956; Mary Hitchcock Hospital Ophthalmic Surgery Staff Nurse 1970-80; Dartmouth Co Dean of Summer Prgms 1972-79; NH Tech Coll at Claremont Ass of Nursing 1982-; *ai:* Cntrl Fac Senate NH Post Scndry Coll Recorder, Campus Registration; Comm Hlth Clinical Liaison A Amer Nurses Assn, Natl League for Nursing 1982-; NH Nurses Ass Comm on Nursing Ed; NH Nurses Fnd 1992-, Founding Mem; F Hopkins Ctr, Past Pres; Norwich Arts Assn, Past Pres; Norwich Club, Schlsp Comm; Upper Valley Comm Band, Exec Comm; St Episopal Church Vestry, Sec; Mem Test Writing Panel 1st Compu RN Licensing Exam; *home:* 198 Dutton Hill Rd Norwich VT 0505

GRIGORESCU, VIOLETA TANASE, Physics Teacher; *b:* Suceava, Romania; *m:* Marius; *ed:* Univ of Bucharest (MS) Physic MI St Univ Grad Courses in Telecommunications; *cr:* Various Romania Physics Tchr 1986-92; Poltechnic Inst of Bucharest Tch 1990-92; Leelanau Schl Physics, Calculus Tchr 1993-95; Collegia Physics Tchr 1995-; *ai:* Outing Club Mentor; AAPT, Physics Club 1995-; *home:* 350 W 85th St Apt 46 New York NY 10024*

GRILL, JOHN JOSEPH, Social Studies & Science Tchr; *b:* Sidn *m:* Kathleen Mary Bruno; *c:* Matthew, Sarah; *ed:* St Univ of NY at C (BA) Soc Sci Ed 1982; St Univ of NY at Albany (MA) Soc Stud Ed *cr:* Saint Josephs-Saint Johns Acad 7th & 8th Grd Soc Stud & S 1985-; *home:* 30 Western Ave Watervliet NY 12189

GRILLO, JAMES J., Prof & Bus Admin Dept Chm; *b:* Hornell, Michelle; *ed:* Alfred Univ (BS) Mrktg 1971, (MS) Cnslng Psych 1 Hrs Doctoral Stud St Univ Albany; *cr:* Alfred St Dean of Admiss Records 1972-90, Dept Chair 1991-; *ai:* Mrktg Club & Phi Theta Hnr Soc Adv; Rugby Coach; Amer Mrktg Assoc 1972-; Alfred Lio 1972-, Pres; Chancellors Awd for Prof Excl 1981; Alumni Tchr of & 1995; *office:* Alfred St Coll Brown Hall 421 Alfred NY 14802*

GRILLO, PAUL STEPHEN, Portuguese & Spanish Teacher; River, MA; *m:* Paula; *c:* Michael, Christopher; *ed:* Univ MA at Da (BA) Span 1974, (MA) Biling Ed 1978; Brown Univ Summer Inst in Ed; *cr:* Fall River Pub Schls Home-Schl Biling Pgm Cnslr 1974-75; MS Biling Tchr 1975-76; Durfee HS Portuguese & Span Tchr 19 Various Comms 20 Yrs; NEA 1975-; St John of God Church Confirmation Tchr, Lector & Choir Mem; Cursillo Movement Dio r 1992-, Past Chprsn; Spon Trips to Portugal; *office:* B M C S 360 Elsbree St Fall River MA 02720*

, PAULA OCCHIUTI, Chemistry Teacher; *b:* Fall River, MA; *m:* : Michael Paul, Christopher Paul; *ed:* Univ of MA at Dartmouth 74; Grad Level Courses in Cmptr Intro; *cr:* James Morton MS Sci 4-78; B M C Durfee HS Chem Tchr 1978-; *ai:* HS Girls Vlybl & ch 1974-77; Run Trips for Stdnts During Vacation; NEA; MTA; n God Church Choir 1989-, Pres, Tchr Confirmation 1989-93; M C Durfee HS 360 Elsbree St Fall River MA 02720

INDA SUE (ROTH), Third Grade Teacher; *b:* Allentown, PA; *m:* c: Taylor W.; *ed:* Kutztown St Coll (BS) Elem Ed 1972, (MED) 1976; *cr:* Kutztown Elem Schl 6th Grd Tchr 1972-77, 3rd Grd 5-; *ai:* Sci Curr Comm; Resource Person for New Tchr Induction A, PSEA, Kutztown Area Tchrs Assn 1972-77, 1986-; Kutztown l Soc 1993-; *office:* Kutztown Elem Schl 40 Normal Ave PA 19530

PATRICIA ANN, Fifth Grade Teacher; *b:* Reading, PA; *ed:* Univ (BS) Elem 1968; Masters Equivalence; *cr:* Roosevelt Elem chr 1968-91; Birdsboro Elem Ctr 5th Grd Tchr 1991-; *ai:* Daniel d Assn, PSEA, NEA 1968-; PTC Grant; Childrens Book nial 1776-1976; Nibor's Travel Challenge Bd Game for Children; hallenge US Trivia Game Questions 5th Grd Stu; *office:* Daniel hl Dist 400 W Second St Birdsboro PA 19508

ROBERT E., Soc Studies Tchr & Dept Chair; *b:* Madison Mills, Charlotte A. Morris; *c:* Irven; *ed:* Univ of MD (BA) Govt, Politics vier Univ (MED) Schl Admin 1969; Cert Schl Supt, HS Prin, Elem , Guid Cnslr; 90 Post Grad Credit; *cr:* USAF Sgt. 1958-62; & Company Insurance Adjuster 1965-67; Miami Trace HS Tchr : Jr Class Adv 1975-; Miami Trace Ed Assn 1967-VP 1994-; OH NEA 1967-; New Holland Lodge #392 Free & Accepted Masons utstdng Mem, Comm Svc, Worshipful Master 1982-83; Sons of terans of the Civil War 1988-, OH Dept Comm 1994; OH Soc of of 1812 1988-, St Pres 1993-; Jaycees Outstdng Young Edctr Awd R Tchr of Yr 1995; Ashland Oil Inc Golden Apple Achiever Awd rtha Jennings Fnd Scholar 1975; *office:* Miami Trace HS 3922 St V Washington Court H OH 43160

VALERIE PEARCE, Science Teacher & Coach; *b:* Frederick, John J.; *c:* John, Jason, Ashley; *ed:* Frostburg St Univ (BS) Bio, 83; Univ of MD (BS) Sci Ed 1986; MD St Dept of ED (APC) Bio, 92; Univ of CA at Berkley 6 Hrs 1992; Miami Univ of OH 4 Hrs rdue Univ 10 Hrs 1983; *cr:* Middletown HS Sci Tchr 1986-; *ai:* ls Track Coach; Field Hockey, WMTOA Track Ofcl; NEA, MSTA, 86-; NFIOA 1992-; Frederick Flute Chair 1990-; Pangea USA, Track Coach 1994, 1991; ACS Chem Com Resource Tchr; tive Learning Cadre Trainer; Partners Terrific Sci Participant; Yr 1990, 1992; *office:* Middletown HS 200 High St Middletown 59*

LDI, ALFONSINA ALBINI, French & Italian Teacher; *b:* New y, NY; *c:* Angela, Vincent; *ed:* Barnard Coll (BA) Italian 1933; a Univ (MA) Italian & Fr 1934, (PHD) Educl Research 1957; *cr:* Coll Italian Dept Asst & Lecturer 1946-50; Hoboken HS Italian & 951-82; Rogosin Yeshiva HS Span Tchr 1982-83; Acad of Sacred & Italian Tchr 1983-; *ai:* Italian Club Adv; NEA 1952-; AATI AAUW 1994-; Received Schlsp for Masters; Articles in Italian ; Pub Doctoral Dissertation as The Universal Humanity of ista Vico 1958; *office:* Acad of Sacred Heart 713 Washington St NJ 07030*

S, NANCY GENTZLER, 5th Grade Teacher; *b:* Barberton, OH; ; *ed:* Wittenberg Univ (BA) Elem Ed 1971; Ashland Univ (MA) v 1993; *cr:* Manchester Schls 3rd-5th Grd Tchr 1971-; *ai:* Phi appa 1984-; Kappa Kappa Iota 1991-; John Knox Presbyn Church ffice: Manchester MS 760 W Nimisila Rd Akron OH 44319*

S, PAULA CADOGAN, Sixth Grade Science Teacher; *b:* re, MD; *m:* John C.; *c:* John Paul, Katharyn Leigh; *ed:* Anne Comm Coll (AA) Gen Stud 1974; Towson St (BS) Elem Ed 1976; it Hrs Univ of MD; 3 Credit Hrs Loyola Coll; *cr:* St John the ist Schl Sci Tchr 1978-83; Magothy River Mid Sci Tchr 1983-84; Park Mid Sci Tchr 1984-; *ai:* Kent Island Yth Soccer League TAAAC 1983-; MSTA 1983-; NEA 1983-; Loyola Coll Study mental Sci Grant; WBAL TV Outstdng Tchr Class Act Awd; *office:* Park MS 450 Jumpers Hole Rd Severna Park MD 21146

S, ROY M., Algebra & Geometry Teacher; *b:* E Liverpool, OH; *m:* e E. Willman; *c:* Daniel, Kathryn; *ed:* Miami Univ (BSEd) Math mptr Programming 24 Credit Hrs; *cr:* Univ of Dayton Cmptr Instr 1983-85; Centerville HS Math Tchr 1964-; *ai:* Wright St cl Tchrs of Math 1993-; Rotary Club Man of Yr 1971; *office:* ille HS 500 E Franklin St Centerville OH 45459

, DONA BURHANS, English Teacher; *b:* York, PA; *m:* Barry R. arry R. Sr., Susan Bossi, Jonathan, Brian; *ed:* York Coll of PA (BA) ; 18 Addl Hrs; Berean Bible Schl Diploma Bible Mission 1965; Lion Chrstn Schl Eng, His Tchr 1980-87; Chrstn Schl of York Eng 88-; *ai:* Tenth Grd Class Adv; Frgn Culture Club; EF England Trip slr; Amer Chrstn Schl Intnl 1989-; Keystone-Chrstn Schl Assn g Tchr Awd; *office:* Christian Schl Of York 907 Greenbriar Rd York 4

, DONNA LEA, English & French Teacher; *b:* New Castle, PA; boro St Coll (BSEd) Comprehensive Eng 1964; Slippery Rock St S) Eng 1971; Edinboro St Coll (BSEd) Fr 1978; *cr:* Allen HS Eng hr 1964-66; Laurel Jr Sr HS Eng & Fr Tchr 1966-; *ai:* Laurel Ed PA St Ed Assn 1966-; NEA; United Meth Church, DANK, Home ary US 1964-66; Outstanding Young Women of America 1965; R 1 Box 452 New Wilmington PA 16142

MER, JOLENE MICHELE, German Teacher; *b:* Oneida, NY; *m:* s Kurt Hohenberger; *c:* Erika Glenn Hohenberger, Kelsie Nicole erger; *ed:* SUNY at Fredonia (BA) Ger 1985; 30 Post Grad Hrs; 28 Hrs Christian-Albrechts Universitat; *cr:* Southwestern Cntrl HS Ger 85-89; Glen Burnie Sr HS Ger Tchr 1989-; *ai:* Ger Club Adv; Amity r-Amer Parnership Prgm Coord; Fac Cncl; Schl Promotion, Schl ne Comms; NEA 1985-; TAAAC 1989-; *office:* Glen Burnie Sr HS alto Annapolis Blvd SE Glen Burnie MD 21060

STED, ERIC F., Mathematics Teacher; *b:* Jamaica, NY; *c:* Laura, ; *ed:* SUNY at Geneseo (BS) Math Ed 1970; Grad Work at Russell oll, SUNY at Albany; *cr:* US Army Spec 4th Class 1970-72; land HS Math Tchr 1972-; *ai:* Focus Prgm Tchr; NYSUT, NCTY AMTNYS 1983-; Mary E. Fraley PTA Comm Svc Awd; Peer ition Awd by Schl Bd; Key Club Awd for Outstanding Dedication *office:* Guilderland HS School Rd Guilderland Center NY 12085

AL, CLARE FIFIELD, English Instructor; *b:* Castine, ME; *m:* ; *c:* Aaron, Darcy; *ed:* Univ of ME (BA) Eng 1966; *cr:* Stonington Tchr 1966-76; Deer Isle-Stonington Jr HS Eng Tchr 1976-78; Deer onington HS Eng, His Instr 1979-; *ai:* Sr Class Adv; Attendence Re-Accredidation Co-Chair; Deer Isle-Stonington Tchrs Assn Sec & Negotiator; MTA, NEA 1966-; Blue Hill Soc for Aid to n 1992-, VP.

GRINDROD, JEFF ALLEN, English & Reading Teacher; *b:* Cincinnati, OH; *m:* Sue Schmidt; *c:* Meghann, Alexis; *ed:* Denison Univ (BA) Comm, Eng 1976; Xavier Univ (MED) Rdng Specialist 1982; *cr:* Newark HS Eng, Rdng Tchr 1976-; *ai:* Asst Ftbl, Track Coach; NEA 1976-; NCTE 1993-; OH Ftbl, Track Coaches Assn; RSVP Licking Cty 1993-, Bd Mem; St Francis de Sales Parish Cncl 1995-, Bd Mem; *office:* Newark HS 314 Granville St Newark OH 43055

GRINDSTAFF, JAMES R., Math & Cmptr Sci Teacher; *b:* Fremont, OH; *m:* Mary Rose Percy; *c:* Kathryn L., Kristin A.; *ed:* Bowling Green St Univ (BS) Ed 1976; *cr:* Eastwood Schl Dist 7th-8th Grd Gen Sci Tchr 1976-90; Otsego Schl Dist Math, Cmptr Sci Tchr 1990-; *ai:* Jennings Fnd Master Tchr; OH Venture Capital Grant Co-Author; *office:* Otsego HS PO Box 290 Tontogany OH 43565

GRIPPALDI, DENISE M. (KOZINSKI), Math Teacher; *b:* S Amboy, NJ; *m:* Joseph; *c:* Joseph Jr.; *ed:* Trenton St Coll (BS) Early Chldhd, Math Ed 1978; Georgian Ct Coll (MA) Supervision 1995; *cr:* Lincoln Elem Schl 3rd Grd Tchr 1978-79; Sayreville Jr HS Math Tchr 1979-80; Herbert Hoover MS Math Tchr 1981-88; Edison HS Math Tchr 1988-; *ai:* Key Club Adv; Odyssey of Mind Coach; Alternative Assessment Pilot Project Co-Chprsn; Math, Sci, Tech Month Act Comm Chprsn; AMTNJ, NCTM, NEA, NJEA, MCEA 1978-; ASCD, NCSM 1990-; Cedar Grove PTO 1995-; St Joe's Parish 1990-; NJ Governor's Tchr Recognition Awd 1987-88; New Brunswick Bus, Prof Women's Org Young Career Woman of Yr Awd 1990; *office:* Edison HS Boulevard Of The Eagles Edison NJ 08817

GRIPPO, JOSEPH ANTHONY, Mathematics Teacher; *b:* New London, CT; *ed:* Providence Coll (BA) Math, Ed 1978; Southern CT St Univ (MS) Elem Ed 1986; *cr:* Eliot MS Math Tchr 1978-83; The Morgan Schl Math Tchr 1983-; *ai:* Coach Vlybl, Bsktbl, Sftbl; Jr Class Adv; NEA, CHSCA 1978-; *office:* Morgan HS Rt 81 Clinton CT 06413

GRISCHOW, A. LYNNE STEFFEN, Sociology Teacher; *b:* Rochester, NY; *m:* Andrew Thomas; *c:* Bryan Thomas, Andrew Gregory; *ed:* Mt Union Coll (BA) Ed & Sociology 1971; Kent St Univ (MA) Ed Admin 1980; *cr:* Warren City Schls Soc Stud 1973-; *ai:* Vol Coord; SADD Adv; Schl Improvement & Blue Ribbon Comms; NEA, NEOTA & WEA 1973-; Delta Kappa Gamma 1989-; Awds: Tchr of the Yr Warren Chamber of Commerce 1992, OH NE Region Vol of the Yr 1992, Hwy Safety Task Force 1994, Honorary Recruiter for the US Army 1995; *office:* Warren G Harding Sr HS 860 Elm Rd NE Warren OH 44483*

GRISE, DEBORAH WALDIN, Fifth Grade Teacher; *b:* Woodbury, NJ; *m:* Howard David; *c:* Lauren, David; *ed:* Univ of DE (BS) Elem Ed 1971; 34 Addl Hrs; *cr:* Marshallton Elem Schl 6th Grd Tchr 1971-72; IRSD Selbyville MS 5th & 6th Grd Tchr 1972-80; Lord Baltimore Elem Schl 5th Grd Tchr 1980-; *ai:* Math 301 Rep; Rdng, Lang Arts Piloting Teach; St Sci Conf Rep; NEA, IREA 1971-; LB PTA 1980-; Beta Sigma Phi 1979-, Past Pres, Girl of Yr; Tchr of Yr; *office:* Lord Baltimore Elem Schl PO Box 21 Rt 26 Ocean View DE 19970

GRISETO, TONI HARZINSKI, Fifth Grade Teacher; *b:* Kingston, PA; *m:* Vincent P.; *c:* Vincent Jr., Anthony, Mary; *ed:* Bloomsburg St Coll (BS) Elem Ed 1981; Wilkes Coll & Coll Misrecordia Grad Credits; *cr:* WY Vly West Schl Dist Sub Tchr 1982; Sacred Heart Schl 3rd Grd Tchr 1982-91, 7th Grd Tchr 1991-92, 5th Grd, 4th Grd Sci & Rdng Tchr 1992-; *ai:* Sci Fair Coord; Safety Patrol Coord; After-Schl Care Tchr; Yrbk Staff; NCEAA 1982-; BSA 1995-, Den Ldr; AAA Traffic Safety Poster Contest Tchr Recognition 10 Yrs; Scranton Diocese Inservice Presentations 1991, 1992 & 1993; Wkshp Presenter 1993; *office:* Sacred Heart School-Luzerne 545 Charles St Luzerne PA 18709

GRISIN, SUZETTE ALINE, Band Director; *b:* Johnstown, PA; *ed:* Indiana Univ of PA (BS) Music Ed 1985; Attnd Duquesne Univ & Villanova Univ Grad Credits; *cr:* Gr Johnstown Vo-Tech Choir & Band Dir 1986-87; Conemaugh Twp HS Band Dir 1988-; *ai:* HS Marching Band; Schl Musicals Instrumental & Vocal Dir; Stu Assistance Prgm Team Mem; Strategic Planning Comm Mem; PMEA, NEA, MENC & PSEA 1986-; St Nicholas Serbian Church, dir, VP & Choir Dir; Amer Fed of Musicians; *office:* Conemaugh Township Area HS West Campus Ave Davidsville PA 15928*

GRISSINGER, ARTHUR DAVID, Asst Professor of Mathematics; *b:* West Reading, PA; *m:* Connie Campbell; *c:* Rose, Tracy, Mark; *ed:* Shippensburg St Coll (BS) Math 1963; Univ of KS (MA) Math 1969; 12 Credit Hrs George Washington Univ, 9 Credit Hrs Columbia Univ, 21 Credit Hrs Univ of KY, 30 Credit Hrs VA Tech, 3 Credit Hrs Univ of Va; *cr:* KY St Univ Ass Prof of Math 1969-78; Defense Mapping Agency Cartographer 1978-84; Liberty Univ Asst Prof of Math 1984-92; Lock Haven Univ Asst Prof of Math 1992-; *ai:* Math Study Groups; Math Assn of Amer 1986-; Fundamental Bible Church 1993-, Sunday Schl Tchr; IBM Watson Rsrch summer Flwshp; Defense Mapping Agency; OUtstdng Stu in Instr Trng Course; *home:* 306 E Walnut St Clearfield PA 16830

GRIST, RODNEY W., HS Theatre Arts Teacher; *b:* Columbus, OH; *c:* Cory J.; *ed:* OH St Univ (BS) Speech, Theatre, Eng Ed 1990, (MA) Speech, Theatre Ed 1994; *cr:* Brookhaven HS Theatre Tchr, Dir 1990-; *ai:* Theatre Dir; Thespian, Radio Club, Magazine Asst Adv; Schl Restructuring Comm; Intervention Assistance Team; CATCO Partnership 1991; OEA, NEA, CEA 1990-; *office:* Brookhaven H S 4077 Karl Rd Columbus OH 43224

GRISWOLD, JACQUELINE MARIE, Human Svcs Pgm Professor; *b:* Palmer, MA; *c:* Adam Schlesinger, Zachary Schlesinger; *ed:* Univ of ME (BS) Child Dev 1972, (MS) Human Dev 1977; Northeastern Univ (EDD) Higher Ed Admin 1987; *cr:* Northeast Combat Consumer Ed Consultant 1975-76; Richmond Jr Sr HS Tchr 1976-77; Cumberland Cty CETA Cnslr & Trainer 1977-80; Univ of ME Cnslr & Stu Svcs Coord 1980-86; NH Tech Coll Prof & Dep Chair 1986-; *ai:* Phi Theta Kappa Adv; Various System-Wide Comms; NOHSE 1994-; Burch House Bd of Dirs; Human Svcs Research Inst Human Svcs Skills Standards Project Ed & Trng Team; Project Dir NH Comm Tech Coll System FIPSE Grant; *office:* NH Tech Coll At Berlin 2020 Riverside Dr Berlin NH 03570*

GRISWOLD, LISA M., 7th-8th Grade Science Teacher; *b:* St Albans, VT; *m:* Kerry L.; *c:* Kristen, Shannon; *ed:* Johnson St Coll (BS) Life Sci, Ed 1974; Grad Courses Johnson St Coll, St Michaels Coll, Univ of VT; *cr:* St Albans Elem Schl 8th Grd Sci Tchr 1974-80; Bellow Free Acad 7-10th Grd Sci Tchr 1980-; *ai:* Class Trip; Fund Raise; Organize Week of Stud Environmental Ctr; 8th Grd R&R; Sci Fair; Together Time Adv; NEA, VEA 1974-; First Bapt Church 1966-, Chrstn Ed, Planning Team, Schl Tchr, Summer Bible Schl Tchr; Outstdng Tchr of Yr 1991.

GRISWOLD, ROBYN HALLOWELL, Social Studies Teacher; *b:* Boston, MA; *m:* Dr. William A.; *ed:* Wheaton Coll (BA) His 1987; Harvard Univ (MA) His 1988, (MED) Tchng & Curr 1989; *cr:* Nashua Sr HS Soc Stud Tchr 1989-; *ai:* NH Cncl for Soc Stud, NCSS 1995-; AFT 1989-; Co-Author of Cooperative Learning Basics-Strategies & Lessons for US His Tchrs Golden Owl 1995; Presenter of Wkshps on Cooperative Learning & Using Primary Sources to Teach His at the Local, St, Regnl & Natl Levels; Author of Article Pub in Horizons Journal of NHCSS 1992; *office:* Nashua Sr HS 36 Riverside Dr Nashua NH 03062*

GRISWOLD, ROCK LOWELL, Business Education Teacher; *b:* Blossburg, PA; *m:* Jennifer Jo Eck; *ed:* Shippensburg Univ (BS) Bus Admin 1988; Bloomsburg Univ (BS) Bus Ed 1990; *cr:* Northern Tier Yth Svcs Educl Cnslr 1989-92; *ai:* PA Future Bus Ldrs of Amer Adv; Girls Track Head Coach; Prof Dev Comm; PBEA 1990-; NBEA 1990-; PSEA 1990-; YMCA 1993-; PA Free Enterprise Schlsp; *office:* Jersey Shore Area Sr HS 701 Cemetery St Jersey Shore PA 17740

GRITEMAN, CATHY LEATHERMAN, Nursing Instructor; *b:* Liberty Ctr, OH; *m:* Bruce; *c:* Robin, John; *ed:* Bowling Green St Univ (BS) Nursing 1979; Med Coll of OH (MS) Nrsng 1996; *cr:* Med Coll Hosp Pediatric Staff Nrsng 1979-86, Staff Dev Instr 1986-88; Northwest St Comm Coll Nrsng Fac 1990-; *ai:* Liberty Chapel United Meth Sunday Schl Tchr; Sigma Theta Tau 1993-, News Reporter; Amer Cancer Soc 1992-, OH Nurse of Hope 1st Alternate 1992-93; Grad Ceremonies Nrsng Speaker X 2; Poster Presenter for Nrsng Conf; *office:* Northwest State Comm Coll 22600 State Route 34 Archbold OH 43502

GRITSAVAGE, LAUREN MILLER, HS Math Teacher; *b:* Rochester, NY; *m:* William H.; *c:* Jeffrey, William Jr., Shana; *ed:* SUNY at Albany (BA) Math, Scndry Ed 1970; *cr:* Sacred Heart Schl 1st-4th Grd Math Tchr 1970-71; St Lukes Schl 7th-8th Grd Math Tchr 1971-72; Perth Cntrl Schl 7th-12th Grd Math Tchr 1976-87; Broadalbin-Perth MS 6th-8th Grd Math Tchr 1987-95, Dept Chm 1992-95; Broadalbin-Perth HS Math Tchr 1995-; *ai:* SADD Adv; AFT, NYSUT 1982-; BPTA 1987-; Perth TA 1982-87, Treas; Nathan Littauer Hospital Auxiliary 1980-, 2nd VP; *office:* Broadalbin-Perth HS Bridge St Ext Broadalbin NY 12025

GRITZER, PATRICIA ANN, Second Grade Teacher; *b:* Johnstown, PA; *ed:* IN Univ of PA (BS) Elem Ed 1964; Cooperative Tchr of Stu Tchrs 1965-92 Credits Earned; John Hopkins Cooperative Learning; Univ of Pittsburg at Johnstown Elem Trainee of Process Writing Prgm, Asst to Univ Prof; *cr:* Bheam Elem Schl Grd 2 Tchr 1964-77; Bhean Westwood West Side Schl Cooperating Tchr of Stu Tchrs 1966-90; West Side Elem Schl Grd 2 Elem Tchr 1977-; *ai:* Curr Planning Cncl; Schl Improvement, Rdng is Fundamental, Tech, Pub Relations Comms; GU Curr Core Comm, Lang Arts, Cncl Mem of Tech; Strategic Planning Action Team; Staff Dev Participant; NEA, PSEA, Greater Johnstown Ed Assn, IUP Alumni Assn 1964-; Comm Arts Ctr 1990-; Friends of Lib 1986-; Comm Advy Bd 1994-; Partners in Ed 1964-; Bus & Prof Women 1969-; Tchrs Expectations & Stu Achvmt Cert 1986; Supts Nom Cert 1988; Cert in Instrl Support & Adept CBA, Cert of Achvmt John Hopkins Cooperative Learning 1991; Core Curr Comm Ldr 1977; Recipient of 2 Mini-Grants for Improving Instruction in Lang; *office:* Westside Elem Schl 196 Westgate Dr Johnstown PA 15905

GRKMAN, LOUIS, Sixth Grade Teacher; *b:* Greensburg, PA; *m:* Darla Williams; *c:* Louis III, Matthew; *ed:* CA Univ of PA (BS) Elem Ed 1969; WV Univ (MA) Elem Ed 1972; *cr:* Maxwell Elem Schl Sixth Grd Tchr 1969-91; West Hempfield MS Sixth Grd Tchr 1991-; *ai:* NEA, PSEA, HAEA 1969-; *office:* West Hempfield MS Northumberland Dr Irwin PA 15642

GROBE, DANIEL, Physical Education Teacher; *b:* Pittsburgh, PA; *m:* Jane SKirtich; *c:* William Jennifer, Elizabeth, Matthew, Andrew; *ed:* Slippery Rock Univ (BA) PE, Hlth 1973; Attnd Indiana Univ of PA; *cr:* Greater Latrobe Schl Dist PE Tchr 1973-; *ai:* Head Coach Girls' Var Soccer, Jr HS Wrestling; Unity Soccer Pres; NEA, PSEA, GLEA 1973-; PA West Soccer Club 1991-, Pres Local Club; Local, St Natl Coaches Assn Soccer 1993-; Demonstration Site Tchr PE Life St Curr; *office:* Baggaley Elem Schl Rd 6 Box 495 Latrobe PA 15650*

GROBE, RONALD S., High School Science Teacher; *b:* Newark, NJ; *m:* Shelley Ferdinand; *c:* Adam, Amy; *ed:* Rutgers Univ (BS) Bio 1971; Montclair St (MA) Stu Prsnl 1975; *cr:* Carteret HS Sci Tchr 1972-; *ai:* Meteorology Club; Sci Olympiad; NJ Sci Tchrs Bio Comm; NEA, NJEA 1972-; NJSTA 1980-; NJ Realtors Assn 1979-; Grants: Ecolob, Eisenhower, to Attend a Conf in Moscow 1991; *office:* Carteret HS 199 Washington Ave Carteret NJ 07008

GROBECMY, MICHAEL JOHN, Guidance Director & Counselor; *b:* Camden, NJ; *m:* Dorothy; *c:* Dana; *ed:* Glassboro St Coll (BA) Math 1968, (MA) Stu Prsnl Svcs 1972; 30 Hrs Schl Bus Admin, Prin, Chief Schl Admin; *cr:* Eastern Regnl HS Math Tchr 1968-71; Clayton HS Guid Cnslr 1971-76, Guid Dir, Cnslr 1976-; *ai:* Fin Adv; Clayton Ed Assn 1971-; NJEA, NEA 1968-; NJSCA 1985-; Knights of Columbus 1980-; *office:* Clayton HS 350 E Clinton St Clayton NJ 08312

GROCOTT, DORENE MITCHELL, English Teacher; *b:* Stoke-on-Trent-Sta, England; *m:* Francis John; *c:* Steven John, Mark Jason; *ed:* Stoke-on-Trent-N-Stech (BA) (MA) PE 1952) PE; Attnd Athl Lilleshall Hall AENUAENC Athl 1954; Caulden Coll WAAA Sr Olympic Level Coaching 1966; WAAA Natl Athl 1960; Intnl AAA Advanced PE 1962 Coaching Degree; *cr:* Queensberry Girl's Schl PE, Hlth Tchr 1952-62; Thistley Hough Girl's Schl PE, Bio Tchr 1964-65; Caulden Coll Ath, PE Dir 1965-66; Univ of N Staffs Head Women's Dept PE 1967; *ai:* Supvr Willingboro Recreation Dept; Sports Dir Girl's Gymnastics; Olympic Track Coach 1960-68; WAAA 1954-, VP, BAAB; Middle St Cncl for Soc Stud 1990-; Track, Field Trial Olympic Level 1948; Played Netball England; Assessor to His Royal Highness Duke of Edinburgh; Eng Coach; Umpire for Netball; Life VP to WAAA, BAAB of Great Britain, Commonwealth; Nom Sacrd Hrt Tchr of Yr 1994-95; Nom Trenton Diocese to Rprsnt Cty & Cnty 1994-95; Mstr Tchr Awd 1994; Nom Tchr of Yr Trenton Diocese; State Rcgnzd; *home:* 176 Tiffany Ln Willingboro NJ 08046

GRODE, LINDA DOWNING, MS Math & Social Studies Tchr; *b:* Pittsburgh, PA; *ed:* Mercyhurst Coll (BA) Elem Ed 1973; Edinboro Univ (MED) Schl Admin 1978; Prin Cert 1978; *cr:* Union City Area Elem Schl Grd 3 Tchr 1973-78; St Leo Schl Grd 4-8 Math Tchr 1980-91; St Paul Cathedral Schl Grd 4, 6-8 Tchr 1991-; *ai:* Diocesan Spelling, Geography Bees Spons; Natl Geographic Soc; Schl Testing Comm; FPDT 1992-; Fulbright Fellowship England 1978-79; *office:* St Paul Cathedral Schl 136 N Craig St Pittsburgh PA 15213

GRODE, MARCIA NELSON, French & Spanish Teacher; *b:* Erie, PA; *m:* John Neal; *ed:* Penn St Univ (BS) Scndry Fr Ed 1967, (MED) Scndry Ed Curr & Fr 1974; Stud Work on Counseling High Risk Youth Cert; *cr:* Memorial MS Fr & Span Tchr 1972-79; Grover Cleveland Elem Schl Eng as Second Lang Tchr 1981-83; Academy HS Fr & Span Tchr 1983-92; Central HS Fr & Span Tchr 1992-; *ai:* Stu Cncl & Fr Club Adv; Mentoring Pgm Coord 1993-; Svc Lrng Coord 1994-; NEA, PEA & EEA 1972-, Bldg Rep; Pi Lambda Theta 1975-; Delta Kappa Gamma 1981-, Pres; ACTFL; AAUW; PSMLA; MLA; AATF; Erie Playhouse Bd 14 Yrs, Several Offices Held; Erie Intnl Inst Bd 2 Yrs, Sec, VP; Central HS & Academy HS Foreign Lang Dept chprsn; Organized 3 Stu Trips to Europe; Svc Lrng Pioneer Awd, Erie City Schl Dist 1995; *office:* Central HS 3325 Cherry St Erie PA 16508*

GROELLER, MARY DAMIANO, Fifth Grade Teacher; *b:* Passaic, NJ; *m:* Adolph A.; *c:* Greg, Jennifer; *ed:* William Patterson Coll (BA) Elem Ed 1969; *cr:* West Freehold Elem 4th Grd Tchr 1981; St Rose of Lima Elem 6th Grd Tchr 1981-89; Winfield Twp Schl 5th-8th Grd Sci Tchr 1989-; *ai:* Safety Patrol Adv; NJEA 1989-; NJ Sci Tchrs Assn 1989-; NJ Governors Tchrs Recognition Awd 1992; *office:* Winfield Township Schl Gulfstream Ave Winfield Park NJ 07036*

GROENING, LEANNE MCLELLAN, Social Studies Teacher; *b:* Calais, ME; *m:* Steven; *ed:* Univ of ME (BS) Scndry ed 1989; *cr:* MSAD 56 Soc Stud Tchr 1989-; *ai:* NEA & MEA 1989-; *office:* Searsport Dist HS 20 Church St Searsport ME 04974

GROFF, JIM, Secondary Lifeskills Teacher; *b:* Pottstown, PA; *m:* Kathleen; *c:* Adrienne Ogden Saul, Jennifer Ogden, Wesley Ogden; *ed:*

East Stoudsburg Univ (BS) Hlth & PE 1970; West Chester Univ (MED) Hlth & PE 1978; Kutztown Univ Spcl Ed Cert 1980; *cr:* Berks Cty Intermediate Unit Adapted PE & Spcl Ed Tchr 1974-92; Hamburg Area Schl Dist Spcl Ed Tchr 1992-; *ai:* Spcl Olympics Spon & Coach; PSEA-PA 1974-; NEA 1974-; Winner; Anne Sullivan Awd for Berks Cty, CEC Natl Practicioners Awd; St of PA Tchr of Yr Nom; *office:* Hamburg Area HS Windsor St Hamburg PA 19526*

GROFF, JOHN WILLIAM, Eng Dept Chm & Teacher; *b:* Sellersville, PA; *m:* S. Kathleen; *c:* Emily, Jeremy; *ed:* SUNY at Binghamton (BA) Eng 1974; U of WA (MA) Eng 1976; *cr:* The Amer Boy Choir Schl His Tchr 1978-79; The Cheshire Acad Eng Tchr 1979-84; Ethel Walker Schl Eng Tchr 1984-; *ai:* Outdoor Adventure Supv; Lit Magazine Fac Adv; Curr Comm; NCTE; NEH Ind Study Flwshp 1988; Article Pub 1994; *office:* Ethel Walker Schl 230 Bushy Hill Rd Simsbury CT 06070

GROFF, KRISTIN F., 6th Grade Teacher; *b:* Erie, PA; *m:* William J.; *c:* Jennifer J. McCurdy, Kelley M., Timothy W.; *ed:* Edinboro Univ of PA (BS) Elem Ed 1971, (BS) Spcl Ed 1972; Lake Erie Coll (MS) Curr Supervision 1991; Johnson-Johnson Cooperative Learning; Mastey Learning; *cr:* Pymatuning Vly Mid Jr High Spcl Ed Tchr 1971-86, 6th Grd Tchr 1986-88, 5th Grd Tchr 1988-89, 6th Grd Tchr 1989-; *ai:* HS Girls Sftbl Coach; Pymatuning Vly Ed Assn 1971-, Sec & Negotiator Bldg Rep; Order of Eastern Star 1976-; Girl Scouts 1980-, Bd of Dirs & Assoc Dir.

GROGG, KATHLEEN KNISELY, Fourth Grade Teacher; *b:* Fremont, OH; *m:* Howard D.; *c:* Renee, Gary, Anne, Douglas; *ed:* Mary Manse Coll (BA) Elem Ed 1965; Univ of Toledo (MED) Elem Cnslng 1970; *cr:* St Joseph Schl 3rd Grd Tchr 1964-66; Green Springs Schl 5th Grd Tchr 1966-68; Sandusky Cty Project Pupil Elem Cnslr Intern 1968-69; Perkins HS Cnslr 1969-70; Clyle Elem Cnslr 1970-71; Centerville Bd of Ed All Schl Tutor 1971-75; St Peter Schl 4th Grd Tchr 1987-; *ai:* Rel In-Svc Right to Read; Rosary Wkly Lay Minister; Peace Talks; Cath Schls Wk; OCEA 1986-; Whole Lang Group 1987-; Sci Org 1996-; CCL 1981-, Pres & Treas; Yth Group 1994-; Carrolleer Band Parent 1992-; Grants: OSU, ADD, AD HD; Project Pupil Intern MS in Elem Cnclng; Outstdng Young Edctrs 1971; *home:* 1800 N Central Dr Beavercreek OH 45432

GROLLER, RICHARD J., Band Director & Asst Principal; *b:* Allentown, PA; *m:* Diana; *ed:* Philadelphia Musical Acad (BMEd) Music 1975; Temple Univ (MS) Music 1993; Scndry Prin, Music Supervisory Cert; *cr:* Harrison-Morton MS Gen Music Tchr 1985-86; Raub MS Instrumental Music Tchr 1987-95, Asst Prin, Band Dir 1995-; *ai:* Band; Orch; Stage Band; Brass Choir; AEA, PA MS Assn 1994-; ASCD 1993-; Allentown Symphony 1968-, Musician; *office:* Raub MS 102 S Saint Cloud St Allentown PA 18104

GROMBACHER, RAYMOND T., 7th & 8th Grade Art Teacher; *b:* Youngstown, OH; *m:* Susan; *c:* Andy, Jimmy, Casey; *ed:* OH Univ (BFA) Art & Photography 1967; Toledo Univ (ME) Admin 1980; 50 Hrs Towards Masters from Bowling Green; *cr:* Longfellow Jr HS Art Tchr 1967-80; Deveaux Jr HS Art Tchr 1980-; *ai:* Bsktbl Coach 28 Yrs; Art Club; Toledo Fed Of Tchrs 1967-, Bldg Rep 11 Yrs; *office:* Deveaux Jr HS 2626 W Sylvania Ave Toledo OH 43613

GRON, ROSEMARY ELAINE, Fourth Grade Teacher; *b:* Martins Ferry, OH; *ed:* OH Univ at Athens (BS) Elem Ed 1969; Dayton Univ (MS) Admin, Supervision 1979; OH Univ at Belmont (BS); Attnd Jefferson Tech Coll, Univ of Steubenville, OH Univ at Belmont; *cr:* Buckeye Local Schls Corrective Rdng Tchr, Adult Basic Ed Tchr, Head Start Tchr, Summer Intervention Tchr, 1-4, 6th Grd Tchr, 2-4 Grd Enrichment Classes Tchr, Spec Ed Classes Tchr, Critic Tchr for Several Stu Tchrs, Tutor, 4th Grd Tchr; *ai:* NEA, OEA, CTA 1966-; Jefferson Cty Schls Mini Grant 6 Yrs; Buckeye Schls Tchr of Yr 1992; Jennings Scholar 1993-; Lecture Prgm Kent St Univ; Several Courses of Stud & Textbook Comms Jefferson Cty Bd of Ed, Gifted Curr; *home:* PO Box 197 325 Hill St Smithfield OH 43948

GROOMES, WARREN EDWARD, Mathematics Teacher; *b:* Washington, DC; *m:* Judith Lockwood; *c:* John, David; *ed:* Univ of MD (BA) Math Ed 1963; *cr:* White Oak Jr HS Math Tchr 1963-71; Springbrook HS Math Tchr 1971-; *ai:* NEA, MSTA, MCEA 1963-; *office:* Springbrook HS 201 Valleybrook Dr Silver Spring MD 20904

GROPMAN, RICHARD, Anatomy Teacher; *b:* Medford, MA; *m:* Maureen C. Burns; *c:* Jeffrey, Leann; *ed:* Suffolk Univ (BS) Bio 1967, (MA) Ed 1970; 15 Hrs Beyond Masters; *cr:* Tewksbury Meml HS Tchr 1967-; NH Voc Tech Coll Instr 1972; *ai:* Tewksbury Schls Hlth Ed Comm; NEA, MA Tchrs Assn 1967-; Tewksbury Tchrs Assn 1967-, Pres; Middlesex Cty Ed Assn, Bd of Dirs; NSF Grant Sci & Soc 1972; Article Pub in Kalidescope Magazine 1970; *office:* Tewksbury Memorial HS 320 Pleasant St Tewksbury MA 01876*

GROSHOFF, JAN K., High School Counselor; *b:* Berea, OH; *m:* Herman; *c:* David A.; *ed:* Univ of Cincinnati (BS-Hnrs) Eng & Soc Stud 1971; Xavier Univ (MED) Cnslng 1984; *cr:* Turpin HS Eng Tchr 1976-87; Anderson HS Cnslr 1987-; *ai:* NEA 1976-; OH Cnslng Assn 1987-; *office:* Anderson HS 7560 Forest Rd Cincinnati OH 45255

GROSS, ALFRED,JR., Sixth Grade Teacher; *b:* Jackson, KY; *m:* Bambi Lynn Thomas; *c:* Trisha, Greg, Christina, Juliana; *ed:* Lees Jr Coll (AS) Ed 1972; Morehead St Univ (BA) Ed 1974; Xavier (MS) Admin 1983; Attnd Drake Univ, Seattle Pacific Univ; *cr:* Clermont North Eastern Schl Sixth Grd Tchr 1974; Ross Local Schls Sixth Grd Tchr 1975-; *ai:* Ross MS Newspaper Team Ldr; Intervention Assitance Team; Environmental Club; Bldg Ldrshp Cncl; Ross Educ Assn 1995-, Treas; NEA 1995-; *office:* Ross Local Schls 3371 Hamilton Cleves Rd Hamilton OH 45013

GROSS, BARBARA E., Band Director; *b:* Abington, PA; *ed:* Bucknell Univ (BS) Music ed 1964; Eastman Schl of Music of Univ of Rochester (MM) Music Lit, Performance 1966; Bassoon Performer's Cert; Post Grad Stud Conducting; *cr:* St Rd Elem Schl Instrumental Music Tchr 1967-80; Schroeder Sr HS Band Dir, Instrumental Music Tchr 1977-84; Schroeder JR HS Band Dir, Instrumental Music Tchr 1979-84; Webster Sr HS Band Dir, Instrumental Music Tchr 1984-; *ai:* Music Curr Assessment Comm; MENC 1964-; NYSSMA, NYSUT, WTA 1967-; NYSBDA 1982-; Rochester Musicians Assn 1966-; Past Mem Penfield Symphony Orch Comm; Past Mem Univ of Rochester Symphony Orch Advy Comm; Univ of Rochester, Penfield Symphony Orchs; Webster Theater Guild Pit Orch; Performed with Rochester Philarmonic, Brookport Symphony, Greece Symphony Orch; Former Conductor Brighton Symphony Orch; *office:* Webster HS 875 Ridge Rd Webster NY 14580

GROSS, BARBARA MARY, Eighth Grade Teacher; *b:* Holyoke, MA; *ed:* Westfield St Coll (BS) Elem Ed 1973; Holyoke Comm Coll (AS) Cmptr Inf Systems 1987; Westfield St Coll (MED) Educl Admin 1996; *cr:* Blessed Sacrament Schl 4th Grd Tchr 1973-81; Holy Trinity Schl 4th Grd Tchr 1981-84; Holy Name Schl 7-8 Grd Tchr 1984-; *ai:* Schl Store Adv; NCEA; ASCD; Pioneer Vly Rdng Cncl; MA Audubon Soc 1979-; *office:* Holy Name Schl 37 Alderman St Springfield MA 01108

GROSS, CAROL L., Health & Physical Ed Teacher; *b:* Doylestown, PA; *ed:* East Stroudsburg Univ (BS) Hlth & PE 1965, (MSEd) Hlth & PE; *cr:* Delhaas HS Hlth & PE Tchr 16 Yrs; Harry S Truman Hlth & PE Tchr 14 Yrs; *ai:* Class Adv; Soccer & Chrldng Coach; NEA 1965-; PSEA 1965-; BTAA 1965-; Red Cross Vol; Speaker on Travel Experiences with Emphasis on 3rd World Travel; *home:* PO Box 461 Levittown PA 19058

GROSS, DAVID IAN, Retired Professor; *b:* Boston, MA; *m:* Mary Margaret Griffith; *c:* Kenneth, Jennifer, Barbara; *ed:* GA Inst of Tech (BCE) Chemical Engr 1959; AFIT (MS) Reliability Engr 1965; Univ of Dayton (MSCE) Enviromental Engr 1995; *cr:* USAF Flight Operations 1952-65, Prgm Mgr 1966-75, System Prgm Dir 1975-78; Univ of Dayton Dept Chair, Prof 1981-95; *ai:* Part-time Instr; ACS; AICHE; EX; ASEE; AWWA.

GROSS, DEBBIE PALMIERI, Sixth Grade Teacher; *b:* Manhattan, NY; *m:* Steve; *c:* Alexa Marielle, Hunter Ian, Jake Brandon; *ed:* CUNY at Queens Coll (BA) Elem Ed 1984, (MS) Elem Ed 1988; *cr:* Louis Armstrong MS IS227 Sixth Grd Tchr 1984-; *ai:* AFT, UFT 1984-; Hadassah 1988-90, VP Membership; Core 5-6th Grd Coord 1986-89; *office:* Louis Armstrong MS 32-02 Junction Blvd East Elmhurst NY 11369

GROSS, DEBORAH MC GARRY, Second Grade Teacher; *b:* Bridgeport, CT; *m:* Scott D.; *ed:* Elizabethtown Coll (BS) Elem Ed 1984; Millersville Univ (MS) Elem Ed 1994; 12 Post Grad Credit Hrs; *cr:* Exeter Twp Schl Dist 1st Grd Tchr, Long Term Sub Tchr 1985-85; Derry Twp Schl Dist 2nd Grd Tchr 1985-; *office:* Hershey Primary Schl PO Box 898 Homestead Rd Hershey PA 17033

GROSS, GEORGE ROSS, Chemistry Teacher; *b:* Paterson, NJ; *m:* Judith M. Ott; *c:* Tammy, George Jr.; *ed:* Montclair St (BA) Chem 1964, (MA) Sci Ed 1966; Syracuse Univ (MS) Biological Sci 1970; Rutgers Univ (EDD) Sci Ed 1977; Attnd Rider Coll, SUNY at Plattsburgh, UCAL at Berkeley; *cr:* Union HS Chem Tchr 1964-; *ai:* Ecology Club; NJ Sci League; Chem Olympics; Natl Sci Bowl; ACS 1979-, Cnslr 1989-91; Alt Cnslr 1991-; Merril Awd 1986; NEA, NJEA 1964-, NJ Sci Convention 1976, Steering Comm; NSTA 1964-; NJSTA 1964-, Pres 1978, Fellow Awd-Citation Scroll; BSA 1980-, Scout Master 14 Yrs; WY Civic Assn 1974-1990; WY Presbyterian Church; Montclair St Coll Distinguished Alumni Awd; Berkeley NSF Summer 1965; Syracuse NSF Summer 1968-70; Woodrow Wilson-Dreyfus Master Tchr 1987; Chem 5 Team 1988; NJ Outstanding Chem Tchr; NJ Presidential Awd Winner; MCA Regnl Awd for Excl in Chem Tchng; Homer J. Hall Awd HS Chem Tchng, AIC; Irwin Jaeger Chair of Sci Union Twp 1995; Co-author "A Demo A Day" 1995; *office:* Union H S N 3rd St Union NJ 07083

GROSS, JOHN C., 6th Grade Math Teacher; *b:* Coudersport, PA; *m:* Shirley Capwell; *c:* Sherri, Sheila, Shelley; *ed:* Mansfield Univ (BS) Ed 1965; 30 Post Grad Hrs Penn St Univ; *cr:* Sayre Area Schls Tchr 1965-; *ai:* Tech Comm for Strategic Planning; Cmptr Comm; PSEA, NEA 1966-; Sayre-Athens Lions 1987-, Treas; Tioga Point Museum 1990-, VP; *office:* H Austin Snyder Elem Schl 130 Warren St Sayre PA 18840*

GROSS, KATHLEEN FRANCES, Mathematics Teacher; *b:* Philadelphia, PA; *ed:* St Joseph's Univ (BS) Elem Ed 1968; 27 Grad Credits from Various Colls & Univs; *cr:* St Edmond's Grd Schl 3rd & 4th Grd Tchr 1964-68; St Maria Goretti HS Math Tchr 1968-71; Holy Spirit HS Math Tchr 1971-; Atlantic Comm Coll Adjunct Math Tchr 1989-; *ai:* NCEA, NCTM, AMTNJ, SCTO 1972-; AAUW, ASCD, AMA 1992-; Wrote Grant 1988; Plan, Conduct In-Service Day at Holy Spirit 1992; *office:* Holy Spirit HS California Ave & New Rd Absecon NJ 08201

GROSS, LAWRENCE WAYNE, PE Tchr, Chairman & Golf Coach; *b:* Elgin, IL; *m:* Marilyn Louise; *c:* Lori, Kristi, Stacy; *ed:* Mt Union Coll (BA) Eng, Hlth & PE 1966; Slippery Rock Univ (MED) PE 1975; *cr:* State St Jr HS Eng Tchr 1966-67; Wiley Jr HS Hlth & PE Tchr 1967-70; Arnold Jr HS Eng Tchr 1970-71; Valley HS Hlth & PE Tchr 1971-; *ai:* Dept Chprsn 7-12 Grd Hlth & PE; Stu Assistance Prgm; Golf Coach; NKAEA, PSEA 1970-; NEA 1966-; AFCA 20 Yrs; Bsbl Coaching Strategies Article Published in Coaching Clinic Magazine 1971; *office:* Valley H S Stevenson Blvd New Kensington PA 15068

GROSS, LINDA ANN, Reading & English Teacher; *b:* Valley Stream, NY; *ed:* St Univ of NY at Oswego (BA) Eng, Sec Ed 1966, (MA) Eng 1969; Univ of WI at Madison (MS) Curr, Instruction 1979; ESL Cert Prgm; *cr:* Sachem Cntrl Schls Eng, Rdng Tchr 1966-; Samoset Jr HS Eng Dept Chprsn 1971-74; Sachem North HS Rdng, Eng Tchr 1975-; *ai:* Cmptr Tech Comm 6 Yrs; Mentor Team Stu Mem; Sachem Cntrl Tchr Assn 1966-, Bldg Rep; NYSUT, AFT 1966-; IRA; Brookhaven Meml Hosp 1980-, Vol.

GROSS, LINDA HOLMES, English Teacher; *b:* Washington, DC; *c:* Derek J., Michael D.; *ed:* Univ of MD at College Park (BA) Eng 1979; *cr:* Atholton HS Eng & Film Arts Tchr 1979-; *ai:* Speech Club Adv; African Amer Awareness Club Spon, Adv; NHS, Awds Comms; NEA 1979-; NCTE 1993-; Outstanding Tchr Awd 1990; Who's Who in Amer Ed 1996-; *office:* Atholton HS 6520 Freetown Rd Columbia MD 21044

GROSS, LOU ANNE DEWITT, 5th Grade Teacher; *b:* Oakland, MD; *m:* Michael Edward; *c:* Joshua Michael, Ashley Lynne, Emily Anne; *ed:* Kent St Univ (BA) Elem Ed 1989; *cr:* Heritage Chrstn Schl 5th Grd Tchr 1989-; *ai:* Chrldr Coord, Jr HS Adv; Safety Patrol Dir; Sci Curr Comm; Living Water Flwshp 1994-, Praise, Worship, Prophetic Dance Teams, Yth Ldr; Kids Are Authors 1991 AWd; Comm Television Consortium Video Contest Mayor's Awd; *office:* Heritage Christian Schl 2107 6th St SW Canton OH 44706*

GROSS, MONIKA E., Assistant Professor of English; *b:* Germany; *m:* Louis Maurice; *c:* Billie Renee, Sydney Tyler; *ed:* VA Commonwealth Univ (BA) Eng 1975, (MA) Eng Ed 1979; Working Toward Higher Ed Admin George Washington Univ; *cr:* J. Sargant Reynolds Comm Coll Instr 1976-78; Chesterfield Cty Pub Schls Eng Tchr 1978-83; Bowie St Univ Eng Prof 1983-; *ai:* Queen Ann Schl Vol Comm; Rel Ed Instr; NCTE 1987-; VCU Alumni Cncl, VCU Afrian Amer Cncl 1990-; MADE 1991-; *office:* Bowie St Univ 1400 Jericho Park Rd Bowie MD 20715

GROSS, PHYLLIS JEAN, Sixth Grade Teacher; *b:* Erie, PA; *ed:* Westminster Coll (BA) Elem Ed 1966; Edinboro Coll (MED) 1970; *cr:* Fox Chapel Fifth Grd Tchr 1966-68; Deer Lakes Fourth-Sixth Grd Math, Spelling, Stud Skills, Writing Tchr 1968-; *ai:* Math, Spelling Bee Spon; PSEA, NEA 1966-; DLEA 1968-; Westminster Coll Womens Club of Pittsburgh1967-, Soc Publicity; Church Daycamp Cnslr 1956-92; *office:* Deer Lakes Schl Dist PO Box 10 E Union Rd Russellton PA 15076

GROSS, RICHARD ALLEN, Computer Sci Tchr & Technician; *b:* Cambridge, OH; *m:* Rose Ann Shaw; *ed:* Otterbein Coll (BA) Math, Ed 1971; Ashland Univ (MED) Admin, Supervision 1981; 20 Hrs Ed, Cmptr; Akron Univ 12 Hrs Math; *cr:* Crestview Local Schls Math, Cmptr, Tech Tchr 1971-; *ai:* North Cntrl Accreditation Evaluation Team; Crestview Tech Comm Chm; Math Dept Chm; OH Schl Net Comm Chprsn; Acad Boosters Outstdng Tchr Awd; Cmptr Prgms Pub; Future Net Cmptr Labs Grant; Cmptr System Admin; Ashland Univ Adj Prof; Pub Internet Pages; *office:* Crestview Local Schls 1575 State Route 96 Ashland OH 44805*

GROSS, ROGER SULLIVAN, Social Studies Teacher; *b:* Tarrytown, NY; *m:* Virginia Barry; *c:* William, Matthew; *ed:* William Penn Coll (BA) Pol Sci, Ec 1971; Fairfield Univ (MA) His 1972, (CAS) Admin Supervision 1976; Fordham Univ Post Grad Credits Admin; Western CT Univ His Credits; *cr:* Brewster Schls Tchr 1973-; *ai:* Dist Liaisons Soc Stud; Ninth Grd Class Adv; Westchester Cncl of Soc Stud 1984-; UFW 1988-; Vietnam Veterans Bronze Star, Army Commendation Medal; Col NY Air Natl Guard, Retired, Air Force Commendation Medal, AF Meritorious Svc Medal; *office:* Brewster HS Foggintown Rd Brewster NY 10509

GROSSI, RAOUL P., US History Teacher; *b:* Rochester, NY; *m:* Andrea Dotterweich; *c:* Stacie, Dan, Jackie; *ed:* Univ of Dayton (BS) Scndry Ed 1969; SUNY at Brockport (MS) Scndry Ed 1975, (EAS) Ed Admin 1981; *cr:* Greece Cntrl Schl Dist Tchr 1970-; *ai:* Asst Ftbl Coach; NEA 1970-; NEA NY 1970-; GTA 1970-; *office:* Greece Athena HS 800 Lon[g Pond Rd] Rochester NY 14612*

GROSSMAN, SHANA R., ESOL Teacher; *b:* Perth Amboy, N[J]; Wilson; *ed:* Tufts Univ (BA) Intnl Relations & Span 1987; Geo[rge Washington] Univ (MED) Eng as Second Lang & Bilin Ed 1992; Doctoral Stud at Univ of Costa Rica; *cr:* SHARE Fnd Asst Dir Montgomery Blair HS Tchr 1991-; *ai:* Intnl Club Spon; Admi[n] Comm Mem; WATESOL, TESOL 1991-; Rotary Intnl Grad Sc[h] VII Fellow; *office:* Montgomery Blair HS 313 Wayne Ave Sil[ver Spring] MD 20910

GROSSMAN, SHEILA C., Assistant Professor of Nursing; *b:* S[...] MA; *m:* Robert; *c:* Lisa, Beth; *ed:* Univ of CT (BSN) Nursing [...] of MA (MSN) Nursing 1976; Univ of CT (PHD) Prof Higher [...] 1985; Advanced Cardiac Life Support Cert; *cr:* St Francis Medical Ctr Critical Care Nursing Instr 1976-77; Univ of CT [...] Prof 1978-84; Mt Sinai Hospital Nursing Ed Coord 1987-89, Hospital Critical Care Nursing Instr 1989-91; Fairfield Univ 1991-; *ai:* Sigma Theta Tau Mu Chi Chapter 1976-, Pres 1995 Nurses Assn 1976-; CT Valley Girl Scouts, Troop Ldr; Hlth Ed[...] Dept Traineeship; Research Grant; Tchr Appreciation Awds; Pu[b] Chapters in 6 Books; Heart, Lung Journal Expert Consultant & M[...] Reviewer for Image; Journal of Nursing Schlshp; Mem Bd of [...] for Nursing St of CT 1995-; *office:* Fairfield Univ Schl of N[ursing] Benson Rd Fairfield CT 06430

GROSSO, DAWN SEIBERT, Business & Law Professor; *b:* Bu[...] *m:* James Charles; *ed:* Alfred Univ (BS) Acctng 1987; Pace Law Jurist Doctor 1991; *cr:* Chase Manhattan Bank Trust Tax A[...] 1987-88; Law Office of Dawn Seibert Grosso Attorney 1992-; [...] Bus Inst Instr 1995-; *ai:* Monroe Cty Bar Assn 1992-; NY St [...] 1991-; MCBA 1991-, Young Lawyer Section, Real Estat[e] Bankruptcy Comm; Pace Law Schl Amer Jurisprudence Awd in [...] Advocacy 1991; *office:* Rochester Bus Inst 1850 Ridge Rd E Roch[ester] 14622

GROSZKOWSKI, JACQUELINE WAJTKUS, Kindergarten T[eacher]; Buffalo, NY; *m:* Leon T.; *c:* Sandra Rera, Darlene Ulatowski; *e[d:]* Coll at Buffalo Ed (BS) 1965, (MS) 1992; *cr:* Iroquois Cntrl Sch[l] Tchr 1965-68; Sub Tchr at Various Schls 1968-74; Cleveland Hill [...] Grd, 3rd Grd Tchr 1974-; *ai:* AFT 1974-; Cleveland Hill Tchrs As[sn] Bldg Rep; Cleveland Hill PTA 1974-, Pres 1977-79; 10 Gall[on] Donor for Red Cross; *office:* Cleveland Hill Elem Schl 105 Mapl[e] Cheektowaga NY 14225

GROTH, THOMAS A., Dir of Bands & Dept Chair; *b:* Warren[...] Brenda S.; *ed:* Youngstown St Univ (BMUSIC) Music [...] Vandercook Coll of Music (MMUSIC) Music Ed; Grad Stud OH[...] Kent St Univ, Bowling Green St Univ, Youngstown St Univ, Ash[land] Otterbein Coll; *cr:* Jefferson Area Schls Music Dir 1963-66; Edge[...] Dir of Bands 1966-69; Boardman HS Dir of Bands, Dept Chair [...] Dir Marching, Symphonic, Concert, Frosh Bands, Jazz, Music En[...] Spartan Spirit Pep Band; Boardman Alumni Band Dir; Ba[...] ParentsAssn, Friends of Boa rdman Band Fac Adv; OH Music [...] 1963-, Dist Pres 10 Yrs; BEA, NEA, IAJE, NBA, ASBDA, AFM, [...] Mu, Pres Elect, MENC 1963-; Boardman Civic Assn, Comm [...] 1980; Boardman PTA, Tchr of Yr Awd 1987; Tchr of Yr 19[...] Packard Concert Band Guest Conductor; Conductor & Music D[...] Bdmn Park Concert Band; *office:* Boardman HS 7777 Glenw[ood] Boardman OH 44512*

GROTHMAN, MICHAEL RICHARD, Band Dir, Instrumental M[...] Philadelphia, PA; *m:* Marta Ann Arnoldi; *ed:* Temple Univ (BA) [...] 1972, (MMEd) Music Ed 1986; PA Music Supervisory Cert [...] Cardinal Dougherty HS His Instr 1972-76, Asst Band Dir 1972-77 Penn Jr HS Band Dir 1978-81; Pennsbury HS Band Dir 1[...] Marching, Jazz Bands; Theatre Orch; NEA 1978-; Penna Music 1981-; Natl Band Assn, Natl Assn of Jazz Edctrs 1992-; American Marine Corps League; Pub Svc Awd Lions Club Intnl; Jazz, Conce[rt] Perform Penna St Music Edctrs Conventions; Marching Band Pe[...] Rose, Orange Bowl Parades, China, France, Japan; Ensembles Pe[...] World's Disneylands; *office:* Pennsbury HS 705 Hood Blvd Fairl[ess Hills] PA 19030

GROTHOUSE, MARK ANTHONY, 4th-5th Grd SLD Teacher; OH; *m:* Veronica L.; *c:* Sydney, Logan, Justinn; *ed:* Univ of Day[ton] Elem Ed, Sci 1985; Spec Ed, EMT-P Paramedic Trng; *cr:* Rushm[ore] Schl 4th Grd Tchr 1985-87, 5th Grd Tchr 1987-94, Inclusion Cl[...] Tchr 1994-; *ai:* Huber Hts Dist Advy, Bldg Inclusion Comm Facilitator; Huber Hts In Home Tutoring; HHEA, OEA, NEA 1[...] Peter Schl Ed Commission 1994-, Councilmen; *office:* Rushmo[re] Schl 6701 Berchman Dr Huber Heights OH 45424

GROTON, JACQUELYN MCCALL, Social Studies Teac[her]; Savannah, GA; *m:* Bennett Brooks; *c:* Andrew Brooks, Alison Reb[...] Salisbury St Coll (BS) Ed 1981; Salisbury St Univ (MS[...]) Concentration Cnslng 1987; *cr:* Riverview MS Sci Tchr 1982-8[...] Dorchester Mid Lang Arts 1983-88, Soc Stud 1991-; Vienna Ele[m] 5th Grd Tchr 1988-90; Hurlock Elem 5th Grd Tchr 1990-91; *ai:* 1982-; NEA 1982-; DE Dorchester Edctrs 1983-; *office:* North Do[rchester] MS 5745 Cloverdale Rd Hurlock MD 21643*

GROTTANO, AGATHA TINA, Social Studies Teacher; *b:* Brook[lyn] *m:* Mark James; *c:* Lisa Grottano Frizol, Mark B.; *ed:* Hofstra U[niv] Elem Ed 1963; Stonybrook Univ (MA) Lbrl Stud 1980; *cr:* Union F[ree] Dist 13 Elem Tchr 1963-64; Smithtown Cntrl Schl Dist Ele[m] 1974-79; St Anthony's HS Soc Stud Tchr 1979-; *ai:* Math & [...] Behavorial Objectives Dist Comms; Discipline Acad Revie[w] Nominating Comms; Mid St Evaluation Philosophy & Goal Co[mm] Tchrs Lead Tchr; 9th Grd Soc Stud Coord; NEA; Long Island Cnc[l] Stud; NCSS; St Pius X Awd for Svc in Rel Ed; Citation of M[...] Citizenship; *office:* St Anthony's HS 275 Wolf Hill Rd S Hunting[ton] 11746

GROTTO, DOUGLAS, 8th Grade Music Teacher; *b:* Staten Isla[nd] *ed:* Concordia Coll (BS) Music Ed 1989; 3 Credit Hrs; *cr:* Zion L[utheran] Tchr 1989-; *ai:* Band, Handbell Choir, Musical, Jr Choir, Sr Choir [...] Group Cnslr; Yrbk Adv; Bsktbl Coach; *office:* Zion Lutheran Sch[l] Ave Westwood NJ 07675

GROUP, KIMBERLY HOWLAND, English & Speech Teac[her]; Dayton, OH; *m:* Robert A.; *c:* Andrew, Maxwell; *ed:* Wright St Un[iv] Eng Ed 1978, (MS) Rdng 1988; *cr:* Randolph Eastern Schl Corp Speech Tchr 1978-79; Kettering Schls Eng & Speech Tchr [...] Symmes Valley Eng & Speech Tchr 1984-85; Beavercreek Schls En[g] & Speech Tchr 1985-; *ai:* NCTE, WOCTELA & OCTELA 1987-; to People Intnl 1993-, Delegation Ldr; *office:* Ankeney Jr H[S] Shakertown Rd Beavercreek OH 45430*

GROUT, NANCY FRITZ, English Teacher; *b:* Kittery, ME; *m:* J[...] *ed:* Keene St Coll (BA) Eng 1983; VT Coll of Norwich Univ (MA) Tchng Writing 1995; Antioch Coll Critical Skills; Writing Process Portfolio Assessment; *cr:* Portsmouth Jr HS Eng Tchr 1983-86; M[...] Vly Regnl HS Eng Tchr 1986-, Eng Dept Chprsn 1989-92; *ai:* Class [...] & Oratorical Adv; Gifted & Talented, Curr & Instr Accred[itation] Statement of Purpose Accreditation Comms; NEA 1983-; NCTE 198[...] Assn of Tchrs of Eng 1991; ASCD 1993-; USPC 1971-, A Grad[...]

aminations; Co-Ed of Rsrch Booklet; Author of Styles Booklet; :trs Awd; *office:* Mascoma Valley Reg Sr HS PO Box 168A W H 03741*

BERNADETTE JOANNE, Business Education Teacher; *b:* ı, PA; *m:* Wayne K. Jr.; *c:* Shawn M., Alexa T.; *ed:* Coll dia at Dallas PA (BS) Bus Ed 1968; PA St Univ (MA) Trng, Curr ; *cr:* Salisbury HS Bus Ed Tchr 1968-71; South Hills Bus Schl 4-75; Adelphia Bus Schl Tchr 1976-78; Great Vly HS Bus Tchr · FBLA Adv 1980-; Women with Purpose Adv 1994-; Prin Advy 'ork Stud Coord; Assignes Tchrs Mentor; AFT 1978-90; Sub PA ssn 1978-, Sec 1982-; NEA 1990-; ASCD 1990-; Great Vly Schl ıtegic Planning Comm; Assn Children & Adult with Learning ies; *office:* Great Valley HS 225 N Phoenixville Pike Malvern PA

CAROL MC DANIEL, Math Teacher & Dept Chprsn; *b:* n, PA; *m:* Thomas W.; *ed:* Univ of Pittsburgh at Johnstown (BS) ath 1973; Attnd IN Univ of PA; *cr:* St Patrick's Schl Tchr 1978-81; Ic Cort HS Dept Chair, Math Instr 1981-; *ai:* Mu Alpha Theta r; AP Coord; Pep Club Adv; NCTM 1993-; PCTM 1995-; LHMA ?; Tchr of Yr, Great Tchr Recognition Awd St Vincent Coll 1993; shop Mc Cort HS 25 Osborne St Johnstown PA 15905

DOUGLAS EDWARD, Mathematics Teacher; *b:* Hagerstown, Mary Lushbaugh; *c:* Douglas, Alex; *ed:* Towson St Coll (BS) Psych od Coll 30 Credit Hrs Master Equivalency; *cr:* Peace Corps at Math Tchr 1976-78; North Hagerstown HS Math Tchr 1978-; *ai:* ; NEA 1978-; MSTA 1978-; WCTA 1978-; NCTM 1984-.

GEORGE WADE, Mathematics Teacher; *b:* Frostburg, MD; *c:* Rhodes, Chet Rhodes, Georgiana, John Rhodes, Aaron; *ed:* g St Univ (BA) Math 1965; 30 Credit Hrs Beyond BA; *cr:* Prince Bd of Ed Tchr 1964-65; Snap-on Tool Dealer Owner 1965-86; :ty Bd of Ed Tchr 1986-; *ai:* Emergency Med Club Spon; GCTA, NEA 1986-; MCMT 1990-; Lions Club 1988-, Sec & VP; *office:* Garrett HS 1100 E Oak St Oakland MD 21550

, JOHN G., Assistant Principal; *b:* Johnstown, PA; *m:* M. Cathy ; *ed:* CA Univ of PA (BS) Industrial Arts Ed 1969; PA St Univ Educl Admin 1973; 30 Addl Grad Credits; *cr:* DuBois Area HS l Arts Instr 1969-74; Selinsgrove Area HS Asst Prin 1974-; *ai:* PA ıdry Schl Prins 1974-; PA Schl Bds Assn 1981-; NASSP 1994-; s H & L FD 1975-, Engr; D H & L Ambulance League 1975-, Pres, Awd; Shamokin Dam FD 1978-, Chief; Hummels Wharf FD 1991-, ef; Governors Hwy Safety Awd Comm of PA for Pub Svc 1985; Stadium Med Squad Cardiac Supvr; Indianapolis 500 Motor y Med Staff; Reviewer for Amer Red Cross CPR Instrs Course, cy Care 7th Edition & Natl EMT Course of Stud Project; *office:* ove Area H S 500 Broad St Selinsgrove PA 17870

, LYNN ALLEN, Eighth Grade Mathematics Tchr; *b:* Alliance, Diana Jean Price; *c:* Jeffrey, Jerrod, Justin, Jessica; *ed:* Mount oll (BA) Ec & Bus 1973; *cr:* West Branch 8th Grd Math Tchr : Var Golf Coach; Jr Var Bsktbl Coach; Alliance Area Chamber of ce Tchr of Month 1994; Jennings Scholar 1994; West Branch Awd 1989; *home:* 4980 Knox School Rd Homeworth OH 44634

, MISSI HEMM, Math Teacher; *b:* Bucyrus, OH; *m:* David; *c:* *ed:* Univ of Findlay (BA) Math 1994; *cr:* Wynford HS Math Tchr *ai:* Var Sftbl Coach, Jr HS VLybl Coach, Stu Cncl Adv; Sftbl Assn 1994-; *office:* Wynford HS 3288 Holmes Center Rd Bucyrus 20

, M. LOUISE SMITH, Biology Tchr & Sci Dept Chm; *b:* ırsburg, PA; *m:* William R.; *c:* Steven R.; *ed:* Shippensburg St Univ) Chem 1957; Univ of PA (MS) Bio Chem Ed 1961; 65 Addl Hrs niv; Western MD Coll Admin Cert; *cr:* Chambersburg Area Schl Tchr 1957-60, Advanced Bio Tchr, Sci Dept Chm 1962-; *ai:* Sci hm; Sci Curr Revision Comm; CEAE, PSEA, NEA 37 Yrs; ırsburg Town Cncl, Fleeted Mem 8 Yrs; Bd of Hlth 4 Yrs; Order of Star, Worthy Matron 1987-88; Women of the Moose; Elks Aux; s Democratic Club 10 Yrs, Schlsp Chrmn; Chamber of Commerce Yr 1995; 3 Noms NSF Schlsp 1992, 1994; *home:* 217 Sherwood Dr rsburg PA 17201

, NILA F., Fifth Grade Lang Arts Tchr; *b:* Shippensburg, PA; *ed:* sburg St Coll (BS) ELem Ed 1967, (MED) Elem Ed 1969; Rdng ppensburg Univ 1986; Jr Great Books Ldrshp Trng Course 1989; G. Rice Elem Schl 5th-6th Grd Lang Arts Tchr 1967-75; South on MS 6th-8th Grd Rdng Tchr 1976-82; Boiling Springs Jr, Sr HS Grd Rdng, TELLS Rdng, Dist HS Remedial Rdng Tchr 1983-95; ge Educl Ctr 5th Grd Lang Arts Tchr 1995-; *ai:* PA Cncl of Tchrs & Lang Arts 1995-; South Middleton Ed Assn 1967-, Sec, Dir; PA Assn, NEA 1967-; Shippensburg Univ Alumni Fnd Phonathon s; Prince Street United Brethren in Christ Church 1955-; *office:* Iron ducl Ctr 4 Forge Rd Boiling Springs PA 17007

, TIMOTHY SHAWN, World Cultures Teacher; *b:* Morocco, IN; ia Lynn; *c:* Sean Douglas Drake; *ed:* Slippery Rock Univ (BS) Ed & Soc Stud 1987, (MED) His 1988; *cr:* Lebanon Schl Dist ı Grd Tchr 1989-; *ai:* Ftbl Asst Coach; Var Wrestling Head Coach; SEA 1995-; Outstanding His Grad Stu; *office:* Lebanon Sr HS 1000 Lebanon PA 17042*

E, VIRGINIA MORRIS, Fifth Grade Teacher; *c:* Pamela Jane rg, Robert Charles, Wendy Carol Kedzierski; *ed:* Univ of MD (MA) Dev 1981; *cr:* Medina Cty Schls First Grd Tchr 1962-63; Manatee ıls Fifth Grd Tchr 1969-72; Garrett Cty Schls 2-3, 6, 4, 5 Grds Tchr *ai:* NEA 1969-; League of Women Voters 1989-, Sec, Pres; Habitat manity 1985-, Sec; *office:* Broad Ford Elem Schl 607 Harvey s Rd Oakland MD 21550

E, WILLIAM ALLEN, High School Tech Ed Teacher; *b:* rgh, PA; *m:* Melanie A. Medanowsky; *c:* William A. Jr., James B., Mc George, Randy Mc George; *ed:* California Univ of PA (BS) Arts 1963, (MS) Indstrl Arts 1968; Attnd Duquesne Univ, Univ of : Chartiers Vly HS Tchr 1963-; *ai:* Girls HS Tennis Coach; Audio Club; Mentor Comm; AFT 1970-, VP; *home:* 186 Old Ridge Rd olis PA 15108*

ES, EDGAR S., Adjunct Lecturer; *b:* Leechburg, PA; *m:* Merry Ann *c:* Edgar J., Heather J.; *ed:* IN Univ of PA (BS) Music Ed 1957; inster Coll (MS) Ed 1962; Prins Cert 1980; *cr:* Hermitage Schl Dist Music Tchr 1959-93; Penn St Shenango Campus Instr 1985-; Grove oll Lecturer 1993-; *ai:* Penn St Shenango Singers; Shenango Valley e; MENC, PMEA 1957-; Shenango Valley Arts Cncl 1991-; ille Symphony 1993-, Bd of Dirs; PA Tchr of Yr Finalist 1991; PA & Senate Awd for Svc to Ed; PA Governors Schl for Tchng Fac; Intnl Who in Music; *home:* 570 Carley Ave Sharon PA 16146

ES, PATRICIA HAHN, Art Teacher & Department Chair; *b:* a, NY; *m:* Richard; *ed:* Buffalo St Coll (BS) Art Ed 1974; 30 Hr Grad erm Cert; 9 Addl Grad Hrs in Related Courses; *cr:* Brockport Cntrl S Art Tchr & Dept Chr 1986-; Gen-Wyo Boces Shared Itinerant Art 986; SUNY at Brockport Adjunct-Instr Interdisc Arts for Children 995; *ai:* Art Club Adv; Co-Dir Class Acts Talent Show; Staff Dev r Cncl Mem; WNY Regnl Scholastic Tchrs Advy Cncl Mem; Soc Chair Brockport Tchrs Assn; NYSUT 1976-; NYSATA 1978-; Gen-Wyo Boces Art Tchrs 1982-86, Pres; WNY Scholastic Tchrs Advy Cncl 1993-; Advy Bd-Young Audiences Rochester 1992-; Roch Meml Art Gallery 1990-, Mem; Cert of Achvmt from Scholastic Inc for Excl in Tchng 1995; *office:* Brockport Centrals Schls 40 Allen St Brockport NY 14420

GROW, ANN GUTEKUNST, Art Teacher; *b:* Allentown, PA; *m:* Glenn C.; *c:* Timothy; *ed:* IN Univ of PA (BS) Art Ed 1972; Kutztown Univ of PA (MS) Art Ed 1981; *cr:* West Chester Schl Dist Art Tchr 1972-81; Daniel Boone Schl Dist Art Tchr 1990-; *ai:* Art Dept Head; Acad Cncl; NEA, NAEA 1972-; Owen J. Roberts Friends of Arts 1992-; *office:* Daniel Boone HS 501 Chestnut St Birdsboro PA 19508

GROZIER, GARY W., Social Studies Instructor; *b:* Berwick, PA; *m:* Sheri Miller; *ed:* Bloomsburg Univ (BS) Scndry Ed, Soc Stud 1991; 24 Addl Credit Hrs Schl Cnslng Univ of Scranton; *cr:* Abramas Schl Tchr, Head Bsktbl Coach 1991-92; Hazleton Cath Prep 7-8 Grd Soc Stud Tchr 1992-93; Berton Area Schl Dist 9-12 Grd Soc Stud Tchr, Head Boys Bsktbl Coach 1993-; *ai:* Jr Class Adv; Stu Asst Prgm Team; NEA 1991-; *office:* Benton Area Schl Dist Park St Benton PA 17814*

GRUBB, JILL ROBINSON, English Teacher; *b:* Olney, MD; *m:* Thomas Christman Jr.; *c:* Joshua Thomas, Elizabeth Ruth, Benjamin Robinson; *ed:* Swarthmore Coll (BA) Eng 1966; Univ of Wi (MA) Eng & Ed 1969; OH Univ Summer Media Inst, Math Courses for Addl Cert; Wright St Experience of Writing; 18 Credits Post Grad; *cr:* Barneveld HS Eng Tchr 1969-71; Highland HS Sub Tchr 1979-89; Mount Gilead HS Eng Tchr 1989-; *ai:* Yrbk & philosophy Club Adv; In-The-Know Team Coach; Stu Involvement Comm Chair; Venture Capital & Renaissance Fair Comms; NCTE 1969-71 & 1989-; NEA 1989-; PTO 1990-; OH Arts Cncl Grants; Schl Bd Grant; *office:* Mount Gilead HS 338 W Park Ave Mount Gilead OH 43338

GRUBBS, THOMAS GENE, Economics & Government Teacher; *b:* Danville, VA; *m:* Linda Rash; *c:* Melissa, Jason; *ed:* West Chester St (BS) Ed & Soc Stud 1964, (MED) Ed & Soc Stud 1972; Penn St Univ 45 Post Grad Credits; *cr:* Avon Grove HS Tchr 1964-65; Phoenixville Area HS Tchr & Soc Stud Dept Chair 1965-; *ai:* Stu Cncl & Schl Store Adv; Publisher Phantom Ftbl Pgm 1982-93; Class Adv 1989-90; PASD Comm Co-Chair 1994-95; Sec Space Comm 1995-; NEA 1964-; PSEA 1964-; Phx Area Ed Assn 1965-, Treas 1969; Kimberton Yth Ath League 1986-, Treas 1993-95, Exec Bd 1993-; Kimberton Fire Co Aux 1990-; People to People Stu Amb Pgm 1992-, Delegation Ldr; Outstndg Edctr Awd 1974; *office:* Phoenixville Area HS Gay St & City Line Ave Phoenixville PA 19460

GRUBE, JOYCE ANNE, Program Director & Instructor; *b:* Lancaster, OH; *ed:* The OH St Univ (BS) Allied Med 1986; 28 Credit Hrs; *cr:* Lee Rd Radiology X-Ray Technologist 1986-87; Mt Carmel East Hosp Sonographer 1988-90; Cntrl OH Tech Coll Pgm Dir of Diagnostic Med Sonography 1990-; *ai:* Fac Dev & Acad Bd Comms; Soc of Diagnostic Med Sonographers 1988-; Cntrl OH Ultrasound Soc 1988-, Pres; Successfully Completed the Amer Registry of Radiologic Technologist 1986 & Amer Registry of Diagnostic Med Sonographers 1988; *office:* Central OH Tech Coll University Drive Newark OH 43055

GRUBER, EDWARD J., Chemistry Teacher; *b:* Brooklyn, NY; *m:* Irene; *c:* Nicole; *ed:* NY Inst of Tech (BS) Natural Scis 1991; Working Toward MSEd in Chem Ed at Queens Coll; *cr:* Valley Stream North HS Chem Tchr 1991-; *ai:* Theater Lighting Crew Adv; Sci Hnr Soc Co-Adv; NSTA, STANYS, ACS Affiliate 1991-; Chem Demo Shows for Girls Scouts, HS, Elem Schl Stdnts; *office:* Valley Stream North HS 750 Herman Ave Franklin Square NY 11010

GRUBER, IRENE LOMBARDI, High School Chemistry Teacher; *b:* Brooklyn, NY; *m:* Edward; *c:* Nicole; *ed:* Iona Coll (BS) Chem 1990, (MS) Multicultural Ed 1992; *cr:* Ciba-Geigy Part-time Lab Technician 1988-90; Lehman HS Chem Tchr 1990-; *ai:* Al Chem E 1992-; Chem Club of NYC, Amer Chemical Soc 1994-; Iona Coll Cncl on Arts 1990-91, Stu, Alumna Mem; STANYS Westchester Section New Sci Tchr Awd 1995; Honorary Tchr of Yr 1995-; *office:* Herbert H Lehman HS 3000 E Tremont Ave Bronx NY 10461

GRUBER, LINDA SARA, Second Grade Teacher; *b:* New York City, NY; *m:* Martin N.; *c:* Scott, Ross; *ed:* Queens Coll (BA) Elem Ed 1962; Masters Equivalent; AACO Courses; Attnd George Washington Univ; *cr:* PS 102 6th Grd Tchr 1962-63; Crofton Woods Elem 2nd, 4th, & 6th Grd Tchr 1971-; *ai:* Worked on Schl Yrbk Comm; Coached Olympics of the Mind; NEA 1971-; TAAC 1971-; Anne Arundel Co Rdng Cncl 1986-; PTA Crofton Woods 1971, Fac Rep; *office:* Crofton Woods Elem Schl 1750 Urby Dr Crofton MD 21114

GRUBICH, SAMUEL, History Teacher; *b:* Export, PA; *m:* Carol Minkovich; *c:* Amy Halloran, Melissa Lara; *ed:* CA St Univ (BS) Soc Stud Ed 1964; OH St Univ 15 Grad Credits; Ball St Univ 13 Credits; IN Univ of PA 6 Credits; Carnegie Mellon Univ 12 Credits; *cr:* Bellefontaine HS Tchr, Bsktbl Coach 1964-69; Bexley HS Tchr, Coach 1969-73; Mt Pleasant HS Tchr, Coach, Soc Stud Dept Chair 1974-; *ai:* Bsktbl Coach St Vincent Coll; Stu Cncl Adv; Org of His Edctrs; NCSS; NEA; Natl Assn of Intercollegiate Aths; Mt Pleasant Polish Falcons 1979-, Schlsp Chm; Natl Hum Fnd Seminar Carnegie Mellon Univ; *home:* RR 7 Mount Pleasant PA 15666

GRUEN, JUDY ANN, Mathematics Teacher; *b:* Scranton, PA; *ed:* Marywood Coll (BS) Math, (MS) Math; Penn St Univ (BS) Cmptr Sci; *cr:* Technic Corp Cmptr Specialist; Scranton HS Math Tchr; Scranton Cntrl HS Math Tchr; *ai:* Sr Class Adv; AFT; PCTM; NECTM; NCTM; Kappa Mu Epsilon; Phi Delta Kappa; Penn St Mentor Prgm; *office:* Scranton HS Adams Ave & Gibson St Scranton PA 18510

GRUENBERG, ALEX T., English Teacher; *b:* New York, NY; *c:* Daelyn, Ginny; *ed:* Lycoming Coll (BA) Eng 1976; Bucknall Univ (MA) Eng 1991; Commonwealth Partnership Summer Inst Tchng Fellow 1986; *cr:* Selinsgrove Area HS Eng Tchr 1978-; PA Coll of Tech Adj Eng Instr 1984-; *ai:* Newspaper Adv 1981-94; PA Schl Press Assn 1987-, Contest Dir; Numerous Articles Pub; *office:* Selinsgrove Area HS N Broad St Selinsgrove PA 17870*

GRUGEL, BARBARA CHESLER, Asst Prof of Ed Department; *b:* Garfield Hts, OH; *m:* Kenneth E.; *c:* Eric, Amy; *ed:* OH St Univ (BA) Elem Ed 1974; Clarion Univ (MS) Sci Ed 1987; IN Univ of PA (EdD) Elem Ed 1993; *cr:* Triway Local Schls Classroom Tchr 1975-76; Huntingdon Local Schls Classroom Tchr 1976-81; St Michael Parish Schl Classroom Tchr 1988-89; Clarion Univ Asst Prof 1989-; *ai:* Adv to Stu Org; PA St Ed Assn; Numerous Grants; Articles Pub; *office:* Clarion Univ Of PA 201 Stevens Hall Clarion PA 16214*

GRUHN, CHRISTINE MAE, Assistant Professor of Biology; *b:* Chicago, IL; *m:* Dr. Robert S. Byrd; *c:* Noah Byrd, Seth Byrd; *ed:* Univ of CA at Davis (BS) Botany 1981; Univ of GA (MS) Plant Pathology 1983; VA Tech (PHD) Botany 1989; *cr:* Morris Brown Coll Asst Prof 1989-91; Nazareth Coll of Rochester Asst Prof 1992-; *ai:* Mycological Soc of Amer 1985-; *office:* Nazareth Coll Of Rochester 4245 East Ave Rochester NY 14618

GRUMMAN, ROBIN SYKES, 7th & 8th Grade Teacher; *b:* Lowell, MA; *m:* Eugene Victor; *c:* Jonathan Bennett Root, Justen Gregory Root, Nathan Parker Root; *ed:* Keene St Coll (BED) Elem Ed 1972; Boston Univ Character & Citizenship Ed Course; Math Assessment; *cr:* Bluff Schl 1st Grd Tchr 1972-74; North St Schl 5th Grd Tchr 1975-76; Daycare Provider 1976-86; Unity Elem Schl 6th-8th Grd Tchr 1986-; *ai:* Yrbk, 8th Grd Class, Peer Outreach Adv; Memorial Day Prgm, Comm Svc Projects Coord; NEA, NEA-NH 1986-; Unity Ed Assn 1986-, Pres; NH Advy Bd on Character Ed 1992-; Sugar River Vly Tech Ctr Day Care Trng Facility 1994-, Advy Comm; Jaycees Women, Outstdng Young Woman 1985; *office:* Unity Elem Schl HCR 66 Box 175 Newport NH 03773

GRUNDER, SCOTT KENRAL, History Teacher; *b:* Canton, OH; *ed:* OH Univ (BS) Ed 1983; 12 Hrs Ed at Univ of Cincinnati; 18 Hrs Bus, Admin, His at OH Univ; 3 Hrs Cmptr Lit, Information Processing at Dartmouth; *cr:* Princeton Jr HS Amer His Tchr 1985; Dater Jr HS Soc Stud Tchr 1985-89; Peter H. Clark Acad US His Tchr 1989-90; Walnut Hills HS His Tchr 1990-; *ai:* Class of 1997 Co-Adv; Local Shared-Decision Making Comm Del OH Fed of Tchrs Exec Cncl; AFT, OFT, CFT 1985-, Area Coord, Bldg Rep; SWOCSS 1990-; NCSS 1983-; OH Univ Summer Scholar; Lester Crowe Awd for Outstdng Stu Tchng; Edctr of Yr; Outstdng Tchr; Learning Links Grant from Cincinnati Fnd; *office:* Walnut Hills HS 3250 Victory Pkwy Cincinnati OH 45207*

GRUNDY, KAREN TRACY, 7th Grade Math Teacher; *b:* Lockport, NY; *m:* James; *c:* Jennifer Covell, Brian, Joel; *ed:* SUC at Brockport (BA) Math 1974; Buffalo St Coll (MS) Math; *cr:* North Park MS 7th Grd Math Tchr 1974-; *ai:* LEA, NYSUT, AFT 1974-; St Patricks Church, Former CCD Tchr, Eucharistic Minister; *office:* North Park MS 160 Passaic Ave Lockport NY 14094

GRUNENWALD, MICHELE WAPLES, Chemistry Teacher; *b:* Youngstown, OH; *m:* James Paul; *c:* Patricia, Elizabeth; *ed:* Youngstown St Univ (BA) Chem 1972, (MSEd) Rdng 1977; *ai:* NHS Adv; Diocese of Youngstown Confederation of Tchrs 1983-, VP; NSTA 1983-; SECO 1989-; Oaktree Cntry Club Ladies Golf Assn 1990-, Pres; Ursuline HS Home & Schl Assn 1994-, Comm Chair; NSTA Grant 1988; Tandy Comp Awd Honorable Mention; *office:* John F Kennedy HS 2550 Central Pkwy Warren OH 44484*

GRUNEWALD, JAMES PAUL, Biology Teacher; *b:* Youngstown, OH; *m:* M. Michele; *c:* Patricia Anne, Elizabeth Anne; *ed:* Youngstown St Univ (BS) Bio, Ed 1972, (BSEd) Soc Principalship 1975; Attnd Clarion St Univ; *cr:* Wilmington Area HS Tchr, Coach, AD 1972-; *ai:* Stu Cncl Adv; Ath Dir; Golf Coach; Audio-Visual Coord; NEA, PSEA 1972-; Wilmington Area EA 1972-, Pres 15 Yrs; *office:* Wilmington Area HS 350 Wood St New Wilmington PA 16142

GRUSECK, DAVID JOHN, History Teacher; *b:* Pittsburgh, PA; *m:* Kathleen Hilinski; *c:* Stacy Taparro, Laryn Weaver, Paul; *ed:* Univ of Pittsburgh (BA) Scndry Ed 1976, (MS) Scndry Ed 1976; *cr:* Pittsburgh Cath Diocese Tchr 1970-74; Pittsburgh Pub Schls Tchr, Coach 1974-; *ai:* Girls Soccer, Asst Girls Bsktbl, Boys Bsbl Coach; Ctr for Advanced Stud Mentor; Conflict Resolution Prgm Mediator; Hlth Tech Initiative; Applied Learning Interdisciplinary Initiative; AFT, Pittsburgh Fed Tchrs 1974-; *office:* David B. Oliver HS 2323 Brighton Rd Pittsburgh PA 15212

GRUSECK, GARY F., Civics Teacher; *b:* Pittsburgh, PA; *c:* Ben, Jacob, Rebecca; *ed:* Indiana Univ of PA (BA) Soc Sci, Ed 1971; Edinboro Univ, PA St Univ MS Equiv Ed 1976; *cr:* Warren Cty Schl Dist 12th Grd Tchr 1973-85; Greensburg-Salem Sch Dist 12th Grd Tchr 1986-87; Burrell Schl Dist 8th Grd Tchr 1987-; *ai:* Var Track Coaching; Educl Support Team; Promotion Retention, Discipline Comm; Time-Out Prgm Supvr; NEA, PSEA 1973-; BEA 1987-, Bldg Rep; Warren Cty Educ Assn 1973-85; Jr Achvmt 1987-; *office:* Burrell Schl Dist Puckety Church Rd Lower Burrell PA 15068

GRUSSENMEYER, MARK LEO, Mathematics Teacher; *b:* Camden, NJ; *m:* Shirley Pollard; *c:* Jon-Mark, Timothy; *ed:* Rutgers Univ (BA) Geology 1976; Glassboro St Coll 37 Credits; NJ Cert; *cr:* Diocese of Camden Parochial Schls 7th & 8th Grd Math & Sci Tchr 1976-82; Buena Regnl HS Math & Sci Tchr 1983-85; Vineland HS Math Tchr 1985-; *ai:* Math Curr Comm; NEA & NJEA 1983-; VEA 1985-; Luth Church 1983-; *office:* Vineland HS North 3010 E Chestnut Ave Vineland NJ 08360

GRUST, PATRICIA L., Nursing Instructor; *b:* Floral Park, NY; *m:* Alan A.; *c:* Jennifer Grust-Lamoreaux, Heidi; *ed:* Broome Comm Coll (AAS) Nrsng 1983; Working Towards BS, MS in Nrsng SUNY at Utica, Rome; Western Suffolk Schl of Nrsng Diploma 1969; Coronary Care Cert 1978-; *cr:* St John's Smithtown Hosp Staff Nurse 1970-71; Med Office Facility Clinic Nurse 1975-83; Delaware Vly Hosp Charge, Staff Nurse 1983-86; SUNY Delhi Clinical Instr, IST 1986-; *ai:* Delhi Chptr Natl Stu Nurses Assn Co-Adv; Ethics Comm; First Aid, Paramedic Curr Dev Comm Chprsn; Walton HS Summer Colorguard Asst Coach; United Univ Professions 1986-; Amer Nurses Assn, NY St Nurses Assn 1988-; Phi Theta Kappa 1982-; Amer Heart Assn 1983-, Instr, Trainer, Regnl Fac 1995-; Ada West Nytch Nrsng Awd 1983; Presenter Documentation in the 90's Wkshp 1996, Nrsng Process for Schl Nurse Tchrs Wkshp 1993; *office:* S U N Y Coll Of Tech At Delhi Rt 10 Delhi NY 13753*

GRUSZKA, DONALD LEONARD, Third Grade Teacher; *b:* Buffalo, NY; *m:* Joyce Uschold; *c:* Michelle A.; *ed:* St Univ Coll at Buffalo (BS) Elem Ed 1970, (MS) Elem Ed, Rdng 1974; *cr:* Parker Elem Schl Sixth Grd Tchr 1970-72, Fourth Grd Tchr 1972-77; Ledgeview Elem Schl Third Grd Tchr 1977-90, Primary Dept Chprsn 1986-90; Sheridan Hill Elem Schl Third Grd Tchr 1990-; *ai:* AFT, NEA, NYSUT, CTA 1970-; *office:* Sheridan Hill Elem 4560 Boncrest Dr E Williamsville NY 14221

GRUYTCH, GAIL HURLEY, English Teacher; *b:* Rahway, NJ; *m:* Stephen Richard; *c:* Jennifer Sue; *ed:* Fitchburg St Coll (BA) Eng 1983, (BS) Eng 1986; Bentley Coll Paralegal Cert; NH Hum Cncl Inst Shakespeare in Global Perspective; *cr:* Londonderry HS Eng Tchr 1986-87; Saint Bernards HS Eng Tchr 1987-89; Bishop Guertin HS Eng Tchr 1989-; *ai:* Frosh Class Moderator; Organized & Chaperoned 3 Stdnt Trips England; Honors Night Prgm Co-Chprsn; Yrbk Adv; NEATE, NCTE 1986-; *office:* Bishop Guertin HS Almont St & Lund Rd Nashua NH 03060*

GRZEGORZEWSKI, BARBARA HAGEN, English & Reading Teacher; *b:* Rochester, NY; *m:* Steven; *c:* David Shoup, Steven Shoup, Megan Shoup, Jan; *ed:* Allegheny Coll (BA) Eng, His 1973, (MAEd) Ed 1975; Univ of Edinboro (MS) Rdng Specialist 1978; *cr:* Cleveland Schl Dist Tchr 1973-74; Crawford Cntrl Schl Dist Tchr 1974-; Allegheny Coll Grad Writing Tchr 1979-92; *ai:* Jr Class Adv; Schl Improvement; Stu Assist Team; NEA, PSEA, NCTE 1974-; Literacy Bd 1983-, Sec; League of Women Voters 1973-87, VP; Duplicate Budge 1973-, Pres, VP; Tchr of Month 1983; *office:* Meadville Area Sr HS North St Ext Meadville PA 16335

GRZELAK, DIANE ZIMMERMAN, Family & Consumer Sci Tchr; *b:* Erie, PA; *m:* Edward; *c:* Pam Kuhar, Paula, Paige, Penny; *ed:* IN Univ of PA (BS) Home Ec Ed 1966; Attnd Edinboro Univ, Penn St Univ, IN Univ of PA; *cr:* Wattsburg HS Home Ec Tchr 1966-67; Harborcreek HS Home Ec Tchr 1967-70; Mc Dowell Inter HS Fashion, Clothing Tchr 1983-; *ai:* Var Chrldrs Coach; NEA, PSEA, MEA 1983-; Perkins Grants 1994-95; *office:* Millcreek Township Schl Dist 3320 Caughey Rd Erie PA 16506

GRZESIK, KAREN L., Physical Education Teacher; *b:* New Bedford, MA; *ed:* Southern CT St Coll (BS) Hlth, PE, Rec 1972; Univ of MA at Amherst (MS) PE, Tchr Preparation 1990; Fitchburg St Coll, Mt Wachuseh Comm Coll, MA Martine, Greenfield Comm Coll 42 Credit Hrs Hlth, PE, Sports Medicine, Adventure Ed 1976-86; *cr:* Ralph C. Mahar Reg Schl JV Sftbl Coach 1972-75, Var Track Coach 1976-80, Var Bsktbl Coach 1972-84, Var Field Hockey Coach 1972-, PE Tchr 1972-, 7-12 Grd Dept Coord 1975-, JV Sftbl Coach 1984-90; *ai:* Bsktbl Ofcl; Track, Field Starter Ofcl; Ski Club Co-adv; S.O.S. Co-adv; CTAPE West 1989-, Treas;

MAHPERD 1972-; AAHPERD 1972-; NFICA, NFIOA 1979-; Mahar Tchr Assn, MA Tchr Assn, NEA 1972-; Womens SPorts Fnd 1995-; USFHA 1979-; Yth Ldr of Yr 1995; *office:* Ralph C Mahar Regional HS S Main St Orange MA 01364*

GUADAGNO-AKARTUNA, ROSEMARY, Biling Spanish & Math Teacher; *b:* Brooklyn, NY; *m:* Faruk Akartuna; *ed:* York Coll at CUNY (BA) Span, Ed 1972; Pace Univ at NYC (MS) Ed Admin, Supervision 1980; Adelphi Univ (MA) Biling Spec Ed 1996; Addl Hrs Doctoral Stud in Span, Latin Amer Lit; *cr:* Hillcrest HS Span, Biling Math, Biling Spec Ed Resource Room Tchr 1974-; *ai:* Islamic Club Fac Adv; Biling Math Tutor; AATSP 1979-; NCTM, ATM-NYC 1993-; Sigma Delta Pi 1972-; Kappa Delta Pi 1994-, Anadolu Club 1989-; Reliance Awd Excl in Tchng, Ed 1993; Nom Awd; *office:* Hillcrest HS 160-05 Highland Ave Jamaica NY 11432*

GUARDINO, CAROL-JANE PILTZ, Eng & Creative Writing Tchr; *b:* Jersey City, NJ; *m:* Joseph L.; *ed:* Chestnut Hill Coll (BA) Eng Lit 1966; Wroxton Coll of Fairleigh Dickinson Univ (MA) Eng Lit 1975; *cr:* Glen Rock Jr Sr HS Eng, Pub Speaking & Drama Tchr 1966-67; Westwood Regnl Jr Sr HS Eng & Creative Writing Tchr 1973-; *ai:* Natl Jr Honor Soc; Educl Cncl for Gifted Stdnts; Peer Mediation & Conflict Resolution Adv; Mid Sts Steering Comm; Minimum Basic Skills Comm; WEA, NJEA, NCTE 1973-; Nom for Governors Tchr Awd 1988; Whos Who in Scndry Ed 1996; Wrote Creative I & II Writing Courses 1989 & 1994; Outstanding Scndry Tchrs of Amer 1974; Attnd Several Writing Wkshps & Wrkshps on Authentic Assessment; Pub Lit Magazine for Creative Writing Classes; Wrote 7th & 8th Grd Gifted Curr; *office:* Westwood Regional Jr Sr High 701 Ridgewood Rd Westwood NJ 07675*

GUARINO, DANITA CRONIN, Tchr of Multiple Handicapped; *b:* Morristown, NJ; *m:* Ronald J.; *c:* Kristen, Kerry; *ed:* Coll of Saint Elizabeth (BA) Elem Ed 1973; 6 Credits Each at Rutgers Univ, Jersey City St Coll & Seton Hall Univ; *cr:* Mendham Twp Elem Reg Tchr 1973-75; Sussex Wantage Schl Dist Reg Tchr 1976-77; Eatontown Schl Dist Reg Ed Tchr 1984-88; East Windsor Regnl Schl Dist Tchr of Spec Ed & Sci Content Specialist 1988-; *ai:* CPR Instr & Trainer; Liberty Sci Ctr Tchr Connection Steering Comm; Staff Dev & Curr Comm; Spec Ed Review Comm; NJBISEC Comm Mem; NJEA, EWEA 1986-; APAST, SEPA, AAAS 1994-, Presidential Awd; CESI, NJSSA, CESNJ, NJAET, ANJEE 1989-; Englishtown & Manalapan 1st Aid 1985-, Capt, Line Officer; NJ Critical Incident Stress Debriefing Team 1989-, Team Mem; Geraldine Dodge & Merck Fellowships; Presidential Awd for Excl in Math & Sci Tchng; Governors Recogniation Awd; Dist Tchr of Yr; Winner of 16 Grants in 3 Yrs; Pub Jointly 2 Tchrs Guides; *office:* Ethel Mcknight Elem Schl 58 Twin Rivers Dr S East Windsor NJ 08520*

GUARNEIRI, ANTHONY CHARLES, High School Guidance Counselor; *b:* Rockville Ctr, NY; *m:* Deborah Anne DelNero; *c:* Christopher, Vincent, Sarisha; *ed:* SUNY at Brockport (BS) Philosophy, Hlth Ed 1971; Syracuse Univ (MS) Guid, Cnslng 1980; Guid, Cnslng Cert of Advanced Stud 1992; *cr:* Strough Jr HS 8th Grd Hlth Ed Tchr 1973-87; Staley Jr HS 8th Grd Hlth Ed Tchr 1973-87; Rome City Schl Dist Substance Abuse Prevention Specialist 1987-93; Fort Stanwix Elem Schl Elem Guid Cnslr 1993-94; Rome Free Acad HS Guid Cnslr 1994-; *ai:* Rome Tchrs Assn, NYSUT 1973-, Rep 1992-93; Mohawk Vly Cnslrs Assn, NY St Cnslrs Assn 1988-; HS Music Boosters 1993-, Corresponding Sec; Knights of Columbus 1982-, Communion Comm Chair; St Patrick's Parish 1989-, Rel Ed Tchr; Parent's Supporting Educl Excl 1996-, Spokesperson, Facilitator; Copyrighted Pamphlets; *office:* Rome Free Acad 500 Turin St Rome NY 13440*

GUASP, SUSAN GUIHAN, Art Teacher; *b:* Brooklyn, NY; *m:* Ralph; *c:* Sarah Veronica; *ed:* Queens Coll (BA) Art 1987, (MS) Art Ed 1989; Summer Landscape Pgm 1980 & 1987; *cr:* Kings Park Schl Dist HS Art Tchr 1987-; *ai:* Art Club & Stage Design Adv; Dist Art Shows Coord; Prof Artist in Landscape & Portrait Drawing, Painting & Photography; Art Shows; Coord Stu Art Show Exhibit at Vanderbilt Museum; *office:* Kings Park HS 200 Route 25A Kings Park NY 11754

GUCCIA, BART GEORGE, Chemistry Teacher; *b:* Johnson City, NY; *m:* Francene Iacovelli; *c:* Sarah, Andrea, Lindsey; *ed:* Hobart Coll (BS) Chem 1971; SUNY System Permanent Tchng Cert 1975; Attnd SUNY at Binghamton, SUNY at Cortland, Boston Univ; *cr:* Union-Endicott HS Chem Tchr 1971-; *ai:* Head Var Ftbl, Var Lacrosse Coach; NY St Cntrl Area for Empire St Games Head Lacrosse Coach; NYS United Tchrs 1971-; Amer Ftbl, NYS Coaches Assn 1974-; Sons of Italy 1989-; Alhambra 1980-; NSF Grant for Grad Work; Section 4 Lacrosse Coach of Yr 1991, 1993, Ftbl Coach of Yr 1995; *office:* Union Endicott HS 1200 E Main St Endicott NY 13760

GUCCIARDO, JUDITH POVSE, Math Teacher; *b:* Cleveland, OH; *m:* Patrick J.; *c:* Patrick S., Anthony, Lisa; *ed:* Bowling Green Univ (BSEd) Math 1966; Univ of Toledo 27 Hrs; *cr:* Euclid HS Math, Geometry Tchr 1966-68; Jefferson Jr HS 8th Grd Math Tchr 1968-69; Whitmer HS Math, Algebra Tchr 1978-; *ai:* NHS Adv 1986-90; NEA, OCTM 1978-; TAWLS 1978-, Bldg Rep; *office:* Whitmer HS 5601 Clegg Dr Toledo OH 43613

GUCHEMAND, MARGARET KELSO, Assoc Prof Music & Dept Head; *b:* Knoxville, TN; *m:* Jerry Robert; *c:* John Edwin; *ed:* Univ of TN (BA) Eng 1961; Towson St Univ (MED) Music 1973; *cr:* Essex Comm Coll Acting Head of Music Dept 1983-84, Head of Music Dept 1984-; *ai:* Advise All Incoming Music Majors; Meet with Mems of Stu Advy Cncl Music Majors; Minority Stdnts Mentor; Natl Assn of Tchrs of Singing 1974-, MD & DC Chapter Pres 1989-91; MENC 1972-, St Stu Membership Chm 1973-80; Sigma Alpha Iota 1960-; Recitalist Performing in Baltimore Area Including Harford Opera Theatre, Handel Choir of Baltimore & Solo Recitals; *office:* Essex Comm Coll 7201 Rossville Blvd Baltimore MD 21237*

GUDEMAN, EARL G., Jr HS Math & Science Teacher; *b:* Rankin, IL; *m:* Eloise Wagler; *c:* Raquel Ekarius, Rosana Sphon, Michael, Jonathan; *ed:* Univ of IL (BS) Voc Ag 1964, (MS) Ed 1968; *cr:* Manlius HS Voc Ag, Bio Tchr 1964-66; Brocton HS Voc Ag Tchr 1966-67; Milford Jr HS Sci Tchr 1976-77; Onarga HS Voc Ag, Horticulture Tchr 1977-78; Alpha-Omega Chrstn Schl Jr, Sr HS Tchr 1978-82; Bethel Bapt Chrstn Acad Jr HS Math, Sci Tchr 1982-; *ai:* ACSI 1991-; *office:* Bethel Baptist Christian Acad 200 Hunt Rd Jamestown NY 14701

GUDENIUS, BARBARA HAMAKER, English Department Head; *b:* Baltimore, MD; *m:* Donald Martinn; *ed:* Towson St Univ (BSC) Eng 1968, (MED) Scndry Ed 1972; Attnd Johns Hopkins U, Loyola U, U of Baltimore, U of MD Coll Pk; *cr:* Hamilton MS Drama Tchr 1968-70; Willows HS 1969-71; Walkbrook HS Eng Tchr 1974-79; Southwestern HS Eng Tchr & Dept Head 1979-88; *ai:* NCTE; *office:* Western H S 4600 Falls Rd Baltimore MD 21209*

GUEIROS, JOAS C. B., Spanish Teacher; *b:* Rio De Janeiro, Brazil; *m:* Laura Jane Jones; *ed:* Faith Theological Sem (MDiv) Theology 1964; Post Grad Stud Penn St Univ, Bloomburg Univ; *cr:* Central Bucks HS-West Span Tchr 1962-1969; Central Bucks HS-East Span Tchr 1969-; *ai:* NEA, PSEA, CBEA 1962-; *office:* Central Bucks HS-East PO Box 405 Buckingham PA 18912*

GUELI, JOHN GEORGE, Administrator; *b:* Brooklyn, NY; *m:* Ruthlyn; *c:* Christine, Heather, Matthew; *ed:* C W Post Coll of Long Island Univ (BA) Pol Sci 1973; Dallas Theological Seminary (ThM) Pastoral Theology 1977; Denver Theological Seminars (DMin) Pastoral Theology 1993; *cr:* North Fork Bapt Church Pastor, Tchr 1974-82; New Dorp Chrstn Acad Admin 1982-; NY Schl of Bible Tchr 1987-; Seminary of the East Prof Homiletics 1993-; *ai:* Natl Assn of Evangelicals 1982-; ACSI 1985-, Admin; MACSA 1982-; Conservative Bapt Assn of Amer 1982-; Heart Resuscitation Unit Vol 1982-, 1st VP, Bd Mem; MI Theological Seminary 1992-, Bd Mem; Crisis Pregnancy Ctr of NY 1986-, Bd Mem; Article Pub in MI Theological Journal; *office:* New Dorp Christian Acad 259 Rose Ave Staten Island NY 10306

GUENDEL, CAMILIA A., Russian & French Teacher; *b:* Bay Shore, NY; *m:* Neal; *ed:* Georgetown (BS) Frgn Lang 1967; SUNY at Stony Brook (MA) Fr Lit 1975; Universite de Grenoble Fr Tchng Cert 1965; Herzen Inst St Petersburg Russian Stud Cert 1990; 75 Hrs Tchng Methods & Philosophies; *cr:* Sayville HS Frgn Lang Tchr 1967-; *ai:* NY St Natl Olympiad of Spoken Russian Co-Chm; Frgn Lang Night Co-Chm; ACTR 1985-; NEH Grant Russian Seminar Bryn Mawr Coll; Ford Fndtn Grant Stud Tchr Exch Pgm St Petersburg; *office:* Sayville HS Brook St Sayville NY 11782

GUENTHER, KATHY R., Home Economics Teacher; *b:* Elizabeth, NJ; *c:* Kirsten, Brian; *ed:* Glassboro St Coll (BA) Home Ec 1977; Masters Equivalency & 60 Credits; *ai:* Coord Teen Pregnacy & Parenting Pgm; Mem Hall of Fame Comm; NEA & Local Chapter 1984-; *office:* Kenwood HS 501 Stemmers Run Rd Baltimore MD 21221

GUENTHER, THERESA A., Librarian; *b:* Rochester, NY; *m:* John Henry; *c:* Elsa, Kristen, Katharine; *ed:* SUC at Geneseo (BA) Eng 1976, (MLS) Lib Sci 1977; Attnd Univ of Nottingham, Alfred Univ; *cr:* Hornell Pub Lib Childrens Librn 1977-85; Arkport Cntrl Schl Librn 1985-; *ai:* NHS; Acad Soc; Lib Cncl; ALA 1980-; NYLA 1977-; NEA 1985-; Hornell Cntry Club Bd 1995-, VP; *office:* Arkport Central Schl 35 East Ave Arkport NY 14807

GUENTHER, WAYNE NORMAN, Fifth Grade Teacher; *b:* Syracuse, NY; *m:* Deborah King Avery; *c:* Aaron James, Emily Katheleen; *ed:* St Univ of NY at Geneseo (BS) Ed 1970; St Univ of NY at Brockport (MS) Ed 1990, (MS) Ed Admin 1991; *cr:* Oakfield-Alabama Cntrl Schl Elem Tchr 1970-; *ai:* 5th Grd Chprsn; AFT, NEA 1970-; NYSTU 1970-, Local Pres; Batavia City Schl Bd of Ed 1981-90, Bd Pres; Batavia Youth Bureau 1994-,; *home:* 64 Tracy Ave Batavia NY 14020

GUERIN, ADELINE PALADINO, First Grade Teacher; *b:* New York City, NY; *w:* John Joseph (dec); *c:* Sean Michael (dec), Hung Tran, Lien Tran, Hiep Tran, Anh Tran, Hong Tran; *ed:* Fordhan Univ Schl of Ed (BSEd) Elem Ed 1957; *cr:* PS 42 Manhattan Schl 2nd-4th Grd, 6th Grd Rdng Tchr 1958-66; Stony Lane Schl 1st, 3rd, 4th-5th Grd Tchr 1968-; *ai:* Ed Assn of Paramus 28 Yrs, 2nd VP 3 Yrs, Chief negotiator 3 Yrs, Neg Team 6 Yrs; BCEA, NJEA 28 Yrs; UFT, AFT 1958-66, Assoc Represen; NJ Governor Tchr Recognition 1988; *office:* Stony Lane Schl 110 W Ridgewood Ave Paramus NJ 07652

GUERINI, JODY LYN (PLANK), Business Teacher; *b:* Mansfield, OH; *m:* David F.; *ed:* OH Univ (BBA) Small Bus Admin 1991; OH St Univ (MA) Bus Ed 1992; 2 Semester hrs Kent St Univ; 3 Semester Hrs Walsh Univ; 1 Semester Hr John Carroll Univ; *cr:* Pioneer Voc Schl Adult Office Tech Tchr 1993; Maple Heights HS Voc Bus Tchr 1993-; *ai:* Bus Prof of Amer Club Adv; Class 1997 Co-Adv; Cleveland Area Bus Tchrs 1993-, Distinguished Svc Awd; NEA, OEA, OH Bus Tchrs Assn, Maple Hts Tchrs Assn 1993-; Acknowledged Participant Automated Acctng Textbook; *office:* Maple Heights HS 5500 Clement Dr Maple Heights OH 44137*

GUERINO, VINCENT JAMES, 6th Grade Teacher; *b:* North Adams, PA; *m:* Kathleen Lapine; *c:* Matthew, David, Gina; *ed:* North Adams St Coll (BA) His 1971; Post Grad 60 Credit Hrs; Attnd Univ of VT, Castleton St, St Michaels Coll; *cr:* St Stanislaus Kostka Schl 7th-8th Grd Tchr 1971-78; Catamount Elem 6th Grd Tchr 1978-; *ai:* Sci & Comp Comms; SWVEA Bldg Rep; Trng Tchrs New Sci Curr; NEA 1978-; VEA 1978-; Sacred Heart St Francis Choir 1984-; BSA, Merit Badge Cnslr; *office:* Catamount Elem Schl 230 School St Bennington VT 05201

GUERNERIE, FRANK WALTER, Science Teacher; *b:* Brooklyn, NY; *ed:* William Paterson Coll (BA) Sci Ed 1975; Seton Hall Univ Scndry Ed, Bio 1979; Addl Grad Stud Montclair St Univ, Rutgers Univ, Jersey City St Coll, Univ of ME in Bio; *cr:* Eisenhower HS Sci Tchr 1975-; *ai:* NEA, NJEA 1975-; NJ Sci Tchrs Assn 1985-; NJ Governors Tchr Recognition Awd 1994; Four Articles Pub Science Scope Magazine; *office:* Eisenhower MS 47 Eyland Ave Succasunna NJ 07876

GUERRA, CLARA TIERNAN, Physics & Chemistry Teacher; *b:* Nashua, NH; *m:* Richard James; *c:* James R., Joseph F., Ann M.; *ed:* Univ of NH (BA) Chem 1963; Antioch Coll (MED) Ed 1993; Univ of MA at Lowell 10 Credits Physics; *cr:* Mount St Mary Seminary Tchr 3 Yrs; Nashua Sr HS Tchr 18 Yrs; *ai:* Fac Advy Cncl 1988-92; OM Coach 1986-87; US First Coach 1991; AFT 1978-; New England Assn of Chem Tchrs 1985-; Lowell Alliance of Physics Tchrs 1992-; NH Sci Tchrs Assn 1980-; St John the Evangelist Parish, Cantor Choir, Cantor; Article Pub 1987; W. R. Grace Co Hands on in Sci Instruction Awd 1989-90; Presidential Math, Sci Awds St Nom 1992; NH 21st Century Awd Tchr of Yr 1995; *office:* Nashua Sr HS 36 Riverside Dr Nashua NH 03062

GUERRA, JAMES E., Adjunct Professor of Saxophone; *b:* Pittsburgh, PA; *m:* Patricia A.; *c:* Colin Jason; *ed:* Berklee Coll (BA) Music 1969; Advanced Stud at The New England Conservatory of Music 1969, US Navy Schl of Music 1970; *cr:* Duquesne Univ Prof of Saxophone 1988-; City of Pittsburgh Music Ctr Jazz Ensembles Artistic Dir for Jazz Ensembles 1991-; *ai:* Pittsburgh Musicians Union AFL-CIO #60-471 1973-, Exec Bd Mem; Founder & Ldr Pittsburgh Saxophone PAC; *office:* Duquesne Univ Schl of Music 600 Forbes Ave Pittsburgh PA 15282

GUERRA, REBEKAH D., History, Lit & Algebra Teacher; *b:* Glen Cove, NY; *m:* Frank; *c:* Frank, Erick, Kimberly, Lynn, Michael; *ed:* Lesley Coll Working on MS Spcl Ed; *cr:* St Annes Schl Dorm & Eng Tchr 1975-76; Middlesex Schl Eng Tchr & Asst Coach 1976-77; Covenant Schl 7th-8th Grd Algebra, Lit & His Tchr 1984-; *ai:* Orton Onslexia Soc 1994-; Learning Disabilities Network 1994-; Covenant Church 1975-; *office:* Covenant Schl 26 Udine St Arlington MA 02174

GUERRIERI, DAVID ALAN, Technology Education Teacher; *b:* Rillton, PA; *m:* Linda Miller; *c:* Angela, Jeffrey; *ed:* CA Univ of PA (BS) Indstrl Arts Ed 1983; Grad Credits Shippensburg Univ of PA; *cr:* Gettysburg Sr HS Tech Ed Tchr 1983-; *ai:* Sftbl, Jr HS Ftbl Coach; Asst & Head; Stu Cncl Adv; Staff Dev Comm; Schl Improvement Team; GAEA, PSEA, NEA 1983-, Pres, VP, Co-Chair Negotiations; ITEA, TEAP 1984-; *office:* Gettysburg Sr HS Lefever St Gettysburg PA 17325*

GUEST, LEONARD GEORGE, Industrial Arts Teacher; *b:* Buffalo, NY; *m:* Kathleen Laurence Covert; *c:* Darin, Megan, Jennifer, Troy; *ed:* St Univ Coll at Buffalo (BS) Industrial Arts Ed 1968, (MS) Industrial Arts Ed 1973; *cr:* Iroquois Cntrl MS Industrial Arts Tchr 1968-69; Aurora MS Industrial Arts Tchr 1969-; *ai:* Ftbl Supervision; Var Boys, Girls Bsktbl Timer; AFT, NYSUT 1968-; Lancaster Tchr Assn 1969-, Exec Bd; *office:* Aurora MS 148 Aurora St Lancaster NY 14086

GUESTO, MARIE FRANCES, World & Amer Literature Tchr; *b:* Wilkes-Barre, PA; *ed:* Marywood Coll (BA) Eng 1972; Lehigh Univ (MA) Eng 1974; 24 Post Grad Credit Hrs PA St Univ; *cr:* Lehigh Univ Tchng Asst 1972-74; Hanover Area Schl Dist Scndry Eng Tchr 1974-80; East Stroudsburg Area Schl Dist Scndry Eng Tchr 1980-88; Hanover Area Schl Dist Scndry Eng Tchr 1988-; *ai:* Mentor Tchr; NEA, PSEA 1974-; NCTE 1983-; Phi Delta Kappa 1981-; Northeast PA Writing Cncl 1989-; Kappa Gamma Pi 1972-, Local Pres; Church Vol; *office:* Hanover Area 1600 Sans Souci Pky Wilkes Barre PA 18702

GUEVARA, WILFORD, Guidance Counselor; *b:* Lima, Peru; *m* Alcalde; *c:* Barbara, Jessie; *ed:* San Marcos Univ (MA) Psy Montclair St Univ (MA) Counseling 1980; *cr:* Mental H Psychologist 1970-73; San Marcos Univ Prof 1970-73; Bergen Inc Voc Assessment Couns 1974-85; Passaic Co Comm Coll Ed 1985-89; Passaic Co Tech Inst Cnslr 1989-; *ai:* Children Helping & Hispanic Parents in Action Dir; Youth Adv for Blessed S Church; Paterson Intnl Consultant and Lecturer; ACA, NJCA 198 1990-; Prof Experience in USA 1993 San Marcos Univ; *office* County Tech & Voc HS 45 Reinhardt Rd Wayne NJ 07470

GUFF, R. BENT C., Senior Army Instructor; *b:* Providence, RI; Hickok; *c:* Allison, Robins, Brian, Stacey; *ed:* Univ of ME (BA) Univ of New Hampshire 3 Hrs His; Wilson Coll 36 Hrs Ed; Command & Ger Staff Coll; *cr:* Harvard Univ Asst Prof 1969-70 New Hampshire Asst Prof 1970-73; US Army Armor Schl Co Tchr 1978-84; LaSalle Military Acad Sr Army Instr 1994-; *ai:* Dept Head; Bd of Mahagers; Assn of US Army 1965-; *office:* Military Acad 500 Montauk Hwy Oakdale NY 11769

GUFFEY, JULIE ANNE MYERS, Language Arts & Reading Tiffin, OH; *m:* Michael J.; *c:* Ryan M.; *ed:* Kent St Univ (BA) Speech 1974, (MA) 20th Century Amer Writers & Adolescent Addl 21 Grad Hrs Beyond Masters Including Cert to Teac Correspndence Courses Various Univs; *cr:* Kent St Univ Tchng As 1974-78; Kent City Schls Tchr 1976-79; Streetsboro City Sc 1978-79; Akron St Univ Instr Instr 1978-83; Kent City Schls Tc *ai:* Drama Coach, Asst Drama Coach Roosevelt HS; Power of P 1995-; NCTE 1995-; Kent Jr Mothers 1993-, Bd; Nom for Ashland of Yr 1994; *office:* Davey MS 196 N Prospect St Kent OH 44240

GUGGER, GISELA MACHIN, Spanish & French Tea Cienfuegos, Cuga; *m:* Robert; *c:* Paul, Daniel; *ed:* Montclair St C Eng Lit 1975-; NJ St Tchr Cert Span 1994, Fr 1995; Addl 33 Cre Grammar, Lit, His Through Thomas Edison Coll & Montclair St C Advanced Grammar United Nations Geneva Switzerland Currently Taking Grad Fr Lit Montclair St Coll; Addl 12 Credi Intnl Comm of the Red Cross Del 1978-81; NJ St Courts Free-Lar Interpreter Span, Fr 1984-91; Montclair Kimberley Acad HS Span 1991-; *ai:* Sophs 1991, Jrs 1992, Srs 1993-94 Adv; Jr Var Chrld 1991-92; Model UN Club Adv, Span Club Adv; *office:* Kimberley Acad 201 Valley Rd Montclair NJ 07042

GUGINO, ELIZABETH TERMER, Science Teacher; *b:* Buffalo Anthony J. Jr.; *c:* Matthew, Megan; *ed:* Canisius Coll (BA) B SUNY at Buffalo (EDM) Scndry Sci 1979; *cr:* Amherst Cntrl Tchr 1978-79; Oakfield AL Cntrl Sci Tchr 1980-85; LeRoy Cntrl Tchr 1987-; *ai:* NHS & Frosh Class Adv; AFT 1978-; NYSTA 19 1987-; Tchr of the Yr 1994; Excl in Scndry Schl Tchng 1994; *o* Roy Jr Sr HS 2-6 Trigon Park Le Roy NY 14482

GUGLIELMONE, VIRGINIA BUDDENHAGEN, Math Tea Callicoon, NY; *m:* Tito W.; *c:* Lisa Gillis, Karen, Daniel; *ed:* St NY at Albany (BA) Soc Stud, Math 1959, (MA) Soc Stud 1960; Hrs In-Svc, Grad; *cr:* Shaker Jr-Sr HS Soc Stud Tchr 1960-61; Sayville, Long Beach Schls Soc Stud, Math Sub Tchr 1961-66, Sayville Pub Schls Soc Stud, Math Tchr 1975-; *ai:* Frosh Class Ad SAT Prep Class After Schl; NYSTA 1970-, Union Rep 6 Yrs; Say 1970-; *office:* Sayville HS 20 Brook St Sayville NY 11782

GUHR, BETH TIMMONS, German Teacher; *b:* Chambersburg, Russell; *c:* Tara Nicole, Taylor Timmons; *ed:* Millersville Univ 1981, (MA) German 1989; *cr:* Greencastle Antrim HS Ger Tc Edgewood HS Ger Tchr 1982-; *ai:* Ger Club; Ger NHS AATG; MS 1982-; AATG 1996; Good Shephard Luth Church 1995-; *office:* E HS 2415 Willoughby Beach Rd Edgewood MD 21040

GUIAO, RAYMOND PAUL, English Teacher; *b:* Cleveland, OH; Western Reserve Univ (BA) Eng 1986; Mundelein Coll (BA) Mus Univ of MI Schl of Music (MM) Vocal Performance 1992; Loyola Chicago Jesuit Philosophy Stud Pgm 1988-90; *cr:* St Ignatius HS Eng I & III & Theology 1992-95; *ai:* Yrbk Adv; Co-Moderator Ch Comm; Liturgical Music Coord; Jesuit Scndry Ed Assn Fac Rep Jesuits Detroit Province 1986-, Jesuit Scholastic Seminarian; *hom* Carroll Ave Cleveland OH 44113

GUIDO, GREGORY J., Physics & Math Teacher; *ed:* Cornell Un Physics 1986; SUNY at Stonybrook (MA) Math 1993; *cr:* Amer London Sci Tchr 1986-87; St Dominic HS Physics, Math Tchr 19 Sci Olympiad; Physics Olympics; Math League; AAPT; NSTA; NCTMA; Chrstn Educator of Yr 1992; *office:* Saint Dominic Anstice St Oyster Bay NY 11771

GUIDO, LISA MARIA, French & Italian Teacher; *b:* Detroit, William John Cibulka; *c:* Ruby Vittoria, Maeve Laura; *ed:* Wayne (BA) Fr, Ed 1933, (BSEd) Fr 1983, (MED) Childrens Lit 1985; Rochester (BS) Italian; Cert of Stud Universite Aix-En Prvence 1981, Centro Linguistico Florence Italy 1981; *cr:* Mont C Montessori Schl Fr Tchr 1982-84; Washington Elem Schl Fr Tchr 1 Ferndale HS Fr Tchr 1986-87; Ivondequoit HS Fr & Italian Tchr 19 Italian Club, Mediation Team Adv; Preseason ATh Trainor; C Citizens Visitation Day; Awds Comm; AATF 1983-; Ital Tchr Assn Assn For Lang Tea1987-; Amer Red Cross 1980-, 10 Yr Merit Aw Cncl of Exercise 1990-; *office:* Irondequoit HS 260 Cooper Rd Ro NY 14617

GUIDOTTI, JENNIFER LYNNE, Biology Teacher; *b:* Camden, Univ of DE (BA) Biological Sci Ed 1994; Organic Chem I Astronomy 3 Cr; Working on Phy Sci Cert; *cr:* Cinnaminson HS B 1994-; *ai:* Girls, Boys Tennis Coach; Frosh Class Adv; Schl Spirit Asst Chrldng Adv; NJEA, CEA, NEA 1994-; *home:* 1621 W Haddon Heights NJ 08035

GUIDRY, GAIL KEITH, Math, PE & Hlth Teacher; *b:* Wilmingt *m:* Mark Allen; *c:* Todd Allen, Tyler Adam, Cydni Joy; *ed:* Liber (BS) PE 1984; Univ of DE 9 Hrs Toward Masters; *cr:* New Cast Acad Var Field Hockey, Bsktbl, Sftbl Coach 1984, K4-12 Grd PE T Field Hockey, Bsktbl, Sftbl Coach 1984-87, Jr HS Math, Geog, P JV Field Hockey, Var Chrldng Coach 1988-, Asst Ath Dir 199 Organized Stu Missions Trip 1994-95; Math League Spon 1993- 1995-; USFHA 1992-; Outstdng Concern for Well Being of Stdn 1990; Classroom Mngmt Seminar Given & Material Pub; *office* Castle Baptist Acad 901 E Basin Rd New Castle DE 19720*

GUILER, JEFFERY KENT, Asst Prof of Management; *b:* New Yo *ed:* Franklin & Marshall Coll (BA) His 1971; Indiana Univ of PA Indstrl Relation 1988; *cr:* Robert Morris Coll Asst Prof of Mngmt *ai:* Soc Advancement Mngmt Fac Adv; Acad of Mngmt 1992-; Advancement of Mngmt 1989-; *office:* Robert Morris Coll Narro Road Coraopolis PA 15108

GUILFORD, DEBRA KAY, Second Grade Teacher; *b:* Hicksville, Bruce E.; *c:* Amy E.; *ed:* Ball St Univ (BS) Elem Ed K-8th 1979; I at Ft Wayne (MS) Elem Ed 1981; Addl 12 Hrs Elem Ed 1993; *cr:* Hic Elem Schl Second Grd Tchr 1979-89, 1991-; *ai:* Land Lab Sci HEA, OEA, NEA 1980-; Grace United Meth Church 1980-, Vacatio day Schl Tchr; Scipio Meth 1994-, Vacation Bible Schl Tchr, 'hoir, Act Chm; *home:* 1209 Hidden Brook Dr Hicksville OH

YLE, ROSEANNE KAMINSKY, Secondary Mathematics *b:* Binghamton, NY; *m:* Thomas L.; *ed:* SUNY at Oswego (BS) SUNY at Binghamton (MST) Ed & Math 1985; *cr:* Vestal Jr High ath Tchr 1968-81; Vestal HS Scndry Math Tchr 1981-; *ai:* NEA YEA 1968-; Enjoie Ladies Assn 1990-; *office:* Vestal Sr HS 205 n Dr Vestal NY 13850

N, RICHARD F.,JR., Band Director & Music Teacher; *b:* NJ; *ed:* Kean Coll of NJ (BS) Music Ed 1989; *cr:* Hawthorne s Drum & Bugle Corps Brass Instr 1993; Dutch Boy Drum & rps Brass Instr 1993; Central Regnl HS Band Dir, Music Tchr 'horus Dir 1991-95; Sunrisers Drum & Bugle Corps Brass Coord, Instr 1991-; Copiague HS Music Arranger-Marching 95-; *ai:* Jazz Band, Indoor Color Guard, Pit Orch Dir; MENC tnl Assn of Jazz Edctrs 1995-; Comm New Tchrs Testing by NJ d; Completed ITIP Trng; *office:* Central Regional H S Forest Hills yville NJ 08721

T, ABBE NATHANSON, French Teacher; *b:* New York, NY; *m:* ie M.; *c:* Philip, Stephanie; *ed:* Goucher Coll (BA) Fr 1973; Univ (MA) Fr Lit 1974; Univ De Provence Aix En Provence *r:* Medill Bair HS Fr & Span Tchr 1974-75; C. C. De Versailles 1975-77; Lycee Francais De Eng Tchr 1977-78; C. W. Baker HS 988-; *ai:* AATF 1988-, Pres; FLACNY & NYSFLT 1988-; PTA *office:* C W Baker HS 29 E Oneida St Baldwinsville NY 13027

T, MARIE MIRANDA, French, Italian & Latin Tchr; *b:* le, NY; *c:* Michel, Marc, Matthew, Martin; *ed:* Univ of NY at BA) Latin & Fr 1961; Dowling Coll (MS) Ed 1983; Attnd Univ of mherst, CUNY Grad Ctr & SUNY at Stony Brook; *cr:* Smithtown in & Fr Tchr 1961-65; Farmingdale HS Latin & Fr Tchr 1966-67; e Schls Latin & Fr Tchr 1984-85; Plainedge Schls Latin, Fr & chr 1985-; *ai:* MS Site-Based Planning Team; Tchr Ctr Policy Bd; 961-; NYSAFLT 1983-, Dir; LILT 1983-, Pres 1994-; Amer League 1985-; Rockefeller Fellowship 1990; NDEA Grants *office:* Plainedge Schls Wyngate Dr North Massapequa NY

ND, ROBERT W., Professor of Biology; *b:* Fall River, MA; *m:* rodie; *c:* Jefferson Brodie, Jameson Moran; *ed:* Univ of RI (BA) , (PHD) Physiological Ecology 1970; New England Schl of Law 1978; Scndry Tchr Cert RI Coll 1961-63; *cr:* E. S. Brown Jr HS i Tchr 1961-64; Univ of RI Asst Zoology Prof 1970-71; Boston St Prof 1971-82; Univ of MA at Boston Bio Prof 1982-; *ai:* Bio Dept ergraduate Advising; Univ Human Subjects Review Comm Coll s Comm on Admissions, Retention; Coord Anatomy, Physiology m Physiological Soc, Am Forestry Assn 1971-; Am Bar Assn IEA 1974-; Benevoletn, Protective Order Elks 1971-; Fraternal Eagles 1994-; NASA Pre-Doctoral Flwshp 1965-69; Distngd Svc cl Tchng 1982, 1987, Univ Svc 1983; Pub Articles; Contributed Book on Comparative Respiration in Vertebrates; *office:* Univ Of Boston Biology Dept 100 Morrissey Blvd Boston MA 02125

Y, PATRICIA ELLEN, English Teacher; *b:* Bronx, NY; *ed:* an Coll (BA) Eng, Elem Ed 1993; *cr:* Ursuline Schl Eng Tchr *i:* Schl Dance Coord; Co-Moderator Pegasus Magazine; Personal r; Alcohol Prgm Cnslr; *office:* Ursuline Schl 1354 North Ave New NY 10804

RICH, MARY ANN (WANNEMACHER), 4th Grade Teacher; *b:* OH; *m:* Dale A.; *c:* Carol Mertz, Kimberly, Christopher, Kelly; *ed:* is Coll (BS) Elem Ed 1980; Mt St Joseph Coll (MS) Elem Ed 1983; t Hrs Beyond Masters Degree at Wright St Univ & Drake Univ; *cr:* City Schls 1st Grd Tchr 1964-65, 4th Grd Tchr 1985-; *ai:* Young Festival; NEA 1986-; CEA 1986-; Phi Beta Psi Iota Gamma Chptr 'reas; Project Discovery for Sci & Math; *home:* 7745 State Route na OH 45822

A, MELODIE DICKERSON, Pvt Voice Instr & Choir Dir; *b:* Ft TX; *m:* Gregg Arthur; *c:* Gabriella, Griffin; *ed:* Sanford Univ (BM) 978; Southwestern Theological Seminary (MM) Voice 1982; *cr:* uston HS Voice Instr 1983-85; Tarrant Cty Jr Coll Voice Instr ; Performer 1985-89; Pvt Voice Tchr 1989-; Millis Church of Minister of Music 1993-; *ai:* Yth Choir to Produce Musicals; AEA Stage Source 1990-; Millis Arts Cncl 1995-, Schl Liason; Appeared erous Prof Theatrical Productions; Directed Over 40 Prof & r Theatrical Productions; Own Enchanted Evenings 7 Yrs; Who's mong Americas Young Women; *home:* 6 Holbrook Way Millis MA

ARD, FAYETTA LAFTON, Health & Physical Ed Instr; *b:* burg, SC; *w:* Jervie Jr. (dec); *c:* Jervie M. III; *ed:* Claflin Coll (BA) PE 1964; Trinity Coll (MS) Ed 1972, (MS) Admin 1979; UOC 30 alt Ed 1982; 12 Hrs Comptr Sci; 6 Hrs Aids Ed; Stress Mgmt 6 Hrs; Houn Cty Schls Tchr 1964-66; DC Pub Schls Tchr 1966-; *ai:* Track, Coach; Debutante 1st in Pub Schl 1980-87; Dean of Girls; WI Tchr DC AAPHER 1970-; Delta Sigma Theta 1964-; Outstanding Tchr 10 Yrs; *office:* Mc Kinley-Penn Sr HS 2nd T St NE Washington 02

, JUDITH L., World Geography Teacher; *b:* Philadelphia, PA; *ed:* Coll (BA) His 1966; Lehigh Univ (MA) Ed 1968; Attnd Penn St, St Joseph's Univs; *cr:* Richard E. Strayer MS Classroom Tchr *ai:* Dept Chm; Chrldng, Yrbk Adv; Geog Bee Coach; Quakertown Ed Assn 1966-, Pres 1968-70; PSEA, NEA 1966-; NCSS 1968-; PA r Soc Stud 1970-; Quakertown Bus & Prof Women's Club 1985-, es; Bucks Cty Republican Exec Comm 1976-; Bucks Cty Housing orp 1989-, VP; Quakertown Zoning Hearing Bd 1995-; *office:* E Strayer MS 349 S 9th St Quakertown PA 18951

AL, MAHINDERPAL SINGH, Adj Lecturer of English Lit; *b:* a, India; *ed:* Univ of Calcutta (BCom) Commerce 1986; York Coll (BS) Bus, Eng 1992; Columbia Univ Tchrs Coll (MA) Tchng Eng Working on MA Eng Lit Queens Coll CUNY; 18 Grad Credit Hrs Towards 3rd Masters Prgm; *cr:* Boricua Coll Adj Lecturer Eng 4; Layvardia Comm Coll Adj Lecturer Eng 1993-94; York Coll Lecturer Eng 1993-; *ai:* Poems Pub; *office:* City Univ Of NY York -20 Guy Brewer Blvd Jamaica NY 11451*

, JAMES ROBERT, Language Arts Teacher; *b:* Wilkes-barre, PA; esa A.; *c:* James, Alison, John, David; *ed:* Kings Coll (BA) Eng Hrs Beyond Masters in Eng from Penn St 1990; Attnd Naval War Norfolk & Army War Coll at Carlisle; *cr:* Newtown Jr HS Eng Tchr Hanover Area Jr-Sr HS Eng Tchr 1979-; *ai:* Jr & Sr Class & Ski Club Project 2000 WBAUTS; PSEA, NEA, HAEA 1972-; US Naval 1970-, Retired 20 Yrs Svc; North East Pa Writing Cncl Fellowship; n & Persian Gulf Eras; *home:* 311 1st St Wilkes Barre PA 18702

, JOHN A., Director of Bands; *b:* Pittsburgh, PA; *ed:* Duquesne BS) Music Ed 1973, (MS) Music Ed 1976; Post Grad Stud Kent St *cr:* A. E. Oblock Jr HS Music Tchr 1973-76; Plum Sr HS Dir of 1976-; *ai:* Marching Band; Jazz Ensemble; Musical Pit Orch; Sr lay; Educl Comm; Tech Comm; NEA, PSEA 1973-; MENC, PMEA Dist Pres, State VP; ASBOA, Phi Beta Mu; St Gerard R. C. Church Parish Cncl Pres; Guest Conductor, Adjudicator in Tri-State; *office:* Plum Sr HS 900 Elicker Rd Pittsburgh PA 15239

GULDIN, MARYANN L., Family & Consumer Science Tchr; *b:* Lebanon, PA; *m:* Joel G.; *c:* Joanna, Rachel, Rebecca; *ed:* PA St Univ (BS) Home Ec Ed 1978; Mansfield St Univ (MS) Home Ec Ed 1986; *cr:* Northern Lebanon HS Jr HS Tchr 1978-81, Sr HS Tchr 1982-; *ai:* Dist MS Steering, Curr, Dist Steering Comms; Dept Chair; NLEA, PSEA, NEA, PAFCS, AAFCS, Leb Co HomeEc Assoc 1978-; Suedberg Church of God 1968-; Penn St Alumni Assoc, Blue Band 1978-; *office:* Northern Lebanon HS PO Box 100 School Rd Fredericksburg PA 17026

GULICH, SUSAN CAROL, Business Teacher; *b:* Cleveland, OH; *ed:* Bowling Green St Univ (BSED) Bus Ed 1969, (MED) Bus Ed 1973; *cr:* Solon HS Cooperative Bus Ed Coord 1969-72; Bowling Green St Univ Grad Asst 1972-73; Toledo Pub Schls Bus Tchr 1973-; *ai:* Club Adv of Bowsher Chapter of Bus Profs of Amer; Delta Pi Epsilon, OH Bus Tchrs of Amer, AFT 1973-; Toledo Art Museum 1990-; *office:* E. L. Bowsher HS 3548 S Detroit Ave Toledo OH 43614

GULICK, DEBRA EDELKRAUT, Mathematics Teacher; *b:* NJ; *m:* Mark; *c:* Laura, Mark, Erika, Peter; *ed:* LaFayette Coll (BA) Engrng 1985; Trenton St Alternate Rt Classes; *cr:* Procter & Gamble Mfg Co Mgr 1985-87; St Marys Regnl HS Math Tchr 1988-93; East Brunswick HS Math Tchr 1993-; *ai:* NJEA & NEA 1988-; NCTM & AMTNJ 1988-; *office:* East Brunswick HS 380 Cranbury Rd East Brunswick NJ 08816*

GULICK, PETER L., Social Studies Chairman; *b:* Chicago, IL; *m:* Ruth P.; *c:* Phebe, Robin, Peter Jr.; *ed:* Hobart Coll (AB) His 1963; Univ of ME (MA) His 1969; Plymouth St Coll (MED) Guid 1993; Dartmouth Coll CAS; *cr:* ME Cntrl Inst Dean of Stdnts 1963-70; New Hampton Schl His Dept Chm 1970-90; Franklin HS His Dept Chm 1990-93; Plymouth Regnl HS His Dept Chm 1993-; *ai:* JV Girls Field Hockey Coach; NH NEA 1990-; NCSS 1970-; Elks 1996; NDEA Flwshp at Dartmouth Coll; Sec New Hampton Planning Bd; Chief New Hampton Rescue; *office:* Plymouth Regional HS 1 Old Wardbridge Rd Plymouth NH 03264*

GULINO, ROSANNE M., Latin Teacher; *b:* Cincinnati, OH; *ed:* St Louis Univ (BA) Latin 1970; NY Univ (MA) Span 1974; Univ of MN (MA) Classical Stud 1977, (PHD) Classical Stud 1987; Attnd Amer Schl of Classical Stud, Amer Acad at Rome; Univ of MI Traveling Scholar Prgm Classical Stud 1978; *cr:* Mariemont HS Fac, Latin, Span Tchr 1970-74; Univ of MN Tchng Assoc, Instr 1975-87; Breck Schl Fac, Latin, His, Span Tchr 1984-88; Stanford Univ Lecturer 1985; Walnut Hills HS Fac, Latin Dept Tchr 1988-; *ai:* 7-8 Grd Latin Club Spon 1989-; 9-12 Grd Antiquitas Spon 1995-; Frgn Lang Curr Cncl Latin Dept Rep; AFT 1988-; Archaeological Inst of Amer 1974-; Women's Classical Caucus 1990-; Fac Travel Grants 1988-92; Parent Bd Stu Grant 1990; Univ of MN Doctoral Dissertation Flwshp 1980-81; Numerous Reviews, Articles Pub; *office:* Walnut Hills HS 3201 Victory Pkwy Cincinnati OH 45207

GULLETTE, E. ANNE, First Grade Teacher; *b:* Cambridge, MD; *ed:* George Washington Univ (BA) Art His, Theory 1967; Advanced Fr Stud Alliance Francaise Paris, Mediterranean Ctr for Fr Stud; *cr:* The Cntry Schl 2-3 Grd Tchr 1970-80; Golden Shore Chrstn Schl 1-2 Grd, Fr Tchr 1983-; *ai:* Instrl Arts Tchr; Dorchester Arts Ctr, Dir; Nature Conservancy; Friends of Dorchester Cty Lib; *office:* Golden Shore Christian Schl 201 Mill St Cambridge MD 21622

GULTNEH, YILMA, Associate Professor of Chem; *b:* Gohatsion Shewa, Ethiopia; *m:* Muna Tesfaye; *c:* Taitu Y., Ethiopia Tobia; *ed:* Haile Sellasie I Univ (BS) Chem 1969; Northern MI Univ (MA) Chem 1976; IA St Univ (PHD) Inorganic Chem 1981; *cr:* Ethiopian Imperial Hwy Auth Chemist 1972-74; Rsrch Found SUNY Rsrch Assoc 1982-85; Univ of Pittsburgh Asst Prof 1985-90; Howard Univ Lecturer 1990-92, Assoc Prof 1992-; *ai:* Amer Chemical Soc 1983-; Co-Authored, Pub Numerous Articles; *office:* Howard Univ 525 College St NW Washington DC 20059

GUM, SUSAN EDWARDS, Pub Relation Coord & Yrbk Tchr; *b:* Washington, DC; *m:* Steven Lawrence; *c:* Jordyn, Mallary; *ed:* CA St Univ at Fullerton (BA) Graphic Art, Illustration 1981; Addl Credit Hrs DE Tech; *cr:* Sussex Tech HS Yrbk Tchr, Pub Relations Coord 5 Yrs; Naticoke Meml Hosp Admin Asst to VP of Mrktg, Dev 3 Yrs; Heineken Group Graphic Designer 2 Yrs; Peninsula Press Layout Artist 4 Yrs; *ai:* Pub Relations Soc of Amer 1996-; Natl Schl Pub Relations Assn 1996-; Amer Cancer Soc 1988-, Pub Information; Mt Olivet UMC 1990-, Yth Adv; Articles Pub; *office:* Sussex Technical HS Rt 9 PO Box 351 Georgetown DE 19947

GUMIENNY, SHERRIE A., English Department Chairperson; *b:* Lanstowne, PA; *m:* Leo E.; *c:* Lee, Autumn; *ed:* West Chester St Coll (BS) Scndry Ed in Speech & Theatre & Eng 1972; Natl Inst of Chrstn Schl Admin; *cr:* Norristown HS Eng & Speech Tchr 1972-73; Marple-Newtown HS Theme Ed 1978-80; Sunlight Chrstn Acad Admin & Founder 1981-87; Ambassador Chrstn Acad Eng, Dept Chprsn 1987-88; Life Ctr Acad Eng & Dept Chprsn 1988-; *ai:* Yrbk Adv; MACSA 1988-; Numberous Articles Pub; *office:* Life Ctr Acad 2045 Burlington Columbus Burlington NJ 08016*

GUMINA, CARMEN F., Biology Teacher; *b:* Rochester, NY; *m:* Sheri Kittredge; *ed:* St Univ of NY at Binghamton (BS) Bio 1986; Univ of Rochester (MS) Microbiology & Immunology 1988; *cr:* Pittsford Mendon HS Bio Tchr 1989-90; Pittsford Sutherland HS Math Tchr 1989-90; Webster HS Bio Tchr 1990-; Monroe Comm Coll Adjunct Bio Prof 1992-; *ai:* Sr Class Adv; Natural Helpers & Charity Drive Coord; NYSUT, Webster Tchrs Assn 1991-; Webster Arboretum Bd 1995-, Dir; Rochester Birding Assn 1994-, Dir; Tchr Ctr Grant 1996; Dist PTSA Tchr of Yr 1994; *office:* Webster HS 875 Ridge Rd Webster NY 14580*

GUMLAW, ELAYNE (KRAVEROTIS), English Teacher; *b:* Springfield, MA; *m:* Roger D.; *c:* Stephanie, Nicholas; *ed:* Westfield St Coll (BSEd) Elem Ed 1973, (MED) 1982; Admin Grad Courses; Rsrch-Based Instruction, Effective Tchng in Cooperation Learning Strategies Inservice Courses; *cr:* Fausey Elem Schl Fourth Grd Tchr 1973-82; MA Migrant Prgm Fourth Grd Eng Tchr 1979-81; West Springfield Jr HS 8 Grd Eng, Rdng Tchr 1982-, Eng Dept Chprsn 1995-; *ai:* WSEA, HCTA, MTA, NEA 1973-; West Springfield Bus Partnership Grants; Convener Comm Arts Curr Writing; Safety Cncl of Western MA Comm Safety Svc Awd 1991; Blue Cross, Blue Shield Life Saver Medal 1992; Agawam Police Life Saving Awd 1991.*

GUMPPER, TERRENCE, Professor of Criminal Justice; *b:* Drexel Hill, PA; *c:* Terrence J., Sean M.; *ed:* La Salle Univ (BA) Pol Sc, Amer Gov 1971; West Chester Univ (BS) Criminal Just Mgt 1982; Police Exec dev Inst Penn St Univ; *cr:* Delaware Cty Comm Coll Co-Adj Criminal Justice Prof 1988-; *ai:* Founder, Adv Criminal Justice Clb; Stu Adv Admin Justice Prgm; Gould Awd Nom Excl Tchng 1991-93, 1995; *home:* 367 Bennett Rd Springfield PA 19064

GUNDERMAN, RICK ALLEN, HS Learning Support Teacher; *b:* Harrisburg, PA; *m:* Karen Antes; *c:* Drew A., Kara Alaine; *ed:* Millersville St Coll (BS) Spec Ed; *cr:* Susquenita HS Learning Support Tchr 1980-; *office:* Susquenita HS 1725 Schoolhouse Rd Duncannon PA 17020

GUNDERMAN, THERUN E., Chem Tchr & Sci Dept Chm; *b:* Catskill, NY; *m:* Lisa Ann Martin; *c:* Tracey Golini, Blayne A. Coryer; *ed:* SUNY at Oneonta (BS) Chem Ed 1964; AZ St Univ (MA) Chem Ed 1968; Penn St Nuclear Inst 1982 4 Hrs; SUNY at Brockport Dept of Energy Inst 1980 4 Hrs; SUNY at Potsdam NSF Inst 1966 6 hrs; *cr:* Coxackie-Athens HS Earth Sci, Chem Tchr 1964-87; Amer Comm Schls 1985-87; Coxsackie-Athens HS Dept Chair, Sci, Chem Tchr 1987-; *ai:* Curr Cncl; Sci Dept Chair; Honor Soc Adv; NEA, AFT, NYSUT 1970-; CATA 1964-, Negotiating Chrm, VP; Jaycees 1964-, VP 13 Yrs; Local Fire Co 1970-; Town Planning Bd 1980-; Comm Bd; Bd of Dir, Catskill Golf Clb; 3 Natl Sci Fnd Awds & 1 Energy Dept Grant Summer Insts; Taught Overseas 1985-87 Athens Greece; *office:* Coxsuckie Athens Central Schl Sunset Blvd Coxsackie NY 12051

GUNDY, JEANNE SMITH, School Counselor; *b:* New Kensington, PA; *m:* Herbert; *c:* Jill, Kyle; *ed:* IN Univ of PA (BSEd) Elem Ed 1971, (MSEd) Cnslr Ed 1975; 15 Credits Scndry Cnslr Ed; *cr:* Burrell Schl Dist Grd 3 Elem Tchr 1971-82, MS Cnslr 1984-85, Grd 1 Elem Tchr 1985-86, 1989-90, HS Cnslr 1990-; *ai:* Strongland Chamber of Commerce Ed Comm; PA Schl Cnslrs Assn, Westmoreland Cty Cnslrs Assn 1990-; PSEA; NEA; BEA; PTA Saltsburg Elem 1988-, VP 1994-, Sec 1992-94; Gift of Time Awd 1995.

GUNN, EVELYN JENKINS, English Teacher; *b:* Whitfield, AL; *m:* Lenton Jr.; *c:* Jean Hathman, Lenton III, Lisa Gail, Kimberly; *ed:* Stillman Coll (BA) Eng, Soc Stud 1962; John Carroll Univ (MAT) Prof Rdng 1972; Attnd Cleveland St, Rider Coll, Meso Amer Inst, IN Univ; *cr:* Eastside HS Eng Dept Chair 1962-63; Glenville HS Eng 1965-69; James Ford Rhodes Eng Dept Chair 1969-77; Pelham Memorial HS Eng Tchr 1980-; *ai:* Co Chair Eng Lang Arts New Compact for Lrng; Adv Comm NY St Tchr Cert; Exam Reader Natl Tchr Exam 1984-; Originator PNN; NYSUT 1980-; NCTE 1989-; NYSTE 1993-; Delta Sigma Theta 1974-; NBTC 1975-, VP; Presby Women 1963-, Vice Moderator; Comm of Women of Color, Lucy Laney Awd; Grant 1993-94; Lucy Craft Laney Awd 1994; NYS St Recognition New Compact for Learning; *office:* Pelham Memorial HS Colonial & Corlies Ave Pelham NY 10801*

GUNNIP, JAMES P., Phys Education Teacher & Coach; *b:* Syracuse, NY; *m:* Elizabeth; *ed:* Cortland St (BS) PE 1986, (MS) PE 1993; *cr:* Union Springs CS PE Tchr 1986-88, 1990-; Liverpool CS PE Tchr 1989-90; *ai:* Girls Soccer, Bsktbl, Boys Bsktbl Coach; AFT, NYSUT 1986-; Lacrosse Fnd 1990-; *office:* Union Springs Central HS 27 N Cayuga St Union Springs NY 13160

GUNTHER, PHILIP, Art & Architecture Teacher; *b:* Troy, NY; *m:* Mary Anne Balasco; *c:* Alison; *ed:* SUNY at Albany (BA) Studio Art 1973, (MS) Educl Comm 1978; 15 Credits CAD D Hudson Valley Comm Coll; Pratt Inst 1969-71; *cr:* Griffin Schl Tchr 1974; Albany HS Tchr 1974-; *ai:* Labor, Mngmt Comm 3 Yrs; Schl Dist Steering Comm on Shared Decision Making; Effective Schls Comm Chrprsn 1987-91; Prof Dev, Restructuring Comms; Albany Pub Schls Tchrs Assn 1974-, Exec at Large; AFT, NYS Art Tchrs Assn 1974-; PTA Lifetime Mem Awd 1994; NYS Olympus of Visual Arts 1st Place 1993, 1995, 2nd Place 1994; Art & Math Grant 1987; *office:* Albany HS 700 Washington Ave Albany NY 12203*

GUNTHER, VIRGINIA F., Social Studies Teacher; *b:* Brooklyn, NY; *m:* Thomas E.; *c:* Nicole, Emily, Anna; *ed:* Fordham Univ (BA) His 1972; New York Univ (MA) His 1975; Long Island Univ Eng as Second Lang Cert; *cr:* New York City Soc Stud Tchr 1972-80; Briarcliffe HS Soc Stud Tchr 1985-86; Mamaroneck Cont Ed General Ed Diploma & Eng as Second Lang Instr 1988-93; New Rochelle HS Soc Stud Tchr 1993-; *ai:* Womens Issues Club Fac Co-Adv; TESOL, NYSCSS; Jr League of Westchester on Sound 1984-, Pres, Vol of Yr; Woodrow Wilson Inst Participant 1994 & 1995; Tchng Guide for Ec; NY St Grant Recipient 3 Times; Wkshp Presenter; *office:* New Rochelle HS 265 Clove Rd New Rochelle NY 10801*

GURECKA, LOU, Associate Professor of Spec Ed; *b:* East Vandergrift, PA; *m:* Sandra Daily; *c:* Jeffrey L.; *ed:* Clarion St Coll (BS) Spec, Elem Ed 1969; Clarion Univ of PA (MS) Spec Ed 1971; Duquesne Univ (MS) Schl Admin 1978; Working Toward EDD in Spec Ed IN Univ of PA; *cr:* Westmoreland Intermediate Unit Spec Ed, LD, EMR Tchr 1969-75, Regnl Mgr, Elem Prin, Intern 1975-78; Clarion Univ of PA Asst Prof 1978-83, Dept Chair 1983-87, Assoc Prof of Spec Ed 1987-; *ai:* Supvr Campus Scholars; NEA, PSEA 1969-; CEC 1969-, Pres, MR Div, PA Fed Adv; Phi Delta Kappa 1980-; Assn Ret Citizens 1987-; Kiski Vly Opport Unlimited 1969-, Bd Mem, Pres; Ducks Unlimited 1988-; PA Campus Compact Grants; Article Pub; *office:* Clarion Univ Of PA 108 Special Education Ctr Clarion PA 16214*

GURGA, ROSEMARY, Spanish Teacher; *b:* New Haven, CT; *m:* Joseph J. III; *c:* Rosina-Maria Lucibello, Gianna Luisa; *ed:* Albertus Magus Coll (BA) Span 1975; So CSU (BS) His 1984; *cr:* Foran HS Span Tchr 1975-76; Hillhouse HS Span Tchr 1976-77; Wilbur Cross HS Span Tchr 1977-; *ai:* Jr Class Adv; Schl Climate, Diploma Comms; CT Org of Lang Tchrs 1976-; AFT 1975-; CORE 1995-; Chef Du Jour 1988 Waterbury Republican-Amer; Who's Who in Amer Ed; *office:* Wilbur Cross HS 181 Mitchell Dr New Haven CT 06511

GURKF, ELIZABETH, Third Grade Teacher; *b:* Paterson, NJ; *m:* Harry Donald; *ed:* Wm Paterson Coll (BS) Elem Ed 1958; Kean Coll (MA) Behavioral Scis 1971; 60 Addl Credits Fordham, Columbia, Fairleigh, Dickinson, Rutgers, Montclair Univ; *cr:* Glen Rock Schls Tchr 1 Yr; Overseas Dependent Schl France Tchr 2 Yrs; East Orange Schls Tchr 7 Yrs; North Caldwell Schls Tchr 25 Yrs; *ai:* NCEA, NJEA, NEA 1958-; NJ Mini Grant 1977; Ec Ed Joint Cncl Hnr Awd 1978; Columbia 1st Place Medalist Awd; Adv to SPACE Lit Magazine 1982-84; Fnd for Free Enterprise Awd for Excl in Tchng Ec; NJ Gifted Ed Exemplary & Demonstration Grant 1987; NJ Governors Tchr Recognition Awd 1990; *office:* Grandview Schl Hamilton Dr North Caldwell NJ 07006

GURKIN, JOELLEN ZYGO, First Grade Teacher; *b:* East Orange, NJ; *m:* Larry R.; *c:* Jami Lee; *ed:* Kean Coll (BA) Ed 1969; Fairleigh Dickinson Univ (MA) Ed 1987; *cr:* Woodbridge Schl #2 & 16 Fifth Grd Tchr 1969-70; Woodbridge Schl #15 First Grd Tchr 1970-75; Woodbridge Schl #18 First Grd Tchr 1975-; *ai:* Family Writing Tchr; Stu of Month Comm; I Am Lovable And Capable Self-esteem Vol; NEA, NJEA, Middlesex Cty Educl Assn 1969-; Amer Assn of Univ Women 1976-, Pres, Sec, Educl Fnd, VP Mbrshp; PTO 1965-, Tchr Rep; Governor's Tchr Recognition Awd for 27 Yrs; *office:* Indiana Avenue Schl #18 Indiana Ave Iselin NJ 08830*

GURNEY, HENRY J., Bus, Accounting Dept Chair; *b:* Belfast, ME; *m:* Polly; *c:* Gary, Robert; *ed:* Boston Univ (BS) HPER 1960; IN Univ (MS) Ath Trng 1964, (HSD) Hlth, Safety Ed 1966; *cr:* Bridgewater St Assoc Prof 1971-76; Mid St Coll Instr 1977-87; Casco Bay Coll Bus & Accounting Chair 1988-; *ai:* Phi Beta Lambda Adv; Delta Phi Epsilon 1988-; 7 Books Pub; *office:* Casco Bay Coll 477 Congress St Portland ME 04101

GURUBATHAM, GLADSTONE P., Professor of Social Sciences; *b:* IN; *c:* Elizabeth Norris, Lena; *ed:* Andrews Univ (BA) Ed, His 1961, (MA) Ed, His 1963; Univ of MI at Ann Arbor (MS) Information Sci 1964; Cath Univ of Amer (MA, PHD) Geography, Psych 1974; Certified Addictions Specialist; Amer Acad of Pain Mngmt Diplomate; Amer Bd of Examiners Crisis Intervention; Amer Acad of Behavioral Medicine, Clinical Psych Fellow; *cr:* Andrews Univ Instr 1962-63; Univ of MI Instr 1964-65; Columbia Union Coll Prof 1965-; *ai:* Summer Curr Comm; Amer Acads Pain Mngmt, Behavioral Medicine, DC Counseling Assn 1989-; Natl Geographic Soc 1984-; US Dept of Aging Bd, Chrpsn 1994-, Vice Chair 1992-93; Sligo Church, Elder; Cath Univ Fellowship; Univ of MI Grants; *office:* Columbia Union Coll 7600 Flower Ave Takoma Park MD 20912*

GUSCIORA, RICHARD W., Science Department Chairperson; *b:* Passaic, NJ; *m:* Ilse C.; *ed:* C W Post Coll of Long Island Univ (BA) Bio 1969; Attnd Rider Univ & Mercer Cty Comm Coll; *cr:* Notre Dame HS Bio

& Environmental Sci Tchr 1969-, Sci Dept Chprsn 1981-; *ai:* Dept Supvr; Ecology & Outdoor Club; Acad Review Bd; Curr Cncl; NCEA 1970-; ASCD 1981-; NJ Sci Tchr Assn 1975-; NJ Sci Supvrs 1981-; Delaware Valley Radio Assn 1991-; Wooden Canoe Heritage Assn 1993-; Assn of Interpretive Naturalists 1977-87; Consultant for EPA-Educl Pamphlet Booklets for Water & Water Treatment; *office:* Notre Dame HS 601 Lawrenceville Rd Lawrenceville NJ 08648*

GUSTAFSON, CYNTHIA, Science Teacher; *b:* Rochester, NY; *m:* Peter A.; *ed:* SUC at Buffalo (BS) Ed 1987; SUNY at Albany (MS) Bio; *cr:* Plattsburgh HS Long Term Sub Tchr 1990; Voorheesville HS Long Term Sub Tchr 1993-94; Rensselaer Mid HS Bio, Earth Sci Tchr 1995-; *ai:* Ski Club, Soph Class Adv; NYSUT; STANYS 1995-; Rsrch Allegheny River Drainage 1986; *office:* Rensselaer Mid HS 555 Broadway Rensselaer NY 12144

GUSTAFSON, DAVID BRUCE, English Dept Program Leader; *b:* Worcester, MA; *ed:* Univ of PA (BA) Eng-Cum Laude 1985, (MSEd) Scndry Ed Prgm 1985; Attnd Cambridge Univ; *cr:* Masconomet Regnl HS Eng Tchr 1986-87; West Boylston MS, HS Eng Dept Prgm Ldr 1987-; *ai:* Class Adv; Restructuring Comm; NCTE, NEA, MA Tchrs Assn 1987-; First Congregational Church 1978-, Chair Mem; *office:* W Boylston MS 125 Crescent St West Boylston MA 01583

GUSTAFSON, KRAIG L., US History Teacher; *b:* Manchester, NH; *ed:* UNH at Durham (BA) His 1985, (MED) Scndry Ed 1991; *cr:* Nashua Sr HS Soc Stud Dept Fac 1987-90; The Derryfield Schl His Fac 1991-; *ai:* JV Boys Bsktbl Coach; Schl Newspaper Adv; Pub Magazine 1992; *office:* Derryfield Schl 2108 River Rd Manchester NH 03104

GUSTAFSON, NANCY ANN, Secondary English Teacher; *b:* Monessen, PA; *ed:* CA Univ (BA) Scndry Ed 1971; Univ of Pittsburgh (MS) Curr & Supervision 1979; *cr:* Pemberton HS Scndry Eng Tchr 1971-76; Fox Chapel Area HS Scndry Eng Tchr 1977-; Comm Coll of Allegheny Cty Writing Prof 1990-; Fox Chapel Adult Ed Prgm Eng Instr 1991-94; *ai:* Newspaper & Poetry Magazine Spons; WPCTE 1988-, Eng Stud Awd; NEA & PSEA 1977-; Great Ideas Grant Recognition; Bd of Schl Dirs Cert of Merit; *office:* Fox Chapel Area HS 611 Field Club Rd Pittsburgh PA 15238

GUSTAFSON, SANDRA LYNNE, Spanish Teacher; *b:* Philadelphia, PA; *ed:* Temple Univ (BS) Span, Scndry Ed 1969; 27 Addl Credit Hrs; *cr:* Lincoln HS Span Tchr 1969-78, 1985-88; Germantown HS Span Tchr 1978-80; Germantown-Lankenau Motivation HS Span Tchr 1980-85, 1988-; *ai:* NHS Spon; Peer Cnslrs; Peer Tutors; Frosh Orientation Prgm Coord; Big Sis, Big Bro Pgm Spon; AFT 1969-, Del to St & Natl Conventions 1973-74; MLA, Kappa Delta Epsilon 1969-; PASE 1992-; Sigma Delta Pi 1971-; Who's Who of Amer Women 1993-; *office:* Germantown-Lankenau Mtvtn HS 201 Spring Ln Philadelphia PA 19128

GUSTAVSEN, LAURA ANN, Symphonic Band Director; *b:* Brooklyn, NY; *m:* Gary George Sr.; *c:* Gary Jr., Grant Geoffrey; *ed:* C. W. Post Coll of LIU (BFA) Music Ed 1977; SUNY at Stony Brook (MMA) Music Performance 1989; *cr:* Brentwood Schl Dist Band Dir; Ward Melville HS Band Dir, Woodwind Instr 1989-; *ai:* Tri-M Hnr Soc Chptr Spon; Marching Band Asst Dir; SCMEA 1990-; NYSSMA, MENC 1993-; Long Island Flute Club, Pres; Natl Flute Assn 1986-; Artists Intnl Chamber Music Competition Winner 1989; NFA Newly Pub Music for Prof Flutists 1986, Master Class 1989, Prof Flute Choir 1989-90 Comp Winner; *office:* Ward Melville HS 380 Old Town Rd East Setauket NY 11733

GUSTAVSON, ELISABETH BUSTARD, Fourth Grade Teacher; *b:* Teaneck, NJ; *m:* Paul Frederick Jr.; *c:* Susan Esteri, Lisa Ann, Jonathan Paul; *ed:* George Peabody Tchrs Coll (BS) Elem Ed 1966; Columbia Tchrs Coll (MS) Elem Admin 1970; *cr:* Eugene Field Elem Schl Fourth Grd Tchr 1966-70; Kit'n Kaboodle Craft Store Owner 1977-81; Timberlane Schl Bd Chprsn 1975-88; Danville Elem Schl Fifth-Fourth Grd Tchr 1989-; *ai:* Math Comm; Cmptr Liason; Epping Comm Church, Chm-Diaconate, Bell Choir Dir, Yth Group Adv; *office:* Danville Elem Schl 283 Main St Danville NH 03819*

GUSTAVSON, ERIC PAUL, History Dept Chm & Ath Dir; *b:* Bethlehem, PA; *m:* Ann Marie LaPalme; *c:* Abraham, Benjamin; *ed:* OH Wesleyan Univ (BA) His 1981; Univ of CT His Instr Co-Op Prgm; *cr:* Marianapolis Prep Schl His Dept Chair 1982-; *ai:* Ath Dir-Bd of Dirs; Boys Soccer Coach; NHS Fac Chm; Ski Club Adv; NEA, Natl & CT Assn of Ath Dirs, Natl & CT Soccer Coaches Assn 1990-; Benevolent & Protective Order of Elks 1992-; Marianapolis Bd of Dirs 1987-; Univ of CT Instr Co-Op Pgrm; *office:* Marianapolis Prep Sch Rt 200 PO Box 368 Thompson CT 06277

GUSTIN, SANDRA L., English Teacher; *b:* Albany, NY; *c:* Eric, Carla Lewis, Chad; *ed:* Coll of St Rose (BA) Eng 1961, (MA) Eng Lit 1971; 20 Hrs Post Grad at SUNYA; 15 Hrs Post Grad Spec Ed at Coll of St Rose; 20 Hrs at Greater Capital Region Tchr Ctr; 6 Hrs Assertive Discipline at Long Island Univ; *cr:* South Colonie Schls Tchr 1961-; *ai:* SCTA 1961-, Grievance Chprsn; AFT, NYSUT 1961-; NYALD 1975-, Bd Mem, Camp Chm; Families of ROI 1991-; *home:* 12 Harold Ave Latham NY 12110

GUT, FLORENCE T. SERAFIN, Business Ed Coord & Teacher; *b:* Garfield, NJ; *m:* Robert E.; *c:* Karen E. Gut Giblin; *ed:* William Paterson Coll (BS) Bus Ed 1955; Montclair St Univ (MA) Bus Ed 1967; 31 Post Grad Credits; Prins, Supvrs Cert; Tchr, Coord Cooperative Voc Tech Ed Prgms Cert; *cr:* Garfield HS Bus Ed Tchr 1958-79, Bus Ed Dept Chprsn 1966-79; Montclair St Univ Adj Prof 1979-81; NJ Dept of Ed Schl Prgm Coord 1979-81; Garfield HS Coop Bus Ed Prgm Coord 1981-; *ai:* Steering, Aux Svcs Comm; Middles Sts Eval Team Prin Speaker; NHS Induction Ceremony 1995; Judge DECA NJ Northern Regnl Contest 1996; Chprsn NJCBECA, Bergen Cty Sector 1994-; CBE Club Adv; NEA, NJEA, GEA 1958-79, VP; NJBEA 1958-; NJCBECA 1967-, Pres, Cor Sec; AFT, GFT 1981-; Hnr Fraternities NHS, Pi Omega Pi, Kappa Delta Pi, Delta Pi Epsilon; Scholars Recognition Awd William Paterson Coll 1994; NJ Governor's Tchr Recgntn Awd 1995-; *office:* Garfield HS 500 Palisade Ave Garfield NJ 07026

GUTH, HOWARD, Earth Science Teacher; *b:* Baltimore, MD; *m:* Linda Lea Smith; *c:* Ryan, Lindsay; *ed:* Salisbury St Coll (BA) Geog 1977; Western MD Coll (MED) Ed Admin 1981; Attnd Towson St Univ, Univ of MD; *cr:* North Hagerstown HS Sci Tchr 1977-84; Easton HS Sci Tchr 1984-; *ai:* Head Track, Field, Asst Cross Cntry Coach; Var Club Adv; Sci Curr Comm; Many Schl-Based Comms; NEA, NSTA 1977-; TCEA 1984-; MD Earth Sc Tchr Ambassador Prgm; Local Coach of Yr 1991-95; *office:* Easton H S 723 Mecklenburg Ave Easton MD 21601

GUTHRIE, ELAINE, Mathematics Teacher; *b:* Jamaica, NY; *c:* Debra, Michael, Marla Michel; *ed:* Hofstra Univ (MA) Ed 1986; Queens Coll Ed 1983; 30 Addl Credits Above Masters; *cr:* Cardozo HS Paparofessional 1977-82, Tchr 1982-83; Grover Cleveland HS Tchr 1983-; *ai:* UFT 1977-; NCTM 1983-; Youth Bd of Comm Planning Bd II 1990-; *office:* Grover Cleveland HS 2127 Himrod St Flushing NY 11385

GUTHRIE, HELEN ROSS, Fourth Grade Teacher; *b:* Mc Keesport, PA; *m:* William F.; *c:* Robert, Barbara Kovacs, Kathleen Marino; *ed:* Lake Erie Coll at Painesville (BS) Elem Ed 1971; 22 Grad Level Credit Hrs; *cr:* Willoughby Eastlake City Schls Elem Tchr 1963-; *ai:* Third, Fourth Grd Dept Chair; In-Schl Stu Popcorn Bus Spon; Curr Revision Comm; Supt Advy Cncl; NEA 1972-; OEA, NEOEA, WETA 1963-; Friendship Force Intnl 1985-, Hosting Dir; Chrstn Ministries 1996, Sewing Project, Appalachia; PTA Tchr of Yr 1990; Great Expectations Awd 1990; *home:* 8521 Forestview Ave Mentor OH 44060

GUTHRIE, REBECCA CARTER, English, Speech & Lit Teacher; *b:* Chillicothe, OH; *m:* Steven Blake; *ed:* OH St Univ (BS) Eng Ed 1993; Working on Ed Master Degree Curr, Instruction; *cr:* Adena HS Eng Tchr 1993-; *ai:* COEDY 1993-; Chrldr Adv 1994-95; Fac Advy Comm 1995-; NCTE 1992-; *office:* Adena HS 167 W High St Frankfort OH 45628*

GUTIERREZ, CAROL L., Seventh Grade Teacher; *b:* Detroit, MI; *m:* Raymond F.; *c:* Kirsten, Kristopher, Courtney; *ed:* MI St Univ (BA) Scndry Ed, Eng 1972; Univ of Toledo (BA) Elem Ed 1984; *cr:* Waite HS ESL Tchr 1972-75; Devilbis HS Tchr of Vision Impaired 1979-80; Little Flower Schl 6th Grd Tchr 1982-83; All Saints Cath Schl 3rd, 5th, 7th-8th Grd Tchr 1983-; *ai:* Yrbk, Chrldng Adv; Girl Scout Ldr; Sci, Math Ldrshp Cncls; Hispanic Liaison; OCEA 1983-; *office:* All Saints Catholic Schl 134 Maple St Rossford OH 43460

GUTKNECHT, MARYANNE, First Grade Teacher; *b:* Philadelphia, PA; *m:* James E.; *c:* Allison; *ed:* PA St Univ (BS) Elem, Spec Ed 1973; Trenton St Coll (MA) Spec Ed 1975; 60 Post Grad Credits Penn St, Temple, Bloomsburg & Marywood; *cr:* Bensalem Schl Dist 2nd Grd Tchr 1973-74, Spec Ed Tchr 1974-77, GATE Tchr 1977-89; Medford Lakes Schl Dist GATE Tchr, Coord 1989-90; Tchr 1990-95; Bensalem Schl Dist Grd 1 Tchr 1995-; *ai:* NEA 1973-; PAGE 1977-95; *office:* Cornwells Elem Schl 2400 Bristol Pike Bensalem PA 19020

GUTMANN, NANCY, English Teacher; *b:* Columbia, SC; *m:* Sam; *c:* Eric, David; *ed:* Duke Univ (BA) Eng 1964; Northeastern Univ (MA) Eng 1969; *cr:* Marblehead HS Eng Tchr 1965-68; Brookline HS Eng Tchr 1978-; *ai:* Chess Club & Team Adv; BEA, NEA 1978-; Natl Endowment for Hum Rdng Grant; Amer Cncl of Learned Socs Team Grant; *office:* Brookline HS 115 Greenough St Brookline MA 02146

GUTOWSKI, PHYLLIS JEAN, Associate Professor of Science; *b:* Bridgeport, CT; *c:* Michael; *ed:* Univ of VT (BS) Medical Tech 1964; Univ of Bridgeport (MS) Sci & Bio 1976; *cr:* Bridgeport Hosp Medical Technologist 1964-65; Coldwater Com Hlth Ctr Medical Technologist 1965-67; Tri St Univ Chem Instr 1967-69; Housatonic Comm Tech Coll Assoc Prof 1974-; *ai:* Emergency Medical Tech Trumbull EMS Vol; Charter Oak St Coll Consulting Examiner; ASCLS 1975-, Omicron Sigma; CSCLS 1975-, Pres & VP; CAMLE-CT 1975-, Chm & Vice Chair; Recognition as Exemplary Tchr Com-Coll Ldrshp Pgm at Univ of TX; Deans Awd & Merit Recognition Housatonic Comm Tech Coll; *office:* Housatonic Comm-Tech College 510 Barnum Ave Bridgeport CT 06608

GUTSHALL, MARY KATHRYN, High School Counselor; *b:* Lancaster, PA; *ed:* Shippensburg Univ (BSEd) Eng 1989, (MSEd) Scndry Counseling 1991; *cr:* Penn Manor HS Scndry Cnslr 1991-; *ai:* NEA, PSEA 1991-; ACA, ASCA 1990-; PSCA 1990-; *office:* Penn Manor HS PO Box 1001 Millersville PA 17551

GUTZWILLER, DEBORAH S., Marketing Education Coord; *b:* Greenfield, OH; *m:* Ronald A.; *ed:* Bowling Green St Univ (BS) Ed 1968; Xavier Univ (MBA) Mrktg 1994; *cr:* Sycamore HS Mrktg Ed Coord 1968-; *ai:* DECA 28 Yrs, Mentoring Prgm, Schls North Cntrl Planning Comm Adv; DECA Alumni Club, HS Bookstore Spon; NEA, OEA, SEA 1968-; Mrktg Educ Assn 1989-; AVA, OVA 1990-; Indian Hill Historical Soc, Sec, Treas, Regent; Ashland Oil Golden Apple 1998, 1995; OH Cncl Retail Merchants 25 Yr Recognition; *office:* Sycamore HS 7400 Cornell Rd Cincinnati OH 45242

GUY, AVA GREENE, English Teacher; *b:* Weimar, TX; *c:* Deirdre T., Danielle A.; *ed:* TX A&M Univ (BA) Eng 1973, (MA) Eng 1984; Post Grad Stud Jersey City St Coll; *cr:* Bryan HS Eng Tchr 1973-84; Monmouth Univ Adj Prof Eng 1987-89; Ocean Cty Coll Adj Prof Eng 1992-; Lakewood HS Eng Tchr 1984-; *ai:* Class Spon 1988-94; African Amer Soc, Interact, Stu Govt Assn, Peer Mediator Advs; PTO; Lakewood Comm Coalition; Upward Bound Project Cnslr; City Schls of Excl Core Team; Lakewood Ed Assn, NJ Ed Assn, NEA 1984-; Delta Sigma Theta 1988-, Sec; NAACP 1990-; United Meth Women 1988-; Monmouth Univ Career Day Pub Svc Awd; Alpha Phi Alpha Teen Pregnancy Forum Pub Svc Awd; *office:* Lakewood HS 855 Somerset Ave Lakewood NJ 08701

GUY, GERALDINE RUTH (WILHELM), High School Spanish Teacher; *b:* Youngstown, OH; *m:* David E.; *c:* Erich D., Karl A.; *ed:* Mt Union Coll (BA) Span, Fr 1969; Univ of Dayton (MS) Ed 1988; *cr:* East Palestine HS Span Tchr 1969-75; Columbina HS Span Tchr 1980-81; East Palestine HS Span, Fr Tchr 1981-, Span Tchr 1996-; *ai:* Stu Cncl Adv; Acad Challenge Team Adv; Mentor Tchr; NEA, OEA 1969-; EPEA; *office:* East Palestine HS 360 W Grant St East Palestine OH 44413*

GUY, RICHARD LEE, High School Guidance Counselor; *b:* Philadelphia, PA; *m:* Margy Lorraine Whitaker; *c:* Kenneth, Kimberly; *ed:* Eureka Coll (BS) Math 1971; West Chester Univ (MA) Guid Ed 1975; *cr:* Penn Wood West Jr HS Math Tchr 1971-83, Guid Cnslr, Math Tchr 1984-93; Penn Wood HS Guid Cnslr 1994-; *ai:* Girls Cross Cntry, Indoor, Outdoor Coach; NEA, PSEA, WPEA 1971-; Omega Psi Phi 1969-; NAACP 1985-, Role Model Awd; DE Cty Girls Track Assn Coach of Yr; *home:* 11 Elder Ave Yeadon PA 19050

GUY, ROBERT D., English Instructor; *b:* Wheeling, WV; *m:* Cheryl H.; *c:* Bobby; *ed:* West Liberty St Coll (AB) Eng, Soc Stud 1969; Kent St Univ (MED) Adult Learning 1990; *cr:* Ringgold Schl Dist 7-12th Grd Eng Tchr 1969-76; Buckeye North HS 9-12th Grd Eng Tchr 1976-89; Buckeye Local HS 11-12th Grd Eng Tchr 1990-; *ai:* Eng Dept Chari; Asst Sftbl Coach; BLCTA, OEA 1976-; NEA 1969-; Ruritan Club 1995-; Tchr of Yr 1988; Martha Holden Jennings Scholar 1986; *office:* Buckeye Local HS Rd 2 Box 475 Rayland OH 43943*

GUYTON, CONSTANCE GAINES, English Teacher; *b:* Washington, DC; *m:* Marion Edward; *c:* John, Joseph; *ed:* Howard Univ (BA) Eng 1969; Amer Univ (MA) Eng 1971; 760 Hrs Post Grad Stud Johns Hopkins Univ, Univ DC, Trinity Coll; *cr:* Francis Jr HS Eng Tchr 1 Yr; Coolidge Sr HS Eng Tchr 1 Yr; Mc Kinley Sr HS Eng Tchr 24 Yrs; *ai:* NHS Chprsn, Spon; Sr Awds Comm Chprsn; Testing Coord 1987-95; NCTE 1989-; Delta Sigma Theta 1968-, Keeper of Records; NACCP 1990-; Most Appreciated Tchr Awd; Penn HS 1989 Intern-Mentor; Prgm Participant 1988 Intern Lead Tchr 1995; Nom Agnes Meyer Outstdng Tchr Awd; *office:* Mc Kinley Penn Sr HS 2nd & T Street N E Washington DC 20002

GUZOFSKY, DAVID P., Earth & Environmental Sci Tchr; *b:* Wilkes-Barre, PA; *m:* Eleanor B.; *ed:* Bloomsburg Univ (BS) Earth & Sp Sci 1972; Penn St Univ (MED) Earth & Mineral Scis 1985; Sc Supvr Cert Scranton Univ 1977; 60 Addl Hrs; Environmental Specialist Cert PA Wilkes Univ; 9 Bloomsburg Univ; 9 Addl Hrs Pocono Environmental Ed Ctr; 4 Hrs Inservice; *cr:* Penn St Univ Geology, Meterology Instr 12 Yrs; Greater Nanticoke Area Schl Dist Earth & Env Sc Tchr 24 Yrs, Sci Chm 16 Yrs; *ai:* Jr Engrng T Soc; Environmental Olympics Coach; NAGT 1984-; LCSTA 1980-; PSTA 1994-; *office:* Greater Nanticoke Area HS 427 Kosciuszko St Nanticoke PA 18634

GUZOWSKI, JANE ISABELLE, Language Arts, Eng & Rdng Tchr; *b:* New York, NY; *m:* John; *ed:* Hunter Coll (BA) Elem Ed 1954; Grad Courses; *cr:* St Josephs Schl Kndgtn Tchr 1954-57; NYC Pub Schls K-6th Grd Tchr 1961-69; Dicoese of Brooklyn & Marys Nativity Schl Various Levels & 5th-8th Grd Tchr 1969-; *ai:* Pgm of Dev of Human Potential Facilitator; Mid Sts Steering Comm Chprsn; L A & Rdng in Schl Coord; NCEA 1975-; Poetry; *office:* Mary's Nativity Schl 14628 Jasmine Ave Flushing NY 11355

GUZZETTA, JAN, Third Grade Teacher; *b:* N Tonawanda Buffalo St Tchrs Coll (BS) Exceptional Ed 1970, (MS) Ed 197 Hrs Russia, Siberia Univ of CO, NASA, Cal Tech, Univ of AL; *c* Tchr 1 Yr; Huth Road Schl 4th Grd Tchr 10 Yrs, 2nd-3rd Grd T 3rd Grd Tchr 2 Yrs; *ai:* AFT, GITA 1970-; NSTA 1985-; First U Church, Bd, Handbell Ringer, Choir, Parish Cncl, Treas, Sunday Rotary Club 1995-; Challenger Ctr 1987-, Founding Mem; Ame Prgm 1987-; Life Membership NYS PTA: Aerospace Ambassa Resource Prgm NASM Smithsonian 1988-92; Speaker's Bureau Ctr; Inspiration Awd 1993-95; Nom Apperson-Hearst O Educator; Attnd Tchr in Space Confs; *office:* Huth Road Schl Rd Grand Island NY 14072*

GWALTHNEY, FRANK JAMES, Math Dept Chair; *b:* Philade *m:* Helen MacKay; *c:* Jonathan, Amy; *ed:* Rutgers Coll (BA) G Credit Hrs; 3 Credit Hrs Univ of ME; 15 Credit Hrs Gloucester 12 Credit Hrs Rowan; *cr:* Clayton HS Math & Eng Tchr Wilmington Friends Schl Math Tchr & Comp Coord 1980-89; HS Math Tchr & Dept Chair 1989-; *ai:* Frosh Ftbl Coach; Stee & Standards, Bldg Tech, & Cty Tech Comms; CARN; Clayto 1969-80, Pres & Negotiations Chair; NEA 1969-80, 1989-; AM Mbrshp Chair & Treas; NCTM 1990-; Woodbury Bd of Ed 19 Glassboro HS Joseph L Bowe Blvd Glassboro NJ 08028*

H

HAAG, ALANA Z. (FORRY), French Teacher; *b:* York, PA; Eugene; *c:* Mariana, Michael; *ed:* Millersville Univ (BS) Fr 1970 1975; 32 Credits Post-Grad Stud; *cr:* Northeastern HS Fr Tchr Stu Tours to Europe Spon; Stu Assistance Team; NEA, PSE Northeastern Ed Assn 1970-, Legislative Chprsn; York Twinn 1975-; Southern York Co Democratic Club 1974-, Former Sec; Manor PTO 1991-; Gift of Time Awd; *office:* Northeastern HS 30 Manchester PA 17345

HAAG, ELIZABETH A., Orch String Instrumental Tchr; *b:* Br PA; *m:* John A.; *c:* Matthew, Jacqueline; *ed:* Wittenberg Univ (Ed '965; Attend Clinics; Mem Prof Orch, Ensembles; *cr:* Cin Twp Instrumental, Vocal, Gen Music Tchr 1965-70; Pvt Str 1970-77; Moorsetown Twp Schl Orch String Instrumental 4-8th 1977-; *ai:* Stu Mentor; Original Opera Orch Dir, Arranger; GA Ensemble Dir; South Jersey Orch Audition Judge; MENC 196 String Tchrs Assoc; Springfield Symphony, Haddonfield Symp Pops Orch, South Jersey Chamber Orch 1st Violon Section; Stdnt South Jersey Orch, NJ Yth Pops Orch, Burlington Cty, St Festivals; GATE Ensembles Perform for Comm Svc; *office:* Mo MS N Stanwick Rd Moorestown NJ 08057

HAAG, HARVEY EUGENE, Physics Instructor; *b:* DuBois, PA; Postlewait; *c:* Elizabeth Ann, Christian J. W.; *ed:* PA St Univ (BS Ed & Physics 1971, (MED) Curr & Instruction 1979; Post Masters Instructional Systems; *cr:* Moshonnon Valley HS Physics, Math Tchr 1971-75; Haags Photography Service Owner & Photograph Clearfield Area HS Physics, Engr, Math & Cmptr Tchr 1975-; PA Part-Time Cmptr Instr 1979-; *ai:* Photography Club Adv; Form Dept Head; Investigatory Grds Comm Chm; Clearfield Area HS Cncl Rep; Clearfield Ed Assn 1975-, Pres 1978; PA St Ed Assn 1 Coordinating Pres 1975; NEA 1971-; PA Sci Tchrs Assn & NST Clearfield Masonic Lodge #314 1985-, Master 1989; BSA 1959-, Cncl Adv & Chm 1989-, Silver Breaver Awd 1991; Lake Glendal Club 1985-, Instr 1990-; Altoona Consistary & Jaffa Shrine 1986- Presbyn Church 1979-, Elder 1987-90; USPS, Borough Cncl; PJA & St Judge 1978-80; PA Sci Olympiad Region & St 3rd Pl Team Judge 1988-89; Clearfield Area HS & Penn St Stdnts Mentor Tchr *office:* Clearfield Area HS P O Box 910 Clearfield PA 16830

HAAGEN, BENJAMIN F., Mathematics Teacher; *b:* Monmouth Maryann Woomer; *c:* Rachel; *ed:* Lock Haven Univ (BS) Scndry 1976; Mansfield Univ (MED) Spec Ed 1990; Attnd Penn St Univ; Haven HS Math Tchr 1976-90; Bald Eagle-Nittany HS Math Tch *ai:* Math Dept Head, Math Bldg Prgm Ldr, Stu Cncl Adv 19 Assistance Prgm Team 1991-; Phi Kappa Phi 1975-; ACCE, PSE 1976-; PCTM, NCTM 1979-; West Branch Rabbit Breeders, Wes Rabbit Breeders 1994-, VP; Walker Grange 1980-, Pres; Walker Club 1973-, Orgnl Ldr; Centre Co 4-H Dairy Club 1987-, Project Cncl Tchr of Math Speaker Annual Meetings 1994, 1996.*

HAAK, KENNETH J., Global Studies Teacher; *b:* Lockport, Patricia J. Jordan; *c:* Kenneth Jr., Stephen; *ed:* Western KY Univ Lib Sci 1975; Niagara Univ (MSEd) Sec Ed 1984; 30 Addl Hrs; *cr* Cntrl Schl US His, Global Stud Tchr 1976-; *ai:* AFT, NYSU NYSCSS 1980-; *home:* 89 Lincolnshire Dr Lockport NY 14094*

HAAS, AL JOHN, Business Teacher; *b:* Hamilton, OH; *m:* Ca Bolser; *c:* Michael, Kathleen; *ed:* Ball St Univ (BS) Bus 1966; Xa (MED) Bus 1993; *cr:* Finneytown Local Schl Dist Bus & Indust Tchr 1966-; *ai:* Dept Chm; OH Ed Assn 1966-; NEA 1966- Finneytown HS 8916 Fontainebleau Ter Cincinnati OH 45231

HAAS, JUDIE SULLIVAN, English Teacher; *b:* Springfield, IL; A.; *c:* Anne Elizabeth, James, Andrew, Jonathan, Robert; *ed:* M Univ (BA) Eng, Drama 1957; St Louis Univ, Bloomsburg Univ Laboure HS Eng Tchr, Speech, Drama 1957-62; Pawnee HS E 1959-60; North HS Eng Tchr, Speech, Drama 1962-65; Glendora Tchr 1965-66; Tunkhannock Area HS Eng Tchr 1979-; *ai:* Newspa 1986-; NEA 1980-; WY Vly Montessori Schl, Founding Mem 1970, 2 Yrs; *office:* Tunkhannock HS 120 W Tioga St Tunkhannock PA

HAAS, KATHERINE HSU, 4th Grade Teacher; *b:* Berlin, Germ Raymond Thomas; *c:* Susan, Carola, Pamela; *ed:* Univ of ND 1974; *cr:* Solen Schl in Sioux Reservation Elem Tchr 1972-74; K Elem Tchr 1974-; *ai:* Friends of Quiet Waters Park 1991-, VP; Permitee in Bird Banding; *office:* The Key Schl 534 Hillsm Annapolis MD 21403*

HAAS, LINDA KATHRYN (CANDEL), Teacher, Math & Science *b:* Bucyrus, OH; *m:* Larry D.; *c:* Derek, Erin; *ed:* OH St Univ (BS & Mid Chldhd Ed 1977, (MA) Elem Ed 1987; Miami Univ of OH of WY Field Stud 1989, 1994, 1995; *cr:* St Mary Schl 5th & 8th G 1978-80; Holy Trinity Schl 5th-8th Grd Tchr 1981-85; St Matthi 6th-8th Grd Tchr 1985-; *ai:* Sci Club, NEED Project, Environment & Drug-Free Winners Choice Camp Coord; NSTA & NESTA 1986-;

1987-; NMSA 1991-; CDEA 1985-, Pres 1991-; Sci Ed Cncl of); NCEA; Natl Audubon Soc 1990-; Sierra Club 1991-; OH Acad 5-; Disabled Amer Vets 1975-; Natl Arbor Day Soc 1988-; World und; Natl Parks Assn; Nature Conservancy; Governors Awd for 1990; Whos Who in Young Profs 1988; Geology Field Stud sidential Tchng Awd Nom 1992; Columbus Tech Cncl MS Prgm 2,1994,1995; MS Bio Wkshp at OH St 1986; Project Disc Physics St; *office:* Saint Matthias Schl 1566 Ferris Rd Columbus OH

.INDA MARLENE (RUNK), Sixth Grade Teacher; *b:* sburg, PA; *m:* Louis J.; *c:* Andrew, Gretchen; *ed:* Notre Dame of Elem Ed 1970; Addl 12 Credit Hrs Toward Masters Degree; *cr:* the Archangel Schl 1, 6 Grd Tchr 1964-68; St Francis of Assist l Tchr 1968-69; Battle Monument Schl Spec Ed Tchr 1969-71; hapel Chrstn Acad K-12 Grd Tchr 1979-; *home:* 326 Broadview en Burnie MD 21061

IARILYN BRICKWEDEL, High School Science Teacher; *b:* y, NJ; *m:* David W.; *c:* David Jr., Russell, Donald; *ed:* William Coll (BA) Bio Sci 1969; Gen Sci Cert 1969 7-12; Gen Elem Cert *cr:* North Bergen Dist 7th-8th Grd Tchr 1982-88, HS Tchr 1988-; ical Co-Chairlady North Bergen HS; AFT 1982-; NEA 1994-; Eastern Star of NJ 1972-, Worthy Matron 4 Times, Gra nd Ofcr NJ Chorale 1993-, Publicity Chairlady; North Bergen HS Tchr of 5; *office:* North Bergen HS 7417 Kennedy Blvd North Bergen NJ

AUL THOMAS, Social Studies Teacher; *b:* Akron, OH; *m:* Ann *l:* Kent St (BSEd) His, Eng 1967; *cr:* Stow HS Soc Stud Tchr Cuyahoga Falls City Schls Soc Stud Tchr 1972-; *ai:* NEA, OH Cuyahoga Falls Ed Assn, VP 1974-75; *office:* Cuyahoga Falls HS St Cuyahoga Falls OH 44221

RICHARD ALAN, Math Teacher; *b:* Williamsport, PA; *m:* Sue Rohland; *ed:* Clarion Univ (BS) Scndry Math 1990; *cr:* Beaver Area Schl Dist Math Tchr 1990-; *ai:* Video Hunt Club; Planning Steering Comm; PSEA, NEA 1990-; *office:* Western rea Schl Dist 216 Engle Rd Industry PA 15052

ICHARD M., Mathematics Teacher; *b:* New York, NY; *m:* Cheryl Bryan, Suzanne; *ed:* Manhattan Coll (BS) Math 1968; Adelphi) His 1971; Long Island Univ 30 Credits Post Grad Stud; *cr:* St Math Tchr 1968-84; Sachem HS Math & Cmptr Tchr 1984-94; HS Math Tchr 1994-; *ai:* SAT Club; NEA 1984-; SAT Prep c; *office:* Meade Sr HS Clark Rd Fort Meade MD 20755*

ROBERT WILLIAM, Science Teacher; *b:* Cleveland, OH; *ed:* Green St Univ (BS) Bio Sci 1969, (MA) Ed Admin 1973; Addl 45 s Cmptrs, GATE; *cr:* Shaker MS Sci Tchr 1969-; *ai:* Lomond Capital Math, Sci Team; Facilitator for Staff Dev Prgms, Sci Fair; cal Sci Fair Judge; Project Wild, Protective Wet, Project Carving Facilitator for OH; SHTA 1969-; NABT, CRABS 1995-; SECO orth Royalton Bsbl Boosters 1986-; CWRU Institutional Comm 8-; Nom for Ashland Inc Tchr Achvmt Awd OH 1996; PTO Awd Plant, Game Buffet 1995; Fnd Awd for Rainstick Act 1995; CCEE ock Market Game Winner 1993; ADDU Cmptr Schlsp 1985; Nom ire Magazine Excl in Tchng 1986; *office:* Shakers MS 20600 lvd Shaker Heights OH 44122*

THOMAS ALLEN, English Teacher; *b:* Annapolis, MD; *m:* Linda thryn E., Christopher A.; *ed:* Univ of DE (BAED) Eng 1973; West niv (MED) Rdng 1979; 60 Credit Hrs; *cr:* Downington Sr HS Eng 3-; *ai:* READ Club Adv; Stu Assistance Svc Team; NEA 1973-; 3-, Den Ldr; Poetry Pub; *office:* Downingtown Sr HS 445 Manor ningtown PA 19335*

CHARLES PAUL, Director of Bands; *b:* Mountainside, NJ; *m:* zabo; *ed:* Upper IA Univ (BA) Music Ed 1974; Jersey City St Coll Music Ed 1978; *cr:* Linden HS Dir of Bands 1974-81; ater-Raritan Regnl HS Dir of Bands 1981-87; David Brearley HS ands 1987-92; Elibabeth HS Dir of Bands 1992-; *ai:* Tri-M Music Band Act Fac Adv; NEA, Music Eds Natl Conf, Natl Band Assn ffice: Elizabeth HS Jefferson Performing Arts Hous 27 Martin ing Jr Plaza Elizabeth NJ 07201

KER, TERRY WILLIAM, Physical Education Teacher; *b:* er, NY; *m:* Susan Blair; *c:* Julia Habecker-Green, Tracy r-Kamrat, Erin; *ed:* Ithaca Coll (BA) PE 1969; St Univ Coll at (MS) PE 1978; *cr:* DeWitt Jr High PE Tchr 1969-85; Ithaca HS 1986-96; Ithaca City Schls PE Tchr 1969-; *ai:* Boys Var Soccer 973-95; Girls Var Vllybl Coach 1986-; NY St Tchrs Assoc 1969-; 59-; Natl Soccer Coaches Assoc 1975-, All-NYS Slection Sect IV ner Vllybl Coaches Assoc 1988-; Ithaca United Soccer Club 1975-, ; Ithaca Vllybl Club 1993-, Club Rep; NY St Class A Soccer onship 1978; NY St Soccer Coach of the Yr 1978; Coll Division g All-Amer 1969; US Triatholon Fed Age Group All-Amer 1994; haca HS 1401 N Cayuga St Ithaca NY 14850

GER, MARTHA (KIRKPATRICK), Retired Elementary *b:* Celina, OH; *m:* Orval J.; *c:* Kirk Louis, Teresa K. Frysinger; ital Univ (BA) Lower Elem 1943; Ball St Univ (MS) Elem, Lang ; IU, PU at Ft Wayne 3 Credit Hrs 1956; *cr:* Rockford Elem Schl rd Tchr 1943-46; Hartford Twp 1-2nd Grd Tchr 1949-52; Jefferson 2nd Grd Tchr 1952-54; Adams Cntrl Elem Schl 1st Grd Tchr ; *ai:* IN STA 1949-86; NEA 1943-86; Pi Lambda Theta 1970-; IN ecialists 1970-86; East Cntrl Cty IRA 1970-86, VP 2 Yrs, Pres 2 l Scout Ldr 1948-51; Adam Cntrl Schl Team Ldr Open Classroom ; Outstdng Elem Tchrs of Amer 1973; Ball St Univ Outstdng s Tchrs Awd 1973; Master Tchr's Awd 1985-86; *home:* P.O. Box 51 d OH 45882

, ARTHUR, Chemistry Professor; *b:* New York, NY; *m:* Margery *c:* Davida C.; *ed:* Polytechnic Inst of Brooklyn (BS) Chem 1972, nem; U of IL at Urbana (PHD) Organic Chem 1977; SUNY Coll at Scndry Ed; *cr:* U of MI Lectuer, Rsrch Assoc 1977-80; Frederick Fac Scientist 1980-82; Bristol-Myers Rsrch Scientist 1982-86; ville Coll Assoc Prof 1988-; *ai:* Aristotle Prgm Coord; Fac ss; Acad, Stu Affairs Comms; Westewater Cert Instr; UUP, NYSUT Amer Chemical Soc 1972-92; Amer Assoc Adv Sci 1972-92; Phi Upsilon 1971-; NY St Bsbl Umpires Assn 1983-, VP; Young Israel Torah 1984-, Pres, Treas; NIH Predoctoral Trainee Cellular, lar Bio; NY St Challenger Awd; *office:* SUNY Coll at Morrisville ept Morrisville NY 13408

, CATHERINE M., First Grade Teacher; *b:* Kingston, NY; *ed:* St NY at New Paltz (BS) Ed 1964; Home, Schl & Comm Relationship es of Rsrch; *cr:* Red Hook Cntrl Schl Dist 1st Grd Tchr 1964-65; t Vly Cntrl Schl Dist 1st Grd Tchr 1965-; *ai:* Portfolio Comm; t Vly Tchrs Assn 1965-89; Rondout Vly Fed 1989-; Altar-Rosary 3-, Sec; *office:* Marbletown Elem Schl PO Box 9 Accord NY 12404

, JAMES FREDERICK, Computer Science Teacher; *b:* gton, DC; *m:* Kathleen Ann Reynolds; *c:* Joseph William, Rebecca Peter James; *ed:* Univ of MD (BS) Industrial Arts Ed 1974; mery Cty Pub Schls (ME) Cmptr Sci 1984; *cr:* Prince Georges Pub ndustrial Arts Tchr 1975; Montgomery Cty Pub Schls Industrial Arts 975-84, AP C S Tchr, Cmptr Sci Dept Head 1984-; *ai:* Cmptr Sci Club Spon; Wallace Meml Church PCA 1974-92, Elder 10 Yrs, Sunday Schl Tchr 8 Yrs; Good Hope Church PCA Elder, 1992-; Reader Scholastic Aptitude Bd; AP C S; Co-Author Capek Robotica; *office:* Springbrook H S 201 Valley Brook Dr Silver Spring MD 20904

HABERBERGER, NANCY J., English & Reading Teacher; *b:* Kane, PA; *m:* Charles; *c:* Thomas, Karen Taylor; *ed:* Clarion St (BSEd) Eng, Rdng, Speech 1964; *cr:* Beaty Jr HS 7th Grd Eng Tchr 1964-65; St Marys HS 7th-8th Grd Eng Tchr 1965-67; Sheffield HS 9th Grd Eng, 7th Grd Rdng Tchr 1970-; *ai:* 7th Grd Class Adv; Plays Co-Dir; PSEA 1970-; NEA; WCEA; *home:* RR 2 Box 48 Kane PA 16735

HABIBULLAH, MOHAMED, Assoc Prof in Coll Bus Admin; *b:* Dhaka, Bangladesh; *m:* Seheli Sultana; *c:* Masud, Yusuf; *ed:* Univ of Guelph Canada (MS) Statistics 1980; Univ of MO at Columbia (PHD) Statistics 1988; *cr:* Univ of WI at Superior Assoc Prof 1988-94; Northeastern Univ Visiting Fac 1994-; *ai:* Amer Statistical Assn 1985-; Pub in JASA Biometrika JRSS; *office:* Northeastern Univ 219 Hayden Hall Boston MA 02115

HABLITZEL, PATRICIA DICKMAN, 5th Grade Teacher; *b:* Lima, OH; *m:* Philip; *c:* Amy, Matt, Sara; *ed:* St Francis Coll (BA) Ed 1973; *cr:* St Peter Upper Sandusky Schl 2nd Grd Schl 1973-74; St Mary's Schl 2nd Grd Schl 1976; St John's Schl 4th-5th Grd Tchr 1982-95; *ai:* NEA; St John Fac Staff Treas; CD of A; *home:* 1301 Gilliland Ave Delphos OH 45833

HACE, DENNIS EDWARD, 11th & 12th Grd Soc Stud Tchr; *b:* Cleveland, OH; *ed:* Kent St Univ (BSEd) Soc Stud Comp 1969; Masters Equivalent John Carroll, Cleveland St; *cr:* Willoughby-Eastlake Schls Tchr 27 Yrs; *ai:* Model United Nations-Cncl on World Affairs; Frosh Boys Bsktbl Coach; NEA, OEA 1969-; WETA 1969-, Exec Comm, Bldg Rep; Maryla Holden Jennings Scholar; *office:* North HS 34041 Stevens Blvd Eastlake OH 44095

HACH, LELAND J.,SR., Math & Comp Programming Tchr; *b:* Medina, OH; *m:* Peggy May Davis; *c:* Leland Jr., Gretchen, Jennie; *ed:* Vly Forge Chrstn Coll (BS) Ministry 1976; SUNY New Paltz Comp Sci; *cr:* Dwaarkill Cntry Store Partner 1989-; High Tech Semi-Conductor Programmer 1991-; Harmony Chrstn Schl Scndry Math Tchr 1992-; *ai:* Jr Class Adv; Shawangunk Vly Fire Dept 1990-94, EMT; *office:* Harmony Christian Schl RD #2 Box 730 Rt 211E Middletown NY 10940

HACK, TRACIE L., Business Education Teacher; *b:* Palmyra, NY; *ed:* SUNY At Oneonta (BS) Bus Ec 1989; Nazareth Coll (MS) Ed 1996; *cr:* Monroe Comm Coll Adjunct Prof 1993; Livonia HS Bus Ed Tchr 1993-; *ai:* Class Adv; Various Bldg Comm; Monroe Cty Bus Educators Assoc 1992-; NBEA 1992-; Bus Tchrs Assn Of NY 1994-; Palmyra Comm Ctr 1992-, Bd of Dir, Recorder; *office:* Livonia HS PO Box E Livonia NY 14487

HACKATHORN, ANGELA M., English Teacher; *b:* Norwalk, OH; *ed:* Bowling Green St Univ (BSEd) Eng 1983, (MA) Eng 1991; *cr:* Norwalk City Schls Sub Tchr 1983-84; Huron Cty Schls Sub Tchr 1983-84; Cardinal Stritch HS Eng Tchr 1984-; *ai:* Yrbk; Newspaper; Photo Club; Writing Lab; Dept Chair; NCTE 1986-; Articles & Poem Pub; *office:* Cardinal Stritch HS 3225 Pickle Rd Oregon OH 43616

HACKENBERG, BARRY MILLER, 11th & 12th Grd Soc Stud Tchr; *b:* Penns Creek, PA; *m:* Elaine Roberta Schraeder; *c:* Erick, Justen Drue; *ed:* Susquehanna Univ (BA) His, Eng 1962; Bloomsburg Univ 6 Hrs; Kutztown Univ 36 Hrs; *cr:* Milton Area HS Eng Tchr 1962-63; Daniel Boone Area Schls 6th Grd Tchr 1963-71; Jim Thorpe Area Schls 6th Grd Tchr 1971-78; North Schuylkill Jr Sr HS 11st, 12th Grd Soc Stud Tchr 1978-; *ai:* Head Ftbl Coach Jim Thorpe HS 1971-76, North Schuylkill HS 1980-85; PSEA, NEA 1963-; NSEA 1978-, Legislator Contact Team, Coord 1991; Commencement Speaker 1992; Duquesne Univ Cert Recognition Excl Tchng, Commitment Univ Values, Traditions; *home:* Box 137-D Acorn Dr Lake Hauto Nesquehoning PA 18240

HACKENSON, CHERYL HESKE, Business Educator; *b:* Lowell, MA; *m:* James G.; *c:* Andrew James; *ed:* Salem St Coll (BS) Bus Ed 1982; Anna Maria Coll (MBA) Bus Admin 1990; Champlain Coll Sec Cert Secretarial 1978; *cr:* Old Sturbridge Village Admin Asst 1982-84; French River Schl Word Processing Instr 1985; Tantasqua Regnl Sr HS Bus Educator 1984-; *ai:* Bus Club Adv; Bus Competition Coord; TTA 1984-, Asst Treas & Treas; MTA & NEA 1984-; Dudley-Webster Boys & Girls Club, Bd of Dirs; Grant From MA Dept of Ed for Remediation & Reinforcement Software 1986; Mini-Grant for Worcester Area Tchrs for Annual Bus Competition; *office:* Tantasqua Regnl Sr HS 319 Brookfield Rd Fiskdale MA 01518

HACKER, GREGORY CHARLES, Science Teacher; *b:* Columbus, OH; *m:* Luanne Kay Harmer; *c:* Darron, Bryce, Tyler; *ed:* Bob Jones Univ (BS) Sci, PE 1976; Continuing Ed Classes; *cr:* Northside Chrstn Schl Hlth, Physical Sci, Bio, Chem, Physics, Earth Sci, Bible Tchr Jr, Sr High 1976-; Franklin Univ Adj Prof, Sci Tchr 1986-; *ai:* Coach; Camping Ministries; Calvary Bible Church Adult Sunday Schl Tchr; Amer Red Cross 1986-, First Aid, CPR Instr; Calvary Bible Church Chrstn Ed comm; Physics Lab Course Re-Org; Tchr for Higher Ed Cncl of Columbus; GATE Tchr 1996; BCSA Tchr Conf Tchr.

HACKETT, ARLEATHA WALSTON, Second Grade Teacher; *b:* Philadelphia, PA; *c:* Lori Niccole, Kyle Jameison; *ed:* Cheyney St Univ (BS) Elem Ed 1967; Bowie St Univ (MS) Elem Ed 1982; 3 Credit Hrs Trinity Univ 1982; *cr:* Edgar A. Poe Elem Schl Third Grd Tchr 1967-68; Heilbronn Dependent Schl Second Grd Tchr 1969-72; Capital Hghts Elem Schl Head Start Tchr 1973-75; Beaver Hghts Elem Schl Head Start Tchr 1975-77; Lake Shore Elem Schl First Grd Tchr 1977-81; Ft Smallwood Elem Schl First, Second, Fifth Grd Tchr 1981-; *ai:* TAAAC 1977-; MSTA 1975-; NEA 1975-; Anne Arundel Cty, Human Relations Adv Comm; United Meth Church, Women's Pres, Ushers, Sunday Schl Tchr; Mills King Human Relations Ed Awd 1990; Human Relations Outstdng Svc Awd 1995; *home:* 7605 McNamara Dr Glen Burnie MD 21061

HACKETT, DEBRA ANNE, Special Education Teacher; *b:* Queens, NY; *m:* Eric; *c:* Benjamin; *ed:* Adelphi Univ (BA) Psych 1978, (MS) Spec Ed, Elem Ed, Nursery Schl 1979; *cr:* Ahavat Shalom Nursery Prgm Toddler Prgm Coord 1991-93; Computertots Cmptr Tchr 1992-93; Alpha Schl Life Skills Curr, Spec Ed Tchr 1993-; *ai:* PIE Coord; Fac Spokesperson; Ruth K. Newman Awd for Excl Presented by The Cncl of Private Schls for Children with Spec Needs 1995; Tchr of Month 1994; *home:* 127 Andover Dr Jackson NJ 08527

HACKETT, DONALD W., 6th Grd Math & Sci Tchr; *b:* Claremont, NH; *m:* Kathleen S.; *c:* Olin (dec); *ed:* Univ of NH (BA) Govt 1966; Attnd Keene St Coll, Univ of Vermont at Springfield, Bridgewater St Coll, Castleton St Coll, Anna Maria Coll; *cr:* Maple Avenue Schl Tchr 1966-68; Newfields Elem Schl Tchr & Prin 1968-70; Springfield VT Pub Schls Tchr & Prin 1970-75; Boys & Girls Camps Inc Camp Dir & Asst Exec Dir 1975-86; Sandwich MA Pub Schls Tchr 1986-; *ai:* NEA; MTA; Sugar River Ed Assn 1966-68, Pres; Sandwich Ed Assn 1986-, Treas; The Compassionate Friends 1986-, Facilitator, Newsletter Ed; Authored Saying Olin to Say Goodbye a Book Sold by The Compassionate Friends; Co-authored Now Childless also Distributed Through The Compassionate Friends.

HACKETT, ELIZABETH S., First Grade Teacher; *b:* Newark, NJ; *m:* Paul; *c:* Paul III, Kelly, Kristin; *ed:* William Paterson Coll MS Elem Ed 1978; Rdng Cert, Presch Cert 1978; *cr:* Canfield Ave Schl Classroom Tchr 1978-; *ai:* Family Sci Tchr; Presenter at Wkshps; NJEA, NEA 1978-; Tchr of Yr 1988; A+ For Kids Grant; *office:* Canfield Ave Schl Canfield Ave Mine Hill NJ 07801

HACKETT, HAROLD B.,JR., Retired Adj Professor of Math; *b:* Coudersport, PA; *m:* Sandra Louise Perry; *c:* Michael, Michelle Louise Brown; *ed:* Mansfield St Univ (BS) Math, Sci Ed 1957; Alfred Univ (MS) Ed 1962; Montclair St (MA) Math 1965; St Univ Coll at Geneseo Math Grad Stud; *cr:* Alfred Almond Cntrl Schl Sr HS Math Tchr 1957-64; Suny Coll of Tech at Alfred Prof of Math 1964-73, Math Dept Chair 1974-76, 1978-94, Acting Dean Schl of Lbrl Stud 1976-78, Acting VP for Acads 1994-95; *ai:* NYSMATYC Math Contest Campus Coord; NYSMATYC 1967-, Sec 1969-71, VP 1971-72, Pres 1972-73; Alumni Tchr of Yr 1987.

HACKETT, MAJEAN BOWLES, Fifth Grade Teacher; *b:* Sioux City, IA; *m:* Thomas Dean; *c:* Thomas Jr., Jerome, Brian; *ed:* Liberty Univ (BS) Ed Elem 1982; *cr:* Temple Chrstn 3rd-4th Grd Tchr 1983-85; Toledo Chrstn PE, Art, 5th Grd Tchr 1985-; *ai:* Jr Class Adv; Girls Bsktbl, Vlybl, Jr High Cheerleading Coach; Asst Track Coach; Chrstn Bus Women 1985-, Chm; *office:* Toledo Christian Schl 2303 Brookford Dr Toledo OH 43614

HADAM, JACK J., Biology Teacher; *b:* Needham, MA; *m:* Diana Lynn Delano; *c:* Jared M., Elijah J.; *ed:* Univ NH (BA) Zoology 1983; OR St Univ (MS) Entomology 1986; 9 Credits Ed Univ New England; *cr:* Univ NH Rsrch Asst 1980-83; OR St Univ Rsrch Asst 1983-85; Kennett HS Sci Tchr 1986-; *ai:* Fac, Admin, Staff Accreditation Comm; NHSTA 1995-; First Bapt Church 1993-, Outreach Dir; Tchr of Yr 1990; Articles Pub 1984, 1986; *office:* A. Crosby Kennett HS Main St Conway NH 03818

HADDAD, ALHAM S., Mathematics Teacher; *b:* Salt, Jordan; *m:* Isam J.; *c:* Shadi, Sheren, David; *ed:* (BA) Math 1983; *cr:* St Mary HS Math Tchr 1983-85; Dickinson HS Math Tchr 1985-; *office:* Dickinson HS 2 Palisade Ave Jersey City NJ 07306

HADDAD, DIANE LYNN, English Teacher; *b:* Beaver Falls, PA; *ed:* IN Univ of PA (BS) Eng Ed 1988; CA Univ of PA (MA) Eng 1995; *cr:* Corey Area HS Scndry Eng Tchr 1 Yr; Waynesburg Coll Adj Eng Instr 1 Yr; Brownsville Area HS Scndry Eng Tchr 5 Yr; *ai:* PSEA, NEA 6 Yrs; ACUWPET 4 Yrs; Human Rights Campaign 1 Yr; Great Ideas Grant 1992.

HADDAD, MARK H., Music Teacher; *b:* Worcester, MA; *m:* Cynthia R.; *ed:* Boston Coll (AB) Psych & Music 1987; Lesley Coll (MED) Creative Arts 1991; Univ of MA 5 Credits Music Ed; *cr:* Walpole Pub Schls 6th Grd Tchr 1991-92; Newton Cntry Day Schl Music Tchr 1992-94; Newton Cntry Day Schl Music Tchr 1994-; *ai:* MS & HS Drama & Musical Pgm Producer & Dir; Select Choir; Admissions Interviewer; MENC 1994-; MMEA 1994-; ACDA 1995-; SpeakEasy Stage Co 1993-, Box Office Mgr & Music Dir Resident; SpeakEasy Stage Co Best Small Prof Theatre in Boston & Musical Production Awd for One of Ten Best 1995; *office:* Newton Cntry Day Schl 785 Centre St Newton MA 02158*

HADDEN, GEORGE STEVEN, 8th Grade Soc Stud & Sci Tchr; *b:* Middletown, NY; *m:* Sandra L.; *c:* Adam, Paige; *ed:* Orange Cty Comm Coll (AAS) Lbrl Arts 1966; SUNY at Geneseo (BS) Ed N-9 1968; SUNY at New Paltz (MS) Elem Ed 1985; Attnd Long Island Univ, CCNY; *cr:* NY St Division for Yth New Hampton Trng Schl Inst Tchr 1968-71; North Rockland Cntrl Schl-Haverstraw MS Tchr 1971-; *ai:* Schl Improvement Planning Team; A-V Club Spon; AFT 1971-; Middletown Jaycees 1974-81, Dir, Jaycee of Yr; Johnson Fire Dept 1976-, Pres, Fireman of Yr; Minisink Vly Yth Soccer 1983-, Coach; Minisink Vly Little League 1985-, Coach; Impact II Developer Grant; *office:* Haverstraw MS Grant St Haverstraw NY 10927

HADDEN, SUSAN BABULA, Fifth Grade Teacher; *b:* Stamford, CT; *m:* Jeffrey Alan; *c:* Michael, Meghan; *ed:* Univ of Hartford (BS) Elem Ed 1974; OH St Univ (MA) Ed, Rdng 1981; 15 Sem Hrs Grad Stud Ed; *cr:* Anderson Schl Dist #5 5th-6th Grd Tchr 1974-76; Cntrl OH Schl Dist Sub Tchr 1976-78; Big Walnut Local Schls 5th-6th Grd Tchr 1978-; *ai:* Outdoor Ed, Instrl Media Comms; NEA, OEA, BWEA 1978-; Phi Delta Kappa 1981-; OH Dynamo Soccer Club 1993-, Team Admin; *office:* Big Walnut Local Schls 4121 Miller Paul Rd Galena OH 43021*

HADDIX, PATRICIA GRIMM, Language Arts Teacher; *b:* Connellsville, PA; *m:* Rick R.; *c:* Heath, Kimberly; *ed:* Univ of SC (BA) Eng, Ed 1971; Bowling Green St Univ (MA) Eng 1979; *cr:* Baron Dekalb HS 7-9th Eng Tchr 1971-72; Fostoria HS 9-11th Eng Tchr 1972-95; Fostoria MS Lang Arts Tchr 1995-; *ai:* Dist Writing Comm; Curr Cncl VP, Fac Concern Cncl; NEA, OEA 1991-; OCTELA 1993-; Alpha Delta Kappa; PTO, YMCA; Eng Tchr of Yr 1985; *office:* Fostoria MS 1001 Park Ave Fostoria OH 44830

HADDLE, DEANNA CHIRILLO, Chemistry Teacher; *b:* Johnstown, PA; *m:* John E.; *c:* John, Matthew; *ed:* IN Univ of PA (BS) Chem Ed 1970; Attnd Univ of Pittsburg & Penn St Univ; Addl Grad Work Done in Cmptrs Earth-Sci, Curr Dev & Sci Ed; *cr:* GJA Voc-Tech Chem Tchr 1970-77; Greater Johnstown Area Post Scndry Chem Tchr 1981-82; Bishop McCort HS Chem Tchr 1989-92; Mt Aloysius Coll Chem Tchr 1991; Conemaugh Twp Area HS Chem Tchr 1992-; *ai:* Sci Club, Stu Congress, PA Jr Acad of Sci Adv; Strategic Planning Comms Curr Dev; PSEA & NEA 10 yrs Negotiator; Amer Chemical Soc 23 Yrs Outstanding Ed Stu; Kappa Delta Pi 24 Yrs; St Benedict Ed Comm, Chm; St Vincent Coll Tchr Recognition Awd 1993; PA Chemical Industry Ed Fnd Appointee.

HADGE, KENNETH MICHAEL, Marketing Professor; *b:* Jamaica Plain, MA; *m:* Lorena Cataldo; *c:* Darren, Janine; *ed:* Suffolk Univ (BBA) Mrktg, Mngmt 1967, (MBA) Mrktg 1968; *cr:* Newbury Coll Prof 1981-; *ai:* SBA Stu, Club Adv; Person, Tchr of Yr Awds; *office:* Newbury Coll 129 Fisher Ave Brookline MA 02146

HADJIMINAS, ELIAS E., HS Chemistry Teacher; *b:* Jamaica, NY; *ed:* NY Univ (BS) Sci Ed 1994; *cr:* Bryant HS Sub Tchr 1994-95, Chem Tchr 1995-; *ai:* UFT 1994-; NSTA 1996-.

HADLEY, STEPHEN PHILIP, Social Studies Teacher; *b:* Shirley, MA; *m:* Cynthia E.; *c:* Allison Oswald, Kristen; *ed:* SUNY at Geneseo (BA) His 1976; MI St Univ (MA) His 1982; SUNY at Brockport (CAS) Educl Admin 1989; *cr:* Perry Cntrl Schl Soc Stud Tchr 1979; Letchworth Cntrl Schl Soc Stud Tchr 1979-; *ai:* Jr Class Adv; Stu Support Team; NEA & Geneseo Valley Cncl for Soc Stud 1979-; Phi Delta Kappa 1988-; Univ of Rochester Tchr of Yr Awd 1993; *office:* Letchworth Cntrl Schl 5550 School Rd Gainesville NY 14066*

HAEMMERLE, SANTINA ASPROMONTE, 2nd Grade Teacher; *b:* Brooklyn, NY; *m:* Richard Henry Sr.; *c:* Richard Jr., Christine Shickler, Karen Sullivan, Thomas; *ed:* St John's Univ (BS) Elem Ed 1963; Adelphi Univ (MS) Spec Ed 1982; Long Island Univ (PD) Educl Admin 1992; Cmptr Courses; *cr:* Commack Pub Schls 1st Grd Tchr 1963-64; Baldwin Pub Schls 1st Grd Tchr 1964-65; Westbury Friends Schl Mid Primary Tchr 1973-74; Diocese of Rockville Centre 2nd Grd Tchr 1979-83; Merrick Pub Schls 1st Grd Tchr 1983-84; East Meadow Pub Schls 1st, 2nd Grd Tchr 1984-; Friends Acad Summer Acad Dir 26 Yrs; *ai:* Chprsn Parkway Planning, Mngmt Team; East Meadow Policy Bd; Pol Action Comm East Meadow Tchrs Union; Phi Kappa Theta 1991-; Nassau Rdng Cncl, IRA, NY St Rdng Assn 1984-; Order Sons of Italy in Amer 1984-, St Trustee; NYS Commission for Soc Justice 1986-, Vice-Chm; Anti-Defamation Arm OSIA; Holocaust Meml Comm of Long Island 1996; Maria Regina Parish 1993-, Eucharistic Minister; *office:* Parkway Schl 465 Bellmore Rd East Meadow NY 11554*

HAENSCH, KAREN S., English Teacher; *b:* Beaver Dam, WI; *c:* Lisa Hines, Mark McKay, Todd McKay; *ed:* Valparaiso Univ (BA) Eng 1961; Attnd Bowling Green St Univ, Univ of Toledo, Chicago St Univ & Ashland Univ; *cr:* Bowling Green HS Eng Tchr 1961-1962; Woodmore HS Eng Tchr 1978-; Many Yrs Sub Tchr; *ai:* Jr Class, Pep Club & Prom Adv; Ath Aide;

Fac Advy & Curr Revision Comms; N Cntrl Evaluation Subcommittee Chm; Acad Boosters; NEA, OEA 1978-; WEA 1978-, Treas; OCTELA, NCTE; *office:* Woodmore HS Ames & Fremont Sts Elmore OH 43416

HAFER, SONYA JANE, Fifth Grade Teacher; *b:* Bellwood, PA; *m:* Paul Carl; *ed:* Shippensburg Univ (BS) Fr 1959; Mansfield Univ (MED) Elem Ed 1980; 2 Summers Canadian Stud Univ of VT; Post-Grad Stud Penn St Univ, Ball St Univ & Univ of ME; *cr:* Bedford HS Span & Eng Tchr 1959-62; Roaring Spring Jr HS Span & Eng Tchr 1962-63; Pangborn Elem 6th Grd Tchr 1963-64; 10th St Elem Schl 3rd Grd Tchr 1964-67; Rock L Butler MS 5th Grd Tchr 1968-; *ai:* PSEA, NEA, Wellsboro Area Ed Assn 1968-; Phi Delta Kappa 1986-; Natl Cncl for His Ed 1994-; Wellsboro Area Schl Dist MS Outstanding Tchr 1988; *office:* Rock L Butler MS 9 Nichols St Wellsboro PA 16901

HAFF, JULIE M., Director of Public Relations; *b:* Sydney, NY; *ed:* Hartwick Coll (BA) Eng 1994; Wesleyan Univ 3 Credit Hrs; *cr:* Miss Hall's Schl Admissions Asst Dir 1994-, Head Lacrosse Coach 1995, Pub Relations Dir, JV Vlybl Coach 1995-; *ai:* Sr Class Adv; Stdnt Life Comm; *office:* Miss Halls Schl 492 Holmes Rd Pittsfield MA 01201

HAFNER, BERNADINE SCHAFNER, Eighth Grade Teacher; *b:* Madison, IN; *m:* Robert A.; *c:* David, Michael; *ed:* Ursuline Bellarmine Coll (BA) Ed 1968; Fordham Univ (MA) Rel Ed 1970; Xavier Univ (MA) SLD Ed 1992; 12 Credit Hrs; *cr:* St Clement Schl at Vly Sta 5th Grd Tchr 1962-64; St Ann Schl 7th & 8th Grd Tchr 1964-68; St Mary Schl 5th Grd Tchr 1968-69; St Clement Schl at St Bernard 8th Grd Tchr 1972-74; Southern OH Coll Instr 1981-88; Our Lady of the Rosary 5th-8th Grd Tchr 1988-; *ai:* Algebra Readiness Pgm Afterschl Tchr; Math Comm Participant; Washington DC Class Trip Chaperone; Cooperating Tchr; ADD Cncl Greater Cincinnati 1990-; CEC 1992-; NCTM 1994-; BSA 1984-, Vol; *office:* Our Lady Of Rosary Schl 19 Farragut Rd Cincinnati OH 45218*

HAGADORN, THOMAS W., Secondary Math Teacher; *b:* Hornell, NY; *m:* Deborah Fierle; *c:* Kyle, Lindsay; *ed:* Addl 27 Hrs SUC Geneseo, 3 Hrs Elmira Coll; *cr:* Haverling Cntrl Schl Scndry Math Tchr 1970-; *ai:* Boys Var Soccer Coach; Steuben Cty Boys Soccer Coord; NHS Selection Comm; NSCAA 1984-; Bath Lodge of Elks 1973-; Amer Legion 1978-; Bath Hope for Youth Co-Founder, First Pres; Bath Kiwanis Youth Soccer League Founder, League Coord; Section V Boys Soccer Coach of Yr 1984-87, 1989-90, 1993-95; Pres Awd for Excl in Tchng Sci, Math Nom 1990-91, 1993; Steuben Cty Pres Awd 1993; NSCAA Soccer Coach of Yr 1994; *home:* 15 Locust St Bath NY 14810

HAGAN, ANN J., Third Grade Teacher; *b:* Hackensack, NJ; *ed:* William Paterson Coll (BA) Elem Ed 1975; Ramapo Coll Project SPACE Courses 15 Credit Hrs 1985-89; Pascack Valley Ed Cncl Insvc Trng in Collaborative Ed 1993; *cr:* Meadowbrook Schl Second Grd Tchr 1976; Memorial Schl First Grd Instrl Aide 1976-77, Fourth Grd Tchr 1977, First Grd Instrl Aide 1977-78, First Grd Tchr 1978, Kndgtn Tchr, 5-8 Grd Title I Math Instr 1978-79, Fieldstone MS Kndgtn Tchr, 5-8 Grd Title I Math Instr 1978-79; Memorial Schl 2-4 Grd Title I Math Instr 1979-81, Third Grd Tchr 1981-; *ai:* NEA, NJEA, Bergen Cty Ed Assn 1978-; Montvale PTO, Corresponding Sec 1990-92; Governors Tchr Recognition Awd 1992; *office:* Memorial Elem Schl 53 W Grand Ave Montvale NJ 07645

HAGAN, CHERYL LYNN, Fourth Grade Teacher; *b:* Dover, NJ; *ed:* Fairleigh Dickinson Univ (BA) Elem Ed 1977; East Stroudsburg Univ (MA) Elem Ed 1985; 12 Credit Hrs 1988-89; Univ of HI at Manoa 18 Credit Hrs; *cr:* Roxbury Twp Bd of Ed 4th, 5th Grd Elem Tchr 1977-; *ai:* NJEA, REA, NEA, MCCEA 1977-; *office:* Jefferson Elem Schl 35 Corn Hollow Rd Succasunna NJ 07876

HAGAN, CHRISTINE GENOVESE, English Teacher; *b:* Springfield, MA; *m:* Daniel C.; *c:* Daniel C. Jr.; *ed:* Univ of MA (BS) Recreational Mgmt & Eng 1972; Westfield St Coll (M Sec Ed) Scndry Ed 1976; *cr:* North MS Eng Tchr 1973-81; Westfield MS Eng Tchr 1981-82; Westfield HS Eng Tchr 1984-; *ai:* Supts Task Force Advy Comm; Westfield Ed Assn & MA Tchrs Assn 1973-; Most Favorite Tchr 1993 & 1994; *office:* Westfield HS 177 Montgomery Rd Westfield MA 01085

HAGAN, ELEANOR NILES, Retired Elementary Teacher; *b:* Boston, MA; *ed:* Lesley Coll (BS) Elem Ed 1960; Bowie St Coll (MS) Admin, Supervision 1982; Addl Hrs Univ of MD; *cr:* Malden Elem Schl Tchr 3 Yrs; P. G. Cty Elem Schl Tchr 31 Yrs; *ai:* Sci Fair; Grd Level Chm; Schl Based Mngmt; Amer Ed Week Chm; PGCEA, MSTA 1963-; NEA 1960-; AAUW, Sec; *home:* 4001 Wakefield Ln Bowie MD 20715

HAGAN, MARYALICE, 8th-9th Grade English Teacher; *b:* Philadelphia, PA; *m:* Philip S.; *c:* Moira; *ed:* Temple Univ (BA) Comm 1975, (MED) Scndry Ed 1979; 30 Addl Credits; *cr:* Neshaming Sr HS Eng Tchr 1980; Holicong MS Eng Tchr 1980-87; Cntrl Bucks West HS Eng Tchr 1987-88; Holicong MS Eng Tchr 1988-; *ai:* Media Club Adv; Optimist Club Oratorical Contest Coach; Schl Paper, Drama Club Past Adv; NEA 1980-, Pres; PA St Ed Assn 1980-, Pres; Newtown Lib Co, Historic Assn Vols 1976-; Bucks Cty Comm Coll Lib Friends 1989-, Bd of Dir; Natl Freedoms Fnd Schlsp; Awded Cmptr Software Educl Grant 1983; *home:* 203 Washington Ave Newtown PA 18940

HAGAN, THERESA JEAN, Secondary English Teacher; *b:* Philadelphia, PA; *c:* Jennifer Kikia, Lianne Kikia, Jamie; *ed:* Univ of Pennsylvania (BA) Eng, Sociology 1973; Univ of Abidjan Ivory Coast African Lit Baoule; *cr:* Cherry Hill HS Scndry Eng Tchr 1973-76; Peace Corps Eng as Scndry Lang Tchr 1976-79; Cinnaminson HS Scndry Eng Tchr 1979-80; Pemberton Twp HS Scndry Eng Tchr 1981-; *ai:* Jr Human Rights Commission, Conflict Resolution Team Advs; NEA 1973-; Natl Endowment of Hum Tchr Scholar 1991-92; *home:* 120 Chippewa Trl Browns Mills NJ 08015*

HAGANY, JUDITH MARIE, 8th Grd Mathematics Teacher; *b:* New Brunswick, NJ; *m:* Lawrence G.; *ed:* Trenton St Coll (BA) Math Ed 1974, (MA) Math Ed 1982; NJ Prin, Supervision Cert 1987; 30 Addl Hrs at Jersey City St Coll, St Peter's Coll, Kean Coll; *cr:* Manalapan-Englishtown Regnl Schl Dist 7th-8th Grd Math Tchr 1974-; *ai:* Math Curr Guide Revision Comm 1995; Math Challenges Prgm Coord, Coach; Math Team, League, Counts Team Coach; MEEA, NJEA, NEA 1974-; NCTM, AMTNJ 1976-; MAA, ASCD 1980-; Governors Outstdng Tchr Awd 1987-88; Distngd Jr HS Math Tchr Edyth May Sliffe Awd 1995; *office:* Manalapan Englishtown MS 155 Millhurst Rd Manalapan NJ 07726

HAGAR, TERESA LYNN, English Teacher; *b:* Kirksville, MO; *ed:* Cntrl MO St Univ (BFA) Theatre 1981; *cr:* Saint Mary HS Eng Tchr 1988-; *ai:* Jr Class Adv; Forensic League, Highlander Schl Newspaper & Drama Club Moderator; NCTE; Soka Gakai Intnl-USA; Actors Equity Assn; Recognized by the MO House of Reps for Educl Theatre; Archdiocese of Newark Tchr Recognition Awd 1994; *office:* Saint Mary HS 64 Chestnut St Rutherford NJ 07070*

HAGEDORN, DEBORAH COLLINS, First Grade Teacher; *b:* Hartford, CT; *ed:* Eastern Nazarene Coll (BS) Elem Ed & Spcl Ed 1976; Cntrl CT St Coll (MS) Early Chldhd Ed 1980; *cr:* Pleasant Vly Schl Kndgtn Tchr 1976-77, 1st Grd Tchr 1977-80 & 1986-, Pre-Primary Tchr 1981-86, 2nd Grd Tchr 1980-81; *ai:* Early Chldhd Cncl Presenter; Scheduling & Time Mgmt Comm; Stu Tchr Mentor; Cooperating Tchr; SWEA 1976-; CEA 1976-; NEA 1976-; Church of the Nazarene 1968-; S Windsor Jaycees Outstdng Edctr of the Yr 1985-; Celebration of Excl Honorable Mention 1988-90; Soc Stud Curr & Photography for Books: Simply Wonderful & Suburban Ways; Articles Pub; *office:* Pleasant Valley Elem Schl 591 Ellington Rd South Windsor CT 06074

HAGEMAN, DONALD F., Choral Director; *b:* Montvale, NJ; *c:* Keith, Jahn Marie; *ed:* Ithaca Coll (BA) Music 1972; Montclair St Coll (MA) Music 1985; *cr:* Rush Henrietta Jr HS Choral Dir 1972-73; Pascack Vly HS Choral, Musical Dir 1973-82; Harrington Park Comm Church Choral Dir 1981-86; Pascack Hills HS Choral, Musical Dir 1982-; *ai:* Sr Class Adv; Choral, Musical, Set Dir; JV Soccer Coach; NEA, BC Music Tchr Assn, NJ Music Tchr Assn 1973-; *office:* Pascack Hills HS 225 W Grand Ave Montvale NJ 07645

HAGEMAN, THOMAS, Junior High Teacher; *b:* Buffalo, NY; *ed:* Buffalo St Coll (BS) Scndry Ed, Soc Stud 1971, (MS) Scndry Ed, Soc Stud 1974; 17 Credit Hrs Post-Grad Stud in Tchng Rdng, Driver Ed, Soc Stud; *cr:* St Andrews Schl Ath Dir, Jr HS Tchr 1971-72; All Saints Schl Ath Dir, Jr HS Tchr 1972-74; Hamburg Sr HS Tchr 1975-82; St Ann's Schl Jr HS Tchr 1983-88; Our Lady Help of Chrstns Schl Soc Stud, Lit, Lang Arts Tchr 1989-; *ai:* Girls Bsktbl, Track Team Coach; Spelling, Geog Bee Coord; AFT 1975-82; *home:* 951 Riverview Blvd Tonawanda NY 14150

HAGEN, RICHARD CARL, 9th-12th Grade Math Teacher; *b:* Cleveland, OH; *m:* Nancy; *c:* Christine, Rick, Jeff; *ed:* U of Pittsburgh (MED) Curr, Supervision 1970; *cr:* Riverside HS Math Tchr 1962-66; Brush HS Math Tchr, Coach 1966-; *ai:* Boys, Girls Var Tennis Coach; Ski Club; NEA, OEA 1962-; SELTA 1966-; OH Tennis Coaches 1968-, Past Pres, Hall of Fame, 600 Wins; *office:* Brush HS 4875 Glenlyn Rd Cleveland OH 44124

HAGER, CLAUDETTE P., Science Teacher; *b:* Rochester, NY; *m:* James R.; *c:* Thomas; *ed:* Erie Comm Coll (AA) Lab Tech 1974; SUC at Buffalo (BA) Sci Ed 1978, (MS) Sci Ed 1982; SUNY at Buffalo (MS) Geology 1986; *cr:* Lancaster Cntrl Schl Sci Tchr 1980-; *ai:* Ski Club, Chess Club, Earth Day Adv; NSTA 1988-; NYSUT 1980-; NYS MS Assn 1990-; Adirondack Club 1985-; ADK 46R 1993-, Cert of Accomplishment; NYS Conservation Cncl Awd; Energy Ed Awd; Cert of Trng Awd for Drugs & Alcohol.*

HAGER, DEBBIE STOLL, Guidance Counselor; *b:* Cincinnati, OH; *m:* John; *c:* Sarah, Jeff; *ed:* OH Univ (BSEd) Elem Ed 1972; Xavier Univ (MED) Guid 1974; *cr:* Norwood View Elem Schl 3rd Grd Tchr 1972-75; Norwood Jr HS Guid Cnslr 1975-80; Clermont Northeastern HS Guid Cnslr 1987-; *ai:* NEA, OEA, CNEA 1972-; OACAC, OSCA 1987-; *office:* Clermont Northeastern HS 5327 Hutchinson Rd Batavia OH 45103

HAGER, JOAN DIANE SMITH, Tchrs Aide & Study Hall Supvr; *b:* Gallipolis, OH; *m:* John Daniel; *c:* Jodie Diane, Jennifer Danielle; *ed:* OH Vly Chrstn Schl Tchrs Aide, Study Hall Supvr 6 Yrs; *cr:* OH Valley Christian Schl Tchrs Aide and Study Hall Supervisor 6 Yrs.

HAGER, PEGGY MC ADAM, 6th Grd Math & Reading Teacher; *b:* Philadelphia, PA; *m:* Bruce R.; *c:* Adam Taylor, Amy, Drew; *ed:* West Chester Univ (BS) Elem 1976; Working on Masters Degree in Hlth; *cr:* County Lines Magazine Account Exec 1977-80; Peggy Taylor Catering Owner 1980-84; Brandywine YMCA Fitness Instr 1984-91; Coatesville Area Schl Dist Tchr 1987-; *ai:* PSEA, NEA 1988-; Bd of Dir Brandywine YMCA 1981-84, Team Ldr, Annual Support Campaign, Nom Comm 1986-; Instrl Grant; One of 2 Tchrs Who Created the Scholar Dollars Prgm; Initiated, Supervised Pen Pal Project with Canadian Stdnts; *home:* 841 Monteith Dr Wayne PA 19087*

HAGERTY, ROBERT E., Associate Professor of Art; *b:* Charleston, WV; *ed:* Auburn Univ (BFA) Graphic Design 1972; Univ of Cincinnati (MFA) Painting 1981; *cr:* Tuskegee Univ Instr of Art, Graphic Designer 1973-86; Univ of Cincinnati Professor of Art 1986-; *ai:* Acad Adv; Collge Art Assn 1992-; AAUP 1986-; Intnl Visual Literacy Assn 1993-; Numerous Shows of Artwork In Natl, Intnl Juried Exhibitions; *office:* Univ Of Cin R Walters Coll 9555 Plainfield Rd Cincinnati OH 45236

HAGEY, HARRIET ELIZABETH, 8th Grade Phys Sci Teacher; *b:* Akron, OH; *m:* Earl; *ed:* Univ of Akron (BS) Ed 1965, (MS) Ed 1980; *cr:* Akron City Schls Elem Tchr 1965-70; Norton City Schls MS Tchr 1970-; *ai:* Natl Jr Hnr Soc; Alternate Learning Tutor; NCTA, NES, OEA 1970-, Bld Rep 1980; AEA, NEA, OEA 1965-69, Bldg Rep 1967; Phi Delta Kappa 1986-; Organ Guild Akron Civic Theatre 1983-; Akron Civic Theater 1995-, Vol; *office:* Norton City Schls 3390 Cleveland Massillon Rd Norton OH 44203

HAGGERTY, EILEEN MARIE,SSJ, Kindergarten Teacher; *b:* Phila, PA; *ed:* Chestnut Hill Coll (BS) Elem Ed 1971, (MED) Early Chldhd 1984; *cr:* Parochial Schl 1-8 Grd Elem Ed Tchr 1956-82, Early Chldhd, Kndgtn Tchr 1983-; *ai:* Early Chldhd Comm Phila Diocese 1986-88; Instructed Tchrs Wkshps; NCEA 1960-; Consultant for Silver Burdett & Ginn Inc 1987-88; *office:* Christ The King Schl 3205 Chesterfield Rd Philadelphia PA 19114*

HAGGERTY, MARY KATHLEEN, Fourth Grade Teacher; *b:* Brunswick, ME; *ed:* Univ of ME at Orono (BS) Elem Ed 1970, (MED) Ed, His 1976; *cr:* Longfellow Schl Fifth Grd Tchr 1970-72; Jordan Acres Schl Fourth Grd Tchr 1972-; *ai:* MTA, NEA, BTA 1970-; ME Cncl for Soc Stud 1990-; Pejepscot Historical Soc 1990-; *office:* Jordan Acres Schl 75 Jordan Ave Brunswick ME 04011

HAGLOCK, JILL KINSEY, HS Lead Science Teacher; *b:* Dennison, OH; *m:* Robert Edwin; *c:* Travis, Melissa; *ed:* Malone Coll (BA) Sci Comprehension, Scndry Ed 1991; *cr:* Sandy Valley HS Sci, Lead Sci Tchr 1991-; *ai:* Jr Class, Sr High Stu Cncl, Ecology Club Adv; Summer Sci Acad Organizer & Instr; Kappa Delta Pi 1990-; *home:* 3838 Cletus Ave SW Navarre OH 44662

HAGUE, BRADFORD BARBER, Science Teacher; *b:* Glens Falls, NY; *m:* Ann Louise Weidner; *c:* Erika Sisel, Nathan Barber; *ed:* Maryville Coll (BA) Bio 1974; George Williams Coll (MS) Environmental Ed 1978; Plattsburgh St Univ 12 Semester Hrs; *cr:* Maryville Coll Environ Ed Ctr Environmental Edctr 1975-76; George Williams Coll Outdoor Ed Prgm Specialist 1977-79; St Mary's Acad Earth Sci, Bio Tchr 1981-84; Queensbury MS 7-8 Grd Sci Tchr 1984-; *ai:* Regnl NY St Mid Level Sci Mentor; NY St Tech Ed Network Lead Mentor; Queensbury UFD Shared Decision Making Steering Comm; AFT, NYSUT 1984-; NYS Sci Tchrs 1990-; NSTA, NYSSSA, ASCD 1993-; NMLSTA 1995-; Regnl Bd of Cooperative Educl Svcs Compact Cncl 1994-; Warren Cty Mountain Bike Trail Comm 1993-; Regents Challenge Excl in Mid Level Ed; Greater Capital Dist Tchrs Ctr Applied Sci & Tech 1990; Co-Author Syllabus; *office:* Queensbury MS 455 Aviation Rd Queensbury NY 12804*

HAGUE, RICHARD, Eng Dept Chair & Writing Coord; *b:* Steubenville, OH; *m:* Pamela C. Korte; *c:* Patrick C., Brendan T.; *ed:* Xavier Univ (BS) Eng 1969, (MA) Eng 1971; Attnd Northwestern Univ Summer Inst 1964, Oxford Univ 1990; *cr:* Purcell Marian HS Eng Dept Chair 1969-; Edgecliff Coll Adjunct Lecturer 1980; Xavier Univ Adjunct Lecturer 1981-86; *ai:* Acad Cncl; Schl Literary Magazine Adv; Creative Writing Wkshp Moderator; Associated Writing Prgms 1989-; Southern Appalachian Writers Coop 1986-, Coord; Tchrs & Writer Collaborative 1994-; NCTE; OCTELA; Cincinnati Comm Gardens 1984-, Site Mgr; OH Arts Cncl 1984-88, Lit Panelist; Individual Artist Fellowship OH Art Cncl 1994; NEH Summer Tchrs Seminar 1990; First Prize Poetry; Master Tchr Awd; Fac Awd 1986; Co-Poet of Yr OH Poetry Day Assn 1985; Tchr Awd Grant Greater Cincinnati Fnd 1984; Books OH St U Press 1984, Cleveland St Univ 1988; Cncl for Basic Ed Arts in Ed Grant 1995; Pub a Bk 1991; *office:* Purcell Marian HS 2935 Hackberry St Cincinnati OH 45206*

HAGUE, ROBERT GRAHAM, 8th-9th Grd Soc Stud T Pittsburgh, PA; *m:* Susan; *c:* Robert, Brian, Annie Elizabeth; Univ (BS) Scndry Ed 1979; *cr:* Quaker Vly Schl Hr HS Soc 1979-; *ai:* Co-Spon, Chaperone 9th Grd Wash DC Trip; Spon, Ger Club Trip Germany; Co-Spon Mock Trial Team; QVEA, P 1979-; 60th Royal Amer Regiment Ft Pitt Re-Enactment Gr Sewickley Borough Cncl 1994-, Councilman; Distngd Tchr *home:* 307 Logan St Sewickley PA 15143

HAHN, DIANE IRVING, Chemistry Teacher; *b:* Binghamto John W.; *c:* Michael, Peter; *ed:* SUNY at Oneonta (BS) Bio & C (MS) Sci Ed 1968; Coll of St Rose (MS) Schl Guidance Cnslr Syracuse Univ, Ithaca Coll, SUNY at Albany, Long Island Un Sage; *cr:* Binghamton North HS Chem Tchr 1964-66; Bethl Schl Bio Tchr 1966-67; Columbia HS Chem Tchr 1967-; *ai:* Sci Coach; EGTA Pub Relations Comm; Benevolence Comm Chm; for Curr Stud; Key Club Adv 1994-; EGTA 1967-; NYSUT 1 1972-; STANYS 1984-, Treas; NSF Grants for Grad Stud; Sabba 1990-91 to Stud Dropout Rate; Selected as an Exceptional Tc at Columbia In the Albany Times Union 1995 & 1996; *office:* Co Luther Rd East Greenbush NY 12061*

HAHN, ELIZABETH R., English Teacher; *b:* Milwauke Frederick L.; *c:* Robert Bailey, Amy Brauchli, Julie Brau Brauchli; *ed:* Seton Hall Univ (BA) Eng 1975, (MA) Ed Post-Grad Credit Hrs; *cr:* East Stroudsburg HS Eng Tchr 1987-; Ed Assn 1988-; NEA 1988-; ASCD 1993-; NTE 1995-.

HAHN, ELLEN K., Third Grade Teacher; *b:* Wilmington, DE; DE (BS) Elem Ed 1972; Glassboro St Coll (MA) Rdng Ed Pennsville Schl Dist 3rd Grd Tchr 1972-; *ai:* Schl Based Planni Numerous Textbook Adoption Comm; NEA 1972-; Delta Kap 1982-, Corresponding Sec, 1st Vp, 2nd Vp; Winterthur Muse Advy 1992-; Governors Recognition Prgm; Penn Bch Tchr of th *office:* Penn Beach Schl 96 Kansas Rd Pennsville NJ 08070

HAHN, EWALDINE M., Second Grade Teacher; *b:* Footeda Regis A.; *c:* Brian A.; *ed:* Waynesburg Coll Stu 1959-62; 15 Waynesburg Coll, WV Coll; *cr:* Laurel Highlands Schl Dist Tchr Cheerleaders Club Spon 1962-63; Yrbk Spon Kennedy Schl; PS Highlands Educl Assn 1962-, Sec 1962-63; NEA 1962-; PTA Trained Stu Tchrs 25-28 Yrs.

HAHN, JEFFREY WILLIAM, English Teacher; *b:* Hartford, C Ann Vigaretti; *c:* Eric, Stephen; *ed:* Marietta Coll (BA) Speech 1 of MD (MED) Scndry Ed 1974; Post Grad Course Work at St U at Brockport; *cr:* Greece Olympia HS Tchr 1968-69; Greece A Tchr 1969-; *ai:* Ski Club, Schl Announcements, Schl Mgmt Tea Drug & Alcohol Awareness Team; Greece Tchrs Assn 1968-, 1968-; Presbyn Church 1975-, Elder; Spencerport Soccer Club 1 Pres, Coach; Participation in Tchr in Space Prgm 1985-86; S Resource Tchr NY St Dept of Ed 1970; *office:* Greece Athena HS Pond Rd Rochester NY 14612

HAHN, MARY LEE, Fifth Grade Teacher; *b:* Burlington, CO; Denver (BA) Eng, Elem Ed 1983; OH St Univ (MA) Children's *cr:* W. A. Blair Elem Schl 4th Grd Tchr 1983-85; Deer Run Elem Grd Tchr 1986-95; Daniel Wright Elem Schl 5th Grd Tchr 1995- Cncl; Multicultural, Ethnozraphic Study comms; NCTE 1985 1995-; EECO 1990-; City of Dublin Solid Waste Advy Comm 19 OH Wildlife Ctr 1990-94; Sherex Awd; 2 Excl in Ed Grants; Grant.

HAHN, NICHOLAS T., English Teacher; *b:* Somerville, NJ; *m:* Summer; *c:* Nicole Larisa, Victoria Rose; *ed:* Wesleyan Univ (M Lit 1978; *cr:* Northern Valley Regnl HS 10th, 12th Grd Eng Instr Adv of Relections, Schl Lit Magazine; NEA, NJEA, BCEA, NC *office:* Northern Valley Regnl HS 25 Central Ave Old Tappan NJ

HAHN, SARAH STEELE, English as Second Lang Te Cincinnati, OH; *m:* A. William; *c:* Adam, Katie, Jennifer; *ed:* Dayton (MS) Elem Ed 1985; TESOL Cert 1985; Attnd Univ o Intnl Inst; *cr:* Oakwood Pub Schls ESL Tchr 1984-89; Eng Multicultural Inst ESL Tchr 1984-89; Wright Patterson AFB 1985-87; Dayton Pub Schls ESL Tchr 1989-; *ai:* Schl Newspaper Tech Comm; Hum Bldg Chprsn; Multicultural Chair Bldg; Mul Festival Chair; Stu Tchr, Young Authors Mentor; NEA, OEA, DE OH TESOL 1995-; TWIGS 1993-; Martha Holden Jennings Wright St Univ TESOL Methods Annual Speaker; City-Wide Bic Rep 2003 Comm; Speaker, Author St Eng Lang Tchrs Conventi Peer Esl Methods Wkshps; *office:* Miami Chapel Elem Schl 16 Chapel Rd Dayton OH 45408*

HAHN, SUSAN MARY, Business Teacher; *b:* Port Chester, Norman J.; *c:* Lindsey, Nicholas; *ed:* Niagara Cty Comm Co Secretarial Sci 1969; SUNY at Buffalo (BS) Bus Ed 1973, (MS 1973; Post Grad Stud Buffalo St Coll; *cr:* Niagara Wheatfield HS 1971-92; Niagara Cty Comm Coll Bus Tchr 1974; Lewiston Porte Tchr 1992-; Niagara Wheatfield HS Bus Tchr 1992-; *ai:* NY S Tchrs, NEA 1971-; NY St Bus Tchrs Assn; Alpha Delta Kapp Corresponding Sec, Altruistic; Advy Bd Bus, Industry Cncl *home:* 1061 Baseline Rd Grand Island NY 14072*

HAHN, W. TODD, 4th Grade Teacher; *b:* Rochester, NY; *m:* Andr *c:* Chad; *ed:* St Univ Coll at Geneseo (BS) Ed 1967; Grad Work S Geneseo; *cr:* Barker Road Elem Schl 5th Grd Tchr 1967-84; Thorn Elem Schl 4th Grd Tchr 1984-; *ai:* NY St United Tchrs, Pittsf Tchrs Assn, PTSA 1967-; E Rochester Recreation 1983-, Vi WHEC-TV Heros in Our Schls; PTSA Life Mbrshp 1991; *home:* 9 St P O Box 44 East Rochester NY 14445*

HAHNE, REGINALD ALLAN, Computer Science Chair; *b:* Australia; *m:* Mary Ann Levant; *ed:* Mitchell Coll of Advanced Ed 1978; Johns Hopkins (MS) Cmptr Ed 1985; *cr:* Atholton HS Cr Chair 1985-; *ai:* Var Soccer Coach; SR Class Adv; Cmptr Educat MD 1992-93; *office:* Atholton HS 6520 Freetown Rd Columbia M

HAIDET, TRENT L., Fifth Grade Teacher; *b:* Canton, OH; *m:* Cashell; *c:* Chad; *ed:* Bluffton Coll (BA) Elem Ed 1973; Univ of (MS) Ed 1989; *cr:* Emerson Elem 4th-6th Grd Tchr 1970-92; Low 5th Grd Tchr 1992-; *ai:* DARE Booster Club; PTA Ofcr; Schl Boo Bldg Level Asst Team; Soc Stud Comm; NEA, OEA & LEA 1970-; Comm; PTA Ofcr 1970-, Pres, VP, Treas & Comms; Numerous Tas & Schl Comm; *office:* Lima City Schls 615 S Clamut Lima OH 45

HAIGH, ROSEMARY PASSANNANTE, French Teacher; *b:* N City, NY; *m:* Ian; *ed:* St John's Univ (BA) Fr 1964, (MA) Fr 197 Sorbonne, Middlebury Coll; *cr:* Sewanhaka Cntrl HS Tchr 1964-; Univ Adjunct Lecturer 1977-; *ai:* Fr Club Adv; Amer Assn Tch 1980-, Pres; NYS Foreign Lang Tchrs Assn, Long Island Lang Tch 1977-; NEA 1970-; League for Animal Protection 1984-; Amer Dowsers 1992-; FulbrightSchlsp; Author of 3 Fr Textbooks; Assistantship; US Govt Foreign Exch Grant Poland Elmont Meml of Yr; VFW Elmont's Comm Svc Awd; *office:* Elmont Memorial Ridge Rd Elmont NY 11003

HAIGHT, DAVID FREDERICK, Professor; *b:* Polson, MT; *m:* M Ann Gey; *c:* Lara; *ed:* Stanford Univ (BA) Philosophy 1963; North Univ Philosophy (MA) 1965, (PHD) 1968; Oxford Univ Philosoph iv Instr 1968; IA St Univ Asst Prof 1969-71; Plymouth St Coll ?rof 1971-; *ai:* Stu Intnl Meditation Soc Adv; Intnl Congress of 88-; Northern New England Philosophy Assn 1976-; Citizens ct-Free Politics 1992-; BA with Honors in Philosophy & ı; Fulbright Scholar; Phi Kappa Phi; Intnl Soc of Poets US Senate Nom; Numerous Articles & Poems, Book Pub; *office:* H Plymouth St Coll Department of Philosophy Plymouth NH

RICHARD L., Professor of Law; *b:* Boston, MA; *ed:* Boston Modern Langs 1962, (LLM) Taxation 1966; Sullfolk Univ (JD) *cr:* Practice of Law Attorney US Govt & Pvt 1966-84; OH niv Law Prof 1984-; *ai:* American Bar Assn 1966-, Admitted to f MA, Dist of Columbia & Federal Courts; Books: Taxes in eveloping Basic Income Tax Concepts, Problems in Federal ation; Stu Bar Assn Most Effective Tchr Awd 1994 & 1995; Northern Univ College Of Law Ada OH 45810

, JERILYNN, English Teacher; *b:* Canonsburg, PA; *ed:* CA (BS) Eng 1977, (BS) Elem 1991; Writing Curr; *cr:* Chartiers S Eng Tchr 1978-79; Ft Cherry HS Eng Tchr 1979-; *ai:* NEA ting Across Curr; Gift of Time; Mentor Tchr; *office:* Fort Cherry c Donald PA 15057*

CAROL ENGLE, 6th Grade Social Studies Tchr; *b:* Canton, enneth D.; *c:* Shaun, Eric; *ed:* Waynesburg Coll (BA) Elem Ed Univ (MS) Rdng 1978; *cr:* Cntrl Greene Schl Dist Elem Tchr *ce:* Central Greene Schl Dist 126 E Lincoln St Waynesburg PA

DAVID L., At-Risk Teacher; *b:* Philadelphia, PA; *m:* Katherine : Ryan, Zachary; *ed:* Kutztown St Univ (BS) Scndry Ed & Soc ; Post Grad Credits in Guidance & Counseling from Rowan St Ed Cert; *cr:* Middle Twp MS Tchr 1973-; *ai:* Stu Act Dir; Stu nl Store Adv; Bsbl Coach; NEA, NJEA 1973-; Sunday Schl Tchr; n for Stu Fund Raising Awds; Act for Amer Cancer Soc; Cape d Grant Recipient; Middle Twp Cultural Educl Grant; *office:* wnship MS 300 E Pacific Ave Cape May Court Hou NJ 08210

G. W.,JR., Social Studies Teacher; *b:* Washington, PA; *m:* Helen nnon, Billy; *ed:* Univ of Pittsburgh (Bach) Soc Stud 1974; 30 lits; *cr:* Trinity Schl Dist Tchr 1975-; *ai:* Soccer Coach; SADD 1975-; McGuffy Schl Bd 1990-, Pres (twice); *office:* Trinity HS Washington PA 15301

HARRY J., Biology Teacher; *b:* Philadelphia, PA; *m:* Susan Mc *c:* Laura, Peter; *ed:* Millersville Univ (BS) Bio 1970; West niv (MA) Bio 1975; Rosemont Coll 27 Credits Cmptr Sci; *cr:* e Area Schl Dist Bio Tchr 1970-73; Upper Merion Area SD Bio -76; Penn Wood HS Bio Tchr 1976-; *ai:* Phi Delta Kappa 1986-; 73-; NEA, PA Ed Assn 1970-; William Penn Ed Assn 1976-, Bldg 1985-, Asst Scoutmaster; Nat Archery Assn 1992-; Svc Awd Sci Tchr Ed Prgm 1984-86; Nat Sci Tchrs Cmptr Awd 1985; nn Wood HS 100 Green Ave Lansdowne PA 19050*

JAMES BARR, Professor of English & Spanish; *b:* Pittsburgh, artha Scull; *c:* James B., Thomas W.; *ed:* Dartmouth Coll (AB) 2; Brown Univ (MA) Span 1964; Univ of Pittsburgh (MA) Eng D) Eng 1975; Univ of Salamanca 9 Credits; *cr:* The Mercersburg n Instr 1964-67; Point Park Coll Eng & Span Prof 1975-; *ai:* Coll MLA 1971-; ACTFL 1994-; NDEA Title IV, Mellon Pre-Doctoral Article on Twain; *office:* Point Park Coll 201 Wood St Pittsburgh

ROBERT E., High School English Teacher; *b:* Kingston, NY; at New Paltz (BS) Ed, Eng 1962; 39 Post Grad Credit Hrs Ed, Red Hook Central Schl Scndry Eng Tchr 1962-; *ai:* NY St United ner Fed of Tchrs AFL, CIO, Faculty Assn 1962-; Daguerreian Soc YSCE Union 1955-, VP, Trustee, Camp Dir, Editor; High Woods d Church, Lay Pastor 1974-76; Kingston Lodge 1974-; oble Awd 1966; Hardscrabble Dedication 1985 & 1996; Dev Curr ngway Stud Pub 1983; *home:* Vista Alegre 287 W Chestnut St NY 12401

ENNETH C., Math & Computer Teacher; *b:* Carlisle, PA; *m:* *c:* Jodi, Juli, Chad; *ed:* Shippensburg Univ (BS) Math, Physics mple Univ (BS) Math 1968; Cmptr Specialist Cert 1982; *cr:* d HS Math, Cmptr Tchr 1966-81; Cumberland Vly HS 1982-; *ai:* ub; Work with Adults to Earn Diploma; Match GED Prgm Tchr; EA, CUEA 1980-; United Meth CHurch 1972-; Tandy Outstdng r Nom 1995; 1st, 3rd Place Harrisburg Area Cmptr Contest; *office:* and Valley HS 6746 Carlisle Pike Mechanicsburg PA 17055*

, SHERRY S., English & Journalism Teacher; *b:* Marion, OH; *c:* Jessica; *ed:* Baldwin-Wallace Coll (BA) Eng 1969; Ball St Univ nlsm 1975; *cr:* Scotch Plains Fanwood HS Eng, Jrnlsm Tchr Dow Jones Newspaper Fund Asst Dir 1980-86; North Plainfield Jrnlsm Tchr 1986-; *ai:* Schl Newspaper Adv; NEA, NJEA 1969-; Ed Assn 1969-, Cert Jrnlsm Edctr, Regnl Dir, Bd; Garden St c Press 1980-, Co-Founder, Pres, Exec Bd; Contributing Jrnlsm *e:* North Plainfield HS 34 Wilson Ave Plainfield NJ 07060

KO, J. MICHAEL, Dist Tech Dir & Asst Principal; *b:* Akron, OH; Pickrell; *c:* Michael John, Khrista Elise; *ed:* Univ of Akron (BA) Arts 1972; OH St Univ (MA) Educl Admin 1979; Attnd OH Univ, Univ, Columbus St Univ 90 Hrs Grad, Post Grad Credit; *cr:* d St Joseph HS Cmptr Sci, Ind Arts, Eng Tchr 1973-74; New n City Schls Tech Ed, Eng Tchr 1974-94, Dist Tech Dir, Asst MS 4-; *ai:* NASSA, OASSA 1994-; Macgahan Cultural Soc 1978-, ect; Mentor Tchr 1993, 1995; Co-Authored Dist Tech Plan & Schlnet Plus Grants; *office:* New Lexinton City Schls 310 1st St xington OH 43764*

, LINDA HOLCOMB, Fourth Grade Teacher; *b:* Newark, NJ; *m:* Lesley, Steven; *ed:* Kean Coll (BA) Elem Ed 1971, (MA) Rdng zation 1973; *cr:* Inman Ave Schl Kndgtn Tchr & Media Specialist , 3rd Grd Tchr 1972-79; Ross St Schl 4th Grd Tchr 1987-; *ai:* Writing Prgm Instr; EOSHI Trng with Rutgers; Alpha Delta Kappa Chapter Mem, Corresponding Sec; Kappa Delta Pi, NEA 1971-; y Parent 1996, Mem; Grant to Implement Calculators in om; 1st Place Awd Dist Wide for Class Involvement in mental Unit; Many Articles, Poems & 1 Song Pub in Educl es; *office:* Ross Street Schl Ross St Woodbridge NJ 07095*

RSTADT, AVIS (LEVY), Math Teacher; *b:* New Bedford, MA; *m:* Adam; *ed:* Univ of RI (BA) Ed & Eng 1967; Masters Equivalency Grad Credits; *cr:* Fitzgerald Schl 1st-3rd Grd Tchr 1967-70; Tobin -3rd Grd Tchr 1970-74; Shipleys Choice Elem Schl 6th Grd Tchr ; Magothy River Mid 7th Grd Math Tchr 1990-; *ai:* Math Magic on; Mem of Fin, Comp & Advy Comms; NEA 1985-; MTA 1985-; A 1985-; NCTM 1991-; GTE Tchng Fellow, Grant 1993; Prentice Mid Yrs Magazine Team Tchng Awd 1995; Contributor to When eets Sea; *office:* Magothy River MS 241 Peninsula Farm Rd Arnold 012

ANNETTE J., English Teacher; *b:* Allentown, PA; *c:* Julie Willis, Willis; *ed:* Thiel Coll (BA) Eng 1965; Lehigh Univ (MA) Eng 1970; vn Univ PA LIb Cert; *cr:* Dieruff HS Eng Tchr 1965-67; Whitehall HS Eng Tchr 1975-; *ai:* Scholastic Scrimmage Coach; NCTE 1976-; *office:* Whitehall HS 3800 Mechanicsville Rd Whitehall PA 18052

HALE, CARL E., English Teacher; *b:* Galion, OH; *m:* Marie Elaine; *ed:* Univ of Akron (BA) Eng 1970, (MS) Scndry Ed 1982; Univ of MO 18 Grad Hrs; *cr:* Buchtel HS Lang Arts, Eng Tchr 1971-; *ai:* Hall of Fame, NHS Selection Comms; Akron Ed Assn 1971-, Bd of Trustees 1988-; NCTE 1980-; Tchr of Yr 1993; *office:* John R. Buchtel Sr HS 1040 Copley Rd Akron OH 44320

HALE, DORIS M., Spanish Teacher; *b:* Jackson Heights, NY; *m:* James E.; *c:* Nicholas, Andrew; *ed:* SUNY at Fredonia Rdng 1979; SUNY at Cortland Nursery & Elem Ed N-6, Span 7th-12th 1979; *cr:* St Peter & Paul Schl Kndgtn Tchr 1981-85; Jamestown HS Span Tchr 1985-86; Maple Grove HS Span Tchr 1986-; *ai:* Lang Club; Hnrs Project Comm; Hnr Soc Selection Comm; NEA 1986-; CCFLTA 1993-, Treas; Our Lady of Victory Church 1993-, Choir; *office:* Maple Grove HS Dutch Hollow Rd Bemus Point NY 14712

HALE, GARY, High School English Teacher; *b:* Ft Leonard Wood, MO; *m:* Aliecia Mason-Hale; *c:* Christopher, Terrence; *ed:* CO Coll (BA) Bus, Ec 1982; Southern CT St Univ (MS) Eng Lit 1986; St Peters Coll 15 Credit Hrs; *cr:* Essex Cty Coll Basic Skills Instr 1984-87; Princeton Univ Eng Precitor, Buyer 1987-88; Sci HS Eng Tchr 1988-91; Immaculate Conception HS Eng Tchr 1992-93; East Orange HS Eng Tchr 1993-; *ai:* Schl Newspaper Adv; Bsbl, Bsktbl Coach; NJEA Tchrs Assn, East Orange Educl Assn 1993-; *office:* East Orange HS 34 N Walnut St East Orange NJ 07017

HALE, STEPHEN MICHAEL, Campus Ministry Director; *b:* Boston, MA; *ed:* Springfield Coll (BS) Scndry Ed 1993; *cr:* Cathedral HS Campus Ministry & Asst Athletic Dirs 1993-; Springfield YMCA Camp Dir 1995-; *ai:* Var Ftbl & Sftbl Asst Coach; ROOTS Adv; YMCA 1995-, Camp Dir; NCEA 1993-; Cath Relief Svcs Dev Schlsp to the Ghanbia Africa; *office:* Cathedral HS 260 Surrey Rd Springfield MA 01118*

HALE, SUSAN ANDREWS, 2nd Grade Teacher; *b:* Lock Haven, PA; *c:* Abbey; *ed:* Lock Haven Univ (BS) Elem Ed 1972; 67 Credits Beyond Degree at PA St Univ & Millersville Univ; *cr:* West Branch Area Schl Dist 3rd-6th Grd Tchr 1972-75; Bellefonte Area Schl Dist 2nd & 4th Grd Tchr 1975-; *ai:* Schl Fundraiser Chprsn; Cooperating Tchr; Publicity for Schl Carnival; PSEA 1972-, Bldg Rep; NEA 1972-; BAEA 1975-; *office:* Pleasant Gap Elem Schl 230 S Main St Pleasant Gap PA 16823

HALESEY, ELAINE DIRISIO, Radiography Prof & Dept Chair; *b:* Schuylkill Cty, PA; *m:* Peter M.; *c:* Peter, Christopher; *ed:* Coll Misericordia (AAS) Radiologic Tech 1978, (MS) Human Svcs Admin 1986; Bloomsburg Univ (BS) Radiography 1983; Nora Southeastern Univ Pursuing an Ed D Higher Ed; Continuing Ed Cert ASRT; *cr:* Bone & Joint Assoc Radiographer 1978-82; Geisinger Med Ctr Radiographer 1982-84; Coll Misercordia Pgm Dir Radiography 1984-; Mercy Hosp Staff Radiographer 1988-89; *ai:* Rho Tau Adv; ARRT 1978-; ASRT 1984-; AERS 1984-; PSRT 1985-; Westside Voc-Tech Schl, Advy Bd Mem Hlth Related Tech, Steering Comm; Hanover Area HS, Steering Comm; Hanover Green PTA 1992-; Authored & Co-Authored Grant 1986, 1988; *office:* Coll Misericordia 301 Lake St Dallas PA 18612

HALEY, JANE MATTHEWS, English Teacher; *b:* Philadelphia, PA; *m:* Franklin M.; *ed:* St Univ Coll of NY at Fredonia (BA) Eng Ed 1969; Attnd Niagara Univ, SUNY at Buffalo, SUCNY at Geneseo, Coll of St Rose; *cr:* Barker Cntrl Schl Eng Tchr 1969-; *ai:* Newspaper Club, Yrbk Adv; Team Ldr; Discipline, MS, Report Card, Negotiations, Shared Decisionmaking, Prin Selection, Stu Recognition Comms; NY St United Tchrs 1969-, Bldg Rep; AFT 1969-; Delta Kappa Gamma 1989-, 2nd VP; *office:* Barker Central Schl 1628 Quaker Rd Barker NY 14012*

HALEY, RICHARD JOHN, Band Director; *b:* Buffalo, NY; *m:* Andrea Ruth Levitt; *ed:* SUC at Fredonia (BM) Music Ed 1982, College of St Rose (MS) Music Ed 1988; *cr:* Liberty Cntrl Schls 7-12th Grd Band Dir 1983-84; New Berlin Cntrl Schls 5-12th Grd Band Dir 1985-93; Portville Cntrl Schls 7-12th Grd Band Dir 1993-; *ai:* Dir Concet, Marching Bands, Jazz Ensemble; NYSSMA, MENC 1986-; NYSSMA Cert Adjudication 1988-; *office:* Portville Central Schl Elm St Portville NY 14770*

HALI, HENRY HIAMA, Science Teacher; *b:* Bolahun, Liberia; *c:* Tamba L., Saah M., Tamba B., Kumba W.; *ed:* Cuttington UNiv Coll (BS) Chem, Math 1976; Farleigh Dickinson Univ (MS) Chem 1980; *cr:* Cuttington Univ Coll Chair Sci Div 1980-85; Dominican Acad Sci, Math, Cmptrs Tchr 1986-88; Dwight Morrow HS Sci Tchr 1988-92; Teaneck HS Sci Tchr 1992-; *ai:* Chess Coach; Ham Radio Operator; Cmptr Consultant; ARRL 1983-; LRAA 1972-, Pres; NEA, NJEA, BCEA 1989-; Wilkins Forum Univ of MN 1985-; Minority, Dodge Flwshp; Fulbright Flwshp Operations Cross Roads Africa.*

HALIBURTON, BRENDA WOOD, Six Grade Math & Lang Teacher; *b:* Washington, DC; *m:* Bruce Earl; *c:* Tiffany, Troy; *ed:* Morgan St Coll (BS) Elem Ed 1972; Bowie St Univ, Trinity Coll 36 Addl Credit Hrs Disabled Learner; *cr:* Flintstone Elem Fourth-Sixth Grd Tchr 1973-95; *ai:* Schl Base Mngmt Team 1993-; Elem Math Contact Tchr; Sci, Math After Schl Club; Maryland Cncl Tchrs of Math 1994-; Asst Cub Scout Ldr for Pack 505 1993-; *office:* Flintstone Elem Schl 800 Comanche Dr Oxon Hill MD 20745

HALKETT, SANDRA TRUE, Sixth Grade Teacher; *b:* Bangor, ME; *ed:* Univ of ME at Farmington (BS) Elem Ed 1976; Univ of ME at Orono (MS) Mid Level Ed 1989; *cr:* Bangor Schl Dept 1, 3, 6th Grds Elem Ed Tchr 1976-; *ai:* Stu Cncl Adv; Intnl Days Co-Chm; Local Bangor Educl Assn 1976-, Many Chairs; Bus & Prof Women's Club, Local Pres, Many St Comm Chairs, Over 10 Yrs; Awarded by Girl Scouts of Amer; Bus & Prof Women Several Awds; Outstdng Young Woman of Amer Twice; *office:* Garland Street MS Harlow St Bangor ME 04401*

HALL, ALDEN B.,JR., Jr & Sr High Teacher; *b:* New York, NY; *m:* Pamela Elizabeth Malley; *c:* Allison Brooke, Patricia Michelle; *ed:* Quinnipiac Coll Schl of Law (JD) 1980; *cr:* CT Judicial Dept Law Clerk 1988-89; Parrett, Porto & Parese PC Atty 1989-90; New Hope Chrstn Acad Tchr 1991-; *office:* New Hope Christian Acad 18 Clapboard Ridge Rd Danbury CT 06811

HALL, ANNA LOUISE, Third Grade Teacher; *b:* Shepherdstown, WV; *m:* Alvin Hall; *c:* Alvina King, Alvin Jr., Thomas, Veleka; *ed:* Medgar Evers Coll (BA) Ed 1977; Adelphi Univ (MA) Ed 1990; 128 Credit Hrs at Comm Bible Inst; *cr:* Bd of Ed Pub Schl 46 Tchr 1980-; Brooklyn Tabernacle Del Ctr Tchr 1991-; *ai:* Pregnant Teen Adv; Brooklyn Tabernacle Del Ctr 1980-, Minister; Childrens Church Pastor; Rel Ed Master Prgm, Bible Schl Tchr; *home:* 139-20 Laurelton Pklyn Rosedale NY 11422

HALL, BERYLE FRANCINE, Fifth Grade Teacher; *b:* Washington, DC; *m:* John Russell Jr.; *c:* DeVonne Annette Chapman, David Allen, Juanita Jeanette; *ed:* Bowie St Univ (BS) Elem Ed 1972, (ME) 1979; Working on MA Guid Cnslng; *cr:* Calvert Elem Schl 3-5 Grd Tchr 1972-83; Beach Elem Schl 4-5 Grd Tchr 1983-; *ai:* Mt Hope United Meth Yth Choir Dir, Lay Speaker; Dunkirk Warrior Yth Club, Chrldrs, PomsCoach; Foster Parent; NEA, MSTA 1972-; CEA 1972-, Sec, Act Chprsn; Dels Schlsp Comm 1990-; *office:* Beach Elem Schl 7900 Old Bayside Rd Chesapeake Beach MD 20732*

HALL, BRENDA BASINGER, Second Grade Teacher; *b:* Bluffton, OH; *m:* James L.; *c:* Ryan; *ed:* Bluffton Coll (BA) Elem Ed 1968; Wright St Univ (MS) Rdng Specialist 1975; *cr:* Sidney City Schls 1st-3rd Grd Tchr 1968-; *ai:* SEA 1968-, Treas; OEA, NEA 1968-; 1st Presbyn Church 1971-, Sunday Schl & Bible Schl Tchr; Kodak Tchng Tip Awd 1982; Sidney Ed Tchr Grant 1984; Martha Holden Jennings Scholar 1986; Sidney Citys Tchr of Yr 1991; Ashlands Golden Apple Awd 1988; *office:* Emerson Elem Schl 901 Campbell Rd Sidney OH 45365

HALL, CANDACE JOAN (COGLEY), Business Teacher; *b:* Seyberttown, PA; *m:* William Bruce; *c:* Sarah April, Kristin Dawn; *ed:* IN Univ of PA (BS) Secretarial, Marketing 1970, (MEQ) Acctng, MIS 1987; Cmptr Courses; *cr:* Cogleys Insurance Agency Sec Part-time 1967-70; Arin Film Svc Clerk Part-time 1967-70; Livingston NJ Parks & Rec Cashier, Food Svc Part-time 1968-69; Armstrong Schl Dist Bus Tchr 1970-; *ai:* ASD Tech Assessement Comm & Strategic Planning, Prep Curr Planning Comm; NEA, PBEA 1970-; PSEA 1970-, Prof Rights & Respons Commissioner; Armstrong Ed Assn 1970-, Mbrshp Chair, Bldg Rep, PR & R Chair, Spec Svcs Chair; Cowansville Hlth Ctr, Pres, Treas, Fin Chair; First Presbyn Church 1962-, Elder, Mission Chair, Session Mem; Amer Ed Week Articles Local Newspaper; *office:* Kittanning Sr HS 1200 Orr Ave Kittanning PA 16201

HALL, CASSANDRA WEST, Jr HS Reading & Tchr of Gftd; *b:* Masontown, PA; *m:* James A.; *c:* Richard James, Carol Hall Oravetz; *ed:* Seton Hill Coll (BA) Eng 1965; Univ of Pittsburgh (ME) Rdng & Lang Arts 1969; *cr:* Mount Pleasant Area Jr HS Tchr Rdng & Eng 31 Yrs; Sr HS Gifted Prgm; *ai:* Jr HS Yrbk Adv 12 Yrs; Schl Camera Club Adv 1993-; NEA, PA St Ed Assn 1965-; *office:* Mt Pleasant Area Jr Sr HS RD 4 Mount Pleasant PA 15666

HALL, CHARLES LOUIS, Army JROTC Instructor; *b:* Prestonsburg, KY; *m:* Gertrud Elisabeth Schluter; *c:* Cindy L. Stahl, Leona G. Hellner; *ed:* Attnd Univ of KY, Univ of South AL; *cr:* Patch Amer HS Army Jr Reserve Ofcrs Trng Corps Instr 1985-86; Osterholz Amer HS Army Jr Reserve Ofcrs Trng Corps Instr 1986-92; Baumholder Amer HS Army Jr Reserve Ofcrs Trng Corps Instr 1992-; *ai:* Var Rifle Team, Drill Team Coach; Schl Improvement Comm; NHS Selection Comm; Fraternal Order of Masons 1968-, Master; Scottish Rite Mason 1969-, Master; Germany Order of Merit Medal Lower Saxony 1981; *office:* Baumholder American HS Cmr 405 Box 1220 APO AE 09034

HALL, DANIEL, Math Dept Chairman; *b:* Amityville, NY; *m:* Donna Ann Brooks; *c:* Daniel Jr., Maureen, William, Suzanne; *ed:* Providence coll (BA) Math, Ed 1959; Long Isl Univ (CW POST), (MA) Math, Ed 1964; SUNY at Stony Brook (MS) Math 1986; 27 Hrs Math Univ of VT; 6 Hrs Math Univ of CA at San Diego, 12 Hrs Math Fordham Univ; 3 Hrs Math Harvard Univ; *cr:* Massapequa HS Math Tchr 1959-72; Rocky Point HS Math Chm 1972-; *ai:* Tennis Coach 1967-72; Honor Soc Adv 1973-; Math Team Coach 1974-; SCMTA 1972-; NEA 1976-; NYSTA 1960-; Amer Contract Bridge League 1962-; Boy Scout Ldr 1979-; CYO 1980-; Life Master ACBL 1976; Long Island Champ Bridge Mens Pairs 1968; Amplification Harvard Univ 1987; *office:* Rocky Point HS Yaphank Rd Rocky Point NY 11778

HALL, DAVID ASHWORTH, Supervisor of Student Tchrs; *b:* Philadelphia, PA; *m:* Jane Ellen; *c:* David, Linda Gibian; *ed:* Ursinus Coll (BA) His 1963; Temple Univ (MED) Ed Admin 1970; *cr:* Springfield Schl Dist 8th Grd Soc Stud 1963-95; West Chester Univ Stu Tchr Supvr 1996-; *ai:* MS Bsktbl & Bsbl Coach 1968-81; HS Var Bsbl Coach 1985-92; Past Stu Cncl Adv, Dept Mgr, Ath Dir; Home & Schl Dist Curr Comms; PSEA 1963-; Positive Tchng Awd 1986; Chamber of Commerce Var Bsbl Sportsmanship Awd Cntrl League 1991; Delaware Cty Ec Ed Awd of Excel 1992; E J Richardson Home & Schl Outstdng Svc Awd 1995; *home:* 130 Crestwood Rd Landenberg PA 19350

HALL, DAVID WAYNE, Social Studies Teacher; *b:* Saint Marys, OH; *m:* Deborah Getz; *c:* Jeffrey, Amanda; *ed:* Univ of Toledo (BED) Intensive Soc Scis-Summa Cum Laude 1978, (MED) Admin & Supervision 1982; Attnd Univ of Toledo Law Schl 1978; *cr:* Springfield HS Soc Stud Tchr 1978-79; Whitmer HS Soc Stud Tchr 1979-82; Perrysburg HS Soc Stud Tchr 1982-; *ai:* Bsbl Head Coach 1986-; Ftbl Asst Coach 1982-; SWAT Team Mem; NEA, OEA 1979-; Kappa Delta Pi; Pi Gamma Mu; Phi Beta Kappa; OH HS Bsbl Coaches Assn 1979-, Bd of Dir for Northwest OH; Toledo Metro Bsbl Coaches Assn 1979-, Pres 3 Times; OHS Ftbl Coaches Assn; Perrysburg Booster 1982-; Tchr of Month; *office:* Perrysburg HS 550 E South Boundary St Perrysburg OH 43551

HALL, DEAN B., Social Studies Teacher; *b:* Lewiston, ME; *m:* Marie; *c:* Eric, David; *ed:* Univ of ME (BA) His & Pol Sci 1970; Univ of Southern ME (MSEd) Counseling 1982; ACEP; *cr:* Durham Elem Schl 6th-8th Grd Soc Stud Tchr 1974-78; Lisbon HS Tchr 1978-; *ai:* Boys & Girls Track Head Coach; Athletic Asst Dir.

HALL, DIANNE MARGARET, Teacher; *b:* Paterson, NJ; *ed:* William Paterson Coll (BA) Elem Ed 1984, (MED) Math 1989; Supvrs Cert 1991; 30 Addl Grad Credits Admin & Supvr; *cr:* Yanticaw Schl Perm Sub Tchr 1984-85; Clifton Elem Schl 12 Grd Tchr 1985-86, 9th Grd Tchr 1986-87; Clifton HS Tchr 1987-88; Woodrow Wilson MS Tchr 1988-; *ai:* Clifton Tchrs Assn, Passaic Cty Ed Assn, NJ Ed Assn, NEA 1985-; *office:* Woodrow Wilson MS 1400 Van Houten Ave Clifton NJ 07013

HALL, DONALD RICHARD, Physical Education Teacher; *b:* Atlantic City, NJ; *m:* Renee T. Solari; *c:* Dino Matthew, Alicia Maria, Nicholas Domenic; *ed:* Glassboro St Coll (BA) PE, Hlth, Recreation 1982; *cr:* Cleveland Browns Prof Ftbl Player 1979-85; Portland Breakers Prof Ftbl Player 1979-85; Pleasantville Pub Schls Tchr 1985-; *ai:* Weight Trng Club; Head Bsbl Coach; NJEA, NEA, PEA 1985-, Negotiating Team; GTAA 1990-, Vol Coach; Ftbl Coach of Yr Lions Club 1987; *office:* Pleasantville HS 350 S Franklin Blvd Pleasantville NJ 08232

HALL, DONNA LYNN, 9th-11th Grade English Teacher; *b:* Woodbury, NJ; *ed:* Camden Cty Coll (AA) Lbrl Arts 1990; Rider Coll (BA) Eng Lit & Sec Ed 1993; *cr:* Rancocas Vly Regnl HS Eng Tchr 1993-; *ai:* SRA Panel Chaperone; Eng Team Tchng Mem; NEA 1993-; *office:* Rancocas Valley Reg HS Jackson & Ridgeway Mount Holly NJ 08060

HALL, ELEANORA T., Social Studies & Spec Ed Tchr; *b:* Baltimore, MD; *m:* Wade; *c:* Aaron; *ed:* Morgan St Univ (BA) His, Soc Stud 1972; Johns Hopkins Univ (MED) Ed 1973; 30 Addl Hrs; 9 Hrs Loyola Coll; 3 Hrs Towson St Univ; *cr:* Pikesville Jr HS Soc Stud Tchr 1 Yr; Lemmel Jr HS Soc Stud Tchr 9 Yrs; Lida Lee Tall Res Ctr Resource Tchr 1 Yr; Perry Hall HS Spec Ed, Soc Stud Tchr 13 Yrs; *ai:* Our Voices Minority Club, Step Squad, Mentoring Adv; Class Spon 1988, 1993, 1995; NEA 1972-; Multi-Culture Diversity Awd; Awd for Excl in Ed; *office:* Perry Hall HS 4601 Ebenezer Rd Baltimore MD 21236*

HALL, GARRY ALLEN, Work Adjustment Coordinator; *b:* Wayne, WV; *m:* Brenda McClain; *c:* Kelsey; *ed:* Marshall Univ (BA) Hlth & PE 1975, (MS) Voc & Tech Ed 1982; 15 Credit Hrs; *cr:* South Point HS Hlth Tchr 1975-79; Wellston HS Occupational Work Adjustment Coord 1979-; *ai:* Discipline Comm; Band 200 Club; Career 100 Club; NEA 1979-; OH Ed Assn 1979-; Wellston Tchrs Assn 1979-; Amer Legion Post 371 1982-; Columbus Assn Performing Arts 1990-; *home:* 2683 Glen Roy Rd Wellston OH 45692

HALL, GEMMA MAHONEY, 1st Grade Teacher; *b:* Louisville, KY; *m:* John H. Jr.; *c:* John H. III; *ed:* Queens Coll (BA) Ed 1969; Hufstra Univ (BS) Spec Ed 1974; Addl 12 Hrs Cmptr Courses, 6 Hrs Grad Credit Coll of St Rose, 9 Hrs Inservice Courses; *cr:* W S Mount Schl 1st Grd Tchr 1969-77, 2nd Grd Tchr 1977-85, 3rd Grd Tchr 1985-; *ai:* Three Village Tchrs Assn Chprsn in Charge of In-service & Staff Dev; PTA Fac Rep;

AFT, NYS United Tchrs 1969-; Three Village Tchr of Yr 1986-87; Mentor in NY St Mentor Intern Prgm; *office:* William Sidney Mount Elem Sch 50 Dean Ln Stony Brook NY 11790*

HALL, GEORGIANN MAUD, Science Teacher; *b:* Scranton, PA; *c:* Amy Kristin, Erin Courtney; *ed:* Taylor Univ (BA) Bio 1971; St Univ of NY at Albany (MS) Bio 1988; Grad Hrs Dev Bio Cntrl MI Univ 1974; *cr:* AuSable Inst for Environmental Stud Instr 1978-89; Ballston Spa HS Sci Tchr 1981-; *ai:* Envirothon Competition Coach; AFT 1981-; NABT 1994-; *office:* Ballston Spa HS 480 Garrett Rd Ballston Spa NY 12020

HALL, GLEN, Social Science Teacher; *b:* McKeesport, PA; *m:* Robin; *c:* Ashley; *ed:* California Unvi of PA (BS) Scndry Ed, Soc Sci 1988; Working on MS Schl Psych; *cr:* Turkeyfoot Valley Schl Dist Tchr 1989-; *ai:* Stu Cncl, SADD Adv; Stu Assistance Prgm; Head Bsbl Coach; Asst Ftbl Coach; Weightlifting Coach; Soc Stud Chprsn; NEA, PSEA 1989-, VP; Natl Assn of Stu Cncl Adv 1990-; ASCD 1989-; *office:* Turkeyfoot Valley Area Schl Rd 1 Box 78 Confluence PA 15424*

HALL, HOLLYS EASTERLING, French Teacher & Dept Chair; *b:* Elyria, OH; *m:* Heath A; *c:* Austin; *ed:* OH St Univ (BA) Fr Ed 1986, (MS) Admin 1994; 35 Addl Hrs; *cr:* Dublin Coffman HS Tchr 1986-95; Dublin Scioto Tchr 1995-; *ai:* Dept Chair; Fr Club Adv; OFLA 1986-; Grant to Promote Foreign Lang in Elem; *office:* Dublin Scioto HS 4000 Hard Rd Dublin OH 43016

HALL, J. TIM, Biology Teacher; *b:* Middletown, OH; *m:* Tamara L. King; *c:* Katie; *ed:* Eastern KY Univ (BS) Bio 1975; Attnd Miami Univ, Univ of Cincinnati, Mt St Joseph, Wright St Univ; *cr:* Lakota HS Tchr 1975-; *ai:* NEA; NSTA; *office:* Lakota HS 5050 Tylersville Rd West Chester OH 45069*

HALL, JACK SHELBURN, Professor of Music; *b:* Manchester, KY; *ed:* Univ of KY (BA) Music 1962; Eastern KY Univ (MA) Music 1969; Indiana Univ of PA (DED) Music 1981; *cr:* Fayette Co Schl Orch Dir 1962-69; Clarion Univ Prof of Music 1970-; *ai:* Brass Ensemble Conductor; Fulbright & Music Ed Comm Mem; PA Music Educators Assn 1978-; Natl Trpt Guild 1985-; Music Educators Natl Conf 1972-; Kappa Kappa Psi Music 1970-; KY Colonels 1970-; Schubert Music Club 1995-; 50 Music Publications From 1970-; St of PA Out-Svc Grant 1981; Whos Who Among Amer Writers; *office:* Clarion Univ Of PA Clarion PA 16214

HALL, JACQUELYN L. (FIELD), Guidance Counselor; *b:* Portland, ME; *m:* Harold James; *c:* Stephen M., Joshua D., John M.; *ed:* Gordon Coll (BS) Elem Ed, Scndry Ed, Soc Stud 1968; Univ System of NH (MED) Guid, Cnslng 1985; Attnd Boston Univ; *cr:* Claremont Schl Dist Grd 4 Tchr 1968-69; Unity Schl Dist Grds 1-6 Tchr 1969-72; Claremont Schl Dist Grd 4, HS Civics Tchr 1975-85, Grds 7-8 Guid Cnslr 1985-; *ai:* Inst for Reality Therapy 1980-; NEA, NHEA, SREA 1968-; Amer Schl Cnslng Assn 1992-; NH Guid, Cnslng Assn 1986-; Amer Curr Dev Assn 1994-; Vestry-Trinity Episcopal Church 1990-, Vestry; Trinity Episcopal 1990-, Sunday Schl Tchr, Co-Dir; Young Career Woman from NH to Natl BPW Conf 1990; Reality Therapy Certfd 1980; Practicum Supvr for Level 1, 2; Designed, Implemented Dropout Prevention Prgm at 9th Grd Level 1975.

HALL, JAMES E., Social Studies Teacher; *b:* Fukuoka, Japan; *m:* Victoria Annette Wright; *ed:* Lock Haven St Univ (BA) Scndry Ed Soc Stud 1980; Western MO Univ (APC) Scndry Ed 1991; Attnd Towson St Univ, Charles Cty Comm Coll; *cr:* Hobart Coll Ftbl Asst Coach 1980-81; Northern HS Soc Stud, Civics, US His, World His & Law Ed Instr 1981-; *ai:* Head Golf Coach 1989-; Asst Track Coach; Japanese Exch Coord; Grad Exercise Comm; Calvert Ed Assn 1981-; Christmas in April 1992-; Elks 1994-; *office:* Northern HS 2950 Chaneyville Rd Owings MD 20736

HALL, JON MICHAEL, Science Teacher; *b:* Manchester, NH; *m:* Maureen Cote; *c:* James; *ed:* Keene St Coll (BED) Bio 1973; *cr:* Pinkerton Acad Sci Tchr 1973-84; Raymond High Sci Tchr 1990-; *ai:* NEA 1990-; NH Track & Field Coach of Yr 1978; *office:* Raymond HS 45 Harriman Hill Rd Raymond NH 03077

HALL, KATHLEEN SUSAN, English Teacher; *b:* Philadelphia, PA; *m:* Tod O. Dagle; *ed:* West Chester Univ (BS) Scndry Ed 1977; 48 Credits MA Equivalency Kutztown Univ, Penn St Univ, Temple Univ, St Joseph's Univ; Stud in England; *cr:* Northwest Jr HS 7th, 9th Grds Eng Tchr 1978-79; Reading HS 9th-12th Grd Eng Tchr 1979-; *ai:* NEA, PSEA, REA 1978-; NCTE 1982-; *office:* Reading Sr HS 801 N Thirteenth St Reading PA 19604*

HALL, LANNA PENDLETON, Art Teacher; *b:* Bryan, OH; *m:* Clarence; *ed:* Univ of Toledo (BSEd) Art Spec K-12 1972; Bowling Green St Univ (MA) Art, Painting 1982, (MFA) Art, Painting 1984; Working on Permanent Tchng Cert; Attnd Arrowmont Schl of Arts & Crafts at Gatlinburg; *cr:* Edon Northwest Local Schls Art Instr 1972-; Bowling Green St Univ Grad Tchng Asst 1981-82; *ai:* Sr Citizens Art Classes; OH Art Ed Assn, OH Ed Assn, NEA 1972-; Edon Northwest Tchrs Assn 1972-, Sec, Treas, Pres; Toledo Museum of Art 1974-; Ft Wayne Museum of Art 1985-; Tri St Artists Assn, Pres, Sec; Numerous Art Exhibits; *office:* Edon Northwest Local Schls Box 188 Edon OH 43518

HALL, LARISSA JO, Multi-Age Classroom Teacher; *b:* Chillicothe, OH; *m:* Frank; *c:* Tammy Cautela, Brett, Heath; *ed:* OH St Univ (BS) 1st-8th Grd Elem Ed 1986, (MA) Children's Lit, Lang Acquisition 1994; 15 Addl Hrs Children's Lit, Rdng, Writing; *cr:* Happy Hour Presch Tchr 5 Yrs; Liberty Schl 2nd Grd Tchr 1 Yr, 2nd-3rd Grd Multiage Tchr 1 Yr; Granby Schl 5th Grd Tchr 4 Yrs; Evening Street Schl 6th Grd Tchr 1 Yr, 5th-6th Grd Multiage Tchr 3 Yrs; *ai:* Dist of Worthington Lang Arts Cncl, Lang, Soc Stud Curr Comm; Math Ldr; Peer Mediation Comm; NEA, OEA 1986-; NCTE 1990-; OCTELA 1988-; Worthington Ed Assn 1986-, Local Level Treas 1 Yr, Schls Rep; All Saints Luth 1969-, Comms, After Guild Nursery Sunday Schl Tchr; PTA 1967-, Fund Raising Comms, Schl Rep; Twigs for Childrens Hosp 8 Yrs; Article Pub; *home:* 253 Heischman Ave Worthington OH 43085*

HALL, LAURENCE PENNELL, Mathematics Teacher; *b:* Westerly, RI; *ed:* Univ of RI (BA) Ed 1976; *cr:* Chariho Regnl Schl Math Tchr 1976-; *ai:* MS Girls Bsktbl Coach 1980-; MS Girls Sftbl Coach 1979-; Class Adv 1979-91; NEA 1976-, Treas; Phi Kappa Delta 1976-; St James Folk Group 1980-, Dir; Hope Vly Ambulance 1990-95, Vol; Chariho Schlsp Comm 1993-, Co-Chair, Treas; Chariho Strategic Planning Comm 1993-; *office:* Chariho Regnl MS 455B Switch Rd Wood River Junctio RI 02894

HALL, LINDA R., Music Educator; *b:* Baltimore, MD; *c:* Kristi; *ed:* Shenandoah Conservatory of Music (BME) Music Ed 1976; Coppin St Coll Spcl Ed; Morgan St Coll Choral Conducting; Peabody Conservatory; Univ of MD; Post-Grad Stud 30 Credit Hrs; *cr:* Montebello Elem Music Edctr 1976-82; Garrett Hgts Elem Music Edctr 1978; Glenmount Elem Music Edctr 1979-82; Baltimore Coty Coll HS 1987-; *ai:* Mixed Chorus, Concert Choir, The Singing Knights, Chamber Ensemble, The Knights & Dames Show Dir; Intnl Baccalaurate Comm Choir; MENC 1976-; MMEA 1977-; ACDA 1987-, Repertoire & Stan Chr St of MD Sr High; St John AME Church, Minister of Music 1986-95; Trinity Presbyn Church, Minister of Music 1995-; Awd of Distinction of Excl in Music Ed; Clinician for MD Music Edctrs Assn Division Conf; Awd for Svc in Pub Interest FBI; Several Articles Pub; Groups Have Won 1st & 2nd Place Hnrs in Natl Competition in FL, Myrtle Beach, GA & Canada; Stdnts Choir Mems Recorded The Whats Best About Balitmore Commercial Performed for the Pre-Inaugural Gala 1993; *office:* Baltimore City College HS 480 3220 The Alameda Baltimore MD 21218

HALL, LUJEAN E., Math Teacher & Associate Head; *b:* Norfolk, NE; *m:* Terry F.; *c:* Chanda, Cliffton; *ed:* Univ of NE at Lincoln (MS) Math & Fr 1969, (MAT) Math 1971; Univ of PA Credit Hrs in Ed 1972-73; *cr:* Westbrook Jr High Tchr 1971-72; Roland Park Cntry Schl Math Tchr 1973-, Math Dept Chair & Math Tchr 1975-82, Upper Schl Head & Math Tchr 1979-93, Assoc Head & Math Tchr 1993-; *ai:* Cum Laude Soc Sec; Tech Comm Chair; Evaluation Steering Comm Chair; NASPG 1994-.

HALL, MARY, Assistant Professor of English; *b:* Pittsburgh, PA; *ed:* Univ of Pittsburgh (BA) Lit 1977, (MFA) Writing, Fiction 1981, (PHD) Lit 1990; *cr:* Univ of Pittsburgh Part-time Instr 1986-88, Instr 1988-93, Asst Prof 1993-; *ai:* Stu Adv; Host Prof for Visiting HS Stdnts; Learning Ctr Writing Assistance Dir; NCTE 1991-; Assn Bus Comm 1990-; Assn for Tchrs of Eng Grammar 1990-, Sec 1992-94; Articles Pub; Regnl, Natl, Intnl Presentations; *home:* 417 W Walnut St Titusville PA 16354

HALL, MELVIN RAYMOND, Adjunct Professor; *b:* New York, NY; *c:* Denise; *ed:* Audrey Cohen Coll Schl of Human Svcs (BPS) 1986; Hunter Coll Schl of Soc Work (MSW) 1988; James W. Teamer Schl of Rel (PHD) Pedagogy 1993; *cr:* Semple-Rieger Co Inc Exec Sec 1948-69; Gaylords Corp Payroll Mgr Asst 1969-74; Grace Meth Church Dir Motivation Wkshps 1974-75; NYC Dept of Soc Svcs Mgr III 1976-92; *ai:* Human Relations, Motivation Wkshp Dir; Cnslr; NASW 1980-; Grace United Meth Church 1962-, Crisis Cnslr, 4 Plaques; NAACP; HRA Grant to Hunter Coll Schl of Soc Work; *home:* 19812 115th Ave Saint Albans NY 11412*

HALL, MICHAEL JOHN, Math Teacher; *b:* Warren, OH; *ed:* Kent St Univ (BS) Math 1992; 14 Grad Credit Hrs Admin Cert; Trained Conflict Mgmt Mediator; *cr:* Wickliffe HS Math Tchr 1992-; *ai:* Head Bsbl Coach; Var Asst Ftbl Coach; Weight Room Coord; NEA, WEA, NEOCTM 1992-; OCTM 1993-; Lake Cnty Coaches Assn for Ftbl & Bsbl 1992; *office:* Wickliffe HS 2255 Rockefeller Rd Wickliffe OH 44092*

HALL, NANCY MARVIN, Writer & Consultant; *b:* Three Rivers, MI; *c:* Jeffrey Marvin, Jennifer Wynne; *ed:* Middlebury Coll (AB) Amer Lit 1956; Lesley Coll (MA) Learning Disabilities 1975; Childrens Hosp Lang Therapist Cert 1965-67; *cr:* Concord Pub Schl Spec Needs Tutor 1966-68; Carlisle Pub Schls Resource Room Tchr 1967-74; Writer of Educl Materials 1970-; The Fenn Schl Tchr, Dir of Intensive Lang Prgm 1974-88; Educl Evaluations Testing Svc Evaluator, Sole Proprietor 1979-; Truro Pub Schl Itinerant Tutor Spec Needs 1993-95; Harwich Pub Schl Itnerant Tutor Spec Needs 1994-; *ai:* Orton Soc 1967-; Co-Author Explode the Code Series; Author Ready Set Go Series, Spellwell Spelling Series Grd 2-5.*

HALL, PATRICIA MARY, Computer Instructor; *b:* Waterbury, CT; *ed:* Cntrl CT St Univ (BS) Bus Ed 1977, (MS) Counseling 1982; Fairfield Univ (CAS) Admin 1991; *cr:* Woodbury MS Cmptr Instr 1 Yr; Nonnewaug HS Bus Instr 16 Yrs; Acad for Bus Bus Instr 1 Yr; *ai:* Cmptr Club Adv; Quality Team; Bldg Comm; Class & Stu Cncl Adv; Attendance Comm; CBEA, NEA, NTA 1979-; Jaycees 1977-80, VP; Colitis Fnd 1982-, Newsletter; Phi Delta Kappa 1989-, Mem; Wrote Time Mgmt & Career Planning Articles for St of CT; *office:* Woodbury MS 67 Washington Ave Woodbury CT 06798

HALL, PATRICIA NOWAKOWSKI, Earth Space Science Teacher; *b:* Erie, PA; *m:* Michael; *c:* Amy, Brian; *ed:* Edinboro Univ (BS) Earth Sci 1972, (MED) Earth Sci 1975; *cr:* Erie Planetarium Dir 1973; Mc Dowell Intermediate Earth Sci Tchr 1973-; *ai:* NEA, MEA 1973-; *office:* Mc Dowell Intermediate HS 3320 Caughey Rd Erie PA 16506

HALL, PENDLETON, German & English Teacher; *b:* Wilmington, DE; *m:* Lawrence LaTour; *c:* Carter Nixon, Elizabeth Nixon; *ed:* Randolph-Macon Womans Coll (BA) Ger 1965; Univ of NC Ger 1968; *cr:* Phillips Jr HS Eng Tchr 1968-69; North Kingstown HS Eng Tchr 1970-71, Eng, Ger Tchr 1978-; *ai:* Past Drama Club Adv; Skills Commission; Student Success, Scholarship, Curr Comms; NEA 1978-; RI Foreign Lang Assn 1978-; American Assn Tchrs of Ger 1981-; South Cty Coalition Against Racism 1980-, Pres, VP; Westminster Unitarian Church 1984-, Soc Action Comm; Goethe Inst, AATG Fellowships for Seminars; *office:* North Kingstown HS 150 Fairway Dr North Kingstown RI 02852*

HALL, RICK LEE, Health & Physical Ed Teacher; *b:* Curwensville, PA; *m:* Kristen Lyn Cronemiller; *ed:* Indiana Univ of PA (BS) Hlth, PE 1989; Need 12 Grad Credits for MS in Sports Admin; *cr:* Curwensville HS Head Girls Bsktbl, Bsbl Coach 1984-88; Indiana HS Hlth, PE Tchr 1989; Indiana Univ of PA Asst Women's Bsktbl Coach 1989-91; Pocono Mountain HS hlth & PE Tchr, Head Girls Bsktbl, Softbl Coach 1991-; *ai:* Bsktbl & Sftbl Intramural, Var Letterwinner Club Adv; PSEA, NEA 1991-; Women's Bsktbl Coaches Assn 1990-, Male Coaches in Women's Bsktbl Comm HS Rep; PA Scholastic Girls Bsktbl Coaches Assn 1993-; Tchr of Week 1994; Coach League All-Stars in Annual Tournament 2 Times; *office:* Pocono Mountain Schl Dist Box 200 Swiftwater PA 18370

HALL, SHERRI SHORT, English Teacher; *b:* Wauseon, OH; *m:* Ellis Franklin III; *ed:* Heidelberg Coll (BA) Music, Eng, Speech 1980; Bowling Green St Univ (MA) Eng 1987; *cr:* Van Buren Schls Eng Tchr 1981-85; Shadyside Schls Eng Tchr 1986-; Wheeling Jesuit Coll Adjunct Eng Fac 1989-; *ai:* Spelling Bee Coord; Cty Rules Judge; Gifted & Talented Liason; Stu Newspaper Adv; NEA 1981-; NCTE 1984-; Towngate Theatre Bd 1988-; Delta Kappa Gamma 1990-; Martha Holden Jennings Scholar; *office:* Shadyside HS 3890 Lincoln Ave Shadyside OH 43947*

HALL, TAMARA LYNN (KING), Health Education Teacher; *b:* Benham, KY; *m:* John Timothy; *c:* Katharine Nicole; *ed:* Miami Univ (BS) K-12 Hlth Ed 1975; Univ of Cincinnati; Coll Mt St Joseph, Miami Univ, Univ of Dayton Ed; Wright St Univ Working Towards Masters Ed; *cr:* Lakota HS Tchr 1975-; *ai:* Hlth Dep Chprsn; NEA, OEA 1975-; AAHPERD 1990-; PTO 1988-; Tchr of Yr 1988-89; Classroom Tchr of Yr Spec Ed 1986.*

HALL, THOMAS J., English Teacher; *b:* Elmira, NY; *m:* Geraldine Cristofard; *c:* John, Alexandra; *ed:* Union Coll (BA) Eng Lit 1963; Purdue Univ (MA) Amer Lit 1969; Attnd Univ of NH, Elmira Coll, Ithaca Coll; *cr:* George Washington Schl Eng Tchr 1963; Ernie Davis Jr HS Eng Tchr 1964-66; Portsmouth Sr HS Eng Tchr 1967-68; Elmira Southside HS Eng Tchr 1968-; *ai:* NCTE; US Power Squadrons 1989-, AP; NEH Inst Elmira Coll Mentor; NEH Seminar on Huck Finn Elmira Coll; WYE Inst Ithaca Coll; *office:* Elmira Southside HS 777 S Main St Elmira NY 14904

HALL, THOMAS W., US History & Global Stud Tchr; *b:* Syracuse, NY; *m:* Sally Hoffman; *c:* Christine O'Neil, Stephanie, Geoffrey, Sarah; *ed:* Cortland Coll (BS) His 1963, (MS) Soc Stud 1967; *cr:* Fayetteville-Manlius HS Soc Stud Tchr 1963-; *ai:* Var LaCrosse Coach; NYSUT, NYSCSS, CNYCSS 1963-; Onondaga HS League 1973-, LaCrosse Chm 1973-; Section 3, LaCrosse Chm 1976-; NYSPHSAA, St LaCrosse Chm 1986-; Natl Interscholastic LaCrosse Assn, Initial Pres 1978-88; US LaCrosse Coaches Assn, Scndry Schl Chm 1978-, Coach of Yr Awd 1969, 1972, 1988, 1993; NILA Man of Yr Awd 1987; Natl Fed Outstdng Coach Awd for NYS 1990; Upstate NY LaCrosse Hall of Fame 1993; *home:* 315 Center St Fayetteville NY 13066

HALL, VICKIE LYNN, Third Grade Teacher; *b:* Athens, OH; *m:* John William; *c:* Erin Lynn, Matthew Ross; *ed:* OH Univ (BSE) Ed 1974; 150 Hrs Ed; *cr:* Poston Elem 4th-6th Grd Tchr 8 Yrs, 3rd Grd Tchr 12 Yrs; Hocking Valley Comm Residential Ctr; *ai:* Jr HS Cheerleading Coach 3 Yrs, First in St, Third in Nationals 1993; Connett United Methodist Chrch 16 Yrs; NEA, OEA 1974-; OH Eastern Star 1980-84, Esther, Martha; Schls Intervention Team; Child Abuse Prevention Team; Comm Awds Recipient 1990; *office:* Poston Elem Schl 14455 Kimberly Rd Nelsonville OH 45764

HALL, WADE, 8th Grade Social Studies Tchr; *b:* Baltimor
Eleanora T. Clark-Hall; *c:* Wade A.; *ed:* Morgan Univ (BA) H
Credit Hrs Towson Univ, Morgan Univ; *cr:* Loch Raven Acad
Ldr 1970-; *ai:* Schl Base Mngmt Comm; Step Squad, Our Vo
African-Amer Achvmt Club; NEA, TABCO 1970-; Excl in Ed,
Svc, Baltimore Cty Pub Schls Svc Awds; Participation, Cur
home: 2900 Placid Dr Baldwin MD 21013*

HALL, WILLIAM ROY, Professor; *b:* Philadelphia, PA; *m:*
Ellmer; *ed:* La Salle Coll (BS) Chem 1968; Univ of PA (PHD
Chem 1974; Grad Credits Chem at Princeton 1968-69; Mc M
Post-Doc Rsrch 1974-75; *cr:* Smith Klein & French Lab
1965-68; Inst for Sci Info Indexer 1969-71; Comm Coll All
South Campus Prof 1975-; *ai:* ACS 1968-; APS 1972-; AAPT
Cmptr User Group 1982-, Sec; Numerous Articles Pub in Che
Journals; *office:* Comm Coll Algny Co South Cmps 1750 Clairto
Mifflin PA 15122

HALLADAY, JANE EASTMAN, Home Ec Teacher & FHA
Watertown, NY; *m:* Rex; *c:* Joshua, Kyle; *ed:* SUNY at Plattsb
Home Ec Ed 1985; OH St Univ (MS) Home Ec Ed 1989; *cr:* Ro
Schl Home Ec Tchr 1985-87; Gereral Brown HS Home Ec Tch
OH St Grad Rsrch Asst 1988-89; Johnson City HS Home Ec T
ai: FHA Adv, Star Events Dist, St, Natl Judge; Antique Costume
Owner, Curator; Broom Cty Home Ec Tchrs Assn 1989-, Comm
Noms & Tchr of Yr, Tchr of Yr; Family & Consumer Sci Tchr of
NYS Tchrs Assn 1985-; Natl Tchrs Assn; Grad Rsrch Asst;
Home Ec Tchr of Yr 1995; NYS Home Ec Curr Writer 19
Johnson City HS 666 Reynolds Rd Johnson City NY 13790*

HALLBACH, CAROL ANN, American History Teacher; *b:* M
CT; *m:* Pual; *ed:* Univ of CT (BA) His & Lang Arts 1968; Cntrl
(MA) Guid 1973; *cr:* Berlin HS His & Eng Tchr 1968-69; McGee
His Tchr 1969-; *ai:* Upbeat & Retention Policy Comm; Golf C
1968-; Berlin Ed Assn 1968-; CT Ed Assn 1968-; *office:* Mc Ge
Norton Rd Berlin CT 06037*

HALLBERG, DOUGLAS JAMES, PE & Hlth Ed Tchr; *b:* Sea
ed: SUNY at Cortland (BSE) PE 1992, (MSE) Hlth 1996; *cr:*
Cntrl Schl Hlth, PE Tchr 1992-; *ai:* Watkins Glen Var Ftbl As
NEA 1992-; Honary Mem Bradford Cntrl Honor Soc; *office:*
Central Schl 2820 Rt 226 Bradford NY 14815

HALLEN, BETTIE S., Writing & English Teacher; *b:* Worceste
Gary Linsky, Jane Taylor, Amy Oser; *ed:* Vesper Geo Schl of
Commercial Art 1957; Western New England Coll (BA) Eng-Su
Laude 1970; Amer Intnl Coll (MAT) Eng, Tchng-Max Hnrs 197
MA Doctoral Worlk; *cr:* Cathedral HS Art Dept Chair 1969-70
Eng Dept Chair 1970-86; Central HS Writing Lab, Eng Tchr 198
Curr Comm 16 Yrs; Schl Based Mngmt Team 3 Yrs; Lit Magazi
Yrs; Earth Action Club Adv 6 Yrs; CSL Bd of Dirs, Coord; Sr C
AFT 1970-; NEA 1970-; Springfield Tchrs Assn 1979-; NCTE;
Tchrs of Eng; MA Cmptr Using Educ; Vol Tutor 1986-; ADK 199
Players Theater 1984-, Exec Bd; WNEC Alumni Assn 1970-,
Kellog Natl Peer Comm Svc Learning Consultant; Springfiel
Multicultural Curr Awd; Outstdng Young Women of Amer 197
Springfield Central HS 1840 Roosevelt Ave Springfield MA 011

HALLENBECK, LINDA SUE, Fifth Grade Teacher; *b:* Indepenc
m: Theodore Ray; *c:* Robert Courtney, Elizabeth Rae; *ed:* Ken
(BS) Early Chldhd Ed 1974, (MS) Early Chldhd Ed 1976; Math
Cert; 60 Addl Hrs; *cr:* Hudson Elem Schl 3rd Grd Tchr 1976-77;
Elem Schl 1st Grd Tchr 1977-86; Mc Dowell Elem Schl 5th
1986-92; East Woods Schl 5th Grd Tchr 1992-; *ai:* Math Chprs
Forum Rep; Tech Acad; Fac Advy Comm; PTO 1976-; NCTM,
Tchrs of Math 1986-; Hudson Ed Assn 1976-, Treas; PEO 198
Comm; Pres's Club KSU; Ski Club 1993-, Adv; Presidential M
1993; Presenter NCTM Natl Confs 1994-; Distngd Tchr Awc
Schls; OH Tchr of Math; Model Tchr North Cntrl Ed Labs;
Writing Consultant; Jennings Grant; NSF Internet Pilot Projec
East Woods Schl 120 N Hayden Pkwy Hudson OH 44236*

HALLER, NORMA RAE, Fourth Grade Teacher; *b:* Frederick,
Frostburg St Coll (BA) Elem Ed 1974, (MA) Elem Ed 1977; 60 Ac
Hrs; *cr:* Waverley Elem 4th Grd Tchr 1974-90, 3rd Grd Tchr 1
Frederick Cty Tchrs Assn, NEA 1974-; *office:* Waverley Elem
Waverley Dr Frederick MD 21702

HALLER, TOM, Middle School Teacher; *b:* Syracuse, NY; *m:* L
Tejay; *ed:* IN Univ (BS) Bus Schl 1972; Syracuse Univ (MS)
Oswego St Univ Coursework in Stdnts Self-Esteem & Hand
Coursework; *cr:* Santa Cruz Gymnastics Schl Owner & Hea
1974-84; Univ of CA Santa Cruz Gymnastics Prgm Head Coach
Syracuse Univ Asst Gymnastic Coach 1984-86; Cntrl Square Sc
6th Grd Tchr 1986-94, Co-Dir Course in Self-Esteem 1994-;
Tchrs Assn 1986-; Amer Soc of Trainers & Developers Forus 197
Org Focusing on Human Potential & Breakthroughs; NCAA
Gymnastics IN Univ 1971; Town of Liverpool Hall of Fame Induc
Liverpool HS Ath of Yr & Hall of Fame 1968.

HALLER, WILLIS FLOYD, Earth Science Teacher; *b:* Waterto
ed: Cornell Univ (AB) Physics 1969; Wesley Theological S
(MDIV) Theology 1972; Wesley Theological Seminary (DMIN)
1975; Grad Stud Scndry Ed SUNY Oswego, SUNY Potsdam; C
Sci, Physics, Soc Stud; *cr:* Grace U Meth Church Assoc Pastor
General Brown HS Earth Sci Tchr 1983-; *ai:* Earth Sci Lab As
General's Guard Historic Reenactment Group Co-Advisor; NYS
1983-; Brown's Brigade Reenactments 1982-; Gen Brown Histo
1982-, Chm of Trustees; *office:* General Brown HS Cemetary R
NY 13634

HALLETT, JAMES W., SS Dept Chm & Admin Asst; *b:* Erie, PA
Gladstone; *c:* Catherine DeLorenzo, J. Andrew; *ed:* Alfred Univ
1964, (MS) Ed 1966; SUNY at Plattsburgh 30 Hrs Beyond Mas
Scio Cntrl Schl Scndry Soc Stud Tchr 1964-, Soc Stud Dept Chr
HS Admin Asst 1982-; *ai:* Schl Improvement Team Coord; Scio T
Past Pres; NY Ed Assn; NY St Cncl on Soc Stud; Scio United Meth
1970-, Pres Admin Cncl, Fin Chm; Scio Campus Life Tchr of the
Scio Lions Club Edctr of the Yr 1988; *office:* Scio Central Schl Was
St Scio NY 14880

HALLEY, LEWIS EDWARD, History Teacher; *b:* Easton, PA;
Catherine Kosa; *c:* Kristin, Pamela; *ed:* Moravian Coll (BA) Soc S
East Stroudsburg Univ (MS) His 1978; *cr:* Easton Jr HS His Tchr
Shawnee Intermediate Schl His Tchr 1979-; *ai:* NEA, PSEA, EAE
Outstanding Scndry Educators of Amer 1974; Tchr of Yr Awd 197
Shawnee Intermediate Schl 1010 Echo Trl Easton PA 18042

HALLEY, MARTHA WILLIAMS, Fourth Grade Teacher; *b:*
ME; *m:* Robert P.; *ed:* Simmons Coll (BS) His 1964; Russell Sage
Grad Hrs; *cr:* Rockland Jr HS 7th Grd Soc Stud Tchr 1964-65; C
Elem Schl 4th-5th Grd Tchr 1966-; *ai:* NY St United Tchrs 1966-
Coxsackie Elem Schl 24 Sunset Blvd Coxsackie NY 12051

HALLIDAY, JOHN CARROLL, Mathematics & Physics Tea
Columbus, OH; *m:* Penne Pensyl; *c:* Heather; *ed:* Purdue (BS)
1971, (MS) Ed 1975; *cr:* East Nobor HS Math, Physics Tchr
Miami Trace HS Math, Physics Tchr 1975-; *ai:* Math Dept Head; M

n; Fayette Cty Life Squad 1985-, EMT-Advanced; Tau Beta Pi; Scholar; *office:* Miami Trace HS 3722 State Route 41 NW n Court H OH 43160*

N, JOHN ALFRED, Fifth Grade Teacher; *b:* Syracuse, NY; *m:* se; *c:* Brian T., Erin M.; *ed:* SUNY at Oswego (BA) His 1972; 1976; *cr:* L. Pearl Palmer Elem Schl Second Grd Tchr 1976-78, Tchr 1978-82, Fifth Grd Tchr 1982-; *ai:* 174 Fighter Wing 973-, Logistics Exec Ofcr.

Y, JEREMIAH JOSEPH, Retired Dean of Stud, Lecturer; *b:* H; *m:* Alison M. Warriner; *c:* Dawn Warriner; *ed:* Dartmouth Eng 1961; Yale Law Schl (JD) 1964; Stanford Univ (PHD) Eng, 1976; Attnd Goethe Inst at Steufen Germany 1966-67, Univ of in France 1967; *cr:* Stanford Univ Tchng Asst, Instr 1970-72; l Instr 1973-74; Mills Coll Instr, Asst Prof, Assoc Prof 1974-83, n of Fac, Dir Grad Stud 1983-89; Manhattanville Coll Dean of urer 1991-94; *ai:* NH Bar Assn 1964-, Inactive Status; Modern 1972-; NCTE 1974-; *home:* PO Box 559 Amagansett NY 11930

Y, SHEILA MARY, English Teacher; *b:* Lowell, MA; *ed:* St Coll (MS) Scndry Ed 1996; Fitchburg St Coll Working on ry Ed; *cr:* Lowell HS Eng Tchr 1969-; *ai:* AFT; *office:* Lowell Morrissette Blvd Lowell MA 01852

ELL, DAVID DEAN, Science & Language Arts Tchr; *b:* CT; *m:* Susan Bent; *c:* Justin, Hannah, Robert, Henry; *ed:* Boston Speech, Theater, Sec Ed 1976; Southern CT St Univ (MS) 88; Sacred Heart 6th Yr Elem Ed 1992; Schl Cnslr Cert Courses; m; *cr:* Chalk Hill MS Drama Tchr, Dir 1976-91; Downtown heater Tchr 1978-79; Chalk Hill MS Lang Arts, Soc Stud Tchr Lang Arts, Sci Tchr 1993-; *ai:* Drama Dir; Lang Arts Curr Comm; ance Prgm; NEA 1976-; Actors Equity Assn 1988-; Monroe Town -, Councilman, Minority Ldr; New England Repertory Theatre ; Democratic Town Comm 1990-; Outstdng Arts Edctr 1991; Nat at Arts Grant 1976; Pub Article; *office:* Chalk Hill MS 345 Fan onroe CT 06468*

N, RICHARD DOUGLAS, Assistant Principal & Sci Tchr; *b:* Ontario, Canada; *m:* Diane Brower; *ed:* Univ of Waterloo (BA) 4; Hunter Coll CUNY (MA) Biological Sci 1987; Supervision, Cr Hrs; *cr:* Lovell-Belcher Surveyors Land Surveyor Technician JHS 123 Sci, Math Tchr 1981-83; Forest Hills HS Bio Tchr Asst Prin & Sci Tchr 1992-; *ai:* Westinghouse Sci Talent Search Howard Hughes Medical Inst Wkshp Coord Hunter Coll CUNY; Tchrs Assn 1985-; UFT 1981-93; CSA 1993-; NYS Bio Mntr ooklyn Museum, Brooklyn Botanic Garden 1988-; Schlsps: City 1968, Govt Ontario 1969; NY St Regents Fellowship 1985; Am em, Mol Bio Fellow 1991.

N, ROBERT RICHARD, Ninth Grade English Teacher; *b:* , PA; *m:* Sally; *c:* Gregg, Todd; *ed:* Lehigh Univ (BA) Eng 1970; Univ (MA) Eng 1977; *cr:* Nazareth Area Schl Dist Eng Tchr NEA 1974-; NCTE 1994; Sierra Club, Wilderness Soc 1989-; an Trail Conf 1988-; Lehigh Valley Fac Partnership 1989; *home:* 6042 Stroudsburg PA 18360

AN, VINCENT E., Principal; *b:* Cincinnati, OH; *c:* Sean, d: Univ of Cincinnati (MED) Admin Curr 1985; *cr:* LaSalle Tchr Asst Prin 1987-94; McNicholas Prin 1995-; *office:* Mc Nicholas Beechmont Ave Cincinnati OH 45230*

IS, BRENDA REYNOLDS, 6th Grade Math Teacher; *b:* on, DC; *m:* John Leon; *c:* John II; *ed:* DC Tchrs Coll Elem Ed orge Washington Univ Math Resource 1991; Rdng Specialist; Coaching; Cmptr Lit; Math Resource; Conflict n;Responsive Classroom; *cr:* Washington Highland Schl Cmptr ; Ferebee-Hope Schl 6th Grd Tchr; *ai:* Black His, Hospitality Restructuring Comm; WTU 1985-; Kettering Boys & Girls Club *fice:* Ferebee-Hope Comm Schl 777 Yuma St SE Washington DC

N, JANET SIMON, 7th Grd Language Arts Teacher; *b:* n, DE; *m:* Morris; *c:* Lynn, Rachel; *ed:* Univ of MI (BA) Eng & 1964; St Peters Coll Grad Courses; *cr:* Romulus Jr HS Eng & Soc 1964-65; Bridgewater-Raritan Schls Eng Tchr 1965-67; Temple Religious Schl Prin 1978-84; Warren MS Lang Arts Tchr 1983-; Dev Steering Comm; WTEA, NJEA, NEA & NCTE 1987-; Hannah non Awd 1979 for Vol Work on Planning the Somerset gewater Branch Lib; *office:* Warren MS 100 Old Stirling Rd J 07059

RN, JEAN KAMMEN, English Teacher; *b:* Indianapolis, IN; *m:* Joseph; *ed:* Columbia Univ (BS) Geography 1964; City Univ NY g Ed 1970; 62 Addl Credits; *cr:* JHS 22 Eng Tchr 1967-69; JHS Tchr 1970-71; Burroughs JHS Eng Tchr 1971; Gorton HS Eng 1-; *ai:* Coach Acad Bowl Team 1988-93; Steering Comm Mid St ation; Schl Improvement Plan Comm Mem 1992-; Cycle I Eng em 1992-93; AFT 1967-; NYSEC; WCEE 1989-; ASCD 1990-; t Shakespeare 1988; NYSEC Tchr of Excl Awd 1993; *office:* E. Gorton HS 100 Shonnard Pl Yonkers NY 10703*

IST, SHAWN ALLEN, Instrumental Music Teacher; *b:* Kane, PA; na; *c:* Cody, Noah; *ed:* St Univ of NY at Binghamton (MM) Performance 1983; Edinboro Univ Trumpet Performance 1982, ert K-12 Music 1984; *cr:* Millcreek Twp Schls Instrumental Music 5-; *ai:* Marching, Jazz Bands; NSOA 1995-; PMEA, MENC 1985-; mpet Guild 1979-; NBA 1993-; Phi Beta Mu 1995-; *office:* Mc MS 3320 Caughey Rd Erie PA 16506

LL, MARY KATARSKI, Science Teacher; *b:* Chicago, IL; *m:* H. H. Mark, Jody; *ed:* AZ St U (BA) Microbiology 1967; UCLA crobiology 1970; Tchng Cert Univ of Cincinnati 1990; 45 Addl Oak Ridge Natl Lab Rsrch Asst 1970-74; Cheviot UM Church Dir 1975-80; Univ Cincinnati Med Schl Rsrch Asst 1980-90; ti Pub Schls Sci Tchr 1990-; *ai:* North Cntrl Acrediting Comm; Spon Acad Team 1992-; Environmental Club Spon 1992-; Sci l; AFT, CFT, ACS 1991-; *office:* Hughes Ctr for Excl 2515 Clifton cinnati OH 45219

Y, KEVIN EDWARD, Mathematics Teacher; *b:* Oswego, NY; *ed:* Oswego (BS) Ed 1989; SUNY at Oneonta (MS) Math 1994; *cr:* dge-Guilford Cntrl Schl Math Tchr 1989-; *ai:* Var Wrestling, Ftbl Coach; 7th Grd Class Adv; *office:* Bainbridge-Guilford Cntrl Juliand St Bainbridge NY 13733

ED, NATALIE KOWALSKI, 8th Grade Civics Teacher; *b:* IL; *m:* Donald Halsted; *c:* Alicea; *ed:* Douglass Coll (BA) His Montclair Coll (MA) Soc Sci 1972; Kean Coll (MA) Admin, ion 1978; *cr:* Conamack MS Soc Stud Tchr 1968-71; Schor MS Tchr 1971-; *ai:* 8th Grd Team Ldr 1992-; NEA, NJEA 1968-; 993-; Girl Scouts 1991-, Troop Ldr; Schor Tchr of Yr 1991; *office:* e Schor MS 243 N Randolphville Rd Piscataway NJ 08854

I, PATRICIA DEFORT, Business Teacher; *b:* Sayreville, NJ; *c:* arski, Thomas, David, Eric; *ed:* Trenton St Coll (BS) Bus 1958; MHS Tchr 1958-62, 1966-; *ai:* Class Adv 1962, 1972; Custodian nds; NEA, NJEA 1958-; MCEA 1958-, LAT Rep; SEA 1958-, Sec, AT Chprsn; SMCTFCU Bd of Dir 1982-, Sec; *office:* Sayreville morial HS 810 Washington Rd Parlin NJ 08879

HALTON, SUSAN HIGLEY, First Grade Teacher; *b:* Sayre, PA; *m:* Charles; *c:* Bridget, Benjamin; *ed:* Keuka Coll (BS) Elem Ed, Psych 1968; Elmira Coll (MS) Ed 1973; 18 Addl Hrs; *cr:* Waverly Cntrl Schls Second Grd Tchr 1968-70; Cuyahoga Falls City Schls First Grd Tchr 1970-72; Sayre Area Schls Fourth, Third, First Grd Tchr 1972-; *ai:* NEA 1968-; PSEA, SAEA 1972-; Delta Kappa Gamma 1994-; St John Luth Church 1989-, Choir; Vly Chorus 1995-; NY PA Apartments Assn 1994-; Gift of Time Tribute.

HAMAD, NANCY L. (FIORINO), First Grade Teacher; *b:* Youngstown, OH; *m:* Richard J.; *c:* Julie Coghill, Lisa, Bryon; *ed:* Kent St Univ (BS) Early Chldhd 1963, (MS) Early Chldhd 1971; 30 Post Grad Hrs; *cr:* Akron City Schls Elem Tchr 1963-66; Cochise Cty Schls Elem Tchr 1967-68; Faith United Meth Church Nursery Schl Tchr 1977-78; Nordonia Bills City Schls Elem Tchr 1978-; *ai:* Math, Tech Comms Nordonia Hills; PTA Rep; Mentor; Stu, Cooperating Tchr; Tech Acad Summity Cty; NHEA, OEA, NEA 1995-; Assn Chldhd Ed 1988-; Nordonia Hills City Schls Fnd Advy Bd 1995-; Martha Holden Jennings Scholar 1991; *office:* Northfield Elem Schl 9374 Olde Eight Northfield OH 44067*

HAMEKA, CHARLOTTE PROCACCI, Chemistry Teacher; *b:* Jessup, PA; *m:* Hendrick F.; *ed:* Penn St Univ f(BS) Chem 1969l Univ of Scranton (MS) Chem 1972; 24 Credit Hrs Post Grad Stud Univ of PA; 15 Credith Hrs Post Grad Stud Cmptr Sci Rosemont Coll; 12 Credit Hrs Post Grad Stud Chem, Statistics Villanova Univ; *cr:* Carbondale HS Chem, Physics Tchr 1969-71; Strath Haven HS Chem Tchr 1973-; *ai:* Peer Tutoring Club Fac Supvr; Site Based Mngmt Task Force; NEA 1969-; In Charge of AP Chem Prgm 1978-; *home:* 1503 Argyle Rd Berwyn PA 19312*

HAMEL, DOROTHY, Third Grade Teacher; *b:* Pittsburgh, PA; *m:* John A. Schirra; *ed:* Northwest MO St Univ (BA) Elem Ed 1969; Duquesne Univ (MED) 1971; *cr:* Upper St Clair Schl System Tchr 1969-; *ai:* Univ of Pittsburgh Mentor Prgm 1991-; Upper St Clair Mentor Prgm 1994-, Strategic Planning Comm for Curr Stans; PSEA 1969-; AFT 1983-; Outstdng Elem Tchr of Amer 1974.*

HAMEL, JO-ANN MARCONE, 9th-12th Grd Mathematics Tchr; *b:* Yonkers, NY; *m:* Richard P.; *c:* John P., Renee; *ed:* Herbert H. Lehman Coll of CUNY (BA) Speech 1976; Kean Coll Post BAC Math Tchr Cert 1996; *cr:* St John The Apostle Math Tchr Grds 6-8 1990-92; Rahway HS Sub Tchr f1992-94; Mother Seton Regnl HS Math Tchr Grds 9-12 1994-; *ai:* St Mary's Church 1981-, Lay Minister of Eucharist, Lector, Choir Mem; *office:* Mother Seton Regional HS Valley Rd Clark NJ 07066

HAMEROFF, GLENN L., HS Social Studies Teacher; *b:* Brooklyn, NY; *m:* Evelyn Knight; *c:* Ian; *ed:* SUNY at Stony Brook (BA) His & Ed 1969, (MA) Lbrl Arts 1974; *cr:* Ward Melville HS Tchr 1969-; *ai:* AFT 1969-; LI Soc Stud Cncl 1969-; 3 Village Schl Dist Tchr of the Yr 1989-90; *office:* Ward Melville Sr HS 380 Old Town Rd East Setauket NY 11733*

HAMERSCHLAG, PATRICIA MYERS, Fifth Grade Teacher; *b:* Brooklyn, NY; *m:* Wain; *c:* MIchael, Christopher, Susan; *ed:* Notre Dame Coll (BA) Pol Sci, Eng 1965; Wagner Coll (MS) Ed 1968; 30 Credits Beyond Masters; *cr:* PS 14R Fourth Grd Tchr 1966-68; PS 55R Third Grd Tchr 1968-72; PS 55R Third Grd Tchr 1985-86; PS 36R 4th-5th Grd Tchr 1986-; *ai:* Sci Fair Dist Judge; Tennent Coop Nurery Schl 1979-85, Pres; Manalapan, Englishtown Schl Reorganizational Comm 1990-; Chm Demographics Comm; *office:* PS 36 R 255 Ionia Ave Staten Island NY 10312

HAMERSCHLAG, WAIN, Science Teacher; *b:* New York City, NY; *m:* Patricia; *c:* Michael, Christopher, Susan; *ed:* Wagner Coll (BA) Ed 1966, (MS) Ed 1971; Georgian Ct Coll Admin Cert; *cr:* PS 55 Richmond Tchr 1966-; *ai:* Cub Scout Chm; Carlton League Coach; L. L. Coach, Umpire; UFT 1967-; Manalapan Englishtown Bd of Ed 1982-88, VP 1987; Manalapan Little League Bd of Dirs 1984-, Sr League Coord; Judge S. I. Sci Fair.*

HAMEZA, NICHOLAS, Industrial Arts Teacher; *b:* Carbondale, PA; *m:* LuAnn; *c:* Jennifer, Emily; *ed:* CA St Coll (BS) Industrial Arts 1974; PA St Univ (MED) Voc, Industrial Ed 1977; Prof Cert Driver Ed East Stroudsburg Univ 1983; *cr:* Lakeland Tchr 1974-; *ai:* Pub Safety Article Schl Shop 1984; Spon Seat Belt Awareness Prgm Elem 1986; Organized Earth Day Prgm 1990; Teen Issues Lackawanna Drug Ctr Comm 1993; Epsilon Pi Tau 1973-; Lakeland Tchrs Assn, NEA 1975-; *office:* Lakeland Jr Sr HS R D 1 Jermyn PA 18433

HAMILL, DONALDINE P., English Teacher; *b:* Springfield, MA; *m:* Irvin; *c:* Peter, George, Kelly, Jean; *ed:* Boston Univ (BA) Eng Lit 1964; *cr:* Bartlett HS 11th Grd Eng Tchr 1972-; Pinkerton Acad 10th Grd Eng Tchr; Tewksbury HS 10th & 12th Grd Eng Tchr; *ai:* Travel Club Adv; *home:* 324 Mason Rd Dudley MA 01571*

HAMILL, LEITA VOSS, English Teacher; *b:* Jackson, TN; *m:* William H. B.; *c:* Sarah, Jane, Will; *ed:* Duke Univ (BA) Eng 1970; Univ of MI at Ann Arbor (MA) Eng 1974; Columbia Univ towards PHD Eng; *cr:* Buckley Cntry Day Schl Eng Tchr 1974-79; Lawrenceville Schl Eng Tchr 1979-; *office:* The Lawrenceville Schl Main St PO Box 6008 Lawrenceville NJ 08648

HAMILL, MARJORIE RAILEY, Retired 4th Grade Teacher; *b:* Mc Henry, MD; *c:* Linda Ropka, Stuart III, Elizabeth Hart, Geoffrey S.; *ed:* (BS) Ed 1944; Post Grad Rdng, Career Ed, GATE; *cr:* Elem Ed 4th Grd Tchr 1965-90; *ai:* Civic Club of Oakland 1958-, Past Pres; Friends of Ruth Enlow 1991-.

HAMILTON, BATTLE M., Dean of Students & His Tchr; *b:* Bronxville, NY; *m:* Gale C. Flynn; *c:* Ashley E., Ian C., Adam, Luke; *ed:* Vanderbilt Univ (BA) His 1966; Univ of MA (MA) His 1970; Sussex Univ of England Ancient His; *cr:* Rumsey Hall Schl His Tchr 1967-69; St Andrews Schl His Tchr 1970-73; Tatnall Schl Stdnts Dean, His Tchr 1973-; *ai:* Class Ofcr Adv; Fac Stu Judiciary; Boys Tennis Coach; Amnesty Intnl; *office:* The Tatnall Schl 1501 Barley Mill Rd Wilmington DE 19807

HAMILTON, CHERYL LYNN, English & Theater Teacher; *b:* Pittsburgh, PA; *m:* Kevin M. Mc Laughlin; *ed:* Slippery Rock Univ (BS) Scndry Ed 1974; 28 Grad Credits; *cr:* Oil City Schl Dist 9 Grd Eng Tchr 1976-77; Chartiers Houston Schl Dist 11 Grd Eng Tchr 1978-80; Ft Cherry Schl Dist 8 Grd Eng Tchr 1980-81; Peters Twp Schl dist 9 Grd Hon Eng, Theatre, 12 Grd Acad Eng Tchr 1981-; *ai:* Directed Drama Productions; Stu Asst Prgm Team; AFT 1981-; Slippery Rock Alumni Assn; Amer Cancer Soc 1980-, Bd, Jewelled Sword Awd; Great Tchr Recognition Prgm; St Vincents Coll Awd; Ed Cty Newsletter Amer Cancer Soc 12 Yrs; *office:* Peters Township HS 264 E Mcmurray Rd Mc Murray PA 15317

HAMILTON, JOAN T., 6th Grade Social Studies Tchr; *b:* White Plains, NY; *m:* Alphonso M.; *c:* Nichele Carter, Stephen, Lisa, Peter, Timothy; *ed:* Mercy Coll (BA) Speech & Elem Ed 1971; Manhattan Coll (MS) Spcl Ed 1975; CCNY SAS Cert Pending; Attnd NYU, Columbia Univ, Manhattanville Coll, Marymount Coll, Pace Univ, SUNY at Oneonta; *cr:* George Washington Elem 5th-6th Grd Tchr 1971-79; White Plains Inter 6th Grd Tchr 1979-91, K-6th Grd Spcl Ed Staff Developer 1990-92; White Plains Mid 6th Grd Soc Stud Tchr 1991-; *ai:* Comp & Tech Comm; WPTA 1971-, Exec Sec; WCSS 1990-, Co-Vice Pres; AFT; NYSUT; NYSCSS; NGA; MSCSS; NYGA; NEA; N Elmsford Civic Assn; Pathfinder Club, Asst Dir; Girl Scouts of Amer, Ldr; PTA Jenkins Memrl Awd 1993; Tchr Consultant Grant from Natl Geog Soc; Dir of GED Pgm in Mt Vernon NY; *home:* PO Box 85 Elmsford NY 10523

HAMILTON, JOYCE BARTOLI, Math Teacher; *b:* Scranton, PA; *m:* Patrick J. Sr.; *c:* Amy Cipollone, Patrick Jr.; *ed:* Univ of Bridgeport (BA) Math 1969; Wesleyan (MAIS) Math 1977; *cr:* Stratford HS Tchr 3 Yrs; North Haven HS Tchr 3 Yrs; Southern Ct St Univ Tchr 4 Yrs; Trumball HS Tchr 4 Yrs; *ai:* Key Club Adv; NCTM 1990-; CEA & NEA 1992-; PIMMS Fellow; *home:* 18 Rolling Meadow Dr Wallingford CT 06492*

HAMILTON, JOYCE ELAINE, Social Studies Teacher; *b:* Abington, PA; *m:* George W.; *c:* Keith, Leigh; *ed:* Bloomsburg Coll (BS) Scndry Ed Soc Stud 1972, (ME) Scndry Ed 1978; Psych Ed 6 Credits Beaver Coll, Research with Psychologist 1993-; *cr:* Pennsbury HS Tchr, SAP Organizer 1972-80; Intermediate Unit Montgomery Cty Teacher, Autistic, SPMR 1989-91; Upper Moreland HS Tchr 1992-; *ai:* Interact Rotary Affiliation, Vol Tutor Prgm Spon; Intensive, Scheduling, Mid States Evaluation, Bldng, image Comm; Liason Between Mid & HS; Sr Projects; NEA 1972-, Bldg Rep; APA, TOPSS 1991-; Scndry Soc Stud 1972-; PSA 1994-, Pres, VP; Therapy Dogs Intnl 1994-; Rutgers Univ Lecturer 1995-; Work with Brain Injred, Elderly, Mentally Disabled, Dog Therapy; schl Wide Bake Sale for Needy Families in Dist; Setup Vol Tutoring Prgm Between HS Stdnts & Remedial Stdnts at Dist Elem Schl; Assist in 2 Fac Dev Fund Awds at Beaver Coll in Chmosensory Directional Tracking By Dogs; *office:* Upper Moreland HS 3000 Terwood Rd Willow Grove PA 19090*

HAMILTON, JULIA, Associate Professor; *b:* Ft Gorden, GA; *ed:* St Pauls Coll (BA) Soc Work 1965; Case Western Reserve Univ (MSSA) Soc Admin 1970; Yeshiva Univ (PHD) & (DSW) 1992; Columbia Univ & Yale Univ Post Grad Stud; *cr:* Yale Med Ctr Soc Work Consultant 1970-, Co-Dir Child Abuse Pgm 1975-; Southern CT St Univ Assoc Prof 1989-; *ai:* Stu Advy; BSW-MSW Pgm; Cultural Diviersity & DEC Univ Comms; NASW 1980-, Soc Worker of the Yr Awd 1980; Ambulatory Corp 1980-; AAWP 1985-; New Haven Bd of Ed 1985-89, Curr Chair, Outstdng Bd Mem Awd; New Haven Welfare Bd 1994-; Numerous Articles Pub; Writer for New Haven Newspaper; 10 Pub Svc Awds; *office:* Southern CT St Univ 501 Crescent St New Haven CT 06515*

HAMILTON, KATIE HILL, English Teacher; *b:* Boston, GA; *m:* Dwane J. Sr.; *c:* Dwane Jr., Khalil; *ed:* Wilberforce Univ (BA) Eng Ed 1973; Cheyney Univ (MS) Eng Ed 1978; Widner Univ Course Work Rdng; Marywood Coll; *cr:* Shaw Jr HS Eng Tchr 1973-81; Edison HS Eng Tchr 1982-83; Fitzsimons MS Eng Tchr 1983-; *ai:* Yrbk, Amer Music Theatre Festival Spon; NCTE 1993-; PFT 1974-; Nom Tchr of Yr; *office:* Thomas Fitzsimons MS 2601 W Cumberland St Philadelphia PA 19132*

HAMILTON, KAY FRANCES, 8th Grd Language Arts Teacher; *b:* Rome, GA; *c:* Bernadette; *ed:* Savannah St Coll (BA) Ed 1964; 30 Credit Hrs Long Island Univ 1984; *cr:* St Marys Cath Schl 6th Grd Tchr 1964-67; Chatham Cty Bd of Ed 6th Grd Spcl Ed Tchr 1968-75; John J Pershing Jr High 8th Grd Eng Tchr 1980-; *ai:* Lang Arts Bookroom Coord; 8th Grd Lang Arts Commnctn Coord; Organizer for Grad; AFT 1980-; NEA 1980-; UFT 1980-; John J Pershing Jr High Voted Star Tchr.*

HAMILTON, LAWRENCE EDWIN,JR., History Teacher; *b:* Loveland, OH; *m:* Linda S. Duncan; *c:* Lawrence III, Cicely, Erika, Jonathan; *ed:* Central St Univ (BS) His Ed 1971; Wright St Univ (MS) His Ed 1977; Univ of Dayton Post Grad Stud; *cr:* Piqua HS His Tchr 1971-; *ai:* Past Golf 17 Yrs, Ftbl 3 Yrs Coach, Soc Stud Dept Chprsn; Soc Stud Competition Adv; NEA; Alpha Phi Alpha 1968-, Delta Xi Chapter Pres; Park Ave Bapt Church 1973-, Sunday Schl Tchr; Dev, Pub Current Event Game News or Lose; WDTN Daytons Class Act Tchr Recognition Awd; *office:* Piqua HS 1 Indian Trl Piqua OH 45356

HAMILTON, MARY MICHAELEEN,RSM, Latin & Religion Teacher; *b:* Providence, RI; *ed:* Cath Tchrs Coll (EDB) Ed 1956; Boston Coll (MA) Latin 1965; Providence Coll Theology Cert; *cr:* St Joseph 6-9 Grd Tchr 1951-57; St Xavier Acad Latin, Eng, Religion Tchr, Guidance Head, Vice-Prin 1957-75; St Mary Acad Bay View Latin, Religion, Eng Tchr 1975-93; *ai:* Amer Classical League 1957-; Most Influential Tchr; *office:* Saint Mary Acad Bay View 3070 Pawtucket Ave Riverside RI 02915

HAMILTON, PATRICIA ANN, Fourth Grade Teacher; *b:* Oil City, PA; *ed:* Slippery Rock St Coll (BS) Elm Ed 1973, (MED) Elem Ed 1980; *cr:* Utica Elem Schl 4th Grd Tchr 1973-; *ai:* Franklin Area Ed Assn, PA St Ed Assn, NEA 1973-; *home:* PO Box 33 Utica PA 16362

HAMILTON, ROBERT M., Principal; *b:* Carlisle, PA; *m:* Deborah Jane Yingling; *c:* Brian; *ed:* Univ of MT (BS) Wildlife Bio 1969; Shippensburg Univ (MED) Educl Admin 1993; 38 Addl Credits; IN Univ 3 Credits; *cr:* Dover Area Intermediate Schl Life Sci Tchr 1973-84; Dover Area HS Bio, Environmental Sci Tchr 1984-93, Asst Prin, Stu Act Dir 1994-95, Prin 1995-; *ai:* Ath Dir; Former Var Head Bsbl Coach 7 Yrs; NSTA 1976-; DAEA, PSEA, NEA 1973-; *office:* Dover Area HS W Canal St Dover PA 17315

HAMILTON, SANDRA K., 9th-12th Grade English Teacher; *b:* Lyons, NY; *ed:* SUNY at Brockport (BS) Eng 1971; Permanent Cert 30 Hrs; Post Grad 9 Hrs Writing Process; *cr:* Sub Tchr 5 Yrs; Red Creek Cntrl Eng Tchr 1 Yr; Wayne Cntrl Eng Tchr 1 Yr; Ganada Cntrl Eng Tchr 17 Yrs; *ai:* Soph Class Adv 15 Yrs; *office:* Gananda Schl 1500 Dayspring Rdg Walworth NY 14568

HAMILTON, SUSAN CLARK, Physical Education Teacher; *b:* Rochester, NY; *m:* Ray J.; *c:* Lyn Michelle Hamilton Milliman, Mathew David; *ed:* Morehead St Univ (BA) PE, Hlth & Rec 1967; Nazreth Coll 36 Hrs Gen Ed & Eng; *cr:* Pittsford MS PE Tchr 29 Yrs; *ai:* Ski & Outing Clubs; Wellness Team; NEA 1967-; NYSTA 1967-; PTSA 1967-, Lifetime PTSA Awd; Amer Red Cross 1966-, 30 Yr Pin; American Heart 1990-, Head Walk Pgm; Amer Cancer 1995-, Camp Cnslr for Kids with Cancer; Womans Club Svc Awd; 25 Yrs of Tchng Recognition; 30 Yr Red Cross Vol; *home:* 317 Main St Penn Yan NY 14527

HAMILTON, THOMAS MICHAEL, High School Vice Principal; *b:* Jersey City, NJ; *m:* Theresa Girardi; *c:* Kimberly, Thomas Jr.; *ed:* St Peters Coll (BS) Mrktg 1972; Jersey City St Coll (MA) Urban Ed, Admin, Supvision 1987; 30 Addl Credits; *cr:* Lincoln HS Bus Tchr 1972-77; Kearny HS Mktg Ed Coord 1978-80; Lacey Twp HS Mktg Ed Coord 1981-95; *ai:* Girls & Boys Soccer Coach; DECA Adv; Ftbl Game Announcer; Bsktbl Scorekeeper; NJASSP 1995-; NJAMETC 1978-, Regnl VP, Regnl Pres, Bd of Governors, St VP, St Tchr of Yr 1984; DECA 1978-, Outstdng Svc, Honary Life Mem; Kiwanis Club, Outstdng Citizen of Yr 1995; *office:* Lacey Township HS Haines St Lanoka Harbor NJ 08734*

HAMILTON-HARRISON, JANINE GAYLE, Eleventh Grade English Teacher; *b:* Cleveland, OH; *c:* Brittish Leigh; *ed:* Bowling Green St Univ (BS) Eng 1973; Youngstown St Univ (MA) Eng 1993; Numerous Continuing Ed Units; *cr:* Liberty HS Eng Tchr 1974-; *ai:* Chrldng, Multicultural Org Adv; Coord, Contact Person Youngstown St Univ's Eng Festival; Steering Comm; Curr Restructuring Prgm Visiting Team; NEA, OEA, LEA 1974-; Delta Kappa Gamma; Delta Sigma Theta 1972-; Ballet Western Reserve 1994-, Bd Mem; Youngstown St Univ Liberty Local Sch Partnership 1995-; Bibliography, Article Pub; *office:* Liberty HS 317 Churchill Hubbard Rd Youngstown OH 44505*

HAMLET, ROSA JANETTE, English as Second Lang Teacher; *b:* Dominica British, West Indies; *m:* George J. N.; *c:* O'Donnell, Derevaughn, Svetlana; *ed:* Queens Coll (BA) K-6th Early Chldhd 1988, (MS) Tchng Eng as Second Lang 1991; 30 Addl Credits; *cr:* Dominica Tech Coll Classroom, Eng Tchr, Act Prin 20 Yrs; Little Friends Schl Group Tchr 5 Yrs; Springfield Gardens HS ESL Tchr 8 Yrs; *ai:* Afternoon Prgm Coord; Voc,

Tech Educl Asst Prgm; Community of Caring Comm; Eng, Application Completion Tutoring; UFT, AFT 1989-; Grace United Meth Church 1985-, Class Ldr, Choir Mem; United Meth Women; Empire St Schlsp; *office:* Springfield Gardens HS 143-10 Springfield Blvd Springfield Gdn NY 11413*

HAMLET, WAYNE L., Biology Teacher; *b:* Acushnet, MA; *m:* Cynthia A. Jennings; *c:* Drew, Beth; *ed:* Univ of Bridgeport (BS) Sci, Hlth & Phys 1974; Addl 21 Plus Credit Hrs; *cr:* Roosevelt Jr HS Sci Tchr 1974-76; New Bedford HS Bio Tchr 1976-; *ai:* Ftbl Head Coach 1992-; Sftbl Asst Coach 1978-; Schl Assessment Comm 1995-; NEA, MTA, NBEA, MIAA, New England Coaches Assn 1974-; Ftbl Asst Coach 1974-92; Class Adv 1984-94; Schl Curr Comm 1992-95; Coach of Yr 1993-94; *office:* New Bedford HS 230 Hathaway Blvd New Bedford MA 02740

HAMLIN, MICHELLE SPARRE, Mathematics Teacher; *b:* Los Angeles, CA; *m:* Edmund Gardner; *c:* Jayme, Jennifer, James; *ed:* St Josephs Coll (BA) Math 1969; Univ of ME 34 Credit Hrs; Univ of NH 8 Credit Hrs; *cr:* Brunswick HS Math Tchr 1970-73; Fryeburg Acad Math Tchr 1973; Th S A D #72 Librn & Media Specialist 1974-76; Westbrook HS Math Tchr 1977-78; Kennett HS Math Tchr 1978-; UNH Coll for Lifelong Learning Math Instr 1983-; *ai:* NEA & CEA 1970-; ME Schl Bd Assn 1975-93; NCTM 1980-; ME Muncipal Assn 1994-; Brownfield Lib Assoc 1980-, Librn 1980-90; Lit Vol 1991-, Trustee; Town of Brownfield 1994-, Selectman; MSAD #72 Chm 1987-93; NEWMAST Participant at Goddard Space Flight Ctr 1989; *office:* Kennett HS Main St Conway NH 03818*

HAMM, HELEN HUGHES, First Grade Teacher; *b:* New York City, NY; *m:* Robert E.; *c:* Douglas, Gregory; *ed:* Danbury St Coll (BS) Elem Ed 1964; Univ of Bridgeport (MS) Elem Ed 1971; 100 Hrs Prof Dev, CPR, Cmptrs, Spec Ed, Ed of Blind, Sci, Math, Lang Arts, Music; *cr:* Riverside Schl Second Grd Tchr 1964-69; Stratfield Schl Rdng, Math Tchr 1977-81, Kndgtn, Math Resource Tchr 1982-83, First Grd Tchr 1983-; *ai:* After Schl Homework Club;FEA Schlsp, Schl Sunshine Comms; Fairfield Ed Assn; Kappa Delta Pi 1962-, VP 1963-64 Local Chptr; Delta Kappa Gamma 1994-; FEA, CEA, NEA 1982-; Church Soc Concerns Ministry 1982-, Emmaus Comm 1983-, Newsletter Co-Ed; US Dept Ed Excl Ed 1987, 1993; *home:* 75 Bennett St Fairfield CT 06432

HAMM, JOANN ELLIS, English Teacher; *b:* Rochester, NY; *c:* Tobin, Scott; *ed:* SUNY at Geneseo (BS) Eng, Elem Ed 1962; SUNY at Brockport (MA) Eng 1986; *cr:* Pittsford Cntrl Schls 6th Grd Tchr 1962, Eng, Pub Speaking, Black His, Lit Tchr 1962-69; John C. Fremont HS Eng Tchr 1969-70; Westmont HS Eng, Pub Speaking Tchr 1970-81; John Marshall HS Eng, Soc Stud Tchr 1981; Webster HS Eng, Pub Speaking Tchr 1981-; Monroe Comm Coll Eng Asst Adjunct Prof 1987-; Eng Dept Ldr 1995-; AP Rdr 4 Yrs; *ai:* Forensics Head Coach; Morning TV Show News Anchors, Commencement Speakers Coach; Brainstormers Co-Coach; Natl Forensic League 1970-; NY St United Tchrs, AFT 1981-; NCTE; Phi Delta Kappa; Genesee Valley Forensic League 1987-, Pres 5 Yrs; Phi Delta Kappa 1990-; NY St Forensic League Reg Dir 7 Yrs; Diocesan Dir & Co-Founder of GVFL 1992-; NEA Fellowship 1966; Yrbk Dedications: Pittsford Cntrl Schl 1968, Westmont HS 1978; Westmont PTSA Service Awd 1977; NY St Eng Tchrs Cncl Tchr of Excl in Drama 1983; Personalities of West, Midwest; World Who's Who of Women; Univ of Richmond Outstanding Educator Awd 1992; Advanced Placement Reader in Eng Lit 1993-94; National PTA Phoebe Hearst Awd 1994; *home:* 300 Rock Beach Rd Rochester NY 14617*

HAMM, ROSE MARIE (HAFER), Second Grade Teacher; *b:* Reading, PA; *m:* Edgar A.; *c:* Rebecca Lynn, Stacey Marie; *ed:* Kutztown Univ (BED) Elem 1966, (MED) Elem 1969; Addl 30 Post Grad Credits; *cr:* Hamburg Area Schl Dist 1st Grd Tchr 1966-68; Albany Elem Schl Dist Kndgtn Tchr 1968-77, 2nd Grd Tchr 1977-; *ai:* NEA, PSEA 1966-; Church Act Music & Worship Comm 1993-, Chprsn; *home:* 9110 Kistler Valley Rd Kempton PA 19529

HAMMANN, RALPH R., Drama & Film Instr; *b:* Pittsfield, MA; *ed:* North Adams St (BA) Theater & Eng 1976; Goddard Coll (MA) Theater 1986; *cr:* Pittsfield HS Drama, Film & Eng Instr & Drama Dir 1976-; Metroland Magazine Theater & Film Critic 1987-; The Advocate Theater Critic 1995-; *ai:* Drama Soc Dir & Adv; British Film Inst 1972-; Amer Theater Critics Assn 1990-; MA Cultural Cncl 1988-95, Pres 1 Term; New Phoenix Inc Dir & Producer; Film Reviews & Articles Pub; *office:* Pittsfield HS 300 East St Pittsfield MA 01201

HAMME, MARTA NELSON, US History Teacher; *b:* Carlisle, PA; *m:* Randall L.; *c:* Jessica, Katelyn; *ed:* Penn St (BS) Scndry Soc Sci 1976; 15 Hrs Grad Credits; *cr:* Cedar Cliff HS World Cultures Tchr 1979-80; Red Land HS World Cultures Tchr 1980-81; Lemoyne MS Career Ed Tchr 1981-82, Eastern Hemisphere, US His Tchr 1983-87, US His Tchr 1987-; *ai:* Adv Stu Cncl, Forum; Mini Curr Rep; NEA 1988-; Girl Scouts 1994-, Ldr; Cancer Soc Fundraiser; Lung Assn Fundraiser; *office:* Lemoyne MS 701 Market St Lemoyne PA 17043

HAMME, RONALD EDWARD, Fine Arts & Humanities Teacher; *b:* Carlisle, PA; *m:* Virginia Langenhop; *c:* Christopher F.; *ed:* Penn St Univ (BS) Art Ed 1970; Penn St at Harrisburg (MA) Hum 1991; 24 Credits Post Scndry for Cert; *cr:* Upper Dauphin Area Schl Dist Art & Hum Tchr 1970-; *ai:* AP Art His Club Adv; Prof Dev Comm Adv; Class Adv 1972-73 & 1976-77; NEA, PSEA & UDAEA 1970-, Pres 2 Yrs; NAEA 1986-90; Jaycees, Sec 3 Yrs, Service Awd; Church Cncl, Deacon 6 Yrs; *home:* Mayfield St Elizabethville PA 17023*

HAMMEL, SUSAN RIDGWAY, Multi-Age Teacher; *b:* New York, NY; *m:* Jeffrey H. Benjamin; *c:* Kirby, Brin; *ed:* Hollins Coll (BA) Psych 1973; Shippensburg Univ (MED) Elem Ed 1981; 24 Credit Hrs in Cnslng; *cr:* Hamilton Elem 5th Grd Tchr 1973-83; Bellaire Elem 4th Grd Tchr 1984-90, 3rd Grd Tchr 1990-91, Multiage Tchr 1991-; *ai:* Taught Eng as a Second Lang to Austrian Stdnts in England; *office:* Bellaire Elem Schl 623 W Penn St Carlisle PA 17013

HAMMER, CATHY E., 6th Grade Block Teacher; *b:* Lancaster, PA; *m:* Todd L.; *c:* Tracy Fornwalt, Ashley, Erica; *ed:* Millersville Univ (BS) Elem Ed 1979; *cr:* Millersville Univ Sec 1969-79; Providence Elem Schl 1st Grd Tchr 1979-84; Swift MS 6th Grd Tchr 1984-85, 1989-; *ai:* Stu Cncl Adv; Fund Raising Chprsn; NEA, PSEA, SEA 1980-85, 1989-; Solanco Little League 1991-, Asst Coach, Coach, Dst Minor League Winners; *office:* Swift MS 1866 Robert Fulton Hwy Quarryville PA 17566

HAMMER, DONALD P., Chemistry Teacher; *b:* Alum Bank, PA; *m:* Shirley R. Caswell; *c:* James, Karen Vatral, Nancy; *ed:* Clarkson Univ (MS) Chem 1965; 60 Addl Hrs; *cr:* Holbrook HS Chem, Sci Tchr 1959-61; Oceanside HS Chem Tchr 1961-; *ai:* Oceanside Fed Tchrs 1970-; Church of the Nazarene 1961-, Bd Trustees, Chm; NSF Summer Insts Clarkson Coll of Tech, Brown Univ, Bowling Green St Univ; Rsrch Participant City Coll of NY; *office:* Oceanside HS Brower & Skillman Aves Oceanside NY 11572

HAMMER, JOHN J.,JR., 4th Grade Teacher; *b:* Danbury, CT; *m:* Rita Mc Guire; *c:* Tracey, John III; *ed:* Danbury St Coll (BS) Ed 1961; Univ of Bridgeport (MS) Ed 1969; 6th Yr Cert Ed, Guid 1978; Numerous Confs, In-Service Credits Cmptr, Math; *cr:* Woodbury Jr HS Tchr 1961-66; Cornet Instr Films Ed Sales Rep 1966-69; Great Plain Schl Tchr 1969-71; Stadley Rough Schl Tchr 1971-; *ai:* Tchrs Fund; NEA Alternate; NEA, CEA 1961-; NEH Danbury 1969-, Bldg Rep; Tchr Ed, Prof Stans, Various Comm Chairs; Exch Club of Danbury 1987-, Treas, Pres, Past Pres Club, Ct Dist Ex Awd, Best Club; *office:* Stadley Rough Elem Schl 25 Karen Rd Danbury CT 06811

HAMMER, PHYLLIS ELAINE, Mathematics Teacher; *b:* Passaic, NJ; *ed:* Syracuse Univ (BS) Ed 1959; Fairleigh Dickinson Univ (MA) Ed, Human Dev 1974; Addl 45 Post Grad Credits; *cr:* Passaic Summer Schl Math Tchr 1959-64; Roosevelt #10 Schl Tchr 1959-69; Adult Ed HS ESL Tchr 1960-66; Lincoln MS #4 Math Tchr 1969-; *ai:* Assembly Pianist; Music Dir Drama Club; Head Dafety Patrol, Chrldng, FUnd Raising, 8th Grd Trips; Extra Voluntary Math Class Advanced Stdnts in Algebra; EAP Local, Cntry 1959-, Rep, Cert of Commendation 25 Yrs Tchng; NJEA, NEA 1959-; Time-Out Club 1995-; Womens Coll Club of Passaic 1988-; Letter of Commendation Supt Schls; Cert Achvmt Bd of Ed; Tchr of Month 1988; Tchr of Yr Governors Tchr Recognition Prgm St of NJ 1988; *home:* 152 Van Houten Ave Passaic NJ 07055

HAMMERTON-MORRIS, LINDA KAY, Spanish Teacher; *b:* Stamford, CT; *m:* Dean R.; *c:* Robin M., Todd M.; *ed:* Bowling Green St Univ (B A) Span & Bus Admin 1984; SUNY at Geneseo (MS) Span & Scndry Ed 1990; *cr:* US Peace Corp Vol in Small Enterprise Dev 1984-86; Waterville Vly Acad Span Tchr 1986-87; Oakfield-AL Cntrl Schl Span Tchr 1987-93; Clarence Cntrl HS Span Tchr 1993-; *ai:* Peace Corps Partnership Pgm Coord; WNYFLEC 1987-, Treas; AFT 1987-; Clarence Tchrs Assn 1993-; NYSAFLT; Regnl Chprsn Ldrshp Awd 1995; *office:* Clarence Central HS 9625 Main St Clarence NY 14031

HAMMETT, LINDA C. (PERRY), Former Secretarial Sci Intsr; *b:* Radville SK, Canada; *m:* Doran Wayne; *c:* Jason, Mandi, Jeremy; *ed:* David Lipscomb Univ (BA) Secretarial Sci 1972; Addl 6 Hrs Comm WV Univ at Parkersburg; *cr:* Great Lakes Chrstn Coll Bus Dept Tchr 1972-74; Harding Univ Exec Sec, Bible Dept 1974-78; First Natl Bank Asst Bank Cash Mngmt 1978-79; OH Vly Coll Secretarial Sci Instr 1992-94; WA St Comm Coll Adj Instr 1995-; *ai:* Elem Schls Yrbk Adv; OH Vly Yrbk Adv, Instr; Church of Christ Yth Comm, Ed Ladie's Newsletter; Most Valuable Mem Phi Beta Lambda 1972 David Lipscomb Univ; *home:* Rt 1 Box 249Aa Vincent OH 45784

HAMMILL, CHARLES P., Assoc Professor of Psychology; *b:* Pittsburgh, PA; *m:* Joanne L. Zolet; *c:* James P., Nancy J.; *ed:* Adams St Coll (BA) Psych, Anthro, Soc 1968, (MA) Psych, Cultural Stud 1969; 45 Credit Hrs Towards EDD Rutgers Univ; *cr:* Burlington Cty Coll Psych Assoc Prof 1969-; *ai:* Fac Senate; SPOC Club Adv; NEA 1975-; APA 1991-; APS 1992-; NJEA 1974-; ECCSSA 1983-; Tchr of Yr 6 Yrs; Chi Iota Fclty Schlr Hall of Honor 1991 & 1995; *office:* Burlington County Coll Rt 530 Pemberton NJ 08068

HAMMILL, TIMOTHY SEAN, Music Teacher; *b:* Latrobe, PA; *m:* Jaqueline Geibel; *ed:* Duquesne Univ (BS) Music Ed 1988; Grad Stud Duquesne Univ, Carlow Coll, OH St Univ; *cr:* CA Area Schl Dist Instrumental Music Tchr 1990-93; Greensburg Salem Schl Dist Instrumental, Choral Music Tchr 1993-; *ai:* Vocal Ensemble; Schl Musicals; MENC, PA Music Edctrs Assn, Westmoreland Cty Music Edctrs 1990-; Greensburg Cultural Trust 1994-; PA Cncl Arts Residency Prgm Grant; Prof Musician.*

HAMMITT, KATHY JO MCMURRAY, Second Grade Teacher; *b:* Toledo, OH; *m:* William Todd Jr.; *c:* Nathan B., Shaun M.; *ed:* Univ of Teledo (BE) Primary K-8th 1973; *cr:* Toledo Pub Schl Kndgtn Tchr 1973-76; Rosary Cathedral Kndgtn Tchr 1979-80; St Angela Hall Kndgtn Tchr 1983-85; St Agnes Schl K-1st Grd, Jr High 2nd Grd Tchr 1985-; *ai:* Sci Leadership, Soc Stud Leadership Comms; Mission Coord; Stu Cncl Adv; 8th Grd Class Trip Tchr Coord; NCEA 1985-; OCTELA 1992-; SECO 1993-; *office:* St Agnes Schl 3891 Martha Ave Toledo OH 43612

HAMMOND, CAROL HOWARD, Fourth-Fifth Grade Teacher; *b:* Knoxville, TN; *m:* James M.; *c:* Endea Thibodeaux, Renata, Rona Smith, James Jr.; *ed:* Oakwood Coll (BA) Sec Ed, Fr, Rel 1957; Univ of MD (MED) Elem Ed, Rdng, Psy 1981; Howard Univ PHD Educ Psy 48 Cr Hrs; *cr:* Ephesus Jr Acad Tchr Grd 7-10 1957-60; Bekwai Sec Schl Tchr Eng, Grds 1-8 1961-74; Columbia Union Coll Loan Supvr 1974-76; Sligo Adventist Schl Tchr Grd 5 1976-; *ai:* ASCD 1993-; Educamus; *home:* 3200 Fullerton St Beltsville MD 20705

HAMMOND, DONNA HOGELAND, Art Teacher; *b:* Rochester, NY; *m:* John Edward Jr.; *c:* Daniel, Aimee Hammond Vasquez; *ed:* SUNY at Potsdam (MS) Tech; Tech Applications 6 Hrs; Cmptr Graphics 6 Hrs; Video, Sound 3 Hrs; *cr:* St Joseph Schl 5th Grd Tchr 1967-69; Liverpool Elem Schl 2nd Grd Tchr 1969-70; Alexandria Cntrl Schl Art, Graphics Tchr 1972-; *ai:* Class, Cmptr Club, Art Club Adv; Frameworks, Tech, Model Schls Liaison Comms; Tchr Ctr Planning Bd; NYS Art Tchr Assn 1988-; NYS Cmptr & Tech Edctrs 1990-; Natl Art Tchrs Assn 1982-; *office:* Alexandria Central Schl 34 Bolton Ave Alexandria Bay NY 13607*

HAMMOND, KATHLEEN M., Middle School Associate Prin; *b:* Lawrence, MA; *c:* David Gibson; *ed:* Lowell St (BAEd) Ed 1969, (MED) Rdng 1975; Salem St (MED) Guidance, Counseling 1981; Cert Prin K-6th, 5-9th; *cr:* Town of Methuen Tchr 1969-94, Assoc Prin 1994-; *ai:* Drama Club; Peer Meditation; MTA, MESPA 1969-94; NELMS 1990-; Multi-Cultural Tchr Awd 1991; Lucretia Crocker Finalist 1985; *office:* Comprehensive Grammar Schl 100 Howe St Methuen MA 01844

HAMMOND, KENT DOUGLAS, Assoc Prof & Tech Coord; *b:* Northampton, MA; *ed:* OH St Univ (BS) Landscape & Horticulture 1972; MI St Univ (MS) Ornamental Horticulture 1974; *cr:* MI St Univ Grad Tchng Asst 1973-74; OH St ATI Landscape Contracting Fac 1975-; *ai:* Schl Adv; Little League Asst Coach; OH Nursery & Landscape Assn 1975-, St Cert Comm, Stu Act Comm, Schlsp; Assoc Landscape Contractors of Amer 1978-, Natl Landscape Technician Cncl, Curr Comm, Field Day Comm; BSA Troop #68 Asst Scoutmaster; OH St ATI Outstdng Adv Awd 1995; Coll of Food, Ag & Environmental Sci OH St Outstdng Adv Awd 1995; *office:* OH St Univ Agri Tech Inst 1328 Dover Rd Wooster OH 44691

HAMMOND, ROSELYN BROWN, College Biology Professor; *b:* Grambling, IN; *m:* Ernest C.; *ed:* Grambling Coll (BS) Bio 1959; OH St Univ (MA) Sci Ed 1965; Cornell Univ (PHD) Sci Ed 1992; *cr:* Grambling Coll Supervising Tchr Grambling L Lab HS 1961-67; Morgan St Univ Sci Ed, Bio Prof, Phys Sci-Sci Ed Prof 1989-; *ai:* Math Clinic Dir; Bio Club Spon; Arts & Sci Curr Comm; Med Tech Selection Comm; Co-Course Bio 101-102 Coord; NSTA 1962-; Natl Assn for Res in Sci Tchng 1987-; MD Assn of Sci Tchrs 1987-; Alpha Kappa Alpha 1958-, Chair, Salute to Outstdng Young Women; Epsilon Omega 1992-; Herbert Frisby Historical Soc, VP; Links Inc 1987-, Recording Sec, Natl Trends Chair; Morgan St Univ Women 1991-, Past Pres; Philomathians, Recording Sec; Shell Merit Flwshp Stanford Univ 1964; NSF Fac Dev Awd 1985; Handbook for Tchrs of Sci; *office:* Morgan State Univ Cold Spring Ln & Hillen Rd Baltimore MD 21239

HAMMOND, SUSAN WOJNO, English & Literature Teacher; *b:* Akron, OH; *m:* David G.; *c:* Michael, Mary, Kathryn; *ed:* Mt Union Coll (BA) Eng Lit 1972; Univ of Akron (MA) Ed Admin 1990; Columbia St (PHD) Ed Admin 1995; Kent St Univ, Harvard Univ; *cr:* Loudonville HS Tchr 1975-83; Coll of Wooster Instr 1975-76; The Univ of Akron Part-time Instr 1983-; Archbishop Hoban HS Eng Lit Instr 1986-; *ai:* Chldr Coach 2972-86; Class Adv 1986-95; Class Trip Coord 1987-; OEA, NEA, NCTE 1972-; Jr League 1982-; Akron Woman's City Club 1986; Grant OH Arts Cncl; 8 Grants Mc Ginty Fnd; Tchr of Yr 1987, 1990; Articles Pub; *office:* Archbishop Hoban HS 400 Elbon Ave Akron OH 44306*

HAMMOND, WILLIAM SANDIN, Mathematics & English T Kenosha, WI; *m:* Cristina Sandin; *c:* Cristina Rich, Thomas Dartmouth Coll (MALS) Math & His 1990, (AB) Eng Lit & Writing; *cr:* Hanover HS Math & Eng Tchr 1983-84; The Maret & Eng Tchr 1984-86; Hanover HS Math & Eng Tchr 1986-; *a* Club Adv; Guitar Club Co-Adv; Lighting Crew & Sr Class C NEA 1983-; NH-ATMNE, HPM 1986-; Youth-in-Action 1989- 1995-; Fulbright Tchr Exch 1991-92; NSF Grant-Math Acros Through Dartmouth 1995-; *office:* Hanover HS 41 Lebanon St H 03755*

HAMMONDS, JAY A., Soc Stud Tchr & Dept Chprsn; *b:* Cons PA; *m:* Susan A. Earl; *c:* Elizabeth A.; *ed:* West Chester St C Scndry Ed & Soc Stud 1965, (MED) Scndry Ed & Soc Stud 1 Univ of DE, St Joseph's Univ & Univ of WA; *cr:* Felton Pub Schl Tchr 1965-67; P.S. duPont HS Soc Stud Tchr 1967-78; Glasgo Stud Tchr, Dept Chair 1978-; *ai:* Former Yrbk Adv; Sen R Leadership Conf Coord; Dragons Amateur Radio Club Adv Admin Stu Writing Lab & Mac Micro-Lab; Clinical Stud Cooper Univ of DE; Co-Chair Mid Sts Accred Steering Comm; NEA 1 Felton EA, Pres 1967; Christina EA; DE St EA; NCSS; DE Coun World His Assn Centered on Tchng Comm; Amateur Radio Eme 1982-; Asst Emerg Coord 1985-87; Chester Cty BSA, Merit B 1963-71, NC 1968-71; Keizai Koho Ctr Fellowship 1992; ICA F Del Rep 1992; DeWitt-Wallace Reader's Digest Fellowship Wilson Inst, Princeton 1991; Robert A. Taft Inst on Govt Fellow Eastern Coll Amer Stud Fellowship 1987; DE Tchr Historian 19 Tchr of Yr 1991; HS Tchr of YR, Christina SD 1987; Tchr of Y HS 1987; World His Assn Bulletin; Multimedia Software; *office* HS 1901 S College Ave Newark DE 19702*

HAMP, JOHN HARRY, Mathematics & Science Teacher; *b:* J PA; *m:* Ila Darlene Thomas; *c:* Melanie Dawn, Amy Elizabeth; *e* of PA (BS) Math 1973, (MS) Math 1979; Physics 1976, General Various Military Schls, Correspondence Courses 1977-; *cr:* US 1965-69; IN Univ of PA Grad Asst 1973-74; Southview HS M 1974-76; Saltsburg Jr Sr HS Math, Sci Tchr 1976-; *ai:* Coach Boys Bsktbl 1976-,Jr HS Girls Bsktbl 1980-, Girls Var 1989; N PSEA 1976-; BSEA 1976-, Building Rep 3 Yrs; Chrstn M Alliance Church 1981-, Elder 13 Yrs, Church Sec 12 Yrs, Ush Choir 3 Yrs, Sunday Schl Tchr, Financial Sec 2 Yrs; PA Army N 1977-, Section Sgt, Various Awds & Medals, Attnd Various Serv Grad Asst IN Univ of PA 1973-74; *office:* Saltsburg Jr Sr H S 84 Saltsburg PA 15681*

HAMPP, MICHAEL ALLAN, Band Director; *b:* Zanesville Shelley Ann; *c:* Andrew, Emily; *ed:* Kent St Univ (BM) Music Ed Hrs Bowling Green St Univ; *cr:* Heidelberg Coll Part-Time Low 1979-93; Tiffin Pub Schls Band Dir 1974-; *ai:* Jr HS Stage Band; NEA, OHIOEA, OMEA, MENC 1974-; National Band Assn 19 Legion Pub Svc Awd 1992; *office:* Tiffin Jr HS 138 E Market St 44883

HAMPSEY, MAUREEN HORAN, High School English Te Brooklyn, NY; *m:* Charles; *c:* Meghan; *ed:* Coll of the Holy C Eng 1988; SUNY at Stony Brook (MA) Eng 1993; *cr:* Ward M Eng Tchr 1992-93; Ft Lee HS Eng Tchr 1993-; Sleepy Hollow HS 1995-; *ai:* Yrbk & Newspaper Adv; *office:* Sleepy Hollow H Broadway Tarrytown NY 10591

HAMPSHIRE, STEVE FRANK, Learning Disabilities Te Fremont, OH; *m:* Candice A Anspach; *c:* Zachary; *ed:* Bowling Univ (BS) Spec Ed, PE, Drivers Ed 1980; Post Grad 45 Credi Fremont City Schls Subing 1980-82, Spec Ed LD 1982-; *ai:* Coac 1980-94, Girls Track 1980-87; Girls Bsktbl 1980-86, Boys Bsk Drivers Ed 1980-; NEA 1980-; *office:* Fremont Ross HS 1100 Fremont OH 43420

HAMPSON, ROBERTA BUDURA, Junior HS Reading Te Bethelhem, PA; *m:* John Freeman; *c:* James; *ed:* Univ of Linguistics 1976, (MS) Ed, Rndg, Lang Arts 1977; Working Tow Writing Project Fellow Whole Lang; Attnd Georgetown Un Linguistics Schl; *cr:* Univ of PA Rdng Clinic Cnslr 1976-77; Ch Schl Rdng Specialist 1977-79; Daniel Boone Schls Rdng S 1979-80; Conrad Weiser Jr Sr HS Rdng Tchr 1980-; Rdng Area C Instr 1982-83; *ai:* Former Stu Cncl, Acad Challenge Team Sp Chm; Vol Clb; CWEA, PSEA, NEA, IRA, NCTE 1977-; Phi Bet Pi Lambda Theta; Reading PA Jr League Inc 1977-92, Bd Mem; A Women Assn 1979-; Rdng Symphony Orch 1982-90, Bd Mem; S Friends 1980-92 1St VP; Cty Pub Ed Fnd Grant; *office:* Conra Jr/Sr HS RR 1 Box 7 Robesonia PA 19551

HAMPTON, LISA MARIE, English Teacher; *b:* Melrose, MA; *m* Keith; *ed:* Harvard-Radcliffe Coll (AB) Eng, Amer Lit & La Harvard Grad Schl of Ed (EDM) Tchng & Curr 1991; *cr:* A Gakuin Eng Tchr 1989; MA Bar Assn Law Related Ed Asst Stoneham HS Eng Tchr 1991-; *ai:* Time & Learning Comm; S Stoneham Tchrs Assn 1992-, Prof Rights & Responsibilities Com 1992-; Stoneham Team Working on NEH Grant; *office:* Stoneham Franklin St Stoneham MA 02180*

HAMRICK, CHRISTINA ANN, English Teacher; *b:* Monroe Jarrett, Lindsay; *ed:* Cntrl MI Univ (BA) Eng 1968; Potsdam C Eng 1992; *cr:* Midland HS Eng Tchr 1968-69; Crestwood HS 1969-75; Colon HS Eng Tchr 1984-87; Norwood Norfolk HS 1987-; *ai:* Yrbk Adv; NCTE 1987-; NNCTA 1987-, VP; *office:* Norfolk HS Rt 56 Norwood NY 13668

HAMRICK, KIMBERLY KAE, Math Teacher; *b:* Dayton, OH; A.; *c:* Chrystal, Richard; *ed:* Liberty Univ (BS) Math Ed 1981 Bowie St Univ Grad Schl; *cr:* Elk Vly Chrstn Schl Math Tchr Sherman Sr HS Math Tchr 1983-84; Riverdale Bapt Schl Ma 1984-94; AACS Math Tchr 1994-; *ai:* Jr Spon; Curr Team; S Comm; NCTM; ASCD; NASSP; Riverdale Bapt Church 1960-; Tc Yrbk Dedication Nom PAESMT Awd; *office:* Annapolis Area Chr 716 Bestgate Rd Annapolis MD 21401

HAMROCK, ARDAITH ALDERMAN, History & English Tea Bluffton, OH; *w:* Thomas J. (dec); *c:* Jennifer L., Thomas C., Jo Phillip R.; *ed:* Youngstown St Univ (BS) Elem Ed, DH-LD, BD 1 Youngstown Pub Schls DH Unit Auxiliary Svcs 1990-91; St Patr 7th Grd Tchr 1991-; *ai:* YSU Eng Festival Judge, Tchr-Coach; Oratorical Coach, Judge; St Patrick Church 1983-, Eucharistic New Tchrs Mentorship; *office:* St Patrick Schl 38 E Water St Hubb 44425

HAMSTRA, JODI GROSSER, Spanish Teacher; *b:* Kalamazoo Jeffrey Todd; *ed:* Grand Vly St Univ (BA) Eng 1991; Seeking Degree Scndry Ed Towson St Univ Tchng Rdng, Writing, Adult Southwestern MI Coll Eng Instr 1992-93; Randallstown HS Sp 1993-; *ai:* Class of 1997 Spon; Chrldng Coach; *office:* Randallst 4000 Offutt Rd Randallstown MD 21133*

HAN, S. BRUCE, Asst Professor of Management; *b:* Seoul, K Unae Kim; *c:* Christina, Michelle; *ed:* Cornell Univ (BS) Operatio 1978, (ME) Operations Rsrch, Indstrl Engrng 1979; The Univ of M Operations Mngmt 1990; PHD Prgm Mngmt Sci Univ of RI; *cr:* Kodak Co Indstrl Engr 1979-85; The Univ of MI Tchng Asst, Resea

TRW Inc Mngmt Assoc 1990-93; Merrimack Coll Asst Prof Bus Stdnts Adv; Sunday Schl Dir; Decision Sci Inst 1994-; vd Excel Tchng; MI Bus Schl Flwshp; Cornell Univ & Hartford Schlsp; *office:* Merrimack Coll 315 Turnpike St North Andover

NG, High School Teacher; *b:* Dalian, Liaoning, China; *ed:* v of Tech (BS) Math, Sci 1982; Temple Univ (MS) Sci 1988; E Grad Schl Engrng Stud; *cr:* Jr Mongolia HS Advanced Inst Tchr 1975-82; Temple Univ Math, Sci Instr 1986-88; Harrisburg Instr 1990-95; Lebanon Cath High Math, Sci Tchr 1990-; *ai:* ay Club Adv; Lebanon Cty Excl in Ed 1992-94; DaLian China 1976, 1980; *office:* Lebanon Catholic HS 1400 Chestnut St A 17042

AN, Chinese Department Chairperson; *b:* Shanghai, China; *m:* uang; *c:* Joy, Liz; *ed:* Foreign Lang Inst at Shanghai China (BA) aistics 1965; OH St Univ Foreign lang Inst (MA) Chinese 1984; OH St Univ (PHD) Chinese Linguistics 1991; Univ of Eng Lit; Malone Coll Post BA Eng Lit; *cr:* East-China Univ air, Foreign Lang Tchng & Rsrch Ctr 1978-81; OH St Univ vidualized Inst Ctr 1982-86; Merrimack Coll Chinese Adjunct 88; Phillips Acad Chinese Dept Chair 1988-; *ai:* NY Acad of ; Chinese Tchrs Assn 1986-; Chinese Bible Church 1986-, ncl Sec; Grants: Kenan, Abbot, Prof Dev; *office:* Phillips Acad Andover MA 01810*

RGH, KEVIN, Guidance Counselor; *b:* Englewood, NJ; *m:* mity, Amber; *ed:* Villanova Univ (BS) Ed 1973; Montclair St ance 1981; *cr:* Hackensack MS Sci Tchr, Guidance Cnslr 1973-; BCEA, NEA 1973-; Character Coalition; Distinguished Svc Awd e: Hackensack MS 360 Union St Hackensack NJ 07601

JUDITH MC LAINE, 5th Grade Teacher; *b:* Highland Twp, PA; th Richard; *c:* Kristine Evankovich, Kaleen Marino, Katrina : Clarion ST (BS) Soc Stud 1964, (BS) Elem Ed 1980; *cr:* -Clarion Vly Schl 6th Grd Tchr 1964-68, Tchr of Elem Gifted 6th Grd Tchr 1988-; *ai:* Mentor Tchr; Lead Tchr; PSEA, NEA nday Schl Tchr 1968-; Emlenton Civic Club 1972-; *home:* 224 # 253 Emlenton PA 16373*

ALTA ANN MYERS, Second Grade Teacher; *b:* Mishawaka, IN; n Elizabeth; *ed:* Mid TN St Univ (BS) Elem Ed 1966; Addl 3 Multicultural Ed Prince George's Comm Coll 1996; *cr:* Bell Third Grd Tchr 1966-67; Lanning Elem Schl Second Grd Tchr V. J. Trapp Elem Schl Third Grd Tchr 1968-69; Gateway Gardens Scnd Grd Tchr 1971-73; Mount Calvary Cath Schl Second Grd -; *ai:* Mid Sts Self-Stud Comm; NCEA 1981-.

CATHY KYER, Art Teacher; *b:* Gouverneur, NY; *m:* Garnold se, Travis; *ed:* Canton Coll (AAS) Cmptr Sci 1970; Potsdam St Art 1986; (MST) Instrl Media Tech 1991; *cr:* Massena Cntrl Schl 986-; *ai:* Liberty Photo Club Adv; Kappa Delta Pi 1985-; Friends Gallery 1986-, Sec 1994; Art Tchrs Network 1986-, VP 1988; ssena Cntrl HS 290 S Main St Massena NY 13662

R, PEGGY ARLENE (SCOTT), 2nd Grade Teacher; *b:* , OH; *m:* Ronald Carl; *c:* Scott, Justin; *ed:* OH Univ (BSEd) 1969, (MED) Spec Ed 1974; 30 Addl Grad Hrs Supervision *r:* Pt Pleasant Schls Tchr of Primary Mentally Retarded 1969-71; rg Schls Tchr of Intermediate Mentally Retarded 1971-73; Dist Tchr of Intermediate Mentally Retarded 1973-74; City Schl 1-3 Grd Learning Disabilities Tchr 1995-; *ai:* Medill on Assistance Team Bldg, Dist Rep; Discipline, Medill y, Site-Based, Social Media, Lang Arts Assessment Selection Medill Visions Team; NEA 1969-; Lancaster Ed Assn 1974-75; 969-73; OEA 1974-; Alpha Delta Kappa 1990-, Publicity, Ed; *office:* Medill Elem Schl 1151 James Rd Lancaster OH

CH, MARIANN E., Fourth Grade Teacher; *b:* Passaic, NJ; *m:* *c:* Charles, Cathleen; *ed:* Paterson St Coll (BA) Elem Ed 1966; se of Newark Catechist Preparation; *cr:* Wallington Pub Schl 5 1966-69; Sacred Heart Elem Schl 5 Grd Tchr 1971-74; St Kostka Schl 4 Grd Tchr 1982-; *ai:* NCEA 1982-; Archdiocese Tchr Recognition Awd 1993; *office:* St Stanislaus Kostka Schl Ave Garfield NJ 07026

CK, FRANK FOX, Retired Teacher; *b:* Milan, NH; *m:* Virginia Bradford, Bryana, Laveroni, Brandon; *ed:* Univ of NH (BA) His, 1954; 32 Credits Univ NH Grad Schl; 9 Credits Keene Tchrs Coll ; 27 Credits USNY at New Paltz; Elem Admin Cert; Lib Media AFT, NYSUTA, OTA 1963-; NEA 1955-; OREO; ONTEORA; dctrs Assn 1994-; Amer Legion 1945-; PTA 1955-; NY PTA Meml Awd 1955; *home:* 27 Mill Hill Rd Woodstock NY 12498

CK, H. STEPHEN, Social Studies Teacher; *b:* Bellefonte, PA; *m:* ckelner; *c:* Amy Richardson, Elizabeth Eckley, Katharine *ed:* Lock Haven St Coll (BS) Scndry ed & Soc Sci 1967; rg St Coll (MA) US His 1979; *cr:* Loyalsock Twp HS Scndry Soc 1967-81; Hughesville HS Scndry Soc Stud Tchr 1981-; *ai:* Asst Coach; Phi Kappa Phi 1979-; ELEA 1981-; *home:* 2435 Blair St port PA 17701

CK, JUDY PFILE, Music Professor; *b:* Monongahila, PA; *m:* : Carlow Coll (BA) Music Ed 1963; Univ of Pittsburgh (MA) gy 1969; *cr:* Pittsburgh Pub Schls Instrumental, Vocal Music Comm Coll of Allegheny Cty 1969-; *ai:* Musicians Club Adv 20 ural Advy Bd Chprsn 1990-93; AFT 1970-; Outstanding Svc Awd l Choir Founder, Dir 1969-; US Steel Chorus Dir 1971-77; *office:* oll of Allegheny Cty 808 Ridge Ave Pittsburgh PA 15212

CK, LOUIS J., Dir of Bands & Music Dept Chm; *b:* Pitcarn, PA; sburg Coll (BS) Music Ed 1974; Attnd Duquesne Univ, Univ of Whitewater, PA St, IL St Univ; *cr:* Norwin Jr HS Band Dir ntal Music 1974-76; Norwin Sr HS Band Dir 1976-, Duquesne junct Prof-Music Ed 1983-; Norwin Sr HS Music Dept Chair : Concert, Jazz, Marching Bands; Small Ensembles; Stage Crew; MENC 1970-; PSEA, NEA 1974-; Bands of Amer Contest ion 1983-88, Exec Sec; Bands of Amer Educl Adv Bd 1993-; onductor ETSU; Adams Cty OH, Adams Cty PA; Sudler Shield t; *office:* Norwin Schl Dist 251 Mc Mahon Rd North Huntingdon 2

CK, NANCY H., Special Education Teacher; *b:* Summit, NJ; *m:* W. Jr.; *c:* Jillian, Frederick; *ed:* Adelphi Univ (BS) Elem Ed IS) Spec Ed 1981; Dowling Coll (SDA) Educl Admin 1996; *cr:* r HS Self Contained Spec Ed Tchr 1980-86; Shoreham-Wading S Resource Room, Spec Ed Tchr 1987-89; Eastport HS Self d, Resourse Room, Soc Stud Tchr 1989-; *ai:* Septa VP; Dist ecision Making Comm; Dist Schl to Career Partnership; Sr Class i Delta Kappa 1996; *office:* Eastport HS 390 Montauk Hwy NY 11941*

X, RICHARD ANDREW, Math Teacher; *b:* Franklin, PA; *m:* Ann; *c:* Richard C., Keeley Kathryn; *ed:* Westminster Coll (BS) 71; *cr:* Greenville HS Math Tchr 1972; Sharon HS Math Tchr Franklin Area HS Math Tchr 1980-; *ai:* Boys & Girls Head Track Coach; Var Club & Class of 1997 Adv; NEA 1972-94; *office:* Franklin Area HS RR 4 Box 325 Franklin PA 16323

HAND, MAUREEN, English Teacher; *b:* Amsterdam, NY; *m:* John; *c:* Debra Metz, Betsy Cosentino; *ed:* SUNY at Albany (BA) Eng, (MA) Eng; *cr:* Amsterdam HS Eng Tchr 1977-; *ai:* Jrnlsm Adv; AFT, NYSUT 1977-; NCTE 1980-; Tchr Research Inst Participant 1993; Chosen Tchr at Scholars Recognition Prgm 1995; *office:* Amsterdam HS Saratoga Ave Amsterdam NY 12010

HAND, ROBERT DONALD, English Teacher; *b:* Canton, NY; *m:* Tammy Ellen Voorhees; *c:* Logan; *ed:* St Lawrence Univ (BA) Eng Lit 1982; SUNY at Potsdam (MS) Scndry Eng Ed 1989; *cr:* Heuvelton Cntrl Schl Sub Tchr 1984; Sackets Harbor Cntrl Schl Eng Tchr 1984-; *ai:* Forensics Club, Speech Team Adv & Coach; Speeling Bee Coord; Shared Decision Making & Curr Advy Comm Mem; Sackets Harbor Tchrs Assn 1984-, Exec Bd; NEA 1984-; NCTE 1989-; *office:* Sackets Harbor Central Schl Broad St Sackets Harbor NY 13685*

HANDFIELD, ANGELA HERNANDEZ, Reading Specialist; *b:* Bayonne, NJ; *m:* John Joseph; *ed:* Jersey City St Coll (BA) Elem Ed 1973; Georgian CT Coll (MA) Elem Ed, Rdng Spec 1987, (MA) Admin, Mngmt 1996; *cr:* Newark Bd of Ed 3rd Grd Tchr 1973-74; St Dominic's Schl 5th Grd Tchr 1976-79; Jackson Bd of Ed Rdng Tchr 1979-93, Rdng Specialist 1993-; *ai:* Celebration of Excl, Inservice, Acad Awds Banquet, Read, Rap & Rally, Mentoring Comms; PTA Rep; JEA 1979-, Corresponding Sec, Assoc Rep; OCCEA 1979-, Assoc Rep; NJEA, NEA 1979-; IRA 1990-; Mistreams Project Owners Assn 1983-, Sec, Trustee; Tchr of Yr 1994-95; *office:* C. W. Goetz MS Patterson Rd Jackson NJ 08527*

HANDLEY, CHARLENE BALLARD, Sign Language Teacher; *b:* Baltimore, MD; *m:* Brian Darrell; *c:* Erin, Kellie; *ed:* Western MD Coll (BA) Psych, Elem Ed 1986, (MS) Deaf Ed 1995; *cr:* Hampstead Elem Schl 3rd Grd Tchr 1986-90; Westminster HS Sign Lang Tchr 1991-; *ai:* Sign Lang Club Adv; Carroll Cty Outstdng Tchr Awd 1989; *office:* Westminster HS 1225 Washington Rd Westminster MD 21157

HANDLEY, MARYANN SCHNEIDER, Science & Reading Teacher; *b:* Columbus, OH; *m:* Stephen M.; *c:* Helen, Grace; *ed:* Miami Univ (BS) Elem Ed 1980; OH St Univ Spec Ed Cert; Attnd Ashland Coll; *cr:* Watkins MS Tchr of Dev Handicapped, 6th Grd Tchr 1985-92; Gahanna MS West 8th Grd Tchr 1992-; *ai:* Sci Dept, Assembly Comm Chm; Dist Sci Curr Comm Rep; Career Ed Comm; GJEA 1992-; OEA, NEA 1985-; *home:* 3770 McCutcheon Rd Columbus OH 43230*

HANDY, MARION LEE GORDY, World Culture & History Tchr; *b:* Philadelphia, PA; *c:* Deborah Gaines, Andrea Turner, Andrew Turner, Flora Handy; *ed:* Salisbury St (BA) Sociology, His, Eng 1977; Western MD Coll (MS) Behavioral Modification 1992; Ed That is Multicultural; Lay Speakers Schl The Bible in Relationship to Todays Wld; Greater Salisbury Comm Ldrshp Inst; ACES; *cr:* Bennett MS Admin Specialist 1970-74; Salisbury St Coll Stu 1974-77; Pittsville MS Hist, Eng Tchr 1977-87; Bennett MS Wld Cultures, His Tchr 1987-; *ai:* Bd of Dir Chipman Fnd; OUV Comm; Maple Shade Boys Home Spon; Sunday Schl Tchr; Speaker at Prison Ministries, Hosp Visitation; Prayer Group Ldr, Union Gospel Group Sr Choir; NEA 1977-, Del; MSTA 1977-, Del, Minority Affairs, Wms Ldrshp; Wicomico Cty Ed Assn 1977-, Del, VP, Bd of Dirs; NASALH 1973-, Bd of Dirs; Chipman Fnd 1980-, Bd of Dirs, Exceptional Svc; Wicomico Cty Ext 1985-, Bd of Dirs; Union United Meth Church 1969-, Lay Ldr 10 Yrs; United Meth Women Peninsula Conf, Past VP; WJDY Comm Achiever 1978; Daily Times Newspaper Pub Speaker List; NASALH Magazine SSU Career Day Presenter; United Meth Women SSU Black His Conf Organizer 1975; Peninsula Co NP Del; Laurel Delmar Charge; *home:* 304 Woodlawn Ave Delmar MD 21875*

HANDY, ROBERT ALAN, Soc Stud Tchr & Dept Chair; *b:* Baltimore, MD; *m:* Janet Bush; *c:* Lynn, Gregory, Beth; *ed:* Univ of MD (BA) Amer Stud, Ed 1975, (MA) Amer Stud 1979; Attnd Inst in Civic Ed, Harvard Univ at Cambridge 1988; De Witt Wallace Natl Leadership Prgm for Tchrs Princton Univ 1990; *cr:* Archdiocese of Baltimore Tchr 1975-76; Fallston Mid, HS Tchr 1976-90; Bel Air HS Tchr, 1990-; *ai:* Amer Historians ORg 1991-; MD His Alliance 1992-95; PTSAMD 1976-, Lifetime Mem; Woodrow Wilson Fnd Princton Univ 3 Grants; TORCH Dir; Numerous Articles, Curr Guides, Tchr Awds; Econ Tchr of Yr 1986; MD Tchr of Yr 1988; Pres Reagan Visited Class 1985; Natl Finalist Name the Orbiter Pgrm NASA Endeavor; AP Consultant for ETS; *office:* Bel Air HS 100 Heihe St Bel Air MD 21014*

HANES, DEBORAH FRY, Eighth Grade English Teacher; *b:* Buffalo, NY; *m:* Michael F.; *c:* Christine, Mark; *ed:* SUC at Fredonia (BS) Elem Ed, Scndry Eng 1976; SUC at Buffalo (MS) Elem Ed, 7-9 Eng 1979; *cr:* Annunciation Schl Sixth Grd Tchr 1977-78; Orchard Park MS Seventh Grd Eng Tchr 1979-82, Eighth Grd Eng Tchr 1989-; *ai:* Wellness Comm; Kid Connection; World Affairs Club Adv; AFT; NYSUT; *office:* Orchard Park MS 60 S Lincoln Ave Orchard Park NY 14127

HANESS, ROSEMARY, Fine Arts Educator; *b:* Union City, New Jersey; *m:* Salvatore Guadagnino Jr; *ed:* Montclair Coll (BA) 1963, (MA) 1970; NYU Post-Grad; NJ Cert Tchr; Cooperating Tchr NJ St Coll 1965, 1993-94, Fairleigh Dickenson Univ 1969-70, Montclair St Coll 1970-71, Kean Coll 1971-72, Columbia Univ 1972-73; *cr:* Fairleigh Dickinson Mid Coll Tchr 1987-92, Art Pgm 1989-93; Caldwell Coll Lectr, Part-Time Fac Ed Dept 1989-90; Mid Sts Comm on Fine Arts & Staff Admin Chprsn 1993; New Providence HS; *ai:* Fine Arts Fest Exhibit & Display 1975-89; NASDTEC Evaluation Ramapo Coll 1976, Georgian Court Coll 1977, Montclair St Coll 1979; AENJ Conf Presenter 1976; Alt Ed for Stdnts 1978-80; Art Stu of Week Rcgntn Pgm 1988-; Yrbk Adv 1982-; Craft Sale for Art Schlsp 1988-; His Tour Guide Bks Designer & Illus 1983-87; Plainfield 300 Bk 1985-88; Croquet-The Art & Elegance of Plyng the Game Loc Coord 1988; Set Designer for Schl Productions 1988-92; Natl Art Hnr Soc Mem, New Providence Chptr Adv 1988-; NEA & NIAE 1993-; New Providence Ed Assn, Fac Rep 1990-91, Chair, Sec; Comms Coun Chair 1989-; Instrnl Coun; Kappa Delta Pi, Hon Soc Ed; Phi Delta Kappa; New Providence Bd of Ed Recipient Cert of Excl 1989-90, 1992; NJ Dept of Ed Cert of Merit 1989-90; NJ Gen Assmbly Resolution of Rcgntn 1989; Tchr of Yr 1989; *office:* New Providence HS 35 Pioneer Dr New Providence NJ 07974

HANESY, MICHAEL JOHN, Physical Education Teacher; *b:* Manchester, IA; *m:* Kathryn R. Thellman; *c:* Madison, Haley, Hunter; *ed:* Edinboro Univ of PA (BS) Hlth, PE 1987; St Bonaventure Univ (MS) Admin 1993; *cr:* Warren Cty Schl Dist Tchr, Coach 1988-93; Millcreek Twp Schl Dist Tchr, Coach 1993-; *ai:* Head Wrestling Coach; *office:* Millcreek Township Schl Dist 3580 W 38th St Erie PA 16506

HANEY, CAROL ANNE, Mathematics Teacher; *b:* Salem, MA; *m:* Francis E.; *c:* Maggie, Mary, Christine, Stephen, Thomas, Paul; *ed:* Emmanuel Coll (BA) Math 1954; Salem St Coll (MED) Guid 1980, (MED) Admin 1988; *cr:* Revere High Math Tchr 1975-; *ai:* NHS Adv; Equity Ofcr; NEA 1975-; MTA 1975-; NCTM 1980-; *office:* Revere HS 101 School St Revere MA 02151

HANEY, EDWARD F., Civics & Leadership Teacher; *b:* Pittsburgh, PA; *ed:* Indiana Univ of PA (BS) Soc Sci 1969; Duquesne Univ (MS) Ed 1976; Addl Credits Univ of Pittsburgh; *cr:* Oliver HS Tchr 1969-; *ai:* 9th Grd PALS Team Ldr; Food, Clothing Drive Coord; Nem Amer Schls Lead Tchr Comm; Pub Relations Coord; AFT, PAFT, PFT 1969-; Pittsburgh Comm on Ed; Election Bd 1982-, Inspector of Elections; Neighborhood Assn 1993-95, VP; Democratic Comm 12 Yrs; World Affairs Cncl of Pittsburgh 1994-; Constitution of Allegheny Cty, BiCentennial Comm; Lions Club 1990-91; Outstdng Scndry Edctr Amer Awd 1974; Jr Achvmnt SW PA 25 Yr Svc Awd; WTAE-TV Exceptional Edctr; USAF Recruiter Edctr Awd 1984; Thanks to Tchr Nom 1991-92; Mini Grant Awd; *office:* Oliver HS 2323 Brighton Rd Pittsburgh PA 15212*

HANEY, ELEANOR HUMES, Retired Humanities & Rel Prof; *b:* Milford, DE; *c:* David; *ed:* William & Mary Coll (BA) Eng 1953; Wellesley Coll (MA) Eng 1954; Yale Univ (PHD) Theological Ethics 1965; *cr:* VA Union Schl Hum Lecturer 1957-60; Yale Univ Chrstn Ethics Tchng Asst 1962-65; Concordia Coll Assoc Prof Rel 1965-77; Harvard Divinity Women's Stud Visiting Prof 1977-78; ME Coll of Art Lbrl Arts Fac 1980-95; *ai:* Soc of Chrstn Ethics 1963-; Ctr for Vision & Policy 1985-, Coord, Bd; Main Share 1988-, Bd; NEH Flwshp; Co-Edited Articles; *home:* HC 32 Box 89 Bath ME 04530

HANEY, JAMES E., Theatre Department Chairman; *b:* Boston, MA; *m:* Anne Price; *c:* David, Kathleen, Sarah; *ed:* Boston Univ (BA) Eng 1961, (MFA) Theatre Directing 1962; Attnd Duke Univ, Harvard Univ; *cr:* Wheelock Coll Instr 1962-1964; Garland Jr Coll Assoc Prof 1962-74; Lasell Coll Dir of Dramatics 1964-75; Middlesex Comm Coll Prof, Chm of Theatre Dept 1964-; Lesley Coll Grad Schl Adj Prof 1978; *ai:* NEA, MTA 1979-, St Dir, Pres Local; Actors Equity Assn; Assn for Theatre in Higher Ed; Theatre Commnctn Group; Prof Actor, Dir & Designer; Dir & Designed Plays; Tchr of Yr 7 Times; Governors Awd for Excl of Svc; *office:* Middlesex Comm Coll Springs Road Bedford MA 01730

HANEY, KATHI D. (CADY), 4th Grade Teacher; *b:* Dennison, OH; *m:* William E.; *c:* Todd W., Shannan R.; *ed:* Kent St Univ (BA) Elem Ed 1974; 13 Addl Hrs; *cr:* Claymont City Schls 4th Grd Elem Tchr 1974-95; *ai:* United Meth Lay Ldr, Sunday Schl Tchr; MYF Ldr; Tech Comm; CTA, Sec; OEA; NEA 1974-; PTO, Sec; *office:* Claymont City Schls 115 N 3rd St Dennison OH 44621*

HANEY, ROSLYN PACIFICI, Retired Sixth Grade Teacher; *b:* New London, CT; *m:* Charles M.; *ed:* Eastern CT St Univ (BA) Elem Ed 1961; Univ of CT (MA) Elem Ed 1964; *cr:* Cohanzie Elem Schl Sixth Grd Tchr 1961-94; *ai:* Wide Math, Curr Comms; Worked With Drug Abuse Resistance Ed; NEA, CT Ed Assn, Waterford Ed Assn 1961-94; NCTM 1986-94; *home:* 310 Boston Post Rd Unit 153 Waterford CT 06385

HANFORD, ALLEN FREDERICK, Industrial Arts Teacher; *b:* Norwalk, CT; *m:* Eleanor Lynn Bond; *c:* Allen Frederick, Krista H. Diggins; *ed:* Salem Coll (BA) Indstrl Arts 1964; *cr:* Sistersville HS Indstrl Arts Tchr 1964-65; Pennsville HS Indstrl Arts Tchr 1965-66; Hopewell Twp Schl Indstrl Arts Tchr 1966-73; Lower Alloways Cr Twp Schl Indstrl Arts Tchr 1973-; *ai:* NJEA, NEA 1965-; LACEA 1973-; Upper Deerfield Historic Comm 1975-; South Jersey Gas Engine Club 1980-; Odyssey of Mind 1980-91, Coached Regnl, St, World Competitions, Won 1st Place in St Competition 1990; *office:* Lower Alloways Creek Schl 967 Main St Canton Salem NJ 08079

HANGE, ANN WENDLING, 4th Grade Teacher; *b:* Defiance, OH; *m:* Don; *c:* Jeffrey, Andrew; *ed:* Bowling Green St Univ (MA) Ed 1978; BGSU (BS) Ed l(&#; *cr:* Hicksville Elem 4th Grd 1973-; *ai:* NEA 1974-, Co-Pres; Delta Kappa Gamma 1979-, Pres Beta Zeta Chptr; *home:* 110443 Slough Defiance OH 43512

HANGEN, MARILYN ANN EDGAR, Assistant Principal; *b:* East Meadow, NY; *c:* Devin, Carrie; *ed:* Hofstra Univ (BS) Elem Ed 1967; Russell Sage Coll (MS) Elem Ed 1971; City Univ of NY Advanced Cert Schl Dist Admin 1991; 9 Post Grad Credits Univ of ME; *cr:* Bell Top Elem Schl Grd 1 Tchr 1968-76; ME Migratory Prgm Schl K-6 Grd Tchr 1977-82; Caribou MS 7-8 Grd Lang Arts Tchr 1982-88; Northern Parkway Elem Schl Grd 6 Tchr 1988-92; *ai:* Elem Chprsn Schl to Work Comm; Aids Curr Comm; Dist Coord CTY Testing Prgm; Conflict Mediator; Safety Patrol Spon; Supervision & Curr Dev Assn 1993-; Admins & Supvrs Cncl 1992-; UAA, CAA 1991-; NEA 1988-; Caribou Recreation Dept Outstdng Vol; SED Consultant: SEPTA Uniondale, PTA Uniondale 1988-; Coauthored Application & Earned 1994 NYS Schl of Excl Awd; *office:* Walnut Street Elem Schl 1270 Walnut St Uniondale NY 11553*

HANGEY, JON DEAN, Geography Teacher; *b:* Chestnut Hill, PA; *m:* Kathleen Colavita; *c:* Jon D. Jr., Daniel, Damien; *ed:* St Joseph's Univ (BS) Pol Sci 1972; Temple Univ at Phila Post-Grad Stud; *cr:* His Tchr 1976-82; Stewart MS His, Geog Tchr 1983-; *ai:* Coach Head Ftbl 1991-, Asst Ftbl 1983-90, Asst Var Bsktbl 1995-; PSEA, NEA, Ed Assn Norristown Area 1976-; Nor-Gwyn Yth Bsbl 1982-92, Little League Coach 10 Yrs; St Joseph's Univ Bsktbl Alumni Club 1980-; *office:* Stewart MS 1315 W Marshall St Norristown PA 19401

HANIK, GERALD H., Middle School Science Teacher; *b:* Paterson, NJ; *m:* Robin Katz; *c:* Robert, Allison; *ed:* Rutgers Univ (BA) Sci, Bio 1969; Montclair St Coll (MAT) Ed 1972; William Paterson Coll (MED) Admin, Supervision 1976; Post Grad Stud Career & Consumer Ed Jersey City St Coll; *cr:* Roosevelt Schl 6-8 Grd Sci Tchr 1969-84; Lincoln MS 6-8 Grd Sci Tchr 1984-; *ai:* Bsbl Card, Autograph Club Advs; NEA, NJEA, Hawthorne Tchrs Assn 1969-; Fair Lawn Soccer 1995-, Asst Coach; Fair Lawn T-Ball 1995-, Asst Coach; Midland Park Little League 1973-, Head Coach; Tchr or Yr 1991-92; *office:* Lincoln MS Hawthorne Ave Hawthorne NJ 07506

HANITZ, DIANE MARIE, Spanish Teacher; *b:* Buffalo, NY; *m:* Eugene M.; *c:* Michelle, Lisa; *ed:* D'Youville Coll (BA) Span 1971; Univ of Buffalo (EDM) Span Ed 1973; 3 Hrs ITIP; 3 Hrs Ed Psych; 3 Hrs Inservice Cmptr Courses & Cooperative Learning; *cr:* West Seneca Cntrl Schls Span Tchr 1971-78; Hamburg Cntrl Schls Span Tchr 1984-; *ai:* SDM Comm; AFT & WNYFLEC 1975-; NYSUT & NYSAFLT 1971-; Hamburg Tchrs Assn 1984-; AATSP 1971-78; Altar & Rosary Soc 1983-, Sec 1 Yr; TWST Swim Team 1992-95, Bd Mem; *office:* Hamburg Sr HS 4111 Legion Dr Hamburg NY 14075

HANKERSON, HOPE NADINE, Instructor of Writing; *b:* New York, NY; *ed:* Touro Coll (AA) Lbrl Arts 1982; Empire St Coll (BA) Eng 1987; The City Coll (MA) Lit, Creative Writing 1990; *cr:* Touro Coll Prof Tutor, Eng, Lbrl Arts Tchr 1980-87, Instr of Lang, Lit 1991-; Coll of New Rochelle Instr of Writing, Letters 1992-; *ai:* Writing Evaluator Eng Dept; Coll of Rochelle Rdng, Writing Specialist, Evaluator Dept of Letters; Grad, Baccalaureate Qualification Comm; Amer Assn of Univ Women 1995-; Coll of Rochelle Ind Stud Lit Mentor 1993-95; Ind Stud Lit Mentor 1993; Articles Pub; *office:* Touro Coll 240 E 123rd St New York NY 10035*

HANKERSON, ROBERT, Mathematics Teacher; *b:* Neptune, NJ; *m:* Elizabeth Mc Coy; *ed:* Jersey City St Coll (BA) MAth Ed 1971, (MA) Admin Supvr 1988; 36 Addl Hrs; *cr:* Westside HS Math Tchr 1971-91; Univ HS Math Tchr 1991-; *ai:* ASCD 1990-92; *office:* University HS 55 Clinton Pl Newark NJ 07108*

HANKINS, VERNON HARRISON, Art Teacher; *b:* Point Pleasant, NJ; *m:* April Kammerl; *c:* Donald, Alyssa, David; *ed:* Monmouth Coll (BA) Fine Arts 1974; Tchr Cert 1975; *cr:* Veterans Meml MS 6th-8th Grd Art Tchr 1980-88; Minerva Tire Mgr 1988-89; Veterans Meml Elem Schl 1st-6th Grd Art Tchr 1989-90; Brick Twp HS 9th-12th Grd Art Tchr 1990-; *ai:* Bsktbl Coach; Regaler Adv; NEA, NJEA, OCCEA 1980-; Art Alliance of Red Bank 1992-, Featured Artist 1994; Laurelton Art Soc 1992-; Monmouth Cty Arts Cncl Statewide Juried Show Mixed Media Winner

1994, Honorable Mention 1996; Various NJ Gallery Shows; *home:* 1 Nejecho Dr Brick NJ 08723

HANKINSON, SUSAN JANE GIFFEN, Retired Eng & Lit Teacher; *b:* Shadyside, OH; *m:* Russell E.; *c:* Beau, Ty, Slade; *ed:* Muskingum Coll (BA) Eng 1975; 12 Grad Hrs OH St Univ; 22 Grad Hrs OH Univ; 12 Grad HRs Ashland Univ; *cr:* West Muskingum Local Schl Dist 3rd-5th Grd Tchr 1975-79; Franklin Local Dist Kndgtn Tchr 1979-82, 6th Grd Tchr 1982-87, Jr HS Tchr of Gifted 1987-90, Jr HS Eng, Lit Tchr 1990-95; *ai:* Power of Pen Team Coach; Stu Cncl Adv; Delta Kappa Gamma 1985-; NCTE 1993-; Trinity United Presbyn Church; Rogge Grant 1986; Martha Holden Jennings Scholar 1976; *home:* 125 Sally Rd Headley Corners Zanesville OH 43701*

HANKLE, ROBERT GLENN, Band Director; *b:* Connellsville, PA; *m:* Marcia Griglak; *c:* Matthew, Benjamin; *ed:* Duquesne Univ Berklee Schl of Music (BSME) Music, Jazz 1971; *cr:* Prof Trombonist NYC, Broadway Theater, Recordings, Concerts 23 Yrs; *ai:* Jazz, Concert, Marching Bands; Pit Orch; NEA, MENC 1989-; IAJE 1993-; Little League 1985-, VP, Championships; Jr Soccer 9185-, VP, Championships; Performances Lincoln Ctr, Carnegie Hall; *home:* 193 Larch Ave Teaneck NJ 07666*

HANLEY, GEORGE H., 8th Grade Teacher; *b:* Hartford, CT; *m:* Pauline Levesque; *ed:* Univ of ME at Fort Kent (BS) Ed 1971; Univ of ME (MS) Ed; *cr:* Champlain Schl 4th, 5th Grd Tchr 1971-73; Medway MS 6th, 7th, 8th Grd Tchr 1973-; *ai:* Boys Soccer, B-Team Bsktbl Coach; MEA, NEA, MTA 1973-, Treas; NMSA 1988-; NELMS 1988-, Tchr Rep 1988-91; ME Assn of Mid Level Ed 1988-, Pres, Treas, Founder, Tchr of Yr 1993; Hillcrest Golf Course 1984-; Natl, Regnl, St Confs Presenter; *office:* Medway MS PO Box L Medway ME 04460*

HANLEY, JONI BARBARA, Kindergarten Teacher; *b:* Boulder, CO; *ed:* Frostburg St Univ (BA) Early Chldhd Ed 1966; Stud Human Dev Univ of MD; 73 Hrs Various Courses; MD St Artist, Tchr Summer Inst 1995; *cr:* Fairland Elem Schl 1st Grd Tchr 1966-71; Cold Spring Elem Schl Kndgtn Tchr 1972-; *ai:* Earl Chldhd Evaluation, Rdng & Lang ARts Evaluation Comms; Odyssey of Mind 1985-; St, Natl, Local Judge & Area Coord 1990-; NEA, MSTA, MCEA 1966-; MCCIRA 1990-, Chair of MD Book Awd Comm; IRA 1995-; NAEYC 1994-; *office:* Cold Spring Elem Schl 9201 Falls Chapel Way Rockville MD 20854

HANLEY, MICHAEL P., Reading Teacher; *b:* Weymouth, MA; *m:* Stacey Johns; *ed:* Westfield St Coll (BA) Eng 1987; *cr:* Frolio Jr HS Tutor 1987-88; Our Lady of the Assumption Eng Tchr 1988-92; Memorial Jr HS Rdng Tchr 1992-; *ai:* Jr HS Girls Bsktbl Coach; Spelling Team Adv; MA Educ Assn 1992-; *home:* 329 Canton St Randolph MA 02368

HANLON, CLAIRE, Social Studies Educator; *b:* Lawrence, MA; *m:* Paul; *c:* Michelle Mailhot; *ed:* Suffolk U (AB) His 1965, (MA) Admin 1975; Univ of MA at Lowell (CAGS) Admin; *cr:* Lawrence HS Tchr 1965-86, Admin 1986-89; Kingswood Regnl HS Edctr 1990-; *ai:* Sr Hnrs Prgm; Strategic Plan; Performance Task; Curr; NEA; ASCD; I Connect Mini-Grant Awd 1996; *office:* Kingswood Regional HS S Main St Wolfeboro NH 03894

HANLON, JOSEPH P., Guidance Counselor; *b:* Scranton, PA; *ed:* Univ of Scranton (BS) Cnslng 1978, (MS) Educl Cnslng 1981; Post Grad Stud at Harvard Univ, St Univ of NY at New Paltz, Coll of New Rochelle, New Schl for Soc Rsrch & Cornell Univ; *cr:* St Francis De Salles HS Rel Stud Tchr 1978-79; Middletown Jr HS Guid Cnslr 1981-88, Guid Chprsn 1988-92; Pearl River HS Guid Cnslr 1992-; *ai:* Class of 96 Adv; Bldg Ldrshp Team; Stu Activities Comm; Youth at Risk Cncl; Discipline Comm; AFT 1981-; NY St Unified Tchrs 1981-; NY St Schl Cnslrs Assn; NJ Buddies Inc 1993-, VP of Bd of Trustees; NY St Dept of Ed Home & Career Skills Curr Writer & Guid Cnslng Consultant; Middle Sts Evaluation Team; Youth at Risk Ryan White Title I Grant Writer; *office:* Pearl River HS 275 E Central Ave Pearl River NY 10965*

HANLON, PAIGE PULICE, Third Grade Teacher; *b:* Erie, PA; *m:* David P.; *c:* Collin, Peyton; *ed:* Edinboro Univ of PA (MED) Elem Ed, Rdng 1990; *cr:* Grandview Elem Schl 3rd Grd Tchr 11 Yrs; *office:* Grandview Elem Schl 4301 Lancaster Rd Erie PA 16506

HANLON, TERESA VETRULLI, Sixth Grade Teacher; *b:* Philadelphia, PA; *m:* Gavin E.; *c:* Kathleen, Colin; *ed:* West Chester St Coll (BS) Ed 1970; Beaver Coll (MED) Educl Leadership 1986; *cr:* Abington Schl Dist 2-6 Grd Tchr 1970-; *ai:* NEA, PSEA 1970-; Abington Ed Assn 1970-, Sec; Amer Cancer Soc Reach to Recovery 1989-; *office:* Overlook Elem Schl 2001 Old Welsh Rd Abington PA 19001

HANLON, VALERIE L., Social Studies & Business Tchr; *b:* Mineola, NY; *m:* Les; *ed:* Hofstra Univ (MA) Ed & Guid 1960; MA +60 Credit Hrs; *cr:* West Babylon HS Bus Tchr 1958-61; Walt Whitman HS Bus & Soc Stud Tchr 1974-; *ai:* Schl Store Adv; NYSBTA 1974-; NYSUT 1974-; NCSS 1984-; *office:* Walt Whitman HS 301 W Hills Rd Huntingtn Sta NY 11746

HANNA, C. SUE, Fifth Grade Teacher; *b:* Burbank, OH; *c:* Katie, Iris; *ed:* Ashland Coll (BSEd) Ed 1964; Univ of Akron (MSEd) Ed 1984; *cr:* Hatton Schl Tchr 1964-; *ai:* Primary Room Monitor, All Stu Helpers, Safety Patrol Supvr; Akron Ed Assn 1964-; Silver Acorn Awd Local PTA; *office:* Otis C. Hatton Schl 1933 Baker Ave Akron OH 44312

HANNA, JOHN E., Mathematics & Computer Teacher; *b:* Teaneck, NJ; *m:* Barbara; *c:* Eric, Amy, Mark; *ed:* Montclair St Univ (BA) Math Ed 1970; Fairleigh Dickinson Univ (MA) Cmptr Ed 1989; 6 Hrs OH St Univ, 6 Hrs Sam Houston St Univ, 25 Hrs Jersey City St Coll; *cr:* Teaneck HS Tchr 1970-; Network Admin Cmptr Dept, THS 1980-; Tchrs Tchng with Tech Instr 1993-; *ai:* Acad Decathlon Coach 7 Yrs; Tech Mngmt Comm; NEA, NJEA 1970-; NCTM, AMTNJ 1992-; T3 Instr 1993-; Co-Author Geometry Text 1974-78; Co-Author: Larson Hostetler Algebra 1993; Presenter Math Confs; *office:* Teaneck HS 100 Elizabeth Ave Teaneck NJ 07666*

HANNA, JOSEPH PATRICK, Amer Gov & Economic Tchr; *b:* Lock Haven, PA; *m:* Susan Marie Daley; *c:* Joseph P. Jr., Brian M., Sean E., Stephen T.; *ed:* Lock Haven Univ (BA) Pol Sci, Soc Stud-Summa Cum Laude; Masters Equivalency; *cr:* Clinton Cty Juvenile Probation Ofcr 1976-80; Jersey Shore HS soc Stud Tchr 1980-82; Lock Haven HS Soc Stud Tchr 1982-; *ai:* Var Ftbl Coach 16 Yrs; Jr HS Bsktbl Coach 1980-82, 1991-; NEA 1980-; PA Ftbl Coaches Assoc 1982-, AAA Dist Champs 1991-94; Regnl Champs 1992; St Semi-Finalists 1992; Lock Haven HS Key Club Adv 1986-, Tchr Adv; Dist Svc Awd 1982-; *office:* Lock Haven HS 301 W Church St Lock Haven PA 17745

HANNA, KEVIN PAUL, Math Teacher & Counselor; *b:* Long Island, NY; *m:* JoAnn DeMicco; *c:* Jessica, Caitlin, Matthew; *ed:* SUNY at Stony Brook (BA) Math, Ed 1980; SUNY at Brockport (MS) Cnslr Ed 1985; NY St (CAS) Cnslr Ed 1996; *cr:* Wellsville MS 7-9 Grd Math Tchr 1980-81; Brighton MS 7-9 Grd Math Tchr 1981-84; Brighton HS 9-12 Grd Math Tchr 1984-, 9-12 Grd Cnslr 1995-; *ai:* Var Boys Vlybl Coach 1985-; JV Girls Vlybl Coach 1986-; Welcoming Comm Adv; NEA 1980-; Monroe Cty Cnslr Assn 1995-; Coach of Yr 1994; Sportsmanship Awd 1995-; *office:* Brighton HS 1150 Winton Rd S Rochester NY 14615*

HANNA, MARGARET VOLTZ, French & Spanish Teacher; *b:* Butler, PA; *m:* Ronald E.; *c:* Jennifer, Ronald C., Sharon, Lorraine, Lynette; *ed:* Carnegie-Mellon Univ (BS) Span, Fr 1964; Credit Hrs Gannon Univ 6, Penn St Univ 20; *cr:* Knoch HS Span, Fr Tchr 1964-70; Butler Co Comm Coll Span Tchr 1971-72; Fox Chapel Schls ESL Tchr 1990-91; Highlands HS Span, Fr Tchr 1991-; *ai:* Fr, Span Club; HEA 1992-; PSEA, NEA 1964-; Trinity Luth Church 1969-, Acolyte Chm; A-K Mother of Twins 1980-, Pres, Treas, 10 Yr Mem Awd; *home:* 149 Iron Bridge Rd Sarver PA 16055

HANNA, MARSHALL W., Business & Social Studies Tchr; *b:* Pittsburgh, PA; *m:* Carol A. Kranak; *ed:* Robert Morris Coll (BS) Bus Admin 1970; Bus Ed Cert 1973; California Univ of PA Soc Stud Cert 1971; *ai:* PIAA Bsbl & Sftbl Ofcl; PSEA 1973-; Saint Vincent Coll Tchr Recognition Prgm 1990; *office:* Burgettstown Area Jr/Sr HS 99 Main St Burgettstown PA 15021

HANNA, MARY KING, Mathematics Teacher; *b:* Baston, MA; *m:* James L.; *c:* Dr.Janemarie Dolan, Judith O'Flynn, Mary Beth Dignam; *ed:* Emmanuel Coll (BA) Math 1958; Boston St Coll (MED) Ed & Math 1972; Boston Univ 6 Credit Hrs, Central CT St Coll 6 Credit Hrs, Bridgewater St Coll 6 Credit Hrs; *cr:* Solomon Lewenberg MS Math Tchr 1966-68; Atlantic Jr HS Math Tchr 1968-72, Resource Tchr & Math Dept Head 1972-83; Quincy HS Math Tchr 1983-85; N Quincy HS Math Tchr 1985-; Acting Dean of Stu 1996; *ai:* N Quincy tardy Prgm Chm; City-Wide Attendance-tardy, N Quincy HS Handbook Comms Stu Lrng Time Comm; Quincy Ed Assn 1968-, Exec Bd 1 Yr, Rep 5 Yrs; Quincy Ed Assn Accreditation Bd 1980-; MTA & NEA 1968-; NCTA 1968-; NCTM 1995-; St Frances Cabrini 1973-, Lay Minister 8 Yrs; Natl Sci Fnd at Cntrl CT Coll; Mediator N. Quincy High; *home:* 14 Bishops Ln Scituate MA 02066

HANNA, MICHIKO SHARON, 8th Grade English Teacher; *b:* Naha City Okinawa, Japan; *m:* John; *c:* Jonathan, Joseph; *ed:* SA PolyTechnic Univ (BA) Lbrl Arts 1976; Nazareth Coll 9MS) Ed 1987; *cr:* Palmyra-Macedon MS 8 Grd Eng Tchr 1981-88; Martha Brown MS 6th Grd Tchr 1989-95; Johanna Perrin MS 8 Grd Eng Tchr 1995-; *ai:* Drama Club Dir; AFT 1988-; Delta Kappa Gamma 1990-; BSA 1993-, Comm Chprsn; Pace Awd; *office:* Johanna Perrin MS 85 Potter Pl Fairport NY 14450

HANNA, TONI COCCIARDO, Learning Disabilities Instr; *b:* Uniontown, PA; *c:* Christopher; *ed:* CA Univ of PA (BS) Spec Ed 1975, (MED) Mentally, Physically Handicapped 1978; Currently Completing Internship Cert Schl Psych 1996; *cr:* Connellsville Schl Dist Learning Disabilities Instr 1975-; *ai:* NEA, PSEA 1975-; NASP 1996-; Cncl for Exceptional Children, Local Pres 1977-78; Wrkshps, Inservices Ed Learning Disabled Stu; *office:* Dunbar Twp Elem Schl 711 Ridge Blvd Connellsville PA 15425*

HANNAFORD, ARTHUR G., Mathematics Teacher; *b:* Biddeford, ME; *ed:* Univ of ME (BS) Scndry Ed 1989; *cr:* Bonny Eagle HS Math Tchr 1989-; *ai:* Stu Cncl Adv; Asst Golf Coach; NEA, MEA 1995-; *office:* Bonny Eagle HS 700 Saco Rd Standish ME 04084

HANNAH, ANN M., Special Education Teacher; *b:* Toledo, OH; *m:* Jack G.; *c:* Scott, Karen; *ed:* Univ of Toledo (BS) Elem Ed, DH 1972; Bowling Green St Univ (MA) Spec Ed 1991; SLD Cert; *cr:* Benton Carroll Salem Schl Intermediate DH Tchr 1972-77; Lake Local Schls Sub Tchr 1978-84; Wood Cty Bd of Ed SLD, DH Tchr 1984-; *ai:* Safety Patrol Adv; Intervention Asst Team; Right to Read Comm; Phi Delta Kappa 1994-; St Mark Luth Church, Sunday Schl Confirmation Tchr, Alter Guild; Outstdng Tchr of Learning Disabilities Natl Awd Cncl for Learning Disabilities 1990; Bowling Green St Univ Rural Amer Inst Project 1990-91; Jennings Scholar 1991-92; Outstdng Tchng Lake Ed Assn 1995; OH St Grant Mentor; *office:* Walbridge Elem Schl Union & Grove St Walbridge OH 43465*

HANNAH, FRED HOMER, Quest Teacher; *b:* Hamersville, OH; *m:* Louise Simmons; *c:* Eric Brown, Cara; *ed:* Asbury Coll (BA) His 1970; Xavier Univ (MED) Scndry Admin 1976; *cr:* Hillsboro City Schls Soc Stud Tchr 1970-71; US Army Admin Specialist 1971-73; Bethel-Tate Schls Tchr 1973-; *ai:* Coach Girls & Boys Bsktbl 1973-92, Fast Pitch Sftbl 1988, Cross Cntry & Track 1973-82; Nazarene Church 1992-, Special Prgm Dir; Church Bd 1995-; Article Pub Scholastic Coach 1977; *office:* Bethel-Tate MS 150 Fossyl Dr Bethel OH 45106*

HANNAH, MARY JOAN ALICE, Retired Mathematics Teacher; *b:* Niagara Falls, NY; *ed:* Niagara Univ (AB) Math, End 1957, (MA) Guid 1958; Attnd Canisius Coll, St Univ at Buffalo, Guadalajara Mexico; *cr:* Lewiston-Porter HS Math Tchr 1958-93; *ai:* Mentor Prgm 2 Yrs; Outcome Based Comms; Hnr Soc, Class Adv; Lamp of Learning, Mid Sts Eval Comms; Chr for Revising Chourse 1 & 2 Workbooks Through Local BOLES; NYSTMA 1958-; DES, Local Chptr Pres; Alpha Delta Kappa 1991-; Amer Cancer Soc Daffodil Drive; Aging Cncl 1992-, Means On Wheels; Heart Assn Fund Raiser Comm; Lib Drive Worker; Adult Ed Classes 30 Yrs; *home:* 549 Lake Rd Youngstown NY 14174*

HANNAH, RUTH ANN, 3rd Grade Teacher; *b:* Hampton, IA; *c:* Barbara, Michael, Susan Kochy, Cynthia Rossi; *ed:* Drake Univ (BS) Elem Ed 1951; Kent Univ Renew Cert in Elem Ed 1976; *cr:* Yankton Co Schls 3rd-4th Grd Tchr 1951-52; Hansell Consolidated Schls 3rd Grd Tchr; Cleveland City Schls 1st Grd Tchr 1954-56; Jefferson Area Schls 3rd Grd Tchr 1977-; *ai:* OEA 1977-; NEA 1977-; Jefferson Tchrs Assn 1977-, Sec; Travelers Club 1974-, Pgm Chm; Rock Creek Church Bd 1980-, Chm; Delta Kappa Gamma 1994-.

HANNAH, SHARI K., High School Mathematics Tchr; *b:* Middletown, OH; *ed:* Miami Univ (BS) Scndry Math Ed 1990; 21 Post Grad Hrs; *cr:* St Pauls Country Day Schl 7th-12th Grd Math Tchr 1990-92; Lakota HS Math Tchr 1992-; *ai:* Var Vlybl Asst Coach; Greater Cin Cncl Tchr of Math 1995-; *office:* Lakota HS 5050 Tylersville Rd West Chester OH 45069

HANNAM, SUSAN ELIZABETH, Assoc Prof of Allied Health; *b:* Annapolis Royal, NS Canada; *ed:* Acadia Univ (BS) PE 1974; IN Univ (MS) Ath Trng 1979 (HSD) Coll, SChl Hlth 1992; *cr:* Acadia Univ Instr-Head Ath Trainer 1979-81; Western IL Univ Adj-Head Women's Ath Trainer 1981-82; IN Univ Instr, Head Women's Ath Trainer 1982-85; Slippery Rock Univ Assoc Prof 1986-; *ai:* Coord Coll Assessment, Research Ctr; 2 NATA Task Forces; Univ Continuous Improvement Ofcr; Dir Ath Trng Curr; Natl Ath Trainers Assn 1978-; Amer Schl Hlth Assn 1991-; Amer Alliance Hlth 1994-, Phys Educ, Recreation, Dance; Amer Red Cross 1995-, Hlth, Safety Advy Bd; Grants Obtained US Dept of Educ, 5 St; Pub Articles; Edited One Booklet; Served as Exchange Prof to S. Korea; *office:* Slippery Rock Univ Of PA Allied Health Dept Slippery Rock PA 16057*

HANNEMAN, DARLENE CULLER, Second Grade Teacher; *b:* Chicago, IL; *m:* Dennis Franklin; *c:* Tamara, Beth Ann, Eric, Angela; *ed:* Bowling Green Univ (BS) Elem Ed 1971, (MS) Rdng, Supervision 1977; *cr:* Ottoville Local Schl 2nd Grd Tchr 1971-74, 1980-89, 1st Grd Tchr 1974-80, 1-3rd Grd Large Class Tchr 1989-95; Split 1st & 2nd Grd Tchr 1994; *ai:* Lang Arts Course of Study, Right to Read Week & Portfolio Assessment Comms; New Tchr Mentor; Mth & Soc Stud Coarse of Stud; Local, St, Natl IRA 1971-, Past Pres; United Ed Profession 1972-, Pres; OH Cncl Tchrs of Eng Lang Arts 1992-; OH Sci Tchr Assn; 4-H Adv 1971-; Cath Ladies of Columbia 1971-, Sec; Amer Legion Auxiliary 1979-, 2nd VP; Kalida Band Boosters Club 1982-, Flag Comm; Putnam Co Soccer League 1984-, Pub Chprsn; Tch Choice Awd Comm; Findlay Coll Mazza Enthusiasts-Children Illustrators Collection; Detla Kappa Gamma; Jennings Lecture Series Awd; Putnam Co Rural Literacy Authors Intervention Project; *office:* Ottoville Local Schl Rt 224 Box 248 Ottoville OH 45876*

HANNES, FLORENCE BLUEGLASS, Assoc Prof of Occuptnl Thrpy; *b:* New York, NY; *m:* Andrew P.; *c:* Amy, Jeffrey; *ed:* NY Univ (BS) Occupational Therapy 1970; Long Island Univ (MS) Comm Mental Hlth 1985; *cr:* Orange Cty Comm Coll Assoc Prof OTA Prgm 1978-; Occupational Therapy Practitioner Consultant 1970-; *ai:* OTA Prgm Club Adv; Consortium Advancement Hlth Careers; Amer Occupation Assn 1970-; NEA 1978-; NY St OT Assn 1980-, Recognition Av Hlth Assn Bd Dirs 1994-, VP Resource Dev; Accredita Occupational Therapy Ed; AOTA Essentials Review Comm; Pr Occupational Therapy Tech Level; Textbook Occupational The Pediatrics; *office:* Orange County Comm Coll 115 South St M NY 10940*

HANNIGAN, SUSAN M., Physical Ed Teacher & Coach; *b:* Por *ed:* Univ of ME at Orono (MS) Ed 1988; Working on Masters Gorham HS Tchr 1988-; *ai:* Var Field Hockey, JV Sftbl, G Coach; Ldrshp Team; MTA, NEA, US Field Hockey Assn 1988- Hockey Assn 1988-, Regnl Rep; Amer Heart Assn 1994-, In Coaching Effectiveness Prgm 1995-, First Aid Instr; PTA Gran Prgm Stdnts, Staff; *office:* Gorham HS 41 Morrill Ave Gorham M

HANNON, JOSEPH JAMES, 7th Grade Reading Teacher; *b:* PA; *m:* Patty Osborne; *c:* Alysa, Jordan; *ed:* Boston Coll (BA) E Philosophy 1971; Temple Univ (MED) Scndry Eng 1974; 60 G Hrs Rdng Specialist Cert; *cr:* Haddonfield Jr HS Eng, Rdng Tch Pocono Mt Junior HS Rdng Tchr 1987-93; Pocono Mt Intermed Tchr 1993-; *ai:* Discipline, Expectation Comm; Instrl Support Prgm; NEA; NJ Governors Tchr Recognition Awd 1987; *offic* Mtn Intermediate School PO Box 200 Swiftwater PA 18370

HANNUM, KRAIG B., 8th Grd Social Studies Teach Leavenworth, KS; *m:* Michele Eaton; *c:* Robby Eaton, Schuyler; at Oswego (BA) Pol Sci 1986; Castleton St Coll (MED) Ed Poultney HS Civics & US His Tchr 1993-95, 8th Grd Soc Stud T *ai:* Co-Adv Stu Cncl; Manchester Historical Soc 1995-.

HANNUM, THOMAS PATRICK, Assc Band Dir-Percussion Chester, PA; *m:* Linda Jeanette Paul; *c:* Gregory James; *ed:* We Univ (BS) Music Ed 1980; Univ of MA (MME) Music 1984; *c* MA Percussion, Minuteman Bands Assoc Dir 1984-; *ai:* Conduc Mobile Percussion Seminar Dir; Star of IN Brass, Percussion (Arranger; Percussive Arts Soc 1982-, Marching Percussion Comr MMEA 1984-; Kappa Kappa Psi 1988-; Tau Beta Sigma 1989-; I 1982-, Clinician, Endorser, Educl Advy Bd 1990; Avedis Z 1982-, Clinician, Endorser, Educl Advy Bd 1995; J. D. Calato M Clinician, Endorser; Mike Balter Mallets 1991-; Dstngd Svc A Books: Championship Concepts for Marching Percussion 19 Video: Fundamental Techniques for Marching Percussion 19 Univ Of MA At Amherst Dept of Music & Dance Fine Arts Ct MA 01003*

HANOVER, MARGARET KELLNER, Social Studies Te Buffalo, NY; *m:* Paul S.; *c:* Julie A. Knight, Laurie A.; *ed:* Dae (BA) His 1960; Nazareth Coll 24 Addl Credit Hrs Post Kensington HS Soc Stud Tchr 1960-61; Kenmore Pub Schls Sub Tchr 1975-80; Mt St Mary's HS Temporary Soc Stud Tchr 1981; Soc Stud Tchr 1981-; *ai:* Frosh Class, UN Club Moderator; Fac A Mid Sts Steering, prsnl, Schlsp Comms; Chrmn Block Sched C St Soc Stud Cncl 1982-; Univ of Rochester Mercy Tchr of Yr 1989; *office:* Our Lady Of Mercy HS 1437 Blossom Rd Roch 14610

HANOVER, ROY, Science Teacher; *b:* Brooklyn, NY; *m:* Caryl Jason; *ed:* Brooklyn Coll (BA) Ec 1964; Ed Courses at City U Coll, Univ of IA; *cr:* PS 196 Tchr 1964-72; PS 1 Tchr 1972- Coach; After Schl Ctr; AFT, UFT 1967-, Chapter Ldr; Bd of Ed Pres 2 Yrs; Sci, Tech Grant; Nom Sci Tchr of Yr 1995; *offi* Tottenville 58 Summit St Staten Island NY 10307

HANRAHAN, BARBARA MORAN, Retired High School Te Chicago, IL; *w:* Thomas E. (dec); *c:* Thomas M., Catherine, Jan Maura Mountain, Lynne; *ed:* Mundelein Coll at Chicago (BS 1954; Attnd Loyola Univ at Chicago; Trinity Coll at Washingto 1986-89; *cr:* Acad of Holy Cross Physics, Math Tchr 1974-95; Swim Team Coach 13 Yrs; Math Club Moderator 5 Yrs; SADD M 6 Yrs; MCTM, NMTA, NCEA, NISCA 1976-; MCSL, Cty Swim *home:* 11418 Hounds Way Rockville MD 20852

HANSBERRY, KENNETH MICHAEL, History Department Waltham, MA; *ed:* Dartmouth Coll (BA) Govt, Ed 1990; Stanf (MA) Ed 1991; *cr:* Wooster Schl His Chair, Coll Cnslr, Coach I Coach Boys' Soccer, Girls' Bsktbl & La Crosse; NEACAC 1993 Wooster Schl 55 Ridgebury Rd Danbury CT 06810*

HANSCOM, STACIE JANE (SHOPPELL), Biology, Geograp Tchr; *b:* Portsmouth, VA; *m:* Daniel Nathan; *c:* Deric Nichola Janelle; *ed:* Univ of ME at Farmingham BS Scndry Ed, Bio Scarborough HS Bio, Geog-Sci Tchr 1993-; *ai:* Assistance JV Sft 1994; Ronald Mc Donald Funding Raising Comm Adv; NEA, SE MEA 1994-, Rep Assembly; *office:* Scarborough HS 20 Go Scarborough ME 04074

HANSEL, ELIZABETH ANNE, Learning Disabilities Tea Columbus, OH; *m:* Charles; *ed:* Kenyon Coll (AB) Eng & Thea Keene St Coll Cert Eng 1993; *ai:* Drama Club, Jr Class Cncl A 1994-; *office:* Keene Sr HS 43 Arch St Keene NH 03431

HANSELL, ELEANOR WILLIAMS, Retired Elementary Tea Dodge City, KS; *m:* Robert E.; *c:* Robert E. Jr., John W., Eleanor Cunningham; *ed:* Trenton St Coll (BA) Ed 1965; Penn St (MS) 60 Hrs Post Grad Penn St Univ, Marywood Coll, Villanova U Schoen Schl Dist Tchr 1950-51; Bristol Twp Schls Elem Tchr 19 Gesell Evaluator Emilie Chrstn Day Schl; Amer Cancer Soc Pub Ed PASR 1991-; AAUW 1985-; Amer Cancer Soc 1984-, Bd of Dir Lake Nature Cntr 1988-, Bd of Dirs; Emilie United Meth Churc Admin Bd & Lay Ldr; *home:* 903 Hilary Ave Croydon PA 19021

HANSELMAN, JEANNE MARIE, High School Principal; *b:* OH; *m:* William Hanzelman; *c:* Todd, Erin, Nashon; *ed:* Youngs Univ (BS) Ed; *cr:* Corinth Chrstn Acad Math Tchr 1983-88; Victor Schl Math Tchr 1988-95, Prin 1995-; *ai:* Vlybl Coach; *office:* Christian Schl 6759 State Route 5 Kinsman OH 44428

HANSELMANN, MARIA, Mathematics Teacher; *b:* Philadelp *ed:* Immaculata Coll (AB) Math, Physics 1970; Temple Univ Math; Boston 6 Credits Sci; *cr:* West Philadelphia Cath HS for Gi 1971-89; W Philadelphia Cath HS Tchr 1989-92; Bishop McDe Tchr 1992-; *ai:* Mathletes; NCEA 1970-; NSTA 1980-; ACT Immaculate Conception Church Reader 1948-; West Extraordinary Minister 1985-91; *office:* Bishop Mc Devitt HS 12 Ave Wyncote PA 19095*

HANSEN, BARBARA LOUISE, English Professor; *b:* Indianap *ed:* Ball St Univ (BS) Eng 1963, (MA) Eng 1964, (PHD) Eng 1971; St Univ Eng Instr 1964-72; Univ of Cincinnati Assst Prof 1972-78 Prof 1978-90, Eng Prof 1990-; *ai:* AAUP 1978-; Venture Cl Outstanding Handicapped Stu; Grad, Doctoral Tchg Fellowship; Awd Handicapped Prof Woman of 1972; Univ of Cincinnati Fac Awd; Two Books Developing Sentence Skills, Picking up the Pi Articles Pub in Journals; Dir of Amer Scholars; World Whos Women; Intnl Whos Who in Education; *office:* Univ Of Cin Plainfield Rd Cincinnati OH 45236

HANSEN, JOHN BRYAN, 7th Grade Science Teacher; *b:* Erie, Kathleen Therese Ott; *c:* Nathan Thomas, Victoria Anne, Sarah K abeth; *ed:* Penn St at Behrend (BS) Bio 1986; Edinboro Univ t in Ed 1987; *cr:* Cathedral Prep HS 10th Grd Bio Tchr 1986-89; Wilson MS 7th Grd Sci Tchr 1989-; *ai:* Ath Dir; Girls Bsktbl Dowell HS; Fac Adv Schl Newspaper; NEA 1989-; St Josephs l Bd 1991-, Sec; Male Ath of Yr Penn St 1986; *office:* James S S 901 W 54th St Erie PA 16509

, MICHELLE LOUISE, Music Teacher; *b:* Ft Riley, KS; *ed:* H (BM) Music Ed 1992; Stud at Univ of Paris at Sorbonne; *cr:* Acad Music Tchr 1992-; *ai:* Musical Dir; Sr Class Adv; Music l Conf 1989-; Intnl Assn of Jazz Edctrs 1990-; Amer Choral Dirs -; ME Music Edctrs Assn 1994-, All St Auditions Chair 1994-95; ornton Acad 438 Main St Saco ME 04072*

, RICH C., Director of Athletics; *b:* Bayonne, NJ; *m:* Elisse .oster; *c:* Rich, Nicole, Dan, Kelsey; *ed:* Jersey City St Coll (BS) 985; NSCA Strength, Conditioning 1988; 9 Credits MA Admin; er's Prep Schl PE Tchr 1983-88, Hlth Ed Tchr 1985-87, Ath Dir Head Ftbl Coach; Head Strength, Conditioning Coord; NJFCA y Represent, Coach of Yr; HCIAA 1988-, Past Pres, Svc Awd; 35-; HC5thQC 1983-, Past Pres, VP, Treas; Freehold Pop Warner 1995-, Bd Mem, Coaches Dir; Playbook 1995 Publication Coach 3-89, 1993-95; City Resolution 1992-95; City Citation 1994-95; s Achvmt 1993-94; Mayor's Awd 1988-89, 1994; Dinardo Comm 1993-94; *office:* St Peters Preparatory HS 144 Grand St Jersey 7302*

, RICHARD NEIL, Eighth Grade Math Teacher; *b:* Auburn, NY; e Delmar; *c:* Stephanie, Michele; *ed:* Univ of MD (MA) Inst Sys Univ of Cntrl MI 30 Grad Hrs 1988-90; *cr:* USAF Security, Law ent 1969-73, Electronic Warfare Ofcr 1973-84, Intelligence 984-90; Newfield MS Eighth Grd Math Tchr 1992-; *ai:* Coord St n-a-thon; Class of 1998 Adv; Shared Decision Making, Chair comms; AFT 1992-, Treas; NCTM 1992-; *office:* Newfield MS St Newfield NY 14867*

, ROBERT EDWIN,JR., 8th Grade English Teacher; *b:* Joplin, Terri Semmelhack; *c:* Robert F., Elizabeth; *ed:* OH Univ (BA) 1968; Akron Univ (MA) Rdng Supervision 1989; *cr:* Cleveland Soc Stud Tchr 1968-75; Medina Cty Youth Vcs Alternative Schl 82; Cleveland Pub Schls 8th Grd Eng, Soc Stud, Rdng Tchr 8th Grd Core Ldr; Carnegie Pilot Project Coord; Newspaper, on Adv; OFT, AFT 1982-; Carnegie Pilot Project Team Grant, St Creative Curr Dev Awds; *office:* Lincoln Intermediate Schl le Ave Cleveland OH 44113

, SANDRA MUELLER, 5th Grade Teacher; *b:* Washington, DC; ; *c:* Neandra Marie, Robert Neil; *ed:* Towson St Univ (BS) Elem George Washington Univ (MA) Ed, Human Dev 1984; *cr:* eanes Elem Schl 5th-6th Grd Tchr 1972-74; Cooper Lane Elem 3rd Tchr 1974-75; Naylor Rd Elem Schl Prin 1977-82; Capitol ad 4th Grd Tchr 1982-86; Benjamin D. Foulois Traditional Acad Tchr 1986-; *ai:* Bantams, Preps, Majors Bowling Leagues Coach NEA, MSTA, PGCEA 1986-; Amer Legion 1994-; Women of 78-, Sr Regent, Coll of Regents; *home:* 11909 Green Tee Turn arlboro MD 20772

, THOMAS JOSEPH, English Teacher; *b:* New Brunswick, NJ; Marie Dudenhoefer; *c:* Gregory, Eric, Matthew; *ed:* Univ of Notre) Ec 1974; Edinboro Univ (BA) Ed 1986; 15 Addl Grad Credits; drew's Grd Schl 6th-8th Grd Tchr 1974-76; Cathedral Prep Eng, Tchr 1976-86; Mc Dowell HS Eng Tchr 1986-; *ai:* Coach Var Bsktbl; Amer Legion Bsbl; NEA, PSEA 1986-; NCTE 1993-; 6-, Exec Bd; NWTF 1980-, Exec Bd; *office:* Mc Dowell HS 3580 Erie PA 16506

, COLLEEN ANN, 6th Grade Teacher; *b:* Johnstown, PA; *m:* arah, Erick; *ed:* Edinboro Univ of PA (BS) Elem Ed, ECE 1976; Haven Cath 6th Grd Tchr 1985-; *ai:* Arts in Ed Rep; Phi Delta 90-, Newsletter Ed.

, CONNIE B., 8th Grade Science Teacher; *b:* Albany, NY; *m:* c: Heather, Harry Jr.; *ed:* Allegheny Coll (BA) Psych 1969, (MA) , k-12 Gifted Validation; *cr:* Cranwood Schl Tchr 1069-89; Young Schl Tchr 1989-; *office:* Whitney Young Intermediate Sch rvard Ave Cleveland OH 44128

, DAVID ALAN, Music Instructor; *b:* Bryan, OH; *m:* Lori Rae *d:* Bowling Green St Univ (BM) Music 1968; Univ of MI (MM) 72; 30 Hrs Post Grad Studs; Attnd Brevard Music Ctr 1967, Aspen hl 1976; *cr:* Findlay City Schls Orchestra Dept Chair 1968-; g Coll Part-time Music Instr 1974-; *ai:* Chamber, Musical Orch in Ed Comm; FEA, OEA, NEA 1968-; MENC, OMEA 1968-, NW hair; OSOA 1968-, Pr; NSOA, ASTA, OSTA 1968-; Findlay Area 1978-, Bd Mem; Jaycees Outstanding Young Educator Awd 1977; s Honor Medal Mid-West Intnl Band, Orch Clinic 1979; MENC Music Educator; Pub 4 Articles Pr of Music Magazines; OH Schl n 1995 Tchr of Yr Awd; *office:* Findlay Sr HS 1200 Broad Ave H 45840*

, DONALD T., Assoc Prof of Acctng & CPA; *b:* Astoria, OR; *m:* Ryder; *c:* Thomas, David; *ed:* Univ of ME (BS) Bus Admin 1967; ern Univ (MBA) Fin 1970; Bentley Coll Post Grad Acctng Stud; eastern Univ Instr 1969-70; Merrimack Coll Assoc Acctng Prof : Fac Grievance, Dept Division Coll & Normal Fac Comms; Rank & Tenure, Curr & Accreditation Stud Comms; Amer Inst of)-; MA Soc of CPA 1980-; Amer Acctng Assn 1992-; MA CPA; & Instr Coord Lambers CPA Review; Author of Various CPE or Certfd Pub Accountants; Co-Author Textbooks : Lambers CPA Fin Acctng & Reporting, Lambers CPA Review-Acctng & g; *office:* Merrimack Coll Dept of Acctng & Fin 315 Turnpike St dover MA 01845

, JAY ROGER, Soc Studies Curriculum Coord; *b:* Fayetteville, usan Brooks; *c:* Heather, Claire, Benjamin; *ed:* Univ of Cincinnati g 1965; Temple Univ (MED) Ed 1967; Grad Schl Pol Sci Univ of ti 1968-70, 1974, Miami Univ 1987, St Univ of NY at Stony Brook : Fitzsimon Jr HS Eng Tchr 1965-67; Univ of Cincinnati Grad 1969-70; Madeira HS Tchr, Curr Coord 1971-; *ai:* Sr Class, Mock m Adv; NEA, OH EA 1975-, Past Local Pres; Amer Civil Liberty 990-; OH Democratic Party 1975-, Precinct Exec; HS Design urr Planning; COE Fellow SUNY at Stony Brook; OH Writers c Univ of Cincinnati Law Related Educ Fellow; *office:* Madeira Jr 65 Loannes Dr Cincinnati OH 45243*

, L. DEAN, Secondary Science Teacher; *b:* Syracuse, NY; *m:* . Mac Intosh; *c:* Scott, Christopher, Daniel; *ed:* St Univ Coll at (BA) Bio 1982; St Univ of NY at Fredonia (MS) Bio 1991; *cr:* own Cntrl Schl Scndry Sci Tchr 1986-; *ai:* Class Adv; Sci d Coach; Discipline, Schl Reorganization Comms; Sci Dept Chm; 1986-; Trinity Luth Church 1987-88, Yth Group Coord; NYS Sci Winner; *office:* Germantown Central Schl 123 Main St own NY 12526

, MICHELLE ALWARD, English & Yearbook Teacher; *b:* WA; *m:* Timothy R.; *ed:* WA St Univ (BA) Eng 1988; Eastern WA A) His 1992; *cr:* North Cntrl HS Tchr of Eng, Soc Stud 1989-92; Roosevelt HS Tchr of Eng, Yrbk 1993-; *ai:* Yrbk Spon 1993-; NEA 1989-; MEA 1993-; Eastern WA Univ Terry Lokken Aed Best Grad Stu Paper 1992; Article Pub 1992; *office:* Eleanor Roosevelt HS 7601 Hanover Pky Greenbelt MD 20770

HANSON, SUSAN JANE, Social Studies Department Chm; *b:* York, PA; *m:* Scott Bryant; *ed:* Towson St Univ (BS) His & Soc Stud 1972, (MA) Scndry Ed 1978; 47 Grad & In-Svc Hrs Beyond Masters Degree; *cr:* Middle River MS Tchr 1972-85; Chesapeake HS Tchr 1985-92; Perry Hall HS Tchr 1992-94, Dept Chm 1994-; *ai:* Svc Learning Coord; Multicultural-Interdisciplinery Coord; Stu Govt, Law Mentor Adv; Mid Sts Visiting Comms Mem 3 Yrs, Asst Chm 2 Yrs; NASSP 1985-; Curr Wkshp 5 Yrs; Christe McAuliffe Fellowship Awd for the St of MD 1991-92; *office:* Perry Hall HS 4601 Ebenezer Rd Baltimore MD 21236*

HANSON, THOMAS RAY, Social Studies Teacher; *b:* Collingswood, NJ; *m:* Lisa; *c:* Erik, Lindsay; *ed:* Glassboro St Coll (BA) His, Ed 1980; *cr:* East Camden MS Soc Stud Tchr 1980-81; Camden HS Soc Stud Tchr 1981-; *ai:* Inst for Political & Legal Ed Coord; JV Bsbl Coach; 4-8th Grd Night Bsktbl Coord; Chess Team; Class Adv 1986; Ftbl Coach 1982-93; Wrestling Coach 1982-86; NEA, CEA 1980-; New England Gynelogical Soc 1993-; Collingswood Little League 1987-, Safety Ofcr; Pub Family His; Curr for the Holocaust Stud of the Dept of Ed; *office:* Camden HS Park & Baird Blvd Camden NJ 08104*

HANSON-HARDING, BRIAN, English & Journalism Teacher; *b:* Kingston, NY; *m:* Alexandra Laing; *c:* Moses, Jacob; *ed:* UC at Berkeley (AB) Eng 1980; Rutgers Univ (MA) Eng 1989; 5th Yr Single Subject Tchng Credential 1980-81; Bay Area Writing Project; MS Classes at NYU; Art His at the New Schl; *cr:* Orange MS Eng Tchr 1981-82; NVRHS at Old Tappen Eng Tchr 1982-; *ai:* HS Newspaper Adv; NJEA 1981-; NCTE 1988-; JEA 1995-; Article Read at Berkshire Womens His Conf 1990; NJ Governors Tchr Awd 1995; E Dickinson & W Whitman NEH Summer Flwshp 1995; Christa McAuliffe Flwshp NJ Winner 1995-; *office:* Nrthn Vly Reg-Old Tappan HS 100 Central Ave Old Tappan NJ 07675

HANTHORN, JEFFREY W., Elementary Principal; *b:* Toledo, OH; *m:* Susan R. Susor; *c:* Sara, Alissa; *ed:* Bowling Green St Univ (BS) Elem Ed 1976; Univ of Toledo (MED) Rdng, Elem Ed, (EDS) Admin Supervision 1981; *cr:* Collingwood Learning Ctr Remedial Rdg Tchr 1976-77; Riverside Elem Schl Remedial Rdng Tchr 1977-78, Elem Tchr 1978-85, Asst Prin 1985-87; Larchmont Elem Schl Prin 1987-; *ai:* OH Assn Elem Schl Admins 1988-; NAESA 1994-; BPO Elks USA 1990-; *office:* Larchmont Elem Schl 1515 Slater St Toledo OH 43612

HANTO, HELEN MARY, English, Jrnlsm Tchr & Chair; *b:* Whitehall, PA; *ed:* Holy Family Coll (BA) Eng 1966; Villanova Univ (MA) Eng 1976; 3 Credits OK Univ Schl of Jrnlsm; *cr:* Colegio Espiritu Schl Eng Tchr 1963-73; Ryan Girls HS Eng Tchr 1976-77; Peirce Coll Comm Tchr 1976-; St Basil Acad Chair, Eng, Jrnlsm Tchr 1977-; *ai:* Moderator Schl Newspaper; Eng Dept Chair; Frosh HomeroomF; NCEA, NEA 1960-; Greater Phila Dog Fanciers Assn 1988-, Sec; Suburban Dog Trng Club, Border Terrier Club Amer 1990-; Good Neighbor Dog Trng 1992-; Wall St Journal; Book: Anthology of College Teachers; Articles Pub; *office:* St Basil Acad HS 711 Fox Chase Rd Jenkintown PA 19046

HANTZIDIAMANTIS, PATRICIA ANN, Special Educator; *b:* Brooklyn, NY; *m:* Christos; *c:* Ashley, Paris, Dean; *ed:* Geneseo St (BS) Spec Ed, Psych 1984; Adelphi Univ (MS) Spec Ed 1987; Post Grad Work Prof Diploma Educl Admin Long Island Univ at Greenvale; *cr:* Lyons HS Resource Rm Tchr 1 Yr; Hicksville HS Resource Rm Tchr 12 Yrs; *ai:* Soph Class Adv; NEA 1984-; Wrote Curr Introduction Acctng & Bus For Spec Ed; *office:* Hicksville HS 200 Division Ave Hicksville NY 11801

HANY, SUSAN LOEFFLER, His, Sociology & Psych Teacher; *b:* Cleveland, OH; *m:* Frederick Carl II; *c:* Joan, Elizabeth; *ed:* Denison Univ (BA) His 1981; Univ of Toledo (MA) Early, Elem Chldhd Ed 1993; Post Grad Work Cnslng; *cr:* Eastwood HS Eng Tchr 1984-88; Oak Harbor HS Tchr 1989-; *ai:* Prom Comm Adv; NEA; *office:* Oak Harbor HS 11661 W State Route 163 Oak Harbor OH 43449

HANZELY, STEPHEN, Prof of Physics & Astronomy; *b:* Satorajaujhely, Hungary; *m:* Brigitta Strammer; *c:* Melinda, Erika Hanzely-Layko; *ed:* Kent St Univ (BS) Physics 1962; Univ of Toledo (MS) Physics 1964; NM St Univ (PHD) Physics 1969; *cr:* Youngstown St Univ Asst Prof 1968-74, Assoc Prof 1974-80, Prof 1980-, Dir of Fac Relations 1993-; *ai:* Youngstown Area Physics Alliance, Co-Dir; Amer Assn of Physic Tchrs, Amer Phys Soc 1980-; Sigma Yi 1975-, Youngstown St Univ Chapter Treas Twice; Fulbright Alumni Assn 1995-; Hungarian Presbyn Church Refugee Resettlement Bd, Treas; Fulbright Fellowship to Hungary 1994; Youngstown St Univ Distinguished Prof Twice; NSF Grants for Summer Wkshps 1979 & 1980.*

HAPP, MARIE K., Biology Teacher; *ed:* Molloy Coll (BA) Bio Ed 1970; C.W. Post Coll (MS) Bio, Ed 1976; *cr:* St Agnes Schl Sci Tchr 1968-72; St John the Bapt HS Bio Tchr 1972-; *ai:* Sci Chprsn; NHS Moderator; STANYS; NSTA; NABT; *office:* St John the Bapt HS 1170 Montauk Hwy West Islip NY 11795

HARASTY, KENNETH JAMES, Teacher of Gifted; *b:* Brownsville, PA; *m:* Cathleen Rhodes; *c:* Matthew, Amanda, Kayla; *ed:* CA St Coll (BS) Scndry Ed 1971; California Univ of PA (MS) Earth Sci 1987; Addl Credits at Penn St Univ 1973-76; *cr:* Brownsville Area HS Sci Tchr & Tchr of the Gifted 1973-; *ai:* Southwestern Area Acad League Team Coach; Falconer HS Newspaper, Lit Magazine & HYPE Cable Television Schl News Prgm Adv; Audio-Visual Svcs Dir; NEA, PSEA, Brownsville Ed Assn 1973-; Veterans of Foreign Wars Natl Band 1964-; 6 Mon Valley Ed Consortium Grants; 1 Accu-Weather-Talcott Mt Sci Ctr Grant; 1 Star Schl Satellite Television Equipment Grant; CNN- Turner Educl Svcs Inc Natl Fac; Natl Tchr Trng Inst Master Tchr; *office:* Brownsville Area HS 1300 Brashear Ave Brownsville PA 15417*

HARBAUGH, KELLY DENISE, Spanish Teacher; *b:* Lewistown, PA; *c:* Shippensburg Univ (BA) Span 1984; *ed:* Shippensburg Univ (BA) Span 1984; *cr:* Palmyra MS Span Tchr 1986-87; Lower Dauphin HS Span Tchr 1987-89; Palmyra MS Span Tchr 1989-; Palmyra HS Span Tchr 1989-; *ai:* Stu Assistance Team Ldr 1988-; Comm Drug Task Force Comm 1995-; PSEA Tchrs Assn 1988-; Tiny Tim Awd 1995; *office:* Palmyra Area Schl Dist 1125 Park Dr Palmyra PA 17078

HARCAR, RAYMOND ANDREW, 5th-12th Grade Band Director; *b:* Cleveland, OH; *m:* Janis Lee Blinkie; *c:* Kristen, Joel; *ed:* Kent St Univ (MMEd) Music 1973, (BS) 1969; *cr:* Perry Local Schls Band Dir 1968-70; Field Schls Band Dir 1970-71; Waterloo Local Schls Band Dir 1971-; *ai:* Marching Band, Jazz Ensemble Dir; Private Instr Kent Roosevelt HS, Wadsworth HS; NEA, OEA 1969-; Waterloo Ed Assn 1972-, Treas 1983-88; OH Music Ed Assn 1969-; Newman Ctr 1964-, Ed Comm; Directed Bands to Numerous Awds and #1 Ratings; *office:* Waterloo Local Schls 1464 Industry Rd Atwater OH 44201

HARCLERODE, BETH DIANE, High School Art Teacher; *b:* Lancaster, PA; *ed:* Kutztown Univ (BS) Art Ed 1985; MD Inst Coll of Art 17 Grad Credits; *cr:* James Craik Elem Art Tchr 1986-89; Mauriec J. McDonough HS Art Tchr 1989-; *ai:* Class & Art Club Spon, MD Stu Asst Team Mem; EACC 1989-; NEA 1989-; *home:* 1602 Boyle St Alexandria VA 22314

HARCLERODE, PRUDENCE D., Business Education Teacher; *b:* Bedford, PA; *m:* Terrance K.; *c:* Sonja, Jerome; *ed:* IN Univ of PA (BS) Secretarial, Accounting 1960; *cr:* Chadds Ford-Unionville Bus Ed Tchr 1960-61; Penn Manor HS Bus Ed Tchr 1961-63; Laurel HS Bus Ed Tchr 1963-65; Penn Manor HS Bus Ed Tchr 1965-69; Chestnut Ridge HS Bus Ed Tchr 1984-; *ai:* FBLA Co-Adv; PA Bus Ed Assn 1990-; FBLA Bd Dirs 1992-, Sec; Bedford Grange 1945-; Chestnut Ridge Booster 1980-, Sec; Pacesetter Bowling League 1976-, Pres; FBLA Article Pub; *office:* Chestnut Ridge Sr HS RD 1 New Paris PA 15554

HARDEN, HENRY, Earth Science Teacher; *b:* Schenectady, NY; *m:* Sally Gillette; *c:* Eric J., Joel R.; *ed:* Univ of Rochester (BA) Geology 1972, (MS) Scndry Sci Ed 1973; 30 Addl Credit Hrs; *cr:* Waverly Cntrl Schls Sci Tchr 1973-; *ai:* NEA 1973-, Grievance Chair; Valley Arts Soc 1992-; 1st Novel 10,000 Copies Pub, 2nd Under Consideration; *office:* Waverly Jr-Sr HS 1 Frederick St Waverly NY 14892

HARDESTY, JOSEPH ROBERT, Business & Accounting Teacher; *b:* Canton, OH; *ed:* Malone Coll (BA) Bus Admin 1987, (BA) Scndry Ed 1990; Univ of Cincinnati (MA) Ed Admin 1995; *cr:* Turpin HS Tchr 1990-; *ai:* Class Adv 1990-94; Dept Chm; Mem Prin Adv Bd; N Cntrl Ed Team; *office:* Turpin HS 2650 Bartels Rd Cincinnati OH 45244*

HARDESTY, TODD HARPER, Math Tchr & Asst Ath Dir; *b:* Sandusky, OH; *m:* Deborah Stansberry; *c:* Emma Jane; *ed:* OH St Univ (BSEd) Elem Ed 1989; Ashland Univ (MED) Ed Admin 1996; *cr:* Dublin Sells MS Tchr, Coach 1989-92; Dublin Coffman HS Tchr, Coach 1992-95; Dublin Scioto HS Tchr, Coach, Asst Ath Dir 1995-; *ai:* Asst Ath Dir; Var Girls Bsktbl Coach; Sr Class Adv; NEA, OEA 1988-; OCTM 1989-; OHSBCA, NIAAA 1995-; Paul Douglas Tchrs Schlsp 1987-89; *office:* Dublin Scioto High School 4000 Hard Rd Dublin OH 43016

HARDIE, THOMAS AUSTIN, English Teacher; *b:* Providence, RI; *m:* Claudette; *c:* Solon, Orran, Aiden; *ed:* Univ of RI (MA) Lbrl Arts, Eng 1968; *cr:* Bristol HS Eng Tchr 1969-94; Mt Hope HS Eng Tchr 1994-; *ai:* NEARA 1973-; St Coord; NEA 1969-; Amer Legion 1975-; *office:* Mount Hope HS 151 State St Bristol RI 02809

HARDING, CATHERINE M., Music Teacher; *b:* New York City, NY; *c:* Thomas P., Kelly C. Harding D'Amico, Marijude; *ed:* Marywood Coll Music (BM) 1958, (MS) 1965; 20 Hrs Post Grad Ithaca Coll, SUNY at Cortland, Binghamton Univ; *cr:* Susquehanna Valley Schl Dist Music Tchr 1958-; Piano Studio Piano Tchr 1960-; St Andrews Church Choir Dir 1976-; *ai:* Choir Dir; Pub Relations Comm Chm; Sunshine Chm; Crises Response Team Mem; Natl Piano Guild 1987-, Chm 5 Yrs, Adjudicator; MTNA 1988-; Mid St Tchrs Assn 1990-; BCMEA 1970-; STMTA 1995-; NYSSMA, NEA, MENC 1960-; Presser Fnd Music Schlsp.

HARDING, CHARLES DOUGLAS,JR., HS Chemistry & Physics Teacher; *b:* Bethesda, MD; *m:* Susan Elizabeth; *c:* Ashley, Amanda; *ed:* Univ of MD (BS) Emergency Hlth Services 1990; Hood Coll (MED) Ed 1994-; Nutrition Sci Inst Course Dev 1995; Paramedic Instr Univ of MD; *cr:* Mont Cty Fire & Rescue Fire Officer & Paramedic 1970-90; Drexel Hghts Fire Dept Fire Chief 1990-93; Linganore HS Tchr 1993-; *ai:* SGA Adv; Ftbl, Swimming Coach; Career Tech Comm Co-Chair; NEA 1994-; Rapid PT Assessment & Transport Pub; Article Univ of MD & IFSTA; EMT an Objective Approach Pub Book; Assimilated Statistics System Data Base Cmptr Prgm; *office:* Linganore HS 12013 Old Annapolis Rd Frederick MD 21701

HARDING, EDWARD, Business Professor; *b:* Boston, MA; *ed:* Middlebury Coll (AB) Geog 1968; Dartmouth Coll (MBA) Finance 1977; Univ of MA (PHD) Mngmt 1989; *cr:* Plymouth St Coll Bus Prof 1983-; *ai:* Cmptr Advy Bd; IBSCA 1992-; Beta Gamma Sigma 1989-; *office:* Plymouth State Coll Dept of Business Hyde Hall Plymouth NH 03264

HARDING, FRED A., 9th-12th Grd Electronics Instr; *b:* Eaton Twp, PA; *m:* Donna F. Giberson; *c:* Scott, Faye; *ed:* Millersville UNiv (BS) Indstrl Arts 1974; 42 Addl Credits; *cr:* US Navy Nuclear Trained Electrician 1964-70; Tunkhannock Area HS Electronics Instr 1974-; *ai:* Tech Stdnts Assn Asst Adv; Tech Ed Assn of PA 1974-; Triton Hose Co #1 1974-; *office:* Tunkhannock Area HS 120 W Tioga St Tunkhannock PA 18657

HARDING, JOHN DOUGLAS, Second Grade Teacher; *b:* Waynesburg, PA; *m:* Robin Lee Mullen; *c:* Allison Kate, John Douglas Jr.; *ed:* Waynesburg Coll (AA) Chrstn Ed 1980, (BA) Elem Ed 1982; 24 Credit Hrs; *cr:* West Greene Schl Dist Elem Tchr 11 Yrs; *ai:* Head Tchr; NEA, NSTA 1993-; Sugar Grove Union Bible Church 1991-, Pastor; Bapt Ordination Pastor; *office:* Springhill-Freeport Elem Schl Star Rt Box 15 New Freeport PA 15352

HARDING, KAREN MACKEIGAN, Business Teacher; *b:* Lakewood, OH; *m:* Ralph John; *c:* Paul W., Elizabeth M., Daniel J.; *ed:* TN Temple Univ (BS) Scndry Ed 1985; *cr:* Open Door Chrstn Schl Bus Tchr 1986-; *ai:* Attendance Officer; ACSI 1986-; *office:* Open Door Christian Schl 8287 W Ridge Rd Elyria OH 44035

HARDING, MARGARET TRAINOR, Sixth Grade Soc Stud Teacher; *b:* Pittsburgh, PA; *c:* Cynthia M. Kouvaras; *ed:* IN Univ of PA (BA) Elem 1969; Slippery Rock Univ (MS) Elem 1974; Attnd Frostburg Univ, Butler Cty Comm Coll; *cr:* Mars Area MS 7th Grd Tchr 1970-81, 6th Grd Tchr 1985-; Adams Elem Schl 4th-5th Grd Tchr 1981-85; *ai:* Schl Dist Ath, Spec Events Videotaper; PSEA, NEA 1970-; PA Geographic Alliance 1990-, Tchr Consultant; Mars Area Ed Assn 1970-, Treas; DARE Spon 1991-, Cranberry Twp Commendation 1995; PA MS Assn 1988-; Butler Cty Elem Tchr of Yr, PA Tchr of Yr Nom 1988-89; Navy Citation Honorary Crew Mem USS Mars; Stu Cncls PA Assn Dist 2 Adv of Yr, USAF Cert of Appreciation 1991; *office:* Mars Area MS 1775 Three Degree Rd Mars PA 16046

HARDING, SANDRA T., Physical Education Teacher; *b:* Baltimore, MD; *ed:* Salisbury St Coll (BS) PE 1978; Masters Equivalency Psych, Cnslng Loyola Coll; *cr:* Mercy HS US His, PE Tchr 1979-81; Archbishop Keough HS Soc Stud, PE, Hlth Tchr 1981-88; Balto Cty Pub Schls K-12 Grd PE Tchr 1988-94; Hereford HS US His, 11-12 Grd Psych Tchr 1994-95, 9-12 Grd PE Tchr 1995-; *ai:* JV Girls Vlybl, Lacrosse Coach; Var Club Asst; MAHPERD 1978-; Most Outstdng Tchr 1983; *office:* Hereford HS 17301 York Rd Parkton MD 21120*

HARDING, TREASURE KINGAN, PE Instructor & Key Club Adv; *b:* Pittsburgh, PA; *m:* Gary J.; *c:* Andrea Nicole, Alisha; *ed:* SUNY at Cortland (MS) PE 1988; *cr:* Eisenhower MS Soc Stud Instr 1 Yr; Van Vleck HS PE Instr 1 Yr; General Brown HS PE Instr 12 Yrs; *ai:* Key Club, Class of 93, SADD Adv; NYSA, AAHPERD, NYAPERD 1983-; Dexter Fireman Aux 1980-81; Ranked 3 in Intnl Key Club Svc Projects 1993; *office:* General Brown HS Cemetary Rd Dexter NY 13634*

HARDISON, BRANDON KIETH, Minority Studies Director; *b:* Camden, NJ; *m:* Donna Gail Johnson; *c:* Shawn, Keyina, Kai; *ed:* Univ of WI (BA) Scndry Ed 1975; Marquette Univ (MFA) Radio, TV Broadcasting 1977; Jersey City St Coll 42 Credit Hrs; *cr:* Trenton Cntr HS US His I, II, Coll Prep; Ewing HS US His II Coll Prep 1989-90; Red Bank Regnl HS Minority Stud Dir, World, Black His Tchr 1990-; *ai:* Ftbl, Asst Boy's Spring Track, Head Chrldr Winter Var Coach; Black Stu Union Adv; Pub Adress Announcer Boy's, Girl's Bsktbl, Wrestling; Mock Trail, Debate Adv; Tutor; NAACP 1979-; Urban League 1981-; Concerned Black Men 1990-; NJ Black Edctrs Assn 1989-; Ctr for Civic Ed Flwshp 1992; Tchr of Yr Top Ladies of Dist 1992, Trenton Bd of Ed 1988; Minortiy Tchr of Yr NJ Black Edctrs Assn 1990; Melon Grant Princeton Univ 1989; *office:* Red Bank Reg HS 101 Ridge Rd Little Silver NJ 07739

HARDMAN, PATRICIA LYNN, Math Teacher; *b:* Nurenberg, Germany; *ed:* Providence Coll (BA) Math, Ed 1986; Notre Dame Coll 6 Addl Credits Towards MED; *cr:* Pinkerton Acad Tchr 1986-; *ai:* Var Girls Tennis; Bsktbl

Referee; IAABO 1990-; NHWBO 1994-; Tchr of Yr 1994; *office:* Pinkerton Acad Pinkerton St Derry NH 03038*

HARDT, LAURIE FEY, 5th Grade Teacher; *b:* Rome, NY; *m:* Norbret; *c:* Erich, Kevin; *ed:* St Univ at Potsdam (BA) Eng 1983; *cr:* Salmon River Central Cmptr Assisted Instruction Lab 1 Yr; Allenstown Schl Dist 4th-5th, 7th-8th Grd Tchr 8 Yrs; *ai:* Alpha Delta Kappa 1996-; *home:* 357 Pittsfield Rd Loudon NH 03301

HARDTKE, KAREN SUE PEET, Mathematics Teacher; *b:* Cincinnati, OH; *w:* Charles Blades (dec); *c:* Larry, Ron, Charles, Krista Thompson, Merideth; *ed:* OH St Univ (BS) Math & Fr Ed 1966; Xavier Univ (MA) Cnslng Sncndry Ed 1994; *cr:* Dater Jr HS Math Tchr 1967-68; Delhi Jr HS Math Tchr 1969-73; Oak Hills Local Schls Sub Tchr 1973-78; Delhi Jr HS Math Tchr 1978-; *ai:* Natl Jr Honor Soc & Math Competition Team Spon; Math Bldg Subject Coord; NCTM 1966-; Presenter Hamilton Cty Office Ed Summer Wkshp 1993-94; PTA Educator of Yr 1993; Oak Hills Local Schls Employee of Month; Church Choir 1980-95, Cncl Mem 1994-; *office:* Delhi Jr HS 5280 Foley Rd Cincinnati OH 45238*

HARDWIG, MICHAEL JAMES, Instructional Support Teacher; *b:* Somerset, PA; *m:* Brenda J. Berkstresser; *c:* Brooke A., Lauren E.; *ed:* Univ of Pittsburgh (BS) Elem Ed 1972, St of PA (Masters Equivalency) Elem Ed 1983; PA St Instrl Support Initiative; *cr:* Somerset Elem Schls 4th-6th Grd Classroom Tchr 1972-90, 3rd-5th Grd Instrl Support Tchr 1990-; *ai:* Elem Ski Club Adv; Schl Kids in Need Fund & Instrl Support Team Chm; PSEA 1972-; Somerset Ed Assn 1972-; Wesley Chapel United Meth Church 1981-, Asst Sunday Schl Supt, Chm of Church Bldg Comm & Family Coord; Historical & Genealogical Soc of Somerset Cty Inc 1987-, Bd Mem & Sec; Co-Chm of Mid Sts Accreditation Somerset; Trainer of ADAPT; Presenter to Area PTA & Kids & Co Conf Seven Springs Resort; *home:* RR 3 Box 289 Rockwood PA 15557*

HARDY, BROOKE D., Fifth Grade Teacher; *b:* Brooklyn, NY; *m:* Alice L. Lasewicz; *c:* Derek, Heather; *ed:* IN St Univ (BS) Elem Ed 1967; *cr:* Cozy Lake Elem Schl Rdng Instr 1967-69, 4th Grd Tchr 1969-76, 5th Grd Tchr 1976-92; White Rock Elem Schl 5th Grd Tchr 1992-95; E T Briggs Elem Schl 5th Grd Tchr 1995-; *ai:* North Jersey Regnl Math Comm; Twp Rep Cable Television Refranchise Comm; NEA, MCCEA 1967-; Jefferson Twp Ed Assn 1967-, VP 1980-84, Pres 1984-86; Jeffeson Twp Comm Television 1983-, Dir & Host, ARC Media Awd 1994; Jefferson Twp Arts Comm 1986-; White Rock Lake Assn 1978-, Pres 1986-88; NJ St Governors Tchr Awd 1987; Jefferson Twp Tchr of Yr Awd 1990-91; Jefferson Twp Mayors Awd 1987-88; Amer Legion Comm Svc Awd 1992; *office:* E T Briggs Elem Schl Espanong Rd Lake Hopatcong NJ 07849

HARDY, DEBORAH, Bilingual School Counselor; *b:* Sao Paulo, Brazil; *ed:* Rider Coll (BA) Lbrl Arts 1988; Long Island Univ (MSEd) Cnslng & Dev 1993; Credits for Permanent Cert; *cr:* Berlitz Lang Tchr 1988-89; Dominican Coll Admissions Cnslr 1989-91; Berkeley Coll Admissions Cnslr 1991-92; Sleepy Hollow HS Biling Schl Cnslr 1992-; *ai:* Supvr for Schl to Work Transition Pgm; Adv for ESL Group & Peer Ldrs; WPRCAD 1991-, Liaison Region IV; NYSSCA 1994-, Region IV Governor; Inspirational Cnslr of the Yr 1994; Book: En Camino a La Universidad; Consultant for ESL Inst for Cnslrs; Coll Conf Speaker on Hispanics Entering Coll & Hispanic Heritage Month Celebration; *office:* Sleepy Hollow HS 210 N Broadway Tarrytown NY 10591*

HARDY, FRED E., Science Teacher & Dept Head; *b:* Huntington, WV; *m:* Charla Sites; *ed:* OH univ (BA) Ed 1972; Marshall Univ (MS) Ed 1975; *cr:* Chesapeake-Union Exempted Village Schls Sci Tchr 1972-, Sci Dept Head; *ai:* Sci Dept; Head Ath Comm; NEA 1972-; Sci Ed Cncl of OH 1985-; Project Disc; Capatol Venture Comm; SECO; Ed Climate Comm; TESA; Martha Holden Jennings Scholar; *office:* Chesapeake-Union Exmpt Vlg Sch PO Box 10 Chesapeake OH 45619

HARDY, JANET JARZEBOSKI, First Grade Teacher; *b:* Toledo, OH; *m:* James E.; *c:* James R., Jeffrey A.; *ed:* Univ of Toledo (AS) PT Asst 1968, (BED) Elem Ed 1971; Univ of Dayton (MSEd) 1995; *cr:* St James Schl First Grd Tchr 1968-70; St Michael Schl First Grd Tchr 1970-72; Sacred Heart Schl First Grd Tchr 1980-; *ai:* OH Cath Ed Assn, NEA 1980-; OH Cncl Tchr of Math 1992-; Juvenile Diabetes Fnd 1970-; Leukemaia Fnd 1982-; Neighborhood Block Watch 1990-; Youth for Understanding 1988-; *office:* Sacred Heart Schl 824 6th St Toledo OH 43605*

HARDY, JEANNE CAREY, Math Teacher & Dept Head; *b:* Plattsburgh, NY; *m:* Philip J.; *c:* Carrie Prevo; *ed:* SUNY at Plattsburgh (BS) Ed 1969, (MS) Sec Math Rd 1971; Woodrow Wilson Summer Insts Functions, Geometry, Statistics, MS Math; *cr:* AuSable Vly Cntrl Schl Math Tchr 1969-; Clinton Comm Coll Adj Assoc Prof 1981-; *ai:* NY St Math Mentor, Educ Turnkey Trainer; Math Dept Chair; Assn Math Tchrs of NY 1985-, Cty Chair; NYSUT, AFT 1969-; NCTM 1986-; NYS Math Supvrs 1995-; Holy Name Church 1948-; AuSable Forks Rotary, Frgn Exch Stdnts Adv; Math Line of the North Cntry, Goals 2000 Rural Consortium Adv; *office:* AuSable Vly Mid-HS Rt 9N Clintonville NY 12924*

HARE, ROBERTA M., Social Studies Teacher; *b:* Canton, OH; *ed:* Kent St Univ (BS) Soc Stud 1969; Over 15 Post Grad Hrs; *cr:* St Joan of Arc Schl Tchr 1970-; *ai:* Stu Cncl Adv; OH Cncl Soc Stud 1990-; Massillon Womans Club 1985-, Treas; Massillon Heritage 1990-; *office:* St Joan Of Arc Schl 120 Bordner Ave SW Canton OH 44710

HARELLA, SHELDA J., First Grade Teacher; *b:* Altoona, PA; *c:* Shelby; *ed:* Penn St Univ (BS) Elem Ed 1980; Masters Equivalency; *cr:* C-K Elementary 1st Grd Tchr 1981-; *ai:* Lead Tchr; PSEA, NEA 1981-; Hollidaysburg Area Music Parents 1989-, VP; *office:* Claysburg-Kimmel Elem Schl RR 1 Box 931 Claysburg PA 16625

HAREN, THOMAS EDWARD, Biology Teacher & Coach; *b:* Canton, OH; *ed:* Kent St Univ (BA) Bio, Zoology 1978, (MA) Bio 1987; 1 Hr Univ WY 1992; 2 Hrs Ashland Univ 1992; 1 Hr Univ of MI 1993; Doctoral Candidate in Sci Ed Curtin Univ in Western Australia 1994-; *cr:* Edison Jr HS 8th Grd Sci Tchr 1978-82; Mc Kinley Jr HS Anatomy, Physiology Tchr 1982-84; Lehman Jr HS 7th-9th Sci Tchr 1984-89; Mc Kinley Sr HS Bio Tchr 1989-; *ai:* Coach Boys, Girls Tennis; NARST 1993-; NABT 1990-; NSTA 1991-; ASIH 1986-; NEA 1978-; Amer Cancer Soc 1987-, Ridership Chm; Mc Kinley Museum S & I 1991-, Ed Consultant; Fellowships Woodrow Wilson Fnd 1991, NABT Wake Forest Univ 1992; Canton Women's Garden Ctr Schlsp 1987, 1992; OH Outstdng Bio Tchr of Yr 1994; NSTA Natl Certified in Bio 1994; *office:* Mc Kinley Sr HS 2323 17th St NW Canton OH 44708*

HARENDZA, ELIZABETH GARABEDIAN, Art Teacher; *b:* Binghamton, NY; *m:* Christopher; *ed:* Univ of Arts (BFA) Painting & Drawing 1988; Tyler Schl of Art at Temple Univ (MED) Art Ed 1995; *cr:* Bywood Elem Schl Art Tchr 1988-92; Upper Darby HS Art Tchr 1992-; *ai:* Equity Issues Comm of Upper Darby Schl Dist 1988-, Recording Sec; NEA, PSEA, NAEA, PAEA 1988-; Delivered Research Thesis at 3rd Penn St Intnl Conf on His of Art Ed 1995; *office:* Upper Darby HS 601 N Lansdowne Ave Upper Darby PA 19082

HARGADON, JOSEPH M., Associate Prof of Accounting; *b:* Philadelphia, PA; *m:* Noreen E. Blake; *c:* Kelli, Casey, Joe Jr.; *ed:* Widener Univ (BS) Acctg 1980, (MS) Taxation 1982; Drexel Univ (PHD) Acctg 1993; *cr:* DuPont Co Cost Accountant 1980-81; Widener Univ Instr 1981-86, Asst Prof 1986-94, Assoc Prof 1995-; *ai:* Acctg Soc Stu Group Adv; Acad Skills Prgm Spon; Frosh Seminar Ldr; Fac Affairs Comm Chair; Introductory Acctg Coord; Amer Acct Assn 1989; Inst of Mngmt Accountants 1980-, VP of Ed; CPA; CMA; Distngd Prof of Yr 1984, 1987, 1991, 1995; Stu Gardes Fin, Managerial Acctg Co-Author; Articles Pub; *office:* Widener Univ One University Pl Chester PA 19013*

HARIZAL, SUSAN MAY, Music Director; *b:* Cleveland, OH; *m:* George; *c:* Melinda; *ed:* OH Univ (BM) Music Ed 1972, (MM) Musicology 1974; *cr:* Federal Hockin Music Tchr 1972-74; Clearview HS Music Tchr 1974-85; Southview HS Music Tchr 1985-; *ai:* High Tech Music Studio; OEA, NEA 1984-; Hlth Trust Trustee 1993-, Vice Chair; Multi Grant for Magnet Prgm; *home:* 6314 Coen Rd Vermilion OH 44089

HARKER, KENNETH H., Computer Graphics Teacher; *b:* Camden, NJ; *m:* Nancy L.; *ed:* Trenton St Coll (BA) Industrial Ed, Tech 1970; Georgian Court Coll (MA) Curr, Supervision 1984; 30 Grad Credits Above Masters Degree; *cr:* Toms River HS Tchr 26 Yrs; *ai:* Ocean Cty Cmptr Cncl Adv; NJ Ed Assn, Toms River Ed Assn, Ocean Cty Ed Assn, NEA 1971-; *office:* Toms River HS East Raider Way Toms River NJ 08753

HARLAN, DAVID L., Technology Teacher; *b:* Zanesville, OH; *m:* Linda S. Kimpel; *c:* Kara, Nathan; *ed:* The OH St Univ (BAEd) Art Ed 1972, (MA) Ed 1988; *cr:* John Glenn HS Industrial Arts & Tech Ed Tchr 1975-; *ai:* 1998 Class Adv; Trek Team; E Muskingum Schl Dist Tech Comm; COTGA; St Johns Luth Church 1977-; BSA 1991-, Asst Scoutmaster; BSA Order of the Arrow 1995-; *office:* John Glenn HS 13115 John Glenn School Rd New Concord OH 43762

HARLAN, FRANCIS RAYMOND, Ec, US History & POD Teacher; *b:* Johnstown, PA; *m:* Barbara Eberhart; *c:* Jeffrey; *ed:* Clarion Univ (BS) Soc Stud 1969; Attnd Univ of Pittsburgh at Johnstown; *cr:* Chestnut Ridge HS Tchr 1969-; *ai:* Head Girls Track Coach; Dept Chprsn; Jr Class Adv; NEA, PSEA, CREA 1969-; BSA, Merit Badge Cnslr; *office:* Chestnut Ridge HS RD 1 New Paris PA 15554*

HARLAN, REBECCA JANE, 11th Grade Social Studies Tchr; *b:* Dallas, TX; *ed:* Rutgers Univ (MA) Amer His 1993; *cr:* Atlantic City HS Tchr 1973-80; Mainland Regnl HS Tchr 1984-; *ai:* NEA 1973-; NJEA, MREA 1984-; Goverors Tchr of Yr Awd 1989; *office:* Mainland Regional HS 1301 Oak Ave Linwood NJ 08221

HARLAND, MADELYN SHAFFER, Second Grade Teacher; *b:* Memphis, TN; *m:* James Lamar; *c:* Marlena Smith, Jamar, Marlynda; *ed:* Cleveland St Univ (BSEd) Ed 1977; Urban Stud Ed; Current Issues in Ed; Conflict Mngmt; Alternatives to Violence; Historical View of Cath Church; African Stud; *cr:* St Adalbert Schl Tchr 1977-93; IA Maple Schl Tchr 1993-; Primerica Fin Svcs Sales Rep 1994-; *ai:* Schl Cntrl Region, 2nd Grd Level, Union Conf Comm, Office Support Chm; Spec Act Tchr for Creative Arts; Tchr Enhancement Elem Math; ACEI 1980; OCEA, NEA 1977-; Intnl Trng in Comm 1978-, All Elected Offices, Speech Contest Runner Up; WECO 1992-; Ladies Aux KPC 1980-; Sec, Vol Svc Awd; Fin Cncl 1995-; Articles Pub; Newsletter Top Gun Awd Sales Rep Primerica Fin Svcs; *office:* Iowa-Maple Elem Schl 12510 Maple Ave Cleveland OH 44108*

HARLEY, LISA DAWN, English & Psychology Teacher; *b:* Portsmouth, OH; *m:* William Lynn; *c:* Madison Lynn; *ed:* Shawnee State Univ (AA) English 1986; Univ of Rio Grande (BS) English 1986; Univ of Dayton (MS) Educational Adminstration 1991; *cr:* Fayetteville-Perry HS Eng & Psych Tchr 1990-96; *ai:* Class Spon; Yrbk, Pep Club, Prom Adv; Tennis, Chrldng Coach; *home:* 18736 Huber Rd Fayetteville OH 45118

HARLOS, CAROL ANN BRUNNER, Mathematics Teacher; *b:* Buffalo, NY; *m:* James P.; *c:* Kasia Jones, Taia, Elena Golde; *ed:* St Univ Coll at Buffalo Bio & Math 1963, (MS) Bio & Math 1968; Univ of Buffalo Post Grad Courses; *cr:* Bennett HS Tchr 1963-68; Acad Challenge Tchr 1981-84; Dr Charles R Drew Tchr 1984-; *ai:* Math Club Coach, Chess Club; Internet Group; Exam Writing Comm; Liaison to Tchr Ctr; AMTNYS 1985-; NCTM 1987-, Mary Polciani Awd; Phi Delta Kappa 1993-; Herb Growers of West NY 1994-, Writer; Awded Mini-Grants; Articles Pub; Wkshp Ldr; *office:* Dr Charles R Drew Sci Magnet 1 N Meadow Dr Buffalo NY 14214*

HARLOW, ELIZABETH MARY, Vocal General Music Teacher; *b:* Boston, MA; *c:* William H. Gunn; *ed:* Western CT St Univ (BS) Music Ed 1959; Attnd Southern CT St Univ, NY Univ, Yale Univ Schl of Music; *cr:* Guilford Bd of Ed Music Tchr 1959-62; North Haven Bd of Ed Music Tchr 1962-65; Hamden Bd of Ed Music Tchr 1976-; *ai:* Swing Choir Dir; Marching Band Flag Team Coach; Staff Dev Schl Rep; NEA, CEA, MENC 1977-; *office:* Hamden Bd of Ed 60 Putnam Ave Hamden CT 06517

HARMAN, ABBE CLICK, Third Grade Teacher; *b:* Columbus, GA; *m:* John; *ed:* Frederick Comm Coll (AA) Gen Stud 1984; Towson St Univ (BS) Elem Ed 1987; Hood Coll 9 Grad Credit Hrs Sci Ed; Western MD 6 Grad Credit Hrs Cnslng; *cr:* Emmitsburg Elem Schl Third Grd Tchr 2 Yrs, Second Grd Tchr 1 Yr; Lauderhill Paul Turner Elem Schl First Grd Tchr 1990-92; Walkersville Elem Schl B Bldg Fourth Grd Tchr 1992-93, A Bldg Third Grd Tchr 1993-95; Glade Elem Schl Third Grd Tchr 1995-; *ai:* Vol Scuba Diver; Scuba Instr; NEA 1987-; *office:* Glade Elem Schl 9525 Glade Rd Walkersville MD 21793*

HARMAN, MARILYN SOINSKI, English Teacher; *b:* Cleveland, OH; *ed:* Lake Erie Coll GATE 1984, 2ndary Cert 1974; Kent St Univ Cert DE VocEd 1980; Univ of Pittsburgh Eng, Hum 1969; *cr:* Willoughby Eastlakes Schls Eng Tchr 1974-; *ai:* NEA, OEA 1974-; WETA 1974-, Local Rep; First Bapt Church 1950-, Various Bds, Sunday Schl Tchr, Chandel Choir, Bell Choir, Voice-Trio; Involved with Speakers Bureau & Local Plastic Surgeon Speaking to Media about Recovery from Spouse Abuse; *office:* Willoughby South HS 5000 Shankland Rd Willoughby OH 44094

HARMAN, MARY ELIZABETH (BELSER), Third Grade Teacher; *b:* Bellefontaine, OH; *m:* Steve; *c:* Erin Roberts, Joe, Wes, Jason; *ed:* BGSU (BS) Elem Ed 1978; Writht St (MA) Tchr, Ldr Ed 1989; Addl 9 Hrs Math Ed; *cr:* Bellefontaine City Schls Third Grd Tchr 1978-; *ai:* Southeastrn Stu Cncl Adv; K-6 Grd Math Resource Specialist; Cmptr, Tchr Evaluation, Supts Advy Comms; Peer Mediation Adv; Mentor Tchr; NEA; OEA; BEA; Luth Church 1956-; Southeastern PTO 1978-; Mary Florence Sours Grants; Logan Cty Educl Grants; Amer Legion Comm Svc Awd 1995; Rotary Excl in Tchng Awd 1994-95; Golden Apple Achvmt 1995; *office:* Southeastern Elem Schl Ludlow Rd Bellefontaine OH 43311*

HARMAN, YOLANDA MICHELLE (FORNO), 10th & 12th Grd Bio Instructor; *b:* New Brighton, PA; *m:* Keith Edward; *c:* Blake Edward; *ed:* Gannon Univ (BS) Bio 1987; Scndry Ed Cert Frostburg St 1989; 30 Addl Misc Credits; *cr:* Newmacolin Woodlands Conf Coord 1987-90; Garreh Cty Hlth Dept Intave Coord, Case Mngmt 1990; Northern HS Bio Instr, Chair 1990-; *ai:* Class, Stu Cncl Adv; Chprsn; Lead Tchr; After Prom; Pep Club; War of Classes; Sci Fair Co-Coord; Chrysalis, Blood Mobile; Schl Improvement Tm, NHS Selection Comm; Garret Cty Assoc of Stu Cncl Regional Adv; NEA, GCTA, MAST 1990-; MABT, NASSP; St John's Church 1989-; Accident Cultural Historical Soc Bd; OBTA Nom 1993; Who's Who 1990-; Outstanding Young Woman 1987; Frostburg Outstanding Tchr Awd 1994.*

HARMANOS, GEORGE, Mathematics Teacher; *b:* Pittston, PA; *m:* Mary Ann Konopka; *c:* David, Mark, Laura; *ed:* King's Coll (BS) Math 1970; Lehigh Univ (MA) Ed 1973; 5 Credits; Calculus Reform Project US Military Acad; *cr:* Bethlehem Cath HS Math Tchr 1970-; *ai:* Mens & Womens Tennis Coach; Weekend Retreat Coord; NCEA 1970-; ADLTA 1975-, Sec; EPCTM 1977-; BSA 1983-, Cnslr; Musikfest Assn 1987-; *office:* Bethlehem Catholic HS 2133 Madison Ave Bethlehem PA 18017

HARMANOS, STEPHEN A., AP American History Teacher; PA; *m:* Kathy; *c:* Michael, Kyra; *ed:* Bloomsburg Univ (BS (MED) Scndry Ed 1976; 36 Credits Univ of VA, LaSalle, Wilkes of Scranton, & WV Univ; *cr:* WY Area Scndry Ed Ctr Educator Key Club Adv 1980-; NEA, PSEA, WAEA 1971-; WY Area Kiw Pres 1992, Div 15 Lt Gov 1993, Distinguished Lt Gov Awd; P 1982-, Key Club Comm, Key of Honor Awd 1990; Bell Atlant 1991; Mellon Fnd Scholar Awd 1988, 1990; *home:* 1230 Wy Exeter PA 18643

HARMELING, GAIL A., Mathematics Teacher; *b:* Cincinna Univ of Cincinnati (BS) Ed 1974, (BA) Math 1974; Xavier U Supervision 1992; *cr:* Cincinnati Pub Schls Tchr 1975-; *ai:* A Girl Scouts 1959-, Bd Treas, 1st Class Awd; Cincinnati Mus 1985-, Bd Mem; Cincinnati Metropolitan Orch Concert Mas Woodward HS 7001 Reading Rd Cincinnati OH 45237

HARMER, BRYAN R., Social Studies Teacher; *b:* Ogdensbur Jefferson Comm Coll (AA) Liberal Arts 1986; SUNY at Broc His, Scndry Soc Stud 1988; SUNY at Potsdam (MS) Instruct 1995; *cr:* Parishville-Hopkinton CS Soc Stud Tchr 1990-; *ai:* B & Bsbl Coach; Class Adv; NEA 1990-; BCANY 1989-; Action Comm 1992-, Section Rep to NYS; *office:* Parishville Hopkint PO Box 187 School St Parishville NY 13672

HARMON, CAROL DEL TUFO, Art Teacher; *b:* Newark, NJ; R.; *c:* Lisa Stefanacci; *ed:* William Paterson Coll (BA) Art Montclair St Univ (MA) Art 1987; Addl 30 Credits Beyond MA; Schl System Art Tchr 1969-; *ai:* Portfolio Club; Art Gallery AP P NEA, NJEA 1969-; Books Pub: Weaving Without A Loom, Wh Say To A Naked Room; Participated in Metropolitan Area Showhouses; Free Lance Artist for Interior Designers; *office:* 333 Colfax Ave Clifton NJ 07013

HARMON, PATRICIA JEANNE, Mathematics Teacher; *b:* Ca *m:* David M.; *c:* Michael; *ed:* Kent St Univ (BS) Math 1976; Work Ed, Math, Bus & Cmptr Sci; *cr:* Mc Kinley HS Tch Stow-Munroe Falls HS Tchr 1978-; *ai:* Bldng Fac Advy Comm N Tchrs Assn 1978-, Trea 1994-; NEOEA 1976-; OEA, NEA 1976 Assembly 1995; NCTM, OCTM 1978-; *office:* Stow-Munroe Fal Darrow Rd Stow OH 44224*

HARMON, SANDRA JEAN, First Grade Teacher; *b:* Toledo John; *c:* Hope, Jonathan; *ed:* Bowling Green St Univ (BS) Elem Univ of Toledo Elem Ed 1975; *cr:* George F Ackermans Homemaker Shop Sales 1971; Coy Elem Tchr 1972-; *ai:* Soc AFT 1972-.

HARNDEN, LAURA DAUENHEIMER, Cosmetology Inst Yonkers, NY; *m:* Richard W. Sr.; *c:* Richard W., Rachel E.; *ed:* N at Oswego (B S) Voc Tech Ed & Spclty Cosmetology 1989; BOCES Vo-Tec Ctr Cosmetology Instr 1987-; *ai:* NY St VICA A United Tchrs 1987-; NY St Cosmetology Assn 1989-; Vol Edctr Cancer Soc Pgm 1989-, Vol Svc; *office:* Ulster Cty BOCES Vo Box 601 Rt 9W Port Ewen NY 12466

HARNED, JOSEPH E., Biology & Anatomy Teacher; *b:* Wes PA; *c:* Shawn, Melanie, Darren, Alayna; *ed:* Westchester Univ Ed, Bio 1969; SUNY at Stony Brook (MS) Lbrl Stud 1975; *cr:* Union Free Schl Dist Tchr 1969-74; Amer Schl of Isfahan Tch HI Prep Acad Tchr, Dept Chm 1978-79;Green Mountain Union Dept Chm 1979 -; *ai:* Var Bsbl; Class Adv; NSTA, VT Ed Assn 19 1969-; Chester Ed Assn 1979-, Pres 1995-; *office:* Green Moun HS Rte 103 Chester VT 05143

HARNESS, EVELYN CHRISTINA (BEGLEY), Fourth Grade *b:* Vaihingen, Germany; *m:* Martin Glen; *c:* Lisa Marie, Jen Martin John-Bradley; *ed:* Univ of Dayton (BS) 1st-8th Grd Elem Wright St Univ (MS) Intnl Childrens Lit 1993; Sinclair Comm C Liberal Arts 1979; *cr:* Wright Patterson AFB Sec 1967-78; Do Elem Tchr of Gifted Resource 1983-92, Fourth Grd Tchr 1992- Strategic Planning Comm Elem Rep; Odyssey of Mind Coach & Captain; Tecumseh Ed Bldg Rep; Dist In-Svc Bd; Bldg Liais Kappa Delta Pi 1993-; Tecumseh Ed Assn 1983-, Bldg Rep; Eng Assn & Terrific Partners in Sci 1990-; Tecumseh Ed Fn Convention Speaker; Coaches Odyssey of the Mind Teams Competition 1984 & 1990; *home:* 11273 Troy Rd New Carlisle

HARNEY, SHAUN M., Chemistry & Physics Teacher; *b:* Salem Rebecca Braddish; *c:* Taylor, Kyle; *ed:* Springfield Coll (BS) Stony Brook Univ (MS) Sci 1988; *cr:* Chippewa Elem PE Instr Sagamore Jr High Sci Tchr 1984-; *ai:* 8th Grd Ftbl, Bsbl & Bskt

HARP, MARILYN BRYANT, Honors English Teacher; *b:* Cleve *m:* Ormond; *c:* LaTanya, David; *ed:* Nyack Coll (BA) Eng Cleveland City Schls Tchr 1977-; Case Western Reserve Univ, Ad 1971-76; *ai:* NHS; Right to Read Comm; Stu Support Club Sp 1977-; Outstdng Tchr Awd 1995-, Cleveland Assn of Black Sch *office:* John Hay HS 2075 Stokes Blvd Cleveland OH 44106

HARP, RANDALL L., Language Arts Teacher; *b:* Inglewood Carol Mc Laughlin; *c:* Katherine, Emily; *ed:* AZ St Univ (BA) 1981; Villanova Univ (MA) Eng 1991; *cr:* Aqua Fria Union 1981-82; Mesa Pub Schls Tchr 1982-84; Ampex Corp Human Rep 1984-87; Rose Tree Media Schl Dist Tchr 1988-; *ai:* Ftbl C Magazine Spon; Bldg Tech Coord; Rose Tree Media Ed Assn 19 Rep; Villanova Univ Tuition Schlsp 1988-89; *office:* Springton 1900 N Providence Rd Media PA 19063

HARPER, BRIAN DOUGLAS, Mathematics Teacher; *b:* Painesv *ed:* Taylor Univ (BS) Math 1980; John Carroll Univ (MA) Math Cumberland HS Math Tchr 1982-83; Lafayette HS Math Tchr Edgewood Sr High Math Tchr 1991-; *ai:* Ftbl Coach; Jr Class A Selection Comm; NEA, OEA, NCTM, OCTM 1991-; Phi Del 1996; *office:* Edgewood Sr HS 2428 Blake Rd Ashtabula OH 440

HARPER, DEAN, Seventh Grade English Teacher; *b:* Zanesville Patricia Jean Abele; *c:* Doug, Jill; *ed:* Xavier Univ (MS) Guidan Attnd OH Univ Post Grad Stud; *cr:* Milford Schls 9th Grd 1972-75; Duncan Falls Jr High 7th Grd Eng Tchr 1975-; *ai:* NCT Optimist Club 1987-; *office:* Duncan Falls Jr HS 254 Mill St Dun OH 43734

HARPER, EDITH BAER, Retired 6th Grade Teacher; *b:* Hamil *ed:* OH St Univ (BS) Elem Ed 1958; Xavier Univ (MS) Cnslng Addl Credit Hrs; *cr:* Northwest Schl Dist 6th Grd Tchr Finneytown Schl Dist 5th, 6th Grd Tchr 1964-92; *ai:* Var Sftb K-6th Grd Math Curr Chprsn; Mentor Tchr; NEA, OEA 1958-; F Assn 1964-, Pres, VP; Kindervelt 1992-, Pres; 2 Yr Schlsp; *ho* Washington Cir Cincinnati OH 45215*

HARPER, EVAN S.,JR., Physical Education Teacher; *b:* Potsdam Connie J. Hickok; *c:* Michael; *ed:* SUNY Coll at Cortland (BS) Post Grad Stud SUNY at Potsdam; *cr:* Edwards Cntrl PE, AD Parishville-Hopkinton Cntrl PE, AD 1970-; *ai:* Coach Girls Va Sftbl; Adv Var Club; NYSUT, NYSAAPER 1967-; NSCA Parishville Fire Dept 1972-, Treas 10 Yrs; Parishville Rescue Squ Amber Lodge #395 F&M 1980-; *office:* Parishville Hopkinton School St Parishville NY 13672

, JIMMIE L., Teacher; *b:* Sumter, SC; *m:* Freddie H.; *c:* Darrell, iller, Gladys; *ed:* Allen Univ (BS) Elem Ed 1955; Credit Hrs at , *cr:* ICCC Day Care Early Chldhd 1958-60; Union City 2nd Grd -62; Middletown Twp 1st & 2nd Grd Ungraded & Developmental :hr 1963-65; *ai:* MTEA 1963-, Bldg Rep, 25 Yrs of Excl Svc to Stdnts Awd 1989; NJEA 1963-; NEA 1963-; Natl Cncl of Negro :c 1990-, Various Comms; St Stephen AM&Z Church, Chrstn Ed y Schl Tchr; WH & OM, Soc Pres & Supt of Buds of Promise ist; Church Awds; Thank You for Being a Beautiful Reflection ppreciation Devoted & Dedicated Svc 1993; Dept of Army Cert ciation 1976; *office:* Harmony Elem Schl 100 Murphy Rd vn NJ 07748

, LESLIE, Reading Recovery Teacher; *b:* Clairton, PA; *ed:* oll (BA) Ecs 1964; Purdue Univ (MA) Ec Ed 1968; Pace Coll min 1976; Brooklyn Coll 30 Credits Early Chlhd Ed; ugh Coll 16 Credits Gen Ed; Polytechnic of London 6 Credits Univ of London 3 Credits Drama, Theatre; *cr:* PS 138 Schl Tchr, Acting Asst, Prin, Tchr-In-Carge ECC 1964-82; PS 169 sroom & Movement Cluster Tchr 1982-92, Rdng Recovery Tchr UFT 1968-; Brooklyn Rdng Cncl 1992-; Soc of Cildren's Book 995-; NY Coalition of 100 AL Women 1994-; NAACP 1995-, Children's Books: Carla's Ribbon, Carla's Breakfast, Traffic Jam; due Univ 1967-68.

, MARIA CHAMPAGNE, 8th Grade Earth Science Tchr; *b:* nia, PA; *m:* Haviland Jr.; *c:* William, Laura; *ed:* Lincoln Univ 1978; Temple Univ (MED) Sci Ed 1981; St Josephs Univ & ll 32 Post Grad Credits Hrs; *cr:* Philadelphia Schl Dist 7th & 8th Tchr 1979-80, 1982-85; Plymouth Whitemarsh HS Bio Tchr Triumph Chrstn Schl 5th & 6th Grd Tchr 1987-88; Cheltenham 8th Grd Sci Tchr 1989-; *ai:* Sci Fair Coord & Spon; 8th Grd Girls key Coach; Current Schl Prin Fac Advy Comm; MCSTA 1989-; 94-; *office:* Cedarbrook MS 300 Longfellow Ave Wyncote PA

, PEGEEN LEE, Science & Mathematics Teacher; *b:* nia, PA; *m:* George Thomas; *c:* Shane, Kelly Erin; *ed:* Trenton St Elem Ed 1985; Catechist Rel Ed Cert Credit Hrs; *cr:* St Peters Sci, Math Tchr 1985-89; Sacred Heart Schl MS Sci, Math, Soc 1990-, K-* Grd Sci Coord 1992-; *ai:* Sci, Sci Fair Coord; Stu ety Patrol Adv; NCEA 1985-; Grant wo Work with Rohn & Haas ists; Book of Experiments Pub 1994; Nom for 1995 Natl Cath sh Tchr Awd; Nom for 1995- NJ Cath Tchr of Yr; *office:* Sacred 1 250 High St Mount Holly NJ 08060*

, RAYMOND KEITH, Eighth Grade Science Teacher; *b:* , KY; *m:* Susan Jo Hattan; *c:* Abby, Kate; *ed:* OH Univ (BA) Elem Coll of Mount Saint Joseph (MA) Ed 1984; Attnd Miami Univ, St Univ & Shawnee St Univ; *cr:* Adams Cty-OH Valley Schls 8th chr 19 Yrs; *ai:* Odyssey of Mind Coach; Curr Comm; Pee Wee Sftbl Coach; Local & Dist Sci Fair, Budget & Eisenhower Grant OVLEA, NEA, OEA 1977-; SECO 1985-; The Golden Apple Awd Ashland Oil 1995; Sci Ed Cncl of OH 1992; Adams Cty OH hl Odyssey of Mind Awd 1995; *office:* West Union Jr-Sr HS 201 St West Union OH 45693

, TERESIA ANN (HALL), Elem Physical Education Tchr; *b:* d, OH; *c:* Randall, Rabiah; *ed:* Eastern KY Univ (BS) PE, Hlth v of Dayton (MS) PE 1979; Addl Course Work Ashland Coll; *cr:* re Elem Schl Elem Phys Edctr 1970-, PE Tchr Grds K-6 1995-; Coll Part-time Lecturer 1992-; *ai:* Bolt BuddiesClub Adv; Delta eta 1988-, Arts & Letters Commission; NEA, OEA, NDEA 1970-; D 1975-, VP of Dance Div 1981, 1991; AAHPERD 1979-, Dist Edctr of Yr 1995, Honored by NDA for Svc in Dance 1995; pt Church 1970-; Gem City Gliders Ski & Bike 1993-, Pres; Jump Heart Coord 1974-; Who's Who Among Young Amer Profs Who's Who in Amer Ed 1992-93; OAHPERD Dance Edctr of Yr AHPERD Young Prof Awd 1983; *office:* Northmoor Elem Schl Salem Rd Englewood OH 45322*

, HAZEL F., Computer & Accounting Teacher; *b:* Fredonia, PA; as; *ed:* Westminster Coll (BBA) Bus 1966; PA Free Enterprise oming Coll Tech Updates 24 Credits & Permanent Cert; *cr:* Penn Sec 2 Yrs; Reynolds HS Tchr 2 Yrs, Sub Tchr 7 Yrs; Seneca s AVTS Comp Tchr 1980-; *ai:* Yrbk; Dept Responsibilities; Help hrs with Tech Matters; Taught Adult Comp Classes 15 Yrs; PSEA 1966-, Sec; NEA 1966-; Penn York Tchrs Assn 1988-; New Club 1980-; PA Womens Club 1980-, 2 St Awds Historical & Quilt; Century Singers 1985-89; Church Choir 1996; PA Free e Week Schlsp 1995 Lycoming Coll; *home:* 3 Pine St Coudersport *

, THOMAS A., Counselor & Athletic Director; *b:* Greenville, azel F. Shelhamer; *c:* Todd, Amy; *ed:* Slippery Rock Univ (BSEd) Soc Stud 1966; Westminster Coll (MSEd) Cnslng 1969; St ure Cert Supt 1986; Wright St Univ Scndry Prin; *cr:* Lakeview Stud Tchr, Bsktbl Coach 1966-73; Sidney MS Cnslr 1973-75; urg-Osceola Schl Soc Stud Tchr, Bsktbl Coach 1975-80; ort Schls Cnslr 1980-; *ai:* Ath Dir; Head Var Girls Bsktbl; NEA, 66-; PSADA 1985-; PGBCA 1993-; PSCA 1981-; Coudersport 1982-, Pres; Coudersport Recreation Bd 1990-, Sec; PIAA Dist 1993-; Bsktbl Coaching Clinic Article Pub 1972; Law Democracy 967; Northtier Coach of Yr 1990, 1993-; Big 30 Coach of Yr 1994; League Coach of Yr 1976; *office:* Coudersport Schl Dist 698 t Coudersport PA 16915

'ER, FRANKLIN SCOTT, Math Teacher; *b:* Bellefonte, PA; *m:* owes; *c:* Franklin S. Jr., Michelle L.; *ed:* Penn St Univ (BS) Math *cr:* US Navy Auxilary Division US Nuclear Sunbmarine 1979-83; gle Nittany HS Math Tchr 1988-89; Penns Vly HS Math Tchr : SADD Adv; NEA 1989-; PA Cncl Tchng Math 1991-; Ctr Area n Partnership 1995-, Bd; VFW 1987-; 4H Woodworking 1993-, ker Twp Grange 1983-; *office:* Penns Valley Jr Sr HS RD 2 Box ng Mills PA 16875

LL, CHARLIE MANNING,III, 7th Grade Geography Teacher; ord, NC; *ed:* East Carolina Univ (BS) Intermediate Ed, Soc Stud, s & Fr 1976; MI St Univ (MA) Curr & Instruction 1986; Stud of MS Acad; Madeline Hunters Theory into Practice; TESA; *cr:* HillCarrboro City Schls 5th Grd Tchr 1976-81; Dept of Defense nts Schls England 5th Grd Self-Contained Tchr 1981-83, 6th Grd Eng Tchr 1983-86, Compensatory Ed Tchr 1986-87; Dept of Dependents Schls Japan 6th Grd Tchr 1987-88; Dept Of Defense nts Schls Germany 6th Grd Tchr 1988-90, 7th Grd Geography 0-; *ai:* 7th Grd Chprsn & Spon; NEA 1976-; Honor Tchr 1980; d Superior Performance Awd 1984, 1987 & 1993.*

GAL, MAUREEN HOLLERAN, English Dept Chprsn & Teacher; land, OH; *m:* Jerome M.; *c:* Danielle Mandala; *ed:* Kent St Univ & Fr 1969; 12 Post Grad Hrs Jrnlsm & Cmptrs; *cr:* Our Lady of Fr Tchr 1971-75; St Vincent-St Mary HS Eng Tchr 1979-; *ai:* Eng Jrnlsm Adv for Schl Newspaper; Adv for Acad Challenge; Soc NEOTA 1982-; Helped Judge Spelling Bees for Akron Journal Yrs; Grant to Attend Course Focused on Co-Operative Learning; aint Vincent-Saint Mary Schl 15 N Maple St Akron OH 44303*

HARRIGAN, JOHN COLEMAN, 5th Grade Teacher; *b:* Syracuse, NY; *m:* Nancy; *c:* Mike, Brian, Andrea; *ed:* SUC at Cortland (BS) Elem Ed 1971; 30 Addl Hrs SUC at Binghamton, Cortland; 60 In-Svc Credits Schl Dist; *cr:* Ross Corners Elem 5th Grd Tchr 1971-80; Tioga Hills Elem 6th Grd Tchr 1980-83; Clayton Ave Elem 5th Grd Tchr 1983-; *ai:* 9th-10 Grd Ftbl, 11th-12th Grd Lacrosse Coach; Schedule, Spec Events Comms; NEA, NYSEA 1971-; PTA Pres 1974-76; Dist BSA Rep 1971-75; *home:* 365 Pitkin Hill Rd Johnson City NY 13790

HARRIGAN, TIMOTHY JAMES, Social Studies Teacher; *b:* Johnstown, PA; *m:* Sheree Drzewiecki; *c:* Timothy Jr., Brandon; *ed:* Shepherd Coll (BS) Hlth, PE 1978; Univ of Pittsburgh at Johnstown Permanent Cert; Penn St Univ Career Enhancement Courses; *cr:* Visitation Elem Schl Soc Stud Tchr 1978-84; Bishop Mc Cort HS Soc Stud Tchr 1984-; *ai:* Weight, Strength, Var Ftbl Coach; Cath Ed Assn 1984-; Windber Recreation Assn 1990-, Bd Mem; Amer Yth Soccer Org 1990-, Chief Coach, Bd Mem; Windber Yth Ftbl Assn 1994-, Bd Mem, Coach; *home:* 603 Park Ave Windber PA 15963

HARRIMAN, JEFFREY GLENN, Band Director & Music Teacher; *b:* Columbus, OH; *m:* Margaret Huiet; *c:* Matt, Mark, John, Elizabeth; *ed:* OH St Univ (BA) Music Ed 1976; *cr:* AK Pipeline-Fluor Corp Fin, TimeKeeper 1976-77; Fluor Continental at Iran Chief Time Keeper, Payroll 1977-78; Whitehall City Schls Instrumental Music Tchr 1979-; *ai:* Marching, Pep, Drill Team Bands; Solo & Ensemble; Musicals; NEA, OEA, WEA 1979-, Bldg Rep; MENC 1979-; OMEA 1979-, S & E Contest Chm; *home:* 2587 Caroline Ave Bexley OH 43209

HARRINGTON, GEORGE EMILE, Mathematics Teacher; *b:* Bald Mountain, NY; *m:* Susan E. Hicks; *c:* Michael David; *ed:* NY St Univ at Plattsburgh (BS) Math, Sci 1968; SUNY at Plattsburgh Math, Ed 15 Hrs; SUNY at Oswego Math, Ed 12 Hrs; SUNY at Potsdam Ed 6 Hrs; Bryant & Strattion Cmptr Programming 24 Hrs; Coll of St Rose Ed 3 Hrs; *cr:* Cambridge Cntrl Schl Eighth Grd Math Tchr 1968-69; Belleville Cntrl Schl Sr High Math Tchr 1969-; *ai:* Jr Class Adv; NHS Advy Bd Mem Jr-Sr Societies; HS Grd Level Comm Mem; Math Dept Chm; NYSUT, AFT 1976-; BHEA 1968-; NYSC & TE 1984-; Cornell Cooperative Extension Assn 1993-; Adams Cmptr Club 1989-; Prof Circle Ldr; Effective Tchng Trng; Supts Selection Comm; Cub Scout Ldr; *office:* Belleville-Henderson Cntrl Sch 2500 Academy St Belleville NY 13611*

HARRINGTON, IVY, Sixth Grade Teacher; *b:* Forest Hills, NY; *m:* T. Donal; *c:* Leigh Kayne, Pamela, Jill Daire; *ed:* Albertus Magnus Coll (BA) His, Eng; Hofstra Univ (MS) Elem Ed; 66 Post-Grad Credits Southern Meth Univ; Post-Grad NY Univ; *cr:* Hewitt Schl 6th Grd Tchr; Fannin Schl 6th Grd Tchr; Kew Forest Schl Math Tchr; Stratford Schl 5th-6th Grd Tchr; Garden City MS 6th Grd Math Tchr; *ai:* Dist Math Comm; NEA, NYST 1962-; GC Tchrs Assn 1974-; NCTM 1990-; Mercy League 1972-, VP; TWIGS 1975-, VP.

HARRINGTON, JAMES S., English Teacher; *b:* Springfield, PA; *m:* Sherian Ann Mc Campbell; *c:* Heather Greyno, James, John, Michael, Matthew; *ed:* Univ of NC (BA) Eng 1966; Beaver Coll (MS) Ed 1982; Attnd PA St Univ, West Chester Univ, Temple Univ; *cr:* Wissahickon Schl Dist Eng Tchr 1966-69; Merck & Co Supvr 1970-71; Central Bucks West HS Eng Tchr 1971-89; Unami MS Eng Tchr 1989-91; Tamanend MS Eng Tchr 1991-; *ai:* C.B. West HS Ftbl Coach; Track Coach; Ski Club; NEA, PSEA 1966-; CBEA 1971-; Stonebridge Civic Assn 1973-, Pres; PA & Natl Blue Ribbon Schl of Excl; *office:* Tamanend MS 1492 Stuckert Rd Warrington PA 18976*

HARRINGTON, JOHN FRANCIS, Band Director; *b:* Lowell, MA; *m:* Kyriaki Goranites; *c:* James F., Mary K.; *ed:* Lowell St Coll (BS) Music Ed 1972; Attnd Univ of Mass; *cr:* Hood Jr HS General Music & Chorus 1972-74; Amherst MS Instrumental Music 1975-76; Band Dir, Coord Music 1980-85; *ai:* Jazz Band Dir; Vol Jr High Musical; Active Prof Musician; MENC 1976-; NHMEA 1976-; Staff Dev Comm; Reviewing Comm Chm 1982-24, Chair; Awd of Gratitude From VFW & Amer Legion.*

HARRINGTON, LINDA SHEA, Professor of English; *b:* Holyoke, MA; *m:* Thomas; *c:* Kimberly, Shaun; *ed:* Coll of Our Lady of the Elms (BA) Eng 1972; Westfield St Coll (MA) Eng 1978; Harvard Schl of Ed PG Stud; *cr:* Chicopee Schl Dept Eng Tchr 1972-77; Amer Intnl Coll Eng Instr 1978-82; Springfield Tech Comm Coll Eng Prof 1978-; *ai:* Soccer Coach; Creative Writing Seminars; NCTEA, CCGS, MTA 1982-; Jr League of Holyoke 1977-79; Seminars on Tchng Stdnts with Learning Disabilities; Creative Writing Workshops for Adults, Children; *office:* Springfield Tech Comm Coll 1 Armory Sq Springfield MA 01108*

HARRINGTON, LOUISE DRAPEAU, Biology Teacher; *b:* Holyoke, MA; *m:* Richard D.; *c:* Anne Haight, Daniel J., Sarah Searles, David A.; *ed:* Rivier Coll (BA) Bio 1964, (MS) Bio 1989; Tchr Cert 1982; *cr:* Univ of MA at Amherst Rsrch Asst 1964-65; Water Dairy Product Industry Lab Mgr 1965-66; Nashua HS Bio Tchr 1982-; *ai:* NABT 1982-; NSF Microbiological Concepts Summer Prgm ATCC 1992; *office:* Nashua Sr HS Riverside Dr Nashua NH 03060

HARRINGTON, MAJORIE HENDERSON, French & Spanish Teacher; *b:* Boston, MS; *m:* Richard; *ed:* Boston St Coll (BA) Fr, Span 1969, (MS) Fr 1972; 45 Hrs Beyond Masters; *cr:* City of Boston Tchr 1969-; *ai:* Jr NHS Adv; Union Bldg Rep; Fac Senate; Ma FLA 1970-; AATF 1993-.

HARRINGTON, MITZI B., Kindergarten Teacher; *b:* Moultrie, GA; *m:* Timothy J.; *c:* Kathleen, Jacob; *ed:* Abraham Baldwin Agricultural Coll (AA) Early Chldhd Ed 1980; Valdosta St Coll (BA) Early Chldhd Ed 1983; 30 Credit Hrs; *cr:* Hartly Elem Schl Second Grd, Kndgtn Tchr 1984-95; South Elem Schl Kndgtn Tchr 1995-; *ai:* Tech Comm 1995-; NEA, CEA, DSEA 1984-; DE St Rdng Assn; West Dover PTO 1993-; Hartley PTF 1985-; *office:* South Dover Elem Schl 955 S State St Dover DE 19901

HARRINGTON, RICHARD ALEXANDER, English Teacher; *b:* Springfield, PA; *ed:* Tarkio Coll (BA) Eng 1972; Beaver Coll (MA) Eng 1976; Univ of PA (PHD) Eng 1988; *cr:* Phoenixville Area HS Eng Dept Coord 1974-; *ai:* Dir of Writing Ctr; Lit Magazine Spon; NEA 1975-; Grant Writing for Writing Ctr; *office:* Phoenixville Area HS Gay & City Line Ave Phoenixville PA 19460

HARRINGTON, RICHARD E., Prof of Building Technologies; *b:* Worchester, MA; *m:* Linda M. Garafolo; *c:* Rebecca, Lindsay; *ed:* SUNY Delhi (AAS) Construction Tech 1971; SUNY Oswego (BS) Tech Ed 1984; SUNY (MS) Wood Products Engrng 1990; *cr:* SUNY Delhi Prof 1978-; *ai:* Dept Chprsn; *office:* S U N Y Coll Of Tech At Delhi Delhi NY 13753

HARRINGTON, STEVEN J., English Teacher; *b:* Windsor, VT; *m:* Marianne Kotch; *ed:* Lyndon St Coll (BS) Eng 1982; Post Grad Stud at Univ of VT; *cr:* US Navy Technician & Naval Security Group 1971-77; St of VT Dept of Employment & Trng Veterans Cnslr 1982; Hazen Union Schl Tchr 1982-; *ai:* Soph Class Adv; NEA, VTNEA 1982-; Tech Comm 1993-95; Univ of VT Tchr of Yr Orleans Southwest Dist 1985; NHS Tchr of Yr 1991; Hazen Grad Commencement Speaker 1990 & 1994; *office:* Hazen Union Schl N Main St Hardwick VT 05843

HARRINGTON, VICKY IOCCO, Third Grade Teacher; *b:* Lyons, NY; *m:* Ronald E.; *c:* Shannon, Bradford; *ed:* SUNY at Oswego (BS) Elem Ed 1973; Perm Cert Elem Ed, Sec Eng 1978; *cr:* Mexico Acad & Cntrl Schl Rdng Tchr Asst 1982-83; Altmar Parish Williamstown Cent Schl 3rd Grd Tchr 1985-95; *ai:* Tchr Ctr Liaison; Storytelling Coord; APW Elem Advy Bd; Effective Schl Team; AFT, NYSUT 1982-; Pulaski Congregational Church 1990-, Choir; *office:* Altmar Elem Schl PO Box 146 Altmar NY 13302

HARRINGTON, WILLIAM THOMAS, Submaster; *b:* Everett, MA; *m:* Ann Leosheena; *c:* Christine, Cronin; *ed:* St Anselm Coll (BA) Philosophy, Ed 1964; Salem St Coll (MA) Ed Admin, Guid 1970; 60 Addl Grad Credits; *cr:* Everett Jr HS PE Tchr 14 Yrs; Pavlin Jr HS Guid Cnslr 14 Yrs; Everett Schls Coord of GATE 14 Yrs; Paulin Jr HS Submaster; *ai:* PTO; Boston Coll Sporting Events Security; ETA; NEA; Everett Historical Soc, Pres 6 Yrs; *office:* Parlin Jr HS 587 Broadway Everett MA 02149

HARRIS, AMY L., Second Grade Teacher; *b:* Pittsburgh, PA; *m:* Robert J.; *c:* Erika, Erin; *ed:* Muskingum Coll (BA) Ed 1980; Kent St Univ (MA) Ed 1994; *cr:* New Philadelphia City Schls 1st-2nd Grd Tchr 1980-93; Dover City Schls 1st-2nd Grd Tchr 1993-; *ai:* Robert E. Wilson Fellow; *office:* Dover City Schls 280 Shafer Ave Dover OH 44622*

HARRIS, BRYANT ANDROCLES, Social Studies Teacher; *b:* St Louis, MO; *c:* Toussaint, Bryant Floyd, Maya; *ed:* Lincoln Univ (BA) Pol Sci 1974; Howard Univ Law Schl (JD) Legislation 1978; *cr:* Bedford Stuyvesant Outreach Tchr Comp & His 1985-88; CEC at Boys Harbor HS Cntr Admin 1988-92; John Jay HS Tchr & Law Coord 1992-; *ai:* Mock Trial & Mock Court Coach; UFT 1985-; AFT 1985-; Phi Alpha Heta 1973-; Hon His; Natl Endowment for the Hum Grant; Law & Morality Seminar 1995; *home:* 341 10th St Apt 5K Brooklyn NY 11215

HARRIS, DAVID L., Social Studies Teacher; *b:* Tarentum, PA; *m:* Diane (Ferrante); *c:* David Jr., Ryan; *ed:* Edinboro Univ (BA) Soc Scis 1970; Univ of Pittsburgh (MED) His 1978; US Constitutional Stud; Tchng of Holocaust; Ind Stud WW II; *cr:* New Brighton HS Civics, Amer His Tchr 1973-87; NB MS Soc Stud Chm, tchr 1987-; *ai:* Acad Games, Mr Pres; NEA, NBEA, PSEA 1973-; *office:* New Brighton Area MS 3225 43rd St New Brighton PA 15066

HARRIS, DONALD EUGENE, 4th Grade Sunday School Tchr; *b:* Akron, OH; *m:* Judith Kay Mc Coy; *c:* Benjamin Eric; *cr:* US Postal Svc Letter Carrier 12 Yrs; *ai:* Apostolic Express Dir; Natl Assn of Letter Carriers 1984-, Trustee, Steward; BSA 1986-, Committeeman, Commissioner; Natl Brotherhood of Scout Campers 1993-.

HARRIS, DOREEN THERESA, Fourth Grade Teacher; *b:* Queens, NY; *m:* John K.; *c:* Nicole Marie; *ed:* Queens Coll (BA) Elem Ed 1983, (MS) Spec Ed 1986; *cr:* St Pascal Baylon Schl 4th Grd Tchr 1983-84; PS 29Q 1st Grd Tchr 1984-85, 4th Grd Tchr 1985-; *ai:* AFT 1984-, Tchr; Vol Sub Tchr CCD Classes.*

HARRIS, DURIEL ESTELLE, High School English Teacher; *b:* Chicgao, IL; *ed:* Yale Coll (BA) Lit 1991; NY Univ (MA) Eng & Amer Lit 1993; *cr:* On Location Ed Location Tutor, Instr 1992-93; NY Univ Eng Instr 1992-93; Dalton Schl HS Eng Tchr 1993-; *ai:* House, Peer Ldrshp Advs; Another Perspective Conf Moderator; Mentoring Prgm Fac Support, Diversity Comms; Yale Alumni Assn of Metropolitan NY 1996; The Lang Act Collective Co-Founder; Dalton Prof Dev Grant Summer 1994-95; Poetry Pub; *office:* Dalton Schl 108 E 89th St New York NY 10128

HARRIS, ELIZABETH DAGROSA, English Teacher; *b:* Hartford, CT; *m:* Jonathan Holden; *ed:* Univ of RI (BA) Comm & Eng 1990; Grad Coursework; *cr:* Fleet Natl Bank Corporate Trust Admin 1990-93; Tiverton HS Eng Tchr 1994-; RI Dept of Ed Interstate New Tchr Assessment & Support Consortium Participant 1995-; *ai:* The Tigers Roar Schl Newspaper Adv; Spotlight Enrichment Prgm UMASS-Dartmouth Group Ldr; NEA 1994-; RI Cncl of Tchrs of Eng 1993-; West Broadway Neighborhood Assn 1992-; *office:* Tiverton H S 100 N Brayton Rd Tiverton RI 02878

HARRIS, ERNEST C., Social Studies Teacher; *b:* New Haven, CT; *m:* Shirley Ranney; *c:* Christopher, Jonathan; *ed:* Syracuse Univ (BA) His 1967; SUNY Cortland (MS) Soc Stud Ed 1983; Attnd New Haven Coll, Southern CT ST Univ, SUNY Oswego; *cr:* Cntrl HS Soc Stud Tchr 1967-70; Auburn HS Soc Stud Tchr 1970-74; East MS Soc Stud Tchr 1984-; *ai:* Stu Govt Org Adv; Effective Schls Comm; Auburn TA; NYSUT; AFT; Knights of Columbus; NY Cncl for Hum His Tchr Inst Schlsp; *office:* East MS Franklin St Auburn NY 13021

HARRIS, FLORENCE ANN, Computer Tchr & Coop Coord; *b:* Brooklyn, NY; *ed:* Brooklyn Coll (AAS) Shorthand & Typing 1961; City Coll (BS) Ed 1968; NYU (MS) Ed 1974; *cr:* Exxon Corp Sec 1961-66; Curtis HS Bus Tchr 1968-69; Susan E. Wagner HS Bus Tchr 1969-95, Coop Coord 1995-; *ai:* Awds Comm; NBEA, BEA, UFT 1968-; Who's Who Among Stdnts in Colls & Univs; *office:* Susan E Wagner HS 1200 Manor Rd Staten Island NY 10314

HARRIS, HARRIET, Second Grade Teacher; *b:* Long Branch, NJ; *w:* Frank Sr. (dec); *c:* Frank Jr., Cheryl L. Harris-Hargrove, Ricardo (dec); *ed:* Brookdale Comm Coll (AA) Early Chldhd Ed 1981; Kean Coll (BA) Early Chldhd Elem Ed 1981, (BA) Spec Ed 1983; *ai:* NEA 1981-.*

HARRIS, JOHN AARON, Physics Prof & Chair; *b:* Muenchenweiller, W Germany; *m:* Penny Jean Keefer; *c:* Stephanie, Aaron; *ed:* Saint Francis Coll (BA) Math & Chemistry 1982; PA St Univ (MS) Nuclear Engrng 1985, (PHD) Nuclear Engrng 1988; *cr:* Saint Francis Coll Assoc Prof of Chem & Phys Sci 1988-; *ai:* JTA Club Adv; Girls Soccer Coach; Resource Comm; Infonet Comm; Pres Fac Senate; AACE 1992-; CUR 1993-; AAHE 1994-; NCTM 1994-; NSF-ILI Chem Labs Grant; Kern Grad Schl Flwshp; *office:* Saint Francis Coll Chem, Math, Phys Sci Dept Loretto PA 15940

HARRIS, KATHLEEN KLINE, Teacher of Gifted Support; *b:* Rochester, NY; *m:* Paul L.; *c:* Jennifer Tepe, Michael; *ed:* Grove City Coll (BA) Elem Ed 1966; California Univ of PA (MA) Elem Ed; 24 Addl Credits Univ of CO, Wayne St, Washington & Jefferson; *cr:* Livonia Pub Schls 6th Grd Tchr 1966-68; Sub Tchr; Mc Guffey Schl Dist 1st Grd Tchr of Gifted Support 1979-; *ai:* Acad Team; Schl Newspaper; MEA, PSEA, NEA 1979-; *office:* Mc Guffey Schl Dist 86 Mc Guffey Dr Claysville PA 15323

HARRIS, LAURA MARIE, Jr High & Elem Choral Teacher; *b:* Fairmont, WV; *m:* Ralph William; *ed:* IUP (BS) Music Ed 1984; St Francis Coll 15 Addl Credit Hrs; IUP 9 Credit Hrs Guidance; *cr:* Tyrone Area Schl Dist Jr High & Elem Choral Tchr 1984-; *ai:* Jr High Show Choir Dir; MENC & PMEA, PSEA & NEA 1984-; TAEA 1984-, VP 1993-; Allegheny Chorale 1985-, Dir 1990-; *office:* Tyrone Area Schl Dist Lincoln Ave & Clay Ave Tyrone PA 16686

HARRIS, LINDA JACQUELINE (GAY), English Teacher; *b:* Philadelphia, PA; *c:* Jason, Jakasha; *ed:* Howard Univ at Washington (BA) Eng 1974; Temple Univ Grad Schl Rdng 3 Credit Hrs; *cr:* Philadelphia Schl Dist Eng Tchr 1976-78; Carneys Point Regnl Schl Dist Eng Tchr 1980-; *ai:* Renaissance Club Adv; Founder, Chprsn Renaissance Club Schlsp Fund; Drama Coach Club Grad Awds Comm; SRA Panel; NJEA 1980-; Darby Area Branch NAACP Salem 1994-; NAACP Cty Branch 1993-; Penn Wood HS Band Boosters 1993-; Salem Cty Branch NAACP Outstdng Tchr Awd 1992-; Article Pub; *office:* Penns Grove HS 334 Harding Hwy Carneys Point NJ 08069

HARRIS, MARY-LOUISE, Professor; *b:* Henderson, NC; *ed:* Durham Bus Coll (AA) Secretarial Stud 1969; Univ of DC (BS) Bus Ed 1975, (MBE) Bus Ed 1976; George Washington Univ (EDD) 1994; *cr:* Fed Govt Admin Asst 1969-74; DC Pub HSs Tchr 1974-81; Univ of DC Assoc Prof 1981-; *ai:* Univ Advy Team; Honda Team Coach; Amer Soc for Trng & Dev; NBEA; Phi Delta Kappa; Neighborhood Advy Comm; Recent Rsrch of Workforce 2000; *office:* Univ Of The Dist Of Columbia 4200 Connecticut Ave NW Washington DC 20008

HARRIS, MICHAEL S., Social Studies Teacher; *b:* New York, NY; *ed:* Kenyon Coll (BA) Rel 1982; Seton Hall (MA) Ed 1993; *cr:* Wallkill Vly Soc Stud Tchr 1986-; *ai:* Head Girls Bsktbl & Golf Coach; Peer Ldrshp Prgm & Acad Bowl Adv; Drug Alcohol Core Team; Schlsp & Scholar-Ath Comm; NEA 1986-; Governors Tchr of the Yr Nom 1993; *office:* Wallkill Valley Reg HS 9 Grumm Rd Hamburg NJ 07419*

HARRIS, PAMELA SLAUGHTER, Health & Physical Ed Teacher; *b:* South Charleston, WV; *c:* Matthew Cooper Wilks, Lindy Alyson Wilks, James Franklin; *ed:* Marshall Univ (AB) Hlth, PE 1970, (MA) Cnslng, Rehabilitation 1973; *cr:* Chesapeake HS Hlth, PE Tchr 1970-74; Oxford Coll of Emory Univ PE Instr 1975-76; Chesapeake HS Hlth, PE Tchr 1977-; *ai:* Stu Assistance Team; Peer Assistance Ldrs Coord; Chrldng, Bsktbl, Vlybl Coach; Honor Soc Comm; PE, Hlth Dept Chprsn 1980-; Jr Class Adv; NEA, OEA, CLTA 1970-; Phi Delta Kappa; Musical Arts Guild 1995-; Rome Presbyn Church, Elder; Mary Kay Cosmetics 1990-, Sales Dir; Hlth Ed Grant Awd by St of OH; St of OH Hlth Ed Conf Del.*

HARRIS, RICHARD A., English Teacher; *b:* Derby, CT; *m:* Patricia; *c:* Alyson, Brendon; *ed:* B. Lyndon St Coll (BS) Eng, Ed 1970; Wesleyan Univ (MA) Lbrl Stud 1978; Southern CT St Univ 6th Yr Admin 1982; *cr:* Littleton HS Eng Tchr 1970-71; Broadview MS Eng Tchr 1971-92; Danbury HS Eng Tchr 1992-; *ai:* Lit Magazine Adv; NEA 1971-, Chair Exec Bd Pub Relations; CEA 1971-, Del Annual Convention; NCTE 1993-; Article Pub; Portfolio Assessment in Lit Co-Author; *office:* Danbury HS Clapboard Ridge Rd Danbury CT 06811*

HARRIS, RICHARD DWIGHT, History Teacher & Coach; *b:* Doylestown, PA; *m:* Betty Jo Grabill; *c:* Tara Jean Lopez, Richard, Nathan, Brittany; *ed:* Bob Jones Univ (BS) His Ed 1980; Kutztown Univ 3 Grad Credits; Harvard Univ 3 Grad Credits; *cr:* Upper Bucks Chrstn Schl Tchr & Transportation Dir 1980-; *ai:* His Curr Comm Chm; Jr High Boys Bsktbl Coach; Evening Adult Classes Tchr; Keystone Chrstn Ed Assn 1980-, Tchr of the Yr Awd; Upper Bucks YMCA 1983-, Past Chm; *office:* Upper Bucks Christian Schl 754 E Rockhill Rd Sellersville PA 18960

HARRIS, ROBERT H., Social Studies Teacher; *b:* Carbondale, PA; *m:* Joanne Wasielewski; *c:* Doreen; *ed:* SU Coll at Buffalo (BS) Soc Scis 1967, (MS) Soc Scis, Concentration in His 1968; 103 Career Credit Hrs Kenmore Staff Dev Ctr; *cr:* Herbert Hoover Jr High Soc Stud Tchr 1969-80; Benjamin Franklin MS Soc Stud Tchr 1980-; *ai:* Stu Cncl Adv; His Trivia Club Spon; Dist GT Comm 3 Yrs; Staff Senate; past Asst Track Coach, Schl Planning Team; Kenmore Tchrs Assn 1969-; NYS United Tchrs 1970-; AFT 1980-; Natl Historic Trust 1989-92; Golden Apple Awd 1993; *office:* Ben Franklin MS 540 Parkhurst Blvd Buffalo NY 14223

HARRIS, RUTH ANN SUDOL, Second Grade Teacher; *b:* Passaic, NJ; *m:* Douglas; *c:* Kimberlee; *ed:* William Paterson Coll (BA) 1968; Nursery Schl Cert 1986; *cr:* Schl Twelve First Grd Tchr 1968-69, Third Grd Tchr 1969-70, Second Grd Tchr 1979-; Radburn Nursery Schl Pre-K Tchr 19865-86; *ai:* Yth Week Rep; Clifton Tchrs Assn 1968-, Schl Del; NJ Ed Assn, NEA 1968-; PTA 1968-, Historian; Allendale Historic Soc 1993-; Bergen Cty Historic Soc 1991-; Natl Historic Preservation 1995-; 25 Yr Svc Honoree; 1992 Governor's Tchr Recognition Awd; *home:* 209 W Allendale Ave Allendale NJ 07401

HARRIS, STEPHANIE FARA, 6th & 7th Grade Teacher; *b:* Waynesboro, PA; *ed:* Charles Co Comm Coll (AA) Gen Stud 1990; Salisbury St Univ (BS) Elem Ed 1992; *cr:* Grace Brethren 6th-7th Grd Tchr 1992-; *ai:* Spon Sr HS Prayer Meeting; Kappa Delta Pi 1991-; *office:* Grace Brethren Christian Schl 6501 Surratts Rd Clinton MD 20735

HARRIS, TODD ELLSWORTH, Middle School Science Teacher; *b:* Canandaigua, NY; *ed:* Syracuse Univ (BA) Sci Ed & Chem 1990, (MS) Sci Ed & Chem 1992; *cr:* Syracuse Univ Grad Asst 1990-91; York Cntrl Schl Mid Level Sci Tchr 1992-; *ai:* Asst Var Bsktbl Coach; Class of 98 Adv; Mid Level Sci Mentor; Stu Speaker Commencement Ceremony Syracuse Univ 1991; Bristol Myers Squib Chem Schlsp; Analytical Chem Awd Amer Chem Soc; Empire St Challenger & Paul Douglas Tchng Schlsps; *office:* York Central Schl Rt 63 Retsof NY 14539

HARRIS, TRUDI, Assistant Professor; *b:* Washington, GA; *c:* Lynzi A. Richardson; *ed:* Bowie St Univ (BS) Elem Ed 1972; Trenton St Coll (MED) Stu Prsnl Svc 1977; 33 Credit Hrs Nova Southeastern Univ Adult Ed; *cr:* Ramapo St Coll Acad Adv 1980; Teaneck Bd of Ed Cnslr 1981-82; Hillside Bd of Ed Tchr, Cnslr 1982-83; Middlesex Cty Coll Cnslr 1983-; *ai:* Assn for Multicultural Cnslng & Dev; Amer Assn for Cnslng & Dev; NJ Comm Coll Cnslrs Assn; NJ Educl Opportunity Fund Prgm Assn; ASTEP 1995-96, Cnslr for Tutoring Prgm; Church of the Living God 1993-, Trustee, 1985-, Diocese Sec, Advy Bd Educl Consultant; *office:* Middlesex County Coll PO Box 3050 155 Mill Rd Edison NJ 08818

HARRIS, TY, Ninth Grade Science Teacher; *b:* Dennison, OH; *m:* Amy Hoffer; *c:* Shelby Ann; *ed:* Otterbein Coll (BA) Hlth, Sci Ed 1982; *cr:* West Holmes HS Ninth Grd Sci Tchr; *ai:* Frosh Class Adv 1994; Asst Var Wrestling Coach 1995-; Jr HS Wrestling Coach 1990-92; Var Sftbl 1988-89; Frosh Ftbl Coach 1986-89; SECO 1988-; WHEA 1986-, Bldg Rep 1987; West Hill Bapt Church 1993-; *office:* West Holmes HS 10901 State Route 39 Millersburg OH 44654

HARRIS, VICTOR A., History Department Chairman; *b:* Penn Yan, NY; *ed:* Finger Lakes Comm Coll (AA) Hum 1979; SUNY at Geneseo (BA His 1981, (MLS) Lib Sci 1982; 21 Addl Grad Hrs in His; *cr:* DeSales HS His Tchr 1985-; *ai:* Var Ftbl & Sftbl Coach; NCEA 1985-; Amateur Sftbl Assn; Finger Lakes Lakers 1994-, VP; NHS Excl in Tchng Awd; Named Awd Stu Cnl Excl in Tchng Awd; *office:* Desales Reg High School 90 Ulteney St Geneva NY 14456

HARRIS, VICTOR LEON,JR., Social Studies Teacher; *b:* Dayton, OH; *ed:* Miami Univ (BS) Comprehensive Soc Stud 1989; Xavier Univ 5 Grad Hrs; Drake Univ 3 Credit Hrs; *cr:* Hughes Ctr World & Amer His Tchr 1989-90; Sycamore Jr High Soc Stud Tchr 1990-; *ai:* 7th Grd Ftbl, Frosh Girls Bsktbl & Jr High Bsbl Head Coach; Co-Chair Dist Multi-Cultural Comm; Chair Dist Socio-Ec Comm; Dist Diverse Staffing Team; NEA & SW OH Bsbl Coaches 1990-; SW OH Bsktbl Coaches Assn 1993-; Outstanding Young Men in Amer 1990; PTO Incentive Awd 1992; *office:* Sycamore Jr HS 5757 Cooper Rd Cincinnati OH 45242

HARRIS, VINCENT ANDREW, Chemistry Teacher; *b:* Montclair, NJ; *m:* Delia A.; *ed:* Montclair St Coll (BA) Phys Sci 1962; Seton Hall Univ (MA) Admin Supervision 1968; 24 Credits Natl Sci Fnd Chem at Stevens Inst Tech & 16 Credits Sci; *cr:* Belleville HS Sci Tchr 1962-; *ai:* NEA & NJEA 1962-; NSF 1965-; Knights of Columbus 1965-; Friendly Sons of the Shillelagle 1992-, Pres; Natl Sci Fnd Grant 3 Summers to Stevens Inst of Tech; *office:* Belleville HS 100 Passaic Ave Belleville NJ 07109*

HARRIS, WAYNE RUSSELL, Fifth Grade Teacher; *b:* Manchester, NH; *m:* Florence Louise Lemire; *c:* Elizabeth R., Jeffrey W., Rebecca M., Catherine V.; *ed:* Keene St Coll (BA) Psych 1972; 27 Credits Ed; 52 Credits Inservice Wkshps; PBS Mathline 1994-; *cr:* Rindge Meml Schl Second Grd Tchr 1972-83, Third Grd Tchr 1983-94, Fifth Grd Tchr 1994-; *ai:* Collaborative Mem with Franklin-Pierce Coll 1993-; PBS Mathline Act Ldr 1994-; Cross-Country Skiing Coach 1992-; Chrstn Doctrine Tchr 1983-95; BSA Merit Badge Adv 1992-; NEA 1975-; NCTM 1995-; Rindge Historical Soc 1984-; *office:* Rindge Memorial Grade Schl 45 School St Rindge NH 03461*

HARRIS, WILLIAM GILBERT, Retired Math & Science Teacher; *b:* Birmingham, England; *m:* Hilda Armstrong; *c:* David, Peter, Timothy, Joy (dec), Paul; *ed:* Bordesley Green Coll (ONC) Engrng Design 1946; Univ of Aston (HNC) Engrng Design 1953; Educl, Tchr Trng City of Bham Ed Dept UK 1975; Theological Trng Refomred Episcopal Church 1977; *cr:* Cadbury LTD Sr Mechanical Designer 1969-75; Castlevale Comprhensive Schl Craft, Design Tchr 1975-83; Reformed Episcopal Church Priest in Charge 1983-90; Scarborough Chrstn Schl Math, Sci Tchr 1991-1996; *ai:* Lay Minister Angelican Church; Adv Scarborough Chrstn Schl on Maintanance; Advising, Making Stage Sets, Props; Inst of Materials Mngmt 1970-, Midlands Branch Ofcr; Inst of British Engrs 1971-, Assoc Mem; Ins of Engrng Designers 1975-, Fellow, Midlands Branch Ofcr; Scarbrough Choral Soc 1993-; Delivered Paper, The Mind of The Creator, to Creation Sci Assn of Ontario; *home:* 740 Kennedy Rd TH 49 Scarborough ON M1K 2C5 Canada CN *

HARRISON, ANNE ELIZABETH, Education Professor; *b:* Columbia, SC; *c:* Maia Ciesluk, Jay Ciesluk; *ed:* Smith Coll (BA) Ed 1975, (MED) Ed 1976; Univ of MA (EDD) Curr Stud 1989; *cr:* Smith Coll Campus Schl Tchr 1975-83; Natl Evaluation Systems Project Mgr 1983-84; Univ of MA Project Admin 1984-88; Elms Coll Prof 1988-; *ai:* Amherst A Better Chance 1985-94, Bd Mem; *office:* Elms Coll 291 Springfield St Chicopee MA 01013

HARRISON, BEVERLY M., Seventh Grade Geography Tchr; *b:* Charlotte, NC; *c:* Trachelle; *ed:* UNC at Charlotte (BA) His 1974; Univ of MD at Baltimore Cty (BA) Ed 1975; Trinity Coll (BA) Ed 1982; Cmptr Literacy, S4RD, Spec Ed, TAG, Drug & Alcohol Abuse Credit Hrs; *cr:* Laurel Jr HS Civics, Core Tchr 1974-79; Andrew Jackson MS Civics, US His Tchr 1979-84; Charles Carroll MS US His Tchr 1984-87; Lord Baltimore Acad Geog Tchr 1987-; *ai:* Soc Stud Dept Chprsn; SPMT Mem; PGCEA, MSTA, NEA 1974-; RMBC Pastor's Aide Club 1988-, Pres; *office:* Lord Baltimore Acad 8700 Allentown Rd Fort Washington MD 20744

HARRISON, BOBBIE MANIECE, Health Education Professor; *b:* Gainsville, AL; *ed:* Tuskegee Univ (BSN) Nursing 1962; NY Univ (MA) Hlth Ed 1972; Tchrs Coll Columbia Univ (EDM) Nursing Ed 1980; NY Univ (EDD) Hlth Ed 1990; *cr:* Veterans Admin Hospital Staff Nurse 1962-66; NY Bd of Ed Instr 1966-70; Borough of Manhattan Comm Coll Prof 1971-; *ai:* Phi Theta Kappa Adv; PE, Hlth Dept Curr Comm; MBCE Honor Comm; APHA, Kappa Delta Pi, Sigma Theta Tau 1979-; SOPHE 1986-; William F. Ryan Comm Hlth Ctr 1983, Bd of Dir, Chrprsn; Greater Harlem Nrsng Home 1990-, Bd of Dir; NY Coalition of 100 Black Women 1981-, Co-chair Ed 1987-91 Comm; *office:* Borough Of Manhattan Comm Coll 199 Chambers St New York NY 10007*

HARRISON, CAROL SHARON, Second Grade Teacher; *b:* Nanticoke, PA; *ed:* Lycoming Coll (BA) His, Elem Ed 1973; Addl Grad Credits Temple Univ, PA St Univ; *cr:* Lincoln Schl 2nd Grd Tchr 1973-79, 3rd Grd Tchr 1980-92; Logan Schl 2nd Grd Tchr 1993-; *ai:* Staff Dev Comm; IST Team; Basal Sel Com Math Rdng; PSEA, NEA 1973-; Gift of Life 1994-95; *home:* 320 Garfield St Tyrone PA 16686*

HARRISON, DANIEL, Associate Professor of Music; *b:* Chappaqua, NY; *m:* Anne Charlotte Turnburke; *c:* Glenn Palmer, Theodore Brooks, Charlotte Collins; *ed:* Stanford Univ (BA) Music 1981; Yale Univ (PHD) Music Theory 1986; MPhil Music Theory 1984; *cr:* Univ of Rochester Asst Prof 1986-93, Assoc Prof 1994-; *ai:* Soc for Music Theory 1984-, Publications Comm, Young Scholar Awd 1995; St Pauls Episcopal Church 1987-, Vestryman; *office:* Univ Of Rochester 205 Todd Union Rochester NY 14627

HARRISON, DIANE MANNING, 8th Grade US History Teacher; *b:* Cincinnati, OH; *m:* Charles P.; *c:* Michael Manning, Steven Manning; *ed:* Univ of Cincinnati (AA) Pre-Elem Ed 1979, (BS) Ed-Summa Cum Laude 1981; Post Grad Work Coll of Mt St Joseph; *cr:* New Richmond Elem Schl 6th Grd Tchr 1984-85; New Richmond MS 8th Grd US His Tchr 1985-; *ai:* Dist Imput Comm; Girls Bsktbl Coach; Soc Stud Dept Chm; Soc Stud Curr Comm; Mentor Tchr; Bicentennial Constitution Grant Presenter in Dists Commission; NEA 1984-; OH Cncl for Soc Stud; NCSS; Southwestern OH Cncl for Soc Stud; Kappa Delta Pi; Sunday Schl Tchr, Camp Cnslr, Church Clerk 25 Yrs; Vacation Bible Schl Tchr 20 Yrs; Nom OH Soc Stud Tchr of Yr; Awded Dist Tchr Grant for Stu Museum; Awded Fin Bicentennial of Constitution Fed Grant for Museum; Clermont Cty Schls In-Svc Day Presenter; Martha Holden Jennings Fnd Scholar; New Richmond Schl Dist Tchr of Yr 1991-92; Nom OH Tchr of Yr 1991-92; Nom Clermont Chamber of Commerce Tchr of Yr; *office:* New Richmond MS 1135 Bethel New Richmond Rd New Richmond OH 45157*

HARRISON, DOROTHY DUNSEN, Vice Principal; *b:* Bel Air, MD; *ed:* Bowie St Univ (BS) Elem Ed 1962; George Washington Univ (MA) Admin & Supervision 1969, (EDD) Higher Ed Supervision, Curr, Cnslng & Support Fields 1986; *cr:* Kettering Elem Vice Prin 1975-79; Heather Hills Tchr of Talented & Gifted 1985-86; Suitland HS Support Tchr 1989-90; Eleanor Roosevelt HS Vice Prin 1995-; *ai:* Alpha Kappa Lambda & Frosh Class Spon; Flwshp of Chrstn Ath; Natl Urban League 1975-, Guild Mem; Assn of Supervision 1980-; Church of Atonement, Vestry, Flwshp & Finance Comms; Empowerment Pgm, Bd Mem; Ford Fndtn Schlsp; Kwanis Awd.*

HARRISON, GINA HEINTZ, 3rd Grade Teacher; *b:* Albany, NY; *m:* William; *c:* Joshua; *ed:* SUNY at Potsdam (BA) Math, Ed 1987; SUNY at Plattsburgh (MA) Elem Ed 1991; Post-Grad Stud Math Ed; *cr:* Salem Cntrl Schl 6th Grd Tchr 1987-93, 3rd Grd Tchr 1994-; *ai:* Elem Stu Cncl Adv; Bldg Level Planning, Family Life, Math Comms; *office:* Salem Central Schl E Broadway Salem NY 12865

HARRISON, JENNIFER BOECKMANN, HS Mathematics Teacher; *b:* Huntington, WV; *m:* Timothy Wayne; *ed:* Coll of Mt St Joseph (BA) Math 1994; *cr:* William Henry Harrison HS Math Tchr 1994-; *ai:* Frosh Transition Comm; Girls Jr Var Soccer Coach.*

HARRISON, JOYCE DECESARE, Fourth Grade Teacher; *b:* Lawrence, MA; *m:* Thomas L.; *c:* Michael, Mary, Steven; *ed:* Lowell St Coll (BA) Elem Ed 1971; Univ of Lowell (MS) Rdng, Lang 1976; *cr:* J. K. Tarbox Schl Title I Rdng Tchr 1971-72, Grd 4 Tchr 1972-86; Leahy Schl Grd 4 Tchr 1986-87; J. K. Tarbox Schl Grd 4 Tchr 1987-; *ai:* AFT 1971-; Nom Tchr of Yr 1991; *office:* John K Tarbox Elem Sch 59 Alder St Lawrence MA 01841

HARRISON, KARIN CLAYPOOL, Fourth Grade Teacher; *b:* Freeport, PA; *m:* James R.; *c:* Christopher; *ed:* Indiana Univ of PA (BS) Soc Stud 1963; Attnd Penn St, Univ of MD, Slippery Rock Univ; *ai:* Prof Dev Action, IST Teams; Lead Tchr Rep; 178, Bldg Environmental Ed Comms; PSEA, NEA 1963-; FEA 1963-, VP 1993; Comm Food Bank; *office:* Buffalo Elem Schl 500 Sarver Rd Sarver PA 16055

HARRISON, LANCE EDWARD, PE Teacher & Coach; *b:* Buffalo, NY; *m:* Linda Waring; *c:* Scott W., Sean Burke; *ed:* SUNY at Buffalo (BS) Hlth, Recreation, PE 1973; 36 Credit Hrs Grad Work; *cr:* Serfilippi & Sons Construction Foreman 1963-67; Equitable Assurance Soc Regnl Dir 1967-70; Marc Equity Corp Recreation Dir 1970-73; Lake Shore Cntrl Schl Tchr, Coach 1973-; *ai:* Girls Vlybl St Champions 1994-95; Boys Vlybl Division Champions 1982-87, 1989-94, Sectional Champions 1983-87, 1989, 1992-93, Regnl Champions 1986, 1992-93; US Vlybl Assn 1982-; Western NY Vlybl Coaches Assn 1987-, Coach of Yr 1986; *office:* Lake Shore Cntrl Schls Rt 5 Angola NY 14006

HARRISON, LEDA HAMMOND, Language Arts Teacher; *b:*
OH; *m:* Trent D.; *ed:* Univ of Rio Grande (BS) Comprehensive
1988, (MS) Classroom Tchng & Rdng 1993; Project
Concentration in Phys Sci; *cr:* Kyger Creek HS Lang Arts Tchr
Yr; Huntington HS Lang Arts Tchr 7 Yrs; *ai:* Jr HS Right to R
HLEA 1989-, Pres Elect & Election Comm Chair; OEA & N
Church of Christ 1981-; Edctr of the Yr 1993-94; Completed
Masters Project; *home:* 8500 State Route 7 S Gallipolis OH 45

HARRISON, RICHARD, Art Teacher; *b:* New York City, NY
Paltz Coll (BAEd) Art 1962, (MS) Art Ed 1972; Attnd Univ
1963-64, Schl of Visual Arts 1988-92, Coll at Purchase; *cr:* Na
Art Tchr 1962-63; Scotia-Glenville Schls Art Tchr 1965-69; An
London Supply Tchr 1969-70; Carmel Schl System Art Tchr
NYSUT, Carmel Tchrs Assn 1970-; NYS Art Tchrs Org 1970-
Co-Pres 1977-79; Putnam Arts Cncl Bd; Soft Sculpture Art
Stores, Galleries; Photography Pub; Drawings, Prints Shown
Purchase, Putnam Arts Cncl, Garrison Art Exhibit; *home:* E
Carmel NY 10512

HARRISON, THOMAS FRANCIS, Principal; *b:* Sharon, PA
Ellen Stewart; *c:* Amy, Katie, Julie; *ed:* St Bonaventure Univ (
1976; Coll of Mount Saint Joseph (MA) Ed 1987; Scndry Educl A
Youngstown St Univ 1995; *cr:* Kennedy Chrstn HS Bio, Genera
1976-79; Lakeview HS Bio II Tchr 1980-95; Bloomfield HS P
ai: Stud Cncl Adv; OASSA 1995-; Howland Comm Church
Deacon; *office:* Bloomfield HS 2077 Park Rd W N Bloomfield

HARRITY, LINDA (DALZIEL), English Teacher; *b:* Montcla
Thomas W.; *ed:* Douglas Coll (BA) Eng Ed 1972; Kean Coll o
Lbrl Stud 1993; *cr:* Middlesex HS Eng Tchr 1972-; *ai:*
Academically Talented Prgm; NEA, NJEA 1972-; NCTE 1980-;
Phi 1993-.

HARRIZ, MARGARET D., Retired Adjunct Instructor; *b:* Lu
PA; *m:* James W.; *c:* J. Thomas, J. Kimberly, J. Eric, Jeffery L.
Haven Univ (BS) Elem Ed 1955; Widener Univ (MS) Ed, Gifte
ABD Schl Admin; Supervision, Curr Cert; Elem, Sec Prin Cert;
Specialist; *cr:* Derry Twp Schl 6th Grd Tchr 1955-57; W Chest
Grd Tchr 1966-68; Avon Grove Schl Tchr, Coord Gift Ed
Millersville Univ Adj Instr 1975-95, Summer Happening Coor
ai: Chrstn Ed Chprsn St Michael Church; PSERS; NEA; Finali
Tchr of Yr 1986; Who's Who in Amer Ed 1989; *home:* 97 State Rd
PA 19311

HARROD, LOIS MARIE, English Teacher; *b:* Coshocton, OH;
c: Jonathan, Katherine; *ed:* Capital Univ (BA) Eng 1964; PA St
Eng 1966; Trenton St Coll Tchng Cert Eng 1984; Addl 30 Hrs
Univ & Rowan Coll; Natl Endowment of Hum; *cr:* PA St Univ
1964-66; Trenton St Coll Adjunct Prof 1968-70; Rider Coll Ad
1978-84; Trenton St Coll Adjunt Prof 1980-84; Gov Schl of Ar
St Coll Poet in Residence Summers 1986-; Trenton St Coll Ad
1994-95; *ai:* Lit Magazine & Dead Poets Soc Adv; NEA 198
1984-; US 1 Writers Cooperative, NJCTE 1986-; Over 200 Po
Geraldine Dodge Fnd Celebration of Teac; Dodge Poet & Tchr
Cncl of Arts Fellowship in Poetry 1993-94; Natl Endowment Hu
1994; Hunterdon Cty Tchr of Yr 1994-95; Princeton Univ Dist
Scndry Tchr 1991; 2 Books of Poetry Every Twinge a Verdict 198
Alice 1991; *office:* Voorhees HS 256 County Road 513 Rt
Gardner NJ 08826*

HARROLD, JANIS MCMILLEN, English Teacher; *b:* Punx
PA; *m:* Douglas C.; *c:* Tonya R., Dane C.; *ed:* Salem Coll (BS) H
Eng 1971; IUP Masters Eng 1977; *cr:* Punxsutawney Area PE T
& Eng Tchr 20 Yrs; *ai:* NEA, PSEA & PAEA 1970-; WPTE 19
of Eastern Star; *home:* RR 6 Box 370 Punxsutawney PA 15767*

HARRY, STEVE R., Environmental Sci & Bio Tchr; *b:* Cham
PA; *m:* Linda M. Secrest; *c:* Nicole Gentile, Brandi; *ed:* Shippens
(BSEd) Bio 1967, (MEd) Bio 1970; Attnd Univ of MA; Various
& Seminars in Ecology; Outdoor Ed; *cr:* James Buchanan HS T
Chrprsn 1967-; *ai:* Sci Dept Chrprsn 15 Yrs; Safari Club Intl; Mas
Ch Bd Mem & Ed Rep; Tuscarora Wildlife Ed Project Dir; Trout
1995-, Conservation Project Judge; Frontier Cntry Gun Club 198
Treas; Natl Parks & Conservation 1993-; Dir of YCC 8 Yrs; Re
for the Selection & Placement of Stus & Tchrs in Various Conse
Wilderness Schls From the Amer Wilderness Schl; Devel
Environmental Ed Pgm in Tuscarora Schl Dist; *office:* James Buc
4773 Fort Loudon Rd Mercersburg PA 17236*

HARRY, VICKIE D. SMITH, Assistant Professor; *b:* Oil Cit
Richard K.; *c:* Brian Fry, Thomas Fry, Richard J., Lance, Am
Clarion Univ of PA (BS) Elem Ed 1981, (ME) Sci Ed 1986; Pen
(PHD) Curr & Instruction 1996; *cr:* Oil City Area Schl Dist
1981-93; Penn St Grad Tchng Asst 1993-94; Clarion Univ Instr
Asst Prof 1995-; *ai:* PSEA Adv; Fnds & Curr Comms; NSTA, PS
Conf Presenter; NCTM, PCTM 1994-, Conf Presenter, Pres Awd
1990; AMTONP 1994-, Conf Presenter; AETS; Good Shephe
Meth Church 1993-, Childrens Choir Dir, Sunday Schl Supt,
Bible Schl Dir; PA Tchr of Yr St Finalist 1993; Consultant for
Inc; DODDS Worldwide Inservice Presenter; Articles Pub in T
Child Today & The TNT Newsletter; *office:* Clarion Univ O
Stevens Hall Clarion PA 16214*

HARSH, JEFFREY GILBERT, 5th Grade Teacher; *b:* Dover
Melanie Mae McCoul; *ed:* Kent St Univ (BA) Elem Ed 1977; Ma
MS Curr & Instruction 1996; *cr:* Avondale Elem Schl Tutor of LD
Canton St Pauls 6th-8th Grd Soc Stud & Math Tchr 1978-85; Ma
5th Grd Tchr 1985-; *ai:* Bsktbl & Ftbl Coach; Spelling Bee & Q
Coord; ASCD 1996; Young Life Ldr 10 Yrs; Jackson Friends Chur
Sunday Schl Tchr; First Friends Church 1980-87, Sunday S
Impact II Dissemenator Grant 1995; *home:* 7350 Marelis Ave N
OH 44721

HARSH, MICHAEL GERARD, Associate Prof of Huma
Williamsport, MD; *m:* Linda Colleen Hartnett; *c:* Katy, Rachael, L
Towson St Coll (BS) Speech, Drama 1973; Western MD Coll (M
1983; George Mason Univ (CAS) Comm Coll Ed 1995; Certfd Ld
Phi Theta Kappa, Kellogg Fnd; *cr:* St Maria Goretti HS Tchr
Maryland Theatre Exec Dir 1979-83; Hagerstown Jr Coll Assoc Pr
ai: Dir Drama Club; Fac Prof Assn, Pres; NCTE 1995-; TO
1975-88; St Maria Goretti HS Bd Trustees 1995-; *office:* Hage
Coll 11400 Robinwood Dr Hagerstown MD 21741*

HARSHBARGER, LAURENE FETHER, Elem Tea
Administrator; *b:* Roaring Spring, PA; *m:* James; *c:* Lance, Jenic
St Univ (BS) Elem & Kndgtn Ed 1977; 24 Credit Hrs for Perma
cr: Mifflin Cty Schl Dist Remedial Math Tchr 1977-79, 2nd
1979-81; Riverside Chrstn Acad Kndgtn Tchr 1986-90, 3rd-4th
1990-93, Tchr & Admin 1993-; *ai:* Stu Cncl Adv; AWANA 19
office: Riverside Christian Acad RR 4 Box 61A Johnstown PA 1

HARSHBARGER, NANCY JANE (CONWAY), Sixth Grade Te
Columbus, OH; *m:* Eugene L.; *c:* Amy, Chris, Ken, Beth Mar
Wright St (BS) K-8th Grd Ed 1977, (MED) Ed Class Tchr
Semester Hrs Continuing Ed; *cr:* Ansonia Local Schl 4th
1977-78; Bradford Ex Village Schls 1st, 4th & 6th Grd Tchr 1
Tech, Sci & Math Comms; NEA, BEA; Bradford Church of Brethr

Chm, Sec; Coached 1978-89; *office:* Bradford Ex Village Schls ami Ave Bradford OH 45308*

EVERLY ANN, Mathematics Teacher; *b:* Lancaster, NH; *ed:* St Coll (BS) Math Ed 1978; Worcester Polytechnic Inst (MM) 6; *cr:* Groveton HS Math Tchr 1977-78; Conant HS Math Tchr NCTM 1989-; NEA 1992-; *office:* Conant HS 3 Conant Way H 03452

RENDA LEE, 8th-12th Grd Math & Sci Tchr; *b:* Valparaiso, IN; st Univ (BS) Physics 1980, (MA) Physics 1981; Bob Jones Univ sic Ed 1985; *cr:* Temple Chrstn Schl 1-12 Grd Music Tchr Faith Chrstn Schl Sci, Math, Music Tchr 1987-, Band 1993-; *ai:* h Acad Adv; Guid Cnslr; IN Rdng Quarterly Article Pub 1991; ith Chrstn Schl PO Box 475 Russ Rd Greenville OH 45331

. EDWARD, Professor of Biology; *b:* St Thomas ON, Canada; *m:* Carr; *c:* Derek, Cameron; *ed:* Univ of Western Ontario (BS) Bio S) Bio 1967; Carleton Univ (PHD) Bio 1971; *cr:* Can Med Res st Doc Fellow Endocrinology Res Unit 1971-73, Nat Inst of Hlth iv of Waterloo Asst Bio Prof 1973-77; D'Youville Coll Asst, of of Bio 1977-; *ai:* Fundraiser Autistic Svcs Inc; Fac Mem of Yr rs-Roebuck Fnd Tchng Excl & Campus Ldrshp Awd 1990; Educl in Human Gross Anatomy Co-Author 1993; *office:* D'Youville Porter Ave Buffalo NY 14201

ELMAR RAY, Biology Teacher; *b:* Lewistown, PA; *m:* Joyce imond; *c:* Leah, Thomas, Lydia, Timothy; *ed:* Shippensburg Univ 1976; Bucknell Univ (MS) Ed 1988; PA St Univ (DEd) Ed Admin Lewisburg Area MS General Sci 1976-77; Tuscarora Jr HS ci 1978-81; E Juniata HS Bio & AP Bio Tchr 1981-; *ai:* Jr Class, ss & Yrbk Adv; Ath Dir; Phi Delta Kappa, PA ST Ath Dir Assn; 371 1977-; E Salem United Meth Church 1969-; Harrisburg y AASR 1993-; Research Work Pub in Journal of Ed Research; uniata HS Box 60 Cocolamus PA 17014*

ARY CHARLES, Social Studies Teacher; *b:* Tiffin, OH; *ed:* Green St Univ (BS_ Compre Soc Stud 1989; 2 Credit Hrs Amer y 1992; *cr:* Tiffin Calvert HS Soc Stud Tchr 1989-; *ai:* Soph Class or; Kids Voting Coord; Tchr of Month Jan, Oct 1992; Tchr of Yr *home:* 303 1/2 Coe St Tiffin OH 44883

NGRID DZENIS, Mathematics Teacher; *b:* Willimantic, CT; *m:* Sr.; *ed:* Keene St Coll (BSEd) Math 1975; Univ of CT (MED) 1981; *cr:* Tolland HS Math Tchr 1975-76; Keene HS Math Tchr Edwin O. Smith HS Math Tchr 1977-; *ai:* BEST Prgm Support A, NEA 1977-; ATOMIC; ATMNE; Imeria Stu 1974-, Treas; O Smith HS 1235 Storrs Rd Storrs Mansfield CT 06268*

EAN KRAUSS, High School Science Teacher; *b:* Norwich, CT; n Hoult; *c:* Julia, Nathan W.; *ed:* Clark Univ (BA) Bio 1960; niv (MST) Bio 1978; Newark St Sci Cert 1972; Numerous Dist mptrs Courses; *cr:* Arthur D. Little Rsrch Tech, Preclinical logy 1960-61; Unin Coll Lab Rsrch Asst 1965-66; Bridgewater egnl HS Bio Tchr 1972-; *ai:* NHS Fac Cncl; NJ Sci League on Bio I & II Coach; BREA, NJEA, NEA 1972-; NJSTA 1980-; Johnson & Johnson Club Outstdng HS Tchr Awd 1986; Hoffman Inc Biological Sci Tchr Grant 1984; Participant NIH, NASA Curr ent Evaluation Steering Panel 1990; NJ Governor's Outstdng vd 1994; *office:* Bridgewater-Raritan Regnl HS PO Box 6569 ter NJ 08807

OANNE S., 6th Grade Math & Rdng Teacher; *b:* New Haven, CT; t E.; *c:* Robert E. Jr., Kelly; *ed:* Southern CT St Univ (BS) Ed S) Ed, Rdng 1976; *cr:* Branford-Canoe Brook Schl Grd 5 Tchr Branford Jr HS Grd 7-8 Rdng Tchr 1970-71; Short Beach Schl hr 1971-72; Adams MS Grd 6-8 Lit Tchr 1976-86; Baldwin MS th Tchr 1986-; *ai:* Guilford Edn Assn; NEA; *office:* Baldwin MS r Guilford CT 06437

ODY MACIOGE, Alternative Education Teacher; *b:* Ellwood *c:* Jordan F., Samuel M.; *ed:* Westminster Coll (BA) Ed & Soc 24 Grad Credits PA Level II Cert; *cr:* Villa Maria HS Soc Stud 9-80; Moon Area Schls Soc Stud Tchr 1980-86; Riverside Beaver tud Tchr 1988-90; Prevention Project CCBC Alternative Ed Tchr : New Brighton HS SADD Club Spon; Beaver Cty March of alkathon Chm; PA Midwest Cnslrs 1995-, Lecturer; NOW 1993-; ic Natl Comm 1994-; Thanks to Tchrs Awd 1996.*

KENNETH E., Language Arts Dept Chairperson; *b:* Newark, NJ; e; *c:* Abbee; *ed:* William Paterson Coll (BA) Eng 1975, (MA) Ed 993; *cr:* Union Coll Adj Tchr 1990-92; Paramus Cath Boys HS 1981-85; Wood-Ridge HS Eng Tchr 1985-87; Mt Olive HS Dept g Tchr 1987-; *ai:* Debate Team Coach; ASCD, NJSPA 1993-; arious Short Stories, Poems Publication, Broadcast; *office:* Mount 19 Corey Rd Flanders NJ 07836*

LISA SCHENCK, German & Reading Teacher; *b:* Akron, OH; *m:* mes; *ed:* Bowling Green St Univ (BSE) Eng 1989; Univ of Akron dng; *cr:* West Carrollton Sr HS Eng Tchr 1989-91; Glen Oak HS , Rdng Tchr 1991-; Kent St Univ Instr 1995-; *ai:* Ger, Book Club Coach; NEA, OEA, NCTE 1989-; Article Pub Kappa Delta Pi Phi Delta Kappa Grant Innovation in Ed; *office:* Glen Oak HS n St NW Canton OH 44709

MARIAN JANICE, American History Teacher; *b:* Bronx, NY; *ed:* Coll of City Univ of NY (BA) His 1964, (BA) His 1965; 30 Addl Credit Hrs Anthropology; *cr:* Glen Cove HS World His Tchr Simon & Schuster Educl Division Editorial Asst 1969-70; Sr HS Soc Stud Tchr 1970-; *ai:* Curr Cncl; Baldwin Tchrs Assn dg Rep, 10 Yr Cert of Recognition; *office:* Baldwin HS 841 High r Baldwin NY 11510

MARLA KAY, Pre-K Teacher; *b:* Danville, IL; *m:* Gene A.; *c:* Dalton; *ed:* Eastern IL Univ (MS) Elem Ed 1977; IN St Univ (BA) 1987; *cr:* Judith Giacoma Elem Schl Title 1 Rdng Tchr 1978-80, Tchr 1980-86, 2nd Grd Tchr 1986-95; Winnie-The-Pooh Pre-K 95-; *ai:* IEA, NEA, WEA 1980-; *home:* 1334 Cedar Point Ct OH 45102

MARY KAY, Assistant Professor; *b:* Utica, NY; *m:* Daniel Whyte; nan, Kathleen; *ed:* Hudson Valley Comm Coll (BA) Cmptr Sci; Geneseo (BA) Ed; St Univ of NY at Albany (MS) Ed; Attnd Union Rochester Inst of Tech; *cr:* Finserv Co Programmer; Albany Authority Systems Analyst; NY St Energy Office Systems ner; Hudson Valley Comm Coll Asst Prof; *ai:* Albany Parks U10 ccer Team, Coach; Montessori Schl, Pres; *office:* Hudson Valley oll 80 Vandenburgh Ave Troy NY 12180

MIRIAM ANNE (UTTER), Fourth Grade Teacher; *b:* Monroe, Michael; *ed:* MI St Univ (BA) Soc Stud 1958; Eastern MI Univ em Ed 1964; *cr:* Custer Consolidated Schl 3rd Grd Tchr 1958-62; Schl 4th Grd Tchr 1962-; *ai:* AFT 1982-; Delta Kappa Gamma psilon Chapter 1973-, Record Sec; St Pauls Luth Church, Organist Toledo Pub Schls Exemplary Level Status in Career Ladder for 991 & 1994; Dev & Dir 2 Schl Bus Partnerships at Home hurst Elem; (PIE) Bd of directors Mem; *office:* Elmhurst Elem edo Pub Schls 4530 Elmhurst Rd Toledo OH 43613*

HART, RANDALL LEE, Engineering Technology Teacher; *b:* Ellwood City, PA; *m:* Cindy Frankenstein; *c:* Jon, Justin, Jackie; *ed:* CA S Univ (BS) Ind Arts 1974, (MS) Ind Arts 1977; 24 Credit Hrs; Adm Cert 1980; *cr:* North Allegheny Tchr 1974-80, Adm Support Svcs 1980-83, Tchr 1983-, Schl Dir; *ai:* Outdoor & Lifetime Acts; Natl Coord Amer Sport Climbing Fed Jr Div; AFT 1974-; Jaycees 1980-83, St Winner 4 Projects; Boro Cncl 1978-79; Cty Assn 1978-79, VP; PA Fish Comm 1983-, Boat Safety Instr; YMCA Advy Bd 1988-; Safari Club Intl Outdoors Tchr Natl Winner 1993; Jaycees Outstanding Educator 1990; PA Tchr of Yr Nom 1991; 4 PA St Senate Citations Excl in Ed 1989-92; 4 Articles Outdoor Ed; 1st Place Jaycees Programming for Handicapped Stdnts 1983; *office:* North Allegheny Interm HS 350 Cumberland Rd Pittsburgh PA 15237

HART, ROBERT LEE, Professor of English; *b:* Phiadelphia, PA; *m:* Valerie Jean Shroeder; *c:* Jeffrey R., Daniel P.; *ed:* West Chester U (BS) Eng 1960; Temple U (EDM) Eng Ed 1970; Nova Southeastern U (EDD) Higher Ed 1993; *cr:* Clearview HS Eng, Soc Stud Tchr 1962-70; Gloucester Cty Coll Eng Prof 1970-; *ai:* Phi Theta Kappa Co-Adv; Awds, Schlsp Comms; NCTE, CCCC 1970-, Tchng Eng in Two-Yr Coll 1980-; Eric Documents Pub; Co-Author Composition Textbook; Tchr of Yr Awd; Collaborative Learning Wkshp Presentations; *office:* Gloucester County Coll 1400 Tanyard Rd Sewell NJ 08080

HART, SHERYL MCNOLDY, Transitional First Grade Tchr; *b:* Lykens, PA; *m:* Lawrence J.; *c:* Shannon Hart Wenrich, Shawn; *ed:* Shippensburg Univ (BS) Elem Ed 1975; Kutztown Univ (MEd) Rdng Ed 1978; *cr:* Williams Valley Schl Dist Elem Classroom Tchr 1975-79, Remedial Rdg Specialist 1979-86, 1st Grd Tchr 1986-93, Transitional 1st Grd Tchr 1993-; *ai:* Summer Rdng Prgm Coord; Spelling Bee Comm Chm; Williams Valley Ed Assn 1975-, Treas; NEA, PSEA 1975-; Trinity United Church of Christ Counsel 1993-, Pres; *office:* Williams Valley Jr Sr HS Rt 209 Box 189-B Tower City PA 17980

HART, SILVIA MARY (SALVI), Kindergarten Teacher; *b:* Passaic, NJ; *m:* William J.; *c:* Lisa M., William S.; *ed:* William Paterson Coll (BA) Elem Ed 1960, (MA) Lang Arts 1965; 6th Yr Level 1970; *cr:* Clifton Schl Eight Kndgtn Tchr 1960-65; Clifton Schl Eleven Kndgtn Tchr 1966-69; Clifton Schl Fifteen Kndgtn Tchr 1974-; *ai:* Affirmative Action Coord; Home & Schl Exec Bd; Admins Kndgtn Rep Liason; NEA, NJEA 1960-; CTA Tchrs Assn 1960-, Bldg Rep 1961-64; NJAKE; Kappa Delta Pi 1966-; Pi Lambda Theta 1982-; Clifton Boys & Girls Club 1984-, Bd of Dirs; Who's Who Among Stdnts in Amer Univs & Colls 1959-60; Clifton Edctr of Yr Awd 1979; Jaycee's Distngd Tchr Awd 1980; Govenor's Recognition Awd 1983; *home:* 184 Abbe Ln Clifton NJ 07013*

HART, TANYA R., PE Tchr & Coach; *b:* Amory, MS; *ed:* Liberty Univ (MS) PE 1986; *cr:* Trinity Chrstn Schl PE Tchr, Coach 1986-94; Intnl Chrstn Acad PE Tchr, Coach 1995-; *ai:* Yrbk, Sr Class, NHS Adv; Vlybl, Bsktbl, Sftbl Coach; Summer Tchng Brazil, France; Kappa Delta Pi 1985-; NCCAA Eastern Region Bsktbl Coaches Awd 1993; *home:* 801 N Hills Dr Ayden NC 28513

HART, TOBY SHAPIRO, Fourth Grade Music Teacher; *b:* New York, NY; *m:* Edward; *c:* Dina Marks, Benjamin; *ed:* Brooklyn Coll (BS) ECC 1957, (MS) ECC 1968, (MS) Spec Ed, LD 1986, (PHD) Admin, Super 1989; 6 Credits Music; 46 Credits Bd of Ed NYC; LeSablier Rdng Method Canada; *cr:* Bd of Ed NYC Kndgtn Tchr 1956-59; Coram Schl Kndgtn Tchr 1967-70; Coces II Music Tchr 1970-72; Oldfield Jr HS Music Tchr 1973-76; North Babylon Sch Music Tchr 1973-76; PS 164Q Bd of Ed PE Tchr 1983-84; Dist 25 Tchr 1984-85; PS 24Q Grd 4 Music Tchr 1985-; *ai:* Recorder Ensemble Dir; UFT, AFT, NEA 1980-; Kappa Delta Pi 1986-, Schlsp Awd; SOMEA 1970-; Angela Zirapedes Tchr Awd 5 Short Stories; NYS Tchr of Yr Awd Finalist 1989; Dir Rsrch Children's Book Rdng Method; Crisis Dir; *home:* 9 Woodmont Rd Melville NY 11747*

HART, WILLIAM HENRY, Eighth Grd Phys Science Tchr; *b:* Warren, OH; *m:* Brenda Lau; *c:* Carrie, Eric; *ed:* Baldwin Wallace Coll (BA) Hlth, Sci, PE 1978; Attnd Kent St; *cr:* Kenston Local Schls 8th Grd Sci Tchr 1978-80; Newbury Local Schls 7th-12th Grd Hlth Tchr 1980-81; Southington Local Schls 7th-12th Grd Sci Tchr 1981-84; Weathersfield Local Schls 7th-12th Grd Hlth Tchr 1984-87; North Royalton 7th-12th Grd PE Tchr 1987-88; Hubbard-Reed Mid 8th Grd Sci Tchr 1988-; *ai:* Sci Olympics; Ftbl; Sci, Hlth Curr, Behavior Code Dev; Sci Fair; Levy Comm; NEA, OEA, HEA, OHSFCA 1978-; Little League LAC 1993-, Coach; Stu Nom Star Tchr 1995; Tchr of Yr Nom 1993; *office:* Reed MS 150 Hall Ave Hubbard OH 44425

HART, WILLIAM T., Athletic Director & Math Tchr; *b:* Falla River, MA; *m:* Pauline W. Lavoie; *c:* Martha Reed, Amy; *ed:* Univ of MA at Dartmouth (BA) His 1969; 15 Plus Credit Hrs Towards Masters in His; 15 Plus Credit Hrs Towards Masters in Scndry Admin; *cr:* Holy Family HS Eng, US His & Latin Tchr 1969-72; Bishop Stang HS Math Tchr 1972-; *ai:* Bingo & Spartan Ath Bingo Mem-in-Charge; NIAAA 1985-; MSSADA 1985-; *office:* Bishop Stang HS 500 Slocum Rd North Dartmouth MA 02747

HARTE DMITRIEV, SHEILA H., Social Studies & Russian Tchr; *b:* Jamestown, NY; *m:* Vladimir V.; *ed:* Univ of CO (BA) Intnl Affairs 1986; St Univ of NY at Albany (MA) Russian Ed 1992; *cr:* Associated Press Bookkeeper 1987-89; Australian Embassy Account Clerk 1989; Office of US Senator Case Worker 1991-92; Champaign Cty Circuit Clerk Account Clerk 1992-93; Clymer Cntrl Schl Tchr 1993-; *ai:* AFS Adv; Var Sftbl Coach; Var Bsktbl Chrldng Adv; NEA 1993-; Amer Cncl of Tchrs of Russian 1995-; NEH Summer Seminar 1995; *home:* 16 Columbia Ave Jamestown NY 14701*

HARTEMANN, RONALD, German & Spanish Teacher; *b:* Hackensack, NJ; *m:* Sandra; *c:* Doug, Sue; *ed:* Fairleigh Dickinson Univ (BS) Ger & Chem 1967, (MAT) Ger & ESL 1971; Span Cert; Working on Masters in Cnslng & Guidance; Stu Assistance Cnslr Cert; *cr:* Garfield HS Ger Tchr 1967-69; Leonia HS Ger & Sci Tchr 1969-71; Kinnelon HS Ger & Span Tchr 1971-75; Kittatinny Regnl HS Ger, Span & Sci Tchr 1975-; *ai:* Ger Club; Facilitator of Peer Leadersip; Peer Support Network; Teen Inst of Garden St; Adventure Based Cnslng; NEA 1967-; AATG 1991-; *office:* Kittatinny Regnl HS 77 Halsey Rd Newton NJ 07860

HARTENSTEIN, ALICE L., English Teacher; *b:* York, PA; *m:* Wayne G.; *c:* Julia, Jacob, Adam; *ed:* Millersville St Univ (BS) Scndry Eng 1970; Western MD Coll 21 Credits Guidance; Penn St York 9 Grad Credits; Millersville St Univ 6 Grad Credits; *cr:* York Suburban MS 7-8th Grd Eng Tchr 17 Yrs; *ai:* ACT Team; EXPO Adv; Acad Team Ldr; Alice C. Brader Schlsp Chprsn; Project Harmony Organizer; York Suburban Ed Assn, PA St Ed Assn, NEA 1970-; *office:* York Suburban MS 455 Sundale Dr York PA 17402*

HARTER, JEAN ANN, Sixth Grade Teacher; *b:* Williamsport, PA; *ed:* Lycoming Coll (BA) Sociology, Elem Ed 1970; *cr:* Fairfield Elem Schl Third Grd Tchr 1970-74; Livingword Acad Fourth Grd & 7-9 Eng Tchr 1981-84; Smoketown Elem Schl Fourth & Sixth Grd Tchr 1985-; *ai:* NEA 1987-; CVEA 1987-, Bldg Rep; Manheim Twp Lib 1995-, Vol; *office:* Smoketown Elem Schl 2426 Old Philadelphia Pike Lancaster PA 17602*

HARTER, MARY LOU CLARK, Fourth Grade Teacher; *b:* Galeton, PA; *c:* Allison Leigh, E. Kenneth III, Robert James; *ed:* SUNY at Geneseo (BA) Elem Ed 1958; Post Grad Hrs SUNY at Brockport; *cr:* Richmond HS Fifth Grd Tchr 1959-60; Harlingen Cntrl Schl Fifth Grd Tchr 1960-61; Marcus Whitman Schl PE Tchr 1966-68; Manchester-Shorsville Cntrl Schl Fourth Grd Tchr 1968-; *ai:* NYSUT, RJCS Fac Assn 1968-; *office:* Manchester Shrtsvle Cntrl Schl Rt 21 Canandaigua St Shortsville NY 14548

HARTER, MOLLIE, English Teacher; *b:* Bloomsburg, PA; *m:* Richard S.; *c:* Rod A., Jeff R., Louise M.; *ed:* Bloomsburg Univ (BS) Bus, Eng 1955, Soc Stud 1961; *cr:* Danville Jr HS Eng, Gifted 1958-82; Danville Sr HS Eng, Honors & Coll Prep, General 1982-; *ai:* Danathos Chapter of NHS Adv; Danville Ed Assn 1958-, Pres 1977-94; PSEA 1958, St Leadership Dev Comm; NEA 1958-; PSEA Northeastern Convention Comm 1980-; Code Appeals Bd Chair 1982-; Dem Comm Person 1984-; Beta Sigma Phi 1952-; PSEA Innovative Tchng Awd; Danville Schl System Innovative Grant; Supts Awd; Looking to Learn Prgm; BSA Merit Badge Certifier; *office:* Danville Sr HS 600 Walnut St Danville PA 17821

HARTFORD, FLORA MARINO, Humanities Teacher; *b:* Queens, NY; *m:* Donald George; *c:* Devon F.; *ed:* Marywood Coll (BA) Soc St, Sec Ed 1969; St John's Univ (MA) African Stud 1971; 6 Credits African Stud Univ of CA at Chico; 6 Credits African Stud Howard Univ; 6 Credits Japanese Stud Sophia Univ; *cr:* Farmingdale HS Soc Stud Tchr 1970-; *ai:* Coord Grd 10 Renaissance Prgm; Selection Comm HS Honor Soc; AFT, UFT 1970-; Coll Level Entry Placement Awd Hum Prgm; Prgm of Excl NY St Eng Cncl; HS Tchr of Yr Jenkins Awd; *office:* Farmingdale HS 150 Lincoln St Farmingdale NY 11735

HARTH, DOROTHY FELDMANN, Professor of Spanish; *b:* New York, NY; *m:* Erich M.; *c:* Peter, Richard; *ed:* Queens Coll (BAE Latin Amer 1947; Columbia Univ (MA) Span 1948; Syracuse Univ (PHD) Span 1957; Univ of Havana at Cuba Cert; 45 Post Grad Credits; *cr:* Syracuse Univ Span Instr 1951-54; Duke Univ Span Instr 1954-57; Onondaga Comm Coll Span Prof 1962-; *ai:* Womens Stud Comm Coord; ULA 1958-88; AFT 1962-; Span Action League 1973-78 Bd of Dirs; SUNY Chancellors Excl in Tchng Awd 1994; Numerous Articles Pub; *home:* 4451 Lafayette Rd Jamesville NY 13078

HARTH, MARSHALL STEPHEN, Professor of Psychology; *b:* New York City, NY; *c:* Cara, David; *ed:* City Coll of NY (BS) Psych 1964; Rutgers Univ (PHD) Psych 1970; *cr:* Ramapo Coll Psych Prof 1972-; *ai:* Psych Assn Fac Adv; Convener Coll Seminar Prgm, Substance Abuse Minor; Rockland Co Psychol Assn 1984-, VP; Bergon Cty Holocaust Ctr 1985-, Bd of Trustees; NIMH Pre-Doctoral Flwshp; MICHHD Post Doctoral Flwshp; Alumni Assn Outstdng Fac Awd; *office:* Ramapo Coll Of NJ 505 Ramapo Valley Rd Mahwah NJ 07430

HARTING, ARNOLD R., English & TV Comm Teacher; *b:* Cleveland, OH; *m:* Elisa Tutone; *c:* Nicole Panna, Michelle Mc Nally, David, Peter; *ed:* The Defiance Coll (BS) Speech 1965; Buffalo St Coll Eng Ed 15 Hrs; St Univ of NY Buffalo Speech Comm 30 Hrs; 56 Post-Grad Hrs; *cr:* Ravenna HS Speech, Eng 1965-67; East HS Eng 1967-78; Bennett HS Eng 1978-88; Buffalo Raditional Schl Eng, TV Comm 1988-; *ai:* X-Country, Girls Track, A-V Dept Head Coach; NEA 1965; BTF 1965, Delegate Chair; Newman Bd 1978-, VP; Newman Bd of Dir 1985-; Western NY Summer Dev Track Assn 1978-, Coach, Meet Dir, High Point Scorer 4 Yrs; Publisher of Bards Bits BTS, Pub The Beacon, HS Papers, Local Comm Newspapers; *office:* Buffalo Traditional Schl 450 Masten Ave Buffalo NY 14209

HARTJE, ALVIN CARL, Science Teacher; *b:* Manhattan NYC, NY; *m:* June Hagen; *c:* Allison, Amanda, Erik; *ed:* Staten Island Comm Coll (AAS) Bus Tech 1964; Pace Coll (BBA) Bus Admin, Mrktg 1969; Coll of Staten Island (MSE) Ed 1988; *cr:* Mission of Immaculate Virgin Schl Childcare Cnslr 1967-86; St Aloysius Elem Schl 1st-8th Grd Sci Tchr 1969-79; Mount Loretto Outdoor Ed Dir 1979-82; Our Lady of the Sea Schl 6th-8th Grd Sci Tchr 1982-; *ai:* Local Sci Fairs Judge; Local Conservation Ctrs, Nature, Indian Stud, Paleolithic Artifacts Speaker; Phi Delta Kappa 1988-; Fed of Cath Tchrs, Staten Island Sci Tchrs Assn 1982-; NSF Grant 1978; Staten Island Continuum of Ed Edctr of Yr 1992; *office:* Our Lady Star Of The Sea Sch 5411 Amboy Rd Staten Island NY 10312

HARTLE, BRIAN L., Instrumental Music Director; *b:* Bethesda, MD; *m:* Joan M.; *ed:* The Cath Univ of AM (BA) Music Ed 1973; Undergard Stud Luther Rice Coll; Grad Masters Prgm Univ of MD; *cr:* Montgomery Hills Jr HS Music Dept Chair 1973-76; Randolph Jr HS Music Dept Chair 1976-80; Takoma Park Jr HS Music Dept Chair 1980-81; M. L. King MS Music Dept Chair 1981-; *ai:* North Cty Honors Band, Stage Tech Dir; NEA; MCEA; MENC; MBDA;MODA; Tri-M Music Honor Soc; Higher Level Thinking Skills Lesson Featured Tchng Video; *office:* Martin Luther Kins Jr HS 11700 Neelsville Church Rd Germantown MD 20876

HARTLE, SALLIE E., Eng II & American Lit Teacher; *b:* New Kensington, PA; *m:* William A.; *c:* Megan Lindsey, Robin Courtney; *ed:* Clarion Univ (BS) Eng, Rdng 1967; PA St Univ (ME) Eng, Comm 1972; *cr:* Kiski Area HS Eng Tchr 1967-69; Elizabeth Forward HS Tchr of Eng, Gifted 1969-; *ai:* Natl Acad Games Project Coach, Consultant; AFT 1979-; Pittsburgh Youth Ballet Exec Bd 1994-; Jrnlsm Ed Assn Past St Dir; Jim Davis Outstanding Coord; *office:* Elizabeth Forward HS 1000 Weigles Hills Rd Elizabeth PA 15037

HARTLEP, DOROTHY KOSMACH, MS Language Arts Teacher; *b:* Pittsburgh, PA; *m:* William L.; *c:* Billy, Christopher; *ed:* St Francis Coll (BA) Eng 1976; 27 Post Grad Credits; 3 Non-Credited Cmptr Classes; *cr:* St Francis Acad HS Eng Tchr 1980-81; St Gabriel of Sorrowful Virgin Schl MS Lang Arts Tchr 1982-; *ai:* Stu Publication Comm; FPDT 1991-; NCTE 1992-; WPCTE 1993-; Davey Goes to Day Care Book; *home:* 1095 ORourke Dr Pittsburgh PA 15236

HARTLEY, NANCY NORTON, Social Studies Teacher; *b:* Lewistown, PA; *m:* David N. II; *c:* Jacqueline, Kristy, Stephanie; *ed:* Juniata Coll (BA) His 1973; Post Grad Stud for Permanent Cert; *cr:* Mifflin Cty Schl Dist Tchr 1973-; *ai:* Soc Stud Club; Adv to His Day; Coord of Newspapers in Ed; NEA 1973-; First Church of Brethren in Lewistown 1964-, Asst Organist, Jr Church; Coord of Upward Bound; *office:* Indian Valley HS 700 Cedar St Lewistown PA 17044

HARTLEY, STEPHANIE, First Grade Teacher; *b:* Paterson, NJ; *ed:* William Paterson Coll (BA) Kndgtn, Primary 1969; *cr:* Haskell Schl Tchr 1969-72; Wanaque Elem Schl Tchr 1972-; *ai:* NJ St Stu Tchr Mentor Prgm; NEA, NJEA 1969-; WBEA 1969-, Corresonding Sec.

HARTLINE, REBECCA SUE (BOYD), English & Psychology Teacher; *b:* Canton, OH; *m:* Neil Edward; *ed:* (BA) Eng 1980; (BA) Psych 1980; *cr:* Massillon Chrstn Schl Eng, Psych Tchr 1980-; *ai:* NHS Adv; Chapel Pianist, Fund Raiser Chprsn; Church Orchestra 1970-; 1st & 2nd Grd Youth Group Ldr 1978-90.

HARTLINE, STEPHANIE KANE, Language Arts Teacher; *b:* Reading, PA; *m:* Bradley J.; *c:* Emily, Alex; *ed:* Ursinus Coll (BA) Eng 1983; Kutztown Univ (MS) Telecommunications 1988; Holy Guardian Angels Schl Lang Arts Tchr 1983-; *cr:* Holy Guardian Angels Schl Lang Arts Tchr 1983-; *ai:* Lang Arts Coord; 8th Grd Play Dir; Allentown Diocese Lay Tchrs Assn 1993-; *home:* 1 Mill Rd Myerstown PA 17067*

HARTLING, RENEE JOHNSON, Title I Math Teacher; *b:* Lockport, NY; *m:* Richard; *c:* Rachael Marie, Rebecca Grace; *ed:* St Bonaventure Univ (BS) Elem Ed 1984; Columbia Univ (MA) Curr & Tchng 1992; SUNY at New Paltz (CAS) Educ Admin & Super 1996; *cr:* Totaro Elem Schl Kndgtn Tchr 1984-87, Fourth Grd Tchr 1987-88; Roscoe Cntrl Schl Fourth Grd Tchr 1988-90, Sixth Grd Tchr 1990-94, Grds 2-10 Title I Math Tchr 1994-; *ai:* JV Girls Bsktbl, Var Sftbl Coach; Bldg Ldrshp Team; Class Adv; Tech Comm Mem; ASCD 1986-; NYSUT 1988-; Roscoe PTA 1988-; *office:* Roscoe Central Schl 10 Academy St Roscoe NY 12776*

HARTMAN, BRYAN G., Chemistry Teacher; *b:* Shartlesville, PA; *m:* Gayle c. Eyrich; *c:* Natalie, Pamela Baker, Bryan; *ed:* East Stroudsburg St (BS) Chem 1958; Univ of MI (MA) Chem 1961; Fresno St Coll Atomic Energy; Brown Univ Chem; *cr:* Tulpelocken Schl Dist Sci Tchr 1958-60; Wyomissing HS Chem, Math Tchr 1960-61; Gov Mifflin HS Chem Tchr 1962-69; William Allen HS Chem Tchr 1969-; *ai:* Odyssey of the Mind, 4 St Champions, 2nd & 4th in World Competitions; NEA; PSEA; AEA; Acad Yr Inst; Grants.

HARTMAN, CINDY MERCER, High School English Teacher; *b:* Xenia, OH; *m:* Richard James; *c:* Renee, Craig; *ed:* Wright St Univ (BS) Eng, His, Sec 1979, (MS) Rdng 1990; Antioch Univ 15 Hrs Multiple Intelligences; Mentor Trng, Implementation; *cr:* Greenview HS Eng Tchr 1983-; Univ of Dayton Prof 1991; *ai:* Adv Jr Class, Prom, Girls Var G; TEAMS, Jr High Vlybl Coach; Block Scheduling Comm; NCTE 1990-; WOCTELA 1989; ASCD 1995-; Grape Grove Church of Christ 1965-; Martha Jennings Scholar 1995; Masters Prgm Hon Stu; Tchng Content Rdng Wksbp Ldr; *office:* Greeneview H S 53 N Limestone St Jamestown OH 45335*

HARTMAN, GWEN TATALEBA, Family & Consumer Science Tchr; *b:* Meyersdale, PA; *m:* John Harry; *c:* Ashley, Evan; *ed:* Penn St Univ (BS) Home Ec Ed 1982; Frostburg St Univ (MS) Interdisciplinary Ed 1991; *cr:* Chestnut Ridge MS Home Ec Tchr 1982-83; Chestnut Ridge Sr HS Home Ec Tchr 1983-84; Somerset Jr HS Home Ec Tchr 1984-91; Somerset Sr HS Family & Consumer Sci Tchr 1991-; *ai:* Baby Think It Over, Children's Latch-Key Programmer; Musical Costum, Fashion Show, Soph-Sr & Prom Gown Sale Dir; Bears for Bosnia Spon; AAFCS, PAFCS 1991-; NEA, PSEA, SAEA 1982-; Somerset Cnty FACS 1984-; Berlin Brethren Church 1986-, Vacation Bible Schl Coord, Sunday Schl Tchr; FASCS Dept Coord; *office:* Somerset Sr HS 835 S Columbia Ave Somerset PA 15501*

HARTMAN, JOYCE STAPLETON, 7th Grd Life Science Teacher; *b:* Goshen, NY; *m:* James A.; *c:* Jennifer, Jordan; *ed:* LadyCliff (BA) Bio & Chem 1971; St Univ at New Paltz MS Educl Admin; *cr:* Tri Valley Regents Bio Tchr 1973-90, Admin Intern 1990-91, MS Sci 1990-; *ai:* New Tchr Mentor; Peer Mediation Coord; Bldg Ldrshp Team; NYSUT 1971-; Phi Delta Kappa 1991-; ASCD 1991-; NYS Regnl Bio Tchr Mentor 1991-92; *home:* RR 1 Box 164E Woodbourne NY 12788*

HARTMAN, LEONARD DAMON, Eng, Jrnlsm Tchr & Yrbk Adv; *b:* Warren, OH; *m:* Holly Kuchta; *ed:* OH St (BA) Eng 1992, (MA) Eng Ed 1994; *cr:* Coventry HS Eng Tchr 1994-; *ai:* Jrnlsm Yrbk Adv; Asst Ftbl Coach; *office:* Coventry HS 3257 Cormany Rd Akron OH 44319

HARTMAN, MICHELLE MARIE, Health & Phys Ed Teacher; *b:* Lebanon, PA; *ed:* Eastern KY Univ (BS) PE 1975, (MA) PE 1979; 6 Post Grad Hrs PA St Univ; 6 Credits Regnl Trng Ctr Gratz Coll; 3 Credits Tchr Ed Inst Carlo Coll; *cr:* Cedar Crest HS Career Ed Adv 1979-80, Hlth, PE Tchr 1980-83; Manheim Cntrl HS Hlth, PE Tchr 1983-; *ai:* JV Hockey Coach 1985-91; Jr HS Bsktbl Coach 1985-89; Fitness Team Coach 1989-92; Stu Proficiency Comm, Mentor 1996; Class Adv 1986-90; 9th Grd Teaming; NEA 1984-; YMCA 1991-; Quentin United Church of Christ 1983-, Deacon; *office:* Manheim Central HS 71 N Hazel St Manheim PA 17545

HARTMAN, WANNETTA JANE, Sixth Grade Teacher; *b:* Memphis, OH; *m:* Ed; *c:* Jessica Jae, Miles Jeremy; *ed:* Southern St Comm (Assoc) Ed 1986; Wilmington Coll (BA) K-8th Ed 1988; Miami Univ (MA) Elem Ed 1993; *cr:* Clinton Cty Sub Tchr 1989; East Clinton Local Schls 6th Grd Tchr 1989; New Vienna Schl Sixth Grd Tchr; *ai:* Lang Arts, Soc Stud Curr & Spelling Bee Comms; Action Rsrch Network; CORE Team; IAT; Judging Power of the Pen; Green Key Hnr Soc 1988-; OEA, NEA & ECEA 1989-; Phi Delta Kappa 1992-; NCTE 1994-; OCTELA 1995-; Childrens Comm 1990-; Outstndng Tchr of Yr 1991; Article Pub 1994; Paul & Kate Farmer Writing Awd; NCTE Presentation; *home:* 4699 Prairie Rd Wilmington OH 45177

HARTMANN, HOLLY LYNN, High Schl Mathematics Teacher; *b:* Lorain, OH; *ed:* OH Univ (BS) Math Ed 1993; *cr:* Lorain HS Math Tchr 1993-94; Southview Schl Math Tchr 1993-95; Sandusky HS Math Tchr 1995-; *ai:* Proficiency Tests Tutoring; OEA, NEA 1994-; SEA 1995-; *home:* 536 Maple Creek Dr Amherst OH 44001*

HARTMANN, SANDRA HORNBY, US History & Anthropology Tchr; *b:* Passaic, NJ; *m:* William A.; *c:* Jennifer; *ed:* Fairleigh Dickinson Univ (BS) Soc Sci 1969; Montclair St Univ (MA) Anthropology 1978; Addl 30 Plus Hrs Post Grad Stud in Supervision; *cr:* Christopher Columbus MS 7-9 Grd His Tchr 1969-84; Clifton HS 11-12 Grd Amer His & Anthropology Tchr 1984-; *ai:* Sr Class Adv; Acad Decathlon Coach; Curr Comms; NEA, NJEA, PCEA 1969-; Clifton Tchr Assn 1969-, Recording Sec, 25 Yrs of Svc; West Patterson Lib Bd 1985-, Recording Sec; Clifton Jr W C 1977-83, Past Pres; *office:* Clifton HS 333 Colfax Ave Clifton NJ 07013*

HARTMANN, SUSAN, Fifth Grade Teacher; *b:* Easton, PA; *m:* Joseph W.; *c:* Jennifer, Joey; *ed:* Rider Univ (BA) Elem Ed 1975; *cr:* Holy ANgels Schl Seventh Grd Tchr 1975-77; Timberlane Jr Schl Eighth Grd Tchr 1978-79; Hopewell Elem Schl Fifth Grd Tchr 1979-; *ai:* Stu Cncl Adv; Fifth Grd Musical Production Dir; Schl Dists Writing Comm; NJEA 1978-; Tri-Cty Rdng Cncl 1991-; Comm Ed Awd 1984; Governor's Tchr Recognition Awd 1988; *office:* Hopewell Elem Schl 35 Princeton Ave Hopewell NJ 08525

HARTNETT, MARIE GRISKY, Math Teacher & Supervisor; *b:* Scranton, PA; *m:* Ronald J.; *c:* Christine Hartnett Camilli, Jeffrey; *ed:* Georgian Court Coll (BA) Math 1968, (MS) Supervision & Admin 1991; Attnd William Paterson, Kane Coll, Rutgers Univ, Univ of VA, James Mason; *cr:* Hamilton HS Math, Sci Tchr 1968-70; Woodson HS Math Tchr 1978-79; Red Bank Catholis Math, Cmptr Tchr 1980-85; Middletown HS South Math Tchr & Supvr 1985-; *ai:* Math Dept Supvr; AMTNJ, NCTM 1985-; ADK 1993-, Correspondence Sec; PDK 1995-; Ed Fnd Grant; *office:* Middletown HS South 501 Nutswamp Rd Middletown NJ 07748

HARTNETT, MAUREEN ANN, First Grade Teacher; *b:* Syracuse, NY; *m:* James P.; *c:* James M., Beth T.; *ed:* LeMoyne Coll (BS) His 1962; Syracuse Univ (MA) Elem Ed 1964; 30 Addl Hrs; *cr:* Pitcher Hill Schl First Grd Tchr 1962-64; Smith Road Elem Schl First Grd Tchr 1965-69; Onondaga Road Elem Schl First Grd Tchr 1970-; *ai:* NYSUT 1962-; West Genesee TA 1970-, Bldg Rep; Vol Work; Church Svc Work; Nom for Outstdng Tchr West Genesee Dist Schl Bd Mem 25 Yr Awd; *office:* Onondaga Road Elem Schl 703 Onondaga Rd S Syracuse NY 13219*

HARTRANFT, KAREN ROHRBACH, Phys Ed & Health Teacher; *b:* Reading, PA; *m:* Craig Harold; *c:* Nicole Marie; *ed:* East Stroudsburg Univ (BS) Hlth, PE K-12 1974; 26 Grad Credits at Kutztown Univ, West Chester Univ, East Stroudsburg Univ, Berks Cty Intermidate Unit; *cr:* Rdng Schl Dist Permanent Sub Tchr 1974-75; Holy Name HS Hlth, PE Tchr 1976-86; St Catharines of Sienna Schl Elem PE Tchr 1991-92; Rdng Cntrl Cath HS Hlth, PE Tchr, Asst AD 1992-; *ai:* Sr Class Adv; Producer of Sr Video Yrbk; Asst Ath Dir; sports Rep to Allentown Diocese; Head Sftbl Coach; PIAA Field Hockey Ofcl, Berks Cty Field Hockey Ofcls 1980-; US Field Hockey Assn, NCEA 1992-; Oley Vly Yth League 1990-, Sftbl Commissioner, Field Hockey Clinic Coord; *office:* Reading Central Cath HS 1400 Hill Rd Reading PA 19602

HARTS, MIRIAM V., Student Activities Coordinator; *b:* Brooklyn, NY; *ed:* Hofstra Univ (BA) Eng, Ed 1969; Long Island Univ (MA) Eng, Ed 1978; Columbia Univ Cert Mediation, Conflict Resolution; *cr:* IS 33 Eng Tchr; Manhattan Voc Tech Grd Adv, Rdng Coord 1974-83; Forest Hills HS Stu Act Coord; *ai:* Stu Govt, Sing Advs; Mediation Prgm, Toys for Tots, Blood Drive, Food Drive, Walk Amer Coords; Consultative Cncl; Security, Schlsp Comms; UFT 1969-; NASAA 1990-.

HARTSBURG, SUSAN C., English Teacher; *b:* Bridgeport, CT; *m:* Walter; *c:* Kathryn, Matthew; *ed:* Western CT St Coll (BS) Scndry Ed 1971, (MS) Ed 1976; *cr:* Bethel HS 9th-12th Grd Eng Tchr 1971-78; St Joseph's Elem Schl Eng, Rel Tchr 1981-84; Immaculate HS 9th-12th Grd Eng Tchr 1984-93; Bethel HS 9th-12th Grd Eng Tchr 1993-; *ai:* NEA, BEA, CEA 1993-; PDK 1992; Tchr of Yr Awd 1992; *office:* Bethel HS 300 Whittlesey Dr Bethel CT 06801

HARTSCHUH, JEAN F., High School Mathematics Tchr; *b:* Tiffin, OH; *ed:* Heidelberg Coll (BS) Math 1967; Bowling Green St Univ (MA) Elem Ed 1979; Attnd Kent St Univ, NSF Summer Inst 1968; OH Univ Post Grad Cmptr Classes; *cr:* Northmor Local Schl HS Math Tchr 1967-72; Wynford Local HS Math Tchr 1972-73; Wayside Chrstn 2nd & 3rd Grd Tchr 1973-76; Willard City 8th Grd Math Tchr 1976-78; Seneca East Local Schls HS Math Tchr 1979-; *ai:* NHS Adv; NEA, OEA, NWOEA, SEEA & NCTM; *office:* Seneca East HS PO Box 462 Attica OH 44807

HARTSHORN, THERESA MARIA, Occupational Therapy Professor; *b:* Niskayuna, NY; *ed:* Univ of NH (BS) Occup Therapy 1987; Attnd Sage Grad Schl; *cr:* Russell Sage Coll Instr 1992-; *ai:* Tech Comm; AOTA 1993-; ASHT 1994-; Numerous Articles Pub; *office:* Russell Sage Coll At Troy Ricketts Hall Troy NY 12180*

HARTWELL, ANDREA S., High School Resource Teacher; *b:* Albany, NY; *m:* Daniel J.; *c:* Abigail Faith; *ed:* Coll of St Rose (BA) Sec Ed, Eng 1986, (MS) Spec Ed 1991; *cr:* St Josephs-St John Acad 7th-8th Grd Eng Tchr 1987-89; Albany HS Resource Tchr 1989090; Cicero-N Syracuse HS Resource Tchr 1991-; *ai:* Conflict Resolution Coord; Dec Making Comm; Process consultation; NYSUT 1989-; *office:* Cicero N Syracuse HS Northstar Dr Cicero NY 13039

HARTWELL, SUSAN CLARK, Business Education Teacher; *b:* Skowhegan, ME; *m:* William G.; *ed:* Thomas Coll (BS) Bus Ed 1971; NH Coll (MS) Bus Ed 1988; *cr:* Portsmouth HS Bus Ed Tchr 1973-, Bus Ed Dept Head 1987-92; *ai:* Co-Adv FBLA; NEA, NHEA, APT, NHBEA 1973-; EBEA 1985-; NHSPCA 1990-; Humane Soc of US 1992-; *office:* Portsmouth HS Jarvis Dr Portsmouth NH 03801

HARTWICK, A. REUBEN, Adjunct Professor; *b:* Korsnas, Finland; *m:* Thelma M. Barth; *c:* Melvin, Darrell; *ed:* Cntrl Bible Coll (ThB) Theology 1951; Reformed Presbyn Theo Sem (MDiv) Pastoral Stud 1966; Du Quesne Univ (MA) His 1972; North Cntrl Bible Coll Pastoral Stud Diploma 1949; 3 Credits Villanova Univ; *cr:* Mt Zion Full Gospel Church Pastor 1952; Mc Keesport Assembly of God Asst Pastor 1952-53; Ellwood City Assembly of God Pastor 1953-60; Coraopolis Assembly of God Pastor 1960-69; Valley Forge Chrstn Coll Prof Div Chr 1969-; *ai:* ETS 1975-; Soc Pent Stud 1978-, Mbrshp Comm; Red Hill, PA Boro Cncl 1974-78, Pres; Ed Qualifications Comm 1959-, Chr; PA-DE Dist Assemblies of God; Several Chptrs & Books; *office:* Valley Forge Christian Coll 1401 Charlestown Rd Phoenixville PA 19460

HARTWICK, PATRICK JAMES, Assoc Prof of Spec Education; *b:* Buffalo, NY; *m:* Christine R. Brinkworth; *c:* Alexandria, Jonathan; *ed:* Buffalo St Coll (BS) Exceptional Ed, Elem Ed 1978, (MSEd) Exceptional Ed 1984; WV Univ (EDD) Spec Ed 1987; *cr:* New Medico Rehabilitation Ctr Ed Coord, Tchr 1988-90; SUNY Asst Prof 1990-93; Daemen Coll Assoc Prof, Chair 1993-; *ai:* Ed Policy Comm Chair; Kappa Delta Pi Adv; NY Chptr of Amer Assn on Mental Retardation Pres; Coll Human Subject Rsrch Comm; AAMR 1984-, NYS Pres, VP, Treas; CEC 1986-; NYS Head Injury Assn 1988-; St Rsrch Grant; Three Chptrs, Two Articles Pub; *office:* Daemen Coll 4380 Main St Amherst NY 14226

HARTWIG, MICHAEL J., Ethics Professor; *b:* Dallas, TX; *ed:* Univ of Dallas (BA) Theology, Philosophy 1977; Gregorian Univ (STL) Theology 1980; Southern Meth Univ (PHD) Rel Ethics 1991; *cr:* Holy Trinity Seminary Vice Rector 1983-87; Univ of Dallas Adj Fac 1983-86; Eastern CT St Univ Asst 1989-91; Albertus Magnus Coll Asst Prof, Assoc Dean 1991-; *ai:* Adv to Gay, Straight, Bi Stu Union; Amer Acad of Rel 1985-; Cath Theological Soc 1992-; Soc for Scientific Stud of Sexuality 1995-; Yale-Mellon Flwshp 1995-; Articles Pub; Papers Given at Prof Meetings; *office:* Albertus Magnus Coll 700 Prospect St New Haven CT 06511

HARTY, LARRY DUANE, English Teacher; *b:* Richmond, IN; *m:* Patricia Mary Wagner; *c:* Abigail, Alexander, Stephanie; *ed:* Ball St Univ (BS) Eng & Speech 1961-65, (MA) Eng 1965-68; Attnd Miami U, Wright St U, OH Weselyan; 30 Additional Hrs; *cr:* Franklin City Schls Tchr 1965-; *ai:* Frosh Class Adv; Saturday Schl Supvr; NEA, OEA, SWEA & FEA 1965-; *office:* Franklin Sr HS 750 E 4th St Franklin OH 45005

HARTZ, JANET MORROW, English Teacher; *b:* Brooklyn, NY; *m:* John; *c:* John, Kerry; *ed:* SUNY at Cortland (BA) Elem Ed, Early Sec Eng 1969; SUNY at Stonybrook (MA) Lbrl Stud 1973; *cr:* Robert Moses Jr HS Tchr 1969-75; Peter J. Brennan Jr HS Tchr 1978-79; North Babylon HS Tchr 1981-; *ai:* Acad Team Adv; NCTE; NY St Cncl of Eng Tchrs; NYSTU; NY Times Writing Contest First Place Winner 1995; *office:* North Babylon HS 1 Phelps Ln North Babylon NY 11703*

HARTZEL, NORMAN D., Math Teacher; *b:* Sellersville, PA; *m:* Judy; *c:* Nathan, Jonathan, Kristin Pepper; *ed:* West Chester Univ (BS) Math 1966; Temple Univ (MED) Math 1970; *office:* Souderton HS 41 N School Ln Souderton PA 18964

HARTZEL, PAUL FRANKLIN,JR., High School Drafting Teacher; *b:* Danville, PA; *m:* Sandra Hopkins; *c:* Adam, Karla, Tiffany; *ed:* CA St Coll (BS) Industrial Arts Ed 1972; Troy St Univ (MS) Spcl Ed 1974; Courses in Ed Admin & Behavoral Scis; *cr:* Dale E Ranck Funeral Home Staff Mem 1968-72; US Air Force SSgt Hq AFROTC 1972-76; Williamsport Area HS Drafting Tchr 1976-; W Branch Motor Boat Assn Gas Dock Proprietor 1985-; *ai:* Adv: Natl Engrng Design Challenge, Petros & Class of 1980; NEA 1976-; Williamsport Ed Assn 1976-, Ed; PA Ed Assn 1976-; Deputy Civil Defense Dir 1976-78; Amer Legion Post 71 1976-; Cntrl PA Conf United Meth 1978-, Certfd Lay Speaker; Dietrick Lamade Lodge F & AM 1978-, Past Master & Sec; Amer Red Cross, Retired 1990 22 Yrs Vol Svc; Small Beginning Day Care 1996, Bd of Dirs; *office:* Williamsport Area HS 2990 W 4th St Williamsport PA 17701

HARVATH, LESLIE MARK, History & World Cultures Tchr; *b:* Greensburg, PA; *m:* Jane Ann Mizikar; *c:* Schuyler Edan; *ed:* Duquesne Univ (BS) Ed 1969, (MED) US His Ed 1973; Penn St Univ 6 Hrs; Univ of Pittsburgh 3 Hrs; *cr:* Norwin HS Soc Stud Tchr 1969-; *ai:* Head Bsbl Coach; Scndry Advy Comm & Rodgers Schlsp Comm Mem; NEA 1969-; PA Bsbl Coaches Assn; Henry C. Frick Educl Schlsp; Free-lance Writer of Sports & Features; *home:* RR 2 Box 328 Jeannette PA 15644

HARVEY, AMINIFU R., Assistant Professor; *b:* Jersey City, NJ; *c:* Malkia, Safiya; *ed:* St Peter's Coll (BA) Sociology 1966; Univ Southern CA (MSA) Soc Work 1972; Howard Univ (DSW) Soc Work 1983; Dept of Hlth & Welfare Flwshp Tulane Univ 1976; *cr:* CA St Univ at Chico Asst Prof 1974-78; Univ DC Adj Assoc Prof 1982-85; MAAT Ctr Exec Dir 1986-; Univ MD at Baltimore Asst Prof 1992-; *ai:* NASW, CSWE 1970-; NABSW 1970-, Natl Assoc SW Awd; Coll Acad Schlsp; Martin Luter King Fellow, Woodrow Wilson Fnd; Cncl on Soc Work Ed Flwshp; 3 Books; Articles; *office:* Univ Of MD At Baltimore 525 W Redwood St Baltimore MD 21201

HARVEY, CRAIG STEPHEN, Director of Bands; *b:* Washington, DC; *m:* Karen Renee Koch; *ed:* Frostburg St Coll (BS) Music Ed 1984; Working on MS in Music Ed Towson St Univ; *cr:* Fallston HS Band Di Baltimore Colts Band Musical Dir 1989-92; Fallston HS Band *ai:* 3 Concert Bands; Competitive Marching Band; Jazz, Ensembles; Piano Labs; Music for Listening; Freelance M Baltimore-WA Metropolitan Area; Work as Clinician & Gu Studio Musician; Marching Bands Drill Designer & Arrang Fallston HS 2301 Carrs Mill Rd Fallston MD 21047*

HARVEY, DIANE CALIO, Spanish & Latin Teacher; *b:* Ph PA; *m:* Robert J.; *c:* Joseph R., Christopher J.; *ed:* West Chester Scndry Ed, Sp, Lat 1967; Post Grad Stud Supvr Rowan Coll; *c* HS Span, Latin Tchr 1967-; *ai:* Newspaper, Span Club Adv; Fo Tchrs Assn 1968-; *office:* Palmyra HS 5th St & Delaware Ave F 08065*

HARVEY, GARY M., Fifth Grade Teacher; *b:* New York Ci Beryl Stair; *ed:* SUNY at Fredonia (BS) Elem Ed 1985; St B Univ (MS) Rdng 1990; *cr:* North Hill Elem Schl Fifth Grd Tchr Soc Stud, Ed Fair Comms; Dist Rubrics & Stans Team; Olean T NEA 1985-, Bldg Rep; Phi Delta Kappa 1989-, Sec; Bartlett Awd 1985; Outstdng Achvmt Awd Dept of Rdng 1990; Eagles of Yr 1992; *office:* North Hill Elem Schl 102 W Forest Ave 14760

HARVEY, GLORIA MARIE, Music Teacher; *b:* Baltimor Leonard Frieson, Jr.; *ed:* Morgan St Coll (BS) Music Ed 1970; Univ (MS) Music Ed 1977; Addl 25 Credit Hrs; *cr:* Deep Cree Music Tchr 3 Yrs; North Point Jr HS Music Tchr 2 Yrs; South Dept Chprsn, Team Ldr, Music Tchr 23 Yrs; *ai:* Gospel Choir Musician; MSTA, NEA 1970-; TABCO 1970-, Tchr Recogn 1995; *office:* Southwest Acad for Arts & Sci 6200 Johnr Baltimore MD 21207*

HARVEY, JAYNE HAUKE, 5th Grade Classroom Teacher; *b:* OH; *m:* Stephen L.; *ed:* Miami Univ (BS) Ed 1971; 46 Addl Se Univ of Cincinnati, Coll of Mount St Joseph, Univ of Dayton; *cr:* Northeastern Schls 3-5 Grd Non-Graded Tchr 1971-75, 5th 1975-; *ai:* Clermont Co Sci Ldrshp Team; Judy Stanforth M Trustee; NEA, OEA 1971-; Delta Kapa Gamma 1988-; Correspo *office:* Clermont Northeastern Schl 5347 Hutchinson Rd Batavia

HARVEY, RONALD WILLIAM, German Teacher; *b:* Hunting Joyce Johanning; *c:* Erin; *ed:* Manchester Coll (BA) Ger & Eng St Univ (MA) Comparative Lit 1976; Attnd Phillipps Univ Pickerington HS Ger Tchr 1976-, Foreign Lang Dept Chm 198 Club Spon; Prins Advy Comm; NEA, OEA, OFLA, AATG 1976- Heritage Assn 1978-, Bd of Dirs; Peace Action of Lancaster 199 VP; Jennings Scholar 1986-87; Tchr of Yr 1987 & 1991; Dist 1991; *office:* Pickerington HS 300 Opportunity Way Pickeri 43147

HARVEY, STEVEN CRAIG, Biological Sciences Instructor; OH; *m:* Ann T.; *c:* Craig, Talley, Becky, Andrew; *ed:* Marshall Bio Sci 1976, (MS) Bio Sci 1981; Trinity Seminary (MDiv) T Stud 1987; *cr:* OH Univ Southern Campus Bio Sci & Chem Ins *ai:* Chaplain HS Ath; IM Ath; Stu Adv & Tutor; Ironton City Schl Pres; Lawrence Cty Citizen of the Yr 1989; *office:* Ohio Un Branch 1804 Liberty Ave Ironton OH 45638

HARVEY, TORANCE NEIL, Guidance Counselor; *b:* York, PA Ann Keeny; *ed:* York Coll of PA (BS) Bus Mgmt 1984, (BS) Bus Western MD Coll (MS) Cnslr Ed 1991; West Chester Univ Drive Ed Cert 1994; *cr:* Solanco HS Bus Tchr 1985-86; Red Lion HS 1986-94; York Suburban HS Guidance Cnslr 1994-; *ai:* Project Adv; Var Sftbl Coach; PA Cnslr Assn, York Cty Cnslr Assn 1994- Lodge #649 1994-; *office:* York Suburban Sr HS 1800 Hollywoo PA 17403

HARVEY, WILLIAM SCOTT, Social Studies Teacher; *b:* K WV; *m:* Tina Denise Mason; *ed:* WV Univ (BS) Ed 1986; 30 Pos at Garrett Comm Coll & Frostburg St Univ; *cr:* Southern Garre Ed Tchr 1987-90; Southern Garrett MS Soc Stud Tchr 1991-; *ai:* Coach; *office:* Southern Garrett County MS 605 Harvey W Oakland MD 21550

HARWELL, LYNNE CAROL, English Teacher; *b:* Chicag Emory Univ (BA) Eng & His 1985; Rutgers Univ (MA) Eng Northfield Mt Herman Schl Admissions Ofcr 1986-87; DeLaSall Placement Coord & Tchr 1987-90; Fieldston Schl Dean of Stdn 1990-; *ai:* Stdnts Unified for Multicultural Efforts Adv; Mu Pgms Dir; Natl Assn of Ind Schls 1991-, Admissions & Mrktg Co *office:* Fieldston Schl Fieldstone Rd Bronx NY 10471*

HARWIN, MARIE L. JABLONSKI, Art Teacher; *b:* Newar Lenard C. (dec); *ed:* Newark St Coll (BS) Fine Arts 1953; Mar Beyond Masters Equivalency; *cr:* Roselle Park Bd of Ed Jr HS Tchr 1953-54; Union Twp Bd of Ed K-8 Grd Art Tchr 1954-; *ai:* Curr Permanent Action Comm; Festival of Arts; Displays Ye Participation in Municipal, St Environmental, Drug Abuse Prever Prevention, Dental Hlth, Energy Contests & Projects; Work w Scouts; UTTA, UCEA, NJEA, NEA 1954-; NJAEA; Alpha De 1966-, Treas 4 Yrs, Sargent at Arms 2 Yrs, 25 Yr Silver Mbr Montclair Art Museum; Morris Art Museum 1994-; 25, 30, 35 & Svc Awds By Union Twp Bd of Ed; 25 Yrs of Svc Awd by Union Assn; Attendance Awd; Cooperating Tchr for Kean Coll, Mo Univ, William Patterson Coll; *office:* Washington Elem Washington Ave Union NJ 07083*

HASE, JAMES ROBERT,SR., United States History Te Cleveland, OH; *m:* Gail Ellen Pannent; *c:* Lauren, James, Jr.; *e* Univ (BS) Comprehensive Soc Stud, His 1975 Magna Cur Cleveland St Univ (MS) Rdng Specialist 1981; Post Grad Hrs, Green St Univ, OH Univ, Baldwin Wallace Coll, Kent St Univ, Coll, & Coll of Mt St Joseph; *cr:* West Muskingum Schls Lang Stud 1975-77; North Olmsted City Schls Summer Schl His Tchr of Mt St Joseph Ed Coll Instr 1986-87; North Ridgeville City Sch Tchr 1977-; *ai:* Head Ftbl & Girls Track Coach; Building Inv Team; Soc Stud Curr Comm; MS Planning Comm; WA DC Field Stud Competency Tutor; Inclusion Comm, Soc Studies Dept He Team Facilitator; Presenter at OH MS Assn St Conf & MS Nut Symposium in Boulder, CO; NEA 1975-, Building Rep 1980, Mi 1987-88; Natl MS Assoc 1993-; Hot Stove Bsbl 1971-, Coach & 1971-; OH HS Ath Assn 1975-; OH Bsbl Umpires Assn 197 Ridgeville City Schls Tchr of Yr 1978; North Ridgeville Jaycee Yr 1978; North Ridgeville UNICEF Coord 1977-, 4th Highest C in Natn 1995; Received Two Group & Seven Individual Prof Gra Marquis Who's Who In Amer Ed 1993; St of OH Commendat Track Coach 1994; Commendation for Ed Excellence OH St Assembly 1995; Two Natl Citations from UNICEF 1991 & 199 North Ridgeville City Schls 35895 Center Ridge Rd North Ridge 44039

HASEBROOK, CHRISTOPHER L., English & Speech Tea Westerville, OH; *m:* Melissa E. Johnson; *c:* Alexander C., Mackenzie E.; *ed:* OH St Univ (BA) Comprehensive Comm 19 Educl Qualitative Rsrch 1994; *cr:* Linworth Alt Prgm 9th-12th Speech Tchr 1988-; *ai:* NEA 1988-; Worthington Ed Ass ns Team 2 Yrs; Articles Pub; *office:* Linworth Alternative HS ublin Granville Rd Worthington OH 43085

Y, PHILLIP A., Professor of Anthropology; *b:* North a, NY; *ed:* SUC Geneseo (BA) Anthropology 1974; SUNY A) Anthropology 1977, (PHD) Anthropology 1984; *cr:* Niagara Coll Instr 1984-86, Asst Prof 1987-88, Assoc Prof 1989-93, Prof NEA 1984-, Rank & File; Amer Schl Classical Stud Athens Amer Paleontological Soc 1995-; NY Cncl on Evolutionary Ed Mem 1985-86; Numerous Articles Pub; Pres Awd for Tchng Excl Y Chancellors Awd for Tchng Excl 1993; NISOD Natl Tchng *office:* Niagara County Comm Coll 3111 Saunders Settlement n NY 14132

NE, RODMAN DAN, Junior High School Teacher; *b:* Lower A; *m:* Lynn Bowers; *ed:* Cedarville Coll (BS) PE 1990; *ai:* Var sst Indoor Soccer, Jr High Bsktbl Coaches; *home:* 3534 Ln Brookhaven PA 19015

NE, SHARON OCONNOR, Second Grade Teacher; *b:* Troy, illiam; *c:* Alonna Susanne, Christopher William; *ed:* SUNY at n NY (B) Ed N-6 1972, (MS) Ed N-6 1976; 30 Credit Hrs Beyond Ed; *cr:* Elizabethtown-Lewis Cntrl Schl 2nd & 3rd Grd Tchr NHS, Yrbk & Jr Class Adv; NYSUT 1972-; AFT 1972-; ELCSTA SA 1980-; Math Wkshps for BOCES; *office:* Elizabethtown Schl Court St Elizabethtown NY 12932

BARBARA LUNDBERG, 2nd Grade Teacher; *b:* Lanes Mills, harles C.; *c:* Dwight Kline, Paul Kline, Jeanne Iddings, Mark y Kline; *ed:* Clarion Univ (BS) Elem Ed 1964; Penn St Univ Ed 1969; +30 Credits Post Grad Work; *cr:* DuBois Area Schls chr 1964-; *ai:* Supervised Stu Tchrs from Clarion Univ 1972-85; Bd of Mental Hlth DRMC 1978-82; NEA, PSEA & DAEA 1964-; pa Gamma 1975-, Recording Sec, Corresponding Sec; Historical *home:* 1740 Meadow St Brockway PA 15824

DANA, Social Studies Teacher; *b:* Flushing, NY; *ed:* Fordham His 1990; Queens Coll (MS) Scndry Ed, Soc Scis 1995; *cr:* Jr oc Stud Tchr 1991-; *ai:* Coach Debate Team; *office:* Stephen HS #157 6400 102nd St Flushing NY 11374

, ALYCE L. HILTON, First Grade Teacher; *b:* Camden, NJ; *c:* Karen L. Haskins Davis, Keith T., Kenneth W.; *ed:* Glassboro St K-8th Grd Elem Ed 1978; 3 Grad Credits; *cr:* Camden Bd of Ed 1972-78, Summer Schl Instrl Asst 1972-78, 1st-2nd & 4th Grd Sub Tchr 1978-79, 1st Grd Tchr 1979-; *ai:* African Amer His m Comm Active Mem; NEA 1979-; NJEA 1979-; Camden Ed -, Assn Rep, Rep of Month; Camden Bible Tabernacle 1971-, Yth , 1982-, Pres of the Missionary Bd, 1995-, Asst Treas of Church; Schl 1st Grd Level Chprsn for 12 Yrs; Tchr of Yr Davis Schl by Governor Florio; *office:* H H Davis Elementary School 34th St Camden NJ 08105

, MARION BADER, Physics & Earth Science Tchr; *b:* Munich, *m:* Leland Royce; *ed:* SUNY Morrisville Coll (AS) Chem 1981; rtland St (BS) Chem 1986, (MS) Sci Ed 1988; Comm within *r:* Owen D. Young Schl Sci Tchr 1988-89; Hamilton Cntrl Schl 987-; *ai:* Sr Class Adv 1993-; NYSUT 1986-; *office:* Hamilton hl W Kendrick Ave Hamilton NY 13346

, MERLE LOWELL, English Teacher; *b:* Cuba, NY; *m:* Karen mma, Samuel, Eli, Alice; *ed:* Jamestown Comm Coll (AA) Hum Y at Oswego (BA) Eng, Writing Arts 1983; St Bonaventure Univ Lit 1986; Critical Skills Classroom; Character Ed; Inst of unications; *cr:* St Bonaventure Univ Adj Prof 1984-89; Comm Coll Adj Prof 1985-89; St Johnsbury Acad Tchr 1989-; Writing Lab; Wireless Radio Club Adv; Tech Long Range Comm; T-Ball Coach; NCTE, ASCD; *office:* St Johnsbury Acad Saint Johnsbury VT 05819*

T, ETHEL MAE, Senior High English Teacher; *b:* Akron, OH; Nazarene Coll (BA) Eng 1967; Akron Univ (MA) Lit 1972; *cr:* Hills Bd Ed HS Eng Tchr 1967-71; Cuy Valley Chrstn Ac HS Eng -79; Rex Humbard Fnd Writer, Proofreader & Tutor 1979-81; Chrstn Ac HS Eng Tchr 1981-; *ai:* Head Dept of Eng; Ski Club ished Pamphlet Entitled Writing A Research Paper; Published 21 otional Articles, 2 Poems, 1 Short Story & 1 Non- Fiction *ffice:* Cuyahoga Valley Christian Acad 4687 Wyoga Lake Rd Stow

GER, PATRICIA A., English Teacher; *b:* Buffalo, NY; *m:* ; *c:* Amy Catherine, Kristie Lynn, Matthew Samuel; *ed:* Coll of BS) Eng 1969; St Univ (MS) Eng 1971; *cr:* Tonananda Jr HS g Tchr 1969-71; Orchard Park HS Scndry Eng Tchr 1984-; *ai:* ub Bus Mgr; NYSTA 1984-.

ROBERTA GENE, Mathematics Teacher; *b:* West Orange, NJ; rs Univ (BA) Math 1988; Montclair St Univ (MA) Learning s 1996; *cr:* George Washington Jr HS Math Tchr 1988-; *ai:* saic Cty E A, Wayne E A 1988-; *office:* George Washington Jr HS Rd Wayne NJ 07470

WILMA HAHN, English Professor; *b:* West Haven, CT; *m:* William; *c:* Lizbeth, Michael, Andrew; *ed:* Univ of CT (BA) Eng Coll (MAT) Eng 1975; Univ of WI 15 Grad Credits; Univ of CT edits; *cr:* Old Saybrook HS Eng & Civics Tchr 1947-51; CT Coll chl Tchr 1957; Ledyard Jr HS Tchr 1974-75; Mitchell Coll Assoc -; *ai:* Field Hockey, Bsktbl, Sftbl Coach; Coll Fgn Lang Adv 4 Adv 10 Yrs; Phi Kappa Theta Adv; Theatre Club; AFT 1976-, Sec; CCCC 1976-; AARP; 2nd Cong Church 1955, Deacon 2 Terms, mm; Amer Field Svc 1970-; PTA; Ed Books; Articles Pub; *office:* Coll 437 Pequot Ave New London CT 06320*

L, JEAN TREVERTON, Assoc Prof Food & Nutrition; *b:* , PA; *m:* Gordon E.; *c:* Karen Hoeman, Megan Erickson; *ed:* Univ (BS) Food, Nutrition 1951; Kent St Univ (MS) Food, 1974; OH St Univ Post Grad Stud, Kellogg Residency Med 1980; *cr:* Trumbull Meml Hosp Schl of Nrsng Tchng Dietitian Clinical Dietitian 1975-79; Gastroenterology Clinic Consulting 1975-83; Youngstown St Univ Assoc Prof, Coordinated Prgm in Coord 1975-; PA St Univ Visiting Lecturer 1980-84; *ai:* Stdnts in Adv; Coll of Hlth, Human Svcs Lib Comm; Grad Fac Policy hys Therapy Stu Selection Interviewing Comm; Hospitality ac Search Comm; Advy, Admissions, Clinical Coordinating PD; Amer Dietetic Assn 1974-; OH Dietetic Assn 1974-, Pub , Awds, Schlsps Comms Chair; Mahoning Vly Dietetic Assn es, Sec, Adv, Media Rep; OH Dietetic Edctrs of Practitioners air; Amer Soc of Parenteral, Enteral Nutrition 1990-; Mahoning Area Hlth Ed Network 1991-, Bd Mem; Women's, Infant's, WIC Advy Bd 1987-; Numerous Peer Reviewed Articles in Prof ons; Grants: MSAHEN 1980, 1993-95, Ross Labs 1991, OH Dept 4-95, Univ Rsrch 1982; *office:* Youngstown St Univ 410 Wick Ave wn OH 44555

MAN, SAN D. SCHOENFELD, Art Teacher; *b:* Brooklyn, NY; *ed:* Montclair St (BA) Fine Arts 1971; Kean Coll (MA) Lbrl Arts n Coll Eng Cert 9-12 1990; *cr:* Union Cty Regnl Dist #1 Art Tchr *i:* Art Club, Writers' Wkshp, SAGES, Class of 1997 Adv; nt Specialist ACT Prgm; AFT 1981-; Arts for Every Kid Grant 1995; Governor's Recognition Tchr of Yr 1989; RI Schl of Design Honoree 1985; *home:* 976 Mountain Ave Berkeley Heights NJ 07922*

HASSEMAN, BRIAN LEE, High School Guidance Counselor; *b:* Canton, OH; *m:* Janice Sayre; *c:* Brent L., Traci L.; *ed:* Miami Univ (BA) His 1966, (MS) Pol Sci; Xavier Univ (MED) Guidance & Counseling 1980; Impact Trng, Drug Counseling & Intervention; *cr:* Fairfield Jr High Classroom Tchr 1966-69; Fairfield Sr High Tchr & Cnslr 1969-83; Fairfield Frosh Guidance Cnslr 1983-; *ai:* Improvement, Impact Drug Comms; Intervention Assistance Team; Critical Thinking Chm; NEA 1966-, Ambassador Awd; OE, SWOEA 1966-; *office:* Fairfield City Schls 211 Donald Dr Fairfield OH 45014

HASSENPLUG, MARY P., English Teacher; *b:* Pittsburgh, PA; *ed:* Bloomsburg Univ (BS) Ed 1984-; Thesis Shy of Masters Degree; *cr:* Morris Knolls HS Eng Tchr 1984-87; High POint Regnl HS Eng Tchr 1987-; *ai:* Var Sftbl Coach; NCTE, NEA 1984-; NJCTE 1994-; HPEA 1987-; Tchr of Yr 1994; *office:* High Point Reg HS 299 Pidgeon Hill Rd Sussex NJ 07461

HASSER, JULIA M., Mathematics Teacher; *b:* Paterson, NJ; *ed:* Richard Stockton Coll (BA) Math 1989; Rutgers Univ (EDM) Educl Admin 1992; *cr:* Hillsborough HS Math Tchr 1989-91; Amsterdam Elem Math Tchr 1991-92; Porter MS Math Tchr 1992-93; Clermont Northeastern HS Math Tchr 1993-; *ai:* Yrbk Adv & Fastpitch Sftbl Coach 1993-; *office:* Clermont Northeastern HS 5327 Hutchinson Rd Batavia OH 45103

HASSETT, ROBERT ANDREW, Science & Biology I & II Tchr; *b:* Cambridge, MA; *m:* Janine M. Morris; *c:* Robert, Emily; *ed:* Boston Coll (BS) Bio, Scndry Ed 1973; Suffolk Univ (MED) Admin, Supervision; 30 Addl Credits in Psych-Physiological, Neuro, Animal Behavior, Schl Law; *cr:* Framingham North HS Bio I Tchr 1973-74; Melrose HS Bio I & II Tchr 1974-75; Melrose Jr HS Gen Sci Tchr 1975-77; Melrose HS Bio I, II, AP Tchr 1977-; Melrose Wakefield Hosp Patient Care Technicians Tchr; Newbury Coll Anatomy & Physiology Tchr 1994-; *ai:* Stu Govt Supvr 14 Yrs; Sr Class Adv 1 Yr; SADD 10 Yrs; Bus, Investment Clubs 3 Yrs; Jr Class Adv 1 Yr; Pol Club 1 Yr; Fac Comm Chprsn; Bloodmobiles Spon 28 Yrs; Comm Svc Club Founder, St Grant 3 Yrs; MTA, MEA 1973-; Bridge 2 Yrs, Treas; Commonwealth of MA House of Reps Recognition for Tireless Devotion to Stdnts; *home:* 37 Damon Ave Melrose MA 02176

HASSMANN, JONI ALEXANDER, Kindergarten Teacher; *b:* Mansfield, OH; *m:* Robert; *c:* Morgan, Abbey, Ryan; *ed:* OH St Univ (BS) Elem Ed 1984; Ashland Univ (MS) Curr, Inst 1996; *cr:* Lincoln Hts Elem Schl Fourth Grd Tchr 1985-91; Madison South Schl Kndgtn Tchr 1993-; *ai:* OEA, NEA 1985-, Bldg Rep; Literacy Grant Altrusa 1995; *office:* Madison South Elem Schl 700 S Illinois Ave Mansfield OH 44907*

HASTINGS, DEBORAH KAY (BRITTON), Consultant & Teacher of Gifted; *b:* Springfield, OH; *m:* Wayne L.; *c:* David, Elizabeth; *ed:* OH Univ (BS) Elem Ed 1971; Kent St Univ (MED) Gifted Ed 1985; Gifted Ed Addl Hrs; *cr:* Alger Jr HS Sci, PE Tchr 1969-70; Canton Local Schls 6th Grd Tchr 1972-75; Sandy Valley Local Gifted Ed Coord, Tchr 1984-87; Graham Local Schls 5th-8th Grd Gifted Ed Tchr 1987-88; Urbana City Schls Gifted Ed Coord, Tchr 1988-; *ai:* Amer Assn Univ Women, Bd Mem; OH Assn Gifted Children 1984-; Consortium Coord for Gifted 1988-; Gifted Ed Topics Speaker; St Grant for Gifted Children 1994; PTA Educator of Yr 1993; Ed Excl 1991; Graham Local Schls Tchr of Yr 1994; Who's Who in Amer Ed 1993; *office:* North Elem Schl 626 Russell St Urbana OH 43078

HASTINGS, KATHERINE KLINEFELTER, High School Math Teacher; *b:* Washington, DC; *m:* Timothy; *c:* Kimberly, Jacqueline; *ed:* 6 Hrs Western MD Coll; 21 Hrs Loyola Coll; 3 Hrs Towson St Univ; *cr:* Balto Cty Bd of Ed Tchr 1980-84; Seton HS Tchr 1984-88; Mt de Sales Acad Dept Chprsn 1988-95; Walkersville HS Tchr 1995-; *ai:* NCTM, MCTM 1979-; RGEF Comm 1993-, Sec; Alpha Gamma Delta 1979-, Province Dir Arc of Epsilon Pi Undergraduates; *home:* 6225 Pinyon Pine Ct Eldersburg MD 21784

HASTINGS, MARGARET MC CLURE, Second Grade Teacher; *b:* Lebanon, OH; *m:* Robert L.; *c:* Robert R., Trimothy L., Joseph M.; *ed:* Otterbein Coll (BS) Ed K-8 1954; Many CEVS; *cr:* Wilmington Elem Schl Kndgtn Tchr 1954-55; Wahiawa Elem Schl 2nd Grd Tchr 1955-56; Enon Elem Schl 2nd Grd Tchr 1956-57; Bremen Elem Schl Kndgtn-3rd Grd Tchr 1957-59; Lake Park Schl Kndgtn Tchr 1972-74; Montessori Schl Pre Schl-Kndgtn Tchr 1979-81; Powell Elem Schl Kndgtn-2nd Grd Tchr 1984-; *ai:* Positive Kids, Curr Comms; NEA, OEA, NBEA 1984-; Pride of Toledo 1990-; Jennings Schl 1991-; *home:* 1628 Clough St Bowling Green OH 43402

HASTINGS, SALLY HARBAUGH, 8th Grade Language Arts Tchr; *b:* Hanover, PA; *m:* Herbert D.; *c:* Lori Spencer, Jeff Atwell; *ed:* Towson St (BS) Elem Ed 1978; Masters Equivalency, Advanced Prof 1986; 9 Credits 1990-; *cr:* William Paca Elem Schl 4th Grd Tchr 1978-80; Southampton MS 6th Grd Tchr 1981-83, 8th Grd Tchr 1984-88, 7th Grd Tchr 1988-93, 8th Grd Tchr 1993-; *ai:* Human Relations Comm; Schl Newspaper; Schl Photomontage; 8th Grd Play; Spelling Bee Coord; Kappa Delta Pi 1978; Articles Pub; *office:* Southampton MS 1200 Moores Mill Rd Bel Air MD 21014

HATCH, SUSAN JANE, Title I Rdng & Lang Arts Tchr; *b:* Mt Vernon, OH; *m:* Virgil A.; *c:* Jacquelyn, Mark, Bethany; *ed:* Otterbein Coll (BA) Speech Comm, Ed 1979; Ashland Univ Master Curr & Instruction; *cr:* Northridge Local Schls Title I Rdng Tchr 1980-87; North Fork Local Schls Title I Lang Arts, Math Tchr 1993-; *ai:* Mentor Tchr; North Fork Ed Assn; Highwater Congregational Church, Music & Worship Comm & Choir; *home:* 11150 Reynolds Rd Utica OH 43080*

HATCHER, RAYFIELD, Computer Sci & Math Teacher; *b:* Florence, MI; *m:* Christal; *c:* Cheryl; *ed:* Jackson St Univ (BS) Sci, Math Ed 1972; Attnd John Carroll Univ Physic for Tchrs, Cleveland St Univ Ed Admin, Cuyahoga Comm Coll Real Estate Law; *cr:* Addison Jr HS Math, Sci Tchr 1972-76; Jane Addams HS Bio Tchr 1976-79; Newton D. Baker Jr HS Asst Prin, Sci Tchr 1979-84; John Marshall HS Cmptr, Math Tchr 1984-; *ai:* Boys, Girls Bsktbl, Girls Track, Boys Ftbl Coach; Photographic, Cmptr, Chess Club Adv; AFT 1992-, Bldg Chprsn; GCCMT 1972-; Tchr of Yr 1977; Outstdng Tchr of Math, Sci 1978; St Dept Ed Curr Evaluation Team Cmptr Sci Mem; *office:* John Marshall HS 3952 W 140th St Cleveland OH 44111

HATCHER, SHELIA PARKER, Elementary Science Teacher; *b:* Philadelphia, PA; *m:* Frederick Douglas; *c:* Karen Taylor, Lisa, Natasha Parker; *ed:* Essex Cty Coll (AS) Elem Ed 1970; Jersey City St Coll (BA) Elem Ed 1972, (MA) Urban Ed, Supervision 1987; NJ Great Ideas of Sci Prgm 24 Credits Earth Sci; Skygazer Prgm of NJ BISEC Globe Prgm W Chester Univ; Thirteen WNET Natl Tchr Trng Inst Math, Sci, Tech; *cr:* Newark Pub Schls Elem Tchr 1973-91, Elem Sci Tchr 1991-; *ai:* Tech Support Comm; Globe Weather, Environment Club; Outside Living Lab; New Tchrs Mentor; NJSTA 1991-; NTU 1973-; NTA, NEA 1974-; Mamas Inc 1991-; Natl Garden Assn Winner 1993; Natl Garden Assn Bulb Winne 1994; NJ BISEC, PSE&G Environmental Ed Winner; Globe Winner; Article Pub; *office:* Harriet Tubman Elem Schl 504 S 10th St Newark NJ 07103

HATFIELD, BARBARA SCOTT, Assoc Professor of Mathematics; *b:* Richmond, KY; *m:* Steven Hunter; *ed:* Mississippi St Univ (BS) Math 1971; Univ of Southern Mississippi (MED) Scndry Ed 1976; Mississippi St Univ (EDS) Scndry Ed 1980; Univ of KY (PHD) Math 1991; *cr:* Meridian Pub Schls math Tchr 1971-82; Univ of Southern MS Instr 1982-83; Univ of KY Tchng Asst 1983-90; Univ of Rio Grande, Rio Grande Comm Coll Math Prof 1990-; *ai:* Math & Sci Club Co-spon Univ of Rio Grande; Fin Adv Delta Gamma; MAA 1992-; AMA 1984-; NCTM, OCTM 1995-; Delta Kappa Gamma 1981-; *office:* Univ Of Rio Grande 585 E College Ave Rio Grande OH 45674

HATFIELD, DANNY L., Sixth Grade Teacher; *b:* Williamsburg, KY; *m:* Marjorie Young; *c:* Michael; *ed:* Cumberland Coll (BS) Elem Ed 1968; Xavier Univ (MED) Admin 1977; *cr:* Brantner Elem Schl Tchr 1968-88; Glen Este MS Tchr, Team Ldr 1989-; *ai:* Homework, Assignment Comm; NEA, OEA, WCEA 1968-; KY Colonel 1985-; *office:* Glen Este MS 4342 Glen Este Withamsville Rd Cincinnati OH 45245

HATFIELD, JANICE FORD, English Teacher; *b:* Washington, DC; *m:* William Floyd; *c:* Andrew, Leslie; *ed:* Concord Coll (BS) Scndry Ed 1962; Bowling Green St Univ (MA) Eng 1965; WV Univ 36 Hrs in PHD Prgm Eng 1977-80; *cr:* Alderson HS Tchr 1963-64; Beverly HS Tchr 1964-65; Charles Town HS Tchr 1965-67; WV Univ Instr 1967-69; Marshall Univ Instr 1969-70; King's Coll Tchr 1974-75; NC St Univ Instr 1975-76; WV Univ Tchng Fellow 1977-80; Fairmont St Coll Part-time Instr 1980-81; West Green Schls Tchr 1981-; *ai:* WAC & PCRP Coord; NHS, Lit Magazine Adv; Strategic Planning, Assessment Comms; NEA 1981-; WPCTE 1988-; NCTE 1975-, Convention Participant; ACUPWET 1991-, Exec Cncl; Tchng Fellow WVU 1977-80; Western PA Writing Project Fellow Summer 1993; *office:* West Green Sr HS RD 5 Box 36-A Waynesburg PA 15370

HATHAWAY, MARILYN MANDOFF, Fifth Grade Teacher; *b:* North Conway, NH; *ed:* Univ of ME at Orono (BA) Elem Ed 1971; *cr:* Strong Elem 1st Grd Tchr 1971-87; Benton Elem 5th Grd Tchr 1988-; *ai:* MTA, NEA 1971-; Local SAD #49 1987-.*

HATHAWAY, SANDRA DEPPEN, Math Teacher; *b:* Allentown, PA; *m:* William W. Jr.; *ed:* Kutztown St Coll (BS) Ed & Math 1973, (MA) Math 1977; E Stroudsburg Univ 15 Post Grad Credits in Ed; *cr:* Parkland Schl Dist Math Tchr 1974-; *ai:* Math Contest & Competition Adv; NEA 1974-; Cedar Crest Coll Math Conn; Eisenhower Grant Presenter; Nom Presidential Awds for Excl Math & Sci Tchng 1995; *office:* Springhouse Jr HS 1200 Springhouse Rd Allentown PA 18104*

HATHAWAY, VICKY GROUT, English & Theater Arts Teacher; *b:* Denton, TX; *m:* Robert; *c:* Kyle, Elann; *ed:* Phoenix Coll (AA) Med Lab Tech 1977; Univ of RI (BA) Eng 1992, (BS) Scndry Ed 1992; Working Toward Masters Eng Ed; *cr:* AZ Childrens Hosp Med Lab Tech 1977-78; Porter Memrl Hosp Med Lab Tech 1978-79; Martin Marietta Comp Trainee 1979-80; Portsmouth HS Eng & Theatre Tchr 1993-; *ai:* Writers Wkshp Adv; Fine Arts & Lang Arts Curr Cncl; Portsmouth Arts Planning Team; NCTE 1991-; Phi Kappa Phi 1991-; Phi Beta Kappa 1992-; NEA 1993-; Portsmouth United Meth 1983-, Lay Ldr; *office:* Portsmouth HS Education Ln Portsmouth RI 02871

HATT, MICHELE ELAINE, English Teacher; *b:* Reading, PA; *ed:* Penn St Univ (BA) Speech Comm 1988; Kutztown Univ Cert Scndry Eng Ed 1992; *cr:* Berks Cty Schls Sub Tchr 1992-93; Reading Area Comm Coll Eng Tutor 1991-; Reading HS Eng Tchr 1993-; *ai:* Head Field Hockey Coach; PA HS Field Hockey Coaches Assoc 1995-; Berks Cty Field Hockey Coaches Assoc 1994-; PSEA, NEA, NCTE 1991-; Penn St Chptr of Alumni Soc 1994-, Sec; *office:* Reading HS 13th & Douglass Sts Reading PA 19604*

HATTALA, KATHERINE JANE, English Teacher; *b:* Binghamton, NY; *m:* Carl S.; *c:* Kacy Haskell; *ed:* SUNY at Cortland (BA) Scndry Eng, (MA) Eng 1984; *cr:* Susquehanna Vly Sr HS 11th-12th Grd Eng Tchr 1981-; *ai:* Peer Ldrshp, Class Adv; Discipline Comm; NEA 1981-; Tchr of Yr Awd; *home:* 995 Park Ave Binghamton NY 13903

HATTON, DAWN MARIE (RICE), 5th Grade Teacher; *b:* Columbus, OH; *m:* Gregory Joseph; *c:* Kyle Gregory; *ed:* Miami Univ (BS) Elem Ed 1988; OH St Univ (MA) Early Mid Chldhd Ed 1995; *cr:* Prairie Lincoln Elem Schl 5th Grd Tchr 1988-90; North Franklin Elem Schl 5th Grd Tchr 1990-92, 4th Grd Tchr 1992-93, 5th Grd Tchr 1993-; *ai:* NEA, OEA, SWEA 1988-; *office:* North Franklin Elem Schl 1122 N Hague Ave Columbus OH 43204

HATZFELD, JILL ANNE, Biology & Chemistry Teacher; *b:* N Massapequa, NY; *m:* Mark Castiglia; *ed:* Hofstra Univ (BA) bio 1990; SUNY at Stony Brook (MA) Lbrl Stud 1996; *cr:* Mac Arthur HS Bio, Chem Tchr 1990-; *ai:* Sci Olympiad Club Coach; Renaissance, Summer Schl Comm; Levittown Union of Tchrs, NYSUT, AFT 1990-; *office:* General Douglas Mac Arthur HS Old Jerusalem Rd Levittown NY 11756

HAUB, CHARLES L., Eng & Pre-College Writing Tchr; *b:* Phila, PA; *c:* Charles, David, Michael; *ed:* Villanova Univ (MA) Philosophy 1970-; Writing Sypmosiums for Personal, Sndry Schl Dev; *cr:* ST John Neuman HS Eng, Bus, Soc Stud Dept's Tchr 1967-; *ai:* Union Rep; Assn Cath Tchrs 1969-, VP; Spruce Hill Comm Assn 1978; Spruce Hill Historical Soc 1986-; Friends of Clark Park 1990-; Francie de Sales Chorale 1987-; *office:* Saint John Neumann HS 2600 Moore St Philadelphia PA 19145

HAUBERT, JOHN ELLIS, 7th Grade Social Studies Tchr; *b:* Akron, OH; *ed:* Univ of Akron (AAS) Comm Svcs Tech, (BA) Soc Stud Comp 1991; *cr:* Sill MS 7th Grd Soc Stud Tchr 1991-; *ai:* 7th Grd Bsktbl Coach 7 Yrs; Asst Girls Var Track 7 Yrs; Var Ftbl, Soccer, Bsktbl Announcer 3 Yrs; Soc Stud Comm 1 Yr; NEA, OEA, CFEA 1991-; Cuyahoga Falls Jaycees 1987-, Pres, Mbrshp Comm Svc VP, Jaycee of Yr 1991, Keyman Awd 1988-92, 1994; PTA Tchr of Yr 1994, 1996; *office:* Sill MS 1910 Searl St Cuyahoga Falls OH 44221

HAUBRICH, NANCY, Mathematics Teacher; *b:* New York City, NY; *ed:* Marilac Coll (BS) Math, Natural Sci 1970; Herbert H. Lehman Coll (MS) Math 1976; NY Univ Post-Grad Cmptr Sci; *cr:* St Jude's Schl 7th-8th Brd Math, Sci Tchr 1970-; Aquinas HS Algebra, Geometry, Trig Tchr 1980; Trinity HS Med Drawing, Alg, Geo, Trig Tchr 1980-; *ai:* NCEA 1970-; PCMT 1993-; Holy Spirit Hosp 1980-, Vol; NSF Grant Cmptr Sci NYU; *office:* Trinity HS 3601 Simpson Ferry Rd Camp Hill PA 17011

HAUCK, ANNE BRANCA, Teacher of Gifted & Talented; *b:* New Rochelle, NY; *m:* Carl W. Jr.; *c:* Carl W. III, Ryan M.; *ed:* Coll of MT at St Vincent (BA) Eng 1965; Seton Hall Univ Prof Ed; *cr:* Holy Family Schl Fourth Grd Tchr 1965-67; Collegiate Schl Fourth Grd Tchr 1967-71; Collegiate Schl Eng Tchr, SAT Preparation 1975-76; St Philip the Apostle Schl Tchr of Gifted & Talented Lit, Math 1985-; *ai:* Gifted Prgm, MS, Rdng Curr Coords; Dir of Mentorship Alternate Route Tchr Candidates; Adv Paterson Schl Dist on MS & Gifted Ed; Curr Comm Dioceses of Paterson; Stu Cncl Moderator; NCEA 1985-, Tchr of Yr 1995; ASCD 1994-; FAC 1985-; Innovations, MADD 1989-; St Peters Haven 1994-; Passaic Interfaith Network Hospitality 1995-; MCEA Distinguished Tchr Awd 1995; NJ Non Pub Schl Tchr of Yr 1995; Paterson Diocesan Fed Distingushed Edctr 1995; Natl Tchr Recognition Pres Clinton; NJ Seante Recognition; NJ Bar Assn Awd; Lecturer Monclair St Univ, Johns Hopkins City Tchr Recognition; *home:* 152 Rowland Ave Clifton NJ 07012

HAUCK, CANDACE ANN, Business Education Teacher; *b:* Everett, PA; *ed:* Allegany Comm Coll (AS) Office Tech, Med 1991; Frostburg St Univ (BS) Bus Ed 1993; Attending Frostburg St Univ Masters Ed Interdisciplinary; *cr:* Claysburg-Kimmel HS Bus Ed Tchr 3 Yrs; *ai:* FBLA 3 Yrs, Diversity Club Co-Adv; Dist Strategic Steering Comm; NEA, PSEA 1993-.

HAUCKE-DAVIS, MARY HELEN, French Teacher; *b:* Springfield, OH; *m:* Nicholas E. Davis Jr.; *ed:* Bowling Green St Univ (BS) Fr 1986; Summer Grad Prgms at Univ of Northern IA, Univ of Southern MS; Attnd Cavilam; *cr:* Springfield South HS Fr Tchr 1990-91; Oak Hills HS Fr Tchr 1991-; *ai:* AFS Fac Adv; AATF, OFLA 1995-; Ashland Oil Tchr Achvmt Awd Honorable Mention 1994; *office:* Oak Hills Sr HS 3200 Ebenezer Rd Cincinnati OH 45248*

HAUGH, DONNA ARENDT, 8th Grade Reading Teacher; *b:* Waynesboro, PA; *m:* Anthony A.; *c:* Michelle, Robert, Jeremy; *ed:* Shippensburg Univ (BSEd) Elem Ed, Eng 1983, (MS) Elem Ed, Rdng 1990; *cr:* Waynesboro Schl Dist Substitute Tchr 6 Months; James Buchanan MS Eng Tchr 1/2 Yr, 8th Grd Rdng Tchr 1985-; *ai:* Stu Org Fac Adv 1989-; SAP Care Team 1991-93; Staff Dev Comm 1990-; NEA, TEA 1985-; Eastern Star, Cancer Soc 1983-; *office:* James Buchanan M S 5191 Ft Loudon Rd Mercersburg PA 17236

HAUGHT, MARGARET TANK, Fmly & Consumer Sciences Tchr; *b:* Toledo, OH; *m:* John Edward; *c:* Jennifer Barry, Melissa Ann; *ed:* Bowling Green St Univ (BSEd) Voc Home Ec 1964; Kent St Univ (MA) Individual Life & Family 1994; *cr:* Kirtland HS Jr Sr HS Home Ec Tchr 1964-67; Painesville City Schls 3rd Grd Tchr 1967-70, Sub Tchr 1980-88; Fairport Harbor Harding HS Family & Consumer Scis, Home Ec Tchr 1988-; *ai:* FHA-HERO Adv; OEA, NEA 1964-70, 1988-; AAFCS, AHEA, OVA, AVA, OAFCS, OHEA 1964-; *office:* Fairport Harding Jr-Sr HS 329 Vine St Painesville OH 44077

HAUGNER, PAMELA HUTLEY, Spanish Teacher; *b:* Warren, PA; *ed:* Edinboro Univ of PA (BSEd) Span 1972, (MED) Guid & Cnslng 1976; Attnd Fredonia St Univ of NY, Univ of Pittsburgh, Penn St Univ, Univ of Valencia; *cr:* Oil City HS Span Tchr 8 Yrs; Oil City HS, Jr HS Span & Eng Tchr 1 Yr; Mayville HS Span Tchr 1 Yr; Montessori Schl Span Tchr 1 Yr; Jmst Hs, MS Span Tchr 12 Yrs; *ai:* Span Club Adv; Stu Trips to Mexico & Spain; Discipline, Schl Climate Comms; Natl Jr Hnr Soc Adv Lincoln & WA Schls; NEA 1972-; NYSAFLT 1984-, JTA, CCFLTA, AAUW 1984-; PSEA 1972-; Am Assn of Sec Cnslrs & Prins 1976-; Jmst Women's Club; South Hills Cntry Club; New Comers Org; Vikings, Thule & Moose Clubs; Nom Fr of Yr; Stud Jr Yr Valencia Spain; *office:* Jamestown HS 350 E 2nd St Jamestown NY 14701*

HAUMACHER, JOSEPH CHARLES,II, World & US History Teacher; *b:* Newark, NJ; *m:* Anne Marie Vrubliauskas; *c:* Joseph III; *ed:* Univ of Scranton (BS) Scndry Ed, Soc Stud 1984, (MA) His 1986; Eagleton Inst Rutgers Univ; *cr:* Univ of Scranton Tchng Fellow 1985-86; Woodbridge Twp Sub Tchr 1986-88, North Brunswick HS Soc Stud Tchr 1988; Hillsborough HS Soc Stud Tchr 1988-89; Bishop George Ahr HS Soc Stud Tchr 1989-; *ai:* Adv to Close Up; Eagleton Fellow, Taft Inst Fellow 1993-; Quiet Mans Soc 1984-, Founder, Pres; *office:* Bishop George AHR HS 1 Tingley Ln Edison NJ 08820

HAUMAN, EUGENE, Social Studies Teacher; *b:* Patchogue, NY; *c:* Glenn; *ed:* Clarion Univ (BS) Soc Stud 1966; Adelphi Univ (MA) Scndry Ed 1971; Addl 90 Hrs; *cr:* Centereach HS Tchr 1966-; *ai:* Mid Cntry Tchrs Assn 1966-, Grievance Chm; AFT 1967-; *office:* Centereach HS 43rd St Centereach NY 11720

HAUN, CATHERINE MARY, High School Guidance Counselor; *b:* St Petersburg, FL; *c:* Brian; *ed:* Salem Coll (BS) Elem Ed 1975; WV Univ (MA) Rdng 1979; 30 Addl Hrs; Supvr, Stu Prsnl Svcs Certs; *cr:* Doddridge Cty Schl Elem Rdng Specialist 1975-80; Salem Coll Rdng Specialist, Instr 1981-84; Mt Olive Twp Schls HS Rdng Tchr 1984-95, HS Guid Cnslr 1995-; *ai:* Amnesty Intnl Adv; NHS Fac Selection Comm; NEA, NJ Ed Assn, Educ Assn of Mt Olive Twp 1984-; Tchr of Month 1994; Tchr of Yr 1995; *office:* Mount Olive HS Corey Rd Flanders NJ 07836

HAUN, DIANE PIXLEY, Mathematics Teacher; *b:* Olean, NY; *m:* William; *c:* Karen, Kristi; *ed:* SUNY at Geneseo (BS) Scndry Ed Math 1967; 35 Addl Hrs; *cr:* Holland Cntrl Schl 8th Grd Math Tchr 1967-68; Pioneer HS Math Tchr 1970-; *ai:* NHS Fac Cncl Sec; Class Adv; NCTM 1990-; AMTNYS 1980-; Pioneer Fac Assn 1970-; Delta Kappa Gamma 1991-, Fin Sec; Tchr of Yr 1992; *home:* 257 Route 39 W Arcade NY 14009

HAUNER, TAMMY S., Emotional Support Teacher; *b:* Wheeling, WV; *ed:* Kent St Univ (BS) Spcl Ed & Severe Behavior Disorders 1991; Franciscan Univ at Steubenville Pursing MS in Educl Admin; *cr:* Fox Run Hosp Tchr & Educl Coord 1991-93; South Side HS Emotional Support Tchr 1993-; *ai:* Dance Team & Var Chrldr Coach; Safe Schls Comm; HS Strategic Plan Team Ldr; NEA 1993-; Chi Omega Alumni 1989-, Treas; Peer Mediation & Safe Schls Grants; Fox Run Hosp Quality Ldr of Yr 1992-93; *office:* South Side HS 4949 St Rt 151 Hookstown PA 15050*

HAUPT, SAMUEL W., Supervisor of Guid & Counselor; *b:* Sunbury, PA; *m:* Roberta L. Hoyt-Haupt; *c:* Alison; *ed:* Bloomsburg Univ (BSEd) Bio 1960; Lehigh Univ (MSEd) Cnslng 1967; Syracuse Univ CAS Prgm; *cr:* Weedsport Cntrl Schl Bio Tchr, Cnslr 1960-72; Lewisburg Schl Dist Cnslr 1972-73; Tri-Cities Comm Owner, Mgr 1973-76; Shikellamy Schl Dist Guid Supvr, Cnslr 1976-; *ai:* NHS, Schl & Comm Svc Club Adv; Amer Schl Cnslrs Assn 1989-; PA Schl Cnslrs Assn 1976-; Amer Psychological Assn 1968-; Kiwanis 1981-, Pres, Distngd Pres; Suncom Industries 1985-, VP, Treas.

HAUSCHILD, PATRICIA SNYDER, Mathematics Teacher; *b:* Dayton, OH; *m:* Douglas; *c:* Kimberly, Robert, Michael; *ed:* Univ of Dayton (BS) Scndry Ed 1981; Masters Pgm Admin, Guid, Ed & MBA Stud; Drake Univ Ed Stud; *cr:* Magsig MS Sci & Math Tchr 1981-83; Northmont HS Math Tchr 1983-; *ai:* Dist Math Comm; Univ of Dayton Mens & Womens Bsktbl, & Ftbl Statistician; OCTM 1984-; NDEA; OEA; NEA; Project Gemma 1991; *office:* Northmont Sr H S 4916 National Rd Clayton OH 45315*

HAUSER, DEBRA SHUKIN, Business Education Teacher; *b:* Manhattan, NY; *m:* Scott; *c:* Ricky, Joey; *ed:* Westchester Comm Coll (AA) Lib Arts, Soc Sci 1977; SUNY at Albany (BS) Bus Ed 1979; Coll of New Rochelle (MS) Rdng Ed 1982; Participated & Received In-Svc Credit for Project Turnkey & Worknet 2000; Credit Hrs in Natl Prgm to Teach Applied Math; Cmptr Programming; *cr:* Lakeland HS Bus Ed Tchr 1979-; *ai:* Adv to Class of '99, Future Bus Ldrs of Amer; Frosh Chrldng Coach; Ldrshp Adv, Instr; Adult Ed Tchr; Principal Selection Comm; Mentorship Prgm; WCBEA, NYSBTA, AFT, NYSUT 1979-; Natl Future Ldrs of Amer Adv Recognition Cert; Westchester Bus Inst Recognition for Influence on Stdnts Dev; *office:* Lakeland HS E Main St Shrub Oak NY 10588*

HAUSER, JAMES, Professor of English; *b:* Philadelphia, PA; *m:* Joyce Hinnefeld; *ed:* Univ of PA (BA) Psych 1965, (MA) Eng 1966, (PHD) Eng 1973; *cr:* Wm Paterson Coll Prof of Eng 1970-; *ai:* WAC Co-Dir; Frosh Seminar Participant; AFT; Photography Shows in Galleries & Corporate Ctrs; *office:* William Paterson Coll 300 Pompton Rd Wayne NJ 07470

HAUSER, WILLIAM F., Health & PE Teacher; *b:* Philadelphia, PA; *m:* Janice Guttzeit; *c:* Bethany, Wil; *ed:* Glassboro St (BA) Hlth, PE 1974, (MA) 1992; Ath Dir Cert; Supvr, Admin Cert 1996; *cr:* Gloucester Twp Pub Schls, Glen Landing MS Hlth, PE Tchr 1974-; *ai:* Dept Chprsn; Hd Coach Girls Bsktbl; Asst Coach Boys Sftbl; Stu Asst Cncl; Peer Group Ldr; Dist Curr Comm; NEA, NJEA, CCEA, GTEA 1974-; NJ Ftbl Ofcl Assn 1980-, Mechanics Chprsn, VP; Articles Pub; *office:* Glen Landing MS 85 Little Gloucester Rd Blackwood NJ 08012

HAUSER-CRAM, PENNY, Associate Professor; *b:* Detroit, MI; *m:* Bestov; *c:* Lacey Barbara, Slater Ernesto; *ed:* Denison Univ (BS) Psych 1968; Tufts Univ (MA) Child Stud 1976; Harvard Univ (EDD) Human Dev 1983; *cr:* Wellesley Coll Asst Prof 1982-84; Tufts Univ Dir & Lab Schl Tchr 1984-87; Boston Coll Assoc Prof 1991-; *ai:* SRCD 1981-; APA 1982-; CAC 1990-; Articles & Book Chptrs Pub; *office:* Boston Coll Schl Of Ed Chestnut Hill MA 02167

HAUSHALTER, SUSAN M., First Grade Teacher; *b:* Coraopolis, PA; *ed:* PA St Univ (BS) El Ed 1971; Masters Equivalency; *cr:* Hopewell Area Schls First Grd Tchr 25 Yrs; *ai:* Hopewell Ed Assn, NEA 25 Yrs; W PA Prof Horseman's Assn; Natl Horseman's Assn; *home:* 632 Golf Course Rd Aliquippa PA 15001

HAUSLER, J. WILLIAM, High School Language Arts Tchr; *b:* Gummit, NJ; *m:* Gail Hannas-Hausler; *c:* William, Peter, Eric; *ed:* Rutgers Univ (BS) PE 1962; Kean Coll (MA) Admin & Supvr 1975; *cr:* Wash Twp MS PE, Eng & His 1962-64; Mountain HS West Orange & West Orange HS Lang Arts 1965-; *ai:* WOEA, NEA & NJEA 1965-; SCOA 1969-, 25 Yrs Svc; NV Bsbl Ump Assn 1974-, 20 Yrs Svc; ISOAAJ 1977-; Founder & Head of Chatham Borough Boys Soccer Pgm 1970-79.

HAUSMAN, MARY LOU GRIMSHAW, Eighth Grade Teacher; *b:* Fremont, OH; *m:* Leonard J.; *c:* Lynn Jump, Tricia, Jennifer, Katie; *ed:* Coll of Mt St Joseph (BS) Soc Stud 1964; 32 Hrs Grad Work Towards MS Ed; Sci Cert 1984; *cr:* Our Lady of Good Counsel 7-8 Grd Tchr 1964-66; Our Lady of Victory 4th Grd Tchr 1966-67; St Aloysius 6-8 Grd Tchr 1979-; *ai:* 7-8 Grd Academic Teams; Jr Achvmt Co-op Tchr; Girl Scouts 1965-, Leader 1965-85, 20 Yr Service Awd.

HAUSMANN, HOWARD STRATTON, Retired Elementary Teacher; *b:* Pitman, NJ; *m:* Henrietta Hitman; *c:* Glenn David, Lorin Sue Antonelli, Keryl Ann; *ed:* Rowan Coll of NJ (BS) Elem Ed 1958, (MA) Adm-Sup Elem Ed 1964, Adm-Sup Scndry Ed 1970, Stu Prsnl Svcs 1973; Nova Southeastern Univ (EDD) 1994; 3 Yrs Post-Grad Ed Univ of PA; *cr:* Glocester Twp Pub Schls Elem Tchr 1957-58; Washington Twp Pub Schls Elem Tchr 1959-63, Elem Prin 1963-85, Elem Tchr 1985-95; *ai:* Gloucester Cty Ret Edctrs Assn 1995-; NJ Assn of Elem & MS Prins, VP 3 Yrs; Amer Legion 1995-; VFW; Governor's Awd for Excl in Tchng 1988; Numerous Articles Pub; Instrumental in Legislation for NJ Schls to Install Automatic Fire Detection Equipment.*

HAUSS, MARYANN E., Biology Teacher; *b:* Philadelphia, PA; *m:* Allen F.; *c:* David, Deborah; *ed:* Rutgers Univ (BA) Bio 1965; Rowan Coll (MS) Environmental Sci 1989; *cr:* Cinnaminson HS Bio Tchr 1965-70; Bio Digest Abstract Writer 1979-81; Cherry Hills Schls Bio Tchr 1981-; *ai:* Nature Defense Club Adv; Earth Ed Partnership Coord; Phi Delta Kappa, NJ Env Ed Alliance 1989-; NJ Sci Tchrs 1985-; NJ Dep, Bldg Env Ed Solutions Grants; *office:* Cherry Hill HS West Chapel Ave Cherry Hill NJ 08002

HAUZE, CATHERINE ANNE, Secondary English Teacher; *b:* Hazleton, PA; *m:* William Richard; *c:* Marisa, William Jr., Jason; *ed:* Bloomsburg Univ (BS) Scndry Eng Ed 1970, (MS) Scndry Eng Ed 1975; 60 Credit Hrs Beyond Masters; *cr:* West Hazleton Jr-Sr HS 7th Grd Eng Tchr 1970-71; Freeland Jr-Sr HS 9th & 12th Grd Eng Tchr 1971-92; Hazleton Area HS 11th & 12th Grd Eng Tchr 1992-; *ai:* NEA, PHEAA 1970-; NCTE 1995-; Friends of the Lib 1980-, Pres; Freeland Little League 1990-, Ladies Auxiliary Pres; Freeland Bsktbl Boosters 1980-86, Treas; Past Sr Class Adv, Drama Club Dir, Cheerleading Coach, Pep Club Adv, FHS & HAHS Care Team; *office:* Hazleton Area HS 1601 W 23rd St Hazleton PA 18201

HAVAY, STEPHEN LAWRENCE, Navy JROTC Instructor; *b:* Johnstown, PA; *c:* Stephen, Debra; *cr:* Truman HS NJROTC Instr 6 1/2 Yrs; Rancocas HS NJROTC Instr 2 1/2 Yrs; *ai:* NJROTC Drill Team, Color Guard Coach; *office:* Rancocas Vly Regnl HS Jacksonville Rd & Ridgway St Mt Holly NJ 08060

HAVEN, MARY PAT, Art Teacher; *b:* Erie, PA; *m:* John F.; *c:* Kim, Brian; *ed:* Mercyhurst Coll (BA) Art 1968; Indiana Univ of PA (MA) Art 1971; Related Arts Grant 6 Credits Temple Univ; Cmptr 6 Credits; Writing Childrens Books 5 Credits; Graphic Arts 6 Credits; Watercolor 6 Credits; Papermaking 3 Credits; Jewelry 6 Credits; *cr:* Erie Pub Schl System Elem, MS, Scndry Levels Art Tchr 1969-; *ai:* Schl for Performing & Visual Arts Exhibits Visual Arts Tchr; NEA, PSEA, EEA 1970-; NAEA, PAEA 1990-; Flwshp for Masters Degree in Art; Related Arts Grant; *office:* Central HS 3325 Cherry St Erie PA 16508

HAVENS, A. GLORIA (MOSCA), Music Teacher; *b:* Manhattan, NY; *m:* Charles E.; *ed:* Douglass Coll Rutgers Univ (BA) Music Ed 1959; *cr:* Clark NJ Bd of Ed Music Tchr 1959-; *ai:* Chorus, Band & Instrumental Stdnts; NEA, NJEA, UCEA, CEA 1959-, Cncl Rep; MENC, NJMEA, CJMEA, PTA 1959-; Clark Jaycees Outstanding Young Educator of Yr 1972; Hehnly PTA Natl Outstanding Educator of Yr 1986 Nom; *office:* Frank Hehnly Elem Schl 654 Raritan Rd Clark NJ 07066

HAVILAND, DOROTHY MAGGIO, Biological Sciences Teacher; *b:* Passaic, NJ; *m:* Arthur Pierce Jr.; *ed:* Glassboro St Coll (BA) Biological Sci 1978; Grad Courses St Peters Coll, Montclair St Univ, William Paterson Coll; *cr:* Mullica Hill Friends Schl K-12 Grd Sci, Math Tchr 1978-86; The Friends Schl Dir of Admis 1982-86; Henery P. Becton Regnl HS Biological Sci Tchr 1986-; *ai:* Sci League, ERASE, Becton On Line Club Adv; Negotations Comm; Custodian of Stu Activity Funds; NJ CDL Bus Driver; Project Grad; Stu Cncl; Stock Market Club; Becton Ed Assn 1986-, VP; NJ Sci Tchrs Assn; NEA; NJEA; New England Morgan Horse Assn, VT Morgan Horse Assn, Amer Morgan Horse Assn 1994-; Amer Rottweiller Club 1996-; The Friends Schl Alumni Assn 1983-; NJ Governors Tchr of Yr Awd 1995; Becton & Dickenson Comm Svc Grant Awd for Project Grad; Div of Hwy Safety Grants Project Grad; *office:* Henry P. Becton Regnl HS Paterson Ave & Cornelia St East Rutherfo NJ 07073*

HAVILAND, GEORGE PATRICK, Band Director; *b:* New York City, NY; *m:* Marianne Dwyer; *ed:* Jersey City St Coll (BA) Music Ed 1981; *cr:* Sunrise Presch Music Tchr 1981-82; North Bergen HS Choral Dir 1982-83, Band Dir 1983-; *ai:* Jazz Band & Fame All-Schl Musical Dir; Talent Show & Summer Music Prgm Dir; Comm Band & Fame Orch Dir; Project Grad & Grad Comms; MENC 1990-; AFT 1983-; Governors Awd for Outstanding Tchng 1993; *office:* North Bergen HS 7417 Kennedy Blvd North Bergen NJ 07047*

HAVLICE, RONALD ANTHONY, Chemistry Teacher; *b:* Cleveland, OH; *m:* Nancy Hanko; *c:* Noah; *ed:* OH St Univ (BS) Zoology 1972, (MA) Educl Stud 1989; *cr:* Cleveland Pub Schls Environmental Mngmt Tchr 1976-77; Strongsville City Schls Bio, Physics Tchr 1977-80; Rutherford B. Hayes HS Chem, Bio Tchr 1980-83; Kwajalein Jr Sr HS Bio, Earth Sci Tchr 1983-85; Dublin HS Chem Tchr 1985-; *ai:* Graded Course Stud Comm; Sci Dept Chr; Sci Educator Cncl of OH; Dublin Educators Assn; DEA; NEA; OEA; Eisenhower Math Sci Awd 1993; Whitco Shevex Tchr Scholar 1992; Ashland Chemical Tchr Intern 1991; *office:* Dublin HS 6780 Coffman Rd Dublin OH 43017

HAWBAKER, DAVID GEORGE, Art Teacher; *b:* Iwakuni, Japan; *ed:* Westminser Coll (BA) Art, Art Ed 1980; Carnegie Mellon (MAT) Fine ARts 1987; *cr:* North Allegheny Schl Dist Art Tchr 1980-; *ai:* Tenth Grd Class Cncl, Intermediate HS Lit Magazine Adv; AFT 1980-; Pub Book The Old North Hills; Art Exhibitions Pittsburgh Fund for Arts, Tchrs Exhibition at PPG Wintergarden 1991, 1993, 1995, Art Festivals 3 Rivers 1995, North Hills Best in Show 1994, Cranberry 1st Place Drawing 1995; *office:* North Allegheny Intermed HS 350 Cumberland Rd Pittsburgh PA 15237

HAWES, SUZANNE LAW, Prof of Community Health Dept; *b* NY; *m:* John Kennedy; *c:* Mary Jane, John Brenden; *ed:* Seto (BA) Bio 1956; Dept of Nrsng Columbia (BS) Nrsng 1959; Columbia (MA) Nrsng Ed 1964; Rutgers (EDD) Sociolgy of E for Modern Psychoanalytic Stud Cert Psychoanalysis 1995; Corps Malaysia Vol 1964-66; Charles E. Gregory Schl of Nrsng Dir Perthamboy Gen Host 1966-75; Rutgers Asst Prof Nrsn William Paterson Coll Dean Schl of Hlth Prof 1978-85, Prof C 1985-; *ai:* Alumni Rutgers; AFT; Columbia U Nrsng Alumn Alumni Columbia U Dept of Nrsng; Roll of Hnr NJ St Nurses A William Paterson Coll 300 Pompton Rd Wayne NJ 07470

HAWK, BRENDA KAY, Home Economics Teacher; *b:* Young *ed:* Youngstown St Univ (BA) Scndry Ed, Voc Consumer & H Ed 1991; Addl 28 Hrs Toward Masters in Scndry Ed; *cr:* Bell- IMPACT Tchr 1991-93; McDonald HS Home Ec Tchr 1993-; Adv; SADD Adv; NEA, OEA, MEA, 1993-; *office:* Mc Dona Iowa Ave Mc Donald OH 44437

HAWK, LAURA KATHRYN, Tax Collector; *b:* Kittanning, P Jones Univ (BS) Scndry Ed 1959; Attnd IN Univ of PA, G Seminary; *cr:* Bob Jones Univ Tchr, Prof 1959-67, 1972; Bob J Tchr 1959-67, 1972; Chrstn Schl Assn Greater Harrisburg Ad Tchr 1967-72, 1973-81; Worthington Bapt Acad Prin, Tchr 19 Worthington Bapt Church, Sec, WBCA, Choir Dir, Sunday Chrstn Tchr Articles; Mt Lou-San Bible Camp Plaque 30 Yrs of PO Box 124 Kittanning PA 16201

HAWK, MARY ELLEN WATTO, Kindergarten Teacher; *b:* Co *m:* Nathan H.; *c:* Madelyn; *ed:* East Stroudsburg Univ (BS) Ele PA St Univ (MED) Elem Ed 1978; *cr:* Jim Thorpe Schl Dist K 21 Yrs; *ai:* Sftbl Coach; Majorette, Patrols Schl Safety Prgm A PSEA, NEA 1975-; Girl Scouts 1987-, Ldr; *office:* L B Morris 150 W 10th St Jim Thorpe PA 18229*

HAWKES, RONALD, Kndgtn & Rdng Recovery Tchr; *b:* Por *m:* Katherine Elizabeth Hufnagel; *c:* Joanne, Susan, Stephen; St Tchrs Coll (BS) Elem Ed 1965; Univ of ME (MS) Ed 1974; Univ, AZ St Univ 1970-72; Post Grad Cert Master Adult Ed, Tc Second Lang Univ of Southern ME; *cr:* Peace Corps Tchr Class US Army Hawk Missile Unit S Korea, Demonstration Tchr T 1967-69; Prides Corner Schl Grd 6 Tchr 1969-70; Tuba City Pu 3 Tchr 1970-71, Grd 1 Tchr 1971-72; *ai:* Staff Dev Comm; Bl NEA, ME Tchrs Assn 1969-; Westbrook Ed Assn 1969-, Rep A Amer Rdng Recovery 1992-; Casco Lib 1989-, Pres, Bd of Knights of Columbus 1978-; Svc Awd Westbrook Schl Bd 1986

HAWKINS, ANDREW ALBERT, High School Computer T Canton, OH; *ed:* Conisius Coll (BS) Scndry Ed 1992; *cr:* Stark Sub Tchr 1992-93; Saint Thmas Aquinas HS Cmptr Tchr 1993-; Bsbl Coach; Schl Newspaper Adv; Tech Comm Chm; NCEA 1 Cty Coaches Assn, OSHAA Coaches Assn 1992-; Tchr of Mo Saint Thomas Aquinas HS 2121 Reno Dr Louisville OH 44721

HAWKINS, CHARLES HOWARD, History Teacher; *b:* Tuffi Sharon Ann Williams; *c:* Jennifer, Jason; *ed:* The OH St Univ Govt 1966; Dayton Univ (MS) Scndry Ed 1993; 19 Credit H Green St Univ; *cr:* North Union Local Schls His, Govt Tchr 19 HS His Tchr 1978-; *ai:* Former Fr Bsktbl Coach; OEA, NEA Ed Assn 1978-, Pres; Lions Club 1978-, Pres; VFW 1980-; Scholar; *home:* 97 State Route 309 Alger OH 45812

HAWKINS, CLINTON MATTHEW, History & Social Wor Pittsburgh, PA; *ed:* Univ of Pittsburgh (MSW) Soc Work 1985 Mellon Univ (MA) Policy His 1993; ABD Policy His; Doctoral *cr:* Univ of Pittsburgh Schl Soc Work Prof 1993-; *ai:* Inst of Univ of Pittsburgh Consultant; Pi Kappa Delta 1978-; Bradd Hitorical Soc 1995-, Bd Mem; Co-author & Co-Ed Aliqui Co-Author Steel People 1986; Contributing Ed for The Report; Ardmore Blvd Pittsburgh PA 15221

HAWKINS, DONALD A., Special Education Teacher; *b:* Roch *m:* Susan A.; *c:* Sara, Lindsay, Joshua; *ed:* Eastern NM Univ 1972, (MS) Spec Ed 1973; Brockport SUC (CAS) Educl Admin Albuquerque Pub Schl Spec Ed Tchr 1973-79; Batavia HS Spe 1979-; *ai:* Coordinate Bldg Responsibilities Part-Time Chm; AF 1973-, Bldg Rep, Pub Relations; St Mary's Church 1994-, Lect Batavia HS 260 State St Batavia NY 14020*

HAWKINS, GARY L., Fourth Grade Teacher; *b:* Jersey Shor Sandra E. Myers; *c:* Marc R.; *ed:* Lock Haven Univ (BS) Elem Bloomsburg Univ (MS) Elem Ed 1972; *cr:* Salladasburg Elem 4th 1967-70; Jersey Shore Elem 4th Grd Tchr 1970-; *ai:* PSEA, N Masonic Lodge 1995-; BPO Elks Club 1969-; Church, Trustee, C *office:* Jersey Shore Area Elem Schl 601 Locust St Jersey Shore

HAWKINS, GWENDOLYN GAIL, English Teacher; *b:* Annap *c:* Jordan Bosques; *ed:* Morgan St Univ (BA) Eng & Ed 1975; Coll; *cr:* Arundel HS Eng Tchr 1975-76; Meade Sr HS Eng Tchr South River Eng Tchr 1977-86; Glen Burnie Eng Tchr 1986-; Comm.

HAWKINS, JOY CAROLE, 7th Grd Language Arts Te Clarksburg, WV; *m:* Charles Joseph Sr.; *c:* Charles Joseph Jr.; *ed:* St Coll (BA) Eng, PE 1964; Ashland Univ (MA) Curr, Instruction Addl Credit Hrs; *cr:* Lorain Sr HS Eng, PE Tchr 1964-66; Barrac Eng, PE Tchr 1966-68; Edison Jr HS Lang Arts Tchr 1968-69; E MS Lang Arts Tchr 1969-; *ai:* Asst Refereeing Girls Vlybl Ga Schl Dances; Marion Ed Assn, OH Ed Assn, NEA 1964-94; Alliance Church, Group Ldr, Sunday Schl Tchr, Deacon, D Comms; Tchr of Yr; *office:* Eber Baker MS 400 Pennsylvania A OH 43302

HAWKINS, KATHLEEN, 4th Grade Teacher; *b:* Philipsburg Robert; *c:* Brian; *ed:* St Francis Coll (BS) Elem Ed & Lib Sci Grad Creds; *cr:* Moshannon Valley Elem 5th Grd Tchr 1974-77 Tchr 1977-; *ai:* NEA 1974-; MVEA 1974-; *home:* PO Box 188 PA 16680

HAWKINS, MARVIN CURTIS, 7th Grade Teacher; *b:* Newar Robin Kilgore; *c:* Tamesha, Charlese, Autumn; *ed:* Seton Hall Elem Ed 1978; *cr:* Sacred Heart Schl 5th Grd Tchr 1979-80; Sacrament Schl 7th Grd Tchr 1980-82; Mt Vernon Ave Schl B Tchr 1982-83, 7th Grd Tchr 1983-; *ai:* X-Cntry, Winter & Spr Track Coach at Irvington HS 1991-; NJEA & NEA 1982-; Phi B 1989-; Asst Coach of the Yr Northern Hills Conf for Essex Cath All Area Coach of Yr 1994-95; *office:* Mt Vernon Ave Schl 36 Ave Irvington NJ 07111

HAWKINS, MARY PENDERGRAFT, Family & Consumer Scie *b:* Pond Creek, OK; *m:* Requa Dean; *c:* Pamela Kay Ringdahl, Lee Hanneman; *ed:* Univ of OK (BS) Home Ec 1963; *cr:* OK City Home Ec Tchr 1963-66; Lowell HS Parenting Tchr 1986-95, Consumer Sci Tchr 1995-; *ai:* Healthy Life Skills Grant; Advy Educl Frameworks Comm; United Tchrs of Lowell 1991-; Lo Coalition 1986-, Chprsn 1991-93; *home:* 13 Westwind Rd Lo 01852

HAWKINS, RENEE DELA VEGA, 7th Grade Health Ed Te Bethesda, MD; *m:* Roy E. Jr.; *c:* Roy III, Stephanie; *ed:* Towso

977; Grad Work & 30 Addl Hrs St Cert in Hlth Ed; *cr:* Walker gh PE Tchr 1978-79; Oxon Hill Jr High PE Tchr 1978-79; Gwynn Hlth Ed Tchr 1979-94; Benjamin Tasker MS Health Ed Tchr MS Implementation Team; Instructional Team Ldr; Fac Advy e Co & Talent Show Dir; Tchr Insvc Instr; Curr Writing; Tchr r Hlth Ed; DMAD Metro Dance champion Coach; Southern Dist mpions & Chrldng Coaches 1979; MS Evaluation Team; PGCEA m for Outstanding Tchr Awd for the Agnes Myer, Washington GCPS; Lions Club Educator Awd; *office:* Benjamin Tasker MS ington Rd Bowie MD 20715*

S, SANDRA KEMP, Third Grade Teacher; *b:* Allentown, PA; *m:* *c:* Jennifer, Daniel, Carly; *ed:* Kutztown Univ (BS) Elem 1982, em 1988; Dale Carnegie Course Grad Asst; *cr:* Fleetwood Area Elem Tchr 1987-; *ai:* NEA, PSEA 1987-; Dale Carnegie Course chvmt Awd 1993; *office:* Fleetwood Elem Schl 109 W Vine St PA 19522

CAROL MC CONCHIE, Vocal & Instrumental Teacher; *b:* Spa, NY; *m:* W. Bruce; *c:* Deborah, Christopher; *ed:* SUC at BS) Music 1964; SUC at Albany (MS) Ed 1974; Coll of St Rose C at Potsdam 12 Hrs; *cr:* Schuylerville Cntrl Schl K-12 Grd Vocal 1966-68; St Clements 4-12 Grd Vocal Tchr 1973; Saratoga ity Schls K-8 Grd Vocal Tchr 1975-79; Greenwich Cntrl Schl trumental Tchr 1981-; *ai:* Drama Club; Choraliers; Guys & Gals; ted Tchrs Exec Comm; Shared Decision Making; MENC, NYSUT 1964-; ACDA 1981-; WCAMTA; Schuylerville Comm *office:* Greenwich Central Schl 10 Gray Ave Greenwich NY

, GEORGE JOSEPH,JR., Music Teacher; *b:* New Haven, CT; rn CT St Univ (BS) Music Ed 1976, (MS) Music Ed 1982; *cr:* n HS Choral Music Dir 1976-; *ai:* HS Music Act; NEA, MENC, 76-; Adv of Yr CT Fed of Stu Cncls 1989; *office:* Watertown HS h St Watertown CT 06795

, LESTER EDWARD, Assistant Principal; *b:* New Haven, CT; Marie Giannotti; *c:* Sharmane, Ianthia, Jesse; *ed:* Southern CT BS) His 1972, (MS) Urban Ed 1976; 6th Yr Admin & Supervision US Marine Corps Infantry Officer 1972-75; Carrigan MS Tchr West Haven HS Tchr 1983-95; Bailey MS Asst Instructional Ldr NAESP 1996; AFT 1976-; *office:* Bailey MS 106 Morgan Ln en CT 06516

, PATRICIA PENNINGTON, HS Mathematics Teacher; *b:* a, VA; *m:* William Thomas; *ed:* SUNY at Oneonta (BS) Scndry 1985, (BS) Math 1985; SUNY at Cortland (MS) Rdng 1989; Psych 1985; *cr:* Liverpool HS Math Tchr 1985-; *ai:* Soc Coord Math Cncl, Vote Cope Chprsn, United Way Chprsn, Curr nt 1985-; NYSTU 1985-; Nom Tchr of Yr 1994-95; *office:* HS 4338 Wetzel Rd Liverpool NY 13090

TH, SHERRY HUMPHREYS, Substitute Teacher; *b:* Chicago, dney George; *c:* Gregory, Jeffrey, Rebecca Haworth Olivieri; *ed:* v (BA) Eng, Span 1961; Grad Credit Ed at IN St Univ; Grad Sociology, Cmptr Literacy at Univ of Cincinnati; Grad Credit Ed at Mt St Joseph Coll; *cr:* Oak Hills Pub Local Schls Summer Eng, Amer Lit, 7th-8th Grd Sci, Math, Soc Stud Tchr 1988-93, 1995-; Cincinnati Pub Schls Sub Tchr 1979-; *ai:* AFT, CFT ater, Western Hills 1977-; HS PTAs 1984-; *home:* 5896 lls Dr Cincinnati OH 45233

IK, EDWARD S.,JR., High School Science Teacher; *b:* New T; *ed:* Cntrl CT St (BS) Bio 1975; Addl 30 Credits MS Prgm Bio; ville HS Sci Tchr, Coach 1977-; *ai:* Girls Cross-Cntry Coach; Jr ; Sports Booster Club; Aux Treas PTSA; Pep Club Adv; Bsbl Seasons; Girls JV & Var Bsktbl 6 Yrs; Girls & Boys Bsktbl Scorekeeper; Curr Dev AP Bio Prgm; NEA, CEA, PEA 1977-; CHSCA 1978-; NSTA, Past Mem; PTSA, Past Treas; Booster -, Past Treas, Booster of Yr 1991; SADD Chapter Adv, Past Mem; ree Grad Comm, Past; ABCA, BCA Coaching Bsbl Awds; *office:* HS N Main St Terryville CT 06786

ELLY L., Business Education Teacher; *b:* Piqua, OH; *m:* Greg; w, Casey, Emily; *ed:* Sinclair Comm Coll (AA) Exec Sec 1977; ayton (BA) Scndry Ed 1986; Wright St Univ (MA) Ed 1993; *cr:* obins HS Tchr 1986-90; Miami Vly Career Tech Ctr Tchr 1990-; rofs Amer Region III Asst Adv 1995-; Bus Profs Amer Cptr Adv Bus Prof Amer 1986-, Adv, CEAC Rep Region III; Vol Spec Greater Dayton Area 1986-; *office:* Miami Vly Career Tchnlgy Hoke Rd Clayton OH 45315

WILLIAM PATRICK, Chemistry Teacher; *ed:* Alvernia Coll (BS) stry 1986; Temple Univ (ME) Ed 1992; Mercer Cty Comm Coll uneral Dir 1988; *cr:* Dougherty Funeral Home Funeral Dir Harry S. Truman HS Tchr 1989-; *ai:* Mgr of Falls Legion Bsbl EA 1989-.*

ORNE, DEBBIE DIERKES, Certified Dental Asst Instr; *b:* , WV; *m:* Walter G.; *c:* Tabatha N.; *ed:* Curr Courses Taken at at Athens; *cr:* Dr Robert J Kolanski Certified Dental Asst Belmont Career Ctr Certified Dental Instr 1990-; *ai:* Stu Cncl, mm Adv; OEA, NEA 1990-; ADAA 1983-; OVA, AVA 1990-; 95-; EMT 1991-; New Athens Ladies Firemans Auxiliary 1989-, Rep 1995-; *office:* Belmont Career Ctr 110 Fox Shannon Pl Saint e OH 43950*

ANNE (DURST), Math, Science & Health Teacher; *b:* Westfield, ichael; *ed:* Slippery Rock Univ (BS) Elem Ed 1971, (BS) Hlth, Clarion Univ (MED) Elem Ed 1973; 60 Addl Hrs Miami Univ of St Univ, Penn St, East Stroudsburg Univ, Ashland Univ; *cr:* Kane nl Dist K-6 Grd HPED, Classroom Tchr 1971-83; Gahanna Coll Dir 1984-87; St Brendan Schl Advances Math, H & Ped 7-88; Merrill Publishing Copy Ed, Consultant 1985-; Columbus Coll Part-Time Instr 1987-; St Pius X Schl 8th Grd Math, Sci, r 1988-; King Thompson Realtor 1989-; *ai:* Prins Advy Comm; Math, Sci Course of Stud Comm; Natl Mid Level Sci Tchrs Assn, ncl of OH, NSTA 1989-; Columbus Diocesan Ed Assn 1987-; Natl rshp Assn 1995-; Natl Realtors Assn, OH Assn of Realtors 1989-; Discovery & Partners for Terrific Sci Grant; Excl Tchng Sci s Awd; Diocesan Schl Bd Exemplary Rel Awd; Tchr of Yr; ial Awd Nom; Ashland OH Tchr of Yr Nom; *office:* St Pius X Schl ggoner Rd Reynoldsburg OH 43068

NCY LANDIS, Physical Education Teacher; *b:* Meyersdale, PA; John; *c:* Jennifer, Christy Jo; *ed:* Slippery Rock St Coll (BS) Hlth 1, (MS) Hlth & PE 1974; CA Univ of PA Scndry Prin Cert 1986; ay HS PE Tchr 1971-74; Somerset HS PE Tchr 1975-; *ai:* Jr High tbl & Yth Bsktbl Coach; Maple Princess & Yth Corps Advs; Dept EA, PSEA, SEA 1974-; Sunday Schl Tchr Sr High Classes; Yth Corps Bsktbl Bd of Dir 1993-95; Tri-Cty Golf Assn Bd of Dir 980; Honored One of Tri-Cty Tchr of Yr 1993; Honored as BPW Woman of Yr 1987; *office:* Somerset High School S Columbia erset PA 15501*

OTT, High School English Teacher; *b:* Fitchburg, MA; *m:* Donna rd; *c:* Keith, Timothy; *ed:* Boston Coll (BA) Eng & Ed 1971; g St Coll (MS) Cnslng; *cr:* Chatham MS Eng Tchr 1971-74; Leominster HS Eng Tchr 1974-; *ai:* Var Ftbl Asst Coach, Defensive Coord; Lit Magazine Adv; Restructuring Comm; Leominster Tchrs Assn 1974-; MA Tchrs Assn 1974-; NEA 1974-; *office:* Leominster HS 122 Granite St Leominster MA 01453

HAYAS, GALYE LYNN, Teacher, Advisor & Coach; *b:* Cleveland, OH; *m:* Jim; *c:* Amy, Kimberly; *ed:* Univ of Akron (BA) Comm Ed 1990; Credit Hrs Legal Updates Edctrs, Integrating Arts Curr, Tech Ed, Co-Operative Ed, Learning; *cr:* Medina Co Career Ctr Cmptr Coord 1980-90; *ai:* Acad Challenge Team Coach; NHS Adv; Schl Improvement Comm Sec; Schl Levy Comm; Outward Bound Team; OASSA, DSA 1990-, St Adv Comm Mem; Medina Co Lang Arts Cncl Steering Comm 1995-; Nom Ashland Inc Tchr Achvmt Awd; Nom CHS Tchr of Yr; *office:* Cloverlead HS 8525 Friendsville Rd Lodi OH 44254

HAYDEL, C. C.,III, English & Literature Teacher; *b:* Washington, DC; *ed:* Xavier Univ of LA (BA) Lang Ed 1989; Columbia Univ (MA) Eng Ed 1990; Inst de Filologia Hispanica 1984; *cr:* Mabel Dean Bacon HS Eng Tchr 1990; Robert Frost Jr HS Eng Tchr, Dept Chair 1990-92; South Mecklenburg HS Eng Tchr 1992-93; Woodlands HS Eng Tchr 1993-; *ai:* Ftbl, Vlybl, Track & Field Coach; Woodlands Individualized Sr Experience Adv; AFT 1991-; NYSUT 1993-; NCTE 1990-; Alpha Phi Alpha 1982-; Mellon Fellows-in-Tchng Scholar 1989-90; Minority Fellows Scholar 1989-90; *office:* Woodlands HS 475 W Hartsdale Ave Hartsdale NY 10530*

HAYDEN, ALICE B., Kindergarten Teacher; *b:* Pittsburgh, PA; *m:* David L.; *c:* Beth; *ed:* Duquesne Univ (BS) Music 1969, (MS) Elem Ed 1972; *cr:* West Mifflin Area Schls Elem Tchr 1970-; *ai:* Delta Kappa Gamma 1983-; AFT 1985-; Park Vly Handbell Ringers 1988-; *home:* 4733 Little St Munhall PA 15120

HAYDEN, DARYL J., Math Teacher; *b:* Garfield, NJ; *c:* John Newcomb, Daniel Newcomb, Peter Newcomb; *ed:* Univ of RI (BA) Eng 1963; *cr:* West Greenwich Elem Schl First Grd Tchr 1963-64; Summit Ave Schl First Grd Tchr 1966-67; Reading Schl Third Grd Tchr 1967-68; Pitman Schl Sixth Grd Tchr 1969-70; Washington Twp Schl Sixth Grd Tchr 1972-; *ai:* Sixth Grd Class Adv; Team Ldr; NEA 1969-; WTEA 1972-; Pitman Womens Club; *office:* Orchard Valley MS 405 Pitman Downer Rd Sewell NJ 08080*

HAYDEN, MARY ELAINE, First Grade Teacher; *b:* Philadelphia, PA; *m:* Howard F.; *ed:* Gwynedd Mercy Coll (BA); *cr:* St Genevieve Schl 1st Grd Tchr 1963-71; St Agnes 1st Grd Tchr 1974-78; St Leo the Great Schl 1st Grd Tchr 1978-; *ai:* Early Chldhd Curr Coord; Rdng & Math Textbook Comms Adv; NCEA 1980-; Middletown Soc Svc, CCD Tchr, RCIA Mem Vol; Rdng, Math Tutor Vol; Cath Edctr of the Yr 1996.*

HAYER, PATTI A., Fourth Grade Teacher; *b:* Stockdale, OH; *m:* Tom; *c:* Kaci, Corey; *ed:* OH Univ (BS) Elem Ed 1970; OH St Univ (MA) Elem Ed, Rdng, Lit & Lang Arts 1992; *cr:* Vernon Local Schl Rdng Tchr 1967-69; Scioto Darby Schls Rdng Tchr 1970-72 & 1975-76; Grace Brethren Chrstn Schls 4th Grd Tchr 1982-; *ai:* Rdng Comm Competency Based Ed Chrprsn; Sci Curr Comm Mem; Lang Arts Curr Comm Mem; OH Cncl Tchrs of Eng Lang Arts 1987-; *office:* Grace Brethren Elem Schl 50 Westview Ave Columbus OH 43214

HAYES, CHRISTINE YVONNE, Social Studies Teacher; *b:* Cambridge, OH; *ed:* Miami Univ (BS) Scndry Ed 1983; OH St Univ (MA) Educl Stud 1991; *cr:* South Webster Schls Soc Stud Tchr 1984-85; Upper Arlington Schls Soc Stud Tchr 1985-; *ai:* Var Chrldng Coach; NEA 1985-; *office:* Upper Arlington HS 1650 Ridgeview Rd Columbus OH 43221

HAYES, EILEEN HAWKES, English Teacher; *b:* Rochester, NY; *m:* Andrew; *ed:* Syracuse Univ (BA) Eng Ed 1981; Elmira Coll (MS) Rdng 1986; *cr:* Newfield Cntrl Schls Mid HS Eng, Remedial Rdng Tchr 1981-86; Caledonia-Mumford Cntrl Schls 7-12 Grd Remedial Rdng Tchr 1987-89, 9-12 Grd Eng Tchr 1987-89; Honeoye Falls-Lima Cntrl Schls 7-8 Grd Eng Tchr 1990-; *ai:* Natl Stans Project Portfolios Pilot; *office:* Honeoye Falls-Lima Cntrl Schls 20 Church St Honeoye Falls NY 14472*

HAYES, MARIE ROYCE, French Teacher; *b:* Charlottesville, VA; *m:* Joseph Edward Sarneski; *c:* Hilary Bishop Sarneski, Jackson Reilley Sarneski; *ed:* George Peabody Coll for Tchrs (BA) Fr 1966; Univ of NC Chapel Hill (MA) Fr 1970, (PHD) Fr Lang & Lit 1976; *cr:* Chopticon HS Fr Tchr 1966-67; UNC-Chapel Hill Asst fr Tchr 1967-72; Francis Marion Coll Instr of Fr & Eng 1973-77; Ludlowe HS Fr, Italian Latin Tchr 1977-87; Tomlinson MS Fr Tchr 1987-92; Fairfield HS Fr Tchr 1992-; *ai:* Amer Field Svc 1979-87; Fr Hnr Soc Fac Adv 1993-; NEA, CEA & FEA 1977-; AATF 1981-; Trinity Episcopal Church 1985-, Sunday Schl Tchr; *office:* Fairfield HS 755 Melville Ave Fairfield CT 06430

HAYES, RONALD JOSEPH,JR., Mathematics & Computer Teacher; *b:* Charleston, SC; *m:* Jody; *ed:* St Univ of NY at Cortland (BS) Math 1990; St Univ of NY at Albany (MA) Math 1995; *cr:* Corinth Cntrl Math & Cmptr Tchr 1990-; Albany Medical Ctr Bio Statistician 1995-; *ai:* Var Track Coach 1990-; AFT, NYSUT 1990-; The Polygon Star & Graphing Koch Curves in AMECS Journal 1995; *office:* Corinth Cntrl Schl 105 Oak St Corinth NY 12822*

HAYES, TIMOTHY COLLINS, Biology Teacher; *b:* Hanover, NH; *m:* Carole Lefeber; *c:* Andrew, Patrick, Collin, Kathleen; *ed:* St Univ of NY at Brockport (BS) Bio 1988, (MSEd) Ed & Bio 1993; *cr:* Letchworth HS Scndry Sci Tchr 1988-92; Geneseo HS Bio Tchr; *ai:* Var Swim Team Head Coach; Var Ftbl Team Asst Coach; Sr Class Adv; HS Discipline Comm; AFT, NYSUT, Geneseo Fac Assn 1992-; USGA 1995-; *office:* Geneseo Central Schl 4050 Avon Rd Geneseo NY 14454*

HAYLE, MARGARET G.,OP, Second Grade Teacher; *b:* New York, NY; *ed:* Holy Family Coll (BA) Elem Ed 1974; Queens Coll (MS) Elem Ed 1991; Diocese of Bklyn Prof Dev Courses; City of NY Bd of Ed Dev of Human Potential Prgm; *cr:* Brklyn Dioceses Grd Schl Tchr 1963-76; Rockville Centre Dioceses Grd Schl Tchr 1963-76; Kelly Svcs Inc Recept, Supvr, Acct Rep, Mgr 1976-80; May Merchandising Corp Asst Prsnl Directress 1980-83; St Margaret Schl Second Grd Tchr 1983-; *ai:* Intermediate Grds Rel Coord; Mission Moderator; Dev of Human Potential Facilitator Prgm; Commission on Elem Schls Mid Sts Evaluation Team; Fac Meetings Sec; NCEA, Cath Sci Cncl, Home Schl Assn 1983-; Queens Coll Elem, Early Chldhd Departmental Hnrs; Bishop's Awd for Rel Ed; *office:* St Margaret Schl 6610 80th St Middle Village NY 11379*

HAYNES, JULIA ANN, Spcl Educ & Lrngn Supprt Tchr; *b:* Bossier City, LA; *ed:* OH Valley Coll (AA) Ed 1984; OK Chrstn Coll (BA) Spec Ed 1987; 24 Credits Penn St Univ at York; *cr:* West York Area Schl Dist Scndry Spec Ed 1987-; *ai:* Head Coach Field Hockey, Track; Tchr Advy Comm; NEA 1987-; WYEA 1987-; Easter Seals SMILE 1984-, Dir; Gift of Time Tribute 3 Yrs; Articles Pub; *office:* West York Area HS 1800 Bannister St York PA 17404*

HAYNES, RANDALL WALTER, Eng, Cmptr, His & Bible Tchr; *b:* Asheville, NC; *m:* Christine Ruth Pinkham; *c:* Leta, Megan, Carla; *ed:* Harvest Christian Coll (BS) Chrstn Ministry 1994; 12 Addl Hrs Chrstn Ed; *cr:* Chrstn Heritage Acad Coach 1981-85; Emmanuel Chrstn Schl Tchr 1987-89; Coastal Chrstn Schl Tchr, Ath Dir 1989-, Dean of Stdnts 1989-93; *ai:* Coll Trip Spon; Handbell Choir Conductor; MCBASO 1986-, MASO Rep; MASO 1993-, Sec, Treas; IAABO 1994-; ACSI 1994-, Scndry Cert; Seminar Presenter NEACS Conventions 1990, 1991, 1993, 1995; *home:* 578 N Nobleboro Rd Waldoboro ME 04572

HAYNES, RICHARD G., Social Studies Teacher; *b:* Cincinnati, OH; *m:* Jennifer Lynn Cobb; *c:* Jared, Kathryn, Emily; *ed:* Univ of Dayton (BS) Scndry Ed 1984; 15 Hrs Univ of Cincinnati 2 Hrs Wrigth St Univ; 31 Addl Hrs; *cr:* Springfield City Schls MS Soc Stud Tchr 1984-85; Centerville City Schls HS Soc Stud Tchr 1986-89; Loveland City Schls HS Soc Stud Tchr 1989-90; Northwest Local Schls HS Soc Stud Tchr 1990-; *ai:* Asst Var Ftbl Coach; Southwest OH Ftbl Coaches Assn 1989-; Partners in Ed 1995-, Bldg Rep; Grant to Univ of Cincinnatis Admin Dev Acad; *office:* Colerain Sr HS 8801 Cheviot Rd Cincinnati OH 45251

HAYS, CAROL LYNN (BAKSA), History & Psychology Teacher; *b:* Plainfield, NJ; *m:* James Hendrickson; *c:* John James II; *ed:* Geneva Coll (BA) Soc Sci 1969; Kean Coll Psych, His Cert 1972, Elem Ed Cert 1992; *cr:* Beaver Co Ct Domestic Relations Ofcr 1969-71; Rahway St Prison Tchr, Cnslr 1972-75; Carteret HS Tchr 1976-; *ai:* Core Team Drug, Alcohol Chprsn; NEA 1976-; CEA 1976-, VP, Bldg Rep; Juvenile Conf Comm Somerset 1994-; *home:* 7 Kirkstall Ct Somerset NJ 08873*

HAYS, CHRISTINA M., Mathematics Teacher; *b:* Salem, OH; *c:* Beth; *ed:* Muskingum Coll (BA) Elem Ed, Sec Math 1981; Coll of Mt St Joseph (MA) Ed 1988; *cr:* Salem HS Math Tchr 1981-; *ai:* Yrbk Adv; *office:* Salem HS 1200 E 6th St Salem OH 44460

HAYS, DENNIS JAMES, Health Teacher; *b:* Cincinnati, OH; *m:* Marcia Lee; *c:* Andrew, Travis; *ed:* OH Univ (BS) Hlth Ed 1974; Univ of AZ (MS) PE 1975; +30 Credit Hrs beyond MS; *cr:* Austin HS Tchr & Ath Trainer 1975-77; Centerville HS Tchr & Ath Trainer 1977-; *ai:* Natl Ath Trainer Assn 1969-; Greater Dayton Ath Trainers Assn 1988-; OH Ath Trainers Assn 1990-; Knights of Columbus 1995-, 1st Degree; *office:* Centerville HS 500 E Franklin St Centerville OH 45459*

HAYS, LAUREL ANN, Secondary Coordinator; *b:* Tuscumbia, AL; *ed:* Univ of North AL (BS) ELem Ed 1980; BJU (MED) Elem Ed 1989; *cr:* Florence Chrstn Acad Jr HS Tchr 1981-87; Bob Jones Univ Press Composition Asst 1987-89; Odenton Chrstn Schl Tchr, Coord 1989-; *ai:* Fine Arts Coord; Amer Assoc of Chrstn Schls 1989-; *office:* Odenton Christian Schl 8410 Piney Orchard Pky Odenton MD 21113

HAYS, NANCY GUNTHER, 8th Grade Science Teacher; *b:* Upper Darby, PA; *c:* Richard, Erin, Jesse; *ed:* Univ of Pittsburgh (BS) Elem Ed 1971; Sacred Heart Univ (MS) Tchng 1990; Duquesne Univ 21 Credits Guid Cnslng; *cr:* Eisenhower Elem Schl 2nd Grd Tchr 1971-74; JHS 165 8th Grd Eng, Span Tchr 1984-85; Hopeville Elem Schl 2nd-5th Grd Tchr 1985-86; Gil Martin Elem Schl 2nd Grd Tchr 1987-88; Wallace MS Earth 8th Grd Sci Tchr 1989-; *ai:* Waterbury Schl Dist Sci Fair Co-Chm 1995-; Sci Fair Chm 1994-; CPEP Coord 1993-; Environmental Caretaker 1987-; CEA, NEA 1987-; CT Pre-Engrng Prgm 1993-; Theatre & Dance Tchr at YMCA; Performed in The Nutcracker Ballet in Nyack NY; Performed in Coppelia in Waterbury's Performing Arts Ballet; Oil Painting Show at Silas Bronson Lib; *office:* Wallace MS 3465 E Main St Waterbury CT 06705*

HAYS, PHILLIP GEORGE, World Geography Teacher; *b:* West Reading, PA; *m:* Theresa Marie Manbeck; *c:* Rachael E., Megan A.; *ed:* Millersville Univ (BS) Ed, Soc Stud 1975; Temple Univ (MS) Ed 1980; 21 Addl Hrs; *cr:* Pine Grove HS Soc Stud Tchr 1976-77; Conrad Weiser Jr HS Soc Stud Tchr 1977-; Conrad Weiser Sr HS Soc Stud Tchr 1977-; *ai:* Ski Club, Geog Club Adv; Nature Club Co-Adv; EA, PSEA, NEA 1977-; PA Geographic Soc, Natl Cncl Geog Educ 1985-; Kiwanis Club 1978-, Key Club Adv; Natl Endowment for Hum Grant; Jr HS Tchr of Yr; *office:* Conrad Weiser Jr/Sr HS 347 E Penn Ave Robesonia PA 19551*

HAYS, THOMAS EUGENE, Associate Prof of Mathematics; *b:* Williamsburg, KY; *m:* Joan Bradford; *c:* Brad, Craig, Aaron, Elaind, Hila; *ed:* Cumberland Coll (BS) Math 1963; Univ of TN (PHD) Math 1971; *cr:* Williamsburg HS Math Tchr 1963-67; OH St Univ Math Tchr 1972-; *ai:* OSUN Acad Affairs Comm; Math Coord; AMS & AMATYC; Church of Jesus Christ of Latter Day Saints 1969-, Bishop, Sunday Schl Tchr, Seminary Tchr; NDEA Flwshp; NSF OH Stipend for Project Discovery Thomas J Evans Tchng Excellance Awd & Julius and Joette Greenstein Svc Awd; *office:* OH St Univ At Newark 1179 University Dr Newark OH 43055

HAYWARD, ADAM PATRIC, English Teacher; *b:* Los Angeles, CA; *m:* Clarissa Rice; *c:* Aidan; *ed:* Princeton Univ (BA) Eng Lit 1988; *cr:* Bassick HS Eng Tchr 1992-; *ai:* Sr Class Adv; Lit Magazine Club; 2 Bridgeport Mini-Grants 1993-94; A. P. Mellon Flwshp 1995; Tchr of Yr 1994-95; Svc Awd 1993-94; *office:* Bassick HS 1181 Fairfield Ave Bridgeport CT 06605

HAYWARD, CHRIS, Mathematics Teacher; *b:* Presque Isle, ME; *ed:* Univ of ME (BA) Math 1989; 2nd Yr Stu MST Prgm at UNH; *cr:* Presque Isle High Math Tchr 1989-91; Scarborough High Math Tchr 1991-; *ai:* Class of 1997 Adv; Fresh Boys Bsktbl; Var Bsbl; NEA 1989-, Mem; Pi Mu Epsilon 1988-, Mem, Natl Math Hono; Fac Mem PIHS 1990; Natl Schl of Excl; *office:* Scarborough HS 20 Gorham Rd Scarborough ME 04074

HAYWARD, JOHN CHARLES, Vocal Music & Drama Director; *b:* Erie, PA; *m:* Jennifer Catazaro; *c:* Zachary, Jeremy, David, Jon; *ed:* Westminster Choir Coll (BME) Voice, Choral 1968; Attnd Peabody Conservatory of Music, Trenton St, Kent St, Eastern KY, George Mason Univs; *cr:* St Anthony HS Vocal Music Tchr 1968-; N Carroll HS Vocal Music Tchr 1971-72; Lehman HS Vocal Music Tchr 1972-76; Woodbridge HS Vocal Music Tchr 1977-81; Mc Kinley HS Vocal Music Tchr 1981-84; Hoover HS Vocal Music, Drama Tchr 1984-; *ai:* Produce, Dir Annual Broadway Musical; Drama Club Spon; Dir Annual Schl Play; Dir Select Ensemble Hoover Hi-Lo's, Annual Competition Trip; OMEA, NEA, MENC, ACDA 1971-; Canton Ballet Co 1993-; Canton Players Guild 1981-; Sharon Lane Chap 199 Vietnam Vets of Amer 1981-; Amer Legion Meritorous, Mayor's Citation for Ed Svcs; Tchr of Yr 1979; Tchr of Yr Runner-up 1989; *office:* Hoover HS South 605 Fair Oaks SW North Canton OH 44720*

HAYWARD, RUTH ANN, Fourth Grade Teacher; *b:* Mt Pleasant, IA; *ed:* St Univ of IA (BA) Jrnlsm, Elem Ed 1960; St Univ of NY at Geneseo (MS) Elem Ed 1964; IA Wesleyan Coll 2 Yr Normal Elem Ed 1955; 6 Credit Hrs Toward MBA Northeastern Univ; 3 Credit Hrs Xerox Corporate Trng Prgm; *cr:* Cntrl Schl Dist 3 Grd Tchr 1955-58; The Instructor Magazine Sr Ed 1960-69; D C Heath & Co Sr Ed, Rdng 1969-72; Harcourt Brace Jovanovich Inc Ed-in-Chief 1972-76; Freelance Writer, Ed, Consulant 1976-77; Harper & Row, J B Lipincott Co Exec Ed, Rdng & Lang Arts 1977-80; Ginn & Co Rdng & Lang Arts Dir 1980-82; Freelance Writer, Ed, Consultant; Wayland-Cohocton Cntrl Schl Dist 4 Grd Tchr, K-8 Grd Gifted Resource Tchr; 8-12 Grd Writing Tchr, 8 Grd Career Ed Tchr 1983-95; Publicom Inc Project Dir 1995-; Wayland-Cohocton Cntrl Schl Dist 4 Grd Tchr 1996; *ai:* NEA, NY St Tchrs Assn, Wayland Tchrs Assn 1983-; Book Pub: What's Cooking? Favorite Recipes from Around the World 1981; *office:* Wayland-Cohocton Cntrl Schl Di Cohocton Elem Schl Cohocton NY 14826

HAYWARD, SANDRA TRACY, Math & Computer Science Tchr; *b:* Providence, RI; *ed:* Univ MA at Dartmouth (BA) Hum, Soc Scis 1978; 21 Credit Hrs Cmptr Sci Prgm Bridgewater St Coll; Post-Grad Prgm Educl Computing, Tech Ldrshp Johnson & Wales Univ; *cr:* Dighton-Rehoboth HS Tchr Aide 1972-78; Taunton HS Math Tchr 1978-84; Mansfield HS Math, Cmptr Tchr 1984-; *ai:* Prof Dev, Schl Improvement Comm; Frosh Field Hockey Coach; MTA, NEA 1978-; *office:* Mansfield HS 250 East St Mansfield MA 02048

HAYWARD, THOMAS E., 7th Grade Math Teacher; *b:* Manchester, NH; *ed:* Rivier Coll (MED) Schl Admin 1995; *cr:* Auburn Village Schl 7th-8th Grd Math Tchr 1990-95; Timberlane Regnl Jr HS 7th Grd Math Tchr 1996; *ai:* Jr HS Girls Bsktbl, 7th Grd Girls Soccer, Asst Jr HS Track Coach; WBC 1996; TAB 1996, Exec Comm; At Risk Comm 1996; *home:* 633 Fremont Rd Chester NH 03036

HAYWARD, WILLIAM GERARD, Rel Dept Head & Sci, Rel Tchr; *b:* Syracuse, NY; *ed:* SUNY Coll of Env Sci & Forestry (AAS) Forestry 1978; Assumption Coll (BA) Bio 1985; Pontifical Inst of St Thomas (BST) (MS) Theology 1989; Credit Hrs Cntrl WA Univ at Ellensburg, Onondaga Comm Coll at Syracuse; *cr:* US Forest Svc Timber Inventory Specialist 1978-79; Cutts Surveying & Staking Slope Staking Crew Chief 1980-82; Marianapolis Prep Sci, Rel Tchr, Rel Dept Head 1989-; *ai:* Tutors, Retreat Prgm Coord; Marianapolis Trustee, Dir 1992-; Thompson Ecumenical Empowerment Group 1992-, Dir; Willimantic Orch 1992-, Prsnl Mgr, Instrumentalist; *office:* Marianapolis Prep Sch PO Box 368 Thompson CT 06277*

HAYWOOD, BARRY O., Instrumental Music Teacher; *b:* Dansville, NY; *m:* Mary S.; *c:* Laurie Stanton, Cheryl Haberly, Janine; *ed:* Ithaca Coll (BS) Music 1958; Univ of Buffalo (MED) Music 1967; *cr:* Holland Cntrl Schl Music Dir 1958-67; Dansville HS Music Dir 1967-; *ai:* Dir: HS Concert Band, Marching Band & Jazz Ensemble; NYSUT 1958-; AFT 1962-; Genesee Vly Tchrs Assn 1967-; Dansville TA 1967-; United Way 1967, Pres 17 Yrs; Dansville Dogwood Festival 1969-, Gen Chm 27 Yrs; Lions Intnl 1971-, Dist Governor, 5 Intnl Pres Awds; Dansville Village Bd 1983-, Trustee; Phillip Morris Co NY St Citizen of the Yr 1992; Dansville Chamber of Commerce Citizen of the Yr; Melvin Jones Fellow Lions Intnl; Pres NY St & Bermuda Lions Fndtn 1995-; *home:* 235 Main St Dansville NY 14437

HAYWOOD, GAYLE L., Language Arts Teacher; *b:* Dayton, OH; *ed:* Wright St Univ (BS) Ed 1972; Univ of Dayton (MS) Rdng 1981; Wright St Univ (MS) Schl Lib Media 1992; *cr:* Longfellow MS Lang Arts Tchr 1972-76; Jefferson Elem Schl Lang Arts Tchr 1976-82; Stivers MS Lang Arts Tchr 1982-89; Fairview MS Lang Arts Tchr 1989-; *ai:* GATE, Techs Comms; NEA 1972-; OELMA 1992-; Natl Museum of the Amer Indian 1994-; Martha Holden Jennings Scholar 1983-84; Wright St Univ Grad Stu Excl Awd 1992.

HAZAN, MARVIN ERIC, Law Teacher; *b:* Brooklyn, NY; *m:* Jane Factor; *c:* Rachel, James Pomeranz; *ed:* Hofstra Univ (BBA) Acctng 1964, (MSEd) Bus Ed 1966; 60 Credit Hrs Beyond Masters Degree; *cr:* Diamond & Charles CPA Accountant 1964-66; Plainview-Kennedy HS Tchr 1966-; *ai:* Moot Ct Club & Wall St Investors Club Adv; HS Auditor; Herb Levy Schlsp & Diana Watson Obey Schlsp Comms; NEA 1966-; SUNY at Albany Schl of Ed Outstdng Tchr of Excl Awd 1986; *home:* 2 Robert Townsend Dr Setauket NY 11733*

HAZELTINE, RUSSELL GENE, Social Studies Teacher; *b:* Conneaut, OH; *ed:* Kent St Univ (BA) Soc Stud Comp; Edinboro St Univ (MS) Scndry Ed 1987; 15 Addl Hrs Scndry Admin Cert PA & OH; 3 Addl Hrs; *cr:* Town & Country Driving Schl Classroom & In Car Instr 1976-77; Rowe MS 8th Grd Amer His Tchr 1978-89; Conneaut HS Glob Geo, Govt, Sociology Tchr 1993; *ai:* MS Track Coach; Key Clb Adv; Conneaut Ed Assn 1978-, Bldg Rep & Legislative Chm; OH Educ Assn 1978-; OH Assn Soc Stud Tchrs 1992-; Gideons Intnl 1991- Chaplin; Gideons Intnl 1991-; Federated Church 1960-, Usher, Media Coord; *home:* 471 Liberty St Conneaut OH 44030

HAZELTON, R. LOIS, Asst Dean, Soc Stud & His Tchr; *b:* Rockville Centre, NY; *m:* Michael; *c:* Michael R., Kari; *ed:* SUNY at New Paltz (BS) Soc Stud 1964, (MS) Ed 1968; 66 Credit Hrs; *cr:* Statsburg Cntrl Schl Soc Stud & Eng Tchr 1964; Coprague Jr HS Soc Stud Tchr 1964-71; Hewlett Schl Soc Stud Tchr, Asst Dean 1979-; *ai:* Yrbk Adv; Mid Sts Chm; Steering Comm; Natl Soc Stud Cncl 1981-; League of Women Voters 1970-, Treas; Pilot Club Babylon Village 1992-; Babylon Womens Club 1994-; *office:* Hewlett Schl 74 Suffolk Ln East Islip NY 11730

HAZLETT, ALEC E., Head of Ceramics Dept; *b:* Chicago, IL; *ed:* Schl for Amer Craftsmen Rochester Inst of Tech (MFA) Sculpture 1972, (BFA) Ceramics 1971; Stud Traditional Ceramics India 1988-89, 1972, Japan 1970; *cr:* Univ of Rochester Meml Art Gallery Ceramics Instr 1967-, Head of Ceramics 1983-; *office:* Univ of Rochester Meml Art Gallery 500 University Ave Rochester NY 14607

HAZLETT, BETTY EALY, English Teacher; *b:* Lewisburg, TN; *m:* David H.; *ed:* Univ of Akron (BA)Lbrl Arts 1969, (MA) Eng 1971; *cr:* Univ of Akron Eng Dept Grad Asst 1969-71; Rootstown Local Schls 10th-11th Grd Eng Tchr 1971-; *ai:* Northcentral Evaluation Comm; Target Area Sub-Comm Choir; Rootstown Tchrs Assn 1969-, Pres, Sec; Church of Good Shepherd, United Meth 1957-, Choir Mem; *office:* Rootstown Local Schls 4170 State Rt 44 Rootstown OH 44272

HAZUDA, JULIANA, Math Seminar Leader & Sub Tchr; *b:* Williamstown, PA; *ed:* Coll Misericordia (BA) Eng 1949; Villanova Univ (MA) Ed 1964; *cr:* Our Lady's Elem Tchr 1940-46; St Marys Elem Tchr 1946-50; St Francis Xavier Elem Tchr 1950-53; St Joseph Elem Tchr 1953-56; Bishop Mc Devitt HS 10th Grd Eng Tchr 1956-60; Sacred Heart Prin 1960-66; St Teresa Jr High Tchr 1966-68; St Francis Harrisburg Prin 1968-72; St Francis Gettysburg Jr High Tchr 1972-; *ai:* Taugh Church & Schl Choirs; NCEA; Received Frederick Noel Distngd Edctr Awd by Diocese of Harrisburg 1993.

HAZZARD, BARRY DAVID, English Teacher; *b:* Leominster, MA; *m:* Margaret Jane Karcher; *c:* Katherine L., Scott B.; *ed:* Univ of MA (BA) Theatre 1970 & (MAT) Ed 1971; *cr:* Chelmsford High Eng Tchr 1971-; *ai:* Georgetown Historical Soc 1974-, Recording Sec; Manuscript Soc 1992-; *home:* PO Box 814 Georgetown MA 01833

HEAD, LAWRENCE V.,JR., English Teacher; *b:* Dayton, OH; *c:* Lauren S. Smith, Lindsey S. Smith; *cr:* Wogaman Elem Schl Eng Tchr 1964-71; E. J. Brown Elem Schl Eng Tchr 1971-77; Alternative West HS Eng Tchr 1977-82; Miami Jacobs Coll Adj Prof 1975-93; Wilberforce Univ Adj Prof 1983-85; Belmont HS Eng Tchr 1982-; *ai:* NEA, OH Ed Assn 1967-; Dayton Ed Assn 1967-, Bldg Rep; Xenia Boys & Girls Club 1992-94, Ed Dir; Dayton Boys & Girls Club 1993-94, Interim Unit Dir, Tutor; Tchr of Yr 1978; Outstdng Young Man of Amer 1980; Good Neighbor 1975-76.*

HEADEN, ROBERT JAMES, PE Teacher & Athletic Dir; *b:* Washington, DC; *m:* Gail Jenkins; *c:* Lesha, Dana, Robert Jr., Nikki; *ed:* St Augustine's Coll (BA) Hlth, PE 1963; Bowie St Coll (MA) Ed 1971; *cr:* Cardozo HS Tchr, Coach 1964-71; H. D. Woodson Sr HS Tchr, Coach, Ath Dir 1971-; *ai:* Head Ftbl, Girls Bsktbl Coach; Dean of Stdnts; NHSACA 1972-, Bd Chm DC; DCIAA 1964-, Pres, Coach of Yr; WA Tchrs Union 1964-; Inferno's Inc 1968-, Pres 6 Yrs; DC Coaches Assn, NFCA, Natl HS Coaches Assn; Kappa Alpha Psi, DC Fed of Clubs 1975-80; DC Pub Schl Ath Advy Comm 1980-, Vice Chm; Pigskin Club of WA DC 1983-; Clinic Speaker Natl HS Coaches Assn, VA HS Coaches Assn; Expert Prgm Coord, Office of Asst Commissioner, Coord; Ad-Hoc Comm on Drug Abuse; Yth Opportunity Svc, Prgm Evaluator 1970-71, Dir Specialist 1974; BRIC Summer Yth Prgm Dir 1984-87; 1962 Ath of Yr, All Conf Back; Coach of Yr Pigskin Club 1968, 1975, 1982, 1994; Eastern Bd of Ofcls Coach of Yr 1968, Ftbl 1978, 1987, 1994, Girls Bsktbl 1979, 1984; Coach of Yr DC Coaches Assn Ftbl, Bsktbl 1994; Natl HS Ath Coaches Assn Hall of Fame 1996; Outstdng Contribution to Comm 1969, AEADNMS Inc & Inferno's Inc; Who's Who Among Stdnts in Amer Univ & Coll 1971-72; *office:* Howard D Woodson Sr HS 55th & Eads St NE Washington DC 20019

HEADINGS, MARK ELMER, Associate Professor; *b:* Halsey, OR; *m:* Mary Kathryn Wenger; *c:* Lisa Amstutz, Leon, Bruce; *ed:* Goshen Coll (BA) Bio 1964; MI St Univ (MS) Entomology 1971, (PHD) Entomology 1975; Hesston Coll Gen Stud 1956-57; *cr:* Ag Div of Rhodia Inc Prod Dev Rep 1974, Project Ldr for Insecticide Dev 1975-76; Univ of Guam Asst Prof of Ent 1976-78; OH St Univ Ag Tech Inst Asst, Assoc Prof 1978-, Division Chair 1982-93; *ai:* Fac Senate VP; Rsrch Creative & Other Scholarly Activity Comm, Intnl Comm Chair; Distngd Tchng Comm; Entomological Soc of Amer 1974-; Natl Assn of Colls & Tchrs of Ag 1979-; Caribbean Food Crops Soc 1989-; Phi Beta Delta 1987-; Wayne United Chaplain Ministeries 1988-, Governing Bd Chair; OH Agrobusiness Assn, Tri Cty Beekeepers Assn 1979-; Distngd Tchng Awd 1995; OSU Coll of Ag & Environmental Sci Excl in Tchng Awd 1995; NISOD Excl in Tchng Awd 1996; Guam EDA Cert for Outstdng & Remarkable Contributions to Guams Pesticide Applicator Cert Trng Prgm; *office:* OH St Univ Agri Tech Inst 1328 Dover Rd Wooster OH 44691*

HEADLEY, JACQUELINE JACKMAN, Fifth Grade Teacher; *b:* New York, NY; *m:* Harold; *c:* Adrienne H., Monique H., Christopher H., Courtney H.; *ed:* CUNY at Hunter Coll (BA) Sociology, (MS) Elem Ed; *cr:* CES 63 1st-6th Grd, Rdng Specialist Cmptr, Sci Labs, 5th Grd Tchr; *ai:* Pupil Prsnl, Prin's Consultative Advy Comms; AFT; UFT; NAACP; Zeta Phi Beta; Jamaican Amer Cultural & Civic Assn Rockland; Tops for Tots Daycare Ctr, Bd of Dirs; Several Alumni Awds.

HEADLEY, JANICE MARIE, Home Economics Teacher; *b:* Rochester, NY; *ed:* St Univ COll of NY at Oneonta (BS) Home Ec Ed 1967; 33 Credit Hrs Grad Work Russell Sage Coll Hlth Ed; *cr:* Catskill Cntrl Schls Home Ec Tchr 1967-; *ai:* Prof Practices Comm; HS Shared Decision Making; Prof Dev Comm; NYSUT, NYSTA 1967-; NYSHETA 1967-75; NYS Mentoring Assn 1990-; BPW 1974-78, Yth Adv; Own Silver Threads & Golden Needles Creative Sewing; *office:* Catskill HS 343 W Main St Catskill NY 12414

HEADLEY, RUSSELL MATTHEW, English Teacher; *b:* Paden City, WV; *m:* Kelly Howell Headley; *c:* John Franklin; *ed:* Bethany Coll (BA) Eng 1989; WV Univ (MA) Eng 1992; *cr:* WV Univ Grad Tchng Asst 1988-90; La Plata HS Eng Tchr 1990-; *ai:* Ftbl Coach 1990-91; Alpha Beta Gamma 1988-; Natl Rifle Assn 1991-; Helped Design, Implement AP Lang, Composition Curr; *home:* 1648 Pin Oak Dr Waldorf MD 20601

HEALD, MARY BROWN, Eng, Philosophy & Lit Teacher; *b:* Ticonderoga, NY; *m:* Frank; *c:* Amy, Ann, Gabriel; *ed:* Cameron Univ (BA) Eng 1972; SUNY at Plattsburgh (BA) His 1973, (MA) Ed & Commnctn 1991; Smith Coll at Northampton Curr Dev 1986; Oxford Univ at England Stud TS Eliot & WB Yeats 1991; *cr:* St Bernards & St Patricks Schls 2nd & 4th Grd Tchr 1968-71; Vly News Denton Publications News Reporter & Feature Writer 1979-81; Sylvanbrook Spinnery Home Bus Part-Time Sheep Flock Mgr & Spinnery Technique Tchr 1975-; *ai:* Stu Cncl Adv; First Essex Cty Assn of Stu Cncl Organizer; NCTE; NYSUT; Bus & Prof Womens 1993-; Westport Cntrl Schl Bd of Ed, Past Pres; Cooperative Extension Bd of Dir 6 yrs, Treas 3 Yrs; Adirondack Mountain Handspinners Guild, Founder & Past Pres; Treadwell Flwshp to Stud at Oxford Univ; Intnl Paper Edcore Awd for Best Written Hinman Grant; Cooperative Extension Recognition Awd for 6 Yrs Svc on Bd of Dirs; *home:* RR 1 Box 1170 Westport NY 12993*

HEALEY, CAROLYNNE EARL, Mathematics Teacher; *b:* Brooklyn, NY; *c:* Ryan; *ed:* St Francis Coll (BS) Elem Ed 1975; Jersey City St Coll 30 Credits Supervision & Admin; *cr:* Village Schl 6-8 Grd Lang Arts & Math Tchr 1975-76; Haskell Schl 4th Grd Tchr 1977-80; Wanaque Schl 7th Grd Sci & Math Tchr 1977-80; West Jefferson HS 9-12 Grd Math Tchr 1980-81; Hasbrouck Hghts Jr-Sr HS 8-12 Grd Math Tchr 1986-; *ai:* NHS Adv; HHEA Bldg Rep; AMTNJ, NCTM 1993-; Hasbrouck Hghts Tchrs Ed Assn 1986-; MSDC St Catharine's Church 1981-, Founder 1981-86, Eucharistic Minister 1986-92, CCD Tchr 1993-94; Math Tchr of Yr Awd 1990; Adjunct Prof Montclair St Coll Critical Thinking Project; The Algebra Project Tchr Trainer Algebra I Consultant, Co-Author Algebra II; Pres Awd Nom 1992; *office:* Hasbrouck Hghts Jr-Sr HS 365 Boulevard Hasbrouck Hts NJ 07604*

HEALEY, LISA BATTISTA, High School Math Teacher; *b:* Worcester, MA; *m:* Thomas J.; *ed:* Worcester Polytechnic Inst (BS) Math 1990; 27 Credit Hrs Scndry Schl Cert Worcester St Coll; *cr:* Southern New England Telephone Budget, Depreciation Analyst 1990-94; Paul Revere Insurance Co Actuarial Analyst 1994; Holy Name Cntrl Catholic HS Math Tchr 1994-; *ai:* Coach Var, Frosh Math Teams; Adv Class of 98; *office:* Holy Name Central Catholic HS 144 Granite St Worcester MA 01604

HEALEY, PATRICIA ANNE, Spanish Teacher; *b:* Scranton, PA; *m:* John Paul; *c:* Erin, Kelly, Shannon; *ed:* Mansfield Univ (BS)Span 1971; Attnd Penn St Univ; *cr:* North Pocono HS Span Tchr 1971-80; Abington Hghts HS Span Tchr 1988-; *ai:* Skills in Scranton Grant for Tchrs; *office:* Abington Heights HS Noble Rd Clarks Summit PA 18411

HEALY, ANN CONSIDINE, English Teacher; *b:* Dorchester, MA; *m:* Kenneth T.; *ed:* Merrimack Coll (BS) Eng 1985; Salem St Coll (MA) Eng 1993; *cr:* Woodstock Union HS 8th Grd Eng Tchr 1985-87; St Louis Acad HS Eng Tchr 1988-92; Lowell Cath HS Eng Tchr 1992-; *ai:* Yrbk Adv; NCTE 1985-; *office:* Lowell Catholic HS 530 Stevens St Lowell MA 01851*

HEALY, DANIEL JOSEPH, Math Instructor; *b:* Pittsfield, MS; *w:* Karen Ann White (dec); *c:* Corin Lee (dec); *ed:* Berkshire Comm Coll (AA) Engrng 1982; North Adams St Coll (BA) Math 1985; Amer Intnl Coll (MED) Scndry Ed 1993; USAF Tech Schl Air Passenger Specialist; *cr:* MA Hwy Dept Grd 1 Engr 1985-86; Berkshire Comm Coll Instr 1988-; *ai:* Calculus Math Tutor; MTA 1988-; *home:* 64 Circular Ave Pittsfield MA 01201

HEALY, JANE E. NEWELL, Home Ec & Home Careers Teacher; *b:* Glens Falls, NY; *m:* Edmund M.; *c:* Ryan, Kathleen; *ed:* SUNY at Plattsburgh (BS) Home Ec 1967; SUNY at New Paltz (MS) K-12, Rdng 1984; *cr:* Long Beach City Schl Dist Home Ec Tchr 1967-71; Onteora Cntrl Schl Home Ec Tchr 1971-73; Ellenville Cntrl Schl Home Ec Tchr 1973-77, 1981-84; Monticello Cntrl Schl HS Rdng Tchr 1984-86; Ellenville Cntrl Schl Home Ec Tchr 1986-; *ai:* Home Ec Dept Chm 1990-; Stu of the Month Coord; Yrbk Photographer; Bldg Level Team Chm 1995-; Ellenville Tchrs Assn, Rep; AFT, NEA, NYSTA 1967-; NYSAFCSE 1986-; Ulster Cty Rdng 1984-; *office:* Ellenville Central Schl 28 Maple Ave Ellenville NY 12428

HEALY, JOHN WILLIAM, 6th-8th Grade Art Teacher; *b:* New York City, NY; *m:* Patricia; *c:* Ryan, Christopher; *ed:* Long Island Univ (BA) Art Ed 1971; Columbia Univ (MS) Art Ed 1973, (MED) Art Ed 1975, (EDD) Art Ed, Coll Tchng 1977; Schl Dist Admin Permanent Cert 1992-; *cr:* Woodland MS Tenured Art Tchr 1988-; *ai:* Art Club; Kappa Delta Pi 1978-; Natl MS Assn 1994-, Conf Speaker 1995; Bd of Jewish Ed of Greater NY; US Army 1073-75, First Lt., Paratrooper, Honorable Discharge; Schl of Educl Ldrshp, Admin Outstdng Stu Awd 1992-93; Order Sons ofof Italy in Amer Golden Lion Awd; Nassau Cty Office of Exec Citation 1990; AT&T, East Meadow Kiwanis, Litton Applied Tech, Coca Cola Bottling Co Grants; *office:* Woodland MS 690 Wenwood Dr East Meadow NY 11554

HEANEY, KAREN CARONE, Middle School Counselor; *b:* Geneva, NY; *m:* Michael; *c:* Shannon, Jason, Brianne; *ed:* SUNY at Brockport (BS) Developmental Psych 1982; Univ of Rochester (MSEd) Ed & Schl Cnslng 1989; 30 Credit Hrs NYS Permanent Cert 1992; *cr:* SUNY Employee Assistance Coord 1982-87; Rochester City Schls Child Dev Specialist 1987-88; Brockport Cntrl K-5th Grd Sub Tchr 1988-89; Arcadia MS 6th-8th Grd Schl Cnslr 1989-; *ai:* Schl Bd Mem 1987-89; CARE Team Chprsn 1991-93; Yth to Yth Adv 1989-93; Kappa Delta Pi 1989-90; NEA 1989-; ASCA 1995-; ACA 1995-; NBCC 1995-; NIMH Grant SUNY EAP Conf 1982; United Univ Profs Awd for Svc 1987; United Way Cert of Achvmt 1984; *office:* Arcadia MS 130 Island Cottage Rd Ro 14612*

HEANEY, MARGARET D., Sixth Grade Teacher; *b:* Buffal Medaille Coll (BS) Ed 1970; 36 Post Grad Hrs St Univ NY Buffalo St Univ at Buffalo, Christ the King Seminary; *cr:* Buffa Primary Tchr for Hard of Hearing 1970-72; Buffalo Schl # 23 5t 1972-73; Buffalo Schl #31 3rd, 4th Grd Tchr 1973-76; Buffal 5th Grd Tchr 1976-78; Buffalo Schl #54 Kndgtn, 4th Grd Tch Buffalo Schl #12 5th Grd Tchr 1980-81; Buffalo Schl #33 1st, 2 Tchr 1981-85; Family Care Svcs Dir Human Resources 1985-8 Schl #33 5th, 6th Grd Tchr 1987-94, 1994-, Magnet Schl 1994-95; *ai:* Site Base Mngmt, Crisis, Conflict Resolution Te 1970-; Buffalo Tchrs Fed 1970-, Del Chprsn, Bldg Comm; Buff 1985-86, Advy Bd; Southtowns Cath 1991-, VP, Schl Bd; Er 1978-, Advy Bd Pres, Instr; St Vincent DePaul 1986-92, Vol P Pres; Guiding Eyes for Blind Donated Labrador Retriver D Raisers Inst; Buffalo Kennel Club 1994-, Bd of Dir; Buffalo Environmental Group; Org Help Buffalo River Feature Geographic Environmental Documentary; *office:* Biling Ctr Sc Elk St Buffalo NY 14210*

HEANEY-HUNTER, JOANN CATHERINE, Assoc Pr Theology; *b:* Bronx, NY; *m:* Gregory S. Hunter; *c:* Bethanne, *ed:* St John's Univ (BA) Psych 1978, (MA) Theology 1981; For (PHD) Historical Theology 1988; *cr:* St John's Univ Fin Aid Of Fordham Univ Grad Asst 1983-87; St John's Univ Theology Pro Undergradute Policy, Univ Mission Effectiveness Comms; Dev First Yr Experience; Coll Theology Soc 1987-; Cath Theolog Amer 1989-; St Aidan's Parish 1988-, Pres Parents Assn, Pres Bd; Fnd Grant to Dev Marriage Preparation Prgm; 1 Book; 1 Outstdng Undergraduate Tchr 1995; Inducted in Skull & Circ 1990; *office:* Saint Johns Univ 8000 Utopia Pkwy Jamaica NY

HEARN, DOLORES ANN (DOLGAS), High School English Passaic, NJ; *m:* Brian R.; *ed:* Coll Misericordia (BA) Eng 1963 Hrs NY Univ; 15 Credit Hrs William Paterson Coll; 3 Credit City St Coll; *cr:* East Paterson HS Eng Tchr 1964-69; Glen Rid Tchr 1970-; *ai:* NHS Adv; NEA, NJEA 1964-; GREA 1970-; *o* Ridge HS 200 Ridgewood Ave Glen Ridge NJ 07028

HEARST-WEISSMAN, JUDI, English Teacher; *b:* Long Bea Leonard; *ed:* Hofstra Univ (BA) Eng Ed 1974; Stony Brook Psych, Eng 1978; South Oaks Hosp Inst of Ed (EDC) Eating Cnslng 1987; 40 Credit Hrs Post Grad; *cr:* Brentwood HS Eng Brentwood Evening HS Eng Tchr 1976-82; Eating Disorders C Founder, Dir 1989-; *ai:* Body Image Group Founder & Adv; P Class 1982-84, Jr Class 1981, 1984; Track Coach 1980; Tw 1976-81; AFT, NYSUT, Brentwood Tchrs Assn 1974-; Natl Assn Disorders Cnslrs 1989-; Tchr of Yr 1982-83, 1992-93; Tchr of M Schl Improvement Team 1992-93; One of 200 Teachers Nationwide to Attnd 1995 Conf for Edctrs of Holocaust Holocaust Museum; *office:* Brentwood HS Sonderling Center NY 11717

HEASTINGS, BARBARA MILLER, Choral Music Di Waynesburg, PA; *m:* Richard James; *c:* Joanna L. Dragan, Step Dragan; *ed:* West Chester Univ (BS) Music Ed 1971; Level I Grad Classes at WV Univ & Duquesne Univ; *cr:* Washington Schl General Music & Orff Ens Tchr 1971-86; Saint Mary & Organist & Choir Dir 1977-92; Washington Park MS General M Dir 1986-; *ai:* After-Schl Ensemble Dir; PMEA, MENC 19 PSEA, NEA 1971-; Alpha Delta Kappa 1996; Pub Composer; H Sing Festival at PMEA Convention at Pittsburgh PA 19 Washington Park MS 801 E Wheeling St Washington PA 15301

HEATH, DAVID MARTIN, Professor; *b:* Philadelphia, PA; *e* HS Equivelancy 1953-54; Wkshps W. Eugene Smith; *cr:* Dayt Instr 1965-67; Moore Coll of Art Asst Prof 1965-70; Ryerson 1970-; *ai:* Guggenheim Fellow 1963-64, 1964-65; Book A Dia Solitude 1965.

HEATH, DOUGLAS EDWIN, Geography & Geology Pro Beverly, MA; *m:* Ellen Rosemary Morris; *c:* Laura E.; *ed:* Buc (BS) Geology 1971; Syracuse Univ (MA) Geography 19 Geography 1978; *cr:* St Univ of NY at Cortland Adjunct Inst 1973-75; St Univ of NY at Buffalo Temporary Asst Prof Northampton Comm Coll Instr 1977-, Prof 1987-; *ai:* Long Learning Task Force; Fac Tech Trng Group; Lib Adv Internationalism Task Force; Assn of Amer Geographers 1974-; for Geographic Ed 1980-, Tchng Awd 1983; AFT 1977- c; S 1973-, Former Local Chapter Prgm Chm; Unitarian Soc of 1989-, Ministerial Relations Comm Chair; Northampton Comm Awd 1983; Northampton Comm Coll Institutional Stud fo Reaccreditation Dir 1985, General Ed Core Revision Curr Co 1990; Pub Various Research Articles, Pedagoical Articles Chapters; *office:* Northampton Comm Coll 3835 Green Pond Rd PA 18017

HEATH, ELISABETH LAURA, Music Tchr & Dir; *b:* Shrev *ed:* Univ of NC at Greensboro (BM) Music Ed 1980; Duquesne Music Ed & Conducting 1990; *cr:* Douglas Byrd Jr & Sr HS 1980-88; Duquesne Univ Adj Prof of Music 1990-; Jewish Music Tchr 1990-, Dir of Perlow Schl of Music 1996; *ai:* Conduc Orchestra & Ovations Yth Orch; Guest Conductor & Clinician NCMEA Band & Orch Festivals; Mu Phi Epsilon 1976-, Pres 19 1980-; Phi Beta Mu 1984-; *office:* Jewish Community Ctr 5738 Pittsburgh PA 15217*

HEATH, JOAN HUDNELL, 6th Grade Teacher; *b:* Mobile, AL; Anthony; *ed:* Jackson St Univ (BS) Elem Ed 1967; Wright St Elem Prin 1978; Univ of Dayton Working Toward PHD Admin; Pub Schl Elem Tchr 1967-68; Cleveland Pub Schl Elem Tchr Dayton Pub Schls Elem Tchr 1969-; Montgomery Cty Children S Ldr 1972-74; *ai:* NEA, Dayton Ed Assn 1967-; Deborah Chptr # of Easters Stars 1976-, Past Matron; Daughter of Iris 1977-; Alp Alpha 1978-, Adv; Mt Alive Bapt Church; *home:* 801 Creekside OH 45427*

HEATH, KRISTIN HARTFORD, Math, Computer & Scienc Philadelphia, PA; *ed:* PA St Univ (BS) Sci 1989; Long Island Math Ed 1993; Brookhaven Natl Lab Tchr Rsrch Prgm; *cr:* Norde Assoc Software Engr 1992-93; Ward Melville HS Math, Cmpt 1993-; *ai:* Project Women Sci, Engrng Adv; Phi Beta Kappa 19 Mu Epsilon 1994-; *office:* Ward Melville HS 380 Old Town R NY 11733

HEATH, LINDA SUSAN, 9th-12th Grade Math Teacher; *b:* Stat NY; *m:* Stephen T. Sr.; *c:* William Andrew, Stephen T. Jr.; *ed:* Ru (BA) Math 1974; 6 Grad Credits Univ of DE; 1 Grad Credit W Univ; *cr:* Maple Shade HS 7th-8th Grade Tchr 1974-75; Glouc HS 9,10, 11th Grd Tchr 1976-77; Incarnate Word HS 9,12th 1983-84; Bishop Eustace Prep Schl 9,12th Grd Tchr 1978-8 Tutoring Rutgers Univ, Greenberg, Haddonfield; Torch Sum 1994; *ai:* Debate Moderator; Cum Laude Adv; Mock Trial Team Companion; Litrgcl Mnstr; NCTM 1974-; MAA 1991-; NJ Tchrs NCEA 1990-; Cub Scouts 1988-, Tiger Scout Moderator, 1 Y

Parish 1987-, Lector, CCD Tchr, Cantor; Unsung Hero 1982; :oach of Yr 1977; Cert Svc, CCD Tchr; Nom for Outstanding of DE Valley; *home:* 15 Woodland Ave Clementon NJ 08021*

MARY, Guidance Director; *b:* Littleton, NH; *m:* Thomas; *c:* ny, Chelsea; *ed:* Plymouth St Coll (BS) Elem Ed 1978, (MED) ; Attnd Northeastern Univ 1973-76; *cr:* Lisbon Regnl Schl 1 Grd -89, Kndgtn Tchr 1989-90, Elem Guid Cnslr 1989-91, HS Guid *ai:* Curr Steering, Staff Dev, Littleton Area Wrap Around Svcs d Comms; Cultural Diversity Comm Adv; Lisbon Tchrs Assn arn, Serve Amer Grant; Baker Stoll Family Grant; NY St Cncl on onoosuc Region Arts Cncl Grant; *office:* Lisbon Regional Schl nd Ave Lisbon NH 03585

WILLIAM RALPH, Professor of English; *b:* Youngstown, OH; :aminals; *ed:* Case Western Reserve Univ (MA) Amer Stud 1967, ier Stud 1971; *cr:* Kenyon Coll Instr 1967-69; Transylvania Coll 1969-74; Vassar Coll Asst Prof 1974-79; Univ of Seville Prof 1979-81; Mt St Mary's Coll Assoc Prof 1981-; *ai:* Ed Vly Review; Adv Lighted Corners; Ath Review, Lib Comms; :l; MLA; AWP; Pub Book of Related Poems 1994, Novel 1995, *fice:* Mount Saint Marys Coll Emmitsburg MD 21727

Y, KATHERINE EILEEN, Kindergarten Teacher; *b:* New York, therine Eileen Rose; *c:* Shana, Jesse; *ed:* Adelphi Univ (BA) Soc , (MA) Elem Ed 1973; 30 Post Grad Credit Hrs; *cr:* Quague Elem 14 Yrs; *ai:* Quague Tchrs Assn 1982-, Sec; Pending Childrens , *office:* Quogue Elem Schl PO Box 957 Edgewood Rd Quogue

, DALENE JONES, Mathematics Teacher; *b:* Oak Hill, OH; *m:* :: Bryan, Christopher; *ed:* West Liberty St Coll (BA) Math Ed v of Dayton (MA) Educl Admin 1982; Attnd Ashland Univ, OH rs Post Grad Stud; *cr:* Buckeye Cntrl Jr High Math Tchr 1976-77; 'ntrl HS Math Tchr 1977-79; Buckeye North H S Math Tchr Buckeye Local HS Math Tchr 1990-; *ai:* Sci Bowl Spon; NEA :TM 1979-; NCTM 1988-; Delta Kappa Gamma 1990-; *office:* .ocal HS Rd 2 Box 475 Rayland OH 43943

, RENATE R., 5th Grade Teacher; *b:* Rendsburg, Germany; *m:* ; *c:* Jennifer S.; *ed:* Northeastern Univ (BA) Eng, Ger, Ed 1969; am St Coll Working on Masters; General Psych 4 Credit Hrs; ical Fnds of Ed 4 Credit Hrs; Rdng & Stud Skills in Mid Schl 4 ; Children's Lit 4 Credit Hrs; Writing Fluency in Mid Schl Level Hrs; *cr:* Mindess MS 7th & 8th Grd Lang & Rdng Tchr 1969-83, chr 1969-, 5th Grd Lang Arts, Rdng, Math Tchr 1983-; *ai:* Headed coring Team; Class Adv; Report Card Dev Comm; Chief Reader Ldr Ashland Basic Competency Testing; Great Books, Curr, Lang g Comms; Stu Newspaper Adv; DARE Prgm; Parade Across Amer A 1969-, Nominating Comm Sec; NEA 1969-; New England Mid 1986-; Ashland Tchrs Org 1969-; Friends of Lib 1975-, Sec, ork; Nobscot Rdng Cncl, Comm Work; Teenage Suicide Hot Line one Call Organizer, Trng Callers; Alzeimhers Assn Local Chapter , Book Research; Needham Pub Lib, Story Hour, Book Reviews; ng Educator in Local Metro West Region 1993; Tchr Nom & on in Metro West Area 1988; Holistic Scoring of Basic cy Testing in MA & Ashland; Creative Stud Writing Lang Arts *ne:* 50 Wedgewood Dr Hopkinton MA 01748

, SHEILA HAYES, Middle School Science Teacher; *b:* NY; *m:* Michael; *c:* Matthew; *ed:* Niagara Univ (BS) Bio 1990; St (ME) Ed 1994; *cr:* Cuba Cntrl Schl 7th-9th Grd Sci Tchr Poland Cntrl Schl 7th & 8th Grd Sci Tchr 1991-; *ai:* Sr Class Adv; AFT 1991-; MS Assn 1993-; Tchr of Yr Runner Up 1994; *office:* entral Schl Rt 8 Box 8 Poland NY 13431*

R, LEE PERRY, Agricultural Education Teacher; *b:* nd, MD; *m:* Deborah Ann Crone; *ed:* Potomac St Coll (AA) Ag ' Univ (BS) Ag Ed 1973; Univ of MD at College Park 15 Grad rostburg St Univ 15 Grad Credits; *cr:* Broad Run HS Agricultural 1974; Francis Scott Key HS Agricultural Ed Tchr 1974-76; HS Agricultural Ed Tchr 1976-; *ai:* FFA Adv; Teach Hunter H Vol Adv; Allegany Co Soccer Ofcl 1980-; NEA, MSTA, ACTA) Ag Tchrs Assn 1974-, Treas, Sec, VP, Pres 1982; Allegany Co eau 1980-, Bd of Supervisions; Soil Conservation Dist 1979-, egany Co; East Gate Lodge 217 AF&AM 1995-; St of MD Young Ag Tchr 1978, Outstdng Ag Ed Ldrshp Awd 1982; Amer FFA Degree 1983; Svc to Allegany Co Ag Farm Bureau ce: Flintstone HS 22000 National Pike Flintstone MD 21530*

.D, RONALD WALTER, 9th Grd Physical Science Tchr; *b:* :S; *m:* MaryJane Abbuzzese; *c:* Veronica Ashley; *ed:* SUNY at (BS) PE 1984; 39 Credit Hrs Exercise Physiology San Diego St Credit Hrs Multicultural Ed & 6 Credit Hrs Admin at IONA; *cr:* Vly MS PE Tchr 1991-92; Vly Cntrl HS 9th Grd PE Sci Tchr Var Track Coach 1987-93; Head Coach 1993-; Indoor & Outdoor Track Coach; NYSUT 1993-; *office:* Valley Central HS Rt 17K ery NY 12549*

CH, DARALYN DUQUETTE, Eighth Grade English Teacher; *b:* e, MA; *c:* Joelle Meunier, Nicholas; *ed:* Lesley Coll (BS) Ed dgewater St (MA) Ed 1990; *cr:* Masconomet Regnl Jr, Sr High 9-81; Sandwich Jr, Sr High Tchr 1981-87; Oak Ridge Schl Tchr NEA 1978-; SEA 1981-; Natl Sci Fnd Fellowship; *office:* Oak nl 260 Quaker Meeting House Rd Sandwich MA 02563

,E, JANET MILLER, Business Education Teacher; *b:* n, PA; *m:* Raymond R.; *c:* Sarah; *ed:* IN Univ of PA (BS) Bus Ed S) Bus Ed 1967; Attnd Duquesne Univ Supervisory I Cert Bus Ed, Cert Scndry Ed 1977; *cr:* Sharpsburg HS Bus Tchr 1962-64; ea HS Bus Tchr 1964-; *ai:* Staff Dev Comm; Bus Ed Dept Chm; EA 1962-; SAEA 1964-, Sec 2 Yrs; PBEA, Tri St Bus Ed Assn; chlsp Recognition Excl in Grad Stud IN Univ of PA; *office:* Shaler IS 381 Wible Run Rd Pittsburgh PA 15209*

', KATHERINE CAMPBELL, English Department Head; *b:* ce, RI; *m:* Adrien W.; *c:* Molly Opiekun, Brendan Opiekun, drien Jr.; *ed:* Emmanuel Coll, Schl of Irish Stud (BA) Eng 1972; l, Univ Coll (MA) Irish His 1983; Providence Coll (MS) Scndry 89; 30 Addl Credit Hrs Eng, Spec Ed, Ed; *cr:* Coventry HS Eng 3-74; Attleboro HS Eng Tchr 1974-, Eng Dept Head 1985-; *ai:* gazine Adv; NEA; MA Tchrs Assn; MA Cncl of Tchrs Eng; New Assn Tchr of Eng; NCTE; Outstanding Young Amer Woman 1982; eral Articles on Travel & His; *office:* Attleboro HS Rathbun)r Attleboro MA 02703

', RONALD A., Orch Director & District Coord; *b:* Yonkers, NY; E.; *c:* Shawn, Seth; *ed:* SUNY at Potsdam (BS) Music Ed 1968, sic Ed 1971; SUNY at Cortland (CAS) Educl Admin 1989; Attnd 3 Hrs & Elmira Coll 3 Hrs; 21 Addl Hrs & 3 In Service Credits; th Inst & Central Jr HS Orch Dir 1968-70; Malone Cntrl Jr HS Music 1971; Utica City Schls Orch Dir & String Tchr 1971-82; lle-manlius Central Schl Orch Dir, String Tchr & Dist Coord : Musical Theater Dir & Orch Conductor; Showboat Producer; lle-manlius Chamber Orch Dir; HS Curr Cncl & Bldg Comm ist Curr Cncl; AFT, NYSUT, ASTA, NSOA & PDK 1971-; \ 1968-, Exec Cncl, All St Orchestra Asst Chr 1994-1995, Chr MENC 1968-, Nationally Registered Music Educator Awd 1990, 1992; Onondaga Cty Music Educators Assn, Pres 1990-; CPP-BELWIN 1st Yr Popular Solos & 1st Yr Christmas Solos for Strings Awd; All-St & All Cty Orchs Guest Conductor & Adjudicator; *home:* 4653 Glencliffe Rd Manlius NY 13104*

HECHLER, SANDRA SHERMAN, French Teacher; *b:* Willimantic, CT; *m:* Stephen H.; *c:* Miriam P., Howard S.; *ed:* Brandeis Univ (BA) Fr Lit 1961; Columbia Univ (MA) Fr Lit 1963, (PHD) Fr Lit 1968; *cr:* Walton HS John Adams HS Fr Tchr 1962-64; Cleveland St Univ Asst Prof of Fr 1968-73; *ai:* AATF 1988-; LILT 1988-; *office:* Half Hollow Hills HS East 50 Vanderbilt Pky Dix Hills NY 11746*

HECHT, RICHARD, Seventh Grade Science Teacher; *b:* Baltimore, MD; *m:* Cindy Joy Bleakman; *c:* Bradley, Matthew; *ed:* Univ of MD (BS) Elem Ed 1976; Loyola Coll (ME) Guidance & Counseling 1985; *cr:* Winand Elem Schl Tchr 1976-85; Old Court MS Tchr 1985-93; Pikesville MS Tchr 1993-; *ai:* Sci & Hlth Liaison; NEA, TABCO, MSTA 1976-; Baltimore Cty Chamber of Commerce Excl in Ed Awd 1990; Sci Recognition Awd 1989-90 & 1993-94; *office:* Pikesville MS 7701 7 Mile Ln Baltimore MD 21208

HECHTMAN, SYLVIA SCHMER, Social Studies Teacher; *b:* Bronx, NY; *c:* Jennifer; *ed:* Hunter Coll (BA) His-Cum Laude 1963; Queens Coll (MS) His 1969; 30 Credit Hrs in Prof Dev 1995; *cr:* Walton HS Soc Stud Tchr 1963-66; I. S. 231 Queens Sub Tchr 1967-81; I. S. 237 Soc Stud Tchr 1986-; *ai:* Magnet Schl Comm; African Amer His Comm; Holocoust Comm Adv & Coord of Schls Prgm; Phi Beta Kappa, Phi Delta Kappa, Natl Assn Soc Stud Tchrs 1963-; *office:* IS 237 Rachel Carson 4621 Colden St Flushing NY 11355

HECK, DENNIS MICHAEL, Physical Education Teacher; *b:* Philadelphia, PA; *m:* Ellen Mary Jennings; *c:* Kristen Ann, Joseph Brendan; *ed:* Univ of RI (BA) PE 1981; Montclair St Univ Masters Grad Stud; *cr:* DePaul HS PE Tchr, Ftbl Coach 1981-83; Clifton HS PE Tchr, Ftbl Coach 1982-88; Teaneck HS PE Tchr, Ftbl Coach 1988-; *ai:* Pupil Asst Comm Mem, Head Ftbl & Golf Coach; NJEA 1981-; Bergen Cty Coaches Assn 1988-; NJ Ftbl Coaches Assn 1982-; *office:* Teaneck HS 100 Elizabeth Ave Teaneck NJ 07666*

HECK, KAREN MILLER, Business Teacher; *b:* Olney, MD; *m:* David J.; *c:* Amy Michele; *ed:* Univ of MD at College Park (BS) Bus Ed 1976; 30 Credit Hrs Toward Advanced Prof Cert Western MD Coll, Loyola Coll; *cr:* Mt Hebron HS Bus Teach 1976-77; Hammond HS Bus Tchr 1977-82; Howard HS Bus Tchr 1982-, Bus Dept Coord 1986-; *ai:* Tech, Co-Chair New Tchr Support Comm; Project Bus Spon; HCEA, MSTA, NEA 1977-; MBEA; Elders Bapt Church 1982-, Nominating Comm; Cooperating Tchr for Stu Tchrs; Presenter Wkshps; *office:* Howard HS # 108 8700 Old Annapolis Rd Ellicott City MD 21043

HECKARD, IDA ROSE (DOENNG), School Psychologist; *b:* San Diego, CA; *m:* George W.; *c:* George, Charissa, David; *ed:* Natl Univ (BA) Human Behavior 1987; Millersville Univ (MS) Psych 1990; 24 Grad Hrs Schl Psych Cert; 10 Hrs Doctoral Stud; *cr:* Cornwall-Lebanon Schl Dist Schl Psych Intern 1990-91, Schl Psych 1991-93; Penn St Univ Coll of Medicine Instr & Schl Psych 1993-94; Harrisburg Area Comm Coll Instr 1994-95; Wilson Schl Dist Schl Psych 1995-; *ai:* NASP 1989-; ASPP 1992-; Psi Chi NHS in Psych; NCSP Nationally Certfd Schl Psych 1995.

HECKATHORNE, DEBORAH KATHRYN (GARMONG), Mathematics Teacher; *b:* Oil City, PA; *m:* Robert Kenton; *c:* Amy, Andrew; *ed:* Edinboro Univ (BS) Math & General Sci 1974; Post Grad Stud at Clarion St Coll; *cr:* Victory MS Math Tchr 1974-75; Franklin HS Math, Bio & Chem Tchr 1975-78; Oil City HS Math Tchr 1984-; *ai:* Strategic Planning Comm; Clarion Univ Comm on Stu Tchrs; NEA, PSEA 1974-; OCAEA 1984-; NCTM 1991-.

HECKELMAN, DONALD DAVID,JR., Asst Prof of Engineering Sci; *b:* Huntington, NY; *m:* Nicole Christine Mozjesik; *ed:* Hudson Valley Comm Coll (AS) Engrng Sci 1979; Rensselaer Polytechnic Inst Mechanical Engrng (BS) 1981, (MS) 1982; ABD Mechanical Engrng 1985; *cr:* Power Kinetics Inc Design Engr 1983-84; NYS Dept of Ed Regents External Deg Examiner Consultant 1989; Hudson Valley Comm Coll Asst Prof 1985-; DIATECH Inc Engrng Design Consultant 1989-; *ai:* Engrng Sci Club Adv; ENS Curr Review Comms; SUNY-TYESA 1985-; Pres Awd for Excl in Tchng 1994; Article STLE Trans 1988; *office:* Hudson Valley Comm Coll 80 Vandenburgh Ave Troy NY 12180

HECKER, ZEKE, English Teacher; *b:* Newark, NJ; *m:* Linda Feigenbaum; *c:* Anna; *ed:* Harvard Coll (BA) Eng 1969; Univ of Hartford (MED) Urban Ed 1971; *cr:* Conn Correctional Inst Tchr 1969-71; Brattleboro Union HS Eng Tchr 1971-; *ai:* NHS Adv; Coord Metropolitan Opera Schl, Mbrshp Prgm; Family, Schl Partnership Comm; NEA 1974-; WSEA 1974-, Bd Dir; Friends of Music 1969-, Founder, Trustee; Consortium VT Composers 1989-, VP; Pioneer Vly Symphony 1973-, Prin Oboist; Windham Orch 1971-, Prin Oboist; Cncl Black Ed, NEH Summer Fllwshp; Summer Seminar Scndry Schl Tchrs; Newsletter Pub; Grants NEA, VT Cncl Arts, Meet Composer; Commissions Musical Compositions; Tchr of Yr 1973; *office:* Brattleboro Union HS 50 Fairground Rd Brattleboro VT 05301

HECKLER, DONALD WARREN,JR., Social Studies Teacher; *b:* Allentown, PA; *m:* Christine Johnson; *c:* Karen, Pamela; *ed:* Kings Coll at Wilkes-Barre (BA) His, Ed 1968; Loyola Coll at Baltimore (MED) Spec Ed 1972; Western MD Coll 30+ Post MA Hrs 1994; *cr:* Bel Air Jr HS Spec Ed Tchr 1968-70; Southampton MS Spec Ed, Eng, Soc Stud Tchr 1970-; *ai:* Schl Morale, Lib Book Review Comms; NEA; MSTA; HCEA; *office:* Southampton MS 1200 Moores Mill Rd Bel Air MD 21014

HECKMAN, ROSANNE FLAMISCH, Mathematics Tchr & Dept Chair; *b:* Northampton, PA; *m:* Kenneth R.; *c:* Richard K., Todd M.; *ed:* East Stroudsburg Univ (BS) Math 1968; Kutztown Univ (MED) Math 1972; Masters & 15 Addl Credits; *cr:* Parkland HS Math Tchr 1968-, Math Dept Chm 1980-; *ai:* Math Team & Scholastic Scrimmage Team Coach; Bldg Leadership Team Comm; NCTM 1995-; Outstanding Educator at Parkland HS; *office:* Parkland HS 2675 Pa Route 309 Orefield PA 18069

HECKMAN, RUTH WASINGER, Bio, Anatomy & Physiology Tchr; *b:* Hays, KS; *m:* James L.; *c:* James M., Amy E.; *ed:* Catholic Univ of Amer (BA) Bio 1969; Southern CT St Univ (MS) Environmental Ed 1988; Southern CT St Univ Educl Fnds Specialist 1990; *cr:* Kirby Jr High Sci Tchr 1969-78; Guilford HS Sci Tchr 1982-; *ai:* Attendance Appeals Comm; Fac Liason Comm; NEA, CEA & GEA 1982-; *office:* Guilford HS New England Rd Guilford CT 06437

HEDBERG, JACQUELINE HOPE, Social Studies Teacher; *b:* Honga, MD; *m:* James D.; *ed:* Western MD Coll (BA) His 1961; MI St Univ (MA) European His 1971; Johns Hopkins Univ (MLA) Liberal Arts 1993; 60 Addl Credit Hrs Beyond 2nd Masters Degree; *cr:* Overseas Dependent Schls Soc Stud Tchr 1964-70; Perry Hall HS Soc Stud Tchr 1974-80; Overlea HS Soc Stud Tchr 1980-82; Dulaney & Towson HS Tchr of GATE 1982-83; Dulaney & Perry Hall HS Tchr of GATE 1983-91; Dulaney HS Soc Stud & Hum Tchr 1991-; *ai:* NHS Co-Spon; NEA, MSTA & TABCO 1961-; NCSS 1974-; MD Writing Project 1985-, BACWAC Steering Comm 1987-90; League of Women Voters 1974-; Freedom to Read Fnd; Baltimore Cty Bd of Lib Trustees 1979-89, Sec 1982-85, Treas 1987-88; Balto Cnty Gftd & Tlntd Extrnl Evltn Steering Comm 1994-95; Cncl for Basic Ed Fellowship 1986; NS Capitol Historical Soc Baltimore Cty Tchr Historian 1986; Finalist Thanks to Tchrs Awd 1990; Baltimore Cty Chamber of Commerce Cert for Excl in Tchng 1987; Dept of Defense Outstanding Tchng Awd 1968; 2 Articles Pub in Soc Ed; MD St Dept of Ed Project, "Writing To Learn Module" 1993; Excl in Tchng Awd 1994; Hum Curr Prjct 1995; *office:* Dulaney H S 255 Padonia Rd Timonium MD 21093

HEDBERG, LORI JEAN, Physical Education Teacher; *b:* Springfield, OH; *ed:* Univ of Dayton (BS) K-12 PE 1985, (MS) PE 1993, (EDS) Admin 1994; *cr:* Bridgeview MS PE Tchr 1990-; *ai:* Var Boys, Girls Head Cross Cntry Coach; 8th Grd Girls Bsktbl Coach; Asst Var Girls Track Coach; PE Instr; Sidney Ed Assn 1990-, VP; Western OH Ed Assn 1990-, Teps Chprsn; AAPHERD; FCA 1983-, VP; *office:* Bridgeview MS 320 E North St Sidney OH 45365*

HEDDEN, BRIAN LEE, Social Studies Teacher; *b:* Akron, OH; *c:* Katie, Alison, Abby; *ed:* Rio Grande Coll (BSS) Amer His 1976; OH Univ (MSS) Pol Sci 1990; Attnd Ashland Univ 1990; *cr:* Oak Hill HS Soc Stud Tchr, Ftbl Coach 1977-; *ai:* Var Ftbl; Fellowship of Chrstn Stu; NEA, OEA, Oak Hill Tchrs Assn 1978-; OH Cncl Soc Stud 1993-; Phi Alpha Theta 1984-; Jackson Cty Red Cross Bd 1990-, Pres, Awd of Appreciation 1990; Martha Holden Jennings Scholar 1986; All-OH Stu Cncl Adv 1989; Regnl Rep OH Geographic Alliance 1989; *home:* PO Box 265 620 Market St Piketon OH 45661*

HEDESH, LYNN POWELL, Teacher of the Gifted; *b:* Bryn Mawr, PA; *m:* Andrew J.; *c:* Jennifer, Andrew; *ed:* Mount Union Coll (BS) Math & Scndry Ed 1968; *cr:* Broward Cty Sci Tchr 1969-70; Plymouth-Whitemarsh Math Tchr 1970-74; Harrisburg Sub Tchr 1974-76; Hazleton Sub Tchr 1981-85; Hazleton Area SD Math Tchr & Tchr of Gifted 1988-; *ai:* PA Jr Acad of Sci & Math Spon; Mathcounts Team Competition Coach; NEA 1988-; PTA Dist Cncl 1980-, Treas; Womens Coalition 1985-, Sec; Elected Councilwoman 1985-89; AAUW & LWV 1986-; Co-Commission for Women 1988-, Treas; Implemented Comp Course & Family Life Pgm; Supt Curr & Parent Advy Cncls; *office:* Hazleton Area Schl Dist 700 N Wyoming St Hazleton PA 18201

HEDGEPETH, JOYCE YATES, English Teacher; *b:* New York, NY; *m:* Robert G.; *c:* Janet H. Lawton, Brenda H. Patron, Dana H. Williams; *ed:* City Coll at NY (BS) Elem Ed 1973; Bank Street Coll (MS) Elem Ed 1974; 46 Credit Hrs Lehman Coll, Columbia Tchrs Coll; *cr:* CES 53 4th Grd Tchr 1974-75; PS 179 2nd Grd Tchr 1975; Christopher Columbus HS Eng Tchr 1975-76; Evander Childs HS Eng Tchr 1976-77; Adlai E. Stevenson HS Eng Tchr 1977-; *ai:* UFT, AFT 1974-; NCTE, NYCATE 1980-; NAACP, Urban League 1975-; Sarah Lawrence coll, Univ NM, Duke Univ NEH Summer Participant; Tchr of Yr; *office:* Adlai E Stevenson HS 1980 Lafayette Ave Bronx NY 10473*

HEDGES, DENNIS RANDALL, Social Studies Teacher; *b:* Columbus, OH; *m:* Kay Neeham; *c:* Amanda, Timothy; *ed:* Otterbein Coll (BA) His, Govt 1968; OH St Univ (MA) Soc Stud Ed 1974; *cr:* Hamilton Twp HS Eng Tchr 1968-69; Lincoln Jr HS Soc Stud Tchr 1969-76; Gahanna Lincoln HS AP, US His, Soc Stud Tchr 1976-; *ai:* NEA, OH Educ Assn, Gahanna Jefferson Educ Assn, OH Cncl of Soc Stud, NCSS 1974-; Cntrl Coll Presbyn Church 1990-, Elder; Habitat for Humanity 1990-; OH St Univ Stud Tour to USSR 1984; Led Stu Tours to USSR, CIS 1989, 1993; Capital Univ Jennings Scholar 1986; *office:* Gahanna Lincoln HS 140 Hamilton Rd Gahanna OH 43230

HEDGES, SHARMAN KLINE, Music, Speech & Drama Director; *b:* Massillon, OH; *c:* Andrew, Aaron; *ed:* Mount Union Coll (BM) Music, Voice 1972; Post Grad Stud in Elem Music, Real Estate; *cr:* Massillon Chrstn Schl Music Dir 1975-77, 1979-80, Music, Speech & Drama Dir 1987-; *ai:* Travelling Music & Drama Group, Plays, Concerts Dir; Sr Class Adv; OMEA; Canton Civic Opera; MacDowell Club; Massillon Bapt Temple, Soloist; Alpha Delta Pi; Mu Phi Epsilon; Helped Comm Soccer, Bsbl Teams; Article Pub.

HEDIGER, DONALD, Supervisor of Science; *b:* Hackensack, NJ; *ed:* Fairleigh Dickinson U (BS) Chem 1959, (MA) Eng 1963; Post Grad Courses at Fairleigh Dickinson U, OH Wesleyan U, Bowdoin Coll, San Diego St & Montclair U; *cr:* US Rubber Co Chemist 1959-61; St Michaels HS Sci Instr 1961-65; Mother Seton Reg HS Sci Instr 1965-66; Pascack Hills HS Supvr 1966-; *ai:* Sci League Adv; NSTA 1966-; NJSTA 1966-; NJSSPA 1978-; NSF Grants; *office:* Pascack Hills HS Grand Ave Montvale NJ 07645

HEDMAN, JOHN HENRY, Alternative Ed Program Teacher; *b:* Kirkland Lake ON, Canada; *c:* Kevin, James; *ed:* Laurentian Univ (BA) His 1965; Mc Master Univ (BPE) PE 1966; *cr:* Sheridan Tech HS PE, His Tchr 1966-68; Fort Frances HS PE, His, Math Tchr 1968-80; Alternative Schl Math, PLM, Career Planning, Eng Tchr 1980-; *ai:* Local Citizen's Advy Comm; All Sports Coach 15 Yrs; OSSTF 1966-; Ontario Fed of Anglers & Hunters 1970-, Pres; Sportsmen's Club 1970-, Pres; NORWOSSA Ath Assn, Pres; Ont Fed of Sec Sch Ath Cert; NORWOSSA Appreciation Plaque; Huntington Coll Paddle Awd 1965; Article Pub; *office:* The Alternative Schl Prgm 1050 Walker Ave Fort Frances ON P9A 1Y4 Canada CN

HEDRICK, ANDREW ROY, Third Grade Teacher; *b:* Roaring Spring, PA; *ed:* Penn St (BA) Sec Ed, Math 1990; Wilson Coll Elem Cert 1995; 6 Credits Univ AK at Ancourage; 4 Credits Sports Acad; *cr:* Everett Area HS Math Tchr 1990-93; Mann Monroe Elem Schl Third Grd Tchr 1993-; *ai:* Asst Jr HS Ftbl, Jr HS Bsktbl Head Coach; NEA, PSEA 1990-; Paul Douglas Tchng Schlsp; *office:* Mann Monroe Elem Schl RR 2 Clearville PA 15535

HEDRICK, DOUGLAS FRANK, Science Teacher; *b:* Conneaut, OH; *ed:* OH Univ (BSEd) Biological Sci 1991; Grad Credit San Jose St Univ, Lake Erie Coll; *cr:* Conneaut City Schls Sub Tchr 1991-92; St John HS Sci Tchr 1992-; *ai:* Sr Class Adv; Asst Bsbl Coach; BSA 1995-, Merit Badge Cnslr, Asst Scout Master; *office:* St John HS 3320 Station Ave Ashtabula OH 44004

HEDRICK, RICHARD W., Middle School Art Teacher; *b:* Middletown, CT; *m:* Linda Toli; *c:* Matthew; *ed:* Univ of NH (BS) Art Ed 1975; 35 Credit Hrs; *cr:* Hooksett Meml Schl Visual Art Tchr 1978-; *ai:* Unified Arts Team Ldr; Crisis Mgmt Team; Supervised Elective Time Comm; Art Club Adv; Teach Cmptr Courses to Dist Tchrs, Staff, Adult Ed at Night; NEA 1979-; Hooksett Conservation Comm 1992-, Commissioner; Nom NH Tchr of Yr 1992-93; *office:* Hooksett Meml MS 1550 Hooksett Rd Hooksett NH 03106*

HEEDER, RUTH SAMSON, World History & French Teacher; *b:* Cortland, NY; *m:* Carl John; *c:* Paummi, Carl John III; *ed:* St Univ of NY at Albany (BA) Soc Stud & Fr 1964, (MA) Fr 1965; McGill Univ Fr Summer Schl Montreal Canada Undergraduate & Grad Stud; *cr:* Ravenna-Coeymans-Selkirk His & Fr Tchr 1965-66; Guilderland HS Fr Tchr 1966-67; West Boylston MS His, Fr & Eng Tchr 1978-81; Notre Dame Acad World His & Fr Tchr 1981-82 & 1986-; *ai:* MCSS, NCSS 1986-; MAFLA 1994-; Edward E Ford Fnd AISNE Sr Tchng Fellow 1995; Model United Nations Club Adv 1986-94; *office:* Notre Dame Acad 425 Salisbury St Worcester MA 01609*

HEENEY, HELEN CULLETON, English Supervisor; *b:* Paterson, NJ; *m:* James; *c:* James; *ed:* William Paterson Coll (BA) Eng 1964; Farleigh Dickinson (MA)-Magna Cum Laude 1968; 60 Addl Credits; *cr:* St Therese Schl Tchr; Kinnelon HS Tchr, Supvr 29 Yrs; *ai:* NCTE, NEA, NJEA, MCEA 1965-; Kinnelon Lib Bd 1986-, Sec, VP; *home:* 6 Fiddlers Elbow Trl Kinnelon NJ 07405

HEERY, JANICE MARIE, Junior High Science Teacher; *b:* Woodbury, NJ; *ed:* Mt St Mary Coll (BA) Math, Elem Ed 1966; Seton Hall Admin; *cr:* St Brendan's Schl 3rd Grd Tchr 1956-60; St Rose Schl Jr HS Tchr 1970-74; Cathedral Schl Jr HS Tchr 1960-70; St Rose Schl Jr HS Tchr 1970-74; St Cecelia's Schl Jr HS Tchr 1975-80; St Rose Schl Jr HS Tchr 1981-; *ai:* Music Ldr; Peer Mediator; Stu Cncl Moderator; Initiated GATE, Guid Prgms; NCEA 1960-; Written up in IHM Missionary Magazine; *office:* St Rose Of Lima Schl 300 Kings Hwy Haddon Heights NJ 08035*

HEFFELFINGER, HAROLD H., Hlth & PE Dept Chair; *b:* Darby, PA; *m:* Barbara L. King; *c:* Donna L. Sellnow, Ronald J.; *ed:* W Chester St Coll (BS) Hlth & PE 1962; Purdue Univ (MS) PE 1963; 36 Credit Hrs Above Masters Degree; *cr:* Bristol Twp Schl Dist Sci & PE Tchr 1963-67; Centennial Schl Dist PE Tchr 1967-68; Neshaminy Schl Dist Hlth & PE Tchr 1968-, Dept Chprsn 1983-; *ai:* Retired Coach of Boys Soccer; Boys Bsktbl Asst Coach; Girls Sftbl & Girls JV Soccer Coach; Dir of Gym Night; Comms: Bldg, Curr & Dist One Soccer Steering; Natl Soccer Coaches Assn of Amer Inc 1968; Suburban Phila Soccer Coaches Assn 1969-, Treas, VP & Pres, Coach of the Yr & Svc Awd; AFT & NFT 1971-; PA Soccer Coaches Assn 1973-, VP & Pres Coach of the Yr 1989; DE Co Hall of Fame 1992; Svc Awd Suburban Philadelphia Ofcl Soccer; *home:* 550 Crescent Ave Penndel PA 19047*

HEFFERN, ROBERT JAMES, Social Studies Teacher & Coord; *b:* Buffalo, NY; *m:* Kathleen Byron; *c:* Dennis, Mary, Maureen, Julia; *ed:* Canisius Coll (BS) Pol Sci 1962, (MS) Soc Stud Ed 1968; 44 Addl Hrs His, Pol Sci, Sci, Ec; *cr:* Huron Portland Cement Inside Sales 1963-64; Extension Lay Vol Tchr 1964-65; Bishop Turner HS Tchr 1965-68; Maryvale HS Tchr 1968-; *ai:* MODEL United Nations; FEO Challenge; NCSS, NY Council Soc St, Niagara Frontier Soc Stud 1974-; Assoc, Super, Currie Dev 1990-; Buffalo Council on World Affairs 1994-; Buffalo Historical Soc; Bridges for Ed Eng Tchr Lithuania 1995 Vol Prg; *office:* Maryvale HS 1050 Maryvale Dr Cheektowaga NY 14225

HEFFERNAN, COR IMMACULATUM, Assoc Prof of Art; *b:* New York City, NY; *ed:* Marywood Coll (BA) Eng 1954; Univ of Notre Dame (MA) Art, Sculpture 1963; Marywood Coll (MS) Cnslng; Syracuse Univ (MFA) Illustration; Parsons Schl of Design Art Stdnts League; *cr:* Bishop O'Reilly HS Art Tchr 1963-65; Congregation of IHM Art Supv 1965-69; Bishop Hannan HS, Bishop Klonowski HS Art Tchr 1969-75; Marywood Coll Art Tchr 1978-, Art Dept Chair 1979-95; *ai:* Adac Adv; Schl of Continuing Ed Policy, Operations, IHM Heritage, Sponsorship Comm; Dorm Cnslr, Adv; NASAD 1980-, Comm on Accreditation; NAEA, PAEA 1979-; CFAS 1965-; Lacawanna Regnl Cultural Cncl 1988-, Chprsn 1988-90; Sr Craftsmen Shop 1993-, Bd Mem; Commission on Arch, Urban Design 1979-, Chprsn; CASE Prof of Yr 1994-95; Northeast Woman Scranton Times 1992; Scranton Distngd Citizen for Arts 1986; Star Achiever: Outstdng Svc in Northeast PA; Multiple Natl, Intnl Exhibits; *office:* Marywood Coll 2300 Adams Ave Scranton PA 18509

HEFFERNAN, JOAN ELIZABETH, Integrated Day Teacher; *b:* New Haven, CT; *m:* Edward J.; *c:* December, Jessica; *ed:* Western Ct St Coll (BS) Ed 1971; Southern CT St Univ (MS) Rdng 1976; Univ of CT 6th Yr Admin 1985; Rdng Consultant Cert Endorsement 1996; Art Courses CT Coll; *cr:* Norwich Pub Schl 1st Grd, K, Preschl Tchr 1971-82, Rdng Consultant 1982-87; Norwich Buckingham Schl Asst Prin 1983-86, 5th, 6th Grd Integrated Day Instr 1988-; *ai:* Coord Integrated Day Prgm; Grant Writing; Before, After Schl Stud Hall; Parent Wkshps; Speaker TPA Meetings; NEA 1971-; ASCD; Delta Kappa Gamma; IRA 1990; St Dept of Ed Improvement Initiative Grant 1996; Best Mentor Cooperating Tchr Trng 1991-; Inst Educl Innovation 1995; *office:* Buckingham Elem Schl 182 Cedar St Norwich CT 06360*

HEFFERNAN, KERRISSA JANE, Assoc Prof & Director; *b:* Heidelberg, Germany; *ed:* FL St Univ (BA) Studio Arts 1980; Boston Univ (MED) Curr, Tchng 1990, (EDD) Curr, Tchng 1992; *cr:* Lasell Coll Asst Prof Ctr Dir 1992-95, Assoc Prof, Ctr Dir 1995-96; *ai:* Adv; Various Comm Affiliations; Dir Spring Break Svc Experience; Co-Dir Camp Colors; NSEE, AAUW; Wellesley Ctr for Rsrch on Women; Gay & Lesbian Tchrs Assn; MA Campus Compact 1996-; MA Advy Cncl on Svc Learning 1994-; MS Consortium on Svc Learning 1994-; In the Best Interest of Children Inc Pediatric HIV Advocacy, Bd Mem; Numerous Articles Pub; Numerous Grants; *office:* Lasell Coll 1844 Commonwealth Ave Newton MA 02166*

HEFFLIN, PATRICK, Physics & Calculus Teacher; *b:* Pittsburgh, PA; *m:* David T.; *c:* Marquita, LaTashia, Davina; *ed:* Mansfield Univ (BS) Physics 1989; Duquesne Univ (MS) Scndry Sci Ed 1990; *cr:* Pittsburgh Pub Schls Sr Physics, Calculus Tchr 1990-; *ai:* Tech Comm Chprsn; *office:* Peabody HS 515 N Highland Ave Pittsburgh PA 15206*

HEFFNER, LEE STANLEY, Assistant Principal; *b:* Hamburg, PA; *m:* Rebecca L. Seidel; *c:* Connie L. Nabozny, Matthew L.; *ed:* Kutztown St Coll (BS) Elem Ed 1969, (MED) Elem Ed 1974; LeHigh Univ Prin Cert Elem 1981; Addl Credits; *cr:* Perry Elem Schl Fourth Grd Tchr 1969-84; Hamburg Elem Fourth Grd tchr 1982-92; Perry Elem Schl Ass't Elem Prin 1992-; Hamburg Elem Schl Ass't Elem Prin 1992-, Upper Bern Schl Ass't Elem Prin 1992-, Tilden Schl Ass't Elem Prin 1992-; Struasstown Schl Ass't Elem Prin 1992-; *ai:* Facilitator Elem Sco Studs Com; Prof Dev Advy Cncl; PAESP, NAESP, PAFPC, IRA 1992-; PDK 1994-; Berks Co Fersommling Dirs 1985-; Virginville Grange 1990-; Head Tchr PTA Life Mem; *office:* Hamburg Elem Schl Hamburg Area Schl Dist 680 E State St Hamburg PA 19526

HEFTER, LILLAIN, 3rd Grade Teacher; *b:* Berlin, Germany; *m:* Israel; *c:* Tzvi, Malkiel, Yossi; *ed:* Cleveland Bd of License 1953, Torah Umesorah 1955 Permanent Tchr Licenses; *cr:* Hebrew Acad All Grds Hebrew Tchr 1944-; Taylor Road Synagogue Hebrew Tchr 1950-55; Warrensville Ctr Syn Hebrew Tchr 1955-60; *ai:* Writing, Productions Schl Plays; Agudah Israel; Torah Umesorah; Honored 50th Anniversary 1993; *home:* 3626 Bendemeer Rd Cleveland OH 44118

HEGAN, MICHAEL K., Sixth Grade Teacher; *b:* Lynn, MA; *m:* Linda Mc Laughlin; *c:* Michelle, Brian; *ed:* Suffolk Univ (BS) Elem Ed 1971, (MEd) Schl Admin 1976; 6 Credit Hrs Salem St Coll; *cr:* Lewis Schl Sixth Grd Tchr 1971-73; Callahan Schl 5th-6th Grd Tchr 19730; *ai:* Schl Improvement Cncl; Intramural Bsktbl, Bsbl Clinic Dirs; AFT 1971-; Lynn Tchrs Union 1971-, Bldg Rep; Assn of NE Ftbl Ofcls `978-, HS Super Bowl, Agganis All-Star; Ancient Ordr of Hibernians; *home:* 80 Winnepurkit Ave Lynn MA 01905

HEGE, STEPHEN K., 6th Grd Math, Sci & Hlth Tchr; *b:* Chambersburg, PA; *m:* Debra Reeder; *c:* Brent A., Adam J.; *ed:* Hagerstown Jr Coll (AA) Ed 1970; PA St Univ (BED) Elem Ed 1971; Shippensburg Univ (MED) Elem Ed 1976; *cr:* West Perry Schl Dist Sixth Grd Tchr 1971-; *ai:* IMAST Team; JV Bsbl Coach; Ftbl Statistician; Lions Club 1980-, Pres, VP; *home:* RR 2 Box 202A New Bloomfield PA 17068*

HEGENDERFER, DEBBIE STUART, Fourth Grade Teacher; *b:* Delaware, OH; *m:* Terry Lee; *c:* Joshua C.; *ed:* OH St Univ (BA) Elem; *cr:* Fairbanks Elem Schl 4th Grd Tchr 1986-90, 1992-; *ai:* Intnl Friendship Assn; NEA 1986-; *home:* 11160 Crottinger Rd Plain City OH 43064

HEHER, ROSEMARY PATAKY, Math Department Chairman; *b:* New York City, NY; *m:* Joseph; *c:* Ashley; *ed:* Univ of MD at College Park (BS) Elem Ed-High Hnrs 1968; Salisbury St Univ (MED) Math Ed 1988; Attnd Univ of Guam Grad Schl 1969-70, Hofstra Univ 1965, Wor Wic Comm Coll; *cr:* Agana Elem Schl 5th Grd Tchr 1968-70; Yorktown Elem Schl 5th Grd Tchr 1971-73; Salisbury St Univ Instr Math, Stu Tchrs Supvr 1987-89; Parkside HS Math Dept Chair, Tchr 1989-; *ai:* Womens Caucus Chair; Schl Improvement Team; Cmptr Club Adv; NEA, MSTA, NCTM, MCTM, WCEA 1988-; Eastern Shore Dental Assn 1980-, Exec Sec, 15 Yr Appreciation Awd; Bethesda United Meth Church 1993-, Sec; Mid Atlantic Soc Oral, Maxillofacial Surgeons, Admin Bd 1981-, Exec Sec; Numerous Publications; Grant Delmarva Power Co; *office:* Parkside HS 1015 Beaglin Park Dr Salisbury MD 21804*

HEIBY, LORI ANN, Agricultural Education Instr; *b:* Coldwater, OH; *ed:* OH St Univ (BS) Ag Ed & Animal Sci 1991; *cr:* Old Fort HS Ag Ed Instr 1992-; *ai:* FFA Adv; OH Voc Ag Tchrs Assn 1992-; Natl Voc Ag Tchrs Assn 1992-; FFA Alumni 1987-; Farm Bureau 1987-; *office:* Old Fort HS 7635 N County Road 51 Old Fort OH 44861

HEID, ALICE WILSON, English & Latin Teacher; *b:* Carnegie, PA; *w:* George S. (dec); *c:* Walter W., Stephen F., David G.; *ed:* Grove City Coll (BA) Eng 1948; 9 Credit Hrs 1949; Attnd Univ of Pittsburgh 3 Credit Hrs 1949; *cr:* Forest Hills Jr HS Eng, Latin & Soc Stud Tchr 1948-50; Springdale HS Eng, Latin & Jrnlsm Tchr 1950-53; Highlands MS Eng & Latin Tchr 1967-; *ai:* NEA & PSEA 1967-; Grace United Meth Church, Pastor, Staff comm 1981-, Chprsn 10 Yrs, Nominations, Prsnl Comm 1981-, Admin Bd 1972-, Worship Work Area 1983-, Cathedral Choir 1960-; Amer Legion Citizen of Yr Awd; *office:* Highlands M S Highlands Schl Dist Argonne Dr Natrona Heights PA 15065

HEIDENREICH, BETH A., English & Theater Teacher; *b:* Galion, OH; *m:* Christopher P.; *ed:* Bowling Green St Univ (BS) Comm Ed 1989; OH St Univ (MA) Speech, Theatre Ed 1996; *cr:* Crestview Local Schls Eng Tchr 1990; Lancaster City Schls Sub Thcr 1990-91; Berne Union Schls Sub Tchr 1990-91; Watkins Meml HS Eng Tchr, Theatre Dir 1991-; *ai:* Ninth Grd Class Adv; Performing Arts Comm; Pvt Saxophone Instr; NCTE 1988-; Heisey Wind Ensemble 1992-; Tchr of Yr 1994-95; *office:* Watkins Meml HS 8868 Watkins Rd SW Pataskala OH 43062

HEIDENREICH, CHRISTOPHER PAUL, Director of Bands; *b:* Fairview Park, OH; *m:* Beth Ann Ogden; *ed:* Bowling Green St Univ (BM) Music Ed 1989; 9 Grad Hrs in Music Ed at OH St Univ; *cr:* Anthony Wayne Local Schls Bands Asst Dir 1989-90; Berne Union Local Schls 5th-12th Grd Instrumental Music Tchr 1990-92; Lancaster City Schls Bands Dir 1992-; *ai:* Music Educators Natl, OH Music Ed Assn 1989-; Natl Eagle Scout Assn 1984-, Lifetime Mem; Heisey Wind Ensemble 1991-; Lancaster Music Club 1993-, Stage Mgr; 6 of 7 Superior Ratings at St Marching Band Finals OMEA; 5 of 6 Superior Ratings at St Concert Band Contests OMEA; Nom for Amer Schl Band Dir Assn; Performance for St Rdng Clinic by Symphonic Band 1996; *office:* Lancaster HS 1312 Granville Pike Lancaster OH 43130*

HEIDER, CHRISTOPHER G., Social Studies Teacher; *b:* Dayton, OH; *m:* Maryann Lafosse; *c:* Zachary, Benjamin, Caroline; *ed:* Univ of Dayton (BS) His 1982; *cr:* St Charles Borrome MS His, Bio Tchr 1982-83; Carroll HS Soc Stud Tchr 1983-; *ai:* Broadcast Club Moderator; Planning Music for Schl Liturgies; NCEA; Who's Who; *office:* Carroll HS 4524 Linden Ave Dayton OH 45432*

HEIDKAMP, TERESA A. SCHUERMANN, Elementary Position Educator; *b:* Cincinnati, OH; *m:* Robert E.; *ed:* Xavier Univ (BS) Elem Ed 1977; Attnd Humboldt Univ; *cr:* Our Lady of Visitation Edctr 1977-; *ai:* Bldg Construction & Awd Comm; Just Say No Moderator; Curr Ldr; NCEA 1977-; OHCEA 1977-; *office:* Our Lady Of Visitation Schl 3180 South Rd Cincinnati OH 45248*

HEIDLEBAUGH, RANDY LYNN, Instrumental Music Director; *b:* Mansfield, OH; *m:* Cindy Lou Rock; *c:* Lindsey, Chelsea; *ed:* Vandercook Coll of Music (BMEd) Music Ed 1975; Murry St Univ & Ashland Univ Post Grad Hrs; *cr:* Caldwell Cty Schls Band Dir 1975-79; Calloway Cty Schls Band Dir 1980-82; Sidney City Schls Band Dir 1982-84; Lexington Local Schls Instrumental Music Dir 1984-; *ai:* Marching Band Dir; NEA 1975-; OH Music Ed Assn 1984-; Music Edctrs Natl Conf 1975; *office:* Lexington HS 103 Clever Ln Lexington OH 44904

HEIDLOFF, FREDERICK C., K-6th Grade Art Teacher; *b:* Charlottesville, VA; *ed:* Richmond Prof Inst (BFA) Art Ed 1963; Attnd Montclair St Coll Grad Ed, Ind Tech; *cr:* Bluestone HS 8-12 Grd Art Tchr 1963-65; Waldwick Jr-Sr HS 7-12 Grd Art Tchr 1966-92; Traphagen & Crescent HS K-6th Grd Art Tchr 1992-; *ai:* Jr Schl Transition Stu Comm 1996; NEA 1965-; NJ Ed Assn, Bergen Cty Ed Assn, Waldwick Ed Assn 1966-; NJ Dept of Ed St Schls Evaluation Comm 1995; Writing, Pub Music Stu Guid; Design & Work in Stained Glass; Tech Data for Stained Glass Craft; Pub Short Stories; *office:* Waldwick Jr Sr HS 155 Summit Ave Waldwick NJ 07463

HEIDORN, KENNETH A., Athletic Dir & Bible Teacher; *b:* Abington, PA; *m:* Jeanne E. Thurman; *c:* Brian, Brent, Heather; *ed:* Columbia Intnl Univ (BA) Bible 1971; Attnd St Josephs Univ; *cr:* PNC Bank Teller 1971; Phila Gear Corp Office 1972; Cedar Grove Chrstn HS Tchr, Coach & Ath Dir 1972-; *ai:* Coach Girls Soccer, Boys Bsktbl, Bsbl; Founder, Dir Indoor Soccer Prgm 1982-92; Girls Soccer Coach of Yr 1995; *office:* Cedar Grove Chrn HS 413 E Tabor Rd Philadelphia PA 19120

HEIDRICH-STROHL, CHARLENE WILLIAMS, 9th Grade English Teacher; *b:* San Diego, CA; *c:* Brian Heidrich, Bradley Heidrich; *ed:* Mt St Mary's Coll (BS) Eng Ed 1976; Attnd Lehigh Univ, Shippensburg Univ, Marywood Univ; *cr:* Harrison-Mortton Schl Eng Tchr 1977-80; William Allen HS Eng Tchr 1986-88; Springhouse Jr HS 9th Grd Eng Tchr 1988-; *ai:* Stu Support Team; NEA, PEA 1988-; CTE 1978-; Bath-East Allen Yth 1986-; Northampton Ath A 1993-; Cub Scouts 1986-, Den Mother, Asst Ldr; *office:* Springhouse Jr HS 1200 Springhouse Rd Allentown PA 18104*

HEIGLEY, CAROL RUTH, Mathematics & Computer Teacher; *b:* Crawford Cty, OH; *m:* Bernard A.; *c:* Rebecca L., Joel D., Andrew S.; *ed:* OH St Univ (BS) Math & Ed 1962; Northwestern Univ (MS) Math & Ed 1969; *cr:* Dublin Jr HS Math Tchr 1962-63; Barrett Jr HS Math Tchr 1963-71; Crooksville K-8th Grd Tchr of Gifted & Talented 1981-83; Crooksville HS Math & Comps Tchr 1983-; *ai:* Soph Class Adv; OCTM 1986-; NCTM 1986-; MCCTM 1993-; Deavertown UM Church 1971-.

HEIL, DAVID C., Mathematics Teacher; *b:* Philadelphia, PA; *m:* Linda; *c:* Christine, Laurie; *ed:* PA St Univ (BS) Math 1964; Westchester Univ (MS) Math Ed 1977; Univ of CA at Berkeley Grad Credits Geometry, Geometers Sketchpad; *cr:* William Tennent HS Math Tchr 1964-; *ai:* Bucks Cty Interscholastic Math League Pres, Problem Author; Centennial Educ Assn 1964-, Pres 1980-84; *office:* William Tennent HS 333 Centennial Rd Warminster PA 18974

HEILES, NANCY SANTORO, Global Education Director; *b:* Italy; *m:* Sigfried; *c:* Ander, Sonja; *ed:* Coll of Mount St Vincent (BA) Fr & Italian 1970; NY Univ (MA) Italian 1971; Candidate for Doctoral in Italian; *cr:* St Edmun HS Fr & Italian Tchr 1971-78; Xavier HS Fr & Italian Tchr & Global Ed Dir 1978-; *ai:* Exch Prgm Dir; Moderator of Fulbright Mentoring Prgm & Intnl Club; Greater NY Chapter of Fulbright Assn 1986-; Home Schl Assn of St Anselm, Pub Relations Comm; Fulbright Exch-Italy-1978; *office:* Xaverian H S 7100 Shore Rd Brooklyn NY 11209*

HEILIG, FAEANNA WILLAUER, Third Grade Teacher; *b:* Easton, PA; *m:* Ralph E.; *c:* Dawn, Karen Decker, Susan Krupkowski; *ed:* West Chester Univ (BS) Elem Ed 1956; Attnd Shippensburg Univ; *cr:* Bellwood-Antis Schl Dist Second Grd Tchr 1956-57; Cntrl Fulton Schl Dist Sub Tchr 1964-70; Forbes Rd Schl Dist Third Grd Tchr 1970-; *ai:* Instrl Support Team; Fulton Cty Historical Soc.

HEILMANN, DIANE MAUREEN, Mathematics Teacher; *b:* C OH; *ed:* Miami Univ (BA) Math 1971; Xavier Univ (MED) Sc Admin 1983; Addl Grad Hrs; *cr:* Oak Hills HS Math Tchr 1971- Adv 1983-; NCTM 1974-; Oak Hills Ed Assn 1971-; NEA 19 Kappa Gamma 1985-, Treas, 2nd VP; Westwood First Presby 1963-, Elder, Deacon, Trustee; Tchr of Yr 1989; Jennings Schola Western Hills Jaycees Outstanding Young Educator 1978.

HEIM, ANNE (FATKIN), Tchr & Math Dept Chprsn; *b:* Camd Thomas G.; *c:* Thomas Jr., Susan, James, Christopher; *ed:* Che Coll (BS) Math 1968; Holy Family Coll (MED) Ed 1996; *cr:* C Cath HS Math Tchr 1969-71, 1985-89, Math Dept Chprsn 199 Cncl Moderator; Educl Staff Mem; NCEA 1985-; NCTM 1988 1990-; Kappa Delta Pi 1994-; Neighborhood Dispute Com Distngd Tchr of Yr 1993-94; *office:* Gloucester Catholic HS 333 St Gloucester City NJ 08030*

HEIM, JEFFERY PAXSON, Teacher; *b:* Philadelphia, PA; *m.* Nemec; *c:* Allison K., Karen D.; *ed:* Penn St (BS) Scndry Ed 19 His 1968; Villanova Univ 18 Credits Pol Sci; West Chester Univ Cultural Stud; Temple Univ 38 Credits His in Doctoral Prgm; *cr.* HS His Tchr 1966-69; East Schl Afro, Asian Cultures Tchr 196 HS Afro, Asian Cultures Tchr 1977-; *ai:* World Affairs Club Spon Co-Chair; AFT 1969-90, Treas; NEA 1991-; NEH Fellow 1986; to India 1989; Annenberg Fellow Frgn Policy Rsrch Inst Conf on 1992; *office:* East HS 450 Ellis Ln West Chester PA 19380

HEIMBERGER, ROLAND L., Dept Chair & Economics T Mansfield, OH; *m:* Gail Younglove; *c:* Matthew; *ed:* Roberts (BA) Soc Stud 1962; Spring Arbor Coll Lib Arts 1960; Attnd Br Univ, SUNY at Oswego, Univ of Rochester, St John Fisher Coll; Cntrl Schl Ec Tchr 1962-; *ai:* Soc Stud Dept Chair; Cross Cntr Track Coach; NEA 1962-; Republican Party Inspector 1975- Recreation Commission 1974-80, Chair; Ontario Recreation & 1965-73, Supt; Outstdng Project Legal Edctr 1986; Tchr of Cntrl; Tchr of Significance 1993; Tchr of Excl Univ of Rochester *office:* Wayne Central HS Ontario Ctr Rd ONTARIO CENTER

HEIMLICH, JUDY NICHOLAS, Fourth Grade Teacher; *b:* Mc PA; *m:* Joel G.; *c:* Sarah; *ed:* CA Univ of PA (BS) Elem Ed 1974; of PA (MED) Elem Ed 1978; Univ of Pittsburgh Tchrs Consult Western PA Writing Project; Univ of HI Dev Approach for Sci, H Trng; *cr:* Cntrl Elem Schl 6th Grd Tchr 1976-91, 5th Grd Tchr 4th Grd Tchr 1995-; Elizabeth Forward MS 8th Grd Lang 1993-95; *ai:* 8th Grd MS Career's Prgm; Elizabeth Forward HS N 1976-, 4th KSRA Keystone 1976; NCTE 1991, 1996, St Rd Western PA Writing Project 1990-, Project Fellow, Tchr C Carlow Coll Woman of Spirit 1996, Vol; Mc Keesport Coll Cl Keystone St Rdng Assn 1976-, Confraternity of Chrstn Doct 1989-90; Outstdng Edctr of Yr 1990; Phoebe Apperson Hearst F Awd; *home:* 118 Penncrest Dr White Oak PA 15131

HEINCELMAN, DOROTHY CORSON, Retired Second Grade *b:* Montoursville, PA; *m:* Norman Feigles; *c:* N. Edward, Terre He Belt; *ed:* Lycoming Coll (BA) Eng, Elem Ed 1963; 13 Credits Bl Univ; *cr:* Lyter Schl Second Grd Tchr 1963-87; *ai:* MAEA 196 Co Chapter 1988-; PA Assn Schl Retirees 1988-, Life Mem; PS PTO 1958-59, Pres, Sec 1962-63; Muncy Bus, Prof Women 1962

HEINE, CAROLYN HARRISON, Retired French Teacher; *b* Park, MD; *m:* Walter F. II; *c:* Susan Wallace, Julia, W. F. III Cheek; *ed:* OH St (BSEd) Fr 1963, (MS) Guid 1979; Attnd Bowl at Dayton; *cr:* Pleasant HS Fr, Guid Tchr 1963-84; Olentangy H 1984-94; *ai:* Fr Club Adv 9 Yrs; OH Mod Lang Tchrs Assn 1963- OH Lang Tchr of Yr 1994, Elem 2nd; ACTFL 1972-; OEA, NE Girl Scout 6 Yrs, Troop Ldr; Sunday Schl Tchr 22 Yrs; Tchr of Yr Amer Assn for Higher Ed Acad Alliance of Frgn Lang Tchrs Cc 1992; *home:* 304 E High St Ashley OH 43003

HEINE, JUDITH G., Social Studies Teacher; *b:* Santa Rosa, CA W.; *ed:* Colby Coll (BA) European His 1967; Bridgewater St Cc His 1978; 90 Credit Hrs Beyond Masters Degree Framingham S MA, Boston Coll, Boston Univ & Harvard; *cr:* Avon Jr-Sr High Grd Soc Stud Tchr 1967-69; Canten HS 9th-12th Grd Soc Stud T *ai:* Girls Swim Team Coach 1971-76; Scheduling, Curr Revi Crisis & Stu Advy Comms; Class Adv; Schl Advy Cncl; NEA Canton Tchrs Assoc 1969-, Local Union Sec & Grievance Com 1969-; Norfolk Cty Tchrs Assoc 1969-, Tchr of Yr 1990; MS Stud; Greater Boston Cncl Soc Stud; Colby Alumnae Assoc 19 Sec; Medfield Historical Soc 1980-; Medfield Womens Assoc 198 Woman of Yr 1991; Colby Coll Class Sec; Five Coll Ctr for A Flwshp to Japan Summer 1987; Fulbright Travel to China Sumr Harvard NEH Summer Seminar Women in US His; Frequent Pr NERC Soc Stud Conf; *office:* Canton HS 960 Washington St Ca 02021*

HEINE, MARGARET EDMUND, Theology Teacher; *b:* Min *ed:* Chestnut Hill Coll (BA) Span 1980; Lasalle Univ (MA) Rel S *cr:* St Elizabeth's Schl Tchr 1964-65; Holy Child Schl Tchr 19 Gabriel's Schl Tchr 1968-73; Archbishop Ryan HS for Girls Tchr Lancaster Cath HS Tchr 1975-80; Our Lady of Perpetual Help 1980-82; Bethlehem Cath HS Tchr 1982-; *ai:* Theology Dept Cha Soph Class Moderator; Coord Frosh, Soph Retreat Prgm; PA ME NCEA; For God & Yth Awd Diocese of Allentown 1993; *office:* B Catholic HS 2133 Madison Ave Bethlehem PA 18017

HEINEMAN, ROBERT ALLEN, Professor of Political Science; IL; *m:* Alice Faye Sandstrom; *c:* Philip, Karen, Cheryl; *ed:* Brad (BA) Pol Sci 1961; The American Univ Govt (MA) 1963, (PhD) Eastern WA St Coll Asst Prof 1964-67; Bradley Univ Asst Prof Alfred Univ Prof 1971-; *ai:* Amer Pol Sci Assn 1963-; NYS Pol 1985-, Pres 1992-93; Allegany Cty Legislature 1995-; Author P Introduction 1995, Authority and the Liberal Tradition 1994; C Amer Govt 1995, The World of the Policy Analyst 1990; *offic* Univ Saxon Dr Alfred NY 14802

HEINES, JESSE M., Assoc Prof of Computer Science; Brunswick, NJ; *c:* Scott, Russ; *ed:* MA Inst of Tech (SB) Earth Univ of ME (MS) Sci Ed 1974; Boston Univ (EDD) Educl Me Post Doc Stud Brown Univ, Open Univ; *cr:* Anglo Amer S 1970-72; Digital Equipment Corp Ed Specialist 1974-84; U MA Assoc Prof 1985-; *ai:* Asst to Provost; SALT 1990-; ACM 198 Dive Club 1993-, All Offices; Speaker at Natl Conf Cmptr-Bas *office:* Univ Of MA At Lowell 1 University Ave Lowell MA 018

HEINES, MARY GARDNER, First Grade Teacher; *b:* Melrose Richard Jr.; *c:* Richard F., Bethany S. Burns; *ed:* RI Coll (EDB) E Ed 1957; Univ of CT (MA) Ed 1965; *cr:* Bradford Elem Schl 1st 1957-61, 1964-68; USAF Dependents Schl 1st Grd Tchr Hampden Meadows Schl Tchr 1962-64; Charlestown Elem Sch Tchr 1975-; *ai:* NEA 1975-; IRA; RI Rdng Cncl 1990-, Public First Bapt Church of Charlestown 1975-, Sunday Schl Supt, Cho Delta Pi; *home:* PO Box 15 Wood River Jt RI 02894

HEINEY, DEBRA ANN, Band Director & Music Teacher; *b:* A PA; *ed:* Mansfield St Univ (BS) Music Ed 1978; 30 Grad Credits Central CT St Univ & Vandercook Univ; *cr:* Dix Pub Schls Ba Music Tchr 1978-79; Instrumental Music Prgms Band Dir 1979-8

ınd Dir & Music Tchr 1988-; *ai:* Jazz Ensemble Dir; Co-Adv Natl Soc; Music Educators Natl Conf 1986-; PA Music Educators Assn 'itation of Excl 1993; Women Band Dirs Natl Assn 1994; NEA, BSEA 1988-; Ed Article Pub PA Music Educators Journal; *office:* r HS BHS Box 2069 Rd 2 Bangor PA 18013*

', DIANE L., English & Drama Teacher; *b:* Trenton, NJ; *m:* Garry; *c:* Philip Wagner, Curtis Wagner; *ed:* Goucher Coll (BA) 958; Univ CT (MA) Theatre 1976; NY Univ (PHD) Drama 1980; Township HS Tchr 1958-59; Blackhorse Regnl Tchr 1959-68; aus Regnl Tchr 1969-; Dowling Coll Prof 1975-76; Wocester St '7-78; *ai:* Local, MA, Natl Tchrs Assn 1969-; MA Arts Cncl, Matching, Natl Hum Arts Grants; *office:* Minnechaug Regional H St Wilbraham MA 01095*

K, DAVID G., Prof of Composition & Music; *b:* Allentown, PA; Lynn Wilke; *c:* Susan Park; *ed:* Eastman Schl of Music (BM) tion 1976, (MM) Composition 1977; Cath Univ (DMA) tion 1986; *cr:* U of MD Visiting Lecturer 1978-79; St Marys Coll rof Music 1979-89; Crane Schl of Music Prof Composition & 989-; *ai:* Dept of Theory, Lit, Composition & Conducting Chair; omposers Inc 1980-; ASCAP 1985-; Compositions Pub; Works ed Throughout US & Canada; Broadcast on NPR & CBC; Appear ffice: Crane School Of Music Potsdam NY 13676

K, THOMAS KARL, Instrumental Music Teacher; *b:* Allentown, larcia Becker; *c:* Thomas J., William A.; *ed:* Temple Univ (BMEd) ntal Music 1983; Addl 4 Grad Credits; 21 Grad Credits ok Coll; 3 Grad Credits Univ of The Arts; *cr:* Allentown Schl Dist ic Tchr 1983-86; Palmerton Area HS, Jr HS Elem Inst Music Tchr, 1988-; *ai:* HS Marching, Concert, Jazz Bands; Jr HS Bands; sembles; NEA, PSEA, PAEA 1988-; MENC, PMEA 1988-; AF of ; Marine Band of Allentown 1978-, Soloist, Asst Dir, Svc Awd; 'alley Youth Band 1993-, Dir; *office:* Palmerton Area HS 3525 Rd Palmerton PA 18071

:, MARY ELISE SCHEIBE, Retired 4th Grade Teacher; *b:* NY; *w:* Robert E. (dec); *c:* Alan, Kevin, Karen Kehrley; *ed:* SUNY altz (BS) Elem Ed 1956; Rdng, Tests, Measurements; *cr:* Liberty il 3rd Grd Tchr 1956-60; Jeffersonville-Youngsville Schl 4th Grd 0-89, 3rd Grd Tchr 1981; St Peter's Regnl Schl 4th Grd Tchr 1990; Spelling Bee Coach; Elem Choir Accompanist; Show Pianist for na Productions; Asst Girls Sftbl Coach; Delta Kappa Gamma res, VP, Sec; NYSTA 1970-; First Luth Church 1978-, Organist, ; Cub Scout Den Mother 1981-83.

, MARK DAVID, 4th-12th Grd Orchestra Dir; *b:* Reading, PA; *m:* ee Roberts; *c:* Matthew Paul, Joshua Daniel, Kaitlyn Alison; *ed:* ster Univ (BS) Music Ed 1982; Towson St Univ (MED) Music Ed Aberdeen Elem, MS, HS Orch Dir 4-12 Grd 1982-86; North Elem, MS, HS Orch Dir 4-12 Grd 1986-; *ai:* Orch Spon; Harford umental Music Curr Comm; NEA, MSTA 1982-; *office:* North HS 211 Pylesville Rd Pylesville MD 21132

, SHARALYN ROBERTS, Pre-School & Sign Lang Tchr; *b:* 'ille, KY; *m:* Mark David; *c:* Matthew Paul, Joshua Daniel, lison; *ed:* David Lipscomb Univ (BS) Elem Ed 1984; Western MD D) Deaf Ed 1985; *cr:* William Paca Old Post Rd Elem Schl 2nd 1984-87, Wakefield Elem Schl Interpreter 1994-95; Harford ll Adj Fac Teach Amer Sign Lang 1989-; Emmorton Elem Schl chr Total Comm Classroom 1995-; *ai:* Differing Abilities Day ffice: Harford Comm Coll 401 Thomas Run Rd Bel Air MD 21015

CH, BRUCE G., Mathematics Teacher; *b:* Cleveland, OH; *m:* Marie Cordisco; *c:* Brandt; *ed:* OH Univ (BS) Math 1971; Wallace (MA) Ed 1983; Attnd Ashland Univ, Drake Univ & John niv; *cr:* Padua Franciscan Math Tchr & Ftbl Coach 1972-80; Math Tchr 1980-; *ai:* Math Curr Bd; Alt Schedule Comm; Greater Ftbl Coach 1972-, Mem, 20 Yr Awd; OH Cncl Tchrs of Math em; OH HS Athletic Assn 1975-; Solon Ed Assn 1980-; Holy 1978-; Ftbl, Bsktbl, Bsbl & Math Club Coach; *office:* Solon HS vood Dr Solon OH 44139

CHS, STEPHEN CONRAD, Physical Education Teacher; *b:* OH; *m:* Karen S.; *c:* Jacob, Katherine; *ed:* OH St Univ (BS) PE) Ed 1978; Attnd Univ of Dayton; *cr:* Northmont Tchr 1974-76, & 1992-; OH St Univ Tchng Asst 1976-78; Delmar Coll Tchng -92; *ai:* Table Tennis & Roller Hockey Club Adv; NEA 1974-; 4-; AAPHERD 1974-; Northmont Recreation Task Force 1995-, arge; Ashland Oil Tchr Achvmt Awd 1995; Founded PE Gym & ecialities Instruction to Parents on Developmentally Appropriate e: Northmont Sr H S 4916 W National Rd Clayton OH 45315

.ISA COOK, Tchr of the Talented & Gifted; *b:* Portsmouth, OH; S.; *ed:* OH Univ (BA) Elem Ed 1984; Univ of Dayton (MS) Guid 988; Supervision Cert 1994; Working on Prin Cert; OH St Univ Cert 1992; *cr:* Minford Local Schls 5th Grd Tchr 1984-90; St Univ Governor's Summer Inst, Summer & Winter Enrichment -95; Minford Local Schls 3rd-8th Grd GATE Tchr 1990-; *ai:* Jr Quiz Bowl Coach; Odyssey of Mind; Newspaper; Yrbk; United dv; Arrange Trips; OH Ed Assn, NEA 1984-; *office:* Minford ls PO Box 204 Falcon Rd Minford OH 45653

ES, JOHN P., Social Studies Teacher; *b:* Patterson, NJ; *m:* Ellen ; *c:* John, David; *ed:* William Paterson Coll (BA) His, Eng Ed ntclair St Univ (MA) Colonial Amer His 1976; Rutgers Univ rr Theory, Dev 1986; *cr:* Cntrl MS Soc Stud, Eng Tchr 1973-89; y Hills HS His Tchr 1989-95; Parsippany HS His Tchr 1995-; *ai:* 976-; PDK 1979-; NCSS 1985-; Dissenation 1986.

ELMAN, DAVID G., Chemistry Teacher; *b:* Winchester, KS; *m:* oore; *ed:* Univ of ME (BA) Bio, Chem 1984, (BS) Scndry Ed king on Post Grad Stud; *cr:* Surrattsville HS Chem Tchr 1986-; Girls' Vlybl 1986-, USVBA Jr Olympic Vlybl Coach; Marathon Kayaking; Mountain Climbing; Sci Fair Chprsn 1988-93; NEA 1986-; *office:* Surrattsville HS 6101 Garden Dr Clinton MD

BRIAN JAMES, 6th Grade Science Teacher; *b:* Brooklyn, NY; . Candelora; *ed:* Suffolk Cty Comm Coll (AA) Lbrl Arts 1966; Stony Brook (BA) Ed 1974, (MLS) Lbrl Stud 1976; Addl 75 Grad dits Sci, Ed, Fine Arts, Lbrl Stud; Grad of Inst of Children's Lit; ntry Schl Dist 2-4 Grd Tchr 1974-78; NY St Ed Dept Sci Bureau m Sci Mentor Tchr 1985-95; SUNY at Stony Brook Adj Instr Wm Floyd Schl Dist Tchr 1978-; *ai:* 6th Grd Math Oympiad for ls Adv; Stu Act Comm; East End Children's Book Writer, s 1991-, Chprsn; Soc of Childrens Book Writers, Illustrators St United Tchrs 1978-; Sci Tchrs Assn of NY St 1981-; NY St Assn 1988-; NY St Elem Sci Tchr of Yr; Books Pub: Beachcraft 986, Beachcrafts, Too 1988, The Alley Cat 1993, Introduction to 4, The Wolves 1996, Kayuktuk 1996, The Monsters' Test 1996; ub; *office:* Nathaniel Woodhull Elem Schl Francis Landau Pl Y 11967

IAROLD J., Language Arts Instructor; *b:* New Brunswick, NJ; et Kistler; *c:* Laura, Carrie, Meggan; *ed:* Rutgers Univ (BA) Eng Cert Registered Holistic Scorer; *cr:* Churchill Jr HS 9th Grd Eng -68; Jamesburg HS 9th-12th Grd Tchr 1968-79; Monroe Twp HS 10th & 11th Grd Eng Tchr 1979-; *ai:* Acad Team Adv; MTEA, MCEA, NJEA & NEA 1967-; NJ Cncl of Tchrs of Eng 1985-; Local #204 Fed of Musicians 1967-; *home:* 13 Little Brook Ln Jamesburg NJ 08831

HEINZELMAN, GERALDINE MILETICH, Adj Professor of Math & Psych; *b:* Newburgh, NY; *c:* Kristine, Mark; *ed:* Univ of Rochester (BA) Scis 1961; Long Island Univ (MS) Cnslng 1992; 60 Grad, Post Grad Hrs SUNY at New Paltz, NYU; 450 Clock Hrs Alcoholism, Substance Abuse Cnslng Skill Credential; *cr:* Vly Cntrl HS Math Tchr 1961-62; Goshen Cntrl HS Math, Sci Tchr 1962-66; Harriman Coll Math Instr 1970-72; Washingtonville HS Scndry Math, Sci, Cmptr Tchr 1973-95, Substance Abuse Prevention Tchr 1985-90; Private Cmptr Conslt Bus Tchr, Cnslr 1995-; Mt St Mary's Coll Adj Prof Math, Psych; *ai:* NYSUT, WTA 1972-; NSF Grant; Tri Summer Sabbatical.

HEINZER, NICHOLAS JAMES, English Teacher; *b:* Butler, PA; *m:* Cecelia M. Cretella; *c:* Nicholas Jr., Louis, Jonathan; *ed:* Youngstown Univ (BS) Elem, Eng 1967; Youngstown St Univ (MA) Guid, Cnslng 1974; 15 Addl Hrs; *cr:* Ursuline HS Tchr 1967-70; St Edward's Jr HS Tchr, Guid Cnslr 1970-72; Liberty HS OWA Coord, Tchr 1972-; *ai:* Girls Sftbl Coach; NEA, OEA 1972-; LEA 1972-, Bldg Rep; NCTE 1984-; Knights of Columbus 1970-; BSA 1985-, Asst Scoutmaster; *office:* Liberty HS 317 Churchill Rd Youngstown OH 44505

HEINZMANN, KAREN L., French & Mathematics Teacher; *b:* Atlanta, GA; *ed:* Dartmouth Coll (BA) Fr 1990; *cr:* Thetford Acad Fr Tchr 1991-94, Fr & Math Tchr 1996-; St Stephens & St Agnes Schl Math & Sci Tchr 1994-95; *ai:* Bsktbl & Soccer Timer; Asst Track Coach; Exch Co-Coord; NCTM 1994-.

HEIPP, RAYMOND THOMAS, Cura Personalis Director; *b:* Cleveland, OH; *ed:* Univ of Dallas (BA) Classical Langs 1986; John Carroll Univ (MED) Rdng 1990; Attnd NC St Univ; *cr:* St Ignatius HS Latin, Cmptr, Rdng Tchr 1986-91, Dir Cura Personalis, Rdng Tchr 1993-; NC St Univ Grad Asst 1991-93; *ai:* Boys Cross Cntry, Track, Girls Bsktbl Coach; Moderate Early Eightees Preservation Soc; Bd of Regents; IRA 1989-; NCTE, ASCD 1993-; Fac Mem of Month; Articles Pub; *office:* Saint Ignatius H S 1911 W 30th St Cleveland OH 44113*

HEISCHMANN, THEODORA DIFRANCO, English Teacher; *b:* New York, NY; *m:* Paul J.; *c:* Theodora Weik, Michael P.; *ed:* SUNY at Stony Brook (BA) Elem Ed 1976, (MALS) Spcl Ed 1981; Long Island Univ (MLS) Lib Sci 1988; Marymount Manhattan Coll Eng Major 1965-67; *cr:* Ward Melville HS Asst Librn 1979-85; Smithtown HS Eng Tchr 1985-87; RC Murphy Jr HS Eng Tchr 1987-; *ai:* NYSUT 1976-; TVTA 1976-; NCTE 1985-; *office:* Robert C Murphy Jr HS 351 Oxhead Rd Stony Brook NY 11790

HEISER, HEATHER (FOURMAN), Math Teacher; *b:* Dayton, OH; *m:* Gregory Aaron; *ed:* Wittenberg Univ (BA) Math 1992; *cr:* Cr Coblentz Local Schls Math Tchr 1993-; *ai:* Conservation Club Adv; CCTA 1993-; NEA 1993-; OEA 1993-; OCTM 1993-; Norman E Dodson Awd for Excl in Math Tchng 1992.

HEISER, JANET D., Health, PE Tchr & Dept Chrprsn; *b:* Myerstown, PA; *m:* S. Joseph; *c:* Kelly, Kori, Kasey; *ed:* Penn St Univ (BS) Hlth & PE 1969; West Chester Univ (MEd) Hlth & PE 1972; 52 Credits Post Masters Degree at Millersville Univ; *cr:* Eastern Lebanon Co Schl Hlth & PE Instr 1969-, Dept Chrprsn 1993-; *ai:* Coached Jr High Bsktbl 10 Yrs & Var Bsktbl 3 yrs; Coached Hockey at All Levels 15 Yrs; Brownie Ldr; Sunday Schl Tchr; Rec Coach; NEA, PSEA & ELCEA 1969-; AAHPERD 1969-, 1993-; St Pauls UCC in Schaefferstown 1980-, SS Tchr; 2 St Runner-Up Titles 92 & 94 & 2 Dist Titles 92 & 94 in Hockey; *office:* Eastern Lebanon Cty Schl Dist 180 Elco Dr Rd #2 Myerstown PA 17067

HEISER, RICHARD R., History Professor; *b:* Sarasota, FL; *m:* Joanne Ruth Murray; *c:* Rebecca, Jeffrey, Matthew, Susan; *ed:* Nyack Coll (BA) His 1984; FL St Univ (MA) His 1988, (PHD) His 1993; *cr:* Nyack Coll His Prof 1990-; *ai:* Korean Stdnts Club Adv; Hum Division Chm; NAIA Fac Ath Rep; Alpha Chi NHS Spon; Amer His Assn; Medieval Acad; Charles Homer Haskins Soc; Park Evangelical Freedom Church 1991-, Elder, Tchr; Numerous Articles Pub.

HEISS, LAURA STAINKAMP, Visual Art Teacher; *b:* Yonkers, NY; *m:* Robert Thomas; *c:* Alexandra, Christopher; *ed:* Cortland St Univ (BA) Art 1975; Coll of New Rochelle (MA) Art Ed 1982; Addl 60 Credits Hum, Post Grad Courses; *cr:* Trinity Elem Schl Art Tchr 1976-82; St Lukes Schl Art Tchr 1982-85; Ward Elem Schl Art Tchr 1985-90; Albert Leonard MS Art Tchr 1990-; *ai:* Art Svc Club; Scenic Design Club for Spec Performances; Peer Mediation Mentor; NAEA; *office:* Albert Leonard MS 25 Gerada Ln New Rochelle NY 10804

HEISS, RALPH E., Counselor; *b:* Philadelphia, PA; *m:* Susan Schanche; *c:* Shawn, Ryan, Tyler; *ed:* Drexel Univ (BS) Soc Sci 1975; West Chester Univ (MED) Cnslng 1977; *cr:* Salesianum Schl Soph Cnslr 1977-; *ai:* Head Cross Cntry, Spring Track Coach; Chess Club Moderator; Music Ministry; ASCA, ACA 1977-; Penn Relays, Sec Schl Comm 1992-, Advy; USA Track & Field 1993-, DE Rep; US Trach Coaches Assn 1993-; Cross Cntry Coach of Yr St 1990, Cty 1990-92, 1994-95; Track Coach of Yr St 1991, 1993, Cty 1993-94; St Champions Cross Cntry 1989-92, 1994-95, Cty 1990-92, 1994-95; St Champions Track 1991, 1993-94, Cty 1993-94; Indoor St Champ 1992; Level I Cert, USA Track & Field; *office:* Salesianum Schl 1801 N Broom St Wilmington DE 19802

HEIST, MICHELLE (SHARGA), Secondary Biology Teacher; *b:* Allentown, PA; *m:* Ralph Charles; *c:* Ashleigh, Michael, Ian, Bryan, Shaun; *ed:* Villanova Univ (BS) Bio 1991; Lehigh Univ Working on MED Scndry Sci; *cr:* Lifeguard, Child Dir Seasonal 1985-92; Lehigh Vly Hosp Microbiologist, Phlebotomist 1988-93; Lehigh Vly Child Care Tchr1993-94; Parkland HS Bio Tchr 1995-; *ai:* Field Hockey, Cathedral Schl Soccer, Sftbl Coach; Northern Vly Soccer League Dir of Referees; Stu Support Team Trng; NSTA; *office:* Parkland HS PA Rt 309 Orefield PA 18069*

HEITMANN, JONATHAN ERIC, Special Education Teacher; *b:* Bronx, NY; *ed:* Albany Univ (BA) Psych 1991; Manhattan Coll (BS) Spec Ed 1993; *cr:* Washington North Schl Tchrs Asst, Autisitic Prgm 1991-92; PS 156 Bronx Spec Ed Tchr 1992-93; PS 65 Bronx Spec Ed Tchr 1993-94; Fairlawn HS Spec Ed Tchr 1994-; *ai:* Var Ftbl Coach Defense Line; Weightroom Supvr; JV Girls Sftbl Coach; NJEA 1994-; Kappa Delta Pi; *office:* Fair Lawn HS 14-00 Berdan Ave Fair Lawn NJ 07410*

HEITZ, CATHERINE RUEN, 6th Grade Teacher; *b:* Ottovillewp Ottovi, OH; *m:* Melvin J.; *c:* Kevin, Rodney; *ed:* Mary Manse Coll (BA) Elem Ed 1964; Bowling Green St Univ 9 Credit Hrs; Toledo Univ 1 Credit Hr; Ashland Coll 1 Credit Hr; Univ of the St of NY 3 Credit Hrs; *cr:* Rosary Cathedral Schl Grd 6 Tchr 1963-64; Ottoville Schl Grd 5 Tchr 1964-68; Ft Jennings Schl Grd 6 Tchr 1969-70; Ottoville Schl Grd 6 Tchr 1970-; *ai:* Christmas Prgm Coord 1994; Elem Advy Comm 1995-; NEA 1970-; NWOEA 1970-, NWOEA Outstndng Svc; Ottorville Local Ed Assn 1970-, Pres, Negotiations Chm; Vol EMT Middlepoint 1992-, Pres; Jenning Scholar 1985-86; Mary L. Sheeley Cncl Literacy Awd 1994; *office:* Ottoville Schl Box 248 Ottoville OH 45857*

HEITZ, JUDITH MEARNS, Third Grade Teacher; *b:* Wilmington, DE; *m:* Michael W.; *c:* Jonathon, Heather; *ed:* Bloomsburg Univ (BS) Elem Ed 1966; Goucher Coll (MA) Elem Ed 1995; Towson St Univ Masters Equivalency Elem Ed 1974; *cr:* William Paca Elem 4th Grd Tchr 1966-71; Churchville Elem 2nd Grd Tchr 1978-86; Harford Comm Coll ABE Prgm Prof 1975-76; Hickory Elem 3rd Grd Tchr 1986-; *ai:* SEM Enrichment Ldr; St & Local Odyssey of the Mind Judge; Hickory Highlight Lit Magazine Ed; NEA, MSTA, HCEA 1966-; Church, Childrens Sunday Schl Bd 1974-; Harford Cty MD Environmental Tchr of Yr 1995; Goucher Coll Self-esteem Research Paper; Environmental Play Everyday is Earthday Curr First Place Awd & Honorable Mention from Natl Geographics World Magazine in Washington DC; *office:* Hickory Elem Schl 2100 Conowingo Rd Bel Air MD 21014*

HEITZ, MICHAEL WILFORD, Chemistry Teacher; *b:* Germantown, PA; *m:* Judith Mearns; *c:* Jonathon Mearns, Heather Sabra; *ed:* Univ of MD (MA) Chem 1969; Addl 30 Hrs Beyond Masters in Chem at TX A&M & Syracuse Univ 1971; *cr:* Bel Air HS Chem Tchr 1966-79; C Milton Wright HS Chem Tchr 1979-; *ai:* Chem Club Adv; Sci Fairs Chprsn; Bsktbl Coach; NEA, MSEA 1966-; HCEA 1966-, Cty Rep; Church 1970-, Deacon 3 Yrs; Natl Sci Fnd Internships at TX A&M, Syracuse Univ & Univ of MD; *office:* C Milton Wright HS 1301 N Fountain Green Rd Bel Air MD 21015

HEIZMAN, MIKE W., 7th & 8th Grade Math Teacher; *b:* Cincinnati, OH; *m:* Cathy Wissinger; *c:* Cara, Brad, Brian; *ed:* IN Univ (BS) Math 1972; Xavier Univ (MA) Admin 1986; *cr:* Northwest HS Math Tchr 1972-77; Harrison HS Math Tchr 1977-84; Indian Hill HS Math Tchr 1984-86; Colerain MS Math Tchr 1986-; *ai:* Asst Ftbl Coach, Offensive Coord; Computer Coord; NEA 1972-; NWTA 1986-; OH Valley Ofcls Assn 1976-, Pres; *office:* Colerain MS 4700 Poole Rd Cincinnati OH 45251

HEKKER, RITA FRANCES, Senior Theology Teacher; *b:* Passaic, NJ; *ed:* St Tchrs Coll (BS) Ed 1953, (MS) Ed 1956; St Charles Seminary (MA) Dogmatic Theology 1974; 1 Credit Prayer & the Adolesant; 3 Credits Spiritual Direction; 1 Credit Cnslng Teen Agers; *cr:* St Rose HS Theology Tchr 1969-74; John Carroll HS Theology Tchr 1974-78; Little Flower HS Theology Tchr 1978-82; Archbishop Carroll Theology Tchr 1982-; *ai:* Dept Chprsn; Acad Bd; Theology Self Study for Mid Sts Chair; NCEA 1960-.*

HEKLER, BARBARA AHLERS, High School Math Teacher; *b:* Cincinnati, OH; *m:* Robert A.; *c:* Rob, Krista, Mark, Michael; *ed:* Xavier Univ (BA) Math 1971; Mount St Joseph Coll (MAEd) 1983; *cr:* McAuley HS Math, Cmptr Programming Tchr 1984-, Math Dept Chprsn; *ai:* Chemical Dependency Core Team; OCTM, GCCTM 1985-; NCEA 1984-; NCTM 1993-; *office:* Mc Auley H S 6000 Oakwood Ave Cincinnati OH 45224

HELBLING, STEPHEN JOSEPH, Chemistry Teacher; *b:* Aberdeen, OH; *ed:* Xavier Univ (MED) Cnslng 1984; 15 Addl Grad Hrs; *cr:* Anderson Jr HS Sci 1967-71; Anderson HS Sci & Chem 1971-; *ai:* Various Comms; FHTA 1967-, Bldg Rep; OEA, NEA 1967-; Amer Orchid Soc 1975-; *office:* Anderson HS 7560 Forest Rd Cincinnati OH 45255

HELCOSKI, JACK E., Supervisor of Pupil Services; *b:* Scranton, PA; *m:* Jane McAndrew; *c:* Brad, Lynne; *ed:* Univ of Scranton (BS) Math Ed 1969, (MS) Cnslr Ed 1972; Supvry Cnclr Ed 1976; *cr:* Riverside Schl Dist Math Tchr 1969-74, Guid Cnslr 1974-80, Supvr of Pupil Svcs 1981-; *ai:* Golf Coach; Stu Asst Team Mem; HS Golf League Treas; PSCA 1980-; Jefferson Little League 1982-; N Pocomo Biddy Bsktbl 1986-; *office:* Riverside Schl Dist 310 Davis St Taylor PA 18517

HELD, DONNA SCHMIDT, Math Teacher; *b:* Chicago, IL; *w:* William F. (dec); *c:* Jennifer, Matthew, Kathryn; *ed:* IL St Univ (BSEd) Speech 1957; Attnd Carroll Coll, OH Wesleyan Univ, OH Dominican Coll, Univ of Dayton; *cr:* St Mary Schl Elem Math, Sci Tchr 1968-70, 1972-95; *ai:* Stu Cncl Adv; Spelling Bee; Tchrs Negotiations, Columbus Diocesan Math Curr Comm; NCEA 1968-; *office:* St Mary Schl 66 E William St Delaware OH 43015

HELD, KATHLEEN (VARANO), Spanish Teacher; *b:* Tarentum, PA; *m:* Richard J.; *c:* Joseph; *ed:* Seton Hill Coll (BA) Span, Fr 1971; SUNY at Buffalo (MA) Span 1975; Steon Hill Coll Eng Cert 1993; *cr:* Mercyhurst Prep Schl Span, Fr Tchr 1971-73; Kiski Area Schl Dist Span, Eng Tchr 1988-; *office:* Kiski Area HS 200 Poplar St Vandergrift PA 15690

HELEEN, WALTER WILLIAM, Mathematics Chairperson; *b:* Acushnet, MA; *m:* Judith Carla Olson; *c:* Jason K.; *ed:* Univ of Bridgeport (BA) Math 1964, (MS) Math Ed 1965; 6 Hrs Harvard Univ Awded Harvard Practitioner; 27 Hrs Boston Coll NSF Institut; Addl 15 Hrs; *cr:* Long Lots Jr HS Math, Sci Tchr 1965-66; Holbrook Jr Sr HS Math Chprsn 1966-83, 1987-, Asst Prin 1983-87; *ai:* Math Club; NHS Adv; NEA, MTA, HEA 1966-; NCTM, ATMIM 1972-; ACSD 1991-; Abington Youth Soccer; Holbrook Chapter Amer Heart Assn; Harvard Practitioner Awd 1988; One of 12 Math Tchrs MA Selected NSF Yr Inst; *office:* Holbrook Jr/Sr H S 245 S Franklin St Holbrook MA 02343*

HELFAND, SCOTT E., Social Studies Teacher; *b:* Brooklyn, NY; *m:* Diane DiCanio; *ed:* SUNY at Stonybrook (BA) His 1986; CUNY at Brooklyn Coll (MA) His 1992; Post Grad Stud in His & Spcl Ed; *cr:* NYC Bd of Ed Spcl Ed Tchr 1987-89, Soc Stud Tchr 1989-92; Jefferson Twp MS Soc Stud Tchr 1992-; *ai:* Soccer Coach; Acad Team Coord; Jefferson Twp Yth Hockey 1992-, Coach; *office:* Jefferson Twp MS Weldon Rd #2 Oak Ridge NJ 07438

HELFENSTEIN, DEBORAH REIS, Guidance Counselor; *b:* New Hyde Park, NY; *ed:* St John's Univ (BS) Ed 1975, (MS) Cnslr Ed 1986; *cr:* St Joseph's Schl Pre-K, Kndgtn Tchr 1977-81, 5th, 6th Grd Tchr 1981-86; Mary Louis Acad Guid Cnslr 1986-87; H. F. Carey HS Guid Cnslr 1987-88; Elmont Meml HS Guid Cnslr 1988-; *ai:* Key Club Co-Adv; Drug Free Schls Comm; NEA, NCA 1986-; *office:* Elmont Memorial HS 555 Ridge Rd Elmont NY 11003

HELFRICH, HAP, Science Teacher; *b:* Columbus, OH; *m:* Suzie Retterer-Helfrich; *c:* Rachel Anne, Sarah Elizabeth, Mary katherine, Margret Jane; *ed:* OH St Univ (BS) Ed 1984, (MA) Educl Admin 1990; *cr:* Worthington City Schls Head Ath Trainer, Sci Acad Asst 1983-87; Marysville Exempted Village Schl Ath Trainer 1988-94; Olentangy Local Schls Sci, PE & Hlth Tchr 1987-; *ai:* Track, Bsktbl, Ftbl, Golf, Ath Trainer; Envirothon Spon; Phi Delta Kappa 1990-; NEA; OEA; Olentangy Tchrs Assn 1987-, Pres; OH Wildlife Ctr 1990-, Raptor Rescue & Rehab; Sierra Club; Audubon; Nature Conservancy; Chemlawn Grant 1991; *office:* Olentangy HS 675 Lewis Center Rd Lewis Center OH 43035

HELGESON, DONNA SANDBURG, Former Math Tutor; *b:* Muscatine, IA; *m:* Douglas T.; *c:* Virginia; *ed:* IA St Univ (BS) Math-Distinction 1987; 3 Grad Credit Hrs AR Math Crusade; *cr:* Oakdale Jr HS, Rogers Pub Schls Math Tchr 1989-95; *ai:* NCTM 1987-; *home:* 38 Florence St Ellington CT 06029

HELLER, HARLAND EDWARD, 7th-8th Grade Teacher; *b:* Chicago, IL; *m:* Karen Ruth; *c:* Darla Gayle; *ed:* Piedmont Bible Coll (BRE) Ed 1972; Moody Bible Inst Commnctn 1970; Bapt Bible Coll; 23 Credit Hrs; *cr:* Harbor Chrstn Tchr & Soccer Coach 1972-78; Emmanuel Bapt Soccer & Bsktbl Coach & Tchr 1978-83; Arlington Bapt Soccer Coach & Tchr 1983-; *ai:* Frosh Class Adv; Var Boys Soccer & Var Girls Bsktbl Scorekeeper; ACSI 1991-, Cert; Article Pub 1968; Sunday Schl Supt of Yr 1975; Whos Who 1976, Outstdg Citizens of SC; *office:* Arlington Baptist Schl 3030 N Rolling Rd Baltimore MD 21244

HELLER, JAMES R. X., Art Teacher; *b:* Allentown, PA; *m:* Teresa A. Wessner; *c:* James R. V., Suzanne M. Cottrill; *ed:* Univ of AZ (BA) Anthropology 1969; Kutztown Univ (MEd) Art 1973; Attnd Ringling Schl of Art 116 Credits, Muhlenberg Coll 15 Credits, Moravian Coll 9 Credits, Univ of the Americas 9 Credits; *cr:* Grammes Inc Artist 1966-67; The Shire

Gallery Owner 1967; Pine Grove Area Schl Dist Art Tchr 1970-; *ai:* NEA, PSEA, PGAEA 1971-; Scholylkill Cty Art Assn 1975-, VP & Pres 1977-80; Church Youth Group Adv 1980-; Penn St, Gwynedd Mercy Coll, Holland House of Art, Shire Gallery, Bach Shows; *office:* Pine Grove Area HS School St Pine Grove PA 17963

HELLER, WILLARD ALLEN, Spanish Teacher; *b:* Niagara Falls, NY; *ed:* SUNY Coll at Buffalo (BSEd) Ed 1977; SUNY Coll at Oenota (MSEd) Elem Ed 1983; 18 Hrs Ed Admin Suny Coll at Brockport; *cr:* Warsaw Elem Schl 5-6 Grd, GATE Tchr 1978-87; Perry Jr, Sr HS 8-12 Grd Span Tchr 1987-; Genesee Comm Coll Adj Instr 1990-; *ai:* Span Club Adv; NYSAFLT, AFT, NYSUT 1988-; FLATOWLS 1990-, Past Sec; 4H Camp Owachta 1993-, Staff Dev Dir; Genesee Vly Tchrs Ctr 1988-91, Policy Bd Chair; Amer Red Cross 1996, CPR Instr; GVTA Warsaw Edctrs Tchr of Yr 1984; Univ of Rochester Awd for Excl in Scndry Ed 1993; Tchr Reviewer Mc Dougall Litell Textbook; *office:* Perry Jr Sr HS 33 Watkins Ave Perry NY 14530*

HELLERT, PATRICIA L., 4th Grade Teacher; *b:* Albion, NY; *m:* Francis; *c:* Laurie Sherrill, Leigh; *ed:* SUNY at Geneseo (BA) Ed 1960; *cr:* Waterport Elem Schl 4th Grd Tchr 1971-89; Albion Primary 4th Grd Tchr 1989-; *home:* 409 East Ave Albion NY 14411

HELLING, GRACE MARIE, School Instrumental Music Tchr; *b:* Rochester, NY; *ed:* SUNY at Buffalo (BA) Music Ed 1986; SUNY at Brockport (MALS) Arts, Lbrl Stud 1991; 3 Post Grad Credit Hrs Coll of Saint Rose at Albany; *cr:* Honeoye Cntrl Schl 4-12 Grd Instrumental Music Tchr, Fine Arts Dept Chair 1987-; *ai:* Conduct Sr HS Jazz Ensemble, Marching Band, Schl Musical Pit Orch; Var Girls Soccer, Jr Var Girls Bsktbl Coach; AFT 1987-; Honeoye Tchrs Assn 1987-, VP, Pres; Ontario Cty Music Ed Assn 1987-, VP 2 Terms; NY St Schl Music Assn 1987-; Womens Bsktbl Coaches Assn 1990-; Music Edctrs Natl Conf 1987-; Intnl Assn of Jazz Edctrs 1996; Parent, Tchr, Stu Assn, Hemlock Sportsmans Club 1990-; Honeoye Auditorium Project 1995-; Honeoye Sports Boosters 1992-; Honeoye Band Boosters 1987-; SUNY at Buffalo Arts Dept Outstdng Svc Awd; Composer Grant Eastman Schl of Music; *office:* Honeoye Central Schl 86 E Main St Honeoye NY 14471*

HELLMAN, CAROL MARIE (WILEY), 4th Grade Teacher; *b:* Delphos, OH; *m:* George J.; *c:* Glenn, Robert, Renee Hellman Peters, Lisa Hellman Recker; *ed:* OSU, Bowling Green St Univ, Univ of Dayton Grad Courses; *cr:* Kalida Elem 3rd Grd Tchr 4 Yrs, Kndgtn Tchr 7 Yrs, 4th Grd Tchr 10 Yrs; *ai:* Curr, Book Adoption Comms; Attnd Wkshps; OEA 1984-, Recruited Most New Mems; KEA 1984-, Pres, VP, Sec, Treas; NRTA 1994-; Amer Legion Post 715 1978-, Sec; OSU Alumni Assn 1977-; Parish Coord 1995-; Poem Pub; Comparative Lit Awd 1971; *home:* 565 N Water St Fort Jennings OH 45844

HELM, ANNE, 5th Grade Teacher; *b:* Malone, NY; *ed:* SUNY at Potsdam (BA) Interdisciplinary Soc Scis 1972, (MS) Ed 1976; *cr:* Chateaugay Cntrl Schl 5 Grd Tchr 1973-; *ai:* NYSUT, Chateaugay Tchrs Assn 1973-; Alice Hyde Auxiliary; Malone Women's Coll Club; *office:* Chateaugay Cntrl Schl River St Chateaugay NY 12920

HELME, SUSAN B., 6th Grade Science Teacher; *b:* Cobleskill, NY; *m:* Donald K.; *c:* Lindsey, Alyssa; *ed:* Marymount Coll of VA (AS) Ed 1970; St Univ of NY at Plattsburgh (BS) Ed 1972; St Univ Coll at Oneonta (MS) Ed 1977; Attnd St Univ of NY at Albany, Coll of St Rose; *cr:* Cobleskill-Richmondville Cntrl Schl Grd Six Tchr 1992-; *ai:* NYSUI, Soc Chprsn; Cobleskill-Richmondville Tchrs Assn; 4-H 1994-; *office:* Cobleskill-Rchmndvl Cntrl Schl 44 E Main Richmondville NY 12149

HELMER, JEAN MARIE, Psychology Teacher; *b:* Vineland, NJ; *c:* David; *ed:* Richard Stockton (BA) Psych 1982; Trng as Consultant for Governors Cncl on Holocaust Ed; Lifespring Trng; Human Factors Ldrshp Trng; *cr:* Mill Road Schl Consultant 1983-84; Atlantic Comm Coll ESL Tchr 1984-86; Mainland Regnl Psych Tchr 1986-; *ai:* Core Team; Schl Effectiveness Trng Chprsn; GATE Convocation Adv; Task Force on Team Tchng Tolerance; NJEA 1984-; TOP 1994-; *office:* Mainland Regional HS 1301 Oak Ave Linwood NJ 08221

HELMRICH, EARL SPENCER,JR., Social Studies Teacher; *b:* Baltimore, MD; *m:* Barbara Hogan; *ed:* Catorsville Comm Coll (AA), Univ of MD at Baltimore (BA); 39 Post Grad Credits; *cr:* St William of York Soc Stud Tchr 1972-; *ai:* Soc Stud Dept Chair; Mid SChl Level Coord; Asst Prin 1984-95; Elem Schl Tchrs Assn; Amer Legion 1995-; *office:* St William Of York Schl 600 Cooks Ln Baltimore MD 21229

HELOCK, JAMES KEVIN, Biology Teacher; *b:* Philadelphia, PA; *m:* Lisa Beth Gentile; *c:* Christopher; *ed:* Millersville Univ of PA (BS) Bio 1993; 6 Grad Credits at IN Weslyn Univ; 3 Credits Cmptr Prgm; *cr:* Elizabethtown MS Long-term Sub Life Sci Tchr 1993; Annville-Cleona HS Grds 10-12 Bio Tchr 1993-; *ai:* NSTA 1993-; United Meth Church 1975-; Lancaster Cty Conservancy 1993-; *office:* Annville-Cleona HS 500 S White Oak St Annville PA 17003

HELON, DAVID JOSEPH, HS Visual Communcations Tchr; *b:* Monessen, PA; *m:* Amy Lampus; *c:* David S., Christopher M.; *ed:* CA St Univ (BA) Tech Ed 1960, (MA) Tech Ed 1972; 30 Addl Hrs; *cr:* Pittsburgh Schl Dist Tchr 1960-, Instrl Tchr Ldr 1985-; *ai:* Fac Pres; Yrbk Adv; Asst Ftbl Coach; AFT 1964-; St, Local Curr Comm; *office:* Perry Traditional Acad 3875 Perrysville Ave Pittsburgh PA 15214

HELSEL, MELANIE COLLINS, Social Studies Teacher; *b:* Washington, DC; *m:* Timothy Dean; *c:* Ashley Yvette, Travis Austin; *ed:* Penn St Univ (BS) Scndry Ed His 1978; Various Post Grad Courses; *cr:* Our Lady of Lourdes Schl 6th-8th Grd Soc Stud Tchr 1978-; *ai:* Odessy of the Mind Competition Judge; 6th Grd Spelling Bee & Thinking Cap Bowl Quiz Competition Supvrs.

HELSINGER, JAMES DAVID, American History Teacher; *b:* OH; *m:* Pamela Sue Haught; *c:* Christina, Laurie; *ed:* Miami Univ in OH (BA) Soc Stud 1974, (MED) Ed & His 1980; *cr:* Lebanon City Schls Amer His Tchr 1974-78; Carlisle HS Amer His & AP Amer His Tchr 1978-; *ai:* Sr Class & Stu Cncl Adv; Boys Bsktbl, Golf & Tennis Coach; NHS Adv; Carlisle Tchrs Assn 1978-; NCSS & OH Cncl for Soc Stud 1974-; *home:* 10080 El An Ja Dr Miamisburg OH 45342*

HEMBREE, JAMES ROBERT,III, History Teacher & Coach; *b:* Alton, IL; *m:* Cynthia Ann Herron; *c:* Rob, Brian, Mark; *ed:* Evangel Coll (BS) PE, His & Soc Stud 1974; *cr:* Evangel HS Tchr & Coach 1976-79; Barry HS Tchr & Coach 1979-89; Family Chrstn Acad Tchr & Coach 1989-93; Cincinnati Chrstn Tchr 1993-; *ai:* Bsbl, Bsktbl Head Coach; 8th Grd Spon; His Dept Chm; IL Coaches Assn 1979-; OH Coaches Assn 1993-; *office:* Cincinnati Christian Schools 825 Waycross Forest Park OH 45240

HEMER, NANCY PEARSON, Fourth Grade Teacher; *b:* Greenville, OH; *m:* Peter Fremont; *c:* Jeffrey, Pamela Walpole, David, Christopher; *ed:* Wrigth St Univ (BSEd) Elem 1976; 40 Addl Hrs in Lang Arts, Classroom Mngmt, Bus & the World of Work; *cr:* Ansonia Schls 4th Grd Tchr 1976-; *ai:* Dist Task Force; St Regnl Testing & Assessment Comm; Educl Assn Sec; Discipline & Advisory Comm; Spelling Bee Coord; Lang Arts Co Curr Mem; Math Tchr Ldr Prgm; Writers Conf Presenter; NEA 1976-, Sec, Bd Rep; Phi Delta Kappa; MRDD Bd Mem 1989-, Vice Chm; Church Schl Tchr; Pol Activities; Venture Capital Grant Comm; Supt Interview Comm; Selected Jennings Scholar by Admin in Recognition of High Performance of Educl Responsibilities; Dist Tchr of the Yr Awd 1994; *office:* Ansonia Local Schls W Cross St Ansonia OH 45303*

HEMINGER, LINDA FOUST, First Grade Teacher; *b:* Urbana, OH; *c:* Amanda, Brooks, Drew; *ed:* OH St Univ (BS) Elem Ed 1973; Wright St Univ (MS) Tchr Ldr 1991; *cr:* Columbus Pub Schls LD Tutor 1976-82; West Liberty-Salem Schl 1st Grd Tchr 1983-; *ai:* Income Tax Levy Comm; WL-SEA Negotiating Team; NEA 1983-; OEA 1983-; WL Salem EA 1983-, Negotiating Team; Kingscreek United Meth Church 1983-, Ed Comm, Pastor Parish Relations, Trustee; *office:* West Liberty-Salem Schl 7208 N Rt 68 West Liberty OH 43357

HEMINGWAY, DENISE BOWIE, Fourth Grade Teacher; *b:* Paterson, NJ; *w:* Michael (dec); *c:* Maya, Noelle; *ed:* William Paterson Coll (BA) Elem Ed, Early Chldhd 1977; Grad Stud Early Chldhd; *cr:* Pub Schl #24 Tchr 1978-79; Pub Schl #4 Tchr 1979-82; Pub Schl #28 Tchr 1982-; *ai:* Fourth Grd Tutorial Prgm; NJEA, NEA 1977-; NAACP 1992-; Ed Comm 1990-; St Luke Church; PTA 1992-, Pres, Outstdng Ldrshp Awd; Awded Primary Position of Federal Prgm Even-Start; Nom Tchr of Yr 1992-93, 1995; *office:* Pub Schl 28 Clinton St Paterson NJ 07522*

HEMKES-ROSS, NORVEL M., Jr Computer Accounting Teacher; *b:* Syracuse, NY; *m:* Randy J. Crandall; *c:* Harold Skip Ross, Aaron W. Ross, Samuel J. Crandall, Stuart A. Crandall; *ed:* Onondaga Comm Coll (AAS) Math, Sci 1983; Le Moyne Coll (BA) Acctng 1985; 9 Credit Hrs SUNY at Oswego Grad Prgm; *cr:* Mexico HS 9-12 Grd Bus Tchr 1986-90; Mid East OH Voc Schl Dist Customized Office Trng, Ad Ed 1991-94; Morgan HS Jr. Computer Acctng Tchr 1994-; *ai:* Bus Prof of Amer Club Adv; OH Voc Assn, NEA 1994-; *office:* Morgan HS 800 Raider Dr Mc Connelsville OH 43756

HEMLER, MARY PATRICIA, Mathematics Teacher; *b:* Gettysburg, PA; *ed:* St Joseph Coll (BA) Math 1970; Masters Equivalency; 30 Addl Hrs; *cr:* Old Court Jr HS Math Tchr 1970-85; Randallstown HS Math Tchr 1985-; *ai:* Var Sftbl Asst Coach; Fac Cncl; NEA, MSTA, TABCO 1970-; NCTM, MCTM 1991-; Parish Cncl 1986-, Pres; MD Governors Acad for Tchrs of Math, Sci, Tech Grad 1993; *office:* Randallstown HS 4000 Offutt Rd Randallstown MD 21133

HEMLOW, LANCE EDWARD, Mathematics Instructor; *b:* Poughkeepsie, NY; *ed:* Dutchess Comm Coll (AA) Math 1981; St Univ of NY at Albany (BA) Math 1983; Western CT St (MA) Math 1992; 15 Credits Toward Doctors at Rutgers Univ; *cr:* Interglobal Tech Svcs Mgr 1985-88; Emory Air Freight Pricing Analyst 1988-89; Fishkill Correctional Fac Adjunct Instr 1990-92; Raritan Valley Comm Coll Instr 1993-; *ai:* Chess Club Adv; Arithmetic, Intermediate Algebra & Pre-Calculus Comms; Reform Project for Applied Calculus; Fac Rep for Tech-Preparatory Grant with Local Area HS; *office:* Raritan Valley Comm Coll PO Box 3300 Somerville NJ 08876*

HEMMERICH, CAROL JEAN, Retired English Teacher; *b:* St Henry, OH; *m:* Gary Lynn; *c:* Kevin, Krisann; *ed:* Univ of Dayton (BSEd) Elem Ed 1966; Wright St Univ Lib Sci Grad Work; *cr:* St Christopher 4th Grd Tchr 1963-64; Queen of Angels 5th Grd Tchr 1964-65; St James 6th Grd Tchr 1965-66; Coldwater Exempted Schls 2nd Grd Tchr 1966-71; Ansonia Local Schls 6-8th Grd Lang Arts Tchr 1971-94; *ai:* Stu Cncl Adv; Staff Dev; Darke Cty Young Authors Steering Comm; Negotiating Team; Local Task Force; OEA; NEA; Local AEA; ORTA; Beta Sigma Phi 1974-, Sec, VP, Pres.

HEMMINGER, G. WILLIAM, English Teacher; *b:* Carlisle, PA; *m:* Joyce A. Gross; *ed:* Shippensburg Univ (BS) Eng, Theatre 1977, (MA) Lib Sci 1982; *cr:* Carlisle Area Schl Dist Eng Tchr 1977-; *ai:* Stage Club Adv; NEA, PSEA 1977-; *home:* 40 Graham Rd Newville PA 17241

HEMPEL, STEVEN PAUL, Science Teacher; *b:* Bayonne, NJ; *ed:* St Peter's Coll at Jersey City (BS) Bio 1980, (MA) Ed, Rdng 1990; *cr:* St Peter's Coll Chemical Technician 1980-93; Meml HS Sci Tchr 1994-; *ai:* Schl Musical Position Dir; Tutorial Achvmt Prgm; Project Grad Comm; Asst Schl Colorguard, Sci Fair, Key Club Adv; NEA, NJEA, WYNEA 1994-; St Mary's Church Store 1990-, Mgr; *office:* Memorial HS 5501 Park Ave West New York NJ 07093

HENAULT, LOUISE BERNIER, Third Grade Teacher; *b:* Lewiston, ME; *m:* Paul; *c:* David, Amanda; *ed:* Univ of ME at Farmington (BS) Elem Ed 1980; *cr:* Jordon Schl Chptr I Tchr 1976-77; Montello Schl Chptr I Tchr 1977-79; Longley Schl Classroom Tchr 1982-; *ai:* Support Team; Sun Journal Partnership; MEA, NEA 1982-; Music Boosters, Hockey Assn 1990-94; *office:* Gov James B Longley Elem Sch 145 Birch St Lewiston ME 04240

HENCEROTH, WILLIAM A., 4th Grade Social Studies Tchr; *b:* Salem, OH; *m:* Christina M. Davis-Henceroth; *c:* Nathan W., Roy M., Jesse C.; *ed:* Kent St Univ (BA) Elem Ed 1977; *cr:* Mc Kinley Elem Tchr 1977-; *ai:* Jr HS Bsktbl Coach Boys 3 Yrs, Girls 2 Yrs; Mahoning Vly Soccer Ofcls 1988-; United Soccer Assn 1990-, Pres; Salem Jr Bsbl 1986-90, VP; Acad Yr in Amer 1995-, Local Coord; *office:* Mc Kinley Elem Schl 441 E Chestnut St Lisbon OH 44432

HENCHBARGER, BURTON LEE, In School Suspension Teacher; *b:* Clearfield, PA; *m:* Colleen M.; *c:* Charles T., Karen B.; *ed:* DuBois Bus Coll (ASB) Acctng 1966; Penn St Univ (BS) Scndry Ed & Soc Stud 1991; Grad Courses with Performance Learning Systems Inc Leading to Masters Degree Gannon Univ; *cr:* Philipsburg Osceola Sr High Soc Stud & In Schl Suspension Tchr 1994-; *ai:* Co-Adv NHS & Soc Stud Club; PSEA 1994-; NEA 1994-; BPOE #540 1971-; John Lewis Shade Post #6 Amer Legion 1994-, Fin Ofcr; *home:* 919 S 6th St Clearfield PA 16830

HENCK, JOAN E., 5th Grade Teacher; *b:* New York City, NY; *m:* Michael; *c:* Susan, John, Stephen; *ed:* Mt Union Coll (BA) Ed 1961; Kent St Univ (MED) 1986; 36 Hrs Over Masters at Ashland Coll; *cr:* Garfield Hts Tchr 1961-65; West Geauga Tchr 1975-; *ai:* Elem Ski Adv; 5th Grd Head Tchr; Math Chm; NEA 1961-; OEA 1961-; OH Tchrs of Math; Greater Cleveland Cncl of Math; West Geauga Tchrs Assn 1975-, Negotiation Team; Beta Sigma Phi 1982- Pres, Treas, Girl of the Yr for 10 Yrs; Nu Aplha Chapter; West Geauga Recreational Cncl; Outstdng Tchr of the Yr at West Geauga; Outstdng Math Tchr 1991 at Northeast OH Elem; Speaker at Sessions of NCTM, OCTM Prof Meetings; Grants Awd to me by West Geauga Ed Fndtn; *office:* Robert C Lindsey Elem Schl 11844 Caves Rd Chesterland OH 44026*

HENCKEL, GEORGE LEE, Principal; *b:* Elkton, MD; *m:* Wanda Lee Moore; *c:* Tami Lynn, Kelley, Travis Lee; *ed:* WA Coll (BA) Eng, Lit 1971; Western MD Coll (MAS) Ed Admin 1976; Univ of MD 6 Hrs PG; *cr:* Sudlersville MS 7th, 8th Grd Read, LA, SS Tchr 1971-93, Prin 1993-; *ai:* Recreation & Parks Instr 1971-93; NEA, MSTA 1971-; Queen Anne's Co Ed Assn 1971-, Past Pres, VP; *office:* Sudlersville MS 201 N Church St Sudlersville MD 21668

HENDERSHOT, DOUGLAS LLOYD, Eighth Grade Math Teacher; *b:* Marietta, OH; *m:* Ruth Ann Baker; *c:* Mark, Jull; *ed:* OH Univ (BSEd) Math 1968; Xavier Univ (MA) Admin 1973; *cr:* Zanesville City Schl Eighth Grd Math Tchr 1968-75; Licking Vly Schl Eighth Grd Math Tchr 1975-88; Tri-Valley Schl Eighth Grd Math 1988-; *ai:* Math Counts Coach; Muskingum Cty Math Course of Stud Comm; NEA, Local OEA 1968-; OH Math Tchrs 1988-; Little League Coach 1987-; Yth Soccer Coach 1988-; Hunter Soc Instr 1980-; Jennings Scholar Awd; Acker Awd; *home:* 6265 Tanglewood Dr Nashport OH 43830

HENDERSON, BARBARA LAWTON, 7th & 8th Grd Rdng Consultant; *b:* Middletown, CT; *m:* James III; *c:* James IV, Susan Cianfarani, Sharon; *ed:* Cntrl CT St (BA) Elem Ed 1964, (MA) Rdng 1978; Westfield St (CAGS) Admin 1993; *cr:* Cromwell Elem Kndgtn Tchr 1964-65; Elem Kndgtn Tchr 1966-67; Dublin Montessorri Kndgtn Tchr Somers Elem 1st Grd Tchr 1976-78; Mabelle Avery Rdng C 1978-; *ai:* NEA 1976-, Pres, Treas; ASCD 1982-; Island Pond As Pres; Cromwell Womens Club & PTA Schlsp; *office:* Mabelle B A Ninth District Rd Somers CT 06071

HENDERSON, BRIAN,FSC, Assistant Prin & Sr Rel Philadelphia, PA; *ed:* LaSalle Coll (BA) Rel, Psych 1981, (MA) Stud 1992; Loyola Coll (MED) Ed, Admin 1995; Archdiocese of B Prof Catechist Cert 1992; *cr:* St Gabriel's Hall Child Care Worker West Cath HS for Boys Rel Tchr, Cncl Moderator 1984-88; St Acad Rel Tchr, Dean of Stdnts 1988-95, Asst Prin 1996; *ai:* Pari Presenter; Confirmation Group Teen Preparation Instr; Calvert HS 1995-, Bd Mem; Article Pub; *office:* St Frances Academy 501 St Baltimore MD 21202

HENDERSON, CECELIA BROWN, Prevention Ed Speci Hampton, VA; *m:* Leon; *c:* Celia H. Settles, Leon Jr., Tanya; *ed:* Buffalo (EDB) Hlth Ed 1963; St Univ of NY at Buffalo (EDM) 1973; Drug Prevention Counseling; Chemical Awareness, Interve Buffalo Bd of Ed Hlth Tchr 1963-86, Drug Ed Specialist 1986- Relations Club, DARE Adv; Peer Ldrs Trng Tchr; Buffalo Tchrs St Ed Assn 1963-; Stu Assistance Profs 1990-; Links Inc 1973- Area Dir; Buffalo Philharmonic Orch 1994-, Bd of Dir; NY St L 1990-, Bd of Dir, Svc Awd; Alpha Kappa Alpha 1963-, Chapter P Adv, Outstanding Svc; Outstanding Young Women of Amer 1973 Ambassador 1991; *office:* Riverside HS 51 Ontario St Buffalo N

HENDERSON, CHARLOTTE A., French & Spanish Tea Cleveland, OH; *c:* Stephanie, Lindsay, Christie; *ed:* OH St Univ (1972, (BS) Ed 1974; Master of Ed Curr & Instruction 1996; *cr:* C Jr HS Fr, Span Tchr 1974-77; River View HS Fr, Span Tchr 1977-8 *ai:* Fr Club, NHS Adv; North Cntrl, Tchr Evaluation Comms; F NEA, OEA, Frgn Lang Tchrs Assn 1974-; Sacred Heart Schl Bd Pres; Sacred Heart PTO 1988-89, Pres; Raised Funding Which Two Grants for Art Cmptr; *home:* 22197 Valley View Dr West Lafa 43845

HENDERSON, DINAH COLEMAN, Second Grade Tea Maysville, KY; *c:* Morehead St Univ (BA) Elem Ed 1969, (MA) 1973; *ed:* Manchester Elem Schl 4th Grd Tchr 1969-72; Mt Orab Grd Tchr 1972-; *cr:* NEA, OEA, SWOEA 1969-; Western Brown 1973-; *home:* 2273 Bardwell West Rd Mount Orab OH 45154*

HENDERSON, DONALD H., Science Department Chairman; NY; *m:* Mary Elizabeth Karam; *c:* Jonathan, Geoffrey, Brianne; Coll of Syracuse Univ (BS) Chem 1974; SUNY of Cortland (MS) (CAS) Admin 1994; *cr:* John F Kennedy HS Chem & Phys 1974-87, Sci Dept Chm 1986-87; Utica Coll Chem Instr 1982-84, John F Kennedy Jr HS Bio Tchr & Sci Dept Chm 1987-88; Utica Proctor HS Chem Tchr & Sci Dept Chm 1988-; *ai:* BOCES Tech Dev Team 1994-; Utica City Schl Dist Curr Comm; NY St Che 1994-; NY St Sci Tchrs, Utica Tchrs Assn 1974-;NSTA 1973-; Supvrs Assn 1987-, Sec; ASCD 1989-; Phi Delta Kappa 1989- N Ed; Mohawk Vly Sci Tchrs Ass n 1974-; Whitesboro Alumni As Pres 4 Yrs, Newsletter Ed 11 Yrs; Yorkville Little Leagu Westmoreland Road Elem Schl PTA Treas 3 Yrs, Playground Tr Rotary Intnl Awd for Excl in Tchng 1985-87; Golden Awd for Yrbk Adv from Herff-Jones 1986; Presidental Awd for Excl in Tc & Sci Nom; *office:* Thomas R. Proctor HS 1203 Hilton Ave 13501*

HENDERSON, DOUGLAS LESLIE, English Teacher; *b:* New CT; *m:* Janet Franklin Shinn; *c:* Kerry, Sally, Brooke; *ed:* Cntrl C (BS) Soc Sci, Eng 1970; Wesleyan Univ (MALS) Lit, Art 1978, (Art 1986; Addl 30 Hrs Hum; *cr:* Robert E. Fitch Jr HS Eng Tchr Robert E. Fitch Sr HS Eng Tchr 1986-; *ai:* Schl Newspaper A 1986-; North Stonington Bd of Ed 1994-; *office:* Robert E Fitch S Groton Long Point Rd Groton CT 06340

HENDERSON, ELIZABETH KARINA, Professor; *b:* Sweder Herald; *c:* Joanna, Wlodawer; *ed:* Warsaw Polytechnic (BA) Ar (MS) Arch, Urban Planning; *cr:* Montgomery Coll Prof 18 Yrs; P Constr Corp Chief Arch 5 Yrs; Lowell Lisk Assn Arch 2 Yrs; *ai:* Imersity Comm; AAUP; Arch Ctr First Place; *office:* Montgome Mannakee St Rockville MD 20850*

HENDERSON, EMILY KING, 6th Grade Teacher; *b:* Philippines; *m:* William; *ed:* Coll of the Holy Spirit (BA) 1957; Univ (MS) Ed; Attnd Jesuit Univ; *cr:* Anglo-Chinese Schl 3rd 1957-58; Espiritu Santo Parochial 5th Grd Tchr 1958-62; St Jude 2nd, 5th Grd Tchr 1962-; Our Lady of Sorrows 1968-69; PS 124 Tchr 1970-; *ai:* Presenter Sci, Staff Dev; Accompanist Calligrapher for Grad; Vol for Dist 2 Environmental Prgm 1972 AFT 1970-; Cath Tchrs Guild; Vol Xavier Soc for Bling 1976-78 Plateau Neighborhood Assn 1984-; Participant NY Acad of S Recipient of Grants; *home:* 5308 66th St Maspeth NY 11378*

HENDERSON, JEAN VICTORIA, Sixth Grade Teacher; *b:* W DC; *c:* William P.; *ed:* DC Tchrs Coll (BS) Elem Ed 1975; 30 Trinity Coll; *cr:* Scott Montgomery Elem Clerk Typist Educational Aide 1969-78; Merritt Elem 4th-5th Grd Tchr 1979 Montgomery Elem Rdng Tchr Title i 1980-81, 6th Grd Tchr Safety Patrols; Awd Comm Mem; Jr Honor Soc Comm Mem; W Tchrs Union, AFT 1979-; Nominated for Agnes Meyers' Tchr Awrd 1995-(ranked 18th of 20th); *office:* Scott Montgomery Elem P Street NW Washington DC 20001

HENDERSON, JILL BRODOCK, PE Teacher; *b:* Rome, NY; *c:* Molly, Matthew Kingdon; *ed:* Springfield Coll (BS) PE T SUNY at Cortland (MS) Hlth Ed 1985; 68 Post Grad Hrs; *cr:* Ro Y Gymnastics & Swimming Tchr 1971-76; Valley Gymnastics Head Coach 1976-; New Hartford HS Gymnastics Coach 1980-; Schls PE Tchr 1987-; *ai:* Head Coach; Valley Gymnastics; USA 1977-, Svc Awd 1990; NAWGJ 1979-, Bd Mem; USA Gym St Bd Mem; NYSPHSA 12 Yrs, Coach of Yr 1994; USA Gym NAWGJ Assn; USA Sr Natl AA Champion & Natl HS Champ 1993; NYSPHS Coach of Yr 1994; AA NYSPHS St Champi 1986-; Coached Over 15 Ath to Div I Schlrshps; *office:* Valley G 215 Clinton Rd New Hartford NY 13413*

HENDERSON, JOYCE HEROD, Principal; *b:* Morgantown George Douglas; *c:* Emily, Laura; *ed:* CA St Univ of PA (B Pathology, Audiology 1975; San Jose St Univ (MA) Educl Cns Univ of OK (BS) Electrical Engrng 1985; Admin, Prins Cert IN 1995; PA Scndry Cnslrs Cert 1993; Pupil Prsnl Svcs Credentia St Univ 1979; *cr:* CA Univ of PA Intermediate Unit #1 Deaf Speech Therapist 1975; Intermediate Unit #22 Buck Cty PA Speech Therapist 1975-77; Evergreen Schl Dist Lang, Speech 1979-80; Wright Patterson AFB Electrical Engr, Comm 1985-89; IN Cty Vo-Tech Schl Prin 1993-; *ai:* Strategic Plannin Comm Authentic Assessment Team Chprsn; Recycling Comm 1994-; PA Schl Cnslrs Assn, IN Cty Cnslrs Assn, IN Cty Prins A Leaguè of Women Voters 1991-; Air Force Inspector Gens Av Patterson AFB 1986; *office:* Indiana Co Area Voc Tech Sch 441 Indiana PA 15701

RSON, MARSHA JANE, Fourth Grade Teacher; *b:* Medford, Bloomsburg St Univ (BS) Elem Ed 1969; 36 Credit Hrs Bus Cmptr Work, Math, Sci, Rdng, Humanistic Ed, Visitation to Schls e & England; *cr:* Alfred I. Du Pont Dist Tchr 1969-71; Cecil Cty hr 1972-; *ai:* CCCTA Rep; Fac Advy, Soc Comms; Geog Bee IEA, MSTA 1973-; CCCTA 1973-, Fac Rep; PTA 1973-; Church o-Chair Bd of Ed, Task Force Comm Learning Ctr 8 Yrs; Sunday r 16 Yrs, Comm Transportation Vol; Dorset Condo Cncl 3 Yrs, Sec; 01 N Harrison St Apt 504 Wilmington DE 19806

RSON, RICHARD L., Language Arts Instructor; *b:* Washington, anice Emerick; *c:* Andrew; *ed:* CA Univ of PA (BA) Soc Stud 1972, g 1980; *cr:* Chartiers-Houston Jr & Sr HS; *ai:* Yrbk Spon; Role in AFT 1990-, Negotiations; NCTE; Short Stories & Brief Bio of esident Pub; *office:* Chartiers Houston Jr Sr HS 2050 W Pike St PA 15342*

RSON, ROBERT BRUCE, History Teacher; *b:* Norfolk, VA; *ed:* g St Univ (BS) Speech Comm 1990; Bowie St Univ (BS) (BA) d, His 1994; *cr:* Leonardtown HS His Tchr 1994-; *ai:* Var Soccer, g, JV Bsbl Coach; NEA 1995-; *office:* Leonardtown HS Rt 1 Box nardtown MD 20650

RSON, ROBERT FREDRICK, French & English Teacher; *b:* s, OH; *m:* Pamela Watkins; *c:* Brian, Katy; *ed:* OH St Univ (BSE) , (MA) Foreign Lang Ed 1969; Attnd OH Acad for Schl nent Strategies & Cooperative Learning Ctr; *cr:* Amanda Clear hls Fr & Eng Tchr 1967-70; W Muskingum Schls Fr & Eng Tchr : Stu Cncl Adv; NEA & WMEA 1972-, Pres 1972 & 1976; ASCD lta Kappa 1987-; Muskingum Schls Tchr of Yr 1990-91; OH Tchr om 1991; OH Effective Schls Grant 1990; Venture Captl Grant *ice:* W Muskingum HS 200 Kimes Rd Zanesville OH 43701*

RSON, SALLY KRAMS, English & Theater Teacher; *b:* Trenton, onald R.; *c:* Libby, Aland, Jean Shulick; *ed:* Univ of Rochester eral Arts Eng 1952; CA Univ of PA 32 Hrs Ed Cert; Colombia urs; Ricks Coll 6 Hrs; PA St Ext 6 Hrs Theater; Univ of PA 8 Hrs *cr:* Convair, Combustion Engnrng, Westinghouse Nuclear Engrng riter 1953-62; Mt Lebanon HS Eng Tchr 1971-72; Bethel Park HS eater Tchr 1972-; *ai:* Dir of Class Play, Broadway Musical; Stage asque Thespians, Sr Class Spon; AFT 1972-; Tchr of Yr 1983; Awd 1978; *home:* 5933 Glen Hill Dr Bethel Park PA 15102*

ICK, PAUL M., English Teacher; *b:* Niagara Falls, NY; *m:* Marcia *d:* Colgate Univ (BA) Eng Lit 1957; Harvard Univ (MAT) Scndry 8; Attnd Univ of Cincinnati, Cincinnati's Xavier Univ; *cr:* HS Scndry Eng Tchr 1959-61; Woodward HS Eng Dept Chm St Xavier HS Scndry Eng Tchr 1976-; *ai:* Liturgy Planning airos Retreat Prgm; Hands Across The Nation; Phi Beta Kappal shed Tchr Sve Awd 1973; Article Pub in Eng Journal 1993; *office:* HS 600 North Bend Rd Cincinnati OH 45224

ICKS, ANDREW MICHAEL, Marketing Tchr & Coordinator; *b:* OH; *m:* Linda Kay Pyles; *c:* Braden; *ed:* OH Univ (BA) Psych & 67; Kent St (VOEd) Mrktg Ed 1972; Wright St Mrktg, Cincinnati William Mason HS Tchr, Coord & Dept Chair 1967-; *ai:* DECA for 21st Century Comm; MEA 1967-, VP, Grievance, Legislative EA, NEA 1967-; United Meth Church 1990-, Bldg Comm; ro United Meth 1990-, Staff, Parish, Youth Ministry Comms; eza Alumni Assn 1986-, Adv; Golden Apple Awd Outstanding Awd 3 Times OH Retail Merchants Assn; Outstanding Achvmt hoes; Over 600 Stu Winners St Mrktg Competive Events & 6 Natl *office:* William Mason HS 770 S Mason Montgomery Rd Mason 0

CKS, DONALD L., Chemistry & AP Chemistry Tchr; *b:* le, PA; *m:* Esther E. Strehle; *c:* Jennifer L. Hendricks Williamson, ; *ed:* PA St Univ (BS) Chem 1964; Univ of Northern IA (MA) 1969; Purdue Univ 30 Credit Hrs; *cr:* Boyertown Area Schl Dist Bio, Chem & AP Chem Tchr 1970-; *ai:* Boys & Girls Cross Cntry Winter Track Coach; Former Class Adv; IM Bsktbl Dir; NSTA EA, PSEA & BAEA 1970-; St Joseph Hill Luth 1970-, Former VP; Planning & Zoning Commission, Former Chair; Flwshps: 2 NSF nst, NSF Acad Yr Inst; NSTA & DuPont Industry Hnrs Wkshp in r Bio; *office:* Boyertown Area Schl Dist 4th & Monroe St n PA 19512

CKS, M. MARIE POE, Bio, Chem & Earth Sci Teacher; *b:* St VA; *m:* George; *c:* Phyllis, Elizabeth; *ed:* Union Coll (BA, BS) Marshall Univ (MS) Bio 1970; Capital Univ 6 Semester UG Hrs; 21 UG Qtr Hrs, 36 Qtr Hrs; Miami Univ 10 Semester G Hrs; Kent Semester UG Hrs; Shawnee St Univ 15 Qtr UG Hrs; *cr:* Big ocal Schls Jr HS Sci Tchr 1955; Beaver Elem 3rd Grd Tchr Eastern HS Bio, Chem, Earth Sci Tchr 1964-; *ai:* Past Sci, Rocket i Fairs Adv; ELCTA 1970-, Pres, Neg Chm, Grievance; OEA, 4-; SEOEA 1964-, Pike Co Exec Comm; NSTA 1979-; Beaver l UM Church 1959-, Lay Del 7 Yrs, Sec 6 Yrs, Sunday Schl Tchr NSF Grants: Chem Capital Univ 1965, Bio Stud Marshall Univ th Sci OH Univ 1969; OH Bd of Regents & NSF Sci is Fun, n Sci Miami Univ 1992-93; *home:* 291 Van Fosson Rd Beaver OH

CKS, PATRICIA MARY, English Teacher & Chairperson; *b:* t, NY; *ed:* Notre Dame Coll of MD (BA) Eng 1965; Villanova) Eng 1971; Addl Hrs Notre Dame Univ; *cr:* Mt Carmel Schl Eng -68; St John Lit Inst Eng Tchr 1968-69; Notre Dame Prep Schl 1969-70; Paul VI HS Eng Tchr 1970-88, Eng Tchr, Dept Chair Creative Writing Tchr; NCEA 1965-; NCTE 1970-; *office:* Paul l Hopkins Rd Haddonfield NJ 08033

CKSON, CHERYL (BARNER), HS Math Tchr & Computer Liberty, NY; *m:* Richard; *c:* Kurt Scheibe, Kristen Scheibe; *ed:* Albany (BS) Math 1969; SUNY at New Paltz (MS) Educl Admin S) Educl Admin 1991; *cr:* Liberty Cntrl Schl 7th-12th Grd Math -72, 1974-76; Tri-Vly Cntrl Schl HS Math, Cmptr Coord 1981-; Tech Comm; Tchrs Ctr; Tech Comm; Tri-Vly Tchrs Assn 1981-, r 1989; ASCD, Phi Delta Kappa 1990-; Delta Kappa Gamma hurch 1985-, Organist, Choir Dir, Sunday Schl Supt, Tchr; NYSCATES Confs 1994, 1995; Co-Winner NYNEX Tech Grant *ce:* Tri-Vly HS Rt 55 PO Box 420 Grahamsville NY 12740

CKSON, GARY LEE, Mathematics & Physics Teacher; *b:* nd, MD; *m:* 21502; *c:* Lindsey Aron, Alex Ethan; *ed:* Frostburg BS) Math, Physics 1967, (MED) Math Ed 1972; Univ of MD rr, Instr 1986; Frostburg St Univ 30 Addl Credit Hrs; Governor's 1D 4 Weeks Summer 1992; *cr:* Fort Hill HS Math Tchr 1967-69; Cty Bd of Ed Adult Basic Ed GED 1973-81; Allegany Comm Coll Math Tchr 1981-90; Allegany HS Math Dept Chair, Physics Tchr : Gifted & Talented Schl Coord, Spectra Math Prgm; Schl Comm Co-Chm; Ski Club Co-Adv, Math Team Co-Adv, NHS Adv; 8-; Phi Delta Kappa 1988-; NCTM, MCTM 1989-; Sigma Pi 75-; Appalachian Environmental Lab Bd of Visitors 1988-; First urch 1974-, Church Schl Supt 1978-79; Environmental Concern 90-, Chm 1992; Allegany Co Tchr of Yr 1991; Fnlst St of MD 1991; Phi Eta Sigma Recognition of Outstanding HS Educators *e:* 1007 Brown Ave Cumberland MD 21502

HENDRICKSON, HOWARD RAY, Computer Science Teacher; *b:* Springfield, MO; *m:* Rebecca Kohn; *c:* Scott A., Staci L.; *ed:* Bloomsburg Univ (BS) Math 1972; Trenton St Coll (MED) Math 1974; PA St Univ 30 Grad Credits; *cr:* Pennsbury HS Math & Cmptr Sci Tchr 1972-, Cmptr Sci Chprsn 1990-; *ai:* Mathletics Spon; Cmptr Sci Team Spon; Internet Dist Comm Chprsn; NEA, PSEA, BCTM 1972-; *office:* Pennsbury HS 705 Hood Blvd Fairless Hills PA 19030

HENDRICKSON, JOHN T.,JR., Social Studies Teacher; *b:* Long Branch, NJ; *m:* Barbara Rost; *c:* Stephanie, Sheryl; *ed:* Rutgers Univ (BA) His 1966; Lehigh Univ (MA) His 1967; Addl 60 Credit Hrs in Post Grad & In-Svc at: Monmouth, Jersey City St, Rowan, Kean, Georgian Court, St Peters Colls; *cr:* Middletown HS North Soc Stud Tchr 1967-; *ai:* Scholar Ath; Schlsp Comm; NEA, NJEA, MonmouthCty EA 1967-; Middletown Twp Ed Assoc 1967-, 25 Yr Svc Awd; NJSIAA Soccer Official 1977-; Shore Soccer Officials Assoc 1977-, Past VP, 15 Yr Svc Awd; NJ Comm for Hum Summer Symposium 1992, Worlds of 1492; *office:* Middletown HS North 63 Tindall Rd Middletown NJ 07748

HENDRICKSON, LINDA LEE, Global Stud & Government Tchr; *b:* Oceanside, NY; *ed:* Hofstra Univ (BA) His, Scndry Ed 1969; Long Island Univ (MS) Lib Sci, Multi Media Ctrs 1974; 20 Cred Hrs Sco Stud, Admin; *cr:* Tripp Lake Camp Ath, Head Cnslr 1968-84; Freeport HS Tchr, Coach 1969-; *ai:* Girls Tennis, Bsktbl Coach; Devil Pride Club; Author Local Paper; Global Stud Regents Review; NCSS 1970-; Nassau Cty Girls Bsktbl Coaches Assn 1985-, Sec, Outstanding Svc Awd; Natl Trust Historical Preservation 1980-; AAHPERD 1971-; Nat Fed Interscholastic Coaches, Ofcls 1988-; Freeport United Meth Church 1969-, Ed Work Area Chprsn, Trustee, Treas; Red Cross 1988-, CPR, First Aid Instr; Freeport Ldr 1987-, Columnist; FUM Church 1969-, Adopt A Family Chprsn; Civic Leadership Awd, Rotary Club 1985; Distinguished Coaching Awd 1986; Sftbl Coach of Yr 1987; *office:* Freeport HS S Brookside Ave Freeport NY 11520*

HENDRICKSON, SCOTT D., Sec Math Teacher; *b:* Warren, PA; *m:* Deanne M. Chambers; *ed:* Penn St Univ (BS) Forest Sci 1983; Edinboro Univ Math Ed Cert 1989; Addl Hrs Gannon Univ Ed; *cr:* Warren Cty Chrstn Schl Math, Sci Tchr 1983-89; Eisenhoewr HS Math Tchr 1990-91; Youngsville Mid, Sr HS Math Tchr 1991-; *ai:* Var Soccer Coach at WAHS; YMSHS Track Coach, Action Team for Mid States, Math Counts Coach; NEA, PSEA, WCEA l((l_; Evang United Meth Church, COM Chprsn,Worship Ldr; *office:* Youngsville Mid, Sr HS 227 College St Youngsville PA 16371

HENERY, GLENN M., Biology Teacher & Ath Dir; *b:* Brookville, PA; *m:* Margaret Smith; *c:* Kaye D. Standing Rock, Kevin T., Greg M.; *ed:* IN Univ of PA (BS) Bio Ed 1965; Bloomsburg Univ (MS) Bio Ed 1970; NSF Credits; Grad Credits Elmira Coll, Mansfield Univ; *cr:* Towanda Area HS Tchr, Ath Dir 1965-; *ai:* FB, Bsktbl Asst Coach; Sr Sci Club Adv; NEA, PSEA 1965-; Towanda Ar Ed Assn 1965-, Pres, VP, Chief Negot; Penna St Ath Dirs 1973-, Rep; Towanda Boro Recreation Bd 1995-; *home:* 7 Barstow Ave Towanda PA 18848

HENGELSBERG, RAYMOND C., History & Pol Sci Assoc Prof; *b:* Pittsburgh, PA; *m:* Susan; *c:* Karl, Thomas; *ed:* Duquesne Univ (BA) His 1964, (MA) European His 1967; *cr:* Adirondack Comm Coll His Instr 1966-68; Monroe Comm Coll His, Pol Sci Assoc Prof 1968-; *office:* Monroe Community College 1000 E Henrietta Rd Rochester NY 14623

HENKEL, KAREN LYNN, English Teacher; *b:* Jersey City, NY; *ed:* Rider Coll (BA) Eng & Ed 1971; *cr:* Manville Intermediate Eng Tchr 1971-73; Notre Dame HS Eng Tchr 1973-; *ai:* NHS & Art-Lit Magazine Advs; Amer Stud Interdisciplinary Curr & Fac Liaison Comms; NCEA 1973-; *office:* Notre Dame HS 601 Lawrence Rd Lawrenceville NJ 08648

HENKEL, KATHY M., Mathematics Teacher; *b:* Pittsburgh, PA; *w:* Robert A. (dec); *c:* Jennifer, Melissa, Shawn; *ed:* IN Univ of PA (BS) Math 1966; 30 Hrs Post Grad; 3 Hrs Post Grad Univ of Pittsburgh; *cr:* West Allegheny Sr HS Math Tchr 1966-; *ai:* Mentor for New Tchrs; WAEA, PSEA; NEA; NCTM; Eastern Star.

HENMAN, BETH ANNE, Spanish Teacher; *b:* Midland, MI; *m:* Brian K.; *ed:* Ohio St Univ (BS) Span, Eng Ed 1992; Working Master Prgm Wright St Univ; *cr:* Westerville North HS Span Tchr 1992-; *ai:* Frgn Lang Dept Head; *office:* Westerville North HS 950 County Line Rd Westerville OH 43082

HENN, CAROLYN (BRANAGAN), Principal; *b:* New York, NY; *m:* Theodore L. II; *c:* Tedd, Craig, Jeff; *ed:* Concordia Tchrs Coll (BA) Ed 1968; Coll of Notre Dame of MD (MA) Mgmt 1994; *cr:* Immanuel Luth Schl 4th-5th Grd Tchr 1967-70, 2nd Grd Tchr 1980-89; Augsburg Luth Home Vol Svcs Dir 1989-94, Admissions, Mrktg Dir 1993-95; Calvary Luth Schl Prin 1995-; *ai:* Immanuel Luth Church Altar Guild; LEA 1995-; Masters Chapter of Alumnae Assn Coll of Notre Dame 1995-, Bd Mem; *office:* Calvary Luth Schl 2625 E Northern Pkwy Baltimore MD 21214

HENN, CHRISTINE J., English Teacher; *b:* Neptune, NJ; *m:* Thomas; *ed:* Shippensburg Univ (MED) Eng 1979; Scndry Prin Cert 1996; *cr:* Chambersburg Sr HS Eng Tchr 1976-; *ai:* Supervision, Attendance Comms; Grad Comm Chm; NCTE 1994-; NEA, CAEA 1976-; Nom CAEA Tchr of Yr 1994; *office:* Chambersburg Sr HS 511 S 6th St Chambersburg PA 17201

HENN, NANCY BASS, Third Grade Teacher; *b:* Albany, NY; *c:* Travis; *ed:* SUNY at Oswego (BS) Elem Ed 1971; Syracuse Univ Perm Cert Elem Ed 1976; *cr:* Stonehedge Elem Schl Fifth Grd Tchr 1971-77; MONY Fin Svcs Systems Analyst 1983-89; Wheeler Schl Sixth Grd Tchr 1989-93, Third Grd Tchr 1993-; *ai:* Grd 6 Chair 1990-91; Budget Comm 1992-93; Lang Arts Bldg Comm 1995-; NYSUT 1971-; *office:* Wheeler Schl 4543 S Onondaga Rd Nedrow NY 13120

HENNEMAN-BARTLETT, DENISE, 7th-12th Grd Girls PE Teacher; *b:* Endicott, NY; *m:* David Alan Bartlett; *c:* Austin Alexander Bartlett; *ed:* SUNY Coll at Cortland St (BS) PE 1985; Lock Haven Univ (BS) Hlth & PE 1990; Manfield Univ (MED) Spec Ed 1990; *cr:* Pine Ridge Schl PE, Adv & Hlth 1985-86; The Harley Schl PE, Coaching & Adv 1986-88; Bishop Newmann HS PE & Stu Cncl Adv 1993-; *ai:* 7 & 8th Grd Girls Bsktbl Coach-Curtain MS; Stu Cncl Adv; *office:* Bishop Neumann HS 901 Penn St Williamsport PA 17701*

HENNEOUS, MARION KOUTNIK, Second Grade Teacher; *b:* Little Neck, NY; *m:* Theodore F.; *c:* Andrew, Steven, Sean, Erin, Ann Marie; *ed:* Queens Coll (BA) Elem Ed & Psych 1961, (MS) Elem Ed & His 1963; Addl 3 Credits in Native Amer Culture & 3 Credits in Tchng Gifted Children; *cr:* Commack Pub Schls 1st Grd Tchr 1961-68; Jefferson Cty Schls 1st Grd Tchr 1968-70; Saint Brendans Elem Schl 2nd Grd Tchr 1983-84; East Providence Schl Dept 2nd Grd Tchr 1984-; *ai:* Kits in Tchng Elem Sci Tchr; East Providence Schls Rep; Prins Advy Bd; Univ of RI & RI Coll Stu Tchr Cooperating Tchr & Supvr; East Providence Ed Assn, NEA-RI 1984-; PTA 1975-, VP, Treas, Sec, Life Membership Awd; Bayview Parent Assn 1993-, Pres; *office:* Waddington Elem Schl Burnside Ave Riverside RI 02915

HENNESSEY, MARILYN JOAN, Biology Teacher; *b:* Chelsea, MA; *ed:* Univ of RI (BA) Bio 1967, (MAT) Sci Ed 1975; Attnd RI Coll, Salve Regina Univ; *cr:* Newton Weeks Jr HS Bio Tchr 1967-68; Rogers HS Bio, Earth Sci, Phys Sci, Physiology Tchr 1968-; *ai:* Peer Cnslng Prgm Adv; NEA 1967-; *office:* Rogers HS Wickham Rd Newport RI 02840*

HENNESSEY, RADCLIFFE WILLIAM, Global Studies Teacher; *b:* Long Branch, NJ; *m:* Gail Ellen; *ed:* Hartwick Coll (BA) His 1971; SUNY at Binghamton (MST) Soc Stud 1980; Russian Lang Stud SUNY at New Paltz; *cr:* Harpursville Cntrl Schl Soc Stud Tchr 1972-, Night Schl GED Tchr 1982-; *ai:* Adv Grd 10 1985-, Ski Club 1982-; NYSUT 1973-; PDK; NHS First Fac Inductee Stu Selection; *home:* 647 Welton St Harpursville NY 13787*

HENNESSEY, THOMAS H., Teacher; *b:* Fitchburg, MA; *m:* M. Jane Pellegrini; *c:* Patrick, Sean; *ed:* CA St Coll at San Bernardino (BA) Sociology 1971; Fitchburg St Coll (MED) Ed Admin 1973; 60 Semester Hrs Beyond Masters; *cr:* City of Riverside Electrical Overhd Estimator 1962-64; US Army Co Clerk 1964-66; City of Riverside Planning Dept 1966-71; City of Fitchburg Schls Tchr 1972-; *ai:* NEA, MA Tchrs Assn 1972-; *office:* Memorial MS 615 Rollstone St Fitchburg MA 01420

HENNESSY, LAURA JEAN, PE & Health Teacher; *b:* Washington DC ; *m:* James; *c:* Christopher, Sean, Patrick; *ed:* Univ of MD (BS) PE 1991; 15 Credit Hrs completed towards MA in Hlth; *cr:* Woodlin Elem PE Tchr 1991-92; Poolesville HS Dept Hea, PE & Hlth Tchr 1992-; *ai:* Girls Var Soccer Coach; JV Field Hockey Coach; Sr Class Spon; NEA; USFHA; Simon McNeely Tchng Merit Awd 1994; *office:* Poolesville Jr Sr HS 17501 W Willard Rd Poolesville MD 20837

HENNIGAN, ALEXANDRIA, Sixth Grade Teacher; *b:* Scranton, PA; *m:* Paul J.; *c:* Shana, Kara; *ed:* East Stroudsburg Univ (BS) Elem Ed 1973; Univ of Scranton (MS) Rdng; *cr:* North Pocono Schl Dist 6th Grd Tchr 1975-; *ai:* Trojan Tracker Newspaper Club Adv 20 Yrs; PSEA 1975-; *home:* RR 7 Box 7346 Moscow PA 18444*

HENNING, ALBERT KARL, Adj Assoc Professor of Engrng; *ed:* Dartmouth Coll (AB) Physics 1977, (AM) Physics 1979; Stanford Univ (PHD) Electrical Engrng 1987; *cr:* Intel Corp Device Physicist 1979-82; Dartmouth Coll Asst Prof of Engrng 1987-93, Assoc Prof of Engrng 1993-; Redwood Microsystems Pgm Mgr, Refrigeration 1996; *ai:* Yth Soccer & Bsktbl Coach; Guest Tchr in Sci & Math; Singing Choral & Close Harmony; IEEE 1979-; Sigma Xi 1979-; Awded US Patent; IBM Fac Dev Awd 1987-91, Analog Devices Career Dev Prof Fed & Industrial Sources 1990-92; Grants & Contracts for Scholarly Act Including Grad Rsrch & Undergraduate Tchng & Rsrch; Numerous Articles Pub; Adv for PHD, MS & Undergraduate Stdnts on Rsrch Projects.*

HENNING, JOHN EDWARD, English Teacher; *b:* Canton, OH; *m:* Maria; *c:* Carl, Alex; *ed:* PA St Univ (BS) AG 1977; Kent St Univ (MED) Voc Ed 1982; Stark Tech Coll (AS) Cmptr Programming 1986; Kent St Univ Doctoral Stu Ed, Psych; *cr:* West Branch HS Voc Ag Tchr 1978; Marlington HS Voc Ag Tchr 1978-87, Eng Tchr 1987-; *ai:* Tech, Inservice Comms; Boundary Breakers; NEA, OH Ed Assn, Marlington Ed Assn 1978-; Phi Delta Kappa 1992-, Pres; Martha Holden Jennings Scholar 1993; Stark Cty Tchr of Yr Finalist 1993; Tchr of Yr 1992.

HENNING, JUDITH VAN FLETT, Family & Consumer Sci Tchr; *b:* Scranton, PA; *m:* George F.; *c:* Adam, Aaron, Susan; *ed:* PA St Univ (BS) Family Stud 1971; Univ of WI (MS) Home Ec Ed 1972; Attnd Alumni Coll; *cr:* Upper Darby HS Tchr 1973; Chichester Jr HS Tchr, Dept Chair, Adult Ed 1974-76; Montrose HS Tchr, Dept Chair 1977-; *ai:* Strategic Planning Steering Comm; Grad Requirements Comm Chair; Support Group Cnslr; Dept Chm; Fac Rep Stu Liason Comm; NEA, PSEA, MEA, AAUW 1973-; Amer Assn Family & Consumer Scis 1971-; Susq Co Lib, Vol; Article Pub; 2 Grants St of PA Family; Pub Master's Thesis; Who's Who in Amer Ed 1995; *office:* Montrose Area HS RR 3 Box 28 Montrose PA 18801

HENNING, MARIA COLAIZZI, American Government Teacher; *b:* San Pietro Avella, Italy; *m:* John; *c:* Carl, Alex; *ed:* Mount Union Coll (BA) Ed & Pol Sci 1970; Kent St Univ (MED) Ed & Pol Sci 1978; Ashland Univ 15 Post-Grad Credit Hrs; *cr:* Marlington HS Soc Stud Tchr 1970-95; *ai:* Ralph Regula Stu Congressional Cncl Adv; Class Adv 1982; Citizens Bee & OH First Vote Coord; NEA & OEA 1970-; MEA 1970-, Sec; PDK 1980-; OH Cncl Soc Stud 1990-; Soc Stud Dept Chair 1989-; Stark Cty Soc Stud Comm 1990-95; Martha Holden Jennings Scholar 1987; Marlington HS Tchr of Yr 1993; Stark Cty Bar Assn Tchr of Yr 1993; Alliance Chamber of Commerce Tchr of Month 1994; *home:* 1051 Briarcliff Ave Alliance OH 44601

HENNINGER, FRANCIS JOSEPH, Director of Amer Studies Prgm; *b:* Jamaica, NY; *m:* Elinore Craven; *c:* Mary Haddad, Thomas, Francis, James, Kathryn; *ed:* Univ of Notre Dame (AM) Eng 1958; Univ of PA (MA) Amer Stud 1961, (PHD) Amer Stud 1965; *cr:* Siena Coll Instr 1958-61; Univ of Dayton Asst Prof, Assoc Prof, Prof of Eng 1965-; *ai:* Amer Culture Assn; Amer Assn Univ Prof 1958-; Articles Pub; *office:* Univ Of Dayton 300 College Park Ave Dayton OH 45469

HENNINGER, ROBERT H., Ec & World Cultures II Tchr; *b:* Renovo, PA; *m:* Elizabeth Lydia Kniowski; *c:* Jonathan, Katie, Abby, Amanda; *ed:* IN Univ of PA (BS) Soc Stud 1971; Bob Jones Univ (MS) Theatre 1979; Carnegie Mellon 9 Credits Grad Ed; Gannon Univ 6 Credits Grad Ec; Edinboro 3 Credits Grad Cmptr; *cr:* Bethel Chrstn Schl Tchr, Coach & Drama Dir 1979-89; McDowell Intermediate HS Tchr 1989-; *ai:* Campus Store & FCA Dir; Lead Tchr; New Tchr Mentor; NEA 1989-; 1st Assembly of God 1988-, Dir of Drama, Christmas & Easter Musicals Writer & Dir; Writer of 30 Pub Musical Dramas; Dir of Summer Grace Theatre Prgm; Natl Speaker for Chrstn Schls Intl; *home:* 1950 Lakeside Dr Erie PA 16511*

HENRICH, CHRISTINE ROSSETTI, 8th Grd American History Tchr; *b:* Lynn, MA; *m:* Stephen P.; *c:* Michael, Kristen; *ed:* Merrimack Coll (BA) His Tchng 1975; 30 Addl Hrs; *cr:* Saugus Jr HS His Tchr 1975-77; Saugus HS His, Law Tchr 1977-78; King Philip HS His, Govt Tchr 1981-82; King Philip North Jr HS His, Cultural Stud Tchr 1983-; *ai:* Team Ldr; KP Tchrs Assmn 1981-, Tchrs Rep; Norfolk Cty Tchrs Assn 1981-; NEA; Franklin Bsktbl Assn 1991-, Coach, Sec; Horace Mann Grant; NELMS Wkshps; Interdisciplinary Hnrs Prgm Co-Orginator; *office:* King Philip North Schl 18 King St Norfolk MA 02056

HENRICH, WILLIAM ROBERT, Ninth Grade Earth Science Tchr; *b:* Cleveland, OH; *m:* Pamela; *c:* Julie, Caitlin; *ed:* Miami Univ (BS) Comprehensive Sci 1982; Cleveland St Univ (MED) Curr, Inst 1989; *cr:* Springfield Pub Schls Sci Tchr 1983-84; Mentor Exempted Village Schls Sci Tchr 1984-; *ai:* Sci Dept Chm; 7th Grd Girls Bsktbl; Paper Recycling Club; March of Dimes Walk Amer Team; Talent Show, PTA Tchr Adv; Mentor Tchrs Assn 1984-; Camp Sue Osborn 1995-, Bd Mem; March of Dimes 1996, Comm Mem; Excl in Tchng Awd Mentor Pub Schls 1996; Martha Holden Jennings Scholar 1990; PTA Lake Cty Tchr of Yr Nom 1995; Kent St Univ Admin Wilson Fellow; Coalition Essential Schls Chicago, New York Roundtable Presentations; *office:* Mentor Ridge Jr HS 7860 Johnnycake Ridge Rd Mentor OH 44060*

HENRICK, KENNETH ALBERT, High School Guidance Counselor; *b:* Lawrence, MA; *m:* Mary Loughlin; *c:* William, Kenneth, Timothy, Michael, Brian; *ed:* Fitchburg St Coll (BSIs) Ind Eng 1975, (MED) Cnslng 1979; Addl Courses Salem St Coll, Northern Essex Comm Coll; *cr:* Military USMC 1956-58; Bay St Foods Supvr 1958-62; Raytheon Mfg Co Supvr 1962-77; Greater Lawrence Tech HS Guid Cnslr 1977-; *ai:* Schl Admissions Comm; Former Ath Fac Mgr; Yth Coach 15 Yrs; AFT 1977-; Northeast Cnslrs Assn 1980-; Methuen Schl Comm 1984-90, Bd Sec; Greater Lawrence Cncl for Children 1980-82; *office:* Greater Lawrence Technical Sch 57 River Rd Andover MA 01810

HENRIQUES, MICHAEL ALAN, 8th Grd Life Science Teacher; *b:* New Bedford, MA; *m:* Susan Partington; *c:* Heather, Ross; *ed:* Univ of Bridgeport (BA) His 1968; Attnd Bridgewater St Coll & Univ of MA at

Dartmouth; *cr:* Fairview Pub Schls Tchr 1968-81, Attendance Ofcr & Guid Cnslr 1982-83, Vice Prin 1984-85; Life Sci Tchr 1986-; *ai:* Ftbl & Bsktbl Coach; IM Acts; NEA 1968-; MTA 1968-; March of Dimes 1990-, Team Capt; Greater New Bedford Regional Voc Tech HS Excl in Tchng Awd; *office:* Hastings MS 7 Scholl St Fairhaven MA 02719

HENRIQUES, ZELMA WESTON, Professor; *b:* Kingston, West Indies; *m:* Gerald; *c:* Lisa Baron, David; *ed:* Morgan St Univ (BA) Sociology 1963; Columbia Univ (MSC) Soc Work 1975, (MED) Applied Human Dev & Cnslng Psych 1975; Doctor of Ed 1979; *cr:* NY City Dept of Soc Svcs 1964, 1967-71; Women's Prison Assn Dir of Soc Svcs 1965-67, 1971-74; NY Inst of Tech Asst Prof 1975-80; Cornell Univ Adj Prof 1981-82; Fordham Univ Adj Prof 1981-82; John Jay Coll Prof 1983-; *ai:* Nu Gamma Sigma, Stu Govt Fac Adv; Acad of Criminal Justice Sc; Amer Soc of Criminology; NE Assn of Criminal Jus Sc; Manna House Inc 1976-, Bd of Dirs; South Forty Corp 1994-, Bd of Dirs; Columbia Univ Post Doctoral Fellow Ctr for Stud of Human Rights; Peer Rview Consultant Natl Inst of Justice; Book: Imprisoned Mothers & Their Children 1982; Articles Pub.

HENRY, ARBA L., Agricultural Ed Dept Chm; *b:* Laurel, DE; *m:* Martha L. Lynch; *c:* Elizabeth Lyn, Brian William; *ed:* Univ of DE (AAS) Ag Mechanization 1967, (BS) Ag Ed 1970; PA St Univ (MED) Ag Ed 1975, (DED) Ag Ed 1984; *cr:* Solanco Schl Dist Dept Chair Appointment 1978; PA St Univ Grad Tchng Asst 198-83; Solanco Schl Dist Ag Tchr 1970-; Univ of DE Appt Adjunct Asst Prof of Ag Sci 1993; *ai:* Solanco FFA Adv, Dairy Judging Club Coach; Alpha Tau Alpha & Phi Delta Kappa 1975-; NEA & PSEA 1970-; Zoning-Hearing Bd 1986-93, Chm 1991; Fulton Grange & Solanco Fair Assn 1971-, Bd; Vol Fire Dept 1977-, Pres 1982; Octorara Watershed Assn Dir; NVATA Outstanding Ag Prgm St Winner 1987; Penn St Cooperating Tchr of Yr Awd 1987; Honorary Amer FFA Degree 1982; AATEA Eastern Region Outstanding Publication Awd 1979; *office:* Solanco Schl Dist 585 Solanco Rd Quarryville PA 17566*

HENRY, CAROLYN LEHMAN, Math Teacher; *b:* Castorland, NY; *m:* Donald O.; *c:* Adonia; *ed:* Goshen Coll (BA) Math, S S Ed 1960; SUNY at Potsdam (MS) Math Ed 1967; *cr:* Watertown Acad Math Tchr 1962-65; Lowville Acad Cntrl Math Tchr 1965-68; Pulaski Cntrl Math Tchr 1968-70; New Hartford Cntrl Math Tchr 1983-85; Poland Cntrl Math Tchr 1985-95; *ai:* Poland Tchrs Assn 1985-, Treas 3 Yrs; NYSUT, NEA 1962-; Church Work; *home:* 4348 Saunders Rd Clinton NY 13323

HENRY, CHRISTINE DECKER, Social Studies Teacher; *b:* Sussex, NJ; *m:* Donald Vincent; *c:* Devin Johnson, Logan Devereau; *ed:* Rider Coll (BA) Sociology 1980; Montclair St Coll (MA) Soc Stud 1988; *cr:* Sussex Cty Voc-Tech Sch Sub Tchr 1980-83; Kittatinny Regnl HS Soc Stud Tchr 1984-90; High Point Regnl HS Soc Stud Tchr 1991-; *ai:* Var Chrldng, Ftbl & Competition; Asst Mock Trial Coach; Mock Trial Coach; Class Adv; NEA & NJEA 1984-; HPEA 1991-; Hpea VP 1994-; Tchr of the Yr 1987; Governors Tchr Recognition Awd 1987; High Points Tchr of the Yr 1993; *office:* High Point Regional HS 299 Pigeon Hill Rd Sussex NJ 07461

HENRY, CINDY FLOYD, HS Teacher & Chairperson; *b:* Pittsburgh, PA; *m:* Thomas W.; *c:* Ryan D., Kyle C.; *ed:* Thiel Coll (BA) Bio, Chem 1969; Univ of Pittsburgh (MA) Tchng Sci 1970; Gannon Univ (MS) Cnslng Psych 1995; 12 Credits Performance Learning Systems; *cr:* Churchill Schl Dist Bio, Phys Sci Tchr 1969-70; Dept of Defense Biol, Math Tchr 1970-72; Fairview Schl Dist Bio, Hnrs Bio, Chem, Hnr Chem, Anatomy & Physiology, Microbiology, Phys Sci, Physics, Advanced Bio Tchr 1972-; *ai:* PA Jr Acad Sci Spon; Sci Dept Chprsn; PSEA, NEA, PA Jr Acad Sc 1972-; NSTA, PSTA 1974-; Delta Kappa Gamma 1995-; WELCA 1974-, Pres; Honored by Edinboro Univ Excl in Ed; *home:* 536 Hilltop Rd Erie PA 16509*

HENRY, CONSTANCE H., 1st Grade Teacher; *b:* Carlisle, PA; *m:* Kurt L.; *c:* Kyle L.; *ed:* Elizabethtown Coll (BS) Elem Ed 1978; Shippensburg Univ (MED) Educl Admin 1984; Elem Prin Cert 1985; *cr:* Cumberland Vly Schl Dist 2nd Grd Tchr 1979-90, 4th Grd Tchr 1990-92, 1st Grd Tchr 1992-; *ai:* Good Hope Civic Assn, Pres 1989-90; PA Comission on Crime & Delinquency Cert of Achvmt; *office:* Silver Spring Elem Schl 6746 Carlisle Pike Mechanicsburg PA 17055*

HENRY, DARREN DEL, Third Grade Teacher; *b:* Findlay, OH; *m:* Jill Knepper; *c:* Chandlar; *ed:* Bowling Green St Univ (BA) 1st-8th Elem Ed 1987; *cr:* Leipsic Pub 3rd Grd Tchr 1988-; *ai:* Girls Asst Bsktbl & Asst Bsbl Coach; NEA; OEA; *home:* 326 Center Leipsic OH 45856

HENRY, DONALD SCOTT, Band Director; *b:* Philipsburg, PA; *ed:* Clarion Univ of PA (BS) Music Ed 1992; Attnd Penn St Univ, Allentown Coll, Gannon Univ; *cr:* Philipsburg-Osceola HS Band Dir 1992-; *ai:* Marching, Summer Bands; Spring Musical; Natl Band Assn 1993-; PA Music Ed Assn 1992-; Natl Guild of Piano Tchrs 1990-; Guest Conductor Mercer Summer Comm Band; Guest Lecturing Clarion Univ Scndry Methods Class; *office:* Philipsburg-Osceola Area HS 502 Philips St Philipsburg PA 16866*

HENRY, DOUGLAS A., Science Teacher; *b:* Fort Littleton, PA; *m:* Donna Bishop; *c:* Dirk, Darci, Darin; *ed:* Shippensburg Univ (BS) Bio, Chem 1964, (MED) Bio 1967; 55 Addl Hrs; *cr:* Cumberland Vly Schl Dist Sci Tchr 1964-; *ai:* NEA, PSEA 1964-; 4 NSF Grants; *office:* Good Hope MS 451 Skyport Rd Mechanicsburg PA 17055

HENRY, ELLEN E., Social Studies Teacher; *b:* Buffalo, NY; *m:* Mark; *c:* Scott, Melissa, Kelly; *ed:* Canisius Coll (BA) Ed 1973, (MS) Ed 1977; *cr:* Frontier MS 7th Grd Soc Stud Tchr 1987-; *ai:* Stu Govt Adv; NYSUT 1987-; NY Cncl for Soc Stud 1989-; *office:* Frontier MS 2751 Amsdell Rd Hamburg NY 14075

HENRY, FREDERICK ANDREW, US History Teacher; *b:* South Amboy, NJ; *c:* Kristen, Erin, Fred III; *ed:* Middlesex Comm Coll (AA) Lbrl Arts 1970; Trenton St (BA) Soc Stud 1973; *cr:* St Mary's Elem Schl Soc Stud Tchr 1974-81; South Amboy MS Soc Stud Tchr 1982; H. G. Hoffman HS His, Eng Tchr 1982-; *ai:* Ath Dir; Cross Cntry, Girls Bsktbl, Boys Bsbl Coach; So Amboy Ed Assn 1982-; City Cncl 1992-, VP; *office:* H G Hoffman HS 240 John St South Amboy NJ 08879

HENRY, GARY RICHARD, Fifth Grade Teacher; *b:* Brookville, PA; *m:* Darla J. Barger; *c:* Neil, Deanna, Jenna; *ed:* Clarion Univ of PA (BS) Elem Ed 1977, (MS) Elem Ed 1981; *cr:* Keystone Elem Schl 3rd Grd Tchr 1978-89, 4th Grd Tchr 1989-90, 5th Grd Tchr 1990-; *ai:* PA Hunter Ed Instr: Elem Intramural Instr; Comm Drug, Alcohol Comm; Knox Little League Coach; PSEA, NEA 1978-; Knox United Meth Churh 1982-, Comm Mem, Youth Act; Clarion Cty Conservation Educator of Yr 1985; *home:* PO Box 81 Knox PA 16232

HENRY, HYDEN HAROLD, Mathematics Teacher; *b:* Trinidad, West Indies; *ed:* Fairleigh Dickinson Univ (BS) Bio 1982; 18 Credit Hrs Bio; *cr:* St Anastasia Elem Schl Sub Tchr 1986-87; Intnl Mrktng Supvr 1987-88; Paul VI Regnl HS Math, Sci Tchr 1988-90; Paterson Cath HS Math Tchr 1990-; *ai:* Stu Cncl Adv; Stu Mentor; St Anastasia Church 1987-, Retreat Ldr, Parish Cncl, Folk Group Dir, Yth Svc; Articles Pub; *office:* Paterson Catholic HS 764 11th Ave Paterson NJ 07514

HENRY, LUCYE BOSTIC, Fourth Grade Teacher; *b:* FL; *c:* Jeffrey O. Baker, Juan S. T.; *ed:* FL A&M Univ (BA) 1-6 Elem Grds 1953; Ball St Univ BA Plus; Boston Univ, City Univ, Univ of West FL, Univ of MD 15/30 1-8 Grds Elem 1993; Cooperative Learning; Cur Issue Rdng, Lang; Kitchen, Garage, Garbage Sci; Love & Logic; Music in Early Chldhd; Instrl Techniques Elem Sci; Early Chldhd, Spec Ed; *cr:* Trinity Gardens Elem Schl 1st Grd Tchr 1953-54; Spady Elem Schl 1st, 2nd, 4th Grd Tchr 1955-63; Washington Elem Schl 4th Grd Tchr 1963-67; Westward Elem Schl 1st Grd Tchr 1967-68; Hainerberg Elem Schl 2nd, 4th Grd Tchr 1969-; *ai:* Grd Level, Ethnic Comm Chprsn; Stu Cncl Spon; Cooperative Learning Mentor; Spelling Bee Coord; Edctrs Day Presenter; OEA, WEA, PTO 1970-; Wiesbaden Ed Assn 1970-, VP; Phi Delta Kappa 1993-; Comm Minority Steering Comm Black His Prgms; Gulf War Support; Stu Cncl OK Bombing Donation; Bosnia, Hungary Support; DODDS Performance Monetary Awds: Superior 1977, Exceptional 1993; Many Appreciation Certs; *office:* Hainerberg Elem Schl 07778 Texasstrasse Wiesbaden Germany XX*

HENRY, MARY COLETTE, Middle School Health Teacher; *b:* Wilmington, DE; *ed:* West Chester St Coll (BS) Hlth, PE 1982; Wilmington Coll (MS) Human Resources Mngmt 1989; *cr:* Fred S. Engle MS Hlth, PE Tchr 6 Yrs; New Castle MS Hlth, PE Tchr 6 Yrs; Gunning Bedford MS Hlth Tchr 2 Yrs; *ai:* Peer Ldr, Mediation Adv; Discipline, Colonial Schl Dist Drug-Free, Hlth Curr Comms; Peer Mediation Advy Bd Chprsn; Colonial Ed Assn, DE Ed Assn, NEA 1989-; DE Army Natl Guard 1980-Major; Community Works, Bd Mem; Team Participation, Chprsn 24 Hr Relay Challenge; Fulbright Tchr Exch 1986-87; Mid Tchr of Yr 1990-91; NE Region Awd 1993-94; *office:* Gunning Bedford MS Cox Neck Rd Delaware City DE 19706

HENRY, MAUREEN P., Asst Principal & Math Teacher; *b:* New York City, NY; *ed:* Adelphi Univ (BS) Ed 1980; St John's Univ (MS) Spec Ed 1982; Brooklyn Coll (PHD) Educl Admin, Supervision 1994; *cr:* St Edmund HS Math, Sci Tchr 1980-85; John Adams HS Math Tchr, Stu Affairs Coord, Math AP 1985-; *ai:* Var Chrldng Coach; Sr, Stu Org Adv; Schl Based Planning Cncl; NCTM; Assn Math Tchrs NYS; Assn Math Asst Prin NYC; ASCD; CO Outward Bound Schl Grant; *office:* John Adams HS 101-01 Rockaway Blvd Ozone Park NY 11417*

HENRY, MICHAEL SCOTT, Adv Placement US His Tchr; *b:* Mt Vernon, IL; *m:* Ann; *c:* Kimberly; *ed:* Univ of MD (BA) Ed 1968, (MA) Ed 1971, (MA) US Hist 1977, (PHD) Curr Instr 1985; *cr:* Cntrl HS Intnl Stud Coord 1989-90; Parkdale HS Tchr & Dept Chair 1968-89; Bowie HS Tchr 1990-; *ai:* NCSS 1968-, Honorable Mention Dissertation Awd 1985; Several Articles Pub; *office:* Bowie HS 15200 Annapolis Rd Bowie MD 20715*

HENRY, PATRICIA ANN, Fifth Grade Teacher; *b:* Akron, OH; *ed:* Univ of Akron (BS) Elem Ed 1964, (MS) Elem Admin 1976; *cr:* Lincoln Schl Tchr 1966-; *ai:* NEA, OEA, NEOEA, CFEA 1966-; Fellow to Aeneid Inst 1986; St of OH Grant to Dev Sci Lab; Hiram Summer Scholar; Cuy Falls City Schls Commitment to the Profession Awd; Project Learn Literacy Prgm for Summit Cty Pub Svc Tutor; *office:* Lincoln Elem Schl 3131 Bailey Rd Cuyahoga Falls OH 44221*

HENRY, RICHARD F., Sixth Grade Teacher; *b:* Rochester, NY; *m:* Marilyn J.; *c:* Timothy, Scott, Christina; *ed:* SUNY at Buffalo (BA) Psych 1967; Addl 30 Hrs in Ed; *cr:* Attica Cntrl Schl 6th Grd Tchr 1969-; *ai:* Ftbl Coach 27 Yrs; Attica Tchrs Assn 1969-; United Presbyn Church 1975-, Elder 3 Yrs; *home:* 3373 Black St Caledonia NY 14423

HENRY, SARA WALLACE, 1st Grade Teacher; *b:* Covington, KY; *m:* Joseph P.; *c:* William P., Dove K.; *ed:* Univ of KY (BA) Elem Ed 1981; St Univ of NY at Oneonta (MS) Elem Ed 1987; *cr:* Gilboa-Conesville Cntrl Schl 4th & 5th Grd Tchr 1984-89, 1st Grd Tchr 1991-; *ai:* AFT 1984-, VP, Pres 1994-; Grants to Publish Local His Book, Design Puppets, Plant & Encourage Gardening & Old Town & Bldg of Dam Slides Conversion to Photo for Class Use; 2 Grants to Begin Preschl Library Nights and a Kindergarten Intro Program; *office:* Gilboa-Conesville Cntrl Schl Wycof Rd Gilboa NY 12076*

HENRY, SHARON LOUISE, Sr HS Mathematics Teacher; *b:* Lewistown, PA; *ed:* Univ of PA at Shippensburg (BSEd) Math Ed 1991; 30 Post Grad Hrs Toward Masters in Tchng & Curr; *cr:* Mechanicsburg HS Math Tchr 1991-92; Milton Hershey Schl Math Tchr 1992-; *ai:* Asst Var Sftbl Coach; Fac Observer & Mentor; NCTM, PCTM, NEA, PSEA 1991-; *office:* Milton Hershey Schl 300 Hotel Rd Hershey PA 17033

HENRY, SHEILA CALLAN, High School English Teacher; *b:* Boston, MA; *m:* Richard H.; *ed:* Salem St Coll (BA) Eng; U MA at Lowell (BA) Eng 1971; Southern CT St Univ (CAS) Ed 1995; *cr:* JFK Jr High Eng Tchr 1971-77; Peachtree HS Eng Tchr 1977-85; Wilton HS Instrl Ldr & Eng Tchr 1985-; *ai:* NHS Fac Advy Comm; NEA 1971-; NCTE 1985-; WEA 1985-; Star Tchr 1981, 1982, 1984; Tchr of Yr 1985; U Chicago Outstdng Tchr 1987; Tufts Outstdng Tchr 1996; *office:* Wilton HS 395 Danbury Rd Wilton CT 06897*

HENRY, THOMAS DAVID, Social Studies Teacher; *b:* Westbury, NY; *m:* Dr. Allison Evans; *c:* Caitlin, Colleen; *ed:* Roberts Wesleyan Coll (BA) Soc Stud 1976; SUNY at Geneseo (MS) His 1984; Amer His Doctoral Candidate Syracuse Univ; *cr:* Byron-Bergen Cntrl Schls Soc Stud Tchr 1977-84; Syracuse Univ Tchrs Asst 1984-85; Liverpool Cntrl Schls Soc Stud Tchr 1986-; Adj Prof of Hist, Sunny Cortland, Syracuse; *ai:* Model United Nations Adv; Chess Club Adv; UMOJA Adv; Cultural Diversity Task Force Chm; Rugby Coach; NCSS 1986-; NYS Soc Stud Cncl 1977-; NYS United Tchrs 1977-, Pres 1981-83; AFT 1977-; CNY Cncl for Soc Stud, Treas 1982-84, Sec 1994-; Baldwinsville Crop Comm 1988-, Publicity 1988-91; Luth Advocacy 1988-; Amer Historians Org 1985-; NY Historical Assn 1984-; A Peoples Guide to Citizenship Author 1990; A Distant Thunder Cntrl NY Civil War Guest Historian; Hist Consultant; *office:* Liverpool H S 4338 Wetzel Rd Liverpool NY 13090*

HENRY, WILLIAM DEAN, Social Studies Teacher; *b:* Brookville, PA; *m:* Helen Elizabeth Gilder; *c:* Kristin, Mark; *ed:* Cedarville Coll (BA) His 1973; Dallas Theological Seminary (ThM) Historical Theology 1984; Kent St Univ 15 PHD Hrs in His; *cr:* Willo Hill Chrstn Schl Kndgtn, Jr High Tchr, Soccer Coach 1973-75; Frederick Chrstn Acad 4th Grd Tchr, Bsktbl Coach 1975-77; Valley Chrstn Acad Scndry His, Eng, Math, PE, 5th Grd Tchr, Soccer, Bsktbl Coach 1985-89; Real Life Chrstn Acad Scndry Soc Stud, Speech, Hlth, PE Tchr, Soccer, Bsktbl Coach 1993-; *ai:* Var Girls Bsktbl Coach; Speech Adv; Greater Youngstown Coalition of Chrstns 1993-; *home:* 4957 E Calla Rd New Middletown OH 44442

HENSCHEL, SANDI, English Teacher; *b:* Brooklyn, NY; *c:* Lisa, Rachel, Sarah Piccione; *ed:* SUNY at Potsdam (BS) Ed, Eng 1960, (MS) Eng 1966; SUNY at Brockport (MA) Creative Writing; U of CA at Santa Barbara PG in Theatre; *cr:* Northern IL Univ Univ Supvr 1968-69; Kendall HS 1974-; SUNY at Brockport 1974-; Genesee Comm Coll Intro to Theatre 1993-; *ai:* NHS Co-Adv; Class Adv 1978, 1984, 1991; Drama Club Adv 1976-93; NEA, Kendall Fac Assn 1974-; NYS Eng Cncl 1993-, Edctr of Excl 1995; Shipping Dock Theatre 1990-, Vol Coord, 2 Excl in Acting, 1 Excl in Directing; Rochester Comm Players 1988-90, Bd of Dirs; Natl Endowment Hum Grant Stud Gilganesh; Extensive Bibliography Available Poetry, Articles, Plays; U of R Excl Tchng Awd 1980; NDEA Arts & Hum Grant 1967; EXtensive Theatrical Resume Available; *office:* Kendall Jr Sr HS 1932 Roosevelt Hwy Kendall NY 14476*

HENSCHEN, LARRY REUBEN, Math Teacher; *b:* Celina, OH; *m:* Karen Lynn Brown; *c:* Jennifer Lynn Wilkerson, Christina Elizabeth; *ed:* OH St Univ (BS) Math Ed 1966; Bowling Green St Univ (MAT) Math Ed 1972; *cr:* Roosevelt Jr HS Math Tchr 1966-81; Springfield North HS Math Tchr 1981-; *ai:* OEA, NEA 1966-; SEA 1966-, Bldg Rep; Clark Cty Dem Exec Com 1983-; Clark Co Dem Cntrl Com 1984-; Truman Kennedy Club 1986-, Trustee; Friends of Clark Co 1992-; Montgomery-Fairborn Libs 1978-; Southwestern OH Antique Bottle-Jar Club, VP; Federated Antique Bottle-Jar Club 1984-; Fed Historical Bottle Collectors; NSF St 1970-72; *home:* 3222 Delrey Rd Springfield OH 45504

HENSELER, SUZANNE MC GOLDRICK, Social Studies T Brookline, MA; *m:* John L.; *c:* Sean Patrick, Warren Paul, Timo *ed:* Boston Coll (BA) His, Ed 1964; Attnd Univ of NC at Chapel Ldrshp Coll at Kenan, Flager Bus Schl; *cr:* Pilgrim HS Soc 1964-65; St Benedict Elem Schl Soc Stud Tchr; St Rocco Sch Tchr; *ai:* Newsbowl Moderator; RI St Legislature 1983-, St Rep Whip 1993-; N Kingstown Democratic Town Comm 1974-; Legis Equity Commission, Quinset Point Davisville Corp Ec Dev Commission on Women 1995-, Womens Hlth Comm Co-Chair Women Legislators Women in Govt; Who's Who Amer Politic Who'sWho in Amer; *office:* St Rocco Schl 931 Atwood Ave Jo 02919

HENSHAW, PAUL J., Soc Stud Tchr & Chairperson; *b:* Yonke Fordham Coll, Fordham Univ (BA) His 1985; Fordham Univ (M Stud Ed 1994; Admin Prgm; *cr:* Transfiguration Schl 8th Grd 1988; St Matthew Schl 6-8 Grd Soc Stud Tchr, Chprsn 1988-; 1988-; ASCD 1994-; *office:* St Matthew Schl Broadway & Vi Hastings On Hudson NY 10706*

HENSLEY, SUSAN WOLLET, Second Grade Teacher; *b:* Pott *m:* William Thurman; *c:* Donna Fay; *ed:* Salisbury St Univ (BA 1962; 36 Post Grad Stud; *cr:* Fruitland Primary Schl Second 1962-; *ai:* Chorus Primary; NEA, WCEA 1962-; PTA 1962-, Ex MYF Church 1970-, Ldr, Sunday Schl Tchr 1968-; *office:* Primary Schl 301 N Division St Fruitland MD 21826

HENSON, JACQUELINE MCKEAN, Biology Teacher; *b:* Ga *m:* Michael A.; *c:* Ira Dane; *ed:* Urbana Univ (BS) Sec Ed & Scis 1976; Cntrl St Univ 3 Qtr Hrs; Kent St Univ 3 Qtr Hrs; M of OH 3 Qtr Hrs; Univ of Dayton 3 Qtr Hrs; *cr:* Cath Cntrl HS B Sc Dept Chair 1978-89; Clark MS Gen Sci Tchr 1989-90; Tria Tchr 1990-; *ai:* Ecology Club Adv; Champaign Cty Sci Cu Co-Chprsn of Triad HS Steering Team; Support Group Facilit Prins Advy Cncl; Stream Quality Monitoring; EECO 1979-; Me Church 1984-; Citizens for Toxic Action 1991-; Urbana Univ Alu 1992-; Shotokan Karate SKA 1994-; Outstdng Young Womar 1979; NSF Schlsp 1979, 1993; DOE Schlsp 1981; Clark Cty Co Tchr of the Yr 1989; *office:* Triad HS 7941 Brush Lake Rd North OH 43060*

HENSON, KIM ALLEN, Guidance Counselor; *b:* Hagerstow Lora L. Gouff; *c:* Jared, Emily; *ed:* Hagerstown Jr Coll (AA) Ger Frostburg St Univ (BA) Psych & Scndry Ed 1973, (MED) G Counseling 1979; Attnd MD Inst of Alcohol & Drug Abuse Stu *cr:* Flintstone Schl 7th-12th Grd Soc Stud Tchr 1973-82; Allegan Dept Addiction Cnslr 1984-85; Oldtown Schl 7th-12th Grd Soc 1985-92; Fort Hill HS Guidance Cnslr 1994-; *ai:* Schl Improvem Allegany Cty Tech Prep Steering Comm; Drug & Alcohol Prev Assistance Comm; MD Schl Cnslrs, MD Assn for Counseling & NEA 1973-, Cty Exec Bd; Oldtown Tchr of Yr 1990 & 1993; Hill HS 500 Greenway Ave Cumberland MD 21502

HENTZ, DEAN THOMAS, HS Social Studies Teacher; *b:* Se PA; *ed:* Bloomsburg Univ (BSEd) Ed 1988; Beaver Coll (MA) *cr:* Pennsbury Schl Dist Tchr 1989; Pennridge Schl Dist T Council Rock Schl Dist Tchr 1991-; *ai:* Council Rock Ed Assn Relations; *home:* 50 S 3rd St Apt 210 Perkasie PA 18944*

HEPBURN, DAVID ROGER, 5th Grade Teacher; *b:* Hartfor Linda Hebert; *c:* Caroline O'Brien, Michael, Julie; *ed:* LaSalle His 1962; Univ of Hartford (ME) Ed 1970; Univ of VA at Stra Fellow 6th Yr Credits; *cr:* Noah Wallace Schl Elem Tchr, Soc S 1964-; *ai:* Soc Stud Comm Town Curr; Cutlural Comm; Farm Assn 1964-, Pres 1976-80, Schl Tchr Rep, Negotiator Conventions; Natl Ed Assn 1964-, Delegate St Conventions; N Delegate Natl Conventions; Archaeological Work M Williamsburg, Poplar Forest, Jamestown Ft Rediscovery, Other *office:* Noah Wallace Elem Schl 2 School St Farmington CT 06

HEPBURN, DEBORAH HATCH, English Teacher; *b:* Poughke *ed:* Ithaca Coll (BA) Eng 1973; VT Coll of Norwich Univ (MA Ed 1986; *cr:* Stoughton Jr HS Eng Tchr 1973-74; Franklin HS 1974-81; Newington HS Eng Tchr 1981-83; Lakewood Jr HS 1984; Clinton Cntrl Schl Eng Tchr 1985-87; St Joseph's HS Eng T North Allegheny Eng Tchr 1988-89; Clinton Cntrl Schl Eng T *ai:* Drama Club Adv; AFT 1989-; NYSUT 1985-87, 1989-; Kirk Golf 1994-, Pres; NCTE Annual Convention Speaker 19 Observer-Dispatch All-St Tchr 1993; NY Cncl for Hum Liv Knowing Biography Discussion Grants 1993-95; RotarY Outst Awd 1994; Outstdng Tchr Tufts Univ 1994, Univ of Chicago 19 Clinton Cntrl Schl 75 Chenango Ave Clinton NY 13323*

HEPFER, FRED E., Guidance Counselor; *b:* Gloversville, NY; S.; *c:* Fred S., Tara S.; *ed:* SUNY at Brockport (BS) Ed 1965; Oneonta (MS) Cnslng 1969; 9 Credit Hrs; *cr:* Park Terr Elem Sc Tchr 1965-69; Howard L. Goff MS 7th & 8th Grd Cnslr 1969-; Hopkins Talent Search Coord; Howard L. Goff Child Stud T 1965-; NEA 1965-; NYSUT 1965-; EGTA 1969-; ASCD 1990-; F Elks Assn 1985-, Yth Act Chm; Key Bank Career Opportunites fo Grant; Multiple Sclerosis Assn Chmn; *home:* 1479 Van H Castleton NY 12033

HEPLER, CATHERINE C., Assistant Principal; *b:* August Michael; *ed:* SUNY at Oswego (BA) Scndry Ed 1978; Johns Hop (MA) Schl Admin 1992; 9 Hrs Loyola Coll 1995; 32 Hrs Salamanca 1977; *cr:* Alleghany Cty Schls Span Tchr 1978-81; Schls Span Tchr 1981-83; Cecil Cty Pub Schls Span Tchr 1984-9 Cty Pub Schls Asst Prin 1992-; *ai:* Gen Curr, Soc Stud Stee Ldrshp, Bus Advy Comms; Dimensions of Learning Advy Bd MASSP, ASCD 1992-; Harford Ldrshp Assn 1992-, Bd Mem; A of Univ Women 1988-, Bd Mem; Perryville HS Tchr of Yr 1991; of Yr Nom 1992; *office:* Havre De Grace HS 700 Congress Ave Grace MD 21078*

HEPLER, MARYJO, 8th Grade Social Studies Tchr; *b:* Allianc Robert W.; *c:* Jessica; *ed:* Kent St Univ (BS) Elem Ed 1973, (M Curr & Inst 1993; *cr:* Regina Coeli Schl 5th Grd Tchr 1973-7 Heart of Mary 2nd Grd Tchr 1974-75; Parkway Elem 4th & 5th 1977-89; Stanton HS 8th Grd Soc Stud Tchr 1989-; *ai:* Team Ldr Adv; Behavior Pgm Comm Chair; AEA, OEA & NEA 1977-; OM OCSS 1989-; Mayors Commission on Historic Preservation for 1991-, Sec; Martha Holden Jennings Scholar 1984; Alliance Ch Commerce Tchr of Month 1993; *office:* Stanton MS 311 S L Alliance OH 44601*

HEPNER, BARBARA E., Music Instructor; *b:* Pittsburgh Carnegie Mellon U (BFA) Music, Music Ed 1968;, (MFA) Music Pvt Trumpet Lessons Music Tchr 1963-; Riverview Schl Dist M 1968-; *ai:* Alle-Kiski Arts Consortium; Elem, Scndry Orch D Edctrs Natl Conf, PA Music Edctrs Assn, Amer Strings Tchrs As Natl Schl Orch Assn; Prof Trumpet Player; *office:* Riverview Hulton Rd Oakmont PA 15139

, KATHRYN ELLA, Accounting & Mathematics Prof; *b:* Butler, lippery Rock Univ (BS) Math, Cmptr Sci 1986, (BS) Scndry Ed BA Candidate; Mount Saint Marys Coll-Emmitsburg MD 22 Completed as of May 1996; *cr:* Butler Cty Comm Coll Instr Susquenita Schl Dist Tchr 1988-90; Harrisburg Area Comm Coll)-90; Cntrl Penn Bus Schl Prof 1990-; *ai:* Westshoremen Drum & rps; Cntrl Penn Accounting Club Adv; Inst of Mgmt Accountants ol Local Pub Television Station WITF; *office:* Central Penn Schl College Hill Rd Summerdale PA 17093*

, MARY KAY MOONEY, Third Grade Teacher; *b:* Darby, PA; m M.; *c:* Kevin J., Maureen E.; *ed:* Trenton St Coll (BS) Early d 1982; Temple Univ 9 Credits Post Grad; Rowan St Coll 15 ost Grad; St Joseph's Univ 3 Credits Post Grad; *cr:* Sacred Heart Schl 6th Grd Tchr 1983-85; Loring Flemming Schl 3rd Grd Tchr : NEA 1985-; Gloucester Twp Mini-Grant 1988-89; Pamphlets *ce:* Loring Flemming Elem Schl 135 Little Gloucester Rd d NJ 08012

ODY BERRY, Vocal Music Teacher; *b:* Smyrna, TN; *m:* Joseph; *ed:* OH St Univ (BME) Vocal Music 1990; *cr:* Pike Schl Vocal hr 1990-95; Delta Schl Vocal Music Tchr 1990-95; York Schl sic Tchr 1990-95; Bryan City Schls Vocal Music Tchr 1995-; *ai:* oir; Musical; Delta Show Choir, Chrldrs, Flag Corps; OMEA CDA 1994-; OMEA St Events 4I Superior Ratings; *office:* Bryan s 150 S Portland St Bryan OH 43506

, RICHARD A., English Teacher; *b:* New Brunswick, NJ; *m:* right; *c:* Elise Miko, Katherine Eiko, William Richard; *ed:* SUNY o (BA) Eng, Spec Ed 1981, (MS) Ed 1985; Ornithology Cornell Oswego Pub Schl Sub Tchr 1980-81; Seneca Falls Cntrl Schl Eng 1-; *ai:* BSA Merit Badge Instr; SFTA Negotiations Team; NEA RA 1982-; SFTA 1981-, Grievance Chprsn, Negotiations 1992; chr Hobart Wm Smith Coll, SUNY at Oneonta, Wells Coll; *office:* Acad 105 Troy St Seneca Falls NY 13148

ELAINE M., Fourth Grade Teacher; *b:* Youngstown, OH; *m:* *c:* Christopher Helm; *ed:* Youngstown St Univ (BSEd) Elem 69, (MSEd) Cnslng 1985; Basic Chrstn Beliefs Ursuline Coll 2 At Risk Stdnts Ashland Univ 3 Sem Hrs; *cr:* John F. Kennedy HS 1984-85; St Patrick Schl Third Grd Tchr 1989-90; Bishop Ready us Minister 1990-91; St Patrick Schl Eighth, Fourth Grd Tchr *fice:* St Patrick Schl 1400 Oak Hill Ave Youngstown OH 44507

IARK RAY, Life Science Teacher; *b:* Pottsville, PA; *m:* Rebecca ni; *c:* Marisa, Lauren; *ed:* Millersville St Coll (BA) Elem, Spec (MS) Elem Ed 1981; *cr:* Blue Mountain HS 9th-12th Grd Spec 975-76; Blue Mt Schl Dist, Auburn Elem 4th Grd Tchr 1976-80; MS 6th-8th Grd Sci Tchr 1980-; *ai:* Past Boys Jr Var Bsktbl Girls Var Bsktbl 1983-94, Boys Var Track 1975-93 Coach; SEA, NEA 1975-; Blue Mt Recreation Comm 1993-, Vol Girls ktbl Coach; Tchr of Yr 1982-83, 1991-92; Blue Mountain All ll of Fame Inductee 1995; *office:* Blue Mountain MS Red Dale sburg PA 17961

K, DALE A., Communications Professor; *b:* Chicago, IL; *ed:* a Coll (BA) Pol Sci 1980; Univ of IA (MA) Communication 1982, ommunication 1988; *cr:* Boston Coll Forensics Instr & Dir Forensics Asst Prof & Dir 1988-91, Forensics Assoc Prof & Dir Assoc Prof 1994-; *ai:* Fulton Debating Soc; Argumentation & , Communication Quarterly & Free Speech Yrbk Editorial Bds er Communication Assn 1994-, Bd of Dirs; Amer Forensic Assn es, VP, Natl Cncl; AEJMC, CSCA, ECA, SCA; Commission on of Expression 1982-, Vice Chair, Research Awd; ECA Past Pres ; ADA Svc Awd 1994; O'Neill Awd for Excl in Research 1993; Awd for Stu Dev 1989; Articles in Argumentation, Argumentation acy, Free Speech Yrbk, Forensic Educator & Natl Forensic *ffice:* Boston Coll Lyons Hall 215 Chestnut Hill MA 02167

ICK, AGNES, Eighth Grade Teacher; *b:* Lyndora, PA; *ed:* Coll dia (BS) 1973; Univ of Dayton (MS) Elem Ed 1979; Yth Ministry n; Master Catechist Cert; Pittsburgh Pastoral Inst; Inst of Applied heology; Bridge to Success; Continuing Ed Units; *cr:* St John the 5-6 Grd Tchr 1964-65; St John the Bapt 5-6 Grd Tchr 1965-68; he Bapt Schl 3-4 Grd Tchr 1068-70; Northend Elem Schl 6 Grd)-72; St Stephen Cath Schl 4 Grd Tchr 1972-74; St Mary Cath d Tchr 1974-76; St Nicholas Cath Schl 3-4 Grd Tchr 1976-78, 7-78; St John the Bapt Schl 5-8 Grd Tchr 1978-79; St John Schl 7-8 Grd Tchr 1979-87; St Mary Byzantine Schl 5-8 Grd 7-; *ai:* North Cntrl Assn of Schls & Colls Self Stud; NCEA; *home:* kney Ave Cleveland OH 44109

, LAURENCE LEE, 4th Grade Teacher; *b:* Pottsville, PA; *m:* Thomas; *c:* Ryan, Amy; *ed:* East Stroudsburg (BS) Elem 1972; Equivalency 1975; *cr:* Pine Grove Schools 4th Grd Tchr 24 Yrs; Boosters Pres; BSA Asst Scout Master; NEA, PSEA 1972-; 972-, Past VP; Pine Grove Fire Co 1970-, Past Pres; Pine Grove e Assn 1970-, Past Sec; Church Cncl 1976-, Past Treas; Pine cl 1976-80, VP; *home:* 24 Hillside Dr Pine Grove PA 17963

RT, REMBERT B., English Teacher; *b:* Sumter, SC; *m:* Rebecca ner; *c:* Mary Emily Brouer; *ed:* Amer Univ (PHD) Lit 1976; *cr:* ongress Music Specialist, Music Div 1976-86; Sacred Heart HS 1987-90; Hunter Coll HS Eng Tchr 1991-; *ai:* Author, Lecturer, egnias Chant; Assn of Anglican Musicians 1990-; NEH Summer or Coll Tchr 1985; Marsden Fnd GrantChart Stud 1986; *office:* oll HS 71 E 94th St New York NY 10128

RT, SCOTT ALAN, Adv Bio & Chemistry Teacher; *b:* Fairborn, aura Simons; *ed:* Miami Univ (BS) Sec Ed Bio 1988; Hypercard; nseh HS Bio, Chem Tchr 1991-; *ai:* Head Wrestling Coach; NEA EA, OEA 1991-.

RT, WILLIAM JOHN, Instructor of Law Enforcement; *b:* Bronx, ynn Mary; *ed:* Sate Univ of NY (AAS) Police Sci 1968; NY Inst BS) Behavioral Sci 1979; C. W. Post-LIV (MPA) Pub Admin 1986; ern ME Tech Coll Instr 1990-; *ai:* Homeowners Assn 1993-95, *ce:* Southern ME Tech Coll Fort Road S Portland ME 04106*

, CORA SUE HEDGES, Second Grade Teacher; *b:* Philadelphia, ynn E.; *ed:* Millersville Univ (BS) Comprehensive Lib Sci 1969; burg Univ (MSLS) Lib Sci 1976; 24 Credit Hrs Elem Cert; 21 s Elem Ed; *cr:* Darby Colwyn Schls Elem Librn 1969-70; Martin b Asst 1971-72; Red Lion Area Schls Elem Librn 1972-82, 2nd 1982-; *ai:* K-12th Grd Tutoring Children at Risk; Soc Comm 3-88; Collinsville Lib Summer Vol; PA St Ed Assn 1982-; NEA ed Lion Area Ed Assn 1982-, Pub Relations Chair & Bldg Rep; orough Cncl, VP & Recreation Chprsn; Sign of Whippet Antiques, r; Amer Lung Assn, Vol; Gift of Time Awd; *home:* 34 Main St 17322*

, JUNE ALEXANDER, 2nd & 3rd Grade Teacher; *b:* Brooklyn, ohn R. Sr.; *c:* Michael, Elizabeth, Barbara Snow, June Biondi, r.; *ed:* Southern CT St Univ (BS) P-6 Elem Ed 1974, (MS) K-12 9; Addl Stud Rdng, Lang Arts, Consultant 1981; *cr:* Lewin G. Joel Schl K-2nd Grd Tchr 1974-92, Rdng, Lang Arts Consultant 2-3 Grd Integrated Day Tchr 1995-; *ai:* AFT 1975-, Pres; NEA 1990-; *office:* Lewin G. Joel Jr. Elem Schl 137A Glenwood Cr Clinton CT 06413

HERBSTRITT, ELEANOR RUPPRECHT, Chemistry Teacher; *b:* St Marys, PA; *m:* Maurice G.; *c:* Christopher J., Matthew G., Gregory T.; *ed:* Seton Hill Coll (BA) Bio, Chem 1961; Penna St Univ (MED) Bio Ed 1970; 6 Cr Nuclear Sci, 3 Cr Cmptrs; IN Univ of Penna 12 Cr Sci Ed; Clarion Univ 3 Cr Cmptr Sci; *cr:* St Marys Cntrl HS Sci Tchr 1961-62; Elk Cty Chrstn HS Sci Tchr 1962-66; Queen of World Schl Elem Tchr 1976-80; Elk Cty Chrstn HS Sci Dept Chair, Tchr 1980-; *ai:* NHS Fac Adv; Jr Class Adv; Fac Senate; Parish Allnc Comm; NCEA 1980-; NSTA 1994-; ASCD 1992-; Eucharistic Minister 1991-; Sacred Heart Lector 1990-; Sacred Heart Adult Choir 1988-; Amer Cancer Soc 1993-; St Vincents Coll Tchr of Yr Awd; Penn St 4 NSF Grants, 25 Yr serv Awd; *office:* Elk County Christian HS 600 Maurus St Saint Marys PA 15857*

HERCEG, ROBERT ANTHONY, Earth Science Teacher; *b:* Johnson City, NY; *m:* Katharine R. Granger; *c:* Jeff, Colleen, John, Julie, Susan, Katie; *ed:* St Univ NY at Oneonta (BS) Elem Ed, Sci 1967; Franklin & Marshall Coll (MA) Geology 1972; Driver, Safety Ed; Geology Courses; *cr:* Henry Bendicott Jr HS 7th-8th Grd Sci Tchr 1967-75; Union Endicott HS Summer Schl Driver Ed, Earth Sci Tchr 1975-; *ai:* NYSUT 1967-; AFR, STANYS; Endicott Tchrs Assn 1967-, Negotiator 1977-79; Church Act; SPEBSQSA 1980-82; Jr HS Bsktbl 1968-75, Frosh Ftbl Asst 1974-75 Coach; *home:* 1706 Summit St Endicott NY 13760*

HERCZEG, MARILYN SMITH, 2nd Grade Teacher; *b:* Philadelphia, PA; *m:* Stephen A.; *ed:* Millersville St Coll (BS) Elem Ed 1974; West Chester Univ (MED) Elem Ed 1986; 31 Addl Hrs El Ed; *cr:* Spring Ford Area Schl Dist ESL Tchr 1975-79, 1-3 Grd Tchr 1979-; *ai:* PSEA, NEA 1982-; United Meth Women 1986-; *office:* Oaks Elem Schl PO Box 396 Oaks PA 19456

HERIGAN, PATRICIA R., English Teacher & Dept Chair; *b:* Harrisburg, PA; *m:* William R.; *c:* Jennifer Fink, Matthew Fink; *ed:* Elizabethtown Coll (BA) Eng 1968; Johns Hopkins Univ (MS) Ed Tech; 30 Grad Credit Hrs Temple Univ; 6 Grad Credit Hrs Shippensburg Univ; *cr:* Cntrl Dauphin East HS Eng Tchr 1968-71; Cntrl Dauphin HS Eng Tchr 1971-, Eng Dept Chair 1990-; *ai:* Bldg Comp Coord; Chaperone Eng Hnrs European Trips; Dist Tech Comm; Dist Strategic Design Team; Dist Assesment Task Force; NCTE 1970-; PSEA, NEA 1974-; ASCD 1990-; PA Computing Edctrs Outstdng Edctr Awd Runner-Up 1991; Cntrl Dauphin Schl Dist Distngd Svc Awd 1991.

HERKERT, MICHELLE STUEBER, Chemistry Teacher; *b:* Lakewood, NJ; *m:* William F. Jr.; *c:* Megan; *ed:* Georgian Court Coll (BS) Biochemistry 1977; 9 Grad Credits; *cr:* Vineland HS Chem Tchr 1977-83; Toms River Regnl Schls Chem Tchr 1983-; *ai:* Sci Clb Adv Vineland HS 1977-83; NHS adv 1990-92; Sci League, Acad Challenge Advs; NEA, NJEA 1977-; NJSTA 1993-; *office:* Toms River Regnl Schls Raider Way Toms River NJ 08753

HERLEY, BETTYANN MURPHY, 4th Grade Teacher; *b:* Floral Park, NY; *m:* Michael; *c:* Jennifer, Melissa, Mickey; *ed:* Immaculata Coll (BA) Eng 1978; Elem Ed Cert 1989; PA Framework; Math Grad Level Course; *cr:* Coatesville Area Schl Dist Sub Tchr 1978-80; St Agnes Schl 4 Grd Tchr 1986-; *ai:* Soc Comm 1980-; *office:* St Agnes Schl 211 W Gay St West Chester PA 19380

HERLIHY, GERARD WALTER, English Dept Chairman; *b:* Haverhill, MA; *ed:* Boston Coll (BA) Eng 1967; UW at Madison (MA) Eng 1968; *cr:* Marian HS Eng Tchr & Dept Head 1973-; *ai:* NHS Adv; Music Ministry; Long Range Planning & Share the Faith Comm; NCEA; BATA 1974-; *office:* Marian HS 273 Union Ave Framingham MA 01701

HERLIHY, THOMAS MICHAEL, Music Teacher; *b:* Rockville Centre, NY; *m:* Annemarie Vetter; *c:* Anne; *ed:* SUCNY at Fredonia (BM) Music Ed 1973, (MM) Music Ed 1989; Attnd Guildhall Schl of Music & Drama at London, Coll of New Rochelle, Long Island Univ, Drake Univ; *cr:* Lake Shore Cntrl Schl Band Dir 1973-; Camp Pioneer Music Dir 1981-84; Chautaugua Inst Music Camp Asst Conductor & Trumpet Tchr 1980; Pyramid Dance Band Dir & Co-Founder 1993-; *ai:* Jazz Ensemble; Marching Band; MENC & NYSSMA 1973-; United Fed of Musicians; *office:* Lake Shore Cntrl Schls 8855 Erie Rd Angola NY 14006

HERMAN, DAVID HENRY, Retired Orchestra Director; *b:* Brooklyn, NY; *m:* Sandra Pinker; *c:* Lori Frommer, Tammy, Deanne; *ed:* NYU (BS) Music 1961; Brooklyn Coll (MA) Music 1970; Trained as Fine Artist, Painting at the Art Stdnts League of NY; *cr:* JHS 210 Orch Dir 1961-64; Elmont Meml HS Orch Dir 1964-95; Violin Restorer, Dealer 1975-; Fine Artist Exhibiting 1991-; *home:* 1511 Dieman Ln East Meadow NY 11554

HERMAN, DONNA COOK, Second Grade Teacher; *b:* Westfield, MA; *m:* Allan M.; *c:* Kara Beth, Tracey Michelle; *ed:* Westfield St Coll (BS) K-8 Ed 1963, (MED) Elem Ed 1967; Masters +15; Working Toward 6th Yr Level; *cr:* Dept of Defense Germany 3rd Grd Tchr 1967-68; Fishing Creek Schl 5th Grd Tchr 1968-69; Main St Schl 2nd Grd Tchr 1971-72; Tatham Schl 3rd Grd Tchr 1963-67, 2-5th Grd Tchr 1972-; *ai:* HS Stu Ambassador Prgm Western MA Coord, Instructed & Coordinated Trips to E Block Countires 1989, Russia & Ukraine 1990, Russia & the Baltics 1992, Australia 1993; Westfield Evening News Photojournalist 1978-83, British Isle 1995, Australia/ New Zealand 1996; West Springfield Ed Assn 1963-, Sec & VP; MA Tchrs Assn, NEA 1963-; MA Arts Ed Advy Comm 1982, W MA Rep; Westfield Arts Cncl 1981-; Westfield Zoning Bd of Appeals 1980-; Westfield City Cncl 1983-, Pres 1989-, Citations from House of Reps & St Senate; Tchr of Yr 1992; Hlth Curr Dev Grant; Project US Grant; Whole Lang Presenter & Lecturer; Pioneer Valley Pomona Grange Pub Svc Awd; Newspaper Photojournalist 1978-83; Articles Pub; Great Recipiant 1995; *home:* 491 Montgomery Rd Westfield MA 01085*

HERMAN, JOANN MAY, Retired Teacher; *b:* Jersey Shore, PA; *m:* Kenneth L.; *c:* Kay J., Karl R.; *ed:* Lock Haven Univ (BS) Elem Ed 1953; Penn St Univ (MED) Elem Rdng 1961; *cr:* Walnut St Elem Schl Third Grd Tchr 10 Yrs; Jersey Shore HS Rdng Specialist 4 Yrs; Jersey Shores Schls Elem & Sec Rdng Supvr 8 Yrs; Nippenose Elem Schl Third Grd Tchr 14 Yrs; *ai:* Sr HS Class Adv 1967-70; *home:* RR 2 Box 336 Jersey Shore PA 17740

HERMAN, JOSEPHINE NANCY, Foreign Language Teacher; *b:* New York City, NY; *ed:* Queen's Coll (BA) Ed, Span 1976; St John's Univ (MS) Ed, Span 1981; Prof Dip Admin, Supervision 1985; *cr:* St Raphael Schl Tchr 1976-77; St Peter's HS Tchr 1977-78; Archbishop Molloy HS Tchr 1978-82; Bishop Ford CCHS Tchr 1982-; *ai:* Acad Probation, Dentention Dir; SADD Moderator; Italian Tchrs Assn, NYSAFLT 1976-; LFA 1996.*

HERMAN, MARK WESLEY, Asst HS Principal; *b:* Hanover, PA; *m:* Kathleen Rosso; *c:* Elizabeth Grace, Katie Leigh, Jesse Daniel, Stephen James, Paul Wesley; *ed:* Messiah Coll (BA) Behavioral Sci 1985; Shippensburg Univ (MA) & Principal's Certification 1992; *cr:* Prince Georges Cty Pub Schls Tchr 1985-86; Greencastle-Antrim HS Tchr 1986-90, Acting Asst Prin 1990-91, Tchr 1991-92, Tchr & Assist Prin 1992-94; Acting Prin 1994-95, Asst Prin 1995-; *ai:* Drama Club Dir; Stu & Tchr Assistance Teams Mem; Dist Long Range Plan Steering Comm Service Supvr; Dir Greencastle Young Life Adv Comm; Prof Devp Comm; NEA, PSEA, GAEA 1985-92; NCSS 1986-; ASCD 1987-; Phi Delta Kappa 1992-; NASSP, PASSP 1992; Young Life of S Cntrl PA 1989-, Ldr 7 Yrs; Evangelical Free Church Tri-St Fellowship 1992-; Bethany Evangelical Free Church 1986-91, Bd Mem 5 Yrs, Chm 2 Yrs; Greencastle Antrim Cmbr of Commrce Bus Ed Comm; Franklin-Fulton-Adams Cty Tchr Induction Prgm Annual Presenter 1987-94; PA Tchr of Yr Awd Semi-Finalist 1990; NCSS Natl Convention Facilitator 1991; Greencastle-Antrim HS Favorite Male Tchr 1987-90.*

HERMAN, NICHOLAS RALPH,II, Powerplant Teacher; *b:* Toledo, OH; *m:* Jayne E. Thurber; *c:* Scott, Matthew; *ed:* Bowling Green St U (BS) Indstrl Edu 197k; Univ of Toledo (ME) Voc Educ 1995; *cr:* The Herman Co VP 1971-90; Toledo Pub Schls Aviation Mechanics Instr 1990-; *ai:* Voc Indstrl Clubs of Amer Adv; Aviation Safety Cnslr FAA Vol; AFT, Toledo Fed of Tchrs 1990-; Phi Kappa Phi, Iota Lambda Sigma 1995-; *office:* Bowsher HS 11791 W Airport Service Rd Toledo Express Swanton OH 43558

HERMAN, RICHARD CHARLES, High School Math Teacher; *b:* Rochester, NY; *m:* Cathleen Marg Mc Avinney; *c:* Jileen, Matthew, Katrina, Stephanie; *ed:* Roberts Wesleyan Coll (BS) Math 1972; 36 Hrs Gen Ed; 15 Hrs Math; *cr:* Webster Cntrl Math, Sci Tchr 1972-76, Math Tchr 1977-; *ai:* Boys Var Soccer & Track Coaches; Dist Tech Prep Comm; AFT, NEA, WTA 1972-; East Williamson Free Meth Church 1974-, Tchr, Yth Dir; Monroe Cty Coaches 1973-, Coach, Coach of Yr; NY St Coaches Assn, Coach, Honor Awd 100 Club; *office:* Webster Cntrl Schl Ridge Rd Webster NY 14580

HERMAN, SUSAN LEIGH, Assistant Professor; *b:* Philadelphia, PA; *m:* William L.; *c:* Katie Leigh, William Lane; *ed:* Lock Haven Univ (BS) Hlth, PE, Recreation 1979; Slippery Rock Univ (MED) Admin 1980; 18 Hrs Admin Univ of Pittsburgh; *cr:* SW Butler Schl Dist Hlth, PE Instr 1979-80; Slippery Rock Univ PE Asst Prof 1980-; *ai:* Delta Psi Kappa Campus Adv; Var Women's Lacrosse Coach; Russell Wright Fitness Ctr Dir; PA St Assn HPERD 1980-, Presidential Planning Comm; PA St Ath Conf 1980-, Lacrosse Pres; Midwest Women's Lacrosse Assn 1985-, Sec, All Amer Comm; United Way 1993-, Campaign Team; PTO 1996, VP; Little League Bsbl 1989-, Coach; Western PA Soccer 1995-, Coach; YMCA 1985-, Coach, Aerobics Instr, Advy Bd; Articles Pub; Aerobic Marathon Fundraiser Women's Ath Schlsps, Teeball All-Star Day, Yth Fitness Wkshp Coord; *office:* Slippery Rock Univ Of PA Slippery Rock PA 16057*

HERMAN, TAD, Physics Instructor; *b:* Poughkeepsie, NY; *m:* Sue; *c:* Corley; *ed:* Dutchess Comm Coll (AS) 1984; Univ of AZ (BS) Physics 1986; SUNY at New Paltz (MED) Physics 1991; *cr:* Sharpe Outdoor Ed Ctr Planetarium Dir, Outdoor Edctr 1988-93; Dutchess Comm Coll Physics, Astronomy Instr 1993-; *ai:* Hiking Club Coord; Coll Life Comm; The Planetary Soc 1988-; AAPT 1996; *office:* Dutchess Comm Coll Pendell Road Poughkeepsie NY 12601

HERMANN, HELEN, Principal & 6th Grade Teacher; *b:* Evans Mills, NY; *ed:* SUNY at Potsdam (BA) Lbrl Arts 1972; Niagara Univ (MS) Ed, Admin 1978; *cr:* Diocese of Ogdensburg Schl System Tchr 1966-81; Holy Name Schl Grd 4 Tchr 1981-83; Trinity Cath Schl Grd 5 Tchr 1983-84; St Augustines Schl Tchr, Prin 1984-; *ai:* Drama Club; Music; Liturgy Team; Pastoral Cncl; Cncl of Prins; CSAANYS, NCEA 1986-.

HERMILLER, JOHN THOMAS, Mathematics Teacher; *b:* Lima, OH; *ed:* OH St Univ (BS) Math 1990, (MA) Math 1992; 3 Grad Credits TI3 Summer Class 1995; *cr:* OH St Univ Grad Tchng Assoc 1990-92; Bishop Ready HS Math Tchr, Bsktbl, Track Coach 1992-; *ai:* Asst Frosh Girls Bsktbl, Asst Boys & Girls Track Coach; Beta Club Selection Comm 1994, Chm 1996; NCTM 1991-; NCEA 1992-; *home:* 836 Bricker Blvd Columbus OH 43221

HERMONAT, SUE KRENNING, Sixth Grade Teacher & Team Ldr; *b:* Medina, NY; *c:* Heidi H. Glosser, Bruce S., Amy H. Smith, Craig A.; *ed:* Marietta Coll (BA) His 1960; Southern CT St coll (MS) Intermediate Ed 1980; Sixth Yr Prof Diploma Classroom Specialist; Tchrs Coll Writing Project; Marilyn Burns Math Inst; Tchng Multiple Intelligences; *cr:* Bunnell HS Soc Stud Tchr 1960-61; Dr. R. H. Brown Schl 6-8 Grd Title I Co-Dir 1976-77; Dr. R. H. Brown MS Grd Six Tchr 1977-, Team Ldr 1989-91, 1994-; *ai:* Schl Improvement Team; Co-Author Mission Statement; Promoting Challenging Act for all Stdnts-Mentor-Mentee Prgm Comm; Math Curr Comm & Co-Writer Comm; CT Dept of Ed Celebration of Excl Advy Cncl; ASCD 1985-; NCTM 1992-; NEA, CEA, MEA 1977-; First Congregational Church 1973-; Vol Amer Cancer Soc, Amer Diabetes Assn 1980-; Madison Tchr Excl Fund Grant 1988; CT Dept of Ed Celebration of Excl Awd Explempary Projects 1993; Brochures: Study Skills, Schl Comm Parents Projects 1993; Impact II Star 1992; Presenter of East Coast Conf on Schl Restructing 1993; First Tchrs Summit 1993; NELMS 1994; *office:* Dr Robert H Brown MS 980 Durham Rd Madison CT 06443

HERMOSILLO, CARMEN, Spanish Teacher; *b:* Harbor City, CA; *ed:* UC Irvine (BA) Span 1980; UCLA (JD) Law 1984; CSU Northridge (MA) Educl Admin 1994; *cr:* San Fernando Jr HS His Tchr 1985-87; Monroe HS Span, ESL Tchr 1987-88; Birmingham HS Span Tchr 1989-995; Amer Intnl Schl, Dhaka Span Tchr 1995-; *ai:* 10th Grd Adv; Span Honorary Soc Spon; Fulbright Assn, ACTFL 1993-; UTLA 1985-95; AATSP 1992-; CFLTA, MCLASC 1990-; Assoc Tchrs Span & Portuguese 1993-; Delta Kappa Gamma 1993-; NEH Summer Seminar 1993; Fulbright Tchr Exch 1992-93; Taught EFL Universidad Nacional de La Plata, Liceo Victor Mercante; NEH Flwshp Ind Study Argentina 1995-; AP Rdr, Span, Clemson Univ 1995-; *office:* Amer Embassy Dhaka Bangladesh Dept of State Washington DC 20521

HERNANDEZ, JOSE, Prof & Coord Puerto Rican Stud; *b:* Jersey City, NJ; *c:* Xavier, Nilza, Shani; *ed:* Fordham Univ (BA) Sociology 1958-, (MA) Sociology 1960; Univ of MN (PHD) Sociology 1964; *cr:* Univ Puerto Rico Asst Prof 1964-65; Ford Fndtn Pgm Adv 1966-69; Univ of AZ Assoc Prof of Sociology 1970-74; US Comm on Civil Rights Rsrch Dir; 1975-76; Univ of WI Prof of Sociology 1976-83; Latino Inst Rsrch Dir 1983; Hunter Coll Prof & Coord of Puerto Rican Stud 1984-; *ai:* Amer Sociological Assn 1961-, Chair Comm on Comms; Puerto Rican Stud Assn 1992-, Founder; SGI-USA Buddhist Org 1987- Group Ldr; Books: Conquered Peoples in America; Puerto Rican Yth Employment; People Power & Policy; Return Migration to Puerto Rico; *office:* City Univ Of NY Hunter Coll 695 Park Ave New York NY 10021

HERNANDEZ, WILSON RAFAEL, 7th Grd Bilingual Ed Teacher; *b:* Ingenio Montellano, Dominican Repub; *m:* Lisa Perlson-Hernandez; *c:* Philippa J., Eli J., Max J.; *ed:* SUNY at Stony Brook Univ (BA) Span Lang, Lit 1982; Tchr Cert Trenton St Coll; Kean Coll Enrolled in MA Prgm Biling Ed; *cr:* William C. Mc Ginnis Tchr 1991-; *ai:* Bsbl Coach; Multicultural Awareness Stu Alliance MASA Adv; EPIC Ldr, Facilitator; NJEA Minority Involvement Comm; NEA 1995-; AFT 1991-; Coach of Yr 1994; *office:* William C Mcginnis MS 271 State St Perth Amboy NJ 08861*

HERNANDO, BELLA, Math Dept Chairperson; *b:* Bangued Abra, Philippines; *m:* Eric P. Madrid; *c:* Jennifer, Francis, Eribel Madrid; *ed:* Philippine Coll of Arts & Trades (BS) Math 1970; Philippine Normal Coll (MA) Math 1975; *cr:* Pasay City HS Math Tchr 1970-74; Manila City HS Math Tchr 1974-80; Nigeria Scndry Schl Math Tchr 1980-85; Mother Cabrini HS Math Tchr 1986-, Math Dept Chprsn 1992-; *ai:* Soph Class Moderator 1993-; NCTM 1988-; Assn of NY City Math Tchrs 1994-; *home:* 1840 Holland Ave Bronx NY 10462

HERO, GEORGE ASTOR, Dir of Social Science Research; *b:* Brooklyn, NY; *ed:* Fordham Univ (BA) His 1980, (MA) His 1982; *cr:* Long Island Univ Prof of His 1994-; Midwood HS His Tchr 1985-, Dir of Soc Sci Rsrch 1988-; *ai:* Founder, Adv Historical, Hellenic, Slavic Heritage, Italian

Heritage Soc; Founder, Coach Wrestling Team; Hellenic Edctrs 1990-; Co-Author: Let's Review Global Studies, Global Studies II; *office:* Midwood HS at Brooklyn Coll Bedford Ave And Glennwood Rd Brooklyn NY 11210*

HEROLD, BRUCE WALTER, Spanish Teacher; *b:* Philadelphia, PA; *m:* Mary Hile; *c:* Bruce, Laura; *ed:* Rutgers Univ (BA) Span 1966; Penn St Univ (MA) Span 1968, (PHD) Span 1977; *cr:* Kennett Consolodiated Schls Span Tchr 1966-67; Bald Eagle Area Schl dist Span Tchr 1973-; *ai:* Span Excursion Club; Bald Eagle Area Educ Assn 1973-; Natl Endowment for Hum Grant; *home:* 637 Devonshire Dr State College PA 16803

HERR, CASSIE RENE, Health & Physical Ed Teacher; *b:* Lancaster, PA; *ed:* Univ of DE (BS) PE, Hlth 1993; Guid Cnslng Credits; *cr:* Pequea Vly HS PE, Hlth Tchr 1993-; *ai:* Vars Field Hockey Coach; SAT Team; Interact Adv; CPR, First Aid Cerfld Instr; Aids Awareness Adv; NEA, PSEA, PVEA 1993-; Cert to Facilitate Support Groups; *office:* Pequea Valley HS 4033 E Newport Rd Kinzers PA 17535

HERR, JAMES R., Retired Teacher; *b:* Salunga, PA; *m:* Joyce E. Dissinger; *c:* Hans M.; *ed:* Elizabethtown Coll (BA) Psych, Sociology 1953; Univ of WY (MA) Ed, Guid 1964, (PHD) Pupil Personnel, Ed 1972; Addl 12 Hrs Temple Univ, 10 Hrs Univ of Rochester, 6 Hrs Millersville Univ; *cr:* Hempfield HS Soc Stud Tchr 1955-58; Eastern York HS Guidance Supv, Cnslr 1958-93; *ai:* NEA, PSEA 1955-; Psi Chi 1965-; Wrightsville Rotary Club 1962-, Pres, Treas; Historic Wrightsville 1988-; Hasn Herr House Fnd; York, Lancaster Cty Hist Socs; Riverside Lodge 503 F+AM; Scottish Right Mason; Amer Legion; Chprsn Founders Comm Kreutz Creek Lib; VP-E York Schl Bd.

HERR, JUDY ANN (GORNDT), Teacher of the Gifted; *b:* Elmhurst, IL; *w:* Richard Zinn (dec); *c:* David, Daniel, Douglas; *ed:* Purdue Univ (BS) Elem Ed 1961; Wilkes Univ (MS) Ed 1990; Attnd Shippensburg Univ, Millersville Univ; In-Svc Credits; *cr:* Glen Ellyn Schl Dist 1st Grd Tchr 1961-64; Ben Franklin Schl 1st Grd Tchr 1961-64; Glen Oak Schl 1st Grd Tchr 1961-64; Fairview Schl Tchr of GATE 1978-; Hooverville Schl Tchr of GATE 1978-; Coord of GATE 1991-94; *ai:* Parents Comm Wkshps; Math Club Adv; WAEA, PSEA, NEA 1980-; GATE PA Assn 1982-, Finalist Tchr of GATE of Yr; Waynesboro Coll Club 1975-90, Sec, Comm Chm; United Way Bd 1990-94; Amer Cancer Soc Vol 1995-; PASCD Confs, Lincoln Intermediate Unit Wkshps; Nom Who's Who in Amer; Lead Tchr, Curr Cncl 3 Yrs; *office:* Fairview Elem 220 Fairview Ave Waynesboro PA 17268

HERRERA, ANDREA O'REILLY, Asst Professor of Literature; *b:* Philadelphia, PA; *m:* Martin; *c:* Alexandra, Nicole, Martin; *ed:* St Josephs Univ (BA) Lit 1980; West Chester Univ (MA) Lit 1988; Univ of DE (PHD) Lit 1993; *cr:* SUNY Coll at Fredonia Asst Prof 1993-; *ai:* Fac Adv Latinos Unidos & Womens Field Hockey Team; Judge Rosa Parks Schlsp Awd, Best Grad Paper for Fredonias Rsrch on Women Conf & Conf of Amer Women Writers of Color; Acad Affairs & Curr Comms; Co-Chprsn Coalition of Fac & Staff of Color; MLA 1988-; NEMLA 1990-; UUP 1993-; NWSA 1993-; SSSS 1994-; Numerous Articles Pub; Novel: Pearl of the Antilles; Anthology: Little Havanna Blues; *office:* S U N Y Coll At Fredonia Dept of Eng 277 Fenton Hall Fredonia NY 14063

HERRICK, BRIAN DOUGLAS, Math Teacher; *b:* Grove City, PA; *m:* Susan; *ed:* Grove City Coll (BA) Math 1987; 26 Credit Hrs Penn St Univ; *cr:* Greenville HS Math Tchr 1987-; *ai:* Ftbl, Track Coach; *office:* Greenville HS 9 Donation Rd Greenville PA 16125

HERRICK, CHRISTOPHER L., HS Physics & Math Teacher; *b:* Salem, MA; *m:* Susan B. Talbot; *c:* Jesse, Heidi; *ed:* Princeton (BSE) Civil Engng 1968; Stamford (MA) Math & Ed 1972; Attnd NSF, UVM, USM & Santa Clara Univ; *cr:* Lynbrook HS Math Tchr 1972-79; Cape Elizabeth HS Math Tchr 1981-83; Falmouth HS Math & Physics Tchr 1983-; *ai:* Math Team; Engng Team; Golf Team; Amer Tour De Sol 1995-; NCTM & ATOMIN 1985-; Pi Cone Math League 1987-91, Treas; *office:* Falmouth HS 52 Woodville Rd Falmouth ME 04105*

HERRICK, GEORGE FRANK, Bio, Anatomy & Physiology Tchr; *b:* Cuyler, NY; *m:* Linda Wilson; *c:* Wendy; *ed:* SUNY at Cortland (BS) Ed & Bio 1963, (MS) Ed & Bio 1965; 25 Credit Hrs Beyond Masters; *cr:* Vestal HS Tchr 1963-, Soccer Coach 1964-; *ai:* Var Soccer Coach; NEA & VTA 1963-; Natl Soccer Coaches Assn 1969-; US Soccer Coaches Assn USSF A License; Olympic Dev Pgm Soccer Coach; FC Broome Soccer Coach; SUNY at Cortland Soccer Schl Dir; NYS Soccer Coach of the Yr 1981, 1982 & 1990; Natl Soccer Coach of the Yr 1990; *office:* Vestal HS Woodlawn Dr Vestal NY 13850

HERRICK, PATRICIA MC CONNELL, 8th Grade Math Teacher; *b:* Nelsonville, OH; *m:* Stephen E.; *c:* Frances, Eli, Michaela; *ed:* OH Univ (AA) Mental Hlth Tech 1973, (BSEd) Elem Ed 1976, (MSEd) Elem Ed 1986; Project Discovery 1994; OCTM Conf 1994-95; Childrens Literative Conf 1990-93; Martha Jennings Holding Math Inst; *cr:* Logan-Hocking City Schls Third Grd Tchr 1982-84, Kndgtn, 4th Grd Tchr 1984-88, 6th Grd Tchr 1988-91, EDK Tchr 1992-93, 5th Grd Tchr 1993-94, 8th Grd Math Tchr 1994-; *ai:* Math Club Share Responsibility; Sci Clubs, Stu Cncl, Schl Newspaper Spon; St Marys Cath Church 1988-, Parish Cncl, CCD Tchr; St Marys Schl 1986-, Fundraisers, Vol; *office:* Logan-Hocking City Schls 57 S Walnut St Logan OH 43138

HERRICK, RICHARD E., Professor of Physical Sciences; *b:* Schenectady, NY; *m:* Phyllis Smith; *c:* Richard, Dean, Seth; *ed:* Bowdoin Coll (AB) Physics 1950; Univ of Rochester (MS) Ed 1962; RPI (MS) Natural Sci 1967; Clarkson Univ (MS) Engrng Sci 1972; Diploma in Photography from Rochester Inst of Tech 1956; Addl 1 Yr Post Grad Work 1951; Addl 40 Credit Hrs in Horticulture at St Univ of NY at Cobleskill; *cr:* Eastman Kodak Co Engr & Statistician 1951-62; Rochester City Schls HS Physics Tchr 1962-65; Middleburgh HS Chem & Physics Tchr 1965-67; *ai:* Amer Assn of Physics Tchrs 1962-; Astronomical Soc of the Pacific 1986-; Natl Speleological Soc 1993-; Hudson Mohawk Prof Geologists Assn 1995-; NSF Grants for Prof Stud Summers of 1963-67, 1969-71; *office:* S U N Y Coll Of A & T Cobleskl Cobleskill NY 12043

HERRING, BARNELLE ROBINSON, Bus Ed Teacher & Coordinator; *b:* Whiteville, NC; *m:* Donald Ray; *c:* Donald Robin, Charmia Udana; *ed:* Elizabeth City St Univ (BS) Bus Ed 1965; Univ of MD (MED) Bus Ed 1972; NY Univ 6 Credit Hrs; Loyola Coll at Baltimore 12 Credit Hrs; *cr:* Prince Georges Comm Coll Bus Prof 1975-92; Peebles Dept Store Fashion Adv 1992-94; *ai:* FBLA; Diversified Occupations Fundraiser; Stu Mentorship Spon; NEA, MSTA 1965-; TAAAC 1970-; Delta Sigma Theta 1962-, Undergrad Pres, Historian, Treas, Comm Chprsn, Eliza P. Shippen Awd 1995; Delta Sigma Theta Fnd 1994-; Garnett HS Alumni Assn Hall of Fame Inductee; *office:* Meade Sr HS Clark Rd Fort Meade MD 20755

HERRING, CAROL WOLFGANG, Third Grade Teacher; *b:* Romy, NY; *m:* Wayne E.; *ed:* St Univ Coll at Oswego (BS) Elem Ed 1969; 90 Grad Credit Hrs; *cr:* De Witt Clinton Elem Schl 2nd Grd Tchr 1969-86; John E. Joy Elem Schl 2nd Grd Tchr 1986-90, 1992-93, 1st Grd Tchr 1991-92, 3rd Grd Tchr 1990-91, 1993-; *ai:* AFT; NYSUT, Rome Tchrs Assn 1969-; St John's Luth Church, Usher, Trustee, Asst, Altar Guild, Stewardship Comm; *office:* John E Joy Elem Schl 8194 Bielby Rd Rome NY 13440

HERRING, MARILYN PARKS, English IV Teacher; *b:* Philadelphia, PA; *m:* Robert C.; *c:* Laura, Michael; *ed:* Coll of Mount St Joseph (BA) Fr, Ed 1972; Xavier Univ (MED) Eng 1989; 40 Quarter Hrs in Fr Lit Sorbonne, Univ of Cincinnati; *cr:* Ursuline Acad Fr Tchr 1972-76, Fr Tchr 1984-89, Fr & Eng Tchr 1989-92, Eng Tchr 1992-; *ai:* Sr Class of 1996 Mentor; Schl Lit Magazine Moderator; Head Discipline Review, North Cntrl Steering Comms; *office:* Ursuline Acad 5535 Pfeiffer Rd Cincinnati OH 45242

HERRINGTON, LEONARD DUDLEY, Social Studies Teacher; *b:* San Antonio, TX; *m:* Gina Marie Calabria; *c:* Brandon James; *ed:* Univ of Pittsburgh (BA) Soc Sci 1983; Duquesne Univ (MS) Scndry Ed 1990; Six Credit Hrs Admin; *cr:* Springdale HS Soc Stud Tchr 1989-; *ai:* Head Jr HS Bsktbl Coach; Stu Cncl Spon; Suspension Monitor; Dept Rep Curr Coordinating Comm; AP US His Tchr; NEA, PSEA, AVEA 1989-; Natl Assn Stu Act Advs 1992-; PA St Ed Assn; Allegheny Vly Ed Assn; Realtors Assn Metropolitan Pittsburgh 1995-; Guest Speaker Duquesne Univ; *office:* Springdale Jr Sr HS 501 Butler Rd Springdale PA 15144

HERRMANN, MARGARET ELLSWORTH, Reading Teacher; *b:* Pittsburgh, PA; *m:* Richard Karl; *c:* Karl, Thomas; *ed:* Miami Univ of OH (BSEd) Elem Ed, LD, BD Tchr 1974; Univ of Pittsburgh (MED) Mildly, Physically Handicapped Ed 1979; Rdng Recovery Trng & Cert OH St Univ 1994; *cr:* Wickliffe Elem Schl Learning Disabilites Tutor 1986-89; Fairland Elem Schl Learning Disabilites Resource Tchr 1989-90; Wickliffe Elem Schl Learning Disabilites Tutor 1990-94; Columbus Schl for Girls Rdng Recovery, Early Literacy Groups 1-3 Grd Tchr 1994-; *ai:* Support Svc Comm; Learning Disabilities Assn 1974-; Rdng Recovery Cncl of North Amer 1994-; Prof Presentations Summer Inst Columbus OH 1991; *office:* Columbus Schl For Girls 56 S Columbia Ave Bexley OH 43209

HERRMANN, PATRICIA PAULICK, Fifth Grade Teacher; *b:* Pittston, PA; *m:* Richard G.; *c:* Keith, Jeffrey; *ed:* Coll Misericordia (BS) Elem Ed 1968; Coll of New Paltz (MS) Elem Ed 1975; 60 Addl Credit Hrs; *cr:* Randolph Cntrl Schl 3rd Grd Tchr 1968-69; Rhinebeck Cntrl Schl 4th-6th Grd Tchr 1969-; *ai:* Aerobics; Crafts; Rhinebeck Tchrs Assn 1969-, Bldg Planning; AFT 1969-; Marist Coll Red Fox Club 1983-; Summer Stud Grant; Rhinebeck Cntrl Local His BOCES Booklets; *home:* 7 Ackert Hook Rd Rhinebeck NY 12572

HERRMANN, RICHARD EDWARD, English Teacher; *b:* New York, NY; *m:* Bette Jean Blake; *c:* Richard, Robert; *ed:* Iona Coll (BA) Eng 1958; Univ of Miami (MA) Eng & Ed 1959; NYU, Hofstra & LIU 45 Credit Hrs Beyond MA; *cr:* Vly Stream Cntrl HS Eng Tchr 1960-; *ai:* Vly Stream Tchrs Assn 1960-, Pres 1974-; AFT 1965-, Convention Del; NY St United Tchrs 1972-, Convention Del; *office:* Valley Stream Central Sr HS Valley Stream Tchrs Assn 33 Merrick Rd Valley Stream NY 11580

HERRMANN, WILLIAM ANTON, Secondary Soc Studies Teacher; *b:* Pittsburgh, PA; *m:* Tina Marie Stephens; *c:* Stephen, Stanley, Stuart; *ed:* Edinboro (BA) Scndry Soc Stud 1968, (MA) His 1970; *cr:* Wilkinsburg Schl Dist Scndry Soc Stud Tchr 1970-; Herrmanns Ground Maintenance Owner, Operator 1970-; *ai:* WEA, PSEA, NEA 1970-; Cross Roads Cemetery Bd 1993-; Class of 1993 Most Interesting Tchr 1988, Favorite Tchr 1989; Class of 1994 Most Interesting Tchr 1989; Class of 1995 Favorite Tchr 1990; *office:* Wilkinsburg MS 747 Wallace Ave Pittsburgh PA 15221

HERROD, CATHERINE I., Bio, Anatomy & Physiology Tchr; *b:* Greensburg, PA; *m:* Clay F.; *c:* Amanda; *ed:* Otterbein Coll (BA) Life Sci 1971; Univ of Pittsburgh (MAT) Scndry Sci 1972; *cr:* Latrobe Sr HS Tchr 1972-; *ai:* Bridges Projects with Latrobe Brewery; Comm Partnerships Greenhouse Project; Alwine 4-H Comm Club, ldr; Control of Microbial Contamination in Food Industry Article Pub Through Bridges Project; *office:* Greater Latrobe Sr HS Country Club Dr Latrobe PA 15650

HERROLD, SHARON DINSMORE, 3rd Grade Teacher; *b:* Buffalo, NY; *m:* Thomas E.; *c:* Stephen, Lauren Herrold Bredickas; *ed:* Wright St Univ (BSEd) Elem Ed 1968; St of PA Dept of Ed (Masters Equiv) Elem Ed 1985; *cr:* Jane Addams Schl 5th Grd Tchr 1968-69; Simpson Street Schl 6th Grd Tchr 1975-77; Upper Allen Schl 3rd Grd Tchr 1977-81; Shepherdstown Schl 3rd Grd Tchr 1981-; *ai:* Sci Curr Comm; NEA 1975-; PSEA 1975-; Mechanicsburg EA 1975-, Schlsp Chprsn; St Pauls United Church of Christ 1970-, Sunday Schl Tchr; Mechanicsburg Outstdng Svc to Pupils Awd 1985; Shippensburg Univ Schl Stu Cncl Outstdng Tchr Awd 1995; *office:* Shepherdstown Elem Schl 1849 S York St Mechanicsburg PA 17055

HERRON, MARY ANNE, Admissions Dir & Geometry Tchr; *b:* Philadelphia, PA; *ed:* St Joseph's Univ (BA) (BS) Theology, Elem Ed 1983; Chestnut Hill Coll (MA) Elem Ed 1995; Scndry Math Ed Cert; *cr:* St Patrick's Schl Fourth-Seventh Grd Math Tchr 1983-85; Waldron Mercy Acad Fourth Grd Tchr 1985-87, Jr HS Math Tchr 1987-91, Admissions Dir, Algebra I, II, Geometry I Tchr 1991-; *ai:* Mathletes Instr; Cmptr Network Admin; Designer Schl Newspaper; Pre-Prep Pgm Coord; NEA 1985-; NCTM 1990-; CYO Yth Group 1983-90, Adv; S. Cehas Awd Distngd Tchng 1990; *office:* Waldron Mercy Acad 513 Montgomery Ave Merion Station PA 19066*

HERRON, MURIEL L. (WOOD), Math Teacher; *b:* Corning, NY; *m:* David; *ed:* SUNY at Geneseo (BA) Math 1990; Elmira Coll (MS) Scndry Ed 1994; *cr:* Savona Cntrl Schl Math Tchr 1990-92; Campbell-Savonal Cntrl Schl Math Tchr 1992-; *ai:* Hnr Pass, Disciplinary Comm; Ath Events Chaperone; *office:* Campbell-Savona Central Schl 8455 County Rt 125 Campbell NY 14821

HERRON, PATRICK RICHARD, Social Studies Teacher; *b:* Syracuse, NY; *m:* Ann Elizabeth Wojenski; *c:* Timothy, Dennis, Patrick; *ed:* St Bonaventure Univ (BA) His 1968; Syracuse Univ Perm Cert Sdndry Edu 1969; *cr:* Chrstn Brothers Acad Soc Sci Tchr 1969-71; Solvay HS Soc Sci Tchr 1971-; *ai:* AFT 1971-; Solvay Tchrs Assn 1971-, Pres 1994-; Excl in Tchng Awd Syracuse Univ Dept of Ed; *office:* Solvay High School 600 Gertrude Ave Solvay NY 13209*

HERSH, LYNN CASSELBERRY, Librarian; *b:* Norristown, PA; *m:* John; *c:* Nathaniel, Nicholas; *ed:* Millersville Univ (BS) Lib 1971; Master's Equivalency; *cr:* Methacton Schl Dist Librn K-5 24 Yrs; *ai:* Comm Work; NEA, PSEA 1971-; Pa Schl Librns Assn 1975-; Lower Providence Comm Lib Bd 1990-, Sec; Church Women's Org 1978-; BSA; *office:* Arrowhead Elem Schl 1001 Kriebel Mill Rd Norristown PA 19408

HERSH, MORTIMER BENNETT,JR., Social Science Asst Prof; *b:* New York City, NY; *m:* Vicki Lynn Dobbs; *c:* Eric, Justin; *ed:* WV Wesleyan Coll (BA) His 1964; Univ of MI (MS) Ed 1968; 10 Addl Credits Univ of KY; *cr:* LAnse Crouse Pub Schls Tchr 1964-69; Alice Lloyd Coll Tchr & Asst Prof 1969-70; Westmoreland Cty Comm Coll Asst Prof 1971-; *ai:* Westmoreland Cty Comm Coll PA 1972-, Sec, Prof Awd of Yr; PSEA, NEA 1972-; Comm Nursing of Greensburg Inc 1986-, VP; Friendship II Investment Club 1984-, Pres; *office:* Westmoreland County Comm Coll Armbrust Rd Youngwood PA 15697

HERSH, VICKI DOBBS, English Teacher; *b:* Wheeling, WV; *m:* Mortimer B. Jr.; *c:* Eric Shawn, Justin Daniel; *ed:* Marshall Univ (BA) Eng, Span 1966; Univ of MI (MA) Rdng Specialist 1969; Addl Post Grad Stud Univ of Pittsburgh, Westchester Univ; *cr:* L'Anse Creuse Pub Schls Tchr 1966-69; Alice Lloyd Coll Tchr 1969-71; Westmoreland Cty Comm Coll Tchr 1971-76; Greensburg Salem Schl Dist Tchr 1977-; *ai:* NEA, PSEA, GSEA 1977-; *home:* 405 Sheffield Dr Greensburg PA 15601

HERSHBERGER, JENNIFER DIANE, Instructional Media Coord; *b:* Lebanon, IN; *ed:* Ball St Univ (BS) Radio, TV 1972; Xavier Univ (MED) Instrl Svcs Specialist 1977; Cable in Classroom Innovations & Applications; *cr:* Wm Henry Harrison HS Instrl Media Coord, Media Dept Chprsn 1972-; *ai:* Dist Media Coord; Instrl TV, Dist News Dirs; Prin Lead Team; NC Evaluation Chrprsn 1980, 1987, 1994; Supt Advy Comm; AECT 1977-; OELMA 1975-; PBS Curr Advy Comm 1975-; Directed & Produced Documentaries Passing Schl Tax Levies; 10 Grant Awds; Marth Jennings Scholar 1983; Natl Schl of Excl Awd; Tchr of Yr 19 Lectures on Media Production; *office:* Wm Henry Harrison HS 9 Rd Harrison OH 45030

HERSHBERGER, MAUREEN H., Seventh & Eighth Grade Te Primavera, Paraguay; *m:* Stanley James; *c:* Bernard J., Leonard S K., Lawrence E.; *ed:* Ed & Eng at Univ of WV; *cr:* Darvell Sussex England 7th & 8th Grd Tchr 1988-91; Spring Valley Schl Grd Tchr 1992-; *ai:* Bruderhof; *home:* RR 2 Box 446 Farmington

HERSHEY, JEFFREY B., Language Arts Instructor; *b:* Lancaste Elizabeth M. Schweitz; *ed:* PA St Univ (BA) Jrnlsm 1987; M Univ Eng Cert 1992; Master of Ed in Eng Prgm Allentown Coll; *c* Mountain HS Lang Arts Instr 1992-; *ai:* Yrbk Adv; Spec Need Track Ofcl; NEA, PMEA 1992-; Tech-Prep Consortium Northa Monroe Ctys 1992-95; Gift of Time Awd 1995; *office:* Pocono Sr HS PO Box 200 Swiftwater PA 18370*

HERSHFELD, VIRGINIA W., General Science Teacher; *b:* Grace, MD; *m:* J. David; *c:* Matt, Todd; *ed:* Towson St Coll (BS) Post Grad Stud; *cr:* Ridgely Jr High 7th Grd Sci Tchr 1964-68; Lo MS 8th Grs Sci Tchr 1985-; *ai:* NEA 1964-68, 1985-; NJEA, W Sci Tchrs 1985-; Local Nursery Schl Bd Mem 1995-; PEO 1981- Research Excl Tchng Awd 1994; *office:* Long Valley MS 51 W Long Valley NJ 07853*

HERSHKOWITZ, ROBERT PHILIP, Biology Instructor; *b:* U NJ; *m:* Carol; *c:* Scott, Brian; *ed:* Muhlenberg Coll (BS) Pre-M Hahnemann Med Schl & Hosp (MD) Med Dr 1971; *cr:* Monmouth Asst Prgm Dir 1983-85; Monmouth Univ Bio Instr 1994-; Advising Comm; Pre-Med Comm; *office:* Monmouth Univ Ceda Long Branch NJ 07764*

HERSHNIK, MARK KARL, English Teacher; *b:* Mt Holly, NJ; (BS) Eng, Scndry Ed 1982; Wesleyan Univ (MA) Liberal Stud, Ps Fairfield Univ (CAS) Admin, Super 1990; 15 Credits Towards Fin Admin; *cr:* R. H. Brown MS Eng Tchr 1983-; *ai:* Stu Cncl, Yrbk A Trip Coord; Debate Coach; Pub Relations, Prof Dev Cncl; Coo Mentor; Grouping, Strategic Planning, Curr Comm; NEA, CE 1983-; Pub Faulkners Legacy, Sympathetic Character, Wesle 1988; Rotary Club 1995 Outstanding Comm Effort as Fac Adv in *office:* Dr Robert H Brown MS 980 Durham Rd Madison CT 06

HERSHWITZKY, PATRICIA ANN, Math & Social Studies Te Los Angeles, CA; *m:* Lloyd; *c:* Alexander, David; *ed:* CA St Univ Sci 1973; CA St Univ at San Bernardino Tchng Credential Subject 1992; *cr:* Where Magazine Asst Ed 1973-75; Lewis Account Exec & Office Mgr 1975-85; St George Schl Tchr 1989 of Visitation Tchr 1995-; *ai:* Yrbk Adv; Math Club; RCAR 1977- & Co-Founder; Articles Pub; *office:* Acad of the Visitation 200 Frederick MD 21701

HERSPERGER, SUSAN LYNN, 7th Grade Language Arts Greensburg, PA; *m:* Jeffery A.; *c:* Kasey Leigh, Alexandra Indiana Univ of PA (BS) Scndry Ed, Eng 1988; 33 Credits Towar in Scndry Guid Cnslng at Kutztown Univ; *cr:* East Penn Schl Dis Lang Arts Tchr 1988-, Team Ldr 1994-; *ai:* 9th Grd Glass Ad Coord; SAP; Fac Senate; NEA, EPEA 1988-; NMSA, PMSA 199 Emmaus Jr HS 660 Macungie Ave Emmaus PA 18049*

HERSTON, KEVIN ROY, History Teacher; *b:* Akron, OH; *m:* M.; *c:* Stephen M., Emily P.; *ed:* Univ of Akron (BA) Scndry Ed 6 Credit Hrs Post Bachelor; *cr:* Orange Chrstn Acad Tchr 1991-; Vlybl & Var Sftbl Coach; Frosh Class Adv; Var Ladies Bskt *office:* Orange Christian Acad 27200 Emery Rd Cleveland OH 4

HERTER, BETTY LOU K., Computer Instructor; *b:* Bath, NY; Jr.; *c:* John W. Beh III; *ed:* Univ of HI (BS) Ec & Bus 1961; S (MS) Scndry Credential 1967; *cr:* Harbor HS His Tchr 1970-74; Voc Bus Tchr 1975-78; Bath Cntrl Schl Bus & Cmptr Tchr Cheerleading Coach; Occ Ed Dept Chair; Tech Trainer & Plar 1980-, Dir of Legislation 1991, Pres, Regnl 8 Dir; Natl Pinto As Amer Saddlebred Assn 1970; Red Cross; NATC Pinto Assn Saddlbred Assn 1970; Ride Class; *office:* Haverling H S 25 Ellis NY 14810

HERTLING, PETER A., Music & Band Director; *b:* Brookly Chester Anne; *c:* Laura Rosler, Hollye; *ed:* Ithaca Coll (BS) Mu C.W. Post Coll (MS) Music 1971; Poetry, Art Stonybrook Merrick HS Band Dir 1964-65; Brentwood HS Band Dir Northport HS Band Dir 1969-72; Rocky Point Schls Music Dir Chess Coach; NYSSMA 1964-; NYSSMA MENC; Articles Pub; Sunset Blvd Wading River NY 11792*

HERTZFELD, ELIZABETH NORA, Elem Principal; *b:* Roche *ed:* Green Mountain Coll (AA) Ed 1970; Keene St Coll (BS) Elem Ed 1972; Univ of NH (MED) Admin 1990; *cr:* Pittsfield HS Spe 1972-75, 5th, 6th Grd Tchr 1975-79; Underhill Schl 3rd, 4th 1979-86; Northwood Schl 6th Grd Tchr 1986-87, Asst Prin 198 1989-93; Effingham Elem Schl Prin 1993-; *ai:* Early Literacy Tech; NHASP, NACSP, ASCD 1986-; Hospice, Mediation 1985- Matther 1993-, Exec Bd; *office:* Ossipee Central Elem Schl Main Ossipee NH 03814

HERTZOG, DIANE LEE, Mathematics Teacher; *b:* Patuxent MD; *m:* Rory Carl; *c:* Ryan Carl; *ed:* Lebanon Vly Coll (BS) M Shippensburg Univ 3 Grad Stud Credits; Millersville Univ 3 Credits; Penn St Univ 18 Grad Stud Credits; *cr:* Solance HS Ma Sci Tchr 1990-91; Cntrl York HS Math Tchr 1991-; *ai:* Strategic Final Exam Comms; NEA, PSEA, CYEA 1990-, Mbrshp Chprs Time Awd.*

HERTZOG, M. JUDINE, Fifth Grade Teacher; *b:* Gallitzin, P Francis Coll (BS) Elem Ed 1970, (MED) Ed 1988; Working Master Catechist Cert; *cr:* Holy Name Schl 5th Grd Tchr Eucharistic Minister; St Patrick Church Lector; NCEA 1971- Schl Advy Cncl 1990-, Sec; St Patrick Parish Cncl 1990- Geographical Soc Tchr Recognition Pgm 1992; *office:* Holy N 215 W Horner St Ebensburg PA 15931

HERVEY, DARLENE PLOTTS, First Grade Teacher; *b:* Ste OH; *m:* Thomas D.; *c:* Shawn; *ed:* West Liberty St Coll (BA) 1972; Dayton Univ (MA) Admin 1980; *cr:* Indian Creek Schl Dis Tchr 1973-; *ai:* Odyssey of Mind Judge; NEA, OEA 1973-; Al Kappa; Martha Holden Jennings Scholar; *office:* Wintersville 125 Fernwood Rd Steubenville OH 43952

HERVOL, JOANNE (DUSZA), Chemistry Teacher; *b:* Pittsburg Theodore R.; *ed:* IN Univ of PA (BS) Chem Ed 1989, (MED) 1990; *cr:* Hempfield Area Schl Dist Chem Tchr 1990-; Westmor Comm Coll Chem Instr 1992-; *ai:* Chem Club Adv; PA Jr Acad c Olympiad Spon; NSTA, PA Sci Tchrs Assn 1989-; Soc of A Chemists of Pittsburgh, Spectroscopic Soc of Pittsburgh Aiken-Psak Meml Schlsp Comm 1990-, Sec; SACP Equipment Grants; *office:* Hempfield Area Sr HS Rd 6 Box 77 Greensburg P

HERWEG, DAVID JAMES, Social Studies Teacher; *b:* Burlingto Patricia; *c:* Heather, Jessica, Andrew; *ed:* Univ of NY at Fredonia Stu 1973; St Univ Coll at Buffalo (MS) Scndry Ed 1980; *cr:* Rich

Tchr 1975-76; Springville GI Cntrl Schl Soc Stud Tchr 1977-78; ıs HS Soc Stud Tchr 1979-82; Oakfield-Alabama HS Soc Stud 3-; *ai:* Var Ftbl Asst Hd Coach; Var Boys & Girls Bsktbl & Boys ıch; Model U.N. 1976; Class Adv 1994; AFT 1983-; NYSUT ɛstern NY Ftbl Coaches Assn; Erie Schl Bd Assn, Mem; Cleveland l Dist, Cheektowaga, NY, Trustee; *office:* Oakfield-Alabama ıchl 7001 Lewiston Rd Oakfield NY 14125

S, CHARLENE MASON, Guidance Counselor; *b:* Wilmington, ɪrank; *ed:* Lee Coll (BA) Music Ed 1976; Salisbury St Univ (MED) ɪslng 1985; *cr:* Washington HS Choral Dir 1981-86; Wicomico MS ɪir 1986-87; Tandy Corp Educl Consultant 1987-88; Washington Cnslr 1988-; *ai:* Stdnts Need Assistance Prgm; Schl Improvement ·isis Team; Pupil Prsnl Comm; Self-Esteem, Sexual Harrassment ; Choral Dir; Delta Kappa Gamma 1991-, Recording Sec; MD St ısn, NEA 1977-; Chrstn Prof Women 1988-, Chm; Parkway Church 959-, Choral Dir; Wor Wic Comm Coll Gen Stud Comm; Lower omm Employment of People with Disabilities; *home:* 5250 Ln Salisbury MD 21801*

IS, FRANK JAMES,JR., Social Studies Teacher; *b:* New york, Charlene M.; *ed:* Salisbury St Coll (APC) His 1977, Hiram Scott) Soc Stud 1969; *cr:* WA HS Soc Stud Tchr 1969-; Amer Inst for d Summer Pgm Coord, Regnl Coord, NY City Liaison 1977-80; . Cty Summer Schl Prin 1991-; *ai:* Bus Partnerships Coord; Prom & After Prom Alcohol Free Pub Coord; NEA 1970-; MSTA 1970-; 970; Natl Assn of Stu Cncl; Jaycees 1969-84, Dir, Ofcr of Month, Young Men of Amer, Speak Up Awd; Lesson Plan Pub; *office:* on H S 10902 Old Princess Anne Rd Princess Anne MD 21853

G, ROBERT MARK, Science Teacher; *b:* Pittsburgh, PA; *m:* y; *c:* Erin, Zach; *ed:* Mansfield St Univ (BS) Ed 1977; Towson St S) Ed 1985; 30 Credits Beyond Masters, Including 12 Grad Credits ɔnmental Issues from Southern IL Univ; *cr:* Bel Air HS Bio & Sci Tchr 1978-79; Aberdeen MS Phys Sci Tchr 1979-81; Bel Air & Life Sci Tchr 1981-91; Harford Cty Bd of Ed MSPP Sci Curr st 1991-92; Bel Air HS Environmental Sci Tchr 1992-; *ai:* ıental Club Spon; NEA 1978-; Harford Cty Environmental Sci 'r 1995; Wrote & Teach 3 Credit Course for Sci Tchrs; *office:* Bel 00 Heighe St Bel Air MD 21014

TH, THOMAS, Science Teacher; *b:* New Bedford, MA; *m:* Janet s; *c:* Laurie J., Lynelle M.; *ed:* Fitchburg St Coll (BSEd) Bio 1970, Sci Ed 1975; 6 Credits Operation Progress 1994; Inst for Chem Ed *cr:* Ayer HS Sci Instr 1970-75; Old Colony Reg Voc HS Sci Instr i: FAC Cncl Hnr Soc; Disciplin Comm; NSTA 1970-; MASS *fice:* Old Colony Reg Voc Tech Schl 476 North Ave Rochester MA

R, VICKIE WILLIAMS (CARTER), 6th Grade Teacher; *b:* KY; *m:* Terry; *c:* Michelle, Jay Carter, Denise Carter, Michael, *d:* Morehead St Univ (BA) Elem Ed 1970; Univ of Dayton (MS) 982; Math Ed Wright St Univ; Math, Arts Ed Univ of Dayton; Western KY Univ; *cr:* Franklin-Monroe Elem Schl 4th-5th Grd 0-71; Hardin Cty Schls 5th-6th Grd Tchr 1972-76; H. V. Bear Elem Grd Tchr 1977-93; Neff Bldg Schl 6th Grd Tchr 1993-; *ai:* Math under, Adv; OH St Proficiency Content Review, Fourth Grd y Rangefinder, Report Card, Math Comms; Dayton Daily News cy Advy Bd, Writer; Math Wkshp Presenter; Dayton Area Tchr 1-, Chair 1995-; OH Cncl Tchrs of Math 1992-, West Dist Dir, air, Outstdng Elem Math Tchr; MCTA, OEA, NEA 1976-; Hesler Tool's, Founder, Ed Division, New Product, Miracle Slate, Office rtha Holden Jennings Scholar; Dayton Area Excl in Tchng Awd; Oil Golden Apple Achiever Awd; Muse Machine Outstdng Arts iamisburg's Exemplary Tchr Awd 1993, 1995; Who's Who 1992; For Ed, Smart, Dist Grants; Project Discovery; *office:* Neff Elem 5 6th St Miamisburg OH 45342

GA, VIRGINIA RIPOSTA, 3rd-5th Grade Teacher; *b:* Newark, erry D.; *c:* Joshua, Joy; *ed:* Widener Univ (MA) Ed 1988; *cr:* Pine Schl 6th-8th Grd Tchr 1976; Mid Twp Schls 1st-5th Grd Gifted chr 1984-; *ai:* Sign Lang & Span Club; NEA 1988-; First Bapt 984-, Kids Choir Dir, Jr High Sun Schl Tchr; *office:* Middle Twp em #2 W Pacific Ave Cape May Ct House NJ 08210*

K, DENNIS WILLIAM, Science Teacher; *b:* Jamestown, NY; *m:* nnont; *c:* Kristen J., Nathan G.; *ed:* SUNY at Buffalo (BS) ɔe Engrng 1971; SUNY at Fredonia (MS) Ed Math 1977; 27 Hrs sters; *cr:* US Air Force Instr Pilot 1972-75; Chautauqua Cntrl Schl hr 1977-81; Clymer Cntrl Schl Sci & Math Tchr 1981-; *ai:* Asst ch; Master Tchrs Cncl Co-Chm; Schlsp Comm Mem; Sci Tchrs 'S 1983-; NSTA Assn 1985-; Clymer Hill Reformed Church 1959-, eacon, Sunday Schl Thcr 1976-, Supt; Cast & Co Theater 1991-, *office:* Clymer Cntrl Schl 8680 E Main St PO Box 580 Clymer NY

DAVID SCOTT, Mathematics Teacher; *b:* Erie, PA; *m:* Christine Young; *c:* Eric, Scott; *ed:* Penn St at Behrend (BS) Bus 1984; Univ Tchng Cert Math Ed 1987; Addl 24 Post Grad Stud in Math, ronmental Sci; *cr:* Harborcreek HS Math Tchr 1987-; *ai:* Asst Ftbl, ıch; Weightlifting Club, Prom, Homecoming Advs; Stu Act Comm; ıss Adv; NEA, PSEA 1987-; Penn St Ftbl Org 1980-; NABC 1990-; l Coach of Yr Natl Dist 8; Bsbl Articles; *office:* Harborcreek HS ffalo Rd Harborcreek PA 16421

DIANE M., Secondary Science Teacher; *ed:* Annhurst Coll (BA) 3; Adelphi Univ (MA) Scndry Ed 1972; Dowling Coll K-12th Grd rt; *cr:* Plainedge Pub Schls Scndry Sci Tchr 1968-; *ai:* Staff Dev; 'f Relations Comm Rep; AFT 1968-; Plainedge Fed of Tchrs 1968-, p; PTA; Church, Rel Ed; Homework Club, Gardening Prgm for Vol; *office:* Plainedge HS 241 Wyngate Dr North Massapequa NY

DOLORES JEAN, Sixth Grade Language Arts Tchr; *b:* North i, PA; *m:* Clarence K.; *c:* Susan E. Nickler, Todd I., Dianne F. ott M.; *ed:* CA Univ (BS) Elem 1974, (MS) Rdng Specialist 1978; pvr 1980; Univ of Pittsburgh Classroom Discussion 1991; Dept of coring A Writing Sample 1992; Carlow Coll Self Esteem 1994; *cr:* em Center Elem Lang Arts Tchr 1975-78, 4th, 5th Grd Lang Arts 78-80; Bethlehem Center Jr HS Rdng Supvr 1980-82, 7th-9th Grd hr 1982-89; Bethlehem Center MS 6th Grd Lang Arts Tchr 1989-; A, NEA 1974-, VP, Bldg Rep, Treas, Sec; AAUW 1986-; Delta Gamma 1992-; Keystone St Rdng, CA Rdng 1973-; CA Univ tial Schlsp 1980; *home:* PO Box 67 Beallsville PA 15313

JOHN MARVIN, Social Studies Teacher; *b:* Lancaster, PA; *m:* Myers; *c:* Susan, Steven; *ed:* MIllersville Univ (BS) Scndry Ed niv of DE (MA) His 1969; *cr:* Garden Spot HS Ninth Grd Eng Tchr ɔlanco HS Soc Stud, Eng Tchr 1966-; *ai:* Asst Girls Sftbl Coach; 66-; Church.

OY MORGAN, Choral Music Teacher; *b:* Lewistown, PA; *m:* D. Jr.; *ed:* IN Univ of PA (BS) Music Ed 1994; 6 Grad Credit Hrs uquesne Univ; *cr:* Tyrone Elem Schls Music Stu Tchr 1994; Tyrone 5 Music Stu Tchr 1994; Purchase Line HS Choral Music Dir 1994-; lause Adv, Dir; Annual All-Schl Musical Dir; PSEA, NEA 1994-; usic Edctrs Assn 1990-; Delta Omicron 1991-, Music Adv, Sr Hnr Pin; Founder Ascotti Madrigal Quartet; *office:* Purchase Line Jr Sr HS RR 1 Box 374 Commodore PA 15729

HESS, LINDA JANE (HOLLOWAY), Fifth Grade Classroom Teacher; *b:* Camden, NJ; *m:* Edward William; *c:* Rachel, Matthew; *ed:* Eastern Coll (BA) Elem Ed 1974; *cr:* Oaklyn Pub Schl Classroom Tchr 1974-; *ai:* Pupil Assistance Comm; Yrbk Co-Ed; Intergenerational Prgm Coord; NJEA, NEA 1975-; Oaklyn Ed Assn 1975-, Sec, Treas; IRA, NJRA 1993-; Camden Co Girl Scouts; Various Church Bds; Co-Founder Haddonfield Child Care; Pastoral Nominating Comm; Tchr of Yr Awd 1995; *office:* Oaklyn Public Schl 136 Kendall Blvd Oaklyn NJ 08107*

HESS, LORI BARKLE, Spanish Teacher; *b:* Lancaster, PA; *m:* Timothy A.; *ed:* Millersville Univ (BSE) Span, Sec Ed-Summa Cum Laude 1990; 36 Addl Grad Credits; *cr:* Middletown Area Schl Dist Span Tchr 1990-; *ai:* NEA, Amer Assn of Tchrs of Span & Portuguese 1990-; PA St Modern Lang Assn 1995-; *office:* Middletown Area HS 1155 N Union St Middletown PA 17057*

HESS, MARK A., High School Spanish Teacher; *ed:* Millersville Univ (BA) Span 1990; Univ of DE (MS) Span Lit 1996; Univ of Madrid 1989, 1991; *cr:* Warwick HS Span Tchr 1990-.

HESS, MEGAN, 2nd & 3rd Grd Classroom Tchr; *b:* Lancaster, PA; *m:* Sid Cook; *c:* Kiri Cook, Custer Cook; *cr:* Kennett Consolidated Schls Eng as a 2nd Lang Tchr 1976-77; Plymouth Meeting Friends Schl Combined 1st-2nd Grd Tchr 1977-85, 4th Grd Tchr 1988-89; Germantown Friends Schl 6th Grd Tchr 1989-93, 2nd-3rd Grd Tchr 1993-; *ai:* Math, Prof Evaluation, Spirtual Life Comms; NCTM 1994-.*

HESS, NORMA M., Spanish Teacher; *b:* Buffalo, NY; *ed:* SUC at Buffalo (BS) Span, Scndry Ed 1981; SUNY at Buffalo (MED) 1995; *cr:* St Francis HS Span Tchr 1981-; *ai:* Span Club Moderator; Foreign Langs Dept Chprsn; Acad Cncl; NYSAFLT 1983-; WNYFLEC 1985-; AATSP 1994; St James Church Folk Group 1992-; *office:* St Francis HS S 4129 Lake Shore Rd Athol Springs NY 14010

HESS, PAUL, High School Art Teacher; *b:* Akron, OH; *ed:* Harding Coll (BA) Art Ed 1966; Rutgers Univ (MA) Studio Art, Drawing & Painting 1976; *cr:* Manville HS Art Tchr 1966-83; Ridge HS Art Tchr 1983-; *ai:* Career Counseling; Curr Dev; Mid Sts Evaluation; Mentor for Gifted & Talented Stdnts; NEA, NJ Ed Assn 1966-; Bernards Twp Ed Assn 1983-; Art Educators of NJ 1994-; Carversville Historical Soc 1994-, Road Rally Coord; Fighting AIDS Continuously Together 1991-; Grant to Start Peer Leadership at Ridge HS 1992; Local PTO Tchr of Month Awd; *office:* Ridge HS S Finley Ave Basking Ridge NJ 07920

HESS, SUZANNE K., L D Support Specialist; *b:* Greenwich, CT; *ed:* Miami Univ of OH (BSEd) Elem Ed 1971; Cert Learning Disabilities K-12 1986; 30 Addl Undeclared Grad Hrs OH Writing Project 1995; *cr:* Middletown City Schls Sub, L D Tutor 1981-84; Miami Univ at Middletown Dept of Continuing Ed Aerobic Dance Instr 1983-; Madison Local Schls Learning Disability Support Specialist 1984-; *ai:* Drill Team Adv; NEA, OEA, Madison Ed Assn 1986-; Southwestern OH Balloon Competition Club 1994-, Charter Mem; *office:* Madison HS 1368 Middletown Eaton Rd Middletown OH 45042

HESSERT, GARY LEE, Science Teacher; *b:* Williamsport, PA; *m:* Jean Ann Pontious; *c:* Aimee Sue, Gregory Jacob; *ed:* Lock Haven St (BS) Hlth & PE 1974; Drivers Ed Cert 1975; General Sci Cert 1985; Bio Cert 1987; Grad Level Courses; *cr:* Wallenpaupark HS Drivers Ed Tchr 1975-77; Mifflinburg HS Drivers Ed Tchr 1978-87, Bio & Sci Tchr 1987-; *ai:* Sci Dept Lead Tchr 1991-; Stu Asst Prgm Team Mem 1992-; NEA, PSEA 1974-; Mifflinburg Area Ed Assn 1978-; Mifflinburg Jaycees Outstanding Educator of Yr 1987; *office:* Mifflinburg Area HS 1st & Market Sts Mifflinburg PA 17844

HESSION, JULIA CHEETHAM, 6th Grade Teacher; *b:* Springfield, MA; *m:* Richard P.; *c:* Scott, Gregg; *ed:* Elms Coll (BA) Ed 1964; Southampton Coll (MS) Soc Stud Ed 1984; 75 Addl Hrs; *cr:* Springfield Schls 3rd-4th Grd Tchr 1964-65; Longwood Schls 3, 4, 6th Grds Tchr 1965-; *ai:* House Captain; Club Adv, Broadcast News Radio; NYSTA 1965-; Middle Island Tchrs Assn 1965-, Sec; Mini Grant for Stu Wkshps in Radio Broadcasting; *office:* Longwood MS 41 Middle Island Yaphank Rd Middle Island NY 11792*

HESSMILLER, JOANNE M., Former Director; *b:* Scranton, PA; *m:* David Trego; *ed:* Marywood Coll (BA) Eng 1981; Loyola Univ of Chicago (MSW) Soc Work 1985; Working Towards PHD in Soc Work Univ of MD at Baltimore; *cr:* Coppin St Coll Instr 1989-92; Millersville Univ Asst Prof 1992-93; Messiah Coll Asst Prof, Acting Dir Soc Work Prgm 1993-94; *ai:* Natl Assn of Soc Workers; Amer Assn Univ Prof; Bertha Cupen Reynolds Soc; Neighborhood Dispute Settlement, Mediator; Camp Hill Schl Dist Strategic Planning Rep; Fulbright-Hays Grant to Stud in West Africa; Articles Pub.

HESTER, EUGENE WILLIAM, Science Teacher; *b:* Plymouth, PA; *m:* Barbara M. Blumenkrantz; *c:* Bonne Jean Rochester, Gerald; *ed:* CA St (BS) Ed 1962; Wilmington Coll (MS) Ed 1992; *cr:* Los Angeles City Schls Sci Tchr; Ridley Schl Dist Sci Tchr; Kirk MS Sci Tchr; *office:* George V. Kirk MS 140 Brennen Dr Newark DE 19713

HESTER, JEFFREY M., 5th Grade Teacher; *b:* Muncy, PA; *ed:* Williamsport Area Comm Coll (AA) Ed Sociology 1973; Lycoming (BA) Sociology 1975; Villanova (MA) Admin 1979; *cr:* East Goshin Elem Schl 5th Grd Tchr 1976-92; Westtown Thornbury Elem Schl 5th Grd Tchr 1992-; *ai:* IST Tchr; Site Based Mgmt Team; NEA, PSEA 1973-; PA St Archery Assn 1992-; Nom Tchr of Yr 1991; *office:* Westtown-Thornbury Elem Schl 950 Westbourne Rd West Chester PA 19373*

HESTER, PATRICIA JEAN, High School Math Teacher; *b:* Cincinnati, OH; *m:* Fred Eugene; *c:* Franklin, Laura; *ed:* Univ of Cincinnati (BSEd) Scndry Math 1974, (MAT) Math 1974; Morehead St Univ (AMEd) Scndry Ed 1978; *cr:* Norwood HS Math Tchr 1974-; *ai:* Math, Sci Club Spon; NEA, OEA, SWOEA, NTA 1974-, Past Pres; NCTM; Zeta Tau Alpha 1971-; Kappa Delta Pi 1974-; Natl Sci Fnd Schlsp; Hewlett Packard Grant Recipient; *home:* 11705 Schmidt Ln Walton KY 41094*

HESTON, FRANK CRAIG, Social Studies Teacher; *b:* Philadelphia, PA; *m:* Anne Quirk; *c:* Frank, Scott, Elizabeth, Katherine; *ed:* Dartmouth (BA) His 1965; Univ of MA (MA) His 1970; 40 Addl Credit Hrs His, Govt, Ger & Local Stud from Smith Coll, Greenfield Comm Coll & Dartmouth; *cr:* Northfield-Mt Hermon Assoc Dir of Dev 1965-66; Hawley Jr HS Soc Stud Tchr 1966-69; Frontier Regnl HS Soc Stud Tchr 1970-; *ai:* Gateways Gifted & Talented Coord; Tennis Coach; Hiking Club Dir; Class of 1996 Adv; Frontier Tchrs Assn Co-Pres; NEA 1982-; MIAA 1973-; Northampton Citizens Schlsp Fnd 1974-, Founder, Tres, Former Pres, 140,000 Dollar Endowment; Northampton Historical Commission 1993-; Kiwanis, Past Pres; Leeds School PTO, Past Pres; Amnesty Intnl, Greenpeace & Northampton Survival Ctr, Democratic Comm; Kennedy Lib Prize (Pioneer Valley Native-Amer Unit Later Pub by Univ of MA); Kennedy Lib Grand (MA Reforms 1783-1865; Natl Hum Grant (Black Stud-New England 1800's); Carnegie Local His Grant; Smith Coll Native Amer Studs; *office:* Frontier Regional Schl N Main St South Deerfield MA 01373

HETHERINGTON, JAMES JOSEPH, History Teacher; *b:* West Chester, PA; *m:* Barbara Ann Pacitti; *c:* Stefanie, Denise; *ed:* West Chester St Coll (BA) His 1967; *cr:* Bishop Shanahan HS His Dept Tchr 1967-; *ai:* Co-oord Audio-Visual Hardware, Channel One Contact Person; Channel Two Moderator; NCEA 1967-; *office:* Bishop Shanahan HS 103 N Everhart St West Chester PA 19380

HETNER, ROBERT F., Social Studies Instructor; *b:* Williamsport, PA; *m:* Kathleene Louise Kroft; *c:* Nicole Swanne, Andrea Lynn, Melissa Louise; *ed:* Williamsport Area Comm Coll (AS) Ed, Soc Work 1974; Lycoming Coll (BA) Sociology 1976; Mansfield Univ (MS) Execeptional Persons 1986; Act 120 Municipal Police Ofcrs Trng Course for PA; *cr:* Borough of S Williamsport Part-time Ofcr 1981-; Lycoming Cty Career Consoritum Protective Svcs Instr 1993-; East Lycoming Schl Dist Soc Stud Tchr 1982-; *ai:* Sr Class Adv 1982-; Citizen's Fire Dept s Williamsport 1971-; *office:* East Lycoming Schl Dist 505 W Central Ave S Williamsport PA 17701*

HETRICK, DENNIS R., Computer Technology Instructor; *b:* Pottstown, PA; *c:* Veronica Orth, Sara; *ed:* Voc Ed 1988 at Temple Univ 1988; Cmptr Sci at Penn St; Electrical Engrng at Belvoir Engrng Schl; Mechanical Design Stevens Tech Schl; *cr:* Arlans Dept Stores Retail Mrktg, Operations 1966-68; Angel Manufacturing Product Design, Cost Estimating 1968-72; Birdsboro Corp Asst VP Engrng Support 1972-84; Rdng Muhlenberg Voc Schl Tchr 1984-; *ai:* Assist Voc Indstrl Clubs of Amer; NEA, PSEA 1984-; *office:* Reading-Muhlenberg Voc Schl PO Box 13068 Reading PA 19612

HETRICK, FRANK WILLIAM, Physical Education Instructor; *b:* Hershey, PA; *m:* Donna; *ed:* Huron Coll (BS) PE 1968; West Chester Univ (MA) Hlth 1975; Addl 68 Credits Above Masters; *cr:* Cedar Crest HS Ftbl Line Coach 28 Yrs; Cedar Crest MS PE & Hlth Tchr 28 Yrs; *ai:* Ice Hockey 43 Yrs; Mountain Biking; Farming; NEA 1968-; PA Hlth & PE Assn 1975-; *office:* Cedar Crest MS 101 E Evergreen Rd Lebanon PA 17042

HETTERICK, KENNETH, Health & Physical Ed Teacher; *b:* Oceanside, NY; *m:* Marjorie Hoblin; *ed:* Cortland St Univ (BSE) PE 1968; Adelphi Univ (MS) Hlth Ed 1973; Post Grad Stud at NY Univ; *cr:* Dutch Broadway Elem Schl PE Tchr 1968-70; Elmont Meml HS Hlth & PE Tchr 1970-; *ai:* Jr Var Ftbl & Var Lacrosse Coach; NEA 1970-; Nassau Cty Ftbl Coaches Assn 1968-; Nassau Cty Lacrosse Coaches Assn 1969-.

HETTICH, DONNA M., Business Teacher; *b:* Troy, PA; *m:* Robert L.; *c:* Doreen, Renee, Darin, Denise; *ed:* Bloomsburg Univ (BS) Bus Ed 1958; 15 Credit Hrs Elmira Coll; *cr:* Upper Perkiomen HS Bus Tchr 1958-60; Horseheads HS Bus Tchr 1960-62; Canton Area HS Bus Tchr 1971-72; Towanda Area HS Bus Tchr 1972-; *ai:* FBLA Adv 15 Yrs; *home:* 13 Locust Ave Towanda PA 18848

HETTINGER, GILLIAN R., High School English Teacher; *b:* Harrogate, England; *m:* Norman; *c:* Jonathan, Caitlin; *ed:* William Paterson Coll (BA) Honors Eng & Hum 1979; Drew Univ (MA) Eng 1982, (MPhil) Eng 1994; *cr:* William Paterson Coll Adjunct Instr 1979-86; Montclair St Coll Adjunct Instr 1982-85; Pequannock Twp HS Eng Tchr 1986-; *ai:* NHS Adv; NCTE 1986-; Geraldine Dodge Fnd Awd; Garden St Fellowship; NEH Summer Seminar on Victorian Childrens Lit at Princeton; NEH Inst on India at Columbia; *office:* Pequannock Township HS 85 Sunset Rd Pompton Plains NJ 07444

HETTINGER, JOANNE SCHREINER, Kindergarten Teacher; *b:* Allentown, PA; *m:* Alfred K.; *ed:* Kutztown Univ (BS) Elem Ed 1969; Credit Hrs for Permanent Cert; *cr:* WHitehall-Coplay Schl Dist First Grd Tchr 1969-82, Kndgtn Tchr 1982-; *ai:* Instrl Support Team; Strategic Planning Comm; NEA, PSEA 1969-; Whitehall-Coplay Ed Assn 1969-, Fac Rep; PTO, Bd Mem; *office:* C M Gockley Elem Schl 2932 Macarthur Rd Whitehall PA 18052*

HETZLER, PATRICIA ANN, 2nd Grade Teacher; *b:* New Wilmington, PA; *ed:* Westminster Coll (MS) Guidance, Counseling 1970; Youngstown St Univ (BS) Elem Ed, Eng 1968; *cr:* Roosevelt Elem McDonald Tchr 1968-; *ai:* SOS Club; Blat Team; Textbook Selection Comm; Curr Coord; NEA, OEA, MEA 1968-; NEOEA; MEA, Sec 1968-76; Contact Trumbull 1970-; Delta Kappa Gamma 1972-; Animal Welfare; *home:* 1045 North Rd SE Warren OH 44484

HEURING, AMY SPAULDING, English & Speech Teacher; *b:* Oregon, OH; *m:* Paul; *ed:* Univ of Findlay (BA) Theatre, Speech, Eng, Scndry Ed 1984; Univ of Findlay Summerstock 1995; OCTA Miami Univ Theatre Conf 1990; *cr:* Genoa HS Musical Dir 1984; Clay HS Eng, Speech, Theatre Tchr, Drama Dir 1985-; *ai:* Limelighters Drama Club Adv; HS Plays, Musicals Dir; EAgle News Network Adv; AFT 1985-; OH Theatre Alliance 1986-, Scndry Schls Rep; OE Comm Theatre 1987-, Founding Mem; Genoa Civic Theatre 1985-, OCTA Rep; Rosary Cathedral Choir 1995-; Old West End Assn 1991-; OR Comm Theatres Production Dir 1987; OTA Awds; Directed Awd Winning Production Genoa Civic Theatre; *office:* Clay HS 5665 Seaman St Oregon OH 43616

HEUSINGER, EARLE CHARLES,JR., Instrumental Music Director; *b:* Buffalo, NY; *m:* Sylvia Puskarich; *c:* Earle III, Stephanie Lynn; *ed:* Youngstown St Univ (BMED) Music Ed 1975, (MMED) Music Ed 1982; Armor Officeros Basic, Advance; US Army Command, Gen Staff, Bandmasters Qualification; *cr:* Farmington Local Schls K-12th Grd Music Tchr 1975-78; Ashtabula Area City Schls Dir Instrumental Music 1978-; *ai:* Jazz Ensemble; Pep Band; NEA, OEA 1975-; MENC, OMEA 1978-; IAJE 1982-; Phi Mu Alpha 1971-; Ashtabula Orch 1994-; *office:* Harbor HS 221 Lake Ave Ashtabula OH 44004

HEUSSER, JOHN A., Art & Art History Teacher; *b:* Philadelphia, PA; *m:* Beverly Belcher; *c:* Douglas, Erica; *ed:* Temple Univ (BA) Art, Art Ed 1970; Tyler Schl of Art (MED) Art Ed 1974; Addl Post Grad Stud Cmptr Graphics; *cr:* Girard Coll Summer Prgm Instr, Cnslr; Rutgers Univ Adj, Art Ed Tchr; Moorestown Twp Pub Schl Elem Art Tchr 1970-82, MS Art Tchr 1982-83, HS Art Tchr 1983-; *ai:* Art Club Adv; Hnr, Svc Soc; Burr Cty EA, NJ EA, NEA, Moorestown EA 1970-; First United Meth Church 1980-; Perkins Ctr for Arts; Art Ed Dept Awd 1970; Trained Many Stu Tchrs; NJ Governors Tchr Recognition Awd 1989; 25 Yr Recognition Awd; *office:* Moorestown HS 350 Bridgeboro Rd Moorestown NJ 08057*

HEUSSER, ROBERT ERNEST, Biology Teacher; *b:* Derby, CT; *m:* Karen; *c:* Danielle Nicole; *ed:* Kings Coll (BS) Bio 1973; Pittsburg St Univ (MS) Microbiology 1975; *cr:* York Cath HS Bio Tchr 1975-78; Middletown Area HS Bio Tchr 1978-; *ai:* Var Boys Bsktbl Coach; NEA 1983-; PSEA 1983-; *office:* Middletown Area HS 1155 N Union St Middletown PA 17057

HEUSTON, LINDA DUTROW, 2nd Grade Teacher; *b:* Duncansville, PA; *m:* Ronald N.; *c:* Ted, Brad, Wade, Suzann Burk; *ed:* Lock Haven Univ PA (BS) Elem & Early Chldhd 1961; Univ of PA at IN 12 Credit Hrs 1963-64; *cr:* Allegheny #2 1st & 3rd Grd Tchr 1961-63; Blair Twp 1st Grd Tchr 1963-65; Spring Cove Schl Dist Kndgtn, 2nd & 3rd Grd Tchr 1966-; *ai:* Spring Cove Ed Assn 1966-; Roaring Spring Jr Womans 1964-77, VP 1969-70, Pres 1970-71; *office:* East Freedom Elem Schl PO Box 210 East Freedom PA 16637

HEVENER MILLER, SUSAN GENE, German & Spanish Teacher; *b:* Baltimore, MD; *m:* Gregory Michael; *c:* Nathan Daniel, Meghan Susannah; *ed:* Western MD Coll (BA) Ger, Span, Sec Ed 1980; Towson St Univ (MED) Scndry Ed 1984; Credit Hrs MD Dept of Ed; Frgn Lang Proficience Inst Univ of MD; Grad Classes Western MD Coll; *cr:* South Carroll HS Ger & Span Tchr 1980-90, Frgn Lang Dept Chair 1990-; *ai:* Ger Club Adv; Curr & Performance Assessment Comms Pub Schls; Awds Comm Mem; Amer Assn Ger Tchrs 1985-; MD Frgn Lang Assn 1980-; Johnsville United Meth Church Sunday Schl Tchr; Outstdng Young Women of Amer 1983; *office:* South Carroll HS 1300 W Old Liberty Rd Sykesville MD 21784

HEVNER, KATHY ANN, Social Studies Teacher; *b:* York, PA; *ed:* York Coll (BA) Scndry Ed Soc Stud 1981; 42 Grad Credits Masters Equivalency 1991; *cr:* Littlestown HS Soc Stud Tchr 1984-; *ai:* Stu Assistance Team; Awds, Recognition Comm; NEA, PSEA, LEA 1984-; PA Rangers 1994-; *office:* Littlestown HS 200 E Myrtle St Littlestown PA 17340*

HEWETT, SANDRA LEE, Health & PE Instructor; *b:* Wilmington, NC; *ed:* Winston-Salem Univ (BS) Hlth, PE 1968; 18 In-Svc Credits Offered by Schl Dist; *cr:* West Side HS PE Instr 1969; Saint Vincent Acad Hlth, PE Instr 1970-75; Barringer HS Hlth, PE Instr 1975-80; University HS Hlth, PE Instr 1980-; *ai:* Violence & Vandalism, Drug Comms; Schl Core Team; PTSO Activity Schl Beautification; Boys Bsktbl After Schl Tutor; Soc Comm Treas; Big Brother & Big Sister Prgm Coord; Girls Vlybl, Sftbl Coach; Bd of Tchrs-Newark Media Work 1985-87; Essex Cty Tournament Bsktbl Champions 1989; All City Bsktbl, Vlybl Champions 1987; North Jersey Section II Group I Champions 1989.

HEWITT, HENRY CHARLES, Religious Educator Teacher; *b:* Elizabeth, NJ; *m:* Linda Ann Siko; *c:* Henry III, Timothy, Amy (dec), Wendy; *ed:* Univ of Scranton (BA) Philosophy 1972, (MS) Ed 1982; Marywood Coll (MS) Rel Ed 1987; Grad Work in Cnslng; *cr:* St Marys Lang Arts Tchr 1972-73; St Patrick Sci, Lang Arts & Rel Tchr 1973-75; St Paul Math & Rel Tchr 1976-80; Scranton Prep Rel Ed Tchr 1981-; *ai:* Prep Plays Tech Dir; Scranton Prep IM Bowling League; Dept Chm; NCEA 1981-; ASCD 1994-; Compassionate Friends 1981-, Pres; Article Pub; Selected for Symposium on Ignation Ed; Selected as Ignation Ldrshp Seminars Participant; *office:* Scranton Prep Schl 1000 Wyoming Ave Scranton PA 18509*

HEWLETT, JOHN A., Social Studies Teacher; *b:* Woodmere, NY; *m:* Linda Hansel; *c:* Richard M., John A. Jr.; *ed:* Guilford Coll (BA) His 1960; Attnd Hofstra Univ, C. W. Post Coll; *cr:* Nassau Cty Museum Asst Curator 1960-63; Malverne MS Tchr 1963-69; Candlewood MS Tchr 1969-; *ai:* Comm to Establish a MS Co-Chm 1987-89; Malverne Tchrs Assn 1963-69; Half Hollow Hills Tchrs Assn 1969-; AFT 1977-; Three Village Historical Soc 1974-, Lecturer; Numerous Articles Pub; Hofstra Univ, Suffolk Cty Comm Coll, Historical Socs in Nassau & Suffolk Ctys, Schl Dists Classes Lecturer; *office:* Candlewood MS 1200 Carlls Straight Path Dix Hills NY 11746

HEY, SHIRLEY STAHLER (CHILDS), 7th Grade Language Arts Tchr; *b:* Boston, MA; *m:* Allan E.; *c:* Susan Prokop, Carol Tobey, Paula Hovey, Fred Childs; *ed:* Merrimack Coll (BA) Eng 1966; Cambridge Coll (MA) Integrated Stud 1991; *cr:* Schl Dept Eng Tchr 1966-; *ai:* Co-Team Ldr of Grd 7 Purple Team; NCTE 1970-; MA Tchr Assn, Danvers Tchr Assn 1966-; *office:* Dunn MS 62 Cabot Rd Danvers MA 01923

HEYD, SUZANNE H., 11th-12th Grd English Teacher; *b:* Terre Haute, IN; *m:* Daniel P. O'Connor; *ed:* Ithaca Coll (BA) Eng 1988; Columbia Univ (MA) Eng Ed 1990; *cr:* Danbury HS Eng Tchr 1990-; *ai:* Creative Writing Club Adv; NCTE 1990-; NEA, CEA 1991-; Article Pub; Presented at NCTE Conf 1993, CCTE Conf 1994; Research Projects; *office:* Donbury HS 43 Clapboard Ridge Rd Danbury CT 06811

HEYEL, DAVID CRAIG, Athletic Trainer; *b:* Bethesda, MD; *m:* Gabrielle Chinnici-Heyel; *cr:* Delsea Regnl HS Athletic Trainer & Strength Asst Coach 1989-; *ai:* Athletic Trng Prgm Adv; Natl Athletic Trainers Assn 1987-, Cty Rep, Nominations Comm; Natl Strength & Conditioning Assn 1988-; *office:* Delsea Regional HS Friesmill Rd PO Box 405 Franklinville NJ 08318

HEYL, LINDA S., Hum, Speech & English Teacher; *b:* Dayton, OH; *m:* Kenneth; *c:* Nancy; *ed:* OH St Univ (BS) Eng 1965; Ashland Univ Grad Course Work; *cr:* Newcomerstown HS 10th Grd Eng Tchr 1966; Philo HS Eng, Speech & Dramatics Tchr 1966-81; North Cntrl Tech Coll Hum & Eng Tchr 1993-; Hillsdale HS Eng, Speech & Hum Tchr 1986-; *ai:* HEA, OEA, NEA, OCTEALA, NCTE 1966-; Ashland Wayne Cty Arts Adv Cncl; Ashland Cty Ed Fndtn Comm; Hilssdale Acad Cncl Mem; Ashland Symphony Orchestra Spon; Ashland Symphony Women's League; Alpha Delta Kappa Chaplain, Sgt at Arms; Mini Growers Garden Club; Trinity Luth Church Cncl; MS Tchr of Yr 1989.*

HEYLER, MARTIN C., Agri & Industrial Arts Tchr; *b:* Wellsboro, PA; *m:* Joyce Elaine Lehman; *c:* Benjamin, Janna Sue; *ed:* SUNY Alfred St Coll (AAS) Agri Engrng 1977; Univ of GA (BS) Agri Ed 1979; Indstrl Arts Cert Millersville Univ; Grad Courses Agri Penn St Univ; *cr:* Towanda HS Vo-Ag Tchr 1980-81; Penn St Univ Grad Stu-Dev Curr Mat Tchr 1981-82; Penn Manor HS Vo-Ag Tchr 1982-83; Cowanesque Vly HS Vo-Ag, Indstrl Arts Tchr 1983-; *ai:* FFA Adv; St FFA Bd of Dir; St FFA Land Judging Contest Co-Chm 983-; PVATA 1983-, Regnl VP, Outstdng Young Mem; NVATA, NTEA, PSEA, NEA 1983-; Crary Hose Co 1983-, Asst Chief, Rookie of Yr, Fireman or Yr; Cty Extension Bd 1993-; Jemison Vly Church 1995; Tioga Cty Fair, Swine Show Chm; Sabinsville Fireman, Amb 1987-; PA St Young Ag Tchr of Yr Awd 1986; *office:* Cowanesque Valley HS Rt 49 W Westfield PA 16950*

HEYMSFELD, DANIEL, Studies & English Teacher; *b:* New York, NY; *ed:* Bethany Coll (BS) Elem Ed 1971; *cr:* East Side Torah Ctr 5th-8th Grd Tchr 1972-77; Yeshiva Mesivta Tifereth Jerusalem 4th-6th Grd Tchr, HS Soc Stud Tchr 1980-; *office:* Mesivta Tifereth Jerusalem 145 E Broadway New York NY 10002

HEYWOOD, GARY DOUGLAS, High School Math Teacher; *b:* Phila, PA; *m:* Ruthann Boyd; *c:* Lori, Jeffrey, Michael; *ed:* Bloomsburg St Univ (BSEd) Math 1969; Trenton St Univ (MED) Guid 1977; *cr:* Hatboro-Horsham Jr HS 8th Grd Math Tchr 1969-72; Keith Vly MS 8th Grd Math Tchr 1972-73; Hatboro-Horsham HS Algebra I, II, Geometry Tchr 1973-; *ai:* Asst Var Wrestling Coach; IM Vlybl Dir; *office:* Hatboro Horsham Sr HS 899 Horsham Rd Horsham PA 19044

HIBBARD, MAX A.,JR., English Teacher; *b:* Fayette, OH; *m:* Donna Stocker; *c:* Joshua, Aaron; *ed:* Bowling Green St Univ (BS) Ed 1970, (MS) Scndry Ed 1982; 30 Addl Hrs; *cr:* Bradford HS Eng Tchr 1970-74; Gorham-Fayette HS HS & Jr High Eng Tchr 1974-76; Paulding Exempted Village Schls HS & Jr High Eng Tchr 1976-; *ai:* NEA 1970-; OEA 1970-; PEA 1976-; OCTELA 1986-; First Chrstn Church 1985-, Elder & Deacon; Paulding Comm Theater 1987-, Pres & Trustee; Paulding Lions Club 1989-, Pres & VP; *office:* Paulding Exempted Village Schl 405 N Water St Paulding OH 45879

HIBBARD, SUSAN CLAYTON, Biology Teacher; *b:* Trenton, NJ; *m:* Peter C.; *c:* Krista S., Stephen J.; *ed:* Trenton St Coll (BA) Sci Ed 1970; Univ of DE (MS) Bio 1972; *cr:* Allentown HS Sci Tchr 1972-78; St Joseph HS Sci Tchr 1978-82; Ocean Cty Coll Adj Inst 1991-93; Tomes River Regnl Schls Sci Tchr 1982-; *ai:* Jr Class, STEPS Adv; NEA 1972-, Bldg Rep; Ocean Co Citizens for Clean H2O 1984-, Tech Adv; Tr Presbyterian Church 1979-, Choir; Ocean Co Philharmonic Chorus 1988-90; Christa Mc Auliffe Flwshp 1989 for Dev of STEPS Prgm; *office:* Toms River HS South Hyers St Toms River NJ 08753*

HIBBERD, JOSIAH, Retired Social Studies Teacher; *b:* West Chester, PA; *ed:* West Chester Univ (BA) Scndry Elem 1950, (MS) Elem 1973; Attnd Temple Univ; *cr:* Malvern Elem Schl Tchr, Prin 29 Yrs; Sugartown Elem Schl Tchr 1 Yr; Gen Wayne MS Tchr 11 Yrs, Vol 3 Yrs; *ai:* IM Sports Dir; Club Sponsorships; NEA 1952-; PSEA 1952-, VP 1956-60; Sanderson Museum 1970-, Sec; VFW, Amer Legion 1947-; Italian Soc Club 1990-; Freedom Fnd Admins Awd 1975; Two Four Chaplain Awds 1976, 1978; Chrstn Sanderson Awd 1975; Malvern Citizen of Yr 1975; Malvern Bus Assn Pres 1978-80; *home:* 609 W Miner St West Chester PA 19382

HIBBERT, ERROL LEROY, Adjunct Asst Prof & Acad Adv; *b:* Kgm Ja, West Indies; *c:* Edson, Donohue; *ed:* NY Inst of Tech (BFA) Comm Arts 1975; NYU (MA) Comm 1978, (PHD) Comm 1996; Diploma Trng & Cert of Remedial Edctrs Tri St Inst; *cr:* NY Inst of Tech Dir of Spec Prog 1980-91; Bronx Comm Coll Instr 1991-92; Ramapo Coll of NJ Adj Asst Prof, SMR Acad Adv 1992-; *ai:* Caribbean Club Adv; Acad Schlsp, Affirmative Action Comms; AFT 1992-; NADE 1982-; Intl Comm Assn 1990-; Ed Policy Fellow 1989; Ed Policy Minority Flwshp 1989-93; Outstdng Fac Awd Estra Curr 1995; Distngd Svc Awd NYS Ed Dept; *office:* Ramapo Coll Of NJ 505 Ramapo Valley Rd Mahwah NJ 07430

HIBBS, JEAN, First Grade Teacher; *b:* Flushing, NY; *m:* Harry; *c:* Amy Hibbs Wagner, Susan; *ed:* Trenton St Coll (MA) Kndgtn & Primary Ed 1964; *cr:* West Windsor Schl System 1st Grd Tchr 1964-67; East Amwell Schl Supplemental Tchr 1972-77, 1978-81, 1st Grd Tchr 1981-; *ai:* Math Comm; NEA 1964-; NJEA 1964-; East Amwell Tchrs Assn 1981-; PTA 1972-, Voted Lifelong Mem; *office:* East Amwell Twp Elem Schl PO Box A Wertsville Rd Ringoes NJ 08551

HIBBS, LINDA COLANGELO, 6th-8th Grd Math Teacher; *b:* Camden, NJ; *m:* Robert F.; *c:* Erik, Jeffrey; *ed:* Camden Cty Coll (AA) Liberal Arts 1972; Glassboro Coll (BA) Elem Ed 1974; *cr:* Strawbridge Elem 5th Grd Tchr 1974-75; Pennsauken MS Sub Tchr 1982-85; St Francis DeSales 1st-2nd Grd Tchr 1985-93, 6th-8th Grd Math Tchr 1993-; *ai:* Stu Cncl Adv; Math Comm; Oaklyn Midget Ftbl Assoc; Tutoring; CS Tchr; SJ Rndg Cncl; Oaklyn Democrat Club 1995-.

HIBBS, MICHAEL EDWARD, English Teacher; *b:* Washington, DC; *ed:* Univ of MD at College Park (BA) Eng Lit 1985; 3 Credit Hrs in 17th Century Lit at Univ of MD Grad Schl; *cr:* DeMatha HS Eng, Math & Comp Tchr 1985-92; The Bullis Schl Eng Tchr 1992-; *ai:* Var Boys Bsktbl Head Coach; JV Ftbl Asst Coach; Honor Code & Stu Compartment Comms; Tchr of the Yr at Bullis Schl 1993; *office:* Bullis Schl 10601 Falls Rd Potomac MD 20854

HIBBS, TODD WILLIAM, Student Assistance Coordinator; *b:* Steubenville, OH; *m:* Karen Kane; *ed:* Mt Union Coll (BA) Psych, Bio 1989; MI St Univ (MA) Sport Psych 1992; *cr:* Wooster HS Stu Assistance Coord 1992-; *ai:* Coach Boys Cross Cntry, Wrestling, Girls Lacrosse; Citizens Drug Free Yth 1992-, Sec; *office:* Wooster HS 515 Oldman Rd Wooster OH 44691

HIBLER, ALFRED WILLIAM, History Teacher & Dept Chair; *b:* Rabat, Morocco; *m:* Cynthia Jane Murphy; *c:* Sarah, Nate, Tommy; *ed:* Bridgewater St Coll (BA) Geography 1973; Suffolk Univ (MA) Ed; *cr:* Duxbury Pub Schls Soc Stud Tchr 1974-88; Vermont Acad His Tchr 1988-; *ai:* Girls Var Bsktbl; NCSS 1980-; Rotary-Duxbury Chapter, Past Mem; West Duxbury Meth Church, Past Trustee; Tarkiln Comm Ctr, Past Trustee; Little League Coaches 1990-, Treas; Donald T Brodine Awd for Outstanding Tchng; *home:* PO Box 500 Saxtons River VT 05154*

HIBNER, CONSTANCE WOOLSLAYER, English & Study Skills Teacher; *b:* MD; *m:* John; *ed:* Clarion Univ (BS) Elem 1966; Gannon Univ (MED) Ed 1991; Attnd Penn St Univ; *cr:* Warren Cty Schl Dist 3rd Grd Tchr 1966-67; Biloxi Schl Dist 3rd Grd Tchr 1967-68; Warner Robins AFB 6th Grd Tchr 1968-69; Izmir Turkey 6th Grd Tchr 1969-70; Warren Cty Schl Dist 4th-6th, 8th Gifted Tchr 1970-; *ai:* WCEA, PSEA 1966-; *office:* Beaty Warren MS 2 E 3rd Ave Warren PA 16365

HIBSCHWEILER, JANE BARONE, Literature & Lang Arts Tchr; *b:* Tucson, AZ; *m:* Paul; *c:* Ellen, Suzanne, Greta; *ed:* Daemen Coll (BA) Eng 1967; St Univ of NY at Buffalo (MS) Scndry Eng Ed 1970; 12 Hrs Toward Masters of Sci in Schl Admin at Canisius Coll; *cr:* West Seneca Cntrl Schl 7th Grd Eng Tchr 1967-73; Mount Saint Joseph Acad 9th Grd Eng & 12th Grd Advanced Placement Eng Tchr 1986-87; Turner Carroll HS 11th-12th Grd Eng Tchr 1987-89; Mount Saint Joseph Acad 6th-8th Grd Lit & Lang Arts Tchr 1989-; *ai:* Strategic Planning Comm; 8th Grd Class Adv; Newspaper Coord; Visions Comm; NYSEC 1995-, Tchr of Excl 1995; Phi Delta Kappa 1994-; Turner Carroll Rel Educator of Yr 1989; NYS 4th-8th Grd Lang Arts Trainer 1990; *office:* Mt St Joseph Acad 2064 Main St Buffalo NY 14208*

HIBSHMAN, CLINTON BENJAMIN, English Teacher & Coach; *b:* Schaefferstown, PA; *ed:* Kutztown Univ (BSEd) Ed 1993; *cr:* Lebanon HS Eng Tchr 1993-; *ai:* Soccer Coach; NEA 1993-; *office:* Lebanon Sr HS 1000 S 8th St Lebanon PA 17042

HICHBORN, PETER COOPER, Middle School Eng Dept Chair; *b:* Boston, MA; *m:* Mary Bagdasarian; *c:* Michael, Matthew; *ed:* Bucknell Univ (BS) Ec 1968; Salem St Coll (MSD) Tchng & Admin 1972-73; Accredited Tchr of Jr Grant Bks, Instrumental Enrichment an Israeli Dev at Hadassa Univ in Tel Aviv; *cr:* Parker MS Eng Tchr & Dept Chair 1968-88; Coolidge MS Eng Tchr & Dept Chair 1988-; *ai:* Pub Cartoonist & Poet; NCTE 1976-; Town Meeting Mem Elected 1978-86; By Law Comm 1981-86, Chmn Reservation Comm 1983-86; North Andover Schlrshp Fndtn 1982-92; Book: Limitless Learning; *office:* AW Coolidge MS 89 Birch Meadow Dr Reading MA 01867*

HICKERSON, DIANNE, 3rd Grade Teacher; *b:* Rochester, NY; *m:* J. Douglas; *c:* Cherie Cretney Delmerico, Timothy Cretney; *ed:* SUNY at Brockport (BS) Math 1964, (MS) Ed 1969; Aesthetic Ed Inst 10 Yrs Summer Stud, Carry-Over Prgms; *cr:* Brockport Cntrl Schl Tchr 1964-; *ai:* AFT, NEA 1964-; Brockport Tchr Assn 1964-, Comm Chair; Hosp Auxiliary Lakeside Hosp Twig Assn 1965-85, Chair Woman 2 Yrs; *office:* Brockport Cntrl Schl 40 Allen St Brockport NY 14420*

HICKEY, BERNARD JOHN, Sixth Grade Teacher; *b:* Delphos, OH; *m:* Janet Henshow; *c:* Michael, Allyson, Craig, Shannon; *ed:* OH St Univ (BSEd) Eng 1971; Bowling Green St (MED) Admin 1984; 40 Addl Post Grad Hrs in Sci & Math; *cr:* Sacred Heart Schl Tchr 1971-1974; Stamm Elem Schl Tchr 1974-80; Lutz Elem Schl Tchr 1980-1984; Hayes Elem Schl Prin 1984-1986; Stamm Elem Schl Prin 1986-88; Hayes Elem Schl Tchr 1988-; *ai:* Jr Var Soccer Coach; Fremont Ross Core Group Comm; Tech Comm Fremont City Schls; NEA, Ohio Ed Assn, Fremont Ed Assn 1992-; Moose 1992-; Ballville Twp Parks Bd 1994-; Fremont Rec Dept Soccer Bd 1995-, VP; *home:* 2916 Darr Rd Fremont OH 43420

HICKEY, DEBORAH PEENEY, Latin & English Teacher; *b:* Lancaster, PA; *m:* Patrick; *c:* Patrick, Maura, Michael; *ed:* Saint Mary's Coll (BA) Classical Lang 1962; Cert Eng; Rel Ed Inst; *cr:* Turtle Hook Jr HS Latin, Eng Tchr 2 Yrs; Notre Dame HS Latin, Eng Tchr 13 Yrs; *ai:* Sr Class Adv; Stu Assistance Team; Peer Listener Moderator; Amer Classical League; Amer Assn Univ Women; *office:* Notre Dame HS 60 Spangenburg Ave East Stroudsburg PA 18301

HICKEY, JEFFREY CHARLES, Social Studies Teacher; *b:* Bridgeport, CT; *ed:* Sacred Heart Univ (BA) His 1981; Univ of Bridgeport (MA) Schl Cnslng 1992; 24 Credits Schl Psych Prgm Fairfield Univ; *cr:* Bullarhd Havens Schl Soc Stud Tchr 1982-; Bullard Havens HS Scl Cnslr, Summer Prgm 1994-; *ai:* Coach Var Bsbl 1982-85, Asst Bsktbl 1981-85; Ath Dir 1982-84; AFT 1982-; *office:* Bullard-Havens HS 500 Palisade Ave Bridgeport CT 06610

HICKEY, LAUREL GUARINO, Special Education Teacher; *b:* Everett, MA; *m:* Stephen; *ed:* Salem St Coll (BS) Early Child Ed 1973, Boston Univ (MED) Ed 1979; 29 Addl Credits; *cr:* St Anthony's 1, 3 Grd Tchr 1973-75; Evans Schl Resource Tchr 1975-78; Everett HS Resource Tchr 1978-; *ai:* Everett Tchrs Assn 1975-, Former Exec Bd Mem; MA Tchrs Ass Cncl for Exceptional Children 1996-; Revere Beach Assn 199 Everett Schl Bd Golden Apple Awd; Federal Grant Awded for P *home:* 474 Revere Beach Blvd Revere MA 02151*

HICKEY, MARSHA STAZIE, Kindergarten Teacher; *b:* Albion Gerald F.; *c:* Caitlin, Brendan; *ed:* St Univ Coll of NY at Brock His & Elem Ed 1973; St Univ Col of NY at Geneseo (MS) Earl Ed 1977; *cr:* Liverpool Cntrl Schls Kndgtn Tchr 1973-74; Brock Schls Kndgtn Tchr 1974-; *ai:* Elem Report Card Revision Comm Shared Decision Making Comm; AFT & NYSUT 1973-; Brockp Assn 1974-; *office:* Brockport Ginther Schl Allen St Brockport N

HICKEY, MARY ELIZABETH, Jr High Science Teacher; *b:* OH; *ed:* OH Dominican Coll (BS) Bio 1973; Univ of Toledo Tow Drug Alcohol Cnslng; Grad Hrs Univ of SC Methods, Physics Charleston Psych, Admin, Kent St Univ Genetics & Human Project, Heidelberg Coll Methods, Writing; *cr:* Immaculate Co Schl Tchr 1974-78, 1989-90; Beaufort Cty Schl Tchr 1978-87; Elem Schl Tchr 1991-; *ai:* Toledo Diocese Sci Curr Dev, Sci Ldrs Inservice Provider Sci Fair Coord; Tech Comm; Stu Cncl Adv 1974-; NEA 1978-87; St Vincent de Paul Soc 1993-; Amer R 1993-, Instr; Drug, Alcohol Cnslng 1994-, Cnslr; I Can Cope Support Group 1994-; ISEF Finalist Spon; SC Commission or Conservation; Alumax Industry; Sci Promotion Edctr; Sea Islan Tchr of Yr 1982 Nom; Beaufort HS Tchr of Yr 1982; *office:* St Jose Schl 716 Croghan St Fremont OH 43420

HICKEY, SARAH ANN (TORRANCE), English Teacher; *b:* Ind *m:* William J.; *c:* Timothy, Thomas, Brian, Andrew, Michael, Co Clarion St Coll (MS) Lib Sci & Speech 1973; Elmira Coll (MS) Schl Pgm Specialist Cert 1982; Eng Ed Cert 1984; 24 Post Grad *cr:* Sayre Area HS Librn 1973-77, Librn & Speech Tchr 1977-82, Eng Tchr 1983-88, Eng Tchr 1988-; *ai:* Class Play & Christmas P Schl Musical Asst Dir; Forensics Team Coach; Spelling Bee Pron Coach; NEA & PSEA 1973-, St Conv Del; Evening Times Spe Pronouncer 1984-; Delta Kappa Gamma 1993-; Dist Pub Rela 1991-93; Gift of Time Awd 1994; Dist Strategic Planning Com *office:* Sayre Area Jr Sr HS 331 W Lockhart St Sayre PA 18840

HICKEY, WILLIAM LAWRENCE, Social Studies Tea Brooklyn, NY; *m:* Elizabeth A. Sweeney; *c:* Brendan, William; *ed* Univ (BA) His 1965, (MS) Scndry Ed 1968; 90 Grad Credits 1 Newfield HS Soc Stud Tchr 1967-70, Guid Cnslr 1970-72; Cente F Soc Stud Tchr 1972-; *ai:* MC Tchrs Assn, NEA, NCSS 1967-; Order of Hibernians 1975-; Assistantship Grad Level Niagara Uni Centereach HS 14 43rd St Centereach NY 11720

HICKMAN, JODI KAY (WATKINS), Fourth Grade Teacher; *b* OH; *m:* Matt; *c:* Anthony; *ed:* Urbana Univ (BS) Elem Ed Fairlawn Schl 4th Grd Tchr 1992-; *ai:* Reserve Vlybl; 7th & 8th Bsktbl; NEA 1992-; *office:* Fairlawn Local Schls 6838 Palestin Box 24 Pemberton OH 45353*

HICKMAN, SUSAN JANICE, French & Spanish Teacher; *b:* Ith *ed:* Middlebury Coll (BA) Fr 1987; WV Univ (MA) Span 1993; Credit Hrs Span Middlebury Lang Schls; 12 Grad Credit Hrs E Univ; *cr:* Wellsville Cntrl Schl HS Fr, Span Tchr 1987-92; WV U Tchng Asst, Fr & Span Tchr 1992-93; Marcus Whitman Cntrl Sc & Span Tchr 1994-; *ai:* NYSAFLT 1987-; WAFFLE 1995-, V Marcus Whitman Cntrl Schl Dist Baldwin Rd Rushville NY 1454

HICKS, DARLA JEAN, Fifth Grade Teacher; *b:* Garrett, Randolph; *c:* Jessica Lynn, L. Rondel; *ed:* OH St Univ (BA) Elem Credit Hrs Bowling Green St Univ, Asland Univ; *cr:* Ridgedale E Tchr 1977-; *ai:* Chprsn PPR Comm Morral U M Church; RTA 19 Rep; OEA, NEA 1977-; Pythian Sisters 1972-, EC Dist Deputy Ridgedale Elem Schl 3105 Hillman Ford Rd Morral OH 43337

HICKS, JANE FRANCAVILLA, Title I Coordinator & Teacher York City, NY; *c:* Keri Lynn, Stephen, Ryan; *ed:* St Bonaventure U Math 1969; NY Univ (MS) Operations Research 1971; City Co (MED) Math Ed 1992; *cr:* Floyd C. Fretz JHS Math Tchr 1968 Rochelle HS Math Tchr 1971-74; Isaac E. Young JHS Math Tchr Sacred Heart Schl Math, Cmptr Tchr 1983-89; Clarkstown HS No Title I Tchr, Coord 1989-; *ai:* Fac Adv Math League, Peer M ADD-ADHD Dist Comm; NCTM; NYSACE, ASCD 1993-; Roc Assn for Hearing Impaired 1986-; *office:* Clarkstown HS N Congers Rd New City NY 10956

HICKS, LOUIS, Sociology Professor; *b:* Port Arthur, TX; *m:* Pa Howard; *ed:* Univ of MD (BA) Soc Stud 1989, (BS) Mngmt St (MA) Sociology 1991, (PHD) Sociology 1994; *cr:* St Mary's Co Asst Prof of Sociology 1993-; *ai:* AAUP; Amer Sociologic IUSAFS; Book Pub Systems of War and Peace; *office:* Saint Mary MD St Marys Cy MD 20686

HICKS, NORMAN W., 6th Grade Science Teacher; *b:* Middlet *m:* Charlene; *c:* Meredith; *ed:* Eastern CT St Coll (BS) Ed, Sci 19 CT St Coll (MS) Ed 1977; Southern CT St Univ 6th Yr Scndry Sci CT Coll Physics Inst in Residence; *cr:* East Hampton Schls Tchr WLIS-AM Radio Talk Show Host 1992; Guilford Schls Tchr 1 Staff Dev; Stu Cncl; Curr Comm; Assn Rep; Guilford Ed Assoc 1 NSTA; Comm Assoc of Brands of Ed 1996; Durham Ag Fair Ass Treas, Exec Comm; Regnl Schl Dist 13 Bd of Ed 1996; Guilford C 1976-, Bd of Dir; Durham Zoning Bd of Appeals 1984-, Vi Magazine Consultant; Inst for Sci Instructive Stud Southern CT Nominee Presidential Awd for Ex Sci & Math; Flwshp Chm As Fairs Schlsp Comm; Chm Durham Ag Fair Schlsp Comm; *office:* Baldwin MS 69 Bullard Dr Guilford CT 06437

HICKS, PAULINE E., Social Studies Teacher; *b:* Newport, RI; J. Jr.; *c:* Peter J. III; *ed:* Bristol Comm Coll (AA) Lbrl Arts 1971 MA at Dartmouth (BA) His 1973; Bridgewater St Coll 18 Addl Cr *cr:* Somerset HS Soc Stud Tchr 1975-86; Thorton Central Schl Tchr 1991-; *ai:* 8th Grd Class Adv; 1-4 Grd After Schl Act Co-Co 1976-; NH Tchrs Assn 1991-, Treas; Thornton Tchrs Assn 1991 1995; *office:* Thornton Cntrl Schl RR 1 Box 275 Campton NH 03

HICKS, REGINA ALESI, English & Journalism Teacher; *b:* Hur PA; *m:* Larry B.; *c:* Kelli Hicks Scalia, Aaron, Ashley; *ed:* Ship Univ (BS) Eng, Lib Sci 1964; Masters Degree Prgm; *cr:* Huntingdon Cty HS Enrichment Classes Tchr 1964-; *ai:* Eng De Speech League, Press Club, Yrbk, Sr Class Adv; NEA; PSEA PAGE; Hosp, Fire Company Auxiliary; Zi Zeta Omicron, Pres, Se Epsilon; Poetry Pub; Amer Legion Svc Awd Essay Competition; Democracy Svd Awd Oratorical Contest; *office:* Southern Huntin HS RR 1 Box 1124 Three Springs PA 17264*

HICSWA, KATHLEEN DONNA (HROBAK), Biology Tea Passaic, NJ; *m:* Ronald D.; *c:* Kevin, Kerri; *ed:* Fairleigh Dickinso Bio Ed 1968, (MAS) Bio 1972; Univ of Bridgeport Cnslng; *cr:* H Heights Jr-Sr HS Tchr 1970-; *ai:* Stu Cncl, Key Club, Jr Class Ad NJEA, BCEA 1970-; NJ Sci Tchr Assn 1977-; Fair Lawn HS P FLHS Parents for Ath 1995-; FLHS Soccer Parents Assn 1992- Tchr of Yr in NJ Governors Tchr Recognition Prgm; Key Club Citation; *office:* Hasbrouck Heights Jr Sr HS 365 Boulevard H Heights NJ 07604*

AN, MICHELLE LAYNE (MONTAGUE), Fourth Grade
b: Massillon, OH; m: David; c: Shawn, Tad; ed: Kent St Univ
ı Ed 1969; cr: Allen East Schls Fourth Grd Tchr 1969-78; Elida
ls Fourth Grd Tchr 1978-; ai: PTO; Bsktbl Mothers Pres; Post
s; NEA, OEA, EEA 1969-; OH Arts, Crafts Guild 1977-; home:
mingbird St Elida OH 45807

OHN STEPHEN, Eleventh Grade English Teacher; b:
n, NJ; m: Katherine Jambor-Hier; ed: William Paterson Coll of
Eng 1989, (MA) Eng 1991; cr: Passaic Cty Comm Coll Adj Prof
-93; Clifton HS Eng Tchr 1993-; ai: End Racism & Sexism
re, Cooperative Alternatives Learned from Mediation Adv;
fton H S 333 Colfax Ave Clifton NJ 07013

YNN DELBIANCO, Mathematics Teacher; b: Proctor, VT; m:
c: Evan; ed: Univ of VT (BS) Ed 1977; 6 Credit Hrs Univ of VT;
Hrs Lesley Coll; 6 Credit Hrs Johnson Coll; 3 Credit Hrs St
cr: Otter Vly Union High Math Tchr 1977-78; Mt Saint Joseph
h Tchr 1978-81; Colchester High Math Tchr 1981-; ai: Var Sftbl
u Cncl & Soph Class Adv; Block Scheduling Comm; VTNEA
Cncl of Tchrs of Math 1981-; VT Sftbl Coaches Assn 1986-;
l of Fame Comm 1995-; CHS Tchr of the Yr 1995; Metro League
h of the Yr (6 Times); office: Colchester HS Laker Ln Colchester

S, ALICE FISHER, Ret 6th Grd Sci & Rdng Tchr; b: Sunbury,
omas J.; c: Cheryl Dorman, Tammy Meckley; ed: Bloomsburg St
ll (BS) Elem Ed 1955; Cert Credits; Prof Dev Wkshps; cr:
ort Cochran Schl 2nd Grd Tchr 1955-56; Millersburg Area Schls
chr 1956-58; Millersburg MS 6th Grd Sci & Rdng Tchr 1964-95;
ncl Adv; Curr Guideline & Long Range Planning Comms;
rg Ed Assn 1964-, Pres 1969-70 & Sec 1976; PA St Ed Assn &
4-; St Pauls Luth Church 1960-, Cncl Pres 1985-86 & 1993;
ng Elem Tchrs of America 1975.

S, DEANNA J. FRANK, English Teacher; b: Vineland, NJ; m:
.; ed: Rutgers Univ (BA) Eng 1990; Rowan Coll (MA) Stud
Svcs, Stud Personnel Svcs Cert 1995; ai: Class Adv; Delsea Ed
Atheneum League Adv; NEA, NJEA 1990-; NCTE 1991-; office:
gional HS Blackwoodtown Rd Franklinville NJ 08322*

S, EUGENE THOMAS, Social Studies Teacher; b: New York
m: Jean Perrillo; c: Jessica, Lauren, James; ed: C. W. Post Coll
ry Ed 1982, (MS) Cmptr Ed 1987; 30 Addl Inservice, Grad Credit
Maria Regina DHS Soc Stud Tchr 1983-84; Sachem South HS Soc
r 1984-; ai: JV Boys Vlybl, 9th Grd Boys Bsktbl, JV Boys
9th Grd Boys LaCrosse Coach; NCAA Coll Ftbl, Suffolk Cty HS
SCTA 1984-; ECAC, ECFOA, NASO 1995-; SCFOA 1989-;
chem HS South 245 Union Ave Holbrook NY 11741

S, JANE EDGINGTON, Art Teacher; b: London, England; m:
c: Devon; ed: Framingham St Coll (BA) Art Ed 1977; MA Coll
MSAE) Art Ed 1996; cr: Danforth Museum of Art Registrar
Lashaway Jr HS Art Tchr 1986-87; David Prouty HS Art Tchr
Newspaper Adv; NAEA 1987-; MAEA 1987-; office: David
302 Main St Spencer MA 01562

S, MARY MCFADDEN, Eighth Grade Teacher; b: Philadelphia,
homas J.; c: Thomas, Barbara, Kathleen, Maureen, Patrick,
Sheila; ed: Gwynedd Mercy Coll (BS) Elem Ed 1980; St Joseph
edits Permanent Cert; cr: Saint Callistos 4th Grd Tchr 1964-66;
BVM 3rd Grd Tchr 1966-72; Saint Laurence 8th Grd Tchr 1976-;
Coord; Marketing Mem Chm; After Schl Care Founder;
nia Archdiocesan Marketing Team; NCEA 1980-; Homework Clb
office: Saint Laurence Schl 8245 W Chester Pike Upper Darby

S, MATTHEW KEITH, Algebra Teacher; b: Clinton, IA; m: Erin
ks; c: Brianna Marie; ed: Mount Saint Clare Coll (AA) Math
not St Univ (BS) Math Ed 1987; 6 Hrs Sinclair Comm Coll; 12
r Univ; cr: Berry Jr HS Math Lab, Cmptr Sci Tchr 1987-89, 7th
Tchr 1989-90; Lebanon HS Math Tchr 1990-; ai: Var Asst Ftbl,
ys Bsktbl Coach; Sr Career Ed Adv; Mu Sigma Eta 1984-, Sci,
; Phi Theta Kappa 1984-; NEA 1987-; United Ed Prof 1992-;
banon HS 25 Oakwood Ave Lebanon OH 45036

S, PAMELA K., Elementary Principal; b: Sidney, OH; ed:
Green St Univ (BS) Ed 1975; Wright St Univ (MA) Admin 1981;
te Hill Schl 4th Grd Tchr 1975-78; Bridgeview Schl 6th Grd Tchr
Northwood Schl 6th Grd Tchr 1980-93; Bridgeview MS Asst Prin
Parkwood Elem Prin 1995-; ai: Asst Prin; Delta Kappa Gamma
RVW 1993-; OERSA 1995-; Sidney-Shelby Cty Yth Svcs Bd
MCA Bd 1996; OCEE Tchrs in Amer Enterprise Awd Winner
Sidney City Schls Tchr of Yr 1987-88; office: Parkwood Elem 315
Rd Sidney OH 45365

S, SUE NUNNALLY, Asst Prof of Cmptr Stud & Info; b: Little
; w: Joe (dec); c: Michael, Donald; ed: Univ of AR (BS) General
; Univ of RI (MS) Bus Ed 1981; Assoc Cmptr Prof Cert Inst for
mptr Prof; 10 Credits Toward MBA; cr: Comm Coll of RI Asst
-; ai: Curr, Judicial, Fac Dev, Acad Advy Comms; Stu Mentor
EA 1975-; Phi Kappa Phi; Delta Pi Epsilon; Gamma Delta
office: Community Coll of Rhode Island 400 East Ave Warwick

S, TERRY H., 8th Grd Lang Arts & Rdng Tchr; b: Sidney, OH;
Matthews; c: Angela, Elizabeth King, Christopher, Emily King,
OH Northern Univ (BA) Eng 1970; Wright St Univ (MED) Curr,
on 1975; Bowling Green St Univ (PHD) Educl Admin 1983; cr:
r Local Schls 8th-9th Grd Eng Tchr 1970-76; Paulding Cty Schls
976-79; Montpelier Ex Vill Schls Asst Supt, Math Tchr 1979-82;
Heights Local Schls Supt 1982-85; Southwest Licking Local Schls
-92, 8th Grd LA, Rdng Tchr 1992-; ai: Dist Insurance Comm;
A, SWLEA 1992-; BASA 1982-; Lions Club 1985-; Etna Twp
994-, VP; office: Watkins MS 8808 Watkins Rd SW Pataskala OH

S, THOMAS DANIEL, Religion Department Chairman; b:
NJ; ed: St Peter Coll (BS) Eng 1966; St John Seminary (MDIV)
1985; Fairfield Univ Ed Admin; NY Univ Eng Lit; cr: Holy
chl Tchr, Asst Prin 1969-76; Christopher Columbus HS Asst Prin,
Stud 1976-77; St Jean Baptiste HS Chm Rel Dept 1986-; ai:
86-; NSF Grant 1972; office: St Jean Baptiste HS 173 E 75th St
NY 10021

S, WILLIAM JOSEPH, Associate Professor of Zoology; b:
d, OH; ed: Boston Coll (BS) Bio 1969; FL St Univ (PHD)
gy 1973; cr: Univ of MD Asst Prof Zoology 1973-78, Acting Asst
dergraduate Stud 1982-85, 1986-87 Assoc Prof Zoology 1979-,
an Coll of Life Scis 1989-; ai: 18 Grant, 12 Fac Dev Wkshps on
oftware; Kappa Delta Adv; Human Anatomy & Physiology Soc
; Amer Assoc for Advancement of Sci 1995-; Metropolitan Bsbl
Assn 1985-; Coll Park Boys & Girls Club 1984-, Coord Sports
Extramural Awd to Support Ed; 8 Excel Tchng Awds; Major Adv,
air for 10 PHD, 18 MS, 7 Undergraduate Hrs, Individual Stud
ffice: Univ Of MD 1212 Symons Hall College Park MD 20742

SON, GEORGE G., Honors English Teacher; b: New York, NY;
arie Burnham; c: Sarah Beth, Tyler; ed: SUNY at New Paltz (BA) Lit 1965; SUNY at Stony Brook (MA) Lbrl Stud 1972; SUNY at Farmingdale (AA) Math 1980; 75 Grad Credits Coll of St Rose, Hofstra Univ, Queens Coll, C. W. Post Coll; PHD Candidate Univ of Sarasota; cr: Hicksville HS Eng, Hum, Math Tchr 1965-; ai: Conflict Mediation Coord; NCTE, NEA 1965-; NY St Hum Cncl 1969-70; office: Hicksville HS Division Ave Hicksville NY 11801*

HIGH, EDWARD WILLIAM, Biology Teacher; b: Williamsport, PA; m: Kim; c: Eric E., Jennifer L. Sheffer, Erin E., Jordan S. Sheffer, Zachary Ellis; ed: Juniata Coll (BS) Bio 1969; Scndry Tchng Cert Lycoming Coll 1970; cr: Mc Call MS Bio Tchr 1970-; ai: PSEA, NEA 1970-.

HIGH, STEPHEN J., Business Marketing Mgmt Instr; b: Waterloo, NY; m: Wanda Fisher; c: Jennifer; ed: Auburn Comm Coll (AAS) Bus Admin 1969; Northern MI Univ (BS) Scndry Ed & Bus 1971; Post Grad Work at SUNY Geneseo, Cornell Univ, Nazareth Coll, Buffalo St Univ; cr: Wayne Finger Lakes BOCES Bus Mrktg Instr & DECA Adv 1971-; Finger Lakes Comm Coll Adj Advertising Instr 1980-85; ai: Bus Skills Cooperative; WFL Tchrs Assn 1971-, V P; DECA NY 1973-, VP & Spcl Adv, Outstdng Svc Honorary Life; T&C Plaza Merchants Assn 1991-; Geneva Chamber of Com 1991-; office: Finger Lakes Area Voc Ctr 3501 County Road 20 Stanley NY 14561*

HIGHFIELD, HARLAN EDWARD,JR., Social Studies Teacher; b: Wilmington, DE; ed: Univ of DE (BA) Soc Sci Ed 1968; cr: Thomas McKean HS Soc Stud Tchr 1968-69; US Navy Active Duty 1969-71; Thomas McKean HS Soc Stud Tchr 1971-86; Henry C. Conrad MS Soc Stud Tchr 1986-87; Thomas McKean HS Soc Stud Tchr 1987-; ai: Head Soccer, Bsbl Coaches; Annual Schl Play Author, Dir; Audio Visual Coord; DE HS Soccer Coaches Assn 1986-; DE HS Bsbl Coaches Assn 1979-; Red Clay Consolidated Schl Dist Tchr of Yr Finalist; Presidential Scholars Prgm Distinguished Tchr 1985, 1993; DE Soccer Coach of Yr 1990, 1993; Blue Hen Conf Bsbl Coach of Yr 1984, 1986, 1988, 1989, Soccer Coach of Yr 1992-94; office: Thomas McKean HS 301 McKennans Church Rd Wilmington DE 19808

HIGNEY, CHRISTINA MOULSON, High School English Teacher; b: Ware, MA; m: Wayne R.; c: Robert, Lauren; ed: Westfield St Coll (BA) Fr, Eng, Ed 1973; Addl 45 Credits Eng-Rdng Cert; UMASS-Amherst Fellowship Process Writing; cr: Ware HS Fr Tchr 1973-74, Eng Tchr 1973-; ai: Lit Magazine Adv; Steering Comm for St Evaluation Co-Chair; Fac Advy Comm; Planning Bd for Coalition of Essential Schls Investigation; NCTE 1973-; WTA; MT Assn; office: Ware HS 237 West St Ware MA 01082

HIKIDA, ROBERT SEIICHI, Prof of Biological Sciences; b: Long Beach, CA; m: Geraldine Karen Oki; c: Stephen Michael; ed: Univ of IL (BS) Zoology 1963, (MS) Dev Bio 1965, (PHD) Cell Bio 1967; Post-Doctoral Research at Columbia Univ Dept Biological Scis; cr: OH Univ Asst Zoology Asst Prof 1969-73; Columbia Univ Bio Visiting Prof 1971; OH Univ Zoology Assoc Prof 1973-77, Prof of Bio & Vice Chm 1977-; OH Univ Coll Osteopath Med Prof of Microanatomy 1991-; ai: Planned Parenthood of SE OH Fund-Raising Act; Help Run Local Rd Races; Amer Soc of Zoologists 1966-; Amer Soc Cell Bio 1972-; Amer Assn of Anatomists 1971-; Athens Band Boosters 1982-86; 120 Publications & Presentations; Research Grants from Pub Hlth Svc & Natl Sci Fnd; Coll of Arts & Scis Jeanette G Grasselli Fac Tchng Awd; OH Univ Outstanding Grad Fac Awd; Coll of Osteopathic Med Outstanding Fac Awds 1992-95; office: OH Univ Dept Biologiacal Stud Athens OH 45701

HILBERT, JEAN ANN BROWN, 5th Grade Teacher; b: Lancaster, OH; m: Larry L.; c: Jennifer, Courtney; ed: OH St Univ (BS) Elem Ed 1966; Univ Dayton (MS) Education 1994; Specliazation Rdng Univ of Dayton; cr: Columbus Pub 1st-2nd Split Tchr 1966-70; groveport Madison Schls 1st-5th Grd Tchr 1977-; ai: HS Reserve Girls Tennis Coach; Stu Cncl Adv; Elem PTO Tchr Liason; Back to Schl Co-Chprsn Dist Wide; GMLEA Exec Bd; GMLEA 1977-, Back to Schl BR; NEA 1966-70 & 1977-; OEA 1966-70 & 1977-; Groveport United Meth Church 1957-, Trustee, Soc Concerns & Ed Chprsn, Sunday Schl Supt, Bible Schl Coord & SS Tchr Choir; Groveport Village Cncl 1994-1995; Honory Mention Ashland Oil 1989; home: 814 Main St Groveport OH 43125*

HILBORN, JENNIFER LYNN, English Teacher; b: Pittsburgh, PA; ed: Bucknell Univ (BA) Eng 1989; Univ of MD (MED) Schl Counseling 1991; cr: Cranford HS Eng Tchr 1993-; ai: Yrbk Production Adv; Publicity Comm; NEA, NJEA, NCTE 1993-, Mem; JEA 1995-, Mem; Cranford Dramatic Club 1992-, Bd of Governors; office: Cranford HS West End Pl Cranford NJ 07016*

HILBORN, L. RICK, Band Director & Music Teacher; b: Allentown, PA; m: Carol A. Werkheiser; c: Lauren A., Crione C.; ed: West Chester Univ (BS) Music Ed 1984; (MM) Percussion Performance 1990; cr: Dieruff HS Band Dir, Music Tchr 1984-88; Whitehall HS Band Dir, Music Tchr 1988-; ai: Direct Marching Band, Wind, Jazz Percussion Ensembles, Pit Orch; MENC, PA Music Edctrs Assoc, NEA 1984-; Natl Band Assoc 1988-; Percussion Ensemble Selected to Perform at PA Music Edctrs Assoc St Conf Twice, MENC Eastern Regnl & Natl; office: Whitehall HS 3800 Mechanicsville Rd Whitehall PA 18052*

HILBUN, JAMES ROBERT, Language Arts Tutor; b: Knoxville, TN; m: Linda; c: Robert, Mark; ed: Youngstown St Univ (BSEd) Eng 1960; Saint Francis at Fort Wayne IN (MS) Guidance & Counseling 1971; cr: McDonald HS Tchr & Coach 1960-65; Crestview HS Tchr & Coach 1965-67; Republic HS Tchr & Coach 1967-68; Lima Shawnee HS Tchr & Coach 1968-70; Lakeview HS Tchr & Coach 1970-74; Southington HS Tchr & Coach 1974-91; Howland Chrstn Tchr & Coach 1991-; ai: Southington Ed Assn 1974-, Pres 2 Yrs; OH Ed Assn 1960-; home: 133 N Colonial Dr Cortland OH 44410

HILD, ELIZABETH MC MILLAN, Second Grade Teacher; b: Auburn, NY; m: Arthur R.; c: Steven A.; ed: Auburn Comm Coll (AA) Lbrl Arts 1966; SUNY At Brockport (BS) Elem Ed 1969; Permanent Cert N-6 Grds 1973; 60 Post Grad Credit Hrs Elem Ed; cr: Jefferson Ave Elem Schl 2-5 Grd Tchr 1969-; ai: Mem Shared Decision Making Team; SOS Hlth & Safety Comm; CORE Drug, Alcohol Prevention Comm; NYSUT, AFT 1969-; home: 5 Fresh Meadow Run Penfield NY 14526

HILDEBRAND, DALE A., Instrumental Music Teacher; b: Elyria, OH; m: Jane O.; c: Jeremy, Janet, Joely; cr: St Bernadette Schl Band Dir 1980-82; Avon HS Band Dir 1982-88; Kenmore HS Instrumental Music Tchr 1988-91; Brookside HS Instrumental Music Tchr 1991-; ai: OH Music Ed Assn, NEA 1980-; BSA, Cubmaster, Asst Cubmaster; First United Meth Church, Orch Dir; Edctr of Yr 1994; office: Brookside HS 1812 Harris Rd Sheffield Lake OH 44054

HILDEBRAND, JOHN CARROLL, German & Latin Teacher; b: Arlington, VA; m: Elisabeth Sandifer; c: James Alexander, Sarah; ed: PA St Univ (BA) Ger 1977; Addl 50 Credit Hrs Ger, Latin, Classics; Second Cert in Latin; cr: Park Forest Jr HS Ger Tchr 1979-81; Bellefonte Area HS ger, Latin Tchr 1982-; ai: AATG 1980-; Sping Semester Sabbatical in Europe 1995; office: Bellefonte Area HS 830 E Bishop St Bellefonte PA 16823

HILDEBRAND, LLOYD BURTON, English Lecturer; b: Charleston, WV; m: Margaret Ann Conway; c: Paul, David, Mark, Timothy, Jeffrey; ed: Glassboro St Coll (BA) Ed 1968; James Madison Univ (MS) Ed 1974; Grad Stud Eng; cr: Park Jr HS Eng Tchr 1968-70; Montevideo HS Eng Tchr 1972-74; Mary Baldwin Coll Asst Dir, Career & Personal Counseling Ctr 1974-76; Logos, Bridge & Victor Pubs Edit, Writer 1977-; Marywood Coll Eng Tchr, Lecturer; ai: Oxford Twp Bd of Ed 1980-87, VP; Articles, Books Pub; home: 126 Maple Ave Clarks Summit PA 18411

HILDING, REBECCA GUTH, Coordinator of Career Services; b: Philadelphia, PA; m: Mark Stephen; c: Chelsea, Jake; ed: Bloomsburg St Coll (MS) Deaf Ed 1977; Flwshp Parent Infant Trng; Univ of DE 15 Credits, Keane St Coll 6 Credits, CAES Ed Admin; Intrepreter Trng 21 Hrs; cr: Intermediate Units 21 & 25 Tchr, Therapist 1977-80; NY St Schl for Deaf Pre-Primary Tchr 1980-81; DE Schl for Deaf MS, HS Tchr 1981-89; Austine Schl for Deaf Prin, Coord Career Svcs 1989-; ai: Prsnl Policies, Educl Policies, Evaluation Comms; CEC 1994-; Battleboro Chamber of Commerce 1994-, Ed Comm; Alliance Lifelong Learning 1995-; Madyar Muzika 1990-; US Dept Ed Grant; Supported Employment Prgm Individuals Severe Disabilities; office: Austine Schl For The Deaf 120 Maple St Brattleboro VT 05301*

HILDRETH, SANDRA JEAN, Jr-Sr High School Art Tchr; b: Milwaukee, WI; c: Jennifer, David; ed: Western Ky Univ (BFA) Fine Arts Painting & Tchr Cert 1969; Grad Work Pratt Inst; St Univ of NY at Potsdam 60 Hrs; cr: DuPont Manual Jr-Sr HS 7-8th Grd Art Tchr 1969-70; Franklin Cty BOCES K-12th Grd Art Tchr 1971-72; Madrid-Wadding Cntrl Schl 7-12th Grd Art Tchr 1972-; St Lawrence Univ Art Methods Instr 1990-; ai: AFT, Madrid-Waddington Tchrs Assn 1972-; Christa McAuliffe Fellowship 1988; Reynolds Metals Excl in Ed Grants 1990-91, 1993, 1995; Sony, THE Journal Multimedia in Ed Awd 1993; Exhibit Art Work in Juried Natl Exhibitions 1980-; St Lawrence Valley Chapter Phi Delta Kappa Tchr of Yr 1994; office: Madrid Waddington Central Sch PO Box 67 Madrid NY 13660

HILEMAN, LINDA L., 4th Grade Teacher; b: New Castle, PA; m: Douglas L.; c: Courtney, Shannon, Cody; ed: IN Univ of PA (BS) Elem 1968; Slippery Rock (MS) Elem; cr: New Castle Schl Dist 2nd & 4th Grd Tchr 1968-69; Highlands Schl Dist 2nd Grd Tchr 1970-78; Freeport Schl Dist 4th & 6th Grd Tchr 1991-; ai: FEA 1993-; NEA 1993-; PSEA 1993-; office: Buffalo Elem Schl 500 Sarver Rd Sarver PA 16055

HILEMAN, ROBERT L.,JR., Math Teacher; b: Philadelphia, PA; m: Anne Murry; ed: East Stroudsburg St Coll (BS) Math Ed 1976; Trenton St Coll (MED) Math Ed 1980; cr: Father Judge HS Math Tchr 1976-78; Bishop Egan HS Math Tchr 1978-81; North Cath HS Math Tchr 1981-85; Bishop Egan HS Math Dept Chprsn 1985-93; Conwell-Egan HS Math Tchr 1993-; ai: Head Cross Cntry, Indoor Track, Asst Outdoor Track Coach; Explorers, Outdoors Clubs Adv; NCEA 1976-; NCTM 1988-; Natl Fed Interscholastic Coaches Assn 1989-; PA Tchrs Induction Plan 1990-; ASCD 1984-; NSF Presidential Sci, Math Tchng Excl Awd Nom; Cty Cross Cntry Coach of Yr 1986; office: Conwell-Egan HS 611 Wistar Rd Fairless Hills PA 19030

HILES, HELEN ADELE, 6th Grade Reading Teacher; b: Darby, PA; m: Fredrick Peter; c: John; ed: West Chester Univ (BS) Early Chldhd 1983, (MED) Rdng, Elem 1986; PA St Univ Studying Prin Cert; cr: Salem Schl Dist 2nd Grd Tchr 1987-88; Spring-Ford Schl Dist 5th Grd Tchr 1988-94, 6th Grd Rdng Tchr 1994-; ai: Stu Assistance Prgm Team; Hlth, Rdng, Writing, Communication Comms; Phi Delta Kappa 1983-, Chptr Schlsp; Kappa Delta Pi 1985-; Who's Who Among Stdnts Amer Univ & Coll 1986-87; home: 539 Pickering Station Dr Chester Springs PA 19425*

HILGENDORF, MARK STEVEN, High School History Teacher; b: Milwaukee, WI; m: Cynthia; c: William, Kirsten; ed: Univ of WI (BA) Philosophy 1970; Northwestern (MA) His 1974; Duke Univ (PHD) His 1982; 24 Hrs Harvard Univ Divinity Schl; cr: Univ Schl His Tchr 1974-77; Duke Univ Grad Asst 1977-79; Cincinnati Cntry Day Schl His Tchr 1979-82; Milton Acad His Tchr 1982-; ai: Black Stu Union Adv; OAH 1982-; Woodrow Wilson Fellowship 1989; Duke Fellowship 1981; office: Milton Acad 170 Centre St Milton MA 02186*

HILIN, MARLENE N., Math Teacher; b: Erie, PA; m: Edward P.; c: Amy M., Lori M.; ed: Villa Maria Coll (BS) Ed 1964; Lake Erie Coll (MS) Ed 1982; Grad Work Kent St Univ; cr: Erie Diocesan Schls Tchr 2 Yrs; Millcreek Twp Schls Tchr 2 Yrs; Painesville & Ashtabula Schls Tchr 18 Yrs; Ashtabula Area City Schls Cmptr Coord 4 Yrs; Kent St Univ Tchr 3 Yrs; Lake Erie Coll Tchr 3 Yrs; ai: AATA 1978-, Newsletter; OEA, NEA, OCTM 1978-; Several Grants; Co-Authored Textbook; Twice Presenter at OH St Dept of EdConfs; Natl Awd for Ec in Ed; home: 7340 Scenic Dr Ashtabula OH 44004

HILKER, DIANE NURKO, Assistant Professor of Biology; b: Princeton, NJ; m: Donald A.; ed: Rutger-Cook Coll (BS) Bio Chem 1978; Jersey Shore Med Ctr (MT) Med Tech 1978; Seton Hall Univ (MS) Bio 1982; cr: Carter-Wallace, Wampole Labs Tech Affairs Mgr 1979-85; Mercer Cty Coll Asst Prof 1989-; ai: Co-Adv Phi Theta Kappa; Div Prsnl, Acad Stans Comm; ASCP 1978-; ASM 1980-; NJEA 1989-; Boy Scouts 1993-; Millstone Twps Women's Org 1991-; office: Mercer County Comm Coll PO Box B Trenton NJ 08691

HILL, AURA M., English & Journalism Teacher; b: E. Stroudsburg, PA; m: Leonard I. Jr.; ed: East Stroudsburg Univ (BS) Ed 1971; Univ of DE (MA) Theatre Arts 1975; Comm, Jrnlsm Shippensburg Univ; Ed Allentown Coll, Wilkes Coll; Elizabethtown Coll; cr: Warren Hills Reg HS Eng Tchr 1971; Milford HS Eng, Drama Tchr 1971-75; Palmyra HS Eng, Jrnlsm Tchr 1975-; ai: Yrbk, Newspaper Adv; Mentor Prgm; Middlestates, Strategic Planning Steering Comms; PSEA, NEA 1975-; PA Schl Press Assn 1985-, Bd Mem; Scholastic Writing Awds 1987-, Sec, VP; Lebanon Cty Educl Hnr Soc 1985-; Delta Kappa gamma 1987-; PSEA Grant; office: Palmyra HS 1125 Park Dr Palmyra PA 17078*

HILL, BRIAN, Biology & Chemistry Teacher; b: Peekskill, NY; m: Maureen Kingsley; ed: St Univ of NY at Albany (BS) Bio 1970; Western CT St Univ (MS) Sci Ed 1976; 60 Addl Credits beyond MS; cr: Carmel HS Bio, Chem Tchr 1970-; office: Carmel HS 30 Fair St Carmel NY 10512

HILL, CHARLOTTE JOZWIAK, Spcl Ed Inclusion Teacher; b: Fairpoint, OH; m: Charles Gary; ed: OH Univ (BS) Elem Ed 1974. (ME) Spec Ed, Learning Disabilities 1980; cr: St Mary's Cntrl Schl Second Grd Tchr 1974-79; St Clairsville MS Seventh-Eight Grd Learning Disabilites Tchr 1980-84, Fifth-Sixth Grd Learning Disabilities Tchr 1984-94, Sixth Grd Inclusion Tchr 1994-; ai: OEA, NEA 1984-; OH Univ Alumni 1983-, Bd Mem; St Marys Cntrl 1990-, Schl Bd; St Joseph Church Cath Womens Club 1990-; Bellaire City Hosp 1995-, Auxilary Bd; office: St Clairsville MS 108 Woodrow Ave Saint Clairsville OH 43950*

HILL, CONNIE D., Fourth Grade Teacher; b: Dayton, OH; m: Larry O.; c: Larissa Graham, Christopher A.; ed: OH Univ at Athens (BA) Ed 1971; Mount St Joseph (MS) Ed 1988; 15 Addl Hrs Ashland Univ; cr: Buckskin Local Schls Third Grd Tchr 1962-64; Adena Local Schls Fifth Grd Tchr 1968-71, Rdng Tchr 1971-76, Fourth Grd Tchr 1976-; ai: 4-H Adv 9 Yrs; NEA, OEA 1962-; AEA 1962-, Tchr of Yr 1992-93; home: 7310 Westfall Rd Frankfort OH 45628

HILL, DEBORAH TULLEY, 5th Grade Teacher; b: Cleveland, OH; m: Brookes C.; ed: Lake Erie Coll (BA) Elem Ed 1977, (MS) Curr & Instruction Ed 1991; Post Grad Hrs in TOM in Ed; cr: Orchard Hollow Elem 5th-6th Grd Tchr 1978-89, 4th Grd Tchr 1985-90, 5th Grd Tchr 1990-; ai: Stu Cncl Adv; Schl Improvement Plan & Learning Cncl Mem; Schl Ldrshp; Kent St Stu Tchrs Mentor Tchr; Orchard Hollow Sci Tchr of Yr 1995-; office: Orchard Hollow Elem Schl 8700 Hendricks Rd Mentor OH 44060*

HILL, DONITA SHAEFFER, Latin Teacher; *b:* Lancaster, OH; *m:* Robert Allan; *c:* Seth, Joshua, Elizabeth; *ed:* OH Wesleyan Univ (BA) Latin & Ger 1968; Attnd OH St Univ; *cr:* OSU Ger TA Tchr 1968-69; Geo Washington Jr High Lang Arts & Ger Tchr 1970-74; Granville HS Latin Tchr 1978-; *ai:* Latin Club; Honor Soc; OH Jr Clasical League; Climate Ct; NEA & OFLA 1978-; GEA 1978-, Bldg Rep; Amer Field Svc 1986-, Sec; Greater Cols Latin Club 1979-, Sec, Treas & Pres; OH Classical Conf 1978-, Liaison, Hildeseim Vase Awd; Centenary Meth Church 1980-, Nomination Ct; Parish Rltns Ct Staff; Ldrs for Learning; Dow Chem Tchng Awd; *office:* Granville HS 248 New Burg St Granville OH 43023

HILL, DONNA BUTLER, Vocal Music Director; *b:* Newark, OH; *m:* Tracie Lynn; *ed:* Mt Union Coll (BME) Music 1988; *cr:* Welsh Hills Schl K-8th Grd Music Specialist 1987-93; Northridge Local Schls K-12th Music Specialist 1993-; *ai:* Dir Children's Choir Centenary Church, Musical, Swing Choir; Pvt Piano Instr; OMEA, MENC 1988-; OCDA, ACDA 1994-; NEA 1993-; Alpha Xi Delta 1984-, Province Pres; Centenary Church 1991-, Children's Cncl Rep; *office:* Northridge HS 6066 Johnstown Utica Rd Johnstown OH 43031

HILL, HOWARD DUGAN, Science & Health Teacher; *b:* Zanesville, OH; *m:* Sharon Sue Cox; *c:* Brian Phillip, Ashley Elizabeth; *ed:* Marietta Coll (BS) Bio 1979; *cr:* Caldwell Exempted Village Schls Jr Hi Sci, Hlth Tchr 1979-; *ai:* Head Track, Head Cross Cntry Coach; OH Assn of Track & Cross Cntry Coaches 1980-, VP, Pres, Elected Hall of Fame 1996; St Stephens Cath Parish 1983-, Parish Cncl; *office:* Caldwell Exempted Village Schl 516 Fairground St Caldwell OH 43724*

HILL, JEANNE, 8th Grade Teacher; *b:* Philadelphia, PA; *m:* Christopher; *c:* Bryan; *ed:* Saint Joseph Univ (BS) Elem Ed 1971; St of PA MS Equiv Elem Ed 1990; PA St Univ Post Grad Stud; *cr:* Special People in Northeast Tchr 1971-82; Saint Anselm Schl Tchr 1969-; *ai:* Math Dept, Field Day Coord; Stu Cncl, Grad Acts Moderator; Stu of Month Prgm Dir; Mid Sts Steering Comm; NCEA 1969-; NCTM; *office:* Saint Anselm Schl 12670 Dunksferry Rd Philadelphia PA 19154

HILL, JEANNE DELIA SCIUBBA, Chemistry Teacher; *b:* Philadelphia, PA; *m:* Ronald Gray; *c:* Gregory Gray; *ed:* Immaculata (BA) Pre-Med 1972; West Chester Univ (MA) Phys Sci 1990; Attnd Drexel Univ, Gratz Coll; *cr:* B. Reed Henderson HS Bio Tchr 1974-76, Chem Tchr 1976-; *ai:* Mentor Tchr; NEA, PSEA 1974-; PSTA 1991-; NSTA 1975-; PA Writing Project Fellow 1987; *office:* B. Reed Henderson HS Lincoln & Montgomery Aves West Chester PA 19380

HILL, JOHN F., Sixth Grade Teacher; *b:* New Rochelle, NY; *ed:* Providence Coll (BA) Hum-Magna Cum Laude 1970; Univ of CT (MA) His 1972; Hofstra Univ 30 Grad Credits Ed; Long Island Univ 9 Grad Credits TESOL; Elmont Union Free Schl Dist 6 In-Svc Credits; *cr:* St Raymond Schl 5th Grd Tchr 1972-74; Elmont Pub Schls 6th Grd Tchr 1974-; Sewanhaka Evening Schl ESL & ABE Tchr 1987-; *ai:* 6th Grd Chprsn; Stu Cncl Adv; Delta Epsilon Sigma 1970-, Hnr Soc Mem; NYSUT 1974-, Union Rep (Twice); LI Soc Stud Assn 1980-; Elmont Citizens Comm 1970-; DBTA 1974-, Pres (Twice); Broadway Tchrs Assn; Flwshp & Assistantship Univ of CT His 1970-72; ESL Grant Elmont Pub Schls 1979; Numerous BOCES Coop Area Projects; *office:* Dutch Broadway Elem Schl 1880 Dutch Broadway Elmont NY 11003*

HILL, JUDITH RHODES, Social Studies Teacher; *b:* Chicago, IL; *c:* Christopher, Kathrine; *ed:* Palomar Coll (AA) Lbrl 1974; Univ of Pittsburgh (BA) Ed 1989; Cambridge Coll (MED) Ed 1994; *cr:* Mt Lebanon HS Stu Tchr 1 Yr; North Allegheny Schl Dist Soc Stud Tchr 7 Yrs; *ai:* AFT 1989-; NEA Stu Tchr of Yr Natl 1989-; *office:* North Allegheny HS 305 Cumberland Rd Pittsburgh PA 15237

HILL, JUNE LOGAN, Vocal & General Music Teacher; *b:* Lexington, KY; *m:* Jerry Keith; *c:* Martha, Jacob; *ed:* Georgetown Coll (BMEd) Music Ed 1973; Radford Univ (MA) Piano Performance 1976; Grad Hrs at Miami Univ; Inservice Hrs at Hamilton Cty, Cincinnati Pub Schls & Oak Hills Local Schls; Summer Stud Intnl Thespian Conf; *cr:* Montgomery Cty Schls K-8th Grd Vocal & Gen Music Tchr 1973-78; The Willows Acad 7th-8th Grd Vocal Music Tchr 1979-80; Cincinnati Pub Schls 9th-12th Grd Vocal & Keyboard Music Tchr 1986-89; Oak Hill Local Schls 7th-9th Grd Vocal & Gen Music Tchr 1990-; *ai:* Spectrum Select Choir; Del Hi Lites Coord; Spring Play & 7th-9th Grd Choir Dir; Vol for Ath; MENC & OMEA 1973-86; NEA, OEA & OHEA 1990-, Sec & Bldg Rep; Church Choir & Comms 1986-, Vol & Choir Dir; WOUMC Comms 1986-, Steering Comm; AIDS Vols of Cincinnati 1987-, Vol; Knothole Bsbl 1991-, Coach; Phi Kappa Phi; Whos Who Among Elem Tchrs; Yth Choir Clinician; Accompanist; Select Choirs & Competitions; Cooperating Tchr Coll of Mt St Joseph, Miami Univ & Cincinnati Conservatory of Music; *home:* 263 Senator Pl Cincinnati OH 45220*

HILL, KATHLEEN L., Dance Teacher & Support Cnslr; *b:* Minneapolis, MN; *ed:* Univ of UT (BFA) Dance 1973, (MFA) Dance 1977; Certfd Trager Practitioner; *cr:* Univ of UT Dance Assoc Instr 1971-77; Stanford Univ Dance Instr 1977-82; Prof NYC Dance Studios & Schls Co & Prof Instr 1982-86; Packer Collegiate Inst K-12th Grd Dance Tchr & Peer Support Leader & Trainer 1986-; *ai:* Fac & Staff Advy Comm; Head Search Comm; Producer Annual Dance Concert; Amer Coll Dance Festival Guest Adjudicator; Pvt Practice Instr; *office:* Packer Collegiate Inst 170 Joralemon St Brooklyn NY 11201*

HILL, KATHY E. (NULL), Science Teacher; *b:* Dayton, OH; *m:* Richard L.; *ed:* Univ of Findlay (BA) Scndry Ed 1990; OH St Univ Post-Grad Credit Hrs; *cr:* Taft MS Sci Tchr 8th grd 1991-96; Wynford HS Girls Head Bsktbl Coach 1993-; *ai:* Head Bsktbl Coach; OH Coaches Assn 1993-; *home:* 695 Girard Ave Marion OH 43302

HILL, LINDA VALERIE, Director & Teacher; *b:* Kyoto, Japan; *c:* Zachary; *ed:* Howard Univ (BA) Ed 1974; Boston Univ (MA) Educl Tech 1978; Attnd Columbia Tchrs Coll, St Johns Univ, Hunter Coll; *cr:* PS 144 Manhattan Pre K-6th Grd Tchr 1974-76; Better Ed Through Alternative Schl 4th-6th Grd Tchr 1978-84; JHS 117 Manhattan Dean of Stdnts 1984-86; Dist Office CSD 4 Chap 53 Screening Dir 1986-87; Coll for Human Svcs JHS Dir 1987-; *ai:* SPINA BIFIDA Assoc of Amer Mem; AIDS Walk Team Ldr; NEA 1974-; UFT 1974-; Schl Vols of NY Awd; Governors Drug Awareness Video Awd; *home:* 205 Clinton Ave Apt 9G Brooklyn NY 11205*

HILL, MARK DAVID, HS Social Studies Teacher; *b:* Cleveland, OH; *m:* Julie Anne Doyle; *ed:* Univ of VT (BA) Pol Sci 1990; John Carroll Uiv (MED) 1994; *cr:* Brush HS Soc Stud Tchr 1994-; *ai:* Yrbk Asst Adv; NCSS, OCSS 1994-; Sallie Mae First Class Tchr Awd Nom; *office:* Brush HS 4875 Glenlyn Rd Cleveland OH 44124

HILL, MAUREEN KINGSLEY, English Teacher; *b:* Staten Island, NY; *m:* C. Brian; *ed:* St Univ of NY at Albany (BA) Eng & Ed 1970; Western CT St Univ (MS) Ed 1976; 60 Post Grad Credit Hrs; *cr:* George Fischer MS Eng Tchr 1971-; *ai:* Spotlight Lit Magazine; MS Site Based Team; Arts in Ed Comm; Carmel Tchrs Assn 1971-, Ed Newsletter; NYSUT & AFT 1970-; NCTE 1980-; *office:* George Fischer MS 275 Fair St Carmel NY 10512

HILL, MELVIN J., 7th Grade Science Teacher; *b:* Chester, MD; *c:* Robin, Melvin Jr., Kendra; *ed:* MD St Coll (BS) Hlth PE, Biological Sci 1963; Grad Stud Trenton St Coll; *cr:* Sampson G. Smith Schl Sci Tchr 1966-; *ai:* Homework Club Spon; Fac Advy, Fac Festival Day Comms; NEA, NJSTA 1966-; NST 1971-; Coll Alumni 1963-, VP 1988-90, Pres 1990-; Church Family Comm 1989-, Chprsn; Geology Inst Princeton Univ 1985; Tchr Mentor Prgm 1995; *office:* Sampson G Smith Interm Sch 1649 Amwell Rd Somerset NJ 08873

HILL, MICHAEL E., Social Studies Teacher; *b:* Glens Falls, NY; *m:* Nancy Conklin; *c:* Bethany, Michael Jr.; *ed:* Adirondack Comm Coll (AA) Liberal Arts 1970; SUNY at Brockport (BS) His 1972; Cntrl MO St Univ (MS) Safety Ed 1976; *cr:* Johnsburg Cntrl Schl Driver Ed Tchr 1973-87, Soc Stud Tchr 1977-; *ai:* Schl Photographer; JCSTA, NYSUT, AFT 1973-; Warrensburg Cntrl Schl BOE 1984-94, Pres; Cornell Cooperative Ext Warren Co, Bd of Dir; First United Meth Church, Trustee; St Ed Dept on Curr Writing, PBS Station on Adirondack His Consultant; *office:* Johnsburg Central Schl Main St North Creek NY 12853*

HILL, RAMONA MABE, 1st Grade Teacher; *b:* Yards, VA; *w:* John Paul Hill (dec); *c:* Paula, Audine; *ed:* St Francis Coll (BA) Ed 1977, (MS) Ed 1984; Attnd Johnson Bible Coll 1951-53, Concord Tchrs Coll 1949-51; *cr:* Hicksville Elem Schl 1st Grd Tchr 1977-; *ai:* NEA 1977-; ACT 1983-, Sec 1985, Chm 1987-88 1990-; *office:* Hicksville Elem Schl W Arthur St Hicksville OH 43526

HILL, RONALD SALVATORE, Special Education Teacher; *b:* Vineland, NJ; *m:* Tiziana Alberico; *c:* Ronald; *ed:* Glassboro St Coll (BA) His 1980; *cr:* Blessed Sacrament Schl Soc Stud, Sci Tchr 1984; St Joseph Schl Math, Soc Stud, Sci Tchr 1984-89; Cleary MS Spec Ed 1989-; *ai:* HS Ftbl Coach 18 Yrs; HS Girls Bsktbl Coach 5 Yrs; NEA, NJEA 1989-; BREA 1989-, VP 1995-; *office:* Dr J P Cleary M S Central Ave Minotola NJ 08341

HILL, SUZANNA LEILANI, Physical Education Teacher; *b:* Las Vegas, NV; *m:* Thomas; *c:* Aubrey Eblin, Jesson; *ed:* OH Univ (BA) Elem Ed 1980, (MS) PE 1994; *cr:* Zane Trace Jr HS Tchr 1981-93, 5-8 Grd PE 1994-; *ai:* Jump Rope for Heart Coord; Vlybl, Bsktbl, Gymnastics Coach; ZTEA 1981-, Tchr of Yr 1993; OEA, NEA 1981-; Coord of 7th Grd Svc Learning Projects; *office:* Zane Trace HS Box 615 Kingston OH 45644

HILL, THELMA L., English Teacher; *b:* Philadelphia, PA; *ed:* Lincoln Univ (BA) Eng 1971; Rutgers Univ (EDM) Urban Ed 1973; Cmptr Sci, Real Estate; *cr:* Newark Schl Dist Eng Tchr 1971-73; Philadelphia Schl Dist Eng Tchr 1973-; Lincoln Univ Upward Bound Resident Dir 1980-84; Philadelphia Comm Coll Part-time Eng Instr 1989-; *ai:* NHS Spon; Philadelphia Fed of Tchr, AFT, PA Fed of Tchrs 1973-; Lincoln Univ Alumni 1971-, Natl Pres, First Woman Pres; Rutgers Univ Alumni 1973-; Delta Sigma Theta 1983-; Ebenezer Bapt Church 1963-, Trustee; *office:* Germantown HS Germantown Ave & High St Philadelphia PA 19144*

HILL, WALTON B., President Asst & Math Coord; *b:* Girardville, PA; *m:* Marie Helene Savidge; *c:* Donna, Kathy Wild, Jerry Louise Bucknam, Walton F.; *ed:* Bloomsburg Univ (BS) Math, Sci Physics 1937; Bucknell Univ (MS) Supv, Admin 1941; Temple Univ (EDD) Psych, Guidance, Admin 1964; Univ of Penna Math; Drexel Univ Graphics; *cr:* East Chillinquaque HS Math, Sci Soc St Instr; Hatboro HS Math, Sci Instr 1938-41; Haverford Twnp HS Boys Dean, Math Instr 1941-67; Drexel Univ Evg Prgm Math Tchr 1946-67; Delaware Cy CC Asso Dean Studnts 1967-71; West Chester Univ Lead Prgm Guidance Coord 1971-79; Penna Inst of Tech Asst to Pres, Coord 1979-; *ai:* Coord Red Cross Blood Bank, Office of Employment, Trng; Phi Theta Kappa Spon; Teach Math Alg to Calculus; Who's Who in Amer Jr Colls; Intnl Stdnt Adv; Working on Grants; NEA 1965-, Life Mem; Kappa Delta Pi 1970-, Life Mem; Rotary Club Media PA, Pres, VP, Secy; Fnd Media Rotary Club, Secy; Red Cross, Bd Mem; Pub Articles; *office:* PA Institute Of Technology 800 Manchester Ave Media PA 19063

HILL, WEBSTER C., Social Studies Coordinator; *b:* Harrison City, PA; *m:* Marie; *c:* Courtney; *ed:* CA Univ (BS) Soc Stud 1965, (MED) Soc Sci 1974; West VA Univ Ed Ad; *cr:* Greater Latrobe Schls 4th Ward Tchr 1 Yr; Greater Labrobe Jr HS Tchr 25 Yrs; Greater Labrobe Sr HS Tchr 4 Yrs; *ai:* Wildcat for Kids Day; ASCD; NCSS; St Cncl of SS; Latrobe Area Chamber of Commerce Ec Comm; *office:* Greater Latrobe Sr HS 131 Country Club Rd Latrobe PA 15650*

HILL, WILLIAM FRANCIS,III, Science & Mathematics Teacher; *b:* Winsted, CT; *m:* Kimberley; *c:* Kristoffer, Shauna, Kasea; *ed:* FL Inst of Tech (AS) Marine Sci 1973; Lyndon St Coll (BS) Broad Field Sci 1976; 30 Post Grad Credits; *cr:* Concord HS Sci Tchr 1978-83; Summer Upward Bound Sci & Math Tchr 1981-91; Concord Schl 7th-8th Grd Sci, Math & Cmptr Sci Tchr 1984-; *ai:* Tech Club; 8th Grad Class & Yrbk Adv; North Cntry Trio Educators Tchr of Yr 1992; *office:* Concord Schl RR 1 Box 1b Concord VT 05824

HILL, WILLIAM FRANK, History Teacher; *b:* E Liverpool, OH; *ed:* Bowling Green St Univ (BSEd) Amer Stud 1969; Post Grad Work; *cr:* Mc Cord Jr HS His Tchr 1969-77; Southview HS His Tchr 1977-; *ai:* Class, CougaReview Adv; Military Strategy Club; Discipline Comm; Sylvania Ed Assn 1969-, VP, Bd of Dirs; NW OH, OH Ed Assns, NEA 1969-; NW OH Soc Stud Cncl, VP; Toledo Personal Rights Org, Bd of Dirs 1987; OH Historical Soc 1975-; Univ of Chicago Tchr Awd; Phi Alpha Theta; Lucas Co Schls I Make A Difference Awd 1990, 1992, 1995; *office:* Sylvania Southview HS 7225 Sylvania Ave Sylvania OH 43560*

HILLA, NANCY, Eighth Grade Teacher; *b:* Jersey City, NJ; *ed:* Chestnut Hill Coll (BS) Ed 1968; Univ of Scranton (MS) Elem Ed 1973; Fordham NY 3 Credits Toward Admin; *cr:* Most Holy Redeemer 7th Grd Tchr 1980-83; St Marys Lebanon 8th Grd Tchr 1983-86; Immaculate Heart of Mary 8th Grd Tchr 1986-88; Queen of Peace 8th Grd Tchr 1988-; *ai:* Yrbk Adv; Soc Stud, Field Day Coord; NCEA, Mid St Cncl for Soc Stud, NCSS; Amer Heart Assn 1992-; Calling Earth Correspondent Quest; Tchr of Yr 1995; *home:* 17 Franklin Pl North Arlington NJ 07031

HILLARD, SAMUEL MARC, Soc Stud, Civics & Geog Tchr; *b:* Jamestown, NY; *ed:* Edinboro Univ of PA (BSEd) Soc Stud 1961, (MSEd) Soc Stud 1965; *cr:* Westmont Hilltop Schl Dist MS Tchr 1961-; *ai:* MS Advy Team; Stu Govt Co-Adv; Jr High Sports Equipment & Game Mgr; Clock Operator; Score Keeper & Ticket Taker; Band Adv; Jr Wrestling Coach 1976-81; Newspaper Adv 1968-81; In Charge of Stu Ushers, Flag Raising & Daily Announcements; NEA, PSEA & WHEA 1961-; NCSS; NC Geog Ed; PCSS; PCGE; Mid Sts Cncl for Soc Stud; PA Historical Assn; Johnstown Jaycees 1965-69; Westmont Fire Co & Fire Police 1981-86; Westmont Church of Brethen, Bd 1991-, Dr of Deacons 1994-; Remedial Pgm Cert of Merit Johnstown Jaycees 1965-69; PA Cncl of Geog Outstndg Tchr 1979; Run for Liberty Pgm Cert of Merit 1986; Johnstown Tribune Person of the Week 1995; *home:* 762 Sunset Ave Johnstown PA 15905

HILLER, JUDITH SUSAN, Mathematics Teacher; *b:* Lawrence, MA; *ed:* Salem St Coll (BA) Math 1968, (MED) Admin 1972; 60 Addl Credits Calculus, Algebra, Connecting Math & Sci, Learning Styles; *cr:* Methuen Jr HS Math Tchr 1968-72; Tenney HS Math Tchr 1972-75; Methuen HS Math Tchr 1975-; *ai:* Block Scheduling, Screening for New HS Prin, AP Tchrs Comms; MTA, NEA 1968-; NCTM 1982-; Assn Tchrs of Math in MA 1982-; Assn of AP Math Tchrs 1990-; Excl in Tchng Awd Bentley Coll; *office:* Methuen HS 1 Ranger Rd Methuen MA 01844

HILLER, KAREN LYNNE, Business Education Teacher; *b:* Durham, NC; *m:* John T.; *c:* Taylor Anne, Andrew; *ed:* Bloomsburg St Coll (BS) Bus Ed 1977; Addl 24 Credits Cmptr Tech, Psych; *cr:* Sharon Hill HS Bus Ed Tchr 1977-80; Downington Area HS Bus Ed Tchr 1980-; *ai:* Stu Assistance Svc Intervention Crisis Cnslng; NEA, PDEA 1977-; *office:* Downingtown Area HS 445 Manor Ave Downingtown PA 19335

HILLER, NANCY ELBERG, Retired Teacher of GATE; *b:* Ci OH; *m:* Jack Gillen; *c:* Julia Hosea, Nancy Wathen, Stephen; *ed* Univ (BS) Elem Ed 1969, (MED) Diagnostic, Remedial Ed 1 Gifted, Native Amer Stud; *cr:* Princeton City 4-5 Grd Tchr 196 Grd GATE Tchr 1982-94; *ai:* NEA 1969-, Bldg Rep; Delta Kappa 1991-, Treas; *home:* 3 Arbor Ct Cincinnati OH 45246

HILLER, SUSAN, Social Studies Teacher; *b:* Wareham, Bridgewater St Coll (BA) Span 1979; *cr:* Old Rochester Regnl S Tchr 1979-82; Jr, Sr HS Chptr I Rdng, Math Tchr 1982-87; Carver Tchr 1987-90, Soc Stud Tchr 1990-; *ai:* NEA, MA Tchrs Ass Kappa Delta Pi 1978-; Order of Eastern Star 1977-; Intnl Order of 1968-; Tchr of Month Awd; Favorite Tchr Awd by Class of 199 Carver HS 60 S Meadow Rd Carver MA 02330

HILLERY, ROSE MICHAEL, Third Grade Teacher; *b:* Brook *ed:* Molly Coll (BA) Eng Lit 1973; *cr:* Our Lady of Guadalupe 3rd-4th Grd Tchr 1937-43; St Nicholas HS Eng, Coml Law, Boo Tchr 1943-44; St Boniface Schl 7th-8th Grd Tchr 1944-63; Lor Cath Schl 7th-8th Grd Tchr 1963-73; Holy Spirit Schl 7th-8th 1973-84, Third Grd Tchr 1984-; *ai:* Cath League for Rel & Civ Educl Comm; Mission Moderator; Sunday CCD Tchr; NCEA; Cre Awd by Cath League Ed Comm 1993; *office:* Holy Spirit Schl 13 New Hyde Park NY 11040

HILLERY, SHARON STEWART, Chem Teacher & Sci Dept Parkersburg, WV; *m:* Paul; *c:* Anne, Alice, John; *ed:* WV Wesle (BS) Chem 1966; Univ of VA (MS) Organic Chem 1969; Univ of Stu in Ed 1984-85; *cr:* Prince George's Comm Coll Chem I 1978-85; Acad of the Holy Cross Chem Tchr 1985-87; Gec Visitation Chem Tchr 1987-; *ai:* Sci Dept Chair; Fac Liaison Com Jr Level Tchrs Comm Co-Chair; Amer Chem Soc; NSTA; NDEA Flwshp 1966-69; NSF SGER Grant Recipient 1991; Georgetown Tandy Schlr 1991-92; *office:* Georgetown Visitatn Prep Schl 152 NW Washington DC 20007

HILLEY, WILLIAM ALLEN,III, Social Studies Teac Murfreesboro, TN; *m:* Toni Lynn; *c:* William Allen, George Earl; Univ (BA) His 1965; RI Coll (MAT) His 1971, (CAGS) Sec Admi Navy Lt Ensign Officer 1965-70; Narragansett Schl System Tch Head 1971-; *ai:* Stu Cncl Adv 7 Yrs; NFL Speech Coach 7 Yrs Coach 7 Yrs; Model Legislative Adv 4 Yrs; NEA 1971-; Tiverton Bd 1970-79, Chm 1 Term; Cub Scouts Ed 1980-84, Den Mother, Ldr; BSA 1982-92, Asst Scoutmaster & Scoutmaster; Youth Socc 1981-83; Presidential Scholar Tchr; *office:* Narragansett HS 245 S Narragansett RI 02882

HILLIARD, BRIAN FRANCIS, Fourth Grade Teacher; *b:* Bronx SUC at Geneseo (BA) Psych, Sociology 1995, (MS) Advanced Tch 75 Addl Credits; *cr:* Frank P. Long Schl Fourth Grd Tchr 9 Y Blake Elem Schl Fourth Grd Tchr 1 Yr; *ai:* AFT, UTFU 1986-; Cabin Ln East Setauket NY 11733

HILLIARD, CAROL, Asst Prof of Nrsng, Med & Surg; *b:* New *ed:* Bronx Comm Coll (AAS) Nrsng 1971; Coll Hunter-Bellevue Nrsng (BSN) Nrsng 1981, (MSN) Nrsng Ed 1983; Working on PH Rsrch Columbia Univ; *cr:* Fordham Hosp RN Staff Nurse, Me 1971-73; NY Med Coll Flower & Fifth Ave Hosp Operating Ro 1974-78; Harlem Hosp RN Emerg Rm ICU, Nrsng Supvr Conti 1779-90; Hostos Comm Coll Asst Prof Nrsng 1990-; *ai:* Nurse Co Prof Tutoring Svc; AFT 1990-; ANA 1971-; EDNA, CCRN NYSBNA 1991-; Amer Red Cross 1988-, CPT Instr; John F. Meml Citizenship Awd; Outstdng Tchr Awd; *office:* Hostos Co Allied Hlth Bldg 500 Grand Concourse Bronx NY 10451

HILLIARD, EUNICE PURNELL, Guidance Department Newark, MD; *m:* Leroy; *c:* Lee, Susan; *ed:* Morgan St Univ (BS) E Johns Hopkins Univ (MED) Ed 1974, (CASE) Cnslr Ed 1 Baltimore City Pub Schls Eng Tchr 1962-78, Guidance Tchr Guidance Dept Head 1988-; *ai:* Curr, Schlsp, Mid Sts HS Visiti Evaluations, Staff Efficacy Comms; Mental Hlth, Staff D Improvement Teams; Honor Soc; Afro-Amer Initiative; Pupil Team Chair; Peer Mediation Coord; Phi Delta Kappa 1986-, Honor, Prof Membership; Pi Lmabda Theta 1977-, Pres, Treas, Ho Membership; Amer Counseling Assn 1977-; Natl Distinguis Registry 1989-, Svc Awd; Epworth United Meth Church 1980-, Girl Scouts 1978-, Cookie Mother, Svc Awd; Natl Certified Cns *office:* Paul L. Dunbar HS 1400 Orleans St Baltimore MD 21231

HILLIARD, NANCY, Social Studies Teacher; *b:* Columbia, SC; Janowitz; *c:* Justin, Sarah; *ed:* Univ of CO (BS) Jrnlsm 1971; No Coll (ME) Curr, Rsrch 1992; 36 Addl Hrs; *cr:* Univ of CO Ad 1978-79; Manhattanville Coll Finance 1979-81; Paralegal, Self-employed 1982-90; Nashua HS Tchr 1991-; *ai:* Co-Adv Odyssey of the Mind Coach; Dist Assessment Comm; SNTAS; AF Natl Cncl on Soc Stud 1995-; NH Cncl on Soc Stud 1994-, Exec Journal Horizons; Nashua Yth Lacrosse League 1993-, Exec Bd; Lacrosse League 1995-, Bd; Dist Grant to Write Proposal for Al Schl; Ed of Horizons; NH Prof Journal for Soc Stud; Presenter of *office:* Nashua Sr HS 36 Riverside Dr Nashua NH 03063

HILLIARD, VICKI LYNN HALL, Chemistry Teacher; *b:* Day *m:* Jim; *c:* Amber, Aaron; *ed:* Fl Southern Coll (BS) Bio & Che Attnd Wright St Univ, Univ of Dayton, Mimai Univ; *cr:* Howard Analyst 1980-81; W Carrollton HS Tchr 1981-; *ai:* Adv Home Parade; WOEA, NEA 1981-; Partners for Terrific Sci; Collegiate Support Group; Tchr Initiative Grant; WC Ed Fnd Grant; *offic* Carrollton H S 5833 Student St West Carrollton OH 45449

HILLIER, CYNTHIA PETERSON, Art Teacher; *b:* Mansfield, Russell; *c:* Jason, Jennifer, Abigail; *ed:* Taylor Univ (BS) Art Ed Grad Hrs; *cr:* Fremont City Schls DPPF Tutor 1977-79; Templ Acad Art Tchr 1980-86; Wee Care Presch Tchr 1986-89; Tiffin C Art Tchr 1989-; *ai:* Prins Advy Comm; Venture Cap Grant Ld Enrichment Club, Prom Adv; Chrstn Edctrs Assn 1994-, Comm Art Ed Assn 1993-; TEA, OEA, NEA 1989-; Voices of Grace 19 Summer Art Inst Grant 1992-93; *home:* 712 Tucker Rd Fremont O

HILLIGOSS, RAYMOND, Culinary Arts Instructor; *b:* Woodbur Bridget Ann Johnson; *c:* Jaclynn Elizabeth, Brittany Ann; *ed:* Comm Coll (AA) Hotel, Motel, Restaurant; MD St Dept Ed Equivolent; *cr:* Bay & Beyond Inc Cafe & Catering Chef, Pres, Legends Restaurant Exec Chef; Garden Gourmet Restaura Wicomico Applied Tech Ctr Culinary Arts Instr; *ai:* Wico Co Bd Awds Comm Head; VICA Prgm, Wor-Wic Comm Coll Hotel Restaurant Prgm Adv; Hearts Disease Prgm; Delmarva Chefs Assn 1988-, Pres; Amer Culinary Fed 1986-, Bd of Dir; S Restaurant Assn 1991-; Grant a Wish Fnd 1995-, Chprsn, Support; MD VICA 1992-, Bd of Dir, Outstdng Svd; Salisbury Cncl 1991-, Chprsn, Participating Chef; Easter Seal Celebrati Presenter, Participating Chef; 1992 Delmarvas Chefs & Cooks A of Yr; 2 Bronze Medals ACF Hot Food Competitions, Taste Peoples Choice Awd 1995; Bay & Beyond Catering Awded Certfd Chefs Amer Culinary Fed 1993; *office:* Wicomico Applied Tech Morris St Salisbury MD 21801

HILLIS, LUCILLE GIBSON, Kindergarten Teacher; *b:* Butler Richard D.; *ed:* IN Univ of PA (BS) Elem Ed 1975; 24 for Perman

:eau Schl Dist 5th Grd Tchr 1975-76; Karns City Schl Dist Kndgtn 76-; *ai:* NEA, PSEA 1975-; KCEA 1976-; Treble Clef Music Club ays, Means Mbrshp; Church, Organist, Sunday Schl Supt, Comms; 2 S Argyle St Petrolia PA 16050

AN, BARBARA HALL, Sixth Grade Teacher; *b:* Summit, NJ; *m:* ; *c:* Eric, Greg; *ed:* Grad Stud Rutgers & Jersey City St Coll; *cr:* of Lima Elem Ed Tchr 1968-74; Wall Twp Schls Elem Ed Tchr *i:* Staff Cncl; Poetry Across Curr Project Coord; NJEA, NEA TA 1982-, Treas, Life Mem; IRA 1989-; Cub Scouts 1986-90, Pack reation Commission 1990-; Co-Pres; Wall Twp Fnd for Educl Excl Aini-Grant; *office:* West Belmar Elem Schl 925 17th Ave Wall NJ

AN, ELIZABETH TRENT, Tchr of Acad Prgm for Talented; *b:* ille, WV; *m:* Larry W.; *c:* Melissa Moss; *ed:* Marshall Univ (BA) 1961; Miami Univ of OH (MA) Supervision & Curr 1974, (PHD) Curr 1982; *cr:* Fairfield City Schls Elem Tchr 1961-64; Princeton s Elem Tchr, Tchr of Acad Prgm for Talented 1964-; *ai:* Ind Stud, ield Stud Critical Thinking Wkshp, Staff Dev Math Wkshp; Tchrs Assn; OEA, NEA 1961-; ASCD 1974-; Phi Delta Kappa ifted Assn; Superintendents Grant; Student Council Grant; Article

DAVID RICHARD, Sixth Grade Teacher; *b:* Trenton, NJ; *m:* erns; *c:* Laura; *ed:* IN Univ of PA (BS) Elem Ed 1976; Rider Univ ucl Admin 1989; Environmental Sci 18 Addl Grad Credits Penn r Sci 12 Addl Grad Credits Penn St, Villanova Univ, Millersville Penn Vly Elem Schl Sixth Grd Tchr 1978-80; Warren Snyder l Fifth Grd Tchr 1980-86; Quarry HIll Elem Schl Fourth Grd Tchr William Penn MS Sixth Grd Tchr 1995-; *ai:* NEA; PSEA; PEA; Bucks Cty Courier Times Coach of Yr Girls Var Sftbl 1981-82; illiam Penn MS 1524 Derbyshire Rd Yardley PA 19067

MICHAEL A., Mathematics Teacher; *b:* Watertown, NY; *m:* Cloutier; *c:* Ashley L., Ryan R., Marissa B., Michaela A.; *ed:* St Coll (BA) Math & 7th-12th Grd Ed 1986; Albany St Univ (MA) 1991; *cr:* Broadalbin-Perth Cntrl Schl Math Tchr 1987-; *ai:* Jr Var Modified Bsbl Coach; Team Ldr; FL Trip Adv; NJHS Selection NYSUT, Natl Fed of Tchrs 1987-; NCTM 1990-; Rube Goldberg Grant 1993 & 1994; Presenter at NYS MS Conf-Rube Goldberg 995; *office:* Broadalbin-Perth Cntrl Schl Cty Hwy 107 Amsterdam 0

SUZANNE ROBSON, Mathematics Teacher; *b:* Philadelphia, PA; ew W.; *c:* Christopher R., Heather J.; *ed:* Beaver Coll at Wyncote th 1966; Attnd Edinboro Univ Scndry Cert 1982; *cr:* Fairview Twp 6th Grd TELLS Tchr 1985-86; Halifax Area Schl Dist Geometry 87-; *ai:* Sr Class & Yrbk Adv; NEA, PSEA 1987-; HEA 1987-, CTM 1993-; Democratic Women 1988-; *office:* Halifax HS 3940 ountain Rd Halifax PA 17032

R, DIANE CAROL, Associate Professor of Math; *b:* Stoneham, Clayton; *c:* Clayton, Sam; *ed:* Univ of Lowell (BS) Acctng 1983; St Univ (MS) Math 1988; *cr:* East Cath HS Math Tchr 1987; ter Comm Tech Coll Assoc Prof of Math 1987-; *ai:* Tenure, Prof rch Chprsn, Awds Reception Planning, Screening for Women wds, Eta Mu Lambda Selection Comms; Mentor Adj Instr; Dev Ed e; MATYCONN; NCTM; *office:* Manchester Comm Tech Coll 60 St Manchester CT 06040*

R, SARAH COSTELLO, Second Grade Teacher; *b:* Canton, OH; M. Jr.; *c:* Megan, Karen; *ed:* Kent St Univ (BS) Elem Ed 1966; 30 St, Cleveland St, Ashland Coll, OH St Univ; *cr:* Springfield City 5 Grd Tchr 1966; Marion City Schls Grd 2 Tchr 1966-67; s Pub Schls Grd 1, 2, 3 Tchr 1967-72; Northwest Local Schls L-D 1981; Aurora City Schls 2nd Grd Tchr 1983-; *ai:* Intervention e Team; Soc Stud Curr Comm; OEA; NEA; AEA 1983-, Sec; Four Swim Team 1982-93, Pres; Outstanding Elem Tchrs of Amer 1972; 7 Parkview Dr Aurora OH 44202

BRAND-WARD, JANET LOUISE (PAULI), First Grade *b:* Massillon, OH; *m:* James Andrew; *ed:* Malone Coll (BS) Elem Attnd Ashland Coll, Coll of Mt Saint Joseph & Univ of Akron xual Abuse Inst; *cr:* Massillon Local Schl System 4th Grd Tchr Tuslaw Local Schl System 1st Grd Tchr 1976-; *ai:* Schl Grdng, uthors Comms; Tuslaw Classroom Tchrs Assn, OEA, NEA 1971-; Holden Jennings Schlr Awd; Ashland Oil Tchr of Yr Nom; PTA ing Tchr Nomination; Stark Cty Local Schl Elem Citizenship Law Ed Svc Wkshp IV.

, JOHN MARTIN, Physics Teacher; *b:* Carlisle, PA; *m:* Anne N. *ed:* Millersville Univ (BSE) Physics 1991; DE St Univ (MS) 1996; *cr:* Lee-Davis HS Physics Tchr 1991-93; Cape Henlopen HS Tchr 1993-; *ai:* Vlybl Coach; NHS Spon; Odyssey of Mind Judge; 91-; DSEA, CHEA 1993-; *office:* Cape Henlopen HS Kings Hwy E 19958

N, KENNETH H., District Social Studies Dir; *b:* Dunkirk, NY; *m:* Anne Olson; *c:* Katherine, Margaret; *ed:* Hiram Coll (BA) Pol 1970; Syracuse Univ (MA) His 1972, (PHD) His 1991; *cr:* Rose dia Schl Dist Soc Stud Tchr 1972-80; Rush-Henrietta Cent Schl Stud Dir 1980-; Nazareth Coll Adjunct Prof 1988-; *ai:* Org Amer 0-; NCSS 1972-; ASCD 1980-; Rotary 1981-; Author Prof Articles nercial Publications; *office:* Rush-Henrietta Cntrl Schl Dist 1799 ta Rd Henrietta NY 14467

N, MARJORIE SYLVIA, Kindergarten Teacher; *b:* Newton, MA; ard Pratt; *c:* Aimee-Michelle Hilton Pratt; *ed:* Boston Univ (BA) Harvard Univ (MA) K-8 Ed; Leslie Coll Lit Courses, Wheelock, elling; Boston Univ Lit and the Law; 60 Addl Credits; Music at Royal Acad Music & Drama; *cr:* Frankfort Intnatl Schule t GR;Allyn & Bacon Publishers 4-8 Grd Soc Sci Textwriter & Ed; Schl Grd Two Tchr 1978-85, 5th Grd Tchr 1982-84; 2nd Grd Tchr ; Third Grd Tchr 1985-89, Lit Tchr, Lib Specialist 1989-91, Tchr 1991-; *ai:* Curtis MS Talent Show, Schl Prgms Stage Lighting; EA; Girls Scouts of Amer, Troop Ldr; Khal B'raira, Exec Comm, -Large; Awded Responsive Classroom Grant to Study at Northeast d; Grant to Upgrade Study of Chicken Embryology & Incubation ems K-pgms; *office:* Haynes Schl Haynes Rd Sudbury MA 01776

N, REBECCA (SMITH), Reading & English Teacher; *b:* New PA; *m:* James III; *c:* Elaine Hilton Mains, James M., Michael J.; *ed:* Rock Univ (BA) Eng 1969; Addl Post Grad Stud; *cr:* Ben Franklin ig, Rdg Tchr 1969-; *ai:* Tall Class, Ben's Pen, Youngstown St Univ estival Spon; AFT, PAFT 1981-; New Castle Fed of Tchrs 1981-, KA Thanks to Tchrs Finalist 1995; *office:* Ben Franklin Jr HS ham Ave New Castle PA 16101

N, SUSAN M., Department of Comm Asst Prof; *b:* Franklin, PA; nis R.; *c:* Elizabeth, Eric, Michael, Sara; *ed:* Clarion St Coll (BS) Ed 1973, (MS) Comm 1978; Working on EdD in Higher Ed, Comm, tnd Nova Southeastern Univ; *cr:* Clarion Univ of PA Asst Prof of 986-; *ai:* Multimedia Production Adv; Soc for Coll Journalist Curr Fac Senate Comm on Cmptr Operations; SCAP 1992-, Newsletter CT; Allegherry Valley Trails Assn 1991-, Newsletter Ed; YMCA oosters 1994-; Franklin HS Booster Club 1991-; OH Region Soccer Club 1994-; Blomsburg Univ Multimedia Production Grant; *office:* Clarion Univ Of PA G-3 Becker Hall Clarion PA 16214

HILTY, ANN ESTELLE, Family & Consumer Sci Tchr; *b:* Indianapolis, IN; *ed:* Bluffton Coll (BA) Ed, Home Ec 1965; 15 Hrs OH St Univ; 20 Hrs Bowling Green Univ; *cr:* Danbury Tw HS Family & Consumer Sci Tchr 1965-68; Celina Sr HS Family & Consumer Sci Tchr 1969-; *ai:* FHA Adv; OH Ed Assn, NEA, Amer Assn of Family & Consumer Sci 1965-; AVA 1969-; Univ Womens Club 1969-, Treas; Alpha Delta Kappa 1973-; First Presbyn Church; Amer Cancer Soc, Amer Heart Assn Vol; *home:* 532 E Fulton St Celina OH 45822

HILTY, PAUL ALLEN, 6th Grade Math Teacher; *b:* Findlay, OH; *m:* Morry Anne; *c:* Tanya, David; *ed:* OH Univ (BA) Ed 1965; Kent St Univ (MS) Admin 1969; *cr:* Bedford City Schls Tchr 1965-; *ai:* 8th Grd Girls Vlybl Coach; Bedford Ed Assn 1965-, VP 1 Yr, Pres 4 Yrs; OEA; NEA; Y's Mens Intnl 1969-, Sec, Treas, VP, Pres; *office:* Aurora Schl 24200 Aurora Rd Bedford OH 44146

HILTY, SUSAN L. SHICK, Math & Computer Science Tchr; *b:* Greensburg, PA; *m:* Robert A.; *c:* Christi Dawn, Tracey Lynn; *ed:* IN Univ of PA (BS) Math Ed 1970; OK St Univ (MS) Statistics 1972; *cr:* Hempfield Area Sr HS Math, Cmptr Sci Tchr 1972-; *ai:* NEA, PSEA, NCTM 1972-; *office:* Hempfield Area Sr HS Rd 6 Box 77 Greensburg PA 15601*

HIMES, KENNETH FRANKLIN, High School Math Teacher; *m:* Barbara Ann; *c:* David, Alan, Clifford, Mary; *ed:* Clarion Univ (BS) Math 1965; Cntrl MI Univ (MA) Bus 1975; Addl Hrs; *cr:* US Air Force Ofcr 1960-80; Keystone HS Tchr 1983-; *ai:* KEA 1983-, Pres; NEA, PSEA 1983-; NCTM, MT of PA 1990-; Order of Eagles 1975-; NRA 1970-; *office:* Keystone HS Beatty Ave Knox PA 16232*

HIMES, LINDA A., Second Grade Teacher; *b:* York, PA; *ed:* Millersville Univ (BA) Elem Ed 1981; *cr:* Northeastern Schl Dist 5th-6th Grd Tchr 1981-83, 2nd Grd Tchr 1987-; Adept Corp Sec 1984-85; York Cty Assistance Office Income Maintenance Worker 1985-87; *ai:* Comm Action, Strategic Plan Comms; PSEA, Northeastern Ed Assn, NEA 1987-; York Cty Red Cross, Co-Piloted Fire Safety Prgm; Co-Recipient Shippensburg Univ Schl of Stud Cncl Exemplary Prgm Awd; *office:* York Haven Elem Schl Cassel Rd York Haven PA 17370

HIMMLER, CHARLES JOSEPH, Coordinator of USST Program; *b:* Cumberland, MD; *m:* Suzanne P.; *c:* Brian, James Anthony; *ed:* Allegany Com Coll (AA) Gen Stud 1972; Frostburg St Univ (BA) Sociology, Soc Sci 1974, (MED) Guid, Counsel 1976; WV Univ Cnslng Psych 6 Hrs; *cr:* Allegany Comm Col Career Dev Coord 1976-85; Northern Garrett HS Coord Voc Support Serv 1986-; *ai:* Coach Boys, Girls Cross Cntry, Girls Track & Field; AARP 1996; GCTA, NEM, MSTA 1986-; Natl Certfd Career Cnslr; *office:* Northern Garrett HS 86 Pride Pkwy Accident MD 21520

HIMMLER, SUZANNE PALETTA, English & Reading Teacher; *b:* Frostburg, MD; *m:* Charles Joseph; *c:* James Anthony, Brian Joseph; *ed:* Frostburt St Univ (BS) Eng 1968, (MA) Rdng 1972; 18 Addl Credit Hrs; *cr:* WA Jr HS Rdng Tchr 1968-77; Flintstone Schl Eng Tchr 1983; Westmar MS 9th & 10th Grd Rdng Tchr, Rdng Specialist 1984-; *ai:* Project Basic, Staff Dev, Wellness, Individual Schl-Based Lib, Media Stans Comms; Allegany Co Spell-a-Thon, Knights of Columbus Spelling Bee, MD Functional Writing Test Schl Coord; Allegany Co Tchrs Assn, MD St Tchrs Assn, NEA 1968-; MS Tchrs Assn 1993-; Church Comms 1979-; March of Dimes 1995-; Playground Assn 1978-90; Master's Project MD Functional Rdng Allegany Co Bd of Ed Functional Rdng Prg Dev; Tchr of Yr 1993-94; *office:* Westmar MS Philos Ave Westernport MD 21562*

HINCHBERGER, TERRY DALE, Soc Studies Dept Head & Tchr; *b:* Butler, PA; *m:* Cynthia J.; *c:* Bradley, Douglas, Kaitlyn; *ed:* Butler Comm Coll (AA) Elem Ed 1973; Slippery Rock Univ (BS) Elem Ed 1975; Westmister, Slippery Rock (MS) Elem Ed 1978; *cr:* Clearfield Elem 4th Grd Tchr 1975-79, 5th Grd Tchr 1979-80, 6th Grd Tchr 1980-; Emily Brittain Elem 2nd Grd Tchr 1985-86; *ai:* Coach S Butler Little League Bsbl Assn; BEA, PSEA, NEA 1975-; *office:* Clearfield Elem 621 Clearfield Rd Butler PA 16001

HINCKS, PATRICIA SUE, Fifth Grade Teacher; *b:* Bainbridge, GA; *c:* Sharon Lynn, Sheryl Rae, Lauren Frances; *ed:* RI Coll (BED) Early Chldhd 1965, (MED) Early Chldhd, Elem 1975; 3 Hrs Rdng Univ of RI; *cr:* Glen Hills Elem Schl Second Grd Tchr 1965-67; Rocky Hill Schl Firs tGrd Tchr 1981-82, Rdng Tchr 1983-84; East Greenwich Schls Sub Grd K-6 Tchr; Frenchtown Elem Schl Grd 4 Tchr 1986-90; Hanaford Elem Schl Grd 5 Tchr 1990-; *ai:* Stu Evaluation Comm; NEA 1986-, Bldg Rep; Little Shepherd Presch 1988-, Bd of Dirs Sec; *office:* Hanaford Elem Schl 100 Lebaron Dr East Greenwich RI 02818*

HINDENLANG, JAMES GRANT, 7th Grade Science Teacher; *b:* Shelby, OH; *m:* Kelley Sue Lepley; *ed:* Bowling Green St Univ (BA) Bio 1990; Comm Coll of Air Force 46 Hrs AS Logistics; Walsh Coll 3 Hrs; *cr:* OH Air Natl Guard 179th AW, APS Transportation Ofcr 1985-; Maple Hghts Bd of Ed 6th-8th Grd Sci Tchr 1990-93; Shelby City Schls Sub Tchr 1993-94; Maple Hghts Bd of Ed 7th-8th Grd Sci Tchr 1994-; *ai:* Asst Var Track Coach; Lead After Schl Sci Clubs; Sci Curr Writing Comm; Mentor MS Sci Tchr; NEA, OEA 1990-; Air Force Assn, Natl Guard Assn 1994-; Partnership Ed in OH Air Natl Guard 179 AW 1994-; OH Air Natl Guard Commission 2nd LT 1994; Recipient NCO 179APS; Acad Achvmt 179APS; 179 Airlift Wing USAF Outstdng Unit Awd 1995; *office:* Mikovich MS 5460 West Blvd Maple Heights OH 44137*

HINDERLITER, CARL M., Instructional Support Teacher; *b:* Warren, PA; *m:* Carol J.; *c:* Miles, Sean, Brandon; *ed:* Edinboro Univ of PA (BS) Elem Ed 1976-Cum Laude; Slippery Rock Univ of PA (MED) Spec Ed 1980; Westminster Coll 1 Yr Undergraduate; *cr:* Reynolds Schl Dist 4th Grd Tchr 1982-87, Learning Support Tchr 1987-90, Instructional Support Tchr 1990-92, Learning Support Tchr 1992-93, 5th Grd Tchr 1993-94, Instructional Support Tchr 1994-; *ai:* Past Mentor Tchr 1991-92, Asst Track Coach 1980-90; Head Track Coach 1990-, Elem Hlth & Sci Curr Chprsn 1986-91 & 1996; NEA, PSEA 1976-; REA 1976-, Treas; Greenville Wrestling Club 1986-, Pres; Gift of Time 1994; Dist 3 St Champions Track 1994-95.

HINDES, PAUL D., Civics Tchr, Coach & Act Spon; *b:* Meadville, PA; *m:* Mary Kay; *c:* Megan, Kevin, Katie; *ed:* Duquesne Univ Master Equivalency 1987; *cr:* Whitehall Jr High, Harrison Mid Schl & Baldwin HS Tchr, Coach & Act Spon 1971-; *ai:* Founder & Co-Spon of TI Sparks and Awd-Winning Drug & Alcohol Alternative Pgm; Co-Founder & Co-Dir of Family Tyes-501-C-3; Head Sftbl & Asst Ftbl Coach; NEA 1993-; WEA 1993-; Fund-Raising with Make-A-Wish & Easter Seals; Co-Dir of Family Tyes; Coach of Yr (3 Times); All-Star Edctr 1993; Baldwin TI-Sparks Pgm Schl of Yr 1993; *office:* Baldwin HS 4653 Clairton Blvd Pittsburgh PA 15236*

HINDI, NITHAM MOHAMMAD, Asst Professor of Accounting; *b:* Amman, Jordan; *m:* Sawsan Siam; *c:* Haneen N., Basel N.; *ed:* Univ of Jordan (BS) Acctng 1981; Univ of AL (MA) Acctng 1985; MS St Univ (DBA) Acctng 1991; *cr:* Jordanian Army Fin Accountant 1981-83; MS St Univ Tchng Asst 1990-91; Miles Coll Assoc Prof of Acctng 1991-94; Shippensburg Univ Asst Prof of Acctng 1994-; *ai:* Stu Chptr Inst of Mgt Acctg Fac Adv; Inst of Mgt Acctng 1990-, Ed & Prof Dev VP, Harrisburg Chptr Pres-Elect; Amer Acctng Assn 1988-; Inst of Internal Aud 1991-; Beta Alpha Psi 1985-; Certfd Mngmt Accountant; Articles Pub; Presentations to Local & Intnl Confs; Awded Outstdng Svc Awd for Participating & Coordinating Vol Income Tax Assistance Site; *office:* Shippensburg Univ 1871 Old Main Dr Shippensburg PA 17257

HINDIE, PETER JOHN, English & Language Arts Tchr; *b:* Cairo, Egypt; *m:* Carmen Brondo; *c:* Nicolas, Harriette Hindie Slavik, Anne, Magdalene; *ed:* Georgetown U at DC (BA) Eng 1953; Xivier Univ (MED) Ed 1961; MD Univ 33 Hrs; Columbia Univ 30 Hrs; *cr:* Greenhills HS Eng, Latin, Fr 1960-65; Ashara HS Eng, Latin, Fr 1965-67; Forrest Sherman HS Eng, Fr 1967-72; DGF HS Eng, Soc Stud 1972-; *ai:* Newspaper Spon; NEA 1960-65; AFT 1968-78; Knights of Columbus 1989-94; Sustained Superior 1979, 1981, 1983; Tchr of Yr 1981; Rota Naval Base Sr Tennis Singles Champ 1984.

HINDLE, PETER GAGE, Mathematics Teacher; *b:* New Bedford, MA; *ed:* Amherst Coll (BA) Math 1956; *cr:* Deerfield Acad Math Tchr 1956-; *ai:* Sr Class Adv; Morehead & Jefferson Schlsp Nominating Comm; Coord Soccer Prgm; JV Golf Coach; Dormitory Assoc; AP Reader; NCTM 1960-; First Church of Deerfield 1956-, Moderator, Auditor; NSF Grant Univ of ME: Co-Wrote Article; Former Pres CVS-ATMNE; *office:* Deerfield Acad Main St Deerfield MA 01342

HINDLEY, LEAH ROMETO, Mathematics Teacher; *b:* Middletown, NY; *ed:* Orange Cty Comm Coll (AA) 1989; SUNY at Binghamton (BA) Math 1990; City Coll of NY (MSEd) Math Ed 1995; SUNY at New Paltz Tchr Cert Math Ed 1992; Columbia Univ Tchrs Coll Pursuing MED in Math Ed; *cr:* Middletown HS Math Tchr 1993-; *ai:* Bldg Rep; Attendance Comm; NCTM 1992-; *office:* Middletown HS Gardner Ave Ext Middletown NY 10940*

HINDS, AGNES VERONICA, Mathematics Teacher; *b:* Georgetown, Guayna; *m:* Querino S'Abreli; *c:* Jinelle, Melissa, Simone; *ed:* Cyril Potter Coll (AS) K-12 Ed Tchr 1978; Brooklyn Coll (BA) Elem Ed 1988; NY Univ (MS) Scndry Math 1993; City Coll 21 Credit Hrs Admin, Supervision; 34 Credit Hrs Math Tchng, Scndry Brooklyn Coll, City Coll; *cr:* Dolphin Comm HS Math, Sci Tchr 1978-83; John Jay HS Educl Assoc 1983-88; Jackie Robinson Jr HS Math Tchr 1988-90; Margaret Douglas Jr HS Math Tchr 1990-; *ai:* Church Fund Raising, Pgrm Planning Comm; AFT, UFT 1988-; Kappa Delta Pi 1987-; Neighborhood Civil group 1988-; Colation of Block Assocs 1985-; *office:* IS 292 Margaret Douglas 300 Wyona St Brooklyn NY 11429*

HINE, MARIE (PETGRAVE), Retired Elementary Teacher; *b:* Orange, NJ; *ed:* Beaver Coll (BS) Early Chldhd Ed 1954; Columbia Univ Tchrs Coll (MA) Curr, Tchng Young Children 1967; Kean Coll Supvr Cert 1988; Addl Grad Stud Univ of Southern CA, Cornell Univ, Cortland St Univ, Kean Coll; *cr:* St Cloud Schl Kndgtn Tchr 1954-57, Second Grd Tchr 1957-58; Gregory Schl Kndgtn Tchr 1954-57, Second Grd Tchr 1957-58; Washington Schl Kndgtn Tchr 1954-57, Second Grd Tchr 1957-58; USAF Dependent Schls First Grd Tchr 1958-60; Newfield Cntrl Schl First Grd Tchr 1960-64; Boyden Schl Fourth Grd Tchr 1964-65; Jefferson Schl First Grd Tchr 1965-67; Roberts Schl First Grd Tchr 1967-70; Grant Schl First Grd Tchr 1970-80; Riley Schl First Grd Tchr 1980-94; *ai:* NEA, NJEA 1954-; NEA, NJEA Retired 1995-; NY St Ed Assn 1960-64; Newfield Cntrl Schl Tchrs Assn 1962-63, Pres; Union Cty Literacy Vol, Plainfield Resident Reader 1995-; Governor's Tchr Recognition Prgm 1991; *home:* 247 New Providence Rd Mountainside NJ 07092

HINEBAUGH, DEBRA K., Title I Resource Teacher; *b:* Dola, WV; *ed:* Frostburg St Univ (BS) Elem Ed 1975; (MS) Ed 1983; 30 Addl Hrs; *cr:* Tunnelton Elem Schl First Grd Tchr 1976-79; Dennett Road Elem Sch Sp Ed Tchr 1979-80, 2nd, 5th Grd Tchr 1980-82; Bradford Elem Sch 5th Grd Tchr 1982-93, Title I Resource Tchr 1993-; *ai:* NEA, MSTA 1976-; GCTA 1976-, Assn Rep; *office:* Broad Ford Elem Schl 607 Harvey Winters Rd Oakland MD 21550

HINEBAUGH, DONNA BUCKEL, 4th Grade Teacher; *b:* Oakland, MD; *c:* Christopher Shane Buckel, Alison Renee Buckel; *ed:* Garrett Comm Coll (AA) Elem 1984; Frostburg St Univ (BS) Elem 1985; Advanced Prof Cert; 30 Credits; *cr:* Broadford Elem Schl Kndgtn Tchr 1986-87; Accident Elem Schl 4th Grd Tchr 1987-; *ai:* Soc Comm; MSTA 1986-; Eisenhower Grant; *home:* PO Box 166 Accident MD 21520

HINER, DONALD JOHN, 7th-12th Grade Choral Director; *b:* Toledo, OH; *m:* Barb; *c:* Stephanie, Matthew; *ed:* Bowling Green St Univ (BA) Music Ed 1986; *cr:* Toledo Pub Schls Jr HS General Music Tchr 1986-87; Rossford HS Choral Dir 1987-; Rossford Jr HS Choral Dir 1987-; *ai:* Drama Vocal Dir; OEA, OMEA, NEA 1986-; ACDA 1996-; MENC 1986-, Outstanding Contributions Music Ed Awd 1992; SPEBSQSA 1986-, Intnl Quartet Champion 1991; Hunt-Wesson Performance Grant 1995; *office:* Rossford HS 701 Superior St Rossford OH 43460

HINES, AVON ADAMS, First Grade Teacher; *b:* Triplet, VA; *m:* Murphy R.; *ed:* Temple Univ (MS) Ed, Rdng 1976; Elem Gradwork Penn St; *cr:* Meherrin Powelton Schl Second Grd Tchr 1966-67; Lauer's Pk Schl Second Grd Tchr 1967-75; Thomas Ford Schl Second Grd Tchr 1975-77; 13th & Union Grds 4-6th Rdng Tchr 1977-79; 5th & Spring Schl Grds 4-6th Rdng Tchr 1977-79; 12th & Marion First Grd Tchr 1979-; *ai:* REA 1967-, Bldg Rep, Spec Svcs Chair; NEA 1967-, Del 8 Yrs; PSEA 1967-, Many Comms; SEW-N-SEW Club 1975-, Pres, Treas; PFO; *home:* 215 N Tulpehocken Rd Reading PA 19601*

HINES, DEBRA RHEN, Social Studies Teacher; *b:* Lebanon, PA; *m:* Anthony Jude; *c:* Lisa J., Daniel A.; *ed:* Shippensburg Univ (BS) Soc Stud 1982; 24 Grad Credits at Wilkes Coll & Millersville Univ; *cr:* Carlisle Area Schl Dist 1985-; *ai:* Stu Cncl Adv; CAEA, PSEA & NEA 1985-; St Patricks Cath Church Cncl 1994-, VP; *office:* Carlisle Area Schl Dist 623 W Penn St Carlisle PA 17013

HINES, FLORENCE ELLEN, Business & Marketing Ed Tchr; *b:* New Brunswick, NJ; *ed:* (BA) Bus Ed 1975; Mrktg Ed Cert 1986; Addl 20 Credit Hrs; *cr:* Ortho Diagnostics J. & J. Prsnl Sec 1975-; Rutgers Univ Sec 1976; South Brunswick HS Tchr, Coord 1976-; *ai:* Distributine Ed Clubs of Amer Adv; Manage Schl Store-Stu Trainees; Curr Comm; NJBEA, NJEA 1976-; SBEA 1976-, Dept Rep; NJMEA 1986-; NJEA-Caucus 1982-, Recording Sec; Pub Articles; Grant for Start-Up Mrktg Prgm Ed; *office:* S Brunswick HS Major Rd PO Box 183 Monmouth Junction NJ 08852

HINES, MARYANN, English & Journalism Teacher; *b:* Sharon, PA; *ed:* Kent St Univ (BS) Eng, Jrnlsm 1983; OH St Univ (MA) Eng Ed 1991; Post Grad Work Youngstonn St Univ, Otterbein Coll; *cr:* Westerville North HS Tchr, Adv 1985-; Southern Scholastic Press Assn Contest Judge 1993-; Great Lakes Interscholastic Press Assn Instr, Judge 1993-; *ai:* Schl Newspaper Adv; Tech Comm Mem; Jrnlsm Dept Head; Westerville Ed Assn 1985-, Fac Rep; NEA, NCTE 1985-; Jrnlsm Assn of OH Schls 1988-, Bd of Dir, Sec; St Stephens Comm Ctr, Columbus Museum of Art, Spec Project News Ed, Easter Seals Org; Ed Assn Educator of Yr; Martha Holdings Jennings Scholar; Natl Endowment for Hum Prgm Participant; *office:* Westerville North HS 950 County Line Rd Westerville OH 43082

HINES, PATRICIA A., Assistant Principal; *b:* Providence, RI; *m:* Salvatore V. Manforte; *c:* Tracy Manforte, Amanda Manforte; *ed:* RI Coll (BA) Eng 1972; Middlebury Coll (MA) Eng 1978; Providence Coll (MED) Scndry Admin 1991; Courses Taken in Schl Plant Planning, Gender-Ethnic Expectations, Stu Achvmt, Labor Relations in Ed; *cr:* East Providence HS Eng Tchr 1972-93; South Kingston HS Asst Prin 1993-; *ai:* Mentor Steering Comm; Schl to Work Coord; NASSP, RIASP 1993-; NECEL 1995-; *office:* South Kingstown HS 215 Columbia St So Kingstown RI 02879

HINES, ROBERT JOSEPH, English Teacher; *b:* Boston, MA; *m:* Marguerite R. Tortorici; *c:* Shawn C., Robert Blaise; *ed:* Boston Coll (BA) Eng 1967; Salem St Coll (MA) British Lit 1971; Suffolk Univ 15 Credit Hrs Admin; Malden HS 60 In-Service Credits Ed; *cr:* Brocton HS Eng Tchr 1967-69; Newbury Coll Continuing Ed, Eng Instr 1973-95; Malden HS Eng Tchr 1969-; E. F. Educl Tours 1990-; *ai:* Frgn Travel Cnslr; Bsbl Coach; Class, Newspaper Adv; NEA 1969-; MEA 1970-; Peabody Little League Coach 1976-80; Peabody Babe Ruth League Coach 1980-85; Summa Cum Laude 1990-, E. F. Educl Tours; Grant to Write Book 1988-90; Yrbk Dedication Tchr of Yr 1990.

HINES, SAMANTHA LEE, English Teacher; *b:* Newport, RI; *m:* Donald T. Farias II; *ed:* Univ of RI (BS) Ed, Eng 1990, (MA) Eng 1994; Attnd Flim Class 1995, Univ of London British Lit, Drama, Culture 1992, Roger Williams Univ Schl of Law Contracts, Torts, Legal Methods I 1995-; *cr:* Middletown HS Tutor 1990-91,Eng Tchr 1990-, SAT Preparation Instr 1991-93, Jrnlsm Tchr 1993-95; *ai:* Middletown NEA 1990-, Bldg Rep 1993-; Phi Kappa Phi, Kappa Delta Pi 1990-; Women's Resource Ctr 1993-95, Bd of Dirs, Pub Relations, Media Comm Chprsn, Vol Advocate; Eng Speaking Union Schlsp Univ of London; Deans Schlsp Roger Williams Univ Schl of Law; *office:* Middletown HS 130 Valley Rd Middletown RI 02842*

HINES, SUSAN KOHLER, German & Civics Teacher; *b:* Wooster, OH; *m:* Thomas J.; *ed:* OH St Univ (BSEd) Soc Stud 1974; Goethe Inst in Frankfurtam Main 1981; *cr:* Frankfurt Intnl Schl Soc Stud Tchr 1975-76; Frankfurt, M. Volkshochschule Schl EFL Tchr 1975-81; Xenopoulos Schl EFL Tchr 1983-84; Tuscarawas Vly HS Ger, Soc Stud Tchr 1986-; *ai:* OFLA, AATG 1986-; *office:* Tuscarawas Vly HS 2637 Tusky Vly Rd NE Zoarville OH 44656

HINES, VERNA J., Reading Specialist; *b:* Columbus, OH; *m:* Claude; *c:* Janet Ruark, David; *ed:* OH Wesleyan Univ (BS) Elem Ed 1972, Rdng Specialty 1973; 30 Hrs; *cr:* Big Walnut Local Rdng Spec & Classroom Tchr 1975-; *ai:* B W Ed Assn, Treas; NHS Adv; Carver Ed Bldg Rep Best Comm Steering Comm; Lit Ed & Advocacy Forum, Sec; IRA 1975-; Career Ed Assn 1980-; Big Walnut Ed Assn 1983-; Career Ed Conf 1985, OH Cncl of Intnl Rdng Assn Conf Presenter; *office:* Big Walnut HS 555 S Old 3c Hwy Sunbury OH 43074*

HINKLE, BRIAN DARYL, 9th-12th Grd Soc Stud Teacher; *b:* Columbus, OH; *m:* Maura Attridge; *c:* Kelly, Jennifer; *ed:* OH St Univ (BS) Soc Stud Ed 1979; 30 Hrs Post Grad Stud Univ of MD; *cr:* Elmwood Local Schls Soc Stud Tchr 1980-81; Montgomery Cty Pub Schls Soc Stud Tchr 1984-; *ai:* NEA; MSTA; *office:* Montgomery Blair HS 313 Wayne Ave Silver Spring MD 20910

HINKLEY, BRIAN DAVID, Band Director & Music Teacher; *b:* Waynesboro, VA; *ed:* Oberlin Coll (BA) Trombone, Euphonium Performance 1985, (BA) Music His 1985, (MA) Music Ed 1986; Addl Stud Cleveland St Univ, Baldwin Wallace Coll, Western MD; *cr:* Maple Heights Schls Band Dir 1986-91; Linganore HS Band Dir 1991-95; Hood Coll Band Dir, Brass Instr 1994-; Urbana HS Band Dir, Arts Chprsn 1995-; *ai:* Instrumental Music Ensembles Coord; NEA, MENC 1986-; Outstanding Tchr Awd Frederick Cty Chamber of Commerce 1994-95; *office:* Urbana HS 3471 Campus Dr Ijamsville MD 21754

HINMAN, ROBERT GUY, 5th Grade Classroom Teacher; *b:* Akron, OH; *m:* Margaret Ann; *c:* Amy Shade, Robert M., Leigh Ann; *ed:* Akron Univ (BS) PE & Earth Sci 1968 & Elem Ed; 150 Post Grad Hrs; *cr:* Barberton City Schls 6th Grd Tchr 16 Yrs, 5th Grd Tchr 12 Yrs; *ai:* Prins Asst; Various Textbook Comms; Math Textbook Comm Chair; Barberton Ed Assn, OH Ed Assn & NEA 1968-; Whos Who in Elem Ed; Jaycees Young Educator of Yr Nom; Barberton Educator of Yr 1988; *office:* Woodford Elem Schl 315 E State St Barberton OH 44203

HINO, LYNN (PAQUIN), Fifth Grade Teacher; *b:* Watertown, NY; *m:* John B.; *c:* David; *ed:* SUNY at Cobleskill (AAS) Nursery Ed 1970; SUC at Potsdam (BA) Elem Ed 1972; BUC at Buffalo (MS) Elem Ed 1979; 6 Addl Hrs; *cr:* St Leo the Great Tchr 1972-74; Lewiston-Porter Tchr 1981-; *ai:* AFT, NYSUT 1987-; *home:* 755 Scovell Dr Lewiston NY 14092

HINOTSKY, GEORGE PHILIP, 6th Grade Teacher; *b:* Ilion, NY; *m:* Susan G.; *c:* Justin E., Jocelyn M.; *ed:* SUC at Oneonta (BS) Elem Ed 1991; 30 Credit Hrs Permanent Tchng Cert SUNY at Cortland; *cr:* Poland Cntrl Schl 4th Grd Tchr 7 Yrs, 5th Grd Tchr 1 Yr, 6th Grd Tchr 17 Yrs; *ai:* Bowling Adv; NY St Bsbl Umpire; Mohawk Vly Bsbl Umpire 5 Yrs; AFT, NYSUT 1971-; Associated Poland Tchrs 1971-, Treas; NYSBUA, MVBUA 1991-; Herkimer Little League 1984-90, Bd Mem; Elem Tchr of Yr Runnerup 1994-95; *office:* Poland Central Schl Rt 8 Poland NY 13431*

HINRICHS, RAYMOND D., Latin Teacher; *b:* Martinton, IL; *m:* Kathleen A. Kinsella; *c:* Kara, Amie; *ed:* Holy Cross Seminary (AB) Philosophy 1962; IL St Univ (MA) Ed Admin 1968; OH St Univ (PHD) Stu Dev 1974; *cr:* OH Dept of Ed Ed Consultant, Planning, Evaluation 1973-79; Cath Conf of OH St, Fed Ed Pgrms Coord 1979-82; St Joseph Montessori Schl Dir 1982-84; Columbus Pub Schls Latin Tchr 1984-; Pontifical Coll Josephinum Lectureer in Latin 1986-; *ai:* Latin Club Adv; Greater Columbus Latin Club 1985-, Treas; Amer Classical League, OH Classical Conf 1985-; OH Historical Soc 1980-; Nature Conservancy 1985-; Involved in Music over 35 Yrs.

HINSDALE, DENNIS MINFORD, Girls JV Basketball Coach; *b:* Corry, PA; *m:* Carole Lictus; *c:* Kyle James, Sarah Marie; *ed:* Northwood Univ (BA) Hotel, Restaurant Mngmt 1975; Buffalo St Univ Cert Water Systems Operator License; *cr:* Clymer Cntrl Schl Girls JV Bsktbl Coach 1990-; Lictus Keystone Inc VP; *ai:* Schl Bldg Comm; Core Team; Sports Boosters Club; NYS Water Operators Assn, Rural Water Assn 1979-; Empire St Petroleum Assn 1988-; Vol Fire Dept 1976-, Sec; United Meth Church 1976-, Trustee; *home:* PO Box 202 Clymer NY 14724

HINTON, KEITH MILTON DUANE, 7th & 8th Grd English Teacher; *b:* Bushkill Twp, PA; *m:* Suzanne Harr; *c:* Kimberly, Joshua, Erik; *ed:* Kutztown Univ (BS) Eng 1975; Masters Equivalency in Eng & Lit at Millersville Univ; *cr:* South Eastern MS 6th-8th Grd Eng & Lang Arts Tchr 1975-; *ai:* 8th Grd Team Ldr; Stu Assistance Prgm; Boys Jr HS Var Bsktbl Coach; Schl Dist Tech Comm; Gymnastics Club & Cmptr Club Adv; NEA, PSEA, SEEA 1975-; SAA Bsbl, Barrens Soccer 1985-, Coach; *home:* 20 Ovelton Ave Stewartstown PA 17363

HINTON, REBECCA STINGLEY, Lecturer in English; *b:* Dayton, OH; *m:* Huland Orville Jr.; *c:* Catherine Dykster, Michael, Joseph, Rosemary, Sean; *ed:* Univ of Dayton (BA) Eng 1967; Wright St Univ (MA) Eng 1984; Miami Univ (PHD) Eng 1990; Course in Old Testament Lit at Athenaeum of OH 1996; *cr:* Wright St Univ Grad Asst 1982-84; Miami Univ Tchng Fellow & Visiting Asst Prof 1984-93; IN Univ East Instr 1993-95; Clermont Coll Lecturer 1994-; Xavier Univ Lecturer 1995-; *ai:* Eucharistic Minister; INADE 1994-95; Miami Univ Sinclair Alumni Flwshp 1984-85, Dissertation Flwshp 1989-90; Numerous Articles Pub; *office:* Clermont Coll UC 4200 Clermont Coll Dr Batavia OH 45103

HINTZ, CATHERINE COOK, 3rd Grade Teacher; *b:* Providence, RI; *m:* David C.; *c:* Katharine, Julie; *ed:* SUC at Geneseo (BS) Elem Ed 1969; Addl 30 Credit Hrs; *cr:* Solvay Elem Schl 3rd-5th Grd Tchr 1969-; *ai:* AFT, NEA, STA 1969-; West Genesee Jaycettes 1979-82, Sec, VP; Cntrl NY Art Guild 1994-; *office:* Solvay Elem Schl 701 Woods Rd Syracuse NY 13209

HINTZE, STACEY (BURKE), HS Art Teacher; *b:* Brooklyn, NY; *m:* James L.; *ed:* Sarah Lawrence Coll (BA) Art, Art His 1985; Columbia Univ (MA) Art Ed 1987; *cr:* Monroe Woodbury HS Art Tchr & Drama Coach 1988-; *ai:* Drama Club Adv, Dir; Frosh Class Adv; Prom Comm; Musical Productions Dir; Extracurricular Policies Comm; NAEA, NEA 1987-; NYSUT; Natl Gallery Grant 1993; Pursuit of Excl Awd 1996; *office:* Monroe-Woodbury Sr HS Old Dunderberg Rd Central Valley NY 10917

HIRSCH, JANET LOUISE, English Department Chairperson; *b:* Warren, OH; *ed:* Mount Union Coll (BA) Eng Ed 1968; Post Scndry Grad Hrs at Univ of Akron, Ashland Univ; *cr:* Salem Jr HS Eng Tchr 1968-69; Louisville HS Eng Tchr 1969-; *ai:* Lang Arts & Composition, Curr Comms; NEA 1968-; NCTE 1995-; Delta Kappa Gamma 1978-; Mount Union Coll Women's Club 1980-; Louisville Lion's Club Tchr of Month 1995; *office:* Louisville Sr HS 1201 S Nickelplate St Louisville OH 44641

HIRSCH, MARY EDITH, Pastoral Minister; *b:* Erie, PA; *ed:* Mercyhurst Coll (BS) Elem Ed 1962; Gannon Univ (MA) Rel Ed 1977; 18 Credit Hrs Mercyhurst Coll; 9 Credit Hrs IN Univ at Bloomington; 8 Credit Hrs KS St Univ at Manhattan; 8 Credit Hrs Carlow Coll; *cr:* Mc Kean PA Post Office Clerk 1937-41; Erie Resistor Corp Shipping Dept 1941-47; Erie Diocesan Schls Tchr, Rel Ed Tchr, Coord 1947-91; St Titus Church Pastoral Minister 1991-; Neighborhood House Taught 1 Summer; *ai:* Schl Supervising; Mission Club Act; Altar Servers; Parish Cncl 1970-71, 1991-; Schl Bd 1970-, Chprsn Nominating Comm, Sec 1985-87; Parish Staff 1991-; Altar Rosary Soc 1991-, Spiritual Adv; PTC 1970-; Few Poems & Articles Pub; *home:* 506 W Spring St Titusville PA 16354

HIRSCHBEIN-BODNAR, SUSAN B., Home Economics Teacher; *b:* Brooklyn, NY; *m:* Perry Bodnar Jr.; *c:* Eric; *ed:* OH St Univ (BS) Home Ecs 1968; Hofstra Univ (MA) Scndry Ed 1973; C. W. Post Coll (MS) Nutrition 1980; Brooklyn Coll Cert of Certification for NY Admin Tchrs; *cr:* Longbeach MS Home Ecs Tchr 1968-80; Long Beach HS Home Ecs Tchr 1980-86; Longbeach MS HE Tchr 1986-87; Long Beach HS Home Ecs Tchr 1987-, Hlth Ed 1987-; *ai:* Boys, Girls MS Tennis Coach; AFT, Long Beach Tchrs Assn 1968-; US Tennis Assn 1980-; Cty Hm Ec Tchrs Assn; Kappa Delta Pi; *office:* Long Beach HS 322 Lagoon Dr W Lido Beach NY 11561*

HIRSCHFIELD, JANE E., Biology Teacher; *b:* Perth Amboy, NJ; *m:* Joseph; *c:* Marc, Lisa; *ed:* Univ of WI (BS) Microbiology, Chem 1962; Long Island Univ (MS) Med Microbiology 1984; 30 Addl Hrs; *cr:* White Plains Hosp Med Technologist 1962-63; Leder Le Labs Rsrch Biologist 1963-67; North Rockland Pediatrics Med Technologist 1977-80; Adlai Stevenson HS Bio Tchr, Med Lab Techniques 1981-; *ai:* Biomedical Prgm; AFT, UFT 1981-; AAM 1962-; New City Jewish Ctr 1973-, VP Programming, VP Fund Raising; ORT 1973-, Pres; Articles Pub; *office:* Adlai E Stevenson HS 1980 Lafayette Ave Bronx NY 10473*

HIRSCHHORN, RONNIE RIBACK, HS Social Studies Teacher; *b:* New York City, NY; *m:* Daniel; *c:* Zev David, Jeremy Beth; *ed:* Hunter Coll (BA) His 1966; Queens Coll (MS) Ed, Soc Stud 1968; 60 Post Grad Credits; *cr:* James Monroe HS Soc Stud Tchr 1966; Forest Hills HS Soc Stud Tchr 1966-73; Somers HS Soc Stud Tchr 1983-; *ai:* Diversity Comm; HS Food Patch Coord; Fac Assn Bldg Rep 3 Yrs; Westchester Cncl for Soc Stud, NCSS 1980-; Participating in Year Long Grant; *office:* Somers HS Rt 139 Lincolndale NY 10540

HIRSHLAND, JUDY L., Spanish Teacher; *b:* Reading, PA; *ed:* Kutztown Univ (BA) Span, (BA) Pol Sci 1985; Cert Scndry Ed 1988; *cr:* Lackawanna Trail Schl Dist Span Tchr 1989-90; Eastern Lebanon Cty Schl Dist Span Tchr 1990-; *ai:* Span Club Adv; *office:* Eastern Lebanon Co Sr HS 180 Elco Dr Myerstown PA 17067*

HIRSHSON, JANET, Third Grade Teacher; *b:* Bronx, NY; *m:* Stanley; *c:* Scott; *ed:* Queens Coll (BA) Elem Ed 1967, (MA) Elem Ed 1972; OWL Courses; Attnd Hofstra Univ; *cr:* Parkside Elem Schl Second Grd Tchr 1967-79; Parliament Place Elem Schl Third Grd Tchr 1981-; *ai:* Grd Level Chm; Lang Arts, Soc Stud Comm; AFT, NEA, North Babylon Tchrs Assn 1967-; ORT 1974-; B'Nai B'Rith Women 1974-, Life Mem; Temple Beth El 1986-93, Bd of Ed; *office:* North Babylon Elem Schls 5 Jardin Pl North Babylon NY 11703*

HISSONG, JEFFREY KEITH, Spanish II, IV & Psych Tchr; *b:* Canton, OH; *ed:* Malone Coll (BA) Ed, Span, Psych 1971; Kent St Univ (MED) Ed, Span 1978; Italian, Ger, Eng; Univ of Valencia in Spain Span 1969-70, Post Grad Span 1972-79; Conducted Stu Stud Tours of Spain, Mexico; Cert Mentor Tchr; *cr:* Fairless HS Span I- IV, Psych Tchr, Lang Arts Dept Chm 1971-; Adult Ed Intnl Bus Span Local Bus Instr, Course Designer 1978-82; *ai:* Lang Arts Dept Chm; Advanced Placement Coord; Lang Arts Curr Dev, Stu Proficiency Test Intervention Prgm Chm; Stu Testing Assessment, Supts Communication Comms; Chess Club Adv; NEA, OEA 1971-; Fairless Educators Assn 1971-, VP 1976; OH Foreign Lang Assn 1971-, Annual Conf Presenter; Milone Coll Alumni Assn 1971-, Dist Fund Raising; Am Heart Assn 1990-, Fund Raising; Sons of Union Veterans of Civil War 1989-; Stark Cty Tchr of Week 1992; Elected by Sr Class Tchr of Yr 1984; Elected by NHS Tchr of Yr 1979; Jennings Scholar 1978-79; OH Schl Bds Assn Outstanding Stu Proficiency Test Intervention Prgm Chm 1993; *home:* 724 Circle Hill Rd SE North Canton OH 44720

HITCHEN, MARRILEE VAN CLEVE, 4th Grade Teacher; *b:* St Marys, OH; *m:* David; *c:* Douglas, Andrew; *ed:* Delta St Coll (BSE) Elem Ed 1961; Univ of Toledo (MSE) Rdng, Elem Ed 1983; 12 Addl Hrs; OH St Univ Pre-Nrsng; *cr:* Middletown Schls 1st Grd Tchr 1961-63; Genoa Schls 1st-4th Grd, Rdng Tchr 1963-66, 1978-; Oregon Schls 1st Grd Tchr 1966-68; *ai:* Textbook Selection Comms; Spec Needs Stdnts Intervention; GAAFT Pub Relations; OEA, NEA 1961-, Sec; GAAFT, AFT 1990-; OCIRA, IRA 1980-, Sec, Treas, Pres; Belle Ami 1970-, Pres, Treas, Sec; Ottawa Co Bd of Ed Math Grant; *home:* 22903 W Walnut Ln Genoa OH 43430

HITCHENS, GRACE WILLIAMS, Fourth Grade Teacher; *b:* Clarksville, DE; *m:* Billy J.; *c:* Tammy Murray, Kevin, Keith, Gregory; *ed:* Salisbury St (BS) Elem Ed 1964; Addl 40.40 Credit Hrs; *cr:* Georgetown Elem Schl 3rd Grd Tchr 1964-65, 2nd Grd Tchr 1966-67; Lord Baltimore Elem Schl 4th Grd Tchr 1967-; *ai:* NEA 1964-; Order of Eastern Star 1960-, Worthy Matron 1969; Amer Legion Auxiliary 1979-, Sec 1980-84; Tchr of Yr 1982; Indian River Schl Dist Order of Excl 1991; *home:* RR 2 Box 101D Dagsboro DE 19939

HITCHMAN, KELLY PATRAW, Guidance Counselor; *b:* Massena, NY; *m:* Donald; *c:* Kale, Tyler; *ed:* Potsdam St (BA) Psych 1987; St Lawrence Univ (MS) Cnslng 1988; *cr:* Carthage Cntrl Schl Elem Cnslr 1988-90; Clifton-Fine Cntrl Schl Guid Cnslr 1990-; *ai:* Aids Peer Ldrshp Ldr; NHS Adv; HS Shared Decision-Making Team; Benchmarking Comm; Alpha Team; Bsktbl Timekeeper; Stu Cncl Co-Adv; NYSUT, NACD 1988-; Church Liturgy Reader 1994-; *home:* PO Box 177 Star Lake NY 13690

HITE, ANN M., English Teacher; *b:* Whiteville, NC; *m:* Anderson B.; *c:* Latoya; *ed:* NC Cntrl Univ (BA) Eng & Ed 1967; Tchng Rdng 3 Hrs; Tchng the Spcl Needs Child 3 Hrs; *cr:* Gordon Jr HS Eng Tchr 1967-74; IBM Corp Software Analyst 1974-93; Crossland HS Eng Tchr 1993-; *ai:* NHS Spon; After Schl Tutorial Rdng & Writing Pgm; 11th Grd Team Ldr; SAT Prep Team Ldr; Numerous IBM Awds for Outstdng Svc; *office:* Crossland HS 6901 Temple Hill Rd Temple Hills MD 20748

HITE, MARY SIMMS, Business Education Teacher; *b:* Powhatan, VA; *m:* Monroe C. Jr.; *c:* Monroe C. III, Monique C.; *ed:* St Pauls Coll (BS) Bus Ed 1967; Cntrl MI Univ (MA) Prsnl Mgmt 1986; Continuing Ed Leadership at Univ of DE; *cr:* S C Abrams HS Bus Ed Tchr Northeast HS Bus Ed Tchr 1968-69; Christiana HS Bus Ed Tchr Bus Prof of America Adv; NEA, DSEA & CEA 1968-; DE Bus 1969-; AVA 1971-; Wilmington Alumnae Chapter of Delta Sig 1969-; NAACP 1969-; 8th St Bapt Church 1969-; Notary Pub 1 Bus Prof of Amer Brd of Trustee; St Bus Prof of Amer Brd of Dir of Amer Alumni Mem; *home:* 1322 Barksdale Rd Newark DE 1

HITE, NAN E., History Teacher; *m:* William; *c:* Stephen, Mark *ed:* Heidelberg Coll (BA) Soc Stud, His 1976, (MA) Ed; *cr:* Detention Ctr Head of Schl 1977-79; TIffin Jr HS His Tchr 1 OEA, NEA 1978-; *home:* 59 Harvest Ln Tiffin OH 44883

HITZEL, SUSAN HERBERT, 3rd Grade Teacher; *b:* Atlantic *m:* Edward R.; *c:* Nicholas, Natalie; *ed:* Glassboro St (BA) Elem *cr:* H. Russell Swift Schl 3rd Grd Tchr 1976-91; C. J. Davenpor Grd Tchr 1991-; *ai:* NJEA 1976-; Alpha Delta Kappa 1994-; C Achvmt Awd.*

HIXON, JAMES THOMAS, Retired Business Ed Teacher; *b:* Cl OH; *ed:* OH Univ (BBA) Bus Admin 1966; Xavier Univ 6 Cred *cr:* Huntington HS Bus Ed Tchr 1970-95; *ai:* Bus Stu of Month Comm; Ath Hall of Fame Organizational & Selection Comm, Me Huntingto Local Ed Assn 1970-, Pres 1973, Outstanding Tchr of Educator of Yr 1987; RCEA, COTA, OEA, NEA 1970-; OH Assn; Ross Cnty Ret Tchrs Assn; Ross Cty Humane Soc 1990-, Soc; Pump House Art Gallery, AARP 1991-; OH Univ Lindley S Friends of Hospice; Comm Schl Bus Advy Cncl Rep Selected by Supt of Schls.

HIXSON, HEATHER A., Fifth Grade Teacher; *b:* Springdale Salem Coll (BS) Elem Ed 1986; Edinboro Univ (MS) Elem Ed Conelway Elem 5th Grd Tchr 1986-; *ai:* Elem Girls Bsktbl Coach CAEA, PSEA & NEA 1986-; *office:* Conelway Elem Schl 18700 Rd Corry PA 16407

HIZNAY, JEROME JOSEPH, Social Studies Teacher; *b:* You OH; *m:* Ann Marie E. Kozar; *c:* Ann Marie N., Jessica; *ed:* Youn Univ (BA) His 1973, (MA) His 1986; 30 Credit Semester Hrs of Stud in Ed from Ashland Univ, Walsch Coll, Drake Univ, & Seattle-Pacific; *cr:* Portland Jr High Eng & Soc Stud Tchr Springfield HS Soc Stud Tchr 1976-; *ai:* Stu Cncl Adv; Acad Ch Quiz Bowl Team Adv; Soc Stud Course of Stud Comm; OEA & N SLCTA 1976-, Negotiator 1995; OH Cncl of Soc Stud 1981-; 1986-92; Phi Delta Kappa 1991-; Ohaska Bsktbl Official 1992-; S Apostle Parish Cncl 1993-; YSU Marion E Blum Outstdng Grad E 1985; Martha Holden Jennings Scholar 1991; Mahoning & Sher Industrial Inst for Ed Outstdng Tchr 1995; *office:* Springfield Youngstown Pittsburgh Rd New Middletown OH 44442*

HIZNY, KIMBERLY ANN KUBISA, HS Mathematics Te Johnson City, NY; *m:* Michael Paul; *c:* Kassandra Lynn; *ed:* Broo Coll (AS) Bus Admin 1987; SUNY at Cortland (BS) Scndry M Binghamton Univ (MSEd) Math Ed 1995; *cr:* Maine Union-Endicott Sub Tchr 1990-91; Vestal Schl Dist Sub Tchr Owego-Apalachin Cntrl Schls HS Math Tchr 1991-; *ai:* B Instructional Strategies Comm; NYSUT 1991-; Owego-Apalac Assn 1991-; *office:* Owego Free Acad George St Owego NY 138

HLADIO, PAUL R., Physics & Math Teacher; *b:* Sewickley, PA M. Masciola; *ed:* Duquesne Univ (BS) Physics 1988, (MS) Ed Ambridge Area HS Physics, Math Tchr 1992-; *ai:* Documentary Co-Spon; Stage Crew Spon; NEA, PSEA, AAEA 1992-; Duque Tamburitzans Alumni Assn 1988-, Pres 1994-95; *office:* Ambridge 909 Duss Ave Ambridge PA 15003

HLADKY, CAROLYN WELCH, First Grade Teacher; *b:* Mem *m:* Roger F.; *c:* Holly Jeanne Pruitt; *ed:* Harding Univ (BA) Elem *cr:* Southampton Elem Schl 2nd Grd Tchr 1963-65; Shamong Schl 1st Grd Tchr 1965-66; Southampton Elem Schl 2nd Grd Tchr Green Bank Elem Schl Remedial Rdng Tchr 1972-80, 1st Grd Tc *ai:* Annual Art Contest, Halloween Parade, Annual Christmas Prgm Spons; Yrbk Co-Spon; Tchr in Charge; NEA, NJEA, BCE GBEA 1972- Mbrshp Chprsn, Treas, VP; Delaware Vly Chrstn Assn 1972-; *office:* Green Bank Elem Schl 2436 Route 563 Eg City NJ 08215

HLASTA, CHESTER PAUL, 8th Grd Amer History Tea Youngstown, OH; *m:* Mary Gail Crumpler; *c:* Melissa; *ed:* Sou Univ (BSE) Soc Stud 1973; Youngstown St Univ (MSE Principalship 1980; Occptnl Wk Adjmnt 1995 OH St Univ; *cr* Local Schl Dist 8th Grd Amer His Tchr 1973-; Occptnl Wk Adj Coord; *ai:* Boy's Var, Jr Var, 8th Grd Bsktbl Coach; Ski Club; His Asst Girls Var Bsktl; NEA, OEA, Liberty Ed Assn 1973-, F Trumbull Cty Coaches 1973-, OH St Coaches Assn 1987-, Bsk Coach of Yr, Golf Coach of Yr; Girard Recreation Dept 199 Coach; Liberty Ath Boosters 1973-; Girard Ath Boosters 1993-; Tchr of Yr; 5 Liberty Educl Endowment Fund Grants; OH Voc *office:* W S Guy MS 4115 Shady Rd Youngstown OH 44505

HLAVATY, NANCY, Math Teacher; *b:* Scranton, PA; *m:* Paul; Wendy; *ed:* Univ Scranton (BS) Ed Math 1986, (MA) Ed Math 19 Wood Coll Admin Cert 1994; *ai:* Natl & Jr Hon Soc; NCTM 1986- Tchr Math 1986-; N Eastern Pa Cncl Tchr 1986-, Cty Rep; PA Dep Prep Grant; *office:* Lackawanna Trail HS PO Box 85 RD 1 Factor 18419*

HLAWATY, HEIDE, Chemistry Teacher; *b:* New York City, SUNY at Stony Brook (B S) Biochemistry 1987; Hunter C Biochemistry 1993; Tchng Cert at Marymount Manhattan Coll 1 Grad Stud at Coll at St Rose NY in Spcl Ed; Credit Hrs For Liscense at Queens Coll NY; *cr:* NY Blood Ctr Rsrch Technician John Adams HS Chem & Bio Tchr 1991-; *ai:* Yrbk, Peer Mediatic Drama Advs; HIV Edctr; AFT 1991-; NEA 1991-; GTEV Schlie Stamm 1988-, VP; Fulbright Exchange Tchr to Germany; *home:* St Elmont NY 11003*

HLIVKO, RICHARD PAUL, Math Teacher; *b:* Steubenville, OH Ann Parker; *ed:* Jefferson Tech Coll (AAD) Drafting & Design 1 Liberty St Coll (BS) Math 1984, (BS) Scndry Ed 1985; 13 C Towards Masters Math; *cr:* East Liverpool HS Math Tchr 1985 Forensics 1986-; *ai:* Debate Coach; E Liverpool Ed Assoc 198 Dirs; OH Ed Assoc 1985-; NEA 1985-; *office:* East Liverpool Maine Blvd East Liverpool OH 43920

HLOPKO, JANE A., Assoc Prof of Hlth Tech Pgm; *b:* Johnson *m:* Gerald D.; *c:* Andrea M.; *ed:* Broome Comm Coll (AAS) Record Tech 1974; Binghamton Univ (BS) Applied Soc Sci 198 Soc Sci 1987; *cr:* River Mede Manor Nursing Home Medical Re 1974-76; Broome Comm Coll Instr, Asst Prof Hlth Information T 1976-; *ai:* Writing Across Campus, Stu Act Coll Comms; A Information Tech Club; Amer Hlth Info Mgt Assn, NY Hlth Info M NY St Hlth Info Mgt 1975-; Active St John Evangelist Schl; Par Guild 1989-, Chm Hospitality Comm; Outstanding MASS Binghamton Univ 1987; *office:* Broome Community College PO Binghamton NY 13902

JACQUELINE ELIZABETH, 8th Grade Science Teacher; *b:* OH; *m:* John Harry Jr.; *c:* Christopher Daniel, Tiffany Marie; *ed:* Coll (BA) Sci 1973; MALL Marietta Coll (MA) Liberal Learning : Warren Local 7th-8th Grd Tchr 1973-74; Belpre City Schls 8th Tchr 1974-; *ai:* 8th Grd Team; OEA, NEA, BEA 1973-; *office:* S Stone Rd Belpre OH 45714

, KEVIN ANDREW, Associate Professor of Art; *b:* Akron, OH; aret Mary; *c:* Kendra Meret, Mathew Quinn; *ed:* Kent St Univ (BS) 973, (MFA) Ceramics, Sculpture 1978; *cr:* St Cloud St Univ Art f 1979-82; Montgomery Coll Art Assoc Prof 1982-; Kenyatta Univ Fulbright Lecturer 1985-87; Yarmouk Univ Visiting Fulbright 1992-93; *ai:* Coll Art Assn 1995-; MD St Art Cncl Individual NEA Ceramics Exhibition Grants; *home:* 102 E 8th St Frederick)1

OSEPH MICHAEL,JR., Social Studies Teacher; *b:* Passaic, NJ; of NV (BS) PE 1964; Montclair St Admin; *cr:* E. Otis Vaughn Jr, chr, Coach 1964-67; Wallington HS Tchr, Coach 1967-; *ai:* Stu ord; WEA, BCTA, NJEA, NEA 1964-; Hillside Soc Ath Club P, Treas; Knights of Columbus; Amer Legion.

MARY NERI, Kindergarten Teacher; *b:* Bridgeport, CT; *m:* ichard; *ed:* Southern CT St Univ (BS) Early Chldhd Ed 1969; Univ eport (MS) Elem Ed 1976; 6th Yr Cert Classroom Tchr Specialist ern CT St Univ 1996; *cr:* Garden Schl First Grd Tchr 1969-70; on Schl First Grd Tchr 1970-72; Franklin Schl Kndgtn Tchr 1972-; Improvement Comm; Stratford TAWL Mbrshp Chair; PTA Tchr er Schl Story Hour; NEA 1969-; Stratford Ed Assn 1969-, Human s Comm Co-Chm; Phi Delta Kappa 1995-; Kndgtn Assn of CT Milford Newcomers 1979-84; *office:* Franklin Schl 1895 Barnum tford CT 06497

SANDRA JEAN, Fourth Grade Teacher; *b:* Fulton, NY; *m:* Bruce p F.; *ed:* SUNY at Oswego (BA) Elem Ed 1963, (MS) Elem Ed ddl 33 Hrs Beyond Masters Degree; *cr:* Walter Hurst Elem Schl 2nd r 1963; Chestnut Hill Elem Schl 3rd Grd Tchr 1964; Weatherly 3rd Grd Tchr 1965; Craven Crawford Schl Primary Lvels Tchr Coram Elem Schl 3rd Grd Tchr 1970-71; Elmcrest Elem Schl 3rd Tchr 1972-; *ai:* Dist Math, Dist Soc Stud, Author Comms; Schl ects; 4th Grd Act Coord; AFT, NYSTA 1963-; ULFA 1963-, Schl YSSC 1988-; Boy Scout Merit Badge Cnslr 1985-; 1995 Impact II Grant; *office:* Elmcrest Elem Schl 350 Woodspath Rd Liverpool 0*

AND, JANICE HONAKER, Math Teacher; *b:* Xenia, OH; *m:* Russell; *c:* Jessica, Erin; *ed:* Muskingum Coll (BS) Math Ed 1980; St Univ (MED) Ed 1994; *cr:* Cedar Cliff MS Math Tchr 1980-82; nt HS Math Tchr 1982-86; Mad-River HS Math Tchr 1986-; *ai:* mpetition Club Adv; OFT & AFT 1989-; WSUATM & NCTM ffice: Greenon H S 3950 S Tecumseh Rd Springfield OH 45502*

THOMAS C., 7th Grd World History Teacher; *b:* Westmoreland *m:* Ruth Ann Spencer; *c:* Ashley Lyn; *ed:* CA State Coll (BSEd)); Duquesne Univ (MSEd) His 1975; *cr:* Norwin 6th St Jr High is Tchr 1970-87; Norwin MS East World His & Amer His Tchr i: Cheetak Team Ldr; Field Trip Coord & Spon; Norwin Ed Assn SEA 1970-; NEA 1970-; N Huntingdon Rescue 8 Squad 1972-, ustee, Sec & Heavy Rescue Technician, 10, 15 & 20 Yr Svc Awds; Schl Dist 20 & 25 Yr Svc Awds; *office:* Norwin MS East 1 Main St untingdon PA 15642

PATRICIA ANN, English Teacher; *b:* Cincinnati, OH; *m:* Mark bastian, Kerry; *ed:* Coll of MT St Joseph (BA) Eng, Scndry Ed Addl Hrs in Eng Lit; *cr:* Seton HS Eng Tchr 1992-; *ai:* Frosh Class or; Collaboriation Coord; NCTE 1992-; Cincinnati Archdiocese Miami Univ; OH Writers Project; *office:* Seton HS 3901 Glenway cinnati OH 45205*

TIMOTHY JOHN, Physics Instructor; *b:* Milford, MA; *m:* Susan llard; *c:* Catherine M., Jessica L., T. Matthew; *ed:* Univ of MA at (BS) Fisheries Mgmt 1970; Worcester Polytechnic Inst (MNS) Sci 1979; 12 Credit Hrs; 6 Credit Hrs MA Marine Consortium; 11 rs Framingham St Coll; 6 Credit Hrs Fitchburg St Coll; *cr:* Eagle Sci, PE Instr, Tutor & Coach 1970-71; Franklin Jr High Sci Tchr Franklin HS Physics & Sci Instr 1991-; *ai:* MA Tchrs Assn EA 1971-; FEA 1971-; UPDATE 1993-; MSTA 1994-; AAPT lks 1974-78; Franklin Conserv Comm 1974-76, Sec; *office:* HS 218 Oak St Franklin MA 02038

T-KOVATCH, JOAN, Accounting & Business Teacher; *b:* d, OH; *m:* Duane; *ed:* Bowling Green St Univ (BS) Bus Ed, Admin ke Erie Coll Working on Masters; *cr:* Willoughby-Eastlake Schls nensive Bus Ed, Cmptr Sci Tchr 1976-; *ai:* NEA 1976-; Local PTA; vded; Advy Comm for Voc Bus Prgms 1976-84; *office:* Willoughby S 5000 Shankland Rd Willoughby OH 44094*

, DIANE ROSSI, First Grade Teacher; *b:* NYC, NY; *m:* Henry T.; el, Allison, Scott; *ed:* Hunter Coll (BA) Pol Sci 1970; Queens Coll m Ed 1973; Adelphi Univ (MS) Spec Ed 1995; Great Books; Space ions with NASA; Family Living, Sex Ed; Tchng the ESL Child; buse; Columbia Writing Process; *cr:* PS 15 K First Grd Tchr PS 94 K Third Grd Tchr 1971-73; PS 18 Q Cross Graded Gifted Tchr 1983-86, Third Grd Tchr 1986-91, First Grd Tchr 1991-; *ai:* y Chldhd Comm; Presenting Dist-Wide Wkshp for Tchrs Coords, FT; NYSUT; BSA 1995-, Sec; Church of St Aidan 1994-, Sub Tchr; lliston Book Discussion Group 1984-; Won Dist Mini-Grant tions 1985-94; Schl, Dist Prsnl Wkshps Presenter; *office:* PS 18 5th Ct Bellerose NY 11427*

, LORRA RHODES, Guidance Counselor; *b:* Harrisonburg, VA; han Wendell; *c:* Kyle, Wendell, Nobbs; *ed:* Bowie St Univ (BA) 1972, (MS) Guidance & Counseling 1976; Anne Arundel Cty Bd ert in Admin & Supervision; *cr:* Millersville Elem Tchr 1972-75; kelen Elem Tchr 1975-93; Baltimore City Comm Coll Instr 1991-; d City Elem Guidance Cnslr 1993-; *ai:* Anne Arundel Cty Parks & on Asst Dir; Human Relations Chm; NEA 1972-; TAAAC 1972-, entor Prgm 1992-, Mentor, Cert of Appreciation; Alpha Kappa 971-; Comm Assn, Sec, Outstanding Svc Awd; Whos Who in Amer niv 1972; Bowie St Bsktbl Team Guard Cert of Appreciation; Miss State 1972; Public Svc Rep; *office:* Maryland City Elem 3359 n S LAUREL MD 20724

, ROBERT G., Dept Chair & Spanish Teacher; *b:* Flushing, NY; h E.; *c:* Christopher, Mark; *ed:* Queens Coll (BA) Span, Ed, Eng st Grad Ed, Eng; *cr:* US Army Specialist 4th Class 1961-63; St mew's R C Schl 4th-8th Grd Lang Arts Tchr 1963-87; Msgr Mc Meml HS Span Tchr Level 1-3 1987-, Dept Chm 1989-; *ai:* or Span NHS; Asst Ath Dir; AATSP, NYS Frgn Lang Tchrs Assn ishop Mugavero Man of Yr Awd Outstdng Svc Yth; 25 Yr Cert Hnr Diocese Bklyn 1987; *office:* Msgr Mc Clancy Meml HS 71-06 31st lmhurst NY 11370

PAUL G., Chemistry Teacher; *ed:* Mount Union Coll (BS) Chem Miami Univ (MAT) Chem 1968; *cr:* Brunswick HS Chem Tchr; HS Chem Tchr 1968-; *ai:* NHS Adv; Sci Olympics Coach; NEA VA Puritan Club 1975-, Pres, VP, Treas, Outstndg Club Pres 1984; Outstdng Edctr N Cantor Endowment Fund; Short Notes Pub 1979, 1982 & 1993; Woodrow Wilson Fndtn Wkshp Princeton 1986.

HOBGOOD, MARABETH B., Third Grade Teacher; *b:* Utica, NY; *m:* Charles Stewart; *c:* Laurie, Todd; *ed:* Westminster Coll (BA) Elem Ed 1966; 12 Hrs El Schl Guidance Counseling; The Defiance Coll 10 Hrs Cert Courses; *cr:* Pleasant Hills Third Grd Tchr 1966-67; Gill Hall Third Grd Tchr 1967-68; Oakview Schl Fourth Grd Tchr 1968-69; Oakwood-Paulding Schl Sy Chapter I Rdng Tchr 1977-80; Anthony Wayne Schl First Grd Tchr 1980-85, Fourth Grd Tchr 1985-90, Third Grd Tchr 1990-; *ai:* NEA 1980-; Article Title I Rdng Prgm Recognized & Pub OH St Dept of Ed 1980; *office:* Anthony Wayne Schl 1745 S Clinton Defiance OH 43512

HOBSON, MARY ANN, Instructional Teacher Leader; *b:* Pittsburgh, PA; *ed:* Univ of Pittsburgh (BS) Elem Ed 1970, (MED) Elem Ed 1972, Admin Cert 1996; Post Grad Credits 50; Attnd Carlow Coll, Penn St, Univ of Pittsburgh Intermed Unit; *cr:* Pittsburgh Parochial Schls 4-8th Grd Tchr 1965-70; Pittsburgh Pub Schls ITL Tchr 1970-, Tchr Sp Assign Admin Duties 1995-; *ai:* Instructional Tchr Ldr; Instructional Cabinet; Responsible Tchr; Parent Schl Comm Cncl; Safety Patrol Spon; CEIP Comm; Middle States Evaluator; ITL Cert Team Mem, Team Ldr; AFT, PAFT, PFT; NCTM, PCTM, PSTA, NSTA; ASCD; Natl Arbor Day Fnd 1991-; Smithsonian Inst 1986-; PTO 1971-; Natl Wildlife Assn 1990-; Excl in Math & Sci Ed Awd 1991-92; Thanks to Tchrs Nom 1990-93; Listed in Marquis Who's Who in Amer Ed 1994-95; *office:* Bon Air Elem Schl 252 Calle St Pittsburgh PA 15210*

HOBSON, STEPHEN CHARLES, World Studies Teacher; *b:* Washington, DC; *m:* Cathrine Evans; *c:* Stephanie, Charles; *ed:* Newberry Coll (BA) His 1973; George Washington Univ (MA) Ed 1975; Attnd Azuza Pacific Coll, Montgomery Coll, Univ of MD; *cr:* Whitter Woods Elem Tchr 1974-77; Bells Mill Elem Tchr 1977-86; John F. Kennedy HS Tchr 1977-79; Phoenix Schl Alternative Ed 1982-; Fox Chapel Elem Tchr 1986-93; Gaithersburg MS Tchr 1993-; *ai:* Mens Bsktbl Coach Montgomery Coll; *home:* 12730 Jesse Smith Rd Mount Airy MD 21771

HOCE, JOANELE VANZANT, Primary Multi-Age Teacher; *b:* Richmond, IN; *m:* Charles E.; *c:* C. J.; *ed:* Miami Univ (BSED) Elem Ed 1984, (MA) Elem Ed 1987; Post-Grad Stud; *cr:* C. R. Coblentz Local Schls Elem Tchr 1984-; *ai:* NEA, OEA 1986-; ASCD, NAME 1995-; Ware's Chapel Church 1989-, Missions Choir; Miami Vly OUtstdng Educator, Franklin B. Walter Outstdng Educator 1994.

HOCHMUTH, SUSANNE M., Spanish Teacher; *b:* Buffalo, NY; *m:* Ronald J.; *c:* Eric, Christine; *ed:* St Univ Coll at Buffalo (BS) Scndry Ed Span 1976; East Carolina Univ (MA) Eng 1990; *cr:* Eb Aycock Jr High Span, Eng Tchr 1976-87; Watertown HS Eng Tchr 1987-90; Sackets Harbor Span Tchr 1990-; *ai:* Stud Cncl, Span Club, Jr Class Adv; NYSAFLT, NYSUT 1990-; NYSAFLT, Embassy of Spain Schlsp.

HOCHSPRUNG, GEORGE WERNER,III, 5th Grade Teacher; *b:* Bronx, NY; *m:* Janet Elizabeth; *c:* Elizabeth, Amy, Anne; *ed:* Western CT St Univ (BS) Elem Ed 1972; 30 Addl Credits; *cr:* South Street Elem 4-6 Grd Tchr 1972-87; Roberts Avenue Elem 5th Grd Tchr 1988-; *ai:* Celebration of Excl Awd St of CT 1993, 1995; *home:* 79 Putnam Park Rd Bethel CT 06801

HOCK, MERRILLIE SIBBALD, Second Grade Teacher; *b:* Clevelad, OH; *m:* Larry George; *c:* Christopher, Jonathan R.; *ed:* Defiance Coll (BS) Soc Stud Scndry Ed 1968; 15 Grad Credit Hrs from Ashland Univ; OSU Retaining Cert K-8 1972, Kndgtn Cert 1973; *cr:* Archbold OH Reading Tchr 1968; Mansfield Elem Schls K-4 Grd Tchr 27 Yrs; *ai:* Comm Mem of our Mentor Pgm 5 Yrs; Staff Dev & Curr Adv Comm Bd Mem; Drug & Alcohol Rep in Bld for 3 Yrs; NEA 1968-, Bld Rep; MSEA; Friends of The Lib; Wkshps on Lang Enrichment Through Lit Throughout OH.*

HOCK, SETH ALLEN, Computer Science Professor; *b:* Columbus, OH; *m:* Mary Lynelle Harms; *c:* Jon, Michelle; *ed:* OH St Univ (BS) Cmptr Sci 1969, (MBA) Fin 1975; *cr:* Columbus St Comm Coll Instr 1973-75, Dept Chm 1975-85, Prof 1985-; *ai:* Author Using Computers Today Study Guide, World of Computing Study Guide, Understanding & Using PFS First Choice; Co-Author Computers & Computing; *office:* Columbus St Comm Coll 550 E Spring St Columbus OH 43215

HOCK, SHEILA JOAN, Math & Religion Teacher; *b:* Queens, NY; *ed:* St John's Univ (BS) CAS 1987; Brooklyn Coll 15 Addl Grad Credits; Basic & Intermediate Cert Parish Rel Prgm; *cr:* St Luke's Schl 5th, 6th Grd Math, Rel Tchr 1989-; *ai:* NCEA 1988-; Bridge to Life 1993-; Right to Life Comm 1992-; Poems Pub; *office:* St Luke Schl 16-01 150th Pl Whitestone NY 11357*

HOCKENBERRY, JAMES OWEN, 7th Grade Science Teacher; *b:* Mt Vernon, OH; *m:* Susan Swanson; *c:* Carrie; *ed:* Olivet Nazarene Univ (BA) Bio 1970; *cr:* Licking Vly Schl 7th Grd Sci Tchr 26 Yrs; *ai:* Track & Field; Church of the Nazarene 1970-, Bd Mem, Bus Capt, SS Tchr; *office:* Licking Vly Schl Dist 1379 Licking Valley Rd NE Newark OH 43055

HOCKENBERRY, NANCY CAROL (HAINES), Teaching Fellow; *b:* New Eagle, PA; *m:* Gerald L.; *c:* Christopher, Theresa, Allison, Matthew; *ed:* Edinboro St Coll (BS) Elem Ed 1973; Youngstown St Univ (MS) Early Chldhd 1990; Enrolled Doctoral Stu Kent St Univ; High, Scope Rsrch Fnd Univ of MI; *cr:* Youngstow St Univ Adj Fac 1990-92; Youngstown St Univ Instr 1992-94, Adj Fac 1994-95; Kent St Univ Tchng Fellow 1995-; *ai:* NAEYC, OAEYC, Tru-Mah-Col 1989-; *home:* 4048 Shelby Rd Youngstown OH 44511

HOCKER, GARY LYNN, Amer History & Economics Tchr; *b:* Chambersburg, PA; *m:* Jeanine Lougee; *c:* Brandon; *ed:* Shippensburg Univ (BS) Ed & Pol Sci 1977, (MS) Pub Admin 1981; Addl 60 Credits Beyond Masters in Ed Course Work; *cr:* Central Jr HS Civics Tchr 4 Yrs; Chambersburg MS Geography His Tchr 2 Yrs; Chambersburg Area Sr HS His & Ec Tchr 12 Yrs; *ai:* Sr Class & Ec Club Adv; NEA, PSEA, CAEA 1978-; Mason Dixon Cncl for Soc Stud 1994-; PEMS 1984-; Elks 1977-; Simulation Exercise Govt Regulation & Productivity Pub in Govt Costs & Benefits Publisher Private Enterprise Market System 1991; *office:* Chambersburg Area Sr HS 511 S 6th St Chambersburg PA 17201

HOCKING, MELANIE E., Chemistry & Biology Teacher; *b:* Martins Ferry, OH; *ed:* Marietta Coll (BS) Chem 1973; Univ of Dayton (MS) Counseling 1976; Duquesne Univ (JD) Law 1986; Univ of VA (LLM) Oceans Law & Policy 1987; Grad Courses Ed Univ Northern CO Greeley 1973-74, Chem Ohio Univ 1973; Post Grad Stud Ed Univ Dayton 1976-; *cr:* Indian Creek HS Chem Tchr 1975-; Jefferson Tech Coll Auxiliary Hlth Tech Instr Anatomy & Physiology; Engrng Tech Inorganic Chem Instr 1992-; *ai:* Fac Cncl; Indian Creek Elem Talented & Gifted Sci Act Prgm, 3rd Grd Sci Enrichment Prgm Co-Dir; Ohio Acad Competition St & Regnl Comm; Jefferson Cty Schl Dist Sci Curr Comm; NHS Fac Comm; Schlsp Comm; NEA, Ohio Ed Assn 1975-; Indian Creek Ed Assn 1975-, Sec 1980-82, Prof Rights & Resp Chm 1987-; PA Bar Assn 1986-; AAUW 1992-; Amer Assn of Univ Women 1993-; Duquesne Univ Law Schlsp 1984-86; Grad Chem Fellowship Ohio Univ 1973; Grants Spectroscopy Soc Pittsburgh HS Equipment 1988-89, Educl Prgm Support 1990; Jefferson Cty Schl Dist Grants 1988-89, 1993; Most Influential Tchr Gold Key Honor Stu 1989-92; Natl Convention Sci Tchrs Assn Presenter; Ogio Assoc For Gifted Children Presenter; Council for Acad Excellence Presenter; Natl Assoc for Gftd Children Presenter; OH Tchr of Yr 1995; Milken Family Fndtn Natl Edctr 1995; *office:* Indian Creek HS 200 Park Dr Wintersville OH 43952

HODDER, ROBERT KENNETH, History Teacher; *b:* Cleveland, OH; *m:* Jo Anne Rouse; *c:* Kelly, Amy; *ed:* OH Univ (BSED) Eng, His, Pol Sci 1966; John Carroll Univ (MA) Classroom Tchng 1977; Post-Grad Stud Cleveland St Univ; *cr:* Richmond Hghts HS Soc Stud, Eng Tchr 1966-; *ai:* Coach Var Vlybl, Girls' Var Bsktbl; Adv Sr Class, Acad Challenge; Rich Hghts Ed Assn 1966-, 5 Term Pres, Negotiator; NEA, OEA, NEOEA 1966-; Rich Hghts PTA, Treas; Church 1966-, PPR Comm; Parents Comm, Euclid Rec Bd; Great Lakes Interscholastic Press Assn 4 Term Pres; Columbia Scholastic Press Assn 18 Yrs; Taught Wkshps Columbia Univ CSPA Conventions; *office:* Richmond Heights HS 447 Richmond Rd Richmond Heights OH 44143

HODEL, MARGARET M., English Teacher; *b:* Middlebury, VT; *ed:* Ithaca Coll (BA) Eng 1962; 72 Addl Hrs St Univ Coll at Oneonta, Syracuse Univ, Utica Coll, Union Coll, Ithaca Coll; *cr:* Chittenango HS Eng Tchr 1962-, Eng Dept Chair 1966-80, 1983-86; *ai:* Soph Class Adv; AFT 1962-; NCTE 1990-; NDEA Inst Hum; NYS Inst Pub Speaking; *office:* Chittenango HS 100 Genesee St Chittenango NY 13037

HODEN, BETH A., Asst Prof of Early Chldhd Ed; *b:* Warren, PA; *m:* John Mickinak; *c:* Molly, Alexander; *ed:* Univ of Pittsburgh (BS) Psych 1974, (MED) Ed 1979; *cr:* Westmoreland Cty Comm Coll Adj Fac 1980-87, Fac 1987-; *ai:* Early Chldhd Club Adv 1987-; Annual WCCC Early Chldhd Conf 1987, Annual Parent Fare 1990 Chprsn; NAEYC 1986-; ACCESS, NEA, PSEA 1987-; Parents Anonymous 1990-, Pres of Bd; *office:* Westmoreland County Comm Coll 413 Founders Hall Youngwood PA 15697

HODGE, JANICE KAY, Occupational Work Coordinator; *b:* Lancaster, OH; *ed:* Capital Univ (BA) Hlth & PE 1978; Ashland Univ (MA) Sports Sci & Admin 1986; Supervision Cert at Univ of Dayton 1992; HS Prin Cert 1993; Occupational Work Experience Cert at Kent St Univ 1995; *cr:* Bloom-Carroll HS Tchr 15 yrs, HS Prin 2 Yrs, Occupational Work Experience Coord 1 Yr; *ai:* NASSP 1993-; *office:* Bloom Carroll HS 69 S Beaver St Carroll OH 43112

HODGE, MAUREEN A. (DOYLE), Guidance Counselor; *b:* Portland, ME; *m:* Gerald F.; *c:* Adam (dec); *ed:* Univ of ME (BS) Ed 1969, (MS) Ed 1970, (MED) Cnslr Ed 1983; *cr:* Bangor HS Tchr 9-12 1970-88, Guidance Cnslr 1988-; *ai:* Schlsp Comm Chprsn; Stu Support Accreditation Comm; Crisis Team Mem; BEA, MEA, NEA 1970-; Ronald McDonald House 1993-, Extensions Pgrm Chair, Bd of Dirs; Pathfinders Bd of Dir 1993-95, Founding Mem; Bently Coll Cnslr of Yr.

HODGE-BANNER, LILLIAM, Counselor of Stu Support Svcs; *b:* Santo Domingo, Dominican Repub; *m:* Bruce A.; *c:* Bruce Alexander; *ed:* World Univ (BA) Psych 1980; Andrews Univ (MA) Comm Cnslng 1990; *cr:* Camcare Comm Mental Hlth Cnslr, Psychologist 1992; Cumberland Cty Coll Cnslr, Adv 1992-; *ai:* Multicultural Club Adv; Intnl Ed Comm; NJCPA, HAHE 1993-; Big Brother-Big Sister 1995-; Bethany 7th Day Adventist Church 1992-, Family Life Dir.

HODGELL, BONNIE COLLEEN, English Teacher; *b:* Philadelphia, PA; *ed:* Univ of Scranton (BA) Eng 1991; *cr:* The Girls Schl Eng Tchr 1993-; *ai:* Drama Dir; Schl Newspaper Adv; Alternative Scheduling Comm; *office:* The Girls Schl 2765 Huntingdon Pk Bryn Athyn PA 19009

HODGES, ANN TAYLOR, Second Grade Teacher; *b:* Red Bank, NJ; *m:* Herbert B.; *c:* Troy T., Tara T.; *ed:* Cheyenne Univ (BS) Elem Ed 1967; Post Grad Credit Hrs; *cr:* Mary C. I. Williams Headstart-Sixth Grd Tchr 1975-77; Baltz Elem Schl Third, Sixth Grd Tchr 1977-79; Richey Elem Schl Second Grd Tchr 1979-80; Highlands Elem Schl Second Grd Tchr 1980-; *ai:* Second Grd Team Ldr; DSEA, NEA 1980-; *office:* Highlands Elem Schl 2100 Gilpin Ave Wilmington DE 19806

HODGES, GARY HOWARD, Music Educator & Band Director; *b:* Marion, OH; *m:* Jeana Laurelle Jeckell; *ed:* OH St Univ (BME) Music Ed 1974; 31 Quarter Hrs; *cr:* Reynoldsburg City Schls Music Edctr, Band Dir 1974-81; Dublin City Schls Music Edctr, Band Dir 1982-; *ai:* Marching Band; Percussive Arts Soc 1972-; NEA, OMEA 1974-; Brass Band of Columbus 1987-; Worthington Civic Band 1978-; Tchr of Month 1995; *office:* Dublin Scioto HS 4000 Hard Rd Dublin OH 43016

HODGES, JEANA JECKELL, Third & Fourth Grade Teacher; *b:* Columbus, OH; *m:* Gary Howard; *ed:* OH St Univ (BS) Elem Ed 1969, (MS) Informal Ed 1976; 40 Addl Hrs; *cr:* Fishinger Elem Schl 2nd Grd Tchr 1969-70; Greensview Elem Schl 1st-2nd Grd Tchr 1970-88; Wickliffe Elem Schl 1st-4th Grd Tchr 1988-; *ai:* North Cntrl Comm; Tech Team; Schl Cncl; Upper Arlington Ed Assn 1969-, Schl Rep; OEA, NEA 1974-; Chi Omega Housing Corp 1971-, Treas; Tchr of Yr 1981; Golden Apple Awd 1990; Greenhills HS Hall of Fame 1993; *office:* Wickliffe Elem Schl 2405 Wickliffe Rd Columbus OH 43221

HODGES, RAYMOND PHILIP, High School Mathematics Tchr; *b:* Middletown, NY; *m:* Lisa Mary Martin; *c:* Matthew, Michael; *ed:* Pace Univ (BBA) Mngmt Info Systems 1985-; City Coll of NY (MA) Scndry Math Ed 1992; 12 Credits Grad Ed SUNY at New Paltz; *cr:* Orange Cty BOCES Cmptr Programming Instr 1985-89; John S. Burke Cath HS Math, Cmptr Tchr 1985-91; Monroe Woodbury HS Math Tchr 1991-; *ai:* Chess Club Adv; NHS Selection Comm; Boy's JV Soccer Coach; AMTNYS Mem 1993-; Woodbury Vol Ambualance Corps 1991-; NY St Empire Schlsp Awd for Tchng 1986-87; *office:* Monroe Woodbury Cntrl Schls Rt 32 Central Valley NY 10917*

HODGKINS, PATRICIA MARION, French Teacher & Dept Head; *b:* Temple, ME; *ed:* Keene St Coll (BE) Fr, Latin 1961; Cntrl CT St Coll (MS) Fr 1968; Span, Cmptr Literacy Courses; *cr:* Wooster Jr HS Fr, Latin Tchr 1961-63; West Rocks Jr HS Fr Tchr 1963-69; Weston HS Fr Tchr 1969-70; Weston MS Fr Tchr 1970-72; Timberline Regnl HS Foreign Lang Dept Head 1974-; *ai:* Celebration of Learning Comm Chm; Duty Coord; Foreign Lang Curr; Cnslr, Chaperone France Trip; NHATFL 1974-, Pres 1976; AATF, ACTFL, MLA; *office:* Timberline Regional HS 36 Greenough Rd Plaistow NH 03865

HODGKINSON, PATRICIA MC GUIRE, Middle School English Teacher; *b:* Albany, NY; *m:* Seamus; *c:* Catie, Bridget, Daniel; *ed:* Boston Coll (AB) Scndry Ed, His 1982; Univ of Albany (MA) Rdng 1994; *cr:* Doane Stuart Schl MS Tchr 1982-; *ai:* MS Co-Coord; MS Newspaper; NCOG Evaluation Comm; MS Comm Svc Coord; NCTE 1993-; Numerous Articles Pub; *office:* Doane Stuart Schl 799 S Pearl St Albany NY 12202

HODGSON, DEBORAH ANASTASIA, English Teacher; *b:* Boston, MA; *m:* John Gerard III; *ed:* 15 Post Grad Credits Hrs Toward Masters; *cr:* Wareham HS Stu Tchr 1991; Wareham MS Permanent Sub, Lang Arts Tchr 1992-93; Wareham HS Eng Tchr 1993-; *ai:* Class of 1996, Frosh & Soph Hnr Soc Adv; Awds Comm; NEA, WEA, MTA 1993-; *office:* Wareham HS 1 Viking Way Wareham MA 02571

HODGSON, LYNDA GAYLE, English Teacher; *b:* West Islip, NY; *ed:* Univ of the South (BA) Art His 1991; SUNY Stony Brook (MA) Eng, Lib Stud 1992; *cr:* BOCES Pub, Private Sec Asst 1993; Greenwich Cntrl Schls 11th Grd Eng Tchr 1994; Mechanicville Cntrl Schls 9th, 12th Grd Engl Tchr 1994-; *ai:* Yrbk Adv; 10th Grd Soph Class Adv; Ski Club Adv; Soccer Coach 1994; NYST RS 1993-; MTA 1994-; Long Island Womens Lax Assn 1993-, Sec; *office:* Mechanicville HS 25 Kniskern Ave Mechanicville NY 12118*

HODGSON, MATTHEW, English Teacher; *b:* Galion, OH; *ed:* Univ of Cincinnati (BA) Eng Lit 1992; Post Grad Work Scndry Ed; *cr:* Archbishop Moeller HS Eng Tchr 1994; *ai:* Asst Moderator for Crusader Newspaper;

NCTE 1994-; *office:* Archbishop Moeller High School 9001 Montgomery Rd Cincinnati OH 45242

HODGSON, THOMAS SALKALD, Philosophy & Rel Stud Dept Chm; *b:* Summit, NJ; *m:* Susan Wrathall Brownell; *c:* Thomas Jr., Katherine; *ed:* Williams Coll (BA) Philosophy, Religion 1974; Yale Univ (MA) Philosophy 1976; *cr:* Phillips Acad Philosophy Instr 1976-; Williams Coll Visiting Philosophy Instr 1982, Visiting Asst Philosophy Prof 1989; *ai:* Head Tennis, Boys Var TennisCoach; Prgm Adv; Day Stu & Acad Adv; APA 1985-; Miller Prize in Philosophy Williams 1973-74; Kent Fellowship Yale 1977; Sterns Tchng Chair 1995-; *office:* Phillips Acad 180 Main St Andover MA 01810

HODSKIEVIC, KERRY P., Teacher & GATE Coordinator; *b:* Cleveland, OH; *m:* Christine; *c:* Elizabeth, Abbey; *ed:* Bowling Green (BSEd) PE, Hlth 1975; Kent St (MS) Ath Adm 1986; Attnd Youngstown St; *cr:* Conneaut City Schls Wrestling, Track Coach, OWA 1975; Bedford City Schls Wrestling Coach, Ath Dir, OWA 1976-77; Trinity HS OWE, Asst Ftbl, Wrestling Coach 1977-78; Warren City Schls SBD, Asst Ftbl Coach 1978-80; Cleve Hts OWE, Head Ftbl Coach; Barberton Schl HPE, Head Ftbl Coach; Allegheny Coll Asst Ftbl, Track, Strength Coach; Upper Arlington City Schls Tchr 1995-; *ai:* AAUP; NEA; OEA; Local Ed Assn; ASSA; Coach of Yr; *office:* Upper Arlington HS 1650 Ridgeview Rd Upper Arlington OH 43221

HODUM, ROBERT A., Spanish Teacher; *b:* Rockville Ctr, NY; *m:* Maria Jose Llorens; *c:* Ryan, Paul, Christopher; *ed:* Stony Brook Univ (BA) His & Span 1975, (MS) Ibero Amer His 1984; Cert in Italian, Span, Soc Stud Grds 7-12; *cr:* Half Hollow Hills HS East Span Tchr 18 Yrs; *ai:* Amnesty Intnl Adv 4 Yrs; Span Honor Soc 13 Yrs; Dir of Open Door Stu Exch 5 Yrs; AATSP 1980-; LILT 1992-, Presentor at 4 Confs; Tech Comm of Port Jefferson Schl Dist 1992, Co-Chm; Writer & Ed of ASTROLBIO; St Josephs Coll Span & Latin Amer Instr 5 Yrs; *office:* Half Hollow Hills HS E 50 Vanderbilt Pkwy Dix Hills NY 11746*

HODZIEWICH, GABRIEL ANTHONY, Biology Teacher; *b:* Cheverly, MD; *c:* Erika; *ed:* Prince Georges Comm Coll (AA) Gen Stud 1977; George Mason Univ (BA) Bio 1978; Attnd Howard Univ ABT Botany 1978-80; *cr:* St Andrews Episcopal Bio Tchr 1982-; *ai:* Recycling Club; Boys Var Tennis Coach; NIH, ADAMHA Flwshps 1991-92; *office:* St Andrew's Episcopal Schl 8935 Bradmoor Dr Bethesda MD 20817

HOEBERLEIN, TERESA MARIE, Assistant Professor; *b:* Rockville Centre, NY; *ed:* Nassau Comm Coll (AAS) Phys Therapist Asst 1975; St Univ of NY at Brooklyn (BS) Phys Therapy 1981; St John's Univ (MS) Schl Psych 1993; *cr:* Bernard Fineson Dev Ctr Phys Therapist Asst 1975-78; Nassau Cty Med Ctr Sr Phys Therapist 1981-85; N Shore Univ Hosp Sr Phys therapist 1985-93; St Univ of NY at Brooklyn Asst Prof 1993-; *ai:* Long Island Dist of NY Phys Therapy Assn Chair Vendor Fair 1996; Amer Phys Therapy Assn 1981-, Nom Comm of Long Island Dist, NY St Del 1995; Prof Dev & Quality of Working Life Awd from NY St United Univ Profs Union; *office:* SUNY Hlth Sci Cent Brooklyn # 93 450 Clarkson Ave Brooklyn NY 11203

HOEFLINGER, ANTON J., Fifth Grade Teacher; *b:* Butler, NJ; *m:* Eleanor Smmk; *c:* Galen, Beth; *ed:* Rutgers Coll (BA) His 1964; *cr:* Franklin Twp Bd of Ed 5th Grd Tchr 1964-; *ai:* Head Womens Soccer Coach; NJEA & NEA 1964-; NSCAA 1989-; NJGSCA 1990-; Franklin Twps Soccer Club 1982-, Pres 1984-90; 1994 Somerset Cty Coach of the Yr; The Star Ledger & The Courier News; *home:* 6 Hilltop Ln Somerset NJ 08873

HOEFS, MONA RAE BARTLETT, Elem Instrumental Music Tchr; *b:* Franklin, NH; *c:* Christopher; *ed:* Plymouth St Coll (BS) K-12 Music Ed 1985; Berklee Coll of Music; *cr:* Plymouth Area Schls K-8th Grd Gen & Instrumental Music Tchr 1986-86; Newfound Area Schls 4-6th Grd Instrumental Music Tchr 1986-89, 5-8th Grd Instrumental Music Tchr 1989-91, 5-12th Grd Instrumental Music, Music Therapy Piano, Guitar Tchr 1991-94; Inter-Lakes Schls 4-6th Grd Instrumental Music Tchr 1994-; *ai:* Beginning, Advances, Jazz Band Dir; Private Lessons; Summer Band Progms; Music Bo oster Club Founder; NEA, MENC 1986-; Lioness Club 1987-90; Unitarian Universal Congregation 1992-; NARAL 1991-; *office:* Inter-Lakes Elem Schl 21 Laker Ln Meredith NH 03253*

HOEFT, MARY COOKE, Advanced Placement Eng Teacher; *b:* Glendale, CA; *m:* John S.; *ed:* St Univ Coll at Oneonta (BA) Eng 1968; 30 Grad Hrs for Permanent NY St Tchng Cert at St Univ of NY at New Paltz 1973; *cr:* Onteona Jr Sr HS Tchr 1968-; *ai:* Stu Support Team Adv & Trainer; Creative Arts Magazine Adv; Onteona Tchrs Assn 1968-; AFT 1985-; NY St Tchr of Yr Finalist 1993; Jenkins Awd-Lifetime PTA Membership awded by the Parents of the Schl Dist; *office:* Onteora Jr Sr HS Rt 28 Boiceville NY 12412*

HOENEVELD, DIANE MARIE (PAPPAS), Sixth Grade Teacher; *b:* New York City, NY; *m:* Robert; *c:* Robert, Diane Hoeneveld Quinn; *ed:* Hunter Coll (BA) Ec, Psych 1955, (MS) Elem Ed 1965; Iona Coll (SAS) Schl Admin, Supvr 1987, (SDS) Schl Dist Supvr; Post Grad Credits in GATE Ed at Coll of New Rochelle; 60 Addl Credits Elem Rdng, GATE, Elem Ed, Psych, Tchr Ed at Hunter Coll, Lehman Coll; *cr:* South Orangetown Cntrl Schl Dist Third Grd Tchr 1965-66; Birchwood Elem Schl Fifth Grd Tchr 1966-67; Strawtown Elem Schl Sixth Tchr 1967-86; Clarkstown Cntrl Schl Dist Admin Intern, Acting Prin 1987-88; Strawtown Elem Schl Sixth Grd Tchr 1989-; *ai:* Project MC-Extend-Goals 2000 Rockland Mentor; Site-Based Mngmt, Mid Level Ed, Bldg Advy Comm; PTA Schlsp Comm for Bldg; NYSUT 1965-; ASCD, Phi Delta Kappa 1988-; Clarkstown Tchrs Assn, PTA 1966-; West Nyack Free Lib 1986-, Pres of Bd of Trustees 1987-89, 1995-, AIA Awd to WNFL 1996; Hnrd by Stdnts for Important Contribution in Ed at Elem Level; *home:* 19 Sable Ct West Nyack NY 10994*

HOENIE, NANCY E. (TEWELL), Third Grade Teacher; *b:* Findlay, OH; *m:* David F.; *c:* Valerie Stauffer, Dean; *ed:* OH Northern Univ (BS) Elem Ed 1970; Wright St Univ (MED) Rdng 1981; Addl Stud Rdng Supvr; Gifted Ed; *cr:* St Henry Consolidated Schls First Grd Tchr 1965-68, 1970; West Jefferson Local Schls First Grd Tchr 1971-79, Chptr I Rdng Tchr 1979-83, Tchr of Gifted 1983-92, Third Grd Tchr 1992-; *ai:* West Jefferson Ed Assn 1970-, VP 1993-94; OEA, NEA 1970-; Delta Kappa Gamma 1978-, Pres of Local Church 1984-86; Zion Luth Church 1970-; Tchr in Space Applicant; Assisted with Starting the Gifted Prgm in West Jefferson Schl Dist; *office:* Norwood El-Jefferson Local Sch 906 W Main St West Jefferson OH 43162

HOENING, EUGENE FRANK, Biology Teacher; *b:* Ft Smith, AR; *m:* Sandra Gerlach; *c:* Ethan, Erin; *ed:* Wilmington Coll (BS) Bio 1979; Univ of Dayton (MS) Educl Admin 1988; *cr:* Ansonia Local Schls Bio Tchr 1980-; *ai:* Head Ftbl Coach; NEA 1980-; Holy Name Soc 1976-, Treas; Cross Cnty Conf Ftbl Coach of Yr 1988-90, 1992-93; Assocd Press SW Dist Ftbl Coach 1990; *home:* PO Box 68 Burkettsville OH 45310

HOEPFER, DONALD CHARLES, Professor of Philosophy; *b:* Camp Hill, PA; *m:* Julie L. Parson; *c:* Joshua T., Kaycee L.; *ed:* Lebanon Valley Coll (BA) Philosophy 1989; Penn St Univ (MA) Philosophy 1990; Temple Univ PHD Prgm; *cr:* Harrisburg Area Comm Coll Instr & Admin 1990-; Coll of Saint Francis Philosophy Adjunct Instr 1991-95; Lebanon Valley Coll Philosophy Adjunct Instr 1992-; Penn St Univ Philosophy Adjunct Instr 1996; *ai:* Amer Philosophical Assn 1996; Cntrl Dauphin Band Boosters 1994-; East Jr PTA 1996; Lebanon Valley Coll Alumni Chorale 1994-; Oliver P. Butterwick Philosophy Awd; Tchng Assistantship Penn St Univ; Prof Dev Awd; *office:* Harrisburg Area Comm Coll Lebanon Campus 735 Cumberland St Lebanon PA 17042

HOEPP, RITA D., English & Journalism Teacher; *b:* Indianapolis, IN; *m:* Joseph T.; *c:* Caroline, Natalie; *ed:* Butler Univ (BA) Eng 1967; Univ of IL (MA) Lit 1969; *cr:* Robert Morris Coll Composition, Speech Tchr 1982-90; Comm Coll of Beaver Co Composition, Speech Tchr 1985-90; Quaker Valley Sr HS Eng, Journ Tchr 1990-; *ai:* Sr Class, Newspaper Spon; Amer Assn Univ Women 1980-; NEA, PSEA, NCTE, WPCTE 1990-; Columnist; Chosen to Accompany presidential Scholr Wash DC Outstdng Tchr; *office:* Quaker Valley Sr HS 625 Beaver Rd Leetsdale PA 15056

HOEY, ANN MARIE, College Instructor; *b:* Flushing, NY; *m:* Stephen D. Elgert; *c:* Devin, Caitlin, Emily; *ed:* Univ of Rochester (BA) Eng 1977; Syracuse Univ (MA) Eng 1982; 9 Addl Credit Hrs; *cr:* Syracue Univ Instr 1980-83; Plymouth St Coll Instr 1983-; Plymouth Friends of the Arts Publicist & Assoc Dir 1986-89; *ai:* Women Stud Cncl Comm Mem; Presidents Commission on Status of Women Comm Mem; Phi Beta Kappa 1976-; Plymouth Friends of the Arts 1984-, Bd Mem; *office:* Plymouth State Coll Reed House Rounds Hall Plymouth NH 03264

HOFF, CAROLE WELCH, 3rd Grade Teacher; *b:* Salem, OH; *m:* Fred H.; *c:* Christopher, Kyle; *ed:* Youngstown St (BS) Elem Ed 1967; Ashland Univ (MED) Curr 1995; *cr:* Crestview Schls 3rd Grd Tchr 1966-68; South Range Schls 3rd Grd Tchr 1983-; *ai:* Future Tchrs of Amer; OEA, NEA 1966-; South Range Ed Assn, Negotiating Team 1993; Crestview Ed Assn 1967-, Sec; AAUW; YSU Alumni Assn; OCIRA; Presenter OCTELA, OH Tchng, Learning Conf; *office:* South Range East Elem Schl 11836 South Ave North Lima OH 44452*

HOFF, ROBERT J., Professor of Criminal Justice; *b:* Catskill, NY; *m:* Susan J.; *c:* Paul, Alec; *ed:* Northeastern Univ (BS) Crim Justice 1972; Eastern KY Univ (MS) Crim Justice 1974; Occassional Courses Albany St Univ; *cr:* Schenectady Co Comm Coll Instr 1973-81, Asst Tchr 1981-87, Assoc Tchr 1987-92, Prof 1992-; *ai:* Criminal Justice Club Adv; Curr; Campus Safety; Fac Dev; Cont Appt; Crim Justice Ed of NYS 1984-, VP; NEA 1973-; Acad of Crim Just Sci 1995-; *office:* Schenectady County Comm Coll 78 Washington Ave Schenectady NY 12305

HOFFER, KATHLEEN MARIE, 2nd Grade Teacher; *b:* York, PA; *m:* Peter T.; *ed:* York Coll (AS) Medical Tech 1967; Shippensburg Univ (BS) Elem Ed, Lib Sci 1969; 51 Grad Credits; *cr:* Northeastern Schl Dist 3rd Grd Tchr 1969-73; Abington Heights Schl Dist 2nd Grd Tchr 1974-; *ai:* Soc Stud Curr Comm; NEA, PSEA 1969-; PTA, Tchr Liaison; Smithsonian 1990-, Natl Trust for Historic Preservation 1985-; Awded Dolbear Schlsp to Stud in Italy, Greece; Wrote Article.

HOFFERT, FRANK, Social Studies Teacher; *b:* Cleveland, OH; *m:* Geraldine Siat; *c:* Stephen, Susan, Paul; *ed:* Western Reserve Univ (BA) His 1959, (MA) His 1964; Inst of Rome Soc of Dante Alighieri 9 Hrs; Williams Coll 6 Hrs; Cleveland St Univ 6 Hrs; 12 Hrs; Westminster Coll 6 Hrs; Univ of CO 6 Hrs; John Carroll Univ 24 Hrs; *cr:* Euclid HS Soc Stud Tchr 1959-, Soc Stud Dept Chair 1969-; *ai:* Stu Cncl, Hum Club Adv; Greater Cleveland Cncl for Soc Stud 1963-, Pres; OH Cncl for Soc Stud 1963-, Exec Bd; NCSS 1963-, House of Dels Mem; NEA, OH Ed Assn, Euclid Tchrs Assn 1960-, Outstanding Educator; Common Cause 1990-; Charles R. Keller Awd; Jennings Scholar; Univ of Chicago Outstanding High Schl Tchr Awd Twice; *office:* Euclid HS 711 E 222nd St Euclid OH 44123

HOFFMAN, ADELE KATZOWITZ, Elementary & MS Strings Tchr; *b:* New Rochelle, NY; *m:* Barry Charles; *ed:* Hartt Schl of Music (BM) Music Ed 1976; Hunter Coll (MM) Performance 1989; *cr:* Stamford Pub Schls Strings Tchr 1976-80; Greenwich Pub Schls Strings Tchr 1980-; Mannes Coll of Music Prep Div Violin Tchr & Ensemble Instruction 1985-87; Norwalk Yth Symphony & Orch Dir 1987-89; *ai:* MS Chamber Orch Dir; Townwide String Festival Co-Chm; PTA Orchestral Enrichment Activities Coord; Music Edctrs Natl Conf 1976-; Amer Sting Tchrs Assoc 1976-; Fairfield Cty Sting Tchrs Assoc 1976-; Greenwich Symphony Orch 1981-, Violinist; Westchester Chamber Orch 1987-, Violinist, Bd Mem 1992-; Westchester Choral Soc 1995-; Philharmonic Symphony of Westchester Musical Contribution Awd 1971; Natl Schl Orch Assn Awd 1971; Deans List Hartt Coll of Music 1972-76; *home:* 501 Pelham Rd Apt 4A New Rochelle NY 10805*

HOFFMAN, ANN DENKIN, English Teacher; *b:* Cambridge, NY; *m:* Joseph Charles; *c:* Jeffrey, Alan Noznesky, Douglas Noznesky; *ed:* Temple Univ (BSEd) Soc Stud & Eng 1962; West Chester Univ (MS) Rdng 1983; Masters Plus 30 Credit Hrs; *cr:* Avon Grove HS Eng Tchr 1962-65, 1975-; *ai:* NEA, PSEA & AGEA 1962-, Bldg Rep; NRA & Chester Cty Rdng Assn 1983-; NCTE 1985-; NH Lit Soc 1982-; NCJW 1991-; Adult Literacy Pgm 1996; *office:* Avon Grove HS 257 State Rd West Grove PA 19390*

HOFFMAN, ANNE SHIELDS, School Counselor; *b:* Altoona, PA; *c:* Katie, Evans; *ed:* PA St Univ (BS) Individual, Family Stud 1974, (MED) Elem Schl Cnslng 1980, (MED) Scndry Schl Cnslng 1990; *cr:* Penn Cambria HS Cnslr 1986-; *office:* Penn Cambria HS 401 Linden Ave Cresson PA 16630

HOFFMAN, BARBARA A., English Professor; *b:* Rochester, NY; *ed:* D'Youville Coll (AB) Eng 1963; Cath Univ (MA) Eng, Drama 1965; Duquesne Univ (ABD) Eng 1969; *cr:* Marywood Coll Asst Eng Prof 1969-; *ai:* RCIA Team Ldr; Scribblers Club Moderator 1969-92; AAUP 1969-; Urasenke Chanoya Soc 1980-; Sears Tchn Excl Awd 1990; Presidential Schlsp 1992; Who's Who in Amer Ed 1993; Poetry Book; *office:* Marywood Coll 2300 Adams Ave Scranton PA 18509

HOFFMAN, BARBARA ELLEN, Mathematics Teacher; *b:* Lock Haven, PA; *m:* Arthur J.; *c:* Benjamin U., Amy Jo; *ed:* Lock Haven St Univ (BS) Math Ed 1977; Masters Equivalency Ed PSU, East Stroudsburg 1989; *cr:* Bellefonte Area MS 8th Grd Math Tchr 1977-83; Bellefonte Area HS Math Tchr 1983-95; *ai:* 9th Grd Team Svc Learning Club Advs; Phi Kappa Phi, Kappa Delta Pi 1976-; ARC 1985-, Bd Dirs 6 Yrs; Grad Magna Cum Laude; *office:* Bellefonte Area HS 830 E Bishop St Bellefonte PA 16823*

HOFFMAN, BARBARA NESTLER, English Teacher; *b:* New York City, NY; *m:* Craig A.; *c:* Nathan, Samuel; *ed:* Univ of Buffalo (BA) Eng 1969; Queen Coll (MA) Eng 1973; *cr:* Berkshire Comm Coll Eng Tchr 1973-74; WBEC Radio Station Copy Writer 1973-74; Herricks HS Eng Tchr 1969-.

HOFFMAN, BARBARA S., Fourth Grade Teacher; *b:* Martins Ferry, OH; *c:* Steven Thomas, Sean Steffik; *ed:* OH Univ (BS) Elem Ed 1974, (MS) Ed Admin 1988; Attnd Univ of Dayton 1978, Wheeling Jesuit Coll Math & Sci Prgm 1984-85; WV Northern Comm Coll, Cmptr Courses; *cr:* Steeple Valley Schl 5th Grd Tchr 1974-75; Hilltop Schl 4th Grd Tchr 1975-92; North Elem Schl 4th Grd Tchr 1992-; *ai:* Sci Fair Coord; Rdng & Math Comms; 7th & 8th Grd Boys Rec Ctr Bsktbl Coach; NEA, OEA, EOTA & MFEA 1974-; Red Cross 1976-, Gallon Club 1991; Alphi Pi Sigma 1988-; Parents Without Partners 1988-, VP 1989-91; Pi Delta Kappan 1987-; St OH Tchr in Space Candidate; *office:* North Elem Schl 500 N 5th St 72559 Colerain Martins Ferry OH 43935

HOFFMAN, BARRY L., 5th Grade Teacher; *b:* New York, NY; *c:* Dara, David, Cheryl; *ed:* Univ of WI (BA) His, Pol Sci 1968; Temple Univ (MA) Elem Ed 1970; *cr:* Mc Daniel Schl 6th Grd Tchr 1970-73; Greenfield Schl Media Specialist 1974-75, 5th-6th Grd Tchr 1976-; *ai:* Discipline Comm; PFT Bldg Comm Rep; Eisenhower Grant; Mayor & City Hall Merit Cert for Greenfield Expressive Arts Prgm, St Grant; Ed Gauntlet Magazine; Writer, Producer, Dir Plays for Greenfield Expressive Arts Prgr Albert M Greenfield Elem Sch 22nd & Chestnut St Philadelphia

HOFFMAN, BETH M., Math & Computer Science Tchr; *b:* Jc PA; *m:* John C.; *ed:* Univ of Pittsburgh at Johnstown (BS) Natu Math 1990; IN Univ of Pennsylvania 30 Credit Hrs Working Tov *cr:* Hollidaysburg Area Sr High Tchr 1990-; *ai:* Soph Class A PSEA 1990-; Pike Grace Bretheran Church 1990-; *office:* Holli Area Sr HS 1510 N Montgomery St Hollidaysburg PA 16648*

HOFFMAN, CHRISTINA C., Business Education Tea Morgantown, WV; *ed:* Rider Coll (BS) Bus Ed 1972; *cr:* Ranc Adult Schl Bus Ed Tchr 1973-76; Pemberton Twp HS Bus Ed Tc *ai:* FBLA; NEA & NJEA 1973-; SJBEA 1980-; NJBEA; *office:* P Township HS Arneys Mt Rd Pemberton NJ 08068

HOFFMAN, DAN G., Physics Teacher; *b:* Pittsburgh, PA; *ed* Univ (BS) Comprehensive Sci, Psych 1969; Edinboro Univ (M 1976; 15 Credits Law Enforcement Mercyhurst Coll; *cr:* Fort LeI Physics Tchr 1969-; Dept of Conservation & Natural Resou Ranger II 1976-; *ai:* Track, Strength Coach; Physics Club Adv Tchr; PSTA 1974-; PSEA, NEA 1969-; 70 St Medals Won B Coached; *office:* Ft LeBoeuf HS 931 High St Waterford PA 1644

HOFFMAN, ELFRIEDE SCHANZ, Mathematics Teacher; *b:* C OH; *m:* Fred; *ed:* Capital Univ (BA) Math 1966; Kent St (ME Specialist 1975; 36 Hrs Post Grad Ed, Math; *cr:* Berea Schls Tchr Willoughby-East Lake Schls Tchr 1967-70; Berea Schl Tchr 1970- Geauga Schls Tchr, Dept Chair 1971-; *ai:* Math Competition Coa NEA 1966-; OCTM, NCTM 1977-; Beta Sigma Phi 1980-, Sec, S Math Club Fnd Grant; *home:* 13410 Walnut Trce Chardon OH 44

HOFFMAN, ELSA M., Fifth Grade Teacher; *b:* Philadelphia, West Chester St Univ (BS) Elem Ed 1967; Temple Univ (MS) Edu 1971; 66 Addl Credit Hrs Educl Field Penn St Univ; *cr:* Colonial Third Grd Tchr 1967-75, Fifth Grd Tchr 1975-76, Sixth Grd Tchr Fifth Grd Tchr 1982-; *ai:* Fifth Grd Trips Coord; PTO Tchr Rep; Curr, Various Dist, Textbook Selecting, Writing Benchmarks PSEA, NEA, CEA 1967-; PW Alumni Assn 1995-, Co Ed, Bd Me Established Alumni Assn; Red Cross Blood Donor; Montgomery H Soc; Shuylkill Cntr for Environmental Ed; Whitemarsh Jr Wom Excl Ed Awd for Elem Ed 1986; New Standard Portfolio Comm for of Ed; *office:* Colonial Elem Schl 230 Flourtown Rd Plymouth Me 19462*

HOFFMAN, EUGENE WILLIAM, Health Ed, Math & PE Baltimore, MD; *ed:* Towson St Univ (BS) Hlth Sci 1974; Att Comm Coll, Chapman Coll & Adelphi Univ Credit Hrs; Post G *cr:* Holy Rosary Schl Sci Dept Head & Tchr 1974-77; Essex Co Track Coach 1986-91; Archbishop Curley HS Hlth Ed, Math & 1977-; *ai:* Cross Cntry, Indoor Track, Track & Field Coach; Moderator 1995; NC Tchrs Ed Assn 1980-; Baltimores Ed Water 1985-; Archbishop Curley Alumni Assn 1980-, Treas 1985-86; Lo Optimists 1993-, VP 1994; Baltimores Best Nom 1982 & 1983; S Cross Cntry Coach of Yr 1984 & 1990; NJCAA Region XX Coa 1990-1991; ArchCurley Tchr of Yr 1993; *office:* Archbishop Cu 3701 Sinclair Ln Baltimore MD 21213

HOFFMAN, FLORENCE ANNE DOHERTY, First Grade Te Woodbury, NJ; *m:* David John; *c:* David John (dec), Heidi Anne Shawn Jonathan; *ed:* Rowan Coll (BA) Gen Elem Ed 1976; *cr:* A 5th Grd Tchr 1976-78, 3rd Grd Tchr 1978-79, K Grd Tchr 1979-87 Tchr 1987-92, 1st Grd Tchr 1992-; *ai:* ETEA Pride in Ed Comm NEA, Gloucester Cty Ed Assn 1976-; Elk Twp Ed Assn 1976-, Sec Pres 1992-; Clayton Bapt Church 1970-, Bd of Chrstn Ed 1982-8 Aura Elem Schl RD 1 Box 338 Glassboro NJ 08028

HOFFMAN, GARY L., Instrumental Music Director; *b:* Warren, Youngstown St Univ (BSME) Instrumental Music 1977, (M Instrumental Music 1984; Post Grad Work in Ed Admin; *cr:* S Schls Band Dir 1977-79; Spruce HS Band Dir 1979-80; Warren C Band Dir 1980-92; Newton Falls Schls Band Dir 1992-; *ai:* M Concert & Jazz Bands; AFT; OFT; OMEA; MENC; ASBDA; Symp Concert Bands Have Consistently Achieved Superior & Excl R Dist, St & Natl Competitions; Bands Have Performed at Cotto Orange Bowl Parades & at OH Music Ed Assn St Convention Newton Falls HS 907 Milton Blvd Newton Falls OH 44444*

HOFFMAN, HARVEY F., Electrical Engineering Prof; *b:* New Y *ed:* CCNY (BEE) Electrical Engr 1964; NYU (MEE) Elect Engr 19 Elect Engr 1972; Hartford Grad Ctr (MS) Mgmt 1985; *cr:* Br Engrng Inst Prof 1973-94; Fairfield Univ Elect Engr Dept Cha United Techs Engrng Mgr; *ai:* IEEE, Eta Kappa NU 1965-; Sigma Fellow; UTC Horner Awd; Several Tech Articles Pub; *office:* Fairfi McAuliffe Hall Fairfield CT 06430*

HOFFMAN, JOAN, Economics Professor; *b:* Gary, IN; *ed:* Du (BA) Math 1965; New Schl for Soc Rsrch (MA) Ec 1968, (PHD) Attnd Univ of Freiburg Germany 1962-63; *cr:* Chase Manhattan Rsrch Asst 1964-68; Newbery Coll Asst Prof of Ec 1968-72; John of Criminal Justice Assoc Prof 1972-; *ai:* Ec Division Coord; Stud Comm; Urban Ec; Pub Sector Ec, MPA Prgms; Introductory E Methods; URPE 1972-; Pi Mu 1961-; Delta Gamma Phi 1964- Racial Discrimination And Economic Development; Duke Univ 1960; New Schl for Rsrch Tuition Grant 1968; Luth Church of Ar Grant 1970; Appointment To Urban Challenge Seminar CUNY Bil Seminar on City Columbia Univ; Rsrch Release Time Awded by G Rsrch Comm 1987; Columbia Univ Full Employment 1988; Philosophy of Thought Mellon Seminar; PSC-CUNY Rsrch 1989-90; CUNY Selection for Women's Stud Comm 1990-92; Justice Rsrch Ctr Grant 1992; Books, Pamphlets, Articles Pu Presentations; Keynote Speaker.

HOFFMAN, KARL WILLIAM, Coord of Medical Biology Bronx, NY; *m:* Linda Indelicato; *c:* Jonathan, Elaina; *ed:* City C Bio 1973; St Johns Univ (MS) Admin, Supervision 1977; Addl LaGuardia Coll Cmptr Classes, 9 Credits Queensborough Coll Nursing Classes; *cr:* JHS Tchr 1973-82; Forest Hills H Westinghouse Seminar 1987-89, Coord, Med Bio Pgrm 1990-; *ai:* Internship Prgm, Laguardia Hosp Queens 1991-, Parkway Hosptial 1993-; Forest Hills HS Schlrsp Com 1992-; AFT 1973-; PS 174 Assn 1993, 1995 Safety, Security Bd; Tv Channel 9 Apple Polish 1981; Amer Zoologist 1972; Teratology 1974; Amer Assn Advance 1972; 46th Westinghouse Talent Search Tchr Recognition Aw *office:* Forest Hills HS 67-01 110th St Forest Hills Flushing NY 1

HOFFMAN, MARC THOMAS, Senior English Teacher; *b:* Allian *m:* Janice L.; *c:* Michael, Melissa; *ed:* Walsh Univ (BA) Scndry 1968, (MA) Cnslng 1983; *cr:* Lake HS Eng IV Tchr 1968-; Kent Eng Instr 1992-; *ai:* LLEA, ECOEA, OEA, NEA 1968-; *office:* I 1025 Lake Center St NW Uniontown OH 44685*

HOFFMAN, MARILYN MEYER, K-1 Transition Teacher; *b:* NY; *m:* Robert; *ed:* SUNY at Albany (BA) Scndry His 1968; SUNY Paltz (MS) Elem Ed 1972; 64 Addl Credit Hrs; *cr:* Kings Ele First-Fourth, Sixth Grd Transition Tchr 1968-; *ai:* AFT, NYSUT Warwick Vly Tchrs Assn 1968-, Sec 1973-76, Bldg Rep I Colleague of Yr 1976; OR Co NY Schl Employees Fed Credit Unio rs 1993, Sec 1993; Kings Elem PTA 1968-, Treas 1988-89, Mbrshp 1994-, NYS Life Mbrshp 1989; Jaycees Outstdng Educator 1977; · Warwick Vly Cntrl Schl PO Box 595 Warwick NY 10990

FMAN, MARILYN PATRICIA, Guidance Counselor; *b:* Weymouth, *ed:* Bridgewater St Coll (BSEd) Eng, Ed 1955, (MED) Guid, Cnslng Attnd Northeastern Univ; *cr:* Hunt Schl 4th-5th Grd Tchr; Nash Schl ·d Tchr; East Jr HS Eng Tchr, Guid Cnslr; Weymouth South HS Guid ; Weymouth HS Guid Cnslr; *ai:* Prin Schlsp, Prof Dev, HS ditation Steering Comms; NEA; MTA; WTA; MA Schl Cnslrs Assn; Shore Guid Assn; Abigail Adams Historical Soc; Sacred Heart Schl acred Heart Parish Cncl; Eucharistic Minister, Lector; St Matthew's

FMAN, MARILYN-LEE HOLLEY, Elementary Teacher; *b:* ille, PA; *m:* Roger Lee; *c:* Amy Lee, James Whitehead, Derek, 'er; *ed:* Shippensburg St Coll (BA) Elem 1968; 24 Credit Hrs; *cr:* erland Vly Schls Elem Tchr 1968; Milton Schl Dist Elem Tchr 1971-; tor Individual Stdnts; NEA 1971-; MAEA 1971-; Eastern Star 1969-; : White Deer Elem Schl General Delivery West Milton PA 17886

FMAN, MARY HILLS, English Teacher; *b:* Elizabeth, NJ; *ed:* g Hill (BS) Sociology 1967; Sonoma St (MA) Eng 1980; Lander Univ ; Cert Sci & Soc Sci; *ai:* NCTE; Sierra Club; Founded Sonoma ala Lit Rev; SC Fiction Project Awd; SC Tchrs Awd Grant; *office:* sburg Area Comm Coll Cumberland Lebanon PA 17046

FMAN, MICHAEL ANTHONY, Agriculture Instructor; *b:* Fremont, *n:* Beth Rene Hord; *c:* Taylor; *ed:* MI St (BS) Ag, Nat Resource Ed Ashland (MS) Schl Admin 1991; Attn OH St; *cr:* Wynford HS Ag 1985-; *ai:* Asst Ftbl; Frosh Class, FFA Adv; AVA, OVATA, NVATA , Dist AG Tchr 1985-, VP, Sec-Treas; Traine 5 Stu Tchr in eration with OH St Univ; *office:* Wynford HS 3288 Holmes Center Rd rus OH 44820

FMAN, ROBERT S., Social Studies Teacher; *b:* New York, NY; *m:* elle Lindell; *c:* Andrew; *ed:* SUNY at Oswego (BA) Commnctn & His Queens Coll 30 Credit Hrs Towards MA in His; *cr:* SHS 204 7th-9th Soc Stud Tchr 1989-93; Rensselaer MHS 12th Grd Soc Stud Tchr ; Schalmont HS 10th Grd Soc Stud Tchr 1995-; *ai:* JV Ftbl Coach; Sr nar Adv; AFT 1989-; Amer Soc His Project Making Connections; : Rensselaer Mid HS 555 Broadway Rensselaer NY 12144*

FMAN, ROSE MARIE, Sixth Grade Teacher; *b:* Wheeling, WV; *m:* E.; *c:* John E. Jr., Ellen Bradley, Thomas, Karen Rohe; *ed:* OH nican Coll (BA) Chem 1957; Univ of Dayton (MS) Ed 1982; *cr:* St h Cntrl 4th-6th Grd Math Tchr 1971-75; Steeple Valley Schl 5th-6th Math Tchr 1975-90; Elm MS 6th Grd Math Tchr 1990-; *ai:* OEA, NEA ; OCTM 1980-; *office:* Elm MS Euclid Ave Martins Ferry OH 43935

FMAN, ROSE MARY, Instr of Devlpmntl Handicapped; *b:* Laurel, *n:* Milton III; *c:* Rayna, Milton Trevon; *ed:* Bowling Green St Univ Spec Ed, EMR DH 1973, (MS) Spec Ed 1978, (EDS) Rdng 1984; *cr:* usky HS Tchr 1973-78; Bowling Green St Univ Intern 1978-79; ensville Hghts Schl Tchr 1979-; *ai:* Warrensville MS Chrldng Adv; Del; Warrensville Hghts Educ Assn 1979-, Sec, Pace Setter; NEOEA , Election Chair; Natl Cncl Negro Women Inc 1984-, Corresponding 2nd VP, Pres Awd, 1995-, Bethune Recognition; PTA 1991-, Treas; Tchr Walked the Walk NEOEA 1996; *office:* Warrensville Hghts MS Warrensville Ct Rd Cleveland OH 44128

FMAN, SUE ELLEN, Fifth Grade Teacher; *b:* Dayton, OH; *m:* ence W.; *ed:* Univ of Dayton (BS) Elem Ed 1963; Wright St Univ .d) Rdng 1988; Attnd Loyolla Coll at Baltimore 1977, Eastern MI at Ypsilenti 1980; *cr:* St Anthony Schl 5th Grd Tchr 1967-68; W sville Elem 5th Grd Tchr 1968-71; Ranchland Hills 6th Grd Tchr -74; Emerson 3rd Grd Tchr 1976; St Joan of Arc 3rd Grd Tchr 78; Our Lady of Good Counsel 3rd Grd Tchr 1979-80; St Helen Schl rd Tchr 1980-; *ai:* Intermediate Play Coord; IRA 1986-; OH Rdng 1988-; Dayton Area Rdng Assn 1991-; Kappa Delta Pi 1988-; AARP ; *office:* St Helen Schl 5086 Burkhardt Rd Dayton OH 45431

FMAN, SUSAN LINDEMANN, 8th Grade Soc Stud Teacher; *b:* ay, NY; *m:* Robert John; *c:* Sarah, Emily; *ed:* Univ at Albany (BA) His (MA) Soc Stud Ed; Hudson Vly Comm Coll Assoc Lbrl Arts 1970; erlin Jr & Sr HS 8th Grd Soc Stud Tchr 1988-; *ai:* MS Stu Cncl Adv; rd Team Ldr; NCSS; NY St Cncl for Soc Stud; AFT 1988-; Girl Scouts -94, Ldr & Trainer; Hoosick Twp Historical Soc 1985-, Sec; Literacy 990-93, Bd Mem; *office:* Berlin Central Jr Sr HS PO Box 259 Berlin 2022

FMAN, TERRY L., Business Teacher; *b:* Dayton, OH; *m:* Sandra S. ing; *c:* Lori K., Chad E.; *ed:* Wright St Univ (BS) Bus Ed 1969, (MS) Ed 1975; *cr:* Houston HS Bus Ed 1969-70; Northmont Jr HS Bus Ed -77; Northmont HS Bus Ed 1978-; *ai:* HS Stadium Message, board Operator; Detention Supvr; NEA, OEA 1969-; Local NDEA -, Membership Chair 8 Yrs; Phillipsburg Luth 1970-, Treas 5 Yrs, 1 Yr; Phillipsburg Rescue 1978-, Pres 2 Yrs, Treas 4 Yrs; AAL #7002 -, Treas 5 Yrs; Dayton Montgomery Co Excl Tchng Awd 1987-88; mont HS Tchr of Yr 1987; Brookville Masons #596 Comm Builder 1988; *office:* Northmont Sr H S 4916 W National Rd Clayton OH 5

FMANN, ELIZABETH MARY (CRONIN), 7th & 8th Grade her; *b:* New York, NY; *m:* Kenneth J.; *ed:* St Johns Univ (BS) K-12 Ed ath 1990, (MS) Rdng Specialist 1993; *cr:* St Fidelis Schl 8th Grd Math i Tchr 1990-, 7th Grd Math & Sci 1995-; *ai:* NCTE 1988-; Kappa Pi 1990-, VP Kappa Eta Chptr 1989-90; NCEA 1990-; Empire St enger Awd in Math; *office:* St Fidelis Schl 124-06 14th Ave Flushing 1356

FMANN, KATHRYN VINCENT, 5th Grade Teacher; *b:* Balston Spa, *m:* Michael; *c:* Derrick; *ed:* Trenton St Coll (BS) Early Chldhd Ed -81; *cr:* Lounsberry Hollow Schl Compensatory Ed 1978-81, 5th Grd 1981-; *ai:* Schl Comm Assn; Budget Comm; NJEA, NEA 1981-; Prin *office:* Lounsberry Hollow MS Box 219 Sammis Rd Vernon NJ 2*

FRAGE, PHOEBE ANN, 4th Grade Teacher; *b:* Winchester, MA; *m:* has Frederick; *c:* Kristin ELizabeth Couch, Thomas Matthew; *ed:* or Univ (BS) Elem Ed 1971; *cr:* Marion Pub Schls 3rd, 6th Grd Tchr -72; Harvard Pub Schl Spec Needs Tutor 1982-83; The Imago Schl 4th Tchr 1985-; *ai:* Chrstn Schls Intnl 1985-.

IUS, ANN IRENE, Tchr & Soc Stud Dept Chprsn; *b:* Grove City, PA; mothy M.; *ed:* Edinboro Univ (BS) Sec Ed, Soc Stud 1976; 30 Hrs ired for Permanent PA Tchng Cert; *cr:* Reynolds Area HS Soc Stud 1977-78; Kennedy Chrstn HS Tchr 1978-; *ai:* Chrldr Adv; Soph Class erator; NCEA 1978-; Eastern Star 1974-, Worthy Matron; Rainbow 1971-, Grand Cross of Color; Ducks Unlimited 1982-, Area Chm, PA Projects Chm; *office:* Kennedy Christian HS 2120 Freeway nitage PA 16148*

MAN, BARBARA HARTUNG, Mathematics Teacher; *b:* Long d, NY; *m:* Robert; *ed:* Trenton St Coll (BA) Elem Ed 1964; Attnd is Cty Comm Coll, Seton Hall Univ, Univ of MD, Trinity Coll; *cr:* dolph Twp Schl 4th, 5th Grd Tchr 1964-69, 7th, 8th Grd Math Tchr -84; Charles Cty HS Math Tchr 1984-85; Montgomery Cty HS Math 1985-; *ai:* Stu Govt Adv; Cooperating Tchr; Schl Assembly Comm; 1964-; MCEA 1985-; MEA 1984-; PTSA 1985-; US Lighthouse Soc 1993-; Natl Capital Area Collectors Club 1992-; *office:* Montgomery Blair HS 313 Wayne Ave Silver Spring MD 20910*

HOFMANN, SHEILA ARMSTRONG, Health & PE Teacher; *b:* West Chester, PA; *m:* Edward G. Jr.; *ed:* West Chester Univ (BS) Hlth, PE 1974; Beaver Coll (MA) Hlth Ed 1980; 40 Credit Hrs Post Grad; *cr:* Neshaminy HS Hlth, PE Tchr 1974-; *ai:* Var Women's Tennis Coach; IM Dir; Gym Night Sr Supvr; AFT 1975-; *office:* Neshaminy HS 2001 Old Lincoln Hwy Langhorne PA 19047

HOFSAESS, FREDRICK ROGER, Professor of Animal Science; *b:* Summit, NJ; *m:* Elizabeth Haldimann; *c:* Edith, Robert; *ed:* DE Valley Coll (BS) Animal Sci 1967; VPI Animal Sci (MS) 1969, (PhD) 1970; *cr:* DE Valley Coll Asst Prof 1970-76, Prof & Chm 1976-; *ai:* Block & Bridle Adv; Amer Soc of Sci 1967-; Natl Assn of Coll Tchng in Ag, NE outstanding Tchr Awd; US Trotting Assn; *office:* Delaware Valley Coll 700 E Butler Ave Doylestown PA 18901

HOGAN, BARBARA E., Cmptr Sci Dept Chm & Math Tchr; *b:* Suffern, NY; *m:* Joseph J. Jr.; *c:* Joseph, Brian, Geoffrey; *ed:* Coll Misericordia (BS) Math Ed 1971; Wilkes Univ (MS) Math Ed 1975; 18 Credit Hrs Acctng; 12 Credit Hrs Cmptr Programming; *cr:* Penn St Univ at Wilkes Barre Adj Math Prof 1981-91; Bishop Hoban HS Math Tchr 1971-; *ai:* Mu Alpha Theta Spon; SADD, Prom Comm Adv; Ski Club Moderator; Curr Comm; NEPA Cncl Tch of Math 1971-; Scranton Dioc Tchr of Math 1981-, Pres; Army Natl Guard Aux, Pres, Svc Awd; Cub Pack 456, Webelos Ldr; Tandy Scholar Outstdnt Tchr Awd; Outstdng Young Woman of Amer; *office:* Bishop Hoban HS 159 S Pennsylvania Ave Wilkes Barre PA 18701

HOGAN, BONITA L., Spanish Teacher; *b:* Troy, NY; *ed:* Buffalo St Coll (BS) Eng Ed 1972, (MS) Eng Ed 1975; 31 Undergraduate Hrs Span Cert; 30 Grad Hrs Spec Ed Cert; 2 Summers of Study in Salamanca Spain; 1 Summer Mexico City; 24 Grad Hrs Toward Admin Cert; *cr:* Hamburg Cntrl Schls Eng, Spec Ed Tchr 1981-82; Orchard Park MS Span, Eng Tchr 1982-88; Buffalo City Schls Span Tchr 1988-90; Frontier HS Span Tchr 1990-; *ai:* Span Club; Intl Club; NYSAFLT 1988-, Bd of Dirs; WNYFLEC1988-, Former VP; Phi Delta Kappa 1982-; ASCD 1990-; Delta Kappa Gamma; PTA 1982-; NY St MCES Fellowship for Summer Study in Salamanca Spain 1990; Fulbright Study in Mexico City 1992; Pilot Prgm Summer ESL in Poland Sponsored by Kosciusko Fnd & UNESCO 1991; *office:* Frontier Central HS S-4432 Bay View Rd Hamburg NY 14075*

HOGAN, CATHERINE J., Business Education Teacher; *b:* Gloversville, NY; *m:* Charles P.; *c:* Meghan, Daniel; *ed:* Siena Coll (BS) Mngmt, Mrktg, Acctng 1975; Niagara Univ (MS) Ed 1979; NYS Soccer, Sftbl, Bsktbl Coach Certfd; *cr:* Lydonville Cntrl Schl Bus Ed Tchr 1975-; Genesee Comm Coll FYE Instr 1995-; *ai:* Schl Store, NHS, NJHS, Acad Decathlon Adv; Girls Soccer, Bsktbl, JV Sftbl Coach; Tech Comm; NYSUT 1975-, Local Treas; PTA 1988-, Tchr of Yr 1990; St Joseph's Church 1985-; Yrbk Dedication, Staff Appreciation Awd 1992; Tchr Coll Credit Class on HS Campus First Yr Experience; *office:* Lyndonville CHS Housel Ave Lyndonville NY 14098

HOGAN, DIANE UTOFT, 6th Grade Teacher; *b:* Tyler, MN; *m:* Frank; *c:* Molly, Kate; *ed:* Grandview Coll (AA) General Ed 1964; Pacific Luthern Univ (BA) Eng 1966; East Stroudsburg Univ Elem Cert; *cr:* Cntrl Park Elem Kndgtn Tchr 1966-67; Hopkins Jr HS Eng Tchr 1967-68; United Cerebral Palsy Classroom Tchr 1970-72; Coll Hill Nursery Schl Head Tchr 1980-85; Union Twp Schl Eng, Gifted Tchr 1987-95; *ai:* NJ Ed Assn 1987-, VP; NCTE 1987-; Assn of Elem Ed, Pres; Whos Who Among Coll Stdnts 1987; Lenape Tchrs of Whole Lang 1990; *office:* Union Twp School 165 Perryville Rd Hampton NJ 08827

HOGAN, DONNA BERTE, English Department Chairperson; *b:* Springfield, MA; *m:* Peter; *c:* Peter, Sean; *ed:* Amer Intnl Coll (BA) Eng 1973; Westfield St Coll (MA) Cnslng, Guid 1978; Amer Intnl Coll CAGS Rdng 1981; *cr:* Ludlow Jr HS Eng Tchr 1973-81; Paul R. Baird MS Eng Dept Chprsn 1981-; *ai:* Rdng, Lang Arts Curr Stud, Bldg Needs Assessment Comms; Curr Ldrshp Team; Tchr Mentoring Prgm; Ludlow Ed Assn 1973-; MA Tchrs of Eng; MA Tchrs Assn; NEA, NCTE; AIC Alumni Assn 1973-; GATE Stdnts Grant Writer MA Ed Dept 1996; Tchr Appreciation Awd Our Lady of the Elms Coll 1984; *office:* Paul R Baird MS 109 Sportsmans Rd Ludlow MA 01056*

HOGAN, ELIZABETH ANN, Pre-Kindergarten Teacher; *b:* Brooklyn, NY; *ed:* St Josephs Coll (BA) Child Stud 1964; Brooklyn Coll (MS) Early Chldhd Ed 1968; 30 Addl Credit Hrs; *cr:* PS 58K Kndgtn Tchr 1964-88, Pre-Kndgtn Tchr 1988-; *ai:* AFT, Cath Tchrs Assn 1964-; *office:* PS 58K Carroll Schl 330 Smith St Brooklyn NY 11231*

HOGAN, JUDITH ANN, Business Education Teacher; *b:* Morristown, NJ; *m:* Ethan; *c:* Kristen, Kelly; *ed:* Trenton St Coll (BA) Bus Ed 1970; *cr:* Hanover Park HS Bus Ed Tchr & COE Coord 1970-78; Hanover Park HS Bus Ed Tchr 1988-95; Whippany Park HS Dept Coord 1995-; *ai:* FBLA Adv; NEA 1970-; NJBEA 1970-; MCBEA 1978-; *office:* Whippany Park HS 165 Whippany Rd Whippany NJ 07981

HOGAN, LOUISE A. (LOUANNE), Third Grade Teacher; *b:* Oswego, NY; *ed:* SUC at Oswego (BS) Elem Ed 1970; SUC at Buffalo (MS) Ed 1987; *cr:* Lyndonville Cntrl Schl Second Grd Tchr 1970-72, Third Grd Tchr 1972-; *ai:* Delta Kappa Gamma 1987-; AFT & NYSUT 1970-; PTA 1989-; *office:* Lyndonville Cntrl Schl Housel Ave Lyndonville NY 14098

HOGAN, MICHAEL C., Mathematics Teacher; *b:* Meadville, PA; *m:* Terry A. Beinard; *c:* Ashley, Russell, Jeffrey; *ed:* Penn St Univ (BA) Scndry Ed & Math 1988; 36 Credit Hrs IN Univ of PA; *cr:* Bellwood-Antis HS Math & Comp Tchr 1989; Northern Cambria HS Math Tchr 1990-; *ai:* Boys Bsktbl & Girls Vllybl Head Coach; NEA 1989-; PSEA 1989-; *office:* Northern Cambria HS 807 N 11th St Barnesboro PA 15714*

HOGAN, ROSEMARY, Teacher of Gifted; *b:* Pittsburgh, PA; *ed:* Carlow Coll (BA) Fr 1969; Masters Equivalency in Credit Hrs Spcl Ed & Gifted Ed; *cr:* St Xavier Acad Fr Tchr 1969-70; Diocese of Pittsburgh Elem Tchr 1970-72; Shaler Area Schl Dist 1st Grd Tchr 1972-81, Tchr of Gifted 1981-; *ai:* Odyssey of Mind Founding Spon; NEA 1973-, Fac Rep & Newsletter Ed, 2nd Pl Newsletter in PA; Renaissance & Baroque Soc of Pittsburgh 1986-, Bd Mem 1992-; 2 Grants for Schl Dist Renaissance Music Groups; *office:* Shaler Area Schl Dist 1800 Mt Royal Blvd Glenshaw PA 15116

HOGAN MAC EVOY, LISA ANNE, Health Occupations Instructor; *b:* St Marys, NY; *m:* Steven; *c:* Adam, Michael, Eric; *ed:* Trocaire Coll (AAS) Nrsng 1978; Buffalo St Coll (BSEd) Voc Ed, Ed 1995; NCCC Intermeiate, Advanced Cardiac Arrthymias; ARC Instr Comm CPR, First Aid, Prof Rescuer; *cr:* BCS Janitor 1975-76; ICMH Nurse Asst 1976-78, LMH Staff, Charge Nurse 1978-92; O-N BOCES Tchr, Clinical Instr 1991-; *ai:* Lead Adv VICA, CCD; Asst Coach Bsbl; Amer Red Cross Instr; Prof, Basic Life Rescuer, First Aid; PTSA; ANA 1978-; NYS PHE, NYS HOE 1992-; PTSA 1995-, Pres 1993-94; PTA 1985-, VP 1991-93; Amer Red Cross 1982-, Instr; Amer Red Cross Comm Svc Awd; *office:* Orleans-Niagara Boces 4232 Shelby Basin Rd Medina NY 14103*

HOGENAUER, DAVID E., Social Studies Teacher; *b:* Mt Vernon, NY; *m:* Claire; *c:* Rebecca Horne, Ken, Heather; *ed:* Haverford Coll (BA) Sociology 1955; Harvard Schl of Educ (MAT) Soc Stud 1956; Seton Hall Univ (MA) His 1976; NYU Course to India; NDEA Grant Univ of NH; *cr:* Vly Rd Schl Tchr 1956-64; Columbia HS Tchr 1964-; *ai:* NEA; NJEA; Prospect Presbyn Church 1966-, Ruling Elder, Sunday Schl Supt, Homeless Prgm Coord; Lesson Plan Chosen for Holocaust Wkshp Presentation 1992; *home:* 9 Cedar Ln E Maplewood NJ 07040

HOGUE, AMANDA J., 8th Grade Algebra & Math Tchr; *b:* Dover, OH; *ed:* OSU (BA) PE & Bio Sci 1984, (BA) Elem, Ed & Math 1986; Ashland Coll (MS) Curr Dev 1996; *cr:* Norton MS 7th Grd Sci 1986-89, 9th Grd Math & Algebra 1989-; *ai:* Coach Bsktbl & Track; Pal; BCC, Bldg Curr & Dis Math Comm; Eisonhour Grant Team; NEA 1986-; OEA 1986-; Schl Bell Awds; *office:* Norton MS 215 Norton Rd Columbus OH 43228*

HOGUE, BARBARA SQUEGLIA, 9th Grd Learning Support Tchr; *b:* New Castle, PA; *m:* Brian; *c:* Samuel; *ed:* Slippery Rock St Coll (BS) Spec, Elem Ed 1979; Slippery Rock Univ (MED) Spec Ed 1983; *cr:* I U #9 Learning Disabilities Tchr 1979-82; Head Start of Lawrence Cty Spec Needs Coord 1982; United Cerebal Palsey Prgm Specialist 1982-83; Mercer Area Schl Dist Learning Support Tchr 1983-; *ai:* Strategic Planning Comm; Parents As Educl Partners Advy Bd; Mentor Tchr for Newly Hired Tchrs; NEA, PSEA 1979-; Mercer Educl Assn 1983-, Sec, Membership Chprsn; Children's Aide Soc 1994-, Auxillary Bd; *home:* 215 S Pitt St Mercer PA 16137

HOGUE, DONALD ROBERT, English Teacher; *b:* Woonsocket, RI; *m:* Paula J. Lafond; *c:* Amy, Adam; *ed:* Brandeis Univ (BA) Eng, Amer Lit 1980; Univ of St Andrews (MPhil) Eng Lit 1987; Medieval Stud Prgm; 20 Credit Hrs in Scndry Ed RI Coll; St Coll 1993; *cr:* Greater Woonsocket Cath Regnl Schls 7-9 Grd Eng Tchr 1980-82; Mount St Charles Acad 7-9, 11-12 Grd Eng Tchr 1982-; *ai:* Jr HS Girls & Boys Cross Cntry Coach; CCD Tchr; NCEA 1980-; Rotary Intnl Flwshp 1 Yr Stud Abroad 1985; Natl Endowment for the Hum Summer Inst Participant 1988; 1st Natl Tchrs Conf on the Holocaust Washington DC Holocaust Museum 1993; Evergreen Tchrs Wkshps on Comm OH Ctr for Learning 1991; Brown Univ Inst for Scndry Edctr Eng 1992; Articles Pub; *office:* Mount Saint Charles Acad 800 Logee St Woonsocket RI 02895

HOGUE, ROBERT A., Computer Sci Asst Prof; *b:* Pittsburgh, PA; *ed:* Grove City Coll (BA) Math 1969; Bucknell Univ (MA) Math 1970; PA St Univ (MS) Cmptr Sci 1983; *cr:* PA St at Shenango Instr 1983-85; Univ of West FL Instr 1985-86; Youngstown St Univ Asst Prof of Cmptr Sci & Information Systems 1988-; *ai:* Assn for Cmptr Mach 1988-; Amer Meteorological Soc 1994-; Golden Key Natl Honor Soc Honorary Mem.

HOGUE, RUSS EUGENE BOBBY DAN,JR., English Teacher & Bsktbl Coach; *b:* Kenton, OH; *m:* Margaret Mc Cullough; *c:* Russ Eugene Bobby Dan III; *ed:* Wilmington Coll (BA) Eng, His 1986; Wright St (MS) Ed 1994; *cr:* Fairfield Union HS Tchr, Coach 1986-91, IN Lake HS Tchr, Coach 1991-; *ai:* Boys Bsktbl Head Coach; NEA, OEA 1986-; ILEA 1991-; *home:* 305 E Torrence St Belle Center OH 43310*

HOHMAN, HEIDI SUE, Fourth Grade Teacher; *b:* Wheeling, WV; *ed:* West Liberty St Coll (AB) Elem Ed 1988; *cr:* St Mary Cntrl Schl Fourth Grd Tchr 1988-; *ai:* Co-Coord Right-to-Read Week Act; Fac Rep SMC 2000; Kappa Delta Pi 1986-, Honorary Ed Soc Awd; NCEA 1988-; Beulah Boyd Schlsp Assn of Amer Univ Women; Paul Douglas Tchr Schlsp; WLSC Outstdng Ed Major; OH Tchr of the Yr Awd Candidate 1992; *home:* RR 1 Box 227 Triadelphia WV 26059*

HOHN, DIANE L., English & Psychology Teacher; *b:* Bowling Green, OH; *m:* John; *c:* Laurie, Kyle, Lindsey; *ed:* Univ of Findlay (BA) Eng 1970; Re-Cert; *cr:* Riverdale HS Eng Tchr 1970-71; Our Lady of Consolation Eng & Rdng Tchr 1971-73; Riverdalle HS Eng & Psych Tchr 1984-; *ai:* Var & JV Chrldng Adv; *office:* Riverdale HS 20613 State Route 37 Mt Blanchard OH 45867

HOHWIELER, ELIZABETH VOSS, Vocal Music Teacher; *b:* Abington, PA; *m:* Donald G.; *c:* Bevin Elizabeth; *ed:* Temple Univ (BMUSED) Music Ed 1977, (MM) Vocal Performance 1980; 11 Post Masters Credits from Various Colls in Music; *cr:* Pennsbury Schls 9th & 10th Grd Vocal Music Tchr 1986-; *ai:* Coach & Prepare Stdnts for Select Choruses on Cty, Dist, Region, St & Natl Levels; Music Dir & Coach for Broadway Type Musical Production Yearly; MENC 1986-; PEA 1986-; AGMA 1993-; Mem of the Philadelphias Singers & Singers Chorale; *home:* 1493 Woodview Rd Yardley PA 19067

HOISL, ANDREA DEVITO, Campus Ministry Dir & Rel Tchr; *b:* Hartford, CT; *m:* Thomas P.; *c:* Matthew, Rebekah; *ed:* Salve Regina Univ (BA) Rel Stud 1986; St Joseph Coll (MS) Ed 1988; Scndry Sci St Cert; *cr:* South Cath HS Rel Tchr & Campus Ministry Team Mem 1986-89; Xavier HS Rel Tchr & Campus Ministry Dir 1989-; *ai:* Soph Class Moderator, Right to Life Group & Peace & Justice Group Moderator; Pastoral Cnslr; Svc & Retreat Coord; NEAC 1986-; Cath Yth Org 1988-, Coord; *office:* Xavier HS 181 Randolph Rd Middletown CT 06457*

HOKE, DALE E., Instrumental Music Teacher; *b:* Chambersburg, PA; *m:* Gail L. Sigafoos; *c:* Corey L., Adam J.; *ed:* Susquehanna Univ (BS) Music Ed 1972; Grad Stud in Music Ed West Chester Univ; *cr:* Ceaser Rodney Schl Dist Music Tchr 1972-73; Mechanicsburg Area Schl Dist Music Tchr 1973-76; Emmaus Schl Dist Music Tchr 1979-80; Mechanicsburg Area Schl Dist Music Tchr 1980-; *ai:* 7th & 8th Grd Bands Dir; Intermediate & Sr HS Jazz Ensemble Dir; Sr HS Musical Pit Orch Dir; Dept Coord; Intermediate Bldg Cmptr Coord; NEA, PSEA, Amer Fed of Musicians; Monaghan Presbyn Church; Outstanding Svc to Pupils Awd by Mechanicsburg Schl Dist 1981, 1995; *office:* Mechanicsburg Area Interm Sch 500 S Broad St Mechanicsburg PA 17055

HOLBERT, BARBARA ELLEN, Vocal Music Tchr & Dept Head; *b:* Honesdale, PA; *m:* James Joseph; *c:* James Robert, Elizabeth Marie; *ed:* Mansfield Univ (BS) Music Ed 1979; Post Grad Cert 1982; *cr:* Elk Lake Schl Dist Voc Music Tchr 1979-, Grds 5-12 Gen Music, Spec Ed Music Tchr 1979-80, 1995-; *ai:* Springville Women's Club Talent Show; Schlsp Banquet Comm; Dist Orch Host 1994; Susquehanna Cty Music Festival Host 1990, 1995; ELEA, PMEA, MENC 1979-; *office:* Elk Lake Schl Dist PO Box 100 Dimock PA 18816

HOLCOMB, JOANNE HURLEY, English Teacher; *b:* Bethpage, NY; *m:* Ernest G.; *c:* Katherine, Meghan, Michael; *ed:* Bridgewater St (BA) Eng & His 1979; Attnd Univ of MA Writing Project, Bridgewater Coll & Lesley Coll Curr; NJ Wrtng Project; Bard Coll Inst for Wrtng & Thinking; *cr:* Falmouth Acad Eng & His Tchr 1979-82; Lawrence Jr High Eng Tchr 1982-93; Falmouth HS Eng Tchr 1993-; *ai:* Field Hockey Coach; Yrbk & Writing Club Adv; Acad Team Chprsn; Dist Writing & Summer Rdng Comms; Stu Activity Coord; MA Tchrs Assn, Falmouth Educators Assn & Barnstable Cty Ed Assn 1982-; NCTE 1985-; VNA Bd of Dir 1980-; Supt Awd for Distinguished Svc 1985; Horace Mann Tchr for Writing Process 1986-87; Tchr of Yr 1989-90; *office:* Falmouth HS 874 Gifford St Falmouth MA 02536*

HOLDAN, GREGORY, Math & Computer Science Tchr; *b:* Pittsburgh, PA; *ed:* Indiana Univ of PA (BS) Ed 1969; Penn St (MA) Math 1971, (PHD) Curr & Instruction 1985; Scndry Prin & Math Supvr Certs; *cr:* Mount Lebanon HS Math & Cmptr Sci Tchr 1971-; Penn St Instructional Design Adjunct Fac 1990-; Duquesne Univ Ed & Math Adjunct Fac 1993-; *ai:* Acad Games Spon; NCTM 1968-; NEA, PSEA & MLEA 1971-; AERA & ASCD 1985-; *office:* Mount Lebanon HS 155 Cochran Rd Pittsburgh PA 15228

HOLDAWAY, STACEY TARANTO, Mathematics Teacher; *b:* Baltimore, MD; *m:* David A.; *ed:* Univ of MD (BA) Ec, Math 1985; Loyola Coll (MED) Ed 1993; 9 Credits Towards Ed Doctorate; *cr:* Bel Air HS Math Tchr 1988-93; North Harford HS Math Dept Head, Tchr 1993-; *ai:* NCTM

1993-; Governors Acad 1993; Rutgers Univ Discrete Math Summer Prgm 1992-93; *office:* North Harford HS 211 Pylesville Rd Pylesville MD 21132

HOLDEN, JAMES E., Computer Information Sci Prof; *b:* Erie, PA; *m:* Caryl A. Winkler; *c:* John A., Timothy J., Shane Ross, Shauna Kush; *ed:* Edinboro Univ (BS) Math 1961; PA St Univ (MED) Math 1966; Cmptr Software Engineering Trng Prgm 2 Yrs; Cmptr Industry Trng 11 Yrs; 75 Post Grad Stud Computing; *cr:* Rocky Grove HS Math Tchr 1961-69; General Electric Co Software Engr 1969-73; United Data Svcs Inc Programmer, Analyst 1973-80; Clarion Univ of PA Asst Prof of CIS 1980-; *ai:* Users Group Adv; General Ed Cncl; APSCUF 1980-; Allegheny Valley Trails Assn 1991-, VP, Pres; Fac Prof Dev Grant 1994; Man of Yr Franklin Chamber of Commerce 1993; Rails to Trails Project Grants & Donations; *office:* Clarion Univ Of PA Clarion PA 16214

HOLDEN, MARYELLEN ROSSVALL, Frgn Lang Chpsn & Span Tchr; *b:* Hartford, CT; *m:* Kevin S.; *c:* Patrick, Eileen; *ed:* Southern CT St Coll (BS) Span, Scndry Ed 1977; Univ of Salamanca Span Cert 1975; 12 Credit Hrs Admin, Supervision Cntrl CT St Univ; *cr:* St Margaret's Mc Ternan Schl Part-time Span Tchr 1977-78, Span Tchr 1980-, Frgn Lang Dept Chair 1992-; Notre Dame Acad Span Tchr 1979-80; *ai:* Span Club Adv; Sr Class Head Adv; Peer Tutoring Prgm Co-Coord; Hlth, Wellness Comm; Physically Challenged Awareness Comm Coord; Ct Org Lang Tchrs 1980-; Forestville Little League 1988-, Sec, Benvenuto Vol of Yr 1995; Eastern Regnl Little League Bsbl Tournament Comm 1996-; Bristol Kiwanis 1995-; Little League Bsbl 1996-, Asst Dist Admin; *office:* St Margaret's Mc Ternan Schl 565 Chase Pkwy Waterbury CT 06708

HOLDEN, RANDALL O.,III, Math Teacher; *b:* Elmira, NY; *m:* Kimberly A. Irvine; *c:* Lindsey, Thomas; *ed:* Mansfield St Univ (BA) Scndry Ed, Math 1978; Elmira Coll (MA) Ed 1989; *cr:* Troy MS Math Tchr 1978-83; Corning-PP East HS Scndry Math Tchr 1983-; *ai:* Ftbl Var, JV Head Coach; Var Lacrosse Asst Coach; IM Weight Trng, Plyometrics Coord; Mentoring Prgm At-Risk Yth Tchr; NEA, AFT 1978-; NYSUT 1983-, NYS HS Ftbl Coaches Assn 1994-; *office:* Corning Painted Post East HS 201 Cantigny St Corning NY 14830

HOLDEN, SUE MALABY, Cooperative Bus Ed Coordinator; *b:* Crestline, OH; *c:* Karen Frisina, Roger Hardgrove; *ed:* Lake Erie Coll (BA) His 1971; Kent St Univ (MED) Voc 1975; Baldwin-Wallace Coll Bus 1954-57; *cr:* Mentor HS Bus Tchr 1971-74; Willloughby-Eastlake Tech Ctr & CBE Coord 1975-; *ai:* CBE Club Adv; NEA 1971-; WETA 1975-; UUSWR 1990-, Chair.

HOLDER, CHARLES RICHARD, Social Studies Teacher; *b:* Hagerstown, MD; *m:* Trudie Louise Keller; *c:* Helen Gertrude, Elizabeth Anne; *ed:* Frostburg St Univ (BA) Scndry Soc Stud Ed 1965, (MED) Ed 1969; Univ of South (TEE) Theology 1978; *cr:* Williamsport HS Soc Stud Tchr 1965-; *ai:* Stu Cncl Adv; Schl Improvement Team; Cty Finals Comm; Washington Cty Tchrs Assn 1965-, MD St Tchrs Assn 1965-, NEA 1965-; NCSS 1985-; Antietam Lodge AF&AM 1972-, Sec; Olive Branch Chptr 1972-, Past Patron; Pleasant Vly Ruritan 1987-; *office:* Williamsport HS 5 S Clifton Dr Williamsport MD 21795

HOLDER, MARGARET C., English & Spanish Teacher; *b:* Pittsburgh, PA; *m:* Robert; *ed:* Duquesne Univ (BA) Eng 1978, (MSEd) Scndry 1984; 6 Addl Hrs Univ of Pittsburgh; *cr:* Keystone Oaks HS Jrnlsm Tchr, PR Dir 1984; Chatham Coll Composition Instr 1984-85; Greenway MS Spanish, Pol Tchr 1985-86; Elizabeth Forward HS Eng, Span Tchr 1986-; *ai:* Schl Newspaper Adv 1986-91; Prof Leadership Cncl Mem; Drama Club; NCTE 1988-; AFT 1985-; Univ of Pittsburgh All Star Educator 1991; St Vincent Coll Great Tchr Awd 1991; Feature Articles Pub in Pittsburgh Magazine; PA Youth Apprenticeship Prgm Curr Team; First Pratitioner in Residence at Duq Univ a Sabbatical Position; *office:* Elizabeth Forward H S 1000 Weigles Hill Rd Elizabeth PA 15037*

HOLDERBY, LINDA (HEROLD), 4th Grade Teacher; *b:* Elyria, OH; *w:* O. Perry Jr. (dec); *ed:* Bowling Green St U (BS) Ed 1973; Wright St Univ (MS) Ed 1988; 15 Addl Sem Hrs; *cr:* Northridge Elem Schl Tchr 1973-; *ai:* NEA 1973-; Warder Literacy Ctr 1991-, Tutor; Kappa Delta Pi; Alpha Delta Kappa; *office:* Northridge Elem Schl 4445 Ridgewood Rd E Springfield OH 45503

HOLDRIDGE, CAROL G., 2nd Grade Teacher; *b:* Newark, NY; *m:* Richard A.; *c:* Mark Sheridan, Brent Ellis; *ed:* SUC at Potsdam (BA) Elem Ed 1967; Attnd Syracuse Univ, SUNY at Oswego; *cr:* Red Creek Cntrl 1st Grd Tchr 1967-71; Phelps Clifton Springs 2nd Grd Tchr 1971-; *ai:* P-CS Fac Assn 1971-; AFT, NYSUT 1967-; AE Comm Ctr, Bd Dir; Newark Ctry Club; Songbook Songs 2nd Grd Curr; *office:* Phelps Primary Schl 1 Banta St Phelps NY 14532

HOLDRIDGE, DONALD WESLEY,SR., Bible & Greek Professor; *b:* Middletown, CT; *m:* Sandra Joy Reak; *c:* Donny; *ed:* Univ of RI (BS) Electrical Engr 1980; Capital Bible Seminary (MDIV) Theology 1985, (THM) Old Testament 1986; Dallas Theological Seminary (PHD) Bible Exposition 1993; US Army Command & Gen Staff Coll 1996; *cr:* Bapt Bible Coll Asst Prof 1993-; *ai:* Cross Cntry, Track Asst Coach for Coll Lib Comm; Evangelical Theological Soc 1993; *office:* Bapt Bible Coll of PA 538 Venard Rd Clarks Summit PA 18411

HOLESKO, JOAN KANTOR, Third Grade Teacher; *b:* North Tonawanda, NY; *m:* Stephen Paul; *c:* Patrick, Stephen; *ed:* St Univ Coll at Buffalo (BS) Elem Ed 1966; Arts in Ed WNY; *cr:* Wurlitzer Elem Schl First, Second Grd Tchr 1966-76; OH Elem Schl First Grd Tchr 1976-79, Third Grd Tchr 1979-; *ai:* Mentor Prgm; Schl Improvement Team; Congruency, Scrap Book, Schlsp Comms; Shared Decision Making Team; NT United Tchrs 1966-, Building Rep; NYSUT, AFT 1966-; Delta Kappa Gamma 1991-; Ghostlight Theater Co 1988-; DeGraff Memorial Hosp Auxiliary; Ideas Pub; Presenter NY St Rdng Assn Conf 1991; *home:* 1253 Bowen Cir North Tonawanda NY 14120

HOLFORD, JANE ANN, Fifth Grade Teacher; *b:* Dayton, OH; *m:* Steven Betts; *c:* Stephanie Betts-Broussard; *ed:* Otterbein Coll (BS) Ed 1971; 28 Grad Hrs toward Masters in Curr & Instruction at Ashland Univ; *cr:* Whittier Elem 6th Grd Tchr 1971-72; Cherrington Elem 5th Grd Tchr 1972-75; Huber Ridge Elem 3rd, 5th & 6th Grd Tchr 1975-; *ai:* Dist 5th Grd Math Tchr Ldr 1993-; Curricular Pathways Team to Integrate Sci & Math 1995-; Acad Adv 1987-90; NCTM 1986-; NEA, OEA, WEA 1976-; Nom for Presidential Awd for Sci & Math Tchng 1994-95; *office:* Huber Ridge Elem Schl 5757 Buenos Aires Blvd Westerville OH 43081*

HOLGATE, KEITH SILVERA, English Teacher; *b:* Portland Jamaica, West Indies; *m:* Mitzi M. Myrie; *c:* Maza, Kia, Keisha; *ed:* Brooklyn Coll (BA) Commnctn 1982, (MS) Guid Cnslng; Attnd Univ of WI; *cr:* Jamaica Citizens Bank Sr Teller & Customer Svc Rep 1970-74; Jamaica Telephone Co Acctng Clerk 1974-77; Chase Manhattan Bank Verification Clerk 1977-82; Malmonides Med Ctr Comp Opr Lab 1982-; IS 285 Meyer Levin Tchr 1987-; *ai:* Schls Peer Tutoring Pgm Supvr; Schls Compact Team Active Mem; Amer Tchr 1987-; UFT 1987-; Kingston Coll Old Boys Assn 1977-; Jamaica Telephone Co Ex Employees 1990-, Founding Mem; *home:* 1160 E 52nd St Brooklyn NY 11234*

HOLIDAY, ISAAC S., Jr HS Dance Teacher; *b:* Manhattan, NY; *c:* Tunesia; *ed:* SUNY at New Paltz (BS) Dance 1987; SUNY at Brockport Visiting Dance 1988-89; SUNY at Fredonia Flwshp Dance 1988-89; Lehman Coll 6 Credit Hrs in Early Chldhd Ed; Coll of St Rose 6 Credit Hrs in Spcl Ed; *cr:* Dance Tchr for Several Marching Bands 1992-95; Off-Broadway Asst Choreographer 1993-94; Quest Club Dance Instr 1993-95; Kips Bay Boys & Girls Club Dance Instr 1993-95; *ai:* Coaching Boys & Girls Bsktbl; Tutoring Stdnts for HS Performing Arts Test; Dance Dir; UFT 1989-; NY Lancers 1979-, Horn Sgt Rookie of Yr; Knight Club 1993-, Pledge Dean, The Knightly Knight; NY Bd of Ed Dance Tchrs for Achvmt 4 Yrs; Laban Inst Movement Stud Summer Dance Tchr Trng; *office:* JHS 141 Riverdale/David Stein 660 W 237th St Bronx NY 10463*

HOLIDAY, JAMES E., Teacher of Handicapped; *b:* Monessen, PA; *m:* Janice Bauer; *c:* Suzette, Erin Patrick, Roderick Morgan; *ed:* Westminster Coll (BS) Psych 1959; CA St Univ (MS) Mental Retardation 1972; WV Univ 60 Hrs; Duquesne Univ 12 Hrs; *cr:* Westmoreland Intermediate Univ Tchr 25 Yrs; *ai:* Blue Shirts; Jr HS Ski Club; PA Spec Olympics Alpine Dir; PSEA 1972-, Local VP; Phi Delta Kappa 1975-; CEC; Free & Accepted Masons 1965-; BPO Elks 1970-; City Monessen Enterprise Zone 1990-; Mon Vly Cath HS, Coach, Trainer; Monessen Midgt Ftbl; Assn for Retarded CitizensTchr of Yr; *office:* Mt Pleasant Scndry Schl Rd 4 Mount Pleasant PA 15666*

HOLIDAY, WILLIAM, HS Social Studies Teacher; *b:* Brattleboro, VT; *m:* Lyle Streeter; *c:* William III, Daniel Patrick, Brieanna Allison; *ed:* Windham Coll (BA) Amer Stud 1972; Keene St Coll (MED) Ed 1975; Through Keene St Coll Attnd Saint Johns Coll at York England & thomand Coll at Limerick Ireland; Schl of World Learning in Brattleboro VT; Dartmouth Coll; *cr:* Dummerston Schl 6th-8th Grds Soc Stud & Lang Arts Tchr 1972-84; Brattleboro Union HS Soc Stud Tchr 1984-; Keene St Coll Adjunct Fac 1992-; *ai:* Stdnts Global Concerns Adv; Close Up Fnd Adv; White Rose Proj; VTNEA 1972-; Tchr of Yr 1989-90 & 1990-91; *office:* Brattleboro Union HS 50 Fairground Rd Brattleboro VT 05301*

HOLIHAN, DEBORAH DAWN, 6th Grade English Teacher; *b:* Syracuse, NY; *ed:* Towson St Univ (BS) Eng Lang, Lit 1991; Johns Hopkins Univ 24 Credit Hrs Towards MS Schl Admin, Supervision; *cr:* Ellicott Mills MS Eng Tchr 1992-95; Clarksville MS Eng Tchr 1995-; *ai:* Modern, Cntry Dance Coach; Show Choir Choreographer; IM Bsktbl Spon; NEA 1992-; PTA 1995-, Tchr Rep; Class Act Awd; *office:* Clarksville MS 6535 Trotter Rd Clarksville MD 21029*

HOLINGER, DOROTHY B., Mathematics Teacher; *b:* Baltimore, MD; *ed:* CT Coll (BA) Pol Sci 1960; Post Grad Stud at Univ of PA, Villanova Univ; *cr:* Friends' Cntrl Schl Math Tchr 1962-70; Agnes Irwin Schl Math Tchr 1970-77; Acad of Notre Dame Math Tchr 1977-; *ai:* Mathcounts 1988-, Mathletes 1990- Coach; Photography Instr 1988-; ATMOPAV 1970-; NCTM 1962-; Photographic His Comm MCC 1994-; NSF Swarthmore Coll, St of PA West Chester Univ Tech Grant 1994; *office:* Acad of Notre Dame 560 Sproul Rd Villanova PA 19085*

HOLLAND, CARDEN, Art Teacher; *b:* Arlington, VA; *ed:* RI Schl of Design (BFA) Painting 1969, (MAT) 1970; *cr:* Warwick Schl Dept Elem Art Tchr 1970-81; Ledyard Bd of Ed HS Art Tchr 1987-; *ai:* Art Curr Comm; NAEA; CAEA; NEA; CEA; LEA; Exhibit Art Work Local, Regnl Juried Art Shows; Co-Recipient Celebration Excl Awd 1989; *office:* Ledyard HS 24 Gallup Hill Rd Ledyard CT 06339

HOLLAND, GREGORY MATTHEW, Social Studies Teacher; *b:* Erie, PA; *m:* Jennifer Ann Gross; *c:* Griffin T., Madison M.; *ed:* Edinboro Univ of PA (BA) Scndry Ed 1990; *cr:* US Navy Quatermaster 1983-88; *ai:* Girls Tennis & Bowling Coach; Model UN & Soph Class Adv; NEA 1992-; US Navy 1983-88; *office:* Erie Cntrl HS 3325 Cherry St Erie PA 16508

HOLLAND, JAMES R., Science Teacher; *b:* Cheyenne, WY; *m:* Claudette Anne Lancaster; *c:* John, Maria, James, Anne; *ed:* Univ of ME (BS) Ed 1954; Saint Marys Coll (MS) Bio 1968; St Univ of NY at Albany DNA Inst; St Univ of NY at Columbia Grn Forensic Chem; St Univ of NY at Oswego Energy Inst; Univ of ME Pollution; Saint Joseph Coll NSF Bio Tech; St Univ of NY at New Paltz Anatomy & Physiology; *cr:* US Army Airborne Capt & Korean Veteran 1954-56; NY Military Acad Bio Tchr 1957-68; Catskill Cntrl HS Bio Tchr 1968-; *ai:* AFT, NYSTA, CTA 1968-; 3rd D Knights of Columbus 1964-; 4th D Knights of Columbus 1964-, Faithful Navigator; Amer Legion 1975-; Korean War Veterans of Amer 1988-; TAC Athletic Assn 1980-; Received Natl Sci Fnd Grants 6 Summers; St Univ of NY at Columbia-Greene for Nurses Anatomy & Physiology Tchr; St Univ of NY at Albany Advanced Bio Tchr; Former Coach of Track, Cross Cntry, Var Bsktbl, Frosh Bsktbl, Var Vlybl & Var Swimming; *office:* Catskill HS 347 W Main Catskill NY 12414

HOLLAND, JOAN MARIE, Secondary Mathematics Teacher; *b:* Philadelphia, PA; *ed:* La Salle Coll (BA) Math, Ed 1975; Master Equivalent 1993; *cr:* Archdiocese of Phila Scndry Math Tchr 1975-; *ai:* ACT, NCEA, Alpha Epsilon Alumni Soc 1975-; Amer Legion Auxiliary 1963-; *office:* Cardinal Dougherty HS 6301 N 2nd St Philadelphia PA 19120

HOLLAND, JONATHAN PERRY, Music Director; *b:* Bridgeport, CT; *m:* Vicki Lynn Eveland; *c:* Lauren M., Carolyn R., Jonathan P. Jr., Timothy J.; *ed:* Western CT St Univ (BS) Music Ed 1979; 18 Credit Hrs at Garden St Bible Schl; *cr:* Chrstn Heritage Schl Music Tchr 1979-81; Bethel Chrstn Schl Music, Fr & Span Tchr 1981-84; Annapolis Area Chrstn Schl Music, Fr & Span Tchr 1984-85; The Pilgrim Acad Music Dir & Ger Tchr 1985-; *ai:* Emmanuel Congregational Church 1988-, Music Comm Chm; *office:* The Pilgrim Acad Moss Mill Rd PO Box 322 Egg Harbor NJ 08215

HOLLAND, KATHLEEN SHECKE, Resource Ctr & Spec Ed Tchr; *b:* Jersey City, NJ; *c:* Kelly; *ed:* Jersey City St Coll (BA) Gen Elem 1964; Farleigh Dickinson Univ (MA) Learning Disabilities 1979; *cr:* Brielle Elem Schl Tchr 1964-69; Weehawken Pub Schls Tchr 1969-71; Brielle Elem Schl Tchr 1974-; *ai:* Proctor Control Detention; NEA, NJEA, BEA 1964-; *office:* Brielle Elem Schl 605 Union Ln Brielle NJ 08730

HOLLAND, NAN COBBS, English Teacher & Dept Chprsn; *b:* Goldsboro, NC; *m:* Roy E.; *c:* Ursula Cobbs; *ed:* Fayetteville St Univ (BS); *cr:* Woodstown HS Eng Tchr 1970-72; Glassboro HS Eng Tchr 1973-87; Milton Jr HS Eng Tchr 1987-88; Williamstown HS Eng Tchr 1988-90; Camden HS Eng Tchr 1991-; *ai:* Career Ctr Coord; FT 2000 Club Adv; Schl Improvement Team Sec; Tech Comm Co-Chair; Hnr Roll Stdnts Recognition; NEA 1970-; NJEA 1970-; DE Tchrs Assn 1988; NCTE 1995-; Local Church, Choir, Stewardess Bd, Lay Org; Overbrook Regnl HS Parent Org; Yrbk Dedication 1988; Glassboro HS Svc Awds; *office:* Camden HS Park & Baird Blvd Camden NJ 08104*

HOLLEN, ROBERT B., Art Teacher; *b:* Akron, OH; *m:* Sandra E. Harris; *c:* Carrie J., Shaun D.; *ed:* Univ Findlay (BS) Art Ed 1977; *cr:* Granville HS Art Tchr 1977-; *ai:* Coached Boys & Girls Cross Cntry, Track & Field & Indoor Track & Field; OH Assn Track & CC Coaches 1980-, Dist Rep; Cntrl Dist Track & CC 1980- Pres; *office:* Granville HS 248 New Burg St Granville OH 43023

HOLLENBACH, STEVEN GLENN, Music Teacher; *b:* Reading, PA; *m:* Maria Magdalena Albino; *c:* Glenn Paul; *ed:* Millersville Univ (BS) Music Ed 1985; 16.5 Credit Hrs Villanova Univ Music 1995-; 3 Credit Hrs Cadow Coll Ed 1994; *cr:* Hamburg Area Schl Dist 4-6 Grd Instrumental Music Tchr 1 Yr; US Army Band Lead Trumpet, Jazz Band Dir 3.5 Yrs; Reading Schl Dist 9-12 Grd Instrumental Music Tchr 1 Yr; Schl Dist of Lancaster 10-12 Grd Dir of Bands; 1-6 Grd Music, Orchestra, Chorus, Bands, A P Music 4 Yrs; *ai:* Band, Jazz Band, Chorus, String Ensemble Curr Comm; MENC 1981-; AF of M Local 292, IASE, NBA, PBA, ITG 1985-; NEA, PSEA, PMEA 1991-; ASCD 1994-; Natl Judges Assn 1991-, Music Judge; US Military Schl of Music Hnr Grad; Berks Jazz Orchestra Founder, Dir; Dave Stahl's Standard Issue CD Asst Producer; Performed for US Pres's; Atlantic Brass Band Live BBC Solo Flugel Hornist; Performed for Numerous Musicians; Ringgold Band Trumpeter; *home:* 1713 Winds[illegible] Lancaster PA 17601*

HOLLENBAUGH, DAVID K., PE & Drivers Ed Teacher; *b:* Ogden[illegible] NY; *m:* Mary Ann Kirlauski; *c:* Michele, Lindsey; *ed:* Hudson Vall[illegible] (AAS) Rec Supv 1973; SUNY at Brockport (BS) PE 1976; SU[illegible] Cortland (MSEd) PE 1986; 18 Grad Hrs Ed Admin; 9 Grad Hrs Dri[illegible] SUNY Buffalo; *cr:* Parochial Elem Schls K-8th Grd PE Tchr 19[illegible] Holley Cntrl Schl Driver Ed & PE Tchr 1981-86; Deposit Cntrl Schl [illegible] Ed & PE Tchr 1986-87; Downsville Cntrl Schl Driver Ed & PE Tchr [illegible] *ai:* Var Sftbl Coach; AV Liason; Dist Shared Decision Making [illegible] C-Chm; WSKG TV Pub Television; Educl Advy Comm; Downsville [illegible] Assn 1987-, VP; NEA NY 1987-; Natl Soccer Coaches Assn 1988-; [illegible] Downsville Central Schl PO Box J Downsville NY 13755*

HOLLENDER, DIANE FEIGENBLUM, Spanish Teache[illegible] Montevideo, Uruguay; *c:* Len, Lisa; *ed:* Brooklyn Coll (BA) Span [illegible] Rutgers Univ (MA) Span 1990; *cr:* JHS 263 Eng & Span Tchr 19[illegible] North Brunswick HS Span Tchr 1977-78; Woodbridge HS Span[illegible] 1978-82; Colonia HS Span Tchr 1982-; *ai:* Club Adv; SODA; Assistance & Fac Advy Comm; NJEA 1982-; FENJ 1990; Elected Me[illegible] Sigma Iota; *office:* Colonia HS East St Colonia NJ 07067*

HOLLERAN, JOSEPH PAUL, Principal; *b:* Elmira, NY; *m:* Ma[illegible] Rose Scott; *c:* Judy, Michael, Brian; *ed:* Cornell Univ (BS) Sci [illegible] Nazareth Coll (MS) Ed 1979; Working On Admin Cert; *cr:* Various[illegible] Elem Jr High Sci Tchr 1973-90; Northeastern Cath Sci Tchr 19[illegible] Northeastern Cath Vice Prin 1991-94; Northeastern Cath Prin 1994 [illegible] Natl MS Assn, NCEA 1994-; Selected One of Outstanding Tchrs of [illegible] *office:* Northeastern Catholic Jr HS 125 Kings Hwy S Rochester NY

HOLLERAN, MARY ANNE QUATRANO, Fifth Grade Teach[illegible] Elmira, NY; *m:* Eugene Patrick; *c:* Sean P., Matthew, Meghar[illegible] D'Youville Coll (BS) Ed, His 1970; Elmira Coll (MS) Ed 1976; Ac[illegible] Grad Hrs; *cr:* F Carder Elem Schl Tchr 1970-; *ai:* Children At[illegible] Educationally Comm; 5th Grd Stu Job Corps Monitor; 5th Grd S[illegible] Musical Dir; Acad Achvmt Comm; Corning Tchrs Assn, NEA, N[illegible] 1970-; Horseheads HS Choir Parents 1991-, Sec; St Mary Our M[illegible] Childrens Liturgist 1977-; Amer Red Cross 1993-, Vol; Amer Lung [illegible] 1985-, Vol; Amer Cancer Soc 1985-; Intnl Forum Quality Ed Dis[illegible] 1993; *home:* 313 West Ave Horseheads NY 14845*

HOLLERAN, SUSAN DEGENNARO, Italian & Spanish Teach[illegible] Hoboken, NJ; *m:* Michael Edward; *c:* Sara Grace, Andrew Jame[illegible] Moravian Coll (BA) Span, Italian 1980; St Peter's Coll (MA) [illegible] Supervision 1983; *cr:* Marist HS Span Tchr 1980-84; Montville Tw[illegible] Span, Italian Tchr 1984-88; St Thomas Aquinas HS Span Tchr 19[illegible] Montville Twp HS Span, Italian Tchr 1992-; *ai:* Field Trip Organizer [illegible] Lang Dept; NEA 1984-; Frgn Lang Tchrs of NJ 1995-; Tchr Recog[illegible] Awd Univ of Richmond; 1994 Recipient Parent's Cncl Awd; [illegible] Montville Twp HS 100 Horseneck Rd Montville NJ 07045

HOLLEUFFER, LESLIE PATTERSON, French Teacher; *b:* Denve[illegible] *m:* Alan J.; *c:* Nicole A.; *ed:* Montclair St Univ (BA) Fr 1976; Ad[illegible] credits in Span, Guid, Cnslng; L'Univ d'Aix-en-Provence France, L[illegible] de Montpellier Summer Courses; *cr:* St Thomas Aquinas HS Fr [illegible] 1976-80; Carteret HS Fr Tchr 1980-; *ai:* Fr Club Adv; Curr Cncl; [illegible] 1980-; FLE NJ 1976-; Clifton PTA 1991-; Phi Kappa Phi; *office:* Ca[illegible] HS 199 Washington Ave Carteret NJ 07008

HOLLEY, EZRA JOHN, English Teacher; *b:* Franklin, NJ; *m:* Mary [illegible] Roe; *c:* John, Anthony, Clinton; *ed:* Drew Univ (BA) Rel 1967; 30 [illegible] Grad Credit Hrs; *cr:* Greenwich Twp Pub 7th-8th Grd Eng Tchr 196[illegible] High Point Regnl HS 9-12 Grd Eng Tchr 1970-73; Montclair HS 9-1[illegible] Eng Tchr 1974-; *ai:* Stu Govt Adv 1980-; NEA 1975-; NJ Ed Assn [illegible] Montclair Ed Assn 1974-; Weston Awd Tchng Writing 1993; Endowment for Hum Summer Scholar Awd 1995; *office:* Montclair H[illegible] Chestnut St Montclair NJ 07042

HOLLEY-SHEPPARD, CAMILLE J., 8th Grd Lang Arts & Rdng [illegible] *b:* Norfolk, VA; *m:* George J.; *c:* Isaiah J.; *ed:* Penn St Univ (BS) S[illegible] Ed Eng 1989; Univ of PA (MS) Ed, Culture & Soc 1992; Univ of N[illegible] Exch Stu 1987-88; *cr:* Philadelphia Schl Dist Long Term Sub [illegible] 1990-92; Scott Intermediate HS 10th Grd Eng Tchr 1993; [illegible] Brandywine MS 8th Grd Lang Arts & Rdng Tchr 1993-; *ai:* Lateral [illegible] Curr Team Mem; PA New Stans Writing & Assessment; PSEA 1993-; 1993-; NAACP 1986-; *office:* North Brandywine MS 200 Reecevil[illegible] Coatesville PA 19320*

HOLLIDAY, DIANE F., Secondary Math Teacher; *b:* Cincinnatti, O[illegible] Cornelius E. II; *c:* Cornelius III, Kelly Holiday Zinn, Joel Christophe[illegible] Univ of Pittsburgh (BS) Psych 1982; *cr:* Ctr Chrstn Acad Scndry Math[illegible] 1982-; *ai:* Sr Class Spon; Model UN Adv; *office:* Ctr Christian Acad [illegible] Washington Pike Bridgeville PA 15017

HOLLIDAY, JOSEPH WILLIAM, Ret Chem Tchr & Sci Dept Ch[illegible] Charleroi, PA; *m:* Helen Kennedy; *ed:* Mt Union Coll (BS) Chem [illegible] 1958; Univ of Pittsburgh (MED) Chem & Ed 1963; Attnd CMU, Per[illegible] Yale; *cr:* Har-Brack HS Chem Tchr 1958-68; Highlands HS Chem T[illegible] Sci Dept Chm 1968-95; *ai:* Ftbl Field Announcer 35 Yrs; Num[illegible] Dist-Wide Comms; Spnsr Academic Triathlon 1988-94; NEA, PSE[illegible] HEA 1958-; ACS 1968-; SACP 1968-; Cheswick Boro Zoning Commi[illegible] 1982-88, Asst Chm; 2 Natl Sci Fnd Fellowships; Pittsburgh Section [illegible] Keivin Burns Awd for Outstanding Tchr; Pittsburgh Press & Un[illegible] Pittsburgh Schl of Ed All Star Tchr; Several Fellowships, Several Aw[illegible] Equipment Grnats from SACP.

HOLLIDAY, MELINDA BARTHELSON, English Dept Chprsn & [illegible] *b:* Erie, PA; *m:* Jonathan Haskell; *ed:* Indiana Univ of PA (BS) V[illegible] 1991; Edinboro Univ of PA Scndry Eng Cert 1991; Masters Equival[illegible] Ed 1991; 24 Credits Toward Masters in Eng at Gannon Univ Including [illegible] PA Writing Project; *cr:* Tech Meml HS Dental Assisting Instr 197[illegible] Acad HS Eng Tchr 1991-92; Cntrl HS Eng Tchr 1992-, Dept Chair [illegible] *ai:* Sr Class Adv; EEA, PSEA, NEA 1976-, Bldg Rep; Delta Kappa G[illegible] Soc 1989-, 2nd VP, 1st VP Elect; NCTE, NWPCTE 1992-; Lead [illegible] Wkshps-Portfolios, Assessment, Site-Based Mgmt, Cooperative Lear[illegible] Tech, Etc; Cntrl HS Tchr of Yr 1994; Wkshp Presentations-Writing A[illegible] the Curr, Process Writing, Portfolios, Cooperative Learning; N[illegible] Consortium of Lead Tchrs Lead Tchr; *office:* Central HS 3325 Cher[illegible] Erie PA 16508*

HOLLINGER, DAVID L., 7th & 8th Grd Math Tchr; *b:* Greenville, [illegible] *m:* Linda K. Bright; *c:* Aaron, Amy, Jason; *ed:* Manchester Coll (BS) [illegible] Ed 1971; Univ of Dayton (MS) Ed 1983; Attnd Wright St Univ & M[illegible] Univ; *cr:* Arcanum-Butler Local Schls 7th & 8th Grd Math & Algebra [illegible] 1971-; *ai:* 8th Grd Class Adv; Jr HS Detention; North Cntrl Ste[illegible] Comm; Chm Adv Cncl; NEA, OEA & ABCTA 1989-; Castine Chur[illegible] the Brethren 1971-, Lifetime Deacon, Church Bd Chm, Sunday Schl [illegible] Bldg Comm Chm, Choir Mem; *home:* 2429 Gordon Landis Rd Arc[illegible] OH 45304

HOLLINGER, DOUGLAS DAVIS, Chemistry & Physics Teache[illegible] Rochester, NY; *m:* Kathryn; *c:* Noel, William, Ruth, Joseph; *ed:* SUN[illegible] Potsdam (BA) Scis 1979; Univ of Rochester (MS) Sci Ed 1986[illegible] Pavilion HS Tchr 12 Yrs; *ai:* JV & Var Soccer Coach; Schl Newspaper [illegible] St Agnes Schl Bd 1990-93; Lions Intnl 1991-; Scouts; Summer Sc[illegible] Little League; NHS U of R Tchr of the Yr; *office:* Pavillio Central [illegible] 7014 Big Tree Rd Pavilion NY 14525

LINGER, JANET ZORTMAN, Business Education Teacher; *b:* PA; *m:* Richard C.; *c:* Karla Heilman, Nedra Johnstone, Kurt; *ed:* ehanna Univ (BS) Bio 1960; York Coll of PA (BS) Bus Ed 1976; ensburg Univ 15 Grad Credits; *cr:* York Hosp Histology Technician 62; York Co of Pub Assistance Caseworker 1962-63; York Co AVTS Ed Bus Tchr 1970-77; York Co Area Voc-Tech Schl Bus Tchr 1977-; HS Selection Comm; Hlth Occupation Stdnts of Amer Medical tarial Area Competition St, Second Pl Natl Winner Instrl Trainer; Crisis Prevention Cert; York Co VT Ed Assn, PA St Ed Assn, NEA ; *office:* York Co Area Voc Tech Sch 2179 S Queen St York PA 17402*

LINGSHEAD, OPHELIA ENSOR, Retired Physical Ed Teacher; *b:* s, MD; *m:* Richard Martin; *c:* Elizabeth Hollingshead Furlong; *ed:* dsburg Univ PA PE, Hlth Ed 1958; Towson Univ 12 Hrs; Univ of MD ; *cr:* Parkville Sr HS PE Tchr, Coach 1958-62; Towson Town Jr HS chr 1964-70; St Paul's Schl for Girls PE Tchr, Coach 1970-86, Ath Dir -; *ai:* At Retirement MS Coaching of Hockey, Bsktbl, Lacrosse; Ath Adv Upper Schl Cnslr; Sr Project Admin Staff; Sr Cncl; AAHPER -; MAAHPER; USW Lacrosse Assn; USW Field Hockey Assn; ey UM Church 1951-, Church Act; Green Apple Awd 1995, SPSG ni Assn; Parents Assn Gold Pin 1992; Hollingshead Sportsman Awd 1996 SPSG; Outstdng Alumni Awd By Sparks, Hemford HS Alumni 1994; *home:* 14600 Western Rd Sparks Glencoe MD 21152

LINGSWORTH, MADELINE KELLY, Third Grade Teacher; *b:* ic, NJ; *m:* John Kent; *ed:* Wm Paterson Coll (BA) Elem Ed 1970,) Early Chldhd Ed 1981; 45 Credit Hrs Writing, Math, Sci, Rdng, Mngmt, Family Problem Solving, Schl Law; *cr:* Paterson St Coll nship Tchng, Kndgtn Tchr 1969; Clifton Schl 55 Grd 1 Tchr 1970-88; Paterson Presch, Daycare Internship 1980; Clifton Schl 5 Grd 3 Tchr -; *ai:* Amer Ed Week Events, City Yth Week Liason, Home-Schl Assn Trustee In-Schl Comms; NEA, NJEA, PCEA 1970-; Passaic Cty Ed , Clifton Tchrs Assn 1970-, VP, Del, Grievance Chair, Negotiated 2 racts, Blood Drive Chair; Local Lib, Vol; Passaic Cty Clifton Tchr of om 1984.

LOMAN, CHARLOTTE CUMBO, Third Grade Teacher; *b:* New ans, LA; *c:* Madeleine M., Glynnis P.; *ed:* Univ So Mississippi (BS) Ed 1972; Natl Louis Univ (MA) Curr, Instr 1990; 3 Hrs Bay Area ng Course Berkley Branch Univ CA; 3 Hrs Ger 111 & Ger 112 Univ D Germany Branch; 6 Hrs Fr I & II Pensacola Jr Coll FL 1982; *cr:* eville Acad 4th-6th Grd Eng Tchr 1974-76; Spencer Bibbs Elem Schl th Grd Tchr 1976-80; AA Dixon Elem Schl 5th Grd Tchr 1980-82; asens Amer Schl 5th, 3rd Grd Tchr 1983-95; Ramstein E S 3rd Grd 1996; *ai:* Soc Comm Chprsn; NEA; Overseas Ed Assn 1983-, Sec; acola Jaycettes 1976-80, 1st VP 1 Yr, Sec 2 Yrs, Outstdng 1st Yr Mem, of Yr, Mem of Quarter, Pub Chpsrsn, Prgms Chprsn, Newsletter Ed, iss St of FL; Selection Comm Tchr of Yr Awd; Math Task Force Dist 1; Exceptional & Commendable Ratings Performance; Kaiserslautern Early Chldhd Comm; *home:* PSC 2 Box 10204 APO AE 09012*

LOWAY, BARBARA CHAMBERS, Dept Chprsn Business ation; *b:* Pensacola, FL; *w:* John F. Jr. (dec); *c:* Frederick Dwayne, ris Jeanette; *ed:* Bishop Coll (BS) Bus Ed 1960; Cleveland St Univ) Ed 1979; Trenton St Univ Data Processing 1969; Kent St Univ Voc Voc Supvr Certs; *cr:* Pennsauken HS Tchr 1969-72; Sawyer Bus Coll 1972; John Adams HS Tchr, Adv 1972-73; Bedford HS Coord, Tchr -; Tri-C Comm Coll Tchr 1976-82; *ai:* Bus Profs of Amer Adv 1972-; ure Capital Proposal Comm 1994; Prins Selection Comm; Supts Advy m; Staff Dev Comm Chprsn; Bedford Tchrs Assn 1973-; NEA 1969-; eland Area Bus Tchrs 1973-, Sec; Prof Dev Comm 1980-82, 1993-95, sn, Sec; Alpha Kappa Alpha 1960-; Phi Delta Kappa 1982-, Treas; gewood Golf Assn 1989-, Pres; Lambda Phi 1979-, Sec; Bedford torship Prog 1988-; Bus Tchr of Yr Northeastern OH 1979, 1986; 's Who Among Amer Women 1987; OH Advy Cncl Voc Ed 1981-84; nguished Tchr Awd United Meth Church 1977; OH Voc Ed Team on ival Skills; *office:* Bedford HS 481 Northfield Rd Bedford OH 44146*

LOWAY, LEWISTINE CONN, 5th Grade Teacher; *b:* Vienna, GA; uidajean, Jamesetta; *ed:* Cnrl St Univ (BS) Elem Ed 1967; Akron Univ ning Disability; *cr:* Wells Elem Schl 1st Grd Tchr 1967-71; Allen Elem 3rd Grd Tchr 1973-74; Washington Elem 1st, 4th-6th Grd Tchr 1974-, Grd Tchr; *ai:* Math Olympic Bldg Coord; Union Bldg Rep CPEA; 5th Boys Bsktbl Adv; Beginning Tchrs Mentor; NEA, OEA, CPEA 1967-; ees 1976-77; NAACP 1980-; Urban League 1981-; Writing Team Grant s, 3 Yrs; *office:* Washington Elem Schl 1220 9th St NE Canton OH 5*

LLOWAY, ROSALIND DAVIS, 5th Grade Teacher; *b:* Albany, GA; *c:* ney; *ed:* Coppin St Coll (BS) Elem Ed 1973; *cr:* Edgecombe Cr Elem Tchr 1973-; *ai:* Schl Improvement, Support Teams; Sci Ldrshp Tchr; Delta Kappa 1993-; Tchr of Yr 1990; *office:* Edgecombe Circle Elem 2835 Virginia Ave Baltimore MD 21215

LLY, KATHY P., Health Teacher; *b:* Philippi, WV; *m:* Timothy James; hristine Holly Welch, Kimberly, Katie; *ed:* Univ of Cinti (BS) Hlth, ogical Sci, PE 1965; Addl 20 Hrs; Miami Univ 5 Hrs; *cr:* Delhi Schl Tchr 1965-67; Durrett HS Hlth Tchr 1967-68; Forest Hills Elem Schl Tchr 1968-69; Anderson HS Hlth Tchr 1989-; *ai:* 7th-8th Grd Vlybl ch; Natl Jr Hnr Soc Adv; Core Team; 7th-8th Grd Act Comms; FHTA, , OEA 1987-; Zeta Tau Alpha Alumnae 1965-, House Bd Pres; Mortar Alumnae; Dad's Club Awd 1967 Delhi Schl; Top Hat Awd 1994.

LLY, TERRANCE W., English Teacher; *b:* Olean, NY; *m:* Laraine nson; *c:* Paige Irwin, Bethany Warner; *ed:* Univ of Pittsburg (BA) Eng Magna Cum Laude 1969; Olean Bus Inst Cert 1963; NY St Permanent ng License 30 Grad Hrs St Bonaventure Univ; *cr:* Smethport HS Span r 1969-70; Olean Jr HS Eng Tchr 1970-88; Olean HS Eng Tchr 1988-; Var Ftbl Offensive, Defensive Line Coach; Discipline Comm Chprsn; Safety Comm; Educl Fair Participant; Olean Tchrs Assn 1970-, ; NEA 1970-; Olean Sports Boosters; *home:* 95 Kansas Branch Rd Duke ter PA 16729*

LM, JENNIFER SUSAN, Science Teacher; *b:* Cambridge, MA; *ed:* gheny Coll (BS) Environmental Sci 1991, (MA) Ed 1992; *cr:* Mascoma Regnl HS Sci Tchr 1992-, Curr Coord 1994-; *ai:* Class Adv 1992-; JV s Bsktbl Coach 1992-, Vllybl Coach 1994; Head of Stu Cncl & Adv 4-; Facilities Accreditation Comm; NHTA 1992-; NEA 1992-; NHSTA 2-; Humane Soc 1995-.

LMAN, RICHARD F., Professor of Physics; *b:* Burlingame, CA; *m:* dence R. Grimes; *c:* Nissa, James; *ed:* Harvey Mudd Coll (BS) Math 8; Johns Hopkins Univ (MA) Physics 1980, (PHD) Physics 1982; *cr:* SA Goddard Space FH Ctr RRC Postdoctoral Fellow 1982- 83; Univ of at Gainesville Postdoctoral Assoc 1983-85; Fermilab Astrophysics up Postdoctoral Assoc 1985-87; Carnegie Mellon Univ Physics Prof 7-; *ai:* Amer Phys Soc 1982-; AAAS 1989-; *office:* Carnegie Mellon v 5000 Forbes Ave Pittsburgh PA 15213

LMES, CANDACE ELAINE DIXON, Fifth Grade Teacher; *b:* nge, NJ; *c:* Ernest Quinn, Shayne Jacqueline; *ed:* VA Union Univ (BA) m Ed 1972; Creative Dance 6 Credits; *cr:* Washington DC Alcoholic se Consultant 1971-72; Heywood Ave Schl 2-6th Grd Tchr 1972-; nmer Schl Tchr 7th & 8th Grd 1993-95; *ai:* Schl Patrol Adv 1985-; CAD Drug Prgm Adv 1989-; Cheerleading Squad Coach 1975; er-Schl Tutorial Tchr 1989-93; After-Schl Prgm Dance Instr 1976-; Summer Enrichment Prgm Drama Tchr; NEA, NJEA 1973-; Alpha Kappa Alpha 1975-; Tchr of Yr 1987; *home:* 246 Hilton Ave Vauxhall NJ 07088

HOLMES, DOREA B., Social Stud & Humanites Tchr; *b:* Buffalo, NY; *c:* Gregory; *ed:* SUNY at Buffalo (BS) Elem Ed 1958, (MS) Scndry Soc Stud 1963; Cert Admin, Supervision; 60 Addl Hrs His, Sociology, Anthropology, Arts; *cr:* Lincoln Elem Schl 6th Grd Tchr 1958-61; Jr HS 7th-8th Grd Soc Stud Tchr 1961-62; Kaegebein Elem Schl 5th Grd Tchr 1963-64; Jr HS 7th-8th Grd Soc Stud Tchr 1964-67; Sr HS 10th-12th Grd Soc Stud Tchr 1967-; *ai:* NHS, Hum Clubs Adv; NYSCSS Curr, Assessment Comm; Joint Comm Prof Dev; ASCD, AFT, NYSUT, Grand Island Tchrs Assn; NCSS 1975-; NY St Cncl Soc Stud 1968-, Chair, Curr, Assessment Comm; NYS Soc Stud Supvrs Assn 1986-, Sec, VP; Niagara Frontier Cncl Soc Stud 1972-, Sec, Pres; Orchard Park Symphony 1955-, First Flute, 40 Yr Svc Awd; Amherst Symphony Orch 1986-; Outstdng HS Tchr Harvard Univ; Natl Endowment for Hum Seminar, Plato Inst, Classical Greece; COE Flwshp US Constitution; Freedom Fnd Valley Forge, Lit, His; Stratford Hall, Monticello Seminar Tchrs, Colonial Amer; Cornell Univ Outstdng HS Tchr; *office:* Grand Island HS 1100 Ransom Rd Grand Island NY 14072

HOLMES, EDWIN M., Mathematics Teacher; *b:* Mansfield, OH; *m:* Dianne Osgar; *c:* Jeffrey, Jennifer; *ed:* OH St Univ (BS) Math Ed 1971; Ashland Univ (MS) Schl Admin 1984; *cr:* Madison Comprehensive HS Math Tchr 1971-; *ai:* Dept Chprsn; Natl Hnr Selection Comm; NEA, OEA, MLEA 1971-; *office:* Madison Comprehensive HS 600 Esley Ln Mansfield OH 44905

HOLMES, GERALD T., 3rd Grade Teacher; *b:* Jamestown, NY; *m:* Jeanne V.; *c:* Courtney, Cara; *ed:* SUNY at Brookport (BS) Elem Ed 1969; SUNY at Fredonia (MS) Elem Ed 1971, (SAS) Admin 1980; *cr:* Southwestern 5th Grd Tchr 1969-71, 4th Grd Tchr 1971-73, 3rd Grd Tchr 1977-; SUL Fredonia Asst Prof Elem Ed 1973-76; *ai:* NEA 1969-; NEA NY 1969-; Southwestern Tchrs Assn 1976-, Pres, Chief Negotiator; Southwestern Area Soccer 1991-94, Bd Mem; *home:* 10 Holly Dr Lakewood NY 14750

HOLMES, HELENE, 5th Grade Teacher; *b:* Providence, RI; *m:* Steven Dunlap; *c:* Carl Joseph, Abigail; *ed:* Univ of MA (BA) Elem Ed 1970; *cr:* Georgetown Pub Schls Sub Tchr 1971; Stanley Home Products Sec 1971-74; Butterfield Schl 5th Grd Tchr 1975-; *ai:* 5th & 6th Grds Chorus Dir; Prgms Lighting Dir; Grds 4-6 Bsktbl Prgm Dir & Coach 1976-; Sftbl Prgm Dir & Coach; NEA, MA Tchrs Assn & Orange Elem Tchrs Assn 1976-; Orange Recreation Assn 1976-, Sec; Orange Little League Sec 1995-; Cntrl Congregation Church of Orange Music Comm 1993-; *home:* 350 Holtshire Rd Orange MA 01364

HOLMES, JAMES ROBERT,JR., Social Studies Teacher; *b:* Erie, PA; *m:* Sherlyn Sue Loyd; *c:* Jennifer Lynn, Amy Christine Holmes Huffman; *ed:* Edinboro Univ of PA (BS) Scndry Ed, Comprehensive Soc Stud 1965; Xavier Univ (MED) Guidance Cnlsr 1980; OH Northern Univ COE Fnd Fellowship 9 Credit Hrs, Cnslrs Cert 6 Credit Hrs; Univ of IL Correspondence Psych 6 Credit Hrs; Ashbland Ashbrok schlsp Instructional Inst 6 Credit Hrs; *cr:* Danville Local Schls Soc Stud Tchr 1965-; *ai:* Sr Class Adv; Mock Trial Coach; Knox Net Govt Project Fac Ldr Cmptr Tech; Stu Emergency Response Team Coord; Danville Vol Fire Dept 1977-, Fire Fighter; Danville Vol Emergency Squad 1980-, Advanced EMT-AED; Danville Vol Fire Dept Inc, 1981-, Sec, Treas; Danville Church of Christ 1966-, Elder, Sunday Schl Tchr; COE Fellowship 1968; Capital Univ Jennings Fellowship; Ashland Univ Ashbrook Constitutional Fellowship; *office:* Danville Local Schls 10 Rambo St PO Box 30 Danville OH 43014*

HOLMES, JOAN ELIZABETH, Spanish & English Teacher; *b:* Long Branch, NJ; *m:* Dale; *c:* Tim, David; *ed:* Cedarville Coll (BA) His, Govt 1967; Attnd Cntrl St Univ of OH, Detroit Bus Inst, Univ of Akron; *cr:* Reimer Rd Bapt Chrstn Utility Tchr 1976-77; First Bapt Chrstn MS Tchr 1977-78; Brunswick Chrstn Utility Tchr 1978-79; First Bapt Chrstn 7th-12th Grd eng, Span Tchr 1982-; *ai:* ACSI 1989-; NCTE; First Bapt Church 1982-; Articles Pub; *office:* First Baptist Christian Schl 3646 Medina Rd Medina OH 44256

HOLMES, KATHY DIANE, 7th-12th Grd PE Teacher; *b:* Madison, WV; *ed:* WV Univ (MA) Comm Stud 1993; Concord Coll at Athens (BSEd) Ed, PE, Eng 1974; *cr:* Clay Jr HS PE Tchr 1 Yr; Belpre HS PE Tchr 18 Yrs; *ai:* Jr HS Girls Vlybl Coach; OH Vlybl Coaches Assn Vlybl Coaches Achvmt Awd 1985-86; *office:* Belpre HS Stone Rd Belpre OH 45714

HOLMES, LAURA MARIE, Art Teacher; *b:* New Brunswick, NJ; *m:* David S.; *c:* Lindsie; *ed:* Univ of WY (BS) Art 1981; Coll of New Rochelle (MA) Art Ed 1991; Saint Thomas Aquinas K-12th Grd Art Tchng Cert 1987; Attnd Comm Coll of NY 6 Credits, Coll of Saint Rose 6 Credits, NY Inst of Tech 6 Credits, NYSUT at Liv 18 Credits; TEI 9 Credits; *cr:* North Rockland HS 9th-12th Grd Art Tchr 1988-; *ai:* Girls Swimming Coach 1987-; Aquatic Club PAL 1988-; Rockland Art Educators Assn 1995-; North Rockland HS Boys Swimming Coach 1987-95; *office:* North Rockland HS Hammond Rd Thiells NY 10984

HOLMES, LAURA REIMER, Reading & Science Teacher; *b:* Harrisburg, PA; *ed:* Rosemont Coll (BA) Psych 1987; Working Towards Masters Tech; *cr:* Prince Georges Cty Schl 3rd Grd Tchr 1989-90; Lemoyne MS 7th Grd Life Sci Math Tchr 1990-92, 7th, 8th Grd Sci & Soc Stud Tchr 1992-93, 6th Grd Rdng Tchr 1993-95; New Cumberland MS 6th Grd Rdng, 7th Grd Sci Tchr 1995-; *ai:* Ski Club Adv; Bldg Profession Mem; Instrl Support Team Mem; PSEA, NEA, WSEA 1993-; Habitat for Humanity 1994-, Laborer; Comm United Meth 1994, Nom, Prsnl Comm; *home:* 22 Meadow Dr Camp Hill PA 17011*

HOLMES, PAUL A., Asst Prof of Religious Studies; *b:* Newark, NJ; *ed:* Seton Hall Univ (BA) Sociology 1977; Pontifical Gregorian Univ (STB) Theology 1980; Pontifical Lateran Univ (STL) Moral Theology 1982; Yale Yniv (STM) Liturgy 1986; Pontifical Univ of St Thomas Aquinas (STD) Dogma 1991; *cr:* St Mathew Church Assoc Pastor 1982-84; Sacred Heart Cathedral Assoc Pastor 1984-86; Archidocese of NY Assoc Dir Worship Office 1988-91; Seton Hall Univ Asst Prof 1988-; *ai:* Chaplain, Phi Kappa Theta; Fac Rep, Priest Advy Cncl; Ethics Consltnt, St Marys Hosp, Passaic, NJ; Magna Cum Laude Gregorian Univ 1980; Summa Cum Laude Lateran Univ 1982; Magna Cum Laude Angelicum Univ 1991; Articles Pub in Ecclesia Orans Journal of Ritual Stud & Ephemerides Liturgicae, Amer, the Furrow; *office:* Seton Hall University 400 S Orange Ave South Orange NJ 07079

HOLMES, PETER JOHN, US History & Soc Studies Tchr; *b:* Providence, RI; *m:* Janet Ruth Blasse; *c:* Travis, John, Patrick, Peter, Ryan, Thomas; *ed:* RI Jr Coll (AA) Lib Arts 1966; Roger Williams Univ (BA) Hist, Lib Arts 1970; RI Coll ITE Cert; 36 Hrs Providence Coll, Un of RI, RIC, Brown Un; *cr:* Riverside Jr HS US His Tchr, Ftbl Coach 1970-78; Ed R. Martin Jr HS Civic Tchr, Ftbl Coach 1978-85; East Prov Sr HS His Tchr, Ftbl, Swim Coach 1985-; *ai:* Ftbl, Swimming Coach; Asst Alternate Chief Examiner of GED's; Head Supvr Recreation Dept; EPEA, RIEA, NEA 1970-; RI His CA Soc 1990-; RI Swim Coaches Assn 1986-; RI Police Chiefs Assn 1985-; EPFO Police Assn Lodge #1, Am Legion Post 10 1975-; EP K of C #1528 1961-; NSF Grant Local EP His Pub Svc Awd for Over 23 Yrs Work with Children For Rec Dept; *office:* East Providence Sr HS 2000 Pawtucket Ave East Providence RI 02914

HOLMES, ROBYN MICHELE, Psychology Professor; *b:* Neptune, NJ; *m:* Richard J. Jr.; *ed:* Rutgers Coll (BA) Bio 1980; Rutgers Univ (MA) Anthropology 1986, (PHD) Anthropology 1988; *cr:* Rutgers Univ Adj Lecturer 1989-92; Monmouth Univ Adj Lecturer 1989-92, Asst Prof 1993-; *ai:* Consulting Editorial Staff for Child Study Journal; Editorial Review Bd for Ed & Treatment of Children; Am Anthro Assn 1986-, Fellow; Am Psy Assn 1994-; Am Psy Soc 1993-; TASP 1988-; 2 Grant-in-Aid for Creativity; Book Pub: How Young Children Perceive Race; Numerous Articles Pub; Svc Awd 504 Accessibility Comm.

HOLMES, SAMMIE L., Social Studies Teacher; *b:* Williston, SC; *c:* Rhonda, Stacy, Travis, Tyler; *ed:* Benedict Coll (BA) Soc Sci 1963; Working Toward MS Admin; Attnd Brooklyn Coll, Trenton St Coll, Ocean Cty Coll; *cr:* Jackson Jr HS Soc Stud Tchr 1967-69; Nottingham Jr HS Soc Stud Tchr 1969-75; Hamilton East HS Soc Stud Tchr 1975-; Hamilton Adult Schl Soc Stud Tchr 1976-; *ai:* Excl Through Ed Pres, Treas; Recreation Dir; Summer Day Camp Supvr; NEA, ATEA 1967-; NJEA 1967-, Strategt Comm; NAACP Sec; Bapt Church 1967-, Trustee Bd; Assn Superintenant S Schl 1994-; Giedons 1993-; Laymen of Amer 1900-, Sec; Rider Univ Human Rights Awd; *office:* Steinart HS 2900 Klockner Rd Trenton NJ 08690*

HOLMES, SAMUEL LOUIS, Art Teacher; *b:* Pittsburgh, PA; *ed:* Edinboro Univ (BS) Art Ed 1960; Univ of Pittsburgh (MA) Humanities 1963; *cr:* Chagrin Falls Art Tchr 2 Yrs; Milton Art Tchr 1 Yr; Bemus Point Art Tchr 32 Yrs; *ai:* Bd Mem: Chautauqua Art Assn, Bemus Point Lib & 4th Sup Credit Union; NEA 1960-.*

HOLMES, WILLIAM EDWARD, Mathematics Teacher; *b:* Warren, OH; *m:* Antoinette Kolasinski; *c:* Jennifer, Deborah; *ed:* OH St (BA) His 1966, (BS) Math 1967; Univ of MD; *cr:* Eliot Jr HS Tchr 1967-68; William Wirt Jr HS Tchr 1968-71; Bowie HS Tchr 1971-; *ai:* Chm Awds & Mid Sts Comms; NEA, MSTA 1967-; PGCEA 1967-, Fac Rep; Saint Peters Church 1974-, Sr Warden Vestry Man; *office:* Bowie HS 15200 Annapolis Rd Bowie MD 20715

HOLMES, WILLIAM H., Choral Director; *ed:* Rutgers Univ (BA) Music Ed 1978; *cr:* Watchung Hills Rgnl HS Choral Dir 1980-; *ai:* 2 Chorus, All St Chorus Comms; Spring Musical; MENC 1974-; *office:* Watchung Hills Regional HS 108 Stirling Rd Watchung NJ 07060

HOLMQUIST, DONALD W., Advanced Placement Bio Teacher; *b:* Point Pleasant, NJ; *ed:* Rider Coll (BA) Scndry Ed Sci 1976; *cr:* Toms River HS North Bio Tchr 1976-; *ai:* Greenhouse Club; Sci League, Acad Challange Teams; NEA, NJEA 1977-; Governor's Mentorious Tchr Awd & Grant 1988; Toms Regnl Schls Tchr of Yr 1989; *office:* Toms River HS North Old Freehold Rd Toms River NJ 08753

HOLOWATHY, ANNMARIE, Science Teacher; *b:* Easton, MA; *ed:* Temple Univ (BS) Scndry Ed 1971; Kutztown Univ (MS) Bio 1980; *cr:* Central Bucks HS West Bio Tchr 1971-; *ai:* Knowledge Master Open Adv; NEA, PSEA, CBEA 1971-; Conservation Educator of Yr Bucks Cty 1981; *office:* Central Bucks HS West 375 W Court St Doylestown PA 18901

HOLQUIST, BEVERLY SMITH, Mathematics Teacher; *b:* Franklin, PA; *m:* L. Thomas; *c:* Corey D., Kimberly R.; *ed:* Clarion St Coll (BS) Math 1973, (MED) Math 1977; *cr:* Cranberry Area HS Math Tchr 1973-; Clarion Univ Upward Bound Instr 1983; *ai:* Usherette Adv; SAP Team; Cooperating Tchr for Stu Tchrs; New Tchrs Mentor; NEA, PSEA, CEA 1973-; Zion Luth Church 1987-, Sunday Schl Tchr; *office:* Cranberry Area HS 1 Education Dr Seneca PA 16346*

HOLSCHER, ELIZABETH DAVISON, Physiology & Biology Teacher; *b:* Vineland, NJ; *m:* William Jerome; *ed:* Geneva Coll (BS) Bio 1961; Univ of CO (MS) Zoology 1963; Attnd Villanova Univ 15 Hrs, Wilkes Coll 9 Hrs, Randolph- Macon Womens 6 Hrs, IN Univ 4 Hrs, Alfred Univ 6 Hrs & Widner Coll 2 Hrs; *cr:* Univ CO Grad Asst Bio Instr 1961-62; Yuba City HS Bio Tchr 1963-64; Swarthmore HS Bio Tchr 1964-74; Parkway HS Psych & Bio Tchr 1974-; *ai:* NEA 1964-, Life Mem; PA Ed Assn 1964-; OH Ed Assn & Parkway Ed Assn 1974-; NABT 1963-; Delta Kappa Gamma 1988-; OH Historical Soc 1985-; Audubon Soc 1974-; Humane Soc 1980-; Natl Wildlife Fed 1974-; Bowling Green St Univ Jennings Scholar 1991; Articles Pub in NABT Journal; Natl Sci Fnds Grants 5 Summers; Phi Sigma Biological Honorary; *home:* 5570 Ross Rd Rockford OH 45882

HOLSHUE, EDWARD JOSEPH, Biology Teacher; *b:* Shamokin, PA; *m:* Martha Wheeler; *c:* Jennifer, Kathleen; *ed:* Hagerstown Jr Coll (AA) Ed 1967; Towson St Coll (BS) Bio Ed 1969, (MED) Sec Ed 1978; *cr:* Wilde Lake MS Sci Tchr 1969-71; Mt Hebron HS Sci Tchr 1971-; *ai:* Head Ftbl, JV Boys Bsktbl Coach; HCEA, MSTA, NEA 1970-; MD St Ftbl Coaches Assn 1991-; Natl Ftbl Fnd 1975-, Bd of Dirs; Tchr of Yr 1993-94; Ftbl Coach of Yr 1980, 1982, 1993; *office:* Mount Hebron HS Rt 99 Ellicott City MD 21042*

HOLSHUE, MARTHA ANN, Art Teacher & Dept Coordinator; *b:* Baltimore City, MD; *m:* Edward Joseph; *c:* Jennifer, Kathleen; *ed:* MD Inst Coll of Art (BFA) Art Ed 1975, (MFA) Art Ed 1980; *cr:* Glenwood MS Art Tchr 1975-80; Mt Hebron HS Art Tchr 1981-82; Howard HS Art Tchr 1980-84, 1981-; *ai:* Art Dept Coord; Site Based Mngmt Team; *office:* Howard HS # 108 8700 Old Annapolis Rd Ellicott City MD 21043

HOLST, EDWARD C., Religion Teacher; *b:* Brooklyn, NY; *m:* Elizabeth M. Donahue; *c:* Jennifer Cartwright, Sarah, Edward M.; *ed:* Brooklyn Coll (BA) Ec 1980; Iona Coll (MS) Tchng, Soc Stud 1996; *cr:* John S. Burke Cath HS Religion Tchr 1993-; *ai:* Soc Awareness Comm; Phi Delta Kappa, Lay Fac Assn, NCEA 1993-, Mem; US Soccer Fed 1989-, Ref; Town of Minisink UPCH Club 1989-93; Juvenile Diabetes Fnd 1985-, Pres 1991; *office:* John S Burke Catholic HS Fletcher St Goshen NY 10924

HOLSTE, BENJAMIN E., Music Director; *b:* Pittsburgh, PA; *ed:* Duquesne Univ (BS) Music Ed 1969, (MM) Music Performance 1974; *cr:* Sencea Jr HS Band & Orch Dir 1969-78; Penn Hills HS Music Dir, Music Apprec, Theory, Choir, Band, Orch 1978-; *ai:* Marching & Jazz Band; Musical Orch; PMEA & MENC 1969-, VP & Pres Dist 1; NBA 1980-; Musician Union 1969-; PMEA All St Festival Coord 1994-; *office:* Penn Hills HS 12200 Garland Dr Pittsburgh PA 15235*

HOLT, BARBARA P., Latin & French Teacher; *b:* Bridgeport, CT; *m:* John M.; *c:* Amanda, Melissa; *ed:* Vassar Coll (AB) Latin 1966; Yale Univ (MAT) Classics 1967; Attnd Rivier Coll, St Anselm's Coll; Univ of IL; Univ of VA; *cr:* Glastonbury HS Latin Tchr 1967-69; Prospect Day Schl Latin Tchr, Dept Head 1969-70; Nashua HS Latin Tchr 1971, Nashua Jr HS Latin, Eng Tchr 1971; Milford HS Latin, Fr Tchr 1979-; *ai:* Cultural Stud Adv; Bldg Facilities Comm; FL Dept; NEA, CANE, ACL 1967-; AATF 1978-; NEH Summer Stud Pgrms; *office:* Milford HS 100 West St Milford NH 03055

HOLT, CAROLYN ANN (FALCK), Biology Teacher; *b:* Pittsburgh, PA; *c:* James S., Ann Roy; *ed:* PA St Univ (BA) Bio 1960; 60 Addl Credits; MA Equivalancy Bio 1993; *cr:* Mars Area HS Bio, Jr HS Sci Tchr 1960-63; State College HS Bio Tchr 1981-; *ai:* Sci Olympiad Coach; Chess Club, British Exchange Adv; State College Ed Assn 1981-, Exec Cncl, Fac Rep; PSEA, NEA 1981-; Phi Delta Kappa 1991-; NSTA; NABT; Commonwealth Bio Initiative Fellow 1991; Howard Hughes Sci Inst Fellow 1993; *office:* State College Sr HS 650 Westerly Pky State College PA 16801

HOLT, HELEN H., Reading Consultant & Eng Tchr; *b:* Philadelphia, PA; *c:* Timothy P., Megan D.; *ed:* Rosemont Coll (BA) Elem Ed 1960; Villanova Univ (MA) Elem Ed 1982; Univ of PA (MS) Rdng 1984; Univ of PA (PHD) Lang in Ed, Rdng & Writing 1992; Rdng Specialist Cert; Rdng Supervisory Cert; *cr:* Springhill Schl 3rd Grd Tchr 1960-63; Agnes Irwin Schl Rdng Consultant & Eng Tchr 1979-; Univ of PA Lit Plus Tchr 1985-87; *ai:* Admission & Rdng Testing; Lib Comm; Mentor; NCTE 1980-; IRA Assn

1980-; DVRT Assn 1980-; Ronald McDonald House Vol; Mentor Tchr; Article Pub; *office:* Agnes Irwin Schl PO Box 407 Bryn Mawr PA 19010

HOLT, JOHN R., English Teacher; *b:* Arlington, VA; *ed:* James Madison Univ (BS) Comm Arts & Eng 1984; Western MD Coll (MS) Curr & Instruction 1992; *cr:* Clarke Cty HS Eng Tchr 1984-87; Westminster HS Eng Tchr 1988-; *ai:* Speech Team & Soc for the Promotion of the Hum Spon; Carroll Cty Tchr of Yr 1993-94; Articles Pub in MD Eng Journal & The Speech Comm Tchr; *office:* Westminster HS 1225 Washington Rd Westminster MD 21157

HOLT, PETER A., 7th-8th Grade Science Teacher; *b:* Fall River, MA; *m:* Jo Ann Bentley; *c:* Kayleigh, Bentley; *ed:* Bridgewater St Coll (BS) Elem Ed 1976; Cambridge Coll (MED) Ed 1991; 30 Addl Credit Hrs Past Masters; *cr:* Biship McVinney Regnl Schl 6th-8th Grd Tchr 1977-83; Westport Comm Schls 6th-8th Grd Sci Tchr 1983-; *ai:* Sci Club Adv; Watershed Alliance Ed Comm; Diman HS Sci Advy Bd; AFT 1984-; Co-Author From Farms to Fish 1989; Mustard Seed Fellowship; CESEME 1992 Grant; Co-Author of River Restoration 1995; Natl Sci Fnd, Bridgewater St Coll & Southeast Schl, Coll Consortium Regnl Wkshp for Elem & MS Sci Tchrs; Environmental Vol of Yr Awd 1993; MA Exec Office of Envrionmental Affairs Excl in Environmental Ed Awd 1995-; *office:* Westport MS 400 Old County Rd Westport MA 02790

HOLTER, NORMA C., Assoc Prof of Acctng & Auditng; *b:* Baltimore, MD; *c:* Melissa, David; *ed:* Univ of Balto (BS) Acctng 1981, (MS) Fin 1984; Geo Washington Univ (PHD) Acctng 1992; *cr:* Essex Comm Coll Visiting Asst Prof 1983-88; Towson St Univ Visiting Asst Prof 1984-88, Asst Prof 1988-95, Assoc Prof 1995-; *ai:* Teach CPA Review Course; AICPA 1985-; MD Assn of CPA 1985-, Auditing Stds, Outstdng Tchr of Yr; Inst of Internal Auditors 1990-, Bd of Governors; IMA; NAFE; AAUW; AAUP; Beta Gamma Sigma; CPA Licensed St of MD; Cert Internal Auditor; Pub: Great Ideas For Teaching Introductory AccountingJrl of Ed for Bus; *office:* Towson St Univ Towson MD 21204*

HOLTHAUS, DEBRA HOEHNE, Business Teacher; *b:* Piqua, OH; *m:* Alfred; *c:* Amanda, Dean, Lauren; *ed:* Wright St Univ (BS) Ed 1986, (MS) Ed 1990; 18 Post Grad Hrs Cmptr Appl Soft; *cr:* Wapakonata City Schls Bus Tchr 1086-93; Apollo Career Ctr Bus Tchr 1993-94; Minster Local Schls Bus Tchr 1994-; *ai:* Bus Profs of Amer Adv; Newletter Ed; OH Bus Tchr Assn 1984-; Minster Tchr Assn 1994-; OH Ed Assn, NEA 1986-; Ft Laramie Gym Comm 1992-; March of Dimes 1995-; Stu Tchr of Yr 1986; Wright St Univ Grad Schlsp; *office:* Minster HS 100 E 7th St Minster OH 45865

HOLTHOUSE, JEANINE MARIE, Mathematics Dept Chairperson; *b:* Richmond, IN; *ed:* Coll of Mt St Joseph (BA) PE 1954; Univ of Detroit (MATM) Math 1967; 30 Credit Hrs Scndry Admin, Math; Math, PE, Bio, Hlth, Eng, Soc Stud, Scndry Admin; *cr:* St Bridgitt HS Tchr 1956-58; Shrine HS Tchr 1958-60; Cathedral HS Tchr 1960-69; Elizabeth Seton HS Tchr, Asst Prin, Prin 1969-82; Seton HS Tchr, Asst Prin, Dept Chair 1982-; *ai:* Chance Dr Chprsn; Mini-Festival Schl Chair; Spiritual Life Comm; NATM 1982-; NCEA 1954-; Amer Cancer Soc 1980-; Chaired All City Archdiocesan Sci Fairs; Pres Denver Cncl of Tchrs of Math; NSF Grant for Masters at UD in Detroit; *office:* Seton HS 3901 Glenway Ave Cincinnati OH 45205

HOLTMEIER, JOANNA THARP, 12th Grade English Teacher; *b:* Easton, PA; *m:* Keith; *c:* Bradford, Gregg; *ed:* Moravian Coll (BA) Eng 1971; 54 Addl Credits Lehigh Univ, Wilkes, West Chester, East Stroudsburg Univ; *cr:* Phillipsburg HS Eng Tchr 1971-75; Palisades HS Eng Tchr 1981-; *ai:* Scholars Bowl Coach; Portfolio, Mentoring Comm; Palisade Ed Assn, PA Ed Assn, NEA 1981-; *office:* Palisades HS 35 Church Hill Rd Kintnersville PA 18930

HOLTON, RICHARD L., Calculus Teacher; *b:* Marysville, OH; *m:* Karla J. Williams; *c:* Narthan W., Benjamin J., Bethany J.; *ed:* Ashland Coll (BS) Math Ed 1976; OH St Univ (MA) Math Ed 1987; *cr:* Marysville HS Math Tchr 1976-; *ai:* Boys JV Bsktbl; NEO, OEA, MEA 1976-, Tchr of Yr 1993; NCTM, OCTM 1976-; *office:* Marysville HS 800 Amrine Mill Rd Marysville OH 43040

HOLTRY, JOHN R., Chemistry Teacher; *b:* Chambersburg, PA; *m:* Winifred C.; *ed:* Shippensburg Univ (BS) Chem 1977; Wilson Coll (BSEd) Chem 1987; Wilkes Univ (MS) Ed 1988; Addl 60 Grad Credit Hrs; *cr:* Production Foreman AMP Inc 1977-87; Shippensburg HS Tchr 1987-; *ai:* Stu Cncl Adv; Bsbl Asst Coach; Sci Dept Chprsn; Head Cross Cntry Coach; NEA, SA Tchrs Assn 1987-; ACS 1989-; F&AM 1976-; Tall Cedars 1982-; Consistory 1985-; Cmptr Software Toshiba Grant; *office:* Shippensburg Area Sr HS 317 N Morris St Shippensburg PA 17257

HOLTRY, WINIFRED CATHERINE, 8th Grd Math Teacher; *b:* Lewistown, PA; *m:* John R.; *ed:* Shippensburg Univ (BSEd) Math Ed 1977; Wilkes Coll (MSEd) Ed 1987; 52 Credit Hrs Beyond Masters; *cr:* Shippensburg Area Jr High Math Tchr 1977-; *ai:* Peer Mediation Adv; 9th Grd Girls Vllybl Coach; NEA 1977-; PSEA 1977-; SAEA 1977-; *office:* Shippensburg Area Jr HS 101 Park Pl Shippensburg PA 17257

HOLTZ, VERNON ANDREW,OSB, Chairperson of Psychology Dept; *b:* Hastings, PA; *ed:* Lock Haven St Univ (BS) Ed 1953; Cath Univ of Amer (MA) Psych 1969; St Vincent Seminary (MA) Theology 1973; Duquesne Univ (PHD) Psych 1984; Latrobe Psychotherapy Assoc Licensed Psychologist; *cr:* St Vincent Preparatory Schl Asst Headmaster 1968-70; St Vincent Archabbey Priesthood Formation Dir 1971-74; St Vincent Coll Cnslng Ctr Dir 1971-75, Psych Chprs n 1975-80, 1987-; *ai:* Psychotherapy in Part-time Practice; Rank, Tenure, Humn Resource Comms; Amer Pysch Assn 1969-; PA Psych Assn 1975-; Nat Register of Hlth Svc Providers 1986-; St Vincent Archabbey 1956-; Roman Cath Priest; Awds Alumni of Distinction, Dean's Fac; *office:* St Vincent Coll 300 Fraser Purchase Rd Latrobe PA 15650

HOLTZMAN, NANCY BANGS, Business Education Teacher; *b:* Danville, PA; *m:* Rudolph V.; *c:* Lori L., David E.; *ed:* Bloomsburg Univ (BS) Bus Ed 1955; *cr:* Warrior Run HS Bus Ed Tchr 1970-; *ai:* NEA, PSEA 1970-; WREA 1970-, Treas; Watsontown Guild 1977-, Pres; *home:* RR 3 Box 451 Watsontown PA 17777

HOLTZMAN, SAMUEL MARK, High School Science Teacher; *b:* Sharon, MA; *m:* Marilyn E. Mc Keever; *c:* Laura, Jessica, Samantha; *ed:* Barrington Coll (BA) Bio 1979; Providence Coll (MED) 1991; Univ of RI Working Towards MS Labor Relations; 36 Addl Credits Math, Physics; *cr:* Pilgrim HS Physics, Gen Sci Tchr 1980-; New England Inst of Tech Adj Fac of Math, Physics 1987-; *ai:* AFT, RI Fed of Tchrs 1980-; Warwick Tchrs Union 1980-, Treas 1990-; *office:* Pilgrim HS 111 Pilgrim Pky Warwick RI 02888

HOLUB, NANCY DENNIS, High School Science Teacher; *b:* Warren, OH; *m:* Michael; *ed:* Youngstown St Univ (BS) Scndry Ed 1989; Kent St Univ Masters Prgm; *cr:* Alliance HS Sci Tchr 1990-; *ai:* Sci Fair Coord; NEA, OEA, Alliance Ed Assn 1990-.

HOLWELL, JEAN ANN BERNHARD, Social Studies Teacher; *b:* Bay Shore, NY; *m:* Gerard; *c:* Amanda; *ed:* Russell Sage Coll (BA) His, Govt, Cum Laude 1969; Hofstra Univ (MA) European His 1974; 30 Credit Hrs in Ed, Soc Stud, His Coursework; *cr:* West Islip Sr HS Soc Stud Tchr 1969-; *ai:* Mid Sts Evaluation Comm for Soc Stud Chprsn 1975, 1985; AFT 1969-; LI Cncl of Soc Stud 1980-; St Mary's Church 1982-91, Rel Tchr; St Mary's Church 1973-, Pre-Cana Moderator; Bay Shore Yacht Club 1978-, Wife of Vice Commodore; *office:* West Islip HS Lions Path West Islip NY 11795

HOLYCROSS, SUSAN SCHRADER, Business Teacher; *b:* Kenton, OH; *m:* Michael W.; *c:* Bryce Landon, Kayli Rae; *ed:* Bowling Green St Univ (BS) Bus Ed 1981, (AS) Secretarial Admin 1981; Wright St Univ (MS) Tchr Ldr 1989; Attnd Ashland Univ, UNiv of Dayton, Edison St; *cr:* Sub at Area Schls 1982-84; OH Hi-Point JVS Bus Adult Ed Instr 1983-85; Riverside HS Dept Head Bus Tchr 1985-; *ai:* Schl Newspaper Adv; Tchr Mentor; Grd, Attendance Comms; OH Bus Tchrs Assn; Nom for Excl Tchng Awd 1994; *office:* Riverside HS 200 W Moore St De Graff OH 43318

HOLZAPFEL, DAVID JAMES, 5th & 6th Grade Teacher; *b:* Elizabeth, NJ; *m:* Michelle Chasse; *c:* Simon, Forrest; *ed:* Marlboro Coll (BA) Italian Poetry, Translation 1972; Attnd Middlebury Coll Lang Inst; *cr:* Applewoods Studio Furniture Maker, Scupltor 1976-; St of VT Artist-in-Residence Prgm 1980-84; Marlboro Elem 5th-6th Grd Tchr 1988-; Schl for Intnl Trng Grad Stdnts Mentor Tchr 1990-; *ai:* Cycling Club; NCTM 1990-; Marlboro Bd of Civil Authority 1986-, Chprsn.

HOLZEN, JANICE RAYMONT, Math Tchr & Gifted Facilitator; *b:* Tarentum, PA; *m:* Luke S.; *c:* Stephen, Paul, Thomas; *ed:* Penn St Univ (BS) Math Ed 1971; Univ of Pittsburgh (MAT) Scndry Ed 1972; 30 Credit Hrs; *cr:* Westinghouse HS Math Tchr 1971-72; Knoxville MS Math Tchr 1972-76; Brashear HS Math Tchr & Gifted Facilitator 1976-; *ai:* CEIP Comm Recorder; AFT 1972-; NCTM; *office:* Brashear HS 590 Crane Ave Pittsburgh PA 15216*

HOLZER, RALPH ADAM, English Teacher; *b:* Pittsburgh, PA; *m:* Andrea; *c:* Ralph Jr., Daniel, Michael, Michele, Stephanie; *ed:* Duquesne Univ (BA) Eng 1964; Univ of Pittsburgh 15 Grad Credits; Duquesne Univ 10 Grad Credits; Carlow Coll 16 Grad Credits; *cr:* Canevin HS Eng Tchr 1964-; *ai:* Wrestling Coach; Ath Dir; NATC 1964-.

HOLZMAN, GARY NEIL, College Instructor; *b:* Reading, PA; *m:* Cheryl L. Walenta; *c:* Jake; *ed:* Boston Univ (BA) Pol Sci 1974; New England Schl of Law (JD) Law 1980; *cr:* DeSantis, Koch Attorneys-at-Law Assoc 1981-83; Self-Employed Lawyer 1983-88; Penn State Univ Undergrad Instr 1985-88; Albright Coll UndergradInstr 1986-88; Fis her Coll Undergrad Instr 1989-; *office:* Fisher Coll 118 Beacon St Boston MA 02116

HOLZSCHUH, DONNA ROSS, Second Grade Teacher; *b:* Rochester, NY; *c:* Jeffrey, Chris, Scot; *ed:* SUNY at Brockport (BS) Ed 1959; *cr:* Penfield Schl Dist Tchr, Harris Hill Schl Primary Tchr & Cobbles Schl 2nd Grd Tchr 31 Yrs; *ai:* Math Bldg Coord 1990-95; Shared Decision Team 1993-95; AFT 1962-; NYSTA 1962-; *office:* Cobbles Elem Schl Gebhardt Rd Penfield NY 14526

HOMAN, CINDY RENEE, 4th Grade Teacher; *b:* St Marys, OH; *ed:* Univ of Cincinnati (BS) Elem Ed 1984, (MED) Curr, Instruction 1990; *cr:* Deer Park Schls 5th Grd Tchr 1984-86, 4th Grd Tchr 1986-; *ai:* Bldg Career Ed Coord; Prin Advy Cncl; Acad Excl, Meritorious Svc Awds; *office:* Amity Elem Schl 4320 E Galbraith Rd Cincinnati OH 45236

HOMAN, DOLORES R., Health Occupations Ed Tchr; *b:* Pottsville, PA; *m:* Calvin R.; *ed:* Temple Univ (BS) Ed 1975; Hahnemann Hosp Schl of Nursing RN Nursing 1960; *cr:* Hahnemann Hospital Staff Nurse 1960-61; Comm General Hospital Staff Nurse 1961-65 & Head Nurse 1965-69; Reading-Muhlenberg Area Voc Tech Schl Tchr 1969-; *ai:* Hlth Occupations Stud of Amer & Voc Industrial Clubs of Amer adv; NEA & PSEA 1969-; Rdg-Muhl Tchrs Assn 1969-, VP & Pres; AVA 1993-; PVA 1993-, Outstanding Tchr of Yr in PA; Amer Red Cross; Keystone Comm Blood Bank; HOSA Task Force Mem for PA, Coord for St Ofcr; PA Voc Tchr Recognition; *office:* Reading Muhlenberg Vo-Tch Schl PO Box 13068 Reading PA 19612

HOMAN, KERRY BOSTELMAN, Mathematics Teacher; *b:* Greatfalls, MT; *m:* Kevin Matthew; *c:* Kendall Marie, Brandon Michael; *ed:* Bowling Green St Univ (BA) Math & Scndry Math 1989; *cr:* Liberty Ctr Schls Jr HS & HS Tchr 1991-; *ai:* Jr HS Girls Track; Chrldng Adv; NCTM 1991-; *office:* Liberty Ctr Local Schls Parrish St Liberty Center OH 43532

HOMBURGER, GAIL D., Algebra Teacher; *b:* Brooklyn, NY; *m:* Paul A.; *c:* Allison; *ed:* 27 Credit Hrs Towards MALS SUNY at Stony Brook; *cr:* North Shore Chrstn Schl 3rd, 5th, 8th Grd Math, Pre-K, Nursery Schl, Algebra Tchr 1983-; *ai:* Handbell Choir Dir; Yrbk Adv; *office:* North Shore Christian Schl 324 Jayne Blvd Port Jefferson Sta NY 11776

HOMEN, PETER JOHN, Social Studies Dept Chair; *b:* New Bedford, MA; *m:* Mary Jane Skurka; *c:* Gregory J.; *ed:* St Coll at Bridgewater (BA) His & Scndry Ed 1970; Univ of RI (MA) Non-Western His 1972; Post-Grad Courses; *cr:* Apponequet Reg HS Soc Stud Tchr 1972-, Soc Stud Dept Chair 1987-; *ai:* Golf & Bsbl Former Coach; Initiated European Stu Travel Pgm 1983; NEA 1972-; MA Cncl Soc Stud 1980-; New England His Tchrs Assn 1984-; Fall River Citizens Schlsp Fndtn 1989-, Bd of Dirs; St Stanislaw Schl 1994-, Parent Advy Cncl; European Travel Lecturer; Numerous Pub Svc Grants & Flwshps; Project Ed Wkshps; *office:* Apponequet Reg HS 100 Howland Rd Lakeville MA 02347

HOMER, CAROLYN FREDERICK, Fourth Grade Teacher; *b:* Hancock, NY; *m:* Clark H.; *c:* Melissa, Kyle; *ed:* Univ of TN (BS) Early Chldhd & Elem Ed 1975; 57 Grad Credits; Masters Equivalency; *cr:* Susquehanna Comm Schl Dist Tchr 1976-; *ai:* IST Team Mem; NEA 1976-; PSEA 1976-; *office:* Susquehanna Comm Schl Dist RR 3 Box 5a Susquehanna PA 18847

HOMER, DOUGLAS MARTIN, Associate Professor of Eng; *b:* Lapeer, NY; *ed:* Ithaca Coll (BFA) Music 1974; Syracuse Univ (MA) Speech, Theatre 1965; *cr:* CA St Coll Asst Prof of Theatre 1965-72; SUNY at CortlandSpeech Instr 1975-85; SUNY at Morrisville Assoc Prof of Eng 1986-; *ai:* Friars' Drama Club Adv; Theatrical Productions Dir; Frosh Experience, Distance Learning Comms; Alpha Psi Omega; Kappa Gamma Psi; Theater Assn of NY St; *office:* St Univ of NY at Morrisville Morrisville NY 13408*

HOMER, FRANK M., Chemistry & Physics Teacher; *b:* Paterson, NJ; *m:* Carol Ann Backus; *c:* Patricia, Robert, Frank; *ed:* Rutgers Univ (AB) Chem 1965; Harvard Univ (MAT) Sci Ed 1966; 100+ Grad Credits from NSF Grants, Industrial & US Army Rsrch; *cr:* West Morris Cntrl HS Physics & Chem Tchr 1966-; *ai:* Dist Right-To-Know Coord; NJEA 1966-; NEA 1966-; ACS 1988-; NNJSDA 1992-, VP; Rsrch Pub; Woodrow Wilson Fndtn Dreyfus Schlshp Awd; Rudolph Awd for Sci Excl (Twice); *office:* West Morris Central H S Bartley Rd Chester NJ 07930*

HOMER, SANDRA WASS, English Teacher; *b:* East Liverpool, OH; *m:* Clayton T.; *c:* Douglas Ray, Jonathan, Samuel; *ed:* Clarion St Univ (BS) Eng 1972, (MED) Rdng 1976; Post Grad Edinboro Univ 12 Credits, Slipper Rock 3 Credits, 6 Addl Credits; *cr:* Franklin Area HS 9-12 Grd Eng, Grd 8 Rdng, Remedial Rdng Tchr 23 Yrs; *ai:* Cmptr Coordinating Comm; Instrl Support Model; Scndry Instrl Support; NEA, PSEA, FAEA 1972-, Bldg Rep; NCTE 1993-; Cub Scouts 1994-, Den Ldr, Comm; *office:* Franklin Area HS RD 4 Pone Ln Franklin PA 16323

HOMES, PHYLLIS R., Guidance Cnslr & Coll Adv; *b:* North Adams, MA; *m:* Joseph M.; *c:* Jon S., Amy M.; *ed:* George Washington Univ (BA) US His 1947; Amer Univ (MED) Counseling Psych 1977; Johns Hopkins 2 Post Grad Courses in Individual & Group Counseling; Art Therapy at NIH Grad prgm; Many Other Continuing Ed Courses Locally; *cr:* Amer Univ Supvr & Cnslr 1977-78; Charles E Smith Jewish Day Schl Cnslr & Coll Adv 1978-; *ai:* SADD & SAFE Clubs Adv; Lit Discussion Group Mem; NACAC 1980-; Natl Endowment Hum grant 1993; *office:* Charles E Smith Jewish Dy Schl 1901 E Jefferson St Rockville MD 20852

HOMOVEC, KATHLEEN MCKINLEY, 2nd Grade Teache Manistee, MI; *m:* Richard Edward; *c:* Michael, Katherine; *ed:* Easte Univ (BS) Elem Ed 1967; Kent St Univ (MA) Ed 1990; 12 Semest Beyond Masters; *cr:* Trenton Pub Schls 1st Grd Tchr 1967-70; Eucli Schls 1st Grd Tchr 1970-74; Painesville City Schls 2nd, 4th, & 5t Tchr 1987-; *ai:* MS Tennis Coach; OEA, NEA, PCTA 1987-; Phi Kappa 1993-; PTA 1987-; Jennings Scholar 1990-91; OH PTA D Outstanding Educator 1993; *office:* Lathrop Elem Schl 61 Roosev Painesville OH 44077

HONAKER, J. WAYNE, Mathematics Dept Chm & Teacher; *b:* Rich VA; *m:* Linda Sue Hollen; *c:* Sarah Lynn, Erin Michelle; *ed:* Bere (BA) Math 1970; Xavier Univ (MED) Math Ed 1973; Cmptr Sci C OH St Univ, Univ of Cincinnati, Xavier Univ, Ashland; *cr:* Marysvi Tchr 1970-; Mill Creek Golf Course Mgrs Asst & Consultant 19 Columbus St CC Math & Cmptr Lit Instr 1976-86; *ai:* Math & Cmp Dept Chair; Math, Cmptr Sci Clubs; Marysville Schl Dists Partners Ed Tech Comm; North Cntrl Evaluation Chm; NEA, OEA 1970-; 1970-, Chair Negotiation, Tchr of Yr; NCTM 1985-; Jr Golf Prog Ldr; OH Dept of Ed Schl Net Reader; OH Dept of Ed for Tech Articles Pub; *office:* Marysville HS 800 Amrine Mill Rd Marysvil 43040*

HONCHARSKI, BARBARA A., Math & Computer Science Tc Philadelphia, PA; *m:* Robert; *c:* Paul, Beth; *ed:* Marietta Coll (BS) 1975; SUNY at Oswego (MS) Ed-Curr 1984; *cr:* Baldwinsville Cntrl 7th-8th Grd Math, Sci Tchr 1976-77; Auburn City Schls Math, Cmp Tchr 1978-; *ai:* Tech Comm; NYSUT, Auburn Tchtrs Assn Skaneateles Ski Club 1987-, Treas 1994-95, Pres Cup 1995; Skaneateles 1989-; Girl Scouts 1991-, Ldr; *office:* Auburn HS Lak Auburn NY 13021

HONER, MARY BOSHART, 8th Grd English Teacher; *b:* Lowville *m:* David; *c:* David II, Robert; *ed:* Goshen Coll (BA) Eng 1965; Tchrs Columbia Univ (MA) Eng Ed 1970; *cr:* Lowville Acad & Cntrl Schl S Eng Tchr 1965-69; Beaver River Cntrl Schl Scndry Eng Tchr 1970 Pub Speaking Contest Dir; Organizer for Local World Vision Famine; Conflict Mgmt; NYSUT 1980-; NCTE 1990-91; Church Sunday Schl Tchr, Church Ed Coord, Pianist; Pub 2 Articles in C Publications; *home:* RR 1 Box 42 Castorland NY 13620

HONEY, ERIN ELLEN, Psychology & World His Tchr; *b:* Anna MD; *ed:* Univ of DE (BA) Psych Ed 1993; Anne Arundel Comm Coll Soc Stud Cert; Bowie St Univ Working Toward (MA) Cnslng Psych Broadneck Sr HS Psych & World His Tchr 1993-; *ai:* JV Cheerle Coach 1 Yr; Stu Govt Adv 2 Yrs; NEA, MSTA, AACCSS 1993-; TOPSS, NASAA 1994-; *home:* 1170 Bay View Vis Annapolis MD 21

HONEY, JOHN H., Biology Teacher; *b:* New York City, NY; *m:* J Spencer; *c:* Laura Lowe, Andrew Payne; *ed:* Western CT St Univ (BS 1966; Univ of Bridgeport (MS) Bio 1972; Fairfield Univ 6th Yr Admin 1992; Cert Advanced Stud; NSF Grant Bowdoin Coll Marine Southern CT St Univ Drug Inst; *cr:* Fairfield HS Bio Tchr 1966- Tennis Coach 1972-; *ai:* Stu Cncl Adv 1966-76; NEA, CEA, Fairfie Assn 1966-; Democratic Town Comm 1994-; *office:* Fairfield HS Melville Ave Fairfield CT 06430*

HONNICK, DOROTHY M. (REYNOLDS), Retired PE Teache Coach; *b:* Los Angeles, CA; *m:* Richard E.; *c:* Tina M. Baylor, Timot *ed:* Ithaca Coll (BS) Hlth, PE, Recreation 1960, (MS) Hlth, PE, Recre 1964; 30 Addl Hrs Bryon MS, Ithaca Coll, Inservice Course Ed 1970-80; Coaching Course Updates; CPR First Aid BLS 195 Swimming & Water Safety Inst Red Cross 1956-95; *cr:* George H. Nic Elem Schl PE Tchr 1960-62; Jenny F. Snapp Elem, Jr HS PE Tchr 196 Union Endicott HS PE Tchr, Coach 1964-95; *ai:* Bowling Coach U Endicott HS; Var, JV Boys, Girls Teams; Girls Var, JV Chrldng C Bsktbl, Ftbl, Girls JV, Var Chrldng, Var Swimming, Girls Track C Section IV Swim Chm for Girls NYS; AFT, NEA, Endicott Tchrs AAHPER Tchrs & Coaches 1960-; Lady Elks, Amer Legion 1980-.

HONTZ, KRISTA HOCH, Second Grade Teacher; *b:* Wilson, PA William Jacob III; *c:* Jennifer, Lindsay; *ed:* Lebanon Vly Coll (BS) Ed 1981; Master Equivalency 36 Credit Hrs; ESU Wilkes Coll IU 2 Floyd R. Shafer Kndgtn Tchr 1983-85, Second Grd Tchr 1985-; *ai:* S Quality Team; NEA 1983-; St John's Ev Luth Church 1972-; Naz YMCA 1977-; *office:* Floyd R Shafer Elem Sch 49 N Liberty St Naz PA 18064

HOOD, BARBARA LANDERS, Kindergarten Teacher; *b:* Springf MA; *w:* Leonard (dec); *ed:* Our Lady of Elms Coll at Chicopee (BA) Ed 1963; 135 Prof Dev Credits; *cr:* Frank Freedman Schl 2nd, 3rd Grd 1963-74; Daniel B. Brunton Schl 2nd, Combination 2nd, 3rd Grd 1974-87, Kndgtn Tchr 1987-; *ai:* Kndgtn Curr Comm; SEA, N Springfield Tchrs Club 1963-; Pioneer Vly Elms Alumnae Assn 1 Cntrl HS Boosters Club 1992-; *office:* Daniel B. Brunton Schl 1801 P St Springfield MA 01128

HOOD, BONNIE HOLQUIST, French & World Studies Teacher; *b:* K PA; *m:* Joseph L.; *c:* Erin, Christopher; *ed:* Grove City Coll (BA) Fr 1 Attnd Youngstown St Univ, Kent St Univ; *cr:* Maplewood HS Tchr Fr III, IV, World Stud 1974-; *ai:* NHS; Fr Club; Peer Tutor, Intervention Team Coord; NEA, OEA, MEA 1974-; OMLTA; A+ Tchr Awd W Tribune Chronicle; *office:* Maplewood HS 2414 Greenville Rd Cortland OH 44410

HOOD, CRAIG ROBERT, Social Studies Teacher; *b:* Detroit, MI Priscilla Whitford; *c:* Casey; *ed:* The Amer Univ (BA) His Antioch-New England Grad Schl (MED) Elem Ed 1978; *cr:* Hol Headstart Tchr 1971-72; Greenfield Child Dev Ctr Tchr 1972-73; Li Hill Schl Tchr 1974-77; Chesterfield Schl Tchr 1981-; *ai:* Stu Cncl SAU 29 Soc Stud Curr Comm; Amer Heritage Tour Group Ldr; 7th & Grd Team Ldr; Lead Tchr; NEA 1981-; *office:* Chesterfield Schl Chesterfield Rd PO Box 205 Chesterfield NH 03443

HOOD, CRISTY, French Teacher; *b:* Jeannette, PA; *ed:* IN Univ of (BS) Fr for Intnl Trade 1989; Tchr Cert Fr Ed 1992; 12 Addl Credit Eng Cert; *cr:* Penn-Trafford HS Fr Tchr; *ai:* Fr Club Adv; Chrldng S Asst Coach; NEA, PA St Modern Langs Assn, Allegheny Frgn Lang 1992-; *office:* Penn-Trafford HS Rt 130 Box 366 Harrison City PA 15

HOOD, R. ELIZABETH PAQUIN, 8th Grade Science Teacher; *b:* River, MA; *c:* Matthew, Eric; *ed:* Univ of Bridgeport (BS) Sci Ed 196 Credits Span; 30 Credits Fr; Attnd Univ of WA; *cr:* Narragansett Jr HS Tchr 1963-65; Plainfield HS Bio Tchr 1965-67; Waggner Jr Sr HS Phys Tchr 1967-68; Swansea Jr Sr HS Fr, Span, Sci Tchr 1984-; *ai:* C Assistance Support Team; Stu Cncl, Drama Club Asst Adv; Sci Ldr Comm; Sci Liaison; Natl Honorary Span Soc; NEA 1984-; SEA, 1984-, Sec; MAST 1992-; Little Theater 1987-; PALMS Summer Golden Apple Awd; *office:* Joseph Case Jr HS 195 Main St Swansea 02777

HOODBHOY, OZDEN KARAKURUM, Chemical Enginee Professor; *b:* Bursa, Turkey; *m:* Alamin I.; *c:* Mehlika, Nilgun, Neslin; Robert Coll at Istanbul (BS) Chemical Engrng 1964; Tufts Univ (Chemical Engrng 1966; Scndry Tchng Cert 1973; 21 Credit Hrs in Prgm at Univ of CT in Chemical Engrng; *cr:* Uni Royal Inc Rsrch 1966-68; Sacred Heart HS Chem Tchr 1974-78; NVCT Coll Prof 19 Harkness Industries VP 1985-; *ai:* Amer Chemical Soc Club Adv; A

; Comm; *office:* Naugatuck Vly Comm Tech Coll 750 Chase Pky rbury CT 06708*

)E, TOM NORMAN, Professor of Biology; *b:* Evansville, IN; *m:* E.; *c:* Tom, Jill Hooe-Twetten, Todd; *ed:* Univ of Evansville (BA) Bio ; Drake Univ (MA) Bio 1970; Univ of MD Doctoral Stud 1972-77; *cr:* e HS Bio Tchr 1964-70; Towson St Univ Bio Instr 1970-75; Baltimore Comm Coll Prof 1975-; *ai:* HAPS 1992-; Intnl Tchng Excl Awd TX; d Excl in Tchng Awd; MAHE Outstdng Edctr Awd; Author of Chptr 5 C Monograph; *office:* Baltimore City Comm Coll 2901 Liberty hts Ave Baltimore MD 21215

)GMOED, JANYCE MARIE, Eng, Art & HS Foods Teacher; *b:* 'son, NJ; *m:* Walter Leonard; *c:* Pamela De Ruiter, Patricia Logan, er L. Jr., Janine, Deborah S.; *ed:* William Paterson Coll (BA) Elem Ed ; *cr:* Browns Mills Elem Schl Pre-First Tchr 1962-1963; US Army HS Math, Sci, Eng, His Tchr 1963-64; Shire of Whittlesea Home Help r 1968-69; Netherlands Reformed Chrstn Schl Eng Gram, Comp, Art 1977-95, Eng, Art, HS Foods Tchr 1995-; *ai:* Art Curr Coord; Bolivia ion Comm Chprsn; Compiled, Wrote 4th-8th Grd Art Curr for School; : 10 Jahn Ct Mahwah NJ 07430

)K, DONNA JEAN, English Teacher; *b:* Toledo, OH; *m:* Richard ard; *c:* Anthony, Deana; *ed:* Univ of Toledo (BA) Eng 1973, (MS) Ed ; *cr:* Whitmer HS Eng Tchr 1977-; *ai:* OEA 1977-, Tchrs Assn WA il Schls 1977-, Oustdng Tchr 1984-85; *office:* Whitmer HS 5601 Clegg oledo OH 43613

)K, FRANK JOSEPH,JR., 2nd Grade Teacher; *b:* New Britain, CT; andra Janowski; *ed:* Cntrl CT St Coll (BS) Elem Ed 1971, (MS) Curr apvr 1978; *cr:* Linden Street Elem Schl 2nd Grd Tchr 1971-; *ai:* NEA -; CEA 1971-; Ed Assn of Plainville 1971-, Chief Negotiator; Kappa a Pi 1969-; GSLC Lit Coalition Literacy Advocate Awd 1991; Stdnts ry Pub Edition of Anthology of Poetry by Young Americans 1994; *e:* Linden Street Elem Schl 69 Linden St Plainville CT 06062

)K, LARRY R., Biology Teacher; *b:* Osceola, IA; *m:* Paula L. Paul; icole, Arron, Lindsee; *ed:* Central Coll (BA) PE, Bio 1977; Xavier MS Degree Ed Admin August 1994; *cr:* Radcliffe HS PE Tchr, Ftbl, k Coach 1977-79; Evangel Coll Exercise Physiology Tchr, Ftbl Coach)-82; IA St Univ Ftbl Coach 1982-83; Hutchinson Comm Coll Housing Ftbl Coach 1983-86; Univ of MI at Morris PE Tchr, Ftbl, Track Coach i-88; Morehead St Univ PE Tchr, Ftbl Coach 1988-89; Milford HS Bio , Ftbl, Track Coach 1990-; *ai:* Var Offensive Coord, Ftbl, Head Track ch; Track Meet Dir; Dev Tchr Classroom Mngmt Skills Inservice Prgm; *e:* Milford HS 1 Eagles Way Milford OH 45150

)OKER, BETH ANN LAMBEIN, Vocal Music Edctr; *b:* Biloxi, MS; stephen John; *c:* Kristin Hooker Howard, Nicole Beth; *ed:* SUNY at dam Crane Schl of Music (BS) Music Ed, Voice 1967; Attnd SUNY at ego, Geneseo, Brockport, Potsdam & Saratoga-Potsdam Choral Inst; Oakfield-AL Cntrl Schl K-6 Grd Elem Vocal Tchr 1967-68; dwinsville Cntrl Schl Elem K-6 Grd Vocal, HS 9-12 Grd Vocal, Strings 1968-73; LeRoy Cntrl Jr, Sr HS 7-12 Grd Vocal Music Tchr 1973-; *ai:* or Guard Adv Marching Band, Winter Color Guard; Jr Sr HS Dir, ducer Musicals; AFS Adv; Stage Crew Adv; Auditorium Supvr; SSMA, MENC, AFT, NEA, NYSUT 1967-; OACS, LeRoy Tchr Assn 7, 1973-; Baldwinsville Tchr Assn 1968-, VP; Onondaga Music Ed 1 1968-;Genesee-Wyoming Music Ed Assn 1967-, Publicity Chm Librn 3; Batavia Players Inc 1973-, Wardrobe Chm, VP Bd, Dir, Music Dir; oming Co Bicentennial Singers 1982-, Bd Mem, Costumer, Dir, Music 1st United Meth Church 1967-88, Yth & Sanctuary Choirs Dir; esee Arts Cncl 1976-80, Bd Mem; Notre Dame HS Musicals Dir 1995-; NYSSMA St Chprsn; *home:* 1987 Kingsley Rd Wyoming NY 14591

)KS, NANCY CAROL, 6th Grade Teacher; *b:* Paterson, NJ; *m:* iam Charles; *c:* Michael, Shawn, Brian; *ed:* Univ of Findlay (BS) Elem 1972; Post Grad Stud Bowling Green St Univ; *cr:* Arcadia Local Schl 5 Tchr 1972-80; St Michael Schl Grd 6 Tchr 1985-; *ai:* Stu Cncl Adv rs; Tech Comm; Soc Stud Curr Team; NEA, OEA, NWOEA 1972-80; EA 1985-; Blanchard Vly Hosp Auxiliary 1995-; DAR 1993-; Nom al Golden Apple Tchrs Awd 3 Times; *office:* St Michael MS 701 Adams indlay OH 45840

)OPENGARDNER, MARION RICE, Third Grade Teacher; *b:* tstone, MD; *m:* Barry F.; *c:* Barry M., Beth M.; *ed:* Frostburg St (BS) m Ed 1962; Frostburg St Tchrs Coll (MED) Elem Ed 1967; *cr:* Havre Grace Elem Schl 4th Grd Tchr 1962; Piney Plains Elem Schl 3rd & 4th Tchr 1965-67; Penn Avenue Schl 4th Grd Tchr 1967-70; Bel Air Elem 1 2nd Grd Tchr 1971-72; Parkside Elem 3rd & 4th Grd Tchr 1972-74; tstone Schl 3rd Grd Tchr 1974-; *ai:* NEA, MSTA 1962-; ACTA 1972-; *e:* Flintstone Schl Main St Flintstone MD 21530

)OPER, ANN SIMMONS, First Grade Teacher; *b:* Syracuse, NY; *c:* chael, Nancy, John; *ed:* Elmira Coll (AAS) Bus 1956; SUC Oswego (BS) m Ed 1977; Nazareth Coll (MS) Rdng 1981; *cr:* Sodus Cntrl Schl Fifth Tchr 1977-78, Second Grd Tchr 1978-; *ai:* Team Ldr; Task Force; Math nm; Conflict Resolution; Delta Kappa Gamma 1989-, Prof Growth Chm 2-94, Mbrshp Chm 1994-; *home:* 109 Prospect St Newark NY 14513*

)OPER, BARBARA, European & US History Teacher; *b:* Glen Ridge, *ed:* Montclair St Univ (BA) His, Anthropology 1972, (MA) Soc Sci 6; Addl 30 Hrs Soc Sci 1984; *cr:* Westfield HS Soc Stud Tchr 1972-74; L. Johnson RHS Soc Stud Tchr 1974-84; Gov Livingston RHS Soc Stud ır 1984-; *ai:* Acad Team, Peer Ldrshp Adv; AFT 1980-; NCSS 1975-; *e:* Gov Livingston Reg HS 175 Watchung Blvd Berkeley Heights NJ 22

)OPER, DALE THOMAS, Career, Drafting & CAD Teacher; *b:* New ndsor, MD; *m:* Carolyn Brust; *c:* Robert, Deborah Hooper Holmer, nifer; *ed:* Catonsville Comm Coll (AA) Mortuary Sci 1990; Univ of MD 1993; *cr:* South Carroll HS Voc, CAD Tchr 1984-87, 1993-; *ai:* Voc strl Club of Amer Adv; MD Stu Asst Prgm Comm; Track & Field, Cross ry Coach; *home:* 102 Paradise Ave Mount Airy MD 21771

)OPER, DOUGLAS L., Broadcast Journalism Tchr; *b:* Plainfield, NJ; Judith A. Nicholson; *c:* Jon, Tim, David; *ed:* William Paterson Coll A) Speech Arts, Dramatics 1967, (MA) Lang Comm 1968; 30 Addl edits; Television; Comm; Acting; *cr:* William Paterson Coll Grad Asst 57-68; Scotch Plains-Fanwood HS Speech Arts, Dramatics Tchr 1968-; 34 News, Stage Crew, Dramatic, Bible Clubs Adv; NEA 1968-; Royal ngers Outpost 55 1983-, Sr Commander; Frontiersman Camping Flwshp)0-, Scribe; Produce 3 Television Prgms for Local Comm Access annels; *office:* Scotch Plains Fanwood HS 667 Westfield Rd Scotch ains NJ 07076

)OPER, FRED GRANT, Choral & Classroom Music Tchr; *b:* merton, PA; *m:* Kay D. Shroyer; *c:* Allison E.; *ed:* Susquehanna Univ A) Music Ed 1973; Bloomsburg Univ (MED) Rdng Ed 1994; Penn St iv (MED) Music Ed 1994; Post-Grad Stud Westminster Choir Coll; *cr:* linsgrove Area MS Choral, Classroom Music Tchr 1973-81; lingsgrove Area HS Choral, Classroom Music Tchr 1981-; Selingsgrove ea Schl Dist Music Dept Chair 1985-; *ai:* Curr, Stu Assistance, Tech mms; Instrl Support Team; Stu Cncl Co-Adv; MENC 1973-, HS Curr, truction Rep; ACDA 1980-, PA Newsletter Ed; Phi Delta Kappa 1989-; A 1992-; Choral Conductor US Music Ambassadors; Accompanist Fred aring US Chorus; Newsletter Ed; Guest Conductor Numerous Choral stivals; *home:* 1003 Orange St Selinsgrove PA 17870*

HOOPER, LESLIE BARBER, High School Math Teacher; *b:* Albany, NY; *m:* Gerald Thomas; *c:* Jacob, Carrie; *ed:* St Lawrence Univ (BS) Math 1970; SUNY at Oneonta 30 Grad Hrs; *cr:* Duanesburg Cntrl 8th-9th Grd Math Tchr 1970-78; Middleburgh Cntrl HS Math Tchr 1978-; *ai:* NHS Adv; Booster Club Corresponding Sec; Hnrs Banquet Comm; AFT & NYSUT 1970-; Mid Cent Tchrs Assoc 1978-, Treas; Delta Kappa Gamma 1989-; Town Planning Bd 1978-92; Boy Scout Ldr 1982-88; Girl Scout Ldr 1988-93; *office:* Middleburgh Central HS 181 Main St Box 400 Middleburgh NY 12122

HOOPES, SCOTT MICHAEL, Guidance Counselor; *b:* Woodbury, NJ; *m:* Elizabeth Wdzieczkowski; *c:* Geoffrey, Trevor, Corinne; *ed:* Glassboro St (BA) Hlth & PE 1989; Rowan Coll (MA) Stu Prsnl 1994; Attending Widener Univ for Doctorate in Schl Admin; *cr:* Haddon Twp HS Hlth Tchr 1989-94; Highland Regnl HS Guidance Cnslr 1994-; *ai:* Jr Var Bsktbl Coach; Camden Cty Schl Cnslrs, NJ Schl Cnslr 1994-; NJEA 1989-, Mem; Kappa Delta Pi Honor Soc, Mem; *office:* Highland Regional H S 450 Erial Rd Blackwood NJ 08012*

HOOPS, JUDITH KAY, English Teacher & Dept Head; *b:* Jackson, OH; *m:* Troy W.; *c:* Brent, Eric; *ed:* OH Univ (BA) Eng 1964; Coll of Mt St Joseph (MA) Rdng 1983; Various Classes through Ashland Coll & Ohio Univ; *cr:* Plains HS Tchr 1964-66; Circleville Jr HS Tchr 1966-67; Unioto HS Eng Tchr 1967-; *ai:* NHS Comm; Mentor Tchr; NEA, OEA & COTA 1964-; USEA 1964-, Pres 2 Times; Ross Cty Tchrs, Tchr of Yr Awd; Unioto Ath Boosters 1980-, Treas 6 Yrs; Attnd Various Wkshps at OH Univ, Ashland Coll & Coll of Mt St Joseph; *office:* Union HS 1432 Egypt Pike Chillicothe OH 45601

HOOTEN, ROSEANNE, 1st Grade Teacher; *b:* Philadelphia, PA; *ed:* Immaculata Coll (BA) Psych, Early Chldhd Ed 1983; Philadelphia Coll of Textiles, Sci Grad Credits; *cr:* St Timothy Schl First GRD Tchr 1983-; *ai:* Schl Integrated Lang Arts Comm; Schl Spirit Day Adv; NCEA 1983-; Mid Sts Assn of Colls, Schls 1994, 1996, Visiting Team Mem; *office:* St Timothy Schl 3033 Levick St Philadelphia PA 19149

HOOTMAN, DAN WINFIELD, Biology & Ecology Teacher; *b:* Sewickley, PA; *c:* Julie Fusco, Vicki Truchan; *ed:* (BS) Bio 1975; (MS) Ed 1981; Prin Cert Admin 1978; *cr:* Meadville HS Tchr 20 Yrs; *ai:* NEA & PSEA 1976-; Pine Town 1988-, Supvr; *office:* Meadville Area Sr HS North St Ext Meadville PA 16335

HOOVER, ALLEN M., Mathematics Teacher; *b:* Hesston, PA; *m:* Patricia Ann Price; *c:* Scott, Brian, Craig, Brent; *ed:* Shippensburg Univ (BS) Math 1962, (MED) Math 1994; Credit Hrs Received From Millersville Univ, LaSalle Univ, Salem St & Boston Univ; *cr:* Milton Hershey Schl Math Tchr & Dept Chair 1962-; *ai:* NHS Adv; Math Dept Chm; NEA, PSEA, MHEA, NCTM & PCTM; Reader for AP Test in Calculus; *office:* Milton Hershey Schl PO Box 830 Hershey PA 17033

HOOVER, ANN LOUISE, Spanish Teacher; *b:* York, PA; *ed:* Millersville UNiv (BS) Sec Educ, Fr-Cum Laude 1977; Span 1978; Masters Equivalency Foreign Lang 1992; *cr:* Manheim Cntrl Sr HS Fr Tchr 1977, Fr, Span Tchr 1978-83, Span Tchr 1984-86, Fr, Span Tchr 1987-88, Span Tchr 1989-90, Fr, Span Tchr 1991, Span Tchr 1992-; *ai:* Drama Asst Dir 1978-81; Dept Chm 1991; Coached 3 First, 2 SecondPlace Group in 4 Latino Competitions at Millersville Univ; Train Srs to Teach Span to Gifted El em Class; PSMLA 1977-82; AATSP 1992-94; NEA, PSEA MCEA 1977-; York Cty 4-H 1965-75, Pres 1971-72, Outstdng Toast Mistress 1973, Natl Schlsp, Outstdng Cty Mem 1974; Pub Speaker Svc Clubs, Dedication York 4-H Ctr, 4 Televised Speeches, Ldrshp Seminar at Natl 4-H Ctr; Time, Caring Awd by Amer Family Inst 1991; S cndry Tchry of Yr 1992; Voted Most Motivating Female Tchr by Class of 1995.

HOOVER, BEVERLY MARIE, Sixth Grade Teacher; *b:* Logan, WV; *m:* Paul Clinton; *c:* Wendy Joy Hoover Smith; *ed:* Kent St Univ (BS) Elem Ed 1972; Baldwin-Wallace Coll (MA) Ed, Remedial Rdng Cert 1981; 40 Addl Semester Hrs; *cr:* Elyria City Schls 5th Grd Tchr 1972-73, 4th Grd Tchr 1973-83, Title I Rdng Tchr 1983-87, 6th Grd Tchr 1987-; *ai:* Sweet Adelines 1981-, Pres, Sweet Adeline of Yr; *home:* 41815 Rambler St W Elyria OH 44035*

HOOVER, DANIEL ZERAH, PE Teacher & Athletic Trainer; *b:* Sandusky, OH; *m:* Dodi Adams; *c:* Cody Adams, Lauren Adams, Galen DuPrae, Benjamin; *ed:* OH St Univ (BA) Ed, PE K-12-Cum Laude; Attnd Toledo Univ Tchr Ed, Vanguard Emergency Medical Tech; *cr:* Oak Harbor HS Tchr, Ath Trainer 1987-, Adapted Phys Ed Tchr; *ai:* Cert Athl Trainer Intramural; Open House, Final Exam, GPA Comms; AAHPERD, NEA, OEA 1987-; Oak Harbor Ed Assn 1987-, Bldg Rep, 5 Yr Awd; NATA, OATA, GLATA 1986-; Mid Cty EMS 1994-; Obertorfer, Ernie Biggs Schlsps; New Games Publication; Phi Lambda Theta; *office:* Oak Harbor HS 11661 W SR 163 Oak Harbor OH 43449*

HOOVER, DOUGLAS E.,II, History & Government Teacher; *b:* Harrisburg, PA; *m:* Colleen A. Cook; *ed:* Penn St (BS) Admin of Justice 1984, (BS) Scndry Ed & Soc Stud 1989; 30 Credits Towards MPA; *cr:* Dover Area HS Tchr 1989-; *ai:* Stu Govt & Yrbk Adv; NEA 1989-; Mason-Dixon Cncl of Soc Stud 1989-, Ofcr; *office:* Dover Area HS W Canal St Dover PA 17315*

HOOVER, DUANE PAUL, Scndry Art Education Teacher; *b:* Altoona, PA; *m:* Marjorie K.; *c:* Tracy, Thad, Amanda; *ed:* Edinboro Univ (BS) Art Ed 1969; 24 Hrs PA St Univ; *cr:* Indian Valley HS Scndry Art Ed Tchr 1969-; *ai:* Art Club Supvr; Mifflin Co Ed Assn, PSEA, NEA 1969-; *office:* Indian Valley Sr HS 700 Cedar St Lewistown PA 17044*

HOOVER, ERIC DOUGLAS, Advncd Plcmnt Studio Art Tchr; *b:* Columbus, OH; *c:* Zachary, Ashley, Benjamin; *ed:* Marietta Coll (BA) Art 1974; Fitchburg St Coll (MED) Educl Tech 1989; *cr:* Maple Hts Jr HS Art Tchr 1974-76; Marshall Simonds MS Art Tchr 1976-79; McCarthy Jr HS & Parker Jr HS Art Tchr 1980-81; Chelmsford Pub Schls K-12th Grd Art Dept Head 1982-89; Chelmsford HS AP Art & Comp Graphics Tchr 1989-; *ai:* Schl Pub Adv; Fine Arts Curr Review & Long Range Tech Planning Comms; MA Alliance For Arts Ed, Arts Edctr of Yr 1989; MA Art Ed Assn; Chelmsford Cultural Cncl 1988-89, Pres; Rebello Memorial Art Schlrshp 1986-, Chief Admin; MA Art All St Festival Steering Comm Founding Chm; Developed Curr for AP Art, Comp Graphics & Studio Art; Chief Consultant to Architects in Bldg New HS Art Studios; Co Founder of Murals Pgm; Co Developer of Hum Pgm; *office:* Chelmsford HS 200 Richardson Rd North Chelmsford MA 01863*

HOOVER, JAMES PATRICK, Assistant Principal; *b:* Sewickley, PA; *m:* Irene J.; *c:* Jason M.; *ed:* Edinboro Univ of PA (BS) Ed 1973; Robert Morris Coll (BSBA) Bus Admin 1977, (MBA) Bus Admin 1986; Youngstown St Univ Cert Ed Admin 1991, Supt Cert; Univ of PI Doctoral Prgm Ed Admin; *cr:* Beaver Area Schl Dist Tchr 1973-94; West Allegheny Schl Dist, Asst Prin 1974-; *ai:* PA Math Assessment Advy, Dist Math Curr, Safe Schls Comms; NAESP, PAESP 1994-; PCTM 1993-; McKee PTA, Wilson PTA 1994-; *office:* West Allegheny Schl Dist 205 W Allegheny Rd Imperial PA 15126

HOOVER, KAYLEEN (KIN), Kindergarten Teacher; *b:* Upper Sandusky, OH; *m:* Stephen A.; *ed:* OH Dominican Coll (BS) Ed, Kndgtn Cert 1975; *cr:* St Joseph Schl Kndgtn Tchr 1975-; *ai:* OCEA 1975-.

HOOVER, LYNN ANN, Math Teacher; *b:* Rochester, PA; *m:* Robert C.; *ed:* Clarion Univ (MS) Math 1974; Edinboro Univ (BS) Elem 1970; Cmptr Sci Credit Hrs; *cr:* Hopewell Area Sch Dist Tchr 1970-77; Cntrl Greene Sch Dist Math Tcr 1977-; *ai:* NEA, PSEA 1970-; Mathematical Assn Amer 1990-; NCTM, PA Cncl Tchrs of Math, Midwestern Math Cncl of PA 1977-; Cntrl Greene Curr Cncl 1980-; Math Dept Chprsn 1980-; Lead Tchr Cntrl Greene 1991-; Who's Who Amer Ed 1991-; *home:* RR 5 Box 71 Waynesburg PA 15370

HOOVER, MARK FRANCIS, Natural Science Instructor; *b:* Altoona, PA; *ed:* Penn St Univ (BS) Bio 1983; IN Univ Of PA (MS) Bio 1988; Columbia Pacific Univ (PHD) Biological Scis 1991; 22 Credit Hrs Physiology Doctoral Pgm; *cr:* Mt Aloysius Coll Tutorial Specialist for TAPSTAR Pgm 1992-93; Natural Sci Instr 1993-; *ai:* Mt Aloysius Coll Comm Svcs Comm; First Luth Church Altoona 1973-, Sunday Schl Tchr & Supt, Church Cncl; St James Luth Church 1993-, Sunday Schl Tchr; Chrstn Ed Comm; Awd for Tchng Excl Mt Aloysius Coll 1993; *office:* Mount Aloysius College 1 College Dr Cresson PA 16630*

HOOVER, MICHAEL JAY, Language Arts Teacher; *b:* Baltimore, MD; *m:* Sherry Irvine; *c:* Jamie, Bryan, April; *ed:* Univ of MD (BA) Eng 1973; 36 Hrs Masters Equiv Millersville Univ 1981-85; *cr:* St Francis Prep Eng Tchr & Dept Chair 1973-85; South Carroll HS Eng, Lang Arts Tchr 1985-, Wrtng Ctr Co-Dir 1994-; *ai:* Drama & Co-Stage Dir; Literary & Art Magazine Adv; Co-Chair Staff Dev Comm; NCTE 1978-; NEA, MSTA & CCEA 1985-; MAWCA 1994-; *office:* South Carroll HS 1300 W Old Liberty Rd Sykesville MD 21784

HOOVER, NANCY J. (CORDES), Third Grade Teacher; *b:* Napoleon, OH; *c:* Nickolas, Kirk; *ed:* Valparaiso Univ (BS) Ed 1970; Post Grad Stud Bowling Green St Univ, Eastern MI Univ, Northwest St Comm Coll; *cr:* Cook CO #144 4th Grd Tchr 1970-71; Northeastern Local Schls 5th Grd Tchr 1971-74; Patrick Henry Local Schls 3rd, 5th-6th Grd Tchr 1975-; Four Cty Joint Voc Schl ABLE Instr 1993-; *ai:* Curr, In-Svc Comms; OEA, NEA 1971-, Bldg Rep; OH Child Conservation League 1980-, Sec, Cncl Pres; AAL Branch 794 1978-, Pres; COSI Young Experimental Scientist Tchr Intern 1987; *office:* Malinta Elem Schl 204 N Henry St Malinta OH 43535

HOOVER, NANCY ROYER, High School Business Teacher; *b:* Philipsburg, PA; *m:* J. Timothy; *c:* Ashley Marie, Ian Matthew; *ed:* Bloomsburg St Coll (BS) Bus Ed 1983; 35 Credit Hrs; *cr:* West Branch HS Sub Bus Tchr 1984-; Clearfield HS Bus Tchr 1984-; *ai:* PSEA, NEA 1984-; Clearfield Ed Assn 1984-, Mbrshp Chair 1989-91; Westover Ath Assn 1990-, Asst Coach; *office:* Clearfield Area HS PO Box 710 Clearfield PA 16830

HOOVER, RICK LANE, Physical Education Instructor; *b:* Toledo, OH; *m:* Debra; *c:* Chad, Eric; *ed:* Bowling Green St Univ (BA) Kndgtn-Prin Elem Ed 1st-8th Grd & PE K-12th Grd 1974; *cr:* Woodmoore 3rd Grd Tchr 1975-83, 7th & 8th Grd Sci Tchr 1984-87, 3rd Grd Tchr 1988-90, K-6th Grd PE Tchr 1990-; *ai:* Boys & Girls Track, Field & Cross Cntry Asst Coach; Intervention Asst Team; Jump Rope for Your Heart Adv & Coord; NEA 1975-, Bldg Rep; OAHPERD 1990-; Phi Delta Theta 1970-, Pledge Pres; Cub Scouts, Den Ldr, Comm Chrprsn 8 Yrs; BSA, Adv Merit Badge Mem 4 Yrs; Civil War, His Living Group 6 Yrs; Boosters Club 19 Yrs; Sci Fair Judge; Woodmore Tchr of the Yr 1978 & 1981; Martha Holden Jenning Awd 1982-83; 35 Season Longevity Awd Columbus OH; Assn of Track & Field & Cross Cntry 1994; Coach of the Yr 1986-87; *office:* Woodmore Pub Schl System 708 W Main Woodville OH 43469

HOOVER, SHARON, Asst Professor of English; *b:* Evansville, IN; *m:* Dean; *c:* Mark, Hadine Hoover Mandolang, Kimberly; *ed:* Kent St Univ (BS) Eng 1960; MT St Univ (MS) Linguistics, Ed 1969; SUNY at Buffalo (MA) Eng 1990, (PHD) Eng 1992; SUNY at Brockport Schl Admin; Buffalo St Coll Linguistics; *cr:* Alfred-Almond Cntrl Schl Tchr, Prin 1971-78; Freelance Ed, Writer 1978-83; Alfred Univ Assoc Prof, Writing Ctr Dir 1983-; *ai:* Stu Newspaper; Modern Lang Assn 1988-; NCTE 1970-; Narrative Theory 1992-; WCPM 1986-; Western Amer Lit 1988-; ALA 1990-; Rel Soc of Friends; Research Grant, Fellowship; Big Book of Rdng; Numerous SCHLR Tchng Articles; *office:* Alfred University 26 N Main St Alfred NY 14802

HOOVER, STEPHEN J., Retired Science Teacher; *b:* Albany, NY; *m:* Sheila N.; *c:* Kalista Dubiel, Sarah Barnum; *ed:* Hartwick Coll (BA) Bio 1962; Castleton St Coll (MA) Sci Ed 1983; Attnd Univ of MN at Benidji, Worcester Poly Tech, SUNY at Albany, SUNY Plattsburgh; NYS Coll at Env Sci & Forestry; *cr:* Pine Valley CS Sci Tchr 1962-65; Burlington HS Sci Tchr 1965-69; Adirondack Comm Coll Adjunct in Bio 1980-86; South Glens Falls HS Sci Tchr 1970-94; Castleton St Coll Adjunct Botany 1983-96; *ai:* Girls Track, Cross Cty Coach; Stu Cncl, NHS Adv; AFT, NYSST 1970-94; Elks 1991-; Jaycees 1968-, Outstanding Young Educator 1969; Natl Ski Patrol 1975-, Patrol Dir, Regnl Candidate, Adv, Natl Awd #7350; Winter Olympics 1980, Asst Chief Alpine Venue; World Cup 1994, Ski Patrol; Natl Sci Fnd 1965, Worceser Poly Tech; Natl Sci Fnd 1968, Univ of MN at Bemidji.

HOPKINS, BARBARA MC FARLAND, Bible, Soc Stud & Span Tchr; *b:* Fruita, CA; *m:* R. Jay; *c:* Martie; *ed:* Geneva Coll (BA) Span 1967; Soc Stud Cert; Attnd Univ of Madrid Spain Summer Inst; Trinity Episcopal Seminary MAR Candidate; *cr:* Western Beaver Schl Tchr 1967-68; Seneca Vly Schl Tchr 1968-72; Beaver Vly Chrstn Acad Tchr 1980-; *ai:* Fin Comm; ACSI 1980-; ACSI Edctrs Conf Russia; *office:* Beaver Valley Chrn Acad 350 Adams St Rochester PA 15074

HOPKINS, BYRON J., Mathematics Teacher; *b:* Bristol, PA; *m:* Renee F.; *c:* Bryan, Paul, Blake, Grant, Mason; *ed:* Bloomsburg St Univ (BS) Math 1966; Post Grad Ed Temple Univ 1966-68, Penna St Univ 1968-70; *cr:* Pennsbury HS Math Tchr 1966-70; John F. Kennedy HS Math Tchr 1970-74; Willingboro HS Math Tchr 1974-; *ai:* Head Var Bsbl, Asst Boys Var Bsktbl Coaches; NEA 1966-; NJEA, Burlington Co Ed Assn 1970-; Wrote Book Team Baseball 1974; *office:* Willingboro HS John F Kennedy Way Willingboro NJ 08046

HOPKINS, GARY A., 6th Grade Teacher; *b:* Brookville, PA; *m:* Vickie Lynn Zimmerman; *c:* Matthew W., Courtney B.; *ed:* Edinboro Univ of PA (ACSA) Admin, (MED), (BS) Elem Ed; *ai:* NEA; PSEA; CASD; Shrine 1984-; Masons 1984-, PM; *office:* Sparta Elem Schl Water St Spartansburg PA 16434

HOPKINS, JAMES R., Mathematics Teacher; *b:* Baltimore, MD; *m:* S. Elizabeth Williams; *c:* James E., Benjamin R., Jonathan R.; *ed:* Towson St Univ (BS) Math 1966; George Washington Univ Masters Equivalency in Math 1972; 48 Post Grad Credits in Math & Ed Scndry; *cr:* Arundel Jr HS Math Tchr 1966-77; South River HS Math Tchr 1977-; *ai:* Fac Cncl; Finance Comm; NEA, MSTA, TAAAC 1966-; *office:* South River Sr HS 201 E Central Ave Edgewater MD 21037

HOPKINS, JEAN ANN, Junior High Math Teacher; *b:* Poughkeepsie, NY; *m:* John W.; *c:* Robert, Margaret, Matthew, James; *ed:* SUNY at Albany (BS) Math 1970; Attnd William Paterson Coll; *cr:* St Thomas Jr HS Math Tchr 1985-; *ai:* Math Coord; Homeroom Act Monitor; Grad Fundraiser; *office:* St Thomas Apostle School 50 Byrd Ave Bloomfield NJ 07003*

HOPKINS, JOHN GOODWIN, Retired Teacher; *b:* Boston ; *c:* Thomas S., Cynthia C.; *ed:* Harvard Coll (BA) Eng 1954; Univ of VA (MBA) Banking, Fin 1960; Harvard Univ (MA) Ed 1964; *cr:* Peddie Schl Eng Tchr 1960-63; Woodstock Union HS Eng Tchr 1964-66; Cushing Acad Chm, Eng Dept 1966-75; Pike Schl Eng Tchr 1976-94; *ai:* Crotched Mountain Rehab Ctr Tchng Asst Vol.

HOPKINS, MARIE KATHERINE, Special Education Teacher; *b:* Waterbury, CT; *m:* Michael M.; *c:* Seth M.; *ed:* Cntrl CT St Univ (BS) Elem

Ed 1969, (MS) Spec Ed 1972; Fairfield Univ (CAGS) Ed Admin 1986; Univ of CT Post Grad Stud 1989-; *cr:* Spaulding Schl 5th Grd Tchr 1969-70; USAF Dependents Schl Rdng Tchr 1970-71; Saint Marys Schl Jr HS Math Tchr 1972-73; Torrington HS 9th-12th Grd Spec Educator 1978-; Cntrl CT St Univ Dept of Spec Ed Adjunct Fac 1987-; Univ of Hartford Coll of Ed Adjunct Fac 1990-; *ai:* Team Tchng; Curr Comm; 9th Grd Restructuring Comm; Mentor Tchr; Phi Delta Kappa 1985-; CT Educators Assn 1978-; CT Assn for Supervision & Curr Dev 1992-; Waterbury Hospital Auxiliary 1979-; Waterbury Jr League 1975-85, VP; Blessed Sacrament Church 1974-, Parish Cncl Sec; Torrington HS Tchr of Yr 1986; Univ of CT Alumni Tchr Awd 1986-; *office:* Torrington HS Major Besse Dr Torrington CT 06790

HOPKINS, STEPHEN EDWARD, History Teacher; *b:* Philadelphia, PA; *ed:* LaFayette Coll (BA) His 1991; *cr:* Oratory Prep Schl His Tchr 1993-; *ai:* JV Soccer; Yrbk Adv; Chess Club Team; *office:* Oratory Prep Schl 1 Beverly Rd Summit NJ 07901

HOPKINS, THOMAS CLAYTON, Guidance Department Chair; *b:* Houtzdale, PA; *m:* Paulette Jean Motawski; *c:* Thomas, Craig; *ed:* Lock Haven St Univ (BS) Hlth & PE 1965; IN Univ of PA (MED) Guid & Cnslng 1973; *cr:* Bald Eagle Schl Dist Elem PE Tchr 1965-66; Moshannon Vly Jr & Sr HS 8th Grd Soc Stud Tchr 1966-67, PE Tchr 1967-72, Guid Cnslr 1972-; *ai:* Upward Bound Coord; MUEA, PSEA & NEA 1966-; *office:* Moshannon Valley Jr Sr HS RR 1 Box 314 Houtzdale PA 16651

HOPKINS, THOMAS DUVALL, Professor of Economics; *b:* Spring Valley, IL; *m:* Jane Eveleth; *c:* Edward, Catherine; *ed:* Oberlin Coll (BA) Ec 1964; Yale Univ (MA) Ec 1965, (PHD) Ec 1971; *cr:* US Office of Mgmt & Budget Deputy Admin OIRA 1981-84; Univ of MD Visiting Assoc Prof 1984-87; American Univ Assoc Prof of Ec 1987-88; Rochester Inst of Tech Arthur J Gosnell Prof of Ec 1988-; *ai:* Amer Ec Assn 1964-; AAUP 1969-; Phi Beta Kappa; US Admin Conf 1994-95, Pub Mem; Consultant to OECD Paris 1994-; Co-Authored Book Tanker Spills; Lecturer at US Bus Schl in Prague Czech Republic 1992-; Natl Research Cncl Transportation Research Bd Comm; *office:* Rochester Inst Of Tech 92 Lomb Memorial Dr Rochester NY 14623

HOPKINS, THOMAS FRANKLIN, Retired Professor; *b:* Culpepper, VA; *c:* Thea Louise, Thomas M., Charles M., Michael, Arthur G.; *ed:* Calvin Coolidge Coll (BS) Physiology 1955; MI St Univ (MS) Physiology 1971; Boston Univ (PHD) Physiology 1970; *cr:* Worcester Fnd for Experimental Bio Rsrch Tech 1949-59, Rsrch Scientist 1961-70; Univ of CT Assoc Prof of Bio 1970-75; Univ of MD Dept Chm 1975-88, Prof 1975-94; *ai:* Chipman Cultural Ctr Exec Dir; EPA Consultant; Amer Physiological Soc 1961-; NSTA; NSF; Population Cncl; UCONN Rsrch Fnd; EPA; Natl Marine Fisheries; Articles Pub; *home:* 1602 Camden Ave Salisbury MD 21801

HOPKINSON, CONSTANCE MC KINNEY, Learning Support Teacher; *b:* Columbia, PA; *m:* Myron D. Bird; *c:* Michael; *ed:* Millersvillea Univ (BS) Spec, Elem Ed 1967; 25 Addl Credits; Trained Teach TESA; Trained Serve on SAP Teams; *cr:* Jackson Elem Schl Tchr of Mentally Retarded 1967-70; Ferguson Elem Schl Emotional Support Tchr 1970-73; Cntrl York HS LS Tchr 1980-; *ai:* SADD Adv; Alternative Assessment Comm; NEA, PSEA 1967-; CYEA 1980-, Bldg Rep; DUI Advy Bd 1987-, VP; Amer Assn of Univ Women, VP, Ed Chm; Underage Drinking Forum, Kid's Expo 1990-; Cooperating Tchr of Yr 1985, 1996; Cntrl York Schl Dist Tchr of Yr; Enrique Camarena One Person Can Make a Difference Awd 1994; TREND Ldrshp, MADD Comm Awds 1995; CEC St Convention Speaker; *office:* Central York HS 300 E 7th Ave York PA 17404*

HOPPLE, MARY WEAVER, Science Educator; *b:* Lock Haven, PA; *m:* Gary R.; *c:* Jason M., Patrick L.; *ed:* Lock Haven Univ (BS) Chem, Bio 1981; Divine Providence Schl of Medical Tech Cert 1982; Penn St Addl 6 Cr 1992, 4 Cr 1994; *cr:* Jersey Shore Hospital Medical Technologist 1982-84; Divine Providence Hospital Medical Technologist 1984-87; PA Coll of Tech Anatomy, Physiology Lab Instr 1989-91; Jersey Shore Sr HS Sci Educator 1990-; *ai:* Jr Class, Envirothon Adv; Asst Jr High Girls Bsktbl Coach; Grad Criteria, Intensive Scheduling Comms; Site Based Decision Making Comm Archivist; Fac Rep; NSTA 1993-; NEA, PSEA 1990-; JSAEA 1190-, Fac Rep; NSF Grant to Attnd Penn St 1992; *office:* Jersey Shore Area Sr HS 201 S Broad St Jersey Shore PA 17740*

HOPPMANN, PETER C., English Teacher & Coach; *b:* Milwaukee, WI; *ed:* Univ of WI at Madison (BA) His 1986; Long Island Univ (MA) Eng Lit 1995; *cr:* Chengdo Univ of Sci & Tech Eng Tchr 1987-88; Long Island Univ TA 1992-95; JHS 258 Eng Tchr 1989-; *ai:* Girls Bsktbl Coach; Bedford-Stuyvesant Lions Club Tchr of the Yr 1992.

HOPSON, WILLIAM ALBERT, Head Teacher; *b:* Point Pleasant, NJ; *m:* Susanne M. Fenimore; *c:* Lori Bates, William Jr., Valerie Bills, Robert Bausum, Lauren Zanella, Kimberly Bausum; *ed:* Univ of DE (BS) Bus Admin 1956; Monmouth Coll (MED) Schl Admin 1974; *cr:* US Naval Reserve Supply & Fiscal Ofcr 1956-60; Cntrl Regnl HS Math & Sci Tchr 1961-62; LaVallette Elem Schl Tchr & Head Tchr 1962-; *ai:* Sci Curr Coord; Tech Comm; NEA 1962-; NJEA 1962-; LaVallette EA 1962-, Pres, VP & Negotiation Chair; Seaside Hghts Vol Fire Co 1960-, LT & Sec; Concerned Citizens of Brick 1990-, Treas; Governors Tchr Recognition Awd 1987-88; LaVallette Founders Day Awd 1994; *office:* Lavallette Elem Schl 105 Brooklyn Ave Lavallette NJ 08735

HORAN, DIANE WHITEHEAD, Associate Professor of English; *b:* Philadelphia, PA; *m:* William R. Sr.; *c:* James W., William Jr.; *ed:* Glassboro St Coll (BA) Eng, Ed 1964; Villanova Univ (MA) Eng, Lit 1966; Post-Grad Credits Lehigh Univ 9, Temple Univ 6, Northeastern Univ 3; *cr:* William Tennent HS Eng Tchr 1964-65; Villanova Univ Grad Asst 1965-66; Cntrl Bucks HS-West Eng Tchr 1966-68; Montgomery Cty Comm Coll Eng Tchr 1968-; *ai:* AFT 1980-; *office:* Montgomery County Comm Coll 340 Dekalb Pike Blue Bell PA 19422*

HORAN, JOHN THOMAS, Social Studies Dept Chair; *b:* New York, NY; *m:* Eleanor Goeller; *c:* Sean; *ed:* St Peters Coll (BA) His 1972; Seton Hall Univ (MA) His 1974; Rutgers Univ (EDM) Educl Admin 1980-; Thomas Edison Coll 3 Credit Hrs Ec; Jersey City St Coll 6 Credit Hrs Eng; Raritan Vly Coll 12 Credit Hrs Comp Programming; *cr:* US Army Reserve, Military Police Ofcr 1974-80; Jersey City Pub Schls Sub Tchr 1974-75; Seton Hall U Law Schl Evening Admin 1976-78; Oratory Prep Schl Tchr, Dept Chair, Asst Headmaster, Tech Coord 1976-; *ai:* Comp Club Moderator; Bowling Team Coach; Amer His Assn 1975-; NCEA 1985-; St John Neumann Parish 1983-, Cantor, Rel Ed Tchr; Lebanon Twp Ath Assn 1988-, Coach; BSA 1989-, Troop Comm Chair; Oratory Prep Newark Archdioscese Tchr of the Yr 1995 & 1996 Nom; *office:* Oratory Prep Schl 1 Beverly Rd Summit NJ 07901*

HORAN, MIKE, Oceanography Teacher; *b:* Phila, PA; *m:* Barbara J. Moore; *c:* Brian; *ed:* Penn St (BS) Chem, Sec Ed 1973; 15 Addl Hrs; 3 Hrs Fairfield Univ, Glassboro Univ; *cr:* Ocean City HS Sci Tchr 1979-80; Absegami Sci Tchr 1980-83; Oakcrest HS Sci Tchr 1980-83; Stockton St Coll Adj Math Tchr 1983-84; Egg Harbor Twp HS Sci Tchr 1983-; *ai:* Hiking Club Adv; NEA 1973-; NJEA 1979-; Marine Mammal Stranding Ct 1978-; Cub Scouts 1994-, Cub Master; Beachcomber Guid SIC 1993-; Audubon Field Ecology Wkshp 1987; Regnl Environmental Ed Prgm 1990; NOAA Tchr at Sea Prgm 1993; Articles Pub; *office:* Egg Harbor Twp HS 24 High School Dr Egg Harbor Townshi NJ 08234

HORAN, TOM, High School Musical Director; *b:* Staten Island, NY; *m:* Martha Hill; *c:* Amelia, Thomas; *ed:* Lowell St Coll (BMUS) Classical Guitar 1975; Post Grad Stud in Motivation, Discipline & Legal; *cr:* Franco Amer Schl Music Tchr 1976-77; Amesbury MS Music Tchr 1977-89; Amesbury HS Music Dir 1989-; *ai:* Pep, Marching, Concert & Jazz Band Dir; Concert Choir & Select Chorus Dir; MENC 1979-; *office:* Amesbury HS 5 Highland St Amesbury MA 01913

HORAN, VIRGINIA ELIZABETH, Asst Prof of Communications; *b:* Bay Shore, NY; *m:* James G.; *c:* Ryan James; *ed:* Univ of Dayton (BA) Comm 1987; NY Univ (MA) Speech Comm 1991; 9 Credits Hum; *cr:* NY Univ Adj Instr 1990; Suffolk Comm Coll Asst Prof 1991-; *ai:* Curr, Enrollment Mngmt Comms 1994-; Speech Comm Assn 1990-; *office:* Suffolk Comm Coll Western Cmps Crooked Hill Road Brentwood NY 11717

HORAN KNEIS, SHARON TERESA, Reading & Social Studies Tchr; *b:* Paterson, NJ; *m:* Paul Emil; *c:* Matthew Paul; *ed:* William Paterson Coll (BA) Elem Ed, Tchr of Handicapped 1975; Grad Credits Jersey City St Coll, St Peter's Coll; *cr:* Franklin Elem Schl Fifth Grd Tchr 1975-80; Washington Elem Schl 2nd, 6th Grd Tchr 1982-86; Lincoln MS 6-8 Grd Rdng, Soc Stud Tchr 1986-; *ai:* Eighth Grd, Stu Cncl, Var Clubs Adv; Hawthorne Tchrs Assn 1975-, Sec, 2nd VP: Passaic Cty Ed Assn 1975-, Cty Rep; North Jersey Intnl Rdng Assn 1989-; *office:* Lincoln MS Hawthorne Ave Hawthorne NJ 07506

HORCHLER, JUDITH BECK, Social Studies Chairman; *b:* Sandusky, OH; *m:* Jeffrey; *c:* Todd; *ed:* OH Univ (BSEd) His & Govt 1972; Bowling Green St Univ (MA) His 1980; Natl Geographic Soc Summer Inst 6 Credit Hrs at Univ of MO; *cr:* Fremont Ross Soc Stud Tchr 1972-76; St Marys Cntrl Cath Soc Stud Chair 1978-83; Huron HS Soc Stud Chair 1984-; Bowling Green St Univ Geog Instr 1996; *ai:* Geog Club; Comms: Action, Grant, Restructuring; NCSS & OCSS 1972-, St Advy Bd; OEA 1972-; PDK 1980-; DKG 1985-; NCGE 1992-; OH Geographic Alliance Bd Mem 1991-; Milan Historical Museum 1991-, Trustee; Natl Geographic Soc Summer Inst Recipient; Wrote 15 Sociology Lessons for Textbook Publisher; Natl Endowment for Hum Russian Inst; NAEP Geog Stan Setting Team; NCGE Natl Conf Presenter 1994; *office:* Huron HS 710 Cleveland Rd W Huron OH 44839

HORDINER, LINDA ZIMMERMAN, Biology Teacher; *b:* New York City, NY; *m:* Charles H.; *c:* David E.; *ed:* Brandeis Univ (BA) Bio 1964; Harvard Univ (MAT) Ed 1965; 60 Hrs In Service Stud Herricks Tchr Center, Summer Wkshps Curr Dev, Recombinant DNA Wkshps Cold Spring Harbor Laboratory, Adelphi Univ Stud Physiology of Exercise; *cr:* Driscoll Schl Sci Tchr 1965; Herricks HS Bio Tchr 1965-; *ai:* Herricks Tchrs Assn 1965-, HS Rep 1991-; AFT, NEA, NYSUT 1965-; Mem Comm To Dev First Lab Manual Molecular Bio Recombinant DNA Beginners at Cold Spring Harbor Lab CSH NY; Dev Curr Physiology Exercise & Medical Tech Summer Wkshp; Dev Sci Research Prgm at Herricks HS; Natl Sci Fnd Leadership Institute in Human and Molecular Genetics 1993; Planning Activities to Train Tchrs in DNA SciTchr od DNA Courses in Local Tchr Cntr; Dev 5th Grd DNA-Genetics Curr for Dist; *office:* Herricks H S Shelter Rock Rd New Hyde Park NY 11040

HORENSTEIN, MARK N., Electrical Engrng Assoc Prof; *ed:* MIT (SB) Electrical Eng 1973; UC at Berkeley (MS) Electrical Eng 1975; MIT (PHD) Electrical Eng 1978; *cr:* Boston Univ Asst Prof 1979, Assoc Prof 1986; *ai:* Amateur Radio Club Adv; Electrical Engrng Sr Design Projects; IEEE 1978-; Excl in Tchng of Engrng Stdnts Awd 1984; Tchr of Yr 1980; Author Micro Electronic Circuits and Devices 1996; *office:* Boston Univ 44 Cummington St Boston MA 02215

HORGAN, JUDITH MARCIA (HARRIS), First Grade Teacher; *b:* Fitchburg, MA; *m:* Michael J.; *c:* Kelly K., Michael J., Tara Horgan Hanley; *ed:* Fitchburg St Coll (BSEd) Ed 1972, (MED) Rdng 1978; 25 Addl In-Service & Grad Credit Hrs; *cr:* Spaulding Meml Schl Primary Grds Tchr 1972-; *ai:* Staff Club Pres; North Middlesex Regnl Schl Dist Tchrs Assn, MA Tchrs Assn, NEA 1972-; *office:* Spaulding Memorial Schl 1 Whitcomb St Townsend MA 01469

HORGAN, MICHAEL H., Health & Spanish Teacher; *b:* Chelsea, MA; *m:* Judith April; *ed:* Salem St Coll (MA) His 1989; Cert 5-12 Hlth; *cr:* Marblehead HS Soc Stud Tchr 1989-94, Span Tchr 1992-, Hlth Tchr 1993-; *ai:* Model UN & Young Democrats Adv; Tobacco Cessation & Ed Adv; Span Rdng Group Facilitator; Soccer Coach; Gender Equity Stud Comm; Natl His Tchrs Hnr Soc 1989-; NEA, MA TA & Marblehead TA 1989-; MA DOE Safe Schls Comm; *office:* Marblehead HS Duncan Sleigh Sq Marblehead MA 01945*

HORLANDER, JUDITH ANN, Math & Algebra Teacher; *b:* Port Arthur, TX; *m:* Dennis; *c:* Holly, Daniel; *ed:* Stephen F. Austin St Univ (BS) Math 1972; Post-Grad Stud Wright St Univ at Dayton, Bowling Green St Univ & DISCOVERY PROJECT 1995 at Lima; *cr:* St Gerard Schl 6-8th Grd Math & Sci Tchr 1984-86; St Charles Schl 7-8th Math & Algebra Tchr 1986-; *ai:* Math Counts Coach; Math Curr Comm Chprsn; NCTM 1992-; OCTM 1991-; GTCTM 1995-; Outstanding Tchr 1990; *office:* Saint Charles Schl 2175 W Elm St Lima OH 45805

HORN, DAVID E., Professor of Chemistry; *b:* Palmerton, PA; *m:* Susan Martin; *c:* Jennifer, Amanda; *ed:* Franklin & Marshall Coll (BA) Chem 1962; Villanova Univ (MS) Biochemistry 1964; Univ of VT (PHD) Organic Chem 1967; Loyola COll of MD (MBA) Mngmt 1983; *cr:* Goucher Coll Asst Prof 1967-73, Assoc Prof 1973-79, Prof of Chem 1979-; Univ of VT Visiting Prof, Summer 1975-; *ai:* Am Chemical Soc 1967-; York Yth Symphony, Pres 1989-91; *office:* Goucher Coll Towson MD 21204

HORN, DAVID THOMAS, 12th Grade AP English Teacher; *b:* Philadelphia, PA; *ed:* Georgetown Univ (BSFS) Intnl Affairs 1960; Univ of PA (MA) His, Philosophy 1961; Balliol Coll (MA) Phil, British His 1965; Post Grad Stud Harvard Univ 1966; *cr:* Freedoms Fnd Seminar Ldr, Tchr on Constitution 1974-78; Chestnut Hill Coll Lecturer, Pub Speaking Seminar 1978-88; Bishop Mc Devitt HS Eng Fac 1961-; *ai:* Dir Churchilliam Forensic Soc 1965-92; Admin Century III, Hoby Awd 1985; Moderator World Affairs Club 1992-; NCFL 1965-, Natl Pres; Natl Conf Eng Tchrs, Natl Comms Soc 1961-; Knights of St Lazarus 1986-; Philadelphia Georgraphic Soc 1965-; Alliance Francaise, Eng Speaking Union 1990-; Finalist Distngd Cath Edctr Archdiocese of Phila 1989-90; George Washington Medal Freedoms Fnd; Natl Tchng Awd 1974; Rochambeau Medal Knight of St Lazaros 1986; Triest Medal 1987; *home:* 7720 Doe Ln Glenside PA 19038*

HORN, JAMES BERNARD, Social Studies Teacher; *b:* Columbia, PA; *m:* Ann Katherine Hilton; *c:* Katelyn Marie, James Francis; *ed:* Mt St Mary's Coll (BS) Soc Stud & Ed 1982; Attnd Western MD coll & Millersville St Coll; *cr:* South Carroll High Soc Stud Tchr 1982-; *ai:* Head Girls Soccer Coach; Schl Improvement & Climate Comms; Prime Time Chm; Coord for South Carroll of Congressional Natl Yng Ldrs Conf; Stud Recognition Comm; Schl Climate Comm; MD Assn of Soc Stud 1989-; MD Assn of Coaches of Soccer 1992-, Women's VP; MD St Soccer Comm 1992-, Carroll Cty Rep; Natl Soccer Coaches Assn of Amer; Carroll Cty Coach of Yr 1992, 1995; MD Soccer Coach of Yr 1994; *office:* South Carroll HS 1300 W Old Liberty Rd Sykesville MD 21784

HORN, MARTI MEYER, Teacher of the Gifted; *b:* Allentown, PA; *m:* John Alden; *c:* Todd Gavin, Jonathan Meyer; *ed:* Kutztown Univ (BS) Elem Ed 1961; 40 Addl Post Grad Hrs Masters Equivlency Millersville Univ, Temple Univ; *cr:* Kutztown AreaSchls 3rd Grd Tchr 1961-62; Upper perkiomen Schl Dist Kndgtn Tchr 1970-77, 5th-8th Grd Tchr of Gifted 1977-; *ai:* Paideia Comm Chprsn; Russian Stud Group Adv; 8th Grd Future Problem Solving Coach; Blue Ribbon Comm 1993; Peer Coaching; U PSEA, NEA 1970-; PA Gifted Ed Assn 1977-, Runner Up Outstar Gifted PA Tchr 1986; Village Calligraphers Guild 1984-; Upper Perki PA Gifted Parent Assn 1988-, Bd Adv; Stud Schls Russia, Hungry Awded 4 Schl Dist Mini Grants; Took Stdnts to Russia, Netherlands Sweden 1995, Scotland & Eng 1996; Snag in the River Awd by DE V Assn 1994; *office:* Upper Perkiomen MS Jefferson St East Greenvill 18041

HORN, PAMELA VIVIAN, Foreign Language Teacher; *b:* New Roc NY; *ed:* Hunter (BA) Fr 1969, (MA) Fr 1971; Fordham (MA) Span Stonybrook (MA) Ger 1984; Coll of New Rochelle (MS) Guid, C 1992, (PD) Admin, Supervision 1995; *cr:* Concordia Coll Sp, Fr 1971-74; Mamaroneck HS Tchr 1974-; *ai:* Mentor Sr Project Int WPRC, W Cncl Self Esteem 1993-; AHTG; ATTS; ATTF; Mamar Tchr Inst, Learning Disabled Child, Self Esteem Grants; *o* Mamaroneck HS 1000 W Boston Post Rd Mamaroneck NY 10543

HORN, SANDRA (BOOTH), Med Lab Technician & Instr; *b:* Paints KY; *m:* Otas Jackson; *c:* Jennifer, Hulbert, Leslie Ann; *ed:* Pikeville (BS) Med Tech 1969; Cntrl MI Univ (MS) Hlth Admin 1989; *cr:* Cla Comm Coll Instr 1985-; Comm Hosp Schl of Nrsng Instr 1986-88; *ai:* St Med Lab Technicians Advy, Curr Comms; ASCP 1969-; Adj Fac T Excl Awd; *office:* Clark State Comm Coll 570 E Leffel Ln Springfie 45505

HORN, T. SCOTT, Chemistry Teacher; *b:* Amityville, NY; *m:* Kar Williams; *c:* Julie A., Matthew S.; *ed:* Oswego St (BS) Ed; Johns Ho (MS) Admin, Curr & Supervision 1985; *cr:* Kenwood HS Chem 1976-78; Lakeland MS 8th Grd Sci Tchr 1978-83; Goddard MS 8th Gr Tchr 1985-93; Roosevelt HS Chem Tchr 1993-; *ai:* PGCEA 1985-; 1995-; *office:* Eleanor Roosevelt HS 7601 Hanover Pky Greenbelt 20770

HORNBECK, MARIANNE MASSI, Computer Science Teache Ashtabula, OH; *m:* James Keith; *c:* Ryan, Joshua, Tyler; *ed:* Kent St (BSEd) Math, Elem Ed 1977; Post Grad Stud Cmptr Tech 1980-93; Ashtabula HS Math Tchr 1977-82; Kent St Univ Cmptr Tech Tchr 198 Part-Time Cmptr Tech Tchr 1984-; Ashtabula-Harbor HS Cmptr Sci 1984-87; Harbor HS Cmptr Sci Tchr 1987-; *ai:* Tech Team; KSU Ashta Cmptr Tech Advy Comm; NEA, OEA, Ashtabula Tchrs Assn 1977-; Processing Mngmt Assn 1988-, Bd Mem; *office:* Harbor HS 221 Lake Ashtabula OH 44004

HORNBECKER, CHARLES ROBERT, Psychology & Govern Tchr; *b:* Hagerstown, MD; *m:* Donna Lynn Middlekauff; *c:* Brian, Ama *ed:* Hagerstown Jr Coll (AA) Ed 1970; Towson St Univ (BS) Soc; Equivalency Western MD Coll, Mount St Marys Coll; *cr:* S Hagerstown HS Tchr 1973-; *ai:* Cross Cntry Coach, Track Asst C Acting Dept Chair; WA Co Tchrs Assn, MD St Tchrs Assn, NEA 1 MCSS 1993-; Wildcat Acad Boosters 1993-, VP; Wildcat Ath Boo 1995-; Rebel Action Cncl 1973-; *home:* 10829 Clinton Ave Hagers MD 21740

HORNBERGER, DANIEL LUKE, English Teacher; *b:* Reading, PA Virginia E. Jackubowski; *c:* Elizabeth, Jean Louise, Thomas; *ed:* Te Univ (BA) Comm, Radio, TV, Film 1984; Millersville Univ Eng Ed 1990; Lehigh Univ 16 Hrs Educl Leadership; *cr:* US Tennis Assn Video Producer, Dir 1985-89; Schuylkill Valley Schl Dist HS Eng 1992-; *ai:* Var Girls, Boys Tennis Coach; Acad Challenge Coach, NEA, PSEA 1992-; NCTE 1994-; *office:* Schuylkill Valley HS RR 2 2165 Leesport PA 19533

HORNBERGER, PAUL M., Fifth Grade Teacher; *b:* Buffalo, NY Dawn Vara-Hornberger; *c:* Chad Mikel; *ed:* SUNY at Fredonia (B Elem Ed 1988, (MSEd) Curr Instruction 1992; *cr:* Lake Shore Cntrl S Grd 5 Tchr 1988-91, Kndgtn Tchr 1991-94, Grd 5 Tchr 1994-; *ai:* NY AFT 1988-; *office:* JT Waugh Intermediate Schl 100 High St Angola 14006

HORNCASTLE, MEGAN ABBOTT, English Teacher; *b:* Peasen England; *m:* Terence; *ed:* Univ of Nottingham (BED) Ed-Honors Miami Univ at Oxford (MED) Ed; St Osyths Coll Cert Ed in Eng & 1978; *cr:* Westbourne HS-U K Eng Tchr 1978-79; The Hatton Schl-u K Tchr 1979-83; The Darwin Schl-U K Eng Tchr 1983-85; Lakota HS Tchr 1985-; *ai:* NEA; *office:* Lakota HS 5050 Tylersville Rd West Ch OH 45069*

HORNE, DAVID CHARLES, Music Teacher; *b:* Warren, PA; Lafayette Coll (AB) Intnl Affairs 1978; *cr:* St Mary's Parish Music 1980-84; Taft Schl Choral Dir 1984-88; Best Intnl ESL Instr 1988-90; Trinity Schl & Parish Choral Music, Mass Music Dir 1990-; *ai:* Choruses; Liturgy Comm; Mid Sts Decenial Evaluation Steering Co Sec; Christmas Show; Spring Show; Phi Mu Alpha 1975-; Phi Alpha T 1978-; AFM 1981-; Poly Hymnia 1993-.*

HORNE, LORI JO (BUTZ), Third Grade Teacher; *b:* Urbana, OH Aaron; *ed:* Bowling Green St Univ (BS) Elem Ed K-8 1976; Addl Miami Univ at Oxford; *cr:* Urbana City Schls Sixth Grd Tchr 1976 Ross Local Schls Third, Fourth Grd Tchr 1979-; *ai:* NEA, OEA, 1976-; *office:* Morgan Elementary 3427 Chapel Rd Hamilton OH 450

HORNE, PATRICIA CLEMMONS, Second Grade Teacher; Williamston, NC; *c:* Pamela, Michael; *ed:* Nassau Comm Coll (AS) 1972; Hofstra Univ (BA) Elem Ed 1975, (MS) Spec Ed 1985; Hempstead Schl Dist #1 Tchr 23 Yrs; *ai:* NY St Tchrs Assn; Ordai Minister 1996; Sunday Schl Tchr 1984-; *home:* 388 Pennsylvania Freeport NY 11520*

HORNE, RITA LITZINGER, 2nd Grade Teacher; *b:* Johnstown, PA; Francis A.; *c:* Dennis, Kathryn Reeser; *ed:* 30 Post Grad Credit Hrs; Queen of Peace Parish Dir of Rel Ed 26 Yrs; *ai:* Area Aerobic Dance T 1984-92; Lifetime Sports Project Dir 1974-77; Delta Kappa Gam Recording Sec; Rel Edctr of the Yr Awd in Altoona-Johnstown Dioc 1976; *office:* Cambria Heights Elem Schl 1 E Campbell St Carrolltown 15722

HORNER, ANN PETRAK, Sixth Grade Teacher; *b:* Nyack, NY; Joseph F. (dec); *c:* Joseph S., Kristie, Katie; *ed:* SUNY at Oswego Elem Ed 1962; SUNY at New Paltz (MS) Elem Ed 1987; 24 Addl Hrs; Ramapo 1 Schl Fifth Grd Tchr 1962-63; South Orangetown Cntrl S Sixth Grd Tchr 1963-64; Monroe Woodbury Cntrl Schl Fourth Grd T 1973-78, 1981-94, Third GrdTchr 1979-81, Sixth Grd Tchr 1994-; *ai:* S Bldg Team; Sixth Grd Yrbk; Souza Schlsp Plays Stage M Monroe-Woodbury Tchr Assn, Sr Bldg Rep; NYSUT 1973-; AFT; Cntrl United Meth Church 1980-, Sunday Schl Tchr, Choir; *office:* North M Street Elem Schl 212 N Main St Monroe NY 10950

HORNER, BARBARA L., Third Grade Teacher; *b:* Johnstown, PA; Terry; *c:* Michelle; *ed:* Clairon Univ (BS) Elem Ed 1969; *ai:* PSEA, N 1969-; *office:* United Schl Dist PO Box 168 Armagh PA 15920

HORNER, DONALD H., Chemistry & Physics Teacher; *b:* Ft Worth, *m:* Susan Mc Grath; *c:* Sean, Andy, Megan; *ed:* Univ of Rochester (Sci, Chem 1971, (MS) Ed, Sci Curr 1976; 6 Credit Hrs Excl in Tchng Sci Fnd Fellowship; Environmental Research SUNY at Brockport & Sci Fnd Fellowship; *cr:* Brighton HS Sci Tchr 1971; East Rochester HS Tchr 1971-78; Fairpot HS Sci Tchr 1978-; *ai:* Boys Var Soccer Coach; B Rep; Soccer Ultramural Coord; Past Sr, Jr, Soph Class Adv; NY St Uni Tchrs 1971-, Pres, VP, Grievance Chm, East Rochester Tchrs A

78; Natl Soccer Coaches of Amer 1988-; St of New Sci Sci Tchrs Org -; Love the Children 1982-; Fellowship Cmptr Applications in room Ithaca Coll & Natl Sci Fnd 1990; Grant Scientific Research of Rochester's Ctr for Photo Induced Charge Research Natl Sci Fnd Writer Regnets Physics Questions 1990, 1992; Internship Career Ed *office:* Fairport HS 1358 Ayrault Rd Fairport NY 14450*

NER, KEITH WILLIAM, Social Studies Teacher; *b:* Paulding, OH; nnie Lea; *ed:* OH St Univ (BS) Soc Stud Ed 1990; Univ of Dayton Educl Admin 1995; *cr:* Lima City Schls Tchr 1991-; *ai:* Var Asst Ftbl; rd Boys Bsktbl; Acad Adv.

NICK, CHRIS C., Band Director; *b:* Johnstown, PA; *m:* Mary Louise ns; *c:* Christy, Matthew, Ryan; *ed:* Indiana Univ of PA (BS) Music Ed , PA St Univ (MM) Music Ed 1971; *cr:* Allentown Schl Dist Elem umental Dir 1968-69; Connellsville Area Schl Dist Elem Instrumental 969-73; Connellsville Jr HS East Band Dir 1973-; *ai:* Marching Band, Ensemble Dir; CAEA, PSEA, NEA 1969-, Comm, Chm; PMEA 1973-; 1990-; YMCA Bsktbl 1992-, Coach; Music Confs Symphonic Band rm MENC Eastern Division 1993, PMEA St 1995; PMEA News zine Adjudication Article; California Univ of PA Jazz 1993; Jazz East Promising Ensemble; *office:* Connellsville Jr HS East Locust St Ext ellsville PA 15425

NICK, MARIE FUNICELLO, HS English Teacher; *b:* Glens Falls, *n:* William F.; *c:* Daniel Aton, Adam Nathan; *ed:* Coll of St Rose (BA) 1965; Univ of MN (MA) Amer Stud 1969; 45 Hrs Interdisciplinary ce; 6 Hrs Grad Credits Amer Stud Fellowship Eastern Bapt Coll 1966; s Grad Credits Syracuse Univ Advanced Composition Stud 1991; *cr:* e-Savannah Cntrl Schl 9-12 Grd Scndry Eng Tchr 1965-68; heesville Cntrl Schl 10-12 Grd Scndry Eng Tchr 1969-74; Schalmont Schl 11-12,Grd Coll Fr Scndry Eng Tchr 1982; Syracuse Univ nct Prof; *ai:* NHS, Stdnt Forum Adv; HS Bldg Planning Team for based Decision Making, Co-Chrprsn; NCTE 1965-; Schalmont Tchrs 1982-, Bldg Rep 1992; AFT 1992-; NYS Eng Cncl 1995-; *office:* lmont HS 1 Sabre Dr Schenectady NY 12306*

RNICK, NORMA MURDOCK, Elementary Music Teacher; *b:* eesport, PA; *m:* Michael P.; *c:* Sally, James; *ed:* Indiana Univ of PA Music Ed 1971; PA St Univ 24 Credits Ed 1972-74; Duquesne Univ edits Music Ed 1974, 3 Credits 1995; Master's Equivalency 8 Credits 992; *cr:* West Mifflin Area SD Jr HS General Music, Choral Tchr -72; Greater Latrobe Area SD Jr HS General Music Tchr 1972-74; ver United Meth Church Children's Music Coord 1982-90; South Side SD Elem General Music Tchr 1990-; *ai:* Girl Scout, 4-H Ldr; NEA -74; PSEA, SSEA 1990-; MENC, PMEA 1971-; Amer Assn of Univ nen; Beaver United Meth Church 1974-; Western Beaver HS Band nts Assn 1988-; North Amer Gladiola Cncl 1988-, Judge; PA Gladiola 1986-, Pres 1989; PTA 1990; Amer Autism Assn 1992; Delta Omicron ic; GAMA-NAMM Guitar Schlsp 1995; *home:* 303 Ridgemont Dr stry PA 15052

RNICK, STEPHANIE BALTA, Kindergarten Teacher; *b:* Camp une, NC; *m:* Ronald; *c:* Brandon; *ed:* Univ of Pittsburgh (BS) Elem Ed , (MED) Rdng Ed 1996; *cr:* St Agnes Schl 6th Grd Tchr 1988-91; The les Tale Cnslng Ctr Prevention Specialist 1991-92; Pittsburgh Pub s Tchr 1992-; *ai:* PFT & AFT 1992-; IRA 1995-; NSTA 1995-; *office:* Cleary Elem Schl 5251 Holmes St Pittsburgh PA 15201*

RNING, JOHN BYRON, English Teacher; *b:* Ridgway, PA; *ed:* knell Univ (BA) Eng 1977; Addl 3 Credits 1977; 30 Credits Mansfield / 1977-86; 9 Credits Williamsport Area Comm Coll North Campus 3-84; *cr:* Mansfield Jr Sr HS Eng Tchr & Coach 1977-; *ai:* Mansfield / Mens Bsktbl Asst Coach; Fac Cncl; PSEA, Southern Tioga Tchrs Assn 7-, Union Rep; NEA 1977-; Masonic Lodge 1989-; *home:* RR 3 Box 3 Mansfield PA 16933

RNING, ROBERT C.,II, High School Band Director; *b:* Elmira, NY; llen Hyde; *ed:* Mansfield St Coll (BSME) Music Ed-Cum Laude 1982; sfield Univ (MA) Music-Summa Cum Laude 1985; *cr:* Pub Schls in WV, NJ, NY Instrumental Music Tchr 1982-90; Campbell-Savona Cntrl Instrumental Music Tchr 1990-; *ai:* Directs 2 Concert Bands, 2 Jazz ds, Saxophone Quartet, Woodwind & Brass Quintet, Panther Marching ; Weekly Instrumental Music Lessons; Music Edctrs Natl 1982-; NY f St Schl Music Assn 1988-; Steuben Cty Music Tchrs Assn 1990-; BSA 1-, Eagle Scout Awd, God & Cntry Awd; Order of Arrow 1976-, Vigil n; Directed HS Band Tours of Canada, CA, Mexico; Major Natl Parades icipation; Small & Medium Class Marching Units 1st Place Awds in l-Western NY; Musicology & Pedagogy Stu of Dr. William M. Goode; *ne:* 18 Gratton Dr Bath NY 14810*

RNISH, DONALD THOMAS,JR., Social Studies Teacher; *b:* Milford, *m:* Donna Magdee; *ed:* Seton Hall Univ (BS) Ed 1971; Rutgers Univ ED) Ed 1980; ABD Soc Stud Ed; NEH Grant So Asian Stud Columbia v 1992-93; Holocaust Ed, Prejudice Reduction Stud Kean Coll; *cr:* rris Cath HS Soc Stud Tchr, Track Coach 1971-72; Westfield HS Soc d Tchr, Track, Cross Cntry Coach 1973-; *ai:* Coach: Var Girls Cross ry 1978-, Track 1978-91, Winter Track 1976081; Asst Coach: Var Girls ck 1991-, Cross Cntry 1973-78; NEA, NJEA, WEA, NCSS 1973-; stfield Adult Schl 1989-, Instr; Track Friends 1980-, Advy Bd; Sts Peter aul RO Church 1980-, Bd of Dirs Chm; PTO Tchr of Yr 1988; Selected Attend NJ Tchr Enrichment Prgm Princeton Univ, Monmouth Coll; ader ETS AP European His Exam 1995-; Star Ldr Courier News Union 1995; Cross Cnrty of Yr; *office:* Westfield HS 550 Dorian Rd Westfield 07090*

RNSPERGER, ELLEN L., Business Education Teacher; *b:* Dayton, ; *m:* Karl J.; *ed:* Bowling Green St Univ (BS) Bus Ed 1971; *cr:* Fremont ss HS Bus Tchr 1971-, Bus Dept Chair 1982-; *ai:* Various Comms; OH s Tchrs Assn; NEA; OH Ed Assn, Fremont Ed Assn 1971-; Sports Car b of Amer 1977-; *office:* Fremont Ross HS 1100 North St Fremont OH 420

RNYAK, DEBRA LOUISE, Third Grade Teacher; *b:* Bay Village, OH; Cumberland Coll (BS) Elem Ed 1979; Bowling Green St Univ (MS) m Ed 1988; 15 Credit Hrs; *cr:* Oakwood Elem Schl 2nd Grd Tchr 79-94, 3rd Grd Tchr 1994-; *ai:* Girl Scouts; Yth for Christ Vol; Yth Act Bible Schl Church; NEA 1979-; OEA 1979-; PEA 1979-; Yth for Christ Mem 1992-, Sec; Girl Scouts 1994-, Ldr.

ROHOE, MARTHA MARY, French & Spanish Teacher; *b:* Buffalo, ; *m:* Keith Dackson; *ed:* Grove City Coll (BA) Fr, His 1981; Purdue iv (MA) Fr 1984; Working Doctoral Dissertation Modern Lang Fr, Span ddlebury Coll; Attnd Universite de Nice, Universide de Grenoble, Amer iv of Paris; Tchng Eng as Frgn Lang Pilgrim's of Canterbury England; an Intnl House Barcelona Spain; Humboldt Inst Ger; *cr:* Grove City Coll m Seminar Ldr 1979-80; Purdue Univ Fr Tchng Asst 1981-83; Leysin ner Schl Fr, ESL Tchr, Frgn Lang Dept Chair 1984-92; The Mercersburg ad Fr, Span Tchr 1992-; *ai:* Schl Newspaper, Fr Club, Stu Adv; Walking ub Spon; Learning Strategies Comm Chair; Residence Hall Floormaster; CTFL 1993-; AATF, SAMLA 1994-; AAUW, Alliance Francaise 1995-; ropean Cncl Intnl Schls 1986-; Purdue Univ Schlsp Stud Univ of icago, Universide de Grenoble; Fr Prize Grove City Coll; *office:* The ercersburg Acad 300 E Seminary St Mercersburg PA 17236

OROWITZ, ALAN GEORGE, Technology Chairman; *b:* New York ty, NY; *m:* Anita Simpson; *c:* Brian, Katherine; *ed:* SUNY at Oswego S) Ind Arts, Tech 1968; Montclair St (MA) Indstrl Tech 1973; St Univ of NY at New Paltz (CAS) Admin 1983; Attnd Coll of New Rochelle 1976, NY Univ 1970; *cr:* Clarkstown Cent Schl Dist Ind Arts, Tech Tchr 1968-, Tech Chm 1981-; *ai:* Solar Car Club, Video Yrbk, Talent Show Adv; NY St Tech Ed Assn 1968-, VP, Pres Elec, Pres; Rockland Orange Sul 1968-, Treas, VP, Pres Elect, Pres, Tchr of Yr; Clarkstown Teach Assn 1968-; NYSUT, AFT 1968-; Intnl Tech Ed Assn 1986-; Amer Red Cross 1977-, Comm Dir, Numerous; Rockland Repeater Assn 1976-, Sec; Radio Amateur Civil Emergency Svc 1980-; Contributing Author Living With Tech; Regnl Tchr of Yr SUNY New Paltz; Epsilon Pi Tau Tech Honor; Numerous Tech Articles; *office:* Felix V Festa Jr HS 30 Parrott Rd West Nyack NY 10994

HOROWITZ, MARTIN L., Social Studies Teacher; *b:* Brooklyn, NY; *m:* Edith; *c:* Susan Jacobs, Gail Greenbaum; *ed:* Brooklyn Coll (MA) His 1967; 90 Post Grad Hrs NY Univ, Brooklyn Coll; *cr:* JHS 117 Tchr 1963-68; IS 27 Tchr, Chprsn 1968-; *ai:* AFT 1963-, Del, Chapter Chprsn; *office:* IS 27 11 Clove Lake Pl Staten Island NY 10310

HOROWITZ, PAMELA SUE, Spanish Teacher; *b:* Pittsburgh, PA; *m:* Domenic Macioce; *c:* Amy Beth Naughton; *ed:* Univ of Pittsburgh (BA) Eng & Span-Cum Laude 1963; *cr:* Pgh Pub Schls Eng Tchr 1 Yr; Shan HS Span Tchr 1 Yr; Euclid Cntrl Jr HS Span Tchr 1 Yr; Mt Lebanon HS Span Tchr in Hnrs Pgm 28 Yrs; *ai:* NEA; PSEA 1968-, Budget Chprsn; Italian Heritage Soc 1986-, Schlsp Comm; ISDA 1995-, Schlsp Comm; Pi Lambda Theta Ed Honorary 33 Yrs; *office:* Mt Lebanon HS 7 Horsman Dr Pittsburgh PA 15228

HOROWITZ, RUTH, Sixth Grade Teacher; *b:* Bronx, NY; *c:* Gayle, Brian; *ed:* Queens Coll (MS) Elem Ed 1985; 30 Addl Grad Credits; *cr:* PS 72 Fourth Grd Tchr 1967-70; PS 152 Sixth Grd Tchr 1981-; *ai:* UFT 1967-; *office:* PS 152 Gwendeline Alleyne 33-52 62nd St Woodside NY 11377

HORSEY, MAJOR FRANKLIN, Fourth Grade Teacher; *b:* Crisfield, MD; *m:* Geraldine Warren; *ed:* Bowie St Univ (BS) Elem Ed 1968; George Washington Univ APC, Elem Ed; *cr:* Mt Hope Elem 5th Grd Tchr 1968-71; Port Tobacco Elem 4-5th Grd Tchr 1971-84; Dr. James Craik Elem 4th Grd Tchr 1984-; *ai:* Grd Level Chprsn 1994-95; Test Coord, Site Base Team 1994-95; Sci Fair Chprsn, Career Ed Chprsn Coord; Safety Comm Team Mem; EACC, MSTA, NEA 1968-; Masonic Lodge #99 Master Master Mason 1985-, Pomfrot Estates Civic Assn 1976-, Treas 1976; GAND-M Inc 1995-, VP Family Bus; Exemplary Tchr Awd 1991; 25 Yr Tchr Svc Awd 1994; US Dept Interior Performance Awd 1990, 1993-95; Comm Svc Awd for ANC 8-C Black, Gold Awds 1992; US Dept of Interior, Outstdng Site Mgrs Awd 1991.

HORSKY, AL G., Retired Band Director; *b:* Dillonvale, OH; *m:* Joanne L. Kiehne; *c:* Debra Jo Hamrick, David Alan; *ed:* OH Univ (BFA) Instrumental Music 1953, (MED) Ed 1955; *cr:* Plains HS Band Dir 1954-64; Logan HS Instrumental Music Tchr 1964, 6-12 Grd, HS Band Dir 1984; *ai:* AARP, Awd 1984; Phi Beta Mu 1983-; Friends & Alumni of OU Schl of Music Bd; Natl Band Assn 1967-; Logan Hall of Fame 1993-; Logan Hall of Fame Outstdng Alumni Awd 1986; Citation Excl OH House Rep, OH Senate 1983; Logan Alumni Band Dir; Established Endowment Schlsp His Honor OH Univ 1994; *home:* 33 Hill St Logan OH 43138

HORSLEY, WAYNE D., Social Studies Teacher; *b:* Dayton, OH; *m:* Allyson Pappas; *ed:* OH Univ (BA) Soc Stud Ed 1993; 30 Hrs Towards a Master in Ath Admin; *cr:* Jackson HS Soc Stud Tchr 1994-; *ai:* Asst Var Ftbl Coach 2 Yrs; Asst Var Bsktbl Coach 2 Yrs; NEA 1994-; *office:* Jackson HS 21 Tropic St Jackson OH 45640

HORST, BLANCHE MOHLER, Retired Third Grade Teacher; *b:* Ephrate, PA; *m:* Nevin L.; *c:* Adelle Ward, Philip M., Phyllis Nofziger, Rachel Mc Laughlin, N. Timothy; *ed:* Eastern Mennonite Univ (BS) El Ed 1953; 8 Credit Hrs Millersville Univ 1978; 5 Credit Hrs Villanova Univ 1983; *cr:* Bedeno Schl 7-8 Grd Eng Tchr 1955-58; Nazareth Bible Acad 9-10 Grd Eng Grammar Tchr 1966-69; Locust Grove Mennonite Schl 3 Grd Tchr 1978-95; *ai:* Mennonite Missionary 19 Yrs; *home:* 360 E Church St Stevens PA 17578

HORST, LINDA QUIETMEYER, Physical Education Teacher; *b:* Norristown, PA; *m:* Robert B.; *c:* Bobbi-Jo, Steven, David; *ed:* West Chester Univ (BS) Hlth, PE, Coaching 1975; PA St Univ Pursuing MS; *cr:* Pine Grove Area Schl Dist Tchr & Coach 1976-; *ai:* Pregnancy Task Force; Drug & Alcohol Advisory Comm; Peer Ed Soph Class Adv; Varsity Club & Intramural Co-Adv; Stu Assistance Team; Coach Comm Soccer & Schuylkill Co Select Teams; PA Aware Anti-drug & Alcohol Assembly Group Adv; PSEA, NEA, AAHPERD 9 Yrs; Schuylkill Cty Youth Soccer Assn 1987-, Rep 5 Yrs; Grace Brethren Church 1981-; EPYSA 1987-, Coach; Schuylkill Cty Referee Assn 1988-, Referee; *office:* Pine Grove Area H S School St Pine Grove PA 17963

HORT, VICKIE PARK, Eng & Advncd Composition Tchr; *b:* Huntingdon, PA; *m:* Robert Craig; *c:* Christopher Craig, Nicole Ann; *ed:* Lock Haven Univ (BS) Eng 1968; Attnd Penn St Univ, Bloomsburg Univ, Mary Wood Coll, Clarion Univ, Millersville Univ; *cr:* Milton Sr HS Eng, Composition Tchr 1968-72; Warrior Run HS Rdng 1978-79; Milton Sr Hs Eng, Composition Tchr 1980-93; *ai:* NHS, Class of 1994 Adv; Stu of The Month Selection Comm; Grad Speakers Adv; PSEA, NEA, Milton Ed Assn 1968-; NCTE 1980-; *office:* Milton Area Schl Dist 700 Mahoning St Milton PA 17847

HORTA, THERESA CHIAPPONE, Mathematics Teacher; *b:* New York City, NY; *m:* Efrain; *c:* Danielle, Scott; *ed:* Trenton St Coll (BA) Math Ed 1975; Attnd Mercer Cty Comm Coll, Rutgers Univ, Stevens Inst of Tech; *cr:* Hightstown HS Math Tchr 1977-; *ai:* Coach Cdhrldng, Boys Frosh Bsbl; Jr Class Adv; Curr Comm; AMTNJ, NCTM 1987-; Mentoring Prgm; Dist Tech Grant; *office:* Hightstown HS 25 Leshin Ln Hightstown NJ 08520*

HORTMAN, DAVID JONES, Technology Education Teacher; *b:* Washington, DC; *m:* Ellen Shea Johnston; *c:* Melissa, Gregory, Jeffery; *ed:* Millersville Univ (BS) Industrial Arts Ed 1976; *cr:* Susquehannock HS Tech Ed Tchr 1982-; Gichner Mobile Systems Tool Designer 1980-82; Kennard Dale HS Industrial Arts Tchr 1976-79; *ai:* Engineering Club Adv; York Cty Tech Ed Assn 1982-, Pres; Tech Ed Assn of PA 1984-, Regnl VP, Tchr of Yr 1992-93; Intnl Tech Ed Assn 1991-, Tchr Excl Awd 1993; Jaycees 1978-, Pres; Phi Delta Kappa 1994-; Accepted Who's Who Amer Ed 1993; *office:* Susquehannoch Sr HS PO Box 128 Glen Rock PA 17327

HORTON, JAMES CHRISTOPHER, K-12th Grd Hlth Ed Tchr, Coord; *b:* Norwich, CT; *m:* Marilyn Jean Martinelli; *c:* Helen; *ed:* Southern CT St Univ (BS) Hlth, PE 1972; Cntrl CT St Univ 36 Hrs Guid, Cnslng; *cr:* East Hampton Pub Schls K-8th Grd Hlth, PE Tchr 1972-80, 9th-12th Grd Hlth, PE Tchr 1980-86, 5th-8th Grd Hlth Ed Tchr 1986-90; Cromwell Pub Schls L-12th Grd Hlth Tchr, Coord 1990-; *ai:* Peer Advocacy Adv; Renaissance Comm Co-Chair; NHS Selection Comm; NEA, CEA, AAHPERD 1972-; Natl Peer Helpers Assn 1991-; CEA Human, Civil Rights Comm 1992-; AHM Yth Svcs Substance Abuse Task Force 1988-, Recognition Cert; New England League of Mid Schls Natl Conf Presenter 1993, 1995; Middlesex Cty Bsktbl Coach of Yr 1980; *office:* Cromwell HS 34 Evergreen Rd Cromwell CT 06416

HORTON, JAMES R., Math & Reading Teacher; *b:* Albany, NY; *m:* Ellen A.; *c:* John, Laura, Jessica; *ed:* Morehead St U (BA) Elem Ed 1967; Wright St U (MS) Principalship 1975; 60 Addl Semester Hrs; *cr:* Brantwood Elem Schl 5th Grd Tchr 1969-72; Brookville MS 6th-8th Grd Tchr 1973-; *ai:* Inculusion Comm; NEA; WOEA; Brookville Tchrs Assn; *office:* Brookville MS 128 S Hill St Brookville OH 45309

HORTON, JOHNNYE MARIE, Inter Disciplinary Math Tchr; *b:* Shreveport, LA; *ed:* Stillman Coll (BS) Math 1968; Rutgers (MSEd) Math 1974; Grad Hrs ESOL Univ of MD at Baltimore; *cr:* Brookwood HS Math Tchr 1968-74; Bucklodge MS Math Tchr 1974-86; Nicholas Orem MS Math Tchr 1986-95; Kettering MS Inter Disciplinary Math Tchr 1995-; *ai:* OSAIS Tutor; MSTA, NEA 1974-; NCTM 1986-; Washington Post Grant 1984; Outstdng Ed PG Cty 1992; *office:* Kettering MS 65 Harrington Dr Upper Marlboro MD 20772

HORTON, LUCILLE MARIE, Business Education Teacher; *b:* Ashtabula, OH; *m:* William Charles; *c:* Melissa Marie, Laurie Ann MC Coy; *ed:* Kent St Univ (BS) Bus Ed 1977; Youngstown St Univ (MS) Master Tchr Bus Ed 1986; 20 Semester Hrs Kent St Univ, Ashland Coll, FL St Univiv; *cr:* Harbor HS Bus Tchr 1977-; Kent St Univ Part-time Office Tech Instr 1988-; *ai:* Bus Club Adv; OH Ed Assn, NEA 1977-; Delta Kappa Gamma 1990-; Past Mem Jaycess Wives, Buckeye Music Boosters, League of Women Voters, Amer Assn of Univ Women; *office:* Harbor HS 221 Lake Ave Ashtabula OH 44004

HORVATH, BROOKE KENTON, Associate Professor of English; *b:* Elyria, OH; *m:* Janet Lee Stone; *c:* Susan, Jordan; *ed:* Kent St Univ (BA)-Summa Cum Laude Eng 1975; St Univ of NY at Binghamton (MA) Eng 1977; Purdue Univ (PHD) Eng, Amer Lit 1986; *cr:* Purdue Univ Visiting Asst Prof 1986-88; Kent St Univ Asst Prof 1988-93, Assoc Prof 1993-; *ai:* Wick Poetry Prgm; Adv Campus Lit Magazine; Akron Cty Schls Sci Materials Selection Comm K-1; Sport Lit Assn 1986-, Journal's Book Review Ed; Natl Book Critics Cir 1995-; Assn Lit Scholars, Critics 1995-; Associated Writing Prgms 1991-; Challenger Bsbl 1995-, Mgr; Books: Consolation At Ground Zero; Poems: In A Neighborhood of Dying Light, Co-Edited Books on Writers Henry James, William Goyen; Assoc Ed Review of Contemporary Fiction; Essays, Reviews, Poems in Perodicals Poetry Amer Lit, Washington Post, Denver Quarterly, Amer Poetry Review; *office:* Kent St Univ Stark Cmps 6000 Frank Ave NW North Canton OH 44720

HORVATH, JOYANNE HODGES, Guidance Counselor; *b:* Paterson, NJ; *m:* Eugene Bruce; *ed:* Geneva Coll (AB) Speech, Drama 1963; Rider Univ (MA) Cnslng Svcs 1986; Substance Awareness Coord Cert 1992; 48 Addl Credits Grad Schl; Hypnotherapy Cert 1995; Rutgers Univ Drug, Alcohol Stud 1988-90; IN Univ Mid Atlantic Addiction Trng Inst 1991-92; WY Seminary Summer Inst Dev Wellness in Families 1990-91; *cr:* Woodbridge HS Eng, Drama, Pub Speaking Tchr 1966-85, Crisis Cnslr 1985-86, Guidance, Crisis Cnslr 1994-95, Guid Cnslr 1995-; John F. Kennedy HS Crisis Cnslr 1986-88; Woodbridge Twp Schls K-12th Grd Substance Awareness Coord 1988-94; *ai:* Achieving Sexual Equity Through Stdnts 1994-; Peer Mediation, Peer Role Models, Stdnts Against Substance Abuse 1990-94; Natl Forensic Soc, Drama Club 1975-89; Natl Forensic Soc 1968-, Degree of Distinction; NEA, NJEA 1970-; Amer Univ Women 1980-; Amer Bd of Hypnotherapy, Intnl Assn of Cnslrs, Therapists 1996; Amer Assn for Cnslng Dev, Middlesex Cty Cnslrs Assn 1986-; Assn of Stu Assistance Profs, NJ Prof Cnslrs Assn 1988-; Amer Mental Hlth Cnslrs 1990-; The Task Force on Compulsive Gambling 1991-; Substance Awareness Coord Grant Recipient 1988-91; Eoodbridge Twp Excl in Ed Awd 1992; NJ Cncl of Compulsive Gambling Ed Awd for Contribution in Field of Prevention, Ed Awareness 1993; *office:* Woodbridge HS Kelly & Freeman Sts Woodbridge NJ 07095*

HORVATH, KATHLEEN MAC DONALD, Reading Teacher; *b:* Toledo, OH; *m:* John Andrew; *c:* Doreen Kay Aldrich, John Andrew, Scott Michael; *ed:* OH Univ (BSEd) Elem Ed 1962; OH St Univ (MA) Rdng 1994; *cr:* Ottawa Cty Schls 1st Grd Tchr 1958-59; Columbus Pub Schls 1st-2nd Tchr 1963-70; Newark City Schls 1-4 Grd Rdng Tchr 1975-; *ai:* Rdng Club; Tech Comm; NEA; OEA; NTa; IRA; NCTE; Newark Org Tchrs Eng, Pres Elect; *office:* Newark City Schls 85 E Main St Newark OH 43055*

HORVATH, LAURA HUTCHISON, Research Asst & Univ Supvr; *b:* Clearwater, FL; *m:* David J.; *ed:* FL St Univ (BS) Eng Ed 1989, (MS) Eng Ed 1990; George Washington Univ (EdD) Curr & Instruction; FL Writing Project Summer 1991; Shakespeare in Ashland at NEH Inst 1992; *cr:* Cntrl HS Classroom Tchr 1990-94; Pasco-Hernando Comm Coll Adjunct Fac 1991-94; George Washington Univ Research Asst & Univ Supvr 1994-; *ai:* Mentoring Project Supervision; Phi Delta Kappa 1994-; ATE, ASCD, AERA 1995-; NCTE 1989-; Hernando Cty Supts Awd of Excl 1993; Paul & Kate Farmer Natl Awd for Excl in Writing 1993; Article Eng Journal 1993; *office:* George Washington Univ 2134 G Street NW Washington DC 20052*

HORVATH, MADELON TOFT, English & Drama Teacher; *b:* Cincinnati, OH; *m:* Roger J.; *c:* Brent, Stacey H. Roberson; *ed:* Kent St Univ (BS) Eng 1977; Theater, Drama & Ed Post Grad 30 Credit Hrs; *cr:* Grand Vly 7th-8th Grd Eng Tchr 1978-80; Chardon HS 9th-12th Grd Eng & Drama Tchr 1980-; *ai:* Drama Coach; Play Dir; Thespian Spon; Sr Adv; NEA, OEA & CCTA 1978-, Bldg Rep; Educl Theatre Assn 1980-, St Bd, St Dir & Regnl Dir; OTA 1982-, St Bd, Scndry Ed Rep; Performed at OH ETA St Conf (Twice); OH Theatre Alliance Superior Rating for One-Act Play; *office:* Chardon HS 151 Chardon Ave Chardon OH 44024*

HORVATH, VALERIE VOLPI, Mathematics Teacher; *b:* California, PA; *m:* Nicholas Dale; *c:* Kimberly, Ryan; *ed:* CA Univ of PA (BS) Math Ed 1972; St Univ of NY at Stony Brook (MALS) Math ed 1988; 75 Addl Credit Hrs; *cr:* Elizabethtown HS Math Tchr 1972-73; Bellport MS Math Tchr 1986-; *ai:* Bellport Tchrs Assn, NYSUT, AFT 1986-; *office:* Bellport MS Kreamer St Bellport NY 11713

HORWITZ, PHYLLIS, Math Resource Teacher; *b:* New York City, NY; *ed:* Brooklyn Coll (BA) Speech, Theatre 1968, (MS) Instrl TV Production 1971; *cr:* NY City Bd of Ed Tchr 1968-; *ai:* Parent Wkshps; Staff Dev; 100th Day Celebration Coord; UFT; AFT; NCTM; MENSA; IMPACT; NYS Math Mentor; Recognizedby NY City for Stdnts Achvmt; *office:* PS 152 Annex 1800 Utica Ave Brooklyn NY 11234*

HORYL, JANE (NELLIGAN), Physical Education Teacher; *b:* Buffalo, NY; *m:* Vladimir; *c:* Steven, Kristin; *ed:* Lorain Co Comm Coll (AA) Lbrl Arts 1971; Bowling Green St Univ (BS) PE, Hlth 1973; 30 Grad Hrs at SUNY Coll at Cortland, Brockport; *cr:* Jordan-Elbridge Jr-Sr HS Hlth, PE Tchr 1975-; *ai:* Girls Jr HS Soccer Coach; Var Club Fac Adv; Pre-Test De-Stress Day Act Chprsn; JETA, NEA, NYSUT 1975-; Tchr of Yr 1994; *home:* 2351 Lawrence Rd Marcellus NY 13108

HOSACK, JOHN LEROY, Mathematics Teacher; *b:* Sidney, OH; *m:* Ruth Iris Black Kotwica; *c:* Donna Jean Kotwica Martin, Donald Theodore Kotwica, Leigh Ann; *ed:* OH Northern Univ (BA) Math 1967; Attnd Wright St Univ 12 Credit Hrs, Bowling Green St Univ 18 Quarter Hrs, OH Northern Univ & Univ of Dayton 4 Credit Hrs; *cr:* Houston HS 8th-10th Grd Math & 8th Grd OH His 1968-70; Elmwood Jr HS 7th Grd Math 1972-79; OH Hi-Point JVS Math Specialist 1985-86; Sidney HS Math & Cmptr Tchr 1986-; *ai:* Asst Wrestling & Head Track Coach; OEA, NEA; Moose Lodge; Elks Lodge 1985-, Exalted Ruler, Chairs, Trustee; *office:* Sidney City Schls 1215 Campbell Rd Sidney OH 45365

HOSEY, MARION BARTLETT, Soc Stud Tchr & Coord; *b:* Springfield, MA; *m:* Gary R.; *c:* Anne, David; *ed:* Cornell Univ (AB) His-Cum Laude 1969; Johns Hopkins Univ (MAT) His 1971; Grad Stud Univ of MD, Bowie St Univ, Univ of MA, Syracuse Univ, Univ of Ghana at Accra; *cr:* Bowie HS His Tchr 1970-93, Tchr Coord 1993-; *ai:* Adv Newspaper, Stu Govt Assn, Key Club, Soph Class; Fac Recognition Comm Chprsn; Schl Based Mngmt Team; Stu Awds Comm; NEA, NCSS 1970-; IRA 1980-; ASCD

1991-; MD Ed Coalition 1993-; Wrote Curr for World His & Advanced Placement European His; Consulting Ed for Textbook; Outstanding Educator 1985-86; *office:* Bowie HS 15200 Annapolis Rd Bowie MD 20715*

HOSKINS, MARYANNE FOULKE, K-3rd Grade Facilitator; *b:* Ridley Park, PA; *m:* John M.; *c:* Lauren, Stacie Dale; *ed:* Montgomery Cty Comm Coll (AS) Early Chldhd Ed 1982; Gwynedd-Mercy Coll (BS) Elem Ed 1985; Cabrini Coll (MED) 1988; Educl Adm Penn St 1995; 60 Credits; *cr:* Norristown Area Schl Dist Kndgtn Tchr 1985-87, 3rd Grd Tchr 1987-95, Grds K-3 Facilitator 1995-; *ai:* Prof Dev Cncl Co-Chair; Staff Dev Presenter; NEA 1985-; Sev Summer Sci Camp Elem Stdnts; Tchr Trng Video; *office:* Norristown Area Schl Dist 401 N Whitehall Rd Norristown PA 19403*

HOSKINS, SHARON HOY, Business Education Teacher; *b:* Columbus, OH; *m:* Jack; *c:* Jay; *ed:* Otterbein Coll (BA) Ed 1975; Attending Univ of Dayton; Bus Ed Cert Fairmont St Coll; *cr:* Bellefontaine MS Span, Lang Arts Tchr 1975-77, 1979-81; Whitehall Adult Ed Bus Ed Tchr 1988-90; Groveport Madison HS Bus Ed Tchr 1990-; *ai:* Scheduling Team; NEA 1975-; GMLEA 1990-; Rally's Tchr of Month 1993; *office:* Groveport Madison HS 4475 S Hamilton Rd Groveport OH 43125

HOSLER, GAIL E., 9th-12th Grd Bus & Tech Tchr; *b:* Irvington, NJ; *m:* Edward T. Sr.; *c:* Eddy, Corey, Jenna; *ed:* Ocean Cty Coll (AS) Bus 1970; Trenton St (BS) Bus Ed 1978; CEU Credits Cmptr Related Courses; *cr:* Toms River HS North Bus Ed Instr 1978-; *ai:* FBLA Adv 15 Yrs; JV Cheering Coach Manchester Twnshp HS 1995-; NEA, NJEA, TREA 1978-; United Meth Church of Island Hghts 1985-, Cncl of Ministires 1985-, Chprsn of Educ, Dir of Vacation Bible Schl 1989, Meth Youth Fellowship 1992-, Dir; Pop Warner Ftbl 1992-93, Head Team Mother; *office:* Toms River HS North Old Freehold Rd Toms River NJ 08753

HOSMER, PATRICIA CRAIN, Retired Third Grade Teacher; *b:* Cleveland, OH; *m:* Phillip Wayne; *c:* Philip Bucher, Paul Bucher, Elizabeth; *ed:* Kent St Univ (BSEd) Elem Ed 1960; John Carroll Univ (MA) Tchng Skills 1969; 15 Addl Hrs in Supervision, Curr, His; *cr:* W. Geauga Schls 3rd-4th Grd Tchr 1955-65; Hawken Schl 3rd Grd Tchr 1970-90; *ai:* Remedial, Enrichment Vol Tutor; Jail Tutor 3 Yrs; KDPi 1954-; League Women Voters 1990-, VOTER Ed; Geauga Cty Historical Soc 1962-, Trustee, Founder of Famous Pioneer Schl; Geauga Park System 1990-, Vol Recruiter; Amnesty Intnl 1990-, Letter Writing Campaign; Natl Assn Ind Schls Conventions Presenter; Articles Pub.

HOSP, J. RUSSELL, Science Teacher; *b:* Kearny, NJ; *ed:* Murray St Univ (BA) Sci, Soc Sci 1966; Attnd Seton Hall Univ Sci; *cr:* Keyport HS Sci Tchr 1966-70; Green Brook HS Sci, His Tchr 1970-90; Watchung Hill Reg HS Sci Tchr 1990-; *ai:* Acad Team Adv; NEA, NJEA 1966-; NJ Sci Tchr 1990-; Bd of Hlth 1985-, Chm; Environment Bd 1990-; Schl & Cty Tchr of Yr 1992; Whos Who Among Amer Coll & Univ Stdnts 1966; *office:* Watchung Hills Regional HS 108 Stirling Rd Watchung NJ 07060

HOSP, ROSE FUOCO, Spanish Teacher; *b:* Utica, NY; *m:* Jack L.; *c:* John L. IV; *ed:* Utica Coll (BA) Span 1964; Middlebury Coll (MA) Span 1967; 62 Addl Post Grad hrs Ed, Theory, Practice; *cr:* Holland Patent Cntrl Schl Tchr, Frgn Lang Dept Chair 1964-; Mohawk Vly Comm Coll Tchr 1970-72; *ai:* Span Club Adv; Peace Corps Project Partner; Tchnr, Learning Ctr Policy Bd Mem; Tchrs Assn Hospitality Co-Chm; HPTA Negociation Cncl Mem; NYSAFLT 1964-, Summer Wkshp Schlsp, James E Allen Awd; FLACNY 1985-; HP Tchrs Assn 1964-, Treas; Delta Kappa Gamma 1991-, Sec; Amer Legion Auxilary 1995-; St Leo's Altar & Rosary Soc 1967-, Treas, Sec, VP, Pres; HP Chptr AFS 1964-, Pres, VP, Sec; Foothills Rural Comm Ministry 1994-; *office:* Holland Patent Central HS 8079 Thompson Rd Holland Patent NY 13354*

HOSSELKUS, SANDRA BEITSINGER, Fifth Grade Teacher; *b:* Imperial, PA; *c:* Nichole Feldhues; *ed:* Slippery Rock St (BS) Elem 1963; Penn St Univ (MA) Elem 1976; 3 Credit Hrs Cal St at Long Beach; 9 Credit Hrs Slippery Rock St Coll; *cr:* Union Free Schl Dist #7 4th Grd Tchr 1963-65; Moon Area Schls 4th Grd Tchr 1965-68; Buena Park Schl Dist 5th Grd Tchr 1968-69; Manteca Schl Dist 5th Grd Tchr 1970; Moon Area Schls 4th, 5th, 6th Grd Tchr 1971-; *ai:* Odessey of Mind Judge; Battle of Books Mgr; Prime Time Rdng Spon; Prof Staff; Schlsp Comm; Classtrip Spon; NEA, MEA Tchrs Assn 1965-; Bicentennial Comm 1986-; Family Inst Awd 1991.

HOST, KATHLEEN E. FLANAGAN, French & English Teacher; *b:* Pittston, PA; *m:* William D.; *ed:* Univ of Scranton (BA) Fr, Eng 1981, (MS) Ed 1985; Univ of Lourain Rotary Fellowship Fr 1983; Working Toward MA FR Middlebury Coll; FIAP Paris France 1981; Fulbright Fellow 1985; *cr:* Elk Lake HS Fr, Eng Tchr 1985-; *ai:* NEA, AATF 1985-; ASCD 1990-; Rotary Fellow 1983; Fulbright Fellow 1985; Modern Lang Awd Univ of Scranton 1981; Who's Who Among Amer HS Tchrs 1993; Summer Internship Northeast-Midwest Inst W DC 1989; Publication in LaBor Notes 1989; *home:* RR 6 Tunkhannock PA 18657*

HOSTA, LUANN KATHLEEN, Math Teacher; *b:* NY; *ed:* SUNY at Fredonia (BA) Math Ed 1969; Kent St Univ (MA) Philosophy 1980; *cr:* Kent Roosevelt HS Math Tchr 1969-; *ai:* Delta Kappa Gamma 1987-; *office:* Roosevelt HS 1400 N Mantua St Kent OH 44240

HOSTAGE, DAVID W., Director & Sci Dept Head; *b:* New Haven, CT; *m:* Susan Duncan; *c:* Christopher, Andrew; *ed:* Middlebury Coll (BA) Bio 1976; Wesleyan Univ (MALS) Sci 1981, (CAS) Sci 1991; Grad Work at USC, CCSU, West Hartford & Curtin; *cr:* The Cate Schl Sci Tchr 1976-80; Mooreland Hill Schl Sci & Math Tchr 1983-84; The Taft Schl Sci Tchr 1984-; *ai:* Coaching; Independent Stud Adv; Educl Policy & Tech & Resources Comms; ACS; NEACT; NSTA; CAST; CSSA; CVISSTA; First Congregational Church, Trustee; Watertown Fire Dist, Zoning Bd of Appeals; Cub Scouts Pack 76, Comm; *office:* Taft Schl 110 Woodbury Rd Watertown CT 06795

HOSTETLER, ELIZABETH ANN, Dir of Tchr Ed & Prof of Ed; *b:* Lima, OH; *m:* George Edward; *ed:* Bluffton Coll (BS) Elem Ed 1968; Wright St Univ (MED) Elem Admin 1972; Univ of Toledo (PHD) Curr & Instruction 1981; *cr:* Hwalien Chrstn Schl K-6th Grd Tchr 1968-70; Bath Elem 2nd & 5th Grd Tchr 1970-74; Bluffton Coll Elem Ed Prof 1974-, Tchr Ed Dir 1981-, MAE Prgm Dir 1995-; *ai:* The Lion & Lamb Peace Arts Ctr Dir & Founder 1987; Delta Kappa Gamma 1989-, Chair, World Affairs; OH Assn of Private Colls of Tchr Ed 1981-, Pres; OH Dept of Ed Standards Comm 1993-; NCTE; IRA, NCSS; Bluffton Pub Lib Bd 1993-, Pres; Girl Scouts of Amer 1992-, Chair, Women of Achvmts Comm, Woman of Achvmt 1992; Lima Mennonite Church 1995-, Chair, Spiritual Cncl; Martha Holden Jennings Outstanding Tchr Educator; OH Arts Cncl, OH Hum Cncl & Honda of Amer Grants; Invitations to Speak Abroad in Japan, Taiwan & Serbia; Chosen as Staley Lecturer at Malone Coll Who Recognizes People in Higher Ed Who Have Made Significant Contributions to Their Stdnts & Inst 1996; *office:* Bluffton Coll 280 W College Ave Bluffton OH 45817*

HOSTETLER, JAMES DWIGHT, History Teacher; *b:* Hooversville, PA; *m:* Gloria Schmalz; *c:* Mike, Greg; *ed:* Lock Haven St Univ (BS) His & Sci 1959; IN St Univ (MS) Soc Stud & Ed 1965; *cr:* Bedford Area Tchr 1959-; *ai:* PSEA, NEA 1960-; Pioneer Historical Soc 1990-; *office:* Bedford Area Schl Dist 440 E Watson St Bedford PA 15522

HOSTETLER, ROBERT JAY, English Teacher; *b:* Ephrata, PA; *m:* Lisa Wiebe; *c:* Zachary, Lauren; *ed:* Goshen Coll (BA) Eng 1983; Houston Bapt Univ (MLA) Lbrl Arts 1989; *cr:* Houston ISD Eng Tchr 1983-85; Cypress-Fairbanks ISD Eng Tchr 1985-90; Houston Comm Coll Eng Tchr 1987-90; Comm Coll of Philadelphia Eng Tchr 1991-92; Haverford Twp Schl Dist Eng Tchr 1992-; *office:* Haverford Twp Schl Dist 200 Mill Rd Havertown PA 19083

HOSTETLER, RONALD E., Wellness Teacher; *b:* Lancaster, PA; *m:* Holly Ann Baltzer; *c:* Janna, Jared, Belcah, Kensi; *ed:* Penn St Univ (BS) HPER 1977; Millersville Masters Equivilency Clinical Psych & Behavioral Sci 1988; *cr:* Milton Hershey Schl Wellness Tchr 1983-; *ai:* Ftbl Coach; NSBA, PSBA 1992-; ASCD 1996-; Derry Twp Schl Bd 1992-, Pres; Family Impact Fnd 1991-, Founder, Pres; Penn St Lettermans Club 1990-; Co-Author There is No Joy in Grantsville, but Theres Plenty to Learn; *home:* 24 Tice Ave Hershey PA 17033

HOSTETLER, SHARON POETA, English Teacher; *b:* Johnstown, PA; *m:* James L.; *c:* Brittany; *ed:* Univ of Pittsburgh (BA) Comm 1973; St Francis Coll (MED) Scndry Ed 1978; *cr:* Central Cambria HS Eng Tchr 1973-80 & 1990-; *ai:* Japanese & German Facilitator; CCEA & PSEA.

HOSTETTER, ALLYN E., Business Education Teacher; *b:* Camden, NJ; *m:* Barbara L. Davidson; *c:* Jennifer L., Brad A.; *ed:* Bloomsburg Univ (BS) Accounting 1966; Villanova Univ (MA) Admin 1977; 45 Grad Credits Beyond Masters; *cr:* Interboro HS Tchr 1966-77, Asst Prin 1978-82, Tchr 1983-89, Dir Info Svcs 1990-93, Tchr 1994-; *ai:* Adult Ed Dir; Stu Cncl Adv; Delta Pi Epsilon 1992-; IEA 1966-, Treas, VP,Chief Negotiator; NEA 1966-; PSER 1966-, Region Exec Bd, Leadership Dev; *office:* Interboro HS 16th & Amosland Rd Prospect Park PA 19076

HOSTETTER, KATHERINE BALSLEY, Eng, Advanced Composition Tchr; *b:* Pittsburgh, PA; *m:* Harold H.; *ed:* Bowling Green St Univ (BSEd) Eng 1966; Post Grad Stud John Carroll, Lake Erie Coll; *cr:* Willowick Jr HS Eng Tchr 1966-75; North HS ENg Tchr 1975-; *ai:* NHS Adv; Acad Decathlon Asst Coach; Sunshine Comm Chm; Mentor Tchr Frosh at Risk Prgm; NEA, OEA, NEOA, WETA 1966-; NASSP; Co-Author Tchng Manual; Favorite Tchr 20 Yrs; *office:* North HS 34041 Stevens Blvd Eastlake OH 44095

HOSTETTER, TIMOTHY J., Scndry Soc Stud Tchr & Prin; *b:* Suffern, NY; *m:* Barbara A. Zeith; *ed:* Houghton Coll (BS) His & Bus Admin 1984; SUNY Coll at New Paltz 33 Hrs Grad Work Towards MA; *cr:* Tabernacle Chrstn Acad Soc Stud & Math Scndry Tchr 1984-92, Soc Stud Scndry Tchr & Asst Admin 1993-95, Prin & Soc Stud Scndry Tchr 1995-; Tianjin Intnl Schl Soc Stud & Math Scndry Tchr 1992-93; *ai:* Bsktbl & Soccer Coach; Ski Club Supvr; Field Trip Coord; Choir Mem; Tabernacle Bapt Church 1974-, Missions Cncl 1985-90, Pulpit Comm 1990-92, Deacon 1993-95; *office:* Tabernacle Christian Acad 153 Academy St Poughkeepsie NY 12601

HOTALING, ERIC J., High School Art Teacher; *b:* Honolulu, HI; *m:* Susan Hoellrich; *ed:* Coll of Saint Rose (BS) Art Ed 1980; Eastern MI Univ (MFA) Multi-Media 1982; *cr:* Oak Hill Schl Art Tchr 1982-84; Saratoga Springs Elem Schl Art Tchr 1984; Saratoga Jr HS Art Tchr 1985-87; Saratoga Springs HS Art Tchr 1987-; *ai:* Ski Club; Fresco Soc; Coll Art Assn 1982-; NYSTA 1984-; NYS Arts Cncl Grant; Skidmore Coll Arts in Ed Fellowship; Solo Exhibitions & Performances; *office:* Saratoga Springs Sr HS 186 West Ave Saratoga Spgs NY 12866

HOTCHKISS, ANITA PRUZAN, Psychology Professor; *b:* Bielsko, Poland; *m:* Frederick H. C.; *c:* Debra Pruzan, Daniel Pruzan, Grace, Emily; *ed:* Hunter Coll of CUNY (BS) Psych-Magna Cum Laude 1969; Grad Schl of CUNY (PHD) Psychobiology 1975; Monell Chemical Senses Inst of Univ of PA Post Doctoral Fellow 1975-77; *cr:* Hunter Coll of CUNY Instr 1970-73; SUNY Coll Instr 1973-75; Rutgers Coll Asst Prof 1977-81; Fitchburg St Coll Prof 1981-; *ai:* Psi Chi, Psych Club, Adelphian Soc Fac Adv; Sigma Xi 1970-; Amer Men, Women in Sci; Columbia Univ Elected Assoc Population Bio Seminar; Behavior Genetics Assn; Society for Study Evolution; Amer Soc of Naturalists; Animal Behavior Soc; Amer Assn for Advancement of Sci; NY Entomological Soc; Amer Psychological Soc; Psi Chi Hnr Soc, Phi Beta Kappa 1969-; CUNY Dissertation 1974-75, NIH Postdoctoral 1975-77, Rutgers Univ Rsrch Cncl Summer 1979 Flwshps; Rutgers Univ Rsrch 1977-80, NSF Instrl Scientific Equipment19 79, Natl Inst of Mental Hlth Rsrch 1979-81, Fac Dev 1981-82, 1985-86, New England Telephone Rsrch 1992, Berman Fund 1977-79 Grants; Rutgers UnivTchng Merit Awd 1979; Nom Tchr of Yr 1992; Nom Vincent J. Mara Awd Excl in Tchng 193-94; FSC Dev Fund 1982-83; Peer Reviews Behavior Genetics, The Amer Naturalist, Genetics, Evolution, Sci; Invited Speaker Univ of CA, Behavior Genetics Assn, Columbia Univ Seminar, Monell Chemical Senses Ctr 1974, Drew Univ, SUNY Coll at Purchase, Hunter Coll of CUNY 1975, Univ of PA Psych Seminar, Columbia Univ Seminar 1976, Drew Univ Zoology Colloquium 1977, Animal Behavior Soc NE Regnl; *office:* Fitchburg St Coll 160 Pearl St Fitchburg MA 01420*

HOTMIRE, PHILLIP GENE, Science & Social Studies Tchr; *b:* Muncie, IN; *m:* Juanita Niswander; *c:* Kurt, Jesse, Erik, Ben; *ed:* Ball St Univ (BS) Sci Ed 1967; St Francis Coll (MS) Ed 1977; Bowling Green St Univ Admin Post Grad Hrs; United Theological Seminary 1 Yr Ministry Stud Ordained Deacon; *cr:* Selma MS 8th Grd Sci Tchr 1970-71; Paulding MS 7th Grd Soc Stud, 8th Grd Sci Tchr 1973-; *ai:* Fed Govt Title VI Prgm Coord; Bldg Tchrs Mentor; NEA 1973-; United Meth Men 1976-, Treas.

HOUCHARD, CAROLEE WEISS, Cooperative Business Ed Coord; *b:* Portland, OR; *c:* John, David, Andrea, Heather; *ed:* Lewis & Clark Coll (BS) Bus Admin 1960; Wright St Univ (MS) Ed 1995; Portland St Univ 1960-62 Grad Courses; Univ of Southern CA Grad Schl of Bus Admin 1962-63; *cr:* Forest Grove HS Bus Tchr 1960-62; Jonathan Alder HS Bus Tchr 1966-69; West Jefferson HS Bus Tchr 1975-80; Tolles Tech Ctr Bus Tchr, COE, CBE Coord 1980-; *ai:* Bus Prof of Amer Adv; Mentor Tchr; Bus Professionals of Amer 1980-; OBTA; OEA, nEA 1989-; OVA, AVA; Plain City Lib Bd of Trustees 1991-94, Sec; Liberty Presbyn Church 1995-; Plain City Presbyn Church 1991-94, Elder; Sweet Adelines 1983-84; Capital Univ Comm Chocir 1977-79; Article Pub OH Bus Tchr Asso Beacon.

HOUCHEN, CHARLES RICK, Tchr & Dir of Christopher Pgm; *b:* Parkersburg, WV; *ed:* Capital Univ (BS) His & Govt 1970; Xavier Univ (MED) Ed Admin 1976; *cr:* Eastmoor HS Tchr 1970-91; Christopher Pgm Tchr & Dir 1991-; *ai:* NEA, OEA, CEA 1970-; Together 2000 1995-; Hlth Smart 1995-; *office:* Christopher Pgm 52 Starling St Columbus OH 43215

HOUCK, DALE CHARLES, Music Teacher & Orchestra Dir; *b:* Wilkes-Barre, PA; *m:* Linda Mc Closky; *c:* Marcella, Sarah, Dale, Amy; *ed:* Berklee Coll of Music (BMUS) Music Ed 1979; Univ of Scranton (MA) Music Ed 1983; 60 Addl Hrs; *cr:* Riverside Jr, Sr HS Music Tchr, Band Dir 1979-82; WY Vly West MS Music Tchr, Orch Dir 1983-; *ai:* Hnrs Orch Dir; NEA, PSEA 1979-; AFM 1970-; WY Vly Band 1970-; *office:* Wyoming Valley West MS 201 Chester St Wilkes Barre PA 18704*

HOUCK, DEAN R., Music Teacher & Band Director; *b:* Pottstown, PA; *m:* Nancy B.; *c:* Joshua; *ed:* Wilkes Coll (BS) Music Ed 1972; Pottsdam Univ, Mansfield Unv, Penn St Univ & Marywood Univ 30 Addl Grad Credits; *cr:* Montrose Music Tchr 1972-; *ai:* HS & Stage Band; Brass Ensemble; NBA & Phi Beta Mu 1985-; MENC & PMEA 1970-, Pres Dist 9, Excl Awd; Kiwanis 1975-80; Music Verein 1990-, Conductor; *office:* Montrose Area Jr/Sr HS RD 3 Box 28 Montrose PA 18801

HOUCK, MAXINE WENZLER, English Teacher; *b:* Cleveland, OH; *c:* R. James Owen, Christopher B. Owen, Gregory L. Owen, Stephanie H. Owen, Melora K. Owen; *ed:* Oberlin Coll (BA) Govt 1958; Youngstown St Univ (MA) Eng 1980; Attnd Western Reserve Univ, NM Highlands Duke Univ; *cr:* Las Vegas City Schls Eng & Soc Stud Tchr 19 Canadian Army in Germany Provost Corps Office Mgr 1960-61; We City Schls Eng Tchr 1961-64; Howland Schls Eng & Soc Stud Tchr *ai:* Lit Magazine Adv; YSU Eng Festival Coord; NEA, OEA, HCTA League of Women Voters 1971-, Former Bd; Saint Johns Episcopal Vestry, Comm Svc Board Head; Mahoning Valley Civil War Roun 1984-, Pres; Planned Parenthood 1992-, Bd Mem, VP of Fundra Ashland Oil Outstanding Tchr Awd 1990; Fulbright Tchr Exch to Hu 1990-91; NEH Fellow at Duke Seminar 1993; 2 Articles in OH Jour Eng Lang Arts; Youngstown Poetry; Mahoning Valley Poetry Re *office:* Howland HS 200 Shaffer Dr NE Warren OH 44484*

HOUGH, CHERYL MOORE, Fine Arts Teacher; *b:* Nurielly-Sur-S France; *m:* J. Allan; *c:* Erin; *ed:* Kean Coll (BA) Fine Arts Studio, Ed Montclair St Coll 24 Grad Credits Ceramics; *cr:* Warren Cty Adult Ed 1980-86; North Warren Reg HS Fine Arts Tchr 1979-; *ai:* Sr Class A Warren Regnl Ed Assn Pres; Art Educators of NJ 1980-; Natl Art Ed Peters Valley Craftsmen, NJ Designer Craftsmen 1976-; NEA 1 Montclair St Coll Alumni Assn Grant 1978-79; Research of Contemp Grant; Czech Ceramics 1978-79; *office:* North Warren Regiona Lambert Rd PO Box 410 Blairstown NJ 07825

HOUGHTON, RUTH B.F., Mathematics Teacher; *b:* Concord, N Winthrop P.; *c:* Winthrop, Theodore; *ed:* Radcliffe Coll (AB) Math Several Credit Hrs in Ed Courses; *cr:* Lincoln Jr HS Math Tchr 196 Biddleford HS Math Tchr 1967-; *ai:* NHS Adv; Stud Performance C Chair; NEA 1964-; NMTC 1995-.

HOUK, ALAN LEE, Band Director; *b:* Columbus, OH; *m:* Cons Fitch; *c:* Nathan, Andrew, Paul, Matthew, Stephen; *ed:* Youngstow Univ (BME) Music Ed, Tuba 1978, (MME) Music Ed 1988; *cr:* Well HS 5-8 Grd Band Dir 1978-83; Ukarumpa HS 5-12 Grd Band Dir 198 United HS 5-12 Grd Band Dir 1985-; *ai:* Marching Band Dir; Asst Coach; MENC, OMEA 1978-; Registered Music Edctr; *office:* U Local HS 8143 St Rt 9 Hanoverton OH 44423

HOUK, DOLORES JEAN (GASPAREC), Fifth Grade Teache Sharon, PA; *m:* George H. Jr.; *c:* Christopher G.; *ed:* PA St Univ (B Elem, Kndgtn Ed 1973; Youngstown St Univ (MSEd) Early Chldhd Addl 15 Sem Hrs Rdng, Gifted Courses; *cr:* Area Dist Sub Tchr 197 Brookfield Local Schl Dist 2nd Grd Tchr 1974-76, 3rd Grd Tchr 197 5th Grd Tchr 1995-; *ai:* Stu Cncl Adv 4th, 5th Grds; Appreciatior Parents, Vols Taking Stock Survey Comm 1994-95; AFT, Brookfield F Tchrs 1974-; Penn St Alumni Assn, Lifetime Mem; Coll Womens As Hermitage 1992-, Ways Means Comm; PTO 1989-, Key Homeroom M 1993-94; Mini Grant Trumbull Cty Bd of Ed; *office:* Addison Elem 900 Judson Rd Masury OH 44438

HOULE, MARK STEVEN, School Psychologist; *b:* Lawrence, MA Salem St Coll (BA) Psych 1980, (MEd) Guid, Cnslng 1984; Northeastern Univ 1989; *cr:* Hampstead Hosp Psychiatric Cnslr 198 Town of Methuen Schl Psychologist 1984-; *ai:* Newspaper, Collectors Adv; Staff Support Team Co-Ldr; Natl Assn Schl Psychologists 1 Merrimack Vly Philharmonic Soc 1993-, Advy Bd; *office:* Methuen C Grammer Schl 100 Howe St Methuen MA 01844

HOULE-MADDEN, LEE, Sixth Grade Teacher; *m:* Skip; *ed:* Easter St Univ (BA) Elem Ed; St Joseph Coll (MA) Spec Ed; *ai:* Team Ldr; Dev Ctr Coord; Stu Tchr Supvr; NEA; CT Ed Assn; WE Assn; Lib Bd, Celebration of Excl Awd, Excl St Screener.

HOULIHAN, GAIL LYNN, Special Education Teacher; *b:* Waterbury, *m:* Thomas Sr.; *c:* Thomas Jr., Ryan, Chelsea; *ed:* Southern CT St (BS) Spec Ed 1984, (MS) SPec Ed 1992; *cr:* W. F. Kaynor Tech Schl Ed Tchr 1984-; *ai:* Pub Relations Comm, Visions Competition, Ka Outstdng Stu Prgm Co-Chprsn; AFT 1984-; VICA 1988-; Natl PTA 1 Children's Village Parent Advy Bd 1993-; Wolcott 200 Comm 1 *office:* W. F. Kaynor Tech Schl 43 Tompkins St Waterbury CT 06708*

HOULIHAN, SHEILA M., Latin Teacher; *b:* Old Saybrook, CT Andrew L. Wizner; *c:* Sarah M. Wizner, Eamon J. Wizner; *ed:* George Univ (AB) Classics, Govt 1985; Univ of MA at Amherst (MAT) Lat Classical Hum 1992; *cr:* Banneker HS Latin Tchr 1985-88; E. Hartfor Latin Tchr 1989-90; Guilford HS Latin Tchr 1992-; *ai:* Class of 1997, L Hnr Soc Adv; A Better Chance Acad Adv; Amer Class League 1988-; C Assoc of New England 1990-; Class Assoc of CT 1990-, Sec; Wethers Yth Advy Bd 1994-, Vice Chprsn; Georgetown Univ Club of CT 1 Treas; *office:* Guilford HS New England Rd Guilford CT 06437

HOULTON, CAROL ANN PRATT, Physical Education Teache Albany, NY; *m:* William E. Jr.; *ed:* Russell Sage Coll (BA) PE 1965, (Hlth Ed 1973; *cr:* Springfield Tech HS PE Tchr 1965-66; Ichabod C Cntrl Schls PE Tchr 1966-67; Emma Willard Prep Schl PE Tchr 1 Shenendehowa Cntrl Schls PE Tchr 1968-; *ai:* IM & Extramurals F Hockey, Soccer, Bsktbl, Vlybl, Track & Field, Sftbl; Girls Ath Assn S NYSAHPERD 1968-, Amazing People in PE; NYSUT 1968-; PTSA 1 Honorary life Mbrshp Awd; *office:* Koda Jr HS Rt 146 Clifton Park 12065*

HOURANI, MOUJALLI C., Civil Engineering Professor; *b:* Marjyo Lebanon; *m:* Jacqueline Jaudes; *c:* Nadia, Stephanie, Gregory; Manhattan Coll (BE) Civil Eng, Math 1981; Rose Hulman Inst of (MS) Civil Eng 1983; WA Univ (PHD) Civil Eng 1987; *cr:* Marjy Lebanon Chem Tchr 1975-77; Washington Univ Instr 1986-87; Manha Coll Assoc Prof 1988-; *ai:* Fac Adv Tau Beta Pi; ASCD 1989-, Fac A Sigma Xi 1989-; James M. Robbins Excl Tchng Awd Chi Epsilon; Tch Yr Schl of Engineering 1992; *office:* Manhattan College 4513 Manha College Pkwy Riverdale NY 10471

HOUSE, CAROL ELAINE, Mathematics Teacher; *b:* Boston, MA; William Milton Sr.; *c:* William Jr., David, Wendy, Stanley James; *ed* Coll at Boston (BA) Ed 1966; Lib Sci; Counseling; *cr:* Cambridge Rin & Latin Tchr 1970-76; Title I Acting Dir 1976-80; Cambridge Rindg Latin Tchr 1981-; *ai:* Mass Pep Team; Concerned Black Staff; Pol Ac Comm; Dental Fund Bd of Trustees; NEA, MTA 1970-; Cambridge T Assn 1970-, Sec, VP; Civic Unity Comm 1987-; Zeta Phi Beta 1992-; F in Comm; Schl Comm Classroom Incentive Awd; Schl Improvement Gr Women's Month Awd 1991; *office:* Cambridge Rindge & Latin Schl Broadway St Cambridge MA 02138

HOUSE, GALE (FELLENSER), High School Teacher & Coach; Philadelphia, PA; *ed:* Ursinus Coll (BS) Hlth, PE, Latin 1967; Temple U (MED) Hlth, PE 1970, (PHD) PE, Biomechanics 1983; *cr:* Ursinus C Part-time Vlybl, Sftbl, Bsktbl Coach 1971-79; Temple Univ Part-t Vlybl Coach 1981-86, Adj Prof 1984-; Phila HS for Girls Tchr, Co 1967-; *ai:* Var Coach Bsktbl, Sftbl; AAHPERD 1967-; PSAHPERD 19 HS PE Tchr of Yr 1995; ABO-NAGWS 1963-, Sftbl Exam Dir, Natl Ho Awd 1989; Girl Scouts Amer 1952-, Asst Ldr; Chapel fo Four Chap 1985-, Honor Mbrshp; Magnet Schl Grant Physics in PE; PATHS Gr Anatomy for Artists; Chptr Pub; Textbook Adj Author; *office:* Philadelp HS for Girls 1400 W Olney Ave Philadelphia PA 19141*

HOUSE, KATHLEEN BURKE, Mathematics Dept Chairman; Washington, DC; *m:* William H. II; *c:* Elizabeth K. House-DeVale, Su Russell House-Schrock, Mark William, Andrew Burke; *ed:* M Washington Coll of UVA (BS) Math 1965; U of VA (MED) Math Ed 19 Hood Coll (MS) Comp Sci; Grasping Calculators in Math Ed; *cr:* Fair

A Ballston Spa NY Math Tchr 1965-66; Waterford CT Math Tchr -67; John Tyler & J Sargeant Reynolds CC Math Instr 1972-76; rick Comm Coll Math Instr 1979-81, 1983-84; Frederick Co MD Tchr 1984-; *ai:* Acad Team, Sci Bowl Team & AFS Club Spon; M 1984-; MCTM 1984-; NEA, MSTA & FCTA 1984-; Church; MD St Tchr of the Yr; MD Semi-Finalist Presidential Tchr of Excl in Tchng ; Hewlett-Packard Grant; Tchr of a Presidential Scholar; *office:* rick HS 650 Carroll Pky Frederick MD 21701

SE, MAXINE B., Latin & English Teacher; *b:* Eau Claire, WI; *m:* rt F.; *c:* James; *ed:* Univ of WI (BS) Latin, Eng 1960; Wm Paterson (MA) Eng 1981; Addl 15 Credit Cert in Rdng, 15 Credits Eng Courses, edits Latin; *cr:* Ramapo HS Latin Tchr 1960-67; Indian Hills HS Eng 1977-, Latin Tchr 1993-; *ai:* Latin Club Adv; Stategic Gaming Club ; NEA, NJEA, BCEA, RIHEA 1978-; NJ Classical Assn 1993-; Circus Assn of Animals 1962-; SEAS 1991-; *office:* Indian Hills HS 97 o Ave Oakland NJ 07436

SE, NANCY CATHERINE, English & Publications Teacher; *b:* ilton, OH; *m:* Ernie; *ed:* Miami Univ (BA) Eng 1983, (MS) Rdng Ed ; OH Writing Project Jrnlsm Hrs at Ball St Univ; *cr:* Toledo Pub Schl Tchr 1983-87; Goshen Local Schls Eng Tchr 1987-93; Milford Schls & Publications Tchr 1993-; *ai:* Stu Newspaper, Yrbk, Lang Arts Adv; & Tech Comms; Desktop Publishing Consultant for Dist; NCTE -; CSPA, NSPA 1993-; NEA 1987-; Article Pub in Eng Journal; Martha en Jennings Scholar 1992-93; *office:* Milford H S 1 Eagles Way rd OH 45150

SEKNECHT, MARY JEAN, Fifth-Sixth Grade Teacher; *b:* Wilkes , PA; *m:* Donald; *c:* Jill, Donald; *ed:* Luzane Cty Comm Coll (AS) Childhood 1977; Millersville St Coll (BS) Elem, Early Childhood ; Spec Ed Cert Marywood Coll; *cr:* Holy Trinity Schl 3rd-4th Grd Tchr -83; St Nicholas St Mary's Schl 5th-6th Grd Tchr 1983-; *ai:* Childrens r Asst; 5th-8th Grd Svc Club Moderator St Deminic; Forensics Stdnts h; NCEA 1983-; SDACT 1986-; Sing for Weddings.*

JSEMAN, BARTON L., Prof of Chemistry Emeritus; *b:* Silver ngs, MD; *m:* Doris Vanderee; *c:* Mark, Jeanne Houseman Maguire; *ed:* in Univ (BA) Chem 1955; Wayne St Univ (PHD) Phys Chem 1961; *cr:* Alamon Natl Labs Visiting Scientist 1966076; Univ of CA at Berkeley Prof of Chem 1969070; Goucher Coll Prof of Chem 1961-95; *ai:* orth Assoc 1963-79; 15 Articles, 3 Patents, 1 Book Pub; *home:* 17 oway Ave Cockeysville MD 21030

JSER, DEBRA A., Counselor; *b:* Philadelphia, PA; *m:* Scott E.; *c:* ifer, Michael; *ed:* West Chester Univ (BS) Ed 1974, (MED) Cnslng ; *cr:* Upper Dublin HS Schl Cnslr; N Wales Elem Schl 5th Grd Tchr; *e:* Upper Dublin HS 800 Loch Alsh Ave Fort Washington PA 19034

JSER, JAMES C., Science Teacher; *b:* Columbus, OH; *ed:* OH Univ Botany 1968; Post Grad Stud Univ of Dayton, Wright St Univ; *cr:* on Union Schls Sci Tchr 1968-; *ai:* Interact-Local Rotary Adv; Tchr of 990, 1993-95; Chosen for Project Discovery 1994; Tchr of Yr Local r Legion 1994.

USER, JO ANN H., English & Writing Teacher; *b:* Chicago, IL; *m:* er N.; *c:* Jennifer Maraschky, Jill Giesey, Glenn, Keith; *ed:* hwestern Univ (BA) Brit Lit, Writing 1958; IN Univ (MS) Scndry Ed, ing 1974; 52 Addl Hrs Hum, Ec; *cr:* Homestead HS Eng Tchr 1969-70; ston HS Eng Tchr 1974-75; West Geauga HS Eng Tchr, Dept Chair 7-; *ai:* Acad Decathlon Coach; Curio Lit Magazine Spon; NEA, OEA -; WGEA 1977-, Pres; Sohio Tchr of Yr; Runnerup Asland Tchr of Yr; ha Holden Jennings Grants, Outstdng Tchr; Tchr of Tchrs; Natl Grant ng Family Issues; *office:* West Geauga HS 13401 Chillicothe Rd sterland OH 44026*

USER, LILLIAN DRAG, Science Teacher; *b:* Painesville, OH; *m:* es E.; *c:* Kelly, Jeffrey; *ed:* Bowling Green Univ (BS) Bio 1971; veland St Univ (MA) Bio 1979; 9 Grad Hrs at Case Western Reserve; 5 d Hrs at John Carroll Univ; 3 Grad Hrs at OK St Univ; *cr:* John Hay Sci Tchr, Dept Chair 1971-; *ai:* Sci Club Co-Spon; Sci Olympiad Adv; Sci Dept Chair; Sci Fair Comm; AFT 1971-; Natl Assn of Sci rs 1995-; Sci Tchrs Org of OH 1980-; PTA 1987-, Corresponding Sec; rch Orgs 1980-; Sunday Schl Tchr 1985-; 2 Impact II Grants; 2 veland Clinic Grants; Newmast Participant Johnson Space Ctr 1995; sented at NSTA Convention in Philadelphia 1995; *office:* John Hay HS 5 Stokes Blvd Cleveland OH 44106*

USER, RICHARD MORRISON, Guidance Director; *b:* San Jose, ta Rica; *m:* elizabeth Nute; *c:* Cynthia Lynne; Sheri Elizabet; *ed:* Master Univ (BA Anthropology 1975-; Univ of Toronto (BEd) Scndry 1976-; Ontario Bible Coll Diploma in Chrstn Ed 1967; *cr:* Ottawa stn Schl 5th-6th Grd Tchr 1976-79; Muskoka Chrstn Schl Admin 9-81; The Christian Acad Tchr, Guidance 1981-; *ai:* Ascend Inc Bd of ; Soccer Coach; Church Mem; Missions Comm Chair; *office:* The istian Acad 704 S Old Middletown Rd Media PA 19063

USER, ROY G., Accounting & Business Teacher; *b:* San Diego, CA; Linda Messer; *c:* Kelly Houser Lenz, Julie Houser Snow; *ed:* nberland Coll (BA) Bus, Soc Stud 1965; Xavier Univ (MS) Admin 2; *cr:* Maimisburg HS Tchr, Coach 1965-; *ai:* Head Coach Var Girls tpitch Sftbl; NEA, OEA, MCTA 1965-; Mid-Miami League Coach of Yr 5, 1987, 1993-95; *home:* 1311 Lord Fitzwalter Dr Miamisburg OH 42

USER, SCOTTI BLACKMON, Third Grade Teacher; *b:* Washington, ; *m:* Jon; *c:* Jon S., Matthew S.; *ed:* Frostburg St Univ (BS) Early dhd Ed 1971; Post Grad Stud; *cr:* Hill Street Schl Kndgtn Tchr 1971-73; khart Schl Kndgtn Tchr 1973-74; Salisbury Elk Lick 1st-3rd Grd Tchr 4-; Frostburg St Univ Saturday Gifted Pgm Tchr 1984-86; *ai:* St Judes thathon Coord 1988-91; Lead Tchr 1991-93; Rainforest Curr Comm 4-95; Strategic Planning Comm 1995-; NEA 1974-; PSEA 1974-; LEA 1974-, Sec 1988-90; PTA 1974-, Pres 1978-82; Northern Ath osters 1988-, Pres 1988-90, Sec 1991-; Lib Bd 1996; *office:* Salisbury Lick Schl PO Box 68 Smith Ave Salisbury PA 15558*

USMAN, JAN LURIE, Teacher; *b:* Altoona, PA; *m:* Jack K.; *c:* Heidi, ; *ed:* Penn St Univ (BS) Elem Ed 1974, (MA) Curr, Instruction 1980, A) Elem Guid 1981; *cr:* Northern Bedford Elem Schl Tchr 1974-; *ai:* EA 1974-; Storytellers of Blair Cty 1992-; *office:* North Bedford Elem hl HCR 1 Box 200A Loysburg PA 16659*

OUSTON, CARLA JEAN (FOREMAN), Fifth & Sixth Grd Science hr; *b:* Spring Valley, NY; *m:* C. Thomas; *ed:* St Thomas Aquinas Coll S) Ed 1970-; Immaculate Conception Seminary (MA) Moral Theology 81; Fairfield Univ 9 Credit Hrs Ed; Univ of NY 21 Cred Hrs Ed; *cr:* St egory Barbarigo Schl Elem Tchr 1970-80; Paramus Cath Girls HS eology, Philosophy Tchr 1981-83; St Joseph's Schl Second Grd, 7-8th d Sci, Eng Tchr 1984-87; Annunciation Schl 7-8th Grd Math, 5-6th Sci hr 1987-; *ai:* Sci Coord; STANYS 1990-; *home:* 196 Garth Rd Scarsdale Y 10583*

OUSTON, CARLENE PEARCE, American History Teacher; *b:* ilipsburg, PA; *m:* Edward N. Jr.; *c:* Ashley, Dustin; *ed:* Lock Haven Univ s) Soc Sci, Geog 1973; Safety Ed Cert; Credits in Cmptr Sci NC St; *cr:* est Branch Area Schl Tchr 1975-; *ai:* NEA PSEA, WBEA 1975-; Pals H Club 1988-, Ldr, Outstdng 4-H Ldr; Agway Inc 1980-, Bd of Dir; PFB 88-, Outstdng Farm Woman; *home:* Painted Hills Farm Kylertown PA 847

HOUSTON, JOOANNE, Music Director; *b:* New Haven, CT; *ed:* Univ of CT (BS) Music Ed 1980; Univ of NH (MED) Admin, Supervision 1994; *cr:* Windham Cntrl Supervisory Union Music Edctr 1980-84; Spaulding HS Music Dir 1984-; *ai:* SADD Adv; Masque, Dagger Drama Club Music Dir; Marching, Concert Bands, Chorus Dir; AFT; NHMEA; ASCD; NEBDA; Tchr of Yr 1992; Amer Legion Patriotic Citizen Awd 1996; Mayoral Outstdng Comm Contribution Awd 1993; Plymouth St Coll Stu Ldrshp Clinician; *office:* Spaulding H S N Wakefield St Rochester NH 03867*

HOUSTON, LINDA S., Assoc Prof of Comm Skills; *b:* New York, NY; *m:* Daniel B.; *c:* Eric, William; *ed:* Syracuse Univ (BS) Speech Ed 1963, (MS) Speech Ed 1968; *cr:* Jr Highs & HS Eng Tchr 1963-70; OH St Ag Tech Inst Assoc Prof 1971-; *ai:* Writing Lab, Comm Skills, Minority Stdnts Tchng Comm Coords; Fac Senate ATI; Univ Senate; NCTE; Mid West Regnl 2 Yr Coll Pres; OH Assn of Two Yr Coll, Ed, Journal; Natl Two Yr Coll Cncl, Past Secy; City Cncl 1984-92; Wayne Cty Alcoholism Svc 1992-, Pres; United Way; Every Womans House, Ahena Woman of Achvmnt Awd; Day Care; 15 Articles Pub; 40 Professional Presentation; *office:* OH St Univ Agri Tech Inst 1328 Dover Rd Wooster OH 44691*

HOUSTON, TYRUS C., MS Geography & History Teacher; *b:* Concord, NH; *m:* Linda E. Schneider; *ed:* Plymouth St Coll of Univ of NH (BE) Ed 1968; Credit Hrs; *cr:* Timberlane Regnl HS Tchr 1968-72, 1977-81; Marthas Vineyard Regnl HS Tchr 1972-76; Franklin Jr Sr HS Tchr 1976-77; Hopkinton MS HS Tchr, Coord 1981-; *ai:* MS, Travel Coord; Admin Cncl; ASCD; NCSS; Local Historical Soc; Presentor Intl Conf Ulster, Amer Folkpark 1995, Lowell Natl Park 1994; HS Principals Awd 1994; *office:* Hopkinton MS HS 297 Park Ave Contoocook NH 03229

HOUT, GRANT D., High School French Instructor; *b:* Crestline, OH; *ed:* Berea Coll KY (BA) Fr 1982; Attnd Univ of Cincinnati; *cr:* Cinti Pub Schls Fr Instr 1982-84; Princeton City Schls Fr Instr 1985, 1987-; *ai:* Adv Fr Club1985-91; Travel Adv; OH Foreign Lang Assn 1984-; Cinti Pub Schls Grant 1983.

HOVAN, JAMES M., Science Teacher; *b:* Anaston, AL; *ed:* Temple Univ (BA) Bio 1993; Univ of PA (MSEd) Scndry Bio & Eng 1994; *cr:* Schl Dist of Philadelphia Stu Tchr 1993-94; South Western Schl Dist Sci Tchr 1994-; *ai:* Soccer Coach; York Cty Sci Fair, Thespian Soc & Outdoor Adventure Club Adv; Earth Day Planning Comm Organizer; NEA & PSEA 1994-; NSCAA 1996; Trout Unlimited 1995-; Sierra Club 1996; Presented Rsrch at Intnl Ethnography in Ed Conf; Univ of PA Moore Flwshp; Temple Smith Scholar; Golden Key NHS; *office:* South Western Sr HS 225 Bowman Rd Hanover PA 17331*

HOVENKOTTER, DALE R., Math, Science & Computer Tchr; *b:* Yakima, WA; *m:* Mary F. Duckett; *ed:* Cntrl WA Univ (BAEd) Gen Sci 1986; *cr:* Willapa Vly HS Sci, Math, Cmptr Tchr 1986-89; Schweinfurt Amer MS Sci, Math, Cmptr Tchr 1989-; *ai:* IM Spon.

HOVERMAN, PHILIP THOMAS, Band Director; *b:* Van Wert, OH; *m:* Carla Fae Fogt; *c:* Ryan, Trent; *ed:* Bowling Green St Univ (BM) Music Ed 1975, (MM) Music Performance, Conducting 1979; *cr:* Antwerp Local Schls Band Dir 1975-77; Bowling Green St Univ Band Asst Grad 1977-79; Archbold Area Schls Band Dir 1979-; *ai:* Marching, Pep, Jazz Band; Church Handbell Dir; OH Music Ed Assn, Music Ed Natl Conf 1975-; Amer Schl Band Dir Assn 1989-; *office:* Archbold HS 600 Lafayette St Archbold OH 43502

HOVEY, ARTHUR, Physics Teacher; *b:* Southampton, NY; *m:* Carol Carbone; *c:* Lyrica, Daniel, Philip; *ed:* Yale Coll (BA) Physics & Math 1964; Yale Univ (MAT) Ed 1965; *cr:* Hillhouse HS Physics & Math Tchr 1965-67; Amity Reg HS Physics Tchr 1967-; *ai:* Physics Jazz Band, Aerospace Club; AFM 1965-; AAPT 1966-; TUBA 1974-; CT Symphonic Band 1990-, 1st Tubist; *office:* Amity Regional HS 25 Newton Rd Woodbridge CT 06525*

HOWANITZ, EUGENE J., Staff Dev Dir & English Instr; *b:* Glenn Lyon, PA; *ed:* King's Coll (BA) Eng 1964; 36 Credit Hrs PA Dept of Ed; 18 Grad Hrs Bloomsburg Univ; *cr:* Pottstown Schl Dist Eng Instr 1964-66; Dallas Schl Dist Eng Instr 1966-; Luzerne Co Comm Coll Adjunct Instr 1984-86; Wilkes Univ Adjunct Instr 1988-89; *ai:* Staff Dev Dir, Facilitator; Dallas Ed Assn 1966-; NEA, PSEA 1964-; *office:* Dallas Schl Dist PO Box 2000 Dallas PA 18612

HOWARD, CHARLES ANTHONY,SR., Program Specialist; *b:* Brooklyn, NY; *m:* Valerie Carter; *c:* Charles Jr.; *ed:* SUC at Buffalo (BA) Jrnlsm 1983; SUNY at New Paltz (MS) Educl Admin 1993, CAS Educl Admin 1995; Doctoral Candidate NY Univ; *cr:* Newburgh Acad HS Cnslr, Coach, Prgm Specialist 1986-; *ai:* Var Vlybl, Asst Var Girls Bsktbl Coach; NTA, NYSUT, AFT 1986-; NASSP 1995-; DARE 1988-, Bd of Dirs, Comm Svc; Neighborhood Based Alliance 1991-, Bd of Dirs; Fellowship Grad Work Ed Admin, Supervision; *office:* Newburgh Free Acad 201 Fullerton Ave Newburgh NY 12550

HOWARD, DONALD EVERS,JR., 8th Grd American History Tchr; *b:* Albany, NY; *m:* Doris Marie Eitzen Crain; *c:* Scott Crain, Marcia Crain, Kelly, Susan Crain, Todd; *ed:* Union Coll (BA) His 1963; 46 Grad Credit Hrs St Univ Coll at Oneonta; *cr:* Cooperstown Cntrl Schl 12th Grd Psych Tchr 1979-92, 8th Grd Soc Stud Tchr 1964-; *ai:* Jr HS Bsktbl 1964-69, JV Bsktbl 1969-95, Jr HS Track 1964-70, Cross Cntry 1985-91, Var Track 1971- Coach; NEA 1964-; NYSUT 1964-76; Rotary Tchr of Yr 1992; NY St Coaches Assn Awd 1995; *office:* Cooperstown Central Schl 38 Linden Ave MS HS Bldg Cooperstown NY 13326

HOWARD, GEOFFRY STANTON, Assoc Prof of Information Sys; *b:* Parkersburg, WV; *m:* Cindy Smith; *c:* Adam, Amy; *ed:* Univ of Cincinnati (BSEE) Electrical Engrng 1972; Univ of Pittsburgh (MBA) Mgmt 1973; Kent St Univ (DBA) Information Systems 1984; *cr:* Youngstown St Univ Sr Systems Analyst 1979-82; ID St Univ Asst Prof 1984; Kent St Univ Assoc Prof 1984-; *ai:* Curr Coord Information Systems; Air Force Reserve 1982-, Col; Distinguished Tchng Awd Finalist KSU Alumni Assn 1988 & 1989; Mortar Bd Tchng Recognition 1986-90; Paul Pfeiffer Creative Tchng Awd 1995; *office:* Kent St Univ Coll of Bus Kent OH 44242

HOWARD, GLORIA BRESLIN, Head of Gifted Prgm & His Tchr; *b:* Toronto ON, Canada; *m:* Hersh; *c:* Rick, Andrew; *ed:* Dalhousie Univ (BA) Hnr His 1958; Univ of Toronto Specialist, Spec Ed 1982; *cr:* Gordon Graydon Schl His, Geog Tchr 1961-66; Earl Haig Scndry Schl His Tchr 1967-; *ai:* Model UN Assembly; Eva's Place for Abused Women; Ldrshp Cncl; OSSTF 1959-; Governor Gen Commemorative Medal 1993; Tchr of the Yr Toronto Sun Newspaper 1991; Tchrs Models of Excl Joyce Nesker; *home:* 131 Beecroft Rd #905 North York ON M2N 6G9 Canada CN *

HOWARD, JAMES, Science Teacher & Coach; *b:* Port Jefferson, NV; *m:* Florence Seibold; *c:* Elyse, Kerrie, James, Aimee; *ed:* SUNY at New Paltz (BS) Scndry Ed 1966; SUNY at Stony Brook (MA) Lbrl Stud 1970; 30 Grad Credits; *cr:* Brentwood HS Sci Tchr 1966-; *ai:* Girls Var Cross Cntry, Track Coach; Brentwood Tchrs Assn 1966-; NY St United Tchrs Assn 1966-; AFT 1966-; Suffolk Cty Coach of Yr 1995; *office:* Brentwood HS 1st St & 5th Ave Brentwood NY 11717

HOWARD, JANE C., French Teacher; *b:* New Orleans, LA; *m:* Hampton W; *c:* Troup; *ed:* TX Chrstn Univ (BA) Fr, Studio Art 1967; Vanderbilt Univ (MA) Fr, Art His 1971; Art Stdnts League NYC 1975-80; *cr:* R. B. Stall HS Art Tchr 1969-; Job Corps HS Equivalency Tchr 1971-73; Art Stdnts League NYC Office 1975-80; Conant HS Fr Tchr 1987-; *ai:* Adv NHS; Prof Dev Comm; AATF, NEA 1987-; Natl Fr Exam Prize Winning Prof 1992-95; *office:* Conant HS 109 Stratton Rd Jaffrey NH 03452

HOWARD, JOANNA, English Composition Assistant; *b:* Boston, MA; *m:* William Olexik; *ed:* Univ of MD (BA) Eng Lit 1989; Georgetown Univ Working Towards BA in Eng Lit; *cr:* Montgomery Cty Schls Eng Composition Asst 1983-; Montgomery Coll Basic Writing Instr 1991-92; Freelance Writing Mentor, Tutor 1993-; *ai:* Lit Magazine Spon; NCTE, CCC 1983-; AAUW 1990-; The Writer's Ctr 1984-; Writing Ctr Assoc Flwshp Georgetown Univ 1989-90; Montgomery Arts Cncl Grant 1987; Presenter at Band Inst for Writing & Things 10 Yr Anniversary 1992; NCTE, Merlyn's Pen, MD Stu Press Assn Awds for Lit Magazines 1989, 1991, 1995; *office:* Watkins Mill HS 10301 Apple Ridge Rd Gaithersburg MD 20879

HOWARD, JOHN LOUGHERY, Science Teacher; *b:* Philadelphia, PA; *m:* Nancy M.; *c:* Kristina; *ed:* Villanova Univ (BS) Psych, Bio 1963; North AZ Univ (MA) Soc Ed 1976; Attnd Harvard Univ, Northeastern Univ; *cr:* Brookline HS Bio Tchr 1971-; *ai:* Schl Cncl; NABT 1990-; *office:* Brookline HS 115 Greenough St Brookline MA 02146

HOWARD, JOHN WILLIAM, 8th Grd American History Tchr; *b:* Sandusky, OH; *m:* Patricia Ann Butchko; *c:* Jason, Amber; *ed:* Defiance Coll (BS) His 1975; Bowling Green St Univ Grad Work; *cr:* Bellevue Jr HS 7th Grd Geog, OH His Tchr 1975-; *ai:* NEA, OH Educl Assn 1975-; *office:* Bellevue Jr HS North St Bellevue OH 44811

HOWARD, JOYCE SATTLER, Second Grade Teacher; *b:* New York City, NY; *m:* Philip Laurance; *c:* Robert, Douglas; *ed:* Nassau Comm Coll (AA) Lbrl Arts, Eng 1972; Adelphi Univ (BS) Elem Ed 1974, (MA) Humanistic Ed 1979; 75 Addl Hrs; NCHE Growing Healthy Trainer; NCCJ Cert Conflict Resolution; *cr:* Massapequa Schls K-8th Grd Sub Tchr 1976-81; N Bellmore Schls K-6th Grd Sub Tchr 1981-87; Saw Mill Rd 3, 6th Grd Tchr 1987-92; Dinkel Meyer Schl 5th Grd Tchr 1992-94; Park Ave Schl 2nd Grd Tchr 1994-; *ai:* Shared Decision Making Comm; CPR Cert; Family Math, Sci Day Prgm Facilitator; N Bellmore Tchrs Assn 1986-, Hlth, Safety, JPPC Exec Bd; Natl Cncl for Hlth Ed; Natl Conf of Chrstns, Jews; PTA 1966-; Smithsonian 1995-; Fire Island Preservation Soc 1988-; Curr Dev Mini-Grants; Growing Healthy Tchr, Trainer; Listed in Anthology; Lit Group; Tchr Ctr Facilitator; *office:* Park Ave Schl 1599 Park Ave N Merrick NY 11566*

HOWARD, LILLIAN D. WHEELER, Reading Specialist; *b:* Washington, DC; *m:* Robert F.; *c:* Robert H., Katira C.; *ed:* Howard Univ (BA) Eng 1970; Edinboro St Coll (MED) Rdng Specialist 1974; State, Rowan Colls Grad Courses; Howard Univ 24 Cred Hrs Master of Arts Prgm Eng Dept 1970; *cr:* Howard Univ Grad Fellow Frosh Eng Tchr 1970-71; Northern HS 10th Grd Eng Tchr 1971-73; Henry C. Beck MS 8th Grd Dev Rdng Tchr 1974-78; Edward T. Hamilton Elem Schl K-5th Grd Rdng Specialist 1978-; *ai:* Voorhees Dist Rdng Specialists, Rdng Curr Review, Spec Needs Pupil Asst Comms; Intnl Rdng Assn; West Jersey Rdng Cncl; Rdng Assessment, Evaluation, Enrichment, Curr Dev, Instruction, Resource, Strategy, Instrl Ideas for Large, Small Group Lessons; NJ ED Assn 1974-; West Jersey Rdng Cncl 1991-, Lit Awd 1993; Mt Zion United Meth Church 1974-, Soc Concerns Chair 1979-80; Howard Univ Grad Flwshp 1970-71; Edinboro St Coll Grad Flwshp 1973-74; Selected Citizen Ambassador Prgm to Visit Peoples Republic of China For Sixteen Days 1994; *office:* Edward T Hamilton Elem Schl 23 Northgate Dr Voorhees NJ 08043*

HOWARD, NANCY MALLISON, Bio Tchr & Acad Team Ldr; *b:* Binghamton, NY; *m:* John L.; *c:* Kristina; *ed:* St Univ of NY at Buffalo (BA) Bio & Geology 1961, (MS) Bio & Chem 1968; Post Grad Credit Hrs at Syracuse Univ, St Univ of NY at Albany, Univ of CA at Berkeley, Harvard Univ, Northern AZ Univ & Univ of NY at Stoney Brook; *cr:* Eden Cntrl HS Bio Tchr 1961-67; Brookline HS Bio Tchr 1967-, Bio Acad Team Ldr 1994-; *ai:* NABT 1988, Outstdng Bio Tchr MA 1989; Various Local Grants for Curr Writing for the Sci Dept; *office:* Brookline HS 115 Greenough St Brookline MA 02146*

HOWARD, NANCY N., US His & Mathematics Teacher; *b:* Troy, NY; *m:* Merton W.; *c:* Merton, Catherine, Timothy; *ed:* Gorham St Tchrs Coll (BS) Ed, His & Math 1965; Eastern CT St Univ (MS) Ed 1974; *cr:* John S. Tapley Schl 8th Grd Sci & Math Tchr 1965-66; Hebron Elem Schl Sub Tchr 1973-83; Gilead HS Tchr 1973-83; Horace Porter Schl 8th Grd US His Tchr 1984-; *ai:* Taught Substance Abuse Classes; Yrbk Adv; Stu Advy Team; BEST Tchr; NEA 1984-; *office:* Horace W Porter Elem Schl School House Rd Columbia CT 06237

HOWARD, RALPH J., English & History Teacher; *b:* Philadelphia, PA; *m:* Diane; *c:* Dana, Susan, Ralph; *ed:* Univ of New England (BA) His 1965; Villanova Univ (MA) His 1974, (MED) Scndry Admin 1988; *cr:* St Katharine HS Tchr 1965-67; St Thomas More HS Tchr 1967-69; Archbishop Carroll HS Tchr 1969-; *ai:* Speech & Debate, T E Yth Soccer Coach; Chm Fac Coord Comm; NCEA 1965-, Schl Rep; Natl Historical Soc 1965-; Best Tchr of Yr Awd Suburban & Wayne Times 1992; *office:* Archbishop John Carroll HS 211 Matsonford Rd Radnor PA 19087

HOWARTH, ROSE ANN BORICHEWSKI, Principal; *b:* South River, NJ; *m:* Ronald E.; *c:* Marilyn V., Ronald J.; *ed:* Douglass Coll (BA) His 1959; Ed Courses Rutgers Univ 1959-60; Admin, Supervision Univ of MA 1985; *cr:* Sayreville Pub Schls K-1, 3-4, 1-8 Transitional I Tchr 1959-70; Rutgers Prep Schl Asst Prin, Dept Chair, Tchr 1970-85, Prin 1985-; *ai:* Storytelling; Exercise Club; NJAIS, Div Heads; Amer Assn Univ Women; NAIS; NJCTE; NJRA; Orton Dyslexia Soc; ASCD; NAEYC; NAESP; Chldhd Intnl; Douglass Alumnae, Bd Mem 1990-91, Pres of Class 1990-95; Ronald Mc Donald Childrens Charities; NJ Connection; Middlesex Cty Fair, Photography Chair; NJAIS St Conf Chair 2 Yrs; Richard C. Malley Prof Dev Awd for NJAIS; Mid Sts Schl Evaluation Comm Chair 5 Yrs; Numerous Articles Pub; Arts Awd; *office:* Rutgers Preparatory Schl 1345 Easton Ave Somerset NJ 08873

HOWE, ANN MARIE, Third Grade Teacher; *b:* Endicott, NY; *m:* Judson D.; *c:* Kyle E., Jason J.; *ed:* SUNY at Oneonta (BS) Ed 1970; Attd SUNY at Cortland, Elmira Coll, Suny at Binghamton; *cr:* Owego Elem Schl Third Grd Tchr 1970-; *ai:* Grd Level Chm; AFT, NYSUT 1970-; *office:* Owego Elem Schl George St Owego NY 13827

HOWE, ELIZABETH MILLER, 3rd Grade Teacher; *b:* New Bedford, MA; *m:* Herbert D.; *c:* Travis Douglas, Keven C.; *ed:* New England Coll (BA) Elem Ed 1968; *cr:* Town of Dartmouth 2nd Grd Tchr 1968-72, 3rd Grd Tchr 1974-; *ai:* Bristol Cty Tchrs; MA Tchrs Assn 1968-; NEA 1968-; *office:* George Potter Elem Schl 185 Cross Rd North Dartmouth MA 02747

HOWE, JUDITH YODER, English Teacher & Dept Chprsn; *b:* Quakertown, PA; *m:* Edward S.; *ed:* Finch Coll (AA) Art His, Eng 1969; Cedar Crest Coll (BA) Eng, Fine Arts 1971; Lehigh Univ (MED) Scndry Ed 1976; 16 Hrs Eng; 16 Hrs Bus Muhlenberg Coll; 12 Hrs Finance Cedar Crest Coll; *cr:* Troxell Jr HS Eng Tchr 1971-; *ai:* PA St Writing Assessment Project Reader, Scorer 1993-; Curr Review, Writing Assessment Comms, Eng Curr Guide WRiter, Ed Parkland Schl Dist; Dept Chprsn; Amer Assn Univ Women; Fundraising Projects for Local Hospitals, Colls; Spec Olympics Vol.

HOWELL, BARBARA BROWN, Retired Elementary Teacher; *b:* Plainfield, NJ; *m:* Robert C.; *ed:* Boston Univ (BS) Elem Ed 1957; *cr:* Washington Schl 6th Grd Tchr 1957-72, 5th Grd Tchr 1972-77, 6th GrdTchr 1977-92, 5th Grd Tchr 1992-93, Reitred 1993; *ai:* NEA, NJEA 1957-; Delta Sigma Theta 1960-, Natl Assn of Univ Women 1987-; Stu Tutorial & Mentoring Prgm 1994-; Frontiers Intnl Excl Educ Awd 1989; NJ Governors Tchr Recognition Prgm 1989; *home:* 1339 E Front St Plainfield NJ 07062

HOWELL, BURTON CLARK, Science Teacher; *b:* Lockport, NY; *m:* Barbara Ann Rubens; *ed:* SUC at Brockport (BS) Earth Sci 1988, (MA) Lbrl Arts 1992; *cr:* Batavia HS Sci Tchr 1988-; *ai:* Ftbl & Sftbl Coach; Sci Olympiad Adv; NYSUT 1988-; BTA 1988-, Elections Chair & Negotiations Comm, Tchr Recognition Awd 1993; *office:* Batavia HS 260 State St Batavia NY 14020*

HOWELL, DOROTHY VANDUSEN, Retired Elementary Teacher; *b:* Elmira, NY; *m:* Robert A.; *ed:* SUNY at Geneseo (BS) Ed 1970; Elmira Coll (MS) Ed 1975; Turn-Key Trainer; *cr:* Cohen MS 6th Grd Tchr 1970-71; Hammondsport Cntrl Schl 2nd-3rd, Pre-1, 6th Grd Tchr 1972-94; *ai:* NEA, NEANY 1970-; NYS Cncl of Pre-1st Tchrs 1981-, Sec; Highlands Co FL Amer Cancer Soc, Strides Against Cancer Walk Co-Chair; Tyrone United Meth Church.

HOWELL, ELIZABETH JEAN, Health & PE Teacher; *b:* Philadelphia, PA; *ed:* Atlantic Comm Coll (AA) Lbrl Arts 1972; Rowan Coll (BS) Hlth, PE 1974; CORE Credits Emergency Med Technician, EMT Instr, CPR Instr; *cr:* Greater Egg Harbor Regnl HS Dist Hlth, PE Tchr, Coach 1974-; Dept of Transp of NJ EMT Instr 1985-; *ai:* Head Sftbl Coach; Grad Coord; Mid St Auxillary Svcs Chm; Project Grad Comm; Prins Advy Bd; NEA, NJEA, ACEA 1974-; Absecon VFW Vol Am 1970-, Sec, Treas, Lifetime Gold Mem; Red Cross 1985-; Natl Red Cross Dir 1990-; Miss Absecon Team Schlsp Comm 1996; Chosen as Local Hero to Represent NJ in Carrying Olympic Torch on its Journey Across the Country; Distngd Woman of 1995 by Atlantic City Press; *office:* Oakcrest HS 1824 Vienna Ave Mays Landing NJ 08330*

HOWELL, JACQUELINE DUNPHY, Eighth Grd Mathematics Tchr; *b:* Kearny, NJ; *m:* Richard; *c:* Alana Jeanne, Molly Reed; *ed:* Rosemont Coll (BA) Psych & Ed 1979; Saint Peters Coll (MA) Ed & Cmptr Sci 1984; *cr:* Ind Child Stud Team K-8th Grd Tchr 1979-84; Kearny Schl System 3rd, 5th, 7th & 8th Grd Math Tchr 1984-; *ai:* NEA, NJEA, KEA 1984-; *office:* Lincoln Schl 121 Beech St Kearny NJ 07032

HOWELL, JOHN SCOTT, Business Education Teacher; *b:* Greenburg, PA; *ed:* Univ of Pittsburgh (BA) Bus Admin 1986; Indiana Univ of PA (BS) Bus Ed 1993; *cr:* Irwin Bank & Trust Co Credit Analyst 1986-88; Westinghouse Electric Co Contract Admin 1988-92; Central Westmoreland C & TC Automated Office Tech Instr 1994-; *ai:* Visual Coord, Lead Techician Marching Band; NEA, Tri-St Bus Assn 1992-; Trinity Branch #8470 1984-, Pres, Treas, VP; Police Ath League 1983-, Treas; PA Interscholastic Ath Assoc 1986-, Referee; Winter Guard Intnl 1994-, Judge; Chancel Bell Choir 1976-, Ringer; Loyal Order of Moose 1984-; PFCJ 1984-, Judge; Vol of Yr Awd Westinghouse 1991; Irwin Businessman of Month; *office:* Ctl Westmoreland Vo Tech Schl 240 Arona Rd New Stanton PA 15672

HOWELL, MARSHA PEASPANEN, First Grade Teacher; *b:* Ashtabula, OH; *m:* Frank Jr.; *c:* Gail, Jodi; *ed:* Kent St Univ (BA) Elem Ed 1976; Edinboro Univ (MS) Early Chldhd Ed 1986; *cr:* Southeast Elem Schl 2 Grd Tchr 1977-82, 1 Grd Tchr 1982-; *ai:* Mentor Tchr; Conneaut Ed Assn 1977-; OCTELA 1993-; Ashtabula Cty Lang Arts Ldrshp Team 1994-; Federated Church Mem; Mrktg Our Schls Awd 1991; Supt Ldrshp Awd 1993; *home:* 7777 Berkshire Rd Conneaut OH 44030*

HOWELL, MICHELE CHARNA, Family & Consumer Science Tchr; *b:* Cincinnati, OH; *m:* John Wesley Sr.; *c:* John, De'mond Jay Ranessalechele, Edward PUllen, Erin Pullen; *ed:* Univ of Cincinnati (BS) Home Ec Ed 1976; Coll of Mt Saint Joseph (MS) Ed, Rdng Specialty 1985; *cr:* Regina Parchoical Home Ec Tchr 1976-77; Cincinnati Pub Schl Family, Consumer Sci Tchr 1978-; *ai:* Yrbk, Sr Class, FHA Adv; Drill Team Asst Adv, VP; Parent Booster; CFT, AFT 1978-; FHA 1990-; Local Schl Decision Making Comm, Alumni Bd 1995-; Hall of Fame; *office:* Withrow HS 2488 Madison Rd Cincinnati OH 45208

HOWELL, MICHELLE ELANE (DAVIS), Reading & Language Arts Tchr; *b:* Wash Ct House, OH; *m:* Chris W.; *c:* Nathan, Rachel, Adrianne; *ed:* OH Univ (BSED) Elem Ed Comprehensive 1988; Miami Univ (MED) Elem Ed Comprehensive 1994; OH Writing Project 1992; *cr:* Clinton Massie Elem 1st Grd Tchr 1989; E Clinton MS MS Schl Rdng & Lang Arts 1989-; *ai:* Mentor Tchr; Lang Arts Tchr-Ldr; Intervention Assistance Team; Stu Cncl Adv; Lang Arts Curr Comm; NEA, OEA, & ECEA 1990-; NCTE 1991-; OCTELA 1992-; Outstdng Edctr of the Yr E Clinton Schl Dist 1994; Poems Pub; *office:* E Clinton MS 246 W Washington St Sabina OH 45169*

HOWELL, NORMA JEAN GRANDFIELD, Physics Teacher; *b:* Bourne, MA; *m:* Edwin I.; *c:* David E., Thomas G.; *ed:* Wright St UNiv (MED) Scndry Ed 1987, (BS) Engineering 1978; Univ of Dayton EDT 646 3 Credit Hrs 1992; Youngstown St Univ Couns 822L 3 Credit Hrs 1992; OH St Univ ED STDS 3 Credit Hrs 1991; Miami Univ CHM 699 5 Credit Hrs 1989; Univ of CO 3 Grad Credit Hrs 1995; *cr:* Troy Jr HS Phys Sci Tchr 1987-89; Wayne HS Physics Tchr 1989-; *ai:* Physics Club, Sr Class Adv; Sci Bowl, Sci Fair, JETS Teams Coach; Renaissance Comm; AAPT, Huber Heights Ed Assn 1989-; OH Ed Assn 1987-; Jennings Scholar 1993; Honored by Dayton Engineering & Sci Hall of Fame 1993; DOE-TRAC Tchr Research Grant 1992; Excel in Tchng Aw; Alliance for Ed, Wright Labs 1995; *office:* Wayne HS 5400 Chambersburg Rd Huber Heights OH 45424*

HOWELL, STEVEN J., English Teacher; *b:* Cleveland, OH; *m:* Kirstein; *ed:* Kent St Univ (BS) Eng 1993; *cr:* Cleveland Hebrew Acad Eng Tchr 1994-95; James A. Garfield HS Eng Tchr 1995-; *ai:* Lit Magazine; Golden Key Natl Honor Soc 1993-; *office:* James A. Garfield HS 10233 State Route 88 Garrettsville OH 44231*

HOWELL, THOMAS C., Mathematics Teacher; *b:* Cleveland, OH; *m:* Joyce Ann Bombay; *c:* Thomas J., Jennifer; *ed:* St Vincent Coll (BA) His 1967; Kent St Univ (MED) Math, Ed 1974; Attnd Keene St, John Carroll Univ, Toledo Univ, OH Univ; *cr:* Berea City Schools Tchr 1968-; *ai:* 8-9th Grd Boys, Girls Bsktbl; 8-9th Grd, Var Asst Girls Track; Cmptr, Chess Club; NCTM, OCTM 1969-; OEA 1968-, Life Mem; Educl Cmptr Consortium of OH 1975-, Vice Chair; BSA 1975-, Scoutmaster, Eagle; NSF Grants Kent St 1970-73, OH U 1978; *office:* Midpark HS 7000 Paula Dr Middleburgh Hts OH 44130*

HOWENSTEIN, MARK S., Asst Prof of Law & Society; *b:* Kirkwood, MO; *m:* Karen S.; *ed:* St Louis Univ (BA) Philosophy 1977; Tulane Univ Schl of Law (JD) Law 1981; WA Univ (MA) Lib Arts 1986; UC at Berkeley (PHD) Juris Prudence & Soc Policy 1993; *cr:* Civil Cts Law Clerk 1981-83; Klutho, Cody, Kilo & Flynn Attys Inc Assoc Attorney 1984-86; UC at Berkeley Tchng Asst 1986-92; Ramapo Coll of NJ Asst Prof 1993-; *ai:* Prelaw Adv; Fac Rep to Pad; Anthropology Search Comm Lit Chair; Campus Wide Information Systems; Law & Soc Masters Lib Stud; Law & Soc Assn 1988-; MO & IL Bar Assn 1981-82; NE Assn of Prelaw Advs 1995-; AFT 1993-; Hands of Help 1993-, Dir, Natl Adv; Intnl Comm of Lawyers for Tibet 1988-, Founding; Berkeley Prof Stud Abroad 1989-90; Tchng Asst of Yr 1990-91; *office:* Ramapo Coll Of NJ 505 Ramapo Valley Rd Mahwah NJ 07430*

HOWES, MARY WHEELER, Retired Teacher; *b:* Utica, NY; *m:* Raymond T.; *c:* Laura, Paul, Katherine Reynolds, Timothy Reynolds; *ed:* Colgate Univ (BA) Sociology 1970; 30 Post Grad Hrs; Cornell Univ 3 Undergraduate Yrs; Syracuse Univ 12 Undergraduate Hrs; *cr:* Hamilton Co-Op Nursery Schl Head Tchr 1963-68; Sherburne-Earlville Cntrl Schl Tchr of Kndgtn, 4th-5th Grds Learning Disabled, GATE 1970-90; Sherburne Pub Lib Dir 1990-91; Colgate Univ Resident Supvr 1992-93; *ai:* NEA 1970-; Hamilton Co-Op Nursery Schl, Bd of Trustees; Comm Meml Hosp, Bd of Trustees; Hamilton Rel Soc of Friends, Clerk, Recording Clerk; Invited to Give Commencement Address Sherburne-Earlville CS 1992; Election to Phi Beta Kappa Colgate Univ 1970; *home:* RR 2 Box 211A Hamilton NY 13346*

HOWETT, RICHARD A., Soc Studies Tchr & Asst Prin; *b:* Wilsonboro, PA; *ed:* Penn St Univ (BS) Scndry Ed 1965; Trenton St Coll (MA) His 1973; Rider Coll Admin Cert 1978; *cr:* Lower Moreland MS Soc Stud Tchr 1968-; Lower Moreland HS Soc Stud Tchr 1968-, Ath Dir 1978-87; Lower Moreland MS Ath Dir 1978-87, Asst Prin 1979-80; Lower Moreland HS Asst Prin 1986-88, 1993-; *ai:* Winter Track Coach 1977-92, Head Coach 1981-82; MS Track Coach 1977-88; HS Head Boys Track Coach 1988-92; Lower Moreland Ed Assn 1968-, Pres 1973-76; Lower Bucks Track & Field Ofcls 1986-, Pres 1989-; PSEA, NEA 1968-; Wrightstown Lib Bd 6 Yrs, Pres; Wrightstown Planning Commission 9 Yrs, Chm; Spec Awd for Svc to Track & Field from Track Coaches Assn of Greater Philadelphia.

HOWEY, WILLIAM CALVIN, Soc Stud, His & Ec Teacher; *b:* Hazleton, PA; *m:* Margaret Ann Lilly; *c:* Kimberly, Dianna; *ed:* Chapman Coll (BA) Soc Stud 1974; Pepperdine Univ (MA) Human Resource Mgt 1977; Kutztown Univ PA St Tchrs Cert 30 Hrs; *cr:* US Marine Corps Lt Col 1954-86; Boyertown Area Schl Dist Sub Tchr 1988-89; Boyertown Area Sr HS Soc Stud Tchr 1989-; *ai:* Yrbk Adv, Ath Ldr 1989-; NEA, PSEA, Boyertown Area Ed Assn 1989-; VFW 1959-, Amer Legion 1987, Retired Off Assn 1986; Niantic Christ Luth Church 1992-; Chapman Coll Cum Laude Gray Key; Kutztown U Deans List; Defense Superior Svc Medal; *office:* Boyertown Area Sr HS 4th & Monroe St's Boyertown PA 19512

HOWIE, ALAN C., PE Teacher & Coach; *b:* Milton, MA; *m:* Winifred J. Everbeck; *c:* Michael, Andrea, Sarah; *ed:* Span Cert Harvard Univ; 15 Hrs Northeastern Univ; *cr:* Sharon Pub Schls PE Instr 1969-; *ai:* Head Coach Boys Var Soccer; Bsktbl Timer, Scorer; NEA; MAPHER; NSCAA 1978-; NSCAA 1978-; EMASS Soccer Coaches Assn 1986-, Ex Bd; Weymouth Soccer Club 1978-90, Pres, Exec Bd; South Shore Soccer League 1985-, Past Bd, Outstdng Contribution; Coach of Yr 1993; Div II E. MA SCA; Outstdng Contributor 1992; EMASS Soccer Coaches Assn; *office:* Shaorn Pub Schls 75 Mountain St Sharon MA 02067

HOWLAND, C. WILLIAM, Principal; *b:* Ware, MA; *m:* Janice; *c:* Jeff, Wendy, Karen, Robert; *ed:* Worc St Coll (BS) Elem 1961, (MS) Admin 1964; *cr:* Rice Schl Tchr 5 Yrs; Dawson Schl Asst Prin 3 Yrs; Rice Schl Prin 28 Yrs; *office:* Margery Rice Elem Schl 48 Phillips Rd Holden MA 01520

HOWLAND, CRAIGIN BARTLETT, English Teacher; *b:* New Haven, CT; *m:* Janice E.; *c:* Susan, Stephen Jewell; *ed:* Hartwick Coll (BA) Eng 19d75; Worcester St Coll (MED) Eng Ed 1992; 50 Credit Hrs Scndry Eng Cert Plymouth St Coll; *cr:* Hyde Schl Eng Tchr 1984-85; Bartellt HS Eng Tchr 1986-; *ai:* Yrbk Co-Adv; Websters Edctrs Assn, MA Tchrs Assn, NEA 1986-; Trustees Nichols Acad 1991-; *office:* Bartlett HS Lake Pkwy Webster MA 01570

HOWLAND, TAMMY, Math Teacher; *b:* South Bend, IN; *m:* Brent; *ed:* IN Univ (BS) Math Ed 1992, (AS) Cmptr Sci 1992; *cr:* Dayton Chrstn HS Math Tchr 1992-; *office:* Dayton Christian HS 325 Homewood Ave Dayton OH 45405*

HOWLEY, KATHLEEN M., Asst Professor of Counseling; *b:* Harrisburg, PA; *ed:* Penn St Univ (BS) Sci, Bio 1984, (MED) Cnslr Ed 1985; Doctoral Candidate in Adult Ed; *cr:* Keystone Jr Coll Act 101 Cnslr 1985-87; Penn St Univ Stu Act Dir 1987-89, Adult Cnslr 1989-90; Harrisburg Area Comm Coll Asst Prof, Counseling 1990-; *ai:* Natl Acad Advising Assn; PA Governor's Advy Cncl on Deaf & Hard of Hearing; Natl Inst for Leadership Dev; Passed Natl Bd for Cert Cnslrs Exam 1994; *office:* Harrisburg Area Comm Coll 1 Hacc Dr Harrisburg PA 17110

HOY, ELDON WAYNE, Secondary Math Teacher; *b:* Myrtle Beach, SC; *m:* Lori Ann Young; *c:* Zachary, Kira; *ed:* Lock Haven Univ (BA) Math 1988; Shenandoah Univ 18 Credit Hrs Cmptrs in Ed Grad Prgm; *cr:* Mifflinburg Area SD Scndry Math, Cmptr Tchr 1988-; *ai:* Class 1995 Adv; Asst Track, Boys & Girls Bsktbl Coach; Key Club Adv; Fac Treas; Fac Schlsp Comm; NEA, PSEA, MAEA 1988-; *office:* Mifflinburg Area Schl Dist 1st & Market Sts Mifflinburg PA 17844

HOY, MARGARET TROYANOSKI, 7th & 8th Grade Gen Sci Tchr; *b:* Frackville, PA; *m:* Daniel D.; *c:* Victoria M. Yeager; *ed:* PA St Univ (BS) Med Tech 1972; 37 Post Grad Credits Toward Scndry Ed Cert in Bio, Gen Sci 1976-77; *cr:* Schuylkill Intermediate Unit #29 Schl Tchr of Gifted 1978-82; Shenandoah Valley Jr, Sr HS 7th-8th Grd Gen Sci Tchr 1982-; *ai:* Discipline Comm; Mentor Tchr; NEA, PSEA 1978-; *office:* Shenandoah Valley Jr Sr HS 805 W Centre St Shenandoah PA 17976

HOY, MICHAEL J., Chemistry & Physics Teacher; *b:* Philadelphia, PA; *m:* Robin Schieber; *c:* Lisa, Karin, David; *ed:* Univ of Notre Dame (BS) Chem Engrng 1972; Univ of Tulsa (MS) Chem Engrng 1975; 42 Credit Hrs Temple Univ in Ed; *cr:* Neshaminy HS Sci Tchr 1990-; *ai:* Jr Var Bsbl Coach; Bucks Cty Sci Tchrs 1993-; *office:* Neshaminy HS 2001 Old Lincoln Hwy Langhorne PA 19047

HOYE, DAVID C., Social Studies Teacher; *b:* New Castle, PA; *m:* Judith Jackson; *c:* Matthew A.; *ed:* Slippery Rock Univ (BS) Soc Stud 1967, (ME) Soc Stud 1973; 33 Hrs Beyond Masters; *cr:* Lakeview HS Soc Stud Tchr 29 Yrs; *ai:* Chess Club Adv; NEA, PSEA, LEA 1967-, Pres Chief Negotiator; Presbyn Elder 1985-88; Presbyn Deacon 1991-93; Camera Club 1981-, Exec Bd 1981-; Natl Sci Fnd Awd in Psych Shippensburg St Coll; Schlsp Westminster Coll Summer Inst in Pol Sci; 1991 Receipient of 10 Exemplary Ec Tchrs in Pa by Joint Cncl of Ec; Citizen of Yr Sandy Lake Rotary 1982; Strategic Plnng for Schl Dist Mem; Coop Tchr for 20 Stu Tchrs; *office:* Lakeview H S RD 1 Stoneboro PA 16153*

HOYE, GWENDOLYN SANDERS, 7th Grade Teacher; *b:* Philadelphia, PA; *m:* Lionel S.; *c:* Maisha, Atiya, Ayana; *ed:* Cheyney Univ (BS) Elem Ed 1964; Attnd Drexal Univ, Sci Resource Ldr Inst; 15 Credits Beaver Coll; 20 Credits Temple Univ; *cr:* Pratt Arnold Tchr 1964-70; Rhodes MS Tchr 1972-78; Fitler Acad Plus Tchr 1980-; *ai:* 24 Challenge Spon; Concerned Black Men Black His Bee Spon; Penn St Univ Math Options 1994 Spon; Canaan Bapt Bowling Club Coach; Chevney Univ CHAMP-MENTOR United Negro Coll Fund Vol; PA Cncl of Tchrs of Math 1985-; ATMOPAV 1987-; PAESTA 1990-; Stu Welfare Cncl 1990-, Bd; Pinochle Bugs Soc & Civic Club 1976-, Natl VP; Alpha Kappa Alpha 1963-; Chapel of Four Chaplains Comm Awd; United Negro Coll Fund Svc Awd; *office:* Fitler Academics Plus Schl Seymour & Knox Sts Philadelphia PA 19144

HOYE, JUNE M., English Teacher; *b:* Derby, CT; *m:* John T.; *c:* John T. Jr., Lauren Hoye Collins, Kathleen Hoye Mingo; *ed:* CT Coll (BS) Zoology 1957; So CT St Coll (MS) Schl Psych 1967; 30 Credit Hrs 6th Yr Eng 1967; *cr:* Wesleyan Univ Bio Tchng & Research Asst 1957-58; Seymour HS Eng Tchr 1967-69; Ledyard Jr HS Eng Tchr 1969-70; Waterford HS Eng Tchr 1970-, Dir of Adult Ed 1980-; *ai:* AFT 1969-; Ansonia Lib Bd 1963-65, Pres of Dirs; North Stonginton Recreation Bd 1967-70, Sec; *office:* Waterford HS 20 Rope Ferry Rd Waterford CT 06385*

HOYECKI, MARIE CAHILL, Retired Teacher; *b:* Manhattan, NY; *m:* Victor J.; *c:* Ellen Nelson, Susan Scholler, Victor, Tricia Rosin, Robert; *ed:* Fordham Univ (BS) Elem Ed 1952; *cr:* Norwalk Pub Schls Mid Grd Tchr 1953-57; Rockville Centre Schls Mid Grd Tchr 1963-91; *ai:* AFT 1963-, Elem Rep; *home:* 136 Argyle Rd West Hempstead NY 11552

HOYER, DEXTER CRAIG, Principal; *b:* Lockport, NY; *m:* Connie Ann Lathers; *c:* Kelly Dawn Taulbee, Amy Lynn Butler, Todd Allen, Scott Zachary; *ed:* Concordia Jr Coll (AA) Ed 1967; Concordia Coll (B 1969; Univ of Akron (MS) Elem Admin 1983; *cr:* Trinity Luth 1969-71; St John Luth Tchr 1971-75; St Peter Luth Prin, Tchr 19 Redeemer Chrstn Schl 8th Grd Tchr 1981-94, Prin 1994-; *ai:* Clev Prins Assoc Schl Bsktbl Coach; LEA 1981-; OAESA 1994-; Redeemer Chrstn Schl 2141 5th St Cuyahoga Falls OH 44221

HOYER, EDGAR, Retired Math & Economics Tchr; *b:* Washingtor *m:* Aline Sowers; *ed:* Trinity Coll (BA) Ec 1956; Post Grad Stud G Washington Univ, Amer Univ, Shippensburg Coll; *cr:* St James Schl Tchr 1959-95.

HOYER, KRISTINA KRSTULICH, English & Writing Teacher; Petersburg, FL; *m:* Edgar Thomas; *c:* Hollister, Shawn; *ed:* Washington Coll(BA) Eng 1968; Penn St Univ (MS) Ed 1972; *cr:* Hig Falls HS Eng Tchr 1968-70; Keith Jr HS Eng, Writing Tchr 1970-; *ai* Jr Hnr Soc Spon; Applied Acad Steering Comm; AAEA, PSEA, NCTE 1970-; ASCD 1990-; Cntrl PA Writers Assn 1990-; Blair Cty Festival 1990-, 1st Pl Poetry Awd; Article Pub; *office:* Keith Jr HS 19th Ave Altoona PA 16601*

HOYER, LAWRENCE COSWELL, Science Teacher; *b:* Washir DC; *m:* Phyllis Scarborough; *c:* Brian, Andrew; *ed:* Wesleyan Univ Bio & Chem 1958; Frostburg Univ (MED) Bio & Ed 1966; Johns Hc Univ (SCD) Med Entomology 1974; Attnd NIH, Oak Ridge Assoc Un Inst of Marine Sci, Univ of MD, AZ St Univ, Hood Coll; *cr:* St James Sci Tchr & Dept Head 1958-66; Hood Coll Asst Bio Prof 1966-72 Cancer Inst Rsrch Scientist 1975-84; Wilde Lake HS Sci Tchr 1985 Jr Class Spon; MD Bio Tchrs Assn 1966-, VP & Pres; AAAS 1975-; MTA & HCTA 1984-; Heart Assn Bd 1966-67; Frederick Y Swim 1972-74, Bd of Trustees 1979-82, VP for Pgms, Chm for Annual M Drive, Fin Comm, VP for PR, United Way Rep; 30 Journal Publica Cosip Grant; NIH Rsrch Grant; NIH Post Doctoral Rsrch Flv Frederick YMCA Vol of the Yr; *office:* Wilde Lake High School State Route 108 Clarksville MD 21029*

HOYLE, CAROL A., English Teacher; *b:* Providence, RI; *m:* John Kerri Duquette, John Jr., Jason; *ed:* RI Coll (EDB) Ed 1959; Univ (MA) Amer Lit 1970; Post Grad Stud Film Making RI Schl of Desig Comm Schl 8 Grd Tchr 1961-67; B. F. Norton Schl 8 Grd Tchr 196 Cumberland MS 7-8 Grd Tchr 1969-71; North Cumberland MS 7-8 Tchr, Curr Coord 1971-90; C umberland HS Eng Tchr 1990-; *ai:* C CHS Annual Gala 1995-; Asst Adv Debate Team 1993-95; Grad C 1995-; HUGS Adv 1991-94; Cumb Tchrs Assn 1962-, VP 1988-92; NEA RI 1962-; Cumberland-Lincoln Comm Chorus 1987-, Pres 198 Producer 1992-; Barrington Boys Choir 1978-85, Bd Mem.

HOYT, CHRISTINA HESS, Language Arts & Math Teacher; *b:* Bu NY; *m:* Jon; *c:* Trisha, Mitchell; *ed:* Univ of Pittsburgh at Johnstown Elem Ed 1981; Edinboro Univ (MED) Schl Admin 1983; Schl Admin *cr:* St Thomas Schl 1-8 Grd Tchr 1981-82; North East Mid Schl 8th Lang Arts & Math Tchr 1983-; *ai:* NEA, PSEA, NEEA 1983-; Wa Church, Chrstn Ed, Deacon, Elder 1969-; Candidate for Natl MS Bd *office:* North East MS 1903 Freeport Rd North East PA 16428*

HOYT, DEBRA JEAN (KNAPP), Second Grade Teacher; *b:* Joh City, NY; *m:* Edwin Dasal; *c:* Jennifer, Justin; *ed:* St Univ Coll at Cor NY (BS) Elem Ed 1982, (MS) Rdng, Elem Ed 1989; *cr:* Windsor Schls 3rd Grd Tchr 1984-92, 2nd Grd Tchr 1992-; *ai:* Schlsp, C Prevention, Prin Interview, Tchr Hiring, Hlth & Wellness Comm; C Vlybl Adult Ed Instr 6 Yrs; Schl Sunshine Person 2 Yrs; K-2 Comm Schl Report Card; AFT, NEA, WTA 1984-; Autumn Vly Golden Retri Club 1994, Sec, Corresponding Sec, Mem of Yr 1994; *home:* 234 Pag Windsor NY 13865

HOYT, WILLIAM CHESTER, Chemistry Professor; *b:* Beverly, MA Lorraine Merlene Crockett; *c:* Joanna, Zachary; *ed:* Univ of IA (BS) C 1966; Univ of KS (MS) Inorganic CHem 1969, (PHD) Inorganic C 1976; *cr:* Hudson Vly Comm Coll Prof Chem 1976-78; Ricker Coll Chem 1978-79; Saint Joseph's Coll Prof Chem 1979-; *ai:* After Schl A Conservation Commision; Amer Chem Soc 1974-; Phi Lambda Eps 1966-; New England Assn of Chem Tchr 1988-; Numerous Articles *office:* Saint Josephs Coll 278 White's Bridge Rd Standish ME 04084

HRADIL, BARBARA ELIZABETH, 8th Grd Language Arts Teache Irvington, NJ; *ed:* William Patterson (BA) Ed, Early Chldhd 1 Montclair Univ (MA) Environmental Ed, Sci 1976; Attnd Seaton Univ, St Peters, Jersey City St; *cr:* Hopatcong Borough Schl Dist 3rd Tchr 1 Yr, Kndgtn Tchr 6 Yrs, 6th Grd Tchr 2 Yrs, 1st Grd Tchr 10 Yrs Grd Tchr 2 Yrs, 7-8th Grd Tchr 4 Yrs; *ai:* Class Adv; Talent Show Co Hopatcong Ed Assn 1969-, Pres, Treas; NJEA; NEA; *office:* Hopatcong Box 1029 Hopatcong NJ 07843*

HRAPCHAK, STEVE J., Guidance Counselor; *b:* Nanty Glo, PA; *m:* Krawcion; *c:* Deborah Roberts, Carol Myers, Steve Don, Tammy; *ed* Univ of PA (BS) Bus Ed 1957, (MS) Guid Ed 1968; Penn St Univ; Adams Summerhill HS Bus Tchr 11 Yrs; Forest Hills HS Guid Cnsl Yrs; *ai:* Dept Chm; NEA 1958-; PSEA 1958-; FHEA 1958-; NHS L Awd; US Air Force Recruiting Appreciation Cert; *home:* 670 Pike Johnstown PA 15909

HREVNAK, MATTHEW J., Mathematics Teacher; *b:* Perth Amboy, *m:* Lilians Vera; *c:* Cassandra; *ed:* Rutgers Univ (BA) Math 1989, (M Ed Admin 1994; *cr:* Our Lady of Hungary 6th, 8th Grd Tchr 1984 Herbert Hoover MS Math Tchr 1992; John P. Stevens HS Math Tchr 19 *ai:* Asst Girls Bsktbl Coach; Acad Team Adv; NJEA, NEA, NC AMTNJ 1990-; NJ St Coaches Assn 1995-; NJ Fed of Bsbl Umpires 19 US Naval Acad Alumni Assn 1984-; Holy Name Soc Our Lady of Hung 1995-; Comm to Interview, Select Prin; Math Dept Rep on Curr Char *office:* John P Stevens HS Grove Ave Edison NJ 08820

HRIC, ANNE JOAN, Retired Elementary Teacher; *b:* New Castle, PA; John; *c:* Raymond, Kathleen, Marlene Crocco, Jerome; *ed:* Youngst Univ (BS) Elem Ed 1981; Clarion Slippery Rock Univ (ME) Ed 1984; Sci Microcomputer Interface; Marine Sci, Oceanography; Westinghouse Gen Acctng 1944-45; Lever Brothers Office Wo 1949-50; Admiral Corp Payroll 1950-51; St Joseph Schl Elem 1964-95; *ai:* Mid Sts Comm 1982, 1992; PTO, NCEA, Former Mem; G Ldr 8 Yrs; Choir 1965-; St Joseph's Adult Variety Shows; St Josep Children's Variety Show, Dir; Natl Pastoral Musicians Conf Philadelp 1st Place St Joseph's Choir; St Joseph's Parish Awd 1992; 30 Yr Tc Awd; *home:* 634 Spencer Ave Sharon PA 16146

HRNCIAR, ANGIE IORIO, Fourth Grade Teacher; *b:* Jersey City, NJ; Steve; *c:* Steve, Joseph, Mary, Jennifer Ferry, Kimberly; *ed:* Jersey City Coll (BS) Elem Ed 1954; Long Island Univ (MS) Elem Ed 1991; Addl Credits; *cr:* Washington Schl 6th Grd Tchr 1954-57; Maywood Av S 2nd-5th Grd Tchr 1978-93 4th Grd Tchr 1993-95; 6th Grd Sci & Rdng T 1995-; *ai:* Textbook, Report Card, Centennial Comms; NEA, MEA, NJ 1978-; Governor's Awd; Tchr of Yr 1991; *office:* Maywood Avenue S 452 Maywood Ave Maywood NJ 07607

HROBAK, MARY K. RAMAGE, Retired Elementary Teacher; *b:* Don Twp, PA; *m:* Albert C.; *ed:* California St Coll of PA (BS) Elem 1961; St 3 Credit Hrs; *cr:* Canton Twp Schl 5th Grd Tchr 1961-62; Warren C Schl 1-4 Grd Primary Ed Tchr 1962-90; *ai:* NEA 1962-; OEA 1962-, L Mem; WEA 1962- Bldg Rep; Ret Tchrs Assn 1991-, Life Mem; Natl Tole Decorative Painters; Warren Women's Bowling Assn; Warren Optim

-, Pres, 1st Women Awd; Cntrl Chrstn Church 1968-, Ed Bd; Young Ed arren Awd; *home:* 4060 Aleesa Dr SE Warren OH 44484

MISIN, JEROME THOMAS, English Teacher; *b:* Pittston, PA; *m:* Ellen Hoban; *c:* Patrick, Thomas; *ed:* King's Coll (BA) Eng-Magna Laude 1971; Univ of Scranton (MA) Eng 1975; *cr:* G. A. R. Meml HS Tchr 1971-; *ai:* Mid States Evaluation Philosophy-Objectives Comm Instr Upwd Bnd Prm Wilkes Univ; NEA, PSEA 1971-; PA Cncl of s of Eng 1972-; Knights of Columbus 1980-; Outstanding Scndry ator of America 1973; *office:* G A R Memorial H S Grant & Lehigh St es Barre PA 18702

SKO, SUE GLADIEUX, English Teacher; *b:* Toledo, OH; *m:* John; li, Jennifer, John; *ed:* Mary Manse Coll (BA) Eng & His 1969; *cr:* uley HS Eng Tchr 1969-71; Stritch HS Eng Tchr 1989-91; Cntrl Cath Tchr 1991-; *ai:* NHS Moderator; Kappa Gamma Pi 1969-; Fnd for Life -75, Trustee; *office:* Central Catholic HS 2550 Cherry St Toledo OH 8

BY, JOSEPH C., Graphic Design Assoc Professor; *b:* Cleveland, *m:* Mary Ann Rudlowski; *c:* Joseph Jr., Sara Lynn, Victoria Grace; *ed:* ing Green St Univ (BS) Art Ed 1962; Case Western Reserve Univ Art His 1974; *cr:* Cooper Schl of Art Dean 1970-73, Dir 1973-76; rnby Studio Creative Dir 1977-83; Univ of Akron Part-time Visiting Prof 1981-88, Asst Prof Graphic Design 1983-89; Colby-Sawyer Coll c Prof, Dir of Gr Des 1989-; *ai:* Electronic Pre Press Consultant, ier; Lib Advy, Tech, Prsnl Comms; Tech Coord Frances Bailey wood Cmptr Studio; Friends of the Lib 1989-; Summer Music Assn -, Bd of Dirs; *home:* PO Box 43 Wilmot NH 03287

SCHKA, PETER DANIEL, Sociology Professor; *b:* Canandaigua, *m:* Judith Kay Driver; *c:* Daniel, Thomas; *ed:* Univ of MD (BA) ology 1967; Univ of WI (MS) Sociology 1969, (PHD) Sociology 1975; Jniv of MD Instr 1969-71; New Coll Instr, Asst Prof 1973-75; OH hern Univ Asst Prof, Prof 1975-; *ai:* ONU Symphonic Band & Comm us; Amer Sociological Assn 1966-; Phi Beta Kappa, Alpha Kappa a, Phi Eta Sigma, Phi Kappa Phi, Kappa Kappa Psi & Kappa Delta Pi Societies; *home:* 138 S Johnson St Ada OH 45810

CHYNSZYN, CAROL PONTERDOLPH, Speech Therapist; *b:* ey City, NJ; *m:* John; *c:* Tracy, Jill; *ed:* Jersey City St Coll (BA) Speech apy, Sp Ed 1975; Kean Coll (MA) Speech, Lang Pathology 1994; Cert linical Competence Amer Speech & Hearing Assn 1995; *cr:* Mary J. ohoe Schl Classroom Tchr 1978-89; Walter F. Robinson Schl Speech apist 1989-; *ai:* After Schl Non-Pub Speech Prgm Speech Therapist; A 1994-; NJEA 1978-; Wrote & Received Several Mini-Grants; *office:* Walter F. Robinson Schl 31st St & Kennedy Blvd Bayonne NJ 07002

CIK, PAULINE EMILY, 8th Grd English Teacher; *b:* Buffalo, NY; Niagara Univ (BA) Eng & Ed 1973; Canisius Coll (MSEd) Scndry Ed ; Univ of Baffalo Admin Cert; NYS Drug & Alcohol Edctr Cert; *cr:* ous Parochial Schls 2nd, 3rd, 5th & 7th Grd Tchr 1968-73; Our Lady ourdes Prin 1973-75; St Joachim Schl Prin 1975-78; Buffalo Pub Schl rant Tchr 1978-80; Royalton-hartland Schl Tchr & Admin Asst)-87; Wise MS 8th Grd Tchr 1987-; *ai:* Spelling Bee Coord; Dist chment Comm Chprsn; Peer Mediation Trainer; NYSUT 1980-; NYS Cncl 1980-, Tchr of Excl 1982; Medina Tchrs Union 1987-; 3 Articles ; Whos Whos of Amer Edctrs 1990-; NY St Tchr Cert Examination rer 1991-; *office:* Clifford Wise MS 1016 Gwinn St Medina NY 14103*

J, DR. SAMUEL, Professor of Music; *b:* Shanghai, China; *ed:* adelphia Coll of Bible (BS) Bible, (BMus) Music 1969; Univ of CA a Barbara (PhD) Historical Musicology 1972; Post-Grad Stud Piano liard Schl, Univ of Southern CA; *cr:* Westmont Coll Instr Piano 1-72; Philadephia Coll of Bible Prof of Music 1972-; CSEHY Summer of Music Chair Piano 1974-; *ai:* Amer Musicological Soc 1972-; adelphia Music Tchrs Assn 1974-; Session of Tenth Presbyn Church of adelphia 1990-, Parish Elder; *office:* Philadelphia Coll of Bible 200 or Ave Langhorne PA 19047

, ERH-WEN, Computer Science Dept Chprsn; *b:* China; *m:* Hsiao-Mei : Arthur, Jessica; *ed:* Cheng Kung Univ (BS) Electrical Engrng 1967; Univ of NY at Stony Brook (MS) Materials Scis 1972; Univ of cinnati (MS) Electrical Engrng 1973; Polytech Inst of NY (PHD) ctrical Engrng 1976; *cr:* Polytechnic Inst of NY Research Asst Prof 6-78; William Paterson Coll Assoc Prof 1978-; *ai:* Org of Chinese er, NJ Chapter Sec; IEEE 1970-; NJ Table Tennis Club, Sec; Merit Awds William Paterson Coll-1-Paper Referred, 3-Conf Presentations; *office:* liam Paterson Coll 300 Pompton Rd Wayne NJ 07470*

, HELEN LI-JEN (CHANG), Mathematics & Cmptr Sci Tchr; *b:* ng King, China; *m:* Michael C.; *c:* Michael P., Andre M.; *ed:* Carlow l (BA) Music 1962; WV Univ (MM) Applied Music 1964; Univ of WI Madison K-12 Math Tchng Cert; Univ of PA Ed Grad Stud; Villanova v Ed Grad Course; Rutgers Univ Math Courses, Satisfied MA quirements; *cr:* St Maria Goretti HS Math Tchr 1964-65; Winnequah Jr Math Tchr 1966-67; Mount Horeb HS Math Tchr 1967-70; Smedley Jr Math Tchr 1972-74; Cherry Hill HS East Math, Cmptr Sci Tchr 1975-; Strategic Planning Comm; Acad Comm; Asian Stu Club Adv; PTA 2-74; WITA 1965-72; NEA, NJEA, NCTM, ATMNJ 1975-; St Thomas re Church 1989-, Womens' Club, Choir; Philadelphia Calligraphers Soc 39-; Philadelphia Museum of Fine Arts, British Museum, Natl Trust of g 1994-; Full Four-Yr Schl Mt Mercy Coll; WV Univ Tchng sistantship; *office:* Cherry Hill HS East Kresson Rd Cherry Hill NJ 003*

ARD, PAUL G., English Teacher & Curr Coord; *b:* Manchester, NH; Kathy A. Rysnik; *c:* Rebecca, Amy; *ed:* Keene St Coll (BED) Eng 1970, ED) Rdng 1978; *cr:* Hillsboro Schl Dist Tchr 1970-73; Salem Schl Dist hr 1973-; *ai:* Class of 1999, NHS Adv; NEA, NHEA, SEA 1970-, Fac p; NCTE, NHATE & NEATE 1985-; Dollars for Scholars 1978-, Sec ist Funds; NH Soccer Ofcls Assn 1978-; NH Bsktbl Ofcls Assn Boys & rls 1986-, Boys Exec Bd; Pub Leaflet NEATE Journal; NH Poet-at-Large nner New England Assn Of Tchrs of Eng Contest; *office:* Salem HS 44 remonty Dr Salem NH 03079*

JART, EILEEN, MS English & Reading Teacher; *b:* Woonsocket, RI; Mount St Joseph Coll (BA) Elem Ed 1970; Providence Coll (MA) Spec 1982; Addl 30 Post Grad Credits in Ed; *cr:* Woonsocket Ed Dept Grd 2 em Ed Tchr 1970-73, Grd 4 Elem Ed Tchr 1973-74, Grd 5 Elem Ed Tchr 74-87, Grd 6 Elem Ed Tchr 1987-90; Grd 6 Tchr 1990-; *ai:* Tchrs aluation Comm 1988-; AFT #951 1970-, Rep Assembly; Alpha Delta apa 1990-, Sgt at Arms; Group Ldr Young Authors Conf; *office:* oonsocket MS 357 Park Pl Woonsocket RI 02895

UBBARD, KATHLEEN BOYD, Vocal Music Teacher; *b:* Wantagh, NY; Shaun; *c:* Jennifer; *ed:* SUNY at Potsdam (BM) Music & Piano 1973; Lawrence Univ (MA) Ed Admin 1993; 30 Hrs Ed Music Towards Cert YS; *cr:* Madrid Waddington Cntrl HS 7th-12th Grd Vocal Music Tchr 74-95, 6th-12th Grd Vocal Music Tchr 1996; *ai:* NYSUT-MW Tchrs ssn 1992-; Small Ensemble Coach 18 Yrs; Drama Production Musical Dir Yrs; NYSUT 1974-, Pres; MENC, NYSSMA 1974-; *office:* Madrid addington Cntrl HS PO Box 67 Madrid NY 13660

UBBARD, RANDY ALLEN, Physics, Zoology & Bio Instr; *b:* Pierre,); *m:* Page Thielemann; *ed:* Univ of NE at Lincoln (BS) Ed, Bio 1971; niv of Northern CO at Greeley (MS) Sci Ed 1976-78; *cr:* Northwest HS str of Earth Sci, Phys Sci, Bio, Anatomy, Phys, Drivers Ed 1972-83; Key Schl Life Sci, Math Amer His Tchr 1983-85; Arundel Sr HS Phys Sci, Marine Bio, Bio, Physics Zoology, Unified Sci Tchr 1987-; *ai:* Wrestling Coach 3 Yrs; NE Acad of Tchrs 1980-83, VP, Pres; NABT 1980-83; NEA 1972-; *home:* 548 Pinedale Dr Annapolis MD 21401

HUBER, JOAN RAPHAEL, Assoc Prof of English; *b:* Johnstown, PA; *m:* Nardo J. Berardinelli; *ed:* Duquesne Univ (BA) Eng 1959; Univ of Pittsburgh (PhD) Eng 1968; *cr:* Univ of Pittsburgh Asst Prof 1974-77; Davis & Elkins Coll Asst Prof, Eng Chprsn 1987-91; Clarion Univ of PA assoc Prof Eng 1991-; *ai:* NCTE 1987-; WPCTE 1991-, Bd; *office:* Clarion Univ Of PA Venango Campus W 1st St Oil City PA 16301*

HUBERT, MARIANNE GERILYN, Junior High Teacher; *b:* Buffalo, NY; *ed:* Daemen Coll (BS) Elem Ed 1981; SUNY at Buffalo (MS) Soc Stud Ed 1991; Working Towards MS Arts Pastoral Ministry Christ the King Seminary 12 Credits; *cr:* Daemen Coll Admin Asst, Sec to VP Stu Affairs 1981-82; Diocese of Buffalo Sub Tchr 1982-83; St Benedict Schl Jr HS Tchr 1983-; *ai:* Soc Svc, Liturgy Prgm; SS Peter & Paul Church, Soc Action Comm; Cath Diocese of Buffalo Rel Edctr of Yr Awd 1991; *home:* 120 Reist St Williamsville NY 14221

HUBERT, ROBERT JOHN, Sci Dept Chair & Physics Tchr; *b:* New Brunswick, NJ; *ed:* IA St Univ (BS) Bio 1975; *cr:* US Marine Corps Ofcr 1975-87; IA St Univ Asst Dir IA Space Grant Consortium 1993; *ai:* Fac Adv Stu Cncl; Sci Club Adv; NCEA 1994-; US Marine Corps Reserve 1987-, Various; Elijahs Promise Soup Kitchen 1993-, Vol Coord; Middlebush Reformed Church 1995-, Deacon; Navy Achvmt Medal US Marine Corps 1983; *home:* 125 Clyde Rd Somerset NJ 08873*

HUBINA, LYN M., Third Grade Teacher; *b:* Bridgeport, CT; *ed:* Univ of ME (BS) Ed 1971; Southern CT St (MS) Ed 1977; St Joseph Coll 6th Yr Ed 1988; *cr:* Abbie Fowler Schl 2nd Grd Tchr 1971-72; Chapel Stocet Schl 4th Grd Tchr 1972-78; Eli Whitney Schl 3rd Grd Tchr 1978-; *ai:* NEA 1971-; CEA, SEA 1972-; ATOMIC 1985-, Presenter; *office:* Eli Whitney Elem Schl 1130 Huntington Rd Stratford CT 06497

HUBLER, FREDA-LEE, English Department Chairperson; *b:* Montreal, Canada; *m:* Beno; *c:* Eric Michael, Ingrid Leila; *ed:* Jewish General Hospital (RN) 1962; Saint Thomas Aquinas Coll (BA) Eng 1975; Fairleigh Dickinson Univ (MA) Eng 1978; 9 Post Grad Credits in Eng at Fordham Univ; *cr:* Fairleigh Dickinson Univ Grad Tchng Fellow 1976-78; Saddle River Day Schl Eng Tchr 1978-85, Eng Dept Chprsn 1985-; *ai:* Acad Decathlon Team Coach; NCTE 1978-; NJCTE 1985-; Hadassah, Sisterhood Temple Emanuel 1965-; Bard Coll Seminar on Writing & Thinking; Advanced Placement Summer Seminar Eng Lit & Comp; Woodrow Wilson Natl Fellowship Fnd Awd 1985; Wkshp on Writing & the Cmptr; 3 Articles Pub in the Record 1985-90; Articles in Journal of the NJ Cncl of Tchrs of Eng & Compassionate Friends Magazine; Tchng Fellowships at Fairleigh Dickinson Univ & Fordham Univ; *office:* Saddle River Day Schl 147 Chestnut Ridge Rd Saddle River NJ 07458

HUBLER, JOAN KEPPLER, Math Teacher & Dept Chairman; *b:* Mansfield, OH; *m:* Randall Lee; *ed:* OH St Univ (BS) Comprehensive Math 1976; Ashland Univ (ME) Supervision 1989; Mentor Tchr Trng; *cr:* Lakewood Local Schls Jr HS, HS Math Tchr 1976-78; Clear Fork Vly Local Schl HS Math Tchr 1979-; *ai:* Prin Adv Team; Schlsp Comm; Ath Events Announcer; NCTM 1991-; OCTM 1994-, North Cntrl Dist Outstdng Math Classroom Tchr; Mid-OH Cncl Tchrs; AFT; Lexington Grace Brethren Church; Martha Holden Jennings Scholar; Masters Degree with Fac Hnrs; Wkshps Tchrs Coaching Tchrs; Selected Srs Celebration of Excl 1992; Speaker OCTM Conf; *office:* Clear Fork HS 987 St Rt 97 Bellville OH 44813

HUBLER, MADALYN WHITE, 4th Grade Teacher; *b:* Philipsburg, PA; *m:* Gary C.; *c:* Kyle, Bethany, Kevin; *ed:* IN Univ of PA (BS) Elem 1975; Post Grad Stud Penn St; *cr:* West Branch Area Schls Elem Tchr 1975-; *ai:* NEA, PSEA, WBA Tchrs Assn 1975-; *office:* West Branch Area Schl Dist RR 2 Box 194 Morrisdale PA 16858

HUBLEY, MELODY A., Biology Teacher; *b:* Lebanon, OH; *m:* Roger; *c:* Susan, Amy, Jill; *ed:* Miami Univ of OH (MED) Biological Sci 1978; *cr:* White Oak Jr HS Sci Dept Chr 17 Yrs; Colerain HS Bio Tchr 7 Yrs; *ai:* Hnr Soc 10 Yrs; Girl Scout Ldr 4 Yrs; NEA 1972-; OEA 1972-; Mason Meth Church; *office:* Colerain Sr HS 8801 Cheviot Rd Cincinnati OH 45251*

HUBSCH, TRISTAN, Physics Professor; *b:* Novi Sad Vojvodina, Yugoslavia; *ed:* Novi Sad Univ (BS) Physics 1981; Univ of MD (PHD) Physics 1987; Zagreb Univ Physics; *cr:* MD Univ Tchng, Rsrch Asst 1984-87; Univ of TX Rsrch Assoc 1987-90; Harvard Univ Rsrch Affiliate 1990-92; Howard Univ Asst Prof of Physics 1992-95, Assoc Prof of Physics 1995-; *ai:* Sci Fairs Judge; Elem, HS Popular Physics Lecturer; DOE Grant Superstrings, Quantum Superfields.

HUBSCHMAN, GAIL GRONAU, 6th Grade Teacher; *b:* Jersey City, NJ; *m:* James W.; *c:* Russell, Tina, Rachael Napier, Jessica Napier; *ed:* William Paterson (BA) Ed 1970; *cr:* Hudson Schl 2nd Grd Tchr 1970-72; H M Potter Schl 6th Grd Tchr 1983-; *ai:* Coach Acad Bowl; Stokes Environmental Pgm; Sci Fair Coord; NJEA 1983-; NEA 1983-; *office:* H M Potter Schl 60 Veeder Ln Bayville NJ 08721

HUCHET, MARY LOU MURPHY, Lang Art Tchr-Media Lit Spclst; *b:* Oneida, NY; *m:* Charles; *c:* Karen Franz, William Franz, Susan, Nicole; *ed:* Rider Univ (BA) Jrnlsm, Eng 1972; Trenton St Coll (MS) Eng, Spec Ed 1978; Attnd Harvard Grad Schl of Ed, Annenberg Schl for Comm, Univ of PA; *cr:* Radio Station WBUD Commercial Writing 1982-83; Lawrenceville HS Tchr Coord, Alternative Prgm 1983-86; Princeton HS Lang Arts Tchr 1986-; *ai:* Fac Adv; TV News Prgm; Consultant to Tchrs on Media Literacy; NJEA 1983-, Tchr Rep; Cultural Environment Movement 1993-, Bd Mem of Natl Org; Article Pub; Conf Presentor Natl Media Literacy Assn; *office:* Princeton HS 151 Moore St Princeton NJ 08540

HUCHITAL, DANIEL H., Chemistry Professor; *b:* Brooklyn, NY; *m:* Helene Hechtman; *c:* Jordana, Andrew; *ed:* City Univ of NY (BSC) Chem 1961; Stanford Univ (PHD) Chem 1965; SUNY at Buffalo Post Doc 1965-66; *cr:* Brookhaven Natl Labs Researcher 1966; Seton Hall Univ Prof 1966-; *ai:* Amer Chem Soc 1966-, NJ Treas; Seton Hall Tchr of the Yr 1992; *office:* Seton Hall Univ 400 S Orange Ave South Orange NJ 07079

HUCKABEE, COLLEEN JENKINS, Enrichment Director; *b:* Washington, DC; *m:* Bill; *c:* Amy H. Koren, Anna, Allen; *ed:* Bates Coll (BA) Bio 1958; Harvard Univ (MAT) Tchng Sci 1959; Validation in Gifted Ed 1992, 175 Credit Hrs in Sci Ed 1990 OH St Univ; *cr:* Newton HS Bio Tchr 1958-61; Weeks Jr HS Bio Tchr 1958-61; The Peddie Schl Bio Tchr 1972-75; Hayes HS Bio Tchr, Sci Dept Head, Enrichment Coord 1975-91; Delaware City Schls Enrichment Dir 1991-; *ai:* Odyssey of Mind Dir; Sci Curr Chm; Artist in Schls Comm Chm; Enrichment Cncl; Natl Assn for Gifted Children, OH Assn for Gifted Children 1990-; Consortium of OH Coord for Gifted 1990-, Appreciation Cert; Delaware Unitarian Universalist Flwshp 1979-; Monday Club 1986-; Delta Kappa Gamma 1980-, Treas; Delaware City Schls Outstdng Tchr 1987; Jennings Scholar Tchr 1980-81; Article Pub; AP Reader in Bio; *home:* 19 Woodland Ave Delaware OH 43015

HUCKEL, JACK R., PE Instructor & Soccer Coach; *b:* Atlantic City, NJ; *m:* Margaret S.; *c:* Abigail C., Daniel F.; *ed:* Grove City Coll (AB) Psych 1968; Univ of Denver (MA) PE 1977; US Soccer Fed A Coaching License; *cr:* Hun Schl Math Tchr & Coach 1977-80; George Mason Univ Asst Soccer Coach 1980-81; ME Maritime Acad PE Assoc Prof & Coach 1981-86; Skidmore Coll PE Instr & Coach 1986-; *ai:* Mens Soccer & Asst Mens Lacrosse Coach; Nat Soccer Coaches 1974-, Hall of Fame Comm Chair & Historian; Intercollegiate Soccer Assn 1981-, Historian; Soc for Amer Soccer His 1993-, Sec; US Team World Cup 1950; *office:* Skidmore Coll Saratoga Springs NY 12866

HUCKNO, WALLY JOSEPH,SR., Athletic Director; *b:* Detroit, MI; *m:* Dixie Lord; *c:* Leslie Ann Baczynski, Wally Jr., MIchelle Lyn Black; *ed:* Edinboro Univ (BS) Ed, Soc Stud, Eng 1962; Grad Stud Fredonia St, Canisus; 42 Hrs; *cr:* Jamestown Pub Schls Eng Tchr 32 Yrs, Ath Dir 2 Yrs, Coach 30 Yrs; *ai:* Head Var Coach 13 Yrs, Record 103-26-1; NEA 1962-; Jamestown Tchrs Assoc 1962-; NYS Ath Admin 1994-; NYS Coaches Assn 1992-; Amer Legion 1975-; VFW 1993-; DeWitt Clinton Masonic, Awd for Comm Svc 1995; Rotary Intnl, Paul Harris Fellow, Rotary Fnd; NY Coach of Yr 1994-95; Team Won St Class A Titles 1994-95, 8 Div I, 9 Rich Stadium Appearances, 6 Rich Stadium Championships; West NY Coach of Yr 1986, 1993, 1994, 1995; Cty Coach of Yr 4 Times; 1994 Team was #23 in USA by USA Today Poll; *home:* 498 Valerie Ln Jamestown NY 14701

HUDAK, ROGER JOHN, Teacher; *b:* Bethlehem, PA; *m:* Sandra Ann Bankowski; *c:* Kathryn Ann, Kristen A.; *ed:* Kertztown Univ (MA) Ed 1994; Attnd LeHigh Univ Eng 1970, West Chester Univ Writing 1993; *cr:* Pennridge Cntrl HS Tchr 1965-69; Liberty HS Tchr 1970-; *ai:* Liberty Life on Schl Newspaper Adv 25 Yrs; NEA, PSEA 1965-; *office:* Liberty H S 1115 Linden St Bethlehem PA 18018

HUDDLE, JOHN E., Biological Sciences Teacher; *b:* Greenville, OH; *m:* Shirley A. Schlimmer; *c:* Michelle L. (Huddle) Billenstein, Bradley J.; *ed:* Anderson Univ (BA) Biological Sciences Ed 1966; Wright St Univ (MS) Curr & Supervision 1979; Addl 24 Hrs Cmptr Sci 1986; Univ of Cincinnati 6 Hrs Environmental Sci 1976; *cr:* Versailles HS Biological Sciences Tchr 1966-; *ai:* Sci Dept Chprsn 28 Yrs; Asst Ath Dir 18 Yrs; Ftbl Video Cameraman 25 Yrs; NSTA 1986-; ABT 1992-; NEA 1966-; VEA 1966-, Pres, Negotiations Chm, Tchr of Yr 1970, 1993; Comm Schlsp Comm 1970-, Chm; Martha Holding Jennings Grant 1977; *office:* Versailles HS 459 S Center St Versailles OH 45380

HUDDLESTON, JOHN ROLAND, American History & Ec Teacher; *b:* Asbury Park, NJ; *m:* Marie Lucille DeLucco; *c:* Colleen Amber, C. J.; *ed:* Colgate Univ (BA) Soc Sci 1967, (MA) Soc Sci 1968; *cr:* Dolgeville Cntrl His Tchr 1968-; *ai:* Ftbl Asst Coach; NEH Summer Inst on Russian Revolution Rollins Coll 1989; Roosevelt Inst Bard Coll & Hyde Park 1990; Independent Stud (NEH) on Pearl Harbor 1991; NEH Summer Inst on George Kennan Brown Univ 1992; *office:* Dolgeville Central Schl Slawson St Dolgeville NY 13329

HUDDY, LYNETTE LUKEHART, First Grade Teacher; *b:* Erie, PA; *m:* Ronald L.; *c:* Eric, Jason; *ed:* Edinboro St Coll (BS) Elem, Spec Ed 1968, (MS) Early Chldhd Ed 1974; Attnd St Univ of NY at Fredonia, Chautauqua Cty Tchrs Ctr, Edinboro Univ; *cr:* Brocton Cntrl Schl Kndgtn Tchr 1975-76, 1979-80, First Grd Tchr1980-, Title I Summer Rdng Tchr 1993-; *ai:* SUNY at Fredonia Elem Advy Comm; Mentor Tchr PTA; Clinical Field Supvr for Stu Tchrs St Univ of NY at Fredonia; Brocton Tchrs Assn, NYSUT, AFT 1979-; Ahira Hall Meml Lib Bd 1993-; Beta Sigma Phi 1973-; Tri Church Parish P. P. R. Bd 1991-; *home:* 6736 Webster Rd Westfield NY 14787*

HUDOCK, ANNE LAWRENCE, Mathematics Teacher & Dept Chm; *b:* Salem, NJ; *m:* Joseph A. Jr.; *c:* Sarah, William; *ed:* Rutgers Univ (BA) Math 1987; Rowan Coll of NJ (MA) Scndry Ed, Math 1996; *cr:* Schalick HS Math Tchr 1987-91; Salem HS Math Tchr 1993-, Math Dept Chm 1994-; *ai:* Class of 96 Adv; Band Front Adv 1993-94; NCTM, AMTNJ, NJEA, NEA 1987-; Quinton Ambulance Corps 1983-, Treas; Quinton Meth Church 1980-, Choir Dir, Sunday Schl Tchr; Governor's Tchr Recognition Awd 1991; *office:* Salem HS 219 Walnut St Salem NJ 08079

HUDRLIK, PAUL F., Chemistry Professor; *b:* Portland, OR; *m:* Anne Marie Bachmann; *c:* Janet, Carol; *ed:* OR St Univ (BS) Chem 1963; Columbia Univ (MA) Chem 1964, (PHD) Chem 1968; Post-Doctoral Rsrch Stanford univ 1968-69; *cr:* Rutgers Univ Asst Prof 1969-76; Howard Univ Assoc Prof 1977-81, Prof 1981-; *ai:* Amer Chemical Soc 1963-; AAAS 1967-; Royal Soc of Chem 1969-; Grants from NSF, NIH, ACS-Petroleum Rsrch Fund; Cyanamid Acad Awd 1988; Pub 7 Book Chptrs, 46 Articles, 5 Book Reviews; *office:* Howard Univ Dept of Chemistry 2400 6th St NW Washington DC 20059

HUDSON, JOAN DENISE, Language Arts Teacher; *b:* Decatur, IN; *m:* Mark Kevin; *c:* Jason; *ed:* Bluffton Coll (BA) Elem Ed 1979; Wright St Univ Elem Ed, Rdng; *cr:* Covington MS Tchr 1979-; *ai:* Schlsp Club Adv; CEA, OEA, NEA 1979-; *office:* Covington MS 25 Grant St Covington OH 45318

HUDSON, PAUL JEFFREY, Band Director & Music Teacher; *b:* Akron, OH; *m:* Amy Campbell Richardson; *c:* Sarah Ann, Matthew Paul; *ed:* Muskingum Coll (BSME) Music 1979; Working Toward Masters with Music Concentration; *cr:* Frontier Local Schls Band Dir 1979-80; West Muskingum Schls Band Dir 1980-85; Muskingum Coll Applied Percussion Tchr 1985-87; East Muskingum Schls Band Dir 1985-; *ai:* OH Music Ed Assn 1979-; *office:* John Glenn HS 13115 John Glenn School Rd New Concord OH 43762

HUDSON, PENNIE HOLLEY, Fifth Grade Teacher; *b:* Waterbury, CT; *m:* Herbert A.; *c:* Michael, Christopher; *ed:* Sacred Heart Univ (BA) His, Ed 1971; Cntrl CT St Univ (MS) Ed 1975; *cr:* Merriman Schl Third Grd Tchr 1971-74; Wendell Cross Schl Second, Fourth Grd Tchr 1974-79; Walsh Schl Fifth Grd Tchr 1980-87; Wendell Cross Schl Fifth Grd Tchr 1987-; *ai:* NEA, CEA, WTA 1971-; *office:* Wendell Cross Schl 1255 Hamilton Ave Waterbury CT 06706

HUDZINA, PATRICIA E., Latin Teacher; *b:* Scranton, PA; *m:* Eugene E.; *c:* Kathryn E., Beth A. Beck, Eugene M.; *ed:* Marywood Coll (BA) His, Soc Stud 1963; Univ of Scranton (MS) Scndry Ed 1994; 3 Post-Grad Stud 1995; 12 Grad Credit Hrs Marywood Coll 1965-66; 6 Grad Credit Hrs Marywood Coll 1989-90; *cr:* South Scranton Jr HS Soc Stud, Lang Arts Tchr 1963-69; Scranton Hebrew Day Schl 1, 4-8, 11-12 Grd Tchr 1974-88; Lackawanna Jr Coll Part-time Soc Sci, Lang Instr 1975-87; Marywood Coll Asst Alumni Dir, GED Instr 1988-90; Scranton Prep Schl Latin, Eng Tchr 1990-; *ai:* NCEA 1990-; Delta Kappa Gamma 1993-, Treas; Kappa Delta Pi 1995-; St Joseph's Ctr Auxiliary 1972-, Pres; Marywood Alumni Assn 1963-, Pres; Univ of Scranton Alumni 1994-; Eucharistic Minister 1981-; St Andrea Soc 1974-; Grant Attend Taft Seminar Tchrs Taft Fellow; *office:* Scranton Prep Schl 1000 Wyoming Ave Scranton PA 18509*

HUDZINSKI, DEBORAH, Third Grade Teacher; *b:* Red Bank, NJ; *m:* John L.; *c:* Laura, Scott; *ed:* Trenton St Coll (BS) Elem Ed 1976; *cr:* Middletown Vlg Schl 5th Grd Tchr 1976-79, 6th Grd Tchr 1979-82; Lincroft Schl 4th Grd Tchr 1987-88, 3rd Grd Tchr 1983-87, 3rd Grd Tchr 1988-; *ai:* NEA, NJEA 1976-; Lit Based Rdng Prgm Grant 1994-95; *office:* Lincroft Elem Schl 729 Newman Springs Rd Lincroft NJ 07738

HUEBLER, KITTY, Third Grade Teacher; *b:* Baltimore, MD; *ed:* Towson St Univ (BS) Elem Ed 1969, (MED) Elem Ed 1974; *cr:* Baltimore Cty Bd of Ed Tchr 1969-; *ai:* Johns Hopkins Children's Ctr, Cultural Enrichment Coord; NEA, TABCO, MSTA 1969-; Church of Nativity 1969-, Yth Adv; *office:* Pot Spring Elem Schl 2410 Spring Lake Dr Timonium MD 21093

HUEBSCH, SUE ALEXANDER, English Teacher; *b:* New York City, NY; *m:* Robert Irwin; *c:* Michelle Huebsch Belcher, Renee Huebsch Belcher; *ed:* Long Island Univ (BS) Early Chldhd Ed & Eng 1963; Attnd Brooklyn Coll, Rutgers Univ; *cr:* PS 32 2nd Grd Tchr 1963-65; PS 261 Kndgtn Tchr

1965-67; Howell HS Eng Tchr 1985-88; Elizabeth HS Eng Tchr 1988-; *ai:* in-Class Support Pgm; Ldrshp Team & Stu Resource Comm Mem; Ed Theme for Restructuring Facilitator; NCTE 1988-; *office:* Elizabeth HS 600 Pearl St Elizabeth NJ 07202*

HUEGEL, DARLENE M., German Teacher; *b:* Erie, PA; *ed:* Thiel Coll (BA) Ger 1967; Gannon Univ Guidance Counseling, Scndry Ed 33 Addl Hrs; *cr:* Mc Dowell Sr HS Ger Tchr 1967-; *ai:* Jr Bowling League Coach; Ger Clb Adv; PSEA, MEA, NEA 1967-; *office:* Mc Dowell Sr HS 3580 W 38th St Erie PA 16506

HUFF, CARL RAYMOND, English Teacher; *b:* Pittsburgh, PA; *m:* Cynthia Louise Bair; *c:* Jon, Kimberly; *ed:* Lock Haven Univ (BS) Eng 1974; Bucknell Univ (MS) Pub Schl Admin 1982; *cr:* C. E. McCall MS Eng Tchr 1974-75, Montoursville HS Eng Tchr 1975-, Admin Asst 1995-; *ai:* Yrbk, Newspaper & Stu Assistance Pgm Class Adv; Ftbl, Bsbl & Bsktbl Coach; Reserve Officers Assn 1982-; Air Force Reserve 46 Aerial Port Sq 1979-, Commander Major; Intnl Whos Who 1994; *office:* Montoursville Area Sr HS 100 N Arch St Montoursville PA 17754*

HUFF, CHARLES C., Assistant Principal; *b:* Ridgely, MD; *m:* Shirley M. Baynard; *c:* Barry, Shane, Charles II, Michael; *ed:* Univ of MD at Eastern Shore (BA) Soc Stud 1969; Norfolk St Univ (MA) Comm 1978; Temple Univ Voc Ed; Univ of DE; DE St Univ Admin Courses; *cr:* St of DE Juvenil Corrections Cnslr, Supvr 1970-72; Wilmington Pub Schl Dist Tchr 1972-78; Christina Schl Dist Admin, Tchr 1978-; *ai:* Intnl Assn of Approved Bsktbl Ofcls Bd Pres; NASSP 1995-; NCSS, ASCD 1985-; *office:* Christiana HS 190 Salem Church Rd Newark DE 19702

HUFF, GEORGE ANTHONY, High School Guidance Counselor; *b:* Elizabeth, NJ; *m:* Kim M.; *ed:* Kean Coll of NJ (BA) Eng 1975, (MA) Stu Personnel Svcs 1985; Spec Ed Cert 1978; Supvrs Cert 1979; *cr:* Northover Cooperative Schl Spec Ed Tchr 1978-79; Bergen Cty Spec Svcs Spec Ed Tchr 1979-81; Cranford HS Spec Ed Tchr 1981-92, Guid Cnslr 1992-; *ai:* Grd 9-12 Peer Dev, Adv, Co-Coord; Girls Bsktbl Grd 9 Coach; NJCA, UCCA, 1992-; NJEA 1978-; CEA 1981-; Spec Olympics NJ 1981-, Vol; Douglass Coll Tchr Appreciation Day 1995; *office:* Cranford HS 201 W End Pl Cranford NJ 07016

HUFF, KELLY SMITH, Rel Ed Coord & Yth Minister; *b:* Toledo, OH; *c:* Susan E., Emily A., R. Patrick, Alexis M.; *ed:* Miami Univ Psych; Intermediate Cert Of Yth Ministry, Cert as Catechist & Coord of Rel Ed; *cr:* St Mary Bookkeeper 1982-85; St Peter in Chain Church, Schl Early Chldhd Classes Supvr, Rel Ed Coord, Yth Minister 1985-; *ai:* Organizing Outreach Projects for Stdnts in Comm; Cinti Yth Minister Assn 1990-; NCEA 1991-; Natl Conf Catechetical Ldrs 1993-; Sojourner Home 1994-, Bd of Dirs; Colleagues of Ft Hamilton Hosp 1994-, Co-Chair Large Comm Fundraiser; Recognition Awd for Comm Svc to Fair Acres Early Chldhd Ctr Presented for Ongoing Svc to Ctr; *home:* 935 Hamilton Cleves Rd Apt #1B Hamilton OH 45013

HUFF, KRISTI ADKINS, Third Grade Teacher; *b:* Hamilton, OH; *m:* Philip M.; *ed:* Miami of OH (BA) Eng, Primary Ed 1992; *cr:* Liberty Elem Schl Third Grd Tchr 1992-; *ai:* NEA 1992-; Nom Ashland Oil Tchr Achvmt Awd.

HUFFMAN, BARBARA J., English Teacher & Dept Chprsn; *b:* E Stroudsburg, PA; *m:* Jay E.; *c:* Jeffrey, Michelle Krajewski, Lori Jo, Deborah; *ed:* E Stroudsburg St Coll (BS) Scndry Ed Eng 1966; Lehigh Univ (MED) Cnslng 1972; 18 Post Grad Credits; *cr:* Stroudsburg HS Eng Tchr 1966-69; E Stroudsburg HS Eng Tchr 1969-, Dept Chprsn 1989-; *ai:* New Tchr Mentor; NEA & PSEA 1969-; NCTE 1969-; Dept of Ed St Evaluation Team Tchr Prep Cert; *office:* East Stroudsburg Sr HS 279 N Courtland St East Stroudsburg PA 18301

HUFFMAN, BEVERLY THACKER, 4th Grade Teacher; *b:* Marion, OH; *m:* Dennis A.; *c:* Heath, Heather; *ed:* Univ of Findlay (BA) Elem Ed 1983, (MA) Ed 1993; *cr:* Riverdale-Forest Elem 4th Grd Tchr 1983-; *ai:* IAT; Cty Course of Stud Comms; Tchr for YES Pgm; Wkshp Presenter; Hull Pottery Assn 5 Yrs; Grant to Dev CLIP; Activity Article Pub; *office:* Forest Elem Schl 311 W Dixon St Forest OH 45843*

HUFFORD, TERRY LEE, Professor of Botany; *b:* Toledo, OH; *m:* Janice Lorene Studer; *c:* Bradley, Christina Simpkins, Gregory; *ed:* Bowling Green St Univ (BS) Bio 1961, (MA) Bio 1962; OH St Univ (PHD) Botany Aquatic Ecology 1972; Scndry Ed Cert Pgm GWU 1988; *cr:* IN Cntrl Coll Bio Instr 1962-63; Cntrl Meth Coll Asst Bio Prof 1963-64; MI St Univ GTA in Bio & Asst Inst Botany 1964-66; Grove City Coll Asst Bio Prof 1966-69; OH St Univ GTA in Botany 1969-72; George Washington Univ Botany Prof 1972-; *ai:* Curr Comm; Frosh Advising Wkshp; Dept of Biological Sciences Sec; AIBS; NSTA; NABT Chair 4 Yr Section; PSA; Sigma Xi; Numerous Articles & Books Pub; Work with Yth Groups, Pub Schl Tchrs & Stdnts; Church Awd; *office:* George Washington Univ Dept of Biological Scis 2023 G Street NW Washington DC 20052*

HUFFSTETLER, CHARLES FREDERICK, World Civilization Teacher; *b:* Gastonia, NC; *m:* Ann Marie Petrofsky; *c:* Laura Gail Guth, Joyce Ann Ley, Michael Edward, William Martin; *ed:* East Carolina Coll (BS) Soc Stud 1960; 30 Post-Grad Hrs Central CT St Coll; *cr:* Cromwell HS 1960-72; Albury North HS Soc Stud Tchr 1972-73; Cromwell HS World Civilization Tchr 1973-; *ai:* Ind Stud Prgm Chm; NEA 1960-; EAC 1960-, Pres 1965-67; CEA, NCSS 1960-; Haddam Democratic Com 1974-, Treas; Haddam Planning & Zone 1994-, Sec; Cromwell Schl System Tchr of Yr 1992; *home:* 36 Haddam View Hts Haddam CT 06438

HUFNAGEL, WILLIAM THOMAS, Technical Drawing Teacher; *b:* Mc Kees Rocks, PA; *m:* Mary Pat; *c:* Tricia Ann, Weston, Matthew; *ed:* CA Univ of PA (BS) Ed 1969; Penn St Safety Ed 15 Cr; CCAC Cmptr Drawing 40 Cr; Univ of Pitt Instrl Design, Tech; *cr:* Hallendale Jr HS Indstrl Arts Tchr 1969-71; Montour Int HS Power Tech Tchr 1971-90; Montour Sr HS Tech Drawing Tchr 1990-; *ai:* Indstrl Arts Dept Head; Audio-Visual Coord; MS Wrestling, Track Coach; Head Swim Coach 1986-90; MEA, PSEA 1971-; Lake Erie Down Riggers 1985-. Treas, Bd of Dirs; *home:* 32 Agnes St Coraopolis PA 15108

HUGEL, JULIE MC COY, Home Economics Teacher; *b:* Ronceverte, WV; *m:* Keivin; *ed:* WV Univ (BS) Family Resources 1990; 54 Addl Hrs Home Ec Ed; *cr:* LaPlata HS Home Ec Tchr 1993-; *ai:* FHA, Class of 99 Adv; Chrldng Coach; Stu Assist Mem; MD Stu Assistance Prgm Profs Assn 1994-; *office:* La Plata HS PO Box 790 Radio Station Rd La Plata MD 20646*

HUGG, C. FRANCES BERMAN, Secondary Social Studies Tchr; *b:* Pittsburgh, PA; *m:* Forrest; *c:* Michael; *ed:* Grove City Coll (BA) His, Ger 1972; Duquesne Univ (MA) His 1974; *cr:* Allegheny Comm Coll His Lecturer 1976; Hollidaysburg Jr-Sr HS Permanent Sub Tchr 1983-85; Altoona Area HS Soc Stud, Ger Tchr 1985-; *ai:* Ger Club Spon 1985-92; Delta Epsilon Phi Founder; NEA, PSEA 1985-; Friends of Altoona Area Lib 1980-, Bd Mem 1980-85; Friends of Hollidaysburg Lib 1980-, Bd Mem, Publicity Chm 1980-85; Wrote Curr AP Ger, European His; Tchng AP Courses Awd; Tchr of Hnrs Stdnts Awd; *office:* Altoona Area HS 415 6th Ave Altoona PA 16602

HUGGINS, JANICE ANNE, Seventh Grade Science Teacher; *b:* Camden, NJ; *ed:* Gloucester Cty Coll (AA) Lbrl Arts 1973; Glassboro St Coll (BA) Elem Ed 1975; Glassboro St Coll K-8 Cert; *cr:* Clayton HS, MS Tchr 1975-; *ai:* MS Stu Cncl Adv; Class of 1996 Adv; Gloucester Cty Educl Expo Chprsn; Clayton's Schl Dist Educl Expo Chprsn; NEA; New Jersey Ed Assn; Clayton Ed Assn; Amer Cancer Soc Road to Recovery Driver 1995-; Clayton Tchr of Yr 1988-89, 1994-95; *home:* PO Box 115 Lincoln Mill Rd Mullica Hill NJ 08062

HUGGINS, VIRGINIA FINNEGAN, First Grade Teacher; *b:* Amherst, OH; *m:* Ronald L.; *c:* L. Thomas Angert, Michelle; *ed:* Kent St Univ (BS) Early Chldhd Ed 1968; Elem Ed Ashland Univ; *cr:* Berea Schls First Grd Tchr 1968-74; Holy Angels Schl Fourth-Sixth Rdng, Soc Stud Tchr 1984-92, First Grd Tchr 1994-; *ai:* NEA, OEA 1968-; NCEA 1984-; *office:* Holy Angels Schl 1603 W Jefferson St Sandusky OH 44870

HUGHES, AGNES T., Professor of Psychology; *b:* Highland Park, PA; *ed:* Immaculata Coll (AB) Theology 1959; Fordham Univ (MA) Psych 1964, (PHD) Psych 1967; Post Grad Stud Jungian Inst Zurich Switzerland 1984; *cr:* Cardinal Dougherty HS Theology Tchr 1956-62; Immaculate Coll PSych Prof 1962-; St Chas Seminary Pastoral Cnslng Prof 1974-88; *ai:* Coll Governance Comms; Amer Psych Assn 1963-; Sigma Xi; Natl Inst of Mental Hlth Flwshp 1965-67; Intnl Inst for Hum Stud Flwshp 1978; *office:* Immaculata Coll King Rd Immaculata PA 19345*

HUGHES, BETH A., High School English Teacher; *b:* Dayton, OH; *m:* Anthony L.; *c:* Ryan, Benjamin; *ed:* Univ of Dayton (BS) Eng Ed 1992; MS Eng Ed 1996; *cr:* Vandalia-Butler HS Eng Tchr 1993-; *ai:* Class Adv 1996; Prom, Homecoming Parade Adv; NEA 1993-; *office:* Vandalia-Butler City Schls 600 S Dixie Dr Vandalia OH 45377*

HUGHES, BETTY QUERQUI, Second Grade Teacher; *b:* Elmira, NY; *m:* Jeptha F. Jr.; *c:* Tina H. Bevilacqua; *ed:* Elmira Coll (BA) Latin Music Cum Laude 1947; Cornell)MED(Elem Ed, Psych Ed 1962; Post Grad TV Seminar Grant at Northwestern Univ; Ed Admin at IN Univ at Bloomington IN; *cr:* Elmira City Schls Early Childhd Tchr 1957-59, Media Specialist, Educl TV 1961-76, Primary Tchr 1976-; *ai:* Sci Proctor, Prgm Testing, Cmptr Tech, Arts Ed Comms; NEA 1957-; NYSUT 1978-; Pi Lamda Theta 1962-; Elmira Symphony 1976-; Choral Soc 1990-; E S & C Soc Bd 1986-, Sec; Grant From Polaroid Camera for Stu Visual Lit Prgm/; Rgnl UTIE Awd from NY St 2 Times; Grant Using Polaroid Camera for Stu Visual Lit Prgm.

HUGHES, BRIDGET MARY, Special Education Teacher; *b:* Lawrence, MA; *c:* Aaron E. Kronstat; *ed:* Fitchburg St Coll (BS) Early Chldhd Ed 1978; Northeastern Univ (MED) Rehabilitation Cnslng 1985; 30 Post-Grad Credit Hrs; PA St Univ Spcl Ed Cert 1981; *cr:* Odyssey House Schl Spcl Edctr 1982-86; Seacoast Learning Collab Liaison Tchr 1986-91; Raymond HS E H Specialist 1991-95; Winnacunnet HS E H Specialist 1995-; *ai:* Class Adv 1991-95; Stu Intervention Team; Raymond Advocacy Pgm Planning Comm; NEA 1991-; Kappa Delta Phi Educl Awd 1986; RHS Yrbk Dedication 1995; *office:* Winnacunnet HS Alumni Dr Hampton NH 03842*

HUGHES, CHRISTINE, ESL Teacher; *b:* Kearny, NJ; *ed:* Cty Coll of Morris (AS) Hum 1985; East Stroudsburg Univ (BS) Elem Ed 1987; 30 Credist & Cert towards Tchr of Eng as Second Lang; *cr:* Somverville Cntrl Schl 1-5 Grd Rdng Tchr 1988-91; Somverville Pub Schls K-12 Grd ESL Tchr 1991-; *ai:* ESL Tutoring; Soc Comm; NEA, NJEA 1987-; Natl Trust for Historic Preservation 1987-; Preservation NJ 1993-.

HUGHES, CORINNE SUZAN, Audio Video Technician & Coach; *b:* Madison, NY; *ed:* Boston Univ (BS) Eng Ed 1992; *cr:* Millis HS Girls Var Bsktbl Coach & Jr Var Sftbl Coach 1992-93; Cohasset HS Girls Var Bsktbl Coach & Audio-Video Technician 1993-; *ai:* AAU 16 & Under Bsktbl Coach; Tech Comm; Univ of MA at Boston Sftbl Asst Coach.

HUGHES, CYNTHIA ANN BROWN, Fourth Grade Teacher; *b:* Barnesville, OH; *m:* Joseph H.; *c:* Joseph W., Laurie Gray, Sherril; *ed:* OH Univ (BSEd) K-8 Elem Ed 1983; Attnd OH Univ Ed 1983-; Muskingum Coll Ed 1991-92; *cr:* Noble Local Schl 2-5 Grds Tchr 1962-63; Barnesville Schl 3rd Grd Tchr 1966-68, K-8 Grd Rdng Tchr 1969-73, 4th Grd Tchr 1984-; *ai:* BEA, OEA, NEA 1972-; ASCD 1991-; *office:* Barnesville Exempted Schl 210 W Church St Barnesville OH 43713

HUGHES, DAWNNE BYROADS, English Teacher; *b:* Dansville, NY; *m:* Michael; *c:* Connor; *ed:* SUNY at Geneseo (BA) Eng 1984, (MS) Ed & Rdng 1990; *cr:* Perry Cntrl Jr & Sr HS 8th Grd Eng Tchr 1984-; *ai:* Vllybl Coach 1992-95; Past Class of 1989 Adv; Comm as Schl & Work to Schl Comms; NYSUT 1992-; AFT 1992-; *home:* 104 Euclid Ave Perry NY 14530*

HUGHES, DIANA CORNELL, Sixth Grade Teacher; *b:* Pittsburgh, PA; *m:* James M. III; *c:* Jason M., Matthew A.; *ed:* Grove City Coll (BA) Elem Ed, Fr 1969; 6 Grad Credits U of CA at Berkeley; 21 Grad Credits at Edinboro Univ of PA; *cr:* Penn Hills Schl Dist 4th Grd Elem Tchr 1969-70; Fairfield Schl Dist 4th Grd Elem Tchr 1970-72; Titusville Schl Dist Elem Tchr 1973-76, Sub Tchr 1979-; *ai:* Textbook Selection Comm; PSEA, NEA 1987-; Titusville Area Educ Assn 1987-, Pres, VP, Sec, Negotiator, Grievance Chair; YWCA Bd of Dirs 1982-88, Sec; Friends Lib Org 1986-, Pres; Main Street PTA 1982-, Pres; *home:* 115 White Oak Dr Titusville PA 16354

HUGHES, EDNA CUNNINGHAM, Fourth Grade Teacher; *b:* Brooklyn, NY; *m:* Thomas; *c:* Thomas, Patricia Weinert, Dr. Janice Culley; *ed:* Saint Josephs Coll (BA) Child Psych & Ed 1942; NY Univ Schl of Engrng 1942-43; *cr:* US Govt Ordinance Dept Inspector 1942-44; Sub Tchr 1960-64; Saint Bernards Schl Tchr 1964-; *office:* St Bernard Schl 2030 E 69th St Brooklyn NY 11234

HUGHES, EDWARD THOMAS, English Department Chairperson; *b:* Elmira, NY; *m:* Judy Lawrence; *c:* Susan, Anne Marie; *ed:* St Univ at Albany (BA) Eng & Soc Stud Tchr 1964, (MA) Eng Ed Tchr 1968; (MS) Educl Admin 1974; *cr:* Horseheads Jr HS 7th & 8th Grd Eng Tchr 1964-67; Shenendehowa MS Eng Chprsn & Tchr 1967-; *ai:* Prof Performance Review Comm Chprsn; Field Tests; Natl Bd Prof Tchng Studies Univ of Pittsburgh; Prof Practices Mediation Panel Chprsn; Capital Dist Eng Supv Assn 1975-, Treas; ASCD 1980-; Shenendehowa Pub Lib 1980-, Bd of Trustees VP; St Edwards Cath Church 1990-, Eucharistic Minister; Outstdng Edctr Cornell Univ; Life Mbrshp Shenendehowa PTA Recipient; *office:* Shenendehowa MS 970 Rt 146 Clifton Park NY 12065

HUGHES, G. GREGORY, Associate Professor; *b:* Montclair, NJ; *m:* Nancy Quarles; *c:* Kathryn, Margret; *ed:* Villanova Univ (BS) Acctng 1973; Univ of VT (MBA) Finance 1975; VT Law Schl (JD) Commercial Law 1984; *cr:* Colgate-Palmolive Inc Fin Analyst 1975-78; Service Enterprises Inc Pres 1978-88; Univ of VT Instr, Lecturer 1988-91; VT Tech Coll Assoc Prof 1991-; *ai:* VT Small Bus Dev Ctr Cnslr; Bethel Schl Bd 1994-; Bethel Zoning Bd of Adjustment 1990-; Grad Research Flwshp; Bus for Russia Grant; *office:* VT Tech Coll Randolph Center VT 05061

HUGHES, GORDON D.,JR., Health Teacher; *b:* Sidney, NY; *m:* Catherine Beckwith; *c:* Tamar, Jason, Jared, Ashley; *ed:* E Stroudsburg (BS) PE 1967; Oneonta St Hlth; *cr:* Edmeston Cntrl Schl PE Tchr 1967-70; Oneonta Elem Schl PE Tchr 1970-71; Bainbridge-Guilford HS Hlth Tchr 1971-; *ai:* Badminton & Table Tennis & Girls Tennis.

HUGHES, HUGH JOSEPH, 8th Grade Soc Studies Teacher; *b:* Ft Devens, MA; *m:* Janet Susan Gelsomin; *c:* Amanda Jayne, Hugh Adam; *ed:* Onondaga Comm Coll (AA) Hum 1985; St Univ of NY Coll at Oswego (BS) Ed 1987, (MS) MS Curr 1990; Addl 36 Hrs MS Ed St Univ of NY; *cr:* North Syracuse Jr HS 8th Grd Soc Stud Tchr 1987-; *ai:* Stu Govt Adv; Jr High Boys-Girls Cross Cntry, Var Girls Winter Track, Girls Track Coach; Bldg Planning, Stu Support Teams; Kappa Delta Pi 1986-; NYSUT, NEA 1987-; NY St Cncl, Cntrl NY Cncl for Soc Stud; Syracuse Chargers 1987-; *home:* 906 Allen Rd North Syracuse NY 13212

HUGHES, JACQUELINE LUCIANI, Retired Elem School Teach New Haven, CT; *m:* W. David; *c:* Kelly, Christopher; *ed:* Southern Coll (BS) Elem ED 1960; Fairfield Univ (MA) Elem Ed 1966; Smit Lbrl Arts 1956-57; Prof Growth & Dev Courses Orange Bd of Ed; *cr:* L. Tracy Schl 5th, 6th Grd Tchr 1960-66; The Bell Schl 5th Grd 1966-67; Turkey Hill Schl 5th-6th Grd Tchr 1967-95; *ai:* NEA, (Assn, Orange Tchrs League 1960-95; Assn of Retired Tchrs of CT Grant Stud Math Webster Coll.

HUGHES, JESSICA BARKASI, 8th Grd Rdng & Lang Arts Tchr; *b.* Kensington, PA; *c:* Loren Deigh Hughes; *ed:* CA St Univ (BS) Ed Grd & Rdng Specialization 1972; OH Wesleyan Univ Post Grad Rdng; OH St Univ Post Grad Stud Voc Ed, Rdng & Alcohol Tobac Other Drugs; Capital St Univ Post Grad Stud Rdng; *cr:* Central HS Specialist 1972-77; Fort Hayes Metropolitan HS Rdng & Comm 1977-91; Southmoor MS 8th Grd Rdng & Lang Arts Tchr 1991-; *a* Grd Team Tchr; Safe & Drug Free Essay Adv; Crisis Intervention C Homebound Tutor; Private Industry Cncl-Employment Skills; Su Schl; NEA, OEA 1972-; Girls Scouts of Amer, Adult Mem; Jewish C Ctr 1987-; YMCA; Voc Ed Rdng & Math Labs Grant Writing 197 *office:* Southmoor MS 1201 Moler Rd Columbus OH 43207

HUGHES, JOHN EDWARD,JR., Eng & Sci Teacher; *b:* Baltimore, *m:* Ann Marie Borowy; *ed:* Loyola Coll (BA) His 1972; John Hopkins (MA) His of Ideas 1976, (MS) Environmental Sci 1992; *cr:* John C Schl Estuarine Ecology Tchr, Coach 24 Yrs; *ai:* Mens Soccer, Wo LaCrosse Coach; GLOBE; Blue Heron Tours, Dir; CBF, Asst Ec 1976-81; Gunpowder River Conservancy, Bd; Comm Preserve Assat Bd; Upper Chesapeake Advy Bd, Appt by St Gov; Osprey Adventure, Naturalist; Tchr of Yr 1990; *office:* John Carroll Schl 703 Churchvil Bel Air MD 21014*

HUGHES, JOYCE MARIE MARTIN, Fourth Grade Teacher; *b:* Hill, OH; *m:* Sheridan W.; *c:* Kelly Sue Curnow, Andrea Kaylene; *ed* St Univ (BSEd) K-8th Grd Elem Ed 1978; Ashland Univ, OH St Univ Credit Hrs; *cr:* Marion City Schls Fourth Grd Tchr 1978-; *ai:* NEA, (MEA 1978-; Chrstn & Missionary Alliance Church 1976-; *office:* Fair Elem Schl 980 Robinson St Marion OH 43302

HUGHES, KAREN J., Chemistry Teacher; *b:* Queens, NY; *ed:* LeM Coll (BS) Bio 1986; Adelphi Univ (MA) Sci Ed 1988; *cr:* NYU Me Ctr Biochemistry Research Technician 1986-87; West Hempstead S Sci Tchr 1988-91; Herricks HS Chem Tchr 1991-; *ai:* Stu Govt Adv Olympiad Coach; *office:* Herricks Sr HS 100 Shelter Rock Rd New Park NY 11040

HUGHES, KATHLEEN, Fourth Grade Teacher; *b:* West Chester, PA West Chester St Coll (BS) Elem Ed 1978; Masters Equivalency in Ele 1994; *cr:* Chichester Schl Dist Sub Tchr 1980-86, Elem Tchr 1986- Instructional Support Team Mem; Elem Soc Stud Moderator; Writir Curr Renewal Comms; PSEA, NEA 1980-; CEA 1986-; *office:* Chich Schl Dist Huddle Ave Linwood PA 19061*

HUGHES, MARY JOE (BREGENZER), Adj Assoc Prof of Humani *b:* Cleveland, OH; *m:* Guy D'Oyly; *c:* Claire, Evan; *ed:* Radcliffe (BA) Lit 1967; Harvard (MA) His 1968, (PHD) His 1976; *cr:* Boston Lecturer in His 1977-79, Lecturer Hnrs Prgm 1979-87, Asst Dir of Prgm 1987-, Adj Assoc Prof, Hnrs Prgm 1992-; *ai:* Women's Stud, Comm; Manchester Coll 1994-, Governing Body; Articles, Papers Whiting Fnd Travelling Flwshp 1983; Ford Fnd women's Stud Grant 1 Phi Beta Kappa Outstdng Tchng Awd 1990; *office:* Boston Coll Ches Hill MA 02167*

HUGHES, PEGGY RILEY, English Teacher; *b:* Elizabeth, NJ; *m:* I *ed:* Upsala Coll (BA) His 1959; *cr:* Burnett MS Eng Tchr 1959- Debating Club & Environmental Club Adv; NEA 1959-; UTTA 19 Burnet PTA 1959-; Tchr of the Yr 1994-95; Nom Chair of Hum 1994.

HUGHES, PRISCILLA POLLY, Second Grade Teacher; *b:* Provide RI; *m:* Charles J.; *c:* Ryan, Kelsey; *ed:* Springfield Coll (BS) Elem 1973; RI Coll Post Grad 38 Hrs; *cr:* Colrain Elem Schl 4th-6th Grd 1973-75; Austin T. Levy Elem Schl 2nd Grd Tchr 1975-95; Steere F Elem Schl 2nd Grd Tchr 1995-; *ai:* Gymnastics Coach 1975-81; N 1973-; *office:* Steere Farm Elem Schl 915 Steere Farm Rd Harrisvill 02830*

HUGHES, REGIS WILLIAM, First Grade Teacher; *b:* Natrona Heig PA; *m:* Marta Mauro; *c:* Ryan, Shannon, Erica; *ed:* IN Univ PA (BS Elem Ed 1968, (MED) ELem Ed 1970; Post Grad 60 Credit Hrs; *cr:* IN A Schl Dist 1st, 2nd Grd Tchr 1968; Oakmont Schl Dist PreK, K-2nd Elem Tchr 1968-71; Riverview Schl Dist Kndgtn, 1st, 2nd, 4th, 6th Gifted Tchr 1971-; *ai:* Jr HS Ftbl, Girls Sftbl Asst Vars Coach; N PSEA, REA 1968-.

HUGHES, RENEE L., Business Teacher; *b:* Michael ; *c:* Jared; Findlay Coll (BA) Bus Ed, Bus Admin 1988; Shippensburg Univ (MS) Ed 1993; *cr:* Forbes Rd Schl Dist Bus Tchr 1988-93; Wilson (Continuing Ed Cmptr Tchr 1992-93; Pine Grove Area HS Bus Tchr 19 *ai:* FBLA Org, Stu Adv; Asst Coach Under 6 Soccer Team; PA Bus Ed A 1988-; Delta Pi Epsilon 1992-, Sec; PSEA, NEA 1995-; Amer Leg Auxiliary 1987-; Order of Easter Star 1986-; *office:* Pine Grove Area School St Pine Grove PA 17963

HUGHES, SUZANNE RAO, French Teacher; *b:* Syracuse, NY; *m:* Dar Tobin; *c:* Shannon, Daniel; *ed:* St Bonaventure Univ (BA) Fr-Ed 19 Syracuse Univ (MS) Fr-Ed 1972; UCONN 6th Yr Degree Admin 19 Addl 30 Hrs Span, Rdgn, Stu Mngmt; *cr:* Baldwinsville HS Fr T 1968-82; J.F.K. HI-MS Fr Tchr, Dept Chair 1987-; *ai:* Quality Plus Co Chair; Dept Chair Cnsl; Foreign Lang Curr Comm; PTO Tchr Liais NEA 1968-; SEA, CT Org of Lang Tchrs 1986-; Town of Southing Diversity 1993-, Comm; Pedagogical Video Using Cmptr Across Cu Mini-Grant Reflexions: Impressionism in Fr Art, Music, His; Tchr of Nom; *office:* J. F. K. MS 1071 S Main St Plantsville CT 06479

HUGHES, WINSTON, Fine Arts Department Chairman; *b:* Perth Amb NJ; *m:* Ruth J. Hagins; *c:* Diane, Donna; *ed:* VA St Univ (BS) Music 1957; Trenton St Coll (MA) Conducting 1966; Attnd Kean Coll, Montc St Coll; *cr:* Thomas Jefferson Schl Vocal Music Tchr 1959-64; Edison Choral Dir 1969-70; Edison Bd of Ed Music Supvr, Choral Dir 1970- Edison HS Fine Arts Dept Chm, Choral Dir 1994-; *ai:* Men's Ensemb Treble Choir; Keytones; Jazz Choir; MENC 1961-; NJACDA 1970-, P 1979-81; NJPSA 1980-; NJMEA 1961-, Chm MCAC 1991; Outstd Young Edctr of Yr 1968; NJ HS All St Chorus Conductor 1977; Region Choir Conductor 1980; Cntrl Jersey Chorus Conductor 1987; *office:* Edis HS Blvd Of The Eagles Edison NJ 08817

HUGO, DANIELLE BIALOBOK, US History & Government Tchr; Amsterdam, NY; *m:* David Arthur; *c:* Aaron, Adrienne; *ed:* Rosary H Coll (BA) His, Govt 1971; Attnd Coll of Saint Rose At Albany NY, SUN at Oneonta; Elmira Coll; *cr:* Broadalbon Cntrl Scndry Soc Stud T 1971-87; Brodalbin-Perth Cntrl Scndry Soc Stud Tchr 1988-; *ai:* Co-A Debate Club; Schl Improvement Team 1989-96; Shared Decision Mk 1994; Broadalbin Tchrs Assn 1972-, Sec 1972, 1988; Mohawk Pathwa Girls Scouts 1986-89, Troop-Ldr; *office:* Broadalbin-Perth HS Bridge Ext Broadalbin NY 12025

HUGO, PATRICIA MC NICHOL, Math Teacher & Dept Chprsn; *b:* N York, NY; *m:* Peter; *c:* Christopher, Daniel; *ed:* Coll of St Elizabeth (B Math 1974; Long Island Univ (MS) Math Ed 1992; Supervision, Admin

;s; *cr:* Great Neck Pub Schls Math Tchr 1984-92; John L. Miller HS Chprsn 1992-; *ai:* Sr Class Spon; Bldg Curr, Rep Group; Shared ion Making Comm; GNTA 1982-; NCTM 1993-; *office:* John L Miller HS 35 Polo Rd Great Neck NY 11023*

:, CAROL PATRICIA, Lecturer; *b:* Tamaica, West Indies; *ed:* Hostos n Coll (AAS) Data Processing 1986; Herbert Lehman Coll (BS) uting, Mngmt 1988; City Coll of CUNY (MS) Cmptr Sci 1994; City Ctr Cmptr Sci; *cr:* J. C. Penney System Svc Statictical Rsrch 1987-88; Rochelle Hosp Data Base Admin 1988-91; Hostos Comm Coll iical Support 1991-, Instr, Adj lecturer 1994-; *ai:* Admission Comm; CIO 1991-; CCNY Alumni Assn 1994-; Alumni Lehman Coll 1988-, Computing Machinery; NY Tchr 1991-; Deans List 1986; Project ss Fund for Improvement of Post Scndry Ed; *office:* Hostos Comm 500 Grand Concourse Room C511P Bronx NY 10451

:, QUENTIN JOHN, Administrative Assistant; *b:* New York, NY; *ed:* Island Univ (MS) Early Chldhd Ed 1990; NY Univ (MS) Ed Admin *cr:* PS 124 Tchr 1983-; Dist 2 Title VII Math & Sci Coord 1991-92; 24 Sci Coord 1992-95, Admin Asst 1992-; *ai:* Sci Club Coord; Bsktbl h; Summer Primary Prgm Coord; NSF 1993-; *home:* 100 Beekman St 2N New York NY 10038

E, THERESA ALBANY, Junior High English Teacher; *b:* Darby, PA; avid P.; *c:* Kevin, Timothy, Kelsey; *ed:* Neumann Coll (BA) Eng Ed ; Rosemont Coll (MED) Educl Tech 1994; 12 Credits Irish Writers, wrights at Univ of Galway Ireland; Childrens Lit, Writing Process at nova Univ; *cr:* St Roberts Schl MS Lang Arts Tchr 1972-78; St Francis ales Jr HS Lang Arts Tchr 1980-; *ai:* Shakespeare Festival Dir; Yrbk erator; Team Ldr; Rdng, Cmptr Coord; Mid Sts Comm Co-Chair; E 1980-; NCEA 1972-; Guid Advy Cncl 1995-; Nominated Cath Tchr 1993; Numerous Articles Pub; *home:* PO Box 72 Chester Heights PA 7

DIE, JOHN JUDE, 7th-8th Grd English Teacher; *b:* Flushing, NY; onna Castronovo; *c:* Cara; *ed:* St Bonaventure Univ (BA) Eng 1968; ns Coll (MS) Tchng Scndry Eng 1972; *cr:* Goshen MS Eng Tchr -, Lang Arts Curr Coord 1974-78, Interdisciplinary Team Ldr 1985-; ideo Yrbk Adv; Tchr Contract Negotiating Comm; Goshen Tchrs Assn, UT, AFT 1968-; Schl Employees Credit Union 1975-, Bd of Dirs; Holy s Church 1971-, Lector; *home:* PO Box 215 Westtown NY 10998

IN, PAUL, Occptnl Work Adjustment Tchr; *b:* Los Angeles, CA; *c:* n, Vanetta; *ed:* Jackson St Univ (BS) Indstrl Arts 1975; Kent St Univ D) Educl Tech 1993; *cr:* Cleveland Pub Schls Ind Arts Tchr 1975-87, tr Lit Tchr 1985-87, Stage Craft Tchr 1982-83, Novell Netwaork p 108 7-88, Owa Tchr Coord 1989-, Ind Art Dept Chm 1995-; *ai:* er Beginnings Initiative; Urban League of Greater Cleveland Tchr, er; AFT, Cleveland Tchrs 1975-; OVA 1993-; *office:* Glenville HS 650 3th St Cleveland OH 44108*

L, JOHN R.,JR., 7th Grd Math, Geog & Rdng Tchr; *b:* Hartford, CT; Vendy Lynne Falck; *c:* Tyler, Brendon; *ed:* Southern CT St Univ (BA) 972; Cntrl CT St Univ (MS) Math Ed 1991; Eastern CT St Univ Elem Cert 1976; *cr:* East Cath HS Math Tchr 1977-87; Sheehan HS Math Tchr 7-89; Dag Hammerskjold MS 7th Grd Tchr 1989-; *ai:* Systemwide Test m; NEA 1977-; CEA 1977-; WEA 1987-, Shining Star of Month; St mpionship Team Coach Cross Cntry 1982 & 1985 & Golf 1984; *office:* Hammarskjold MS 106 Pond Hill Rd Wallingford CT 06492

LL, KAREN (LOCY), English Teacher & Dept Chair; *b:* Columbus, *m:* Daryl E.; *c:* Sean, Matthew; *ed:* Anderson Univ (BA) Eng 1971; land Univ (MED) Curr, Instruction; Scndry Prin, Supvr Certs 1993; *cr:* dleton MS Eng Tchr 1973-74; Reynoldsburg Jr HS Eng Tchr 1975-78; Walnut HS Eng Tchr, Dept Chair 1979-; *ai:* Jr Class Adv; OCTELA 8 SOCTE 4 Yrs; NCTE 18 Yrs+; Cooperative Learning Seminar enter; *office:* Big Walnut HS 555 S Old 3C Hwy Sunbury OH 43074*

LL, LEONARD EMERSON,JR., Social Studies Teacher; *b:* Taunton, ; *m:* Jacqueline Elaine Coelho; *ed:* Bridgewater St Coll (BA) His, Eng, Ed 1980; Paralegal Stud Cert 1983; *cr:* Taunton HS Soc Stud Tchr 3-91; John F. Parker MS Soc Stud Tchr 1991-; *ai:* Taunton HS Acad llenge Bowl, Acad Challenge Bowl Adv; Track Coach; Advy Cncl; th Shore Cncl for Soc Stud 1989-; NEA, MA Tchrs Assn 1983-; Taunton rs Assn 1983-, Bldg Rep; Taunton Substance Abuse Coalition 1989-; nton Chamber of Commerce Tchr of Yr Nom 1995; *office:* John F. ker MS 50 Williams St Taunton MA 02780

LL, MARIA-CATHERINE (DALY), Assoc Prof Indstrl Technology; Schenectady, NY; *m:* Douglas Robert; *c:* Mary Beth, Betty Ann; *ed:* lson Vly Comm Coll (AAS) Indstrl Tech 1982; SUC at Oneonta (BS) 1975; Grad Stud St Univ of NY at Albany, Oneonta; Softwares Certs; Ballston Spa HS Sub Tchr 1975; Shenedehowa HS Sub Tchr 1975; lson Vly Comm Coll Assoc Prof of Indstrl Tech 1982-; *ai:* 4-H Adv; ersity Forum; NY St Eng Tchrs Assn 1984-, VP: HVCC Fac Assn 1982-, Rock Day Spinners Guild 1987-, Pres; Hudson Mohawk Weavers 5-, Pres; Master Tchrs Seminar Participant 1989; *office:* Hudson Valley nm Coll 80 Vandenburgh Ave Troy NY 12180

LL, MARY ELLA, Retired Teacher; *b:* Cambridge Springs, PA; *ed:* St Tchrs Coll (BA) Early Chldhd 1955; *cr:* Peters Twp Schl Second Grd ir 1954-56; Carlynton Schl Dist First, Second Grd Tchr 1956-86; *ai:* EA 1954-; NEA; *home:* 133 Elm Grove Dr Mc Murray PA 15317

LL, SHERRY R., Second Grade Teacher; *b:* Maysville, KY; *m:* lliam S.; *c:* William T., Brady W.; *ed:* Southern St (AA) Elem Ed 1981; Univ (BA) Elem Ed 1982; Univ of Cin (MS) Spec Ed, Presch 1993; st-Grad Hrs; *cr:* Mother Goose Nursery Presch Co-Owner, Tchr 78-80; Adams Co Chrstn Schl Tchr 1981-90; Adams Co OH Vly Schls hr 1990-; *ai:* Ldrshp, Tech, Schl Scheduling Teams; NEA; Exceptional hvmt Awd; Literacy Grant; Prof Women's Schlsp; *office:* Seaman Elem nl PO Box J Broadway St Seaman OH 45679

JLSE, KAREN L., 11th & 12th Grd Med Tech Tchr; *b:* Wilmington, DE; Caleb; *ed:* IN Univ of PA (BS) Bio, Med Tech 1979; Tchng Cert Bio Ed 91; 13 Addl Credits Clinical Lab Sci; *cr:* Lenape AVTS Med Tech Tchr 91-; *ai:* Voc Indstrl Clubs of Amer Adv Hlth Knowledge, Quiz Bowls; A 1995-, PA New Outstdng Tchr of Yr; VICA 1991-, Western Region v of Yr; ASCP 1981-; *office:* Lenape Area Voc Tech Schl 2215 Chaplin e Ford City PA 16226*

JLSE, SHARON A., Fourth Grade Teacher; *b:* Hartford, CT; *m:* Jon; *c:* ra, Meghan; *ed:* Cntrl CT St Coll (BS) Elem Ed, Rdng 1975; Post Grad ld at CA St Coll Stanislaus; *cr:* Don Pedro Schl Tchr Grd 2 1977, imary Tchr Learning Handicapped 1977-78; Green Hills Schl Spec Ed hr 1979; Corpus Christi Schl Grd 4 Tchr 1987-; *ai:* NEASC Steering mm Co-Chm; Accreditation Soc Stud Coord K-6; ATOMIC, NCEA 87-; WHS Band Boosters 1992-, Sec 1994-; Corpus Christi omen'sClub 1992-; Corpus Christi Home & Schl Assn 1987-, Tchr Rep; chr of Two Winning Stdnts in Town-wide & Cty-wide Fire Prevention ster Contest, Received Two Tchr Awds; *office:* Corpus Christi Schl 581 las Deane Hwy Wethersfield CT 06109

JLTS, DEBORAH ANN, Spanish & French Teacher; *b:* Harrisville, MI; Robert L.; *c:* Zeb, Brienne; *ed:* Lock Haven St Coll (BA) Scndry Fr 73; Scndry Span Cert; *cr:* Coudersport Jr Sr HS Fr, Span Tchr 1975-88; reenwood Jr Sr HS Fr, Span Tchr 1988-; *ai:* Europe Trip Planner & Adv; AT Group Adv; NEA, PSEA 1975-, Sec; PMFLA 1992-; Bible Stud Ldr 91-92.

HUME, DEAN B., Teacher & Advisor; *b:* Akron, OH; *ed:* OH Univ (BSEd) Eng, Jrnlsm 1981; Kent St Univ (MA) Jrnlsm 1992; *cr:* R. B. Hayes HS Tchr, Adv, Coach 1981-90; Kent St Univ Assoc Dir 1990-92; Northern OH Schl Press Assn Part-time Fac 1990-92; Lakota HS Tchr, Adv 1992-; Jrnlsm Assn of OH Schls VP, Exec Dir 1994-95; *ai:* Pulse-Journal Weekly, Cincinnati Enquirer Stringer; SPARK Magazine Adv; WEB PR, Mrktg Comm; Contributing Ed Comm Jrnslm Ed Today; Publication Judge; Jrnlsm Ed Assn 1985-, Judge, Speaker; Northeastern OH Schlast Press 1984-, Bd Mem, Adv of Yr 1988, 1989, 1995; Soc of Prof Journalists 1993-; Sitting Bd Mem; Delaware Parks & Recreation Dept, Yth Bsbl Dir 1985-; Cincinnati Historical Soc 1994-; Dow Jones Newspaper Fund Dist Adv Awd 1993; Textbook Pub 1992; Received Proclamation from DE, OH City Cncl Outstdng Jrnlsm Edctr 1986; HS Press Club of Cntrl OH Elected Pres 1985; *office:* Lakota HS 5050 Tylersville Rd West Chester OH 45069*

HUMISTON, GERARD E., Teacher; *b:* Chateaugay, NY; *m:* Jean Desidoro; *c:* Andrew, John, Laura, Kathleen; *ed:* St Michaels Coll (BA) Chem 1961; Niagara Univ (MS) Chem 1963; St Johns Univ (PHD) Chem 1970; Schl Dist Admin Cert; *cr:* Manhattan Coll Asst Prof 1965-70; Harcum Jr Coll Acad Dean 1970-75; Johnson St Coll Acad Dean 1980-85; Greenwich CSD Tchr 1988-; *ai:* Modified Golf Jr Class Adv; Tech Comm; NYSUT 1988-; STANYS 1988-; ASCD 1995-; Lake George Bd of Ed 1989-, VP; Pub Textbook: General Chemistry 1990; *office:* Greenwich Central Schl 10 Gray Ave Greenwich NY 12834*

HUMISTON, JEAN DESIDORO, Guidance Counselor & Director; *b:* Saratoga Springs, NY; *m:* Gerard E.; *c:* Andy, John, Laura, Kathleen; *ed:* SUNY at Plattsville (BS) Elem Ed 1962; Manhattan Coll (MS) Cnslng & Psych 1971; Attnd SUNY at Albany, Empire St; *cr:* Bergenfield Schls 6th Grd Tchr 1965-70; Chittenden Dist K-12th Grd Sub Tchr 1982-85; Washington Cty K-12th Grd Sub Tchr 1985-87; N Warren HS Guid Dir & Cnslr 1987-; *ai:* Peer Cnslr, Natural Helper, SADD Adv; Parenting Pgm Coord; Tennis Coach; Crisis Team; Hlth & Wellness Comm; Drug Free Schls Grant Writer; NYSUT 1987-; Adirondack Cnslng Assoc 1987-, Sec; Washington Cty Comm on Yth at Risk 1991-; *office:* North Warren HS Box 190 Main St Chestertown NY 12817

HUMMEL, CHERYL ANN (COONS), Business Education Teacher; *b:* Huntingdon, PA; *m:* David Lee; *c:* Matthew, Michael, Elaina; *ed:* Shippensburg St Coll (BS) Bus Ed 1981; *cr:* Tyrone Area HS Bus Ed Tchr 1981-82; Forbes Rd HS Bus Ed Tchr 1982-88; Southern Huntingdon Cty HS Bus Ed Tchr 1988-; *ai:* Southern Huntingdon Cty Tchrs Assn 1988-; PTO; *office:* South Huntingdon Cty HS RR 1 Box 1124 Three Springs PA 17264

HUMMEL, RANDY MICHAEL, Social Studies Teacher; *b:* Bradford, PA; *m:* Jennifer S.; *c:* Rachel, Benjamin, Melissa; *ed:* Clarion Univ of PA (BSED) Soc Stud 1977; Addl Hrs Guid, Admin Trinity Coll; *cr:* Dubois HS Tchr 1983; Stoddert MS Tchr 1984-85; Forestville HS Tchr 1985-89; Douglass HS Tchr 1989-; *ai:* Crisis Intervention Team; NEA, MSTA, PGCEA 1988-; Mid Bay Kiwanis 1991-, Charter Mem; Calvert Co Republican Men's Club 1993-, Charter Mem; Calvert Cty Chptr Amer Red Cross 1995-, Bd Dirs.

HUMMEL, ROBERT A., HS Social Studies Teacher; *b:* Phoenix, AZ; *m:* Susan Lee Mauhs; *c:* Christopher, Jeffrey, Deborah; *ed:* Colgate Univ (BA) His & Ed 1980, (MAT) Soc Stud 1984; St Univ of NY at Plattsburgh (CAS) Schl Admin 1994; *cr:* Hackley Schl Soc Stud Tchr 1981-84; Rumson-Fairhaven HS Soc Stud Tchr 1984-87; Queensbury HS Soc Stud Tchr 1987-; *ai:* Boys Var Bsktbl & Frosh Ftbl Coach; Summer Recreation Bsktbl Supvr; QFA, NYSUT, AFT, AFL, CIO 1987-; NYSPHAA, Modified Sports Comm 1995-, St Bsktbl Tournament Comm 1987-; BCANY, Bd of Dirs 1995-; St Univ of NY at Plattsburgh Supervising Tchr 1989; *home:* 17 Lady Slipper Dr Queensbury NY 12804*

HUMPHREY, JEAN WHITCOMB, French Teacher; *b:* Buffalo, NY; *m:* Edward R.; *ed:* Grove City Coll (BA) Fr 1963; Univ of MD (MLS) Lib Sci 1980; 12 Hrs Penn St Univ; 12 Hrs Univ of Pittsburgh; 6 Hrs Univ of MD; 3 Hrs Amer Univ; *cr:* Gaskill Jr HS Fr, Ger Tchr 1963-64; Gateway Sr HS Fr Tchr 1964-66; DEW Jr HS Fr Tchr 1966-68; US Army GED Eng Tchr 1969; Montgomery Cty Pub Schls Fr, Ger, Resource Tchr 1972-; *ai:* Tech Comm; Software Chair; Natl Fr Hnr Soc Spon; NEA 1972-; AATF 1991-; Outstdng Tchr Nom; Agnes Meyer Awd; Grant to Stud in France; *office:* Rockville HS 2100 Baltimore Rd Rockville MD 20851

HUMPHREY, LAURA MASOTTI, French, Span Tchr & Dept Head; *b:* Youngstown, OH; *m:* Raymond; *ed:* Univ of Rochester (BA) Fr Lit 1969, (MA) Fr Lit 1970, (PHD) Fgn & Comparative Lit 1981; SUNY at Brockport SAS 1987, SDA 1987; *cr:* Keuka Coll Asst Prof of Span & Hum 1976-77; SUNY at Geneseo Asst Prof of Span 1977-78; Olympia HS Italian & Span Tchr 1978-79; Sutherland HS Dept Head & Tchr 1979-; *ai:* Instructional Ldrshp Team; Fgn Lang Standards Steering Comm; NHS Co Adv; AATF 1976-; AATSP 1976-; NYSAFLT 1976-, Regnl Conf Coord, Svc Awd; Phi Delta Kappa 1987-; Excl in Tchng Awd Univ of Rochester 1984; NEH Grant Summer Seminar in Paris 1993; Grant Summer Stud Costa Rica 1994; Franco Amer Fndtn Grant for St Supvrs & Coords 1995; *office:* Sutherland HS Sutherland St Pittsford NY 14534

HUMPHREY, ROSEANN SANTANGELO, Curr & Testing Supervisor; *b:* Jersey City, NJ; *m:* John; *c:* Shayne-Alexis, Devon Marie, Taryn Cullen; *ed:* William Paterson Coll (BA) Elem Ed 1972; Montclair St (MA) Learning Disabilities 1983; Prin, Supvr Cert, 32 Addl Credit Hrs 1989; *cr:* Kearny Bd of Ed Elem Tchr 1972-92, Supvr of Curr, Testing K-8 1992-; *ai:* Tech Coord for Grd 7-8th; Dir of Report Card Revision Comms; Dir of Staff Dev, GATE; PSA, ASCD, NCTM 1992-; Parsippany Acad Charter PTA Comm 1994-, Parent Adv; *office:* Kearny Schl Dist 100 Davis Ave Kearny NJ 07032

HUNDLEY, PAMELA EMS, Fifth Grade Teacher; *b:* Philadelphia, PA; *m:* John C.; *c:* Christopher Brad; *ed:* Millersville St (BS) Elem Ed 1968; Grad Stud 48 Credits; *cr:* Centennial Schl Dist 1st Grd Tchr 1968-69; Souderton Area Schl Dist 1st Grd Tchr 1969-72, 4th Grd Tchr 1975, 1st Grd Tchr 1977-78, 4th Grd Tchr 1978-89, 5th Grd Tchr 1989-; *ai:* Safety Patrol Adv; Math Advocate; PSEA, NEA, SAEA 1972-; *office:* E. M. Crouthamel Elem Schl 143 S School Ln Souderton PA 18964

HUNDLEY, RITA P., 1st Grade Teacher; *b:* Balto, MD; *c:* Thomas J., Wm Patton, Anne H. Blakeley, John A., Allison C.; *ed:* Towson St Univ (BS) Primary Ed Comp 1955; (MS) Primary Ed Comp 1990; Attnd Hopkins, Loyola Coll & Goucher, 30 Grad Credit Hrs; *cr:* Towson Elem Primary Tchr 1955-1958; Hampton Elem Primary Tchr 1973-; *ai:* PTA Bd; Cooperating Tchr for Stu Tchrs; Sci Facilitator; TABCO 1973-, Election Bd, Recognition Awd; MSTA 1973-, Outstndg Tchr 1991; NEA 1973-; Jr Chamber of Commerce, Outstndg Tchr Cert; *home:* 1008 Marleigh Cir Baltimore MD 21204

HUNE, THERESA (GAMBON), Introduction to Theater Tchr; *b:* Queens-Bayside, NY; *m:* James Richard; *c:* Clarice Jeanine; *ed:* Clarion Univ of PA (BS) Scndry Ed & Eng 1984; Slippery Rock Univ of PA (MA) Eng 1992; Integrating the Arts 3 Addl Credits; *cr:* Ingomar MS 7th Grd Eng Tchr 1985-86; Miles Bryan MS 7th Grd Eng Tchr 1987-89; Seneca Valley Jr HS 8th Grd Eng & Theater Tchr 1989-; *ai:* Thespian Club Spon; Stage Mgr; NEA 1987-; SVEA 1989-; Pittsburgh Pub Theater 1990-, Vol Usher; St Catherines Church 1990-, Lector; Max Nemner Awd for Clarion Univ Outstanding Eng Grad 1984-85; Slippery Rock Univ Outstanding Eng Grad Masters Prgm 1992-93; Grant Recipient & Participant AZ Shakespeare-Milton Inst Univ of AZ at Tucson 1993; *office:* Seneca Valley Jr HS 122 Seneca Schl Rd Harmony PA 16037*

HUNEKE, MARY KAY (MURPHY), Third Grade Teacher; *b:* Port Clinton, OH; *m:* Jeffrey Robert; *ed:* Bowling Green St Univ (BS) Elem Ed 1972; Post-Grad Stud Ashland Univ; *cr:* Sandusky City Schls 3rd Grd Tchr 24 Yrs; *ai:* Peer Mediation, Beautification, Social, Fire Prevention, Open House Comms; Delta Kappa Gamma 1993-; Sandusky Tchrs Assn, OEA, NEA 1972-; Co-Authored Tchr Resource Book 1992; Alumni Assn Tchr of Yr 1994; *home:* 427 Ohio St Huron OH 44839

HUNEKE, WAYNE, History Teacher & Coach; *b:* Bronx, NY; *m:* Lea Brunetti; *c:* Daniela, Graziella, Paul; *ed:* Lehman Coll CUNY (BA) Ec 1975; Western KY Univ (MA) Ed 1981; *cr:* Amer Comm Schl 3rd Grd & PE Tchr 1975-79; Western KY Univ Scndry Ed Tchng Asst 1980-81; St Pauls Schl Ec, His Tchr & Coach 1980-91; East Woods Schl His Tchr & Coach 1991-; *ai:* Lead Var Bsktbl & Soccer; Asst Var Lacrosse; Stu Cncl Adv; Theater Club Dir; Chess Club; NCSS 1995-; Donna Mayer Flwshp to Stud & Travel in England & Italy; 80 Percent Won-Loss Coaching Record; *office:* East Woods Schl 31 Yellow Cote Rd Oyster Bay NY 11771

HUNNELL, MORGAN A., Civics & Geography Teacher; *b:* Waynesburg, PA; *m:* Virginia Mac Queen; *c:* Sherry Lynn Hunnell Samek, Brian James; *ed:* Waynesburg Coll (BS) Soc Stud, Math 1966; Post Grad Stud Ashland Coll, Penn St Univ; *cr:* Laurel Highlands HS Problems of Democracy Tchr 1966-74; Waynesburg Cntrl HS Civics & Geog Tchr 1974-; *ai:* PA St Ed Assn, NEA 1967-; Selective Svc Bd 1982-; Lions Club, Pres 1979-80; Church Parish Cncl 1993-, Pres 1995-; Uniontown Chamber of Commerce Awd; *office:* Waynesburg Central HS RR 2 Box 39 Waynesburg PA 15370

HUNNIBELL, SHERRILL EDWARDS, Professor of Visual Arts; *ed:* RI Schl of Design (BFA) Art Ed & Illustration 1964; Brown Univ (MAT) Visual Art 1966; *cr:* Lincoln Pub Schls Elem Art Tchr 1964-65; Com Coll of RI Art Dept Prof 1966-; *ai:* CAA; FATE; NEA; MA 4-H Fndtn; RI 4-H All Stars; Banff Centre for the Arts Leighton Studios Fellow; VA Ctr for the Arts Fellow; Fiber Arts Design Book Four 1991; MA St Arts Lottery Grant; *office:* Community Coll Of RI 1762 Louisquisset Pike Lincoln RI 02865

HUNT, CAROLE ELIZABETH, Math Teacher; *b:* Sewickley Heights, PA; *m:* Richard P. Tynebor; *c:* Christopher J., Erik R., Robert M., Kristin K.; *ed:* PA St Univ (BS) Ed 1967; Stony Brook Univ (MALS) Ed 1975; 24 Post Grad Credits PA St Univ 1967-69; St Mary's of CA 6 Credits Amer Field Stud 1975-78; *cr:* H. E. Roberts 6th Grd Schl 1967-69; Hauppauge MS Eng Tchr 1969-73; Pines Schl Eng Tchr 1973-85, Math Tchr 1985-90; Hauppauge MS Math Tchr 1990-; *ai:* GO Adv; NYSUT, Hauppauge Tchrs Assn 1969-; Southold Historic Assn 1990-; *office:* Hauppauge Union Free Schl Dist 600 Townline Rd Hauppauge NY 11788

HUNT, CAROLE MACGREGOR, English Teacher; *b:* Lock Haven, PA; *m:* Brian A.; *c:* Jeffrey Kinley, R. Cory Kinley; *ed:* Lock Haven Univ (BS) Eng Ed 1982; DE St Univ 18 Credits Towards Masters; *cr:* Sussex Cntrl HS Eng Tchr 1985-; *ai:* Yrbk & Newspaper Adv; NEA 1985-; Indian River Ed Assn 1985-; Adult Comm Ed Assn 1986-; *office:* Sussex Central HS 301 W Market St Georgetown DE 19947

HUNT, CHRISTINE HANTZOPULOS, Span, Biling & Soc Stud Tchr; *b:* Brooklyn, NY; *m:* Jeffrey John; *ed:* Cornell Univ (BA) Span Lit 1985; SUNY at Binghamton (MA) Span Lit 1987; *cr:* Edward R. Murrow HS Span, Biling Soc Stud, Astronomy Tchr 1987-; *ai:* Sing Adv 8 Yrs; Fac Adv Sci Fiction Club; UFT, AFT 1987-; Astronomy Soc of Pacific 1994-; Prof Comic Books: Quantum Leap, Lost in Space 1993-94.

HUNT, DAVID MILES, Substitute English Teacher; *b:* Keene, NH; *ed:* Keene St Coll (BA) Eng 1981; *cr:* Salem HS Eng Tchr 1982; Mascenic HS Eng Tchr 1983-94; Conval HS Sub 1994-; *ai:* Drama Dir; NEA-NH 1986-; *home:* 20 Barrett Mountain Rd New Ipswich NH 03071*

HUNT, DEBRA BUCKWALTER, Hotel & Restaurant Mgt Coord; *b:* Williamsport, PA; *c:* Katherine; *ed:* IN Univ of PA (BS) Ed, Food Svc, Nutrition 1973; Educl Fnd Serv-Safe Sanitation Cert 1991; *cr:* Stouffers Restaurant Div Food Production Mgr 1973; Clover Div of Strawbridge & Clothier Dist Coord Food Svc 1973-80; Self Employed Consultant; Montgomery Cty Comm Coll Coord, Asst Prof of Hotel & Restaurant Mngmt 1981-; *ai:* Hospitality Club Adv; Acad Dean, Rsrch Design Specialist Comms Search; Acad Adv Cadre; Phila DE Vly Restaurant Assn 1973-, Bd of Dirs 1979-80; PAFT; Natl Restaurant Assn 1981-; Cntrl Montgomery Cty Tech Schl 1992-, Advy Comm, Adv; *office:* Montgomery County Comm Coll 340 Dekalb Pike #P-214 Blue Bell PA 19422*

HUNT, DENNIS CHARLES, History Teacher; *b:* New Haven, CT; *m:* Karen Spargo; *c:* Jennifer, Matthew; *ed:* Fairfield Univ (BA) Ed 1967; Southern CT St Univ (MA) His 1969; *cr:* Amity Regnl Sr HS His Tchr 1968-; *ai:* Crisis & Sabbatical Comms; Amity Ed Assn 1969-, VP 1978-79; CT Ed Assn & NEA 1969-; Church Garden Food Bank 1987-, Ldr 10 Yrs; Youth & Govt Club 1988-, Club Adv & Legislative Process Chprsn 10 Yrs, Leadership Awd 1989; YMCA Man of Yr Awd 1987; Amity Regnl Sr HS Tchr of Yr Awd 1989 & Gold Pen Awd 1985; Yrbk Dedication 1987; *office:* Amity Regnl Sr HS Newton Rd Woodbridge CT 06525

HUNT, ELOISE J., Language Arts Teacher; *b:* Philipsburg, PA; *m:* Robert J.; *ed:* Lock Haven St Coll (BS) Lang Arts 1963; Attnd Various Colls, Univs Permanent Cert in Lang Arts; *cr:* Tyrone HS Lang Arts Tchr 1963-68; Tamaqua Jr HS Lang Arts Tchr 1968-; *ai:* PSEA 1963-; NEA 1963-; NCTE 1963-; *office:* Tamaqua Area Jr HS High St Tamaqua PA 18252

HUNT, GARY S., High School Mathematics Tchr; *b:* Lowell, MA; *ed:* Lowell St Coll (BS) Ed 1969; Univ of Lowell (MA) Admin 1974; *cr:* Center Elem Schl 6th Grd Tchr 1969-78; Bedford HS Math Tchr 1978-; New England Banking Inst Math Tchr 1995-; *ai:* Bsktbl Coach; NEA, MTA, BEA 1969-; Bedford HS Schl Cncl 1995-; Wkshps in T I Graphing Calculator & Claris Works Software Courses; Univ of Lowell Athletic Hall of Fame; *office:* Bedford HS 9 Mudge Way Bedford MA 01730

HUNT, HAZEL, Chapter I Math Teacher; *b:* Pittsburgh, PA; *m:* Gerald Lamar Brown; *c:* Denise Lynn; *ed:* Point Park Coll (BA) Elem Ed 1971; Penn St Univ (MA) Elem Ed 1975; 3 Addl Credit Hrs in Math; *cr:* Barrett Elem 1-3 Grd Chptr I Math Tchr 1 Yr, 1-5 Grd Chptr I Math Tchr 1 Yr; Park Elem 1-5 Grd Chptr I Math Tchr 1 Yr; Woodlawn MS Metrics, 7th-8th Grd Math, 6th Grd Eng, 8th Grd Sci, 6-8 Grd Chptr I Math Tchr 14 Yrs; St Rita 1-8 Grd Chptr I Math Tchr 2 Yrs; Franklin Elem 2-3 Grd Classroom Tchr 7 Yrs; Calhoun Elem 2 Grd Classroom Tchr 2 Yrs; *ai:* Gen Cnslng; Steel Vly HS Chrldr Spon 10 Yrs; Woodlawn MS Chrldr Spon 3 Yrs; Woodlawn MS Girls Vlybl Coach 3 yrs; Homestead MS Girls Bsktbl Asst Coach; NEA 1971-, Bldg Rep 1975-76; SVEA, PSFA 1971-; MAACP 1965-; Shalimar Womens Club 1966-70, VP; Pastor's Aide Soc 1986-94; Jr Missionary 1959-65; Stdnts Who Had Difficulties in Schl & Adulthood Follow Up.

HUNT, IRENE WALMSLEY, Tchr of Gifted & Talented; *b:* Paterson, NJ; *m:* Brian; *c:* Tara; *ed:* William Paterson Coll (BA) Elem Ed 1963; Fairleigh Dickinson Univ (MA) Human Dev 1981; *cr:* Charles Olbon Schl 3rd Grd Tchr 1963-73; Beatrice Gilmore Schl 4th Grd Tchr 1975-77; Memorial Schl 7th-8th Grd Math & Soc Stud Tchr 1978-81; West Paterson Schl Dist 1st-8th Grd G & T Tchr 1982-; *ai:* Model Congress Adv; Cognetics Coach; Schl Play Dir; NEA 1963-; NJEA 1963-; WPEA 1963-, Sec; West Paterson Tchr of the Yr; Passaic Cty Tchr of the Yr; *office:* West Paterson Meml Schl Memorial Dr West Paterson NJ 07424

HUNT, JAMES CHRISTOPHER, Science Department Professor; *b:* Dawson Springs, KY; *ed:* Murray St Univ (BS) Physics & Astronomy & Math 1987; Univ of MD (MS) Physics 1990, (MA) His of Sci 1996; *cr:* Prince George Comm Coll Instr 1990-93, Asst Prof 1993-; *ai:* Cross-Cultural Educl Advy Comm; Honors Advy Cncl; His of Sci Soc 1993-; CSICOP Assn, Natl Ctr for Sci Ed 1990-; Natl Org of Gay & Lesbian Sci & Tech Prof 1996; Astronomical Soc of Pacific 1990-; Delta Lambda Phi 1991-, Natl Extension Chair; Bd of Dirs, Best Chapter Pres Awd 1993; *office:* Prince Georges Comm Coll 301 Largo Rd Uppr Marlboro MD 20774

HUNT, JOHN DOLMAN, Sixth Grade Science Teacher; *b:* Wuhu Anwhei, China; *m:* Anna Catherine Edmonds; *c:* Shawn, Gregory, Monica, Elizabeth; *ed:* Lamar Univ (BS) Scndry Ed, Bio, PE 1960; Stephen F. Austin St Univ (MS) Zoology, Botany 1968; Baylor Univ (EDD) Curr, Instruction 1973; Univ of MD 2 Credit Hrs; Univ of San Diego 5 Credit Hrs; Wilkes Univ 8 Credit Hrs; Boston Univ 16 Credit Hrs; Univ of Cntrl FL 3 Credit Hrs; Univ of NC 1 Credit Hr; Univ of AZ 1 Credit Hr; Cornell Univ 6 Credit Hrs; SUNY at Oneonta 4 Credit Hrs; TX Tech Univ 27 Credit Hrs; *cr:* Judson HS Chem, Physics Tchr 1986-87; Frankfurt HS Phy Sci Tchr 1987-88; Hanau HS Ed Prgm Mgr 1988-89; Giessen HS Asst Prin 1989-90; Hanau MS 6th Grd Sci Tchr 1990-; *ai:* Schl Advy Cncl VP; Hanau HS Var Soccer Coach; Schl Improvement Plan Co-Chprsn; Sci Club Spon; Advanced Rsrch Project Act Pilot Tchr; Sci Day K-8 Co-Chprsn; Germany ASCD 1973-, Pres, VP, Treas; Natl MS Assn 1993-; NSTA 1960-, STAR Awd, Outstdng Tchr; Germany Phi Delta Kappan 1973-; BSA 1989-, Merit Badge Cnslr; PTSA 1987-; Hanau Protestant Chapel 1988-, Children's Sermon Presentor; Shell Merit Fellow; Directory of Two Natl Sci Fnd Grants; DoDDS US Civilian Employee of Yr Hanau Germany; 24 Articles Pub; *home:* Cmr 470 Box 7706 APO AE 09165*

HUNT, JOHN H., 7th & 8th Grd Science Teacher; *b:* Colechester, VT; *m:* Ruth E.; *c:* Ian; *ed:* Unity Coll (BS) Environmental Sci 1975; Beal Coll (AS) Medical Asst 1987; Univ of ME Ed Cert 1988; *cr:* Caravel MS Sci Tchr 1988-; *ai:* Sci Olympiad Coord; Sci Fair Coach; Sportsman Alliance of ME 1995-, Fishing Advy Comm; *office:* Caravel MS Rt 1 Box 2970 Carmel ME 04419

HUNT, LINDA ANN, Advanced Placement Bio Teacher; *b:* Warrington, England; *ed:* Glassboro St Coll (MA) Environmental Sci 1981; Coll of Notre Dame (BA) Bio; Biological Scis K-12th Grd Cert; 20 Credit Hrs Post Grad Stu Sci Ed; *cr:* Naval Air Engineering Ctr Environmental Bio 1983-86; Paul VI HS Bio, Anatomy & A P Bio Tchr 1978-92; Sterling HS Summer Bio Tchr 1986-93; Sterling HS 1992-; Camden Cty Coll Anatomy & Physiology Part Time Tchr; *ai:* NHS Faculty Cncl; Chemcl Hygn Ofcr, Mntr; NSTA & Mid Sts Evaluation Team; Nat Sci Fnd Grant & Fellowship; PSEG Grant Physics; Stevens Inst of Tech Schlsp; Cath Edcuator of Month; *office:* Sterling HS Warwick Rd & Preston Ave Somerdale NJ 08083*

HUNT, MARTHA ANNE, Professor of Bus & Banking; *b:* Keene, NH; *m:* Nestor N. Deshaies; *ed:* Univ of NH (BS) 1970; Univ of WI at Madison Diploma Banking 1983; Attending NH Coll Schl of Bus; *cr:* City of Concord Schl Lib Admin Asst 1970-72; Bank of NH VP, Compliance Officer 1973-85; NH Tech Inst Bus Prof, Dept Head Banking, Fin 1985-; *ai:* Workload, Dept Head Comm; Amer Inst of Banking 1973-, Various; Sigma Lambda Mu, Adv; Concord Regnl Food Prgm 1984-, Trustee; Yrbk Dedication for Outstdng Contribution Stu Life; *office:* NH Tech Inst 11 Institute Dr Concord NH 03301*

HUNT, MICHAEL LEE, Band Director; *b:* Washington, DC; *m:* Connie Elaine Smith; *ed:* Columbus Coll (BM) Music Ed 1988; Duquesne Univ (MM) Music Performance 1990; 15 Addl Credit Hrs Music Ed; *cr:* Duquesne Univ Grad Asst 1988-90; Randolph-Clay HS Band Dir 1990-92; Albany Symphony Orch Principle Horn 1990-92; Bishop Mc Namara HS Band Dir 1992-; *ai:* MENC, Phi Mu Alpha 1988-; Pittsburgh Musicians Union 1989-; Intnl Horn Soc 1985-; *office:* Bishop Mc Namara HS 6800 Marlboro Pike Forestville MD 20747

HUNT, ROBERT J., Instrumental Music Teacher; *b:* Philipsburg, PA; *m:* Eloise J. Lutz; *ed:* Mansfield St (BS) Music Ed 1964; Post Grad Work at Penn St, Ithaca Coll, Bloomsburg St & W Chester St; *cr:* Tamaqua Area Schl Dist Band Dir 1964-76, Elem Inst Music Tchr 1976-; *ai:* Elem Bands Dir; PSEA 1964-; NEA 1964-; MENC, PMEA 1964-; *office:* Tamaqua Area Schl Dist Box 112 Tamaqua PA 18252

HUNT, SUE HEATH, English Teacher; *b:* Kinston, NC; *c:* Ruskin; *ed:* East Carolina Univ (BS) Eng 1960; Long Island Univ (MS) Ed 1992; CSW Cert Soc Worker; NCAC Natl Cert Addictions Cnslr; CADC Cert Alcohol, Drug Cnslr; *cr:* Rutherford Jr High Eng Tchr, Chair 1960-65; Maywood Ave Schl Eng Tchr 1966-; Beth Israel Hospital Family Prgm Addictions Dir 1983-90; Private Practice Addictions Therapist 1989-; *ai:* Peer Counseling Coord; Prin Advy Cncl; K-8th Grd Affirmative Actions Officer 1993-; Maywood Ed Assn 1966-; NEA 1969-; NCTE 1960-; AAUW 1991-; *office:* Maywood Avenue Schl 452 Maywood Ave Maywood NJ 07607*

HUNT, THERON L., Bio, Ecology & Life-Sci Tchr; *b:* Geneva, OH; *m:* Virgie A. Fry; *c:* Darren, Chad; *ed:* Ashland Coll (BS) Bio 1965; Univ of WI Bio; OH St U Natural Resources; Ash Coll Dr Ed Cert 1970; *cr:* South Cntrl HS Bio, Life Sci, Ecology & Dr Ed 1965-; *ai:* Stu Cncl Adv 21 Yrs; SADD Adv 9 Yrs; Coached Bsbl 25 Yrs, & Bsktbl 10 Yrs; Ath Dir 13 Yrs; OEA 1965-; SCEA 1965-94, Pres 1983-84; OH Archeological Soc 1970-; U of WI NSF Grant 1968-70; *office:* South Central HS 3305 Angling Rd Greenwich OH 44837*

HUNTER, ALLEN DALE, Associate Professor; *b:* Prince George, BC Canada; *m:* Susan F.; *c:* April; *ed:* Univ of British Columbia (BC) Chem 1981, (PHD) Chem 1985; Post Doctoral Fellow Australian Natl Univ 1986 & Univ of Alberta 1987; *cr:* Univ of Alberta Asst Prof 1987-92; Youngstown St Univ Assoc Prof 1992-; *ai:* Amer Chemical Soc 1980-; AAAS 1982-; Amer Crystallographic Soc 1984-; Grants Univ of Alberta & Youngstown St Univ; Papers Refereed Chem Journal; *office:* Youngstown St Univ 410 Wick Ave Dept of Chemistry Youngstown OH 44555*

HUNTER, ANDREW JOHN, Social Studies Teacher; *b:* Syracuse, NY; *m:* Kathlene Ann Miller; *ed:* LeMoyne Coll (BA) Pol Sci 1989; SUNY at Cortland (MS) Soc Stud Ed 1996; *cr:* NY St Assembly Legislative Asst 1989; Liverpool HS Scndry Soc Stud Tchr 1991-92; Central Sq MS Scndry Soc Stud Tchr 1992-93; Marcellus HS Scndry Soc Stud Tchr 1993-; *ai:* Soph Class Adv; AFT, Cntrl NY Cncl for Soc Stud, NYSUT 1991-; NEH Summer Grant 1994; *office:* Marcellus Sr HS Reed Pkwy Marcellus NY 13108

HUNTER, COLLEEN F., English Department Chair; *b:* Fountain Hill, PA; *m:* Robert L.; *c:* Thomas R., Erin C. Roman; *ed:* Kutztown St Coll (bSEd) Eng 1963; Kutztown Univ (MED) Eng 1989; *cr:* Fountain Hill HS Eng Chprsn 1963-64; Nitschmann Jr HS Curr Aide & Permanent Substitute 1977-79; St Francis Acad Eng Chprsn 1979-87; Northampton Comm Coll Adjunct Prof 1988-; Allentown Cen Cath HS 1987-, Eng Chprsn 1989-, Dir of Studies 1996-; *ai:* Scholastic Scrimmage Coach; Broadway Show Dir; NCEA 1979-; NCTE 1988-; Allentown Diocese Lay Tchrs Assn 1987-, Sec 2 Yrs; ASCD 1992-; Bethlehem Pub Lib Bd, Sec 7 Yrs.*

HUNTER, DONALD SCOTT, Instructor & Coord; *b:* Baltimore, MD; *m:* Sandra Kaye; *c:* Karen, Cheryl; *ed:* Camron Newman Coll (BA) Amer His 1964; Towson St Univ (MA) Personnel, Ed 1972; LaSalle Univ Ed 1992; *ai:* Golf, Girls Bsktbl Coach; Key Club, Model UN, Youth, Govt Adv; Kiwanis 1984-, Pres, District Ad, Mem of Yr 1992; Pres Church Bd 1970-, Bd of Dir; Fac Mem of Yr; Dist Awd MD, DEL, VA; Vly Forge Freedom Flwshp; Harvard Stud Grant Amer His; *home:* 1806 Reuter Rd Timonium MD 21093*

HUNTER, GARY R., Chemistry Teacher; *b:* Warren, PA; *m:* Linda Tiernan; *c:* Tabatha Peters, Stephanie Palmer, Lindsey Palmer; *ed:* Clarion Univ (BS) Phys Sci & Math 1963; Duke Univ (MAT) Chem 1967; Post Grad Slippery Rock Univ, Penn St & WI St at Oshkosh; *cr:* Mercer Area Schl Math Tchr 1963-67; Hickory HS Chem Tchr 1967-; *ai:* PSEA 1963-, NEA 1963-; HEA 1967; Mercer Amer Legion 1963-; Brandy Springs Pk Bd 1970-, VP; JCI Senator 1970-; Mercer Cty YABA 1975-, Pres; NSF Grants 5 Yrs; *office:* Hickory HS 640 N Hermitage Rd Hermitage PA 16148

HUNTER, JERRY LEROY, Business Administration Tchr; *b:* Farmington, ME; *m:* Tracy L.; *c:* Kristen, Taylor; *ed:* Univ ME at Machras (BS) Bus Tchr Ed 1986; NH Coll (MS) Bus Tchr Ed 1993; *cr:* Brunswick HS Bus Ed Tchr 1986-92; MVR #10 Bus Admin Tchr 1992-; NH Coll Assoc Prof 1993-; *ai:* FBLA St & Yrbk Adv; RTTA Pres; Negotiations Chair; Cert Comm; Bus Ed Assn of ME 1982-, Pres Elect, Newsletter Ed & Region Dir; FBLA 1981-, St Adv; FBLA Adv of Yr; *office:* ME Voc Schl Region #10 68 Church Rd Brunswick ME 04011

HUNTER, MARILYN K., 11th & 12th Grade English Tchr; *b:* Pittsburgh, PA; *m:* William Richard; *c:* Erin, Lauren; *ed:* Clarion St Coll (BA) Eng & Rdng 1968; Carnegie Mellon Univ (MA) Eng 1971; Tesa Prgm; *cr:* Penn Hills Schl Dist 7th Grd Core, Eng & Soc Stud Tchr 1968-71, 11th-12th Grd Eng Tchr 1971-; Comm Coll of Allegheny Cty Eng Instr 1990-; Profession Experience Program Tchr 1994-; *ai:* Curr Cncl; SADD Spon; Discipline Policy Bd for Dist; Climate Renewal Comm for Dist; PHEA, PSEA, NEA & NCTE 1968-; Penn Trafford Soccer Booster 1992-, Comm Chprsn; Church 1980-, Lector, CCD Tchr & Choir; Allegheny Intermediate Unit Guest Speaker 1993; *office:* Penn Hills Sr HS 12200 Garland Dr Pittsburgh PA 15235

HUNTER, MARY WILLIAMS, Medical Office Asst Teacher; *b:* Merigold, MS; *m:* David; *c:* David C., Christopher D.; *ed:* Cleveland St Univ (MS) Bus Ed, Curr & Instruction 1978; Comp Sci & Employment Skills; *cr:* Valena C Jones HS Tchr 1965-67; Jane Addams Bus Career Tchr 1968-; *ai:* Bus Prof of Amer; CTU Election, Prin Awd & Mrktg Comms; NEA; CABTA; Bright Star Bapt Church 1972-; Share Pgm; *home:* 15716 Oakhill Rd East Cleveland OH 44112

HUNTER, NATHAN ANDREW, Youth Pastor; *b:* Lock Haven, PA; *m:* Shari Lynn Kratche; *c:* Christian, Tiffany, Derek; *ed:* Cedarville Coll (BA) Biblical Stud 1983, (BA) PE 1985; Working on Masters in Ministries Moody Bible Inst; *cr:* Evangel Bible Church Minister of Yth & Chrstn Ed 1985-86; Flwshp Bible Church Yth Pastor 1986-; *ai:* Bsktbl Coach; Natl Network of Yth Ministers 1991-; *office:* Fellowship Bible Church Schl 16391 Chillicothe Rd Chagrin Falls OH 44023

HUNTER, ROBERT RANDALL, 6th Grd Science & Math Tchr; *b:* London, OH; *m:* Toni Anita Mere; *c:* Maxwell R.; *ed:* OH Univ (BA) Sports Sci 1986; OH St Univ (MS) Elem Ed 1988; *cr:* Jefferson Local Schls MS Sci Tchr 1988-; *ai:* Head Var Boys Bsktbl & Co-Ed Tennis Coach; Advy Comm; *office:* Jefferson Local Schls 177 S Frey Ave West Jefferson OH 43162

HUNTER, THOMAS C., Second Grade Teacher; *b:* Johnstown, PA; *m:* Christine Helen Fornadel; *c:* Julie, Megan, Tommy; *ed:* Univ of Pittsburgh at Johnstown (BS) Elem Ed 1975; Univ of Pittsburgh (MED) Elem Ed 1980; *cr:* Forest Hills Elem Schl 2nd Grd Tchr 1976-; *ai:* Boys & Girls Var Cross Cntry Coach 1977-; NEA 1976-; Adams Twp Girls Sftbl League 1990-, Mgr, League Sec; 1889 South Fork Hunting & Fishing-Historical Preservation Soc 1987-, Sports Dir; *office:* Forest Hills Elem Schl 547 Locust St PO Box 156 Sidman PA 15955

HUNTER, TODD LEE, Music Dept Chprsn & Band Dir; *b:* Phoenixville, PA; *m:* Deborah A. Johnson; *c:* Lauren Elizabeth; *ed:* Mansfield Univ (BS) Music Ed 1976; West Chester Univ (MM) Music Ed 1983; 18 Credit Hrs Beyond Masters; *cr:* Minersville Area HS Band Dir & Music Tchr 1977-80; Berwick Area Sr HS Band Dir & Music Tchr 1980-87; Cntrl Buck West HS Band Dir & Music Tchr 1987-88; Dallas Sr HS Band Dir, Music Tchr & Dept Chprsn 1989-; *ai:* Marching, Jazz & Pep Bands; NEA, PSEA, Amer Fed of Musicians 1977-; MENC, PMEA 1980-; Bloomsburg Univ Comm Orch 1976-, Prin Trombone; Berwick Colonial Band 1980-; Whos Who in Amer Ed-Marquis; Preformed with Group Daddy-O & the Sax Maniax for Pres & First Lady Hillary Clinton 3 Times-2 at the White House, PA Governor Robert Casey 1994, Governor Tom Ridge 1995 & Numerous Charity Performances; Appeared in People Magazine with Pres Clinton 1995; *office:* Dallas Sr HS PO Box 2000 Dallas PA 18612*

HUNTER, WILDA FAISON, Fifth Grade Teacher; *b:* Jeannette, PA; *m:* James E.; *ed:* Clarion Univ of PA (BS) Elem Ed 1963; *cr:* DuBois Area Schls Tchr 1963-65; Monroe Cty Schls Tchr 1965-67; Norwin Schl Dist Tchr 1967-; *ai:* Cooperative Learning Trainer; NEA 1963-; PSEA, Norwin EA 1967-; DKG Soc Intnl 1989-; PCTM 1991-; Tchr of Yr 1986; Shaw PTA Phoebe Apperson Hearst Outstdng Edctr Awd 1994; *office:* Shaw Elem Schl 281 Mc Mahon Dr N Huntingdon PA 15642

HUNTLEY, REID DEBERRY, English Professor; *b:* Charlotte, NC; *c:* David, Maria Huntley Warmke; *ed:* Duke Univ (AB) His 1957; Yale Divinity Schl (MDiv) Theology & Ethics 1961; NNC at Chapel Hill (PHD) Eng 1969; Munich Germany Jr Coll Yr 1955-56; *cr:* The Coll of Wm & Mary Presbyn Campus Minister 1961-64; OH Univ Eng Prof 1968-; *ai:* Scioto Valley Presbyn 1968-, Ordained; Danforth Assoc of OH 1981-, Chair; Assn for Psychological Type 1985-; Fulbright Visiting Prof Univ of Madras India 1975-76; Univ Prof (Twice); Thomas Wolfe Review Contributor; Intnl Assn for Psychological Type Presenter; *office:* OH Univ Ellis Hall 314 Athens OH 45701

HUNTSINGER, DONALD ROSS, American Cultures Tchr & Adv; *b:* Altoona, PA; *m:* Janice Kay Daniels; *c:* Jeffrey Ross; *ed:* Millersville Univ (BS) Geog 1968, (MS) Cnslr Ed 1972; Widener Univ Courses Toward Comprehensive Soc Stud Degree 1976; *cr:* Warwick Schl Dist Tchr 1968-; *ai:* Ed Comm Discipline; Stu Assistance Prgm; NEA, PSEA, NCSS 1968-; Warwick Ed Assn 1968-, Negotiator 1972-, Chief Negotiator 1976; East Petersburg Boro Cncl; Nom Tchr of Yr Jaycees.

HUNTZINGER, JANICE ZIEGLER, Education Director; *m:* Joseph F.; *c:* Christopher J., Kali R.; *ed:* Luzerne Comm Coll (AAS) Erl Ed 1980; Bloomsburg Univ (BS) Elem Ed 1982; *cr:* Wilkes-Barre Acad Kndgtn Tchr 1983-86, 1st Grd Tchr 1986-88, 3rd Grd Tchr 1988-89, 8th Grd Tchr 1989-90, 5th-8th Grd His Tchr & Dir 1990-; *ai:* Ski Club Adv; Geography Bee Spon; *office:* Wilkes-Barre Acad 20 Stevens Rd Wilkes Barre PA 18702

HUPE, RICHARD CARTER, Regents Biology Teacher; *b:* Hempstead, NY; *m:* Andrea Theresa Casale; *c:* Matthew, Scott; *ed:* Saint John's Univ (BS) Bio 1966; Hufstra Univ (MS) Ed 1969; *cr:* St Raymond's HS Bio, Math Tchr 1966-69; Lynbrook HS Bio Tchr 1969-; *ai:* Cross Cntry, Winter Track, Spring Track Coach; Nassau Track Coaches Assn 1969-, Sportsmanship Awd; *office:* Lynbrook H S 9 Union Ave Lynbrook NY 11563

HUPKA, JOSEPH MICHAEL, High School Art Instructor; *b:* Pottsville, PA; *m:* Trudy; *c:* Elayne, Jennifer, Michael; *ed:* Kutztown Univ (BS) Art Ed 1966, (ME) Art 1994; *cr:* Schuylkill Haven HS Art Instr 1966-; *ai:* Graphic Arts Dept Chm; Newspaper Adv; SHEA, PSEA, NEA 1966-; *office:* Schuylkill Haven HS 120 Haven St Schuylkill Haven PA 17972

HURD, PATRICIA MONDRUT, English & Speech Teach Youngstown, OH; *m:* John K.; *c:* Emily S, Erica S., John K.; *ed:* Univ at Oxford OH (BA) Speech & Eng 1966; Post Grad at Xavier U Miami Univ; *cr:* Brecksville HS Eng & Speech 1966-67; US Army 4 Tchr 1968-69; Indian Hill HS Eng & Speech 1969-75, 1982-; U Cincinnati Speech Instr 1980-82; *ai:* NHS & Key Clb Adv; NEA 1969; CTA Classroom Tchrs Assn 1969-, Corresponding Sec 1991-; 1985; NASSP 1990-; Cinncinati Bar Assn Auxiliary 1974-; PTC Colonel 1988; OH Writing Project Fellow 1984; Dev of Acad Interv for Stdnts at Risk 1990; Classroom Tchr hon of Distinction for W with LD Stdnts 1989; Madeline Hunter Mastery Tchng I & II 19 Clinical Supvr 1988; Inservice Materials on Peer Groups, Journals, F Writing as Process; *office:* Indian Hill H S 6845 Drake Rd Cincinna 45243

HURD, PHILIP L., 4th Grade Teacher; *b:* Brooklyn, NY; *m:* Barbar Walker; *c:* Kristen; *ed:* Plattsburgh St Univ Coll (BS) El Ed 1968, (M Ed 1973; *cr:* Peru Cntrl Schl 4th-6th Grd Tchr 1968-; *ai:* NEA & NY Peru Assn of Tchrs 1968-; *office:* Peru Cntrl Schl New York Plattsburgh AFB NY 12903

HURDLE, ELIZABETH CONROY, Basic Skills Teacher; *b:* Washir DC; *m:* William T.; *ed:* Univ of DE (BS) Ed 1956; Univ of South FL Rdng Ed; 6 Credit Hrs Univ of MD; 24 Credit Hrs George Washi Univ; *cr:* Montgomery Cty Schl Elem, Rdng Tchr 1956-66; Pinella Schl Scndry Rdng Tchr 1966-78; Indian River Schl Elem Tchr 198 Numerous Comm Local, State Level; NEA 1954-; DSEA, IREA Intnl Rdng Assn 1963-78; 1966-78; FL Rdng Assn 1966-78; Pinella Rdng Assn 1966-78, Sec 1976, Treas 1977, VP 1978; Amer Assn Women 1957-65, Sec Schlsp Chm; Jr HS Tchr of Yr; Rdng Tchr of Y Math Tchr Awd 1963; Co-Author Pendulum Press Activity S Illustrated Classics 1976-78.

HURFF, RICHARD PAUL, English Teacher; *b:* Camden, NJ; *ed:* U Coll (BA) His 1964; LeHigh Univ (MA) Eng 1970; Columbia Pacific (PHD) Fine Arts 1996; 30 Grad Credits Eng at Rowan Coll; *cr:* Tritor HS His Tchr 1965-67; Camden Cty Coll Eng Tchr 1968-75; Audubo Eng Tchr 1967-, Eng Dept Chair 1979-88; *ai:* Concert Club; Newspaper Adv; Stu Cncl; Ind Stud Prgm; Schl Photographer; Audub Assn 1967-, Treas 8 Yrs; NJEA, CCEA, NEA 1967-; BSA 1958-, Exp Adv, Asst Scoutmaster, J. T. Ashe Awd; Tchr of Yr 1989; *office:* Aud Jr-Sr HS 350 Edgewood Ave Audubon NJ 08106

HURLBURT, LAUREN MCGEE, French Teacher; *b:* Rochester, N Dana; *c:* Addison; *ed:* St Univ of NY at Potsdam (BA) Fr 1987; Middl Coll (MA) Fr 1991; *cr:* Letchworth Cntrl Schl Fr Tchr 1987-; *ai:* Fo Lang Club Adv; Foreign Lang Trips Coord; Phi Delta Kappa 1994-.

HURLBUT, ARTHUR GLENN, Professor; *b:* Ogdensburg, NY; *m:* L. Kelsey; *c:* Andrew, David, Kimberly; *ed:* SUNY Agri & Tech (AAS) Air Cond Engr Tech 1965; Clarkson Coll (BSME) Mecha Engrng 1969, (MSME) Mechanical Engrng 1970, (PHD) Engrng Sci *cr:* Landis & Gyr Powers Svc Tech 1965-67; Carrier Corp Design En 1970=-73; SUNY Canton Prof 1973-; *ai:* ASHRAE Stu Chptr at Ca Adv; Tau Alpha Pi at Canton; Appt & Promotion, Coll Assn Cor ASHRAE1973-, Energy Comm Chair; Pi Tau Sigma 1967-, Pres Clar Chptr; Tau Beta Pi 1968; Experimental Aircraft Assn 1970-, Pres, VP, Letter Ed; First Bapt Church 1960-, Sunday School Tchr, Deacon; In Press Awd Air Conditioning 1965; Clarkson Coll Flwshp 1969-70; F Element Solutions to Composite Materials-ASME Transactions; *offic* U N Y Coll Of Tech At Canton Cornell Dr Canton NY 13617

HURLBUT, BRUCE ALAN, Business Education Teacher; *b:* N Adams, MA; *m:* Christine Ellen Nelson; *c:* Chris, Jessica; *ed:* Southea MA Univ (BS) Mgmt 1971; North Adams St Coll (MED) Scndry A 1977; *cr:* Monument Mountain Regnl HS Bus Ed Tchr 1971-; *ai:* Berks Crafts Fair Treas; NEA 1971-; Bd of Dirs Cath Youth Ctr 19 Fundraising Chprsn, Vol of Yr 1993; Cath Youth Ctr 1986-, Bsktbl Co YMCA 1986-, Soccer Coach & Ofcl; HS-MS Parent Advy Comm 19 Chprsn; Natl Tandy Scholar Awd; *office:* Monument Mountain Re Schl Rt 7 Great Barrington MA 01230

HURLEY, JOSEPH, Science Teacher; *b:* Worcester, MA; *m:* Kathlee Fitzgerald; *c:* Kimberly Markey, Elizabeth, Joseph, Sarah; *ed:* Holy C Coll (AB) Bio 1969; Suffolk Univ (MA) Ed & Bio 1970; T Coll-Columbia Univ (MED) Sci Ed 1974; Doctoral Stud; *cr:* St P Marian HS Bio Tchr & Sci Dept Chprsn 1974-87; Auburn HS Bio 1987-; Quinsigamond Comm Coll Part-Time Anatomy & Physiology 1988-; *ai:* Boys Var Bsktbl & Girls Var Tennis Coach; NEA 1987-; 1987-; ATA 1987-; MBCA 1994-; Tchrs Coll Columbia Univ Sci Flwshp; 2 Horace Mann Educl Grants for Rsrch in Sci Ed; Major Spe at St Stu Cncl Convention; Numerous Speaking Engagements at Sch Church Groups.*

HURLEY, JOSEPH D., English & Latin Teacher; *b:* Boston, MA; *m:* L Whelan; *c:* Jason, Shauna, Jennifer; *ed:* Iona (BA) Classical Langs 19 Northeastern Univ (MS) Sociology 1974; *cr:* New England Teleph Mngmt, Bus Office 1969-71; Cath Meml HS Eng, Latin Tchr 1971-; Multi Cultural Club Coord; Jr Prom Adv; Girl's AAU Bsktbl Asst Co *home:* 18 Phyllis Rd Foxboro MA 02035*

HURLEY, JOSEPH PATRICK, Math Teacher; *b:* Rochester, NY Jennifer, James; *ed:* SUNY at Brockport (BA) Math 1979; Nazareth (MS) Ed 1988; *cr:* Mercy HS Math Tchr 1979-80; Camden HS Math T 1983-84; Caledonia-Mumford HS Math Tchr 1984-; *ai:* Var Golf Coa ARFT, NEA, NYSUT 1983-; Univ of Rochester Excl Scndry Tchng A 1995; *office:* Caledonia-Mumford HS 99 North St Caledonia NY 1442

HURLEY, RICHARD KEVIN, Science Teacher; *b:* Bayshore, NY; Judith A.; *c:* Kevin, Karen; *ed:* SUNY Suffolk C. Coll (AA) Earth Sci 19 Elmira Coll (BS) Environmental Sci 1977, (MS) Ed, Bio 1986; Bradford Cntrl Schl Sci Tchr 1986-; *ai:* Photo, Garden Club Adv; N 1986-, Treas; Natl Tchr Trng Inst Master Tchr; BOCES NYS Water W Grant 1996-; Pub Report NYSDEC; Natl Gardening Grant 1994; Hills D Store Grant; *office:* Bradford Central Schl Rt 226 Bradford NY 14815*

HURLEY, SUE A. BOGENSCHUTZ, Junior High Teacher; *b:* Covingt KY; *w:* Robert E. (dec); *c:* Jeremiah, Robert, Lawrence; *ed:* Our Lady Cincinnati (BA) Sociology 1954; Cmptr, Tax, Scripture, Lit Courses; Ch Abuse; *cr:* Saint Dominic Schl Tchr 1954-61; Pub, Parochial Schls S Tchr 1967-71; Saint Jude Schl Tchr 1971-74; Saint Ignatius 8th Grd t 1974-; *ai:* Jr HS Acad Team Moderator; Parish, Schl Ed Commission R Mentored Tchrs; Math Dept Chprsn; NCEA 1971-; Natl Math Tchr As Parish Org 1966-; Addressed Natl Parent Tchr Assn; Archdiocesan M Curr Comm for Course of Stud; Planned, Organized Jr HS Prgn Organize, Chaired Testing Explanation Prgm for Parents.

HURLING, GWENYTH HILL, HS Guidance Counselor; *b:* Glen Rid NJ; *c:* Kathy A., Wendy R.; *ed:* Fisk Univ (BA) Math 1943; Montclair Univ (MA) Stu Prsnl Svcs, Cnslng 1969; Supervision & Admin Cert Credits Kean Coll of NJ; *cr:* West Kinney Jr HS Math Tchr 1965-66; J. Kennedy HS Math Tchr 1966-68; J. F. Kenndey HS Guidance Cnslr 196 *ai:* NEA, Paterson EA, Passaic Co EA 1966-; Passaic Cty Prsnl & G Assn 1975-, Recording Sec 6 Yrs; Montclair Alumnae 1962-, 1st Pr Charter Mem; Passaic Cnty Prsnl & Cnslr Assn of NJ Cnslr of Yr 199 William Patterson Coll of NJ Schlrs Recognition Awd 1994; *home:* 51 Willow St Montclair NJ 07042

SEY, JACQUELINE ELLIS, 4th Grade Teacher; *b:* Greene Cty, OH; rest Glen; *c:* Jennifer Beth Hursey Gantz, Forest Clinton; *ed:* OH St BSE) Elem Ed 1965; 15 Credit Hrs earned through Ashland Univ; *cr:* western City Schls 3rd& 4th Grd Tchr 1965-70; Licking Hghts Schls 4th Grd Tchr 1984-; *ai:* NEA 1965-; OEA 1965-; LHEA 1984-; Summit Elem 6539 Summit Rd Summit Station OH 43073

ST, JOHN ANTHONY, English Teacher & Theater Mgr; *b:* Atlanta, : Gillian M., Shane M.; *ed:* Emory Univ (BA) Eng 1966; Univ of AZ Stud; Univ of London Cert Asian Art 1991; *cr:* Green Fields Schl Head, Eng Tchr 1969-73; Am Embassy Schl Eng, Drama Tchr 78; Intnl Schl of Islamabad Eng, Drama Tchr 1978-80; St Mary's Eng, a, Soc Stud Tchr 1980-82; Singapore Amer Schl Eng, Drama, Soc Tchr 1982-; *ai:* Train Stdnts Tech Theater; Tucson Teen Theater 72, Bd Mem; Delhi Comm Theater 1977-78, Dir; Islamabad Comm er 1980-82, Dir.*

ST, W. SHELDON, Visual Arts Gallery Director; *m:* Karen P.; *c:* S.; *ed:* Wheaton Coll (BA) Sociology 1967; Andover Newton ogical Schl (MDIV) Theology 1971; Boston Univ (MA) 20th Century 976; Andover Newton Theological Schl (DMIN) Art, Church 1984; mer Bapt Churches USA Pastor 1971-; Hyde Collection Ed Curator 94; Adirondack Comm Coll Asst Prof of Art, Dir Visual Arts Gallery ; *ai:* Coll Art Assn 1994-; Lake George Chamber Orch, Pres; Lake ge Arts Project, Selection Comm; Hyde Collection 1986-, Ed Comm; Tchng Excl Awd 1996; *office:* Adirondack Comm Coll Bay Rd nsbury NY 12804

T, KRYSTAL ANITA, English Teacher; *b:* Detroit, MI; *ed:* Univ of on (BS) Ed & Eng 1979, (MS) Guidance Counseling 1984; *cr:* Kemp Schl Eng Tchr 1979-82; Patterson Career Ctr Eng Tchr 1983-93; *ai:* or Soc Adv; Grad Comm; NEA 1979-; *office:* Patterson Career Ctr 118 St Dayton OH 45402

T, ROGER A., Social Studies Teacher; *b:* Franklin, PA; *m:* Nancy L. in; *c:* Drew A., Joe R., Jennifer T. Boscia, Benjamin A. Boscia, odore V. Boscia; *ed:* Clarion Univ of PA (BS) Scndry Ed & prehensive Soc Stud 1966; Post Grad Clarion Univ & Mansfield univ; ustin Area HS Soc Stud Instr 1966-; *ai:* NHS Chptr Adv; PSEA 1966-; 1966-; Austin Area Ed Assn 1966-; Coudersport Golf Club 1969-, Dir; : Austin Area Schl RR 1 Box 7 Austin PA 16720

RTACK, JAMES THOMAS, Fourth Grade Teacher; *b:* Colver, PA; *m:* n Jean Wild; *c:* Bryan, Nicole; *ed:* St Francis Coll (BS) Elem Ed 1967; St Univ (MEQ) Elem Ed 1973; 15 Total Credit Hrs at Univ of AK, ow Coll, IN Univ of PA; *cr:* Blacklick Valley Elem 4th Grd Tchr 1967-; PSEA 1967-, Mem; NEA 1967-, Mem; BVEA 1967-, Bldg Rep & otiations Team; Knights of Columbus 1990-, 4th Degree; *office:* klick Valley Elem Ctr 1000 W Railroad St Nanty Glo PA 15943

RTACK, STEPHEN GEORGE, Spanish Teacher; *b:* Cleveland, OH; eslie Hirth; *c:* Daniel, Sarah; *ed:* Kent St (BA) Eng & Span 1969, (MA) 1971; Attnd Universidad de las Americas, Cleveland St Univ & eland Comm Coll; *cr:* Eastlake North HS Span & Eng Tchr 26 Yrs; *ai:* Modern Lang Assn; Saint Gabriel Parish Saint John & Saint Jerome -, Eucharistic Minister; *office:* Eastlake North HS 34041 Stevens Blvd lake OH 44095

RVITZ, RANDEE KRONE, English Teacher; *b:* Philadelphia, PA; *m:* ey R.; *c:* Steven, Julie; *ed:* PA St Univ (BA) Eng Lit, Lang 1974; ple Univ (MED) Psych of Rdng 1991; Scndry Eng Cert Beaver Coll ; 33 Post Grad Hrs; *cr:* Harding Jr HS Tchr of Eng, Mentally Gifted 5-92; George Washington HS Eng Tchr, Mentally Gifted Prgm Mentor -; *ai:* Rdng, Eng Curr Resource Team; PA Acad Decathlon Judge 1996; Magazine Fac Adv; Mordechai Anielewicz Creative Arts Contest, kespeare Oratorical Competition Spon; Mid Sts Evaluation Comm rsn; Natl Ctr on Ed, Ec; AFT, Philadelphia Fed Tchrs 1975-; NCTE 2-; Philadelphia Young Playwrights, Veteran Tchr; Pew Charitable st Entrepreneurial Tchrs Grant 1991-92, Stagewrite Grant 1995-; adelphia Alliance for Tchng Hum in Schls Grant; William Penn Fnd nt 1992-95; *office:* George Washington HS 11000 Bustleton Ave adelphia PA 19116

SBAND, DALTIA, Speech Improvement Teacher; *b:* Panama City, ama; *c:* Erika Blackman, Alissa Mayers; *ed:* Hunter Coll (BA) Comm s 1975, (MA) Speech Pathology 1980; *cr:* Governeur Hosp Biling ech Pathologist 1980-84; NYC Bd of Ed Speech Tchr 1984-; *ai:* Amer ech, Lang, Hearing Assn 1981-; Girl Scout, Troop Ldr; *home:* 1221 E n St Brooklyn NY 11234

SCHAK, IRENE TIMURA, Technologies-Software Dev Tchr; *b:* ndber, PA; *m:* Regis F.; *c:* Mary Kaufman, Regina Horwat, Daniel, nifer; *ed:* CA Univ of PA (BS) Scndry Math 1967; Nova Univ (MS) ptr Based Learning 1992; Doctoral Prgm; *cr:* Portage Area Schl Dist dry Math Tchr 1967-94; Mount Aloysius Coll Cmptr Sci Instr 1986-; oona Area Schl Dist Technologies Tchr 1994-; *ai:* NEA 1968-; PAEA 8-94, VP; AAEA 1994-; Portage Schl Dist Tech Awd 1990; *office:* oona Area Schl Dist 1415 6th Ave Altoona PA 16602

SEMAN, BRIAN EDWARD, PE & Health Teacher; *b:* Ft Thomas, KY; Linda Marie Fischer; *c:* Nicholas Brian; *ed:* Northern KY Univ (BA) h, PE 1986; 9 Addl Hrs Sports Admin Xavier Univ; *cr:* Princeton HS r, Coach 1988-; *ai:* Mens, Womens Swimming & Water Polo Head ach; Coach of Yr 1990-95; Amer Swim Coaches Assn 1990-; Natl ersch Swim Coaches 1988-; US Swimming 1992-; Comm Ed 1988-, tr; Apples for Excl PTA Awd; *office:* Princeton HS 11080 Chester Rd ncinnati OH 45246

SLER, KENNETH MICHAEL, Music Teacher; *b:* Harrisburg, PA; *m:* nda Barber; *c:* Matthew, Kristen; *ed:* Millersville Univ of PA (BS) Music 1975; West Chester Univ of PA (MS) Music Ed 1987; K-12 Music pervisory Cert; *cr:* Manheim Twp Schl Dist Music Tchr 1976-; *ai:* HS rching Band Prgm; NEA, MENC 1976-; PMEA 1976-, Dist 7 Pres, tation of Excl Dist 7 1996; PA Music Edctrs Assn; Artisles Pub, anherm Twp K-12 Music Dept Chprsn 1986-94; *office:* Manherm Twp hl Dist Box 5134 Schl Rd Lancaster PA 17601

USSA, RICK, HS Math Teacher; *b:* Bryn Mawr, PA; *m:* Sarah R.; *c:* nily, Benjamin; *ed:* Cornell Univ (BA) Ec 1970; SUNY at Albany (MA) ath 1972; *cr:* Warwick HS Tchr 1972-74; Kaiserslautern HS Tchr 74-76; GLen Falls HS Tchr 1976-; *ai:* Math, Quiz Team Adv; Yrbk Bus gr; *office:* Glens Falls HS 10 Quade St Glens Falls NY 12801

USSE, CAROL ANN, 8th Grd Social Studies Teacher; *b:* Columbus, OH; Univ OH St (BS) Soc Stud, Pol Sci, Bus, Acctng, Amer His 1960; Post Soc Stud Univ of HI 1965; Post Credit Black Stud OH St 1970, 1980; : Utica HS Problems of Dem Grd 12 Tchr 1960-61; Franklin Alt MS h-9th Grd, Soc Stud, Current Events, Bus Law, World Bus, Amer His Tchr 961-; *ai:* Ski, Hum Club; 8th Grd Party & Promotion, End of Yr Class Trip omms; Chrldng Coach 16 Yrs; NEA 1961-; OEA; COSS; CEA; COTA; h Worker 1961-; Church Vol Neighborhood Watch; Inter-City Vol Worker Yrs; *office:* Franklin Alternative MS 1390 Bryden Rd Columbus OH 205

USSEL, DAVE W., PE Tchr & Athletic Director; *b:* Cincinnati, OH; *m:* na S.; *c:* Jason, Justin; *ed:* Miami Univ At Oxford Hlth, PE (BS) 1972, IE) 1978; *cr:* Colerain MS Hlth Tchr 1972-1985, PE Tchr 1986-; *ai:* tramural Dir 1985-1994; 7th-8th Grd Track Coach 1985-, Frosh Ftbl Head Coach 1972-; OEA, NEA 1980-; *office:* Colerain MS 4700 Poole Rd Cincinnati OH 45239

HUSSEY, GEORGE ERNEST, Chem & Earth Sciences Teacher; *b:* Hardwick, VT; *m:* Sandra M. Delle; *c:* Peter, Emily; *ed:* Worcester Polytechnic Inst (BS) Chem 1971; Lesley Coll (MED) Cmptrs in Ed 1992; *cr:* Mason Rsrch Inst Pharmacology Lab Supvr 1977-73; Bay Path Regnl Voc Tech HS Bio, Physics Tchr 1973-75; Falmouth HS Chem, Earth Sci Tchr 1975-; *ai:* Sci Club Adv; MA Tchrs Assn, NEA 1973-; Falmouth Tchrs Assn 1975-; NSTA 1992-; BSA Explorer Post 40 1978-, Adv; HS Tchr Summer Fellow in Rsrch Wondo Hole Oceanographic Inst 1993-95; JASON Project Curr Writer 1988-91; Woodrow Wilson Flwshp Fnd Princeton Univ His of Chem Fellow 1992; Text, Lab Book Contributor Chemistry Study of Matter 1996; Rsrch Publications 1971, 1974; *office:* Falmouth HS 874 Gifford Street Ext Falmouth MA 02540*

HUSTED, LOUIS CHARLES, English Teacher; *b:* David, Rep of Panama; *m:* Robyn Lee; *c:* Kyle, Brian, Colleen; *ed:* Canal Zone Coll (AA) Span 1969; Rutgers Univ (BA) Span 1971; Univ of Miami (MS) Biling Ed 1979; Addl 35 Post Masters Credit Hrs; *cr:* Balboa HS 12 Grd Eng Tchr 1972-73; Curundu Jr HS 8-9 Grd Eng Tchr 1973-95; Balboa HS 10, 12 Grd Eng Tchr 1995-; *ai:* Ftbl, Soccer, Track Field Head Coach; AFT 1972-; Flwshp of Chrstn Ath 1994-, Huddle Coach; Articles Pub; Outstdng Tchr of Yr 1991; *home:* PSC Box 2 Box 482 APO AA 34002

HUSTH, GERALDINE WEISS, Mathematics Teacher; *b:* Newark, NJ; *c:* Darcie Husth Badnar, Jeanelle, Gordon; *ed:* Newark St Coll (BA) Math Ed 1967; *cr:* Crossroads Schl Math Tchr 1967-70; Trenton Cntrl HS Math Tchr 1985-; *ai:* Stu of the Month Selection Comm; SRA Review Comm; Tech Prep Environmental Ed Project; Dist Site Based Comm; Trenton Ed Assoc 1985-, Greivance Comm, Svc Awd 1995; NJEA 1985-; NEA 1985-; *office:* Trenton Central HS 400 Chambers St Trenton NJ 08609

HUSTON, JOAN BONFIGLIO, HS Psychology & History Tchr; *b:* Jamestown, NY; *m:* Dale E.; *c:* Tara, Lana; *ed:* Jamestown Comm Coll (AA) Lib Art 1968, (BA) Soc Stud & Ed 1970; SUNY at Fredonia (MA) His 1974; CA Coast Univ of Santa Ana (pHD) Psych 1987; *cr:* Jamestown HS Psych & His Tchr 1970-; Hynotherapist 1992-; *ai:* JTA, NEA, NYEA 1970-; Amer Guild Hypnotherapists 1988-; Amer Bd of Hypotherapy 1992l-; Fenton Historical Soc 1980-; PTA 1970-; Fredonia Alumni Assn 1971-; Pub Articles; *office:* Jamestown HS 350 E 2nd st Jamestown NY 14701

HUSTON, KATHRYN L., Fifth Grade Teacher; *b:* Johnstown, PA; *m:* Kevin R.; *c:* Elizabeth, Rebecca; *ed:* Univ of Pittsburg (BS) Elem Ed, Eng 1970; *cr:* United Schl Dist Elem Tchr 1971-; *ai:* NEA, UEA 1971-; Zion Luth Church Cncl 1995-, VP.

HUSZAR, CARL GEORGE, Amer His & US Geog Tchr; *b:* Greensburg, PA; *m:* Kathleen Kovac; *c:* Stephanie, Zachary; *ed:* Univ of Pittsburgh (BA) His 1970, (MED) Scndry Ed 1976; Scndry Ed Cert Univ of Pittsburgh 1973; Scndry Prin Univ of Pittsburgh 1982; Asst Supt Univ of Pittsburgh 1984; *cr:* Norwin Jr HS East US His, Civics Tchr 1974-85; Norwin Jr HS West Asst Prin 1985-87; Norwin HS US His, World His, Govt, Applied Gov, Ec, Psych, Civics Tchr 1987-; Norwin Schl Dist Norwin MS East Tchr 1995-; *ai:* NEA, PA St Ed Assn, Norwin Ed Assn 1974-; Norwin Historical Soc 1994, Pres, Exec Bd Pres; Norwin Soccer Assn 1990-; Early Amer Coppers 1989-; *office:* Norwin MS East 1 Main St North Huntingdon PA 15642*

HUSZCZA, CELESTE MARY, Latin & Italian Teacher; *b:* Brooklyn, NY; *ed:* Manhattan Coll (BA) Ed 1954; St Mary's Coll (MA) Theology 1961; Middlebury Coll (MA) Span 1978; (MA) Italian 1985; (DML) Span & Italian 1988; Institutum Pontigicium Regina Mundi Mag in Scientiis Sacris 1957; Univ of GA at Athens Two Summer Sessions, 3 Correspondence Courses in Classical Stud; Univ of PR Span Stud 1965-70; *cr:* Sabbatical in Spain DML Prep 1978-79; Generalate of CSFN New Constitution Prep 1979-80; Nazareth Acad Lang Dept Head, Tchr 1980-95, Latin & Italian Club Adv 1980-; *ai:* Evaluation Team Comms & Reports 1990; Conduct Mardi Gras & Lang Week Act; Natl Latin & Italian Exams Coach; NCEA 1980-; AATI; Jr Classical League; AATSP; NEH Grants to Stud Cicero St Olaf Coll 1989, Stud Plutarch & Athens Univ of KY at Lexington 1993; Schlsps & Grants to Attend Latin Convention; *home:* 4001 Grant Ave Philadelphia PA 19114*

HUTCHINGS, ANTOINETTE JANNOTTI, Business Education Teacher; *b:* Newburgh, NY; *m:* Richard A.; *c:* Kevin, Susan, Brian; *ed:* Fairleigh Dickinson Univ (BS) Bus Ed 1974; Attnd Marywood Coll, St Univ at Albany, Coll of St Rose; *cr:* Minisink Vly Schl Dist Bus Ed Tchr 1968-; Orange Cty Comm Coll Assoc Prof Evenings 1978-; *ai:* YAC Adv; Amer Cancer Soc 1984-, Bd Mem; Alumni Assn of Orange Cty Comm Coll 1996, Bd Mem; Helped to Edit Acctng I & II Automated Acctng South Western Pub Co; *office:* Minisink Vly Cntrl Schl Dist Rt 6 PO Box 217 Slate Hill NY 10973

HUTCHINS, RONALD L., Engineering Professor; *b:* Dayton, OH; *m:* Roberta Fox; *ed:* Sinclair Comm Coll (AAS) Manufacturing Engr 1984; Univ of Cincinnati (BS) T&I Ed 1984; Addl Hrs Univ of Dayton; *cr:* Dayton Pub Schls Tchr 1977-81; Sinclair Comm Coll Prof 1981-; *ai:* Stebbins HS Advy Bd; Step II Prgm Creator; OH Instrl Grand Admin; Dayton Tooling & Machining Assn 1980-, Sec, Treas, Trng Comm, Assn Exec; Dayton Soc of Assn Exec, Pres; Text Author; Natl Tooling & Machining Assn Host; Created Dayton Industrial Exhibition, Dayton Tooling & Machining Schlsp Fund; *office:* Sinclair Comm Coll 444 W 3rd St Dayton OH 45402*

HUTCHINS, SUSAN ELIZABETH, Chemistry & Physics Teacher; *b:* Kane, PA; *ed:* Seton Hill Coll (BA) Chem 1972; Clarion Univ Scndry Cert Chem; Penn St Univ Scndry Cert Physics; St Bonaventure Univ Grad Work Ed; *cr:* Sheffield Mid, Sr HS Chem, Physics Tchr 1974-; *ai:* NHS Adv; JETS Team Adv; Sci Dept Head; NEA, PSEA 1974-; Court Callistus 66 CDA 1990-, Vice Regent, Regent; Diocesan Comm 1993-, Treas; Parish Vitality Stud 1996, Chm; *office:* Sheffield Jr Sr HS Star Rt Sheffield PA 16347*

HUTCHINS, THOMASENIA MYERS, Asst Prof of Literature; *b:* Bronx, NY; *ed:* Fordham Univ (BA) Eng 1973, (MS) Ed 1976; Columbia Univ Tchrs Coll 70 Credits Toward EdD; *cr:* Malcolm-King Coll Writing & Critical Thinking Instr 1974-78; Purchase Coll-SUNY Asst Prof Lit 1977-; *ai:* Westchester Colls Project on Racial Diversity Pres 1994; Womens Stud & Black Stud Pgms Acad Adv; NEH Local & Regnl Resources Exploration Project 1995-96; UUP 1977-; NYSUT 1977-; AFT 1977-; Fordham Univ Grad Flwshp 1973; NEH Summer Flwshp 1986; Purchase Coll Stdnts Union Awd-Outstdng Fac Mem 1988-89; NYSUUP Awd-Excl in Tchng 1990; Dr Nuala McGann Drescher Fund Awd Doctoral Stud 1990; Amer Century NEH Noted Scholars Lecture Series 1993; *office:* Purchase Coll, S U N Y 735 Anderson Hill Rd Purchase NY 10577*

HUTCHINSON, DENIS DURWARD, Biology & Chemistry Teacher; *b:* Buffalo, NY; *c:* Raymond; *ed:* Cornell Univ (BS) Bio 1966, (MS) Chem 1967; Canisius Coll (MED) Ed 1972; *cr:* IN St Univ Asst Tchr 1962-63; Depew Pub Schls Tchr 1966-; *ai:* AFT 1966-; HEA 1966-; NYSUT 1966-; Wildlife Rehab Ctr 1976-, Pres; NSF Roswell Park Experimental Rsrch Cancer Inst; *office:* Depew HS 5201 S Transit Rd Depew NY 14043

HUTCHINSON, ELAINE FRANCES, Soc Stud & Gifted Hum Teacher; *b:* Nanticoke, PA; *ed:* East Stroudsburg St (BS) Biological Sci 1959; West Chester St (MED) Soc & Behavioral Sci 1971; Rosemont Coll Cmptrs 6 Credits; Beaver Coll Ecology 4 Credits; PA St Univ Ecology & Ed 35 Credits; *cr:* Phoenixville Area Jr HS Classroom Tchr 1959-92; Phoenixville Area MS Classroom Tchr 1992-; *ai:* Acad Team 6 Yrs; Ecology Club; Acad Stud; E-Mail Pen Pals to Turkey; PA St Ed Assn, NEA 1959-; Phoenixville Area Ed Assn 1959-, Pres; NSTA 1965-; PA Sci Tchrs Assn 1990-, Presentor; NCSS, PA Cncl for Soc Stud 1991-; ASCD 1990-95; Amer Assn of Univ Women 1992-; Sci Tchrs Assb of NY St 1995-; Delta Kappa Gama 1969-, VP & Pres, Coordinating Chapters 1980-, Pres; Chesmont Bus & Prof Women's Club 1968-, VP & Pres; Friends of Pocono Environmental Ed Ctr 1987-; Natl Audubon Soc 1985-; Order of Eastern Star 1980-; Acad Boosters Club 1990-, Co-Comm Chair; Bapt Church Outreach Comm 1992-, Sec; Chrstn Ed Comm 1980-, Schlsp Chair; Stepping Stone Ed Cntr Bd Member; Outstanding Ldr in Elem & Scndry Ed 1976; Who's Who in the East; JC's Outstanding Sci Tchr Awd; Articles Pub; Antartica Curr Circulated by Antartctica Women's Expedition; Beaver Coll Schlsp to Dev & Learn REEP; Attnd NSTA & Moscow Sci Tchrs Convention at Moscow St Univ 1991; Pub in Sci Scope Magazine 1991; World's Who's Who of Women 1995; Dictionary of Intnatl Biography 1995; Who's Who in Amer Ed 1995; Women's His at STANMYS 100th Convention; Phoenixville Area MS Team Leader 1991; *home:* 1211 Harrison Ave Phoenixville PA 19460

HUTCHINSON, FREDERICK EVERARD, 6th Grade Teacher; *b:* Beverly, MA; *m:* Lori Ann Nelson; *c:* Danielle, Tyler; *ed:* Salem St Coll (BS) Elem Ed 1985; *cr:* North Salem Elem Schl 6th Grd Tchr 1985-; Walter Haigh Elem Schl 6th Grd Tchr 1985-; Woodbury MS 6th Grd Tchr 1985-; *ai:* Soccer, Bsktbl Coach; NEA 1985-; New Hampshire Bsktbl Coaching Assn 1994-; *office:* Woodbury Schl 206 Main St Salem NH 03079

HUTCHINSON, JOHN FULLER,JR., Community Service Director; *b:* Monterrey, CA; *m:* Elizabeth Mather; *ed:* Amherst Coll (BA) Ec 1984; 15 Credit Hrs Wesleyan Univ GLSP Prgm; *cr:* Canterbury Schl His & Religion Tchr 1984-85; Choate Rosemary Hall Schl Ec, Religion Tchr & Comm Service Dir 1985-; *ai:* Boys Var Soccer, Wrestling & Lacrosse Coach; Choate Chrstn Fellowship & Choate Assn for Reaching Out to Others Adv; Athletic Advy Comm Head; Literacy Vols of Amer 1992-, Bd Mem; Habitat for Humanity 1994, Bd Mem; Wallingford Shelter 1994, Bd Mem; WNEPSA Coach of the Yr 1993; *office:* Choate Rosemary Hall Schl 333 Christian St Wallingford CT 06492*

HUTCHINSON, JOSEPH FREDERICK, Geog & World History Teacher; *b:* Toledo, OH; *m:* Linda; *ed:* Univ of Toledo (BE) Soc Stud & Comprehensive 1987; Working on MS Scndry Ed; *cr:* Jesup W Scott HS Bldg Sub Tchr 1987-88, 1991-92, Soc Stud Tchr 1988-91, 1992-; *ai:* Asst Bsbl Coach; TFT 1987-; AFT 1987-; Toledo 200 1993-; Humane Soc of the US 1995-; Hum 1996; *office:* Jesup W Scott HS 2400 Collingwood Blvd Toledo OH 43620*

HUTCHINSON, RUBY NERISSA, Ec & Global Studies Tchr; *b:* Porus, Jamaica; *ed:* Univ of West Indies (BS) Ec 1971, (DIP ED) Ed, Soc St 1976; Simon Fraser Univ (MED) Ed 1981; IN St Univ (PHD) Curr 1989; Substance, Child Abuse Prevention; *cr:* St Joseph's Tchrs Coll Prin Lecturer 1972-92; Coll of Arts, Sci & Tech Lecturer in Research 1991-92; Catherine Mc Auley HS Ec, Global Stud Tchr 1993-; *ai:* Curr Dev Comm; 4H Club Adv; Cath Ed Assn 1993-; Cncl for Amer Private Ed 1995-; Fulbright Scholar 1989; Jr Reader 1995; *office:* Catherine Mc Auley HS 710 E 37th St Brooklyn NY 11203*

HUTCHINSON, SUSAN M., Physical Education Teacher; *b:* Concord, MA; *ed:* Plymouth St Coll (BS) PE 1984; *cr:* Pembroke Acad PE Tchr 1986-; *ai:* Var Field Hockey, Jr Var Sftbl Coach; *office:* Pembroke Acad 209 Academy Rd Pembroke NH 03275

HUTCHISON, ALICE LEEANN, Science Teacher; *b:* Flint, MI; *m:* James Maurice; *c:* Heather, Sarah, Jaime; *ed:* Univ of MD (BS) Pre-Vet, Animal Sci 1981; Johns Hopkins Univ (MS) Interdisciplinary Sci 1995; WA Coll Tchr Cert Ed 1988; *cr:* Anne Arundel Comm Coll Vet Sci Tech Instr 1981-86; Johns Hopkins Univ Cancer Research Assoc, Tchng Asst 1981; Easton Sr HS Sci Tchr 1988-; *ai:* Ecology Club Adv; Sci Curr Team Mem; Admin Environmental Camp; NEA, TCEA 1988-; MAEOE 1990-; Waterfowl Trust of North Amer 1993-, Bd Mem; MD Assn of Bio Tchrs, NSTA 1988-; Christa McAuliff Schlsp; Natl Facilitator Curr; Chesapeake Bay Trust Environmental Action Projects Grants; Cert Scuba Diver; *office:* Easton H S Mecklenburg Ave Easton MD 21601

HUTCHISON, JAMES H., Sixth Grade Teacher; *b:* Butler, PA; *m:* Susann K.; *c:* Tracy Sue Derouin, Betsy Ann Vogel, James Eric; *ed:* Clarion Univ (BS) Elem 1963, (MS) Elem 1973; Attnd Penn St Univ, Slippery Rock Univ; *cr:* South Butler Co Schls Elem Tchr 33 Yrs; *office:* South Butler Cty Schls Knoch Rd Saxonburg PA 16056

HUTCHISON, JANICE LUND, English Teacher; *b:* Perth Amboy, NJ; *m:* John Reid; *c:* Carrie Lynn, Tracy Marie; *ed:* Upsala Coll (BA) Eng & Ed 1969; 3 Credit Hrs in Jrnlsm at Rutgers Univ; *cr:* South River MS Eng Tchr 1969-85; South River HS Eng Tchr 1985-; *ai:* The Ram Newspaper Adv; NEA, Middlesex Cty Ed Assn, NJEA 1969-; South River Ed Assn 1969-, Sec; Stagecrafters Inc 1983-, Bd Mem; *office:* South River HS Montgomery St South River NJ 08882

HUTCHISON, SUSAN K., First Grade Teacher; *b:* Leechburg, PA; *m:* James H.; *c:* Tracy Sue Derouin, Betsy Ann Vogel, James Eric; *ed:* Clarion Univ (BS) Elem 1962; Attnd Penn St, Slippery Rock Univ; *cr:* Freeport Area Schls Elem Tchr 28 Yrs; *ai:* PSEA, NEA 1962-; FEA 1962-, Past Pres; Girl Scouts of Amer 1971-, Ldr, 10 Yr Pin; Coll Club 1970-, Past Sec; Sons of Union Veterans 1989-, Past Pres, Sec, Treas; Clara Cockerille Rdng Cncl 1994-; *office:* Freeport Area Schls South Pike Dr Freeport PA 16229

HUTCHISON, THOMAS C., Biology Teacher; *b:* New Castle, PA; *m:* Lynn; *c:* Kyle, Kerri; *ed:* Slippery Rock Univ (BS) Bio, Ed 1989; 20 Hrs Post Grad Stud; *cr:* West Middlesex HS Bio Tchr 1990-; *ai:* Asst Track Coach Ecology Team Adv; NABT 1988-; PA Jr Acad of Sci 1989-; NEA 1989-; *office:* West Middlesex HS Rt 18 West Middlesex PA 16159

HUTH, KAREN MARIE, Second Grade Teacher; *b:* Baraboo, WI; *ed:* Dominican Coll (BA) Eng, Ed 1962; Diocese of Columbus Dept of Ed Tchr Enrichment Series, Bureau of Ed, Rsrch Strengthening Your Second Grd Prgm 1993; Columbus Cath Dept of Ed Where the Wild Things Are 1994; Columbus Pub Schls Math Updating, Manipulitives 1995; Univ of CA 12 Semester Hrs Ed 1970, 1972, 6 Grad Semester Hrs Comparative Ed, USSR, Poland 1973; 1 CEU Math Their Way 1991; Stevenson Lang Prgm, Rdng, Writing 1992; Simple Math 1992; Bldg Today Tomorrow 1993; *cr:* WI Schls Primary Tchr 1960-66; Newark Schl System Primary Tchr 1966-68; Saint Piux X Schl Primary Tchr 1968-; *ai:* Schl Bd 1975-; Prin Advy Comm 1994-95; CDEA 1968-; Girl Scouts of Amer 1969-88, Ldr; Alverno coll Stu Tchrs 1960-; Dominican Coll Stu Tchrs 1980-; Hidden Heira 1976; Tchr of Yr 1985; *office:* St Pius X Schl 1061 Waggoner Rd Reynoldsburg OH 43068*

HUTSON, RONALD LEE, Associate Prof of Fine Arts; *b:* St Louis, MO; *ed:* Univ of MO at Columbia (BS) Chem 1968; WA Univ at St Louis (BS) Eng 1976, (MA) Eng Lit, Drama 1977; Doctoral Work Eng; *cr:* Point Pk Coll Assoc Prof 1979-; Pittsburgh Dance Alloy Schl Carnegie Museum Instr; Oakland Schl of Performing Arts Instr 1980-; *ai:* African Dance, Drum Ensemble of Pittsburgh Performer, Choreographer; Intnl Night Adv; Curr Comm Dance Dept Chm; Grad Flwshp WA Univ 1976-79; *office:* Point Park Coll 201 Wood St Pittsburgh PA 15222*

HUTTNER, MICHAEL TODD, Mathematics Teacher; *b:* Islip, NY; *m:* Wendy Harrington; *c:* Leah, Emily, Eve; *ed:* Buffalo St Coll (BA) Ed 1982; SUNY at Buffalo (MS) Math Ed 1989; Math Courses; *cr:* Gate Way United Meth Group Home Spec Ed Tchr 1982-85; Amherst Cntrl Schl Spec Ed Tchr 1984-85; BOCES Math Tchr 1985-86; Starpoint HS Math Tchr 1986-; *ai:* Acad Stans Comm; Class, Chrstn Club Adv; NYSSBA 1993-; NYSUT 1982-; Clarence Schl Bd 1993-; Kappa Delta Pi; *office:* Starpoint Jr Sr HS 4363 Mapleton Rd Lockport NY 14094*

HUTTON, DEALE A., Librarian; *b:* St Paul, MN; *m:* Robert F. Marcuson; *ed:* Regis Univ (BA) Pol Sci, Sociology-Magna Cum Laude 1981; Syracuse Univ (MLS) Lib Sci-Magna Cum Laude 1990; Ed Courses 12 Hrs; *cr:* Wayne co Dept of Soc Svcs Caseworker 1985-88; Wayne MS Librn 1990-; *ai:* Stud Weaving, Spinning, Art, Yoga, Ayurvedic Med; Friends of Lib Adv; Wellness Comm; NEA 1990-; Alpha Sigma Nu 1980-, Ntl Jesuit Hnr Soc; Craemer Awd Excl in Pol Sci; *office:* Wayne MS 6076 Ontario Center Rd Ontario Center NY 14520*

HUTZELL, LARRY WILLIAM, American History Teacher; *b:* Somerset, PA; *m:* Carol Balla; *c:* Molly H. Newton, Lucas; *ed:* CA Univ of PA (BS) Elem Ed 1962; 12 Credit Hrs; Penn St Univ 3 Credit Hrs; IN Univ of PA 3 Credit Hrs; *cr:* Somerset Area Schls Tchr 1962-64; Forbes Area Schl Dist Tchr 1964-66; ABC USD Tchr 1966-67; Vly Schl of Ligonier 1967-; *ai:* Soc Stud Chm; Coaching; PPSTA 1967-; *home:* PO Box 207 Laughlintown PA 15655*

HUTZLEY, CAROL JO, Frgn Lang Dept Chair & Fr Tchr; *b:* Baltimore, MD; *m:* Frederick Grant; *c:* Bradford David, Cara Lynn; *ed:* Anne Arundel Comm Coll (AA) Frgn Lang 1974; Univ of MD at Balto (BA) Fr, Ed 1976, (MA) Intercultural Comm 1990; Spec Session at Univ de Caen France 1976; Attnd Loyola Coll 1982; *cr:* Catonsville Comm Coll Eng as Second Lang Instr 1990-92; Baltimore Cty Bd of Ed Frgn Lang Tchr 1976-; *ai:* Human Relations Comm Chm; Schl Improvement Team; Baltimore Symphony Orch Partnership Steering Comm; Societe Honoraire de Francais Spon; Phi Kappa Phi 1976-; AATF, NEA 1980-; Severna Park United Meth Church 1988-; *office:* Lansdowne HS 3800 Hollins Ferry Rd Baltimore MD 21227*

HUXLEY, SHARON JONES, Associate Prof of Accounting; *b:* New Haven, CT; *m:* Richard A.; *c:* Robert; *ed:* Univ of Hartford (BA) Pol Sci 1971, (MBA) 1976; Addl Post Grad Stud Accounting; *cr:* Post Coll Teikyo Post Asst & Assoc Prof 1978-; *ai:* Accounting Club Adv; IMA, AAA; Bethany Planning & Zoning Commission 1985-, Vice Chm; South Cntrl CT Regnl Planning Commissions 1987-; Bethany Horserman 1984-, Treas; *office:* Teikyo Post Univ 800 Country Club Rd Waterbury CT 06708

HUZICKA, MARY ANN (REESEN), 5th-6th Grade Science Teacher; *b:* Youngstown, OH; *m:* William G.; *c:* Mary Bridget, Shannon, Meghan; *ed:* Youngstown St (BS) Elem Ed 1976; *cr:* St Christine 2nd Grd Tchr 1976-80, 5th Grd Sci Tchr 1981-82, 5th & 6th Grd Sci Tchr 1985-; *ai:* Lake to River 1989-; Seton Club 1994-; Governors Awd of Excl for Sci; Outstdng Sci Tchr Proclamation from Boardman Twp; *office:* St Christine Schl 3125 S Schenley Ave Youngstown OH 44511

HY, PHILIP J., Spanish Teacher; *b:* N Tonawanda, NY; *m:* Susan E. Anderson; *c:* Joseph Philip, Bethany Rose; *ed:* SUNY Coll at Buffalo (BA) Ed 1991; SUNY Coll at Brockport (MS) ED 1996; *cr:* Haverling Cntrl Schl Span Tchr 1991-; *ai:* Var Cross Cntry Coach 1992-94; Asst Girls Track Coach 1994, 1996; Span Club Adv 1995-; NY St Frgn Lang Tchrs Assn 1992-.

HYBERTSON, BEVERLY BLAISDELL, Elementary Teacher; *b:* Augusta, ME; *m:* Larry D.; *c:* Linda Lee, Geoffrey Dean; *ed:* Eastern Nazarene Coll (BS) Elem Ed 1956; Attnd Point Loma Coll 1972-73, Eastern Nazarene coll, Fitchburg St Coll 1974-; *cr:* Grace Farrar Cole Schl 2nd Grd Tchr 1956-59; Adams Elem Schl 2nd Grd Tchr 1959-60; Willagillespie Schl 2nd Grd Tchr 1961-63; City of Tallahassee Sub Tchr 1963-65; Eastern Nazarene Coll Art Methods Instr 1966-69; Kingston Elem Schl 2nd Grd Tchr 1969-71; City of Pasadena Schl Elem Sub Tchr 1971-73; Kingston Yth Commission Cmptr Tchr 1983-90; Kingston Elem Schl 3rd Grd Tchr 1973-76, Primary Tchr 1976-86, 3rd Grd Tchr 1986-; *ai:* NEA, MA Tchrs Assn 1974-; Plymouth Cty Ed Assn 1974-, Meritorius Citation 1993; KTA 1974-, Negotiating Team 1974-; United Church of Christ 1974-94, Deacon 1985-88, Chrstn Ed Bd 1993-94; UCC Hanover 1994-; Elected to Who's Who in Amer Ed 1992-; *home:* 86 Larchmont Ln Hanover MA 02339

HYDE, ANTHONY JOHN, Band Master & Dir of Bands; *b:* Milford, CT; *m:* Anne Marie Fiore; *c:* Michael, Christopher; *ed:* Boston Conservatory of Music (BM) Music Ed 1964, (MM) Music Composition 1967; Univ of MA at Boston (CAGS) Educl Admin 1990; Arranging Berklee Coll of Music 1960-64; 3 Credit Hrs Marching Band Symposium Univ of WI 1970-87; *cr:* Stoneham HS Band Dir 1970-77; Cohasset HS Band Dir 1977-80; Millis HS Band Dir 1980-83; Dennis-Yarmouth Reg HS Band Dir 1983-84; Somerville HS Band Dir 1984-; *ai:* Music Consultant Jazz Ensembles; Marching Band; Drum Corps, Jazz Ensemble Judge; Prof Band Ldr; MICA 1987-, Marching Band Supvr; MMEA 1970-; IAJE 1972-, Treas, Pres; STA 1984-, Bldg Rep; Porsche Club of North Amer 1988-; Pub Composer; Boston Globe Jazz Festival Coord 1979; *office:* Somerville HS 81 Highland Ave Somerville MA 02143*

HYDE, ELISE CONNELLY, Secondary Soc Studies Teacher; *b:* Buffalo, NY; *m:* Charles E.; *c:* Andrew C., Robert L.; *ed:* St U of NY Coll at Buffalo (BS) Scndry Soc Stud 1965, (MS) Scndry Soc Stud 1971; Credit Hrs Univ of MD at Coll Park 1976-77, Plymouth St 1995, Univ of NH; *cr:* PS #60 Buffalo 5th Grd Elem Tchr 1965-66; PS #77 Buffalo Jr HS Soc Stud Tchr 1966-73; Spaulding Jr HS Soc Stud Tchr 1977-80; Spaulding HS Soc Stud Tchr 1980-; *ai:* AFT, Rochester Tchrs Assn 1980-; NH Cncl Soc Stud 1995-; Delta Kappa Gamma 1990-; Natl Endowment Hum Grant 1987; *office:* Spaulding HS Wakefield St Rochester NH 03867

HYDE, JESSE DANIEL, Art Teacher; *b:* Pittsburgh, PA; *m:* Colleen Tabacchi; *c:* Jesse Jr., Nathan Lee; *ed:* IN Univ of PA (BS) Art Ed 1976; 24 Addl Hrs Painting; *cr:* Penn Hills HS Art Instr 1976-80; Oswayo Valley Art Instr 1980-; *ai:* NEA 1976-; PSEA 1976-, Local Pres; NAEA 1980-; Artist: Ofcl 1993-94; US Open, Meml Golf Tournaments; Jack Nicklaus Artwork Pub 1990 US Open Magazine; Artwork Pub Yearly Pebble Beach CA Golf; Artwork Sold Japan, Australia, Scotland; US Open Golf Trnmt 1995-96; Tchr of Yr; *home:* RR 1 Box 472 Shinglehouse PA 16748

HYDE, KATHLEEN SCULLY, Peer Mediation Coordinator; *b:* Astoria, NY; *ed:* St Univ Coll at Brockport (BSEd) Hlth, PE 1968; Bowie St Univ (MED) Guid, Cnslng 1994; Addl Admin 1995-; Natl Crisis Prevention Inst Certfd Instr; Amer Heart Assn Certfd CPR Instr; *cr:* Churchville-Chili Jr, Sr HS Hlth, PE, Coach 1968-74; Penn Yan Acad Hlth, PE, Coach 1974-76; Prince George's Cty Pub Schls Hlth, PE, Coach, Nutrition Specialist Cnslr; Peer Mediation Coord 1976-; *ai:* SADD Adv; Crisis Intervention Team Chprsn; Grad Night Fac Adv; Stu Svc Learning Opportunities Liaison; AFT 1976-; Amer Schl Cnslrs, Amer Cnslrs Assn 1993-; Assn for Supervision, Curr Dev 1995-; Lions Club Intnl 1994-, Chrprsn, Ed, Schlsp; P. G. Cty Chamber of Commerce Oustanding Tchr 1994; P. G. Journal Coach of Yr in Sftbl 1992; Grant for Schls Against a Fearful Enviroment, Office of Govenors of MD 1995; *office:* Frederick Douglass HS 8000 Croom Rd Upper Marlboro MD 20772*

HYDE, RICHARD ALBERT, Mathematics Teacher; *b:* Defiance, OH; *m:* Joyce Gossman; *c:* Richard II, Russell, Randall; *ed:* Ashland Coll (BA) Math 1964; Ashland Univ (MED) Curr & Instruction 1990; Akron Univ Grad Math 6 Hrs; Kent St Univ Grad Math 18 Hrs; *cr:* Elyria Tchr 1964-68; Wellington Tchr 1968-; *ai:* Var Bsktbl Scorekeeper 20 Yrs; North Cntrl Assn Comm Co-Chm; 7th Gr, Fr, JV Bsktbl Coach; HS Bsbl Ump 28 Yrs; OEA & NEA 1964-; WEA & NEOEA 1968-; NCTM 1990-; Lorain Cty Fair Bd 1977-, Treas; 1st Bapt Church, Treas; *office:* Wellington HS 629 N Main St Wellington OH 44090

HYDE, ROBERT LIVINGSTON, Humanities Instructor; *b:* New York City, NY; *m:* Faith Perrin White; *c:* Peter S., Mark W., Matthew H.; *ed:* Yale Univ (BA) Eng 1952; Episcopal Theological Schl (MDiv) Moral Reasoning 1955; Univ of Dayton Russian His 1959-60; Columbia Univ Tchrs Coll Methods Eng 1968; Harvard Univ Grad Schl of Linquistics Transformational Grammar 1970; *cr:* Episcopal Church Ordained Minister 1955-68; Hackley Schl Instr in His & Eng 1967-68; Hamden Hall Cntry Day Schl Instr in Eng & Soc Stud 1968-84, Dir of Admissions 1969-79; Cape Cod Acad Instr in Hum, His, & Eng 1984-; Dennis-Yarmouth Regnl HS Summer Session Instr in Eng 1994-95; *ai:* Ed Comm & Fac Adv to Stdnts; A.F.& A.M.1957-; Distinguished Tchng Awd Hamden Hall Cntry Day Schl & Cum Laude Soc 1984; Certified Eng Grds 9-12; *office:* Cape Cod Acad 50 W Barnstable Rd Osterville MA 02655*

HYDER, THOMAS L., US His & Economics Teacher; *b:* Huntington, NY; *ed:* Cortland Coll (BA) His 1970, (MA) US His 1973; Univ of SC at Columbia PHD Cand; *cr:* Smithtown HS Soc Stud Dept 1970-; *ai:* HS Girls Cross Cntry, Indoor Track, Spring Track Coach; Org Amer Historians, AFT, NYSTA 1970-; Amer Conf Irish Stud 1980-; Suffolk Cty Track Coaches Assn 1974-, Pres 1993-; *office:* Smithtown HS 100 Central Rd Smithtown NY 11787*

HYLAND, MARYBETH, Fifth Grade Teacher; *b:* Brooklyn, NY; *ed:* Boston Coll (BA) Elem Ed 1987; Coll of Staten Island (MS) Elem Ed; 150 Credit Hrs Prof Dev Stud, Resolving Conflict Creatively Prgm; *cr:* P S 205 Schl 5th Grd Tchr 1992-94, 4th Grd Tchr 1988-; *ai:* AFT, UFT 1988-; US Master Swimming 1995-; *office:* PS 205 Clarion 6701 20th Ave Brooklyn NY 11204

HYLAND, MARY LOU, Head Science Teacher; *b:* Boston, MA; *ed:* Bridgewater St Coll (BS) Earth Sci & Scndry Ed 1968; Boston Coll (MS) Geology 1971; Post Grad Stud at Northeastern Univ; *cr:* Joseph H Martin Schl 7th-8th Grd Sci Tchr 1974-; *ai:* Schl Talent Shows Dir & Producer; Schl Cncl; Project BEST Schl Coord; PALMS Leadership Team; Sci Curr Comm; Sci Fair Coord; NEA, MTA, TEA 1974-; NSTA, MAST 1990-; *office:* Joseph H. Martin School 131 Caswell St East Taunton MA 02718*

HYLAND, THOMAS, Math Teacher; *b:* Allentown, PA; *m:* Sharon; *c:* Jodi, Brett; *ed:* East Stroudsburg Univ (BS) Math 1966; Rutgers Univ (MST) Math Ed 1972; 30 Addl Post Grad Credits; *cr:* Middlesex HS Math Tchr 1966-70; West Milford HS Math Tchr 1970-; *ai:* Co-Chm Negotiations Comm; Screening Comm for Prin Applicants; NEA, NJEA 1966-; *home:* PO Box 26 Glenwood NJ 07418

HYLLESTAD, SUSAN JANET OLIVIERI, Fifth Grade Teacher; *b:* Brooklyn, NY; *m:* Craig Lewis; *c:* Ryan; *ed:* Molloy Coll (BA) Elem Ed, Span 1971; C.W. Post Coll (MS) Elem Ed 1972; *cr:* Hempstead Schl Dist Grds 3-6 Tchr 1972-74; Patchogue-Medford Schl Dist Grds 5-6 Tchr 1974-; *ai:* Lang Arts Festival Comm; Fifth Grd Fundraisers; NYSUT, AFT, NEA 1972-; Patchogue Medford Congress of Tchrs 1974-; Eagle Elem PTA 1974-85, Recording Sec 2 Yrs; Bay Elem PTA 1987-; Mt Sinai PTO 1990-; Patchogue-Medford SD Citation Cert 1995.

HYMAN, MURRAY, Biology Teacher; *b:* New York, NY; *m:* Rita Markowicz; *c:* David, Julie; *ed:* Staten Island Comm Coll (AA) 1961; Hunter Coll (BA) Bio 1964; City Coll (MA) Ed 1966; *cr:* DeWitt Clinton HS Tchr 1964-; Julia Richmond HS Tchr 1982; *ai:* Bio Tutor; AFT, UFT 1964-; Work Stud Prgm Cooperative Coord 4 yrs; Sex Ed Tchr; Tchr Mentor for Spec Ed Tchrs Trng in Sci; *office:* Dewitt Clinton HS 100 W Mosholu Pky S Bronx NY 10468*

HYMAN, VIVIAN MARIA (SILVERIO), 6th-8th Grd Soc Stud Tchr; *b:* Bronx, NY; *m:* Alan Stephen; *ed:* Bergen Comm Coll (AAS) Sci 1976; Felician Coll Rel; *cr:* Our Lady of Lourdes Tchr 1987-; *ai:* Co-Chair, Moderator Civic Achvmt Awd Prgm; Close-Up Fnd; Fac Rep Curr Coord Cncl Paterson Dioceses; Craft Prgm Coord; Amer Legion Auxiliary 1986-; Diocese of Patterson Soc Stud Curr; Soc Stud Dept Chm; *office:* Our Lady Of Lourdes Schl 186 Butler St Paterson NJ 07524

HYMES, PATRICIA EDITH, Violence Preventn Educl Coord; *b:* Columbus, OH; *m:* Eric M.; *c:* Carmen; *ed:* Bowling Green St Univ (BS) Eng 1971; Cntrl CT St Univ (MS) Educl Ldrshp 1994; 12 Sem Hrs Educl Ldrshp; 9 Sem Hrs Violence Prevention; *cr:* Scott HS Eng Tchr 1972-76; HS for Performing & Visual Arts Eng Tchr 1976-88; Windsor HS Eng Tchr 1989-95; The Partnership Educl Coord 1995-; *ai:* Dist Prof Dev Comm; NCTE 1978-; NEA 1972-; ASCD 1991-; Edctr of Yr Windsor HS 1991.

HYMON-PARKER, SHIRLEY, Acting Chair; *b:* Warrenton, NC; *m:* Eugene Parker; *c:* Jocelyn, Alex; *ed:* NC Cntrl (UBS) Clothing & Textiles 1979; Cornell Univ (MS) Design & environmental Analysis 1981; Univ of MD at Coll Park (PHD) Ed Admin 1993; *cr:* Hecht Co Asst Buyer 1981-83; Univ of MD Lecturer 1983-87; Hood Coll Instr 1987-88; Univ of MD Eastern Shore Fashion Merchandising 1988-94, Acting Chair Prgm Coord 1994-; *ai:* Kappa Omcron Nu Adv; Costumer, Fashion Show, Fashion Stud Tour Coord; AAFCS 1985-; ACRA 1993-; ACE 1994-, Institutional Rep; KON 1979-, Nom Comm Former Dorothy Mitsfier Flwshp 1988-90; United Way Lower 1995-, Eastern Shore Bd of Dir; MD A Assn Family & Consumer Scis 1985-, Chair Coll & Univ Section; Natl Coalition on Black Dev in Home Ec 1993-, Chair Educl Stans; Cncl of Admin in Family & Consumer Sci 1995-; Assn of Admin in Human Scis 1994-; Admin in Family & Consumer Scis 1980-; Outstdng Scientist Rsrch Paper; Assn of Rsrch Dir Symposium; Outstdng Tchr Scholar of Yr 1985; *office:* Univ Of MD Eastern Shore Department of Human Ecology 2101 Richard Henson Center Princess Anne MD 21853*

HYNES, JOHN PATRICK, High School Soc Studies Tchr; *b:* Jersey City, NJ; *ed:* Jersey City St Coll (BA) Pol Sci 1979, (MA) Urban Ed 1996; 9 Credit Hrs San Francisco St Coll; Attnd NY Inst of Fin; *cr:* Jersey City Bd of Ed Tchr 1980-82; Dean Witter Reynolds Operations Mgr, Pension Consultant 1982-87; Garben Ltd Bond Broker 1987-89; Jersey City Bd of Ed Tchr 1989-; *ai:* Bsktbl Coach Asst Var; Chprsn Site Base Mngmt Team; Merril Lynch Shadowing Prgm Moderator; NEA, NJEA 1989-; Summer Skills Acad 1990-, Job Placement Ofcr; Tchr of Yr 1995-; Pub Article; *office:* William Dickinson HS 2 Palisade Ave Jersey City NJ 07306*

HYNES, LAWRENCE ROBERT, English Teacher; *b:* Oil City, PA; *m:* Carol Mumford; *c:* Shannon, Sean; *ed:* Clarion Univ of PA (BS) Soc Stud 1964; Cortland Univ (BS) Eng 1971; 30 Hrs Master's Equivilent St Univ of Cortland; *cr:* Union Endicott HS Eng Tchr 1964-; *ai:* Var Cross Cntry, Modified Track Head Coach; AFT, NYSUT, Endicott Tchrs Assn 1964-; NFICA 1970-; Soc for Preservation & Encouragement of Barbershop Quartet Singing in Amer 1080-; *office:* Union Endicott HS 1200 E Main St Endicott NY 13760

HYNES, SHEILA GEGOGEINE, Reading Specialist; *b:* Oil City, PA; *c:* Alison Ann, Kate Elizabeth; *ed:* Clarion Univ (BS) Elem Ed 1975, (MED) Elem, Rdng Specialist 1989; Shippensburg Univ; *cr:* Riverview Schl Abraxas Rdng Specialist 1990-91; Jefferson Cty Jail Rdng Specialist, GED Tchr 1990-92; Brockway Area Schl Dist 1-12 Grd Rdng Specialist 1991-; *ai:* JV Chrldng Adv; Seneca Rdng Cncl 1989-.*

HYTREE, MARYSUE MASON, Second Grade Teacher; *b:* Pain OH; *m:* David; *c:* Rick, Sarah; *ed:* Allegheny Coll (BA) Elem Ed Lake Erie Coll Post Grad; *cr:* McGuffy Local Schls 3rd Grd Tchr 19 Painesville Township Schls 2nd Grd Tchr 1965-66; Madison Local 2nd Grd Tchr 1979-; *ai:* Land Lab Adv; Parent Comm Co-Chair; V Capital Grant Comm; Intervention Assessment Comm; Madison E 1979-, Sec; OH Ed Assn 1979-; NEA 1979-; *office:* Red Bird Eler 1956 Red Bird Rd Madison OH 44057

I

IACCHETTI, RAFFALINA FRANCES, Middle School Science Te *b:* Pittsburgh, PA; *m:* Attilio Delfo; *c:* Riccardo, Stefano; *ed:* Carlov (BA) Music, Ed 1966; Univ of Pittsburgh Post Bac Degree Elem Ed 30 Credit Hrs; *cr:* Pittsburgh Cath Diocese Elem Ed Tchr 1966-; *ai:* Acad Spon, Judge 9 Yrs; St Margaret Schl Sci Coord, SAP Core Team Mem; NCEA 1966-; *office:* Saint Margaret Schl 915 Ali Pittsburgh PA 15220*

IACCIO, FRANK LOUIS, American Government Teacher; *b:* Qu NY; *m:* Linda Sue George; *c:* Christa, Jennifer; *ed:* St Johns Univ Scndry Ed 1968; C. W. Post Coll LIU (MS) His 1972; Brown Coalition Essential Schls Seminars; *cr:* Amityville Pub Schls His 1968-84; Southampton Pub Schls Govt Tchr 1988-; *ai:* Coach Var Sftbl; NYSTA 1968, Tchr; NEA 1968-, Tchr; AFT 1968-, Tchr; *home* Sebonac Rd Southampton NY 11968

IACOBACCI, PHILIP JOSEPH, Mathematics Teacher; *b:* Boston, *c:* Philip Jr., Sandra, Michael; *ed:* Bridgewater St Coll (BA) Math Cambridge Coll (MS) Comp Ed 1990; 50+ Grad Credit Hrs in Law, Sci, Admin, Acctng & Tchng; *cr:* Stoughton HS Math & Comp Tchr 1 *ai:* Past Class Adv; Past Comms; MTA 1973-; NEA 1973-; NCTA 1 STA 1973-, Exec Bd, Newsletter Ed; NCTM 1990-; Fall River Better Assn 1988-, Pres; Wrote Comp Sci Curr for Raytheon Schl 1979; 844 Hood St Fall River MA 02720

IACOVAZZI, DOMINICK C., Science Teacher; *b:* Endicott, NY Marjorie Gaul; *c:* Nicole; *ed:* SUNY at Oneonta (BA) Sci Ed Binghamton Univ (MS) Sci Ed 1994; *cr:* Jennie F. Snapp Jr HS Eart Tchr 1968-75; Union -Endicott HS Earth Sci Tchr 1976-; *ai:* Wres Coach; Weather Watch, Helios Adv; *office:* Union-Endicott HS 12 Main St Endicott NY 13760

IACOVELLI, NICHOLAS, History & Social Studies Tchr; *b:* Provid RI; *m:* Lynn Ullrich; *c:* Nicole, James; *ed:* Providence Coll (BA) HIs Stud, Scndry Ed 1975; Cntrl CT St Univ (MS) Scndry Ed 1986; Cert Roger Williams Coll 1975; *cr:* St Joseph HS His, Soc Stud Tchr 197 Good Hope Schl His, Soc Stud Tchr 1976-79; CT Regnl Dist 10 Schl Soc Stud Tchr 1979-82; RHAM Schl His, Soc Stud Tchr 1982-; *ai:* Co-Adv; Dist Wide Soc Stud Task Force; NEA 1979-; East Had Historical Soc 1985-; East Haddam Bd of Ed 1995-; Article Pub; *o* Rham HS 67 Rham Rd Hebron CT 06248

IACOVELLI, RAYMOND JOSEPH, English Teacher; *b:* Jersey City *m:* Jean Marie Doyle; *c:* Scott, Ryan; *ed:* BA & 15 Eng Credit Hrs Memorial HS Eng Tchr 1974-; *ai:* PCBS Tchr St Peters Coll; Mode Acad Team; NEA 1974-; Parent Advy Cncl 1994-.

IACOVONE, DENISE FUSCO, Art Teacher; *b:* Brooklyn, NY; *m:* R John; *ed:* NY Univ (BS) Art Ed & Fine Art 1978, (MA) Art Ed for Level 1992; 12 Post Grad Credit Hrs in Art & Advertising; *cr:* Frank E Advertising Art Dir 1980-85; Garcia Advertising Sr Art Dir 1985-87; Grant Advertising Sr Art Dir 1987-89; Xavier HS Visual Arts Dept C & Tchr 1989-; Dzines by Denise Sole Proprietor 1990-; *ai:* Port Preparation; Create Retreat Crosses with Art Stdnts for Schl Wide Re Prgm; NAEA, NY St Art Tchrs Assn 1992-; Jewelers & Silversmith Amer 1990-; ASCD 1992-; Theater Guild 1976-; Saks Fifth Avenue Designer of Yr; Intnl Advertising Festival 3rd Place Print Media; Packaging 2nd Place Awd; Whos Who in Advertising, Women in Bus, & Engrng; *office:* Xavier HS 30 W 16th St New York NY 10011*

IAGULLI, THOMAS LOUIS, Eighth Grade English Teacher Youngstown, OH; *m:* Susan Mary Weller; *c:* Jonathan Jay, Jill A Jeffrey Thomas; *ed:* Salem Coll (BA) Eng, Comm 1970; PA St, Uni Pittsburg Ed Credits; *cr:* Liberty HS Scndry Eng Tchr 1970-72; Ches Ridge HS Scndry Eng Tchr 1972-83; Chestnut Ridge MS 8th Grd Eng T 1983-; *ai:* HS Boys Track Coach; 8th Grd Team Ldr; CREA, PSEA 19 NEA 1970-; MS Tchr of Decade; 1994 Tchr of Yr.

IALENTI, FRANCIS VINCENT, World Language Department Chm Weymouth, MA; *ed:* Stonehill Coll (BA) Fr 1963; Boston Coll (M. Modern Langs 1968; Attnd Univ of Louisville, Univ of CO, Rutgers, U of WA, Middlebury, Rollins Coll, SUNY, Univ of Lyon; *cr:* Oliver A HS World Lang Tchr 1963-; *ai:* France, Spain Exch; MA Tchrs, N 1963-; ACTFL; AATF; Lions Club Tchr of Yr; *office:* Oliver Ames HS Lothrop St North Easton MA 02356*

IALONGO, VIC, High School English Teacher; *b:* Ellwood City, PA; Janice DePola; *ed:* Geneva Coll (BA) Eng 1969; Westminster Coll (M Eng Ed 1975; Elem Ed Cert Post-Grad Stud at Slippery Rock Univ; Massanutten Military Acad Eng Tchr, Yrbk Spon 1969-70; Lincoln Eng, Jrnlsm, Schl Newspaper Spon 1970-78, 10th-12th Grd Eng T 1978-; *ai:* NHS, Prin Advy, Planned Course Guide Comm; Schl D Identity; PSEA 1970-84; AFT 1984-; Chrstn Assembly Church 1961-, of Trustees 1992-; Duquesne Univ Cert for Excl in Tchng, Commitm 1992; *office:* Lincoln HS 501 Crescent Ave Ellwood City PA 16117

IAMAIO, JOHN JOSEPH, Bible, Psych Tchr & Fam Cnslr; *b:* Fult NY; *m:* Betty Stewart; *c:* John M., Stephanie J.; *ed:* Piedmont Bible C (THB) Theology 1971; Luther Rice Seminary (MA) Biblical Stud, Gr 1987, (MA) Counseling 1990; NY St Coaching License; NY FIrst Aid CPR Courses; Susquehanna Univ Mental Hlth Ed Cert; *cr:* Calvary B Church Pastor 1971-87; Heritage Bapt Church Pastor 1987- Northumberland Chrstn Schl Bible & Greek Tchr 1980-86; Webster P Schls Wrestling Coach 1988-93; Webster Chrstn Schl Sftbl & Soc Coach 1990-95, Bible & Psych Tchr 1991-; *ai:* Wrestling, Soccer & Sf Coach; Booster Club Pres 1990-94; Weekly Radio Prgm on WMHN 199 Natl Chrstn Counseling Assn Clinical Mem; ACSI 1990-; Westside B Church 1990-; Republican Party; Webster Pub Schl Wrestling Coach of *office:* Webster Christian Schl 675 Holt Rd Webster NY 14580*

IAMES, MARY STEINER, Guidance Counselor; *b:* Bluffton, OH; Jeffery; *ed:* Bluffton Coll (BA) Math 1988; Bowling Green St Univ (ME

& Cnslng 1992; Univ of Toledo Working Toward PHD; *cr:* Perry HS Tchr 1988-91; Bowling Green St Univ Grad Asst 1991-92; Perrysburg ɔsh Cnslr 1992-93; Perry Elem Schl K-8th Grd Cnslr 1993-; *ai:* Ftbl Adv; Dance Team Coach, IDAA Co-Adv; TLC Adv; Perry PALS ƆEA & NEA 1988-; NWOCA, OCA & ACA 1993-, Sec NWOCA; 1994-, Grant; Shawnee United Meth Church 1994-; *office:* Perry Schl 2770 E Breese Rd Lima OH 45806

ONTE, BRUNO, Science Teacher; *b:* Calabria, Italy; *m:* Mary Noel rthy; *c:* Tina, Trish; *ed:* Univ of WV at Charleston (BS) Bio 1969; Rutgers Univ, Jersey City St Coll, Montclair St Coll & William on Coll; *cr:* Kearny Schl System Sci Tchr 27 Yrs; *ai:* Dev & mented Summer Environmental Awareness Prgm; Conducted Tchr ice; Organized Sci Fair Earth Day Prgm; Ecology Field Trips; NJEA , HMDC Environmental Ctr 1990-, Selection Comm for NJ Critical for Tchrs; Monsato Chem Co Summer Prgm, NJ BISEC, NY NJ r Estuary, Environmental Endowment for NJ Inc Grants; Awd from E; Sci Lesson Pub in Sci Scope Magazine & HMDC Envirnmental olid Waste Act Book; Tchr of Yr; *office:* Lincoln Schl 121 Beech St y NJ 07032

PIETRO, LORAINE ARLYN, Humanities Teacher; *b:* Oneonta, NY; cholas; *c:* Jared, Jacob, Arlynn; *ed:* Keuka Coll (BA) Elem Ed 1977; le Univ (MA) Spec Ed 1978; *cr:* Bristol Twp Schl Dist Tchr of Spec earning Disabled 1978-80; Cncl Rock Schl Dist Tchr of Gifted Stdnts ; *ai:* Stu Cncl Adv; Drama Club Dir; Yrbk Ed; Schl Act with Parent Coord, Vol; Comm Svc with Stdnts; Gifted Ed Comm; PSEA 1978-; s Who in Amer Univs, Colls 1976-77; *office:* Richboro Elem Schl 125 Holland Rd Richboro PA 18940

ACONE, JOHN A., English Teacher; *b:* Paterson, NJ; *m:* Lucy J. ; *c:* Mary Y.; *ed:* Georgetown Univ (BA) Eng 1964; Fairleigh nson Univ (MAT) Tchng 1966; Supvrs Cert Eng; 30 Post Grad Credits Stud; *cr:* Indian Hills HS Tchr, Head Tchr 1966-; *ai:* Writing Ctr l; Stu Cncl, Lit Magazine Adv; NEA, Local Assn 1966-; NCTE 1985-; lastic Inc 1992-, Editorial Adv; Pub 2 Articles Eng Journal; NJ rnor's Tchr Recognition Awd 1992; *home:* 259 Standish Rd ewood NJ 07450*

DIORIO, EDWARD A.,JR., Tchr of the Hearing Impaired; *b:* burgh, PA; *m:* Eileen Kerston; *c:* Tracey, Lauren; *ed:* Univ of burgh (BA) Anthropology 1982, (MED) Hearing Impaired 1985; *cr:* A Tchr of the Hearing Impaired 1985-87; ARIN-Homer Ctr Jr, Sr HS of the Hearing Impaired 1987-; *ai:* Dir Homer Ctr Sign Lang rmance Group, Spiritual Hands Sign Lang Chrstn Performing Group; Dir Pitcairn Presbyn Church Vacation Bible Schl 8 Yrs; NEA, PSEA -; PA Edctrs of Stdnts Who are Deaf & Hard of Hearing 1994-; Chrstn tion; Anne Sullivan Awd; *office:* Homer-Center HS 20 Wildcat Ln er City PA 15748

NELLI, BARBARA DIANE, 1st Grade Teacher; *b:* Philadelphia, PA; ne L.; *ed:* Kutztown Univ (BS) Ed Elem 1969; *cr:* Stevens Elem Schl Tchr 1969-74; Fountain Hill Elem Schl Grd 1 Tchr 1974-79; Lincoln Schl Grd 1 Tchr 1979-; *ai:* Various Dist Comms; NEA, PSEA, BEA -; Church, Sunday Schl Tchr, Vestry, Church Ed Comm Chair, Choir, hip Comm; Welcom Pl Bd 1992-; Bethlehem Raiders Little League 1984-88, Sec; BASD Bell for Outstdng Performance 1985; Howard L. p Awd 1987; *office:* Lincoln Elem Schl 1810 Renwick St Bethlehem 8017*

NIELLO, TERESA M., PE & Health Teacher; *b:* Hempstead, NY; *ed:* au Comm Coll (BA) PE 1982; East Stroudsburg Univ (BS) PE, Hlth 984; Hofstra Univ (MS) Hlth 1990; Attending Long Island C. W. Post Masters Admin; 18 Inservice Credits; *cr:* East Rockaway HS nanent Sub Tchr, Coach; St Fracis of Assissi PE Tchr; Elmont HS PE, Var Vlybl, Bsktbl, Sftbl, LaCrosse Coach 11 Yrs; *ai:* Liason Comm; Corps Advy; Sports Night Adv; Drug Free Schls; Aids Advy, Hlth, es Comms; NEA 1987-; SFT, Booster Club 1986-; SEICUS 1989-; au Vlybl Coaches Assn, Nassau Bsktbl Coaches Assn 1986-, Treas; nen in Sports Fnd Grant Girls LaCrosse Team; *office:* Elmont HS 555 e Rd Elmont NY 11003*

NONE, VINCENT JOSEPH, Music Teacher; *b:* Philadelphia, PA; *m:* ces M.; *c:* Joe, Lauren; *ed:* West Chester Univ (BS) Music 1969, (MM) ic Ed 1973; New England Conservatory of Music 1969-70; *cr:* Philip or Acad Woodwind Instr 1969-70; Collingdale Schl Dist Instrumental ic Dir 1970-72; Music Village Woodwind Tchr 1972-73; Tatnall Schl rumental Dir 1973-74; DE Cty Comm Coll Music Theory Instr 4-75; Southeast Delco Schl Dist Elem Classroom Music Tchr 1975-; naculata Coll Continuing Music Ed Tchr 1986-; *ai:* Chorus; NEA 1970-; Cty Symphony 1992-, Principle Clarinet; Performance & Publication riginal Music Composition; *office:* Sharon Hill Elem Schl 701 Coates haron Hill PA 19079

NOTTI, JOHN DAVID, Social Studies Teacher; *b:* Providence, RI; St Univ Coll at Oneonta (BS) Ed 1976; St Univ Coll at New Paltz (MS) 1979; 12 Hrs Beyond Masters in His & Pol Sci; *cr:* Edmeston Cntrl ls Soc Stud Tchr 1976-7; Kingston City Consolidated Schls Soc Stud r 1977-80; Onteora Cntrl Schls Soc Stud Tchr 1980-; *ai:* Mock Trial m Adv; Asst Track Coach, 1983-93; Cross Cntry Coach 1984-87; Indoor ck Coach 1986-89; Jr Class Adv 1982; Sr Class Adv 1983, 1984, 1985, 7; Stu Affairs Cncl Adv 1989-90; Onteora Tchrs Assn & NYSUT 1980-, gotiator 1990; St Catherine Laboure 1962-, Commentator Usher 4 Yrs; ter Zoning Bd of Appeals 1991-93, Vice Chm 1 Yr; Ulster Republican b 1990-, VP 1 Yr; Town of Ulster Cnclman & Deputy Adv 1994-; nell Modek Congress Adv; Ulster Bd of Cooperative Educl Services cessful Fundraisers & Co-Author of 3 Tchng Manuals; National lowment for Hum Fellowship 1992 Aristotle's Nicomachean Ethics; ce: Onteora Sr HS Rt 28 Boiceville NY 12412*

NNUCCI, JEANETTE ROSE, 7th-8th Grd Math Teacher; *b:* New York y, NY; *m:* Paul Anthony; *c:* Jennifer, Christopher; *ed:* Nassau Comm A) 1969; Queens Coll (BA) Math 1972; Hofstra Univ (MS) Spec Ed 76; Queens Coll (PD) Admin 1990; *cr:* SUNY at Westburg Instr 1989; and Trees Schls Summer Elem Prin 1990-94; Island Park Schl Math Tchr 72-; *ai:* Mathletes; Stu Cncl; Yrbk; NYSTA 1972-, Bldg VP; NCMTA; ng Island Collectors Club 1981-, Charter Pres, VP, Treas; *office:* Lincoln ens Schl Trafalger Blvd Island Park NY 11558*

NNUCCI, JOHN, Career Programs Coordinator; *b:* Rockville Centre, ; *m:* Marilyn Kohl Butler; *c:* Elaine Lisa, John William; *ed:* NY Univ S) Ed-Cum Laude 1968, (MA) Ed 1972; Berean Schl of the Bible ploma 1982; *cr:* NY Univ Adj Instr & Asst Prof 1968-80; Baldwin Pub hls Tchr 1968-69; NY Pub Schls Tchr 1969; Westbury Pub Schls Tchr 59-; *ai:* Bldg Advy Comm Chprsn; Epsilon Pi Tau 1967-, Pres 1972-75; Univ Founders Day Awd 1968; Article Pub; *office:* Westbury HS 1 Post Old Westbury NY 11568*

ROSSI, FRANK E., HS Math Teacher; *b:* New York City, NY; *ed:* CNY (BS) Mechanical Engr 1970, (MS) Chem Engr 1973; *cr:* Thalle Inc gr 2 Yrs; Yonkers Bd of Ed Math Tchr 23 Yrs; *ai:* Scarsdale Golf, Vllybl Wrestling Coach; ASME 1970-; *office:* Saunders Schl 183 Palmer Rd nkers NY 10701

SEVOLI, PAUL, Spanish Teacher; *b:* Port Jefferson, NY; *ed:* IA St (BA) an & Ed 1978; Univ of IL (MA) Latin Amer Lit 1981; Attnd Univ Laval inte Foy; Univ De Salamanca; *cr:* Hofstra Univ Assoc Prof 1981-82; oly Cross HS Span Tchr 1983-86; Bethpage HS Span Tchr & Dir of Dist Adult Ed 1986-; *ai:* NYSAFLT 1983-; SCOPE 1994-; MCES NYS Awd 1989; NYSAFLT Journal Article; *office:* Bethpage H S Cherry Ave Bethpage NY 11714

IBE, PATRICK NNEIBE, Chemistry Teacher; *b:* Mgbowo, Nigeria; *m:* Helen; *c:* Ike, Ama, Kike; *ed:* Univ of Ibadan (BS) Chem 1974; Univ of IA (MS) Medicinal Chem 1980, (PHD) Sci Ed 1985; *cr:* TX Coll Asst Prof Chem 1985-88; The Lawrenceville Schl Chem Tchr 1988-; *ai:* Asst Coach JV Soccer; Assoc Housemaster Hamill House; Rsrch Corp Partners in Sci Chem Rsrch Awds 1992-93; Pub Paper Rsrch Corp; *office:* The Lawrenceville Schl 206 Main St Lawrenceville NJ 08648

ICKES, LESLIE J., History & Physical Ed Tchr; *b:* Somerset, PA; *ed:* Pensacola Chrstn Coll (BA) 1988; 3 Credits Ed Psych, 3 Credits His & Philosophy of Ed Liberty Univ; 3 Credits US Hist; *cr:* Riverside Chrstn Acad His, PE Tchr 1988-; *ai:* Yrbk Adv; Vlybl Coach; Stu Cncl Adv; Elem Bsktbl Coach; *home:* RR 2 Box 55 Hollsopple PA 15935

ICONIS, LUCILLE F., Reading Specialist; *b:* Brooklyn, NY; *m:* Arthur P.; *c:* Joseph, Philip; *ed:* Hofstra Univ (BA) Elem Ed, His 1976, (MS) Rdng 1979; Educl Admin Prof Diploma 1991; Jr Great Books Ldr; *cr:* Hofstra Univ Rdng Clinician 1979-80; Washington St Schl Classroom Tchr 1976-88, Rdng Specialist 1988-; *ai:* Curr Cncl; Grd Chprsn 1977-88; Geography Bee Coord; Site Based Mgmt Team; IRA 1985-; Nassau Rdng Cncl, ASCD 1988-; PTA Tchr Awd; *office:* Washinton Street Schl 760 Washington Street Franklin Square NY 11010*

IEZZI, CARL THOMAS, Instrumental Music Dir; *b:* Greensburg, PA; *m:* Lynn Eyermann; *c:* Christoher M., Carmen K.; *ed:* Duquesne Univ (BS) Music Ed 1968, (MM) Fr Horn Performance 1970; Post Graduate Stud Music Theory; *cr:* Conroy Jr HS Instrumental Music 1969-71; D. B. Oliver HS Band Dir 1971-88; Rogers Schl for the Arts Instrumental Music Dir 1988-; *ai:* Natl Jr Hnr Soc; Tchr of Horn Pittsburgh Ctrs for Musically Talented; Pittsburgh All-City Hnrs Orch Conductor; Instrl Tchr Ldr; AFT 1969-; Pittsburgh Muscians Univ 1970-; PMEA 1988-; *office:* Rogers Creative Sch Perf Arts 5525 Columbo St Pittsburgh PA 15206*

IFFT, WILLIAM EDWARD, 7th Grade Social Studies Tchr; *b:* Warren, OH; *m:* Renee Beth Beveridge; *ed:* Youngstown St Univ (BSEd) Comprehensive Soc Stud 1983; Credit Hrs Grad YSU 15 Qt Hrs; Oh Univ 14 Qr Hrs; *cr:* Austintown Fitch HS Asst Ftbl Coach 1981; Niles City Schls Asst Ftbl Coach 1983-91, Dean of Stdnts 1993; Mineral Ridge HS Asst Ftbl Coach 1993; Niles City Schls Soc Stud Tchr 1983-; *ai:* Coach Ftbl; Niles Classroom Tchrs, OEA, Trumbull Cty Coaches Assn 1983-; Trumbull Cty Coaches Assn Asst Coach of Yr 1987; Recognized for Saving A Stdnts Life 1989; Cooperating Tchr 1991-92 YSU Dept of Ed; *office:* Edison Jr HS 360 W Church St Niles OH 44446

IFKOVIC, EDWARD J., Professor of English; *b:* N Branford, CT; *ed:* Southern CT St Univ (BS) Eng 1965; Univ of NC (MA) Amer Lit 1966; Univ of MA (PHD) Amer Lit 1972; PostDoctoral Stud-Columbia Univ; *cr:* Tunxis Comm-Tech Coll Prof 1972-; *ai:* Adv Poetry Review; MELUS 1974-, Pres; MLA 1972-; Books Written Anna Marinkovich, For Love of Country, Mr. Dooley & Mr. Dunne, Dream Street, Yugoslavs in America; Edited Amer Letter- Immigrant Writing; *office:* Tunxis Comm-Tech Coll 271 Scott Swamp Rd Farmington CT 06032

IFKOVITS, DAVID JOHN, Director of Choral Activities; *b:* Allentown, PA; *m:* Kathleen Marie Fennimore; *ed:* Moravian Coll (BA) Music Ed, Voice 1983; Hartt Schl of Music (MMUS) Choral Conducting 1988; *cr:* St Jane Frances de Chantal Parish Music, Liturgy Dir 1983-86; Notre Dame HS Band Dir 1983-86; Archmere Acad Choral Act Dir 1988-; St Joseph the Brandywine Parish Choirs Dir 1992-; *ai:* Asst Drama, Drama Dept Tech Dir; Amer Choral Dirs Assn, Music Edctrs Natl Conference, Pastoral Musicians Assn 1983-; DE Sr All St Choir Chm 1994-95; Choirs Invited to Perform at Carnegie Hall, Madrid Spain, London England, Vienna Austria; *home:* 2336 Jamaica Dr Wilmington DE 19810*

IGLESIAS-CARDINALE, VINCENT PAUL, English Instructor; *b:* Oakland, CA; *m:* Marie; *c:* Morgan Collins; *ed:* Humboldt St Univ (BA) Philosophy 1991, (MA) Eng 1993; Currently Working Toward MFA in Fiction Writing at VT Coll; *cr:* Humboldt St Univ Eng Instr Part-Time 1992-93; Genesee Comm Coll Eng Instr Part-Time 1994-; Monroe Comm Coll Eng Instr Part-Time 1995-; *ai:* Writing Lab Tutor; AWP 1996; Poetry Pub in Poetalk & Babble On; *office:* Genesee Comm Coll 1 College Rd Batavia NY 14020

IGO, MARGARET CULLEN, Third Grade Teacher; *b:* Whitinsville, MA; *m:* John F.; *c:* Ellen, Michael; *ed:* Emmanuel Coll (BA) Psych, Ed 1958; Worcester St Coll (ME) Ed 1960; Attnd Harvard, Boston Univ, Coll of New Rochelle; *cr:* Northbridge Jr HS 7th Grd Eng, Sci Tchr 1958-62; Nipmuc Regnl Schl 7th, 10th Grd Eng Tchr 1962-64; St Thomas of Canterbury 3rd Grd Tchr 1981-; *ai:* Textbook Comm; NCEA 1981-; Friends of Lib 1978-; *office:* St Thomas of Canterbury Schl 336 Hudson St Cornwall On Hudson NY 12520

IHASZ, DANIEL L., Asst Professor of Voice; *b:* Racine, WI; *m:* Helen M.; *ed:* Univ of WI at Madison (BM) Vocal Performance 1985; Eastman Schl of Music (MM) Vocal Performance 1992; Performers Cert; *cr:* St Univ of NY Coll at Fredonia Asst Voice Prof 1992-; Houghton Coll Voice Lecturer 1992-93; *ai:* Phi Kappa Lambda; Phi Mu Alpha Sinfonia Adv; NYSSMA 1992-; NATS 1993-; CCMTA 1993-; *office:* S U N Y Coll At Fredonia 2166 Mason Hall Fredonia NY 14063*

IHLEFELD, SANDRA LUCILLE, Frosh English & Jrnlsm Tchr; *b:* Rock Island, IL; *m:* Richard O.; *c:* Craig L., Dirk A.; *ed:* Augustana Coll (BA) Scndry Eng 1961; St Univ of NY at Buffalo (MS) Information & Lib Stud 1985; Columbia Univ Jrnlsm Sem 1983; Buffalo St Coll Arts Seminar 1986; *cr:* Washington Jr HS Eng Tchr 1961-62; South East Jr HS Eng Tchr 1962-64; Park Ridge Schl for Girls Eng 2nd Art Tchr 1966-70; Willowbrook Schl Eng Tchr 1970-71; Clarence Jr-Sr HS Eng & Jrnlsm Tchr 1972-; *ai:* Schl News Magazine & Wales UK-Clarence Exch Adv; Alpha Delta Kappa 1980-, Historian; Beta Phi Mu 1985-; NCTE 1961-; NY St Engl Council; Dow Jones Jrnlsm Fellowship 1983; World Univ Games Stu Press Corps Mentor 1993; Poetry Pub; Presenter, Global Conversations on Lang and Literacy 1996; *office:* Clarence Sr HS 9625 Main St Clarence NY 14031

ILARIA, DORIS, 8th Grade Teacher; *b:* Jersey City, NJ; *ed:* Jersey City St Coll (BA) Elem Ed 1973; Montclaire St Grad Pgm 12 Credit Hrs; *cr:* St Margaret of Cortona 4th Grd Tchr 1973-83, 8th Grd Tchr 1983-86; St Matthew Schl 4th Grd Tchr 1987-88, 8th Grd Tchr 1988-91; Notre Dame Interparochial 8th Grd Tchr 1991-; *ai:* Stu Cncl Adv; Dir of Schl Plays; Moderator of Boys Bsktbl Team; Rainbow Pgm; Mentor Tchr; NCEA 1974-; Hackensack Med Univ 1992-, Vol; *office:* Notre Dame Interparochial Sch 312 1st St Palisades Park NJ 07650

ILER, ELISABETH, Program Director; *m:* Kama Krishna; *ed:* Peoples Coll of Law (JD) Law; *cr:* CUNY York Coll Prgm Dir 1982-; *ai:* Assn Amer Med COlls, AFT, NEA 1982-.

ILER, PAULA DIANE, 2nd Grade Teacher; *b:* Bucyrus, OH; *m:* Stephen; *c:* Audra, Nathan; *ed:* OSU (BA) Elem K-8 1974; Ashland Univ (MA) Curr & Instruction 1991; 21 Addl Hrs; *cr:* Bacyrus City Schls 1st Grd Tchr 1974-77, Head Start Tchr 1980-81, Col Crawf Schls 2nd Grd Tchr 1986-89; Galion City Schls 2nd Grd Tchr 1989-; *ai:* Safty Patrol Advison; Dept Chm, Tchr Ldr Math & Sci; Mentor; CCIRA 1991-, Bldg Rep; OCTELA 1992-94; Altar Guild 1992-; Jennings Schlr; Article Pub; Awded 2 Math Grants; *office:* Galion City Schls 200 Westgate Galion OH 44833*

ILES, MARK ANDREW, American His & Govt Teacher; *b:* Cincinnati, OH; *m:* Doreen Elaine Matthis; *c:* Kathryn, Lauren, Kerry; *ed:* Miami Univ (BA) Bus 1983, (BA) Scndry Ed, Soc Stud, Bus 1991; *cr:* Hancock Fabrics Mgr 1984-88; J C Penney Sales 1988-91; LaSalle HS Tchr 1992-; *ai:* Stu Newspaper, Yrbk Adv; Lancer Day Gay, Cert Comms; NCSS 1990-; tchr of Month; Dir Cmptr Curr Buckeye St Jrnlsm Wrkshp; *office:* La Salle HS 3091 W North Bend Rd Cincinnati OH 45239

ILES, MARY LOU, English & Social Stud Teacher; *b:* Boonville, NY; *m:* Kenneth W.; *c:* Jennifer Searey, Kenneth A., Daniel; *ed:* St Lawrence Univ (BA) Eng 1959; SUNY at Cortland (MS) Eng Ed 1975; 30 Addl Hrs in His & Eng; *cr:* Burnt Hills NY Tchr 1959-60; Oriskany NY Tchr 1960-63; Westmoreland Tchr 1969-; *ai:* Schl Quality Review Initiative Co-Chair; NYSCSS 1990-; *office:* Westmoreland Cntrl Schl Rt 233 Westmoreland NY 13490

ILG, CHRISTOPHER PAUL, 6th-12th Grd Vocal Music Tchr; *b:* Rocky River, OH; *ed:* Cleveland St Univ (BMUS) Ed 1990; *cr:* St Joseph Church Prin Organist 1979-87; Our Lady of Peace Music Minister 1987-88; Ascension Church Music Dir 1988-90; Highland Local Schls Vocal Music Tchr 1990-; *ai:* 8th Grd Guys, Girls Chorus Dir; HS Guys, Women's Chorus Spring Musical; OMEA, MENC, NEA 1990-; ACDA 1995-; *office:* Highland Local Schls 3880 Ridge Rd Medina OH 44256*

ILIESCU, SORIN, Asst Prof of Fire Sci Dept; *b:* Romania; *m:* Ruxandrda Popescu; *ed:* Univ of Bucharest Romania (MS) Mech Engrng 1977; Univ of New Haven (MS) Fire Sci 1992; *cr:* Valley Engrs Field Engr 1985-86; D. C. Allen Fire Protection Designer 1987-92; Univ of New Haven Asst Prof 1992-; *ai:* Undergraduate Adv Fire Sci Dept; Core Curr Comm; Acad Stans Comm; Office of Acad Svcs Adv; NFPA 1992-; SFPE 1990-; *office:* Univ Of New Haven 300 Orange Ave West Haven CT 06516

ILLSLEY, ARTHUR E., Social Studies Teacher; *b:* Brockton, MA; *m:* Mary Jane Frost; *c:* Nathan; *ed:* Bridgewater St Coll (BA) His 1978; Natl Geographic Geography Ed Prgm; *cr:* East Bridgewater HS Soc Stud Tchr 1984-; *ai:* Adv Class of 1998; Co-Adv Amer Field Svc; Schl Cncl; Mission Statement & Core Values Comm; NEA, MTA & New England His Tchrs Assn; Plymouth Cty Ed Assn, Honor Awd 1991; Southeast MA Geography Network, Founding Mem; Phi Alpha Theta; Wkshp Presenter Tchng About S Africa; *office:* East Bridgewater HS 11 Plymouth St East Bridgewater MA 02333

ILLUZI, JAMES V., 7th Grade Social Studies Tchr; *b:* Buffalo, NY; *m:* Andrea Di Giori; *c:* Lori; *ed:* Univ of Buffalo (BA) Ed 1970, (MS) 1974; *cr:* Kenmore MS Tchr 20 Yrs; *ai:* Sr Fac & United Way Reps; Interview & Fac Adv Comms; KTA, NYSUT & APT 1970-; Golden Apple Awd 1993; Spec Cty Ed Awd 1995.

ILLUZZI, JAMES VICTOR, Social Studies Teacher; *b:* Buffalo, NY; *m:* Andrea DiGiore; *c:* Lori; *ed:* (BA) Ed 1970; (MS) 1974; *cr:* Kenmore-Tonawanda Pub Schls Tchr 1970-; *ai:* Jeopardy Activity Adv; Quiz Bowl Coach; Bldg Advy, Interview Comms; Sr Bldg Rep; NYSUT, AFT 1970-; Kenmore Tchrs Assn 1970-, 25 Yr Awd; Golden Apple Awd 1993.

ILOV, LAURA ANN, Reading & History Teacher; *b:* Rochester, PA; *ed:* Slippery Rock St Coll (BS) Elem Ed 1974; Duquesne Univ (MS) Rdng, Lang Arts 1995; Post Grad Stud Carlow Coll, Duquesne Univ, Boston Coll; *cr:* Mount Gallitzin Acad Intermediate Tchr 1974-75; St James Primary Tchr 1975-76; St Raphael Schl Upper Elem Tchr 1978-84; Holy Rosary Schl Upper Elem Tchr 1984-95; St Benedict the Moor Schl Upper Elem Tchr 1995-; *ai:* African Amer His Bowl Adv; Bsktbl, Swimming Coach; NCEA 1976-; NCNW 1992-; Dev African Amer His Bowl, African Amer Lit Prgm; Nom Golden Apple Tchr Awd 1994; Nom Natl Cncl of Negro Women Tchr of Yr African Amer His 1992; *office:* St Benedict the Moor Schl 2900 Bedford Ave Pittsburgh PA 15219*

ILYES, MARK ALLEN, Physics Teacher; *b:* York, PA; *m:* Kathleen Renee Dick; *ed:* Grove City Coll (BS) Applied Physics 1990; Millersville Univ (MED) Math 1995; *cr:* Meadville Area Sr HS Physics Tchr 1990-91; Dallastown Area HS Physics Tchr 1991-; *ai:* NHS Adv; Co-Spon Physics Olympics; AAPT; New Fairview Church of the Brethern 1980-, SS Tchr Asst, Organist & Yth Ldr; Article to be Pub; *office:* Dallastown Area HS 700 New School Ln Dallastown PA 17313*

IMBORNONE, JANET S., English Teacher; *b:* Sharon, PA; *c:* Michael; *ed:* Grove City Coll (BA) Eng Ed 1971; Clarion Univ of PA (MS) Comm 1982; *cr:* Chelsea HS Eng Tchr 1971-76; Mahar Regnl HS Eng Tchr 1976-77; Wilmington Area HS Eng Tchr 1978-; *ai:* Sr, Jr Class Adv; Dept Ldr; CARE Team; Fac Advy; WAEA 1978-, Sec 4 Yrs; PSEA, NEA 1978-; BSA Parents Comm 1991-95; Carnegie Mellon Inst AP Tchrs Eng Grant.

IMBRIACO, MARYANN SADLIK, English Teacher; *b:* Derby, CT; *m:* Val Anthony; *c:* Matthew, Andrea; *ed:* Univ of Cntrl CT (BS) Eng Ed 1970; Attnd Glassboro St Coll; *cr:* Catherine Magee Schl Eng Tchr 1970-76; Edgewood Jr HS Eng Tchr 1976-85; Overbrook Sr HS Eng Tchr 1985-; *ai:* NEA 1970-; LCCRHSD 1976-, AR; *office:* Overbrook Regigonal Sr HS Turnesville Rd Pine Hill NJ 08021

IMBRIGLIO, THOMAS F., HS Pupil Services Chairman; *b:* Fall River, MA; *m:* Suzanne M. Lapointe; *c:* Adam, Andrew; *ed:* Boston Coll (BA) Scndry Ed, His 1970; Boston Univ (MED) Cnslng 1972; Northeastern Univ Post Grad Stud; *cr:* Burlington HS Guid Cnslng 1972-85, Pupil Svcs Chm 1985-; *ai:* Var Bsktbl Coach 1981-93; Schlsp Prgm Chm; NEA, MA Tchrs Assn 1972-; Burlington Edctrs Assn 1972-, Pres 1981-; MA Schl Cnslrs Assn 1985-; Teuksbury Yth Bsktbl Assn 1992-, Coach; *office:* Burlington HS 123 Cambridge St Burlington MA 01803

IMFELD, KATHY SCEARCE, Second Grade Teacher; *b:* Middletown, OH; *ed:* Miami Univ (BA) Elem Ed 1972; Xavier Univ (MS) Guid 1977; Attnd Univ of Dayton; *cr:* Cntrl Schl Second Grd Tchr 1969-74; Gerke Schl Second-Third Grd Tchr 1974-76; Schenck Schl Third Grd Tchr 1976-80; Pennyroyal Elem Schl 1st-3rd Grd Tchr 1980-; *ai:* NEA, OEA, FEA 1972-; YMCA; Middletown Area YMCA St Striders; Holy Family Parish Church; *office:* Pennyroyal Elem Schl 4203 Pennyroyal Rd Franklin OH 45005

IMHOF, DAVID CHARLES, Band Director; *b:* Glen Ridge, NJ; *m:* Jill Alderton; *c:* Ryan Charles, Andrew John, Jessica Joan; *ed:* William Paterson Coll (BS) Music Ed 1982; Ithaca Coll (MM) Music Ed 1988; Post Grad VanderCook Coll of Music, Villanova Univ; *cr:* Seaford Jr HS Instrumental Music Instr 1983-85; Hackensack HS Band Dir 1985-88; Hillsborough HS Band DIr 1988-90; Hunterdon Cntrl HS Band, Orch Dir 1990-93; Hackettstown HS Band Dir 1993-; *ai:* Marching Band; Jazz Ensemble; MENC 1984-; Natl Band Assn 1988-; Natl Fed Interscholastic Music Assn 1994-; NJ Music Edctrs Assn 1985-; Cntrl Jersey Music Edctrs Assn Symphonic Band Conductor 1992; Hunterdon Cty Teen Arts Festival Instrumental Music Coord 1991-92; *office:* Hackettstown HS Warren St Hackettstown NJ 07840

IMM, NANCY MAXWELL, Retired Elementary Teacher; *b:* Athens, OH; *m:* Robert R.; *c:* Thomas, Laura Imm Hanzel; *ed:* OH Univ (BSEd) Elem Ed 1958; 9 Grad Hrs at OH St Univ; *cr:* Newark City Schls Third Grd Tchr 1953-64; Worthington City Schls Third Grd Tchr 1964-65; Portsmouth City Schls Seventh, Third Grds 1971-91; *ai:* Scioto Cty Retired Tchrs 1991-; OH Retired Tchrs 1991-; Alpha Delta Kappa 1975-, Sec, Treas, Historian, Schlsp Comm; *home:* 5531 Kentland Ave Portsmouth OH 45662

IMMEL, CHERYL PENDELL, High School Guidance Counselor; *b:* Springfield, OH; *m:* Ivan Lorin; *c:* John Lorin, Kathelyn Thersa; *ed:* MI St

Univ (BA) Ed 1965; Univ of Dayton (MA) Guid Cnslr 1992; Kent St Elem Ed 1967; *cr:* Salem Pub Schls 4th Grd Tchr 1968-69; United Local Schls Elem Tchr 1971-72; Preble Shawnee HS Elem Tchr, HS Guid Cnslr 1972-; *ai:* NEA, OEA, PSLEA 1972-.

IMMOHR, PHILLIP HENRY, Teacher; *b:* New York City, NY; *ed:* West CT St Univ (BS) Elem Ed 1974, (MS) Elem Ed 1979; Confratute 93, 94, 95 Participant 45 Grad Credits; *cr:* John F. Kennedy Elem Schl Tchr 1975-; *ai:* Dist Enrichment, Inclusion Comms; Bldg Sci Liaison; NY St Tchrs, Brew Tchrs Assn 1975-; AFT 1975-, AFL,CIO; Phi Delta Kappa 1983-; Tchr of Yr 1988; Employee of Month 1993; Mem Union Carbide, Sci Math Enrichment; 1987 Finalist NY St Outstdng Sci Tchr; Southeastern Sec Mem Putnam No West Boces; *office:* John F. Kennedy Elem Schl Foggintown Rd Brewster NY 10509

IMPAGLIATELLI, LEONARD M., Sixth Grade Teacher; *b:* Plainfield, NJ; *m:* Patricia Holzapfel; *ed:* Newark St Univ Tchrs Coll (BA) Elem Ed 1966, (MA) Elem Ed & Advanced Specialization 1969; *cr:* John F Kennedy Schl 5th & 6th Grd Tchr 1966-70; Sayerville Jr HS 7th Grd Sci Tchr 1970-71; Quibbletown MS 6th Grd Tchr 1971-, Grd Level Adv 1971-84; *ai:* NJEA, NEA 1964-; MCEA 1966-; PTEA 1971-; Tchr of Yr From Piscataway 1989; *office:* Quibbletown MS 99 Academy St Piscataway NJ 08854

IMPERATO, BILLIE JEAN, English Teacher; *b:* Media, PA; *m:* Nicholas; *c:* David, Danielle; *ed:* Syracuse Univ (BA) Speech, Drama, Eng 1972; Georgian Court Coll (MS) Ed 1981; *cr:* Randolph Twp HS Eng, Drama Tchr 1972-; Wall Twp HS Eng, Hum Tchr 1977-; *ai:* Stu Cncl, NHS Adv; GATE Curr Revision Comm; Fac Advy Comm; NEA, NJEA, WTEA 1972-; Cub Scout Den Ldr 1992-; *office:* Wall Twp HS 18th Ave & New Bedford Rd Wall NJ 07719

IMPERATORE, TERESSA ANN, Substitute Teacher; *b:* Washington, PA; *ed:* Univ of Pittsburgh (BA) Math 1992; Scndry Ed Cert 1993; Working Towards Masters Prgm Math Ed; Comm Coll of Allegheny Cty's Bus Prgm; Working Towards Bus Ed Degree; *cr:* Comm Coll of Allegheny Cty Adult Ed, HS Summer Prgm 1993-; Carlynton Schl 8-9th Grd Long Term Sub Math Tchr 1994-95; Seneca Vly Schl 7-8th Grd Long Term Sub Math Tchr 1994; Canon Mc Millan Schl Long Term Sub Applied Math, Geometry Tchr 1994; *ai:* Diving Coach; NEA, NCTM 1993-; *home:* 601 Franklin Ave Canonsburg PA 15317

IMSCHWEILER, ANITA FRANCES, High School Business Teacher; *b:* Pottsville, PA; *ed:* Shipensburg Univ (BS) Bus Ed 1981; Wilkes Univ Ed (MS) 1990; *cr:* Schuylkill Bus Inst Bus Tchr 1981-85; Blue Mountain HS Bus Tchr 1985-; *ai:* Club Adv; FBLA; BM Tchr Assn 1985-; Amer Assn of Univ Women 1991-, Membership VP; Article Pub in Alumni Tchr Book Wilkes Univ 1993; *office:* Blue Mountain HS RD 1 Box 1215 Schuylkill Haven PA 17972*

INDECK, DOROTHY ZEIDMAN, Retired Teacher; *b:* Brooklyn, NY; *m:* Bernard; *c:* Barbara, Matthew, Andrew; *ed:* Univ of MA (BS) Ed 1945; Addl Classes; Early Chldhd Creditation; *cr:* City of Boston Tchr 1946-49; Bridgewater-Raritan Schl Tchr 1959-60; JCC of Somerset Cty Dir of Nursery Schl 1961-69; Bridgewater-Raritan Regnl Schl Dist Tchr 1970-91; Rutgers Univ Consultant Supvr of Stu Tchrs 1992-94; *ai:* Docent Giving Tours, Wkshps, Out-Reach Prgms at Jane V. Zimmerli Museum; NEA 1970-; IRA Somerset 1970-, VP; Hadassah 1990-, VP; NCJW 1960-, VP; *home:* 270 Rolling Knolls Way Bridgewater NJ 08807*

INDELICATO, MARY VALERA, Special Education Teacher; *b:* New York City, NY; *m:* Angelo; *c:* Jeanmarie Woolley, Stephen, Celeste Ciulla, Matthew, Mark; *ed:* SUNY at New Paltz (BS) Elem Ed 1957; Long Island Univ (MS) Spec Ed 1986; Hofstra Univ Rdng Cert 1991; *cr:* Freeport Pub Schl 6th Grd Tchr 1957-59; Deer Park No Babylon Pub Schl Sub Tchr 1962-86; Roosevelt Jr Sr HS Spec Ed Tchr 1986-; *ai:* Private Tutoring; AFT, NEA, NYSTA 1957-; RTA 1986-; Deer Park Coop Presch 1965-71, VP, Pres, Dir; SSCyril & Methodius Rel Ed 1960-85, Bd, Tchr; *office:* Roosevelt Jr Sr HS 1 Wagner Ave Roosevelt NY 11575

INDERBITZEN, MARJORIE MOHR, Chemistry Teacher; *b:* Buffalo, NY; *m:* Paul E.; *c:* Katherine Eileen; *ed:* Canisius Coll (BS) Chem 1972; Rivier Coll (MS) 1993; *cr:* Milford Area HS Chem & Bio Tchr 1974-80; Alvirne HS Chem Tchr 1985-; *ai:* AFT & NHSTA 1985-; NEST 1989-; Univ of NH NSF Fellowship; MIT Sci & Engineering Prgm for HS Tchrs; *home:* 2 Timothy Ln Hudson NH 03051

INDERLIED, BARBARA DRINKWATER, Title I Teacher; *b:* Batavia, NY; *m:* H. F. Jr.; *c:* Jeanne LeBlond, Jennifer Barry, Hank, Julie; *ed:* Univ of AZ (BS) Elem Ed-Magna Cum Laude 1962; Lake Erie Coll (MS) Rdng 1980; Addl 3 Hrs Ec; *cr:* Amphitheater Schls 4th Grd Tchr 1962; East Cleveland-Prospect Schl 3rd Grd Tchr 1963-66; West Geauga-Russell Schl 1st Grd & Title I Tchr 1966-88; Park Elem Schl 2nd Grd Tchr 1973; Chardon Schls Title I, Rdng Tchr, Parent Liaison & Tutor Trainer 1988-; *ai:* April 29th Jim Trelease Prgm Organizer; Chardon Staff Aerobics Instr; Strategic Planning Comm Mem; Levi & Calendar Comms; Capts Club Founder Summer Rdng Tutorial; NEA, CCTA 1970-, Insurance Comm; Geauga Panhellenic 1972-, Pres; PEO 1988-; Pilgrim Chrstn Church 1972-, Bell Choir, Missions, Tchr; Charisma Ball for Cancer 1980-, Chm; Geauga Heart Ball 1975-, Chm & Founder; Burlington Green Condo Assn, Pres; Plain Dealer Newspaper Crystal Apple Awd; Ashland Oil Golden Apple Finalist; Chardon Schls Fnd, Geauga Lib Fnd & Rotary Grants; *home:* 105 Clubside Ct Chardon OH 44024*

INDERMUHLE, JOYCE MARIE, Kindergarten Teacher; *b:* New Martinsville, WV; *ed:* Kent St Univ (BA) Early Chldhd Ed 1980; 45 addl Hrs OH Univ; *cr:* Midway Elem Kndgtn Tchr 1980-90; Sardis Elem Kndgtn Tchr 1980-; Hannibal Elem Kndgtn Tchr 1990-; *ai:* Young Authors Conf Comm; Right Read Week Coord; Sci Fair Judge; Monroe Cty Historical 1989-, Pres, VP; *office:* Hannibal Elem Schl PO Box 56 Star Rt 536 Hannibal OH 43931

INDERMUHLE, ROBERT EUGENE, Mathematics Teacher & Leader; *b:* Sardis, OH; *m:* Karen Stoll; *c:* Eric, Trent, Carol; *ed:* Kent St (BS) Math 1965; OH Univ (MS) Cnslng 1968; 30 Credit Hrs Math Ed 1994-95; *cr:* Hannibal Elem 8th Math Tchr 1965-69; Beallsville High Cnslr 1970-79; River High Math Tchr 1980-; OH Univ Tchr Ldr 1994-; *ai:* Teen Inst; Prom Comm; NEA 1965-; OEA 1965-; OCTM 1995-; Apostolic Chrstn Church 1961-; Southeast OH Tchr Ldr 1994, 1995 & 1996; *home:* 50400 Baptist Rdg Sardis OH 43946*

INDOVINO, MICHAEL, Social Studies Teacher; *b:* Brooklyn, NY; *m:* Cathy Holl; *c:* Christopher, Zachary; *ed:* St Johns Univ (BA) Soc Stud 1981, (MA) Scndry Ed 1986; *cr:* Our Lady of Mercy Elem Schl 6th-8th Grd Soc Stud Tchr 1981-83; Floral Park Memrl HS Soc Stud Tchr 1983-89; Elmont Memrl HS Soc Stud Tchr 1990-95; *ai:* Var Sftbl & JV Bsktbl Coach; Long Island Cncl of Soc Stud 1994-; Elks Club 1987-; Spearheaded Interdisciplinary Curr for Global Stud 9th-10th Grd; *office:* Elmont Meml HS 555 Ridge Rd Elmont NY 11003

INDRIKOVIC, MARINA VOTTA, Dance Coordinator; *ed:* Allentown Coll (BA) Dance 1989; Amer Dance Festival 1991, 1993, 1995; *cr:* Mercer Cty HS of Performing Arts Dance Prgm Coord 1989-; Mercer Cty Comm Coll Modern Dance Instr 1990-; *ai:* NJEA 1989-; NJA, AAHPERD 1990-; PDA 1991-; *office:* Mercer County HS Prfrmng Arts 1200 Old Trenton Rd Trenton NJ 08690

INFANTE, NEIL DOMINIC, Human Anatomy, Physiology Tchr; *b:* Buffalo, NY; *m:* Catherine; *c:* Jason; *ed:* St Bonaventure Univ (BS) Bio 1968; SUC at Buffalo (MS) Bio Ed; *cr:* Frontier Cntrl Bio, Human Anatomy Psych 1970-; Erie Comm Coll Human Bio, Nutrition Instr 1991-; *ai:* NYSUT 1970-; *office:* Frontier Central HS S-4432 Bay View Rd Hamburg NY 14075

INFANTE, NEIL JOSEPH, 5th Grade Teacher; *b:* Bagnoli Irpino, Italy; *m:* Susan Diane Hansgen; *c:* Andrew, Matthew; *ed:* Buffalo St Coll (BS) Elem Ed 1973, (MS) Elem Ed 1976; *cr:* Orchard Park Cntrl Schls 5th Grd Tchr 1973-; *ai:* O P Modified Soccer Coach 1980-90; Schl Safety Patrol Adv; Sci Instructional Ldr; Bldg Communications; Var Soccer Coach 1995-; AFT, NYSUT & Orchard Park Tchrs Assn 1973-; Boston Emergency Squad 1980-85; St Bernadette Holy Name 1985-, St Bernadette's Baptism Prgm 1985; Usher 1986; Dist 5 Soccer Club 1980-; *home:* 87 Old Orchard Ln Orchard Park NY 14127

INFANTE, PAUL R., Instrumental Music Teacher; *b:* New York City, NY; *m:* Sharon E.; *c:* Crystina L.; *ed:* Ithaca Coll (BM) Music Ed 1985; Queens Coll (MS) Ed 1990; Specialist Diploma Admin, Supervision 1994; *cr:* Brentwood Schl District Music Tchr 1985-86; Lawrence HS Instrumental Music Tchr 1986-87; S. Middle Schl Instrumental Music Tchr 1987-; *ai:* Brentwood Schl Dist Gen Music Tchr 1985-86; Lawrence HS Instrumental Music Tchr 1986-87; S MS Instrumental Music Tchr 1987-; Jazz Band; Dir of Band; Front For HS Marching Band; Music Curr Comm; Suffolk Cty Music Edctrs Assn 1985-, Chm SW Div II; Brentwood Tchrs Assn 1985-; Music Edctrs Natl Convention 1985-; Phi Mu Alpha Prof Music 1985-; Kappa Delta Pi; *office:* South MS 785 Candlewood Rd Brentwood NY 11717*

INFANTI, RONALD ANTHONY, Industrial Technology Teacher; *b:* East Liverpool, OH; *m:* Amy J. Salsberry; *ed:* Kent St Univ (BS) Indstrl Arts, Ed 1975, (MA) Indstrl Tech 1978; *cr:* Conrail Comm, Signals 1975-83; Geer Realty Realtor 1975-; Kent St Univ Instr 1984-85; Southern Local Schl Dist Tchr 1987-; *ai:* NEA, OTA 1987-; Sons of Italy 1994-; Phi Gamma Delta 1973-; Safety Dir City of Wellsville 1986-90; Svc Dir City of Wellsville 1985.

INGE, GREGORY E., History Teacher; *b:* New Brighton, PA; *m:* Christine A.; *c:* Jeb Stuart, Jacob Jasper; *ed:* Edinboro Univ (BS) Ed, Soc Stud 1979; Indiana Univ of PA His 1983; *cr:* Blairsville HS His Tchr 1979-90; Beaver HS His Tchr 1990-; *ai:* Blairsville Civil War Club 1979-90; Beaver Civil War Club 1990-; Blairsville HS Wrestling Coach, Asst 1982-88; Beaver Jr HS Ftbl Coach 1991-; PSEA, NEA 1979-; Assn for Preservation of Civil War Sites 1990-; Unsung Hero Awd 1982; *office:* Beaver HS Gypsy Glen Rd Beaver PA 15009*

INGELLIS, MARIAN L., Honors English Teacher; *b:* Bristol, CT; *ed:* Coll of St Elizabeth (BA) Eng 1966; Villanova Univ (MA) Eng 1972; 6 Credit Hrs Admin at Montclair St; NEH Grants at Skidmore Coll Greek Classics 1986 & SUNY at Oswego Poetry of WB Yeats 1992; *cr:* St Joseph HS Eng, His & Bus Tchr 1961-65; Paul VI HS Eng Tchr & Dept Head 1966-76; Villa Victoria Acad Eng Tchr & Dept Head 1976-89 Villa Walsh Acad Honors Eng Tchr 1990-; *ai:* Homeroom Tchr; NEA; *office:* Villa Walsh Acad Western Ave Morristown NJ 07960

INGERSOLL, JED SAMUEL, English Teacher; *b:* Rotterdam, NY; *m:* JoAnne Merola; *ed:* SUNY at Cortland (BA) Scndry Eng Ed 1982; SUNY at Albany (MS) Scndry Eng Ed 1985; *cr:* Broadalbin-Perth HS Eng Tchr 1982-; *ai:* Adv Creative Writing Club; NY State United Tchrs 1982-; *home:* 1013 Horvath St Schenectady NY 12303*

INGERSOLL, JUDITH ANN RUMINSKY, Mathematics Teacher; *b:* Lorain, OH; *m:* Charles I.; *c:* Chip; *ed:* Kent St Univ (BS) Math 1969; 32 Hrs Post Grad Stud Bowling Green St Univ, Ashland Coll, Notre Dame Coll, Baldwin Wallace, Coll of Mt St Joseph; *cr:* Marion L. Steele HS Math Tchr 1970-77, 1986-; Bay Village HS Math, Cmptr Sci Tchr 1986; *ai:* Math Stud Course Revision Comm; NEA, OEA, Amherst Tchrs Assn, NEOEA, NCTM 1970-; Sandstone Summer Theatre 1993-, Bd Mem; Golden Apple Awd; Educl Fnd Graphing Calculator Overhead Grant; FTA Favorite Tchr Honoree; *office:* Marion L Steele HS 450 Washington St Amherst OH 44001

INGERSOLL, RENEE THERESA, Music Teacher; *b:* Watertown, NY; *ed:* SUNY at Potsdam (BM) Music Ed 1986; MI St Univ (MM) Applied Music 1989; SUNY at Buffalo (MLS) Schl Lib Media Specialist 1996; *cr:* Malone Cntrl Schl K-5th Grd Music Tchr 1989-92; St Lawrence Cntrl Schl 7th-12th Grd Music Tchr 1992-94; North Cntry Schl 4th-8th Grd Music Tchr 1994-95; Orchard Park MS 6th-7th Grd Music Tchr 1995-; *ai:* Musicals Vocal Dir, Accompanist; MENC, NY St Music Assn 1990-; Western NY Music Edctrs Assn 1995-; NY Lib Assn 1996; Sigma Alpha Iota 1985-; St Lawrence Cty Jr HS All Cty Chorus Conductor 1994; *home:* PO Box 312 Martinsburg NY 13404*

INGERSON, BRADFORD I., Assistant Principal; *b:* Blaine, ME; *m:* Cindy; *c:* Marcus, Holly; *ed:* Gorham St Coll (BS) Math, PE 1964; Univ of South ME (MS) Schl Admin 1970; *cr:* Granite St Schl 5-6 Grd Tchr 1964-87; MS Asst Prin 1987-; *ai:* NAESP 1980-; Elks 1980-, Exalted Ruler Leaving Knighk; Congregational Church Trustee; Recreation Comm 1995-; *office:* Millinocket MS Katahdin Ave Millinocket ME 04462

INGINO, ELAINE BERKOWITZ, 5th Grade Teacher; *b:* Bronx, NY; *m:* Manuel; *c:* Michele, Michael; *ed:* Sullivan Cty Comm Coll (AS) Lbrl Arts, Ed 1967; Long Island Univ (BS) Elem Ed, Math 1969, (MS) Elem Ed, Rdng 1974; 30 Addl Credits Spec Ed, LD Fordham Univ, Brooklyn Coll; *cr:* PS 73K 1st, 2nd, 5th Grd Tchr 1970-73; PS 95K 2nd Grd Tchr 1982-83; PS 216K 3rd-6th Grd Tchr 1983-; *ai:* New Tchr Staff Dev Tchr Trainer 8 Yrs; UFT 1970-, Del 1993-; AFT 1982-; *office:* PS 216 Arturo Tuscanini 350 Avenue X Brooklyn NY 11223

INGLE, ROBERT WESLEY, Art Instructor; *b:* Dayton, OH; *m:* Diane Marie; *c:* Jennifer Marie; *ed:* Wright St (BS) Art Ed 1977, (MS) Art Ed 1985; 81 Additional Qt Hrs; OH St 4 Additional Qt Hrs; Univ of Dayton 7 Additional Qt Hrs; *cr:* Brookville Elem Schl Art Instr 1977-79; Brookville HS Art Instr 1979-; *ai:* Art Club Adv; NEA 1977-; OEA 1977-; OAEA 1977-; BTA 1977-; Natl Rifle Assn 1980-; Brookville Optmist 1994-; Honorary Chptr Farmer; Brookville Cert of Commendation; Brookville Bd of Ed Outstdng Tchr Awd; NHS 1992, 1994, 1995; *office:* Brookville HS 106 S Hill St Brookville OH 45309

INGLIS, CHRISTINE CHERIE, High School Guidance Chprsn; *b:* Brooklyn, NY; *ed:* Coll of Mount Saint Vincent (BA) Sociology 1974; Hofstra Univ (MS) Ed 1982; *cr:* Our Lady of Mercy Acad HS Guidance Cnslr 1983-, Soc Stud Tchr 1991-95, Guidance Chprsn 1995-; *ai:* Stu Advy Comm Mem; Drug & Alcohol Comm Chprsn; Weigting Comm Chprsn; ASCD, Nassau Cnslrs Assn, Western Suffolk Cnslrs Assn; *office:* Our Lady Of Mercy Acad 815 Convent Rd Syosset NY 11791

INGRAFFIA, RICHARD JAMES,JR., Vice Principal for Discipline; *b:* Hoboken, NJ; *ed:* St Peter's Coll (BS) Ec 1984; 15 Credit Hrs Univ of PA, Grad Schl Ed Admin; *cr:* Sacred Heart Schl Jr HS Tchr 1984-85; Queen of Peace HS Soc Stud Tchr, Var Bsktbl Coach 1985-92, Vice Prin for Discipline 1993-; *ai:* Frosh Bsktbl; Little League Bsbl; NASSP, ASCD 1993-; Natl Yth Sports Coaches Assn 1991-; Lyndhurst Bd of Ed 1995-; Natl Cath Ed Assn Distngd Grad Awd; *office:* Queen Of Peace HS 191 Rutherford Pl N Arlington NJ 07071*

INGRAHAM, CHRYS M., Asst Professor of Sociology; *b:* Syracuse, NY; *ed:* Syracuse Univ (MPA) Pub Admin 1986, (MA) Sociology 1988, (PHD) Sociology 1992; Grad Cert Women's Stud at Syracuse Univ; BA Policy Stud, Nonviolent Stud; *cr:* Ithaca Coll Asst Prof 1991-93; Russell Sage Coll Asst Prof 1993-; *ai:* Co-Dir Allies Ctr for Stu of Difference & C Curr Comm; Fac in Residence; Womens Stud Advy Brd; Amer Socic Assn, Soliologists for Women in Soc 1990-; Co-Ed ASA Theory S Newsletter; Rsrch Grant 1994-95; Dean's Awd 1994-95; Article *office:* Russell Sage Coll At Troy 45 Ferry St Troy NY 12180

INGRAM, LINDA FOGLIA, Chemistry Teacher; *b:* Rochester, N Gary; *c:* Donald, Stephanie; *ed:* Nazareth Coll (BS) Bio 1975; SU Brockport (MS) Ed 1989; *cr:* Greece Schl Dist Chem Tchr 1989- Class Adv; NEA 1989-; NSTA 1990-; *office:* Greece Athena HS 80 Pond Rd Rochester NY 14612

INGRAM, W. BRUCE, Theology Teacher; *b:* Philadelphia, P LaSalle Univ (BA) Psych 1981; Villanova Univ (MA) Liberal Stuc WA Theological Union New Schl for Soc Research 44 Credits Gra in Theology & Psych; *cr:* Monsignor Bonner HS Eng & Theolog 1982-85; Archbishop Wood HS Eng Tchr 1985-86; Holy Ghost Prepa Schl Eng Tchr 1988-89; Archbishop Ryan HS Theology Tchr 1989 Marks HS Theology Tchr 1990-; *ai:* Yrbk Editor; Soph Level NCEA 1982-; Summa Cum Laude; Augustinian Schlsp for Grad Stu Schl for Soc Research; Grad Fac Schlsp; LaSalle Univ Alumni Schlsp; Recipient of the Mark of Excellence Awd for Distinguished 1994; *office:* Saint Marks H S Pike Creek Rd Wilmington DE 1980

INMAN, JOANN NASUTA, English Teacher; *b:* Passaic, NJ; *m:* Priestley; *c:* Harold H. III, Mary Alice; *ed:* Ricker Coll (BA) Eng Post Grad Courses Related to Tchr Cert in ME; *cr:* Saint Marys Lan Tchr 1962-65; Christ the King Lang Arts Tchr 1965-66; Hodgden H Tchr 1974-; *ai:* Jr Class Adv; NEASC Accreditation Comm; Eng Chprsn; NEA, MEA 1973-; MSAD 70 Educators Assn 1973-, Pre Aroosook General Hospital Free Bed & Aid 1965-, VP, Pres; ME Fnd 1991-; Houlton Regnl Hospital Auxiliary; Linneus Sno-Sports Reporter; *office:* Hodgdon HS RR 4 Box 1870 Houlton ME 04730

INMAN, JOHN G., English Teacher; *b:* Altoona, PA; *m:* Krumenaker; *c:* Juliana, Jaime; *ed:* Lock Haven Univ (BS) Scndr Stud 1972; St Francis Coll Cert Elem 1975, Scndry Eng 1977; *cr:* Cambria Schls Eng Tchr 1974-; Altoona Schls Continuing Ed ABE & Tchr 1981-; *ai:* Speech Var Coach; PSEA 1974-; PCEA 1974-; NEA Knights of Columbus 1990-; St Brigids Lector 1973-; Book Pub Mira Melody Malone 1988; Numberous Articles Pub; *office:* Penn Cambria School 401 Linden Ave Cresson PA 16630

INNAURATO, LAWRENCE D., Mathematics Teacher; *b:* Philade PA; *m:* Marie B. Smargisso; *c:* Lawrence Jr., Robyn Ann; *ed:* West C Univ (BS) Math 1961; Attnd Penn St Univ, Univ of PA, Villanova Uni Penn Delco Schl Dist Tchr 1961-65; Peirce Jr Coll Tchr 1965-67; M Newtown Schl Dist Tchr; *ai:* Stu Cncl; Yrbk; IMs; Bsbl; NEA, 1961-; MNEA 1967-; NSF Grant Univ of Penna 1963; *office:* M Newtown Sr HS 120 Media Line Rd Newtown Square PA 19073

INNERS, DANIEL J., Sixth Grade Teacher; *b:* York, PA; *m:* Con Miller; *c:* Lauren, Kari, Brady; *ed:* Shippensburg Univ of PA (BS) Ed 1986; Western MD Coll (MS) Elem Guidance 1993; *cr:* Spring Int Schl Sixth Grd Elem Tchr 1987-; *ai:* Golf, Bsebl Coach; SGEA, P NEA 1987-; *office:* Spring Grove Intermediate Schl RD 4 Box 4 Roths Church Rd Spring Grove PA 17362

INNOCENZI, DARRYL A., Associate Principal; *b:* Cleveland, OH John Carroll Univ (BA) Eng 1975; Cleveland St Univ (MED) Instruction 1979; Cnslng Cert 1984, Admin Supvr Cert 1992 John C Univ; Trng in Integrated Curr; *cr:* Cleveland Hts-Univ Hts Eng 1975-90, Guid Cnslr 1988-90; South Euclid-Lynhurst Guid Cnslr 199 Assoc Prin 1992-; *ai:* Venture Capital Grant Governance Comm; Dist Comm; Phi Delta Kappa, ASCD 1992-; OH PTA, Lifetime Mem; *o* Greenview Upper Elem Schl 1825 S Green Rd Cleveland OH 44121*

INNOCENZI, DAVID RICHARD, History Teacher; *b:* Trenton, N Donna Codd; *c:* Jenna & Nina; *ed:* Stockton St Coll (BA) His 198 Grad Credits Rider Coll; *cr:* Hamilton HS West Tchr 1987-; *ai:* Stu & Sr Class Adv; Dramatic Productions Producer; NJEA 1987-; Cond of Trustees 1989-93, Pres; Tchr of Yr 1991; Governors Tchr Recogn Awd 1991; *office:* Hamilton HS West 2720 S Clinton Ave Trento 08610*

INNOCENZI, KATHLEEN WSZOLEK, Social Studies & Psych Tch Trenton, NJ; *m:* Scott; *c:* Megan, Brian; *ed:* West Chester Univ (BSEd Stud, Psych 1986; Trenton St Coll Working Towards MS in Counse Currently Taking Courses Related to Guidance, Counseling; *cr:* Ste HS Soc Stud Tchr 1987-; *ai:* Drill Team, Peer Leadership Adv; H Instruction Tutor; NEA, NJEA, HTEA 1987-; ACA 1996; *office:* Ham East HS 2900 Klockner Rd Trenton NJ 08690

INSLEY, LAWRENCE DAVID, Social Studies Supervisor; *b:* Pate NJ; *m:* Kathleen; *c:* Kendra, Tyler; *ed:* Rutgers (BA) Ec 1969; Fair Dickenson (MAT) Tchng 1973; Soc Stud, Eng, Supvr Cert; *cr:* Milford HS Tchr 1973-77; Indian Hills HS Tchr 1977-78; Bogota HS T Supvr 1978-; *ai:* Stu Congress, Sr Class Adv; Soc Stud St Multi-Cultural Coord; Affirmative Action Officer; GBCSS; Natl Ass Stu Activity Adv; NCSS; Organized and Directed Prgms for Dru Alcohol Awareness, ERASE, SADD, Conflict Resolution; Cooper Learning; Critical Thinking; Stu Leadership; Multi Cultural; Model Affirmative Action; *office:* Bogota HS 2 Henry C Luthin Pl Bogota 07603

INSTINE, NANCY O'BRIEN, Special Education Teacher; *b:* Springf OH; *m:* William J. Jr.; *c:* Angela, Christopher; *ed:* Wittenberg Univ Hlth, PE 1969; Wright St Univ Specific Learning Disabilities; Northeastern HS Hlth, PE Tchr 1969-732; Triad HS Spec Ed Tchr 19 *ai:* Acad Advy Comm; AFT, OFT, TEA 1994-, VP; OH HS Vlybl Coa Assn 1990-; Eastern Star 1975-, Worthy Matron; *home:* 1375 Yocum Cable OH 43009*

INTERSIMONE, NANCY S., Sixth Grade Teacher; *b:* Hartford, CT Richard A.; *c:* Courtney S., Lindsay S.; *ed:* Vassar Coll (BA) Ec 1 Hofstra Univ (MS) Elem Ed 1976; Prof Diploma Rdng 1981; *cr:* G Neck North HS 9-12th Grd Rdng Specialist 1981-82, 7-8th Grd R Specialist 1982-83; J. F. Kennedy Elem Schl 3rrd Grd Tchr 1983-84, Grd Tchr 1984-86; Great Neck North MS Sixth Grd Tchr 1986-; *ai:* Stu Govt; *office:* Richard S Sherman-North MS 77 Polo Rd Great Neck 11023

INYA, CHRISTOPHER NWACHI,SR., Assoc Professor of Econom *b:* Afikpo Abia State, Nigeria; *c:* Chinyere, Chris, Uche-nna; *ed:* Rutg Univ (BA) Ec 1976; Long Island Univ (MBA) Mngmt 1978; Colum Univ (PHD) Higher Ed Fin 1984; *cr:* A & P Supermarkets Fin Ana 1976-78; Manulife Pension Consultant 1978-83; MCC St Univ Assoc P of Ec 1984-; *ai:* Intnl Stu Club Adv; Fac Senator Rep Bus, Ec Dept; F Dev Comm; AFT 1984-, Voting Mem; NYSEA 1986-; United Way 19 Vol Fac; Ldrshp Svc Awd; Vol Svc Awd; Co-Author Introduction to Ma System, Introduction to Principles of Microeconomics 2nd Ed; One of Prof in Nations Diversity Resource Directory; *office:* Monroe Commun Coll 1000 E Henrietta Rd Rochester NY 14623*

IOGHA, RUTH HENRY, Professor of Music; *b:* Winfield, KS; *m:* Fra *c:* Marc, Diane Iogha Stratton; *ed:* Univ of KS (BM) Music Performa 1956; Tchrs Coll Columbia Univ (MA) Music ed 1957; City Coll of N Meadowmount Schl of Music Violin Performance; *cr:* Orange NJ F Schls Music Tchr 1957-58; Kaliski Schl Music Dir, Remedial Thr 1958-

IA Pub Schls String Tchr 1969-70; Crane Schl of Music Prof of 1970-; *ai:* Acad Adv; UUP, AFT 1970-; Music Dir, Fnd of Celebrity Series Potsdam NY; Book: Structured Dramatics for Children with ng Disabilities 1971; *office:* Crane Schl of Music Pierrepont Avenue m NY 13676*

LO, ROBERT JAMES, Classics Instructor; *b:* Bridgeport, CT; *ed:* m Univ (BA) Classics 1969; Princeton Univ (MA) Classics 1971, Classics 1973; Columbia Post Grad Stud Eng Lit, Italian ssqnce Art, Northern Renaissance Art; *cr:* Mrau-a-Pula Classics, Eng 1977; The Hill Schl Classics Instr 1973-; *ai:* IM Tennis; Dormitory 22 Yrs; Occasional Dept Chair; Amer Philological Assos 1970-; Book ws; Woodrow Wilson Fellow; Fordham & Princeton Flwshps; Hill srch Fnd Grants; *office:* Hill Schl 717 E High St Pottstown PA 19464

E, MARILYN TERJESEN, First Grade Teacher; *b:* Staten Island, : Merton L.; *ed:* Richmond Coll (BA) Psych, Early Chldhd 1974; St Univ (MS) Rdng Ed 1979; 30 Addl Credits; *cr:* YMCA Presch Tchr 75; St Joseph's Schl 5 Grd Tchr 1975-80; St Mary of the Assumption Tchr 1980-84; South Londonderry Schl 1 Grd Tchr 1986-; *ai:* NEA; NEA; GSRA; *office:* South Londonderry Elem Schl 88 South Rd nderry NH 03053

E, THERESA LIVATINO, 7th Grade English Teacher; *b:* Brooklyn, *d:* CW Post Coll of Long Island Univ (BA) Eng Ed 1972; Suny Stony (Masters) Lbrl Stud; *cr:* Oakdale Bohemia Rd Jr HS Eng Tchr 1972-; SL; Inculturating Frgn Stdnts to Amer Life; AFT 1972-; NYSUT ; Written Fiction Short Stories Professionally, Freelance.

LITO, JOSEPH ANTHONY, History & Economics Teacher; *b:* City, NJ; *m:* Michele Felice; *c:* Dean, Gina; *ed:* Seton Hall (MA) n & Guid 1976; *cr:* Ridgefield Park Tchr 29 Yrs; *ai:* Project Grad; Club; NEA, NJEA, BCEA 1968-, Treas; RPEA 1968-; NJ St Chess 976-, VP, Sec, Pres; Bergen Cty Flwshp.*

KI, DENNIS MICHAEL, Guidance Counselor; *b:* Nanticoke, PA; nna Sue William; *c:* Tara Dawn, Jill Lynnette; *ed:* King's Coll (BA) 1972; Towson St Univ (MED) Scndry Ed 1975; Loyola Coll (MED) & Cnslng 1981; Six Credits Eng Harford Comm Coll; *cr:* Aberdeen pan Tchr 1972-82, Guid Cnslr 1982-95; Havre de Grace HS Guid 1995-; *ai:* Peer Helpers, Mediation; Harford Ed Ldrshp Prgm; *office:* e Grace HS 700 Congress Ave Havre De Grace MD 21078

AND, DIANA LEHMANN, Jr HS Science Teacher; *b:* Delphos, OH; chard Paul; *c:* John C., Jane Robinson, Patricia L. Carmichael; *ed:* t Univ (BS) Elem Ed 1970; 1 Credit Hr Cmptrs Ashland Univ; 5.2 t Hrs; *cr:* St Charles Schl Jr HS Sci Tchr, Coord 1970-; *ai:* Sci Fair, urr Coord; Lima Cath Schls Positive Addiction Prgm Co-Dev; NCEA ; Reg Cncl Alcoholism 1982-83; Inst for Drug & Alcohol Awareness 1981-91, 10 Yr Svc Awd; Allen Cty Hlth Dept Advy Cncl 1981-82; le Pub 1984; Natl Tchr Magazine; Woman of Yr 1986; Honored US ressional Recep 1988; Governor's Awd Excl in Youth Sci rtunities 1992-93; Honored at White House by Mrs. Reagan 1988; OH e Commendation 1983; Governor's Awd for Excel in Yth Sci rtunities 1991-94; *office:* Saint Charles Schl 2175 W Elm Lima OH 5

N, JOHN V., Physical Ed Teacher & Coach; *b:* North Plainfield, NJ; atricia; *c:* Hannah, Holly, Hope; *ed:* SUNY at Cortland (BS) PE 1982, PE 1986; *cr:* Hancock Cntrl Schl Sub Tchr 1982; Cntrl Sq HS PE 1982-; *ai:* Head Var Ftbl, Head Var Boys Winter, Outdoor Track, ngth Coach; NYSUIT 1982-; NSCA 1996-; NYSFCA; *home:* 206 rest Dr Central Square NY 13036

N, MARY SEELEY, Spanish Teacher; *b:* Columbus, OH; *m:* Frank ence; *c:* Nathan; *ed:* OH St Univ (BS) Span Ed 1988; Univ of Dayton ad Credits; Otterbein Coll 2 Grad Credits; *cr:* Lehman Cath HS Span & Asst Var Vllybl Coach 1991-94; Olentangy HS Span Tchr 1994-; pan Club & Ski Club Adv; Co-Adv In the Know Quick Recall Team; n Tours & Homestays Tour Adv; OFLA 1993-; Linc OH Frgn Lang p 1994-; Wright St Univ Span Culture Day Guest Speaker 1994; *e:* Olentangy HS 675 Lewis Center Rd Lewis Center OH 43035

H, ALLEN M., Chemistry, Science Topics Tchr; *b:* Ft Meade, MD; *c:* n, Samuel; *ed:* Colby Coll (AB) Chem 1968; PA St Univ 6 Credit Hrs Grad Stud; Univ of ME 15 Credit Hrs Post Grad Stud; *cr:* Freeport HS Tchr 1971-; *ai:* Women's Soccer, Sftbl Coach; Prof Dev, NEASC ms; NEA 1971-78, 1981-; 2 Articles Co-Authored, Pub; *office:* port HS 30 Holbrook St Freeport ME 04032

H, JOY HANSON, Director; *b:* Fargo, ND; *m:* Robert; *c:* Joy Ann; Univ of WI (BA) Elem Ed 1967; Coll of St Rose (MA) Elem Ed 1971; redit Hrs Educl Admin; *cr:* Guilderland Cntrl Schl Dist Tchr Grds 4 & 967-73, Math Coord Bldg 1970-73; Bethlehem Cntrl Schl Dist, derland Cntrl Schl Dist Sub Tchr Grds K-5 1973-81; Children's Schl nma Willard Tchr K-3 1981-92, Asst Dir, Tchr 1992-94, Dir 1994-; *ai:* A 1969-80; ASCD 1994-; Jayncees 1968-81; Girl Scouts 1980-82 p Ldr; Bethlehem Tomboys 1987-91, Dir; Troy Boys & Girls club 5-, Dir; *office:* Emma Willard Children's Schl 285 Pawling Ave Troy 12180*

SH, LINDA HOGERHUIS, HS Family & Consumer Sci Tchr; *b:* aic, NJ; *m:* William Bruce; *c:* Kristy, Nathan; *ed:* Montclair St Univ Home Ec Ed 1969; Master Equivelency Issued by St of PA; 36 Grad dits; *cr:* OK St Univ Rsrch Asst 1969-70; Glen Rock HS Adult Schl 1972-74; BOCES of NY Adult Schl Tchr 1975-77; Easton Area Schl Family & Consumer Sci Tchr 1979-; *ai:* Teen Parenting Task Force; ily & Consumer Sci Tech Prep Curr, Grad & Mid Sts Accreditation uation Comms; NEA 1979-; PSEA 1979-; Celtic Classic, Comm Mem; *e:* Easton Area HS 2601 William Penn Hwy Easton PA 18045

SH, NANCY HATTER, Ret Lang Arts & Lit Teacher; *b:* New nswick, NJ; *m:* Donald; *c:* Kevin, Shannon Hirsch; *ed:* Trenton St Coll) Eng, Lib Sci 1958; *cr:* Linwood Jr HS Tchr 1958-60; Jonas Salk MS r, Lang Arts Coord 1969-94; *home:* 58 Colfax St South River NJ 08882

BACHER, DAVID E., Principal; *b:* Pittsburgh, PA; *m:* Katharine Lou ner; *c:* Jennifer, Scott, Rebella; *ed:* Edingoro Univ (BS) Elem Ed 1973; uesne Univ (MS) Admin 1978; Attnd Carlow Coll, Univ of Pittsburgh, Univ of PA, Clarion Univ, Slippery Rock Univ, The Principals Acad of stern PA; *cr:* Wilson Street Schl Tchr 1973-86; Burchfield Schl Tchr 6-91; Reserve Schl Prin 1991; Marzolf Schl Prin 1991-95; ESPE Schl 1995-; *ai:* Specialist for Sci; IM; Ecology Club; Conflict Resolvotion n Comm Chair; Gifted Advy Comm Elem Rep; NAESS, PAESSP 2-; NSTA, PSTA 1988-; PA Schl Bds Assn 1991-; Edinboro Univ mni Assn 1973-, Sec, VP, Pres; BSA 1988-, Cubmaster, Distngd Svc d; Distngd Prin Awd; The Principals Acad of Western PA United Way npaign Chair 3 Yrs; *office:* ESPE Schl 8711 Old Perry Hwy Pittsburgh 15237

ONS, FAITH EISENHUTH, Lead & Home Economics Teacher; *b:* San onio, TX; *m:* John Joseph; *c:* Daniel, Leslie; *ed:* Univ of DE (BS) Home Ed 1973; Immaculata Penn St 24 Credit Hrs; *cr:* Haverford Jr HS Home Tchr 1973-84, Field Hockey & Lacrosse Coach 1973-84, Asst Ath Dir 9-82; Haverford HS Home Ec Tchr 1984-, Lead Tchr 1994-; *ai:* Stu sistance Pgm; Strategic Planning Comm Haverford Schl Dist; Steering Curr Comms; NEA 1973-; PSEA 1973-; HTEA 1982-; Westgate Hills ic Assn 1982-; Hilltop Swim Club 1989-, Bd of Dir; Haverford Alumni ant; Clothing Construction Classes Make Quilts for HIV Babies & Infants in Long Term Care Situations in Nearby Hosps; *office:* Haverford HS 200 Mill Rd Havertown PA 19083

IRONS, JAMES C., Social Studies Teacher; *b:* Monaca, PA; *m:* Joanne Armstrong; *c:* James, Julie Leo; *ed:* Geneva Coll (BS) Soc Stud 1963; Univ of Dayton (MS) Admin Sec, Elem 1986; Attnd PA St, Western CO St; *cr:* Norwalk HS Tchr 1963-65; Western Reserve HS Tchr 1965-69; Freedom Area HS Tchr 1969-79; East Liverpool HS Tchr 1979-; *ai:* Sr Washington DC Trip, Sr Spring Trip Spon, Chaparone; Jr Achvmt Adv; Discipline, Soc Stud Comms; NEA 1963-; OEA 1963-67, 1979-; PSEA 1969-79; Beaver Hall of Fame Com 1995-, Bd Mem; YMCA, Bd Mem; First Presbyn Church of Monaca 1969-, Deacom, Elder, Session, Youth Dir; Beaver Cty Hall of Fame 1992; *office:* East Liverpool HS 100 Maine Blvd East Liverpool OH 43920

IRVIN, E. DIANE, Health & PE Teacher; *b:* Waynesboro, PA; *m:* Harry James Jr.; *c:* Aileen; *ed:* East Stroudsburg Univ (BS) Hlth & PE 1970; Masters Equivalency; Addl Post Grad Credit Hrs; *cr:* Parkland Schl Dist Springhouse Jr HS Hlth & PE Tchr 1970-75; Gateway Schl Hlth & PE Tchr 1980-84; Saucon Valley HS Hlth & PE Tchr 1984-; *ai:* Grad Awds Comm; Prins Advy Cncl; Stu Assistance Prgm; Saucon Valley Ed Assn 1984-, Pres; PA St Ed Assn 1970-; NEA; Pub Article; *office:* Saucon Valley HS 2100 Polk Valley Rd Hellertown PA 18055

IRVINE, CAROLE WALTER, 4th Grade Teacher; *b:* Pittsburgh, PA; *m:* John B. II; *c:* John B. III, Jeffrey W.; *ed:* West Liberty St Coll (BS) Dental Hygiene 1963; The Johns Hopkins Univ (MS) Admin & Supervision in Ed 1976; West Liberty St Coll DH Cert Dental Hygiene 1959; *cr:* Springfield Local Bd of Ed 2nd Grd Tchr 1960-61; Jefferson Union Bd of Ed 1st Grd Tchr 1961 & 1962-64; Steubenville City Bd of Ed 1st & 2nd Grd Tchr 1964-69; Anne Arundel Cty Pub Schls 1st, 2nd & 4th Grd Tchr 1969-; Anne Arundel Cty HS Adult Ed Tchr 1969-; *ai:* Differentiated Staffing Comm Anne Arundel Co; 10 Yr Plan for Educl Excl Comm 1980-90; Spon Co Tchr for ATF; OH Ed Assn 1960-69; NEA 1960-, Natl Del; Anne Arundel Co Tchrs Assn 1969-, Bd of Dir 1994-96; MD St Tchrs Assn 1969-; Phi Delta Kappa 1980-; Auxiliary Anne Arundel Gen Hosp, Pink Lady Ball Chm & Co Chm 1991-93; AACPS Pub; *office:* Bodkin Elem Schl 8320 Ventnor Rd Pasadena MD 21122

IRVINE, MARION HACKMAN, Retired Sixth Grade Teacher; *b:* Abington, PA; *m:* Richard Dale; *c:* Richard, Robert; *ed:* Penn Hall Jr Coll (AA) 1953; Goucher Coll (BA) Soc, Anthrop Minor Psych 1955; 24 Credits Post Grad Work Glassboro St Coll Ed Courses; *cr:* Zane North Elem Schl 5th-6th Grd Tchr 1969-94; *ai:* Past Safety Patrol Adv 13 Yrs; Ran Schls Geog Bee; Collingswood Ed Assn 1970-, Sec, Bldg Rep, Tchr of Yr; NJ Ed Assn 1970-, Cty Rep; NEA 1970-, Del to 2 Conventions; NJ Retired Ed Assn 1994-, VP of Cty Assn; Camden Cty Retired Ed Assn 1994-; Camden Ed Assn 1970-, Pub Relations Chair, Pride Chair; Delta Kappa Gamma Intnl, Legislative Chair for St Chptr; Tch Sunday Schl; Sing in Choir; Tchr of Yr 1990; *home:* 240 Buckner Ave Haddonfield NJ 08033

IRWIN, ADRIENNE TOTH, Teacher of Gifted & Talented; *b:* Pittsburgh, PA; *m:* Christopher L.; *c:* Gregory, Jeffrey; *ed:* Indiana Univ of PA (BS) Ed 1973; Duquesne Univ (MA) Eng 1978; Carnegie-Mellon Univ Cmptr Aids in Writing Classroom 1985; OK St Univ, Aerospace Ed 1994; *cr:* Woodlawn MS Eng Tchr 1973-82; Steel Valley HS Tchr of Gifted & Talented 1982-; Woodlawn MS Math Tchr 1988; *ai:* Mock Trial Team & Acad Bowl Team Spon; Project STAR Coord; Mr Wizard-Ms Wiz Sci Demonstrations; Host of Creative Convention; Tech Planning Comm Mem; PA Assn for Gifted Ed 1982-; Steel Valley Ed Assn 1973-, Sec; PSEA & NEA 1973-; E Allegheny PTA 1989-; Interboro Coll Club 1977-, Past Pres; Carnegie Sci Ctr 1991-, Ed Ambassador; Steel Valley Tchr of Yr 1989; Semi-Finalist PA Tchr of Yr 1990; Finalist "Thanks to Tchrs" 1990; Recipient of 5 Great Idea Grants From Mon Valley Ed Consortium; Conducted Wrkshps for PA Dept of Ed Bureau of Curr & Univ of Pittsburg Inst for Practice & Research in Ed; NASA Ed Wkshp, Goddard Space Flight Ctr 1994; *office:* Steel Valley HS 3113 Main St Munhall PA 15120*

IRWIN, ELMO, English Teacher & Dept Chm; *b:* Curwensville, PA; *m:* Carolyn Eshelman; *c:* John T., Christopher J.; *ed:* Lock Haven Univ (BS) Eng 1969; Penn St Univ (MA) Ed 1990; Addl 9 Credits Carlow Coll, 6 Credits Ganna Univ; *cr:* Clearfield Jr HS Eng Tchr 1969-70; Curwensville HS Eng Tchr 1970-; Curwensville Area HS Eng Dept Chm 1992-; *ai:* SAT Preparatory Activity Spon; Core Team for Stdnts Assistance Prof; Past Asst Ftbl Coach; Judo Instr Intramurals 3 Yrs; NEA, PSEA, CEA 1969-; PA Assn of Stdnt Assistance Profs; Little League 17 Yrs; Cub Scouts, Weblo Scouts 4 Yrs Svc; Tchr of Yr 1986; *home:* 442 Scofield St Curwensville PA 16833*

IRWIN, JAMES ROBERT, Elem PE Teacher; *b:* New Kensington, PA; *m:* Elizabeth Anna Subasic; *c:* Brian Joseph, Stephanie Elizabeth; *ed:* Slippery Rock Univ (BS) Hlth & PE 1969; Univ of Pittsburgh (MED) PE 1973; Track & Field Coaching Cert; *cr:* IN Area Schl Dist Elem PE Tchr, Cross Country & Track Coach 1969-; IUP Cooperating Tchr for PE Stu Tchrs 1974-; *ai:* Coach Cross Country & Track 27 Yrs; PSEA 1969-; IAEA 1969; NEA 1970; Lions Club 1990-; *office:* East Pike Elem Schl 501 E Pike Indiana PA 15701*

IRWIN, JOHN JAY, Physics Teacher; *b:* Mc Donald, PA; *m:* Susan K. Mc Givern; *ed:* Grove City Coll (BS) Physics 1975; Univ of Pittsburgh (MED) Sci Ed 1976; *cr:* Waynesboro Area Schl Dist Physics Instr 1976-80; CCAC Evening Division Part-time Physics Instr 1983-86; Upper St Clair Schl Dist Physics Instr 1980-; *ai:* AFT, PAFT, USCEA 1980-; Physics Alliance, PSTA 1990-; *office:* Upper Saint Clair HS 1825 Mc Laughlin Run Rd Pittsburgh PA 15241

IRWIN, REBECCA SUIT, Second Grade Teacher; *b:* Leonardtown, MD; *m:* Robert Wayne; *c:* Katie Lind, Brett Wayne; *ed:* Charles Cty Comm Coll (AA) Gen Stud 1979; Frostburg St Coll (BS) Early Chldhd Ed 1981; Advanced Prof Cert; *cr:* Dr G. Brown Elem Schl First, Second Grd Tchr 1981-; *ai:* Team Ldr; Tchr Assistance, Site Mgmnt Teams; *office:* Dr Gustavus Brown Elem Schl University Dr Waldorf MD 20602

ISA, GENEVA A. COOPER, Science Resource Teacher; *b:* Kingstree, SC; *ed:* Voorhees Coll (BA) Soc Stud 1973; Univ DC (MA) Admin, Supervision, Elem Ed 1986; Trinity Coll at WA DC 40 Hrs Grad Credits; Cal-Tech at Pasadena 8 Hrs Grad Credits; George WA Univ 6 Hrs Grad Credits; DC Law Schl 12 Hrs 1980; *cr:* Rosemary MS Elem Tchr 1974; Parkview MS Adult Ed Tchr 1975; Dillard HS Soc Stud Tchr 1975; Southeastern Univ Asst Registrar 1976-77; C&P Telephone Co Operator 1978-80; DC Pub Schl Sci Res Tchr 1983-; *ai:* After Schl Sci Fair Prgm; Young Astronauts; Energy Patrol; Tutor; AFT 1985-; DC Sci Ed Assn 1985-, Chprsn of Mbrshp; NSTA 1987-; Delta Sigma Theta 1974-; Big Sis of WA 1978-, Recruiter Person, Sisters of Yr 1980; NAACP 1969-, Section Coll, Rep St Convention; Chrstn Interreligious concerns 1994-, Co-Chprsn; Asbury United Meth Church; Lay Speaker, Young Adult Cncl, Voices of Praise Choir, Women Group, Children's Ministry, Outreach Ctr; 1994 Tchr to Tchr Awd; 1993 Outstdng Tchr; Applied to Fulbright Tchr Exchange Prgm; Mc Gill Univ 1993; *office:* Benjamin Orr Elem Schl 22nd St & Minn Ave SE Washington DC 20020*

ISAAC, PATRICIA, Art Teacher; *b:* Boston, MA; *m:* Donald Tileston; *c:* Cheryl Isaac Murphy, Diana Isaac Johnson, Deborah Isaac Blair; *ed:* MA Coll of Art (BFA) Drawing & Painting 1954; Bridgewater St Coll Tchng Cert Art Ed 1970; 32 Credit Hrs Beyond BA Art Inst of Boston, MA Coll of Art; *cr:* Rockland Pub Schls Elem Art Tchr 1968-79, Jr High Art Tchr 1979-82, HS Art Tchr 1982-, Art Dir 1983-; *ai:* Goals & Objectives Comm for Ed Reform; Scenery Adv to Drama Club; Schl Cncl for HS Curr Frameworks; MTA, NEA 1968-; MA Dir of Art Ed 1984-; MA Alliance for the Arts 1992-; Southeastern Philharmonic Orch 1975-, Pres; So. Shore Art Ctr 1986-; No. River Arts Soc 1987-; Outstanding MA Art Educator 1986; Horace Mann Grant for Curr 1988; Awds for Own Work in Local Shows; *office:* Rockland HS Godard Ave Rockland MA 02370*

ISAACS, MELVIN A., Principal; *b:* New York City, NY; *m:* Goldie Stern; *c:* Susan Winton, Joseph, Bonnie; *ed:* Brooklyn Coll (BA) Elem Ed 1961, (MS) Elem Ed 1967; Yeshiva Univ (EDD) Schl Admin 1991; Hofstra Univ Educl Admin 1978; *cr:* PS 169 Brooklyn Elem Tchr 1961-68; Merrick Schl Dist Elem Tchr 1968-81; Cong Ohar Sholom Religious Schl Prin 1974-; Merrick Schl Dist Coord, Instr Gifted Prgm 1981-94; Hebrew Acad Prin; *ai:* Dist Wide Testing 1992-, Chm Dist Report Card 1973 Comms; Fac Cncl; Speaker Numerous PTA & Septa Prgms; Inservice Staff Tchng Gifted 1-; NYSUT 1961-; Educators Cncl Amer 1979-, Treas, VP, Pres; ASCD 1992-; AGATE 1981-; Hebrew Acad Nassau Cty 1967-, Bd of Ed, Achvmt Awd; Merrick PTA 1968-, Life Membership; Natl Cncl Synagogue Youth 1976-, Achvmt Awd; Pub Article Pedagogic Reporter 1980, 1990; Presenter NYS Agate Conventions 1986, 1988, 1991, CEC Convention 1990; Chm ECA Conventions 1984, 1986; *office:* Hebrew Acad Nassau Cty 25 Country Dr Plainview NY 11803

ISAACSON, ELAINE SCHULMAN, String Instrumental Music Tchr; *b:* New Brunswick, NJ; *m:* Harold; *c:* David, Mark; *ed:* Douglass Coll (BA) Music Ed 1960; *cr:* Highland Park Schls Vocal, Gen Music Tchr 1960-61; Baltimore Cty Schls Vocal, Gen Music Tchr 1961-62; West Hempstead Jr, Sr HS Instrumental Music Tchr 1962-65; Tomes River Schls Instrumental Music Tchr 1976-; *ai:* All-Schl Orch Dir; NEA, NJEA, MENC, Amer String Tchrs Assn 1978-; Silver Bay Schl Tchr of Yr.

ISAACSON, MATTHEW OKE, Sixth Grade Teacher; *b:* Jamestown, NY; *ed:* St Univ Coll at NY at Brockport (BS) Elem Ed 1976; St Univ Coll of NY at Fredonia 30 Grad Hrs; *cr:* Jamestown Pub Schls Headstart Aide 1975, 4th Grd Tchr 1977; Bemus Point Elem Schl 5th Grd Tchr 1977-80, 6th Grd Tchr 1980-; *ai:* Play Dir; Elem Schl Enhancement Team; NEA, NYEA & Bemus Point Fac Assn 1977-; Town of Ellery Youth Recreation Prgm Commissioner 1988-; Bemus Point Pub Lib Trustee 1987- Pres 1989-95; Honorary Life Mem of PTA; WJTN Rado Apples for Tchr Awd 1987; Recognized as Spec Tchr with Educl Impact by SUC; Fredonia Pres Donald Macphee 1991 & 1992; *office:* Bemus Point Elem Liberty St Bemus Point NY 14712

ISABELLA, BOBBE WHITEMAN, Acctng & Computing Sr Instr; *b:* Warren, OH; *m:* Gary L.; *c:* Brian J. Bitler, Christy M. Bitler; *ed:* Kent St Univ (BS) Bus Ed 1990; Ashland Univ MS Ed & Curr 1996; Attnd Columbus Bus Univ; *cr:* Adia Temporary Svc Mgr & Coord 1971-81; Trumbull Cty JVS Acctng & Computing Instr 1983-; *ai:* Bus Profs of Amer Chptr & Bus Profs of Amer Acctng Class Adv; NEA, OEA & TCJVTA 1983-; Yth Ldrshp Cncl Adv of Yr 1991-94; *office:* Trumbull County Joint Voc Schl 528 Educational Hwy NW Warren OH 44483

ISABELLE, LINDA LEE (BELL), Health & Human Services Instr; *b:* Winchester, MA; *m:* Scott D.; *c:* Amy; *ed:* St Anselm Coll (BSN) Nrsng 1982; Keene St Coll Alt IV Cert 1995; *cr:* Beth Israel Hosp Clinical Nurse II 1982-84; Nashua Meml Hosp Dir Comm Ed, Charge Nurse 1984-93; Nashua Schl Dist Hlth Occ Instr 1993-94; Gov. Wentworth Regnl Schl Dist Hlth, Human Svcs Instr 1994-; *ai:* Hlth Occupations Stdnts of Amer Adv; Instrl Practices Task Force; Signa Theta Tau 1982-, Pres; NHNA, NAACOG 1984-; NHVTA, NEA 1994-; YWCA Bd of Dirs 1991-94, VP; Nurse of Month 1993; Outstdng Hlth Occupations Stdnts of Amer Adv 1995; *home:* 41 Pleasant St Wolfeboro NH 03894

ISAKS, MARTIN, Assoc Professor of Chemistry; *b:* Riga, Latvia; *m:* Ruth E. Tanner; *ed:* Purdue Univ (BS) Chem 1957, IA St Univ (MS) Organic Chem 1960; Univ of Cincinnati (PHD) Organic Chem 1963; *cr:* Georgia Inst of Tech Rsrch Assoc 1963-64; Brown Univ Post Doctoral Rschr Fellow 1964-65; Univ of MA at Lowell Asst Prof 1965, Assoc Prof 1970-; *ai:* Fac Advs Amer Chem Soc Stud Affiliate, Sports Car Club; Chem Dept, Coll of Sci & Hum Comms; Amer Chem Soc 1955-; The Royal Soc of Chem 1959-; Amer Assoc of Univ Profs, New England Assn Chem Tchr 1967-; Many Publications; *office:* Univ Of MA At Lowell Dept of Chemistry 1 University Ave Lowell MA 01854

ISALY, FRAN HEDGPETH, Second Grade Teacher; *b:* New River, NC; *m:* Charles William; *c:* Britt, Russell; *ed:* Miami Univ (BS) Ed 1966; Attnd Northwestern Univ 1962-64; *cr:* Fairfax Cty Schls Third Grd Tchr 1966-67; Churchill Area Schls Fourth Grd Tchr 1967-69; Forest Hills Schl Dist Second Grd Tchr 1984-; *ai:* FHTA, OEA, NEA 1984-; Jr League of Cincinnati 1981-; Mt Washington Presbyn Church, Elder; *office:* Maddux Elem Schl 943 Rosetree Ln Cincinnati OH 45230

ISENBERG, ANNETTE JANICE BIEBER, Spanish Teacher; *b:* Chicopee Falls, MA; *m:* Edward A.; *ed:* Lycoming Coll (BA) Span Ed 1992; Attnd Bucknell Univ Pursuing MS Instructional Specialist; *cr:* Berwick HS Span Tchr 1993-; *ai:* Span Club Co-Adv; Phi Sigma Lota 1991-; AATSP 1994-; *office:* Berwick Area HS 1100 Fowler Ave Berwick PA 18603

ISIDOR, JULIA NAWROCKI, Theology & Ethics Teacher; *b:* Fall River, MA; *m:* John L.; *c:* John, Daniel, Edward, David, Katherine; *ed:* Emmanuel Coll (BA) Ed, Sociology 1967; Univ of NC at Chapel Hill (MED) Ed, Sociology 1970; *cr:* Fall River Pub Schls 5th Grd Tchr 1967-68; Orange Cty Pub Schls 4th-5th Grd Tchr 1969-70; Seton Hall Univ Adjunct Child Psych Prof 1979-80; Archdiocese of Newark Family Life Ministries Assoc Dir 1979-85; Lacordaire Acad Theology, Ethics Tchr 1985-; *ai:* Liturgy, Retreat Coord; Family Life Wkshps Speaker; *office:* Lacodaire Acad 155 Lorraine Ave Montclair NJ 07043

ISLAM, M. MAHABUB-UL, Assoc Professor of Economics; *b:* Khulna, Bangladesh; *m:* Farhana; *c:* Illiyuna, Sameen; *ed:* Jahangirnagar Univ (BS) Ec 1980, (MS) Ec 1981; Northeastern Univ (MA) Ec 1987, (PHD) Ec 1989; *cr:* Chittagong Univ Lecturer 1981-82; Northeastern Univ Lecturer 1986-88; Univ of RI Lecturer 1988-90; St Francis Coll Asst Prof 1990-94, Assoc Prof 1994-; *ai:* Ec Adv Bangladesh Dev Initative; Amer Ec Assn 1982-; Pub Several Articles; *office:* Saint Francis Coll Loretto PA 15940

ISLER, WILLIAM CONRAD, 7th Grade Science Teacher; *b:* Warren, OH; *m:* Ruth Ann Mizner; *c:* William P., Gregory C.; *ed:* Hiram Coll (BA) PE & Physical Sci 1963; Kent St (MED) Counseling; Attnd Cornell Coll at IA 5 Hrs, John Carroll 8 Hrs & Southwestern OK St Univ 6 Hrs; *cr:* Twinsburg Schls 9th-12th Grds Phys Sci Tchr 1963-68; Hudson Schls 7th Grd Sci Tchr 1968-; *ai:* OEA & NEA 1980-; 2 NSF Grants; 1 NEH Grant; Oh Ed Assn Ideal Classroom task Force 1990; *office:* Hudson MS 120 N Hayden Pkwy Hudson OH 44236

ISLES, CHERYL A., Biology Teacher; *b:* Schenectady, NY; *m:* Peter J. Braun; *ed:* St Univ of NY at Albany (BS) Bio 1977, (MS) Bio 1980, (PHD) Bio 1984; Siena Coll Tchr Cert Prgm; *cr:* Univ of Albany Bio Dept Tchng Asst 1978-80, Bio Dept Rsrch Asst 1980-83; Cohoes HS Sci Tchr 1986-; *ai:* Sci Club Adv; NHS Selection Fac Cncl; Bldg Ldrshp Team Chprsn; Sci Tchrs Assn of NY St; NSTA; NABT; Numerous Articles Pub; Greater Capital Region Tchr Ctr Grant Molecular Bio for Tchrs Grant; Scholars Recognition Pgm 3 Times; *office:* Cohoes HS 1 Tiger Cir Cohoes NY 12047

ISMAIL, ZAFAR A., Professor of Physics; *b:* Keymore, India; *m:* Syeda F. Zafar; *c:* Atif Zafar, Khurram Zafar, Faiza Zafar, Mona Zafar; *ed:* Panjab

Univ at Pakistan (MSc) Physics 1952, (MA) Math 1954; Cambridge Univ UK (BA) Physics-Honors 1958; Oxford Univ UK (DPhil) Nuclear Physics 1964; Degree of Masters Awarded by Cambridge Univ UK in Lieu of Honors Degree 1961; *cr:* SIND Univ of Pakistan Lecturer to Prof 1958-71; Tripoli Univ at Libya Physics Prof 1971-82; Daemen Coll Physics Prof 1983-; *ai:* Sci First Tech Adv; Inst of Physics 1965-; Amer Phys Soc 1985-; Amer Assn of Physics Tchrs; The NY Acad of Sci; Smithsonian Inst; Coll Pres Awd of Outstanding Fac 1995; Books Motion Theory & Experiments Printed by McGraw Hill for the Co Sci First; Dev a Microprocessor Controlled Electronic Timer For Coll & Schl Stdnts With Sci First Co; *office:* Daemen Coll 4380 Main St Amherst NY 14226

ISNER, KARIN KRAULAND, Mathematics Teacher; *b:* Queens, NY; *m:* Robert Sr.; *c:* Robert Jr., Erika Marie; *ed:* Univ of CT (BS) Math, Ed 1985; Wesleyan (MALS) Math 1992; *cr:* Southington HS Math Tchr 1985-; *ai:* Math Team Coach 1985-93; Class of 89, 93 Adv; NCTM 1985-; SEA; CEA; Kappa Kappa Gamma 1985-.*

ISRAEL, DONALD KIRK, Head Wrestling Coach; *b:* Ames, IA; *m:* Karen Elizabeth; *c:* Bjorn J., Jessica Marie; *ed:* Univ of NE at Omaha Architectural Engrng 21 Credit Hrs; Mgmt, Basic & Sports First Aid, Wrestling, Coaching, Motivational Clinics for Further Stud; *cr:* US Army 54th Engrs 1977-81; VT Dept of L&I-Fire Prevention Fire Inspector 1987-89, Regnl Mgr 1989-; *ai:* Ath Booster Club Pub Relations Rep; Parent-Comm Group; NFPA 1987-; USA-Wrestling 1989-, Registered Coach, Prof; VT Wrestling Assoc 1994-, Area Chptr Pres; Ministry Team 1995-; VT Haz-Mat Team 1996; NE Emergency Mgmt Team 1996; *office:* Otter Vly Union HS Rt 7 S Box 1115 Brandon VT 05733

ISRAEL, RICHARD WILLIAM, 7th Grade Social Studies Tchr; *b:* Hazleton, PA; *m:* Sherry Smith; *c:* Craig, Marc, Todd; *ed:* Moravian Coll (BA) Scndry Ed, Soc Stud 1978; Post Grad 24 Credit Hrs Kutztown St Univ; *cr:* Nazareth Area Schl Dist 7th Grd Soc Stud Tchr 1979-; *ai:* Just Ret from 17 Yrs of Coaching Var, JV Ftbl, Wrestling; NEA 1979-; *home:* 1957 Kingsley Dr Bethlehem PA 18018*

ISSA, JOSEPH G., Fifth Grade Teacher; *b:* Brockton, MA; *m:* Marcia M.; *c:* Sarah E.; *ed:* Stonehill Coll (BS) Acctng 1972; Bridgewater St Coll (MS) Schl Admin 1981; *cr:* George S Paine Schl 5th-6th Grd Tchr 1973-74; St Colmans Schl 6th Grd Tchr 1974-81; Keith Schl 4th-5th Grd Tchr 1981-83; Oscar F Raymond Schl 5th Grd Tchr 1983-93; Winthrop Schl 5th Grd Tchr 1993-; *ai:* Brockton Ed Assn 1973-; MA Tchrs Assn 1973-; NEA 1973-.

ISSEKS, FRED, English Teacher; *b:* Middletown, NY; *m:* Denise Shelby; *c:* Sodie; *ed:* SUNY at Albany (BA) Eng 1970, (MA) Eng 1975; New Schl for Soc Rsrch (MA) Media Stud 1994; Tchng Cert SUNY at New Paltz 1975; *cr:* Middletown HS Tchr 1976-; Long Island Univ Adj Prof 1990-93; NYIT Adj Prof 1994-; *ai:* Environmental Club Adv; Worked with Stdnts Produce Investigative Documentaries Solid Waste Issues; Documentary Work Written UP Columbia Jrnlsm Review, NY Times, Village Voice; *home:* 17 Rockwell Ave Middletown NY 10940

ISSELMANN, M. CARROLL,IHM, Undergraduate Academic Dean; *b:* Harrisburg, PA; *ed:* Immaculata Coll (BS) Home Ec Ed 1972; Drexel Univ (MS) Nutrition & Human Behavior 1979; Rutgers St Univ (EDD) Sci & Hum 1982; *cr:* Imaculata Coll Prof, Nutrition Ed 1988-, Dept Fashion, Foods, Nitrition Chair 1988-90, Grad Div Nutrition Ed Chair 1993-, Undergrad Acad Dean 1996-; *ai:* Amer Dietetic Assn Site Visitor; ADA Review Panel for Approval of Preprofessional Practice Prgms; Presbyn Hosp Geriatric Initiative Steering Comm; DE Vly Chptr Soc for Nutrition Ed 1982-, Bd of Dir, Pres, Treas; Philadelphia Dietetic Assn 1981-, Bd of Dir; PA Dietetic Assn 1981-, Outstdng Dietetics Edctr; Amer Dietetic Assn 1981-, Outstdng Dietetics Edctr; Presbyn Med Ctr 1993-, Steering Comm; Alumni Schlsp & Grad Assistantship Rutgers St Univ; Article Pub Journal of Amer Dietetic Assn 1993; Poster Session Abstracts NJ Dietetic Assn & PA Dietetic Assn; Nutrition Ed Grants; *office:* Immaculata Coll PO Box 662 Immaculata PA 19345

ITALIANO, DONA, Language Arts Teacher & Coord; *b:* Jersey City, NJ; *m:* Anthony; *c:* Frank, Anthony Jr.; *ed:* St Peters Coll (BA) Eng 1975; Beaver Coll (MA) Eng 1991; Fellow of PA Writing Proj; Addl 15 Post Grad Credits; *ai:* Newspaper, Lit Magazine Adv; HS Cabinet; Curr, Assessment Comm Strategic Planning; SAEA, PSEA, NEA, NCTE 1986-; PA Dept of Ed Comm Design Team; *office:* Souderton Area HS 41 N School Ln Souderton PA 18964*

ITO, KEITHA SUE (SNODGRASS), Latin Teacher; *b:* El Dorado, AR; *m:* Max Akira; *c:* Laura, Mari, Jamie; *ed:* Univ of OK (BA) Latin 1976, (MA) Latin 1978; 15 Hrs Eng KS St Univ; 12 Hrs Undergrad Math Auston Comm Coll; *cr:* Univ of OK Grad Tchng Asst Classics 1976-78; KS St Univ Grad Tchng Asst Eng 1979-80, Med Terminology Instr 1980; Aiea Comm Schl for Adults ESOL Tchr 1990-91; HI Pacific Univ Ad Hoc Instr, Bus Eng Tchr 1991; Hyd Pk Bapt HS Latin, Eng Tchr 1991-94; Montgomery Cty Pub Schl Latin Tchr 1995-; Walter Johnson HS Latin Tchr; *ai:* Latin Club Spon; Amer Classical League 1992-; Protestant Women of Chapel 1984-90, Pres 1987-89; PTA 1986-, Treas 1989-90; *office:* Sherwood HS 300 Olney Sandy Spring Rd Sandy Spring MD 20860

ITTERLY, G. FREDERICK,JR., School Counselor; *b:* Nazareth, PA; *m:* Kathleen Claire; *c:* Itterly; *ed:* Lafayette Coll (AB) Psych 1972-; U of UT (MED) Educl Psych 1978; U of MA (CAGS) Cnslng 1992; Licensed Mental Hlth Cnslr Commonwealth of Massachusetts; *cr:* Northampton HS Schl Cnslr 1989-; Job Corps Administator1976-89; Westover Job Corps; *ai:* JV Girls Bsktbl Coach 1989-; MA Schl Cnslrs Assn, New England Assn of Coll Adm Cnslrs 1989-; Northampton Chptr Dollars for Scholars 1989-, Bd of Dir; *office:* Northampton HS 380 Elm St Northampton MA 01060

ITZKOWITZ, LEONARD M., Science Teacher; *b:* Brooklyn, NY; *m:* Linda Sandman; *c:* Eve, Hope; *ed:* Brooklyn Coll (BS) Chem 1968; Stanford Univ (MS) Chem 1969; Colby Coll (MS) Physics 1976; *cr:* Elmont Mem HS Sci Tchr 1969-76; New Hyde Park Mem HS Sci Tchr 1976-79; H. Frank Carey HS Sci Tchr 1980-; Nassau Comm Coll Adjunct Chem Prof 1990-; *ai:* NSF Grants; Pub Article J Phys Chem; Co-Authored Curr Guides, Lab Manual.*

IVANCIC, KARITA, Vocal Music & Religion Teacher; *b:* Cleveland, OH; *ed:* Notre Dame Coll of OH (BA) Music, Ger 1971; IN Univ (MME) Music Ed 1981; Akron Univ Vocal Pedagogy Grad Work; Purdue Univ NEH Grant Ger Grad Work; Cleveland Music Schl Settlement Music Composition; *cr:* Regina HS Religion Tchr, Music Dept Chair, Choral Dir 1971-73; Notre Dame Coll Elem Tchrs Music Fundamentals Summer Instr 1971-73; Notre Dame Acad Notre Dame Cathedral Latin Schl Religion, Ger, Choral Tchr, Music Dept Chair 1973-90; Lorain Cath HS Religion, Ger, Choir Tchr 1990-95; *ai:* Dir of Various Vocal Ensembles; ACDA 1981-90; AATG 1980-90; Natl Pastoral Musicians 1978-90; MENC, OMEA 1994-; Liturgical Music Composition Natl, Local Awds; NEH Ger Grant Awd 1985-86; Pub Music Compositions; Cleveland Diocese 20 Yr Tchng Svc Awd; Appointed Music Coord Sisters of Notre Dame Natl, Intnl Congress; Translator Intnl Congress; *office:* Notre Dame Cathedral Schl 760 Tower Blvd Lorain OH 44052*

IVASKA, DALIA SKUDZINSKAITE, Chemistry Teacher; *b:* Alytus, Lithuania; *m:* Raymond D.; *c:* Nijole, Darius, Ramunas, Dalia Marija; *ed:* Newton Coll (AB) Chem 1955; Boston Coll Univ (MED) Ed 1967; Worcester Polytechnic Inst (NMS) Physics, Chem 1978; MIT Pre-Coll Tchrs Sci, Engrng Prgm 1990; Boston Univ Sci Fellow 1984; *cr:* Lithuanian Schl Lithuanian Lang Tchr 1955-66; Hyde Park HS Chem Tchr 1966-72; Boston Latin Schl Chem Tchr 1972-; Wellesley Coll Assoc in Ed Tchr 1988-93; *ai:* NEACT 1969-, N Eastern Section ACS Lyman Newel Awd; NEST 1990-; LAEAA 1978-, Chptr Pres; Amer Astronomical Soc 1989-, Astronomer for Day Awd; Worcester Polytechnic Inst Partial Schlsp for Acad Merit 4 Yrs; *office:* Boston Latin Schl 78 Avenue Louis Pasteur Boston MA 02115

IVERSEN, DORIS MARIE, Choral Director; *b:* Jamaica, NY; *ed:* SUNY at Fredonia (BA) Music & Voice 1972; SUNY at Stony Brook (MA) Hum 1976; 75 Credit Hrs Music; *cr:* Rocky Point Schl Dist Music Tchr 1972-74; Wm Floyd Schl Dist Music Tchr 1974-; *ai:* Select Choir; NYSSMA Solo Preparation; SCMEA 1972-, VP Classroom Music; Wm Floyd Tchr Assn, NYSSMA & MENC 1974-; ACDA; ARS; LIAOSA, Past Pres; Nathaniel Woodhull Schl Tchr of the Yr 1988; *office:* William Floyd Schl Dist 240 Mastic Beach Rd Mastic Beach NY 11951

IVERSEN, NANCY A. (GORMAN), Former HS Biology Teacher; *b:* Newark, NJ; *m:* Robert W.; *c:* Christopher L., Timothy R.; *ed:* Nassau Comm Coll (AA) Lbrl Arts & Scis 1968; Hofstra Univ (BA) Bio 1974; SUNY at Oneonta (MS) Scndry Sci Ed 1979; 60 Addl Hrs Grad Stud in Bio, Prof Ed; Addl Sabattical Stud in Landscape Design & Plant Scis; *cr:* Syosset HS Bio Tchr 1974; Richfield Springs HS Bio, Life Sci Tchr 1974-80; Cooperstown HS Bio Tchr, Dept Chair 1980-; *ai:* NHS Comm; Sci Olympiad Coach; STANYS 1974-; NEA, NSTA 1979-; Access Excl Fellow Genentech 1995; Bio Tchrs Fellow Cornell Inst 1990-94; SEPA Bassett Advy Bd 1990-94; Catskill Area Tchr Ctr Enabling Grants 1980, 1990.*

IVERSON, GREGORY ALLEN, Math & Science Teacher; *b:* Watervliet, MI; *m:* Cheri Ann Rilea; *c:* Carrie Ann, Grant Andrew; *ed:* Grad Tchng Asst Univ of WY PE Classes; 21 Hrs Motor Learning, Water Safety Instr; 18 Hrs Math; *cr:* Voc Rehabilitation 1982-87; Tri-City SDA Schl Head Tchr, 5th-8th Grd Tchr 1987-89; Fredericksburg Jr Acad 5th-8th Grd Tchr 1989-91; Eastern Shore Acad 7th-10th Grd Tchr 1991-; *ai:* Co-Spon Yrbk, Newspaper; Curr Comm; NCTM, MCTM 1993-; Phi Delta Kappa 1994-; Vol Fire Fighter 1986-; NAVI Scuba Diver 1969-; MD Dellow AT&T Sci, Tech Inst 1995; NSA Math Inst Particpant; *office:* Eastern Shore Jr Acad 407 Dudley Corners Rd Sudlersville MD 21668

IVES, KAREN SPANG, Sixth Grade Teacher; *b:* Rochester, NY; *m:* William Roland; *c:* Michael W., James B., Christine K.; *ed:* Nazareth Coll (BA) His, Elem Ed 1982; *cr:* St Matthias 4th Grd Tchr 1963-65; St John 6th Grd Tchr 1965-68; St Ambrose Kndgtn, 1st, 4th Grd Tchr 1968-72; Corpus Christi Schl 1st, 2nd Grd Tchr 1979-83; Christ the King Schl 3rd, 6th Grd Tchr 1983-; *ai:* Math Dept Chprsn; Dismissal Prgm Monitor; Intermediate, Primary Curr Follow Through Coord; NCEA, CSAANYS, WEN, NEA 1990-; Irondequoit Local His 1990-, Schl Coord; Tchr Learning Ctr 1990-, Wkshps Coord; Comm Outreach Curr Integrating Schl & Comm; *office:* Christ the King Schl 445 Kings Hwy S Rochester NY 14617*

IVEY, JESSICA, Physical Education Teacher; *b:* Akron, OH; *ed:* Towson St Univ (MS) Hlth Ed; TN St Univ (BS) Hlth & PE; 24 Credit Hrs Beyond Masters; *cr:* Forest Park HS Tchr 1969-73; Frederick Douglass HS Tchr 1974-84; Baltimore City Coll Tchr 1985-; *ai:* Vllybl & Badminton Coach; Dance Dir; Noble Mystics Club; Previous Bsktbl & Track & Field Coach; MS Co-Chair; Gifted & Talented Pgm Tchr; PE Dept Chair; AFT; Delta Sigma Theta; *office:* Baltimore City Coll HS 3220 The Alameda Baltimore MD 21218*

IVINS, RONALD TRACY, Math & Computer Teacher; *b:* Belvidere, NJ; *m:* Dolores Ann Brodka; *c:* Tracy, Tim, Abby; *ed:* ESU (BS) Math 1961; Sci Fnd Courses; *cr:* West Milford Schl System Math Tchr 1961-62; Blairstown HS Math Tchr 1962-70; North Warren Regnl HS Math Cmptr Tchr 1970-; *ai:* Bsktbl, Photography Coach; Stu Cncl; Jr, Sr Class Adv; NEA, NJEA 1961-, Pres; *office:* North Warren Regional HS Lambert Rd Blairstown NJ 07825

IWAN, THOMAS MICHAEL, Eighth Grd Math & Alg Teacher; *b:* Cleveland, OH; *m:* Marilyn Krakowski; *c:* David, Daniel, Sarah; *ed:* John Carroll (BS) Math 1969; Akron Univ (ME) Admin 1988; 30 Addl Credit Hrs Ashland Univ, John Carroll, Drake, Cleveland St; *cr:* Benedictine HS Math Tchr, Coach 1970-76; Maple Hts Schl 8th Grd Math Tchr, Coach 1981-82; Solon Schl 8th Grd Math Tchr, Coach 1982-; *ai:* Coach Asst Ftbl, Bsktbl, Head Track; IM Dir; SEA, OTAFC 1982-; GCFC 1970-; PTA 1982-; Coach of Yr Conf Track 6 Times, NE OH Track; Asst Coach 4 St Play-off Ftbl Teams; St Track Coach Runner-up; *office:* Solon Schls 33425 Arthur Rd Solon OH 44139*

IWORSLEY, ARTHUR WILLIAM, Physical Education Teacher; *b:* Lawrence, MA; *m:* Katherine Graves; *c:* Joy Katherine, Eric Paul; *ed:* Doane Coll (BA) PE, Ed 1970; Univ of MA at Lowell (MA) Ed 1974; Fitchburg St Post Grad Credit Hrs; *cr:* West Elem Schl PE Tchr 1970-76; Andover HS Boys Track Coach 1974-, Girls Vlybl Coach 1983-; *ai:* Boys, Girls Indoor, Outdoor Trach Coach; NEA 1969-; MA Tchrs Assn, MA Hlth, PE, Dance Assn 1970-; Andover Ed Assn 1970-, Tchr Rep; Vlybl Hall of Fame 1983-, Bd of Dirs; Stone Environmental Schl 1975-85, Bd of Dirs; PE Tchr of Yr 1977; Coach of Yr 1992-93; *home:* 8 Rindge Rd Andover MA 01810*

IYENGAR, MARIA HREBENAK, Fifth Grade Teacher; *b:* Mc Kees Rocks, PA; *m:* Ramesh; *c:* Luke; *ed:* Univ of Pittsburgh (BS) Elem Ed 1982; Duquesne Univ Perm Cert Theology 1984; *cr:* St Peter Schl Elem Tchr 1993-; *ai:* Math-A-Thon Coord; Holy Chldhd Assn Coord; NCEA 1983-; *office:* St Peter Schl 711 W Commons Pittsburgh PA 15212

IYENGAR, SRIDHARAN S., Professor of Chemistry; *b:* Madras City, India; *m:* Lakshmi; *c:* Aneesh; *ed:* Univ of Madras (BS) Chem 1966, (MS) Chem 1968; Univ of CA (PHD) Organic Chem 1974; Johns Hopkins Univ (MS) Cmptr Sci 1985; *cr:* Anne Arundel Comm Coll Chem Prof 1978-; *ai:* Fac Adv; Stu Affiliate Chptr of Amer Chem Soc Advy Bd; Amer Chem Soc 1978; MD Section of ACS 1978-, Chm 1993; Tchng Fac Org 1978-, Pres 1991-92; S. G. Theater Group 1993-, Pres; Quarterfield Farms Homeowners Assn 1995-, Sec; Tchng Excl Awd 1987; Honorable Mention Outstdng Edctr Awd 1993; Short Stories, Two Novels, Articles, Books Pub; Several Plays Written; *office:* Anne Arundel Comm Coll 101 College Pky Arnold MD 21012

IZER, ANASTASIA TEHANSKY, Retired Teacher; *b:* McAdoo, PA; *m:* Robert L.; *c:* Robert B., Barbara Ann Homan; *ed:* East Stroudsburg (BA) Hlth, PE 1940; Attnd Bloomsburg; *home:* 400 High St Milton PA 17847

J

JABARO, JUDITH NIXON, Fourth Grade Teacher; *b:* Bellefonte, Frederick Michael; *ed:* Penn St Univ (BS) Elem Ed 1973; East Strou Univ (MS) Rdng 1979; 42 Grad & Inservice Credits Beyond Maste Barrett Elem Ctr ECIA Title I Spec Rdng 1974; Coolbaugh Elem C Grd Tchr 1974-87; Barrett Elem Ctr 4th Grd Tchr 1987-; *ai:* Soc Stu Revision Comm; Wellness Comm Rep; Jr Field Observers Adv; Poco Ed Assn 1973-, Bldg Rep; NEA, PSEA 1973-; Colonial Northamp Rdng Educators; Food Pantry for Meth Church 1995-; Tang Soo Do 1987-91, Black Belt; Nom by Former Stdnts Gift of Time Tribute Recipient 1994, 1995; *office:* Barrett Elem Ctr Rt 390 Mountainho 18342

JABERS, PRISCILLA SALOME, Second Grade Teacher; *b:* Barre, PA; *ed:* Bloomsburg Univ (BS) Elem Ed 1985, (MED) Rdng *cr:* ST Hedwig's Schl 2nd Grd Tchr 1985-; *ai:* Rdng Coord; M Chprsn; NCEA 1985-; Luzerne Cty Rdng Cncl 1992-; *office:* St He Schl 207 Zerby Ave Wilkes Barre PA 18704

JABLONSKI, CAROL WAWRZYNEK, Mathematics Tchr & Chprsn; *b:* N Tonawanda, NY; *m:* John; *c:* Thomas, Gregory; *ed:* B St Coll (BS) Math 1972, (MS) Math 1975; Addl 27 Hrs Sci, Tech & *cr:* Sweet Home HS Tchr 1972-; *ai:* Dept Chprsn; SHEA, NYSUT *office:* Sweet Home HS 1901 Sweet Home Rd Amherst NY 14228

JABLONSKI, FRANCIS JAMES, Biology & Human Anatomy Tc Framingham, MA; *m:* Joyce M. Avedisian; *ed:* MS St Coll at Framir (BA) Bio 1970; *cr:* Milford HS Bio, Anatomy Tchr 1970-; *ai:* NEA, 1970-; Tchr Awd 1995; Tchr Recognitions Worcester Polytechni 1994, Northeastern Univ 1995, Bowdoin Coll 1993, Simmons Coll *office:* Milford HS 31 W Fountain Milford MA 01757

JABLONSKI, MARIE LORINI, English Teacher; *b:* New York City *m:* Thomas C. J.; *ed:* Rutgers Univ (BA) Eng Ed 1969, (MED) Instruction 1971; 60 Credit Hrs Post Grad Stud EDD in Educl Admin as Supvr & Prin; *cr:* Hillsborough HS Eng Tchr 1969-; *ai:* Middle Sts Comm; NEA, NJEA, Somerset Cty & Hillsborough EAS 1969-; N Presbyn, Princeton Fitness Ctr 1986-; Dir of Publications 197 Articles Pub; *office:* Hillsborough HS Raider Blvd Belle Mead NJ 0

JABLONSKI, MICHAEL JUDE, Social Studies Teacher; *b:* We MA; *ed:* Merrimack Coll (BA) Pol Sci 1989; Fitchburg St Coll (M Working Towards MA in Cnslng Framinghan St Coll; *cr:* St Bernard HS Soc Stud Tchr 1989-; *office:* St Bernards Cntrl Catholic HS 45 Ha St Fitchburg MA 01420

JACK, STEPHEN DOUGLAS, Fifth Grade Teacher; *b:* Portland, M Joyce Elizabeth; *c:* Amy, Kevin; *ed:* Univ of Southern ME (BS) Ed 1972; *cr:* Arundel Schl Grds 5-8 Tchr 1972-74; Sanford MS Grds 5-6 1974-87; No Yarmouth Meml Schl Grds 5-6 Tchr 1987-; *ai:* Stu Assis Team; Sci Task Force; NEA 1987-; *office:* North Yarmouth Memorial 25 Memorial Hwy North Yarmouth ME 04097

JACK, TIMOTHY JAMES, Social Studies Teacher; *b:* Zanesville, *m:* Beth Spicer; *c:* Lauren, Shannon; *ed:* Univ of Akron (BA) Scndr 1981, (MA) Scndry Prin 1984; 20 Post Grad Hrs; *cr:* Highland HS Stud, PE tchr 1983-89; Medina Sr HS Soc Stud 1990-; *ai:* Boys Var Bsktbl 13 Yrs; Run Pitching Clinics Local Yth; OH Ed Assn, NEA 11 2 Most Influential Tchr Spec Letters; *office:* Medina Sr H S 777 E U St Medina OH 44256*

JACKES, KATHLEEN MC COURT, Fourth Grade Teacher; *b:* Nev NJ; *m:* Richard C.; *c:* Richard, Courtney; *ed:* Jersey City St Coll (BA) Ed 1968; 16 Post Grad Credits; *cr:* Lincoln Schl 5th Grd Tchr 1968 Blairstown Elem Schl 4th Grd Tchr 1981-; *ai:* NEA, NJEA, WWC 19 Blairstown Tchr Assn, Sec; Lib Comm 1982-, Childrens Book Selec CCD Tchr 1980-81; 4-H Ldr 1986-90; *office:* Blairstown Elem Sc Sunset Hill Rd Blairstown NJ 07825*

JACKMAN, FRANCES LOUISE, Music Teacher; *b:* Akron, OH; Univ of Akron (BM) Music Ed K-12 1982, (MM) Music Ed K-12 1988 Stow-Munroe Falls City Schls Music Tchr 1984-; *ai:* HS Musical, Con Orch Dir; ATAP Comm; Vol Concerts Nrsng Homes, Libraries; ME Amer String Tchrs Assn 1982-; Akron Feds of Musicians 1980-; 1984-; Orch Parents Group 1994-, Co-Treas; PTA Mini Grant 1996; A Grant 1994; OSTA Mini Grant 1993; Chptr II Grants 1989-92, 1994; *of* Stow-Munroe Falls City Schls 1819 Graham Rd Stow OH 44224

JACKOWICZ, URSEL HAFFER, Teacher; *b:* Freudenstadt, Germ *m:* A. John; *c:* John Andrew, Krista Marie Grose; *ed:* Univ of Akron Elem Ed 1983; Frgn Lang Credits; *cr:* Immaculate Conception 6th Tchr 1966-67; St Adalbert 6th Grd & 7th & 8th Sci 1984-85; Brunswic Adalbert & St Ambrose Sub Tchr 1985-87; St Ambrose 4th & 6th Grd 1987-92; St Ambrose & Brecksville-Broadview Hghts Sub Tchr 1992- PSR Cath Rel 1992-, Tchr; Parma Symphony Orch 1995-, Violin; H Fund 1993-, Vol; *home:* 1695 Cortland Ln Broadview Heights OH 44

JACKSON, AARON CICERO, Director of Bands; *b:* Columbus, OH Lori Anne Slade; *c:* Miranda Elise, Megan Alexandra; *ed:* OH St U (BME) Music Ed 1977; 50 Percent Masters; *cr:* Lancaster Cath S Instrumental Music Dir 1977-78; Crestview Jr HS Dir of Instrumental 1979-80; Columbus East HS Dir of Bands 1980-88; Briggs HS Dir of Ba 1988-; *ai:* Sftbl, Ensemble & Solo Coach; Admin Responsibilities Co OEA, NEA, CEA, MENC, OH Music Ed Assn 1978-; Greater Hilltop Commission 1981-, Chair; St Lands Planning & Facilities Comm; West Kiwanis; OH St Univ Alumni Band TBDBITL 1977-; West HS Alu Band Assn 1978-, Dir 1978-81; Ingram Grant; *office:* Briggs HS 2 Briggs Rd Columbus OH 43223

JACKSON, ANNE MARTIN, Early Learning Skills Teacher; Pittsburgh, PA; *m:* Andrew James Jr.; *c:* Monica Farrell-Adams, Nic Tiffany, Kimberlee, Cheryl Johnson; *ed:* Univ of PA (BA) Elem Ed 19 (MED) Elem Ed; Elem Ed Johnson C. Smith Univ 1958-61; *cr:* Frick E Schl 7-8th Grd Tchr 1974-80; Phillip Murray Elem Schl 5th Grd T 1980-81; Boggs Elem Schl 4th Grd Tchr 1981-82; Phillips Elem S 4th-5th Grd Tchr 1982-85; Brookline Elem Tchrs Ctr Third Grd T 1985-91; Brookline Elem Schl Early Learning Skills Tchr 1991-; *ai:* C Human Resources Co-Chair; Discipline Comm; Eureka Project 19 Co-operative Tchr for Stu Tchrs 1995; PFT 1975-; NAACP; Delta Sig Theta 1960-; Featured on KDKA TV'S Evening Magazine Black Month 1986; Instrl Team Ldrs Cert Team Mem; Monitoring Ach Pittsburgh Project Tchr Trainer 1982; Brookline Tchr Ctr Clin Resident, Dev Demonstration Tchr 1985-91; *office:* Brookline Elem S 500 Woodbourne Ave Pittsburgh PA 15226*

JACKSON, BASIL P., Cmptr Information Systems Prof; *b:* Richmo VA; *m:* Ann Alexander; *c:* Julian Basil; *ed:* VA St Univ (BS) Math 19 George Washington Univ (MBA) Acctng 1978; *cr:* Strayer Coll Cmptr I Systems Prof 1978-; *ai:* Tutor; Assn Cmptr Manufacture Adv; *offi* Strayer Coll 6830 Laurel Ave NW Washington DC 20012

JACKSON, CARMEN LONGO, Biology Teacher; *b:* Ithaca, NY; Donald Edward; *c:* Anne Metz, John; *ed:* Cornell Univ (BS) Bio 19

Bio 1961; cr: Irondequoit HS Bio Tchr 1955-61; Ithaca HS Bio Tchr 56; Ithaca Coll Bio Tchr 1966; Montgomery Coll Bio Tchr 1976-90; lly Schl of Holy Child 1981-; ai: MBTA, NABT 1981-; Georgetown Biotechnology Stud Grant 1988; office: Connelly Sch Of The Holy 9029 Bradley Blvd Potomac MD 20854*

SON, DEBORAH HENSHALL, Fifth Grade Teacher; b: San Diego, Leigh-Anne, Ryan Joseph; ed: Elon Coll (BA) Elem Ed 1975; 15 Hrs Salisbury St Univ, Loyola Coll, Western MD; cr: St Matthews Schl 3rd Grd Tchr 1975-78; North Salisbury Elem Schl Fifth Grd 1986-; ai: Schl Improvement Team Chm; MD St Teach Assn, NEA ; Wicomico Educ; office: North Salisbury Elem Schl 201 Union Ave ury MD 21801

SON, DEBORAH MARIE, English Teacher; b: New York, NY; ed: an Coll (BA) Sociology 1972; Rutgers Univ (MA) Ed 1978; 42 Addl s; cr: CES 104 Elem Tchr 1972-76; Richmond Hills HS Eng Tchr Coord of Stu Acts 1989-; ai: Grd Adv 1983-89; Eng Fac Adv ars Club; Fashion-Talent Show, Sing & Dome Magazine Lit Adv; & UFT 1972-; Phi Delta Kappan 1978-; Impact II Grant, Made mar Handbook for Stdnts; office: Richmond Hill HS 89-30 114th St nond Hill NY 11418

SON, DIANE LOUISE, 4th Grade Teacher; b: Oil City, PA; m: t L.; c: Lisa, Mark; ed: Clarion Univ (BA) Elem Ed 1979; cr: nption BVM Schl 5-6th Grd Tchr 1969-70; St. Patrick Schl 1-3rd Grd 1970-80; Pinegrove Elem 4th Grd Tchr 1982-93, 3rd Grd Tchr 94, 4th Grd Tchr 1995-; ai: Math Comm; Act 178 Comm; PSEA, NEA ; Keystone Rdng Cncl; Commonwealth Elem Sci Tchng Alliance Ldr 4 Yrs; Math Comm; home: 202 Manor Dr Franklin PA 16323

SON, ELAINE SANDRA, Fourth Grade Teacher; b: Brooklyn, NY; rooklyn Coll (BA) Sociology 1969; Post-Grad Stud Brooklyn Coll, Island Univ 45 Hrs 1970-95; cr: Bushwick Neighborhood dinating Cncl Soc Worker 1969-70; PS 45 K Schl Third Grd Tchr 74; PS 384 Schl Fourth Grd Tchr 1974-; ai: Stu Cncl Adv; After-Schl Prgm Tchr; Vol Tchr for After-Schl Homework Helper Prgm; AFT, 1970-; Block Assn 1970-, Pres 1971-75; Comm Newsletter 1970-, Ed 76.

KSON, FRANCES LONG, Math Teacher; b: Schenectady, NY; ed: Y at Albany (MA) Math Ed 1975; 12 Addl Hrs; cr: Saratoga City Schls Tchr 1975-80; SUNY at Albany Supvr for Stu Tchrs; Schalmont Schl Tchr 1990-95; ai: Environmental Club, Natl Jr Hnr Soc Adv; Speaker umerous Confs; Awded Grant with Conjunction of Union Coll, nectady Cty; office: Schalmont MS 2 Sabre Dr Schenectady NY 12306

KSON, GAIL POMPEY, Developmental Reading Teacher; b: ville, PA; m: William F.; c: Maggie E.; ed: Kutztown Univ (BS) Elem 977) Marywood Coll (MS) Rdng Ed 1991; cr: Valley View Schl Dist Tchr 1977-79; St Mary's Schl Second Grd Tchr 1979-83; Scranton St for the Deaf Sub Tchr 1984-85; Mt View Schl Dist Rdng Tchr 1985-; duction Coord; Jr Class Adv; MVEA Social Chprsn; MVEA, PSEA, 1985-; IRA 1987-; NSRA 1989-; office: Mountain View HS RR 1 Box Kingsley PA 18826*

KSON, GERMAINE D., Assistant Principal; b: Mobile, AL; m: ence L.; c: Felicia Y., Marjon A.; ed: Fisk Univ (BA) Math 1973; ta Univ (MS) Math 1972; Post Grad Stud Kent St Univ, Cleveland St for Admin Cert; cr: IBM Systems Programmer 1972-73; Oberlin Coll Applications Programmer, Lecturer in Math 1973-76; Lorain City Math Tchr 1985-93, Dean of Stdnts Ldr 1993-95, Asst Prin 1995-; hrldng Adv; Act Coach; LAA 1993-; Jack & Jill of Amer Inc 1986-, Sec, Fin Sec; LCABSE 1988-, Bldg Rep; Stu Nominated Outstdng Awd; Outstdng Young Women of Amer; office: Lorain Admiral King 600 Ashland Ave Lorain OH 44052

KSON, GUSTAV E., Prof of Environmental Studies; b: Guyana; m: an Joseph; c: Javan, Gea, Mighel, Dewa; ed: Northern IL Univ (BS) ogy 1969; Univ of Chicago (MS) Geophysical Sci 1972; Union Inst D) Geoscience 1974; cr: Cntrl U Coll Instr Phys Sci 1969-74; St of MD of Natl Resources Hydrogeologist 1974-76; Howard Univ Asst Prof eology 1970-81; Sojourner-Douglass Coll Prof of Sci & Ed 1985-; ai: ts for Environmental Equity Org Adv; Citizens Clearinghouse for ardous Wastes 1992-, Consultant; E of the River Cons Assn 1992-, Bd ; Rain Forest Consultants Assn 1994-, Exec Dir; Inducted into The ssroots Movement for Environmental Justice Hall of Fame.*

KSON, JAMES HENRY, Sixth Grade Science Teacher; b: Elizabeth , NC; m: Barbara Ann White; c: James, Kendric; ed: Elizabeth City St (BS) Elem Ed 1965; Salisbury St Univ (MS) Ed 1975; Attnd WA Coll; Ross St Elem Schl 5th Grd Tchr 1965; US Army Soldier 1965-68; DC of Correction Guard 1968-69; Dorchester Cty Bd of Ed Tchr 1969-; Girls Bsktbl Coach; HS & MS Sci Chprsn; NEA 1969-; MD St Tchrs -; Dorchester Tchrs Assn 1969-; Omega Psi Phi 1963-, Basileus, ega Man of Yr; NAACP 1969-; Wesley Temple Meth Men 1977-, Pres; ation Army Boys & Girls Club 1977-; Dist 10 MD Jaycees Speak Up 1971-72; Pi Alpha Chptr Omega Psi Phi Outstdng Svc Awd 1983-; ation Army Boys & Girls Club Cadet Bsktbl Coach of the Yr 1985-86; re-Ups Med Transportation Driver of the Yr 1987; office: North chester MS 5845 Cloverdale Rd Hurlock MD 21643

CKSON, JOHN A., Science Teacher; b: Norwich, NY; ed: SUNY at hi (AAS) Veterinary Sci Tech 1988; Cornell Univ (BS) Animal Sci 1; SUNY at Cortland (MAT) Ed 1992; AIDS Turnkey Trainer; Ithaca Cmptr Interfacing; cr: New Berlin Cntrl Schl Sci Tchr 1992-; ai: ironmental Sci Club Advy; Jr Var Boys Bsktbl Coach; AFT 1992-; ohanna Bd of Bsbl Officials 1996; office: New Berlin Cntrl Schl School ew Berlin NY 13411

CKSON, KAREN PENNYPACKER, Mathematics Teacher; b: Upper by, PA; m: Albert Terry; c: Kimberly Ann Dumont, Sharon Lee Locke, y Donald; ed: Moravian Coll (BS) Math 1964; Wesleyan Univ (MALS) h 1981; cr: Salisbury Twp Jr Sr HS Math Tchr 1964-65; Middletown Math Tchr 1977-; ai: Former Mem Math Team; Former NEML Coord, S Adv; Atomic 1979-; NCTM 1985-; Pub Article 1991; Cty, St Team ch Awds1985-87; Outstdng Svc & Dedication Tchr Awd 1984; office: ddletown HS Hunting Hill Ave Middletown CT 06457

CKSON, KAREN TOOHIG, Fifth Grade Teacher; b: Cleveland, OH; Kevin, Craig; ed: Kent St (MED) Elem Ed 1963, (MS) Curr & Instruction 0; cr: Warren City Schls Tchr 1964-68, 1976-; ai: NEA, OEA 1976-; A 1976-, Bldg Rep.

CKSON, KAREN TOSLOSKY, Eng & Creative Writing Tchr; b: zleton, PA; m: W. Kent; c: Lauren, Colin; ed: Wilkes Univ (BA) Eng Ed 74, (MS) Ed 1992; 60 Credits Beyond Masters Degree; cr: West zleton HS Tchr 1978-92; Hazleton Area HS Tchr 1993-; ai: Schl wspaper Adv; NEA 1978-; office: Hazleton Area HS 1601 W 23rd St zleton PA 18201

CKSON, KATHRYN RENEE, English Teacher; b: Painesville, OH; ed: e Erie Coll (BS) Ed, Eng 1979; Kent St Univ (MA) Eng 1988; 20 Addl ctoral Level Work Eng; cr: Madison HS Eng Tchr 1979-85; Kent St Univ ng Fellow & Asst in Lit, Psychoanalysis Dept 1985-87; Madison HS g Tchr 1987-; ai: Adv Acad Competition Team; Yrbk Adv; Madison Ed sn 1979-, Past Pres; OH Ed Assn, NEA 1979-; Distinguished Tchng Awd 87; Paper Delivered at Midwestern Modern Lang Assn Conf 1988; Natl Endowment for Hum Grant 1991; office: Madison HS 3100 Burns Rd Madison OH 44057

JACKSON, LARRY THOMAS, Band Director; b: Cumberland, MD; ed: WV Univ (BS) Music Ed 1987; Frostburg St Univ (MBA) Mngmt 1991; cr: North Garrett MS Music Tchr 1988-90; Westmar HS Band Dir 1990-94; Allegany HS Band Dir 1994-; ai: Symphonic, Marching Band; Jazz Ensembles, Indoor Percussion & Guard; MENC 1988-; Int Assn of Jazz Ed 1990-; NEA 1987-; Cumberland Jazz Soc Inc 1987-, VP; Allegany Cty Music Advocacy Cncl 1995-, Natl, St Liason; Tournament of Bands 1990-, Asst Coord; MD Music Ed Assn 1988-; Co-Authored Curr; Presenter at St Music Conf; office: Allegany HS 616 Sedgwick St Cumberland MD 21502*

JACKSON, LYNNE BERRYMAN, Third Grade Teacher; b: Salem, OH; m: Roy Allan; c: Jeffrey, David; ed: Bowling Green St Univ (BS) Elem Ed 1974; Youngstown St Univ Grad Work in Early Chldhd Ed; cr: Salem City Schl Dist 3rd Grd Tchr 1974-; office: Reilly Elem Schl Salem Pub Schl Dist 491 Reilly Ave Salem OH 44460

JACKSON, MARGARET K., History Teacher; m: George M. Jr.; c: George III, Gretchen; ed: Glassboro St (BS) Soc Stud & Eng 1963; cr: W Deptford HS Tchr 1963-65; Triton Regnl HS Tchr 1966-67; Highland Regnl HS His Tchr 1967-; ai: His Club & Presidential Classroom Adv; Alumni Service & Career, Mid Sts Evaluation Act, US Constitution Bicentennal Schl & Columbus Quincentennial Chprsn; NEA & NJEA; NCSS 1963-; NJ Cncl of Soc Stud 1983-; World Affairs Cncl 1989-; Normandy Museum 1988-, Charter Mem; NJ Governors Tchr Recognition Awd 1986; Amer Legion Outstanding Service 1986-87; VFW VOD Service Awd 1981; office: Highland Regional H S Erial Rd Blackwood NJ 08012

JACKSON, MARJORIE A., Science Teacher; b: Hartford, CT; m: V. W. Smith; c: Heather Lane; ed: Cntrl CT St Univ (BS) PE 1981, (MS) Gen Sci 1988; Univ of Hartford at West Hartford Doctoral Candidate; cr: St Brigid Schl 7th, 8th Grd Sci, Math Tchr, K-12 Grd PE Tchr 1981-83; Lewis Fox MS Pool Asst 1983-84, PE Tchr 1984-88, Sci Tchr 1988-92; South MS Sci Tchr 1992-; ai: Sci Lead Tchr; Interdisciplinary Curr Dev Team; Chprsn Hartford MS; Sci Curr Dev Team; NSTA, ASCD 1993-; Act Integrating Math, Sci 1994-; Village of Children, Families Foster Parent 1994-; Schl Tchr of Yr, South MS Tchr of Yr 1995-; home: 34 Hillside St Newington CT 06111*

JACKSON, MICHELE YVONNE, Home Economics Teacher; b: Akron, OH; ed: Univ of Akron (BA) Ed 1979; cr: Robinson Elem Tchr 1979; Litchfield MS Tchr 1979-83; Firestone HS Tchr 1983-95; The Univ of Akron Nursery Schl Tchr Summer Pgm 1990-95; East HS Tchr 1995-; ai: FHA Adv; Past Adv Future Tchrs of Amer & Black Cultural Club; GAHEA 1990-; Alpha Kappa Alpha 1986-; office: East HS 80 Brittain Rd Akron OH 44305

JACKSON, NANCY SLONEKER, French Teacher; b: Hamilton, OH; m: Robert; c: Patrick, Brett; ed: Miami Univ (BS) Fr & Eng 1975; 175 Cred Hrs; OH Writing Project 1995; cr: Madison HS Fr & Eng Tchr 1976-78; Fairfield MS Fr Tchr 1983-; ai: Wrestlette Coach, Liaison & Stu Cncl Adv; Quebec Trips; Rewards Comm; OEA & NEA 1983-; Hamilton High Boosters 1993-; office: Fairfield MS 255 Donald Drive Fairfield OH 45014*

JACKSON, NEELIA THOMPSON, 7th Grade Mathematics Teacher; b: Columbus, OH; m: Leslie E.; c: Bryan, Michelle, Kathleen; ed: Cntrl St Univ (BS) Math, Educ 1969; Youngstown St Univ (MS) Guid & Counsel, Educ 1982; Attnd Cleveland St Univ, Boston Univ; cr: Cleveland Hghts Schl Math Tchr 1969-70; Warren City Schls Math Tchr 1971-85; Concord Carlisle Reg HS Math Tchr 1986-88; Comm Learning Ctr Math Coord 1986-87; Boston Pub Schls Math Tchr 1988-; ai: Boston Pub Schls MS Math Comm; AFT, MFT 1988-; Bedfprd Chrstn Church 1985-, Dir of Missions; office: James Timilty MS 205 Roxbury St Roxbury MA 02119*

JACKSON, PRESTON,JR., Air Science Teacher; b: Chicago, IL; m: Linda Vincentia Kersh; c: Preston III, Genifer L.; ed: SUNY (BS) Bus & Mgmt 1981; Cambridge Coll (MED) Mgmt 1993; cr: Baltimore Polytechnic Inst Tchr 1993-; ai: Aerospace Sci Adv 1993-; Tennis Coach 1994-; AFT 1993-; Balt Tchrs Assn 1993-; Taunton Jaycees 1980-82, Pres, Adv Mgmt Awd; Outstding Young Man 1981; office: Baltimore Poly Tech Inst 403 1400 W Cold Spring Ln Baltimore MD 21209*

JACKSON, ROBERT A.,JR., Social Studies Teacher; b: Phila, PA; c: Dedra, Robert III, Samantha; ed: Cheyenne Univ (BS) Scndry 1974; ai: 2nd Asst Var Ftbl, Track; JV Bsbl; AFT 1976-; Mt Zion Bapt Church 1966-, Bd of Deacons; Northeast Boys & Girls Club 1970-, Bd of Mgrs; office: Central HS Ogontz & Olney Aves Philadelphia PA 19141

JACKSON, STEVEN K., Science Teacher; b: Hamilton, OH; ed: Miami Univ at Oxford (BA) Earth Sci Ed 1992; cr: Fairfield HS Earth Sci Tchr 1992-93; Lakota HS Sci Tchr 1994-; ai: Asst Var Ftbl, Jr HS Head Wrestling Coach; Lakota Ed Assn, OH Ed Assn, NEA 1994-; SWOFCA Ftbl 1994-; SWOWCA Wrestling 1995-; office: Lakota HS 5050 Tylersville Rd West Chester OH 45069*

JACKSON, VIVIAN BUTLER, Developmental Rdng & Ed Prof; b: Greensboro, NC; c: Ralph; ed: Columbia Univ Tchrs Coll (MA) Applied Linguistics 1982; CUNY City Coll (MSEd) Dev Rdng 1996; Addl 12 Credit Hrs Linguistics; cr: Columbia Univ Law Schl Exec Sec 1977-82; CUNY Bronx Comm Coll Rdng, Stud Skills Coord 1982-88, Assoc Dir Spec Progs Office 1988-89, Dev Rdng, Ed Prof 1989-; ai: Ed Soc Fac Adv; Rdng, Dept of Ed, ESL Team Ldr; Bronx Tech Prep Prgm Wkshp Presenter; NYMADE, NADE 1984-; ASCD 1992-; AFT 1989-; Unity, Strength Assn 1986-; Ed Soc Cert of Honor Svc Awd; CCTIP Most Valuable Instr Awd 1991; Stu Govt Svc Awd 1988-89; Stu Support Svcs Most Valuable Employee 1983; office: Bronx Comm Coll W 181 St & University Ave Bronx NY 10453*

JACKSON-BAYTOPS, LORRAINE MALLORY, First Grade Teacher; b: Philadelphia, PA; c: Martin K. Jackson, Monica Jackson Taylor; ed: Cheyney St Coll (BS) Elem Ed 1966; Post Grad Stud Temple Univ, Cabrini Coll; cr: Schl Dist of Phila Tchr 1966-; ai: Extended Day Prgm Tchr; Rdng, Lang Arts, Sci Comms; New Tchrs Mentor; PFT, NEA 1966-; IRA 1996-; Zoological Soc of Phila 1989-; Amer Family Inst Positive Tchng Tribute; Phila Schl Dist Commendation; office: Lewis Cassidy Elem Schl Lansdowne Ave E of 66th St Philadelphia PA 19151

JACOB, CHRISTINA F., Sixth Grade Teacher; b: Hooksett, NH; w: Henry A. (dec); c: Virginia Ann Kern; ed: Keene St Coll (BA) Elem Ed 1957; Attnd Albany St 1958-60, Cornell 1959-60 Grad Work; cr: Middleburg Cntrl Schl Grd 6 Tchr 1957-60; Johnson City Schl Grd 4 Tchr 1960-61; Broad Street Schl Grd 6 Tchr 1961-95; ai: Friendly Helpers Ldr; Math Club Adv; Fleet Bank Yth Ldr; Math, Sci Coord; AFT 1973-; NH Math Tchrs Assn 1985-; NH Sci Tchrs Assn 1990-; Friends of Bedford Pub Lib, St Elizabeth Seton 1973-; GFWC Vol; New England Telephone Pioneer Vol 1996-; W R Grants; Sci Awd; Cash Awds; Delta Sci, Math; Addison Wesley Reviewer, Cert of Merit; home: 18 West Dr Bedford NH 03110

JACOB, MONIQUE, French Teacher; b: Montreal Quebec, Canada; ed: Queen's Univ in Ontario BComm Mrktg, Prsnl 1985; Univ of RI Fr, Scndry Tchng Cert 1988; Working on Fr MA; Eng as 2nd Lang; cr: Central Falls HS Fr Tchr 1988-; ai: Frosh Class Adv; RI Skills Commission; RIFLA, AATF, AFT 1988-; office: Central Falls Jr Sr HS 24 Summer St Central Falls RI 02863

JACOBOWITZ, E. LUNN, Assistant Professor; b: Brooklyn, NY; ed: Gallaudet Univ (BA) Psych 1976; Univ of MD (MED) Educl Comm 1981; Doctorate Candidate Gallaudet Univ Admin & Supervision, Spec Ed Admin; cr: Hilda Knoff Schl for the Deaf Tchr 1977-79; Gallaudet Univ Instr 1981-89, Asst Prof 1989-; ai: Natl Assn of Deaf-Amer Sign Lang Tchrs Assn Pres; Deaf Employees Caucus Sec; Intnl Visual Literacy 1990-; ASLTA 1976-, VP, Evaluator, Pres; Natl Assn of Female Execs 1988-; Metro WA Assn of Deaf 1985-; Montgomery Cty Assn of Deaf 1990-; Alice Teegarden Awd; Fac Dev Awds; Articles Pub; office: Gallaudet Univ Dept of Amer Sign Lang 800 Florida Ave NE Washington DC 20002

JACOBS, ANDREW, PE Tchr & Coach; b: Canandaigua, NY; m: Lynn M.; ed: Finger Lakes Comm Coll (AA) PE 1983; SUNY at Cortland (BSE) PE 1985; Canisius Coll (MS) PE 1990; 9 Hrs Post Grad Ed Admin; cr: St Andrews Cntry Day Schl PE Tchr Grds K-8 1985-86; Iroquois Cntrl Schl PE Tchr Grds 4-8 1986-; ai: Boys 4 Yrs, Girls 6 Yrs Var Soccer, Boys JV Bsktbl 10 Yrs, Boys Var Tennis 4 Yrs, Girls Var Track 2 Yrs Coach; NEA 1986-92; NYSUT 1992-; NSCAA 1988-, Soccer Coaches Mem; home: 11214 Porterville Rd East Aurora NY 14052

JACOBS, BEVERLY SUE, Spanish Teacher; b: Brooklyn, NY; ed: Brooklyn Coll (BA) Span 1965, (MA) Ed, Scndry 1966; NY Univ (PHD) Medieval Span Lit 1975; Post Grad Stud Span, Italian, Fr 1980, 1986; cr: Hudde Jr HS Span, Eng Tchr 1965; Brooklyn Coll Evening Sub Span Tchr, Summer Schl Span Tchr 1965; F.D. Roosevelt HS Span, ESL Tchr 1965-; ai: UFT 1965-; New Tchr Mentor; Stu Tchr Trainer; Lead Tchr; Jr Grd Sing Adv & Grd Adv; Textbook Consultant; Col Univ Scholastic Press Assn 1st Pl Elbuen Vecino 1972, 1974; Article Pub 1983; Presented Medieval Span Autobiography Paper Fourth Medieval Forum Plymouth St Coll 1983; office: Franklin D Roosevelt HS 5800 20th Ave Brooklyn NY 11204

JACOBS, DONALD LEE, Science Teacher & Dept Chair; b: Marietta, OH; ed: OK Chrstn Coll (BSE) Ed & Sci 1978; Central St Univ (MS) Ed & Admin 1983; OH St Univ Physics Class 1986-87; cr: Oklahoma City Schls MS Earth Sci Tchr 1978-80; Piedmont Jr HS General Sci Tchr 1980-85; Berne Union HS AP Bio, Chem & Physics Tchr & Sci Dept Head 1985-; ai: Sci Club Adv; NEA 1985-; Fairfield Physics Tchrs Alliance 1986-; OH Natl Guard 1987-, Sergeant, Army Achvmt Awd 1991; Lancaster Church of Christ 1986-, Deacon 7 Yrs; Awded Grant to Attnd NSF Wkshp for Chem Tchrs 1990; Awded Grants to Purchase Equipment for Classrooms; NSF Wkshp for Dev of Elem Tchrs 1993; Project Discovery Classes to Change Innovate Sci Tchng; office: Berne Union HS 506 N Main St Sugar Grove OH 43155

JACOBS, ETHEL BOWDEN, Instructor of Communications; b: San Diego, CA; c: Emily A., Nathaniel S.; ed: Colby Coll (BA) Eng 1978; Univ of Southern ME (MS) Adult Ed 1996; Inst Tech Comm Hinds Comm Coll 1995; cr: East Orange HS Eng Tchr 1978-83; Roselle Cath HS Eng Tchr 1983-85; Lewiston Adult Ed Eng Tchr 1987-88; Cntrl ME Tech Coll Comm Instr 1988-; ai: Stu Magazine Adv; Advy Comm Ctr for Tchng; NCTE, Convention Reader of Wkshp Proposals 1995; ATTW 1995-; MCELA; Pub Theater 1993-, Friend; Newcomers Club 1995-, Sec; TETYC Presenter 1995; Stud Guide, Article Pub 1995; office: Central ME Tech Coll 1250 Turner St Auburn ME 04210*

JACOBS, JANET M., English Teacher; b: Dayton, OH; ed: Miami Univ (BS) Eng 1972; Wright St Univ (MED) Eng 1974; 24 Semester Hrs Post-Grad Stud; cr: Milton-Union HS Tchr 1972-; ai: North Cntrl Assn Comm Chair; North Cntrl Core Team; Venture Grant BBudget Comm; Author OH Venture Capital Grant; NCTE 1970-; NEA 1972-; Dayton Art Inst 1990-; Honorary Tchr of NHS; office: Milton Union HS 221 S Jefferson St West Milton OH 45383

JACOBS, JAYNE C., Special Education Teacher; b: White Plains, NY; m: Ronald; c: Brett, Adam; ed: Univ of Southern CT (BS) Spec Ed 1984; Iona Coll (MS) Urban Ed 1987; 9 Credits Schl Law; cr: Vitam Schl Math Tchr 1984-86; Edgemont Jr-Sr HS Spec Ed Tchr 1986-; ai: AFT 1986-; CEC 1984-86, 1995-; office: Edgemont Jr Sr HS 199 White Oak Ln Scarsdale NY 10583

JACOBS, JUDY RUTH (ANTHONY), Sixth Grade Teacher; b: Cleveland, OH; m: Jack R.; c: Kevin, Jennifer Gardner; ed: Bowling Green St Univ (BS) Elem Ed 1965; 12 Credit Hrs in Math, Art Ed OH St Univ; 8 Credit Hrs in Lit, Rdng Ed Ashland Univ; cr: Grand Blanc Schls 4th Grd Tchr 1965-66; Madison Local Schls 2nd, 4th Grd Tchr 1966-68; Ft Huachuca Schls 5 Grd Tchr 1968-70; Madison Local Schls Sub Tchr 1979-84, 4-6 Grd Tchr 1985-; ai: NEA, OEA 1979-; YWCA 1976-, Pres 1 Yr; PTO 1980-, VP; BSA 1978-82, Den Mother; office: Madison Local Schools 1379 Grace St Mansfield OH 44905*

JACOBS, MARY JUREWICZ, Tchr Aide & Learning Lab Coord; b: Buffalo, NY; m: Edward W.; c: Leslie, Stephen, Nicole; ed: D'Youville Coll (BA) Soc Stud 1962; Univ at Bflo (MA) Soc Stud, Ed 1967; cr: Bflo Pub Schls Soc Stud Tchr, Dept Chair 1962-67; W Seneca Cntrl Schls Sub Tchr 1978-79, 1986-93; W SR Aide, Learning Lab Coord, Peer Tutoring Group Tchr 1994-; office: West Seneca West Sr HS 3330 Seneca St West Seneca NY 14224

JACOBS, MARY JOAN,CSFN English Teacher; b: Philadelphia, PA; ed: Holy Family Coll (BA) Eng 1984; Villanova Univ (MA) Eng 1990; cr: St John Cantius First Grd Tchr 1974-76; St Brendan Eighth Grd Tchr 1976-78; St Kunegunda Eighth Grd Tchr 1978-79; Visitation BVM Trooper Sixth Grd Tchr 1979-81; St Mary Sixth Grd Tchr 1981-84; Nazareth Acad 9-12 Grd Eng Tchr 1984-; ai: Yrbk, Quill & Scroll Moderator; Schlsp Comm; NCTE 1984-; Three Pub Pamphlets; office: Nazareth Acad 4001 Grant Ave Philadelphia PA 19114

JACOBS, MICHAEL D., Business Dept Chairperson; b: Pottstown, PA; m: Diane Sharrow; c: Max, Andrew, Sarah, Olivia, Nick; ed: Shippensburg St Univ (BS Ed) Bus Acct Ed & Data Proc 1973; Kutztown St Univ (MED) Scndry Guid Cnslr 1982; Comp Network Trng 7 Credits; cr: Daniel Boone HS Tchr, Dept Chair, Network Admin, Ftbl & Bsbl Coach & FBLA Adv 1973-; ai: Sr High Var Asst Ftbl Coach; Bsbl Coach; Jr High Asst FBLA Adv; NEA 1973-; PSEA 1973-; NBEA 1992-; Boyertown Midgit Bsbl Coach 1984-86; Daniel Boone & the News of Southern Berks Tchr of Yr 1994; office: Daniel Boone HS 501 Chestnut St Birdsboro PA 19508

JACOBS, NANCY LOEB, Assistant Prof of Child Dev; b: Cleveland, OH; m: Sanford; c: Leslie Jacobs Yaussy; Ellen Jacobs Wagner; Jennifer Jacobs Vorell; ed: CWRU Schl of Applied Soc Sci (MSSA) Case Work, Child Welfare 1953; Kent St Univ (PHD) Early Chldhd Ed, Curr, Instruction 1984; Miami Univ at Oxford Sociology; Cleveland St Univ 2 Hrs; Univ of Akron 3 Hrs; 90 Hrs Continuing Ed; cr: Jewish Comm Ctr of Cleveland Presch Tchr 1967-71, Presch Dir 1971-76; Bellefaire Jewish Childrens Bureau Dir of Early Chldhd Svcs 1976-91; Univ of Akron Asst Prof of Child Dev 1991-; ai: NAEYS 1971-, Accreditation Rep; NASW 1971-; ACEI 1991-; Kappa Delta Pi Natl Ed Honorary 1984-; Pub Articles; office: Univ Of Akron 215 Schrank S Carroll St Akron OH 44325

JACOBS, PAULA, Social Studies Teacher; b: Needham, MA; ed: Westfield St Coll (BA) Ed & Hist 1976; Univ of AR at Fayetteville (MED) Ed & Soc Stud 1985; Attnd Amer Intnl Coll, Univ of MA at Boston; cr: St Boniface Schl Tchr 1977-84; Cathedral HS Tchr 1984-85; Southwick Tolland Regnl HS Tchr 1985-; ai: Debate Team; Class & NHS Adv; NEA 1985-; MTA 1985-; New Eng His & Tchr Assn 1985-; US Golf Assn 1994-; office: Southwick-Tolland Regional HS 93 Feeding Hills Rd Southwick MA 01077

JACOBS, ROBERT S., Chemistry Teacher; *b:* New York, NY; *m:* Janet Elaine DeMeo; *c:* Bruce, Beth Justin, Stephen; *ed:* Lafayette Coll (BA) Chem 1966; St Johns Univ (PHD) Phys Chem 1972; *cr:* Wilton HS Chem Tchr 1969-; Wilton HS Girls Tennis Coach 1972-; *ai:* Girls Var Tennis Coach; NEA & CEA 1969-; WEA 1969-, Chm of Negotiating Team; Doctoral Dissertation Pub; Wrote Wilton HS Sci Handbook & Chem Prgm; Distgshd Tchr Awd by the White House Comssn on Pres Schlrs 1995; *office:* Wilton HS 395 Danbury Rd Wilton CT 06897*

JACOBS, RONALD J., Mathematics Teacher; *b:* Wilkes-Barre, PA; *ed:* Wilkes Univ (BS) Math 1971, (MS) Math 1974; *cr:* Newton Jr HS Math Tchr 1971-79; Hanover Area Jr-Sr HS Math Tchr 1979-; *ai:* Gifted Math Instr; Spon for Math Projects for PA Jr Acad of Sci; PA Jr Acad of Sci Treas; PA St Ed Assn, NEA, & Hanvoer Area Ed Assn 1971-; Luzene Cty Math Assoc of PA Cncl of Tchrs of Math 1995-; YMCA 1978-; *office:* Hanover Jr/ Sr HS 1600 Sans Souci Hwy Wilkes Barre PA 18702

JACOBS, ROSE MARY, 8th Grade Teacher; *b:* Amsterdam, NY; *m:* Benedict M.; *c:* Kara, BJ; *ed:* Fulton-Montgomery CC (AA) Lbrl Arts 1969; SUNY at Oneonta (BA) Ed 1971; 30 Addl Credit Hrs; *cr:* St Stanislaus Schl 8th Grd Tchr 1971-74, 1981-; *ai:* 8th Grd Act Adv; NYSSTA 1989-; *home:* 3051 State Highway 5 Fonda NY 12068

JACOBS, SUSAN SHAMBO, Elementary Teacher; *b:* Watertown, NY; *m:* Thomas G.; *c:* Thomas G. II; *ed:* SUNY at Potsdam (BA) Math 1986, (MS) Elem Ed Concentration Comps 1988; *cr:* John F Kennedy Elem 5th Grd Tchr 1986-87; Grant C Madill Elem 6th Grd Tchr 1987-91, 4th Grd Tchr 1991-94, 5th Grd Tchr 1994-95, 4th Grd Tchr 1995-; *ai:* Schl Store Adv; Arts & Crafts T-Shirt Ldr; PARP, Math & Activity Club Comms; OEA 1986-; AFT 1986-; NEA 1986-; Presidential Awd for Excl in Sci & Math Tchng Nom; *office:* Grant C Madill Elem 800 Jefferson Ave Ogdensburg NY 13669*

JACOBS, TIM, Anthropology & Sociology Instr; *b:* Quincy, MA; *m:* Theresa Warren; *c:* Star Gibbs, Thorin, Travis, Tyler; *ed:* Mohegan Comm Coll (AA) Liberal Arts 1982; Wesleyan Univ (BA) Anthropology, Sociology & Linguistics 1985, (MA) Anthropology 1985; Univ of CT Antrhopology PHD Prgm; *cr:* Mattatuck Comm Coll Adjunct Instr 1986-92; Univ of CT Adjunct Instr 1992; Naugatuck Valley Comm Tech Coll Anthropology, Sociology & Gerontology Instr 1992-; *ai:* Acad Stans Comm Chair; Archaeology Soc Adv; Living His Assn 1992-; Phi Beta Kappa; Etherington Fellowship Wesleyan Univ; *office:* Naugatuck Valley Comm Coll 750 Chase Pky Waterbury CT 06708

JACOBS, WILLIAM DAVID, Biology Teacher; *b:* Lock Haven, PA; *m:* Mary Cillo; *c:* Kirstin, Ryan; *ed:* Shippensburg Univ (BS) Math & Bio 1972; Kutztown Univ (MED) Bio 1975; 42 Addl Credits; *cr:* Upper Perkiomen HS Bio & Math Tchr 1972-; *ai:* Girls Tennis Coach 20 Yrs; Tabor United Meth Church 1973-, Pres Trustees 5 Yrs; Nom Outstanding Young Educator for Upper Perkiomen Area; Won 9 League Championships in Tennis; *office:* Upper Perkiomen H S 2 Walt Rd Pennsburg PA 18073

JACOBSEN, RUTH BOWLES, English Teacher; *b:* Bangor, ME; *c:* Joy Jacobsen Petrich, Richard Jr.; *ed:* Univ of ME (BS) Ed, Eng 1968; 30 Hrs SUNY Potsdam 1973; *cr:* Carthage Cntrl HS Eng Tchr 1968-; *ai:* Mentor; EAP, Awd, NY St RCT Review Comms; Peer Cnslng; Curr Cncl; CTA 1968-, Pres 5 Yrs; NYSUT 1958-; Jeff Lewis Tchrs Assn 1987-, Sec 7 Yrs; NCTE 1992-94, Tchr of Excl 1992; Presented Numerous Wkshps; *office:* Carthage Cntrl HS 36500 NYS Rt 26 Carthage NY 13619*

JACOBSON, ALAN JOEL, High School Guidance Counselor; *b:* Clinton, MA; *ed:* Hamilton Coll (BA) Psych 1972; Northeastern Univ (MED) Cnslr Ed 1974; *cr:* Waltham Pub Schls Guidance Cnslr 1974-; Work Family Directions Coll Cnslr 1993-; *ai:* Waltham Educators Assn 1974-, VP; MA Schl Cnslrs Assn, MA Tchr Assn, NEA 1974-; *office:* Waltham HS 617 Lexington St Waltham MA 02154

JACOBSON, DOROTHY TROUP, English Teacher; *b:* Providence, RI; *c:* Donald, Deborah Karczewski; *ed:* Boston Univ (BA) Eng 1952; SUNY (MA) Ed 1965; NYC 12 Hrs Hum; 12 Hrs Ed Policy & Admin; *cr:* Western Penn Zionist Youth Commission Exec Dir 1951-52; Troy Schl Dist Tchr 1967-95; Suny at Albny Adj Prof 1996-; *ai:* Tchr Trng in Cooperative Small Group Learning; AFT, NCTE 1967-; TTA 1967-, VP, Rep 7 Yrs; Bethany Homeless Shelter 1988-, Pres 6 yrs; Troy Human Rights Commission 1988-, 6 Yrs; Temple Berith Sholom 1960-, Pres, VP 5 Yrs; COTE Outstanding Tchr Educator for NY; *office:* W. K. Doyle MS 1976 Burdett Ave Troy NY 12180*

JACOBSON, FRANKLIN PAUL, Music Department Chair; *b:* Wappingers Falls, NY; *m:* Jeanette Helen Kees; *c:* Paula Helen; *ed:* Eastman Schl of Music (BME) Music His, Organ 1964; Grad Stud Musicology 1965-66; Westminster Choir Coll Summer Stud; West Chester Univ Electronic, Cmptr Applications, Music; IL St Jazz Ed; *cr:* St Luke's Episcopal Church Organist, Choir 1963-67; The Harley Schl Music Tchr 1965-67; Princeton Day Schl Music Dept Chair 1967-; Calvary Episcopal Church Organ, Choir 1982-; Bar Harbor Festival Harpsichordist 1989-; *ai:* Bicycle Club 1972-; Annual Musical Comedy Dir 1969-; AGO 1985-; ACDA 1982-; Fellow, Rutgers Athenaeum for Early Music 1992; *office:* Princeton Day Schl PO Box 75 The Great Rd Princeton NJ 08542*

JACOBSON, JONATHAN LEE, Arts & Humanities Acad Leader; *b:* Baltimore, MD; *m:* Donna M. Bowens; *ed:* Univ of Bridgeport (BA) His 1967; 30 Credit Hrs Towson St Univ 1970-; *cr:* Douglass HS Soc Stud Tchr 1970-92; Patterson HS Dept Head, Soc Stud Tchr & Arts & Hum Acad Ldr 1992-; *ai:* Tennis Coach; Sr Class Adv; Mid Sts Evaluation Team Chm; Schl Improvement Team; Exec Cabinet Mem; Homecoming Comm; Steering Comm Chm; Wkshp Citizenship Preparation; Balto Tchrs Union 1975-; AFT; US Tennis Assoc 1975-; Action for Homeless 1992-; US Prof Tennis Assoc 1993-; Tchng Tennis Prof 1970-; Recognized by Schl Bd Dev Twilight Schl; Action for Homeless Awd; Amer Red Cross Recognition for Blood Donor Drives 15 Yrs; Mid Sts Dev a Guide for First Time Evaluators; *office:* Patterson Sr HS 100 Kane St Baltimore MD 21224

JACOBSON, WENDEE ELIZABETH, English Professor; *b:* Quincy, MA; *m:* Julie Scholman; *ed:* Lake Erie Coll (BA) Eng 1981; Univ of IA (MA) Eng 1986; *cr:* Cntrl AZ Coll Eng Instr 1988-89; Pima Coll Writing Instr 1988-89; Alfred St Coll Eng Instr 1989-95; *ai:* Poem Pub 1990; Article Pub.*

JACOBY, JOSEPH HAROLD, English Teacher; *b:* Fostoria, OH; *ed:* Bowling Green St Univ (BA) Music 1969; Kent St Univ (MA) Eng 1989; Free-Lance Piano Stud London, England 1971-73; OH St Univ Tchng Cert 1978-79; *cr:* Roosevelt Jr HS Music Tchr 1969-71; Bowling Green St Univ Piano Instr 1973-77; Lakewood HS Music, Eng Tchr 1979-; *ai:* Acad Challenge Adv; NEA 1979-; Martha Holden Jennings Scholar 1984-85; *home:* 12700 Lake Ave Apt 1301 Lakewood OH 44107

JACOBY, TERRY PENNELL, Kindergarten Teacher; *b:* Richmond, VA; *m:* Ronald Kent; *c:* Jessica L., Jordan K.; *ed:* Kutztown St Univ (BS) Spec Ed 1973, (MEd) Elem Ed 1976; 41 Credits in Post Grad Stud Including Effective Tchng Practices, Learning Styles, Assertive Discipline, Developmental Appropriate Practices in Classroom; *cr:* Quakertown Comm Schl Dist Kndgtn 1973-; *ai:* TPO Finance Comm; QCEA 1973-, Past Sec; PSEA, NEA 1973-; *office:* Richland Elem Schl 500 Fairview Ave Quakertown PA 18951

JACOVINO, JOSEPH JOHN,JR., Music Director; *b:* Waterbury, CT; *m:* Roberta Velykis; *c:* Sara, Joseph III; *ed:* Hartt Schl of Music (BSME) Piano Performance 1973; Manhattan Schl of Music (MMusEd) Ed 1976; *cr:* St Lucys R. C. Church Organist, Cantor & Choir Dir 1970-; Holy Cross HS Dir of Music 1980-; Naugatuck Valley Comm Tech Coll Adjunct Fac in Theory & Jazz Band 1988-; *ai:* Jazz Band & Spring Musical Conductor; MENC & CMEA 1980-; Intnl Assn of Jazz Educators 1988; Music Educators Natl Conf; CT Music Educators Assn; Amer Fed of Musicians; Amer Guild of Organists 1975-; Waterbury Symphony Orch 1988-91, Bd of Dirs & Music Comm; Staff Pianist; Univ of Hartford Regents Awd 1972; Active Piano & Organ Recitalist Throughout CT Area; Prof Piano Accompanist for CT Choral Soc; *office:* Holy Cross HS 587 Oronoke Rd Waterbury CT 06708

JACQUES, KATHLEEN CLEARY, HS Social Studies Teacher; *b:* Buffalo, NY; *m:* Denis J.; *c:* Denis Jr., Brian; *ed:* Canisius Coll (BA) His 1970, (MS) Soc Stud Ed 1975; 30 Credit Hrs Beyond MS; *cr:* Maryvale HS Soc Stud, Global Stud, Law, Rights & Constitution America Tchr 1970-; *ai:* Model UN Adv; Schl Improvement Team; Policy Bd Mem; MAPS Var Club Co-Adv; Maryvale Tchr Assn 1970-; Niagara Frontier Cncl of SS 1990-; NYS Cncl of SS 1990-; Mount Mary Alumnae Assn 1988-94, Bd of Dirs; Attnd Taft Inst of Govt; *office:* Maryvale HS 1050 Maryvale Dr Cheektowaga NY 14225

JACQUES, LINDA MARIE, Professor of Law; *b:* Millis, MA; *ed:* MA Bay Comm Coll (AS) Bus, Ed 1979; Bryant Coll (BS) Bus, Ed 1981; Creighton Univ (JD) Law 1990; *cr:* Katharine Gibbs Schl Instr 1981-92; Middlesex Dist Attorneys OfficeAttorney 1990-93; MA Bay Comm Coll Prof 1993-; Comm Legal Svcs Attorney 1995-; *ai:* MA Bar 1990-; Northeastern Univ Outstdng Fac Awd1995; *office:* MA Bay Comm Coll 19 Flagg Dr Framingham MA 01701*

JADD, MARSHA J., School Counselor; *b:* Buffalo, NY; *c:* Kristofer; *ed:* Univ of Buffalo (BA) Amer Stud 1962; St Univ of NY at Buffalo (MED) Schl Cnslng 1965; 30 Addl Hrs; *cr:* Buffalo Bd Ed Tchr 1963-66, Cnslr 1966-; *ai:* Adv NHS, Schl Newspaper; Buffalo Tchrs Fed, NEA 1963-; Phi Beta Kappa; *office:* Seneca Vocational HS 666 E Delavan Ave Buffalo NY 14215

JAEGER, ALFRED ADAMS, 6th-8th Grd Lang Arts Teacher; *b:* Sussex, NJ; *m:* Dale Margaret; *c:* Alexander, Katherine, Ronald, Adam, Brad; *ed:* Delhi Tech (AAS) Agri-Economics 1967; ND St Univ (BS) Eng 1970; William Paterson Coll (MED) Elem, Lang, Arts 1979; Montclair St Tchng Cert 1971; *cr:* Frankford Twp Schl Lang Arts Tchr 1971-; *ai:* Schl Yrbk Adv, Founder 1971; Frankford Tchrs Assn, NJEA, NEA 1971-; Frankford Plains United Meth Church 1960-, Pres, Trustees; Sussex Area Jaycees 1975-85, Sec; NJ Gov Tchr of Yr Frankford Twp Schl Dist 1989; *office:* Frankford Township Schl PO Box 430 Branchville NJ 07826

JAEGER, GALE A., Assistant Professor; *b:* Pueblo, CO; *m:* Robert H.; *c:* Robert Jr., Marjoree, Kristin Hudspeth; *ed:* St Univ of NY (BS) Sociology Work, Industry 1984; Adelphi Univ (MA) Ed 1990; Enrolled ABD Temple Univ; Grad Stud NY Univ Orgnl Sociology; *cr:* R. H. Macy & Co Dir Prsnl 1977-89; Mngmt By Enrichment Pres Consulting Bus 1989-91; Employment Opportunity, Trng Ctr Employment Coord, Trainer 1991-93; Marywood Coll Asst Prof 1991-; *ai:* Adv Kappa Omicron Mu, Retail Merchandising Club; Admissions, Educal Effectiveness, Policy, Procedure Comms; Mrktg Ed Assn, Natl Assn Female Execs, Delta Epsilon Delta 1991-; Retail Edctrs Assn 1996; SHINE 1992-, Bd; PA Landtrust Conservancy 1994-; Awds Outstdng Contributions to Retail Women, Outstdng Achvmt Orgnl Sociology; Article Pub; *office:* Marywood Coll 2300 Adams Ave Scranton PA 18509*

JAEGER, JANET LYNN, Varsity Volleyball Coach; *b:* Cincinnati, OH; *ed:* Univ of Cincinnati (BS) Bio 1991; Med Tech Pgm ASCP Cert 1993; *cr:* MND Var Vllybl Coach 1992-95; Childrens Hosp Med Ctr Med Tech 1993-; *ai:* Jr Olympic Vllybl Club Dir & Coach; Tutor & Mentor; ASCP 1993-; *office:* Mount Notre Dame HS 711 E Columbia Ave Cincinnati OH 45215

JAEGLE, DEBORAH JUSTEN, Rel Teacher & Campus Minister; *b:* Toledo, OH; *m:* David R.; *c:* Chad, Alison, Justen; *ed:* Lourdes Coll (BA) Rel Stud 1993; *cr:* St Catherine Parish Yth Ministry Dir 1986-91; Diocese of Toledo Yth & Schl Svcs Area Coord 1992-94; St Wendelin HS Rel Tchr, Campus Minister & Rel Dept Chprsn 1994-; *ai:* Today Production Producer; Today Productions 1993-, Historian; Diocese of Toledo for God & Yth Awd 1990; *office:* St Wendelin HS 533 N Countyline St Fostoria OH 44830

JAFFE, MARVIN R., Professor; *b:* New York City, NY; *ed:* Brooklyn Coll (BS) Chem 1960, (MA) Chem 1965; Fordham Univ (PHD) Analytical Chem 1970; *cr:* Bronx Comm Coll Instr 1965-68; Borough of Manhattan Comm Coll Asst Prof 1970-76, Assoc Prof 1976-85, Prof 1985-; *ai:* Fac Senate; *office:* Borough Of Manhattan Comm Coll 199 Chambers St New York NY 10007

JAGODOWSKI, MAUREEN KENNEDY, Lang Arts, Latin & Span Tchr; *b:* Holyoke, MA; *m:* Thomas George; *c:* Thomas, Todd (dec), Troy; *ed:* Our Lady of the Elms (BA) Span, Ed 1971, (MAT) Eng, Ed 1990; *cr:* Blessed Sacrament Schl 6th Grd Lang Arts Tchr 1986, 5th Grd Tchr 1986-87, 7th Grd Lang Arts & Span Tchr 1987-90, 8th Grd Latin, Lang Arts & Lit Tchr 1990-; *ai:* Drama Club; Self-Evaluation & Self-Growth Process Comm; Yrbk Adv; NCEA, Pioneer Valley Cncl Rdng 1986-; Five Colls Partnership 1988-; Pompeiana Classical Stud 1989-; *office:* Blessed Sacrament Schl 21 Westfield Rd Holyoke MA 01040

JAILER, BERNICE PONGER, English Teacher; *b:* Elizabeth, NJ; *m:* Warren; *c:* Judith Bluysen, Todd, Laura Jansen; *ed:* Montclair St TC (BA) Eng 1947; 36 Credit Hrs Advanced Stud Post Grad; *cr:* Hackensack Bd of Ed Tchr 1947-51; Middletown Twp Bd of Ed Tchr 1961-; *ai:* South Offers Svc Adv; Alpha Delta Kappa 1981-; NJEA, MCEA, MTEA, NEA 1961-; Grad Schl of Ed Harvard Fellowship; Adjunct Instr Brookdale Comm Coll; Book Reviewer Women's Reporter; Panelist Holocaust Symposium Brookdale Coll; Governor's Teacher Recognition Awd 1992; *office:* Middletown HS South 501 Nutswamp Rd Middletown NJ 07748

JAKOBI, STEVEN RICHARD, Assistant Prof of Biology; *b:* Budapest, Hungary; *m:* Toni Walzer; *c:* Matthew, Robert, Steven; *ed:* Univ Cincinnati (BS) Bio 1976; West Chester Univ (MA) Bio 1984; WV Univ Phd Candidate Plant Pathology; Univ PA Hosp HTL, ASCP Histotechniques 1980; *cr:* WV Univ Bio Lab Instr 1987-90; MAssachusetts Bay Comm Coll Bio Instr 1991-93; Alfred St Coll Asst Prof Bio 1993-; *ai:* Amer Inst Biol Sci 1991-; Amer Phytopathol Soc 1985-, Tchng CTE Mem; *office:* SUNY Alfred St Coll Dept Physical & Life Sci Alfred NY 14802*

JAKOBS, CATHERINE, Fifth Grade Teacher; *b:* Otisville, NY; *m:* Gustav; *c:* Deborah Gallagher, Patrina Denaro, Carol Denaro, Theresa Keyes, Andrew Denaro; *ed:* Queens Coll CUNY (BA) Sociology, Urban Stud 1988, (MS) Elem Ed 1992; *cr:* Our Lady of the Cenacle Schl Fifth Grd Tchr 1988-91, Seventh-Eighth Grd Tchr 1991-95, Fifth Grd Tchr 1995-; *ai:* Math League Coord; Math Cncl; NCEA 1988-.*

JAKOWICKI, VIOLETTA ANNA, ESL Teacher; *b:* Monticello, NY; *ed:* SUNY at Stony Brook (BA) Fr, Ed 1993; Currently Completing MA Eng as Second Lang, Linguistics, Ed 27 Credit Hrs; 6 Credit Hrs Span Lang; *cr:* Hewlett Schl 7-12 Grd Fr Tchr, Admissions Rep, Adv 1993-94; Lindenhurst Pub Schls K-12 Grd ESL Tchr 1994-; *ai:* Key Club Adv; Admission, Schl Rep; Translator; NYSADLT, LILT 1992-93; Amer Soc for Eighteenth Century Stud 1993.

JAKYMIW, NICOLE J., English Teacher; *b:* Astoria, Queens, NY; *m:* Stephen Mounkhall; *ed:* Fordham Univ (BA) Eng 1991; Lehman Coll (MS) Eng Ed 1995; *cr:* Lerhman HS Tchr 1991-; *ai:* Shared Decision M Comm; NCTE 1991-; Rsrch Awd for Thesis in Eng Ed.

JALBERT, SANDY, Eng Dept Chair & Writing Tchr; *b:* Van Bure *ed:* Univ of ME at Presque Isle (BS) Ed & Eng 1970; Univ of Southe (MS) Scndry Rdng & Literacy 1982; *cr:* Sabattus Elem Schl Jr H 1971-82; Brunswick Jr HS 7th & 8th Grd Tchr 1982-; *ai:* Recogni Progress Report Comms; Staff & Stu Cncls; Stu Assistance Team; ME Ed Assn, ME Cncl of Eng Lang Arts, NCTE, Intnl Rdng Ass Rdng Assn; Coastal Humane Soc, Bd of Dirs; *office:* Brunswick Jr Columbia Ave Brunswick ME 04011

JAMES, ANITA MARIE (YOUNG), Retired Teacher; *b:* Zanesvill *m:* Donald Earl; *c:* Donald E., Dana E., Amy James Krec; *ed:* OH (BSEd) K-8 1967; Attnd Ohio Univ, Muskigum Coll, Garrett Evan Theological Seminary, Duke Divinity Schl; 5 Yrs, 2 1/2 Yrs Se Work; *cr:* Maysville Schl Dist 4, 5, 6, 8 Grd Tchr 1963-; *ai:* Chrld. Sports, Stu Cncl Adv 1994-95; OH Ret Tchrs Assn, Muskingum Co Assn 1996; United Meth Church Pastor Parish, Sunday Schl Laymember Annual Conf, Lay Speaker; *home:* 1318 Arch St Zanesvi 43701

JAMES, BEVERLY HOLTON, Third Grade Teacher; *b:* Meshoppe *m:* Richard J.; *ed:* Mansfield St Coll (BS) Elem Ed 1975; Univ of Sc (MS) Elem Ed 1980; 30 Addl Grad Credits; *cr:* Mehoopany Elen 2nd-4th Grd Tchr 1975-; *ai:* Instrl Support Team; NEA, PSEA TAEA 1975-, Exec Bd Mem; *office:* Mehoopany Elem Schl RR 2 B Mehoopany PA 18629

JAMES, DONALD L., Math & Bible Teacher; *b:* Ridley Park, F Susan Hastie; *c:* Rebecca, Daniel, Matthew, Abigail, Mical LeTourneau Coll (BS) Welding Eng Tech 1978; *cr:* Chicago Bridge Welding Eng 1979; Budd Co Design Eng 1979-86; West Chester Schl Math, Bible, Sci Tchr 1986-; *ai:* Bible Bapt Church 1987-, D 1991-; *office:* West Chester Christian Schl 1237 Paoli Pike West C PA 19380

JAMES, ELEANOR D., English Coordinator; *b:* Chingford, engla Ronald James; *c:* Michael, Carolyn; *ed:* Univ of British Columbia Eng & Philosophy 1963; Univ of MA Eng 1966; Villanova Univ Credits; *cr:* Temple Univ Instr Eng 1965-69; Montgomery CCC Asso Eng 1969-; *ai:* Bd Mem Philadelphia Youth Orch, DE Cty Youth Orc Cty Concerts Assn.*

JAMES, JEFFREY R., Communication Arts Teacher; *b:* N Versaille *ed:* Clarion Univ (BS) Communication Arts, Scndry Ed 1990; Allegheny HS Eng Tchr 1990-91; Franklin Regnl SD Eng, Rdng, T Arts Tchr 1991-; *ai:* Ftbl, Track, Bsbl, Wrestling Coach; Thespians, Team, Chess Club, Yrbk Spon; PSEA, NEA 1990-; *office:* Franklin Schl Dist 3210 School Rd Murrysville PA 15668*

JAMES, KRISTEL SHUTT, English Teacher; *b:* Gettysburg, P Kenneth A.; *c:* Chelsea, Nathan; *ed:* Bluffton Coll (BA) Eng, Hum Bowling Green St Univ Cert Scndry Ed 1988, Addl 8 Hrs; 3 Hrs U Toledo; Cooperative Learning Seminars; *cr:* Luma Art Assn Admin 1984-86; Woodmore HS Tchr 1988-89; Northwood HS Tchr 1989-; *a* Cncl Adv; North Cntrl Assn Comm, Fac Co Chair; Eng Dept OCTELA 1991-; NCTE 1988-; Brancroft Mennonite Church 1994-, S Schl, Drama Team; *office:* Northwood HS 600 Lemoyne Rd Northwo 43619

JAMES, LINDA D., Resource Teacher; *b:* Newark, NJ; *m:* Herbe Shawn, Aaron; *ed:* Newark St Coll (BA) Elem Ed 1972; Kean C Credit Hrs; Montclair St Univ 27 Credit Hrs; *cr:* Newark Bd of Ed T Yrs; *ai:* Solid Rock Bapt Church, Deaconess Bd Sec, Pres Ed, S Comm; *office:* Mc Kinley Schl 1 Colonnade Pl Newark NJ 07104

JAMES, LINDA S., Professor of Psychology; *b:* Meadville, P Kristina Goodwin, Shauna, Carlton, Davy; *ed:* Univ of KY (BS) 1963; IN Univ (PHD) Psych 1968; Cert Family Therapy; Lic Practicing Psychologist NJ; *cr:* Univ of TX at Austin Adj Instr 196 Trenton St Coll Adj Instr 1971-74; Geogrian Court Coll Prof 1974-; *a* Psi Chi NHS in Psych Adv, Assembly Chair 1995-95, Exec C Planning Team; Mentor Undergraduate Research; Chair Psych Dept; A on Cnslng Psych; Mentor NJ MAC Undergrad Flwshp Prgm; Psychological Assn 1975-; AAUP; Intnl Soc for Stud of Dissoci 1989-; Amensty Intnl 1991-; 3 Week Conf Tchng Undergrauate Psyc St Univ; Presented Paper at APA San Francisco 1992; Several Articles *office:* Georgian Court Coll 900 Lakewood Ave Lakewood NJ 08701

JAMES, MICHAEL D., Math Teacher; *b:* Chelsea, MA; *m:* Nancy C *c:* Matthew Joseph; *ed:* Univ of RI (BA) Ed 1973, (MA) Math, Soc 1978; *cr:* RI Coll Upward Bound Math Prgm 1979-87; *ai:* Stu Fac Se Gymnastics Club, Comm Forum Adv; AFT; *office:* Classical HS Westminster St Providence RI 02903*

JAMES, PEGGY JOYCE, Fourth Grade Teacher; *b:* Jamestown, OH Central St Univ (BSEd) Elem Tchng 1971; Wright St Univ (MED) Specialist 1987; Mercy Cntrl Hosp LPN Nrsng 1960; *cr:* Greene Hosp LPN 1960-66; Greenview Schl Dist Tchr 1971-; *ai:* Schl Dist Me Cedarville Coll Tchr Ed Advy Comm 1991-; Ross Chapel AME Ch 1951-; Friends of Lib; Kappa Delta Pi; Martha Holden Jennings Sc 1974-75, 1986-87; Outstdng Elem Tchrs of Amer 1974; Lion's Club C Svc Awd 1986; *office:* Greenview Schl Dist 1795 S Charlesto Jamestown OH 45335*

JAMES, PETER C., 8th Grade Social Studies Tchr; *b:* Buffalo, NY Nancy Pristia; *c:* Randy, Kristie; *ed:* Morehead St Univ (BA) His 1 Buffalo St Coll (MS) Ed 1975; 32 Addl Hrs; *cr:* Hamburg Cntrl Schls 1967-; *ai:* Hamburg Tchrs Union, NEA, NY St Tchrs Union, NY Cnc Soc Stud 1967-; Hamburg Jr Bsbl League 1972-, Field Supvr, Recrea Dept Mem; Fredonia St Coll Adjunct Prof, Certified Field Supvr for Tchrs; Hamburg Schls Career Milestone 25 Yrs; Modified Bsbl C 1969-91; modified Soccer Coach 1976-77; *home:* 134 Meadow Hamburg NY 14075

JAMES, VELDA M. H., Mathematics Teacher; *b:* St Vincent, W I; Univ of the West Indies (BA) Math, Ec 1974; Dip Ed Math 1977; Scndry Schl Barbados W I Tchr of Math 1976-85; Scndry Schl St Maa Tchr of Math, In Charge of Coord Dept 1985-; *ai:* Supervising Correc of Examination Papers; Carribbean Examinations Cncl Asst C Examiner; ASCD Intnl 1990-, Bd of Dir; ASCD SXM Affiliate 1990-, Elect 1996; Schl Awd Perfect Attendance & Dedication to Duty 1993; Awd for Meritorious Svc & Commitment for 10 Yrs 1979-88; Schl Awc Excellent Results in CXC Math Exam 1990; *office:* St Maarten Acad L Scots Rd St Maarten Nethrlnds Antilles XX

JAMESON, AMY R., Physics Teacher; *b:* Lackawanna, NY; *m:* Stever Adriane, Anthony; *ed:* Univ of Cincinnati (BS) Comprehensive Sci 1985; Grad Hrs Xavier Univ; *cr:* Western Hills HS Physics & Chem 1985-88; Shroder Paideia Schl 8th Grd Sci Tchr 1990-91; Hughes Physics Tchr 1991-; *ai:* Past Sci Club, Environmental Club Spon; 1985-; AAPT 1993-; Kappa Delta Pi 1983-; Marion Merrell Dow Runner Up Innovation Sci Tchng Awd 1991; *office:* Hughes Ctr HS 2 Clifton Ave Cincinnati OH 45219*

JAMESON, ELLA C., Language Arts Teacher; *b:* Rocky Mount, NC Carl; *c:* Sharron Latham, Carlette Adams, Everton, Kimberly; *ed:* NC C Univ (BA) Eng, Fr 1962; Long Island Univ (M) Eng Ed 1973; St John's (M) Hum 1978; Attnd Brooklyn Coll, Hunter Coll; *cr:* Wise HS Eng T

Pinetops HS Eng Tchr 1 Yr; Decatur Jr HS Lang Arts Tchr 25 Yrs; Garnett Jr HS 324 Lang Arts Tchr 4 Yrs; *ai:* AFT; UFT 1970-; Alpha Alpha 1961-; NAACP 1980-; Astor Flwshp; *home:* 15 Maple St yn NY 11225*

SON, PATRICIA GALLEY, Psychology Instructor; *b:* sport, PA; *c:* Robert III, Thomas, Joseph; *ed:* Carlow Coll (BA) gy & Psych 1986; Duquesne Univ (MA) Psych 1987; Working on al Dissertation in Psych; Certfd Hypnotherapist Amer Hypnosis Acad; Nuturing Pgm Consultant; Family Dev Resources; *cr:* kley Vly Hosp Therapist 1987-89; Barton Psych Therapy Assn ist 1987-; Family Resources Phys Abuse & Prevention Treatment 1989-94; Carlow Coll Adj Fac 1989-; Luth Yth & Family Svcs tant 1994-; *ai:* Womens Spirituality Group for Young Women & ns Journey Through Mid-Life Facilitator; Hilltop Comm Childrens 89-, Pres & Bd of Dir; Emory UM Church for Family Dev Project Consultant; Tchng Flwshp at Duquesne Univ; Federal, St & Comm for Child Abuse Prevention & Treatment Pgms; Alternative Pgm for ilitation of Drug Addicted Mothers & Children Grant.*

SON, RONALD E., Social Studies Teacher; *b:* Pottstown, PA; *m:* Jane Mest; *c:* Keith, Brian; *ed:* West Chester Univ (BS) ehensive Soc Sci 1971, (MED) Educl Media 1975; 45 Addl Hrs Penn West Jr HS 7th Grd SS Tchr 1971-, Audio, Visual Dir, Stage Mgr , Team Ldr 1996; *ai:* Coach Jr HS Ftbl 1973-, Sr HS Var Bsbl 93, Jr HS Bsktbl 1972-76; NEA, PSEA 1971-; Colebrookdale Chapel 39, Sec, Bldg Comm; Exeter Bible Church 1989-; Bsbl 5 League, 2 PIAA St Championships 1991; *office:* Boyertown Jr HS-WEST 2nd lison Sts Boyertown PA 19512*

SON, ROY M., HS Mathematics Teacher; *b:* Ritchie Cty, WV; *m:* Oliver; *c:* Kelli Burdette, Matt, Kristen; *ed:* Marshall Univ (BA) Ed OH St Univ (MA) Math 1992; *cr:* Warren Local HS Math Tchr 1966-; st Ftbl Coach; WA Cty Math Curr Comm; NEA, OEA, WLTA 1966-; 1 1994-; *office:* Warren Local Schl Rt 1 Vincent OH 45784

EL, JOHN, Theatre Dept Visiting Instr; *b:* Orange, NJ; *ed:* William on Coll (BA) Speech, Theatre 1974; Brooklyn Coll (MFA) Acting Trained with Master Tchrs Uta Hagen, F. Murray Abraham in NY ; *cr:* Brooklyn Coll Tchng Fellow 1989-90; Berea Coll Guest Artist 1992-93; Buffalo Studio Arena Guest Artist 1995; Wagner Coll ng Instr 1994-; *ai:* Acting Tchr, Coach; Directed, Fac Adv Stu ctions; Supvr Speech Profiencey Test; ATHE, ECTC 1990-; SETC ; Actors Equity Assn; Screen Actors Guild; Prof Actor 20 Yrs rming Off-Broadway, Regnl Theatre, Summer Stock, Commercials; Wagner Coll 631 Howard Ave Staten Island NY 10301

ESON, CAROLYN EILENE, Health Career Instructor; *b:* Van Wert, ; Roger L.; *c:* Michael Lee, Jody Paula, Gary David; *ed:* OH St Univ Nursing 1964, (MSN) Nursing Ed 1965; Lima Mem Schl of Nursing ma Nursing RN 1962; *cr:* OH St Univ Hospitals Staff Nurse 1963-64; Vert Cty Hospital Staff Nurse & Inservice 1966-72; Vantage Voc Adult ursing Classes Tchr 1972-75; Vantage Voc Schl Hlth Careers Instr ; *ai:* Voc Clubs Of Amer Adv; NATP Primary Instr; Vantage Tchrs Org , Schlrshp Comm; OVA, AVA 1976-; RN Assn; Amer Red Cross Vol ; Amer Heart Cardiac Pulmonary Resusitation Instr 1990-; Numerous nps, Seminars for CEUs; *home:* 7272 Monmouth Rd Van Wert OH

IESON, KAREN TOPER, High School Math Teacher; *b:* Watertown, *n:* Tedd R.; *c:* Jenna, Kristin; *ed:* SUNY at Cortland (BSE) PE, ning 1981; SUNY at Potsdam (MS) Ed 1986; NYS 7-12 Math Cert; ding SUNY Oswego for (CAS) Admin; *cr:* Binghamton YMCA tics, Women's Membership Dir 2 Yrs; Carthage HS Math Tchr 14 Yrs, n Intern 1995-96; *ai:* NY Math League Adv; Stu at Risk Team; ate Comm; Site Based Mngmnt Team; NYSUT Tchrs Union 1983-; Math Assn 1981-; ASCD 1995-; AIAW Division III All Amer mer SUNY Cortland 5 Var Records; *office:* Carthage Central HS) NYS Rt 26 Carthage NY 13619*

ISON, CONNIE ELAINE, Vocal Music Teacher; *b:* Chillicothe, OH; avid Earl; *c:* Shaun David, Christina Louise; *ed:* OH Univ (BED) Elem 72, (MED) Curr & Instruction 1987; Post Grad Stud at Capital U, OH Rio Grande U & Wright St U; *cr:* Zane Trace Elem 3rd & 4th Grd -72; Adena Local Schl Vocal Music K-8th Grd 1975-77; Huntington Schl Vocal Music K-6th Grd 1978, 4th Grd 1978; Zane Trace Schl Music K-8th Grd 1978-82, K-12th Grd 1982-86, Vocal Music K-4th 1-12th 1987-; *ai:* Voice-Piano Pvt Stdnts; Church Organist; Church Dir Comm Choral Dir; NEA 1969-; OMEA & NMEA 1977-; ACDA -82; Curr & Instruction Assn 1987-89; Delta Kappa Gamma 1993-; : Zane Trace HS 946 Rt 180 Chillicothe OH 45601*

ISON, MARJORIE ANN, US Soc Stud Tchr & Dept Chm; *b:* sburg, MD; *ed:* Hagerstown Jr Coll (AA) Ed 1965; Shepherd Coll Scndry Ed, S S 1967; Shippensburg St Coll (ME) Ed 1970; Hood Coll edit Hrs; WV Univ 3 Credit Hrs; *cr:* Boonsboro MS Tchr Grd 8th US Functional Math, Lang Arts, 7th Grd Eng, 6th Grd Rdng, 6-7 Grd Soc 1967-; *ai:* Attendance, Discipline Comm; Mentor for Beginning s; WA Co Tchrs Assn, MD St Tchrs Assn, NEA 1967-; MD St Soc ghters of Amer Revolution Awd Outstanding Accomplishment Tchng r His 1987-88; Letter Recognition Peter G. Callas Mem MD House Former Dir Admin for Bd Ed Washington Co; *office:* Boonsboro M S H. Wade Dr Boonsboro MD 21713

ISON, NORMAN HARVEY,SR., 7th & 8th Grd Science Teacher; *b:* burg, PA; *m:* Delma Jean Holt; *c:* Kimberly Ann Carter, Kelly Lynn y, Tracie Yvonne Mangum, Tammy Jean, Norman H. Jr., Meghan , Erin Nicole; *ed:* Thiel Coll at Greenville (BSEd) Biological Sci ; Univ of Toledo Drug Ed; *cr:* Toledo Pub Schls Tchr 1965-; St aels Med Ctr Dir Fire & Safety 1984-85; Univ of Toledo Dir NYSP ts Prgm 1993-95; *ai:* OH St Univ, Jr Manners Coop Prgm; Scott HS s Asst Track Coach; Toledo Fed of Tchrs 1969-; Phi Delta Kappa; : 2639 Glenwood Ave Toledo OH 43610*

IISON, WILLIAM EDWARD,III, Chemistry & Physics Teacher; *b:* on, OH; *m:* Judy R. Jackson; *c:* William IV, Danielle, Ryan, Nathan; Kent St Univ (BS) Bio 1974; Wright St Univ (BS) Chem, Cert 1976; tr Sci Courses; *cr:* Grandview Hosp Med Records Analyst 1975-77; brook HS Sci Tchr 1977-; Sears Automotive Sales Assn Sales Assoc 8-; *ai:* Cmptr Trng Stu, Staff; NEA, OEA 1977-; Falcon Club 1986-, m Chair; Chosen Most Influential Tchr by Valedictorians 4 Times; *e:* Bellbrook HS 3491 Upper Bellbrook Rd Bellbrook OH 45305

IDERCHICK, CRISTAL S., Vocal Music Teacher; *b:* Mechanicsburg, *c:* Jessica, Julie; *ed:* IN Univ of PA (BS) Music Ed 1982; Cr Hrs Hartt of Music; Westminster Choir Coll, Vandercook Coll of Music; *cr:* St. y's Schl Elem Instrumental Music Tchr 1983-85; Milton Hershey Schl ic Tchr 1985-; Hershey 1st United Meth Church Flute, Children's ir Dir 1990-; *ai:* New Horizons Jazz-Show Choir; MENC, PMEA, MEA 1990-; PSEA, MHEA 1994-, Bldg Rep; Delta Omicron 1980-; tral PA Symphony 1990-, Principal Flutist; Voice Care Network 1994-; Excl Awd Milton Hershey Schl 1991; *office:* Milton Hershey Schl PO 830 Sr Hall Hershey PA 17033

IECEK, KAREN KEARNEY, Second Grade Teacher; *b:* Sewickley, *m:* Richard; *c:* Rene Mauder, Gayle Sklarsky, Darlene Fowler, Patrick; IN Univ of PA (BA) Elem Ed 1966; Univ of Pittsburgh (MS) Voc Ed); *cr:* Moon Schls 2nd Grd Tchr 1966-68; Duarte Schls 4th Grd Tchr 1968-70; Parkway Voc Tech Mrktg Tchr 1977-80; North Allegheny Intermed Gifted Tchr 1981-82; North Allegheny HS Mrktg Tchr 1982-83; Espe Elem Schl 2nd Grd Tchr 1983-; *ai:* 2nd Grd Mentor & Facilitator; Southwestern PA Ctr for Tchr Ldrshp Bd Mem; NAFT 1981-; Hampton Lib 1990-, Lib Bd; Northland Lib 1980-, Vol; Deacon Hampton Presby Church 1970-; *home:* 24 Cedar Ridge Road Ext Allison Park PA 15101*

JANECZEK, MARY, Mathematics Teacher; *b:* New Haven, CT; *ed:* Boston Coll (BA) Scndry Ed, Math 1977; Southern CT St Univ (MED) Rdng Ed 1981; Fairfield Univ Cert of Advanced Stud-Educl Admin & Supervision; *cr:* Dr Carl C Giannotti Jr HS Math Tchr, Master Tchr 1977-83; West Haven HS Math Tchr 1983-; *ai:* NHS Fac Cncl; NFT, WHFT, ATOMIC 1977-; DKG 1987-, Treas; *office:* West Haven HS 1 Circle St West Haven CT 06516*

JANEK, NANCY REESE, English Teacher & Dept Chair; *b:* Sharon, PA; *m:* James Allen; *c:* Jean Jerina, Mary McFarland, Jay; *ed:* Westminster Coll (BA) Speech 1959; CA St Univ at Dominquez Hills (MA) Hum 1979; Attnd Youngstown St Univ; Earlham Coll; OH Wesleyan Univ; Kent St Univ; Ashland Coll; OH St Univ; West Virginia Univ; Cabe- Western Reserve Univ; *cr:* Shaker Heights Pub Schls 7th Grd Lang Arts Tchr 1959-60; Columbia Station Pub Schls HS Eng & Speech Tchr 1960-61; Crestline Pub Schls HS Eng & Speech Tchr 1972-73; Beaver Local Pub Schls MS Lang Arts Tchr 1975-86, HS Eng Tchr 1986-, Dept Chair 1987-; *ai:* Y-Teens Adv; North Cntrl Self Esteem Comm; Prin Advy Comm; WROTE 1991-; NEA & oEA 1959-; OCTELA & NCTE 1980-; Salem Presbyn Church 1978-; Pub in Theory Into Practice; NCTE Notes Plus; OH Journal; NE OH Chrs Ldrs Network; Jennings Scholar; Two Federal Grants, English Journal (publication); *office:* Beaver Local HS 13187 St Rt 7 Lisbon OH 44432*

JANEKA, RHONDA ROARK, Science Educator; *b:* Wilmington, DE; *m:* Thomas Sr.; *c:* Thomas Jr., Laurie, Zachary; *ed:* Univ of DE (BSEd) Spec Ed-Cum Laude 1981, (MED) Scndry Spec Ed 1984; 45 Credits in Tech, Hlth, Psych, Curr Design; *cr:* Glasgow HS Spec Ed Tchr 1983; Christiana-Salem Elem Team 2nd Grd Tchr 1984; Glasgow HS Spec Ed Tchr 1984-; *ai:* Dept Chprsn; Head Field Hockey Coach; Bldg Ldrshp Team; Stu Assistance Team; Dist Sci Curr Comm Co-Chair 1994, Chair 1995-; NEA 1983-; DE Ed Assn 1983-, Bldg Rep; CEC 1989-; NSTA 1995-; Amer Assn of Univ Women 1991-; CHADD 1995-; Continuing Ed Stu Awd Univ of DE 1995; Tech in Ed Grant 1991; New Directions in DE St Inservice Presenter 1993; Grad Tchng Assistantship 1982-83; *office:* Glasgow HS 1901 S College Ave Newark DE 19702*

JANELLE, DIANE L. ST. CYR, Former Third Grade Teacher; *b:* Manchester, NH; *m:* Marc Andre; *ed:* Notre Dame Coll (BS) Elem Ed 1984; *cr:* St Anthony Schl 1 Grd Tchr 1984-85, 2 Grd Tchr 1985-90, 3 Grd Tchr 1990-95; Self-Employed Free Lance Childrens Writer, Wkshp Presenter 1995-; *ai:* Sponsoring, Coaching Stu Steck-Vaughn's Publish-a-Book Contest; Tutoring 2 Stdnts Math, 1 Stu Rdng; NCEA 1984-95; St Anthony Church 1994-, Folk Group; *home:* 117 Bittersweet Dr Manchester NH 03109

JANESAK, MARY KODY, Child Devlopment, Home Ec Tchr; *b:* Passaic, NJ; *m:* Charles P.; *c:* Christine A.; *ed:* Rutgers Univ (BA) Home Ec, Child Dev 1969; Douglas Coll Ed; St Peter's Coll Urban Ed; Jersey City St Coll Supervision Degree; *cr:* North Bergen HS Home Ec, Child Dev Tchr 1969-; *ai:* Presch, Playschool Child Dev Prgm Supvr; Play Wardrobe Designer; AFT, Amer Home Ec Assn 1969-; Humane Soc of US 1985-; Ortley Beach Property Assn 1978-; NJ St Ed Grant for Early Chldhd Presch Prgm Dev; *office:* North Bergen HS 2417 Kennedy Blvd North Bergen NJ 07047

JANICKI, MARY ANDERSON, Learning Tchr for At Risk Stud; *b:* Columbus, OH; *m:* Donald J.; *c:* Matthew, Julie; *ed:* OH Univ (BA) Elem Ed 1978; OH Valley Coll Assoc 1968; Learning Disabilities Cert; *cr:* Zanesville City Resource Tchr 1979-80; Chandlersville & DFSH Resource Tchr 1980-81; Duncan Falls Jr HS Resource Tchr 1980-; *ai:* North Amer Riding for the Handicapped Assn; N Terrace Church of Christ 1995-; 2 Grants from Cntrl OH Coal Comp; *office:* Duncan Falls Jr HS Cedar St Duncan Falls OH 43734

JANIGA, JEFFERY ALLAN, Govt, Econ & Hnrs History Tchr; *b:* Barberton, OH; *m:* Teressa Pilgrim; *c:* Bryan, Kyle, Todd Michael; *ed:* Kent St (BS) Comprehensive Soc Stud & PE 1977; Akron Univ Post Back; Chemical Substance Abuse; Sports Medicinie; *cr:* Barberton HS Tchr 1977-; *ai:* Var Girls Bsktbl 1978-; Mem Ath Bd; Stud Discipline Class; Touchdown Club Mem 1985-; Barberton Ath Booster 1977-;OH Coaches Assn 1977-; Womens Tri-Cty Coaches Assn 1992-, Pres 1993-; Barberton Sports Hall of Fame 1991; Summit Cty Coach of the Yr 1989, 1994; OHSAA 300 Wins 1995; Metro Coach of the Yr 1988, 1995; UPI OH Coach of the Yr 1983; *office:* Barberton HS 489 W Hopocan Ave Barberton OH 44203

JANIS, JOANN BRAMBLE, Business Teacher; *b:* Wilmington, DE; *m:* Michael J.; *c:* Michelle Schram, Michale J. Jr., Jonathan A.; *ed:* Goldey Beacom Coll (AA) Med Sec 1964; DE St Coll (BS) Voc Ed 1989; Bus Ed, Med Office Asst Certs; *cr:* Drs. Bancroft & Cannon Med Sec 1962-68; DE St Hosp Med Sec 1968-69; Wilmington Med Ctr Exec Sec 1969-71; Drs. Straughn & Resurreccion Med Sec 1972-79; Talmo Real Estate Agent 1976-81; Hodgson Voc Tech HS Tchr 1979-; RCI Owner, Pres 1987-; *ai:* HOSA, VICA, BPA Clubs Adv 1979-; Information Systems, Svcs Advy Bd; Tchrs' Sunshine Comm; NEA, DSEA 1979-; NCCVTEA 1979-, Treas, Recording, Corresponding Sec, Negotiations, Supplemental Pay Comms; DE Tech & Com Coll Advy Bd; DE Chptr Amer Assn of Med Transcrip 1993-; DE Chptr Alzheimer's 1995-; Franciscan Care Ctr 1995-, Vol; New Castle Cty Chamber, DE Chamber of Commerce 1987-; Tchr of Yr 1986-87; *office:* Hodgson Voc Tech HS 2575 Summit Bridge Rd Newark DE 19702*

JANISHEFSKI, VICTOR FRANK, Art Teacher; *b:* Danville, PA; *m:* Christine H. Parks; *c:* Monica Logan, Lisa, Brendan; *ed:* MD Inst of Art (BFA) Fine Arts 1963; *cr:* Glen Burnie HS Art Tchr 1963-66; Calvert Hall Coll Art Tchr 1967-; *ai:* Archery Coach; Art Club Moderator; NCEA 1967-; Sabbatcal 1991-92; *office:* Calvert Hall College Schl 8102 Lasalle Rd Baltimore MD 21286

JANJIGIAN, ANAHID, Fine Artist & Art Instr; *b:* Boston, MA; *c:* Adrienne Kooyoumjian; *ed:* Art Stu League of NY; *cr:* Janjigian Art Studio Art Instr 1963-; *ai:* Art Stu League Schlrshp; Whos Who in the East; Armenian Painters & Sculptors, Numerous Exhibitions Displayed; *office:* Janjigian Art Studio 16416 Lithonia Ave Fresh Meadows NY 11365

JANKOWSKI, BARBARA LOU (CHAMBERS), Teacher; *b:* Toledo, OH; *m:* David J.; *c:* Julie B.; *ed:* Mary Manse Coll (BA) Elem Ed; Eastern MI Univ (MA) Lang Arts 1987; Attnd Toledo Univ & Bowling Green St Univ; *cr:* Hillview Elem Schl 2nd Grd Tchr; Greenwood Elem Schl 2nd Grd Tchr 1964-69; Christ the King Schl 2nd Grd Tchr 1976-77; Shoreland Elem SChl 5th Grd Tchr 1977-; *ai:* Rdng Curr, Soc Stud Curr Comms; Dept Chm; NEA; OEA; TAWLS; Delta Kappa Gamma; Intnl Rdng Assn-City & Natl Level; Whole Lang Support Group; OH Cncl of Tchrs of Eng Lang Arts; Outstanding Classroom Tchr Awd 1988-89; *office:* Shoreland Elem Schl Suder & E Harbor Dr Toledo OH 43611

JANKOWSKI, MADELYN ANN, Art Teacher; *b:* Upper Darby, PA; *m:* Ronald; *c:* Jason; *ed:* Glassboro St Coll (BA) Art Ed 1971; 15 Grad Credit Hrs; *cr:* Pine Hill Schl Art Tchr `171-76; Trinidad Schl for the Deaf Art Tchr 1977-80; St Bernadettes Art Tchr 1977-80; Woodbury Pub Schls Art Tchr 1986; Chews Elem Schl Art Tchr 1987-; *ai:* Art Club; Latch Key Art Class; AENJ South 1987-Recording Sec; Glouscester Twp Scenic & Historical Preservation Comm 1995-; Governor's Tchr Awd; Resloution by NJ St & Gen Assembly Honoring Art Night 1995; Perfect Attendeace Awds; *office:* Chews Elem Schl 600 Somerdale Rd Blackwood NJ 08012

JANNARONE, JANE, English Teacher; *b:* Montclair, NJ; *c:* Robyn Narayouski; *ed:* Marietta Coll (BA) Eng 1969; Monmouth Univ (MSEd) Stu Prsnl Svcs 1993; *cr:* Freehold Regnl HS Dist Eng Tchr 1969-; Freehold Adult HS Guidance Cnslr 1995-; *ai:* NEA 1969-; NCTE 1985-; Tchr of Yr 1991; *office:* Howell HS Squankum Yellow Brook Rd Farmingdale NJ 07727*

JANNOTTA, DOREEN PATRICIA, Volunteer Substitute; *b:* Chicago, IL; *m:* Anthony Joseph; *c:* Dana Marie, Anthony; *ed:* Dallas Peace Inst Conflict Resolution 1993; Miami Peace Inst 1993, Formation in Ministry 1978-81; *cr:* Lincoln Jr HS Eng, Soc Stud Tchr 1965-67; St Mary's Schl 4th Grd Tchr 1981-82; Holy Family of Nazareth 8th Grd Tchr 1991-95; Vol Sub All Grds Span & Mediation 1996-; *ai:* Hispanic Children; Montgomery Cty Homeless Vol; St Rose Lima Church, Vol; TEETH 1992-, Coord, Comm Svc; Texans for Emergency, Tooth Hlth; CasaRicardo Refugee Resettlement 1989-92; Peace & Justice Commission OK & TX 1980-85; Nom Dorothy Day Awd Diocese of FT Worth 1992; Nom Ft Worth Vol of Tr 1992-93; Comm Svc Awd in Tulsa Svc 1989; Rerum Novarem Awd; *home:* 9 Sterling Ct Rockville MD 20850*

JANNUZZELLI, GERALD JOSEPH, Band Director; *b:* Jersey City, NJ; *m:* Diane C. Marianacci; *ed:* Jersey City St Coll (BA) Music 1968, (MA) Music 1971; Columbia Univ Tchrs Coll (MED) Music Ed 1974; VanderCook Coll of Music 12 Semester Hrs 1992; Univ of the Arts 9 Semester Hrs 1993; Attnd US Naval Schl of Music; *cr:* Sayreville Jr HS Lang Arts Tchr 1968-69; Lincoln Elem & Locust MS Instrumental Music Tchr 1969-75; Kean Coll Adj Music Instr 1973; Abraham Clark HS Band Dir & Inst Music Tchr 1975-80; Middletown HS North Band Dir & Inst Music Tchr 1980-92; *ai:* Marching Band Dir 11 Yrs; NJ Ed Assoc 1968-; NEA 1968-; NJ Music Edctrs Assoc 1980-; Music Edctrs Natl Conf 1980-; US Naval Reserve 1957-, Chief Musician, 5 Medals; US Army Reserve 1976-, Warrant Ofcr, 3 Medals; Navy Musicians Assoc 1995-, Region Coord; Thorne MS Governors Tchr Awd Recepient & Tchr of Yr 1995; US Army Reserve Bandmaster 78th Division Band NJ Lightning; Roselle Bd of Ed & Middletown Twp Bd of Ed Letters of Commendation; *office:* Thorne MS 70 Murphy Rd Middletown NJ 07748

JANOSKE, WILLIAM E., Science Teacher; *b:* Oakland, MD; *m:* Lisa Hawker; *c:* William E., Jena N.; *ed:* Frostburg St Coll (BS) Elem Ed 1974, (MED) Elem Ed 1980; *cr:* Accident Elem Schl 6th Grd Tchr 1974-77; Southern MS Sci Tchr 1978-; *home:* 733 Mason School Rd Oakland MD 21550

JANOSS, FRANK S., 8th Grade Math Teacher; *b:* Pittsburgh, PA; *m:* Janet L. Simon; *c:* Jenifer; *ed:* Clarion Univ (BS) Math Ed 1970; Univ of Pittsburgh, Cmptr Sci; *cr:* Chartiers Valley Schl Dist Scndry Math Tchr 1970-; *ai:* Steering Comm; Tchr In-Svc Trainer; Union VP; AFT, CVFT 1985-, VP; *office:* Chartiers Valley HS 50 Thoms Run Rd Bridgeville PA 15017*

JANS, ANTON, Former Teacher; *b:* New York, NY; *m:* Suzanne Groll; *c:* Michael; *ed:* NY Univ (BA) Psych 1986; CUNY Queens Coll (MA) Psych 1995; Hofstra Univ Driver Ed 16 Credits; *cr:* Christ the King RHS Sci, Cmptr Sci Tchr 1988-95; *ai:* Speech, Debate Coach 1988-; Driver Ed 1989-95; TACK 1988-, Treas; BQCFL 1988-, VP Stu Congress.

JANSEN, SHEREE BYERS, 11th & 12th Grd English Tchr; *b:* Chambersburg, PA; *m:* Mark Lee; *c:* Matthew, Patrick; *ed:* Shippensburg Univ (BA) Eng, Comm 1975, (MS) Eng, Media 1981; *cr:* James Buchanan HS Eng Tchr 1975-; *ai:* Sr Class Adv 1975-79; Girls Bsktbl Coach 1975-77; NEA, PA's 1975-; Cub Scout Ldr 1985-91; Parish Cncl of Cath Women 1983-; *office:* James Buchanan HS 4773 Ft Loudon Rd Mercersburg PA 17236

JANTZI, MARY HOLTHOUSE, Science Teacher; *b:* Jamestown, NY; *m:* Brian; *ed:* Alfred St Coll (AAS) Agicultural Sci 1987; Fredonia St Univ (BS) Bio, Scndry Ed 1989, (MS) Elem Ed 1993; *cr:* Chautauqua Jr Sr HS Sci Tchr 1989-; *ai:* Jr HS Chrldng; HS Bowl Acad, Sci Olympiad, Envirothon Teams; NEA 1989-; *office:* Chautauqua Jr Sr HS PO Box 1097 Chautauqua NY 14722

JAQUAY, JORDAN ERIC, Social Studies Teacher; *b:* Cobleskill, NY; *m:* Melissa Stiles; *c:* Kyle Aran; *ed:* SUNY at Geneseo (BA) His & Commnctn 1989; Siena Coll Scndry Ed Cert 1991; Grad Stu SUNY At Albany Soc Stud Ed; *cr:* Cairo-Durnham CS Soc Stud Tchr 1991-92; Gilboa-Conesville CS Soc Stud Tchr 1992-93; Cherry Valley-Springfield CS 1993-; *ai:* Class of 1996 Adv; Var Boys Soccer; JV Boys Bsktbl; Var Track Boys & Girls; NYSCSS; NYSUT; Boy Scouts of Amer; Cherry Valley Fire Dept; Sigma Nu; Masonic Lodge; US Holocaust Museum Seminar.*

JAQUES, CLARK ROBERT, Computer Coordinator; *b:* Olean, NY; *m:* Rebecca Lee Miller; *c:* Jessica; *ed:* St Univ Coll at Geneseo (BS) Elem Ed 1965; *cr:* Bolivar Cntrl Schl Elem Tchr 1965-94; Bolivar-Richburg Cntrl Schl Comp Coord 1994-; *ai:* Schl Newspaper Adv; NEA & NYEA 1975-; *office:* Bolivar-Richburg Central Sch 100 School St Bolivar NY 14715

JAQUETTE, FLORENCE EVELYN, 6th Grd Communications Teacher; *b:* Philadelphia, PA; *ed:* West Chester Univ (BS) Elem Ed, Psych 1966; Trenton St Coll (MS) Guid, Cnslng 1979; Attnd Temple Univ; *cr:* Herbert Hoover Elem Schl 5th Grd Tchr 1966-68; Fed Govt DPSC Contract Admin 1968-69; Snyder MS 6th-7th Grd Soc Stud, Rdng, Comm Tchr 1969-; *ai:* Broadway Musicals Co-Dir, Choreographer, Instrumental Dir 1970-86; Pride Prgm Writing Curr; 6th Grd Multicultural Festival Dir; After Schl Tutoring; Mentor Prgm; Discipline, Prof Dev Comms; Entertainment Dir; PSEA, BETA, NEA, PTO, Kappa Delta Pi 1966-; Church Choir, Jr Choir Dir 1979-; Singles Svc Org, Pet Therapy Prgm 1986-; Nrsng Home Geriatric Ministry 1993-; Subject of Co-Worker's Doctoral Stud on Tchng Effectiveness; *office:* Cecelia Snyder MS 3330 Hulmeville Rd Bensalem PA 19020

JARCZYNSKI, MARY ANN DOOLEY, HS Bus & Social Stud Teacher; *b:* Leonardtown, MD; *m:* James P.; *c:* Jeffrey, Amy, Ryan; *ed:* St Marys Coll of MD (BA) Soc Sci & Sec Ed 1977; George Washington Univ MA Human Resource Dev 1982; *cr:* St Marys Cty Adult Ed Bus Tchr 1977-79; Comm Coll at St Marys Bus Tchr 1979-81; St Marys Tech Ctr Voc Support Tchr 1985-89; Great Mills HS Bus & Soc Stud Tchr 1989-; *ai:* SADD Spon 1989-90; Bank Teller Pgm 1990-; Schl Fin 1990-; NEA 1988-; Bd of Dir Breton Bay Rec 1984-, Elected Ofcr; Breton Bay Recreation Swim 1986-92, Chpsn; Citizens Schlsp Fndtn 1988-93; Adult Literacy Pgm 1996-, Chrpsn, Vol; Great Mills HS Tchr of Yr 1994; Univ of NC at Chapel Hill, Inst in the Hum Summer 1996; *home:* 131 Meadow Ct Leonardtown MD 20650*

JARMUSIK, THERESE RILEY, Principal; *b:* Malden, MA; *c:* Matthew, Kristin, Brian; *ed:* Salem St Coll (BS) Ed 1973; Suffolk Univ (MPA) Admin 1985; *cr:* Comm of Mass Admin 1975-87; Our Lady Mt Carmel Schl Tchr 1989-94; St Patrick Schl Prin 1994-; *ai:* NCEA 1989-; Who's Who in Excecs & Profs; *office:* St Patrick Schl 20 Pleasant St Stoneham MA 02180

JAROLEN, MARK JOHN, Soc Studies Dept Chair & Tchr; *b:* Nanticoke, PA; *ed:* Wilkes Univ (BA) Pol Sci 1976; St of PA (ME) Ed 1990; 42 Addl Credits; *cr:* Crestwood HS World Cultures Tchr 1980-, Dept Chm 1990-;

ai: Golf Coach 1985-; NEA, PSEA 1978-; Crestwood Ed Assn 1988-; NCSS; *home:* 105 Raymond St Nanticoke PA 18634

JAROSZ, LARRI VREELAND, Span Tchr, Frgn Lang Dpt Chair; *b:* Middletown, NY; *m:* Ray; *c:* Ray; *ed:* SUC at Oneonta (BA) Sec Ed, Span 1970; Syracuse Univ (MA) Span Lit 1972; SUC at New Paltz Educl Admin 1991; Univ of Valencia Spain 30 Hrs; *cr:* Cornwall HS Span Tchr, Frgn Lang Dept Chair 1973-86; Minisink Vly HS Span Tchr, Frgn Lang Dept Chair 1986-; *ai:* Jr Class Adv; NYSAFLT, NYSUT 1973-; MV Tchrs Assn 1986-; Minisink Cares 1989-, VP; NYSUT Comm Svc Awd; *office:* Minisink Valley HS Rt 6 Box 217 Slate Hill NY 10973

JAROSZ, RAY, 7th Grade Math Teacher; *b:* Warwick, NY; *m:* Larri Vreeland; *c:* Ray; *ed:* Syracuse univ (BS) Prsnl Mngmt 1972; SUC at New Paltz 30 Hrs Ed; *cr:* Ellenville HS Bus, Math Tchr 1976-77; Washingtonville Jr HS Bus, Math Tchr 1977-86; Minisink Vly MS Math Tchr 1986-; *ai:* JV, AAU Bsktbl Coach; Modified Ftbl Coach; NYSUT 1976-, Del; MV Tchrs Assn 1986-; NY Bsktbl Coaches Assn of NY 1991-; MV Little League 1992-, T-Ball Dir, Minor, Major League Coach; *office:* Minisink Vly MS Rt 6 Box 217 Slate Hill NY 10973

JAROT, PAULA BURGET, 5th Grade Teacher; *b:* Joliet, IL; *m:* Paul; *c:* Christopher, Michael, Nathan; *ed:* Univ of IA (BS) Spec Ed, Elem Ed 1973; Natl Coll of Ed (MED) Learning Disabilities 1979; *cr:* Valley View Schls 6th-8th Grd Spec Ed Tchr 1973-74; Plainfield Spec Ed Coop Consultant of LD 1976-79; Aurora Chrstn Kndgtn Tchr 1979-86; Numonohi Chrstn Schl 1st-2nd, 5th Grd Tchr 1986-; *ai:* 11th Grd Class Spon; Curr Dev; New Tribes Mission 1986-; Child Centered Classrooms, Individulized Instruction, Learning Styles 4 Intnl Wkshps Presenter; *office:* Numonohi Chrstn Acad PO Box 1079 EHP Goroka Papua New Guinea XX 00000*

JARRELL, WILLIAM A., Mathematics Teacher; *b:* Dayton, OH; *m:* Carole Anne King; *c:* Craig Allen; *ed:* OH St Univ (BS) Math Ed 1970, (MS) Math Ed 1973; *cr:* Bexley HS Tchr 1971-; *ai:* Ski Club Adv; NCTM 1972-; *office:* Bexley H S 326 S Cassingham Rd Bexley OH 43209

JARRELLE, AUDREY LEE, Associate Dean; *b:* Washington, DC; *ed:* Longwood Coll (BS) Home Ec Ed 1966; Univ of NC (MSHE) Textiles, Cloghing 1968, (PHD) Textiles, Clothing 1973; Fashion Inst of Tech; *cr:* Univ of NC Rsrch Asst 1966-67; Univ of CT Instr 1967-73, Asst Prof 1973-78, Assoc Prof 1978-, Assoc Dean 1988-; *ai:* Univ Senate; Enrollment Mngmt Retention Comm; Inter Textile Apparel Assn 1967-; Phi Kappa Phi 1990-, Pres, UCONN Chptr; Kappa Omicron Phi 1965-; *office:* Univ Of CT 348 Mansfield Rd #U-58 Storrs CT 06169

JARRETT, CYNTHIA WALBURN, Business Teacher; *b:* Piqua, OH; *m:* Robert E.; *c:* Jeffrey J., Jason R., Jeremy R.; *ed:* Kent St Univ (BS) Comprehensive Bus Ed 1970; *cr:* Southeast HS Bus Ed Tchr 1970-74, 1976-; *ai:* Pep Club Adv 21 Yrs; NEA, OEA 1970-; SELDTA 1970-, Local Assn Sec; *office:* Southeast HS 8423 Tallmadge Rd Ravenna OH 44266

JARRETT, PETER J., 7th Grade Life Science Teacher; *b:* Allentown, PA; *m:* Terry R.; *c:* Lisa; *ed:* Millersville Univ (BSEd) Bio 1976; Penn St (MSEd) Ed 1985; *cr:* Quakertown Comm Schl Dist Sci Tchr 1979-; *ai:* Girls Track Coach; Outdoor Schl Coord; Ski Club, Sci & Oceanography Fieldtrip Spon; SAP Team; QCEA 1979-; PSEA 1979-; NEA 1979-; Quakertown Optimist Club 1981-, Bd Mem, Life Mem; *office:* Richard E Strayer MS 349 S 9th St Quakertown PA 18951

JARRETT, RODNEY LYNN, Fourth Grade Teacher; *b:* Zanesville, OH; *c:* Christopher; *ed:* Heidelberg Coll (BA) Elem Ed 1988; 8 Credit Hrs of Ocean Focus Prgm from Bowling Green St Univ; *cr:* Lutz Elem 4th Grd Tchr 1988-; *ai:* Var Bsktbl Asst Coach at Clyde HS; Tech Comm; Stu Cncl Adv; NEA, OEA, FEA 1988-; *office:* Lutz Elem Schl 1929 Buckland Ave Fremont OH 43420

JARUSIEWICZ, JANE L., Elementary Guidance Counselor; *b:* Elizabeth, NJ; *m:* Richard; *c:* Lindsay; *ed:* Kent St Univ (BS) Elem Ed 1973; Kean Coll (MA) Stu Prsnl Svcs 1981; Schl Soc Worker Cert; *cr:* Port Monmouth Elem Schl Tchr 1973-83; River Plaza Elem Schl Tchr 1984-87; Bayshore MS Soc Worker 1987-88, Lang Arts Tchr 1988-94; Ocean Ave Schl Elem Guid Cnslr 1994-; Middletown Vlg Schl Elem Guid Cnslr 1994-; Leonardo Schl Elem Guid Cnslr 1994-; Lincroft Schls Elem Guid Cnslr 1994-; *ai:* Dev Guid Comm Mem Middletown Twp Schl Dist; NJEA 1973-; NJ Schl Cnslrs Assn, Monmouth Cty Schl Cnslrs Assn 1995-; *office:* Middletown Vlg Schl King's Hwy Middletown NJ 07738

JARVI, LOIS A. PERUGINE, Second Grade Teacher; *b:* Ashtabula, OH; *m:* Dennis A.; *ed:* Kent St Univ (BS) Early Chldhd Ed 1970; 20 Credit Hrs; *cr:* Ashabule Area City Schls 1st Grd Tchr 1970-71, 2nd Grd Tchr 1971-73, Title One Rdng Tchr 1974-75, 2nd Grd Tchr 1975-; *ai:* Schl Soc, Sci Comm; NES, OEA, AATA 1970-; Ashtabula Yacht Club; Chapel Hills Golf Club 1996-; GIC Investment Club 1995-; Article Germany, Scotland; *home:* 2116 Ashbrook Dr Ashtabula OH 44004

JARVIS, JAY ALLEN, Bible Teacher; *b:* Gallipolis, OH; *m:* Cheryl Jones; *c:* Joshua, Johanna; *ed:* Bob Jones Univ (BA) Bible Ed 1981; *cr:* OH Vly Chrstn Schl Bible Tchr 1981-; *ai:* Ath Dir; Girls Jr Var, Var Vlybl Coach 15 Yrs; Honor Soc, Alumni Assn Adv; Yth Soccer League coach; Pee-Wee, Litle League Bsbl Asst Coach; Amer Assn of Chrstn Schls 1981-; *home:* 10 Evans Hts Gallipolis OH 45631

JARVIS, REBECCA S. MAIKRANZ, Guidance Counselor; *b:* Youngstown, OH; *ed:* Youngstown St Univ (BS) Educ 1979; OH Univ (MS) Educ, Guidance 1988; 30 Addl Hrs; *cr:* Pennsville Elem 7th, 8th Grd Self Contained Tchr 1979-89, 1-4 Grd Eng 1989-91; Windsor Elem 7th, 8th Grd Adv, Lang Arts, Eng Tchr 1991-95; Morgan HS Guid Cnslr 1995-; *ai:* Curr Advisory Cncl, Class Adv, Negotiations Team; Chrldng Adv; MLEA Sec; MLEA, OEA, NEA 1979-; Phi Kappa Tau 1988-; PTO Pres, Treas; Good Apple Winner Excl in Ed; Tchr of the Wk; *home:* 110 5th St Malta OH 43758*

JARZYNKA, BARBARA MERCER, Fifth Grade Teacher; *b:* Pittsburgh, PA; *m:* Jerome J.; *ed:* Slippery Rock Univ (BS) Elem Ed, Socially Emotionally Maladjusted 1970, (MS) Elem Ed 1973; *cr:* Franklin Regnl Schl Dist 2nd-6th Grd Tchr 1970-; *ai:* 4th-6th Grd Natl Lang Arts, 5th-6th Grd Natl Spelling Bee Spon; Tchr Mentor; K-6th Grd Curr Writing for Math; Spec Svcs Cyclical Rev; Instructional Support Team Mem; Tchr PTO Rep; Franklin Regnl Ed Assn, PSEA, NEA, SR Alumni Assn 1970-; First United Meth Church of Murrysville 1968-, Ed, Worship, Outreacg Commissions, Youth Ldr, Sunday Schl Tchr; *office:* Sloan Elem Schl Sardi Rd Murrysville PA 15668*

JARZYNSKI, JOHN S., English Teacher; *b:* Angola, NY; *ed:* Daemen Coll (BA) Theatre 1985; SUNY at Fredonia (MSEd) Eng Ed 1996; *cr:* Gowanda Cntrl Schl Eng Tchr 1991-; *ai:* Fall Play Dir; Spring Musicla Producer; Co-Chm Tech Comm; AFT; *office:* Cowanda Cntrl Jr, Sr HS 24 Prospect St Gowanda NY 14070

JASINSKI, JOHN S., Vice Principal; *b:* Gardner, MA; *m:* Anne Dubzinski; *c:* Kathleen, Peter; *ed:* Fitchburg St (BSEd) Math 1974, (MED) Ed 1980; Addl Hrs; *cr:* Narragasett Reg Schl Math Tchr 1974-86, Vice Prin 1986-; Bsbl, Bsktbl Coach 1974-87; *ai:* Schl Event Attendance; NEA, MTA, Dist Ed Assn 1974-; Natl Assn Sec Schl Prins, MA Sec Schl Adm Assn 1987-; MA Bsktbl Coaches Assn 1975-; Wachuskit Bsktbl League Coach of Yr 1986-87; *office:* Narragansett Reg Jr Sr HS 464 Baldwinville Rd Baldwinville MA 01436

JASKULSKI, JUDITH CATHCART, Accounting Instructor; *b:* Pittsburgh, PA; *m:* James J.; *c:* Jodi, Jami; *ed:* Grove City Coll (BA) Bus Ed 1963; 16 Credit Hrs for Permanent Tchng Cert Penn St; *cr:* West Mifflin Area HS Bus Ed Tchr 1963-68; Comm Coll of Allegheny Cty Bus Ed Tchr 1970-79; Steel Center Accounting Instr 1980-; *ai:* FBLA Club Adv; PA AFT Steel Center 1980-, Sec Treas 1990-91; Iota Lambda Sigma 1982-; Lebanon Womens Club 1975-, VP 1987, Pres 1988-90; West MIfflin Boosters 1989-, Sec 1990; Church Organist; PA Tchr of Yr Nom 1989; *office:* Steel Center Area Vo Tech Schl 565 Lewis Run Rd Clairton PA 15025*

JASLOW, JEFFREY, Teaching Assistant Principal; *b:* New York, NY; *m:* Linda Lewis; *ed:* SUNY at Stony Brook (BS) 1975; Univ of Bridgeport (MS) Bio 1981; *cr:* Freeport HS Bio Tchr 1976; Ridgefield HS Bio Tchr 1976-91, Bio Tchr & Asst Prin 1991-; *ai:* NSTA 1976-; NASSP 1991-; ASCD 1991-; AFSA & CFSA 1991-; Western CT Supts Assn & Union Carbide Corp Recognition as Outstdng Tchr; BEST Assessor; *office:* Ridgefield HS 700 N Salem Rd Ridgefield CT 06877*

JASPER, MINNIE R., Eng as a Second Lang Teacher; *b:* Cincinnati, OH; *m:* Philip R.; *c:* Karen Davis, Philip II, Darryl; *ed:* Univ of Cincinnati (BA) Ed 1975; Univ of Findlay Grad Stud Credit Hrs in Tchng ESL Stdnts; *cr:* Cincinnati Pub Schls Sub Tchr 1975-76; Swifton Primary Schl Kndgtn Tchr 1976-77; Vine Elem Schl 3rd-4th Grd Tchr 1978-82; Acad of World Langs ESL Tchr 1982-; *ai:* Interracial-Intercultural Comm Club; AFT 1985-; Awd of Inspiration for Excl in Tchng.

JASSEN, ALISON PUTNAM, Instructor of Chemistry & Bio; *b:* New York City, NY; *m:* Kerry Robert; *c:* Amy, Karl; *ed:* Charter Oak Coll (BA) Natural Scis 1990; Cntrl CT St Univ (MS) Chem 1993; *cr:* Northwestern CT Comm Coll Sci Lab Supvr 1987-93; Northwestern CT Comm Tech Coll Instr 1993-; *ai:* Pre-Nrsng Adv; Schl, Career, Acad Policy, Commencement Comms; Bio Dept Self-Stud; Sci Tech-Prep Coord; Amer Chem Soc 1995-; CT Breast Cancer Coalition 1994-, Chair Sci, Med Rsrch; Outstndg Grad Stu; Women's Hlth Issues Seminar; CT St Univ Fac Rsrch Conf Presenter; *office:* Northwestern CT Comm Tech Coll Park Place Winsted CT 06098

JASTRAB, SANDRA LEE (KAIN), School Social Worker; *b:* Baltimore, MD; *m:* Robert F.; *c:* David, Ann-Marie; *ed:* PA St Univ (BA) Soc Welfare 1963; MI ST Univ (MSW) Soc Work 1966; *cr:* NY City Welfare Dept Soc Worker 1963-64; Flint Mental Hlth Clinic Soc Worker 1966-67; Mohawk Vly Comm Coll Instr 1872-76; Rome Dev Ctr Soc Worker 1977-79; Whitesboro Cntrl Schls Soc Worker 1979-; *ai:* Natl Assn of Soc Workers 1966-; Acad of Ceritfied Soc Workers 1978-; Phi Beta Kappa; Phi Kappa Phi; Phi Sigma Iota; Pi Gamma Nu; *office:* Whitesboro Cntrl Schls 67 Whitesboro St Yorkville NY 13495

JAVERSAK, ALICE MATHIESON, English & Speech Teacher; *b:* Steubenville, OH; *m:* David Thomas; *c:* Grant C., Meredith A.; *ed:* West Liberty St Coll (BA) Scndry Ed, Eng, Speech 1967, (MA) Eng Ed 1980; Grad Courses Guidance, Cnslng 1981-82, Comm 1987-89; *cr:* Ewa Beach Intermediate Schl Eng Tchr 1967-68; OH Cty & Brooke Co Schls Sub Tchr 1978-80; West Liberty St Coll Writing Specialist-Stu Special Svcs 1980-84; Martins Ferry HS Eng, Speech Tchr 1985-; *ai:* Fac Cncl Hnr Soc; Jr Class Adv; Natl Cncl Tchrs of Eng 1980-; NEA, OEA, MFEA 1967-; *office:* Martins Ferry HS 614 Hanover St Martins Ferry OH 43935

JAWORSKI, NANCY LYNN, First Grade Teacher; *b:* Paterson, NJ; *m:* Bruce; *ed:* Univ of MD (BS) Early Chldhd Ed 1978; Long Island Univ (MS) Elem Ed 1992; *cr:* Saddle Acres Nursery Schl Tchr 1978-79; Elmwood Park HS Basic Skills Instruction Tchr 1979-81; Haskell Schl Kndgtn Tchr 1981-92, First Grd Tchr 1992-; *ai:* PRIDE Comm Chprsn; NEA 1978-; NJEA; Wanaque Boro Educ Assn; PTA, Tchr Rep, Life Mem Awd; Wanaque Boro Tchr of Yr 1991; Co-Authored Mini Grants Parent Educ; Up Cty Early Chldhd Cncl Comm Work; Designed Parent-Tchr Resource Room; Co-Managed Dist Fire Safety Fair, Early Chldhd Art Shows Implementation.

JAYE, IRWIN, 5th Grade Teacher; *b:* Bronx Cty, NY; *m:* Barbara Sirota; *c:* Jennifer Jaye; *ed:* Hunter Coll of the City Univ of NY (BA) Psych & Ed 1964, (MSEd) 1970; 60 Credit Hrs in Psych & Cmptr Sci; *cr:* PS 127 Queens 4-6 Grd Tchr 1965-69; Branch Brook Elem 4, 6 Grd Tchr 1970-71; Great Hollow Elem 6 Grd Tchr 1972; Great Hollow MS 6 Grd Tchr 1973-86; Accompsett Elem 5 Grd Tchr 1987-; *ai:* HS Girls Var, JV Bsktbl Coach; Involved in Classroom Cmptr Testing Prgms, New Operating System; Girls Var Soccer, Bsktbl Ofcl Scorer 12 Yrs; Drama Club Dir 10 Yrs; AFT, UFT 1965-; Smithtown Tchrs Assn 1970-, Schl Rep; NCTE; ASCD; Hauppauge Yth Org 1978-85-, Coach; *home:* 64 Holiday Park Dr Hauppauge NY 11788

JAYNES, DANNY, Bandmaster, Dir Instrmntl Mus; *b:* Crossnore, NC; *m:* Mary Alice Siqmon; *c:* Alice Ann Merle, D. Thomas; *ed:* US Navy Schl of Music 1959; US Armed Forces Schl of Music 1968, 1973; Attnd Austin Peay St Univ, Mc Neese St Univ, Northwestern LA St Univ; *cr:* US Army Instrumentialist, Group 1DR 1959-63, Band Ldr 1963-72, Bandmaster 1973-86; Vly Forge Military Acad, Coll Bandmaster, Dir of Instrumental Music 1986-; *ai:* Guest Conductor, Adjudicator; Adjudicator for Yth Music of World, London England; MENC 1965-; PAMENC, NBA, Ret Military Musicians Assn 1986-; KY Colonel 1985-; *office:* Valley Forge Military Acad 1001 Eagle Rd Wayne PA 19087

JEANNIS, INGRID, Counselor; *ed:* Lehman Coll (BA) Psych 1988, (MS) Spcl Ed 1990; NY Univ (MA) Schl Cnslng 1994; *cr:* PS 140 Spcl Ed Tchr 1988-93; CODA Inc ESL & GED Tchr 1989-93; John Dewey HS Cnslr 1993-; *ai:* African-Amer Caribbean Unity Club Adv; *office:* John Dewey HS 50 Avenue X Brooklyn NY 11223*

JECK, DOUG ALAN, Art Professor; *b:* Jersey City, NJ; *m:* Delia Seigenthaler; *c:* Henry Alan, William Jacob; *ed:* Appalachian Ctr for Arts & Crafts (BFA) Art, Ceramics 1986; Schl of Art Inst of Chicago (MFA) Art, Ceramics 1989; *cr:* Schl of Art Inst of Chicago Adj Prof 1994; Alfred Univ Asst Prof 1994-; *ai:* NCECA 1995-; Article Pub; Visual Artist Flwshp, Natl Endowment for Arts 1990, 1992; IL Artist Flwshp Awd 1990; NEA Travel Grant La Napoule Fnd 1993; *office:* Alfred Univ 2 Pine St Alfred Station NY 14803

JECKAVITCH, CAROL ROTH, Vocal Music Director; *b:* Johnstown, PA; *m:* Jeffrey A.; *c:* Laura, Steven, Mark; *ed:* Edinboro Univ (BS) Music Ed 1978; Youngstown St Univ (MS) Music Ed 1983; *cr:* Salem HS Vocal Music Dir 1978-; *ai:* NHS Adv 1990-94; Music Edctrs Natl Conf 1978-; OH Music Edctrs Assn 1978-; Amer Choral Dirs Assn 1978-; *office:* Salem HS 1200 E 6th St Salem OH 44460*

JECKOT, JOHN JOSEPH, MS Choral Music Teacher; *b:* Albany, NY; *m:* M. Christine; *c:* Elizabeth Lee, John; *ed:* West Chester Univ (BS) K-12 Music 1973; *cr:* Countryside Elem Schl K-5th Grd Music Tchr 22 Yrs; T. E. Harrington MS 7th-8th Grd Music Tchr 1 Yr, 4th-8th Grd GATE Music Tchr 13 Yrs; *ai:* GATE Music Prgm; Summer Theatre Wkshp; Fall Choral, Spring Performing Arts Clubs; NEA 1973-; PTO, PTA 1973-; Governor's Tchr Recognition Awd for Countryside Schl 1989; Governor's Tchr Recognition Awd Twice Nom; Wrote Original Songs; *office:* T. E. Harrington MS Mt Laurel Rd Mount Laurel NJ 08054*

JEFFCOAT, JOANNE THERESA, Assoc Prof & Fieldwork Coord; *b:* Altoona, PA; *m:* William P.; *c:* Jill A., William T.; *ed:* Mt Aloysius Coll (AS) Occupational Therapy 1973; Coll Misericordia (BS) Occupational Therapy 1991; Penn St Univ (MED) Ed, Hlth Ed 1995; *cr:* Therapeutic Specialists P-T Staff Therapist 1985-87; Comm Coll Allegheny Co Fieldwork Coord 1985-; Comm Coll of Allegheny Co Assoc Prof 1991-; Horizon Mental Hlth Mgt Mental Hlth Consultant 1992-95; *ai:* Fac Adv Stu Occupational Therapy Assn; Amer Occupational Therapy Assn 19 Occupational Therapy Assn 1973-, Recognition Awd 19 Bartholomew Ath Assn 1991-, Sec, Chrldr Adv; Penn Hills Socc 1986-, Sec; Indian Roundballers Bsktbl Assn 1994-, Sec, Treas; Comm Coll Algny Co Boyce Cmps 595 Beatty Rd Monroeville PA

JEFFERIS, JAMES B., Social Studies Teacher; *b:* Coatesville, Kristine M. Hulshart; *ed:* York Coll of PA (BA) Scndry Ed Millersville Univ Ed 1994; *cr:* Red Lion Area Jr HS Soc Stud Tchr *ai:* Head Jr High Ftbl & Jr Var Wrestling Coach; NEA 1987-; *offi* Lion Area Jr HS 200 Country Club Rd Red Lion PA 17356

JEFFERIS, PAUL EDWARD, High School Math Teacher; *b:* Wilm DE; *m:* Patricia Anne Heckman; *c:* Pat Lucas, Edward, David Jose Lehigh Univ (BS) Indstrl Engrng 1956; Templ Univ, Immaculat Kutztown Ed Courses; *cr:* Mack Truck Inc Employee; St Matthe Tchr, Coach 1962-65; Lansdale Cath HS Tchr, Coach, Admin 196 ATMOPAV 1980-; *office:* Lansdale Catholic HS 7th & Lansda Lansdale PA 19446

JEFFERS, LESLIE CAROLYN, 8th Grade Science Teach Frederick, MD; *ed:* Coll of William & Mary (BA) His 1978; 3 Credits; *cr:* Gov Thomas Johnson Jr Sr HS 8th-12th Grd Mat 1978-79; North Carroll MS 8th Grd Sci Tchr 1979-; *ai:* As Choreographer Schl Musicals 1990-93; Carroll Co Ed Assn MD St Assn, NEA 1978-.

JEFFERSON, CHERI TYLER, English Teacher & Dept Co Baltimore, MO; *m:* Jeffrey L.; *c:* Meredith, Amy; *ed:* Anne Arundel Coll (AA) Gen Stud 1984; Univ of MD at Baltimore (BA) Eng 1987 Hopkins Univ (MS) Ed Sci 1994; Loyola Coll 30 Addl Credit H Owen Brown MS 7-8th Grd Eng Tchr 1987-89; Patuxent Valley MS Grd Dept Chair 1989-93; Atholton HS 9, 11th Grd Dept Coord 1993 of MD Part-time Instr 1993-; *ai:* Schl Improvement Team; Grace Comm; 9th Grd Cross Curricular Team; NEA, HCTA 1987-; MC NCTE 1986-; MD Middle Schl Eng Tchr of Yr 1992; *office:* Atholt 6520 Freetown Rd Columbia MD 21044*

JEFFERY, J. ELMALENE, Vocational Spec Ed Coord; *b:* Malver *m:* Bill; *c:* Carissa; *ed:* Bowling Green St Univ (BS) Bus Ed 1976; Specific Learning Disabilities 1995; Curr Dev, Cmptrs, Gui Counseling, Spec Ed Addl Coursework; *cr:* Four Cty Joint Vo Secretarial Svcs Instr 1977-95; Spec Ed Coord 1995-; *ai:* Bus Prof o Co-Adv; Honor Soc, Textbook Selection, Enrollment, Retention, Bus Ed Advy, Curr Comms; Delta Pi Epsilon 1985-; Pi Omega Pi VP; NEA, OH Ed Assn 1977-; Northwest OH Bus Tchrs Assn 1980-; Four County Joint Voc Schl 22-900 SR 34 R 1 Box 245-A Archbo 43502

JEFFREY, NADINE WOOLLEY, Retired K & 1st Grd Teacher; *b:* Branch, NJ; *m:* Donald R.; *c:* Cindy Rosemont, Jill Kuser; *ed:* Mon Jr Coll (AA) 1953, (BS) Ed 1960; *cr:* Middletown Schl Elem Tchr 19 Long Branch Gregory Schl Elem Tchr 1960-61; Wolf Hill Schl Eler 1962-95; *ai:* Take Chldrn to Liberty Sci Ctr, Fossiling; NEA; Mon Cty Kndgtn Assn; *home:* 35 Wyandotte Ave Oceanport NJ 07757*

JEFFRIES, BESSIE WEYAND, Mathematics Instructor; *b:* Bellevu *m:* Kevin D.; *c:* Cassandra; *ed:* Butler Cty Comm Coll (AAS) Acco 1977; Chatham Coll (BA) Bus & Admin 1980; Slippery Rock Univ (Math & Scndry Ed 1991; Univ of NH (MST) Math 1996; US Space 1992; Ecology Educators Natl Audubon Soc 1994; *cr:* Napc Production Scheduler 1981-88; Butler Cty Comm Coll Math Instr *ai:* ACT 101 Adv Bd; NCTM; GSA 1985-, Trainer, Thanks B Outstanding Vol; Renew 1992; Outstanding Fac Mem Nom 1995; Butler County Comm Coll PO Box 1203 Butler PA 16001*

JEFFRIES, JOHN E., 8th Grade Social Studies Tchr; *b:* Elizabet *ed:* St Francis Coll (BA) Soc Stud 1973; Kean Coll (MA) Libera 1990; *cr:* St John the Apostle Schl Tchr 1973-76; Bridgewater-R Schls Tchr 1977-; Kean Coll Adjunct Instr 1990-; *ai:* Girls Sftbl C In-Service Course & Attendance Comm; Stu Cncl Adv 1981-87; 1977; NCSS 1985; NJCSS 1994; *office:* Bridgewater-Rarita Merriwood Dr Bridgewater NJ 08807

JEFFS, JEANNE L., Intrvntn, Eng & Dev Rdng Tchr; *b:* Philadelphi *m:* Thomas Y.; *ed:* Bucknell Univ (BS) Eng & Soc Stud 1964; Wester Coll (MLA) Eng & His 1976; Univ of Dayton Guidance & Counseling Bowling Green St Univ Developmental Rdng Cert; Numerous Courses at Various Univs; Comp Sci Cert; *cr:* Batavia City Schls Eng 1964-65; Shikellamy Schls Eng & Rdng Tchr 1965-66; Baltimor Schls Eng & Drama Tchr 1970-73; Tehran-Amer Schl Iran Rdng 1973-74; Shiraz Univ Iran Eng Tchr 1974-75; Bluffton Schls Eng Rdng, Soc Stud Intervention Tchr 1977-; *ai:* Class Adv; Prom; Stu Se OCTELA 1989-; Bluffton Ed Assn 1977-, Pres & VP 7 Yrs; NEA & 1977-; Uniserv Area OEA Cncl 1980-, Pres 2 Yrs; NCTE 1980-; AS 1993-; ACLU & MS Soc 1989-; Focal 1991-; People for the Amer 1989-; AAUW 1991; NARAL OH 1992-; League of Women Voters BGSU Original Cmptr Prgm 2nd Pl; *office:* Bluffton Exempted V Schl 106 College Ave Bluffton OH 45817*

JEGGE, THOMAS C., Social Studies Teacher; *b:* Paterson, N William Paterson Coll (BA) K-12, Jr HS 1977; Grad Stud East Strouds Univ, Jersey City St Coll; *cr:* Great Gorge Dir of Skiing 1982-84; V Vly Ski Instr 1973-81; *ai:* Tchng In-Service Course Roxbury Twp S Prof Ski Instrs of Amer; Candian Ski Instrs Alliance; NEA 1977-; *o* Eisenhower MS 47 Eyland Ave Succasunna NJ 07876*

JEGOU, GREGORY CHARLES, Health & Physical Ed Teacher; *b:* Brunswick, NJ; *m:* Ivy Wexler; *ed:* Trenton St Coll (BA) Hlth, PE (MS) Ed 1989; *cr:* Sayreville MS 6th-8th Grd Hlth, PE Tchr 1989-9 Grd Hlth, PE Tchr 1991-; *ai:* Partner Leading Awarness In Dive Monthly Reward Prgms Coord; Stu Mentor; Var Boys HS Soccer, Coach; 7th-8th Grd Boys Bsktbl Coach; 6th-8th Grd Floor Hockey; N NJHPERD 1989-; Cty Soccer Coaches Assn 1993-, Sec; Middlesex Soccer Coach of Yr 1990; *office:* Sayreville MS Washington Rd Parli 08859

JELAGIN, BARBARA ZLICESKI, Social Studies Teacher; *b:* Eliza NJ; *m:* Victor; *c:* Andrew; *ed:* Neward St Coll (BA) Scndry Soc Stud Keane Coll (MA) Contemporary Civilizations 1981; 15 Post Grad Cr Rutgers Univ, Keane Coll; *cr:* Raritan HS Soc Stud Tchr 1962-; *ai:* Trial Adv; Renaissance Comm; NEA, NJEA, HTA, MCEA, NJCSS 1 Tchr of Yr; *home:* 776 Holmdel Rd Holmdel NJ 07733

JELLIFF, EVELYN GAIL NUTT, First Grade Teacher; *b:* East Or NJ; *m:* Kenneth George; *c:* Eliza Kathleen; *ed:* Monmouth Univ (BS) Ed 1967; 8 Hrs UCLA Extension; 4 Hrs Ithaca Coll; 3 Hrs; *cr:* Bradle Elem Schl First Grd Tchr 1967-68; Cntrl Elem Schl First Grd 1968-72; West Belmar Elem Schl First-Second Grd Tchr 1972-; *ai:* Resource Cncl; NEA, NJEA, MCEA 1967-; WTEA 1968-; Women's of Sea Girl Fire Co 1980-, Corresponding Sec; Sea Girt Real Estate A Sea Girt Lighthouse Comm; NJ Grant Nutitional Ed 1979-80; *office:* Belmar Elem Schl 925 17th Ave Wall NJ 07719*

JEMO, DAVID NICHOLAS, Social Studies Chairman; *b:* Hazleton, *m:* Linda; *c:* Nicholas, David; *ed:* Penn St (BS) Soc Stud 1969; Maryw (ME) Ed 1983; *cr:* Weatherly HS Soc Stud Tchr 1969-; *ai:* Golf, Coach; Video Yrbl Dir; NEA, PSEA 1969-, Local Treas 2 Yrs; Jayce Yrs; *office:* Weatherly Area HS 6th Street Weatherly PA 18255*

INS, CARL H., Music & Band Director; *b:* Brooklyn, NY; *m:* Jane an; *c:* David, Matthew; *ed:* Montclair St Univ (BA) Music Ed 1970; bia Univ-Tchrs Coll (MA) Music Ed 1972; 45 Credits Beyond 's; Dir of Fine & Performing Arts Cert; *cr:* North Adams Pub Schls nstrumental Dir 1973-76; Drury HS Band & Music Dir 1976-; *ai:* sical Music Dir & Producer; NEA, MENC 1973-; MA MENC 1973-, Mgr & Dist Mgr; IAJE 1976-, Dist Chm; Williams Coll Adjunct Prof phonic Winds Conductor; Berkshire Symphony Orch Prin Oboe.

INS, CATHIE S., 8th Grade English & Lead Tchr; *b:* Lewistown, William K.; *c:* Andrew, Rhett; *ed:* Wilson Coll Eng 1971; Grad Stud nple & Shippensburg Univs; *cr:* Carlisle Jr HS 7th Grd Eng Tchr '8; Wilson MS 8th Grd Eng Tchr 1979-; *ai:* Assessment Strategic ng Team Head; 8th Grd Team Ldr & Lead Tchr; Cross Cntry Coach; 1990-; CAEA, NEA 1971-; Friends of Bosler Lib 1980-; Wilson Coll 971-, Pres; Outstanding Educator & Guest Lecturer Shippensburg ud Cncl 1995; Article on Rubric NMSA; *office:* Wilson MS 623 W t Carlisle PA 17013*

INS, DONALD EUGENE, Instrumental & Vocal Teacher; *b:* field, OH; *m:* Bonita Sue Jackson; *c:* Jennifer, Ben, Wendy; *ed:* Univ of OH BM) Music Ed 1968, (MM) Music Ed 1978; *cr:* gton Exempted Schls Instrumental Tchr 1968-70; C.R. Coblentz nstrumental Music Tchr 1970-71; Newton Local Schls Instrumental, Music, Dr Train Tchr 1971-78; Troy City Schls Instrumental Music 978-86; Anna Local Schl Instrumental Music Tchr 1986-87; Newton Schl Instrumental, Vocal Music Tchr 1987-; *ai:* Marching, Concert, and; Mens & Girls Chorus; Negotiations Comm; OH Ed Assn 1968-, 978, Newton Assn; NEA, NTA 1976-; OH Music Ed Assn 1968-, Dist 982-85; MENC, ASBDA, Phi Beta Mu, Phi Mu Alpha; First Bapt h Deacon Bd, Sunday Schl Tchr; Honor Bands Dir; OME St ntions, OH St Ftbl Game, Disney World Performer; Marching Band Championships Winner; Dist Concert, Marching Band Contests or; *office:* Newton HS Long St Pleasant Hill OH 45359*

INS, GEORGIA ANN (BERSHEE), High School Math Teacher; *b:* s Barre, PA; *m:* Thomas E.; *c:* Marybeth, Janine; *ed:* Wilkes Coll Math 1966; Post Grad Studs Wilkes Univ, Penn St Univ; *cr:* Wyoming West Schl Dist HS Math Tchr 1966-74; Lake Lehman Schl Dis Sub Tchr 1983; Dallas Schl Dist Scndry Math Tchr 1983-; King's Coll ct Fac Ed Dept 1987-; *ai:* Newspaper Club Adv; Luzerne Cty Math 1992-; PA Cncl of Math Tchrs 1993-; Cider Painters of Amer 1987-; Options Comm 1993-, Comm Mem; *office:* Dallas Sr High PO Box Conyngham Ave Dallas PA 18612*

INS, GLORIA JACKSON, Eighth Grade Lang Arts Teacher; *b:* WV; *m:* Willard L.; *c:* Roderick, Tracie; *ed:* WV St Coll (BA) Elem 67; Univ of Dayton (MS) Ed 1981; *cr:* Residence Park Elem Schl h Grd Tchr 1968-71; Fairview Elem Schl 4th-5th Grd Tchr 1971-75; Elem Schl 2nd-4th, 7th-8th Grd Tchr 1975-82; Fairview MS 7th-8th chr 1982-84; Roth MS 7th-8th Grd Tchr 1984-; *ai:* Dist Curr Comms, In-Svc Coord 1973-; Young Authors' Comm 1980-; Great Books Dir, 1982-88; Lang Arts Dept Chprsn 1982-84; Natl Annie CAsey Fnd ter Enrichment Prgm 1990-93; Dayton Ed Assn, OH Ed Assn, NEA ; *home:* 3100 Marlay Rd Dayton OH 45405

INS, MELINDA ANN, Math Teacher; *b:* Ypsilanti, MI; *m:* Dennis; mothy, Christina; *ed:* Towson St Univ (BS) Math 1991; *cr:* minster HS Math Tchr 1991-; *ai:* NHS Adv; NEA & CCEA 1991-; A 1990-; Mary Hudson Scarborough Awd for Excl in Field of Math; for Carroll Cty Tchr of Yr 1992; *office:* Westminster HS 1225 ngton Rd Westminster MD 21157

INS, ODESSA, Title I Comm Arts Teacher; *b:* New York, NY; *ed:* Univ of NY (BS) Psych 1961; Pace Univ (MS) Educl Admin, vision; *office:* PS 92 Mary Mcleod Bethune 222 W 134th St New York 0030*

INS, RONALD LEE, Geography & History Teacher; *b:* Kingston, ; Judith Neidjaco; *c:* Wendy L., Cindy S. Veldon; *ed:* Bloomsburg St (BA) Soc Stud 1965; *cr:* Southampton Twp Schls 4th Grd Tchr -70, 7th Grd Geog, His Tchr 1970-; *ai:* NJEA, NEA 1965-; ampton Twp NJ Tchr of Yr Awd 1987.

KS, DENISE J. DEVER, 4th Grade Teacher; *b:* Cincinnati, OH; *m:* ; *c:* Chris, Marissa; *ed:* Bowling Green St U (BED) Elem Ed 1970; of Dayton Credits; Wright St MS Pgm; *cr:* Walter Shade 1st Grd Tchr 75; Frank Nicholas 3rd Grd Tchr 1976-79; Harry Russell 3rd-5th Grd 1980-; *ai:* Soccer Coach 1986-90; BSA Comm Chair 1987-; Cub Chair 2 Yrs; Quality Sch Comm; Right to Read Coord; St Tchr Spon; A, WOE & DEA 1970-, Bldg Rep; Ashland Oil Golden Apple Achvmt W Carrollton Significant Tchr 6 Yrs; *office:* Harry Russell Elem Schl Elementary Dr West Carrollton OH 45449

NER, BRYAN H., Band Director; *b:* Mineola, NY; *m:* Andrea Beth h; *c:* Christopher; *ed:* SUNY at Potsdam (BM) Music Ed 1985; Grad SUNY at Stony Brook, Adelphi Univ, Jersey City St Coll; *cr:* Saxton Band Dir 1986-87; Baldwin Sr HS Co-Band Dir 1987-89; Hasbrouck hts Jr Sr HS Band Dir 1989-92; North Brunswick Twp HS Band Dir -; *ai:* Marching, Jazz Band; Winter Guard; Pit Orch; NJMEA, NEA, A 1989-; MENC 1984-; Rutgers Univ Outstdng Tchr Awd 1995; les Pub; *office:* North Brunswick Township HS 98 Raider Rd North swick NJ 08902*

NER, EILEEN KAPICA, Spanish Teacher; *b:* Brooklyn, NY; *m:* ew; *ed:* Queen Coll (BA) Span, Ed 1969; Middlebury Coll (MA) Span (MA) Italian 1985; 30 Credit Hrs Span Lit; *cr:* Island Trees HS Span 1969-70; John Dewey HS Span Tchr 1970-; *ai:* Needlecrafts Club AATSP 1970-, Bd of Dirs, VP; St Stanislaus Kostka 1955-, Choir, or, Euchristic Minister, RCIA Tchr; Stu Org Avc Awd; Tchr of Yr; : John Dewey HS 50 Avenue X Brooklyn NY 11223

NERJOHN, MARILYN RINKER, English Teacher; *b:* Easton, PA; ederick A.; *c:* D. Gregory Witmer, Stephanie R. Witmer; *ed:* Lebanon y Coll (AB) Eng 1962; PA St Univ (MA) Jrnlsm 1976; 24 Addl Credit Past Masters Wilkes, Allentown & Carlow Colls General Ed; 6 Addl it Hrs Past Masters Breadloaf Schl of Eng Writing & Lit; *cr:* Manheim HS Eng Tchr 1962-66; York Coll of PA Adjunct Eng Instr 1977-78; ng Grove HS Eng Tchr 1978-; *ai:* NEA, PSEA & Spring Grove EA -; NCTE 1985-; Tchrs & Writers Collaborative 1992-; Church Choir -, Alto Soloist; Two Articles Pub "the Round Table" Eng Journal 1992 94; Idea Pub Ideas Plus Book Eleven; *office:* Spring Grove HS Jackson anover Sts Spring Grove PA 17362

NINGS, BARBARA JEAN, Cooperative Ed Coord & Teacher; *b:* New ans, LA; *c:* Leslie Reid, La Tonya Reid, Rodney Reid; *ed:* Coll of New nelle (BA) Lib Arts 1986; Bernard Baruch (MSEd) Bus Ed 1991; *cr:* ts Fnd Inc Office Mgr 1969-72; Bd of Ed Schl Sec 1972-92, Tchr -; *ai:* Hnr Soc Coord; Amnesty Prgm Grd Adv; Chrldr Coach, IS 183 x for Sports Fnd Inc; BEA 1990-; AFT 1972-; UFT1972-, Del 1996; Cncl of Negro Women 1985-; Empire St Flwshp 1989; Sports Fnd Inc Achiever Awd; *home:* 129-33 W 147th St #6L New York NY 10039

NINGS, CAREEN SCHMIDT, HS English Teacher; *b:* Decatur, IL; eorge, Shannon, Eric (dec); *ed:* Univ of CT (BA) Eng 1965; Purdue (MA) Eng 1969; Univ of NH 4 Hrs Amer Lit; *cr:* South Side HS Eng 1967-69; Norwich Free Acad Eng Tchr 1969-; *ai:* NEA 1969-; Delta Kappa Gamma 1989-; Natl Org for Women 1980-; *office:* Norwich Free Acad 305 Broadway Norwich CT 06360

JENNINGS, CAROLE BEHRENS, English Teacher; *b:* Lancaster, PA; *m:* Louis G.; *c:* Laurie Kear, Karen Longenecker, Janet LaSpina, David Dusman; *ed:* Univ of PA at Millersville Scndry Eng (BS) 1970, (MS) 1974; 30 Post Grad Hrs Lang Arts; *cr:* Manheim Central HS Eng Tchr 1970-74; Manheim Central Jr HS Eng Tchr 1975-87; Manheim Central HS Eng Tchr 1988-; *ai:* Teens Taking Charge Adv; MCEA, NEA 1970-; NCTE 1980-; AAUW 1993-; *office:* Manheim Central High School Adele Ave & Hershey Dr Manheim PA 17545

JENNINGS, ELIZABETH LOUISE, Director of Alumnae Affairs; *b:* Mt Vernon, OH; *ed:* Kenyon Coll (BA) Eng & His 1990; *cr:* The Eisenhower Inst Asst to Exec Dir 1990-93; Georgetown Visitation JV Field Hockey Coach 1992; Oldfields Schl Alumnae Dir, Coach & Dorm Parent 1993-; *ai:* Var Field Hockey, JV Soccer & Squad III Lacrosse Coach; Adv to 5 Stdnts; CASE 1993-; APC 1993-; *office:* Oldfields Schl 1500 Glencoe Rd Glencoe MD 21152*

JENNINGS, JOANN CONSOLETTI, Kindergarten Tchr; *b:* Milford, MA; *ed:* Northeastern Univ at Boston (BS) Ed-Cum Laude 1957; Town of Holliston (MS) 1984; Attnd Harvard Univ, Leslie Coll, Framingham St, Oxford Univ, Boston Univ 1958-85; *cr:* Santa Barbara Schl Elem Tchr 1958-59; Berkley Schl Elem Tchr 1963-64; US Govts Overseas Prgm Germany, Italy, Japan 1959-62; Wayland Pub Schl System Elem, Kndgtn Tchr 1964-68; Holliston Pub Schl System Elem, Kndgtn Tchr 1976-; *ai:* Holliston Elem Cncl, Sr Citizens of Holliston Elem Rep; Select, Screen New Supt Comm 1995; Study New Lang Arts, Hlth St Frame Works Comm; NEA, AFT 1976-, Rep 10 Yrs; Nobscott Rdng Assn 1976-; Newport Preservation Soc 1987-; Newport Garden Soc 1989-; Potter Animal Soc 1986-; Animal Rights, Environment Org; Master Tchr for Practice Tchrs from Framingham St Coll 1976-95; Amatuer Theatre Group; *office:* Andrews Schl School St Holliston MA 01746

JENNINGS, JULIA MC CULLOUGH, Fifth Grade Teacher; *b:* Boston, MA; *m:* Wyatt Delano; *c:* Pamela; *ed:* Boston St Coll (BS) Elem Ed 1957; Attnd Kean Coll, Anderson Univ, Boston Univ; *cr:* Boston Pub Schls 2-3 Grd Tchr 1957-59; Montclair Pub Schls 3-4 Grd Tchr 1959-67; Plainfield Pub Schls 2 Grd Tchr 1967-68; Roselle Pub Schls Pre, Kndgtn Tchr 1970; Scotch Plains, Fanwood PS 2-3 Grd Tchr 1971-; *ai:* Strategic Planning Action Plan Facilitator; PTA Office Holder Mem; Sci Curr Dist Comm; NEA, NJEA 1959-; Scotch Plains, Fan EA 1971-, Rep, Pub Relations; Natl Assn of Univ Women 1968-, Sec; SP,F YMCA, Bd of Dirs Cert; Nom 1st Joan Vagelos Curry Distngd Tchr Awd; Mini-Grant Integrated Stud Tech; *office:* School One Willow Ave Scotch Plains NJ 07076*

JENNINGS, KATHRYN M., Head Teacher; *b:* Sioux Falls, SD; *ed:* Univ of ME (BS) Elem Ed; Harvard Univ (MED) Tchng, Learning, Supervision 1983; *cr:* James Bean Schl 6th Grd Tchr 1979-84; Hope Schl Tchng Prin 1984-86; Riley Schl Head Tchr 1986-; *office:* Riley Schl Warrenton St Glen Cove ME 04846

JENNINGS, MARK A., Assistant Principal; *b:* Montclair, NJ; *m:* June Venson; *c:* Thayer; *ed:* Univ of Dayton (BSEd) Elem Ed 1974, (MSEd) Ed Admin & Sup 1975; Seton Hall Univ Ed D Candidate; *cr:* Montclair HS & Mt Hebron MS Asst Prin 1991-; *ai:* NASSP 1991-; *home:* 1 Kimberly Ct Springfield NJ 07081

JENNINGS, NANCY E., Fourth Grade Teacher; *b:* Akron, OH; *m:* Laurence C.; *c:* Charles Gibson; Cindy Laikos, Stephen Gibson; *ed:* Univ of Akron (BS) Elem ed 1968; Post Grad Stud Ashland Univ; *cr:* Sherman Elem Schl Fourth Grd Tchr 1969-81; Norton Intermediate Schl Fourth Grd Tchr 1981-; *ai:* Sci Curr Comm Chprsn; Intervention Assistance Comm; Tchrs Assn Bldg Rep; Grd Level, Recognition Banquet Chprsn; Norton Classroom Tchrs Assn, NEA, OEA 1969-; *office:* Norton Intermediate Schl 4138 Cleveland Massillon Rd Norton OH 44203

JENNINGS, ROBERT M., United States History Tchr; *b:* Boston, MA; *m:* Pauline Houlihan; *c:* Mary Elizabeth, Elaine Buckley, Michael, Davia Leverton, Anne Marie, Stephen, Christine; *ed:* Boston Coll (BS) His & Govt 1956; Boston Univ (MA) Amer His 1957; 40 Hrs Grad Credits Beyond Masters; *cr:* Lewis Jr High 7th & 8th Grd Math Tchr 1957-58; Westwood Jr High 7th & 8th Grd Math Tchr 1958-59; Milton HS Soc Stud Tchr 1959-; *ai:* Former Driver Ed Instr 1963-85; Milton Edctrs 1958-, Former Bldg Rep; Norfolk Cty Tchrs 1958-; NEA 1973-; Weymouth MA Town Meeting 1974-, Elected Mem; *home:* 38 Idlewell St Weymouth MA 02188

JENNINGS, SYBILLYN H., Psychology Professor; *b:* Albany, NY; *m:* Kenneth H.; *ed:* Bennington Coll (BA) Lit 1963; San Jose St Coll (MA) Psych 1968; Univ of CA at Santa Barbara (PHD) Psych 1975; Univ of Denver Post Doctoral Fellow 1980; *cr:* Russell Sage Coll Asst Prof, Assoc Prof 1976-; *ai:* Amer Psychological Assn 1978-; Jean Pizyet Soc 1982-; Amer Ed Rsrch Assn; Flwshps; Grants; Awds; Articles Pub; *office:* Russell Sage Coll At Troy Dept of Psychology Troy NY 12180

JENNINGS, VAUGHN M.,III, Teacher & Principal; *b:* Terre Haute, IN; *m:* Marlene J. Todd; *c:* Jonathan D. T., Kathleen G. Merkt, Jennifer F. Milton; *ed:* Andrews Univ (BS) Elem Ed & Art 1974, (MAT) Elem Ed 1990; *cr:* WI Conf of SDA Elem Tchr, Prin 1965-76; NY Conf of SDA Elem Tchr, Prin 1976-78; WI Conf of SDA Elem Tchr, Prin 1978-82; OH Conf of SDA Elem Tchr, Prin 1982-85; PA Conf of SDA Elem Tchr & Prin 1985-; *ai:* PA Conf Exec Comm; Blue Mountain Acad Bd Mem & Prsnl Comm Mem; PA Conf Comm Mem; PA Conf Prins Comm 1985-, Pres; Thoams & Violet Zapara Excl in Tchng Awd 1990; Author of Primary Sabbath Schl Lessons for SDA Church 1985; *office:* Gettysburg Sda Church Schl 246 Hanover St Gettysburg PA 17325*

JENSEN, MICHAEL KEITH, Professor of Mechanical Engrng; *b:* Ft Collins, CO; *m:* Lois M. Horak; *c:* Melissa A. Jacobson, Leigh N., Kelsey R.; *ed:* Univ of MO at Columbia (BS) Mechanical Engrng 1972; IA St Univ (MS) Mechanical Engrng 1976, (PHD) Mechanical Engrng 1980; *cr:* Univ of WI at Milwaukee Asst & Assoc Prof 1980-86; Rensselear Polytechnic Inst Assoc & Full Prof 1987-; *ai:* ASME Stu Group Fac Adv 9 Yrs; Sigma Xi 1976-; ASME 1980-, Tech Comm Chair, Local Section Chair; AAAS 1982-; ASHRAE 1987-; AICHE 1986-; SAF 1993-95, Teeton Tchng Awd; Sierra Club 1975-, Local Group Chair, St Exec Bd 1 Yr; Assini Undergrad Tchng Awd 1990; 85 Publications; 16 Grants; 11 Multi Yr Grants; 20 Invited Lectures; Adv to 16 Masters & 6 Doctorate Stdnts; Licensed Prof Engr WISC; *office:* Rensselaer Polytechnic Inst Dept of Mech Engrng Troy NY 12180

JENSEN, PAMELA MARIE, HS Speech, Drama & Debate Tchr; *b:* Silver Spring, MD; *m:* Philip L.; *ed:* Liberty Univ (BS) Speech 1984; Western MD Coll Grad Stud Curr, Instruction; *cr:* Riverdale Bapt Schl HS Tchr 1990-; *ai:* NHS Adv; Asst Stu Govt Assn Spon; fac Soc Comm; Debate Coach; Chapel Coord; NCTE, Ed Theatre Assn 1993-; Natl Assn of St Advs 1994-; VFW 1990-, Voice of Democracy Speech Contest Coord; *office:* Riverdale Baptist Schl 1133 Largo Rd Upper Marlboro MD 20774

JENSEN, SVEN, Social Studies Dept Head; *b:* Uppsala, Sweden; *m:* Vera R. Henneuse; *c:* Kristoffer, Maria; *ed:* Uppsala Univ (BA) Politics, Ec 1969; Loyola Russian His; Towson St African His; *cr:* Kfum Uppsala Head Bsktbl Coach 1970-81; Solna IF Head Bsktbl Coach 1981-83; Sodertalje BBK Head Bsktbl Coach 1983-84; Swedish Bsktbl Fed Natl Team Head Coach 1979-84; Oldfields Schl Head Soc Stud Dept 1985-; *ai:* Head Vars Bsktbl Coach; Current Issues Forum Adv; Prof Dev, May Prgm, Curr Comm; NCSS 1994-; *office:* Oldfields Schl 1500 Glencoe Rd Glencoe MD 21152

JENSEN, THOMAS JUDE,CFC, Classical Studies & Math Tchr; *b:* New York City, NY; *ed:* Iona Coll (BA) Classical Lang, Lit 1962; Manhattan Coll (MA) Classical Lant, Lit 1968; Permanent NYS Cert Grds 7-12 Latin, Fr, Math 55 Credit Hrs; *cr:* Essex Cath HS Instr & Bsktbl Coach 1962-66; Cardinal Hayes HS Instr 1966-67; Power Meml Acad Instr, Dean & Ath Dir 1967-76; Iona Preparatory Schl Instr, Bsktbl & Bsbl Coach 1976-84; Bergen Cath HS Instr, Ath Dir, Bsbl & Bsktbl Coach 1984-; *ai:* NCEA 1980-; NY Cath HS Ath Assn Hall of Fame; *office:* Bergen Cath HS 1040 Oradell Ave Oradell NJ 07649

JENSON, MARY SHULETSKY, Business Instructor & Chprsn; *b:* Hazleton, PA; *m:* Charles T.; *c:* Deborah T. Dickison, Jodi E.; *ed:* Bloomsburg Univ (BS) Bus Ed 1959; *cr:* Susquehanna Twp Sr HS Bus Tchr 1959-63; Cntrl Dauphin East Sr HS Bus Tchr 1963-67; Salt Lake City Tech Coll Bus Instr, Chprsn 1968-70; Weber Coll Bus Instr, Chprsn 1970-72; Stony Brook Sporting Goods Store Owner 1976-82; Consolidated Schl of Bus Chprsn, Bus Instr 1982-; *ai:* Yrbk Co-Adv; Class of 1961 Adv; PA St Ed Assn, NEA 1959-67; Local Ed Assn 1959-67, Sec; Beta Sigma Phi 1972-82, Treas, Sec, VP, Pres, Woman of Yr 1978; *home:* 2159 Eden Rd York PA 17402

JEONG, JOYCE CHIH-CHEN, Engineering Assistant Prof; *b:* Taipei, Taiwan; *m:* David Yuen; *ed:* Soochow Univ (BS) Math 1982; Univ of SC (MS) Math 1986; Lehigh Univ (MS) Applied Mechanics 1993; *cr:* North Shore Comm Coll Instr 1990-93, Engrng & Industrial Techs Asst Prof 1993-; *ai:* Curr Comm; AAPT 1993-; *office:* North Shore Comm Coll 1 Ferncroft Rd Danvers MA 01923

JEPSEN, KATHLEEN HAGERTY, English Teacher; *b:* Philadelphia, PA; *m:* William G. Jr.; *c:* Erika Robertson, Haakon, Britta; *ed:* Cath Univ (BA) Speech, Drama 1969; Johns Hopkins Univ (MA) Lbrl Arts 1992; Towson St Univ (MS) Instrl Tech, Schl Media 1994; *cr:* George Fox MS Lang Arts Tchr 1983-87; Northeast Sr HS Eng Tchr, Drama Coach 1987-89; George Fox MS Lang Arts Tchr 1989-91; Southern Sr HS Eng, Drama Tchr 1991-93; Meade Sr HS Eng Tchr 1994-; *ai:* Citizens Advy Cncl Tchr Rep; Multicultural Affairs Liaison; Human Relations, Tech Comms; MD Cncl Tchrs of Eng, Lang Arts 1989-, Featured Speaker 1990; NCTE 1994-, Books for You Annotator; MD Educl Media Org 1994-; Anne Arundel Cty Pub Lib 1995-, Vol; Anne Arundel Cty Tchr of Yr Nom 1989; Maude Broils Lit Excl Awd Nom Towson St Univ 1994; *office:* Meade Sr HS 1100 Clarke Rd Fort Meade MD 20755

JERBERT, MARILYN BAKER, Business Teacher; *b:* Westerly, RI; *m:* Arthur H.; *c:* Evelyn B. Hale, Carolyn Baker Reck, Daniel L. Baker; *ed:* Bryant Coll (BSEd) Bus Ed 1962; Univ of RI (MS) Bus Ed 1980; *cr:* Wheeler HS Bus Tchr 1968; New London Schl of Bus Dir of Ed, Bus Tchr 1977-88; Griswold HS Bus Tchr 1988-; *ai:* NHS Co-Adv; Tech Prep Liaison; Natl DPE Mbrshp Comm; NEBEA 1977-, 2nd VP; Delta Rho Epsilon 1977-, Past Pres; NBEA, EBEA, CBEA 1977-; CEA 1988-; Muriel Fletcher Outstdng Bus Edctr Awd; Univ of CT Alumni Outstdng Tchr Awd; *office:* Griswold Jr-Sr HS 267 Slater Ave Jewett City CT 06351

JERDON, WILLIAM H., Photography Teacher; *b:* Hamilton, OH; *m:* Cecilia Cerutt; *c:* Colby, Melissa, Ian, Giuliana, Edward; *ed:* Bowling Green St Univ (BS) Art Ed 1966, (MA) Painting 1972, (MFA) Painting 1972; *cr:* Belle Cntrl Schls Art Supvr 1966; Cleveland Heights HS Art Tchr 1966-70; Bowling Green St Univ Tchng Fellow 1971-72; Cleveland Heights Art Tchr 1972-; *ai:* Photography Club Adv; Curr Adv Comm; Art Dept Liaison; K-12th Grd Art Task Force; AFT 1966-; Kennedy Ctr Fellowship; Pres Cncl on Ed Distinguished Tchr; RI Schl of Design Fellowship; Cncl for Basic Ed Fellowship Grant; *office:* Cleveland Heights HS 13263 Cedar Rd Cleveland Heights OH 44118

JERIC, RICK HENRY, Campus Minister; *b:* Cleveland, OH; *m:* Theresa Nigborowicz; *c:* Richard, Christian; *ed:* John Carroll Univ (BA) Pol Sci 1980; Ed Cert 1990; 9 Post Grad Hrs Toward Admin; *cr:* Bainbridge Colonial Lanes Operations Mgr 1980-87; Internal Revenue Svc Taxpayer Svc 1987-88; Agency Rent-A-Car Office Mgr 1988-89; Cleveland Cntrl Cath Schl Tchr 1990-91; Notre Dame Cathedral Latin Schl Tchr, Campus Minister 1991-; *ai:* Fac Advy Bd; Prins Exec Cncl; NCEA 1991-; St Joan of Arc Parish Schl, Chair of Future Planning; *office:* Notre Dame Cathedrl Latin Schl 13000 Auburn Rd Chardon OH 44024*

JERMAN, ELIZABETH FAYE, 5th Grade Teacher; *b:* Elkton, MD; *m:* Jerry; *c:* James; *ed:* DE St Coll (BS) Elem Ed 1978; *cr:* Lake Forest 5th Grd Tchr 14 Yrs, 6th Grd Tchr 4 Yrs; *ai:* NEA 1978-; *home:* RR 4 Box 429 Georgetown DE 19947

JERNIGAN, JANICE REDMOND, Business Education Teacher; *b:* Edenton, NC; *m:* Charlie H. Jr.; *c:* Amber Jenay, Jason Haywood; *ed:* Rutgers Univ (MS) Ed 1979; Winston Salem St Univ (BS) Bus Ed 1975; *cr:* SCS Bus & Tech Inst, Bus Ed Tchr 1981-84; Katharine Gibbs Schl Bus Ed Tchr 1985-89, Dean of Continuing Ed 1986-87; Plainfield Pub Schl Bus Ed Tchr 1989-90; Monroe Twp HS Bus Ed Tchr 1990-; *ai:* FBLA Adv; Core Team Mem; Tchr Mentoring Prgm; NEA; *office:* Monroe Township HS 1629 Perinneville Rd Jamesburg NJ 08831

JERNIGAN, PRINCE DAVID, History & Social Studies Tchr; *b:* Edenton, NC; *m:* Nancy Celestine Patterson; *c:* Alison, David; *ed:* Winston-Salem St Univ (BA) His 1973; Morgan St Univ (MS) His, Soc Sci 1976; Credit Hrs Appalachian St Univ 14, Bowie St Univ 21, Loyola Coll 3; *cr:* Andover Sr High 1973-81; Anne Arundel Cty Pub Schls Soc Stud & His Tchr 1973-; Severna Park Evening HS Tchr 1976-; Glen Burnie Summer Schl Admin 1978-; Hartofrd Comm Coll Instr 1978; Old Mill Sr HS 1981-; *ai:* Class Adv 1978-77, 1985; Citizens Advy Comm; Asst Band Dir; Drama Coach; NEA, MD St Tchrs Assn, Tchrs Assn of AA Cty 1973-; WSSU Balto Alumni Chapter 1980-, VP, Corr Sec; Mem of St. Martins 1990-; *office:* Old Mill Sr HS 600 Patriot Ln Millersville MD 21108

JEROME, JOHN LUCKNER, Assistant Professor; *b:* Cazale, Haiti; *m:* Jacqueline O. Brathwaite; *c:* Jaimie, Janelle; *ed:* Long Island Univ (BS) Math 1986, (MS) Math 1988; Univ of TN (MS) Aviation Systems 1992; 6 Credits at Hunter Coll; 3 Credits at NY Univ; 3 Credits at Stony Brook; *cr:* Episcopal Church Ctr Refugee Specialist 1987-90; Univ of TN Grad Asst 1990-92; Suffolk Comm Coll Asst Prof 1992-; *ai:* Math Club Adv; Comm Relations & Encourage Appreciation of Diversity Comms; Multiculturalism; Schlsp Comm; AFT 1992-; AMATYC 1993-; NASBE Chapter 1991-, VP; KME Chapter 1986-, VP; Bishop Comm 1986-, Sec; Long Island Philomonica 1984-, Viola Player, Schlsp; NASSAU POPS Symp 1995-, Viola Player; Step & Liberty Partnership Prgms; Tech-Prep Consortium Coll Liaison; *office:* Suffolk Community Coll Crooked Hill Rd Brentwood NY 11717*

JEROME, MARLENE S., 6th Grade Teacher; *b:* VanWert, OH; *m:* J. David; *c:* Emmalyn, Matthew, Benjamin; *ed:* Lima Meml Schl of Nrsng (RN) 1970; Attnd OH Northern Univ; *home:* 1797 Holton Rd Grove City OH 43123

JESCHKE, MARLIN, Ret Prof of Philosophy & Rel; *b:* Laird, Canada; *m:* Elizabeth Ann Bixel; *c:* Eric, Margaret, David; *ed:* Tabor Coll (BA) Eng 1954; Garrett Seminary (BD) Theology 1958; Northwestern U (PHD) Rel 1965; Visiting Schloar Post-Doctoral Harvard U Divinity Schl 1968-69, Fuller Theological Seminary 1988-89; *cr:* North Park Coll Lecturer 1959-61; Goshen Coll Asst Assoc Prof 1961-94; *ai:* Amer Theological Soc 1967-, Pres; Mennonite Histocial Soc 1961-, Book Review Ed, Sec;

Writing Book Reviews, Books in Theology; Flwshp in Asian Rels 1968-69; Lilly Endowement Summer Stipend 1990; Pub Book, Discipling in the Church 1972, 1988; Over 200 Book Reviews in Various Periodicals.

JESEK, CHARLES JERRY, Fifth Grade Teacher; *b:* Pittsburgh, PA; *m:* Carol Ann Bushem; *c:* Bridgette, Chad; *ed:* CA Univ (BA) Elem Ed 1968; PA St Univ (MS) Ed 1990; *cr:* Court Elem Schl 5th-6th Grd Tchr 1968-80; Carnegie Elem Schl 5th Grd Tchr 1980-; *ai:* 7th-9th Grd Bsktbl Coach; HS Gold Coach 1986-88; Union Building Rep 1968-70; Patrol Spon 1969-74; IM Dir 1972-78; AFT 1972-; PTA 1968-; *home:* 446 Morrow St Carnegie PA 15106

JESERSKI, DIANE D., Business Teacher; *b:* Holyoke, MA; *m:* Frederick; *c:* Lindsey, Mark; *ed:* Amer Intnl Coll (BA) Bus Admin 1975; 15 Addl Credit Hrs; Courses Taken At Westfield St Coll; Springfield Tech Comm Coll; *cr:* Mt Holyoke Coll Sec 1971-75; Agawam Jr HS Bus Tchr 1975-76; Minnechaug Regnl HS Bus Tchr 1976-; *ai:* Future Bus Ldrs of Amer Adv 6 Yrs; Field Trip Comm; MA Tchrs Assn 1975-; *office:* Minnechaug Regional HS 621 Main St Wilbraham MA 01095

JESS, DIANE THOMPSON, Mathematics Teacher; *b:* Piqua, OH; *m:* Thomas Allan; *c:* Jaclyn, Jennifer, Janelle; *ed:* Wittenberg Univ (BA) Math 1974; Wright St Univ (MED) Tchr, Ldr 1984; Post Grad Stud Univ of Dayton, Wright St Univ; *cr:* Graham Local Schls Math Tchr 1974-; *ai:* Math Counts Coach; Stu Cncl Adv; Promotion Ceremony Coord; Jr DARE Adv; Kappa Delta Pi 1983-; Phi Delta Kappa 1984-; Graham Ed Assn, NEA, OEA 1974-, Bldg Rep, Treas; 4-H Adv 11 Yrs; Champaign Cty 4-H Comm Mem 1993-; After Prom Parents Publicity Chm 1994-; United Meth Church Sunday Schl Tchr 1977-; Diamond Chapter 84 Order of Eastern Star; After Prom Prnts Pres 1995; Untd Meth Women Mem; Child Culture Club; *office:* Graham Local Schls 370 E Main St Saint Paris OH 43072

JESSEE, LINDA CRAMPTON, 5th Grade Teacher; *b:* Hagerstown, MD; *m:* Steve W.; *c:* Susan Ulsh; *ed:* Towson St Univ (BA) Elem Ed 1969; Shippensburg St Univ (MA) Elem Ed 1973; *cr:* Clear Spring Elem 4th Grd Tchr 1969-75, 5th Grd Tchr 1985-; Hickory Elem 4-5th Grd Tchr 1975-85; *ai:* NEA, MSTA, WCTA 1969-; Clear Spring Historical Soc 1989-; Washington Cty Tchr of Yr Awd Nom 1991; *home:* 12921 Keefer Rd Big Pool MD 21711

JESSOP, KATHLEEN DUGGAN, English & Language Arts Tchr; *b:* Middleboro, MA; *m:* John W.; *c:* Sarah, Catherine; *ed:* Bridgewater St Coll (BA) Eng 1971; *cr:* Meml Jr HS Eng, Lang Arts Tchr 1971-; *ai:* Schl Cncl Rep; Middleboro Ed Assn Exec Bd; MTA, NEA, 1971-; MEA 1971-, Treas, Citation 1989; PCEA; Friends of Lib; Soule Homestead; *office:* Memorial Jr HS 219 N Main St Middleboro MA 02346

JESSY, CARL WILLIAM, Social Studies Teacher; *b:* Pittsburgh, PA; *c:* Michael William; *ed:* Thiel Coll at Greenville (BA) His 1967; 37 Credit Hrs; *cr:* Kane Jr HS 9th Grd Civics & PA His Tchr, Jr HS Bsktbl Coach 1967-82; Yeshiva Schls Soc Stud Tchr, His Dept Chprsn 1983-; *ai:* Bsktbl Coach; PA Soc Stud Cncl 1991-; PSEA 1967-; PA St Historical Soc; Natl Cncl of Social Studies Tchrs; Luth Br Fraternal Soc 1964-, Former Consultant; GSLC Church Cncl 1987-, Property Chm; Pittsburgh JCC Bsktbl Assn 1984-86, Coach, Coach of Yr 1984-86; *office:* Yeshiva Achei Tmimim Schl 2100 Wightman St Pittsburgh PA 15217

JESTER, KELLY WILSON, Social Studies Teacher; *b:* Chestertown, MD; *m:* Richard P.; *ed:* Western MD Coll (BA) His, Art His 1988; Univ of MD Baltimore Cty (MA) Instrl Systems Dev 1994; 30 Addl Credits; *cr:* Franklin MS Tchr 1991-92; Franklin HS Tchr 1991-; *ai:* Class of 1998 Adv; NHS Fac Cncl; Cross Cntry Coach; *office:* Franklin HS 12000 Reisterstown Rd Reisterstown MD 21136

JETTE, BETH HUNTER, Middle Schl Mathematics Tchr; *b:* Saint Albans, VT; *m:* Andre M.; *c:* Jessica L., Andrea M.; *ed:* Castleton St Coll (BS) Math 1973; Univ of VT (MED) Ed 1988; *cr:* Missisquoi Valley Union Math Tchr 1973-, Summer Ed Dir 1981-85; *ai:* Firebirds Team Ldr; VT Cncl of Tchrs of Math, NEA 1973-; VT MS Assn 1986-; Swanton Jaycee Womens 1984-; ATMNE Conf Presider; Dev of Gifted Summer Prgm; Natl ASCD MS Consortium Tchr Rep; Effective Tchng Conf Presenter; Curr Cluster; Math Challenge League, Parent Support & Rewarding Excl in Math Grants; *office:* Missisquoi Valley Union HS RR 2 Box 268 Swanton VT 05488*

JEWELL, VICTORIA FIOCCA, Fifth Grade Teacher; *b:* Lakewood, OH; *m:* Dennis; *c:* Greg, Janine Journey; *ed:* Bowling Green St Univ (BS) Elem Ed 1967; 30 Grad Semester Hrs; *cr:* Cleveland Pub Schls Fifth Grd Tchr 1967-70; Southington Local Schls Fifth Grd Tchr 1970-71; Champion Local Schls All Elem Grds 1982-.

JEWETT, BARBARA JOANNE, Sci Dept Chprsn & Chem Tchr; *b:* Cleveland, OH; *ed:* Univ of NH (BA) Chem 1964; John Carroll Univ (MST) Physics 1971; 15 Credit Hrs Duke Univ; 9 Credit Hrs Univ of MN; *cr:* Andrews Schl Sci Dept Chprsn 1968-73; Bucks Cty Comm Coll Bio, Chem Instr 1973-74; Oakland Mills HS Sci Dept Chprsn 1974-; *ai:* NHS; Its Acad; NEA 1974-; NSTA 1977-; Amer Chemical Soc Outstdng HS Chem Tchr MD 1988, Mid-Atlantic Region 1989; *office:* Oakland Mills HS 9410 Kilimanjaro Rd Columbia MD 21045

JEWETT, FRANKLYN WAYNE, Health & Physical Ed Teacher; *b:* Waltham, MA; *m:* Mary Mulgrew; *c:* Amy, Brian, Patrice; *ed:* Boston Univ (BA) Hlth, Recreation & PE 1971, (MS) Scndry Ed & Admin 1972; 15 Hrs Toward Doctorate Degree; *cr:* Roberts Jr HS PE Tchr 1972-78; Medford HS Hlth & PE Tchr 1978-; *ai:* HS Ftbl Coach 1972-80; HS Golf Coach; Jr-Sr Class Adv; Commissioner of Outdoor Track Ofcls for the Greater Boston League; Medford Tchrs Assn 1972-; MA Tchrs Assn 1972-; Natl Tchrs 1972-; Medford Coaches Assn; MA Coaches Assn, Pres, VP & Treas; *office:* Medford HS 489 Winthrop St Medford MA 02155

JEWUSIAK, JOHN A., Physical Science Teacher; *b:* Englewood, NJ; *m:* Ingrid Elise Endreson; *ed:* Ocean Cty Coll (AA) 1968; Trenton St Coll (BA) Phys Sci 1971; 16 Addl Credits; *cr:* Wall Intermediate Schl Phys Sci Tchr 1971-; *ai:* NJEA, WTEA 1971-; Tchr of Yr 1988 Under Governors Recognition Prgm; *office:* Wall Intermediate Schl Allaire Rd & Baileys Corner Rd Wall NJ 07719

JIAMACHELLO, THOMAS A., French Teacher; *b:* Brockway, PA; *ed:* IN Univ of PA (BSEd) Ed, Fr-Magna cum Laude 1994; Univ of VT (MAT) Ed, Fr-Summa Cum Laude 1977; 42 Addl Credits; Univ de Poitiers Fulbright Schlsp 1974-75 Fr Lang; *cr:* Univ of VT Continuing Ed Division Fr I-II, 51-52 Tchr 1977-79, 1981-83; Essex HS Fr I-VI, AP Tchr 1977-; *ai:* Co-Chair Chittenden Cntrl Stan Bd 1995-98; Var Boys Tennis Coach 1983-; Org Fr Exch 1991-; SAT Prep Course Verbal Instr 1988-; NEA 1977-; VT Frgn Lang Assn 1977-, Bd of Dir 1980-; Essex Junction Educl Assn 1977-, VP; Fleming Museum Univ of VT Antique Appraiser; Tchr of Yr 1987-88; Presenter VFLA Annual Convention 1990-; *office:* Essex Junction HS 2 Educational Dr Essex Junction VT 05452*

JILES, KATHRYN GAMBILL, 2nd Grade Teacher; *b:* Richwood, WV; *m:* Fred A. Jr.; *c:* Shaun, Eric, Savannah; *ed:* Glenville St Coll (BA) Elem Ed 1983; WV Univ (MA) Elem Ed 1994; *cr:* Fairplains Elem Schl 5th Grd, 4th-6th Grd Music Tchr 1984-86; Salem Liberty Elem Schl 2nd, 6th Grd Tchr 1988-; *ai:* NEA 1984-; FFTA 1988-; *office:* Salem Liberty Elem Schl PO Box 37 Lower Salem OH 45745*

JILES, SAVILLA WEAVER, Civics Teacher; *b:* Chamersburg, PA; *m:* Lester G. Sr.; *c:* Lester G. Jr., Isaiah W.; *ed:* Lincoln Univ (BA) Ed & His 1972; Shippensburg Univ Masters in Ed; *cr:* Cntrl Jr HS Amer His Tchr 1973-86; Chambersburg Area MS Amer His Tchr 1986-92; J Frank Faust Jr HS Amer His & Civics Tchr 1992-; *ai:* STEP Pgm Adv; PA St Ed Assn 1990-; NEA; Chambersburg Comm Improvement Assn 1990-; Coyle Free Lib Friends 1995-; *office:* J Frank Faust Jr HS 1957 Scotland Ave Chambersburg PA 17201

JILLSON, JILL, 3rd Grade Teacher; *b:* Boston, MA; *ed:* Bates Coll (BA) His 1968; Univ of MA (MED) Rdng 1972; Attnd Univ of Hartford, N Adams St Coll, Worcester S C, Westfield S C, Salem S C; *cr:* Riverview HS His, Eng Tchr 1968-70; Berkshire Hills RSD 3rd-5th Grd Sp Ed 1972-; *ai:* Fac Adv to Supt; Soc Stud Task Force; Fac Rep PTO; Tchrs Assn, Sec; NEA, MTA 1972-; BHEA 1972-, Pres 1984-88, Sec 1980-84, 1995-; Church Life Mem, Rel Ed Tchr, Pres Parish Cncl; Berkshire Camera Club 1988-, Exec Bd, Comm Head, Photograph of Yr 1990; Bates Alumni Assn 1968-, Pres Local Bates Alumni Club 1986-90, Bates Fundraising; *office:* Bryant Elem Schl 16 School St Great Barrington MA 01230*

JIMERSON, SANDRA E., Seneca Language & Culture Tchr; *b:* Salamanca, NY; *c:* Wm J. Crouse Sr., M.W. Crouse Jr., Jacqueline Crouse, Brandon Crouse; *ed:* Jamestown Comm Coll (AA) 1980; *cr:* Salamanco City Schls Seneca Lang & Culture Tchr 11 Yrs; *office:* Salamanca HS 50 Iroquois Dr Salamanca NY 14779

JINKS, KATHLEEN CASEY, Language Arts Teacher; *b:* Easton, PA; *m:* Roger A. Sr.; *c:* Maria, Kathleen, Roger Jr.; *ed:* Centenary Coll (BS) Elem Ed 1985; East Stroudsburg Univ (MED) Prof, Scndry Ed 1995; *cr:* Sts Philip & James Schl Grd 2, 4 Tchr 1978-86; Stewartsville Elem 3, 6-8 Grd Tchr 1986-; *ai:* Stu Cncl Adv; NCTE 1993-; ASCD 1994-; NJEA, WCEA, GTEA 1986-; Girls Scouts 1980-, Diocesan Coord; St Mary's Church 1993-, CCD Tchr, Lector; NJ Governor Tchr Recognition Awd 1990; Warren Cty Tchr of Yr 1995; A Plus for Kids LRE Grant 1995; Unit Published A Plus for Kids Idea Catalog; *office:* Stewartsville Elem Schl 642 S Main St Stewartsville NJ 08886*

JIRA, ROSE MARI CHINIGO, 6th Grade Teacher; *b:* Cleveland, OH; *m:* Paul L.; *ed:* Kent St Univ (BA) Elem Ed 1988; Basic Catechist Certfd; 9 Credit Hrs; *cr:* St Patrick Schl 6-8th Grd Tchr 1989-; *ai:* IA Testing Coord; Initiated Frgn Lang Exploration Prgm; Stu Mediation Trnr Summer Schl Prgm; OCEA 1989-; NCTE 1990-; *office:* St Patrick West Park Schl 17720 Puritas Ave Cleveland OH 44135*

JOBIN, DOROTHY MARTIN, Kindergarten Teacher; *b:* Marlborough, NH; *m:* Raymon A.; *c:* Monique Jobin Harmon; *ed:* Keene St Coll (BED) Elem Ed 1962; *cr:* Chesterfield Elem Schl First Grd Tchr 1962-66; St Joseph Schl Kndgtn Tchr 1972-, Interim Prin 1994-95; *ai:* NCEA; NH Cath Schl Edctr of Yr Awd 1993; *home:* 4 Willow St Keene NH 03431

JOCHNOWITZ, JOHANN MICHAEL, Prof of Fine Arts; *b:* New York, NY; *m:* Carol Lipson; *c:* Abby Hunt, Nina, Gabrielle Clisold; *ed:* NYU (BS) Fine Art & Ed 1957, (MS) Fine Art 1959; Visual Arts; Cooper Union; Art Stdnts League; *cr:* Jewish Guild for the Blind Ceramic & Sculptur Coord 1960-64; Buck Rock Work Camp Gift Adolescents Dir & Tchr 1960-80; South HS Scndry Art Prof 1964-65; Univ of Madras Gov Art Inst Visiting Prof 1965-67; Queens Coll FA Asst Prof 1967-68; Kean Coll Fine Arts Prof 1968-; *ai:* Fine Arts Club Dept Adv; AFT 1972-; Org of Holocaust Artists & Scholar 1990-; Historic Comm of So Orange 1985-, VP; Gallery of So Orange 1993-, Founding Mem & Bd of Dirs; Fulbright Scholar to India Sr Grantee; Ford Fndtn Grant to Japan; *office:* Kean Coll Of NJ Morris Avenue Union NJ 07083

JOCHUM, BRIDGETT WHITTAKER, Third Grade Teacher; *b:* Johnson City, TN; *m:* Jerry; *c:* Jessica; *ed:* Univ of MD (BS) Elem Ed 1985; Bowie St Univ (MA) Spec Ed 1993; Elem Ed; *cr:* Eva Turner Elem Schl 3rd Grd Tchr 1986-90; William B. Wade Elem Schl 3rd Grd Tchr 1990-; Chades Cty Comm Coll PT, Rdng Instr 1993-; *ai:* Prof Dev Team Ldr; NEA 1986-; *home:* 16900 Driftwood Pl Hughesville MD 20637

JOEDICKE, JOAN M., Library Media Specialist; *b:* Stamford, NY; *m:* Frederick H.; *c:* Kelly Joedicke Lawrence, Kimberly, Kristy; *ed:* WV Wesleyan Coll (BS) PE, Hlth 1964; SUNY Albany (MLS) Lib Media 1987; *cr:* Oneonta HS PE Tchr 1965-66; Stamford CS Jefferson CS PE Tchr 1966-71; Jefferson CS Gilboa CS Lib Media Specialist 1984-89; South Kortright Cntrl Schl Lib Media Specialist 1989-; *ai:* NHS Adv; Tech Comm; Dollars for Scholars; NEA 1965-; DE Cty Yth Bd 1990-, VP, Yth Worker; Tchr of the Yr 1988.

JOERIGHT, DIANE BUDAN, 7th-8th Grade English Teacher; *b:* Cleveland, OH; *m:* Charles; *c:* Chad, Craig, Colin; *ed:* Kent St Univ (BS) Elem Ed 1971; Attnd Univ of Dayton, Kent St, Baldwin Wallace; *cr:* St Columbkille Schl 2nd Grd Tchr 5 Yrs; St John Bosco Schl 4th-5th Grd Sci, Rdng Tchr 1 Yr; Incarnate Word Acad 7th-8th Grd Eng Tchr 5 Yrs; *ai:* Speech Team Coach 15 Yrs; Drama, Ski Clubs Adv; Retreat Coord; AAUW 1991-; N Royalton Planning, Rep; *office:* Incarnate Word Acad 6618 Pearl Rd Cleveland OH 44130

JOFFE, PATRICIA DEMPSEY, Assistant Professor; *b:* Summit, NJ; *m:* Edward M.; *c:* Edward, Brian, Sean; *ed:* Rutgers St Univ (BSN) Nursing 1969, (MS) Maternal-Child Nursing 1979; Jersey City St Coll Schl Nurse Cert Prgm; *cr:* Charles E. Gregory Schl of Nursing Instr 1970-75, Chprsn, Coord 1975-77; Middlesex Cty Coll Instr 1980-81; Kean Coll of NJ Asst Prof 1986-91; Jersey City St Coll Asst Prof 1991-; *ai:* Sigma Theta Tau, Kappa Eta Chapter Fac Cnslr; Visiting Nurse Assn Pediatric Team Nurse; Rutgers Alumni Assn 1969-; Amer Nurses Assn 1969-; NJ St Nurses Assn 1969-; Sigma Theta Tau 1979-; NHS, Cnslr; BSA 1989-; Westfield PTA 1982-; Sigma Theta Tau NHS for Nursing; Amer Nurse Credentialing Ctr Pediatric Nurse Cert; Licensed NJ Clinical Nurse Specialist.

JOFFRAY, DONALD MARSHALL, Math Teacher; *b:* Richmond, VA; *m:* Suzanne Clum; *c:* Rexford, Jeffrey; *ed:* Wesleyan U (AB) Math 1950; *cr:* Loomis Chaffee Math Tchr 1950-; US Navy LTJG 1952-56; *ai:* Ftbl, Wrestling, Track & Hockey Coach; Outing Club Adv; Whitewater Slalom C-1 US Natl Champion 1960; *office:* Loomis Chaffee Schl Batchelder Rd Windsor CT 06095

JOFTIS, FRANK JAY, Eighth Grade Teacher; *b:* Philadelphia, PA; *m:* Bess Fall; *c:* Cara J.; *ed:* Temple Univ (BA) Pol Sci 1969, (MED) C & I 1972; Prins Cert Univ of PA 1978; 30 Addl Hrs Toward EDD, MBA Prgm Temple Univ (MBA) 1994; *cr:* Phila Bd of Ed Educator 1969-; *ai:* Grd Chrm; Yrbk, Saftey Patrol Spon; Girls, Boys Bsktbl Team Coach; AFT, Bnai Brith 1969-; Warrington Ath Assn 1978-; Rose Linderbaum Awd for Tchng Exel 1994; *office:* Fitler Academics Plus Seymour & Knox St Philadelphia PA 19144*

JOHANNES, PAULA MARIE, Elem Teacher of Gifted Stdnts; *b:* Pittsburgh, PA; *m:* Robert; *c:* Lindsay, Ross; *ed:* PA St Univ (BS) Elem Ed 1979; PA Masters Equivalency Degree 1994; 6 Addl Grad Insvc Credits; *cr:* Aliquippa MS 8th Grd Bio Tchr 1979-80; Ramsey Schl 6th Grd Tchr 1980-81; South Fayette Elem Schl 1-2, 4-5 Grd Tchr 1981-88, Elem GATE Tchr 1988-; *ai:* Elem Tech Team; PSEA 1980-; Girl Scouts of Amer 1995-, Daisy Scout Ldr; Nom Stu Tchr of Yr 1979; *office:* South Fayette Elem Schl 2248 Old Oakdale Rd Mc Donald PA 15057

JOHN, DAN WAYNE, Gifted Support Teacher; *b:* Monaca, PA; *ed:* Clarion Univ of PA (BSEd) Eng 1966; Univ of Pittsburgh (MA) Eng Lit 1971; 39 Addl Hrs at Bearen Coll, Widener Univ, Marywood Coll; *cr:* St Marys HS Eng Tchr 1966-67; Freedom Area HS Eng Tchr 1967-70; Hatboro-Horsham HS Eng, Gifted Support Tchr 1970-; *ai:* Golden Pen Lit Magazine; PSEA, NEA 1966-; PA Assn for Gifted Ed 1981-90; Advanta Corp Grant for Pentium Cmptr, Internet Hook-up; *office:* Hatboro Horsham Sr HS 899 Horsham Rd Horsham PA 19044

JOHN, MICHELLE HAND, Math Teacher; *b:* Norfolk, VA; *m:* Rob *c:* Laura E.; *ed:* Liberty Univ (BS) Math, Ed 1990; 15 Credit H Sussex Cntrl HS Math Tchr 1991-; *ai:* Asst Sftbl Coach St Char 1995; Staff Dev Comm; DE Cncl of Tchrs of Math 1993-; Attendanc 1992, 1995; *office:* Sussex Central HS 301 W Market St Georgeto 19947

JOHNCAR, DEREK KENT, Mathematics Teacher; *b:* Saint Joseph *m:* Alicia Louise Norris; *ed:* Grove City Coll (BA) Math & Scnc 1992; Slippery Rock Univ 9 Grad Level Hrs; *cr:* Grove City Admissions Cnslr 1992; Grove City HS Tchr 1993-; *ai:* Asst Var & 9th Grd Ftbl Coach; 7th Grd Boys Bsktbl Coach; Bible Club Adv 1993-; *office:* Grove City HS 511 Highland Ave Grove City PA 161

JOHNDRO, MARCIA MAE, History Teacher; *b:* Ft Kent, M Stephen; *c:* Kevin, Kenneth, Carrie, Rolande; *ed:* Univ of ME at F (BS) His 1971; *cr:* St Francis Elem Jr HS Kndgtn, 3rd, 6th, 7th, 8t His Tchr 1975-; *ai:* NEA, ME Ed Assn 1975-; *office:* St Francis E HS PO Box 57 Saint Francis ME 04774*

JOHNS, CAROL ROMA, English Teacher; *b:* Orange, NJ; *m:* Peter Kevin H., Aimee N.; *ed:* Brookdale Comm Coll (AA) Eng 1984; Do Rutgers Univ (BA) Eng, Ed 1992; Brookdale Comm Coll Bio; *cr:* N Acad Sci & Tech Eng Tchr 3 Yrs; *ai:* Beacon Lit Magazine; NEA NCTE 1993-; Phi Beta Kappa; *office:* Marine Acad Of Sci & Tec Gunnison Rd Sandy Hook NJ 07740

JOHNS, DORIS E., Math Teacher; *b:* Mt Pleasant, PA; *m:* Donald Eric, Darrell, Diane; *ed:* IN Univ of PA (BS) Math, Physics Ed Columbia (MS) Radiological Physics 1968; *cr:* Natl Cancer Inst Phy 1965-70; Clover Creek Bapt Schl Tchr 1982-83; Mt Zion Chrstn Aca 1985-.

JOHNS, FRANK ROBERT, Biology Teacher & Sci Chair; *b:* Glenn NY; *m:* Sara Kelly; *c:* Anthony F., Ryan K., Tyler J.; *ed:* Adirondack Coll (AS) Bio 1966; Potsdam St Coll (BA) Biog & Chem 1969; 30 Hrs, Permanent Cert; *cr:* Lake Placid HS Bio Instr 1969-, Sci Chm *ai:* NHS Adv; NYSUT & NEA 1969-; Clarkson Univ Outstandir Tchng Awd 1986; Prentice Hall Bio Text Scndry Reviewer; *home:* P 1340 Lake Placid NY 12946

JOHNS, JEANNE MARIE, English Teacher; *b:* Youngstown, OH Kent St Univ (BS) Eng 1971; Post Grad Stud; *cr:* Southeast HS Eng 1972-; *ai:* NEA 1972-; OEA 1972-; SE Tchrs Assn 1972-.

JOHNS, LOREN L., Asst Professor of Religion; *b:* Goshen, IN; *m:* R Ann Leaman; *c:* Kendra, Jessica; *ed:* Goshen Coll (BA) Bible Goshen Biblical Seminary (MDiv) Pastoral Ministry 1984; PHD Can Princeton Theological Seminary; *cr:* Blough Mennonite Church Co-I 1977-85; Herald Press Theology Book Ed 1985-89; Koinonia Journal Ed 1991-93; Bluffton Coll Rel Asst Prof 1993-; *ai:* Cross-Cultural C Soc of Biblical Lit 1988-; Mennonite Historial Soc 1993-; Co-Aut Article; Co-Edited Hillel and Jesus; *office:* Bluffton Coll 280 W Co Ave Bluffton OH 45817

JOHNS, RICHARD A., Fourth Grade Teacher; *b:* Glens Falls, N Karen Simons; *c:* Nicole A.; *ed:* St Univ of NY at Potsdam (BA) Ele 1972; Grad Hrs at Russell Sage Coll; *cr:* Saratoga Springs City 3rd-5th Grd Tchr 1972-; *ai:* Var Girls Tennis Coach; NYSUT 1 Saratoga Tchrs Assn 1972-, VP 1981-82; USTA 1972-; YMCA, V Mem 6 Yrs; Hawley Fnd 1992-, Trustee; Saratoga Springs Sports H Fame 1993-, Comm, Founder 1993; Pub Articles in World T Magazine; Coaches Select Circle Awd 1987; Inducted into Potsdam S of Fame 1986; U S Tennis Assn Coach of Yr 1985.

JOHNSMEYER, ELLEN GILMARTIN, English Teacher; *b:* New NY; *m:* Charles; *c:* Nell, Nora, Charles; *ed:* Fordham U (BA) Eng SUNY (MS) Ed 1975; 45 Credits Coll of New Rochelle, Un Bridgeport; *cr:* St Anthony's Schl 5 Grd Tchr 1970-73; North Rocklar Eng Tchr 1974-; *ai:* Adv Schl Newspaper, Lit Magazine; NYSUT 1 Westchester ARC, Parents Assistance Comm on Down's Syndrome 1 Haverstraw Elks Club Svc Recognition; SUNY Purchase Off-Site D Enrichment Prgm; *office:* North Rockland HS Hammond Rd Thiell 10984

JOHNSON, AARON S., Health, PE Tchr & Ath Dir; *b:* Youngstown, *ed:* Messiah Coll (BA) Sport & Exercise Sci 1993, (BA) Hlth & PE *cr:* Girard Alliance Chrstn Hlth & PE Tchr & Ath Dir 1994-; PAAHPERD 1992-; AAHPERD 1995-; NSCA 1996; *office:* G Alliance Chrn Acad 229 Rice Ave Girard PA 16417*

JOHNSON, AGNES FRANKLIN, Substitute Teacher; *b:* Lothian, *m:* Joseph Henry; *c:* Deborah Swann, Terry Darnell; *ed:* Inservice Cmptr Evening Class; *cr:* Anne Arundel Cty PS Sub Tchr 1962-; *ai:* Judge Church Act Election; Jury Duty; *home:* 1328 Marlboro Rd Lo MD 20711

JOHNSON, ANN SNOWDEN, His Tchr & 8th Grd Class Dean; *b:* York, NY; *m:* David Collins; *c:* Katherine; *ed:* Wellesley Coll (BA) H Art His 1985; NY Univ (MA) Art His 1989; Attnd China Inst of Am NY; *cr:* Trinity Schl His Tchr & Dean 1988-; *ai:* Asian Stud Point Pe Rsrch Comm; Homeroom & Ancient His Fair Adv; 7th & 8th Grd Trip Coord; Watch Hill Improvement Soc 1985-, 2nd VP; Watch Chapel Soc 1989-, Clerk; Fac Dev Grant for Rsrch on China; *office:* Tr Schl 139 W 91st St New York NY 10024*

JOHNSON, ANNA CISZEWSKI, First Grade Teacher; *b:* Bellaire, *m:* Richard; *c:* Janelle; *ed:* OH Univ (BS) Ed 1969; Salem-Teikyo (MA) Ed 1994; *cr:* Powhatan Elem Schl First Grd Tchr 1969-70, T Tchr 1970-77, First Grd Tchr 1977-; *ai:* Hills Miss School Miss Out Chprsn; NEA, OH Ed Assn 1996-; Switzerland of OH Ed Assn 1969-, Rep; Powhatan PTO 1964-, Sec; Powhatan Lib Bd 1995-; Shady Alumni Assn 1989-; River Band Patrons 1990-, Sec, Treas; Belmont Animal Rescue League 1993-.

JOHNSON, BARBARA KENDER, Family & Consumer Science Tch Homestead, PA; *m:* Robert George; *c:* Tara Marie; *ed:* Western Car Univ (BSEd) Home Ec 1966; Univ of VT at Burlington 6 Credits Bordentown Regnl HS Family & Consumer Sci Tchr 1967-; Bordentown Regnl Ed Assn Tchr Rep Cncl; Bordentown Regnl HS Sunshine Rep; Block Scheduling Comm; NEA 1967-; NJ Ed Assn 19 Amer Home Ec Assn; Bordentown Regnl Ed Assn; Craft Club 19 Bensalem Historical Soc 1976-, Ed, Chprsn; Angels of Amer Club 19 MADD; Bensalem Bicentennial Cookbook; Nom Walt Disney Co A Tchr Awd 1995; Gov Tchr Recognition Awd 1996; *office:* Bordent Regional HS Dunns Mill Rd Box 50 R D #2 Bordentown NJ 08505

JOHNSON, BAYNE F., Social Studies Dept Chair; *b:* Warsaw, NY Carol J.; *c:* Bayne Jr.; *ed:* St Univ of NY at Brockport (BS) Scndry 1968; Post Grad Stu; *cr:* Oakfield AL HS Tchr 1968-; *ai:* Dept Ldr; H Coach Girls Bsktbl; AFT, NEA 1968-; Pittsford Dist Tchrs Assn 19 Greater Rochester Coach of the Yr 1980 & 1991; Univ of Rochester in Tchng Award 1994; Elected to Notre Dame HS Hall of Fame 1 *office:* Pittsford Sutherland HS 55 Sutherland St Pittsford NY 14534*

JOHNSON, BETTY A. (CHIUSOLO), Principal; *b:* Jersey City, NJ Dennis; *c:* Dennis; *ed:* William Paterson Coll (MA) Elem Ed 19 Fairleigh Dickenson Univ in Elem Ed 1972; Early Chldhd Cert; Admi Supervision Cert; *cr:* Norwood Public Schl 1st & 2nd Grd Tchr 1972 5th 7th & 8th Grd Lit Tchr 1988-93, Prin 1993-; *ai:* Rdng & Lang C

3; 8th Grd Adv 1989-93; Initiated Prime Time Friday Rdng Nights 3; NJ Schl Brds Assn, NJPSA, NMSA, BCEMSPA, NVPA 1993-; NEA, BCEA 1972-93; Governors Awd for Tchr of Yr 1990; Nom for Awd 1991; Pres NVPA; *office:* Norwood Elem Schl 177 Summit St od NJ 07675

SON, BEVERLY A., Art Teacher; *b:* Hartford, CT; *c:* Gregory no, Amy Catalano; *ed:* Southern CT St Univ (BS) Art Ed 1977, (MS) Art, Ceramics 1987; Arrowmont Schl of Arts, Crafts; *cr:* Shelton HS chr 1977-; Summer Art Experience Art Tchr 1989-90; Area rative Educl Svcs Tchr, Migrant Children's Prgm 1987-88; *ai:* Adv s Art Club, Stdnts Enraged at Earth's Destruction; AFT 1977-; 1988-95; New Haven Paint & Clay Club 1987-, Exec Bd, Mbrshp Unitarian Soc New Haven 1983-, Aesthetics Comm; Friends of New Animal Shelter 1995-; CT Cat Project 1996; Masters Thesis Art t 1977 SCSU John Lyman Ctr; Juried Group Exhibits New Haven & Clay Club 1986, 1988, 1990; Two Person Exhibit Erector Square y 1988; *office:* Shelton HS 120 Meadow St Shelton CT 06484*

ISON, BRENDA MC QUEEN, First Grade Teacher; *b:* Dover, OH; rk E.; *c:* Jeremiah, Justin; *ed:* Lorain Cty Comm Coll (AA) 1974; St Univ (BA) Elem Ed 1976; Post Grad Stud at Kent St Univ; *cr:* Elem Schl Second Grd Tchr 1976-78, Second-Third Grd Split Class 978-80, Second Grd Tchr 1980-82, Third Grd Tchr 1982-83, First chr 1983-; *ai:* NEA, OEA, Garaway Tchrs Assn 1976-; Baltic Amer Auxiliary 1965-; *home:* 518 Luzern St SW Sugarcreek OH 44681

ISON, CARL, Mathematics Teacher; *b:* Gary, IN; *ed:* Upsala Coll Math 1985; *cr:* Hillside HS Math Tchr 1985-91; Belleville HS Math 991-; *ai:* Conflict Mediator; Intl Club Asst; NEA, NCTM 1985-; Natl Assn of Rocketry 1995-; Jersey Cares Vols 1994-, Proj Coord; at for Humanity 1994-; USAF Reserve 1988-, Staff Sgt, Ground ment Mechanic; *office:* Belleville HS 100 Passaic Ave Belleville NJ

ISON, CARL AWOLOWO, Lecturer in Sociology; *b:* Washington, *n:* Orundun DaCosta; *c:* Mamadou, Djassi, Camara, Djani; *ed:* n Univ (BA) Pol Sci 1969; Attnd City Univ of NY PHD Candidate; S Freedom Schls SNCC Tchr, Organizer 1963-64; Wesleyan Univ er in African Stud 1971-72; Queens Coll Lecturer in Sociology 81; BMCC Lecturer in Sociology 1992-; *ai:* Fac Adv Stu Govt Assn; Abroad Comm; Ford Fnd Fellow 1969-72; *office:* Borough Of attan Comm Coll 199 Chambers St New York NY 10007

ISON, CAROL ANN (MILLER), Fourth Grade Math Teacher; *b:* own, PA; *m:* Bruce Edward; *c:* Kirk Edward, Ross Alan; *ed:* Clarion ll (BS) Elem Ed 1970; IN St Coll (MED) Elem Math 1975; 9 Hrs uter Courses; *cr:* United Schl Dist Elem Tchr 1970-; *ai:* NEA, PSEA, l Ed Assn 1970-; *home:* RR 1 Box 198 Seward PA 15954

SON, CAROL BODDORF, Fifth Grade Teacher; *b:* Du Bois, PA; lliam G.; *c:* Wade E.; *ed:* Clarion St Coll (BS) Elem 1969, (MS) Elem 71; *cr:* Titusville Area Schl Dist Fifth Grd Tchr 1969-88, Sixth Grd 988-89, Fifth Grd Tchr 1989-; *ai:* PSEA, NEA 1969-; Delta Kappa a 1990-; *home:* 406 E Spruce St Titusville PA 16354

ISON, CAROLYN RENITA, Seventh Grade Soc Studies Tchr; *b:* ngeles, CA; *ed:* Notre Dame Coll of OH (BA) Liberal Arts, Soc Stud Cleveland St Univ (MA) Guidance Cnlsr 1995; Case Western ve Univ Women Stud Schlsp Prgm; *cr:* Warrensville Heights City ilwoman 1987-95; BP Standard Oil Bio Lab Technician 1985; Maple ts Bd of Ed Soc Stud Tchr 1986-; *ai:* Soc Stu Chprsn; Stu Cncl Adv; Head Track Coach; Parenting for Ed Facilitator; PTO Mem; E Mt Bapt Church Mem; NEOTA 1985-; Martha Jennings Scholar Tchr African Amer Women Achvmt Awd; Make A Wish Fnd Awd; essman Louis Stokes Youth of Distinction Awd; St of OH House of Awd; *home:* 29500 S Woodland Rd Pepper Pike OH 44124*

NSON, CASSANDRA ANN, English Teacher; *b:* Washington, DC; opher; *ed:* Howard Univ (BA) Eng 1964; Trinity Coll (MAT) Eng *cr:* Ancostia HS Tchr 1967-71; Kramer Jr HS Tchr 1971-75; son Sr HS Tchr 1975-.

NSON, CATHERINE GRAHAM, Campus Minister & Rel Tchr; *b:* s, Greece; *m:* Paul C.; *ed:* Univ of Scranton (BS) Bio 1987; Villanova (MA) Religious Stud 1991; *cr:* Immaculata HS Math, Religion Tchr, Asst Bsktbl Coach 1987-89; Merion Mercy Acad Schl Minister, on Tchr, Soccer & Asst Bsktbl Coah 1991-; *ai:* Moderator of stry Team, Liturgy Club; Var Soccer, Asst Var, JV Bsktbl n;Moderator of Peer Helpers; Natl Assn Pasteral Musicians 1992-; Campus Ministry Assn 1993-; NCEA 1991-;NSCAA 1993-; *office:* n Mercy Acad 511 Montgomery Ave Merion Station PA 19066

NSON, CHARLES WILLIAM, PE Teacher; *b:* Washington, DC; *ed:* ury Univ (BS) PE 1976; Trinity Coll (MS) Spec Ed 1981; Mark Alt Schl 1977-82; Wheaton HS 1982-92; Springbrook HS Adaptive, Ed Tchr 1992-; *cr:* FCA; Girls Bsktbl; Outdoor Track; Acad issance; *ai:* NEA, MCEA 1977-; Mc Donalds Capital Classic mer Bsktbl Cty Champions 1982, 1984, 1986, 1988, 1994-95; *office:* gbrook HS 201 Valleybrook Dr Silver Spring MD 20904

NSON, CRYSTAL PERRY, African Amer, Global Stud Tchr; *b:* sville, PA; *c:* Maya; *ed:* Eastern Coll (BA) Psych, Scndry Ed 1979; edits Hrd Univ of OK; 3 Credits USC; 6 Credit Hrs Immaculat Coll; dits Writing Women into His Sonoma St; Examing Prejudice in the room; Gender Equity Issues; Multicultural Trng with Afrocentric of Ed; *cr:* Coatesville Inter Schl Soc Stud, PSy, Global Stud, African is Tchr, Peer Group 1985-; *ai:* Chrstn Ed Dir; NAACP Work with Yth; n Black His Comm; Peer Group Adv; Sunday Schl Tchr; Tchr or; Stu Assistance Prgm; Chester Cty Authority Bd Mem; NEA 1985-; CP 1995-; Yrbk Dedication 1994; Presenter COBBE Conf; On Black Ed; *home:* 129 Harlan Dr Coatesville PA 19320

NSON, CYNTHIA BRADY, Science Teacher; *b:* Massillon, OH; *m:* .; *c:* Rachel, Andrew; *ed:* Malone Coll (BA) Bio 1970; Bowling Green niv 135 Addl Hrs; *cr:* Bowling Green St Univ Grad Asst 1970-73; illon Chrstn Schl Sci Tchr 1974-76; Heritage Chrstn Schl Sci Tchr -77, Belmont Tech Coll Sci Instr 1982-85; Real Life Chrstn Acad Sci 1985-88; Heritage Chrstn Schl Sci Tchr 1988-; Stark Tech Coll Sci 1989-; *ai:* St of OH Comm to Evaluate 9th Grd Proficiency Tests; : Heritage Christian Schl 2107 6th St SW Canton OH 44706

NSON, DAVID B., Chemistry Teacher; *b:* Providence, RI; *m:* Andrea McMahon; *c:* Ellen J., Andrew D.; *ed:* Tufts Univ (BS) Chem 1965; of NH (MST) Chem 1973; *cr:* Woburn Sr HS Chem Tchr 1967-72; ws Falls Union HS Chem Tchr 1972-; *ai:* Jr Class Adv; VT NEA -; Hooper Golf Club 1974-, Pres 1979-81; Lions Club 1976-89, Pres ; *office:* Bellows Falls Union HS Rt 5 S Bellows Falls VT 05101

NSON, DAVID MARTIN, Lecturer in Ec, Acctng & Bus; *b:* Woburn, *m:* Rosamund; *ed:* Univ at Lowell (BS) Physics 1971; Baruch Coll A) Acctng 1994; NYU Grad Stud Ec 1977-84; *cr:* Combustion Engrng ear Engr 1974-77; Salomon Brothers Researcher 1980-83; York Coll rer 1984-; *ai:* Curr Comm; Dept Curr Comm Chm.*

NSON, DAWN NEVILLE, Spanish & French Teacher; *b:* Providence, ; Megan; *ed:* Quinebaug Vly Comm Coll (AS) Gen Stud 1982; Eastern t Univ (BA) Span, Fr, Scndry Ed 1991; Working Toward Masters; *cr:* wold Jr-Sr HS Span, Fr Tchr 1992-; *ai:* NEA 1991-; *office:* Griswold HS Slater Ave Jewett City CT 06351

JOHNSON, DEBRA ANN (VAULTZ), Fifth Grade Teacher; *b:* Fort Sill, OK; *m:* Collin Michael; *c:* Zanetta D., Darrik L., Joshua D.; *ed:* Univ of OR 3 Hrs Integ Comp Curr; Univ of South FL 3 Hrs Interdisc Team C&I; Trinity Coll 3 Hrs Peer Asst Ldrshp Bldg Admin Tchng; *cr:* Sollar Elem Schl Sixth Grd Tchr 1987-90; Chicksands Elem MS Math Tchr 1990-93; Annapolis Elem Schl Fifth Grd Tchr 1995-; *ai:* TAAAC 1995-; Chesapeake Chrstn Ctr 1994-; Church Yth Tchr; *office:* Annapolis Elem Schl 180 Green St Annapolis MD 21401

JOHNSON, DEBRA LOU, First Grade Teacher; *b:* Pittsburgh, PA; *m:* Med; *c:* Adam, Lindsay, Mackenzie; *ed:* Edinboro Univ (BS) Elem Ed K-8 1976; Kent St Univ M Curr, Instruction 1990; Cert Rdng K-12; *cr:* Ledgemont Elem Schl Kndgtn Tchr 1976-77, 1st Grd Tchr 1977-; *ai:* Yrbk Coord; OEA, NEA, LEA 1976-; Chapel United Meth Church 1983-, Ed Chm; Martha Holden Jennings Scholar 1993; Robert E. Wilson Fellow Kent St 1989; Thanks to Tchrs Awd 1995; *office:* Ledgemont Elem Schl 16200 Burrows Rd Thompson OH 44086

JOHNSON, DELLA DAMERON, Drama Professor; *b:* Jefferson City, MO; *m:* Cleveland L.; *ed:* Lincoln Univ (BSE) Speech, Drama 1971; Northern IL Univ (MA) Theatre His, Criticism 1973; Univ of MD at College Park (EDD) Ed 1989; *cr:* Lincoln Univ Instr 1973-75; Univ of MD Asst Prof 1975-; *ai:* Dir Theatre Prgm; Internship Coord; Drama Soc, Gospel Choir Adv; Black Theatre Network; Naomi Chptr OES 1984-, Worthy Matron; Delta Sigma Theta 1970-; Maple Shade Yth & Family Svcs Bd 1993-; United Way Bd 1995-; *office:* Univ Of MD Eastern Shore Room 1105 PAC UMES Princess Anne MD 21853*

JOHNSON, DENISE RONDEZ, Teacher of the Gifted; *b:* Astoria, NY; *m:* Kenneth; *c:* Kirk, Ryan; *ed:* St John's Univ (BS) Ed 1965; Queens Coll (MS) Ed 1968; *cr:* Merrick Schl Dist 3rd, 5th Grd Fr Tchr 1965-80, Tchr of Gifted 1981-; *ai:* Consultant, Lecturer; AGATE 1981-; NYSUT 1965-; NAGC 1985-; SEAGATE 1988-; Bayside Historical Soc 1980-; Kiwanis Tchr of Yr; *office:* Merrick Schl Dist 21 Babylon Rd Merrick NY 11566*

JOHNSON, DENNIS A., Health & Phys Ed Instructor; *ed:* Marshall Univ (BA) PE 1976, (MS) PE 1977; *cr:* Sheffield Area HS Tchr, Coach 1976-; *ai:* Asst Wrestling Coach at Eisenhower HS; Asst Track Coach; Natl Wr Coachs Assn 1976-; Co-Author of The Coaches Guide to Nutrition & Weight Control; Author of Wrestling Drill Book; *office:* Warren Cty Schl Dist Rt 6 Sheffield PA 16347*

JOHNSON, DENNIS EINAR, Professor of Art; *b:* Philadelphia, PA; *m:* Mary Jo Remsnyder; *ed:* Temple Univ (BFA) Graphic Design 1977; Kutztown Univ (MED) Art Ed 1979; Syracuse Univ (MFA) Advertising Design 1988; Kutztown Univ Graphic Design in Austria 1991; *cr:* J. J. Dugan Advertising Art Dir 1970-71; Silver-Gross Advertising Creative Dir 1971-74; Moravian Coll Art Prof 1979-88; Kutztown Univ Art Prof 1988-; *ai:* Amer Advertising Fed Campus Chptr Adv; NAEA 1979-; AIGA 1991-; Cntrl PA Ad Club 1991-, Educl Comm; Buckinghamshire Coll Taught Contemporary British Advertising & Design; *office:* Kutztown Univ Of PA Comm Design Dept Kutztown PA 19530

JOHNSON, DIANE, 6th Grade Teacher; *b:* Nyack, NY; *m:* Howard Boyd; *c:* Melissa, Jeffery, Melanie, Laura; *ed:* St Univ of NY at Oneonta (BS) Elem Ed 1968; St Univ of NY at New Platz Admin & Supervision 1990; 24 Credit Hrs in Remedial Rdng at Manhattan Coll; 9 Credit Hrs in Rdng at Long Island Univ; 15 Credit Hrs towards PHD in Admin & Supervision; Cert from NYS in Nursery K-6th Grd Elem Ed 1968, Schl Admin & Supervision Cert 1992 & Schl Dist Admin 1993; *cr:* PS #29 Yonkers 3rd Grd Tchr 1968-73; Peekskill City Schls 1986-, Uriah Hills 6th Grd Tchr 3 Yrs, 5th Grd Tchr 2 Yrs, Hillcrest 1st Grd tchr 2 Yrs, Woodside 6th Grd Tchr 2 Yrs & Peekskill MS 6th Grd Tchr at Present; *ai:* AFT 1986-; PFA 1986-; *home:* 14 Elena Dr Cortlandt Manor NY 10566*

JOHNSON, DIANE DEROCHE, 5th Grade Teacher; *b:* Bangor, ME; *m:* Dan Gene; *c:* Jacqueline Gumm, Stephen; *ed:* UW at Milwaukee (BA) Elem Ed 1979; Fairfield Univ (MA) Ed, Prof Improvement 1983; Southern CT St Univ 6 Yr Cert Classroom Specialist 1995; *cr:* new Canaan Pub Schls 6th Grd Tchr 1980-92, 5th Grd Tchr 1992-; *ai:* Stu Cncl Adv 1992-95; Dev Summer Camp for Multiple Intelligences 3-7 Grds 1995-; Best Trained Mentor Tchr 1989-; Team Ldr 1992-93; Chrstn Ed Ldr 1985-; *office:* New Canaan Pub Schls 39 Locust Ave New Canaan CT 06840

JOHNSON, DIANE IRENE (SCAGLIONE), 10th Grade English Teacher; *b:* Altoona, PA; *m:* Steven Michael; *c:* Amanda Irene, Andrew Robert; *ed:* PA St Univ (BS) Scndry Eng Ed 1983; 24 Credits St Francis Coll at Loretto; 9 Grad Credits; *cr:* Altoona Schl of Comm Eng, Speech Tchr 1983-85; Bellwood-Antis HS 10th Grd Eng, AP Eng Tchr 1985-; *ai:* Speech League Coach 4 Yrs; Stu Support Group Facilitator; Mentor Tchr for New Tchrs; Rdng Competition Adv; Stu Congress Coach; NEA, PSEA, Bellwood-Antis EA 1985-; Western PA Cncl of Eng Tchrs 1990-; Natl Forensic League 1991-; St Matthews Church 1987-; Catechism Instr 1991-92; Bellwood-Antis Yrbk Dedication 1993; *office:* Bellwood-Antis HS Martin St Bellwood PA 16617

JOHNSON, DONNELL S., Life Science Teacher; *b:* Tacoma Pk, MD; *m:* Myra Cruz; *c:* Jason; *ed:* St Univ of NY at Brockport (ME) Bio 1993; *cr:* Rochester Jr Acad Sci Tchr 1980-84; Monroe MS Life Sci Tchr 1984-; *ai:* Peer Mediation Prgm Adv; Gospel Choir Dir; Home-Base Guid, Black His Comms; Scndry Schl Tchng Awd for Excl from Univ of Rochester; *office:* Monroe MS 164 Alexander St Rochester NY 14607

JOHNSON, ERIC A., Language Arts Teacher; *b:* North PLainfield, NJ; *m:* Donna Sue Stein; *c:* Rochelle Shanks, Roxanne Hensley, Erica; *ed:* Miami Univ (BS) Ed 1990; Post Grad Studs Miami Univ, Coll of Mt St Joseph, Univ of Dayton; *cr:* Fairfield Mid Schl Math, Sci Tchr 1990-92, Lang Arts Tchr 1990-; *ai:* NEA, OEA 1990-, Kappa Delta Pi 1988-; BSA, Speakers Bureau; Schl Bell Awd 1995; *office:* Fairfield MS 255 Donald Dr Fairfield OH 45014*

JOHNSON, ERVIN JOHN, Industrial Arts Teacher; *b:* Doylestown, PA; *m:* Marjorie; *c:* Kate, Kelly; *ed:* Trenton St Coll (BA) Industrial Arts Ed 1967; *cr:* Hopewell Vly HS Industrial Arts Tchr 1967-; *ai:* Frosh Girls Bsktbl & Var Golf Coach; NJEA 1967-; NEA 1967-; HVEA 1967-; USGA 1990-; Hopewell Vly Tchr of Yr 1992; *office:* Hopewell Vly Cntrl HS 259 Pennington Titusville Rd Pennington NJ 08534*

JOHNSON, FRAN, Biology Teacher; *b:* Lock Haven, PA; *m:* Marilou; *c:* Daniel, Timothy, Rebekah; *ed:* Cedarville Coll (BA) Bio 1969; Xavier Univ (MED) Bio 1971; Penn St Univ 45 Credit Hrs; *cr:* Bald Eagle Area SD Bio Tchr 16 Yrs; Bellefonte Area SD Bio Tchr 6 Yrs; *ai:* Var Wrestling Coach; Sci Dept Chm; Allison Twp Supvr 20 Yrs; Hosp Advy Comm 6 Yrs; Yrbk Dedication 3 Times; Fullbright Exchange to Germany; Governors Schl of Sci Comm; *office:* Bellefonte Area HS 830 E Bishop St Bellefonte PA 16823

JOHNSON, FRANCINE PORTER, Second Grade Teacher; *b:* Darby, PA; *m:* Harold Scott; *c:* Dexter; *ed:* Cheyney St Univ (BS) Elem 1979; *cr:* Aldan Elem 1st Grd Tchr 1979-82, 2nd Grd Tchr 1982-; *ai:* NEA, PSEA 1979-; *office:* Aldam Elem Schl Providence Rd Aldan PA 19018*

JOHNSON, FRANK E., 6th Grade Teacher; *b:* Pualski, NY; *m:* Nancy B.; *c:* Jill B., Kristin L.; *ed:* SUNY at Oswego (BS) Elem Ed 1965; 46 Hrs Grad Credit-Permanent Cert; *cr:* Sandy Creek Elem Schl 4th Grd Tchr 1965-66; Pulaski Cntrl Schl 4th-6th Grd Tchr 1966-; *ai:* Project Smart Math, Scis Prgrms; NVSTA 1965-, Pres, V Pres; Jaycees 1965-, St Dir; Intnl Tchng Flwshp Australia 1978-79.

JOHNSON, FRANK E., HPE Teacher & Dept Chprsn; *b:* Hartford, CT; *m:* Patricia Bower; *ed:* East Stroudsburg SC (BS) Hlth, PE 1974; East Stroudsburg Univ (MS) PE 1982; *cr:* Acad Elem Schl PE Tchr 1975-77; J. M. Hill Elem Schl HPE Tchr, K-6th Grd Dept Head 1978-85; North Courtland Elem Schl HPE Tchr, K-6th Grd Dept Head 1986-92; J. T. Lambert Int Schl HPE Tchr, Int Dept Head 1992-; *ai:* Jr HS Boys Bsktbl Coach; Inramurals; Jump Rope for Heart Coord; Spec Olympics Fundraiser; Chris Taylor PE Awds, Jr Natl Honor Soc Selection, Dist Bldg, HPE Curr Comm; Stu Tchng Prgm; Accredidation Cncl; PSEA, NEA 1978-; AAHPERD 1985-; NASPE, AAHE 1990-; Little League 1981-, Day League Coord; PTSCA 1978-; Outstanding Tchr Aws by PTA 1985; *office:* J. T. Lambert Int School 2000 Milford Rd East Stroudsburg PA 18301

JOHNSON, FRED H.,JR., Chaplain & Teacher; *b:* Columbus, GA; *ed:* Yale Univ (BA) Fr 1965; Yale Univ Divinity Schl (MDIV) Rel 1970; Inst De Phonetique Univ De Paris; *cr:* Choate Rosemary Hall Tchr 1968-73; Packer Collegiate Inst Tchr, Chapel Coord 1973-80; Church of the Intercession Priest Assoc 1980-82; Franklin, Weinrib, Rudell & Vasallo Support Staff 1983-86; Birch Wathen Schl Tchr, Assembly Coord 1986-93; Trinity Schl Chaplain, Tchr 1993-; *ai:* Asian Appreciation Club Adv; Diversity, Cnslng, Hlth, Extra-Curricular Life, Rel Advy Comms; Acad Cncl; Upper Schl Admin Group; Rel Ed Assn 1995-; Common Cause 1980-; Translator; *office:* Trinity Schl 139 W 91st St New York NY 10024

JOHNSON, GARY ROSS, Math, Sci Tchr & Dept Chprsn; *b:* Montreal, Canada; *m:* Kathryn Sproule; *ed:* Mc Gill Univ (BSC) Physics 1972; Concordia Univ (MSC) Physics 1976; *cr:* Marianopolis Coll Physics Tchr 1988-92, Dept Chair 1993-; *ai:* Regnl Sci Fair; Organizer Canada First Robotics Competitions; Mentor Coll Rep; Bell Montreal Regnl Sci Fair 1982-, Pres, Chprsn; Rsrch Tchng of Physics; *office:* Marianopolis Coll 3880 Cote Des Nerges Rd Montreal PQ H3H 1W1 Canada CN

JOHNSON, GLORIA FAYE, Vocal Music Teacher; *b:* Elizabeth City, NC; *ed:* Elizabeth City St Univ (BS) Music Ed 1965; Howard Univ (MED) Early Chldhd 1974; Pupil Prsnl Cert; *cr:* Brawley HS Vocal Music Tchr 1965-66; Chestertown HS Tchr 1966-67; Bradbury Heights Elem Vocal Music Tchr 1971-; *ai:* NEA 1967-; Prince Georges Tchrs 1967-, Fac Rep; Prince Georges Cty MD Outstanding Educator.

JOHNSON, GRACE F., Asst Prof of Mngmt & Acctng; *b:* Jamaica, NY; *ed:* Univ of South FL (BS) Acctng 1983-89, (MAcc) Acctng 1988; *cr:* Poynter Inst for Media Stud Chief Accountant 1983-89; Marietta Coll Asst Prof 1989-; *ai:* Inst of Mngmt Accountants 1988-; WV Soc of CPAs; Book: Information Technology in Accounting 1995; *office:* Marietta Coll Thomas Hall 119 Marietta OH 45750

JOHNSON, HARVEY, Asst Prof of Theater & Speech; *b:* Pittsburgh, PA; *m:* Denise Michelle Marshall; *c:* Bria Walker, Jonathon Walker, Jeremy, Kira; *ed:* Kent St Univ (BFA) Theatre, Acting 1970; Carnegie-Mellon Univ (MFA) Theatre, Directing 1984; *cr:* Allegheny Campus Comm Coll Asst Speech, Theatre Prof 1986-90; Geneva Coll Asst Theatre, Speech Prof, Drama Dir 1991-; *ai:* Alpha Psi Omega Cast Spon; Fine Arts Dir; Chrstns in Theatre Arts 1991-, Northeast Rep; Assn for Theatre in Higher Ed 1991-, Exec Comm Rel Focus Group; United Hosanna Ministries 1994-, Bd of Dir; Henry Mancini Awds 1995-, Adjudicator; *office:* Geneva Coll 3200 College Ave Beaver Falls PA 15010

JOHNSON, HELEN GOBLE, Third Grade Teacher; *b:* Cincinnati, OH; *m:* Robert P.; *ed:* Northern KY Univ (BA) Elem Ed 1981, (MA) Elem Ed 1986; *cr:* St Teresa of Avila Tchr 1981-; *ai:* Tutor; NCEA 1981-; Asland Inc Individual Tchr Achvmt Awd Nom; *office:* Saint Teresa Of Avila Schl 1194 Rulison Ave Cincinnati OH 45238

JOHNSON, JACK ALLEN, Health & PE Teacher; *b:* Columbus, OH; *m:* Pamela Kay Landis; *c:* Denise, Matt, Mark; *ed:* WV Wesleyan Coll (BS) Hlth, PE, Ed 1966; Univ of Dayton (MA) Guid 1980; *cr:* Fairfield Schl for Boys PE Tchr 1966-69; Pickerington HS Hlth, PE Tchr 1969-; *ai:* Head Ftbl, Strength Coach; Hall of Fame Selection Comm; Summer Ftbl Passing League Chm; FCA Adv; OEA, NEA 1969-94; OH Bsbl Coaches 1969-80, Pres 1976-77; OH Ftbl Coaches 1969-, Mid-St Hall of Fame; Numerous Article Pub; *office:* Pickerington HS 300 Opportunity Way Pickerington OH 43147*

JOHNSON, JAMES ROBERT, Science Teacher; *b:* Lancaster, PA; *m:* Nancy Edith Nickel; *c:* Jeffrey Lee, Ryan Lee; *ed:* Temple Univ (MED) Scndry Admin 1986; Scndry Supervisory Cert Millersville Univ 1985; Bio PA Dept of Ed 1974; 103 Addl Hrs; *cr:* Wheatland Jr HS Sci Tchr 1967-; *ai:* Oriental Cultures Club Adv; Team Ldr; NEA, PA St Ed Assn, Lancaster Ed Assn 1967-; PSTA PA St Sci Tchrs Assn 1983-; Sierra Club 1991-; BPO Elks 1968-; World Natural Power Lifting Assn 1994-, Natl Bench Press Champ; Chief Dancer Wheatland Ballet 1970-; Natl Awd Amer Assn Advancement of Sci Photography Contest; Lancaster Summer Arts Festival Photography Exhibitor & Awd; *home:* 323 E Orange St Lancaster PA 17602

JOHNSON, JAN MELAINE, Sixth Grade Teacher; *b:* Washington, DC; *ed:* Amer Univ (BS) Elem Ed 1984; *cr:* Our Lady of Perpetual Help Schl 5th Grd Tchr 1984-85; John H. Bayne Elem Schl 6th Grd Tchr 1985-; *ai:* Afterschool Tutorial Prgm; Grd Level Chprsn; NEA, Prince George's Co Educ Assn 1985-; *office:* John H Bayne Elem Schl 7010 Walker Mill Rd Capitol Heights MD 20743

JOHNSON, JANE B., English Teacher; *b:* Bristol, CT; *m:* Robert H.; *c:* Bryan, Meghan; *ed:* Coll of New Rochelle (BA) Eng 1970; Fordham Univ (MA) Eng 1976, (PD) Rdng & Admin 1981; *cr:* Elmsford Pub Schls Eng Tchr & K-12th Grd Lang Arts Coord 1974-84; Rye City Schls Eng Tchr 1984-; *ai:* AFT 1974-; Rye Tchrs Assn 1984-; Staff Dev Comm 1993-; *office:* Rye City Schls Parsons St Rye NY 10580

JOHNSON, JANET REISSFELDER, Fifth Grade Teacher; *b:* Westwood, MA; *m:* Walworth Jr.; *c:* Jennifer, Julie; *ed:* Keene St (BE) Elem 1968; Univ of NH (MA) Rdng, Cnslng 1970; CAGS Rdng, Cnslng; *cr:* Rye Elem Schl 4 Grd Tchr 3 Yrs; Garrison Schl 4 Grd Tchr 1 Yr; Woodman Park Schl 4 Grd Tchr 16 Yrs, 5 Grd Tchr 2 Yrs; *ai:* Community Schl Choir; SADD, Stu Cncl Adv; Coord Schl Sci Curr: New Math, Sci, His Comms; Delta Kppa Epsom 1986-, Pres; NEA 1970-; Jaycees 1971-, Sec; Mayflower Soc 1971-; Hosp 1990-, Vol; Ford Flwshp.*

JOHNSON, JASON R., American His & Government Tchr; *b:* Orrville, OH; *m:* Lana Odeon Mc Graw; *ed:* OK Chrstn Univ (BA) Soc Sci Ed 1991; Attnd Ohio Univ Spec Ed; *cr:* Warren Local Schls Learning Disability Tutor 1993-94, His, Govt Tchr 1994-; *ai:* Helping Coach Var Bsbl; Curr Dev Comm; NEA 1990-, Stu Tchr of the Yr; Belpre Church of Christ 1991-; Received Cncl for Exceptional Children Masters Stu of Yr; Natl Deans List; *office:* Warren Local HS Rt 1 Vincent OH 45784*

JOHNSON, JENNY EHREN, English Teacher; *b:* Grand Forks, ND; *m:* Jeff; *ed:* Bob Jones Univ (BS) Eng Ed 1991; *cr:* Carolina HS Instrl Aide & Tchr 1991-92; New Castle Bapt Acad Eng Tchr 1992-; *ai:* Stu Cncl Adv.

JOHNSON, JOAN ABELLONIO, Teacher of Visually Impaired; *b:* New York, NY; *m:* Patrick G.; *c:* James; *ed:* Hunter Coll (BA) Ed 1963, (MS) Spec Ed 1965; 30 Credit Hrs Brooklyn Coll 1968-70; *cr:* New York City Bd of Ed Early Chldhd Tchr 1963-65; PS 146K Tchr of Visually Impaired 1966-95; PS 102K Tchr of Visually Impaired 1966-95; PS 10K Tchr of Visually Impaired 1966-95; *ai:* United Cerebral Palsy; AFT, NEA, UFT 1963-; Dist 15 Grant 1989; *office:* Public Schl 10 511 7th Ave Brooklyn NY 11215

JOHNSON, JOHN CLINTON, Math Teacher; *b:* York, PA; *m:* Barbara Dooley; *c:* Michael Clinton, Hydee Lizz; *ed:* Western MD Coll (BA) Ec

1967; Univ of Fl (MA) Ec 1968; Attnd Towson St Univ, Johns Hopkins Univ; *cr:* North Harford HS Math Tchr 1969-; *ai:* Bsbl, Bsktbl Coach; MD Math League Spon; NEA, MSTA, NCTM 1971-; St Ridge Presbyn Church 1970-, Elder; *home:* 216 Main St Delta PA 17314

JOHNSON, JOHN DAVID, Social Studies Teacher; *b:* Brookville, PA; *c:* Miranda, Evie, Jonni; *ed:* Clarion Univ of PA (BS) Scndry Ed, Soc Stud 1989; 3 Addl Credit Hrs Ed, Scndry at Liberty Univ; 18 Addl Credit Hrs Ed, Scndry at Gannon Univ; *cr:* Brookville HS Soc Stud Tchr 1989-; *ai:* Asst Ath Dir; Jr Historians of PA Adv; NEA, BAEA, PSEA 1992-; Stu Ldr of Cty Historical Soc 1990-; Mason Church Act 1981-; Tchr of Yr 1994-95; Wrote Grant Stdnts Involved in Victorian Project; Multiple Newspaper Articles; *home:* PO Box 134 Corsica PA 15829*

JOHNSON, JOHN FRANKLIN, American History Teacher; *b:* Toledo, OH; *m:* Cathy Otremba; *c:* Jamie, Leslie, Melissa, Lindsay; *ed:* Univ of Toledo (BE) PE 1969, (MS) His 1993; *cr:* St Francis HS Driver Ed Tchr, Asst Coach 1967-68; Bowsher HS Amer His Tchr, Asst Coach 1969-77; Macomber HS Amer His Tchr, Head Ftbl Coach 1977-83; Clay HS Amer His Tchr, Head Ftbl Coach 1984-; *ai:* 8th Grd Boys Bsktbl Coach; NW OH Ftbl Coaches Assn 1984-; OH HS Ftbl Coaches Assn 1970-, Regnl Dir; Natl Ftbl Fnd 1995-; Monroe Street Church 1977-, Adm Bd, Schlsp Bd; 1 of 14 OH Tchrs to Germany Spon Armonk Inst 1992; *office:* Oregon Clay HS 5665 Seaman St Oregon OH 43616*

JOHNSON, JOHN K., 7th Grade Math & Science Tchr; *b:* Georgetown, Guyana; *m:* Phyllis T. Swan; *c:* John Jr., Nicole, Bryan; *ed:* City Coll (MED) Sci 1992; Columbia Univ (MA) Sci Methodology 1994; Doctoral Stu; *cr:* Marymount Coll Dir Purchasing 1970-80; Morgan Guaranty Co Accountant 1980-88; NYC Bd of Ed Tchr 1988-; *ai:* Coach, Adv Mind over Matter Schl Team Contest; NYC Chem Club 1989-; NYC Tchrs Assn 1988-; Rockaway Dev Assn 1991-, Bd Mem; Beulah Chuch of Nazarene 1991-, Sunday Schl Supt; Tchr of Yr Queens Cty 1992; Pub Sci Ed Series Cmptr Software Analysis St Johns Univ; *office:* IS 53 Brian Piccolo 1045 Nameoke St Far Rockaway NY 11691

JOHNSON, JOHN WAYNE, 6th Grade Teacher; *b:* Van Wert, OH; *m:* Carla Ann Deitsch; *c:* Kara, Kathryn, Douglas; *ed:* Wright St Univ (BS) Elem Ed 1975; Univ of Dayton (MS) Educl Admin 1982; *cr:* Ansonia Local Schls 4th Grd Tchr 1975-76; Van Wert City Schls 6th Grd Tchr 1976-; *ai:* Stu Cncl Adv; Geog Bee Coord; Schl Insurance Group Trustee; NEA 1976-85; AFT 1985-; *home:* 5432 State Route 117 Rockford OH 45882

JOHNSON, JOHNNY C., Health Teacher; *b:* Covington, GA; *m:* Angela; *c:* Geoffrey, Danielle; *ed:* Ft Vly St Coll (BS) Hlth, PE 1970; Slippery Rock St Univ (MED) Curr, Admin, Hlth, PE 1978; Credit Hrs in Cmptr Tech, Yth Empowerment System; *cr:* Erie City Schl Dist HPE Tchr 1970-; *ai:* Bible Stud Club; Hlth Quest Challenge Adv; tu Assistance Prgm Team; NEA, PSEA, EEA 1971-; BTW Ctr 1989-, Pres of Bd; Alpha Kappa Alpha Edctr of Yr 1989; *home:* 223 Walnut St Erie PA 16507

JOHNSON, JOYCE DELZEITH, Jr High Teacher; *b:* Coldwater, OH; *m:* Thomas E.; *c:* Jeremy C., Christopher T., Philip E.; *ed:* Wright St Univ (BS) Elem Ed 1981; *cr:* St Joseph Schl Jr High Tchr 1981-; *ai:* PTO Treas; Scholastic Bowl Team & 8th Grd Class Adv; 5th-8th Grd Head Tchr; NCEA 1981-; *office:* St Joseph Schl 1101 Lincoln Hwy Wapakoneta OH 45895

JOHNSON, JOYCE YANCEY, English Teacher & Dept Chair; *b:* Clarksville, VA; *c:* David, Holly; *ed:* Elon Coll (BA) Eng 1959; Attnd Coll of William & Mary, Univ of Toledo, Bowling Green St Univ; Ashland Univ; *cr:* Great Bridge HS Eng Tchr 1959-61; Frank Cox HS Eng Tchr 1961-63; Colonel Crawford Jr HS Eng Tchr 1963-66; Colonel Crawford HS Eng Tchr 1966-; *ai:* Eng Dept Chm; Frosh Class Adv; Prins Advisory Comm; Jennings Scholar; *office:* Colonel Crawford HS Rt 602 North Robinson OH 44856

JOHNSON, JUDITH ANN, 2nd Grade Teacher; *b:* Buffalo, NY; *m:* William A.; *c:* Kevin Sullivan, Erin Sullivan, Kerry Sullivan; *ed:* SUNY at Cortland (BA) Elem Ed 1964; SUNY at Buffalo (MS) Curr 1991; *cr:* Green Acres Schl 2nd Grd Tchr 1964-69; Armor Elem 1st, 2nd & 4th Grd Tchr 1987-; *ai:* Lang Arts Coord; HTA 1987-; NYSUT 1987-; Hamburg Antiques Stud Group 1968-, Pres, VP & Sec; Hamburg House & Garden Club 1972-, VP; Southtowns Tchr Ctr Liaison 1993-; Tchr Innovator 1992.*

JOHNSON, JUNE CARVEL, English Dept Chairman & Tchr; *b:* Dayton, OH; *m:* Raphael E.; *c:* Jennifer Johnson Bujazia, James E.; *ed:* Ohio Univ (BS) Eng 1974; 1 Yr of Masters in Counseling; *cr:* Wm. V. Fisher HS Eng Tchr, Yrbk for Jrnlsm 22 Yrs; *ai:* Yrbk Adv; Fac Cncl, Textbook Selection, Curr Comms; NCTE 1982-; Book Ed; *office:* William Fisher Catholic HS 1803 Granville Pike Lancaster OH 43130*

JOHNSON, JUNE THURSTON, First Grade Teacher; *b:* Middlesex, VA; *c:* Timothy M.; *ed:* VA St Univ (BS) Elem Ed 1964; Beaver Coll (MED) Ed 1977; Attnd Various Univs & Colls Addl Stud; SP. ED. PA Supervisory Cert; *cr:* Portsmouth Schl Dist 1st Grd Tchr 1964-65; Camden Schl Dist 1st Grd Tchr 1965-68; Philadelphia Schl Dist 1st Grd Tchr 1969-; *ai:* Loesche Schl Calligraphy Club Spon; 1st Grd Chprsn; Multicultural Lit Club Spon; NEA 1964-; NJEA 1965-; PFT & AFT 1969-; Phi Delta Kappa 1993; Alpha Kappa Alpha 1963-; Sci Ed Division Elem Sci Federal Grant; William C Jacobs Trust Fund Schlsp; Dwight D Eisenhower Math & Sci Act Schlsp; *office:* William H Loesche Elem Schl Bustleton Ave & Tomlinson Philadelphia PA 19116*

JOHNSON, KALLIN A., Director of Music; *b:* Logan, UT; *m:* Linda Lee Celularo; *c:* Christopher; *ed:* UT St Univ (BA) Fr, Music 1978; New England Conservatory (MMA) Piano Performance 1985; Art Mngmt Courses; *cr:* UT St Univ Adj Tchr of Piano 1976-80; Pakachoag Comm Music Schl Dir 1982-86; South Shore Conservatory Piano Instr 1982-85; Notre Dame Acad Dir of Music 1984-; New England Theatre Co Exec Producer 1994-; *ai:* Oversee Concert, Chamber Chorales, Jazz Ensembles, Concert Band, Chamber Orch, Percussion Ensembles Music Act; MA Music Tchr Assn 1985-, Pres; MA Music Ectrs Assn 1989-; Worcester Intnl Artists 1991-, Programming Chm; Arts Worcester 1991-, Bd Mem; Written, Composed for Musical Theater; Received Cultural Enrichment Awd; *office:* Notre Dame Acad 425 Salisbury St Worcester MA 01609*

JOHNSON, KATHERINE MAY, Special Education Teacher; *b:* Woodstown, NJ; *w:* Edward Lee (dec); *c:* Hope Cherette; *ed:* Cumberland Co Coll (AS) Ed 1983; Glassboro St Coll (BA) Tchr of Handicapped K-12 1986; Cooper Med Ctr Cert of Radiology 1970; *cr:* Newcomb Med Ctr X-Ray Technician 1970-73; Marsh Radiology X-Ray Technician 1980-82; *ai:* Stu of Mnth Comm; Stdnts Exhibiting Good Behavior Comm; Vineland Ed Assn, NEA, NJ Ed Assn 1986-; Church Choir 1967-, Pianist; *office:* D'Ippolito HS 1578 N Valley Ave Vineland NJ 08360*

JOHNSON, KATHIE (EVANS), Sr HS English Teacher; *b:* Seneca Falls, NY; *m:* Stephen B.; *c:* M. Kristin, Mike, Jennifer; *ed:* Nazarath Coll (BA) Eng 1969; Elmira Coll (MS) Ed 1973; *cr:* Romulus Cntrl Schl Eng Tchr 1969-71; Waterloo Sr HS Eng Tchr 1971-; *ai:* Class of 1998 Adv; Waterloo Ed Assn, NYSUT 1971-; *office:* Waterloo HS Center St Waterloo NY 13165

JOHNSON, KATHLEEN LEWIS, Social Studies Teacher; *b:* Cuyahoga Falls, OH; *m:* Curt Lee; *c:* Megan, Karen; *ed:* OH St Univ (BS) Home Ec Educ 1965, (MS) Child Dev 1967; Elem Cert Lake Erie Coll; Short Courses Eng, Art, Arch, Eng Educ Oxford; *cr:* Burton Elem Schl Kndgtn Tchr 1966-74, 4th-5th Grd Tchr 1975-94, 5-6 Grd Soc Stud Tchr 1994-; *ai:* PTO Fac Rep; GA Cty Soc Stud Curr Comm; NEA, OEA, BEA 1966-; Delta Kappa Gamma 1984-; Phi Upsilon Omicron 1964-; Burton Pub Lib Bd of Trustees 1974-, Pres; OH St Univ Alumni Assn Geauga Cty 1993-, Pres; Martha Holden Jennings Scholar 1981; *office:* Burton Elem Schl PO Box 406 Burton OH 44021

JOHNSON, KATHLEEN R., Teacher; *b:* New Britain, CT; *ed:* Emmanuel Coll (BA) His 1968; Grad Credits at Univ of RI, Univ of MA, CCSU; *cr:* Holy Cross Schl Tchr 1968-69; St Kevin Schl Tchr 1969-72; Holy Cross Schl Tchr 1972-76, Asst Prin 1975-76; St Joseph Schl Tchr 1976-77; Our Lady of Mt Carmel Schl Tchr, 7 Grd Homeroom 1977-; *ai:* Rel Coord; Accreditation Comm; NCEA.

JOHNSON, KATHY L., Mathematics Department Chair; *b:* Cincinnati, OH; *m:* Robert; *ed:* Miami Univ (BSEd) Math & Psych 1980; Univ of Dayton (MED) Ed 1984; Attnd Univ of Akron, Kent St & Ashland Addl 30 Hrs; *cr:* Newbury HS Math Tchr 1980-; *ai:* Asst Vlybl & Girls Bsktbl Coach; Girls Track Coach; NEA, OCTM & NCTM 1980-; *office:* Newbury H S 14775 Auburn Rd Newbury OH 44065

JOHNSON, KEITH W., Secondary English Teacher; *b:* New York, NY; *ed:* Pace Univ (BA) Lit, Comm 1984, (MS) Ed 1991; *cr:* Suffern HS Stu Tchr 1987; Lakeland Regnl HS Eng, Jrnlsm Tchr 1987-95; Harrison HS Eng Tchr 1995-; *ai:* Participated in Cultural Visits HS Stdnts to Spain, Denmark, Russia; Schl Newspaper Fac Adv; SAT Instr Stanley H. Kaplan Educl Svcs; AFT, NEA, Lakeland Regnl HS Tchrs Assn 1987-95; Harrison Assn of Tchrs 1995-; NYSUT; Sigma Tau Delta 1984-; March of Dimes 1986-, Vol, Chptr Svc Coord; Guest Speaker William Paterson Coll Spring Conf in Response to Stud Dialectical Journal Writing Across the Curr; Written Several Articles; Nom Several Times Govenors Awd for Tchng Excl, Awd Rcpnt 1995; *office:* Harrison Central Dist 50 Union Ave Harrison NY 10528*

JOHNSON, KENITH R., PE Teacher & Coach; *b:* Waynesboro, PA; *m:* Denise Doherty; *c:* Emilie, Abigail; *ed:* Towson St Univ (BS) PE 1975; 9 Addl Grad Credits Western MD Coll; 15 Addl Grad Credits Bowie St Coll; 6 Addl Grad Credits Goucher Coll; *cr:* Owings Mills HS PE Tchr, Coach 1978-82; Randallstown HS PE Tchr, Coach 1985-90; Chesapeake HS Ath Dir, Coach 1990-82; Liberty HS Ath Dir, PE Tchr, Coach 1993-; *ai:* Ath Dir; Head Ftbl Coach; CCEA 1993-, Mem; MD St Ftbl Coaches Assn 1990-, Mem; NEA 1985-, Mem; Baltimore Sun Metro Coach of Yr Ftbl 1995; *office:* Liberty HS 5855 Bartholow Rd Sykesville MD 21784

JOHNSON, KENNETH R., Biology Teacher; *b:* Brockton, MA; *m:* Barbara L. Burgeson; *c:* Kenneth Jr., Douglas, Lynn Madigan; *ed:* Bridgewater St Coll (BS) Bio 1968; 18 Addl Hrs; *cr:* Rockland Jr HS Sci Tchr 1968-74; Rockland HS Sci Coord 1974-79, Bio Tchr 1979-; *ai:* Rockland Tchrs Assn, MA Tchrs Assn, NEA 1968-; Vega Club 1967-, Schlsp Chm; *office:* Rockland HS 52 Goddard Rd Rockland MA 02370*

JOHNSON, KEVIN JOSEPH, English & Journalism Teacher; *b:* Buffalo, NY; *m:* Charlene Zaccagnini; *c:* Michael, Patrick, Tara, Emma; *ed:* St Univ of NY at Buffalo (BA) Eng 1975; Radiation Therapy (AAS) 1985; Working Toward MED; *cr:* Buffalo General Hosp Tech 1986-90; Rosewell Park Cancer Inst Radiation Therapy 1990-92; Clarence Sr HS Tchr 1992-; *ai:* Youth to Youth Adv; Mentor Pgrm Participent; NYS Tchrs Assn, AFT, NCTE 1992-; *office:* Clarence Sr HS 9625 Main St Clarence NY 14031*

JOHNSON, LINDA BAYLISS, Social Studies Teacher; *b:* Oakland, CA; *m:* Stanley E.; *ed:* Wittenberg Univ (BA) Pol Sci 1968; Miami Univ (MED) Curr, Supervision 1975; Addl Work OH St Univ, OH Univ; *cr:* Amanda Clearcreek Local Schls 6th Grd Tchr 1970-74; Heath City Schls 4th, 5th Grd Tchr 1975-83, 10th-12th Grd Tchr 1983-; *ai:* Licking Cty Tchr Dev Cncl; Licking Cty Soc Stud Curr Comm; Heath Ed Assn 1975-, Treas; Cntrl OH Tchrs Assn, OH Ed Assn, NEA 1975-; Marabar Heights Garden Club 1980-, Pres, VP, Sec; Metropolitan Columbus Daylily Soc 1987-; Broad St Presbyn Church; Grad Asst Dept of Ed Miami Univ 1974-75; Martha Holden Jennings Scholar 1971-72, 1986-87; Tchr of Yr 1985, 1988, 1994; Dow Excl Tchng Awd 1988, 1993; *office:* Heath HS 300 Lickingview Dr Heath OH 43056

JOHNSON, LINDA ELIN, Middle School Math Teacher; *b:* Worcester, MA; *m:* Robert A. Jr.; *c:* Sven, Elin; *ed:* Worcester St Coll (BA) Math 1970; Cmptr Programming; *cr:* Bellingham Jr Sr HS Math Tchr 1970-77; Hopedale Jr Sr HS Math Tchr 1983; Whitinsville Chrstn Schl MS Math Tchr 1988-; *ai:* United Meth Women; Yth Dir; Church Choir; NCTM 1992-; Alliance Ed 1995-; *office:* Whitinsville Christian Schl 279 Linwood Ave Whitinsville MA 01588

JOHNSON, LINDA K., Social Studies Teacher; *b:* Steubenville, OH; *m:* Mark F.; *c:* Mark, Holly; *ed:* Univ of Steubenville (BS) Elem Ed, Learning Disabilities, Behavior Disoreders 1978; Kent St Univ Credit Hrs; *cr:* Toronto HS Learning Disabilities Tchr 1978-86; J. T. Karaffa MS Soc Stud Tchr 1986-; *ai:* Stu Cncl Adv; Constitution Bowl Spon; *office:* J T Karaffa MS 1307 Dennis Way Toronto OH 43964*

JOHNSON, LINDA MAKOWSKI, Art Teacher; *b:* Kingston, PA; *m:* Robert E.; *c:* Jennifer, Jessica, Robbie; *ed:* Kutztown (BA) Art Ed 1971; Univ of Scranton (MS) Art Ed 1975; *cr:* Wyalusing Jr-Sr HS Art Tchr 1971-75; Bishop OReilly Schl Art Tchr 1990-; *office:* Bishop O'Reilly HS 316 N Maple Ave Kingston PA 18704

JOHNSON, LISA ANN, Seventh Grade Teacher; *b:* Dennison, OH; *ed:* OH Univ Elem Ed 1985, Stud Elem Math, Ed Courses; *cr:* St Mary Cntrl Seventh Grd Tchr 1987-; *ai:* Sci Fair Dir; Mathcounts Coach; OH Univ Eastern Theatre Mem; Academic Fair Dir; OCEA 1987-; Eisenhower Math Grant 1992; *office:* St Mary Central Grade Schl 24 N 4th St Martins Ferry OH 43935*

JOHNSON, LOUIS BERNARD, History Teacher; *b:* Fayetteville, OH; *m:* Dolores Molitor; *c:* Louis Anthony, Sandra Marie Ladenburger; *ed:* Wilmington Coll (BA) His, Pol Sci, PE & Drivers Ed 1974; 150 Credit Hrs Advanced; *cr:* Fayetteville Perry Schls Tchr 20 Yrs; *ai:* Bsktbl & Bsbl Coach; NEA, OEA 1976-; *home:* PO Box 5 Fayetteville OH 45118*

JOHNSON, LYNN JEFFERSON-WEBB, Sixth Grade Teacher; *b:* Camp Kilmer, NJ; *m:* Kenneth; *c:* Marlon Webb; *ed:* Trenton St Coll (BS) Elem Ed 1974; Rider Univ (MA) Schl Cnslng 1995; 24 Credit Hrs Grad Work in Dev Rdng, ESL; *cr:* Upper Freehold Regnl Elem Schl First Grd Tchr 1974-75, Seventh-Eighth Grd Eng Tchr 1975-87; Allentown HS Eng Tchr 1987-90; West Windsor-Plainsboro Upper Elem Schl Sixth Grd Tchr 1990-; *ai:* Human Relations Comm; Tchrs Assn 1990-; NJEA, NEA 1974-; Article Pub; *office:* Upper Elem Schl WWP 75 Grovers Mill Rd Plainsboro NJ 08536

JOHNSON, MARION OHLIN, Instructional Support Teacher; *b:* St Marys, PA; *m:* Lawrence L.; *c:* Eric, Ann; *ed:* Edinboro Univ of PA (BA) Elem Ed 1972, (MA) Elem Ed & Early Chldhd 1975; *cr:* St Marys Area Schl Dist Elem Tchr 1972-84, Elem Prin 1984-93, Elem Tchr 1993-95, Instrl Support Tchr 1995-; *ai:* Girl Scout Brownie Ldr; Mem Fox Twp & Elk Cty Planning Commissions; St Boniface Parish Cncl, Church Lector; Prof Dev, Prof Relations & Pub Relations Comms; Curr Dev; PSEA & NEA & SMAEA 1972-, Past Bldg Rep; AAUW; PTO, Past Pres; Bldg Renovation Design & Planning; Dev Extended Day Kndgtn; Dev Transitional 1st Grd; Established Instrl Support Pgm; SMART Mem; *office:* Fox Township Elem Schl 376 Main St Kersey PA 15846*

JOHNSON, MARK ANTON, Eng, Speech & Drama Teacher; *b:* Muskegon, MI; *m:* Ruth Elaine Auckland; *c:* Kelly, Travis, Meghan; *ed:* Maranatha Bapt Bible Coll (BS) Scndry Ed 1981; US Sports Acad, Sports Mgmt 31 Hrs; Univ of MI 12 Hrs Internship; *cr:* Maranatha Bapt Bible Coll Tchr & Coach 1981-84; Pennridge HS Coach 1985-95; Faith Chrstn Acad Tchr & Coach 1985-; *ai:* Jr Class Adv; Bsktbl Coach; Head of Eng *home:* 427 Ridge Rd Sellersville PA 18960

JOHNSON, MARTY, Professor of Mathematics; *b:* Allentown, P Kutztown Univ (BS) Scndry Ed Math 1969; Univ of KY (MA) M 1970; Temple Univ (MBA) Cmptr & Info Sci 1982; *cr:* US Intelligence Ofcr 1971-74; Harford Cty Schl Math Tchr 1974-76; Math Prof 1976-; *ai:* AFT 1982-, Local Treas 1983-85; Montgomery County Comm Coll 340 Dekalb Pike Blue Bell PA 19

JOHNSON, MARY ANNE (BLACK), Lang Arts & Soc Stud T Hamilton, OH; *c:* Laura; *ed:* Cntrl MI (BA) Ed, Fr 1973; Miam (MED) Rdng 1983; *cr:* Talawanda City Schls 3rd Grd Tchr 1978- Grd Tchr 1979-80, 6th Grd Tchr 1980-82, 5th Grd Tchr 1982-95; Stud Comm; Lang Arts Textbook Adoption Crisis Comm; NEA *office:* Stewart Schl 315 S College Ave Oxford OH 45056

JOHNSON, MARY BETH HABAS, Professor of Court Reporti Erie, PA; *m:* David R.; *c:* Barrett David; *ed:* Dickinson Coll (BA) Stud 1975; Duquesne Univ (MA) Ed 1995; *cr:* Duffs Buss Inst D Stdnts, Court Reporting Tchr 1978-90; Comm Coll of Allegheny C 1990-; *ai:* Court Reporters Org Spon; Dev Prgm Wherein Court Rep Stdnts Caption Classes for Hearing Impaired Stdnts; Mrktg Retention Task Force; Schl Spirit Sub-Comm; Natl Court Reporters PA Court Reporters Assn; OH Vly Gen Hosp Elegant Auction Co- 1996; Spec Event Mt Lebanon United Meth Church Co-Chprsn 19 Commission Mt Lebanon United Meth Church; Written Several Gr PA Voc Ed Funding; *office:* Comm Coll Algny Co Algny Cmps 808 Ave Pittsburgh PA 15212

JOHNSON, MARY JO PAYNE, English Teacher; *b:* New York Cit *m:* Ellie O. Jr.; *c:* Ellie III, Andrea; *ed:* Shippensburg St Coll (BS Speech 1966; Working Towards MS Curr Supervision at Miami Oxford; Continuing Ed Courses; Voc Ed Courses at Kent St; *cr:* Heir HS Eng Tchr 10 Yrs; Miami U Assoc Prof, Supvr, Coord 2 Yrs; Woo HS Inner City Stu Tchng Prgm, Work Coord, Tchr for Potential Dro 19 Yrs; *ai:* Basic Skills Ed Advy Co; Textbk Comm Chair; Voc Cu Comm; AFT 1970-; OVA, AVA 1977-; City Wide OWE Coords 1977- Bond Hill Child Dev Ctr 1975-, Co-Pres; Progressive Club 1972-, Paddock Hills Assn 1975-; Eng Dept Head; Urban Stu Tchrs; *home*. Westminster Dr Cincinnati OH 45229

JOHNSON, MERI E., Biology Teacher; *b:* Hamilton, OH; *m:* Wayr Miami Univ of OH (BS) Biological Scis 1980; Northern KY Univ Biological Scis 1988; *cr:* Lakota HS Sci Tchr 1981; Clermont Northe HS Bio Tchr 1983-95; Batavia HS Bio Tchr 1995-; *ai:* Sci Olympiad Cincinnati Gas & Electric Advy Comm; SW OH Tchr Ldr Prgm; NEA, NSTA: NBTA, SECO; US Forestry Grant; Partners in Sci Facil Presenter at Tchng-Learning Conf; Exemplary Tchr Awd Cle Northeastern HS; *office:* Batavia HS 800 Bauer Ave Batavia OH 45

JOHNSON, MICHAEL DENNIS, Technical Education Teach Buffalo, NY; *m:* Susan; *c:* Amie, Vinnie; *ed:* Buffalo St Coll Industrial Arts Ed 1984; Working Towards MS Voc Tech Ed; *cr:* M Earle Inc Installer 1986-88; Polestar Renovation & Construction 1988-94; Cuba-Rushford Cntrl Schl Tech Ed Tchr 1994-; *ai:* Frosh Adv; Schl Play Set Builder; NEA 1994-; West NY Home Improv Cncl 1991-; *office:* Cuba-Rushford Central Schl 15 Elm St Cuba NY

JOHNSON, MICHAEL K., Math & Soc Stud Tchr; *b:* Cleveland, O Mary Ann Theado; *c:* Michelle, Matthew, Megan, Melissa; *ed:* OH S (BA) Early, Mid Chldhd 1978; Currently Working for MA Oh St PDS Create Prof Growth Combing Schls, Univ Fac, Stu Tchng Prgr Madison Co Schls Autistic Unit, Spec Ed Aid Tchr 1976-78; Dios Columbus Sci, Math, Rdng Tchr, etc 1978-86; Columbus Pub Sch Math, Soc Stud Tchr 1986-; *ai:* Knights of Columbus; Son's Sch Team Coach; NEA; Knights of Columbus 1993-, Prgm Dir; *home:* Glasgow Pl Columbus OH 43235

JOHNSON, MITCHELL DAVID, Physics Teacher; *b:* Queens, N SUNY at Cortland (BS) Physics 1974; Univ of AZ (MS) Astronomy SUNY at Binghamton (MS) Physics 1994; *cr:* Union Endicott HS Ph Tchr 1974-; *ai:* AAPT 1974-; Tchr Rsrch Assoc at Lawrence Berkele Lab Summer 1995; *office:* Union Endicott HS 1200 E Main St Endico 13760

JOHNSON, MOREI BANKS, Kindergarten Teacher; *b:* Dover, D Michael W.; *c:* Shea, Tiffini, Tyler; *ed:* DE St Univ (BS) Early Chld 1979, (MS) Ed 1985; 25 Addl hrs Ed, Cmptrs; *cr:* Fairview Elem Kndgtn Tchr 1979-81; South Elem Schl Kndgtn Tchr 1979-81; H Elem Schl Kndgtn Tchr 1981-; *ai:* Day Care Comm Chm; Instrl Adv Capital Sch Dist; DSEA, NEA 1979-; PEEC 1995-, Bd of Dirs; Kappa alpha 1983-; Who's Who Outstdng Black Women; Tchr of Yr; 229 N Caroline Pl Dover DE 19904*

JOHNSON, NANCY BOWER, Social Studies Teacher; *b:* William PA; *m:* Thomas W.; *c:* Suzanne; *ed:* Bloomsburg St Coll (BS) Soc 1962; Bucknell Univ (MS) Ed 1967; Attnd Syracuse Univ, Oswego St Brookport St Coll; *cr:* North Rose-Wolcott Soc Stud Tchr 31 Yrs; Class, NHS Adv; DAR Awd Act Chm; NEA 1977-, Del, St Del; Kappa Gamma 1971-, Chair Comms; Lioness Club 1984-, Pres, Pres Presbyn Church 1962-; Tchr of Yr; *office:* North Rose-Wolco Salter-Colvin Rd Wolcott NY 14590*

JOHNSON, NANCY FOURNIER, Fourth Grade Teacher; *b:* Lac NH; *m:* Andrew D.; *c:* Sue-Ellen; *ed:* Keene St Coll (BED) Elem Ed 30 Addl Hrs UNH, PSC, Notre Dame Coll at Manchester; *cr:* Gilford 2nd, 4th-5th Grd Tchr 1962-72; Gilford MS 8th Grd Eng Tchr 197 Gilford Elem 4th Grd Tchr 1978-; *ai:* Chair #30 Staff Dev C Enrichment Coord; Assessment Comm; NEA; Gilford Ed Assoc; *o* Gilford Elem Schl 76 Belknap Mountain Rd Laconia NH 03246

JOHNSON, NANCY OGLES, Second Grade Teacher; *b:* Mc Minn TN; *m:* Russell Keith; *c:* Keith, Kyle Johnson Wille; *ed:* Trenton S (BS) Elem Ed 1976, (MA) Elem Ed 1984; Rutgers St Univ (EDD) Lang Arts 1995; *cr:* West Windsor-Plainsboro Regnl Schls Classroom 1976-88; Princeton Regnl Schls Classroom Tchr 1988-; *ai:* NEA 1 NCTE 1988-, 2 Tchr Rsrch Grants; NJCTE 1988-; NJ Governor's 1989-90; Excl in Eng Prgm Awd Princeton Branch of Eng Speaking U 1993; NJ Alliance for Arts Grant 1995-; Princeton Ed Fnd Grant 1 *office:* Riverside Elem Schl 58 Riverside Dr Princeton NJ 08540

JOHNSON, NORMAN LEE, Phys Therapist Asst Pgm & Prof; *b:* PA; *m:* Nancy Ellen Lenke; *c:* Holly Leight; *ed:* George Washington (BS) Environmental Hlth Sci 1983; Univ of Pittsburgh (BS) Phys The 1984, (MS) Orthopaedic Phys Therapy 1988; PA St Univ 12 Cr Towards DED Adult Ed; *cr:* Braddock Med Ctr Phys Therapy Dir 198 Comm Hosp Phys Therapy Dir 1986-87; CCAC Boyce Campus PTA Dir 1987-; PRO Phys Therapy Co-Owner 1990-; *ai:* Stu Phys Therapy Adv; Phys Therapy Advy Comm; Who's Who Among Coll Stdnts Sele Comm; APTA 1982-; PA Edctrs Network 1990-, Co-Chair; AMSUS, 1984-; Lions Club Intnl 1986-; Fac Mem of Yr 1994-95; Golden Key 1989; Educl Booket Pub 1986; *office:* Comm Coll Algny Co Boyce 595 Beatty Rd Monroeville PA 15146*

JOHNSON, PATRICIA, Assistant Professor of Law; *b:* New York, *ed:* John Jay Coll (AA) Lbrl Arts, (BA) Criminal Justice, (MA) Crir Justice; Cornell Univ Schl of Law Pre-Law Stud; Rutgers Univ Schl of at Newmark Juris Doctorate; *cr:* NYC Court System Judicial Friends

Assoc Counsel Pub Adm Office & Deputy Chief Clerk 1986-91;)ame CLEO & Seton Hall Law Prof of Legal Writing 1993-94; John)ll Asst Prof & Adj Asst Prof 1987-; *ai:* Assn of Bar of Entertainment Law Comm Law Schl Prep Wkshp; Benjamin ao Law Schl Entertainment Law Moot Cour Hnrs Competition nary Rounds Judge; Natl Bar Assn 1985-; Prof Staff Congress NY Bar Assn 1994-; Amer Bar Assn 1994-; Numerous Article Pub; John Jay Coll of Crim Justice 899 10th Ave Rm 422T New York NY

SON, PATRICIA ANNE, Biology Teacher; *b:* Kearny, NJ; *ed:* Heary Coll (BS) Bio 1971; Montclair Tchng Cert; Grad Work at s, William Patterson, St Peters; Working on MS OR St Univ; *cr:* ood HS Sci Tchr 1972-; *ai:* Bio Team Adv; Bio Tchrs Assn of NJ Pres 1994-; NEA, NSTA, NBAT, REA, AAAS NYAS Entire Career; Fnd Earthwatch Espedition 1986; Lead Tchr Modern Bio at Rutgers MIT Book Awd for Excl 1991; Outstdng Bio Tchr of Yr 1995; *office:* ood HS 627 E Ridgewood Ave Ridgewood NJ 07450

SON, PAUL ROBERT, Drama & Choral Director; *b:* Brooklyn, NY; ne Rose Ruberti; *c:* Jesse, Eryn, Joshua, Zachary; *ed:* Alfred Univ Music Ed & Voice 1970; New England Conservatory of Music (MM) 1972; *cr:* Hudson Pub Schls K-12th Grd Choral, Drama & Music 972-; *ai:* Drama Dir 1980-; Acton Comm Chorus 1984-, Founder & t Voice Tchr; Musical Dir Local Comm Theatres; Hudson Drama 1989-, Founder & Dir; NEA 1972-; MMEA 1980-; Huntington e Tchr Adv 1994-; Hudson Arts Alliance 1993-, Advy; *office:* 1 HS Brigham St Hudson MA 01749

SON, PELAGIA DOTILLOS, Kindergarten Teacher; *b:* Bourbon Philippines; *m:* Adolphus; *c:* Christie, Ann D.; *ed:* Lehman Coll Early Chldhd 1988; (BS) in Ed & Elem Ed; *cr:* Tabogon Roosevelt & Eng Tchr 1969-72; Court Of First Instance Clerk 1972-73; Elem E Tchr & Guid Cnslr 1973-78; *ai:* United Fed of Tchrs 1979-; *office:* Majorie H Dunbar 175 W 166th St Bronx NY 10452

SON, PETER HASSELL, Social Studies Teacher; *b:* Plainfield, : Mary Ann Suozzo; : Lisa, Kenneth, Meredith, Peter; *ed:* outh Univ (BS) His, Ed 1968; Attnd Univ of ME Grad Ec; Univ of atdoor Rec; *cr:* Plainfield HS Tchr, Coach 1967-69; Hinckley Schl r, Tchr, Coach 1969-77; L. L. Bean Inc Floor Ldr Fly Fishing Dept 1; Hall-Dale HS Tchr, Coach, Stu Assistance Team 1992-; *ai:* Var Coach, Boys, Girls Var Track Coach; Steering Comm editation; SIFA Group AIDS Awareness; NEA 1992-; St Soccer es Assn 1995-; Notary Pub 1985-89; Bd of Appeals 1979-94; *home:* ool St Gardiner ME 04345*

SON, PHILIP ROY, History Teacher; *b:* Detroit, MI; *m:* E. Cornelia y; *c:* John Charles, William; *ed:* Univ of KY (BA) His 1969; Elmire MS) Ed 1988; *cr:* N Rose-Wolcott Schl Eng Tech 1969-70; Geneva hls His Tchr 1971-; *ai:* Ftbl Coach; Ski Club Adv; Schl Improvement Chprsn; Soc Stud Dept Chair; Geneva Tchrs Assn 1971-, Pres 5; Wayne Finger Lakes Cncl for Soc Stud 1989-, Pres; Pres Geneva Assn 1993-; Chprsn NEA/NY Human Rights Comm; Finger Lakes Derby, Bd of Dirs 1985-; United Meth Church 1960-; Geneva Free d of Dirs; Excl in Tchng Awd from Univ of Rochester 1986; *office:* a HS 101 Carter Rd Geneva NY 14456

SON, RANDALL LAMAR, Asst Prof of Interior Design; *b:* Winter FL; *m:* Robb Walter Yonkin; *ed:* Rochester Inst of Tech (BFA) graphic Illustration 1984, (MFA) Indstrl, Interior Design 1989; *cr:* ster Inst of Tech Adj Instr Cmptr, Design 1989-91; Monroe Comm sst Prof Interior Design 1990-; *ai:* Interior Design Club Adv; Curr ; Amer Soc of Interior Design 1990-; Fac Senate 1995-; South East Coalition Bd of Dirs 1992-, Pres 94-, Sec 1993-; Natl Cncl for Interior n Qualifications Cert; *office:* Monroe Comm Coll 1000 E Henrietta chester NY 14623

SON, REMELLE L. RICHMOND, Spanish Teacher; *b:* New York NY; *m:* Richard W.; *c:* Rita Gail, Lois C.; *ed:* City Coll (BA) Span, 1 Arts 1957; St Johns Univ (MS) Span, Biling Ed 1977; 39 Credits & Scndry Ed 1975; *cr:* Herman Rider JHS98BX Span, Math, Non Eng Tchr 1958-62; Hollis Schl PS 134Q 6th Grd ICG, FLES Tchr 75; PS203Q Kndgtn 3-4 Grd Span Tchr 1977-80; Douglaston Schl PS h Grd Tchr, Span Cluster 1980-87; Louis Pasteur MS 67Q Span Tchr *ai:* Magnet Tutorial Prgm Span Conversation 1991-93; Mentor for pan Tchrs; Mem Hollis Presbyterian Church 1963-; Bd of Chrstn Ed; h Sunday Schl Tchr 1959-62 & 1969-73; AFT 1977-; AATSP 1969-; Coll Graduation, Hispanic Inst Awd Highest Achvmt 1957; St Johns 977 Full Schlsp for MS in Ed, Span St Johns Fellow; Author A Guide Spanish Curriculum for the Middle School (Grades 6-9); *office:* Pasteur Sr H S 51-60 Marathon Pkwy Littleneck NY 11362

SON, RITA T., Art Teacher; *b:* Elizabeth, NJ; *m:* Albert W. Jr.; *c:* A.; *ed:* Slippery Rock Univ (BFA) Fine Art 1987; Westminster Coll Cert; *cr:* USMC Illustrator 1972-78; Neshannock Schl Dist Art Tchr 89; Monhead Schl Dist Art Tchr 1989-90; Mohawk Schl Dist Art Tchr Mars Schl Dist Art Tchr 1990-; *ai:* Class of 1997 Spon; NHS Spon; 1995-; PA S Ed Assn 1989-; NEA 1989-; Various Local Art Shows.*

SON, ROBERT,JR., English Teacher; *b:* New Rochelle, NY; *m:* Bride; *c:* Bryan, Meghan; *ed:* Iona Coll (BA) Eng 1971; Fordham Coll Eng 1975; 45 Grad Credit Hrs; *cr:* Thornton Donovan Schl 8-12 Grd chr 1973-75; Sleepy Hollow MS Grd 8 Eng Tchr 1975-; *ai:* AFT, T 1975-; NYSEC 1975-, Edctrs of Excl; *office:* Sleepy Hollow MS Broadway Tarrytown NY 10591

SON, ROBERT H., Teacher; *b:* Greenfield, MA; *m:* Bessie M.; *c:* el, Kathy, Mark; *ed:* Springfield Coll (BS) Sci 1952; *cr:* Curtis r Chrstn Schl Prin 1977-79; Ellsworth Chrstn Schl Prin 1979-84; as Valley Chrstn Schl Prin 1985-86; SENHCA Tchr 1986-.*

SON, ROBERT S., 5th Grade Teacher; *b:* Hellertown, PA; *m:* Faye : Moravian Coll (BA) His 1964; Lehigh Univ (MED) Elem Ed 1967; afer Elem Schl 6th Grd Tchr 1964-86, 5th Grd Tchr 1986-; *ai:* Schl Mgr; Talent Show Coord; Drama Club; Veterans Meml Coord; Fund for Schl, Comm Org 1994-95; Nazareth Area Ed Assn, PA Ed Assn, 1964-; Honored by Amer Legion, Veterans of Vietnam for Prgms & ans Meml; UNICEF Letters of Appreciation or Fund Raising Efforts; d of Ed by Cty; Honored for Fund Raising for Restoration of Statue erty; *home:* 823 Easton Rd Hellertown PA 18055

SON, ROGER, Science Teacher; *b:* Irvington, NJ; *m:* Leigh ens; *c:* Daniel, Michael; *ed:* Kean Coll (BA) Outdoor & Urban ation 1979; Montclair St Coll, Kean Coll Tchng Cert 1982-84; 6 Grad s Boston Univ Phys Sci Tchrs Wkshp; *cr:* Project Link Educl Ctr MS tud & PE Tchr 1980-82; Maplewood MS Sci Tchr 1984-; *ai:* IM Adv ; Recycling Club Adv 1990-; Planning Comm 1990-92; Discipline 1 1992-93; Sci Dept Resource Coord 1992-93; Sci Curr Assessment 1 1992-93; South Orange Maplewood Ed Assn 1984-; NJ Ed Assn ; Branchburg Roller Hockey League 1995-, Yth Team Coach; hburg Soccer Club 1994-, Yth Team Coach; Branchburg Bsbl Club , Yth Team Coach; Governor's Tchr Recognition Awd 1987; *office:* ewood MS 7 Burnett St Maplewood NJ 07040

NSON, ROGER WILLIAM, Guidance Counselor; *b:* Port Allegany, *m:* Virginia Arlene Wheeler; *c:* Brian Paul, Robin Renee; *ed:* Clarion iv (BS) Elem Ed 1972; Kutztown St Univ (MS) Elem Cnslng 1975; 30 Addl Credits; *cr:* Green Lake Elem Schl 4th Grd Tchr 1972-73; Upper Perkiomen MS 6th Grd Sci Tchr 1973-91, Guid Cnslr 1991-; *ai:* HS Var Sftbl Head Coach; NEA, PSEA, UPEA 1972-; *office:* Upper Perkiomen MS 510 Jefferson St East Greenville PA 18041

JOHNSON, RONALD G., American History Teacher; *b:* Charleroi, PA; *m:* Linda Ann Houseman; *c:* Brian, Karla; *ed:* CA Univ (BA) Industrial Arts 1976, (MS) Industrial Arts 1979, (MS) Soc Stud 1983; *cr:* Bentworth HS Tchr 1977-; *ai:* Stu Asst Team; Sr HS Instructional Cabinet; Staff Bldg Rep; NEA, PSEA 1977-, Bentworth Ed Assn 1977-, VP; HS Tchr of Month 1993; *office:* Bentworth HS 500 Lincoln Ave Bentleyville PA 15314*

JOHNSON, RUSSELL A., 8th Grd Tchr & Guidance Cnslr; *b:* Martins Ferry, OH; *m:* Savaria Dellatore; *c:* Russell, Anthony; *ed:* OH Univ (BSEd) Elem Ed 1962; Kent St Univ (MED) Schl Admin 1968; Post Grad Univ of Akron, Ashland Univ; *cr:* Bridgeport Exempted Village Tchr, Coach 1961-62; Grand Valley Schls Tchr, Coach 1962-64; Plain Local Schls Tchr 1964-67; Lake Local Schls Prin 1967-70; Plain Local Schls Prin 1970-86, Tchr 1986-; Ashland Univ Adjunct Fac 1992-; *ai:* Adv Schl Newspaper; Mgr Schl Store; Lang Arts Dept Head; OEA, Nea 1986-; Local Tchrs Assn 1986-, Organizing Mem 1966, Exec Bd Mem 1986-87; Ohio MS Assn 1994-; Ohio Career Ed Assn 1995-; Amer Heart Educ Steering Comm 1983-; Grad Asst Kent St Univ; Sr Partner Three Views Educ Seminars; Seminar Speaker; Tchr of Yr Finalist Stark Cty; *office:* Middlebranch MS 7500 Middlebranch Rd Canton OH 44721*

JOHNSON, SHEILA FOGARTY, English & Journalism Teacher; *b:* Bridgeport, CT; *m:* Brian J.; *c:* Kirsten E., Gavin T., Brendan J., Brian T.; *ed:* Marietta Coll (BA) Eng 1965; Eastern CT St Univ (MS) Ed 1991; Univ of CT Writing Project Summer Inst 1993 6 Hrs; *cr:* Brooklyn Jr HS Bus, Career Ed Tchr 1987-88; Killingly HS Eng, Jrnlsm Tchr 1988-; *ai:* Newspaper, Yrbk Asst Adv; CT Eng Tchrs Cncl, NCTE 1990-; KEA, CEA, NEA 1988-; Cncl Mem; CTCWP Planning Comm 1993-; Northeast CT Writers 1994-; *office:* Killingly HS Westfield Ave Danielson CT 06239

JOHNSON, SHEILA LABLANCHE, Assoc Prof of Counseling; *b:* Dayton, OH; *m:* James Emory Hunt; *c:* Julian Elliott, Justin Edward; *ed:* Western KY Univ (BA) Music 1977, (MA) Cnslng 1978; Univ of Pittsburgh (PHD) Higher Ed, Acad Admin 1983; *cr:* Carlow Coll Dir Minority Affairs 1982-86; Comm Coll of Allegheny Cty Project Dir 1987-, Assoc Prof 1991-; *ai:* Returning Stdnts Assn Adv; Women's Cncl Mid Sts Diversity Comm Mem; African Amer Fac, Staff Caucus; AFT 1991-; Women Work 1993-; PA Coll Prsnl 1991-, Western Rep; Delta Sigma Theta 1973-, Chptr Pres, Most Outstdng Delta; Western Penn Hills Comm Action 1994-, Grant Writer; Wrote 5 Yr Grant Single Parents; Wrote 2 Yr Grant Western Penn Hills Comm Action; Producer Time of Restoration TV Show; *home:* 969 Garden City Dr Monroeville PA 15146*

JOHNSON, SHEILA SUSAN, 7th-8th Grade Science Teacher; *b:* Rochester, NH; *m:* Paul A.; *c:* Jennifer, Stefanie; *ed:* Univ of NH (BA) Bio 1969; Marine Algae & Math Ed Courses; *cr:* Oyster River MS 6th Grd Sci Tchr 1972-79, 7th-8th Grd Sci Tchr 1979-; *ai:* Ath Co-Dir; ORTG; NHEA; NEA; Recycling Comm 1994-; *office:* Oyster River MS 47 Garrison Ave Durham NH 03824

JOHNSON, STAN ALLAN, Business Teacher; *b:* Milford, DE; *m:* Kathy Mahan; *c:* Scott, Kevin; *ed:* Salisbury St Univ (BA) & (BS) Bus Ad & Psych 1981, (MED) Educl Admin & Super 1991; Soc Cert 1983; Bus Ed Cert 1986; Master of Sci Mgmt Wilmington Coll; 130 Hrs Beyond BS; *cr:* Delmar Schl Dist Soc Stud, Bus Tchr 1983-; Wilmington Coll Part-Time Psych Instr 1993-; *ai:* Strategic Planning Comm Facilitator; BPA, Chess Club, Class of 1998 Adv; Tech, Discipline & Joint Advy Comms; Voc Ed Dept Coord; NEA 1983-; Delmar Ed Assn 1983-, Pres; Bus Prof Amer 1991-, Sussex Cty Rep, Leadership Awd; DE Bus Ed Assn 1994-; Lions Club 1994-, VP; Little League Coach & Property Owners Assn 1994-; PTA 1993-; Tchr of Yr & Outstanding Svc Awds; Outstanding Comm Svc Awd Chamber of Commerce; *home:* PO Box 1101 Allen MD 21810

JOHNSON, STEPHEN,III, Band Director; *b:* Oberlin, OH; *m:* Mary Ann Youngless; *c:* Courtney, Sarah; *ed:* Eastern KY Univ (BME) Music Ed 1972, (MME) Music Ed 1973; Attnd Oberlin Coll, Oberlin Tchrs Acad; *cr:* Massillon Schl Dist Asst Bands Dir 1973-75; US Army Acting Sgt Operations 1975-77; Oberlin Schl Dist Bands Dir 1977-; *ai:* HS Marching, Pep Band; Contests; Concerts; OMEA 1977-, Dist IV Pres; NBA; MENC; Phi Mu Alpha Sinfonia; Soc of Amer Bsbl Rsrch 1992-, Umpire Comm; *home:* 62 King St Oberlin OH 44074

JOHNSON, STEPHEN R., Coll of Arts & Scis Assoc Dean; *b:* Corning, NY; *m:* Denise Wawrejko; *c:* Ashley Ealy, Michael Swyers; *ed:* Mansfield Univ (BS) Music Ed 1976; AZ St Univ (MM) Music Performance 1982; Univ of MD (PHD) Curr, Instruction 1994; Attnd Tanglewood Inst Empire Brass Quintet Symposium; *cr:* Sullivan Cty HS Instrumental Music Tchr 1976-79; New Covenant Acad Music Instr 1982-88; Clarion Univ Bands Dir 1993-95, Arts & Scis Assoc Dean 1995-; *ai:* Fac Dev, Gen Ed Review Comms; Pres Commission on Status of Women; Music Edctrs Natl conf 1976-; PA Music Edctrs Assn, CBDNA 1993-; Presser Fnd Awd; Francis Scott Key Schlsp; Starkey Fnd Schlsp; *office:* Clarion Univ Of PA 177 Carlson Clarion PA 16214

JOHNSON, SUSAN ANN, Second Grade Teacher; *b:* Perth Amboy, NJ; *ed:* Rutgers Coll, Rutgers Univ (BS) Elem Ed 1978; Seton Hall Univ (MAE) Gen Prof Ed 1993; Credit Hrs Tchrs Coll, Columbia Univ, Monmouth Univ, Rutgers Grad Schl of Ed; *cr:* Boundbrook HS Spec Ed Aide, Rdng Tchr 1978-79; Readington Twp Schls GATE Tchr 1979-81; Whitehouse Schl Second Grd Tchr 1981-; *ai:* First Yr Tchr Mentor; Lang Arts, Writing Fair, Report Card, Stans Comms; Family Schl Cncl; Prin Select Comm Chprsn; NJEA 1978-; NCTM 1987-; NCTE 1994-; IRA 1993-; ASCD 1992-; Kappa Delta Pi; Merck Inst for Sci Ed Ldr, Tchr; *home:* 771 Aborn Ave Woodbridge NJ 07095*

JOHNSON, THOMAS JOSEPH, 8th Grade English Teacher; *b:* Buffalo, NY; *m:* Patricia Anne Doorley; *c:* Erin, Jeffrey, Brian; *ed:* St Bonaventure Univ (BA) Eng 1974; SUNY at Buffalo (MS) Curr Stud 1980-; *cr:* Heim MS Tchr; *ai:* Drama; NYSUT, AFT, Williamsville Tchr's Assn 1974-; *office:* Heim MS 175 Heim Rd Williamsville NY 14221

JOHNSON, THOMAS M., English Teacher; *b:* Wilkes-Barre, PA; *ed:* Villanova Univ (AB) Modern Langs 1972; Attnd Centre Universitaire D'Avignon, Exeter Coll, Oxford Univ, Trinity Coll; *cr:* Wilkes-Barre Area Schl Tchr 20 Yrs; *ai:* FBLA Adv; WBEA, PSEA, NEA 1975-; Chicory House Folk Club 1995-, Vol; AATF Schlsp 1983.

JOHNSON, TIMOTHY, Social Studies Teacher; *b:* Corning, NY; *m:* Kelley; *ed:* St Univ of NY at Cortland (BS) Elem & Scndry Ed 1984; Alfred Univ (MS) Cnslng 1988; *cr:* Penn Yan Acad Soc Stud Tchr 12 Yrs, Var Bsbl Coach 4 Yrs; *ai:* JV Bsbl Coach & Var Bsbl Coach 12 Yrs; NEA 1984-; BPOE Elks 1985-; *office:* Penn Yan Acad School Dr Penn Yan NY 14527

JOHNSON, TOMMIE TEMPLETON, High School Counselor; *b:* Huntington, WV; *m:* Gregory L.; *c:* Michalle Ashworth, Susan Arthur, T. R. Hannan; *ed:* Marshall Univ (AB) Voc Home Ec 1971, (MA) Cnslng 1977; 8 Hrs Post Grad Cnslng OH Univ; *cr:* Chesapeake HS Home Ec Tchr 1973-94, Cnslr 1994-; *ai:* Coll Options Prgm Supvr; HS Quiz Bowl Team Reader; HS Promenade Announcer; Class Day & Grad Prgm Participant; Natl Tchr Assn 1974-; Chesapeake Local Tchrs Assn 1974-, Pres; OH Schl Cnslr Assn 1994-; Womens Club of Huntington 1976-, Chairwoman Pub Affairs Comm; Assembly Club 1994-, Nominations Comm; Bsbl Little League 1994-; PTA 1974-; Beverly Hills Bapt Church 1985-; *office:* Chesapeake HS 10181 CR 1 Chesapeake OH 45619*

JOHNSON, VAN ALLEN, Fourth Grade Teacher; *b:* Scranton, PA; *m:* Joyce Ellen Kephart; *c:* Jayna Lyn, Katie Vanessa, Jillian Carli, Benjamin Van; *ed:* Williamsport Area Comm Coll (AS) Lbrl Arts 1973; Clarion St Coll (BS) Elem Ed 1974, (MED) Elem Ed 1978; Lock Haven St Coll Spcl Ed Cert 1976; IN Univ of PA Cert Elem Guid & Cnslng 1992; *cr:* Cntrl Intermediate Unit #10 Tchrs Aide Elem Mentally Retardation 1974-76, Spcl Ed Tchr Mentally Retardation 1976-77; West Branch Elem Schl 4th Grd Elem Tchr 1977-; *ai:* Portfolio Comm; Strategic Planning Comm; Soph Class Adv; Sports Timekeeper; WBFA Pres (2 Times), VP; YMCA Judo Instr; Karate Instr Curwensville Elem; Self-Defense Instr Presbyn Church; WBFA Negotiation Team; Curwensville Elem & YMCA Bsktbl Coach; NEA & PSEA 1976-; W Branch Ed Assn 1977-, Pres (Twice), VP (Twice), Pres-Elect (Twice); PA St Judo Inc 1974-, Comm Chm; USJI 1974-, Comm Mem; USJF 1993-; PA Judo Inc 4th Degree Black Belt, Karate 1st Degree Black Belt; Teach Judo Karate Self-Defense to Women and Children; Demonstrate Martial Arts to Boys & Girls Scouts; Deans List Williamsport Coll, Clarion St & IN Univ of PA; *office:* West Branch Area Schl RR 2 Box 194 Morrisdale PA 16858*

JOHNSON, VAUGHN MONROE, Art Teacher; *m:* Sandra Carey; *c:* Tashana, Tasman; *ed:* Morgan St Univ (BS) Art Ed 1971; Bowie St Univ (MA) 1982; *cr:* Fairmont Hghts HS Art Tchr 24 Yrs; *ai:* Cross Cntry & Track Coach; Peer Mediation; NEA 1973-; Potomac Vly Indoor Track Coach of Yr 1995.*

JOHNSON, VIOLA TOLBERT, Secondary English Teacher; *b:* Evergreen, AL; *c:* Nathan; *ed:* AL St Univ (BS) Eng 1972; UMAS at Boston (MA) Eng 1988; Attnd Wellesley Coll, Harvard Univ, Northeastern Univ, Simmons Coll, Boston St, Boston Univ; *cr:* Charlestown High Eng Tchr SAT Prep 1974-77; East Boston High Eng Tchr 1977-83; Boston Latin Schl Eng Tchr 1983-; *ai:* Fac Senate Sec; Eng Field Trips Coord; BTU Bldg Rep; BLS Rising Broadway Co-Adv; Boston Tchrs Union 1974-, Bldg Rep; NCTE 1983-88; 20th Mag Tchr of Yr; Lead Tchr Honorable Mention; *office:* Boston Latin Schl 78 Avenue Louis Pasteur Boston MA 02115

JOHNSON, VIRGINIA HILTON, Chemistry Teacher; *b:* Syracuse, NY; *m:* Greg; *c:* Karishma; *ed:* Onondaga Comm Coll (AAS) Medical Tech 1971; SUNY at Plattsburgh (BA) Bio 1973; SUNY at Potsdam, SUNY at Oswego Ed Grad Work; SUNY at Syracuse Environmental Stud; *cr:* Jefferson Comm Coll Microbiology Instr 1973-76; Pulaski Cntrl Schl Sci Tchr 1977-78; Mexico Acad Chem Tchr 1978-; *ai:* Peer Group; Operation Reindeer 1990-; *office:* Mexico Acad Main St Mexico NY 13114*

JOHNSON, WALTER J., German & English Teacher; *b:* Philadelphia, PA; *m:* Marion R. Dolan; *c:* Paul D., Eric J., Glen B.; *ed:* La Salle Coll (BA) Ger, Ed 1963; Attnd Temple Univ, Phila Coll of Textiles & Sci; *cr:* Northeast Cath HS Soc Stud, Ger, Eng, Theology Tchr 1963-; West Cath Summer HS Ger Tchr 1967-68, Ger & Eng Tchr 1975-88; Roman Cath Summer HS Asst Disciplinarian, Asst Prin 1989-91; *ai:* Schl Locker Control & Maintaince; Assn Cath Tchrs 1975-; NCEA 1980-; Knights of Columbus 1964-, 3rd Degree Mem, 4th Degree Mem 1972-; 25 Yrs of Tchng Cert 1988; Svc to Class Plaque 1971; Pro Tem Stu Svcs Asst Prin 1994; *office:* Northeast Catholic Boys HS 1842 Torresdale Ave Philadelphia PA 19124

JOHNSON, WAYNE, 7th & 8th Grade Science Tchr; *b:* Upland, PA; *m:* Evangeline; *c:* Tim, Michelle, Daniel, Nicole, Kisha; *ed:* Univ of KY (BS) Elem Ed 1970; West Chester Univ, & Penn St Univ 30 Addl Credits; *cr:* Main Street 5th Grd Tchr 1970-82, Kndgtn Tchr 1983-88, 5th Grd Tchr 1889-93, 6th Grd Tchr 1994-95, 7th & 8th Grd Sci Tchr 1996; *ai:* Mem of Instructional Support Team, Mem of Stu Assistance Prgm; AV Coord & Sci Coord; CUEA 1970-, Bldg Rep; PSEA & NEA 1970-; *office:* Main Street Elem Schl 704 Main St Brookhaven PA 19015

JOHNSON, WILLIAM CARTER,II, Assoc Professor of Biology; *b:* Wakefield, RI; *m:* Catherine Watts; *c:* Eleanor Chase, William Carter III; *ed:* Univ of RI (BS) Zoology 1969, (PHD) Oceanography 1980; *cr:* Univ of RI Asst Prof of Chem 1979-88; Comm Coll of RI Assoc Prof of Bio 1988-; *ai:* NEA 1988-; *office:* Community College of RI 400 East Ave Warwick RI 02886

JOHNSON, WILLIAM LEANDER, 8th Grade Teacher; *b:* Baltimore, MD; *m:* Lorraine Ann Williams; *c:* Alison, Adam, Jay, Maggie; *ed:* Prince Georges CC (AA) Scndry Ed 1980; Salisbury St Univ (BA) His 1982; *cr:* Frederick Douglass HS Ftbl & Wrestling Coach 1982-; St Columba Sch 6th & 8th Grd Tchr 1983-; *ai:* NCEA 1982-; MSFCA 1988-; MWA 1992-; Dion Johnson Comm 1993-; Univ of Md Excl in Tchng Awd 1995; *office:* Saint Columba Schl 7800 Livingston Rd Oxon Hill MD 20745

JOHNSON, WILLIAM M.,JR., High School Health Ed Teacher; *b:* Concord, MA; *m:* Nanci Rockwell; *c:* William III, Meghan; *ed:* Seton Hall Univ (BS) Hlth Sci 1972, (MA) Scndry Ed 1973, (MA) Adolescent Psych 1973; 9 Credit Hrs Drug Ed Yale Univ; 12 Credit Hrs Sexuality Ed Southern CT; *cr:* Fairfield HS 9th-12th Grd Hlth Ed Tchr 22 Yrs; *ai:* Var Sftbl Coach 22 Yrs; Project Reach Adv; Townwide Family Life Prof Comm; LEA 1973-; NEA 1973-; Town of Fairfield Bd of Rec 1988-, Chm; *home:* 88 Rhoda Ave Fairfield CT 06430

JOHNSON-FOSTER, HYACINTH CARMEN, Upper Schl Sci Tchr & Chprsn; *b:* St Ann, Jamaica W I; *m:* Linton A.; *c:* Trudy, Gregg; *ed:* Univ of West Indies at Jamaica (BSC) Chem, Biochemistry 1974; Univ of West Indies Ed Tchng of Bio 1978; NY Cert in Bio 7th-12th Grds; *cr:* Kingston Coll, Queens HS Bio Tchr 1974-82; St Hughes HS Biological Sci Coord 1982-85; Walden Lincoln Schl 4th-12th Grd Sci Tchr 1985-91; Womens Ctr Brooklyn Coll Sci, Engrng Instr 1990-; Brooklyn Friends Schl Upper, Mid Schl Tchr, Sci Chprsn 1991-; *ai:* Sr Acad Adv; NAIS, ATIS 1985-; NYBTA 1986-; Vanderveer United Meth Church 1987-; *office:* Brooklyn Friends Schl 375 Pearl St Brooklyn NY 11201*

JOHNSON-MILLER, RUTH A., English & Reading Teacher; *b:* Columbus, OH; *m:* Leigh M.; *ed:* OH UNiv (BA) Eng, Lit 1978; 45 Credit Hrs Eng Cert; 20 Credit Hrs Rdng Cert; *cr:* Liberty Union MS Educl Aide 1975-77, Tchr 1978-; *ai:* Spelling Bee; Cmptr Lab; OEA, NEA 1978-, Pres 1980, Exec Comm 1978-; Young Farmer's 1987-, Cncl; *office:* Liberty Union MS 600 W Washington St Baltimore OH 43105

JOHNSTON, BARBARA A., Band Director; *b:* Warren, OH; *m:* Dennis A.; *c:* Jessica, Sarah; *ed:* Kent St Univ (BM) Music Ed 1972; Cleveland Inst of Music (MM) Performance 1977; North TX St Univ (PHD) Music Ed 1986; *cr:* Hayes Jr HS Gen Music Dir 1972-75; State Street MS Band Dir 1977-81; Vivian Field Jr HS Band Dir 1981-89; Lisha Kill MS Band Dir 1989-; *ai:* Blue & Gray Civil War Band Dir 1994-; MENC 1992-; NYSBDA 1995-; NYSTA; Article Pub; 1st Place Intnl Chamber Music Competition Belgium 1973; VIP Tchr Awd Carrollton TX; *home:* 17 Rosemary Dr Schenectady NY 12304

JOHNSTON, CHRISTIAN THOMAS, Mathematics Teacher; *b:* Levittown, PA; *ed:* Temple Univ (BS) Math Ed 1993; Villanova Univ Masters of Tchng Math Prgm; *cr:* Wissahickon HS HS Math Tchr 1994; Wassahickon MS Math Tchr 1994-; *ai:* HS Girls & MS Boys Coach; NCTM 1993-; NEA, PSEA, WEA, PCTM, ATMOPAV 1994-; US Soccer Coaching Org 1995-; US Soccer Certified Coach Level C; *office:* Wissahickon MS 500 Houston Rd Ambler PA 19002*

JOHNSTON, CHRISTINE, Business Education Teacher; *b:* Altoona, PA; *m:* Michael; *c:* Nickolas, Kayla; *ed:* IN Univ of PA (BS) Bus Ed 1987; St

Francis Coll (MED); *cr:* Altoona Area HS Bus Tchr 1989-92; Roosevelt Jr HS Bus Tchr 1992-; *ai:* Yrbk & FBLA Adv; NEA 1987-; PSEA 1987-; *office:* Roosevelt Jr HS 1501 7th Ave Altoona PA 16602

JOHNSTON, CHRISTINE LYNNE, Personal Care Teacher; *b:* Philadelphia, PA; *ed:* Mansfield Univ (BS) Home Ec Ed 1982; Edinboro Univ Grad Credits Toward Early Chldhd MS; *cr:* Corry HS Home Ec Tchr 1983-85; Inn at Lambertville Station Gen Mgr, Conf Coord 1985-87; Corry HS Home Ec, Personal Care Tchr 1987-; *ai:* Steering, Stud Act Day, Acad Awds Banquet Comms; Action Planning, TIPS Ldr; Home Ec Dept Head; Amer Home Ec Assn 1995-; NAEYC 1992-; Red Cross 1993-, Bd Mem; Erie Cty Extension 1995-, Bd Mem; *home:* 317 Wright St Corry PA 16407

JOHNSTON, DOROTHY CARR, Resource Center Teacher; *b:* Janesville, WI; *m:* Dennis; *c:* Kristin, Ami; *ed:* Univ of WI (BA) Elem Ed 1962; Kean Coll (MS) Learning Disabilities 1991; Attnd Univ of CO at Denver, Univ of CO at Boulder; *cr:* Jefferson Cty Schls Fifth Grd Tchr 1962-67, Resource Tchr 1967-68; Schl Dist of Chathams Resource Ctr Tchr 1979-; *ai:* NEA, NJEA, Assn Chatham Tchrs 1979-; *office:* Chatham MS 480 Main St Chatham NJ 07928*

JOHNSTON, DWIGHT DAVIS, Physics I & II Instructor; *b:* McKeesport, PA; *m:* Barbara Ann; *c:* Joseph, Erica, Dwight; *ed:* Penn St Univ (BS) Scndry Ed 1970, (MED) Ed 1976; Post Grad Work in Nuclear Concepts & Nutrition Sci; *cr:* Juniata Cty Schl Dist Chem & Physics Instr 1970-89; Spring Grove Area Schl Dist Physics I & II Instr 1989-; *ai:* Acad Comp Team Adv; Dist Tech, Strategies Planning Comms; NEA & PSEA 1973-; Local & Natl Tech Comms; NSTA Convention Presenter; Future Search Comm Participant; *home:* 345 Pulaski Pl Dallastown PA 17313

JOHNSTON, JAMIE, Assoc Professor of Woodworking; *b:* New York City, NY; *m:* Sondra Bogdonoff; *c:* Caitlin, Nemo, Jake; *ed:* Unif of Denver (BS) Eng 1970-; *cr:* Coll of the Atlantic Woodworking Fac 1977-81; ME Coll of Art Woodworking Fac 1984-; *ai:* Maintains Studio Focusing on Commission Furniture, Designing.

JOHNSTON, JEFFREY FRANCIS, Associate Professor of Arch; *b:* Brooklyn, NY; *c:* Rachel; *ed:* Univ of Notre Dame (BA) Arch 1971; Rome Stud Prgm U of ND Rome Italy 1969-70; Photography Nikon Schl; Printmaking Alfred Univ; *cr:* SUNY Instr 1974-80, Adj Lecturer 1981-83, 1988-95, Assoc Prof 1996-; *ai:* Enrollments Mngmt, Campus Beautification Task Force; Fac Senate, Exec Comm; Prof Dev Comm; ABX Adv; UUP; Wellsville Arts Cncl 1995-; Juror Arts Cncl Show of Architectural Perspective Drawings; *office:* S U N Y Coll Of Tech At Alfred 412C Engineering Bldg Alfred NY 14802

JOHNSTON, JEFFREY M., Fifth Grade Teacher; *b:* Toledo, OH; *ed:* Bowling Green St Univ (BS) Elem Ed 1985; Ashland Univ (BS) Curr, Instruction 1993; *cr:* Bowling Green City Schls Fifth Grd Tchr 1987-; *ai:* Stu Cncl, Yrbk Adv; Comm, Post-Vention Teams; PTO, Cmptr Tech Rep; BGEA 1987-, Rep; NSTA 1994-; *office:* Conneaut Elem Schl 542 Haskins Rd Bowling Green OH 43402*

JOHNSTON, JOANNE SANTARONE, 7th Grade Teacher; *b:* Philadelpha, PA; *m:* Anthony Joseph; *c:* Mary Beth Conricode, Craig; *ed:* Chestnut Hill Coll (BA) Eng 1963; Temple Univ 24 Post Grad Credit Hrs; *cr:* Stetson Jr HS 7th Grd Eng Tchr 1963-64; Jacksonville Jr HS 6th Grd Tchr 1964-65; George Washington HS 8th-9th Eng Tchr 1966-68; William Tennent Intermediate 9th-10th Grd Eng Tchr 1977-79; St Joseph St Robert Schl 7th Grd Tchr 1979-; *ai:* Lang Arts Coord; Stu Lectors Coord; New Fac Mentor; NCEA 1979-; Child Home Comm Inc 1987-, Sec, Consultant; Parish Cncl 1992-, Bd Mem; Parish Lector 1985-; Schl Parish Eucharistic Minister 1990-; Outstdng Cath Edctr 1987; Achvmnt in Ed Awd 1990; *office:* Saint Joseph-Saint Robert Schl 1701 Columbia Ave Warrington PA 18976

JOHNSTON, JOY BUTERBAUGH, Music Teacher; *b:* Chambersburg, PA; *m:* Norma Lee; *c:* Ahna Lee, Rebecca Joy Hoffer, Seth Jared, Benjamin Paul; *ed:* Bob Jones Univ (BA) Chrstn Ed 1972; *cr:* Ind Gospel Mission Missionary 1974-79; Bapt World Missions Missionary 1979-94; Homeschooled 4 Children Korea 1979-87; Kimcheon Korea Nurses Coll 1981; Lighthouse Bapt Acad Kndgtn Tchr 1987-88; Liberty Fundamental Bapt Acad 1st-3rd Grd Tchr 1990-91; Mt Zion Chrstn Acad Music Tchr; *ai:* Girls Bsktbl, Cheerleading Coach; KCEA All St Choir, Summer Camp Spon; Yrbk Coord; KCEA St Fine Arts Competition Spon & Coord; Annual Drama Presentation Dir; Church Pianist.

JOHNSTON, KELLIE E., Resource Room English Teacher; *b:* Jersey City, NJ; *ed:* Jersey City St Coll (BA) Spcl Ed 1983, (MA) Cnslng 1994; *cr:* James F Ferris HS Spcl Ed Tchr 1984-; *ai:* Asst Cross Cntry & Track Coach; *office:* James J Ferris HS 35 Colgate St Jersey City NJ 07302

JOHNSTON, KIP ANNE MC CLAURY, Elem Instrumental & Vocal Tchr; *b:* Tarentum, PA; *m:* John Wesley Jr.; *c:* Gabrielle; *ed:* Seton Hill Coll (BS) Music Ed 1979; 12 Credit Hrs Indiana Univ of PA; *cr:* South Butler Co Schl Dist Elem Instrumental, Voc Tchr 1982-; *ai:* Private Lesson Instr; Church Orch; Handbell, Flute Choir Dir; PSEA 1982-; *office:* South Butler Cty Schl Dist PO Box 657 Knoch Rd Saxonborg PA 16001

JOHNSTON, LYNNE LATTER, High School Language Arts Tchr; *b:* Pittsburgh, PA; *m:* Eric R.; *c:* Michelle, Brent; *ed:* OH Univ (BSEd) Eng-Suma Cum laude 1964; Cleveland St Univ (MAEd) Curr, His Instruction 1995; *cr:* Midpark HS Eng, Rdng, Drama Tchr 1964-65; Scribner Jr HS Eng, Drama Tchr 1965-67; Vly Forge HS Eng Tchr 1983-; *ai:* Hugh O'Brien Yth Fnd Adv; NEA, OEA, NCTE 1983-; Perry Lib Bd 1994-; *office:* Perry HS 1 Success Blvd Perry OH 44081

JOHNSTON, M. PAMELA, Elementary Librarian; *b:* Greensburg, PA; *m:* Larry S.; *ed:* St Francis Coll (BS) Elem Ed 1974; *cr:* Hempfield Area Schl Dist Elem Tchr 1974-82, Elem Librn 1982-; *ai:* Hempfield Area Tech Comm Elem Rep; NEA, PSEA, HAEA 1974-; Westmoreland Cty Assn Schl Librns 1982-, Sec; *office:* Stanwood Elem Schl Box 255 Arona Rd New Stanton PA 15672

JOHNSTON, PAMELA KUHN, Biology Teacher; *b:* Hagerstown, MD; *m:* Charles Henry Jr.; *c:* Tina Johnston McVicker; *ed:* Shepherd Coll (BA) Scndry Ed 1974; Hood Coll (MA) Environmental Bio 1983; *cr:* Williamsport High Bio Tchr 1974-; *ai:* Stu Assistance, Schl Improvement Teams; FCA Spon; Envirothon Coach; WCTA 1974-, Union Rep 4 Yrs; MABT 1974-, OBT Semi Finalist; NABT; Black Rock Bible Church 1970-; *office:* Williamsport HS 5 S Clifton Dr Williamsport MD 21795

JOHNSTON, SANDRA, Third Grade Teacher; *b:* Worcester, MA; *ed:* Wheelock Coll (BS) Early Chldhd Ed 1977, (MS) Educl Ldrshp 1979; Tchr Effectiveness Trng; Literacy Vols; *cr:* U of MA Adult Literacy Vol Prgm Dir, Acad Adv 1979-84; Roxbury Children's Svc Family Support Network Dir 1984-85; Mather Elem Schl 1st, 3rd, 5th Grd, Chptr 1 Rdng Tchr 1986-; *ai:* Schl African Heritage Comm; African Heritage Assembly Prgm Dir, Writer, Narrator; Boston Tchrs Union 1986-; Black Edctrs Alliance MA, Chprsn Tchrs Comm; Sidney Fnd Fellow; Impact II Awardee Twice; *office:* Mather Elem Schl 1 Parish St Dorchester MA 02121*

JOHNSTON, STEVEN ERIC, Regents Earth Science Teacher; *b:* Lakeland, FL; *m:* Lisa; *c:* Marcus, Katrina, Jessica; *ed:* NY St Univ at Fredonia (BS) Geology 1978; Univ of ME (MS) Geochemistry 1981; *cr:* Brocton Cntrl Schl Earth Sci Tchr 1981-85; Prince Alfred Coll Physics & Math Tchr 1986-91; Falconer Cntrl Schl Regents Earth Sci Tchr 1991-; *ai:* Var Girls Tennis Coach; Sci Tchrs of NY St 1993-; Amer Astronomical Soc 1994-; 7 Sci Publications; Amer Astronomical Soc Tchr Resource Agent; NY St & Australia Tchr Exch Pgm; *office:* Falconer Central Schl East Main St Falconer NY 14733

JOHNSTON, THOMAS EDWARD, Volunteer Coordinator; *b:* Cheverly, MD; *ed:* Working Toward Psych Degree at Univ of MD at College Park; *cr:* US Navy Airman 1990-92; Vol MD Natl Svc Participant 1993; City of Bowie Vol Coord 1993-; *ai:* Bsktbl Referee; Self Help & Resource Exchange; Governors Citation; Citizens Concerned for Cleaner Cty 1993-95; Served in Desert Shield, Desert Storm & Operation Provide Comfort; Nom for Outstanding Pub Sector Employee; *office:* City of Bowie 2614 Kenhill Dr Bowie MD 20715

JOHNSTONE, TIMOTHY LEON, Mathematics Teacher; *b:* Dover, OH; *m:* Carolyn Anne Rainsburg; *c:* Marianne; *ed:* Univ of Akron (BA) Mechanical Engineering Tech 1982, (MS) Tech Ed 1986; *cr:* Timken Co Dev Expediter 1974-79; Stark Tech Coll Part-time Physics Instr 1983-; Sandy Valley HS Math Instr 1989-; *ai:* Sci Club, Card Club Adv; Jr High Cross Cntry Coach; OEA, NEA 1989-; *office:* Sandy Valley HS Rt 2 Box 100 Magnolia OH 44643

JOINER, DENNIS F., English Dept Head & Teacher; *b:* Colver, PA; *m:* Lynn Allen; *c:* Christopher, Jeremy; *ed:* Indiana Univ of PA (BS) Scndry Ed 1969; Masters Equivalency; *cr:* Delhaas HS Eng Tchr, Tchr of Gifted 1969-81; F. D. Roosevelt Jr HS Eng Tchr, Hum Dept Head 4 Yrs 1981-; *ai:* Rdng Olympics Spon; Bristol Twp Tchrs Assn, PSEA, NEA 1969-.

JOINES, KEITH PERRYMAN, Guidance Counselor; *b:* New York, NY; *m:* Agnes Louise Cruse; *c:* Keith II; *ed:* Univ of Bridgeport (BA) Span 1970, (MS) Counseling 1972, (CAS) Counseling 1983; *cr:* Harding Prep Prgm Job Dev Cnslr 1972-75; Carver Fnd Deputy Dir 1975-76; East Side MS Guidance Coord 1976-81; Bassick HS Guidance Cnslr 1981-; Housatonic C T Coll Cnslr 1983-94; CETA-SYEP Dir 1977-81; *ai:* NHS Adv; Stu Assistance Team; NEA, CEA 1980-; BEA 1980-, Scndry VP; AACD, CACD, CSCA 1981-; AAUP, CCCC 1985-; CALAME 1986-, Awd 1988; NEACAC 1989-; Save Our Babies Comm; Civic Duty Awd; Regnl Coll Bd Presenter; In-Svc Trainer; Big Bros/Big Sis; Comm Ser Awd; Who's Who Among Amer Edu 1992-; *home:* 100 Weaver St Torrington CT 06790

JOLES, LISA, Business Teacher; *b:* Hornell, NY; *ed:* Nazareth Coll of Rochester (BS) Bus Admn 1990, (MS) Bus, Distributive Ed 1995; Amer Sing Lang LoGuidace BOCES NYS; *cr:* Clymer Cntrl Schl Bus, Elem Cmptr Tchr 1990-; *ai:* FBLA, Yrbk Bus Staff Adv; Stu Sec, Job Shadow Prgm, Amer Enterprises Assembly, MS Act Night Coord; Tech Comm; Christmas Tea Chmprsn; NEA, NEANY, Chautauqua Co BTA, NYS Bus Tchrs Assn, Clymer Educ Assoc 1990-; FBLA 1983-, NYS Bd of Trustees 1993-, St Ofcr Adv 1993-, NYS Adv of Yr 1994, Gold Key Awds 1993-95; Led FBLA to 1995 Chapter of Yr, Natl 1st Pl Awd Partnership with Bus Project 1994, 17 Chapter Awds 1993-, at St Level, Natl 9th Pl Awd In Partnership with Bus; *office:* Clymer Central Schl PO Box 580 Clymer NY 14724

JOLIN, MARTIN JOHN, Asst Professor of Theatre Arts; *b:* Lowell, MA; *ed:* Vesper George Schl of Art (AA) Design 1966; Boston Conservatory (BFA) Music Theatre 1976; Univ of MD (MA) Speech, Theatre 1978; Spec Ed Boston Univ; Ed MA Coll of Art; *cr:* Howard Univ Asst Prof 1979-; North VA Comm Coll Instr 1981-82; Prince Georges Coll Instr 1981-86; Montgomery Coll Instr 1983-88; *ai:* Adv; Coach; Dir; Curr Comm Chair; Exec, Awds Comms; AGUA 1986-; NATS 1983-; WA Hospice Death, Dying Cnslr; Episcopal Caring Cap Hill Day Schl, Donation of Boat Cruise Entertainment; Prof Achvmt, Outstdng Svc to Stdnts Merit Awd 1992-93; *home:* 713 D St SE Washington DC 20003*

JOLLES, MITCHELL I., Physics & Mathematics Teacher; *b:* Bronx, NY; *ed:* Polytechnic Inst of Brooklyn (BS) Aerospace Engrng 1973, (MS) Applied Mechanics 1973; VA Polytechnic Inst (PHD) Engrng Mechanics 1976; *cr:* VA Polytechnic Inst Instr 1973-76; Univ of Notre Dame Asst Prof 1976-79; Univ of MO Assoc Prof 1979-82; Naval Rsrch Lab Rsrch Scientist 1982-88; Widener Univ Prof 1988-; Strath Haven HS Physics, Math Tchr 1996-; *ai:* Sigma Xi; Tau Beta Pi; Phi Kappa Phi; Dow Outstdng Young Fac Awd; Ralph R. Teetor Awd; Alan BErman Rsrch Publication Awd; Jimmie Hamilton Awd.

JOLLIFF, SHARON KAY, Kindergarten Teacher; *b:* Lima, OH; *m:* Jack Lee; *c:* Christine, Mark; *ed:* Bluffton Coll (BA) Elem Ed 1983; Attnd Univ of Findlay, Univ of Toledo, Bowling Green Univ & Ashland Coll; *cr:* Arlington Local Schls Kndgtn Tchr 1983-; *ai:* AFT 1983-, Past Treas 2 Yrs; Phi Delta Soc; Hancock Cty Schls Outstanding Educator; Jennings Scholar Awd; *home:* PO Box 425 Arlington OH 45814*

JOLLY, PEGGY SHUPERT, First Grade Teacher; *b:* Seaman, OH; *m:* Dean L.; *c:* John Dane, Brooke Marie, Mark Dean; *ed:* OH St Univ (BA) Home Ed Ed 1978; Univ of Dayton (MS) Ed Admin 1985; Miami of Oxford 15 Hrs; Oh Univ 20 Hrs; Wilmington Coll 15 Hrs; *cr:* Waverly HS Home Ed Tchr 1978-80; Como-Pickton Schl Dist Title, 3rd Grd Tchr 1981-83; Bright Local Schls Kndgtn Tchr 1983-90, 4th Grd Tchr 1990-93, K & 1st Grd Tchr 1993-; *ai:* Jr Class Adv Waverly 1979-80; OEA; NEA; Sugar Tree Ridge Church of Christ 1986-; *office:* Concord Elem Schl 2281 State Route 136 Hillsboro OH 45133

JONES, ADELE LISA, Math Teacher; *b:* Seaford, DE; *ed:* Univ of DE (BS) Math Ed 1983; *cr:* Milford HS Math Tchr 1983-84; Indian River HS Math Tchr 1984-90; Sussex Cntrl HS Math Tchr 1990-; *ai:* Adv Chrldng Ftbl 1983-87, 1989, Bsktbl 1983-84, Soph Class; NEA 1983-, DSEA Exec Bd; DE Cncl Tchrs of Math 1985-; *home:* 23 Heather Dr Lewes DE 19958*

JONES, ALAN DAVID, Choral Music Director; *b:* Columbus, OH; *m:* Joanne; *ed:* Capital Univ (BM) Music Theory, Performance 1977; Eastman Schl of Music (MM) Music Ed 1980; 10 Credit Hrs; *cr:* Downtown United Prebyn Church Music Resource Person 1980-; Spencerport HS Vocal Music Dir 1980-; *ai:* MENC 1980-, St Chair, Vocal Jazz; NYSSMA 1980-, St Chprsn Vocal Jazz 1991-92, Festival Chprsn Vocal Jazz 1994-, All-St Vocal Jazz Adjudicator 1992; Rochester Philharmonic Orch & Brockport Sympony Soloist; Opening Act Bill Cosby, Rich Little, Jackie Mason; *office:* Spencerport HS 2707 Spencerport Rd Spencerport NY 14559

JONES, ALAN ROBERT, Health & Physical Ed Teacher; *b:* Philadelphia, PA; *m:* Meaghan E.; *ed:* Rowan Coll of NJ (BA) Health, PE 1993; *cr:* Gillespie MS Tchr of Hlth, PE 1994-; *ai:* Fund Raising Coord; IM Ftbl, Sftbl; Panther Wrestling Club; Asst Wrestling Coach Frankford HS; Police Ath League Vol; AAHPERD 1993-; NWCA 1996; Patberg Awd Svc to Wrestling; *home:* 8112 Verree Rd Apt B-201 Philadelphia PA 19111

JONES, ANN L., Teacher of Gifted Talented; *b:* Ashland, PA; *m:* Harry B. Perkins; *c:* Jennifer Ann Munro Legacy, Jessica Frances Munro Savoie; *ed:* Salm St Coll (BS) Elem Ed, Sci 1976; Lesley Coll (MED) GATE 1985; Continuing Ed in Prof Dev Courses; *cr:* Merrimac Pub Schls Elem Tchr 1976-84, GATE Tchr 1984-91; Groveland Pub Schls Elem Tchr 1976-84; Dedham Pub Schls GATE Tchr 1991-; *ai:* Act Spon; Comm Television Productions for Ed, Advocacy; NEA, MTA, MA, AIP 1984-; NCTA, DEA 1992-; Dedham Ed Fnd 1993-; Joppa Jazz Dance Co 1980-; Master Tchr; MA Discretionary Grant; *office:* Dedham Pub Schls Whiting Ave Dedham MA 02026*

JONES, BESSIE MILEY, Tech Coord & Computer Teacher; *b:* Greensboro, NC; *c:* Lailah, Aliyah, Khalilah; *ed:* Jersey City St Coll (BA) Fine Arts 1986; *cr:* Luth Parochial Schl Art, Rel Tchr 1983-85; St Anthony Elem Schl 6th Grd Tchr 1985-86; St Rocco Elem Schl Tchr 1990-91; St Aloysius Elem Schl Tchr,Tech Coord 1991-; *ai:* Sci Fair Coord; Patrol, Newsletter Adv; NCTA, NCEA 1990-; Hall of Fam Svc to Yth; *hom* Parkview Ter Hillside NJ 07205*

JONES, BETH CHRIS, English Teacher; *b:* Chillicothe, OH; *m* L.; *c:* Kyle D., Derek Allen; *ed:* OH St Univ (BS) Ed, Eng 19 Chillicothe City Schls 9-12 Grd Eng Instr 1980-84; Union Sciot 9-12 Grd Eng Instr 1990-; *ai:* Coach Yth Bsktbl; NCTE 1993-; *ho* Northfork Dr Chillicothe OH 45601

JONES, BRADLEY K., US His & Amer Govt Teacher; *b:* Pauldin *m:* Stacie A. Arn; *ed:* Ball St Univ (BS) Soc Stud 1991; Post Grad V Educl Admin at Univ of Dayton; *cr:* Lincolnview HS Soc Stud Tchr *ai:* Jr Var Bsbl Coach; Ath Ticket Mgr; OH HS Bsbl Coaches Assn *office:* Lincolnview Jr Sr HS 15945 Middle Point Rd Van Wert OH

JONES, BRYAN DAVID, Biology Teacher; *b:* Philadelphia, PA; *m* Barry Packard; *ed:* Brown Univ (BA) Biochemistry 1989; *cr:* Merc Acad Bio Tchr 1989-92; Maret Schl Bio Tchr 1992-; *ai:* MS Schedu Newspaper Adv; Peer Facilitation Pgrm Trainer; NSTA 1992- Anthony Trust of RI 1989-, Nom Chair; 1991 Johnson Ch Outstanding Young Tchrs; *office:* Maret Schl 3000 Cathedral A Washington DC 20008

JONES, CARLTON LEE, Tech Coord; *b:* Piqua, OH; *m:* Yvo Carriker; *c:* Leah, Carrie, Kelsey, Amy; *ed:* William Penn Coll (BA & PE 1975; Wright St Univ (ME) Cmptr Ed 1988; Attnd Univ of St Univ & Miami Univ, Oxford OH; *cr:* Williamsburg HS Math & Prog 1975-84; Ansonia HS Math & Cmptr Prog 1984-; Ansonia H Tchr Leader for Project Discovery; *ai:* HS Girls Track Coach; NEA OH Ed Assn 1984-; OH Cncl of Tchrs of Math 1987-; Phi Delta 1991-; Tchr of Yr Darke Cty 1990; Martha Holden Jenning's S 1989-90; Participating in OH St's C2PC & TRANSIT Prgms which Using Tech in the Math ClassroomOCTM West Reg Outstndng Sec Math Tchr; *office:* Darke Cty Edu Service Ctr 5279 Educati Greenville OH 45331

JONES, CAROL A., Fifth Grade Teacher; *b:* Granville, NY; *ed* Chester St Univ (BS) Elem Ed 1970; Temple Univ (MS) Rdng 1978 Specialist Cert 1978; 45 Credit Hrs Beyond MS in Ed; *cr:* Delcrof Schl Tchr 1970-; *ai:* NEA, PSEA, Southeast Delco Ed Assn 1970-; Delcroft Elem Schl School Ln Folcroft PA 19032

JONES, CAROLE HUEY, Jr High Math Teacher; *b:* Warren, O Kevin H.; *c:* Chad Ronyetz, Connie Ronyetz; *ed:* Ashland Coll (BS Ed 1971; Post Grad Stud Youngstown St Univ, Kent St Univ, Ashlan Drake Univ, Fresno Pacific Coll; *cr:* Strongsville City Schls Eler 1971-80, Elem Tutor 1989-94, Jr HS Math Tchr 1994-; *ai:* Teens Time to Care Adv; Hnr Soc Comm; NEA 1994-; OH Cncl Tchrs o 1995-; Brunswick United Meth Church 1984-, Ed Chprsn, Woman Jennings Scholar; *office:* Albion Jr HS 13200 Pearl Rd Strongsvi 44136

JONES, CARRYE BOWERS, Gftd & Talented Resource Tc Louisville, KY; *m:* Franklin F. Jr.; *c:* Tami K., Margaret Thomas, F III, Winston K., Carolyn B.; *ed:* Balwin-Wallace Coll (BA) Eng Howard Univ (MAT) Early Chldhd Ed 1986; Univ of CT GAT Dynamic Presentations Trng; Tech, Ldrshp Trng Courses; Conflict Grantsmanship; *cr:* Univ of LA Dean of Girls Upward Bound 1969; Coll Womens Annexes, Lang Houses Dir 1968-69; Rochester A Performing Arts Dir of Preschool Drama, Dance Instr 1980-84; H Cty Pub Schls GATE Resource Tchr 1986-; *ai:* Disability Awarene Coord; Cultural Arts Chair; 20th Anniversary Celebration Chair; Advy Comm; Schl Planning & Mngmt & GATE Liason; Scout Ld Tchr Mentor; Hlth Cadre; Spec Projects Consultant; Kappa Delta Pi Phi Delta Kappa 1988-, Present Rsrch; NEA, HCEA 1987-; The Lin 1972-, Pres, Sec; Jack & Jill of Amer Inc 1974-, Pres, VP, Comm Ch of Dir Nation Capital 1990-, Sec; Area United Way; KY Dance Cncl Urban League Outstdng Svc Awd; Preschool Performing Arts Prgm Pub Article 1990.*

JONES, CHRISTIAN, Math Tchr, Dept Chm, Asst Prin; *b:* Brookly *ed:* Manhattan Coll (BA) Math 1951, (MA) Math 1956; Natl Sc Courses NY Univ, Brooklyn Coll; *cr:* Sacred Heart Schl 6th-8th Gr 1947-57; Bishop Loughlin HS Math Tchr 1957-72; Chrstn Brothers HS Math Tchr 1972-; *ai:* Math Team Moderator; Asst Prin Scheduling; Cath HS Math League Pres; NCTM 1962-; Mathematica of Amer 1965-; Chrstn Brothers 1943-, Golden Jubilee; *office:* Ch Brothers Acad 850 Newman Springs Rd Lincroft NJ 07738

JONES, CHRISTINE, Spanish Teacher; *b:* Charleroi, PA; *c:* C Marie, Carrie Anne; *ed:* CA Univ of PA (BS) Ed, Span 1972; PA S Cert; *cr:* Belle Vernon Area Tchr 1985-86; Van HS Tchr 1986-87 Cntrl Tchr 1987-89; Belle Vernon Area Tchr 1989-; *ai:* Interact Club Lang Club Spons; Belle Vernon AFT 1990-, Pres; Rotary Club of Vernon 1991-; *office:* Belle Vernon Area HS RR 2 Crest Ave Belle PA 15012*

JONES, COLLEEN O'BRIEN, Fourth Grade Teacher; *b:* Easton, Edward; *c:* Erich; *ed:* Lycoming Coll (BA) Music, Elem Ed 198 Mansfield Twp Schl Dist Resource Room Aide 1980-81; Oxford Cnt Dist Compensatory Ed Tchr 1981-82; Diocese of Allentown Schl Fi Tchr 1982-87; Greenwich TWP Schl Dist Fourth Grd Tchr 198 Musical Theatre Singer; NJEA 1987-; NEA 1980-; PA Playhouse Sec, Play Rdng Chm; Children in Theatre Grant; Lycoming Coll Fellow; *office:* Stewartsville Elem Schl 642 S Main St Stewartsvi 08886

JONES, DALE RICHARD, Fourth Grade Teacher; *b:* Wilkes-Barr *m:* Sally Carew; *c:* Jessica, Heather; *ed:* Mansfield (BS) Ed 1971; Coll (MS) Ed 1976; *cr:* Hanover Area Tchr 24 Yrs; *ai:* NEA, 1972-.*

JONES, DAN ETHEL, Math Instr & Dept Chair; *b:* Milwaukee, Ronald B.; *c:* Ronald, Ramoan, Raphael; *ed:* Andrews Univ (BA) El 1968; George Washington Univ (MA) Hum Growth, Dev 1992; George Coll Admin Cert; Spec Ed Cert; Credit Hrs Cert In Mat Harmony Hall Elem Schl 5th Grd Tchr 1975-76; Samuel Chase Ele 5th Grd Tchr 1976-86; Valley View Elem Schl 6th Grd Tchr 1986-94; Hill MS Math Tchr, Chprsn 1994-; *ai:* Chair of Math Dept; Schl Pl Comm; Family Lie Chprsn Dir; MS Contact Person Co Math Me NEA, PGCEA, MEA 1975-; Church Bd Mem 1970; Schl Bd Chair Private Schl; Bd of Elders 1985-, First Women to Serve Office; Sp Bureau for Women 1994-; *home:* 400 Swan Creek Rd Fort MD 207

JONES, DAVID MEREDITH, Journalism Professor; *b:* Anderson, Mary Joan Marsh; *c:* Vincent, Yann; *ed:* Ball St Univ (BS) Jrnlsm (MA) Jrnlsm 1974; Univ of Pittsburgh (PhD) Higher Ed 1978; IN Uni of Law 40 credit Hrs; *cr:* Point Park Coll Prof 22 Yrs; Anderson Bu Newspaper Reporter 9 Yrs; US Army Comm Specialist 4.5 Yrs; *ai:* T Stud Comm; Comm in Informated Classroom; Soc Prof Journalists Kappa Tau Alpha, Jrnlsm Honorary 1974-; Articles Pub; *office:* Point Coll 201 Wood St Pittsburgh PA 15222*

JONES, DELORES DIRESE, Professor of Law; *b:* Lawrenceville, Clifton Brown; *c:* Ashley Brown; *ed:* Howard Univ (BA) Sociology, Just 1982; Rutgers Schl of Crim Just (MA) Criminal Justice 1985; R Law Newark (JD) Law 1986; Rugers Grad Schl (PHD) Criminal Just *cr:* Rutgers Univ Coll Tchng Assist 1985-86; Temple Univ Visiting Prof 1987-90; Rowan Coll Adjunct Tchr 1987-93; John Jay Coll Ass ai: Thurgood Marshall Schlsp, Womens Stud, Stu Judiciary, Stu ›n, Steering Comms; Diamond Flwshp Mentor; NJ St Bar Assn Sec; Acad CJ Scis 1989-, Various Comms; Amer Soc Criminology Various Comms; NSF Travel Awd; Ralph Bunche, Walter C. Russell ; Levine Law Scholar; *office:* John Jay Coll of Criminal Just 899 Ave New York NY 10019

S, DIANA BRANDT, Science Teacher & Coordinator; *b:* Mc ›rt, PA; *m:* William B.; *c:* Jay Mc Cusker, Patrick Mc Cusker, ›ret Mc Cusker; *ed:* Gettysburg Coll (BA) Bio, Gen Sci 1963; Univ sburgh Microbiology 1963-64; Univ of MD Ed 1978-81, Physics *cr:* Carnegie HS Bio Tchr 1964-65; St Francis Xavier Univ Bio Lab 965-66; St Paul's Way Scndry Modern Schl Bio Tchr 1966-67; ›le HS Bio Tchr 1978-80; Oxon Hill HS Sci Tchr, Coord 1980-; *ai:* ›ir Coord; Ski, Space Clubs Spon; NEA, MSTA, PGCEA 1978-, Fac ›ABT, MABT 1978-, Outstdng Tchr Nom; NSTA, MAST 1978-; PTA Cty, Schl Pres, Natl PTA, MD Golden Apple Awds; League of ›n Voters; WA Energy Soc, Amer Soc of Microbiologists Awds; Bio, Physics, Biochemistry, Lab Safety Curr Guides; *office:* Oxon Hill ›01 Leyte Dr Oxon Hill MD 20745*

S, DIANE CRIMMINS, Third Grade Teacher; *b:* Philadelphia, PA; ›rew; *ed:* Mansfield St Coll (BS) Elem Ed 1972; Post Grad Credits ›St Univ, Marywood Coll; *ai:* Soc Stud Comm; NEA, PSEA, PEA Gift of Time Awd 1992; Finalist in NJ Cooperating Tchr Awd 1993; ›Helping Kids 1993; *home:* 163 Hillcroft Way Newtown PA 18940

S, DIANE M., Biology Teacher; *ed:* Coll Misericordia (BS) Bio Wilkes Univ (MS) 1979; 25 Hrs Post Grad Stud Cmptr Sci & Bio; ›shop Hoban HS Bio Tchr 1974-; Luzerne Cty Comm Coll Bio Tchr ›34; Coll Misercordia Bio Tchr 1980-84; *ai:* Luzerne Co Sci Tchrs Sec 1979-83; Coll Misercordia Outstanding Tchr Awd 1984; *office:* ›Hoban HS 159 S Pennsylvania Ave Wilkes Barre PA 18701

S, DIANE WHEELER, Elem Vocal Music Specialist; *b:* Hanover, ›Don Alan; *c:* Edward Merryman, Heather Merryman; *ed:* Houghton ›BME) Music, Piano 1968; Western MD Coll (MLA) Liberal Arts ›shenandoah Univ Post Grad Work; *cr:* NY St Schl for Blind Tchr ›59; South Carroll HS Tchr, Choral Dir 1976-77; Mt Airy Elem Tchr ›34; William Winchester Elem Private Piano Tchr 1984-; *ai:* Guidance ; Childrens Chorus of Carroll Cty Co-Dir; NEA, MSTA 1979-; , MUSIK 1985-; MTNA, MSMTA 1980-, VP; Carroll Cty Arts Cncl Consultant; Carroll Cty Outstanding Tchr of Yr Nom 1995; *home:* ›Winters Dr Westminster MD 21157*

S, DONALD LEONARD,JR., Health Education Specialist; *b:* ›art, Germany; *m:* Jennifer Lin Harris; *c:* Matthew, Mark; *ed:* Malone ›BS) Hlth, PE 1981; Post Grad Ed at Ashland Coll; *cr:* Univ of ›urgh Head Cross Cntry Coach 1981-82; Palm Beach Cty Schls K-6 ›str 1982-85; Malone coll Asst Track Coach 1986-; Canton Cty Schls ›Ed Specialist 1996; *ai:* Young Life Ldrshp; NEA 1982-; Track Ath ›ess 1984-; Promise Keepers 1994-, Ambassador; *office:* Timken Sr ›1 Tuscarawas St W Canton OH 44702

S, DONNA MARLENE, German & English Teacher; *b:* Wiesbaden, ›any; *m:* Shawn M.; *ed:* Univ of MD (AA) 1989; Mansfield Univ Ger, Elem 1992; Univ of Scranton (MS) Eng 1997; *cr:* Elk Lake Schl ›ier, Eng Tchr 1992-; *office:* Elk Lake Schl Dist Box 103 Dimock PA

S, ELIZABETH MCGEE, Kindergarten Teacher; *b:* Staten Island, ›: Kenneth P.; *c:* Lisa M., William K.; *ed:* SUNY at Oneonta (BS) Chldhd Ed 1962; Post Grad Stud SUNY at Cortland; *cr:* Clinton CS ›d Tchr 1962-64; Westmoreland CS 1st Grd Tchr 1964-68, Pre-1st Grd 1968-76, 3rd Grd Tchr 1976-91, Kndgtn Tchr 1991-; *ai:* Elem Sci ›; Oneida Cty BOCES Sci Task Force; Shared Decision Making ›; AFT 1966-; Westmoreland Tchrs Assn 1966-, Sec; Clinton Jaycee ›74; Salvation Army Clinton Unit 1985-, Chprsn; Moses Foote ›ers 1986-, Pres & Sec.

S, ELLEN MEYER, Earth Science Teacher; *b:* Cambridge, MD; *m:* ›t S.; *c:* Lauren E., Kathryn M.; *ed:* Salisbury St Coll (BS) Phys Geog Salisbury St Univ (MED) Scndry Sci 1990; *cr:* Wicomico HS Earth ›Bio 1984-; *ai:* Environmental Club Adv; Instrl Support Team; ›nico Cty Ed Assoc 1984-, Nom Twice for Outstdng Tchr of the Yr; ›St Trackers Assoc 1984-; Bethesda UM Church 1980-; Tchr of the ›; Tchr Who Most Influenced My Life Article; *office:* Wicomico HS Ave Salisbury MD 21801

S, EUGENE, Bsktbl & Sftbl Coach; *b:* Taunton, MA; *m:* Patricia ›; *c:* Christine, Eugene, Timothy; *ed:* Bridgewater St (BS) Educ 1967; ›eastern Univ (MED) Curr & Inst Math 1976; Cert Guid & Cnslng 60 Addl Hrs; *cr:* Bridgewater Elem Schl 5th & 6th Grd ›Contained Tchr 1967-73; Bridgewater MS 5th-8th Grd Math Tchr ›83; Bridgewater Jr HS 7th & 8th Grd Math Tchr 1984-88; ›ewater Elem Schl Guid 1989-90; Bridgewater Jr HS 7th & 8th Skills ›990-; *ai:* Ski Club, IM Adv; Bsktbl, Sftbl Coach; Bridgewater Educ 1967-, Treas; Plymouth Cty Educ Assn 1967-, Bd of Dir, Citation; ›chrs Assn, NEA 1967-; Finance Comm 1980-; Little League 1977-, ›reas; Hockey League 1977-, Bd of Dir; Phi Delta Kappa; Kappa Delta ›*fice:* Bridgewater Jr HS 200 South St Bridgewater MA 02324

S, EUGENE,JR., Professor of Biology; *b:* Atlanta, GA; *m:* Sarah ›beth; *c:* Dwayne E., Jocelyn B.; *ed:* DE St Coll (BS) Bio 1961; ›ard Univ (MS) Zoology 1968, (PHD) Zoology 1974; Hahnemann Med CYTO Tech in Allied Hlth; Cytotechologist Cert by ASCP 1963-; *cr:* ›Bd of Hlth Bacteriologist, Cytotech 3 Yrs; DE St Coll Asst Prof 1 ›V St Coll Asst Prof 1 Yr; Cheyney Univ of PA Prof 19 Yrs; *ai:* Hlth ›ed Professions Coord; Bio Club Adv; Sponsored for Credit Sickle Disease Wkshp for Area Elem, HS Tchrs, Hlth Care Providers; ›CP; NEA 1961-; AFSCUF 1975-; Commonwealth of PA Univ ›gists 1976-, VP 1977-78, Pres 1986-87; Kent Cty Affirmative Action ›n 1993-; Pre Med Comm 1978-, Chprsn; Stu Orgs Awds; Howard Univ ›n Summers Biomedical Rsrch in Hypertension, Food & Drug Admin ›Awds 1981-88; *office:* Cheyney Univ Of PA Box 177 Cheyney PA ›9*

ES, EVELYN I., Guidance Counselor; *ed:* Hofstra Univ (BA) Elem ›MS) Cnslr Ed; Ed Admin Coll of New Rochelle; *cr:* Elem Ed Tchr ›77; Uniondale FSD Elem Ed Tchr 1977-90, Guid Cnslr 1990-; *ai:* ›p Club, Friends, Helpers Club Adv; Big Brothers, Big Sisters Adv 3 ›Uniondale Tchrs Assn 1977-; Nassau Cnslrs Assn 1990-; Delta Sigma ›1980-, Recording Sec; Cntrl Nassau Bus & Prof Women 1981-; ›ns Meml; Grand Ave PTA Awd 1985-86; *office:* Turtle Hook Jr HS ›alem Ave Uniondale NY 11553*

ES, EVELYN (SHEA), Dept Chairperson & Eng Tchr; *b:* Barnesboro, ›: Mike K.; *ed:* IN Univ of Pa (BS) Eng 1967, (BS) Fr 1967; Grad Wrk ›St Univ; *cr:* T. Roosevelt Jr HS Fr Tchr 1967-82, Eng Tchr 1982-90, Chair, Eng Tchr 1990-; *ai:* Chrldrs Spon 1968-80; Spelling Bee ›cipants Coach One Went to Ntl Spelling Bee WA DC; NEA, PA St EA ›; *office:* Theodore Roosevelt Jr HS 1501 7th Ave Altoona PA 16602

ES, FRED G., English Teacher; *b:* Jacksonville, FL; *m:* Judith S.; *c:* ›Lisa, Stephanie, Jefferson; *ed:* Univ of the South (BA) Eng 1960; Univ ›(PHD) Medieval Lang & Lit 1967; *cr:* Univ of FL Instr 1966-67; Of VA Asst Prof 1967; St Univ of NY at Binghamton Asst Prof ›73; John Bapt Meml HS Tchr 1983-; *ai:* Amer Guild of Organists 1973-, Dean; Assn of Anglican Musicians 1984-; Saint Johns Episcopal Church, Organist & Choirmaster 1980-.

JONES, GARY ROBERT, English Teacher; *b:* Schenectady, NY; *ed:* St Univ of NY Coll at Potsdam (BA) Eng 1972, (MA) Eng Lit 1974; *cr:* Burnt Hills-Ballston Lake HS Eng Tchr 1973-; *ai:* NYSUT, AFT 1973-; Hnr Soc Tchr of Yr 1978, 1983, 1988, 1993; *office:* Burnt Hills-Ballston Lake HS Lake Hill Rd Burnt Hills NY 12027

JONES, GEORJEAN RUSSLYN, Bio Tchr & Science Dept Chm; *b:* West Reading, PA; *ed:* Alvernia Coll (BS) Bio, Gen Sci 1976; Kutztown Univ (MED) Sec Ed 1981; *cr:* Nativity B.V.M. HS Bio Tchr 1976-, Sci Dept Chprsn 1981-, Acad Cncl 1981-, Act 195-90 Coord 1992-; *ai:* Stu Govt Adv; Coord for Nativity Sci Fair, Capital Area Sc & Engineering Fair, Earth Day Sci Fair; PA Jr Acad of Sci Schuylkull Cty Coord; NCEA 1976-; PSTA 1993-; NABT 1980-; Natl Wildlife Fed 1977-; Masters Thesis; Natl Congress on Cath Ed Regnl Congress; Mentor Tchr; Nom for Presidential Awds for Excl in Sci & Math Tchng; *home:* 5337 Allentown Pike Temple PA 19560

JONES, JAMES ALAN, Lecturer in Physical Education; *b:* Mansfield, OH; *m:* Amy M. Markley; *ed:* Mount Union Coll (BS) Cmptr Sci 1990; *cr:* Mount Union Coll Track, Cross Cntry Asst Coach 1990-92; Otterbein Coll Track, Cross Cntry Asst Coach 1992-94; Muskingum Coll Track, Cross Cntry Head Coach 1994-; *ai:* Div III Cross Cntry Coach's Assn 1994-; Div III Track Coach's Assn 1994-; Level I USATF Coach's Cert; *office:* Muskingum Coll New Concord OH 43762*

JONES, JAMES EDWARDS, Rel Prof & African Stud Chair; *b:* Baltimore, MD; *m:* Matiniah Yahya; *c:* Shakur, Abdul Nur, Khabirah, Haneefah, Ibrahmis, Muhammad, Abdul Hakim, James Jr., John, Damon, Tracy, Malik, Mustaffah; *ed:* Hampton Univ (BS) His, Scndry Ed 1968; Yale Divinity Schl (MAR) Rel 1983; Hartford Seminary (DMin) Rel, Islamic Stud 1989; Yale Law Schl, Yale Grad Schl 1968-70; LLB-MA Prgm Amer Stud, African Amer His; *cr:* New Hampshire Coll Campus Dir, Assoc Prof of Human Svcs 1979-89; Manhattanville Coll Assoc Prof of Rel, Af Stud Coord 1990-; *ai:* Muslim Stdnts Assn, Black Stdnts Union, Frosh Adv; Hispanic, African Heritage Month Comms; AAR 1990-, Mid Atlantic Region Exec Comm; Assn of Muslim Soc Scientists 1990-; Natl Trng Labs 1979-; Greater New Haven Dawah Comm 1987-, Coord; Islamic Prison Chaplain 1980-, Vol; Vol of Yr Awd; Congressional Citation for Comm Svc; Tchr of Yr Awd; Comm Svc Awds.*

JONES, JAMES PATRICK, Bio, Zoology & Genetics Tchr; *b:* Brooklyn, NY; *ed:* Adelphi Univ (BS) Bio, Sec Ed 1973; Hofstra Univ (MA) Sec Ed 1976; 60 Addl Credits Bio; *cr:* C. P. Weber Jr HS Sci Tchr 1973-83; P. D. Schreiber HS 1984-; *ai:* Frosh Bsktbl Coach; Adv Sci Olympiad; Coord Genetics Prgm; NYSUT 1973-; Residents of P. W. 1985-; Wildlife Conserv, Audubon Soc 1973-; Explorers Club 1996-; RITEC Tchr of Yr 1990; Raptor Survey Bethpage St Park 4 Yrs; Book Spirits of the Harbor; *office:* Paul D. Schreiber HS 101 Campus Dr Port Washington NY 11050*

JONES, JEANNE SARRA, Retired Elementary Teacher; *b:* Frackville, PA; *m:* Ronald E.; *c:* Bradley J.; *ed:* Kutztown St Univ (BA) Elem Ed 1956; 18 Post-Grad Credit Hrs; *cr:* Reading Schl Dist Elem Tchr 1958-61; North Schuylkill Schl Dist Elem Tchr 1963-93; *ai:* PSEA, NEA 1963-; Cath Daughters of Amer 1960-; Ladies of the Elks 1970-; *home:* 250 W Chestnut St Frackville PA 17931

JONES, JEFFREY A., Physics & Chemistry Teacher; *b:* Warsaw, NY; *m:* Carolyn Bresee; *c:* Beth, Rose, David, Andrew; *ed:* Houghton Coll (BA) Bible & Psych 1981; Potsdam Coll (MS) Physics & Scndry Ed 1990; Attnd Indiana Univ of PA, Boston Univ, CO Schl of Mines Numerous Credit Hrs; *cr:* Cornerstone Acad Sci & Math Tchr 1981-83; Beaver Cty Chrstn Schl Sci Tchr 1984-86; Watertown HS Physics & Chem Tchr 1986-; *ai:* Parkside C & MA Church 1986-, Finance Comm 3 Yrs; Elder, Governing Board Mem; *office:* Watertown H S 1335 Washington St Watertown NY 13601

JONES, JOAN A. JOHNSON, Fourth Grade Teacher; *b:* Paris, MD; *c:* Stacy, Quanda, Corey; *ed:* Bowie St Coll (BS) Ed 1972; 30 Hrs MD St Ed Dept, Trinity Coll; *cr:* Even Start Schl Home Base Tchr 1994-; Calvert Cty Adult Ed Schl Tchr 1990-; Huntingtown Elem Schl Tchr 1972-; *ai:* After Schl Math Tutoring Prgm; NEA, MSTA 1972-; CEA 1972-, Rep; Amer Cancer Soc; Bd of Child Care, Rep; WA East Dist, Cncl Sec; Tchr of Yr 1992; 20 Yr Svc Awd CEA; *office:* Huntingtown Elem Schl 4345 Huntingtown Rd Huntingtown MD 20639

JONES, JOAN OAKES, HS Social Studies Teacher; *b:* Rockville Centre, NY; *m:* Robert E.; *c:* Kelly Ann, Kimberly; *ed:* Molloy Coll (BA) His 1969; LIU-CW Post (MS) Spec Ed 1984; Attnd Hofstra Univ Post Grad His 9 Addl Credits; *cr:* Woodmere Acad Soc Stud & PE Tchr 1969-71; WanTagh Jr & Sr HS Sub Tchr 1972-83; Island Trees HS Soc Stud Tchr 1983-; *ai:* Human Relaions Club Founder & Adv; PTSA Island Trees 1983-, NY St Jenkins Awd 1986; Lt Cncl of Soc Stud 1992-; NYSUT & AFT 1983-; Cath Youth Org 1957-, St Williams Exec Bd, CYO Constitution Comm; Nassay Cty Girls Vlybl; USVBA Rated Ofcl Boys; *office:* Island Trees HS 59 Straight Ln Levittown NY 11756

JONES, JOSEPH ALAN, English Teacher; *b:* Gallipolis, OH; *m:* Teresa H. Crabtree; *c:* Erin S.; *ed:* Univ of Rio Grande (BS) Eng 1971; OH St Univ (MA) Eng, Hum 1977; Attnd Great Books Inst; *cr:* Fulton Schl Lang Arts Tchr 1971-83; Amer Inst of Banking Comm Instr 1976-84; Heath HS Eng Tchr 1983-; *ai:* Heath Ed Assn, Pres; Dist Chair EECAP, Curr Revision Comm; Prof Concerns Rep; Heath Ed Assn, OH Ed Assn, NEA 1971-; Newark Band Parents 1992-; First UM Church 1982-; Licking Cty Edctr of Yr; Dow Tchr Excl Awd; Key Club Edctr Awd; *home:* 1379 Pleasant Valley Dr Newark OH 43055*

JONES, JUDY MILLER, Math Tutor; *b:* Cincinnati, OH; *m:* Daniel G.; *c:* Emma, Adam; *ed:* Coll of Mt St Joseph (BA) Elem Ed 1987; Cert Scndry Ed Math 1996; Tchr Effectiveness Trng; *cr:* Our Lady of Visitation Schl 7th Grd Tchr 1987-94; *ai:* Sci Fair Judge; Cincinnati His Day 1988-94; Mt St Joseph Alumni Assn 1987-, Various Comms; *home:* 6369 Suehaven Ct Cincinnati OH 45248

JONES, KAREN, Reading Specialist; *b:* Albany, NY; *ed:* St Univ of NY Coll at Plattsburgh (BS) Elem Ed 1976; St Univ of NY at Albany (MS) Rdng 1978; Addl Credits Russell Sage Coll & Saint Rose Coll; *cr:* Guilderland Cntrl Schl Dist Elem Tchr 1976-77; Lyons Cntrl Schl Dist Grds 7-12 Rdng Specialist 1978-80; Corinth Cntrl Schls Grds 7-12 Rdng Specialist 1980-; *ai:* Commencement Coord; Awds Comm; Homecoming Chprsn; Stu Mentor; NHS Adv; NYS Tchrs Assn 1976-; Iroquois Rdng Cncl 1980-, Bd of Dirs 1981-91, Pres 1987; NY St Rdng Assn, Intnl Rdng Assn 1978-; Natl Assn of Wkshp Dirs 1986-; NASSP Div of Stu Activities 1985-; Corinth Youth Commission 1987-, Bd of Dirs 1987-; Corinth Comm Building Fund COmm 1985-; High Hopes 1989-95; Jessup's Landing Comm 1987-95; Corinth Plan of Action Image Comm 1993-95; Fellowships-Leadership & Co-Curr Activities, 12th World Rdng Congress, 13th- 16th World Rdng Congress, Activity Adv Handbook; Grants-Stu SKills Handbook, Youth at Risk, Alternative Ed Consolidation Stud; *home:* 8 Holly Ln Latham NY 12110*

JONES, KATHLEEN ANNE, English & Journalism Teacher; *b:* Baltimore, MD; *m:* Ronald N. Taylor; *c:* Kara Jackson, Benjamin Taylor; *ed:* St Joseph Coll (BA) Eng 1972; Johns Hopkins Univ (MA) Lbrl Arts 1979; 60 Addl Credits; *cr:* Cockeysville HS Eng, Jrnlsm Tchr 1972-79; Dulaney HS Eng, Jrnlsm Tchr 1979-; *ai:* Newspaper Adv; MSTA, TABCO 1972-; MD Scholastic Press Assn 1979-; *office:* Dulaney HS 255 Padonia Rd Timonium MD 21093*

JONES, KATIE, Former Elementary Teacher; *b:* London, England; *m:* Gregory Rooney; *ed:* Stirling Univ (BA) Bio 1975; Diploma Ed 1975; Waldorf Tchr Trng; Waldorf HS Tchr Trng in Sci; Yr of Trng in Speech & Drama; *cr:* Greenoak Acad HS Tchr 1975-77; Lasoneti Island Schl Elem & HS Tchr 1979-81; Quadra Island Waldorf Schl Elem Class Tchr 1981-85; Marin Waldorf Schl 5-8 Grd Elem Class Tchr 1987-94.

JONES, LAURA ORZECHOWSKI, Sixth Grade Teacher; *b:* Jersey City, NJ; *m:* Bruce A.; *c:* Ryan B.; *ed:* Jersey City St Coll (BA) Elem Ed 1974, (MA) Rdng 1976; *cr:* Holy Rosary Schl Sixth Grd Tchr 1974-77; Washington Schl Rdng Specialist 1977-78; Vroom Learning Ctr Rdng Specialist 1978-79, 8th Grd Tchr 1979-80, Sixth Grd Tchr 1980-; *ai:* Lit-Art Magazine Adv 13 yrs; NJEA, NEA 1979-; *office:* Vroom Learning Ctr 18 W 26th St Bayonne NJ 07002

JONES, LINDA L., Teacher; *b:* Easton, MD; *c:* Sara, Rachel; *ed:* Loyola Coll of MD (MED) Curr, Instruction 1994; Univ of MD, Salisbury St Advanced Prof Rdng Cert 1988; *cr:* Talbot Co Pub Schls Tchr 1971-; Chesapeake Coll Instr 1994-; *ai:* Sit Team; AAUW, NEA, MSTA, TCEA 1971-; Alpha Delta Kappa 1979-, Sec, Treas, Sgt at Arms; MD Alpha Delta Kappa, Southeast Region of US Schlsps; *office:* Easton Elem Schl Moton Bldg Glenwood Ave Easton MD 21601*

JONES, LINDA MILLSAPS, SS & Health Teacher; *b:* Hiddenite, NC; *m:* Glen; *c:* David, Darryl; *ed:* Wilkes Comm Coll at Wilesboro (AAS) Soc Svc, Early Chldhd Dev 1976; Appalachian St Univ at Boone (BS) Elem & MS Specialization, 6-8 Grd SS, LA 1983; OH St Univ 12 Credit Hrs Alcohol & Drugs, Tribes, STARS, Alternatives to Violence Stud; *cr:* Wittenburg Elem Schl Tchrs Aide 1976-80; Hiddenite Elem Schl Headstart Tchr, Coord 1983-84; Stony Point Elem Schl Tchr 1984-87; Clinton MS Acad Proficiency Tchr; *ai:* Yrbk Coord, Adv; Black His Gospel Fest Coord; UNCF Spon; Mentor; Columbus Ed Assn, NEA 1987-; EKKLESIA Bapt Church 1992-, Pastor, Licensed & Ordained; Tchr of Yr Awd 1988; Black Heritage Awd 1988; *home:* 1975 Sharbot Dr Columbus OH 43229*

JONES, LORI ANN, Spanish Teacher; *b:* Clearfield, PA; *m:* William L. Jr.; *ed:* Indiana Univ of PA (BSEd) Span 1990; Currently Working Toward Masters Degree in Span Lit; *cr:* Westwood HS Span Tchr 1990-93; Hempfield Area Sr HS Span Tchr 1993-; *ai:* NEA, Amer Assn of Tchrs of Span & Portuguese 1993-.

JONES, LYNN A., 6th Grade Teacher; *b:* Harrisburg, PA; *m:* Daniel E.; *c:* Lauren Taylor; *ed:* Wright St Univ (BA) Speech, Lang Pathology 1977; Univ of Cincinnati (MA) Speech, Lang Pathology 1979; Elem Ed Cert 1986; 32 Addl Hrs; *cr:* Pvt Speech Pathology 1979-86; Duvall Elem Schl Speech, Lang Pathologist 1979-86; New Burlington Elem Schl Speech, Lang Pathologist 1979-86, Sixth Grd Tchr 1986-; *ai:* Site-Based Mngmt Team Steering Comm; Staff Dev Comm Chm 1992-; Past Spon Just Say No Club; Oratory Contest Coach; New Tchrs Mentor; NEA, OEA, Amer Speech, Hearing Lang Assn 1979-; MHTA 1979-, Sr Bldg Rep; St Michael's Parish 1995-; Mary Help of Chrstns Parish 1965-; New Tchrs Mentor, Facilitator Trng Selection; *home:* 9451 Ambleside Dr Cincinnati OH 45241*

JONES, LYNN ALICE, Chemistry Teacher; *b:* Cincinnati, OH; *c:* Andrew, Kaitlyn; *ed:* Beaver Coll (BS) Chem 1962; Johns Hopkins Univ (MS) Chem 1994; 12 Grad Credits 1963-64; 16 Grad Credits Stanford Univ 1962-63; *cr:* South Carroll HS Chem Tchr 1987-; *ai:* Role Playing Club Adv; NEA 1987-; MAST 1987-; MD Governors Acad of Math & Sci Ambassador 1995; *office:* South Carroll HS 1300 W Old Liberty Rd Sykesville MD 21784

JONES, MARCIA VERN, Latin & Mathematics Teacher; *b:* Springfield, MA; *m:* Dana Whitley; *c:* Kent Whitley; *ed:* Wells Coll (AB) His 1954; 15 Hrs Ed; 3 Hrs Eng Literary Criticism; 12 Hrs Cmptr Programing; *cr:* Berk Athenacum Bookmobile Librn 1957-59; MacDuffie Schl Tchr 1959-60; Berk Cntry Day Schl Tchr 1964-75; Miss Halls Schl Dean of Stdnts 1975-80; Berk Cntry Day Schl Tchr 1983-; *ai:* Bd Ed, Bd Tech, Cmptr Comms; Amer Classical League, Classical Assn New England 1984-; Pioneer Vly Classical Assn 1982-; St Stephens Table 1984-, Chairwoman 1990-91; Literacy Vol 1990-, VP; St Stephens Church 1995-, Vestry Mem; Write, Pub Software; Creator of Latina Blocks Manipulatives for Tchng Latin; *office:* Berkshire Country Day Schl PO Box 867 Lenox MA 01240*

JONES, MARGARET MILLER, Math & Science Teacher; *b:* New Haven, CT; *m:* Barrett W.; *c:* Kenneth, Elizabeth; *ed:* Alfred Univ (BA) Bio, Environmental Sci 1977; Univ of ME (MA) Scndry Ed, Sci 1993; *cr:* Calvary Family Schl HS Eng, Sci Tchr 1987-95; Coastal Chrstn Schl Jr HS Math, Sci Tchr 1996; *ai:* NSTA; Calvary Bapt Church 1985-; *office:* Coastal Chrstn Schl 574 N Nobleboro Rd Waldoboro ME 04572

JONES, MARY BARNES, Team Leader & Guidance Cnslr; *b:* Goldsboro, NC; *m:* Jesse A.; *c:* La Rone; *ed:* Shaw Univ (BS) Natural Scis 1968; Kean Coll (MA) Stu Prsnl Svcs 1971; 9 Credit Hrs Rutgers Univ; 24 Credit Hrs Jersey City St Coll; *cr:* Rutledge Ave Schl Tchr 1968-70; NJ Educl Consortium Cnslr Supervision 1971-73; Orange HS Cnslr 1973-; *ai:* SAVE Staff Adv; Orange Ed Assn, NJ Ed Assn, NJ Cnslng Assn 1973-; Orange Juvenile Conf Comm 1978-; Delta Sigma Theta 1989-; New Point Bapt Church 1985-; Orange Police Dept Svc Awd; No Jersey Shaw Univ Citizen Awd; *office:* Orange HS 400 Lincoln Ave Orange NJ 07050

JONES, MARY LIVI, Special Education Teacher; *b:* Charleroi, PA; *m:* Douglas P.; *c:* Mardy, Diane, Kara, Meghan; *ed:* California Univ of PA (BS) Ed & Eng 1970, (MS) Ed, Physically and or Mentally Handicapped 1994; *cr:* Youth Dev Ctr Cnslr 1970-75; John F Kennedy Schl MS Eng Tchr 1980-94; Trinity HS Inclusion-Learning Support Tchr 1994-; *ai:* PSEA, NEA 1994-; Mayors Commission for Handicapped 1994-; Open Doors for Handicapped 1994-; Phi Delta Kappa Outstanding Grad Stu 1994; PA Jr Acad of Sci Judges Awd; *office:* Trinity HS Park Ave Washington PA 15301

JONES, MATTHEW RICHARD, Physical Education Teacher; *b:* Schenectady, NY; *m:* Mary Catherine Bocchetti; *c:* Christopher, Nicholas, Ryan; *ed:* Cortland St Coll (BA) PE 1977; Castleton St Coll (MS) Sports Medicine, Ath Trng 1983; PE Hudson Vly CC 1975; Credits Educl Admin North Adams St Coll; *cr:* Vanderheyden Hall PE, Hlth Tchr 1978-81; Greenwich Cntrl Schls PE Tchr, Ath Dir 1981-88; Shenendehowa Cntrl Schls PE Tchr 1988-; Colonie Cntrl Schls PE Tchr 1992; Albany BOCES 1993-; Summer PE Instr of Handicapped Children; *ai:* Head Var Cross Cntry, Indoor Track, Boys Track Coach; Bsktbl IM; Section II NY St Boys Indoor Track Coord; AFT, NYSUT 1981-; Natl Track & Field Teams Coach; *office:* Shenedehowa HS 970 RR 146 Clifton Park NY 12065

JONES, MELO E., 6th Grade Teacher; *b:* Halifax, NC; *m:* Jeanette E.; *ed:* Shaw Univ (BA) Elem Ed 1961; City Coll NYC (MS) Spec Ed 1973; Rdng, Permanent Commn Branches Certs; Adm, Supervision For Elem Schl Credits; *cr:* Graham Elem Magnet Schl 6th Gr Tchr 28 Yrs; *ai:* Tutoring Stdtns in Rdng, Math; Adv Schl Safety Patrol, Math, Sci Olympics; AFT 1965-, Local Bldg Rep; CCNY Alumni 1973-; Kappa Alpha Psi 1961-; Phalanx of AA Men 1987-, Pres; Trinity Episcopal Church 1967-, Pre of Men's Club, Lay Eucharistic Minister 1991; *office:* Graham Magnet Elem Sch 421 E 5th St Mount Vernon NY 10553*

JONES, NANCY JANE, Social Studies Teacher; *b:* Wilkes-Barre, PA; *m:* Richard Frampton; *c:* Rebecca, Keri, Eric; *ed:* PA St Univ (BA) LbrlArts 1971; Loyola Coll at Baltimore (MA) Spec Ed 1993; 30 Credit Hrs Howard Comm Coll; *cr:* PA Dept of Welfare Caseworker 1971-73; Soc Security

Admin Houston Claims Rep 1973-75; Ho Co Pub Schls Sub Tchr 1986-90; Good Shepherd Ctr Soc Stud, Spec Ed Tchr 1990-92; Centennial HS Soc Stud Tchr 1992-; *ai:* Class of 1995, 1996 Adv; Spirt Club Spon; NEA 1990-; *office:* Centennial HS 4300 Centennial Ln Ellicott City MD 21042

JONES, NANCY JUSTIN, Teacher; *b:* Cinti, OH; *c:* Jennifer, Ann; *ed:* Stephens Coll (AA) Lib Arts 1966; Univ of Cinti (BA) Ed-K Through 3 1968; Attnd Xavier Univ; *cr:* Bramble Priamry Schl Tchr 1968-70; Newtown Elem Schl Tchr 1979-84; Maddux Elem Schl Tchr 1984-; *ai:* Maddux Express Stu Newspaper Adv; NEA, OEA 1978-; Tchr of Yr; Mem Forest Hills Writing Cncl; Presented Seminars on Writing Various Schl Dists.

JONES, NANCY MARKWORDT, Fourth Grade Teacher; *b:* Baltimore, MD; *m:* John Paul; *c:* Ryan, Derek; *ed:* Bloomsburg Univ (BS) Elem Ed 1976; 36 Addl Credit Hrs St Masters Equivalency; 14 Addl Grad Credits; *cr:* Tamaqua Area Schls 1st Grd Tchr 1976-80, 5th Grd Tchr 1980-82, 1st-2nd Grd Tchr 1982-84, Kndgtn Tchr 1984-85, 4th Grd Tchr 1986-; *ai:* Tamaqua Ed Assn Schlsp & Prof Dev Comms; NEA & PSEA 1976-; Delta Kappa Gamma Soc Intnl 1994-; Gift of Time Tribute 1991, The Amer Family Inst King Prussia PA; *office:* West Penn Elem Schl RR 2 Box 224 New Ringgold PA 17960*

JONES, PATRICIA DIANE, HS Health & Phys Ed Tchr; *b:* Pittsburgh, PA; *ed:* Slippery Rock Univ (BS) Hlth & PE 1977; *cr:* Hempfield Area Schl Dist Tchr 19 Yrs; *ai:* Dept Co-Chair Hlth & PE Ed; Demonstration Site Tchr for PE Life Project PSAHPERD Org; AAHPERD 1977-; PSAHPERD 1976-; NEA, PSEA, HAEA 1978-; *office:* Hempfield Area Schl Dist Rd 6 Box 77 Greensburg PA 15601*

JONES, PAUL S., Assistant Professor of Music; *b:* Moncton NB, Canada; *ed:* Western Ontario Conservatory of Music (AMus) Piano Performance 1986; Philadelphia Coll of Bible (BMus) Music 1992, (BS) Bible 1992; IN Univ (MM) Piano Performance 1993; Doctoral Stud, DM in Choral Conducting; Conducting, Organ, Piano, Composition Pvt Stud; *cr:* Chambers-Wylie Presbyn Church Organist, Choir Dir 1988-92; Csely Summer Schl of Music Choir Dir, Tchng Fac 1995; Arlington United Meth Church Organist, Choir Dir 1992-93, 1995-; Philadelphia Coll of Bible Asst Music Prof, Conductor 1993-; *ai:* Accompanist Bloomington Chamber Singers; Conductors Guild 1993-; IN Univ Doctoral Flwshp; New Brunswick Arts Grant; Presser Scholar; Canada Cncl Arts Grant; *office:* Philadelphia Coll Of Bible 200 Manor Ave Langhorne PA 19047

JONES, PAULA CRAWFORD, 1st Grade Teacher; *b:* Washington, DC; *m:* Frederick C. Jr.; *c:* Frederick C. III, Frances C.; *ed:* DC Tchrs Coll (BS) Elem Ed 1973; 15 Grad Credit Hrs at George Washington Univ; 15 Grad Credit Hrs at Trintiy Coll; *cr:* DC Pub Schls Tchr 23 Yrs; *ai:* Southern Bapt Church Sunday Schl Tchr & Childrens Ministry Tchr; Hope For Life Outreach Ministries Inc Asst Yth Coord; AFT 1973-; Friends of the Lib 1996-; Orr Elem Schl Outstdng Tchr Awd 2 Yrs; Bapt Church Outstdng Sunday Schl Awd 1995; *office:* Orr Elem Schl 22nd & Minnesota Ave SE Washington DC 20020*

JONES, RAYMOND F., Spanish Teacher; *b:* New Castle, PA; *ed:* Youngstown Univ (BA) His, Span 1957; Duquesne Univ (MA) Span, Scndry Ed 1962; Span Classes Natl Univ of Mexico; *cr:* New Castle Pub Schls Span Tchr 1960-64; Youngstown Pub Schls Span Tchr 1964-; *ai:* Span Club; Tour Guide; YEA, OEA, NEA 1980-; Jennings Scholar; *home:* RR 8 Box 311 New Castle PA 16101*

JONES, REGINALD BERNARD, Social Science Teacher & Coach; *b:* Bronx, NY; *m:* Beverly J. Edwards; *c:* Nicole C., Bryan W.; *ed:* Herbert H. Lehman Coll (BA) His 1974; 21 Grad Credits Asst Prin Internship Prgm; 60 Grad Credits Media Specialist, Scndry Ed; *cr:* Northview Ctr Asst Dir, Tchr, Coach 1977-85, Dir of the Schl 1985-87; The Isaac Newton Jr HS Soc Sci Tchr, Coach 1987-, Asst Dir 1993-94; *ai:* Bsktbl Team Coach; Trip Coord; Stu Govt Adv; AFT 1978-; ASCD 1985-; Chestnut Ridge Little League 1993-, Coach, Svc Awd 1995; Ramapo Bsktbl League 1995-, Coach; Co-op City Ftbl League 1977-, Coach, Coaches Awd 1980-81; BSA 1972-, Asst Scoutmaster; Tchr of Yr 1987; Comm Svc & Schl Dir 1986; Schl Dist Tchrs Awd 1983; *office:* The Isaac Newton Jr HS E 116th St & Fdr Dr New York NY 10029*

JONES, RICHARD ALONZO,II, Social Studies Teacher; *b:* Fort Campbell, KY; *m:* LuAnn; *c:* Rebecca, Richard; *ed:* Mount Vernon Nazarene Coll (AA) His 1973; Olivet Nazarene Univ (BS) His 1975; CA St Univ at Domenguez Hills (MA) Hum 1992; *cr:* Mount Gilead HS Stud Hall Monitor 1975-76; River Valley HS Scndry Soc Stud Tchr 1976-; *ai:* River Valley World War Two Commemorative Comm Chair; NEA, OEA 1976-, Local Pres; OH Cncl for the Soc Stud 1989-; Sons of Union Veterans of Civil War 1994-; Univ of Chicago Tchr of the Yr 1990; River Valley Local Schl Outstanding Achvmt Awd 1995; *office:* River Valley HS 1267 Columbus Sandusky Rd N Marion OH 43302*

JONES, RICHARD L., Edith Mc Crea Prof of Theatre; *b:* Chicago, IL; *m:* Mary Jay; *c:* Alexander, Kate; *ed:* San Francisco St Univ (MA) Eng 1969; Grad Schl & Univ Ctr of City Univ of NY (PHD) Theatre 1984; *cr:* Fremont HS Drama Tchr 1968-73; Russell Sage Coll Prof of Theatre 1975-; Somerville Coll Guest Lecturer 1992-; Oxford Univ Guest Lecturer 1992-; *ai:* Sage Colls at Oxford Prgm Dir; *office:* Russell Sage Coll At Troy Troy NY 12180*

JONES, RICHARD WARREN, Chemistry & Physics Teacher; *b:* Coshocton, OH; *m:* Diane A. Zuro; *c:* Robert, Melissa, Alison; *ed:* Hiram Coll (BA) Chem, Physics 1972; Credit Hrs from OH Univ, Kenyon Coll, OH Weslyan Univ, Ashland Univ, Malone Coll, OH Northern; *cr:* River View Schl Dist Jr HS Math Tchr 1972-81; Cntrl OH Tech Coll Math Instr 1992-; River View Schl Dist HS Chem, Physics Tchr 1982-; *ai:* NHS Adv; NEA, OEA 1972-; River View Ed Assn 1972-, Pres 1981-82; SECO 1980-; Coshocton Model Railroad Club 1972-, Treas 1980-; *home:* 214 S 18th St Coshocton OH 43812*

JONES, RICK VAN, HS Social Studies Teacher; *b:* Akron, OH; *m:* Barb; *c:* Nathan, Sara; *ed:* Univ of Akron (BA) Soc St Comp 1970; Continuing Ed Courses 1970, 1980's; *cr:* U L Light Jr HS Soc St Tchr 1970-72; Erwine MS Soc St Tchr 1972-83; Coventry HS Soc St Tchr 1983-; *ai:* NEOEA 1974-, Pres; OEA 1974-, VP; NEA 1974-; CEA, Pres; *home:* 3046 Lindale Dr Akron OH 44312

JONES, ROBERT A., Social Studies Teacher; *b:* Utica, NY; *m:* Eleanor Muraco; *c:* Leslie, Robin, Melissa; *ed:* Utica Coll of Syracuse Univ (BA) His 1972; Grad Work; *cr:* Perry Jr HS Soc Stud Tchr, Coach 1973-; *ai:* Coach Var Ftbl 1977-, Sftbl; Shared Decision Making Team; AFT, NYSUT, New Hartford Tchrs Assn 1973-; *office:* Perry Jr HS Weston Rd New Hartford NY 13413*

JONES, ROBERT H., American History Teacher; *b:* NJ; *m:* JoAnn L.; *c:* Scott James, Glenn; *ed:* SUNY at Plattsburg (BS) Ed 1964; SUNY at Albany (MS) Econ 1970; Grad Stud Long Island Univ, SUNY at Albany & Plattsburgh; *cr:* Greensbury Schls Tchr 1968-96; SUNY at Plattsburg Adj Fac 1976-85; Long Island Univ Adj Fac 1976-85; *ai:* Alpine Ski Prgm Spon; AFT, NYSUT Del; Greater Capital 1982, Chm; Humorous Region Ctr Vice Chmn; Queensbury Fac Assn; Souther Adirondack League of Tchrs Pres; *home:* 200 W Mountain Rd Queensbury NY 12804

JONES, ROBERT JOHN, History Teacher; *b:* Kearney, NE; *c:* Matthew, Elizabeth; *ed:* Defiance Coll (BA) Comp Soc Stud 1966; IN St (MS) Ed 1968; Post Grad Work Cnslng Kent St Univ; *cr:* Gary IN City Schls Tchr 1966-69; Hawthorne Jr HS Tchr 1969-76; Hawthorne HS Cnslr 1977-88; Irving Jr HS Tchr 1989-92; Lorain HSTchr 1992-95; Lorain Admiral Kin g HS Tchr 1995-; *ai:* Stu Cncl Adv, Jr HS Bsktbl Coach, IM Adv; Worked on Many Comms; NEA, OEA 1969-; Lorain Ed Assn 1969-, Ed of Newspaper; Key Employee of Yr Awds 1985-86; 8th Grd Tchr of Yr Irving Jr HS 1988.*

JONES, ROBERT KENNETH, Social Studies Chairman; *b:* Blairsville, PA; *m:* Kathleen Barbara Hill; *c:* Darren, Ryan; *ed:* IN St Coll (BS) His, Ec 1963; IN Univ of PA (MS) Sociology, Psych 1968; PA St Univ 12 Hrs; Attnd WV; *cr:* Burrell Schl Dist Tchr 1963-, Dept Chm 1987-; *ai:* Head Wrestling Coach; Class Spon 15 Yrs; Club Adv 10 Yrs; Burrell Ed Assn 1963-, Exec Comm; PA St Assn 1963-, Del; NEA 1963-; Great Tchr Awd 1982, 1987, 1994; *office:* Burrell HS 1021 Puckety Church Rd Lower Burrell PA 15068

JONES, ROBERTA LYN (BROWN), Physical Ed & Health Teacher; *b:* Corinth, NY; *m:* William Idris; *c:* Kelsey, Colin; *ed:* Cedarville Coll (BA) PE 1979; Univ ME 3 Credit Hrs; Cuyahoga Comm Coll 3 Credit Hrs; TN Temple Univ PE; *cr:* Wayside Chrstn Acad Tchr & Coach 1979-80; Westside Chrstn Acad Tchr & Coach 1981-82; Orange Chrstn Acad Tchr & Coach 1984-86, 1988-; *ai:* Jr Class & Ski Club Adv; Frosh & Var Vllybl Coach; US Vllybl Coaches Assn 1996-; Vly Chrstn Acad 1994-, Personal Comm; *office:* Orange Christian Acad 27200 Emery Rd Orange Village OH 44128

JONES, ROCHELLE R., Art & Photography Teacher; *b:* Watertown, WI; *m:* Mark; *c:* Claire; *ed:* Univ of FL (AA) Pre Phys Therapy 1978; Univ of Cincinnati (BFA) Art Ed 1983; Miami Univ (MA) Art Ed 1989; *cr:* Art Acad of Cincinnati Children's Classes Dir 1983-85; Bridgetown Jr HS Art Tchr 1984-85; Batavia Jr Sr HS Art Tchr 1985-; *ai:* Peer Cnslng, Core Team Chm; Drug Free Schls Grant, Charity Donations Coord; Class Spon; SW OH Art Ed Assn 1983-; NAEA 1981-; Knox Presch Bd 1994-, Treas, Dev Chair; Clermont Cty Tchrs Excl in Ed Grant 1994; Art Acad of Cincinnati Drawing OH Juried Art Show 1990; Univ of Cincinnati DAAP Alumni Art Show 1990; Kennedy Ctr for Performing Arts Imagination Celebration Wkshp Coord 1985; *office:* Batavia Jr Sr HS 800 Bauer Ave Batavia OH 45103*

JONES, ROGER A., Retired Elementary School Tchr; *b:* Hollis, NY; *m:* Mary Myers; *c:* Barbara LaPointe, Sara, Michael, Nicholas; *ed:* Bard Coll (BA) Pol Sci 1950; Russell Sage Coll (MS) Elem Ed 1970; Post Grad Stud Ed Psych at SUNY at New Paltz; *cr:* Bennett Schl 4th-6th Grds Tchr 1967-92; *ai:* Chess Club, Sftbl Team Adv, Coach; Grd Chm 1976-90; NY St Tchr Assn 1967-; AFT; NY St Yth Conservation Corps summer Environmental Prgm Camp Dir; *home:* 6 Mercy Ct Albany NY 12205

JONES, SARAH ANN (CRAWLEY), Art Teacher; *b:* Durham, NC; *ed:* Morgan St Univ (BS) Art Ed 1971; Coppin St Coll (MS) Spec Ed 1976; Attnd Towson St Univ; *cr:* Gen John Stricker Jr HS Art Tchr 1971-83; Patapsco HS Art Tchr 1983-87; Sparrows Point HS Art Tchr 1987-; *ai:* Stu Cncl, Art Hnr Soc Adv; Class of 1998 Co-Adv; Mid Sts Evaluation, Bd of Ed Stu Selection Comm; Schl Improvement, Budget Team; NAAPS; NEA, Tchrs Assn of Baltimore Cty 1971-; NAEA, ASCD 1993-; MD St Tchrs Assn; Baltimore Co Alliance of Black Schl Edctrs; MD Art Ed Assn; Delta Sigma Theta 1970-; Celebrating Diversity Honoree African Amer Stu Achvmt, Multicultural Curr Infusion; Tchr in Excl Nom; Good Fellow Awd Ldrshp Trng Wrkshp; *office:* Sparrows Point HS 7400 N Point Rd Baltimore MD 21219

JONES, SHIRLEY WINDER, Sixth Grade Teacher; *b:* Salisbury, MD; *m:* Matthew Jr.; *c:* Ivan L.; *ed:* Bowie St (BS) Elem Ed 1962; George Washington Univ (MA) Admin & Supervision 1970; Math Specialist Credits; Attnd Morgan St Univ, Bowie St Univ, Univ of DC, Trinity Coll, George Washington Univ, George Mason Univ; *cr:* Nanjemoy Elem Tchr 1962-66; Kenilworth Elem 1966-; *ai:* Gifted & Talented Prgm & Spelling Coord; Telecomm-Distance Learning-TEAMS Coordination; Chrldr Coach & Ad; YAC Adv; Charm-Etiquette Club; Hall Chprsn; Stu Govt Adv; PTA Treas; Youth Asst Dir; Choir/Ensemble Member; Friendship AOH Church; GED Inst; Martial Arts; AFT 1966-, Local Schl Chprsn; NCTM 1988-; NSTA, DCSEA 1994-; ASCD; Smithsonian Assoc 1989-; Library of Congress Assoc; Tchr of Yr; Supts Incentive Awd; PTA Svc Awd; US Park Svc Aquatic Gardens Advy Panel; (LEAD) Program; Housing Curr Writer; TEAMS Natl Advy Bd; Proposal Writer/Awardee; Assesment Team; Peer Sprvsn; *office:* Kenilworth Elem Schl 44th St bet Nash & Ord NE Washington DC 20019*

JONES, STEPHANIE WRIGHT, 10th-12th Grade Health Ed Tchr; *b:* San Diego, CA; *c:* Demetrious; *ed:* Howard Univ (BS) Hlth, PE 1977; Trinity Coll 12 Hrs; Univ of MD at College Park 12 Hrs; Bowie St Univ 12 Hrs; *cr:* Camden City Pub Schl Hlth, PE Tchr 1977-79; Hampton City Pub Schl Hlth, PE Tchr 1979-80; Richmond Co Pub Schl Hlth, Sci, Math, PE Tchr 1980-85; Montgomery Co Pub Schl Hlth, PE Tchr 1985-; *ai:* JV Field Hockey Coach; Wellness Comm; NEA; MCEA 1985-; Delta Sigma Theta 1975-; Co-Authored MD St Hlth Ed Curr; Montgomery Cty Pub Schls Revised Hlth Ed Alternative Prgm; Citizens Advy Comm 2 Yrs; MCPS Hlth Eval of MAt Comm; *office:* Springbrook HS 201 Valleybrook Dr Silver Spring MD 20904*

JONES, SUSAN ELAINE, Middle School Health Teacher; *b:* Portsmouth, OH; *ed:* Mt Vernon Nazarene Coll (BA) PE & Hlth 1986; *cr:* Columbus City Schls Sub Tchr 1986-87; Colonel Crawford Schl Ist Pe Tchr 1987-92; Chillicothe City Schls PE Tchr 1993-95, Hlth Tchr 1995-; *ai:* NEA 1987-; OEA 1987-; CEA 1993-.

JONES, SYLVIA DE STEFANO, 6th Grade Teacher; *b:* Paterson, NJ; *m:* Gerald A.; *c:* Gerald J., Gina Marie; *ed:* Wm Paterson Coll (BA) Elem Ed 1968; Addl 25 Credit Hrs Tchng Strategies for Elem Schl; *cr:* PS #9 Paterson 4th Grd Tchr 1968-73; PS #21 Paterson 6th Grd Tchr 1983-; *ai:* Club Adv for Arts, Crafts Club; Schl Wide Plan, Site Based Shared Decision Making Team Comms; NEA, NJEA, PCEA, PEA 1993-; Article Pub; Math Curr 1995; *office:* Elem Schl 21 322 10th Ave Paterson NJ 07514*

JONES, THOMAS MARSDEN, Retired Teacher; *b:* Mathews Cty, VA; *m:* Audrey Jefferson; *c:* Thomas, Calvin, Kim Norrington, Paul; *ed:* VA St Univ (BS) Indstrl Mngmt 1943; *cr:* Ambae Industries Electrical 1946-70; Roger Putnam Voc Tech HS Tchr, Chprsn Ret 1990-96; Westfield St Coll Tchr in Tchr Trng Prgm; Putnam Voc Tech Evening Prgm Elect Apprentice Tchr; *ai:* Putnam Voc Tech Schl SCDM Team; NEA 1970-; Comm of MA Journeyman Elect 1947-; Comm of MA Master Elect; Third Bapt Church, Trustee, Sunday Sch Tchr, Choir; Alpha Phi Alpha 1978-, VP; *home:* 637 Plumtree Rd Springfield MA 01118

JONES, THOMAS WRIGHT, Professor of Education; *b:* Riverside, CA; *m:* Julie Kay Guker; *c:* Thomas W. Jr.; *ed:* Univ of South FL (BA) Spec Ed 1969; GA Peabody Coll (MA) Spec Ed 1973; Univ of Pittsburgh (PHD) Spec Ed 1978; *cr:* Dade Cty Pub Schls Tchr 1969-73; Regnl Deaf & Blind Ctr Educl Specialist 1973-75; TX Tech Univ Asst Prof 1978-81; Gallaudet Univ Asst & Assoc Prof 1981-; *ai:* CEC 1967-, Cahpt, Pres; Assn of Tchr Educators, Deaf & Hard of Hearing, Pres; Cncl on Ed for Deaf, SIG Chair; Three Federal Prsnl Preparation Grants; 40 Articles, Chapters & Monographs; *office:* Gallaudet Univ 800 Florida Ave NE Dept of Education Washington DC 20002

JONES, VIRGINIA S., Business Education Teacher; *b:* Franklin, NJ; *m:* Robert J.; *c:* Amy E. Bennett, Daryl R., Melissa A.; *ed:* Trenton St Coll (BA) Bus Ed 1966; 15 Credit Hrs Towards Degree in Admin & Supervision at Jersey City St; *cr:* Jefferson Twp HS Bus Ed Tchr 1966-68; Butler HS Bus Ed Tchr 1979-81; Jefferson Twp HS Bus Ed Tchr 1981-; *ai:* NJ Bar Assn Mock Trial Tchr & Coach 1986-; Class Adv 1987; Pupil Asst 1992-; FBLA Adv 1992-93; Middle St Steering Comm; NJBEA, MCEA & NEA 1966-; JTEA 1966-; JTEA 1994-, VP; Delta Kappa (1995-; Wallkill Valley Reg HS Bd of Ed 1987-94; NJSBA 1987-94; V Valley Athletic Booster Club 1983-92; Jefferson Twp Tchr of Yr *office:* Jefferson Township H S Weldon Rd, RR 2 Oak Ridge NJ 07

JONES, WILLIAM I., Principal & Chemistry Teacher; *b:* Lakewoo *m:* Robert Brown; *c:* Kelsey E., Colin I.; *ed:* Cedarville Coll (B. 1981; Univ of Akron 10 Credit Hrs Post Grad Bio; Coll of Atlantic 3 Hrs Post Grad Ecology; *cr:* Westside Bapt Chrstn Schl Tchr, A 1981-82; Orange Chrstn Acad Sci Tchr 1982-94, Ath Dir 1983-87 Tchr 1988-93, Prin 1993-; *ai:* Ed Comm Chm; Stu Govt, Ski Clu Coll, Career Counseling; OH Assn of Coll Admissions Cnslrs Supervision, Curr Dev Assn 1989-; NASSP, Intnl Chrstn Schl Fell Admins 1993-; Bethlehem Bapt Church 1984-, Sunday Schl Tchr; Orange Christian Acad 27200 Emery Rd Orange Village OH 44128

JONES, WILLIAM IRVING,III, Eng & Creative Writing Teac Baltimore, MD; *m:* Jane Croghan; *c:* Sean, Sara, Nathan; Bonaventure Univ (BA) Eng 1973; The Johns Hopkins Univ (ML 1980; Addl 60 Credit Hrs; *cr:* Woodlawn HS Eng Tchr 19 Catonsville HS Eng, Creative Writing Tchr, Dept Chair 19 Pikesville MS Eng Tchr 1979-80; Pikesville HS Eng Tchr 19 Ridgely MS Eng Tchr 1980-81; Loch Raven HS Eng Tchr 19 Dulaney HS Eng, Creative Writing Tchr 1981-92; Towson HS Creative Writing Tchr 1993-; *ai:* Lit Magazine Adv; Site-Based Team; Pub Relations Comm Chair; Renovation Steering Comm; MSTA, TABCO, NCTE 1973-; Baltimore Cty Chamber Commerc Excl in Tchng 1991; Achvmt in Ed Awd 1992 Timonium Optimist Baltimore Artscape Lit Prize Poetry 1992; W. H. Wheeler Awd Poetry Collection Pub 1992; *home:* 204 N Tyrone Rd Baltimore MD

JONES, WILLIAM MICHAEL, Social Studies Teache Collingswood, NJ; *m:* Patricia Ann Dougherty; *ed:* Millersville Uni Scndry Ed, Soc Stud 1977; 25 Credits Post Grad Stud; *cr:* William HS Soc Stud Tchr, 9th Grd Boys Bsktbl, Var Track Coach 19 Reynolds Jr HS Soc Stud Tchr, Track & Chrldng Coach, Stu Cnc 1978-90; Warwick MS Soc Stud Tchr Jr HS Ftbl, Chrldng Coach 199 PTO Pres 1982-83; Var Asst Chrldng Coach 1987-88; Warwick Ec 1990-; NEA 1978-; Reynolds Jr HS Tchr of Yr 1980-81; Lancaster Ne Tchr of Week 1994; *office:* Warwick MS 401 Maple St Lititz PA 17

JONES, ZAINABU NETOSH, Educator; *b:* Guthrie, OK; *c:* T Bryant; *ed:* Cntrl MI Univ (BS) Speech Pathology, Elem Ed 1977; W on MED Rdng Specialist; *ai:* Pres, Founder Melanin Siste Consultants Inc; African Amer Org; Tchng His, Contributions of A People; WA Tchrs Union 1987-; AFT 1982-; African Heritage Stud IRA; ASALH; Melanin Sisters; Comm Orgs in DC; Natl Commissi Commonwealth of Malcolm X; Ile Towa Lona; Ma'at System for Chi Walter E. Fauntroy Comm Svc Awd; Annual Malcolm X Candleligh Founder; Natl Park Ranger.

JOOSS, MARK EDWARD, Seventh & Eighth Grd Sci Tchr; *b:* Haven, CT; *m:* Patricia Clifford; *ed:* Quinnipiac Coll (BS) 1969; So Ct Univ (MS) Ed 1975; Southern CT St Univ Admin, Supervision 1981; *cr:* Fairhaven MS 7th-8th Grd Sci Tchr 1969-; *ai:* New Have of Tchrs, AFT 1969-; CT St Sci Tchrs Assn 1978-; St Francis Schl A Assn 1990-, Dev Cmte; New Haven Schls TAPS Distinguished Sc Awd 1988; *office:* Fair Haven MS 164 Grand Ave New Haven CT 06

JOOSS, PATRICIA (CLIFFORD), 4th Grade Teacher; *b:* New H CT; *m:* Mark E.; *ed:* Southern Ct Univ (BS) Elem Ed 1969, (MS) 1978; *cr:* Bishop Woods Schl 3rd, 4th Grd Tchr 1969-; *ai:* SPMT; Comm; Spelling Bee Coord; AFT, New Haven Fed of Tchrs 196 Francis Schl Alumni Assn 1990-, Dev Bd; New Haven Fnd Excl 1981; Elem Schl Prins Urban-Suburban Exch Grant 1994-95; Bishop Woods Elem Schl 1481 Quinnipiac Ave New Haven CT 065

JORCH, NANCY SUE, English Teacher; *b:* Cleveland, OH; *m:* W C.; *c:* Billy; *ed:* Radford Coll (BS) Eng & His 1966; 30 Grad Hrs H Univ, C. W. Post Univ; *cr:* Windsor Locks Jr HS Eng Tchr 1966-67 K. Jr HS Eng Tchr 1967-80; Burr Jr HS Eng Tchr 1980-82, 19 Commack MS Eng Tchr 1989-92; Commack HS Eng Tchr 1993-; Grd Lit Magazine Adv; R&D Comm for Alternative Scheduling; St Advy, Portfolio Comms; NCTE 1988-; AFT, Commack Tchrs Assn Northport UMC 1982-, Flower Comm Chair; Tchr of Yr 1995; P Magazine; *office:* Commack HS Scholar Ln Commack NY 11725

JORDAN, CARLTON PRESTON,JR., Language Arts Teache Southampton, NY; *m:* Jaqueline Erica Brown; *c:* Carlton III; *ed:* St of NY at Albany (BA) Ec 1985, (MA) Tchng Eng Scndry 1991; *cr:* S at Albany Writing Instr 1990-92, Adjunct Lecturer African Amer 1990-92; Montclair HS Eng Tchr 1992-; *ai:* 9th Grd World Lit C Writing Wrkshp Club Adv; NJCTE 1995-; *office:* Montclair HS Chestnut St Montclair NJ 07042

JORDAN, CAROL DELONG, Language Arts Teacher; *b:* Presque ME; *m:* Philip K.; *c:* Lee-Rae Jordan-Oliver; *ed:* Univ of ME (BS) Ed *cr:* Freeport MS Lang Arts Tchr 1971-72; Littleton Elem Schl Mig Tchr 1972-73; Houlton Jr Sr HS Lang Arts Tchr 1973-; *ai:* ME Tchrs Houlton Tchrs Assn 1991-; Houlton Hosp Auxilary 1971-; *office:* SA Schl 5 Bird St Houlton ME 04730*

JORDAN, DIANE M., Business Teacher & Dept Chm; *b:* Easton, P Frank; *c:* Mark, Erik, Lindsay; *ed:* Bloomsburg Univ (BS) Bus Ed Attnd Lehigh Univ, Allentown Coll of St Francis de Sales, Kutztown *cr:* Freedom HS Tchr 1979-; *ai:* Cross Cntry & Track Asst Coach; Class Adv; Restructuring Comm; *office:* Freedom HS 3149 Cheste Bethlehem PA 18017

JORDAN, IRENE ANN, Elementary Art Teacher; *b:* Brooklyn, N William; *c:* Michael, Ryan, Mackenzie; *ed:* Dowling Coll (BA) A 1978; SUNY at Stonybrook (MA) Elem Ed 1983; 15 Grad Hrs Ass Discipline; *cr:* Our Lady of Mercy Schl 1st-8th Grd Art Tchr 197 Duffield Elem Schl 1st-6th Grd Art Tchr 1981-83; Washington Lea Ctr 1st-8th Grd Ceramics Tchr 1983-84; E J Bosti Schl K-6th Grd Art 1984-; *ai:* ORBAA; Showcase of the Arts; Dowling Coll Hnr Soc Art S CTA; NYSUT; E J Bosti PTA; Pines PTA; Town of Islip Arts Organized Grant for Artist in Residence Boces; *office:* Edward J Elem Schl Bourne Blvd Bohemia NY 11716

JORDAN, JANET E., Fourth Grade Teacher; *b:* Holden, MA Worcester St Coll (BS) Elem Ed 1977; Cambridge Coll (MED) 199 Naquag Elem Schl Rdng Instructional Aide 1977-78, First Grd 1978-79, Fourth Grd Tchr 1979-83, Third Grd Tchr 1983-84, Fourth Tchr 1984-, Cmptr Coord 1991-94; *ai:* Cntrl MA Rdng Cncl 1982-; MAssachusetts Tchrs Assn 1978-; Wachusett Regnl Ed Assn 1 Rutland Tchrs Assn 1978-94, Sec, Treas; Holden Grange #78 1970-, Silver Star; Two Horace Mann Grants; Inclusion Pilot Pgrm at Na Participant; *office:* Naquag Elem Schl 285 Main St Rutland MA 015

JORDAN, JOHN J.,JR., Lang Arts Dept Supvr & Tchr; *b:* Allentown *ed:* Lehigh Univ (BA) Lang Ger 1965, (MA) Ed 1967; Eng & Supervisory Cert; *cr:* Liberty HS Ger Tchr 1965-67; Freedom HS G Eng Tchr, Eng Supvr 1985-92; Eng Chprsn 1981-; *ai:* Freedom Forum Newspaper 1973-92; NCTE; ASCD; *office:* Freedom H S 3149 Cheste Bethlehem PA 18017

AN, KYLE A., Director of Bands & Orchestra; *b:* Lewiston, ME; *m:* ine Adams; *ed:* Plymouth St Coll (BS) Music Ed 1991; *cr:* Houlton Band Dir 1991-92; Dirigo HS Music Dir 1993; Oxford Hills HS Orch Dir 1994-; *ai:* Jazz Ensemble, Marching Band Dir; Tech ; MENC 1990-; MMEA, NBA 1991-; IAJE 1992-; NEA, MTA 1993-; e League of ME Distinguished Svc Awd; *office:* Oxford Hills HS 250 St South Paris ME 04281*

AN, LILLIE M. (RICHARDSON), 1st Grade Teacher; *b:* ston, SC; *m:* Herbert; *c:* Terry Tyrone, Darryl Leonard, Derrick ne; Errol Gerard; *ed:* Allen Univ (BA) Elem Ed, Eng 1960; City Univ (MS) Remedial Rdng 1972; Hunter Coll 30 Credit Hrs; In Svc es 24 Credit Hrs; Fiorella H. LaGuardia Comm Coll Visual Arts 16 Hrs; *cr:* Bonds Wilson HS Lang Arts Tchr 1961-63; Bapt Hill HS Arts Tchr 1963-64; PS 154X Tchr of CB in DES 1966-76; PS 65X f CB in DES 1976-94; PS 40X Tchr of CB in DES 1994-; *ai:* I Love ad Club Adv; Music with Movement Group Coach; Church Sunday Tchr; UFT, AFT 1966-; United Meth Comm Church, Tenants Assn Mother of Yr Awd; 25 Yrs Svc Awd; *home:* PO Box 588 Bronx NY

AN, MARGARET L., Spanish Teacher; *b:* Brockton, MA; *m:* ard E. Jr.; *c:* Hubbard William; *ed:* Wheaton Coll (BA) Span, Ed Schl for Intnl Trng (MAT) Span 1988; 30 Credits Beyond Masters e with Fitchburg St Coll; *cr:* Hingham Pub Schls Span Tchr 1984-88; & Heinle Publishers Lang Specialist 1989-90; Silver Lake Regnl Dist Span Tchr 1990-; *ai:* Organized Trip to Spain with Stdnts 1992; roned Trip to Mexico with Stdnts 1992; NEA, MTA 1984-; Phi Beta 1984-; Delta Kappa Gamma 1992-; *office:* Silver Lake Regnl HS embroke St Kingston MA 02364*

AN, MARK EDWARD, Health Teacher; *b:* Warren, OH; *m:* Linda rkovich; *c:* Zachary; *ed:* Youngstown St Univ (BSEd) PE 1986; *cr:* side HS 8th-10th Grd Hlth Tchr 1986-; *ai:* Boys Jr Var Bsktbl Coach; DEA 1986-; Selected into #1 Club for Tchrs Who Made A ence; *office:* Riverside HS 585 Riverside Dr Painesville OH 44077

AN, MATTIE JOYCE, 4th & 5th Grade Teacher; *b:* Sanford, FL; rold; *c:* Hallison A., Matthew J.; *ed:* Onondaga Comm Coll (AA) Elem Ed 1974; SUNY at Cortland (BS) Early Elem Ed 1976; use Univ (MS) Early Elem Ed 1982; *cr:* Delaware Elem Schl oom Tchr 1977-; *ai:* NYSUT, AFT 1977-; Christ MS Bapt Church *

AN, MICHAEL WILLIAM, Mathematics Teacher; *b:* Quonset Pt I; *m:* Joan E. McGuiness; *c:* Kathryn Elizabeth; *ed:* Glassboro St BA) Math 1989; *cr:* Toms River Regional Schls Math Tchr 1990-; *ai:* rack & Var Ftbl Asst Coach; DECA Activities Personnel; NJEA ; TREA 1990-; ACEP 1993-; *office:* Toms River HS North Old old Rd Toms River NJ 08753

AN, PAMELA LEE, Eighth Grade Teacher; *b:* Toledo, OH; *ed:* of Toledo (BA) Ed 1983; OH St Univ Pre-Med; *cr:* Whitmer Sr HS Sci Tchr 1984-87; Cardinal Stritch HS Math Tchr 1987-88; St e Schl Seventh Grd Tchr 1988-89; St Catherine Schl Seventh Grd 989-91; Blessed Sacrament Schl Eighth Grd Tchr 1991-; *ai:* NCEA NSTA 1991-; Springbrook Civic Assn 1989-, VP 2 Yrs; *office:* ed Sacrament Schl 2216 Castlewood Dr Toledo OH 43613

AN, PATRICK JOSEPH, Social Studies Teacher; *b:* Cleveland, *m:* Susan Sawyer; *ed:* Kent St Univ (BA) His, Pol Sci 1986; Cleveland v Comprehensive Soc Stud 1988; Attending Grad Schl Kent St Univ n Cert; *cr:* C. F. Brush HS Soc Stud Tchr 1989-; *ai:* NHS, Silent Sport Adv; Soc Stud Curr, Sr Project Comm; NEA, OEA, NEOEA 1989-; nrs Soc 1984-86; Providence House Crisis Nursery Vol 1988-91; Larlham Fnd for Physically, Mentally Challenged Children 1993-; and Plain Dealer Editorials Pub, Bd of Contributors; *office:* Brush 75 Glenlyn Rd Lyndhst-Mayfld OH 44124

AN, STEVE, Resource Center Teacher; *b:* Flushing Queens, NY; *m:* erly Kaszak; *c:* Eric, Ryan; *ed:* William Paterson Coll (BA) Spcl Ed *cr:* Bound Brook HS Self Contained Class 1979; Wallington HS rce Ctr Tchr 1979-; *ai:* NEA 1979-; NJEA 1979-; WEA 1979-, VP; Wallington HS 234 Main Ave Wallington NJ 07057

AN, TERRY LYNN, A P American History Teacher; *b:* Mansfield, *m:* Linda Kay Freeman; *c:* Lea, Cali, Cody; *ed:* Taylor Univ (BSEd) rehensive Soc Stud 1970; Cleveland St Univ (MA) His 1981; Post n Ec OH Univ, Human Relations Cleveland St; *cr:* Madison HS Amer JS His Tchr 1970-73; Orange HS AP Amer His Tchr 1973-; *ai:* Track ; Sr Project, Class Adv; NEA; OEA; OTA; Greater Cleveland Cncl tud; YMCA, YWCA 1993-; Indian Guides & Princesses; Outstanding Yrs; *home:* 34741 Southside Pk Dr Solon OH 44139*

AN-COHEN, LAUREEN M., 7th & 8th Grade Science Tchr; *b:* and, NJ; *ed:* Georgian Court Coll (BS) Bio & Ed 1988; Working on Ed Admin; *cr:* E A Tighe Schl 7th-8th Grd Sci Tchr 1990-; *ai:* leading Coach; Summer Theatre Wkshp Drama Instr; After Schl Lib work Club Moderator; Friday Teen Nite Moderator; NEA & NJEA ; *office:* Eugene A Tighe Schl Amherst & Essex Ave Margate City NJ

ANOFF, CHRISTINE (KUNKO), Music Education Chair & Prof; nnstown, PA; *m:* Nicholas; *c:* Richard Iliya, Gregory Philip; *ed:* esne Univ (BSME) Music Ed 1969, (MME) Voice Performance 1970; y Musical Trng Inst Music Ed Diploma 1972; Attnd Liszt Acad of Budapest Hungary; *cr:* Duquesne Univ Prof 1972-; *ai:* Dean's Advy, rgrad Cncls Adv; Curr Revision Chair; MENC 1972-; OAKE 1973-, ACDA 1986-, Rep & Stans St Chair; Bulgarian Nationality Group ; St Bede's Church; children's Festivals Chorus of Pitts, NY Music Tchr ReTrng, Videos Grants; *office:* Duquesne Univ Schl Of Music orbes Ave Pittsburgh PA 15282*

AN-SQUIRE, JEANNINE M., English & Yearbook Teacher; *b:* OH; *m:* David; *c:* Christopher, Megan; *ed:* Univ of Toledo (BA) Eng, a 1982; Bowling Green St Univ (MA) Popular Culture 1987; Univ of o (MED) Scndry Curr; Post Grad Classes Adolescent Lit, borative Learning; *cr:* Bowling Green St Univ Instr, Flwshp 1982-84; of Toledo Ed Perspectives Childrens Lit 1985-86; Lima City Schls Tchr 1986-; Lima Tech Coll Instr 1989-; *ai:* Yrbk Adv; NEA; Delta a Gamma 1990-, Chm, Comm; Trinity House Bookstore Bd of es 1995-, Vice Chair; Ed Columnist Lima News; Ed Newsletter; 228 N Woodlawn Ave Lima OH 45805*

GENSEN, BETH ELLEN, Spanish Professor; *b:* Staten Island, NY; omas S. Covell; *c:* Megan J. Covell, Benjamin J. Covell; *ed:* Oberlin (BA) Span-High Honor 1975; Univ of WI at Madison (MA) Span (PHD) Span, Amer Lit 1986; *cr:* Univ Of Rochester Asst Span Prof 93, Assoc Span Prof 1993-, Mod Lang, Cultures Chair 1994-; *ai:* B. Anthony Inst for Womens Stud Asst; Multimedia Ctr Steering n; Modern Lang Assoc 1985-, Assembly Del; Phi Beta Kappa 1975-, Pres, Bd Mem, Iota of NY Chapter; AATSP 1987-; Book The Writing ena Peniatowska Engaging Dialogues Univ of TX Press 1994; rous Articles in Prof Journals; *office:* Univ Of Rochester Lattimore Rochester NY 14627

GENSEN, DONNA W., English Teacher & Dept Leader; *b:* Darby, *m:* John E.; *c:* Karen, Mark; *ed:* West Chester Univ (BS) rehensive Eng 1969; Villanova Univ (MA) Ed 1984; Lehigh Univ 15 Credit Hrs; Attnd East Stroudsburg, Penn St, Univ of WI; *cr:* Pottstown Northern Jr High Eng Tchr 1969-71; Boyertown Area Sr High Eng Tchr 1976-; *ai:* Mock Trial Team & NHS Adv; Prof Dev Cncl; Instr & Peer Coaching; Eng Dept Ldr; Drama Dir 10 Yrs, Dept Ldr; BAEA, PSEA & NEA 1976-; Keystone St Games 1987-91, Regnl Coord Gymnastics; Sister Cities of Boyertown 1992-, Exch Tchr to Ukraine; PA Tchr of the Yr Nom 1990; Kappa Delta Pi; Exch Tchr to Ukraine; Peer Coaching Trainer; *office:* Boyertown Area Sr HS 4th & Monroe Sts Boyertown PA 19512

JORGENSEN-KIMBALL, MARION, English Teacher; *b:* Boston, MA; *m:* Charles Kimball; *c:* Noah Jorgensen, Luke Jorgensen; *ed:* Emmanuel Coll (BA) Eng 1961; The Cath Univ of Amer (MFA) Theatre 1964; 15 Credit Hrs; *cr:* Mary Grove Coll Eng Instr 1966-70; Siena Heights Coll Eng Instr 1970-73; Massasoit Comm Coll Part-Time Eng Instr 1980-; West Jr HS Prgm for Gifted, Eng Tchr 1974-; *ai:* Performing Arts Comm Fac Chair; Restructuring Steering, Portfolio Assement Comm; NEA 1961-; MTA 1974-; MCCC 1980-; TAG 1974-92; Brockton Outstdng Tchr; Local Pol Campaigns; 11 Articles; Theatre Reviewer 1985-90; *office:* West Jr HS 271 West St Brockton MA 02401*

JORIS, IRENE (GEORGES), Teacher; *b:* Staten Island, NY; *m:* Louis; *ed:* Parsons Coll (BA) Ed 1968; NY Univ (MA) Ed 1969; 26 Credit Hrs Post Grad; *cr:* PS 16 Tchr 1969-70; PS 31 Tchr 1970-80; PS 39 Tchr 1970-80; PS 60 Tchr 1980-; *ai:* UFT 1969-; AFT CA 1970-; Hellenic Univ Club 1972-83.

JORISCH, MARA GOLDMAN, Mathematics Teacher; *b:* Brooklyn, NY; *m:* Robert; *c:* Jordan; *ed:* Hofstra Univ (BA) Ec 1980, (MS) Scndry Ed 1981, (CAS) Ed Admin 1985, (PD) Educl Admin 1988; 120 Credit Hrs Beyond Masters; ABD Eductl Admin; *cr:* Massapequa HS Summer Math Tchr 1982-; Uniondale HS Math Tchr 1982-94, Math Dept Chr 1994-; *ai:* Water Safety & Swim Instr; Lifeguard; Uniondale Tchrs Assn, AFT, Assn Math Tchrs of NY St 1982-; ASCD 1985-; Hofstra Univ Doctoral & Master Fellowship; West Publishing Co Textbook Review; *office:* Uniondale HS 933 Goodrich St Uniondale NY 11553*

JOSBENO, LARRY JOSEPH, Professor of Physics; *b:* Elmira, NY; *m:* Cecile Ann Quatrano; *c:* Deborah, John; *ed:* St Bonaventure (BS) Math 1962; Univ of NH (MS) Chem 1970; Grad Work Physics Cornell Univ, Rensselar; Grad Work Math Elmira Coll; *cr:* Elmira Free Acad Chem Tchr 1962-63; US Artillery & Missle Schl Survey Instr 1963-65; Horseheads HS Physics, Chem, Math Tchr 1965-89; Corning Comm Coll Physics Prof 1989-; *ai:* Fac Assn Chprsn; Observatory Co-Dir; Sci Tchrs Assn of NY St 1965-, Pres, Fellow; NSTA 1981-, Presidential St Awd 1985-86, 1988; AAPT 1979-, Bd of Dirs; Southern Tier Lib System Bd 1994-; Steele Memo Lib Bd 1985-, Pres; Elmira Corning Astronomical 1965-, Observary Dir; NSF Grants NH 4 Yrs, RPI 1 Yr; Princeton Woodrow Wilson Scholar 1983, 1987; Author ARCO Physics Review Book, Nautilius Math for Adults; Visiting Scientist Cornell Wilson Synchiotron 1986-87.

JOSCELYN, WARREN HENRY, Mathematics Professor; *b:* Roscoe, NY; *m:* Marcia E. Pascale; *c:* Thomas, Warren P., Meredith; *ed:* SUNY at Oneonta (BS) Math Ed 1962, (MS) Math Ed 1968; *cr:* Cairo Cntrl Schl Math Tchr 1962-66; Hudson Vly Comm Coll Math Tchr 1966-; *ai:* Little League Coach; Chancelor's Awd for Excl in Tchng 1973; Before Calculus 1981; *office:* Hudson Valley Comm Coll 80 Vandenburg Ave Troy NY 12180

JOSE, CHERYL ANN, Foreign Language Dept Chm; *b:* Uniontown, PA; *ed:* West VA Univ (BA) FR, Span 1974; Loyola Coll of MD (MA) Modern Stud 1989; *cr:* Bruce HS Span, Fr Tchr 1975-81; Archbishop Curley HS Foreign Lang Dept Chm 1981-; *ai:* CORD Adv; Schl Yrbk; Photography Club Moderator; Study Skills Coord; Span NHS Moderator; NCEA 1981-; Natl Assn of Tchrs of Span & Portuguese 1985-; *office:* Archbishop Curley H S 3701 Sinclair Ln Baltimore MD 21213*

JOSEPH, ARLENE, Science Teacher; *b:* New York, NY; *c:* Miriam, Phillip, Robert; *ed:* NY Univ (BA) Sociology, Geology 1952; Fairleigh Dickinson Univ (MA) Human Relations 1983; Attnd Montclair St Coll, Jersey City St Coll, William Paterson Cpoll, Inst for Educl Dev; *cr:* Englewood MS Sci Tchr 1966; Pasack Hills HS Earth Sci Tchr 1967-; *ai:* Environmental Club Adv; Peer Mediation Moderator; NEA 1966-; Natl Assn of Geology Tchrs, NJ Earth Sci Tchrs Assn 1967-; Astronomical Soc of Pacific 1977-; *office:* Pascack Hills HS Grand Ave Montvale NJ 07645

JOSEPH, DEBORAH HILTY, Mathematics Tech Assistant; *b:* Alamesa, CO; *m:* Richard L.; *c:* J. Daniel; *ed:* NCCC (AS) Math & Sci 1982; St Univ Coll at Buffalo (BS) Math, (MS) Educl Computing 1992; *cr:* NCCC Tech Asst Math 1980-; *ai:* NYSMATYL; NYCLSA; Altar Society.

JOSEPH, DOUG, HS Health & Amer History Tchr; *b:* Columbus, OH; *m:* Charlotte Bard; *ed:* Otterbein Coll (BA) Ed 1974; US Sports Acad (MS) Sports Medicine 1994; *cr:* Radnor Jr HS Soc Stud, PE Tchr 1976-81; Ostrander Jr HS Soc Stud, PE Tchr 1984-86; Buckeye Valley HS His, Hlth Tchr 1986-; *ai:* Golf Coach 6 Yrs; Var Asst Girls Bsktbl Coach 2 Yrs; Var Track Coach 9 Yrs; Buckeye Valley Tchrs Assn; OH Ed Assn; *office:* Buckeye Valley Schls 901 Coover Rd Delaware OH 43015*

JOSEPH, KATHLEEN EAMES, Former Teacher; *b:* Brooklyn, NY; *m:* Leslie Joseph; *c:* Lori; *ed:* Marymount Manhattan Coll (BA) Math 1972; Brooklyn Coll at CUNY (MA) Scndry Math 1977; St John's Univ (PD) Ed Admin & Supervision 1995; *cr:* The Mary Louis Acad Math Tchr 1972-93, Chprsn 1977-93; *ai:* OLA Sports Cncl 1980-, Sec, Asst Chprsn, Treas, Governing Bd Awd; OLA Eucharistic Minister 1987-; Tandy Scholar Outstdng Tchr; Who's Who in Amer Ed; Mary Louis Acad Svc Awd.

JOSEPH, KEITH JOHN, LD Aide & PE Teacher; *b:* Youngstown, OH; *ed:* Youngstown St U (BA) Sport Mgmt 1992; Akron Univ (BA) PE 1994; Outdoor Ed 12 Master Hrs; *cr:* Springfield Local Schls Sub Tchr 1993-95; Springfield Local HS LD Tchr 1995-; *ai:* Boys Var Ftbl Coach 1985-; Girls Var Track Coach 1990-; Girls Var Bsktbl Coach 1992-; *office:* Springfield Local HS 11335 Youngstown Pittsburgh Rd New Middletown OH 44442

JOSEPH, KENNETH WYCLIFFE, Mathematics Teacher; *b:* Georgetown, South Amer; *m:* Joycelyn W. Cosbert; *c:* Karen; *ed:* NYC Comm Coll (AAS) Accounting 1974; Baruch Coll (BA) Bus Mgmt 1991; Working on MS in Math Ed; Tchrs Cert Guyana Tchrs Coll 1966; *cr:* Guyana Tchrs Assn Tchr 1957-68; Manufacturers Hanover Trust Systems Officer 1971-87; NYC Bd of Ed Tchr 1990-; *ai:* United Fed of Tchrs 1990-; *office:* Meyer Levin HS 285 5909 Beverley Rd Brooklyn NY 11203*

JOSEPH, LAURA MUELLER, Assistant Professor; *b:* Huntington, NY; *m:* David; *c:* Jennifer; *ed:* Farmingdale Univ (AS) Dental Hygiene 1984; Old Dominion Univ Dental Hygiene (BS) 1985, (MS) 1987; Pursuing EDD at Columbia Univ; *cr:* Fairleigh Dickinson Univ Research Coord 1987-89; St Univ of NY at Farmingdale Asst Prof 1987-; *ai:* Stu Amer Dental Hygienist Assn Club Adv; Research Project Coord; Promotions, Alumni Steering, Bacheloriate Planning Comms; NY St Educators 1987-; Amer Dental Hygienists Assn, LIDHA, NYDHA 1984-; Amer & Intnl Assn Dental Research 1987-; Club Adv of Yr 1995; Pub Book 1995; Pub Articles; *office:* S U N Y Coll Of Tech At Frmgdl Rt 110 Farmingdale NY 11735*

JOSEPH, LAURIE B., Visiting Professor of Biology; *b:* New Haven, CT; *ed:* George Washington Univ (BS) Geology 1969; OH St Univ (MS) Experimental Pathology 1982, (PHD) Experimental Pathology 1986; Post Doctorate Yale Univ 1986-87, Univ of CT 1987-90; *cr:* Jefferson Univ Asst Prof 1990-92; Liposome Scientist 1992-93; Quality Biotech Sr Rsrch Scientist 1993-94; Gwyneed Mercy Coll Instr 1995; Trenton ST Coll Instr 1995; Ursinus Coll Visiting Prof 1994-; *ai:* AAAS 1973-; Sigmi Xi 1981-; Sigma Delta Epsilon; Amer Soc Cell Biologist 1987-; Juvenile Diabetes Fnd Rsrch Flwshp 1987-89; NIEHS Post Doctoral Flwshp 1986-87; Sigma Xi Rsrch Grant in Aid 1984-85; Numerous Articles Pub.

JOSEPH, PATRICIA TALLERICO, 8th Grade Reading Teacher; *b:* Pittsburgh, PA; *m:* Richard A.; *c:* Abbi; *ed:* Duquesne Univ (BS) Spec, Elem Ed 1975, (MS) Rdng, Lang Arts 1994; *cr:* Resurrection Schl Grd 7-8 Tchr 1975-82, Grd 6-8 Tchr 1987-; *ai:* SPFL Moderator; Confirmation Catechist; NCTE, IRA, Three Rivers Rdng Coun, PMSA 1995-; Nom Diocese of Pittsburgh Golden Apple Awd 1996; *home:* 539 Clemesha Ave Pittsburgh PA 15226*

JOSEPH, RICHARD E., Dean of Students; *b:* Far Rockaway, NY; *m:* Clare Stokolosh; *c:* Queens Coll (MS) Scndry Ed 1980; *ed:* 30 Credits Above Masters; 16 Credits Eng Lit & Creative Writing; Halsey Jr HS Eng Tchr 1970-74; Campbell Jr HS Soc Stud & Eng Tchr 1974-76; Leonardo Da Vinci Eng Tchr 1976-86f Dean 1986-88; Glendale Jr HS Eng Tchr 1988-, Dean of Stdnts 1995-; *cr:* After Schl Rdng Pgm; *ai:* United Fed of Tchrs 1970-; Mentor; Cert of Appreciation Supv of NYC Bd of Ed Summer Camp; Article Pub; *office:* Glendale Jr HS 74-01 78th ave GLENDALE NY 11385*

JOSEPH, RICHARD H., Biology Teacher; *b:* Springfield, MA; *m:* Margaret Newman; *c:* Ashlie; *ed:* Westfield St Coll (BS) General Sci 1968; Amer Intnl Coll (MST) Gen Sci 1972; Princeton Univ Woodrow Wilson Fellowship 1992; Hampshire Coll Human Genetics 1993; Cold Sprng Harbor Genetics Prgm 1995; *cr:* Duggan Jr HS Sci Tchr 1968-70; Holyoke Comm Coll Microbio, Zoology Tchr 1982-86; Agawam HS Bio, Physics Tchr 1970-; *ai:* NHS Fac Comm; Educl Assn Schlsp Comm Chprsn; Sci Club Adv; Tchr Acad Decathalon; NEA, MTA 1968-; AEA 1970-; NSTA; NATB; *office:* Agawam HS 760 Cooper St Agawam MA 01001*

JOSEPH, VICTORIA THERESE, Associate Professor; *b:* Springfield, MA; *m:* Patrick A. Baker; *ed:* SUNY at Albany (MLS) Lib Sci 1980; WNEC (JD) Law 1987; *ai:* Acad, Paralegal Placement & Internship Adv; HCBA 1987-; CBA 1989-; AAFPE 1990-; Twice Awded Elms Coll Prof of Yr; AAFPE Journal Ed-in-Chief; *office:* Elms Coll 291 Springfield St Chicopee MA 01013*

JOSLIN, MELISSA ANN, Biology Teacher; *b:* Schenectady, NY; *m:* Randall S. Harris; *c:* Benjamin, Catherine; *ed:* Hartwick Coll (BA) Bio 1975; Vanderbilt Univ (MS) Sci Ed 1980; Ball St Univ 4 Credit Hrs Genethics; Cornell 3 Credit Hrs Molecular Bio; *cr:* US Peace Corps Vol Sci Tchr 1975-79; Prince William Co Pub Schls Sci Tchr 1980-85; Averill Park HS Bio Tchr 1985-; *ai:* NABT, NSTA, AFT; Amer Soc Biochemistry, Molecular Bio Tchr Fellow RPI 1989; Golub Corp Tchr Scholar 1993; *office:* Averill Park HS 146 Gettle Rd Averill Park NY 12018

JOSWICK, DONALD VINCENT, Sixth Grade Teacher; *b:* Somerset, PA; *m:* Marie A. Meholic; *c:* Heather, Ryan; *ed:* Shippensburg Univ (BS) Elem Ed 1970; 3 Credit Hrs; PA St Univ 9 Credit Hrs; Univ of Pittsburgh 21 Credit Hrs; *cr:* Northeastern Schl Dist Fourth Grd Tchr 1970-72; Ferndale Area Schl Dist Second, Fourth, Fifth, Sixth Grd Tchr 1972-; *ai:* Girls Var Bsktbl Head Coach; PSEA, NEA 1970-; Knights of Columbus 1993-; *office:* Ferndale Area Elem Schl 100 Dartmouth Ave Johnstown PA 15905*

JOWETT, LINDA LANGEVIN, Geography Teacher; *b:* Southbridge, MA; *c:* Scott James; *ed:* Annhurst Coll (BA) Fr 1971; Amer Intnl Coll (MA) Ed 1984; His 27 Credits; Global Stud Washington DC; Cultural Stud Through Travel; *cr:* Southbridge HS Fr, His, Geography 1971-; *ai:* Stu Cncl Adv 1987-; Stu Act Coord 1987-; Schl Climate NASC Evaluation Comm Chair; Stu Poll Observer; NEA, SEA 1971-; SHS Sports Booster Club 1993-; Foreign Exch Stu Host 1985-91; World Exch Prgm of Amer Inc Pres; *office:* Southbridge HS 25 Cole Ave Southbridge MA 01550*

JOY, SUSAN CHRISTY, Fourth Grade Teacher; *b:* Pittsburgh, PA; *m:* John A. Jr.; *c:* Jonathan, Christopher; *ed:* Clarion Univ (BA) Elem Ed 1972, (MS) Elem Ed 1974; *cr:* Southwest Butler Cty Schls Elem Tchr 1972-74; A-C Valley Schls Elem Tchr 1975-; *ai:* PSEA, NEA 1972-; First Presbyn Church 1966-, Elder; Clarion Hospital 1965-, Vol; *home:* 4 Glenwood Dr Clarion PA 16214

JOYCE, ANNE JOHNSON, Fourth Grade Teacher; *b:* Cleveland, OH; *m:* Jon Loyd; *c:* Jeffrey, Jan Ahrens, David; *ed:* Wittenberg Univ (BS) Ed 1959; Wright St (MS) Tchr-Ldr 1985; Attnd Univ of Dayton; *cr:* Springfield Local Elem Tchr; Springfield City Teen-Age Pregnancy Prgm; *ai:* NEA; OEA; Grace Luth Church 1990-, Cncl; *office:* Springfield Local Schl Dist 3500 W National Rd Springfield OH 45504

JOYCE, ELLEN, Instructional Support Teacher; *b:* White Plains, NY; *m:* Joseph P.; *c:* Katy Mann, Holly; *ed:* U of MD (BS) Elem Ed 1969, (MS) Spcl Ed 1977; Post Grad Stud at Hood Coll & Western MD Coll; *cr:* Geog Club; Knowledge Master Club; Math Olympiad; *ai:* NEA 1976-; MCEA 1976-; *office:* Cedar Grove Elementary Schl 24001 Ridge Rd Germantown MD 20876

JOYCE, RON, Career Counselor; *ed:* Youngstown St (BA) Philosophy 1966; Kent St (MS) Ed Couns 1968; *cr:* OH Voc Rehab Cnslr 1966-68; Kent St Prof Rehab Couns 1968-69; Titusville Schls Career Couns 1969-; *ai:* Titusville Schls Alumni Assn Dir; NEA, PSEA 1969-; Rotary 1969-; Titusville Chamber 1980-, Bd of Dir; *office:* Titusville Schools 302 E Walnut St Titusville PA 16354

JOYCE, SHARON LEE, 5th Grade Teacher; *b:* Haverhill, MA; *m:* John J.; *c:* Amy, Sara; *ed:* Salem St Coll (BS) Elem Ed 1972; 12 Grad Credits Rdng; 100 Hrs Drug Ed Trainor; 18 Grad Credits Sci, Math, Tchr Effectiveness Trng; *cr:* Danville Elem Schl Tchr 1972-80; Sandown Cntrl Schl Tchr 1980-; *ai:* Chprsn Sci, AIDS, Curr Comms Coord Elem Schls Here's Looking at You 2000 Drug Prgm; AFT, 1991-, VP; NSTA 1987-; TTA 1972-, Pres, Treas, Sec, Co-Chm Negotiating Team; ST Anne's Choir 1987-; Top 25 Tchrs Timberlane Schl Dist; *office:* Sandown Central Schl 293 Main St Sandown NH 03873

JOYCE, TERESA PELLEGRINO, Fifth Grade Teacher; *b:* Passaic, NJ; *m:* Christopher T.; *c:* Maria Perry, Christopher Jr.; *ed:* William Paterson Coll (BA) Elem Ed 1958; *cr:* Franklin #3 Third Grd Tchr 1958-62; Jefferson #1 2nd Grd Tchr 1962-63, Kndgtn Tchr 1968-70; Mario J. Drago #3 Kndgtn, 5th Grd Tchr 1971-; *ai:* PTO; Site Based Mngmt Team; NEA, NJEA, EAP 1971-; Will Paterson Alumni 1959-; Clifton Yth Week 1980-83; Clifton Bd of Recreation 1984-90; Meml Day Parade 1985-, Chm; Clifton 75th Anniversary 1990-92, Sovenir Chm; *office:* Mario J. Drago #3 Schl 18 Belmont Pl Passaic NJ 07055

JOYCE, THOMAS, Pastor & Theology Teacher; *b:* Pittsburgh, PA; *ed:* Passionist Seminary (BA) Philosphy 1965; Fordham Univ (MA) Sociology 1972; 4 Yrs Theology for Ordination as Roman Cath Priest; *cr:* Immaculate Conception Church Asst Pastor, Theology Tchr 1972-78; Passionist Priest & Brothers Asst Provincial 1978-82; Immaculate Conception Schl Theology Tchr 1982-; Immaculate Conception Church Pastor 1982-; *ai:* Teen Club Dir; Brooklyn Tablet 1994-, Bd of Dirs; *office:* Immaculate Conception Schl 179-14 Dalny Rd Jamaica NY 11432

JOYCE, THOMAS C., French Teacher; *b:* Pittsburgh, PA; *ed:* Grove City Coll (BA) Fr, Rel 1978; Gordon-Conwell Seminary (MDIV) Theology 1983; Duquesne Univ (MA) Scndry Ed 1994; 9 Credits Russion Univ of Pittsburgh; 12 Credits Russian Norwich Univ; *cr:* Hengyang Tchrs Coll Eng Tchr 1989-90; Kieve St Pedagogical Inst of Frgn Lang Eng Tchr 1992-93; Falk Schl Fr Tchr 1993-95; Pine-Richland HS Fr Tchr 1994-; *ai:* Frosh Class Spon 1994-95; Soph Class Spon 1995-.

JOYNER, RACHELLE HABIG, Mathematics Teacher; *b:* Cincinnati, OH; *m:* Thomas William; *c:* Jeffrey, Jennifer; *ed:* Miami Univ (BS) Math, Ed 1979; Wrigh St Univ (MS) Scndry Ed 1987; *cr:* Fairfield Schls Math Tchr 1979-80; Springfield Cath Cntrl Schl Math Tchr 1981; Beavercreek HS Math Tchr 1981-82; Carroll HS Math Tchr 1982-84; Beavercreek HS Math 1984-; *ai:* Schlsp Comm; NCTM, OCTM, NEA, OEA, BEA 1979-; *office:* Beavercreek HS 2660 Dayton Xenia Rd Beavercreek OH 45434

JOYNER-GIFFIN, SALLY B., Adj Instr of Psychology & Ed; *b:* Richmond, VA; *m:* John E.; *c:* Holly Anne, John Grey; *ed:* Lyndon St Coll (BA) Behavioral Sci 1977; James Madison Univ (MED) Psyc, Cnslr Ed 1979; Addl 30 Grad Hrs; *cr:* Morgan Cty Schls Elem Schl Cnslr 1986-88; Coolfont Conf Ctr Dir Hlth Svcs 1980-84; Cntrl MD Cath Charities Therapist 1990-; Frederick Comm Coll Adj Instr 1990-; *ai:* Adj Fac Task Force; Natl Bd for Cnslr Cert 1986-; Escape Child Abuse Prevention Ctr, Vol Trainer 1992; James Madison Univ Tchng Flwshp; Lyndon St Coll Rita C. Bole Awd; *office:* Frederick Comm Coll 7932 Opossumtown Pike Frederick MD 21702

JOYNES, BETTY BROWN, Asst Prof & Fac Coord; *b:* Piper, AL; *m:* Embert; *c:* Sabreena, Jonathan Brown; *ed:* VA St Coll (BS) Dietetics 1971; NY Univ (MA) Nutrition 1976; Registered Dietitian 1972; *cr:* Dairy cncl Nutrition Consultant 1976; Stratford Convalescent Ctr Nutrition Consultant; Camden Cty Coll Asst Prof, Fac Coord 1976-; *ai:* Fac Assn Pres; Steering Comm Mid Sts Accreditation; Dietetic Club Adv; Amer Dietetic Assn 1972-; NJ Dietetic Assn 1972-, Cncl Chair; Southern Dist NJDA 1972-, Pres; Alpha Kappa Alpha 1968-; Advy Bd; Cty Head Start Prgm 1990-; Excl in Tchng Awd; Excl in Tchng Medallion Univ of TX; NY Univ Hlth Grant; Outstdng Young Women of Amer Awd; *office:* Camden County Coll Little Gloucester Rd Blackwood NJ 08012*

JOZEFOV, KATHY M., Sub Commercial Art Instructor; *b:* Wilkensburg, PA; *ed:* Art Inst of Pittsburgh (AA) Commercial Art 1978; Point Park Coll (BA) Design, Comm 1989; Seton Hill Coll Cert Mrktg 1993; *cr:* Lehigh Design Artist 1978-82; Westinghouse Electric Designer 1982-90; J-Communicates Art Dir, Owner 1990-94; Forbes Road East AVTS Sub Commercial Art Instr 1994-95; Beaver Vly AVTS Sub Commercial Art, Instr 1995-; *ai:* Allegheny Mountain Tennis Assn Dir of Mrktg 1985-91; Pittsburgh Racquet Club Advy Bd; *home:* 138 State St Wilmerding PA 15148

JUBB, ALICE L., Third Grade Teacher; *b:* New Brighton, PA; *m:* Philip; *c:* Meri, Cari; *ed:* Slippery Rock St Coll (BS) Elem Ed 1969; Masters Equiv Degree; *cr:* Blackhawk Schl Dist 2nd Grd Tchr 1969-81, 3rd Grd Tchr 1981-; Instrctnl Support Team 1995-; *ai:* PSEA, NEA, BEA 1969-; ASCD 1993-; Blackhawk Wellness Connection 1990-; Enon Presbyn Church 1965-; *office:* Blackhawk Intermediate School 635 Shenango Rd Beaver Falls PA 15010*

JUDA, PATRICIA S., HS English Teacher; *b:* Hartford, CT; *m:* Michael S.; *c:* Robert, Peter, Kristen; *ed:* St Joseph Coll (BA) His, Pol Sci 1974; Cntrl CT St Univ (MA) Rdng 1978; *cr:* St Augustine Schl 6th Grd Tchr, Rdng Coord 1974-78; St Mary's Coll 7th Grd Tchr 1979-80, Prin 1980-81; Northwest Cath HS Eng Tchr 1984-; *ai:* Jr Class Moderator; New Tchrs Mentor; NECA 1984-; *office:* Northwest Catholic HS 29 Wampanoag Dr W Hartford CT 06117

JUDD, DOROTHY CORSON, Second Grade Teacher; *b:* Boston, MA; *c:* Orrin C., Stephen, Mary-Ellen; *ed:* Tufts Univ (BA) Eng 1960; Fairleigh Dickinson Univ (MA) Psych 1973; Montclair St Univ; *cr:* 12 Corners Schl Tchr 1960-61; Franklin Schl Tchr 1970-78; South Mountain Schl Tchr 1979-; *ai:* NEA, NJEA 1970-; SOMEA; Pleasantdale Presbyn Church 1990-, Moderator, Bd of Deacons; Mini-Grant Governors Tchr Recognition Pgm 1990; ISOL Grant; Numerous Articles Pub; *office:* South Mountain Elem Schl 444 S Orange Ave W South Orange NJ 07079

JUDD, JEFFREY R., Orchestra Teacher; *b:* Summit, NJ; *m:* Ann K.; *c:* Julie, Jennifer; *ed:* Grove City Coll (BM) Music Ed 1985; Ithaca Coll (MM) Music Ed 1993; *cr:* R E Menzel Violins Inc Violin Maker 1986-89; Williamsport Area Sch Dist Orch Tchr 1989-; *ai:* 6th-8th Grd String Quartets; WASD Summer String Pgm Dir; PMEA 1989-; ASTA 1989-; *office:* Andrew G Curtin MS 85 Eldred St Williamsport PA 17701

JUDD, THOMAS E.,JR., Mathematics Dept Chairman; *b:* Johnson City, NY; *ed:* Ursinus (BS) Math 1969; Math Penn St, Trenton St Univ; *cr:* Hatboro Horsham HS Math Tchr 1969-89, Math Dept Chm 1989-; *ai:* Asst Spring Track Team Coach; Dist OBE Comm Asst Chm; NEA, PSEA, HHEA 1969-; NCTM, PCTM 1991-; Nom Champions of Learning Awd 1990, 1992; *office:* Hatboro Horsham Sr HS 899 Horsham Rd Horsham PA 19044

JUDGE, CHRISTINE M., English Teacher; *b:* Providence, RI; *ed:* Emmanuel Coll (BA) His 1959; Boston St Coll (MED) Ed, Eng 1963; 56 Addl Hrs; *cr:* Robert Earley Jr HS Lang Arts Tchr 1959-64; Lincoln Jr HS Eng Tchr 1964-69; Walsh MS Eng Tchr 1969-85; Framingham HS Eng Tchr 1985-; *ai:* Past Yrbk Adv; Class of 1993 Adv; NEA, MTA, FTA 1964-; *office:* Framingham HS 115 A St Framingham MA 01701*

JUDGE, JON CHARLES, Social Science Teacher; *b:* Littleton, NH; *ed:* Louisburg Coll (AA) Lbrl Arts 1976; Eastern CT St Coll (BA) His 1978; *cr:* A. Crosby Kennett HS Soc Stud Instr 1978-; *ai:* Girls Var Tennis Coach; Stu Cncl Adv; Project Grad Asst; NH Ed Assn, NEA 1978-; Discipline Comm, Curr Dev Comm 1995-; Class I Girls Tennis Coach of Yr 1994; Kneissl White Star Masters Tennis Coach of Yr 1987; *home:* PO Box 1807 Conway NH 03818*

JUDGE, ROBERT ANTHONY, Professor of Fine Art; *b:* Providence, RI; *m:* Janice Birch; *c:* Tracey, Kristen, Eric; *ed:* RI Schl of Design (BFA) Illustration 1961, (MS) Art Ed 1962; OH Univ (MFA) Painting 1966; *cr:* Ponaganset HS Art Tchr 1962-64; Comm Coll of RI Art Prof 1966-; *ai:* NEA 1966-; Mac Dowell Colony Fellow 1975; *office:* Comm Coll of RI 400 East Ave Warwick RI 02886

JUDICE, JOAN KANE, Spanish & English Teacher; *b:* Philadelphia, PA; *m:* Gregory; *ed:* Immaculata Coll (BA) Span & Ed 1972; Marywood Coll (MA) Bi; West Chester & Univ of PA 24 Credits for PA Permanent Cert 1973-75; PA Cert in Eng 1978; Queens Coll NY 6 Credits in Latin Amer Stud; Summer Prgm at Instituto Venezolano de Estudios Sociales Y Politicos Caracas Venezuela 1988; Cmptr Stud at Temple Univ, West Chester Univ & Philadelphia Coll of Textiles & Scis 9 Credits; 30 Plus Beyond Masters; *cr:* West Cath HS Span Tchr 1972-76; Archbishop Carroll HS Span Tchr 1976-90; Saint Joseph Univ Eng as Second Lang Tchr 1984-86; Delaware Cty Comm Coll Span & Eng Adjunct Tchr 1986-88; Haverford Sr HS Span & Eng Tchr 1990-; *ai:* HTEA, PSEA, NEA 1990-; ACT 1976-90; Maryknoll Call & Response 1990-, Vol Work in Summer at Oaxaca MX; Immaculata Coll 1988-, Masters Prgm Mentor; Natl Endowment for Hum-Tchrs Inst for Latin Amer Stud Fellowship; Atlas-Fulbright Fellowship Instituto Venezolano Carcas Venezula; Finalist Rockefeller Fnd for Foreign Lang Tchrs 2 Yrs; Finalist Natl Endowment for Hum 1 Yr; Whos Who Among Latin Amer Scholars 1992; Eng as Second Lang Tchng Awd at Saint Joseph Univ; Article Pub in Hispania; Curr dev & Pub in Eric & Resources in Ed at Columbia Univ; *office:* Haverford HS 200 Mill Rd Havertown PA 19083*

JUDKINS, RUSSELL A., Assoc Prof of Anthropology; *b:* Salt Lake City, UT; *m:* Ann Bunnell; *c:* Alexander, Benjamin, Thaddeus, Samuel, Gabriel, Austin, Briant; *ed:* Brigham Young Univ (BS) Anthropology 1966; Cornell Univ (PHD) Anthropology 1973; *cr:* Hobart Coll Instr 1969-72; William Smith Coll Instr 1969-72; SUNY Coll at Geneseo Asst Prof, Assoc Prof 1972-; *ai:* Native Amer Recognition Week, Prsnl Comm Chair; LDSSA Adv; Amer Anthropological Assn, Fellow; UUP; BSA, Troop Comm Chm; NEA Summer Insts; SUNY Grads Rsrch Initative Visiting Rsrch Prof SUNY at Buffalo; Grants: SUNY, Geneseo Rsrch Fnds, SUNY Conversations in Disciplines, UUP Travel Rsrch; Publications, Series Ed; *office:* S U N Y Coll At Geneseo 1 College Cr Geneseo NY 14454

JUDSON, JANE THRUN, Fifth Grade Teacher; *b:* Port Washington, WI; *m:* Richard D.; *c:* Jesse S., Dana R., Taylor L.; *ed:* Baldwin-Wallace Coll (BS) Elem Ed 1980, (MED) Supv 1993; *cr:* Avon Lake City Schls 5th Grd Tchr 1980-81, 2nd & 5th Grd Tchr 1981-86, 4th & 5th Grd Tchr 1986-95, 5th Grd Tchr 1995-; *ai:* Safety Patrol Adv Mentor; NEA & OEA 1980-; ALEA 1980-; Recognition of Excl Awd 1987, 1988 & 1995.

JUFFEY, ANGELA NINA, 7th-8th Grd Computer Teacher; *b:* Scarsdale, NY; *m:* Daniel A.; *c:* Mark Anthony, Mary Nina; *ed:* Monmouth Coll (BS) Ed 1977; Cmptr Cert Georgian Court Coll 1994; *cr:* D. D. Eisenhower Schl 7-8th Grd Sci Tchr 1977-93, 7-8th Grd Cmptr Tchr 1993-; *ai:* Sci Dept Chprsn 1983-93; Mentor Prgm MS Stdnts; NEA, NJEA 1977-; Natl Kidney Fnd Vol; March of Dimes Vol; Natl Energy Fnd Tchr Recognition, Natl Sci Tchrs Assn Tchr Recognition, Monmouth Coll Alumni Awds; *office:* Dwight D. Eisenhower Schl Burlington Rd Freehold NJ 07728*

JUGLER, BRIAN, Eighth Grd Amer History Tchr; *b:* Havre De Grace, MD; *m:* Cynthia Mc Larty; *c:* Bradley, Katherine; *ed:* Univ of Waterloo at Ontario (BA) His 1971; Univ of Bridgeport (MS) Counseling 1980; Western CT St Univ Ed; *cr:* Rogers Park MS 7th Grd Geography Tchr 1974-79; Danbury HS Amer His Tchr 1979-85; Broadview MS 8th Grd Amer His Tchr 1985-; *ai:* Boys Var Bsktbl Coach North Salem HS 1974-79, Bethel HS 1981-90; NEA, CT Ed Assn 1994-; Fairfield Cty Ftbl Ofcls Assn 1974-; Western CT Stbl Ofcls Assn 1974-, Pres 1988-89; *office:* Broadview MS Hospital Ave Danbury CT 06810

JUILIANO, FRANK J., English Teacher; *b:* Plainfield, NJ; *m:* Susan; *c:* Andrew, John; *ed:* Temple Univ (BS) Eng 1970; Rutgers Univ (MA) Eng Lit 1981; *cr:* Montgomery Twp HS Eng Tchr 1971-; *ai:* Acad League Adv; NJEA; NEA; NJ Cncl of Tchrs of Eng; Natl Endowment for the Hum Fellow 1983; Courier News Favorite Eng Tchr 1983; *office:* Montgomery Twp HS Burnt Hill Rd Skillman NJ 08558

JULESON, MARY RAMEY, Family & Consumer Sci Instr; *b:* Ayer, MA; *m:* Raymond E.; *c:* Raymond, Kelly Anne; *ed:* Manchester Comm Tech Coll (AS) Lbrl Arts, Scis 1070; Univ of CT at Storrs (BS) Home Ec Ed 1973, (MA) Ed Psych 1983; Post Grad Stud Ed GATE; *cr:* Memorial MS Eng, Rdng, Home Ec Tchr 1973-82; Sage Pk MS Tchr of Gifted 1983-85; East Hartford HS Family, Consumer Sci Instr 1991-; *ai:* Comm Svc; NEA, CEA, E Hartford Ed Assn 1991-; Amer Assn of Family, Consumer Sci 1993-; Children's Assoc Summer Theatre 1990-; Dev Original Curr Funded by St Grant; Co-Author Rdng Curr Relating Reading and Recipes, Values Curr Caring About People; *office:* East Hartford HS 869 Forbes St East Hartford CT 06118*

JULIAN, DAVID A., Microcomputer Instructor; *b:* Rochester, NY; *m:* Mary Petitti; *ed:* Bryant Stratton (AOS) Cmptr Sci 1982; Tech Math Undergrad Hrs; Applications Trng; *cr:* Bryant & Stratton Instr 1982-; *ai:* Cmptr Lab Admin; CIR, Course Design, Media Selection, Accreditation Comms; Dept Chair; MCBEA 1986-; Who's Who Among Stdnts in Jr Colls; Tchr of Quarter Awd; *office:* Bryant & Stratton Bus Inst 82 Saint Paul St Rochester NY 14604

JULIAN, MARY ALICE, Second Grade Teacher; *b:* Salem, OH; *m:* Joseph S.; *c:* Steven, Michael; *ed:* OH St (BA) Elem Ed 1964; *cr:* West Branch Schls Third Grd Tchr 1964-66; Salem City Schls Kndgtn Tchr 1984-85, Transistional First Grd Tchr 1985-87, Second Grd Tchr 1987-; *ai:* NEA, OEA, SEA 1985-; Big Brothers, Sisters 1992-, Bd of Trustees; *office:* Buckeye Elem Schl 1200 Buckeye Ave Salem OH 44460

JULIAN, RALPH DAVID, French Teacher & Dept Head; *b:* Southbridge, MA; *m:* Pauline Claire Servant; *c:* Matthew, Marc, Jonathan; *ed:* Assumption Coll (BA) Fr 1970, (MA) Ed 1980; Post Grad Stud Worcester St Coll; *cr:* Austin, Cate Acad Fr Tchr 1970-71; Mary E. Wells Jr HS Dept Head, Fr Tchr 1971-; *ai:* Co-Chm Act Day; Curr Ldrshp Team; Intnl Day Comm; Southbridge Ed Assn, MA Tchrs Assn, NEA 1971-; Southbridge Optimist Club 1985-, VP, Sec, 1st Place Comm Svc Awd; *home:* 24 Riverview Dr Southbridge MA 01550

JULIANO, JOHN CHARLES, Mathematics Teacher; *b:* Yonkers, NY; *ed:* Manhattan Coll (BS) Bio, Math 1960; Columbia TC (MA) Bio, Math 1961; *cr:* Gorton HS Math Tchr 1961-71; Roosevelt HS Math Tchr 1971-; *ai:* JV Acad Team Coach; NHS Selection Comm; Yonkers Fed of Tchrs 1961-; St Bartholomew Church Parish Cncl 1994-; St Barts Lector 1989-; NY St Tchr of Yr 1987; *office:* Roosevelt HS 631 Tuckahoe Rd Yonkers NY 10710

JULIANO, MARY ELLEN GIORDANO, Business & Computer Instructor; *b:* Batavia, NY; *m:* Charles Anthony Jr.; *c:* Jason; *ed:* St Univ Coll at Buffalo (BS) Bus, Distributive Ed 1975, Voc, Occupational Bus, Distributive Ed 1977; *cr:* Batavia HS Bus, Cmptr Instr 1975-; *ai:* Bus Tchrs Assn, Batavia Tchrs Assn, AFT, NEA 1975-; *office:* Batavia HS 260 State St Batavia NY 14020

JULIO, PAMELA SISSON, English Teacher; *b:* Erie, PA; *ed:* Edinboro St Univ (BS) Eng Ed 1988; Masters Equilvelency; *cr:* Fairview HS Eng Tchr 1988-; *ai:* SADD Adv 1988; Stu Cncl Adv 1989-94; Class Adv 1990-93; Dept Chprsn 1993-95; NCTE 1993-; NEA 1988-; *office:* Fairview HS 7460 Mccray Rd Fairview PA 16415

JUNEAU, JANET WANDERSEE, Kindergarten Teacher; *b:* Rochester, NY; *m:* George H.; *c:* Brian W., Michael James; *ed:* Cortland St (BS) Early Chldhd Ed 1960; *cr:* Pub Schl #13 Kndgtn Tchr 1960-64; Pub Schl #7 Part-Time Kndgtn Tchr 1964-65; Pub Schl #35 Part-Time Kndgtn Tchr 1965-66; Pub Schl #34 Kndgtn Tchr 1966-; *ai:* NEA, NYSTA, RTA 1960-; *office:* PS 34 Dr Louis A Cerulli 530 Lexington Ave Rochester NY 14613

JUNGBLUTH, EILEEN OBERNESSER, Kindergarten Teacher; *b:* Utica, NY; *m:* John; *c:* Nicholas, Jeremy; *ed:* SUNY at Geneseo (BA) Early Chldhd Ed 1973, (MS) Early Chldhd Ed 1976; Cnslng; *cr:* Brockport Cntrl Schl Kndgtn Tchr 19 Yrs, 1st Grd Tchr 2 Yrs, 1973-; *ai:* BTA Bldg Rep; Band Booster Pres; Stu Placement, Tech & Kndgtn Stud Comms; NYSUT 1973-; BTA 1973-; *home:* 17 Timber Trl Brockport NY 14420

JUREK, JEAN HAAS, Instr of Hlth Information Tech; *b:* Buffalo, NY; *m:* G. Michael; *c:* Amy, Michael; *ed:* Ithaca Coll Med Record Admin 1982; Grad Prgm at St Univ of NY at Buffalo, 9 Hrs; *cr:* East Pointe Hosp Dir of Med Records 1982-86; Self-Employed Med Record Consultant Long Term Care 1983-86; Naples Comm Hosp Asst Dir Med Records 1986-88; Carolyn Cave Assoc Inc Spec Projects Dir 1989-; Erie Comm Coll Instr Hlth Information Technology 1993-; *ai:* Adv Hlth Information Tech Org; Guest Instr Med Billing Prgm; Amer Hlth Information Mngmt Assoc 1982-; NY Hlth Information Mngmt Assoc 1988-; Hlth Information Mngmt Asso of Western NY 1988-, Ed Chm; Med Records Associative of SW FL 1982-88, Pres, VP; Fnd Rsrch & Ed FORE in Hlth Information Mngmt Grad Schlsp 1995; *office:* Erie Comm Coll North Cmps 6205 Main St Williamsville NY 14221

JURICH, PETER MICHAEL, High School Theology Teacher; *b:* Hempstead, NY; *ed:* St Bonaventure Univ (BA) Theology 1973; Univ of St Michael's Coll aT Toronto (MA) Theology 1980; *cr:* St Anthony's HS Theology Tchr 1984-; *ai:* Girls Var B Tennis, Sftbl Team Moderator; NCEA 1984-; South Huntington Tchr, Parent Resource Ctr, Policy Bd *office:* St Anthony's HS 275 Wolf Hill Rd Melville NY 11747

JURJANS, BAIBA ANNA (DABOLS), First Grade Teacher; *b* Credit ON, Canada; *m:* Peteris; *c:* Artis, Tija, Kaspars; *ed:* Lake Er (BA) Ed 1975, (MED) Ed 1978; Royal Toronto Conservatory of Mus Hillsdale Elem Schl 3rd Grd Tchr 1970-; Maple Elem Schl 3rd Grd, Tchr 1975-; *ai:* Girl Scout Ldr; Taught Latvian Schl, Piano, L Sunday Schl; NEA 1975-.

JURKOUICH, CAROL ANN, Business Education Teacher; *b:* P NJ; *m:* Thomas P.; *c:* Scott, Brett; *ed:* Montcalir St Coll (BA) Bus Ec (MS) Bus Ed Supvr Cert CBE Coord 1991; *cr:* Pompton Lakes HS Tchr 1968-74; Lee T Purcell Assoc Exec Sec 1974-76; Franklin HS Tchr 1976-82; Wallkill Vly Reg HS Bus Ed Tchr 1982-; *ai:* FBLA, Schl Store Adv; CBE Coord; NHS, Schlsp, & Scholar Ath Comm; & NJBEA 1968-, WVEA 1982-, Sec; Delta Pi Epsilon 1988-, Sec, VF Nanassy Awd; Wallkill Vly Booster Club 1982-; Tchr of the Yr 1990 of the Month 1995; FBLA Outstdng Local Adv 2nd Pl 1996; Wallkill Valley Reg HS 9 Grumm Rd Hamburg NJ 07419*

JURY, ROGER ALLEN,II, English Teacher; *b:* Upper Sandusky, C OH St UNiv (BS) Eng Ed 1990; 3 Addl Quarter Hrs; 3 Semest Chapman Coll; 18 Grad Hrs Ashland Univ; *cr:* Old Fort HS Eng 1990-95; Cardington-Lincoln HS 1995-; *ai:* Boys JV Bsktbl Coach Jr HS Var Track Coach; Var Boys Bsktbl, Var Girls Track Coach; NE Ed Assn 1990-; Dist 6 Bsktbl Coaches 1990-95; Central Dist Bsk Bsktbl Coaches 1995-; *home:* 17799 S H 231 Nevada OH 44849

JUST, ROBERT JOHN, Music Teacher; *b:* Newark, NJ; *m:* Trudy *c:* Michelle, Robin; *ed:* Manhattan Sch of Music (BM) Performance (MM) Ed 1961; Post Grad Stud Univ of CO at Boulder, SUNY at Roc *cr:* NYC Bd of Ed Tchr, Supvr of Music 1961-93; Rockland Cntry Da Music Instr 1994-; *ai:* AFT, VFT 1965-; MENC 1961-; NYSSMA 1

JUSTICE, MICHAEL RAY, Math & Physics Teacher; *b:* Ironton, C Lydia Sharb; *c:* Lauren, Lindsay; *ed:* Rio Grande Coll (BS) Math Ed OH Univ (MS) Math 1992; *cr:* Vinton Cty Local Schls Math & P Tchr 1977-79; Amanda-Clearcreek Schls Math & Physics Tchr *office:* Amanda-Clearcreek HS 414 N School St Amanda OH 43102

JUSTICE, RAY EUGENE, Biology Teacher; *b:* Mt Sterling, O Claudia Crockarell; *c:* Lee Ann Reinhart, Lisa Davis; *ed:* Auston P Univ (BA) PE Hlth Bio 1960; Murray St Univ (MS) Arts of Sci 197 Undergraduate Hrs; 50 Graduate Hrs; *cr:* Madison Mills HS Bio PE 1960-61; Madison Plain HS Bio & PE Tchr 1961-73; Hilliard HS Bi 1973-; *ai:* Asst Coach Ftbl 35 Yrs; Coach Bsktbl, Bsbl & Sftbl 35 yrs 1960-; OH Ed Assn 1960-; Local Ed Assn 1960-; First United Meth C 1956-,Chm Official Bd 8 Yrs, Lay Ldr 8 Yrs, Sunday Schl Supt 8 Yrs Finance 4 Yrs, Chm Stewardship 4 Yrs, Sunday Schl Tchr 35 Yrs; S Schlrshp Murray St Univ; Ath Schlrshp Austin Peay Univ; *office:* H HS 5100 Davidson Rd Hilliard OH 43026

JUSTICIA-LINDE, PATRICIA ANN ADAMS, Spanish Teach Rochester, NY; *m:* Jose F.; *c:* Faye Elizabeth; *ed:* Wells Coll (BA) Sp 1970; Univ of Rochester (MA) Span Lit 1973; Credit Hrs St Univ at Buffalo, Buffalo St Coll; Universidad de Granada Spain, Under-Gr Abroad Prgm; *cr:* Orchard Park MS Span, Eng Tchr 1973-87; Orchar HS Span Tchr 1987-, Instrl Ldr, FL Dept 1989-; *ai:* AP Comm; NYSUT, NY St Assn Frgn Lang Tchrs 1973-; Western NY Frgn Edctrs Cncl; Item Writer NY St Regents Span Proficiency Examin *office:* Orchard Park HS 4040 Baker Rd Orchard Park NY 14127

JYRINGI, CRAIG AARNE, Human Anatomy, Physiology Tc Worcester, MA; *m:* Sheryl Lariviere; *c:* Nicole; *ed:* Worcester St Col Bio 1976; Grad Stud Cmptr Programming, Bio; *cr:* Auburn HS Bic 1976-78; David Prouty HS Anat, Physio, Cmptr Tchr 1978-; *ai:* Dir Ed, Audio-Visual; Spencer East Brookfield Tchrs Assn 1978-; MTA, 1976-; Awds Police Good Citizen, Lion's Club Pub Svc; *office:* Prouty HS 302 Main St Spencer MA 01562*

JZYK, LINDA ZONFRILLO, Biology Teacher; *b:* Providence, F John Edward; *c:* Nicholas, Alexander, Peter; *ed:* Brown Univ Biological & Medical Scis 1974; Bryant Coll (MBA) Pub Mngmt Attnd Providence Coll, RI Coll, Univ of RI; *cr:* Woonsocket Jr HS Li Tchr 1974-87; Woonsocket Sr HS Bio-Science Tchr 1987-; Sci Dept 1994-; *ai:* Substance Abuse Prevention, Talent Show Coord; SADD Feinstein Pub Svc Coord; Youth Leadership Spon; Strategic Plan C Schl Imprv Restructuring Tm; AFT #951 1974-; NSTA 1981-; RI Sci Assn 1977-; Educators for Blackstone 1994-; Delta Kappa Gamma 1994; Woonsocket Task Force on Substance Abuse 1992-94, Treas; B Univ Assn of Class Officers 1989-, VP, Brown Univ Class 1974; B Univ Class of 1974 Reunion Comm 1984, 1989, 1994; Boy Scout Tro Saylesville 1993-, Comm Mem; Friends of Blackstone 1992-; Slate Educ Comm 1995; Dept of Energy Residential Energy Inst 1979; Comm Hlth 1986, Bio 1990; Bryant Coll Acad Grievance Comm Woonsocket Ed Dept Exemplary Contribution Awd 1991; Providenc Lab & Demonstrations Coord 1987; RI Teen Inst Cert of Achvmt; RI Amer Natl Del 1987; Woonsocket Task Force on Substance Prevention Awd 1992; Commencement Speaker 1989; MADD RI E the Dolphin Awd; Feinstein Fnd Pub Svc Grant 1993; Con Lrn Energy Grnt 1995; *office:* Woonsocket Sr HS 777 Cass Ave Woonsock 02895*

K

KABALA, STANLEY JOHN, Social Studies Department Hea Webster, MA; *m:* Catherine Mahoney; *c:* James, Daniel; *ed:* Provid Coll (BA) Soc Stud 1963; Rhode Island Coll (MAT) His 1968; 45 C Beyond Masters From Clark Univ, Boston Coll & Worcester St Col Bartlett HS Tchr 1963-, Soc Stud Dept Head 1977-; *ai:* NEA, MTA, 1963-; NDEA Grant at Clark Univ 1968; Summer Study of US Constit at Boston Univ 1995; *office:* Bartlett Jr Sr HS 52 Lake Pkwy Webste 01570

KABALAN, MARY JANE TAMBURINO, Multi-Age Learnin Teacher; *b:* Youngstown, OH; *m:* Raymond T.; *c:* Raymond T. Jr., Pa Marla J., Philip D., Suzanne T.; *ed:* Youngstown St Univ (BS) Ele 1969, (MSEd) Cnslng 1991; 30 Addl Credit Hrs; *cr:* Youngstown Pub Tchr 1968-70, Sub Tchr 1971-74, Tchr 1984-; *ai:* Curr Planning C OH Network Team Assisting Schls & Comm; NEA, OH, Youngstown Assns 1984-; Amer Red Cross 1981-90, Water Safety Instr, Learn to Supvr; Girl Scouts of Amer 1981-85, Day Camp Staff; BSA 1979-85, ach, Den Ldr, Den Ldr Coach, Den Ldr Awd; Sigma Chi Omega; 3420 Kirk Rd Youngstown OH 44511

3, MARIANNE OTILIA, French Tchr & Lang Dept Chprsn; *b:* Czechoslovakia; *m:* Neil A. Crane; *c:* Samantha A. Crane; *ed:* town Univ (BS) Fr 1965; George Washington Univ (MS) Scndry Ed 50 Hrs Post Grad Stud; *cr:* Raymond Elem Schl FLES Fr Tchr); Lafayette Elem Schl FLES Fr Tchr 1970-77; Murch Elem Schl Tchr 1977-78; Shaw Jr HS Fr Tchr 1978-83; Mc Kinley HS Fr Tchr 3; Woodrow Wilson HS Fr Tchr 1983-; *ai:* Dept Chprsn; Curr ; City-Wide Lang Contest Comms; Served on Panels to Evaluate chr Tests; AATF 1980-; Greater Washington Assn of Lang Tchrs NEH Grant 1985; Wrote Video Series for Elem Schl Fr Lang g; *office:* Woodrow Wilson Sr HS Nebraska Ave-Chesapeake St Nw gton DC 20016*

A, KONRAD GRZEGORZ, Chemistry Assistant Professor; *b:* a, Poland; *m:* Lucyna; *c:* Adam; *ed:* Barry Univ (BS) Chem 1988; M (PHD) Chem 1993; *cr:* TX A&M Univ Undergrad Lab Supvr, octoral Position 1993; SUNY Fredonia Lecturer 1993-94, Asst Prof m 1994-; *ai:* Chem Club Adv; Amer Chemical Soc 1989-; AAAS Amer Inst of Chemist Awd 1988; Welch Fnd Rsrch Flwshp 1992; S U N Y Coll At Fredonia Fredonia NY 14063

A, MARY E., High School Art Teacher; *b:* Buffalo, NY; *m:* Richard Heather, David, Gretchen; *ed:* Rosary Hill (BS) Art Ed 1967; ter Inst of Tech (MFA) Painting, Graphis Design, Comm 1968; *cr:* nsille North HS Art Tchr 1968-80; Frontier Cntrl HS Art Tchr; *ai:* ub Adv; Dept Rep; NYSUT, NYSA 1968; Albright Knox; *office:* r Central Sr HS S-4432 Bay View Rd Hamburg NY 14075*

MAR, STEPHEN,JR., Fourth Grade Teacher; *b:* Northampton, PA; hryn F. Smith; *c:* Steven Placid; *ed:* Lehigh Carbon Comm Coll Ed 1972; Kutztown Univ (BSEd) Elem Ed 1974; Lehigh Univ) Elem Ed 1977; *cr:* Cetronia Elem Schl Fifth Grd Tchr 1974-84; y Manor Elem Schl Fourth Grd Tchr 1984-; *ai:* PSEA, NEA 1974-; Parkway Manor Elem Schl 768 Parkway Rd Allentown PA 18104

ULIS, JAMES A., Professor; *b:* Brooklyn, NY; *ed:* Hunter Coll at (BS) Music Ed 1972; Tuft Univ (MA) Music 1994; Indonesian an at New England Conservatory; Hindustani Music at Warren s; *cr:* NYC Pub Schls Chorus, Band, Guitar, Piano, Theory Tchr 6; Tuft Univ Instr 1990-93; Berklee Coll Prof 1986-; *ai:* mental Adv; Stu Club Adv; Stu, Fac Show Producer; Soc for nusicology 1993-; Am Fed of Musicians 1978-; AFT 1972-; NEA rant 1978; Prof Composer, Guitarist; *office:* Berklee Coll Of Music oylston St Boston MA 02215

UR, GEORGANN JERKO, Senior English Teacher; *b:* Indiana, Charles; *c:* Nicholas, Andrew, Christopher; *ed:* Indiana University BS) Eng 1963, (MED) Eng 1980; Post Grad Credits; *cr:* Apollo Schl Eng Tchr 1963-64; Homer Ctr Schl Jr Eng Tchr 1964-65; Indiana chl Sr Eng Tchr 1978-; *ai:* Eng Curr Comm; Former Core Team Former HS Newspaper 10 Yrs; PCTE; NEA, PSEA 1978-; IAEA; Schl Bd Excl Grants; *office:* Indiana Area Sr HS 450 N 5th St PA 15701*

UR, THOMAS MICHAEL, Sr HS Math Teacher; *b:* Windber, PA; Fresch; *c:* Matthew, Stefanie, Nathan; *ed:* St Francis Coll (BA) 969; Shippensburg Univ (MA) Math 1974; *cr:* Hollidaysburg Area Math Tchr 1969-; Penn St Altoona Campus Part-time Evenings Tchr *ai:* HAEA, NEA, PSEA 1969-; NCTM; *home:* 378 Washington St nsville PA 16635

URAK, EDITH ANN, English Teacher & Chairperson; *b:* on, PA; *m:* Joseph J.; *c:* Rachel, Joseph Jr.; *ed:* Wilkes Coll (BA) 967; Univ of Scranton (MA) Eng 1970; *cr:* Deposit HS Eng Tchr 9; Susquehanna Twp HS Eng Tchr 1969-70; Bellefonte HS Eng Tchr 3; Whippany Park HS Eng Tchr 1973-76; Immaculate Heart Acad chr 1987-88; Mary Help of Chrstns Acad Eng Tchr 1988-, Eng Dept 1995-; *ai:* Sr Class & Lit Magazine Adv; NCTE 1995-; NCEA *office:* Mary Help Of Christians Acad 659 Belmont Ave North on NJ 07508

MARCIK, MARCELLA ZIEMBA, English Department Chm & *b:* Yokohoma, Japan; *m:* Paul Michael; *c:* Rose Anna; *ed:* sburg Univ (BS) Scndry Ed & Fr 1970; Univ of Scranton (MS) Ed & Fr 1978; Supvr of Comm at Univ of Scranton; *cr:* Dauphin ch Schl Fr, Eng, His Tchr 1970-72; Fell HS Eng & Fr Tchr 1972-76; ndale Area Jr, Sr HS Eng Tchr, Dept Head 1976-; *ai:* NHS & Lit Club Strategic Planning Comm; Support Group Facilitator & Stu ance Prgm; Peer Mediation Facilitator; NCT of Eng, NEA, PSEA Friends of Carbondale Pub Lib 1996-; Carbondale PTA 1972-; ndale Area Booster 1994-; Article Pub Northeast Writers Newsletter; Carbondale Area Jr Sr HS Rt 6 Brooklyn St Carbondale PA 18407*

MARCZYK, BARBARA BROCHU, Chem, Hlth Tchr & Dept ; *b:* North Canaan, CT; *m:* David D.; *c:* Cheryl, Jon; *ed:* CCSU (BS) en Sci 1966, (MS) Bio 1973; Ed Univ of Bridgeport; Attnd Woodrow n Inst, Univ of Hartford; SMARTNET Sacred Heart Univ; *cr:* ury HS Bio Tchr 1966-71; St Paul CHS Grds 7-12 Bio, Chem Tchr *ai:* Schls Renaissance Prgm Dir; Earth Shuttle Field Trips Ldr; Fac, Schlsp Dir 1994, 1996; GHCEA Pres; NACST 1984-, Bldg Rep, Pres; GHCEA 1984-; Tchr of Yr 1989; CSTA 1990-; NEACT 1995-; ; Local Democratic Party 1980-; Grants Woodrow Wilson, TNET, Merrimac Coll; *office:* Saint Paul Catholic HS 1001 Stafford istol CT 06010*

MAREK, MARIANNE (LOTEMPIO), Earth Science Teacher; *b:* o, NY; *m:* Philip; *ed:* Buffalo St Coll (BS) Earth Sci, Gen Sci, ional Cert 1970-, (MS) Ed 1973; Permanent Cert, Earth Sci, Chem, ci 7-12 1975, Post Grad Stud; Canisusu Coll Post Grad Stud Stu Asst D'Youville Coll Post Grad Stud, React Forum Comm; *cr:* Alden HS Chem Tchr 1970-93, Gen Sci Tchr 1970-93, Earth Sci Tchr 1993-; uffalo Museum Sci Presenter, Vol; Frosh Class Adv 1993-96; lizing & Evergizing Approaches to Chem Tchng Presenter, Sec, PR; rt Teams for At-Risk Stdnts Sec 1991-94; Asst Track & Field Coach 84; NY St Advs Assn 1990-91, Adv; NY St Sci Tchrs Assn 1990-92; Chem Assn 1992-94; Regnl Earth Sci Tchrs 1993-; NY St Tchrs Assn Articles & Photographs Pub; Chem Ed for Pub Understanding Prgm chr 1990; Canisus Yth Connection Stu Asst Prgm 1991; Ldrshp Camp 992; *office:* Alden Cntrl HS 13190 Park St Alden NY 14004*

ZOR, CHERYL HYSONG, Work & Family Life Teacher; *b:* urgh, PA; *m:* Keith; *c:* Elizabeth, Abigail; *ed:* Douglass Coll at rs Univ (BS) Home Ec 1982; *cr:* Teen Challenge Tchr 1985-87; ard Chrstn Flwshp Childrens Ministry Coord 1986-95; Wgh Cath Schl Presch Tchr 1990-92; Union Local HS Work & Family Life Tchr ; *ai:* FHA Adv; NEA, OEA 1992-; Girl Scouts of Amer 1994-, ie Ldr; *home:* 161 N 19th St Wheeling WV 26003

AMANI, ADEL JAMIL, Chemistry Teacher; *b:* Zahle, Lebanon; *m:* bou-Ghanem; *ed:* East Carolina Univ (BS) Chem 1984; City Univ of MA) Polymer Chem 1987; 36 Credit Hrs Astronomy, Anthropology, : Townsend Harris HS at Queens Coll Chem Tchr 1990-; *ai:* Stdnts St Animal Cruelty Club Adv; *office:* Townsend Harris HS 149-11 ourne Ave Flushing NY 11367*

KADDEN, RENANA ROBKIN, English Teacher; *b:* Atlanta, GA; *m:* Ronald M.; *c:* Jonathan, Aytan, Jeremy; *ed:* Brandeis Univ (BA) Eng 1964; Columbia Tchrs Coll (MA) Eng 1965; *cr:* NYC Pub & Pvt Schls 1965-68; Yorktown HS Eng Tchr 1969-73; Westchester Day & HS Eng Tchr 1973-80; Avon HS Eng Tchr 1981-86; Farmington HS Eng Tchr 1987-; *ai:* Sr NHS Adv; NEA 1981-; NCTE 1985-; Phi Delta Kappa 1985-; Bd of Ed, Chprsn; Hebrew HS Bd of Dirs; Article Pub; *office:* Farmington HS 10 Monteith Dr Farmington CT 06034*

KADERLY, PEG A., Title I Teacher; *b:* Cleveland, OH; *m:* Bill; *c:* Sheri Anderson, Wayne, Tracy; *ed:* Ashland Coll (BA) Elem Ed 1967; *cr:* Ashland City Schl 4th Grd Tchr 1967-68, 3rd Grd Tchr 1968-74; Southeast Local Schl 5th-6th Grd, Title I Tchr 1975-; *ai:* Ashland-Wayne Cty Prof Dev Comm; OEA, NEA, SELEA 1990-; Delta Kappa Gamma 1972-; United Church of Christ 1974-, Librn; Materials Grant for Gifted 1980; Selected for Visit by Gov 1984; Wayne Cty Arts Ctr Colonial Christmas Grant 1995, Displayed at Kennedy Arts Ctr; Local Tchrs Org Outstdng Tchr Awd 1988; MS Edctrs Delegation to Russia Team Mem 1995; *home:* PO Box 225 Mount Eaton OH 44659*

KADET, GERALDINE, Retired Primary Teacher; *b:* New York City, NY; *c:* Rickie Kadet Teich, Alan; *ed:* City Coll of NY (BBA) Retailing 1949; Hofstra Univ (MS) Ed 1969; Prof Diploma Hofstra Univ; *cr:* Hewlett-Woodmere Dist #14 Schl Tchr 1970-92; *ai:* Club Adv; 4H Group Ldr; Hewlett Woodmere Tchr Assn, Rep.

KADOR, SUELLEN ANDERSON, Chemistry Teacher; *b:* Pittsburgh, PA; *m:* Peter F.; *c:* Karl E., Heidi E.; *ed:* Capital Univ (BA) Chem 1975; Grad Stud at Univ of MD; Tchr Inservice Courses; *cr:* Madison MS Sci Tchr 1975-76; Cabin John Jr HS Sci Tchr 1976-82; Winston Churchill HS Chem Tchr 1982-; *ai:* Chemathon Competition Spon; NEA 1976-; Washington Saengerbund 1988-; Best HS Tchr Comp Pgm Winner Project Seraphim 1984; *office:* Winston Churchill HS 11300 Gainsborough Rd Potomac MD 20854

KADRA, MARY SHEILA, Asst Coordinator & Teacher; *b:* Malden, MA; *m:* James M.; *c:* James, William, Daniel, Elizabeth Ristain; *ed:* Boston Coll (BSEd) Eng 1957; Cambridge Coll (MED) Ed 1986; Courses Syracuse Univ, Bard Coll, Univ of MA NEH Grant Writing Inst, Southern OR St NEH Grant Shakespeare Perf, Framingham St; *cr:* Midland Park Jr Sr HS 8-10 Grd Eng Tchr 1957-58; Holliston MS 7-8 Lang Arts Tchr 1973-80; Holliston HS 11-12 Grd Asst Coord, Tchr 1981-; Syracuse Univ Adj Instr, Writing, Eng Tchr 1981-; Nichols Coll Adj Inst Writing, Speech Lit 1991-; *ai:* NHS Fac Cncl; Frosh Cabinet; Project Advance; Frameworks Stud Comm Local; AFT, HFT 1973-; NCTE 1975-; MCTE 1995-; ASCD 1990-; Vokes Players 1978-, NETC Festival Best Actress 1986; Co-Author Painting with Words Amaginative Approach to Writing Competency; *office:* Holliston HS 370 Hollis St Holliston MA 01746

KAELI, DAVID RICHARD, Assistant Professor; *b:* Poughkeepsie, NY; *m:* Dianne T.; *c:* Melissa A., Emma T.; *ed:* Rutgers Univ (BSEE) Electrical Engrng 1981, (PHD) Electrical Engrng 1992; Syracuse Univ (MSCE) Comp Engrng 1985; *cr:* IBM Rsrch Advy Engr 1981-93; Northwestern Univ Asst Prof of Electrical & Comp Engrng 1993-; *ai:* IEEE Stu Chapter Adv; ACM 1990-; IEEE 1990-; NSF Career Awd Recipient; *office:* Northeastern Univ 409 Dana Rsrch Ctr Boston MA 02115*

KAEN, JULIE MULRY, Director of Development & Tchr; *b:* New York, NY; *m:* Michael D.; *c:* Daniel, Megan; *ed:* Coll of Mt St Vincent (BS) PE 1980; City Univ of NY (MS) Ed 1988; *cr:* St Barnabas HS AD Tchr & Dev Dir 1980-; NYC EMS Acad Tchr 1982-84; *ai:* SADD & Photography Club Moderator; Ath Dir; Kingsdale Vol Ambulance Corps 1980-88, Lt, Trainer; Bldg Block Childcare 1993-, Bd of Dirs VP; *office:* Saint Barnabas HS 425 E 240th St Bronx NY 10470

KAFALAS, DENNIS J., 8th Grade Language Arts Tchr; *b:* Woonsocket, RI; *m:* Barbara Dethomas; *c:* Daniel, Timothy; *ed:* RI Coll (BA) Eng 1984, (MAT-C) Scndry Eng 1989; *cr:* Woonsocket MS 8th Grd Lang Arts Tchr 1986-; *ai:* Lang Arts Curr Dev; *office:* Woonsocket MS 357 Park Pl Woonsocket RI 02895

KAGAN, MARLIN R., Mathematics Teacher; *b:* Denver, CO; *ed:* Boston St Coll (AB) Math 1974; Univ of Lowell (MS) Math 1982; *cr:* Francis Wyman MS Math Tchr, Team Ldr 1974-81; Marshall Simonds MS Math Tchr 1981-86; Burlington HS Math Tchr 1986-; *ai:* MAML Math League Adv; Advanced Placement Calculus Adv; Math Curr Comm Chprsn; Burlington Edctrs Assn, MA Tchrs Assn, NEA 1974-; Harley Owners Group 1990-; *office:* Burlington HS 123 Cambridge St Burlington MA 01803*

KAHL, JAMES E., Mathematics Teacher; *ed:* CA Univ of PA (BS) Math Ed 1968; OH St Univ (MS) Math 1974; Univ of Pittsburgh (BS) Cmptr Sci 1982; *cr:* East Allegheny Schl Dist Math Tchr 1968-; *ai:* GATE Tchr; PSEA, NEA, EAEA 1968-, Mbrshp Chair; NCTM 1970-; *office:* East Allegheny HS 1150 Jacks Run Rd North Versailles PA 15137

KAHLE, JANICE M., Kindergarten & EDK Teacher; *b:* Glandorf, OH; *ed:* OSU at Lima (BS) Elem Ed 1980; Post Grad Stud Wright St Univ; *cr:* Perry Local Schl Kndgtn Tchr 1980-81; Kalida Local Schl K-1st Grd Tchr 1981-; *ai:* Playground Comm; Jennings Scholar 1991-; Delta Kappa Gamma 1992-; St Michaels Parish Cncl 1994-; Regnl Resource Crt Lang Dev Grant; *office:* Kalida Elem Schl 208 4th St Box 358 Kalida OH 45853

KAHN, HAROLD G., 8th Grd Social Studies Teacher; *b:* Newark, NJ; *m:* Sandra Alterman; *c:* Matthew, Laura; *ed:* Upsala Coll(BS) Pol Sci 1959; Newark St His; Montclair St Eng; *cr:* Newark Schl 11th, 7th-8th Grd Tchr 1959-67; Parsipany-Troy Hills Cntrl MS 7th-8th Grd Soc Stud Tchr 1967-; *ai:* Drama Club Adv, Dir; Curr Planning, Chprsn Soc Stud Comm; NEA, NJEA 1967-, Parsipany-Troy Hill Ed Assn, Svc Awd 1992; Temple Beth Am Ed Comm; Parsippany-Troy Hill Comm Theater, Pres, Producer, Dir; Twp Pro-Ed Comm, Pres; Rho Tau Sigma, Natl Collegiate Ed Broadcast Awd; Gold-U Awd Svs to Upsala Coll; Educl Radio Prgm.

KAHN, JEFF, English Teacher; *b:* New York City, NY; *ed:* Cornell Univ (BA) Eng 1963; John Hopkins, Gaucher (MED) Ed 1964; 22 Hrs Past Masters in Eng, Cmptr Ed; *cr:* Colgate Schl Eng Tchr 1963; Increase Miller Eng Tchr 1964-; *ai:* Dist Curr, Schlsp Fund Comms; Dist Lang Arts Cncl; NEA, NYSTA, NYNEA 1964-; IMFA 1964-, Past Pres; KLDTA 1964-, Past Corresponding Sec; Local Comm Theatre Groups VP; NY St Eng Tchr of Yr 1982; Wrote Off Broadway Musical; *office:* Increase Miller Schl Rt #138 Goldens Bridge NY 10526

KAHRL, BENJAMIN RICHARDS, Social Studies Teacher; *b:* Rochester, NY; *ed:* Harvard Coll (AB) European His 1989; OH St Univ (MA) Military His 1992; Harvard Univ (EDM) Ed, Tchng & Curr 1993; *cr:* Plymouth South HS Tchr, Coach 1993-; *ai:* Frosh Boys Soccer, Head Var Boys & Girls Indoor Track, Head Var Boys Track Coach; MA Tchrs Assn, Plymouth-Carver Tchrs Assn 1993-; Extra Mile Tchng Awd 1995; *home:* 22 Samoset St # 1 Plymouth MA 02360

KAIL, RONALD, Science Resource Teacher; *b:* Wilkinsburg, PA; *m:* Carol Ann Mitterlehner; *ed:* Univ of Pittsburgh (BS) Bio 1972; California Univ of PA Tchng Cert Scndry Ed 1974; Masters Equivalency Western MD Coll, Trinity Coll In Svc Courses; *cr:* Robert E. Peary HS Bio Tchr 1974-81; Walter Johnson HS Bio Tchr 1981-83; Bethesda-Chevy Chase HS Bio & Sci Resource Tchr 1983-88; Gaithersburg HS Sci Resource Tchr 1988-; *ai:* Dept Chm; NEA; MCEA; MABT; MAST; NSTA; *home:* E Stratford Garden Ct Silver Spring MD 20904*

KAIN, JAMES E., Music Teacher; *b:* Lancaster, PA; *m:* Joyce A. Hess; *c:* Jennifer, Jessica; *ed:* Lebanon Valley Coll (BS) Music Ed 1969; Trenton St Coll (MA) Music 1973; Attnd Jersey City St Coll, Central CT St Univ; *cr:* Palmerton Area Schls Music Tchr 1969-71; West Morris Central HS Music Tchr 1971-; *ai:* Marching & Jazz Bands; Samll Ensembles; NEA, MEA, WMREA 1971-; MENC 1965-; North Jersey Area Band, Pres, Conductor, VP, Audition Chm, Mgr; Region I North Jersey Music Ed Assn, Mem Bd Dirs & Treas; All-St Band Procedures Comm; *office:* West Morris Central H S Bartley Rd Chester NJ 07930

KAINDL-RICHER, MARGIT, 8th-12th Grade German Teacher; *b:* Furth Bayern, Germany; *m:* Robert Richer; *c:* Albert; *ed:* Cntrl Coll (BS) Ger, Fr 1976; SUNY at New Paltz (MS) Fr 1978; Attnd Univ of Vienna Austria 1973, Sorbonne Univ of Paris France 1974; *cr:* Lycee Montaigne Mulhouse France Eng Asst 1976-77; Hyde Park Schl Dist Fr Tchr 1977-78; Onteora Jr Sr HS Ger, Fr Tchr 1978-; *ai:* Ger Exch Prgm Coord; AATG 1979-, Treas; NYSAFLT 1979-; Goethe House Outstdng Ger Tchr Awd 1989; *office:* Onteora Jr Sr HS PO Box 300 RR 28 Boiceville NY 12412

KAISER, JAMES F., Science Teacher; *ed:* Boston Univ (BA) Bio 1968; Univ of MA (MED) Sci 1971; CFA Sci Curr Dev Harvard Univ; *cr:* Sharon MS Sci Tchr 1968-; *ai:* IM Coach; Team Ldr; MAST 1993-; NCTA 1969-, Bd; *office:* Sharon MS 75 Mountain St Sharon MA 02067

KAISER, MARTIN, Language Arts Teacher; *b:* Brooklyn, NY; *m:* Elinor A. Ribner; *c:* Louis; *ed:* Brooklyn Coll (BA) Ec 1964; C. W. Port Campus of Long Island (MA) Educl Admin, Supervision 1981; Addl 30 Credits; *cr:* PS 87 Brooklyn Elem Grd Tchr 1965-68; PS 155 Queens Elem Grd Tchr 1968-75; PS 91 Queens Elem Grds Tchr 1973-; *ai:* AFT 1964-, Chptr Chm; NYDUT 1973-, Del; *office:* Public Schl 91 Queens 6810 Central Ave Glendale NY 11385

KAISING, KAREN ANN, Social Studies Teacher; *b:* Cincinnati, OH; *ed:* Thomas More Coll (BA) His, Scndry Ed 1988; *cr:* Anderson HS Short, Long Term Sub Tchr 1988-92; Eastern HS Civics, Amer Govt Tchr 1992-; *ai:* Citizens Bee Adv 1992-93; Stu Levy Comm Adv 1994; Stu Cncl Adv 1993-; Fine Arts Comm 1992-93; NEA, OEA 1992-; ELEA 1992-, Sec 1992-93; St John's Soc Ctr, Repair Affair, St Francis Soup Kitchen, Svc Trip to Carter Cty 1995-, Vol; *office:* Eastern HS PO Box 500 Sardinia OH 45171

KAJDASZ, BONNIE MARIE (PERUZZINI), Fourth Grade Teacher; *b:* Buffalo, NY; *m:* Richard; *c:* Amy, Jason; *ed:* St Univ of NY at Buffalo (BS) Elem Ed 1971, (MS) Educl Psych 1975; Tchng Elem Schl, Cmptr Tech Courses; *cr:* Union East Elem 3 Grd Tchr 1971-72, 6 Grd Tchr 1972-74, 4 Grd Tchr 1974-76, 3 Grd Tchr 1976-79, 4 Grd Tchr 1986-; *ai:* Sci K-6, Math K-4 Curr Coord; Dist Ldrshp, Schl Improvement, CCTA Negotiations, Least Restrictive Enviroment Teams; CCTA Union Rep; Comms; HS Equivalency Tchr; AFT, NYST 1971-; Cheek Cntrl Tchrs Assn 1971-, Bldg Rep, Negotiator; Tchr of Yr 1987; *office:* Union East Elem Schl 3600 Union Rd Cheektowaga NY 14225

KAKABAR, CAROLE M. (LEONARD), Science Teacher; *b:* Johnstown, PA; *m:* R. Timothy; *ed:* IUP (BA) Chem, Criminology 1984, (BS) Med Tech 1985, (BSEd) Chem, Bio 1990; Working on MED Educl Psych; Prin Cert; *cr:* Good Samartian Hosp Med Tech 1987-88; Miners Hosp Med Tech, Generalist 1988-; Penn Cambria HS Sci Tchr 1990-91; Cntrl Cambria HS Sci Tchr 1991-; *ai:* Mock Trial, Ski Club, Healthquest Challenge Adv; Liason, Strategic Planning, Family Life Curr Comms; SAP Team; PSEA Bldg, Negotiating Team Reps; NEA, PSEA 1990-, Bldg Rep, Negotiating Team; ATS, PSTA, NWF 1991-; NASSP, ASCO, PASCO 1996; ASCP 1985-; St Michael's Church 1992-, Lector; IU 08 Equity Team 1994-, Rep; Young Amer Sci Grant 1994; Kappa Delta Pi Inductee; Cert Tchr Assessor LEAP; *office:* Central Cambria HS 208 Schoolhouse Rd Ebensburg PA 15931*

KAKALEY, MICHAEL JAMES,JR., Math Teacher; *b:* Shenandoah, PA; *ed:* Penn St (BS) Mechanical Engrng 1990; Bloomsburg Univ (BS) Scndry Ed & Math 1994; *cr:* Bloomsburg Area HS Math Tchr 1994-; *ai:* Girls Bsktbl Coach; PSEA 1994-; NEA 1994-; NCTM 1996; *office:* Bloomsburg Area HS 1600 Railroad St Bloomsburg PA 17815

KAKAREKA, ARLENE, Latin & Gifted Teacher; *b:* Scranton, PA; *ed:* Marywood Coll (BA) Fr, Latin in Scndry Ed 1966; *cr:* Massena Cntrl HS Fr Tchr 1966-71; North Pocono HS Sub Tchr, Homebound Instr 1972-90, Gifted Instr 1985-, Latin Tchr 1990-; *ai:* Dead Lang Soc Adv; NEA, PSEA 1990-; CAAS-CW 1995-; Moscow Borough Shade Tree Commission 1988-, Chm, Commission Received Tree City USA Status 6 Yrs; N Pocono Pub Lib 1985-, Sec, Paper Folding Origami Sessons; *office:* North Pocono HS Church St Moscow PA 18444

KALADA, PETER RICHARD, Math Teacher; *b:* Jersey City, NJ; *m:* Elaine Rogers; *c:* Christina, Stephen; *ed:* Jersey City St Coll (BA) Math 1965; Monmouth Coll Guid Grad Work; *cr:* St Vincent Acad Math Tchr 1966-77; Essex Cath HS Math Tchr 1978-80; Orange HS Math Tchr 1980-; *ai:* Math Curr Comm; NJEA 1980-, NEA; First Ward Civic Betterment Assn, Environment Comm Chm; Math Tchng Awd 1988; *office:* Orange HS 400 Lincoln Ave Orange NJ 07050*

KALAFARSKI, JOHN MICHAEL, English Teacher; *b:* Providence, RI; *c:* Thomas, Joanna; *ed:* Providence Coll (BA) Eng Ed 1967; RI Coll 36 Grad Hrs in Eng; *cr:* Hong Kwong MS South Korea Eng Tchr 1968-69; Bristol HS Eng Tchr 1970-93; Mt Hope HS Eng Tchr 1993-; *ai:* Acad Decathlon Adv; NEA & BEA 1970-; *office:* Mount Hope HS 199 Chestnut St Bristol RI 02809

KALAN, SHARON (WINIARZ), High School English Teacher; *b:* Brooklyn, NY; *m:* Robert Stewart; *c:* Lana, Erica, Stephanie; *ed:* Queens Coll (BA) Eng 1973, (MS) Ed 1975; 38 Grad Credit Hrs Psych, Eng, Ed & Tchng Skills; *cr:* Woodside JHS Eng Tchr 1981-83; JHS #109 Eng Tchr 1983-86; Jamaica HS Eng Tchr 1986-; LaGuardia Comm Coll Adj Instr for Coll Now Pgm 1993-; *ai:* UFT 1981-; NYSUT 1981-; AFL-CIO 1981-; *office:* Jamaica HS 16701 Gothic Dr Jamaica NY 11432*

KALANJA, ROBERT A., Fifth Grade Teacher; *b:* Trafford, PA; *m:* Cynthia Keselich; *c:* Robert, Elizabeth; *ed:* Slippery Rock Univ (BS) Elem Ed 1974; Univ of Pittsburgh (MS) Elem Ed 1981; *cr:* Gateway Schl Dist Elem Tchr 1974-76; Franklin Reg Schl Dist Elem Tchr 1976-; Univ of Pittsburgh Instr 1993-; *ai:* Admin Asst; NEA 1974-; *office:* Sloan Elem Schl 4121 Sardis Rd Murrysville PA 15668

KALCICH, NORMA JEAN, HS Mathematics Teacher; *b:* Sunbury, PA; *m:* John Imbeck; *c:* Jeston, Matthew; *ed:* Bloomsburg Univ (BS) Math, Scndry 1970; Working on Masters Equivalency 27 Credits; *cr:* Lampeter-Strasburg HS Math Tchr 1970-76; Shikellamy & Lewisburg HS Sub Tchr 1978-83; Selinsgrove HS Math Tchr 1985-; *ai:* Stu Assistance, Instrl Support Team Comm; Peer Ldrshp Coord; Jr Class Adv; PSEA 1985-; PASAP 1993-; Trinity Luth Church 1978-; Liturgist, Pianist Sunday Schl, Lector, Chair; *office:* Selinsgrove Area Schl District Broad St Selinsgrove PA 17870

KALDAHL, BRAD G., Electronic Imaging Professor; *b:* Minneapolis, MN; *m:* Stacy Lynn Rice; *ed:* Mankato State Univ (BS) 1985; Attnd John Hopkins Univ, AZ St Univ, IA St Univ; *cr:* J&J Communications Mgr 1988-90; AM Multigraphics Instr 1990-91; Sierra Vista Pub Schls Instr 1991-92; Montgomery Coll Prof 1992-; *ai:* Ctr for Tchng, Learning; Provide Fac Trng with Multimedia; Consultant for Md Voc Rehab; GATF, IGAEA 1991-; CoAuthor & Implement Distance Learning Grant; Educl

Software Dev; Author of Commercial Image Editing Software; *office:* Montgomery Coll 51 Mannakee St Rockville MD 20850

KALE, TERRI A., 2nd Grade Teacher; *b:* Wilmington, OH; *m:* E. Thomas; *c:* Allyson, Aaron, Andy; *ed:* Bowling Green St Univ (BA) Elem Ed 1980; 21 Credit Hrs; *cr:* St Richards & Swanton 1st & 3rd Grad Sub Tchr 1980-81; St Alousius & 4th Grd Tchr 1981-90; Milton Elem 2nd Grd Tchr 1990-; *ai:* Frosh, JV & Var Ftbl & Bsktbl Chrldng Adv; Little League Mom; Ftbl & Bsktbl Team Mom; Stu Cncl; OEA 1990-; NEA 1990-; St Aloysius Altar Soc 1979-; Homemakers; Bowling Green Ath Boosters 1988-, Sec; Conflict Mgmt Grant OH Bd of Ed; BGSU Summer Frosh Pgm; *office:* Milton Elem Schl 22550 Mermill Rd Custar OH 43511

KALEMBA, JOYCE ANN PASSANTE, Spanish Teacher; *b:* New Brunswick, NJ; *m:* Stanley; *ed:* Upsala Coll (BA) Span 1967; NY Univ (MA) Span, Lang, Lit 1972; 30 Credit Hrs Univ of Madrid Spain; *cr:* Mountain HS Span Tchr 1967-70; Roosevelt Jr HS Span Tchr 1971-77; West Orange HS Span Tchr 1977-; *ai:* Sociedad Honoraria Hispanica Adv; AATSP, ACTFL 1972-; Foreign Lang Educators of NJ 1972-; NEA, NJEA 1972-; NEA & Kodak Grant; Cameras in Curr; Challenge to Tchr Creativity.*

KALERVO, ANGELA DEFILIPPI, 5th-8th Grd Teacher; *b:* Rochester, PA; *m:* David; *c:* Lori, Kristin; *ed:* Villa Maria Coll (BA) Early Chldhd 1979, (BA) Elem Ed 1980; *cr:* Good Samaritan Cath Schl Elem Tchr 15 Yrs; *ai:* Sci Fair, Drama Club Adv; PSTA 1995-; NCEA; NSF Presidential Awds for Excl in Sci & Math Tchng Prgm Nom; Golden Apple Awd Nom; *office:* Good Samaritan Catholic Schl 8th & Glennwood Ave Ambridge PA 15003

KALICICKI, MAJORIE GREENE, Office Technology & Asst Prof; *b:* Rayne Township, PA; *m:* John F.; *c:* Thomas J.; *ed:* IN Univ of PA (BS) Bus Ed 1972; SUNY at Binghamton (MA) Soc Sci 1989; 12 Grad Credits; SUNY at Oneonta 20 Grad Credits; *cr:* Norwich HS Bus Tchr 1972-88; St Univ of NY Asst Prof 1988-; *ai:* Integrated Comm Network Programming Task Force; NYSUT 1988-; UUP 1988-; Delta Kappa Gamma 1992-.

KALIGIAN, PETER LEO, Physical Education Teacher; *b:* Springvale, ME; *m:* Patricia; *c:* Brian, Mark, Lance, Scott; *ed:* Springfield Coll (BS) PE, Sci 1958; MI St Univ (MED) Exercise Physiology 1971; Attnd Univ of NH Guid 1964; *cr:* Pembroke Acad PE, Sci Tchr 1958-70; MI St Univ PE Instr, Coaching 1971-72; Douglas Mc Arthur HS PE, Hlth Ed Tchr 1972-88; Spaulding HS Weight Trng Instr, Hlth Tchr 1988-; *ai:* Var Bsktbl, JV Bsbl Coach; NH Assn PE Hlth Recreation & Dance 1988-; NH Assn Coaches; YMCA 1960-, Pres Bd of Dirs 35 Yrs; *home:* RR 1 Freedom NH 03836

KALINOWSKI, DOUGLAS P., Assistant Professor of Biology; *b:* Queens, NY; *m:* Mary Elizabeth; *ed:* Syracuse Univ (BA) Eng 1980, (BS) Bio 1980; Univ of IL at Urbana-Champaign (PHD) Bio & Genetics 1991; *cr:* St Univ of NY Upstate Medical Ctr Clinical Cytogeneticist 1981-85; Univ of VT Postdoctoral Research Assoc 1990-92; Daemen Coll Asst Prof of Bio 1992-; *ai:* Fac Senate 1995-; Environmental Mutugen Soc 1986-; Amer Assn for Advancement of Sci 1991-; CoAuthored Article in Mutation Research 1995; *office:* Daemen Coll 4380 Main St Amherst NY 14226

KALISKI, JANICE GRAHAM, Physics Professor; *b:* Johnson City, NY; *m:* Burton Stephen; *c:* Burton, Kristen Cassereau John, Karen, Michael; *ed:* SUNY at Albany (BS) Chem 1960, (MS) Ed 1961; NH Coll (MBA) Bus MIS 1985; Various Summer Insts; *cr:* Herricks HS Chem, Phys Tchr 1961-64; Derryfield Schl Chem Tchr 1980-82; Trinity HS Phys Sci, Physics Tchr 1984-85; NH Tech Coll Physics Prof 1985-; *ai:* NH Tech Coll Systemwide Pedagogy Comm; Day Care Ctr Advy Bd Adv; Opticianry Craft Comm; Mentor Part-time Physics Tchrs; Retention AD HOC Comm; Curr Dev; AAPT-NE Region 1987-; NHSTA 1985-; PHOTON 1987-, VP, Coord NH Physics Olypmics; NHSTE 1993-; ST Paul's UM Church 1975-, Church Schl Supt Christ Candle, Chair Bd of Trustees 1987-; Alpha Phi 1978-, Chptr Adv; PTO 1975-; YWCA 1976-81, VP; NSF Ldrshp Dev Wkshp Using Cmptr Algebra Software 1993, Tchng Physics Using Interactive Digitized Media 1994; *office:* NH Tech Coll At Nashua 505 Amherst St PO Box 2052 Nashua NH 03061

KALISTA, NANCY CONCANNON, ESL Teacher; *b:* Manchester, NH; *m:* Thomas W. S.; *ed:* Univ MA at Lowell (BS) Sociology 1975; Univ of MA at Boston (MA) ESL 1992; Royal Soc of Arts British Cncl; EPL Cert Tchng; *cr:* Wall Street Inst EFL Tchr 1983-86; Middlesex Comm Coll ESL Tchr 1992; Brighton HS ESL Tchr 1993-; *ai:* SABES Mem; MATSOL; Ed of From the Heart Collection of my ESL Stdnts Writings; Managing Ed of Four Wind a Collection of Northeast MA Adult Ed Stu Writings; Ed of Four Winds II, III, IV & V; *office:* Brighton HS 25 Warren St Brighton MA 02135

KALKSTEIN, PAUL, English Instructor; *b:* Philadelphia, PA; *m:* Marion Hobart Cale; *c:* Hobart, Molly, Emily; *ed:* Princeton Univ (AB) Eng 1965; Yale Univ (MAT) Eng 1967; *cr:* The Choate Schl Eng Tchr 1965-70; Phillips Acad Eng Instr 1970-; *ai:* Var Bsktbl, Lacrosse Coach; Chair of Tech Advy Cncl; Commission on Composition NCTE 1989-91; Commission on Writing Cncl for Basic Ed 1977-79; Eng Competence Handbook Longman 1976, 1979; Combination for Competence Longman 1982f Good Writing Pitman Learning 1982; *office:* Phillips Acad S. Main St Andover MA 01810

KALLAS, CYNTHIA GRESOCK, Kindergarten Teacher; *b:* Punxsutawney, PA; *m:* David J.; *c:* Stefanie N., Lindsay Y.; *ed:* Indiana Univ of PA (BSED) Elem Ed 1976, (MED) Elem Ed 1980; *cr:* Jenks Hill Elem Schlk 4th-6th Grd Rdng, Lang Arts Tchr 1977-81; Longview Elem Schl 4th-6th Grd Rdng, Lang Arts Tchr 1981-86; Mary A. Wilson Elem Schl 3rd Grd Tchr 1986-94, Kndgtn Tchr 1994-; *ai:* Co-operating Tchr Clarion Univ of PA; PSEA, PAEA 1977-; *office:* Mary A Wilson Elem Schl 407 E Mahoning St Punxsutawney PA 15767*

KALLAS, GEORGE CHRIST, Special Education Teacher; *b:* Washington, DC; *m:* Laura B.; *ed:* Prince Georges Comm Coll (AA) PE 1972; Univ of MD (BS) PE 1974; Spcl Ed 1980; *cr:* Dwight Eisenhower Jr High PE Instr 1974-79; Benjamin Foulois Jr High PE Instr 1979-81; Stephen Decatur MS Spcl Ed Tchr 1980-83; Eleanor Roosevelt HS Spcl Ed Tchr 1983-; *ai:* Var Mens Soccer Coach; Var Golf Coach; Ath Booster Club Comm Mem; Prince Georges Cty Rep to MS Scndry Schls Ath Assn in Soccer; MACS 1980-, Terry Colaw Awd for Svc; NSCCA 1980-; *office:* Eleanor Roosevelt HS 7601 Hanover Pky Greenbelt MD 20770*

KALMAN, GERDA D., History Teacher; *b:* Vienna, Austria; *m:* Aaron; *c:* Sumner; *ed:* Univ of NH (BA) His 1970, (MA) His 1975; 10 Hrs Russian Stud; 40 Hrs Art His; 40 Hrs Mid East; Two Yr Coll in Shanghai China; *cr:* Salem HS Dept Chair, Tchr 1970-84, Tchr, Head 1984-; *ai:* Founded, Run Annual Model UN; NEA, Phi Beta Kappa 1970-; SEA 1984-; Library 1995-; *office:* Salem HS 44 Geremonty Dr Salem NH 03079*

KALMAN, MARCIA ZARACHOFF, Social Studies Teacher; *b:* Brooklyn, NY; *m:* Sidney; *c:* Douglas, Cheryl; *ed:* NY Univ (BA) Fr 1962; Addl 6 Credits; 24 Credits Brooklyn Coll Grad Schl Tchr Ed Prgm; *cr:* Lafayette HS Fr Tchr 1962-65; St John Vianney HS Fr Tchr 1980-90, Fr, Soc Stud Tchr 1990-94, Soc Stud Tchr 1994-; *ai:* Schl Crisis Team; Peer Group, Frosh Class, Fr Club Moderator; NHS Selection, Discipline Bd Stud Skills Comm; Star Ledger Schlsp Comm; Phi Beta Kappa 1962-; Fr, His NHS NY Univ; *office:* St John Vianney Reg HS 94 Line Rd Holmdel NJ 07733*

KALMAN, RONALD JAY, Music Teacher & Band Director; *b:* New York City, NY; *m:* Judith; *c:* Marc, Bruce, Laurie; *ed:* City Coll of NY (BA) Music 1963; Montclair St Coll (MA) Music Ed 1967; *cr:* Elmwood Pk Pub Schls Music Tchr 1963-76; Paramus HS Band Dir 1976-; *ai:* Marching Band; Wind, Jazz Ensemble; Pit Orch; North Jersey Schl Music Assn 1963-, Auditions Host; NJ Music Edctrs, Music Edctrs Natl Conf 1963-; Guest Conductor, North Jersey Marching Band Festival, North Jersey Jr HS Band, North Jersey Jr HS Jazz Ensemble, Bergen Cty HS Band; *home:* 162 Middlesex Ave Paramus NJ 07652*

KALMUS, MITCHEL ELI, Biology Teacher; *b:* Brooklyn, NY; *m:* Blythe Evans; *ed:* Brooklyn Coll (BA) Bio 1987, (MA) Bio 1994; *cr:* Midwood HS Bio Tchr 1990-; *ai:* Bio Med Soc, Introspect, Sing Advs; Peer Mediator Supvr; Teach Elective Molecular Bio of DNA; AFT 1990-; Dev Curr Elective Molecular Bio of DNA; *office:* Midwood HS Bedford Ave & Glenwood Rd Brooklyn NY 11210

KALNINS, DACE, German & English Teacher; *b:* Germany; *m:* Sven; *c:* Grant; *ed:* Temple Univ (MS) Eng Ed 1971; Post Grad Stud Ger West Chester Univ; *cr:* Phoenixville Area Schl Dist Eng, Ger Tchr 1967-; *ai:* Ger Club Adv; NEA, PSEA 1967-; ACTFL-TG; Union of Latvian Bapt in Amer Women's Soc 1993-, Sec; *office:* Phoenixville Area HS Gay St & City Line Ave Phoenixville PA 19460

KALOGERAS, ARETA, Music, Band & Orch Teacher; *b:* Erie, PA; *ed:* Edinboro Univ (BS) Music Ed K-12 1975; Duquesne Univ (MED) Music 1987; Attnd Penn St Univ; *cr:* North Hills Schl Dist Instrumental Music, Strings, Band, Orch, Chorus Tchr 1975-; *ai:* Flagline, Majorette Spon 1975-89; Marching Band Asst Dir 1975-89, Dir 1990-; PSEA, NHEA, NSOA, MENC 1975-; PMEA 1975-, Curr Instr Rep; WBDNA; NBA; ASTA, Membership Chm; Delta Kappa Gamma 1990-; Bus & Prof Woman's Club; North Hills Bus & Prof Women Woman of Yr 1989; North Hills Jaycess Young Edctr of Yr 1988.*

KALOUDIS, GEORGE, Associate Professor; *b:* Kos, Greece; *m:* Penelope; *c:* Stergos, Naomi; *ed:* Panteios Schl of Pol Sci (BA) Pol Sci 1974; CA St Univ Fullerton (MA) Pol Sci 1976; Kaysas Univ (PhD) Pol Sci 1981; *cr:* Daniel Webster Coll Instr 1983-88; Rivier Coll Instr 1985-88, Asst Prof 1988-92, Associate Prof 1992-; *ai:* Adv Pol Camp; Model UN Adv; Dodecouese Soc VP; Bicentennial Comm Chair; Dodecouese Soc 1983; Amer Pol Sci Assn 1990; New England Pol Sci Assn 1990; New Historical Assn 1992; Published Bks, Articles, Essays; Tchr of Yr 1984-85, 1985-86; *home:* 31 Woodland Dr Merrimack NH 03054*

KALP, ROBERT D.,JR., Chemistry Teacher; *b:* Bayshore, NY; *m:* Andrea L.; *c:* Bobbi Jo, Jaci, Jarrette; *ed:* IN Univ of PA (BS) Chem Ed 1967, (MED) Sci 1973; Scndry Counseling Cert; 30 Hrs Beyond Masters; *cr:* Hempfield HS Chem Tchr 1967-68; US Army Criminal Investigation Lab Forensic Chemist 1968-70; Hempfield HS Chem Tchr 1970-; *ai:* Var Bsktbl Asst Coach 27 Yrs; Girls Sftbl Asst Coach 6 Yrs; HAEA, PSEA, NEA 1967-; *office:* Hempfield Area HS Rd 6 Box 77 Greensburg PA 15601

KALTER, EILEEN, French & Spanish Teacher; *b:* Monticello, NY; *m:* Ivan; *c:* Andrew, Sheryl; *ed:* Ithaca Coll (BA) Fr 1965; SUNY at New Paltz (MS) Fr 1971; Sorbonne Univ at Paris 4 Credit Hrs 1964; 6 Credit Hrs 1980; *cr:* Huntington Station Jr HS Fr Tchr 1965-66; Fallsburg Jr Sr HS Fr & Span Tchr 1966-70; Benjamen Cosor Elem FLES 1972-75; Monticello HS Span Tchr 1981-84; Fallsburg Jr Sr HS Fr & Span Tchr 1984-, Dept Coord 1990-95; *ai:* VP Fallsburg Tchrs Assn 1991-; Decorum Comm; NY St Assn of Frgn Lang Tchrs 1970-; Frgn Lang Assn of Sullivan Cty 1989-, Sec 1995-; Hadassah 1970-, Pres 1976-78; Bnai Brith 1966-; Town of Fallsburg Democratic Comm 1985-, Comm Person 1991-; *office:* Fallsburg Cntrl Jr-Sr HS Brickman Rd Fallsburg NY 12733

KALTREIDER, CAROLYN A., 8th Grade English Teacher; *b:* York, PA; *ed:* American Univ (BA) Eng 1969; Attnd Grenoble Univ in France; 36 Credits Masters Equivalency; *cr:* Dover Intermediate 8th Grd Eng Tchr 1970-; *ai:* NEA, PSEA & DAEA 1970-; Saint Paul Luth Church, Church Cncl; Spring Grove Borough, Planning Commission.

KALU-NWIWU, AZUBIKE, Professor; *b:* Aba, Nigeria; *c:* Azubike II, Chioma; *ed:* Univ at Buffalo (MS) Soc Stud 1983, (PHD) Soc Fnd 1988; *cr:* Univ of Buffalo Tchng Asst 1983-88; Erie Comm Coll Prof 1991-; *ai:* Jr League Soccer Coach; NEA 1992-; Pub Book: Educations and National Integrations in Nigeria.*

KAM, SUSAN F., Physical Education Teacher; *b:* Newark, NJ; *ed:* Ithaca Coll (BS) Hlth & PE 1975; Western CT St Univ 65 Grad Credits; *cr:* George Fischer MS 5th-8th Grd PE Tchr 1975-80; Patterson Elem K-4th Grd PE Tchr 1981-82; Kent Elem Schl K-4th Grd PE Tchr 1982-84; Carmel HS Hlth Ed 1984-86, 9th-12th Grd PE Tchr 1987-; *ai:* 5 Yrs MS Sftbl Coach; 8 Yrs Var Field Hockey; 5 Yrs JV & 3 Yrs Var Sftbl; NYSUT 1975-; AFT 1975-; Carmel Tchrs Assn 1975-, Bldg Rep; NYSHPEDR 1991-; New Fairfield Recreation Dept; Danbury Fast Pitch Sftbl League, Coach; New Fairfield Slow Pitch Sftbl League, Coach; *office:* Carmel HS 30 Fair St Carmel NY 10512

KAMAROUSKY, IRENE PETOCK, Sixth Grade Teacher; *b:* Minersville, PA; *m:* Joseph; *c:* Mary; *ed:* Kutztown St Tchrs Coll (BS) Ed 1956; 30 Credits Ed Toward Cert Elem Ed; *cr:* Reading Schl Dist Elem Tchr 1956-63; St Clair Area Schl Dist Elem Tchr 1965-66; North Schuykill Schl Dist Elem Tchr 1966-; *ai:* NEA, PSEA, NSEA 1966-.

KAMB, WILLIAM D., CAD Department Manager; *b:* Cambridge, MA; *m:* Donna M. Westwater; *c:* William Jr., Kaitlyn, Douglas; *cr:* Bristol-Plymouth Reg Machine Drafting Tchr 1994-95; *ai:* MA Tchrs Assn 1994-; *home:* 1414 Central St East Bridgewater MA 02333

KAMEN, RHONDA R., Spanish Teacher; *b:* Miami, FL; *m:* Mark J.; *c:* Marty, Jason; *ed:* Univ of FL (BA) Span 1970; Montclair St Coll (ME) Stu Prsnl Svcs 1974; LIU Coll of St Rose 30 Hrs Post Grad Stud; *cr:* East Ramapo Cntrl Schl Dist Tchr 1970-; *ai:* NEA 1970-; NYSFLT 1970-; *office:* Ramapo Sr HS 400 Viola Rd Spring Valley NY 10977

KAMENSHINE, MEL, Teacher; *b:* Brooklyn, NY; *m:* Roseann Davis; *c:* Sabrina, Chad; *ed:* Long Island Univ (BA) PE; Working on Masters in Guid; *cr:* Ericsson Jr HS #126 Tchr 24 Yrs; *ai:* Dance Team; Chrldrs; Weightlifting Pgm; Performances with Chrldrs for Sr Citizen Org; *office:* JHS 126 John Ericsson 424 Leonard St Brooklyn NY 11222

KAMERER, BARBARA JO, English Teacher; *b:* Lewistown, PA; *m:* James P.; *c:* Anne C., Susan J.; *ed:* Slippery Rock St Coll (BS) Ed 1974, (MA) Eng 1981; *cr:* Butler Sr HS Eng Tchr 1974-77; Butler Intermediate HS Eng Tchr 1978-; *ai:* NEA, PSEA 1974-; Bd of Deacons 1988-, Moderator; Hill Church 1991-, Pulpit Nominating Comm 1993; Lyda Mc Clure Cir 1984-, Ldr; *office:* Butler Intermediate HS 551 Fairground Hill Rd Butler PA 16001

KAMIMURA, IRENE HIROKO, 5th Grade Teacher; *b:* Honolulu, HI; *ed:* Univ of HI at Manoa (BA) Elem Ed, Psych 1983; Prof Degree; *cr:* Kahala Elem Schl ESL K-6th Grd 1983-85, 2nd Grd Tchr 1985-86, 2nd, 6th Grd Remedial Rdng, 1-2nd Grd Remedial Math, 4th Grd Enrichment Math, IRA Project Tchr 1986-88; Aina Haina Schl 4th Grd Tchr 1988-91, 5th Grd Tchr 1991-95; Conant Schl 5th Grd Tchr, Tchr Exch Prgm 1995-; *ai:* Dance Team, Pep-Squad Co-Adv, Choregrapher; Project PRIME NH Math Mem; Tech Comm In-House Mem; *office:* Aina Haina Elem Schl 234 East Side Drive Concord NH 03301

KAMIN, GARY DAVID, Chemistry & Physics Teacher; *b:* Buffalo, NY; *m:* Elizabeth C.; *c:* Scott, Lisa; *ed:* Widener Univ (BS) Chem 1971; Villanova Univ (MA) Scndry Schl Admin 1976; Attnd SUNY at Buff Grad Stud Chem; *cr:* Penn-Delco Schl Dist Sci Tchr 1972-82; W Univ Chem Instr 1982-86; Westchester Area Schl Dist Chem & F Tchr 1982-; PA Sci Tchr Ed Prgm Microcomputer Instr 198 Westchester Area Schl Dist Long Range Planning Comm; NSTA 198 Sci Tchr Assn 1985-; NEA 1972-; Pub in The Sci Tchr 1987; GE Tchr Achvmt Awd 1989; Tandy Tech Scholars & Amer Soc of Ma Outstanding Tchr Awds 1991; *office:* East H S 450 Ellis Ln West C PA 19380

KAMINSKI, FRANK W., History Teacher; *b:* Nanticoke, F Margarite Giudice; *c:* Blythe; *ed:* Kings Coll (BA) His 1967; Rutger (MA) His 1973, (MED) Ed 1977; Stu Prsnl Svcs 3 Credits & Audio- Aids 2 Credits from Kean Coll; *cr:* Iselin Jr HS 7th-9th Grd Soc Stu 1967-81; Colonia HS 9th-12th Grd His Tchr 1981-; *ai:* NEA, Woodbridge Twp Tchrs Assn 1981-; Curr Comms 1970, 1978, 19 Tchr Expectations & Stu Achvmt Ldr 1987; *office:* Colonia HS Colonia NJ 07067

KAMINSKI, JOAN M. JANKOWSKI, 5th & 6th Grade Teac Pittsburgh, PA; *m:* Robert J.; *c:* Jonathan, Christopher, Laura; *ed:* Coll (BA) Eng 1969; Duquesne Univ (MEd) Admin & Supervision *cr:* St Raphael Schl Tchr 1969-75; Immaculate Heart of Mary Tchr *ai:* Fund Raising; Rel Preparation for Sacraments; NASSP 1992-; Immaculate Heart Of Mary Schl 3029 Paulowna St Pittsburgh PA 1

KAMLOT, FRANCES LOPILATO, Fifth Grade Teacher; *b:* Wi MA; *m:* Frederick; *ed:* Boston Sr Coll (BS) Ed 1962; *cr:* C. M. B Schl 5-6 Grd Tchr 1962-83; A. C. Whelan Elem Schl 7-8 Grd Tchr 19 4th Grd Tchr 1992-94, 5th Grd Tchr 1994-; *ai:* Schl Improvement Bldg Based Support Team; NEA, MTA 1962-; *office:* A. C. Whelan Schl 107 Newhall St Revere MA 02151

KAMM, KAREN K., Antmy, Physlgy & Adv Bio Tchr; *b:* Decatur, Douglas C.; *c:* Audra, Amy, Adam; *ed:* Eastern IL Univ (BSEd) Z 1970; Miami Univ (MA) Bio Sci 1993; *cr:* Oglesby Grd Schl 6th Gr 1970-71; Johns Hill MS 7th, 8th Grd Sci Tchr 1972-84; Lakota HS Level Bio, Zoology Tchr 1984-; *ai:* Beta Sigma Phi 1984-, Pres 19 1993-; NSTA; Kappa Delta Phi; MAT Sponsored by Howard Hughes Prgm; *office:* Lakota H S 5050 Tylersville Rd West Chester OH 450

KAMMER, LONNIE D., Social Studies Teacher; *b:* Akron, C Donna; *c:* Lonnie Jr., Jeff, Naomi, Angie, Josh; *ed:* Univ of Akro Soc Stud 1978; *cr:* Goodyear MS Spec Ed Tchr 5 Yrs; Cntrl-How Stud Tchr 1 Yr; Ellet HS Soc Stud Tchr 3 Yrs; *ai:* Var Golf, Girls Track Coach; Coach of Yr 1995; Close-Up Adv; *office:* Ellet HS 309 Ave Akron OH 44312

KAMMERDIENER, HELEN VIRGINIA, Sixth Grade Teach Putneyville, PA; *ed:* IN Univ of PA (BS) Elem Ed 1964, (MED) El 1969; 30 Credit Hrs Beyond Masters; *cr:* Wilkinsburg Schl Dist 2 Tchr 1965; Altoona Schl Dist 5th & 6th Grd Tchr 1965-66, 2nd Gr 1966-67; Redbank Vly Schl Dist 5th Grd Tchr 1967-, 6th Grd Tc RVEA, PSEA & NEA 1965-, Bldg Rep; Putneyville United Meth 1967-, Lay Del to Conf, Chair Admin Bd; New Bethlehem Area Choir 1987-, Narrator; Seneca Rdng Cncl 1993-; Various Poe Newsletters, Local Newspaper, Etc; Book: My Turn to Care; Chr Song Lyrics Used by a Colleague in Church & Comm Functions; *hom* 1 Box 180 New Bethlehem PA 16242*

KAN, BEVERLY REHOR, Eng, French Tchr & Eng Chair; *b:* Clev OH; *m:* Timothy; *c:* Matthew; *ed:* Bowling Green St Univ (BSEd) Fr 1970; 48 Post Grad Hrs; *cr:* Brecksville-BH Mid Eng & Fr Tchr *ai:* Power of Pen Adv, St Sec & Bd of Trustees; Friend of Ed Chair Advy Comm; NEA, OEA & BEA 1970-, Treas, Comm Chair; Alpha Kappa 1982-, Altruistic Chair; Adoptive Families Support Assoc Grant Writer; Jennings Scholar; Awds: Outstdng Young Edctr, Fri PTA, Local Tchr of Yr, Power of Pen; Phi Delta Kappa; Classroom C *office:* Brecksville Broadview Hts MS 27 Public Sq Brecksvil 44141*

KANAGY, MICHAEL T., Mathematics Resource Teache Washington, DC; *m:* Annamarie; *ed:* Capital Radio (AAS) Electroni 1961; Univ of MD (BS) Math Ed 1966; Univ of WY (MS) Math, P 1970; *cr:* Northwood HS Physics, Math Tchr 1966-73; Churchill HS Tchr 1973-75; Walter Johnson HS Math Resource Tchr 1975-; *ai:* Cncl, Global Access Comm; APEX Scholars Comm; NEA, MSTA, 1966-; Montgomery Cty Math Tchrs Assn 1975-, Pres; NSF Acad Y of WY 1969-70; *office:* Walter Johnson HS 6400 Rock Spring Dr Be MD 20814

KANALLEY, ELIZABETH MAHANEY, Second Grade Teach Auburn, NY; *m:* Thomas J.; *c:* Kara, Brian, Kevin; *ed:* SUNY at Bro (BS) Ed, His 1973; SUNY at Cortland (MS) Elem Ed, Rdng 1974; Graw Cntrl Schl Elem Tchr 1973-; *ai:* Assessment Dev; Author Com Stud, Rdng-Writing Curr; Mc Graw Tchrs Assn 1973-, Pres; Seve Rdng Cncl 1986-, VP; Delta Kappa Gamma 1985-, Sec; St Mary Parents Guild 1983-; *home:* 676 Hoy Rd Cortland NY 13045

KANAWADA, LEO VINCENT,JR., Fifth Grade Teacher; *b:* Flu NY; *m:* Carol; *c:* Kristina, Sean; *ed:* Bucknell Univ (BS) Scndry E 1963; Maxwell Schl of Pub Affairs Syracuse Univ (MA) Amer His St John's Univ (PHD) 20th Cent His 1980; *cr:* Hicksville HS GATE Tchr 1968-85; East Street Schl Sixth Grd Tchr 1985-93; Old Cntry R Fifth Grd Tchr 1993-; *ai:* Phi Kappa Psi; Bucknell Univ Alumni Former Pres; Parkway Comm Church 1974-, Elder; Classics of N Suffolk Cty, Governing Body; BSA, Vigil Hnr Mem, Order of Arrow, Scout; Cited in Directory of Amer Scholars, Who's Who in NY; 3 Pub: Franklin D. Roosevelt's Diplomacy, Something Worthwhile L Times of Parkway Comm Church, Some Thoughts Worthwhile; Induc Hicksville Hall of Fame 1992; US Army Capt Vietnam War 19 Bronze Star; *office:* Old Country Road Elem Schl 49 Rhodes Ln Hick NY 11801

KANDALEC, RICHARD ALAN, Dept Coord & Tech Ed Ins Muskegon, MI; *c:* Julie, Jason; *ed:* Muskegon Comm Coll (Industrial Arts 1962; Western MI Univ (BS) Industrial Arts 1971; State Univ Post Grad 45 Credit Hrs; *ai:* Curr Cncl; Venture Capital; P HAL; Mentor Tchrs Assn Rep Cncl; Tech Club Adv; NEA 1972-; C Assn 1972-; OH Tech Ed Assn 1972-; Mentor Tchrs Assn Painesville YMCA Indian Pgm 1985-, Scribe & Chief; Lake Cty Comm 1994-; NE OH Mountain Bike Assn 1995-; James F Lincol Welding Fndtn Contest Judge 1983; *office:* Mentor HS 6477 Cen Mentor OH 44060

KANDEL, LINDA BECK, Math Teacher; *b:* Seattle, WA; *m:* Paul D *c:* Bree Kandel Linton, David Marcus; *ed:* Lewis & Clark (BA) Ed Univ of OR (MA) Ed 1969; *cr:* Cherry Creek Math Tchr 196 Chappaqua Mid Math Tchr 1971-72; Rippowam Cisqua Math 1980-83; John Jay Mid Math Tchr 1983-; *ai:* Riding, Math Count C Games & Breakfast Club; NY Mets Connection; NEA, NYSMTA NEMS 1986-; Midnight Run; *office:* John Jay MS Rte 121 Cross Riv 10518

KANE, BARBARA MORRISON, Associate Professor of Englis Leicester, MA; *m:* Robert G. Sr.; *c:* Kathleen, Robert Jr., Joseph, Emily; *ed:* Worcester St Coll (BS) Ed, Eng 1959, (MS) Ed, Eng 196 Addl Credit Hrs; *cr:* Leicester Elem Schl Grd 6 Tchr, PE Instr 195 ter HS PE Instr, Coach 1962-64; Annhurst Coll Supvr of Stu Tchrs Leicester Jr Coll Eng, Rdng Instr 1970-77; Becker Coll Eng Prof ai: Fac Adv; Phi Theta Kappa, Stu Affairs, Fac Senate Comms; Assn of Univ Women, NCTE; AFT 1978-; office: Becker Coll At ter 3 Paxton St Leicester MA 01524

:, BRENDA CAROLE, Fourth Grade Teacher; b: Providence, RI; m: ; c: David; ed: RI Jr Coll (AA) Liberal Arts 1967; Mount St Joseph BA) Elem Ed 1969; RI Coll (MA) Rdng Ed 1973; Providence Coll Elem Admin 1990; cr: Centredale Schl 4th Grd Tchr 1969-; Johnson es Weekend Coll Rdng Tchr 1976-78; ai: All Stu Theatre Founder, :er 1976-; Spelling Bee Coord 1984-94; AFT 1969-, Union Del; NEA Boosters Assn; PTO 1969-, Pres, Sec 1994-95; Regnl Inclusion Tm; Ed Advy Bd 1980-81; Corresponding Sec; Bldg Comm 1 Yr, Sec; CAP Spec Ed Comm; Peer Advocate, Trained in Crisis Intervention; nding Young Woman of Yr 1977; Tchr of Yr 1988; office: Centredale Schl 41 Angell Ave North Providence RI 02911*

:, BRIAN M., Asst Prof of Moral Theology; b: Newburgh, NY; ed: attan Coll (BA) Eng Lit, Rel Stud 1983; Boston Univ (MTS) Soc 1985; Marquette Univ (PHD) Moral Theology 1994; cr: Iona Prep nstr 1985-88; Edgewood Coll Instr 1989-92; Allentown Coll Asst 992-; ai: Coll Theology Soc 1990-; Soc of Chrstn Ethics 1992-; rous Articles Pub; office: Allentown Coll Of St Francis 2755 Station enter Valley PA 18034

:, DANIEL JOSEPH, Physical Ed Tchr & Coach; b: Ellsworth, ME; nie L. Watson; c: Nicholas R.; ed: Univ of ME at Orono (BA) PE cr: George Stevens Acad PE Tchr 1989-; ai: Var Soccer & Bsbl ; ME St Soccer Coaches, MTA 1989-; MAAPHERD 1988-91; Blue Summer Act 1989-, Bsbl & Soccer Clinics Instr; 2 Eastern ME pion Bsbl Teams Head Coach 1989-94; 1 Eastern ME Champion r Team Head Coach 1995; office: George Stevens Acad PO Box 816 Hill ME 04614

:, DOROTHY BRINJAK, Third Grade Teacher; b: Pittsburgh, PA; mes J.; c: Patrick J., James T., Jennifer L., Brian G.; ed: Duquesne BED) Elem Ed 1959; Attnd Univ of Pittsburg, Allentown Coll, PA St Duquesne Univ, Berks Cty Intermediate U, Allegheny Cty mediate Unit; cr: City of Pittsburgh Schls Elem Tchr 1959-61; Shaler Schls Sub Tchr 1964-74; St Bonaventure Schl First Grd Tchr 84; St Ignatius Loyola Schl Third Grd Tchr 1984-; ai: Sci Coord; 1978-; Mid Sts Evaluation Teams; Compiled Mid Sts Data for Mem ering Comm Evaluation 1986; office: St Ignatius Loyola Schl 2700 Albans Dr West Lawn PA 19609

:, DOUGLAS HENRY, Environmental Design Asst Prof; b: Boston, ed: Cntrl CT St Univ (BS) His, Pol Sci 1971; Univ of MA (BS) onmental Design 1976; Univ of PA (MLA) Landscape Architecture Bridgewater St Coll His Ed Grad Stud 1972-73; cr: Awbury etum Dir 1979-83; Temple Univ Landscape Arch Asst Prof 1983-89; are Valley Coll Environmental Design Asst Prof 1989-; Univ of PA ad Prgm Visiting Prof 1993-; ai: Ecological Landscape Design Club Curr, Campus Planning Comms; Planning & Resource Task Force for t Evaluation; Ecological Exhibit Phila Flower Show Chm; Awd Best ow for Ed; Phila Horticultural Soc; City Park Assn Awbury etum; Soc for Ecol Restn; PA Native Plant Soc; Heritage ervancy 1990-, Natural Areas Register Boardmember; Buck's tiful, Boardmember, Rules Comm Chm; Bowman's Hill Wildflower ve Assoc; Dev Environmental Design Prgm & Campus Master Plan; e Univ Dev Baccalureate Degree in Landscape Architecture Based in cological Philosphy, Sigma Lambda Alpha Landscape Architecture Charter Mem Alpha Rho Chapter 1993; Ecological Design Issues r & Speaker; Buckingham Twnshp Admn Site Usng envnmt-frdly h appl in ecol desgn solutns to stormwater mismngmt issues; office: vare Valley College 700 E Butler Ave Doylestown PA 18901

E, EILEEN MARIE, Kindergarten Teacher; b: Philadelphia, PA; ed: eph Univ (BS) Sociology 1975; Prof Cert in Theology; cr: Mater osa 1st Grd Tchr 1975-78; St Martin of Tours 1st Grd Tchr 1978-83; cilias Schl Kndgtn Tchr 1983-, Pre-kndgtn 1995-; ai: NCEA 1975-; 5128 Castor Ave Philadelphia PA 19124

E, ELIZABETH ANN OPAROWSKI, Rdng, Lang Arts & Rel Tchr; icopee, MA; m: Paul Jerome; c: Christopher D., Michael T., Paul J. Villiam P., Matthew E., Patrick S., Maura Elizabeth; ed: Westfield Elem Ed, Lang 1961; Addl 11 Credits Cmptr; cr: Streiber Elem Schl Tchr 1961-63; Blessed Sacrament Schl 4, 6 Grd Home Ec Tchr ; ai: Stu Cncl Adv 1986-; NCEA 1977-; home: 59 Fairfield Ave oke MA 01040

E, GRACE MULLEN, Teacher; b: Philadelphia, PA; m: James; c: , Jonathan; ed: Boston Coll (BA) Elem Ed 1982; PA Writing Project; aint Barnabas Schl Tchr 1982-87; DE Cty Comm Coll Adjunct Prof 95; Saint Gabriel Schl Tchr 1987-; office: St Gabriel Schl 233 wk Ave Norwood PA 19074*

E, JAMES P., Superintendent; b: Staten Island, NY; m: Maureen J. a; c: Deirdre, Donna; ed: Fordham Univ (BS) Eng Ed 1954; Columbia (MA) Stu Prsnl 1962; Fairleigh Dickinson Univ (EDD) Admin 1974; nbia Univ Prof Diploma Admin 1964; NY Univ Doctoral Candidate; clair St Univ Admin; Hunter Coll Latin Poetry; NJ St Dept of Ed Exec cr: Nyack Prep Schl Tchr, Eng, Dean of Stdnts, Coach Bsktbl 66, Headmaster 1966-75; Hamburg Pub Schl Dist Supt 1975-; ai: Dir rama Soc; Author Schl Plays; NJASA 1975-; Phi Delta Kappa, Kappa Pi 1962-; AASA 1985-; NJ Symphony Orch League 1978-, Pres x Chptr; Sussex Cty Roundtable Assn 1975-, Pres, Pres Awd; Franklin ral Museum 1978-, Trustee; Third Marine Division Assn, Capt CR; Diplomate Educl Admin NJASA; Who's Who Amer Univ & Coll; dtable Distngd Svc, Sussex Arts & Heritage, PTA Life Mbrshp, hardt Distngd Svc, Warren Cummins Distngd Svc Ed, Fordham Univ ni Achvmt 1994, Hamburg Citizen of Yr 1980 Awds; Author 9 Prof als; office: Hamburg Public Schl Linwood Ave Hamburg NJ 07419

E, KATHRYN STRAUB, Instructional Support Teacher; b: es-Barre, PA; m: Martin R.; c: Jared; ed: Coll Misericordia (BS) Elem 971; Univ of Scranton (MS) Elem Ed 1975; 54 Credit Hrs; hampton Cty Comm Coll Mortuary, Funeral Svc Cert 1990; Luzerne mediate Credits; cr: Dodson Elem Schl 5th Grd Tchr 1971-93, Instrl ort Tchr 1993-, Funeral Dir 1991-; ai: W-B Area Women's Club Pres; E Credit Union Bd Mem; Elem IM Bsktbl Coach; PSEA, NEA, EA, LCFDA, PFDA, NFDA 1971-; Luzerne Cty Drug & Alcohol n 7 Yrs; office: Dodson Elem Schl 80 Jones St Wilkes Barre PA 2*

E, KEVIN E., Music Teacher; b: Providence, RI; m: Lila Futernick; shua, Margaret, Sarah; ed: RI Coll (BS) Music Ed 1972, (MAT) Music 976; cr: Scituate Jr Sr HS Music Tchr 1972-; ai: Scituate Tchrs Assn , Negotiations 3 Yrs; RIMEA 1972-, Treas; ACDA RI 1984-, Pres , Pres; Amer Band 1979-, Chm, Bd of Dir; Smithfield Performing Arts 1990-; Southern Regnl Band, Chorus; Jr Hnrs, All City Chorus; nce for Arts Ed Excl Awd; office: Scituate Jr Sr HS 94 Trimtown Rd h Scituate RI 02857

E, MARGARET ANN MAC DONNELL, English Teacher; b: mouth, MA; m: Dennis Michael; c: Stacey, Catherine, Andrew; ed: anuel (BA) Eng 1969; Salem St Coll (MED) Rdng 1978; Attnd Univ owell, Harvard Univ; cr: Medford HS Tchr 27 Yrs; ai: Adv Class of 1984, Frosh 1992; NEA; MTA; NCTE; Wilmington Schl Comm 1990-93, Sec 1992-93; Wilmington Family Counseling Svc Bd of Dirs 1994-95; WHS SAC 1994-; Fac Senate, Sec 1995-; Travel Grant to Japan 1993; World of Difference Awd 1995; office: Medford HS 489 Winthrop St Medford MA 02155*

KANE, MARIE REDDINGTON, English Teacher; b: Scranton, PA; m: Thomas B.; c: Sarah J., Thomas W., Elizabeth M.; ed: Bloomsburg Univ (BS) Eng & Scndry Ed 1973; Beaver Coll (MA) Ed & Writing 1995; West Chester Univ PA Writing Project; PA St Univ Lit Stud; cr: Cntrl Bucks East Eng Tchr 1975-89; Cntrl Bucks West Eng Tchr 1989-; ai: START Mem; NEA 1975-; Cntrl Bucks Ed Assn 1975-; NCTE 1988-; Kappa Delta Pi 1992-; Recognition from Natl Fndtn of Advancement in the Arts; office: Central Bucks HS West 375 W Court St Doylestown PA 18901*

KANE, MICHAEL DEAN, History Teacher; b: Olean, NY; m: Valerie Buckley; c: Alison B., Megan B.; ed: St Univ of NY Cortland (BA) His & Ed 1977; St Bonaventure Univ (MS) ATE His 1984; In-Svc Hrs BOCES; cr: Olean HS Permanent Sub Tchr 1977-79; Hinsdale Cntrl Schl His Tchr 1979-80; Olean HS His Tchr 1980-; ai: Head Var Ftbl Coach; Weight Room Supvr; STAT; NEA & OTA 1980-; Southern Tier Coaches Assn 1994-; Western NY Small Schl Coach of Yr 1994-95; Big 30 Coach of Yr 1995; office: Olean Sr HS 410 W Sullivan St Olean NY 14760

KANE, NANCY DUNCAN, English Teacher; b: Binghamton, NY; m: Anthony; c: Mathew, Timothy; ed: Elmira Coll (BA) Eng 1967; Attnd SUNY at New Paltz 30 Credit Hrs 1968-90 & NY Univ; cr: Chenango Valley Cntrl Schl 10th Grd Eng Tchr 1967-68; Jamesville-DeWitt Cntrl Schl 10th & 11th Grd Eng Tchr 1968-69; Monticello MS 8th Grd Eng Tchr 1970-75; Eldred Cntrl Schl 7th-12th Grd Eng Tchr 1986-; ai: NYS Turnkey Trainer for Writing; 7th & 8th Grd Tchng Team Sr Tchr; Jr & Sr Acad Teams Coach; Schl Improvement Team for Effective Schls Rep; ECS Faculty Assn President 1994-; NYSUT & AFT 1986-; Sullivan Cty Youth Bd 1985-; Forestburgh Youth Bd 1981-86.*

KANE, RICHARD DAVID, History Professor; b: Phila, PA; m: Phyllis Levit; c: Scott, Randi, Gary; ed: Temple U (MA) His 1961; 60 Post-Grad Hrs; cr: Lehigh U Grad Asst 1962-65; Int Amer Instr1965; Rider Coll Instr 1966-68; Jersey City St Assoc Prof 1969-; ai: Phi Alpha Aota Adv; AFT; office: Jersey City St Coll 2039 Kennedy Boulevard Jersey City NJ 07305

KANE, ROBERT JOSEPH, Sr Instructor of Mortuary Sci; b: Boston, MA; ed: Suffolk Univ (BA) His, Ed 1966; New England Inst Cert Mortuary Sci 1961; cr: New England Inst Instr 1966-70; Kane Funeral Home Dir, Founder 1968-; Mt Ida Coll Instr 1989-; ai: Placement Cnslng; Mass Funeral Dirs; Bd of Hlth Easton 1981-, Past Chm; home: 605 Washington St South Easton MA 02375

KANE, SANDRA L., Gen Music Teacher & Choral Dir; b: Rhinebeck, NY; m: Edward F.; c: Peter, Meghan; ed: Dutchess Comm Coll (AS) Lbrl Arts 1977; Coll of St Rose (BS) Music Ed 1980, (MS) Spec Ed 1986; cr: Regina Coeli, St Peter's Schl Music Tchr 1980-81; Phoenix Cntrl Schl Music Tchr 1990-91; Rhinebeck Cntrl Schl K-2nd Grd Music Tchr, 6th-12th Grd Choral Dir 1981-; ai: HS Musical Vocal, Swing Choir Dir; Arts in Ed Coord; AFT 1981-; MENC, Dutchess Co Music Ed Assn 1980-; Rhinebeck-Rheinback Exch Prgm 1988-, Choral Dir; office: Rhinebeck HS PO Box 351 Rhinebeck NY 12572

KANER, CAROL ELIAS, French & Spanish Teacher; b: New Bedford, MA; m: Marc; ed: Boston Univ (BS) Fr 1972; 9 Credit Hrs Elms Coll Immersion Prgm Instensive Stu Fr 1992; cr: Nute HS Fr, Span Tchr 1973-75; Fairhaven MS Fr, Span Tchr 1975-81; Fairhaven HS Fr, Span Tchr 1981-; ai: Sister City Comm; Adv Pen Pal Club, Span Club 1981-94; MAFLA 1981-; Established First HS Exch 1994; Article Pub 1995; office: Fairhaven HS 12 Huttleston Ave Fairhaven MA 02719

KANGANIS, GEORGE E., French & Spanish Teacher; b: Greece; ed: Hunter Coll (BA) Fr 1966; Middlebury Coll (MA) Fr 1967; Sorbonne Univ of Paris Diplome D'Etudes Francaises 2e Degree 1967; cr: Eastview Schl Fr Tchr 1967-70; Bronx HS of Sci Fr, Span Tchr 1970-75; Riverdale Cntry Schl Fr, Span Tchr 1976-78; Darien HS Fr, Span Tchr 1978-80; Hunter Coll HS Fr, Span Tchr 1980-; ai: Northeast Conf Tchng of Frgn Langs Advy Cncl; Dean's Liaison Comm; Men's Issues Forum Adv; AFT, NYSUT 1967-; PSC-CUNY 1980-, Chptr Chair 1987; office: Hunter Coll HS 71 E 94th St New York NY 10128

KANIA, SARAH HODGE, Reading Coordinator; b: New Haven, CT; m: Michael A.; c: Kristen Emeline; ed: Univ of Hartford (BA) Ed 1974; Cntrl CT St Univ (MS) Rdng 1979; 6th Yr Rdng Course 1989; cr: Elmer Thienes-Mary Hall Schl 3rd Grd Tchr 1974-75; Gilend Hill Schl 4th Grd Tchr 1975-76; Elmer Thienes-Mary Hall Schl 3rd Grd Tchr 1976-82, Gifted Prgm Coord 1982-92, 2nd Grd Tchr 1992-95, Rdng Coord 1995-; ai: NEA, CEA 1974-; Marl Ed Assn 1974-, Ofcr 1979-83; Intnl Rdng Assn 1995-; Gilead Congregational Church 1984-, Chrstn Ed Comm 1988-94, Sunday Schl Tchr 1988-94, Mentor Prgm 1994-; office: Elmer Thieres Elem Schl 25 School Dr Marlborough CT 06447

KANIECKI, LINDA PINCHOT, Mathematics Teacher; b: Du Bois, PA; m: John F.; ed: Bloomsburg St Univ (BS) Math, Scndry Ed 1981; Towson St Univ (MS) Scndry Ed 1990; 30 Post Grad Credits Beyond Masters; cr: Joppatowne HS Math Tchr, Dept Chprsn 1981-; ai: Sr Class, Chrldng Adv; Tennis Coach; NEA; MSTA; NCTM; office: Joppatowne HS 555 Joppa Farm Rd Joppa MD 21085

KANIS, SHARON,SSND Religious Studies Asst Prof; b: Baltimore, MD; ed: Coll of Notre Dame of MD (BA) Chem; Fordham Univ (MA) Theology; Attnd Sholem Inst for Spiritual Direction; Union Inst Doctoral Candidate; cr: Notre Dame Acad HS Sci Tchr 1964-69; Archbishop Keongh HS Sci, Rel Tchr 1969-72; St Francis Church Pastoral Assoc 1972-74; Notre Dame Prep Schl Rel, Campus Ministry Tchr 1974-89; Coll of Notre Dame of MD Rel Stud Instr 1989-; ai: Wkshps, Retreats, Lectures Women's Spirituality; Women's Stud Prgm Chprsn; Fros Orientation Course Dev Co-Chprsn; Justice & Peace Commission 1990-, Chprsn; Natl Star Tchr Awd FL 1969; office: Coll Of Notre Dame Of MD 4701 N Charles St Baltimore MD 21210*

KANKOLENSKI, PAUL FRANK, Psychology Prof; b: Niagara Falls, NY; m: Marilyn Ruth Martino; c: Dana Ann Nicole, Paul Craig, Michael Jarrett, Kristen Kankolenski Mayrose; ed: SUNY at Buffalo (BA) Psych 1963, (MA) Experimental Psych 1968; cr: SUNY Rsrch Assoc Biochem, Psychiatry 1963-671 Bell Aerospace Co Human Factors, Asst Mgr Trng Dept 1967-68; Matrix Rsrch Co Rsrch Scientist 1968-71; Niagara Cty Comm Coll Psych Asst Prof, Prof 1971-; ai: Dev Criminal Justice Curr, Phys Therapist Asst Curr; Several Advisorships, Comm Chairmanships; NEA 1980-; J. Psychiatric Rsrch 1970-78; Psychonomic Sci 1967; Eastern Psych Assn Presentation 1966; Soc Reliability Engrs Achvmnt Awd 1970; office: Niagara County Comm Coll 3111 Saunders Settlement Rd Sanborn NY 14132

KANNENBERG, LLOYD CHAMBERS, Professor of Physics; b: Sarasota, FL; m: Susan Lippman; c: Susanna; ed: MIT (SB) Physics 1961; Univ of FL (MS) Physics 1963; Northeastern Univ (PHD) Physics 1967; cr: Lowell Technological Inst Physics Instr 1966-67; Northeastern Univ Physics Instr 1967-68; Lowell Tech, Univ of Lowell, UMA at Lowell Asst Prof Physics 1968-72, Assoc Prof Physics 1972-77, Prof Physics 1977-; ai: Amer Physical Soc, Math Assn of Amer, MSPINE; Pub New Branch of Math; Pub 15 Articles; office: Univ Of MA At Lowell 1 University Ave Lowell MA 01854

KANTROWITZ, BETTY, Mathematics Teacher; b: Flushing, NY; m: William; c: David, Mark, Ira Gordon; ed: Hunter Coll (BA) Math 1962; Math, Ed Grad Courses NY Univ, Hunter Coll, Queens Coll, Harvard, Simmons, Princeton, Boston Univ; cr: Jamaica HS Math Tchr 1963; Brookline Pub Schls Math Tchr 1979-80; Newton South HS Math Tchr 1981-; Coll Bd Consultant 1983-; ai: Math Team Coach; Coll Bd AP Consultant; Brooks Cole VIP Prgm; Test Math Software; NCTM 1974-, NCSM 1994-, Cncl Presidential Awardees in Math 1987-, Schlrsp Comm 1987; Young Israel of Brookline, Photographer; Presidential Awd Excl Math Tchng; Wrote Article 1992; Westinghouse Awd Helping Math, Sci Stdnts; office: Newton South HS 140 Brandeis Rd Newton Center MA 02159

KANZIG, MARIA F., Spanish Teacher; b: Granada, Spain; m: William Ray; c: Ray, Paul; ed: Heidelberg (BA) Span, His 1979; Bowling Green St Univ (MA) Span 1988; Attnd Goddard Coll; cr: Calvert HS Span Tchr 1979-86; Columbian HS Span Tchr 1986-; Heidelberg Coll Span Instr 1994-; ai: Span Club Adv; NHS Selection Comm; Annual Span Trip to Spain Adv, Chaperone; Kappa Delta Pi 1977-, Sec, Treas; Phi Alpha Theta 1977-; NEA 1987-; OFLA 1993-; VP Pres Local Tchr Ed Assn 1994-; Pres of TEA 1996; Sigma Delta Pi; NHS in Span; AAUW 1993-; Comm Intnl Resource Ctr, Bd Mem; Ashland Oil Tchr Awd Nom; office: Columbia HS 300 S Monroe St Tiffin OH 44883*

KANZLER, BARBARA A., US His & World Cultures Tchr; b: New York City, NY; c: Candice Kanzler-Zane; ed: Kean Coll (BS) Spec Ed 1980; Georgian Court (MS) Spec Ed; 30 Hrs Substance Awareness Coord; 40 Hrs Aids Ed; cr: MCVSD CareerCtr Bldg Trades Tchr 1983-85, Baking Tchr 1985-88, Horticulture Tchr 1988-92; MCVSD Kiva HS World Cultures, US His Tchr 1992-; ai: Yrbk; Aids Comm; AA, NA Meetings; Bsktbl Ofcl; VICA; FFA; Holistic Healing; NJEA, NEA 1983-; NJ Women & Aids Network 1990-; NJIAA Bd #4 HS Bsktbl Ofcl 1995-; AA, NA 1988-; NJ Equity Ldr of Yr 1990; NJ Governor's Tchr of Yr 1991, 1993; NJ Equity Restoration Project of Yr 1994; office: Kiva Alternative HS 537 Tinton Ave Tinton Falls NJ 07724*

KAPELA, SANDY, Second Grade Teacher; b: Kingston, NY; m: Gerald; c: Lisa, Noel; ed: SUNY at New Paltz (BS) Elem Ed 1973, (MA) Early Ed 1978; cr: SUNY Campus Learning Ctr Tchr 1973-74; Ellenville Cntrl Schl Tchr 1974-; ai: Drama, Journal Clubs; Math Their Way Follow Up Ldr; IRA; NY St Rdng Assn, Ulster Cty Rdng Cncl 1976-; Ellenville PTA 1975-, Dir; office: Ellenville Central Schl 28 Maple Ave Ellenville NY 12428

KAPFER, MARY ETHNA, Math Teacher; b: Ilion, NY; ed: Coll of St Rose (BS) Sci; Syracuse Univ (MS) Sci 1970; Cmptr Sci; cr: St Francis De Sales 8th Grd Tchr 1941-51; St John's Prin 1951-57; St Mary's 7th-8th Grd Sci Tchr 1962-69; St Jude's Prin 1970-72; St Francis De Sales Jr Math, Sci Tchr 1976-; ai: Parish Cncl; Adult Ed Comm; NCEA 1970-; Neighborhood Watch 1995-; RSVP 1990-; Mohawk Sr Citizenship Club 1994-; Cancer Soc 1994-, Vol; NSF Grant; Calculators Grant; office: Saint Francis De Sales Schl 220 Henry Herkimer NY 13350

KAPILOFF, ALAN LAWRENCE, Social Studies Teacher; b: New York, NY; m: Ruth Perlstein; c: Ellen Shinberg, Bonnie Mamiye; ed: Brooklyn Coll (BA) Pol Sci 1967, (MA) Soc Stud Ed 1970; Prof Cert Scndry Schl Admin at Hofstra Univ 1975; Post Grad Stud in Ec at Stony Brook Univ SUNY; EMT License at Suffolk Cty Comm Coll 1972; cr: Prospect Heights HS Soc Stud Tchr 1967-69; Plainview-Old Bethpage HS Soc Stud Tchr 1969-72; Selden Jr HS Soc St Tchr, Dept Chair 1972-78; Newfield HS Soc St Tchr 1978-; ai: Stu Govt Adv; NHS Former Adv; Yorker Club Adv; Future Tchrs of Amer Adv; Chess, Checkers Club Adv; Class of 91 Adv; AFT, Mid Cntry TA 1972-; Long Island Cncl of Soc Stud Supvrs 1972-78, Founder, Chair; Commack Vol Ambulance Corps 1972-83, Ambulance Driver; Grant to Stud Holocaust in Israel for 3 Weeks 1986; home: 49 Montrose Dr Commack NY 11725*

KAPITANEC, NANCY BATTLES, Sixth Grade Teacher; b: Chardon, OH; m: Ben; c: Larissa, Nick; ed: Univ of Akron (BS) Sec Ed, Span, Home Ec 1980; Cleveland St Univ Elem Cert 1986; cr: Willoughby-Eastlake Schls Home Ec Tchr 1980-88, Span Tchr 1987-88, 6th Grd Tchr 1989-; ai: NEA, OEA 1980-; Mem OH Project Discovery 1993; Ashland Oil Golden Apple Awd 1995; office: Willoughby MS 36901 Ridge Rd Willoughby OH 44094

KAPITANSKY, BARBARA N., Business Education Teacher; b: Brooklyn, NY; m: Stanley; c: Evan, Ross; ed: CCNY-Baruch Coll (BS) Bus Ed 1964; Pace Univ (MS) Educl Admin & Supervision 1983; Brooklyn Coll +30 Credits Masters Equivalency in Psych & Guid; cr: Norman Thomas HS Bus Ed Tchr 1964-70; Thomas Jefferson HS Bus Ed Tchr & Dept Coord 1977-83; James Madison HS Bus Ed Tchr 1984-; Kingsborough Comm Coll Continuing Ed Bus Tchr 1995-; ai: Liberty Partnerships Pgm Cnslr & Advocate; Career Day & LPP Comm Svc Projects Coord; AFT & UFT 1964-; Bus Tchrs Assn 1964-; Pace Alumni Assn 1983-; APC Inc 1970-, Recording Sec, VP, Chprsn Various Comms; Temple Emanuel 1980-; Guy M Stewart Cancer Assn 1985-; Phi Beta Kappa; office: James Madison HS 3787 Bedford Ave Brooklyn NY 11229

KAPLAN, BRUCE JAY, Music Teacher; b: Brooklyn, NY; m: Beth; c: Josh, Andy, Jeremy; ed: Brooklyn Coll (BA) Music 1973; C. W. Post (MS) Music 1976; cr: Lindell Schl Vocal Music Tchr 1973-80; Long Beach HS Vocal Music Tchr 1980-; ai: HS Musical Production; LBCTA 1973-; NMEA, MENC 1980-; AF of L Local 802 1968-; office: Long Beach HS 322 Lagoon Dr W Long Beach NY 11561

KAPLAN, CHESTER FRANK, Band Director; b: New York City, NY; ed: New York Univ (BS) Music Ed 1969, (MA) Music Ed 1971; cr: IS 285 Music Tchr 1969-; Kingsboro Comm Coll Adjunct Lecturer 1980-81; ai: Music Educators Assn of New York City 1990-, Exec Bd Mem; NY St Schl Music Assn 1975-, Adjudicator, Seminar Ldr; Appalachian Mountain Club 1987-, Hike Ldr; office: Meyer Levin HS 285 5909 Beverley Rd Brooklyn NY 11203*

KAPLAN, DIANA, Mathematics Teacher; b: Brooklyn, NY; ed: Hamilton Coll (BA) Math 1990; Univ of NC (MS) Math 1992; cr: Univ of NC Tchng Asst 1990-92; Hackley Schl HS Math Tchr 1992-; ai: Math SAT Course; Comm Svc Club, Sr Class Adv; Hamilton Coll Root Flwshp; office: Hackley Schl 293 Benedict Ave Tarrytown NY 10591

KAPLAN, ENID FERN, English Teacher; b: New York City, NY; c: Lauren Kaplan-Sagal, Deborah Kaplan-Gershenson, Carolyn Kaplan Ward; ed: Smith Coll (BA) Eng 1956; Lehman Coll (MA) Eng, Writing, Ed 1991; Columbia Univ Grad Faculties 30 Cred Medieval Lit, 17C 1962; Fordham Univ Anglo Saxon; SUNY at Purchase Linguistics; Rutgers Univ Linguistics; cr: Forest Hills HS Phys Sci Tchr 1956-59; Walton HS Eng Tchr 1959-61; Mamaroneck Schl Dist Elem Stdnts Poetry Tchr 1978-79, HS Lay Reader 1978-79; Mamaroneck HS Eng, Writing Specialist Tchr 1979-, Schl Newspaper Adv 1979-86; Lehman Coll Adj Writing, Lit Lecturer 1990-; ai: NCTE; Inst for Literacy Stud, New York City Writing Project, Natl Writing Project 1991-; Article, Several Poems Pub; home: 707 Palmer Ct Mamaroneck NY 10543*

KAPLAN, HELEN L., Seventh Grd Mathematics Tchr; b: Brooklyn, NY; m: Frank; c: Lawrence, Deena; ed: Newark St Coll (BA) Elem Ed 1964; NJ Cert as K-12th Grd Math Tchr; cr: Hawthorne Elem Schl Elem Tchr 1964-65; Cleveland Elem Schl Elem Tchr 1966-67; Spotswood HS Math Tchr 1981-82; Linwood MS Math Tchr 1983-; ai: Gender Equity Comm in Sci & Math; Project Renaissance Comm Co-Chair; NEA, NJEA 1981-;

NBTEA 1983-; *office:* Linwood MS 25 Linwood Pl North Brunswick NJ 08902

KAPLAN, LAURIE SMITH, Associate Professor; *b:* Cleveland, OH; *m:* Richard S.; *ed:* St Thomas Hospital Schl of Nursing (RN) 1968; Univ of Miami (AB) Eng 1970, (MLA) Eng 1973, (PHD) 1981; *cr:* Univ of Miami Tchng Asst 1970-, 1973-75; Miami-Dade Comm Coll Tchr 1978-79; Univ of Miami Tchng Asst 1979; Towson St Univ Tchr 1979-80; Goucher Coll Assoc Prof 1979-, Assoc Acad Dean 1993-95; *ai:* Fac Adv Stu Newspaper Quindecim; Fac Adv Goucher Quarterly, Alum Magazine; British Stud Trip During January Break; Janes Austen Soc, Life Mem, Henry Burke Grant; James Joyce Fnd 1976-; Modern Lang Soc 1979-; Goucher Coll Lib, Bd of Dirs-Friends of Lib; Baltimore Bibliophiles; Publications Essays, Scholarly Artilces, Book Reviews, Fiction; Undergraduate Preparation Team, MD St Tchr Ed Task Force; Hewlett-Mellon Summer Research Grant 1987; San Jose Stud Awd Best Fiction 1986; Outstanding Tchr Hums 1982; *office:* Goucher Coll Dulaney Valley Rd Towson MD 21204*

KAPLE, PATRICIA L. (TRAME), High School Science Teacher; *b:* Lima, OH; *m:* John D.; *c:* Travis Horstman, Addie; *ed:* Bowling Green St Univ (BS) Chem 1970, (MED) Scndry Sci Ed 1985; *cr:* Pandora-Gilboa HS Sci Tchr 1971-73; Miller City-New Cleveland Sci Tchr 1973-78; Bath HS Sci Tchr 1978-; *ai:* Sci Olympiad Coach 10 Yrs; SEAC 3 Yrs; Tech Comm; BEA Schlsp Comm Chair; Mentor Tchr; SECO 1993-; SOS, AAPT 1984-; Bath Ed Assn 1978-, Pres, Sec; OCCL Tiny Titans 1983-, Held All Offices; Martha Holden Jennings Scholar & Grant Recipient 1995; Bath Excl Grant Recipient 1994-95; Ball St Univ Lasers & Holography Wkshp; 2 OH St Univ Dreyfus Fnd Wkshps-HS Chem Tchrs; Coll of Mount Saint Joseph PRIDE, TEACH & TLC Wkshps; *office:* Bath HS 2850 Bible Rd Lima OH 45801*

KAPLON, KERRY L., Mathematics Teacher; *b:* Lowell, MA; *m:* Patricia Camenga; *c:* Jeffrey, Jay; *ed:* Univ of MA (BA) US His 1976; Cambridge Coll (MA) Ed; *cr:* Ripley Schl 6th Grd Tchr 1976-86, 6th Grd Head Tchr 1986-89; Melrose MS 6th Grd Math Tchr 1990-, Asst Prin 1993-94; *ai:* NEA, MTA 1976-; Peter Farrelly Awd Excl in Math, Sci 1993; Horace Mann Grants Lit 1990-91, Sci 1988; *office:* Melrose MS 360 Lynn Fells Pky Melrose MA 02176

KAPNER, GEORGE H., Mathematics Teacher; *b:* Freeport, NY; *m:* Kathy Ann Trojanowski; *c:* Diane, Danielle; *ed:* Brown Univ (BA) Psych 1973; Hofstra Univ (MA) Scndry Ed 1975; *cr:* Lawrence Jr HS Math Tchr 1975; Westfield HS Math Tchr 1975-; *ai:* Boys Head Coach Soccer, Swimming, Tennis; NEA, NJEA, NCTM 1975-; NSCAA 1980-; Coach of Yr Soccer 1984, Swimming 1996; *office:* Westfield HS 550 Dorian Rd Westfield NJ 07090

KAPNER, W. MARVIN, Retired History Teacher; *b:* Newark, NJ; *m:* Helen; *c:* Gary, David, Paul; *ed:* Rutgers Univ (BA) His 1957, (EDM) Civics & Instruction 1961; Addl 35 Credits Beyond EDM; *cr:* Kearny Pub Schl Tchr 1957-60; Livingston HS Tchr 1960-66; New Milford HS Dept Chair 1966-67; Saddle Brook HS Admin Asst 1967-68; Emerson Jr Sr HS Tchr, Dept Chair 1968-95; *ai:* Hnr Soc, Class Adv; NJEA 1957-; EEA 1968-, Negotiator; Jewish Family Svc Civics Tchr to Immigrant Population.

KAPORCH, MOYA REGINA, Asst Prin & Eng Lecturer; *b:* Bristol, PA; *ed:* Immaculata Coll (BA) Eng & Scndry Ed 1981; Beaver Coll (MA) Ed & Writing 1988; Attnd Villanova Univ 6 Credit Hrs, Lit Yeats Intnl Summer Schl Sligo Ireland; *cr:* Holy Family Coll Eng Lecturer 1989-; Nazareth Academy HS Eng Tchr 1981-94; Holy Family Coll Spec Asst to the Pres 1992-; *ai:* Schl Lit Magazine, Coll Selection & Guidance Dept Adv; Quill & Scroll & Jr Class Act Co-Moderator; NCEA 1981-; NCTE 1983-; NCTE 1994; NAPAHE 1994; *office:* Holy Family College Grant & Frankford Aves Philadelphia PA 19114*

KAPOSTASY, MARGARET ANN, 1st Grade Teacher; *b:* Painesville, OH; *m:* Dennis; *c:* Jennifer, Daniel; *ed:* Kent St Univ (BS) Early Chldhd Ed 1972; 18 Addl Credit Hrs; *cr:* Mentor Pub Schls 2nd Grd Tchr 1972-78, 1st & 3rd Grds Tchr 1984-; *ai:* Fairfax Portfolio Comm; Sci Grd Lvl Coord; Mentor Tchrs Assn 1972-78; OEA & NEA 1984-, MTA; *office:* Fairfax Elem Schl 6465 Curtiss Ct Mentor OH 44060

KAPP, JUDITH A.,RSM, Mathematics Teacher; *b:* Troy, NY; *ed:* St John Fisher Coll at Rochester (BS) Math 1981; SUNYA (MS) Rdng 1983; Educl Admin Stud; *cr:* Doane Stuart Schl Math, Cmptr Tchr 1981-84; Catskill HS Math Tchr 1984-86; Bishop Maginn HS Math Tchr 1986-91, 1993-; Comm Maternity Svcs Math, Eng Tchr 1992-93; *ai:* Soph Class Co-Adv; *home:* 310 S Manning Blvd Albany NY 12208*

KAPP, LEHMAN E.,JR., Mathematics Teacher; *b:* Steelton, PA; *ed:* Ursinus Coll (BS) Math 1968; *cr:* Methacton HS Math Tchr 1968-; *ai:* Soccr Head Coach; Track, Bsktbl Asst Coach; Mt Bike Club Co-Spons; Nation Cncl of Tchrs of Math 1970-; Math Assn of Amer 1967-; AFT 1983-; *office:* Methacton Sr HS 1001 Kriebel Mill Rd Norristown PA 19403

KAPPLE, NANCY A., Sixth Grade Teacher; *b:* Boston, MA; *m:* Albert W. Sr.; *c:* Christine J., Albert W. Jr., Brian M., Cheryl M.; *ed:* Cumberland Cty Coll (AA) Gen 1986; Glassboro Coll (BA) K-8 Ed 1989; *cr:* Landis Intermediate Schl 6th Grd Tchr 1989-; *ai:* Schl Improvement Team; Peer Mediation Bldg Coord; Crisis Intervention Team; Soc Stud Curr Team; Kappa Delta Pi 1988-; NEA, NJEA, Vineland Ed Assn 1989-; *office:* Landis Intermediate Schl 61 W Landis Ave Vineland NJ 08360

KAPRON, CECELIA FLECKENSTEIN, Dance Teacher; *b:* Pittsburgh, PA; *m:* Edward S.; *c:* Kelly, Edward Jr.; *ed:* Slippery Rock Univ (BS) Hlth, PE 1972; Univ of Pittsburgh (MED) Dance Ed 1975; Attnd American Univ, Wolf Trap Acad for Performing Arts, Loyola Mary Mount Univ, UCLA; *cr:* Mt Lebanon HS Dance Tchr 24 Yrs; *ai:* Dir of Mt Lebanon HS Dance Co; Choreographer, Dance Dir HS Musicals; PSAHPERD 1984-, Outstdng Dance Edctr of Yr 1995; PA Arts Curr Project; PA Dance Cert Comm; PA Dance Ed Comm; Dir Dance Prgm; Best Practices PA Arts in Ed 1995; Cum Laude Soc 1991; Who's Who Among Coll Stdnts 1972; First Pl Holocaust Arts, Writing Competition 1994; *office:* Mt Lebanon HS 155 Cochran Rd Pittsburgh PA 15228

KAPUSTAR, KATHLEEN ANN, German Instructor; *b:* Mansfield, OH; *m:* Alan E.; *c:* Kent, Kara, Kristen, Katie; *ed:* Wilmington Coll (BA) Ger, His, Govt, Pol Sci 1970; Ashland Univ (MA) Rdng 1989; Attnd Kent St Univ, OH St Univ, Drake Univ, Andrews Univ; *cr:* Clinton Massie Schls Soc Stud Tchr 1970-71; Graham Schls Soc Stud Tchr 1971-72; Mansfield City Schls Ger Tchr 1973-75; Lexington HS Ger, Rdng Tchr 1976-; *ai:* Ger Club Adv; Acad Awds Prgm Coord; Acad Challenge Team Asst; Lexington Tchrs Assn, OH Ed Assn, NEA 1982-; OH Frgn Lang Assn 1985-; Pastorius Assn 1993-; Presenter OH Frgn Lang Assn Conf 1990, 1995; *office:* Lexington HS 103 Clever Ln Lexington OH 44904

KARABAIC, MARY JANE TAKACH, 7th Grade Science Teacher; *b:* Martins Ferry, OH; *m:* Ronald E.; *c:* Carolyn, Brad; *ed:* OH St Univ (BS) Elem Ed 1969; William & Mary Univ of Dayton (MS) Elem Ed 1982; *cr:* Hampton Cty Schls Elem Tchr 1969-72; Steubenville City Schls Elem Tchr 1972-; *ai:* Steubenville Ed Assn 1972-, Treas; OH Ed Assn 1972-; NSTA 1981-; NEA; Delta Kappa Gamma 1985-; Jennings Scholar 1990; *office:* Harding MS 1928 Sunset Blvd Steubenville OH 43952

KARABAICH, JOSEPH CRAIG, English & Language Arts Tchr; *b:* Lancaster, PA; *m:* Andrea Kathleen Havlicsek; *c:* Michael, Nicholas; *ed:* Mansfield St Coll (BS) Ed 1966; Elmira Coll (MS) Ed 1971; 18 Addl Hrs; *cr:* Horseheads Jr HS 8th Grd Eng Tchr 1966-87; Horseheads HS 10th-12th Grd Eng Tchr 1987-; *ai:* Adv Stu Cncl 1966-87, Yrbk; IM Dir; Girls, Boys Var Soccer Coach 1975-95; JV Bsbl Coach; NYSUT 1966-; Elks #2297 1970-, Yth Act; Chemung Cty Yth Soccer Assn, Chm, Elk of Yr; *home:* 228 Oriole Dr Horseheads NY 14845

KARABINUS, CYNTHIA MILLER, Soc Stud & Psych Tchr; *b:* Palmerton, PA; *m:* Thomas J.; *ed:* Lycoming Coll (BA) Sociology, Anthropology 1977; 9 Grad Credits Psych Lehigh Univ; 3 Grad Credits Psych Rider Univ; 3 Grad Credits Psych Wilkes Coll; 3 Grad Credits His East STroudsburg Univ; Lafayette Coll Tchr Cert 1980; *cr:* William H. Rohrer Pharmaceutical Sales Rep 1978-79; Bangor Jr Sr HS Soc Stud Tchr 1980-83; Delaware Vly Regnl HS His, Psych Tchr 1983-; *ai:* NEA 1980-; Natl Org for Psych Tchrs 1990-.*

KARAISKOS, MARIA, English Teacher; *b:* Flushing, NY; *ed:* Queens Coll (BA) Eng 1995; Grad Division 15 Credit Hrs; *cr:* Long Island City HS Eng Tchr 1995-; *ai:* Phi Beta Kappa 1991-; Golden Key Natl Hnr Soc, Natl Deans List 1990-; *office:* Long Island City HS 2801 41st Ave Long Island City NY 11101

KARAM, JODY F., Health & Physical Ed Teacher; *b:* Easton, PA; *m:* Karen Werkheiser; *c:* Sage; *ed:* East Stroudsburg Univ (MS) Sport Mngmt; *cr:* Lopatcong Twp Elem Schl K-8th Grd PE Tchr 1990-92; Liberty HS 9-12th Grd Hlth, PE Tchr 1993-; *ai:* Head Wrestling Coach; BEA Tchrs Assn 1993-; Hurricane Wrestling Club 1993-, Adv; Post Prom Party Funding 1994-, Adv; NJ Wrestling Coach of Yr; *home:* 613 Coleman St Easton PA 18042

KARAS, JOHN RICHARD, Science Teacher; *b:* Johnstown, PA; *ed:* IN Univ of PA (BSEd) Sci 1968; Post Grad Stud Shippensburg Univ, Wilkes Coll, Carlow Coll; IN Univ of PA; *cr:* Littlestown Area Schl Dist Sci Tchr 1968-; *ai:* NHS Adv; NEA, PSEA 1968-; Littlestown Ed Assn 1968-, Pres 1976-77, Treas 1983-; PA Scholastic Press Assn 1971-95; *office:* Littlestown H S 200 E Myrtle St Littlestown PA 17340

KARAS, PATRICIA A., Business Teacher; *b:* Pittsburgh, PA; *m:* John; *c:* David, Steven; *ed:* Univ of Pittsburgh (BS) Acctng, Bus, Ger 1961; California Univ of PA (MED) Elem 1995; 24 Addl Credits; *cr:* Glassport Jr-Sr HS Bus Tchr 1961-64; Brentwood Jr-Sr HS Ger Tchr 1964-67; West Mifflin Area HS Bus Tchr 1975-; *ai:* AFT 1976-; *office:* West Mifflin Area HS 91 Commonwealth Ave West Mifflin PA 15122

KARASARIDES, JENNIFER ANNE, 2nd Grade Teacher; *b:* Canton, OH; *m:* Steven; *c:* Stephanie, John; *ed:* Mount Union Coll (BA) Elem Ed 1975; Coll of Mount Saint Joseph (MEd) 1987; Kent St Univ Tenure Elem Ed 1982; Ashland Coll 15 Ed Hrs 1990; 3 Elem Ed Math Hrs 1993 & 1994; Louisville City Schls Continuing Ed Cmptr Units 1991; *cr:* Louisville Elem Schl 2nd Grd Tchr 1975-78, 1st Grd Tchr 1980-82, 2nd Grd Tchr 1982-; *ai:* Grandparents Day & Hlth Book Adoption Comms; Intervention Team Mem; Child Find Comm; Parent Tchr Org Mem; After Schl Tutoring; Mentor Tchr; Mount Union Coll Dept of Ed Advy Cncl 1992-, Mem; OEA & NEA 1975-, Mem; Ashland Oil Golden Apple Awd 1993; *home:* 3779 Maplegrove St Louisville OH 44641

KARASKA, GERALD JAMES, Professor; *b:* Wilkes Barre, PA; *m:* Mary Claire Ennis; *c:* Christine, Mark, Susan Ladd, Carl; *ed:* Penn St Univ (BS) Geog 1954, (PHD) Geog 1962; George Washington Univ (MA) Geog 1957; *cr:* Dept Defense Researcher 1954-57; Villanova Instr 1960-61; Univ of PA Asst Prof 1961-65; Syracuse Univ Assoc Prof 1966-69; Clark Univ Prof 1969; *ai:* Ec Geog Ed 1969-91; SARSA Cooperative Agreement Dir 1982-; *office:* Clark Univ 950 Main St Worcester MA 01610

KARATZ, CAROL STRAKA, English, Rdng & Soc Stud Tchr; *b:* Bayonne, NJ; *c:* Megan, Jill, Brian; *ed:* Glassboro St Coll (BA) Early Chldhd Ed, Elem Ed, Speech Dev & Correction 1978; *ai:* PTA Exec Bd; Brick Meml Girls Track Coach; NEA 1988-; *office:* Lake Riviera MS 171 Beaverson Blvd Brick NJ 08723

KARAZIM, LINDA STASZAK, Coll Prep, AP, English Teacher; *b:* Toledo, OH; *m:* Thomas J.; *c:* Todd Andrew; *ed:* Univ of Toledo (BE) Eng 1973, (ME) Curr & Instruction 1975, (EDD) Curr & Instruction 1987; Cert Soc Stud, Pol Sci, His, Rdng Coll of Ed; Minor in Eng Doctoral Level Coll of Arts & Sci; *cr:* Toledo Pub Schls All Levels Sub Tchr 1970-73; Evergreen Local Schls 9-12 Grd Eng Tchr, Dept Chair 1974-91; Univ of Toledo Grammar, Linguistics Instr 1987, Coll Composition I & II Instr 1990-94; Springfield Local Schls 12 Grd Eng Tchr, Dept Chair 1991-; *ai:* Prime Time Exec Comm for Schl Improvement; North Cntrl Evaluation Steering, Tech Comms; NEA 1974-; Delta Kappa Gamma 1992-95; Phi Delta Kappa 1986-; Block Watch 1995-, Co-Capt; Toledo Zoological Mem 1992-; St Joan of Arc Schl Advy Cncl 1991-, Sec; Univ of Toledo Alumni Assn; Outstdng Eng Tchr Runner Up Northwest OH 1993; Outstdng Staff Mem of Week 1994; Make a Difference Awd 1994; Nom Tchr of Yr 1987; Article Pub 1982; Tchr of Yr Evergreen HS 1978; Martha Holden Jennings Scholar 1976-77; *office:* Springfield HS 1470 S Mccord Rd Holland OH 43528*

KARBOWSKI, JOHN PAUL,JR., Physical Education Teacher; *b:* Schenectady, NY; *m:* Judith Ann Gizzi; *c:* John III, Jared, Jenessa; *ed:* St Univ of NY Coll at Brockport (BS) PE 1978; Russell Sage Coll (MS) Hlth Ed 1985; *cr:* Schenectady Boys Club Aquatic Dir 1980-83; Schenectady Schl Dist 9th-12th Grd Hlth Ed Tchr 1984-86; Mohonasen Schl Dist 9th-12th Grd PE Tchr 1986-; *ai:* Boys Var Bsktbl Coach; NYSUT 1983-; *office:* Mohonasen HS 2072 Curry Rd Schenectady NY 12303

KARCH, PETER B., Professor of Biological Sci; *b:* Urbana, IL; *m:* Lillian Kwasnyca; *c:* Michael, Robert, Laura; *ed:* Univ of Detroit (BS) Bio 1965; Univ of Western Ontario (MSc) Physiology 1967; MI St Univ (PHD) Zoology 1974; *cr:* Lansing Comm Coll Biological Sci Lecturer 1972-75; Penn St Univ at Allentown Biological Sci Lecturer 1976-86; Lehigh Carbon Comm Coll Asst & Assoc Prof of Biological Sci 1975-; Penn Power & Light, Amer Inst Cancer Research Freelance Writing Consultant 1986-87; *ai:* Vineyard-Enology; Playing Flamenco & Classical Guitar; Hiking; Sailing; Tennis; Writing; Penn Assn 2 Yr Coll of Bio 3 Yrs, Newsletter Ed; Bsbl Little League 1977-90, Coach, Asst Coach; BSA, Cub Scouts, Pack & Den Ldrs; Grd & HS Comms; Soccer Coach & Asst Coach; Lilly-Penn Fellow Biological Basis of Behavoir 2 Yrs; Doctorate & Master Dissertations Pub; Several Articles on Food Intake Regulation Pub; Unpublished Anatomy & Physiology Textbook; Environ Compliance, Environ Response Manuel for Penn Power & Light; *office:* Lehigh Carbon Comm Coll 4525 Education Park Dr Schnecksville PA 18078

KARFELT, FRANK JAMES, Sixth Grade Teacher; *b:* Mt Pleasant, PA; *m:* Sandra Brady; *ed:* CA St Coll (BS) Elem Ed 1972, (BS) Scndry Soc Stud 1972; Clarion Univ of PA (MED) Sci Ed 1995; *cr:* Norvelt Elem Schl Sixth Grd Tchr 1976-; *ai:* NEA, PA St Ed Assn 1976-; PA Sci Tchrs Assn 1993-; Westmoreland Co 4-H 1993-, Bd of Dirs; Soc Analytical Chemists Pittsburgh Grant; Article Pub; *office:* Norvelt Elem Schl RD 1 Box 169A Mount Pleasant PA 15666

KARICHNER, JOYCE SHELLY, 6th Grade Teacher; *b:* Williamsburg, PA; *c:* Paul, Kori Pene; *ed:* Lock Haven Univ (BA) Elem Ed 1963; Ed Credits; Kutztown Univ Lib Sci; *cr:* Woolrich Elem Schl Third Grd Tchr 1963-66; Robb Elem Schl Kndgtn Tchr 1966-67; Orviston Elem Schl Fifth-Sixth Grd Combined Tchr 1967-68; Woodward Elem Schl Sixth Grd Tchr 1968-; *ai:* Lock Haven HS Majorette Coach 1986-89; Lock Haven Jr HS Majorette Coach 1968-86; ACCE 1963-, Sec, Treas 1963-65, Bldg Rep 1986-; PSEA, NEA 1963-; PTO, Exec Bd 1981-; Ben Follies 1978-; *home:* RR 3 Box 420 Mill Hall PA 17751

KARIG, RITA REICHMAN, English Teacher & Coordinat Brooklyn, NY; *c:* Stephen Chul; *ed:* City Coll (BA) Eng, Jrnlsm Herbert H. Lehman Coll (MS) Learning Disabilities 1972; Attnd Th Schl; City Coll, Mt St Vincent Coll, Fordham Univ; *cr:* IS 148 En 1966-75; Dist 9 Dist Office Learning Disabilities Specialist 1975-7 7 Dist Office Learning Disabilities Specialist 1977-79; John F. Ke HS Eng Tchr, Rdng Coord Prgm 1980-; *ai:* Gateway to Higher Ed Tutor; Poetry Ctr Project; AFT 1966-; Riverdale Comm Assn; Democratic Party, Dist Ldr; Co-op Amer; Audubon Soc; Natl Endo Hum, NY St Cncl Hum 1995; Behavorial Rsrch Lab Excl Tchng Woodrow Wilson Flwshp; Audubon Ecology Wkshp; *office:* J Kennedy HS 99 Terrace View Ave Bronx NY 10463*

KARIS, CHRISDELL MARIE WATSON, Third Grade Teach Youngstown, OH; *m:* Donald; *c:* Adam, Stacy; *ed:* Youngstown S (BS) Ed, Rdng 1978, (MS) Ed, Rdng 1984; *cr:* Holy Trinity Schl 6 Tchr 1978-79, K-8 Gr Remedial Rdng Tchr 1979-85; Fifth Street Schl 1-3 Grd Tchr 1985-88; Manor Ave Schl 3-5 Grd Tchr 1988-; *ai:* OEA, SEA 1980-; Bethlehem United Church of Christ 1928-, Sunda Tchr; Class Act Awd in Recognition of Outstdng Tchrs in Mah Shenango Vly Spon Giant Eagle, Sleepy Hollow, Channel 21 WFM Martha Holden Jennings Awd 1994-95; *office:* Manor Avenue Elen 230 E Manor Ave Struthers OH 44471

KARKER, CHARLES M., Health & Athletics Coordinator; *b:* Cob NY; *m:* Jane Kniskern; *c:* Philip, C. J.; *ed:* Springfield Coll (BS) PE 32 Grad Hrs Hlth, PE; *cr:* Susquehanna Vly Cntrl Driver Ed Instr 19 Fort Plain Cntrl PE, Hlth Tchr, Driver Ed Instr, Coach 1972-; *ai:* Cntry, Track Coach; AIDS Advy Comm; Comprehensive Schl H Wellness Comm; Ath Coord; League Sec, Treas; Section II Safety C Ofcls Comm; Section II Cross Cntry Comm; League Chprson Cross Ft Plain Tchrs Assn1972-, Negotiators; NY St United Tchrs 1971-; N Admins 1987-; NY St Coaches Assn, Chptr 2; Natl Assn Ath Admin Plain Recreation Comm 1980-, Bd Rep; Town of Minden Yth Org Bd Rep; NY St Coaches Assn Century Club Awd for Track, Cross Scholastic Coach, Franklin Select Circle Awds; Cross Cntry Gold Track Silver Awd; *office:* Fort Plain Central Schl 21 West St Fort Pla 13339

KARKUT, ANNE, Peer Mediation Facilitator; *b:* Binghamton, N Michael Conrad III; *c:* Rachel A., Christopher J.; *ed:* Coll of Artesia Span & Ed 1971; *cr:* Ludlow HS Span Tchr 1971-78; Chicopee HS Tchr; Fairview Veterans Memrl Schl Mediation Facilitator 199 Mediator; NHS; Jr NHS; Class Adv 1990-93; CEA & NEA 1990-; M 1994-; Jr League of Holyoke 1974-, Sec; NHS Stdnts Awds.

KARL, JOY RUARK, Teacher; *b:* Cincinnati, OH; *m:* Mark Stephanie K. Lake, Jason; *ed:* Univ of Cincinnati (BS) Speech Path 1970; Univ of Dayton (MA) Theology 1991; Post Grad Stud Theolog Clermont Co Schls Speech Therapist 1970-71; Vandalia Pub Schls S Therapist 1974-75; Univ of Dayton Grad Asst 1989-91; Carroll HS 1991-; *ai:* Yth in Govt Co-Adv; Project Outreach Adv; Fin Co-Chprsn; NCEA 1991-; AHP 1990-; Christ Child Soc 1980-, Bd; Carroll HS 4524 Linden Ave Dayton OH 45432

KARL, ROBERT EDWIN, US History Teacher & Coach; *b:* Cinci OH; *m:* Amy Farren; *c:* Caitlin Jennifer, Colleen Reann; *ed:* Alle Coll (BA) His & Ed 1970, (MED) Ed 1972; Continuing Ed: Wright St Univ of Dayton; Sinclair Comm Coll; *cr:* Brooklyn HS Tchr & 1970-72; D L Barnes Jr HS Tchr & Coach 1972-76; Fairmont West HS & Coach 1976-84; Sinclair Comm Coll His Instr Part-Time Fairmont HS Tchr & Coach 1984-; *ai:* Head Girls Track-Field C Track Stats Adv; Fac Advy Comm; OEA & NEA 1972-; KEA 1972-; 1975-; Greater Dayton Track Officials 1973-, VP & Sec-Treas, Svc A Yrs; OH Assn of Track & Cross Cnty Coaches 1973-, Asst Clinic Schlsp Comm Chrm; Kettering Schls Consolidation Comm 1984-, C Natl Coaches Awd Track & Field 1989; Finalist Alliance for Ed Ou Tchr 1996; OAT-CCC Longevity Awd 1993; Presentor at OCSS Conve Local Inservice Pgms; *office:* Kettering Fairmont HS 3301 Shroy Kettering OH 45429*

KARLITSKIE, LYNN DEE, First Grade Teacher; *b:* York, PA; *m:* R J.; *ed:* West Chester Univ (BS) Elem Ed 1972; 15 Hrs Towards M Elem Ed 1993; *ai:* Delta Kappa Gamma 1987-; PSEA 1975-; SGEA Sec; *office:* Paradise Elem Ctr RD 1 Box 170-B Thomasville PA 17

KARLSON, C. LYNN HUBERT, Mathematics Teacher; *b:* Hoboke *c:* Gustaf, Eric; *ed:* Fairleigh Dickinson Univ (BS) Math Ed 1965; City St Coll (MA) Math Ed 1984; 41 Addl Credits Math, C Supervision, Admin; *cr:* Palisades Park Jr Sr HS Math Tchr 1965-; *a* Alpha Theat Adv; NHS Fac Review Comm; Acad Decathlon Vol; NJEA, BCEA, PP,EA NCTM 1965-, Mbrshp Chprsn; Glen Rock Gra 1991, 1994; Amer Heart Assn 1988-, Vol; Governor's Tchr Recog Awd 1987; Dist Tchr of Yr 1989; Algebra Project Consultant; Palisades Pk Jr Sr HS 1 Veterans Plz Palisades Park NJ 07650

KARLSON, CONRAD CHARLES, Television Production Teach Lynn, MA; *m:* Judith Ann; *c:* Nicole, Melissa; *ed:* Drew Univ (BA 1966; Boston Univ (MED) Media 1972; Attnd Ivniversite de Nancy F Kutztown Univ, Pennsylvania St Univ, Montclair Coll, Rutgers Fairleigh Dickenson Univ; *cr:* St Joseph Hosp Media Dir 197 Conkarlson Photography Owner 1978-89; Conrad Weiser HS Production Tchr 1987-; *ai:* TV Club; NEA, PSEA, CWEA 1987-; F Grant 1971-72; *home:* 225 Halsey Ave Reading PA 19609

KARLSON, JOYCE V., First Grade Teacher; *b:* Boston, MA; *m:* D *c:* Hugh Mackay, Claudia Kohn; *ed:* St Coll at Boston (BS) Primar Eng 1959; Lesley Coll (MS) Moderate Spec Need 1977; Harvard 1962-64 Gifted Ed; *cr:* Wilmington Schl 1st Grd Tchr 1959-60; Wa Schl Kndgtn Tchr 1963-64; Cambridge Schl 3rd Grd Tchr 196 Arlington Schl Heat Start Coord 1967-68, Kndgtn, Small Spec Needs Grd, 1 & 2 Combination Tchr 1969-; *ai:* Prof Dev Comm; Inclusion Tutoring, Mentor Tchr; Arlington Tchrs Assn 1969-, VP, Ch Negotiations; MA Tchrs Assn, NEA 1969-; Hobart Coll 1964, C Univ 1980, Wheelock Coll 1990-95 Guest Lecturer; Disney Tchr Runner Up 1994; Distngd Svc Awd 1995; *office:* Thompson Elem Sc N Union St Arlington MA 02174*

KARMEN, ANDREW A., Dept of Sociology Professor; *b:* New York *m:* Jessica; *c:* Emily; *ed:* Univ of Rochester (MS) Geology 1968; C (MA) Sociology 1970; Columbia Univ (PHD) Sociology 1977; *cr:* Joh Coll Grad Coord & Prof 1978-; *ai:* Criminology & Criminal Justice Textbook: Crime Victims An Introduction To Victimology; *office:* Univ Of NY John Jay Coll 445 W 59th St New York NY 10019

KARMILOWICZ, FLOYD EDWARD, Sixth Grade Teacher; *b:* B OH; *ed:* Bowling Green St Univ (BSE) Elem Ed 1962; Kent St Univ (Elem Ed 1966; Rel Stud St Mary's Univ of MN 1972-73; *cr:* Parknoll Schl Grd 6 Tchr 1962-64; Koeppe Elem Schl Grd 6 Tchr 1964-65; N Elem Schl Grd 6 Tchr 1965-70; Sacred Heart Jr HS Math Tchr 197 Montini HS Rel Tchr 1972-73; St Adalbert Elem Schl Grd 6-8 1977-84; SS Joseph, John Schl Grd 6 Tchr 1984-; *ai:* NCEA 1977-; M Prof Catechist; Eucharistic Minister; *office:* SS Joseph & John Schl Pearl Rd Strongsville OH 44136

KARMINSKI, BARBARA KAY, Computer Teacher; *b:* Bellepoint, *m:* Lee; *c:* Todd, Terri; *ed:* James Madison Univ (BS) Ed 1961; 2 Grad Credits; *cr:* Balto Co Bd of Ed Music Tchr 1961-66; Mountain C

5 Grd Tchr 1985-90, K-8 Cmptr Tchr 1991-; *ai:* Choir Dir; *office:* ...tain Christian Schl 1824 Mountain Rd Joppa MD 21085

...N, ALLEN RAY, High School Mathematics Tchr; *b:* Dayton, OH; *c:* ...a, Nathan, Holly; *ed:* Manchester Coll (BA) PE 1977; OH Northern ...Math 1981; *cr:* Vly View HS Math Tchr, Coach 1981-83; Greenon HS ...Tchr, Coach 1983-88; Eaton City Schls Math Tchr, Coach 1988-; *ai:* ...tance Var Girls Track, Boys Bsktbl; OCTM, ECTA, OEA 1988-; ...: Eaton City Schls 307 N Cherry St Eaton OH 45320*

...N, ERIC MICHAEL, Social Studies Teacher; *b:* Bellefontaine, OH; ...liami Univ (MA) His 1989, (MAT) Scndry Soc Stud Ed 1992; Stu in ...any & Czechoslavakia; *cr:* Kenton Cty Schls Tchr 1993-94; ...west Local Schls Tchr 1994-; *ai:* NHS Spon; Jr Class Adv; Var Boys ...l Asst Coach; OH Cncl for the Soc Stud 1993-; Natl Cncl for the Soc ...1993-; Alpha Phi Omega 1988-1990; OH Cncl for Soc Stud Presenter

...NES, PHILIP M., Seventh-Eighth Grade Teacher; *b:* Defiance, OH; ...dy Porata; *c:* Casey, Amy, Emily; *ed:* Univ of Toledo (BE) Spec Ed ...(MS) Admin 1996; *cr:* Bryan City Schls Tchr of Sixth-Eighth Grd ...Handicapped 1975-86; Williams Cty Schls Tchr of Behavioral ...icapped 1988-89; Defiance Cty Schls Tchr of Seventh-Eighth Grd ...ing Disabilities 1989-; *ai:* Spec Ed Team Ldr; NEA 1975-; Loyal ...of Moose 1977-; *office:* Defiance Jr HS 629 Arabella St Defiance ...3512

...NS, MARY B., English Teacher; *b:* E Derry, NH; *m:* Harry E. Sr.; *c:* ...Jr., Jeffrey L., Adam L.; *ed:* Shippensburg Univ (BS) Ed & Eng 1969; ...edford HS Eng Tchr 1969-71; Everett Area HS Eng Tchr 1983-; *ai:* Jr ...NHS Adv; Stu Assistance Team Core; EAEA 1983-, Prof Rights & ...onsibilities Chprsn; PSEA 1983-; NEA 1983-; *office:* Everett Area HS ...River Ln Everett PA 15537

...P, BARBARA MOLINARO, 9th Grade English Teacher; *b:* ...ellsville, PA; *m:* Robert G. Jr.; *c:* Daniel J.; *ed:* CA Univ of PA (BS) ...orehensive Eng, Sndry 1973; 36 Addl Credits 1987; *cr:* Connellsville ...Schl Dist 1973-74; Connellsville Jr HS East 1974-; *ai:* NEA, PA St ...ssn, Connellsville Area Ed Assn 1974-; Immaculate Conception ...ch 1960-, Lector 1986-; Sons of Italy Ladies Lodge of Connellsville ...5 1973-; First Cath Slovak Ladies Union, First Cath Slovak Union ...; *office:* Connellsville Jr HS East 710 Locust St Ext Connellsville PA ...5

...PF-FRITTS, CHARLOTTE, Fourth Grade Teacher; *b:* Bronx, NY; ...obert C. Fritts; *ed:* Dowling Coll (BA) Soc Sci 1972, (MS) Ed 1975; ...edit Hrs; 30 Post Grad Hrs; *cr:* Wenonah Elem Schl Tchr 24 Yrs; *ai:* ...Grant Comm Chm; Sci Fair Coord; Bldg Ldrshp Team; Math Club ...d; SCTA, AFT, NYSUT 1972-; *office:* Wenonah Elem Schl 251 ...on Ave Lake Grove NY 11755*

...PIEN, CAROL M., Associate Professor; *b:* Lockport, NY; *m:* Ronald ...Peter W., Elizabeth A.; *ed:* SUNY at Albany (BA) Soc Stud & Eng ...(MA) Ed; *cr:* Berlin Cntrl Schl Scndry Schl Tchr 1970-72; Sub Tchr ...-78; Hudson Vly Comm Coll Eng Instr 1978-; *ai:* Acad Senate; Ad ...Comm on Coll Restructing; Ctr for Effective Tchng Steering Comm; ...Pgm Comm; NERC 1990-; Faith Luth Church 1972-, Treas, Pres, ...h Bd Chair; Acad Advy Comm at Averill Park HS 1992-93, Pres, ...hprsn; Concerned Poestenkill Residents 1994-, Sec; NY St ...cellor's Awd for Excl in Tchng; *office:* Hudson Valley Comm Coll 80 ...enburgh Ave Troy NY 12180

...PIEN, RONALD J., Physics Professor; *b:* Rome, NY; *m:* Carol H. ...ow; *c:* Peter, Elizabeth; *ed:* SUNY at Albany (BS) Physics 1969; ...selaer Polytechnic Inst (MS) Physics 1972; *cr:* North Colonie Schl ...Sci Tchr 1971-82; Hudson Vly Comm Coll Physics Prof 1980-; *ai:* ...T 1983-; Averill Park HS Acad Advy Comm 1992-93; Concerned ...ankill Residents 1994-; NY St Chancellors Awd for Excl in Tchng; ...: Hudson Valley Comm Coll 80 Vandenburgh Ave Troy NY 12180

...PINSKI, BENJAMIN THOMAS, Social Studies Teacher; *b:* Jersey ...NJ; *m:* Ann Marie Faccone; *c:* Thomas, Stephen; *ed:* Newark St Coll ...His 1967, (MA) Sociology 1969; 33 Credit Hrs Hum; *cr:* Newark Bd ...Tchr 1967-71; Chatham Twp Bd of Ed Tchr 1971-91; Chatham Bd of ...chr 1991-; *ai:* Head Golf Coach 1967-68; Asst Bsktbl Coach 1968-83; ...Ftbl Coach 1968, 1974; Charter Mem HS Site Comm; NEA, NJEA ...-; MCCEA 1971-; CEA 1971-, Exec Comm; E Hanover Recreation ...nission, Past Dir Boys Bsktbl; *office:* Chatham HS 255 Lafayette Ave ...nam NJ 07928*

...R, EDYTHE NAOMI, Math, English & Bible Teacher; *b:* Conway, ...; *m:* Alberto B.; *c:* Nerissa, Ursula; *ed:* Oakwood Coll (BA) Eng 1956; ...nam Univ (MS) Elem Ed 1972; *cr:* R. T. Hudson Schl Tchr 1956-59, ...-65, 1972-; NY Pub Lib Proofreader 1959-60; Leo Wolleman Inc Sec ...; Harlem Trailblazers Comm Summer Prgm Dir 1968-72; *ai:* Curr, ...Bible Textbook Steering Comm 3 Yrs; Ephesus Seventh Day ...ntist Church, Asst Treas, Sabbath Schl Tchr; Zapara Outstdng Tchr ...*office:* R. T. Hudson Schl 1122 Forest Ave Bronx NY 10456

...RAS, FOULA KONTONICOLAS, Spanish Teacher; *b:* Piraeus, ...ce; *m:* Dimitrios; *c:* Aphrodite, Irene; *ed:* Queens Coll (BS) Fr, Span, ...ry Ed 1984; Long Island Univ (MS) Ed 1995; 20 Addl Cr; *cr:* ...bishop Iakoros HS Fr, Span tchr 1984-87; St Francis Prep Fr, Span ...1987-88; York Coll ESL Span Tutor 1988-91; Townsend Harris HS ...Tchr 1991-92; Lafayette HS Span Tchr 1992-; *ai:* Span Club Adv ...-94; Multicultural Comm 1991-92; Tutorial Prgm 1994-; UFT 1991-; ...: Lafayette HS 2630 Benson Ave Brooklyn NY 11214*

...RICK, MARY KAY (HUFFMAN), 8th Grd Language Arts Teacher; ...oledo, OH; *m:* Charles Russell; *c:* David Charles, Stephen Russell, ...Michael; *ed:* Bowling Green St Univ (BS) Elem Ed 1965; 40 Grad ...at Univ of Toledo; *cr:* Washington Local 2nd Grd Tchr 1965-66; ...on City Schls 4th Grd Tchr 1966-69; Lake Local L-D Tutor 1978-81; ...nwood Local 8th Grd Lang Arts Tchr 1982-; *ai:* 8th Grd Vlybl Coach; ...3rd Intramural Sports; DKG 1986-; Oregon Comm Theater 1990-, Sec; ...: 3434 Fleitz Rd Oregon OH 43616

...SNER, ANNA JOAN (WAGNER), 2nd Grd Tchr & Primary Coord; ...altimore City, MD; *m:* Joseph R. III; *c:* Joseph R. IV, Michael S., ...aret M.; *ed:* Essec Comm Coll (AA) Summa Cum Laude 1976; Notre ...e of MD (BA) Elem Ed-Magna Cum Laude 1978; Prof Catechist Cert; ...t Anthony of Padua Schl 2nd Grd Tchr, Primary Coord, Sacramental ...d 1964-; *ai:* Primary Coord; Schl Bd Liasion for Fac; Sacramental ...erator Eucharist Prgm; Liturgy Comm; NCEA 1964-; Tchr of Yr.

...SNER, NANCY JANE, Enrichment Teacher; *b:* Philadelphia, PA; *m:* ...t G.; *c:* Joy, Scott, Ryan; *ed:* Glassboro St Coll (BA) Elem Ed 1975; ...an Univ (MA) Elem Ed 1990; Univ of CT Gifted Ed Coursework; ...sboro St Early Chldhd Cert; Rutgers Course in Gifted Ed; G T Cert ...; Speech Cert 1975; *cr:* Bellmawr Pub Schls 1st-3rd Grds Regular ...sroom & Tchr of Gifted 1975-80; Voorhees Pub Schls Tchr of Gifted ...-; *ai:* Various Schl Comms; NEA, NJEA 1975-; VTEA 1988-; NJAGC ...-.

...TAGINER, MARILYN WERMUTH, High School Math Teacher; *b:* ...klyn, NY; *m:* Pinchas; *c:* Ruth, Abraham, Don; *ed:* Brooklyn Coll (BS) ...1972, Richmond Coll (MS) Math, Ed 1976; *cr:* Tilden HS Tchr ...-73; Erasmus Hall HS Tchr 1973-74; FDR HS Math Tchr 1985-; *ai:* ...T 1972-; *office:* Franklyn Delano Roosevelt HS 5800 20th Ave ...klyn NY 11204*

KARUSTIS, MARLENE MAZZETTA, Bio Tchr of Gifted & Talented; *b:* New Haven, CT; *m:* George; *c:* Charles; *ed:* Albertus Magnus Coll (BA) Bio 1961; Seton Hall Univ (MA) Psych 1978; Wood's Hole Biological Lab, Brandais Univ; *cr:* Yale Univ Lib Asst to Head Librn 1961-67; Resolve Youth & Family Counseling Agency Exec Dir 1977-83; Bloomfield Coll Gifted-Talented Tchr 1985; Mount St Mary Acad Bio, Gifted, Talented Tchr 1985-; *ai:* Fac Adv Naturalist's Club, Cum Laude Soc Sci League; Prin's Adv Bd; Curr, Scheduling Comm; Natl Cath Ed Assn 1985-; Intnl Soc for Hist Philosophy & SocSci of Bio 1968-; St Helen's Parish 1968-, Catechism Tchr, Liturgical Comm; St Law Enforcement, HUD Grant; Connally Fndtn Schlsp Boston Coll; *office:* Mount Saint Mary Acad 1645 US Rt 22 W Watchung NJ 07060

KARWACKI, MARGARET WOLSKI, Retired First Grade Teacher; *b:* Baltimore, MD; *m:* Eugene J. Sr.; *c:* Eugene J. Jr., Joan M. Barnhart, Thomas J., William J.; *ed:* St Joseph Coll (BS) Home Ec, Dietetics 1951; Jewish Hospital of Brooklyn NY (ADA) Internship Dietetic Acceptance in Amer Dietetic Assn 1952; Early Chldhd Ed Essex Comm Coll 1971-73, Mt St Agnes Coll 1970, Master Equivalency Loyola Coll 1973-76; Advanced Prof Cert Early Chldhd St of MD; Prof Catechist Cert Archdiocese of Baltimore; *cr:* St Clement Schl Remedial Rdng Tchr ESEA Title I 1967-68; Our Lady of Hope Remedial Rdng Tchr 1968-70; St Clement Schl 2nd & 1st Grd Tchr 1970-94; Mid St Assn Educl Cnsltnt; St John the Evnglst Schl 1st Grd Vol; *ai:* Steering Comm Chprsn; Mid States Evaluation Curr Coord St Clement Schl; Mid St Evaluating Team; NCEA Mini Convention 1988-91, Presenter; Elem & Scndry Tchrs Assn; Steering Comm Chprsn Middle States Evaluation 1983-94; Archdiocese of Balto Service Awd 1988; Service Awd 20 Yrs St Clement Schl.*

KARWATSKY, DONNA J., Mathematics Teacher; *b:* Connellsville, PA; *m:* David P.; *c:* Kelly D., Brian D., Kristen D.; *ed:* California Univ of PA (BS) Scndry Ed 1974; 36 Post Grad Credits; *cr:* Connellsville Schl Dist Sub Tchr 1974-75; Connellsville Jr HS West Math Tchr 1975-; *ai:* SAP Team Mem; NEA & PSEA 1975-; CAEA 1975-, Budget Ch, IPD Ch, Election Ch, Bldg Rep; Delta Kappa Gamma 1983-, Pres, 1st VP, 2nd VP; KDKA Thanks to Tchrs Awd 1993; *office:* Connellsvile Jr HS West 215 Falls Ave Connellsville PA 15425

KARWOSKI, JOSEPH P., Mathematics & Computer Teacher; *b:* Johnstown, PA; *ed:* Univ of Pittsburgh (BS) Math & Sci 1977; Penn St (MA) Math 1985; Tufts (PHD) Cmptrs & Ed 1991; *cr:* Central Cambria HS Math & Cmptr Tchr 16 Yrs; *ai:* Cmptr Team; Cmptr Club; NHS; NEA, PSEA 1978-; CCEA 1980-; Nom for 1992 PA Teach of Yr; Wrote 3 ITEC Grants for Cmptr Equipment; Nom for the Tandy Outstanding Tchr; *office:* Central Cambria HS 208 Schoolhouse Rd Ebensburg PA 15931*

KASAI, JOYCE L., Business Teacher; *b:* Johnson City, NY; *ed:* SUNY at Albany (BS) Commercial Ed 1965, (MS) Commerce 1971; Coord of Diversified Cooperative Ed 1996; Taken Numerous Cmptr Courses; *cr:* Binghamton City Schl Dist Bus Tchr 1965-70; West Canada Vly Cntrl Schl Dist Bus Tchr 1970-; *ai:* West Canada Vly Tech, Herkimer Cty Voc & Tech Ed Assn, Model Schls for Bus Comms; AFT, NY St United Tchrs, NY St Bus Tchrs Assn, NBEA 1965-; *office:* W Canada Valley Ctl Schl Dist PO Box 360 Newport NY 13416

KASCHAK, KAREN MARIE (MEHALKO), Fifth Grade Teacher; *b:* Hazleton, PA; *m:* James Jr.; *c:* Amanda; *ed:* E Stroudsburg Univ (BS) Elem Ed 1988; *cr:* Transfiguration Schl 5th Grd Tchr 1988-; *ai:* Yth Group Adv; Rel Ed Dir; Pa Jr Acad of Sci 1983-; *office:* Transfiguration Schl 217 W Green St W Hazelton PA 18201*

KASCHER, ROSEMARIE ANNE, Teacher; *b:* Youngstown, OH; *ed:* Univ of FL at Miami (BA) Voice-Cum Laude 1958; Columbia Univ (MA) Voice 1970; Cleveland Inst of Mus & Case Western Res Univ; Attended: Rayen Schl, Vienna Conservatory of Music, Oxford Univ, Eastman Schl of Music, Kent St Univ, Felt & Tarrant Bis Schl; Westminster Choir Coll: Saratoga-Potsdam Choral Inst; East Carolina Univ; Hartwick Coll, CA St Univ & Pecs Univ Pecs, Hungary; *cr:* The Eng Ctr Tchr 6Yrs; Austintown Schls Vocal & Music Coord; Youngstown St Univ vocal & Music Tchr 13 Yrs; Kwassui Coll Eng & Music Tchr 4 Yrs; Cleveland St Univ 1 Yr; The Cleveland Inst of Music 1 Yr; St of OH Dept of Ed Permanent Cert; *ai:* Amer Assoc of Univ Prof; Music Edctrs Natl Conf; MCMT; AEA; OEA; Beta Sigma Phi; NEA; Amer Choral Dir Assn; NOTA; Natl Assn of Tchrs of Singing; Amer Orff-Sculwerk Assn; Kodaly Intnl Inst; Amer Choral Dir Assn; Trinity Meth Church; Youngstown Philharmonic Chorus; Concordia Chorus; Amer Recorder Republican Natl Comm; Soloist in Concerts Recitals, & Operas in Europe, Japan, & USA; Conducted Austintown Fitch Concert Choir; Pupil of Eleanor Steber, Margaret Kabil, Yu Kwa Sze, Madame Maria Guidi of Rome Opera House; Kalberine Long Schl of Music; Met Opera Recordings & Television Performances; Temple Israel, Soloist; Sunday Schl Tchr; Saxon Sarngerbund Asst Dir & Accompanist; Miami Opera Guild SChlshp; Wesley Fndtn Flwshp; Columbia Univ Grant; Univ of Miami SchlShp; Freedom Fndtn Tchrs Medal Awd; Whos Who of Amer Women; Intnl Whos of Musicians; Nu Kappa Tau Pres; Alpha SIGma Epsilon Co Ed Ldrshp Honorary; Univ of Miami Hnr Ct: Beta sigma Phi; Sigma Alpha Data; Ibis Outstdng Female Stud Awd; YWCA Chrst Woman Awd; YWCA Tchr Awd Nom; Whos Who in Amer Coll & Univ; Jennings Scholar; Whos Who Among Woman of the World; Pta Tchr of the Yr; Pres Awd 1987; Outstdng Svr, Amvets 1987; Congressional Awd 1987; Admins Plaque, Veterans Affair 1987; Citizen of the Yr, 1st Woman in Area; Edctr of the Yr; Austrian Saxton Vereins Metal.

KASCHULUK, ANN B. C., Guidance Counselor; *b:* Westerly, RI; *m:* Peter J.; *ed:* Univ of RI (BA) Scndry Ed, His 1975, (MA) Guidance, Cnslng 1980; Addl Courses; Addl Courses RI Coll; *cr:* Charibo Regnl Schl Dist 7-8 Grd Eng, Soc Stud Tchr 1977-92; Charibo Regnl MS Guid Cnslr 1992-; *ai:* Stud as Mediators coord, Instr; Natl Jr Hnr Soc Adv; NEA 1977-; Chorus of Westerly, Christ Church Choir 1962-; Westerly Hosp Auxilary 1984-; North East Regnl Ctr Drug Free Schls; *office:* Chariho MS 455B Switch Rd Wood River Jct RI 02894

KASE, SUZANNE LAMANNA, Fifth Grade Teacher; *b:* Reading, PA; *m:* Stephen Albert; *c:* Stephen, Ashley, Erica; *ed:* West Chester Univ (BS) Fr 1975; Univ of Montpelier France Scndry Ed Cert 1973-74; Alvernia Coll Elem Ed Cert 1990; *cr:* Cntrl Cath HS Fr Tchr 1976-78; St Catharine of Siena Seventh Grd Tchr 1991-92, Fifth Grd Tchr 1993-; *ai:* Lang Arts Coord; Spelling Bee, Declamation Moderator; Women's Soc of St Ignatius Parish 1985-, Treas 1985-87; Cath Yth Org 1994-, Bd Mem; *office:* St Catharine Siena Regnl Schl 2330 Perkiomen Ave Mt Penn PA 19606

KASEMAN, JANE LANKFORD, Retired Language Arts Teacher; *b:* Dover, PA; *c:* Debra Raye Kaseman Acosta; Bradrick Scott; *ed:* East Stroudsburg (BS) Elem Ed 1956; 21 Credits Elem Ed Shippensburg; 6 Credits Rdng Millersville; 6 Credits Rdng Penn St; *cr:* Bloomfield-Cntre Tchr 1964-82; Greenpark Schl Tchr 1982-90; *ai:* NEA, WPEA 1964-; NRA; KRA; *home:* PO Box 237 New Bloomfield PA 17068

KASEORU, DIANNE JOY, High School Special Educator; *b:* Torrington, CT; *m:* Peter W.; *c:* Johanna, Anthony; *ed:* Southern CT St Coll (MS) Spec Ed 1973, (BA) Spec ed; St Michaels Coll 3 Credits Spec Ed Assessment; Johnson St Coll 3 Credits Spec Ed Assessment; *cr:* Jefferson MS Mid Level Spec Educator 8 Yrs; Lamoille Union HS Spec Educator 8 Yrs; *ai:* Mem of Restructuring Comm, Grad Comm, Prof Dev Comm & Co- Chair For 1 Yr; Frosh Orientation Prgm Instr; New Tchr Mentorship- Mentor; Lamoille N Stans Bd; NEA 8 Yrs; LUHS 8 Yrs; Bakersfield Lib Vol 1985-87; Sheldon Pub Lib 1988-; *office:* Lamoille Union HS PO Box 304 Hyde Park VT 05655*

KASHATUS, MARY M., Spanish Teacher; *b:* Danville, PA; *ed:* East Stroudsburg Univ (BS) Span 1968; Attnd Penn St & Univ of Hartford; *cr:* Greater Nanticoke Area Schl Dist Span Tchr 27 Yrs; *ai:* Foreign Lang Club Adv; Honor Soc Adv; NEA, PSEA, GNAEA 1968-, PSMLA 15 Yrs; AATSP, NE PA Chapter 10 Yrs; *office:* John S Fine Sr H S Educational Plz Nanticoke PA 18634

KASHIMAWO, TUNDE, Dir of College Discovery Pgm; *b:* Lagos, Nigeria; *m:* Tade; *c:* Tolani, Zaidat, Ade; *ed:* City Coll of NY (BA) Soc Sci 1975; St Univ of NY at Buffalo (MSEd) Coll Prsnl Admin 1978; Schl Admin 1979; *cr:* Queensborough Comm Coll C-STEP Coord 1978-95, Coll Discovery Dir 1995-; *ai:* C-STEP Club Fac Adv; Intnl Womens Assn & Prof Women Assn Mem; Assn of Black Women in Higher Ed 1993-; *office:* Queensborough Comm Coll 222-05 56th Ave Attn Cstep Office Flushing NY 11364

KASHMAN, MARGERY KRANE, English & Journalism Teacher; *b:* Brooklyn, NY; *m:* David S.; *c:* Amy; *ed:* SUNY at Stony Brook (BA) Eng 1971; CUNY at Queens Coll (MLS) Lib Sci 1975; St John's Univ (PHD) Adin, Supervision 1987; *cr:* Woodmere Jr HS South Eng Tchr 1971-78, Eng Chprsn 1979-80; G W Hewlett HS Eng, Jrnlsm Tchr 1980-; *ai:* Spectrum HS Newspaper Adv; NYSUT, NEA 1971-; NCTE 1989-; LISPA 1989-, Bd Mem; Phi Delta Kappa, ASCD 1988-; Hewlett HS Alumni Assn 1993-; SUNY SB Alumni Assn 1971-; Distngd Alumni Awd 1989; Article Pub Eng Journal 1994; NYSEC Eng Tchr Excl 1991; *office:* George W Hewlett HS 60 Everit Ave Hewlett NY 11557

KASHMANN, BETH L., Counselor; *b:* Newark, NJ; *ed:* Trenton St Coll (BA) Math Ed 1970; Syracuse Univ (MS) Cnslg, Guid 1974; Addl 30 Grad Hrs; *cr:* Hightstown HS Math Tchr 1970-73; East Syracuse-Minoa HS Cnslr 1974-; *ai:* Site-based Mngmt Bldg Tchr Ldr; United Tchr 1974-, VP 1993-; NYSUT, AFT 1974-; Multiple Sclerosis Svc Org 1980-; *office:* East Syracuse-Minoa HS 6400 Fremont Rd East Syracuse NY 13057

KASKEY, RICHARD R., High School Social Stud Tchr; *b:* Wilkes-Barre, PA; *m:* Kathleen Patricia Kinney; *ed:* Temple Univ (BS) Sndry Ed & Soc Stud 1992; 16 Credit Hrs Towards Masters Bucknell Univ; *cr:* Montoursville HS Soc Stud Tchr 1993-; *ai:* Asst Athletic Dir; Stu Govt Adv; Bsktbl Asst Coach; *office:* Montoursville HS 100 N Arch St Montoursville PA 17754*

KASKOUN, ELLEN JEAN, High School Art Teacher; *b:* Bayshore, NY; *ed:* SUC NY at Buffalo (BS) Art Ed 1974; 70 Credit Hrs Oriental Art, Philosophy SUNY at Stony Brook; *cr:* Burr Rd Jr HS Art Tchr 1974-76; Commack North HS Art Tchr 1976-79; Mt Siani Jr HS Art Tchr 1979-92; Mt Sinai HS Art Tchr 1992-; *ai:* LI Media Arts Show Adv; Prom Decorating Comm Adv; NY St United Tchrs, AFT 1974-; Stud Travel India, Pakistan, Bali, Borobodur; Art Travel Hermitage Museum St Petersburg Russia, Tretiakoff Art Museum Moscow Russia; *office:* Mount Sinai HS Gertrude Goodman Dr Mount Sinai NY 11766

KASLER, KATHY LYNNE (BEELER), Applied Mathematics Teacher; *b:* Lima, OH; *m:* Brent Alan; *c:* Melissa; *ed:* Ohio Univ (BA) Scndry Ed 1990; 12 Credit Hrs in Masters Educl Admin; Major in Math; Minor in Biological Sci; *cr:* Tri-Cty JVS Math Tchr 1991-; Upward Bound Coll Prep Acad Math Tchr 1994-; *ai:* Passport Ceremony Co-Chprsn; NEA 1991-; OEA 1991-; Martha Holden Jennings Scholar; *office:* Tri-Cty Voc Schl 15676 St Rt 691 Nelsonville OH 45764

KASOLD, STEPHEN JOSEPH, High School English Teacher; *b:* Rockville Center, NY; *m:* Lorraine Seebeck; *ed:* St Francis Coll (BA) Eng & Sec Ed 1973; Hofstra Univ (MA) Eng & Amer Lit 1974; St Univ of NY Theatre Arts 30 CH; *cr:* Sts Peter & Paul Schl Eng Instr 1978-79; Schroon Lake CSD HS Eng Tchr 1979-81; Cazenovia JS HS Eng Tchr 1981-; Cazenovia Coll Lecturer in Eng 1982-; *ai:* Cent NY Schl to Coll Initiative Mem; NYSUT 1979-; Dramatists Guild 1992-; NEH Summer Seminar for HS Tchrs 1993; Local Schls Grants 1984, 1992; *office:* Cazenovia Jr Sr HS 31 Emory Ave Cazenovia NY 13035*

KASPAR, ELIZABETH WEATHERS, Fourth Grade Teacher; *b:* Indianapolis, IN; *m:* John Adam; *c:* Adam, Debbie, Jesse, Albert Voegtlin, Jeanne Voegtlin; *ed:* Beaver Coll (BA) Pol Sci 1964; Elem Cert Glassboro St Coll 1968; Addl 18 Grad Credits Elem Ed; *cr:* Vineland Schl Sys Fourth Grd Tchr 1964-; *ai:* Vineland Ed Assn Rep, Legislative Chprsn; NEA 1964-; NJEA; CCCEA Govt Relations Chprsn 1982-88; VEA; ADK 1978-84; Democratic Party 1988 Candidate for City Cncl, 1984 Del to Natl Convention; 1987-88 Edctr of Yr; *home:* 321 Summit St Vineland NJ 08360

KASPER, DIANE CARR (DICKERSON), Second Grade Teacher; *b:* Elmira, NY; *m:* Laurence H.; *c:* Lynn H. Greatsinger, Barbara L. Dickerson, Kathleen J. Marcus, Laura L. Young, Martin L.; *ed:* St Univ at Geneseo (BS) Elem Ed 1963; Elmira Coll (MS) Ed 1970; *cr:* Higbie Lane ES 3rd Grd Tchr 1963-64; Geo Washington ES 1st Grd Tchr 1965-66; Broadway ES 1st Grd Tchr 1968; Wellsburg ES 3rd Grd Tchr 1979-80; Newfield ES 2nd Grd Tchr 1989-; *ai:* Chprsn Tchr Support Team; NYSUT, AFT 1989-; Southport Recreation Commission, Former Sec; Town of Southport, Former Councilwoman; *office:* Newfield Elem Schl 247 Main St Newfield NY 14867

KASPEREK, CATHERINE A. (BEARDSELL), Marketing Teacher; *b:* Buffalo, NY; *m:* James T.; *c:* John J., Kimille C.; *ed:* St Univ Coll at Buffalo (BS) Bus 1989, (MS) Bus 1994; *cr:* Casey MS Sr Clerk Stenographer 1977-81; Williamsville South Sr Clerk Stenographer 1981-89, Bus & Mrktng Tchr 1989-; *ai:* DECA Adv; AFT & NYSUT 1989-; Natl Bus Ed Assn 1988-; Friends of Lancaster Lib 1988-; Lancaster Opera House 1989-; *office:* Williamsville South HS 5950 Main St Williamsville NY 14221

KASPRISIN-RUS, THEA M., Social Studies Teacher; *b:* Cleveland, OH; *m:* Vladimir J. Rus; *c:* Jacquelyn Kasprisin, Julee Kasprisin; *ed:* Pacific Luth Univ (BA) Elem Ed 1966; Rdng Specialist Cnslng 1989; *cr:* Diocese of Cleveland Tchr 1962-64; Garfield Heights Schl Tchr 1968-69; Maple Heights Schl Tchr 1969-70; Diocese of Cleveland Tchr 1971-84; May Co Sr Exec 1985-86; Solomon Schechter Day Schl Tchr 1986-; *ai:* Stu Cncl Adv; Ed Comm; NEA 1962-; AACDS 1994-; AASST 1980-; Global Issues, Bd Mem; Oral His Intergenerational Viewpoint Grant; Outstdng Soc Stud Tchr OH 1993; *office:* Solomon Schechter Day Schl 19910 Malvern Rd Shaker Heights OH 44122*

KASSEES, MARTHA CADOURA, Social Studies Teacher; *b:* Wilmington, DE; *m:* Samir Saadallah; *ed:* Jacksonville Univ (BA) His 1964; Wilmington Coll (MS) Human Resource Mngmt 1990; 38 Hrs in Ed, His; *cr:* D. U. Fletcher Jr HS Soc Stud Tchr 1964-66; Dela Warr HS Soc Stud Tchr 1966-78; William Penn HS Soc Stud Tchr 1978-; *ai:* Colonial Schl Dist GATE Comm; GATE Comm; Co-Operating Tchr of Stu Tchr; Colonial Ed Assn 1978-; DE Ed Assn 1966-, HS Rep, IPD Awd 1993; Delta Kappa Gamma 1990-, Chptr Pres; NEA 1966-; Univ of DE Dept of His Tchr of Yr 1988; Tchr of Yr 1991; DuPont Mini Grant Prgm 1991; DE Recognition for Tech Ed 1992-93; *office:* William Penn HS 713 E Basin Rd New Castle DE 19720

KASTNER, MARY E., English & Debate Teacher; *b:* Newark, NJ; *ed:* Newark St Coll (BA) Eng; Kean Coll (MA) Hum 1978; 32 Post Grad Hrs Lbrl Stud; *cr:* Dover HS Eng Tchr 1967-71; Heritage Jr HS Eng Tchr 1973-83; Livingston HS Eng, Debate, Media Tchr 1983-; *ai:* Debate Coach; NEA, NJEA 1967-; ECEA, LEA 1973-; NJ Pub Broadcasting Authority 1992-, Treas 1992-94, Commissioner; Parsippany-Troy Hills town Cncl 1983-87, Councilwoman; *office:* Livingston H S 30 Robert Harp Dr Livingston NJ 07039

KASTNER, MICHAEL PAUL, Vocal Music Director; *b:* Tiffin, OH; *m:* Mary E.; *c:* Michelle, Melissa, Matthew; *ed:* Siena Heights Coll (BA) Music Ed 1983; Attnd Heidelberg Coll, BGSU, Kent St Univ; *cr:* St Joseph Schl K-8th Grd Music Tchr 1983-88; Western Reserve HS Vocal Music Dir 1988-; *ai:* Dir, Producer of Musical; 3 HS, 2 MS Show Choirs; OH Music Ed Assn 1983-; W R Tchrs Assn, NEA 1988-; *office:* Western Reserve HS 3841 US Rt 20 E Collins OH 44826

KASTNER, ROXANNE LEE, Fourth Grade Teacher; *b:* Baltimore, MD; *ed:* Averett Coll (BS) Early Chldhd 1976; Bowie St (APC) Spcl Ed 1985; Western MD Elem Ed 1990; *cr:* Great Mills Elem Tchr 1979-80; Lettie Marshall Dent Tchr 1980-; *ai:* Talent Show, Sci Fair & Soc Stud Comm Mem; NEA 1978-; MSTA 1979-; PTA 1979-, Life Mbrshp; Human Soc 1988-; World Wide Life 1988-; PETA 1988-; St Marys Cty Schl Environment Awd; Life Time Mbrshp PTA Awd; *office:* Lettie Marshall Dent Elem Sch 47355 New Market Turner Rd Mechanicsville MD 20659

KASUNIC, MARY CLAIRE, French Teacher; *b:* Darby, PA; *m:* Jon Alan; *c:* Raquel, Elise, Anna, Nicholas; *ed:* Univ of Pittsburgh (BA) Fr 1983, (MA) Ed 1990; *cr:* Frick Intnl Stud Acad Stu Tchr 1989; Oakland Cath HS Fr Tchr 1992-; *ai:* Fr Club Co-Moderator; NEA 1991-; Sacred Heart PTG 1990-, Recording Sec; Alliance Francaise 1995-; *office:* Oakland Catholic HS 144 N Craig St Pittsburgh PA 15213

KATANA, JOHN JOSEPH, Geography Teacher; *b:* Spangler, PA; *ed:* Indiana Univ of PA (BS) Ed, Geog, Soc Stud 1970, (EDM) Ed, Geog 1975; 30 Post Grad Hrs in Ed, Geog; *cr:* Indiana Jr HS Geog Tchr 1971-; *ai:* Geog Club Spon; Geog Bee Local, St Level; Geog Olympiad; Schl, Dist Assessment Comm; Steering Comm for Local Soc Sci Alliance; Tchr Consultant for PA Geographic Alliance; NEA, PSEA 1971-; Natl Cncl Geographic Ed 1977-, DTA 1989, 1994; PA Geographical Soc, Lifetime, Past Pres, Bd of Dirs; Moose 1986-; GCU, Lifetime Mem; Hays-Fulbright Grant; Natl Geographic Soc Schlsp; Tchr Recognition Awd for Curr Dev; Regnl Rand Mc Nally Awd for Curr; Numerous Articles Pub; *office:* Indiana Jr HS 245 N 5th St Indiana PA 15701*

KATARSKI, JOSEPH M., English Teacher; *b:* Danville, PA; *m:* Kathy Hutter; *c:* Mark, Hallie, Brian; *ed:* St Vincent Coll (BA) Eng 1972; Bowling Green St Univ (MA) British & Amer Lit 1974; *cr:* Bowling Green St Univ Tchng Asst 1972-74; St Vincent Coll ESL Instr 1974-76; Blairsville-Saltsburg Schl Dist Eng Tchr 1975; Hempfield Area Schl Dist Eng Tchr 1976-; Seton Hill Coll Continuing Ed Instr 1994-; *ai:* Ecology Club Co-Spon; NEA 1975-; PSEA 1975-; ACUWPET 1990-; *office:* Hempfield Sr HS RD 6 Box 77 Greensburg PA 15601*

KATCHEN, RITA LITWACK, Fourth Grade Teacher; *b:* Newark, NJ; *c:* Steven Marc, Mitchell Larry, Douglas Adam; *ed:* Newark St Tchrs Coll (BS) Elem Ed 1959; *cr:* Abraham Clark Schl 4th Grd Tchr 1959-60; Frank K. Hehnly Schl 4th Grd Tchr 1969-; *ai:* Bernett Rsrch Office Supvr; NEA, NJEA, Clark Ed Assn 1969-; PTA 1964-, Pres; Clark Cncl PTA 1964-70, Pres; Presenter Module Sci Alliance Hunterdon Bus, Ed Partnership; *office:* Frank K. Hehnly Schl 654 Raritan Rd Clark NJ 07066*

KATCHER, MITCHELL SCOTT, Language Arts Teacher; *b:* Brooklyn, NY; *ed:* Queens Coll (BA) Eng 1988, (MS) Scndry Ed, Eng 1994; *cr:* Rockaway Beach Jr HS 180 Lang Arts Tchr 1988-; *ai:* Beach Channel HS Var Girls Sftbl Coach; Arista, Arete Hnr Soc Master of Ceremonies 4 Yrs; AFT 1988-; UFT 1988-, Union Del; Museum of Natural His 1992-; Pub Article 1992; Presented Plaque for Debate Team Champion Coach 1989.

KATEN, SHEILA BLAINE, Math Teacher; *b:* Cornwall, NY; *m:* Karl T.; *c:* Jesse, Katrina; *ed:* SUNY at Oswego (BS) Scndry Ed-Math 1971; 33 Addl Hrs; *cr:* Norwich HS Math Tchr 1971-; *ai:* K-12 Math Comm; HS Instrl Support Task Force; Mentor Interm Prgm; NE, NYNEA 1971-; NCTM 1994-; AMTNYS 1984-; *office:* Norwich HS Midland Dr Norwich NY 13815

KATKO, CHARLOTTE MARTELL, Elementary Teacher; *b:* Brownsville, PA; *m:* Terry W.; *ed:* CA ST Coll (BS) Elem Ed 1968, (MED) Elem Ed 1972; *cr:* Cntrl Elem Schl Tchr 1968-93; Cardale Elem Schl Tchr 1994-; *ai:* PSEA, NEA, BEA 1968-; *office:* Cardale Elem Brownsville Area Schl Dist Grindstone PA 15442

KATSOULIS, ROSINA A. (PANETTA), 5th-8th Grade Science Teacher; *b:* Brooklyn, NY; *m:* George C.; *c:* Andrew; *ed:* Hunter Coll City Univ of NY (BA) His, Geology 1977; Pace Univ (MSE) Supervision, Admin 1988; Attnd Numerous Cath Diocese Prof Dev, NY St, Earth Sci Regents Curr Wkshps; *cr:* St Francis Xavier St Augustine Schl 7th Grd Soc Stud Tchr 1978-79; A. Fantis Greek Amer Schl 7th Grd Sci, Soc Stud Tchr 1979-82; St Demetrios HS Sci Dept Chprsn 1982-88; Regina Pacis Schl Grd 5-8 Sci Tchr 1988-; *ai:* Schl Sci Coord; Enrichment Prgm, Sci Fair Advs; Schl Bd Mem; Pace Univ Alumni, PDK 1988-; *office:* Regina Pacis Roman Cath Schl 1201 66th St Brooklyn NY 11219*

KATUSAK, EDWARD RICHARD, French & English Teacher; *b:* Scranton, PA; *ed:* Univ of Scranton (BS) Scndry Ed 1966, (MS) Scndry admin 1971; 12 Credit Hrs; *cr:* Dunmore HS Fr & Eng Tchr 29 Yrs; *ai:* Fr Club Adv; Quebec Spring Trip; Mid Sts Comm; AFT 1966; AATF; NCTE; Holy Family Church, Parish Soc; *home:* 1121 Clay Ave Apt 1H Dunmore PA 18510

KATZ, CYNTHIA, Photography Instructor; *b:* Newark, NJ; *c:* Dylan Katz Wicks; *ed:* Univ of NH (BFA) Photography 1983; Bennington Coll (MFA) Photography 1987; *cr:* Phillips Exeter Acad Photography Instr 1984-85; The Schl of the Museum of Fine Arts Boston Photography Instr 1988-89; Various Summer Pgms; Concord Acad Phtography Instr 1987-; *ai:* Yrbk Photo & Gay & Straight Alliance Adv; Alternative Forms of Assessment Comm Chair; SPE 1987-; CAA 1987-; GLSTN 1990-; Soc for Photographic Ed; Coll Art Assn; Consultant on Portfolio Based Assessment; Worked on Grad Schl of Ed at Harvard; NY St Art Tchrs Assn; MA Assn of Art Edctrs; NJ Assn of Ind Schls; Studio in a Schl; Presentor on Protfolios at NE Tchrs Conf; NE Tchrs Day; *office:* Concord Acad 166 Main St Concord MA 01742*

KATZ, DAVID RAYMOND,III, Pol Science & History Prof; *b:* Norfolk, VA; *c:* Erin Alexandra, David Raymond 4th, Daniel Martin; *ed:* Camden Cty Comm Coll (AA) Lbrl Arts 1976; Univ of MA (BA) Pol Sci 1978; Villanova Univ (MA) Pol Sci 1980; *cr:* Mohawk Vly Comm Coll Pol Sci, His Prof 1981-; *ai:* Womens Bsktbl Coach; Coordinated Coll Pgrm Local Correctional Facility; Learning Through Writing Course Prof; Our Lady of Lourdes Church 1981-, Lector; AYSO 1990-, Coach; Utica Roadrunners 1996 Competitive Runner; Mohawk Vly Peace Cncl 1988-; Tchng Excl Coll Awd; Tchr Who Made a Difference Awd; Retaining Adult Stdnts Awd Excl in Tchng; *office:* Mohawk Valley Comm Coll 1101 Sherman Dr Utica NY 13501*

KATZ, JANICE FEINZEIG, English Teacher; *b:* Brooklyn, NY; *m:* Marvin; *c:* Michael, Melissa; *ed:* Brooklyn Coll (BA) Eng 1969; 30 Addl Grad Credits 1973; *cr:* Samuel J. Tilden HS Eng Tchr 1969-74; Susan Wagner HS Eng Tchr 1983-; *ai:* 9th Grd Coord Scholars Fair; UFT 1969-74, 1982-; Flwshp to Poland, Israel Holocaust & Jewish Resistance 1993; *office:* Susan E Wagner HS 1200 Manor Rd Staten Island NY 10314*

KATZ, JILL, Math Teacher; *b:* Brooklyn, NY; *ed:* Nassau Comm Coll (AA) Math 1977; SUNY Stony Brook (BS) Math 1979; Hofstra Univ (MA) Ed 1981; Addl Stud BOCES; *cr:* Levittown Meml HS Permanent Sub Tchr 1979-80; Salk Jr HS Permanent Sub Tchr 1980; Long Beach Jr HS Math Tchr 1980-81; Long Beach HS Math Tchr 1981-; *ai:* Sr Class, Ice Hockey Adv; NYSUT 1979-; *office:* Long Beach HS 322 Lagoon Dr W Lido Beach NY 11756

KATZ, JOANNE SEFFENS, Asst Prof of Physical Therapy; *b:* Brooklyn, NY; *m:* Neal B.; *c:* Jason, Daniel; *ed:* SUNY at Buffalo (BA) Bio 1977; Columbia Univ (MA) Applied Physiology 1985; Cert Phys Therapy 1978; NY Univ PHD Candidate Phys Therapy; *cr:* Hosp for Spec Surgery Phys Therapist 1978-82; Visiting Therapy Assocs Phys Therapist, Consultant 1982-83; Queens Ctr, Multi-Handdicapped Children Sr Phys Therapist 1983-84; Phys Therapy Pvy Practice Phys Therapist, Owner 1983-94; Visiting Nurse Svc of NY Phys Therapist Consultant 1985-86; NY Univ Phys Therapy Lab Instr 1993-94; SUNY-HSC Brooklyn Phys Therapy Asst Prof 1994-; *ai:* CHRP Fac of the Assembly Sec 1995-; CHRP Fac Comm 1995-; Centerwide Fac Comm 1995-; CHRP Acad Policy, Qualifications Comm 1994-; Fac Stu Assn Bd of Dir 1994-; CHRP Coll Retreat Comm 1994-; CHRP Curr Comm 1995-; APTA 1977-; AACPDM 1980-; NDTA 1983-; AAUW 1996; Pi Lambda Theta 1995-; UUP Awd 1995; NIH Flwshp Grant 1993-94; NIDRR Grant 1992-93; Katz, Ling & Mc Donough 1994 Phys Ther; Katz & Nelson 1995; World Confederation of PT Congress Proceedings; Balogun, Tang, Hsieh & Katz 1995; Phys Therapy Bd Review Wkdhp; Primary Hlth Care of Wom; Fourth Annual Rsrch Conf 1995; World Confederation for PT Congress 1995; Rsrch in Progress Presentation 1995; Second Joint APTA, CPA Congress 1994; *office:* S U N Y Hlth Sci Cent Brooklyn 450 Clarkson Ave Box 16 Brooklyn NY 11203

KATZ, LIVIA, English Teacher; *b:* Sighetul Marmatiei, Rumania; *ed:* Long Island Univ (BA) Eng 1973; CUNY Grad Schl (MA) Eng 1991; Working Towards PHD in Eng; *cr:* Baruch Coll Tchng Intern 1976-77; Borough of Manhattan Comm Coll Adj Lecturer 1977-78; John Jay Coll of Criminal Justice Adj Lecturer, Lecturer 1978-; Borough of Manhattan Comm Coll Adj Lecturer 1994-; *ai:* Stu Adv; Proficiency Test Proctor; PSC CUNY 1978-; Read Two Papers for Shelley Society on Percy Bysshe Shelley 1976, Wordsworth at North-East MLA Conf 1978; *office:* John Jay Coll of Criminal Just 445 W 59th St Ofc New York NY 10019

KATZ, REGINA MARY, Social Studies Teacher; *b:* Utica, NY; *m:* Steven H.; *c:* Aram, Michael; *ed:* SUNY at Brockport (BS) Amer His 1974; East Stroudsburg Univ (MA) Amer His 1993; SUNY New Paltz Tchng Cert Scndry Soc Stud 1986; St Johns Univ 30 Post Grad Hrs Amer His; *cr:* Roscoe Central Schl Soc Stud Tchr 1987-, Soc Stud Chair 1995-; *ai:* Discipline, Union Pol Action & Union Grievance Comms; NYSUT 1987-, Pres; Sons of Itay 1994-; *office:* Roscoe Central Schl Academy St Roscoe NY 12776

KATZ, ROBERT NATHAN, Chemistry Teacher; *b:* Jersey City, NJ; *ed:* Rutgers Univ (BS) Chemical, Cellular Bio 1974; Univ of CA at San Diego (MS) Inorganic Chem 1976, (PHD) Chem 1978; Columbia Univ Post-Doctoral Fellow 1978-80; *cr:* Engelhard Corp Rsrch Chemist 1980-84; Rockefeller Univ Rsrch Assoc 1984-88; Mount Sinai Schl of Medicine Chemist, Instr 1988-94; Brooklyn Tech HS Tchr 1994-; *ai:* Chem, Sci Olymnpiad; Chem PULSE Tutoring; AAAS 1980-; Amer Chemical Soc 1974-; NY Acad Sci 1977-; Comprehensive Model Schls Project 1995-, Chem Tchr; Sigma Xi; Alpha Zeta; R. W. Herbert Meml Schlsp Rutgers Univ; Earl C. Anthony Schlsp USCD; NJ St Schlsp; *office:* Brooklyn Technical HS 29 Fort Greene Pl Brooklyn NY 11217

KATZ, ROBERTA KARPF, Third Grade Teacher; *b:* Brooklyn, NY; *m:* Howard; *c:* Craig, Nanci; *ed:* Brooklyn Coll (BA) Ed & Speech 1967; Stony Brook Univ (MA) Lbrl Stud 1975; Suffolk Comm Coll 30 Credits Above MS Degree; *cr:* PS 154 Queens 1st-5th Grd Tchr Primarily Grd 3 18 Yrs; PS 183 Brooklyn Preschl, Kindgtn & 1st Grd Tchr 2 Yrs; *ai:* Soc & UFT Comm; AFT & UFT 1967-; Natl Cncl of Jewish Women; Natl Org of Women; *office:* PS 154 Queens 75-02 162nd st Flushing NY 11366

KATZ, SHELDON, Mechanical Engrng Tech Prof; *b:* Brooklyn, NY; *m:* Barbara Powers; *c:* Neal S., Donald B.; *ed:* City Coll of NY (BME) Mechanical Engrng 1963; Rochester Inst of Tech (MS) Engrng Tech 1970; Grad Credits from Saint Lawrence Univ, St Univ of NY at Potsdam, Clarkson Univ; *cr:* Esso Research & Engrng Co Project Engr 193-64; General Dynamics Electronics Division Project Engr 1964-69; St Univ of NY Coll of Tech Asst Prof, Assoc Prof, Prof 1969-; *ai:* Inst of Ind Engrs 1987-; Amer Soc for Engrng Ed 1990-; United Univ Prof 1975-; Exch Prof to City Coll Norwich, United Kingdom 1995; Whos Who in East; Mechanical Engrng Tech Dept Chair 1985-90; *office:* S U N Y Coll Of Tech At Canton Canton NY 13617*

KATZ, THELMA ACKERMAN, Full-Day Kindergarten Teacher; *b:* McKeesport, PA; *m:* Allan; *c:* David, Marcie; *ed:* Univ of PA (BS) Primary Ed 1956; 30 Credit Hrs; *cr:* Overbrook & Rogers Schls 3rd Grd Tchr 1956-60; Piedmont Jr high 3rd Grd Tchr; Knoxville Elem Kndgtn Tchr; Whittier Elem Kndgtn Tchr; Westwood Elem Kndgtn Tchr 1980-; *ai:* Pittsburgh Fed of Tchrs; *office:* Westwood Elem Schl 508 Shadyhill Rd Pittsburgh PA 15205

KATZ, VERA J., Professor; *b:* Richmond Hill, NY; *m:* Dr. Thomas A. Korth; *c:* Anita L. Greenberg, Larry A.; *ed:* Brooklyn Coll (BA) Theatre 1956; Boston Univ (MFA) Theatre & Directing 1958; Attnd Univ of CA at Los Angeles in Film & Univ of Southern CA Division of cinema & Television; 3 Advanced Courses in Schl of Comm Howard Univ; *cr:* Arlington Cty Recreation Ctr Childrens Dramtics Tchr 1962; Eckington Elem Schl Urban Corps Spec Projects Tchr 1963; Howard Univ Prof of Acting & Directing 1969-; Speech & Presentation Private Tchr 1977-85; Multi-Media Inc Acting for Camera 1985-89; Round House Theatre Acting for Adults 1986-87; Acting & Audition Techniques Private Tchr 1986-; Prime Cable of Prince Georges Cty Camera Dir 1987 & 1988; Multi-Media Inc Acting for Camera 1985-89; Rutgers Univ Beginning Directing & Acting Techniques Tchr Fall 1990; *ai:* Arena Stage Intern Prgm Advy Bd Mem 1990-; Playwrights Unit Advy Bd Mem 1989-; Operation Understanding DC Black & Jewish Youths; Natl Coalition Bldg Inst Diversity Trng; AAUP 1970-; Alpha Psi Omega 1969-; African Amer Continium Theatre Coalition 1990-; Directed More than 50 Productions, Originally Working Under the Famed Playwright-Director-Author, Moss Hart, on Broadway; 10th Anniversary of Serenity Players Keynote Speaker 1993; Numerous Wkshps; Smallbeer Theatre Lecture on Black Women Playwrights Past to Present 1989; Dr Andrew A Allen Arts Scholarship Initiator, Coord & Fund Raiser Organizer 1985-; Numerous Publications & Interviews; Brooklyn Coll Alumni Assn 1992, ECTC 1987, Amer Theatre Assn 1979 Confs; Numerous Awds for Productions 1958-84; Grant from DC Hum Cncl in Assn with Afro-Amer Museum Assn; Numerous Other Theatre Experiences in Acting, Directing & Production Asst; *office:* Howard Univ-Coll of Fine Arts 2400 6th St NW Dept of Theatre Arts Washington DC 20059*

KATZMAN, LANNIE S., High School Teacher; *b:* Ft Dodge, IA; *m:* Roanne; *c:* Chari Beth Fogel, Geri Kay Welsh; *ed:* Bowling Green St Univ (BSEd) Speech 1968, (MED) Admin 1971; Spec Admin & Schl Comm Relations 1983; Stud in Jrnlsm & The Law, Publications Law & Effective Ed Against Drugs; *cr:* Toledo Pub Schls Tchr 1968-; Bicentennial Youth Debates Regnl Dir 1974-76; Univ of Toledo Part-Time Instr 1974-96; *ai:* Schl Newspaper & Yrbk Adv; Schl Musical & Play Dir; Phi Delta Kappa 1972-; TFT, OFT, AFT 1974-; *home:* 4227 Todd Dr Sylvania OH 43560

KAUFER, LARINDA DYSON, First Grade Teacher; *b:* Meshoppen, PA; *m:* Neil; *c:* Seth, Adam, Aaron; *ed:* Wilkes Coll (BA) Elem Ed 1975; Wilkes Univ (MS) Elem Ed 1989; *cr:* Mill City Elem Schl Kndgtn, 1st Grd Tchr 1975-78; Evan Falls Elem Schl Kndgtn, 1st Grd Tchr 1978-; *ai:* Readathon Coord; Coll Misericordia Stu Tchng Prgm Cooperating Tchr 1987-; PSEA; Tunkhannock Area Ed Assn 1975-; JCC of WY Vly Children, Comm 1978-, Bd of Dirs Sec; Kingston Little League 1990-, Team C Coll Misericordia Excl in Tchng Awd 1987; *home:* 322 Reynol Kingston PA 18704

KAUFFMAN, BRENDA JOY, Middle School Teacher; *b:* St Louis, *ed:* William Jennings Bryan Coll (BS) Elem Ed 1984; *cr:* Akron C Schl 5-8 Grd Eng, His, Rdng Tchr 1984-; *ai:* Yrbk Adv; Edu Comm; Coord; *office:* Akron Christian Schools 508 Newton St Tallmadge 44278

KAUFFMAN, CRAWFORD, Biology Teacher; *b:* Mt Alto, PA; *m:* S *c:* Mike, Christine; *ed:* Shippensburg Univ (MS) Bio 1969, (MS) Bio Conestoga Vly HS Bio Tchr 1966-; *ai:* NEA, CUEA & NBTA; Wa Twp, Supvr; Jaycees, Outstdng Young Edctr; *office:* Conestoga Vall HS 2110 Horseshoe Rd Lancaster PA 17601

KAUFFMAN, LARRY DALE, Professor of Music; *b:* Elkhart, IN Marjorie Wood; *c:* Jennifer, John, Nathan; *ed:* Bob Jones Univ (BA) M 1969; Cincinnati Conservatory (MM) Music 1970, (DMA) Music Choral Methods at Westminster Choir Coll, Rider Univ at Princeton Bob Jones Univ Music Instr 1970-79; Pillsbury Bible Coll Music 1982-84; Bapt Bible Coll Music Prof 1986-; *ai:* Artist Series Comm; M Interest Fellowship; Calendar Comm; Chapel Pianist; Natl Guild of Tchrs, MTNA 1973-; ACDA 1995-; Summit Bapt Bible Church 1 Deacon, Pianist, Choir Dir; *office:* Bapt Bible Coll 538 Venard Rd C Summit PA 18411

KAUFFMAN, MARY ANN, Mathematics Teacher; *b:* New Cumber PA; *m:* Robert W.; *c:* Stephen Michael, Jeffrey Alan; *ed:* Penn St (BS Math 1959; Univ of Auckland, New Zealand (MA) Ed 1963; Suffolk (CAGS) Leadership 1989; *cr:* Mechanicsburg Math Tchr 1959-61; W Math Tchr 1962-66; Marshfield Math Tchr 1975-; *ai:* Schl Cncl Fac Alternative Schedule Comm; SAT Review; Acad Assembly of Coll Bd England Regnl Del; NEA 1962-; MATA 1975-, Various Jobs, Honor 1994; NCTM 1985-; Math Tchrs New England 1985-; *office:* Marsh HS Forest St Marshfield MA 02050

KAUFFMAN, S. DUANE, Social Studies Teacher; *b:* Mattawana, PA Naomi Hoover; *ed:* Eastern Mennonite Coll (BS) Scndry Ed 1958; Te Univ (MA) His 1964; Attnd Univ of Saint Andrews at Scotland 16 C Hrs; Addl 16 Credit hrs; *cr:* Christopher Dock Mennonite HS Soc Tchr 1958-, Dept Chair 1969-; *ai:* Sr Class Adv; Educl Prgm & Comms; NSSC 1968-; MSEC 1966-; Mennonite Historians of Easter 1965-, Bd of Trustees; PA Historical Soc 1973-; Berks Cty Historica 1988-; Mifflin Cty Historical Soc 1980-; Publication of The Mifflir Amish & Mennonite Story Book 1990; *home:* 1411 Schwenkmil Perkasie PA 18944*

KAUFFMAN, SUSAN ANN (POLAKOWSKI), Art Teacher Cleveland, OH; *m:* Keith P.; *c:* Lyndsey, Megan, Jessica; *ed:* Bov Green St Univ (BS) Art Ed 1976; Ashland Univ & Univ of CT Addit Hrs; *cr:* Evergreen Local Schls 9th-12th Grd Art Tchr 1977-78; Elyria Schls 7th-9th Grd Art Tchr 1978-84; Wellington Ex Village Schls 9th-Grd Tchr 1984-; *ai:* WEA 1984-, Union Pres 1995-; Lorain Schlol Regnl Art Comm Co-Chprsn; *office:* Wellington HS 629 N Mai Wellington OH 44090

KAUFMAN, CAROL FELKER, Assoc Prof of Marketing; *b:* Pottsv PA; *c:* Jennifer, Jeffrey; *ed:* Duquesne Univ (BS) Math 1974; Renss Polytechnic Inst (MBA) Mngmt 1978; Tempel Univ (PHD) Mrktg 1986 Rutgers Univ Assoc Prof of Mrktg 13 Yrs; *ai:* Adv to Mktng Assn; C of Undergraduate Stu Affairs Comm; Chair of Scholastic Standing Co Dir Cynthia Klotzbach Handball Choir; Kindred Joy Womens V Quartet, Haddonfield Meth Church; Amer Mrktg Assn 1989-; Cons Research Assn; Acad of Mrktg Sci 1990-; Numerous Book Chap Articles in Journal of Consumer Research, Journal of Retaling, Journ Advertising Research; Journal of Bus & Psych, Journal of Stra Change; Schl of Bus Tchng Excl Awd; Grant from Intnl Fnd of Shop Ctrs; *office:* Rutgers University Camden Schl of Business 3rd & Pen Camden NJ 08102

KAUFMAN, DOUGLAS JEROME, Social Studies Teacher; *b:* El F TX; *m:* Kathleen Ann Cummings; *c:* Kirsten, Keith; *ed:* Jr Coll of Al (AA) Liberal Arts 1981; St Univ of NY at Albany (BA) His 1983, (Scndry Ed 1985; His of Amer Women, Tchng the Holocaust; Amsterdam HS Soc Stud Tchr 1985-; *ai:* Ldr People to People Exch to Russia; Amsterdam Tchrs Assn 1985-; Holocaust Survivors & Fri 1990-; People to People Foreign Exch Prgm 1992-; Univ of Richn Recognition in Tchng; *office:* Amsterdam HS Saratoga Ave Amsterdam 12010*

KAUFMAN, HOWARD, Prof of Elec, Comp & Engrng; *b:* Sara Springs, NY; *m:* Eve; *c:* David, Jeffrey, Deborah; *ed:* Renss Polytechnic Inst (BEE) Electrical Engrng 1962, (MEE) Electrical En 1964, (PHD) Electrical Engrng 1965; *cr:* Cornell Aeronautical Lab Engr 1965-68; Gen Electric CR&D Systems Engr 1968; Rensse Polytechnic Inst Prof 1969-; *ai:* ECSE Promotion Comm; Internal Re Bd; IEEE 1962, Sr Mem; Book Direct Adapative Control Algorithms 1 Book Chptrs; Journal Articles; *office:* Rensselaer Polytechnic Inst E Dept 110 8th St Troy NY 12180

KAUFMAN, LINDA K. (MARTIN), Fifth Grade Teacher; *b:* Lima, *m:* Timothy A.; *c:* Emily J., Erika J., Tasha J., Tonya L.; *ed:* The Defi Coll (BS) Elem Ed K-8, Elem PE 1984; Saint Francis Coll (MS) Lear Disabilities 1995; Drake Univ 3 Sem Hrs; Bowling Green St Univ 1 Hr; OH St Univ at Lima 4 Sem Hrs; *cr:* Millcreek West Unity Schl C Tchr 1984-86; Ottoville Local Schl Grd 5 Tchr 1986-; *ai:* Var Vlybl C 1987-91; OEA Tchrs Assn 1986-, Treas 1993-94; *home:* 24616 Co Road R Fort Jennings OH 45844

KAUFMAN, MARY ANN BURKE, Second Grade Teacher; *b:* Elmh NY; *m:* Stuart; *c:* Peter Andrew; *ed:* SUNY at Oswego (BS) Elem Ed 1 SUNY at Stony Brook (MMS) Lbrl Arts 1993; *cr:* Sayville Schls 3 Tchr 1965-69, 5, 1, 2 Grd Tchr 1975-; *ai:* Initiated, Co-Chaired Site B Team Booklet on Practical Acts Involving Math; AFT, NYSUT, Say Tchrs Assn 1965-; Long Island Bd of Realtors 1981-; Sayville M Boosters for Arts 1980-, Pres, Schlsp Chm; South Shore Womens Coll 1995; Created Creative Writing Awd Art, Music Annual Awds; *hom* Greenway Ter Sayville NY 11782*

KAUFMAN, MINNA P., Health Occupations Teacher; *b:* Mur Germany; *m:* Lewis J.; *c:* Michael William, Peter Eric; *ed:* SCSU (BS) Stud; CCSU 30 Credits Hlth Ocupations Ed; Bridgeport Hospital Sc Nursing RN Nursing 1970; *cr:* Yale New Haven Hospital Medical, Surg Unit Staff Nurse 1970-71; CT Mental Hlth Ctr Staff, Head Nurse 1971 Milford Hospital Medical, Surgical Unit Staff Nurse 1982-86; Career Hlth Occupations Tchr, Coord 1988-; *ai:* OR Shalom Soc Action Co Hadassuh; CT Assn of Hlth Occupation Educators 1988-, Treas; Yale Haven Partnership 1990-, Liason; *office:* Career HS 21 Wooster Pl Haven CT 06511

KAUFMAN, PAIGE SCOTT, Music Teacher; *b:* Granville, NY; Richard C.; *c:* Amanda Neary, Scott; *ed:* Castleton St Coll (BA) M 1970; 51 Addl Credits; *cr:* West Rutland Elem Schl K-8th Grd Music 1970-71; Barstow Meml Schl K-8th Grd Music Tchr 1974-82; Lot Elem Schl K-6th Grd Music Tchr 1985-; *ai:* Drama Musical Dir; N

A 1985-; MENC 1986-; Trinity Church, Jr Choir Dir 1979-81, Adult r Mem 1978; *office:* Lothrop Elem Schl Main St Pittsford VT 05763

FMAN, RENIE, Teacher & Coordinator; *b:* Paterson, NJ; *m:* David; son Paul, Seth Adam; *ed:* Trenton St Coll (BA) Spec Ed, Deaf, Hard ing, Tchr of Handicapped 1968; William Paterson Coll (MED) Spec Emotionally Disturbed Socially Maladjusted 1975; 12 Credit Hrs ng, Sign Lang; *cr:* Hackensack Prgm for Deaf Presch Tchr 1968-72; and Scndry Hearing Impaired Prgm Comm, Eng Tchr 1980-83; Lake Schl Classroom Tchr 1983-88; Mt Lakes HS Lake Drive Prgm ing Impaired Comm Specialist Cnslr, Mainstream Coord 1988-; *ai:* Jr Natl Assn of Deaf; Project Grad Comm Wayne Schls 1990; NEA -; Grants Dev Effective Comm Hearing Impaired Children 1985-86, Soc Competencies 1987-87; Article Pub 1986; Presenter 1982 Eastern l Conf Edctrs of Hearing Impaired 1985-86; NJ Governor's Tchr gnition Prgm 1989 Recipient; *office:* Mountain Lakes HS Powerville Fountain Lakes NJ 07046

L, KIM PATRICIA, Physical Educator & Coach; *b:* Buffalo, NY; *ed:* sius Coll (BS) PE 1980, (MS) Ath Admin 1985; Post Grad Stud, vice Credit Totaling Masters Plus 40 Addl Hrs; *cr:* Orchard Pk Ellicott Phys Educator 1980-86; Orchard Pk HS Head Girls Bsktbl Coach -, Head Girls Sftbl Coach 1985-; Orchard Pk MS Phys Educator 1986-; th Hall of Fame Comm; MS Girls Intramurals; Natl Ath Trnrs Assn -, Certified Mem; NYSAAHPERD 1980-; NYS United Tchrs 1980-; PE Consortium 1987-; Inducted into Western NY Sftbl Hall of Fame ; Amateur Sftbl Assn All-Amer 1993; US Olympic Festival Sftbl cipant 1993; US Natl Team Tryouts Sftbl 1993; *home:* 8740 Cole Rd en NY 14033

P, SHEKHAR SHETTY, Prof of Bus Administration; *b:* Kaup, India; avasini Pakkala; *c:* Sahana, Shubha Johnson, Saumya, Rajshaker; *ed:* of Bombay (BA) Ec 1956, (MA) Ec 1958; City Univ of NY (MBA) mt 1965; Auburn Univ (PHD) Admin 1969; Attnd Harvard Univ, A, UMCP; *cr:* Univ of MD Prof 1969-, Dept Chair 1969-72, 1984-85, Dean 1972-75, Asst Vice-Chancellor Dean, Grad Stud 1975-80; *ai:* king Engagements; Acad of Mngt 1969-; ASTA; IRRA; IIRA; AEA; CBE; AEIB; Ldrs in Ed 1974; Amer Men, Women of Sci 1974; dng of Amer 1974; *office:* Univ Of MD Eastern Shore Princess Anne 21853

ANAGH, JUSTINE, 8th Grade English Teacher; *b:* Agana, GU; *ed:* cuse Univ (BS) Broadcast Jrnlsm 1990; UMass at Amherst (MED) Ed ; *cr:* Action for Boston Comm Dev Inc GED Instr 1992-93; wsbury HS 8th Grd Eng Tchr 1992-; *ai:* Asst Coach Speech & Debate ; NEA, NCTE 1993-; *office:* Shrewsbury HS 45 Oak St Shrewsbury 01545

ANAGH, ROSANNE LENORE, English Teacher; *b:* Oceanside, NY; Thomas M.; *c:* Bridget; *ed:* Dowling Coll (BA) Scndry Ed 1992, (MS) Ed 1996; *cr:* Brentwood Sr HS Replacement Eng Tchr 1992, Summer Eng Tchr 1992-95; East MS 8th Grd Eng Tchr 1992-94; West MS 8th Grd Eng Tchr 1992-; *ai:* Peer Mediation Prgm Coord & Adv; spaper Co-Adv; SIT Comm Mem; Brentwood Tchr Assn 1992-; *office:* twood West MS Udall Rd Bay Shore NY 11706*

ANAGH, THOMAS J., Social Studies Chair & Teacher; *b:* New York, *c:* Elizabeth Mary; *ed:* Iona Coll (BA) Philosophy 1970, (MS) Ed ; *office:* Cardinal Hayes HS 650 Grand Concourse Bronx NY 10451

IN, DONNA GALVANEK, Music Teacher; *b:* Perth Amboy, NJ; *m:* ; *c:* Kimberla Laura, Michelle Stacy; *ed:* Trenton St Coll (BA) Music 968; *cr:* Woodbridge HS Vocal & Instrumental Tchr 1968-71; John F nedy HS Vocal Tchr 1971-72; Wall Twp Elem Schls Vocal Tchr -87; Freehold Twp Elem Dist Vocal & Instrumental Tchr 1987-; *ai:* eral, Mixed & Concert Chorus Groups Dir; Music Portion of Schl Play; , NJEA, MCEA 1968-; Delta Omicron 1966-; *office:* Dwight D nhower MS 237 Burlington Rd Freehold NJ 07728*

ISH, LINDA L., English & Gifted Ed Teacher; *b:* Mc Keesport, PA; eorge Jr.; *c:* George III; *ed:* IN Univ of PA (BS) Eng Ed 1971; Attnd m Coll of Allegheny Cty; Post Grad Carlow Coll, Wilkes Univ; *cr:* US Tchr GED Prgm 1972-73; Duquesne Cath Schl Tchr 1985; St Joseph's 1982-85; Forensics Coach 1985-88; Duquesne HS Tchr 1988-; *ai:* ate, Stu of the Month, Tchr & Bldg Supply Comms; Dept Head Eng, ms; Duquesen Ed Assoc 1988-, Exec Bd; NEA 1988-; NCTE 1994-.

LICK, KATHRYN ANN, Second Grade Teacher; *b:* Morgantown, *ed:* Charles Cty Comm Coll (AA) Gen Stud 1978; Univ of MD (BS) Ed 1980; George Washington Univ (MA) Ed, Human Dev 1984; *cr:* n Head Elem Schl 1 Grd Tchr 1980-86, 2 Grd Tchr 1986-; *ai:* Soc m; Mentoring Prgm; Clinical Supervising Tchr Fall 1995; NEA, Ed of Charles Co, MD St Tchrs Assn, PTA 1980-; Charles Cty Bd of Ed Elementary Vol IV, No 8 1992; *office:* Indian Head Elem Schl 4200 n Head Hwy Indian Head MD 20640

OOSI, JEHAN GIR, Assistant Professor of Busines; *b:* Mashad, Iran; Mary Clair McCaffrey; *c:* Michelle Farah, Hope Laudan, Andrea een; *ed:* Univ of Mashad (BA) Eng Lit 1962; Northern IL Univ (BS) 1968, (MA) Ec 1970; Post Master Courses; *cr:* GTE Industrial Engr -72; Joliet Jr Coll Bus Instr 1972-74; Clarion Univ of PA Asst Bus Prof -; *ai:* Fac Comms Assoc; Admin Sci Dept & Clarion Univ Comms.

OURAS, PETER GEORGE, Social Studies Teacher; *b:* Middletown, *m:* Jennifer A. Calvert; *ed:* Miami Univ at Ohio (BA) Pol Sci 1983, Ed, Scndry Soc Stud 1983; Wright St Univ (MED) Ed 1994; *cr:* West ollton Sr HS Soc Stud Tchr 1985-; *ai:* Stu Cncl, Asst Grad Avd; NEA, , WCEA 1985-; WOEA 1985-, Area 5 Rep; OH Cncl for Soc Stud -, Treas; WCEA News Publications; 3rd Congressional Dist Coord; m Based Bill of Rights Prgm Project Dir; *office:* West Carrollton Sr 5833 Student St West Carrollton OH 45449

VA, JOHN STANLEY, Fifth Grade Teacher; *b:* Springfield, MA; *m:* nia Ramos Falcon; *c:* John Alexander, Brittney Marie; *ed:* Holyoke m Coll (AS) Liberal Arts 1972; Univ of MA at Amherst (BA) Ed 1975; tfield St Coll (MED) Elem Admin 1987; *cr:* Howard St Elem -Sixth Grd Tchr 1975-76; Brightwood Elem Third-Fourth Grd Tchr -87; Glenwood Elem Fourth-Fifth Grd Tchr 1987-; *ai:* Elem Sci, Soc ; Math Curr, Site Based Mngmt, PTO Chprsn Yrbk Comms; ructuring Task Force; SEA, MTA, NEA 1981-; Holy Name Hockey 1990-; Horace-Mann Tchr Mentor 1989; Grant Recipient Springfield und 1986; *office:* Glenwood Elem Schl 50 Morison Terr Springfield 01104

WALEC, WALTER M., Latin Teacher; *b:* South Amboy, NJ; *m:* stancer Kulczynski; *c:* Laura Schubert, Donna Cardaneo, Joseph; *ed:* n Hall Univ (BA) Fr 1961; Trenton St Coll (MA) Prsnl Svcs 1973; *cr:* dlesex HS Tchr 1961-62; Sayreville HS Tchr 1962-68; Sayreville Mid HS Tchr 1968-93; Sayreville HS Tchr 1993-94; Mount Saint Mary l Tchr & Chm 1994-; *ai:* Knights of Columbus 1986-; *office:* Mount ary Acad 1645 US Highway 22 Watchung NJ 07060

WKA, LENORE C., 5th Grade Teacher; *b:* Rochester, NY; *ed:* areth Coll (BA) Soc Stud 1973; Univ of Brockport Permanent NYS K-6, 7-12 Soc Stud, Earth, Gen Sci; *cr:* St Louis Schl Jr High Sci Tchr -85; Pittsford MS Bio, Earth Sci Tchr 1985-86; Park Rd Schl 6th Grd 1986-87; Jefferson Rd Schl 4th Grd Tchr 1987-88, 5th Grd Tchr -; *ai:* Odyssey of Mind Adv 1988-; Safety Patrol 1988-; Elem Math m; NYSUT; STANYS CW Section; St Stanislaus Rel Ed Tchr 1992-; St Stanislaus Synod Comm 1993-; Polish Festival Co-Chair 1991-; Pittsford PTSA Life Mbrshp Awd 1992.

KAY, ALAN A., English Professor; *b:* Brooklyn, NY; *m:* Jo; *c:* Corinne, Lisa, Adina; *ed:* Brooklyn Coll (BA) Eng 1965; New York Univ (MA) Eng 1967, (EDD) Eng Ed 1975; Acad for Jewish Rel Rabbinic Prgm 1993-; *cr:* NY City Tech Coll Prof of Eng 1968-; *ai:* NCTE; Phi Delta Kappa; Coalition for Advancement of Jewish Ed; Soc of Childrens Book Writers, Illustrators; Simon Wiesnthal Ctr; Beit Hashoah Museum of Tolerance; US Holocaust Meml Museum; Schlr on Campus 1991; Charles Matusik Peace Awd 1994; Ursula Schwerine Intercultural Harmony Awd 1990; Childrens Lit Curr Awd 1990; Books: A Jewis Book of Comfort, The Red in My Fathers Beard, Pebbles on a Stone; Shofar Magazine Founding Ed; Mickey Leland-Ivan Tillem Peace Seminar Founder; *office:* New York Tech Coll 300 Jay St Brooklyn NY 11201

KAY, ELLEN KEMP, Span Teacher & Jr Class Adv; *b:* Massillon, OH; *m:* James; *c:* Andrew, Mary Van Beysterveldt; *ed:* Otterbein Coll (BA) Span, Fr, Eng 1962; Univ of Dayton (BSEd) Ed 1985; *cr:* Western Hills HS Span Tchr 1962; Oakwood HS Fr Tchr 1962-65; Kettering Jr HS Eng Tchr 1983-84; Centerville HS Fr Tchr 1984-85; Miami Vly Schl Fr, Span, Latin Tchr 1983-; *ai:* Jr Class, Lit Magazine Adv; AATSP; Miami Vly FL Alliance; Delta Kappa Gamma 1988-, Treas, VP; Article Pub.

KAY, IAN, Instrumental Director; *b:* Manchester, England; *m:* Ellen; *c:* Sara, Michael; *ed:* Queens Coll (BA) Music Ed 1971, (MS) Music Ed 1974; Admin, Supervision in Ed Cert 1977; 60 Grad Credits; *cr:* JHS 275 Instrumental Music Tchr 1971-73; Erasmushall HS Instrumental Music Tchr 1973-76; Woodmere Acad Instrumental Music Tchr 1976-77; Roslyn HS Instrumental Dir 1977-; *ai:* Auditorium Supvr Lighting, Sound; Festivals Coord; Shared Decision Comm; Nassau Music Edctrs, Long Island String Fetival 1977-; MENC 1968-; Rhythm Fundamental for Band; Scale & Chord Fundamentals for Band Grant for Instrumental Curr K-12; *office:* Roslyn HS Round Hill Rd Roslyn Heights NY 11577*

KAY, KATHY DEE, English Teacher; *b:* Jersey City, NJ; *m:* Richard Alan; *c:* Jeffrey, Michael, Melanie; *ed:* William Paterson Coll (BA) Eng 1972, (MA) Eng 1974; 3 Addl Hrs Understanding Exceptional Child, Critical Thinking, Cmptr Applications; *cr:* Beren Cty Voc-Tech HS Eng Tchr 1974-78; Montclair St Univ Adj Fac 1993-; Cedar Grove HS Eng Tchr 1992-; *ai:* Girls Var Tennis Coach; Yrbk, Class Adv; NEA, NJEA, NCTE 1992-; PTO 1978-; NJ Governor's Tchr Recognition Prgm Awd 1995; *office:* Cedar Grove H S Rugby Rd Cedar Grove NJ 07009

KAY, LINDA L., English Teacher; *b:* Paterson, NJ; *m:* Donald A.; *c:* Aaryn, Dana; *ed:* William Paterson Coll (BA) Eng Lit 1969; Clemson Univ (MA) Eng Lit 1971; Addl 15 Credit Hrs; *cr:* Cresskill HS Eng Tchr 1972-73; In Bus 1981-; Sharon HS Eng Tchr 1994-; *ai:* Kellog Peer Consultant; CSL Trainer; SAT Course Instr; Sharon Tchrs Assn; NEA; Curr Tchng Project.*

KAYE, DANIEL B., English Dept Chairperson; *b:* Philadelphia, PA; *m:* Anne Schleicher; *c:* Ethan I., Thea E.; *ed:* East Stroudsburg St Coll (BS) Scndry Eng Ed 1970; Addl Credit Hrs PA ST Univ; *cr:* Wilson Area HS Eng Tchr 1970-, Eng Dept Chprsn 1981-; *ai:* Drama Club Adv; NHS Adv; Tech Arts Club Adv; NEA, PSEA, WAEA 1970-; NCTE 1973-; Tchr Intern Ingersoll Rand Corp 1982; PA Dept Ed Long Range Planning Simulation Project Participant 1990; Co-Founder The Performers Studio; *office:* Wilson Area H S 22nd & Washington Blvd Easton PA 18042*

KAYE, DEBORAH, Mathematics Teacher; *b:* Brooklyn, NY; *m:* Fred; *c:* David, Steven; *ed:* SUNY at Stonybrook (BS) Math 1973, (MA) Liberal Stud 1976; *cr:* R.C. Murphy JHS Math Tchr 1973-; *ai:* Math Team; Math Counts Adv; NCTM, Suffolk Cty Math Tchrs Assn 1973-; *office:* Robert C Murphy Jr HS 351 Oxhead Rd Stony Brook NY 11790*

KAYE, KATHLEEN PAGE, Lang Arts & Soc Stud Teacher; *b:* Burlington, VT; *m:* John Kaye; *c:* Allison, Lindsey; *ed:* Univ of VT (BA) Eng & His Ed 1973, (MED) Lit Rdng Ed 1978; 60 Grad Credits Beyond Masters Degree; *cr:* Frederick Tuttle MS 6th-8th Grd Lang Arts & Soc Stud Tchr 1973-; *ai:* Stu Cncl Adv; NEA 1975-; MS Tchr of Yr 1988.

KAYE, LORETTA BANDYCH, High School Math Teacher; *b:* Utica, NY; *m:* Ivan A.; *ed:* SUNY at Plattsburgh (BS) Scndry Math 1968; 60 Grad Hrs Colgate Univ, Coll of St Rose, Albany St, Utica Coll, SUNY at Oswego, Oneonta, Cortland, AP Calculus Inst at Allegheny Coll, Eisenhower Inst At Syracuse Univ; *cr:* Remsen Cntrl Schl Jr HS Math Tchr 1968-71; Metropolitan Life Claim Approver 1972-73; Town of Webb Schl HS Math Tchr 1973-; *ai:* Stu Cncl Soc Comm Adv; Soph Homeroom; NYSUT, AMTNYS 1968-; Delta Kappa Gamm 1993-, Treas 1994-; St Mary's Parish Cncl 1991-; Thendara Golf League 1983-, Treas, Co-Pres; Writer of Cmptr Curr.

KAYE, MAXINE TIPTON, Retired Teacher; *b:* Carson, IA; *m:* Ernest Louis; *c:* Lance, Bryce; *ed:* Morris Harvey Coll (BA) Music 1937; Univ of IA (MA) Music 1938; Paterson St Tchrs Coll Elem Schl Ed 12 Credits 1956-57; Fairleigh Dickinson Univ Elem Schl Ed 3 Credits 1956-57; New Paltz St Tchrs Coll Elem Schl Ed 3 Credits 1956-57; *cr:* Jamestown Coll Instr 1938-39; Montvale Pub Schls Elem Tchr 1955-93; Meml Schl Writing Wkshp Vol 1993-; Fuller Elem Schl Supplemental Instruction Vol 1994-; *ai:* MTA; NEA; NJEA; Tchr of Yr Memorial Schl 1987.

KAYES, LISA A., Spanish Teacher; *b:* Olean, NY; *m:* James E.; *c:* Jeffrey; *ed:* Covenant Life Coll (BS) Span & Ed 1987; Empire St Coll (BA) Cultural Stud 1991; Empire St Coll 28 Credit Hrs Toward Grad Degree; *cr:* Brussels Chrstn Schl Span Tchr 1984-87; Olean City Schls Sub Tchr 1987-91; Franklinville Cntrl Schl Span Tchr 1991-; *ai:* Span Club Adv; AFT 1991-; Franklinville Tchrs Assn 1991-; NYSAFLT 1995-; *office:* Franklinville Cntrl Schl 31 N Main St Franklinville NY 14737

KAYS, WILLIAM JOHN, Scndry Sci Tchr & Dept Chprsn; *b:* Scranton, PA; *m:* Maureen Tyrrell; *c:* Conor T., Eamon T., Liam T., Katharine T.; *ed:* Jacksonville Univ (BS) Bio & Chem 1979; St Univ of NY at Oswego (MS) Ed & Sci 1993; Lemoyne Coll Ed Courses; *cr:* Private Industries Analytical Chemist 1979-86; Mexico HS Sci Tchr 1986-; *ai:* Jr Var Ftbl & Var Wrestling Coach; HS Steering & Planning Comms; Alternative Scheduling Comm; NYSUT 1987-; Mexico Little League 1990-, Coach; Saint Marys Church Mexico, Lector; OHSL Metro Conf Wrestling Coach of Yr 4 Times; Honorary Grad Marshall 1995; NHS Induction Speaker 2 Times; OHSL Spec Coaches Awd 1994; *office:* Mexico HS Main St Mexico NY 13114

KAYSER, JUDY, Science Teacher; *m:* Hans Christoph; *c:* Nicole Kayser-Laundry, Mark A., Patrick A.; *ed:* Webster Univ (BA) Bio 1967; SUNY at Brockport (MA) Ed 1986; *cr:* A. D. Oliver MS Sci Tchr 1986-; *ai:* NYSUT, NYSST, NYSTRS 1986-.

KAZAKAVICH, JUDITH EMERSON, Business Teacher; *b:* Boothbay Harbor, ME; *m:* Edward D.; *c:* Edward Jr., Elizabeth, Danya; *ed:* St Joseph's Coll (BS) Bus Ed 1961; NH Coll (MS) Bus Ed; Attnd NY Univ, St Univ of NY, Cty Coll of Morris; *cr:* Kings Park HS Tchr 1962-64; Dover Bus Coll Tchr 1971-78; Mt Olive HS Tchr 1978-79; Pembroke Acad Tchr 1979-; *ai:* Stu Act Funds Dir; Mngmt Team; Frosh Team Mem; NHBEA; NEA; Bedford Lib 1987-, Vol; NH Tchr of the Yr 1993 Candidate; *office:* Pembroke Acad 209 Academy Rd Pembroke NH 03275

KAZANJIAN, CARLA ELISE, HS Social Studies Teacher; *b:* New Haven, CT; *m:* Donald E. Giroux; *ed:* Ithaca Coll (BA) His 1971; Southern CT St Univ (MA) His; 51 Hrs Beyond Masters Degree at Univ of Hartford, SCSU His; Spec NEH Grant Winner for the 1st Harvard Stud on the His of Women in Amer; Study in Erope on Women Wrtrs of 19th Century; *cr:* Shepang Valley Mid HS Soc Stud Tchr 1971-; *ai:* Peer Leadership & Fresh Spec Adv; Womens His Month Coord; Chair of a Comm Report for NEASC; CEA & NEA 1971-; Shepaug Valley Ed Assn 1971-, Exec Comm; Valley Ed Assn, Negotiating Bd; Edith Wharton Restoration Fnd 1989-; Natl Org of Women 1971-, Past Pres; Amer Assn of Univ Women; Regular Guest Speaker on Womens His Topics for Numerous Org; *office:* Shepang Valley Mid HS South St Washington Green CT 06793

KAZEE, LINDA SUE, 8th Grd Math & Algebra Teacher; *b:* Columbus, OH; *m:* Wilfred Lee Jr.; *c:* Bryan, Aaron; *ed:* OH St Univ (BS) Math Ed 1962, (MS) Chldhd Math 1981; *cr:* Prairie Norton Elem Schl 7th & 8th Grd Math Tchr 1962-64; Norton Jr HS 9th Grd Math & Algebra Tchr 1964-69; Westland HS 9th-11th Grd Math & Algebra Tchr 1970-73; Finland MS 8th Grd Math & Algebra Tchr 1974-; *ai:* NEA 1962-; NCTM & OCTM 1972-; Mid-West NFFC 1986-, Pres 3 Yrs; Cavalier Drum & Bugle Corp Booster 1988-; Columbus & Suburban Cncl Tchrs of Math Tchr of Yr 1988; SWSC Bd of Ed Cert of Excl 1986; Natl & Local Math Convention Speaker; OH St Dept of Ed Math Curr Developer 1986-88; *office:* Finland M S 1825 Finland Ave Columbus OH 43223

KAZIMER, DENISE LYNN, Sports Medicine Instructor; *b:* Washington, DC; *ed:* PA St Univ (BS) Exercise & Sports Sci 1993; *cr:* Bishop McNamara HS Athletic Instr & Sports Medicine Instr 1993-; *ai:* MG Action Cncl Spirit Club Moderator; Natl Athletic Trainers Assn 1992-; MD Athletic Trainers Assn 1996; *office:* Bishop Mc Namara HS 6800 Marlboro Pike Forestville MD 20747

KAZIMIERCZYK, LINDA MAI, Music Teacher; *b:* Rahway, NJ; *m:* John; *ed:* Westminster Choir Coll (BS) Music Ed 1979; *cr:* Roselle Park MS Jr HS Music, Choral Tchr 1979-86; So Portland Schl Dist Jr HS Music, Choral Tchr 1986-87; Bow Mem Schl Music, Choral Tchr 1987-; *ai:* Choruses Dir; Private Piano Instr; MENC 1978-; Concord Music Club 1994-; NEA 1979-87; Amer Canoe Assn 1985-, Instr, Trainor; New England Slalom Series 1994-, Coord; Spaleto Festival 1978; Westminster Singers Tour 1982, 1984; Larry Ferrara Orch Lead Singer 1980-86; *home:* 49 Lufkin Rd Weare NH 03281*

KAZINSKAS, VICTORIA HUNTER, Kindergarten Teacher; *b:* Gardner, MA; *m:* John P.; *c:* Stacey, Elizabeth; *ed:* Fitchburg St Coll (BA) Elem Ed 1972, (MA) Elem Ed 1979; *cr:* Templeton Ctr Schl 1st Grd Tchr 1972-73, Kndgtn Tchr 1973-; *ai:* CCD Tchr; Hosp Vol; Musuem Guide; NEA, MTA, NDEA 1972-; Gardner Museum 1980-, Corresponding Sec; Hosp Aid Assn 1988-; Girl Scouts of USA 1956-; *home:* 122 Green St Gardner MA 01440

KEACH, TERRANCE JOHN, Music Teacher; *b:* Corning, NY; *ed:* Nazareth Coll (BS) Music Ed 1983; Ithaca Coll (MM) Music Ed 1988; *cr:* Horseheads CSD Strings Tchr 1983; Diocese of Rochester Cath Schls Vocal Music Tchr 1983-91; Albion CSD Vocal Music Tchr 1991-93; Aquinas Inst Choral Music & Theory Tchr 1993-; *ai:* Select Chorus; Spring Musical Vocal Coach; Sacred Heart Cathedral Choir 1984-, Chorister; Sacred Heart Cathedral Handbell Choir 1992-, Dir; Awd for Excl in Stu Tchng 1993; *office:* Aquinas Inst 1127 Dewey Ave Rochester NY 14613

KEALEY, WALTER G., Principal; *b:* Philadelphia, PA; *m:* Christine Benson; *c:* Laura Elizabeth Weegie; *ed:* Ursinus Coll (BA) Ec 1969; Lehigh Univ (MA) Elem Ed 1972; Walden Univ (EDD) Ed 1986; PA K-8th Grd & NJ K-12th Grd Prin Cert; PA Scndry Prin Cert; *cr:* Fidelity Bank Branch Mgr 1969-70; Council Rock Schl Dist Tchr & Admin Intern 1970-75; Indiana Area Schl Dist Elem Prin 1975-95, Math Curr Coord 1988-93; *ai:* Bsktbl Coach; PA Assn of Elem Schl Prins 1976-, Audit Comm; Phi Delta Kappa 1984-; PA Congress of Schl Admin 1976-; IN Rdng Cncl 1979-; NAACP 1991-, Exec Bd, Ed Chair, Comm Action Awd; PTA 1976-, Indiana Cty Cncl Pres, St Bd of Mgrs, Parent Ed & Involvement St Chm, Dist 8 Newsletter Chm, Outstanding Svc Awd; US Army Reserve 1979-, Lt Col, Meritorious Svc Awd; Amer Legion, Marine Corps League 1976-; Veterans of Foreign Wars, Reserve Office, AMVETS, Life Mem; Church, Sunday Schl Tchr; Human Svc Commission Grant for Parent-Ed Wkshps; Recognized for Excl at FORSCOM Level Campaign Drug Free; Great Amer Family Awd Prgm 1st Army Rep; PA ROA Jr Army Officer of Yr; Lincoln HS Hall of Achvmt; Established USAR-NAACP Scholar-Ath Awd; PA Supt 3 Intermediate Unit Exec Dir Letters of Eligibility; *office:* East Pike Elem Schl 501 E Pike Indiana PA 15701

KEAN, MONICA M. P., Spanish Teacher; *b:* Newark, NJ; *m:* Edward B. Van Houten; *ed:* Orange Cty Comm Coll (AA) Lib Arts 1976; St Thomas Aquinas Coll (BA) Spanish, Elem Ed 1979; Iona Coll (MA) Urban Ed 1987; 30 Credit Hrs Post Grad Admin, Supervision; *cr:* St Gregory Barbarigo Schl 2 & 4th Grd Tchr 1979-83; Albertus Magnus HS Span Tchr 1983; Tappan Zee HS Span Tchr 1984-; *ai:* Bldg Liason, Foreign Lang Review Comms; NY St Assn of Foreign Lang Tchrs 1984-; Phi Delta Kappa 1987-; Oradell Bsbl Assn 1987-, Spon; St Thomas Aquinas Coll Tchr Ed Bd 1990-; *office:* South Orangetown Cntrl Schl Van Wyck Rd Blauvelt NY 10913

KEANE, JOHN PATRICK, 8th Grade Science Teacher; *b:* Old Town, ME; *m:* Mary Ann Elizabeth Furrow; *c:* Lauren, Robert; *ed:* Univ of ME at Orono (BS) Bio 1987; 30 Credit Hrs Towards a Masters in Educl Ldrshp; *cr:* Wells Jr HS 8th Grd Sci Tchr 1987-90; Livermore Falls MS 8th Grd Sci Tchr 1990-; *ai:* Sftbl, Bsktbl & Vllybl Coach; Bsktbl & Soccer Referee; Register ME Guide; NEA 1987-; MEA 1987-; ACA 1987-; ME Innovative Grant Recipient 1989-90; *office:* Livermore Falls MS 1 Highland Ave Livermore Falls ME 04254*

KEANE, KATHLEEN M., English Teacher; *b:* Boston, MA; *ed:* Cardinal Cushing Coll (BA) Eng 1966; Boston Coll (MA) Eng 1981; 45 Credit Hrs Harvard Coll, Tufts Univ, Northeastern Univ; *cr:* Girls HS Eng Tchr 1966-80; Roxbury HS Eng Tchr 1966-80; Boston Latin Acad Eng Tchr 1980-; *ai:* Girls HS Newspaper, Yrbk Adv; Roxbury HS Newspaper, Yrbk Adv; NHS 1992-94; Boston Tchrs Union, NCTE 1966-; NEH Seminar 1990; Mentor Tchr 1994-95; Eng Dept Head 1972-79, 1988-91; *office:* Boston Latin Acad 205 Townsend St Boston MA 02121*

KEANE, STEVEN, Health Teacher; *b:* Bangor, ME; *m:* Marie Corbin-Keane; *c:* Katlyn, Molly, Matthew; *ed:* Unv of ME at Orono (BS) PE 1980; *cr:* Job Corps Dorm Ldr 1981-82; Chewonki Fnd Environmental Ed Tchr 1982-85; Telstar HS Hlth & Outdoor Ed Tchr 1985-; *ai:* HS Boys Bsktbl Coach 7 Yrs; Dev Outdoor Ed Prgm; Instituted a New Schl Wide Chance for Change Prgm; NEA, MEA 1982-; Amer Canoe Assn 1983-; Prof Maine Guide Assn 1994-; Friends of the Androscoggin; St of ME Grant Awd for Outdoor Prgm 1984; *office:* Telstar Regional HS 284 Walkers Mills Rd Bethel ME 04217

KEANEY, JAMES EDWARD, Latin Teacher; *b:* Wilkes-Barre, PA; *m:* Julianne V. Faria; *c:* Erin, James J.; *ed:* Kings Coll (BA) Eng 1967; Shippensburg Univ (MED) Eng 1984; Post Grad Credits at Wilkes Univ, Mansfield Univ & Worcester St Coll; *cr:* Bishop OReilly HS Eng & Latin Tchr 1968-78; Natick HS Eng Tchr 1978-80; Shippensburg HS Latin Tchr 1980-; *office:* Shippensburg Area Sr HS Eberly Dr Shippensburg PA 17257

KEANEY, JONATHAN E., Self Employed Agri-Business; *b:* Liverpool, England; *ed:* Kings Coll at London (BS) Physiology, Biochemistry 1986; Loughborough Univ (MS) Exercise physiology 1987; Post Grad Ed Cert; *cr:* Salt Brook Schl 6th-7th Grd Sci Tchr 1990-91; New Providence MS 7th Grd Sci Tchr 1991-95; *ai:* New Providence HS Var Soccer Coach, Asst Track Coach; Pres Awds 1994-, Bd Mem; New Providence MS Tchr of Yr 1994; Articles Pub 1987.*

KEANEY, KATHLEEN CARBON, Math Teacher; *b:* Providence, RI; *c:* Brian C., Kevin J.; *ed:* Providence Coll (BA) Scndry Ed 1975; Salem St Coll (MED) Scndry Schl Admin 1978; 3 Post Grad Credits Fitchburg St; *cr:* Lynn Voc Tech HS Math, His Tchr 1975-76; Eastern Jr HS Math, His Tchr 1976-78; Attleboro HS 9 Grd Math Tchr 1978-79; North Attleboro HS 9 Grd Math Tchr 1985-86; North Attleboro Jr HS 8 Grd Math Tchr 1986-; *ai:* North Attleboro Fed Tchrs 1985-, Bldg Rep; MFT; AFT; Eisenhower Grant 1995; *office:* North Attleboro Jr HS 45 S Washington St North Attleboro MA 02760

KEARLY, SUSAN NOTO, First Grade Teacher; *b:* Buffalo, NY; *m:* Jack L.; *ed:* Medaille Coll (BS) Elem Ed 1974; SUNY Coll at Buffalo (MS) Elem Ed 1977; *cr:* Tonawanda Pub Schls Elem Tchr 1974-78; NY St Ed Dept Title I Prgm Coord 1979-80; Tonawanda Pub Schls Elem Tchr 1979-83; North Tonawanda Pub Schls Elem Tchr 1983-; *ai:* Bldg Improvement, Dist Rdng Comm; Stu Support, Dist Prin Selection Team; North Tonawanda United Tchrs 1983-; AFT 1974-; Rotary Dist 7090 Yth Exch Newsletter Ed, Dist Conf Co-Chprsn 1990; *home:* 126 Ellicott Creek Rd Apt 9 Tonawanda NY 14150

KEARNEY, ANNA M., HS Librn & Media Specialist; *b:* Kane, PA; *m:* David William; *c:* Karen Howard, Kathleen Yancosek, Kristen, Amy Olsson; *ed:* Edinboro Univ (BA) (BS) Elem Ed, (BA) (BS) Lib Sci 1971; Post Grad Stud at Carlow Coll, Gannon Univ, East Stroudsburg, Clarion Univ; *cr:* Kane Area Schl Dist Elem Elem Tchr; Self-Employed Nursery & Daycare Dir 1981-87; Saint Marys Area Schl Dist HS Librn, Media Specialist 1988-; *ai:* Stu Assistance Prgm; PRIDE; Lib Club Dir; PSEA, NEA 1971-; Cath Chrstn Doctrine 1973-, Vol Tchr.*

KEARNEY, CYNTHIA AGUILAR, Former Jr HS Teacher; *b:* Springer, New Mexico; *m:* Thomas Dinan; *c:* Ricardo, Timothy, Natalia; *ed:* Loyola Marymount Univ (BA) Ed, Sociology 1973; 15 Credit Hrs Ed Courses; *cr:* Santa Teresita Schl 2nd Grd Tchr 1973-74; St Mel Schl Jr HS Tchr, Lang Arts 1986-90; St Margaret Mary Schl Jr HS, Lang Arts 1993-95; *ai:* NCEA 1993-; NCTE; *home:* 32 Kristy Dr Bethel CT 06801

KEARNEY, DORIS MARIE, Eighth Grade Teacher; *b:* Birmingham, AL; *m:* James A.; *c:* Brian, Sheryl; *ed:* St Paul's Coll (BS) Elem Ed 1966; Glassboro Extension T for C Credits 3 Hrs; *ai:* Homework Club 4-8 Grd; Cooking Club 2nd Grd Adv 1970-71; Budget, Redesign, Curr Comms; Pleasantville Ed, NJEA, NEA 1966-; Faith Bapt, Usher Bd Pres 1988-89, Schlsp Club Treas 1987-88; Governor's Awd; Tchr of Yr; *home:* 1001 Iowa Ave Pleasantville NJ 08232*

KEARNEY, JUDITH ARLENE (CARROLL), Spanish Teacher; *b:* Chester, PA; *m:* Robert M.; *c:* James, Sean, Aaron; *ed:* Adelphi Univ (BA) Span 1970; NY Univ (MA) Ed 1973; *cr:* John W Dodd MS Span Tchr 1970-81; Freeport HS Span Tchr 1981-; *ai:* Stu Mentor; Tutor; AFT 1970-; NYSAFLT 1992-; Love Oasis Chrstn Church 1992-, Music Ministry Flutist; Nu-Finmen Swim Club 1985-, Sec; *office:* Freeport HS 50 S Brookside Ave Freeport NY 11520

KEARNEY, LYNN, Social Stud & Humanities Tchr; *b:* Miles City, MT; *m:* James A. Lee; *c:* Maurice Ramirez, Paola Ramirez; *ed:* Duchesne Coll (BA) His 1966; Georgetown Univ (MA) His 1970; 37 Hrs in Lit & His; Grants from Natl Endowment for Hum & Natl Sci Fnd; *cr:* George Norris Jr HS Core Tchr 1966-68; Dunbar HS Tchr 1970-; *ai:* Ed Adv Bd Arena Stage; Intnl Prgm DC Pub Schls; AFT 1972-; Natl Geographic 1987-; Sierra Club 1995-; Arlington Cty Democratic Comm 1993; US Dept of Ed Grant; Seminar Amer and New World Order.

KEARNEY, PAULA F., Owner & Instructor; *b:* Worcester, MA; *c:* Sheryl, Sharlene, Christopher; *ed:* Quinsigamond Comm Coll (AA) Ed 1969; *cr:* Paula Kearney Dance Studio Owner, Instr 1971-; *ai:* Dance Masters of Amer 1973-; Choreographed 10 Musicals for Acad Park HS, Summertime at the Park.

KEARNEY-MC FADDEN, LINDA, 5th Grade Teacher; *b:* New York, NY; *m:* Dovell Mc Fadden; *ed:* South Cntrl Comm Coll (AS) Early Chldhd Ed 1978; Southern CT St Coll (BS) Elem Ed 1981, (MS) Rdng Ed 1989; Self-Esteem Efficacy Prgm; Psych Classes; *cr:* New Haven Child Dev Ctr Tchr 1981-84; New Haven Bd of Ed Tchr 1984-; *ai:* Tutorial Stud for Former Stdnts; PTO, Lead Peer Cnslng, Intrvention Groups; Mentor Individual Stdnts; Provide After Schl Homework, Resource Assistance; Lib Power Comm; New Staff Mentor Tchr; AFT 1984-; CT Cooperative Tchrs 1990-, Stu Tchr Trainer; NCNW 1985-; SCSU Alumni 1981-; Pine Rock Bd of Dirs 1990-, Pres; Bridging Gap Between Elem, Mid Schl Grant; Comm Concerned Citizens Coalition Tchr of Yr; Choir Distngd Svc Awd; BSA Appreciation Awd; *office:* Helene Grant Elem Schl 185 Goffe St New Haven CT 06511*

KEARNS, JAMES LESTER, 5th & 6th Grade Teacher; *b:* Ashland, KY; *m:* Kelli Ann Carmon; *c:* Christopher; *ed:* OH Univ (BS) Elem Ed 1976; Addl 45 Quarter Hrs in Educl Admin; *cr:* Dawson-Bryant Schls 5th-6th Grd Tchr 1976-; *ai:* Sci Curr, Pub Relations, TQM Comms; *home:* 1115 Latonia St Ironton OH 45638*

KEARNS, RICHARD L., Poetry Tchr, Writer & Musician; *b:* Harrisburg, PA; *m:* Valdenice Almeida; *ed:* Millersville Univ of PA (BA) Span 1984; Columbia Univ Schl of Jrnlsm (MS) Print Jrnlsm 1986; *cr:* PA Schl of Art, Design Poetry Tchr 1992-94; Danzante Poetry Tchr, Musician 1992-; Rutgers Univ Adj Instr Poetry of Protest 1995; Art Tech, SCCA Poetry Tchr 1995; *ai:* Harrisburg Artists Cooperative Bd Mem; Natl Assn of Hispanic Jrnlsm 1995-; PR Org Comm 1995-, Bd Mem; Articles Pub; *home:* 3022 N 5th St Harrisburg PA 17110*

KEARNS, ROBERT DEAN,JR., Phys Ed & Drafting Instructor; *b:* Braintree, MA; *m:* Rita Elizabeth Cooney; *c:* Jennifer, Rita Marie; *ed:* Xavier Univ (BS) PE 1969, (MED) PE 1970; Miami Univ (BS) Indstrl Arts 1981; Cincinnati St Beg, Adv Auto CAD 1996; *cr:* St Peter & Paul Schl PE Tchr 1968-70; St Vincent Ferrer Schl PE Tchr, Coach 1968-70; Madeira City Schls Sci Tchr 1970-75; Private Construction Bus 1975-79; Madeira Jr Sr HS Ind Arts, PE Tchr, Ath Dir, Wrestling coach 1979-; *ai:* Head Wrestling Coach, Prgm Coord; Madeira City Schls Planning Commission; SWOWCA 1979-, Coach of Yr 1986; OWCA 1980-; AAHPERD 1995-; *office:* Madeira Jr Sr HS 7465 Loannes Dr Cincinnati OH 45243*

KEARNS, RONALD EDWIN, Instrumental Music Teacher; *b:* Raleigh, NC; *m:* Lillie Broughton; *c:* Tiffany; *ed:* Knoxville Coll (BS) Music Ed 1974; Cath Univ (MM) Music Ed 1985; DMA Stud; Univ of Nairobi African Music Cert 1970; *cr:* Forest Park HS Band Dir 1975-78; Frederick Douglass HS Band Dir 1978-84; John F. Kennedy HS Instrumental Music Tchr 1985-95; Walter Johnson HS Instrumental Music Tchr 1995-; *ai:* Band; Orchestra, Jazz; Dir; Tri-M Adv; MMEA 1975-, Pres, S Cntrl; Tri-M 1975-, W Cntrl Chm; IAJE 1976-; ASCAP 1990-; FMJS 1990-, Advy Bd Mem; Sargent Meml Presbyn Church, Elder; Contributing Writer MMEA, Jazz News Magazine; Record Producer Candid Records, Jazz Karma Records; *office:* Walter Johnson HS 6400 Rock Spring Dr Bethesda MD 20814*

KEARSE, LORRAINE HART, English Instructor; *b:* Washington, DC; *m:* Kelvan Mark; *c:* Mark Alexander, Courtney Alxandra; *ed:* Langston Univ (BS) Bus Mgmt 1983; Quinnipiac Coll (MA) Eng 1994; *cr:* Pan Amer World Airways Flight Attendant 1985-92; Albert I Prince RVTS Eng Instr 1993-; *ai:* Chrldng Coach; Girl Scout & SAT Acad Ldrs; Delta Sigma Theta 1980-; *office:* A I Prince Reg Voc-Tech Schl 500 Brookfield St Hartford CT 06106*

KEATING, MARGARET DEANGELO, Second Grade Teacher; *b:* Pittston, PA; *m:* Michael R. Jr.; *c:* Michael R. III, Charles E.; *ed:* PA St Univ (BS) Elem Ed 1965; Univ of MD (MED) Elem Ed 1980; Loyola Post Grad Stud; *cr:* Belle Grove Elem Schl 2nd-3rd Grd Tchr 1970-72; Rippling Woods 3rd Grd Tchr 1973-93, 2nd Grd Tchr 1994-; *ai:* Tchr Assn Anne Arundel Cty 1970-; Alpha Delta Kappa 1980-; AA Cty Rdng Cncl, Treas; Nom Tchr of Yr Anne Arundel Cty; *office:* Rippling Woods Elem Schl 530 Nolfield Dr Glen Burnie MD 21061*

KEATING, MARY MALAN, Math Teacher; *b:* Camden, NJ; *m:* Richard; *ed:* FL St Univ (BA) Elem Ed 1975; *cr:* Glen Landing MS Tchr & Team Ldr 1975-; *ai:* Track Coach 1988-93; Math Adv; 6th Grd Dist Rep; NJEA 1975-; NEA 1975-; *office:* Glen Landing MS 85 Little Gloucester Rd Blackwood NJ 08012

KEATING, PHYLLIS D., English Teacher; *m:* Charles Edward; *c:* Scott Edward, Misha A.; *ed:* Miami Univ (BSEd) Eng 1965; Attnd OH Univ; *cr:* Logan HS Eng Tchr, Eng Dept Chair 1965-69; Berne Union HS Eng Tchr, Eng Dept Chair 1970-; *ai:* Jr, Sr Prom Adv; Schl Newspaper Adv; NEA; OEA; BUEA; Delta Kappa Gamma.

KEATING, SHARON FLYNN, Fifth Grade Teacher; *b:* Fallriver, MA; *m:* William M.; *c:* Billy, Jimmy, Brian; *ed:* Westfield St Coll (BSED) Ed 1966; Attnd Univ of CT; *cr:* Andover Schl System Kndgtn Tchr 1966-67; Holyoke Schl System 1st Grd Tchr 1967-69; St Patrick's Schl 1st Grd Tchr 1978-88; Chicopee Schl Sub Tchr 1988-93, 5th Grd Tchr 1993-; *ai:* NEA 1993; *office:* Bowie Elementary Schl Dane Way Chicopee MA 01020

KECK, BARTH ALLEN, HS English & Journalism Tchr; *b:* Baltimore, MD; *m:* Peggy; *c:* Zachary, Jared; *ed:* Quinnipiac Coll (BA) Mass Comm 1984, (MAT) Eng Ed 1991; Empire St Coll SUNY Bus & Policy Stud 30 Credits Towards MA; *cr:* Houlton Regnl Hospital Dir of Comm Relations 1984-86; Dansbury Hospital Dir of Pub Relations 1986-90; Haddam-Killingworth HS Eng Tchr 1991-; *ai:* Asst Ftbl Coach; Stu Newspaper Adv; CT Cncl of Tchrs of Eng Mem; Block Scheduling, Schl Restructing Comm; CT Cncl of Tchrs of Eng, NEA, CT Ed Assn 1991-; CT HS Coaches Assn 1993-; *office:* Haddam-Killingworth HS Little City Rd Higganum CT 06441

KECK, JONATHAN ALDEN, English Teacher; *b:* Clinton, IA; *c:* Shannon, Joshua; *ed:* SUNY at Brockport (BA) 1972, (MS) Admin 1975, (CAS) Admin 1980; *cr:* Greece Cntrl Schls Eng Tchr 1972-; *ai:* Soccer Ofcl; Lit Magazine Alpha; Ftbl, Bsbl, Wrestling & Sftbl Coach 1972-90; NEA 1972-; Tchr of Yr 1985; NHS; *office:* Greece Arcadia HS 120 Island Cottage Rd Rochester NY 14612*

KECK, SUSAN STOVER, English Teacher; *b:* Lancaster, PA; *m:* Brian R.; *c:* Justin Ternosky, Jillian Ternosky; *ed:* Shippensburg St Univ (BS) Eng Ed 1980; 33 Grad Hrs in Educl Stud; *cr:* Northwester Lehighh HS Eng Tchr 1 Yr; Norther Lehigh HS Eng Tchr 7 Yrs; *ai:* Ski Club Adv; Assessment Team Comm; Arts & Hum Transition Team Chair; NEA, PSEA, NLEA 1990-; NCTE 1994-; *office:* Northern Lehigh Sr HS 1 Bulldog Ln Slatington PA 18080*

KEDIAN, MARY CARDEN, Second Grade Teacher; *m:* F. Patrick; *c:* Patrick, Katie, Kerry Suter; *ed:* Montclair St Univ (BA) Soc Stud 1963; Attnd Treton St Coll; *cr:* Bergenfield Sr High Soc Stud & Psych Tchr 1963-64; Stony Brook Elem 5th Grd Tchr 1964-66; Bridgewater-Raritan MS Supplemental Tchr 1975-78; Princeton Univ Rsrch Asst 1978-79; *ai:* Yrbk Moderator 1983-84; Stu Cncl Adv; Young Authors Moderator; NCEA 1980-; Rdng Tchrs Assn; St Augustine Schl Diocese of Metuchen Tchr of Yr 1990; *office:* St Augustine Schl Canterbury 45 Henderson Rd Kendall Park NJ 08824*

KEECH, THOMAS N., Seventh Grade Science Teacher; *b:* Coatesville, PA; *m:* Linda S.; *c:* Stephanie, Thomas; *ed:* PA St Univ (BS) Elem Ed 1979; *cr:* South Brandywine MS Math, Sci Tchr 1980-81; Gordon MS Sci Tchr 1982-83; Rainbow Elem 2nd Grd Tchr 1983-84; Gordon MS 7th Grd Sci Tchr 1984-; *ai:* 7th Grd Ftbl, 7-8th Grd Sftbl Coach 1986-; Envirothan Coach 1992-; NEA, PSEA 1981-; Coatesville Tchrs Assn 1981-, VP 1990-94; *office:* William T. Gordon MS 351 Kersey St Coatesville PA 19320

KEEFE, CAROL PASTORE, 4th Grd Self-Contained Teacher; *b:* Derby, CT; *m:* Thomas William; *c:* Thomas Nicholas; *ed:* Southern CT St Coll (BS) Elem Ed 1967; 5th Yr Elem Ed 1973; *cr:* Derby Bd of Ed Head Start Tchr 1967-70, Homebound Instr 1967, 3rd Grd Tchr 1967-77, 4th Grd Tchr 1977-; *ai:* Crisis Team; Hyde Schl Fair Share Chprsn, Performing Arts; DEA 1967-83, 1987-, Negotiating Team; CEA, NEA 1967-83, 1987-; AFT 1983-87; *office:* Bradley Schl David Humphrey's Rd Derby CT 06418

KEEFE, MARY C., Mathematics Teacher; *b:* Lowell, MA; *ed:* Emmanuel Coll Boston (BA) Math 1994; Univ of PA (MSEd) Ed 1959; 27 Credit Hrs Rensselaer Polytech, Univ of New Hampshire, Boston Univ; *cr:* Dracut HS Math Tchr 1949-60; Acton Boxborough Regnlg HS Math Tchr 1960-77, Math Dept Chprsn 1961-73; Keith Cath HS Math Tchr 1985-89; Notre Dame Acad Jr HS Math Tchr 1988-; *ai:* NEA, MTA 1949-; NCEA 1985-; G.E. Flwshp for Math, Sci Tchrs 1952; Natl Sci Fnd Flwshp 1958-59; *home:* 1461F Pawtucket Blvd Lowell MA 01854

KEEFE, MICHAEL LEONARD, Chemistry Teacher; *b:* Syracuse, NY; *ed:* SUNY Coll of ESF (BS) Bio 1975; Syracuse Univ (MS) Sci Ed 1989; *cr:* Corcoran HS Intern 1988-89; Paul V. Moore HS Gen Sci Tchr 1989-90; Jamesville Dewitt HS Chem Tchr 1990-; *ai:* Jr Class Adv; NYSUT 1990-; *office:* Jamesville-Dewitt HS PO Box 606 Edinger Dr Syracuse NY 13214*

KEEFE, PERRI TOLKOFF, HS Physical Education Teacher; *b:* Queens, NY; *m:* Ronald; *c:* Abby, Rebecca; *ed:* Ithaca Coll (BS) PE 1974; Russell Sage Coll (MS) Hlth Ed; *cr:* Red Hook Cntrl HS PE Tchr 1974-; *ai:* Class Adv; NYSAT 1979-; *office:* Red Hook Cntrl HS W Market St Red Hook NY 12571

KEEFE, THOMAS J., Professor of Physics; *b:* Springfield, MA; *m:* Margaret Johnson; *c:* Thomas, Michael; *ed:* Univ of MA at Lowell (BS) Electrical Engrng 1963; Univ of RI (MS) Electrical Engrng 1965; *cr:* Univ of RI NASA Fellow 1963-66, Rsrch Asst 1966-72, Tchng Asst 1972-75; Comm Coll of RI Prof of Physics 1975-; *ai:* NEA, MAA 1976-; Knights of Columbus 1970-; *home:* PO Box 283 Kingston RI 02881

KEEFER, DAWN E., Business Ed & Math Teacher; *b:* Bath, NY; *ed:* Alfred Univ (BA) Math 1975; Elmira Coll (MS) Ed 1979; Numerous Credit Hrs Acctng, Cmptr Ed; *cr:* Gowanda Cntrl Schl Math Tchr 1975-77; Dundee Cntrl Schl Bus Ed, Math Tchr 1977-; *ai:* Occ Ed Dept Chair; AFT, NYSUT 1977-; NYS BTA; Dundee Village Trustee 1995-; Presbyn Church, Asst Treas; Dundee Fire Auxiliary 1994; Alfred Univ Alumni Bd 1994-; *office:* Dundee Central Schl 55 Water St Dundee NY 14837

KEEFER, KRISTIN M., English Teacher; *b:* Corning, NY; *m:* Gregory K.; *c:* Ellen, Bennett; *ed:* Lock Haven Univ (BS) Eng, Comm 1976; PA St Univ (MEd) Curr Dev 1982; Marywood Coll 30 Grad Credits; *cr:* PA St Univ Tchng Asst 1981; Williamsport Area Comm Coll Eng Composition Instr 1984; Montgomery Area Jr Sr HS Eng Tchr 1976-; *ai:* 8th Grd Career Project Coord; NEA, PSEA, MAEA 1976-, Sec, Exec Comm; Lead Tchr; Developed Research, Composition Style Sheet; *office:* Montgomery Area Jr Sr HS 120 Penn St Montgomery PA 17752

KEEGAN, BEATRICE COX, First Grade Teacher; *b:* New York, NY; *w:* Timothy B. (dec); *c:* James, Joseph, Anne, Brendan; *ed:* Hunter Coll (BA) His, Sociology; NY Univ (MA) European His; NYU Schl of Ed Stud Prgm Intnl Stud; *cr:* United Nations Secretariat, Specialized Agencies Staff Mem 1956-69; NY City Bd of Ed Tchr 1972-; *ai:* Phi Alpha Theta 1971-; *h*[illegible] 30 Blenheim Dr Manhasset NY 11030

KEEGAN, CHRISTINE SHAW, French Teacher; *b:* New York City[illegible] *m:* Jackson R.; *c:* Kristin Keegan Bullock, Megan; *ed:* St Univ of N[illegible] Brockport (BA) Scndry Fr 1969; Ithaca Coll (MA) Fr 1974[illegible] Susquehanna Valley Jr HS Fr Tchr 1969-84; Susquehanna Valley [illegible] Tchr 1984-; *ai:* Yrbk, Stu Cncl & Sr Class Adv; NEA, NY St Foreign [illegible] Tchrs 1969-; Jr League of Binghamton, Sustaining Mem; [illegible] Susquehanna Valley Sr HS 1040 Conklin Rd Conklin NY 13748*

KEEGAN, JULIA M., Associate Professor of Nursing; *b:* Philade[illegible] PA; *ed:* Neumann Coll (BS) Nrsng 1970; Cath Univ of Amer (M[illegible] Cardiovascular Nrsng 1977; Attnd NY Univ; *cr:* St Joseph [illegible] Cardiovascular Clinical Specialist 1971-80; Neumann Coll Fac 198[illegible] Nrsng Curr Comm; Numerous Hlth Care Wkshps; Natl League of [illegible] 1981-; Sigma Theta Tau; Phi Delta Kappa; Samuel Eshborn, Tchng [illegible] Awds; *office:* Neumann Coll Concord Rd Aston PA 19014*

KEEGAN, KATHLEEN DUNSHEE, Social Studies & Psych Teach[illegible] Neptune, NJ; *m:* James E.; *c:* Katelyn, Shaun, Tara; *ed:* Glassboro S[illegible] at Rowan (BA) Ed, Soc Stud, Lang Arts 1980; Cert Psych 198[illegible] Freehold Twp HS Soc Stud Tchr 1981-86; Howell HS Soc Stud, Psych[illegible] 1992-; *ai:* Staff Dev; Renaissance Comm; Fr Class Adv; NJEA [illegible] ASCD 1994-; NCSS 1996; Asst Coach Little League; Established [illegible] Ldrshp Prgm.*

KEEGAN, MICHAEL, Fourth Grade Teacher; *b:* Troy, NY; *m:* [illegible] Killelea; *c:* Michael; *ed:* Coll of St Rose (BA) Sociology 1972; R[illegible] Sage Coll (MS) Elem Ed 1978; SUNY at Oneonta Grad Course Wo[illegible] Tchrs, Interns Supervision; *cr:* Green Island St Joseph's Schl 6th Grd[illegible] 1972-76; Rensselaer St Joseph's Schl 4th Grd Tchr 1976-84; Rensselaer Elem Schl 4th Grd Tchr 1984-; *ai:* Article Pub; *office* [illegible] Rensselaer Elem Schl Washington Ave Rensselaer NY 12144

KEEHN, G. THOMAS, Bands Director; *b:* Lancaster, PA; *m:* C[illegible] Reed; *c:* Geoffrey, Timothy; *ed:* Lebanon Vly Coll (BS) Music Ed [illegible] West Chester Univ (MM) Music Ed 1973; Attnd Oberlin Conserv[illegible] Univ of VT; *cr:* Kingston City Schls Elem Instrumental Music [illegible] 1963-70; Kingston Jr HS Instrumental Music Tchr 1970-86; Kingst[illegible] Instrumental Music Tchr 1986-; *ai:* Wind Ensemble, Tiger Marching [illegible] Jazz Band, Pit Orch Dir; Bldg Ldrshp Team; NYSSMA 1963-; UC[illegible] Kingston Tchr Assn 1963-, Pres; AFT 1970-; A F Musicians [illegible] Kingston Jaycees 1963-; Redeemer Luth 1963-, Music Dir; Hudso[illegible] Philharmonic 1965-, Trombonist; Clement Angstrom Civic Svc Awd [illegible] Rotary; Pub Svs Awd Kingston Moose Lodge; *home:* 2 Glen Ln Wood[illegible] NY 12498*

KEEHN, RUDOLPH W., English Teacher; *b:* Pottstown, PA; *m:* Vi[illegible] Lee Freese; *c:* Maria Schaeffer, Nichole, Erik; *ed:* Ursinus Coll (BA[illegible] & His 1965; 30 Credit Hrs in Eng & Related Areas; *cr:* Phoenixville[illegible] Schl Dist Jr HS Eng Tchr 1968-80, Head of Jr HS Eng Dept 1980-9[illegible] Eng Tchr 1993-; *ai:* Yearly Shakespeare Production & Competition [illegible] NEA 1968-; *home:* 32 Alans Ln Boyertown PA 19512

KEELER, MARY DRISCOLL, Sixth Grade Teacher; *b:* Corning, N[illegible] Patrick; *c:* Katie, Kelly, Kristin; *ed:* Corning Comm Coll (AA) [illegible] Oswego St Coll (BA) Elem Ed 1971; Elmira Coll (MA) Elem Ed 198[illegible] Selinsgrove Elem Schl Kndgtn Tchr 1971-72; St Mary's Primary Sch[illegible] Grd Tchr 1980-82; Booth Elem Schl 6 Grd Tchr 1982-; *office:* Arth[illegible] Booth Elem Schl 414 Davis St Elmira NY 14901

KEELER, STEVEN ROBERT, Telecommunications Professo[illegible] Newark, NJ; *m:* Carole Ann Kroll; *c:* Benjamin, Rebecca; *ed:* Un[illegible] Buffalo (BA) Media Stud 1977; Syracuse Univ (MS) Television & [illegible] 1982; Grad Cert Information System 1995; *cr:* W G Publishin[illegible] 1978-80; Brown Univ Media Specialist 1981; New Channels Cable [illegible] Exec Producer 1982-87; Cayuga Comm Coll Fac 1987-; *ai:* Ra[illegible] Television Guild Adv; WDWN-FM Coll Radio Station Fac Adv; [illegible] 1987-, Local Sec; Natl Assn of Cable Programmers 1983-; Broadca[illegible] Assn 1994-; Comm Coll Assn for Instruction & Tech Best Promo[illegible] Video 1994, Presidents Awd Pub Svc Video 1994 & Best Entertair[illegible] Prgm 1993; Cable Ace Awd Nom 1986 & 1986 Sports & 1985 [illegible] Programming; Hometown Video Festival Finalist 1987 & 1994; [illegible] Cayuga County Comm Coll 197 Franklin st Auburn NY 13021*

KEELING, AGNES CURRAN, Fourth Grade Teacher; *b:* Johnstowr[illegible] *m:* Charles M.; *c:* Cara L.; *ed:* IN Univ of PA (BS) ELem Ed [illegible] Duquesne Univ (MS) Elem Ed 1968; *cr:* Baldwin-Whitehall Schl [illegible] Primary Tchr 1964-74; Chatham Coll Cooperating Tchr 1966-70; Sli[illegible] Rock Coll Cooperating Tchr 1966-70; Bethel Park Schl Dist Primary [illegible] 1975-76; St Valentine JR HS Inter Prin 1983-; St Valentine Schl Fourt[illegible] Tchr 1996; *ai:* Elem Dept Chprsn; Sci Fair Comm; Mission Awar[illegible] Coord; NSCST, FPDT 1989-; Bethel Park Lioness Club 1990-92; Beth[illegible] HS Band Boosters 1991-94; *home:* 5362 Madison Ave Bethel Pa[illegible] 15102

KEELS, CARL EUGENE, Science Teacher; *b:* Washington, D[illegible] Eearnell Patricia; *c:* Carmen Anita, Patrice Diana; *ed:* Howard Univ [illegible] Zoology 1971; Fed City Coll (MA) Ed, Supervision 1972; Howard [illegible] (MDIV) Divinity 1992, (DMIN) Ed 1994; 33 Hrs Doctoral Stud G[illegible] Washington Univ; 6 Hrs MDIV Stud Capital Bible Seminary; [illegible] Biotechnological Stud Trinity Coll; *cr:* MD Univ Asst Instr 198[illegible] Ballou Sr HS Sci Tchr 1972-; Maple Springs Bible Seminary Assoc[illegible] 1996; *ai:* Spon Solar Car Project, Human Genome Project, Sci [illegible] BioBlast; BioCom Project; BASMAV 1992-, Asst Recording Sec; Fo[illegible] Fellow; Fnd Advancement Sci Fellow; Natl Inst Hlth Fellow; NI[illegible] Article; Pres US Amer Environmental Merit Awd 5 Times; D. C. Sc[illegible] City Cncl Awds Outstdng Tchng; HS Outstdng Sci Tchr; MD Univ [illegible] *office:* Ballou Sr HS 3401 4th St SE Washington DC 20032

KEEN, CAROL NANCY MUNYON, Second Grade Teache[illegible] Abington, PA; *m:* Richard Allen; *c:* Richard Todd, Tracy Lynn [illegible] Ryzner, Shawn Allen; *ed:* Bucks Cty Comm Coll (AA) Ed 1972; Tr[illegible] St Coll (BS) Ed 1977, (MS) Guidance, Stu Prsnl Svcs 1984; Rider Co[illegible] Prsnl Svcs 6 Credit Hrs; Beaver Stu Prsnl Svcs, Rdng 3 Credit [illegible] Villanova Spec Ed 3 Credit Hrs; Marywood Spec Ed, Prsnl 6 Credi[illegible] *cr:* Trevose Chrstn Day Nursery Nursery Schl Tchr 1968-69; Nesha[illegible] Schl Dist 4th-5th Grd Tchr of Gifted 1977-81; Council Rock Schl Dis[illegible] Grd Tchr 1982-; *ai:* Children Are People Group Co-Facilitator; [illegible] Union Rep; IST; PTO, Fac Rep; Stu Cncl Ldr 2 Yrs; TELLS Instr [illegible] Schl Plays Asst Adv; NEA 1982-; CREA 1982-, Fac Rep; Youth Aide [illegible] Newtown Twp 1990-, Sec, Asst Ldr; Newtown Presbyn Church [illegible] Elder, Deacon; Ladies Auxiliary Newtown Fire Co; Magna Cum [illegible] Grad 1977; *office:* Hillcrest Elem Schl 420 E Holland Rd Hollan[illegible] 18966*

KEENAN, ELLEN M., Sixth Grade Teacher; *b:* Massena, NY; *ed:* S[illegible] at Potsdam (BA) His, Elem Ed 1987, (MS) Elem Ed 1992; *cr:* Low[illegible] Acad Cntrl Schl Sixth Grd Tchr 1988-; *ai:* Modified Girls Soccer C[illegible] Synchronized Swim Club Co-Adv; Odyssey of the Mind Regnl, St J[illegible] Conflict Mngmt, Drug Free Schls Comm Chprsn; AFT 1988-; NY St [illegible] of Tchrs 1988-; Black River Rdng Cncl 1989-; Coll Womens Club [illegible] Assn of Amer Univ Women 1992-93; *home:* 123 Bowers Ave Wate[illegible] NY 13601

KEENAN, JAMES CLINTON, Amer History & Economics Tc[illegible] Warsaw, NY; *m:* Ann zuchowski; *c:* Rene, Ryan, Kenzie; *ed:* Man[illegible]

(BS) Scndry Ed 1971; Elmira Coll (MS) Amer Stud 1973, (MS) Adult 984; *cr:* Horseheads Cntrl Schls Tchr 1971-; *ai:* Wrestling Coach 84; Bsbl Coach 1977-; Dir of Bsbl Camps; BCA 1995-, Dist Chm; : Horseheads Cntrl Schls 1 Raider Ln Horseheads NY 14845

NAN, JAMES N., English & Writing Wrkshp Tchr; *b:* Philadelphia, : Marianne Christine; *ed:* (BA) Eng 1988; Addl 51 Credit Hrs Eng llanova Univ; *cr:* Norristown Area HS Stu Tchr & Sub 1988-89; Sun HS Eng Tchr 1990-; Phoenixville Area HS Eng, Writing Wkshp Tchr ; *ai:* Adv Schl Newspaper; Asst Var Ftbl Coach; NEA 1990-; *office:* nixville Area HS Gay St & City Line Ave Phoenixville PA 19460

NAN, MARJORIE, Vice Principal; *b:* Philadelphia, PA; *ed:* Chestnut Coll (BS) Chem 1972; villanova Univ (MS) Chem 1978; *cr:* St Anne Tchr 1967-68; Holy Name Schl Tchr 1968-71; St Joseph Acad Tchr, Head 1972-77; St Ambrose Schl Tchr 1977-83; Bethlehem Cath HS Vice Prin 1983-; *ai:* NCEA 1967-; NASSP 1986-; NSTA 1983-; : Bethlehem Catholic HS 2133 Madison Ave Bethlehem PA 18017

NAN, MARY L., Third Grade Teacher; *b:* Worcester, MA; *m:* Richard : Emmnauel Coll (BA) Elem Ed 1963; Univ of NH (MS) Music Ed, n 1973; Bridgewater St Coll Addl Credit Hrs; *cr:* St Rita Schl 6 Grd 1960-62; St Mary HS Music Tchr 1962-69; St Joseph HS Prin 73; Williams Elem Schl Music Dir, Tchr 1973-80, 3rd Grd Tchr ; *ai:* Lang Arts Comm; NEA, MA Tchrs, Plymouth Cty Tchrs Assns ; *office:* Williams Elem Schl 200 South St Bridgewater MA 02324

NAN, NANCY, Title I Teacher; *b:* Staten Island, NY; *ed:* St John's (BS) Elem Ed, Ed 1964; Kean Coll (MS) Ed, Contemp Civ, His 1974; of Staten Island 24 Grad Credits in Sp Ed 1984, 6 Yr Cert Supervision, n 1994; *cr:* Public Schl 19 2, 4, 5 Grds Tchr 1964-78, PCEN 2-5 Grds 1978-80, 5 Grd Tchr 1980-90, K-5 Grds Title I Tchr 1990-; *ai:* Chm Prog; Title I Proj Comm; UFT Chptr Chair; Supvr After Schl Prog, room; Coord Stu Cncl, Field Day, Graduation, City Wide Testing UFT 1970-, Chptr Chm; AFT; NYSUT; *office:* PS 19 Curtis 780 Post taten Island NY 10310*

NEY, CAROL GARTNER, First Grade Teacher; *b:* New York, NY; seph; *c:* Bryan, Robert; *ed:* St John's Univ (BS) Ed 1970, (MS) Curr ing, Elem Ed 1974; 30 Addl Hrs; *cr:* PS 75 Tchr 1970-74; PS 71 Tchr ; Coll of New Rochelle Part-time Adj Instr 1 Yr; *ai:* AFT, UFT 1970-; Photographs as Greeting Cards; St Judes Children's Hosp for Cancer Fundraising Fairs Pub Svc Recognition; *office:* Rose E. Scala Schl Roberts Ave Bronx NY 10461*

NEY, JAIME LEIGH, Title I Math & Lang Teacher; *b:* Huntington, : Thomas E.; *c:* Brandon, Britani; *ed:* Marshall Univ at Huntington K-12th Grd Art 1978, (MS) 1st-8th Grd Elem Ed 1986; 45 Hrs Post Stu in Admin Univ of Dayton; *cr:* Fairland Local Schls Art Instr 89, 6th Grd Self Contained Classroom Tchr 1989-92, 7th Grd Lang 1992-93, Title I, Math, Lang Tchr 1993-; *ai:* NEA, OEA 1982-; : Fairland East Elem RR 1 Box 593 Proctorville OH 45669

SEY, MAURICE JAMES, Fifth Grade Teacher; *b:* York, PA; *m:* n-Lynn Burgen; *c:* Erin, Robyn; *ed:* Parsons Coll (BA) Modern Lang Millersville Univ (MED) Elem Ed 1973; Addl 60 Credit Hrs; *cr:* ezer Elem 5th Grd Tchr 1973-83; Cornwall Elem Facilitator of Gifted 88, 5th Grd Tchr 1988-; *ai:* Dist Leadership Team Mem; Lebanon Cty A-Thon Dist Chm; NEA, Cornwall-Lebanon Ed Assn 1973-, Bldg Yrs; Lebanon Cty Educl Honor Soc.

SLER, CAROLE BELINDA, First Grade Teacher; *b:* Portsmouth, : James Edward; *ed:* Cedarville Coll (BA) Elem Ed 1978; OH Univ) Elem Ed 1982; *cr:* Parker Elem Schl Title I Primary Tchr 1978-81, n Tchr 1981-86, Seventh Grd Tchr 1986-93, Chptr I Primary Tchr 95, First Grd Tchr 1995-; *ai:* Grace Bapt Church Pianist; *office:* r Elem Schl 12599 State Route 124 Piketon OH 45661

TLEY, JANICE BARBARA (NOBLE), Third Grade Teacher; *b:* Fall , MA; *m:* David W.; *c:* Jennifer, Meredith; *ed:* Bridgewater St Coll Elem Ed 1969; *cr:* River Street Schl Sixth Grd Tchr 1969-70; owbrook Schl Supplemental Tchr 1980-83, Third Grd Tchr 1983-; *ai:* , NJEA 1980-; ETA 1980-, Tchr Rep; *office:* Meadowbrook Schl ff Rd Eatontown NJ 07724

ELMAN, BERNADETTE, Biology Teacher; *b:* Wilmington, DE; *ed:* of DE (BS) Animal Sci 1986; 12 Addl Post-Grad Hrs in Agricultural emestry; *cr:* Immaculate Heart of Mary Schl Earth Sci Tchr 1988-91; Du Pont MS Earth Sci Tchr 1991-92; St Elizabeth HS Bio, Chem, omy, Physiology Tchr, Sci Dept Chprsn 1992-; *ai:* Acad Cncl; Earth eness Group, Sci Olympiod Team Adv; NSTA 1991-; *office:* St beth HS 1500 Cedar St Wilmington DE 19805*

LER, CAROLYN W., English & Journalism Tchr; *b:* Philadelphia, : Reginald Sr.; *c:* Amaela T. Wiley; *ed:* Cheyney St Univ (BA) Eng Ed Eng 1979; *cr:* Chester-Upland Schls 8th Grd Eng Dept Head s; Vineland Bd of Ed 10th & 12th Eng Tchr 2 Yrs; Chester High Acad 1th Grd Eng & Jrnlsm Tchr; *ai:* Yrbk Staff; Monitors Squad; Former h Grd Advisory Chm; CBC Building Coord; Schl Nwsp Adv; Former 78 Co-Chm & Eng Dept Head; NEA, CUEA, PSEA 1973-; Newspaper he Philadelphia Inquirer; *office:* Chester High Acad 9th & Fulton St er PA 19013*

NE, DAVID ANDREW, English Teacher; *b:* Fredrick, MD; *ed:* on St Univ (BS) Speech 1984, (MED) Scndry Ed 1995; 9 Grad Credits Coll; 6 Grad Credits MD Univ at College Park; *cr:* Towson St Univ Dir of Alumni 1984-88; Univ of MD Dev Dir 1988-90; Baltimore ub Schls Eng Tchr 1990-92; Frederick Cty Pub Schls Eng Tchr 1993-; u Govt Adv 1993-; Schl Improvement Team 1995-; NCTE 1992-; 1990-; *office:* Catoctin H S 14745 Sabillasville Rd Thurmont MD 8

OE, DEBORAH L., Special Education Head Teacher; *b:* Medford, : James E.; *c:* Brian Crowley, Tracey; *ed:* Bridgewater St (BS) Elem 970, (MEd) Ed 1977; Salem St Coll (CAGS) Educl Leadership 1996; Leadership, Spec Ed Stud; *cr:* East Bridgewater MS Elem Tchr, Ldr 1970-76; Salem Pub Schls Elem Tchr 1976-81; Salem HS Spec chr 1981-92, Spec Ed Head Tchr 1992-; *ai:* Comms City-Wide Tech, SC Evaluation, Schls That Work; Class Adv; Mem of Inst for Learning chng; ASCD, CEC 1992-; AFT 1976-; Marblehead Comm Theater -; Honorable Mention Educator of Yr 21st Century 1994; Nom for e Awd Salem Evening News 1993; Selected by Northeast Consortium ttend ASCD Conf in Chicago Emerging Images of Learning 1994; : Salem HS 77 Willson St Salem MA 01970*

OE, JUDITH A. OPIELA, First Grade Teacher; *b:* Buffalo, NY; *m:* F.; *ed:* St Univ of NY at Buffalo (BS) Elem Ed 1963, (MSEd) Admin, rvision 1968; OH St Univ 9 Credit Hrs; Niagara Univ 6 Credit Hrs; W Seneca Schl Kndgtn Tchr 1963-64, First Grd Tchr 1964-65; oldsburg First Grd Tchr 1965-66; Worthington First Grd Tchr 1966; enville First Grd Tchr 1966-67; Amherst Cntrl Schl Dist First Grd 1967-; *ai:* Dist-Shared Decision Team; Curr Cncl 12 Yrs; Stu Tchr sroom Supvr Univ of Buffalo, Daeman Coll, Canisius Coll; AFT, NEA -; Amherst Ed Assn 1963-, Bldg Rep; PTA 1963-; Treas, Sec 16 Yrs, fetime Awd 1982; *office:* Amherst Cntrl Schl Dist 55 Kings Hwy erst NY 14226

RING, LEE A., Art Department Chairperson; *b:* Baltimore, MD; *m:* ; *ed:* Essex Comm Coll (AA) Art Ed 1971; Towson St Univ (BS) Art 975, (MED) Art Ed 1975; US Coast Guard 1966-70; Attnd Engr Schl 1968, Fire Fighting Schl 1967, Outboard Motor Schl 1969; Theories & Practices Educl Ldrshp 1991; Care & Prevention Ath Injuries 1992; *cr:* Perry Hall HS Art Instr 1974-90; Parkville MS Art Instr 1974-76; Overlea HS Art Instr 1990-93; Perry Hall HS Art Instr 1990-91; Patapsco HS Art Instr 1991-93; Overlea HS Art Dept 1993-, Art Dept Chm 1994-; *ai:* Drawing I, II Instr Essex Comm Coll 1993-; Indoor Track Dist Champs 1978; Wrestling Coach 1979; Girls Soccer Coach 1988-89; Var Asst Coach Boys Soccer Cty Champs 1992; Annual Spring Art Show, Schl Mural Painting Spon; TABCO 1974-; NEA 1980-; Biannual Art Exhibit Baltimore Art Museum Oil Painting 1974-75; Art Tchrs Art Baltimore Life Bldg Honorable Mention Painting 1984-85; On Loan Display Paintings St Michael Luth Church New Ed Bldg 1993; Numerous Articles Pub 1971, 1975; *office:* Overlea HS Charles St Towson MD 21204

KEIB, DONNA LEE, 3rd Grade Teacher; *b:* Pittsburgh, PA; *ed:* Cedarville Coll (BA) Elem Ed 1968; Attnd OH St Univ, Ashland Coll, Bowling Green Univ; *cr:* Plymouth Local Schls Rdng Tchr 1967-68; Shelby City Schls 3rd, 4th Grd Tchr 1968-; *ai:* Math, Sci, Hlth, Soc Stud Curr Comms; NEA, SEA, OEA 1968-; Mansfield Bible Galion Alliance Church, Tchr.

KEIL, JUDITH SIMPSON, Second Grade Teacher; *b:* Bay village, OH; *m:* G. Michael; *ed:* OH St Univ (BS) Elem Ed 1972, (MA) Early Mid Ed 1989; Attnd Ashland Univ; Bowling Grn; AIMS wrkshps; Math Their Way; *ai:* Lang Arts, Penmanship & Bldg Advy Comm; Parenting Comm 1993-94; Prnt Night Wrkshp Presenter 1989; Mem Morrow Cnty Intl Rdng Assn Pres, VP, Sec, Prm Chair, By-Laws Comm; Bldg Advsy Comm; Lang Arts Comm; Prvte Tutoring; NEA & OEA 1972-; NCOEA 1972-, Dist Rep, Svc Awd; CLFA 1972-, all Currently Negotiations Chair; St Lit Awd 1970; *home:* 4480 State Route 95 Mount Gilead OH 43338*

KEIL, RENEE ANN GIOVANE, Dance & Acting Instructor; *b:* Pittsburg, PA; *m:* C. Thomas Jr.; *c:* Alixandra Olivia; *ed:* Univ of Pittsburg (BS) Hlth, PE 1970, (MAEd) Hlth, PE 1972; *cr:* Duquesne Univ Dance Instr 1987-89; Chartiers Valley HS Dance, Acting, PE Tchr 1970-; Choreographer for Local Theater Productions at Pittsburgh, Savoyards, Starlight Productions; Acting in Local Productions; *ai:* Majorette Spon; Acting Ensemble; Drill Team Choreographer & Spon; Dance Ensemble; Musical Theater Dir & Choreographer; AFT 1985-; AAHPHERD 1993; ASCD 1995; Mem PA Arts Assessment Design Team; Nom for Choreography, Lighting, & Costume for the Pittsburg Civic Light Operas Gene Kelly Awds 1991; *office:* Chartiers Valley H S 50 Thoms Run Rd Pittsburgh PA 15017*

KEILMAN, CHRISTINE RAWLEY, Mathematics & Science Teacher; *b:* Gary, IN; *m:* John H.; *ed:* IN Univ (BS) Math 1970; Univ of Toledo (MED) Curr & Instrl 1974; Cntrl CT St Univ, Nazareth Coll, St Univ of NY at Brockport, PA St Univ Grad Credit Hrs Sci; *cr:* Whiteford Ag HS Math Tchr 1971-76; Minerva Deland Schl Math, Sci Tchr 1976-83; Gideon Welles Jr HS Math, Sci Tchr 1983-84; Cntrl CT St Univ Math Instr 1984-86; Glastonbury HS Mat, Sci Tchr 1984-; *ai:* Natl Engrng Design Challenge Team St Coach, Adv 3 Times St Winner; Jr Engrng Tech Soc Team Coach, Adv; Assn of Schls, Colls Performance Chm Mentor Tchr; Glastonbury Ed Assn 1983-, VP; NEA, CT Ed Assn 1983-; NSTA, CSTA, St Sci Assn 1980-; NCTM, ATOMIC, St Math Assn 1974-; Sigma Xi Scientific Rsrch Soc Awd; Pub Article; CT Bus, Industry Assn St Dept of Ed Innovative Interdisciplinary Curr Awd; Nom Excl in Sci Tchng Presidential Awd 5 times; Nom Tchr of Yr 6 Times; onorium for Tchng Excl; *office:* Glastonbury HS 330 Hubbard St Glastonbury CT 06033

KEIMACH, BRAD M., Instr of His, Western Culture; *b:* Boston, MA; *c:* Julia; *ed:* The Juilliard Schl (BM) Conducting 1975; SUNY at Purchase (MFA) Conducting 1996; *cr:* Lincoln Ctr Inst Tchng Artist 1979-83; Westfield Symphony Orch Music Dir 1983-; Kean Coll Instr 1994-; *office:* Kean Coll Of NJ 300 W 72nd St #4B New York NY 10023*

KEISER, PATRICIA ELRENA, Seventh Grade Teacher; *b:* Burlington, IA; *c:* Jordan Aubrey; *ed:* Temple Univ (BS) Elem Ed 1986; Penn St Univ (MED) Trng Design & Dev 1993; Penn St Univ Prin Cert 1994; *cr:* Haverford Twp Schl Dist First Grd Tchr 1987-89; Schl Dist of Philadelphia Third Grd Tchr 1989-90, Seventh Grd Tchr 1990-; *ai:* Stu Asst Prgm Tchr Mentor; Ldrshp Team; Lib Power Participant; Women in Ed 1995-; Paths, Prism Crossing the Boundaries, Philadelphia Ed Fund Lib Power Grants; *office:* Theodore Roosevelt MS Washington Ln & Musgrave St Philadelphia PA 19144*

KEITH, DAVID M., PE & Earth Sci Teacher; *b:* Mineola, NY; *ed:* Hunter Coll (BS) Psych 1988; Queens Coll (MS) Sci Ed 1994; Addl Hrs Physics; *cr:* Great Neck South MS Sci Tchr 1990-; *ai:* Long Island Sci Congress Fac Spon; STANYS, AFT 1990-; PTA Grant to Explore Computerized Lab Stations in MS 1996; *office:* Great Neck South MS 345 Lakeville Rd Great Neck NY 11020

KEITH, DIANE MARIE, Mathematics Teacher; *b:* Cohoes, NY; *w:* Leland (dec); *c:* Andrea; *ed:* SUC at Brockport (BS) Math Ed 1971; St Univ of NY at Albany (MS) Educl Communication 1976; *cr:* Averill Park HS Math Tchr 1971-; *ai:* Capital Dist HS Challenge Adv; Scheduling & Attendance Policy Comms; NYST, AFT 1971-; Golub Scholar Recognition Awd; *home:* 5 Phoebe Ct Latham NY 12110

KEITH, RAYMOND J., Business Education Teacher; *b:* Barnesboro, PA; *m:* Gloria F. Whited; *c:* Rae-Anne, Tammy; *ed:* Indiana Univ of PA (BS) Bus Ed 1964, (MS) Bus Ed 1976; 9 Addl Credits; Attnd Penn St Univ 14 Credits, Shippensburg Univ 1 Credit & Bloomsburg Univ 3 Credits; *cr:* Cntrl Cambria HS Bus Tchr 1964-67; Purchase Line HS Bus Tchr 1967-; *ai:* Ret Track & Bsktbl Coach 22 Yrs; Past FBLA, Var Club & Sr Class Adv, Jr Class Adv; Girls Sftbl coach, PIAA Offcl for Bskbl & Track; NEA, PSEA & PBEA 1964-; PLEA Pres 2 Yrs; NBEA; Jaycees, Former Mem; North End Assembly of God Church 1962-, Bd of Dirs 1970-, Treas 1972-; *office:* Purchase Line H S RD 1 Box 374 Commodore PA 15729

KEITH, THOMAS A., Eighth Grade Science Teacher; *b:* Brockton, MA; *m:* Mary Ann Pirani; *c:* Jenna, Betsy, Daniel; *ed:* Cape Cod Comm Coll (AA) Liberal Arts 1967; Bridgewater St Coll (BA) Earth Sci 1971, (MAT) Phys Scis 1988; *cr:* Rockland HS 9th Grd Earth Sci Tchr 1971-78; Nathaniel H Wixon MS 8th Grd Sci Tchr 1982-; *ai:* Dennis-Yarmouth Regnl Sci Curr Team Ldr; 8th Grd Class Adv; MS Tennis Coach; MA Assn of Sci Tchrs 1988-; NEA, MTA 1971-; Intnl Assn of Bsktbl Ofcls 1968-; NSF Grants Inst for Chemical Ed 1988, Bridgewater St Sci Tchr Support 1985-86, Northeastern Univ SEED 1992; Rockland HS Tchr of Yr 1976; *office:* Nathaniel H Wixon MS 901 Route 134 South Dennis MA 02660

KEITHS, LISA K., HS Physical Education Teacher; *b:* Philadelphia, PA; *ed:* Univ of DE (BS) PE, Hlth 1984; Penn St Univ Drug Cnslr Cert; *cr:* Oxford HS Boys & Girls Track Coach 1987-89, PE Grd 9-12 Tchr 1987-, Girls Tennis 1989-93; *ai:* Stud Assistance Team; Adventure Group Explorers Club; AAHPERD 1981-; BSA Explorers, 1993-, Troop Ldr; *office:* Oxford Area HS 301 5th Street Rd Oxford PA 19363

KEKIS, REGINA SBARAGLIA, Spanish Teacher; *b:* Rome, NY; *m:* James Dmitri; *ed:* St Univ of NY at Oswego (BA) Span & Scndry Ed; Elmira Coll (MS) Adult Ed; Working Toward CAS at St Univ of NY at Cortland; Attnd Univ of Spain at Salamanca 6 Grad Credits & Madrid 8 Grad Credits; *cr:* Rome Cath HS Span Tchr 1978-85; Vernon Verona Sherrill HS Span Tchr 1985-; *ai:* Dist-Wide Tech Planning Team; Span Club; Tour Ldr to Spain, France & Mexico; AFT, NYUST 1985-; NYSAFLT 1985-, Hospitality; FLACNY 1985-, Sec, Distinguished Svc Awd; VVSTA 1985-, VP; BPW of Rome 1974-80, Sec, Outstanding Young Career Woman Awd; Church, Sunday Schl Tchr 1980s; NYS MCES Schlsp to Univ of Salamanca; BOCES Mini Grant to Build Classroom Store, to Attend Skidmore Lang Conf; Kenwood Grant to Travel to Spain; NYSAFLT Grant to Attend Skidmore Lang Seminar 2 Times; *office:* Vernon Verona Sherrill HS Rt 31 Verona NY 13478*

KELBAUGH, ROSS J., Social Studies Teacher; *b:* Baltimore, MD; *m:* Nancy Basile; *ed:* Univ of MD (BA) His, Soc Stud 1971; Johns Hopkins Univ (MLA) His 1977; Adv Masters Equivalency 1987; *cr:* Catonsville Jr High Soc Stud Tchr 1971-82; Cantonsville HS Soc Stud Tchr 1982-; *ai:* His Club Adv; Site Based Mgmt Team; Fund Raising Comm; NEA, MSTA, TABCO 1971-; Friends of Natl Parks of Gettysburg 1990-, Bd of Dir; Lib Comm MD His Soc 1989-, Vice Chm; Tchr-Historian of Yr 1988; Natl Capital Historical Soc; Author Introduction to Cival War Photography; Directory of MD Photographers 1893-1900 Directory of Civil War Photographers; Numerous Articles on 19th Century Photography; Excl in Ed Awd from Balto Cty Chamber of Commerce 1995; *home:* 7023 Deerfield Rd Baltimore MD 21208*

KELBER, DAVID ROBERT, Broadcast Comm Coord & Tchr; *b:* Newark, NJ; *ed:* Moravian Coll (BA) Gen Stud 1967; Trenton St Coll Addl Credits Ed Dept; *cr:* WVCH Radio Prgm Mgr 1967-68; WHTG Radio Operations Mgr 1971-75; Hunterdon Cntrl HS Coord of Comm 1975-; *ai:* Head Boys Track, Asst Cross Cntry Coaches; Radio Club, VICA Advs; NJ Television Edctrs Consortium 1992-; Mercer Coll Comm Advy Bd 1989-; NJ Voc Admins & Supvrs Assn; Voc Tchr of Yr Awd 1993; Cross Cntry Coach of Yr Awd 1986; *office:* Hunterdon Central Regional HS RT 31 Flemington NJ 08822*

KELEHER, JAMES MICHAEL, Science Teacher; *b:* Kenmore, NY; *m:* Patricia Schulz; *c:* Kate, Christine, Courtney, Kimberly; *ed:* Buffalo St Coll (BS) Scndry Ed Bio 1978, (MS) Scndry Ed, Bio 1981; *cr:* St Marys HS Sci Tchr 1978-79; Village of Kenmore Prof Firefighter 1979-82; Village of Kenmore Juvenile Ofcr 1982-; Erie I BOCES Sci Tchr 1985-90; Kenmore MS Sci Tchr 1990-; *ai:* Schl Planning Comm & Schl Design Teams; SAIT Comm; Substance Abuse Intervention Team; Kenmore Tchrs Assn 1990-, Rep 1995; NY St Tchrs Assn 1985-; Liberty Bell Awd Erie Cty Bar Assn Comm Srv 1984; Outstdng Young Man of Amer US Jaycees 1983; *office:* Kenmore MS 155 Delaware Rd Kenmore NY 14217*

KELEMEN, ELIZABETH,CDP, 7th & 8th Grade Teacher; *b:* Cumberland, KY; *ed:* Thomas More Coll (BA) Elem Ed 1953; Xavier Univ (MED) Rdng, Elem Ed 1955; *cr:* St Thomas Schl Tchr, Prin; Christ the King Tchr; St Louis Tchr; St John the Bapt Tchr, Youth Dir; *ai:* MathCounts, Acad Teams Coach; Outstanding Contributions Ec Ed Awd 1991; Jr Achvmt Participant 10 Yrs; NCEA Distinguished Tchr Awd 1995; *office:* Saint John The Baptist Schl 5375 Dry Ridge Rd Cincinnati OH 45252

KELLAR, CHERYL, Instructor; *b:* Wilkes-Barre, PA; *ed:* Wilkes Coll (BA) Sociology, Span & Comm Svc 1979; Syracuse Univ (MSW) Soc Work 1981; Licensed Soc Worker; Acad of Certified Soc Workers; *cr:* Northeast Counseling Svcs Psychotherapist & Outpatient Svcs 1981-82, Dir of Intake Svcs 1982-95; Fremont & Assocs Assoc in Private Practice 1989-; Maywood Coll Grad Schl of Soc Work Part-Time Instr 1990-; Homebound Hlth Svcs Soc Work Consultant 1994-; Northeast Counseling Svcs Dir of Outpatient Svcs 1995-; *ai:* NASW 1979-; ACSW 1981-; Hugo V Mailey Awd for Acad Excl in Soc Scis; Natl Inst of Mental Hlth Fellowship; Schlsp from Span Dept for Summer Stud in Mexico; Research Project & Paper Accepted & Presented at the Intnl Gerontological Soc Meeting in Canada; *office:* Marywood Coll 2300 Adams Ave Scranton PA 18509

KELLAR, TINA ANN, Instrumental Music Teacher; *b:* Wilkes-Barre, PA; *ed:* Wilkes Univ (BM) Music Ed 1989; Ithaca Coll (MMEd) Music Ed 1994; Attnd Westminster Choir Coll, Rel Ed Inst Scranton Diocese; *cr:* St Aloysius Elem K-12th Grd Gen Music Tchr 1989-90; Bishop Hoban HS Instrumental Music Tchr & Band Dir 1990-; *ai:* Marching Band, Concert Band & Jazz Ensemble Dir; Elem Band Dir & Coord; Liturgical Music Ensemble; Mid States Sub-Comm; 25th Anniversary Celebration Comm; PMEA 1990-, Recording Sec; NCEA 1990-; Natl Piano Tchrs 1991-; Church Musician; Article Pub; *office:* Bishop Hoban H S 159 S Pennsylvania Blvd Wilkes Barre PA 18701

KELLEHER, JOHN THOMAS, Business Education Faculty; *b:* Brockton, MA; *m:* Jean; *c:* Justin, Jessica; *ed:* Northeastern Univ (BS) Mngmt, Acctng 1973; Cambridge Coll (MS) Ed 1995; Attnd Bridgewater St Coll, Fitchburg St Coll, Suffolk Univ; *cr:* Aetna Casualty & Ins Co Account Rep Natl Account Dept 1973-75; Brockton HS Bus Ed Fac, DECA Adv 1975-; Kelleher Real Estate Svcs Owner, Broker 1993-; *ai:* Yrbk, Class, Schl Bank Adv; NEA, MTA, BEA 1975-, Treas; MA DECA 1987-, Bd of Dirs; NAACP 1993-; *office:* Brockton HS 470 Forest Ave Brockton MA 02401

KELLEHER, JOSEPH EDWARD, Instructor; *b:* Baltimore, MD; *m:* Gloria; *c:* Jaime, Christopher, Kimberly; *ed:* Towson St Univ (BA) Math 1972, (MED) Scndry Ed & Statistics 1974; *cr:* Baltimore City Pub Schls Scndry Math Tchr & Supvr 1969-82; Dundalk Comm Coll Cmptr Prgmng Fac 1982-; *office:* Dundalk Community Coll 7200 Sollers Point Rd Dundalk Sp Pt MD 21222

KELLEHER, KATHERINE MARY, Global Studies Teacher; *b:* Flushing, NY; *c:* Rory Petteys, Daniel Petteys; *ed:* SUNY at Albany (BA) His 1988, (MA) Soc Stud 1991; *cr:* Greenwich Cntrl Schl Eleventh Grd Soc Stud Tchr 1988-89; North Colonie Schls Eighth Grd Soc Stud Tchr 1989; Shenendehowa Cntrl Schls 7th-9th Grd Soc Stud Tchr 1990-; *ai:* Tchr Rel Ed 1992-; Child Stud Team 1993-; Crisis Intervention Team 1993-; Shenendehowa Tchr Assn 1990-, Bldg Rep; NYSUT 1988-, Del; *office:* Koda Jr HS 970 Route 146 Clifton Park NY 12065

KELLER, BARBARA KLEAR, English Teacher; *b:* New Brighton, PA; *m:* Henry Earl; *c:* Joshua Earl, Julie Kaye; *ed:* Westminster Coll (BA) Speech & Eng 1969; Attnd Slippery Rock univ & Univ of Pittsburgh Post Grad Work; *cr:* Seneca Valley Schl Dist Eng Tchr 1969-73; Waldenbooks Bookseller & Mgr 1978-89; Armstrong Schl Dist Eng Tchr 1989-; *ai:* Speech & Debate Coach; Drama Dir; Class Adv; NEA & PSEA 1969-; Armstrong Ed Assn 1989-; PA Speech & Debate Assn 1987-; Musical Theater Guild 1975-; *office:* Armstrong Schl Dist 410 Main St Ford City PA 16226*

KELLER, BEVERLY DARLYNE JONES, Third Grade Teacher; *b:* Camden Cty, NJ; *m:* Richard Fremont III; *c:* Donald Clyde, Richrd Fremont IV, Donna Darlyne Michael; *ed:* Cecil Comm Coll (BA) Elem Ed 1985; Liberty Univ (BS) Elem Ed, Psych 1991; *cr:* Pike Creek Chrstn Schl Second Grd Tchr 1969-79; Fairwinds Chrstn Schl Fifth Grd Tchr 1979-92; Red Lion Chrstn Acad Third Grd Tchr 1992-; *ai:* Missions Comm; Camp Dir; *home:* 7 Hillwood Rd Elkton MD 21921

KELLER, CHERYL SHAYMOW, Spanish Teacher; *b:* New York City, NY; *m:* Marc S.; *c:* Leslie, Meredith; *ed:* SUC at Oswego (BA) Span & Scndry Ed 1974; St Univ of NY at Albany (MA) Span Lit 1977; Instituto Internacional Madrid Spain; 18 Credits at Sorbonne Novvelle Paris France Summer Course; *cr:* Montgomery Cty Pub Schls Span Tchr 1975-82; Akiba Hebrew Acad Span Tchr 1983-86; Harding HS Span Tchr 1989-90; Daniel Hand HS Span Tchr 1991-92; East Haven HS Span Tchr 1992-; *ai:* Stu Advy Comm; NEA 1992-; CT Cncl of Lang Tchrs 1991-; Org for Rehabilitation Through Trng 1979-; *office:* East Haven HS 200 Tyler St East Haven CT 06512*

KELLER, CHRISTOPHER LEIGH, Earth Science Teacher; *b:* Fulton, NY; *m:* Diane Schiefke; *c:* Scott, Kevin, Shannon; *ed:* St Univ Coll at

Oswego (BA) Sci 1967, (MS) Earth Sci; 75 Credits Beyond Masters; *cr:* Mexico Acad HS Earth Sci Tchr 1967; Connetquot Schl Dist Earth Sci & Sci Research Tchr 1967-; *ai:* AFT, NEA, NYSTA, NYSSTA, Connetquot Tchrs Assn 1967-; Patchogue Fathers Club 1992-; Jr Natl Honor Soc Honorary Mem by Stu Body; Stu Cncl & Frosh Adv; Schl Bldg Reporter; *office:* Oakdale-Bohemia Jr HS Oakdale-Bohemia Rd Oakdale NY 11769

KELLER, JENNIFER A., 5th Grade Teacher; *b:* Pittsburgh, PA; *ed:* Clarion Univ (BSEd) Elem & Early Chldhd Ed 1989; Duquesne Univ (MSEd) Rdng Specialty 1995; *cr:* St Bartholomew Schl Kndgtn & Preschl Tchr 1989-91; St Marys Schl 5th Grd Tchr 1991-; *ai:* Yrbk; Cath Schls Week & Spirituality Comm; *office:* St Mary Schl 2510 Middle Rd Glenshaw PA 15116*

KELLER, JOHN CHARLES, Senior High English Teacher; *b:* Wilkes-Barre, PA; *ed:* Univ of CT (BA) Eng 1966; Temple Univ (MS) Ed 1975; Shakespeare Inst; *cr:* Schl Dist Phila 30 Yrs; *ai:* Eng Bookroom Asst; Steering Comm 1997 Mid Sts Eval; AFT; PFT; NCET; *office:* George Washington HS Bustleton Ave & Verree Rd Philadelphia PA 19116

KELLER, KAREN JEAN (WILSON), Family & Consumer Sci Teacher; *b:* Pittsburgh, PA; *m:* Robert Eugene; *ed:* IN Univ of PA (BSEd) Home Ec 1970, (MSEd) Home Ec 1974; 14 Credit Hrs; *cr:* Epworth Woods Camp Asst Cook Summer 1968, Head Cook Summers 1969-70; Moon Area Schl Dist Tchr 1970-; *ai:* KIDS Club Co-Spon; Odyssey of Mind Judge; LEADERS Comm Awd & HS Grad Requirement Comms; NEA, PSEA & Moon EA 1970-; AAFCS & PAFCS 1970-; NAEYC & PAEYC 1992-; Sharon Presbyn Church 1971-, Elder & Deacon; AAUW Coraopolis Sewickley 1990-; *home:* RR 3 Box 301 Aliquippa PA 15001

KELLER, KATHLEEN LIPTAK, Chem Tchr & Sci Dept Chprsn; *b:* Cleveland, OH; *c:* Steven, Thomas; *ed:* Notre Dame Coll (BS) Chem 1965; OH St Univ (MS) Chem 1968; 6-12th Grd Chem & General Sci Cert; 18 Grad Credits WSU, Univ of Dayton, OSU & Xavier Univ; 5 CEU's Univ of Dayton & OH Northern Univ; *cr:* U.D. Research Inst Asst Chemist 1969-71; Dayton Wastewater Treatment Bacteriologist & Chemist 1980-84; Carroll HS Sci Tchr 1985-, Sci Dept Chprsn 1989-; *ai:* Organize & Direct all Sci DayAct; Sci Quiz Bowl Team Coach; Montgomery cty Sci Day & West Dist Sci Day Comm; St Sci Day Judge; Co-Chair of Montg County Sci Day; NSTA 1985-; OH Acad of Sci 1989-; SECD 1994-; Audubon Soc; Kappa Delta Pi; Governor's Awd for Excl in Youth Sci Opportunities 1990, 1992-95; ISEF Commendation 1992-93; Hugh D. Hildebrant Awd 1992; Amer Vacuum Soc Grant 1993; Selected by OH Acad of Sci to Participate in B-Wiser Inst 1993-94; Krecker Awrd for Sci Dept Ohio Acad of Sci, 1994; Miami Vall Cath Schl Tcher of Yr Awrd 1994; Cert of Recog Dayton's Eng & Sci Hall of Fame 1994; *office:* Carroll HS 4524 Linden Ave Dayton OH 45432

KELLER, LORI HENDERSON, 6th Grade Tchr & Cheer Coach; *b:* Washington, PA; *m:* Scott Alan; *c:* Kayla Ann; *ed:* Univ of Akron (BA) Elem Ed 1988; Post-Grad Stud; *cr:* Stow Schls Tchr, Coach 7 Yrs; *ai:* Cheer Coach; NEA, OEA 1989-; Numerous Cheer Titles, 1993 Natl Champs, 1994 State Champs; *home:* 3787 Kay Dr Stow OH 44224

KELLER, PAUL STEPHEN, Chemistry I, II & Physics Tchr; *b:* Portsmouth, OH; *m:* Susan E. Smith; *c:* Shannon, Travis, Nancy; *ed:* OH Univ (BSEd) Sci Comprehensive 1971, (MA) Ec Educ 1977; Attnd OH St Univ, Miami Univ of OH; *cr:* Clay Local Schls Sci Tchr 1971-73; Shawnee St Univ Adj Fac, Chem 1975-86; OH Univ Adj Fac, Chem 1993; Wheelersburg Local Schls Sci Tchr 1973-; *ai:* Sci Curr, Curr Integration Comms; Project NEATWORK Cmptr Facilitator; Phi Delta Kappa 1982-, Pres, Treas, Distngd Past Pres, Charter Mem; Wheelersburg Educ Assn 1973-, Pres, Sec; Wheelersburg Kiwanis Club, Pres, Treas, Distngd Past Pres; Amer Legion Post 622 1971-; Christ's Comm Church, Tchr Sunday Schl; *office:* Wheelersburg HS 701 Pirate Dr Wheelersburg OH 45694*

KELLER, PAULA, Third Grade Teacher; *b:* New York, NY; *m:* Sheldon; *c:* Douglas, Cindy Berman; *ed:* Queens Coll (BA) Ed 1954; 14 Post Grad Hrs; *cr:* Northwest Schl Tchr 1961-82; Park Ave Schl Tchr 1983-; *ai:* AFT, NSUT 1961-; *office:* Park Ave Schl Park Ave & Ireland Pl Amityville NY 11701

KELLER, ROBERT EUGENE, Physics Teacher; *b:* Lock Haven, PA; *m:* Karen Wilson; *ed:* Clarion Univ (BS) Chem 1963; Attnd PA St Univ, Geneva Coll; *cr:* Franklin HS Sci Tchr 1963-64; Moon Area HS Sci Tchr 1964-; *ai:* Odyssey of Mind Coach; Treas User Group; Co-Chair Intra-Inter Communication Comm; PSEA, NEA 1963-; MEA 1964-; Sharon Church 1974-, Deacon, Elder; *office:* Moon Area HS 904 Beaver Grade Rd Coraopolis PA 15108

KELLER, ROBERT W., 5th Grade Teacher; *b:* Mariemont, OH; *m:* Brenda L. Cox; *c:* Ryan, Rebecca; *ed:* Miama Univ OH (BS) Elem Ed 1974; Grad Stud; *cr:* Lakota Jr HS 6th Grd Tchr, Coach 1974-76; Liberty Jr HS 6th Grd Tchr, Coach 1976-80; Adena Elem Schl 5th Grd Tchr 1980-88; Freedom Elem Schl 5th Grd Tchr 1988-, Grd Level Chprsn 1988-90; *ai:* Informal Intervention Assistance Team; APPLE Pgm Instr 1996; OH Ed Assn, NEA, Lakota Ed Assn 1992-; *office:* Freedom Elem Schl 6035 Beckett Ridge Blvd West Chester OH 45069

KELLER, SANDRA, Third Grade Teacher; *b:* York, PA; *m:* P. Joseph; *c:* Joanna, Matthew, Katharine; *ed:* Millersville St Coll (BS) Elem Ed 1975, (MA) Elem Rdng 1981; *cr:* Red Lion Area Schl Dist Grd 4 Tchr 1975-81, Rdng Specialist 1981-82, Grd 3 Tchr 1982-; *ai:* PSEA, NEA 1975-; Collinsville Lib Bd 1986-, Pres; *office:* Clearview Elem Schl RD 1 Box 340 Brogue PA 17309

KELLER, SANDRA KAY, 2nd Grade Teacher; *b:* Galion, OH; *m:* Roger P.; *ed:* OH St Univ (BS) Early, Mid Chldhd Ed 1975, (MA) Ed 1982; Post Grad Work Ashland Univ; *cr:* Wilma Crall Elem Schl 4th Grd Tchr 1976-78, 2nd Grd Tchr 1978-80, 2-3 Split Grd Tchr 1980-81, 2nd Grd Tchr 1981-; *ai:* Soc Stud Graded Course of Stud, Competency Based Ed Comms; NEA, OEA, GEA 1980-; Wilma Crall PTA 1976-, Pres 1991-94, Treas 1994-; Martha Holden Jennings Scholar 1988-89; *office:* Wilma Crall Elem Schl 702 S Boston St Galion OH 44833

KELLER, SANDRA MELLOR, Kindergarten Teacher; *b:* West Orange, NJ; *m:* George W. IV; *c:* Thomas Scott, James Andrew; *ed:* Grove City Coll (BA) Elem Ed 1967; 24 Credit Hrs; *cr:* Riker Hill Elem 2nd-3rd Grd Tchr 1967-69; Potomac View Schl Kndgtn, 2nd Grd Tchr 1969-71; Scenic Hill Elem Schl Kndgtn Tchr 1985-; *ai:* NEA 1985-; *office:* Scenic Hills Elem Kndgtn Ctr 49 W Leamy Ave Springfield PA 19064

KELLER, TONY S., Mechanical Engrng Assoc Prof; *b:* Salzburg, Austria; *m:* Sally Jo Whitehead; *c:* Jeffrey, Sarah, Erin; *ed:* OR St Univ (BS) Gen Sci & Gen Engrng 1978; Univ of WA (MSE) Bioengineering 1983; Vanderbilt Univ (PHD) Mechanical Engrng 1988; Working Towards Dr of Med Sci at Univ of Gothenburg Sweden; *cr:* Veterans Admin Rsrch Biomedical Engr 1981-91; Vanderbilt Univ Rsrch Asst Prof 1988-91; Univ of VT Asst Prof 1991-95, Assoc Prof 1995-; *ai:* ASME Stu Section Fac Adv; VT Space Grant Consortium Co-Dir; Amer Soc of Biomechanics 1983-, Young Scientist Awd; Amer Soc of Mechanical Engrs 1985-; Intnl Soc for Study of Lumbar Spine 1990-, Volvo Awd; CIES Sr Fac Rsrch Awd; Outstdng Paper Pub; Tau Beta Pi; *office:* Univ Of VT & St Agri Coll Burlington VT 05405

KELLER, TRACI LYNN, Assistant Band Director; *b:* Galion, OH; *ed:* OH St Univ (BME) Music Ed 1993; Working on MA; *cr:* Lakewood Local Schls Asst Band Dir 1993-; *ai:* Assisting Pep Band; NEA, OMEA 1993-; Cntrl OH Brass Band 1992-, Librn; Dow Chemical Grant 1995; *office:* Lakewood Local Schls 5222 National Rd SE Hebron OH 43025

KELLER, WANDA DIANE, Mathematics Teacher; *b:* Johnstown, PA; *ed:* Univ of Pittsburgh (BS) Scndry Ed & Math 1971; IN Univ of PA (MED) Math 1975; *cr:* Greater Johnstown Math Tchr 1971-; *ai:* Sr Class Adv; Dist Safety Comm; NEA, PSEA 1971-; GJEA 1971-, Bldg Rep; Delta Kappa Gamma 1982-, Pres IOTA Chapter; NCTM, PCTM, MCWP 1971-; *office:* Greater Johnstown Sr HS 222 Central Ave Johnstown PA 15902

KELLER, WILLIAM EDWARD, 6th Grade Teacher; *b:* Ravenna, OH; *m:* Virginia Ann Brudapast; *ed:* Adrian Coll (BA) His, Pol Sci 1968; Kent St (BS) Elem Ed 1977, (MED) Elem Ed 1982; 6 Post-Grad Hrs Univ of Pacific; *cr:* Fairfax Elem Schl 2nd-3rd Tchr 1977-79; Bellflower Elem Schl 2nd-3rd, 5th-6th Grd Tchr 1979-; *ai:* Playground Supvr; ESP Facilitator Problem Stu Prgm; Math Tutor; MTA 1977-, Elem Co-Chm; OES 1977-, St Del; NEA; VFW 1986-; Lake Cty Historical Soc 1984-, Bd Dirs; WKYC TV-3 Tchng Awd 1990; *office:* Bellflower Elem Schl 6655 Reynolds Rd Mentor OH 44060

KELLEY, CAROLYN GETZ, Guidance Counselor; *b:* Cleveland, OH; *m:* Timothy; *ed:* Denison Univ (OH) Psych 1987; Boston Coll (MA) Cnslng, Psych 1993; 12 Credit Hrs Self-Esteem, Reality Therapy, Disciplining with Dignity, Projective Tests, Individial Testing; *cr:* St Street Bank Fund Accountant 1987-88; Stonehill Coll Admissions Cnslr 1988-91; One With One Tchr, Cnslr ESL Prgm 1992; Boston Coll Grad Admissions, Assistantship 1991-92; Higher Ed Information Ctr Cnslr 1993-; Medway HS Guid Cnslr 1993-; *ai:* Adv Peer Cnslng, Stu Alliance Cultural Awareness; MA Schl Cnsl Assn 1992-; New England Assn Coll Admissions Cnslrs 1989-, Panel Presenter 1990 Conf; MA Peer Helpers Assn 1993-, Bd Mem 1993-95, Conf Chair 1995 Conf; MTA 1993-; *office:* Medway HS 45 Holliston St Medway MA 02053

KELLEY, CHARLOTTE FOWLE, Fifth Grade Teacher; *b:* Wilton, NH; *m:* John Arnold Jr.; *c:* Jill Brown; *ed:* Plymouth St (BED) K-8 Elem 1954; Antioch Univ of New England (MED) Ed 1988; 40 Credits Cooperative Learning, Reality Therapy, Sci in Elem, Behaviors Modification, Tchng Tdng; *cr:* Dr. H. O. Smith Elem Schl First Grd Tchr 1954-57; Ft Devens Elem Schl First Grd Tchr 1957-64; Sutton Elem Schl First, Second Grd Tchr 1968-71; Simonds Elem Schl Fifth Grd Team Ldr 1975-76, Fourth Grd Tchr 1976-77, Fifth Grd Tchr 1977-; *ai:* Soc Stud Curr Comm 1993-; Mindstretch Steering Comm 1990-; Soc Stud Curr R-8th Grd Comm 1967-68; Math Curr R-8th Grd Comm 1976-77; Soc Stud Curr R-8th Grd 1986-91; Soc Stud Curr E-8th Grd Comm 1993-; NHEA, NEA 1954-; Riverbend Rdng Cncl 1989-; KREA Tchrs Assn 1966-, Salary Negotiation Comm 1966-67; Brownies 1954-56, Ldr; Cub Scout 1976-77, Ldr; Zoning Bd of Adjustment 1986-, Bd Mem; Warner Historical Soc 1995-, Exec Bd; *home:* PO Box 245 Kearsarge Mt Rd Warner NH 03278*

KELLEY, CORNELIA A., Assistant Head Master; *b:* Boston, MA; *m:* Luco J. LaCambria; *ed:* Newton Coll the Sacred Heart (BA) Eng 1969; Boston St Coll (MED) eng, Sec Ed 1970, (CAGS) ED Admin 1975; Attnd New England Classics Inst; Boston Univ Ldrshp Acad; *cr:* Brighton HS Eng Tchr 1971-80; Boston Laton Schl Eng, Classics Tchr 1980-87, Asst Head Master 1987-; *ai:* NASSP, ASCD, BASAS 1987-; Phi Delta Kappa 1980-, Historian; Alumni Assn 1987-; Coll Bd 1994-, Del; Notre Dame Acad; New England Assn Schl, Colls Visitng Comms Chair; Class of 1944 Honorary Mem; Boston Univ Flwshp; *office:* Boston Latin Schl 78 Avenue Louis Pasteur Boston MA 02115

KELLEY, EMILY ROORBACH, Science Teacher; *b:* Providence, RI; *m:* Randy L.; *c:* Elizabeth, Anne; *ed:* Northwestern Univ (BS) PE 1981; Plymouth St Coll (MED) Admin 1991; *cr:* Holderness Schl Ath Trainer, Tutor 1985-90; Holderness Cntrl Schl Sci Tchr 1982-; *ai:* Grd 8 Adv; Team Ldr 6-8 Grd; NH Assn Mid Level Ed 1993-, Dir; NELMS 1991-, Mid Level Curr, Recognition Prgm; NSTA, NEA 1986-; Phi Delta Kappa 1991-; NH St Cncl Arts, Film Commission Videography Awd; Article Pub; *office:* Holderness Central Elem Schl RR 3 Box 95 Plymouth NH 03264*

KELLEY, FRANK J., Science Specialist & Team Ldr; *b:* Norwood, MA; *ed:* Univ of MA at Amherst (BS) Enviro Sci 1984; Working on MED Univ of NH; *cr:* Kingswood Regnl MS Edctr 1986-; Johns Hopkins Univ Forest Ecology Instr 1993-; Univ of NH Prgm Asst 1994-; *ai:* Odyssey of Mind Coach; Drama Asst; NH Sci Tchrs Assn 1986-; Lakes Region Conservation Trust 1995-; Calu Winnepesankee Watershed Project, Lakes Region Planning Commission 1995-; TAPESTRY Grant 1995; Conservation Tchr of Yr 1992; Project Wild, Learning Tree Facilitator 1987-; *office:* Kingswood Regnl MS 404 S Main St Wolfeboro NH 03894*

KELLEY, GLORIA JEAN SMITH, Music Teacher; *b:* New York, NY; *m:* Donald M.; *c:* Natasha Love, D'onna Monique; *ed:* William Penn Coll (BA) Music Ed 1980; *cr:* Dr. Charles R. Drew Acads Music Tchr 15 Yrs; *ai:* Gospel Choir; Schl Improvement Comm; Peer Mediation; AFT, UFT 1981-; MENC 1985-; NYSSMA 1983-; Girl Scouts of Amer 1986-, Ldr; *office:* Dr. Charles R. Drew Acads 3630 3rd Ave Bronx NY 10456

KELLEY, JOSEPH GERARD, English & History Teacher; *b:* Boston, MA; *m:* Melanie A.; *c:* Sarah; *ed:* Boston Coll (BA) Eng 1967; Boston Univ (EDM) Ed 1973, (EDD) Ed 1976; *cr:* Malden Cath HS Eng, His Tchr 1967-71; Danvers HS Eng Tchr 1971-72; Action Bokbordogh Jr HS Eng Tchr 1974-75; Diamond Jr HS Eng Tchr 1975-80; Lexington HS Eng, His Tchr 1980-; *ai:* NEA 1975-; MA Tchr of Yr 1982; *office:* Lexington HS 251 Waltham St Lexington MA 02173

KELLEY, JUDITH ANNE, Chemistry Professor; *b:* Boston, MA; *m:* Philip Clark Johnson; *c:* Hope Amory Johnson Weinman, Elizabeth Waitstill Johnson; *ed:* Emmanuel Coll (AB) Chem 1963; Lowell Technological Inst (MS) Chem 1977; Northeastern Univ (MED) Cnslng 1975, (DED) Higher Ed, Admin 1984; Visiting Scholar Lesley Coll Prgm Evaluation & Rsrch Group, Sabbatical 1987-88; *cr:* U Mass Lowell Full Prof Instr 1966-; Consult, Sci Ed Evaluation 1987-; *ai:* Telecommunications Cncl for Improving Tchng & Learning K-12 Acts Coord; Manage Idea; NEACT 1970-, Cntrl Division Chair, Journal Ed; STARS 1986-, Pres; NSTA; ACS; AAAS; MAST; MASS; Indstrl His Ctr Educl Advy Bd 1990-; NSF Grants; NEH Grant; MA Hall of Fame for Sci Edctrs 1994; *office:* Univ Of MA At Lowell 1 University Ave Lowell MA 01854*

KELLEY, KAREN M., 6th Grade Teacher; *b:* Rochester, NY; *m:* Larry; *c:* Kevin, Timothy; *ed:* St Univ at Potsdam (BA) Ed K-6, Eng 7-9 1969, (MS) Ed 1972; Courses in Whole Lang & Spec Ed Topics; *cr:* Chateaugay Cntrl Schl 3-6 Grd Tchr 1970-73, K-12 Grd Sub Tchr 1974-76; Newark Vly Cntrl Schls K-12 Grd Sub Tchr 1976-78; York Cntrl Schl 6 Grd Tchr 1978-; *ai:* Grd Level Chprsn; K-12 Lang Arts Curr Comm; NYSUT; York Tchrs Assn 1979-; St Mary's Church 1979-, Comms.

KELLEY, LYNNE DHIONIS, Chinese Biling & ESL Teacher; *b:* Newton, MA; *m:* Richard G.; *ed:* Boston Univ (BS) Elem Ed 1969; Grad Stud Linguistics Harvard Univ; Grad Stud Haitian Creole IN Univ; Grad Stud TESOL Boston Univ; Grad Stud Biling, Bicultural Ed Lesley Coll; *cr:* Webster Schl Greek Biling ESL Tchr, Curr Dev 1970-78; Graham & Parks Schl Haitian Biling ESL Tchr, Curr Dev 1978-84; M. L. King Schl Korean Biling ESL Tchr, Curr Dev 1984-90, Chinese Biling ESL Tchr 1990-; *ai:* Tchr in Charge; Coord Chinese Biling Multicultural, Schl Multicultural Comms; MA Tchrs Assn, TESOL, NEA 1970-; Coastal Coalition Friends of Scituate NEARO; Grad Flwshp IN Univ Inst Haitian Creole Biling Tchrs; *home:* 10 Orchard Rd Scituate MA 02066

KELLEY, MARY ELIZABETH, English Teacher; *b:* New York Cit *m:* James J.; *c:* James, Christopher; *ed:* Cabrini Coll (BA) Eng 1968 of CT (MA) Scndry Ed 1996; Addl Hrs RI Coll, Univ of RI; *cr:* Co MS Eng Tchr 1984-86; Coventry HS Eng Tchr 1986-; *ai:* Future Comm; NCTE, AFT, RI Cncl of Tchrs of Eng 1984; PTSA 1978-, *office:* Coventry HS 40 Reservoir Rd Coventry RI 02816

KELLEY, MICHAEL JOHN, Language Arts Teacher; *b:* Rutland, V Kim P.; *c:* Devin, Spencer, Alora; *ed:* Univ of VT (BA) His 1979; Cas St Coll (MED) Curr, Instruction 1986; Pacific Inst of Commercial Ar 1981; Account Exec Dev Prog PIA Grad 1981; *cr:* West Rutland HS Grds Eng, Soc Stud Tchr 1984-90; Otter Vly Union HS 7-12 Grds En STud Tchr 1990-; *ai:* Yrbk Adv; Spokesman for Tchrs Union Negot Comm; Schl Climat Comm for Pub Schl Approval; NEASC; NEA VP; Educl Fair Past Chm; Brandon Historical Soc Silver Lake C *office:* Otter Valley Union HS Rt 7 Brandon VT 05733

KELLEY, PATRICIA L., Health & Physical Ed Teacher; *b:* DeLan *c:* Cheri Matincheck, Kendra Seprish, Koreen Bernal; *ed:* PA St (BS) PE 1966; 40 Addl Post Grad Credit Hrs; *cr:* Lower Dauphin Schl Dist PE Tchr 1966-67; Cntrl Dauphin Schl Dist Hlth, PE Tchr 1967-68; Branch Area Schl Dist Hlth, PE Tchr 1969-; *ai:* Head Vlybl Coach; PSEA 1969-; Miffli Cty Search & Rescue Unit 1991-; *office:* West B Area HS Rd 2 Box 194 Morrisdale PA 16858

KELLEY, PETER E., Math Department Chair; *b:* Abington, P Elizabeth Berry Eaton; *c:* Caroline, Matthew; *ed:* Princeton Univ Chem Engrng 1978; *cr:* St Albans Schl Math Tchr 1983-; *ai:* It's Team; Math Team; Sakripisyo; Mathematical Assn of Amer 1995-; Edith May Stiffe Awd 1995; *office:* St Albans Schl Mt St Alban Washi DC 20016

KELLEY, RANDY LEE, Fourth Grade Teacher; *b:* Ironton, OH; *e* Univ (BS) Soc Stud 1974; 5th Yr Elem Ed 1975; *cr:* Lawrence Cty Sub Tchr 1974-76; Ironton City Schl Dist Sub Tchr 1974-76; Rock Elem #2 Schl Tchr 1976-; *ai:* NEA, OEA 1976-; RHEA 1976-, Tre yrs; *office:* Rock Hill Elem Schl #2 4824 St Rt 141 Ironton OH 4563

KELLEY, TERRI, French Teacher; *b:* Lawrence, MA; *m:* George D *ed:* Emmanuel Coll (BA) 1961; Boston Coll Grad Schl (MA) Fr, Ru LeVeille Virtuoso Schl Advanced Diploma Classical Piano 1990; Ur Savoie at Annecy Grad Cert 1982; *cr:* Boston Pub Schls Tchr 19 Lawrence HS Tchr 1962-; *ai:* AFT, Lawrence Tchrs Union, MFT Psychological Ctr 1969-88; *office:* Lawrence HS 233 Haverh Lawrence MA 01840*

KELLEY, WILLIAM DAVID,JR., Seventh Grade Soc Studies Tc Philadelphia, PA; *ed:* Temple Univ (BS) Soc Sci, Ed 1968, (MS) So Ed 1978; *cr:* First Presbyn Church Music Dir 1964-68; Musical Fun of Philadelphia Music Comm 1970-; Cntrl Presbyn Church Musi 1968-81; St Luke Luth Church Music Dir 1981-86; St Thomas of Vill Univ 1989-95; Crystal Cathedral Music Ministry Outreach 1989-9 Stu Cncl, Comm Outreach Moderator; Spring Show Producer; Home Parent Org; Musical Fund Soc of Phildelphia 1970-, Chm Natl Competition; Philadelpia Art Alliance 1970-; Christ Church Philade 1970, Music Comm; PA Glee Club 1985, Honorary Mem; Union Le Philadelphia 1979-85; George Washington Freedom Medal Phoenixville Jaycees Comm Svc Awd 1985; Dogwood Parade C Marshall 1994; CBS WCAV-TV Spirit of Philadelphi Awd 1984; Out Tchrs in Elem, Scndry Schls 1976; *office:* Phoenixville Area MS 1 Main St Phoenixville PA 19460

KELLEY, WILLIAM MICHAEL, Mathematics Teacher; *b:* F Frederick, MD; *ed:* St Marys Coll of MD (BA) Math 1994; Grad o Governors Acad for Math & Sci Instrs 1995; *cr:* Northern HS Geon Algebra Instr 1994-; *ai:* After Math Club; MultiCultural Comm; Review Bd; MD Stu assistance Prgm; Head Coach Girls Track & NCTM 1994-; *office:* Northern HS 2750 Chaneyville Rd Owings 20736

KELLIER, SHIRLEY GLORIA, Physical Education Teache Montego Bay, Jamaica, WI; *c:* Sherard; *ed:* Long Island Univ (BS 1980, (MS) Adaptive PE 1981; Addl 30 Credits Post Grad Stu Therapy; *cr:* Shields Inst Ctr Recreation Therapist 2 Yrs; Boys & Gir PE Tchr 2 Yrs; Springfield Gardens HS PE Tchr 10 Yrs; *ai:* NYC Pub Ath League; Girls Var Sftbl, Jr Var Vlybl, Bsktbl Coach; NY Chrstn Ctr 1991-; NY Coaches Assn 1986-, Merits, Achvmts 1986; NY As Hlth, PE, Recreaton, Dance; United Cerebral Palsy 1981-, Merit; *o* Springfield Gardens HS 143-10 Springfield Blvd Jamaica NY 11413

KELLIHER, JANET SANFORD, Sixth Grade Teacher; *b:* Winch MA; *m:* Joseph Douglas Sr.; *c:* John Laurence, Joseph Douglas Jr.; Joseph's Coll (BA) Elem Ed 1967; Antioch-New England Coll (1990; Conf Character Ed; Integrated Lang Arts Writing Process; *cr:* Vine Street Schl Tchr 1967-68; Wilkins Elem Schl Tchr 196 Bicentennial Elem Schl Sixth Grd Tchr 1975-; *ai:* Discipline, W Portfolio, Lang Arts, St of NH Assessment Comms; Writing Coach; M Prgm; AFT 1975-, Bldg Rep; Alpha Delta Kappa 1994-; Nashua Jr W 1978-, Treas; St Patrick's Adv 1990-, Minister; Tchr of Yr; Writing P Grant; Poem Pub; *office:* Bicentennial Elem Schl 296 E Dunstab Nashua NH 03062

KELLIHER, THOMAS P., Computer Science Professor; *b:* West Ch PA; *ed:* Johns Hopkins (BES) Electrical Eng & Comp Sci 1983; Pe (PHD) Comp Sci 1993; *cr:* Burroughs Engr 1983-86; *ai:* UPE Adv; 1983-; ACM 1984-; Numerous Articles Pub; *office:* Westminster Coll Wilmington PA 16172

KELLNER, LINDA ZUCKERMAN, Spanish Teacher; *b:* Brooklyn *m:* Lesle G.; *c:* Rick, Greg; *ed:* SUC Oneonta (BS) Span, Scndry Ed Adelphi Univ (MA) Span 1978; Attnd Instituto Internacional de Ma *cr:* Baldwin HS Span Tchr 1976-77; Naseau Cty Soc Svcs Bilingua Welfare Examiner 1977-78; Baldwin HS Span Tchr 1978-79, 1988- Sportsnite IM Night Adv, Coord; Class of 94 Adv; Frgn Lang Hnr Soc Ethnic Sharing Comm; Span Book Comm; Stud Skills Mentor; New Mentor; Stu in Jeopardy Men; Spain Trips Chaperone; AATSP, NYS NYSUT 1988-; Temple Avodah 1984-, VP, Ed Temple Topics; 9th Conversation Inhouse Curr; *office:* Baldwin HS 841 High Schoo Baldwin NY 11510*

KELLNER, VERONICA MARIE, English Teacher; *b:* Queens, N Elisabeth, William; *ed:* St Joseph's Coll (BA) Eng 1986; Dowling (MS) Ed 1990; Addl 18 Hrs Admin Courses C. W. Post; *cr:* West Ba HS Leave Replacement 1986; William Floyd HS Leave Replacement Ctr Moriches HS Tchr 1986-; *ai:* Sr Class, Stu Cncl Adv; Ctr Moncre 1987-, Sec; NCTE 1986-; *office:* Ctr Moriches HS 311 Frowein Rd C Moriches NY 11934

KELLO, ROSEANN MARIE, Elementary Vocal Music Teache Binghamton, NY; *ed:* West Chester Univ (BS) Music Ed, Voice 1981, (Music Ed, Orff Concentration 1986; *cr:* Hempfield Schl Dist Elem Music Tchr 1981-82; Conestoga Vly Schl Dist Elem Vocal Music 1982-83; Kennett Consolidated Schl Dist Elem Vocal Music Tchr 1 West Chester Univ Cooperating Tchr 1985-; PA Governor's Schl for T Fac Mentor 1990-93; *ai:* Select Vocal Ensemble; HS Musical Mak NEA, PSEA, KEA, MENC, PMEA, Amer Orff Schulwerk Assn, PA Org of Amer Kodaly Ed 1981-; Kennett Symphony Orch Bd 1 Publicity Dir; Our Lady of the Assumption Choir 1990-, Soloist; Sts ul Choir 1979-, Dir; YMCA 1988-; Top 10 Finalist PA Tchr of Yr; Distngd Alumnus; Sing Natl Anthem at Phillies Game; Bridging the Chester Cty IU Participant; PSEA House of Delegates Soloist; *office:* D Lang Elem Schl Center & Mulberry Sts Kennett Square PA 19348*

LOGG, STEPHEN, Asst Professor of Business Law; *b:* Buffalo, NY; arolyn Karcher; *c:* Stephen Jr., Loren L., Carolyn B., Justin K.; *ed:* ty Coll (BA) Econ 1961; SUNY At Buffalo (MD) Law-Magna Cum e- 1966; US Court of Appeals Law Clerk, Chief Judge Lumbard -67; Davis Polk & Wardwell Assoc 1967-68; Hodgson Russ AW&G er 1968-84; SUNY Coll at Fredonia Asst Prof 1984-89; SUNY At alo Asst Prof of Bus Law 1989-; *ai:* ED-in-chief Buffalo Law Review; : 55 Windsor Ave Buffalo NY 14209

LOW, GLENDA PHILLIPS, Hlth & Physical Education Tchr; *b:* Stroudsburg, PA; *ed:* Lock Haven St Coll (BS) Hlth & PE 1981; es Coll 36 Grad Credits-Masters Equiv; *cr:* Nazareth Jr HS 7th-9th PE Tchr 1982-83; Lower Nazareth Elem Schl & Bushkill Elem Schl n Grd PE Tchr 1983-84; Easton Area HS 10th-12th Grd Hlth & PE Tchr -; Peer Assistance; *ai:* HS Coord Stu Assistance Prgm; PTSA Tchr on; Peer Assistance Prgm Adv; PA St Assn Hlth, PE, Rec & Dance -; PTSA 1981-, Tchr Rep, Pres Honor; NEA & PSEA 1981-; NALSAP -; Alert Partnership for a Drug-Free LeHigh Valley 1994, Schl Action m; Natl Assn for Peer Helpers 1993-; PA Dept of Ed Comm Svc Awd; : 2183 Lake Minsi Dr Bangor PA 18013

LY, ANN, Philosophy Professor; *b:* Cleveland, OH; *ed:* Ursuline Coll His 1955; Univ of Notre Dame (MA) Philosophy 1959, (PHD) sophy 1962; Attnd Cath Univ of Amer, La Salle Coll, Villanova Univ, Carroll Univ; *cr:* Ascension Grammar Schl Third Grd Tchr 1951-52; ed Heart Acad HS His Tchr 1955-56; Ursuline Coll Philosophy Instr -66, Acad VP 1966-73, Prof, Chair Philosophy 1973-; *ai:* Acad ding; Amer Assn Phil Tchrs 1980-; Amer Cath Phil Assn 1966-; Inst of Ethics & Life Sci 1976-; Rel Congregation 1952-, Chair; OH Regents sp; YMCA Women of Prof Excl Awd 1991; Harvard, MIT Awd 1985; Grants Coll Fac Seminar Univ of MD 1980, Univ of AZ 1974; *office:* line Coll 2550 Lander Rd Pepper Pike OH 44124*

LY, ANNA M., Sixth Grade Teacher; *b:* Cincinnati, OH; *m:* David P.; ichael C.; *ed:* Univ of Cincinnati (BS) Elem Ed 1989; 15 Hrs in Grad , Lib & Media Specialist Prgm at Wright St Univ; *cr:* Saint Therese ird Tchr 1990-93; Little Flower Schl 6th-8th Grd Tchr 1993-; *ai:* Stu Adv; Environmental & Cmptr Clubs; Tech Planning Comm Mem; 4th Vlybl Team Coach; Cincinnati Zoo 1988-, Vol; Ashland Tchr Achvmt Nom 1992-93 & 1993-94; Ashland Golden Apple Awd 1994-95; er Cable Tchr Achvmt Awd 1994; Time Warner Crystal Apple Awd ; C-Span Equipment Grant 1994; Learning Links Grant 1995-; *office:* Flower Schl 5555 Little Flower Ave Cincinnati OH 45239

LY, BARBARA E., Assistant Principal; *b:* Newark, NJ; *m:* William; my, William, Melinda; *ed:* Temple Univ (BS) Elem Ed 1980; Beaver (MED) Ed 1996; Cert Environmental Ed; *cr:* St Stanislaus Schl 3rd Tchr 1980-86, 6th Grd Tchr 1986-87, 7th Grd Tchr 1987-93, Acting 1993-94, Asst Prin 1994-; *ai:* NCEA; NSTA; Philadelphia diocese Distngd Cath Edctr 1989; *office:* St Stanislaus Schl 493 E St Lansdale PA 19446

LY, BARBARA POND, Business Education Chairperson; *b:* dhaven, NY; *m:* Joseph M. Campagna; *c:* Donald, Mary Sohm, James; St John's Univ (BS) Curr, Tchng 1968, (MS) Scndry Ed 1971; C. W. (SAS) 1991; 15 Hrs Admin; 9 Hrs Admin Brooklyn; 9 Hrs Guidance hn's Univ; Advanced Mastery Supervision UCLA Madeline Hunter; t John's Univ Adjunct Instr 1969-70; G. W. Hewlett HS Bus Ed Tchr -, Tchr Coach 1989-91, Bus Ed Chprsn 1991-; *ai:* Bus Advy Bd der; Bus Comm Alliance Sec; Dist Tech Comm; Dist Crisis vention Team; HWASA 1991-; Long Island Bus Ed Chprsns 1989-; Advy Bd 1989-, Chprsn; Amer Assn of Univ Women, World Ship Soc, n Ship His Soc of Amer; MS Soc Fund Raising Awds; *home:* 10 dow Ln Rockville Centre NY 11570*

LY, BARBARA WILSON, Basic Skills Teacher; *b:* Atlantic City, NJ; William L.; *c:* Alexa W.; *ed:* Glassboro St Coll (BA) Elem Ed 1984; *cr:* econ Pub Schls Basic Skills & Comp Tchr 1984-86, Basic Skills Tchr -87, 1994-, 4th Grd Tchr 1987-93; *ai:* NJEA 1984-; NEA 1984-; *e:* H A Marsh Elem Schl Irelan Ave Absecon NJ 08201

LY, BARRY NIEL, Science Teacher; *b:* York, PA; *m:* Barbara J. net; *c:* David, Beth, Amy; *ed:* Shippensburg Univ (BS) Elem Ed 1969; ern MD (MS) Ed Admin 1992; *cr:* Spring Grove Tchr 1971-; *ai:* Boys k Asst Coach 1983-84; Boys Track Head Coach 1985-93; Girls Track l Coach 1993-95; NEA 1971-; SGEA 1971-, Pres; Phi Delta Kappa -; *office:* Spring Grove Area Schl Dist 220 W Jackson St Spring Grove 7362

LY, BRIAN JOSEPH,JR., Assistant Professor; *b:* Rome, NY; *ed:* St of NY Coll of Ag & Tech at Morrisville (AAS) Design & Drafting ; Univ at Buffalo (BPS) Arch 1984, (MARCH) Arch 1986; *cr:* Clark k Millis & Gilson Project Architect, Intern 1986-90; El Clark Assoc VP 1990-91; El Assoc Staff Architect 1991-92; Hueber, Hares, Glavin itects Staff Architect 1992; Brian Joseph Kelly Jr. Architect Architect -; SUNY at Morrisville Asst Prof 1993-; *ai:* Arch Club Adv; St Ann's ch Art Auction, MS 150 Bike Tour, Handicap Accessibility Comms; ndaga Cycling Club; Cntrl NY Amer Inst of Architects 1986-, Prgm NYS Assn of Architects 1986-; Onondaga Cycling Club 1991-, Art CNY Multiple Sclerosis Soc MS 150 Tour 1988-, Bd Mem, MS Bike Awd 1991-92; Registered Architect; Natl Cncl Architectural stration Bd; *office:* S U N Y Coll Of A & T Morrisvl Morrisville NY 8

LY, CHARLES, Social Science Instructor; *b:* Waterbury, CT; *m:* nor Martin-Kelly; *ed:* Cntrl CT St Univ (BS) Ed 1976; Southern CT St (MS) Sociology 1979, (MS) Urban Stud 1982; Univ of New Haven A) Mgmt 1988; Cntrl CT St Uni (MA) Psych 1995; Working on ers in Soc Work; *cr:* CT Bus Inst Instr 1982-86; Teikyo Post Univ Soc Instr 1987-; *ai:* NASW 1995-; APA 1988-; CT Cert Bd 1994-; *office:* yo Post Univ 800 Country Club Rd Waterbury CT 06723

LY, CHRISTINA SHAVER, Spanish Teacher; *b:* Schenectady, NY; ohn C.; *c:* Kathleen, Bridget, Fiona, Ann; *ed:* Univ of Rochester (BA) & Span 1972; St Univ of NY at Oneonta-Cooperstown Grad Prgm) His Museum Stud 1981; St Univ of NY at Albany Grad Ed Courses ; Russell Sage Coll Span Courses 1989; *cr:* Glens Falls Historical Curator 1974-75; Rensselaer Cty Historical Soc Curator 1975-77; bridge HS Span & Soc Stud Tchr 1990-91; Hoosic Valley HS Span 1992-; *ai:* Lang Club Adv; Odyssey of Mind Coach; Curr & Alternate eduling Comms; NEA 1990-; NYSFLT 1992-; Rensselaer Cty orical Soc 1975-; Melrose Food Cooperative 1980-, Treas; Bedford ey Homemakers 1980-, Pres, VP & Sec; Town of Schaghticoke 1986-, n Historian; *office:* Hoosic Valley Central HS Rt 67 Schaghticoke NY 54

LY, CHRISTOPHER MICHAEL, Principal; *b:* Washington, DC; *m:* h Lucy Beyer; *c:* Brendan; *ed:* Univ of VA (BA) Sociology 1983; king Toward MA in Educl Admin Cath univ; *cr:* Our Lady of Lourdes After Care Tchr 1987-88; St Thomas More Schl Tchr 1988-89; umption Schl Tchr 1989-94, Prin 1994-; *ai:* Tchr Svc Corps Advy Bd; A 1988-; ASCD 1991-; Outstdng Tchr Awd 1989, 1991-92; *office:* umption Cath Schl 220 Highview Pl SE Washington DC 20032

KELLY, DAVID HARVEY, Professor of History; *b:* Chicago, IL; *m:* Ruth Rielly; *c:* Jennifer Paradise, Elizabeth Paradise; *ed:* Univ of Chicago (BA) Amer, Eu His 1965; IN Univ (MA) Modern His 1968, (PHD) Modern His 1976; *cr:* Univ of WI Rsrch Assoc 1970-74; Rochester Inst of Tech Adj Instr 1974-75; D'Youville Coll Inst Prof 1975-; *ai:* Org Amer His, AMer His Assn 1970-; AAUP 1975-, Pres Local; Buffalo Cncl World Affairs 1993-, Bd Dirs; Fac Mem of Yr 1995; AAUP Schls Awd 1995; Author, Co-Author, Ed Seven Books, Five Monographs, Five Articles; *office:* D'Youville Coll 320 Porter Ave Buffalo NY 14201

KELLY, DIRK THOMAS, USI & World History Teacher; *b:* Orange, NJ; *m:* Jacqueline LaVelle; *c:* Thomas, Steven; *ed:* Fairleigh Dickinson Univ (BA) His 1986; Rutgers Univ Tchng Cert Ed 1988; *cr:* Newton HS Soc Stud Tchr, Coach 1988-; *ai:* Boys Bsktbl Coach; Class of 1997 Adv; NEA 1988-; Coach of Yr Boy's Bsktbl NJ Herald, West Jersey Star Ledger1994-95; *office:* Newton HS 44 Ryerson Ave Newton NJ 07860

KELLY, GINA POYLE, Kindergarten & First Grd Tchr; *b:* Elyria, OH; *m:* Mike; *ed:* OH St Univ (BS) Elem Ed 1987; Ashland Univ (MS) Curr, Instruction 1991; Attnd Ashland Univ, Drake Univ, Bowling Green St Univ; *cr:* Hawthorne Schl K-1st Grd Tchr 1987-95; Longfellow Schl K-1 Grd Tchr 1996; *ai:* Avon HS Vlybl, Bsktbl, Elyria Cath HS Head Bsktbl, Jr HS Bsktbl, Track Coach; CYO Vlybl Ofcl; Assigning Sec; Big Bro; LEA, NEA, OEA 1987-; CYO 1980-, Ofcl.

KELLY, H. TODD, English Teacher; *ed:* Albright Coll (AB) Eng 1985; Kutztown Univ (MA) Eng 1991; *cr:* Muhlenberg HS Eng Tchr 1985-86; Pottsgrove HS Eng Tchr 1986-; *ai:* Drama Dir; Speech Coach; NEA; Limelight Productions 1981-, Pres; *office:* Pottsgrove HS 1345 Kauffman Rd Pottstown PA 19464

KELLY, JAMES MICHAEL, Retired Business Teacher; *b:* Nyack, NY; *ed:* SUNY at Albany (BS) Bus Ed 1961, (MS) Guidance 1962; Addl 45 Credit Hrs in Bus Ed; *cr:* Dover Jr Sr High Bus Tchr 1962-95; *ai:* NHS Adv; Dover/Wingdale Tchrs Assn 1962-; AFT 1967-; EBEA 1961-; Lions 1981-; Knights of Columbus 1965-.

KELLY, JAMES P., Comm Art & Science Trng Instr; *b:* Montclair, NJ; *m:* Mary Ann; *ed:* Montclair NJ Univ (BA) Broadcast, Comms 1981; Attnd Seton Hall Univ; *cr:* Parsipanny Hills HS Maternity Leave Sub Tchr, Jrnlsm Instr 1987-89; Montville-Lazar MS 6th Grd Sci, Rdng, Tchr of GATE, Media Production 1989-91; Clifton HS Comm Art & Sci Trng Instr 1991-; *ai:* Head Ftbl Coach; Television Production Dir; NEA, NJEA 1988-; CTA 1991-; Passaic Cty Audio Visual Assn, Passaic Cty Coaches Assn, NJ Ftbl Coaching Assn 1991-; Aerho Broadcasting Hnr Soc; Nom Ed of Yr 1990; NJEA Tchr Recognition 1991-93; NJ Teen Arts Festival; Svc Awd Success Prgm 1991-93; Svc Awd Appreciation Media Coverage DECA Chptr 1991-95; *office:* Clifton H S 333 Colfax Ave Clifton NJ 07013

KELLY, KENNETH, Social Studies Teacher; *b:* Queens, NY; *ed:* Nassau Comm Coll (AA) Lbrl Arts 1978; Adelphi Univ (BA) His 1981; Queens Coll (MS) Scndry Ed 1991; *cr:* Pvt Schl Soc Stud Tchr, Dean 1982-91; Harry S. Truman HS Soc Stud Tchr 1991-92; F. K. Lane HS Soc Stud Tchr 1992-; *ai:* His Club Adv; RCT Preparation Instr; AFT, UFT 1991-; *office:* F. K. Lane HS 999 Jamaica Ave Brooklyn NY 11208*

KELLY, KEVIN A., Mathematics Teacher; *b:* Montclair, NJ; *ed:* Rutgers Coll (BA) Math, Comp Sci 1990; MIT (MS) Math 1993; Harvard Univ (MED) Tchng & Learning 1994; *cr:* MIT NDSEG Fellow 1990-93; Harvard Grad Schl of Ed Rsrch Asst 1994-; Lexington HS Math Tchr 1994-; *ai:* Schedule Comm Chair; Fac Steering Comm; Instrl Cncl; MAA 1986-; NCTM 1993-; NEA, MTA, LEA 1994-; Writer, Ed Harvard Assessment Task Archive; New Stans Project Consultant; Modern Geometry Project Dir.

KELLY, LAURA, Eng as Second Language Teacher; *b:* Brooklyn, NY; *m:* Joseph William Mc Gee; *c:* Ciaran Edward Mc Gee; *ed:* Working Toward MS in TESOL at Fordham Univ; 30 Addl Credit Hrs; *cr:* E B Shallow 227 Intermediate Schl, Tchr 1987-; *ai:* Portfolio Dev for HS Art Applicants; Project Install Grant; *office:* E B Shallow Intermediate Schl 6500 16th Ave Brooklyn NY 11204

KELLY, LEO J., Educational Coordinator; *b:* Hartford, CT; *m:* Linda C.; *c:* Kristen L., Paul T.; *ed:* Central CT St Univ (BA) Bio, Chem 1970; Quinnipiac Coll (BS) Pathologist Asst 1973, (MHS) Pathologist Asst 1976; *cr:* VA Med Ctr Ed Coord 1973-; *ai:* VA Med Ctr Tumor Bd, Cancer Comm; AAPA 1973-, Pres; CSH 1976-, Treas; NSH 1980-, Ed Resource Chm; Sportmens Club 1994-; Meritorious Svc Awd Hlth Care Prof 1990; Rosemary & Donald Ostermeier Meml Awd 1992; *office:* Quinnipiac Coll Mount Carmel Avenue Hamden CT 06518

KELLY, LORRAINE TOMPKINS, French Teacher; *b:* Philadelphia, PA; *m:* Lawrence A.; *c:* Megan, John; *ed:* St Louis Univ (BA) Fr, Eng 1968; Antioch New Eng Grad Schl (MED) 1996; Post Grad Stud Dartmouth Coll, Paris, St Malo, Avignon; *cr:* Cambridge HS, Latin Schl Fr Tchr 1968-70; Hanover St Schl Third Grd Tchr 1972-78; Marion Cross Schl Fr Tchr 1981-; *ai:* VT Foreign Lang Assn 1985-; NEA 1991-; Norwich Tchrs Assn; Norwich Shared Housing Comm 1993-; United Way of Upper Valley 1979-88, Nominating Comm Chair; *office:* Marion Cross Elem Schl Main St Norwich VT 05055*

KELLY, MARTHA JEAN, Science Teacher; *b:* Ashland, KY; *c:* Victoria, Rachel; *ed:* Morehead St Univ (MS) Sci Scndry Ed 1981; Various Sci Grad Credit Hrs; *cr:* West Carter HS Sci Tchr 1973-85; Arcanum HS Sci Tchr 1986-; *ai:* Sci Dept Chprsn; SADD Adv; Tchrs Assn VP; Negotiations Comm; OEA, WOEA & SECO 1986-; Order of Eastern Star 1970-; Sweet Adelines 1975-; 4-H Adv 1990-; PTO 1986-, Talent Show Coord; *office:* Arcanum HS 310 N Main St Arcanum OH 45304

KELLY, MARY DIANE (BRUNO), Secondary Math Teacher; *b:* Carbondale, PA; *m:* James Paul; *c:* Alex, Barbara, Jeffrey; *ed:* Marywood Coll (BA) Math 1965, (MS) Math 1973; *cr:* Waymart HS Scndry Math Tchr 1965-68; Benjamin Franklin Jr HS Math Tchr 1968-69; Carbondale Area Jr Sr HS Math Tchr 1979-; *ai:* Math Club Adv; PSEA, NEA 1979-; NCTM 1989-; Natl Sci Fnd Grant Univ of Scranton 1970; *home:* 20 10th Ave Carbondale PA 18407

KELLY, MAXINE PETERSON, Mathematics Teacher; *b:* Bridgeton, NJ; *m:* Michael Jos.; *c:* Brian Michael, Michael Patrick, Erin Eliz.; *ed:* Rutgers Univ (BS) Sci & Math 1961; Addl Stud in Tests & Measurements, Educl Psych & Human Behavior & Dev; *cr:* Whitehall Lab Analytical Chemist 2 Yrs; Woodland Day Schl 7th Grd Tchr 3 Yrs; Woodruff Schl Spec Ed Asst 5 Yrs; Saint Mary Magdalen Elem Schl 4, 6, 7, 8th Grd Math Tchr, Curr Coord; *ai:* Saint Jude Mathathon Chprsn; Asst Prin 1993-; Math Club Adv; NCEA 1986-; US Peace Corps 1962; *office:* Saint Mary Magdalen Elem Schl 7 W Powell St Millville NJ 08332

KELLY, NADIA S., English Teacher; *b:* Munich, Germany; *m:* James Laymen; *c:* Matthew James, Gregory Ross, Jessica Nadia; *ed:* Kutzman Univ (BS) Eng & Russian 1969; Masters ESOL 1990; *cr:* Bridgeton Schl Dist Eng Tchr 1969-72; Allentown Schl Dist Eng Tchr 1972-74, 1982-; *ai:* NEA 1982-; PA Comp Grant.*

KELLY, PEGGY LEE DINGUS, Teacher & Coord of Gifted; *b:* Huntington, WV; *m:* Michael Franklin; *c:* Michael Jason, Adam Christopher, Matthew Joseph, Daniel Raymond, Jonathan Isaac; *ed:* OH Univ (BS) Elem Ed 1973, (MED) Elem Ed 1979; Permanent Cert K-8 Elem, K-12 Gifted, Provisional Cert Gen Supervision; 49 Post-Grad Hrs Educl Admin, Career Educ, Gifted, Math, Sci, Cmptr OH Univ, Marshall Univ; Toastmasters of Ashland 1986-89; Comm, Ldrshp Trng; *cr:* OH Univ Primary Hnrs Prgm Tchr 1994-95; Dawson-Bryant Local Schl Dist 1, 2, 3 Elem Classroom Tchr 1973-91, 4-8 Grds Remedial Tchr, GATE Tchr, 1991-; *ai:* Adv Model United Nations, Elem & Jr High Quiz Teams; Rdng, Math, Parent-Tchr, Gifted Prgm, Schl Improvement Comms; Toastmasters 1987-89, Sec, Educl VP, Competent Toastmaster Classification; Bapt Church 1962-, Sunday Schl, Church Classes, Nursery-Teens Tchrs 1965-; Lawrence Cty Right to Life 1990-; River Cities Cultural Cncl 1987-89, Rep; Wrote, Administered Constructive Choices Hlth Grant, Gifted, Developmentally HandicappedGrant; Gifted PACE Grant Team Coord; Provided Tchr Inservice; Organized Rsrch Based Gifted Fairs; Created Yearly Toastmasters Prgm; Taught Speechcraft; Coord, Judged Speech Contests; Creation of Speakers Bureau, Yth Ldrshp Trng; Prepare Annual Gifted Identification, EMIS Reports; *home:* 8321 State Route 243 South Point OH 45680*

KELLY, RICHARD B., Amer His & Pub Affairs Teacher; *b:* Gloversville, NY; *m:* Piret H. Kutt; *c:* Patrick, Michael; *ed:* St Univ NY at Albany (BA) His 1963, (MA) Pol Sci 1964; Addl 60 Hrs; *cr:* Shenendehowa HS Tchr 1964-; *ai:* Stu Fac Admin Senate Adv; AFT 1964-, Natl Convention Del; NYSUT; Capital Dist Cncl Soc Stud 1964-; NEH Fellowship; Taft Inst; PTSA Life Membership; *office:* Shenendehowa HS 970 Rt 146 Clifton Park NY 12065

KELLY, ROBERT J.,JR., Social Studies Teacher; *b:* Port Chester, NY; *m:* Janine Wilkos; *c:* Alison M., Brett R., Grant W.; *ed:* Amherst Coll (BA) His 1966; Univ of MA (MA) Ed 1968; Addl Ed & Soc Stud Courses; *cr:* Amherst Regnl HS Tchr 1967-, Dept Head & Assoc Dept Head 1976-; *ai:* Girls Var Tennis Team Coach; Amherst-Pelham Ed Assn 1970-, Contract Negotiations Head; MA Tchrs Assn, NEA 1970-; Amherst Regnl HS Robert Frost Tchng Chair 1972; Amherst Regnl Schl Dist Merit Tchng Awds; *office:* Amherst Regional Sr HS 21 Matoon St Amherst MA 01002

KELLY, ROBERT P., Theology Teacher; *b:* Astoria, NY; *m:* Maureen Gillen; *c:* David Robert, Matthew Charles, Laura Jean; *ed:* NY Inst of Tech (BS) Behavioral Sci 1977; IMM Conception Seminary (MA) Systematic Theology 1987; Addl 24 Hrs Theology; *cr:* NY City Police Dept Police Ofcr 1966-69; Suffolk Cty Police Dept Police Acad Instr 1970-88; *ai:* Amer Soc of Trng, Dev 1985-; Cub Scouts 161 1975-, Comm Chm; Shoreham Little League 1977-, Mgr, Bd Mem; St Marks Bsktbl 1976-, Coach; Police Prof Awd; Juvenile Investigator; JVC Television Awds; Wrote, Produced Instrl Television Prgms for Police; *office:* St Anthony's HS 275 Wolf Hill Rd Melville NY 11747

KELLY, SHARON R., First Grade Teacher; *b:* Baltimore, MD; *c:* Kelly D. Ruark; *ed:* Salisbury St (BS) Elem Ed 1971, (MED) Early Chldhd 1979; 30 Addl Credit Hrs; *cr:* Fruitland Primary Schl 1st Grd Tchr 1971-73; Westside Primary Schl 1st Grd Tchr 1975-; *ai:* NEA 1975-; ACEI, Alpha Delta Kappa 1995-; Reading Cncl 1993; *home:* 1411 Ard Brac Pl Salisbury MD 21804*

KELLY, SUZANNE BOYD, Reading Specialist; *b:* Hackensack, NJ; *m:* Raymond J.; *c:* Kara, Ryan; *ed:* Boston Univ (BA) Elem Ed 1969; Boston Coll (MED) Rdng 1972; Rivier Coll Rdng Course; Notre Dame 2 ESL Courses; *cr:* Billerica MA Schl Dist 3rd-5th Grd Rdng Specialist 1969-73; Hillsboro Deering HS 9th-12th Grd Rdng Sp 1988-; *ai:* NEASC Steering Comm; IRA 1989-; John Stark Regnl HS 1985-, Schl Bd; *home:* 58 Brown Ridge Rd Weare NH 03281

KELLY, SYLVIA NEAHR, Tchr of the Gifted & Talented; *b:* Grand Rapids, MI; *m:* David M.; *c:* Jordu, Colette, Willow, Esodie Geiger; *ed:* Univ of IA (BA) Eng 1967; 3 Grad Credit Hrs St Bonaventure Univ 1977; 36 Grad Credit Hrs SUNY at Geneseo 1968-77; *cr:* Honeoye Cntrl Schl 7-12th Grd Eng Tchr 1968-78; Avon Schl G T Elem, Part-time Resource Tchr 1979-81; Caledonia G T Elem, Part-time Resource Tchr 1979-81; Livonia Schls G T Elem, Part-time Resource Tchr 1979-81; SUNY Adj Writing Instr 1992-93; Genesco Migrant Ctr Inc Arts Admin Coord Camps; Caledonia Mumford Schl G T K-12 Resource Tchr; *ai:* Head Coach Odyssey of the Mind Prgms 3-12th Grd; Co-Coach Acad Decathlon, Master Minds, Brain Stormers, Acad Challenge Bowl, Battle of the Books; Co-Dir Jr HS Play 10th-11th Grd; Interscholastic Competition in Eng; Adv OM Club, Lit Magazine; Core Comm, Arts in Ed, Genesee Vly Cncl on Arts 1994-, Comm; Genesee Vly Cncl on Arts 1982-85, Bd Mem; Soc for Advancement of Gifted Ed 1978-82, Founding Mem; Lit Vols of Genese Vly 1978-82, Bd Mem; Amer Cancer Soc 1977-79, Bd Mem, 1975-78, Adv Yth Against Cancer; Coord 15 Exhibitions of Traditional Art by Migrant Farm Workers 1984-91; Numerous Articles Pub; Tchr of Excl NY St Eng Cncl 1985; Vol in Trng to Amer Literacy Vols of Amer 1986; NY Fnd for the Arts Fellow In Fiction 1991; OMER Awd for Sportsmanship Odyssey of the Mind 1996; Presented Rdngs of Own Work 1979-95; *home:* PO Box 53 Geneseo NY 14454

KELLY, THOMAS MICHAEL, Biology Teacher; *b:* Woodside Queens, NY; *c:* Timothy, Peter, Thomas C.; *ed:* Duquesne Univ (BS) Ed, Bio 1973; Attnd SUNY at New Paltz, Union Coll; *cr:* Webutuck HS Bio Tchr 1973-; *ai:* AFT, NYSUT 1973-; STANY 1995-; *home:* PO Box 247 Pine Plains NY 12567*

KELLY, WILLIAM JOSEPH, Teacher; *b:* Norristown, PA; *ed:* Gwynedd-Mercy Coll (ASN) Nrsng, Ed 1981; St Charles Seminary Church Ministry Cert 1991; Archdiocese of Philadelphia Tchr Cert Prgm 1992; Working Toward BHSEd Hlth Sci Ed; *cr:* St Matthew Parish Coord of Rel Ed 1987-95; St Matthew Schl Kndgtn Tchr 1988-91, 6th-8th Grd Math Tchr 1988-, 7th Grd Tchr 1991-93, 8th Grd Tchr 1993-95, 6th Grd Tchr 1995-; Vly Forge Military Acad & Coll Registered Nurse-Infirmary 1990-; *ai:* Stu Cncl, Mathletes, Yrbk Moderator; CYO Photographer; Bsktbl Scorekeeper; Eucharistic Minister; Rel Coord; Schl Dance Chprsn; CCD Tchr; Rel Curr Comm 1994-95, Recognition Awd; TAP Prgm Gwynedd-Mercy Coll Stdnts Tchr Mentor; Villanova Univ Nrsng Stdnts Mentor for Hlth Promotion; AT&T Telecommunications Project Mindworks to Stdnts Participated & Taught; *home:* 107 Progress Dr Conshohocken PA 19428*

KELSCH, ROBERT H., Latin Teacher; *b:* Cincinnati, OH; *m:* Barbara Brockwell; *ed:* Georgetown Coll (BA) Latin 1969; Xavier Unv (PHD) Classics 1977; Attnd Vergilian Schl Naples Italy 1970; *cr:* Princeton HS Latin & Fr Tchr 1969-; Notre Dame Grammar Schl Exchange Tchr 1973-74; *ai:* Latin Club; Acad Team Coach; Textbook Adoptions Chair, Latin; Schl Comms Rules, Dress, Attendance, Curr; OH Classical Conf 1970-, Pres, VP, OHs Best Classics Prgm 1978; NEA, OEA, PEA 1970-; Classical League NTL 1975-, St Co-Chair Bd of Dirs; Cresent Ct Assn 1976-86, Bd Pres; North Cntrl Sec Schl Assn on Site Evaluations Chair; Guest Lecturer Schls, Groups, Classes; Grad Organizer; Lib Bd 1975-80; Fulbright-Hays Grant Taught in England 1973-74; Hildescheim Vase OHs Best Lat Prgm 1984; Bd of Ed Proclamations; Golden Apple Awd Hon Mention; *office:* Princeton HS 11080 Chester Rd Cincinnati OH 45246

KELSCH, SHARON G., Asst Professor of Nursing; *b:* New York, NY; *m:* John W.; *c:* John II, Andrew; *ed:* Suffolk Comm Coll (AAS) Nrsng 1976; SUNY at Stonybrook (BS) Nrsng 1982, (MS) Nrsng 1985; 18 Credit Hrs Post-Grad Stud; *cr:* J T Mather Memrl Hosp Staff RN, ER, Med & Surg 1978-85, Coord Employee Hlth Svc 1985-90; Suffolk Cty Office of Employee Med Review Family Nurse Practitioner; Suffolk Comm Coll Asst Prof & Nrsn 1990-; *ai:* Prof Dev, Serving the Needs of Persons with Disabilities, & Evening Common Hr Comms; NY St Coalition of NPS 1985-, Sec LI Chptr 1990, Newsletter Ed & LI Chptr 1988-90; Sigma Theta Tau Intnl Hnr Soc of Nrsng 1985-; Assn of Hosp Employee Hlth Profs 1985-91, Exec VP 1989-91; Infant Jesus Church, Rel Ed Tchr 1994-; Mather Hosp NY St Legislature Nurse of Distinction Nom 1990; Joyce

Safian Natl Role Model Awd 1991; Suffolk Comm Coll For Who Made a Difference Awd Nom 1993; Suffolk Comm Coll For Chancellors Awd Nom 1996; *office:* Suffolk Community Coll Crooked Hill Rd Brentwood NY 11717*

KELSCHENBACH, ANGELA MARIE, Consultant Teacher; *b:* Buffalo, NY; *m:* David Allan; *c:* Caitlin; *ed:* SUCNY at Buffalo (BS) Ed & Art 1977, (MS) Spcl Ed 1990; *cr:* JF Kennedy HS Art Sub Tchr 1977-80, Spcl Ed Self-Contained & Res Tchr 1987-95, Spcl Ed Consult Tchr 1995-; *ai:* Schl Newspaper Adv; Art Club; *office:* John F Kennedy HS 305 Cayuga Creek Rd Cheektowaga NY 14227

KELSEY, MARY HEITMEYER, Sixth Grade Teacher; *b:* Lima, OH; *m:* Kenneth; *c:* Laura; *ed:* Univ of Dayton (MS) Tchng 1987; Coll of Notre Dame 3 Semester Hrs 1993; *cr:* Delphos St Johns 2nd Grd Tchr 1970; Ada Elem 3rd-6th Grd Transitional Tchr 1970-1st Grd Tchr; *ai:* NEA, OEA 1971-, AEA 1971-, Treas; Ada Women's Assn 1980-, Treas, VP, Pres; *office:* Ada Elem Schl 500 Grand Ave Ada OH 45810

KELSEY, MICHAEL ANTHONY, Special Ed, Health & PE Tchr; *b:* Media, PA; *ed:* Glassboro St Coll (BA) Hlth & PE 1991; Rowan Coll Spec Ed Cert, Working Towards Masters Admin; 57 Credits Drafting & Design; *cr:* Cumberland Regnl HS Hlth, PE & Spec Ed Tchr 1993-; *ai:* Spec Ed Resource Ctr & In-Class Support; Cross Cntry; Girls Track & Field; NEA 1993-; *office:* Cumberland Regional HS PO Box 5115 Seabrook NJ 08302

KELSHAW, DELMAR, Math Teacher; *b:* Hazleton, PA; *m:* Margaret M. Matuella; *c:* James, Charles; *ed:* East Stroudsburg Univ Masters Equivalency, 60 Addl Credit Hrs Mostly in Cmptr Sci; *cr:* Hazleton Area Schl Dist Tchr 1972-; *ai:* Head Golf Coach, 1996 Conf, Dist Championship; NEA, PSEA 1975-; *office:* West Hazleton Jr HS 325 North St West Hazleton PA 18201

KELSHAW, RONALD H., Guidance Counselor; *b:* Hazleton, PA; *m:* Lisa Stoudt; *c:* Lauren Diane; *ed:* Moravian Coll (BA) Sociology 1974; Kutztown Univ (MED) Scndry Cnslng 1977; Lehigh Univ Cert Elem Cnslng 1981; Addl Grad Work Penn St, Univ Mansfield Univ, Carlow Coll, Allentown Coll, Wilkes Univ; *cr:* Bloomsburg MS 6-8 Grd Guid Cnslr 1977-85; Bloomsburg Mem Elem Sch K-5 Grd Guid Cnslr 1985-87; Weatherly Area HS 9-12 Grd Guid Cnslr 1987-; *ai:* SD Strategic Planning, Grad, Assessment Comms; Scndry Instrl Support, Stu Assistance Teams; Envirothon Teams Adv; PSEA 1977-; WEA 1987-, Spec Svcs Chm; NEA, PSCA 1977-; LCSCA 1987-; Alumni Assn 1992-, Schlsp Comm Chm; Zions Luth Church 1952-; Carbon Cty Transition Cncl; Helped Dev Potential Dropouts Alternative Ed Prgm; Helped Write Grant Proposal Consumer, Family Sci Equipment, Materials; *office:* Weatherly Area HS 601 6th St Weatherly PA 18255

KELSO, DAVID J., Physical Science Teacher; *b:* Saugus, MA; *m:* Nancy Richmond; *c:* Kevin, Brian, Kristen; *ed:* Salem St Coll (BA) Earth Sci 1974; Notre Dame Coll (MED) Ed 1980; *cr:* Cntrl Hs 9th Grd Phys Sci & 12th Grd Physics Tchr 1974-95; *ai:* US First Robotics Competition Adv; Curr Comm; NEA, NH Ed Assn 1976-; Amer Assn Physics Tchrs 1988-; New England Section Amer Assn Physics Tchrs 1995-; Candia Youth Athletic Assn 1985-, Pres, Coach; Moore Schl Facilities comm 1995-; *home:* 61 Douglas Dr Candia NH 03034

KELTOS, COLLEEN A., Teacher, Cmptr Sci & Tech Dir; *b:* Bridgeport, CT; *m:* Colleen A.Coyle; *c:* Samantha, Alexandra, MicKayla; *ed:* Fairfield Univ (BS) Bio 1980, (MA) Instrl Cmptr Sci 1984; Working Toward MS from RPI Mngmt of Tech; *cr:* Fairfield Coll Prep Schl Tchr 1980-, Cmptr Sci & Tech Dir 1995-; *ai:* ISTE 1994-; SMARTNET 2000 Grant; *office:* Fairfield Coll Prep Schll 1073 N Benson Rd Fairfield CT 06430*

KEMENY, CHERYL E., President & Prof Voice Teacher; *b:* Norwalk, CT; *m:* James Pezza; *ed:* Hartt Coll, Univ of Hartford (MB) Voice, Opera 1973; Franz Liszt Acad of Music Cert Voice 4 Yrs; Wesleyan Alternative Rt to Cert Music Ed 1991; *cr:* Crystal Theatre Inc Pres, Tchr 1987-; Self Employed Prof Voice Tchr 1987-; Mead Schl for Human Dev Music Tchr 1988-90; All Saints Cath Schl Choral Dir 1993-; *ai:* Composer, Playwright in Residence; Wilton Schl System, Creative Summer Multi-Arts Prgm Freelance Writer, Dir; NETC, MENC 1992-; Amer Fed of Musicians, AFL-CIO 1978-; Off-Broadway Musical Composer, Co-Writer 1990; Theatre Arts Prgm St Grant 1990-91; *office:* Crystal Theatre Inc 12 June Ave Norwalk CT 06850

KEMICK, JOSEPH EDWARD, Math Teacher; *b:* Bradford, PA; *m:* Aimee Elizabeth Vecellio; *ed:* Attnd Penn St Univ, Gannon Univ, East Stroudsburg Univ of PA; *cr:* Bradford Area Schl Dist Math Tchr 1987-89; Seton Keough HS Math Tchr 1989-90; Ridgway Area HS Math Tchr 1990-; *ai:* Asst Ftbl Coach; NHS Adv; PSEA 1987-; NCTM 1992-; St Leos Church 1991-; *office:* Ridgway Area HS 1403 Hill St Ridgway PA 15853

KEMMERER, BARBARA ANN, Principal; *b:* Reading, PA; *ed:* Felician Coll (BA) Elem Ed 1970; 6 Credits (MA) His Villanova; Cert K-12 Elem Ed, K-12 Soc Stud; *cr:* Trenton Wallington Schl Tchr 1965-78; St Paul Schl Tchr 1978-80; St Anthony Schl Prin 1980-87; Sacred Heart Schl Tchr 1987-89; St Adalbert Schl Prin 1989-90; Sacred Heart Schl Tchr 1990-92; Sacred Heart Schl Prin 1992-; *ai:* St Jude Math-A-Thon; Schl Yrbk; Latch Key Prgm; NCEA 1980-; Mid States Accred 1994-; Article Pub Cath Tchr 1995; Tchr of Yr 1992; Humanistic, Legal Rights Aids Patients St Peter's Jersey City; *office:* Sacred Heart Schl 229 Cedar St South Amboy NJ 08879

KEMMERER, LESLIE H., History, Bible Tchr & Ath Dir; *b:* Binghamton, NY; *m:* Nancy Walter; *c:* Jennifer, Jeremy, Justin; *ed:* Bapt Bible Coll of PA (BA) Ed, His, Bible 1974; Buffalo St Univ (MS) Soc Stud Ed 1989; *cr:* West Seneca Chrstn Schl Tchr, Coach, Ath Dir 1974-; *ai:* Boys Var Soccer, Bsktbl Coach, Ath Dir; Social Stud His Chm; Sr Class Adv; Golf Club Adv; Drama Club Helper; NY Assn of Chrstn Schls 1988-; Amer Assn of Chrstn Schls 1994-; Word of Life Yth Group 1978-; Group Ldr; Independent Ath Conf 1978-, Pres; *office:* West Seneca Christian Schl 511 Union Rd West Seneca NY 14224

KEMNITZER, THOMAS JOSEPH, Social Studies Teacher; *b:* Flushing, NY; *m:* Judith Hanke; *c:* Keith Petroro, Brian Petroro, Katlyn; *ed:* Nassau Comm Coll at Garden City (AA) General Lib Arts 1972; St Univ of NY at Albany (BA) Soc Stud, Scndry Ed 1974; Hofstra Univ at Hempstead (MA) Scndry Ed 1979, (CAS) Ed Admin 1992; *cr:* West Hempstead Pub Schls Scndry Level Soc Stud Tchr 1974-; *ai:* MS Boys Soccer, Vlybl, Co-Ed Spring Track Coach; NYSUT 1974-, Corresponding Sec 1986-89; St Andrews Church, Cncl, Choir; *office:* West Hempstead Pub Schls 252 Chestnut St West Hempstead NY 11552*

KEMP, DEE ANN, Mathematics Teacher; *b:* Wapakoneta, OH; *m:* Robert Gifford; *c:* Benjamin, Emily; *ed:* Miami Univ (BA) Math 1973; 30 Grad Hrs Ed, Tchr Related; *cr:* Tallmadge Jr HS Math Tchr 1973-77, 1983-87; Tallmadge HS Math Tchr 1987-; *ai:* NEA, OEA, TTA 1993-; OCTM 1988-; United Church of Christ 1980-, Outreach Chm; *office:* Tallmadge HS 486 East Ave Tallmadge OH 44278

KEMP, JANET PAINTER, Retired Teacher; *b:* Ashland, OH; *c:* Kevin, Derek; *ed:* Elem Hrs Ashland Univ, Kent St, Akron Univ; Grad Hrs OH St Univ; *cr:* 1-12 Grd Music Tchr 1 Yr; 4-8 Grd Music Tchr 5 Yrs; 5 Grd Tchr 12 Yrs; 6 Grd Tchr 12 Yrs; *ai:* ACTA; OEA; NEA; *home:* 1320 State Route 96 # R5 Ashland OH 44805*

KEMP, KATHERINE LEE, Jr High Language Arts Teacher; *b:* Delaware, OH; *m:* Mark Allen; *c:* Aaron Michael; *ed:* OH St Univ (BME) Music Ed 1981; Cert Elem Ed 1982; *cr:* Delaware City Schls Sub Tchr 1981-82; Calvary Chrstn Schl Jr High 6-8 Grd Lang Arts Tchr 1985-; *ai:* Stu Ldrshp Cncl Adv; Curr Comm; *home:* 2043 Sherwood Ave Toledo OH 43614*

KEMP, LORI MEESE, Former English Teacher; *b:* Olney, IL; *m:* Kevin L.; *c:* Matthew, Michael; *ed:* IN St Univ (BS) Eng 1981; *cr:* John Glenn HS Eng Tchr 1981-84; Wentzville HS Eng Tchr 1987-92; Pleasant Vly HS Eng Tchr 1993-95; *ai:* NEA 1981-; Wentzville Schl Dist Tchr of Yr 1991-92; *home:* 15 Judith E Ln Methuen MA 01844*

KEMP, MELANIE HAWKS, History Teacher & Principal; *b:* Akron, OH; *m:* Jon F.; *c:* Kristi, Jonathan, Bethany; *ed:* Taylor Univ (BS) Soc Stud 1971; Attnd Akron Univ, Baldwin-Wallace; *cr:* Cuyahoga Falls HS Psych Tchr 1972-77; Cuyahoga Falls-Roberts MS L. D. Tutor 1980-81; Summit Chrstn Schl 2nd Grd Tchr, 6th, 8th Grd His Tchr, Prin 1986-; *ai:* Bsktbl IM; Horseback Riding; Bowling, Ski Club; *home:* 1027 Chestnut Blvd Cuyahoga Falls OH 44221*

KEMPER, B. J., English Teacher; *b:* Houlton, ME; *ed:* UMF (BA) Eng 1992, (BS) Ed 1992; *cr:* Messalonskee HS Eng Tchr 1994-; *ai:* SAT Team; Drug & Alcohol Policy Comm; ME Drama Festival Host Dir; *office:* Messalonskee HS 62 Oak St Oakland ME 04963

KEMPER, JOYCE ANNE KEATON, 6th Grade Teacher; *b:* Greenup Cty, KY; *m:* David E.; *c:* Kathryn R., Matthew D.; *ed:* Warren Wilson Coll (AA) Elem Ed 1960; OH Univ (BS) Elem Ed, DH, SLD 1974; *cr:* Wheelersburg Local Schl Sub Tchr 1970-71; Bloom Local Schl Tchr 1971-72; Green Local Schl Tchr, EMR, SLD 1972-80; Minford Local Schl Tchr 1980-; *ai:* MEA, OEA, NEA 1975-; Alpha Delta Kappa 1992-, Treas; *office:* Minford MS PO Box 204 Minford OH 45653

KEMPER, LINDA WEBSTER, Asst Professor of Education; *b:* Wilkinsburg, PA; *m:* Richard V.; *ed:* Univ of ME at Orono (BSEd) Elem Ed 1965; Boston Coll (MED) Rdng 1978, PHD) Ed Admin & Supervision 1984; *cr:* Bedford Pub Schls Tchr 1970-80; Goffstown Pub Schls Elem Prin 1985-88; Litchfield Pub Schls Elem Prin 1988-93; Rivier Coll Asst Prof of Ed 1993-; *ai:* IRA 1977-; ASCD 1978-; NCTE 1995-; Phi Delta Kappa 1981-; Alpha Sigma Nu; Book Chapter Teaching Reading Letters, Language & Thought LARC Pub; Grants NH Dept of Ed, NH Inst on Disabilities; *office:* Rivier Coll 420 S Main St Nashua NH 03060*

KEMPF, JOHN J., Soc Stud Tchr & Dept Chairman; *b:* Rome, NY; *m:* Alana Beehm; *ed:* Utica Coll of Syracuse Univ (BA) Soc Stud 1969; 33 Credit Hrs; *cr:* Rome Cath HS Soc Stud Tchr 1969-71; St Frances de Sales HS Soc Stud Tchr 1971-76; Notre Dame HS Soc Stud Tchr 1976-; Prof Organist 1991-; *ai:* Acad Cncl Comm; *office:* Notre Dame HS Burrstone Rd Utica NY 13502

KENDALL, JUDITH TOWNSEND, Fourth Grade Teacher; *b:* Rahway, NJ; *m:* George H. Jr.; *c:* George III, Carolyn, Douglas T.; *ed:* Middlebury Coll (BA) Amer Stud 1957; 30 Grad Credit Hrs; *cr:* Mt View Schl Grds 4, 3, 1, 5 Tchr; *ai:* NEA, NJEA, EAMO 1970-; Tchr of Yr 1986; *office:* Mountain View Elem Schl 118 Clover Hill Dr Flanders NJ 07836

KENDALL, SHERRIE R., 7th-8th Grade Comm Arts Tchr; *b:* Philadelphia, PA; *ed:* Oglethorpe Univ (BA) Elem Ed 1974; 60 Hrs GA St Univ Towards Masters in Admin; *cr:* Stoneview Elem Schl Tchr 1974-80; Arthur Rann MS Tchr 1985-; *ai:* Team Ldr; Stokes Coord; ASAP; Yrbk Coord 1985-92; NJEA, NEA 1984-; GEA 1985-; PTA 1974-80 Exec Bd PTA, 1985-; Career Ed Chm 1979-80; Pride in NJ Ed 1995-; SITE Coord 1987-92; Stokes Coord 1989-93; Pub Relations Comm 1974-80; Educl Mngmt Team 1978-80; Sunshine Comm 1976-80; Fernbank Sci Ctr Coord 1976-80; S Jersey Consortium Tchr 1985-93; *office:* Athur Rann MS 8th Ave Absecon NJ 08201

KENDALL, WILLIAM WALTER, Math & Computer Teacher; *b:* West Boylston, MA; *m:* Judith Hickey; *c:* Jonathan, Amanda; *ed:* Boston Coll (AB) Math 1971; Univ of MA at Boston (MS) Math 1978; Boston Univ (MS) Cmptr Sci 1985; Harvard Univ (EDD) Tchng, Curr 1992; *cr:* Half Assini Scndry Schl Math Tchr 1971-73; Braintree HS Math Tchr 1973-; *ai:* MA Tchrs Assn 1973-, Local Pres; NCTM 1973-; Weymouth Yth Soccer 1990-; Weymouth Girls Bsktbl 1995-; Project Zero South African Math, Math Case Stud Projects; Cognitive Skills Stud Group Project Zero; *office:* Braintree HS 128 Town St Braintree MA 02184*

KENDRA, JEFFREY LAURENCE, Mathematics Teacher; *b:* Seattle, WA; *ed:* Western New England Coll (BS) Math 1969; Westfield St Coll (MA) Ed 1974; *cr:* Chicopee Comp HS Math Tchr 1969-; *ai:* Girls Var Tennis Coach 27 Yrs; MTA, NEA 1969-; *home:* 73 Dunsany Dr Longmeadow MA 01106

KENDRICK, RAYMOND H., Diesel Instructor; *b:* Huntington, WV; *m:* Nora Conley; *c:* Harold, Shari Grubbs, Timothy, Kathy; *ed:* OH St Univ (BA) Sci 1988; *cr:* Collins Career Ctr Diesel Mechanic Instr 18 Yrs; Creamer Construction Diesel Mechanic 10 Yrs; Cooper Tire & Rubber Co Maintenance Mechanic 10 Yrs; *ai:* VICA Adv; AFT 1986-, VP 1 Yr; ASE Certfd Master Truck Mechanic; *office:* Collins Career Center 11627 State Route 243 Chesapeake OH 45619

KENEL, SALLY A., Theology Professor; *b:* New York, NY; *ed:* Seat of Wisdom Coll (BA) Natural Sci 1965; Rensselaer Polytechnic Int (MS) Natural Sci 1968; Fordham Univ (MA) Rel Ed 1978, (PHD) Theology 1984; *cr:* Our of Wisdom Acad Sci Chair 1968-70; Mercer Cty Schls Sci Tchr 1970-76; St Johns Univ Theology Prof 1984-; *ai:* AAVP 1986-; CTS 1985-, Bd Mem; AAR 1986-; Templeton Fnd Awd for Article in 1994; *office:* Saint Johns Univ 300 Howard Ave Staten Island NY 10301

KENNA, COLLEEN FRANCES, High School English Teacher; *b:* Stamford, CT; *ed:* St Joseph Coll (AA) Liberal Arts 1973; Southern VT Coll (BA) Ed, Eng 1976; Fairfield Univ 6th Yr Degree CAS; Univ of Bridgeport MS Counseling; *cr:* Stamford HS Eng Tchr 19 Yrs; *ai:* Fac Flower Fund Chprsn; Soc Comm; SEA, CEA 1977-; NCTE 1989-; CCTE 1993-; ASCD 1994-; Phi Beta Kappa 1995-; HSUS; WWF; NPCA; ASPCA; Who's Who 1993-95; Nom Tchr of Yr 1995; *office:* Stamford HS 55 Strawberry Hill Ave Stamford CT 06902

KENNA, KRISTINA WOLF, Elem Instrl Support Teacher; *b:* Pittsburgh, PA; *c:* Brent C., Allison P.; *ed:* Millersville Univ (BS) El Ed, Sp Ed 1973; Working on ME, El Ed; *cr:* Eshleman Elem Schl Three Grd Tchr 1973-75; Conestoga Elem Schl Intermediate Sp Ed Tchr 1975-77; Hambright Elem Schl Spec Ed Tchr 1978-83; Pequea Elem Schl Spec Ed Tchr 1983-87; Intermediate Unit #21 MS Spec Ed Tchr 1987-88; Martic Elem Schl 5 Grd Tchr 1988-93; Cntrl Manor Elem Schl Instrl Support Tchr 1993-; *ai:* Elem Sci Curr, Sci Strategic Planning, Assessment Strategic Planning Comms; NEA, PSEA, PMEA 1973-; Lititz Jaycee Women 1978-87, Pres, Sec, Outstdng Young Woman 1985; PA Jaycee Women 1978-91, St Admin Chair, Regnl Dir, Life Mgrshp, Admin Chm of Yr; Millersville Women of Today 1988-91, St Dir; Outstdng Edctr 1984; Outstdng Young Edctr Millersville Jaycees 1984; Sallie Mae Tchr Tribute Awd 1991.

KENNEALLY, CHRISTOPHER, Chemistry & Physics Teacher; *b:* Buffalo, NY; *m:* Elizabeth M.; *c:* Sean, Andrew, Kathryn; *ed:* SUNY Brockport (BS) Chem 1973; Syracuse Univ (MS) Sci Ed 1984; *cr:* Bishop Ludden HS Chem Tchr 1973-83; Fayetteville Manlius HS Chem, Physics Tchr 1984-; *ai:* Asst Coach Var Lacrosse; USLCA, STANYS 1974-; USLCA Century Club; Coach of Yr Cntrl NY Lax Assoc 1983; *office:* Fayetteville-Manlius HS E Seneca Turnpike Manlius NY 13104

KENNEDY, BRIAN ANDREW, Voc Agrcltrl Mechanics Instr; *b:* Columbus, OH; *m:* Kathie Ann Mayo; *cr:* Share Tractor Svc Mgr 1977-78; Howard Sales Indstrl Truck Mechanic 1978; Barry Equipment co Heavy Equipment Mechanic 1978-85; Eastland Career Ctr Voc Agricul Mechanics Instr 1985-; *ai:* OEA, NEA 1985-; Eastland Voc SD Al Assn 1991-, Trustee; St FFA Degree 1976; Eastland Voc Schls Hall of 1993; Tchr of The Year Nom 1994-95; *office:* Eastland Career Ctr 4 Hamilton Rd Groveport OH 43125

KENNEDY, DAVID W., Social Studies Teacher; *b:* Meadville, PA Patricia Ann; *c:* Mike, Matt, Nick; *ed:* Edinboro Univ (BSEd) Soc 1973, (MED) Soc Stud 1975; Allegheny Coll Grad Course Intermediate Unit 5 Summer Enrichment; *cr:* Meadville Jr HS Soc Tchr 1974-78; Meadville Sr High Soc Stud Tchr 1978-; *ai:* Swim Coach 1974-76; Sftbl Coach 1978-94; Track Coach 1995-; Ou Encounter Adv 1974-78; Stu Cncl Adv 1978-; Jr Class Adv 197 Sucessful Schl Partnership 1990-; NEA 1973-; PA St Assn 1973-; Cent Ed Assn 1973-; PA Cncl of Soc Stud 1973-; Meadville Rotary Foreign Stu Laison 1985-; Red Cross Bd of Dirs 1989-, Dir; Mead Are Bsbl 1990-, VP Amer Cancer Soc; Outstdng Young Edctr Awd 1988; Tchr Designation 1994; Allegheny Coll Collaborative Designation *office:* Meadville HS 800 North St Meadville PA 16335

KENNEDY, DENNIS WILLIAM, English Teacher; *b:* Fall River, M. Mary Kathleen Spring; *c:* Katie Spring, Dennis Thomas, Sean William Stonehill Coll (BA) Eng 1971; Univ of MA at Boston (MA) Eng 1979; of MA at Amherst (PHD) Lit, His 1987; *cr:* Holy Family HS Eng 1972-78; Normandie Jr HS Eng Tchr 1978-79; Univ of MA TA 197 Amherst Regnl HS Eng Tchr 1982-83; Northfield Mount Hermon Sch Tchr 1983-; *ai:* Debate Coach; David D. Hartman Comm Flwshp; Hur Stud Fellow; *office:* Northfield Mount Hermon Schl PO Box Northfield MA 01360

KENNEDY, DIANE, Math Teacher; *b:* Bronx, NY; *m:* James; *c:* Kristina, Michelle, James; *ed:* Stony Brook (BS) Math 1977, (MS 1982; *cr:* Lindenhurst JHS Math Tchr 1978-79; Islip JHS Math 1979-80; North Babylon HS Math Tchr 1980-95; *office:* North Babylo 5 Jardine Pl North Babylon NY 11703

KENNEDY, ELAINE KAHLER, Home Economics Teacher; *b:* El NY; *m:* Dr. Edward E.; *c:* Esther E., Eben K.; *ed:* St Univ of NY at Bu (BS) Home Ec Ed 1958; Cornell Univ (MS) Home Ec Ed 1965; Attnd of Rochester; *cr:* Rochester Schl for Deaf Home Ec Tchr 1958-62; M Whitman HS Home Ec Tchr 1975-; Finger Lakes Comm Coll Adjunc of Psych 1985-; *ai:* FHA-HERO Youth Leadership Adv; Dist S Decision Making Comm; Tech Prep Curr Writing; NYSUT 1 NYSAFCSE 1976-, Several Offices Including St Pres, NYS Outstar Tchr Awd; AVA 1983-; NYSOEA 1983-, Awds Chair, Outstanding Awd, NYSOEA Supporter Awd; Delta Kappa Gamma 1982-, Se Offices, Nominating Comm Chair; United Church of Christ 1960-, Tru United Way, Bd Mem, Vol of Yr Awd; Cooperative Extension 1960-, V Mem; Lions Club Citizen of Yr; Occupational Educl Tchr of Yr; Home Ec Tchr of Yr; *office:* Marcus Whitman Jr Sr H S Baldwi Rushville NY 14544

KENNEDY, GERALD JOSEPH, History Teacher; *b:* Philadelphia *ed:* Duns Scotus-Mercy Coll of Detroit (BA) His 1980; 19 Undergra Grad Hrs Scndry Ed Cert Xavier Univ; 6 Credit Hrs Working Tow Masters Coll of Mt Saint Joseph; *cr:* Seton HS His Tchr 1984-; *ai:* Trial Team 1984-87; Audio Visual Room 1987-89, 1993-95; Stu Work Co-ordinator 1989-93; Sr Parking 1995; Sr Retreats 1985-; *office:* HS 3901 Glenway Ave Cincinnati OH 45205

KENNEDY, JAMES EDWARD, Social Studies Teacher; *b:* Bethle PA; *m:* Bernadette Fritz; *ed:* Wilkes Univ (BA) His 1969; Lehigh (MA) Ed 1976; *cr:* Winfield Schl Dist Soc Stud Tchr 1969-70; Nitsch Jr HS Soc Stud Tchr 1970-71; Liberty HS Soc Stud Tchr 1971-; *ai:* Girls Soccer Coach.

KENNEDY, JAMES JOSEPH,JR., Math Teacher; *b:* Lowell, MA Mary Elizabeth Balas; *c:* Kathleen, James; *ed:* Univ of MA at Lowell Bio 1968, (MED) Admin 1973; Naval OCS (COM) Nautical, Sci 196 Addl Hrs; *cr:* US Navy Officer 1968-71; Lowell HS Biological Sci 1969-87, Chm Sci Dept 1987-90, Math, Sci, Cmptr Tech Chm 1990- Horace Mann Tchr 1986-87; Math, Sci MA Frameworks Comm Lowell Admin Assn 1987-; NEA 1969-84; AFT 1984-87; ASCD 1 Reserve Officers Assn 1975-, Pres, St Sec; Naval Resource Officer 1975-; Wardroom Club of Boston 1978-; Knights of Columbus 1 Horace Mann Fellow; *office:* Lowell HS 50 Fr Morrissette Blvd Lo MA 01850

KENNEDY, JAMES MICHAEL, English Teacher; *b:* Oil City, PA Amrie Zame; *c:* Jonah; *ed:* Youngstown St U (BA) Eng 1969, (MA) 1975; *cr:* Bourdman High Jr & Sr Eng Tchr 1969-; YSU Part-Time Rdng & Study Skills 1984-; *ai:* Boardman Ed Assn 1969-; NEA 1 OEA 1969-; BHS Tchr of the Yr; WK BN Channel 21 Class Act *office:* Boardman HS 7777 Glenwood Ave Youngstown OH 44512

KENNEDY, JAMES MICHAEL, Former Swimming Coach Schenectady, NY; *ed:* Lafayette Coll (BS) Math 1977; Drexel Univ Cmptr Sci 1981; *cr:* Leeds & Northrup Co Systems Programmer 197 Gen Electric Co Sr Software Engr 1984-; *ai:* YMCA Swimming C 1987-; USS 1990-, Coach; 2 Papers Pub.

KENNEDY, JANE A., Reading Teacher; *b:* Fitchburg, MA; *ed:* Fitch St Coll (BS) Elem Ed 1973, (MED) Rdng, Lang Arts 1976, (MED) Spe 1983; Boston Univ Ed Leadership 30 Hrs; Lowell Univ Ed Leaders Hrs; *cr:* Reingold Elem Rdng & Diagnostic Prescriptive Tchr 197 Fitchburg HS Lang Arts Tchr 1977-78, 1981-86; Fitchburg Schl Sy Asst Dir Competency 1978-81; Meml MS Rdng Tchr 1986-; *ai:* Fitch Tchrs Assn, MA Tchrs Assn, Natl Tchrs Assn 1974-; Phi Delta K 1977-; NCTE 1993-; Schl Cncl 1993-; Curr Framewrks Stud Comm; *o* Memorial MS 615 Rollstone St Fitchburg MA 01420*

KENNEDY, JANET CAROL, Biology & Gen Science Teache Philadelphia, PA; *m:* Blair; *c:* Lauren; *ed:* Lebanon Univ (BA) Bio 1 Attnd Penn St Univ; *cr:* Haverford Jr HS Earth, Space, Sci Tchr 196 Haverford Sr HS bio, Gen Sci Tchr 1980-; *ai:* NEA, PSEA 1967-; H 1967-, VP; Chester Cty Hosp Auxiliary 1981-, Treas, VP; *home:* Hillside Dr West Chester PA 19380*

KENNEDY, JANETTE KUHN, 5th Grade Teacher; *b:* Tiffin, OH Michael J.; *ed:* OH Univ (BSEd) Elem Ed 1971; 30 Addl Hrs in Elem, Dev; *cr:* Tiffin Pub Schls 5th Grd Tchr 1971-74; South Western City S 3rd-5th Grd Tchr 1974-; *ai:* NEA 1971-; NCTE 1985-; NCTM 1 ASCD 1995-; *home:* 7669 Old Foxe Ct Columbus OH 43235

KENNEDY, JANICE KAY, Third Grade Teacher; *b:* Lima, OH Timothy E.; *ed:* OH St Univ (BA) Elem Ed 1967; Univ of Dayton Guid 1977; *cr:* Elida Elem Third Grd Tchr 29 Yrs; *ai:* NEA 1967- Books Pub; *office:* Elida Elem Schl 300 Pioneer Rd Elida OH 45807

KENNEDY, JANICE PASCOE, Secondary Counselor; *b:* Pittsburgh, *m:* Thomas E.; *c:* Thomas Jr., Ryan C.; *ed:* Edinboro U of PA (BS) 1970; Univ of Pittsburgh (MED) Cnslng 1974; Attnd PA St Univ Post C *cr:* Thomas Jefferson HS Eng Tchr 1971-74; Bethel Park HS Cnslr 1 *ai:* AFT 1970-; ACCA 1974-, Exec Ofcr 1990-95; PSCA 1980-; Outreach Underprivileged Children 1990-, Charitable Christmas D Chprsn; Gift of Time Recipient 1990; *office:* Bethel Park Sr HS 309 Ch Rd Bethel Park PA 15102

KENNEDY, JEAN C., English Teacher; *b:* Quincy, MA; *c:* Jea Sowers, Kendra Sowers, Derek Sowers, Lindsay Sowers; *ed:* PA St

1964; Westchester Univ (MED) Eng 1970; *cr:* Olympic Financial Corp Alternative Energy 1984-86; Stillpoint Publishing Ed, Chief of Bd -88; Thayer HS Eng Tchr 1988-; *ai:* Coll Ed Majros Methods Tchr; tion of Essential Schls Wkshps; Environmental Club Spon, Adv; oor Club; Jr Adv; Schl Comm Chairwoman; Citibank Fellow, Natl Fac -; Tchrs Assn 1988-; Ford Innovation Awd; Coalition Essential Schls np; Brown Univ Summer HS Grant; *office:* Thayer Jr Sr HS 84 Parker inchester NH 03470*

NEDY, KATHLEEN PATRICIA, Sixth Grade Teacher; *b:* LaCrosse, *ed:* Univ of Toledo (BE) Elem Ed 1956; 27 Addl Credit Hrs; *cr:* Bl ment Schl Sixth Grd Tchr 1956-61; Fall-Meyer Schl Fifth Grd Tchr -66; St Rose Schl Third Grd Tchr 1966-67; Westwood Schl 5-7 Grd 1967-84; Trilby Schl 5-6 Grd Tchr 1984-; *ai:* Intermediate Dept rsn; Safety Patrol Adv; Ventura Capital Steering Comm; NEA, OEA, EA, TAWLS, IRA 1967-; Cath Club Diocese of Toledo Women's Aths Dir, Veteran Coach Awd; TAWLS Outsdng Edctr 1079-80; *office:* y Elem Schl 5720 Secor Rd Toledo OH 43623

NEDY, LARRY KEITH, 6th Grade Teacher; *b:* Gettysburg, PA; *m:* ara Lynne Class; *ed:* Shippensburg Univ (BS) Elem Ed 1963, (MED) Ed 1970; Western MD Coll Admin Cert Elem Prin 1976; 9 Post Grad t Hrs; *cr:* Biglerville Elem Schl 6 Grd Tchr 1963-67; Arendtsville Schl 6 Grd Tchr 1967; Bendersville Elem Schl Prin 1967-86, 6 Grd Tchr 1986-89, 6 Grd Tchr 1989-; *ai:* Strategic Planning Co-Chm; Tchr; IMs; PTA Intermediate Rep; PTA 1967-, Adv; Natl Congress of nts, Tchrs 1967-; PSEA, NEA 1986-; Bendersville Comm Fire Co -; 4-H Ldr 1978-; Masonic Lodge 1968-; BPO Elks 1964-; Outstdng g Tchrs Awd Lions Club 1969; Honorary Life Mem Natl Congress of nts, Tchrs 1990; L. V. Stock Tchr of Excl 1993; Outstdng Tchr Awd ; *office:* Bendersville Elem Schl 137 Carlisle St Bendersville PA 6

NEDY, LINDA LOUISE, Mathematics Teacher; *b:* Albany, NY; *ed:* Univ of NY at Albany (BS) Math 1974; St Univ of NY at Albany (MS) Classroom Tchng in Scndry Math Ed 1983; Syracuse Univ Project nce 3 Credits; Rutgers Univ Ldrshp Prgm in Discrete Math; *cr:* entian Inst Math Tchr 1974-77; NY St Job Corps Math Tchr 1977-78; Cntrl HS Math Tchr 1978-84; Rensselaer HS Math Tchr 1984-; *ai:* Ldrshp Team; Multi Disciplinary Team; Acad Challenge Team Coach; Prep Comm Chprsn, Coord; Class & Club Act Vol; NCTM, AMTNYS -; Delta Kappa Gamma 1990-, Membership Chair; Renss Tchrs Assn -; Who's Who in Amer Ed; *office:* Rensselaer Mid HS 555 Broadway selaer NY 12144*

NEDY, LINDA (SAPPAH), Third Grade Teacher; *b:* Red Bank, NJ; ohn J.; *c:* Jeffrey, Jason; *ed:* Trenton St Coll (BS) Elem Ed 1976; *cr:* atherines 2nd-5th Grd Tchr 1969-72; Holy Family Schl 4th Grd Tchr -77; Keyport Cntrl 3rd & 6th-8th Grd Tchr 1977-; *ai:* Asst JV Chrldng h 1991-; Portfolio Comm; NEA 1977-; NJEA 1977-; Keyport Tchrs 1977-; Keyport PTA 1977-; Keyport Tchr of Yr; Governors Tchr gnition Pgm for NJ 1988-89; *home:* 104 Chingarora Ave Keyport NJ 5*

NEDY, MARGARET WOLF, HS Home Economics Teacher; *b:* ord, CT; *m:* John D.; *ed:* Univ of CT (BS) Home Ec 1975, (MS) Home d 1982; *cr:* Guilford HS Home Ec Tchr 1982-; *ai:* Staff Dev Comm hair; Family & Consumer Scis Ed Focus Group; NEA, CEA 1984-; Practices VIP Awd 1985; Guilford Tchr of Yr 1994; Awded 4 Carl ns Mini Grants for New Prgms in Home Ed; Part of Comm That Wrote for Family & Consumer Scis; Celebration of Excl Winner 1985; *e:* Guilford High School New England Rd Guilford CT 06437

NEDY, MELISSA GREGORY, Mathematics Teacher; *b:* Bayshore, *m:* Bruce; *c:* Justin, Colin, Brendan; *ed:* Beaver Coll (BA) Math 1970; Y at Stony Brook (MA) Math Ed 1975; 37 Addl Hrs; *cr:* Walker Mill Math Tchr 1970-72; Udall Road Jr HS Math Tchr 1972-80; West Islip Math Tchr 1980-; *ai:* 1993 Class Adv; Math Curr Comm; NCTM 1988-; NYSUT, West Islip Tchrs Assn 1972-; Amityville Jr League 1975-, 1981-82; *office:* West Islip HS 1 Lions Path West Islip NY 11795*

NEDY, MICHAEL CURTIS, Junior High Math Teacher; *b:* eroy, OH; *m:* Carrie Ann Harris; *ed:* OH Univ (BSEd) Math, Scndry 989; *cr:* YMCA Camp Campbell Gard Outdoor Ed Instr 1990; Meigs Chptr I Math Tchr 1992-93; Meigs Jr HS Math Tchr 1993-; *ai:* Cross , Eighth Grd Girls Bsktbl, HS Girls Track, Field Coach; NEA, OEA -; OH Cncl of Tchrs of Math 1995-; *office:* Meigs Jr HS 621 S 3rd Ave lleport OH 45760

NEDY, NADA TROUT, Third Grade Teacher; *b:* Harrisburg, PA; *m:* ard R.; *c:* Michael, Douglas; *ed:* Shippensburg Univ (BA) Elem 1965; ost Grad Credits; *cr:* Ickesburg Elem Schl 3rd Grd Tchr 1965-67; n Park Elem Schl 3rd Grd Tchr 1967-68; Blain Elem Schl 3rd Grd Tchr -79; Green Park Elem Schl 3rd Grd Tchr 1979-; *ai:* Bldg Ldrshp -95; NEA, PSEA, WPEA 1965-; Messiah Luth Church 1964-, nist, Evangelism Comm Chprsn; *home:* PO Box 15 Green Park PA 1*

NEDY, NANCY MACRI, High School English Teacher; *b:* klyn, NY; *m:* Thomas Charles; *ed:* Molloy Coll (BA) Eng, Ed 1990; king Towards Masters; *cr:* Marine Midland Bank Head Teller 1981-84; rd Stop Store Mgr 1984-85; First Nationwide Bank Operations Officer -89; St Anthony's HS Eng Tchr 1990-; *ai:* NCTE 1990-; Marine and Personal Best Sales Awd 1984; First Nationwide Bank sperson of Yr 1986; Molloy Coll S. Mary Vining Eng Excl Awd 1990; *e:* St Anthony's HS 275 Wolf Hill Rd Melville NY 11747*

NEDY, PAULINE DANICE (WEST), Second Grade Teacher; *b:* ldletown, OH; *w:* Harold W. (dec); *c:* Candy A. Scribner, Sally Jo n, Harold W. Jr., John F., James A., Teri Lynn Hawkins; *ed:* Miami (BS) Elem Ed 1976-, (MED) Elem Ed 1980; Post Grad 25 Credit Hrs; d Miami Univ, Univ of Dayton; *cr:* Middletown City Schls Tchr Aide -77, Second Grd Tchr 1977-; Oneida Elem; *ai:* MTA Nomination, oting Chprsn; Middletown Women's Tchr Club Pres, VP; MTA, OEA, 1977-; AAUW 1992-95; OCIRA 1992-; Martha Holden Jennings Fnd olar 1986-87.

NEDY, PHILIP WAYNE, Elementary Schl Principal; *b:* Huntington, *m:* Laura Ellen Glover; *c:* Timothy, Douglas; *ed:* CW Post Coll (BS) Ed 1971; Rider Coll (MA) Educl Admin 1991; 30 Grad Credits; *cr:* gle Elem Schl 4th-6th Grd Classroom Tchr 1971-76; Hillsborough Schl 6th Grd Classroom Tchr 1976-86, Math Resource Tchr 1986-93; McKeown Elem Schl Vice Prin 1993-95, Prin 1995-; *ai:* NJPSA & D 1993-; Sussex Co Admin Assoc 1993-; NJ Schoolmasters 1994-; NJ of Ed 1996; *office:* Marian E Mckeown Elem Schl 1 School Rd ton NJ 07860

NEDY, ROBERT WILLIAM, Science Teacher; *b:* Schenectady, NY; iane Marie; *ed:* SUNY at Potsdam (BA) Bio 1983, (MS) Ed 1987; *ai:* ket, Holography Club Advs; Co-Advisor of Music Tech Club, Chess Coach; MENSA Soc 1992-; Awded The Reynolds Metal Company Excl chng 1991-92; *office:* Heuvelton Central Schl Box 375 Washington St velton NY 13654

NEDY, RUTH L. (O'DIAM), Fifth Grade Teacher; *b:* Dayton, OH; Oliver Charles; *c:* Isaac, Sarah, Charlene; *ed:* Manchester Coll (BS) Ed 1971; Liberty Home Bible Inst 2 Yrs, Manahatn Schl of Theology ourses; *cr:* Harford Chrstn Schl 3rd Grd Tchr 1971-72; Ridgeville Chrstn Schl 2nd Grd Tchr 1972-73; Harford Chrstn Schl 3rd Grd Tchr 1973-78; Manahatn Chrstn Kndgtn 4 & 5 Yr Old Tchr 1981-84; Harford Chrstn Schl 4th Grd 1984-91, 5th Grd 1993-; *ai:* Franklin Bapt Church 1994-, Asst Children's Schl Worker, Bible Schl Tchr, Choir; *home:* 810 Ellis Ave Delta PA 17314

KENNEDY, THELMA MARY, Spanish & English Teacher; *b:* Hazleton, PA; *m:* James M.; *c:* James Jr., Patrick; *ed:* Bloomsburg Univ (BS) Scndry Ed 1972; Grad Courses at Penn St Univ, Univ of Scranton; *cr:* Hazleton HS Span, Eng Tchr 1972-; *ai:* NEA 1972; AATSP 1980-; PSMLA 1993; Recognition From AATSP; *office:* Hazleton Area HS 1601 W 23rd St Hazleton PA 18201

KENNEDY, TIMOTHY MURLIN, Advanced Biology Teacher; *b:* Lima, OH; *m:* Sandra Sue Burget; *c:* Brook Erin, Ryan Munlin; *ed:* Miami Univ (BA) Botany 1969; Univ of Dayton (MS) Admin & Counseling 1974; Post Grad Chico St 1970; Credit Hrs OH St Univ 1972, OH Northern Univ 1973 & Wayne St Univ 1971; *cr:* Lima Sr HS Aviation, Bio & Botany Instr 1969-82, Unit Prin 1982-85; Celina Sr HS Advanced Bio Tchr 1985-, Western Field Stud Dir 1985-; *ai:* Environmental, Sci & Aviation Club; Boy Scout Merit Badge Cnslr; NEA, OEA & WOEA 1969-; LEA 1969-82; CEA 1985-, Bldg Rep & Exec Comm; Merdon Union Schl Bd 1986-90; Parkway Schl Bd 1994-97; Lakefield Airport Authority 1986-93; Union Twp Zoning Commision 1988-; Celina Presbyn Church 1970-, Elder; Jennings Conf on Educl Excl Presenter; Classroom Enrichment Grants; Mercer Cty AIDS Task Force; Small Schl Dist Advy Comm Chm; OH Schl Bds Assn; Natl Sci Fnd Research Grant 1970; *office:* Celina City Schls 715 E Wayne St Celina OH 45822

KENNEDY-SMITH, SUSAN M., Secondary English Teacher; *b:* Suffolk Cty, NY; *m:* Ernest Patrick Smith; *c:* Drew Patrick, Conor Patrick; *ed:* Hofstra Univ (BA) Eng 1984; Dowling Coll (MS) Ed 1989; SUNY at Stony Brook Tchr Cert Prgm; *cr:* Longwood Jr HS Eng Tchr 1985-; Longwood HS Eng Tchr 1993-; Bellport MS Eng Tchr 1993; *ai:* Future Tchrs of Amer Club 1996; LJHS Act Adv, Coord, Extra Curr Act Supvr 1987-89; First Suffolk Cty JHS SADD Chptr 1988; NCTE 1985-; Excl Tchng Awd 1988; *office:* Longwood HS 100 Longwood Rd Middle Island NY 11953*

KENNEL, BETH MATTSON, French & German Teacher; *b:* Detroit, MI; *c:* John, Christian; *ed:* Univ of MI (BA) Ger 1965, (MA) Ger 1967; SUNY at Brockport Admin Cert 1991; Attnd Univ of Rochester, Nazareth Coll at Paris Cologne; *cr:* Univ of MI Tchng Fellow 1966-67; Fairport HS Tchr, Facilitator for Gifted Stdnts 1974-; *ai:* Shared Decision Making Team; Acad Decathlon Team Coach; Steering Comm GATE; AATG, NY Tchrs Assn 1975-; AATF 1988-, Pres 1991-93; NYSAFLT 1985-, Regnl Chair, Ldrshp Awds 1994-96; ATAD Bd 1995-, Chair, Rennes; YFU 1961-, School Liaison; Fulbright Tchr in Switzerland 1980-81; DAAD Flwshp 1965-66; Tchr of Month 1993; NY Championship Decathlon Team Coach 1992-95; *office:* Fairport HS 1358 Ayrault Rd Fairport NY 14450*

KENNEY, ANGIE, High School English Teacher; *b:* Columbus, OH; *ed:* OH Wesleyan (BA) Eng Ed 1993; Working Towards MA Curr, Instruction Ashland Univ; *cr:* Big Walnut HS Eng Tchr 1994-; *ai:* Girls Bsktbl Coach; NHS Adv; NEA 1994-, Bldg Rep; *office:* Big Walnut HS 555 Old 3C Hwy Sunbury OH 43074*

KENNEY, JOHN MICHAEL, Athletic Dir & Faculty Instr; *b:* Gouverneur, NY; *m:* Carol Seiple; *c:* Jacob, Derek, Nathan, Adam; *ed:* Univ of VA (BS) Ed 1976; Wheaton Coll (MA) Theology 1985; PHD Pgm at NY Univ 18 Hrs Philosophy; *cr:* Dallas Police Dept Ofcr 1976-79; Stony Brook Schl Fac Mem 1979-; *ai:* LaCrosse Chprsn; Long Island Metro Fndtn; NY St Sectional Comm Mem; Tournament & Policy; Coach: Ftbl, Wrestling, LaCrosse; Suffolk Cty Coaches 1986-, Pres; Natl Ath Admins 1988-, CAA Awd; Natl Interscholastic LaCrosse Assn 1988-, VP; Three Village LaCrosse Club 1985-, Pres; Three Village Times Newspaper Man of Yr 1990; Suffolk Cty Coaches Assn Man of Yr 1993, Coach of Yr 1995; Numerous Articles Pub; *office:* Stony Brook Schl Rt 25 A Stony Brook NY 11790*

KENNEY, LINDA ANN (FREEFIELD), Second Grade Teacher; *b:* Bethlehem, PA; *m:* David Jr.; *c:* Laura, Melissa; *ed:* East Stroudsburg Univ (BS) Elem 1973, (MSED) Elem 1976; 30 Addl Grad Credits; *cr:* Quakertown Schl Dist 1st Grd Tchr 1973-82; Neidig Elem Schl 2nd Grd Tchr 1982-; *ai:* Midget Chrldr Coach; Fac Rep Parent Group; Assembly Planner Schl; PSEA, NEA 1973-; Tchr of Yr Awd 1994; *office:* Joseph S Neidig Elem Schl 201 N Penrose St Quakertown PA 18951

KENNEY, MARGARET J., Professor of Mathematics; *b:* Boston, MA; *ed:* Boston Coll (BS) Scndry Ed, Math 1957, (MA) Math 1959; Boston Univ (PHD) Math 1977; *cr:* Boston Coll Lecturer 1959-; Boston Coll Asst Prof 1970-; Boston Coll Assoc Prof 1979-; Boston Coll Math Prof 1992-; *ai:* NCTM 1962-, Bd of Dirs 1983-86, Numerous Comms 1979-; MAA 1958-; AMS 1963-; Assn of Tchrs of Math in New England 1957-, Pres 1982-84; Alumni Awd for Excl in Sci 1989; Project Dir; NSF Higher Ed Grants; Authored Numerous Books & Articles; *office:* Boston Coll Chestnut Hill MA 02167

KENNEY, MARY, Art Teacher & Chairperson; *b:* Glen Cove, NY; *ed:* Mt St Vincent Univ (BA) Elem Ed 1963; NY Univ (MA) Art Ed 1975; *cr:* St Sylvester Schl Elem Prim Grd Tchr 1963-74; Georgian Ct Coll Adj Art Prof 1975-76; NY Univ Art Dept Asst to Chprsn 1976-82; St Johns Prep HS 9th-12th Grd Instr & Chprsn 1982-; *ai:* HS Lit Magazine Moderator; Phi Delta Kappa 1982-, NYU Chptr; Intnl Color Pencil Soc 1990-; TEACH Awd 1985; Written Up in Local Newspaper to Mary Kenney Art More Than Imitates Life 1989; Numerous Articles & Creative Writing Pub; *office:* Saint Johns Preparatory HS 2121 Crescent St Astoria NY 11105*

KENNEY, MICHAEL WILLIAM, Fourth Grade Teacher; *b:* Philadelphia, PA; *ed:* Univ of MS (BA) Elem Ed 1970; Villanova Univ (MS) Admin 1975; Attnd John Hopkins Univ; *cr:* Woodland Elem 6th Grd Tchr 1972-73; Ancola MS 6th Grd Tchr 1973-82; Eagleville Elem 4th Grd Tchr 1982-95; Audubon Elem 4th Grd Tchr 1995-; *ai:* NEA 1972-; *office:* Audubon Elem Schl 2765 Egypt Rd Norristown PA 19403*

KENNEY, MICHELLE D. ST HILAIRE, Social Studies Teacher; *b:* Manchester, NH; *m:* W. Bruce; *ed:* Notre Dame Coll (BA) His 1974; Educating Exceptional Learner, Emotionally Disturbed Stu; Paralegal Stud; New Hampshire His; *cr:* Southside Jr HS Soc Stud Tchr 1977-, Part-time Curr Coord 1981-82; *ai:* Acad Awds Night Originator, Adv; Dist, Local Staff Dev Comm; Soc Stud Curr Comm City of Manchester; NH Historical Soc, Manchester Historical Soc 1987-; NCSS, NH Cncl for Soc Stud 1981-; ASCD 1982-; NEA, MEA 1977-, Rep 1977-79; Staff Dev Comm; Notre Dame Coll Bd of Alumni 1991-94, Treas; NEA Instrl, Prof Dev Comm; Who's Who in Amer Ed; Schl Curr Dev Comm; Law Related Ed Prgms Initiated Interdisciplinary Tchng Prgm; Boston Globe Bill of Rights Wkshp Presentor; Dev Jr HS Orientation Prgm Stud, Survival Skills; *office:* Southside Jr HS 140 S Jewett St Manchester NH 03103

KENNEY, NANCY ELIZABETH, Algebra Teacher; *b:* Baltimore, MD; *m:* Richard J.; *c:* James J.; *ed:* Towson St Univ (BS) Math 1969; Attnd Loyola Coll, Towson St Univ, Cath Univ; *cr:* Rock Glenn Jr HS Tchr 1970-74; Chinquapin MS Tchr 1974-78; West Baltimore MS Tchr 1978-; *ai:* Eighth Grd Closing, Schl Fund Raiser Comms; Team Ldr; *office:* West Baltimore MS 201 North Bend Rd Baltimore MD 21229

KENNEY, VIRGINIA E., First Grade Teacher; *b:* Elizabeth, NJ; *ed:* Kean Coll (BS) Elem Ed 1973; Cert to Teach Blind, Visually Impaired 1984; Jersey City St Cert Spec Ed 1985; 3 Credit Hrs Orientation, Mobility; *cr:* St Mary's Grammar Schl Primary Grds Tchr 1969-74; St Thomas the Apostle Schl First Grd Tchr 1975-; Bookkepper, Mgr Local Bus; *ai:* NCEA 1975-; POW-MIA 1968-; EIES of NJ 1977-; Outstdng Tchr Recognition Awd 1992; *office:* St Thomas Apostle Schl 60 Byrd Ave Bloomfield NJ 07003

KENNY, JAMES F., Social Studies Teacher; *b:* Wheeling, WV; *m:* Patricia; *c:* Kerry, Cory, Trevor; *ed:* St Francis Coll (BA) His 1971; Trenton St Coll (MAT) Tchng 1974; Attnd Penn St Univ; *cr:* Cncl Rock Schl Dist Tchr 1975-; *ai:* Bsktbl Coach 22 Yrs; Stu Cncl Adv 10 Yrs; NEA & PSEA 1975-; *office:* Holland Jr HS 400 E Holland Rd Holland PA 18966

KENNY, ROSEMARY, Kindergarten Teacher; *b:* Washington, DC; *ed:* Seton Hall (BS) Elem Ed & Early Ed 1973; Span Lang Inst; Pvt Span Classes; Archdiocese of Newark Tchr Inservice Pgm 1970-, Catechist Cert 1991; *cr:* Sacred Heart Elem Schl 3rd Grd Tchr 1967-68; St Henry Elem Schl K-1st Grd & 8th Grd Art Tchr 1968-71; Bender Acad Kndgtn Tchr 1971-; Columbia HS Adult Ed ESL Tchr 1990-92; *ai:* Co-Direct Adult Retreats; Co-Operating Tchr for Stu-Tchrs From Seton Hall; Mbrshp Schl Evaluation Team; Mid Sts Evaluation Comm Mem; NCEA 1968-; *office:* Bender Memorial Acad 416 Linden Ave Elizabeth NJ 07202

KENSECKI, JOHN LEONARD, Social Studies Teacher, Chprsn; *b:* Scranton, PA; *c:* Jonathan M., Amanda M., Matthew J.; *ed:* East TN St Univ (BS) His 1966; West Chester Univ (MED) Instrl Media Ed 1973; Post Grad Staunton Military Acad 1962; Attnd Millersville Univ & Penn St Univ; *cr:* Coatesville Area HS Soc Stud Tchr 1966-72; Staunton Valley HS Soc Stud Tchr, Chprsn 1973-; *ai:* Head Track, Ftbl Coach; PIAA Track Ofcl; NEA, PSEA 1973-; Saucon Vly Ed Assn 1973-, Legislative Chprsn; *office:* Saucon Valley Sr HS 2100 Polk Valley Rd Hellertown PA 18055

KENSICKI, SANDRA A. LACORTE, English Teacher; *b:* Clifton, NJ; *m:* J. Kenneth; *c:* Kevin Joseph, Korinne Mary; *ed:* Northwestern Univ (BA) Eng, Ed 1968; Montclair St Coll Scndry Eng 1969, Eng as Second Lang 1990 Certs; *cr:* Passaic Vly HS Eng Tchr 1968-72; Clifton HS Eng Tchr 1988-; *ai:* Chrldng Coach; Schl Improvement Comm; Scheduling Task Force; Sr Review Assessment Panel; NEA, NJEA 1968-; Clifton Tchrs Assn 1988-, VP; NJ TESOL BE 1988-; Clifton Yth Week Comm 1990-94, Cert of Merit; Clifton Western Division Bsbl-Sftbl 1981-91, Treas; *office:* Clifton HS 333 Colfax Ave Clifton NJ 07013*

KENT, LISA R., 7th-12th Grd PE Teacher; *b:* Rochester, NY; *m:* Keith; *c:* Aaron, Kayla; *ed:* Brockport St (BS) K-12 PE 1977, (MS) 7th-12th PE 1984; *cr:* Lyndonville CntrlSchl 7th-12th Grd PE Tchr 1979-; *ai:* Adv Var Club, Jr Class; Peer Mediation Adv; Prins Adv, Shared Decision Making Comms; NYSUT, AFT 1979-; Lyndonville PTA 1993-; Yates Bapt Church 1994-; *office:* Lyndonville Central Schl Housel Ave Lyndonville NY 14098

KENT, MARNIE JAYNE, Physical Education Teacher; *b:* Oneonta, NY; *m:* Scott; *ed:* St Univ Coll at Cortland (BSE) PE 1991; Masters Degree 12 Credits Toward Gen Scndry Nazareth Coll; *cr:* Spencerport Cntrl Schls PE, Adaptive & K-12th Grd PE Tchr 1992-93; Fairport Cntrl Schls 6th-8th Grd PE Tchr 1993-; *ai:* Var Girls Lacrosse & Modified Girls 7th & 8th Grd Soccer Coach; Ski Club Adv; Stu & Behavior & Support Team; Drug Intervention Team; IM; PE Adv Comm Dist; NYSAPEHERD 1991-; FEA 1993-; NYSUT 1992-; Dollars for Scholars 1995-, Bd of Dir; Brighton Pittsford Post Girls Lacrosse Coach of Yr 1995; Monroe Cty Girls Lacrosse Coach of Yr 1995; Red Cross Swimming Lessons Vol; Comm Lacrosse Vol Coach; *office:* Martha Brown MS 665 Ayrault Rd Fairport NY 14450

KENT, VALARIE ANN, Math Teacher; *b:* Cuba, NY; *ed:* SUNY at Brockport (BS) Math 1987, (MA) Math 1989; Attnd Real World Application Inst at Brockport, Woodrow Wilson Insts; *cr:* Buffalo Bd of Ed Scndry Math Tchr 1989-; Erie Comm Coll Part-Time Math Instr 1990-; *ai:* Drill Team & Class Adv; Asst Girls Sftbl & Girls Bsktbl Coach; Math Mentor; After Schl Tutoring Pgm Math Instr; Lafayette HS Outstdng Svc Awd 1993; TRANSIT Advy Bd Mem.

KENYATTA, JANICE GREEN, Business Education Teacher; *b:* Newark, NJ; *m:* Kamau T.; *c:* Aliya, Ayanna; *ed:* Essex Co Coll (AS) Secretarial Sci 1972; Montclair St Coll (BA) Bus & Secretarial Ed 1975, (MA) Bus & Secretarial Ed 1977; *cr:* Essex Cty Voc & Technical HS Bus Tchr 1976-; *ai:* NEA, NJEA 1976-; Montclair St Grad Fellowship to Complete Masters Degree; Co-Wrote with Husband & Pub Book Entitled Black Folks Hair-Secrets, Shame & Liberation; *office:* Essex Cty Voc & Technical HS 91 W Market St Newark NJ 07103

KENYON, JAMES A., Social Studies Teacher; *b:* Oreonta, NY; *m:* Pamela Conroe; *c:* Olivia, Briana, Annica; *ed:* SUNY at Cobleskill (AAS) Bus Admin 1972; East Stroudsburg Univ (BS) Sec Ed 1974; SUC at Oneonta (MS) Ed 1986; SUNY at Albany 6 Credit Hrs Ed Admin 1995; SUC at Cortland 3 Credit Hrs Ed Admin 1996; *cr:* Oyster Bay HS Coach 1975; Notre Dame HS Tchr 1976-78; Bangor HS Admin Aide 1979-80; worcester Cntrl Schl Tchr 1980-; *ai:* Var Men's Bsktbl, Var women's Soccer Coach; Sr Class Adv; Worcester Tchrs Assn 1980-, Pres; NYS Cncl Soc Stud 1983-; United Meth Church 1983-; Coach of Yr Soccer 1989-; Coach of Yr 1994 Bsktbl; *office:* Worcester Central Schl 182 Main St Box 1C Worcester NY 12197

KENZIG, WILLIAM JOSEPH, English Teacher; *b:* Brooklyn, NY; *m:* Kathleen H.; *c:* Rachel, Allison; *ed:* Stony Brook Univ (MS) Ed 1977; *cr:* Longwood MA Grd 7 Tchr, House Cptn 1986-93, Grd 7 Eng Tchr 1972-; *ai:* 7th-8th Grd Bsbl Coach; Talent Show Coord; Cooking Club; Exercise Club; AFT, NEA, MITA 1972-; Wading River Little League 1993-, Trustee; Tchr of Yr 1986; *office:* Longwood MS 41 Yaphank-Middle Island Rd Middle Island NY 11953

KEOGAN, MARGARET E.,RDC, 8th Grade Teacher; *b:* Bronx, NY; *ed:* Good Counsel Coll Eng 1956; St Joseph's Hartford, Fairfield Univ Ed Adoles Phyc; *cr:* St Bernard's Schl Tchr 1953-62; Mt Carmel Schl Tchr 1962-; *ai:* Moderator Boys Ath Prgms, News, Views Team, Yrbk; *office:* Our Lady-Mt Carmel Schl 59 E Main St Elmsford NY 10523

KEOSSEIAN, JOHN MARK, English Tchr & Mentor Pgm Dir; *b:* Brooklyn, NY; *m:* Ellen J.; *ed:* St Francis Coll (BA) Eng 1971; Coll of Staten Island (MS) Eng & Sec Ed 1976; Cert in Admin & Supvr; *cr:* St John the Evangelist 5th & 6th Grd Eng Tchr 1971-73; St Francis of Assissi 7th & 8th Grd Eng Tchr 1973-75; St Saviour HS 9th-12th Grd Eng Tchr, Dept Chair 1975-79; Calvert HS Eng Tchr, Dir of Mentor Prog 1979-; *ai:* Dir of Comm Mentorship Pgm for Academically Able HS Srs; NCTE 1977-; NEA, MSTA & CEA 1979-; St Marys Coll Exceptional Tchr Awd 1985; Calvert Cty Pub Schl Tchr Yr Awd 1988; *office:* Calvert HS 600 Dares Beach Rd Prince Frederick MD 20678*

KEOUGH, ANDREW WILLIAM, Vice Principal; *b:* New Orleans, LA; *m:* Christine Marie Souza; *c:* Julia, Mary; *ed:* Roger Williams Coll (BA) His 1984; Framingham St Coll (MED) Spcl Needs 1991, (MA) Schl Admin 1994; Northeastern Univ Non-Degree Cert 1988; 30 Credits; *cr:* Douglas HS Spcl Ed Tchr 1988-90; Milford HS Spcl Ed Tchr 1990-95; Blackstone-Millville Regl Schl 7th-12th Grd Vice-Prin 1995-; *ai:* MASSP 1995-; NASSP 1995-; Sherborn Bicycle Comm 1994-; Sherborn Democratic Town Comm 1995-; *office:* Blackstone-Millville Regnl Sch 175 Lincoln St Blackstone MA 01504

KEOUGH, MARGARET MC GAUGHEY, Second Grade Teacher; *b:* North East, PA; *m:* Donald S.; *ed:* Mercyhurst Coll (BS) Elem 1960; Edinboro 9 Credits; Fredonia 6 Credits; ACES 3 Credits; Ripley Cmptr; IU Ctr in Edinboro Cmptr Classes; *cr:* Randolph Schl 3-4th Grd Tchr 1960-62;

Erie Schl 1-3rd Grd Tchr 1962-; *ai:* EEA, PSEA, NEA 1962-; Amer Legion Aux 1980-; Tchr of Yr 1988; *home:* 10308 Irish Rd Ripley NY 14775*

KEPLER, MELANIE HUNT, Mathematics Teacher; *b:* Sharon, CT; *m:* Lance J.; *c:* Louise, Corey; *ed:* SUNY at Brockport (BS) Sendry Math 1979, (MA) Math Ed 1985; 39 Addl Hrs Math, Ed; *cr:* Elba Cntrl Schl Scndry Math Tchr 1980-; *ai:* United Way Chprsn; Schlsp Comm; NYSUT 1981-; NYSTMA; *office:* Elba Central Schl 51 S Main St Elba NY 14058

KEPLINGER, THOMAS LOWELL, 5th Grade Teacher; *b:* Canton, OH; *m:* Carol S. Friedley; *c:* Robert, Jeffrey; *ed:* Ashland Univ (BS) Elem Ed 1979, (MED) Admin 1985; *cr:* Lincoln Elem Schl 5th, 6th Grd Tchr 1981-; *ai:* 8th Grd Ftbl Coach, Elem Sci Coord; Ashland City Tchrs Assn, OEA, NEA 1998-; *office:* Lincoln Elem Schl 30 W 11th St Ashland OH 44805

KEPNER, JOANNE GOLDER, 2nd Grade Teacher; *b:* Philadelphia, PA; *m:* Dale; *c:* Steven, Cynthia, Sharon; *ed:* West Chester Univ (BS) Elem 1956; Geneseo St Univ 30 Hrs Elem; Temple Univ 6 Hrs Comparative Ed; *cr:* Keystone Schl Kndgtn Tchr 1956-58; Garrettford Elem Schl 1st Grd Tchr 1958-59; Honeoye Cntrl Schl 2nd Grd Tchr 1966-; *ai:* Pub Rel Comm; Schl Bldg Team; Grd Level Chprsn; Honeoye Tchrs Assn 1966-, Pres 1977-82, Sec 1993-; NYSUT 1966-, Negotiations Ch; Delta Kappa Gamma Soc Intnl, Pres 1990-91; Youth Bd 1985-, Chprsn; United Church of Bristol 1960-, Women's SocPres; Harmony Circle 1965-, Pres; St Awds Comm 1993-94; *office:* Honeoye Central Schl Main St Honeoye NY 14471*

KEPNER, NANCY M., Fourth Grade Teacher; *b:* Warren, OH; *w:* Perry J. (dec); *c:* Debra J. Duda, Sharon M., Paul J., Maribeth Peters; *ed:* Youngstown St Univ (BSEd) Elem Ed-Cum Laude 1971; Kent St Univ (MSEd) Ed 1980; Post-Grad Stud Ashland Univ; *cr:* Champion Local Schl Dist Tchr 1971-; *ai:* NEA 1971-; OEA 1971-; CEA 1971-; *office:* Champion Central Elem Schl 5759 Mahoning Ave NW Warren OH 44483

KEPPEL, JOHN CHARLES, Social Studies Teacher; *b:* Hibbing, MN; *c:* Erin Marie, Maura Ann; *ed:* Univ of MN (BS) His, Scndry Ed 1971; Univ of MA at Dartmouth (MBA) Bus 1990; *cr:* Edgewood Jr HS Soc Stud Tchr 1973-75; Stoughton HS Soc Stud Tchr 1975-; *ai:* Learning Moddalities & Instructional Methodology Wkshp Faciliator 1995; K-6th Scope & Sequence Consultant 1993; NEA 1973-, MTA, NCTA 1975-; Tufts Univ Outstanding Tchr Recognition Awd 1994; NEH Fellowship in Ecs Univ of N IA 1993; UMA at Dartmouth Scholar Awd 1990; *office:* Stoughton HS 232 Pearl St Stoughton MA 02072

KEPSHIRE, CHERYL ANN (WILSHIRE), Second Grade Teacher; *b:* Pittsburgh, PA; *w:* Thomas S. (dec); *c:* Dax, Derek; *ed:* IN Univ of PA (BS) Elem Ed 1972; MS Equivalency Penn St Univ 1975; *cr:* Berwick Area Schl Grd 2 Tchr 1972-73; Cambria Heights Schl Kndgtn, Grd 2 Tchr 1973-; *ai:* CHEA 1973-; *office:* Cambria Heights Elem Schl 1 E Campbell St PO Box 510 Carrolltown PA 15722

KERCH, FRANK PAUL, Social Stud & Sociology Tchr; *b:* Somerset, PA; *m:* Virginia Marie Deromedi; *c:* Matthew; *ed:* Shippensburg St (BS) Soc Stud 1974; Shippenburg Univ (MED) Soc Stud 1978; *cr:* Shippensburg Schl Dist Tchr 1974-; *ai:* Ftbl & Sftbl Coach; Ath Equipment Mgr; Stu Asst Team; SAEA, NEA & NCSS 1974-; Shippensburg Historical Soc 1980-; Pres of Shippensburg Univ Bsbl Alumni Club 1982-, Pres; Coaching Sftbl; Championships 6 League, 3 Dist, 1 St; *office:* Shippensburg Area Sr HS 317 N Morris St Shippensburg PA 17257

KERDAVID, GISELE, Fifth Grade Teacher; *b:* Manhattan, NY; *ed:* Univ at Albany (BS) Bus Admin 1979; Queens Coll (MS) Elem Ed 1986; 30 Addl Hrs; *cr:* St Farm Insurance Claims Svc Rep 1979-83; St Francis de Sales Fifth Grd Tchr 1984-87; Elmont UFSD Fifth Grd Tchr 1987-; *ai:* Shared Decision Making Comm, Schl & Dist; AFT, NYSUT 1987-; Joint Cncl Ec Ed Awd 1987; Young Consumer Olympics Awd 1989; *office:* Dutch Broadway Elem Schl 1880 Dutch Broadway Elmont NY 11003

KERESTON, JANETTA OVERAND, Fourth Grade Teacher; *b:* Pittsburgh, PA; *m:* Ronald; *ed:* CA Univ (BS) Elem Ed 1972, (MA) Rdng Specialist 1975; *cr:* Belle Vernon Area Schl Dist Remedial Rdng Tchr 1973-75, Open Classroom Ed Tchr 1975-77, Fifth Grd Tchr 1977-80, Fourth Grd Tchr 1980-; *ai:* CA Univ Stdnt Tchng Advy Bd 1992-; *office:* Marion Elem Schl 500 Perry Ave Belle Vernon PA 15012*

KEREZSI, PATRICIA ANN, Fourth Grade Teacher; *b:* Chester, PA; *ed:* West Chester Univ (BS) Spec Ed 1985; Grad Credits St Joes Univ; Credits Del Co I.U., Chester Co. I.U.; *cr:* St Francis de Sales Schl Fourth Grd Tchr 1985-; *ai:* Girl's Bsktbl Coach; Yrbk Comm; NCEA, NCTM 1985-; St Francis Parish 1964-, Eucharistic Minister 1990-; Franciscan Companions in Mission 1990-, Task Form; Outstdng Grad of Cath Schls Awd 1992; Franciscan Companions in Ministry Vol 1992; *office:* St Francis de Sales Schl 39 New Rd Aston PA 19014

KERKOWSKI, SCOTT PAUL, Chemistry Teacher; *b:* Luzerne, PA; *m:* Anita Barton; *ed:* Lock Haven Univ (BS) Sec Ed Bio, Chem 1992; 36 Addl Credit Hrs; *cr:* Lake-Lehman HS Chem Tchr 1993-; *ai:* Asst Var Ftbl, Strength Conditioning Coach; PSEA, NEA 1992-; Knights of Columbus 1996, 3rd Degree; *office:* Lake-Lehman HS 38 Market St Lehman PA 18627

KERN, BARBARA MAE (HUTCHINSON), High School Guidance Counselor; *b:* Bridgeport, CT; *m:* Frederick Paul; *c:* Kelly L., Jason F. (dec); *ed:* Univ of Bridgeport (BS) Elem Ed 1962; Cntrl CT St Univ (MS) Schl Cnslng 1982; *cr:* Loram Elem Schl Tchr 1962-63; Eli Whitney Schl Elem Tchr 1963-66; Moran Jr HS Sixth Grd Tchr 1966-68; Cheshire HS Guid Cnslr 1982-; *ai:* Fac Senate Comm; Transition Group Organizer; CT Ed Assn, NEA 1963-; CT Cnslrs Assn 1985-; Amer Assn of Univ Women 1968-, Pres, VP; CT Chapter of Natl Hemophilia Assn 1971-, Asst Treas; Appointed to Mayor's Yth Svc Bd 1975-; 4 Yr Acad Schlsp to Univ of Bridgeport; Who's Who Among Stdnts in Amer Colls, Univs; Eva Mc Intyre Awd for Svc to Natl Hemophilia Fnd CT Chapter; Lead Partina Documentary Film on HS Stdnts with Strong Potential Narrated by Walter Cronkite; Article Pub; *home:* 1261 E Johnson Ave Southington CT 06489

KERN, ROBERT WILLIAM, High School Math Teacher; *b:* McKeesport, PA; *ed:* Edinboro Univ (BS) Scndry Math 1970; Attnd Pitt, Penn St, AIU #3; *cr:* Homeville Jr HS Math Tchr 1970-82, Dept Head 1980-82; Edison Intermediate Math Tchr, Dept Head 1982-84; West Mifflin MS Math Tchr, Dept Head 1984-90; West Mifflin HS Math Tchr 1990-; *ai:* Long Range Plan, Staff Dev Comm; West Mifflin Fed Tchrs 1973-, Treas 17 Yrs; NCTM 1970-; Local Drug Alcohol Org 1989-; *office:* West Mifflin Area HS 91 Commonwealth Ave West Mifflin PA 15122

KERNER, JOHN E., Mathematics Teacher; *b:* St Marys, PA; *m:* Mary Brunner; *c:* John Declan; *ed:* St Bonaenture Univ (BS) Math 1965, (MS) Adv Tchr Ed in Math 1970; 112 Grad & In Svc Credit Hrs; *cr:* Limestone Union Free SD Math Tchr 1965-68; Allegancy Central Schl Math Tchr 1968-; *ai:* Adv Nevins Math Contest, AHSME, AIME; Timekeeper Var Ftbl, Bsktbl, Vlybl; Scorekeeper Men-Women Bsktbl; Alleg-Limestone Tchrs Assoc 1968-, Pres, Past Treas; Phi Delta Kappa 1990-; NEA 1975-; Olean Tchrs Fed Credit Union 1970-, Past Bd of Dir; YMCA 1993-, Corporate Cup Spirit Awd; St Marys of the Angels Church 1968-, Usher; Colgate Univ Summer Prgm for Advanced Placement, Honor Stnts in Math; NSF Inst for Tech SUNY Brockport; *office:* Allegany-Limestone Centrl Schl N 4th St Allegany NY 14706*

KERNER, KATHLEEN, Business Teacher; *b:* Brooklyn, NY; *c:* Joseph; *ed:* Bernard M Baruch Coll (BS) Ed Commerce 1973; C W Post Coll (MS) Scndry Ed, Guid 1977; Prof Cert Hofstra Univ Cmptr Ed 1989; 50 Credit Hrs Cmptr & Tchr Dev Courses; *cr:* Seaford HS Bus Instr 1973-; David Sanders Dance Dynamics Dance Co Dancer, Instr 1982-84; Nassau Dance Ctr Dancer 1983-89; Greg Burge Dance Studio Instr 1983-85; Seaford HS Tract Prgm Instr 1987-89, 1994-; Hofstra Greywig Dancer & Actor 1991; *ai:* Class Adv 1974-80; Secretarial Svc Prgm 1977-83; FBLA Adv 1982-83; Choreographer Drama Club 1994-; Jazz Exercise Club Instr 1980-83; Curr Writing 1987-88, 1992-94; NBA 1980-; UTS 1780 1973-; *home:* 97 Barnes St Long Beach NY 11561

KERNS, C. MICHAEL, Dir of Vet Svcs & Asst Prof; *b:* Kenton, OH; *m:* Melanie E.; *c:* Eric, Rachel; *ed:* OH St Univ (DVM) Veterinary Medicine 1981; *cr:* Berlin Veterinary Clinic Inc Veterinarian 1981-82; Fort Recovery Veterinary Clinic Inc Veterinarian 1982-87; Findlay Animal Clinic Veterinarian 1987-92; Univ of Findlay Asst Prof of Natural Sci & Dir of Veterinary Svcs 1992-; *ai:* Coordinating Veterinarian for the Hancock Cty Fair; Hancock Cty Advy Bd; Hancock Ldrshp Pgm; OH Bank Advy Bd; OVMA 1981-; AVMA 1981-; HVMA 1987-, Pres, VP & Sec-Treas; Amer Assn of Equine Practitioners 1994-; 4H Adv; Bsbl Coach; Ben Logan HS, Hall of Fame Awd; *office:* Univ Of Findlay 1000 N Main St Findlay OH 45840

KERR, DIANNE LYNNE, Asst Professor of Health Ed; *b:* Canonsburg, PA; *ed:* Slippery Rock St Univ (BS) Hlth & PE 1976; Bowling Green St Univ (MED) Hlth & PE 1981; OH St Univ (MA) Hlth Ed 1987, (PHD) Hlth Ed 1992; *cr:* Bowling Green St Univ Grad Asst 1980-81; Notre Dame Coll of OH Instr & Asst Prof 1981-85; OH St Univ Grad Asst 1985-87; Amer Schl Hlth Assn AIDS Ed Project Dir 1987-90; Kent St Univ Asst Prof 1991-; *ai:* Curr Comm Chair; Fac Advy Comm; Dissertation Awds Comm; Eta Sigma Gamma Rho Chptr Adv; Eta Sigma Gamma 1987-; AAHPERD 1987-; ASHA 1987-; AAUP 1995-; SIECUS 1995-; HIV Comm Planning Group 1994-, Chair & Gen Comm Group; OH AIDS Svc Awd; Pub Article & Column; Directed AMFAR Targeted Ed Grant; CDC Cooperative Agreement; Met Life Project Reach Grant; *office:* Kent St Univ 316 Whitehall PO Box 5190 Kent OH 44242

KERR, JAMES R., Social Studies Teacher; *b:* Daytona Beach, FL; *m:* Terri L. Hill; *ed:* Christian Heritage Coll (BS) His & Scndry Ed 1990; *cr:* The Kings Chrstn Schl Jr HS Lang Arts & Algebra Tchr 1990-92, 7th-12th Grd Soc Stud, Cmptrs & Keyboarding Tchr 1993-; 9th-12th Grd Soc Stud 1995-; *ai:* Jr Var & Var Mens Soccer Coach; Jr Var & Var Womens Bsktbl Coach; Stu Cncl Adv; *office:* The King's Christian Schl Winston Way Cherry Hill NJ 08034

KERR, LINDA, Assistant Professor; *b:* Ithaca, NY; *m:* Daniel W. Toomey; *ed:* Bates Coll (BA) Eng Lit 1980; Lesley Coll (MED) Moderate Spec Needs 1985; Working on Masters in Rdng & Lang, Working on Doctoral in Rdng, Lang & Learning Disabilites at Harvard Univ; *cr:* Landmark Coll Tutorial Dept Chair & Supvr 1985-88; Harvard Univ Tchng Asst 1988-90, Instr 1990-92; Landmark Coll Asst Prof 1993-; *ai:* IRA.

KERR, LINDA SMITH, Second Grade Teacher; *b:* Scranton, PA; *m:* Andrew R.; *c:* Andrew R., Steven A.; *ed:* SUC at Geneseo (BS) Elem Ed, ECE 1975; SUC at Brockport (MS) Ed, Rdng 1980; *cr:* Albion Primary Schl Kndgtn Tchr 1975-80; Albion MS 6th Grd Tchr 1980-82; Albion Primary Schl Kndgtn Tchr 1982-91, 4th Grd Tchr 1991-93, 1st Grd Tchr 1993-94, 2nd Grd Tchr 1994-; *ai:* Lang Arts Comm; Bldg Ldrshp Team; PTA Playground Comm Co-Chprsn; PTA; Greece Cntrl Schl PTA; AFT 1975-; Albion Tchr Assn 1992-, VP; NYSUT 1975-, Ldrshp Awd; Cub Scouts 1989-, Ldr; Friends of Strong 1992-, Vol Pediatrics; Rel Instruction-Catechism Classes 1994-, Tchr; *office:* Albion Primary Schl 324 East Ave Albion NY 14411*

KERR, LOIS JEAN COURTEMANCHE, HS Social Studies Teacher; *b:* Lebanona, NH; *m:* Douglas; *ed:* Plymouth St Coll (BA) Lbrl Arts, His 1971; Dartmouth Coll (MA) Lbrl Stud 1984; Credit Hrs Staff Dev Curr Methods; *cr:* Lebanon Jr HS 7th-8th Grd Math Tchr 1975-81; NIH Voc Tech Coll Math Instr 1981; Claremont Jr HS 7th-8th Grd Math Tchr 1982-83; Windsor HS Math, Resource Room Tchr 1981-84; Lebanon HS Scndry Soc Stud Tchr 1984-; *ai:* Granite St Challenge Coach; NHCSS 1980-; ASCD 1994-; VT Pub Interest Group 1990-; Master Tchr Presented Seminar Dartmouth Coll 1991-92; *office:* Lebanon HS 195 Hanover St Lebanon NH 03766

KERR, MAUREEN CONNELLY, 8th Grd Tchr & Sci Curr Coord; *b:* Philadelphia, PA; *m:* Kenneth H.; *c:* Bridget, Kenneth, Kelly, Michael; *ed:* Immaculata Coll (BA) Bio 1964; Villanova Univ (MS) Bio 1966; Cmptr Programming, Application Courses; *cr:* Villanova Univ Instr 1966-67; Merck & Co Renal Rsrch Assoc 1967-73; Kerr & Assocs Bookkeeper 1973-85; St Stanislaus Schl Cmptr Coord 1985-92, 8th Grd Tchr 1992-; *ai:* Montgomery Co Sci Tchrs Assn 1992-; *office:* St Stanislaus Schl 493 E Main St Lansdale PA 19446

KERR, MAUREEN REILLY, Mathematics Teacher; *m:* John; *c:* Tracy, Kristin; *ed:* St Francis Coll (BA) Math 1975; *ai:* NEA; NCTM; AMTNJ; Tri Boro First Aid Squad 1976-, Life Mem; SSP Emergency Mngmt Team; Superior Tchr Awd 1993; Mayors Awd for Outstdng Civic Contribution 1984; *office:* Central Regional H S Forest Hills Pkwy Bayville NJ 08721

KERR, PRISCILLA WIGGINS, Fifth Grade Teacher; *b:* Barbados, WI; *c:* Brandon C., Derick S.; *ed:* Brooklyn Coll (BA) Ed 1972, (MS) Ed 1977; *cr:* PS 44 Tchr 1972-75; HS Redirection Math Tchr 1975-76; PS 133 Tchr 1976-79; PS 44 Tchr 1979-; *ai:* Comar Team; Urban Systemic Initiative Prgm MST Tchr Ldr; AFT, UFT 1973-; *office:* PS 44K 432 Monroe St Brooklyn NY 11221*

KERRANE, LEONA GIORDANO, 7th Grade English Teacher; *b:* Philadelphia, PA; *c:* Jack, Tom; *ed:* Univ of PA (BS) Eng, Math 1958; Beaver Coll (MED) Eng, Ed 1978; 30 Credit Hrs Bus Ed Cert; Attnd Marywood Coll, Carlow Coll, Gwynedd Mercy Coll, MCCC; *cr:* Hatboro Schl Tchr 1959-63; Colonial Schl Dist Tchr 1974-; *ai:* Scheduling; NEA; PSEA; CEA; ALS; AAUW; *office:* Colonial MS 716 Belvoir Rd Norristown PA 19401

KERRIGAN, MICHAEL ANDREW, English Teacher; *b:* New York City, NY; *m:* Rachelle Schlosser; *ed:* Queens Coll (MA) Eng 1994; *cr:* Benjamin Cardozo HS Eng Tchr 1993-; *ai:* Poetry Club, Lit Magazine Adv; NTE 1993-; *office:* Benjamin N Cardozo High School 57-00 223rd St Bayside NY 11364*

KERRY, JANE ELIZABETH, High School English Teacher; *b:* Marlboro, MA; *m:* David T.; *c:* Seamus; *ed:* Univ of ME (BS) Eng, Ed 1978; Working on MS Ed; Attnd Univ Galway; *cr:* Longmeadow HS Eng Tchr 1978-79; Somers HS Eng Tchr 1979-81; Old Orchard Beach HS Eng Tchr 1981-; *ai:* Substance Abuse Vol Effort Team; NCTE 1978-; Stdnts on Stage Grant; Drug Free Schls Recognition; *office:* Old Orchard Beach HS 40 T For Turn Rd Old Orchard Beach ME 04064*

KERSCHBAUM, JAMES, Chemistry Teacher; *b:* Parma, OH; *m:* Leslie Hill; *c:* John; *ed:* Bowling Green St Univ (BS) Comprehen Sci 1963; John Carroll Univ (MA) Admin 1969; *cr:* Normandy Sr HS Sci Dept Chm, Chem Tchr 1968-; *ai:* NEA, OH Ed Assn, Parma Ed Assn 1963-; PTA Schlsp 1982; *office:* Normandy HS 2500 W Pleasant Valley Rd Parma OH 44134

KERSHAW, PHYLLIS GALE, 5th Grade Teacher; *b:* Brooklyn, NY; *ed:* Hofstra Univ (BS) Ed 1963; Credit Hrs Russell Sage Coll; *cr:* PS 257-BrooklynElem Tchr 1964-67; D. P. Sutherland Schl Elem Tchr 1967-73; Genet MS 5 Grd Tchr 1973-; *ai:* Schl Improvement, Soc Comms; Homework Assistance Organizer; Mentor, Supvr Stu Tchrs Oncorta Coll of St Rose, Russell Sage Coll; AFT; NEA; East Greenbush Tchrs Assn 1967-; Chatham Courier Newspaper 1975-, Correspondent; Merit Awd E. Greenbush Schl Dist Outstdng Tchng; *office:* Genet MS Rt 9 & 20 Greenbush NY 12061

KERSHETSKY, DANIEL F., Music Educator; *b:* Shenandoah, PA; Carole Stauffer; *c:* Julia L., Alexander J.; *ed:* PA St Univ (BS) Mus 1981; West Chester Univ (MM) Music Ed 1994; *cr:* Souderton Are Music Educator 1981-87; Boyertown Area SD Music Ed 1987-; *ai:* Ch Show Choir; NEA; PSEA; MENC; PMEA; ACDA; *office:* Boyertown Schl Dist 200 S Madison St Boyertown PA 19512

KERSHNER, BRUCE S., Science Teacher; *b:* Brooklyn, NY; *m:* H Golden; *c:* Joshua, Libby; *ed:* St Univ of NY at Binghamton (BA 1972; Univ of CT at Storrs (MS) Botany, Ecology 1975; St Univ of Buffalo Tchr Cert Sci, Scndry Educ 1993; Univ of CT 60 Hrs Ecolog Univ of Buffalo Med Schl Sci & Med Ed 1983-87; Great Lakes United Environmental Scientist 1987-93; Grand Island MS Sci Tchr 1994; J Kennedy HS Sci Tchr 1994-; *ai:* Adventure Outings Club Adv; Emp Coll Part-time Fac Sci; AFT 1994-; Friends of Allegany 1981-, Founder, Environmentalist of Yr 1987; Erie Cty Environ Cncl 1983 Mem; Ancient Forest Survey NY 1989-, Co-Chair Founder; Open Comm at Amherst 1989-, Co-Chair; Best Children's TV Show in 1991 NY St Broadcasters Assn; Author of 4 Books; Environmentalist 1988 Sierra Club; Gold Medal for Sci Ed Publishing 1985 Natl Cn Advancement & Support of ED; *office:* John F Kennedy Jr Sr HS Cayuga Creek Rd Buffalo NY 14227

KERSHNER, SUSAN, 2nd Grade Teacher; *b:* Salt Lake City, U Jeffrey L.; *c:* Christina L., Stephanie G.; *ed:* Kent St Univ (BS) Chldhd, Elem 1972, (MS) Elem Ed 1977; Post Grad Stud at John C Univ, Franciscan Univ of Steubenville, Ashland Univ; *cr:* North Ave C Elem Kndgtn Tchr 1973-75; Kennedy Schl for the Gifted Primary Tchr 19 Private Tutoring Elem 1978-84; Columbia Coop Nursery Schl Pre-Sch 1984-85; Crestview Elem Schl 2nd, 4th Grd Tchr 1985-; *ai:* Family Family Sci; CEA, OEA, NEA 1985-, Sec; Phi Delta Kappa 1991-; Kappa Gamma, OCTELA 1990-; Zion Luth Church; Martha H Jennings Scholar 1991; Youngstown St Univ Project Link Grant; OC Presenter at St Conf; Wkshp Presenter at In-Svcs; *home:* 213 Eastwo New Middletown OH 44442*

KERSTETTER, BARBARA REINDOLLAR, Second Grade Teach Gettysburg, PA; *m:* Robert E. Jr.; *c:* John, Rachel, Anna; *ed:* Shippen St Coll (BS) Elem Ed 1975; Bloomsburg St Coll (MS) Elem Ed 198 Penns Creek Elem Schl 2nd Grd Tchr 1976-91; Middleburg Elem Sc Grd Tchr 1991-; *ai:* Odyssey of Mind Adv; PSEA, NEA 1980-; Middleburg Elem Schl 600 Wagenseller St Middleburg PA 17842*

KERSTETTER, HAROLD WILLIAM, Geography Teacher Millerstown, PA; *m:* Nancy L. Mitchell; *c:* Teena M. McCann, Neal R Shippensburg St (BS) Geography 1965; West Chester St (MED) Geog 1970; Numerous Post Grad Courses; *cr:* Pierce MS Geography Tchr 1 *ai:* Soc Sci Dept Chm 1973-; Outdoor Ed Dir 1982-; Tchng Team 19871-; Mentor Tchr 1989-; NEA, PSEA 1965-; Natl Cncl for Geogr Ed 1982-; PA Geographical Soc 1975-; NCGE Distinguished T Achvmt Awd 1983; Lehigh Univ Assocs of Distinction 1982; Whos W Chester Cty 1st Edition; *office:* E N Peirce MS 1314 Burke Rd Chester PA 19380

KERSTETTER, JEFFREY ALLEN, Seventh Grade Science Teach Harrisburg, PA; *m:* Donna Marie Haeberle; *c:* Alycia Marie, Bradley A *ed:* Slippery Rock Univ (BS) Elem Ed 1984; Penn St Univ 3 Credits; Stroudsburg Univ 21 Credits; *cr:* Susquentia Elem Schl Grd 6 1985-92; Susquentia MS Grd 7 Sci Tchr 1993-; *ai:* 4th Grd Bsktb Head Soccer, Girls Track Coach; Deck Hockey Club; Environmental Dauphin Soccer Assn; Micro Soccer Prgm Dir; Wetland, Scheduling, & Parish Relations Comms; PSEA, SEA 1987-; Halifax United Church 1993-; Halifax Bsbl Assn, North Amer Fishering Club, R Grouse Soc 1995-; Sigma Pi 1983-, Sec, Efficiency Awd; DER Wet Grant; Susquenita Soccer Team Sportsmanship Awd for Mid Pen *office:* Susquenita MS 1725 Schoolhouse Rd Duncannon PA 17020

KERVICK, IRENE T., 8th Grade Teacher; *b:* Bristol, PA; *ed:* Immac Coll (BA) Soc Stud; Villanova Univ (MA) His; Attnd La Salle Trenton St; *cr:* St Matthew 8th Grd Tchr 1958-68; St Agnes 8th Grd 1968-72; St Simon-Jude 8th Grd Tchr 1972-76; Blessed Virgin Mar Grd Tchr 1976-82; St Matthew 8th Grd Tchr 1982-87; St Andrew Sc Grd Tchr 1987-90; St William Schl 8th Grd Tchr 1990-; *ai:* Stu Cncl Mid Sts Evaluation Steering Comm; Integrated Lang Arts Curr C NCEA 196-; NCET; Voyages in Eng Workbook; Lang Arts Stud C Diocese of Philadelphia; PACEM Newsletter; *office:* St William Schl Rising Sun Ave Philadelphia PA 19111

KERWAN, DEBRA LEE, English Teacher; *b:* Victorville, CA Michael Patrick; *c:* Patrick; *ed:* Corning Comm Coll (AAS) Para 1984; Utica Coll of Syracuse Univ (BA) Eng, Ed 1988; Elmira Coll Ed 1994; Cooperative Learning; Multiple Intelligences; Authen Portfolio Assessment; *cr:* Paralegal Asst 1984-85; Rome City Schl Tchng Asst 1985-86; Addison Jr Sr HS Scndry Eng Tchr 1990-; Co Comm Coll ACE Tchr 1995-; *ai:* Scheduling, Curr & Assessment C Bldg Level Team; Past JV Vlybl Coach, Class Adv; NEA 1990-; Ass Curr Dev, AAUW 1995-; Utica Coll Alexander Schlsp; Mu Intelligence Paper Used as a Trng Tool; *office:* Addison Jr Sr HS 1 Co St Addison NY 14801

KERWIN, MICHAEL THOMAS, Social Studies Teacher Lachawanna, NY; *m:* Paula Jean Saber; *c:* Andrew Michael, Ch Renee; *ed:* Canisius Coll (BA) 7th-12th Grd Soc Stud Ed 1981; St Un NY at Buffalo (MA) 7th-12th Grd Soc Stud Ed 1991; *cr:* Buffalo Pub Sub Tchr 1980-81; Nativity of Our Lady Schl Soc Stud & Span Tchr & Prin 1981-; *ai:* St Elizabeth Ann Seton Awd 1991; *office:* Nativity of Lord Schl 4414 S Buffalo St Orchard Park NY 14127

KERWOCK, PAUL WILLIAM, French Teacher; *b:* Millinocket, ME Patricia Michaud; *c:* Tatum, Paul C.; *ed:* Univ of ME at Ft Kent (B 1972; *cr:* Ft Kent Elem Schl Fr Tchr 1972-73; Ft Kent Comm HS Fr & Tchr 1973-86; Allagash HS Eng Tchr 1986-87; Mt Desert Island H Tchr 1987-; *ai:* Hearing Comm Tchr Rep; Fr Club Adv; Boys & Soccer Games Timer; IAABO Bsktbl Ofcl 1974-; EMBABO 1974-, Treas & Assingner; MDI Tchrs Assn 1987-, Treas; NEA 1987-; *home* 1 Box 357-Z Ellsworth ME 04605

KERYESKI, MICHAEL PAUL, Fifth Grade Teacher; *b:* Natrona H PA; *m:* Paula Ann; *c:* Michael Garret; *ed:* Edinboro Univ (BS) Ele 1971; 24 Crdit Hrs at PSU; *cr:* Birdview Elem 5th-6th Grd Tchr 14 Grandview Elem 5th Grd Tchr 10 Yrs; Fairmount Elem 5th Grd Tchr *ai:* Schl Newspaper; Flag Ftbl Coach; Soccer Coach; NEA 1971-; P 1971-; Highlands Ed Assoc 1971-, Bldg Rep; Highlands Area S 1994-; Highlands Area Bd of Dir 1996, Asst Dir of Coaching; Gifted Awd; Thanks To Tchrs Nom; *office:* Fairmont Elem Schl 1060 Atlanti Brackenridge PA 15014

KESLER, EDWARD, Elem Schl Principal; *b:* Philadelphia, PA; *ed:* Joseph Univ (BS) Elem Ed 1978; LA St Univ (MED) Schl Admin 1 Post Grad Stud Univ of Cincinnati, Thomas More Coll; *cr:* Presentati Mary Schl Elem Tchr 1969-71; St Anthony Schl Elem Tchr 1971-84; of Ars Schl Prin 1984-89; Immaculate Heart of Mary Schl Tchr, Prin 19 *ai:* Natl Jr Hnr Soc Adv; NCEA 1971-; Brothers of Poor of St Fr 1968-; *office:* Immaculate Heart-Mary Schl 7800 Beechmont Cincinnati OH 45255

.ER, KATHLEEN HARMON, English Teacher; *b:* Sarasota, FL; *m:* Michael; *c:* Ashley, Zachary; *ed:* VA Intermont (AA) Hi, 1966; Wake BA Eng 1968; Univ of MD (MA) Eng 1975; 30 Hrs Ed, Mngmt; *cr:* Lodge Jr HS Eng Tchr, Dept Chair 1968-80; High Point HS Eng Tchr 85; Churchill HS Eng Tchr 1985-87; M. L. King Jr HS Eng Tchr 88; Quince Orchard HS Eng Tchr 1988-; *ai:* Prince George's Cty Ed 1968-85; NEA 1968-; Montgomery Cty Ed Assn 1985-; *office:* Quince rd HS 15800 Quince Orchard Rd Gaithersburg MD 20878

IER, MARYJANE, Head Kindergarten Teacher; *b:* Youngstown, n: George M.; *c:* Kristine Martin, Kraig; *ed:* Youngstown St Univ Elem Ed 1990; Accredited in Early Chldhd Ed; *cr:* St Christine Schl 3rd Grd Tchr 1957-61, Kndgtn Tchr 1970-; Yo Diocese Sub Tchr 70; *ai:* Legion of Mary Soc Club Adv; Write & Dir Play for Kndgtn Yearly; Spllng Clb Adv; Yo Diocesan Confederation of Tchrs 1993-; 989-; Amer Cancer Soc; *office:* Saint Christine Schl 3125 S Schenley 'oungstown OH 44511*

SINGER, THOMAS ANTHONY, Social Studies Teacher; *b:* nouth, OH; *m:* A Jane Pellegrinon; *c:* Amy K. Chelman, Ann M.; *ed:* r Univ (BS) His, Ec 1969, (MED) Rsrch, Curr 1971; Univ of nnati (MA) Medieval His 1978; Working Towards PHD Ec, Ed; *cr:* St rine Schl Edctr 1970-72; Xavier Univ Adj Fac Lecturer Part-Time ; Wyoming HS Edctr 1972-; *ai:* Close Up Club Coord 1985-; Great Japan in Schls Proj Assoc Dir 1987-; NCSS 1977-, Del to Annual ention; OH Cncl for Soc Stud 1977-, Rep, Tchr Of Yr 1985; Natl Cncl eographic Ed 1983-, Outstdng Tchr Awd 1984; Phi Delta Kappa -; Finneytown Civic Assn 1980-, Trustee; Finneytown Schls Fnd , Treas; Finneytown Schls Cncl 1985-87, Pres; US Army Reserves ; Lieutenant Colonel, Chief of Prsnl, Plans, Mngmt; Ec Casebook; n Plans for Jr HS 1995; Articles Pub; *office:* Wyoming HS 106 ry Ave Cincinnati OH 45215*

SLER, CYNTHIA LEE, Biology Teacher; *b:* Cincinnati, OH; *c:* l Robinson, Jeffrey Robinson; *ed:* Purdue Univ (BS) Natural rces, Environmental Sci 1974; Univ of Akron (BA) Scndry Ed 1993; d Credit Hrs; *cr:* Ellet HS Bio, Hnrs Bio Tchr 2 Yrs; *ai:* Hnrs Bio, nomy, Environmental Sci, Eco Comms; Sci Edctrs Cncl of OH 1992-; ., Natl Assn of Bio Tchrs 1994-; Fairlawn Luth Church 1992-, regational Sec 1994-95, Yth Bd Sec 1993-; SECO Conf Decorating DNA Wkshp 1996; *home:* 85 Pineland Dr Copley OH 44321

SLER, KATE, English Teacher; *b:* Carlisle, PA; *ed:* Shippensburg (BS) Psych 1977, (MA) Eng 1981; Indiana Univ of PA (PHD) Eng *cr:* Big Springs HS Eng Tchr 1985-87; Chambersburg HS Eng Tchr ; PA St Mont Alto Eng Instr 1992-; Harrisburg Area Comm Coll Eng 1993-; *ai:* Conflict Resolution Comm; NEA 1987-; NCTE 1989-; Assn of Univ Women 1994-; PA Humanities Cncl 1993-, Particpant :oord; Rel Soc of Friends 1993-; Environmental Defense Fnd 1985-; Music Soc 1993-; Bus & Ed Partnership Grant 1992; Pub Televisions Tchrs Awd 1992; Pub Articles, Chptrs, Books; Freguent Speaker; dng Rsrch Awd Disertation 1993; *office:* Chambersburg Area Sr HS 6th St Chambersburg PA 17201*

SLER, LARRY DOUGLAS, Principal & Chair; *b:* DuBois, PA; *m:* Marie Miller; *c:* Amy Marie, Elizabeth Renee, Mark Douglas; *ed:* oro Univ (BS) Scndry Comp Soc Stud 1974, (BS) Elem Ed 1979; Ed 1979; Supervisory Cert Scndry Soc Stud Elem Prin Ltr; Scndry Ltr; *cr:* DuBois Area HS Soc Stud Tchr 1974; Fairview HS Soc Stud 1975-; Gannon Univ Adjunct Prof for Elem Ed Soc Stud; *ai:* Staff Dev er, Debate & Academic Coach; Dept Chair; Fairview Ed Assn Bd; Cncl Summer Schl Tchr; ASCD, NCSS 1991-; PSEA, FEA, NEA , Many; Natl Cath Foren Leag 1978-, Exec Bd; PHSSL 1980-, Dist hair; Sister VA Coaches & NW Jaycees Young Educator Awds; *office:* iew H S 7460 Mccray Rd Fairview PA 16415*

SLER, SANDRA SCHOENECK, 5th Grade Teacher; *b:* Oneida, NY; ouglas K.; *c:* Hans D., Joel C., Eric S.; *ed:* SUNY at Cortland (BS) 59; Nazareth Coll of Rochester (MS) Elem Ed 1976; Syracuse Univ) Adult Ed 1990; *cr:* New Hartford Cntrl PE Tchr 1959-61; Pittsford 4th-6th Grd Tchr 1971-; *ai:* AAUW Women Helping Girls With es Conf Ldr 1991-; Tchr Ctr Movement 1985-91; YMCA of Greater ester Camp Bd 1991-; NYSUT, ASCD, AAUW & Women in Ed ork; Phi Delta Kappa; Delta Kappa Gamma; *office:* Pittsford Cntrl Thornell Rd Pittsford NY 14534

TER, JAMES MARVIN, Technology Education Teacher; *b:* town, PA; *m:* Kelly Ann Handley; *c:* Nathan J., Leah C., Rachel A.; Millersville Univ of PA (BS) Indstrl Arts 1984; 36 Grad Credit Hrs PA asters Equivalency Cert; *cr:* Northern Lehigh HS Indstrl Arts Tchr -87; Parkland Jr HS Indstrl Arts Tchr 1988-89; Parkland Sr HS Tech chr 1989-; *ai:* Solar Car Team Adv; TEAP, ITEA, NEA 1988-; *office:* and HS 2675 Pa Route 309 Orefield PA 18069

TER, LINDA J., Kindergarten Teacher; *b:* PA; *m:* Bruce D.; *c:* Adam, ssa; *ed:* The Kings Coll (BS) Elem Ed 1976; Elem Ed Credit Hrs; *cr:* Hill Chrstn Schl Kndgtn Tchr 1976-; *ai:* Youth Group Spon.

TER, SUSAN JANE, Fifth Grade Teacher; *b:* Allentown, PA; *m:* in L.; *ed:* Kutztown St Coll (BS) Elem Ed 1970; Lehigh Univ (MED) Ed 1972; *cr:* Walnutport Elem Scl Fifth Grd Tchr 1970-74; Slatington Schl Fifth Grd Tchr 1974-; *ai:* Northern Lehigh Ed Assn, PA St Ed NEA 1970-; *office:* Slatington Elem Schl 1201 Shadow Oaks Ln ngton PA 18080

TNER, CHERYL GLAISTER, Fourth Grade Teacher; *b:* Natrona hts, PA; *m:* Ronald R.; *c:* Ronald R., Tiffany M.; *ed:* Indiana Univ of BS) Elem Ed 1978; Wilkes Univ (ME) Elem 1995; *ai:* St Judes -a-thon for Cancer Rsrch Schl Coord; Stu Support Team; Earth Fnd t-an-Acre Project Coord; Mt St Peter Parent Vol Org; *office:* Mt St Elem Schl 100 Freeport Rd New Kensington PA 15068*

TNER, JANE E., Professor of Psychology; *b:* Huntington, IN; *c:* eline, Jamie, Kyle; *ed:* Ball St Univ (BS) Experimental Psych 1973; Dame (MA) Experimental Psych 1975, (PHD) Experimental Psych ; *cr:* Youngstown St Univ Prof of Psych 1978-; *ai:* Adv Psi Chi; er Tchr Coll of Arts & Sci; Midwestern Psych Assn 1978-; Assn for vior Analysis 1980-, Co-Chair Balance Spec Interest Group; Help ne Inc 1995-, Bd of Trustees; Articles Pub; Papers Presented Confs for Behavior Analysis, Midwestern Psych Assn; *office:* Youngstown iv Dept of Psych 410 Wick Ave Youngstown OH 44555

CHAM, RUSSELL ALAN, Humanities Teacher & Coach; *b:* ola, NY; *m:* Carol Joan Sender; *c:* Todd Richard, Douglas Clark; *ed:* nst of Tech (BFA) Comm Arts 1971; St John's Univ (MSEd) Ed Admin ; Attnd LaSalle Univ Doctoral Stud, NY Univ Doctoral Stud, Hofstra Prof Diploma; *cr:* Old Westbury Schl 6th Grd Tchr 1971-73; Sea Cliff 4th-6th Grd Tchr 1973-82; Glen Head Schl 6th Grd Tchr 1983-89; h Shore MS Hum Tchr 1990-; *ai:* Bsktbl Coach; Chptr 1 Funding d; Pierce Cty Day Camp Supvr, Dir; NY Assn for Comprehensive Ed -, Constitution Chair; Natl Assn of Fed Ed Prgm Admin 1987-; Carle Educl Fnd 1994-, Bd of Dir; Carle Place Ath Boosters 1978-, Bd of Kiwanis Intnl 1986-; Father of Yr Schl for Lang & Comm Dev 1991; osse Coach Awd 1986; Rookie of Yr 1987; *office:* North Shore MS 550 Cove Ave Glen Head NY 11545

CHAM, SANDRA ROBERTS, Assistant Professor; *b:* Pittsfield, *m:* Gerald L.; *c:* Lisa M., Stephen G.; *ed:* North Adams St Coll (BA) Math 1984; St Univ of NY at Albany (MA) Math 1995; *cr:* Berkshire Comm Coll Asst Prof 1984-; *ai:* Planning & Fianance, Stu Standing, Prof Dev Comms; NEA 1987-; MAA 1984-; NCTM 1990-; BCC Alumni & Friends 1985-, Bd of Dirs; *office:* Berkshire Comm Coll 1350 West St Pittsfield MA 01201

KETCHUM, ANDREW SCOTT, Science Teacher; *b:* Boston, MA; *ed:* Princeton Univ (BA) Bio 1984; Harvard Univ (PHD) Cell Bio 1991; John Hopkins Univ (MAT) Scndry Ed 1994; ESL Trng UMBC; Sci for All Amers Loyola Coll; *cr:* John Hopkins Univ Rsrch Fellow 1991-92; Baltimore Polytechnic Schl Sci Tchr 1993-94; Northern HS Sci Tchr 1994-; *ai:* Goucher Coll SMART Prgm; NHS Mentorship; Publicity Comm; AFT, ASCD 1993-; NSTA Presenter 1995; *office:* Northern HS 2201 Pinewood Ave Baltimore MD 21214*

KETCHUM, JOSEPH F., Law & Economics Teacher; *b:* Johnson City, NY; *m:* Marcia Goffa; *c:* Steven, Laurie; *ed:* SUNY at Albany (BA) His 1959, (MA) His 1963; Many Grad Prgms; *cr:* Scotia-Glenville HS Law, Ec, His Tchr 1959-; *ai:* Golf Coach 35 Yrs; Ftbl, Bsktbl Coach 5 Yrs; Mock Trial Team Coach; Scotia Tchrs Assn 1959-, Chief Negotiator, Grievance Chm; AFT, NYSUT 1959-; NYS Law & Yth; Willows Cntry Club 1970-88, Golf Chprsn 8 Yrs; League Affiliation Group 1990-93; Hall of Fame Comm 1990-, Historian; Excl in Tchng Awd SUNY at Albany 1985; PTSA Awd 1996; Foothills Cncl Golf Coach of Yr 1996; Coe Fnd, Woodrow Wilson Flwshp Grants; *office:* Scotia Glenville HS 1 Tartan Way Scotia NY 12302

KETCHUM-COLLETTA, DONNA J., Health Teacher; *b:* Buffalo, NY; *m:* James G.; *c:* Carrie Ketchum, Katherine Ketchum; *ed:* SUC at Brockport (BS) Hlth Ed 1971, (MS) Hlth Ed 1994; SUNY at Fredonia Admin Ed Stud; *cr:* Frontier Cntrl HS Hlth Tchr & Dept Chair 1972-; *ai:* Jr Class Adv; Hlth Advy Cncl Chprsn; NYSUT 1971-; NYS Fed of Prof Hlth Ed, Pres, Outstdng Tchr Awd; St Marks Episcopal Church 1979-, Retreat Chm; Amer Assn of Univ Women 1996; Outstdng Tchr in Erie Cty 1976 & NY St 1988; Metropolitan Life Healthy Me Awd 1987; *office:* Frontier Central Sr HS S-4432 Bay View Rd Hamburg NY 14075*

KETTERER, MARY ATHERTON, Eng Tchr, Lang Arts Dept Chair; *b:* Binghamton, NY; *m:* James Michael; *c:* James Atherton; *ed:* Bucknell Univ (BA) Eng, Sociology 1964; Marywood Coll 3 Grad Credits; Univ of DE 25 Grad Credits; *cr:* Blue Ridge Jr, Sr HS Eng Tchr 1964-65; Christiana Jr HS Eng Tchr 1965-70; Newark HS Eng Tchr 1970-73; Mountain View Schl Eng Tchr 1973-; *ai:* Yrbk; Wrestling Scorekeeper; Mountain View Ed Assn 1973-, VP, Pres; PSEA 1973-; NEA 1964-; St Mark's Thrift Shop 1988-, Vol; *office:* Mountain View Jr Sr HS RR 1 Box 339 Kingsley PA 18826

KETTERING, NANCY LOUISE, Geometry Teacher; *b:* New Kensington, PA; *m:* Charles E.; *c:* Michele, Michael; *ed:* IN Univ of PA (BS) Math 1976; Addl 24 Grad Credits; *cr:* Kiski Area Schl Dist Math Tchr 1977-81; Lenope Vo-Tech Schl Permanent Sub 1982-83; Highlands Schl Dist Permanent Sub 1983; Kiski Area Schl Dist Math Tchr 1983-; *ai:* PSEA, NEA 1977-; *office:* Kiski Area HS 200 Poplar St Vandergrift PA 15690

KETTERMAN, LINDA ANN, US History Teacher; *b:* Cumberland, MD; *m:* Lee Joseph; *c:* LIsa A Teeter, Scott, Russell; *ed:* Frostburg St Univ (BS) Soc Scis 1981; *cr:* Career Ctr Tchr 11 Yrs; *ai:* Prom Adv; NEA 1982-; Eagles 1990-; *office:* Center for Career & Tech Ed 14911 Mc Mullen Hwy SW Cumberland MD 21502

KETTLEWELL, JANE, 4th Grade Teacher; *b:* Akron, OH; *m:* Paul; *c:* Molly, Ben, Jacob; *ed:* Hanover Coll (BA) Elem Ed 1973; Bloomsburg Univ 32 Grad Hrs; *cr:* Lakota Schl Dist 1st Grd Tchr 1973-76; Bowling Green Schl Dist 1st Grd Tchr 1976-77; Danville Schl Dist TELS Rdng Tchr 1987-90, 6th Grd Tchr 1990-93, 4th Grd Tchr 1993-; *ai:* Prof Dev Bldg Rep; Prof Dev Task Force; Tech Task Force; NEA 1987-; PSEA 1987-; DEA 1987-; Grove Presbyn Church 1982-, Bd of Trustees; Camp Dost 1982-, Dir 8 Yrs; Camp Victory 1987-, Exec Bd; Lady of Yr Beta Sigma Phi Intnl; *home:* 16 Charles St Danville PA 17821

KEUPER, CINDY ARCHER, MS Language Arts Teacher; *b:* Zanesville, OH; *m:* William Thomas; *c:* Karen, Daniel; *ed:* Gods Bible Schl (BA) Psych 1985; Univ of Cincinnati (MS) Ed 1987; *cr:* Roberts Jr HS MS Tchr 1985-88; Peoples MS Tchr 1989-; *ai:* Stu Cncl Adv; Future Successes Co-Adv; Play Dir; CFT 1985-; Brighton Ctr of N KY 1990-, Pres; *home:* 26 Elmwood Ave Fort Thomas KY 41075

KEW, KRISTIN LYNN, French & Spanish Teacher; *b:* Mayfield, OH; *ed:* Mt Union Coll (BA) Fr 1994; Institut de Savoie Fr; *cr:* St St MS Part-Time Fr Tchr 1991-92; Regina Coeli Elem Part-Time Fr Tchr 1992-93; St Thomas Aquinas HS Fr & Span Tchr 1994-; *ai:* Fr Club; Span Club; Ski Club Chaperone; OFLA 1994-; MLA 1994-; St Thomas Aquinas HS Tchr of the Month (Twice); *home:* 908 Bell Rd Chagrin Falls OH 44022

KEW, STEPHEN D., Technology Teacher; *b:* Niagara Falls, NY; *ed:* Buffalo St (BS) Indstrl Arts Ed 1988, (MS) Voc Tech Ed 1994; *cr:* Rsrch Fnd Consultant 1986-88; Grand Island C Schl Sub Tchr 1989; Franklinville Cntrl Schl Tech Tchr, Dept Head 1989-; *ai:* Sr Class Adv 1992; 9th Grd Class Adv 1993; Franklinville RC Club Adv 1990-94; TESA 1985-88, VP; Whitetails Unlimited 1992-, VP; Grand Island HS Indstrl Arts Stu of Yr 1984; Several Awds TESA from USTE 1987; Masters of Sci in Ed 4.0 GPA; *office:* Franklinville Central Schl 32 N Main St Franklinville NY 14737*

KEY, HELEN ELAINE, Assistant Principal; *b:* Cleveland, OH; *ed:* WV St Coll (BS) Comprehensive Bus Ed 1968; Cleveland St Univ (MS) Higher Ed Admin 1977; Doctoral Candidate Urban Ed Admin; *cr:* Cleveland Bd of Ed Bus Ed Tchr 1968-95; Cuyahoga Comm Coll Part-time Instr 1969-; Dyke Coll Part-time Instr 1978-88; Cleveland Bd of Ed Asst Prin 1995-; *ai:* Career, Guid Comm Mem; Natl Ass Schl Ad, Assn Sup & Curr Dev 1995-; CABSE 1990-; ITC Eloquent Pearls 1978-, Pres, Treas; Alpha Kappa Alpha 1975-, Treas; *office:* Charles W. Eliot MS 15700 Lotus Dr Cleveland OH 44128*

KEYS, CAROLE LANGMAID, Former French & History Tchr; *b:* Oshawa, Ontario Canada; *m:* Terence H.; *c:* Shannon Elizabeth, Lyndsay Alexandra, Lauren Heather; *ed:* Laval Univ (FSLI) Fr as 2nd Lang Tchr 1972; Toronto Tchrs Coll Cert Elem Tchng 1969; Trent Univ Pol Sci, Native Stud Courses 1976-78, Cert Co-Operative Learning; *cr:* Vincent Massey Elem Schl Fr, 6-8 Grd Tchr 1976-79; Creative Fun for Little Ones Owner, Parents Educator 1983-87; Harmony Heights Elem Schl Fr, 6 Grd Core Tchr 1987; Pringle Creek Elem Schl Intermediate Div Fr, His Tchr 1987-; *ai:* Adv Cncl Comm 1994; Intermediate Chprsn; Schl Trips, Grad Comm Chprsn; Schl Growth Team, Special Days Comm Mem; Durham Elem Tchrs Assn, Fed of Womans Tchrs of Ontario 1972-; Hearth Place 1995-, Bd Mem; Oshawat Dist Breat Cancer Support Grp 1995-, Facilitator; Home & Schl at Schls 1983-, Exec Mem, Past Pres, Treas; Canadian Hearing Soc 1984-, Access 2000 Comm; Canadian Cancer Soc 1984-, Canvasser; Co-Authored Activity Book Young Children Parents-Tchrs, Fr Programmes Evaluation Material, Course Outlines, Resource Materials Fr Programmes; *home:* 12 Trinity Cres Whitby ON L1N 8M1 Canada CN

KEYS, JOSEPH T.,JR., Health Teacher; *b:* Philadelphia, PA; *m:* Connie L. Eisenhower; *c:* Bryan, Kevin, Megan, Gillian; *ed:* CAC; SAC; *cr:* Deptford HS Hist Tchr 1967-70; Clayton HS Hlth Instr 1972-; *ai:* Ftbl; Sftbl, Teen Tchrs; Clayton Place Adv; Tang Soo Do Karate Club; NEA 1967-, NJEA 1967-, Tchr of Yr; Intnl Tang Soo Fed 1988-; NJCA 1994-; Clayton Councilman 1986-, Councilman; Clayton Bd of Hlth 1988-; Clayton Municipal Alliance 1990-; Clayton Planning Bd 1991-92; Gloucester Cty Svc Awd; Intnl Tang Soo Do Karate Dedication & Svc Awd; Clayton Tchr of Yr 1975; NJ Governor Awd for Tchng 1988; *office:* Clayton MS & Sr HS Clinton St Clayton NJ 08312*

KEYS, LORETTA SCHUMACHER, 5th Grade Teacher; *b:* Jersey City, NJ; *m:* Peter J.; *c:* DIanna, Vanessa; *ed:* St Univ at Oneonta NY (BS) ELem Ed 1975, (MS) Elem 1979; *cr:* Cherry Vly Cntrl Schl 1st, 2nd, 4th Grd Tchr 1975-82; Louville Cntrl Sub Tchr 1982-83; Beaver River Sub Tchr 1982-83; Copenhagen Schl Sub Tchr 1982-83; Carthage Schl Sub Tchr 1982-83; Copenhagen Cntrl Schl Elem Librn, Remedial 1983-89; Beaver River Cntrl 5th Grd Tchr 1989-; *ai:* ELem Stu Cncl Adv; 4th, 5th Grd Parents at Rdng Partners Comm; NYSUT 1975; Beta Sigma Phi 1979-, Pres, Sec, Trea, VP Woman of Yr 1985; *office:* Beaver River Central Schl Artz Rd Beaver Falls NY 13367

KEYSER, KEITH ALLEN, Modern European History Tchr; *b:* Honolulu, HA; *m:* June Weischedel; *c:* Jennifer Lee, Amanda Ruth; *ed:* Shippensburg St Coll (BS) European His 1968, (MED) Russian His 1971; Attnd PA St Univ, Villanova U, U of CA at Long Beach, St Josephs U, West Chester U & Temple U 51 Credits Beyond Masters; *cr:* Marple Newtown Schl Dist Soc Stud Tchr 1968-; *ai:* Comp Club & His Day Adv & St & Natl Judge; MNEA, PSEA & NEA 1968-, MNEA Negotiator & Advy Cncl Chm, MNEA Tchr of the Yr 1991-92; PCSS 1970-, Bd of Dir, Tchr of the Yr 1990-91; World Futures Soc 1993-; Trinity Assembly of God Church Bd 1993-, Bd of Deacons; DAR Tchr of the Yr Awd for DE Cty 1982-; PA Cncl for the Soc Stud Tchr of the Yr 1990-91; Marple Newton Ed Assn Tchr of the Yr 1991-92; NEH Flwshp to Cal St at Long Beach for The Englihtenment Revisited 1992; NEH Ind Stud Grant on Medieval Scriptoria 1994; *office:* Marple Newtown Sr HS 120 Media Line Rd Newtown Square PA 19073

KEZAR, WANDA LEIGH, Eighth Grade Science Teacher; *b:* Rochester, NH; *m:* Timothy C.; *ed:* Univ of ME at Farmington (BS) Elem Ed 1990; MAMLE Conf 1995; *cr:* Walnut Hill Child Care & Presch Tchr 1991; Bath, Brunswick Child Care Svcs Presch Tchr 1991-92; Windham Chrstn Acad HS Tchr 1993-95; Sanford Jr HS Sci Tchr 1995-; *ai:* MEA Advy Comm; *home:* RR 1 Box 151 North Berwick ME 03906

KHALIFE-MC CRACKEN, ROSA, Principal & Teacher; *b:* Wilkes-Barre, PA; *m:* Paul Joseph; *ed:* Wilkes Coll (BS) Music Ed 1979; Marywood Coll (MAT) Elem Ed 1991; Prin Cert, Schl Ldrshp; *cr:* SS Peter & Paul Schl 5th Grd, Music Tchr 16 Yrs; St Mary's Sch Prin, 2-8th Grd Tchr 1 Yr; *ai:* Cnsl Jr Mozart Club 1995-; NCEA 1979-; Kappa Delta Pi 1991-; F M Kirley Ctr; WY Vly Oratorio Soc 1984-; St Anghony's Maronite Church Altar & Rosary Soc 1975-; Sr Mozart Club 1995-; Who's Who Among Am Coll & Univ Stdnts 1979; Who's Who Among Bus Exec; *office:* St Mary Our Lady of Czestochow 3357 Greenwood Ave Moosic PA 18507*

KHAN, MANSURUL A., Mathematics Teacher; *b:* Chittagong, Bangladesh; *m:* Nayeema P.; *c:* Aziz; *ed:* Donetsik St Univ USSR (MA) Ec 1977; Univ of Stirling (MS) Ec 1981; New Schl (MA) Ec 1992; PHD Credits Completed; *cr:* Sheapshead Bay HS Math Tchr 1989-90; George Wingate HS Math Tchr 1990-93; HS of Ec Math Instr 1993-; NY Univ Instr 1987-; *ai:* Stu Adv 1988-89; Dir Bangladesh Cultural Ctr; Asia Soc Bangladesh, Bangladesh Ec Assn 1983-; Fulbright Scholar 1985-86; British Cncl Scholar 1978-80; USSR Govt Scholar 1972-77; *office:* Economics & Finance HS 100 Trinity Pl New York NY 10006*

KHANG, MINXIE, Mathematics Instructor; *b:* Tumen, China; *m:* Kim Jin; *c:* Amy Yuanhui, Anna Yuanmee; *ed:* Yanibian Univ (BS) Math 1982; Univ of CT at Storrs (MB) Math 1989, (PHD) Math 1993; *cr:* Yanbian Univ Instr 1982-86; Univ of CT Tchng Asst 1978-93; Cape Cod Comm Coll Instr 1994-; *office:* Cape Cod Comm Coll 2240 Iyanough Rd West Barnstable MA 02668

KHIEL, MARIE O'CONNELL, Instructional Assistant; *b:* Washington, DC; *m:* Omar H.; *c:* Omar Jr., Charles, Anthony; *cr:* Montgomery Cty MD Schl System Title 1 Instrl Asst 1973-; Montgomery Knolls Elem Schl Rdng Lab 1 Yr; Pine Crest Elem Schl 1 Yr; Rolling Terrace Elem Schl Kndgtn-6th Grd Tchr 21 Yrs, Second Grd READ Prgm 3 Yrs; *ai:* Safety Patrol Spon 13 Yrs; *home:* 12513 White Dr Silver Spring MD 20904

KIBELBEK, MARY BOYLE, Elementary School Teacher; *b:* Pittston, PA; *m:* Tony; *c:* Tony, Julie Kibelbek-Junker; *ed:* Coll Misericordia (BS) Home Ec, Sci, Scndry Ed 1953; Addl 30 Credit Hrs; Elem Ed Cert Penn St, Univ of DE Elem Ed Cert 1975; *cr:* DE Hosp Dietitian 1953-54; Henry Conrad HS Home Ec Tchr 1954-55; Alfred I. DuPont Jr HS & Brandywine Sr HS & Adult Ed Home Ec Tchr 1955-59; St Coll Jr HS Home Ec Tchr 1959-61; Bellefonte Penns Vly Sub Tchr 1972-76; Boalsburg Panorama Schl Elem Tchr 1976-95; *ai:* Division, Unit Chairpersonships; Comm Offices; PSEA, NEA 1976-; Palmer Museum of Art Penn St Univ, Friend 1993-, Docent 1995-; *home:* 1108 Karen St Boalsburg PA 16827*

KIBLER, ANDREW PERRY, Professor of Biology; *b:* Pittsburgh, PA; *m:* Kimberly; *c:* Ian; *ed:* Allegheny Coll (BS) Bio 1975; FL St Univ (MS) Botany, Marine Bio 1979; Attnd Fredonia Univ SUNY, Daemon Coll; *cr:* Jamestown Comm Coll Full Prof Bio 1980-; *ai:* Tropical Bio Seminar Field Stud Jamaica; NEA 1992-; Audobon Soc Bd 6 Yrs; Fac Awd Excl Tchng 1982, 1989; Article Pub; *office:* Jamestown Comm Coll 525 Falconer St Jamestown NY 14701*

KICH, MARIE BONSUTTO, 5th Grade Teacher; *b:* Cleveland, OH; *m:* Robert; *c:* Brian, David, Melanie; *ed:* Cleveland St Univ (BA) Eng & Ed 1971; 6 Semester Hrs Capital Univ; *cr:* St Joseph 5th & 7th-8th Grd Tchr 1971-72; Assumption 5th-6th Grd Tchr 1972-74; St Columbkille 7th-8th Grd Tchr 1975-76; Sts Joseph & John Schl 5th & 7th-8th Grd Tchr 1988-95; St Adalbert Schl 5th Grd Tchr 1995-; *home:* 10750 Gate Post Rd Strongsville OH 44136*

KICINSKI, GARY, Math Instructor & Ath Dir; *b:* Bayonne, NJ; *m:* Susan Bock; *c:* Melissa, Lauren; *ed:* Jersey City St Coll (BA) Math 1972; Montclair St Univ (MA) Admin & Supervision 1981; *cr:* Wallington HS Math Tchr 1973-, Bsbl Coach 1981-85, Bowling Coach 1985-, Dir of Ath 1983-; *ai:* NJEA 1973-; WEA 1973-; DDANJ 1983-, Pres; Wallington Hall of Fame 1991-, Treas; Womens Sports Fndtn Grant; NJ Gov Tchr Recognition Awd 1994; *office:* Wallington HS 234 Main Ave Wallington NJ 07057

KICK, STEPHEN PHILLIP, American History Teacher; *b:* Akron, OH; *m:* Kay Ellen Schlessman; *c:* Ellen, Phillip, Andrew; *ed:* Capital Univ at Columbus (BSEd) Pol Sci, His 1964; Bowling Green St Univ (MED) Guidance & Counseling 1968; Course Work in Admin; OH Univ Transportation Admin; Dayton Univ Ed; *cr:* Riverdale HS Tchr, Coach 1964-65; Upper Scioto Valley HS Tchr, Cnslr, Coach 1965-69; Patrick Henry HS Tchr, Cnslr, Admin, Coach 1969-76; Kenton HS Tchr, Coach 1976-83; Ridgedale HS Tchr, Coach 1983-88; Loudonville HS Tchr, Coach 1988-; *ai:* Head Boys Bsktbl Coach, Honor Society Adv; OH HS Bsktbl Coaches Assn 1964-, St Pres 1987-88; OEA 1964-; NEA 1970-; LPEA Pres 1993-; Our Saviors Luth Church Chm 1981-85; Zion Luth Church Chm 1991-; City Recreation Bd Kenton; Dist Coach of Yr 1969, 1973, 1983; Ashland Oil Tchr of the Yr Nom; *home:* 404 Hoffman Rd Loudonville OH 44842

KIDD, CALE A., Sixth Grade Teacher; *b:* Mansfield, OH; *m:* Marcia Ann Riffle; *c:* Richard, Mark; *ed:* OH Univ (BS) Elem Ed 1968; WV Univ (MA) Curr, Instruction 1974; *cr:* Woodsfield Elem Schl Sixth Grd Tchr 1965-; *ai:* Jr HS Ftbl, Asst Bsbl, Bsktbl Coach; Jr HS to Var Resident Outdoor Ed; Hnr Roll Dir; 5th-6th Grd Girls Track, Bsktbl Referee; Switzerland of OH

Ed Assn 1965-, Pres; OEA, NEA 1965-; OH Vly Bd of Ofcls 1983-; East Cntrl OH Bd of Ofcls 1981-, Pres, Exec Bd; *home:* 111 Olin Dr Woodsfield OH 43793

KIDD, TERESA MARIE, First Grade Teacher; *b:* Lancaster, NY; *m:* Franklin; *c:* Nicole, John; *ed:* Medaille Coll (BS) Elem Ed 1969; Canisus Coll (MS) Elem Ed 1974; *cr:* Depew Pub Schls 1st Grd Tchr 1969-; *ai:* Report Comm; Rdng Comm; TEPS; AFT 1969-; NFT 1969-; *office:* Cayuga Heights Elem Schl 1780 Como Park Blvd Depew NY 14043

KIDD-JENNY, ELIZABETH COBLENTZ, Language Arts & History Tchr; *b:* Reading, PA; *m:* Richard; *c:* Megan, Mandi, Molly; *ed:* Muhlenberg Coll (BA) Eng 1969; Trenton St 18 Hrs in Spec Ed; East Stroudsburg, Kutztown Univ Rdng Courses; Intnl Chrstn Univ at Tokyo Japan Japanese Culture; *cr:* New Hope Soleburg HS 9-12th Grd Eng Tchr 1969-72; Stroudsburg HS 9-10th Grd Eng Tchr 1972-73; Brandywine HS 6th Grd Eng Tchr 1984-85; Jewish Day Schl 5-8th Grd Eng Tchr 1985-; *ai:* AAUW; 1st Presbyn Church Sunday Schl Tchr; *office:* Jewish Day Schl 2313 Pennsylvania St Allentown PA 18062*

KIDDY, KEITH RUSSELL, MS Guidance Counselor; *b:* Frostburg, MD; *m:* Amy Sue Dicken; *c:* Justin, Jeremy; *ed:* Frostburg St Coll (BS) Elem Ed 1973, (MS) Guid, Cnslng 1979; *cr:* Barton Elem Schl Third, Fifth Grd Tchr 1975-86; Westernport, Barton Georges Creek Elem Schl Guid Cnslr 1986-88; Westernport Elem Schl Fifth Grd Tchr 1988-94; Westmar MS Guid Cnslr 1994-; *ai:* NEA, MD St Tchr Assn, Allegany Co Tchr Assn 1975-; Lonaconing Republican Club 1971-; *office:* Westmar MS Philos Ave Westernport MD 21562

KIDWELL, ROLLIN JAY, Psychology Professor; *b:* Abilene, TX; *m:* Lisa Ann Beneking; *c:* Katie, Nickie, Erin, Emma; *ed:* Northern KY Univ (BA) Psych 1985; Univ of Cincinnati (MA) Psych 1989; Working Toward PHD in Applied Psych at Union Inst; *cr:* Cincinnati Bible Coll Asst Prof 1988-; *ai:* Book: Instinctive Archery Insights-Secrets from Sports Psych; Various Articles on Sports Psych; *office:* Cincinnati Bible Coll & Sem 2700 Glenway Ave Cincinnati OH 45204

KIEC, KAY SYLOR, AP Erpn & Global Stud Tchr; *b:* Dansville, NY; *m:* Eugene J.; *ed:* Univ of Buffalo (BA) His 1960; Syracuse Univ (MA) His 1967; Attnd Georgetown Univ NDEA Inst 1965; *cr:* Medina HS Soc Stud Tchr 1960-66; Lakeland HS Soc Stud Tchr 1967-69; Williamsville South HS AP European His, Global Stud Tchr 1969-; *ai:* NCSS, Fulbright Scholars 1992-; NYS Cncl Soc Stud 1990-; Fulbright to Netherlands 1992; Natl Endowment for Hum 1995; Overseas Seminar Germany 1995; *office:* Williamsville South HS 5950 Main St Williamsville NY 14221

KIECHLE, DAWN MURPHY, Latin & German Teacher; *b:* Syracuse, NY; *m:* Charles L.; *ed:* St Univ of NY at Albany (BA) Latin 1969; Middlebury Coll (MA) Ger 1973; Amer Acad in Rome Italy; Goethe Insts in Berlin & Freiburg Germany; *cr:* Gelinas Jr High Latin & Ger Tchr 1969-73; Cambridge Cntrl Schl Latin & Ger Tchr 1973-76; Immaculate Heart Cntrl Latin & Eng Tchr, Eng Dept Chair 1984-86; Indian River Cntrl Schls Latin Eng & Ger Tchr 1986-; *ai:* Jr Classical League Adv; Classical Assn of the Empire St 1969-, Treas; Amer Classical League 1969-; Amer Assn of German Tchrs 1991-; Fulbright Grant Italy, Grant From W German Govt; *office:* Indian River HS Rt 11 Philadelphia NY 13673

KIEFER, KATHARIN L., Science Department Chair; *b:* Philadelphia, PA; *m:* James H. Kerr; *c:* Robert D. Kerr; *ed:* FL Atlantic Univ (BS) Microbio 1973; Univ of PA (MS) Ed 1990; *cr:* North Broward Schl Sci Tchr 1974-76; St Andrew's Schl Sci, Math Tchr 1976-80; Hun Schl of Princeton Hnrs, AP Bio Thr, Sci Dept Chair 1980-; *ai:* Running Club, Sr Class Adv; Curr Comm; NSTA 1987-; NJ Sci Tchrs Assn 1990-; Natl Sci Edctrs Ldrshp Assn 1993-; Sierra Club 1993-; Amer Assn Univ Women 1996; NJ BISEC Grant 1993; Tandy Tech Scholars Outstdng Tchr Awd 1993-94; *office:* Hun Schl Of Princeton 176 Edgerstoune Rd Princeton NJ 08540

KIEFF, DOROTHY M., Third Grade Teacher; *b:* Honesdale, PA; *m:* Robert E.; *c:* Maureen Kieff Kjetsaa, Robin, Holly Kieff Mc Ree, Gillian; *ed:* Coll Misericordia (BS) Elem Ed 1962; William Paterson Coll (MA) Elem Ed 1969; 61 Addl Credits; *cr:* Oradell Pub Schl Tchr Grd 3 1962-66; Wallenpaupack Area Schl Dist Tchr Grd 3 1973-; *ai:* After Schl Prgm Math Tutor; NEA, PSEA 1973-; Outstdng Edctr Awd 1991; *home:* RR 2 Box 76 Hawley PA 18428

KIEFFER, DAHLIA KAY, Cosmetology Teacher; *b:* Canton, OH; *m:* David H.; *c:* Erik, Brian, Justin; *ed:* Attnd Kent St Univ, Glemby Intnl Trng Ctr at NY & at Toronto, Zotos Acad; *cr:* Stern & Manns Salon Cosmetologist 1973-80; Imagery Hair Designers Cosmetologist 1980-90; Timken Sr HS Cosmetology Tchr 1990-; *ai:* VICA Adv & Treas; Homecomeing Comm; NHS Comm; Venture Capital Comm; NCA 1973-; OEA & NEA 1990-; OVA 1990-; OVCTA 1990-; Charles A Griggs Schlsp; Parents in Partnership Grant; Henry Kurgle Grant; *office:* Timken Sr HS 521 Tuscarawas St W Canton OH 44702

KIEFFER, DONALD H., Physics Teacher; *b:* Danville, PA; *m:* Gloria Lyons; *c:* Karen R., Warren S.; *ed:* Lock Haven Univ (BS) Physics Ed 1965; Syracuse Univ (MS) Phys Sci 1970; Villanova Univ 12 Grad Credits; Glassboro St 12 Grad Credits; Wilkes Univ 24 Grad Credits; IUP 3 Grad Credits; Clarion Univ 2 Grad Credits; PSU 2 Grad Credits; Carlow Coll 3 Grad Credits; Aurora Univ 3 Grad Credits; Gannon Univ 3 Grad Credits; *cr:* Selinsgrove Area Schls Physics Tchr 1965-66; Woodbury Pub Schls Physics, Math, E Sci Tchr 1966-78; Gloucester Co Coll Adjunct Sci Lecturer 1970-72; Camp Watonka Prgm Dir, Tchr 1981-90; PA St Univ Adjunct Math Lecturer 1979-81; Abington Heights Schl Dist Sci Coord 1978-90, Physics Tchr 1978-; Adult Ed Stained Glass Inst; *ai:* Spon Research Stu PA Jr Acad Sci; Dev, Dir Bridge Bldg Competitions; Spon, Adv Stu PA Sci, Hum Symp; PA Sci Olympiad; NEA, PSEA, AHEA 1990-; PSTA 1978-; PAS 1979-; Clarks Summit Blood Cncl 1994-; NSF Awds; PHEA Stud, ITEC Cmptr Grants; Tandy Tech Natl Tchr Finalist; Distinguished Educator Awd Lock Haven Univ 1992; DOE Inst at Fermi Lab 1992; CItizens Ambassador Prgm to Australia, New Zealand 1989; *home:* 134 Beverly Dr Clarks Summit PA 18411*

KIEFFER, MARITA GREINER, Sixth Grade Teacher; *b:* Altoona, PA; *m:* Don L.; *c:* Susan Gonet, Jana Erb, Laurie Westbrook, Maura Baker, Andrew; *ed:* Carlow Coll (BS) Elem Ed, Soc Sci 1966; Notre Dame Coll (ME) Individualized Instruction 1977; *cr:* Parochial Schls Thr 1966-68; Westinghouse Learning Corp Ed Dir 1968-69; Division of Voc Rehab Cnslr 1969-70; Public Schls Tchr 1971-; *ai:* Spelling Bee, Sixth Grd Play Coach; Org Symposium for Edctrs Funding Pub Schls; Phi Delta Kappa Southern NH 1984-, Pres, Outstdng Kappan; MEA 1971-, Local Rep; NH Germanic Assn 1980-, Schl Bd for Lang Schl; Articles Pub; Wkshps for Tchrs; Artist in Classroom Multicultural Film Making Grant.

KIEHN KIRKEY, CAROL, Math Teacher & Dept Chair; *b:* Bronx, NY; *m:* Terrill L.; *ed:* St Univ of NY at Oneonta (BS) Math 1973, (MS) 1997; Grad Coursework Syracuse Univ; *cr:* Gilbertsville Cntrl Schl Math Tchr 1974-79; Oneonta HS Math Tchr 1979-; Syracuse Univ Adj Instr 1985-; Oneonta HS Math Dept Chair 1989-; hartwick Coll Adj Instr 1990-94; *ai:* NEA; NCTM; AMTNYS; Oneonta Tchrs Assn 1995-, Pres; Outstdng Educator 1991-92; *office:* Oneonta H S Upper East St Oneonta NY 13820

KIEL, ALICE, English Teacher; *b:* Newark, NJ; *ed:* Kean Coll (BA) Eng 1970; *cr:* East Orange HS Eng Tchr 1970-77; Toms River HS North Eng Tchr 1977-; *ai:* Honor Soc Selection Comm; NEA, NJEA, TREA 1970-; Yrbk Dedication; *office:* Toms River HS North Old Freehold Rd Toms River NJ 08753

KIEL, WILLIAM T., Middle School Counselor; *b:* Akron, OH; *m:* Bernadette Carcione; *c:* Lynn, Jon; *ed:* Univ of Akron (BA) Scndry Ed, Math 1970, (MA) Counseling 1977; *cr:* Erwine MS Math Tchr 1970-79, Schl Cnslr 1980-90; Coventry HS Schl Cnslr 1990-93; Erwine MS Schl Cnslr 1993-; *ai:* NEA, OEA 1970-; Summit Cty Cnslrs 1980-, Pres, VP; OSCA 1980-; Outdoor Writers of OH 1986-, Best Radio Show in OH; *office:* Erwine MS 1135 Portage Lakes Dr Akron OH 44319

KIELBLOCK, HENRY FRANCIS, History Teacher; *b:* Plainfield, NJ; *m:* Lenore E. Farley; *c:* Henry J., Elizabeth; *ed:* Rutgers Univ (BA) His, Eng 1966; TrentonSt (MA) His 1971; Montclair 6 Credit Hrs; Rutgers 9 Credit Hrs; *cr:* Hacketts Town Elem Schl Tchr 1966-68; Piscataway Schl Tchr 1968-69; Piscataway HS Tchr 1969-; *ai:* Golf, Chess Coach; NCSS 1989-; NEA 1966-; Natl Aubudon Soc; Trout Unlimited; Collie Club of Amer; Articles Pub; Tchr of Yr 1976.

KIELBLOCK, LENORE FARLEY, Mathematics Teacher; *b:* Pottsville, PA; *m:* Henry F.; *c:* Henry J., Elizabeth; *ed:* Trenton St Coll (AB) Math 1965; 3 Credit Hrs Rutger Univ; *cr:* Piscataway Conazkamozk Tchr 1965-67; South Plainfield HS Tchr 1978-; *ai:* NJMT 1985-; *office:* South Plainfield HS 200 Lake St South Plainfield NJ 07080

KIELBOWICK, FREDERICK JOSEPH, Guidance Counselor; *b:* Spangler, PA; *m:* Debra Jean Reed; *c:* Jeff, Jenna; *ed:* Indiana Univ of PA (BS) Art Ed 1971, (MA) Fine Art 1983; 30 Credit Hrs Scndry Schl Cnslr Cert 1995; *cr:* Ridgeway Area HS Art Instr 1971-95, Guid Cnslr 1995-; *ai:* Sr Class Adv; PSEA, NEA, Ridgeway Tchrs Assn 1971-; Ridgeway Rifle Club 1975-, Pres; PA Rifle & Pistol Assn 1978-, Chm Silhouette, PA St Champion; Natl Rifle Assn 1976-, Silhouette Comm; *home:* RR 2 Ridgway PA 15853*

KIELCESKI, THOMAS AQUINAS, Junior High School Teacher; *b:* Scranton, PA; *ed:* Marywood Coll (BS) Home Ec 1967, (MS) Scndry Eng 1978; Rel Ed 1980-83; Cmptrs 1984; *cr:* St Mary HS 9th-10th Grd Eng Tchr 1958-65; St Dominic HS Vice Prin, 10th-12th Grd Eng Tchr 1969-79; St Paul Schl Prin 1984-88; Msgr Mc Hugh Schl 6th-8th Grd Eng Tchr 1990-; *ai:* Article Pub; *home:* PO Box 568 Cresco PA 18326

KIERNAN, GAYLE T., Health & Family Studies Tchr; *b:* Milo, ME; *m:* John J.; *c:* John Jr., Timothy, Janelle; *ed:* Univ of ME (BS) Home Ec 1963; Hlth Cert 1988; *cr:* East Haven HS Tchr 1963-64; West Genesee HS Tchr 1964-65; Waterville HS Tchr 1983-; *ai:* NHS, Class of 1990, Comm Learning & Stu Svc Advs; Focus Day Chm; NEA, MHEA 1983-; Friends of ME Childrens Home, Comm Chprsn; Parent, Tchrs & Friends ST Johns Church, Chprsn; Waterville Womens Club, Chprsn; Jaycee Wives, Pres; *office:* Waterville HS 1 Brooklyn Ave Waterville ME 04901

KIERNAN, JEFFREY THOMAS, Religion Teacher & Dept Chair; *b:* Bridgeport, CT; *m:* Barbara D'Arcy; *c:* Sean, Brendan, Timothy, Randy, Christopher; *ed:* Univ of Bridgeport (BA) Sociology 1968, (MA) Sociology 1975; Yth Ministry Cert Diocese of Bridgeport Yth Mnstry Inst 1977; *cr:* Unif of Bridgeport Lecturer in Sociology 1975-89; Notre Dame HS Rel Tchr 1975-, Rel Dept Chair 1990-; Housatonic Comm Coll Lecturer in Sociology 1991-; *ai:* Chptr of Amnesty Intnl Moderator; Stu Life Comm Chair; NCEA 1980-; Intnl Thomas Merton Soc 1989-; Pub in Merton Seasonal; *office:* Notre Dame Catholic H S 220 Jefferson St Fairfield CT 06432

KIERNAN, PATRICK THOMAS, Psychology Teacher; *b:* Newark, NJ; *m:* Nancy Moran-Kiernan; *c:* Kayleigh Alexa; *ed:* Bloomfield Coll (BA) Psych 1986; 6 Credits ESL Cert; Supvsr, Prin Cert; *cr:* Blessed Sacrament 1, 2, 4 Grd Tchr 1984-89; Paul VI HS Eng Tchr 1989-91; St Joseph HS Psych Tchr 1991-92; Passaic Vly HS Psych Tchr 1992-93; John F. Kennedy HS Psych Tchr 1993-; *ai:* Var Boys Bsktbl, Frosh Girls Sftbl, Var Ftbl Asst Coaches; NEA 1992-; APA; Amature Sftbl Assn 1995-, Umpire; Middlesex Coaches Assn 1995-, Coach; Amer Psy Assn 1993-; Tchr of Excl Rutgers Univ 1995; *office:* John F. Kennedy HS 200 Washington Ave Iselin NJ 08830*

KIERNAN, THERESA GRILLI, Mathematics Teacher; *b:* Woodhaven, NY; *m:* Bruce; *c:* Sal, Bruce Jr., Clare; *ed:* St Univ of NY at Oneonta (BS) Math 1975; St Univ of NY at Stony Brook (MA) Math 1977; *cr:* Smithtown Schl Dist Math Tchr 1977-80; Saint Anthonys HS Math Tchr 1990-; *office:* St Anthony's HS 275 Wolf Hill Rd South Huntington NY 11747

KIESS, LYNNE KANE, Third Grade Teacher; *b:* Abington, PA; *w:* Thomas (dec); *c:* Amy; *ed:* Univ Of Findlay (BS) Elem Ed 1970; *cr:* Seneca East Schl 2nd Grd Tchr 1970-72; St Augustine Elem Schl 2nd Grd Tchr 1972-73; Patrick Henry Schls Remedial Rdng Tchr 1976-78; Seneca East Schls 3rd Grd Tchr 1978-; *ai:* NEA 1970-; OEA 1970-; SEEA 1978-; Jennings Scholar 1991-92; *office:* Republic Elem Schl PO Box 39 Madison St Republic OH 44867

KIGER, MARCIA MAE (DEEDS), Retired 6th Grade Teacher; *b:* Sugar Grove, OH; *m:* Clarence Robert; *c:* Anna Louise Kiger Wentz, Susan Marie Kiger Ponn; *ed:* OH Univ (BS) ELem Ed 1964, (MED) Rdng 1967; Post Grad Stud 54 Semester Hrs IN Univ, Fl St, John Carroll, OH Univ; *cr:* Liberty Union-Thurston Schl Fourth Grd Tchr 1962-64; Lancaster City Schls Fourth Grd Tchr 1964-67, Rdng-Lang Arts Supvr 1967-78, Sixth Grd Tchr 1978-93; OH Univ Assoc Prof 1967-93; *ai:* Curr Stud Comm; Rdng, Lang, Math, 4-H, Yrbk Adv; March Rdng Prgm; Lit Rdng Tutor; NEA 1962-; Lancaster Classroom Tchrs 1964-, Bldg Rep; IRA 1962-; Bus, Prof Women 1967-, Sec, Pres, Pres's Pin; Emanual Luth Church 1930-, Sunday Schl Tchr, Bible Schl 1992-; Lib Bd 1982-; Deans List OH St; Stu Acad Grants; Rdng Conf Del; Rsrch Articles, Grants; *home:* 291 Tarkiln Rd SE Lancaster OH 43130*

KIGGINS, DONNA MCCURDY, Eng, Pub Speakng & Psych Tchr; *b:* Corning, NY; *m:* Joseph A.; *ed:* St Univ at Albany (BA) Eng 1962; Syracuse Univ (MA) Eng Ed 1967; Colgate Univ Guid Cnslr Permanent Cert 1971; *cr:* Webster Cntrl Schl Jr High Tchr 1962-64; Holland Patent Cntrl Schl HS Tchr 1964-, Guid Cnslr 1968-78; *ai:* NHS; Sr Class Adv; Reinforcement Comm; Holland Patent Alumni Assn 1958-, Recognition Outstdng Tchr; Holland Patent Tchrs Assn 1964-, Bldg Rep; Meth Church 1965-93, Lay Ldr & Speaker; Eastern Star OES 1958-, Matron; Faxton Hosp Vol 1980-85; Outstdng Young Women of Amer 1965-67; *office:* Holland Patent Central HS Thompson Rd Holland Patent NY 13354

KIJANKO, TONY, Health Edctr & PE Dept Head; *b:* Cleveland, OH; *m:* Dolores Castillo; *c:* Angela, Karrah, Joshua; *ed:* Bowling Green SU (BA) HPE 1972, (MA) HPE 1976; Addl Hrs Comm Intervention, Chemical Dependancy Wkshp, AIDS Wkshp, Eating Disorder Wkshp; *cr:* Eastwood HS HPE Inst 1973-74; Hopewell Loudon HS HPE Instr 1974-76; Margaretta HS HPE Instr 1977-79; Tallmadge HS HPE Instr 1979-; *ai:* Ftbl Coach 1973-; Track Coach; Schl Ldrshp Prgms Speaker; NEA, OEA 1973-; The Chapel 1985-, Yth Group Trip Ldr; Summit Cty Coach of Yr 1982; Metro League Coach of Yr 1982; Akron Beacon Clem Caraboolad Coach of Yr Awd 1995; *office:* Tallmadge HS 484 East Ave Tallmadge OH 44278*

KIKENBERY, STEVEN KENT, HS English Instructor; *b:* Dayton, OH; *m:* Tana Marie Gettinger; *c:* Amy Leigh, Bret Mathew; *ed:* Miami Univ (BA) Eng 1969, (MED) Eng, Ind Ed 1973; Antioch Univ 31 Post MED Hrs; *cr:* Preble Shawnee HS Eng Instr 1969-77; West Carrollton HS Eng, Speech Instr 1977-; Sinclair Comm Coll Dev Rdng Instr 1989-; *ai:* Forensic Dir, Track Coach; Curr Comm; NEA 1969-; OEA 1969-, Rep; WCEA 1977-, VP; WCEA 1977-, Exec Comm; Recipient 5 Ed Grants; NFL Natl Qualifier Coach 1995; 4 Gallon donor Comm blood Ctr; Pub 1992; Tchr Awds 1985-; *office:* West Carrollton Sr HS 5833 Student St Dayton OH 45449

KIKER, JANICE A., Mathematics & Computer Teacher; *b:* Akror *ed:* Shippensburg Univ (MS) Math, (BS) Scndry Ed, Math; Harr Comm Coll (AA) Math; *cr:* Trinity HS Tchr; *ai:* Sr Class Moderator Honor Soc, Pep Club Moderator; Asst Track Coach; Retention C NCEA; NASAA; PCTM; *office:* Trinity HS 3601 Simpson Ferry Rd Hill PA 17011

KILBANE, MARY JANE MANAK, 5th Grade Teacher; *b:* Clev OH; *m:* Thomas E.; *c:* Thomas Andrew, Mary Eileen, Sheila Becker, Marie, Martin Joseph; *ed:* Kent St Univ (BS) Elem Ed 1965; Addl John Carroll Univ & Notre Dame Coll; *cr:* Our Lady of Angels Sc 6th-7th Grd Tchr 1959-64; Robinson G. Jones Schl 5th-6th Grd 1964-66; Our Lady of Angels Schl Sub Tchr All Grds 1970-81, 5t Tchr 1981-; *ai:* Co-Founder & Adv to First Saturday Club; Facilita Peace & Justice Infusion Wkshps; Young Authors Conf; Comm Mem Course of Stu & Pilot of New Texts; *office:* Our Lady Of Angels Schl Rocky River Dr Cleveland OH 44111

KILBERG, ESTA LAZARUS, 4th Grd Teacher; *b:* Jersey City, N Samuel Marc; *c:* Jay Scott, Regina Hope; *ed:* Penn St Univ (MS) El 1958; Univ of Bridgeport (MS) Ed 1992; *cr:* Franklin Schl 4th Grc 1958-61; Washington Schl Sub Tchr 1967-77, Gifted & Talented 1977-79, 4th Grd Tchr 1979-; *ai:* SIP Comm; NEA; UTEA; PTA; NHS Recognition Awd Chosen 6 Times; 1 Grant Submitted; *office:* Washi Schl 301 Washington Ave Union NJ 07083

KILBRIDE, PATRICIA KIESA, Eighth Grade Teacher; *b:* Syracuse *m:* James P.; *c:* Patrick, Megan, Andrea, Timothy, Matthew; *ed:* Le N Coll (BA) Eng 1964; Temple Univ (MED) Spec Ed 1966; *cr:* S.A. Dc Schl Spec Ed Tchr 1964-69; Holy Cross 7th, 8th Grd Tchr 1988-; *ai:* Grad, Lang Arts Coord; Home, Schl Rep; NCEA 1988-; *office:* Holy Schl 144 E Mount Airy Ave Philadelphia PA 19119*

KILBURN, SUSAN CANNON, Health Assistant Instructor; *b:* Meac PA; *m:* Ronald; *c:* Douglas Fullerton, Dan Fullerton, David, Cou Christy, Michael, Joshua; *ed:* Slippery Rock Univ (BSN) Nrsng 198 Univ of PA (BSE) Voc Ed 1988; Meadville City Hosp Schl of Diploma Nrsng 1972; Schl Nurse Cert; Master's Equilvalency in Vc *cr:* St Vincent's Hosp Nurse 1976-77; Spencer Hosp Nurse 197 Meadville Med Ctr Recovery Room, Surgery RN 1979-81; Crawfor Area Vo Tech Hlth Asst Instr 1981-; *ai:* Hlth Occupations Stdnts of Adv; PSEA 1981-, Past Sec, Past VP; Amer Cancer Soc 1985-, Bd, of Hope; Hospice 1986-, Bd; Prof Advy to VNA 1980-, Bd, Asst Chai Advy to LPN Schl of Nrsng 1981-, Bd, Chprsn; *office:* Crawford Cty Vo Tech 860 Thurston Rd Meadville PA 16335

KILBY, JILL ANN, Social Studies Teacher; *b:* Andrews Air Force *m:* James G. Jr.; *c:* Christina, Jimmy, Jordan; *ed:* Frostburg St Univ Soc Sci, Scndry Ed 1989; 9 Credit Hrs; *cr:* Benjamin Stoddert MS 6 Grd Soc Stud Tchr 1989-94; Carroll HS Soc Stud, US His, Socic Current Events Tchr 1994-; *ai:* Stu Cncl Adv; Far Hills Bapt Church Sunday Schl Tchr; *office:* Carroll HS 4524 Linden Ave Dayton OH

KILCHENMAN, WILLETTA EMBICK, Retired English & Acctng *b:* Norwalk, OH; *m:* John F.; *c:* Lisa Monroe, Sherry Levergood, Bogart, Doug, Marcia; *ed:* Bowling Green St Univ (BS) Eng 1966 Grad Stud Univ of Akron, Kent St Univ, Bowling Green St Uni Bellevue HS Eng Instr 1966-68; Ridgeville HS Eng Instr 1968-70; Philadelphia HS Eng, Bus Instr 1970-73; Maysville HS Bus Instr 197 Fairless HS Eng, Bus Instr, Dept Chm 1975-; *ai:* NHS, Yrbk, News Chrldrs, Teen Bd Adv; Dept Head; Recognition Prgm Chm; *home:* Cherokee Ave NW North Canton OH 44720

KILCOYNE, LAURA L. (PATTEN), Chemistry & Biology Teach Syracuse, NY; *m:* John; *c:* Jennifer, Joshua; *ed:* North Cty Comm (AAS) Radiologic Tech 1974; Potsdam Coll (BS) Bio 1988; Potsdam (MST) Ed 1989; *cr:* St Lawrence Cntrl HS Sci Tchr 1989-; *ai:* Class, S for Environmental Awareness Adv; Var Swim Team Asst; STANYS, NSTA 1990-; *office:* St Lawrence Cntrl Schl PO Box 307 Brasher Fal 13613

KILE, DEBBIE STEVENS, Fifth Grade Teacher; *b:* Berwick, P Shawna, Brianne; *ed:* Bloomsburg Univ (BA) Elem Ed 1974; Maste Ed Prgm 21 Credit Hrs; Instruction II Cert 24 Credit Hrs; *cr:* Berwick Schl Dist Elem Tchr 1974-; *ai:* Band Front Dir Color Guard, Tw 1972-78; Chrldng Coach 6 Yrs; Choreographer Swing Choir for 8 PSEA, NEA, & BAEA 1974-; *home:* RR 3 Box 3877A Berwick PA

KILEY, EVA CELULARO, History Teacher; *b:* Worcester, MA; *m:* J.; *c:* Paula Kiley Boudreau, Pamela Kiley Donovan; *ed:* Worcester St His, Geography 1957, (MS) Ed 1959; 15 Hrs Beyond Masters US Hi Hopkinton MS His Tchr 1957-; *ai:* Class Adv Sr Class; Hopkinton TA Profile Nom, NEA, MATA 1957-; Ostomy Assn, 1979, Newsletter; Tchr; Tchr Excl Awd, Jiffy Lube; 20 Yr Recognition Hopkinton System; *home:* 15 Gambier Ave Worcester MA 01604*

KILGORE, JENNY SHAFER, English Teacher; *b:* Cincinnati, O Timothy Stuart Kilgore; *c:* Erin, Brian; *ed:* Xavier Univ (BS) Ele 1984, (ME) Gifted Ed 1990; *cr:* Landmark Chrstn Schl Substitute K-12 1979-84; Landmark Kiddie Coll Dir of Daycare 1981-82; Land Chrstn Schl 7-9th Grd Eng Tchr 1984-; Super Saturday (OVATAG) Tchr Winter 1990; *ai:* Comm to Develop Stud Skills Curr; Admin of Youth Sports 1984-90; Natl Honor Soc Adv 1988-; Jr HS Chrldrs 1987-88; Sr Class Adv for Class of 1990 & 1994; NASSP 1988-; *o* Landmark Christian Schl 500 Oak Rd Cincinnati OH 45246*

KILGORE, MARY SPRUILL, Mathematics Instructor; *b:* Nashville *ed:* Vanderbilt Univ (BA) Math 1964, (MA) Math 1966, (PHD) Math *cr:* Fisk Univ Asst Prof 1968-69; Federal City Coll Asst Prof 196 Bowdoin Coll Asst prof 1972; Phillips Exeter Acad Instr 1972-; *ai:* Var Squash Coach; USSRA 1980-; Pub Integrated Math I 1993; *o* Phillips Exeter Acad 20 Main St Exeter NH 03833

KILKELLY, ANNE M., Sixth Grade Teacher; *b:* New York City, N John V.; *c:* Jeannnine Lescoe, Kevin, Maureen Moore, Matthew K Hunter Coll (BS) Math 1957; *cr:* East Lake Schl 2nd Grd Tchr 1957- Barnabas Schl 5th Grd Tchr 1978-92; St Elizabeth Ann Seton Schl 6t Tchr 1992-; *ai:* Cath Tchrs Assn 1978-; Birthright of Nassau Su 1970-, 25th Vol Plaque, Pin; *office:* St Elizabeth Ann Seton Regnl Washington Ave Bellmore NY 11710

KILKENNY, MARTIN J., Science Teacher; *b:* New York City, NY SUNY at Fredonia (BS) Bio 1983, (MS) Bio 1985; *cr:* Cold Spring H Labs Tech 1985; NY Blood Ctr Tech 1986-89; Richmond Hill HS 1989-93; *ai:* Stu Cncl & Russian Exch Adv; Sci Olympiad Coach; *o* George W Hewlett HS 60 Everit Ave Hewlett NY 11557

KILKER, BARBARA M., Academic Affairs Asst Prin; *b:* Cleveland, *c:* Kelly Schlereth, Kristen; *ed:* Ursuline Coll (BA) Eng 1968; Wo Toward Masters in Educl Admin; Attnd Bowling Green St Univ, Carroll Univ, Cleveland St & Baldwin-Wallace Coll; *cr:* Mayfield Eng Tchr 1968-71; Saint Marys Schl 4th Grd Tchr 1980-88; Lorain HS Eng Tchr, Dept Chair & Dean of Women 1988-95; Elyria Cath HS Prin for Acad Affairs 1995-; *ai:* Sr Class Asst Adv; Curr Comm Ch *office:* Elyria Cath HS 725 Gulf Rd Elyria OH 44035

KILKER, JAMES FREDERICK, Theology Teacher; *b:* Carbondale *m:* Mary Tom Crowder; *c:* Erin, Ryan; *ed:* Univ of TX (BBA) Bus 55 Hrs Theology, Ethics, Biblical Stud & Pastoral Cnslng Brite Div Schl, TX Chrstn Univ; *cr:* Stuart Cntry Day Schl Dir of Campus Mir

-87; Immaculate Conception Church Dir of Rel Ed 1987-90; Scranton Schl Theology Tchr, Dir of Sr Svc 1990-; *ai:* Retreat Prgm Asst; dng Tchr Awd from Univ of Chicago 1995; *home:* HC 65 Box 62 ant Mount PA 18453

.EEN, THOMAS F., English Department Chairperson; *b:* Jersey City, *n:* Katherine Suscavage; *c:* Heather; *ed:* Siena Coll (BA) His 1971; am Paterson Coll (MA) Eng 1982, (MED) Admin 1995; 12 Credits seling; *cr:* Wayne Valley HS Eng Tchr 1972-89; High Tech HS Eng Dept Chair 1991-; *ai:* Bstkbl, Bsbl, Bowling, Sftbl Coach; Acad ; NCTE, NJCSS 1991-; Tchr of Yr 1991; Northern Hills Conf Bsktbl h of Yr 1984; *office:* High Tech HS 2000 85th St North Bergen NJ 7*

.LELEA, JOHN M., Art & Video Production Tchr; *b:* Oceanside, NY; rances Genta; *c:* Alison, Danica, Christopher; *ed:* St Johns Univ (BS) 'd 1968; NY Univ (MFA) Film & TV 1976; Attnd Pratt Inst Brooklyn *cr:* Brentwood Schls Art Tchr 1968-72; Various TV Free Lance Work ucer & Asst Producer 1976-80; Compton Advertising Producer -84; Various TV Free Lance Work Producer-Camera 1984-87; ington HS Art & Video Tchr 1987-; *ai:* AFT 1968-; LI Art Tchr Assoc -; NYSCATE 1995-; Several Grants for Tchng Projects; *office:* ington HS Oakwood Rd Huntington NY 11743

.LER, KENNETH MARSH, Honors Bio Tchr & Dept Chair; *b:* walk, CT; *m:* Brenda G. Anderson; *c:* Christine, Craig, Katherine, aeth W.; *ed:* Univ of Hartford (BS) Bio 1963, (MS) Scndry Ed & Sci ; St Josephs Coll (MS) Sci Ed 1988; *cr:* Wilby HS Bio Tchr & Dept r 1963-; *ai:* Girls Var Tennis Coach 25 Yrs; Waterbury Tchrs Assn, & NEA 1963-; CSSA, CSTA, NSTA & ABT 1970-; 8th Army Air e Roundtable 1990-; NSF Grant 1970; Exclnce in Tchng Awd Bentley 1987; Outstndng Tchr Awd Sacred Heart Univ; *office:* Wilby HS ks Hill Rd Waterbury CT 06704

.LIAN, KYLE DAVID, Instr of Human Services Dept; *b:* Midland, MI; anna M. Agathangelou; *ed:* Miami Univ (BA) Psych 1987; Syracuse (MA) Marriage, Family Therapy 1991; Marriage & Family Therapy); *cr:* Syracuse Univ Tchng Asst, Fellow 1988-; Onondaga Comm Coll an Svcs Dept Instr 1991-; Syracuse Univ Resident Coord, Intnl Living 1992-; Onondaga Pastoral Cnslng Ctr Marriage & Family Therapist -; *ai:* RAPE Ctr Advy Bd; Syracuse Univ Eating Disorder Network n; Family Therapy Section Newsletter, Natl Cncl on Family Relations Amer Assn for Marriage & Family Therapy 1989-, Clinical Mem; Natl on Family Relations 1991-; Syracuse Univ Senate 1992-, Senator; cuse Univ Three Yr Doctoral Flwshp; Who's Who Among Stdnts in er Univs & Colls 1991, 1994; Book Chptrs & Articles Pub.

.LIAN, LAWRENCE NEIL, Assistant Professor of Biology; *b:* wick, PA; *m:* Lois Ruth Kennedy; *c:* Tad, Kristl, Erin, Courtney; *ed:* arville Coll (BS) Bio 1964; Cntrl St Univ (BS) Scndry Ed 1965; acuse Univ (MS) Sci Ed 1968; Wright St Univ (PHD) Biomedicine ; *cr:* Springfield Pub Schls Scndry Sci Tchr 1964-65; Linwood Pub s Scndry Sci Tchr 1965-67; Cedarville Coll Assoc Prof of Bio 1968-91; k St Comm Asst Prof of Bio 1992-; *ai:* Fac Senate; Coll Outreach rd; Personnel, Acad Svcs Comms; Flwshps Wright St Univ, Syracuse ; Prof Excl 1990; Fac Mem of Yr Cedarville Coll 1974; *office:* Clark e Comm Coll PO Box 570 Springfield OH 45501

.LIANY, EUGENE FRANCIS, Mathematics Teacher; *b:* Scranton, *m:* Nancy C.; *ed:* Univ of Scranton (BS) Math 1973, (MS) Math 1979; kes Univ 12 Grad Credits Comp Sci; Marywood Coll 4 Grad Credits h Theology & Taft Inst; *cr:* Lackawanna Trail HS Math Tchr 1973-76; anton Schl Dist Math Tchr 1979-; *ai:* Equipment Comm Co-Chrpsn; 'M Annual Conf 1996; AFT 1980-; NPCTM 1987-; NEA 1990-; CCD St Francis Parish 1980-90, Tchr; *office:* West Scranton HS 1201 erne St Scranton PA 18504

.LINGER, MARY MARGARET (COWAN), Kindergarten Teacher; Chambersburg, PA; *m:* Richard Alan; *c:* Eric Alan, Jason Ryan; *ed:* ppensburg Univ (BS) Elem Ed 1969, (MS) Elem Ed 1973; Elem Ed sses Shippensburg Univ, Penn St; *cr:* Fayetteville Elem Schl Kndgtn r 1969-75; Grandview Elem Schl Kndgtn Tchr 1976-; *ai:* VP PTO; ive Parenting Class Helper; Spon PTO, PTA Cncl; NEA, PSEA, CAEA 0-; PTO 1976-, VP; Prince St U B Church 1993-, Yth, Music, Worship nmission; Tchr Recognition Awd 1994; *home:* 704 Charles St ppensburg PA 17257

.LMER, MARY GRACE GRALL, Mathematics Teacher; *b:* Elizabeth John C. Jr; *c:* Kimberly, John C. III; *ed:* Chestnut Hill Coll (BS) Math 3; Fordham Univ (MSTM) Math 1969; Attnd Kean, William Patterson ersey City St 60 Hrs Beyond Masters; *cr:* Union Cty Reg HS Math Tchr 3-70, Part Time 1976-78; Middletown HS North Math Tchr 1980-; liam Patterson 1 Course Summer 1993; *ai:* Adv Math Team; Assn Math rs of NJ, NCTM, NJEA & NEA 1963-; MTEA 1980-; Natl Sci Grant Masters Degree Fordham Univ William Patterson 1992 & 1993; Tchr of Yr Middletown North 1992; *office:* Middletown HS North 63 Tindall Middletown NJ 07748

.MER, JOHN S., HS Guidance Counselor; *b:* Dayton, OH; *m:* hleen Bondy; *c:* Kari, Kasey, John; *ed:* Bowling Green St Univ (BS) 1967; Univ of Toledo (MS) Guidance & Counseling 1975; Post sters in Schl Admin; *cr:* US Army Prsnl Specialist 1968-70; Genoa HS Tchr 1971-75, Guidance Cnslr 1975-95; *ai:* Sr Class Asst Adv; Track ach; OEA, NEA 1971-; *office:* Genoa HS 2980 N Genoa Clay Center Rd noa OH 43430

.LROY, MARY CROWLEY, Department Head & Teacher; *b:* ington, MA; *m:* John F.; *c:* Nancy, William, John; *ed:* Univ MA at ston (BSN) Nrsng 1985; Fitchburg St Coll (MED) Ed 1991; St zabeths Hosp RN Diploma Nrsng 1956; Certfd Hlth Occupations Edctr Credits; *cr:* Pub Hlth Nrsng Geriatric Nrsng 1956-69; Norwood Hosp tical Care Nrsng 1969-74, Inservice Edctr 1974-76; Blue Hills Regnl h Schl Instr 1976-, Dept Head, Hlth Occupations, Early Chldhd Ed m 1992-; *ai:* NHS Fac Cncl; Blue Hills Ed Assn, MA Tchrs Assn, NEA, Voc Tchrs Assn 1976-; Amer Red Cross 1978-, CPR Instr; *office:* Blue ls Regnl Tech Schl 800 Randolph St Canton MA 02021

.LROY, MAUREEN ANNE, Eighth Grade Teacher; *b:* Euclid, OH; *ed:* iv of Dayton (BS) Elem Ed 1986; John Carroll Univ (MEd) Ed 1994; *cr:* Christine Schl 6th, 8th Grd Tchr 1986-; *ai:* Stu Cncl, Yrbk Adv; NCEA 36-; Irish Amer Club 1996; CYO Voluntary Parish Svc Awd; *office:* St ristine Schl 860 E 222nd St Euclid OH 44123*

.LTHAU, JANE F. (THOMAS), Social Studies & Japanese Tchr; *b:* New rk, NY; *w:* Harry G. (dec); *ed:* Queens Coll (BA) His 1964; City Univ NY (MA) European His 1967; Post Grad New Schl for Soc Rsrch, Amer iv in Cairo Egypt, NYU, Cornell Univ, Harvard Univ, Univ of HI, St iv of NY, Hofstra Univ, Univ of ME, St John's, Otani Univ in Kyoto an; *cr:* John Adams HS Soc Stud, Music Tchr 1964-66; Commack HS : Stud, Japanese Lang Tchr, Dean of Discipline 1966-; *ai:* Dean; Fac v Class 1996; Assn of Asian Stud; NE Assn of Tchrs of Japanese; Natl sn of Scndry Tchrs of Japanese, Charter Mem; Japanese Tchrs Network; cks Unlimited 1973-, Treas Western Suffolk; Mountains & Rivers Order n Mountain Monastery 1994-; Japan Soc 1972-; Ki-Sui-An Shakuhachi jo 1995-; NSF; US St Dept Univ of HI East West Ctr; Fulbright-Hays d Amer Univ Cairo Egypt, South Korea; Tchr of Yr 1991, Finalist 1992; *ice:* Commack HS Townline Rd & Scholar Ln Commack NY 11725

KILTY, CORNELIUS FRANCIS,OSFS French & English Teacher; *b:* Philadelphia, PA; *ed:* Niagara Univ (BA) Fr, Span 1964; De Sales Theologate (MA) Theology 1970; Villanova Univ (MA) Classics 1970; *cr:* Northeast Cath Schl Tchr, Coach 1970-72, 1974-78, 1987-; Allentown Coll Classics, Theology Instr 1978-83; Moravian Coll & Seminary Scripture, Greek Instr 1980-82; Father Judge HS Dir of Stud 1983-87; *ai:* NHS Moderator; Head Coach Cross Cntry, Indoor, Outdoor Track; NCEA 1970-; Allentown Coll 1989-, Bd of Trustees; Cncl of Rel Tchrs 1970-, Pres 1984-; Track & Field Coaches Assn of Greater Philadelphia 1991-; Person of Yr Fathers & Mothers Assn 1995; *office:* Northeast Cath HS 1840 E Torresdale Ave Philadelphia PA 19124

KIM, CHANG-SOO S., Finance Professor; *b:* Seoul, South Korea; *m:* Seok-Hee Yoon; *c:* Soo-Ryeon, Soo-Kyeong, Jae-Chun; *ed:* Yomsei Univ (BA) Bus Admin 1983, (MBA) Fin 1985; Univ of Wi at Madison (PHD), (MS) Fin 1991; *cr:* IBM Jr Programmer Analyst 1985-86; Univ of WI Instr 1990-91; St John's Univ Asst Prof 1991-; Yomsei Univ Asst Prof 1995-; *ai:* Amer Fin Assn, Fin Mngmt Assn, Western Fin Assn 1991-; Distngd Paper Awd Midwest Fin Assn; Univ Grants 1992-95; Books: Emerging Markets in Asia 1996, Globalization of Asian Economies and Capital Markets 1995; Numerous Articles Pub.*

KIM, CHONG RAE, Mathematics Professor; *b:* Korea; *m:* Kwang Sup; *c:* Sue Yeun, Eric Joonil; *ed:* Seoul Natl Univ of Korea (BS) Math 1968; Purdue Univ of IN (MS) Math 1970; Purdue Univ (PHD) Math 1973; *cr:* IN Univ Purdue Univ Math Prof 1974-75; Seoul Natl Univ Math Prof 1978-80; Rutgers Univ Math Prof 1980-81; Raritan Valley Coll Math Prof 1981-88; Merrimack Coll Math Prof 1989-; *ai:* Korean Stdnts Club Adv; Amer Math Soc 1970-; Math Assn of Amer 1983-; Amer Assn of Women Math 1990-; Amer Assn of Univ Prof 1993-; North Boston Korean Schl, Prin; Boston Korea Times, Editorial, Writer.

KIM, HESUN, Korean Language Arts Teacher; *b:* Korea; *c:* Yu Bong Ko, Yu Jin KO; *ed:* Kon-Kuk Univ in Korea (BA) Pol Sci, Diplomacy 1962; Presbyn Schl of Chrstn Ed at Richmond (MA) Chrstn Ed 1971; Diploma Sookmyung Women's Coll Korean Lang & Lit 1948; 9 Credits Schl of Soc Work Columbia Univ; 35 Credits Rockland Comm Coll; 9 Credits Dominican Coll; 3 Credits SUNY New Paltz; 6 Credits Coll of New Rochelle; 3 Credits St Thomas Aquinas Coll; 3 Credits Long Island Univ; Tchng & Rsrch Asst Univ of London; *cr:* Soo-Do Girls HS TChr 1953-62; Korean Govt Correspondant Sec 1964-69; Korean Schl of NY Tchr 1973-83; Newtown HS Tchr 1979-; *ai:* Korean Lit Magazine, Korean Club Adv; NY City Pub Schl Dist Offices Translator; AFT 1979-; Amer Assn of Tchrs of Korean 1992-; Korean Tchrs Assn of NY 1992-, Adv; Korean Church & Inst 1975-, Eldership; Tchng & Rsrch Asst; Test Dev; Item Writer; Educl Testing Svc; Essays & Articles Pub; *office:* Newtown HS 48-01 90th St Elmhurst NY 11373

KIM, MIMI T., Tchr of Learning Disabilities; *b:* Youngstown, OH; *m:* Marcus S.; *c:* Amy, Mimi; *ed:* Youngstown St Univ (BA) Ed, Elem, Spec 1978; Kent St Univ Grad Hrs; *cr:* Youngstown City Schls Elem Tchr 1979-82; Hubbard HS 9th-12th Grd Specific Learning Disabilities Tchr 1982-; *ai:* Building Leadership Team 1994-95; Staff Advy Cncl; NEA, HEA 1982-, Sec; Trumbull Cty Bd of Ed Grants 1983-87, 1990, 1992-94.*

KIM, MIN, Asst Prof of Piano & Theory; *b:* Seoul, S Korea; *ed:* Juilliard Schl (BM) Piano Performance 1987, (MM) Piano Performance 1989; Eastman Schl of Music (MMA) Piano Performance 1993; *cr:* Juilliard Schl Tchng Asst 1986-89; Eastman Schl Tchng Asst 1989-91; St Univ of NY at Oneonta Asst Prof 1992-94; Jersey City St Coll Asst Prof 1994-; *ai:* Many Comms, Lectures & Concerts; AFT 1992-; NJEA 1995-; *office:* Jersey City State Coll 2039 Kennedy Blvd Jersey City NJ 07305*

KIMBALL, MARSHALL COLEMAN, Band Dir & Music Dept Chm; *b:* Parkersburg, WV; *m:* Marcia Jo Bogard; *c:* Christopher, Jeremy; *ed:* OH Univ (BM) Music Ed 1972, (MM) Music Ed 1975; *cr:* Hocking Co Schls Band Dir 1971-72; Trimble Local Schls Band Dir 1972-75; Marietta City Schls Band Dir 1975-; *ai:* MS Grd Card & Music Interview Comms; Marching Band & Pep Band Dir; Music Curr Comm Chm; MS Scheduling Comm; NEA, OMEA & MENC 1971-; MEA 1975-; ASBDA; Athens Co Outstanding Young Educator 1972; Marietta City Schls Outstanding Extra Curricular Adv 1985; Received Key to City of Marietta for Music Accomplishments 1987; Acad Excl Recognition as Honor Educator 1988-90 & 1992; Marietta City Schls Outstanding Educator 1993; *home:* 101 Edgewood Dr Marietta OH 45750*

KIMBELL, ALICE E., PAR Consultant & Teacher; *b:* Toledo, OH; *ed:* OH St Univ (BE) Elem Ed 1960, (ME) Counseling Ed 1972; *cr:* Maize Elem 4th-6th Grd Tchr 1960-90; Valley Forge 5th Grd Tchr & PAR Consultant 1991-94; 3rd Grd Tchr Parkmoor 1994-; *ai:* Strategic Planning Comm for Columbus Pub Schls; OEA, NEA & CEA 1960-; Alpha Delta Kappa 1964-, Pres, VP & Treas; Freedom Fnd Awd; Good Apple Awd.*

KIMBLE, KAY JOYCE SMITH, English Teacher; *b:* VA; *ed:* James Madison Univ (BS) Home Ec 1959; MED Eq Eng 1975; Curr, Ed, Eng & Methods Grad Stud; Global Access Trng & Experience; *cr:* Montgomery Cty Pub Schls Tchr 1966-; *ai:* Forensics & Debate Spon & Coach; Evening HS & Summer Schl Tchr; Discipline & Attendance Comms; Chrldrs Past Spon; Co-Dir Schl Plays; Costume Dir; PTSA Fac Rep; MCEA, MSTA & NEA 1966-; PTSA 1966-, PTA Pres; OCA 1968-; *office:* Montgomery Cty Pub Schls 850 Hungerford Dr Rockville MD 20850*

KIMBLE, ROBYN SNYDER, Fourth Grade Teacher; *b:* Cambridge, OH; *m:* Robert Leigh; *ed:* OH Univ (BS) Elem Ed 1983; Zanesville City, Muskingum Cty Schls Learning Team Project 1984-85; *cr:* Westview Elem Schl 3rd Grd Tchr 1983-86, 4th Grd Tchr 1987-; *ai:* NEA 1983-; Martha Holden Jennings Scholar; *office:* Westview Elem Schl 2256 Dresden Rd Zanesville OH 43701*

KIMBROUGH, RENNAE H., Asst Prin & Lang Arts Teacher; *b:* Richmond, VA; *c:* Adanma-Noni Huria; *ed:* VA Union Univ (BA) Pol Sci 1983; Atlanta Univ (MA) Ed Admin 1987; *cr:* Avondale HS Paraprofessional, 8th-9th Grd Title I Rdng Tchr 1986-87; George Washington Jr HS 7th-8th Grd Chptr I Rdng Tchr 1987-88; Hammond Jr HS 7th-8th Grd Chptr I Rdng Tchr 1988-89; Assumption Schl 7th-8th Lang Arts Tchr, Asst Prin 1989-; *ai:* Asst Chrldng Spon; Zeta Phi Beta 1980-; Tchr Svc Corp, Mentor; *office:* Assumption Schl 220 Highview Pl SE Washington DC 20032*

KIMBROW, RUBY EULOLA, Bus Ed Tchr & Dept Chprsn; *b:* Kodak, KY; *ed:* Morgan St Coll (BS) Bus Ed 1972; Cath Univ of Amer (MS) Coll Bus Mgmt Higher Ed 1973; 60 Credit Hrs Beyond MS Degree; *cr:* Baltimore Cty Bd of Ed Bus Ed Tchr 1974-93, Bus Ed Chprsn 1994-; Catonsville Comm Coll Adj Fac & Office of Tech 1980-; Baltimore Cty Adult Ed Tchr; *ai:* Multicultural Awareness, NHS & FBLA Adv; MD St Stu Performance Plan, Goal Setting, Stu Svc Learning, Data Processing & Keyboarding Curr Comms Mem; NBEA & TABCO 1973-; MBE & MD St Tchrs Assn 1980-; Alpha Kappa Alpha 1993-; Awded Cert of Appreciation 1990; Recipient of City of Baltimore Presidential Citation 1993; *office:* Eastern Voc Tech HS 1100 Mace Ave Baltimore MD 21221*

KIME, CAROL A., 3rd Grade Teacher; *b:* Harrisburg, PA; *m:* Gary G.; *c:* Heather Jeanne; *ed:* West Chester Univ (BS) Elem Ed 1963; 12 Credit Hrs; *cr:* Brookline Elem Schl Fourth Grd Tchr 10 Yrs; Oakmont Elem Schl Seminar Tchr 3rd Grd Gifted 1 Yr; Llanerch Elem Schl Seminar Tchr Gifted 4th Grd 1 Yr; Coopertown Elem Schl Seminar Tchr of Gifted, 4th Grd Gifted 2 Yrs; Chatham Park Elem Schl Third Grd Tchr 14 Yrs; *ai:* PBR Rep Brookline Schl 9 Yrs; PTA Rep 3 Yrs; Fund Raising Com Swimming 10 Yrs; Rdng Incentive Comm 2 Yrs; Comm Awd for Beautification of Home; NEA 1963-; PSEA 1963-, Fac Rep 3 Yrs; Sunday Schl Tchr 1 Yr; Bible Schl Tchr 1 Yr; Luth Women 4 Yrs; Mid St Evaluation Team 1971; Tchr of Yr 1972; Curr Awd Grant 1989; Trained 5 Stu Tchrs; Mentor 2 Yrs; Fac Mem Schl of Excl Awd 1986; *office:* Chatham Park Elem Schl Allston & Glen Arbor Rds Havertown PA 19083*

KIME, SUE-ANN MC CARTHY, Supervisor of Student Teachers; *b:* New Haven, CT; *c:* Kevin M.; *ed:* Vassar Coll (BA) His 1960; SUNY at New Paltz (MS) Soc Stud 1965; L Amer Stud; Multi-Culturalism; Authentic Assessment; European Comm; *cr:* Red Hook HS Tchr 1960-63; Arlington HS Tchr 1965-95, Coord of Soc Stud 1982-95; Marist Coll Supvr of Stu Tchrs 1995-; *ai:* Debate Club Adv; MNSSC 1986-, Exec Bd, VP, Pres, Tchr of Yr; NYSCSS 1986-, Global Stud Comm Chair, Outstdng Second Soc Stud; NCSS 1986-; ATA 1965-; AFT 1977-; Phi Beta Kappa 1960-; NEH Flwshp; Virginia Swinburne Brownell Prize in His; GE, Union Coll Flwshp; Cornell Univ Excel in Tchng; Co-Author World Studies, Global Studies A Regents Rev iew Book, Global Studies A Competency Review; *home:* 13 Amber Ct Poughkeepsie NY 12603*

KIMES, KAYE M., Mathematics Teacher; *b:* Pottstown, PA; *ed:* West Chester Univ (BS) Math 1969, (MEq) Scndry Ed 1972; 60 Addl Hrs St Joseph's Coll in Phila, East Stroudsburg, Carlow Coll at Pittsburgh, Penn St Univ; *cr:* Coatesville Area Schl Dist Math Tchr 1969-, Gifted Seminar Facilitator 1996-; *ai:* Yrbk Adv 1982-; New Tchrs Prgm Mentor 1995-; Stu Awareness Prgm; NEA, PSEA, CATA 1969-; Stu Body Yrbk Dedication 1985; Positive Tchng Awd Amer Family Inst 1989; *office:* Coatesville Area School Dist 1425 E Lincoln Hwy Coatesville PA 19320

KIMMEL, JUDITH SNYDER, First Grade Teacher; *b:* Grangetown, England; *c:* Biran L., Ian M.; *ed:* Heidelberg Coll (BA) Elem Ed 1981; Ashland Coll (MA) Ed, Curr & Instruction; 9 Credit Hrs Educl Stud; *cr:* Tiffin City Schls Sub Tchr 1981-82, First Grd Tchr 1983-; *ai:* Sci Curr Comm; NEA, OEA, TEA 1983-; Cooperating Tchr for Stu Tchrs from Heidelberg Coll; *office:* Noble Elem Schl 130 Minerva St Tiffin OH 44883

KIMMEL, PETER BLAIR, Asst Prof of Natural Sciences; *b:* Portland, OR; *m:* Barbara E. Brewer; *c:* Jamie, Holly; *ed:* Portland St Univ (BS) Bio 1979, (MS) Bio 1985; Univ of MA (PHD) Zoology 1990; *cr:* Univ of Saskatchewan Post Doctoral Rsrch 1990-91; Castleton St Coll Asst Prof 1991-; *ai:* Sci Assn Adv; Human Anat, Phys Soc 1993-; Canadian Soc Zoologists 1990-; Human Subjects Institutional, Renew Bd Mem; *office:* Castleton St Coll Seminary St Castleton VT 05735

KIMMER, BEATRICE AYRES, German Teacher; *b:* Morristown, NJ; *m:* Wilton H. Jr.; *c:* Claire Ann, David Lloyd; *ed:* Montclair St Univ (BA) German, Span 1970; 9 Credits, Wilkes Coll; 9 Credits Jersey City St Coll; *cr:* Bridgewater-Raritan MS HS German Tchr 1970-75; Sampson G. Smith MS Span Tchr 1980-81; Warren Hills Regnl MS HS Span, Ger 1981-; *ai:* MS Ger Club Adv; MS Steering Comm; AATG, NEA, NJEA 1970-; ACTFL 1985-; NJ Governor's Tchr Recognition Awd 1990; *office:* Warren Hills Regional HS Jackson Valley Rd Washington NJ 07882*

KIMMER, WILTON H.,JR., Honors Chemistry Teacher; *b:* New Brunswick, NJ; *m:* Beatrice Ayres; *c:* Claire, David; *ed:* Monmouth Univ (BS) Chem 1967; Ripon Coll (NSF) Rsrch Grant 1974; Jersey City St Career Ed 28 Credit Hrs; Middlesex CC & Raritan Valley CC 26 Credits; *cr:* Franklin HS Chem Tchr 1967-; *ai:* Asst Girls Track Coach; Chem League Adv; Past Outdoor Sportsmans Club; Key Club Adv; NEA, NJEA & SCEA 1968-; FTEA 1968-, 2nd VP Chair Negotiations; NSTA 1980-; Kiwanis 1970-91, Pres (2 Yrs), Govs Awd for Outstndg Pres; Cert Trainman Conductor at Steamtown Natl Park; *office:* Franklin HS 415 Francis St Somerset NJ 08873

KIMMET, PAMELA B., Head of Lower School; *b:* Wellsville, NY; *m:* Gary J.; *c:* Darcy, Ryan; *ed:* Cornell Univ (BS) Child Dev 1969; Wheelock Coll (MS) Early Chldhd Ed 1970; Brockport Coll (CAS) Schl Admin 1990; *cr:* Harley School Primary Tchr 1970-87, Asst Head Lower Schl 1987-89, Head of Lower Schl 1989; *ai:* Curr, Long Range Planning, Admins, Chair of Focus Week, Author, Divison Head Comm; Early Chldhd Stud Group; Chair of Coords; Chair Bookfair; Phi Kappa Delta 1987-; NAEYS 1970-; Women in Ed Network 1990-; Vol Work Biweekly with Inner City Child; Cumming Grant for Reggio Emilia Italy Schls Stud; *office:* Harley Schl 1981 Clover St Rochester NY 14618

KIMP, ANNIE COUNTS, Retired Teacher; *b:* Columbia, SC; *c:* Margaret H. English; *ed:* Adult Ed Classes; Completed Schl, Soc Coll Course; *cr:* Build Acad Tchr Aide 1970-85; *ai:* Peoples Comm United Church Clerk 1988-94, Trustee; New Covenant United Church of Christ Clerk 1994-, Womens Flwshp Sec; JFK Advy Bd 1990-; Tchr Aide of Yr 1984-85; 2 Svc Awds from King Solomon Holiness Church; Svc Awds, Plaque 1970-87; *home:* 38 Devon Grn Buffalo NY 14204

KINAITIS, KIMBERLY HARTMAN, French & English Teacher; *b:* Ashland, OH; *m:* Eric K.; *ed:* Bowling Green St Univ (BSEd) Fr & Eng 1990; Kent St Univ (MEd) Lang Arts 1993; *cr:* Cuyahoga Falls HS Fr & Eng Tchr 1990-; *ai:* Key Club Adv; Asst Girls Tennis Coach; Pepsi Say Yes to Work Supvr; Mem of OH Career Passports Pilot Prgm; NEA, DEA 1987; NCTE 1992; Kiwanis 1990-, Sec; *office:* Cuyahoga Falls HS 2300 4th St Cuyahoga Falls OH 44221*

KINBERG, BERNARD D., Physics Teacher; *b:* New York, NY; *m:* Marilyn Moral; *c:* Michael, Peter, Karen DeCross, Jill Hubbard; *ed:* NYU (AB) Physics 1951; Columbia Univ (MA) Physics 1953; Wooster Polytechnic Inst (MA); Attnd Geneva Coll, Univ of CA Berkley, Fordham Univ, Yeshiva Univ, Sarah Lawrence Coll & Wellesley Coll; *cr:* Coll of Physicians & Surgeons Research Assoc 1955-57; Teaneck HS Chem & Physics tchr 1957-58; Amer Dependent Schls Physics, Chem & Bio Tchr 1958-60; Herricks Schls K-12th Grd Sci Coord 1960-83; Westhill HS Physics Tchr 1983-; *ai:* Chess Club; C-Man Ftbl; NEA, NYS Sci Tchrs Assn, CT Supvr & CEA; Flour Stud Dye Dilution Technique Amer Journal of Physiology; Tchr Machine NYS Super & Admin; NSTA Tchng Grant; Sci Wkshp Tchr Grds K-8th; *office:* Westhill HS 125 Roxbury Rd Stamford CT 06902*

KINCAID, GREGORY ROBERT, Elem Phys Ed Teacher & Coach; *b:* Rochester, NY; *m:* Christine E. Richardson; *c:* Gregory Jr., Jeffrey, Michael; *ed:* SUNY at Canton (AS) Hotel Restaurant Mgmt 1986; SUNY at Brockport (BA) PE 1989, (MS) PE 1995; Post Grad Educl Admin Pgm; *cr:* Spencerport Cntrl Schls PE Tchr & Coach 1989-91; Churchville Chili Schl Dist PE Tchr & Coach 1991-; *ai:* Operation Offense Chem Hlth Trainer; Boys JV Soccer, Girls Var Bsktbl Asst, Summer Yth Soccer, & Jr Bsbl Coach; Bldg Effective Schls Team; NYSUT 1989-91; NEANY 1991-; NYSAHPERD 1991-; Ogden Rep Comm 1995-; Spencerport Jr Bsbl Bd of Dirs 1995-; *office:* Chestnut Ridge Elem Schl 3560 Chili Ave Rochester NY 14624

KINCH, LYNNE F. MURPHY, Kindergarten Teacher; *b:* Riverside, NJ; *m:* John R. Kinch; *c:* J. Brian, Jocelyn Kinch Braudt; *ed:* Glassboro St Coll (BS) Elem Ed 1958; Continuing Ed; *cr:* North Plainfield Kndgtn Tchr 1958-59; Warren Township Kndgtn Tchr 1962-63; Branchburg Kndgtn Tchr 1974-; *ai:* Tchrs Comm; NJ Assn Kndgtn Educators, Intnl Rdng Assn, AFT, Branchburg Fed of Tchrs 1974-; Somerset Cty 4-H, Judge Pub Presentations; Bridgewater United Meth Church Admin Bd; Amer Cancer Soc for Somerset Cty Residential Crusade Chprsn 1975; NJ Governors Tchrs Recognition Prgm 1990; 4-H Outstanding Svc Awd 1984; *office:* Old York Schl 580 Old York Rd Branchburg Branchburg NJ 08876

KINDBERG, JANET KATHLEEN, 5th Grade Teacher; *b:* Wheeling, WV; *ed:* Dowling Coll (BA) Elem Ed 1990; SUNY at Stony Brook (MA) Lbrl Arts 1993; 45 Post Grad Hrs; *cr:* West Islip Schl Dist 4th & 5th Grd Tchr 1990-; *ai:* Var Chrldng Coach; Mem Site Based Team; Kappa Delta Phi 1989-; AFT 1990-; West Islip Tchrs Assn 1990-; *office:* Udall Rd MS Udall Rd West Islip NY 11795*

KINDELBERGER, SUE ANN, Retired English Teacher; *b:* Wheeling, WV; *ed:* WV Univ (BS) Scndry Ed Lib Sci & Eng 1965; Univ of Dayton (MS) Scndry Admin 1983; Univ of Steubenville; Kent St Univ; *cr:* W. G. Harding HS Eng Tchr 1965-94; *ai:* Newspaper Adv; NHS Adv; Asst Chrldr Adv; Asst Pep Club Adv; Sports Information Dir; Warren Ed Assn 1965-94 Newsletter Co-Editor 1987-88; NEOTA, OEA, NEA 1965-94; Animal Welfare League 1990-; Sports Hall of Fame 1989-91; 1st Presbyn Church of Warren; Bd of Directors Friends of Warren Lbry; Publication of Poetry & Sports Articles; Prfrdr of Pblishd Articles.

KINDER, JOANNE PANGONIS, LA Dept Head & Teacher; *b:* Shenandoah, PA; *m:* Raymond C.; *c:* Elizabeth A., Amy J., Raymond J., Heather J.; *ed:* Penn St Univ (BAEd) Eng, Soc Stud, Thea Arts 1961, (MA) Theatre Arts 1964; *cr:* Penn St Univ Grad Asst, Dept Thea Arts 1961-63; Tamaqua Area HS Eng Tchr, LA Dept Head 1963-69; Blue Mountain HS Eng, Speech Tchr 1981-86; Tamaqua Area HS Eng Tchr, LA Dept Head 1986-; *ai:* Sr Class, Commencement Adv; TEA, PSEA, NEA 1963-; Tamaqua Lib Bd 1978-, Sec; Lionettes 1982-, Pres, Sec; Woman's Club 1972-88, Pres, VP, Sec; *office:* Tamaqua Area Sr HS Stadium Hill Rd PO Box 90 Tamaqua PA 18252

KINDSVATTER, GEORGE JERRY, Biology Teacher; *b:* Steubenville, OH; *ed:* OH Univ (BS) Zoology 1957; Syracuse Univ (MS) Sci 1961; Attnd NE OH Coll of Medicine, Case-Western Reserve Univ, Univ of CA at Berkeley, Kent St Univ, E Stroudsburg Univ; *cr:* Mentor HS Honors Bio Tchr 1957-; *ai:* Mentor Tchrs Schlsp Assn Comm Chm; MTA, NEOEA, OEA, NEA 1957-; George A. Holly Lodge #745 1958-; PTA 1957-, Treas; Natl Sci Fnd Acad Yr Inst Grant; *office:* Mentor HS 6477 N Center St Mentor OH 44060*

KINENS, LEE ANN N., Third Grade Teacher; *b:* Houlton, ME; *m:* Robert H.; *c:* Abigail; *ed:* Univ of ME at Fort Kent (BSEd) K-9 Soc Scis Elem Ed 1977; *cr:* Houlton Elem Schl 5th Grd Tchr 1977-81, 3rd Grd Tchr 1981-; *ai:* NEA, MTA 1977-; Tchr Cert Comm 1992-, Bd Mem; Houlton Parks & Recreation Advy Bd 1987-93, Bd Mem Chm 1992-93; *office:* Houlton Elem Schl 60 South St Houlton ME 04730

KINER, JOHN C., Graphic Arts Teacher; *b:* Harrisburg, PA; *m:* Linda Swartley; *c:* Jennifer Zimmerman, Kimberly Sheibley, David; *ed:* Millersville Univ (BA) Industrial Arts 1970; *cr:* Cumberland Valley HS Graphic Arts Tchr 1970-95; *ai:* Newspaper Adv; Tech Ed Assn of PA, Intnl Tech Ed Assn 1986-; Mount Gilead United Meth Church 1980-, Admin Bd Chprsn; *office:* Cumberland Valley HS 6746 Carlisle Pike Mechanicsburg PA 17055

KING, B. DIANE COLEMAN, 3rd Grade Teacher; *b:* Portland, OR; *m:* David S.; *c:* Jennifer Coleman, Claire Coleman; *ed:* Willamette Univ (BA) Rel 1967; Univ of AK (MAT) 1972; Harvard Divinity Schl 2 Yrs Study; Southern CT St Univ Gestalt Psychology Cert; *cr:* Fairfield Schl Pre Kndgtn-Kndgtn Tchr, Prgms Coord 1981-82; Foote Schl Kndgtn Tchr 1982-83; Beecher Rd Schl K-3rd Grd Tchr 11 Yrs; *ai:* Kisdng Childens Music Camp Coord 8 Yrs; NEA; WEA; 1st Church of Christ Woodbridge, Bd Mem 1980-82; *office:* Beecher Road Elem Schl 40 Beecher Rd Woodbridge CT 06525

KING, BETSY INGRAM, First Grade Teacher; *b:* Pearisburg, VA; *m:* William Chapman; *c:* Shawn M. Watts, Christopher W.; *ed:* Radford Univ (BS) Elem Ed 1969; Attnd Western MD Univ at Westminster & Wilkes Coll at Wilkes-Barre; *cr:* Fairfax Co Pub Schls 3rd Grd Tchr 1969-70; Gammaflux Inc Sec 1975-76; Amer Newspaper Publishers Assn Govt Affairs Sec 1976-77; Henson Aviation Flight Dept Sec 1977-79; Tuscarora Schl Dist 1st Grd Tchr 1979-; *ai:* TAYSO Youth Soccer Spirit Comm; NEA, PSEA, TEA 1988-; PTO 1979-; Mentor for New Tchrs; *office:* Mountain View Elem Schl 2311 Lemar Rd Mercersburg PA 17236

KING, BETTY (HARNESS), Economics Teacher; *b:* LaFollette, TN; *m:* David J. Sr.; *c:* David, Christina, Frank, Andrea; *ed:* Wittenberg Univ (BA) Sociology, Bus Ed 1971; Capital Univ (MBA) Bus Admin 1996; *cr:* Hamilton Local Schls Tchr 1975-76; Lakewood Local Schls Tchr 1977-; *ai:* Yrbk, Jr Class, OWE Club Adv; OEA, NEA 1977-; Lakewood Tchrs Assn 1977-, Treas; Occupational Work Experience Coords Assn 1983-; Tchr of Yr 1993; *office:* Lakewood Sr HS 5222 National Rd SE Hebron OH 43025

KING, CARLENE WOOSTER, English Teacher; *b:* Rockland, ME; *m:* Dale B.; *c:* Meredith; *ed:* Bob Jones Univ (BA) Eng, Fr 1965; Middlebury Coll (MA) Eng 1967, (MLITT) Eng 1987; Attnd Malone Coll, OH Wesleyan Univ, Magill Univ, Lincoln Coll at Oxford; *cr:* Camden-Rockport HS Eng, Fr Tchr 1965-66; Bob Jones Univ Fr, Eng Tchr 1966-68; Brandon Hall Schl Fr, Eng Tchr 1969; The Tandem Schl Fr Tchr 1970-71; Hong Kong Bapt Coll Eng Tchr 1981-82; Malone Coll Eng Tchr 1973-79, 1983; Cuyahoga Valley Chrstn Acad Eng Tchr 1983-; *ai:* Acad Challenge Coach; Bd's Ed Comm Fac Rep; New Baltimore Comm Church 1973-; Cleveland Museum of Art 1993-; Filene Fnd Grant to Stud at Harvard Univ; Natl Endowment for Hum Grant to Stud in Florence Italy; *office:* Cuyahoga Valley Christian Acad 4687 Wyoga Lake Rd Cuyahoga Falls OH 44224

KING, CARRIE LYNN, Spanish Teacher; *b:* Mc Keesport, PA; *ed:* Bethany Coll (BA) Span, Scndry Ed 1994; Attnd Univ of MD at Coll Park; *cr:* Prince George Cty Pub Schls Span Tchr 1994-; *ai:* Jr Class, Span Class Spon; NEA, MSTA 1994-; *office:* Fairmont Heights HS 1401 Nye St Capitol Heights MD 20743

KING, CHERYL L. (PUGH), Guidance Counselor; *b:* Bainbridge, GA; *m:* Thomas Marshall; *c:* Jarrod, Jayson; *ed:* Rutgers Univ (BA) Commnctn 1979; Trenton St Coll (MA) Tchng; Stu Prsnl Svcs, Supervision & Eng Certs; *cr:* Plainfield Pub Schls 1st Grd Tchr 1985-87; Franklin Twp Pub Schls 7th Grd Eng Tchr 1987-90, 3rd Grd Tchr 1990-91, 2nd Grd Tchr 1991-92, 8th Grd Eng Tchr 1992-94, Elem Guid Cnslr 1994-95, 7th Grd Guid Cnslr 1995-; Trenton St Coll Instr Alternate Route Tchrs Pgm 1990; *ai:* 7th Grd Class Adv; Mem Magnet Schl Steering Comm; Intnl Day Spon; EPIC Pgm Coord; NEA 1985-; NJ Ed Assn 1985-; Somerset Cty Schl Cnslrs Assn 1995-; PTA, PTO & PTSO 1987-; NAACP 1991-, Yth Cncl Adv; Writer Local Newspaper The Franklin Voice Ed Section; 2 Articles Pub; *office:* Sampson G Smith Interm Sch Amwell Rd Somerset NJ 08873*

KING, CLIFFORD MICHAEL, Principal & Spanish Teacher; *b:* Pawtucket, RI; *ed:* Providence Coll (BA) Ed, Lang 1973; St Michael's Coll (MA) Rel Stud 1983; Boston Coll (MED) Educl Admin 1989; *cr:* Bishop Guertin HS Tchr 1974-78; Mt St Charles Acad Tchr 1978-86; St Dominic HS Prin 1986-89; Mt St Charles Acad VP, Prin 1989-; *ai:* Ath Events Bus Driver; NCEA 1986-; RIFLA 1992-; NASSP 1986-; *office:* Mount Saint Charles Acad 800 Logee St Woonsocket RI 02895

KING, CONSTANCE ADELLE, Math, Science, Spanish Teacher; *b:* Dubuque, IA; *m:* Steven C.; *c:* John D., Adelle E., Abigail R., Elizabeth T.; *ed:* Cornell Coll (BSS) Psych, Span 1977; *cr:* Calvary Chapel Chrstn Acad HS Math, Sci, Span Tchr 1991-; *ai:* Music Chapel Comm; *office:* Calvary Chapel Christian Acad 8056 New Cut Rd Severn MD 21144

KING, DEBORAH KAY, High School English Teacher; *b:* McConnellsburg, PA; *m:* Thomas S.; *c:* Andrew T., Lauryn R.; *ed:* Cntrl PA Bus Schl (ASB) Legal Asst 1985; Shippensburg Univ (BSEd) Eng 1988; MEd Shippensburg Univ 1995; *cr:* Forbes Road HS Eng Tchr 1988-; *ai:* Cardinal Care Team (Schls Stu Asst Team); NHS & Natl Jr Honor Soc Adv; *office:* Forbes Road HS HCO 1 Box 222 Waterfall PA 16689*

KING, DEBORAH LYNN, Sixth Grade Teacher; *b:* Dayton, OH; *c:* Brittney, Hayden; *ed:* Cntrl St Univ (BS) Elem Ed 1975; Wright Univ 6 Credit Hrs Math; Univ of Dayton 4 Credit Hrs Ldrshp; *cr:* Loos Elem 1st Grd Tchr 1979-80; Whittier Elem 5th Grd Tchr 1980-81; Eastmont Elem 1st Grd Tchr 1981-82; Residence Park Elem 6th Grd Tchr 1982-88; Carlson Elem 6th Grd Tchr 1988-; *ai:* Fac Cncl; Safety Patrol Adv; Conflict Mgmt Coord; Blach His Comm; Speech Contest Comm; Yr Round Comm; 6th Grd Adv; CCTM News Comm; OEA & NEA 1979-; CEC 1994-, Sec; Brigham-Hoard Reunion Comm 30 Yrs; Metropolitan Civic Women Org 3 Yrs Sec; Project Prime Project Completed 30 Hrs of Enhancement for Improving Math Ed; *home:* 768 Ernroe Dr Dayton OH 45408

KING, DENISE WENDELL, Fifth Grade Teacher; *b:* Pittsfield, MA; *m:* John M.; *c:* Jonathan, Andrew; *ed:* Univ of MA (BS) Human Dev 1968; St Univ of NY at Albany (MS) Curr Dev 1968; *cr:* Pontoosuc Elem Schl Kndgtn Tchr 1968-69; Tucker Elem Schl Second Grd Tchr 1969-72; Chatham MS Fifth Grd Tchr 1988-; *ai:* Natures Classroom Coord; Shared Decision Making Team; Dist Tchr Evaluation, Sci Fair, Wellness Comms; Strategic Planning, Curr Dev; NEA, Chatham Cntrl Tchrs Assn 1988-; NYSMA 1992-, Conf Presenter; NYS Democratic Comm 1993-, 99th Assembly Dist; Columbia Cty Democratic Comm 1980-, Chatham Town Chm; PTA 1982-, Founder, Pres of Local Org; Articles Pub; *home:* 15 Middlebrook Dr Valatie NY 12184*

KING, DENNIS F., Science Teacher; *b:* Boston, MA; *m:* Dana Wood; *c:* Maggie, Abbie; *ed:* Boston Univ (BA) Bio 1987; Univ MA Lowell (MED) Curr & Instr 1988; *cr:* Methuen HS Sci Tchr 1988-; *ai:* Cross Cntry Coach 1989-95; Wrestling Coach 1991-; NEA, MTA 1988-; NSTA 1988-; *office:* Methuen HS 1 Ranger Rd Methuen MA 01844

KING, DONALD S., Social Studies Teacher; *b:* Williamsport, PA; *m:* Sharon Drick; *c:* Christopher, Karen; *ed:* Susquehanna Univ (AB) His 1966; Lycoming Coll Tchng Cert 1967; Penn St at Bloomsburg M Equivalency Soc Stud 1970; *cr:* Jersey Shore HS Soc Stud Tchr 1966-68; Montoursville HS Soc Stud Tchr 1968-; *ai:* Soc Stud Seminar Adv; OME 1985-, Bd Mem; Planning Commission 1986-, Chm; Church Admin Bd 1991-, Chm; Kiwanis 1987-, Sec; Cemetery Bd 1993-, Sec; Author 3 Booklets; *office:* Montoursville Area Sr HS 100 N Arch St Montoursville PA 17754

KING, ELLEN MC GOWAN, 6th Grade Language Arts Tchr; *b:* York, PA; *m:* Robert G.; *c:* Kathleen, Robert P., Kevin; *ed:* St Joseph Coll (BS) Elem Ed 1968; Youngstown St Univ (MS) Ed, Talented, Gifted Specialist 1986; *cr:* St Joseph Elem Ctr 5-6 Grd Lang Arts Tchr 1968-70; Richmond Ave Schl 4th Grd Tchr 1970-73; W. S. Guy Schl 6th Grd Lang Arts Tchr 1973-; *ai:* Power of Pen Adv, Judge 1993-; Lang Arts Curr Advy Comm; Venture Capital Grant Wrtng Comm 1995-; Tlntd & Gftd Advsy Comm 1995-; NEA, OH Ed Assn 1973-; WRITE 1990-; Trumbell Area Rdng Comm 1980-; St Charles Church 1992-, Rel Instr; Cath Collegiate 1990-; Martha Holden Jennings Scholar 1993-; WFMJ-TV Class Act Awd 1993; Limited Svc Grad Instr Youngstown St Univ 1992-; Presentor Trumbell Area Ltrcy Conf 1994-; *office:* W. S. Guy MS 4115 Shady Rd Youngstown OH 44505

KING, GEORGE CURTIS, AP Eng, Lit & Composition Tchr; *b:* Springfield, MO; *m:* Suzanne Adelaide Sutphen; *c:* Kimberly Jean King Houston; *ed:* Amer Univ (BA) Eng 1965, (MA) Eng Lit 1968; Univ of VA, Univ of MD, Montgomery Cty Pub Schls 30 Hrs in Ed; *cr:* Rockville HS Eng Tchr 1968-; *ai:* Girls & Boys Tennis; It's Acad; Steering Comm Mid States Evaluation; NEA; MCEA; US Tennis Assn 1978-, Ranked 7 in Mid Atlantic Region 1989; Apple Cmptr 1989 Scholastic Writing Awd; Recg for Proucing High Scores on AP Eng Test Twice the Rate of Comparable Schls 1995, 1996; Nom Marian Greenblatt Awd for Dedication and Exel 1996; Authored 2 Novels and 1 Contemporary Mythology 1990-96; *home:* 15 Longmeadow Dr Gaithersburg MD 20878*

KING, JANE LOUISE STIDD, Fourth Grade Teacher; *b:* Bellaire, OH; *m:* Edwin William; *ed:* OH Univ (BS) Elem, Spec Ed 1968, (MS) Guid, Cnslng 1983; Post-Grad Stud; *cr:* Bellaire City Schls First Grd Tchr 1968-69; Shadyside Schls Spec Ed Intermediate Tchr 1969-80; Grd Tchr 1980-81; Second Grd Tchr 1981-92; Fourth Grd Tchr 1992-; *ai:* Spontaneous Coach for Several OM Teams; Y-Teen Adv; Priv Tutoring; NEA, OEA, EOTA 1968-; SEA 1968-, Bldg Rep, Sec, VP; Delta Kappa Gamma Psi Chptr 1973-, Chm Various Comms; Order of Eastern Star 1971-, Worthy Matron 1976, 25 Yr Pin; Lincoln Ave United Meth Church 1958-, Active Various Comms; Delta Kappa Gamma Annie Webb Blanton Schlshp 1983; *office:* Leona MS 3895 Leona Ave Shadyside OH 43947*

KING, JANET WELLS, Cooperative Business Ed Coord; *b:* Kankakee, IL; *c:* Anita; *ed:* Trevecca Nazarene Coll (BS) Bus Ed 1974; Univ of Cincinnati (MED) Voc Bus Ed 1978; *cr:* Great Oaks Inst for Tech & Career Dev Bus Tchr 1976-; *ai:* Bus Prof of Amer Club Adv; OVA, AVA 1978-, Exec Bd; OBTA 1979-; Delta Phi Epsilon 1982-, Historian; Univ of Cincinnati Schlsp; *office:* Live Oaks Career Dev Campus 5956 Buckwheat Rd Milford OH 45150

KING, JOHN R., Mathematics Instructor; *b:* Middletown, CT; *m:* Maureen Mulcahy; *c:* Matthew, Joshua, Zachary; *ed:* Cntrl CT St Univ (BA) Math 1969; Wesly Univ (MAT) Math 1971; Trinity Coll (MA) Math Supervision 1974; *cr:* Hartford Pub HS Math Tchr 1969-79; Xavier HS Math Instr 1979-; *ai:* Hamden Hall Cntry Day Schl Soccer, Var Bsktbl Coach; Mercy HS Var Lacrosse Coach; AFT, NCTM 1969-; *office:* Xavier HS 181 Randolph Rd Middletown CT 06457

KING, JULIE DEAN, Counseling Co-Dir & His Tchr; *b:* Cambridge, MA; *c:* Kristina I., Carolyn J.; *ed:* Williams Coll (BA) His 1984; NY Univ (MA) Modern European His 1992; *cr:* Jeffcoat Schoen, Morrell Inc Account Exec 1984-85; Harvey Schl Part-time Tchr 1985-86; Hackley Schl Tchr 1986-, Asst Dir Admissions 1989-91, Co-Dir Coll Counseling 1992-; *ai:* NACAC 1992-, NYSACAC 1992-; NAIS 1986-; Oscar Kimelman Awd Excl Tchng; Yrbk Awd; *office:* Hackley Schl 293 Benedict Ave Tarrytown NY 10591

KING, JULIE MORVAI, American History Teacher; *b:* Akron, OH; *m:* Roy D.; *c:* Justin Lee, Nicholas Morvai, Jacob Alexander; *ed:* 25 Semester Hrs Cnslng 1995; Chemical Intervention Trng 1983; *cr:* Manchester MS 7th-8th Grd LD Lang, Rdng, Math Tchr 1981-85; Manchester Elem Schl 2nd Grd Tchr 1985-86; Gables Elem Schl K-5th Grd Disciplinarian Tchr 1990-91; Hilliard Heritage MS 8th Grd Sci, Soc Stud Tchr 1991-92, 8th Grd Amer His, Intervention Academically At Risk Tchr 1992-; *ai:* Co-Adv FCA; Positive Attitude Winds Coord; Coalition Essential Schls Comm Rep; NEA 1981-; Hilliard Ed Assn 1991-; Pickerington PTO 1993-; MS Educator of Yr 1992; Jennings Scholar Awd 1992; Yth to Yth Drug Alcohol Prevention Honorary Awd Svc 1993; Tchr of Month 1995; *office:* Hilliard Heritage MS 5600 Scioto-Darby Rd Hilliard OH 43026*

KING, KAREN BANVILLE, Science Teacher; *b:* Washington, DC; *m:* Steven Lee; *c:* Christopher, Erin; *ed:* St Mary's Coll of MD (BS) Bio, Natural Scis 1975; Post Grad at Western MD, Trinity; *cr:* Esperanza MS Sci Tchr 1974-; *ai:* Seventh Grd Team Chprsn; Schl Improvement Team Comm; Shenandoah Natural His Assoc; St Mary's Nursing Home Fnd 1995-; Advanced Prof Tchng Cert 1982-; *office:* Esperanza MS 201 Maple Rd Lexington Park MD 20653

KING, KARRIE L., Art Teacher; *b:* Toledo, OH; *m:* Timothy Bowling Green St Univ (BS) Art Ed 1984; Univ of Toledo (ME) 1994; *cr:* Rossford Jr High Art Tchr 1984-92; Anthony Wayne HS Ar 1992-; *ai:* Art Club Adv; OEA, NEA, OAEA 1984-; NWOAEA Newsletter Ed; Northwest OH Outstanding Art Educator 1995-96; Holden Jennings Scholar; Article Pub in School Arts Magazine; Anthony Wayne HS 5967 Finzel Rd Whitehouse OH 43571

KING, KEVIN B., Choral Director; *b:* Baltimore, MD; *m:* Bettye *c:* Chris, Robbie; *ed:* Towson St Univ (BS) Music Ed 1980; M Equivocal Music Performance at Towson St Univ 1987; *cr:* Wir Sandymount Elem Schl Vocal, Gen Music Tchr 1980-82; Heart o Chorus Musical Dir 1988-; South Carroll HS Choral Dir, Orch, Theory, His 1982-; *ai:* Meml Episcopal Church Tenor Soloist Musical Productions 15 Yrs; NEA, MENC 1980-; SPEBSQSA 1977 10 Quartet Finalist Certfd Judge, Singing 1986-; *office:* South Carrc 1300 W Old Liberty Rd Sykesville MD 21784

KING, KIM YVONNE BULMER, French Teacher; *b:* Lockport, N Steven H.; *c:* Christopher K., Brandon S., Arielle L.; *ed:* Univ of B (BA) Fr 1979, (MED) Frgn Lang Ed 1982; Attnd Univ de Gre 1978-79; *cr:* Intensive Eng Lang Inst Univ of Buffalo ESL Instr 198 Cedar Cliff HS Fr Tchr 1984-; *ai:* Fr Club, Frgn Trip Adv; Ski Club; CEC Comms; AATF, NEA, WSEA 1986-; ST Joan of Arc, Rel Ed Tchr; Russian-Amer Tchr Exchange Moscow; *office:* Cedar Cli Carlisle & Warwick Rds Camp Hill PA 17011

KING, KRISTINE LARSEN, Soc Stud & Lang Arts Tchr; *b:* Cleve OH; *c:* Karen Muthusammy, Edward K., Susan K.; *ed:* Kent St (MAEd) Soc Stud 1989; Gifted Cert; John Carroll Univ, Ashland C Cleveland St Univ 10 Credit Hrs; *cr:* St Terese Schl 7th-8th Grd Soc & LA Tchr 1985-91; Emerson MS 7th-8th Grd Soc St & LA Tchr of C & Talented 1991-; Cleveland St Univ Instr 1993-94; *ai:* Ski Classroom of Champions, 8th Grd Power of the Pen & Water Adv; 8t Team Ldr; Schl Plays Coord; Soc Stud Curr Comm; NEA 1991-; 1991-; Lakewood MS Tchr of the Yr 1995; *office:* Emerson MS Clifton Blvd Lakewood OH 44107*

KING, LEANNE CATHERINE, Science Teacher; *b:* Oxford, OH Miami Univ (BS) Scndry Ed & Biological Sci 1993; Univ of Cinci Grad Work in Schl Psych; *cr:* LaSalle HS Sci Tchr 1993-; *ai:* Information Comm; Mens Bsktbl Statatician; Mens JV Tennis C *office:* La Salle HS 3091 W North Bend Rd Cincinnati OH 45239

KING, LINDA DIANE, Guidance Counselor; *b:* Brooklyn, NY; *m:* Dennis Parrott; *ed:* Long Island Univ (BA) Speech & Hearing 1976, Cnslng 1978; Paralegal Stud; *cr:* PS 21 Schl Aide 1972-75; PS 308 2 5th Grd Tchr 1984-89, Guid Cnslr 1989-92; PS 309 Guid Cnslr 1995 Chrldr Coach; Dance Club; AFT 1984-; NEA 1984-; Media Edctrs 1985-; Assn for Cnslng & Dev 1993-; Arthur Mitchell Dance Theat Harlem Schlsp; *office:* PS 309 794 Monroe St Brooklyn NY 11221

KING, LLOYD EUGENE, English Teacher; *b:* Marble, NC; *m:* S Lee Darrell; *c:* Lyndon, Donna, Kevin, Keith; *ed:* Univ of TN (BS) Pol Sci 1960, (MS) Eng, S Stud 1961; William & Mary Eng, Pol Sci E TN St U Eng, Pol Sci 1958; Amer Univ Post M Pol Sci 1965; Pace Post M Pol Sci 1972-73; *cr:* Pensacola Coll Ec Tchr 1960-62; Smyrn Soc Stud Tchr 1962-65; P S Du Pont HS Eng, Soc Stud Tchr 196 Glasgow HS Eng Tchr 1977-; *ai:* Acad Bowl Team; NHS; Shakes Club, Troupe; X-Head Bsbl Coach 12 Yrs; Smyrna Ed Assn 1962-, Newark Ed Assn 1977-, Adult Cty Tchr of Yr; NEA 1960-; Elks Club 1 Moose Club 1980-; NHS, Bd of Dir, Rept Del; NDEA Grants 197 Poem Pub 1978; Tchr of Yr New Castle Cty Adult Schl; *office:* Glas HS 1901 S College Ave Newark DE 19702

KING, LYNNE FONIECZKO, Associate Prof of Nursing; *b:* Lewi ME; *c:* Scott, Caitlin; *ed:* Univ of Southern ME (BSN) Nrsng 1977, Adult Ed 1981, (MSN) Nrsng 1988; *cr:* Univ of ME Assoc Prof N 1982-; *ai:* Acad Advising; Fundamentals Course Math Coord; T Comm Chprsn 1993-95; NEA 1982-; Sigma Theta Tau 1988-; Amer Assn 1986-, Past Mem Affiliate Faculty; PTA 1988-; Spec Pr Assignment to Adapt Nrsng Prgm 1991-93; Pressure Ulcer Preve Rsrch Stud; *office:* Univ Of ME At Augusta University Heights Au ME 04330

KING, MABEL A., Business Education Teacher; *b:* Philadelphia, P Sharon A. Loper-Knox, Dianna E. Loper, Frances A. Goodson, Darc Burt, Stephanie L. Bridgeford, Keith S. Bridgeford, Kelly M. Turner Cheyney Univ of PA (BS) Bus Ed 1981; 18 Grad Hrs; Widener Univ o 6 Grad Hrs; *cr:* Chester HS Bus Ed Tchr 1982-; New Life Schl of Min Admin 1987-88; *ai:* Stu Prayer Org Club Adv; PSEA, NEA 1992-; ST 1994-; World of LIfe Comm Ministries 1992-, Prayer Ldr; Inst Enterprise Internship; *office:* Chester HS 18th & Melrose Ave Cheste 19013*

KING, MARGARET L., Professor of History; *b:* New York City, NY Robert E. Kessler; *c:* David Kessler, Jeremy Kessler; *ed:* Sarah Lawr Coll (BA) His 1967; Stanford Univ (MA) His 1968, (PHD) His 1972 Brooklyn Coll His Prof 1972-; Grad Ctr City Univ of NY His Prof 1 *ai:* Renaissance Quarterly Ed 1984-88; Vol Deacon; AHA 19 Renaissance Soc of Amer 1972-, Exec Dir 1987-; Woodrow Wi 1967-68, Danforth 1968-72, ACLS, NEH, Amer Philosophical Sc Gladys Krieble Delmas Fndtn Grants & Flwshps; Numerous Books *office:* Brooklyn Coll Dept of His 2900 Bedford Ave Brooklyn NY 11

KING, MARK E., Assoc Prof Dept of Child Dev; *b:* Baltimore, MD Virginia Bach; *c:* Shana; *ed:* Univ of MD (BA) Psych 1967; Univ of (MS) Child Dev & Family Relations 1970; Iona St Univ (PHD) Child 1973; *cr:* Ougiene Univ Asst Prof 1973-75; Univ of Pittsburgh Assoc 1975-; *ai:* Amer Psychological Assn 1980-; PA Psych Assn 1992-; 5 B Pub on Cnslng & Clinical Hypnosis; *office:* Univ Of Pittsburgh 1717 of Learning Pittsburgh PA 15260

KING, MARY BILEK, Biology Teacher; *b:* NJ; *m:* Mark O.; *c:* B Brent; *ed:* Univ of DE (BA) Bio & Ed 1965; Attnd West Chester Uni Western CT St Univ.

KING, PATRICIA ANN, English Tchr & Dept Chprsn; *b:* Frederick, *ed:* Frostburg St Univ (BS) Eng, Ed 1963; Towson St Univ Equv Ed 1 *cr:* Sykesville HS Eng Tchr 1963-69; South Carroll Hs Eng Tchr 1969- MCTELA; DKG; NCTE; CCEA; NEA; MSTA; *office:* South Carroll 1300 W Old Liberty Rd Sykesville MD 21784*

KING, RICHARD, English Teacher; *b:* Pittsburgh, PA; *m:* Brenda H. Richard H., John D.; *ed:* Cheyney St Coll (BS) Ed, Eng 1971; Trento Coll (MED) Ed, Eng 1979; Post Grad Temple Univ, Rutgers U Glassboro St Coll; *cr:* Trenton Jr HS Tchr 1971-77; Camden HS 1977-; *ai:* Bsktbl, Vlybl Coach; Class, Yrbk Bus Adv; NJEA 19 Evergreen Bapt Church 1972-, Trustee; Kappa Alpha Psi 1976-; Pri Hall Mason 1979-; Who's Who Among Stdnts in Amer Colls & Univs 1 *office:* Camden HS Park & Baird Blvd Camden NJ 08104*

KING, ROBERT A., English Teacher; *b:* Buffalo, NY; *m:* Elizabeth; St Univ of NY at Buffalo (BA) Eng 1968; Canisius Coll (MS) Eng Ed 1 Post-Grad Ed 60 Hrs SUNY at Buffalo, SUNY Coll at Buffalo; *cr:* Gr Island Cntrl Schls Eng Instr 1968-; *ai:* AFT, NYSUT, GITA, NCTE 19 Awded Two Sabbatical Leaves Advanced Grad Stud; Twice Winne Celebration of Inspiration Awd; Pub; *office:* Grand Island MS 1 Ransom Rd Grand Island NY 14072*

ɡ, ROBERT LEE, 6th Grade Teacher; *b:* Mt Pleasant, PA; *m:* Sandra ; *ed:* CA Univ of PA (BS) Elem Ed 1972; Penn St Univ (MS) Elem Ed IN Univ of PA (MS) Elem Math 1984; *cr:* Southmoreland Schl Dist ird Tchr 1972-; *ai:* PSEA, NEA, SEA 1972-; PCTM 1096-; NCTM ; BPOE 1984-; F&AM 1988-; *office:* Scottdale Elem Schl N Chestnut ottdale PA 15683

ɡ, RONALD LEE, Science Teacher; *b:* Huntington, WV; *m:* Tamara McCoy; *ed:* Marshall Univ (BA) Physics 1986, (MA) Ed Scndry *cr:* Pocahontas HS Sci Tchr 1986-87; Portsmouth HS Sci Tchr -90; Fairland HS Sci Tchr 1991-; *ai:* Coach Chem & Physics lastic Test, Sci Olympiad Team; Coach of Scores Chemistry & ics Test; NEA 1986-; OEA 1987-; OSTA 1991-; Governors Awd Excl ı Sci Opportunities.

ɡ, ROSE HITCHCOCK, Teacher & Coordinator; *b:* Milledgeville, *m:* Zan Jr.; *c:* Joy Lynn, Philicia Lillian; *ed:* OH Univ (BS) Ed, Eng 1973; OH St Univ (MA) Policy & Ldrshp, Curr Inst, Prof Dev 1995; al Univ Law Schl 41 Semester Hrs Juris Doctor; *cr:* Cleveland Pub Edctr 1973-74; Columbus Pub Schl Edctr 1974-75; Franklin Cty are Dept Recertification Wkr 1977-80; Columbus Pub Schls Edctr -; *ai:* Grantwriter; Project Venture Capital Comm; OH Future Edctrs ner, Exec Bd; Columbus Edctrs of Tomorrow Prgm, Adv; NEA, OEA, 1973-, Rep; Girls Scouts of Amer 1987-, Vol, Vol Awd; Framingham Assn 1988-95, Pres; Alpha Kappa Mu 1995-, Acad Excl; Phi Delta 995-, Acad Excl; OH Dept of Ed Project Venture Capital Grant; Tchr r 1988-90; Tchr of Month TV Channel 4 1996; *office:* Northland HS Northcliff Dr Columbus OH 43229

ɡ, SANDRA LEE, Business Ed Tchr & Dept Chprsn; *b:* Everett, PA; seph F.; *c:* Donald, Jodie, Kelsey, Swain; *ed:* Shippensburg Univ (BA) Ed 1972; Frostburg St Univ (MS) Guid & Cnslng 1979; Allegany m Coll Cmptr Sci 1992; *cr:* Mount Savage Schl Bus Dept Chprsn -; *ai:* Schl Store, FBLA Adv; Stu Svc Coord 9th-12th Grd; Bus Dept, Sts Steering Comm Chair; Mid Sts Guid, Curr, Fin Comms; Stu book; NBEA 1993-; MSTA, NEA 1972-; MD Archery Assn 1982-, VP ournaments; Cumberland Bowhunter's 1982-, Sec; Tchr of Yr 1995; of Day for WCBC 1993; MD St Dept of Ed Distngd Voc Bus Ed Prgm 1988, Awd for Excl 1988; *office:* Mt Savage Schl 13201 New School W Mount Savage MD 21545

ɡ, SANDRA (ZIEROLF), Mathematics Teacher; *b:* Findlay, OH; *m:* ld F.; *c:* Thomas W.; *ed:* Bowling Green St Univ (BS) Math, Chem ; NSF Tchrs Trng Tchrs in Discrete Math Demana, Waits Graphing ulator Insts; *cr:* Fostoria City Schls Math Tchr 1964-71, 1981-; *ai:* M 1985-; OH Cncl of Tchrs of Math 1982-; Fostoria Ed Assn 1981-, ; Jennings Scholar; Eisenhower Grant; *office:* Fostoria HS 1001 Park Fostoria OH 44830

ɡ, SELENA FRASER, 9th-12th Grd English Teacher; *b:* Newton, *m:* Benjamin Zehnder; *ed:* William Coll (BA) Eng 1986; Harvard Univ D) Ed & Eng 1990; *cr:* Hopkinton HS Eng Tchr 1990-91; Nauset Regnl Eng Tchr 1991-; *ai:* Newspaper Adv; NEA 1991-; *office:* Nauset Reg School Cable Rd Eastham MA 02651

ɡ, STEPHEN ALAN, English Teacher; *b:* Springfield, OH; *m:* cia Ann DiMartile; *c:* Alison M., Andrew S.; *ed:* Univ of CT (BA) Eng ; Temple Univ (MS) Ed 1977; *cr:* Bishop Mc Devitt HS Eng Tchr -74; Cedar Cliff HS Eng Tchr 1974-; *ai:* Amensty Intnl Club & Lit azine Adv; Ftbl Coach; NEA, PSEA, WSEA 1974-; *office:* Cedar Cliff Carlisle & Warwick Rds Camp Hill PA 17011

ɡ, SUSAN ADELE, Social Studies Teacher; *b:* Toledo, OH; *m:* James n; *c:* Meghan, Ashley, Lindsay; *ed:* Principia Coll (BA) His 1972; *cr:* ania City Schls Soc Stud Tchr 1972-79, 1982-; *ai:* SEA, OEA, NEA -; *office:* Sylvania Southview HS 7225 Sylvania Ave Sylvania OH 50

ɡ, SUZANNE S., Soc Studies, Math & Eng Tchr; *b:* New York, NY; George; *c:* Kimberly King Houston; *ed:* Amer Univ (BA) Eng 1966; l Tchng Courses Univ of VA, Univ of MD; *cr:* Town & Country Schl 1967-78; The Barnesville Schl Tchr, Asst Prin 1978-; Washington Cathedral Staff AIDE, Medieval Wkshp 1992-; *ai:* Study Skills Coord; spaper Spon; Stu Life Comm Co-Chm; MS Drama Dir; Smithsoniana 1995-, Assoc Mem; Natl Cathedral 1992-, Vol; Division Dir Grds 3-6; ring Comm 1993 Accreditation; Prgm Comm, MS Comm Bd of Dirs; ss Presentation Folger Shakespear Lib; *home:* 15 Longmeadow Dr thersburg MD 20878

ɡ, UNITY MACKLIN, Business Education Teacher; *b:* Washington, *m:* R. Burlington; *ed:* Howard Univ (BA) Bus Admin 1961, (MA) Ed ; 60 Addl Grad Hrs Admin Trinity Coll, Univ of DC, Amer Univ; *cr:* ngarn SHS Stay Prgm Bus Ed Tchr 1965-68; Sousa Jr HS Bus Ed Tchr 8-70; Amer Schl Bus Ed Tchr 1971-72; Woodrow Wilson SHS Bus Ed r 1973-; *ai:* FBLA Adv; Career, Consumer Sci Dept Chprsn; NBEA 5-; Eastern Bus Ed Assn 1975-, Scndry Schl Dir; Phi Delta Kappa 1-; Delta Pi Epsilon 1980-; Sec, VP; DC Bus Ed 1975-, Pres; Carter on East Neighborhood Assn 1985-; Sixth Presbyn Church 1985-; con, Ruling Elder; *office:* Woodrow Wilson Sr HS Nebraska -Chesapeake St Nw Washington DC 20016

ɡ, VIRGINIA ANN ROLLI, Elementary Teacher; *b:* Jamaica, NY; *m:* hard A.; *c:* Deborah Ranicar, David Groves; *ed:* St Univ Coll at Oneonta) Ed 1966; *cr:* Fleetwood Schl 1st Grd Tchr 1966-68; Mill Road Schl rant Tutor 1971-76; Astor Learning Ctr Remedial Rdng Tchr 1979-82; e Plains Cntrl Schl Pre-1st, 1st & 4th Grd Tchr 1982-; *ai:* Trainer for h Their Way; Dist & Bldg Level Teams; Working with Schl Plays; Pine ns Fed of Tchrs 1982-, Bldg Rep, VP, Pres; AFT; Nom PTA Tchr of Yr; ervice Credit Hrs in Math Their Way, The Lit Connection, ELIC, operative Learning & Whole Lang; *home:* RR 1 Box 2766 Red Hook NY 71*

ɡ, WALTER CLEMENS, Asst Prof of Illstrtn & Fndtns; *b:* timore, MD; *m:* Tamara Ann; *c:* Daniel, James; *ed:* Columbus Coll Arts es (BFA) Illustration 1981; Boston Univ (MFA) Painting 1985; Wichita Univ 15 Credit Hrs; *cr:* Freelance Illus & Design Artist 1978-90; Cols l of Art & Design Instr 1985-; *ai:* Illustration Dept Acad Advising, iting Artist & Schlsp Comms; Fac Cncl; Cols Art League 1988-, Jean nb Hall Awd for Painting; ACME Art Co 1989-, Advy Bd; EF Educl rs 1994-, Tour Cnslr; AIGA Graphic Design IV 1983; Living Arts of sa OK Solo Exhibition 1993; 3 OH Painters Exhibitions; *office:* umbus Coll Of Art & Design 107 N 9th St Columbus OH 43215*

ɡ, WILLIAM EVERETT, Program Manager; *b:* Dayton, OH; *m:* ndra Louise Hall; *c:* Sherry Muskoff, Julie Riley; *ed:* OH Univ (BS) m Ed, Scndry Eng 1973, (MED) Educl Admin 1980; Post Grad Stud OH iv; *cr:* Portsmouth City Schls Elem Tchr, Adult Ed Instr 1968-73; erview Chrstn Schl Tchr, Prin 1973-75; WV Bible Schl Tchr, Prin 76-91; WV Bible Schl & Coll Pres 1978-91; OH Univ Southern Campus m Mgr 1991-; *ai:* Groups, Orgs, Churches Speaker; OEA, NEA 1968-; stn Ed Assns 1975-; Adult Literacy Prgm 1988-, Tutor; Wesleyan liness Church 1976-, Adult, Yth Tchr, Layminister; Foster Parenting 87-; Editorials & Articles Pub; Educl, Church Confs Presenter; ochial, Pvt Schls Educl Consultant.

NGSBURY, GARY A., 8th Grade Math Teacher; *b:* Onieda, NY; *m:* san McKenna; *c:* Todd, Lisa; *ed:* SUNY at Brockport (BS) El Ed 1967, S) El Ed 1970; *cr:* Albion Ctrl Schl 5th Grd Tchr 1967-70, 6th Grd Tchr 1970-83, 8th Grd Math Tchr 1983-; *ai:* JV Ftbl, 7th & 8th Grd Girls Bsktbl & 7th & 8th Grd Boys Bsktbl Coach.

KINGSDORF, BETTY GLOVER, Retired Elem Teacher; *b:* Bowdoin, ME; *m:* Jerry; *c:* Joseph Andrew Carleton, Frank Austin Thompson; *ed:* Washington St Tchrs Coll (BA) Elem Ed 1957; 15 Credit Hrs; *cr:* Cushing Elem Schl Third Grd Tchr 1962-63; Matinicus Island Schl 1st-8th Grd Tchr 1963-66; Galloway Twp Schls 2nd-6th Grd Tchr 1966-95; *ai:* Matinicus Island Schl Acting Coach, Prin; Cooking Club; NJEA, NEA, PTA 1966-; *home:* 215 Old River Rd Mays Landing NJ 08330

KINGSLEY, JANE WHEATON, English Teacher; *b:* Derby, CT; *m:* James F.; *c:* Jeffrey J., Justin M., James M.; *ed:* Merrimack Coll (BA) Eng Tchg 1969; *cr:* Aetna Casualty & Surety Co Ins Adjuster 1969-70; FAS Inc Adjuster 1985-87; Guilford HS Sub Tchr 1987-92, Tchr 1992-; *ai:* Sr Class Adv; NEA, CEA, GEA 1992-; *home:* 5 Dover Ln Madison CT 06443

KINLEY, BARBARA HERBERT, Third Grade Teacher; *b:* Bronx, NY; *m:* Donald Joseph; *ed:* Lock Haven Univ (BS) Elem Ed 1975; Marywood Coll (MS) Humanistic, Integrative Ed 1983; 15 Credit Hrs; *cr:* Keystone Cntrl Schl Dist Sub Tchr 1975-79; Castanea Elem Schl 2nd Grd Tchr 1979-81; Liberty-Curtin Elem Schl 3rd Grd Tchr 1981-; *ai:* Co-Chair Hlth Fair 1995-; Fac Cncl 1995-; PCTM Math 1995-; Mill Hall Jehovah's Witnesses 1979-; Lock Haven Area Jaycees Outstdng Young Edctr 1983; TU 10 Arts in Ed Grant Co-Chair 1979-80; Tech Proposal; *home:* 114 Palmer Ave Mill Hall PA 17751

KINLOCK, STEVEN F., Psych & Government Teacher; *b:* Easton, MD; *m:* Elizabeth Swaine; *ed:* Washington Coll (BA) His 1980, (MA) His 1987; Working Towards PHD at Univ of MD; *cr:* Washington Coll Instr 1989-; St Michaels HS Tchr 1980-; *ai:* Chess Coach; Schl Improvement Team; Implementation & Evaluation Comm; Republican Cntrl Comm of Talbot 1991-94; Talbot Cnty Cncl 1994; *office:* Saint Michaels H S Seymour Ave Saint Michaels MD 21663*

KINMAN, DAVID J., Spanish & French Teacher; *b:* Pittsburgh, PA; *m:* Cynthia Shoop; *c:* Jennifer, Whitney; *ed:* Geneva Coll (BA) Span, Fr 1973; IN Univ of PA (MA) Span 1976; Attnd Universidad de Valencia; *cr:* Allegheny-Clarion Vly HS Span, Fr, Latin Tchr 1973-; *ai:* Instrl Support Team; Stu Assistance Prgm; Dept Chm; Mentor Tchr; PA Lead Tchr Prgm; A-V Dir; Chess, Span Club Adv; Head Girls Track Coach 15 Yrs; Jr HS Bsktbl Coach 10 Yrs; NEA, PSEA 1973-; AATSP; PSMLA; Amer Camping Assn, Chrstn Camping Intrnl 1986-; St Peters Reformed Church 1979-, Elder; Westminster Highlands Camp 1986-, Summer Resident Dir; NEH Grant Westminster Coll Latin Inst 1984-85; *office:* Allegheny-Clarion Vly HS PO Box 345 Foxburg PA 16036

KINNAN, SONJA (KULJKO), German Teacher; *b:* Salzburg, Austria; *m:* Jon Thomas; *c:* Ryan, Ashley, Stefanie; *ed:* Univ of Akron (BA) Voc Home Ec, Cert Comprehensive Consumer Homemaking & Multi-Area Job Trng-Cum Laude 1977; Grad Schl Coll of Fine & Applied Arts Master's Prgm-Not Complete 1980; Kent St Univ Post-Undergraduate Completion of Work Ger Tchng Cert, Coll of Arts & Sci 1983; *cr:* Summit Cty Schl Sub Tchr; Portage Cty Schl Sub Tchr 1977-78; Stow HS Home Ec Tchr 1978-79; Nordonia HS Home Ec Tchr 1979-82; Harmon MS Home Ec Tchr 1982-85; Aurora HS Ger Tchr; Harmon MS Ger Tchr 1985-; *ai:* Comm Discipline Advy Comm; AATG 1986-; OH Ed Assn, NEA, Amer Home Ec Ed Assn 1978-; OH Frgn Lang Assn 1993-; OH Lang Assn 1990-; Aurora Ed Assn; Phi Kappa Tau Univ of Akron; Kappa Omicron Phi; *office:* Aurora HS W Pioneer Trail Aurora OH 44202*

KINNARD, MICHAEL LANE, Earth Science Teacher & Coord; *b:* Mount Vernon, OH; *c:* Jennifer; *ed:* Bowling Green Univ (BS) Scndry Ed & Earth Sci & Geography 1968; Eastern MI Univ (MA) Soc Sci 1971; *cr:* Zimmerman Jr HS Soc Stud Tchr & Dept Chm 1968-73; Fairfield Frosh Schl Tchr & Sci Coord 1974-; *ai:* NEA, OEA & FCTA 1974-95; Sci Team Placed 1st (Twice) in OH Scholastic Achievement Test in General Sci; *home:* 3709 Riva Ridge Dr Indian Springs OH 45011

KINNEAR, DIANE LASH, Fifth Grade Teacher; *b:* Baltimore, MD; *m:* James; *c:* Michele Kinnear Mc Guire, Gregory, Robert; *ed:* Towson St Univ (BS) Elem Ed 1970; Attnd Western MD Coll, Drake Univ, Shenandoah Univ; *cr:* Saint Marks Schl Fourth Grd Tchr 1970-71; Our Lady of Perpetual Help Schl Fifth Grd Tchr 1983-; *ai:* Math Dept Chair; Mid Sts Reaccreditation Comm; ESTA 1983-, NCTM 1991-; NCEA 1983-; *office:* Our Lady Perpetual Help Schl 4801 Ilchester Rd Ellicott City MD 21043

KINNEAR, KELLI DUCHAK, Religion Teacher; *b:* Kettering, OH; *m:* Keith M.; *ed:* Univ of Dayton (BS) Ed 1992; Working on Masters in Cnslng; *cr:* Chaminade-Julienne HS Religion Tchr 1992-; *ai:* Key Club Adv; Kiwanis Club 1993-; Initiative Grant to Begin Stu Annual Urban Plunge Retreats into Inner Cities; *office:* Chaminade-Julienne HS 505 S Ludlow St Dayton OH 45402

KINNEAR, SHARON RAE, Soc Stud & Rel Tchr; *b:* Union City, IN; *ed:* Capital Univ (BSEd) His, Pol Sci, Music 1971; 30 Credit Hrs in Soc Stud, Rel, Cmptr, Ed; *cr:* Peace Corps, Holy Rosary Sec Schl His, Math, Music, PE Tchr 1973-75; Clyde Jr High 8th Grd OH His Tchr 1975-76; Hazel Green Acad HS Sec, Typing Tchr 1976-79; Clyde St Mary's Schl 7th-8th Grd Soc St, Math, Music Tchr 1971-73, 5th-8th Grd Soc Stud Tchr, 7th-8th Grd Rel Tchr 1979-; *ai:* 5th-8th Grd Dept Coord; Cmptr Lab, Summer Cmptr Camp Coords; OH Cath Ed Assn, Natl Cath Ed Assn; Top Ten Tchr of Yr in Toledo Diocese 1981.

KINNER, LEEANN FOSTER, Music Teacher & Entertainer; *b:* Dayton, OH; *m:* Marion Ray; *c:* Brian M., Brent F., Tori T.; *ed:* Wright St Univ (BA) Music ed 1991; Cincinnati Conservatory of Music Orff Schulwerk Cert 1986; Wright St Univ; Drake Univ; Univ of Dayton; Univ of Cincinnati; *cr:* Kinner Music Studios Private Guitar Tchr, Voice Inst 1974-; Miamisburg, West Carrollton Vocal, Guitar Group Instr, Parks, Recreations Prgms 1976-; Dayton Chrstn Schls Music Tchr 1984-91; Miami Valley Acad of Music Theory, Sight Singing, Orff Schulwerk 1990-95; Miamisburg City Schls Music Tchr, Specialist 1991-; l'Auberge Restaurant Singer, Guitarist 1991-; Sycamore Creek Ctry Club Singer, Guitarist 1992-; *ai:* 4 Team Comm to Rep Schl for Dev of New Fine Arts St Model 1996; 8 Team Miamisburg Schl; Music Dept Re-writing Music Curr Comm 1996; AOSA 1985-; OMEA, MENC, NEA, MCTA 1991-; Playing Guitar As the Entertainment for Bosnia Peace Talk Delegation Pre-Signing of Peace Treaty Party.*

KINNEY, BEVERLY SEEMAN, Teacher of the Gifted; *b:* Toledo, OH; *m:* John P.; *c:* Jeffrey P., John Eric; *ed:* Univ of Toledo (BA) Ed 1962; Univ of Cincinnati (MS) Ed 1972; Univ of DE (MS) Ec Instruction 1983; Attnd Amer Univ, Miami Univ, Montclair Coll NJ, Xavier Cincinnati; *cr:* Toledo Pub Schls Tchr 1962-63; Princeton City Schls Tchr 1969; Univ of Cincinnati Center of Ec Ed Consultant 1983-86; *ai:* Drama Club Adv; Divorce Support Group for Children Ldr; Chair of Dist Curr Cncl for Gifted; Corresponding Sec of Tchr Assn; Grievance Comm of Tchr Assn; Adv and Trainer for Peer Mediation; NEA, OEA, PACE 1971-; YMCA 1975-; Church 1971-, Chair of Several Comm; Church Synod ELCA, Review Comm; Habitat for Humanity; Tchr of Yr in Consumer Ed of OH 1986; Honorable Mention Ashland Tchr of Yr; Wrote Ec Curr for Lesley Coll; Created Opera; Fellowship to Metropolitan Opera NY; *office:* Robert E Lucas Interm Schl 3900 Cottingham Dr Cincinnati OH 45241

KINNEY, GARY M., Science Teacher; *b:* Danforth, ME; *m:* Beatrice Spofford; *c:* Tanya LaPier, Kurt; *ed:* Univ of ME (BS) Biochemistry 1964; Rensselaer Polytechnic Inst (MS) Natural Scis 1971; Topics in Modern Physics; Fermilab; Woodrow Wilson Physics Inst; Gettysburg Coll TRAC Pgm; Lawrence Berkeley Lab; *cr:* Whitesboro Cntrl Schls Sci Tchr 1965-; *ai:* Sci Olypiad Coach; NEA 1968-, Local Pres; STANYS & MUSTA 1970-, Treas; Rotary Outstdng Edctr Awd; *office:* Whitesboro Cntrl Schls 6000 Rt 291 Marcy NY 13403

KINNEY, KEVIN DWAYNE, Fifth Grade Teacher; *b:* Dayton, OH; *c:* Julius M. Howard; *ed:* OH St Univ (BS) Elem Ed 1979; Wright St Univ (MED) Tchr Ldr, Curr, Sup 1995; Miami Univ at Oxford 10.5 Sem Hrs Curr, Supervision; Elem Geometry for Tchrs 2 Sem Hrs; *cr:* Taft Elem Schl 5th Grd Tchr 1979-82; Mc Kinley Elem Schl 5th-6th Grd Tchr 1982-; *ai:* After Schl Tutor; Oratorical Contest, Discipline Comms; Midd Tchrs Assn, OH Ed Assn, NEA 1979-; Big Brothers, Big Sisters Assn 1990-; Southside Optimist Club 1985-; Middletown Comm Fnd Crystal Apple Excl in Tchng Awd 1995; Outstdng Young Men of Amer 1986; Martha Holden Jennings Scholar 1986; Ashland Oil Inc Tchng Awd Nom 1985, 1988, 1995; *office:* Mc Kinley Elem Schl 1210 S Verity Pky Middletown OH 45044*

KINNIER, JAMES ANTHONY, 11th Grd AP Amer History Tchr; *b:* Brooklyn, NY; *m:* Elizabeth; *c:* James, Andrew, Anne Bunone; *ed:* St Johns (BA) His 1961; CW Post (MS) Ed & His 1970; *cr:* Archbishop Molloy Tchr & Alumni Dir 1961-; *office:* Archbishop Molloy HS 83-53 Manton St Briarwood NY 11435

KINOWSKI, KATHRYN LEE, English Teacher; *b:* Gloversville, NY; *c:* Adam John; *ed:* Coll of St Rose (BA) Eng, Scndry Ed 1975, (MA) Eng 1982; *cr:* St Mary's Inst Jr HS Eng Tchr 1979-84; Stillwater Cntrl HS Sr HS Eng Tchr 1984-; Schenectady Cty Comm Coll Adj Fac 1990-; *ai:* Retired Yrbk, Sr Adv to Pursue Writing Career; Articles Pub; *office:* Stillwater HS N Hudson Ave Stillwater NY 12170

KINSER, ANN YELVERTON, Language Arts & Reading Tchr; *b:* Dover, OH; *m:* Donald; *c:* Jennifer, Jeff; *ed:* Bowling Green St Univ (BS) Elem, Eng 1973; Lake Erie Coll (MS) Supervision 1992; Rdng, Supvrs, Kndgtn Certs; 30 Addl Credit Hrs; *cr:* Mansfield City Schls 4th Grd Tchr 1973-75; London City Schls 7th Grd Rdng Tchr 1975-77; Notre Dame Acad 9th Grd Eng Tchr 1977-78; Chardon Local Schl 6th Grd Tchr 1987-; *ai:* NEA, OEA, CCTA 1988-; NCTE 1992-95; Lake Erie Coll Ed 1993-, Recording Sec, Advy Bd; *office:* Chardon MS 424 North St Chardon OH 44024

KINSEY, NEIL R., Career Education Teacher; *b:* Souderton, PA; *m:* Donna Thomasco; *c:* Elizabeth, Robert, Rebecca; *ed:* Millersville Univ (BSEd) Soc Stud 1968, (MED) Spec Ed 1972; *cr:* Edward Hand Jr HS Spec Ed Tchr 1968-72; J. P. McCaskey HS Spec Ed Tchr 1972-88; Schl Dist of Lancaster Substance Abuse Coord 1988-89; J. P. McCaskey HS Career Ed Tchr 1989-; *ai:* PSEA, NEA 1968-, Bldg Rep; PA Coop Voc Ed Assn 1990-; East Hempfield Twp Bd of Supvrs 1990-, Chm; Lane Cty Planning Commission 1980-86, Chm; Coop Tchr of Yr 1982; *office:* J P Mc Caskey HS 445 N Reservoir St Lancaster PA 17602

KINSEY, PATTI ANN, English Teacher; *b:* Philadelphia, PA; *m:* Robert S. Jr.; *c:* Dillon; *ed:* Muhlenberg Coll (BA) Eng Lit 1982; Completing Masters Prgm Eng Lit Beaver Coll; Received Scndry Cert Owynedd Nurey Coll; 30 Inservice Credits; *cr:* North Penn Jr HS Eng, Drama Tchr 1990-93; North Penn HS Eng Tchr 1994-; *ai:* Lit Review Curr Comm; NCTE, PSEA, NEA 1990-; *office:* North Penn HS 1340 S Valley Forge Rd Lansdale PA 19446*

KINSLOE-BYERS, SUSAN, Art Teacher; *b:* Lancaster, PA; *m:* William Byers; *c:* Douglas, Christopher; *ed:* Allegheny Coll (BA) 1966; Penn St Univ (MA) Art Ed 1967; Extensive Wkshp Experience 1979-93; *cr:* South Windsor HS Art Tchr Ceramics 1967-92; Timothy Edwards MS Art Tchr Unified Arts 1992-; *ai:* Best in Show Willimantic Summer Wkshps Ceramics 1979; *office:* Timothy Edwards MS 100 Arnold Way South Windsor CT 06074

KINSTLER, CYNTHIA (BEHR), Teacher & Counselor; *b:* Phila, PA; *m:* Richard Charles; *c:* Scott, Brett, Dana, Brooke; *ed:* Jersey City Coll (MA) Stu Prsnl Ser 1982; Cert Supv, Admin; *cr:* Island Heights Schl Tchr 1972-, Cnslr 1992-; *ai:* Lit Club; Safety Patrol; Kid Power; Curr Comm; Delta Kappa Gamma 1992-, Rec Sec; NJEA, NEA 1972-, Past Pres 15 Yrs; White Pine Twig 1993-, Comm Chair; Fulbright Seminars Egypt, Israel 1991, India 1995; Hands Across Water Russian Tchr Ex 1992; Ocean Cty Tchr of Yr 1995; *office:* Island Heights Grade Schl 115 Summit Ave Island Heights NJ 08732*

KIPHART, ANDREW PAUL, Hlth & Physical Education Tchr; *b:* Ashtabula, OH; *ed:* Baldwin-Wallace Coll (BA) Hlth & PE 1991; Working on Masters Ed in at Youngstown St Univ; *cr:* Harbor HS Hlth & PE Tchr 1993-; *ai:* Frosh Ftbl & Bsktbl Coach; Jr Var Bsbl Coach; OEA 1993-.*

KIPLE, JUDITH CLINE, Sixth Grade Teacher; *b:* Salem, NJ; *c:* Reese Austin, Todd Edward; *ed:* Glassboro St (BA) Ed 1960; *cr:* Field St Schl 4th Grd Tchr 1960-62; Lafayette Pershing 4th Grd Tchr 1964-66; Penns Grove MS 6th Grd Tchr 1971-; *ai:* NJEA, NEA 1960-; Salem Co E A 1960-; PG Ed Assn 1960-, VP, Sec; Carneys Point Recreation Comm 5 Yrs Mem; Tchr of Yr.

KIPP, HENRY M., 8th Grade Math & Algebra Tchr; *b:* Quakertown, PA; *m:* Mary A. Geissinger; *c:* Timothy, Corinne, Tia; *ed:* Bloomsburg Univ (BS) Scndry Ed & Math 1974; Lehigh Univ (MED) Ed 1977; 24 Addl Credit Hrs; *cr:* Intermediate Unit #14 Project Specialist 1974; Saucon Valley schl Dist Tchr 1975-77; Northampton Area Schl Dist Tchr 1977-78; Saucon Valley Schl Dist Tchr 1978-; *ai:* PA Math League Adv; 8th Grd Team Ldr; Soccer Club Coach 1992-; PSEA, NEA & SVEA 1975-; West Swamp Memnnonite Church 1990-, Adult SS Supt 1991-93, Moderator 1994-; *office:* Saucon Valley M S 1050 Main St Hellertown PA 18055

KIPP, ROSE WELLS, English Teacher; *b:* Sayre, PA; *m:* Lamar F.; *c:* Jennifer, Marla; *ed:* Mansfield St Univ (BS) Eng, Ed 1970; 24 Hrs Post Grad; *cr:* Roosevelt Jr HS Eng Tchr 1970-71; Wyalusing Valley Jr Sr HS Eng Tchr 1985-; *ai:* Stu of Month Selection Comm; Principal's Cncl; Tech & Prep Comm; NEA, PSEA, WEA 1985-; *office:* Wyalusing HS R R 2 Box 7 Wyalusing PA 18853

KIPP, SAMUEL JAMES, Fifth Grade Teacher; *b:* Altoona, PA; *ed:* Penn St (BS) Elem Ed 1981; *home:* 220 Gates Rd Fallentimber PA 16639

KIRBY, BARBARA B., Jr High English Teacher; *b:* Cleveland, OH; *m:* Donald N. Jr.; *c:* Christa Lynn; *ed:* St Bonaventure Univ (BA) Eng Lang, Lit 1967; (MA) Ed; *cr:* Coudersport Area Jr Sr HS Eng Tchr 1968-; *office:* Coudersport Area Jr Sr HS 698 Dwight St Coudersport PA 16915

KIRBY, MARK S., 8th Grade History Teacher; *b:* Canton, OH; *m:* Susan D.; *ed:* Anderson Univ (BA) US His 1970; Ball St Univ (MA) US His 1979; Kent St 15 Credit Hrs; *cr:* Hamilton Hghts Jr HS His Tchr 1971-79; Canton City Jr HS His Tchr 1980-83; West Branch Jr HS His Tchr 1985-; *ai:* Chess Club Coach; WBEA, NEA & OEA 1985-; Martha Holden Jennings Scholar.

KIRCHHOFF, HARDING, American History Teacher; *b:* Greenville, MS; *c:* Candace E.; *ed:* Bowling Green St Univ (BS) Soc Stud 1971; OH St Univ (MA) Hum Ed 1977; 33 Addl Hrs; *cr:* East Knox HS Soc Stud Tchr 1971-73; Westerville HS Soc Stud Tchr 1973-75; Westerville North HS Soc Stud Tchr 1975-; *ai:* Acad Quiz Team Adv, Coach; Integrated Team Planning Comm; NEA, OH Ed Assn 1971-; Westerville Ed Assn 1973-, Fac Rep 1976-78, 1995-; Northeast in the Know League 1980-, Founder, Sec; *office:* Westerville North HS 950 Smothers Rd Westerville OH 43081*

KIRCHHOFF, JON R., Chemistry Professor; *b:* Palmyra, NY; *m:* Joanna P. Hinton; *ed:* St Univ of NY at Cortland (BA) Chem 1979; Purdue Univ (PHD) Chem 1985; Post-Doctoral Assoc at Univ of Cincinnati; *cr:* Univ of

Toledo Asst Prof 1989-95, Assoc Prof of Chem 1995-; *ai:* Amer Chemical Soc, Soc for Electroanalytical Chem; Author of 40 Research Publications; *office:* Univ Of Toledo 2801 W Bancroft St Toledo OH 43606

KIRCHNER, CHRISTINE F., Sixth Grd Language Arts Tchr; *b:* Newport, RI; *m:* David W.; *c:* David, Lindsay, Michael; *ed:* Univ of RI (BA) Scndry Eng 1972; Salve Regina Univ (MA) Hum & Spec Ed 1982; *cr:* Wilbur-McMahon 5th-8th Grd MS Lang Arts Tchr 1972-; *ai:* Textbook Selection & Supt Search Comms; 8th Grd Class Adv; LCTA, RIEA 1972-; RI Fnd 1000 Dollar Grant Recipient; Foxfire Trained; *office:* Wilbur-Mcmahon Schl Commons PO Box 178 Little Compton RI 02837

KIRIAN, ELAINE ANN, Science Teacher; *b:* Findlay, OH; *m:* Dane Lee; *c:* Adam, Seth, Brittany; *ed:* Bowling Green St Univ (BS) Elem Ed & LDBD 1984; Grad Work at Dayton Univ; *cr:* Riverdale Local LD & DH Tchr 1984-89, 5th Grd Tchr 1990-93, Sci Tchr 1994-; *ai:* NEA, OEA 1984-; REA 1984-, Past Pres, Negotiations Chair; *office:* Riverdale Jr HS Franklin St Wharton OH 43359

KIRK, BILL,III, Teacher; *b:* San Diego, CA; *m:* Jeanette Goik; *c:* Anne, Katie; *ed:* Akron U (BA) Elem Ed 1977; *ai:* Bsktbl & Golf Coach; Medina Cty Coach of the Yr Golf & Bsktbl; *office:* Highland MS 3940 Ridge Rd Medina OH 44256*

KIRK, CAROL REBECCA, Day Care Dir & Child Dev Instr; *b:* Connellsville, PA; *ed:* Seton Hill Coll (BS) Home Ec 1979; *cr:* Frazier Area Schl Dist Tchr 1979-80; Laurel Highlands Schl Dist Tchr 1980-82; Connellsville Area Schl Dist Tchr 1983-; Designs by Carol Owner, Operator 1985-91; *ai:* Teen Parenting Prgm Advy Cncl; PA Assn Family & Consumer Sci, Amer Assn Consumer Sci 1988-; PSEA, NEA 1986-; Who's Who Among Young Women in Bus; *office:* Connellsville Area Sr HS 125 N 7th St Connellsville PA 15425

KIRK, GEORGE WILLIAM,III, Fifth Grade Math Teacher; *b:* Sweickley, PA; *m:* Wanda Bernice Kroboth; *c:* George IV; *ed:* Slippery Rock Univ (BS) Ed 1963; Univ of NC Undergraduate 32 Credits; Duquesne Univ 12 Grad Credits; *cr:* Moutour Schl Dist Elem Tchr 1963-; *ai:* Montour Ed Assn 1963-, Pres, Sec, Nagotiator; PSEA, NEA 1963-; Church 1964-, Deacon, Trustee, Choir; Valley Forge Tchrs Medal; *home:* 220 Wyngate Rd Moon Twp PA 15108

KIRK, JAN BOECHLER, Biology Teacher; *b:* Milford, DE; *m:* Vernon A.; *c:* Erin Ann; *ed:* Univ of DE (BS) Bio 1970; *cr:* Dover HS Tchr 26 Yrs; *ai:* Vlybl Boosters; Steering, Discipline, Dist Sci Comm; NEA 1970-, DSEA 1970-, St Bio Tchr of Yr; Capital Ed Assn 1970-, Chm Bldg, Mem Hlth; Girl Scouts 1985-, Outdoor Ed Cons Camping, Trip Consultant, Site Monitor, Green Angel Outstdng Ldr, Outstdng Vol; Tchr of Yr; Natl Trng Cadre for Yth Conservation Corps; *office:* Dover HS 1 Pat Lynn Dr Dover DE 19904*

KIRK, KATHRYN A., Biology Tchr & Sci Dept Chm; *b:* Waterloo, IA; *m:* Gregory H. Landis; *c:* Anna P. Landis; *ed:* Bloomsburg St Coll (BSEd) Bio, Sec Ed 1973; Philadelphia Coll of Textiles & Sci (MS) Instructional Tech 1994; Penn St Marywood COll Assorted 24 Grad Credits; *cr:* North Penn Sch Dist 7th Grd Life Sci Tchr 1974-78; Boyertown Area Sr High 7-12 Grd Substitute Tch 1978-85, Bio, Human Physlgy Tchr 1994-; *ai:* Sci Dept Chair 1988-; NEA, PSEA, BAEA, NSTA 1986-; NABT 1988-; *home:* 26 Lenape Rd Barto PA 19504

KIRK, KENNETH H., Mathematics Teacher; *b:* Buffalo, NY; *m:* Maureen P. Bartlett; *c:* Kimberly Zabel, Mary Beth Hoch, Lynn Gibbons, Kelly, Kevin; *ed:* St Bonaventure Univ (BS) Math 1967; Canisius Coll (MS) Ed 1972; 6 P G Credits in Schl Law, Fin Niagara Univ; *cr:* West Seneca Cntrl Schl Math Tchr 1967-; Erie Comm Coll Part-time Math Tchr 1980-; *ai:* Class of 1998, NHS Co-Adv; Var Boys Soccer Coach; Supervision of Ath Act; AFT 1967-; NYSUT 1967-, Local Del, Pension & Retirement St Comm; WSTA 1967-, Past Treas, Educ of Yr-Union; NYSTRS 1967-, Local Del; West Seneca CEFCU 1967-, Bd Mem, Loan Ofce; West Seneca Soccer Club 1978-, Travel Soccer Coach; Buffalo Dist Soccer Club 1994-, Travel Soccer Coach; Svc to Yth in the Educl & Ath Setting Awd; 20 Gallon Blood Donor Red Cross Pheresis; *home:* 215 Tudor Blvd Buffalo NY 14220*

KIRK, KEVIN EDWARD, English Teacher & Dept Chair; *b:* Worcester, MA; *m:* Margaret; *c:* James, Brianna; *ed:* Assumption Coll (BA) Eng 1976; Worcester St Coll (MED) Eng 1992; *cr:* St Peter-Marian HS Tchr, Coach, Dept Chair 1977-; *ai:* Sr Class Adv; Boys & Girls Cross Cntry Head Coach; NCTE; Distngd Tchr of the Yr Awd; *office:* Saint Peter Marian CC H S 781 Grove St Worcester MA 01605

KIRK, PHILLIP WAYNE, Chemistry Teacher; *b:* Robinson, IL; *ed:* Wright St Univ (BS) Chem Ed 1992; *cr:* Fairborn HS Chem Tchr 1992-; *ai:* Sci Club Adv; NEA, OEA, NSTA 1992-; Alliance for Ed Grant.*

KIRK, RICHARD J., History Teacher; *b:* Philadelphia, PA; *m:* Susan; *c:* Jennifer; *ed:* Lock Haven Univ (BS) Soc Stud 1972; Temple Univ (MED) Elem 1975; Coll of Performing Arts 60 Addl Credits, Career Tchr 1992; 60 Addl Credits Gratz Coll, Univ of CA at Hayward; *cr:* Dobbins Randolph HS Tchr, Coach 1989-; *ai:* Jr Var Bsbl, Jr Var Ftbl, Var Bsktbl, Womens AAY Bsktbl Coach; PFT 1972-; *office:* Dobbins-Randolph HS Henry Ave & Roberts St Philadelphia PA 19132

KIRK, WILLIAM V., Administrative Assistant; *b:* Bronx, NY; *m:* Maria; *c:* David, Lauren; *ed:* Marquette Univ (BA) Eng 1965; NYU (MA) TESOL 1967; Montclair St Admin Work; City Coll Post Grad; *cr:* Jr HS 149 CRMD Tchr 1965-68, ESL Tchr 1969-72, Eng Tchr 1973-79, Dean 1980-89, Admin Asst 1989-; *ai:* Phi Delta Kappa 1967-; NDEA to NYU for MA Flwshp, Bergen Cty Schl Bd Mem of the Yr 1986; *office:* Jr HS 149 360 E 145th St Bronx NY 10454

KIRKBY, MICHAEL ROSS, History Teacher; *b:* Scott AFB, IL; *m:* Marlene Mehr; *c:* Andrew, Carly; *ed:* Univ of Ca at Santa Barbara (BA) Math, His 1974; Univ of Ga (MA) His 1977; Univ of Ma Enrolled in PHD Prgm in His 1977-82; *cr:* McFarland Union Elem Math Tchr 1974-75; Clarke Mid Schl Math Tchr 1976-77; Cath Cntrl HS Math Tchr 1984-87; Naugatuck HS His Tchr 1987-; *ai:* Fac Advy, Curr, Instruction Comm; CEA, NEA 1987-; *office:* Naugatuck HS 543 Rubber Ave Naugatuck CT 06770

KIRKENDALL, HELEN ROLF, Sixth Grade Teacher; *b:* Bowling Green, OH; *m:* Kim; *c:* Joseph, Jill, Jeffrey; *ed:* Wright St Univ (MS) Ed 1993; *cr:* Patick Henry Local, Chapter I Rdng Tchr, 4th Grd & Jr HS Rdng Tchr, 2nd Grd Tchr, 3rd Grd Tchr, 5th Grd Tchr & 6th Grd Tchr; *ai:* Hamler Summerfest, Act Dir for Summer Leagues; Jr HS Sunday Schl Tchr; *office:* Hamler Elem Schl PO Box 328 Hamler OH 43524*

KIRKER, LYDIA RICHMOND, Kindergarten Teacher; *b:* West Union, OH; *m:* Tom; *c:* Adam, Aaron; *ed:* Morehead St Univ (BA) Elem Ed 1974; Coll of Mt St Joe (MA); 15 Addl Hrs; *cr:* West Union Elem Schl First Grd Tchr 7 Yrs, Fourth Grd Tchr 8 Yrs, Third Grd Tchr 3 Yrs; West Union Primary Schl Chptr I Rdng Tchr, Rdng Recovery Tchr, Kndgtn Tchr 1 Yr; *ai:* Color Guard Spon; Grant Writing Team; OEA, NEA 1974-.*

KIRKER, ROBERT H., Physical & Gen Science Tchr; *b:* Pittsburgh, PA; *m:* Linda Koftis; *c:* Robert J., Jessica, Korey; *ed:* Slippery Rock Univ (BS) Sndry Ed 1973; Univ of Pittsburgh (MED) Sci Ed 1976; 45 Credits Past MED; *cr:* Chartiers Valley Schl Dist Sci Tchr 1973-; *ai:* Chariers Valley Fed 1973-; PAFT, AFT; PA Sci Tchrs Assn; Western PA Conservancy; NRA; *home:* 183 Cumer Rd Mc Donald PA 15057

KIRKER-LOW, CAROL, Senior English Teacher; *b:* Toledo, OH; *m:* Mark W.; *c:* Zachary, Emma; *ed:* Capital Univ (BA) Eng & Sociology 1974; The Breadloaf Schl of Eng Middlebury Coll (MA) Lit & Writing 1982; Course Work at Ashland, Josepheium Pontifical Coll, OUL & Univ of Dayton; *cr:* Pinkerington HS Eng Tchr 1974-; *ai:* NEA 1974-; OEA 1974-; PEA 1974-; *office:* Pickerington HS 300 Opportunity Way Pickerington OH 43147

KIRK-HULL, TERRI, English & Reading Teacher; *b:* Cleveland, OH; *m:* David; *c:* David K., Jessica M.; *ed:* OH Univ (BSEd) Eng Ed 1972; Kent St Univ (MED) Eng Ed 1976; Speech Cert 1992; Rdng Cert John Carroll Univ 1984; *cr:* Parma Schls HS Eng Tchr 1972-; Cuyahoga Comm Coll Frosh Eng Tchr 1982-83; *ai:* Write Club 1991-, Interact Club 1975-80 Advs; North Cntrl Implementation 1993-, Strategic Planning 1992 Comms; NEA 1972-; OCIRA 1990-; NCTE 1989-; AAUW 1991-, Membership VP; *office:* Parma Sr HS 6285 W 54th St Parma OH 44129

KIRKLEY, DONNA B., Professor of Speech; *b:* Bridgeport, CT; *m:* Mark Merritt Canfield; *c:* David Howe, Douglas Scott; *ed:* Averett Coll (AA) General Stud 1963; Coll of William & Mary (BA) Eng Lit 1965; Univ of MD (MA) Speech, Radio & Television 1967; Fac Dev Inst on Classroom Research 1990; *cr:* Univ of MD Speech Instr 1967-70; Prince Georges Comm Coll Speech Instr 1970-71; Howard Comm Coll Prof of Speech Instr 1971-; *ai:* Fac Forum Exec Cncl; Fac Dev Programming; Natl Cncl for Staff Prgm & Org Dev 1986-, Regnl VP, Distinguished Svc 1992; Individual Merit Awd 1994; Fidos for Freedom 1987-, Demonstration Team; Pet Owners with Aids Resource of Howard Cty 1993-, Co-Founder; 3 Publications in Journals; *office:* Howard Comm Coll Little Patuxent Parkway Columbia MD 21044

KIRKPATRICK, ALLAN K., Choral Music Teacher; *b:* Walla Walla, WA; *m:* Irene Mannheimer; *ed:* MI St Univ (BM) Music Ed 1959, (MM) Music Ed 1962; *cr:* Gull Lake Comm Schl K-12th Grd General & Choral Music Tchr 1960-64; Minot St Coll Music Ed Asst Prof 1964-66; Montgomery Cty Schls Choral & General Music Tchr 1966-; *ai:* MENC, MMEA, MCMEA, ACDA, NEA, MSTA, MCTA 1960-; *office:* Colonel Zadok Magruder H S 5939 Muncaster Mill Rd Rockville MD 20855

KIRKPATRICK, CAROLE ANN (MYERS), Work & Family Life Teacher; *b:* Willard, OH; *m:* F. Eugene; *c:* Chad, Amy; *ed:* Ashland Univ (BS) Consumer Homemaking, Voc Ed & Job Trng 1978; *cr:* Plymouth HS Work & Family Life Tchr 1979-84, 1985-; *ai:* FHA-HERO Adv; Prin Advy Comm; PEA, NEA, OEA 1980-; Greenwich Grange 1976-, Youth Adv Ceres, Lady Asst, 1st-5th Degrees; Grads Advy Bd 1988-; Many CEU Credits for Various Wkshps in Related Areas; Voc Ed Planning Comm 1994-95; Regnl Presenter of Job Shadowing Ideas & Ways to be Successful in Classroom; *office:* Plymouth HS 184 Sandusky St Plymouth OH 44865*

KIRKPATRICK, THOMAS, English Teacher; *b:* Auburn, NY; *ed:* Cayuga Comm Coll (AA) Lbrl Arts 1990; SUNY at Oswego (BA) Scndry Ed 1992; Post Grad Stud SUNY at Cortland; *cr:* Mount Markham HS Eleventh Grd Eng Tchr 1993-; *ai:* Jr Class Adv; Schl Newspaper; Bldg Team Comm; NHS Fac Cncl; AFT, NYSEC, NCTE 1993-; *office:* Mt Markham HS Fairground Rd West Winfield NY 13491*

KIRKWOLD, KORISSA ANN, Music Director; *b:* Waukegan, IL; *m:* Geoffrey W. B.; *ed:* Northwestern Coll (BA) Music 1993; Attnd D'Angelo Schl of Music; *cr:* Home Music Resources Tchr, Dir of Ensembles 1989-92; K and S Conservatory of Music Private Lesson Instr in Voice, Piano, Cello 1991-93; Kirkwold Music Studio Owner, Tchr of Private Music Stdnts in Voice, Cello, Piano 1988-; *ai:* Choir, Show Choir, SCHOLA Liturgical Singing Group, Handbells, Band, Ensemble Coach, String Ensemble Dir; Penn Music Ed 1992-, 1st Place Schlsp Awd; Erie Music Tchrs; MENC; Grace Bapt Church 1993-, Yth Choir Dir; 1st Place Schubert Club Advanced Voice Competition St Paul MN; 1st Place Northwestern Aria & Concerto Comp Roseville MN; Finalist Natl Assn of Tchrs of Singing; 1st Place Erie Music Tchrs Assn Schlsp Awd; *home:* 4054 W 38th St Erie PA 16506

KIROUSIS, LINDA, Second Grade Teacher; *b:* Fitchburg, MA; *m:* Charles; *c:* Kirsten K. Yanco, William; *ed:* Fitchburg St Coll (BSEd) Elem Ed 1963, (MSEd) Ed, Rdng & Psych 1967; Numerous Additional Stud; *cr:* Fitchburg MA at Crocker 3rd Grd Tchr 1963-67; Bermingham MI Rdng Specialist 1967-68; Brandon Schl Rdng Consultant 1969-79; Petersham Ctr Schl 2nd Grd Tchr 1979-; *ai:* Curr Dev; Report Card Comm; PTO; NASA; Smithsonian Rsrch Sci Work; IRA 1988-; NCTM 1988-; NEA & MTA; Parent Advy & Conservation Comms; Tchr Who Made a Difference Stu Nom 1990; Top 40 Tchrs of MA 1990; Nom for MA Tchr of the Yr 1995; Numerous Grants; *office:* Petersham Ctr Schl Spring St PO Box 148 Petersham MA 01366*

KIRSCH, JOHN, Associate Director; *b:* Mineola, NY; *m:* Karen J.; *c:* Kristin, Tim; *ed:* Middlebury Coll (BA) Sociology 1974; Springfield Coll MA Candidate Ath Admin; *cr:* Milton HS Tchr, Var Bsktbl Coach 1974-78; Aetna Life & Casualty Admin 1978-94; MA Mutual Assoc Dir 1994-; *ai:* Var Boys Bsktbl Coach.*

KIRSCH, MARY LOUISE, 5th Grade Teacher; *b:* Cleveland, OH; *c:* Erin, Tara; *ed:* Kent St Univ (BA) Ed 1974; Cleveland St Univ (MS) Curr, Cmptrs 1995; *cr:* Cleveland Cath Schls 2nd-3rd Grd Tchr 1974-89; Cleveland Pub Schls 5th-6th Grd Tchr 1989-; *ai:* Act Chprsn; Cleveland Tchrs Union 1989-; *office:* Mary Bethune Elem Schl 11815 Moulton Ave Cleveland OH 44106

KIRSCH, RITA J., Language Arts & Reading Tchr; *b:* Grand Forks, ND; *m:* Larry J.; *c:* Jeff, Michael, Stephen, Terri; *ed:* Northern St Coll (BS) Elem, Spec Ed 1965; Bowling Green St Univ 11 Addl Semester Hrs; *cr:* East Allen Cty Schls 5th Grd Tchr 1965-66; Queen of Angels Schls 8th Grd Soc Stud, Sci Tchr 1969-70; St Jerome's Schl 8th Grd Soc Stud, Rdng Tchr 1979-80; St Rose Schl 8th Grd Lang Arts, Rdng Tchr 1981-; *ai:* Competency Testing Lang Arts Judge, Co-Anchor 7 Yrs; Singing Folk Group 20 Yrs; Lang Arts Ldrshp Cncl 1990-, Coord; NEA 1980-; *office:* St Rose Schl 217 E Front St Perrysburg OH 43551

KIRSCHBAUM, HAROLD, Eighth Grd Social Stud Tchr; *b:* Jersey City, NJ; *m:* Carol Beth Richter; *ed:* Queens Coll (BA) Pol Sci & Ed 1970; NY Univ (MA) Media Ecology 1973, (PHD) Media Ecology 1979; *cr:* Junior HS #136 Soc Stud Tchr 1970; J. W. Dodd Jr HS Eighth Grd Soc Stud Tchr 1976-; C. W. Post Coll Adjunct Fac 1979-; *ai:* Fac PTA Rep 1975-90; Fac Comm to Study Stu Failure & Retention; NYSUT & AFT 1970-; Upper Room Ministries 1982-, Vol; Grant to Study the Use & Effects of Videotape in Classroom; PTA Jr HS Tchr Awd for Outstandikng Svc; Articles Pub; *office:* J. W. Dodd Jr HS Pine St Freeport NY 11520

KIRSCHLING, WILLIAM N., Soc Stud Tchr & Dept Chprsn; *b:* Woodbury, NJ; *m:* Mary Beth Quinn; *c:* Neil, Megan; *ed:* Trenton St Coll (BA) Scndry Soc Stud 1973; Rowan Coll (MA) Ed Admin 1996; *cr:* Paulsboro HS Soc Stud Tchr 1975-81; Gateway Regnl HS Soc Stud Tchr 1981-82; Kirschling Hydroponics Mgr & Owner 1982-88; Paulsboro HS Soc Stud Tchr & Dept Chprsn 1988-; *ai:* Sr Class Adv; Discipline & Stu of Month Comms; NEA, NJEA 1975-; PEA 1975-, Exec Comm; Prin Advy Comm 1995-; Prof of Yr Nom 1988-95; *office:* Paulsboro Jr Sr HS 670 N Delaware St Paulsboro NJ 08066

KIRSCHNER, CAROL MERRIMAN, 7th & 8th Grade Teacher; *b:* Cleveland, OH; *m:* William S.; *c:* Sandra, William, Suzanne Barnes, Michael, Kelly Ann; *ed:* Ursuline Coll (BA) Elem Ed, Eng 1975; 15 Hrs Admin; *cr:* St Mary Magadalene Schl 4th, 6th Grd Tchr 1955-59; Willoughby Eastlake Sys 4th, 6th Grd Tchr 1960-64; St Anselm Schl 7th, 8th Grd Tchr, Lang Arts, Eng Chprsn 1968-; *ai:* Lang Arts Chprsn; Stu Cncl Moderator; Booster Club Ofcr; Friends of Lib, Amer Lib Assn *home:* 8081 Monterey Dr Kirtland OH 44094*

KIRSCHNER, CAROL ANN MC KINNEY, Family & Consume Teacher; *b:* Kew Gardens, NY; *m:* Bruce; *ed:* Concordia Jr Coll (AS Stud 1966; SUNY at Oneonta (BSEd) Home Ec 1969; SUNY at Brook (MALS) Arts, Lblr Stud 1981; 95 Credits; Cert Home Econon Family & Consuemer Sci; *cr:* Mid Cntry Schl Dist Home Ec Tchr *ai:* Yrbk Co-Adv; Var Girls Bowling Team Coach; Time-Out Comm Cntry Tchrs Assn 1969-, Bldg Rep, Grievance Bldg Rep; NY St Ho Tchrs Assn 1980-, Mbrshp Chair, Area Coord, Tchr of Yr; Sullolk Cty Home Ed Tchrs Assn 1980-, Newspaper, Mbrshp Chair; NYSOEA, NAHVET 1993-; PTA 1969-, Jenkins Awd; Suffolk Cty Home Ec T Yr 1994; *office:* Centereach HS 14 43rd St Centereach NY 11720

KIRSH, FRANCENE K., Spanish Teacher; *b:* Newark, NJ Muhlenberg Coll (BA) Span 1971; *cr:* Belleville Jr HS Span Tchr 197 Belleville HS Span Tchr 1981-; *ai:* NHS, Frgn Lang Club Adv; Prins Comm Conflict Mediator; Mid Sts Evaluation Team; Belleville Ed NJEA, NEA, NJ Frgn Lang Tchr Assn 1971-; Dev & Presented a Inservice Course in Span; *office:* Belleville HS 100 Passaic Ave Bell NJ 07109

KIRSH, ROSLYN M., Guidance Counselor & Math Tchr; *b:* Broc NY; *c:* Mark, Gary; *ed:* Brooklyn Coll (BA) Psych, Math 1960; NY (MA) Psych 1966; St John's Univ (MS) Scndry Math Ed 1987; 30 Hrs Guidance; *cr:* Central Queens Day Schl Math Tchr 1968-78; Cardozo HS Math Tchr 1980-84; John Bowne HS Math Tchr 1984-8 N. Cardozo HS Math Tchr, Guidance Prsnl 1985-; *ai:* Schl, Gui Planning Comms; Jewish Stu Union Adv; UFT 1980-; *office:* Benjar Cardozo HS 57-00 223rd St Bayside NY 11364

KIRSTEIN, RHEA S., Literature & Writing Teacher; *b:* Douglaston *ed:* Queens Coll (BA) Eng Lit 1982; Goddard Coll (MA) Creativity 1996; Brooklyn Coll Grad Stud in Psych; Lehman Coll NYC W Project; Goddard Coll Creativity Theory Ed Reform, Ed Psych; Parsons Schl of Design, Schl of Visual Arts, Hunter Coll; *cr:* Brooklyn Acad Lit Tchr 1990-91; Clara Barton HS for Hlth Professions Writin Tchr 1991-; *ai:* Created Dance Prgm; Schl Based Mngmt, Shared Dec Making; Prof Dev Comm; AFT, UFT 1989-; *office:* Clara Barton H Hlth Prof 901 Classon Ave Brooklyn NY 11225

KIRSTEN, MIRIAM JOAN, Spanish Teacher; *b:* Cuba ; *m:* Edwar *c:* Suzanne Kirsten Lavin, Eric; *ed:* Hunter Coll of City Univ of NY Span, Fr 1965; 30 Addl Credits; *cr:* Nutley HS Span Tchr 1965-; *ai:* Class Adv 1984-88; Span Club Adv, New Tchr Mentor, Honor Soc C NEA, NJEA, NTA 1965-; *office:* Nutley HS 300 Franklin Ave Nutle 07110

KIRTLAND, JOSEPH, Asst Professor of Mathematics; *b:* Auburn, *m:* Cynthia Rice; *c:* Timothy, Elizabeth; *ed:* Syracuse Univ (BS) 1985; Univ of NH (MS) Math 1987, (PHD) Math 1992; *cr:* Marist Coll Prof of Math 1992-; *ai:* Math Club Fac Adv; Organizer of Local Pro Solving Competition; Putnam Team Coach; Math Assn of Amer 1 Amer Mathematical Soc 1990-; 2 Articles Pub in Comm in Algebra; A Pub in Archiv der Mathematik; *office:* Marist College 290 Nort Poughkeepsie NY 12601

KISABETH, LARRY JAY, Guidance Counselor; *b:* Tiffin, OH Deborah Sterling Roth; *c:* Kathleen, C. Jay, Robert; *ed:* Heidelberg (BS) Math, PE 1974; Bowling Green St Univ (MA) Educl Admin Guid, Cnslng 1991; *cr:* Carey HS Math Tchr, Coach 1974-83; East J Math Tchr, Coach 1983-85; Tiffin Columbian HS Math Tchr, C 1985-91, Guid Cnslr, Pupil Prsnl Supvr, Coach 1991-; *ai:* Venture Ca Motivation, Prin Advy, Ath Hall of Fame Comms; Girls Var Bsktbl, Coach; *office:* Tiffin Columbian HS 300 S Monroe St Tiffin OH 4488

KISH, CHRISTINE MARTIN, Mathematics Teacher; *b:* Trenton, N John G.; *c:* Brian, Kristin; *ed:* Trenton St Coll (BA) Math 1974, (M Math 1976; Cmptr Courses 3 Credits; *cr:* West Windsor Plainsboro Math Tchr 1974-79; St Gregory the Great Math Tchr 1986-; *ai:* Mathco Coach; Math Coord; NCTM, AMTNJ 1987-; Trenton St Coll Sr Achvmt Awd 1974; *home:* 2642 Kuser Rd Hamilton NJ 08691

KISH, JOHN B., 6th Grd Inclusion Tchr & Coord; *b:* Potsdam, NY Leslie Anne Hoy; *c:* Kathy Engle, Barbara, Katharine Norwood; *ed:* S at Brockport (BSEd) Elem Ed 1966; Addl 40 Hrs in Elem Ed, 30 H Admin; *cr:* Albion Cntrl HS 6th Grd Inclusion Tchr & Coord 1966- Inclusion Comm; MS Reorganization Team; Dist Curr Cncl; Buffal Comm Mem; USTA & Harness Horse Breeders of NY 1986-; NY St on Exceptional Children St Convention, Presenter; WHY Inclusion Presenter; Niagara BOCES Supt Conf Day Presenter; NY St Mid S Assn St Conf; Educator of the Year 1993, NY St Cncl on Excptnl Chl Published in CEC FORUM 1993; Presenter NY St MS Convention 1 Forum Mem NYS Convention on Exceptional Children 1994; *off* Albion Cntrl Schl 254 East Ave Albion NY 14411

KISH, KATHI ANN, Teacher of Gifted & Talented; *b:* Bellaire, OH; OH Univ (BS) Eng Ed 1976; Univ of Dayton (MS) Jr High, MS Ed 1 10 Credit Hrs GATE OH Univ, WV Univ; *cr:* St Clairsville-Richland Dist 7th, 8th Grd Lang Arts, Rdng Lit Tchr 1976-90, 7th, 8th Grd G Tchr 1990-95, 5th, 6th, 7th, 8th Grds GATE Tchr 1995-; *ai:* 7th, 8th Scholastic Challenge, 7th, 8th Grd Newspaper Staff Adv; Belmont Advy Comm for GATE; Zanes Trace Consortium for Gifted Stdnts; 7th Grd Knowledge Master Open Coach; OH Thinking Cap Quiz Bowl C for 5th, 6th Grds; NCTE; OH Cncl of Tchrs of Eng, Lang Arts; NEA; O St Clairsville Educl Assn; St John Vianney Parish Cath Church; Coac 2 Stdnts who Won Belmont Cty Spelling Bee, Scripps Howard Spelling Bee 1988-90; *home:* 112 Carrie St Powhatan Point OH 4394

KISH, MARY M., Cmptr, Keyboarding & Bus Tchr; *b:* Athens, OH; Robert; *c:* Natalie, Nicole, Brian; *ed:* OH Univ (BSED) Comp Bus 1963; Cmptr Sci Cert Kent St Univ; 26 Sem Hrs Ashland Univ; *cr:* Cha F. Brush HS Tchr 1963-67; Kent St Univ Prof Part-time 1986-89; Berks HS Tchr 1982-; *ai:* Pep Club Adv; North Cntrl Steering Comm; Cmptr Supvr; BEA Tchrs Assn 1982-, VP, Sec; NEOEA, NEA, OBTA 19 Delta Kappa Gamma 1986-, Ed.

KISH, PAUL MICHAEL, English Teacher; *b:* Sharon, PA; *m:* K Marie Leghart; *c:* Kaylee; *ed:* Bowling Green St Univ Scndry Admin Credit Hrs; *cr:* Gateway HS Eng Tchr 3 Yrs; Tiffin Columbian HS Eng T 2 Yrs; *ai:* Asst Ftbl, Bsktbl, Bsbl Coach; NEA 1991-.*

KISH, ROBERT STEPHEN,SR., Assistant Professor of HVAC; Wheeling, WV; *m:* Nancy A. Johnson; *c:* Robert Jr.; *ed:* Mc Kinley Ctr Sheet Metal; Belmont Tech Coll HVAC; West Liberty St Coll Regen Degree; *cr:* OH Cty Schls Instr Adult Ed 1983-85; WA Inst of Tech I HVAC 1993-94; Belmont Tech Coll Asst Prof HVAC 1994-; *ai:* Fac A RSES 1994-, Proctor; ACCA 1995-, Proctor; ASHRAE 1994-; A Legion Post #1 1993-, Adejutant of Post; *office:* Belmont Tech Coll Fox Shannon Pl Saint Clairsville OH 43950

KISH, WHITNEY A., 6th Grade Teacher; *b:* Wadsworth, OH; *m:* Bill Lindsay, Torey; *ed:* Akron Univ (BS) Ed 1974; Grad Schl Cnslng, Attnd Old Dominion Univ, Norfolk St Grad Stud Gifted Enrichment; James Russell Lowell Schl Readiness 1975-76; Sparrow Rd Schl 6th Gifted Tchr 1977-76; St Anthony Parochial Schl 3rd Grd Tchr 1978- Copley-Fairlawn Schls 6th, 8th Grd Sci Tchr 1979-95; *ai:* DARE Co Frgn Lang Dev, Fac Soc, Hall of Fame Comm; Talent Show Chp

ssey of MInd; Copley Tchr Assn, NEOTA 1979-; SECO 1990-; Meth ch 1970-; PTA 1979-; MADD 1990-; Eisenhower Sci, PTA Lang Arts t; *office:* Copley-Fairlawn MS 1531 S Cleveland Massillon Rd Copley 44321

IEL, JOHN CHARLES, Sixth Grade Teacher; *b:* Holyoke, MA; *m:* yl Ann Turner; *c:* Mark Charles, Tara Lynn Gray; *ed:* Holyoke Comm (AA) Liberal Arts 1967; Univ of MA (BA) His 1969; Westfield St Coll Grad Stud; *cr:* Anna E. Barry Schl 7th-8th Grd Tchr 1969-72; Bellamy 5th-8th Grd Tchr 1972-78; Streiber Schl 5th Grd Tchr 1978-84; bert Lavoie Schl 6th Grd Tchr 1984-95; Fairview Veterans Memrl MS Grd Tchr 1995-; *ai:* Schl Cncl Co-Chm; CEA, MTA, NEA 1969-; ghts of Columbus 1969-, Grand Knight, Star Cncl; MA St K of C Cncl -85, Dist Deputy; St Anne Parish Cncl 1969-, Pres 1994-; St Anne Rel 982-87, Coord; *home:* 38 Cherryvale Ave Chicopee MA 01020*

LOSKI, JEFFREY J., Environmental & Earth Sci Tchr; *b:* hamton, NY; *m:* Carolyn Waltman; *c:* Elizabeth, Emily, Matthew; *ed:* Geology 1986; (MAT) Ed 1989; *cr:* Owego Free Acad Sci Tchr 1990-; Alcohol & Drug Stu Information Prgm, Sci Club Advs; Envirothon n Coach; *office:* Owego Free Acad George St Owego NY 13827

PERT, MAUREEN C., Retired Fifth Grade Teacher; *b:* Stillwater, *m:* John H.; *c:* John Jr., Jamin, Mary; *ed:* Univ of MN (BS) Elem Ed ; Southampton Univ (MS) Elem Ed 1974; Attnd St Mary's Coll, Notre ne, IN; *cr:* Sinton Schl Third Grd Tchr 1962-63; Minneapolis MN Sub 1963-67; Cntr Moriches Schl Prefirst, Second Grd Tchr 1974-80; iam Floyd Schls Prefirst, Second Grd Tchr 1980-95; Tangier Smith n Schl Third, Fifth Grd Tchr 1980-95; *ai:* Math Olympiad Tchr; PTO ; Scrabble Club Adv; WFTU; NYSUT; Suffolk Rdng Cncl.

SEL, ANDREA MARIE, HS Social Studies Teacher; *b:* Center iches, NY; *m:* John M.; *c:* Alexis S.; *ed:* Suffolk Cty Comm (AS) Lbrl 1981; SUNY at Plattsburgh (BA) Amer His 1983; Dowling Coll (MA) 989; 3 Credit Hrs in Effective Tchng at Madelin Hunter; 3 Credit Hrs chng Spcl Needs Stdnts; *cr:* Port Jefferson HS Soc Stud Tchr 1985-92; nxville HS Leave Replacement-European Tchr 1993; Mt Sinai HS t, 12th Grd Ec & 10th Grd Global Stud Tchr 1994-; *ai:* Frosh Class Adv; *office:* Mt Sinai HS Gertrude Goodman Blvd Mount Sinai NY 66

SINGER, LORI ANN, Foreign Language Dept Chairman; *b:* York, *m:* Roy H.; *c:* Mignonne, Jenny; *ed:* Susquehanna Univ (AB) Fr & Span 4; Millersville Univ (MA) Fr 1970; Attnd NDEA Inst Goucher Coll, I Inst, AATF & NEH; *cr:* Central High Fr & Span Tchr & Dept Chm 4-69; Upper Perkiomen Mid Fr & Span Tchr 1969-70; Montgomery Cty Schls Fr & Span Tchr & Dept Chm 1972-; *ai:* NEA, PSTA & MSTA 4-; AATF 1989-; MFLA 1985-; AED 1962-; *office:* Poolesville Mid HS ard Rd Poolesville MD 20837

SKO, JOHN MARTIN, Social Studies Teacher; *b:* Torrington, CT; *w:* rea Kocsis; *c:* David, Darrin, James, John; *ed:* Univ of CT (MA) Soc d & Ed 1968; 60 Credit Hrs; *cr:* Litchfield HS Tchr & Dept Head 27 ; *ai:* Citizen Bee Adv; Tech Task Force; NEA 1970-, Local Pres; NCSS 5-; ASCD 1985-; BSA 1968-, Scout Master, Cncl Mem at Large, Silver aver; Philmore B Wass Awd-JCSS; *home:* 206 Red Mountain Ave rington CT 06790*

STLER, CHERYL R., Art Teacher; *b:* Warren, OH; *m:* Keity; *ed:* ngstown St Univ (BS) Ed, Visual Arts 1974, (MS) Ed Art 1987; *cr:* mington Local K-12 Grd Art Tchr 1 Yr; Lakeview Local Schls K-6 Grd Tchr 7 Yrs, 9-12 Grd Art Tchr 14 Yrs; *ai:* 10 Grd Adv 1983-85; Future rs of Amer 1974; Yrbk 1974; Jr Class Adv 1982-84; Girls Track 1974; Bsktbl 1978-79; LTA, NEO, OEA, NAEA, OH Art Ed 1974-; Grants: r Artistic Heritage1981, Integrated Curr Multi-Handicapped 1980; *ce:* Lakeview HS 300 Hillman Dr Cortland OH 44410*

STLER, HEIDI E., Fourth Grade Teacher; *b:* Northampton, PA; *ed:* NY at Cortland (BS) Elem Ed 1965; Attnd Nazareth Coll SUNY at ockport; *cr:* Fairport Cntrl Schls Fourth Grd Tchr 1965-; *ai:* Fairport Ed n Numerous Comms; AFT, NYSUT, Fairport Ed Assn 1965-; Delta ppa Gamma 1973-, Treas; *home:* 1518 Aster Ter Walworth NY 14568

SVER, ANNE NACHBAR, Spanish Teacher; *b:* Newark, NJ; *m:* wrence J.; *c:* David, Lauren; *ed:* CW Post Coll (BA) Ed, Span 1967; +30 edit Hrs Ed & Span; *cr:* Jericho MS Span Tchr 1967-70; Danbury HS n Tchr 1970-; *ai:* Summer Schl Tchr; NHS Comm; Mentor Tchr; Pvt or; Taught Western CT St Univ 1 Semester; NEA 1970-; COLT 1970-; spice Vol 1992-; *office:* Danbury HS Clapboard Ridge Rd Danbury CT 311*

TABJIAN, MARY S., High School Biology Teacher; *b:* Baltimore, MD; David; *ed:* Drexel Univ (BS) Electrical Engrng 1989, (MS) Biomedical grng 1991; Addl 6 Post Grad Credits at Philadelphia Coll of Bible; *cr:* pt of Defense Cooperative Stu Engr 1986-87; Meth Hospital Biomedical grng Technician 1988; Johnson & Johnson Product Dev Scientist 91-94; Plumstead Chrstn HS Bio Tchr 1994-; *ai:* Accreditation & Sci rr Comms; NSTA, NABT 1995-; Grad Fellowship; Masters Thesis; Intnl nf Co-Coord; 2 Pub Articles; *office:* Plumstead Chrstn Schl 5765 Old ston Rd P O Box 216 Plumsteadville PA 18949

TAEFF, MICHAEL, Biology Teacher; *b:* Brooklyn, NY; *m:* Valerie nith; *c:* Nicole; *ed:* Hunter Coll (BA) Bio 1964; Long Island Univ (MA) arine Bio 1968; 60 Credit Hrs Beyond Masters; *cr:* Farmingdale Jr HS eneral Sci Tchr 1965-66; Garden City Jr HS Bio & General Sci Tchr 66-86; Garden City HS Bio Tchr 1986-; *ai:* Class of 1996 Adv; NEA, YSUT, AFT; *office:* Garden City Sr HS 170 Rockaway Ave Garden City Y 11530

TCHEN, DEBORAH L., Art Teacher; *b:* Lexington, KY; *ed:* Miami niv of OH (BS) Art Ed 1985; *cr:* Edgewood Jr Schl Art Tchr 1986-93; adison Jr Schl Art Tchr 1993-; *ai:* 8th Grd Vlybl, Var Womens Bsktbl oach; Womens Basketball Coaches Assn 1995-; *office:* Madison Jr Schl 80 Middletown Eaton Rd Middletown OH 45042

TCHEN, DOUGLAS LEE, English & Social Studies Tchr; *b:* Urbana, H; *ed:* Urbana Univ (BS) Ed, Eng 1989; *cr:* Champaign Cty Schls Sub chr 1989-91; Triad Local Schl Dist HS Eng, Soc Stud Tchr 1991-; *ai:* Jr ass, Mock Trial Adv; OFT, AFT 1994-; Triad Ed Assn 1991-, Pres, Sec, P; *office:* Triad HS 7941 Brush Lake Rd North Lewisburg OH 43060*

ITKO, ANTHONY STEPHEN, Industrial Arts Teacher; *b:* Philipsburg, A; *m:* Genevieve Tatanish; *c:* Brian, Christopher; *ed:* CA Univ of PA (BS) dstrl Arts 1968; PA St Univ (MED) Indstrl Arts 1970; Future of Flight rad Course Clarion Univ of PA; *cr:* Brookville Jr Sr HS Classroom Tchr 968-; *ai:* Equipment Mgr; All Sports Jr High Dir; NEA, PSEA, BAEA 968-; PA St Ath Dir Assn 1991-; Jeff Co Area Agency on Aging, Vol.

ITSKA, SUSAN A., Eng, German Tchr & Dept Chair; *b:* Akron, OH; *ed:* ent St Univ (BSEd) Eng & Ger 1968, (MED) Eng 1974; *cr:* Medina City chls Eng & Ger Tchr 1968-73; Cuyahoga Falls City Schls Eng & Ger Tchr 973-83; Walsh Jesuit HS Eng & Writing Tchr, Lab Coord & In-House Ed 984-88; Southern OH Coll Eng Instr 1984-88; Wooster Bus Coll Eng Instr 987-92; Akron Univ Comm & Tech Coll Eng Instr 1988-90; Rittman xempted Village Eng & Ger Tchr 1988-& Dept Chair; *ai:* Schl ewspaper; AATG, REA & NCTE 1988-; NEA 1968-; St Sebastians hurch 1978-; Delta Phi Alpha KSU Chapter 1966; Ger Consulate Awd for u Excl 1962; Whos Who Intnl 1993 Cambridge England; *home:* 1237 /eathervane Ln Akron OH 44313*

KITSOCK, MICHAEL JOHN, Latin Teacher; *b:* Norristown, PA; *m:* Joan Marie Devine; *c:* James; *ed:* East Stroudsburg Univ (BS) Eng, Scndry Ed 1975; Univ of Scranton (MS) Eng, Scndry Ed 1981; Millersville Univ Latin Cert 1989; Latin Stud Villanova Univ, Univ of Notre Dame of MD; *cr:* Tamaqua HS Eng, Latin Tchr 1975-90; Exeter HS Latin Tchr 1990-; *ai:* Jr Classical League Adv; PA St Ed Assn, NEA 1975-; Classical Assn of Atlantic Sts, PA Classical League 1992-; Schuylkill Historical Soc 1993-; Schuylkill Arts Cncl 1991-; Schuylkill Vol Firefighters Assn 1971-, Sec; NEH Flwshp Grant 1990; NEH Ind Stud Grant 1991; Orbis Romanus Summer Grant NEH 1994; *home:* 2110 Woodglen Rd Pottsville PA 17901*

KITSON, HERBERT WILLIAM, Associate Professor of English; *b:* Wheeling, WV; *m:* Katherine Blystone; *ed:* Wofford Coll (BA) Eng, Fr 1969; Univ of SC (PHD) Comparative Lit 1976; Stud in Eng Ed1979-81; *cr:* Univ of SC Grad Tchng Asst 1969-73; Univ of Grenoble Lecturer in Amer Stud 1973-75; Midlands Tech Coll Adjunct Instr 1980-82; Univ of Pittsburgh Asst Prof of Eng 1982-87, Assoc Prof of Eng 1987-; *ai:* Stu Govt Assn Fac Adv; Theater Club & Fr Club Spon; Univ of Pittsburgh Fac Comm; Fac Senate; Eng, Lang, Hum Adv at Pittsburgh; Phi Beta Kappa 1970-; Crawford Cty Hospice 1992-, Cert Vol; Friens of Lib 1988-; Titusville Leisure Svc Bd 1985-; Titusville Cncl on Arts 1985-, Bd Mem; Crawford Cty Hospice 1992-, Cert Mem; Friends of Lib 1988-; Leisure Svcs Bd 1985-; Univ of SC NEH Grant 1979; NY Univ NEH Grant 1985; Univ of AZ NEH Grant 1990; Poetry Prizes; Univ Press of Amer Books; MAF Press Chapbooks; Natl Library of Poetry 1995 Cntst Semi-Fin; Free Lunch Arts Allnc Yngr Poets Awd; *office:* Univ of Pittsburgh-Titusville PO Box 287 Titusville PA 16354*

KITSON, ROSEANN, Social Studies Teacher; *b:* Yonkers, NY; *ed:* NY Univ (BA) Urban Pub Policy 1987, (MA) Soc Stud Ed 1988; *cr:* Murry Bergtraum HS Soc Stud Tchr, Legal Stud House Adv, Testing Coord 1988-; *ai:* United Fed of Tchrs 1988-; Children Intnl 1989-, Spon; Lincoln Ctr Theater Ed Prgm Grant 1994-; Natl Endow For Hum Temple Univ Philadelphia Grant 1995; Morgan Guaranty Lib Ed Project Pace Univ Grant 1995-; *office:* Murry Bergtraum HS 411 Pearl St New York NY 10038

KITTELBERGER, FREDERICK WILLIAM, Retired Math Tchr & Dept Head; *b:* Mt Vernon, OH; *m:* Mary Lou; *c:* Eric, Jason; *ed:* Case Inst of Tech (BS) Civil Engineering 1959; Univ UT (MSE) Sci, Math 1968; Univ Akron Cert Tchr Ed; *cr:* Fed Aviation Agency Civil Eng 1959-60; US Army Civil Eng 1960-62; Schaaf Jr HS Math Tchr 1963-65; Hillside Jr HS Math Tchr 1965-94; *ai:* Parma Ed Assn, OEA, NEA 1963-94; Natl Sci Fnd Acad Yr Inst 1967-68 to Univ UT.

KITTLE, BARRENT R., Marketing Professor; *b:* Charleston, WV; *ed:* WV Univ (BS) Bus Admin, Mrktg 1968, (MBA) Bus Admin 1973; Univ of AL (PHD) Bus Admin, Mrktg 1989; *cr:* Univ of AL Advertising Prof 1983-90; WV Univ Mrktg Prof 1990-94; Youngstown St Univ Mrktg Prof 1994-; *ai:* Citibank Advertising Compeition, Direct Mrktg Competition, Amer Advertising Fed Competition Adv; Amer Mrktg Assn, Southern Mrktg Assn 1979-; Amer Acad of Advertising 1983-; *office:* Youngstown St Univ 410 Wick Ave Youngstown OH 44555

KITTRELL, JOAN YOCUM, English Teacher; *b:* Belleville, PA; *m:* Edward C.; *ed:* Shippensburg Univ (BSEd) Eng 1968; Masters Equivalency in Ed; *cr:* Owen J Roberts HS Eng Tchr 1968-; *ai:* PSEA, NEA 1968-; Roberts Ed Assn 1968-, Co-Chair Schlsp; Eastern Star 1965-; *office:* Owen J. Roberts HS 981 Ridge Rd Pottstown PA 19465

KITZLER, ELIZABETH ROSEMARY, Fourth Grade Teacher; *b:* Windsor ON, Canada; *m:* Max D.; *c:* Randall, James (dec), Mark; *ed:* Kent St Univ (BS) Ed 1975; Elem Ed Tchng License London Tchrs Coll 1957; 15 Credit Hrs Post Grad; *cr:* Sarnia Pub Schls 2nd-3rd Grd Tchr 1957-59; Midview Schls Sub Tchr 1967-76; Elyria Schls Sub Tchr 1967-76; Grafton Elem Schl 4th Grd Tchr 1976-92; East Carlisle Elem Schl 4th Grd Tchr 1992-; *ai:* NEA, OEA, Midview Ed Assn, NEOTA 1976-; *office:* East Carlisle Schl 1959 Grafton Rd Elyria OH 44035

KITZLER, MELINDA MYERS, Kindergarten & Reading Teacher; *b:* Findlay, OH; *m:* Mark W.; *c:* Holly, Josh, Jay; *ed:* Definance Coll (BA) EL Tchr 1975; 150 Hrs Attnd Ashland Univ, Drake Univ, Findlay Univ; *cr:* Carey Pub Schls 2nd Grd Tchr 8 Yrs, Kndgtn, Rdng Tchr 11 Yrs; *ai:* Concession Adv 1 Yr; Chrldr Adv 3 Yrs; OEA, NEA, CEA 1975-; Altar Guild 5 Yrs; *home:* PO Box 165 Carey OH 43316

KJAERBYE, BARBARA ANN RUBENBAUER, 1st Grade Teacher; *b:* Bay Shore, NY; *m:* Peter Kjaerlyng; *c:* Samantha, Rebecca; *ed:* Molloy Coll (BA) Ed 1972; Adelphi Univ (MA) Ed 1975; 60 Credit Hrs Beyond MA in Ed; *cr:* Our Lady of Poland Schl 2nd Grd & Primary Tchr 1972-79; Frank J Carasiti Sub Tchr 1984-86, Tchr Asst 1986, 1st Grd Tchr 1986-; *ai:* Dist EDC; PGC; Assessement & Textbook Comms; PDC; Dist & Bldg SDM Team Chprsn; Report Card Comm; AFT 1986-; NYSUT 1986-; RP Local Tchrs Union 1986-, Chprsn of Kids in Need Pgm; PTA 1983-; 5 Tchr Ctr Grants; Design Your Own Grant Tchr Insvc; NYS Better Beginnings Tchr Awd Nom 1996; *office:* Frank J Carasiti Elem Schl Rocky Pt & Yaphank Rd Rocky Point NY 11778*

KJERGAARD, SONIA PRADO, Bilingual Social Studies Tchr; *b:* Brooklyn, NY; *ed:* Cornell Univ (BA) Lit, Eng 1975; Mediator Trng Cert; Research for Better Tchng; *cr:* Lansing Schl for Girls Eng Tchr 1975-78; Putnam Voc Tech HS Biling Tchr 1980-; *ai:* Spon Calligraphy Club; SEA, MEA, NEA 1985-; CT Vly Calligraphers 1988-; *office:* Putnam Voc Tech HS 1300 State St Springfield MA 01109

KLANIAN, LILLIAN BERBERIAN, 4th Grade Teacher; *b:* Providence, RI; *m:* Peter; *c:* Michele A., Laura M., Peter J., Christine L.; *ed:* Brown Univ (BA) Sociology 1957; Attnd RI Coll, Framingham St Tchrs, Bridgewater, Comm Coll of RI; *cr:* Lippitt Elem 3rd & 4th Grd Tchr 1958-63; Warwick K-6th Grd Sub Tchr 1979-86; Oakland Beach 2nd-4th Grd Tchr 1986-; *ai:* AFT 1986-; Rdng Assn 1987-; Delta Kappa Gamma 1988-, VP & Pres; Alpha Delta Kappa 1989-; Brown Alumnae Club of Kent Cty 1979-, Sec, Treas, VP & Pres; *office:* Oakland Beach Elem Schl 383 Oakland Beach Ave Warwick RI 02886

KLAPPER, MARGERY MAHLER, English & Journalism Teacher; *b:* Bogota, Columbia; *c:* Elizabeth; *ed:* Penn State Univ (BA) Ger 1969; Temple Univ (MED) Frgn Lang, Ger 1975; Univ of MD 6 Credit Hrs; Prince Georges Comm Coll 9 Credit Hrs; Charles Cty Comm Coll 3 Credit Hrs; *cr:* Abraham Lincoln HS Ger Tchr 1969-73; Bladensburg HS Ger, Eng & Jrnlsm Tchr 1973-; *ai:* Spon Schl Newspaper & Schl Lit Magazine; Awds Comm; Fac Choral Ensemble; NEA 1973-; Article Pub; *office:* Bladensburg HS 5610 Tilden Rd Bladensburg MD 20710

KLASNIC, KATHLEEN CARROLL, 3rd Grade Teacher; *b:* Baltimore, MD; *m:* Jack; *c:* Kathleen J.; *ed:* Towson St Univ (BS, MS) Ed, Elem Schl Sci 1964; Towson St BEBCO (MA) Elem Ed 1973; BEBCO (MSE) 60 Credits; Towson St Univ Post Grad; Tokoyo Mus of Nat His Paleontological Study 1984; *cr:* Wellwood Elem Sci Tchr 1964-71; BEBCO Hands-On Sci Curr Dev Level 5 Ldr 1969-71, Conducted Inservice, Tours & Admin Sci 1970; Ottawa Schls Consultant Hands-On Sci 1970; Seventh Dist Sci Coord, 6th Grd Tchr 1971-75, 3rd Grd Tchr 1977; Prettyboy 3rd Grd Tchr, Sci Coord 1978-; *ai:* Sci Materials Coord; Inservice, Staff Dev Presenter; Facilitator Participatory Decision Making Comm; Supv Stu Tchrs; TABCO, NEA, MSTA 1964-; IAIED 1991-; Commendation BEBCO Dept of Curr, Instruction 1993; Cert of Recognition for Contributions Sci Ed Balto Co 1992; Nom, Candidate Presidential Awd for Excel 1992; Commendations for Conducting Inservices MSPAP, Handson 1992; Commendation Asst Supt Outstdng Tchng Competency 1991; Commendation for Countrywide Professional Study Day; Facilitator Site Based Mgmt 1991-95; Eisenhower Sci Grant 1994-95, "Updating Scientific Knowledge for the Mature Staff"; *office:* Prettyboy Elem Schl 19810 Middletown Rd Freeland MD 21053

KLASS, JUDITH ALEXANDRA, Adjunct Lecturer in English; *b:* New York, NY; *ed:* Sarah Lawrence Coll (BA) Lbrl Arts 1988; Oxford Univ MPhil Pol Sci 1990; *cr:* Borough of Manhattan Comm Coll Adj Eng Lecturer 1991-; *ai:* Truman Schlsp 1986; Book: The Cry of The Oulies; Pub Book of Poems & Stories; *office:* Borough Of Manhattan Comm Coll 199 Chambers St New York NY 10007*

KLASSEN, ROSE RYE, Asst Prof of Comm Dept; *b:* Tulsa, OK; *m:* Robert; *c:* Kristopher, Eric; *ed:* Panhandle St Univ (BA) Speech 1960; Cntrl St Univ (MA) Speech 1964; Univ of GA (MFA) Theatre Design 1982; MI St Univ Doctoral Work 1970-74 ABD Theatre; *cr:* OK City Univ Asst Prof Theatre 1964-65; Allen Univ Asst Prof Comm 1970-71;Lansing Comm Coll Asst Prof, Var Debate Coach 1966-70; Carolina Stritch Coll Assoc Pr of, Dept Chm 1977-85; SUNY at Fredonia NY Asst Prof Comms 1985-; *ai:* Acting, Directing Coach for Stu Video Productions; *office:* S U N Y Coll At Fredonia 302 Mc Ewen Hall Fredonia NY 14063

KLATT, ROGER J., Alternative Education Teacher; *b:* Albion, NY; *m:* Kristen S.; *c:* Emily, Madeline; *ed:* SUNY at Brockport (BS) PE 1984, (MS) Elem Ed 1987; *cr:* Albion HS PE Tchr 1985-86; Albion MS Elem Math Tchr 1986-87, Sixth Grd Tchr 1987-93; Albion HS Alternative Ed Tchr 1993-; *ai:* Var Boys Swim, Var Cross Cntry, Jr HS Track Coach; IM Tennis Coach, Adv; AFT, NYSUT, Albion Tchrs Assn 1985-; Kappa Delta Phi; *office:* Albion HS 302 East Ave Albion NY 14411*

KLAUS, MICHAEL EDWARD, Anatomy, Physiology & Bio Tchr; *b:* Lima, OH; *m:* Susan Budd; *c:* Gavin Michael, Robin Susannah; *ed:* Ashland Coll (BS) Ed 1982; Miami Univ (MA) Ed 1983; *cr:* Miami Univ Grad Tchng Asst 1982-83; Cuyahoga Falls HS Tchr, Head Ath Trnr 1983-90; Elida HS Tchr, Head Ath Trnr 1990-94, Tchr 1994-; *ai:* Responsible for Prevention, Evaluation, Treatment, Rehabilitation all Interscholastic Aths; NABT; Elida Ed Assn, OH Ed Assn, NEA; OH Ath Trainers Assn; OH Licensed Ath Trainer; *office:* Elida HS 101 E North St Elida OH 45807

KLEBANER, BENJAMIN JOSEPH, Professor of Economics; *b:* Brooklyn, NY; *m:* Ruth Perlman; *c:* Simeon Nathan, Josiah Abraham; *ed:* City Coll of NY (BS) Ec-Magna Cum Laude 1945; Columbia Univ (MA) Ec 1947, (PHD) Ed 1952; *cr:* Rutgers Univ Instr 1951-54; City Coll Asst Prof 1954-61, Assoc Prof 1961-66, Prof 1966-, Dir of MA Pgm 1971-; *ai:* Amer Ec Assn 1947-; Ec His Assn 1949-; Bus His 1983-; Phi Beta Kappa-Gamma of NY 1945-, Treas, Sec, VP & Pres; Kappa Delta Pi-Gamma Lota 1945-; Flwshp Columbia Univ 1949-50; Ford Fac Rsrch Seminar 1958; Assoc Columbia Univ Seminar on Ec His; Assoc Ed for Journal of Money, Credit & Banking 1975-79; Numerous Articles Pub; *office:* City Univ Of NY City Coll Convent Ave At 138th St New York NY 10031

KLEE, KATHLEEN MCDERMOTT, Math & Computer Science Tchr; *b:* Syracuse, NY; *m:* Dr. Karl J.; *ed:* St Bonaventure Univ (BS) Math 1970; SUNY at Geneseo (MA) Math 1975; Post Grad Stud at Cntrl St Univ in Edmond Allegheny Coll in Meadville, SUNY at Fredonia & Jamestown Comm Coll in Areas of Math and Cmptr Sci; *cr:* Red Jacket Cntrl Schl Math Tchr 1971-77; Randolph Cntrl Schl Math Tchr Math Dept Chair 1977-; Jamestown Comm Coll Part-Time Math Prof 1980-82 & 1994-; *ai:* Cmptr Coord; Acad Quiz Team Adv; Math Dept Head; Tech, Tchr Evaluation & Gifted-Talented Comms; Randolph Cntrl Tchrs Assn 1977-, Pres & Membership Chair; NCTM, AMTNYS 1971-; NYSUT, AFT 1971-; Participant in People to People Cmptr Sci Delegation to Soviet Union in 1989; 1986 & 1994 Nom for Presidential Awd for Excl in Math Tchng; 1985 Apples for Tchrs Awd; *office:* Randolph Cntrl Schl Main St Randolph NY 14772

KLEEB, ROBERT ALLAN, Social Studies Teacher; *b:* Broken Bow, NE; *m:* Margaret JoAnn; *c:* Shawn, Scott; *ed:* NE St Univ (BA) Boston Univ (MA) Human Svcs 1982; 40 Post Grad Hrs; *cr:* ID St Youth Trng Ctr Tchr 1965-68; Dept of Defense Schls Japan, Germany, Turkey & Italy Tchr 1969-; *ai:* Model US Senate; Debate Team; Knowledge Bowl; AFT 1968-, VP, Pres.

KLEEM, ANTHONY MARK, Social Studies Teacher; *b:* Cleveland, OH; *m:* Mary Loomis; *c:* Sarah, Anthony, Christian; *ed:* Univ of Akron (BA) Ed 1991; Cuyahoga Comm Coll Ed 1988; Addl 12 Credit Hrs; *cr:* OH Boys Town Tchr, Tutor 1991-; North Royalton HS Soc Stud Tchr 1993-; *ai:* Track Coach; NEA 1993-.*

KLEEMANN, NANCY BECKER, Music Teacher; *b:* Vero Beach, FL; *m:* John; *ed:* Adelphi Univ (BS) Music Ed 1992; Currently Enrolled Aaron Caplant Schl of Music MM Music His; *cr:* Waldorf Schl Cooperative Tchng 1992; Sacred Heart Acad Music Tchr 1992-; *ai:* Women's Chorus; Gospel Chorus; Fac Chorus; NUSSMA, NMEA 1994-; Deans List Awd; Acad Excl in Scndry Ed; Hnrs Thesis.

KLEES, JANET POTTER, 4th Grade Teacher; *b:* Philipsburg, PA; *c:* Brett Eric; *ed:* Lock Haven Univ (BS) Elem Ed 1972; *cr:* Williamsport Area Schl Dist Sub Tchr 1973-75; West Branch Area Schl Dist Tchr 1976-; *ai:* PHEAA 1976-; NEA 1976-; WBEA 1976-; BASS 1996-; *home:* PO Box 124 Karthaus PA 16845

KLEIMAN, STEPHEN HARRIS, History Teacher; *b:* Newark, NJ; *m:* Nancy Ulbricht; *c:* Jodi; *ed:* Rider Coll (BA) Soc & Beh Sci 1964; Kean Coll (MALS) Pol Phil, His & Soc 1986; Newark St Tchr Cert 1968; *cr:* Cleveland Schl 5th & 6th Grd Tchr 1966-69; Hillside High His Tchr 1969-; *ai:* PTA Tchr Rep 12 Yrs; Rifle Team Coach 27 Yrs; Various Advisorships; AFT 1966-69; HEA & NJEA 1969-; PTA 1966-; NJI Rifle League 1969-, Sec & Treas, Coach of the Yr 1973, 1981, 1994; Physics & Chem Audio-Visual Aids Demonstrator at NJ Tchrs Convention 1968; Hillside High PTA Life Mbrshp.*

KLEIN, BERNARD S., Physics Teacher; *b:* New York City, NY; *m:* Violet; *c:* Jeffrey, Carrie, Dara, Tamona, Sarah-Ann; *ed:* City Coll of NY (BS) Physics 1966; Yeshiva Univ (MS) Physics 1970; *cr:* Newtown HS Tchr 1966-84; LIC HS Tchr 1992-; *ai:* UFT, AFT 1966-; Nom Nation Sci Fnd Tchr of Yr Awd; Mentoring 2 Yrs; *home:* 167-04 Bridgewater Ave Floral Park NY 11001*

KLEIN, HAROLD STEVEN, Biology Teacher; *b:* Brooklyn, NY; *ed:* CUNY (MS) Environmental Sci 1989; *office:* City AS Scholl 30-00 48th Ave Long Island City NY 11101

KLEIN, JAMES ALLEN, High School Math Teacher; *b:* Cleveland, OH; *m:* Denise Michelle Hanft; *c:* Megan Mary, Erin Emily; *ed:* Miami Univ (BA) (BS) Aeronautics, Math 1984; Cleveland St Univ Tchng Cert 1987; Bowling Green St Grad Courses; OH St Univ Project Discovery; *cr:* Hawthorne Acad Math Tchr 1987-90; Irving MS Acad Math Tchr 1990-94; Lorain HS Math Tchr 1994-95; Lorain Admiral King HS Math Tchr 1995-; *ai:* OH Cncl Tchrs of Math 1987-, Math Club Adv; NCTM 1987-; Trinity Luth Church 1993-, Cncl Mem, VP, Bldg Coord; *office:* Lorain Admiral King HS 2600 Ashland Ave Lorain OH 44052

KLEIN, JEFFREY ALLEN, Social Studies Department Chm; *b:* Irvington, NJ; *m:* Dolores Ann Hornbeck; *c:* Carol, Christine, Kevin; *ed:* Glassboro St Coll (BA) Soc Stud & Lang Arts 1968; *cr:* Deptford Twp HS Soc Stud Tchr 1968-, Dept Head 1980-; *ai:* Asst Sftbl, Girls Soccer, Cheerleading & Bowling Coach; Yrbk Adv; Asst Band Dir; NHS Selection,

Grad & Schlsp Comms; March of Dimes Drive Coord; SGA Adv; NEA, NJEA & GCEA 1968-; Clayton Planning Comm 1986-87; Clayton Bd of Hlth 1988-89; Tchr of Yr 1974 & 1980; NJ Interscholastic Coaches Assn Projec Chm; *office:* Deptford Township H S 575 Fox Run Rd Deptford NJ 08096*

KLEIN, JOHN M., English Chairperson; *b:* Montclair, NJ; *m:* Margaret A. Wisniowski; *ed:* Iona Coll (BA) Eng 1968; Seton Hall Univ (MA) Ed 1974; St Michaels Coll (MAT) Rel Ed 1982; *cr:* Bergen Cath HS Eng Tchr 1969-75; Cath Memrl HS Eng Tchr & Asst Headmaster 1975-82; St Johns Prep Tchr 1983-; *ai:* Winter & Spring Track Coach; A-V Ctr; NCTE 1976-; MCTE 1985-; *office:* St John's Prep Schl 72 Spring St Danvers MA 01923

KLEIN, KAREN HELLE, Math Teacher; *b:* Columbus, OH; *m:* Patrick Alan; *c:* Andrea, Sara, John; *ed:* OH Univ at Athens (BS) Elem Ed 1967-71; Addl 15 Credit Hrs 1991; Univ of Dayton 15 Hrs Educl Admin 1995; *cr:* 4th Grd Tchr 7 Yrs, 5th Grd Tchr 2 Yrs, MS 7th Grd Math Tchr 5 Yrs; *ai:* Lancaster City Schl Dist Tech Comm 1992-; Tech Comm 1992-; Medill Elem Tech Comm 1995; Lancaster City Schl Dist Math Comm Scndry Level, Rewriting Math Curr 1994-, Elem Level 1987-92; NCTM, OCTM 1989-; NEA, LEA, OEA 1986-; Supervision, Curr Dev Assn 1995-; Alpha Delta Kappa 1992-, Chm; ADK Educl Honary for Women Edctrs 1993-, Chm; St Bernadette Cath Church 1980-; Activate Stu Interest Affordable Math Materials, Trainer Wrkshp INtroduction to Windows IBM User Spon Southeastern Regnl Prof Dev Ctr, OH MS Assn 1995; Work Sessession Activity Based Math on Budget 1994; Presidential Awds for Excl Elem Math 1992; *office:* Thomas Ewing Jr HS 825 E Fair Ave Lancaster OH 43130*

KLEIN, KAREN LYNN, English Teacher; *b:* Youngstown, OH; *c:* Mark; *ed:* Youngstown St Univ (BS) Ed, Eng 1984; Kent St Univ (MA) Eng 1994; Post Grad Stud Gifted, Talented; *cr:* Springfield City Schls Eng Tchr 1984-85; Youngstown City Schls Eng Tchr 1986-; *ai:* Youngstown St Univ Eng Festival Facilitator; NEA, OEA, YEA 1986-; Associated Writing Prgms 1995-; *home:* 689 Purdue Ave Austintown OH 44515*

KLEIN, KIMBERLY KEYEK, French Teacher; *b:* Camden, NJ; *m:* Jay S.; *ed:* Rutgers Univ (BA) Fr & Ed 1989; ESL Cert from Kean Coll; *cr:* Millville Sr HS Fr Tchr 1990-92; Greenbrook MS Fr Tchr 1992-93; Hackettstown High & MS Fr Tchr 1993-; *ai:* HS Peer Support Erase, HS Fr NHS & MS Frgn Lang Club Advs; AATF 1990-; FLENJ 1990-; NJEA, NEA & HEA 1990-; Paul Douglass Tchr Scholar; AT&T Tech in the Classroom Grant; Pro-Feld Neighborhood Betterment Grant; *office:* Hackettstown HS 701 Warren St Hackettstown NJ 07840

KLEIN, MARC, Retired Mathematics Teacher; *b:* Newark, NJ; *m:* Dorothy Koumas; *c:* Daniel, Stacy, Diahann, Erica; *ed:* NY Univ (BS) Math 1959; Queens Coll (MS) Math Ed 1963; Attnd Taft Ed Ctr; *cr:* Leonia HS Math Tchr 1959-60; Bethpage HS Math Tchr 1960-95; *ai:* Lucille P. Shaffer Meml Schlsp Fund; AFT 1963-, Pres 4 Yrs; NCTM 1994-; Unitarian Universalist Flwshp 1973-, Bd of Trustees 1980-82.*

KLEIN, PAMELA JEAN, 8th Grade Science Teacher; *b:* Newark, OH; *m:* Steve; *c:* Kyle, Nathan, Nicholas; *ed:* Oh St Univ (BS) Elem Ed 1980; Math & Sci Ashland Univ; *cr:* Logan Elm Schls 8th Grd Eng, Sci Tchr 1980-; *ai:* 8th Grd St Cncl Adv; 7th Grd Vlybl, 8th Grd Track Coach; NEA, OEA 1980-, Co-Pres 1992-93, VP 1990-92; *office:* Logan Elm Schls 9579 Tarlton Rd Circleville OH 43113*

KLEIN, RICHARD H., English & History Teacher; *b:* East Orange, NJ; *m:* Karen Munck; *c:* Richard C.; *ed:* Trenton St Coll (BA) Soc Stud 1968; Addl 15 Hrs Guid Jersey City St; *cr:* H. G. Hoffman HS Tchr 1968-; *ai:* Girls Soccer 1980-, Sftbl 1980-97, 1990-, Boys Soccer 1970-77, Cross Cntry 1969-70, Tennis 1972-77 Coach; South Amboy Ed Assn 1968-, Pres, VP; NEA; South Amboy PTA; Middlesex Cty Softball Coaches Assn 1990-, VP; South Amboy Yth Bsebl Assn 1992-; Middlesex Cty Sftbl Coach of Yr 1984, 1987, 1990; *home:* 324 Walnut St South Amboy NJ 08879

KLEIN, ROSEMARY DIANE, Art Teacher; *b:* Brooklyn, NY; *m:* Ronald; *c:* Diane, Christina; *ed:* Attnd Brooklyn Museum Art Schl, Schl of Visual Arts; *cr:* NY St Commission for Blind Publicity Asst 1962-70; St Patrick Schl Art Tchr 1979-; Our Lady of Good Counsel Art Tchr 1982-86; St Joseph Hill Acad Art Tchr 1986-; *ai:* United Fed of Tchrs, Appreciation Awd 1985, 1989, 1992; NY City Art Tchrs Assn, Spec Awd 1985; NCEA 1979-, Tchr Assoc; Police Ath League, Panel Judge, Tchr Citation 1992; Wagner Coll, NY Univ Alumni Assns, Support Mem; Stdnts Art Festival Channel 13; City of NY Mayor David Dinkins Appreciation Cert 1992; Cardinal O'Connor Tchng Excl Appreciation 1985; *office:* St Joseph Hill Acad 850 Hylan Blvd Staten Island NY 10305*

KLEIN, SHARON BURDICK, Business Teacher; *b:* Troy, NY; *m:* Karl Louis; *c:* Erik Lewis, Laura Beth; *ed:* Hartwick Coll (BS) Bus Sci Ed 1964; 30 Grad Credit Hrs Nursery-6th Grd Cert Rdng North Adams St Coll; *cr:* Dolgeville Cntrl Schl Bus Tchr 1964-67; Warren, Washington, Hamilton Cty BOCES Data Processing Instr 1967-68; Berlin Cntrl Jr Sr HS Tech Tchr 1976-; *ai:* Jr, Sr Hnr Soc Adv; Prin Selection Comm; JOBBS Project; NYS Tchrs United 1964-, Local Sec, Staff Recognition Awd; NYS Bus Tchrs Assn, AFT 1976-; Natl Bus Tchrs Assn 1990-; Berlin Free Town Lib Trustee 1982-, Pres; Watipi Assn 1972-78; Berlin Yth Comm 1971-76; First Bapt Church 1954-, Supt of Sunday Schl; Berlin July 4th Parade Comm 1990-, Sec.*

KLEIN, STEPHEN D., Biology Teacher; *b:* Waterloo, NY; *m:* Hilde Teitelbaum Klein; *c:* Jeffrey Krampf, Susan Krampf, Michael; *ed:* St Univ Coll Plattsburgh (BA) Bio 1970, (MSEd) Bio Ed 1972; Tchrs Coll Columbia Univ (EdM) Instructional Tech 1982; *cr:* Shenendehowa HS Bio Tchr 1972-; *ai:* NABT; NYS Model Schls Mini Grant Cmptr Software, Hardware Project 1992; Writer, Ed of Questions for NYS Regents Bio Exams 1988-; Co-Author of Interactive Educl Software 1987; Authored Two Articles Pub 1980, 1981; *office:* Shenendehowa Sr HS 970 Rt 146 Clifton Park NY 12065*

KLEIN, TERRY MUELLER, Latin Teacher; *b:* Pittsburgh, PA; *m:* Thomas F.; *c:* Scott, Steven; *ed:* Duquesne Univ (BA) Latin & Greek-Summa Cum Laude 1969; Bryn Mawr Coll (MA) Latin & Greek 1973; Attnd Penn St 3 Credit Hrs, Carlow Coll 10 Credit Hrs & Univ of Pittsburgh 18 Credit Hrs; Miami Univ, OH 3 Cred Hrs; *cr:* Beaver Area Schl Dist Latin & Eng Tchr 1970-74; N Allegheny Schls Latin & Eng Tchr 1981-82; Avonworth Schl Dist Latin & Eng Tchr 1982-83; N Allegheny Schls Latin & Eng Tchr & Staff Dev Ldr 1984-; *ai:* Jr Classical League Spon; Prins Advisory & Staff Dev Cncl; AFT 1984-;Classical Assoc of Pittsb 1984; PA Classical Assn 1990-; Amer Classical League 1993-; Clsscl Assoc of Atlantic St 1993; Cranberry Pub Lib Bd 1980-, Pres 8 Yrs, VP 4 Yrs; GFWC Cranberry Jr Womens Club 1976-, Pres 2 Yrs, Clubwoman of Yr Awd 1978; Red Cross Instr 1979-; Butler Cty Federated Lib System Bd 1993-, VP 1 Yr, Pres 2 Yrs; NDEA Title IV Fellowship; PASCD Conf Presenter 1986; Cranberry Jaycees Young Woman of Yr 1977; Appointed to PA Dept of Ed In-Service Advisory Cncl 1990; Natl Task Force on Clsscl Lang Learning Stndrds 1995; *home:* 1 Pinebrook Dr Cranberry Twp PA 16066*

KLEINMAN, ROBERTA W., Professor of Chemistry; *b:* New York City, NY; *ed:* Barnard Coll (BA) Chem 1964; Rutgers Univ (PHD) Organic Chem 1969; Univ MI at Dearborn 12 Credit Hrs; Potters Guild at Ann Arbor MI; *cr:* Rutgers Univ Instr 1970-72; Univ of MI at Dearborn Asst Prof 1972-79; Univ of MI at Ann Arbor Lecturer 1979-82, Visiting Prof 1992-93; Lock Haven Univ Assoc Prof 1982-87, Prof 1987-; *ai:* Undergrad Rsrch Supvr; Tech Comm; Dev Tutorials & Internet Resources; Amer Chem Soc 1969-, Local Sec; AAUW 1985-; NSF & NASA Predoctorial Flwshps; NIH Postdoctorial Schlsp; 10 Grants in Chem Ed; Co-Author Stud Guide; Presentations About Chem Ed; *office:* Lock Haven Univ Dept of Chem Lock Haven PA 17745

KLEIST, DAVID A., English Teacher; *b:* Lansdale, PA; *m:* Lisa J. Zver; *ed:* Lehigh Univ (BA) Engl Lit 1981; Moravian Coll Tchr Cert Ed 1989; Wesleyan Univ Writers Conf 1993; *cr:* Freedom HS Eng Tchr 1989-; *ai:* Arts Lit Magazine Adv; Film Fanatics Adv; Staff Options Comm; NCTE 1989-; NEA, PSEA & BEA 1989-; PCTE 1995-; Pub Author & Poet; Phi Beta Kappa; *office:* Freedom HS 3149 Chester Ave Bethlehem PA 18017

KLEMOW, KENNETH M., Associate Professor of Biology; *b:* Hazleton, PA; *m:* Sheree Fern Zigman; *c:* Meryl Heather; *ed:* Univ of Miami (BS) Bio 1975; St Univ of NY-ESF at Syracuse (MS) Plant Ecology 1979, (PHD) Plant Ecology 1982; *cr:* St Univ of NY-ESF at Syracuse Tchng Asst 1975-82; Onondaga Comm Coll Adjunct Prof 1980; St Univ of NY at Binghamton Adjunct Lecturer 1982; Wilkes Univ Asst & Assoc Prof 1982-; *ai:* Tchr Recognition & Effectiveness Comm; Ecological Soc of Amer 1977-, Ed Section Chair, Certified Sr Ecologist; Sigma Xi 1982-, Wilkes Univ Club Pres, Natl Meeting Del; PA Acad of Sci 1982-, Exhibits Comm Chair, Life Membership; Kirby Park Advy Comm 1991-, Natural Resources Subcommittee Chair; Tubs Natural Area Advy Comm 1987-, Inventory Comm Chair; Wilkes-Barre Chamber of Commerce, Environmental Comm 1994-; Rosenthal Herbarium, Curator; Wilkes Univ Carpenter Outstanding Tchr Awd 1991; EPA Grand of 1 Million Dollars To Create Wetland to Treat Mine Drainage; Articles Pub in Journal of Ecology, Amer Midland Naturalist; Textbook Reviewer for Harper Collins & Wm C Brown; Courses & Wkshps for Tchrs on Ecological & Botanical Topics; *office:* Wilkes Univ 184 South River Street Wilkes-Barre PA 18766*

KLENK-BRANCH, CORNELIA, Fourth Grade Teacher; *b:* Teaneck, NJ; *ed:* Dominican Coll (BS) Ed 1987; Fordham Univ (MS) Admin 1989; 30 Addl Credits Post Grad in Ed at Long Island Univ, Saint Rose Coll; *cr:* Saint Margarets Schl 5th-6th Grd Sci, Rdng Tchr 1987-91; Franklin Ave Elem Schl 4th Grd Tchr 1991-; *ai:* Stu Cncl Adv; *office:* Franklin Ave Elem Schl 48 Franklin Ave Pearl River NY 10965

KLEPADLO, SHIRLEY J., Chemistry Teacher; *b:* Montague, MA; *ed:* Anna Maria Coll (BA) Chem 1966; Rutgers Univ (MS) Radiological Hlth 1968; Bentley Coll (CA) Accountancy 1982; Salem St Coll, Boston Univ, Northeastern Univ, Framingham St Coll, Univ of MA, Antioch New England, MIT, Univ of NH; *cr:* Worcester Found Exp Bio Research Asst 1967-68; Marlborough High Chem Tchr 1968-71; Maynard High Chem Tchr 1971-; *ai:* Fac Cncl; NEA & MA Tchrs Assn 1968-; Maynard Tchrs & MA Assn Sci Tchr 1971-; US Pub Hlth Svc Fellowship; Amer Chem Soc Northeast Outstanding Chem Tchr 1988; ACS Aula Laudis Honor Soc 1990; Batelle Math, Sci Army Internship 1991 & 1993; *office:* Maynard HS 1 Tiger Dr Maynard MA 01754*

KLEPINGER, WILLIAM R., Agriculture Education Teacher; *b:* Dayton, OH; *m:* Beverly; *c:* Amy, Emily; *ed:* Ohio St Univ (BS) Ag Ed 1970; *cr:* Graham HS Ag Ed Tchr 1970-71; US Army Helicopter Pilot 1971-1974; Ridgemont HS Ag Ed Tchr 1974-1975; Miami East HS Ag Ed Tchr 1976-; *ai:* FFA, Class Adv; wrestling Coach; NVATA, OVTA 1986-; OH Cattlemens Assn 1980-; Darke Cty Cattlemens 1990-, Pres; Miami Cty Cattlemens 1986-, pres; Monroe Twp Zoning Bd 1992-; *office:* Miami East HS 3825 N State Route 589 Casstown OH 45312

KLEPPNER, AMY M., English Teacher; *b:* Boston, MA; *m:* Adam; *c:* Bram, Caleb; *ed:* Smith Coll (BA) Philosophy 1952; Mount Holyoke Coll (MA) Philosophy 1954; Columbia Univ (PHD) Philosophy 1960; Attnd Univ of MD, Bowie St Coll, Univ of VT, Univ of CO; *cr:* LaReine HS Eng Tchr 1981-85; John F Kennedy HS Eng Tchr 1985-86; Montgomery Blair HS Eng Tchr 1986-90; Takoma Park Intermed Eng Tchr 1990-91; Walt Whitman HS Eng Tchr 1991-; *ai:* Yrbk Adv; Ethics Comm; NEA 1986-; *office:* Walt Whitman HS 7100 Whittier Blvd Bethesda MD 20817

KLEPS, CHERYL LYNN, English Teacher; *b:* Cleveland, OH; *ed:* Kent St Univ (MED) Rdng Specialization 1974; *cr:* John R. Williams Eng Tchr 1968-; *ai:* NEA, OEA, PTEA & NCTE 1968-; Delta Kappa Gamma 1985-, Pres & Sec; Whos Who in Amer Ed 1989-90, 1991-92; *office:* John R Williams Jr HS 625 Riverside Dr Painesville OH 44077

KLESH, DAVID, 8th Grade Science Teacher; *b:* Hazleton, PA; *m:* Diana Conant; *c:* Deanna, Daniel, Deborah; *ed:* Alma White (BA) His & Ed 1966; Kean Coll (MA) Guid 1974; Paterson St Coll Educl Courses; *cr:* Byram Twp Schls Sci Tchr 1967-1991; *ai:* Skiing & Tennis Adv; NJEA 1967-; NEA 1969-; USTA 1992-; NJ Governors Awd; *office:* Byram Twp Intermediate Schl Mansfield Dr Stanhope NJ 07874

KLEWER, ELAINE LEHMAN, Second Grade Teacher; *b:* Toledo, OH; *m:* Jerry; *c:* Kyle; *ed:* Univ of Toledo (BED) Elem Ed 1961, (MED) Elem Ed 1969; *cr:* Pine St Elem Schl First-Second Grd Tchr 1961-68; Starr Elem Schl Second Grd Tchr 1968-; *ai:* Right to Read; Prof Dev Comm; AFT, OR Fed of Tchrs 1970-; Delta Kappa Gamma 1975-, Chapter Pres 1986-88; Alpha Delta, Convention Registrar 1989; Western Lake Erie Sailing Club 1983-, Sec 1993-95; Beta Sigma Phi 1961-, Pres 1965; Univ of Toledo Tchr Ed Prgm Advy Comm 1984-91; 28 Stu Tchrs; *office:* Starr Elem Schl 3230 Starr Ave Oregon OH 43616

KLEZEK, STANLEY JOSEPH,JR., Social Studies Teacher; *b:* Spangler, PA; *m:* Jana Marie; *c:* Wade, Julie; *ed:* Clarion Univ (BS) Bus Admin 1980; St Francis Coll Soc Stud Cert 1982; *cr:* Bishop Carroll HS Soc Stud Tchr 5 Yrs; Cntrl Cambria HS Soc Stud Tchr 8 Yrs; *ai:* Asst Var Ftbl & Head Jr Var Bsbl Coach; NEA 1988-; CCEA 1988-; *office:* Central Cambria HS 208 Schoolhouse Rd Ebensburg PA 15931

KLIEGER, ALAN BRUCE, Technology Teacher; *b:* Brooklyn, NY; *m:* Barbara Levy; *c:* Michael, Allison; *ed:* NY Univ (BA) Indstrl, Voc Ed 1967, (MA) Supervision, Admin Scndry Ed 1969, (MA) Occupational Safety Admin 1976; *cr:* Floral Park HS Tech Tchr 1967-; *ai:* Tech Club; Dist Shared Decision Comm; NEA NY 1980-, Alt Regnl Dir; Sewanhaka Fed of Tchrs 1967-, VP; *office:* Floral Park Memorial HS 210 Locust St Floral Park NY 11001*

KLIMKO, CECELIA SKOVIRA, Second Grade Teacher; *b:* Uniontown, PA; *m:* John Michael; *c:* David, Michael; *ed:* CA Univ of PA (BS) Elem Ed 1963; 30 Addl Hrs; *cr:* Laurel Highlands Schl Dist Elem Tchr 1963-; *ai:* NEA, PSEA 1963-; LHEA 1966-; *home:* 247 Brown Blvd Uniontown PA 15401

KLINE, A. BRUCE, US History & Govt Teacher; *b:* Fairfax, VA; *m:* Elizabeth Lee Phillips; *c:* Alex M., Ethan P.; *ed:* WV Univ (BS) Scndry Ed, Soc Stud 1984; WA Coll (MA) His 1995; *cr:* BSA Allegheny Trls Cncl Sr Dist Exec 1984-88; Bohemia Manor HS Soc Stud Tchr 1988-; *ai:* Head Bsbl Coach; Soc Stud Dept Chair; Schl Improvement Team; Ath Adv Cncl; NEA, MSTA, CCCTA 1988-; Phi Alpha Theta 1983-; MD Geographic Alliance 1990-; Cecil Cty Historical Soc 1993-; *office:* Bohemia Manor HS 2755 Augustine Herman Chesapeake City MD 21915

KLINE, DALE D., World Cultures & GATE Teacher; *b:* Shenandoah, PA; *m:* Cheryl Horning Kline; *c:* Dale, Matthew; *ed:* Bloomsburg Univ (BS) Scndry Soc Sci 1970, (MED) China, Japan & SE Asia 1971; *cr:* Tamaqua Area Sch Dirs 7th Grd Soc Sci Tchr 1971-86 & 9th & 11th Grd Soc Sci Tchr 1986-; *ai:* Tamaqua Ed Assn, PA St Ed Assn & NEA 1971-; Amer Legion & Loyal Order of Moose 1966-; YMCA Dir Part-Time Svc Awd 21 Yrs; *office:* Tamaqua Area HS PO Box 90 Tamaqua PA 18252*

KLINE, EDWIN, 6th Grade Teacher; *b:* Mineola, NY; *m:* Dia Kamercia; *c:* Derek, Danae; *ed:* Univ of NH (BA) Commnctn Western MT Coll Tchr Ed Stud; Plymouth St Coll Tchr Cert; *cr:* Gi Elem Schl 5th Grd Tchr 1975-77; Shishmoref Schl 10th-12th Grd Soc & Guitar Tchr 1977-78; Ekwok Schl 6th-8th Grd Tchr Tchr 197 Gilford MS 7th Grd Math Tchr 1980-85, 6th Grd Math Tchr 1995-; *a* Grd Team Ldr; MS Vllybl & Bsbl Coach; 6th Grd Math Team Coach Ldrshp Team; NEA 1975-; Ctr Harbor Conservation Commission 1 Treas, Chm; Parks & Recreation Comm; *office:* Gilford Middle H Alvah Wilson Rd Laconia NH 03246*

KLINE, EMMA CATHERINE, Math Teacher; *b:* Zanesville, OH Phillip Arthur; *c:* Melissa Anne Kline-Hess, Jonathon Paul, Justin Michael Taylor; *ed:* Bowling Green St Univ (BS) Math 1970; Heide Univ (MA) Ed 1989; Post Grad OH St Univ in Graphing Calculators; Work in Guid & Cnslng; *cr:* Terra Tech Coll Math Tchr 1972-73; Fre Jr High Math Tchr 1973-74; Rosary HS Math Tchr 1975-76; Bellevu Math Tchr 1976-77; Tiffin Calvert High Math Tchr 1977-83; Columbian High Math Tchr 1993-; *ai:* OCTM 1977-; NEA & TEA 1 Bldg Rep; Martha Holdings Jennings Grant; *office:* Columbian HS 3 Monroe St Tiffin OH 44883

KLINE, GENIE M., Chemistry & Physics Teacher; *b:* New Kensin PA; *m:* Michael; *ed:* Univ of Pittsburgh (BS) Chem Ed 1987, (MS 1990; *cr:* Plum Boro HS Chem, Physics Tchr 1987-88; Everett Are Chem, Physics Tchr 1988-; *ai:* PA Jr Acad Sci Spon; Ski Club Adv Assistance Team; NSTA 1994-; AAPT 1993-; NEA 1988-; *office:* Ev Area HS 12 N River Ln Everett PA 15537

KLINE, JANE LACY, High School Art Teacher; *b:* Saranac Lake, NY Philip Michael; *c:* Catherine F., Benjamin J.; *ed:* Dutchess Commercial Art 1967; New Paltz (BS) Art Ed 1970; 30 Grad Hrs Ru Sage 1975; 38 Credit Hrs; *cr:* Mayfield Elem Schl 1st-6th Grd Art 1970-75; Free Lance Graphics 1970-88; Milford Elem Schl 1st-6th Arts & Crafts Tchr 1975-76, Mayfield Elem 1st-6th Grd Art Tchr 197 Mayfield HS & Jr HS Art Tchr 1988-; *ai:* Sr Class, Prom, Yrbk & D Art Adv; MTA 1970-, Treas 1973-74; NYSUT, AFT 1970; Cmptr C Yrbk Advancement 1995-96; Art Illustration Educl His Books; *of* Mayfield Cntrl Schl 27 School St Mayfield NY 12078

KLINE, MARILYN L., Computer Science Teacher; *b:* Wilkes Barre, *m:* Bruce W.; *c:* Alyssa, Alexander; *ed:* Bloomsburg Univ (BA) Scndry Math 1988; Millsburg Univ 24 Addl Grad Credits; *cr:* Donegan Schl Math, Cmptr Sci Tchr 1992-; *ai:* Network Admin; Recycling Club Co- PSEA, NEA 1992-; *office:* Donegal HS Rt 772 Mount Joy PA 17552

KLINE, PAUL H., Mathematics Teacher; *b:* Lebanon, PA; *m:* Tamm Smith; *c:* Nicholas D., Aaron M.; *ed:* Shippensburg Univ of PA (BS) M 1982; Bloomsburg Univ of PA (BS) Ed, Math 1987; *cr:* Amer Genral Sales Rep 1983-85; Bloomsburg Univ of PA Asst Soccer Coach 198 Coatesville Area Schl Dist Math Tchr, Soccer Coach 1987-91; Ea Lebanon Cty SD Math Tchr, Soccer Coach 1991-; *ai:* Soccer Club, Indoor Soccer Adv; Boys Jr Var, Girls Var Soccer Coach; NSCAA 19 *office:* Eastern Lebanon County HS 180 Elco Dr Myerstown PA 1706

KLINE, RICHARD CHARLES, District Supervisor; *b:* Shickshinny, *m:* Carol A. Kester; *c:* Elizabeth Kester, Richard Jr, Kristin; *ed:* PA St (BS) Ed & Scndry Ed 1972, (MED) Bio Sci 1975; PA Certs in Supervi of Sci, Chem, Bio, Gen Sci, Elem Prin & Scndry Prin; *cr:* Abington Dist Sci Tchr 1972-78; Bloomsburg Schl Dist Sci Tchr 1978-91; Abin Hghts Schl Dist Sci Coord 1991-94; Wissahickon Schl Dist Sci, Elem Ed Dist Supvr 1994-; *ai:* Stu Spon & Judge of PA Jr Acad of Sci; Phi D Kappa 1974-; WASA 1994-; PASCD 1994-; ASCD 1994-; *of* Wissahickon SChl Dist 351 W Skippack Pike Ambler PA 19002*

KLINE, SHARON MYERS, 5th Grade Teacher; *b:* Norristown, PA Gerald Raymond; *c:* Natalie; *ed:* Kutztown St Coll (BA) Elem Ed 1 Beaver Coll (MED) Gifte Ed 1985; *cr:* R. C. Struble Elem Schl 5th Tchr 20 Yrs; *ai:* Sci, Math Comms; BTEA Union Rep-Spec Svcs; N 1995-; NCMT 1994-.*

KLINEFELTER, KAY SMEAL, Business Teacher, Curr Planner Bloomsburg, PA; *m:* D. Kerry; *c:* Kelly Diane, Christopher; Bloomsburg Univ (BS) Bus Ed, 1970, (MS) Bus Ed 1974; Post-C Credits Millersville Univ, Carlow Coll; *cr:* Millersburg Area Schl Bus Tchr, Curr Planner 1970-; *ai:* Mentor Tchr; Class Adv; Past Adv Newspaper 12 Yrs, Yrbk 2 Yrs, Bus Club 12 Yrs; Delta Kappa Gan 1986-, Sec; PSEA 1970-; MAEA 1970-, Sec; PBEA 1993-; Upper Dau Cty Arts Alliance 1994; PA Bus Edctr of the Yr 1994; *office:* Millers HS 799 Center St Millersburg PA 17061

KLINEFELTER, SUZANNE MILLS, Third Grade Teacher; *b:* NYC, *m:* Gary A.; *c:* Bobby, Billy; *ed:* Univ of VT (BS) Elem Educ 1975, (M Environmental, Elem Educ 1980; Addl 18 Credits Tchng, Educ; Bradford Elem Schl Fourth Grd Tchr 1975-77; Barre Town Elem S Fourth Grd Tchr 1977-85, Third Grd Tchr 1985-; *ai:* Sci Curr Comm; N VT-NEA 1975-; Barre Town PTO 1985-, Co-Vice Pres 1992-93; *off* Barre Town Elem Schl RR 2 Box 4323 Barre VT 05641*

KLINEK, LUCY TREBINO, Spanish Teacher; *b:* Neptune, NJ; *m:* Jay Dana, Eric; *ed:* Montclair St Univ (BA) Span, Scndry Ed 1970; Monmo Univ (MSEd) Stu Prsnl 1976; 6 Addl Credits; *cr:* Wall HS Span Tchr 19 *ai:* Stu of Month Prgm Head; Matawan-Aberdeen Schl Dist Curr & Bud Comms 1992-; Wall Tchrs Assn, NJEA, NEA 1970-; *office:* Wall Twp 18th Ave & New Bedford Rd Wall NJ 07719*

KLING, DAVID D., Sociology & Psychology Teacher; *b:* Pittsburgh, *m:* Lynn Ann Roth; *c:* Robert David, Jayme Lynn; *ed:* IN Univ of PA (Comprehensive Soc Stud 1969; 27 Hrs Soc Stud; *cr:* IN Univ of PA G Asst Wrestling Coach 1969-70; Keystone Oaks HS Soc Stud Tchr & Co 1971-; *ai:* Head Wrestling 1973-, Asst Ftbl 1971-92, Asst Track 10 yrs Jr High Wrestling 1971-73 Coach; Asst Golf Coach 1992-95; PSEA, N & KOEA 1971-; WPIAL Wrestling Coaches Assn 1971-, Pres 1982- Treas 1985-; PA Wrestling Coaches Assn 1971-, Exec Comm 1982-85; PA Wrestling Hall of Fame Comm 1991-; 2 Articles Pub Coach & Ath Athl Journal; Indctn into PA Wrestling Hall of Fame; *office:* Keyst Oaks HS 1000 Kelton Ave Pittsburgh PA 15216

KLING, TATIANA, Performing Arts Teacher; *b:* Naternberg, Germa *m:* Andrew Smith; *ed:* Long Island Univ (BS) Elem Ed, His 1967; Brook Coll (MS) Rdng 1970; 30 Addl Credits; 24 Credits Admin, Supervisi Licensed Asst Prin; *cr:* Fordham Univ Instr 1990; PS 130 2nd-6th Rdng, Art, Soc Stud tchr 1967-87, Admin Asst 1987-91, Rdng, Soc Performing Arts Tchr 1991-; *ai:* Natl Dance Inst Tchr Liason 1987-; U 1967-, Chptr Chair, Del; Neighborhood Beautification 1972-, Cash A Animal Rights Groups; Women's Groups; Curr Dev; Co-Author His Workbook; *office:* PS 130M 143 Baxter St New York NY 10013*

KLINGBEIL, CAROLYN LIBERTI, High School Spanish Teacher; Brooklyn, NY; *m:* Donald William; *c:* Megan, Courtney, Caitlin; *ed:* John's Univ (BA) Span, Italian 1977, (MS) Scndry Ed 1990; *offi* Malverne HS 80 E Ocean Ave Malverne NY 11565

KLINGBEIL, LORENE ELIZABETH, 6th Grade Teacher; *b:* Tole OH; *ed:* Bowling Green St Univ (BS) Ed 1966, (MEd) Elem Ed 1971; Genoa Area Local Schls 6th Grd Tchr 1966-; *ai:* Brunner Schl Quiz B Adv; Genoa Area Ed Assn Negotiations Comm; AFT 1990-; OH Ed A Life Mem; Genoa Area Ed Assn; Delta Kappa Gamma 1973-; Ellis United Meth Church Sunday Schl Pianist 35 yrs, Church Organist 25 Y

a H. Jennings Scholar; *office:* Brunner Schl 1224 West St Genoa OH

GER, AMY L., Gifted Education Coordinator; *b:* Toledo, OH; *m:* *ed:* Univ of Toledo (BE) Commnctn 1982-, (ME) Curr 1991; Educl n; Gifted Ed Validation; *cr:* North Baltimore HS Lang Arts Tchr 85; Rossford Jr High Lang Arts Tchr 1985-87; OR City Schls Gifted hr 1987-93, Gifted Ed Coord 1992-; *office:* Oregon City Schls 5721 in Oregon OH 43616

GER, CHARLITA CRAIG, English Teacher & Team Leader; *b:* nnati, OH; *m:* Edward; *c:* Kathleen, Angela; *ed:* OH Univ (BSEd) Eng Grad Hrs: Marietta Coll, Ashland Coll, OH Univ; Working on Cnslng Project Youthlead; Lion's Quest; *cr:* Maysville HS Eng Tchr 1967-72; e MS Eng Tchr 1972-73; Belpre HS Eng Tchr 1984-, 7-12 Grd Lang Team Ldr 1991-; *ai:* Adv Hi-Y, Yth in Govt; Tech Prep; Strategic n Team; NCTE; OCTELLA; OEA; NEA; C. P. Huntington RR rical Soc; Habitat for Humanity 1990-; Rockland United Meth Admin isenhower Grant Participant 1992-94; Ashland Tchr Nom 1996; or; *office:* Belpre HS Stone Rd Belpre OH 45714

GER, JAMES R., Coord of Gifted & Talented Ed; *b:* Williamstown, : Jane McNeal; *ed:* Mansfield St Coll (BS) Elem Ed 1971; Post Grad n Spcl Ed; *cr:* Halifax Area Schl 3rd-5th Grd Tchr 1971-82, Spcl Ed 1982-83, Remedial Math Reader 1983-84, Gifted Coord 1984-; *ai:* tator & Founder IGT Schlsp Pgm; Owner Jr's 1st & Ten Sportsline; 1971-; HEA; NEA; Advocate for the Rights of Spcl Needs Stu; 415 Julian St Williamstown PA 17098*

GER, JUDITH ANN, French Dept Chair & Teacher; *b:* Reading, PA; erry K.; *c:* Erika, Christin; *ed:* Albright Coll (BA) Fr 1969; Kutztown (MA) Fr 1973; Eng Cert Alvernia Coll; 15 Credits Post-Grad Stud Ed; almyra Jr HS Fr Tchr 1969-70; Governor Mifflin Jr HS Fr Tchr -73; Reading Area Comm Coll ESL Tchr 1978-79; Daniel Boone Jr Sr r Tchr, Dept Chair 1979-; *ai:* Fr Club Adv; Acad Counsel; Tour Dir; PSEA 1969-, Exec Bd; *office:* Daniel Boone Jr Sr HS 501 Chestnut rdsboro PA 19508*

NGER, MARGARET J., English Teacher; *b:* Wilkes Barre, PA; *ed:* Chester Univ (BSEd) Comm 1982, (MED) Ed 1989; Credit Hrs West er Univ, Millersville Univ, St Josephs Univ, Carlow Coll; *cr:* Marple on Schl Eng Tchr 1982-84; Downington Sr HS Eng Tchr 1985-; *ai:* Class Adv; NEA; NCTE 1986-; Pi Kappa Delta 1980-; *office:* nngtown Sr HS 445 Manor Ave Downingtown PA 19380

NGER, SUSAN SMITH, Art Teacher; *b:* Norristown, PA; *m:* Michael; millersville Univ (BS) Art Ed 1979; Kutztown Univ (MEd) Art Ed ; 24 Credit Hrs Beyond Masters; *cr:* Perkiomen Valley Schl Dist Art 1980-, Fine Arts Dept Chprsn 1991-; Cabrinia Coll Adjunct Instr -93; *ai:* Educl Planning & Facilities Comm; Curr Advy Cncl; Stu nship Prgm Adv; NEA, PSEA, PUEA 1980-; Greater Norristown Art ue 1984-, Bd of Dir; Perkiomen Valley Art Ctr, Philadelphia rcolor Club 1991-; PA Watercolor Soc 1990-; Lifetime Achvmt Awd Work & Svc in Perkiomen Valley; Cert of Spec Congressional gnition; Gallery Representation of Artwork; *office:* Perkiomen Valley 09 Gravel Pike Collegeville PA 19426

NGLER, PATRICIA ANN, Elementary School Teacher; *b:* adelphia, PA; *m:* Philip; *ed:* Towson St Tchrs Coll (BS) His & Elem Ed ; Nazareth Coll (MS) Learning Disabilities 1974; 6 Addl Hrs; *cr:* more Pub Schls 5th-6th Grd Tchr 1964-68; Massena 6th Grd Tchr ; Rochester Pub Schls 7th Grd Tchr 1968-69; Chesterfield Cty 4th Grd 1969-70; Huntsville 4th Grd Tchr 1970; USDE Nurnburg Amer Elem Grd Ger Tchr 1971-72; Macedon Elem 4th-5th Grd Remedial Rdng 1972-; *ai:* Chosen Tchr of Yr 1991; *office:* Macedon Elem Schl 4 West acedon NY 14502

NGNER, RONALD W., Gifted, Talented & AP Bio Tchr; *b:* Jamaica, *m:* Lorna Hershberger; *c:* Kelley Curran, Heather Curran; *ed:* Univ of MED) Bio Sci & Scndry Ed 1980; 33 Grad Credits in Bio 1993-95; nryu World Karate Headquarters, Tchng License, Okinawa & Karate ; Guild Natural Sci Illustrators Course Work in Botanical Illustration crylic Wash Technique for Butterflys; *cr:* Howard Cty Pub Schl System of Gifted & Talented & AP Bio 1973-; *ai:* Past Stdnts for ronmental Awareness Spon; Comm for Dev Prof Ethics Chair; Mt rons Isshinryu Karate Club Spon & Head Instr; NEA, MSTA 1973-; d of Natural Sci Illustrators 1993-; Isshinryu World Karate Assoc -, 5th Degree Black Belt, Tchng Cert; Nature Conservancy 1976-; ubon Soc 1976-; MD Natural His Soc 1995-; Howard Cty Unsung Hero 1990-, Unsung Hero Awd; Illustrated Zoology I Lab Manual Univ of 1973; Summer Bio Inst Logo Illustrator 1993; Cover Illustration rnal of Lepidopterists Soc 1993; Author Experimental Bio-Using ssroom Skeleton as a Forensic Model; AM Express Outstanding vmt in Creating an Original Project in Geography 1992; *office:* Mt ron HS 9440 State Route 99 Ellicott City MD 21042*

ISCH, DENEA LAURELLI, Guidance Counselor; *b:* Chester, PA; *m:* ph S. Jr.; *ed:* West Chester St Coll (BS) Elem Ed 1973; Villanova Univ) Elem Cnslng 1976; Elem Admin 1992; Rosemont Coll Tech Ed 1994; Eddystone Elem Schl First Grd Tchr 1973-89; Ridley MS Guid Cnslr 9-; *ai:* Kappa Delta Pi 1976-; PSEA, NEA, REA 1973-; *office:* Ridley 1001 Morton Ave Folsom PA 19033

ISOWSKI, CLARA GRUNFELD, French Teacher; *b:* Huedin, nania; *w:* Adam (dec); *c:* Susan M. Sadowski, Elizabeth A. Smith, th E. Paradis; *ed:* Univ of Steubenville (BA) Fr, Chem 1965; Univ of ton (MS) Cnslng 1977; Gen Sci, Data Processing Cert; *cr:* Jefferson on HS Fr, Chem Tchr 1966-67; Steubenville HS Fr, Gen Sci Tchr 1967-; Fr Club Adv; NEA, DEA, STA 1967-; OH Vly Hosp, Vol; *home:* PO Box 5 Wintersville OH 43952

IZA, SUSAN BOWIE, Second Grade Teacher; *b:* Brooklyn, NY; *m:* ert; *c:* Jesse, Sarah, Hannah, Susan; *ed:* Schl of Visual Arts (BFA) Fine s 1980; St Univ of NY Coll at Oneonta (MS) Ed, Rdng 1993; *cr:* Gilboa esville Cntrl Schl Sixth Grd Tchr 1989-91, Second Grd Tchr 1991-; *ai:* ting, Sci Curr Dev Comm; NYSUT, AFT 1989-; Dev Trng Prgm; *office:* boa Conesville Cntrl Schl Wyckoff Rd Gilboa NY 12076*

OBERDANZ, MARYANN MIRANTE, 8th Grade Social Studies Tchr; Brooklyn, NY; *m:* John Henry; *c:* John David, Andrew Christopher; *ed:* nt Johns Univ (BS) Scndry Ed & Soc Stud 1962; Hunter Grad Schl (MA) Sci 1967; *cr:* New York City Jr HS #162 7th-8th Grd Soc Stud Tchr 2-64; Lindenhurst MS 8th Grd Soc Stud, Hum, & Amer His Tchr 1965-; Ecology Club Adv; Schl Play Spon; Tchrs Assn of Lindenhurst 1971-, m; AFT 1971-, Mem; Good Shepherd Choir 1983-, Soprano; denhurst MS PTA 1965-, Mem, Commendation Awd; *office:* denhurst MS 350 S Wellwood Ave Lindenhurst NY 11757

OC, SHEILA SCHWEITZER, Retired Second Grade Teacher; *b:* ndusky, OH; *m:* Norbert F.; *c:* Laura, Jacqueline, Christopher; *ed:* Notre me Coll (BA) Eng 1962; Bowling Green Univ Elem Cert; John Carroll v Cmptr Cert; Cert to Teach Chemical Abuse Prevention Courses; *cr:* dison Schl 1st Grd Tchr 1963-64; Walton Schl 1st Grd Tchr 1964-65; St eph Schl 2nd Grd & Quest Prgm Tchr 1980-; *ai:* Rainbows Prgm cilitator; Sacramental Prgms Tchr.

OCK, TY LEONARD, Physics & Computer Teacher; *b:* Princeton, NJ; Trudy Kathleen Dorry; *c:* Brian David, Daniel Wayne, Robyn Lisa; *ed:* gers Univ (BA) Physics 1973, (MS) Physics 1980; *cr:* Somerville HS Physics & Cmptr Tchr 1973-; *ai:* Adult Ed Sci & Cmptr Tchr 1974-; Engr Day 1975-, Great Adventure Physic Day 1991-, NJ-BISEC King of the Hill Competition 1992- Local Coord; Somerville Cntrl Schl Sci 2000 Lab Resource Tchr 1987-; NJAAPT Physics Bowl 1992- & Sci Olympiad 1992- Local Coord; Physics Sci Olympiad Adv 1992-; Amer Cmptr Sci League Adv 1992-; North NJ Sci Fair Adv 1992-; Physics AP Exam Adv 1989-; Cmptr Sci AP Exam Adv1986-; CML Pascal Cmptr Sci Competition Adv 1988, 1993-; NEA, NJEA, AAPT, SCEA, SEA, NJAAPT; Newsletter Ed; NJCA; Planetary Soc; Rutgers Youth Sports Research Cncl; Rutgers Univ Alumni Assn; NJ-BISEC Lightwave Comm Grant 1987-88; NSF AT&T Ldrshp in Tchng; Co-author of Physics Tchng Modules 1987-91; NST ETS Video Tchng Assessments in Sci; W Pub Cmptr Texts Subject Editor; Sigma Xi Excl in Sci Ed Awd; NJ Governor's Tchr Grant Prgm Nom 1988; Excl in Sci & Math Tchng Presidential Awd Nom 1989, 1993; Math & Sci First Annual Stevens Inst Ldrshp Awd Nom 1990; IBM, Tech & Learning Magazine Tchr of the Yr Prgm; Cncl for Basic Ed & NSF Sci & Math Fellowship Nom 1991-93; MIT Most Influential Tchr 1990-91; *office:* Somerville H S 222 Davenport St Somerville NJ 08876

KLODT, ROBERTA DICARLO, Choral Director & Music Tchr; *b:* Astoria, NY; *m:* Raymond R.; *c:* Lisa Ann DiCarlo, Laura Marie DiCarlo; *ed:* SUNY at Potsdam Queens Coll (BA) Music 1968; SUNY at Stony Brook (MA) Music 1975; Post Grad, 30 Hrs Various Music, Ed Disciplines; *cr:* Baldwin Jr HS Music, Chorus Tchr 1968-69; 3 Village Schls Music Tchr, Choral Dir, Music Dir, Theatre Arts 1975-; *ai:* Vocal Vikings 1990-95; Theatre Arts Music Dir; NYSUT, TVTA 1974-; Organist, Asst Choir Dir St Anthony of Padua Church 1980-91; *office:* Gelinas Jr HS 25 Mud Rd Setauket NY 11733

KLOKUS, MARCIA GONGOL, 4th Grade Teacher; *b:* Salamanca, NY; *w:* Ronald (dec); *c:* Aliza, Ronald; *ed:* SUNY at Geneseo (BSEd) Elem Ed 1964; *cr:* Bryant Elem 4th Grd Tchr 1964-69; Lindley-Presho Elem 2nd Grd Tchr 1969-72; Erwin Vly Elem 4th Grd Tchr 1974-; *ai:* Bldg Ldrshp Team; Schl MATES; NYSUT 1964-; Corning Tchrs Assoc 1969-; *office:* Erwin Valley Elem Schl 16 Beartown Rd Painted Post NY 14870

KLONICKE, MARY ELIZABETH MULCAHY, Sr HS Guidance Counselor; *b:* Windber, PA; *m:* Mark; *c:* April Ann, Alecia Marie; *ed:* Univ of Pittsburgh (BS) Dev Psych 1981; PA St Univ (MED) Cnslr Ed; PA Dept of Ed Cert in Elem & Scndry Guid Cnslng; *cr:* Appalachia Intermediate Unit 08 Schl Elem Guid Cnslr 1982-88; Richland Schl Dist Scndry Guid Cnslr 1988-; *ai:* NHS Adv; Stu Ldrshp Comm Adv; Dept Chprsn Pupil Prsnl, Spec Ed; Stu Assistance Prgm; NASSP, DSA 1991-; PSEA 1982-; *office:* Richland Schl Dist 220 Highfield Ave Johnstown PA 15904

KLONSKY, BRUCE G., Psychology Professor; *b:* New York, NY; *ed:* Herbert H. Lehman Coll (AB) Psych 1971; Fordham Univ (MA) Psych 1973, (PHD) Psych 1978; *cr:* Fordham Univ Tchng Fellow, Psych Dept 1974-76; WV Univ Visiting Asst Prof, Psych Dept; 1978-79; SUNY Coll at Fredonia Psych Dept Asst Prof 1979-85, Assoc Prof 1986-92, Full Prof 1992-; *ai:* Labor & Industrial Relations Concentration Coord; Psi Chi Fac Adv; Psych Dept Merit Awd Comm Chair; Internship Coord Psych Dept; APA 1975-; APS 1990-; AERA 1983-; ASA, TASP, SASP 1978-; PSI Chi 1970-; Sigma Xi 1980-; UUP 1979-, Dept Rep; Research Opportunity Awd from NSF 1988-89; SUNY Research Fdn Grant; 20 Publications, Chapters for 8 Books; *office:* SUNY at Fredonia Central Ave Psych Dept Fredonia NY 14063*

KLOOS, SYDNEY WHITE, French Teacher; *b:* Philadelphia, PA; *m:* Harry; *c:* John, Sandra; *ed:* Catawba Coll (BA) Fr, Eng-Cum Laude 1959; Attnd Rutgers Univ Frgn Lang Inst; Univ of ME 3 Credit Hrs; *cr:* Hatboro HS Fr, Eng Tchr 1959-60; Pennsauken HS Fr Tchr 1960-64; Cherokee HS Fr Tchr 1977-; *ai:* Fr club, La Societe Honoraire de Francais Adv; CORE Team; Fac Cncl Natl Hon Soc; NEA, NJEA, AATF, LDEA 1977-; 4-H 1975-86, Ldr; *office:* Cherokee HS Willow Bend Rd Marlton NJ 08053*

KLOPFER, RONALD G., Prof of Anatomy & Physiology; *b:* Scranton, PA; *ed:* Mansfield Univ (BS) Gen Sci, Geog, Scndry Ed 1972; Bloomsburg Univ (MED) Sci Ed 1973; 60 Post Grad Hrs at Univ of DE, Manhattan Coll; *cr:* Brandywine HS AP Bio Tchr 1973-1991; DE Tech Comm Coll Prof Applied Sci 1991-; *ai:* Commencement, Middle Ath Sts Self-Stud Comms; Mentor Amer With Disabliity Act Funding Comm; Human Anat & Phys Soc 1991-; NEA 1973-; *office:* DE Tech & Comm Coll 400 Stanton Christiana Rd Newark DE 19713*

KLORER, ALISON ELIZABETH, Autism Specialist; *b:* Columbus, OH; *ed:* Quinnipiac Coll (BA) Psych 1993; Currently Enrolled MS Prgm Psych Westfield St Coll; *ai:* Soccer, Track Coach; *home:* 212 Ely Ave W Springfield MA 01089

KLOSSNER, DIANE REESE, Fourth Grade Teacher; *b:* Kingston, PA; *m:* Gary Dennis; *c:* Rebecca, Gregory; *ed:* Penn St Univ (BS) Elem Ed 1973; Cortland St Univ (MS) Elem Ed, Curr Dev 1976; *cr:* Syracuse City Schl Dist Tchr 1974-; *ai:* Team Ldr; Mc Kinley Brighton Magnet Schl; Schl Improvement Team; Math Coach; Syracuse Tchrs Assn, NYSUT, AFT 1974-; Jamesville Federated Church 1977-, Chair Ed Comm; *office:* H. W. Smith Elem Schl 1130 Salt Springs Rd Syracuse NY 13224

KLOTZ, PATRICIA ANN, 8th Grade Teacher; *b:* Allentown, PA; *m:* Bernard Eugene; *c:* Darren, Kevin, Kimberly; *ed:* Allentown Coll Elem, Physics 1993-94; Cedar Crest Elem, Math 1993-94; Kutztown Elem, Rdng Cert 1961; *cr:* St Francis of Assisi 8th Grd Tchr 2 Yrs, 7th Grd Tchr 15 Yrs; South Hill 5th Grd Tchr 1 Yr; Ritter Elem Schl 6 Yrs; *ai:* Sci, Eng, Safety Patrol Coord; Yrbk Comm; Mentor; NEA 1959-; N Cath Tchrs 1979-; Girl Scouts 1981-86; Brownies 1978-81; Cubs 1970-73; BSA 1973-78; *office:* St Francis Of Assisi Schl 1035 W Washington St Allentown PA 18102

KLOTZ, ROBERT PATRICK, Social Studies Teacher; *m:* Lisbeth Young; *c:* Thomas, Julia, Robert Jr.; *ed:* Univ of Dayton (BA) Ed 1975; Working Towards MS Univ of Northern; Attnd Univ of Cincinnati, Univ of Pacific; *cr:* Northwestern HS In-Schl Suspension 1975-76; Richmond HS Soc Stud Tchr, Asst Ftbl 1976-80; Oak Hills Soc Stud Tchr 1981-, Head Ftbl 1986-; *ai:* Teen Breakfast Club; Inclusion, Dist Soc Stud Comms; OHEA 1981-, Bldg Rep; NEA 1979-; SNOFCA 1986-; St Xavier Alumni 1971-; Nom Tchr of Yr Ashland Oil 1996; Coach of Yr 1986, 1988; Edctr of Yr Jaycees 1982; *office:* Oak Hills Sr HS 3200 Ebenezer Rd Cincinnati OH 45248*

KLUCK, TERRY C., French & Spanish Teacher; *b:* Philadelphia, PA; *m:* Robin W.; *c:* Jessica; *ed:* Kutztown Univ (BS) Scndry Ed 1979; Post Grad Work in Span Villanova Univ; Post Grad Work in Ed Beaver Coll, Rider Coll; *cr:* Centennial Schls Span, Fr Tchr 1978-79; Cncl Rock HS Span, Fr Tchr 1979-; *ai:* Fr Club Adv; NEA 1979-; Amer Assn Tchrs Span & Portuguese 1991-; Bucks Cty Assn Tchrs Foreign Lang 1990-; Accompanied Stdnts on Educl Tours to France 1981, 1985; Kiwanis Recognition For Leadership Key Club 1984; *office:* Council Rock HS 62 Swamp Rd Newtown PA 18940

KLUCKHOHN, CARMEN VILLARINI, Third Grade Teacher; *b:* Buffalo, NY; *m:* Carl Frederick; *c:* Emily Marilyn, Hannah Rose, Karl Frederick; *ed:* Fredonia St Coll (BA) Elem Ed 1984; Buffalo St Coll (MA) Rdng Specialist 1988; Instrl Theory into Practice; *cr:* Wayside Presch Tchr 1984-85; Hamburg Cntrl 1st Grd Tchr 1985-86, 2nd Grd Tchr 1986-92, 3rd Grd Tchr 1992-; *ai:* Fredonia Hamburg Tchr Ed Steering, Tech, Least Restrictive Environment, Inclusion Comms; Portfolio Assessment Project; NYSUT 1985-; Hamburg Tchrs Assn 1985-; PTA 1985-; Phi Delta Kappa; Girl Scout Leader 1995-, Co-op Ldr; *office:* Hamburg Cntrl Armor Elem Schl 5301 Abott Rd Hamburg NY 14075

KLUDT, BEHTE HALL, Science Teacher; *b:* Pikeville, KY; *m:* William Ross; *c:* Bethany; *ed:* Pikeville Coll (BS) Bio & Chem 1988; Univ of Dayton (MS) Admin 1994; *cr:* Dillie Clinical Lab Lab Technician 1989; St Teresa Cath Schl Sci Tchr 1989-91; Springfield N HS Sci Tchr 1991-; *ai:* Sci Fair Coord; SECO 1995-; *office:* Springfield North HS 701 E Home Rd Springfield OH 45503*

KLUGH, KRISTEN M., English Teacher; *b:* West Chester, PA; *ed:* West Chester Univ (BSEd) Eng 1988; 30 Grad Hrs Toward Masters in Eng; *cr:* West Chester Univ Eng Tchr 1988-89; Academy Park HS Eng Tchr 1989-90; Upper Darby HS Eng Tchr 1990-; *ai:* Omni Club; NEA, NCTE 1988-; Tchr of Month 1992; Stu Assistance Prgm Coord Recognition Awd 1992; Pub NCTE Notes 1994-95; *office:* Upper Darby HS 601 N Lansdowne Ave Upper Darby PA 19082*

KLUGMANN, SARAH JAROSLAWICZ, Science Teacher; *b:* Brooklyn, NY; *m:* Eli; *c:* Tzipora Pesha, Yehoshua Moshe, Orrin Aryeh, Chaya Fradl, Nechama Margolit; *ed:* Machon Devorah Tchrs Sem Ed License 1981; Working Towards Ed, Psych BA Touro Coll; *cr:* Beth Jacob of Boro Park Grds 4 & 7 Elem Tchr 1981-83; Shulamis HS Grd 10 Bible Stud Tchr 1983-84; Prospect Park Yeshiva Grd 5 Elem Ed Tchr 1983-84; Beth Jacob of Ger Grds 7 & 8 His, Lang Arts Tchr 1984-85; Bnos Yaakov of Pupa Grd 6 Tchr 1985-86; *ai:* Tutor; Coll Adv; Stu Mentor; Prin Talmud Torah Kresses Israel of Sea Gate; *office:* Merkaz Bnos HS 1400 W 6th St Brooklyn NY 11204*

KLUSAS-KING, PAULA A., Spanish Teacher; *b:* Chicago, IL; *m:* Paul C.; *ed:* Purdue Univ (BA) Span & Fr 1965; ID Univ (MAT) Ed & Span 1969; Bridgewater St Coll CAGS Schl Amin 1987; attnd Univ of Iberoamericana 1970, Univ of Valencia Spain 1972; *cr:* Dedham HS Span Tchr 1967-70; Randolph HS Span Tchr 1970-; *ai:* Prin Advy Chcl; Randolph Tchrs Rep Cncl; Span Club Adv; Floor Master, Summer Schl Dir; Schl Cncl Mem; NEA, MTA 1969-; RTA 1969-; MAFLA 1970-; ACTFL 1970-; aSCD 1989-; *office:* Randolph Jr Sr HS 70 Memorial Pky Randolph MA 02368

KLUZ, BETH HILL, Mathematics Teacher; *b:* Erie, PA; *m:* David Timothy; *c:* Maureen, David; *ed:* Edinboro St Univ (BS) Math Ed 1970; Penn St Univ (MED) Math Ed 1975; *cr:* Monaca Jr HS Math Tchr 1970-72; Bensalem HS Math Tchr 1972-75; Harrisburg Mid & HS Math Tchr 1976-87; Harrisburg Area Comm Coll Math Tchr 1979-93; Susquehanna Twp HS Math Tchr 1987-; *ai:* NEA; *home:* 1859 OHara Ln Middletown PA 17057*

KMIEC, ANDREW, Sixth Grade Teacher; *b:* South Amboy, NJ; *m:* Margaret Mullen; *c:* Kara Ann, Kis Andrew; *ed:* Waynesburg Coll (BA) Elem Ed 1968; Trenton St Coll (MS) Urban Ed 1977; 30 Credits Beyond Masters; *cr:* William C McGinnis 6th Grd Sci Tchr 1971-87, 7th Grd Sci Tchr 1987-90, 8th Grd Sci Tchr 1990-94; Shull Schl 6th Grd Sci Tchr 1994-; *ai:* Boys & Girls Bsktbl, Sftbl & Vlybl; 6th Grd Sci Club; Saint Marys Var Girls & Boys Bsktbl Coach; 8th Grd Girls Frosh, Jr Var & Asst Var Bsktbl Coach; 8th Grd Boys, Frosh & Var Receivers Ftbl Coach; Frosh Boys Bsbl Coach; 8th Grd Yrbk Adv; 8th Grd Adv; AFT 1971-; IKE Grants for Sci; Governors Awds for Perth Amboy McGinnis Schl; Tchr of Yr Awd 2 Times; PSEG Sci Grant; *office:* Samuel E Shull Schl 360 Hall Ave Perth Amboy NJ 08861*

KMON, PATRICIA DELNEGRO, 7th Grade Language Arts Tchr; *b:* Springfield, MA; *m:* John David; *c:* Jay Carmine; *ed:* Amer Intnl Coll (BA) Psych, Ed 1966; Westfield St Coll (MED) Guid 1972, (CAGS) Educl Admin 1993; *cr:* Mabelle B Avery MS 6th Grd LA Tchr 1966-91, 7th Grd LA Tchr 1991-, Team Ldr 1992-; *ai:* Class Adv 1991-94; SEA 1966-, Grievance Chprsn; CEA 1966-; NEA 1966-.

KNAAK, RANDY SCOTT, Physical Education Teacher; *b:* Ft Bragg, NC; *m:* Paul Jean Cotter; *c:* Scott, Jennifer; *ed:* Canisius Coll (BS) PE 1986; SUNY at Brockport Master Track, PE; *cr:* Albion Cntrl In School Correction Supvr 1986-90, PE Tchr 1990-; *ai:* Jr High Ftbl, Girls Var Swimming Head, Var Track Head, Asst Coach 10 Yrs; *office:* Albion Central School District 324 East Ave Albion NY 14411

KNABE, MARIE L., Teacher; *b:* Camden, NJ; *m:* Robert F.; *c:* Beth; *ed:* Trenton St Coll (BA) Bus Ed 1964; *ai:* Bus Club; NJEA, NEA 1985-; Tchr of Yr 1994-95.

KNANISHU, JOANNE MARIE, Kindergarten Teacher; *b:* Teaneck, NJ; *m:* Glenn Sander; *c:* Christina; *ed:* Saint Thomas Aquinas Coll (BS) Elem & Early Chldhd Ed 1977; *cr:* Immaculate Conception Schl 7th Grd Tchr & Departmental Head 1977-79; ICS & Saint Marys Sub Tchr 1979-82; Saint Marys Kndgtn Tchr 1982-; *ai:* NCEA 1979-; Amer Legion 1993-, Vol Work; Immaculate Conception Pre-Cana 1988-, Org & Registration; Immaculate Conception 75th Anniversary Comm 1975; Mid Eastern Dance Troupe 1993-; Cath Tchr Recognition Awd 1993; Diagnostic Evaluation Comm 1992-93; Rel Ed Wrksps; *office:* St Mary Schl 300 High St Closter NJ 07624

KNAPP, CAROL S., Lang Arts Chprsn & Teacher; *b:* Sharon, PA; *ed:* Mercyhurst Coll (BA) Lang Arts 1967; Pace Coll (MS) Ed 1983; New Paltz Admin 1975; Northeastern Univ Process Conf Writing 1985; *cr:* Carmel Cntrl Schl Dist Lang Arts Tchr 1967-, Lang Arts Dept Chm 1984-; *ai:* Chrldng, Girls Vlybl Coach; NCTE 1985-; NY St Cncl Tchrs of Eng 1985-, Outstdng Eng Prgm; ASCD, CTA 1989-; Presenter NY St Cncl Tchrs of Eng; MS NY St Tchng Assn; Consultant & Wkshp Ldr, Writing Process; *office:* George Fischer MS 275 Fair St Carmel NY 10512*

KNAPP, JAMES P., Guidance Counselor; *b:* Pittsburgh, PA; *m:* Eileen Abbott; *c:* Casey; *ed:* IN Univ of PA (BS) Comm Media 1984; Univ of Pittsburgh (MA) Higher Ed 1987; Slippery Rock Univ (MS) Scndry Cnslng 1989; *cr:* Ford City HS Guidance Cnslr 1989-90; Washington Vo-Tech Schl Guidance Cnslr 1990-91; North Allegheny HS 1991-92; Bethel Park HS Guidance Cnslr 1992-; *ai:* Coach Girls Head Var Bsktbl 1994-, Asst Sftbl 1992-94, Asst Bsktbl 1979-93; Dance, Key Club Spon; Natl Assn Scndry Cnslrs 1989; Allegheny Cty Cnslrs, PA Schl Cnslrs 1990-; *office:* Bethel Park Sr HS 309 Church Rd Bethel Park PA 15102*

KNAPP, JO-ANNE CATHERINE (WELSH), Vocal & General Music Teacher; *b:* Binghamton, NY; *m:* Michael Patrick; *c:* Mary Catherine; *ed:* Binghamton Univ (BA) Music 1982; SUC at Cortland (MSEd) Rdng 1987; *cr:* Whitney Point Cntrl Schls Tchng Asst 1985-86, Music Tchr 1987-, Music Dept Chm 1992-; *ai:* Select & Women's Chorus Dir; Schl & Comm Productions Dir; Broome Co Music Educators 1989-; NYS Schl Music Assn, Music Educators Natl Conf 1988-; Whitney Point Tchrs Assn 1987-; Amer Choral Dir Assoc 1995-; Castle Creek Meth Church 1981-, Choir Dir; Stevenson Barrett Meml Awd 1982; Tchr of Yr 1992; Whitney Point Rotary Club Merit Awd 1992; *office:* Whitney Point Central Schl PO Box 249 Whitney Point NY 13862

KNAPP, JOHN P., Fourth Grade Teacher; *b:* Rockville Centre, NY; *m:* Marie; *c:* Johnny; *ed:* St Univ of NY at Stony Brook (BA) Elem Ed 1974, (MALS) Elem Ed 1977; 30 Credits Including Admin Internship; *cr:* Sachem Schl Dist Tchr 1975-; *ai:* 11 Yr Old Boys Travel Soccer Coach; *office:* Chippewa Elem Schl 1 David Mello Dr Holtsville NY 11742

KNAPP, ROBERT CHARLES, Fifth Grade Teacher; *b:* Heidelburg, Germany; *m:* Rosemary Morrisson; *c:* Allison, Molly, Sarah; *ed:* Univ of MD (BS) Elem Ed 1974; Loyola Coll (MS) Admin 1987; Attnd Anne Arundel Comm Coll, Salisbury St Coll; *cr:* Tylerton Elem Schl Tchr in Charge 1974-78; Parole Elem Schl Tchr 1979-85; Severna Park Elem Tchr 1986-; *ai:* NEA 1979-; TAAAC 1979-, Tchr Rep; Fnd for Educl Excl

1995-, Chprsn; *office:* Severna Park Elem Schl 6 Riggs Ave Severna Park MD 21146*

KNAPP, ROBERT S., English Teacher; *b:* Arlington, VA; *m:* Jean M. Zupko; *c:* Sarah; *ed:* Drew Univ (BA) Eng Lit 1986; Addl 3 Credit Hrs; Coll of St Elizabeth Tchr Cert 1990; 3 Credit Hrs Rutgers Univ; *cr:* Oratory Cath Prep Schl Eng Tchr 1990-; *ai:* Jr Schl Bsktbl Coach, Dir of Act; NCTE 1994-, NCEA 1990-; *office:* Oratory Cath Prep Schl 1 Beverly Rd Summit NJ 07901

KNAPP, THERESA MARLENE, Health & Physical Ed Teacher; *b:* El Paso, TX; *ed:* Malone Coll (BS) PE 1983; Kent St Univ (MA) Exercise Physiology 1984; *cr:* Injury Reduction Tech Inc Fitness Ctr Mgr, Ed Prgm Coord 1985-91; Norton HS Tchr, Coach 1992-; *ai:* Girls Var Bsktbl Asst Coach; Girls Var Track & Field Head Coach; NEA 1992-; *office:* Norton HS 4138 Cleveland Massillon Rd Norton OH 44203

KNAPP, WILMA CONKEY, Retired Teacher; *b:* Waynesburg, PA; *m:* John Franklin Sr; *c:* John F. Jr., David Michael, Brian Keith; *ed:* Malone Coll (BS) Elem Ed 1974; 150 Hrs Ashland Coll Cmptr Lit, 3rd Grd Guarantee Project Impact, Math; *cr:* Myers Elem Schl 6th Grd Tchr 1969-70; Mt Hope Elem Schl 2-4, 5-6 Grd Tchr 1970-74; Killbuck Elem Schl 4th Grd Tchr 1974-78; Clark Elem Schl 2nd Grd 13 Yrs, 5th Grd 1 Yr Sci Tchr 1979-94, Kndgtn, Act Days Vol 1994-; *ai:* WHEA 1975-94, Sec, Treas 2 Yrs; EHEA 1971-75, Sec, Treas 2 Yrs; Delta Kappa Gamma 1983-, Sec 4 Yrs; Jennings Scholar 1983; *home:* 7008 Cty Rd 68 Millersburg OH 44654

KNAPP WEBSTER, DONALD, Honors, AP & IB Chem Tchr; *b:* Montclair, NJ; *m:* Leslie Gordon Gamble; *c:* Clayton, Leland, Cynthia, Evan, Eric; *ed:* Duke Univ (AB) Chem & Philosophy 1957; Univ of Rochester (AM) Philosophy of Sci 1965; Univ of East Anglia (PHD) Chem Ed 1977; 33 Post-Doctoral Hrs Ed; *cr:* Wash DC Pub Schls Chem Tchr 1961-66; Fairleigh-Dickinson Univ, Montclair Univ & Amer Univ Adj Prof or Summer Sci Pgm Dir 1963-82; Mountain Lakes HS Chem Tchr & Dept Head 1966-85; Berlex Labs, Sandoz Inc, Warner Lambert, Lederle, Union Carbide: Scientific Consultant 1972-87; Newark Acad Chem Tchr 1987-; Lehigh Univ NSF Evaluation Consultant; *ai:* Curr Comm; Tchr Evaluation Comm; Supvr of Experimental Chem Projects for the Intnl Baccalaureate Diploma Extended Essay; NEA 1960-; NJEA 1960-; NJSTA & NSTA 1960-, Chem Coord, NJ Outstdng Chem Tchr, Natl Industry Ed Awd for Innovation; ACS 1960-, Chair Subsection, Councilor NJ Section; Sr Hnrs Thesis Duke Univ; NIH Rsrch Grant; Univ Schlsp UEA England; Publications in Philosophy, Ed & Biochemical Rsrch; Writer of St & Natl Chem Exams.

KNASINSKI, FRANK STANLEY,JR., Life Science Teacher; *b:* Milwaukee, WI; *m:* Patricia Ann Meek; *c:* Tanya Lynn Malak, Jason Michael; *ed:* Ball St Univ (BS) Bio 1971, (MA) Ed, Bio 1974; *cr:* Thomas R. White Adult Ed HS Sci Tchr 1971-72; Greenville Sr HS 9-12 Life Sci, Bio Tchr 1972-79; Greenville Jr HS Seventh Grd Life Sci Tchr 1979-; *ai:* Sci Club Spon Greenville Sr HS; Sci Club Spon 1983-85; NEA, OEA 1977-; GEA 1977-, Bldg Rep, Appreciation Plaque; Main St Chrstn Church 1969-, Deacon, Chrstn Ed Chair; Winchester Lions Club 1989-, Treas, Sec; BSA 1980-90-, Pack, Den, Troop Ldr, Outstdng Troop Ldr 1988; Feather Dissection Lab Kit; *home:* 430 E Franklin St Winchester IN 47394

KNAUFF, GEORGE OAKLAND, Retired Social Studies Teacher; *b:* Williamsport, PA; *m:* Loraine Clifford; *c:* Thaddeus, Damian, Joshua; *ed:* Duquesne Univ (BA) Sci, Ed 1965; Carnegie-Mellon Univ (MA) His 1971; *cr:* Bethel Park Schl Dist Sr HS Tchr, Soc Stud Dept 1965-; *ai:* AFT 1968-; South Hilus Chorale 1988-94, Lighting Dir; NSF Grants African & Asian Stud 1969, Tchng Psych in HS Today 1988; Nom Tchr of Yr Univ of Chic 1987; Svc Awd 1990; Named Outstdng Fac Mem 1992; *home:* 3411 Ashland Dr Bethel Park PA 15102*

KNECHT, BRAD KEVIN, 9th Grade Biology Teacher; *b:* Bethlehem, PA; *m:* Elizabeth Rothrock; *c:* Ben, Gregg; *ed:* Millersville Univ (BS) Bio 1980; Wilkes Univ (MS) Bio 1994; *cr:* Susquehanna Twp Schls Life Sci Tchr 1980-81; Randolph HS Bio & Med Tech Tchr 1981-86; Nazareth HS Bio Tchr 1986-; *ai:* PSEA 1980-; NEA 1980-; NSTA 1981-; Howard Hughes Sci Grant.

KNECHT, KATHY, Third Grade Teacher; *b:* Newark, NJ; *ed:* Univ of DE (BS) Ed 1979; Kean Coll (MA) Spcl Ed 1987; *cr:* Jefferson Schl Sixth Grd Tchr 1979-80, Resource Room Tchr 1980-95, Third Grd Tchr 1995-; *ai:* PTO Tchr Liaison, Stdnt Cncl Adv, Pupil Asst Comm Mem; NEA 1979-; NJEA 1979-; Kappa Delta Phi 1979; Phi Kappa Phi 1979; Govenor's Tchr Recognition Pgm Awd 1986; *office:* Jefferson Elem Schl 110 Ashwood Ave Summit NJ 07901

KNECHT, MARY ANN, American Studies Teacher; *b:* Jamestown, OH; *ed:* Wilmington Coll (BA) His, Govt 1970; Wright St Univ Rdng Ed Cert 1992; *cr:* Bellefontaine MS 8th Grd Soc Stud Tchr 1970-; *ai:* Mentor Tchr for System; Bellefontaine Ed Assn 1970-, Treas 5 Yrs; OH Ed Assn, NEA 1970-; Delta Kappa Gamma 1992-, Sec; OEA Awd for Outstdng Treas for Local Assn; *office:* Bellefontaine MS 509 N Park Rd Bellefontaine OH 43311

KNECHTEL, NANCY, Art History Professor; *b:* Buffalo, NY; *ed:* St Univ Coll at Buffalo (BA) Eng Lit 1979; St Univ of NY at Buffalo (MA) Art His, Italian 1985; *cr:* St Univ of NY at Buffalo Archivist Office for Pres 1988-; Niagra Cty Comm Coll Asst Prof 1989-; Niagra Univ Sr Lecturer; *ai:* Intnl Ed Comm Chair; Art Guild, Stu Senate Adv; College Art Assn 1986-; Natl NISOD Excl Tchng Awd 1994; St Univ NY Chancellors Excl Tchng Awd 1993; *office:* Niagara County Comm College 3111 Saunders Settlement Rd Sanborn NY 14132*

KNEPP, M. ELIZABETH FRENCH, 5th Grade Teacher; *b:* Lewistown, PA; *m:* Walter W.; *c:* Elizabeth, Amy; *ed:* Messiah Coll (BA) Home Ec Ed 1974; Wilkes Coll (MED) Ed 1989; Elem Cert 30 Hrs Penn St Univ 1976; Addl 36 Credit Hrs; *cr:* Brown Twp Elem Schl 1 Grd Tchr 1976-77; Chief Logan MS 6-8 Grd Home Ec Tchr 1977-79; Misc Positions, Bldgs 3-5 Grd Tchr 1987-88; Srodes Mills Elem Schl 5 Grd Tchr 1988-; *ai:* Stone Arch Rdng Cncl 1990-; Mifflin Cty Extension Bd 1995-; *office:* Strodes Mills Elem Schl RD 2 Box 122A Mc Veytown PA 17051

KNIERIEMEN, ELEANOR MARY, Social Studies Teacher; *b:* Brooklyn, NY; *ed:* St Univ of NY at Brockport (BS) His 1975; Lesley Coll (MS) Moderate Spec Needs 1980; 9 Credits Lee Canter Assertive Discipline; *cr:* Warwick HS Eng & Soc Stud Tchr 1976-1977; Goshen HS Soc Stud Tchr 1977-1979, 1980-; *ai:* Womens Vlybl Var Coach; Peer Mediation Adv; Dept Chprsn; NYSCSS 1988-; AFT, NYSUT, GTA 1977-; *office:* Goshen H S Scotchtown Ave Goshen NY 10924*

KNIGHT, DAVID HOLMAN, Asst Professor of Accounting; *b:* Bangor, ME; *m:* Gloria DeLuca; *c:* Christopher; *ed:* Yale (BA) Ec 1965; Rutgers (MBA) Acctng 1966; *cr:* Lehman Brothers Auditing Dir 1975-80; USAID Consultant 1981-85; AICPA Consultant 1985-87; Manhattan Coll Asst Prof 1988-91; Borough of Manhattan Comm Coll Asst Prof 1991-; *ai:* AICPA 1983-, CPA Awd; Co-Author Elementary Accounting 123 1991, 1994; *office:* Borough Of Manhattan Comm Coll 199 Chambers St New York NY 10007

KNIGHT, DOLORES ELAINE, Fifth Grade Teacher; *b:* Coatesville, PA; *c:* Deric Allen, Elizabeth Martha, Rebecca Elaine, Daniel Irvin; *ed:* West Chester Univ (BS) Elem Ed 1975; Cabrini Coll 30 Credit Hrs Early Chldhd; Grad Stud 30 Credit Hrs; *cr:* Chester Cty Head Start Biling Tchr 1974-75; Peirce Elem Schl Biling, Regular Ed Tchr 1975-79; Exton Elem Schl First-Second, Fifth Grd Tchr 1979-; *ai:* WCASD 1975-, Exton Rep; NEA 1975-; Women's Ministry 1990-; Prof Women's Club 1988-; *office:* Exton Elem Schl 301 S Hendricks Ave Exton PA 19341

KNIGHT, HERBERT LINDSAY, English Teacher; *b:* Quincy, FL; *m:* Karen Anne Bailey; *c:* Melissa Yvette, Philip-David Lindsay; *ed:* FL A&M Univ (BA) His & Eng; Cntrl CT St Univ (MS) Supervision & Admin; Attnd East Carolina Univ at Greenville, Cambridge Coll & St Univ of NY at New Paltz; *cr:* USMC Admin Prsnl; Lewis Fox MS Tchr; Hartford Adult Schl Tchr 1990-94; Univ of Hartford Affiliate Fac 1991-; *ai:* Hartford Stage Spon a Stu; Sister Schl Pen Pal Prgm; Tutorial After Schl Prgm; CT St Fed of Tchrs 1978-; Hartford Fed of Tchrs 1978-, Area Chprsn; NCTE 1980-; Kappa Delta Phi; NAACP 1978-; World Cncl Affairs 1980-; Big Brother 1981-; *office:* Lewis Fox MS 305 Greenfield St Hartford CT 06112*

KNIGHT, JANET LYNN, Reading Teacher; *b:* Oswego, NY; *ed:* St Univ Coll at Oswego (BS) Elem Ed 1977, (MS) Rdng Ed 1984; Whole Lang & Cmptr Stud Inservice Hrs; *cr:* Minetto Elem 2nd-3rd Grd Tchr 1977-87, Rdng Tchr 1987-; *ai:* Treas Home & Schl Assn, Schl Soc Fund; Parents as Rdng Partners Co-Ldr; Oswego Classroom Tchrs Assn, AFT 1977-; IRA 1989-; Oswego Rdng Cncl 1990-; Presenter NYS Rdng Conf 1991, Regnl Rdng Conf 1992; Oswego Tchrs Ctr Grant 1989; Oswego City Schl Dist Grant 1989; *office:* Minetto Elem Schl Granby Rd Minetto NY 13115

KNIGHT, JANICE A., Third Grade Teacher; *b:* Philipsburg, PA; *m:* Ronald; *c:* Melinda, Kari; *ed:* 36 Credits Masters Equivalency; *cr:* Wilson Schl Dist First Grd Tchr 1969-71; Lamar Cty Schl Fourth Grd Math Tchr 1971-72; Bradford Area Schl Second Grd Tchr 1972-74; Weathrly Area Schl Third Grd Tchr 1989-; *ai:* NEA, PSEA, WEA 1988-; Nom Tchr of Yr 1974.

KNIGHT, LINDA MARIE COOK, Family & Consumer Sci Tchr; *b:* Port Clinton, OH; *m:* Robert C.; *c:* David; *ed:* BGSU (BA) Home Ec 1971; 15 Hrs Grad Work; *cr:* Oak Harbor HS Home Ec Tchr 1971-72; Genoa HS Home Ec Tchr 1971-72; Toledo Pub Schls Family & Consumer Sci Tchr 1972-; *ai:* FHA, HERO Adv; Dept Chm Family & Consumer Sci; OVA, AVA 1978-; TFT 1976-; *office:* Woodward HS 600 E Streicher St Toledo OH 43608

KNIGHT, MARGIE J., Physical Education & Hlth Tchr; *b:* Baltimore, MD; *ed:* Salisbury St Univ (BS) PE 1979; Attnd Loyola Coll & Towson St Univ; *cr:* Colonel Richardson HS Math & Sci Tchr 1979-80; Federalsburg Elem PE Tchr 1980-83; North Caroline HS PE & Hlth Tchr 1983-; *ai:* Vlybl & Sftbl Head Coach; Athletic Trainer; Booster Club Spon; Natl Sftbl Coaches Assn 1995-; Amer Vlybl Coaches Assn 1990-, 100 Wins Club Awd; Caroline Cty Recreation 1990-, Park Vol; Inducted Into Salisbury St Univ Athletic Hall of Fame 1995; Mid-Shore Vlybl Coach of Yr 1988, 1989, 1990, 1991 & 1993; Sftbl Coach of Yr 1986, 1987, 1988, 1990 & 1992; Pub Article in FastPitch Magazine 1994; *office:* North Caroline HS 10990 River Rd Ridgely MD 21660

KNIGHT, MARY BROWN, Kindergarten Teacher; *b:* Columbus, GA; *m:* Arthur; *c:* Aaron; *ed:* SUNY at Oswego (BS) Elem Ed 1964; Jefferson Comm Coll 21 Hrs Span; Univ of Madrid Spain 12 Hrs Span; *cr:* Adams Cntrl Schl 4th Grd Tchr 1964-65; Rome City Schls 6th Grd Tchr of Emotionally Disturbed 1965-69; E Irondequoit Schls MS Lang Arts Tchr 1969-70; Sackets Harbor Cntrl Schl Kndgtn, 2nd, 4th Grd Tchr 1971-; *ai:* NEA 1971-; Black River Rdng Cncl 1990-; Jeff Lewis Tchrs Ctr 1985-; St Cecilia's Ladies Group 1981-, Pres, Treas; *office:* Sackets Harbor Central Schl PO Box 290 S Broad St Sackets Harbor NY 13685*

KNIGHT, MERLE M., 6th-12th Grd Soc Stud Coord; *b:* Sparta, IL; *m:* Sally J.; *c:* Jeff, Julya, Jamily, Jolene, Janelle; *ed:* Henderson Coll (BA) Ec & Psych 1963; Purdue Univ (MA) Ec 1967; Univ of CO (MA) Psych 1970; Post Grad PHD Candidate; *cr:* Univ of CO Rsrch Economists 1968-71; Univ of NY Asst Prof of Ec 1972-75; Lewis S Mills HS Soc Stud Coord 1976-; Univ of CT Ec Instr 1986-; *ai:* NHS & Sparta Scroll Newspaper Adv; Debate Coach; NEA 1976-; NCSS 1976-; AAUP 1986-; Univ of CT Outstdng Tchr 1994-95; Numerous Articles & Textbook Pub; *office:* Lewis S Mills HS 26 Lyon Rd Burlington CT 06013*

KNIGHT, MOLLY SCHEHR, Univ Supvr of Student Teachers; *b:* Cincinnati, OH; *ed:* Univ of Cincinnati (BS) Elem Ed 1962; Wright St Univ (MED) Tchr Ldr 1981; 30 Addl Hrs Beyond Masters at Univ of Dayton; *cr:* Clovernook Elem 4th Grd Tchr 1962-63; Tinsley Elem 2-8th Grd Remedial Rdng Tchr 1963-64; Stonewall Elem 4th-6th Grd Tchr 1965-67; Brent & Whitaker Schls 3rd-6th Grd Tchr 1967-71; Trenton MS 8th Grd Self Contained Spec Class 1972-71; Normandy Elem Schl 4th-5th Grd Tchr 1971-92; Univ of Dayton Campus Supv of Ed Stu Tchrs 1992- 1992-; *ai:* NEA, OH Ed Assn, 1967-, Rep to St Assembly 1986-92; Kappa Delta Phi 1962-, Sec; Centerville WA Twp Ed Fnd 1971-, Hall of Fame Awd 1990, Tchr of Yr; Friends of Dayton Ballet 1993-, Bd Mem; Waynesville Chamber of Commerce 1993-, Sauerkraut Festival Food Co-Chm, Centerville Americana Festival Festival Tchrs Booth; Habitat for Humanity 1994-, Builder, Supporter; Jennings Scholar 2 Yrs; Nom Excl in Ed Awd 1987; Outstanding Tchr of Yr Hall of Fame Awd 1990; Centerville Washington Twp Ed Fnd Grant to Support Photojournalism; Mentor Tchr; Bausch & Lomb Sci Awd.*

KNIGHT, RAY S., Instrumental Music Teacher; *b:* St Marys, PA; *m:* Mary Grace Hanes; *ed:* Clarion Univ (BA) Music Performance 1979; 3 Hrs Carnegie Mellun, Duquesne, IN Univ; 18 Hrs Gannon Univ; *cr:* ECCHS Dept Chair 1982-; *ai:* Concert, Marching Band Dir Chprsn; NCAA, PMEA, NEMC 1982-.

KNIGHT, RENEE GUMINS, English Teacher; *b:* Buffalo, NY; *m:* David H.; *c:* Rebecca Du, Rachel Silsdorf, Andrew, Daniel, Christopher; *ed:* Case Western Reserve Univ (BA) Eng 1965; Niagara Univ (MS) Ed 1977; 69 Post Grad Hrs in Ed & Hum; *cr:* North Park Jr HS Eng 1974-1978; Emmet Belknap Jr HS Eng 1978-1987; Lockport HS Eng 1987-95; North Park MS 1995-; *ai:* 7th Grd Class Cncl Adv; AFT 1974-; Lockport Ed Assn 1974-, Exec Comm; United Way 1992-, Bldg Coord; Honorary Life Mem Natl Congress of PTA 1995; Fredonia St Univ Pres Commendations for Excl in Tchng 1989 & 1990; Creator of Awd Winning Lit Magazine Mindworks.*

KNIGHTLY, DAVID S., Teacher & Administrator; *b:* Norway, ME; *m:* Cathy; *c:* Jimmy, Elizabeth; *ed:* Houghton Coll (BA) Bible, Span, Ed 1985; Environmental Sci CEUS; *cr:* Oxford Hills HS Sub Tchr 1985-86; Paris Chrstn Acad Sci, Span Tchr, Admin 1989-; *ai:* So Paris Bapt Church 1978-; Deacon, Tchr; Oxford Cty Conservation Tchr of Year 1994; *office:* Paris Christian Acad PO Box 282 South Paris ME 04281

KNIGHTS, CHRISTINE WOLF, English Teacher; *b:* Bronx, NY; *m:* Russell P.; *c:* Christopher, Robyn; *ed:* SUNY at Stony Brook (BA) Scdnry Ed, Eng 1986; NY Inst of Tech (MS) Training, Learning 1991; Long Island Univ, Coll of New Rochelle 45 Addl Credit Hrs; *cr:* Central Islip HS Eng Tchr 1987-89; Ward Melville HS Eng Tchr 1987; Ralph G. Reed Jr HS Eng Hnrs Tchr 1989-; SUNY Stony Brook Coll AIM Eng Tchr 1994; Long Island Inst for Prof Stud Instr Interdisciplinary Curr 1995-; *ai:* Newspaper, Lit Fac Adv; Violence Prevention Prgm Fac Adv; AFT, NCTE, Assn of Curr, Dev 1986-; Grad Flwshp Awded; Dev Courses, Designed Curr for Long Island Inst for Prof Stud; *office:* Ralph Reed Jr HS 200 Half Mile Rd Central Islip NY 11722*

KNIGHTS, CLARISSA RICHARDSON, Reading Teacher; *b:* Lewiston, ME; *m:* James C.; *c:* Tracy Ann; *ed:* Bob Jones Univ (BS) Elem Ed 1979; ME Assn of Chrstn Schls Cert 1981; *cr:* Waterloo Canadian Schls Kndgtn, 1ts Grd Tchr 1979-80; West Sumner Bapt Schl Kndgtn, 1st Grd Tchr 1980-84, Part Time Rdng Tchr 1991-; *ai:* Vol Librn; Yth Group W Nursery Vol; West Sumner Bapt Church Librn.

KNIGHTS, MAYVELLA R., Spanish Teacher; *b:* Caribow, M Joseph C.; *c:* Holly, Kristina; *ed:* Ricker Coll (BA) Span 1971; Ex Travel With Stdnts to Mexico & Spain; *cr:* Massabesic HS Spa 1982-; *ai:* NEA, MEA 1982-; *office:* Massabesic HS PO Box 500 W Waterboro ME 04087

KNIHA, CHARLES MARTIN, English Teacher; *b:* Charleroi, F Veronica; *c:* Mark, Lisa; *ed:* CA Univ of PA (BS) Scndry Eng 1963 Eng 1968; Post Grad Stud Univ of VT; *cr:* Harrold Jr HS Eng Tchr 19 Stanwood Jr HS Eng Tchr 1974-86; Westmoreland Cty Comm Part-time Eng Fac 1982-94; Hempfield Area SHS Eng Tchr 198 Girls, Boys Tennis Coach; Stu Assistance Prgm; WCCC Tennis 1987-94; Hempfield Area Ed Assn, PSEA, NEA 1963-; Amer Musicians 1963-, Bd of Trustees 1980-; Conducted Seminar, W Judged Finals North Amer Convention Intnl Trng in Comms 1994; 195 Stump Dr Belle Vernon PA 15012

KNIPE, FRANK STEPHEN, Spanish Teacher; *b:* Easton, PA; *m:* J May Evans; *c:* Brian J.; *ed:* Kutztown St Coll (BS) Scndry Ed Post-Grad Stud; *cr:* Pennridge Jr High Schls Span & Fr Tchr 19 Pennridge HS Span Tchr 1968-; *ai:* Pennridge Acad Team Coach; Na Soc Selection Comm; Rotary Stu of Month Selection Comm; NEA Bucks Cty Frgn Lang Tchrs Assn 1990-; Whos Who in Bucks C *office:* Pennridge HS 1228 N 5th St Perkasie PA 18944*

KNIPPLE, WILLIAM F.,JR., Mathematics Teacher; *b:* Albany, N Kathleen S. Davin; *c:* Taryn M., Kevin W.; *ed:* Western CT St Univ Math, Scndry Ed 1981, (MA) Math Ed 1991; *cr:* New Milford HS Tchr 1981-; *ai:* 1996 Class Adv; Asst Wrestling Coach; Mentor St Comm; NEA, CEA, NMEA 1981-; NCTM 1985-, ATOMIC 1994- Milford Comm Cncl 1993-; Best Pgm Cooperating Tchr for Stu *office:* New Milford HS 25 Sunny Valley Rd New Milford CT 0677

KNISELY, GEORGE ARTHUR, Agricultural Science Teach Bedford, PA; *m:* Debra Berger; *c:* Zakary Arthur, Jakob Atwood; *ed:* St Univ (BS) Agronomy 1981; Shippensburg Univ (MS) Geoenviron Stud 1992; Penn St Univ Tchr Cert Ag, Sci 1984; Working Toward Educl Admin; *cr:* Littlestown Area Schl Dist Agricultural Sci 1985-86; Chambersburg Area Schl Dist Ag, Sci Tchr 1986-; *ai:* St Judging Team 1994, St Agronomy Team 1995 Coach; Envirothon First Place Teams 1991-93; FFA Adv 1985-; Key Club Adv 1986-90; PVATA 1985-; Audubon Soc, Natl Wildlife 1988-; Conservation Ed Yr Awded by Keystone Chptr of the Soil & Water Conservation Soc Safe Schls Grant 1996; *office:* Chambersburg Area Sr HS 511 S Chambersburg PA 17201*

KNISELY, LINDA SUE, Chemistry & Physics Teacher; *b:* York, P Widener Univ (BS) Chem 1979; SUNY Coll at Brockport (MS) Che Ed 1987; 40 Addl Hrs; *cr:* Dansville HS Chem, Physics Tchr 1983- Charles Borromeo Schl 7th-8th Grd Math Tchr 1984-86; Chesapeak Chem, Physics, Astronomy Tchr 1986-90; Annapolis HS Chem, Pl Tchr 1990-; *ai:* MD Assn of Sci Teach 1993-; ACS 1978-; AAPT MD Space Grant Consortium SSIP Tchr; GLOBE Tchr; Sci, Math & Grad MD's Governor's Acad; *office:* Annapolis Sr HS 2700 Riv Annapolis MD 21401

KNISKERN, DONALD EUGENE, Mathematics Teacher Susquehanna, PA; *m:* Yvonne; *ed:* SUC at Brockport (BS) Math SUNY at Binghamton 30 Grad Hrs; *cr:* Hancock Cntrl Schl Math 1971-80; Windsor Cntrl Schl Math Tchr 1980-; *ai:* Golf Coach; Wi Tchrs Assn 1980-, Chief Negotiator; *home:* 569 Kent St Windsor NY 1

KNITTEL, BETTY TURNER, Intermediate Special Educato Roseboro, NC; *m:* John A.; *c:* John A. II; *ed:* Akron Univ (BS) Sp 1989, (MS) Mastery Tchr Regular Ed 1994; Ashland Univ 3 Sem Hr Buckeye Jr HS Learning Disabilities Tchr 1989; Liverpool Elem Learning Disabilities Tchr 1989-; *ai:* Church Confirmation Spon; Stu Adv; IAT Team; AFT 1989-; CEC 1988-, 5 Yr Awd; *office:* Liverpool Schl 6801 School St Valley City OH 44280

KNITTEL, GREGORY J., Latin, Greek & English Teacher; *b:* Cleve OH; *m:* Catherine Ann Lanning; *c:* Matthew, Mary, Peter; *ed:* John C Univ (BA) Philosophy 1971; Univ of CA at Santa Barbara (MA) Cla 1974; Kent St Univ (PHD) Ed 1991; *cr:* Bishop Garcia Diego HS 1973-74; St Ignatius HS Tchr, Coach & Cnslr 1974-; *ai:* Cnslr; Tchr Comm; ASCD 1985-; CAMWS 1975-; OCC 1975-, Hildesheim Vase 1986-87; Greater Cleveland Soccer Coaches Assn 1976-90, Sec & 1983-84, Coach of Yr Awd 1980, 1993; Coach of the Yr 1980, 1993; of the Yr 1990; *office:* Saint Ignatius H S 1911 W 30th St Clevelan 44113

KNITTEL, MARY JO,OP, Pastoral Associate; *b:* Cleveland, OH; *ed:* Dominican Coll (BA) Chem 1961; Univ of Notre Dame (MS) Physics Jesuit Schl of Theology Cert Spirituality 1993; *cr:* Watterson HS Phy Chem, Drama Tchr 1969-74; Dominican Acad Sci Dept Chprsn 197 St Andrew the Apostle Pastoral Assoc Liturgy 1994-; *ai:* Liturgy, M St Vincent de Paul Soc; RCIA Dir; Chamber Chorus of New York; A 1967-; NSF Grant; *office:* St Andrew the Apostle 6713 Ridge Brooklyn NY 11220

KNOBLE, E. LYNN LANIER, Vocal Music Director; *b:* Gallipolis, *m:* Ronald L.; *c:* Andrew; *ed:* OH Northern Univ (BS) Music Working Toward ME Univ of Rio Grande; Post Grad PA St Univ, Ba Univ; *cr:* Wapakoneta City Schls Vocal Music Tchr 1970-77; Ada HS V Music Dir 1978-; *ai:* Var Singers Show Choir, Musical Dir; OMEA 1 25 Yr Awd; MENC 1970-; Martha Holden Jennings Scholar; Exempla HS Dir; *office:* Ada HS 435 Grand St Ada OH 45810

KNOBLE, PATRICK MICHAEL, Agriscience Instructor; *b:* Obe OH; *ed:* OH St Univ (BS) Agricultural Ed 1994; Grad Credit Agricultural Ed; *cr:* Graham Local Schls Agriscience Instr 1994-; *ai:* A Graham FFA Chptr Adv; OVATA, NVATA, OVA, AVA 1994-; *off* Graham HS 7800 Rt 36 Saint Paris OH 43072

KNODEL, JOHN J.,JR., Mathematics Teacher & Coach; *b:* Newark, *ed:* Glassboro St Coll (BA) Math Ed 1975; Cntrl MI Univ (MA) Bus A 1981; Attnd Kean Coll, Montclair St Coll, Jersey City St Coll, Will Patterson St Coll, NC Univ; *cr:* Washington Twp HS Tchr, Adv 1975 Chatham HS Tchr 1977; Middletown HS South Tchr, Coach, Adv 19 Red Bank Reg HS Summer Schl Tchr 1985; *ai:* Golf, Soccer, Boys & C Soccer & Swimming Coach; Schl Pictures, Soph Class Fundraiser, Club Adv; St Golf Tournament Dir; NEA, NJEA, Monmouth Cty Ed A Middletown Twp Ed Assn 1977-; Shore Conf Golf Comm 1990-, Advy Pritsch Schlsp Fund 1991-, Founder, Dir; Asbury Park Press, Shore C 1987-, Golf Comms; Former Mem Eatontown Bd of Ed Chprsn Comms; Golf Coach Stu Exch Prgm; Newspaper Writer; 1991 Golf Coach of *office:* Middletown HS South 501 Nut Swamp Rd Middletown NJ 077

KNOLL, SUSAN MARIE, Psychology & History Teacher; *b:* Red B NJ; *m:* Raymond G Korver; *c:* David C. Knoll Korver; *ed:* Middleburg C (BA) Psych & His 1974; Fairleigh Dickinson Univ (MA) Clinical Ps 1980; Seton Hall Univ Eds Family & Marriage Therapy; St of NJ C Alcoholism Cnslr 1986; *cr:* Morris Hills HS Tchr 1974-79, Tchr 1980- Substance Abuse Cnslr 1987-92, Tchr 1992-; FDU Cnslr Ctr for Wo 1979-80; Sussex Cty Coll Instr 1990-; *ai:* Fac Advy Comm; NJEA & N

, VP 1982-84; Morris Hills Tchr of Yr 1987; *office:* Morris Hills Regl 20 W Main St Rockaway NJ 07866

TT, MARK A., Counselor & Business Teacher; *b:* Lima, OH; *m:* Jo Beining; *ed:* Defiance Coll (BS) Comp Bus Ed 1979; Univ of on (MS) Schl Cnslng 1988; 9 Addl Post Grad Hrs; Univ of Toledo 2 Sports Med; *cr:* Ottoville Local HS Bus Tchr 1979-, Var Bsbl Coach -85, Var Bsktbl Coach 1985-88, Cnslr 1987-; *ai:* Testing, EMIS Coord; , NEA 1979-; OLEA 1979-, Pres 1991, Uniserve Chprsn 1994-; mbus Grove Eagles, Ottawa Sons of Amer Legion 1982-; Ottoville 1983-; *office:* Ottoville Local HS 580 W 3rd St PO Box 248 Ottoville 45876

TT, PATRICIA C., Art Teacher; *b:* Ambler PA ; *ed:* Pratt Inst (BFA) Arts, Art Ed 1973; Beaver Coll at Glenside Working Towards Masters m; *cr:* Free-Lance Artist 1975-85; Sure-Fit Products Inc Product Dev, e Furnishings 1986-89; Quakertown Schl Dist Art Tchr 1989-91; ridge Schl Dist Art Tchr 1992-; *ai:* Lit, Art Magazine Stu Publication ; Art Co-Dept Coord; NAEA 1989-; *office:* Pennridge HS 1228 N 5th rkasie PA 18944

TT, SUZANNE THERESA, MS Language Arts Teacher; *b:* Delphos, *m:* Timothy Eugene; *c:* Alan Timothy, Michael John; *ed:* Saint Francis (BS) 1st-8th Grd Elem Ed 1972; Dayton Univ (MS) Elem Admin 1978; aint Joseph Elem Tchr 1972-73; Saint Clement Elem Tchr 1973-76; Marys Elem Tchr 1976-79; Leipsic Pub Elem Admin Summer -80; Miller City-New Cleaveland Elem & MS Tchr 1979-; *ai:* Delta a Gamma 1992-; 4-H Adv 5 Yrs; Bible Schl Coord; Saint Anthonys ch Eucharistic Minister, Schl Advy Bd; Putnam Cty Curr Comm; Tchr ce Awds Comm; Sci Fair Judge at Cty, Dist & St Levels; *office:* Miller -New Cleveland Schl Box 38 Miller City OH 45864*

OTTS MOYER, EDITH CLAUDE, Math Specialist; *b:* Baltimore, *m:* Thomas Jerome; *c:* Oliver Knotts Jr., Olin Knotts, Thomas M.; *ed:* of DE (BSED) Elem Ed 1976; Cheyney Univ (MED) Admin, Elem Ed ervision 1982; 12 Hrs Cnslng; 18 Hrs Cmptr Sci; 12 Hrs Math Classes; Drew Pyle Elem Schl Tchr 1977-91; Bancroft Schl Math Specialists -; Schlsp Galore Owner, CEO 1995-; Univ of DE Dir NCAA, Natl h Sports Summer Prgm 1996-; *ai:* Yrbk, Stu Cncl, Schl Store Adv; a Sigma Theta 1976-, Treas, Asst Rec Sec, Cert of Svc; Jack and Jill mer 1984-; NCTM 1988-; NEA 1977-; Wilm Park, Rec 1989-, Bd ; Foster Care Review Bd 1992-; Schl, Local Newspaper Articles; 's Who Among Stdnts in Coll, Univ 1981.

OWLES, CAROLYN BIRCH, Mathematics Teacher; *b:* Washington, *m:* Kenneth Alward Jr.; *c:* LInda Knowles Wright, Ken III, Karyn, ey; *ed:* Coll of William & Mary (BS) Math 1963; Univ of VA (MED) h Ed 1973; *cr:* Warwick HS Math Tchr 1967-68; Henley Jr HS Math 1970; Jack Iouett Jr HS Math Tchr 1970-71, 1972-75; Southern Sr HS h Tchr 1981-; *ai:* Field Hockey Head Coach; Class 97 Spon; NHS, sp Comms; NCTM, MCTM 1983-; TAAAC 1981-; USDHA 1989-; HSFHCA 1991-, Sec; Field Hockey Coach of Yr 1988; *office:* Southern IS 4400 Solomons Island Rd Harwood MD 20776

OWLES, HARVARD VAUGHAN, English Teacher; *b:* Newport, ME; Tufts Univ (BA) Eng 1958; Duke Univ (MA) Eng 1965; Attnd Columbia v 1978-79; *cr:* Loomis Chaffee Schl Eng Tchr 1962-74; Phillips Exeter d Eng Tchr 1974-; *ai:* Acad Newspaper Adv; NCTE 1965-; MLA 1987-; e Ldr; Advanced Placement Reader; Klingenstein Fellowship; NEH inars; *office:* Phillps Exeter Acad 20 Main St. MSC 1144 Exeter NH 33

OWLTON, REGINA PUSTIE, Science Department Coordinator; *b:* erside, NJ; *m:* Reginald K.; *c:* Justin, Megan; *ed:* St Joseph's Univ (BS) 1975, (MS) Ed 1992; *cr:* Inst for Cancer Rsrch Rsrch Asst 1975-81; ner Judge HS Bio Stu Tchr 1991; Little Flower Cath HS Bio, Phys Sci r 1991-93; Bishop Eustace Prep Schl Sci Dept Coord 1993-; *ai:* Acad l; Strategic Planning Comm; NABT 1992-; NSTA 1995-; Articles Pub 7-79; *office:* Bishop Eustace Prep Sch 5552 Marlton Pike Pennsauken 08109*

OX, ANN MANSFIELD, Special Education Teacher; *b:* Beverly, MA; Lyndon St Coll (BS) Spec Ed K-12, Elem Ed K-6 1987; Univ of VT d Courses; Enrolled Masters Prgm Trinity Coll; *ai:* Admin, Stu Support ms; CEC 1987-; ASCD 1995-; St Andrews Episcopal Church 1989-, Jr rden; VT Children's Theater 1989-, Dir Asst; *home:* PO Box 116 Lyndon 05849

OX, BARBARA A., Mathematics Teacher; *b:* Laurinburg, NC; *c:* Karl, en G., Sephanie O.; *ed:* Shaw Univ (BS) Math 1965; Univ of Dist of umbia (MA) Admin & Supervision 1983; Attnd George Washington v, Georgetown Univ; *cr:* Eastern Sr HS Math Tchr 1969-72; Kelley ler Jr HS Math Tchr 1972-73; Francis Jr HS Math Tchr 1973-; *ai:* Natl Hnr Soc, Math Club Spon; AFT 1969-; NCTM 1983-; Delta Sigma Theta 2-; *office:* Francis Jr HS 24th & N Street NW Washington DC 20037

OX, DENISE SCHULTE, Associate Prof of Life Sci; *b:* Toledo, OH; John P.; *ed:* Bowling Green St Univ (BS) Scndry Ed, Bio 1975, (MS) 1979; *cr:* Owens Comm Coll Assoc Prof 1979-; *office:* Owens Comm l 30335 Oregon Rd Box 10000 Toledo OH 43699

OX, PEGGY LABER, First Grade Teacher; *b:* Massillon, OH; *m:* ctor Nelson; *c:* Amy Marie Creel; *ed:* Ashland Univ (BS) Elem Ed 1970, ED) Rdng Supervision 1984; 30 Post Grad Hrs Ashland Univ, Bowling een St Univ, Drake Univ; *cr:* Whetstone Elem Schl Kndgtn-First Grd nr 1970-; *ai:* Dept Chprsn 1990-92; Curr Comms; Right-to-Read Week air; Tchr Mentoring; Presenter North Cntrl OH Tchrs Rdng Conf, IRS, hland Univ Rdng Conf; NEA 1970-; CCIRA 1970-, Treas; Lib Friends 90-; Meth Church 1970-, Jr Church Tchr, Choir, Ed Commission; Martha lden Jennings Scholar 1984; Who's Who in Young Women in Amer 1984; hr of Yr 1995; Nom Martha Holden Jennings Master Tchr 1995; *office:* hetstone Elem Schl 4063 Monnett Chapel Rd Bucyrus OH 44820*

NUPP, DAVID MURRAY, Assoc Prof Environmental Prgm; *b:* Sharon, ; *m:* Candice I.; *c:* Tawnya, Michael; *ed:* Univ of WV (BS) Forestry 70; Univ of ME (MS) Wildlife Mgmt 1974; *cr:* Unity Coll Instr & Assoc of 1972-; *ai:* ME Chptr of Wildlife Soc 1975-; Monroe Lions Club 86-; Winterport Conservation Comm 1989-, Chm; Certfd Wildlife ologist; Licensed Prof Forester; *office:* Unity Coll Quaker Hill Rd Unity E 04988

NUPP, DOROTHY CASTNER, First Grade Teacher; *b:* West iddlesex, PA; *m:* Allan H.; *c:* Debbie Shields, Dorothy, Jim; *ed:* oungstown St (BS) Elem Ed 1960, (MS) Rdng 1978; Kent St Cadet Elem 1958; Post Grad Credits Ashland Coll 21, Chapman Coll 1, Drake Univ 3 Addl Post Grad Credits; *cr:* Hubbard Roosevelt Elem 2nd Grd Tchr 58-62, 1964-70, 1st Grd Tchr 1970-; *ai:* NEA, OH Ed Assn 1958-; ubbard Ed Assn 1958-, Treas; Delta KappaGamma 1979-, Recording Sec; utstanding Elem Tchr of Amer 1975; *office:* Hubbard Roosevelt Elem hl 110 Orchard Ave Hubbard OH 44425

NUTH, DIANA G., French Teacher; *b:* Dallas, TX; *m:* Robert H.; *ed:* TX arstn Univ (MAT) Fr 1972; Math Cert 24 Hrs Math; Gen Ed 36 Post Grad rs; *cr:* Castleberry HS Fr, Eng, Geog Tchr 1965-77; Tarrant Cty Jr Coll Tchr 1976-77; Warrensville HS Eng Tchr 1977-81; Newbury HS Eng chr 1981-82; West Geauga MS Fr Tchr 1982-; *ai:* Frng Lang Dept Chm; ance Stu Trips Spon; Organize, Dir Frng Lang Week Act Yearly; NEA, H Ed Assn 1977-; OFLA 1982-; ACTFL 1995-; *office:* West Geauga MS 611 Cedar Rd Chesterland OH 44026

KNUTH, SANDRA RAE, Tchr of Disabilities Behavior; *b:* Fairview, OH; *ed:* Heidelberg Coll (BA) Hlth, PE, Recreation 1972; IN Univ (MS) Outdoor Ed Admin 1976; OH Univ Specific Learning Disibilities 12 Hrs; Lee Canter Stud 6 Hrs; Low Initiative, Team Challence Trng; *cr:* Newark Pub Schls K-6 Grd PE Tchr 1972-76; Heart of OH Girl Scouts Outdoor Prgm Dir 1976-79; River View Local Schls 9-12 Grd SLD, BD Tchr 1980-; *ai:* Outdoor Ed Cnslrs Training; 6th Grd Outdoor Acad Prgm Dir; Riverview Tchrs Assn 1980-; Martha Holden Jennings Scholar 1989-90; East Cntrl OH Spec Ed RegnlResource Ctr Outstdng Edctr Awd 1990; Raised Money for DH, SLD Stdnts for Disney World 1990, 1992; *home:* 25580 Twp Rd 111 Warsaw OH 43844

KOBA, STANLEY JOSEPH, Social Studies Teacher; *b:* Middletown, CT; *m:* Linda Gail Herbster; *c:* Stacey, Lauren, Nancy, Matthew; *ed:* Cntrl CT St Univ (BS) His 1973; GA Court Coll (MA) Supervision 1984; *cr:* Freehold Boro HS Soc Stud Tchr, Curr Designer 1973-; *ai:* Jr Class Adv; Hum Relations Dir Coord; NEA 1973-; Natl Conf Chrstns & Jews; *office:* Freehold Boro HS Robertsville Rd Freehold NJ 07728*

KOBASA, GREGORY, Fifth Grade Teacher; *b:* Lansdale, PA; *m:* Dorothy Marie Hackman; *c:* Kristin, Kevin, Keath; *ed:* DE St Coll (BS) Elem Ed 1974; Post Grad at Penn St, Villanova, St Josephs; Masters Equivalency; 30 Addl Hrs; *cr:* York Avenue Elem Schl 4th-6th Grd Tchr 1974-; *ai:* Schl Store Adv; Sci Comm; Merck Inst Sci Ed; NPEA, PSEA, NEA 1974-; Norgwyn Bsbl Inc 1995-, Sec; Lansdale Jaycees Outstdng Young Edctr; *office:* York Avenue Elem Schl 700 York Ave Lansdale PA 19446*

KOBBE, NANCY BOLT, Sixth Grade Teacher; *b:* Binghamton, NY; *c:* Sean, Ryan; *ed:* SUNY Coll at Cortland (BA) Elem Ed 1975; Elmira Coll (MS) Ed 1979; *cr:* Frank Pierce Elem Schl 2nd-3rd Grd Tchr 1976; Erwin Vly Elem Schl 5th Grd Tchr 1977-78; Lindley Presho Elem Schl 2nd, 5th Grd Tchr 1978-85; Corning Free Acad MS 6th Grd Tchr 1985-; *ai:* NYSUT, AFT 1975-; *home:* 48 Forest Dr Painted Post NY 14870

KOBE, ALEXANDER WILLIAM, Biology Teacher; *b:* Manhatton, NY; *m:* Judith Royce; *c:* Katie Lynn, Joshua Alexander; *ed:* Plymouth St Coll of UNH (BA) Bio 1977; Dartmouth Coll (MALS) Sci 1986; DNA Sci Cert; *cr:* Lebaron HS Bio Tchr 1978-79; Orford HS Bio, Physics, Earth Sci & Phys Sci Tchr 1979-80; Hartford HS Physics Tchr 1980-85, Bio Tchr 1980-; *ai:* Drugs & Alcohol; NEA 1980-; NABT 1988-; *office:* Hartford HS 1 Highland Ave White River Juncti VT 05001

KOBERNA, CHARLENE, 8th Grade Amer History Tchr; *b:* New Bedford, MA; *m:* Richard J.; *c:* Adam, Benjamin; *ed:* Miami Univ (BSEd) His, Govt, Speech & Drama 1962-66; Kent St Univ (MEd) MS Curr & Instr 1991; Univ of Akron Eng & Learning Disabilities Cert; 30 Hrs Beyond Masters; *cr:* Kenston MS 7th Grd Lang Arts 1967-72; Hudson MS Amer 8th Grd His & Eng 1983-; *ai:* 8th Grd Amer His Dept Chpsn; Adv & Cooperative Appraisal Revision Comms; Summit Cty Tech Acad; NEA 1983-; OEA 1983-; Phi Delta Kappa 1986-; OH MS Assn 1989-; OH Fed of Bus & Prof Women Schlsp 1985; Distngd Tchr Awd 1991; *office:* Hudson MS 77 N Oviatt St Hudson OH 44236

KOBERT, LINDA W., Math Teacher; *b:* Latrobe, PA; *m:* Don; *c:* Mark, Beth; *ed:* Clarion Univ (BS) Math 1969; Addl Hrs Math Ed Miami Univ; *cr:* Mentor Tchr 1993; Stu Tchr Supvr 1990-94; Longaberger Branch Adv 1995; *ai:* Future Edctr Adv; NCTM; *office:* Lakota HS 5050 Tylersville Rd West Chester OH 45069

KOBIK, HENRY NELS, World History Teacher; *b:* New Brunswick, NJ; *ed:* Montclair St Coll (BA) His 1991; Rowan Coll 15 Credit Hrs Schl Admin; *cr:* Perryville MS US His & Geog Tchr 1991-92; Delsea Rgnl HS World His Tchr 1992-; *ai:* Asst Boys Soccer, Asst Golf & Diving Coach; Ftbl Team Statistician; Peer Mediator; Natural Helpers Pgm; NEA 1991-; NJEA 1992-; Gloucester Co Ed Assn 1992-; NCSS 1991-; NJ Cncl for Soc Stud 1995-; *office:* Delsea Regional HS Blackwoodtown Rd Franklinville NJ 08322

KOBLICK, SANDRA POMERANTZ, Fifth Grade Teacher; *b:* New York, NY; *m:* Stephan K.; *c:* Neil, Keith; *ed:* Hunter Coll (BA) Music 1963; Queens Coll (MS) Elem Ed 1976; Brooklyn Coll (SAS) Supervision & Admin 1994; attnd Fordham Univ Practicum Metropolitian Opera Course 3 Addl Credits, Kingsborough Comm Coll Ctr for Tchr Stud- Sci, Microcomputer, Span 12 Addl Credits; *cr:* Berwyn Hghts Schl Sixth Grd Tchr 1964-66; Grissom Elem Schl Third & Fifth Grd Tchr 1966-69; Yeshiva Second Grd Tchr 1973-76; PS 222 & 195 Music Specialist 1981-84; PS 222 Fifth Grd Tchr 1984-; *ai:* Teach Writing in Kingsborough Comm Coll Evenings; Writing Multicultural Curr part of Fed Magnet Prgm in Schls; AFT 1984-; Kappa Delta Pi 1994-; Cert Awded for Participants in Project True; McGraw Hill Book Co Achvmt Awd for Class Particpant 1985; Participant of the Homeless Cert of Appreciation for Class Poject 1989; *office:* P S 222 3301 Quentin Rd Brooklyn NY 11234*

KOBRYN, PAULA, Special Education Teacher; *b:* Bayonne, NJ; *c:* Donna Shannon, Pauline Dyletczuk; *ed:* Jersey City St Coll (BA) Spec Ed 1976, (MA) Spec Ed 1982; Nursery Schl Cert 1981; *cr:* Jersey City Child Dev Ctrs Inc; Head Start Tchr 1977-78; Mt Carmel Guild Tchr 1978-80; Bayonne Bd of Ed Tchr 1980-; *ai:* NJEA 1980-; Hudson Cty Tchrs Recognition 1995.*

KOBUS, STEVEN ALBERT, Algebra & Geometry Teacher; *b:* Pittsburgh, PA; *m:* Gloria Pugh; *c:* Benjamin, Samantha, Allyson; *ed:* Univ of Akron (BA) Scndry Ed 1986, (MA) Scndry Ed 1993; *cr:* OH Army Natl Guard Turbine Engine Mechanic 1981-; Windham HS Math Tchr 1986-; *ai:* Var Track & Frosh Ftbl Coach; Windham Tchrs Assn, OH Cncl Tchrs of Math 1986-; Liquid Crystal Symposium at Kent St Univ; Pub Article on World Wide Web on Applications of Liquid Crystals in Classroom; *office:* Windham HS 9530 Bauer Ave Windham OH 44288

KOCH, BARBARA BORGE, High School English Teacher; *b:* Portland, ME; *m:* Wayne M.; *c:* William, Michael; *ed:* Gordon Coll (BA) Eng 1968; Attnd Pepperdine Univ, Salem St Univ; *cr:* Chelmsford HS 9th Grd Eng Tchr 1968-74; Eastern HS 10th-11th Grd Eng Tchr 1990-; *ai:* AP Tchrs Comm Chprsn; NCTE 1993-; NEA, EEA 1990-; Amer Legion Auxil 1946-65; Presbyn Church 1983-, Church Schl Supt; *office:* Eastern HS Laurel Oak Rd Voorhees NJ 08043*

KOCH, CARRIE KIMMEL, Teacher of the Gifted; *b:* Philadelphia, PA; *m:* Richard Wesley; *c:* Max Richard; *ed:* Pennsylvania St Univ (BA) Phnilosophy 1979; Kutztown Univ (MeD) Scndry Curr & Instruction 1992; Kutztown Univ Elem Tchr Cert 1982; *cr:* Williams Valley Schl Dist Tchr 1985-; *ai:* Stu Cncl & Enrichment Club Adv; NEA, PSEA & Williams Valley EA 1985-; *office:* Williams Valley Jr Sr HS Rt 209 Tower City PA 17980

KOCH, CHRISTINE PFENNIG, Third Grade Teacher; *b:* Reading, PA; *c:* Lindsay K.; *ed:* Millersville St Coll (BS) Elem Ed 1970, (MED) Elem Ed 1976; 6 Credits Carlow Coll; *cr:* Downingtown Area Schl Dist 6th Grd Tchr 1970; Twin Vly Schl Dist 2nd-4th, 6th Grd Tchr 1971-; *ai:* 3-5 Grd Shell Club Spon; NEA, PSEA 1970-; Twin Vly Ed Assn 1971-, Neg Team, Bldg Rep; Friends of Chester Co Lib 1993-; First United Meth Church 1984-, Bell Choir, Chancel Choir, Sub Sunday Schl Tchr, Lay Reader; Conchologists of Amer 1992-; Flwshp to Penn St Univ for Spec Ed 1970; *office:* Twin Valley Elem Ctr RR 3 Box 54 Elverson PA 19520

KOCH, CYNTHIA JEAN, Instrumental Music Teacher; *b:* Holyoke, MA; *ed:* Lowell St (BA) Music Ed 1972; Univ of MA (MA) Music Ed 1986; 15 Credit Hrs Beyond Masters; *cr:* Medford Pub Schls Instrumental Music Tchr 1968-72; Littleton Gen Choral & Instrumental Music Tchr 1972-82; Ludlow Pub Schls HS Beginners Instrumental Music Tchr 1986-; *ai:* Jazz Ensemble; Marching Band; Small Ensembles; Ski Club; NEA, MTA 1972-; MMEA, MENC 1972-; WMEA 1975-76, Pres; MMEA 1992-, Band Mgr.

KOCH, DEBORAH DALESSIO, Fifth Grade Teacher; *b:* Brooklyn, NY; *m:* George J.; *c:* Kristina; *ed:* St Univ of NY at Stony Brook (BA) Ed, Earth & Space Sci 1974; Adelphi Univ (MS) Spec Ed 1976; Addl 78 Credits Both Grad & Inservice Beyond Masters; *cr:* Cayuga Art, Music, PE & Lib Ancillary Tchr 1974-76, 1st Grd Tchr 1976-88, 5th Grd Tchr 1988-93, 1st Grd Tchr 1993-94, 5th Grd Tchr 1995-; *ai:* Elem Girls Early Morning PE & Sports Coach; Sci Comm- Revamped Elem Sci for Dist; SCTA, AFT, NYSUT 1974-; Sachem Spiked Shoe Club 1993-, Historian; Created Read Across the USA Prgm for 1st & 2nd Grd Stdnts; Articles Pub in Frank Schaeffers Schooldays; Wrote Ecology-Recycling Unit for 5th Grd that Entire Dist Uses; Created, Pub & Edited Video Yrbk for Girls Cross Cntry & Winter & Spring Track & Field Teams; *office:* Cayuga Elem Schl 865 Hawkins Ave Lake Grove NY 11755*

KOCH, GARRY R., History Teacher; *b:* Allentown, PA; *ed:* Univ of Scranton (BA) Philosophy 1980; Mary Immaculate Seminary (MA) Theology 1982; Grad Theological Union (PHD) Theology 1992; *cr:* Chrstn Brothers Acad Tchr 1982-; *ai:* NHS Adv; Acad Team Coach; Intramural Sports Prgm Dir; Biblical Archaeological Soc 1992-; *office:* Christian Brothers Acad 850 Newman Springs Rd Lincroft NJ 07738

KOCH, LYNN ARTHUR, Vocal Music Teacher; *b:* Springville, NY; *c:* Gillian, Devon; *ed:* St Univ Coll at Potsdam (BM) Music Ed 1976; Westminster Choir Coll (MM) Music Ed 1981; *cr:* Westminster Choir Coll Music Theory Grad Asst 1979-81; Trenton City Schls Elem Vocal Music Tchr 1982-87; Cincinnatus Cntrl Schl Elem & HS Vocal Music Tchr 1987-; *ai:* Pvt Music Instruction; NEA 1982-; MENC 1979-; Alpha Psi Omega 1991-; Mc Grawville Bapt Church 1991-, Organist, Choir Dir; Folk Singer, Guitarist 1983-; Choosing and Using Folk Songs with Children Pub 1987; Folk Songs of Upstate NY Pub 1990; Recording of The Fox, Old Blue and Dinosaurs Too 1994; *home:* 13 Elm St # 684 Mc Graw NY 13101

KOCH, MADELYN ANN, HS Math & Computer Teacher; *b:* Greensburg, PA; *m:* Dr John A.; *c:* Michael, Matthew; *ed:* Bucknell Univ (BS) Math 1970; Master Equivalency from St of PA 1992; *cr:* Champaign Schl Dist Jr High Math Tchr 1970-76; Wilkes Univ Adjunct Prof & Math Dept 1983-88; Lake Lehman Schl Dist HS Math & Cmptr Tchr 1988-; *ai:* NHS Adv; NEA & PSEA 1989-; Amer Diabetes Assn 1983-, Bd Mem; Newcomers Club 1977-87, Pres; Natl Sci Fnd Summer Grants 1971-72; *office:* Lake Lehman HS PO Box 38 Lehman PA 18627

KOCH, NANCY JOY, Vocal Music Tchr & Choral Dir; *b:* Wellsboro, PA; *ed:* Mansfield St Coll (BS) Music Ed 1962; Trenton St Coll (MA) Voice 1972; 45 Addl Hrs Penn St Univ; 9 Grad Credits MI Univ 1963; Oberlin Conservatory Rockefeller Fnd Grant 1967; *cr:* E Stroudsburg Jr Sr HS Music Tchr, Choral Dir 1962-68; Mc Donald Elem Schl Music Tchr, Choral Dir 1968-72; Log Coll Jr HS Music Tchr, Choral Dir 1972-89, Dept Chair 1987-92; Warminster Presby Church Choir Dir 1987-92; Log Coll MS Music Tchr, Choral Dir, 6th-8th Grd Pvt Voice Coach 1989-; *ai:* 6th Grd Chorus, 7th-8th Grd Chorus, Musical, Vocal Ensemble Dir; Cty Chorus; BCMEA 1972-, Treas 1978-88; NEA, PSEA, PMEA, MENC 1962-; Vocal Ensemble Music in Park 1980-95, Competition 1st Place; Comm Svc YMCA 1981-, Comm Svc Awd; Music in Parks 1989, 1991-94-, Overall Oustdng Trophy; Who's Who in Amer Ed 1996- Ed; Rockefeller Fnd Grant Flwshp Oberlin Conservatory, Soprano Soloist Bach Cantate Robert Fountain Dir 1967; Soprano Soloist Verdi Requiem Trenton St Coll 1972; 1st Place Awd Vocal Ensemble Music in Parks Competitions 1980-95; Soprano Soloist Warminster Symphony Centennial SD Tchr of Yr Achvmt Awd 1992; PMEA Regnl II Choris Host Dir 1968; *office:* Log College MS 730 Norristown Rd Warminster PA 18974*

KOCH, PHILIP FREDERICK, Professor of Fine Arts; *b:* Rochester, NY; *m:* Alice Miriam Spitzer; *c:* Susan Gail; *ed:* Oberlin Coll (BA) Studio Art 1970; IN Coll (MFA) Painting 1972; Art Stdnts League of NY 1968-69; *cr:* Central WA St Univ Painting Instr 1972-73; MD Inst Coll of Art Fine Arts Prof, Painting, Drawing; *ai:* Exhibitions Comm Chair 1990-95; Univ of MD 1993-, Advy Bd, Co-Chair; Baltimore Museum of Art Affilliates 1994-; Solo Painting Exhibitions Saginaw Art Museum 1996, Washington Cty Museum of Fine Arts 1995, Midwest Museum of Amer Art 1995, Butler Inst of Amer Art 1995, Sheldon Swope Art Museum 1995, Cedar Rapids Art Museum 1994; *office:* MD Inst Coll Of Art 1300 W Mount Royal Ave Baltimore MD 21217

KOCHANSKI, DENISE TURCOTTE, Junior HS Teacher; *b:* Fall River, MA; *m:* John L.; *c:* Christopher J., Sarah E.; *ed:* Bridgewater St Coll (BA) K-8th Grd Elem Ed 1971; Buzzards Bay Rim Project UMASS at Dartmouth; *cr:* St John the Evangelist Schl Tchr 1973-74; St Anne Schl Permanent Sub Tchr 1980; Dominican Acad First Grd Tchr 1980-86, Jr HS Tchr 1986-; *ai:* Sci Fair Coord; Natl Jr Hnr Soc Adv; Sci & Soc Stud Chprsn; Sci Lead Tchr; NCEA 1980-; ASCD 1992-; NASAA 1993-; NSTA 1996; Nom Presidential Awd for Excl in Sci & Math Tchng; *office:* Dominican Acad 37 Park St Fall River MA 02721

KOCHANSKI, PATRICIA GALE, Counselor; *b:* Hopewell, VA; *ed:* Trenton St Coll (BS) Early Chldhd & Elem Ed 1978, (MA) Counseling & Stu Prsnl Svcs 1987; 9 Hrs Post Grad Credits; *ai:* Discipline, Scheduling & Curr Dev Comms; ASCA 1984-; NEA, NJEA, BCEA 1979-; MLEA 1979-, Rep; NJ Schl Cncl Assn 1984-, Pres Elect, Past Pres; BCSCA 1984-, Cty Pres, Pres Elect, Cty Cnslr of Yr; NMSA 1994-; Amer Diabetes Assn 1995-; Presenter Wkshps, Seminars, Loss, Moving, Stress; Amer Schl Cncl Assn Conf Albquerque, Pittsburgh; Self-Esteem NJ Schl Cncl Assn Conf Trenton Rider Univ; Operation Desert Storm Ft Dix NJ; *home:* 19 Quail Hollow Dr Mount Holly NJ 08060

KOCHANSKY, MARY COOPER, Chemistry Teacher; *b:* Kingstree, SC; *m:* Jan; *c:* Amanda, Justina; *ed:* Univ of SC (BS) Chem 1965; Univ of CO (PHD) Organic Chem 1991; *cr:* Suitland HS Chem Tchr 1989-; *ai:* ACS 1991-, Editorial Advy Bd for ChemCom III, Soc Comm Ed; NSTA 1989-; MAST 1991-; *office:* Suitland HS 5200 Silver Hill Rd Forestville MD 20747

KOCHENOUR, CHRIS, High School Chemistry Teacher; *b:* Newton, NJ; *m:* Mary E. Remillard; *c:* Sky, Cale; *ed:* North Adams St Coll (BA) Bio 1975, (MED) Admin 1985; 9 Credit Hrs Admin; *cr:* Housatonic Vly Regnl HS Sci Tchr 1976-79; Mt Anthony Union HS Chem Tchr 1979-; *ai:* Former Soccer Referee; Former Track Ofcl; Amateur Radio Adv; NHS Induction Speaker 1982; Grad Speaker 1986 & 1992; Selected as Most Influential Tchr By a Presidential Scholar 1989; Yrbk Dedication 1994; *home:* RR 2 Box 158 Pownal VT 05261

KOCHENOUR, LEE W., First Grade Teacher; *b:* North Adams, MA; *m:* Pamela Terry; *c:* Shannon, Jocelyn, Nathaniel; *ed:* North Adams St Coll Ed (BS) 1972, (MS) 1977; *cr:* New Lebanon Cntrl 1st, 6th Grd Tchr 1972-; *ai:* Girls Var Soccer Coach 1994-; Past Boys Var Soccer 1986-93, JV Soccer 1972-82 Coach; NYSUT 1972-; NSCAA 1988-; Girls Soccer Coach NY St Champions Class D 1994; *office:* Walter B Howard Elem Schl PO Box 38 Rt 20 West Lebanon NY 12195

KOCHENSPARGER, JONATHAN WAYNE, Social Studies Teacher; *b:* New Lexington, OH; *m:* Kellie Ann Burnett; *c:* Anthony, Rachel; *ed:* Wright St Univ (BSEd) Scndry Comprehensive Soc Stud 1987, (MSEd) Cmptr Ed Classroom Tchr 1995; *cr:* Wright St Univ Stu Lib 1982-87, Resident Asst 1984-86; Beavercreek Local Schls Tchr 1987-; *ai:* Class 1996 Fac Adv; Fall Play Tech Dir; Winter Play Dir & Tech Dir; Spring

Musical Tech Dir; NEA, OEA 1988-, Local Treas, Outstanding Treas; Ascension Church 1994-, Lector; *office:* Beavercreek HS 2660 Dayton Xenia Rd Beavercreek OH 45434

KOCHER, DAVID JEROME, Teacher & Science Dept Head; *b:* Canton, OH; *m:* Joan Edmundson; *c:* Kyle, Drew, Jordan, Cory; *ed:* Mt Union Coll (BS) Bio 1970; Akron Univ (MS) Scndry Ed & Bio 1981; 15 Addl Grad Hrs Beyond Masters; *cr:* Louisville HS Tchr 1970-77; Canton City Crenshaw Jr High Tchr 1977-78; Lake HS Tchr 1978-; *ai:* JV Boys Bsktbl Coach; Ticket Mgr; Sci Dept Head; SECO 1980-; NEA, OEA 1970-; Jennings Scholar; *office:* Lake HS 1025 Lake Center St Uniontown OH 44685

KOCHERT, THERESA A., French & Spanish Teacher; *b:* Chambersburg, PA; *m:* Robert C.; *c:* Laura, Keith; *ed:* Shippensburg Unvi (BS) Fr & Span 1972; 39 Credit Hrs at Millersville & Wilkes; *cr:* Central Jr HS Fr Tchr 1973-83; J Frank Faust Jr HS Fr Tchr 1973-89; Chambersburg Area Sr HS Fr Tchr 1989-, Sp Tchr 1994-; *ai:* Fr Club & Bible Stud Club Adv; NEA, PSEA & CAEA 1981-; PA St Modern Lang Assn 1989-; ACTFL & AATF 1989-; Zion Covenant Church 1980-, Sunday Schl Tchr; *office:* Chambersburg Area Sr HS 511 S 6th St Chambersburg PA 17201*

KOCHINSKI, GERALD J., Reading Specialist; *b:* Windber, PA; *m:* Dr. Veronica A. Otvos; *c:* Christine A.; *ed:* Univ of Pittsburgh (BA) Comprehensive Soc Stud 1967, (MAT) Scndry Ed 1968, (EDD) Instruction & Learning 1991; Rdng Specialist Cert 1972; Rdng Supvr Cert 1976; *cr:* Bethel Park Schl Dist Rdng Specialist 1971-; Comm Coll of Allegheny Coll Cmptr Literacy Instr 1981-84, Speed Rdng Instr 1985-; *ai:* IRA 1977-; Keystone St Rdng Assn 1977-, Regnl Dir; Three Rivers Rdng Cncl 1977-, Pres, Treas, Newsletter Ed; MS Rdng Spec Interests Group 1977-, Pres, Newsletter Ed; Disabled Reader Group 1989-, Treas; South Hills Coin Club 1980-; Dir of Federal Basic Skills Prgm Titled MICRO-READ Cmptrs & Remedial Rdng at the Scndry Level; These Worked for me ERIC; Stud of 5 Western PA Schl Dists & Their Scndry Rdng Prgms; *office:* Bethel Park Sr HS 309 Church Rd Bethel Park PA 15102

KOCHMAN, JAMES VINCENT, 7th-8th Grade Math Teacher; *b:* Staten Island, NY; *m:* Helen S.; *c:* James Jr., Brian, Chris, Linda; *ed:* Wagner Coll (BS) Ec 1964; Fairleigh Dickinson Univ (MA) Ed 1974; *cr:* Keansburg Schl System Tchr 1964-; *ai:* Bsbl, Bsktbl, Track, Bowling Coach; NEA, NJEA, MCEA 1964-; Keansburg Tchrs Assn, Former Pres; *home:* 52 Raleigh Ct Eatontown NJ 07724

KOCHMAN, JANET SMITH, English Teacher; *b:* Spangler, PA; *m:* Thomas F.; *ed:* IN Univ of PA (BS) Scndry Eng 1975, (MA) Rhetoric & Linguistics 1985; Attnd Penn St Univ, Wilson Univ, Shippensburg Univ; *cr:* Blairsville Sr High Eng Tchr & Girls BB Coach 1975-76; Purchase Line Jr-Sr High Dept Head, Eng Tchr & BB Coach 1976-87; Shippensburg Area Sr High Eng Tchr 1987-; *ai:* Bearmania Club Adv; NEA 1975-; PSEA 1975-; NCTE 1975-; SAEA 1987-; Tchr Who Made a Differnce Awd 1994.*

KOCI, ADELE KATHERINE, Fourth Grade Teacher; *b:* New York City, NY; *ed:* Fairleigh Dickinson Univ (BA) Elem Ed 1969; *cr:* Yantacaw Schl Tchr 1969-; *ai:* Grd Chprsn; NEA, NJEA, Essex Cty Ed Assn 1969-; Ed Assn of Nutley 1969-, Bldg Rep 4 Yrs.

KOCI, JAN M., 7th Grd Tchr & Sci Dept Chprsn; *b:* New York, NY; *ed:* Montclair St Coll (BA) Fine Arts Ed 1973; Fairleigh Dickinson Univ Elem Ed Cert 1978; *cr:* Bloomfield North Jr HS Art Tchr 1973-76; Washington Elem Schl Tchr 1978-81; Bloomfield Art League Art Tchr 1974-82; Bloomfield Adult Schl Art Tchr 1978-84; Good Shepherd Acad Sci, Rdng, Art Tchr 1979-; *ai:* Sci Dept Chprsn; Art Show Coord; NCEA 1979-; *office:* Good Shepherd Acad 24 Brookline Ave Nutley NJ 07110

KOCUR, EDWARD ALAN, German Teacher & Coach; *b:* Pittsburgh, PA; *m:* Adriana; *c:* Amanda, Alexa; *ed:* Duquesne Univ (BA) Jrnlsm & SP Comm 1982, (MS) Scndry Ed 1986; *cr:* Knoxville MS Tchr & Coach 1986-; *ai:* Girls Sftbl & Soccer Coach; Dir of Parent Ath Assn; Pittsburgh Fed of Tchrs & AFT 1986-; *office:* Knoxville MS 300 Charles St Pittsburgh PA 15210

KODJO, ALBERT K., Chemistry & Physics Teacher; *b:* Lome, Togo; *m:* Rema S.; *c:* Cheryl, Denise; *ed:* Seton Hall Univ (BS) Chem 1967; Univ Libre De Bruxelles (MS) Hospital Admin 1972; Pace Univ (MS) Schl Admin 1981; City Univ of NJ 24 Credits Advanced Chem, Fr, Span; St Univ of NY 12 Credits Tech, Advanced Physics; *cr:* Ecole St Martin De France Chem, Fr Tchr 1967-70; NY City Bd of Ed Chem, Physics Tchr 1972-; *ai:* Tennis Coaching; AFT, UFT 1975-; NYSABE 1978-, Presenter; Eastchester Presbyn Church 1978-, Elder; Woodrow Wilson Summer Inst of Sci Chem & Physics at Princeton Univ; *office:* Washington Irving HS 40 Irving Pl New York NY 10003*

KOEHL, RUTH ANN, HS Chem & Earth Science Tchr; *b:* Buffalo, NY; *ed:* Ursuline Coll (BS) Bio 1961; Notre Dame Univ (MS) Bio 1966; Wesleyan Univ (CAS) Geology 1973; John Carroll Univ 18 Credit Hrs; Cleveland St Univ 28 Credit Hrs; *cr:* Nazareth Acad Chem, Bio & Earth Sci Tchr 1967-79; Cuyahoga Comm Coll Part-time Geology Instr & Full-time Lab Technician 1981-92; St Joseph Acad Chem, Bio & Phys Sci Tchr 1961-67, Chem & Earth Sci Tchr 1992-; *ai:* Discipline Comm; OH Acad of Sci 1966-; Cleveland Museum of Natural His 1984-; Sci Ed Cncl of OH 1993-; Natl Sci Fnd Grant; *office:* Saint Joseph Acad 3430 Rocky River Dr Cleveland OH 44111

KOEHLER, BARBARA JEAN, Teacher of Gifted & Talented; *b:* Orange, NJ; *m:* Walter III; *c:* Tamara, Walter IV; *ed:* Georgian Court Coll (BA) Elem Ed 1976; Georgian Court Coll (MA) Rdng 1983; *cr:* Silver Bay Elem 3rd Grd Tchr 1976-90, Tchr for Gifted & Talented 1990-; *ai:* Stock Market Game Adv; Math Team Coach; Talent Show Dir; Sci Fair Coord; NJEA 1976-; NEA 1976-; TREA 1976-; Alpha Delta Kappa 1981-; VP; Toms River Tchr of Yr 1987; *office:* Silver Bay Elem Schl Silver Bay Rd Toms River NJ 08753

KOEHLER, MICHAEL, Adjunct Professor & Asst Dir; *b:* Concord, MA; *ed:* City Coll of NY (BS) Arch 1989; Attnd Cooper Union Arch; *cr:* Self Employed & Employee Architectural Offices & Engrs Offices 1973-; Inst of Design & Construction Instr 1986-94; City Coll of NY Schl of Arch CCAC, Project Mgr, Facilities Database Project 1990-; *ai:* Fac Adv; Amer Inst of Arch Merit Awd 1989; Goodman Fund Short Story Awd 1988; Housing the Homeless Exhibition City Without Walls Gal 1988; 50 Illustrations Pub 1994.

KOELLING, CHARLES W.,II, AP & General Biology Instr; *b:* Cleveland, OH; *m:* Laurie Smith; *c:* Kristen, Robert; *ed:* Miami Univ (BSEd) Biological Sci 1972; Cleveland St Univ (MED) Ed 1978; Molecular Bio Class Case Western Reserve Univ 1992; Nike Bsktbl Coaching Clinics; *cr:* Willoughby South HS Bio Instr 1972-; *ai:* Asst Girls Var Bsktbl Coach Perry HS; NEA, OEA, WETA 1972-; Nom Lake Cty Sci Tchr of Yr 1994, 1995; Greater Cleveland Conf Girls Bsktbl Coach of Yr 1989; *office:* Willoughby South HS 5000 Shankland Rd Willoughby OH 44094

KOELSCH, RALPH GERALD, Math Teacher; *b:* Boston, MA; *m:* Wendy; *c:* Kevin, Kerry; *ed:* Univ of MA (BA) Ec 1971; Univ of Hartford (MED) Urban Ed 1973; Northeastern Univ 12 Credit Hrs Math; Bridgewater St 30 Credit Hrs Ed; *cr:* Weaver HS Math Tchr 1971-73; Cntrl Jr HS Math Tchr 1973-81; Quincy HS Math Tchr 1981-85; Morgan HS Math Tchr 1985-86; Sterling MS Math Tchr 1987-; *ai:* IM Vlybl, Sftbl; NEA 1971-; Patriot Ledger Golden Apple Awd; *office:* Sterling MS 444 Granite St Quincy MA 02169

KOENIG, ANN CHRISTINE, Biology & Chemistry Teacher; *b:* Reedsburg, WI; *m:* Gordon Muck; *ed:* Univ of WI at LaCrosse (BS) Bio 1983; Elmira Coll (MS) Bio 1989; *cr:* Corning Comm Coll Bio Chem Staff Asst 1983-86; Notre Dame HS Bio & Chem Tchr 1986-; *ai:* FACT; Chem Bowl Quiz Team Adv; Ath Review Bd; ESATYCB 1985-; Indian Hills Golf Club 1986-; Spencer Crest Nature Center 1983-; Visiting Lecturer Bio Corning Comm Coll ACE Prgm; Recipient Empire St Challenger Fellowship Awd; *office:* Notre Dame H S 1400 Maple Ave Elmira NY 14904

KOERNIG, BARBARA RARRICK, 8th-12th Grade French Teacher; *b:* Elmira, NY; *m:* Robert W.; *c:* Felissa, Gregory; *ed:* Mansfield Univ (BA) Fr 1972, (BA) Eng 1975; Grad Work at Millersville; *cr:* Southern Tioga Fr Tchr 1972-; *ai:* Foreign Lang Club Adv; Have Taken 10 Stu Oriented Trips Outside US; NEA 1972-; STEA 1972-, Sec; OES 1968-, Assoc Matron Martha; *office:* Southern Tioga Schl Dist 300 Morris St Blossburg PA 16912

KOESTNER, KEITH ALLAN, Math Teacher; *b:* Aberdeen, MD; *m:* Karen; *c:* Kaitlin, Kyle; *ed:* Univ of IL (BS) Scndry Ed Math 1990; Almost Complete with MA in Ed; Concentration in Curr Completed 35 Credit Hrs at Western CT St Univ; *cr:* H.H. Wells MS Math Tchr 1990-; *ai:* Enrichment Coord; Prin Selection Comm 1994; Enrichment GATE Comm; AFT, NYSUT 1990-; *office:* Henry H Wells MS RR 312 Brewster NY 10509

KOFOET, JUDITH KENNEDY, Assoc Prof & Clinical Coord; *b:* Massena, NY; *w:* Rudolph L. (dec); *c:* Scott Harriman, Ana Harriman, Allison Kofoet Walser, Timothy, Andrew; *ed:* Hagerstown Jr Coll (AA) Radiography 1980; Hood Coll (BS) Radiologic Tech 1983, (MA) Adult Ed 1988; Attnd Monterrey Peninsula Coll at Monterey, George Washington Univ at Washington DC; *cr:* Washington Cty Hosp Staff Radiographer 1980-84; Hagerstown Jr Coll Radiography Tchr 1984-; *ai:* Breast Self Examination, Amer Cancer Soc Instr; Basic Cardiac Life Support; Amer Heart Assn; Cmptr Rsources Steering, Fac Schlsp Comm; MD Soc of Radiologic Tech 1980-, VP, Mbrshp Chair, Charlotte Wade Todesco Meml Lecture; Amer Soc Radiologic Techs 1982-; Assn of Edctrs in Radiologic Sci 1984-; Hagertown Jr Coll Alumni Assn Pres 1992-93; Flower, Garden Show 1995- Chm; Renew Comm St Mary Church 1995-, Chm; Adult Ed 1984-, Chm; Radiologic Tech 1980, Mammography 1992 Certs; *office:* Hagerstown Jr Coll 1140 Woodcrest Dr Hagerstown MD 21742

KOFTON, DIANE WISNESKI, 4th Grade Teacher; *b:* Montclair, NJ; *m:* Paul H.; *c:* Paul Jr., Kimberly; *ed:* Kean Coll (BA) Elem Ed 1969; 30 Addl Credit Hrs; *cr:* Louise Conley Elem Schl 4th Grd Tchr 1969-71; Cntrl Elem Schl 2nd Grd Tchr 1983-90, 4th Grd Tchr 1990-; *ai:* Curr & Staff Cncl; Mainstream Assistance Team; EBEA, MTA, NEA 1983-; *office:* Cntrl Elem Schl 107 Central St East Bridgewater MA 02333

KOGER, DOROTHY DESCHON, Former Teacher; *b:* Pittsburgh, PA; *m:* Thomas Jr.; *c:* Jonathan T., Brian T.; *ed:* Duquesne Univ (BS) Elem Ed 1990; *cr:* St Phillip Schl 4th-8th Grd Tchr 1990-93; *ai:* Stu Cncl Adv; St Philip Yth Group 1990-; *home:* 2029 Crafton Blvd Pittsburgh PA 15205

KOGUT, VIOLETTE KARA, French Teacher; *b:* Paris, France; *m:* Mike; *c:* Alice Mary, Michael John; *ed:* UMCP Coll (BA) Fr & Scndry Ed 1987; 12 Credits John Hopkins U MBC; *ai:* Intl Club Spon; Fr Writer Club 1971-73, Pres; *office:* Wilde Lake HS 12101 State Route 108 Clarksville MD 21029

KOGUTEK, SHARON, Second Grade Teacher; *b:* Buffalo, NY; *ed:* (BS) Ed 1973, (MS) 1976)0; Post Masters 1980; *cr:* Newfane Elem Schl 1st, 2nd Grd Tchr 1973-; *ai:* PTO 1973-; Amer Legion Aux 1960-, Jr Aux Pres, VP, Sec, Treas, Comm Chm; Foreign Relations Chm 1973-92, Awds; Dale Carnegie 1980-, Grad Asst; Nutritional Grant Elem Ed; Inspirational Art Pub; Natl Dairy Cncl Publication; Writing Trophy for Essay from Pub Lib; *office:* Newfane Elem Schl 2909 Transit Rd Newfane NY 14108

KOH, SUSAN GREENFIELD, Assistant Principal; *b:* New York City, NY; *m:* Barry; *c:* Howard, Rebecca; *ed:* Barnard Coll (BA) Psych, Sociology 1961; Post Grad Courses for Cert Univ of MD; Post Grad Courses Johns Hopkins Univ; *cr:* Parkway Elem Schl 1-2, 4 Grd Tchr 1961-64; Comm Day Schl 1 Grd Tchr 1976-79; Park Schl 1-2 Grd Tchr 1979-94, LS Early Child Admissions Coord 1994-95, LS Asst Prin 1995-; *office:* Park HS Old Court Rd Brooklandville MD 21022*

KOHAN, KYLE STAMER, Instrumental Music Teacher; *b:* Buffalo, NY; *m:* Mark; *c:* Justin; *ed:* Univ of Buffalo (BFA) Music Performance & Music Ed 1982, (MA) Master of Arts 1990; *cr:* The Nichols Schl Music Tchr 1983-84; Williamsville North HS Music Tchr 1984-85; Frontier Central Schls Music Tchr 1985-; *ai:* Jazz Ensemble Dir 1984-94; HS Marching Band 1985-88; MS Music Club Adv 1988-94; Hamburg Musician Union 1977-, VP; ECMEA 1982-; MENC 1982-; NYSSMA 1984-; FCTA 1985-; NYSUT; AFT; AFL CIO; Hamburg Village Bd 1977-, Prin Clarinetist & Sec; Steel City Brass Band 1980-; Erie Cty Wind Ensemble 1984-; Clarion Wind Trio 1985-; Freelance Musician Studio Arena Theatre; Sub for Various Groups; Fredonia St Coll Recognition for a Tchr Who Made a Difference; NYSSMA MS Band Evaluation Festival Rating 4A Plus; Selected for Several NEA & NYSCA Recording Projects; *office:* Frontier Central Sr HS S-4432 Bay View Rd Hamburg NY 14075*

KOHANOW, CAROL POLLETTA, Social Studies Teacher; *b:* Waterbury, CT; *w:* Nicholas Everett (dec); *ed:* Univ of CT (BA) Soc Stud, Pol Sci 1966; Southern CT Univ (MS) Rdng 1972; 13 Credits Univ of Hartford; 31 Credits St Jospeh Univ; *cr:* St Mary's Grammar Schl Soc Stud Tchr 1966-67; Crosby HS Soc Stud TChr 1967-; *ai:* Peer Helper; Fac & Class Adv; BEST Pgm, Coop Tchr; TQE Comm; NEA, CEA, WTA 1968-.

KOHL, ANTHONY THOMAS, American Literature Teacher; *b:* Northampton, PA; *ed:* Bloomsburg St Coll (BS) Eng & Fr 1971, (MED) Theatre 1975; 42 Hrs Beyond MED; *cr:* Millville HS Eng & Fr Tchr 1971-73; Emmaus HS 12th Grd Eng Tchr 1973-; *ai:* 1993, 1996 & Yr 2000 Cl Adv; Sr Commencement Speaker Adv; Fac Senate; NEA 1971-; PA EA 1971-; East PA EA 1971-; Tchr in Space Candidate; House Mgr for PA Stage Co; Natl Endowmennt for the Arts Participant (3 Times); Worked with Allentown Civic Little Theatre 1974-; Allentown Prof Theatre Co 1978-83; *office:* Emmaus HS 851 North St Emmaus PA 18049

KOHLER, JEAN STEEHLER, Secondary Math Teacher; *b:* Rochester, NY; *m:* Paul Douglas; *c:* Jeffrey William, Mark Douglas; *ed:* St Lawrence Univ (BS) Math 1966; St Univ of NY at Albany (MS) Math Ed 1970; Amer Sign Lang Level 1; *cr:* Liverpool MS Math Tchr 1966-67; Seneca Falls MS Math Tchr 1971-72; Sidney MS Math Tchr 1985; Bainbridge-Guilford HS Math Tchr 1985-; *ai:* NHS Adv; SAT Math Course Tchr; Ticket Seller for Games; NEA 1985-; NYSTA 1985-; Tri-Town Theatre 1982-; 1st Congregational VCC 1982-, Treas, Comm Chair; Hosp Guild 1990-; Amer Red Cross 1995-, Asst, Treas; Outstdng Young Women of Amer; *office:* Bainbridge-Guilford HS 18 Juliand St Bainbridge NY 13733

KOHLER, MARY ANN, 6th Grade Teacher; *b:* Cannonsburg, PA; *m:* T. Jeffrey; *c:* Kara, Kelsey; *ed:* Indiana Univ of PA (BSEd) Elem 1979, (MED) Elem, MS Math 1980; *cr:* North Star Schl Dist Tchr 1980-81; St Benedicts Schl Tchr 1981-82; Bishop Mc Cort HS Tchr 1982-84; North Star Schl Dist Tchr 1984-; *ai:* Task Force Mid Level; NCTM; PA Cncl of Tchrs of Math; Laurel Highlands Math Alliance; *office:* North Star Schl Dist 1200 Morris Ave Boswell PA 15531

KOHLER, PATRICIA HARGADON, Music Teacher; *b:* Baltimore, MD; *m:* Fillmore T. III; *ed:* Frostburg St Univ (BA) Music Ed 1974; Salisbury St Univ (MED) Educl Admin 1985; Doctoral Candidate Univ of MD, Educl Admin, Supervision; *cr:* Federalsburg Elem Schl Music Tchr 1974-88; Preston Elem Schl Music Tchr 1977-88; Lockerman MS Music Tchr *ai:* Choral Dir; Schl Improvement Team; Staff Dev Comm; NEA MD St Tchrs Assn 1974-, Comm Chair; Caroline Cty Tchrs Assn Pres 1979-80, 1985-86, 1991-92, 1994-; Music Edctrs Natl Conf Tidewater Performing Arts Sox 1989-92, Bd of Dir; Caroline Cty C Arts 1996; Delta Omicron 1971-; PTA Awd Improving Image of Ed Governor's Ed Policy Transition Team 1994; *office:* Lockerman M Lockerman St Denton MD 21629*

KOHLHAAS, DONALD N., Biology Teacher; *b:* Harrisburg, PA Lycoming Coll (AB) Bio; Glassboro St (MS) Scndry Ed 1977; Glas Coll at Rowen Genetics Embryology; *cr:* Beck Jr Schl Sci Tchr 197 Cherry Hill HS West Bio Tchr 1987-; *ai:* Running, Judging Sci Fair; NJEA; CHEA; NSTA; Amer Water Skiing Assn 1990-; *home:* 75 Ol Harbor Rd Sicklerville NJ 08081*

KOHLMAN, M. AVOLENE, Mathematics Teacher; *b:* Toledo, O Calvin; *c:* Kathy Shiets; *ed:* Univ of Detroit (BA) Math 1962, (M Math 1966; 12 Quarter Credit Hrs Univ of UT; 5 Credit Hrs Coope Ed BGSU 1990-92; 9 Credit Hrs Ed Drake Univ 1991-93; 3 Credi Techs in Ed, Discipline Ashland Univ 1991-92; *cr:* Immaculate Conce Schl Elem Tchr 1954-60; St Raphael Schl Math Tchr 1962-64; Ca Stritet HS Math Tchr 1964-69; Cntrl Cath HS Math Tchr 1969-74; Clinton Jr HS Math Tchr 1983-; *ai:* Mathcounts Adv 8 Yrs; Acad Chal Team Adv & Coach 7 Yrs; Math Dept Chair 6 Yrs; NCTM 1980-; O 1988-; AFT 1992-; Nom Presidential Awd 1986, 1990; Jennings Sc 1988-89; Math Grant to NC Cntrl Univ NSF 1972; Title One Grant New Techniques for Tchng Geometry Jr HS Stdnts; *office:* Port Clint HS 110 E 4th St Port Clinton OH 43452

KOHLMANN, JUDY FLEMING, Mathematics Teacher; *b:* Stroudsburg, PA; *m:* Bill; *c:* BJ, Brooke; *ed:* ESSC (BS) Scndry Math 30 Credits Grad Courses ESU, ECY, Wilkes Coll, Penn St; *cr:* Stroud MS 8th Grd Math Tchr 1979-80; West Craven MS 6-9th Grd Math 1980-83; Mumford Elem Schl 5-8th Grd Math Tchr, Math Dept 1983-86; Stroudsburg Area Schl 8th Grd & HS Math Tchr 1986-; *ai:* Counts, Math Conn Spon 1986-90; Scorekeeper HS Girls Bsktbl 1992 Hockey Coach 6-8 Grd 1987-90; Statistician for Cross Cntry & 1993-; NEA, PSEA 1986-; PCTM 1989-; BSA Comm Person 1993-; Girl Scout Ldr 1995-; *office:* Stroudsburg HS 1100 W Main St Strouds PA 18360

KOHMUENCH, MARY THEOHARIS, Computer Multimedia Tea *b:* New York City, NY; *m:* Frederick W. III; *c:* Betty; *ed:* Fair Dickinson Univ (BS) Bus Ed 1975, (MBA) Mrktg 1983; Attnd Mon St Coll, Jersey City St Coll; *cr:* Lakeland Regnl HS Bus Tchr 197 Montclair St Coll Adjunct 1988-91; Lakeland Regnl HS C Multimedia Coord 1992-; *ai:* Multimedia Cmptr Lab Dir; Cmptr Comm; NEA, NJEA, NBEA, NJBEA 1975-; ITEA, ASCD 1992-; Scouts 1988-; Governor Tchr Awd 1992; Data Base Magazine Pub; I Pi Epsilon; Phi Omega Epsilon; *office:* Lakeland Regional HS Conklintown Rd Wanaque NJ 07465*

KOHOUT, DOLORES,CDP, Religion Teacher; *b:* Pittsburgh, PA Duquesne Univ (BS) Music; Boston Univ (MED) Music; 18 Credit Univ of Notre Dame Post Grad Theology, Cert Theology; *office:* Sa Heart HS 399 Bishops Hwy Kingston MA 02364

KOKES, KATHLEEN DONNELLY, K-12th Grd Music Teache Saranac Lake, NY; *m:* David P.; *ed:* Skidmore Coll (BS) Psych, N-12 M Ed 1988; SUNY at Plattsburg (MS) Ed 1991; *cr:* North Colonie Schl Music Tchr 1988-89; Northeastern Clinton Cntrl Schls Music Tchr 19 *ai:* Cheerleading Adv; Chorus Dir; Private Music Tchr; NYSSMA, 1988-; MENC 1985-, Coll Chapter Pres 1986-87; Psi Chi NHS; *of* Northeastern Clinton Cntrl Sch Rt 276 Champlain NY 12919

KOKORAS, VICTORIA, Ret Elementary School Teacher; *b:* Peab MA; *ed:* Boston Univ (BA) Philosophy 1955; NY Univ (MA) Philoso of Ed 1968; Chicago Univ 6 Credit Hrs Philosophy 1955-58; Roose Univ 18 Credit Hrs Philosophy 1965-66; *cr:* NY Pub Schls 4 Grd E Tchr 1967-68; Peabody Pub Schls 5-7 Grd Elem Tchr 1968-92; Tanglewood Concerts Usher; AFT 1967-; ASCD 1986-88; NSTA 1989 Pub Citizen 1992-; People For Amer Way 1987-; Amer Assn of U Women 1995-; Natl Womens His Project 1989-; Natl Org for Wo 1994-; Horace Mann Grant; Natl Lib of Poetry; Nom Who's Who of A Women; *home:* 20 Greenwood Rd Peabody MA 01960

KOLACZ-BELANGER, VILMA, HS Math & Computer Sci Teache Warren, OH; *m:* Allan Belanger; *ed:* Youngstown St Univ (BS) Math 1 (MSEd) Sec Math 1982; Doctoral Stud Leading to PHD in Ed at Ker Univ 1993-; *cr:* Youngstown St Univ Part-time Adj Math Tchr 1982 Hubbard HS Math, Comp Sci, Bio Tchr 1975-; *ai:* Math Contest A EOCTM 1978-, Pres 1992-, Sec 1986-88; OCTM, NCTM 1978-; O 1989-, Co-Newsletter Editor 1989-93; martha Holden Jennigns Sch Phi Kappa Phi; *office:* Hubbard HS 350 Hall Ave Hubbard OH 44425

KOLAK, DANIEL, Philosophy Prof & Dept Chm; *b:* Zagreb, Croatia; Wendy Zentz; *c:* Julia; *ed:* Univ of MD (BA) Philosophy 1978, (M Philosophy 1981, (PHD) Philosophy 1986; *cr:* Towson St Univ Philosophy Prof 1980-87; Univ of WI Asst Philosophy Prof 1987 William Paterson Coll Asst Philosophy Prof 1989-95, Assoc Prof & D Chm 1995-; *ai:* Philosophy Club Adv; Books: in Search of God, Lover Wisdom, Mathematical Thought, Self Cosmos God, Wisdom With Answers, Self & Identify; in Search of Self; From Plato to Witlgevstein Search of Kantz; Numerous Articles Pub; *office:* William Paterson 300 Pompton Rd Wayne NJ 07470*

KOLAKOSKI, DAVID FRANK, Social Studies Teacher; *b:* Terryv CT; *c:* Jennie, Jake; *ed:* Univ of CT (BS) Scndry Ed 1985; Wesleyan U 30 Post-Grad Credits Soc Stud; *cr:* Southington HS Soc Stud T 1985-90; DePaolo Jr HS Soc Stud Tchr 1990-93; Southington HS Soc S Tchr 1993-; *ai:* Quality Plus Comm; Writer's Club Asst Adv; Coord Trip to WA DC; Badminton Club Adv; NEA, CEA, SEA 1985-; AS 1995; CT Cncl on Soc Stud 1985-; Friends of New Haven Free Historical Wooster Square Assoc, Audobon Ctr for the Arts 1995-; Whitney Museum 1994-; *home:* 25 Court St New Haven CT 06511

KOLAKOSKI, DAWN LAYMOND, Early Childhood Education Prof Albany, NY; *c:* Kathryn, Rebecca; *ed:* Coll of St Rose (BS) Music Ed 19 (MS) Music Ed 1984, (MED) Early Chldhd Ed 1993; *cr:* Bethlehem C Schls Music Tchr 1980-83; Magic of Music Owner, Dir 1982-; Maria C Music Lecturer 1989-; Hudson Valley Comm Coll Instr, Field Supvr 19 *ai:* NAEYC 1989-; Orff-Schulwerk Assn 1981-; ACCESS 1995-; *offi* Hudson Valley Comm Coll 80 Vandenburgh Ave Troy NY 12180

KOLANKIEWICZ, SANDRA J., English & Leadership Professor; Pittsburgh, PA; *ed:* Johns Hopkins Univ (MA) Eng 1982; OH Univ (PH Eng 1986; *cr:* Univ of MD Eng Instr 1986-91; Marietta Schl Eng, Ldr Prof, Writing Ctr Dir 1992-; *ai:* Stu Advising; Sigma Sigma Sigma, C Democrats Adv; Better Neighborhood Assn 1992-; Retired Sr Vol Pr 1994-, Bd Mem, Bd Sec; 45 Short Stories Pub; 3 Poems; Yaddo Fell *office:* Marietta Coll 5th St Marietta OH 45750*

KOLB, MARY LOUISE, Math Teacher; *b:* Baltimore, MD; *m:* T. Rona *c:* Adam T., Brian J.; *ed:* Mt St Agnes Coll (BA) Math, Scndry Ed 19 42 Grad Credits Loyola Coll of MD; *cr:* Northern HS Math Tchr 1970- Our Lady of Pompei HS Math Tchr 1982-; *ai:* Jr Class, NHS Adv; Tchr

94-95; *office:* Our Lady of Pompei HS 201 S Conkling St Baltimore 1224

B, ROBERT H., Soc Stud & Geography Teacher; *b:* Scranton, PA; .utztown St Coll (BS) Soc Stud 1971; Lehigh Univ (MED) Rdng alist 1975; Post Grad Kutztown St Univ, Wilkes Coll; *cr:* ehall-Coplay MS Rdng Specialist 1971-92, Geog, Soc Stud Tchr ; *ai:* Geog, Drama Clubs; New Tchrs Mentor; NEA, PSEA 1971-, Fac NCSS 1992-; ASCD 1991-; *office:* Whitehall Coplay MS 2930 rthur Rd Whitehall PA 18052

BE, WILLIAM ANDREW,JR., Spanish Teacher; *b:* Elizabeth, NJ; lma Gloria; *c:* William A. III; *ed:* Univ of MA (BS) Microbio 1973; y Coll (MA) Intnl Stud 1986; Boston Univ (MBA) Pub Admin 1992; ailefihi Coll Math, Sci & Eng Tchr 1973-75; Escuela Nacional de ultura Sci Tchr 1976-79; Andover HS Span & Chem Tchr 1980-; ela Americana Math & Sci Tchr 1985-87; *ai:* Schl Garden Club Tech ultant; Schl Assemblies Musical Consultant; Advanced Placement generational & Cultural Ed Prgm Spon; NEA, MTA & MaFLA 1980-; righted Article on Mayan Math; Outstanding Tchr Awd; Half Schlsp id MBA at Boston Univ; *office:* Andover HS Shawsheen Rd Andover 1810*

CUN, LORRAINE M., Co-Op Work Coordinator; *b:* Carbondale, PA; 'aldwell Coll (BS) Bus Ed 1972; Temple Univ Cooperative Ed Cert; vington HS Bus Ed Tchr 1973-78; Wallenpaupack Area Schl Dist Bus c Tchr 1979-; *ai:* Diploma Pgm; Sr Project & Fac Advy Comms; PSEA -; PVEA 1980-; *office:* Wallenpaupack Area Schl Dist HC 6 Box 6075 ey PA 18428

E, JAMES PATRICK, Assoc Prof of Acad Support Svc; *b:* Abington, *d:* Penn St Univ (BS) Human Dev, Individual & Family 1974, (MED) Ed 1975; Nova SouthEastern Univ (EDD) Higher Ed Admin 1987; 3 its in Hi Ed, Scndry Schl Cnslng cert; Addl Credits in Comm Theory, Realtions, Mssg Design, Comm, Educl Tech, Mgmt, & Prsnl Admin at on Univ of PA; *cr:* Skills of Cntrl PA Residential Mgr Group Home 975-76; Clarion Univ of PA Asst to Assoc VP of Stu Affairs 1976-82, of Guidance Svcs at Venango Campus 1982-90, Assoc Prof, Acad ort 1990-, Univ Coord of 504, ADA, Title IX Part Time; *ai:* Venango pus Distinguished Alumni Awd; APSCUP Departmental Rep; idential Commission on Disabilities; Venango Cty Quality ncement Comm; AFT 1976-; Amer Cnslng Assn 1975-; Natl Career Assn 1995-; Venango Cty Literacy Bd 1990-, Bd Mem; Research wship Nova Univ 1986-87; Grants: Ctr for Smoking Cessation at CUP , Installation of 3 Joint-Use PAR Course Exercise Clusters, Venango pus Smoking Cessation Support Initiative; Pub 6 Articles, Contributed Book; *office:* Clarion Univ Of PA 207 Davis Hall Clarion PA 16214*

ERSKI, CYNDEE BOORAS, Secondary English Teacher; *b:* sena, NY; *c:* Jessia Lee; *ed:* Mater Dei Coll (AA) Lbrl Arts 1985; Y at Potsdam (BA) Eng 1987, (MST) Scndry Eng Tchr 1989; *cr:* rson Lewis BOCES GED Instr Part-time 1990-95; Beaver River Cntrl Scndry Eng Tchr 1990-; *ai:* Dead Poets Soc Adv; Tutor; Prof Dev, itator Shared Decison Making Comm; Thi Beta Kappa 1985-; Kappa a Pi 1987-; NCTE 1989-; Two Poems Pub; *office:* Beaver River Central Artz Rd Beaver Falls NY 13305*

ESAR, CHERYL A. K., French Teacher; *b:* Canton, OH; *ed:* Bowling n St Univ (BS) Ed 1992; *cr:* Mac Donald HS Stu Tchr 1992; Maysville al Schl Dist Fr, Math Tchr 1992-; *ai:* Fr Club, Schl Improvement m; Acad Boosters Officer; Bldg Cncl; NHS; MEA Sec; NEA, OEA -; *home:* 2234 Coopermill Rd Zanesville OH 43701

ESAR, KATHIE L., Business Education Teacher; *b:* Cleveland, OH; Lakeland Comm Coll (AA) Lbrl Arts 1968-76; Bowling Green St Univ Bus Ed & PE 1977; Heidelberg Coll (MS) Ed, Guid & Cnslng 1990 & ; *cr:* Penta Cty Voc Schl Bus Ed Tchr 1981-83; Fremont Jr High Bus Tchr 1983-; *ai:* Yrbk Asst Ed; NEA; NBEA; Big Brother & Big Sister 5-; The Link Cnslr Trng 1995-; First Call for Help 1996; Peer iation Comm Mem; Received Gottshell Rex Schlsp in PE in Coll SU; *office:* Fremont Jr HS 501 Croghan St Fremont OH 43420*

ESAR, LYNN TOTH, Business Teacher; *b:* Cleveland, OH; *m:* Paul; indsay, Lauren; *ed:* Cleveland St Univ (BBA) Bus Ed 1984; Ashland (MED) Curr, Instruc 1994; *cr:* Maple Hghts HS Bus Tchr 1990-; *ai:* ss of 1997, Bus Prof of Amer Adv; Yrbk Bus Mgr; NEA, OEA, OH Bus s Assn, Cleve Area Bus Tchrs Assn, Bus Prof of Amer 1990-; Maple hs Tchrs Assn 1990-, Corresponding Sec; *office:* Maple Heights HS 0 Clement Ave Maple Heights OH 44137

LIS, MAUREEN ELAINE, Guidance Counselor; *b:* Passaic, NJ; *m:* aley J.; *c:* Stanley, Mary; *ed:* William Paterson Coll (MED) Cnslng 7; *cr:* Parsippany Hills HS Guid Cnslr 1987-92; Passaic Vly Reg HS Level Supvr 1992-94; James Cladwell HS Guid Cnslr 1994-; *ai:* Peer or Adv; Sr Awds & Schlsps; NACAC 1987-; NJ Cnslng Assoc 1987-; ce: James Caldwell HS Westville Ave West Caldwell NJ 07006

LLAR, KAREN MARKS, English & Journalism Teacher; *b:* Farrell, *m:* Glenn; *c:* Christine, Matthew; *ed:* Youngstown St Univ (MA) Eng 8; *cr:* Greenville HS Eng, Fr & Jrnlsm Tchr 1972-; *ai:* NHS; Yrbk Adv; vspaper Adv; NEA 1972-; Youngstown St Eng Festival 1985-, Bd Mem; ron Herald Design an Ad Tchr of the Yr; *office:* Greenville HS 9 nation Rd Greenville PA 16125

LLEHLON, KONIA TWENINMII, Assoc Professor of Sociology; *b:* oli Island, Liberia; *m:* Yvonne Denise Buford; *c:* Jacqueline, Kevin; *ed:* ward Univ (BA) Sociology 1974, (MA) Sociology 1976; U of MD at lege Park (PHD) Sociology, Demography 1982; *cr:* U of MD at Eastern ore Lecturer 1983-85, Assoc Prof 1986-89, Assoc Prof 1990-; *ai:* ciology Club Adv; Am Soc Assn, Population Assn of Am, Liberian Stud in 1982-; Pub Articles; *office:* Univ Of MD Eastern Shore Backbone Rd ncess Anne MD 21853

LLMAR, GAIL E., Family & Consumer Science Tchr; *b:* NJ; *m:* R. uglas; *ed:* Messiah Coll (BS) Home Ec Ed 1991; Millersville Univ rsuing MS Clinical Psych; *cr:* Comm Progress Cncl Life Skills Instr 91-92, Dir of Teen Parenting 1992-93, York Even Start Instr 1993; Cntrl k Schl Dist Child Dev Tchr 1993-; *ai:* Natl Cncl on Family Relations 95-; NEA, PSEA 1993-; York Cty Home Ec Assn 1993-; *office:* Central k Schl Dist 300 E 7th Ave York PA 17404*

LMAN, MATTHEW HOWARD, English Department Chairman; *b:* iladelphia, PA; *m:* Flora Perea; *c:* John R., Flori P.; *ed:* Penn St Univ A) Honors Eng, Amer Lit 1977; Boston Univ (MA) Eng, Amer Lit 36 edits; SUNY at albany (MA) Eng Ed 1980; *cr:* Lenope Jr HS Eng Tchr 80-82; Central Bucks West HS Eng Tchr 1983-; *ai:* Schl Newspaper; ys & Girls Tennis Coach; NCTE 1993-; Tufts Univ Tribute Awd; *office:* ntral Bucks-West HS 375 W Court St Doylestown PA 18901*

LODZIEJ, EDWARD JOSEPH, French Teacher & Frgn Lang Chm; *b:* ffalo, NY; *m:* Kathleen Mc Kenna; *c:* Erin, Erik; *ed:* Canisius Coll (BA) 1970; Middlebury Coll Fr Summer Schl, Northwestern Univ Grad Stud Fr; SUNY Fredonia NY Post Grad Stud in Fr, Ed; *cr:* Dunkirk City Schls Tchr 1971-; Dunkirk HS Frgn Lang Dept Chm 1994-; *ai:* Class of 1996, Club Adv; Compact for Learning, Acad Letters Comms; AFT 1971-; SFLTA 1974-; CCFLTA 1995-; WNYFLEC 1985-; BSA 1987-, Troop mm, Cncl VIP Awd; Girl Scouts of Amer 1985-; Alpha Mu Gamma; St ristopher Awd Diocese of Buffalo; *home:* 55 Point Dr N Dunkirk NY 048*

KOLONAY, LOUISE ANNE SCHRENKEL, French Teacher; *b:* Barr Twp, PA; *m:* James F.; *c:* Lisa M., James F.; *ed:* IN St Tchrs (BS) Bio, Fr 1948; Attnd St Francis Coll, Lockhaven Coll; *cr:* Hastings-Elder HS Tchr 1948-60; Cambria Hghts HS Tchr 1980-; *ai:* NEA, PSEA 1949-; CHEA 1980-; *office:* Cambria Heights HS 426 Glendale Lake Rd Patton PA 16668

KOMAN, MARCY FIRESTONE, Third Grade Teacher; *b:* Hershey, PA; *m:* David W.; *c:* Andrew, Scott; *ed:* IN Univ of PA (BA) Elem Ed 1984; *cr:* Lower Dauphin Schl Dist Third Grd Tchr 1985-; *ai:* PSEA, NEA 1993-; Devon Manor Civic Assn 1988-.

KOMAR, JONATHAN DANIEL, Science Teacher; *b:* Cleveland, OH; *m:* Penny A. Palombo; *ed:* Bowling Green St Univ (BA) General, Biological & Earth Sci 1992; Working Toward Masters in Bio at Kent St Univ; *cr:* Parma City Schls Sci Tchr 1992-; *ai:* Key Club Stu Adv; Jr Var Bsbl Coach; NEA, OEA 1992-; *office:* Valley Forge HS 9999 Independence Blvd Cleveland OH 44130*

KOMAR, MARY ANN JAFOLLA, High School Mathematics Tchr; *b:* Philadelphia, PA; *m:* David; *c:* Christina, Candace; *ed:* West Chester Univ (BS) Scndry Ed & Math 1973, (MA) Scndry Ed & Math 1995; *cr:* Ridley Schl Dist Math Tchr 1973-79; West Chester Schls Math Tchr 1992-; *ai:* Math Counts Coach; Cheerleading Head Coach; NCTM 1992-; *office:* Henderson HS Lincoln & Montgomery Aves West Chester PA 19380*

KOMER, JAMES EDWARD, Assistant Prof of Mathematics; *b:* Pittsburgh, PA; *c:* Lori Lee, K. R.; *ed:* Carnegie Inst of Tech (BS) Mechanical Engrng 1958; Clemson Univ (MBA) Bus 1973; CA Univ of PA 2nd Cert Math 1985; Attnd US Army Command, Gen Staff Coll; *cr:* US Army Corps of Engrs Construction Engr 1958-79; Royce Kershaw Co Operations Mgr 1979-81; AL Pub Svc Commission Utilities Engr Specialist 1981-85; Slippery Rock Univ Bus Mgmt Dept Instr 1986-87; Vly Forge Military Acad Math Tchr 1988-; *ai:* Cadet Tutor Pgm Dir; Ski Club Adv; Facilities Planning Comm Mem; Hnrs Ed Pgm Monitor; NCTM 1988-; Old Forge Crossing Condominium Assn 1991-, Property Comm Chm & Exec Bd Mem; Slippery Rock Univ Alpha Kappa Psi Prof of Yr 1988; Vly Forge Military Acad Excl in Tchng Awd 1991 & Order of Anthony Wayne 1994; *office:* Valley Forge Military Acad 1001 Eagle Rd Wayne PA 19087

KOMMER, JOSEPH O., Science Teacher; *b:* New York, NY; *m:* Gina H.; *c:* Michael, Rachael, Taos, Liam; *ed:* SUNY at Binghampton (BA) Bio 1982; SUNY at Stony Brook (MALS) Ed Natural Sci 1993; Curricular Dev 1990-, SUNY at Stonybrook, Coll of New Rochelle; *cr:* Westhampton Beach HS Sci Tchr 1987-; *ai:* Fac Spon CURE Environmental Group; Coach JV Lacrosse; WHBTA 1987-; *office:* Westhampton Beach HS Lilac Rd Westhampton Beach NY 11978*

KOMOCKI, LYDIA V. (POKORNY), High Schl Spanish Instr; *b:* Cleveland, OH; *m:* David S.; *c:* Kirt Edward, Chad Austin, Marla Faye; *ed:* Bowling Green St Univ (BS) Span, Math 1967; Kent St Univ (MA) Span 1979; 3 Credit Hrs Span K-12 Grd Span Cert 1988; Iberoamerica Univ at MC Span 1967; *cr:* Willoughby-Eastlake Schls Span Instr 1967-76; Chemidyne Corp Translator 1988; Kent St Univ Span Instr 1985-91; Willoughby-Eastlake Schls Span Instr 1991-; *ai:* NEA, OEA, WETA, OFLA 1967-; Delta Gamma 1965-, Pres 1986-88; Cleveland Pops People 1995-, Chptr Mem; AAUW 1967-76; Sokol Greater Cleveland 1952-; Holt, Rinehart, Winston Inc Textbook Editor 1990.*

KOMONDOR, GREGORY, Geography & Government Teacher; *b:* Glassport, PA; *m:* Lisa Marie; *ed:* Slippery Rock Univ (BS) Scndry Ed 1990; Attending Loyola Univ to Obtain Masters in Guid 30 Credits; *cr:* Joppatowne HS Tchr & Coach 1991-; *ai:* Head Var Ftbl, Head Boys Track & Asst Bsktbl Coach; Schl Based Instrl Decision Making Team; Stu Assistance & Referral Team; NCA 1973-; NEA 1991-; 9th Grd Tchr of the Yr 1994; Cty Nom for Tchr of the Yr 1995.

KONAWAL, NORMA NAPOLIELLO, Business Education Teacher; *b:* Newark, NJ; *m:* Stephen; *c:* Jennifer; *ed:* Montclair St (BA) Bus, PE 1958; 18 Hrs Montclair St; 12 Hrs Kean Coll; *cr:* Roselle Bd of Ed Bus Ed Tchr 1958-; *ai:* Class Adv 1967, 1972, 1979, 1984, 1997; Yrbk 1988; Color Guard Adv 1960, 1969, 1989, 1996; Mid Sts Coord 1970; TALC 1994-; Roselle Ed Assn 1958-, Rep; NJEA 1958-, Legal Action Rep; NEA, NJBEA 1958-; *office:* Abraham Clark HS 122 E 6th Ave Roselle NJ 07203*

KONAXIS, ANTOINETTE, English Teacher; *b:* Brookline, MA; *ed:* Salem St Coll (BA) Eng 1973; Lesley Grad Schl (MED) Multidisciplinary 1995; *cr:* Gloucester HS Eng Tchr 1973-; *ai:* Elicitor Magazine Adv; NEA, MTA, GTA & NCTE 1973-; MCTE & NEATE; *office:* Gloucester HS Leslie O. Johnson Rd Gloucester MA 01930

KONCAR, GEORGE ALAN, Mathematics Teacher; *b:* Kenton, OH; *m:* Jody Kasler; *c:* Glenda A., Jessica R.; *ed:* Capital Univ (BA) Math Ed 1972; OH Univ (MS) Math 1988; *cr:* Hilliard City Schls 7th Grd Math Tchr 1972-73; Maysville Local Schls 8-12 Grd Math Tchr 1973-; *ai:* All Schl Play Co-Dir; Quiz Team, Environmental Club Adv; North Cntrl Evaluation Steering Comm Q; Maysville Ed Assn 1986-, Pres, Treas; OEA, NEA 1986-; Muskingum Area Cncl of Tchrs of Math 1990-, Pres; OH Cncl of Tchrs of Math 1970-; Aid Assn for Luth 1972-, Pres Local Chptr; Kiwanis 1975-, Outstdng Svc Awd 1980; *home:* 112 Juanita Dr Zanesville OH 43701

KONCHAN, KENNETH J., History & Humanities Tchr; *b:* Cleveland, OH; *ed:* Hiram Coll (BA) His 1963; John Carroll Univ (MA) Hum 1991; Working on MA His Akron, Drake Univs; Seminars Cleveland St, Kent St, Ashland Univ, John Carroll Univ, Akron Univ; *cr:* Greenbriar Jr HS Tchr 1964-71; Valley Forge HS Tchr 1971-; *ai:* Dept Chair Soc Stud; Ath Dir, Curr Writing Tms; Curr Stud Teams, Coach Ftbl, Bsbl, Bsktbl, Girls Bsktbl; Chess Club Adv; Stu Tchr Tec Ctr; Chm Bi-Centennial Comm; Sun Newspapers Advy Bd 1986-, Greater Cleveland Bsktbl Coaches Assn, Ohio Bsktbl Coaches Assn; Natl Bi-Centennial Distinguished; Coach of Yr; Millstone Awd; Victories 100,200,250,300; Marta Holden Jennings Fnd Schlr; Natl Endowment for the Hum Ind Study Grant; Guest Lecturers John Caroll Univ, CSU Holocaust Wkshp, Cuyologa Comm Coll; *office:* Valley Forge HS 9999 Independance Blvd Cleveland OH 44130*

KONDIKOFF, LINDA ANNE, Art Teacher; *b:* Easton, PA; *m:* James; *ed:* Kutztown Univ (BS) Art Ed 1977, (MED) Art Ed 1982; 3 Post Grad Credits; *cr:* Asa Packer Elem Schl Art Tchr 1979-; *ai:* BEA, NEA 1979-; *home:* 499 Grouse Dr Bath PA 18014

KONDOPIRAKIS, EMMANUEL, Professor of Mathematics; *b:* Kastelli Kisamou, Chania Greece; *m:* Irene Vidalakis; *ed:* CCNY (BS) Math, Engrng 1972, (MA) Math 1976; NYU Courant Inst (PHD) Math 1984; *cr:* SUNY at Farmingdale Prof 1972-84; Cooper Union Prof 1984-; *ai:* Mathematical Modeling Natl Competition Fac Adv; Putnam Competition Coach; Math Tutoring Prgm Coord; Natl Statistical office of Greece Decretary Gen 1990-93; *office:* Cooper Union 51 Astor Pl New York NY 10003*

KONDRATH, MARTIN EDWARD, Teacher & Coord of Marketing; *b:* Philadelphia, PA; *m:* Barbara Taylor; *c:* Martin Taylor, Krista Anne; *ed:* Saint Josephs Univ (BS) Accounting 1961; Temple Univ (MED) Mrktg Ed 1965; *cr:* Camden City Schls Bus & Mrktg Ed Tchr 1961-67; Upper Merion Area HS Mrktg Ed Tchr & Coord 1967-; Church Farm Schls Tennis Prof 1980-; *ai:* DECA & Yrbk Financial Adv; NEA, UMAEA, PSEA 1967-; USPTR 1980-; Plymouth Whitemarsh Exch Club 1970-; Tchr of the Yr Awd by Chamber of Commerce 1985; *office:* Upper Merion Area HS 435 Crossfield Rd King Of Prussia PA 19406*

KONECHY, JOAN, Spanish Teacher; *b:* Paterson, NJ; *ed:* Montclair St Univ (BA) Span 1973, (MA) Bus Ed 1983; 15 Grad Credits in Admin & Supervision; Supvrs Cert; William Paterson Coll 18 Grad Credits in Tchng Eng as Second Lang; *cr:* Hawthorne HS Span & Italian Tchr 1973-75; Wayne Bd of Ed Sub Tchr 1976-77, Adult Schl Tchr 1978-79; Kinnelon HS Bus Ed Tchr 1978-79; Neumann Prep Schl Span Tchr 1979-85; Lakeland Regnl HS Span Tchr 1985-; *ai:* Span Hnr Soc Adv 1989-94; NEA 1973-; NJEA 1973-; Amer Assn of Tchrs of Span & Portuguese 1973-; Frgn Lang Edctrs of NJ 1979-; ACTFL 1985-; Nom for NJ Governor Tchrs Recognition Awd (3 Times); Pub Abstract of Rsrch Project for MA; *office:* Lakeland Regional HS 205 Conklintown Rd Wanaque NJ 07465

KONELL, SUSAN L., Seventh Grade Teacher; *b:* Philadelphia, PA; *c:* Jordan; *ed:* Temple Univ (BSEd) Ed 1975, (MED) Ed 1977; Attnd Gratz Coll 30 Credit Hrs Hebrew 1979, Widener Univ 60 Credit Hrs Early Chldhd 1991; *cr:* Schl Dist of Philadelphia Tchr 1975-; *ai:* Schl Newspaper; Creative Dramatics; Tutoring; AFT, PFT 1975-; Cluster Schl Cncl 1995-; Family Resource Network 1995-.*

KONIG, JANET ANN, French Teacher; *b:* Sharon, PA; *ed:* Slippery Rock Univ (BS) Fr, Scndry Ed 1973, (MED) Scndry Counsel 1991; 30 Credits Span Cert Univ of Pittsburgh 1979; Post Grad Stud in Span for Cert 2 Credits Penn St 1974, 4 Credits Youngstown St 1976; *cr:* Sharon Jr HS Fr, Eng Tchr 1973-74; Shenango Vly Schls Sub Tchr 1974-76; Our Lady of Sacred Heart Fr, Span, Art Tchr 1976-80; Shaler Jr HS Fr, Span Tchr 1980; Hampton HS Fr Tchr 1980-; *ai:* Soph Class Spon 1980-84; Var, JV Chrldng Spon 1981-85; Fr Club Spon 1980-; HTEA, PSEA, NEA 1980-; PSMLA 1970-; Allegheny Cty FL Assn; Original Creators, Presentors of Hampton Twp Tchr Ctr; *office:* Hampton Twp Schl Dist 2929 Mccully Rd Allison Park PA 15101*

KONIGSBERG, NOAH JUDAH, Art Department Moderator; *b:* Philadelphia, PA; *m:* Patrice Brennan; *c:* Quinn Dara; *ed:* Philadelphia Coll of Art (BFA) Jewelry, Ed 1982; San Diego St Univ (MA) Art 1988; Tchng Cert; Attnd CA Coll of Arts & Crafts; *cr:* Glenmills Schls Art Dept Head 1988-92; Germantown Friends Art Tchr 1992-93; Chichester Sr HS Art Moderator 1993-; *ai:* Paper Unicorn, Natl Art Hnrs Adv; Philadelphia Museum of Art.*

KONKEL, MARK RAYMOND, English Teacher; *b:* Erie, PA; *m:* Cynthia Ann Thompson; *c:* Joel, Amy; *ed:* Mercy Hurst Coll (BA) Scndry Eng 1979; Gannon Univ (MEqv) Eng 1994; *cr:* St Mark's Seminary Eng Tchr 1978-79; St John Kanty Prep Schl Eng Tchr 1979-80; Gridley MS Remedial Math Lab Instr 1980-81; Girard HS Eng Tchr 1981-; *ai:* Swim Team Coach; AFT 1981-; GFT 1981-, Bldg Rep; *office:* Girard HS 1135 Lake St Girard PA 16417

KONOPKA, MARY VANDYKE, Latin Teacher; *b:* Lackawanna, NY; *m:* Bruce David; *c:* James; *ed:* Univ of PA (AB) Latin 1988; Fordham Univ (MA) Latin 1994; *cr:* The Hun Schl of Princeton Latin Tchr 1988-90; St Josephs Univ Crew Coach 1992-95; Mount Saint Joseph Acad Latin Tchr 1993-; *ai:* Natl Latin Honor Soc; Messores; Jr Classical League; Classical Assn of Atlantic Sts; Philadelphia Classical Soc; PA Classical League; Jr Classical League; *office:* Mt St Joseph Academy 120 W Wissahickon Ave Flourtown PA 19031

KONRAD, CAROL J., Mathematics & History Teacher; *b:* Gas City, IN; *ed:* Millersville St Univ (BSEd) Ed 1979, (MSEd) Ed 1983; *cr:* Math Tchr, Coach 1979-82; Lebanon Cath HS Math Tchr, Coach 1982-83; Largo HS Math Tchr, Coach 1983-; DuVal HS Math Tchr, Coach 1996-; *ai:* Sftbl Coach, AP Test Coord; AFT 1986-; NCTM 1995-; Amer Assn of Univ Women 1996-; Natl SB Coaches Assn 1995-; ASCD 1988-, MASCD, MAA 1990-; Lanham B & G Club 1990-93, Coach; Mc Donalds Kroc Awd; *home:* 7304 Cipriano Springs Dr Lanham Seabrook MD 20706*

KONTOULES, CHARLES JAMES, Reading Teacher; *b:* Saugus, MA; *m:* Luisa Costa; *ed:* Boston Univ (BA) Geology 1976; Gemological Inst of Amer (GG) Gemology 1982; Salem St Coll (MED) Rdng 1992; *cr:* Breed Jr HS Sci Tchr 1978-80; GIA, GEM Trade Labs Staff Gemologist 1980-84; Breed Jr HS Sci Tchr 1989-93; Pickering Jr HS City Rdng Tchr 1993-95; Thurgood Marshall MS Title I Rdng Tchr 1995-; *ai:* Phi Kappa Phi 1992-; *office:* Thurgood Marshall MS 19 Porter St Lynn MA 01902

KONWINSKI, JACQUELINE MARIE KORALEWSKI, History & Economics Tchr; *b:* Toledo, OH; *m:* James R.; *c:* John R.; *ed:* Mary Manse Coll (BA) His 1965; Univ of Toledo (MA) Amer His 1986; 16 Semester Hrs Beyond Masters; *cr:* Summerfield Jr-Sr HS Amer His, Geography, Fr, Sociology & Psych Tchr 1965-66; Central Cath HS Amer His Tchr 1966-67; McAuley HS Amer His, Soc Problems & Religion Tchr 1979-83; Univ of Toledo US His Instr 1984-85; Notre Dame Acad AP Amer His, Ec & Soc Tchngs Tchr 1987-; *ai:* Sr Class Homeroom Tchr; NCSS 1980-; OH Cncl for Soc Stud 1979-; NCEA 1987-; Natl Assn of Stu Activity Advs 1990-94; PASM 1985; *office:* Notre Dame Acad 3535 Sylvania Ave Toledo OH 43623

KONZELMAN, HAROLD, English Supervisor; *b:* Hackensack, NJ; *m:* Jacquelynn Schwarz; *c:* Eric; *ed:* Fairleigh Dickinson Univ (BA) Eng 1973; Seton Hall Univ (MA) Admin, Supervision 1979; 30 Credit Hrs Ed, Writing; *cr:* Queen of Peace Boys HS Eng Tchr 1973-78; High Point Reg HS Eng Tchr 1978-73, Eng Supvr 1983-; *ai:* NCTE 1980-; ASCD 1984-; PSA 1987-; Eng Journal 1987; *office:* High Point Regional HS 299 Pidgeon Hill Rd Sussex NJ 07461

KOOIMA, SEBERT E., Admin, History & Religion Tchr; *b:* Rock Vly, IA; *m:* Ann Katsma; *c:* Paul, Scott, Pamela Ackerman, Krystn Boonstra; *ed:* Dordt Coll (AA) Ed 1957; Calvin Coll (BA) Frgn Langs 1959; MT St Univ (MA) Scndry Ed 1980; *cr:* Manhattan Chrstn HS Tchr & Cnslr 1959-86; Sussex Chrstn Schl Admin & Tchr 1986-; *ai:* Chrstn Schl Intnl Dist 1 1987-, Sec; Sussex Town Cncl 1991-, Councilman; *office:* Sussex Christian Schl 51 Unionville Ave Sussex NJ 07461

KOOISTRA, SUSAN BALMER, Home Economics Teacher; *b:* Long Branch, NJ; *m:* Alan R.; *c:* Kelly Lynn, Kevin Richard; *ed:* Glassboro St Coll (BA) K-12 Home Ec 1977; *cr:* Keyport HS Tchr 1977-; *ai:* Color Guard & Twirling Coach 1978-80; Preschl Pgm Head 1985-; Mentoring Pgm 1991-94; Fac Adv Comm 1995-; KTA 1977-; AHEA 1977-; NEA 1977-; *office:* Keyport HS 351 Broad St Keyport NJ 07735

KOONS, FRANCES JEAN, English Teacher; *b:* Waverly, NY; *ed:* Marywood Coll (AB) Eng 1967; Attnd Elmira Coll, Binghamton Univ; NYS Cert; *cr:* MacArthur Jr HS Eng Tchr 1967-79; Binghamton HS Eng Tchr 1979-; *ai:* NEA, NYSTA, BTA 1967-.

KOONTZ, BETH M., Third Grade Teacher; *b:* Harrisburg, PA; *m:* Dennis; *c:* Kayla, Tasha, Samantha; *ed:* Millersville Univ (BS) Elem Ed 1985; Western MD Coll (MS) Admin 1994; 15 Hrs Elem Prin Cert 1995; *cr:* South Western Schl Dist Grds 2-4 Elem Tchr 1985-; *ai:* Manheim Elem Lead Tchr; Grds K-12 Soc Stud Curr Ldr; NEA, PSEA 1985-; All Saints Episcopal Church 1975-, Sunday Schl Supt 1988-; *office:* Manheim Elem Schl Rd 2 Box 2462 Glenville PA 17329*

KOONTZ, DONALD F., English Teacher; *b:* Somerset, PA; *ed:* Univ of Pittsburgh (BA) Scndry Ed, Eng, His 1967, (EMEd) Eng 1972; Francis Scott Key HS Tchr 1 Yr; North Star HS Tchr 28 Yrs; *cr:* Yrbk Lit Staff Adv; *ai:* EA, PSEA 1968-; NSEA 1968-, Pres; *office:* North Star HS 400 Ohio St Boswell PA 15531

KOONTZ, MARY BETH ANN, Music Teacher; *b:* Johnstown, PA; *ed:* Seton Hill Coll (BM) Music Ed, Voice 1984; *cr:* Word of God Schl Music Tchr 12 Yrs; *ai:* 6th-8th Grd Fine Arts Club Dir; 1st-8th Grd Musical Dir;

NCEA 1984-; MENC 1991-; Westmoreland Symphonic Winds 1986-, Bd Mem; Seton Hill Coll Alumae Club 1993-; Thanks to Tchrs Finalist; *office:* Word Of God Schl 7436 Mcclure Ave Pittsburgh PA 15218

KOOPMAN, DIANA BONAZZA, Mathematics Tchr & Dept Chair; *b:* Hoboken, NJ; *m:* John; *c:* Andrew, Jillian, Samantha; *ed:* Montclair St Univ (BA) Math 1971; Villanova Univ (MA) Math 1974; *cr:* Haverford HS Math Tchr 1971-78; Council Rock HS Math Tchr 1979-82; Villa Joseph Marie Schl Math Tchr 1992-95; *ai:* Jr Class Moderator; NCTM, ATMOPAV 1992-; *office:* Villa Joseph Marie HS 1180 Holland Rd Holland PA 18966

KOOS, ERNEST JOHN, Physics Teacher; *b:* St Petersburg, PA; *m:* Romayne; *c:* Scott, Cheryl; *ed:* Clarion Univ (BS) Math, Physics 1965; Univ of AZ (MS) Chem 1971; Various Insts 51 Post Grad Credit Hrs; *cr:* Leesburg HS Physics Tchr 1965-66; Ridgway HS Physics Tchr 1966-; *ai:* Math Club Adv; Math Chm 1966-75; NHS 1994-; AAPT 1984-; PSEA 1966-, Pres; NEA 1966-; Elk Co Cancer Soc 1968-70; 2 Int Sci, Eng Fair Commendations; Westinghouse Sci Talent Search Commendation; 2 St. Vincent Coll Great Tchr Prgm Recognition; *office:* Ridgway MS HS 1403 Hill St Ridgway PA 15853

KOPAC, PAUL LEWIS, Gifted Program Specialist; *ed:* Slippery Rock Univ (BS) Elem Ed 1966; PA St Univ (MED) Ed 1970, (MED) Admin 1971; *home:* 301 Cedar Blvd Hollidaysburg PA 16648

KOPANIC, MICHAEL J.,JR., Asst Prof of Social Sciences; *b:* Youngstown, OH; *m:* Rebecca Marie Kocurek; *c:* Milenka Anna, Erika Alzbeta; *ed:* Youngstown St Univ (AB) His 1976; Univ of Notre Dame (MA) European His 1977; Univ of Pittsburgh (PHD) E Cntrl European His 1986; Univ of Toronto Doctoral Work 1977; Slovak Lang Trng Slovak Jesuits 1981; Comenius Univ Studia Acad Slovaca 1982; *cr:* Univ of Akron Lecturer Dept Of Gen Stud 1981, 1984-90; Lock Haven Univ of PA Asst Prof of His 1990-91; Teikyo Westmar Univ Asst Prof of Interdisciplinary Stud 1991-92; Mt Aloysius Coll Asst Prof of Soc Scis 1992-; *ai:* Bottleworks Ethnic Arts Ctr Lectures on Slovak Customs; Slavic Festival Exhibits on Slovak Culture at the PA St Univ; Slovak Surname Reference Project Genealogical Data Base Rsrch; Duquesne Univ His Forum Annual Papers on Contemporary Slovakia 1992-; Amer Historical Assn 1978-; Slovak Stud Assn 1980-; Czechoslavak His Conf 1983-; Amer Assn for Advancement of Slavic Stud 1983-; Czechoslovak Soc of Arts & Scis 1984-; Soc for Austrian & Habsburg His 1986-; Assn for Stud of Nationalities 1992-; WAUP Slovak Pgm Radio 1984-90, Dir, Outstdng Broadcaster 1988-89; Bottle Works Ethnic Arts Ctr 1995-; Cressom Area Historical Assn 1995-; Slovak Heritage Soc 1996-; Grants: W Wilson Intnl Ctr for Scholars Rsrch 1994, Universitat Bremen 1988, Intnl Rsrch Exch Slovakia 1982-83; Amer Biographical Insts Intnl Directory of Distngd Ldrshp 1989; Phi Alpha Theta 1989; Stephen B Roman Dissertation Awd 1982, 1986; Numerous Articles Pub; *office:* Mount Aloysius College One College Dr Cresson PA 16630*

KOPCHICK, PATRICIA P., Social Studies Teacher; *b:* Troy, NY; *m:* Daniel A.; *c:* Helena, Jozef; *ed:* Siena Coll (BA) Sociology 1974; Univ of KY (MA) Intnl Relations 1979; *cr:* St Anthony's Schl Fifth Grd Tchr 1974-77; Holy Spirit Schl Soc Stud Tchrs 1981-83; Shenendehowa Schl Soc Stud Tchr 1986-; *ai:* Mentor Prgm for Stdnts-at-Risk; SFA Senate; Ger-Amer Partnership Prgm; NCSS, NYSUT, AFT 1986-; Fresh Air Fund 1988-; Bethlehem Music Assn 1995-; St Nicholas Ukrainian Cath Rel Ed Prgm 1985-, Dir; 1991 Fulbright Scholar, Excl in Ed Awd; Adj Instr Syracuse Univ 1993-; Co-Author: Teaching About China 1992, Global Studies Curriculum Guide 1987; *office:* Shenendehowa Cntrl Schl 970 Route 146 Clifton Park NY 12065*

KOPCHO, CHRISTINE, Biology Teacher; *b:* Pittston, PA; *m:* John; *c:* Jonelle; *ed:* Coll Misericordia (BS) Bio 1970; Wilkes Univ (MS) Bio Ed 1976; *cr:* Lake-Lehman HS Bio Tchr & Dept Head 1970-; *ai:* Environmental Club, Teams Coach; NBTA; NEA; Tchr Awd from Coll Misisicordia; *office:* Lake Lehman HS Market St Lehman PA 18627

KOPCHO, DENISE JERMYN, Math Support Tchr & Coord; *b:* Philadelphia, PA; *m:* Robert M.; *c:* Caroline S. (dec); *ed:* West Chester Univ (BS) Elem Ed 1973, (MA) Tchng Eng Second Lang 1977; 72 Post-Grad Credit Hrs; *cr:* Snyder-Girotti Elem Schl Classroom Tchr 1973-89; Bristol Jr Sr HS ESL Tchr 1991-93; Bristol Borough Schl Dist Math Dist Curr Adv 1991-93; Snyder-Birotti Elem Schl Math Support Tchr, Coord 1989-; *ai:* PSEA, NEA 1973-; NCTM 1995-; UNITE 1994-; *office:* Snyder Girotti Elem Schl 420 Buckley St Bristol PA 19007*

KOPCO, MARILYN KIMMEL, Art Teacher; *b:* Johnstown, PA; *m:* Kenneth; *c:* Brian, Kathleen; *ed:* Mansfield Univ of PA (BS) Art Ed 1975; 17 Credit Hrs PA St Univ; 3 Credit Hrs Duquesne Univ; 4 Credit Hrs PA In-service; *cr:* Bishop Mc Cort HS Art Tchr 1978-81; Westmont Hilltop Schls Sub Tchr 1982-90; Cambria Cty Comm Art Ctr Ed Coord 1986-88; Bishop Mc Cort HS Art Tchr 1990-; *ai:* Art Club Adv; Chrstn Svc Club Co Chm; Stage Crafts Adv; Foreign Travel Adv; NAEA, PA Art Ed Assn 1991-; NCEA 1990-; Cath Schl Tchr Assn 1990-, Asst Rep; Allied Artists 1991-, Co-Chair SUM Show; Cam Comm Art Ctr 1986-; *office:* Bishop Mc Cort HS 25 Osborne St Johnstown PA 15905

KOPE, KATHLEEN M., Mathematics Teacher; *b:* Buffalo, NY; *m:* Peter; *ed:* SUNY at Geneseo (BS) Ed 1973; 33 Hrs SUNY at Oswego; *cr:* A.V. Zogg MS Grds 6-7 Math Tchr 1973-80; Chestnut Hill MS Grd 7 Math Tchr 1981-; *ai:* MS Math League Coach; Yrbk Adv; United Liverpool Fac Assn 1973-; *office:* Chestnut Hill MS Saslon Pk Dr Liverpool NY 13088*

KOPENA, JOLENE FRANCES (ROMBACH), Spanish Teacher; *b:* Martin, OH; *m:* Gerald M.; *c:* Jeremy, Joshua; *ed:* Univ of Toledo (BE) Span 1973, (MA) Span 1989; Iberoamericana Mexico City 1979; IFK Salzburg Austria 1982; *cr:* Continental Schls Span Tchr 1974-78; Genoa HS Span Tchr 1978-; Univ of Toledo Span Instr 1989-93; *ai:* Span Club; Schl Newspaper; AFT 1989-; NEA; Toledo Mothers of Twins Club 1994-, Pgm Chair; *office:* Genoa HS 2980 N Genoa Clay Center Rd Genoa OH 43430

KOPERSKI, CLAUDIA SMITH, Art Teacher & Dept Chairman; *b:* Toledo, OH; *m:* Fred; *c:* Craig, Julie; *ed:* Bowling Green St Univ (BA) Art Ed 1969; Univ of Toledo (MS) Scndry Art Ed 1978; *cr:* Anthony Wayne HS 9-12 Grds Art Tchr 1969-70; Sylvania Southview HS 9-12 Grd Art Tchr 1972-78; Sylvania McCord Jr HS 7-8 Grd Art Tchr 1978-80; Sylvania Maplewood & Whiteford Elem Schls K-6 Grds Art Tchr 1980-85; Sylvania Arbor Hills Jr HS 7-8 Grds Art Tchr 1985-89; Sylvania Southview HS 9-12 Grds Art Dept Head, Tchr 1989-; *ai:* Art Club Adv; Sylvania Ed Assn, OEA, NEA 1972-, Bldg Rep; Northwest Art Ed Assn 1968-, Regnl Dir; OH Art Ed Assn; Sylvania Arts Commission 1989-, Bd Mem; St Joseph's Cath Church 1977-, Cncl Mem; *office:* Sylvania Southview HS 7225 Sylvania Ave Sylvania OH 43560*

KOPF, LINDA LORENZON, 5th Grade Teacher; *b:* Philadelphia, PA; *m:* James; *c:* Jen L., Amy E., Emily M.; *ed:* Millersville St Univ (BS) Elem Ed 1963; Attnd Millersville, Temple, PA St Univs; *cr:* Upper Dublin SD 4th Grd Tchr 1963-64; Lampeter-Strasburg SD K-1 Grd Tchr 1966-71; Solanco SD 3-5 Grd Tchr 1964-65, 1978-; *ai:* Spon Schl Store; Instructional Support Team; Bldg Planning Team; Head Tchr 1995-; Solanco Ed Assn, PSEA, NEA 1963-, Bldg Rep, Sec; Lanc/Leb Reading Cncl; Keystone St Reading Assoc; Lancaster General Hospital Auxilary 1975-; Phi Delta Kappa; Trainer Cooperative Learning, Conflict Resolution, Tchng Children to be Peacemakers; Cooperative Tchr for Millersville Univ Stu Tchrs; ASCD; *office:* Quarryville Elem Schl 211 S Hess St Quarryville PA 17566

KOPP, CAROL ALLBERG, English Teacher; *b:* Cleveland, OH; *m:* Donald J.; *c:* Christina, Kenneth; *ed:* Baldwin-Wallace (BA) Eng 1973; Mt St Joseph (MA) Ed 1987; 48 Addl Semester Hrs; *cr:* Normandy HS Eng Tchr 1974-; *ai:* Adv Schl Newspaper; PEA, OEA, NEA 1974-; League Dir Girls Sftbl 1994-, League Dir; *office:* Normandy HS 2500 W Pleasant Valley Rd Parma OH 44134

KOPPEIS, PATRICIA STEPHENSON, Orchestra Director; *b:* Charlotte, NC; *m:* Francis Joseph Jr.; *c:* Stephanie, Joshua; *ed:* New England Conservatory (BM) Violin, Music Ed 1971; Tchrs Coll Columbia Univ (MA) Music Ed 1976; Cntrl CT St Univ 8 Credits Conducting; *cr:* Somerset Schls String Specialist 1970-72; Charlotte Symphony First Violin, Contract Player 1972-73; Hudson Vly Philharmonic First Violin 1973-74; Syosset Schls 3rd-12th Grd String Tchr 1975-; *ai:* Tri-M Music Hnr Soc; Tri-M NY St Schl Music Assn St Chprsn; MENC 1975-, Tri-M Natl Cncl; Eastern Division Chprsn; Nassau Music Ed Assn 1975-, All-Cty Orch Chprsn; Amer String Tchrs Assn, Natl Schl Orch Assn 1975-; West Islip Chamber Orch 1996; *office:* Syosset HS South Woods Rd Syosset NY 11791

KOPPINGER, MARY HOWLEY, Social Studies Teacher; *b:* Brooklyn, NY; *m:* Thomas; *c:* Thomas III; *ed:* Ripon Coll (BA) Span 1985, Brooklyn Coll (MA) Emotionally Handicapped 1989; *cr:* JHS 198 Spec Ed Span Tchr 1986-90, 6-9 Grd Span Tchr 1990-94, 8 Grd Soc Stud Tchr 1995-; *ai:* Supvr of A Bettery Chance Prgm in JHS 198; Career Day, Discipline, Grading, Compact for Learning Comms; Cath Tchr 1990-, JHS 198 Rep; Rockville Ctr Newcomers Club 1991-, 1st VP; Eng Springer Spaniel Club of LI 1992-, Bd Mem; *office:* JHS 198 Benjamin Cardozo 365 Beach 56th St Far Rockaway NY 11692

KORB, SUZANNE B., Music Educator; *b:* Columbia, PA; *m:* Joseph H. Jr.; *c:* Joshua Paul; *ed:* Elizabethtown Coll (BA) Music 1987; Music Ed Cert 1987; *cr:* Eastern York Schl Dist Elem Vocal Tchr 1988-89; South Eastern Schl Dist MS Vocal Tchr 1989-90, Elem Vocal, Instrumental Tchr 1991-92, HS Instrumental, Elem Vocal Tchr 1992-; *ai:* HS Concert, Jazz Bands Dir; MENC, PMEA 1984-; NEA, PSEA 1991-.

KORBAS, TODD ANDREW, Mathematics Teacher; *b:* Shelby, OH; *ed:* Bowling Green St Univ (BS) Math Scndry 1980; Ashland Univ (MED) Curr, Instruction 1995; *cr:* Lexington HS Math Tchr 1980-; *ai:* Curr Pathways Team; Fac Rep Ath Control Bd; NEA, OEA, LTA, OCTM, MOCTM 1980-; Cath Knights of Columbus 1980-; BGSU Alumni Assn 1990-; Elected by Class 1995 Hand Diplomas at Grad; Wrote Copyrighted Cmptr Prgm; *office:* Lexington HS 103 Clever Ln Lexington OH 44904

KORBEOGO, DITTA WILLIAMS, Chemistry & Science Teacher; *b:* Buff Bay Portland, Jamaica; *m:* Stephane Alassane; *c:* Patricia, Check; *ed:* Univ of West Indies (BS) Chem, Biochem 1978; 3 Credits Tchng Advanced Placement Manhattan Coll 1995; Cmptr Programming, Theory DATAMAC Inst 1984; Post-Grad Diploma Ed, Tchng Chem 1980; *cr:* Clarendon Coll Head Cmptr Dept, Tchr AP Chem, Cambondeg O, Level Chem, Bio, Math, Cmptr Stud 1978-88; Queens Comm Early Chldhd Ctr 3rd-5th Grd Tchr 1988-92; PS 83 Gifted 5th Grd Tchr 1993-94; Samuel J. Tilden HS Regents Chem, Bio Tchr 1994-95, Tchr AP Chem, Regents Chem, Earth Sci 1995-; *ai:* Coord Schls Sci Club; Coach Schl Sci Olympiad Team; UFT, AFT 1993-; Church of God of Prophecy 1974-, Sunday Schl Tchr, Supt, Parish Pub Relations Dir, Camp Dean of Women, Lay Minister; Tchr of Yr 1989; Mellon Fnd Flwshp 1995; Mem Fellon Fnd Selection Comm 1996; *office:* Samuel J Tilden HS 5800 Tilden Ave Brooklyn NY 11203

KORBICH, LEE EDWARD, Accounting Teacher; *b:* Shamorin, PA; *m:* Jane F. Chesney; *c:* Levi; *ed:* Tri-St Univ (BS) Bus Admin 1967; Ball St Univ (MBA) Bus Mgmt 1968; *cr:* Line mountain HS Math Tchr 1967-68; Lourdes Regnl HS Accounting Tchr 1968-; *ai:* Ath Dir; Boys Bsktbl Head Coach; Financial Dir; NCEA, NBEA 1967-; K of C, Admiral, Captain; PA St Bsktbl Champions coach 1990; *office:* Our Lady of Lourdes Regnl HS 2001 Clinton Ave Coal Township PA 17866

KORCHNAK, KAREN H., Business Teacher; *b:* New Kensington, PA; *m:* Lawrence C.; *c:* Lawrence D.; *ed:* Robert Morris Coll (BS) & (BA) Bus Ed 1983, (MS) Bus Ed 1988; *cr:* West Allegheny HS Bus Tchr 1984-85; Comm Coll of Beaver Cty Part Time Bus Tchr 1984-86; Robert Morris Coll Part Time Bus Tchr 1984-85; Ft Cherry HS Bus Tchr 1985-; *ai:* Dist Strategic Planning, Tech & Behavior Comms; Afro-Amer Club Spon; NEA 1986-; FCEA 1986-, Sec; *office:* Fort Cherry Jr Sr HS 110 Fort Cherry Rd Mc Donald PA 15057

KORCINSKY, TERRI ANN, Math & Science Teacher; *b:* Bridgeport, CT; *m:* Joseph P.; *c:* Christine, John J., Mark A., Joseph M., Matt A.; *ed:* Slippery Rock Univ (BS) Elem Ed 1965; Univ of Pittsburgh (MED) Elem Ed 1966; Ursuline Coll (MA) Educl Admin 1996; Prins Cert; *cr:* Colfax Elem 6th Grd Lang Arts Tchr 1966-67; Greenville Schl Dist 1st Grd Tchr & Elem Sub 1967-88; St Michael 7th-8th Grd Math & Sci Tchr 1988-; *ai:* PA Jr Acad of Sci & Math Counts Spon; NCEA 1988-; *office:* Saint Michaels Schl 80 N High St Greenville PA 16125

KOREJWA, PAMELA BROWN, Junior HS Science Dept Chair; *b:* Cambridge, MA; *m:* John A.; *c:* Christian Kaplinger, Matthew Kaplinger, Daniel Kaplinger, Heidi, Richard Kaplinger, Timothy Kaplinger, Jillmarie Metivier, Adam Callahan; *ed:* Massasoit Comm Coll (ABA) Early Chldhd Ed 1969; Bridgewater St Coll (BSEd) Elem Ed 1979; Divine Providence Tchr Trng Inst Elem Ed; Archdiocese of Boston Master Tchr Cert 1980; Sci & Environmental Sci; *cr:* Duxbury Head-Start Tchr 1976-78; Childrens Choice Schl Dir 1980-88; Cape Org for Rights of Disabled Svcs Coord 1988-89; MA Forests & Parks Regn 1 & 2 Interpretive Svcs DEM Coord 1989-94; St Josephs Schl Sci, Lit & Rel Tchr 1989-; Boston Harbor Whale Watch Naturalist & Sci Rsrchr 1990-; *ai:* Holy Family & St Josephs Church Childrens Choir Dir; Girl Scout Ldr; St Theclas Holy Family Church CCD Coord & Tchr; Cath Tchrs Assn 1989-; Ocean Quest Inc 1991-, Co-Founder, Bd of Dirs, Best Boat Awd 1995; MA Assn of Sci Tchrs 1993-; MA Marine Edctrs 1996; South Shore Regn Office for Children 1980-, Bd of Dir 1983-85; Quincy Crisis Ctr 1983-86, Bd of Dir 1983-85; Plymouth Marine Mammal Rsrch Ctr 1986-, Bd of Dir; Project SWIMS 1993-, Advy Bd Mem; US Power Squadron 1993-, Boat Safety Class, Tchng Coord, Merit Mark Awd; Ladies Aux VFW 1995-; Day Care Guide Co-Author 1982; Christa McAuliffe Tchrs Awd Bridgewater St Coll 1989; Gov Dukakis Awd Person of Yr 1989; Boston Coll HS Excl in Tchng Awd 1994; Quincy Patriot Ledger Good Apple Awd 1994 & 1995; Pub Nature Photographer; *home:* 174 North Ave Rockland MA 02370*

KOREN, CHARLES J., High School Principal; *b:* Sheboygan, WI; *m:* Rebecca A. Finkle-Koren; *c:* Amy N., Christina J., Julie E.; *ed:* Juniata Coll (BS) Scndry Ed 1978; Univ of Pittsburgh (MED) Sport Admin 1984; Duquesne Univ ABD Interdisciplinary Doctoral Prgm Educl Ldrs; *cr:* Pittsburgh Cntrl Cath HS Tchr 1978-87, Asst Prin 1987-90; Bishop Carroll HS Prin 1990-; *ai:* Head Ftbl Coach; NASSP, PASSP 1987-; NCEA 1978; Knights of Columbus 1990-; *office:* Bishop Carroll HS 728 Ben Franklin Hwy Ebensburg PA 15931

KORN, RICHARD, 10th Grade Global Studies Tchr; *b:* Suffern, NY; *m:* Linda Blohm; *c:* Edward, Steven, Lisa; *ed:* Fairleigh Dickinson Univ (BA) Ed 1973; *cr:* North Rockland HS 10th Grd Global Stud Tchr 23 Yrs; *ai:* Var Girls Bsktbl Coach; Rockland Cty Umpires Assn; Little League Past Bd Mem; *office:* North Rockland HS 106 Hammond Rd Thiells NY 10984

KORNBAU, JULIA LOUISE, Chemistry Teacher; *b:* Albermarle, NC; *m:* Raymond W.; *c:* Robert Myers, William Myers; *ed:* Westhampton Coll Univ of Richmond (BS) Chem 1960; Bowie St Univ (MA) Guidance, Counseling 1977; *cr:* Chesterfield Co Bd of Ed Tchr 1 1/2 Yrs; Bow[ie] Tchr 25 Yrs; *ai:* Sr Class Spon; Prince George's Cty Area Sci Fair Bd of Dirs; PGCEA 1970-; *office:* Bowie HS 15200 Annapolis Rd MD 20715

KORNBLUTH, AHARON, 7th Grd Religious Studies Tchr; *b:* Bro[oklyn,] NY; *m:* Yette Singer; *c:* Shani, Aryeh, Chaya, Pinchas; *ed:* Brookly[n] (MS) Cmptrs, Chem 1982; Kollel Gur Aryeh Rabbincal Talmud 198[?] Camp Morris Camp Head Cnslr, Dir 1990-95; Rabbi Jacob Joseph sc[hl] Grd Rabbi 1986-.

KORNBLUTH, JANE BERMAN, English Teacher; *b:* Oceanside, N[Y;] Jerry; *c:* Brett, Scott; *ed:* Bowling Green St Univ (BSEd) Eng & His (MAEd) Eng Ed 1975; *cr:* Merrick Ave Jr High Eng Tchr 1967-69; H[...] Carey HS Eng Tchr & Talented & Gifted Mentor 1979-; *ai:* NEA [...] Tchr of Excl Awd Chosen by the Prin; Honor Soc Acad Tchr of Yr Awd; Whos Who in Previous Yrs; Started Womens Issues Group at HS; *office:* H Frank Carey HS 230 Poppy Ave Franklin Square NY [...]

KORNER, MARALYN KENNEDY, Third Grade Teacher; *b:* Bu[...] OH; *m:* Robert Charles; *c:* Pamela Sue Korner Rowland; *ed:* OH St[...] (BA) Elem Ed 1975; Bowling Green St Univ 18 Credit Hrs; Ashlan[d ...] CEU Credits; *cr:* Colonel Crawford Schl Dist Third Grd Tchr 19[...] Head Tchr 1981-86; *ai:* Math Curr, Soc Stud Curr Comms; CCEA, NEA, NCOEA 1976-; CCIRA 1978-; Whetstone Comm Club 1963-, Treas; Eastern Star Bucyrus Chptr 1965-; Good Hope Luth Church [...]

KORNHAUSER, NEIL, Mathematics Teacher; *b:* Queens, NY; *m:* Lynn Tinkel; *ed:* St Univ of NY at Stony Brook (BS) Math 1978; 21 [...] Hrs Math Ed Post-Grad; *cr:* Vineland HS Math Tchr 1978-80; Palmy[ra ...] Math Tchr 1980-84; Cherokee HS Math Tchr 1984-; *ai:* Math Te[am ...] Chess Team Adv; NJEA 1978-; *office:* Cherokee HS Willow Ber[...] Marlton NJ 08053*

KORODE, ED D., Industrial Arts Teacher; *b:* Lisbon, OH; *ed:* Walsh (BA) His, Govt 1970; Kent St Univ Indstrl Art Cert, 30 Addl Hrs; [...] Joseph of Maximo Rdng, His Tchr 1970-71; *ai:* OEA, NEA 1973-; [...] Who Among Stdnts; *office:* James A. Garfield HS 10233 State Rou[te ...] Garrettsville OH 44231

KORODE, RUTH E., English Teacher; *b:* Cleveland, OH; *ed:* Clev[eland] St Univ (BA) Ed 1972; 30 Grad & Post Grad Hrs Kent St Univ[;] Cleveland Pub Schls Tutor 1970-71; James A. Garfield Local Schls 1972-; Portage Co Schls Summer Schl 1992-93; Garfield HS Mentor 1993-; *ai:* Girls MS BB Coach 1979-88; HS Newspaper Adv 1986-; Comm; Wrote Cty Office Project; Adv MS Historica Book; Sr Class 1994-; NEA, OEA, GEA 1972-; Assembly of God Played Piano & C[...] 1976-79; Women's Missions 1975-80; Sunday Schl 1967-72; Child[...] Church 1976-79; Marlboro Assmbly of God Pianist 1994-, Vac Bible Tchr 1989-; Pub Educl Instructional Material, Article on Work in Sc[...] of OH Certified Mentor 1993; Tchr of the Yr Nom 1994; *office:* Jam[es A.] Garfield H S 10233 State Rt 88 Garrettsville OH 44231

KOROL, STEPHEN GEORGE, Science Teacher; *b:* Hazleton, PA[;] JoAnne M. Batcha; *ed:* Bloomsburg St (BS) Comprehensive Sci [...] (MED) Bio 1972; Scranton Univ Scndry Prin Cert 1982; 9 Credit Hrs [...] St Univ Educl Instruction; 11 Credit Hrs King's Coll Data Processing[;] Freeland Jr HS Sci Tchr 1967-; *ai:* Ath Dir; AFT, NSTA 1970-; Free[land] Area Jaycees 1973-, Charter Pres, JCI Senator; Rotary Club of Free[land] 1983-, Pres, Treas Paul Harris Flwshp; Freeland YMCA Bd of Dir 19[...] Pres; Freeland Homecoming Assn 1978-, Chm, Treas; Evolutio[n ...] Thyroid Gland 1972; His of Foster Twp 1976; *home:* RR 1 Box 1[...] Freeland PA 18224*

KOROM, MICHAEL JOHN, German & English Teacher; *b:* [...] Kozarci, Yugoslovia; *m:* Virginia Ann Widger; *c:* Michael, Nikolas; Clarion Univ (BS) Ger 1977; Villanova Univ (MS) Sec Schl Admin [...] St Joseph's Univ Eng Cert; Geothe Inst Ger; Cabrini Coll Post [...] Credits; *cr:* Cntrl Bucks Eng, Ger Tchr 1977-79; Vly Forge Military A[cad] Asst Dir of Admissions 1980-86; Lionville Jr HS Ger, Eng Tchr 1987- Head Ftbl Coach Valley Forge Military Acad; Head Bsktbl Coach; Bsbl Coach; NEA, PSEA 1986-; Vly Forge Military Acad Tchr of Yr 1[...] Coach of Yr Del-Val 1992; *office:* Lionville Jr HS 50 Devon[...] Downingtown PA 19335

KORP, WILLIAM MICHAEL, Math Teacher; *b:* Meriden, CT; *m:* M[...] Leopizzo; *c:* William, Jeffrey, Eric; *ed:* Cntrl CT St Univ (BS) Math 1[...] (MS) Math 1981; *cr:* Wethersfield HS Math Tchr 1971-95; Middle[sex] Comm Coll Part-time Math Tchr 1986-89; *ai:* AFT 1971-; ATOMIC 19[...] Recognition Awd Harvey Mudd Coll; *home:* 210 Deckert Dr Plantsville 06479

KORTAN, JOSEPH JOHN, Mathematics Teacher; *b:* New York City, [...] *ed:* Lorain Cty Comm Coll (AA) Ed 1970; Baldwin-Wallace Coll (BA[)] 1972; Cleveland St Univ (MA) Ec 1978; Univ of Akron Inst for Mili[...] Stud; *cr:* Parma City Schls Math Tchr 1972-; *ai:* NEA, OH Ed Assn, Pa[...] Ed Assn 1972-; Democratic Party 1996, Survey Comm; Railroad C[...] Drama Production of Inherit the Wind 1994; *office:* Parma City Schls 6[...] Ridge Rd Parma OH 44129

KORTENAAR, PAUL, Biology Teacher; *b:* Montreal Quebec, Cana[da;] *ed:* Mc Gill Univ (BS) Bio, Human Genetics 1988; Dip Ed Bio, Ch[...] 1989; Bio Hnrs Specialist Univ of Toronto 1992; *cr:* Brebeuf Coll Schl Tchr 1989-95; Ontario Sci Centre Sci Schl Bio Tchr 1995-; *ai:* Connau[ght] Stu Biotechnology Conf 1996; Bsktbl, Debate Coach 1991-95; OEC[...] 1989-; STAO 1993-, Conf Planner; *office:* Ontario Sci Centre Sci Schl [...] Don Mills Rd Toronto ON M3C 1T3 Canada CN

KORTHALS, WILLIAM H., English Teacher; *b:* North Tonawanda, N[Y;] *m:* Elaine Stachewicz; *c:* William III, Kathleen; *ed:* St Univ Coll at Buf[falo] (BS) 1967, (MS) 1972; Christ the King Seminary (MAPM) 1988; 15 Cr[edit] Hrs Admin; 24 Credit Hrs Rdng Ed; St Bernard Inst 40 Credit Hrs Towa[rd] Masters Theology; 4 Units CPE; Niagara Cty Comm Coll Assoc 1965; Lockport HS Eng Tchr 1967-68; Frontier HS Eng Tchr 1968-; Erie [...] Comm Coll Frosh Eng Tchr 1975; Ford Motor Co Tutor in Writ[...] 1975-78; *ai:* Frontier Chptr of NHS Adv; Forum Club Adv; Former S[...] Play & Musical Adv; Former Schl Newspaper Adv; Frontier Cntrl Tc[...] Assn 1968-; AFT; NYSUT; NACC Certfd Chaplain 1992-; Vol Chaplair[n] 2 Area Hosps; KAIROS Vol; Benedict House Vol Chaplain; Frontier Cr[...] Comm Intervention Team Chair 2 Yrs; Commendation for Vol Work Buffalo Gen Hosps, Ene Cty Med Ctr & Benedict House; *office:* Fron[tier] Sr HS S 3342 Bay View Rd Hamburg NY 14075

KORY, MARY MOORE, Reading Teacher; *b:* Cleveland, OH; William; *c:* Stephan, Larissa Holodick; *ed:* Ursuline Coll (BA) Eng 196[...] John Carroll Univ (MA) Eng 1969; Univ of PA (MED) Rdng 1985; *cr:* Jerome 4th Grd Tchr 1964-65; Roosevelt Jr High Eng Tchr 1966-67; Patrick 6th-8th Lang Arts Tchr 1984; Conemaugh Twp HS Eng & Rd[ng] Tchr 1985-; *ai:* Strategic Planning Action Team; PSEA 1985-, Sec; N[...] 1985-; Tree Advy Comm 1994-; Southmont Borough Comm Arts Ctr 199[...] *office:* Conemaugh Township Area HS West Campus Ave Davidsville [PA] 15928

KOS, ANTHONY J., Instructor of Management; *b:* Phoenix, AZ; [...] Youngstown St Univ (BA) Bus of Admin 1983, (MS) Bus of Admin 198[...] *cr:* Youngstown St Univ Grad Asst Mngmt Dept 1986-87, Mngmt De[pt] Instr 1987-88, Dept of Bus Information Systems Instr 1988-84, Mng[mt] Dept Instr 1994-; *ai:* WCBA Fac Senator 1995-; YSU-OEA Plannir[g ...]

:omm 1995-; Sigma Pi Alpha; *office:* Williamson Coll of Bus Admin :k Ave Youngstown OH 44555

KOWSKI, EUGENE DAVID, Fourth Grade Teacher; *b:* Bayonne, Christine Choromanski; *c:* Janine, Jennifer; *ed:* Jersey City St Coll lem Ed 1972; Kean Coll (MA) Admin, Supervision 1984; *cr:* George gton Schl 4th & 6th Grd Tchr 1972-89; Hurden Looker Schl 4th Grd 990-; *ai:* Stu Cncl, Drama Club Adv; Drug Awareness 1993-94; NJEA 1972-; Elks 1995-; *office:* Hurden Looker Elem Schl 1261 Ave Hillside NJ 07205

KOWSKI, JOANNA C., Mathematics Professor; *b:* Jersey City, NJ; ontclair St Coll (BA) Math 1971; Univ of MA at Amherst (MS) ive Psych 1977; Addl 30 Credits; *cr:* Univ of MA Instr 1973-77; Control Mgr 1977-82; MIT Asst to Dir Sloan Schl 1982-84; Lincoln y Regnl HS Math Tchr 1984-87; Lasell Coll Assoc Prof, Dept Coord *ai:* Curr Comm Chair 4 Yrs; Acad Cncl; Acad Stans, Admissions Undergraduate Full Schlsp 4 Yrs; Grad Schl Full Schlsp 4 Yrs.

KOWSKI, RICHARD JOSEPH, Art Teacher; *b:* Natrona Heights, Diana Lee Hughes; *c:* Kimberly Anne, Richard Keith, Philip John, ew Aaron, David Craig; *ed:* Indiana Univ of PA Art Ed 1972, Master lancy in Ed 1990; *cr:* Ridgway Area Schl Dist Art Tchr 1972-; *ai:* ssistance Prgm Team Mem; Discipline Policy Review Comm; ay Area Tchrs Assn, PA St Ed Assn, NEA 1972-; BSA 1987-, Comm Advancement Comm; *office:* Ridgway Area HS PO Box 447 ay PA 15853*

NOVIC, LESLIE ANN (WAGNER), Life Science Teacher; *b:* ing, WV; *m:* Edward Michael; *ed:* West Liberty St Coll (BA) Sci Ed WV Univ (MA) Schl Counseling 1993; *cr:* Cameron HS Life Sci 989-91; Barnesville HS Bio, Anatomy, General Sci & Biochem Tchr *ai:* Church Admin Bd Sec; Sci Fair Adv; Dist Sci Fair Comm; NEA , BEA 1991-; WV Counseling Assn 1993-; Christ United Meth 1991-; *office:* Barnesville HS Shamrock Dr Barnesville OH 43713*

NOVICH, CONNIE, Biology & Marine Biology Tchr; *b:* rton, OH; *m:* Michael; *c:* Lauren; *ed:* Abilene Chrstn Univ (BS) Pr, 974; Akron Univ (MS) Outdoor Ed 1988; Ashland COll Cmptr es; Kent St Univ Sci Classes; *cr:* Barberton City SChls Sci Tchr 77; Copley HS Bio Tchr 1977-; *ai:* Evvironmental Club Adv; Frosh Adv; SECO 1980-; NSTA 1994; Beautification Comm 1992-, VP; Copley HS 3807 Ridgewood Rd Copley OH 44321

ANOVICH, PETER, Seventh Grade Math Teacher; *b:* Lackawanna, N. Mary; *ed:* Syracuse Univ (BA) Math Ed 1967; St Univ of NY at o (EDM) Math Ed 1971; *cr:* West Seneca East MS Math Tchr 1967-, Dept Chprsn 1969; *ai:* West Seneca Tchrs Assn 1967, Outstanding tor Awd 1986; NY St United Tchrs 1967; AFT 1967; Kiwanis Club st Seneca 1994; March of Dimes Walk America Team Captain 1992-; West Seneca East MS 1445 Center Rd West Seneca NY 14224

AREK, CHERYL L., Home Ec Tchr & Cabinet Member; *b:* Elkhorn, *:* Joseph John; *c:* Kathryn Elizabeth; *ed:* Univ of WI at Stout (BS) Ec Ed 1972; SUNY at New Paltz, UVM at Burlington 30 Grad Hrs; SED, Dist Credits 34 Credit Hrs; *cr:* Big Foot HS Home Ec Tchr 73; Smithtown HS Home Ec Tchr 1973-75; Onteora Jr Sr HS Home hr 1975-, Bus, Home Ec, Tech Dept Chair 1981-95, Prin Cabnt 1995; ist, Bldg Shared Decision Making Stud, Site Comms; Step Adult START Mem; NYSHETA 1978-, Regnl Team Ldr, Cty Tchr of Yr Area Coord; NYSOEA 1992-; OTA, AFT 1975-, Dist Cncl, Awds, Relations Comms; ASCD Mem 1994; PTA 1989-, Soc Comm; PTSA , Sci Fair, Career Day Comm; Tchr Rep; St Exams Test Writer; St Ed Consultant; Regnl Prof Wkshp Presenter 5 Yrs; Honorary DECA Mem 1993; *office:* Onteora Cntrl Schls Rt 28 Boiceville NY 12412

BOTH, ANGELINA VALIANOS, Retired Kindergarten Teacher; *b:* town, NY; *m:* John; *ed:* Cazenovia Jr Coll (AA) Lbrl Arts 1960; Y at Oswego (BS) Elem Ed 1962; Addl 45 Credit Hrs; *cr:* Williamson Schl Kndgtn Tchr 1 Yr; West Irondequoit Schl Kndgtn Tchr 4 Yrs; oye Falls-Lima Schl Kndgtn Tchr 28 Yrs; *home:* 313 Cheese Factory oneoye Falls NY 14472

CHOFF, JOANN MARIE, Hlth, PE & Drivers Ed Tchr; *b:* wissa, PA; *ed:* East Stroudsburg Univ (BS) Hlth & PE 1977, (MED) 983; Safety & Driver Ed Cert; *cr:* Millville Schl Dist Hlth, PE & r Ed Tchr 1978-; *ai:* Field Hockey & Sftbl Head Coach; PSEA, NEA -; Millville Ed Assn 1978-, Pres; USFHA 1983-; Field Hockey Coach 1992; Hlth & PE Dept Chprsn 1990-; *office:* Millville Jr Sr HS PO 260 Millville PA 17846

CINSKI, MICHAEL JOHN, Mathematics Teacher; *b:* Port rson, NY; *m:* Lisa Savino; *ed:* Oneonta St (BS) Elem, Scndry Ed Math ; *cr:* US Coast Guard Reserves 1983-89; Mercy HS; Tuckahoe mon Schl Math Tchr 1995-; *ai:* Mercy HS Math Tchr 3 Yrs; Hope e Ministries Head Tchr 2 Yrs; Var Wrestling, Jr Var Ftbl Coach; Math Amer 1992-, Suffolk Cty Math Assn 1995-; *home:* 63 Senix Ave er Moriches NY 11934*

BENAK, CATHERINE CANNON, Assistant Principal; *b:* Wilkes e, PA; *m:* Theodore L.; *ed:* Univ of PA (PHD) Ed Ldrshp 1985; Eng , El Ed 1975 Wilkes Univ; *cr:* WY Vly West Schl Tchr 1972-86, Cntrl e Curr Coord K-8 1986-93, Asst Prin HS 1993-.

SER, DONALD EUGENE, Business English Teacher; *b:* Mercersburg, *m:* Martha Marie Hoffman; *c:* Barry E., Vivian K.; *ed:* Messiah Coll Eng 1971; *cr:* Dover Area HS Eng Tchr 1971-72; Consolidated Schl Bus Eng Tchr 1984-; *office:* Consolidated Sch Of Business 1605 gston Rd York PA 17404

SHUTA, ANNE DOUGHERTY, Science Dept Chairperson; *b:* dale, PA; *m:* Nicholas W.; *c:* Anne, Nick, Molly; *ed:* Alvernia Coll Bio 1969; Penn St Univ (MED) Ed 1975; Kutztown Univ Elem Ed; of Rochester 2 Summers Biotechnology Inst; *cr:* Panther Valley Schl Bio Tchr 1969-77; Annes Nursery Schl Dir, tchrs 1984; Cardinal nnan HS Physics, Bio Tchr 1984-; *ai:* Sci Club Adv; Ring Day Comm; A 1969-; ADLTA 1984-; Grant Biotechnology Inst; Pub NST ification & Univ of Rochester; *office:* Cardinal Brennan H S Fountain ngs RR 2 Ashland PA 17921*

SHY, ANNAMMA, Science Teacher; *b:* Punalur, India; *m:* George C.; George, Philip; *ed:* Fatima Coll at Quilon (BS) Zoology, Chem 1968; Meml Coll (BS) Ed Sci 1970; Adelphi Univ (MS) Spec Ed 1991; 30 Credit Hrs in Ed; *cr:* Bharat Eng Schl India Sci Tchr 1979-81; Our Eng Schl of UAE Sci Tchr 1982-86; Montessori Acad NY Sci Tchr 6-89; P140 at PS 150 Sci Tchr 1991-; *ai:* Schl Site Mngmt, Schl Pub ations, Schl Mngmt Comms; AFT, UFT, Sci Tchrs Assn 1991-; *office:* 40 at PS 150 364 Sackman St Brooklyn NY 11212

SIBA, PATRICIA ANN, Secondary Health Ed Teacher; *b:* Mineola, *m:* Paul J.; *c:* Kelly Amzler, Caroline; *ed:* West Chester Univ (BS) Hlth E 1979; Adelphi Univ (MA) Hlth Ed 1984; Post Grad Stud 60 Addl dit Hrs; *cr:* Our Lady of Mercy Acad PE Tchr 1979-80; John Phillip sa Jr HS PE Tchr 1980-81; Paul D. Schreiber HS Hlth Ed Tchr 1981-; Coach; SADD Adv; AFT, PW Tchrs Assn 1980-; Nassau Cty SADD Adv Yr; HS Hlth Textbook Contributing Author 1994; *office:* Paul D reiber HS 101 Campus Dr Port Washington NY 11050

SIK, CHRISTINE ZILL, Eng Tchr & Lang Arts Chprsn; *b:* Pittsburgh, *m:* John William; *c:* Jaclyn, Justin, Matthew; *ed:* Univ of Pittsburgh (BA) Eng 1972, (MS) Scndry Ed 1976; *cr:* South Fayette Jr-Sr HS Eng Tchr 1972-, Lang Arts Dept Chair 1985-; *ai:* Spelling Bee Spon; Stu of Month Comm; Lead Tchr; Mentor Tchr; Assesment Comm; PSEA, NEA 1972-; NCTE 1985-; SFE PTA 1992-95; Gift of Time Awds; Thanks To Tchrs Nom; 19 Post Gazette Spelling Bee Winners; *office:* South Fayette Jr Sr HS 2254 Old Oakdale Rd Mc Donald PA 15057

KOSINSKI, CHRISTINE (GORZOCH), Second Grade Teacher; *b:* Phila, PA; *m:* Louis; *ed:* St Josephs Univ (BS) Elem Ed 1968, (MA) Elem Ed 1972; 30 Addl Hrs at Univ of Performing Arts; Cert of Cantorial Stud at St Charles Seminary; Scholum Cantorum Stud Cert at Immaculata Coll; *cr:* St Annes Elem Schl Grd 2 Tchr 1962-68; Whittier Elem Schl Grd 1 Elem Tchr 1968-71; A. Adaire Elem Schl Grd 4, 3, 2 Tchr 1971-; *ai:* Rdng Chprsn; Tops, Honors Comm Chprsn; PFT, AFT 1968-, Past Bldg Rep, Present Sec; Natl Assn of Pastoral Musicians 1991-; Phila Assn of Church Musicians 1981-; Svc Appreciation Awd; 25 Yr Appreciation of Svc Awd; 3 Nominations for Rose Lindenbaum Edctrs Awd; Regnl Finalist for Rose Lindenbaum Awd 1996.*

KOSKI, GLENN LAWRENCE, Instrumental Music Teacher; *b:* New Haven, CT; *m:* Laura; *c:* Megan, Timothy; *ed:* Ithaca Coll (BM) Music Ed 1984;Queens Coll (MM) Music Ed 1991; Long Island Univ (SAS, SDA) Educl Admin 1996; *cr:* Giblyn Elem Schl Instrumental Music Tchr 1987-; Atkinson Elem Schl Music Tchr; Freeport HS Band Tchr; *ai:* Nassau Music Edctrs Assn, MENC 1987-; Seaford Comm Band 1989-, Asst Dir; 2 Brass Ensemble Performances at White House 1995-; *office:* Freeport HS S Brookside Ave Freeport NY 11520

KOSKY, MARY BOEKER, Mathematics Teacher; *b:* New Haven, CT; *m:* Philip G.; *c:* Deirdre, Nicole; *ed:* SUNY at Potsdam (BA) Math 1964; SUNY at Albany (MS) Math 1970; Attnd Univ of CA at Berkeley, Cornell Univ; *cr:* Alameda HS Math Tchr 1964-66; John Mason HS Math Tchr 1966-68; Voorheesville HS Math Tchr 1968-69; Moravian Acad HS Math Tchr 1975-76; Northamptn Comm Coll Math Tchr 1976-77; Burnt Hills Ball St Lake HS Math Tchr 1978-; Union Coll Adj Prof 1993-; *ai:* Class, Math Club Adv; ASMA Contest Mgr; NYSUT, NCTM, NMVC Cncl 1977-; AMTNYS 1977-, Sci Liaison; StANYS 1994-, Math Liaison; STEP 1990-, Wkshp Ldr; Intnl Sci, Engrng Fair Stu Spon 1994; BH-BL Mini Grant 1995; *office:* Burnt Hills Ballston Lake HS Lakehill Rd Burnt Hills NY 12027

KOSLOVSKY, SUE WEIDMAN, 4th Grade Teacher; *b:* Canton, OH; *m:* James Lewis; *c:* Curt W., Craig W., Jennifer L., Kimberly J.; *ed:* Heidelberg Coll (BA) Elem Ed 1966; Univ of Toledo (MA) Elem Ed 1987, (EDS) Admin, Supervision 1989; *cr:* Noble Schl 3rd Grd Tchr 1966-69; Elm St Schl 3rd Grd Tchr 1969-72; Hopewell Schl 5th, 6th Grd Tchr 1978-81; Horace Mann Schl 5th Grd Tchr 1981-82; Trilby Schl 6th Grd 1982-83; Jackman Schl 2nd, 3rd Grd Tchr 1984-92; Meadowvale Schl 2nd, 4th Grd Tchr 1992-; *ai:* TASC Career, Community, Right to Read Comms; Mentor Prgm; NEA, OEA, NWOEA 1966-; Tchrs Assn Washington Local Schls 1978-; Pi Lambda Theta 1987-; Alpha Delta Kappa 1992-; IRA 1978-; Heidelberg Coll, Univ of Toledo Alumnae Assns; St Pius X Church, Parent's Club; St Ursula Parent's Club; CATV Grant 1994-95; *office:* Meadowvale Elem Schl 2755 Edgebrook Dr Toledo OH 43613*

KOSOLA, CHARLES ERIK, Technology Teacher; *b:* Abington, PA; *m:* Maria; *c:* Charles, Carl; *ed:* Cheyney St Coll (BS) Indstrl Arts 1969; Temple Univ (ME) Indstrl Ed 1975; 20 Addl Hrs Dexel Univ of United Kingdom; *cr:* Master Cardantar 32 Yrs, Wood Tech Tchr 2 Yrs; South Philadelphia HS Graphic Arts 19.5 Yrs; Northeast HS Tech Publishing 6.5 Yrs, Carl Perkins Coord 26.5 Yrs; *ai:* Spon Stu Tech Assn; Car Club; Intnl Tech Assn 1990-; Phila Tech Pres 1994-; PA Tech Assn 1970-; St Johns Evergeheal Luth Church 1959-; Sears Bi Monthly TV Tool Sales Show; *office:* Northeast HS Cottman & Algon Ave Philadelphia PA 19111

KOSSICK, SHERRY LYNN, Mathematics Teacher; *b:* New Kensington, PA; *ed:* PA St Univ (BS) Scndry Ed 1991; *cr:* Highlands Schl Dist HS Math Tchr 1992-; *ai:* JV & 9th GrdGirls Bsktbl Coach; A Better Idea Spon; NEA 1992-, Bldg Rep; NCTM 1991-; WPCTM 1993-; *office:* Highlands HS Idaho at Pacific Aves Natrona Heights PA 15065

KOST, DEBORAH ROSE, Upper School Biology Teacher; *b:* Bethlehem, PA; *m:* Michael R. Jr.; *c:* Joshua, Sarah; *ed:* Univ of AZ (BS) Bio 1981; Lehigh Univ (MED) Scndry Ed 1989; Woods Hole Marine Bio Pgm, AP Bio Grad Course; *cr:* Gwyned Mercy Acad Bio & Phys Sci Tchr 1988-89; Yale Univ Rsrch-Spcl Ed 1989-91; Denison Nature Ctr Admin & Edctr Ed Dept 1991-92; Friends Select Bio Tchr 1992-; *ai:* Upper Schl Dean; Admissions Comm; Math Comm Chprsn; Sci Dept Chair; Environmental Club Adv; NSTA 1992-; Howard Hughes Med Inst Grant 1994; *office:* Friends Select Schl 17th & the Parkway Philadelphia PA 19103

KOST, KATHLEEN ANN, Social Work Asst Professor; *b:* Chicago, IL; *c:* Eric Davidoff; Jordan Davidoff; Rose E. Davidoff; *ed:* Univ of WI at Madison (MA) Pub Policy 1990, (MSSW) Soc Work 1993, (PHD) Soc Welfare 1994; *cr:* Schl of Soc Work SUNY at Buffalo Asst Prof 1994-; *ai:* CSWE 1994-; APPAM 1995-; ACOSA1996; Welfare to Work Cncl 1994-; Soc Work Advy Bd 1995-; *office:* SUNY At Buffalo 332 Baldy Hall Box 601050 Buffalo NY 14260

KOSTAL, CAROLYN Z., Mathematics Teacher; *ed:* Northwestern (BS) Math, Ed 1961; Kean Coll (BS) Math, Ed 1995; *cr:* Wheaton Cntrl HS Math Tchr 1961-67; Kent Pl Schl Math Tchr 1987-; *ai:* NCTM 1987-; Phi Kappa Phi; Halsey Grant; Klipstein Fellowship; *office:* Kent Place Schl 42 Norwood Ave Summit NJ 07901

KOSTANSEK, MARY SILVA, Special Education Teacher; *b:* Euclid, OH; *c:* Lisa A., Gina T., Paul A., Lauren A.; *ed:* Kent St Univ (BS) Ed 1967; Cleveland St Univ (MS) Curr, Instr 1989, (MS) Supervision 1991; *cr:* Upson Schl SBD Asst 1981-83; Memorial Park LD Tchr 1983-87; Forest Park SBD Tchr 1988-; *ai:* NEA, NEOTA, ETA 1981-; St Felicitas Schl Dev Bd 1995-, Sec; *office:* Forest Park Elem Schl 27000 Elinore Ave Euclid OH 44132

KOSTECKE, RONALD D., Counselor & Professor; *b:* Rochester, NY; *m:* Carol Hardie; *c:* David; *ed:* SUC at Brockport (BA) Psych 1969; SUNY at Albany (MS) Cnslng 1970; Univ of Rochester (EDD) Cnslng 1990; *cr:* Monroe Comm Coll Cnslr 1970-; Pvt Practice Individual, Marriage & Family Cnslr 1984-; *ai:* Monroe Comm Coll Writing Across the Curr Comm; ACA; ACCA; AMHCA; IAMFC; NYSACD; NYMHCA; NYSCCA; NCC 1984-; *office:* Monroe Community Coll 1000 E Henrietta Rd Rochester NY 14623

KOSTENKO, MICHAEL DAVID, Social Studies Dept Coord; *b:* Paterson, NJ; *m:* Carlin Priscilla Mulcock; *c:* Timothy, William, Kevin, Joshua; *ed:* Seton Hall Univ (BS) Ed, Eng 1969, (MA) Sec Ed 1973; Courses in Psych, Schl Law, Sociology, Ec, Contract Law, Coaching; *cr:* De Paul HS Eng Tchr 1969-70; Kinnelon HS Eng, Soc Stud Tchr 1970-87; Pt Pleasant Beach HS Soc Stud Tchr 1987-; *ai:* Girls JV Tennis Coach; Girls Var Bsktbl Head Coach; Boys, Girls Var Track Head Coach; NEA 1969-; PPBEA 1987-, Pres; ASSP 1994-; *office:* Pt Pleasant Beach HS 700 Trenton Ave Point Pleasant Bea NJ 08742*

KOSTER, EDWARD H.,JR., Chemistry Teacher; *b:* Erie, PA; *m:* Mary Joan Hahn; *c:* Matthew, Jennifer, David; *ed:* Gannon Univ (BA) Chem 1964; Edinboro St Univ (MED) Phys Sci 1971; 18 Credit Hrs Schl Admin; *cr:* West Tech HS Chem Tchr 1964-67; North East HS Chem Tchr 1967-; *ai:* Golf & Bowling Coach; Yrbk & Acad Competition Adv; Sci Dept Head; Ath & Asst Ath Dir; NEA 1967-; PSEA 1967-; PASSP 1988-92; *office:* North East HS 1901 Freeport Rd North East PA 16428

KOSTER, MARY M., 6th Grade Science Teacher; *b:* Morgan City, LA; *m:* John W.; *ed:* Nicholls St Univ (BA) Elem Ed 1978, (MS) Admin, Supervision 1983; Post Grad Stud in Geog, GATE; 45 Credit Hrs in Sci Ed, Environmental Stud; *cr:* Maitland Elem Schl 4th, 6th Grd Tchr 1978-86; Redding MS 6th Grd Tchr 1987-; *ai:* NSTA, NEA, Appoquinimink Ed Assn 1987-; DE Tchrs of Sci 1989-; DE Geographic Alliance 1990-; *office:* Redding MS 201 New St Middletown DE 19709

KOSTER, RHINA, Elem Social Studies Teacher; *b:* Jersey City, NJ; *m:* Robert; *c:* L. Steven, Russell; *ed:* Jersey City St (BA) Elem 1969, (MA) Elem & Rdng Specialist; 33 Credit Hrs; *cr:* S A Roberson Elem Tchr 1969-92; Bayonne HS Basic Skills Rdng 1992-94; Washington Elem Tchr 1994-; *ai:* Multi Cultural, Color Guard, Tchr Recognition, Yrbk Comm; NEA, NJEA, BTA 1975-; AFT 1975-; Humane Soc US 1994-; Humane Soc NJ 1994-; St of NJ Grant for Innovative Pgms; Bd of Ed Bayonne Grant for Innovative Pgm; Tchr Recognition Awd NJ for S A Roberson Schl; *office:* Washington Elem Schl 9 191 Avenue B Bayonne NJ 07002*

KOSTKA, ROBERT RAYMOND, Social Studies Teacher; *b:* Taunton, MA; *m:* Lynne Spence; *c:* Andrew, Allison; *ed:* Salem St Coll (BS) Soc Stud 1970, (MAT) Geography 1976; Attnd Northeastern Univ, Bridgewater St Coll, Plymouth Cty Ed Assn, National Center for Teaching & Thinking; *cr:* Bridgewater Raynham Regna Sociology, US His & Amer Govt Tchr 1970-, Humanities Dept Head 1995-; *ai:* Adv St & Local Stu Govt Days; B-R Tchrs Assn 1970-, Pres, Exec Bd; MA Tchrs Assn & MA Cncl For Soc Stud 1970-; Bd of Water Commissioners 1993-, Commissioner; Kingston Kingdom Playground Comm 1988-90, Co-Chair; Soc Stud Tchr Yr 1990; *home:* 14 Silver Lake Dr Kingston MA 02364*

KOSTYLA, DENNIS J., Mathematics Teacher; *b:* Providence, RI; *m:* Trudy Tessier; *c:* David; *ed:* RI Coll (BA) Math 1967; 39 Credit Hrs Sdncry Ed, Math; *cr:* East Greenwich HS Math Tchr 1967-95; *ai:* Girls Track Coach; Mentor Tchr; NEA, NEARI 1967-; EG Tchrs Assn 1967-, VP 1989-91; Vol Prgm Univ of RI 1986-, 250 Hrs Svc Awd; Scripted, Produced, Edited Two Educl Films for Cable TV; Grants Funding, For Traffic Safety Prgm, Wrote Follow-up Article for Natl Safety Magazine, Five for Drivers's Ed.

KOSZOWSKI, LILLYAN INTROZZI, Art Teacher; *b:* Budapest, Hungary; *m:* Thomas; *c:* Adam, Victoria; *ed:* Hunter Coll (BA) Art Ed 1967, (MA) Art 1971; Temple Gifted Cert; Holy Family Elem Cert; *cr:* Bay Ridge HS Art Tchr; Summit Schl Art Tchr; Temple Univ Stu Tchr Supvr; Bensalem Schls Art Tchr; *ai:* Stu Cncl Yrbk; HS Girls Var Coach; HS Boys Tennis Coach; Stu at Risk Pgm; AFT 1967-; PSEA 1980-; NEA; Glen Ashton Farm Civic Assoc 1975-, Bd; Vol Pgm Coord; *home:* 4444 E Yates Rd Bensalem PA 19020*

KOTCH, JOHN PAUL, Science Teacher; *b:* Northampton, MA; *m:* Diane Martin; *c:* Jessica Anne; *ed:* Univ of MT (BA) Bio 1982; Boston Univ (MAT) Sci Ed 1987; Natl Ctr Microscale Chem Course Work Merrimack Coll; *cr:* Landmark Schl Sci Tchr 1983-85; Bishop Fenwick HS Sci Tchr 1988-94; Hamilton-Wenham Regnl HS Sci Tchr 1994-; Endicott Coll Human Anatomy & Physiology Instr 1992-; *ai:* Sci League Adv; MA Tchrs Assn 1988-; NYNEX Sci & Tech Semifinalist 1994-95; *office:* Hamilton Wenham Reg HS 775 Bay Rd South Hamilton MA 01982*

KOTCH, TIMOTHY JOHN,SR., Middle School Math Teacher; *b:* McKeesport, PA; *m:* Mary M. Luxbacher; *c:* Timothy J. Jr., Amanda E.; *ed:* Univ of Pittsburgh (BS) Metallurgical Engrng 1986; Seton Hill Coll Math Ed 1989; *cr:* Estill HS Math Tchr 1989-94; Norwin HS Math Tchr 1994-95; Norwin MS East Math Tchr 1995-; *ai:* Math Counts Team Adv; NCTM 1988-; ASCD 1988-; Dept of Energy Tchr Rsrch Assoc 1993; *office:* Norwin MS East 1 Main St North Huntingdon PA 15642

KOTCHER, KENNETH JAMES, Social Studies Teacher; *b:* Passaic, NJ; *ed:* Syracuse Univ (AB) His, Soc Stud Ed 1983; Seton Hall Univ 15 Credit Hrs Asian Stud; Natl Geographic 1989, NJ Rutgers 1988 Geog Insts; *cr:* Wayne Hills HS Soc Stud Tchr 1983-84; Hunterdon Cntrl HS Soc Stud Tchr 1984-; *ai:* Bsbl JV, Soccer Asst Var Coach; *office:* Huntedon Central Regional HS 84 Route 31 Flemington NJ 08822

KOTCHICK, MICHELE R., Cmptr Tchr & Rdng Specialist; *b:* Wilkes-Barre, PA; *ed:* Wilkes Coll (BA) Sociology 1974; Scranton Univ (MS) Rdng 1981; Addl 27 Credits Cmptr Sci Wilkes Coll, 18 Credits Cmptr Sci Wilkes Univ; *cr:* Hanover Area Schl Elem Tchr 1974-80, Rdng & Cmptr Scndry Tchr 1980-; *ai:* Act 178 Comm; PJAS Judge; PSEA, NEA 1974-; Luzerne Cty Rdng Assn; St Anns Awd; Excl in Tchng Awd 1990-91; PSPA Yrbk 1st Place Awds 1994-95; Herof Jones Yrbk Awds 1994-95; *office:* Hanover Area Jr Sr HS 1600 Sans Souci Pky Wilkes Barre PA 18702

KOTCHO, JAMES P., HS Social Science Teacher; *b:* Throop, PA; *m:* Nancy Gross; *ed:* Univ of Scranton (BS) His 1967; Montclair St Univ (MA) Soc Sci 1975; Addl 60 Post Masters Hrs; 12 Credits Toward Masters in Archaeology at Rutgers Univ at New Brunswick; *cr:* Jackson Twp Tchr 1967-68; US Army Co Commander 1968-70; Bloomfield HS Soc Sci Tchr 1970-; *ai:* NEA, NJEA 1967-; Bloomfield Ed Assn 1967-, Treas; NCSS 1990-; Soc of Amer Archaeology 1995-; US Army Reserve 1970-, Colonel; *office:* Bloomfield HS 160 Broad St Bloomfield NJ 07003

KOTCHO, NANCY BUSHTA, Kindergarten Teacher; *b:* Scranton, OH; *m:* Joseph; *c:* Katrina; *ed:* Marywood Coll (BS) Elem Ed & Early Chldhd 1985; Masters Equivalency; *cr:* Holy Ghost 3rd-4th Grd Tchr 1985-87, Kndgtn Tchr 1987-88; Vly View 5th Grd Tchr 1988-90, 3rd Grd Tchr 1990-91, Kndgtn Tchr 1991-; *ai:* Curr Steering Comm; VVEA 1988-; PSEA & NEA 1989-; *office:* Valley View Elem Schl 901 Main St Peckville PA 18452*

KOTKIN, JUDITH SAMUELS, Math & Computer Science Tchr; *b:* Bklyn, NY; *m:* Richard; *c:* Lara, Michelle; *ed:* Brooklyn Coll (BA) Math 1966, (MA) Math Ed 1981; Admin Cert 1991; 3 Credits at Colgate Univ Pascal; *cr:* Brooklyn Tech HS Math Tchr 1967-; *ai:* Garden Club 1994-, Pres; NSF Grant in Cmptr Sci at Colgate with Stipend; *office:* Brooklyn Technical HS 29 Fort Greene Pl Brooklyn NY 11217*

KOTKIN, MORTON I., Biology Teacher; *b:* New York, NY; *ed:* City Coll of NY (BA) Sci 1957, (MA) Sci Ed 1960; Pace Univ (MA) Educl Admin 1987; *cr:* Bronx HS of Sci Tchr, Chm 1957-91; Yeshiva Univ HS Tchr, Chm 1961-73, 1991-95; Westchester Hebrew HS Tchr, Chm 1973-87; City Coll of NY Adj Tchr 1988-90; *ai:* Sci Club Projects Adv; AFT 1960-; Synagogue 1963-, Trustee; NSF Grants Loretto Heights Coll 1963, Sarah Lawrence Coll Bio, Chem; *office:* Yeshiva Univ HS For Boys 2540 Amsterdam Ave New York NY 10033

KOTLARZ, VIRGINIA, Dept Chair & Prgm Dir Med Tech; *b:* Olean, NY; *m:* Theodore; *c:* Kathryn; *ed:* SUNY at Fredonia (BS) Med Tech 1976; SUNY at Buffalo (MS) Allied Hlth Ed 1983, (PHD) Educl Admin 1994; *cr:* Millard Fillmore Hosp Med Technologist 1976-82; Daemen Coll Med Tech Fac 1982-88, Dept Chair, Prgm Dir 1988-; *ai:* Lambda Tau Adv; Amer Soc Clinical Lab Sci 1980-; Amer Soc Clinical Pathologists 1984-, Assoc Mem; Presbyn Homes of Western NY 1994-, Bd of Dirs; Articles Pub; *office:* Daemen Coll 4380 Main St Amherst NY 14226

KOTOK, LINDA D., Kindergarten Teacher; *b:* Wilkinsburg, PA; *m:* John M.; *c:* Jaime Leigh, Lisa Marie; *ed:* Edinboro St Coll (BS) Elem Ed & Early Chldhd 1974; Addl 24 Hrs Penn St Univ; *cr:* Penn Elem Kdgn Tchr 1975-76; Sunrise Elem 4th Grd Tchr 1976-77; Harrison Park Elem Kdgn Tchr 1977-; Harrison Park Level Green Kdgn Tchr 1991-92; *ai:* PTEA,

PSEA, NEA 1975-; *office:* Harrison Park Elem Schl 10 Dell Ave Jeannette PA 15644

KOTUN, CAROL ANN, Mathematics Teacher; *b:* Youngstown, OH; *ed:* Kent St Univ (BA) Sec Math, Russian 1970, (MED) Sec Ed 1974; 20 Hrs Post Grad Math; Natl Sci Fnd 1972-80; *cr:* Brown Jr HS 8th-9th Grd Math Tchr 1970-74; Ravenna HS Alg I, II, Geometry, Pre-Calculus Tchr 1974-; *ai:* 22 Yr Adv Acad Challenge Team; NCTM 1985-, Math Dept Sec 1970-74; Ravenna Ed Assn 1970-, Treas 3 Yrs, Sec 3 Yrs; NEA; OEA; Martha Holden Jennings Scholar 1985; Northcentral Evaluation Math Comm Chm 1988; *home:* 1509 Stratford Dr Kent OH 44240

KOTUN, MARTHA ESSEX, Kindergarten Teacher; *b:* Dunkirk, NY; *m:* John J; *c:* Joseph, Heidi; *ed:* Keuka Coll (BS) Elem Ed 1976; Elmire Coll (MS) Elem Ed 1981; *cr:* Nursery Schls Head Start Prgm Tchr 1966-76; Trumansburg Elem Schl Tchr 1976-; *ai:* Parent Edctr for Parents of Teens & Children 4-12; NEA 1972-; NAEYC 1962-, Pres; Natl Trainer for Active Parenting Pub; Newspaper Writer; Advy Bd; *home:* 9386 Congress St Trumansburg NY 14886

KOTZAN, HOLLY WILLS, Fourth Grade Teacher; *b:* PR; *m:* Kip; *ed:* Denison Univ (BA) Eng Lit 1988; Sacred Heart Univ (MA) Tchng 1991; *cr:* Voluntown Elem Schl 4th, 6th, 7th & 8th Grd Tchr 1990-93, 4th Grd Tchr 1995-; US Peace Corps Tchr & Consultant 1993-95; *ai:* NEA; US Peace Corps, Vol; *office:* Voluntown Elem Schl Rt 138 PO Box 129 Voluntown CT 06384

KOTZAN, JANICE MEIER, Spanish & English Teacher; *b:* Johnstown, PA; *m:* Dennis P.; *c:* Nicole; *ed:* Clarion St Coll (BS) Span & Eng 1973; Post-Grad Stud Univ of Valencia & Univ of Southern FL; *cr:* DuBois Area HS Span & Eng Tchr 1973-79; Windber Area HS Eng Tchr 1979-80; Conemaugh Vly HS Span & Eng Tchr 1981-; *ai:* Span Club Adv; Host of Frgn Exch Stdnts; Travel with Stdnts to Mexico; HS Steering Comm Mem; PSEA 1973-; NEA 1973-; Conemaugh Hosp Jr Auxiliary 1990-, Gala Rep; *home:* 1777 Regal Dr Johnstown PA 15904

KOUAME, SHEILA PULLEY, Spanish Teacher; *b:* Rocky Mount, NC; *c:* Qua Shaun; *ed:* Bennett Coll (BA) Span 1980; Georgetown Univ (MAT) Eng as a Frgn Lang 1983; Attnd Univ of Salamanca 1975; *cr:* Smith Berlin Rsrch Firm Ed 1985-86; Calvin Coolidge Sr HS Span Tchr 1986-92; Urban League Ed Specialist 1992-94; Prince George's Cty HS Span Tchr 1994-; *ai:* Tutor, Vol Span, Fr, Eng Bsktbl Team 1987-91; Founder Span Club 1994-; Spon Class 1998; NEA, MD St Tchrs Assn Prince George's Cty Edctrs Assn 1994-; First Bapt Church 1989-; Dean's List 1976-80; Bennett Scholar 1977; Grad Top 20% 1980; Recognized by Alpha Kappa Mu Superior Schlsp Span 1977, 1980, WUSA Dedication Tutorial Svcs 1989; Natl Dean's List 1979-80; *home:* 1616 16th St NW Apt 705 Washington DC 20009

KOUBEK, PAULETTE ANN, English Instructor; *b:* Cleveland, OH; *m:* Charles Yao; *ed:* Cleveland St Univ (BA) Eng 1982; Univ of IL (MA) TESOL 1986; *cr:* Yonsei Coll Eng Tchr 1986-87; Cuyahoga Comm Coll Eng Tchr 1987-88; Union Cty Coll Eng Instr 1988-91; Essex Cty Coll Eng Instr 1991-; *ai:* Stu Newsletter Fac Ed; TESOL 1986-; NEA, NJEA, ASCD, CCCC 1992-; Former Asst Ed NJ TESOL-BE Newsletter; *office:* Essex County Coll 303 University Ave Newark NJ 07102*

KOUKIS, SUSAN ROBINSON, English Teacher; *b:* Delaware, OH; *m:* Vlassis; *c:* Natalie, Alexander, Andrew; *ed:* Ohio Wesleyan Univ (BA) Hum, Classics 1976; OH ST (BS) Scndry Eng Ed 1985; 6 Credit Hrs Rdng; 3 Credit Hrs Portfolio Writing in Classroom; *cr:* Hambakis Schls Cmptr Stud Tchr 1979-84; Pierce Coll Tchr 1983-84; Willis MS 8th Eng Tchr 1985-89; Marysville HS Tchr 1990-; *ai:* NHS Adv; Stu Cncl Adv; NEA 1990-; Undergrad Flwshp; Benjamin Spencer Awd Best Poem; Article in Old Cars; *office:* Marysville HS 800 Amrine Mill Rd Marysville OH 43040

KOULET, CASSANDRA, Tech Prep Coord & Guid Cnslr; *b:* Medford, MA; *m:* Michael L. Capasso; *ed:* Univ of TX at El Paso (BS) Scndry Ed 1969; Suffolk Univ (MA) Cnslng 1972; RI Coll 30+ Grad Hrs; Coll Yr in Athens Greece 1964-65; *cr:* Bel Air HS Soc Stud Tchr 1969-71; N Kingstown HS Guid Cnslr 1972-, Tech Prep Coord 1986-; *ai:* Tech Prep Advy & Exec Comm; Tech Prep Exec Dir; Arts Talk; Tech Prep Stu Adv; NEA 1969-; RI Ed Assn 1972-; N Kingstown Tchrs Assn 1972-; Warwick Museum of Art 1986-, Life Mem; NK Chamber of Commerce 1994-, Bus & Partnerships; Tech Prep Tchrs in Industry 1994-; Southwest Cooperative Educl Lab Curr Dev Grant 1969; PA St Univ Biling Ed Tchr Flwshp Awd 1978; W Bay Voc Tech Schl Child Care Pgm Grant 1984; Bus Ed, TPAD, & Coord RI Tech Prep Grants 1986-95; Comm Coll of RI TPAD Pgm Video 1993; *office:* North Kingstown H S 150 Fairway Dr North Kingstown RI 02852

KOUTSOSPYROS, AGAMEMNON DEMETRIOS, Assoc Prof of Environ Engrng; *b:* Patras, Greece; *m:* Effie Nicoladu; *c:* Demetrios; *ed:* Natl Tech Univ at Athens (BS) Chem Eng 1979; Polytechnic Inst of NY (MS) Environmental Eng 1985; Polytechnic Univ (PHD) Environmental Eng 1990; *cr:* Polytechnic Univ Adj Asst Prof 1989-92; Pratt Inst Asst Prof 1989-92; Univ of New Haven Asst Prof 1992-95, Assoc Prof 1995-; *ai:* Core Curr, Grad Comms; NEF 1984-; AWWA 1992-; IWPRC 1984-; Curr Advy Bd St Demetrios HS 1994-; Pub Several Scientific Articles, Chptr in Book, Biological Treatment of Hazardous Wastes; *office:* Univ Of New Haven 300 Orange Ave West Haven CT 06516

KOUVEL, MAUREEN, Head Guidance Counselor; *b:* Bayonne, NJ; *m:* John H.; *c:* Karen M. Carter; Barbara M. Duff; *ed:* Monmouth Univ (BS) Elem Ed 1976; Kean Coll (MA) Stu Personnel 1985; Soc Work, Supvr Cert; Prin Cert; *cr:* Middletown Bd of Ed Elem Tchr 1977-85, Guid Cnslr 1985-93, Head Guid Cnslr 1993-; *ai:* Jr Hnr Soc Adv; NEA 1976-; ACA 1985-; Awded Parenting Groups Grants; *office:* Bayshore MS 734 Leonardville Leonardo NJ 07737

KOVAC, DONNA SUITS, Business Teacher; *b:* Mohawk, NY; *m:* Allen S.; *c:* Lynne, Charles, Suzanne; *ed:* St Univ of NY at Albany (BS) Bus Ed 1959; Syracuse Univ, Oswego St 30 Hrs; *cr:* Oppenheim Ephratch Cntrl Schls Bus Tchr 1959-60; West Genesee Cntrl Schls Bus Tchr 1960-61; North Syracuse Cntrl Schls Bus Tchr 1969-; *ai:* Mock Trial Coach, Adv; Pathways Team; Conflict Resolution Mediation Trained Mediator; Delta Pi Epsilon 1975-; NSEA, AFT 1970-; Onondaga Cty Yth Court Steering Comm 1993-; *office:* Cicero-North Syracuse HS N Star Blvd Cicero NY 13039

KOVAC, SHIRLEY ANTOS, Second Grade Teacher; *b:* Sharon, PA; *m:* Donald; *c:* Shelly, Karen Cidila, Donald Jr.; *ed:* Slippery Rock Univ (BS) Ed 1972; *cr:* Sharon City Schls Lib Aide 1972-75, Elem Permanent Sub Tchr 1975-76; Hadley Elem Schl First, Second, Fifth Grd Tchr 1976-93; Musser Elem Schl First, Second, Fifth Grd Tchr 1976-93; West Hill Elem Schl First, Second, Fifth Grd Tchr 1976-93; Case Ave Elem Schl First, Second, Fifth Grd Tchr 1976-; *ai:* Ldrshp Cncl; NEA, PSEA 1976-; Coll Club of Sharon 1974-; *office:* Case Avenue Elem Schl 36 Case Ave Sharon PA 16146

KOVACH, CLAUDIA MARIE, Professor of English & French; *b:* Brownsville, PA; *m:* Ronald L.Smorada; *ed:* Seton Hill Coll (BA) Eng, Fr 1973; Purdue Univ (MA) Comparative Lit 1975, (PHD) Comparative Lit 1980; 16 Credits Fr Lang, Quebecois Culuture Universite Laval; *cr:* Neumann Coll Lecturer 1980-83, Instr 1983-85, Asst Prof 1985-88, Assoc Prof 1988-93; Natl Taiwan Univ Visiting Assoc Prof 1990-91; Neuman Coll Prof 1993-; *ai:* Senator Fac Governance; Chair Coll-Wide Curr, Co-Chair Steering Comms; Ed Self-Stud Document NC Commission Higher Ed Mid Sts Region Re-Accreditationf AAUP Pres; Study Abroad Adv; MLA 1978-; NEMLA 1982-; AAUP 1992-; NAB-IAS; ICLA; Medieval Acad of Amer; The Tristan Soc; Sears Roebuck Tchng Excl, Campus Leadership 1990, Growth Schslp Awds; Pub Articles, Book Chapters; *office:* Neumann Coll Concord Rd Aston PA 19014*

KOVACH, GARY, Social Studies Teacher; *b:* Cleveland, OH; *ed:* Cleveland St Univ (BA) His 1992; *cr:* Vly Forge HS Soc Stud Tchr 1993-; *ai:* Girls & Boys Tennis Coach; Stage Crew Dir; Bldg Advy Comm; NEA, OH Ed Assn 1993-; Parma Educl Assn 1993-, Bldg Rep; *office:* Valley Forge HS 9999 Independence Blvd Cleveland OH 44130*

KOVACH, SANDRA, Health Occupations Instructor; *b:* Chicago, IL; *m:* Emil P.; *c:* Kenneth P.; *ed:* MD Univ (BS) Ed-Summa Cum Laude 1973, (MS) Nursing-Summa Cum Laude 1974; Sibley Meml Hospital RN 1959; Advanced Prof Tchng Cert; *cr:* Prince George's Hospital Ctr Staff Nurse 1959, Head Nurse, Emergency Room 1959-60, IN & Out Surgery Supvr 1960-61; Drs Moyers, Cormeau, Carmeron Office Nurse 1961-66; Bladensburg HS Hlth Occupations Instr 1966-; *ai:* Tchr Recognition Comm; Voc Industrial Club of Amer; Hlth Career Promotion chair 3 yrs; Comm Coll Tech Prep Articulation Comms; Dept Chprsn 5 Yrs; Aw Comm 10 Yrs; NHS Comm 10 Yrs; NEA, MD St Ed Assn, Prince Georges Cty Ed Assn, MD Voc Assn 1966-; MD St Hlth Occupations 1966-, Chprsn 1 Yr; Phi Kappa Phi Honor Soc 1973-, Grant 1974; Ioata Lambda Sigma Honor Soc 1973-; Career Tech Dept Chair 5 Yrs; Who's Who Among Stdnts in Amer Univ & Coll 1974-75; Sigma Theta Tau Honor Soc 1974; Hlth Careers Club Spon 8 Yrs; In Svc 3 Yrs, Awds 7 Yrs Comms; Schl Mngmt Team 5 Yrs; In Schl Writing Improvement Team 5 Yrs; Distingnished Prgm Awd Voc Tech Ed 1985; Outstanding Tchr Rotary Club 1970; Outstanding Scndry Ed 1975, 1994; *office:* Bladensburg HS 5610 Tilden St Bladensburg MD 20710

KOVACIC, ROBERT WILLIAM, Senior Army & JROTC Instr; *b:* Cleveland, OH; *m:* Brenda Jean Reynolds; *c:* Robert, Brenda, Brian, David; *ed:* John Carroll Univ (BA) Pol Sci 1970; Univ of Southern CA (MS) Systems Mngmt 1982; Armored Ofcr Advance Course Command & Gen Staff Coll; *cr:* US Army Ldrshp Positions 1970-93; US Army ARmor Schl Instr, Doctrine Analyst 1980-83; US Army Engr Schl Dir Tactics, Ldrshp Dept 1989-91; *ai:* JROTC Drill, Exhibition Team Adv; Raider Challenge Team Coach; UFT 1993-; Ft Hamilton Chapel 1991-; Bronze Star, Meritorious Svc Medals, Ranger Tab, Airborne, Combat Infantryman's Badge, Royal Order of St George, DeFlurry Medal Military Awds; Articles Pub 1981-82; *home:* 117A General Lee Ave Brooklyn NY 11209

KOVACIK, GEOFFREY JOHN, Soc Stud Dept Chm, AP His Tchr; *b:* Butler, PA; *m:* Sara Jane Carmody; *c:* Geoffrey Jr.; *ed:* Slippery Rock Univ (MED) His 1974; *cr:* Moniteau Schl Dist Elem Instr 1968-69; butler Area Schl Dist Soc Stud Tchr 1969-; *ai:* Butler Hockey Club Fac Adv 1973-76; Baccalaureate Comm Chm 1976-95; Butler Ed Assn 1969-; PA St Ed Assn 1968-; NEA 1968-; Thomas Jefferson Meml Fnd 1990-; Col Williamsburg Fnt 1989-; Poplar Forest Fnt 1993-; Natl Mngmt, Historic Presentation 1994-; PA Unique Curr Achvmts 1978-, Comm Rel.

KOVAGE, CARMELA, Spanish Teacher; *b:* Bennington, VT; *m:* Michael; *ed:* Univ of VT (BS) Span 1982; *cr:* Mt Anthony Union HS Frgn Lang Tchr 1982-; *ai:* NEA 1983-; VFLA 1992-; *home:* 503 Jefferson Hts Bennington VT 05201

KOVALCHICK, JOSEPH J., Technology Education Teacher; *b:* Punxsutawney, PA; *ed:* CA Univ of PA (BS) Tech Ed 1985; Attnd Buffalo St Coll, Jamestown Comm Coll, IN Univ of PA; *cr:* Cassadaga Jr, Sr HS Tech Ed 1986-89; Armstrong Schl Dist Tech Ed 1989-90; IN Jr HS Tech Ed 1990-91; Kittanning Sr HS Tech Ed 1991-; *ai:* Equipment Mgr for All Sport Prgms; PSEA, NEA 1989-; Tech Ed Assn of PA 1984-; All Star Edctr 1995; *home:* 215 N Ridge Rd Shelocta PA 15774

KOVALESKI, PAULA HECKMAN, Third Grade Teacher; *b:* Philadelphia, PA; *m:* Donald; *c:* Karyn K. Greengo, Susan K., Diane K.; *ed:* Wilkes Univ (BA) Elem Ed 1979; *cr:* Saint Judes Schl 2nd & 3rd Grd Tchr 1981-; *ai:* Nature Trail Chprsn; Saint Judes Hospital Math-a-Thon; Northeast PA Oral Rdng Competition Coord; *office:* St Jude Schl 422 S Mountain Blvd Mountain Top PA 18707*

KOVALESKY, TONY RAY, American History Teacher; *b:* Steubenville, OH; *m:* Deborah Burch; *c:* Mary, Jenny, Annie; *ed:* Warren Wilson Coll (BA) His, Pol Sci & Scndry Ed 1977; Elem Ed 1st-7th Grd Youngstown St Univ, Kent St & Univ of Steubenville; *cr:* Piney Woods Cntry Life Schl Tchr 1977-78; Springfield HS Tchr 1978-82; Richmond Elem Tchr 1982-87; Edison HS Tchr 1987-; *ai:* Coach Ftbl, Reserve Girls Bsktbl & Boys & Girls Track; Chm Soc Stud Dept; Close Up Prgm Advr; NEA & OH Ed Assn 1978-; Edison Local Ed Assn 1978-, Pres & Sec; East Springfield Ruritans 1982-, Pres, VP, Zone Governor, Outstanding Pres Awd; Jefferson Cty School Grant Pub Guide to Citizenship Proficiency Test; *office:* Edison HS Box 308 Richmond OH 43944

KOVALL, ELIZABETH REINHARDT, Third Grade Teacher; *b:* Rochester, NY; *m:* Richard; *c:* Nicholas, Jessica, Stephen; *ed:* Buffalo St Coll (BS) Elem Ed, Spec Ed 1981; Elmira Coll (MS) Rdng 1986; *cr:* Tioga Cntrl Schl 3rd Grd Tchr 1983-; *ai:* Thematic Instruction Performance Assessment, Bldg Comm; NEA 1984-; Northeast Regnl Lab; *office:* Nichols Elem Schl PO Box 199 Roki Blvd Nichols NY 13812

KOVANES, WILLIAM G., Eighth Grd Language Arts Tchr; *b:* Lorain, OH; *m:* Sandra Dolan; *c:* Christopher; *ed:* Kent St Univ (BA) Eng 1966, (MED) Eng 1972; *cr:* Lorain Cty Schls Eng Tchr 1966-68; Cardinal Local Schls Eng Tchr 1968-; *ai:* Yrbk; Schl Newspaper; NEA, OEA 1966-; Martha Holden Jennings Scholar; *home:* 13049 Old State Rd Huntsburg OH 44046

KOVARY, LORAINE BRITA, Spanish Teacher; *b:* Bethlehem, PA; *m:* Frank; *ed:* Kutztown Univ (BS) Ed 1970, (MA) Span 1973; Univ of Valencia at Valencia Spain 21 Credit Hrs Span; *cr:* Wilson HS Span Tchr 1970-; *ai:* Span Club Adv; Stud Tour to Spain Prgm Head Chaperone & Organizer; AFT 1986-; Amer Assn of Tchrs of Span & Portuguese 1972-; Wilson Fed of Tchrs & Berks Cty Foreign Lang Alliance; Wilson Schl Dist Tchr Appreciation Awd 1986; *office:* Wilson Sr H S 2601 Grandview Blvd West Lawn PA 19609

KOVERMAN, GERALD ALLEN, Agri Ed Teacher; *b:* Dayton, OH; *m:* Ruth Ann Kuether; *c:* Kimberly Ann Mc Eldowney, Christine Marie Brubaker, Kelly Ann Otte, Michael S.; *ed:* OH St Univ (BS) Ag Ed 1962; *cr:* Ansonia Local Schls Ag Ed Tchr 1962-; *ai:* FFA, NHS Adv; NEA, OEA, AVA, OVA, AEA 1962-; OVATA 1962-, Treas 1989-, Outstdng Ag Tchr 1983; Knights of Columbus 1965-; Ansonia Village Cncl 1968-78, Pres 1974, 1976-78; Ansonia Mayor 1975-; Jaycees 1966-79; *home:* PO Box 311 Ansonia OH 45303

KOVITZ, SONDRA E., First Grade Teacher; *b:* New York, NY; *m:* Howard I.; *c:* Debra, Hugh; *ed:* Adelphi Univ (BS) Elem Ed 1962; Long Island Univ Post Grad Stud; Addl Credit Hrs; *cr:* Babylon Meml Grd Schl Sixth Grd Tchr 1962-65; Boardman Elem Schl Fourth Grd Tchr 1985-90, First Grd Tchr 1990-; *ai:* Primary Theater Group, Mathletes Adv; Schl Based Planning, Shared Decision Making, Educl Articulation Teams; AFT, NYSUT, Oceanside Fed of Tchrs 1985-; Women's Amer ORT 1965-, Fin Sec; *office:* Boardman Elem Schl #9E Alice & Beatrice Ave Oceanside NY 11572

KOVOLISKY, ANTOINETTE L., First Grade Teacher; *b:* Kearny, NJ; *ed:* Chestnut Hill (BS) Elem Ed 1972; LaSalle Coll (BS) Religion 1972; Yearly Updates in All Subject Areas Through Wkshps & Mini Course Day Helenas 2nd Grd Tchr 1967-69; Christ the King 3rd, 5th Grd Tchr 1 St Charles Borromeo 1st Grd Tchr 1973-; *ai:* Act 90,195 Co Textbooks; Parish Cncl Tutor; Mid St Evaluation Philosophy NCEA 1967-; Tchr of Yr 2nd Place 1974; *office:* St Charles Borrom 1704 Bristol Pike Bensalem PA 19020

KOWALCZYK, GEORGIANNA C., Chemistry & Physics Teac Detroit, MI; *m:* Chester R.; *c:* Teresa Rose; *ed:* Rosary Hill Coll (1964; Union Coll (MS) Chem 1970; Attnd Niagara Univ, St Univ o Buffalo, Canisius Coll; *cr:* Villa Maria Coll Chem & Physic 1976-79; Villa Maria Acad Bio Tchr 1965-71, Earth Sci Tchr 1 Chem & Physics Tchr 1967-; *ai:* Sci Club Adv; Bloodmobile STANYS & NSTA 1985-; Italian Sons & Daughters of America Orator 31 Yrs, Natl VP 6 Yrs; Presidential Awd Nom for Excl in Tc 1989; *office:* Villa Maria Acad 600 Doat St Buffalo NY 14211

KOWALCZYK, KATHLEEN KERRY, Fourth-Fifth Grade Teac Somerset, PA; *ed:* Univ of Pittsburgh at Johnstown (BS) Elem Ed Univ of Pittsburgh (MED) Elem Ed 1977; *cr:* North Star Schl Dist Tchr 1975-77, 5th Grd Tchr 1977-80, 4th Grd Tchr 1980-91, 4th- Tchr 1991-; *ai:* Fourth Grd Math Curr Dev Comm; North Star Wes Bd; Strategic Planning Intermediate Task Force; Parent & Tchr Con Focus Group; PA St Ed Assn, NEA, North Star Ed Assn 19 Stanislaus Cath Church 1953-, Religious Ed Asst Coord K-6 1976-82; St Vincent Coll 1988-, Retreat Bd; *home:* 212 Susqueha Boswell PA 15531

KOWALCZYK, THERESA ZAPP, English Teacher; *b:* New Bru NJ; *m:* Daniel R.; *ed:* Univ of CT (BA) Eng & Span 1987; Univ (MEd) Eng Ed 1989; 6 Addl Cr Hrs in Eng & Ed at Univ of RI; *cr:* Deering Jr High Eng Tchr 1990-; *ai:* NCTE 1989-; Various Articles Mgrs Magazine in 1987; *office:* John F Deering MS Webster Kni West Warwick RI 02893

KOWALESKI, DONALD JOSEPH, English Teacher; *b:* Elyria, (Cathy Whittaker; *c:* Matthew; *ed:* Univ of Dayton (BA) Amer Stud Wright St Univ (ME) Tchr Ldr 1989; Tchr Cert 1975; *cr:* Centerv Stu Tchr 1975; Lebanon HS Eng Tchr 1976-; *ai:* Past Frosh Bsktbl 10 Yrs; NEA, OEA 1976-; *office:* Lebanon HS 160 Miller Rd Leban 45036

KOWALEWSKI, HOPE CARTER, Aquatics Teacher & Coa Philadelphia, PA; *m:* Anthony John; *ed:* Gettysburg Coll (BA) Psych 24 Credits Instrl II Cert at Penn St Univ; *cr:* York Suburban Schl D Tchr, Asst Var Swim Coach 1987-89; Northeastern Schl Dist Ac Tchr, Head Var Swim Coach 1989-; *ai:* Head Var Swimming Team (Bobcat Swim Club Age Group Team Head Coach; Wellness Comm; PSEA 1991-; Amer Swim Coaches Assn, Natl Interscholastic Coaches Assn 1990-; Jr League of York 1988-91; Swim Coach of Y 1993-94; *office:* Northeastern M S N Hartman St Manchester PA 1

KOWALIK, MICHAEL S., English Teacher; *b:* Schenectady, N Winifred Marie; *c:* Erin, Gretchen, Sean; *ed:* Shippensburg St Col Eng 1970, (MED) Eng 1977; Addl 30 Credits Beyond Masters; *c* Lion Area Schl Dist Eng Tchr 1970-; *ai:* Stu Cncl Adv; RLAEA Pres; PSEA, NEA 1970-; BPOE 1984-; Fulbright Schlsp Awd Exch T Canada; *home:* RR 5 Box 145A Red Lion PA 17356*

KOWALSKI, DEBRA, Coordinator of Pace Program; *b:* Troy, N William LaChapelle; *ed:* SUNY at New Paltz (BA) Psych 1980; SU Albany (CAS) Cnslng, Prsnl Svcs 1984, (MS) Cnslng, Prsnl Svcs; W with Violent Families, Adolescents, Resistance; Alcoholic Family Facilitation; Family Cnslng; Substance Abuse; Trng of Trainers; *cr:* at New Paltz OASIS Dir 1980-82; SUNY at Albany Mid Earth Trng 1982-84; Equinox Substance Abuse Cnslr 1984-87; Hudson Vly Coll PACE Prgm Coord 1987-; *ai:* Sexual Harrassment Advy C *office:* Hudson Valley Comm Coll 80 Vandenburgh Ave Troy NY 12

KOWALSKI, JANET L., High School Guidance Counselor; *b:* Pittsb PA; *ed:* Clarion St Coll (BS) Math Ed 1971; Slippery Rock Univ (Scndry Guid 1984; *cr:* Slippery Rock Area HS Math Tchr 1971-95, Cnslr 1995-; *ai:* PSEA, SRAEA 1971-; PCTM 1980-; PSCA 1995-; YMCA Yth, Govt Prgm; Adv of Yr 1981; *office:* Slippery Rock Ar Kiester Rd Slippery Rock PA 16057

KOWALSKI, ROBERT JOSEPH, English & History Teacher; *b:* City, NJ; *m:* Gretchen Guiler; *c:* Robert, Susan Curto, Jennifer, K Deborah, Victoria, Rebecca; *ed:* Union Coll (AA) Lib Arts 1973; Kea (BA) Ed, Urban Stud, His & Eng 1976; Seton Hall (MED) Ed 1993; *c* Marine Corps Sgt 1955-61; NJ St Police First Class Sgt 1960-85; Cnty Regnl Dist Tchr & Coach 1985-87; Woodbridge Bd of Ed Tchr & Track & Bsktbl Coach 1987-; *ai:* Var Ftbl, Girls & Boys Var Track, Var Bsktbl Coach; NEA 1985-; WTEA 1987-; *office:* Woodbridge HS St Woodbridge NJ 07095

KOWALSKY, GERALDINE RINALDO, 9th-12th Grade En Teacher; *b:* Elizabeth, NJ; *m:* Peter J.; *c:* Jaimie, Lindsey; *ed:* Glas St Coll (BA) Eng 1974, (MA) Scndry Eng Ed 1975; Jersey City St Kean Coll of NJ Supervisory Cert; *cr:* Alexander Hamilton Jr HS Eng 1975-77; Elizabeth HS Eng Tchr 1977-80; Battin Career Ctr Eng 1980-85; Woodbridge Twp HS Eng Tchr, Subject Area Ldr 1989-; Class Adv, Cotillion Comm Chprsn; NEA 1975-; WTEA 1 Woodbridge Twp Strategic Planning Comm 1995-; WA Elem Restructuring Comm 1994-; Holy Spirit Cath Church 1995-, Vol Cate NJ Governors Tchr Recognition Awd 1982, 1992; Woodbridge Chamber of Commerce; Tchr of Yr Nom 1996.*

KOWGIOS, NICK, 10th Grade English Teacher; *ed:* LaFayette Coll Eng 1984; Iona Coll (MS) Ed 1989; *cr:* North Salem Cntrl Schls Te 1989-; *ai:* Schl Newspaper Adv; NY St Eng Cncl Edctr of Excl *office:* North Salem HS Old Rt 124 North Salem NY 10560

KOWITCH, LOUISE F., Social Studies Teacher; *b:* New York City, *m:* E. Mac Campbell; *ed:* Vassar Coll (BA) His 1982; Univ of Par Sorbonne (MA) His 1987; Brown Univ (MAT) Soc Stud 1988 Farmington HS Soc Stud Tchr 1988-; *ai:* Stu Cncl, Debate Club Adv; Day Comm; Phi Delta Kappa 1995-; ASCD 1990-; Amer Assn of His 19 St Semi Finalist CT Tchr of Yr 1994; Farmington Tchr of Yr 1 Prudence Crandall Awd for Human Rights 1994; *office:* Farmington H Montieth Dr Farmington CT 06032*

KOWKER, DONNA, Home Ec & Computer Tech Tchr; *b:* Pottsville, *ed:* Penn St Univ (BS) Home Ec Ed 1981; Lehigh Univ (MS) Instructi Tech Ed 1994; *cr:* Williams Vly Jr Sr HS Home Ec Tchr 1981 Minersville Area Jr Sr HS Home Ec Tchr 1982-89; Hamburg Area Jr S Home Ec, Cmptr Tech Tchr 1989-; *ai:* Cmptr Club; Annual Musical; N PSEA 1981-; Hamburg Area Ed Assoc 1989-, Treas; Phi Delta K 1993-; Penn St Alumni Assoc 1981-; Schuylkill Cty Friend of Ed 1990.

KOZA, BURT T., Social Studies Teacher; *b:* Amityville, NY; *m:* Marg Smolinsky; *c:* Jason; *ed:* Marist Coll at Poughkeepsie (BA) His 1968 Univ of NY at Stony Brook (MA) Liberal Stud 1978; Hofstra Univ 9 C Credits; St Rose Coll 3 Grad Credits; 6 Grad Credits Ed; *cr:* St Jos Schl 8th Grd Soc Stud, Lang, Arts & Rel Tchr 1968-72; Our Lady Perpetual Help Schl 6th-8th Grd Soc Stud Tchr 1972-; *ai:* Soc Stud Co Intnl Peace Site Comm Moderator; Grad Act Coord; Suffolk Ct Democr Comm 1972-, Area Chm; OWL Tchr & Comp Trng Ctr 1985-, Tr ı Town Dept of Consumer Protection 1987-, Dir & Chm, Whos Who Govt Awd; Town of Babylon Planning Bd 1990-; OLPH Comm Svc 85 & 1986; Babylon Town Achvmt Awd 1990; OWL Tchr Ctr Mini ıwd; *office:* Our Lady-Perpetual Help Schl 240 S Wellwood Ave ıurst NY 11757*

K, ANDREW FRANK, Associate Prof of Economics; *b:* lphia, PA; *ed:* LaSalle Univ (BA) Ec 1979; Univ of Notre Dame c 1981, (PHD) Ec 1983; *cr:* St Mary's Coll Asst Prof of Ec 1984-90, Prof of Ec 1990-; *ai:* Hnrs Prgm Asst Dir; Amer Ec Assn; MD ate Hnrs Cncl, VP; Natl Collegiate Hnrs Cncl; St Mary's Cty Comm ırp; Book: Critical Issues In Supply Side Economics 1983; Homer ge Excl in Tchng Awd 1988; Natl Endowment for Hum Summer 1989.*

REC, MARK S., Middle School Art Teacher; *b:* Kettering, OH; *m:* l. Hamilton; *c:* Ellie; *ed:* Univ of Cincinnati (BAAE) Art Ed 1989; Dayton Persuing A Masters Degree in Schl Admin; *cr:* Kettering Tchr 1989-; *ai:* Var Ftbl & Bsbl Asst Coach; Ath Bd of Controls; 989-; NAEA 1989-; Supply Paintings & Drawings for Local ı; *home:* 1525 W Stroop Rd Kettering OH 45439

ATEK, WALTER, Athletic Dir & Graphics Instr; *b:* Owensboro, Dianne Mc Clair; *c:* Cheryl Reno, Keith, Walter; *ed:* Trenton St ıdstrl Ed 1967; *cr:* South River HS Graphic Arts Instr 1967-, Ath Dir *ai:* NEA, NJEA, SREA 1967-; Ath Dirs Assn 1994-; *office:* South IS Montgomery St South River NJ 08882

K, FRANCIS X., Former Teacher; *b:* Washington, DC; *m:* Paula J. ; *c:* Michelle, John; *ed:* Univ of MD (BS) Ed 1970, (MA) Elem Ed *r:* Kenmore Elem Schl Classroom Tchr 1970-76; Greenbelt Ctr Schl Specialist 1976-80; Floating Faculty Resource Classroom Tchr 2; Beach Elem Schl Classroom Tchr 1982-87; Northern MS ɔom Tchr 1987-95; *ai:* Soccer Coach; Girls Bsktbl Calverton MS; ınce Abuse Comm; NEA 1970-; Calvert Ed Assn 1987-, Negotiations Chprsn; MD St Tchrs Assn 1970-.

KOWSKI, LEONA (MALINOWSKI), 3rd Grade Teacher; *b:* ne, NJ; *m:* Allen; *c:* Robert, Thomas; *ed:* Jersey City St Coll (BA) Ed 1972; *cr:* Drum Point Road Schl 3rd Grd Tchr 1972-; *ai:* Ocean ıng Cncl Exec Bd; Stu Invention Through Ed Coord; NJEA 1972-; 1995-; OCRC 1985-, Treas 1 Yr; HEAL 1992-; OC BSA 1983-87, other, Music Merit Badge Cnslr 1988-; Tchr of the Yr 1993; *office:* Point Road Elem Schl 41 Drum Point Rd Brick NJ 08723

OFF, JERALDINE D., Social Studies Teacher; *b:* Far Rockaway, David; *c:* Samuel, Louis, Deborah; *ed:* Wellesley Coll (BA) Pol Sci Univ of PA (LLB) Law 1968; John Hopkins Schl of Advanced al Stud 1 Yr; Albright Coll Ed Cert; *cr:* Berks Cty Court of Common Support Hearing Ofcr, Master in Divorce 1980-86, Child Advocate 37; Wilson HS Soc Stud Tchr; WY Area HS Soc Stud Tchr 1987-; *ai:* Hosp 1 Yrs; Acad Challenge Club Adv; WY Area Ed Fnd Steering , Bd Mem; Prin Advy Comm 1 Yr; NCSS 1989-; WY Area Ed Assn Rep; Tchrs of Psych Scndry Schls 1990; Articles Pub; *home:* 1334 effy Ave Wyomissing PA 19610*

OWSKI, EDMUND EDWARD, Math Teacher; *b:* Winchendon, *n:* Kathryn; *c:* Mark; *ed:* St Anselm Coll (BA) Math 1969; Univ of l (MMT) Math 1976; 12 Credit Hrs Kent St Univ; 3 Credit Hrs ster St; *cr:* Gardner HS Math Tchr 1969-; *ai:* Former Cross Cntry, JV Bsbl, JV Bsktbl Coach; Dist, St Cross Cntry Meet Dir; MTA, 1969-; Gardner Ed Assn 1969-, Treas; Cntrl MA Track Ofcls 1978-; 25 Nelson St Gardner MA 01440

OWSKI, EDWARD T., Mathematics Teacher; *b:* Chester, PA; *ed:* ova Univ (BS) Scndry Ed & Math 1979; Widener Univ (MED) al Ed & Cmptr Sci 1990; Penn St Univ 18 Credits Supervisory Cert; l Univ 4 Credits Heuristic Diagnostic Tchng; *cr:* Penn-Delco Schl Math Tchr 1979-95; Drexel Univ Asst Dir to Diagnostic Math ing Lab 1995-; *ai:* Drama Club; Sun Valley Drama Club; Dir of Sr y Show; 8th Grd Team Ldr; PSEA, NEA; *office:* Northley MS 95 ord Rd Aston PA 19014

MA, TERRY ALAN, Economics Teacher; *b:* Berea, OH; *ed:* Ashland (BS) Ec 1975; Clemson Univ (MED) Admin, Supervision 1980,) Admin, Supervision 1988; *cr:* Strongsville Sr HS Soc Stud Tchr ; *ai:* Track & Field Coach 1979-; Cross Cty Coach; NEA 14 Yrs; land Area Ec Tchr of Yr 1991; *office:* Strongsville Sr H S 20025 Lunn rongsville OH 44136

OL, STEPHEN MICHAEL, Social Studies Teacher; *b:* Hartford, CT; eborah Ann Kozol; *ed:* Brandeis Univ (BA) Amer Stud, African & Amer Stud 1983; George Washington Univ (JD) Law 1986; Scndry ert West Chester Univ 1992; *cr:* Drinker Biddle & Reath Employee fits Attorney 1986-89; Price Waterhouse Employee Benefits Svcs Mgr 91; Upper Merion Area HS Soc Stud Tchr 1992-, Soc Stud Dept Chm ; *ai:* NEA, PSEA 1992-; UMAEA VP Chief Negotiator 1995-; Amer Assn 1986-; Southern Poverty Law Ctr 1987-; *office:* Upper Merion HS 435 Crossfield Rd King Of Prussia PA 19406

UCHOWSKY, MICHAEL EDWARD, Technology Education ner; *b:* Union City, PA; *m:* Pamela Rose Pongratz; *c:* Lauren, Kevin; alifornia Univ of PA Industrial Arts, Tech Ed 1980; Edinboro Univ of Masters Equivalency Instructional Media 1985; Realtor; Working on St for Residential Appraisal License; *cr:* General McLane HS Tech Ed 1980-; *ai:* Tech Prep Ingenuity Challenge Adv; Tech Ed Assn of North ern PA 1980-, Pres, Outstanding Svc Awd; Tech Ed Assn of PA 1980-, 1 VP, Conf Wkshp Chprsn; PSEA, NEA 1980-; Natl & PA Assn of ors 1991-; *office:* General Mclane HS 11761 Edinboro Rd Edinboro 6412

USKO, GENEVIEVE MARY, Physical Education & Hlth Tchr; *b:* gomery Cty, MD; *m:* Andrew J. Jr.; *c:* Andrew J. III, Amy Sue; *ed:* n Coll (BS) Hlth & PE 1969; Penn St Univ Permanent Cert 1973; *cr:* e Creek Area-Woodland Halls Schl Dist Hlth & PE Tchr 1969-73; Josephs Schl PE Tchr 1980-84; The Ellis Schl Hlth & PE Tchr 1984-; ield Hockey, Bsktbl & Lacrosse Coach; Fac Rep Annual Giving issions Comm for MS Stdnts; Mid & Upper Schl Stdnts Adv; PA Tchrs -PSAHERD 1984-; Mid-West Schl Girls Lacrosse Assn 1986-; Whos Amoung Bus & Prof Women of Amer 1976; *home:* 850 6th St Verona 5147*

AEMER, JOSEPH GERARD, Performing & Fine Arts Supvr; *b:* elwood, NJ; *m:* Kim Linshek; *ed:* Jersey City St (BA) Music Ed 1985,) Admin, Supervision 1992; *cr:* Wayne Vly HS Band Dir 1985-86; tville HS Band Dir 1986; Belleville HS Band Dir 1986-82, Supvr 2-; *ai:* MENC 1986-; NJ Music Admins 1972-; NEA 1985-; Knights of ımbus 1992-; Belleville Music Parents Assn 1986-; *office:* Belleville f Ed 100 Passaic Ave Belleville NJ 07109

AFT, DAWN BOVAIS, Teacher & Director; *b:* East Orange, NJ; *m:* iam T.; *c:* Kimberly Kraft Ballantyne, Jennifer Lyn; *ed:* Tarkio Coll) Elem Ed 1964; *cr:* Westboro Elem Schl First Grd Tchr 1964-65; io Elem Schl First Grd Tchr 1965-67; Sherman Nursery Schl 4-5 Yr Tchr, Dir 1974-83; Village Presch Co-Owner, Dir, Tchr 3-5 Yr Olds 3-; *ai:* Storytelling Classes; NAEYC 1983-; EEC of New Milford 5-; *office:* Village Pre-Schl 36 Main St New Milford CT 06776

AFT, DEBORAH DUNKLE, Business Teacher & CBE Coord; *b:* Point ısant, NJ; *m:* William J.; *c:* Jacob William; *ed:* Monmouth Univ (BS) Bus Ed 1975; Montclair St Univ (MA) Bus Ed 1982; 9 Credit Hrs Guidance Svcs; *cr:* Southern Regnl HS Bus Tchr 1975-77; Brick Twp HS Bus Tchr, CBE Coord 1977-; *ai:* FBLA Adv; NEA, NJEA 1975-; BTEA, NJBEA 1977-; NJCBECA, OCCBECA 1989-; Voc Ed Grants 1991-; Featured Speaker on DTP for NJBEA, SJBEA Wkshps 1993; *office:* Brick Township HS 346 Chambersbridge Rd Brick NJ 08723*

KRAFT, KATHRYN M., Fourth Grade Teacher; *b:* Ashland, PA; *m:* Robert C.; *c:* Jennifer; *ed:* Shippensburg St Coll (BS) Elem Ed 1972; Bloomsburg St Coll Master Equivalency; *cr:* Ringtown Elem Schl 4th, 6th Grd Tchr 1972-78; Frackville Elem Schl 4th Grd Tchr 1979-; *ai:* Strategic Planning Comm; Grd Level Chprsn; PSEA, NEA 1972-; NCTM 1995-; Girl Scouts, Svc Team, Ldrs Awd; Friendship Fire Co Lad Aux, Treas; *home:* 534 W Oak St Frackville PA 17931*

KRAFTY, DIANE WERKHEISER, High School Mathematics Tchr; *b:* Palmerton, PA; *m:* Joseph J.; *c:* Joseph C.; *ed:* Kutztown Univ (BS) Math 1974; George Washington Univ (MAEd) Human Dev 1980; Attnd Charles Cty Comm Coll, Univ of MD, Johns Hopkins Univ; *cr:* Spring Ridge MS Math Tchr 1974-1993, Math Dept Chprsn 1974-1993; Leonardtown HS Math Tchr 1993-, Math Dept Chprsn 1995-; *ai:* NHS Spon; SIT, Curr, Scheduling Comms; NCTM, MMSA 1975-; ASCD; BSA, Asst Den Ldr 1989-; Natl Bd Stans Comm MD Outstdng Math Tchr Nom; Project Smart Grant; MMSA Presenter; PACE Article Pub; Outstdng Math Tchr of Yr; *office:* Leonardtown HS Rt 5 Box 49-3 Leonardtown MD 20650*

KRAFTY, JOSEPH JOHN, Social Studies Teacher; *b:* Bethelem, PA; *m:* Diane Louise Werkheiser; *c:* Joseph; *ed:* Kutztown Univ (BS) Ed, Soc Stud 1972; George Washington Univ (MA) Supervision, Human Relations 1980; Attnd St Mary's Coll of MD, Charles Cty Comm Coll; *cr:* Margaret Brent MS Tchr 1974-80; Leonardtown HS Tchr 1980-; St Mary's Coll Cooperating, Stu Tchr 1982-; Charles Cty Comm Coll Instr 1980-82; Bowie Univ Cooperative, Stu Tchr 1994; *ai:* Head Cross Cntry Coach; Final Examination, Acad Awds Comms; Mid States Chrmn, boys Track Coach, Golf Coach; NEA, MSTA, EASMC 1974-; Babe Ruth Bsbl Coach; Tchr of Yr 1992; Boys Cross Cntry Coach of Yr 1988; Girls Cross Cntry Coach of Yr 1989-94; *office:* Leonardtown HS Leonardtown MD 20650

KRAHEL, LINDA SUE MATHEWS, Fourth Grade Teacher; *b:* Martins Ferry, OH; *m:* Peter Paul; *c:* Chad Alan, Paige Alison; *ed:* OH Univ (BS) Elem Ed 1966; Univ of Dayton (MS) Child, Yth Dev 1983; Educl Post Grad Courses OH Univ Eastern; *cr:* St Clairsville-Richland Schl Dist 3rd Grd Tchr 1966-67, 4th Grd Tchr 1968-72, 1974-; *ai:* Chprsn Grd Level 1974-76, Math Curr 1993-95, Sci Course of Stud 1994, Grd Policy 1995; Math Textbook Comm 1993-94; NEA 1966-; SEA 1966-, Grievance Comm 1993-; *office:* St Clairsville Elem Schl 120 Norris St Saint Clairsville OH 43950*

KRAIMECHE, BELKACEM, Electrical Engineering Prof; *b:* Baghlia, Algeria; *m:* Khadija Elallam; *c:* Yassin, Adam, Zakary, Amin; *ed:* Columbia Univ (MS) Electrical Eng 1981, (PHD) Electrical Eng 1984; Pratt Inst (MS) Cmptr Sci 1989; *cr:* Bellcore Tech Staff Mem 1984-86; Pratt Inst Electrical Eng Prof 1982-91; Cooper Union Electrical Eng Prof, Telecom Prgm Dir 1991-; *ai:* IEEE, MSA Adv; IEEE Acts; IEEE 1981-; NY Acad of Scis 1986-88; AFT 1985-; Over 30 Research Papers; Book Project; 2 NSF, 1 Keck Fnd Grants; Flwshps 1st Citicorp Telecommunications 1983, Govt from Algeria 1979-84; *office:* Cooper Union School of Engineering 51 Astor Pl New York NY 10003

KRAJEWSKI, JUNEAN GOURLEY, Education Professor; *b:* Murray, UT; *ed:* Univ of NE at Reno (BA) Elem, Spec Ed, (MED) Spec Ed, (EDD) Curr, Instruction 1987; *cr:* Washoe Cty Schl Dist Tchr 1976-86, Title IV Coord 1986-87, Mentor Tchr 1987-88; Providence Coll Elem, Spec Ed Assoc Prof 1988-; *ai:* Fac Welfare Comm Rep; RI St Dept, Local Schl Dists Coopertive Learning Presentations; CEC 1972-; AAUP 1991-; RI Tech Assistance Project 1992-, Assoc Dir; Numerous Articles Pub 1988, 1992-93; *office:* Providence Coll River Ave Providence RI 02918

KRAJEWSKI, KAREN JONES, Mathematics Teacher; *b:* Buffalo, NY; *m:* Thomas R.; *c:* Eric, Kristopher; *ed:* SUNY Coll at Buffalo (BS) Math Ed 1970; Canisus Coll (MS) Math Ed 1973; *cr:* Hamburg Jr HS Math Tchr 1970-79; Hamburg Sr HS Math Tchr 1981-; *ai:* Scheduling, Attendance Comms; NEA, AFT, HTA 1970-; Eisenhower Grant; *office:* Hamburg Sr HS 4111 Legion Dr Hamburg NY 14075

KRAKER, LESLIE WILSON, Middle School Art Teacher; *b:* Warren, OH; *m:* Gary L.; *ed:* Youngstown St Univ (BFA) Graphic Design 1983; OH St Univ (BAE) Art Ed 1985, (MA) Educl Admin 1992; Addl Stud Towards Prin Cert; *cr:* Columbus Pub Schls Art Tchr 1987-; *ai:* 6th Grd IM Dir; Track Coach 1992-95; Unified Team Ldr 1988-95; NAEA 1989-; PTA, CEA, NEA 1987-; Edctr of Yr 1992; Art Work Exhibited Butler Inst of Amer Art 1983, Bliss Gallery 1983; *office:* Sherwood Regnl Alternative MS 1400 Shady Lane Rd Columbus OH 43227*

KRAKOWSKI, RICHARD A., Math & Computer Teacher; *b:* Cleveland, OH; *ed:* John Carroll Univ (BS) Psych 1969; Ed Hrs at St John Coll, Asland Univ & Baldwin Wallace Univ; *cr:* St Hyacinth Elem Schl 6th-8th Grd Tchr 1969-89; St Stanislaus Elem Schl 6th & 7th Grd Tchr 1989-90, 1st-8th Grd Comp & Jr High Math Tchr 1990-, Asst Prin 1994-95; *ai:* Ath Dir; Bsktbl Coach; Newspaper Moderator; *office:* St Stanislaus Elem Schl 6615 Forman Ave Cleveland OH 44105

KRALY, THOMAS W., 5th Grade Teacher; *b:* Johnson City, NY; *ed:* SUNY at Cortland (BA) Elem Ed & 7th-9th Grd Math 1988; (MS) Rdng; *cr:* Whitney Point Schls Tchr & Coach 1988-; *ai:* Var Bsbl, Legion Bsbl & JV Girls Bsktbl Coach; *office:* Whitney Point Central Schl PO Box 249 Whitney Point NY 13862

KRAMARENKO, GEORGE, Spanish & Italian Teacher; *b:* Allentown, PA; *ed:* Kings Coll (BS) Bio 1976; LaSalle Univ (MA) Ed 1989, (MA) Span, Bi-Cultural; Liceo Scientifico Statale C. Cavour Roma Italy Diploma 1978; Universita Italiano Per Stranieri Perugia Italy Diploma 1976; Universita Degli Studi Di Parma Parma Italy 1978-80; *cr:* St Maria Goretti HS Italian, Span Tchr 1989-93; Harry S. Truman HS Italian, Span Tchr 1993-; *ai:* Italian Club Adv; ACTFL, AATI 1993-; PSMLA 1995-; NYSAFLT 1992-; US Army Commendation, Achvmt Awds; *office:* Harry S Truman HS 3001 Green Ln Levittown PA 19057*

KRAMER, ARLINE SINGER, Third Grade Teacher; *b:* New York City, NY; *m:* Robert M.; *c:* Felicia Shutter, Jamie Shutter, David Kramer; *ed:* SUNY at Cortland (BA) Ed 1969; Long Island Univ Masters Early Chldhd 1991; *cr:* Gardenville Schl Learning Disabled 1969-72; PS 68 Art Cluster Tchr 1986-87; PS 221 3rd Grd Tchr 1987-; *ai:* Soc Comm; UFT, NYS Tchrs, AFT 1986-; *office:* North Hills Schl PS 221Q 57-40 Marathon Pkwy Little Neck NY 11362

KRAMER, BARBARA JEAN (LOTTES), First Grade Teacher; *b:* Corapolis, PA; *m:* Alexander F.; *ed:* Edinboro St Coll (BS) Elem Ed 1970; Penn St Extension 24 Credit Hrs; *cr:* West Allegheny Schls Elem Tchr 1970-; *ai:* Instrl Support Team Mem; Math Curr Comm; Lead Tchr; NEA 1970-; WA Tchrs Assn 1970-, REP Cncl Mem; Amer Cancer Soc Reach to Recovery 1986-; *office:* Wilson Elem Schl 67b Boggs Rd Imperial PA 15126

KRAMER, CAROLYN ELIZABETH, French & Spanish Teacher; *b:* Kansas City, MO; *ed:* Ripon Coll (BA) Fr 1974; CO St Univ (MA) Fr 1976; *cr:* North Brandford Intermediate Fr Tchr 1977-; *ai:* NEA 1977-; COLT 1990-.

KRAMER, CHARLES MARVIN, Professor of Economics; *b:* Boston, MA; *m:* Beverly L. Wine; *c:* Wendy Waida, Jeffrey; *ed:* Boston Univ (BBA) Ed 1954; Northeastern Univ (EDM) Bus Ed 1956; 61 Addl Credits Ec; *cr:* Dean Coll Soc Sci Dept Chair 1967-92, Prof of EC 1954-; *ai:* Steering Comm; Amer Ec Assoc 1958-; Eastern Ec Assoc 1974-; Comm coll Soc Sci Assoc 1978-; Beta Gamma Sigma; Vly Forge Freedom Fnd Awd; *office:* Dean Coll 99 Main St Franklin MA 02038

KRAMER, CHARLES MILLER,JR., PE & Aquatics Instructor; *b:* Norristown, PA; *m:* Christine Manning; *c:* Margaret, Samantha, Charles, Kelly; *ed:* KS St Univ (BS) Hlth, PE 1975; Temple Univ (MED) PE 1992; Addl 30 Credits Prin Cert; Amer Red Cross Lifeguard Trng Instr; *cr:* Montgomery Cty Intermediate Unit Adpt PE, Aquatics Tchr 1978-; Perkiomen Vly Schl Dist HS Var Wrestling Head Coach 1982-; Spring-Ford Schl Dist Soccer Coaching Staff 1995-; Haverford Coll Var Womens Soccer Coach 1984-90; *ai:* Head Wrestling Coach; Tchr MiniGrant Selection Comm; Projects of Self Esteem Through Body Awareness, Outdoor Ed for Physically Challenged, Enrichment of Life Skills for Handicapped Stdnts; Spec Olympic Local Adv; PSEA; NEA; Natl Soccer Coaches of Amer; Natl Assn of Sport & ed; Natl Strenth & Conditioning Assn; PA Wresting Coach Assn; Amer Red Cross 1988-, Vol Hlth, Safety Instr; Norristown Dept Recreation 1978-, Recreation Advy Bd; Legion of Hnr Awd 1981; Young Edctr of Yr 1986; Dist 1 Wrestling Coach of Yr 1984, 1986, 1988, 1990; HS Coach of Yr 1986; *office:* Montgomery Cty Intrmdt Union 1605 W Main Norristown PA 19401*

KRAMER, DAVID MARSHALL, K-3 Music Teacher; *b:* New York City, NY; *m:* Hilary Berger; *c:* Daniel, Ari, Alizah; *ed:* Queens Coll of the City Univ of NY (BS) Music Ed 1975, (MS) Music Ed 1979; *cr:* Andrew Muller Primary Schl K-3rd Grd Music Tchr 1975-; *ai:* HS Drama Dir; Gifted & Talented Playwriting Mentor; Gifted & Talented Play Production Facilitator; Elem Schl Chorus & Recorder Ensemble Conductor; NY St Schl Music Assn 1975-; Music Edctrs Natl Conf 1975-; Suffolk Cty Music Edctrs Assn 1983-; *office:* Andrew Muller Primary Schl 65 Lower Rocky Point Rd Miller Place NY 11764

KRAMER, FRANCIS J., Retired English Professor; *b:* Troy, NY; *m:* Mary Patricia Caldwell; *c:* Francis, Stephen, Jocelyn; *ed:* Champlain Coll (BA) Eng 1953; SUNY at Albany (MA) Ed; *cr:* Hoosick Falls HS 9-10 Grd Eng Tchr 1954-58; Colonie HS 9-10 Grd Eng Tchr 1958-60; Hudson Vly Comm Coll Eng Prof 1960-95; *ai:* Eng Dept Chair 1977-84; Sr Class Adv; Fac Assn 1961-, V-Chair; Troy Civic Svc Commission 1980-; Planning Comm 1977-80, V-Chair; Text-Pub Speaking.

KRAMER, LAWRENCE, Professor of English & Music; *b:* Philadelphia, PA; *m:* Nancy Leonard; *c:* Claire Leonard; *ed:* Univ of PA (BA) Eng 1968; Yale Univ (PHD) Eng 1972; *cr:* Univ of PA Asst Eng Prof 1972-78; Fordham Univ Asst Eng Prof 1978-80, Assoc Eng Prof 1980-86, Eng Prof 1986-, Eng & Music Prof 1995-; *ai:* Amer Musicological Soc 1988-, Natl Cncl; Soc for Music Theory 1991-; Hudson Vly Chamber Music Cr 1989-, Bd of Trustees; Author of 3 books: Music & Poetry, Music as Cultural Practice & Classical Music & Postmodern Knowledge; 50 Articles Pub; Ed 19th Century Music Journal; *office:* Fordham Univ Lincoln Center New York NY 10023

KRAMER, MARGARET KANE, Third Grade Teacher; *b:* Trenton, NJ; *m:* Donald A.; *c:* Kevin, David; *ed:* Trenton St Coll (BA) Soc Stud Ed 1968, (MED) Elem Ed 1980; *cr:* Millstone Twp Elem Schl Fifth Grd Tchr 1965-72; University Heights Elem Schl Third, Fifth Grd Tchr 1980-; *ai:* NEA, NJEA 1965-72, 1980-; MCEA, HTEA 1980-; Amer Assn of Univ Women 1978-, Past Pres; West Trenton Garden Club 1985-, Pres; Zonta Intnl; Zonta Club of Trenton 1990-, Pres Elect; *home:* 12 Maddock Rd Titusville NJ 08560

KRAMER, MARY DUHAMEL, Full Professor of English; *b:* Colombus, WI; *ed:* U of WI (BA) Eng 1966; U of KS (MA) Eng 1967, (PHD) Eng 1969; *cr:* Lowell St Coll Eng Prof 1969-75; Univ of Lowell Eng Prof 1975-92; UMass Eng Prof 1992-; *ai:* Hnrs Prgm; Writers Club; His Competition; NEA, MTA 1975-; Phi Beta Kappa, Phi Kappa Phi 1966-; NDEA Title IV Flwshp; Pub Numerous Articles, Reviews; Co-Author Textbook, Newspaper, Journal Columnist; *office:* Univ Of MA At Lowell South Campus 1 University Ave Lowell MA 01854

KRAMER, MYRNA KLOSK, Fourth Grade Teacher; *b:* New York, NY; *m:* Richard; *c:* Robert, Scott; *ed:* Univ of Bridgeport (BA) Ed 1958; St Johns Univ (MS) Guid & Cnslng 1973; *cr:* New York City Pub Schls Tchr 1959-; *ai:* Grd Ldr; New Tchr Wkshp; AFT; *office:* PS 60 Queens 91-02 88th Ave Woodhaven NY 11421*

KRAMER, NANCY DAVIS, English Teacher; *b:* Kingston, PA; *m:* Michael William; *c:* Sarah, Abigail; *ed:* Lock Haven Univ (BS) Eng Ed 1980, (BS) Commnctns 1980; Wilkes Univ (MS) Ed 1985; *cr:* Wilkes Barre Schl Dist Eng Tchr 1980-82; Wilkes Univ Eng Tchr 1985-87; Juniata HS Eng Tchr 1982-; *ai:* Jr Class & Prom Adv; NEA 1982-; PSEA 1982-; Home & Schl Assn 1993-; *office:* Juniata HS RR 4 Box 99 Mifflintown PA 17059

KRAMER, NANCY KAUFFMAN, Retired English Teacher; *b:* Hamburg, PA; *c:* Patricia G.Greene, E. David, Laurette G.; *ed:* Kutztown Univ (BA) Eng 1967, (MA) Eng; *cr:* Hamburg Area HS Tchr 1967-92; *ai:* NEAR 1967-; *home:* PO Box 191 Shoemakersville PA 19555

KRAMER, SHIRLEY A., 6th Grade Teacher; *b:* Pittsburg, PA; *c:* Robert W.; *ed:* Edinboro Univ (BS) Elem Ed 1968, (BS) Sec Ed, Earth Sci, Geog 1972; St of PA MS Equilivancy Ed 1978; Post Grad Hrs Earth Sci, Oceanography, Guid; *cr:* Titusville Area Schl Dist 2nd Grd Tchr 1968-69; Warrior Rum Schl Dist MS Tchr 1969-71; Dept of Ed 5th Grd Tchr 1972; Millville Area Schl Dist 6th Grd Tchr 1974-; *ai:* Dept Head of Soc St; Run Schl Store; PSEA 1968-; Big Bro, Big Sis 1992-93; First Eng Bapt Church 1992-94; Bd of Chrstn Ed 1996-99; Chaired Mid Sts Evaluation; Presenter San Francisco ASCD; Intnl Tchng Fellow Victoria Australia 1986; *home:* 210 E 10th St Bloomsburg PA 17815*

KRAMER, THOMAS HENRY, Fifth Grade Teacher; *b:* Newark, NJ; *m:* Carol; *ed:* St Univ at Oswego (BS) Ed 1967; Dowling Coll (MS) Ed 1983; *cr:* Robert Seaman Schl Tchr 1967-80; Cantiague Schl Tchr 1980-; *ai:* Schl Newspaper; Night Astronomy Classes; Mock Trial; AFT 1967-; NEA 1967-; JTA 1967-; Cited in: Lang Literacy & the Child; *home:* 6 Baywood Ln Bayport NY 11705

KRAMER, WILLIAM KARL, Honors Geom & Cmptr Sci Tchr; *b:* Dayton, OH; *m:* Beverly Sue Stevens; *c:* Beth Lynn Shumaker, Bret William; *ed:* IN St Univ (BS) Math 1962; Univ of MI (MS) Math 1963; 100 Addl Credit Hrs Univ of OR, Wright St Univ, Univ of Dayton, Sinclair Comm Coll, Miami Univ, Kent St Univ; *cr:* Kettering Fairmont East HS Math, Cmptr Sci Tchr 1963-83; Kettering Fairmont HS Math, Cmptr Sci Tchr 1983-; *ai:* Ftbl Games Scoreboard; Prom Ticket Sales; Lines of March Ldr for Grad; Schl Math & Sci Assn 1963-, Emeritus Membership; Excl in Tchng Awd; *office:* Kettering Fairmont HS 3301 Shroyer Rd Kettering OH 45429

KRANING, TOM, Physical Ed Teacher & Coach; *b:* Baltimore, MD; *c:* Stephen, Daniel; *ed:* Towson St Coll (BS) PE 1974; Loyola Coll (MA) Learning Disabilities 1983; *cr:* Chesapeake HS PE Tchr 1980-, Asst Ftbl Coach 1982-85, Head Bsktbl Coach 1985-93, It's Acad Adv 1988-89, Head Ftbl Coach 1988-; *ai:* Natl Strength, Conditioning 1982-; MD St Tchrs Assn, Anne Arundel Co Tchrs Assn 1981-; Baltimore Ofcls Sportsman of Yr Awd; *office:* Chesapeake HS 4798 Mountain Rd Pasadena MD 21122

KRANKOTA, RICHARD A., Health & Physical Ed Teacher; *b:* Butler, PA; *m:* Teresa Reep; *c:* Christine, Rebecca, Michael; *ed:* Slippery Rock Coll (BS) Hlth, PE 1981; 24 Addl Hrs Hlth, PE, Drivers Ed; *cr:* US Marine Corps Team Ldr 1975-77; Conneaut Schl Dist Tchr 1981-; PA Army Natl Guard Ofcr 1982-; *ai:* Table Tennis Club Adv; Conneaut Ed Assn 1981-, Schl Rep; PA St Ed Assn, NEA 1981-; Natl Guard Ofcrs Assn 1983-; *office:* Linesville Conneaut Summit HS RR 3 Box 135e Linesville PA 16424*

KRANTZ, JOAN SCZAWINSKI, English Teacher; *b:* Bristol, CT; *m:* F. Donald; *c:* Donald, David; *ed:* Albertus Magnus Coll (BA) Eng 1974; CCSU (MA) Eng 1980; Wesleyan (CAS) Arts 1989; *cr:* Terryville High Eng Tchr 1974-75; Swift Jr High Eng Tchr 1975-82; Watertown High Eng Tchr 1982-; *ai:* Newspaper Club & Lit Magazine Advs; NEA 1976-; CT Poetry Soc 1990-; NCTE; Poems Pub; *office:* Watertown HS 324 French St Watertown CT 06795*

KRANZ, HOWARD JOHN, Social Studies Teacher; *b:* Syracuse, NY; *m:* Cheryl Densing; *c:* Michael, Matthew; *ed:* SUC at Geneseo (BS) N-9 & Soc Stud 1969; SUNY at Stony Brook (MS) Continuing Ed 1974; 75 Credit Hrs; *cr:* Bellport MS Tchr 1969-; *ai:* His Team Adv; NYSUUt & NYSTA 1969-; Bellport TA 1969-, Treas & Bldg Rep; *office:* Bellport MS Dunton Ave East Patchogue NY 11772

KRASMAN, ALBERT JAMES,JR., Carpentry Instructor; *b:* Glassport, PA; *m:* Sandra Lee Locke; *c:* Bret David, Todd Daniel; *ed:* CA St Univ of PA (BS) Ed & Industrial Arts 1966; St Francis Gen Stud; Penn St Univ 6 Credit Hrs; Loyola Univ 9 Credit Hrs; Townson St Univ 20 Credit Hrs; *cr:* Franklin Regnl Jr HS Industrial Arts Instr 1966-68; Bohemia Manor MS 7th-12th Grd Industrial Arts Instr 1968-94; Cherry Hill MS 6th-8th Grd Industrial Arts Instr 1994-95; Cecil Cty Schl of Tech House Bldg 1995-; *ai:* NEA 1966-; MSTA 1968-; CCCTA 1968-; *home:* 56 Spring Hill Ln North East MD 21901

KRASONIC, BARBARA L., Cosmetology Supervisor; *b:* Belle Vernon, PA; *m:* John D. Sr; *c:* John D. Jr.; *ed:* Univ of Pitb Ins II Voc Ed 1975; Coiffure Creation Acad Advanced Trg Cos 1965; *cr:* Franco Beauty Acad Cosmetology Tchr 1963; B K's Wig & Beauty Salon Owner 1963-78; North Fayette AVTS Instr 1972-84, Supvr 1984-; *ai:* VICA, Cosmetology Club Adv; PSEA 1972-, Sec; NEA 1972-, Sec; COVET, AVTEC 1976-; *office:* North Fayette Co Voc Tech Sch 720 Locust St Connellsville PA 15425

KRASTEK, ROBERT A., Soc Stud Dept Chair; *b:* Altoona, PA; *m:* Leila McGuire; *c:* Eric, Caroline; *ed:* Duquesne Univ (BA) Pol Sci 1971; Trenton St Coll (MAT) Scndy Ed 1975; Glassboro St Coll Supvrs Cert Scndry Ed 1993; *cr:* Holy Cross HS Tchr & Asst Ath Dir 1973-; Burlington Cty Coll Adjunct Instr 1976-80; Cinnaminson HS Dept Chair/Tchr; *ai:* Model United Nations Moderator; Soccer Coach; Mock Trial Moderator; NASCA 1985-; ACT 1973-; NCSS; Riverside PAL 1980-, VP, Little League Commissioner; Freedom Fnds Schlsp 1989; Taft Inst Schlsp 1975; Speaker at NJ St PTA Convention 1990; Speaker at Region 7 PTA Conf 1990; VSIP Scholarship 1995; *office:* Cinnaminson HS Riverton Rd Cinnaminson NJ 08077

KRASZEWSKI, BARBARA KING, Associate Professor of English; *b:* Pittsburgh, PA; *m:* Lanny J.; *c:* Jonathan, Mark, Elizabeth; *ed:* Duquesne Univ (BS) Eng 1966; Carnegie Univ (MA) Eng 1967; *cr:* Taylor Allderdice HS Eng Tchr 1967-68; Indiana Univ of PA Eng Prof 1969-; *ai:* NCTE; AFT; CCCC; Prospective Tchrs Fellowship; Who's Who Among Amer Colls, Univs; Distinguished Fac Awd for Tchng; PSEA Outstanding Tchng Awd; *office:* Indiana Univ of Pennsylvania 220 Leonard Hall Eng Dept Indiana PA 15705

KRATZMAN, EUGENE L., Math & Algebra Teacher; *b:* Toledo, OH; *ed:* Univ of Toledo (BED) Math, Eng 1971, (MED) Curr Dev 1978; Cmptr Programming Univ of Toledo; Cmptr Langs & Programming Owens Comm & Tech Coll; *cr:* Roxboro Jr HS Math Tchr 1971-72; Gateway MS Math, Alegebra & Eng Tchr 1972-; *ai:* NEA, OEA 1971-; MEA 1972-; Toledo Rose Soc 1981-, Pres, VP, Sec; Pi Kappa Phi Alumni 1971-; Career Edctr of the Yr Awd 1991; NEA Conf on Careers in Math Speaker; MS Interdisciplinary Team Ldr; *office:* Gateway MS 900 Gibbs St Maumee OH 43537*

KRAUS, CAROL WINN, Sixth Grade Lang Arts Tchr; *b:* Fayetteville, AR; *c:* Ryan Charles, Diane Elizabeth; *ed:* Pittsburgh St Univ (BA) Elem Ed 1968; Masters Equivalency plus 15 Hrs; *cr:* Joplin Schl Dist 6th Grd Elem Tchr 1968-69; CO Springs Schl Dist 1st-3rd Grd Elem Tchr 1970-71; North Pocono Schl Dist 6th-8th Grd Math, Eng, & Lang Arts Tchr 1971-; *ai:* Scholastic Bowl; PSEA, NEA 1972-; Presbyn Church 1971-, Deacon & Elder; Long Range Planning for the North Pocono Schl Dist; *home:* RR 7 Box 7531 Moscow PA 18444*

KRAUS, JON P., Professor of Political Science; *b:* Northampton, MA; *m:* Wilma; *c:* N. Kirsten, Wendy; *ed:* Bucknell Univ (BA) Psych & Eng 1960; Johns Hopkins Univ (MA) Intnl Affairs 1962, (PHD) Intnl Affairs 1971; *cr:* Univ of SC Instr 1967-70; St Univ of NY Asst Prof 1970-73, Assoc Prof 1973-80, Pol Sci Dept Prof 1980-; *ai:* Fac Cncl; Budget & Planning Comm; Kasling Awds Comm; Amnesty Intnl Fac Adv; Fredonia Pol Sci Assn Fac Adv; Filmaholics Fac Adv; Canadian Journal of African Studies Assoc Ed; Comm for Acad Freedom in Africa Bd of Spons; African Stud Assn 1963-; Amer Pol Sci Assn 1965-; Amnesty Intnl Fredonia Fac Adv; Numerous Articles pub; 23 Book Chptrs; Written Encyclopedia Articles; Author & Ed of Trade Unions, Democratization and Economic Crisis 1996; Numerous Grants to Conduct Field Rsrch; SUNY at Fredonia Kasling Awd for Scholarly Achvmt 1986; *office:* S U N Y Coll At Fredonia Fredonia NY 14063

KRAUS, LARRY MATTHEW, PE & Bible Teacher & Ath Dir; *b:* Ellwood City, PA; *m:* Carol Ann Gomory; *c:* Amy, Erika, Zephaniah; *ed:* Slippery Rock Coll (BS) Hlth, PE 1972; *cr:* Hopewell Area Schl Dist Hlth, PE Tchr 1972-82; Rhema Chrstn Schl PE, Bible Tchr, Ath Dir 1982-; *ai:* Girls, Boys Bsktbl; *home:* 352 Longs Run Rd Aliquippa PA 15001

KRAUS, SHEILA PETERS, Third Grade Teacher; *b:* Oswego, NY; *m:* Edwin M.; *c:* Elizabeth Koval, Susan, Kathleen, Ed; *ed:* Coll of Saint Rose (BS) Elem Ed 1962; Post Grad Courses From Univ of Louisville at Marywood, Elmira Coll & Mansfield Univ; *cr:* Glenwood Landing Elem 3rd Grd Tchr 1962-63; Crums Lane Elem 1st Grd Tchr 1963-64; Sheshequin Ulster Elem 3rd Grd Tchr 1983-; *ai:* PTO Fac Rep; AAEA 1983-; PSEA 1983-; NEA 1983-; *office:* Sheshequin Ulster Elem Schl 2nd St Ulster PA 18850

KRAUSE, MIKE JOHN, Administrative Intern; *b:* Allentown, PA; *m:* Jill Josephson; *c:* Taylor; *ed:* East Stroudsburg Univ (BS) Hlth, PE 1978; Cedrar Crest Coll Math Cert 1986; *cr:* St Thomas More Schl Hlth, PE Tchr 6 Yrs; Trexler MS Math Tchr 10 Yrs, Admin Intern; *ai:* Vlybl Coach; IMs, Conflict Resolution Prgm Dir; 24 Challenge Adv; Schl Cncl Steering Comm; Head Vlybl Coach Muhlenberg Coll; AEA, NEA 1986-; Amer Vlybl Coaches Assn 1995-; Lehigh Vly HS Summer Bsktbl Tournament 1989-, Bd Mem; *office:* Trexler MS 851 N 15th St Allentown PA 18102

KRAUSE, TERRY L., Instrumental Music Director; *b:* Cleveland, OH; *m:* Polly Moore; *c:* Jessica, Lindsay; *ed:* OH Univ (BFA) Music Ed 1972; Post Grad Stud Univ of Akron, Univ of Toledo; *cr:* Dover City Schls Instrumental Music Tchr 1972-78; Bryan City Schls Instrumental Music Tchr 1978-86, Non Tchng Positions 1984-91; Hilltop Schls Instrumental Music Tchr 1991-; *ai:* Marching, Pep Bands; OMEA, MENC 1972-; *office:* Hilltop Schl 113 S Defiance St West Unity OH 43570

KRAUSER, JOEL, Related Arts Supervisor; *b:* Bronx, NY; *m:* Adelle Levitsky; *c:* Lawrence, Pamela, Rachel; *ed:* Harvard Coll (BA) Liberal Arts 1957; NY Univ (MA) Art Ed 1964; Attnd Cooper Union Schl of Art 1961-63, Art Stdnts League 1959-61; Pratt Graphics Ctr Sabbatical Yr Stud 1971-72; *cr:* Erasmus Hall HS Tchr 1963-64; Northern Valley Regnl HS Tchr 1964-93, Supvr of Related Arts 1993-; *ai:* NAEA; Exhibit Nationally; Listed in Whos Who in Amer Art 1980-84; *home:* 168 Engle St Tenafly NJ 07670

KRAUSKOPF, TERESA LYNN, English Teacher; *b:* Dayton, OH; *m:* James Russell; *c:* Bradley James; *ed:* Wright St Univ (BS) Scndry Ed in Eng 1985; Univ of Dayton (MS) Schl Admin 1993; *cr:* Centerville HS Eng Tchr 1985-; *ai:* NEA, OEA 1985-; Centerville Classroom Tchrs Assn 1985-, Bldg Rep; *office:* Centerville HS 500 E Franklin St Centerville OH 45459

KRAUSS, ART J., Prof & Coord of Communications; *b:* Detroit, MI; *c:* Peter, Emily; *ed:* MI St Univ (BA) Comm 1968, (MA) Art & Graphic Design 1969; 30 Post Grad Credits in Art & Cmptr Graphics; *cr:* Wichita St Univ Prof of Art 1969-72; Fitchburg St Coll Prof of Comm 1980-85; Northeastern Univ Sr Lecturer in Art 1985-; Becker Coll Prof of Comm 1992-; *ai:* WBKR Radio Club Adv; Performance Coffeehouse Producer & Adv; Stu Affairs Comm; Worcester AD Club 1995-; Coll Art Assn 1985-; AFT, NEA; Exhibiting Artist; Musician & Song Writer; Music & Book Publications; Art Gallery Owner & Mgr; *office:* Becker Coll At Leicester 3 Paxton St Leicester MA 01524

KRAUSS, CHARLOTTE CHEATHAM, 3rd Grade Teacher; *b:* Columbia, KY; *m:* Howard; *c:* John, Sally; *ed:* Western KY Univ (BS) Elem Ed 1966; Post Grad Stud Miami Univ; *cr:* Harveysburg Elem 2nd Grd Tchr 1965-66; Houston Elem Remedial Rdng & 2nd Grd Tchr 1966-70; Sacred Heart Schl 3rd Grd Tchr 1976-; *ai:* NCTE; OCTELA; IRA; TWAL; OH Writing Project Presenter & Consultant; *home:* 7623 Fairfield Rd Oxford OH 45056

KRAUSS, DIANA S., English Teacher; *b:* Schenectady, NY; *m:* Jere LaPointe; *ed:* Colby Coll (BA) Eng 1974; Boston Univ (MFA) Theatre 1980; *cr:* Waterville Jr HS Lang Arts Tchr 1974-75; Various Theatres Tech Jobs 1979-87; Dexter Regnl HS Eng Tchr 1988-; *ai:* Stu Cncl Adv; New Tchr Mentor; MTA, NEA 1988-; Delta Kappa Gamma 1993-; SAD 68 Schl Bd 1994-; Monson Lib Bd 1990-; Mellon Grant 1993; MEH Grant 1992; NEH Summer Seminar 1991; MEH Grant 1990; The Coll Bd Advanced Placement Eng Fac Consultant 1994; *office:* Dexter Regional HS 12 Abbott Hill Rd Dexter ME 04930

KRAUSS, LAURIE SUE, 6th Grade Teacher; *b:* Kenmore, NY; *m:* Daniel A.; *c:* Rebecca, Ryan, Connor; *ed:* IN Univ of PA (BA) Elem Ed 1982, (MS) Math Ed 1990; *cr:* Bedford MS 6th Grd Tchr 1983-84; Everett Area Schl Dist 3rd Grd Tchr 1984-92, Kndgtn Tchr 1992-95, 6th Grd Tchr 1996; *ai:* Sci, Health Fairs; TESA; NEA, PSEA 1984-; Cncl on Ministries 1986-, Chm; Womans Club 1985-90; *office:* Everett Area Elem Schl 165 E 1st Ave Everett PA 15537*

KRAVITS, BARBARA A., Sixth Grade Teacher; *b:* Pittsburgh, PA; *m:* Eugene F.; *c:* Jennifer; *ed:* Attnd PA St Univ Ed, Temple Univ Ed, IN St Tchrs Coll Elem Ed, Spec Ed; Extensive Stud Abroad; *cr:* Har-Brack Schl Dist Tchr 1967-93; Gateway Schl Dist Tchr 1967-; *ai:* Owner Truffles Antiquites; NEA, PSEA, GEA 1963-, GEA Sec; *office:* Moss Side MS Mosside Blvd Monroeville Mall PA 15146

KRAVITZ, JEANNE, Health Related Technology Tchr; *b:* Wilkes Barre, PA; *m:* William J.; *c:* Melissa Ann; *ed:* Wilkes Univ (BA) Soc Stud, Ed 1976, (MS) Scndry Ed 1980; Luzeane Cty Comm Coll (AAS) Nrsng Ed 1990; Post Grad Work in Voc Ed Temple Univ; *cr:* Wyoming Vly West Sub Tchr 1976-80; Wilkes Univ Assoc in Reference, Interlibrary Loan 1981-85; Janney Montgomery Scott Sales Asst 1987-95; First Hosp of Wyoming Vly Nurse on Addiction Unit 1990-93; West Side AVT Schl HRT Instr 1989-; *ai:* Hlth Occupations Stu of Amer Club Adv; NEA, PSEA, Tchrs Assn 1989-; ANA 1990-; Girl Scouts 1993-; *office:* West Side Area Voc Tech Schl 75 Evans St Wilkes Barre PA 18704

KRAVITZ, MICHAEL STANLEY, Chemistry Teacher; *b:* Newton, MA; *m:* Cheryl Rose Schultz; *c:* Rachel; *ed:* Amer Univ (BA) Govt, Pub Admin 1969; Post Grad Stud George Washington Univ, Amer Univ, Montgomery Coll, Univ of MD; *cr:* Hyattsville Jr HS Sci Tchr 1970-72; Tilden Jr HS Sci Tchr 1972-81; Charles Woodward HS Sci Tchr 1981-87; Walter Johnson HS Sci Tchr 1981-91; Montgomery Blair HS Sci Tchr 1991-; *ai:* Co-Coach Acad Team; Co-Coach St of MD Panasonic Acad Challenge Team; Montgomery Cty Ed Assn, MD St Tchrs Assn, NEA 1976-; Montgomery Cty Sci Tchrs Assn 1993-; Kodak Outstdng Sci Tchr 1980; Kodak Schlsp to Tilden Jr HS; Co-Coach 2 Natl Champion Acad Teams 1992, 1994; *office:* Montgomery Blair HS 313 Wayne Ave Silver Spring MD 20910

KRAWCZYK, CARL-MICHAL, Assistant Professor; *b:* Bristol, England; *m:* Ruth Ann Gentes; *ed:* Univ of MD (AA) Liberal Arts 1981, (BA) His, Eng 1982; Univ of Houston (MA) His 1985; *cr:* Univ of Houston Tchng Asst 1983-85; WA St Comm Coll His Instr 1991-95, Asst Prof 1995; *ai:* Amer Historical Assn 1992-; Three Natl Lit Awds for Short Fiction 1991-93; Four Short Fiction PIeces Pub Local, Natl Lit Reviews 1991-; Bi-weekly Column; *office:* Washington St Comm Coll 710 Colegate Dr Marietta OH 45750

KRAWIEC, WALTER EDWARD, Soc Studies Chairperson & Tchr; *b:* Passaic, NJ; *m:* Barbara Hasse; *c:* Cindi, Richard; *ed:* Montclair St Univ (BA) Soc Stud 1969, (MA) Soc Sci 1972; Walden Univ (EDD) His Ed 1976; K-12 Admin, Supervision Post Grad Stud; *cr:* George Washington Jr HS Tchr 1969-, Admin Intern 1990-93; *ai:* Jerseymen His, Jrs Clubs Spon, Adv; 9th Grd Frosh Line Ftbl Coach; St Mary's HS Ath Trainer; Paul IV Reg HS; Karate Instr; NEA, NJ, Wayne Ed Assns 1969-; NCSS 1985-; Paul IV Reg HS 1988-, Bd of Ed; Elks Club 1984-; Amer Hapkido Assn 1986-, Instr, Svc Awd; NJ St Mini Grant; NJ Historical Soc Citation; DAR Tchr of Yr 1993, Awds 1988, 1976; *office:* George Washington Jr HS 68 Lenox Rd Wayne NJ 07470*

KREAGER, MARY, English & Enrichment Teacher; *b:* Euclid, OH; *ed:* Notre Dame Coll (BA) Eng Educ 1973, (MED) Ed 1996; *cr:* St Justin Martyr Jr HS Eng Tchr 1973-79; Regina HS Eng Instr 1979-; *ai:* Clown Ministry Dir; Fac Adv Bd; Sr Class Co-Adv; Acad Cncl; Enrichment Coord; Multiple Intelligences Chprsn; Cath Diocese Excl Awd 1990; Prins Ldrshp Awd 1994; Grant from McGinty Fndn 1994; *office:* Regina HS 1857 S Green Rd South Euclid OH 44121

KREBS, GEORGE EDWARD, Industrial Arts Teacher; *b:* Indiana, PA; *m:* Sue Ann Porter; *c:* Tonya Sue, Todd Allen; *ed:* OH Univ (BSEd) Instrl Tech 1985; Attnd Belmont Tech; *cr:* Y & O Coal Co Unit Mgr 1973-80; North Amer Coal Co Section Foreman 1980-87; Cath Cntrl HS Tchr 1987-88; Union Local HS Tchr 1988-; *ai:* Sr Class Trip Adv; Bsktbl Statistician; NEA, ULACT 1988-; Friends Church 1974-, Stewardship Elder, Presiding Clerk; Martha Holden Jennings Awd; *home:* 66754 Glencoe St C Rd St Clairsville OH 43950

KREBS, LEONARD CARL, Chemistry Teacher; *b:* Baltimore, MD; *ed:* SUNY at Stonybrook (BS) Chem & Engrng 1985, (MS) Chem 1991; 12 Credit Hrs Grad Ed; *cr:* SUNY at Stonybrook Dept of Chem Rsrch Asst 1984-85, Rsrch Assoc 1986-91; St John the Bapt DHS Sci Tchr 1992-; *ai:* Radio Station & Ecology Club Moderator; Hnr Soc & Jr Class Adv; Amer Chemical Soc 1984-; STANYS 1993-; NSTA 1993-; SUNY Dept of Chem Rsrch Awd; Excl in Tchng Renaissance Awd; *office:* St John the B[illegible] 1170 Montauk Hwy West Islip NY 11795

KREBS, MARJORI MADDOX, Social Studies Teacher; *b:* Lubbo[illegible] *m:* Paul; *c:* Taylor, Jacob; *ed:* OH St Univ (MS) Elem Ed 1992; Post-Grad Stud; *cr:* Worthington Kilbourne HS Soc Stud 1985-; *ai:* [illegible] Serv Club, Yth in Govt Adv; Scndry Career Ed Ldr; Liberty [illegible] Church 1990-, Sunday Schl Tchr; Ldrshp Worthington 1991-; You[illegible] of Yr Awd 1986; Worthington Ed Fnd Grant 1994; *home:* 178 E G[illegible] Rd Worthington OH 43085*

KREBS, ROBERT KARL, High School German Teach[illegible] Aschaffenburg, Germany; *ed:* Stony Brook Univ (BA) Ger Lit-Mag[illegible] Laude 1970; Hofstra Univ (MA) Eng Lit 1975; *cr:* Smithtown HS G[illegible] 1970-; *ai:* Natl Ger Honor Soc Spon; NYSTA, AFT, AATG & STA[illegible] Natl Ger Honor Soc, VP 1980-81, Pres 1982-94; Articles [illegible] Unterrichtspraxis & Lang and Behavioral Abstracts; Presented the [illegible] Republic of Germanys Prestigious Ger-Amer Friendship Awd [illegible] Ambassador in Washington DC; Created Carl Schurz Schlsp[illegible] Initiated, Sponsored & Directed a Natl HS Poster Exhibit which Tou[illegible] Nation; Spon of Numerous Natl Contests for HS Stdnts & Re[illegible] Recognition; Lectured at Natl Confs for FL Educators; *office:* Sm[illegible] HS 100 Central Rd Smithtown NY 11787

KREBS, WILLIAM J., English Teacher; *b:* St Louis, MO; *m:* Virg[illegible] Martin, Kathryn, Daniel; *ed:* Canisius Coll (BA) Eng 1973; SU[illegible] Buffalo (EDM) Eng 1976; *cr:* West Seneca West Sr HS Eng Tchr [illegible] West Seneca Summer Schl Eng Tchr 1986-; *ai:* Stu Newspape[illegible] Western NY Schl Press Assn 1983-; Springvale Planning Bd 6 Yrs; West Seneca West Sr H S 3330 Seneca St West Seneca NY 14224

KRECK, SUSAN DANA, Third Grade Teacher; *b:* Oneonta, N[illegible] Joseph S.; *c:* Matthew Klafehn, Cory Klafehn; *ed:* SUC at Oneon[illegible] Elem Ed 1973; Grad Credit Hrs; *cr:* Lockport City Schls Sixth G[illegible] 1973-75; Unadilla Elem Schl Sixth Grd Tchr 1976; Oneonta City [illegible] Third Grd Tchr 1985-; *ai:* NEA 1984-; Jaycees, Pres; Atonemer[illegible] Church 1967-; Sweet Adelines 1995-; *office:* Valleyview Elem Sc[illegible] 40 Valleyview St Oneonta NY 13820

KREEGER, KATHY LYNN, French Teacher; *b:* Amherst, OH; *m:* [illegible] *c:* Jennifer, Michael; *ed:* Bowling Green St Univ (BSEd) Fr 1973; 2[illegible] Hrs; *cr:* Lorain City Schls Fr Tchr 1973-; *ai:* Fr III Stdnts Group Ld[illegible] Frgn Lang Comm; NEA, OEA, LEA 1973-; *office:* Lorain Southvi[illegible] 2270 E 42nd St Lorain OH 44055

KREGER, MARILYN DALLING, Fourth Grade Teacher; *b:* Toled[illegible] *m:* Arnold J. Jr.; *c:* Jane, Brad; *ed:* Bowling Green St Univ (BA) Ho[illegible] 1963, (MED) Elem Ed 1969; Tchng Cert 1965; Guid & Cnslng Cer[illegible] *cr:* Lake Local Schls First Grd Tchr 1965-82, Fourth Grd Tchr 198[illegible] Grd Level Ch*prsn; Career Ed Rep; Bldg Advy Comm Mem; Educ[illegible] Chprsn; NEA, OEA 1965-, Life Mem; NWOEA, LEA 1965-; [illegible] Holden Jennings Scholar; Ashland Oil Golden Apple Awd; Tchr of [illegible] Awd Nom; Eisenhower Grant in Math & Sci; Toledo Edison TGIF [illegible] Adaption Grant in Affective Ed; Local Career Ed Grants; *office:* [illegible] Local Schls 28150 Lemoyne Rd Millbury OH 43447

KREGER, PATRICIA DI BELLA, Art, Photo & Theatre Arts Te[illegible] Flushing, NY; *m:* Gary W.; *c:* Alessa; *ed:* Montclair Coll (BA) Fi[illegible] 1973; Boston Univ Schl of Visual Art (MFA) Studio Tchng 1978 Early Modernism at Natl Gallery of Art 1993; Stud Art, Land & Land[illegible] at Smithsonian Inst 1995; *cr:* New Brunswick Tomorrow Office & Admin 1976-83; Smitten & Terse Interior Arts Self Employed Desig[illegible] Painter 1983-87; S Brunswick HS Art, Photo & Theatre Arts Tchr [illegible] *ai:* Backstage Club & Drama Adv; Frosh Team Comm; NEA [illegible] Theatrical Awds for Musical Performance & Costume Design 1989 in Show Awd at Pascack Art Show 1993; Dist Grant Awds to Atten[illegible] Inst 1993-95; Dodge Grant Awd for Tchr as Artist 1994; *office:* Brunswick HS PO Box 183 Monmouth Junction NJ 08852*

KREHELY, ROBERT JOHN, Spanish & World History Tc[illegible] Kingston, PA; *m:* Stephanie Wayslow; *c:* Robert, Brad; *ed:* King[illegible] (BA) Span & Soc Stud 1973; Bloomsburg St Coll (MS) Ed 1975; 12 [illegible] Hrs Post Grad Stud at Penn St Univ; *cr:* Bishop Hoban HS His & Span[illegible] 1973-; *ai:* Admissions & Review Bd Chm; Disciplinary Advy Bd; F[illegible] Asst Bsbl Coach 20 Yrs, Asst Ftbl Coach 8 Yrs & Ski Club Modera[illegible] Yrs; NCEA 1980-; Plains Twp Teener League & Little League 1982-92, Coach, 1986 Playoff Champions; Numerous Dist & L[illegible] Division Championships as an Asst Bsbl Coach Also One Final Fo[illegible] Bsbl Team Champion; *home:* 17 Pine Rd Wilkes Barre PA 18705

KREICK, ELIZABETH LAPLANTE, English Teacher; *b:* Nashua [illegible] *m:* Bradley; *ed:* Providence Coll (BA) Eng 1989; Simmons Coll (MAT[illegible] 1992; *cr:* Nashua Sr HS Eng Tchr 1992-; *ai:* Var Tennis Team Coa[illegible] Class Adv; *office:* Nashua Sr HS 36 Riverside Dr Nashua NH 03060

KREIDER, DAWN DELONG, Health & Physical Ed Teache[illegible] Lancaster, PA; *m:* D. Michael; *c:* Benjamin, Nathaniel; *ed:* Un[illegible] Pittsburgh (BA) Hlth, PE 1986; Millersville Univ Masters Equivalent [illegible] *cr:* Swift MS Long Term Sub 1986-87; Solanco HS Hlth, PE Tchr 1[illegible] *ai:* Field Hockey Coach JV 1987-89, Var 1990-92; NEA, PSEA 1987-; Field Hockey Champions 1990; *office:* Solanco HS 585 Solanc[illegible] Quarryville PA 17566

KREINBERG, PENNY, Staff Developer & Rdng Tchr; *b:* Chicago, IL OH St Univ (BS) Elem Ed 1968; Hunter Coll (MS) Elem Ed 1973; 60 [illegible] Credits; 24 Credits Rdng; *cr:* PS 44 1st-3rd Grd Tchr 1969-86, Rdng [illegible] 1986-92, Staff Developer 1992-; *ai:* Comer Action Team; Dist 13 C[illegible] Facilitator; Peer Tutoring Adv; AFT 1969-; IRA 1986-; Wrote Gra[illegible] Comm for Goals 2000; *office:* P S 44 432 Monroe St Brooklyn NY 1[illegible]

KREINBRINK, GARY WILLIAM, Jr HS Language Arts Teache[illegible] Lima, OH; *m:* Victoria (Kauffman); *c:* Corey, Amanda; *ed:* Bluffton [illegible] (BA) Comprehensive Comm 1983; 20 Addl Hrs Sports Sci Ashland U[illegible] *cr:* East Knox HS Eng Tchr 1983-85; Leipsic HS Lang Arts Tchr 1985-[illegible] Coach Var Girls Bsktbl 1985-, Var Cross Cntry 1985-94, Var T[illegible] 1987-93; NEA 1983-; Ath Booster, Ath Amateur Union 1985-; Knigh[illegible] Columbus 1979-, Schlsp Judge; Fraternal Order of Eagles 1983-; S[illegible] Writer Lima News; Northwest OH Dist 8 Coach of Yr 1983, 1985; Dia[illegible] Cnslr Awd; *office:* Leipsic HS 232 Oak St Leipsic OH 45856

KREINER, DIANE, Family & Consumer Science Tchr; *b:* Cincin[illegible] OH; *m:* Tim; *c:* Allison, Katie; *ed:* Coll of MT St Joseph (BS) Home Educ 1972; Voc Cert FCS 1994; Credit Hrs 6, Miami Univ 10, Univ C[illegible] 12, OH Univ 4; *cr:* Taylor HS 9-12 Grd Home Ec Tchr 1972-77; Rea[illegible] Comm Schls Sub Tchr 1978-80; Casco Inc Specialized Sewing S[illegible] 1984-86; Lockland HS Voc Family, Consumer Sci Tchr 1986-; *ai:* F[illegible] Dept Chprsn; Curr Cncl; Voc Ady Bd; AAFCS, OAFCS 1988-; H[illegible] 1988-, Treas 1995-, Sec 1993-95; AVA, OVA 1994-; NEA, ODA, [illegible] 1990-; MND-Parent Club 1992-; Ec Edctr of Yr; Cert Family, Consu[illegible] Scis; John Wycliffe Fleming Yth Awd; *office:* Lockland HS 249 W F[illegible] St Lockland OH 45215*

KREINER, SANDRA BECKWITH, Social Studies Teacher; *b:* Ak[illegible] OH; *c:* J. Kraig; *ed:* Univ of Akron (BA) Psych, Finance, Comp Soc S[illegible] 1973; Post Grad Psych; *cr:* Cuyahoga Falls HS Soc Stud Dept Tchr 19[illegible] Akron BOE GED, ABLE Tchr 1990-; *ai:* Mentor Entry Yr Tchr Adv 19[illegible] Amer Psychological Assn 1985-; OH Cncl Soc Stud 1976-; NEA 19[illegible] CFEA, OEA 1975-; ASCD 1993-; Sunshine Staff Fund; Soc Stud;

, Zero Tolerance 1995; Collaborative Action Comm 1994; *office:* oga Falls HS 2300 4th St Cuyahoga Falls OH 44221*

SER, LINDA L., Seventh Grade Science Teacher; *b:* Harrisburg, PA; llersville Univ (BA) Bio 1974, (BS) Bio & Gen Sci 1976; Tchr Cert d Credit Hrs 1983; *cr:* Lower Dauphin Schl Dist Work Stud Coord '6, 8th Grd Phys Sci Tchr 1977-81, 7th Grd Life Sci Tchr 1982-; *ai:* ar Sftbl Coach 1976-; Var Field Hockey Coach 1978-; LDGAB r Club Adv 1980-; Asst Varsity Bsktbl Coach 1984-1992; PA St Ed 978-; NEA 1978-; US Field Hockey Assn 1970-, Exec VP of Teams; ose Field Hockey 1974-, Capt; Mid Atlantic Field Hockey Camp Dir PA St Field Hockey Coach Assn 1991-, Selection Comm for All-St 1991-93; AAA St Championship Field Hockey Team Coach 1993; Coach of the Yr 1994; Lower Dauphin HS Commencement Speaker Inducted into Millersville Univ Hall Of Fame 1996; US Field y Assn Natl Team Player; *office:* Lower Dauphin Schl Dist 251 Rd Hummelstown PA 17036

TER, DEE ANDRESS, Title I Reading Specialist; *b:* East sburg, PA; *m:* William Raymond; *ed:* East Stroud Univ (BS) Elem 77, (MS) Rdng 1981; *cr:* East Stroud HS Aide Rdng Room 1977-80; mithfield Elem Schl Rdng Specialist 1981-94; J. M. Hill Elem Schl Specialist 1994-95; *ai:* Pocono Area Transitional Housing 1990-, Bd ; *office:* J M Hill Elem Schl 151 E Broad St East Stroudsburg PA

ZMAN, JERRY, French Teacher; *b:* N Africa; *ed:* Queens Coll (BA) 59, (MS) Fr 1972; 30 Credits Beyond Masters New Schl for Soc FAIIS; Attnd Univ of Rouen Normandy & Univ of Nice; *cr:* Yeshiua ueens Fr Tchr 1969-71; IS 25 Fr, Span & Italian Tchr 1971-76; MS & Multicultural Tchr 1976-; *ai:* St Org Adv; Bsktbl Coach; UFT er Chm 9 Yrs; AATF 1992-; Trachtenberg Awd (Twice); Coach of Yr es; Jr HS Tchr of Yr; French Is Fun Pub; *office:* MS 74 6115 Oceania shing NY 11364

MPASKY, THOMAS FRANCIS, Soc Studies Educator & Chprsn; *b:* on, PA; *m:* M. Renee Canevari, RN, BA; *c:* Thomas, Christina, e, Nicole; *ed:* W TX St Univ (BS) His 1968; Post-Grad Stud wood Coll, Wilkes Univ; *cr:* Blakaly HS Amer His & Eng Educator Valley View HS Sco Stud Ed & Chm 1969-; *ai:* Asst Ftbl Coach; Sr & Prom Adv; Ath Advisory Comm; Acad Advisory Cncl; VVEA, 1968-; Natl Cncl Soc Stud; Ec Advisory Cncl; Cougar Kickoff Org; Valley View Jr-Sr H S Columbus Dr Archbald PA 18403

PPS, KATHLEEN MARIE, Third Grade Teacher; *b:* York, PA; *ed:* wood Coll (BS) Elem Ed, ECE 1983; 24 Grad Credits Ed; *cr:* St Rose na Schl Second Grd Tchr 1983-87; St Patrick Schl Third Grd Tchr ; *ai:* Religion Coord; Rdng Co-Coord; NCEA 1983-; Contemporary Group 1991-; *office:* St Patrick Schl 231 S Beaver RR York PA

SCH, JEFFREY SCOTT, Health, PE Teacher & Coach; *b:* New York, *m:* Erica Lynn Hampel; *c:* William, Meredith Leigh, Matthew; *ed:* ery Rock St (BS) Hlth, Phy Ed 1980; Prof Cert Drivers Ed 1980; St Univ Prof Cert Ath Admin 1988; Montclair St Ath Trng Course 1983; air Lawn Bd of Ed Sub Tchr K-12 Grd, Asst Var Ftbl Coach 1980-82; ouck Heights Bd of Ed PE, Hlth, Drivers Ed Tchr, Coach 1982-; NJ Pub Relations Intern 1986; NJ Devils Pub Relations Intern 1986-87; Giants Pub Relations Dir 1987-; All Cty Ftbl Camp Trng Coord 93; Natl Ftbl League NY Giants Pub Relations Coord 1990-; *ai:* NFL ision Coord 1990-; NEA, NJEA 1980-; BCSL Olympic Division of Yr Girls Track 1990-93, Boys Track 1991-93; Olympic Division pions Boys Track 1989, 1992-94, Girls Track 1987, 1990-93; Penn s Coach Boys, Girls Sprint Relay Teams 1989-; Coach of Yr Track, Northern Amateur Assoc 1985; Olympic Division Ftbl Champions nsive Coord 1985, 1995, Dist Wrestling Champions 1991-94; Boys, St Sectional Track Champions, Boys Cty Relay Champions 1994; St onal Ftbl Champions, Voted Team of Yr Defensive Coord 1995; St onal Wrestling Champions, Voted Team of Yr 1992, 1995; *home:* 57 hung Dr Hawthorne NJ 07506

SHOVER, LINDA (MAYOVER), Sixth Grade Teacher; *b:* delphia, PA; *w:* Neil (dec); *c:* Jesse; *ed:* PA St Univ (BS) Elem, tn Ed 1968; Trenton St Coll (MA) Elem Ed 1972; Attnd Bucks Cty n Coll; *cr:* James Buchanan Elem Schl 2-5 Grd Tchr 1968-78; Thomas son Elem Schl Gifted 1-6 Grd Tchr 1981-83; George Washington Schl Gifted 5-6 Grd Tchr 1981-; *ai:* ACT 178 Comm Staff Dev; NEA, Ed Assn, Bristol Twp Educ Assn 1968-; Employee Achvmt Awd 1989; hower Grants Math, Sci, Classroom, Inservice; *office:* George ington Elem Schl 275 Crabtree Dr Levittown PA 19055

SS, RICHARD MICHAEL, Latin & English Teacher; *b:* Manchester, *m:* Sandra A. Fowle; *c:* Michael, Stephen; *ed:* St Anselm Coll (BA) ics 1969; Univ of Pittsburgh (MA) Classics 1971; *cr:* Traip Acad , Eng Tchr 1972-74; Geneva HS Latin Tchr 1974-76; Lincoln MS , Eng Tchr 1976-78; Deering HS Latin, Eng Tchr 1978-; *ai:* Boys or, Outdoor Track Coach; Latin Club Adv; NEA, PTA 1978-; *office:* ng HS 370 Stevens Ave Portland ME 04103

SSLY, THOMAS C., Science Teacher; *b:* Little Rock, AR; *m:* Linda ebster; *c:* Lynne, Thomas, Timothy; *ed:* Lock Haven St (BS) Bio Ed ; Elmira Coll (MS) Bio Ed 1974; *cr:* Hammondsport Cntrl Schl Bio, n Tchr 1971-, Dept Chm 1991-; *ai:* Class Adv; Wrestling Track Coach; stling Tournament Dir; Tchrs Assn, Pres 1995-, Comms 1971-; Vol ulance Corps 1974-81, Pres, Dir of Operations; Jaycees 1973-79, s; Little League 1981-88, Coach; Summer Yth Prgm 1981-87, Coach; Scouts 1987-92, Comm Mem, Chm; Cty Wrestling Coord 1989-95, dential Awd; Sectional Wrestling Comm 1989-95; Village Justice -; *office:* Hammondsport Central Schl Main St Hammondsport NY 0

ARIS, LORETTA G., History Teacher; *b:* New York, NY; *m:* ules; *c:* Katherine; *ed:* Syracuse Univ (BA) His, Jrnlsm 1958; mbia Univ (MA) His Ed 1960; *cr:* Plainview Old-Bethpage HS Soc Tchr 1960-; Plainview-Old Bethpage John F. Kennedy HS Soc Stud 1960-; *ai:* NEA 1975-; *office:* Plainview John F. Kennedy HS 50 nedy Dr Plainview NY 11803

CH, ELLEN BERNHARD, English & Public Speaking Tchr; *b:* more, MD; *m:* Lee H.; *c:* Dane William, Meryl Anne, Leah Mary; *ed:* rking Towards MALdrshp in Tchng Coll of Notre Dame; *cr:* Bank of imore Dir of PR 1977-85; United Way of Cntrl MD Dir of Mrktg 5-91; Roland Park Cntry Schl Dir of PR 1991, Tchr, Creative Writing oetry 1991-; *ai:* Yrbk, Lit Magazine, Chrstn Flwshp Club Advs; nission, Head of Philosophy Comms; Grant for Creating Rdng & ing Sci Fiction Course; Pub Svc Awd Creating Nurturing Envrnmt for ts; *office:* Roland Park Ctry Schl 5204 Roland Ave Baltimore MD 10

EGEL, MARION NEWIRTH, Art Teacher; *b:* New York, NY; *m:* ; *c:* Alisa, David, Jennifer; *ed:* Pratt Inst (BS) Art Ed 1963; USC phic Arts; UCLA Graphic Arts; Montclair St Art Therapy; *cr:* John r Jr HS Art Tchr 1963-65; Norwood Pub Schl Art Tchr 1979-; *ai:* Art ad, Yrbk Adv; 8th Grd Homeroom Tchr; Norwood Tchrs Assn 1980-, sp Comm Chm; Jamboree Fundraiser 1983-, Producer; NY Tchr of Yr 0.*

KRIEGER, FORD, History Teacher; *b:* Philadelphia, PA; *m:* Carla Jean Repsher; *ed:* Univ of PA (BA) His 1976, (MS) Ed 1984; *cr:* Beth Shalom Acad His Tchr 1984-86; Perkiomen Valley HS His Tchr 1986-; *ai:* Odyssey of Mind Spon, Coach 1986-; NEA 1986-; *office:* Perkiomen Valley HS Rt 29 & Trappe Rd Collegeville PA 19426*

KRIEGER, MICHAEL TROY, English Teacher; *b:* Barberton, OH; *m:* Lori Kay Coats; *ed:* OH St Univ (BS) Eng Ed 1986; Bowling Green St Univ Pursuing MA Rdng Ed; *cr:* Rossford Exempted Village Schls Eng Tchr, Coach 1986-; Owens Comm Coll Writing Instr 1992-95; *ai:* Var Cross Cntry, Jr High Track Coach; Renaissance Coord; Soph Class Adv; RACT 1986-; Spec Olympics 1995-; Pub Novel Melvin Howards Fireside Chats 1992; *office:* Rossford HS 701 N Superior St Rossford OH 43460*

KRIEGER, WILLIAM F., Physical Ed Teacher & Coach; *b:* Buffalo, NY; *c:* Carey Ann, Jessica Lynn, Zoe Elizabeth; *ed:* MO Vly Coll (BS) Hlth, PE, Recreation 1967; Attnd Ithaca Coll, Canisius Coll; *cr:* Lancaster Sr HS PE Tchr, Coach 1967-70; Aurora MS PE Tchr, Coach 1970-; *ai:* NYSUT 1967-, Bldg Rep; Amer Ftbl Coaches Assn 1985-; *office:* Aurora MS 148 Aurora St Lancaster NY 14086*

KRIER, NORMAN JOHN, Environmental Science Teacher; *b:* Trenton, NJ; *m:* Patricia Ann; *c:* Jaime Lyn, Jason Philip; *ed:* Beaver Coll (MA) Ed 1984; 27 Grad Credits Environmental Ed PA St Univ; *cr:* Bishop Egan HS Bio, Env Sci Tchr 1970-93; Conwell-Egan HS Bio, Env Sci Tchr 1994-; *ai:* Outdoors Club Moderator 1970-; Schl Facilities Comm; Environmental Stud Ctr Chm; ACT, Natl Wildlife Fed 1970-; NCEA; Friends Silver Lake Nature Ctr 1978-, Pres, Vol of Yr 1982; Bowman's Hill Wildflower Preserve 1994-; AARK Fnd 1985-, Vol; Tchr of Yr Bishop Egan HS 1990; *office:* Conwell-Egan Cath HS 611 Wistar Rd Fairless Hills PA 19030

KRIER, TIMOTHY JAMES, Secondary English Teacher; *b:* Columbus, OH; *ed:* Vanderbilt Univ (BA) Eng 1989; OH St Univ (MA) Educl Admin 1995; *cr:* The Amer Schl of Pueblo Mexico 7th-9th Grd TESOL Tchr 1990-92; Hamilton Twp HS 11th Grd Basic, Regular, Advanced & Hnrs Eng Tchr 1992-93; Whitehall-Yearling HS 9th-11th Grd Eng & 11th Grd AP Tchr 1993-; *ai:* Environmental Soc; Soccer Coach; North-Cntrl Steering Comm; NCTE 1990-; ASCD 1992-; NEA 1993-; Cty Cntrl Comm for Democratic Party; Publishing Author of Supplemental Materials for Fundamental & Themes of Art.*

KRIKKE, FLORENCE, Sixth Grade Teacher; *b:* Grouw, The Netherlands; *ed:* Cedarville Coll (BA) Elem Ed 1971; Wright St Univ (MED) Classroom Tchr 1975; Cert Supervision, Prin, Asst Supt 1991; *cr:* Park Layne Elem Schl 5th-6th Grd Tchr 1971-76; Westlake Elem Schl 6th Grd Tchr 1976-81; New Carlisle MS 6th Grd Tchr 1981-; *ai:* Chm Tchr Inservice Planning Comm; Optimist Club Speech Contest Coach; Dist Sucess, Dist Liaison Comms; NEA, OEA, TEA 1971-; Tecumseh Ed Assn 1971-, Pres, Newsletter Ed, Negotiations Comm; Phi Delta Kappa 1980-; New Carlisle Optimist 1990-, VP, Speech Contest Comm Work; Sertoma Club 1995-; Clark Cty Continental Cablevision Tchr of Yr 1993; Martha Holden Jennings Scholar 1995-, Grant; *office:* New Carlisle MS 1203 Kennison Ave New Carlisle OH 45344*

KRILL, BRUCE C., High School Math Teacher; *b:* Bryan, OH; *c:* Lindsay, Brent, Alexie; *ed:* Defiance Coll (BS) Math Ed 1980; Univ of Toledo (MS) Admin, Supervision 1986; *cr:* Hardin Northern HS Math Tchr 1982-83; Bryan HS Math Tchr 1983-89; Edon HS Math Tchr 1989-93; Edgerton HS Math Tchr 1993-; *ai:* Math Dept Head; Math Club; Bsktbl, Track Coach; NEA, OEA 1989-; Trinity Luth Church Life Time Mem; Bsbl Assn 1989-; Bsktbl Coaches Assn 1980-, Sec, VP, 100 Win Awd; Dist Bsktbl Coach of Yr Twice; *office:* Edgerton HS 324 S Michigan Ave Edgerton OH 43517

KRINER, HOLLY FREEMAN, Second Grade Teacher; *b:* Buffalo, NY; *ed:* St Univ Coll at Buffalo (BS) Elem Ed 1973; 30 Grad Work Hrs 1977; *cr:* Attica Cntrl Schl Rdng Aide 1974-, 2nd Grd Tchr 1974-; *ai:* AFT, NEA, NYSUT, Attica Fac Assn 1974-; Genesee Region on Whole Lang 1993-; *home:* 51 Wren Ave Lancaster NY 14086

KRINGER, MICHEAL DALE, HS Vocal Music & Drama Teacher; *b:* Whittier, CA; *m:* Janet Lynn; *c:* Daniel James; *ed:* Cath Univ of Amer (BM) Choral Music Ed 1988; Ithaca Coll (MM) Music Ed 1994; Vocal Pedagogy, Hlth for Musicians, Music for Spec Learner & Stu Self-Esteem & motivation; *cr:* Benjamin t Rome schl of Music; Achdioscen Cathedral of Saint Matthew the Apostle Asst Choralve Dir 1984-88; Cath Univ of Amer Production & Scheduling Dir 1986-88; Skaneateles Cntrl Schls HS Vocal Music & Drama Tchr 1988-; Saint Mary of the Lake Church Music Dir 1988-; *ai:* Mens Barbershop Chorus; Womens Chorus; SC8 Madrigal Choir; Drama Club; All Schl Entertainment Tech Adv; NYSUT, AFT 1988-; MENC 1984-; *office:* Skaneateles Cntrl Schls 49 E Elizabeth St Skaneateles NY 13152

KRISA, ANTONIETA, Language Chairperson & Tchr; *b:* Caracas, Venezuela; *m:* Thomas Keith; *c:* Thomas Anthony; *ed:* Stony Brook Univ (BA) Span 1993; Babson Coll ESL 1988; Universidad Metropolitana in Caracas Modern Langs 1987; *cr:* Berlitz Lang Acad ESL, Span Tchr 1988-89; Mercy HS Lang Chprsn, Span Tchr 1989-.*

KRISANTZ, CHERYL KNAPP, Fifth-Eight Grade Teacher; *b:* West Mifflin, PA; *m:* Dale Wayne; *c:* Nicholas Joseph; *ed:* CA St Coll (BS) Elem Ed 1979; Allegheny Interm Unit 32 Credits; Carlow Coll 6 Credits; *cr:* West Mifflin Area Schl Dist 3rd, 5th Grd, GATE Tchr 1979-85; James Lavelle Meml Schl 5th-8th Grd Tchr 1985-; *ai:* Spelling Bee, 8th Grd Fieldtrip Spon; *home:* 2114 Duquesne Ave Mc Keesport PA 15132

KRISHER, MICHELE LE LAIDIER, Teacher of Gifted & Talented; *b:* Warren, OH; *m:* Robert Jr.; *c:* Rebekah Conn, Sarah, Michael; *ed:* Kent St Univ (BS) Early Chldhd Ed 1975, (MED) Early Chldhd Ed 1978; 36 Addl Hrs; Cert of GATE 1989, Supervision 1996; *cr:* Lordstown Schls Kndgtn Tchr 1975-79, Tchr of GATE 1988-; *ai:* Acad Prep Bowl Coach; OAGC, NAGC, AFT 1988-; OH Farm Bureau 1978-; OH Holstein Assn 1978-, Dist Sec, Learning Circle Pre Schl 1985-86, Bd Pres; Innovative Energy Lesson Grants OH Edison Co & East OH Gas 1990; Contributing Author: Home, School, Community 1979; *home:* 1405 Tait Rd SW Warren OH 44481

KRISKA, CYNTHIA LOUISE (SESKES), English Teacher; *b:* Cleveland, OH; *m:* Dean A.; *c:* Scott A.; *ed:* Bowling Green St Univ (BS) Eng Ed 1969; Attnd Univ of Akron, Kent St Univ, Drake Univ; *cr:* North Olmsted Jr HS Eng Tchr 1969-70; Hillside Jr HS Eng, Speech Tchr 1970-82; Parma Sr HS Eng, Speech Tchr 1982-; *ai:* NHS Comm; Acad Decathlon Lit Coach; Parma Ed Assn, OH Ed Assn, NEA 1969-; *office:* Parma Sr HS 6285 W 54th St Parma OH 44129

KRISKO, MARTHA BACON, Kindergarten Teacher; *b:* Salem, NJ; *m:* Thomas F.; *c:* Esteline Templin, Dwayne, Damian, Merri; *ed:* Catawba Coll (BA) Elem Ed 1968; *cr:* Portage Area Elem Schl Kndgtn Tchr 1981-; *ai:* Instructional Support Team Mem; Portage Area Wellness Comm Mem; Mentor Tchr; NEA, PAEA & PSEA 1981-; *office:* Portage Area Elem & MS 84 Mountain Ave Portage PA 15946

KRISPINSKY, LEONARD STEPHEN, Head Varsity Soccer Coach; *b:* Youngstown, OH; *m:* Carmen Y.; *c:* Todd S., Chad M., Ryan K.; *ed:* Kent St Univ (BFA) Graphic Design 1970; *cr:* Cardinal Monney HS Asst Girls Var Soccer Coach 1991, Head Boys Jr Var Soccer Coach 1992-93, Head Boys Var Soccer Coach 1993-; *ai:* Feeder System Establishment, Dev; Bldg Successful Soccer Prgm; Natl Soccer Coaches Assn 1993-; Gr Yo Scholastic Coaches Assn 1993-; St Matthias Holy Name Soc 1981-, Pres 1986-92, Man of Yr; Youngtown Lions Club 1976-, Exec Bd Mem; Mooney Home, Schl 1989-, Pres 1992-93; Mooney Ursuline Campaign for Excl, Chm; Amer Society Prof Graphic Artists Awds; Head Coach Diocese Youngstown Soccer Champions 1991-92; Head Coach Tri Cty Soccer Assn Div III champions 1996; *home:* 805 E Philadelphia Ave Youngstown OH 44502

KRISTA, ELIZABETH COLE, 8th Grade Teacher; *b:* Jersey City, NJ; *m:* Kevin C.; *ed:* Jersey City St Coll (BA) Elem Ed 1972; *cr:* Holy Rosary Schl 5th, 8th Grds Tchr 1972-74; St Aloysius Elem Grds 2, 4, 5, 8 Tchr 1974-81; O. L. of Czestochowa 5th-8th Grds Tchr 1981-85; Queen of Peace 8th Grd Tchr 1985-; *ai:* Cath Schl Week Chair; Yrbk, Newspaper Chrstn Leadership Weekend Adv; Gifted & Talented Planning Comm; Rel Ed Tchr; Spelling Bee Coord; Adv of Stock Mkt Game; NCEA 1972-; Schl Nom Disney Awd 1992-93; 1993 Outstanding Tchr, Newark Archdiocese; *office:* Queen of Peace Elem Schl 21 Church Pl North Arlington NJ 07031

KRISTA, KEVIN CHARLES, History Teacher; *b:* Jersey City, NJ; *m:* Elizabeth A. Cole; *ed:* Jersey City St Coll (BA) His 1972; *cr:* St Aloysius Schl 5th-6th Grd Tchr 1972-76; St Peter Schl 7th-8th Grd Tchr 1977-78; Marist HS His Tchr 1988-93; Queen of Peace HS His Tchr 1993-; *ai:* Chrstn Leadership Weekend Adv; Comm on Stu Dev Chm; Religious Ed Tchr CCD; NCEA 1988-; Knights of Columbus 1981-; *office:* Queen of Peace HS 191 Rutherford Pl North Arlington NJ 07031

KRISTOFF, JOAN M., Business & Computer Teacher; *b:* Minersville, PA; *m:* John; *c:* Michele Marie Mc Keown, Jennifer Kohlmeir; *ed:* Bloomsburg Univ (BS) Bus 1959; *cr:* Pottsville Area Schl Bus Tchr 1959-63; Blue Mountain Schl Bus, Cmptr Lead Tchr 1971-; *ai:* Soph Class Adv; Mentor Tchr; Mid St Evaluation Co-Chprsn; NEA, PSEA, BMEA 1971-; PBEA; *office:* Blue Mountain HS RR 1 Schuylkill Haven PA 17972

KRITZWISER, HELEN P., 5th-8th Grade Lang Arts Tchr; *b:* Springfield, OH; *m:* Verlin N.; *c:* Jeff, Greg, Todd, Amy; *ed:* OH Univ (BS) Elem Ed 1987; *cr:* TX-Mexican Chrstn Inst Tchr 1959-60; Buchanan Elem Schl Tchr 1960-61; Beaver Elem Schl Tchr 1965-70; Pike Chrstn Acad Tchr 1987-; *ai:* Amer Red Cross 1982-, Blood Mobile Vol; Pike Co Historical Soc 1991-, Bd Mem; ACSI 1987-; King's Way Flwshp 1991-; *office:* Pike Chrstn Acad 400 Clough St Waverly OH 45690

KRIX, BARBEL, German & Russian Teacher; *b:* Gustrow, Germany; *m:* Michael Dean; *ed:* Univ of Rostock (BA) Eng & Russian 1989; Attnd Univ of Cincinnati; *cr:* Friedensschule Germany Eng & Russian Tchr 1989-92; 4 Cincinnati HS Asst German Tchr 1992-93; St Xavier HS German & Russian Tchr 1993-; *ai:* Univ Grad Stud from Univ of Cincinnati; *office:* St Xavier HS 600 W North Bend Rd Cincinnati OH 45224

KRIZ, THOMAS EDWARD, English Teacher; *b:* Bridgeport, CT; *ed:* Univ of Dayton (BS) Scndry Ed Eng & His 1972; Sacred Heart Univ (MA) Tchng 1991; *cr:* St Gabriel MS Eng & His Tchr 1973-85; Trinity Cath High Eng & His Tchr 1985-; *ai:* Girls Bsktbl Head Coach; JV Girls Sftbl Coach; NCEA 1973-; CASS & CHCSS 1979-; North Stamford Exch Club 1993-; *office:* Trinity Catholic HS 926 Newfield Ave Stamford CT 06905

KROCK, THERESA ANNE (JOHNSON), Lang Arts & Reading Teacher; *b:* Kenton, OH; *m:* John L.; *ed:* Bowling Green St Univ (BS) Elem Ed 1985; *cr:* Benjamin Logan Schls Rdng, Lang Arts Tchr 1985-; *ai:* Newspaper Staff Adv; Stu Incentive Comm; Intervention Assistance Team; NEA 1985-; Nom Rotary Club Tchr Excl Awd 1994-95; *office:* Benjamin Logan MS 4262 Road 26 Bellefontaine OH 43311

KROEGER, NANCY JANE (HORSTMAN), English & Science Teacher; *b:* Ottoville, OH; *m:* Larry J.; *c:* Jonathon, Anthony; *ed:* Bowling Green St Univ (BA) Hearing Impaired & Elem Ed 1980, (MS) Ed with Guidance 1992; *cr:* Vandalia Comm Schls K-6th Grd Tchr of Hearing Impaired 1980-81; Ottoville Local Schls 7th-10th Learning Disablities Tchr & Tutor 1981-82, Jr HS Eng & Sci Tchr 1982-, Reading Tchr; *ai:* Quest & Sci Fair Adv; OLEA 1981-, Sec; NEA 1980-; Saint John Bapt Church 1982-, Clothing Chair, Sunday Schl Tchr; Landeck Mothers Club 1990-, Sec; Vantage Voc Career Awd 1992; *office:* Ottoville Local Schl Box 248 E 3rd St Ottoville OH 45876

KROEGER, PAUL E., Science Resource Teacher; *b:* Elmhurst, IL; *m:* Vickie Peterson; *c:* Kaitlin, Dean; *ed:* Univ of IL (BS) Geology 1972; MS Equivalency 1978; 30-40 Post Grad Credits; *cr:* White Oak Jr High Sci Tchr 1974-81; Springbrook HS Sci Tchr 1981-92; Montgomery Coll Adj Prof of Chem 1990-; J F Kennedy HS Sci Resource Tchr & Dept Chprsn 1992-; *office:* John F Kennedy HS 1901 Randolph Rd Silver Spring MD 20902

KROEGER, VICKIE PETERSON, Honors & AP Chemistry Teacher; *b:* Pleasanton, CA; *m:* Paul Emil; *c:* Kaitlin, Dean; *ed:* Ferris St Coll (AS) Pre-Sci 1977; Western MI Univ (BS) Sci Ed 1979; *cr:* Parkland MS 1979-80; White Oak Jr High 1980-86; Springbrook HS 1986-89; J. F. Kennedy HS 1989-92; Bethesda Chevy Chase HS 1992-; *ai:* NEA, MSTA, MCEA 1979-.

KROEPIL, KATHY ELLEN (SPANGLER), 2nd Grade Teacher; *b:* Bloomsburg, PA; *m:* Joseph James; *c:* Kevin Eugene, Ellen Elise; *ed:* Shippensburg Univ (BS) Elem & Early Chldhd Ed 1977, (MS) Elem Ed 1980; Masters Plus 60 Credit Hrs Various Insts 1986-90; *cr:* Learning Tree Child Care Tchr 3-6 Yr Olds 1977-79; S Antrim Elem Schl 3rd Grd Tchr 1979; Hamilton Hghts Elem Schl Kndgtn Tchr 1980; Scotland Elem Schl 2nd Grd Tchr 1980-; *ai:* Elem Sci Comm; PTA, Reflections Prgm; Chambersbrug Area Ed Assn, PA St Ed Assn, NEA 1981-; Scotland Ladies Auxiliary 1985-, Sec, Treas; St Luke Luth Church 1990-, Cncl Sec 1994; Sunday Schl 1991-, Tchr Grds 2-4; Chrstn Ed Comm 1991-, Bible Schl 1992-, 1st-6th Grd Tchr; Women of ECLA 1991-, Sec; Center Ideas Pub; *home:* 768 Frey Rd Chambersburg PA 17201

KROEPLIN, CLAIRE, Third Grade Teacher; *b:* Jersey City, NJ; *m:* Edward W.; *c:* Margaret A., Edward J.; *ed:* Seton Hall Univ (BS) Ed 1970; SUNY at Plattsburgh (MA) Ed 1983; Northeast Whole Lang Conf Participant 1991, 1993-95; *cr:* Westport Cntrl Schl Elem Tchr 1979-; *ai:* Westport Tchrs Assn 1979-, Sec; NY St Eng Cncl 1993-; NNYTAWL 1990-, Steering Comm; Hodge-Podge Lit Soc 1993-; *office:* Westport Central Schl 55 Sisco St Westport NY 12993

KROH, ANN C., Kindergarten Teacher; *b:* Harrisburg, PA; *m:* James E.; *c:* Alison; *ed:* Shippensburg Univ (BS) Elem Ed 1966; Addl Credit Hrs Penn St Univ, Millersville Univ, Wilkes Coll; *cr:* Cntrl Dauphin Schl Dist 2nd Grd Tchr 1966-67; Westfield Schl Kndgtn Tchr 1967; Waltimore Cty Schl Kndgtn Tchr 1968; Dept of Defense Schls Kndgtn Tchr 1968-70; Cntrl Dauphin Schl Dist Kndgtn Tchr 1980-; *ai:* PSEA, NEA 1983-; NAEYC 1991-; YWCA of Greater Harrisburg 1991-, Bd Mem; Jr League of Harrisburg 1983-; Ronald Mc Donald House 1984-, Vol Coord; Distngd Svc Awd.

KROH, PENNY JEAN, High School English Teacher; *b:* Marlboro, NY; *m:* William Siddle; *c:* Kristal Nicole Hobbs; *ed:* Fredonia St Univ (BA) Scndry Ed 1973; *cr:* Springville Griffith Inst Eng Tchr 1974-77; North Collins HS Eng Tchr 1982-83; Dunkirk MS Eng Tchr 1984-85; Marlboro HS Eng Tchr 1985-; *ai:* Class of 96, Lit Magazine Advs; Handbook Revision Comm 1996; NEA, AFT 1985-; GSDCA 1979-, Champion Ger Shepherd Dogs; *home:* 465 Lattintown Rd Marlboro NY 12542

KROHN, FRANKLIN BERNARD, Professor of Marketing; *b:* Erie, PA; *m:* Inez Claire Judelsohn; *c:* Lynette, Robert, Debra; *ed:* SUNY at Buffalo (BA) Comm 1971, (MA) Comm 1974, (PHD) Comm 1977; *cr:* SUNY Coll of Fredonia Asst Prof, Assoc Prof, Full Prof, Dist Svc Prof 1978-; *ai:* Adv Amer Mrktg Assn, Stdnts In Free Enterprise; Dept Curr Comm; Dept

Parliamentarian; UUP 1979-, Sec; AMA 1981-, Bd; ISGS 1977-; ABCA 1979-; SUNY Chancellor's Awd Excl Tchng 1987; Bernard & Audre Rapoport Flwshp Amer Jewish Stud; Hebrew Union Coll, Jewis Inst Rel 1992; SUNY Distngd Svc Prof Awd 1993; Sam M. Walton Flwshp Freee Enterprise 1995-; *office:* S U N Y Coll At Fredonia Dept of Business Admin Fredonia NY 14063*

KROK, THOMAS B., Guidance Counselor; *b:* Springfield, MA; *m:* E. Patricia Reardon; *c:* Michael, Nicholas; *ed:* Univ of MA (BA) Sociology 1971; Springfield Coll (MED) Guidance & Psychological Svcs 1974, (CAGS) Guidance & Psychological Svcs 1979; *cr:* Westfield Jr HS Eng Tchr 1971-72; Westfield HS Eng Tchr 1972-75, Occupational Guidance Cnslr 1975-77, Guidance Cnslr 1977-; *ai:* PSAT Admin; Class Adv; Golf Asst Coach; MA Tchrs Assn, NEA 1971-; Westfield Ed Assn 1971-, Bldg Rep; Westfield Little League 1989-, Coach; Westfield Youth Bsktbl 1990-, Coach; Westfield Youth Soccer 1990-93, Coach; *office:* Westfield HS 177 Montgomery Rd Westfield MA 01085

KROL, JANET CHARUBIN, Mathematics Teacher; *b:* Boston, MA; *m:* David F.; *c:* Alicia; *ed:* Boston Coll (BA) Math Ed 1968, (MA) Math 1970; 24 Grad Credits Beyond Masters Math & Ed; *cr:* Stoughton HS Math Tchr 1970-; *ai:* MA Tchrs Assn, NCTM, NEA, STA, NCTA 1970-; *office:* Stoughton HS 232 Pearl St Stoughton MA 02072

KROL, NANCY J. (BOWER), 7th-8th Grd Health & PE Tchr; *b:* Point Pleasant, NJ; *m:* Allen J.; *c:* Courtney, Michael; *ed:* West Chester St Coll (BS) Hlth, Pe, Recreation 1977; Addl Credit Hrs; *cr:* Wall Intermediate HS Hlth, PE Tchr 1977-78; Lakewood MS Hlth, PE Tchr 1978-; *ai:* Sunshine Comm Co-Chprsn; NEA, NJEA 1977-; LEA 1978-, Pub Relations Co-Chprsn 1994-; Girl Scouts 1992-, Ldr 1 Yr; Tchr of Yr Lunch with Governor 1994-95; *office:* Lakewood MS 755 Somerset Ave Lakewood NJ 08701

KROLCZYK, FRANCESCA, Former Business Manager; *b:* Baltimore, MD; *ed:* Coll of Notre Dame of MD (BA) Math 1949; Cath Univ of Amer (MA) Math 1969; Attnd Simmons Coll at Boston, Northeast LA St, Univ of WY; *cr:* Cath HS Math Tchr, Curr Coord 1976-84; Towson St Univ Math Tchr 1984-86; Shrine of the Little Flower 7th-8th Grd Math Tchr 1986-92; Cath HS Bus Mgr 1993-95; Sabbatical 1995-.

KROLICKI, JOLINE DEHART, English Dept Chair; *b:* Baltimore, MD; *m:* Raymond John; *c:* Lori Pierson, Julie Brown; *ed:* Univ of MD (BA) Eng 1965; 30 Addl Hrs; *cr:* Severna Park HS Eng Tchr 1965-66; Arundel HS Eng Tchr 1966-73; Old Mill HS Eng Tchr 1973-80; Southern HS Eng Dept Chair 1980-; *ai:* Yrbk Adv; Schl Improvement Team; Fin Comm; NEA, TAAAC, MSTA 1965-; NCTE 1965-, Writing Judge; Womens AGLOW 1972-, Pres; Columbia Scholastic Press Assn 1984-, Judge; Natl Scholastic Press Assn 1984-, Judge; All-Amer, Gold Medalist Yrbk; Key Player; *home:* 516 Darkwood Ave Ocoee FL 34761

KROLL, LORRAINE STEIN, Fourth Grade Teacher; *b:* Passaic, NJ; *m:* George; *c:* Linda Elfenbein, Barbara Kluger; *ed:* Fairleigh Dickinson (BA) Psych 1956; William Paterson Coll (MA) Soc Stud 1981; 15 Addl Credit Hrs; *cr:* Fairlawn Pub Schls Second Grd Tchr 1956-58; Clifton Pub Schls Fourt, Sixth Grd Tchr 1965-; *ai:* Safety Patrol Adv; NEA, NJEA 1965-; Clifton Tchrs Assn 1965-, Pres; Clifton Boys, Girls Club 1985-, Dir; North Jersey Fed Credit Union 1990-, Dir; Kappa Delta Pi 1956; Pi Lambda Theta 1982; NJ Governor's Tchr Recognition Awd 1990; Hoffman LaRoche Curr Grant 1991; *home:* 42 MacArthur Dr Clifton NJ 07013

KROMER, WILLIAM ANNESLEY, English & Spanish Teacher; *b:* Washington, DC; *m:* Blanca Vasquez; *c:* Rosetta, Isabel; *ed:* Bard Coll (BA) Lang, Lit 1968; SUC at New Paltz (MSEd) Scndry Span; Middlebury Coll (MA) Eng 1986; *cr:* Marlboro HS Span I Tchr 1968-71; Horace Greeley HS Span I Tchr 1971-72; Colegio S. Antonio Abad Schl Eng, Span Tchr 1972-74; Downsville Cntrl Schl Eng, Span 7th-9th Grd, Ad Ed 1984-; *ai:* Jr HS Stu Cncl Co-Adv; Stu Exch Comm Adv; NEA 1968-; NY NEA 1978-; DTA 1974-; Downsville Vol Fire Dept 1976-; Lions Club 1977-, Pres 1982-83; NEH Summer Seminars Scndry Tchrs 1984, 1987, 1991, 1994; Tchr of Yr 1990; *office:* Downsville Central Schl PO Box J Downsville NY 13755

KROMPAK, FRANCES A., Guidance Counselor; *b:* Toledo, OH; *ed:* Univ of Toledo (BE) Soc Stud Ed 1962, (ME) Guidance & Counseling 1993; *cr:* Cntrl Cath PE & Hlth Tchr 1962-92, Bsktbl & Vlybl Head Coach 1970-82, Guidance Cnslr 1993-; *ai:* Support Group Facilitator; Children of Alcoholics; Amer Counseling Assn 1992-; Athletic Bd Cntrl 1985-; Toledo City League 1988-, Hall of Fame Nominating Comm; Ath Halls of Fame at Birmingham-East Toledo, Cntrl Cath 1987 & Toledo City League 1st Woman 1988; *office:* Central Catholic HS 2550 Cherry St Toledo OH 43608*

KRONER, LOUIS RICHARD, Teacher of Gifted & Talented; *b:* Cincinnati, OH; *m:* Mary Kay; *c:* Katie, Alan; *ed:* Univ of Cincinnati (BS) Elem Ed 1972; Coll of Mt St Joseph (MA) Ed 1986; Post Grad Stud Xavier, Miami & OH Univ; *cr:* Roll Hill Elem Schl 3rd-6th Grd Tchr 1972-73; St Aloysius Gonzaga Schl 5th Grd Tchr 1973-79; J F Dulles Elem Schl 4th-6th Grd Tchr 1979-; *ai:* NEA & OEA 1979-; Articles Published Eng Lang Arts Bulletin & Challenge Magazine; OH Journal of Schl Math, Author of Slides, Flips, Turns; *home:* 178 Twain Ave Cincinnati OH 45233

KROSKIE, KAREN A., English Teacher; *b:* Mc Keesport, PA; *m:* Joseph P.; *c:* Shannon, Brandy; *ed:* Muskingum Coll (BA) Eng 1968; California Univ of PA Post-Grad Courses 25 Credit Hrs; Univ of Pittsburgh 4 Credit Hrs; *cr:* Proctor & Gamble Dist Co Marketing Research Supvr 1968-70; Elizabeth-Forward Schl Dist Secondary Eng Tchr 1968-; *home:* 420 Mutich St Belle Vernon PA 15012

KROTEC, MARK CHARLES, Biology Teacher; *b:* Pittsburgh, PA; *m:* Deborah Amodeo; *c:* Kyra, Mara; *ed:* Univ of PA (BA) Bio 1977, (MS) Bio 1981; ASBMB, ASCI, ASCB, PEP Five Summer Rsrch Internships: Molecular Bio, Oncology, Molecular Evolution, Cell Bio; *cr:* Pittsburgh Cntrl Cath HS Bio Tchr 1981-; *ai:* Dir Extracurricular Sci: PJAS Sci Bowl, Sci Olympiad, Carnegie Sci Fair, Penn St Sci Symposium; WPBTA 1988-, Pres, Exec Bd; NABT 1990-; PSTA 1988-; 4-6 Girls Bsktbl 1992-, Vol Coach; Kevin Burns Sci Tchng Awd 1994; Outstdng Bio Tchr of PA Awd 1995; Diocesan Golden Apple Tchng Awd 1995; Curr Pub Read Biology, Sol III An Evolutionary Perspective, Molecular Immunology, Human Disease, A Transformation Mystery.*

KROTZER, MARY HORNER, English Teacher; *b:* Bellefonte, PA; *m:* Allan V.; *c:* Gene, Darla, Daryl, Victoria Angstadt, Natalie Hetzel, Connie Black, Leigh Agnoni, Frederick Nienhueser; *ed:* Lycoming Coll (BA) Eng 1971; Mansfield Univ (EDS) Rdng 1976; *cr:* Liberty HS Eng Tchr, Dept Head 24 Yrs; *ai:* CARE, IST Teams; Class Adv; NEA, PSEA 1971-, Mbrshp Chair; Phi Delta Kappa 1990-; Church Internship 1990-, Chair; *office:* Liberty HS PO Box 135 Liberty PA 16930

KROTZER, SHERYL CLARK, Sixth Grade Teacher; *b:* Toledo, OH; *m:* James G.; *c:* Jamie Lynn, Bradley; *ed:* Bowling Green St Univ (BS) Elem Ed 1970, (MS) Rdng 1973; 30 Credit Hrs Beyond Masters Degree; *cr:* Ashland City Schls 6th Grd Tchr 1970-71; Gibsonburg Exempted Village Schls 5th & 6th Grd Tchr 1971-; *ai:* NEA & OEA 1971-; Gibsonburg Tchrs Assn 1971-, Sec 1 Yr VP; Delta Kappa Gamma 1975-; Phi Delta Kappa 1987-; Zion Luth Church 1974-; Fire Ladies Auxilary 1977-; Welker-Smith Post #17 Amer Legion Auxilary 1988-; Gibsonburg Music Boosters 1989-; Ashland Oil Inc Tchr Achvmt Awd 1988; OH Dept of Ed NET Prgm Grant; OH Dept of Hlth Grant; Honorable Mention from Learning Magazines Best in Prof Leadership; *home:* 817 S Ludwig Ave Gibsonburg OH 43431

KROUSE, CAMILLE ROSSO, 11th Grade American Lit Tchr; *b:* Painesville, OH; *m:* Jeffrey Michael; *c:* Zak; *ed:* John Carroll Univ (BA) Eng 1979, (MA) British Lit 1981; 53 Addl Hrs; *cr:* John Carroll Univ Part-time Prof 1979-85; Cuyhoga Comm Coll Part-time Prof 1980-85; Gilmour Acad Full-time Eng Tchr 1980-87; Lakeland Comm Coll Part-time Prof 1980-; Solon HS Full-time Eng Tchr 1987-; *ai:* Jr Class, Prom Adv; NEO, OEA 1986-; NCTE 1981-, St Coord; Phi Delta Kappa 1992-, Advising Yth Writers; St John's Parish, Confirmation Instr; Jennings Fnd Scholar 1991; Who's Who Prof Bus Women 1987; Nom Ashland Oil Tchr of Yr 1996; Who's Who Amer Coll Stdnts 1979; Who's Who Amer HS Stdnts 1975; *office:* Solon HS 33600 Inwood Dr Solon OH 44139*

KROUSE, JANICE ZAWACKI, Mathematics Teacher; *b:* Sharon, PA; *m:* Raymond E. Jr.; *ed:* Clarion Univ of PA (BS) Scndry Ed, Math 1989; Clemson Univ (MS) Math Sci 1991; Univ of Pittsburgh Doctoral Stu Math Ed; *cr:* Clemson Univ Grad Asst 1989-91; Laurel HS Geometry, Functions, Calculus Tchr 1991-; *ai:* Marching Band Auxiliary Adv; Strategic Planning, Prof Dev Comms; Mentor & Stud Tchr Cooperating Tchr; NEA, PSEA, NCTM 1991-; PCTM 1995-; Clemson Univ Flwshp; *office:* Laurel HS R D 4 Box 30 New Castle PA 16101

KROUSKOFF, JOHN H., English Teacher; *b:* New Rochelle, NY; *m:* Pamela; *c:* Lauren, David; *ed:* SUNY at Oneonta (BS) Speech Comm 1985; Manhattanville Coll (MAT) Ed 1990; Attnd Long Island Univ Cmptr Tech, SUNY at New Paltz Admin, NY Inst of Tech, Rockland Tchr Ctr; *cr:* Felix Festa Jr HS Eng Tchr 1988-89; Clarkstown HS North Eng Tchr 1989-; *ai:* Et Cetera Lit & Art Magazine, Cmptr Club, World Wide Web Site Adv; *office:* Clarkstown HS North 55 Congers Rd New City NY 10956*

KROUT, NOAH EUGENE, Sixth Grade Teacher; *b:* York, PA; *m:* Rebecca; *c:* Heidi; *ed:* Millersville Univ (BS) Elem Ed 1969; Attnd Penn St; *cr:* Cntrl York Schl Dist 6th Grd Tchr 1969-95; *ai:* NEA 1969-; Jacees 1970-74, Sec & Treas, Speak up-Regnl Winner; Lions 1976-82, Tail Twister; Easter Seals Bd 1975-, Prog Personal; Township Supvr 1989-, Vice Chmn; Awds: Governor's for Employment of People With Disabilities, York Cty Distngd Citizen, Svc to Mankind, Distngd Life Time Svc.

KRUCZEK, THOMAS PAUL, Instrumental Music Teacher; *b:* Holyoke, MA; *m:* Dorann Kirp; *c:* Jennifer, Hadley; *ed:* Holyoke Jr Coll (AA) Lbrl Arts 1962; Boston Univ (BM) Music Ed 1965; Columbia Univ (MA) Music Ed 1966; Attnd Berklee Coll of Music, U of MA, Worchester St Coll; *cr:* North JHS Band, Gen Music Tchr 1966-70; Southbridge HS Band Dir 1970-81; Mary E. Wells JHS Band Dir 1981-; *ai:* Var Sftbl Coah; NEA; MA Tchr Assn Southbridge Ed Assn 1970-, Pres 1992-95; Music Edctrs Natl Conf 1966-; Optimisy Intnl 1985-.*

KRUCZYNSKI, WILLIAM JOSEPH, Chem & Physics Tchr & Chprsn; *ed:* The OH St Univ (BSEd) Sci Ed 1978, (BS) Chem 1992; *cr:* Franklin Hghts HS Chem, Physics Tchr & Sci Chprsn 1986-; *ai:* Head Soccer Coach; NSTA; Sci Ed Cncl of OH; Amer Chemical Soc; *office:* Franklin Heights HS 1001 Demorest Rd Columbus OH 43204

KRUECK, SUZANNE LEE, Social Studies Teacher; *b:* Elyria, OH; *ed:* Miami Univ (BA) His 1968; Grad Hrs from Kent St Univ, Coll of Mt St Joseph, Bowling Green St Univ & OH Univ; *cr:* Elyra City Schls 1968-; *ai:* Discipline Comm; NEA 1968-; NOETA 1968-; OEA 1968-; EEA 1968-; Martha Holden Jennings Scholar 1972-73; Elyra Tchr of the Yr 1973; Standard Oil of OH Tchrs in Amer Enterprise Pgm for Excl in Tchng Ec Winning Entry 1978-79; Delta Kappa Gamma Tchr Honorary; *office:* Northwood Jr HS 700 Gulf Rd Elyria OH 44035*

KRUEGER, ANGELA DESANTIS, High School English Teacher; *b:* Niagara Falls, NY; *m:* William J.; *c:* Mikal, Emily, James; *ed:* Syracuse Univ (BA) Eng Ed 1972; Attnd Elmira Coll, SUNY at Geneseo & SUNY at Brockport 36 Grad Hrs; *cr:* Mynderse Acad Scndry Eng Tchr 1973-81 & 1988-; *ai:* Bldg Cncl; Stu Forum Adv; Poets & Writers Adv; NEA 1988-; NCTE; Phi Beta Kappa; *office:* Mynderse Acad Seneca Falls Schl Dist 105 Troy St Seneca Falls NY 13148*

KRUEGER, BARRY A., Mathematics Teacher; *b:* Darby, PA; *m:* Nancy Townsend; *c:* Victoria, Dana; *ed:* Gettysburg Coll (BA) Math 1969; 36 Grad Credits at West Chester Univ; *cr:* Penn Wood HS Math Tchr 1969-; *ai:* Penn Wood Ed Assn 1969-, Treas 1972 & Bldg Rep; PSEA 1969-; NEA 1969-; *office:* Penn Wood HS 100 Green Ave Lansdowne PA 19050

KRUEGER, CECILIA EILEEN, First Grd Rdng Recovery Tchr; *b:* Huntington, WV; *m:* Edwin Richard; *c:* Franklin Seth, Sondra Eileen; *ed:* Cedarville Coll (BA) Elem Ed 1970; Wright St Univ (ME) Tchr Ldr 1985; Appalachian Bible Inst Diploma Bible, Chrstn Ed 1968; *cr:* Springfield Local Schl Dist Third-Fourth Grd Tchr 1970-91, Chptr I, Rdng Recover Tchr 1991-92, First Grd Rdng Recovery Tchr 1992-; *ai:* Intervention Team; PTO Speaker; Right to Read Comm; CILT Instr; SLEA 1970-, Bldg Rep; OEA, NEA 1970-; RRCNA 1996; Kappa Delta Pi 1985-; OCC St Bd 1978-; CEF Local Bd 1976-; Gideon Auxiliary 1990-, Pres 1995-; SYS Parent Bd 1995-; Southgate Bapt Church, Charter Mem; Amer Acad of Human Dev; Springfield Local Tchr of Yr; Cabell Cty Hall of Fame; Clark Cty Excel in Tchng Nom, Tchr Dev Mini Grant; *home:* 2447 E Possum Rd Springfield OH 45502*

KRUEGER, DANIEL W., Vocal Director; *b:* Louisville, KY; *m:* Margaret Wolf; *c:* David Otto, Stacy Marie; *ed:* Eastern KY Univ (BA) Music Ed 1975; Vandercook Coll (MME) Music Ed 1980; *cr:* Glen Este MS Band 1975-85; Glen Este HS Vocal Dir 1975-; *ai:* Show Choir Dir; Feaste Producer; OMEA, NEA 1975-; ACDA 1980-; Clermont Tchrs Credit Union 1979-, Bd of Dirs; *office:* Glen Este HS 4342 Glen Este Withamsville Rd Cincinnati OH 45245*

KRUEGER, ELLEN, English Teacher; *b:* Irvington, NJ; *ed:* Moravian Coll (BA) Eng 1975; Rutgers Univ (MED) Eng, Scndry Ed 1982; *cr:* Bridgewater Rarlton HS Eng Tchr 1975-82; Millburn HS Eng Tchr 1982-; *ai:* Club Adv; Creating Writing Wkshp; Chaperone Overseas Educl Trips; Mentor Tchr; NEA, NJEA 1975-; MEA 1982-, Assn Rep; NCTE Presenter 1994; Outstanding Scndry Educator Clark Univ 1987; *office:* Millburn HS 462 Millburn Ave Millburn NJ 07041*

KRUEGER, MARGARET WOLF, Elementary Music Teacher; *b:* Cincinnati, OH; *m:* Daniel W.; *c:* David, Stacy; *ed:* Morehead St Univ (BME) Music Ed 1976; Xavier Univ (ME) Schl Cnslng 1993; 3 Hrs Univ of Cincinnati 1982; 8 Hrs Vandercook Coll of Music 1980; *cr:* Clough Pike Elem K-6 Grd Music Tchr 1976-90; Bethel-Tate MS Vocal Music, Choirs Tchr 1990-92; Clough Pike Elem K-5 Grd Music Tchr 1992-; *ai:* Stu Cncl, Stu News Correspondents Adv; Career Ed, Drug Awareness Rep; IAT Team; Scheduling Comm; Co-Supervising Tchr; OH Music Ed Assn; West ClermontTchrs Assn; Assn for Advancement of Arts Ed; Batavia 1st Presbyn, Church Choir Dir, Sunday Schl Supvr & Tchr, Yth Group Adv; Child Focus, Parenting, Cnslng Adv; Nom Tchr of Yr 1993, 1996; *office:* Clough Pike Elem Schl 808 Clough Pike Cincinnati OH 45245*

KRUEGER, SUSAN HEIDI, Literature Professor; *b:* Camp Le Jeune, NC; *m:* Peter L. Wallace; *c:* Lucia, Kai; *ed:* Middlebury Coll (BA) Eng, Ger 1976; Yale Univ (MPHIL) Comparative Lit 1979, (PHD) Comparative Lit 1984; Attnd Stockholms Universitet 1974-75, Ludwig-Maximilians Universitat 1979-80; Fr, Ancient Greek New Schl for Soc Rsrch 1991-92; *cr:* Yale Coll Tchng Fellow, Acting Instr 1978-81; Summer Lang Inst Tchng Fellow, Acting Instr 1978-81; Williams Coll Visiting Asst Prof of Ger 1982-83; Lang Coll New Schl for Soc Rsrch Fac in Lit 1983-; *ai:* Fr Yr Prgm Dir 1992-; Fr Wrkshp Coord 1993-95; Exec Comm 1993-; Tchng & Learning 1995-; Comm Acad Stans 1988-95; Stu Life 1995-; Acad Adv 1983-; Univ Lib Comm 1987-; NY City Schl Vc Tutor 1991-92; Modern Lang Assn 1981-; Amer Philological Assn Ford Flwshp Diversifying Curr 1993; Distngd Univ Tchng Awd 199(Flwshp Coll Tchrs 1986-87; Whiting Flwshp Yale Univ 1981-82; Flwshp 1979-80; Articles Pub; *office:* Eugene Lang Coll 65 W 11th York NY 10011*

KRUFKA, JOSEPH J., Retired Teacher; *b:* Kingston, PA; *m:* Mary Mary Jo, Lisa Marie Stanski, Alison Rosandich; *ed:* Penn St (BS Montclair St (MA) Ind Arts 1963; Grad Stud Penn St, Jersey C Glassboro St; *cr:* Hanover Park HS Tchr, Coach 1956-66; Whippa HS, Ind Arts Instr 1967-93; *ai:* GATF 1967-; NEA, NJEA 1956-; Arts Assn Pres, Tchr of Yr 1975; Wrestling Coach 1968-83; US O Wrestling Team 1952; Morris Cty Wrestling Hall of Fame 1986; *h* Nerewood Rd Randolph NJ 07869

KRUG, EDWARD WILLIAM,JR., Criminal Justice Prgm Coc Berwick, PA; *m:* Richards L. Fecher; *c:* Kimberly, Christopher; *ed:* Coll (BA) Sociology 1971; Kutztown Univ (MA) Cnslng 1980; Temple Univ, West Chester, Penn St; *cr:* PA Dept of Corrections 1974-81, Ctr Dir 1981-; Allentown Coll Criminal Justice Adj 1982-87; Moravian Coll Sociology Adj Instr 1987-; Northampton Coll Criminal Justice Prgm Coord 1990-; *ai:* Criminal Justice Clu IARCA 1988-; PAPPC 1987-; Outstdng Performance Awd 1989; Northampton Comm Coll 3835 Green Pond Rd Bethlehem PA 1801

KRUGMAN, DOROTHY STEIN, History Teacher; *b:* Perth Ambc *m:* Marshall H.; *ed:* Douglas Coll (BA) His Ed 1966; Rutgers Univ (His Ed 1971; Supervisory Cert 1981; Post-Grad Stud in Span & Ita Renaissance Art; *cr:* Carteret HS His Tchr 1966-; *ai:* Intnl Travel Trips Abroad With Stdnts; NEA & NJEA 1966-; NCSS 1970-; T Sholom 1976-, Bd of Trustees; Natl Gallery of Art Summer Wkshp Amer Assn of Profs for Peace in the Middleeast Grant Studied in Summer 1977; *office:* Carteret HS 199 Washington Ave Carteret NJ 0

KRULL, STEVEN R., Science Dept Chair; *b:* Bayonne, NJ; *m:* Perlman; *c:* Geoffrey, Kenneth, Sarah; *ed:* Sullivan Comm Coll (Liberal Arts 1966; SUNY at Brockport (BS) Bio 1968, (MS) Ed 198 Advanced Stud Admin 1989; *cr:* Madison HS 7th-10th Grd Sc 1968-74; West Babylon Jr HS 8th Grd Earth Sci Tchr 1974-75; Penfie 10th Grd Bio, 12th Grd Advanced Bio Tchr 1975-, 6th-12th Grd Sc Chr 1994-; *ai:* Shared Decision Making Team; NYSUT 1970-; *hon* Williamsburg Dr Fairport NY 14450*

KRUM, CAROL ANN (LA BAR), Seventh Grade Math Teach Bethlehem, PA; *c:* Jarrod A.; *ed:* Ursinus Coll (BS) Math 1968; T Univ (MS) Ed 1973; Post Grad Credit Hrs Villanova Univ, Wilkes C Joseph's Univ, Allentown Coll; *cr:* North Penn Schl Dist Jr HS Matl 1968-73; Upper Perkiomen Schl Dist MS Math Tchr 1977-; *ai:* Coope Learning, Peer Coaching, Alternative Assessment, Math Interdiscip Comms, Inclusion; UPEA, PSEA, NEA 1977-; Church Orgs 1968-; Women's Club 1980-, Music Chprsn; Bus & Prof Women 1992-, Rec Sec, Treas; Rep Party Comm-Woman 1995; Natl Sci Fnd Phy Sci Outstanding Scndry Educator Awd 1973; *office:* Upper Perkiomen Dist Jefferson St East Greenville PA 18041

KRUML, GARY WILLIAM, Social Studies Teacher; *b:* Rutland, V Diane Lee Fusco; *c:* Kelly Lee, Joshua Grant; *ed:* Univ of VT (BA) 1971; Castleton St Coll (MAE) Guidance & Counseling 1981; 30 Post Hrs Spec Ed, Soc Stud & Driver Ed at Saint Cloud; *cr:* Hartford H Stud Tchr 1971-72; Fair Haven Union HS CORE Prgm Dir 1972-74 Stud Tchr 1974-; Castleton St Coll Sociology Instr 1990-91, 1994-9 Soph Class Adv; Negotiation Comm Co-Chprsn; AFT 1978- Geography Assn 1994-95; NCSS 1990-; Natl Physique Assn 1986, Place Awd; US Powerlifting Assn 1992, St 1st Place Masters; Assn for Cultural Exch Prgm 1993-; Supts Incentive Awd; ARSU Tchr of Yr; for VT Tchr of Yr; Yrbk Sr Class Favorite Tchr; *office:* Fair Haven D Union HS 33 Mechanic St Fair Haven VT 05743

KRUMM, ELEANOR A., English Dept Chprsn & Teacher; *b:* NJ; *e* Johns Univ (BA) Eng 1968; Wagner Coll (MS) Eng, Ed 1974; *cr:* M Cath HS Eng Tchr, Chprsn 1970-84; Msgr Farrell HS Eng Tchr, C 1984-; *ai:* Moderator of Literary Magazine; *office:* Monsignor Farre 2900 Amboy Rd Staten Island NY 10306

KRUMM, JOHN HENRY, Band Director; *b:* Columbus, OH; *m:* S Sue Funk; *c:* Mitchell, Andrew; *ed:* OH Univ (BMEd) Ed 1978; Un Dayton (MS) Ed 1995; Attnd OH St Univ; *cr:* North Fork Local Schls Dir 1978-87; Fairfield Union Local Schls Band Dir 1987-90; Gra Schls Band Dir 1990-; *ai:* Marching, Pep, Jazz Band; Brass Choir Assistance Prgm; OH Music Edctrs Assn 1979-, Contest Chm; Amer of Edctrs 1995-; Excl in Ed Awd 1985-87; Tchr of Month 1992.

KRUMPAK, DIANE L., Chemistry Teacher; *b:* Salem, OH; *m:* Bi Cole; *ed:* OH St Univ (BS) Biological Sci Ed 1984; Youngstown St (MS) Ed 1989; *cr:* Mc Donald HS Chem Tchr, Quest Instr 1984-; *ai* Girls Track & Field Head Coach; OH Tests of Scholastic Achvmt C NEA, OEA, MEA, NSTA 1984-; MC Donald Hlth Awarness Comm 1 Rotary Tchr of Month Awd; *office:* Mc Donald HS 600 Iowa Av Donald OH 44437

KRUMPER, CLAIRE LEVINE, Mathematics Teacher; *b:* New York, *m:* Samuel; *c:* Michael, Neal; *ed:* Hunter Coll (BA) Math 1963; Co New Rochelle (MS) Spec Ed 1991; 30 Addl Credits Lehman Coll, Hu Coll; *cr:* Morris HS Math Tchr 1963-65; Stevenson HS Math Tchr 1 Asst Prgm Chm 1990-; *ai:* Asst Prgm Chm; Holiday Summer Homs 1 Treas; *office:* Adlai E Stevenson HS 1980 Lafayette Ave Bronx NY 10

KRUMPUS, JUDITH ANN, Second Grade Teacher; *b:* Plainfield, NJ Brockport St (BS) Elem Ed, His 1970; Cobleskill Coll A1 Nurser 1968; Oneonta St Grad Work; *cr:* Ichabod Crane Schl Kndgtn, Mod 2nd, Modified 3rd, 2nd Grd Tchr; *home:* 5 Pine Oak Dr Kinderhook 12106

KRUPA, RITA CHRISTINE, Religion Teacher; *b:* Meriden, CT; Albertus Magnus Coll (BA) His 1975; Providence Coll (MA) Biblical 1977; 12 Credits Toward Masters in Rel Stud at Providence Coll; Putnam Cath Acad Religion Tchr 1976-77; St Marys Acad Religion 1977-78; Cathedral HS Religion Tchr 1978-; Elms Coll Adjunct Prof of Stud 1986-90, 1992 & 1996; *ai:* Photography Club Adv; NCEA 1978-; Endowment for Hum Summer Seminar 1995; Cncl for Basic Ed Ind S in Hum 1992; Fullbright Hays Fellowship Summer Seminar in Israel 1 *office:* Cathedral HS 260 Surrey Rd Springfield MA 01118

KRUPA, THOMAS ANDREW, 11th Grade US His & Govt Tchr Nanticoke, PA; *m:* Elizabeth Jane Kasper; *c:* Mary Elizabeth, Anne M Elisa Anne, Joanne Mary; *ed:* Utica Coll (BA) Liberal Arts 1982; S Cortland (MS) Soc Stud 1985; 10 Addl Hrs; *cr:* Utica Schl Dist Sub 1982-83; Notre Dame HS Part-time Tchr 1982-85, Soc Stud Tchr 19 *ai:* Jr Class Adv; Phi Alpha Theta 1983-; *office:* Notre Dame HS Burrs Rd Utica NY 13502

KRUPINSKI, MICHAEL STEVEN, Supervisor of Instruction; Newark, NJ; *m:* Laura Curcione; *c:* Llora McAvoy, Lisa, James Curci Stephanie Curcione; *ed:* Montclair St Univ (BA) Sci 1968; Rutgers U (MS) Zoology 1974; 60 Credits Schl Admin Cert; Enviromental Ed; Davisville Jr HS 7th Grd Sci Tchr 1968-69; Parsippany Hills HS Bio, r 1969-75; Kittatinny Regnl HS Bio, Che, Physics & Enviormental chr 1975-, Supvr of Instruction 1981-; *ai:* Tech, Cmptr, sciplinary Writing, In-Svc, Staff Dev Chair, Tchr Evaluation ; Amer Assn Bio Tchrs, Natl Assn of Sci Tchrs 1981-, Mem; ny Supv Assn 1983-, Pres; NJ Princ, Supv Assn 1984-, Mem; Right v Law 1990-, Coord; Dist In-Svc 1994-, Coord; Parents Adv Gifted, d 1981-82, Mem; NJEA Human Rights 1978-79, Mem; *office:* ny Regional HS 77 Hasley Rd Newton NJ 07860*

INSKI, SANDRA JEAN, Chemistry Teacher; *b:* Leominster, MA; ry J.; *c:* Brian, Jennifer; *ed:* Montclair St Coll (BA) Chem, Sci Ed Rutgers Univ 12 Credits; *cr:* Highland Park HS Chem Tchr 1971-74; uns HS Chem Tchr 1981-86; Highland Park HS Chem Tchr 1986-; l Improvement, Dicipline, Attendance Comms; Sci Team Coach; NJ Tchrs Assn 1981-; NJ Star Ledger Scholar Tchr Awd 1993; HP HS wd; *office:* Highland Park HS N 5th Ave Highland Park NJ 08904

NIK, THOMAS EDWARD, 6th Grd Sci & Lang Arts Tchr; *b:* ide, OH; *m:* Vicky L. Wade; *c:* Jennifer, Mark, Nikki; *ed:* OH Univ lem Ed-Cum Laude 1978; Univ of Dayton (MA) Ed Admin-Summa aude 1984; *cr:* St Francis Xavier Tchr 2nd Grd 1978; Martin's Ferry ist Tchr 1978-; *ai:* Sci Text Comm; NEA; *home:* 221 Frazier Ave e OH 43906*

P, MARLENE COSTA, Mathematics Teacher; *b:* LaVale, MD; *m:* R.; *c:* Robert; *ed:* Kean Coll (BA) Math, Ed 1971; Kean Coll of NJ Math, Supervision 1983; 45 Credits at Various Insts Stressing Cmptr mming; *cr:* Henry P. Becton Regnl HS Math Tchr 1971-; The a Project Consultant 1985-, Co-Author 1992-, Dir 1996; *ai:* Stock Club; Past Yrs Chrldrs; Outdoor Ed, Ski Clubs; Bowling, Girls Coach; NEA, NJEA, BCEA, NCTM, Assn Math Tchrs of NJ 1971-; thor The Algebra Project Alg II 1993; Consultant The Algebra Alg I; Consultant for Schl Dist San Antonio, TX & Seattle, WA; o Attend Summer Inst; *office:* Henry P Becton Reg HS Cornelia St rson Ave E Rutherford NJ 07073*

PA, KRISTAL MARIA, French & German Teacher; *b:* Pt Jefferson Y; *ed:* Binghamton Univ (BA) Fr, Ger 1989, (MAT) Ed 1991; *cr:* s Cntrl Schl Fr Tchr 1991-94; Binghamton HS Fr, Ger Tchr 1994-; t Adv Sister Cities; NEA, Bingham Tchrs Assn, NY St Assn of Frgn Tchrs 1994-; Stu Tchr of Yr Laurens Cntrl Schl 1992-93; *office:* amton HS 31 Main St Binghamton NY 13905

PA, RICHARD ANDREW, Prof of Manufacturing Tech; *b:* ale, PA; *m:* Helen Anne Osborn; *c:* Anneliese Sensini, Andrew; *ed:* St Univ (BS) Industrial Arts 1962; SUNY Coll at Buffalo (MS) rial Ed 1967; OH St Univ (PhD) Industrial Tech 1970; *cr:* Lewiston Cntrl Schl Industry Arts Tchr 1964-67; OH St Univ Research Assoc 59; Bowling Green St Univ Manufacturing Tech Prof 1964-; *ai:* acturing Tech Prgm Chair & Prgm Adv; NAIT 1980-, Regnl Dir, Pres standing Regnl Dir Awds; SME 1980-; 22 Grants; Contributed to 6 ; 22 Journal Articles; 13 Research Reports; 1 Videotape Series; 24 apers; 27 Consultantships; *office:* Bowling Green St Univ Bowling OH 43402*

E, JANE THIER, Retired Third Grade Teacher; *b:* Elmore, OH; *m:* ond K.; *c:* Kathleen Mc Cray, Susan Mc Phillips, Kevin; *ed:* Bowling St Univ (BS) Elem Ed 1969; Univ of Toledo (MS) El Ed 1982; 15 Hrs Early Chldhd Dev, Childrens Lit, Math Elem; *cr:* Genoa Area 3 Grd Tchr 29 Yrs; *ai:* Phi Kappa Phi 1969-; GAEA 1966-, Treas; OEA 1966-; AFT 1988-; DKG 1981-, Treas; ORTA 1995-; Jr Women Pres, Sec; Mothers Club 1985-, Pres, Sec; Article Pub; Jennings ar; *home:* 19033 W State Route 105 Elmore OH 43416

SE, RICK L., English Teacher; *b:* Napoleon, OH; *m:* Sue at-Kruse; *c:* Benjamin, Trevor; *ed:* Bowling Green St Univ (BSEd) 977; 152 Addl Sem Hrs MED; *cr:* Liberty Ctr HS Eng Tchr 1977-81; een HS Eng Tchr 1984; Napoleon HS Eng Tchr 1984-; *ai:* Asst Drama HS Adv, Advy Comm; OH Educ Assn, NEA 1977-; Benevolent Order ks 1993-; Sons of Amer Legion 1989-; *office:* Napoleon HS 701 eath Dr Napoleon OH 43545*

SH, CHRISTOPHER PAUL, Art Teacher; *b:* Pittsburgh, PA; *m:* a Radine; *c:* Paul, Kevin, Lesley; *ed:* Univ of NE at Omaha (BS) Ed 970; *cr:* Omaha Tech HS Art Tchr 1970-73; Thomas Stone HS Art 1973-; *ai:* Wrestling Coach; *home:* 375 Sandgates Rd Mechanicsville 0659

VCUK, SANDRA C., Reading & English Teacher; *b:* Philadelphia, Robert; *c:* Nicole, Heather, Michelle; *ed:* Temple Univ (BS) Scndry 72, (MED) Rdng Spclst 1979; *cr:* Phila Schl Dist Eng Tchr 1973-75; nnial Schl Dist Rdg & Eng Tchr 1975-77; Redeemer Lutheran Rdng g Tchr 1981-; *ai:* Roadrunner Lit Magazine Supv; Redeemer Church ir & Sunday Schl Dir; Redeemer Church Sec; Phila Rdng Cncl 1986-; e Pub; *office:* Redeemer Lutheran Schl 3212 Ryan Ave Philadelphia 136

VCZUK, ROBERT JOSEPH, Earth & Space Science Teacher; *b:* delphia, PA; *m:* Sandra Carol DeWolff; *c:* Nicole, Heather, Michelle; emple Univ (BA) Geology 1974, (MSEd) Sci Ed 1976; Drexel Univ LS) Lib Sci 1983; US Army Infantry Ofcr Basic, Advanced Courses, mand & Gen Staff Schl; *cr:* William Tennent Inter HS Earth, Space chr 1974-79; Long Coll Jr HS Earth, Space Sci Tchr 1979-86; William ent HS Earth, Space Sci Tchr 1986-; *ai:* Jr Class Adv; Sci Dept Chair; iction, Rocket Clubs; NSTA 1984-, Local Leader; NEA 1976-; TA 1992-, Bucks Cty Outstdng Sci Tchr Selection Comm Chair; TA 1990-, Host Philadelphia Area Conv; Satellite Ed Assn 1990-; ve Ofcr Assn 1980-; Amer Legion 1990-; NSS 1984-; NSF Grants 1989; NEWMAST Goddard Space Flight Ctr 1990; *office:* Willian ent H S 333 Centennial Rd Warminster PA 18974*

ZEWSKI, BARBARA J., Math Teacher; *b:* Worcester, MA; *m:* nas J.; *c:* Edward, Michael; *ed:* Boston Univ (BA) Eng 1971; ester St (MED) Math 1982; Harvard Univ Practitioner of Math; *cr:* ett HS Tchr 1971-; *ai:* Math Team Coach; NEA, MTA & Webster s Assn 1971-; WOCOMAL 1982-, Sec; ATMIM 1987-; BSA 1988-, Badge Cnlsr & Den Mother; Quo Vadis Awd; *office:* Bartlett HS Lake way Webster MA 01570*

SA, OLEH, Professor of Violin; *b:* Lublin, Poland; *m:* Tatiana kina; *c:* Andre, Peter, Taras; *ed:* Moscow Convervatory (DMA) Violin ; *cr:* Kiev Conservatory Prof of Violin, Chair, String Dept 1967-73; in Musical Inst Violin Prof, Chair, String Dept 1973-75; Moscow ervatory Violin Prof 1985-90; Manhattan Scl of Music Violin Prof -93; Eastman Schl of Music Violin Prof 1993-; *ai:* Artistic Dir Music inian Inst of Amer New York City; The Way They Play Book; erous Recordings; *office:* Eastman Schl of Music 26 Gibbs St ester NY 14604

SIAK, DORIS PARKS, Fifth Grade Teacher; *b:* Sayre, PA; *c:* ela, Brendalyn, Colleen; *ed:* Mansfield St Coll (BS) Elem Ed 1962; Grad at Penn St, Millersville & Gannon; *cr:* Westfield Elem 5th Grd 962-67 & 1976-; *ai:* NEA, PSEA; CVEEA 1962-, Treas; Order ern Star, Organist; Meth Sunday Schl, Treas; LeCercle Moderne, Past ; *home:* 155 1st St Westfield PA 16950

YSTOWIAK, RANDY JAY, Science & PE Teacher; *b:* Glens Falls, *m:* Catherine E. McLaughlin; *c:* Randy Jay Jr., Tiffany Joy, Jesse d, Jacquelyn Elizabeth; *ed:* Bob Jones Univ (BS) Hlth, PE Ed 1983; *cr:* Upper Bucks Chrstn Schl Hlth, PE Tchr 1983-85; High Point Bapt Acad Sci, PE Tchr 1985-; *ai:* Rocket Club Adv; Jr HS Boys Bsktbl Coach; Summer Camp Asst Dir; Amer Assn Chrstn Schls 1983-, Cert; ASEP, NFICEP 1994-, Cert Coach; High Point Batp Church 1985-, Sunday Schl Tchr, 10 Yr Awd; Amer Red Cross 1981-, Lifeguard, CPR, First Aid Cert Instr; *office:* High Point Baptist Acad PO Box 188 Geigertown PA 19523

KRZESINSKI, PATRICIA SULLIVAN, Dean of Students; *b:* Buffalo, NY; *m:* Stephen E. Jr.; *c:* Karen, Andrew; *ed:* Univ of Buffalo (BA) His 1967; Buffalo St Coll (MA) Ed 1992; *cr:* West Seneca Schls Soc Stud Tchr 1967-73; Cleveland Hill Schl Soc Stud Tchr 1984-94, Dean of Stdnts 1994-; *ai:* Stu Leadership, Anti-Substance Abuse Groups Adv; Shared Decision Making; Oversee Allocation Fed Drug Free Grant; Cleveland Hill Tchrs Assn 1984-; Assn Scndry Schl Prins 1992-; Jr League of Buffalo 1975-, Bd Mem; Jim Kelly Fnd for Kids 1990-, Local Organizing Comm; Erie Comm Coll Bd of Trustees 1995; *office:* Cleveland Hill HS 105 Mapleview Dr Cheektowaga NY 14225

KUBACH, PATRICIA J., Biology Teacher; *b:* Philadelphia, PA; *ed:* LaSalle Univ (BA) Ed & Bio 1984; Temple Univ (MS) Ed & Sci 1990; *cr:* Archbishop Wood HS Bio Tchr 1984-88; St Hubert Bio Tchr 1988-; *ai:* Asst Ath Dir; Jr Prom Moderator; NSTA 1984-; PSTA 1984-; ACT 1984-; NCEA 1984-.

KUBASKO, DENNIS STEPHEN, Mathematics Teacher; *b:* Mocanaqua, PA; *m:* Jeanne; *c:* Gina, Dennis Jr., Derek; *ed:* Mansfield St Coll (BS) Math & Scndry Ed 1965; Penn St (MS); 20 Credits Ed; *cr:* Ridley Schl Dist Math Tchr 1965-, Coach Bsktbl & Bsbl 20 Yrs; *ai:* Schl Discipline & Detention; Tech Comms; DSEA, NEA, REA 1965-, 25 Yr Awd; Ridley Interboro Ath Club 1968-90; Brandywine Youth Club 1990-, Bsktbl Championship; Natl Sci Fnd Grant; Math Stud; *office:* Ridley Sr HS Morton Ave Folsom PA 19033

KUBBS, CHRIS ROBERT, HS Math Teacher; *b:* Mansfield, OH; *m:* Julie Maher; *c:* Corey BoKimble, Kara Ann; *ed:* OH Northern Univ (BS) Math 1980; Ashland Univ (MS) Sports Admin 1993; *cr:* Mt Gilead HS Math, Cmptr Tchr 1980-85; Hebron Lakewood HS Math, Cmptr Tchr 1985-89; Marion Pleasant HS Math Tchr 1989-; *ai:* Head Ftbl, 7th Grd Boys Bsktbl, Head Bsbl Coach; NHS Soc Comm Man; NEA, OEA, Local NFOFCAA 1984-; OHSFCA 1985-, Coach of Yr Div V; *home:* 1225 Marion Cardington Rd E Marion OH 43302*

KUBIAK, JAMES RICHARD, OWA Teacher; *b:* Saginaw, MI; *m:* Janet Huston; *c:* Kateri; *ed:* Eastern MI Univ (BA) Engl Lang & Lit 1969; Wright St Univ (MA) Ed 1987; Post8Grad Courses Ashland Univ, Univ of Dayton, Bowling Green, Andrews Univ; *cr:* Detroit House of Corrections Eng Tchr 1969-70; East Jr HS Eng Tchr 1970-72; Cross Keys HS eng Tchr 1972-74; Indian Lake HS Bus, Cmptr Sci, LD, GATE, OWA Tchr 1974-96; *ai:* Stu Cncl, Quiz Team, OMEGA (GATE) Club Adv; Schl Philosophy Comm; OEA, NEA 1974-94; OVA, AVA 1995-; Huntsville Lions Club 1994-, Budget Comm; Russell Point Knights of Columbus 1990-; *office:* Indian Lake HS 6210 State Route 235 N Lewistown OH 43333*

KUBICKO, STEPHEN J., Social Studies Teacher; *b:* Braddock, PA; *ed:* Clarion Univ of PA (BS) Scndry Ed & Soc Stud 1989; 30 Credits Towards Masters at Univ of Pittsburgh; *cr:* Deer Lakes Jr Sr HS Soc Stud Tchr 1991-; *ai:* Strategic Planning Steering Comm Mem; NEA, PSEA, DLEA 1991-; NCSS 1995-; Alle-Kiski Historical Soc 1995-; W PA Historical Soc 1994-; His & Landmarks W PA 1993-; PA Cncl of Soc Stud 1995-; DER Grant.*

KUBIK, ANN, Fourth Grade Teacher; *b:* Amityville, NY; *ed:* St Univ NY at New Paltz (BS) Elem Ed & Theatre Arts 1968, (MS) Ed 1969; *cr:* Farmingdale Youth Cncl Jr & Sr Coun, Swimming Instr, & Asst Pool Supvr 1959-69; Surflight Summer Theatre Lead Character Actress 1970; Lindenhurst Pub Schls 2-5 Grd Elem Schl Tchr 1969-; *ai:* Prin Advisory Comm; Dist Sci Comm, Audio/Visual Coord; Tchrs Assn Lindenhurst, NYSUT, AFT, PTA 1969-, Tchr of Yr 1989; James Street Players 1974-, Pres 3 Yrs; UMC Bd Trustees 1980-, Sec 3 Yrs; I,C Babylon Chancel Choir 1975-, Conductor; Friends of Montauk Lib 1979-, Storyhour 5 Hrs; Who's Who Among Stdnts Amer Univs & Colls 1968; PTA Founders Day Prgm Emcee & Performer 1972-76; Rdng is Fundamental DaySpecl Character Presentations 1989, 199 1 & 1992; Spec Christmas Presentations Live Performances Selected Childrens Lit 23 Yrs; Owl Tchr Center NYS Ed Grant Hands on Stu of Long Island Geography; *office:* Albany Avenue Schl 180 Albany Ave Lindenhurst NY 11757

KUBIK, ELAINE MARIE, Senior HS Vocal Music Teacher; *b:* Buffalo, NY; *ed:* SUNY at Fredonia (BM) Music Ed Piano, Choral 1982; Ithaca Coll (MM) Music Ed Piano, Choral, Suzuki 1988; *cr:* Addison Cntrl Schl 7-12 Grd Vocal Music Tchr 1982-86; Lindenhurst HS Scndry Vocal Music Tchr 1988-; *ai:* HS Thespians, Charles St Players Adv; Producer, Musical Dir; Odyssey Songbirds; MENC 1978-; ACDA 1988-; PTSA 1988-; Staff Mem of Month 1992; *office:* Lindenhurst Union Free Schl 300 Charles St Lindenhurst NY 11757

KUBILUS, DARYL GEORGE,JR., Instrumental Music Teacher; *b:* Akron, OH; *m:* Bonnie; *ed:* Univ of Akron (BA) Music Ed 1993; Grad Work Ed Admin; *cr:* Highland HS Instrumental Music Tchr 1993-; *ai:* 3 Co-Curr Jazz Ensembles Dir; AFM #4 & #24 1989-; OMEA 1993-; *office:* Highland HS 3880 Ridge Rd Medina OH 44256

KUCH, KATHLEEN MARIE (FILLER), Instrumental Director; *b:* Lakewood, OH; *m:* Gregory M.; *c:* Ariel Collette, Kaitlyn Nicole, Kelzey Alexis; *ed:* Grad Classes at BGSU & Akron Univ; *cr:* Vanlue Schls K-12th Grd Music Tchr 1984-87; Riverdale Schls 5th-12th Grd Instrumental Dir 1987-; *ai:* Marching & Pep Band; OMEA 1984-; NEA 1987-; Avon Lakes Music Tchrs Hall of Fame; *office:* Riverdale HS 20613 State Route 37 Mt Blanchard OH 45867

KUCHARSKI, ANN BRIEDEN, Chemistry & Pre-Algebra Tchr; *b:* Carbondale, PA; *m:* John J.; *c:* Jill, Justin, Angela; *ed:* Marywood Coll (BA) Math 1974; Univ of Scranton (MS) Chem & Physics 1978; 3 Credit Hrs Assertive Discipline; 3 Credit Hrs Microsoft Ware Cmptrs; *cr:* Forest City Regnl Schl Dist Math Tchr 1974-75; Lakeland Schl Dist Math & Chem Tchr 1975-; *ai:* NEA 1974-; LEA 1975-; *office:* Lakeland Jr-Sr H S Rd 1 Rt 247 Jermyn PA 18433*

KUCHARSKI, FRANK W., 7th Grade Science Teacher; *b:* Stamford, CT; *m:* Jill Jones; *c:* Katherine, Lindsey; *ed:* Villanova Univ (BA) Hum, Sci 1972; Southern Ct St Univ (MS) Environmental Ed 1979; Cert Math, Sci 1974; *cr:* Mc Gee Schl Tchr 1974-; *ai:* Sport Memorabilia Show for Muscular Dystrophy Coord; Fishing Club Adv; NSTA 1980-; Chester Little League 1992- Exec Bd; CT Aquatic Resources Ed 1990-, Instr; *office:* Catherine Mc Gee MS 899 Norton Rd Berlin CT 06037

KUCHER-PATENAUDE, JANICE, Choral & Theater Dir; *b:* Irvington, NJ; *m:* Joseph R.; *c:* Emma; *ed:* Ithaca Coll (B Music) Music Ed 1973; Rutgers Univ (MED) Creative Drama 1985; *cr:* Drury Sr HS Choral & Theater Dir 1973-82; Lawrence Twsp Jr & Sr HS Choral Dir 1982-83; Montville HS Choral & Theater Dir 1983-; *ai:* Spring Musical, Choir, Vocal & Drama Coach; MENC 1973-; North Jersey Schl Music Assn 1983-, Region I Choir Dir 1989; Pro Arte Chorale 1994-, Festival Chorus, Chorale, Chamber Singers; *office:* Montville HS 100 Horseneck Rd Montville NJ 07045

KUCHTA, LINDA ZACCARI, Sixth Grade Teacher; *b:* Baltimore, MD; *c:* Steve, Heather; *ed:* UMBC (BA) Elem Educ, Psych 1972; Johns Hopkins Univ (MS) Rdng, Ed 1977; Advanced Catechist Cert; *cr:* Our Lady of Perpetual Help Schl Tchr 1972-79; John Paul Regnl Cath Schl Tchr Grd 6, Math Tchr Grd 5 1979-; *ai:* Archdiocesan Math Curr Comm; Math Coord John Paul Regnl Cath Schl; Co-Chprsn of Mid Sts Evaluation; Dept Head for Intermediate Level Class Schedules; NCEA 1972-; Home School Assn 1979-; Our Lady of Perpetual Help Parish 1985-; Mothers Club Mt St Joseph HS 1994-; Woodbridge Vly Improvement & Civic Assn 1980; Nom for Miriam Joseph Farrel Awd; Nom for Presidential Awd for Excl in Sci & Math Tchng; *office:* John Paul Rgnl Catholic Schl 6946 Dogwood Rd Baltimore MD 21244

KUCICH, KAREN ANN, 7th-8th Grade Latin Teacher; *b:* Cleveland, OH; *ed:* OH St Univ (BS) Ed 1968; John Carroll Univ (MED) Ed 1978; Attnd Kent St Univ, Cleveland St Univ, Notre Dame Coll, Univ of MA, Walsh Univ; *cr:* Shaker Heights City Schls 7-8 Grd Latin Tchr, 1 Yr to 5 Grd GATE, 7-8 Grd Fr Tchr, 4-6 Grd FLES 1968-; *ai:* Recycling Club; Spelling Bee Coach; Sunshine Fund Choir; OH Frgn Lang Assn 1970-; The Amer Classical League 1980-; Shaker Hts Tchrs Assn 1968-; Chagrin Falls Village Recycling Ctr 1987-90, Vol; Federated Church of Chagrin Falls New Beginnings Singles Group 1991-, Soc Chmn; Sierra Club 1995-; Nature Conservancy 1992-; Martha Holden Jennings Scholar 1975-76; Youth Ctr StdntsChoice Tchr of Yr 1994; PTA Cncl Tchr Flwshp 1991; *office:* Shaker Heights MS 20600 Shaker Blvd Shaker Heights OH 44122*

KUCK, F. J. M., 5th Grade Classroom Teacher; *b:* Staten Island, NY; *m:* Elizabeth M. Kessig; *c:* James, Brian, Alysen; *ed:* Seton Hall Univ (BA) Natural Sci 1964, (MA) Fr 1967; Richmond Coll 6th Yr Cert Sup, Admin 1975; *cr:* IS 27 Math, Fr Tchr 1966-67; PS 18 6 Grd Tchr 1967-68 1970-72, 6 Grd Cluster Tchr 1968-70, Dean, 4-5 Grd Spec Ed Tchr 1973-75, 5 Grd Tchr 1976-; *ai:* UFT 1966-; AART 1993-.*

KUCKO, CAROL ZUCHOWSKI, Fourth Grade Teacher; *b:* Cleveland, OH; *m:* Robert; *ed:* Hiram Coll (BA) Elem Ed, Sci 1971; Cleveland St Univ (MA) Rdng Specialist; *cr:* Royal Ridge 5th Grd Tchr 1972; Dentzler 5th, 6th Grd Tchr 1972-79; Dag Hammerskjold 2nd-5th Grd Tchr 1979-; *ai:* Cmptr Club Adv 2 Yrs; St Jude Mathathon Coord 4 Yrs; Classroom Coats for Kids, Hunger Fund Raisers; Curr Writing Comms; Stu Tchrs CTE 10 Yrs; Licensed Foster Parent 2 Yrs; NEA, OEA, PEA 1971-, PEA Sec 6 Yrs; IRA 1989-92; ADK 1986-88; PTA 1971-; Article Pub Exceptional Children; Cox Cable for Creative Dramatics Grant; *office:* Dag Hammarskjold Elem Schl 4040 Tamarack Dr Parma OH 44134*

KUDLA, VIRGINIA WAWRZENIAK, Upper Elementary Science Tchr; *b:* Glassport, PA; *m:* Henry Robert; *c:* Mary J. Molinaro, Henry R., Mark, Ruth Chiappa, Joseph; *ed:* Duquesne Univ (BEd) Bio, Sec Sci 1952, (MS) Elem Ed 1978; 8 Credits in Chem at Univ of Pittsburgh; *cr:* Bureau of Mines Analytical Lab 1952-58; Glassport Catholic Elem 1-8th Grd Tchr 1970-84; Serra Cath HS Sci Tchr 1984-86; St Joseph Regnl Elem 5-8th Grd Tchr 1987-; *ai:* Upper Elem Sci Competitions Adv, Spon; Stdnts-At-Risk Core Team Mem; NEA, NCEA 1970-; NSTA 1994-; Parish Choir 1965-; Chrstn Mothers, Guild 1960-; Rosary Soc 1957-; 1993 Pittsburgh Regnl Schl Sci, Engrng Fair; 1994 Jr Division Tchr With Most Winning Entries Awd; Amer Soc of Mechanical Engrs Awd; Alcoa Fnd Awd; 1995 Soc of Analytical Chemists; Golden Apple Awd; *office:* St Joseph Regional Cath Schl 1125 Romine Ave Port Vue PA 15133

KUDLEY, JOHN JAMES,JR., Social Studies Teacher; *b:* Cleveland, OH; *m:* Barbara Hettinger; *c:* J. J. (John III), Molly, Jeffrey, Stephen; *ed:* Muskingum Coll (BA) His 1969; Kent St Univ (MA) His 1979, (MA) Scndry Admin 1985; *cr:* Cleveland Pub Schl Soc Stud Tchr 1969; Aurora City Schls Soc Stud Tchr 1972-; *ai:* Ath Coord; Girls Var Track Coach; Pres Aurora Ed Assn; Aurora Ed Assn 1972-, Pres; OH Ed Assn, NEA 1972-; OH Cncl for Soc Stud; OH Track & Cross Country Coaches; Aurora City Landmark Commission 1989-, Vice Chair; *office:* Aurora HS W Pioneer Trail Aurora OH 44202

KUDRICK, BENJAMIN L., Science Teacher; *b:* Streator, IL; *m:* Jennifer F. Kozer; *ed:* Harvard Coll (AB) Chem 1986; Clarion Univ of (BS) Ed 1987; 18 Credits Environmental Ed; *cr:* A-C Vly HS Sci Tchr 1987-90; Lutherlyn Environmental Ed Ctr Asst Env Edctr 1990-91; Shandong Polytechnic Univ Eng Tchr 1991-92; King George Cty HS Chem Tchr 1992-93; Hempfield Area Sr HS Sci Tchr 1993-; *ai:* Westmoreland Cty Comm Coll Connecting Links, Bridges Comms; PA Sci Tchrs Assn, PSEA, NEA 1987-; Bridges Small Grant; *office:* Hempfield Area Sr HS Rd 6 Box 77 Greensburg PA 15601

KUDZIA, RENEE M., Womens Basketball Head Coach; *b:* Toledo, OH; *ed:* Lourdes Coll (BS) Bus & PE 1996; *cr:* Ypsilanti Jr HS Bsktbl & Vlybl Head Coach 1987-88; Swanton HS Var Bsktbl Asst Coach 1988-92; Owens Comm Coll Bsktbl Head Coach 1992-; *ai:* Kodak All Amer JC-CC Selection Comm Dist IV; Womens Bsktbl Coaching Assn 1989-; OH Jr Coll Athletic Conf Coach of Yr 1993; *office:* Owens Comm Coll 30335 Oregon Rd Box 10000 Toledo OH 43699

KUDZMA, THOMAS GEORGE, Assoc Prof of Math & Engrng; *b:* Nashua, NH; *ed:* MA Inst of Tech (SB) General Engrng 1957; Harvard Univ (AM) Math Tchng 1957; Attnd Univ MN, Purdue, Harvard Coll, Univ of NH, Syracuse, Lowell Tech Inst & Rivier Coll Advanced Stud Chem & Arts; *cr:* Clinton Comm Coll Head Math & Physics Dept 1957-58; Marmion Military Acad Head Chem Dept 1958-59; Phillips Exeter Acad Sci Instr 1959-61; Univ of MA at Lowell Assoc Prof Math 1961-; Univ of NH Adjunct Lecturer Math 1976-81; *ai:* Hall Math Prize Comm Chm; Lecturer in Paper Conservation & Museum Conservator; MTA, NEA 1974-; Amer Assn of Museums 1983-; Intnl Cncl of Museums 1984-; Nashua Zoning Bd 1967-91, Chm; Nashua Planning Bd 1970-85, Distinguished Svc Awd; Independence Rowing Club 1965-, Trustee; Natl Sci Fnd Fellowship Purdue Univ 1960; Ed Museum News Spellman Philatelic Museum; License du Juge-Arbitre Fed Internationale des Societes dAviron; Invited Exhibitor Principality of Monaco Intnls 1985 & 1987; Book Problems in Applied Math for Chemical Engrs; *office:* Univ Of MA At Lowell 1 University Ave Lowell MA 01854

KUECHLER, LINDA ECKERT, Accounting Professor; *b:* Buffalo, NY; *m:* Karl Louis; *c:* Kelly, Candace; *ed:* Canisius Coll (BA) Eng 1970; RIT (MBA) Acctng 1974; SUNY AB (PHD) Intnl Travel 1996; Tax Cert; *cr:* Rochester Inst of Tech Asst Prof 1974-78; Erie Comm Coll Asst Prof 1978-85; Daemen Coll Assoc Prof 1985-; *ai:* Delta Mu Delta Moderator; Fac Senate Pres; AICPA, IMA 1990-; Intl Assoc of Mngmt 1989-, Track Chprsn; Better Bus Bureau 1988-, Arbitrator; CPA; CMA; Articles Pub; *office:* Daemen Coll 4380 Main St Amherst NY 14226

KUEHL, JOHN THOMAS, Instrumental Music Teacher; *b:* Oak Park, IL; *m:* Kathleen A.; *c:* John M., Sharon v.; *ed:* Gettysburg Coll (BS) Music Ed 1973; Penn St Univ 30 Credit Hrs in Music & Music Ed; *cr:* Mt Union Area Schl Dist Jr High Band Dir 1973-75; Elem & 7th Grd Band Dir 1975-79; Jr & Sr HS Band Dir 1979-; *ai:* Music Edctrs Natl Conf 1973-; NEA 1974-; Natl Band Assn 1975-; *office:* Mount Union Area HS 706 N Shaver St Mount Union PA 17066

KUEHLEWIND, CLARA KRAUS, Radiologic Sciences Professor; *b:* Buffalo, NY; *c:* Charles B. Jr., Baron Leo, Claire Ann Rung, Mary Kay Lyon; *ed:* SUNYAB (BS) Hlth Sci Ed 1973, (MED) Sci Ed 1979; Doctatorial Candidate ABD 60 Credits; *cr:* Sisters of Charity Hosp Radiologic Tech 1950-83; SUNYAB Clinical Assoc Prof Hlth Related Prof Med Schl 1973-; Trocaire Coll Division Hlth Sci Prof 1973-; *ai:* Fac Senator; ASRT Bd Dirs; Radiation Safety Ofcr; Career Consultant Area HS; Empire St Coll Mentor Grad Stdnts; ASRT 1972-, Regnl Dir, Plaque; AERTNYS 1974-; NFSRT 1970-, Treas, Installation Ofcr, Plaque; Christ

King RC Parish 1993-, Eucharistic Minister; Acad Sacred Heart 1984-, Bd Dlrs, Plaque; SUNYAB-HRP Clinical Instr Awd Outstdng Contributions Allied Hlth Ed 1981; *office:* Trocaire Coll 110 Red Jacket Pky Buffalo NY 14220*

KUEHN, DREW W., French Teacher; *b:* Philadelphia, PA; *ed:* Grove City Coll (BA) Fr, Span; Universite Laval (MS) Fr; Attnd Universite Catholique de L'Ouest, Universidad de Barcelona, Universita Caholica di Milano, Penn St Univ, Slippery Rock Univ; *cr:* Butler Area Schl Dist Tchr 20 Yrs; *ai:* Fr Club Adv; ESL Instr for Frgn Stdnts; Stu Trip Organizer; Stu Prgms Abroad; NEA, PSEA, BEA 10 Yrs; Meridian Comm Choir; Blazing Star Symphony Choir; Church Pianist; AFS15 Yrs, Club Adv; Duquesne Univ Excl Tching & Commitment to Univ Values & Traditions Awd 1992; Commissioned by Slippery Rock Univ to Compose, Play Original Piano Tribute to Dr. Martin Luther King; Music Dir; *office:* Butler Sr HS 165 New Castle Rd Butler PA 16001*

KUEHN, MYRNA FOSTER, Speech Communication Professor; *b:* Tulsa, OK; *m:* Scott A.; *c:* Sarah; *ed:* Lynchburg Coll (BA) Speech Comm, Eng 1981; TX Tech Univ (MA) Speech Comm 1982; Penn St Univ (PHD) Speech Comm 1987; *cr:* Clarion Univ Prof 1987-; *ai:* Theta Phi Alpha Fac Adv 1988-94; CUP Women's Conf Co-Chair 1995-; Stu Dev, Comm Wkshp Trainer 1987-; Speech Comm Assn of PA 1985-, Pres; Eastern Comm Assn 1985-, Interst Cncl; Speech Comm Assn 1982-; March of Dimes 1992-, Walk Amer Team Capt; Habitat for Humanity 1995-, Family Nurturance Chair; Carey Brewer Awd Lynchburg Coll; Pub Communication Skills for Surviving Conflicts at Work 1996; CUP Tchng Excl Showcase Using Cmptr Mediated Comm to Enhance Instr; Everett Lee Hunt Awd Comm Eastern Comm Assn Comm of Scholars; *office:* Clarion Univ Of PA SCT Dept Clarion PA 16214

KUENNE, JANET B., Eng Tchr & Learning Specialist; *b:* New York City, NY; *m:* Robert E.; *c:* Christopher B., Carolyn Kuenne Jeppsen; *ed:* Radcliffe Coll (BA) His 1956; SUNY at Oneonta (MS) Elem Ed 1959; Univ of PA (EDD) Educl Psych 1970; Postdoctoral Stud Tchrs Coll, Columbia Univ, Rutgers, St Univ of NJ, Univ of VT; *cr:* Princeton Township Schls 3, 4 Grd Elem Tchr 1957-62; NY Univ Assoc Prof Educ Psych 1972-75; Rider Coll Visiting Assoc Prof 1976-78; The Hun Schl of Princeton Learning Specialist, Eng Tchr 1976-; *ai:* Dir Testing, Evaluation; Phi Delta Kappa 1982-, Rsrch Chair; IRA 1969-, Editorial Bd J of AAL; NJRA 1975-, Editorial Bd RIJ; Orton Ayslexia Soc 1969-; Scndry Rdng Interest Cncl 1976-84, Pres, VP; Princeton Nursery Schl Bd 1975-81, Pres; Radcliffe 1957-82, Pres, VP, Treas; Harvard Club of Princeton 1987-, Bd of Trustees; Articles Pub in J of Ed Psych, Rdng Instruction Journal, Hun Today; Presentations AERA, NJRA, IRA; *office:* Hun Schl Of Princeton 176 Edgerstoune Rd Princeton NJ 08540

KUENNE, LINDA HAASIS, Elementary Helping Teacher; *b:* Perth Amboy, NJ; *m:* Michael L.; *c:* Leigh, Michael, Marybeth; *ed:* Trenton St Coll (BA) Elem Ed 1966; Fairleigh Dickinson Univ (MA) Hum Dev 1988; St of NJ Supvrs Cert; *cr:* Mawbey St Elem Schl 4th-6th Grd Tchr 1966-94; Woodbridge Twp Schl Dist Elem Helping Tchr 1994-; *ai:* Steering Comm: Integrated Lang Arts Fair & Developing Scope & Sequence for Soc Stud & Sci Curr; NEA & NJEA 1978-; Woodbridge Twp Ed Assn 1978-; NJ Rdng Assn 1994-; Middlesex Cty Rdng Assn; *office:* Woodbridge Twp Schl Dist PO Box 428 Woodbridge NJ 07095

KUENZEL, CHARLES A., 9th Grade Science Teacher; *b:* Denver, CO; *m:* Margaret; *c:* Matt, Bryan, Lauren; *ed:* SUNY at Plattsburgh (BS) Sec Ed, Earth Sci 1974; Union Coll (MST) Masters Sci Tchng 1977; *cr:* Saratoga City Schls 9th Grd Sci Tchr 1974-; *ai:* Saratoga Tchrs VP & Exec Comm; NSUT, AFT 1974-, Ed #10 Rep; Capital Region Tchr 1994-; Bd Mem; Ctr Policy Bd; Cub Scouts 1990-, Den Ldr, Comm Mem; BSA 1990-, Merit Badge Cnslr; US Dept Energy Ed Grant Univ of VT 1978; *office:* Saratoga Springs Jr HS W Circular St Saratoga Spgs NY 12866

KUENZEL, DIANNE HUNTER, English Teacher; *b:* Grand Rapids, MN; *m:* Adelbert; *c:* Peter; *ed:* Southern CT Coll (BA) Eng 1967; *cr:* Metuchen HS Eng Tchr 1968-; *ai:* Newspaper Adv; Substance Abuse Comm; Crisis Mngmt Team; NJEA, MEA 1968-; *office:* Metuchen HS 400 Grove Ave Metuchen NJ 08840

KUFFA, ELAINE SMILES, First Grade Teacher; *b:* Wilkes Barre, PA; *m:* Andrew E.; *c:* Megan L.; *ed:* Bloomsburg Univ (BS) Elem Ed 1968; Wilkes Univ (MS) Elem Ed 1974; Inservice, Intermediate 11 Unit Credits; *cr:* Abington Heights Schl Dist Fourth Grd Tchr 1968-79; Wyoming Area Schl Dist Elem Tchr 1989-; *ai:* NEA, PSEA 1968-; 1st United Presbyn Church 1968-, Womens' Assn Sec, Elder, Trustees Sec; *home:* 155 Philadelphia Ave West Pittston PA 18643*

KUHBANDER, KATHLEEN SUE, English, German & Yrbk Tchr; *b:* Hickory, NC; *m:* Daniel; *ed:* Clearwater Chrstn Coll (BA) Eng 1994; *cr:* FCS Eng, Ger, Yrbk Tchr 1994-; *ai:* NHS Advy Comm; Chrldng Adv; Drama Club Ldr; ACSI 1994-; Yth Ldr 1994-; Who's Who in Coll; *office:* Faith Christian Schl 740 E Russ Rd Greenville OH 45331*

KUHL, DAVID SCHUYLER, Computer Science Teacher; *b:* Jersey City, NJ; *m:* Emily Miller; *ed:* Boston Univ (BA) His 1990; *cr:* Egg Harbor Twp HS His & Anthropology Tchr 1992-95; Cyrus Pierce Schl Cmptr Sci Tchr 1995-; *ai:* Mock Trial Team Coach; Stu Assistance Comm Mem; Sailing & Windsurfing Instr; Foreign Lang Comm; Comm Schl Adult Ed Cmptr Tchr; *home:* 12 Hussey St Nantucket MA 02554*

KUHL, JUDITH ANNETTE, Science Teacher; *b:* Pittsburgh, PA; *c:* Sharon Zink Spencer, Amy Zink; *ed:* IN Univ of PA (BSEd) Bio & Ed 1960; Troy St Univ at Dothan (MSEd) Bio & Ed 1987; Grad Course Work at Amer Univ, Auburn Univ, George Washington Univ, Univ of VA, Univ of MD at Coll Park; *cr:* Arlington VA Cty Schl Bio Tchr 1965-78; Houston Cty AL Bio & Life Sci Tchr 1980-81, 1984-85; Wiregrass Rehab Ctr at Dothan Work Adjustment Instr 1985-87; Suitland HS Bio, Physiology & Microbiology Tchr 1988-; *ai:* Internship & Multicultural Comm; Sci Fair; Cty Sci Bowl Judge Coord; MD Assn of Sci Tchrs Presenter; NEA 1960-; MD Assn of Bio Tchrs 1988-, Honorable Mention Outstndg Bio Tchr Awd; NSTA & MSTA 1988-; PGCEA 1988-; NABT & MAST; Alpha Sigma Alpha 1958-; Chesapeake Bay Fndtn 1989-; ASPCA 1992-; Friends of Natl Zoo 1993-; MD Governors Acad for Sci, Math & Tech 1992; Martin Marietta Grad Fellows Pgm Rsrch Fellow 1993; NSF Presidential Awd for Excl in Sci Tchng Nom 1994; Amer Physiological Assn Rsrch Fellow 1995; *office:* Suitland HS 5200 Silver Hill Rd Forestville MD 20747*

KUHLMANN, DIANA OPPERMAN, Fourth Grade Teacher; *b:* New York City, NY; *c:* George Divine, Sharon Divine Laroche; *ed:* SUNY at New Paltz (BS) Ed 1966, (MS) Ed 1983; 56 Credit Hrs Post-Grad Stud; *cr:* Wappingers Cntrl Schls Tchr 30 Yrs; *ai:* Various Curr Comms; Cty Wide Curr Dev; AFT & NEA; Town Ec Dev Comm 1996, Vol Docent; Co-Authored Local His Booklets for Dist use in Tchng 4th Grd Curr; *home:* PO Box 1105 Highland NY 12528

KUHN, GERALD JEROME,JR., Technology Education Teacher; *b:* Fall River, MA; *m:* Bernadette Verrengia; *c:* Elizabeth, Michael, Rachel, Daniel, Sarah; *ed:* RI Coll (BS) Industrial Ed 1978; Dartmouth Coll (MA) Liberal Stud 1985; Over 30 Credits Beyond Masters; *cr:* Attleboro HS Tchr 1978-79; Monadnock Regnl HS Tchr 1979-; *ai:* Odyssey of Mind Coach & Coord; Tech Stu Assn Co-Adv; Drama Production Tech Adv; NEA 1978-; NH Tech Ed Assn, Tchr of Yr 1996; Intnl Tech Ed Assn, Tchng Excl Awd 1996; Saint Vincent De Paul Soc 1980-, Pres; Pub Cadkey Cookbook Jr HS Intro to 3D CAD; *office:* Monadnock Reg Jr Sr HS 580 Old Homestead Hwy East Swanzey NH 03446

KUHN, JACKIE HUMPHREY, 2nd Grade Teacher; *b:* Clarion, PA; *m:* Blaine Norman; *c:* Dana Dianne Baluch, Blaine Darrin; *ed:* Clarion Univ (BS) Elem Ed 1967, (MED) Elem Ed 1970; Attnd PA St Univ; Univ of AK 40 Credit Hrs in Ed; *cr:* Brookville Schl Dist 2nd Grd Tchr 1967-68; Forest Area Schl Dist 1st-2nd Grd Tchr 1968-; *ai:* Forest Area Wellness Dir; Strategic Planning Comm; Phi Delta Kappa, Delta Kappa Gamma 1994-; PSEA, NEA 1967-; Forest Area Planning 1992-; United Meth Church 1970-, Chm Worship Comm; Metropolitan Life Fnd Grant; 2 Growing Healthy Grants; Family Fun Nights Grant; Numerous Other Grants; *office:* West Forest Elem Schl 210 Vine St Tionesta PA 16353*

KUHN, LINDA C., Sixth Grade Math Teacher; *b:* Lancaster, OH; *ed:* OH St Univ (BS) Psych 1981, (BA) Elem Ed 1981, (MS) Elem Ed 1989; *cr:* Brookpark MS 6th Grd Math Tchr 1983-; *ai:* Prof Assistance Ldr; Curr, Tchr Ldr, Venture Capital Planning & Funding, Restructuring Network Comms; Bldg Math Coord; NCTM 1994-; OH Cncl Tchrs of Math 1992-; South-Western Ed Assn 1983-, Bldg Alternate; Schl Bell Awds 1986, 1988-89, 1992-94; Tchr of Yr 1992-93; OSU Honoring Excl in Tchng Profession 1993; *office:* Brookpark MS 2803 Southwest Blvd Grove City OH 43123

KUHN, MARJORIE ANN, 6th Grade Teacher; *b:* Cambridge, MA; *ed:* Notre Dame of Wilton (BA) Elem Ed 1969; Long Island Univ (MA) Elem Ed 1990; 30 Credits Beyond Masters; *cr:* St Patricks 5th Grd Tchr 1965-66; St Bridgets 5th Grd Tchr 1966-68; Lincoln Schl 7th Grd Tchr 1969-70; Warren Point 6th Grd Tchr; Thomas Jefferson MS 6th Grd Tchr 1993-; *ai:* Observation & Evaluation Comm Chair; Soc Stud Comm; NEA, NJEA, BCEA & FLEA 1969-, Past VP & Sec; Annual Kodak Photo Contest Winner; *office:* Thomas Jefferson MS 35-01 Morlot Ave Fair Lawn NJ 07410

KUHN, ROBERT STERLING, Computer Science Professor; *b:* Cambridge, OH; *m:* Patricia Louise Cooper; *c:* Robert, Kathy Pontius, Christopher, Judy Knouff; *ed:* Muskingum Coll (BS) Geology 1955; OH Univ (MS) Higher Ed 1982; Columbia Pacific U (PHD) Cmptr Sci 1993; Elem, Scndry Ed, Chem, Music Muskingum Coll; Certfd Gemologist Amer Gem Soc; Certfd Flight Instr CFII; *cr:* Kuhn's Jewelers Watch Maker 1948-55; Independant Exploration Co Geologist 1955-56; Vanadium Corp of A Rsrch Mineralogist 1956-59; East Muskingum Schls 7-8 Grd Tchr 1959-61; *ai:* Cmptr Operations Oversite Comm MATC; OH Ed Assn 1961-; Amer Gem Soc 1973-; Civil Air Patrol 1980-, Major, Air Rescue; *home:* 1590 Hillcrest Acres Cambridge OH 43725*

KUHNS, MARTHA, Nursing Professor; *b:* Latrobe, PA; *ed:* Womens Med Coll Hosp (RN) Nrsng 1970; Duquesne Univ (BSN) Nrsng 1981; Univ of Pittsburgh (MSN) Nrsng 1984, (PHD) Nrsng 1993; *cr:* St Johns Alcohol & Drug Rehab Charge Nurse 2 Yrs; Woodville St Hosp Psych Nurse I 1 Yr; Stat Nrsng Consultants Psychotherapist 5 Yrs; Duquesne Univ Asst Prof 10 Yrs; *ai:* Curr, Tenure & Promotion Comms; SADD Spon Springdale HS; Sigma Theta Tau 1986-, Stu Cnslr; Natl Nurses Soc on Addictions 1984-, VP Local Level; Alpha Tau Delta, Adv, Adv of Yr, Honorary Mem; Cult Awareness Network 1988-, Advy Bd; Chemical Awareness & Referal Evaluation Svc 1990-, Advy Bd; Sigma Theta Tau Intnl Rsrch Grant; Citizens Ambassador Prgm Del; Appreciation Natl Crisis Prevention Inst Cert; Tchr Awd SGA of Duquesne; *home:* 1874 Saxonburg Blvd Tarentum PA 15084

KUJAWSKI, LUANNE SALVADOR, Business & Computer Teacher; *b:* Buffalo, NY; *m:* James A. Sr.; *c:* James Jr., Melanie; *ed:* Buffalo St Coll (BA) Bus Ed 1984, (MS) Bus Ed 1987; *cr:* Elba Ctrl Schl Bus, Cmptr Tchr 1984-; Voc Ed Chr; *ai:* Schl Store, Jr Class, Mock Trial Adv; Univ of Rochester Tchr of Yr Awd; *office:* Elba Central Schl 57 S Main Elba NY 14058

KUKUK, ELLEN CORDING, Third Grade Teacher; *b:* Washington, DC; *m:* William s.; *c:* Debbie Johnson, Cherie Brewer; *ed:* Miami Univ (BS) Ed 1973; Wright St Univ (MS) Ed 1982; 30 Post Grad Hrs; Staff Dev Hrs; *cr:* Sherman Elem Schl First Grd Tchr 1977-80; Roosevelt Elem Schl Third Grd Tchr 1980-; *ai:* Coord, Adv Conflict Resolution Peer Mediation Prgm; Roosevelt Ldrshp Team; NEA, OEA, MTA 1977-; W. H. Mc Guffey IRA 1984-, Pres 1989-1990; IRA, OCIRA 1984-; Miami Alumni Bd 1985-; Crystal Apple Awd Middletown Comm Fnd 1995; *office:* Roosevelt Elem Schl 2701 Central Ave Middletown OH 45044

KULCZYK, KIMBERLY ANN, Math Teacher; *b:* Buffalo, NY; *m:* James; *c:* David; *ed:* St Bonaventure Univ (BS) Math, Ed 1988; Indiana Univ of PA (MED) Math Ed 1989; *cr:* Iroquois Cntrl Schls 7 Grd Math, Sub Tchr 1989-90m 1991-931 Gowando Cntrl Schl 7 Grd Math Tchr 1990-91; Huntington Learning Ctr Math Tchr 1989-; Bishop Timon-St Jude HS Math Tchr 1993-; *ai:* Jr Cls Adv; Campus Ministry; NCEA, NYSMTA, NYS Lay Tchrs Assn 1993-; *office:* Bishop Timon-St Jude HS 601 Mckinley Pky Buffalo NY 14220

KULHA, DOROTHY J., French Teacher; *b:* Carbondale, PA; *w:* Kenneth (dec); *ed:* Millersville Univ (BS) Fr 1968; 106 Post-Grad Credit Hrs Fr, Ed, Cmptr Tech; *cr:* John Harris HS Fr Tchr 1968-69; Susquehanna Township HS Fr Tchr 1969-71; Middletown Area HS Fr Tchr 1971-; *ai:* Stu Trips; Foreign Lang Dept Chprsn 1990-; Experimental FLES Project; NEA, PSEA, MAEA 1971-; PSMLA; Implementation FLES Prgm; Assessment Acad; In-serviced Fac Authentic Assessment & Outcome Based Ed; Mentor Tchr; Nom Tchr of Yr 1993; Participant in Edctr Exchange Prgrm Wth Victoria, Australia 1996; *office:* Middletown Area HS 1155 N Union St Middletown PA 17057

KULICK, BARBARA MAY, Social Studies Instructor; *b:* Abington, PA; *m:* Frank; *c:* Adam May, Courtney, Sasha; *ed:* Gwynedd Mercy Coll (BA) His & Scndry Ed 1974; Villanova Univ (MA) Philosophy 1979; Widener Law (JD) Law 1981; *cr:* North Penn HS Soc Stud Tchr 1974-83; Rosemont Coll Part Time Bus Law Prof 1982-84; PA Superior Court Law Clerk 1983-84; Villanova Univ Part-Time Philosophy Instr 1984-93; Widenek Law Legal Writing 1984-85; Montgomery Cty Comm Police Trng & Part-Time Law 1983-; Cntrl Bocks HS East Soc Stud Tchr 1993-; *ai:* Jr Class Adv; Republican Party 1975-, Comm Women; Souderton Orch 1995-, Housing Dir; Law Review; Aviation Forum Ed; Moot Court Hnr; *office:* Central Bucks-East HS Holicong & Anderson Rd Buckingham PA 18912*

KULICKI, STEVEN M., 7th-8th Grd Graphic Arts Tchr; *b:* New York, NY; *m:* Mary Thierjung; *c:* Gregory, Stefanie; *ed:* Millersville Univ (BS) Ed 1967; 30 Credit Hrs Guid Kutztown Univ; *cr:* Nazareth Schl Dist Tchr 1967-; *ai:* Sr High JV Wrestling 1969-76; Jr High Head Wrestling Coach 1976-81; NEA 1967-; PSEA 1967-, Negotiation Comm; Lehigh Vly Radio Control Soc, VP, Newsletter Ofcr; Article Pub 1992; *office:* Nazareth Area Schl Dist 1 Education Plz Nazareth PA 18064

KULIG, LINDA COLE, Reading Recovery Teacher; *b:* Ludlow, MA; *c:* Lisa Bachiochi; *ed:* Univ of MA (BAEd) Elem Ed 1967; Amer Intnl Coll (MS) Spec Ed 1977; Rdng Recovery Trng U CT 1995-96; *cr:* Stony Hill Schl 2nd Grd Tchr 1967-70, Sped Classroom 1970-74; Resource Rm 1974-81; Soule Rd Schl Resource Room 1981-91; Meml Schl Resource Room 1991-95; Meml Schl Rdng Recovery Tchr 1995-; *ai:* Delta Kappa Gamma 1983-; *office:* Meml Schl 310 Main St Wilbraham MA 01095

KULIK, GARY, Mathematics Teacher; *b:* Mineola, NY; *m:* Barbara Ann; *c:* Garrett, Lindsay; *ed:* Suny Stonybrook (BS) Applied Math, Statistics 1984, (MA) Coaching, Ath 1990; Woodrow Wilson Fnd Math Modeling; *cr:* Mid Cty Sch Dist Math Tchr 1985-86; Hewlett Schl Math Tchr 1986-87; Mt Sinai Schl Dist Math Tchr 1987-; *ai:* Ftbl Coach 8 Yrs; Boys Bsktbl Coach 9 Yrs; Dwight D. Eisenhow Grant Prgm Problem Solving Technigues; *office:* Mount Sinai HS Gertrude Goodman Dr Mou NY 11766

KULIS, MICHAEL DAVID, Teacher; *b:* Auburn, NY; *m:* Laura G *c:* Michael Jr., Christopher, Kelly; *ed:* LeMoyne Coll (BA) Bus 197 Genesseo, Oswego; *ai:* Golf Coach; Yrbk Bus Mgr; NEA 1995-.

KULJU, WILLIAM DAVID, Health Teacher; *b:* Marquette, MI; *m* *c:* Ashley, Abbie; *ed:* OH St Univ (BS) Ed 1978, (MA) Ed 1984; *cr:* MS PE Tchr 1978-80; Whitter Elem PE Tchr 1980-81; Westervill HS Hlth Tchr 1981-; *ai:* Head Ath Trainer; NEA, OEA, WEA 197 Ath Trainers 1980-; OH Ath Trainers 1986-; Ath Trainer 1993 Wor Games; Ath Trainer Pan Am Games 1995; *office:* Westerville South S Otterbein Ave Westerville OH 43081

KUMMER, IDA, French Teacher; *b:* Tunis, Tunisia; *m:* Bart; *c:* Be Tamara; *ed:* Paris X Nauberne Univ (BA) Lit, Lang 1971; Paris III S Nouvelle (MA) Lang, Linguistics 1974, (PHD) Comparative Lit 19 Mount Holyoke Coll Fr Tchr 1973-75; Brearley Schl Fr Tchr 19 United Nations Intnl Schl Fr Tchr 1976-; *ai:* MLA 1991-; Artic 1995; *office:* United Nations Intl Schl 24-50 E River Dr New Yc 10010

KUMP, LISA S., 9th-12th Grd English Teacher; *b:* Milwaukee, Robert; *c:* Haleigh; *ed:* Gettysburg Coll (BA) Eng 1988; Coll of W & Mary (MA) Scndry Ed 1992; *cr:* Olson Research Assocs Mrktg 1988-90; Glen Burnie HS Eng Tchr 1992-; *ai:* Frosh, Soph, Jr, S Spon 1992-; Schl Promotion Comm 1995-; Stu of the Month Comm TAAC 1992-; Catsonville Area Jaycees 1994-; *office:* Glen Burnie H Baltimore Annapolis Blvd Glen Burnie MD 21060*

KUMPEY, MARIE DOHERTY, Fourth Grade Teacher; *b:* Wo MA; *c:* Rodney Jr, James J.; *ed:* Worcester St Coll (BS) Elem Ed Boston Coll (MED) Elem Ed 1960; 65 Addl Credit Hrs; *cr:* Flagg Fourth Grd Tchr 1960-65; Rice Schl Fourth Grd Tchr 1968-89; Je Schl Fourth Grd Tchr 1989-; *ai:* Math, Sci Task Force; MTA, NEA WREA 1994-; NSAC 1970-; WARC 1985-; Horace Mann Grant; Two Tchr Who Influenced Most; *office:* Jefferson Elem Schl 1745 M Jefferson MA 01522

KUMPIKAS-STRAVINSKAS, GIEDRE, French & German Teac Kaunas, Lithuania; *ed:* Hunter Coll (BA) Fr Lit 1961, (MA) Fr Li Grad Ctr CUNY (PHD) Fr Lit 1974; Queens Coll (MA) Eng Lit 19 Credits Ger, 24 Credits Latin, Regents Equivalency in Span Permane Cert; *cr:* Hicksville HS Fr, Ger, Latin, Span, Eng Tchr 1961-; *ai:* Regents Classes I, II, III, AP in Lit, Coll Fr Intermediate Levels Advanced Conversation, Intnl Baccalaureate Fr; Emphasized Sp Areas of Fr Lit; Taught Scndry Levels Ger, Latin; Conducted In-S Courses Conversational Fr; Chaired Dist Scndry Reorganization C Dist Curr Cncl, Inter-Visitation Comms; Consistent Highest A Regents Scores; Fr Natl Exam; Fr Poetry Contests; Natl Ger Exam Latin Exam Medals, Certs; AATF, Second VP, Nassau & Grand Co Chprsn; AATG; Fr Club, Spon 25 Yrs; Ger Club, Spon 20 Yrs; Bun Yth Exh Prgm NY Selection Comm; Distngd Fr Tchr Awd AATF, N Chptr, Svcs Culturels of Fr Embassy 1994; Commendations Tra France, Field Trips, Tutorials; *home:* 8232 Bell Blvd Jamaica NY 1

KUNIAK, LORRAINE OZIMEK, Mathematics & Science Teach Natrona Hghts, PA; *c:* Jacqueline E., Jeanine M.; *ed:* IN Univ of PA Art Ed 1970; Post-Grad Math PA St Univ 1989-92; *cr:* Mt Pleasan Dist Elem Art Tchr 1970; Highland Schl Dist Elem Art Tchr 19 Margaret Mary Schl 6 Grd Homeroom Tchr 1987-; *ai:* 7-8 Grd Counts Coach; 4-6 Grd Math Curr Comm Greensburg Diocese; 1987-; *office:* St Margaret Mary Schl 3055 Leechburg Rd New Kensi PA 15068

KUNIKIS, MICHAEL ANTHONY, Social Stud Tchr & Dept Cha Cleveland, OH; *ed:* Cleveland St Univ (MA) His 1989; Attnd Univ o His 1969; *cr:* St Mary Schl Soc Stud Tchr 1969-72; Nativity Schl Soc Tchr 1972-85; St Thomas Aquines HS Soc Stud Tchr 1985-88; St J Acad Soc Stud Tchr 1989-; Cuyahoga Comm Coll His Instr 1990-; *a* Stud Dept Chair; Coordinate Stu TV News; His Club Moderator; OH of Soc Stud 1989-; *office:* Saint Joseph Acad 3430 Rocky Riv Cleveland OH 44111*

KUNKA, JOSEPH J., Mathematics Teacher; *b:* Ambridge, PA; *m:* Lee Elger; *c:* Allison, Gregory, Brian; *ed:* Indiana Univ of PA (BS) 1968; Masters Equivalency from Penn St & West Chester Univ; *c* Army Lieutenant 1968-70; Methacton HS Math Tchr 1970-; *ai:* PSEA, Methacton Ed Assn 1970-; PA Cncl Tchrs of Math; *o* Methacton Sr HS 1001 Kriebel Mill Rd Norristown PA 19403

KUNKEL, JANICE LORAYNE, Math Instructor & Dept Chair; *b:* D Hill, PA; *m:* Steven; *c:* Stephanie, Drew; *ed:* PA St Univ (BS) Psyc 1984, (MED) Cnslr Ed 1985; Towson St Post Grad Sci Courses; Go Tchr Inst Courses; *cr:* PA St Univ Ath Tutor, Math Instr 1984-8 Timothy's Schl Sci, Math Tchr 1985-92; Harford Day Schl Math Chair, Instr 1991-; Harford Comm Coll SAT, GED Math Private 1993-; *ai:* Field Hockey, Lacrosse, Bsktbl Coach; Stu Cncl, Comm Adv; Bldg, Grounds Comm; Mathalon Adv; NCTM 1991-; Matl Planning Comm 1993-; PA St Alumni Assn 1986-; St Timothy's Olsso Incentive Awd 1990; Tom Bernhardt Mem Tchng Awd 1993; Guest T Month Harford Cty Chamber of Commerce 1994; *office:* Harford Day 715 Moores Mill Rd Bel Air MD 21014*

KUNKLE, CRAIG ROSS, Social Studies Teacher; *b:* Harrisburg, P Cathy Ann Benfer; *c:* Ryan, Christy; *ed:* Grove City Coll (BA) Hi 1972; Shippensburg Univ (MED) Soc Sci 1976; *cr:* Allen Jr HS 9th His Tchr 1972-78; Allen MS 8th Grd US His Tchr 1978-82; Cedar Cli Soc Stud Tchr 1983-; *ai:* Model UN, Ski Club Adv; PSEA, NEA 1 *office:* Cedar Cliff HS West Shore Schl Dist Carlisle & Warwick Rds C Hill PA 17011*

KUNKLE, LUCILLE FERRACCIO, Secondary Med Assist Teach Vandergrift, PA; *c:* Rosemary K. Bayliss; *ed:* Univ of Pittsburgh Tchng 1976, (MED) 1978, (PHD) 1984 Health Occupations; M Womans Hosp X-ray Tech, 2 Yrs Cert Prgm; *cr:* Univ of Pittsburgh Sun Instr Voc Ed Dept 1980-84; *ai:* Adult Evening Sch Coord, Adult I Boyce Comm Coll; VICA Adv Vol Indstrl Clubs of Amer; Amer Reg of X-Ray Technicians 1966-; PSEA 1978-, Pres; PA St Educl Assn Med Asst Prgm Natl 1st Pl Awd 1988; Med Asst VICA Competition Plac Natl Stdnt Winner; *office:* N Westmoreland Career/Tech Ctr Stevenson Blvd New Kensington PA 15068*

KUNKLE, THOMAS JOSEPH, Music Teacher; *b:* Bethleham, PA Dianne E. Mock; *c:* Beth, Mindy, Joe; *ed:* PA St Univ (BS) Music Ed 1 (MED) Music Ed 1970; *cr:* Philipsburg-Osceola Area Schls Music 1966-78; Spotts Music Cntr Music Store Mng 1978-88; Hollidays Area HS Music Tchr & Dept Chair 1988-; *ai:* Music Dept Chprsn; Ch Choir, Alumni Chorus Dir; NEA 1966-, Resolutions Comm Local P Yrs; MENC 1966-, Dist Pres 2 Yrs; Alumni Assn Comm Svc Awd; *of* Hollidaysburg Area Jr HS 1000 Hewitt St Hollidaysburg PA 16648

KUNS, MELISSA MILBURN, Sixth Grade Teacher; *b:* Hillsboro, OH Michael; *c:* Darren, Amber; *ed:* Wilmington Coll (BA) Elem Ed, K Attnd Bowling Green, Ashland Univs; *cr:* Clearmont Northeastern Ch & 2nd Grd Tchr 1983-85; Clyde-Green Springs 6th Grd Tchr 1985 Margaretta Local 6th Grd Tchr 1988-; *ai:* Beta Sigma Phi 1988-, F

Apple Awd Ashland Oil 1993-94; *home:* 5417 Miller Rd Castalia ›24

Z, DEBBIE, Special Populations Guid Cnslr; *b:* Ellwood City, PA; ›sell Jr.; *c:* Stephanie, Ryan, Melanie; *ed:* Indiana Univ of PA (BS) ›itation Ed 1977; Univ of Pittsburgh (MED) Rehabilitation Cnslng ›MED) Scndry Guid 1992; *cr:* Harmanville Rehab Ctr Voc, Educ ›ir 1985-88; PA Insurance Mgt Co Voc Rehab Specialist 1988-91; ›n Beaver HS Prevention Specialist 1992-; Ctr HS Spec Populations ›nslr 1995-; *ai:* Stu Assistance Team; Comm Advy Cncl; St Felix ›1987-, Lecter; *office:* Western Beaver Co Jr Sr HS 1260 N ›ad Rd Monaca PA 15061

Z, MAUREEN ELIZABETH, 5th Grade Teacher; *b:* North ›anda, NY; *ed:* SUC Buffalo (BS) Elem Ed 1986; SUNY at ›urgh (MS) Elem Ed 1991; *cr:* Sanford St Schl Option Classroom ›987; Hudson Falls Sr HS Resource Room Tchr 1988; Corinth Elem ›rd, 5th & 6th Grds Tchr 1988-; *ai:* Elem Bldg Planning Team; ›al Arts Comm; Stu Mentor; Stu Cncl; Shared Decision Making Team; ›Helping Girls Seminar; Girls Club; NYSUT & AFT 1988-; *office:* ›n Central Elem Schl 105 Oak St Corinth NY 12822*

Z, NAN DECKER, Second Grade Teacher; *b:* Kingston, NY; *m:* ›; *c:* Alyson, Erica; *ed:* St Univ at Oswego (BS) Elem Ed 1966; St ›Albany (MS) Rdng 1985; *cr:* Burnt Hills, Ballston Lola Schl 4th ›hr 1966-70; Niskayuna Cntrl Schl Elem Resource Tchr 1980-85, 2nd ›hr 1985-; *ai:* Niskayuna HS Crew Club Dir 1987-, Crew Club Coach ›3; NYSUT, AFT 1985-; Nisk Tchrs Assn 1985-, Bldg Rep; League ›men Voters 1970-, 1st VP, Sec; Outstdng Woman of Yr 1992; *home:* ›organ Ave Niskayuna NY 12309

Z, RAYMOND L., Computer Science Teacher; *b:* Sewickly, PA; *m:* ›*c:* Donna, Paul; *ed:* Indiana Univ of PA (BSEd) Sec Ed, Chem 1965; ›se Univ (MS) Gen Sci, Chem 1971; PA St Univ (EDD) Phys Chem ›*cr:* Turtle Creek HS Tchr 1969-87; Comm Coll Allegheny Cty Adj ›978-; Woodland Hills HS Tchr 1987-; *ai:* Cmptr Sci Dept Chm; Amer ›Soc 1974-; ACM, IEEE 1988-; Keivan Burns Awd Excl Sci Tchng ›*office:* Woodland Hills HS 2550 Greensburg Pike Pittsburgh PA

ZMANN, ANN LEWINE, Guidance Counselor; *b:* Philadelphia, ›Kenneth J.; *c:* Brian, Laura; *ed:* Penn St (BS) Elem, Spec Ed 1980; ›n St Coll (MA) Schl Cnslng 1988; *cr:* Delta Schl Tchr 1980-82; St ›'s Home for Girls Tchr 1982-83; Cntrl Bucks Schl Dist Spec Ed Tchr ›89, Guid Cnslr 1989-; *ai:* NEA, PSEA, CBEA 1983-; ASCA, ACA ›*office:* Lenape MS 313 W State St Doylestown PA 18901

, MICHAEL W., Elementary Principal; *b:* Karen Nickerson ; *c:* ›ny, Nicole; *ed:* SUNY at Geneseo (BSEd) Ed 1973; (MLS) Lib Sci ›St Bonaventure Univ (MSEd) Educl Admin 1988; *cr:* Friendship ›Schl 4-6 Grd Math Tchr 1973-88; Cuba-Rushford CS Elem Prin ›*ai:* PTA 1988-, Honorary Life Mem; ASCD 1985-; SAANYS 1988-; ›eo Alumni Assn, Life Mem; FFA, Honorary Life Mem; Cuba Circ Lib ›e 1995-; Cuba United Meth Church 1989-, Trustee treas; Allegany ›leighborhood Based Alliance, Charter Mem; Chaired Creative ›ound Effort; Assisted Successful Schl Merger Effort 1991-; Admin ›Cattaragus Allegany Schl Lib System; Numerous Articles Pub; *office:* ›Rushford Cntrl Schl 20 Elm st Cuba NY 14727

ZENDORF, ROBERT GODFREY, Psychology Professor; *b:* ›n, NE; *m:* Elizabeth Ann Ritvo; *c:* Jennifer, Rebecca; *ed:* Yale Univ ›Psych 1973; Univ of VA (PHD) Cognitive Psych 1979; Boston Univ ›& Post Doctoral Courses; *cr:* Univ of MA Asst Prof 1979-85, Assoc ›985-90, Prof 1990-; *ai:* Coord Interdisciplinary Minor in Cognitive ›83; Assoc Dir Hnrs Pgm 1994; MA Soc of Profs & NEA 1979-; APA ›AASMI 1983-, Pres 1990-91; Mason-Rice After Schl Pgm 1989-, bd ›Cambridge Hosp 1983-, Behavioral Medicine Fellow; Co-Ed The ›ophysiology of Mental Imagery 1990; Ed Mental Imagery 1991; ›Hypnosis & Imagination 1996; Numerous Articles & Book Chptrs ›*office:* Univ Of MA At Lowell 1 University Ave Lowell MA 01854

'HA, JOSEPH RICHARD, Chemistry & Physics Teacher; *b:* Perth ›y, NJ; *m:* Christine D'Aquila; *c:* Douglas, Erin; *ed:* Paterson St Coll ›Jr HS Ed 1967; Trenton St Coll (MA) Sci Ed 1981; 30 Post Grad ›Hrs in Sci, Ed Courses; *cr:* John Adams Jr HS Math, Sci Tchr ›85; J. P. Stevens HS Chem, Physics Tchr 1985-; *ai:* Boys Soccer Var ›Christn Flwshp Adv; NEA, NJEA, NJSTA 1967-; First Presbyn ›h 1973-, Elder, Trustee; *office:* J P Stevens HS 849 Grove Ave Edison ›820*

CHIK, MARION E., English Teacher; *b:* Cleveland, OH; *m:* Brian ›n; *c:* Steven, John, Ellen; *ed:* Notre Dame Coll (BA) Eng 1973; ›land St (MA) Eng 1989; 8 CEU AP Seminars, Wkshps Eng, Writing, ›iscipline, Theater; *cr:* Villa Angela Acad Eng Tchr 1973-76; Lorain ›HS Eng Tchr 1989-92; St Joseph Acad Eng Tchr 1992-; *ai:* Moderator ›ss, Key Club; Drama Coord; NCTE 1992-; NCEA 1973-; Channel ›Outstdng Tchr Awd Nomination 1994; Most Influential Tchr 1995; ›Speaking Union Shakespeare Competition Tchr Participant 1996; ›Saint Joseph Acad 3430 Rocky River Dr Cleveland OH 44111

ER, SUSAN D., Eng & Humanities Instructor; *b:* Manhasset, NY; *m:* ›*c:* Savannah, Jeremy; *ed:* IN Univ (BS) Eng, Ed 1985; Univ of ›ers (MED) Soc, Philosophical Fnds of Ed 1993; *cr:* Perth Amboy HS ›Instr 1986-89; Manadepan HS Eng Instr 1989-93; Howell HS Eng, ›Instr 1993-; *ai:* 1st Yr Tchrs Mentor; Renaissance Comm; Scholars ›Curr Wkshp; NJEA, NEA 1986-; *office:* Howell HS 405 Squankum ›wbrook Rd Farmingdale NJ 07727*

ERSMITH, ABRAHAM, English Professor; *b:* Johnstown, PA; *m:* ›Frank; *c:* Lydia; *ed:* Harvard (MA) Amer His Ed 1964; City Univ ›European His 1965; NY Univ (PHD) Amer Civilization 1974; *cr:* ›attan Comm Coll Prof 1967-; *ai:* Prof Staff Congress 1967-; Mark ›n Soc 1994-, Scholar; Mellon Flwshp; NEH Flwshp; Articles Pub Ed; ›Borough Of Manhattan Comm Coll 199 Chambers St New York NY ›7*

INSKI, A. JEAN (HUGHES), Resource Room Teacher; *b:* Syracuse, ›*m:* John; *c:* Peter, Amy; *ed:* LeMoyne Coll (BA) Eng 1974; Syracuse ›(MS) Spec Ed 1985; Working Toward Masters in Educl Admin at ›Bonaventure Univ; *cr:* Jamesville DeWitt MS Eng Tchr 1974-80; ›oran HS Resource Room Tchr 1984-86; Olean HS Resource Room ›1986-; *ai:* Frosh Class Adv; SADD Avd; Spec Ed Comm Mem; Soc ›n Mem; NEA 1986-; NYSUT 1974-86; *office:* Olean HS Sullivan St ›n NY 14760

P, JOHN CHARLES,III, Orchestra Director; *b:* Pottstown, PA; *m:* ›n Nobel; *c:* Tracey, Steven; *ed:* Montclair Univ (MA) Music Ed 1986; ›uehanna Univ (BS) Music Ed 1972; *cr:* Bergenfield Pub Schls ›umental Music Tchr 1972-; *ai:* Jazz, Marching Band, Various ›umental Ensembles; NEA, MENC 1972-; NSOA 1986-, NJMEA ›-; NJ Governors Awd Tchr of Yr 1990; *office:* Bergenfield HS 80 S ›pect Ave Bergenfield NJ 07621

RANGA, ABRAHAM AKANBI, History Professor; *b:* Okutala, ›ria; *m:* Eulin Maria Pullar; *c:* Kemi, Abraham, David; *ed:* ASWA (BA) ›1978; Andrews Univ (MA) His 1979; Elmhurst Coll (BA) Fr 1981; ›ni Univ (PHD) His 1992; *cr:* ASWA Lecturer 1981-86; Miami Univ ›Scholar 1991-92; Earlham Coll Visiting Prof 1992-93; Univ of ›innati Adj Prof 1993-; Cincinnati St Prof 1994-; *ai:* Univ of Cincinnati Adv; Frgn Stu Adv Comm; AHA 1992-; AAUP 1994-; West OH Chrstn Edctrs; Hamilton SDA Church 1987-, Bd, Elder 1987-92; Dissertation Scholar 1991-92; *office:* Cincinnati St Tech & Comm Coll 3520 Central Pky Cincinnati OH 45223*

KURCZ, MARY ANN HERBAL, Science Teacher; *b:* Hazleton, PA; *m:* Robert; *c:* Nathan; *ed:* Bloomsburg Univ (BS) Elem Ed Sci 1972; Lehigh Cty Comm Coll (AA) Ed 1974; Kutztown Univ Guidance; Allentown Coll; *cr:* Most Blessed Sacrament Schl 6-8th Grd Sci Tchr 1977-91; St Paul Schl 6-8th Grd Sci Tchr 1991-; *ai:* Stu Cncl, Drama Club Adv; Sci Coord; Candleligh, Cath Schls Week Comm; NCEA 1977-; PSTA 1993-; *office:* St Paul School 219 Susquehanna St Allentown PA 18103*

KURILLA, MICHAEL ANDREW, Social Studies Teacher; *b:* Kingston, PA; *m:* Marlene Frantz; *c:* Karen, Lisa, Michael, Stephen; *ed:* Kings Coll (BA) Soc Stud 1966; 30 Credit Hrs at Duquesne Univ; Addl 58 Post Grad Credit Hrs; *cr:* Grand Army of the Republic HS Soc Stud Tchr 1969-; *ai:* Jr Class & Prom Adv; Soc Stud Comm Coord; NEA, PSEA & WBAEA 1966-; Larksville Jr Bsktbl League 1972-, Pres & Sec; WY Vly W Schl Bd 1982-86; Luzerne Cty Intermediate Unit 1985-86, Sec; *office:* G A R Memorial Jr Sr HS 250 S Grant St Wilkes Barre PA 18702

KURKE, LANCE BROWNSON, Assoc Professor of Management; *b:* Fargo, ND; *m:* Florence E. Mendelson; *c:* Jamie; *ed:* Stetson Univ (BS) Chem 1974; Cornell Univ (MA, MBA) Org Theory & Behavior, Quantitative Analysis 1979, (PHD) Org Theory & Behavior 1981; *cr:* Carnegie Mellon Univ Asst Prof 1981-86; Wake Forest Univ Asst Prof 1986-89; Duquesne Univ Behavioral Div Chm 1992-95, Assoc Prof 1989-; *ai:* Delta Sigma Pi Adv; Acad of Mngmt; Amer Sociolog Assn; Strategic Mngmt Soc; Pittsburgh Chamber Music Soc 1992-, Bd Mem, Mrktg Comm; Rsrch Grants; Tchng Awds; Articles Pub; *home:* 1218 Squirrel Hill Ave Pittsburgh PA 15217

KURLEY, DOLORES THERESE, Administrative Assistant; *b:* Brooklyn, NY; *ed:* Immaculata Coll (BA) Elem Ed 1967; St Charles Seminary 74 Revelation; Prof Cert PA Dept of Ed; Leisure Time Act 1975; Human Sexuality Parents, Tchrs 1990; *cr:* St CLement Elem Schl Second Grd Tchr 1951-57; St Agnes Demonstration Elem Schl Second, Third Grd Tchr 1957-64; St Agatha Elem Schl First, Second Grd Tchr 1964-70; Immaculata Conception Elem Schl Third Grd Tchr 1970-71; Sacred Heart Elem Schl Third Grd Tchr 1971-76; Transfiguration Elem Schl Second-Fourth Grd Tchr 1976-79; St Martin of Tours Elem Schl Third, Fourth Grd Tchr 1979-83; St Rose of Lima Elem Schl Third Grd Tchr 1983-87; St Cyril Elem Schl Third Grd Tchr, Admin Asst 1987-; *ai:* NCEA; Eng as Second Lang Grant; Co-Author Fourth Grd Math Text, Work Book; Taught Eng to Cambodian, Chinese Women; Taught Bible Stud Black Bapt Children; *office:* Saint Cyrils Elem Schl 716 Emerson Ave East Lansdowne PA 19050

KURRE, JAMES A., Assoc Professor of Economics; *b:* Cincinnati, OH; *m:* Gail A. McGaughey; *ed:* Univ of Cincinnati (BA) Ec 1973; Wayne St Univ (MA) Ec 1975, (PHD) Ec 1982; *cr:* Wayne St Univ Tchng Asst & Research Asst 1973-76; Penn St Univ Instr of Ec 1977-83, Asst Prof of Ec 1983-89, Assoc Prof of Ec 1989-; *ai:* Assoc Dir of Ec Research at Inst of Erie 1982-; Consulting Economist on Wrongful Death & Injury Cases; Regnl Sci Assn Intnl 1977-; Skill Needs Comm of Erie Cty JTPA; Univ Grad Fellow Wayne St Univ 1976-77; Excl in Tchng Awd from Penn St-Erie 1982 & 1986; Excl in Advising Awd from Penn St-Erie 1992; 12 Articles in Referred Prof Jrnls; *office:* PA St Univ Erie-Behrend Coll Schl of Business Erie PA 16563

KURT, EDWARD PAUL, Dean of Students & Ath Dir; *b:* Sandusky, OH; *m:* Kimberly Dawn Rister; *c:* Mandy, Ryan, Victoria, Evan, Jordan; *ed:* OH St Univ (BA) Math Ed 1989; Wright St Univ 15 Hrs Toward Masters in Admin; *cr:* Sandusky HS Math Tchr 1989-91; Madison Plains HS Math Tchr 1991-93, Athl Dir & Dean of Stu 1993-; *ai:* Athl Dir; Head Boys Bsktbl Coach 1990-; NEA 1989-; Local Tchr Union 1989-; *office:* Madison Plains HS 800 Linson Rd London OH 43140*

KURTA, ANN MASON, Fourth Grade Teacher; *b:* Newark, NJ; *c:* Meghan; *ed:* Caldwell Coll (BA) Elem Ed 1979; *cr:* Kearny Pub Schls Basic Skills Tchr 1980-84; Growing Tree Nursery Schl Tchr 1987-89; Kearny Pub Schls 6th Grd Tchr 1989-90, Basic Skills Tchr 1992-95, 4th Grd Tchr 1995-; *ai:* Adult Schl GED Tchr; IM Sports Supvr; NJEA 1989-; *office:* Schuyler Schl Forest St Kearny NJ 07032

KURTZ, ANNE BABIN, 7th Grd Social Studies Teacher; *b:* Drexel Hill, PA; *m:* Joseph; *c:* Joseph; *ed:* West Chester Univ (BA) Pol Sci 1986; Scndry Ed, Soc Stud Cert 1987; *cr:* Harrison-Morton MS Soc Stud Tchr 1989-; *ai:* Stu Cncl Adv; AEA, PTA 1989-; *office:* Harrison-Morton MS 137 N 2nd St Allentown PA 18101*

KURTZ, BARBARA A., Tchr of Mentally Gifted Stud; *b:* Clearfield, PA; *m:* Randall Lee; *c:* Emily, Ryan; *ed:* PA St Univ (BA) His 1970; (MA) Acad Curr & Instruction 1975; 36 Addl Credits; Cert in Elem, Scndry Soc Stud, Spec Ed, Enrichment; Penn St Doctoral Acceptance; *cr:* Clearfield Schl Dist 3rd Grd Tchr; Claysburg Kimmel Schl Dist 2nd Grd Tchr; Chambersburg Schl Dist Spec Ed; St Marys Area Schl Dist Instructional Support, Tchr of Mentally Gifted; *ai:* Odyssey of the Mind Coach; Statewide Mock Trial Competition & Model United Nations Simulations Adv; NEA, PSEA, St Marys Ed Assn; Book of Poetry (self Publication); Logic Puzzle Publication; *office:* St Marys Area HS 977 S Saint Marys Rd Saint Marys PA 15857

KURTZ, DEAN K., Music Teacher & Pastor; *b:* Pipestone, MN; *m:* Brenda Lynn; *c:* Sarah, Colette; *ed:* Pillsbury Bapt Bible Coll (BS) Music Ed 1981, (BS) Bible 1981; Pensacola Chrstn Coll (MA) Sacred Music 1986; Dissertation Pending for Doctor of Ministry Calvary Bapt Theological Seminary; *cr:* Calvary Bapt Schls Music Tchr 1981-, Music Pastor 1987-; Calvary Bapt Theological Seminary Adj Prof 1994-; *office:* Calvary Baptist Schl 1380 S Valley Forge Rd Lansdale PA 19446

KURTZ, MARY CURTIN, Fifth Grade Teacher; *b:* Rockville Centre, NY; *m:* Arthur; *c:* Gregory, Thomas; *ed:* SUNY at Brockport (BS) Elem Ed 1969; SUNY at Stony Brook (MA) Lbrl Stud 1972; 45 Addl Credit Hrs; *cr:* St Brigid's Elem Schl 2nd Grd Tchr 1969; Cntrl Islip Schl Dist 4th-5th Grd Tchr 1969-; *ai:* Tchrs Union Bldg Comm; AFT; NYSUT; *office:* Marguerite L. Mulvey Schl 44 E Cherry St Central Islip NY 11722

KURTZ, RICHARD M., HS Science Teacher; *b:* Toronto, Canada; *m:* Melissa C. Pearlman; *c:* Matthew, Zachary, Abigail, Elliott; *ed:* Univ of Waterloo (BES) Environmental Stud 1980, (MS) Entomology 1984; *cr:* Woodmere Acad Sci Tchr 1984-86; Huntington HS Sci Tchr 1986-; Dowling Coll Adj Prof 1994-; *ai:* Hnr Soc Comm; AP Rdng in Bio Fac Consultant; AFT, Huntington Tchrs Assn, NABT 1986-; TRAC Flwshp Dept of Energy; Cncl for Basic Educ & Natl Sci Fnd, Sci & Math; Amer Soc for Clinical Investigation Flwshp; Amer Soc for Biochemistry & Molecular Bio; *office:* Huntington HS Oakwood & Mc Kay Rd Huntington NY 11743

KURTZMAN, SUSAN WALKER, Kindergarten Teacher; *b:* Columbus, OH; *m:* Dennis; *c:* Derek, Megan; *ed:* OH St Univ (BS) Elem Ed 1977; 9 Semester Hrs Behavioral Stud Drake Univ; 60 Hrs Religious Stud; *cr:* Temple Chrstn Schl 4th Grd Tchr 1977-78; St Mary Schl 5-8 Grd Sci, Rdng Tchr 1978-83, Second Grd Tchr 1983-90, Kndgtn Tchr 1990-; *ai:* Elem Schl St Accreditation Comm; NCEA 1978-; Shenandoah Chrstn Church 1987-, Sunday Schl Tchr; Nom Ashland Oil Co Tchr of Yr Awd 1996; *office:* St Mary Schl 26 West St Shelby OH 44875

KURZ, DANIEL M., Instrumental Music Teacher; *b:* Newark, NJ; *ed:* Jersey City St Coll (BA) Music Ed 1972; Kean Coll of NJ (MA) Guidance & Counseling 1984; Studied Orchestral Conducting at Aspen Music Festival Aspen CO 1980; *cr:* Hillside Pub Schls Elem Vocal Music Tchr 1972-73; Cliffside Park Pub Schls Elem Vocal & Instrumental Music Tchr 1975-82; Perth Amboy Pub Schls MS Instrumental Music Tchr 1982-89, HS Instrumental Music Tchr 1989-; Adult HS Guidance Cnslr 1984-; *ai:* Marching Band, Jazz, Chamber Music Ensembles Dir; AFT 1982-; Music Educators Natl Conf 1985-; Studied Conducting Aspen Music Festival CO 1980; Conducted Vocal Music Inst Concert Production Mozart's Don Giovanni; Assist Conductor Amato Opera Showcase Theatre in NY City 1976-80; *office:* Perth Amboy HS Eagle Ave & Francis St Perth Amboy NJ 08861

KURZ, LINDA ANN, Professor of Mathematics; *b:* Troy, NY; *c:* Jesse Kurz Belleau; *ed:* SUNY at Albany (BS) Math Sec Ed 1964; U Notre Dame (MS) Math 1969; SUC at Oneonta (MS) Math Ed 1987; Retraining Inst Cmptr Sci at Clarkson; *cr:* Harborfields HS Math Tchr 1964-68; Walton HS Math Tchr 1968-69; Coll of Tech Math, Cmptr Sci Prof, Dept Chair 1969-; *ai:* Adv Fac Senate; Various Search Comms; HS Hnrs Prgm; Women in Higher Ed; BSA Vol 1993-; NSF Grants; Chancellors Awd for Excl in Tchng; Numerous Articles Pub; *office:* Coll of Tech 418 Evenden Tower Delhi NY 13753*

KURZ, NANCY PATTERSON, Third Grade Teacher; *b:* Lancaster, PA; *m:* Todd O.; *c:* Emily, Gavin; *ed:* Shippensburg Univ (BS) Elem Ed 1981; Millersville Univ (MS) Cnslr Ed 1992; Cnslr Cert 18 Grad Credits; *cr:* Bergstrasse Elem Schl Second Grd Tchr 1984-85, Third Grd Tchr 1985-95; *ai:* Instrl Support Team; Learning Support Planning, Conflict Resolution Comms; NEA, PSEA 1985-; *office:* Bergstrasse Elem Schl 6 Hahnstown Rd Ephrata PA 17522*

KURZYNOWSKI, KRISTEN PATRICE, Social Studies Teacher; *b:* Jersey City, NJ; *ed:* Rutgers Coll (BA) Sociology, Ed 1992; *cr:* Red Bank Regnl HS Soc Stud Tchr 1993-94; Middletown HS S Soc Stud Tchr 1994-; *ai:* Girls Soccer, Bsktbl Coach; Jr Class Adv; NEA 1993-; NJEA, MTA, NCSS 1994-; Middletown Soccer Club 1992-, Coach; *home:* 72 Main St Port Monmouth NJ 07758*

KUSH, ALAN MICHAEL, Fifth Grade Teacher; *b:* Nanticoke, PA; *m:* Madelyn Wall; *ed:* Mansfield St Univ (BS) Elem 1970; Bloomsburg St Univ (MS) Early Chldhd Ed 1975; Attnd Lehigh Univ, Cedar Crest Coll, Northampton CC; *cr:* Northern Lehigh Schl Dist Tchr 26 Yrs; *ai:* Rotary Club Treas; PTA VP; PSEA 1970-, Treas; NEA, NLEA 1970-; Holy Name 1994-, VP; Heritage Choir 1990-; Assumption BVM Church 1992-, Music Coord; *office:* Northern Lehigh Schl Dist 1201 Shadow Oaks Ln Slatington PA 18080*

KUSH, DAVID J., Fourth Grade Teacher; *b:* Johnstown, PA; *m:* Patricia A. Flowers; *c:* Michelle; *ed:* Univ of Pittsburgh (MS) Elem Ed 1972, (MED); Admin Cert Elem Prin; *cr:* Conemaugh Vly Schl Dist Elem Tchr 1972-; *ai:* Environthon Co-Adv; PSEA 1972-; NEA 1972-; CVEA 1972-; *office:* Conemaugh Valley Elem Schl 1451 Frankstown Rd Johnstown PA 15902

KUSHINSKY, JEANNE ROTHENBERGER, Second Grade Teacher; *b:* Reading, PA; *m:* David L.; *c:* Seth Wallerstein, Gail Wallerstein Melichar; *ed:* Cedar Crest Coll (BS) Elem Ed, Eng 1958; Master Sci Equivalency Kean Coll, Family Life Stud, 33 Addl Credits; *cr:* Elmwood Schl Fourth Grd Tchr 1958-60; Bd of Ed Homebound Tutor 1961-62; LaSierra HS Eng Dept Reader 1963-65; James Madison Intermediate Schl Fourth-Sixth Grd Tchr 1974-76; Dept Testing, Assessment Dept of Ed Ed 1974-76; Piscatawaytown Schl Sixth Grd Tchr 1980-84; James Madison Primary Schl Second-Third Grd Tchr 1976-80, 1984-; *ai:* Curr Coordinating Comm, Rep; ETEA 1974-, Alternate Rep; NJEA, NEA 1974-; Citizens Advy Cncl Ed 1991-92; Borough Improvement League 1991-; Zimmerli Museum 1989-; Governor's Tchr Recognition Awd, Outstdng Tchr 1993; *home:* 119 Turner Ave Edison NJ 08820*

KUSHMAUL, THOMAS R.,JR., Music Teacher; *b:* Springfield, OH; *m:* Patricia; *c:* Stephen, Natalie; *ed:* Heidelberg Coll (BMUS) Ed, Piano 1985; Educl Tech; Wright St Univ; *cr:* Cath Cntrl HS Music Tchr 1993-; *ai:* Drama Club, Pep Band Adv; OMEA, MENC 1995-; AFM 1985-; *office:* Catholic Central HS 1200 E High St Springfield OH 45505

KUSHNER, JOEL, Guidance Counselor; *b:* NYC, NY; *m:* Linda R. Levy; *c:* Seth R.; *ed:* Hofstra Univ (BA) Psych 1966; Long Island Univ Guid & Cnslng 1970; 35 Credits Ed; *cr:* Marcus Jr HS Tchr 1966-75; Grissom Jr HS Tchr 1975-91; Washington Irving HS Guid Cnslr 1991-92; E. R. Murrow HS Guid Cnslr 1992-; *ai:* UFT, AFT 1966-; *office:* Edward R Murrow HS 1600 Avenue L Brooklyn NY 11230

KUSHNER, MICHAEL, Economics Prof; *b:* Brooklyn, NY; *m:* Barbara Susan Bass; *c:* Elissa M., Evan M.; *ed:* Long Island Univ (BA) Ec 1969 (MA) Ec 1970; Scndry Schl Math Cert 1972, Supv, Prin Cert; Attnd Paterson St Coll, Montclair St Coll, Monmouth Coll; *cr:* Eastside HS Math Tchr 1969-73, Freehold HS Math Tchr 1973-; Ocean Cty Coll Adj Ec Asst Prof 1980-; *ai:* Soph Class, Forensic, Black Achiever Adv; NEA, NJEA 1969-.*

KUSHNER, STEPHEN, Music Dept Chair; *b:* York, PA; *ed:* Bucknell Univ (BM) Music His 1982; Univ of MA (mM) Conducting 1987; Klingenstein Fellow Tchrs Coll Columbia Univ 1992-93; *cr:* Former Free Lance Conductor; Riverside Choir Principle Conductor 1993-95; Phillips Exeter Acad Dir Choral Act 1987-; *office:* Phillips Exeter Acad 20 Main St Exeter NH 03833*

KUSHNER, WILLIAM ALAN, English Teacher; *b:* Pittsburgh, PA; *m:* Barbara Jean Yalch; *c:* Christopher Alan, Nicole Mary; *ed:* Allegheny Comm (AA) Arts 1973; Univ of Pittsburgh (BA) Eng 1974, (MA) Scndry Ed 1978; *cr:* Avella HS Grds 9-10 Scndry Tchr 1974-82, Grds 11-12 Scndry Tchr 1982-; *ai:* Golf Coach; PSEA, NEA 1974-; GCU 1946-, Local Lodge Pres; Amer Legion 1988-, Veteran USAF; *office:* Avella HS 1000 Avella Rd Avella PA 15312

KUSKOSKI, JOHN W., Cross Country Coach; *b:* Spangler, PA; *m:* Kathryn M. Quist; *c:* Jason Dillon, Joshua Dillon; *ed:* PA St (BS) Scndry Ed 1975; IN Univ of PA (MED) Comm Media 1981; *cr:* Cambria Heights HS Cross Cntry Coach 1992-; *ai:* Cross Cntry Coach; NEA 1975-; *office:* Cambria Heights HS Rd 1 Box 6 Patton PA 16668

KUSMIN, JESSICA BYRNE, English & Drama Teacher; *b:* Boston, MA; *ed:* Mount Holyoke Coll (BA) Theatre 1993; *cr:* Carrabassett Valley Acad Eng, Drama Tchr, Ski Coach, Dorm Parent 1993-; *ai:* Free Style Ski Coach; Dorm Parent; 7th & 8th Grd Adv; MS Comm; NCTE 1996-; *office:* Carrabassett Valley Acad RR 1 Box 2240 Kingfield ME 04947

KUSTRA, JOELLA ZINGARO, First Grade Teacher; *b:* New Castle, PA; *m:* Walter F.; *c:* Walter, Victor; *ed:* Clarion Univ (BA) Elem Ed 1976; Westminster Coll (MS) Rdng Specialist 1983; *cr:* Shenango Elem Schl 1st Grd Tchr 18 Yrs; *ai:* Mini-Majorettes 18 Yrs; PSEA 1977-; LCRA; TAWL 3 Yrs; *office:* Shenango Area Schls 2501 Old Pittsburgh Rd New Castle PA 16101

KUSTRON, THOMAS P., Mathematics Instructor; *b:* Monongahela, PA; *m:* Linda Bartolotta; *c:* Kimberly, Karey; *ed:* California Univ of PA (BS) Math Ed 1966, (MED) Math Ed 1970; Univ of Notre Dame (MS) Math 1971; 9 Credit Hrs Cmptr Sci Univ of Pittsburgh; St Vincent Coll Tchr Enhancement Inst 1993-94; Seton Hill Univ Cmptr Applications 1989; *cr:* Mon Vly Cath HS Math, Comp Instr 1065-89; Comm Coll of Allegheny Cty

Math Instr 1978-83; Univ of Ca Math Instr 1983-95; Univ of Pittsburgh Adj Comp Instr 1983-87; Canevin Cath HS Math Instr 1989-; *ai:* Stu Assistance Team; Math Cncl of West PA, NCTM 1970-; NSF Grant Univ of Notre Dame; *office:* Canevin Catholic H S 2700 Morange Rd Pittsburgh PA 15205*

KUTA, MARYANN NICOLIA, Home & Career Skills Teacher; *b:* Erie, PA; *m:* Jan J.; *c:* Bryan; *ed:* Villa Maria Coll (BS) Home Ec 1971; Grad Credit Hrs; *cr:* George Staley Jr HS Home Ec Tchr 1971-73; Fairport HS Home Ec Tchr 1973-76; Nutrition Ed & Trng Prgm Area Coord 1978-81; Futuring Project Prgm Specialist, Consultant 1981-83; Sauquoit Cntrl Schl Home, Career Skills Tchr 1982-; *ai:* Goals 2000 Trng; NYS Assn Family, Consumer Sci Edctrs, NYSUT, AFT 1971-.

KUTNER, JACQUELINE R., Art Teacher; *b:* New York, NY; *ed:* Herbert H. Lehman Coll (BA) Art, Ed 1971, (MA) Art Ed 1976; Coll of New Rochelle Ed Gifted Child Cert 1985; Post Grad Work Schl Admin 26 Cr Manhattan Coll; *cr:* PS 79 Early Chldhd Tchr 1973-78; Lee Cty Pub Schls Art Tchr 1978-80; Commodore John Rodgers Schl Early Chldhd Tchr 1980-83; PS 81 Robert J. Christen Schl Second Grd, Art Tchr 1983-; *ai:* After Schl Ctr Dir; Schl Based Mngmt Team Comm; UFT, AFT 1972-; NYC Art Tchrs 1993-, Art Tchr of Year 1994; NYS Art Tchrs 1994-; Bronx Cty Historical Soc 1984-, Pres 1993-; Beneath the Sea 1988-, Ed Mgr; Museums Cncl New York 1993-; Art Edctr of Yr Elem Div New York City Art Tchrs Assn 1994; Photography Show June 1994 Schervier Gallery NYC; *office:* PS 81 Robert J Christen 5550 Riverdale Ave Bronx NY 10471*

KUTNER, RICHARD F., Fourth Grade Teacher; *b:* New York, NY; *m:* Lynn; *c:* Roland, Paul; *ed:* Yale Univ (BA) Fr Lit-Magna Cum Laude 1968; NY Univ (MA) Ed 1979; *cr:* Masters Schl Dobbs Work Prgm Coord, Fr, Eng & Filmmaking Tchr 1970-72; Hamden Hall Cntry Day Schl Fr Tchr 1972-73; Brooklyn Ethical Culture Schl Fr & Soc Stud Tchr 1973-76; Berkeley Inst Fr Tchr 1976-79; United Nations Intnl Schl 3rd Grd Tchr 1979-82, 4th Grd Tchr 1982-; *ai:* After Schl Cmptr Classes; Cmptr E-Mail Link with Geneva Intnl Schl; Fr Translation of 27 Songs for EuroDisney Made Into Cassettes & Compact Disks & Performed at Euro Disneyland; *office:* United Nations Intl Schl 2450 Fdr Dr New York NY 10010

KUTSCHERENKO, SUSAN TERESA, First Grade Teacher; *b:* Stockport, OH; *ed:* Muskingum Coll (BA) Ed 1978; OH Univ (MED) Elem Ed 1984; Addl 30 Hrs; *cr:* Homer Union Elem Schl First Grd Tchr 1978-; *ai:* PTO Treas; NEA, OEA 1978-; MLEA 1978-, Bldg Rep; Martha Holden Jennings Schlrs 1985-86; Good Apple Awd 1988-89; Twin Comm Jaycees Outstdng Young Edctr 1990; *home:* 378 S Cooper Rd NE Mc Connelsville OH 43756

KUTZ, ARLENE CLARKE, English Teacher; *b:* Jersey City, NJ; *m:* Frederick W.; *c:* Mark D., Heather L.; *ed:* Univ of DE (BS) Home Ec 1963; Univ of MD (MED) Scndry Ed 1975; Attnd Loyola Coll; *cr:* Delawarr HS Home Ec Tchr 1963-64; Wilde Lake HS Eng & Home Ec Tchr 1973-84; Oakland Mills HS Eng Tchr 1985-; *ai:* Class of 1988 Spon; Giant Tape Lady; NEA 1973-; NHS, Honorary Mem; Tchr of Yr 1990 & 1995; Tchng Excl Awd 1994; MD Congress of Parents & Tchrs Inc life Membership; *home:* 4967 Moonfall Way Columbia MD 21044

KUTZ, JOHN THOMAS, Health & PE Teacher; *b:* Altoona, PA; *m:* Jill Ann Smith; *c:* Joshua Thomas; *ed:* Rutgers Univ (BS) Sport Mngmt 1989; 18 Addl Credit Hrs Saint Francis Coll; IN Univ of Pennsylvania Cert Hlth, PE 1991; *cr:* Hollidaysburg Area Sr HS Hlth, PE 1991-; *ai:* Head Ftbl Coach 1996; Asst Ftbl Coach 1989-95; Head Girls Track Coach 1991-; PSEA 1991-; *office:* Hollidaysburg Area Sr HS 1510 N Montgomery St Hollidaysburg PA 16648

KUZARA, LINDA MARIE, Math & Computer Teacher; *b:* Poughkeepsie, NY; *m:* Robert; *c:* Michael; *ed:* Coll of Mt St Vincent (BA) Math 1970; Lesley Coll (MED) Cmptrs in Ed 1992; *cr:* IBM Fortran Programmer 1969; Monroe Calculator Co Sales Trng Supvr 1972-75; Victor Bus Products Sales Trng Supvr 1975-78; Lynnfield HS Math Tchr 1988; Bishop Fenwick HS Math, Cmptr Tchr 1988-; *ai:* Tech Planning Comm; NCTM 1988-; ISTE 1992-; NSF Grant; Intergration of Math, Sci 9 Credits Bridgewater St Coll; Curr Guide for Mathcad Math Soft Inc at Cambridge MA; *office:* Bishop Fenwick HS 99 Margin St Peabody MA 01960

KUZICKI, PAULA SCHILLACI, 8th Grade Language Arts Tchr; *b:* Passaic, NJ; *m:* Kenneth J.; *c:* Kenneth, Kelly-Ann; *ed:* William Paterson Coll (BA) Early Chldhd, Elem Ed 1976; *cr:* Walnut Ridge Primary Schl 4th Grd Tchr 1980-81; Lounsberry Hollow MS 5th-6th, 8th Grd Tchr 1985-94; Glen Meadow MS 8th Grd Lang Arts Tchr 1994-; *ai:* NJEA 1980-; Amer League Women's Auxilliary 1987-; *office:* Glen Meadow MS PO Box 516 Rt 517 & Sammis Rd Vernon NJ 07462*

KUZMA, DANIEL FRANKLIN, Social Studies Teacher; *b:* Passaic, NJ; *m:* Diane Elizabeth Howell; *c:* Gregory, Christine; *ed:* Guilford Coll (BA) His 1965; William Paterson Coll (MA) Soc Sci Ed 1968; Attnd Structural Approach Inst Level 1 1992, Advanced Structures Inst Level 3 1993, Coop Facilitators Inst Level 5 1994; *cr:* Indian Hills Regnl HS Tchr, Soc Stud Dept 1965-; Regnl Trng Ctr Instr, Grad Courses 1995-; Kagan Cooperative Learning Consultant, Presneter 1995-; *ai:* Tchr Trainer; NEA, NJEA, BCEA, RIHEA, NJ Cncl for Soc Stud 1965-; St Michael's Church 1965-, Layreader; Bergen Cty Soccer Ofcls Assn 1976-, Immediate Past Pres; Bergen Cty Bsbl 1984-, VP, Chm of Pub Relations Comm; Umpires Assn; Spec Awrd Outstdng Contributions to HS Aths 1987; Hall of Fame Mem Inducted 1978; Mid Sts Visting Evaluator 1990; *office:* Indian Hills Regnl HS 97 Yawpo Ave Oakland NJ 07436

KUZSMA, MARILYN MUSHALKO, Chem Dpndncy Cnslng Asst Prof; *b:* Newark, NJ; *m:* Thomas; *c:* Melissa; *ed:* Duke Univ (BS) Psych 1978; Univ of Notre Dame (MA) Cnslng Psych 1979; *cr:* Dundalk Comm Coll Asst Prof 1990-; *ai:* CACOM 1990-, Ofcr; Mem of Yr 1994; NAADAC 1990-, Bd of Dirs; *office:* Dundalk Comm Coll 7200 Sollers Point Rd Dundalk MD 21222

KVINT, VLADIMIR L., Professor of Management System; *b:* Krasnoyarsk, Russia; *c:* Liza, Valeria; *ed:* Grad Schl of Non Ferrous Metals (MS) Mining, Electrical Engr 1972; Moscow Inst of Natl Economy (PHD) Managerial Ec 1975; Inst of Economics, Acad of Sciences Dr of Ec Sci, Ecs 1988; Artluir Anderson Co Corp Finance 1993; *cr:* scientific Tech Co of Non Ferrous Metals Deputy Exec, Chm 1976-78; USSR Acad of Scis Leading Fellow Researcher 1978-89; Vienna Ec Univ Visiting Ec Prof 1989-90; Badson Coll Distinguished Ec Prof 1991; GBA, Fordham Univ Mgmt Systems, Intnl Bus Prof 1990-; *ai:* Ec Consultant Dir; Muhlenberg Coll Intnl Visiting Comm; Bretton Woods Comm 1993-; Russian Acad of Natural Sci 1993-, Full Lifetime Mem; NY Acad of Sci 1992-; 12 Books, Several Articles Pub; Wesner Heritage Fnd Fellowship; *office:* Fordham Univ Grad Schl 113 W 60th St 6th Floor New York NY 10023*

KWAAK, BARBARA GOWER, Basic Skills Reading Teacher; *b:* New York City, NY; *c:* Kathryn Victoria; *ed:* Hunter Coll (BA) Eng, Ed 1964, (MSEd) Ed 1966; Trenton St 1988-89, St Peter'sColl 1989, Jersey City St Coll 1989-91 Post Grad Prgm Cert in Admin, Supervision 1991; NJ Dept of Ed Acad Prof Dev 1994; *cr:* New York City Pub Schls Tchr 1964-68; Taylor Mills Schl Classroom Tchr 1976; Pine Brook Schl 7-8 Grd BSI Rdng Tchr 1976-83; Lafayette Mills Schl 3-6 Grd BSI Rdng Tchr 1983-92; Manalapan-Englishtown MS 7-8 Grd BSI Rdng Tchr 1992-; *ai:* NJEA, MEEA 1976-; Humane Soc of US 1994-; Natl Defense & Ed Act Rsrch Grant 1965; NJ Dept of Ed Grant 1990; *office:* Manalapan Englishtown MS 155 Millhurst Rd Englishtown NJ 07726

KWAPICH, DEBRA CORNEY, Math Teacher; *b:* Brooklyn, NY; *m:* Mark Kwapich; *ed:* SUNY Binghamton (BS) Math, Ec 1985; Coll of Staten Island (MSE) Math Ed; *cr:* NY Life Ins Co Svc Rep 1985-88; Abraham Lincoln HS Tchr 1988-; *ai:* Regents Review; Basis Collaborative Project in Math; Lincoln Angle Adv; Chptr I Coord; Sr Grd Adv; Supervised Tutors; UFT, AFT 1988-; *office:* Abraham Lincoln HS Ocean Pkwy & West Ave Brooklyn NY 11235

KWARTENG, CHARLES OWUSU, Political Science Asst Prof; *b:* Juabeng, Ghana; *ed:* Univ of Ghana (BA) Pol Sci 1981; Baylor Univ (MA) Pol Sci 1984; Univ of Pittsburgh (PHD) Intnl Affairs 1989; *cr:* Mobay Corp Researcher 1986-89; Morgan St Univ Asst Prof 1992-; *ai:* African Stud Assn 1989-; European Comm Assn, Soc Intnl Dev 1992-; Ghanaian Assn Pittsburgh 1986-, VP; Third World Flwshp; Fulbrigh Hays Scholar; Numerous Articles Pub; *office:* Morgan State Univ Cold Spring Ln & Hillen Rd Baltimore MD 21239*

KWASNY, CARL, 9th Grade Government Teacher; *b:* Windber, PA; *m:* E. Sue Tisdale; *c:* Kelly S., Eric J.; *ed:* Westermoreland Coll (AS) Lbrl Arts 1984, (AS) Bus Mngmt 1986; Univ of Pittsburg (BS) Ed 1988; Univ of Pittsburgh Masters Eqvilacny 1989; Seton Hall Coll Soc Stud 1991; *cr:* Mc Keesport HS Military Sci-NJROTC Tchr 1976-91, Amer His Tchr 1991-92, Amer Govt Tchr 1992-; *ai:* NEA, PSEA, MAEA 1976-; Fleet Reserve Assn, VFM, Amer Legion 1976-; Elks Club 1964-; ASCD 1992-; *office:* Mc Keesport HS 1960 Eden Park Blvd Mc Keesport PA 15132

KWESKIN, HELEN TRUSS, English Teacher & Dept Head; *b:* Essex, England; *m:* Edward Michael; *c:* Abigail, Adam; *ed:* Univ of PA (BA) Eng-Cum Laude, With Dinstinction 1970; George Washington Univ (MA) Eng Lit 1973; Attnd Columbia Univ & Tchrs Coll; *cr:* The Booth Schl Eng Dept Head 1971-73; King & Low-Heywood Thomas Schl Eng Dept Head 1973-; *ai:* Yrbk Adv; Drama Coach; Curr Comm; NCTE 1973-; Cncl for Women in Ind Schls 1985-; Klingenstein Flwshp 1987-88; CT Writing Project Flwshp 1988; *office:* King & Low-Heywood Thomas Sch 1450 Newfield Ave Stamford CT 06905*

KWIATKOWSKI, CHRISTINE, Spanish Teacher; *ed:* Douglass Coll (BA) Span 1971; Attnd Rutgers Univ, Rider Univ, Brookdale Coll; *cr:* Sayreville War Meml HS Tchr 1971-; *ai:* Span Hnr Soc Adv; NEA, NJEA, Sayreville Ed Assn, Tchrs Span & Portuguese 1971-; Governor's Recognition Awd; *office:* Sayreville War Meml HS 820 Washington Rd Parlin NJ 08859

KWON, ANNIE, Assistant Professor of Art; *b:* Seoul, Korea; *m:* Steven; *ed:* CA St Univ (BA) Fine Art 1979; OH St Univ (MFA) Fine Art 1982; Attnd Cntrl CT Univ, CA St Univ MA Prgm 1979; Univ of CA at Davis Undergrad Courses; *cr:* Western CT St Univ Adj Prof 1987-88; Tunxis Comm Coll Adj Prof 1990-93; Wesleyan Univ Adj Prof 1989-96; Teikyo Post Univ Asst Prof 1990-; *ai:* Annual Stu Art Show Org; Stu Art Club Adv; Stu Svcs Comm; CAA 1989, 1996; Editorial Adv Bd 1996; Fiction Novel Pub 1976; *office:* Teikyo Post Univ 800 Country Club Rd Waterbury CT 06708

KWOZKO, ZENON, Math Teacher; *b:* New York City, NY; *m:* Susan Ruisi; *c:* Danielle, Christopher; *ed:* Penn St Univ (BS) Sci 1965; 45 Grad Credits; *cr:* Philadelphia Pub Schls Math Tchr 1965-66; Floral Park Meml HS Math Tchr 1966-; *ai:* Boys, Girls Cross Country, Winter Track, Boys Spring Track Coach; NCTM, Nassau Cty Math Tchrs Assn, NEA, Sewanhaka Fed of Tchrs 1966-; *office:* Floral Park Memorial HS 210 Locust St Floral Park NY 11001

KYE, TERRY LEE, Mathematics Teacher; *b:* Dunkirk, NY; *ed:* SUNY at Fredonia (MS) Math, Scndry Ed 1980; *cr:* Pine Vly Cntrl Schl 7-12 Grd Math Tchr 1975-; *ai:* HS Class Adv 11 Yrs; Compact for Learning Comm; Dept Chprsn 2 Yrs; NY St Math Tchrs Assn 1980-; NY St United Tchrs 1975-; Pine Vly Tchrs Assn 1975-, Treas, Negotiator; *office:* Pine Vly Cntrl Schl Rt 83 South Dayton NY 14138

KYLE, JACQUELYN F. BOWMAN, Second Grade Teacher; *b:* Akron, OH; *m:* Thurman L.; *c:* Marianne; *ed:* Univ of AKron (BS) Elem Ed 1968; Masters Equivalency Elem Ed; 30 Grad Hrs Kent St; *cr:* Crosby Schl Tchr 1967-71; Hatton Schl Tchr 1972; Akron Pub Schls Tchr 1967-; Stewart Schl Tchr 1972-; *ai:* Bldng Ldrshp Team; Schoolwide, Guid, Discipline Comms; Akron Ed Assn 1967-, Bldg Rep; NABSE 1995-; Bldg, PTA Tchr of Yr 1995; *home:* 1153 Oak Tree Rd Akron OH 44320

KYLE, MERLE HURST, Kindergarten Teacher; *b:* Philadelphia, PA; *m:* Howard J.; *c:* Kathryn, Kenneth; *ed:* OH St Univ (BS) Elem Ed 1973; Various Grad Credits Rowan Coll; *cr:* Congregation Beth Isreal Prin 1981-88; Atlantic City Bd of Ed Kndgtn, First Grd Tchr 1974-; *ai:* Multicultural Comm Implementaion of Natl Pilot Prgm Mem 7 Yrs; Certfd Mentor 5 Yrs; Dist Curr Dev Comm 7 Yrs; Pilot Tchr, Consultant 5 Publishing Cos; NEA, NJEA 1974-, Legislative Chm, Rec Sec; Alpha Delta Kappa 1979-88, Sec; Atlantic Cty United Way 1987-92, Allocator; Atlantic City Juvenile Conf 1993-; Roland Rogers PTA 1989-, Corresponding Sec; Tchr of Yr 1995 Chelsea Hts, Venice Park Schl; Spec Ed Prgm for Stdnts Through Writing Grant; *office:* Chelsea Hts Schl 4101 Filbert Ave Atlantic City NJ 08401*

KYSER, PAUL LAVON, Technical Education Teacher; *b:* Bryan, OH; *m:* Barbara Jo Nichols; *c:* Kim Coy, Randy Jewell, Natalie Herring; *ed:* Bowling Green St Univ (BS) Indstrl Arts; *cr:* Aro Corp Carpenters Asst, Spray Painter 1968-79; Northwest Products Trainer 1983-84; Hilltop HS Tech Ed Tchr 1984-; *ai:* Head Track, Strength Coach; Asst Ftbl Coach; OEA; NEA.

KYSER, ROBERT E., Technology CADD Coordinator; *b:* Olean, NY; *m:* Elaine; *c:* Brett C., Nathan R., Jeremy S.; *ed:* St Univ of NY at Buffalo (BS) Indstrl Arts 1970, (MS) Indstrl Arts 1971; 45 Addl Credit Hrs; *cr:* Atomic Energy Comm Shift Foreman 1965-67; Muryvale HS Indstrl Arts Tchr 1971-72; Frontier C. HS CADD Coord 1973-; Erie Comm Coll Voc Tech Instr 1977-81; *ai:* Tech, CADD Clubs; Ath Supervision; AFT, Frontier Tchrs Assn 1971-; NY Tech Assn 1972-, Pres, Life Mem; Western NY Tech Assn 1970-, Outstdng Svc; Environmental Bd 1980-; NY Electric & Gas Grants 1975-76, 1988-90; *office:* Frontier Sr HS S-4432 Bayview Rd Hamburg NY 14075

KYTE, JULIE EVANS, English Teacher; *b:* Ruston, LA; *m:* John R.; *c:* John Evans; *ed:* Marymount Univ (MA) Ed 1992; LA Tech Univ (BA) Eng 1983; *cr:* US House of Rep Caseworker 1985-88; Salt River Project Office Mgr 1988-92; Eleanor Roosevelt HS Eng Tchr 1993-; *ai:* Lit Magazine Adv; Frosh Class Spon; *office:* Eleanor Roosevelt HS 7601 Hanover Pky Greenbelt MD 20770*

L

LAASCH, CAROLE HANIF, English Teacher; *b:* Langley Field, Thomas R.; *c:* Cassie, Jaime; *ed:* Univ of Toledo (BA) Eng 1967; Hrs; *cr:* Palmer HS Eng Tchr 1967-69; Hamilton Schl Jr HS Tchr 1 Sylvania City Schls LD & ESL Tutor 1973-80; Sylvania Southv Tchr 1980-; *ai:* NHS; Vol Focus; Sylvania Ed Assn 1973-, Sec; OH 1973-, Del to St Assembly; NEA 1967-; NCTE 1980-; Chi Omega St Josephs Church 1969-; Dayton Mothers Club 1994-; Sylvan Outstdng Tchr Nom; Mentor 2 Yrs; Area Wide PR Nom; Outstd Finalist; *office:* Sylvania Southview HS 7225 Sylvania Ave Sylva 43560

LABAGH, CHERYL CHRISTINE, Spanish & ESL Teach Waterbury, CT; *c:* Jennifer, Michael, Katharine; *ed:* Mount St Ma (BA) Span & Scndry Ed 1973; Univ of CT (MA) Biling & Bicult 1989; Univ of Hartford ESL Courses; Trinity Coll of VT Ed C Quinnipuc Coll Carnegie Fndtn; *cr:* Waterbury Adult Ed Rdng & Jo Tchr 1985-88, ESL Tchr 1992-; Wallace MS Span Tchr 1987-; *ai:* F in Ed; WTA Bldg Rep; Prins Advy Comm; PTA; Assessment & C Team; Designer & Comm Mem Wallace Project for Succes Assessments for Beginning Tchr CT Stan Setting Stud Comm; NEA CEA 1987-; WTA 1987-; COLT 1990-; CT Trls Cncl of GS 1980 Trainer, Svc Unit Chm, Browie Ldr, Troop Consultant, Outstdng Ld Hill PTA 1985-, Sec, VP & Pres, Svc Awd; St Michaels Altar Guild Flwshp to Univ of CT, WCAT TV Presentation Fiesta 1992; Bldg the Yr 1993; CT MS Tchr of the Yr Nom 1993-94; Article Pub; Wallace MS 3465 E Main St Waterbury CT 06705*

LABARBERA, THOMAS JOSEPH, Scndry Soc Studies Teac Danbury, CT; *m:* Constance J. Anderton; *ed:* Western CT St Univ(B Ed 1992; 10 Credit Hrs Univ of DE; *cr:* New Fairfield Bd of Ed Su 1986-92; Nauatuck Bd of Ed Sub Tchr 1986-92; Christina Sc Full-Time Long Term Sub Tchr 1992-93; West End Neighborhood Cmptr Ctr Dir 1992-93; Caravel Acad Soc Stud Tchr 1993-; *ai:* United Nations, Yth in Govt Adv 1993-; Odyssey of Mind Coach 19 DE Geographic Alliance 1995-; Articles Pub; *home:* 1107 Thorn Newark DE 19702*

LABATO, REGINA M., Kindergarten Teacher; *b:* Youngstown, C Youngstown St Univ (BS) Elem Ed 1980; Post Grad Hrs in Early C *ai:* Chrldng Adv 1980-; *office:* St Rose Schl 61 E Main St Girard OH

LABELLA, VICTOR, Vocational Teacher; *b:* Middletown, CT; *m:* *ed:* Central CT St Univ (BS) Soc Sci, Art 1968; 30 Credit Hrs Voc, Richard C. Lee HS His, Art, Auto Mech, Graphic Arts Tchr 19 Pinkerton Acad Voc Auto Mech Tchr 1980-; *ai:* Bsbl Pitching Coach Club Adv; Comms; *office:* Pinkerton Acad 9 Pinkerton St Der 03038*

LABIANCA, DOMINCIK ANTHONY, Chemical Professor; *b:* Brc NY; *m:* Carol Ann Rudow; *c:* Dominick Karl; *ed:* Polytechnic Uni Chem 1965; The Univ of MI (PHD) Chem 1969; NSF Postdoctoral F at CA Inst of Tech 1969-70; *cr:* Union Carbide Corp Rsrch Chem 19 Brooklyn Coll of CUNY Asst Prof 1972-78, Assoc Prof 1978-82 1982-; *ai:* Chemical Consultant; Amer Chemical Soc CA 1965-; Sig CA 1968-; AAUP CA 1973-; AAAS CA 1974-; NSTA CA 1974-; NY of Scis 1974-; Winner of Ohaus-NSTA Awd for Innoviations in C Tchng 1979, 1982, 1985 & 1993; *office:* Brooklyn Coll of CUNY Bedford Ave Brooklyn NY 11210

LABIENTO, ALETA, Community Health Prof; *b:* Howard Beach NY; *m:* Anthony; *c:* Lorraine, Jason; *ed:* SUNY at Westbury (BS Comm Hlth 1989; Hofstra Univ (MS) Hlth Svcs Ed 1991; Walder (PHD) Infectious Disease Control 1996; Behavior Approach to Lab 1992; *cr:* Nassau Comm Coll Allied Hlth Dep Tech Asst 1986-, Hl De Prof, Hlth, Safety Ofcr 1989-; *ai:* Access Prgm; Extra Help Lab Hlth Stdnts in Anatomy; Women in Sci Club; Womens Fac Stud Prgm Island Infectious Disease Soc 1992-; Amer Red Cross 1990-, Vol; Bloodborne Pathogens Conf Nassau Comm Coll 1992; Grant Funded by Ford Fnd; Womens Fac Bias Free Curr; *office:* Nassau Coll One Education Dr Garden City NY 11530

LABOMBARDE, PATRICIA ANN (BARNICLE), Social Studies Team Ldr; *b:* Montague, MA; *m:* Barry L.; *ed:* Fitchburg St Coll (B His & Eng 1971; Clark Univ, Harvard Univ, Univ of MA at Amh Dorchester Campuses, Smith Coll Grad Credits; *cr:* Athol Jr HS 7th Grd Eng & Soc Stud Tchr, SS & Eng Dept Chm 1971-93; Athol MS 8 Soc Stud Tchr & Team Ldr 1993-; *ai:* 5 Day Washington DC Trip Soc Stud Stans, Prof Dev & Resources Comms; St & Local Resourc Tchrs; Odyssey of Mind Competition Asst; Athol Tchrs Assn 1971-, MA Tchrs Assn 1971-; NEA 1971-; MA Cncl for Soc Stud; Cntrl M Stud Bd of Dirs; Horace Mann Grant (Twice); Tsongas Industrial H NSF Grant; Smith Coll NEH Grant; Clark Univ Blakeslee Fellow Field Ctr for Tchng & Learning Fellow; Global Stud Summer Insts Univ & Univ of MA; 1 of 18 New England Tchrs Selected for Stud T Japan Sponsored by Five Coll Ctr for East Asian Stud Smith Coll; Athol MS 494 School St Athol MA 01331*

LABONTE, CELESTE A. (ROCHELEAU), Music Teacher & Dir; *b:* Providence, RI; *m:* Gerald W.; *c:* Jeremy, Timothy, Alicia; Coll (BA) Music 1984, (MATC) Music Ed 1990; *cr:* Cultural Hom Intnl Tchr Coord 1995-; Comm Coll of RI Adj Fac 1990-; Cumberland MS Music Tchr, Choral Dir 1990-; *ai:* Pvt Vocal Instr, Theatre Performer; Beethoven Club Schlsp Chprsn; Religious Ed NEA, MENC 1990-; RI Music Ed Assn 1990-, Bd; Church Soloist; North Cumberland MS 400 Nate Whipple Hwy Cumberland RI 0286

LABONTE, EMILY E., Theology Professor; *b:* Manchester, NH Notre Dame Coll (BA) Philosophy 1970; Fordham Univ (MA) The 1982; MA Candidate Cnslng & Psychotherapy; *cr:* St joseph Schl Tchr 1970-74; Nashua Cath Jr High Math Tchr 1974-83; Notre Dame Theology Prof 1983-; *ai:* Acad Policies Comm; Acad Affair Comm Bd of Trustees; Comm Cncl; Coll Review Bd; CTS 1984-; ACA *office:* Notre Dame Coll 2321 Elm St Manchester NH 03104

LABONTE, JACQUELINE ANNE, Fifth Grade Teacher; *b:* Hol MA; *ed:* Westfield St Coll (BSEd) Elem Ed 1970; Western New En Coll (MBA) Bus Admin 1983; 46 Post Masters Hrs Contract Law, Ur NH Writing Rdng, Holyore Cntrl CT St Univ Math, Westfield St & C St Univ His; *cr:* Harris Schl Intermediate Level Tchr 1970-74; Washi Schl 5-6 Grd Tchr 1974-85; New North Comm Schl Grd 6 Tchr 198 Warner Schl Grd 5 Tchr 1986-91' Mary M. Walsh Schl Grd 5 Tchr 1 *ai:* Sccelerated Schls Implmentation Team; Math Curr Comm; Ch NEA, MTA, SEA 1970-; Pioneer Valley Rdg Assn 1985-, Treas; M 1990-; NCTE 1988-; Schola Cantorum 1990-; Our Lady of Pergetual Church Choir, Canton 1992-; The Golden Era Sourcebook C 1865-1915; *office:* Mary M. Walsh Schl 50 Empress Ct Springfield 01129*

LA BONTE, LINDA, Fifth Grade Teacher; *b:* Springfield, VT; *m:* An Scott Bladyka; *c:* Marcy Hoyt, Jamie Hoyt, Molly Bladyka; *ed:* Kee

ISE) Elem, Spec Ed 1976; 60 Credits Castleton St Coll, Norwich Univ of VT; *cr:* Molly Stark Schl Spec Ed Tchr 1976-87; Springfield pec Ed, Fifth Grd Tchr 1987-; *ai:* VT Golden Apple Awd; *home:* 54 eld St Springfield VT 05156*

R, JOHN J., Asst Admin & Band Dir; *b:* Westmoreland City, PA; nne C.; *c:* Michelle, Kevin; *ed:* Indiana Univ of PA (BS) Music Ed Univ of DE (MED) Educl Admin 1980; Lancaster Coll of Bible uing Ed; *cr:* Laurel Schl Dist Band Dir 1969-71; Seaford Schl Dist Dir 1973-86; Natl Judges Assn Youth Act Dir 1986-89; Seaford Acad Asst Admin, Band Dir 1989-; *ai:* Eagles Flight Team Coach; Coach; 1st Lt Civil Air Patrol; Acad Excl Project Spon; Class Adv; oach; ASCI 1992-; Tchr of Yr 1980, 1981; *office:* Seaford Christian 10 Holly St Seaford DE 19973*

SSIERE, DONALD G., HS Social Studies Teacher; *b:* Pawtucket, Patricia Bennett; *ed:* Comm Coll of RI (AA) Lbrl Arts 1985; RI Coll oc Sci, Sec Ed 1987, (MA) Cnslng 1996; First Aid Emergency Cert oss; CPR; Pharmacy, Psychiatric Tech US Navy; *cr:* Cntrl Falls HS 988-; *ai:* Class Adv; Event Chaperone; Asst Coach Bsktbl; Time ng Comm; Classroom Alternative Support Team; AFT, RI Tchrs Assn Adj Fac 1990-, Stu, Tchr, Site Supvr; Channel One 1984-, Vice ; Governor's Comm Crime, Juvenile Justice 1988-; Pub Article; RI gazine Short Story, Poems; *office:* Cntrl Falls HS 24 Summer St Falls RI 02863

AKE, DEBORAH MARIE, English Teacher; *b:* Massena, NY; *ed:* Coll at Oswego (BA) Scndry Ed 1989; St Lawrence Univ (MS) Gen 991; *cr:* Massena Cntrl HS Eng Tchr 1989-91; Fallsburg Cntrl HS chr 1991-; *ai:* Var Chrldng, Schl Newspaper, Superteam Adv; Peer ion Co-Coord; Musical Stage Dir; AFT, NYSUT 1989-; FTA 1991-; ess Assn Awd Recipient for 2nd Place Finish in NY St HS Newspaper t; *office:* Fallsburg Cntrl HS PO Box AH Fallsburg NY 12733

ANCHE, DONALD R., Fifth Grade Teacher; *b:* Providence, RI; *m:* Krick; *c:* Jennifer; *ed:* West Chester Univ (BS) Hlth, PE 1972; er Univ (MED) Elem Ed 1985; *cr:* Chichester Schl Dist Swim Coach, h Grd PE Tchr, 3rd, 5th Grd Classroom Tchr 1974-; *ai:* NEA, PSEA NCTM 1990-; PA Writing Project Fellow 1993; *office:* Chichester ist PO Box 2100 Marcus Hook PA 19061*

ANCHE, SHIRLEY LOUISE, English & Social Studies Tchr; *b:* da, MD; *m:* Guy; *c:* Lillie, Luc, Natalie; *ed:* San Diego City Coll Eng 1979; CA St Univ at Chico (BA) Eng 1981; Working Toward 's in Amer & New England Stud at Univ of South ME; *cr:* Acton Schl d Eng & Soc Stud Tchr 1981-85; Mendota Union Schl 7th Grd Eng 1985-; *ai:* Drama Club; ME Innovative, Lifetouch, ME Arts ission & NCTE Grants; *office:* Acton Schl HC 1 Box 528 East on ME 04027

ECQUE, MARGUERITE, 7th Grade Teacher; *b:* Salem, MA; *ed:* nack Coll (BA) Fr 1970; *cr:* St Joseph Schl 7th Grd Tchr 1971-73, 75 & 1976-; St Mary of the Hills 7th Grd Tchr 1975-76; *ai:* Natl Geog oc, Cultural Fair & Lit Fair Schl Chprsn; NCEA 1971-; *office:* St Schl 20 Harbor St Salem MA 01970

REE, LYNDA GOODWIN, Retired Teacher; *b:* Bradford, ME; *m:* e A.; *c:* Victoria LaBree Nevodomsky, Valerie LaBree Westgate; *ed:* of ME at Farmington (BS) Elem Ed 1962; Several Courses Childrens Math Their Way, Writing Process, Exceptional Children, Drug ness, DPA Math; *cr:* Marcia Buker Schl 1 Grd Tchr 1962-63; Jay Schl 1 Grd Tchr 1963-69; Mercer Elem Schl 1 Grd Tchr 1969-95; r Elem Schl Head Tchr 1990-94; *ai:* Rdng Revising Curr; Report Comm; Promoting Annex Mercer Elem Schl; SAD #54 Ed Assn ME Tchrs Assn, NEA 1962-; Supts Awd 1988-; Grange 1979-, r, Lecturer, Sec, Overseer, 10 Plus Awd; Amaranth Order 1993-, Matron, Royal Matron; Eastern Star 1990-, Warder; Emblem Club White Shrine of Jerusalem 1995-, Noble Prophetess; Article Pub; PO Box 95 Industry Rd New Sharon ME 04955

UTTO, MATTHEW ANTHONY, 6th Grade Teacher; *b:* Old Forge, Rosalyn Magistro; *c:* Christopher, Maria; *ed:* Univ of Scranton (BS) 967; Marywood Coll (MS) Guid Cnslng 1972; *cr:* Susquehanna Vly Schl Dist Elem Tchr 1967-; *ai:* NEA 1967-; SVTA 1967-, Bldg Rep, iating Comm; *home:* 21 Mountain Brook Dr Vestal NY 13850*

UTTO, ROSALYN MAGISTRO, Spanish Teacher; *b:* Pittston, PA; atthew A.; *c:* Christopher, Maria; *ed:* E Stroudsburg Univ (BS) Span SUNY at Binghamtom (MST) Span 1975; Addl 20 Hrs Latin; Univ drid Spain Undergraduate Credits 1968; *cr:* Mid Cntry Cent Schl Dist Tchr 1970-71; Johnson City Cent Schl Dist Span Tchr 1971-; *ai:* Span Adv; Chaperone Summer Trip 1996; JCTA 1971-, Bldg Rep; NEA Dos Rios 1986-; *home:* 21 Mountain Brook Dr Vestal NY 13850

DA, STANLEY STEPHEN, Global Studies Teacher; *b:* Camden, Margaret; *c:* Brian, Jeffrey; *ed:* Camden County Coll (AA) Lbrl Arts Glassboro St (BS) Soc Stud 1971; Post Grad Rowan Coll Prof Dev 994-, Saint Josephs Univ Comp Pgmng in Classrooms 1981-82; rs Univ Curr Dev for Gifted & Talented 1981; *cr:* Woodrow Wilson oc Stud Tchr 1971-; *ai:* Rowan Coll Woodrow Wilson Partnership Prof Dev Schl Tchr; NJEA, NEA, Camden Ed Assn & Camden Cty sn 1971-; Natl Geographic Soc 1975-; Woodrow Wilston PTA 1971-; n PTA 1982-; Collingwood PTA 1982-; NSF Grant St Josephs Univ; os Curr NJ His & Acad Talented; *office:* Woodrow Wilson HS 3100 al St Camden NJ 08105*

Z, RONALD MATTHEW, Dept Head & Graphic Comm Prof; *b:* NY; *m:* Carol Altimonte; *c:* SUNY at Oswego (BA) Philosophy The OH St Univ (MA) Philosophy6 1977; Syracuse Univ (MPHIL) 1993, (MA) His of Art 1994; *cr:* Mohawk Valley Comm Coll Prof, Head 1981-; *ai:* Graphic Design Ed Assn 1988-, Treas 1991-93, nations Chair 1988-91; Amer Ctrfor Design 1991-; Typophiles 1985-; s Square Historical Assn 1984-, Sec, Treas 1986-; Boni Fellowship Chancellors Awd Excl Svc 1989; Mohawk Valley Excl in Prof Svc 989; St Univ of NY Fac Exchange Scholar 1990; Outstanding Paper 1990; 9 Books Pub; Over 100 Articles Pub; *office:* Mohawk Valley n Coll 1101 Sherman Dr Utica NY 13501*

AGNINO, EVELYN MOLINARY, Eighth Grade Teacher; *b:* Bronx, : Gerard A.; *c:* Sara, Lauren; *ed:* Brooklyn Coll at CUNY (BS) Psych Fordham Univ (MS) Ed 1978; *cr:* Johns Hopkins Univ Grad Schl of Stud at Bologna Lib Acquisitions 1980-84; ELS Lang Ctr at Wagner Intnl Stu Adv & ESL Instr 1984-90; Assumption Schl 8th Grd Tchr 91; St Sylvester Schl 8th Grd Tchr 1991-; *ai:* Jr Achvmt Tchr ultant; Ldrshp Team Adv; Schl Newspaper Fac Adv; Yrbk Adv; Sci Coord; NYSEC 1995-, Edctr of Excl 1995; NSTA 1995-; SI Rdng Assn ; Conf House Assn 1995-, Bd of Dirs; SI Rotary Ecology Grant 1995; t Permanent Tchr Cert 1993; *office:* St Sylvester Schl 884 Targee St n Island NY 10304*

ASSE, KENNETH MICHAEL, Math & Reading Teacher; *b:* chall, NY; *m:* Kathleen Marie Hawkes; *c:* Jennifer, Michael, Timothy, topher, Bryan; *ed:* SUNY at Plattsburgh (BS) Elem Ed 1970, (MS) Ed 1972; 27 Credit Hrs Past MA in Spec Ed & Effective Tchng Skills; orthside Elem Schl 4th Grd Tchr 1970-72; Cambridge Cntrl Schl 6th Math & Rdng Tchr 1972-; *ai:* Var Soccer Coach; Chaperoning; MS d Decision Making Team; MS Stu Mentoring Prgm; NY St United 1970-, Effective Tchng Prgm Instr; Cambridge Fac Assn 1972-, Negotiater; AFT 1970-; Knights of Columbus 1992-, Charter Mem; St Patrick's Church, Eucharisic Minister; Cambridge Yth Soccer, Travel Team Coach; Math On Line, Videography Curr Writing, Family Life & Human Dev Curr Writing Grants; *home:* Center Cambridge Rd Cambridge NY 12816

LACAVA, MICHAEL M., Music & Band Director; *b:* Wilmington, MA; *ed:* Univ of MA at Amherst (BM) Music Ed 1992; Fitchburg St Coll Fine Arts Dir Cert; *cr:* Gardner Pub Schls Band Dir 1992-, Music Dir 1993-; *ai:* Musical Dir Mass Instrumental Conductors Assn; Marching Dir Schl Cncl; Greater Gardner Comm Band; MMEA 1992-; MICA 1994-, Marching Chair; Narragansett Comm Band 1994-; *office:* Gardner HS 200 Catherine St Gardner MA 01440

LACCETTI, SILVIO R., Professor of Humanities; *b:* Teanceck, NJ; *ed:* Columbia Coll (BA) His 1962, Columbia Univ (MA) His 1963, (PHD) His & Int Politics 1967; Fulbright Rsrch Schlr Univ of Rome; *cr:* Stevens Inst of Tech Prof of Hum 1966-; *ai:* Comm Liaison; Economic Dev Projects; Stevens Ice Hockey & Pre Law Pgm Dir; Admissions & Recruitment Comm; AAUP 1966-; Danforth Assocs 1978-84, Rsrch Grant; Woodrow Wilson Fndtn 1992-, Master Tchr; County Drug Abuse Ed 1969-73, Dir; Comm Svc 1969-, Various Offices; County Bicentennial 1974-76, VP; Fulbright Flwshp; Danforth Tchng Assoc; NJ Dept Comm Affairs Inter Supvr; Dialogue on Drugs, Outlook on NJ & NJ Profiles Pub; Numerous Articles Pub; *office:* Stevens Inst Of Tech Castle Point Station Hoboken NJ 07030

LACEY, KEVIN PATRICK, Social Studies Teacher; *b:* West Mifflin, PA; *m:* Kelley C. Robey; *ed:* Univ of Pittsburgh (BA) Ec 1991; Duquesne Univ (MED) Scndry Ed 1992; Pursuing Doctorate at George Washington Univ; *cr:* Kings & Queens Cntrl HS Tchr & Spcl Asst to Prin 1992-93; Suitland HS Tchr 1993-; *ai:* Saturday OASIS Pgm Tchr; NEA 1992-; NCSS 1992-; Cncl on Ec Ed in MD 1994-; Mellon Advanced Placement Flwshp Grant; Habitat for Humanity Vol; *office:* Suitland HS 5200 Silver Hill Rd Forestville MD 20747*

LACEY, MARIAN HOPEWELL, Kindergarten Teacher; *b:* Danville, PA; *m:* Richard A.; *ed:* Mansfield St Coll (BS) Elem Ed 1971; Elmira Coll (MS); 18 Addl Hrs Penn St, Mansfield; *cr:* Northeast Bradford Schl Dist Kndgtn Tchr 1971-; *ai:* Act 178 Prof Dev Team Sec; Curr & Internal Affairs; Scheduling Comm; NEA, PSEA, NEBEA 1971-, Pres, Sec; NE Region Resolution 1991-; *home:* RR 2 Box 149 Rome PA 18837

LACEY, PATRICIA VERDIECK, Substitute Teacher; *b:* Cleveland, OH; *m:* Edward R.; *c:* Pamela, Michele; *ed:* Immaculata Coll (BA) Math 1967; 4 Grad, 7 Inservice Credits; *cr:* Haverford Jr HS 8th Grd Math Tchr 1967-68; Coatesville Area Cath Elem Schl 5th Grd Math, Sci Tchr 1984-90, 7th, 8th Grd Math Tchr 1990-92, Sub Tchr 1992-; *ai:* Glenmoore Garden Club 1994-, Treas 1994-95, Prgm Co-Chair 1995-; Amer Family Inst Postitive Tchng Awd 1986, 1988; Mid Sts Evaluation Team 1988, 1992; *home:* 160 Lamb Tavern Ln Glenmoore PA 19343

LACEY, THEODORA SMILEY, Eighth Grade Science Teacher; *b:* Montgomery, AL; *m:* Archie Louis; *c:* Archie Jr., Mary Lacey Murphy, Clinton, Nanette; *ed:* AL St Coll (BS) Chem, Math 1953; Hunter Coll NY (MS) Ed 1969; Attnd Rutgers Univ, Fairleight Dickinson Univ, Bank St; *cr:* Carver HS Sci Tchr 1957; Grambling Coll Lab Asst 1959; Natl Sci Fnd Admin Asst 1961; Teaneck Pub Schls Sci Tchr 1970-; *ai:* Co-Chair Pupil Asst Comm; Stu Cncl Adv MS; VP Teaneck Twp Ed Assn; Adv Brd Ethics Twnshp Cncl Teaneck NJ; TTEA, BCEA, NEA 1970-, Local VP; NJSTA 1970-; Delta Kappa Gamma 1970-, Newsletter Ed; Phi Delta Kappa 1969-; Teaneck Fnd for Children 1985-, VP; Cty-Wide Martin Luther King Observance Comm 1980, Chair; Comm Relation Bd 1960's; Rosa Parks Day 1983, Chair; Teaneck Centennial Comm 1995, Chair House Tours; Alpha Kappa Alpha 1952-, Past Pres; Tchr of Yr 1982-83; Comm Human Relations Awd 1986; Del to USSR Rep St of NY 1986; NAACP Branch Svc Awd 1987; Howard Univ Svc to Youth Awd 1987; *office:* Thomas Jefferson MS Teaneck Rd Teaneck NJ 07666

LACH, BARBARA REPOTSKI, First Grade Teacher; *b:* Nanticoke, PA; *m:* Joseph A.; *c:* Elizabeth, Joseph; *ed:* Wilkes Coll (BA) Span 1972; Bloomsburg Univ (MS) Elem Ed 1986; Addl 21 Credits; *cr:* Lincoln Schl 2nd Grd Tchr 1972-77; Kennedy Elem Schl 1st Grd Tchr 1977-88, 1990-91, 1993-; *ai:* NEA, PSEA, GNAEA 1972-; Luzerne Cty Rdng Assn 1988-; Mill Meml Lib 1991-; Bd of Dir & Trustees PTA 1972-; *office:* J F Kennedy Elem Schl 513 Kosciuszko St Nanticoke PA 18634*

LA CHANCE, ANDRE, English Teacher; *b:* Hull Quebec, Canada; *m:* Amy Myers; *c:* Elijah Timmothy, AnnaGrace Therese; *ed:* St Michael's Coll (BA) Jrnlsm 1982; Univ of VA (MED) Eng 1987; 36 Addl Hrs; *cr:* St Michael's Coll Sports Information Dir 1981-84; Univ of VA Asst Sports Information Dir 1984-85; Gloucester HS Eng, Jrnlsm Tchr 1987-89; Champlain Valley Union HS Eng Tchr 1989-; *ai:* Bsbl Coach; Grace Fnd 1994-, Pres; NHS Tchr of Yr 1993; Who's Who 1994; *office:* Champlain Valley Union HS RR 2 Box 160 Hinesburg VT 05461

LACHANCE, ELAINE ESTELLE, 5th-6th Grade Teacher; *b:* Waterville, ME; *ed:* Univ of ME at Farmington (BS) Elem Ed 1973; Thomas Coll; *cr:* Gilbert Schl First Grd Tchr 1973-76; St Augustine Schl 6-8 Grd Tchr 1976-79, 4-5 Grd Tchr 1979-87, 5-6 Grd Tchr 1987-; *ai:* NCEA 1976-; Pub Poems; Who's Who Among Stdnts in Amer Univs, Colls 1971-72; *home:* 2 Davis St Augusta ME 04330

LACHAPELLE, TRACIE ANN, Fourth Grade Teacher; *b:* Providence, RI; *m:* John A.; *c:* Lindsay Jordan; *ed:* CCRI (AA) Early Chldhd Ed 1984-85; RI Coll (BA) Elem Ed, Psy 1988, (MA) Elem Ed 1991; 6 Credit Hrs in Cnslng Prgm; *cr:* Anna Mc Cabe Schl 6th Grd Tchr 1988-89; William Winsor Schl 6th Grd Tchr 1989-90, 4th Grd Tchr 1990-; *ai:* Grd 3 CCD Tchr; Full Schlsp 1st Yr RI Coll; *office:* William Winsor Elem Schl Putnam Ave Greenville RI 02828

LACKEY, NANCY SIMERAL, Retired Elementary Teacher; *b:* Coraopolis, PA; *m:* James Blair; *c:* Karen Mackley, Kimberly Witmer; *ed:* Slippery Rock Univ (BS) Soc Stud, Speech 1950; Univ of Pittsburgh (MA) Elem Ed 1954; *cr:* Moon Schl Dist 6th Grd Elem Tchr 1950-56; Greensburg Salem Schls 4th-6th Grd Elem Tchr 1965-88; Peterson Directed Handwriting Diagnostician Part-time 1988-; *ai:* Westmoreland Hosp Vol; Pvt Tutoring; NEA, PA St Ed Assn, Greensburg Ed Assn 1950-88; Curr Comms; Helped Dev Chptr I Math Prgm for Greensburg; *home:* 629 Welty St Greensburg PA 15601

LACKMAN, CONWAY LEE, Schl of Business Professor; *b:* Chicago, IL; *c:* Eleanor, Abigail; *ed:* OH Wesleyan Univ (BA) Ec & Chem 1962; AZ St Univ (MBA) Bus Admin 1964; Univ of CT (PHD) Ec 1971; *cr:* Mead Paper Co Sr Market Analyst 1966-68; Norfolk Southern Sr Economist 1971-74; R J Reynolds Dir & Strategic Planning 1975-80; CT Insurance Dir & Market Rsrch 1980-84; AT&T Corp Sr Market Rsrch Mgr 1984-91; *ai:* Assoc Adv; Stu Am Mrktg Assn; SIFE Flwshp Alternate; Amer Ec Assn 1971; Amer Mrktg Assn 1975; Duquesne Soc 1993-; Maricopa Bank Flwshp Bureau of Ec AZ St Univ; Omicron Delta Epsilon; Natl Ec Honorary; TAFT Fndtn Rsrch Flwshp; Univ of Cincinatti Flwshp; GSBA; Univ of Chicago.

LACLAIR, RICHARD JAY, English Professor; *b:* Silver Creek, NY; *m:* Mary Jo Uebbing; *c:* James, Jeanne, Jennifer; *ed:* Canisius Coll (BA) Eng 1965; Niagara Univ (MA) Eng 1972; Fredonia Coll Cert 2 Yr Tchng Cert 1974; *cr:* Erie Comm Coll Eng Prof 1974-; *ai:* Element Stu Newpaper Adv 1975-79; Insight Lit Magazine Adv 1988-; Occasional Actor, Stu Plays; NY St Cncl Writing 1985-; Town of Amherst Conservation Advy Cncl 1974-81, Chm; Erie Cty Environmental Advy Cncl 1974-76; Articles Pub; *office:* Erie Comm Coll North Cmps Main St & Youngs Rd Williamsville NY 14221

LACOCK, LYNN A., 5th Grade Teacher; *b:* Washington, PA; *m:* Von; *c:* Lynsey, Von, Maggie, Ty; *ed:* Morehead St Univ at KY Elem, Spec Ed 1969, (MA) Spec Ed; *ai:* NEA, PSEA 1969-.

LACOTTA, JEROME PAUL, Chemistry Teacher; *b:* Peckville, PA; *m:* Ann Marie Dee; *c:* Jerome Michael, Mark William; *ed:* Univ of Scranton (BS) Ed 1963, (MS) Scndry Ed 1971; 8 Credit Hrs Natl Sci Fnd; *cr:* Benton Twp Schl Dist Chem, Math Tchr 1963-64; Lackawanna Trl Dist Sci, Civil Defense Tchr 1964-65; Jessup School Dist Sci, Math Tchr 1965-69; Valley View Schl Dist Sci, Chem, Math Tchr 1969-; *ai:* PSEA 1963-; NEA 1969-; Jessup Tchrs Assn 1965-69, VP, Treas; Valley View Tchrs Assn 1969-, Treas; Lakeland Indian Midget Sports Assn 1976-78, Pres, Treas, Asst Coach; Whitmore Hose Co 1976-; HS Honor Grad 1959; Ted V. Rodgers Schlsp 1959; *office:* Valley View HS Columbus Dr Archbald PA 18403

LACROIX, ROLAND ANDRE, English Teacher; *b:* Fall River, MA; *m:* Elaine Theresa Gagne; *c:* Sara, Wesley; *ed:* Walsh Coll (BA) Eng 1969; 18 Post Grad Hrs in Tchng Rdng; *cr:* Saint Marys Cathedral Schl Sci & Eng Tchr 1968-69; Bishop Connolly HS Eng Tchr 1973-; *ai:* NHS Adv; NCEA, NCTE 1973-; NCEA, NCTE 1973-; *home:* 20 Bourne Rd Swansea MA 02777

LACURTS, CARVEL LEE, Math & Computer Science Tchr; *b:* Salisbury, MD; *m:* Mary Kathryn; *c:* Katrina Leigh; *ed:* Salisbury St Univ (BS) Math 1970, (MED) Math 1972; 50 Grad Hrs; *cr:* Berlin MS Math Tchr 1970-72; Pocomoke HS Math Tchr 1972-; Salisbury St Univ Adj Math Instr 1974-; *ai:* Var Sftbl Coach; NSH Adv; Advanced Placement Coord; NCTM 1976-; NEA, WCTA 1970-; MCTM 1980-; Kiwanis Cub 1980-; Awds Natl Presidenital 1984; Natl Tandy Tech 1990, MD Math Tchr of yr 1982, Salisbury St Univ Distinguished Alumni 1986; *office:* Pocomoke H S 1817 Old Virginia Rd Pocomoke City MD 21851

LACY, ANN WALKER, Speech Communication Prof; *b:* Souderton, PA; *m:* John E.; *c:* Kara; *ed:* WV Univ (BA) Speech & Bio 1969; Univ of Houston (MA) Speech 1971; Post Grad Stud Temple Univ; *cr:* Montgomery Cty Comm Coll Assoc Prof & Speech Coord 1971-; *ai:* AAUP 1972-; AFT 1977-; Univ of Houston Fellowship; *office:* Montgomery County Comm Coll 340 Dekalb Pike Blue Bell PA 19422

LACY, CONSUELLA FRAZIER, Senior Counselor; *b:* Columbia, SC; *m:* Franklin L. Jr.; *c:* Kimberly, Stephanie, Ricardo; *ed:* Univ of DC (BA) Psych 1983, (MA) Cnslng 1993; *cr:* Ford's Theatre Box Office Supvr 1979-88; Atlantic St Shelter Prgm Coord 1987-90; Arch Ballou Sr Cnslr 1990-; *ai:* Assn of Specialists in Group Work 1990-; UDC Peer Cnslng Org 1979-, Pres, VP, Bus Mgr; Ward 8 Outstdng Cnslr 1991, 1993; Outstdng Peer Cnslr 1983; *office:* Arch Ballou Schl 3100 Martin Luther King Ave SE Washington DC 20032

LACY-LIMOGES, ELIZABETH JEAN, Career, Hlth & Home Ec Tchr; *b:* Gunnison, CO; *m:* Mark R.; *c:* Marie Ann; *ed:* Gallaudet Univ (BS) Home Ec 1980; Western MD Coll (MS) Deaf Ed 1994; 3 Credit Hrs Deaf Ed Keene St Coll; *cr:* Keene St Coll Amer Sign Lang Instr 1990-95; Hilltop Montessori Schl Amer Sign Lang Instr 1993-95; Ausine-Project Adventure Amer Sign Lang Immersion ASL Instr, Deaf World Act 1995; Austine Schl for the Deaf Home Ec, Math, Rdnt Tchr 11980-86, Career Ed, Hlth Ed, Home Ec, Outdoor Ed Tchr 1987-; *ai:* ASSA; Bilingl Bicultural Comm; Class Adv; ESDAAT Tournament, Bake Sale Comm; Employee Benefits Dev Comm; Infrastructure Renewal Retreat Comm; Deaf Stud Field Day; Planning, Implementation; Field Hockey, Var Girls Bsktbl Coach; VT Parent Infant Prgm Deaf Mentor; *office:* Austine Schl For The Deaf 120 Maple St Brattleboro VT 05301*

LADA, JUDSON, Guidance Counselor; *b:* Steubenville, OH; *m:* Carol Weekly; *c:* Tawnya, Tiffany; *ed:* Franciscan Univ of Steub (BA) Eng 1976; Univ of Dayton (MS) Ed 1983; *cr:* Conotton Vly Schls Eng Tchr 1976-89, Guid Cnslr 1989-; *ai:* Stu Cncl & Frosh Class Adv; OEA & NEA 1976-; Conotton Vly Tchrs Assoc 1976-; New Phila Band Boosters 1992-, Trustee; *office:* Conotton Vly HS 7205 Cumberland Rd SW Bowerston OH 44695*

LADAS, GERASIMOS, Professor of Mathematics; *b:* Lixouri, Greece; *m:* Theodora A. Stamatatos; *c:* Homer, Andreas; *ed:* Univ of Athens (BS) Math 1961; NY Univ (PHD) Math 1968; *cr:* Univ of RI Asst Prof 1969-72, Assoc Prof 1972-75, Prof 1975-; *ai:* Journal Ed in Chief; AMS 1966-; Excl in Tchng Awd 1987; Books & Articles Pub; *office:* Univ Of RI Tyler Hall Kingston RI 02881

LADD, CULVER S., Classroom Teacher; *b:* Bismarck, ND; *ed:* Univ of MD (BS) Phys Sci, Chem, Math, Physics 1953; Amer Univ (MA) Pol Sci 1978, (PHD) Intnl Relations 1984; Attnd Harvard Univ Summer Schl 1963, Chulakongkorn Univ Bangkok Lang Schl 1965, Oxford Univ 1975-76; *cr:* Dept of Justice FBI Clerk, Photographer 1946-54; COD USAFR Reserve Duty Air Force Ofcr 1954-56, 1965-72; Covington & Burling Lawyers Asst Office Mgr 1956-62; Intnl Schl of Bangkok Tchr 1964-66; Univ of MD Lecturer 1966-74; Payap Univ Spec Lecturer 1974-75; Bus Rsrch Ltd Rsrch Dir 1966-74; DC Pub Schls Classroom Tchr 1978-; *ai:* Harvard Model Congress Adv 1985-; NCTM; MSCSS; NCAPSA; ODK; Pi Sigma Alpha 1962-; DC Young Republicans 1956-62, VP, Natl Committeeman; Mngmt Decision Making with Linear Programming 1967; *office:* Woodrow Wilson Sr HS Chesapeake St-Nebraska Ave NW Washington DC 20016

LADD, THOMAS PAUL, Math & Science Teacher; *b:* Niskayuna, NY; *ed:* Rensselaer Polytechnic Inst (BS) Biomedical Engr 1987; Duke Univ (MS) Biomedical Engr 1989; Union Coll (MAT) Ed 1990; *cr:* Schallmont MS Life Sci Full-time Sub Tchr 1989-90; Averill Park HS Math, Sci Tchr 1990-; *ai:* JV Boys Soccer Coach; Key, Sunday Ski Adv; Staff Dev, ACCESS 21 Comms; Odyssey of Mind Adv; Tau Beta Pi 1986-; Duke Univ, Empire St Challenger Fellowships; NYSTEN MST Mntr; *office:* Averill Park HS 146 Gettle Rd Averill Park NY 12018

LADERER, ANNE F., French Teacher; *b:* Washington, DC; *m:* Bruce P.; *c:* Heidi, Noelle, Matthew; *ed:* RI Coll (BA) Fr 1970, (MAT) Eng 1972; *cr:* Riverside Jr High Fr & Eng Tchr 1971-94; East Prov Sr High Fr Tchr 1994-; *ai:* Mem of Fac Comm; NEA, RIFLA 1970-; PTA 1989-90, Membership Chprsn, Silver Bowl Awd; Jr HS Tchr of Month 1994; *office:* East Providence Sr HS 2000 Pawtucket Ave East Providence RI 02914

LADLEY, PATRICIA POWERS, Theology Teacher; *b:* Buffalo, NY; *m:* Peter G.; *c:* David F., Jonathan F.; *ed:* Trocaire Coll (AAS) Lbrl Arts 1964; Medaille Coll (BA) Eng 1967; Christ the King Seminary (MA) Theology 1975; Canisius Coll Grad Stud; *cr:* Elem Schls Primary Ed Tchr 1963-73; Diocese of Buffalo Pastoral Minister, Consultant, Rel Edctr 1973-77; Cntrl Cath HS Theology Tchr, Comm Svc Adv 1977-78; St Benedicts RC Church Coord of Sco Ministries 1981-85; Notre Dame HS Theology Tchr, Comm Svc Adv 1985-; *ai:* NHS, Amnesty Intnl Moderator; Tchr in Sci Ed; Intnl Thomas Merton Soc 1988-; NCEA 1986-; NASAA 1991-; Amnesty Intnl, Bread for World 1981-; Pax Christ USA 1974-; Friends of Mt Sauror 1990-; Co-authored Cath Worker Houses, Ordinary Miracles 1988, Test We Live In Jesus; Justice Edctr; Outstdng Rel Edctr 1976; *office:* Notre Dame HS 1400 Maple Ave Elmira NY 14904*

LADOPOULOS, MARILYN D., Spanish Teacher; *b:* Pittsfield, MA; *m:* Harry N.; *c:* Cheryl A., Michelle E. Baldani, Nicholas H., Darlene M.; *ed:* Syracuse Univ (BA) Span 1961; NY St Univ at Albany (MA) Advanced Classroom Tchng, Span 1969; Permanent Fr Cert 1985; *cr:* Burnt

Hills-Ballston Lake Jr HS Span, Fr Tchr 1961-62; Various Schls Sub Tchr 1971-83; Schalmont HS Span, Fr Tchr 1984-90, Span Tchr 1990-; Schalmont MS Span, Fr Tchr 1984-90; *ai:* Intnl Club Adv 1985-92; NEA 1985-93; NYSUT 1993-; Schalmont Tchrs Assn 1985-, Bd of Dirs 4 Yrs; *office:* Schalmont HS 1 Sabre Dr Schenectady NY 12306

LADOUCEUR, REGINA QUEALY, Literature Teacher; *ed:* Bridgewater St Coll (BS) Gen Sci, Elem Ed 1967, (MED) K-12th Grd Rdng Consultant 1980; *cr:* E. B. Intermediate Schl 4th-6th Grd Tchr 1967-81; E. B. MS 5th-6th Grd Tchr 1981-83, Rdng, Lit Tchr 1983-; *ai:* DARE Club; Parent Seminars on Quest Prgm; NEA 1967-; MTA; PCEA 1980-90, Exec Bd, Citation, Hnr Awds; EBEA 1990-95, Treas; Natl Rdng, Diabetes, Cancer Assns; Horace Mann Grant; *office:* East Bridgewater MS 435 Central St East Bridgewater MA 02333

LADRACH, JANET MEISNER, 5th Grade Teacher; *b:* Fostoria, OH; *m:* Richard P.; *c:* Claire Allyson White; *ed:* Kent St Univ (BS) Elem Ed 1976; Malone Coll (MA) Curr, Instruction 1992; 12 Addl Hrs; Cmptr, Environmental Sci; WY Tchrs Geology, Botany Courses; *cr:* New Philadelphia City Schl Tchr of Gifted 1985-94, 5th Grd Tchr 1994-; *ai:* Future Problem Solving Coach; Stu Cncl; NPEA 1979-, VP, Bldg Rep; New Towne Cloggers 1989-, Sec 2 Yrs; Phi Delta Kappa, Quaker Grants; Presented at OAGC 1992; *home:* 4043 Boltz Orchard Rd SW Sugarcreek OH 44681

LADUKE, RICHARD MARTIN, Physical Ed Teacher & Coach; *b:* Gourneur, NY; *m:* Kathryn Jean Rann; *c:* Robert, Dona; *ed:* St Lawrence Univ (BS) PE 1975, (MED) Admin 1976; NJ City St Coll Drivers Ed Cert; *cr:* Clifton HS Tchr, Coach 1976-; *ai:* Sftbl, Ice Hockey, Vlybl Coach; Ftbl Defensive Coord; Ski Club Adv; NEA, NJEA, CTA, CHSFO, PCCA, CCA, NEISCA 1976-; NJSCA 1976-, Inducted into Coaches Hall of Fame 1996; Wallkill Vly Bd of Ed 1991-; NJ St Sftbl Coach of Yr 1990; Numerous Sftbl Coach of Yr Awds; *office:* Clifton H S 333 Colfax Ave Clifton NJ 07013

LADY, CHARLES SPURGEON, Retired Music Teacher; *b:* Sandusky, MI; *ed:* Buffalo St Coll (MS) Ed 1983; Study at Univ of NY at Buffalo; Attnd Eastman Schl of Music, Cath Univ; *cr:* Niagara Chrstn Coll Tchr 1963-68; Cleveland Hill Tchr 1966-69; West Seneca Cntrl Schl System Tchr 1969-75; *ai:* MENC; Erie Cty Music Ed Assn; West Seneca Tchrs Assn, Bldg Rep 5 Yrs; Comm Choirs, Dir & Singer; Buffalo Philharmonic Chorus; Erie Yth Choir, Chime Ensemble, Dir; Fort Erie Legion Band; Dev Music Dictation Machine, Used as Masters Project; *home:* PO Box 512 West Seneca NY 14224*

LAEMLEIN, JEAN WAGANKA, Mathematics Teacher; *b:* Troy, NY; *m:* Robert J.; *c:* Jessica, Marie; *ed:* SUC at Oneonta (BA) Math Ed 1967; St Univ of NY at Albany (MA) Math Ed 1968; Addl Hrs Beyond Masters from St Univ of NY at Brockport; *cr:* Niskayuna Pub Schls Math Tchr 1968-69; Fairport Pub Schls Math Tchr 1969-; *ai:* NEA, NYSUT 1968-; Fairport Educators Assn 1969-, Treas 1974-86; NSF Grant 1980; *office:* Fairport HS 1358 Ayrault Rd Fairport NY 14450

LAFAGE, WENDY L., Director of Nursing Programs; *b:* S Weymouth, MA; *c:* Meredith Tiffany; *ed:* Univ of CT at Storrs (BS) Nrsng 1969; AZ St Univ (MS) Maternal Newborn Nrsng, Nrsng Ed 1974; LA St Univ at Baton Rouge (MA) Cnslng 1981; Working Toward PHD Curr & Instruction St Univ of NY at Albany; Registered Nurse MA, NY, VT 1981-; *cr:* Pima Comm Coll Asst Prof of Nrsng 1972-76; Southeastern LA Univ Asst Prof of Nrsng 1977-90; Parkland Psychiatric Hosp Admin Supvr, Nrsng Admin 1985-89; Woman's Hosp Part-time Newborn Nursery Staff Nurse 1988-89; Univ of MA Educl Mobility Prgm Dir 1990-93; Southern VT Coll Nrsng Prgms Dir 1993-; *ai:* US Navy Reserve Lieutenant; Presented Curr Seminar 1993; Nrsng Prgm Accreditation; Critical Thinking in Curr; Curr Bldg, Revision; Nrsng Ed; Testing, Assessment Learners; Maternal, Infant Care; Foster Care Case Reviewer; Hlth Ed Vol; Pub Article; Co-author Womens Health Nursing Examination Review, Test Bank for Essentials of Maternal Newborn Nursing, Clinical Simulations in Nursing II, Clinical Simulations in Nursing III; *office:* Southern VT Coll Monument Ave Bennington VT 05201

LAFAUCI, FRANCES FERRANTE, Professor of Nursing; *b:* Bronx, NY; *m:* Thomas J.; *c:* Jean, Kristin, Lauren, Patricia; *ed:* SUNY at Buffalo (BS) Nrsng 1971; Adelphi Univ (MS) Nrsng 1976; SUNY at Stony Brook (MA) Lbrl Stud 1989; *cr:* Suffold Cty Dept of Hlth Svcs Pub Hlth Nurse 1971-77; Goos Samaritan Hosp Staff Nurse 1974-79; Farmingdale SUNY Instr, Adj 1978-79; Suffold Comm Coll Prof 1980-; *ai:* Schlsp Comm; Course Coord LB42; Nrsng Fac Comm; Suffolk Cty Perenatal Assn 1990-; Suffolk Prof Nurse Assn 1994-; Sigma Theta Tau 1992-; St Thomas More Church 1978-, Coord 2nd Grd Rel; Pius X Awd 10 Yrs Svc; PTA 1979-m Mbrshp Chprsn 1993-; Tchr Who Made a Difference Nom; Nurse of Distinction Awd Nom 1992; *office:* Suffolk Community Coll Crooked Hill Rd Brentwood NY 11717*

LAFAVE, RICHARD P., French & Spanish Teacher; *m:* Linda B.; *c:* Scott Alan, Jeff Christopher; *ed:* Cntrl CT St Univ (BS) Fr & Span 1971, (MS) Guid 1976; *cr:* East Hampton MS Fr & Span Tchr 1971-; *ai:* Ath Dir; Cross Cntry & Vllybl Coach; East Hampton Edctrs Assn 1971-, Bldg Rep; CEA, NEA; East Hampton Tchr of Yr 1988 & Good Apple Awd 1995; *office:* East Hampton MS 19 Childs Rd East Hampton CT 06424

LAFERTY, CRAIG W., Math Dept Chair; *b:* Baltimore, MD; *m:* Betty Eickelberg; *c:* Craig Jr., Jenifer; *ed:* Towson St Univ (BS) Math 1966; Northwestern Univ (MA) Math 1970; 80 Credits Beyond MA Loyola Coll, Johns Hopkins Univ, Towson St Univ; *cr:* Greece Arcadia HS Math Tchr 1966-70; Randallstown HS Math Tchr 1970-77; Towson HS Math Chair 1977-94; Dulaney HS Math Chair 1994-; *ai:* Men's Var Soccer Coach; NCTM 1966-; TABCO, NSTA, NEA 1980-; Young Life Vol Ldr 1963-84, Ldr, Speaker; Towson St Univ Ath Hall of Fame; Coach of Yr 1994; Distngd Tchr Presidential Scholars 1992; Exceptional Tchr Stamford Univ 1983; *office:* Dulaney HS 255 Padonia Rd Timonium MD 21093

LAFFERTY, DRUSILLA KERR, Social Studies & English Tchr; *b:* Cheltenham, PA; *ed:* Rutgers Univ (BA) His 1992; *cr:* Vineland HS South Soc Stud Tchr 1992-95; Vineland Alternative HS Soc Stud, Eng Tchr 1995-; *ai:* Schl Newspaper Adv; Model Congress, Project Grad Chaperone; Soc Stud Curr Review Comm, Schl Crisis Team Mem; NEA, NJEA 1992-; VEA 1992-, Bldg Rep; CCEA; Phi Beta Kappa 1992-; Amer Camping Assn 1995-, Assoc Visitor; NJ Governor's Tchng Schlsp 1988; NJ Tchrs Conf on Holocaust 1995; *office:* Vineland HS 2880 E Chestnut Ave Vineland NJ 08360

LAFFERTY, LINDA, Biology Teacher & Sci Chprsn; *b:* Brooklyn, NY; *ed:* Molloy Coll (BS) Bio 1980; Adelphi Univ (MS) Bio 1982; Addl 15 Credits Ed; *cr:* Sacred Heart Acad Bio Tchr 1983-; *ai:* Sci Hon Soc Moderator; STANYS, NYSTA 1985-; *home:* 55 Vernon Ave Rockville Centre NY 11570

LAFFERTY-JOHN, LAURIE SUE, 6th-12th Grd PE Teacher; *b:* Olean, NY; *m:* Scott David; *c:* Jackson, Tanner; *ed:* Slippery Rock Univ (BS) Hlth & PE 1988; 34 Grad Hrs; *cr:* Salamanca City Schl PE 1990-; *ai:* Girls Var Swimming, Diving, Track & Field Coach 6 Yrs; Asst Drama Club Adv; NEA 1990-; Track & Field Coach of Yr 1994; *office:* Salamanca HS 50 Iroquois Dr Salamanca NY 14779*

LAFFEY, JUDITH SHERIDAN, Spanish, French & Italian Tchr; *b:* Providence, RI; *c:* Kristen, Eric; *ed:* Newton Coll-Sacred Heart (BA) Modern Langs 1972; RI Coll (MA) Agency Cnslng 1991; *cr:* St Mary's Elem 1 Grd Tchr 1972-76; St Mary's Acad-Visitation Frng Langs Tchr 1976-82; Narragansett HS Frgn Langs Tchr 1982-86; LaSalle Acad Frgn Langs Tchr 1986-; *ai:* Music Ministry Directress; Fac Assn Pres Lay; Natl Span Exam RI Coord 1990-; Amer Assn of Tchrs of Span 1984-; Awded Fullbright Grant to Stud in Italy Summer 1985; *office:* LaSalle Acad 612 Academy Ave Providence RI 02908

LAFFOND, WANITA SIOUI, Sixth Grade Teacher; *b:* New York, NY; *m:* William Paul; *c:* Kateri Marie, Jonathan David; *ed:* Our Lady of the Elms (BA) Eng, Ed 1969; U MA (BA) Sci, Math, Ed 1993, (CAGS) Sci, Math, Ed 1994; *cr:* St Thomas Schl 7th Grd Tchr 1960-65; Blessed Sacrament Schl 8th Grd Tchr 1965-71; Frontier Regnl HS Eng Tchr 971-72; Buckland-Shelburne Regnl Schl 6th Grd Tchr 1979-93; Conway Grammar Schl 6th Grd Tchr 1993-; *ai:* Mediation Adv; Lucretia Crocker Scholar 1989; *office:* Conway Grammar Schl Fournier Rd Conway MA 01341*

LAFKAS, KAREN SKINNER, HS Mathematics Teacher; *b:* Middletown, OH; *m:* Robert C.; *c:* Katherine, Charles, David, Abigail, Matthew; *ed:* St Mary of the Wood Coll (BA) Math 1965; Grad Work Xavier Univ; *cr:* Badin HS Math & Sci Tchr 1966-68; Summit Cntry Day Schl Math Tchr 1968-69; St Ursula Acad Math Tchr 1989-; *ai:* Big Sisters Club Moderator; NCTM 1989-; St Mary of the Wood Coll Alumni Bd 1965-, Natl Pres 1978-80; *office:* Saint Ursula Acad 1339 E Mcmillan St Cincinnati OH 45206

LAFLESH, LEROY WILLIAM, Eighth Grade Math Teacher; *b:* Chicopee, MA; *m:* Emily Gnacek; *c:* Michael Leslie, Thomas; *ed:* Amer Intnl Coll (BS) Elem Ed 1969; Westfield St Coll (MA) Elem Admin 1974; *cr:* Alvord Schl Sixth Grd Tchr 1969-92; Betcher Schl Sixth Grd Tchr 92; Selser Schl Sixth Grd Tchr 1969-92; Bellany MS Eighth Grd Math, Alg Tchr 1992-; *ai:* Interact Club Chicopee Rotary Spon; Comm Involvement Prgm Adv; Framework Comm City of Chicopee; Math Club Adv; Chicopee Ed Assn, MA Ed Assn, NEA 1969-; Holy Name Soc, St Stanis Church 1960-, Pres, Man of Yr; Bsbl Little League Coach 8 Yrs; Bsktbl Little League Coach 4 Yrs; 7th-8th Grd Ftbl Coach 4 Yrs; *office:* Edward Bellamy MS 314 Pendleton Ave Chicopee MA 01020

LAFON, MARK ALLEN, Social Science Teacher; *b:* Hungtington, WV; *ed:* Univ of Rio Grande (BS) Soc Sci Comprehensive 1993; Continuing Ed Credits at OH Univ; *cr:* Yth Dev Corp of Amer Voc & Educl Coord 1992-93; Chesapeake HS Soc Sci Tchr 1993-; *ai:* Golf & Womens Bsktbl Head Coach; Boys Bsktbl Asst Head Coach; NEA 1993-; OH Ed Assn 1993-; Chesapeake Local Tchrs Assn 1993-, VP; Tau Kappa Epsilon 1989-, Pres; Chesapeake Local Jaycees 1991-; *office:* Chesapeake HS 10181 Cty Rd 1 Chesapeake OH 45619

LAFOND, JADA MC RAE, Biology & Health Teacher; *b:* Gloucester, MA; *m:* Robert; *c:* Kajsa Marie, Nissa Ann; *ed:* Bridgewater St Coll (BS) Hlth, PE 1977; Cambridge Coll (MS) Ed 1991; Cmptr Trng; *cr:* St Ann's Cath Schl PE Tchr 1977-79; O'Maley MS Sci Tchr 1980-85; Gloucester HS Bio Tchr 1986-; *ai:* Thespians Choreographer; Bsktbl Coach 9 Yrs; Field Hockey Coach 7 Yrs; Track, Field Coach 1 Yr; NEA, Gloucester Tchrs Assn 1980-; *office:* Gloucester HS 32 Leslie O. Johnson Rd Gloucester MA 01930

LAFOND, JOHN PHILIP, Biology Teacher; *b:* Oakridge, TN; *m:* Barbara A.; *c:* Erika, Chad, William, Kirsten, Betsy; *ed:* Univ of Southern ME (BS) Sci 1968; Univ of ME (MS) Ed 1974; Attnd Columbia Univ, Penn St Univ; *cr:* Lincoln Jr HS Sci Tchr 1968-78; Deering HS Bio Tchr 1978-90; Portland HS Bio Tchr 1990-; *ai:* Coach Ftbl, Track, Girls Bsktbl, Frosh Bsktbl, Var Golf; St Rep HSGCA; St Golf Comm; PEA, MEA, NEA 1968-; ME Coaches Assn 1968-, Coach of Yr 1990; *office:* Portland HS 284 Cumberland Ave Portland ME 04101*

LAFORCE, SHIRLEY EDDY, Retired Kindergarten Teacher; *b:* Warsaw, NY; *m:* Dean Edward; *c:* Todd Joslyn, Joel Edward; *ed:* Bapt Bible Seminary (BRE) Chrstn Ed 1956; SUNY at Cortland (MS) Elem Ed 1964; *cr:* Windsor Cntrl Schl Dist K-6 Grd Tchr 1959-64; Bainbridge-Gilford Schl Dist K-6 Grd Tchr 1965-69; Johnson City Central Schl Dist K-6 Grd Tchr 1969-90; *ai:* Beginner Church Ldr, Sub Tchr, Design Crafts, Coord Lesson Materials; AWANA Ldr, Sub Story Teller, Song Ldr; JCTA 1969-; NEA, NYSTA 1959-; Windsor Tchrs Assn; Bainbridge-Gilford Tchrs Assn; J C Dist Tchrs Assn; Outstdng Svc Awd 1973; Delta Kappa Gamma 1979; Primary Grd Hlth Curr Project Master Tchr Trainer 1983, Coordinating Instr 1987; Grant from Broome Dental Soc.

LAFORGE, MARGARET HANSON, Director of Choral Music; *b:* Pittsburgh, PA; *m:* John; *c:* Michele, John, Matthew; *ed:* Univ of NH (BA) Music His 1969; Univ of So ME (MS) Music Ed 1981; 16 Addl Hrs; *cr:* St Anthony's Schl 1962-65; Presque Isle HS 1968-69; Freeport MS & HS Choral Music Dir 1981-; *ai:* Broadway Musical; Cabaret, Springfest; All St Chorus; MEA 11th Grd Hum Comm; MENC, MMEA 1980-; ACDA 1981-, ACDA Choral Tchr of Yr 1992; MEA, MMEA 1981-; Holy Martyrs Cath 1983-95, Choir Dir; Foreside Comm UCC 1974-84, Chair Dir; Greely HS Steering Comm 1992-93, Ski Club; Finalist Tchr of Yr 1995; Hosted 7 Stu Tchrs 1988-95; Articles Pub; Piano Accompanist for All St Choir 1992; *office:* Freeport MS & HS 30 Holbrook St Freeport ME 04032*

LA FOUNTAIN, MARK, Second Grade Teacher; *b:* Watertown, NY; *m:* Sharon Tuck; *ed:* SUNY at Oswego (BA) Elem Ed 1982, (MS) Elem Ed 1987; Earned Cert of Educl Admin 1993 at SUNY Oswego; *cr:* Sackets Harbor Cntrl Schls Sixth Grd Tchr 1982-84; North Rose-Wolcott Schl Dist Second Grd Tchr 1984-; *ai:* Acting Bldg Prin; NEA 1982-; Masonic Lodge 1995-; Knights of Columbus 1978-; *office:* Florentine Hendrick Elem Schl New Hartford St Wolcott NY 14590

LAFRANCE, MARGARET A., Mathematics Coordinator; *b:* Bronx, NY; *m:* Glenn R.; *c:* Helen Corcoran, Richard, Brett; *ed:* 33 Grad Hrs; *cr:* Groton Elem Schl Tchr 1968-; *ai:* Dist Curr Design Team; Admin Cncl; AMTNYS, NCTM 1990-; St Anthony's Church Choir; Sports Booster Club; *office:* Groton Elem Schl 516 Elm St Groton NY 13073

LA FRANCE, MAUREEN MURPHY, Fifth Grade Teacher; *b:* Boston, MA; *m:* William Bernard Jr.; *ed:* St Coll at Boston (BS) Ed 1970; Cambridge Coll (MED) Ed 1991; Attnd Univ of AK, Boston Univ, Tufts Univ, Bridgewater St Coll, Fitchburg St Coll, Framingham St Coll, Emmanuel Coll; *cr:* South Schl 5th Grd Tchr 1969-; *ai:* South Schl Cncl; NEA, MTA, STA 1969-; NCTA 1972-; Castle Island Assn 1986-; Cousteau Soc 1982-; Striar JCC 1994-; Horace Mann Grant Recipient; Life Saver Awd Blue Cross Blue Shield; *office:* South Elem Schl 171 Ash St Stoughton MA 02072

LAFRANCE, PAUL R., Business Teacher; *b:* Providence, RI; *m:* Cynthia Lee Cruciani; *ed:* Bryant Coll (BS & BA) Mgmt & Ec 1983; Univ of RI (BS) Ed 1989; Providence Coll MED Admin Candidate; *cr:* Pilgrim HS Tchr 1989-90; Chariho HS Tchr 1990-; *ai:* Class Adv 1991-95; Jr Achvmt Adv 1991-; FBLA Adv 1992-; RI BEA 1990-; NEA 1991-; Coinesett Meadows Assoc 1987-, Pres; Comm Assoc Inst 1991-; FBLA Adv of Yr Pell Awd 1995; *office:* Chariho Reg HS 453 Switch Rd Wood River Junctio RI 02894

LAFROMBOISE, MARIE B., 3rd Grade Teacher; *b:* Williston, VT; *ed:* Diocesan Srs Coll (BA) Ed 1969; Post Grad Univ of VT & Johnson St Tchr Coll; *cr:* CT Schl Systems 1st Grd Tchr 1961-69; VT Schl Systems 1st, 2nd & 3rd Grd Tchr 1969-84; Visiting Nurse Assn Nurses Aide 1984-85; VT Schl Systems 1st, 2nd & 3rd Grd Tchr 1985-; *ai:* Tchr of Tae Kwon-Do After Schl; Past Girls Summer Sftbl Coach, Womens Sftbl & Mixed Sftbl League; Barbershop Chorus & Quartet; NEA 1970-; Negotiator; Episcopal Church Lay Reader, Played Folk Svc; Recorder Quartet, Singing Quartet & Choir; Communion Server & Bread; Art Pub; Tae Kwon-Do 1st Degree Black Belt, Silver & Gold Medals & Tournaments; Dedication & S by Fed of Tae Kwon-Do; *office:* Milton Elem Schl Herrick Ave Mil 05468*

LAGAN, CHERYL MARIE, Business Teacher; *b:* Rochester, Joseph; *ed:* SUNY at Albany (BS) Bus, Distribute Ed 1981; Ior (MBA) Mrktg 1986; NY St Ed (BS) Scndry Math 1989; *cr:* Maho Bus Tchr 1981-89; Ossining HS Bus Tchr 1989-; *ai:* Class Adv Mahopac Chrldng Adv; Recording Sec Fac Cncl; NYSUT, AFT, W BTA of NY 1981-; St John the Evangelist 1981-, Parishioner; La Pub; *office:* Ossining HS 29 S Highland Ave Ossining NY 10562

LAGATTA, DAVID, Technology Education Teacher; *b:* Columbus, Brenda Lowery; *c:* Stephen, Jeffrey, Kimberly; *ed:* SUNY at Osweg Tech Ed 1989, (MS) Tech Ed 1992; *cr:* Camden Cntrl HS Tech Tchr *ai:* Girls Var Bowling Coach; Epsilon Pi Tau 1988-; Mohawk Vly T Assn, NYS Tech Ed Assn 1987-; *office:* Camden HS Oswego St C NY 13316

LAGATTUTA, DIANE, English Second Language Tchr; *b:* Teane *ed:* Rutgers Univ (MA) Lang Ed 1990; Montclair St Coll (BA) Ho *cr:* Peace Corps El Salvador Hosp Nutrition Edctr 1978-80, Ho Regnl Nutrition Svcs 1980-81; Woodbridge Bd of Ed Home E 1984-90; Rahway Bd of Ed Eng as Second Lang Tchr 199 Multi-Cultural, Prin Advy Comms; NEA, NJEA, REA 1990-, Ass TESOL 1990-; Returned Peace Corps Vol 1981-; *office:* Rahway H Madison Ave Rahway NJ 07065

LAGERMAN, HARRY M., 8th Grade Teacher; *b:* New York City, N Muskingum Coll (BA) Eng, Sociology 1969; Plymouth St (MED) Lang Arts 1984; 33 Addl Credits Wm Patterson, Columbia Tchrs C Dexter City Schl Tchr 1969-71; Meml Schl Tchr, Admin 19 Bloomfield Schl Tchr 1981-82; Child Stud Teams Inc Tchr 19 Eastside HS Tchr 1984-86; Meml Schl Tchr, Admin 1986-; *ai:* St Adv; Bsktbl, Sftbl Coach; Phi Delta Kappa 1983-; NJ Cnc for So 1989-; L. F. Ed Assn 1976-, Governor's Outstdng Tchr 1990; Sons of Legion 1990-, Commander; Lions 1993-, Dir; *office:* Memorial M Liberty St Little Ferry NJ 07643*

LAGERSTEDT, ARTHUR P., Retired Teacher; *b:* Painesville, O Susan E.; *c:* Arthur P. Jr.; *ed:* OH Univ (BSEd) Elem Ed 1964; Lak Coll (MS) Ed 1976; *cr:* Las Vegas Schls Tchr 1964-64; Painesvill Schls Tchr 1965-69; Mentor Schls Tchr 1971-95; *ai:* Former C Charge of Detention Hall; Playground Supvr; OEA 1971-; NEA Mentor Lions 1985-86, Newsletter Chm; Jr Summer Golf League Cmptr Software Grant; *home:* 6202 Dawson Blvd Mentor OH 44060

LAGOY, DENNIS MARK, High School Math Instructor; *b:* Glens NY; *m:* Sharon Clark; *c:* Mark, Jeff; *ed:* Adirondack CC (AA) Lb 1970; Plattsburgh St (BA) Sec Ed 1972; 30 Addl Credits; *cr:* Johr Cntrl Math, Sci Tchr 1972-80; Argyle Cntrl Schl Jr HS Sci Tchr 19 HS Math Tchr 1986-; *ai:* Math Team; Girls Bsktbl Var Coach; NYSUT 1972-; Gideons Int 1973-; *office:* Argyle Central Schl Sheri Argyle NY 12809

LAGRANDE, CHARLES NORMAN, German Instructor; *b:* Roc IL; *m:* Phyllis M.; *c:* Peter Charles; *ed:* Rockford Coll (BA) Ger 1968; St Univ (MA) Ger 1972; Western CO Univ (DA) Ger 1982; Hofstra NDEA Inst Flwshp Grant; *cr:* Kent St Univ Ger Instr 196 Ottawa-Glandorf HS Ger Instr 1969-73; Ruhrtac Gymnasium Eng 1973-75; OH St Iniv Ger Instr 1979-85; Shawnee HS Ger Instr 197 Ger Club Adv; Var Asst Soccer, Bsbl Coach; Dept Frgn Langs Chm; 1968-, Pres 1991-93; ACTFL 1968-; NEA, OEA 1969-; Delta Phi 1969-; Phi Delta Kappa 1976-; Amil Tellers Dramatics 1976-, 1978-79, Acting Awds; Greater Lima Soccer League 1983-90, 1987-89; *office:* Shawnee HS 3333 Zurmehly Rd Lima OH 45806*

LAGRAVE, NANCY GOODWIN, Special Education Teache Portsmouth, VA; *c:* Michelle, Laura; *ed:* Southern CT St Univ (BS) PE, Recreation 1965, (MS) Spec Ed 1991; 15 Credits Beyond Maste Naugatuck HS PE Tchr 1965-71; Central Avenue Elem Schl Kndgtn 1988-89; City Hill MS Spec Ed Tchr 1989-90; Naugatuck HS Spec Ed 1990-; *ai:* NEA, CEA 1988-; CEC 1993-; Raymond K. Foley Awd *office:* Naugatuck HS 543 Rubber Ave Naugatuck CT 06770

LA GREGA, NICHOLAS, Third Grade Teacher; *b:* Port Jefferson, *ed:* C. W. Post Coll (MS) Elem Ed 1982, (PD) Educl Admin 1985; S at Stonybrook Elem Ed 1972; *ai:* Elem Prins Aide; Renaissance, Sc Adv; Drama, Fr Club; PTA Dist 1972-, Legislative Chm; County 1990-, Ed Chm; *office:* Tamarac Elem Schl 50 Spence Ave Holtsvill 11742*

LAGUEUX MCINTYRE, JUNE MARIE, Home Economics Teach Rochester, NH; *c:* David, William, Susan; *ed:* Rivier Coll (BA) Hor 1966; Attnd Univ of NH, Leslie Coll, Notre Dame at Manchester, Un VA, Univ of CO & Univ of GA; *cr:* Marshwood HS Home Econ 1966-67; Farmington Elem 6th Grd Tchr 1971-90; Farmington HS H Economist 1990-; *ai:* Voc Dept Chprsn; NEA 1966-; Farmington Assn 1970-, Pres, VP; Eagle Awd Awded by Peers; *office:* Farmingto Memorial Dr Farmington NH 03835*

LAHEY, MICHAEL EDWARD, English Teacher; *b:* Worcester, M Patricia Ellen Puracchio; *c:* Caitlin, Connor; *ed:* Assumption Coll Eng 1977; Worcester St Coll (MA) Ed 1987; *cr:* Saint Johns High Eng 1978-; *ai:* ICON; Sr Class Moderator; Worcester Cty Young Writers S NCTE, MCTE, NCEA; Emerald Club 1993-; *office:* Saint Johns HS Main St Shrewsbury MA 01545

LAHOOD, MARVIN J., Distngd Tchng Prof of English; *b:* Auburn, *m:* Marjorie Braun; *c:* John, Melissa, Mark; *ed:* Boston Coll (BS) Pre 1954; U of Notre Dame (MA) Eng 1958, (PHD) Eng 1962; *cr:* Niaga Instr & Assoc Prof 1960-61, 1962-64; Buffalo St Coll Assoc Prof & 1964-67, 1967-71; Salem St Coll Prof & Acad Dean 1971-75 DYou Coll Prof & Dean of Fac 1975-78; Buffalo St Coll Prof & Distngd T Prof 1978-95, 1995-; *ai:* SUNY Senate Operations Comm Burchfield-Penney Poetry Series Chair; UUP 1978-; Mt St Marys 1990-94, Chm of Bd; SUNY Chancellors Awd for Excl in Tchng 1 Univ Dortmund Germany 1986, Lille Univ France 1991 Lecturer; Bo Tender is the Night Essays in Criticism 1969, Conrad Richters Amer 1 *office:* Buffalo State Coll 1300 Elmwood Ave Buffalo NY 14222*

LAHR, DALE EDWARD, 8th Grade Mathematics Teacher; *b:* Danv PA; *m:* Linda Susan John; *c:* Melissa Ann, Kristen Sue; *ed:* Bloomsbu Coll (BSEd) Elem Ed 1969, (MED) Elem Ed 1976; *cr:* Stevens Elem 6th Grd Tchr 1969-75; Shamokin Area MS 6th-8th Grd Math Tchr 1 *ai:* Shamokin Area HS Chess Club Adv & Asst Coach; NEA, PSE Shamokin Area Ed Assn 1969-; *office:* Shamokin Area M S 8th & Arc Shamokin PA 17872

LAHTI, SUSAN AINAIRE, Social Science Teacher; *b:* Bangor, ME Eric Reino; *c:* Adam, Hannele; *ed:* Univ of ME at Orono (BA) His 1 (MED) Scndry Ed 1978; *cr:* Carrabec HS Soc Sci Tchr 1972-; *ai:* Sup Team; Hi-Q Team Faculty Adv; Jr Class Adv; Carrabec Ed Assn 1972-, 2 Yrs, Grievance Officer 1981-93; Delta Kappa Gamma 1991-; NE MTA 1972-; WCBB Pub Television, Vol; ME Hlocaust Human Ri Center 1991-; ME Geographic Alliance 1993-; S Poverty Law C 1992-; Amnesty Intnl 1990-; Carrabec Tchr Awd 1984; ME Geogra Alliance Tchr Consultant 1993-.

,AW, MARCIA JEAN, Physical Education Teacher; *b:* ·neur, NY; *ed:* Jefferson Comm Coll (AS) 1969; SUC at Brockport E 1971; SUC at Cortland & Azusa Pacific Coll 30 Credit Hrs; *cr:* ota HS PE Tchr 1972-; *ai:* Field Hockey Coach 23 Yrs; Girls Var Coach 22 Yrs; Jr Olympic Vllybl Coach 2 Yrs; Canastota Tchrs 1972-; US Field Hockey Assoc 1995-; *home:* RR 1 Box 295 ota NY 13032

:, RAYMOND ALAN, Voice & Speech Prgm Coord; *b:* Pittsburgh, Susan Mary Mc Gregor; *cr:* Point Park Coll Asst Prof, Acting, ng, Speech 1979-; *ai:* PPC Co Dir; Pittsburgh Playhouse Theatre Co Dir; AEA, SAG 1964-; AFTRA 1968-; Amer Shakespeare Festival Amer Conservatory Theatre Flwshps; Amer Coll Theatre Festival Merit; *office:* Point Park Coll 201 Wood St Pittsburgh PA 15222

}, ALAN RUDOLPH, Math Tchr & Dept Facilitator; *b:* W sville, PA; *m:* Lucille Ann Esposito; *c:* Amy; *ed:* Geneva Coll (BS) Ed 1962; IN Univ (MAT) Math; BS+81 Semester Hrs; *cr:* Rochester th Tchr 1962-64; Horace Mann Jr HS Math Tchr 1964-67; Lakewood ath Tchr 1967-; *ai:* LTA 1964-; OEA 1964-; NEA 1964-; OCTM IN Univ NSF Flwshp 1968-71; Kent St Univ IFSMACSE Flwshp 1; Author Comp Manual; *office:* Lakewood HS 14100 Franklin Blvd ood OH 44107*

}, STEPHEN BRIAN, Vice Principal & History Tchr; *b:* Rochester, *l:* Atlantic Union Coll (BA) His, Bus Admin 1984; Working Towards ·s in Schl Admin; *cr:* Maplewood Elem Schl Spec Ed Asst 1991-92; Lancaster Acad His Tchr 1992-, Vice-Prin 1995-; *ai:* NHS, ated Stu Body Ofcrs Spon; Dir Stu Mem Gospel Singing Group; , Natl Assn of Stu Act Advs 1995-; NCSS 1994-; *office:* South ster Acad George Hill Rd South Lancaster MA 01561*

PLY, ROBERT LE ROY,JR., Reading & Language Arts Tchr; *b:* ıs, OH; *m:* Sandra Mc Graw; *c:* Jason, Jennifer, Judson; *ed:* OH St BS) Elem Ed 1977; Post-Grad Hrs TESA, Motivating Stdnts, I Can *cr:* Buckeye Cntrl Schls 6th Grd Tchr 1977-78; Bucyrus MS 6th Grd Math Tchr 1978-79, Sci, Math Tchr 1980-; *ai:* Stu Cncl, Drug ation Adv; NEA, OEA, BEA 1977-; OH MS Assn 1991-; Natl ·rs Assn 1992-; OH Speakers Forum 1992; First Presbyn Church Elder; Amer Legion 1978-; *office:* Bucyrus MS 245 Woodlawn Ave ıs OH 44820*

, SANDRA, Retired 12th Grd English Tchr; *b:* Akron, OH; *m:* y A.; *ed:* Jackson Jr Coll (AA) Eng & His 1961; the Univ of Akron Eng & His 1965; Post Grad Stud in Eng Childrens Lit & Rdng Akron *cr:* Barberton HS Soc Stud Tchr 1965; UL Light Jr High Eng Tchr 34; Barberton HS Eng Tchr 1984-; *ai:* Adv for Acad Decathlon & Challenge Teams; Barberton Ed Assn 1970-, Sec; OH Ed Assn, NEA Martha Holden Jennings Scholar; BHS Tchr of Yr 1991-92.

D, FRANK A., Teacher; *b:* Philadelphia, PA; *m:* Virginia K.; *c:* on, Sean; *ed:* BA & 30 Addl Credit Hrs; *cr:* Southern Regnl HS ced Placement Amer His & Psych Tchr 1968-; *ai:* Frosh Bsktbl ; NEA & NJEA 1968-; Governors Tchr Recognition Awd; *office:* ern Regional HS 600 N Main St Manahawkin NJ 08050

D, H. A. SKIP, Business Teacher; *b:* Union City, PA; *m:* Debora *c:* Adrianne Linnea, Deven Bradley, Alissa Lauralee; *ed:* Clarion BS) Bus Admin 1977; 45 Addl Credit Hrs; Mercyhurst Coll Acctng, Tech Bus Ed Cert 1993; *cr:* Corry Area HS Bus Tchr 1993-; *ai:* Head Vlybl, Asst Boys Wrestling Coach 1993-95; Head Coach Boys Golf ; *office:* Corry Area HS 534 E Pleasant St Corry PA 16407

D, LOUIS CALVIN,JR., MS Social Studies Teacher; *b:* Baltimore, *ed:* Univ of MD (JD) Law 1989; *cr:* Baltimore City Pub Schls Tchr ; *office:* Hazelwood Elem Schl 4517 Hazelwood Ave Baltimore MD

D, SUSAN DIANA, Sociology Instr; *b:* Youngstown, OH; *ed:* gstown St Univ)BA) Sociology 1985, (MSEd) Cnslng 1991; Licensed Cnslr Credentialed 1994; Completed Post Grad Prgm 1995; *cr:* gstown St Univ Sociology Instr Limited Svc 1991-; *ai:* Stud Skills ; Independent Tutor HS & Coll; Market St Merchants Assn 1985-, ng Hands; *office:* Youngstown St Univ 410 Wick Ave Youngstown OH *

D, TIM H., English Instructor; *b:* Richmond, IN; *m:* Robin Smith; *c:* e, Mallory; *ed:* Bowling Green St Univ (BS) Eng Ed 1984; *cr:* wood HS Eng Instr 12 Yrs; *ai:* Yrbk & Sr Class Adv; Var Golf Coach; Inservice Comm; Northwood Local Tchrs Assn 1984-; OCTELA ; *office:* Northwood Local Schls 700 Lemoyne Rd Northwood OH *

:SKIE, JILL BRACEY, Teacher of Gifted & Talented; *b:* Nyack, NY; ssandra Lynn; *ed:* St Univ Coll at Oswego (BA) Elem Ed, Art 1969; erkeley Twp Schls 1st Grd Tchr 1969-70; East Brunswick Pub Schls 3rd Tchr 1970-78, 1990-91, 3rd Grd Tchr 1978-85, 5th Grd Tchr 89, 5th, 7th Grd GATE Tchr 1989-90, 3rd, 5th, 7th Grd GATE Tchr 93, 3rd-5th Grd GATE Tchr 1993-; *ai:* NEA 1969-.

:UNESSE, CHARLES ALLEN, Director Dept of Psychology; *b:* psburg, NJ; *m:* Constance Minorics; *c:* Seth, Amber; *ed:* Univ of MO lla (BS) Engrng Mgmt 1971; Univ of MO at Columbia (MED) Cnslng (PHD) Cnslng Psych 1979; *cr:* Fruin-Colnon Corp Sales Trainee -72; SW Bell Co Mgr Commercial Dept 1972-75; Coll Misericordia Full Prof 1979-; *ai:* Psi Chi Adv; Lbrl Arts Core Review Comm ; Amer Psychological 1988-; Tchng of Psych of APA 1988-; PA ological Assn 1995-; Tchr of Yr 1991; Several Articles Pub; Regnl & Conf Presentations; *office:* Coll Misericordia 301 Lake St Dallas PA 2*

)IE, DONNA RANAE HERK, High School Business Teacher; *b:* , MA; *m:* Jeffrey; *ed:* Bryant Coll (BA) Bus Mngmt 1991; Amer Intnl (MED) Scndry Ed 1995; *cr:* Athol HS Bus Tchr 1994-; *ai:* Coach Var yball, Sftbl, Western Mass Jr Olympics Vlybl, Summer League Bsktbl ; *office:* Athol HS 2363 Main St Athol MA 01331

)IE, JOHN WALTER, English Teacher; *b:* Burlington, VT; *m:* erine Brown; *c:* Jack, Daniel; *ed:* Univ of VT (BA) Eng 1972; SUNY ony Brook (MA) Eng 1974; Addl 15 Hrs Post Grad Stud; *cr:* Univ of ıstr 1976-78; Stevens HS Tchr 1980-; *ai:* VP of Ed Assn; NEA 1980-, VT Adaptive Ski Prgm 1995-; IBK 1972; Corse Flwshp 1972; *office:* ens HS 175 Broad St Claremont NH 03743

ATOSH, DEBRA, Spanish Teacher; *b:* Savannah, GA; *ed:* Kutztown (MA) Ed 1982; Studying PA Ger; *cr:* South Mountain Jr HS Span 1977-82; Dodd Elem Schl Span Tchr 1977-79; MOS 1980-83; Dieruff pan Tchr 1982-83; Allen HS Span, ESL Tchr 1983-; Muhlenburg Elem Span Tchr 1992-94; *ai:* Class Adv 1987, 1990-91, 1995; NEA, AEA -; *office:* Wm Allen HS 17th & Linden Sts Allentown PA 18104*

:E, ALBERT CLARK,JR., Science Teacher; *b:* Jacksonville, FL; *m:* on Whittier; *c:* Stephen, Jennifer Clukey; *ed:* Keene St Coll (BEd) Sci, 1964; Purdue Univ (MS) Chem 1969; MT St Univ Radioisotope n; Univ of NH Math & Physics; *cr:* Salem HS Sci Dept Chm 1971-85, n Tchr 1964-71, 85-; *ai:* Schl Dist Tech Day Comm; Cmptr Assisted Comm; Strategic Planning Comm; NEA 1985-; NH Ed Assn 1985-, 1990; Salem Ed Assn 1985-, Pres 1987-90; Hamstead Fire Dept -91, Pres 1973; Hampstead Schl Bd 1974077; Hampstead Budget m 1978-91; Salem Ed Assn Tchr of Yr 1988; Tchr Idea & Information Exchange Article Pub 1989; Local & St Instructional Convention Chm 1989; *office:* Salem HS 44 Geremonty Dr Salem NH 03079*

LAKE, AMY, Social Studies Teacher; *ed:* Southern CT St Univ (BS) Social Work 1981; (MS) Libr Sci 1992; Central CT St Univ Cert His, Soc Stud 1988; *cr:* Wilderness Schl Instr, Outdoor Ed 1980-82; Southeast Schl Ctr for Alterntive Learning Tchr 1982-86; Lee H. Kellogg Schl Soc Stud Tchr 1988-; *ai:* MS Team; 8th Grd, Stu Cncl Adv; NEA 1988-; CT Cncl Soc Stud 1989-; Coalition for Peace, Justice 1989-; Co-Chair; Town Democratic Comm 1991-, Co-Chair; Taconic Learning Ctr 1992-, Advy Bd; Kezai Koho Ctr Flwshp; Outstdng Prgms for Spec Ed; Travel Flwshp to U.S.S.R.; *office:* Lee H. Kellogg School 47 Main St Falls Village CT 06031*

LAKE, BECKY BRENDA, Science Teacher; *b:* Wilmington, DE; *m:* Gary Richard Sr.; *c:* Gary Jr., Desiree; *ed:* Towson St Univ (BS) Bio 1980; 15 Hrs Wilmington Coll; 18 Hrs Univ of DE; *cr:* Harve de Grace MS Sci Tchr 1980-81; North Wast HS Sci Tchr 1981-; *ai:* NEA, MSTA 1980-; CCCTA 1981-; Marylander Awd Yrbk Adv 1989; Yrbks 1st Place 1986-89 Awds; *office:* North East HS 300 Irishtown Rd North East MD 21901

LAKE, CHRISTOPHER JOHN, Language Arts Teacher; *b:* Susquehanna, PA; *ed:* Univ of Scranton (BS) Ed, Comm 1988, (MS) Sec Ed 1996; *cr:* Mountain View HS Tchr 1988-; Luzerne Comm Coll Prof 1992-; *ai:* Drama Club, Yrbk, Class Adv; Spec Events Dir; NEA, PSEA, MVEA 1988-; Alpha Sigma Nu 1988-; Who's Who Among Coll, Univ Stdnts; Keystone Integrated Framework Grant PA; *office:* Mountain View HS RR 1 Box 339 Kingsley PA 18826*

LAKE, DONNA HOUCHIN, Kindergarten Teacher; *b:* Jeffersonville, IN; *m:* John M. III; *c:* Stephen Battersby, Melissa Cronhardt, Jennifer; *ed:* Glassboro St Coll (BA) Elem Ed 1967; *cr:* Field Street Schl Kndgtn Tchr 1967-69, First Grd Tchr 1970-82; Lafayette Pershing Schl First Grd Tchr 1982-84; PW Carleton Schl Fourth-Fifth Grd Basic Skills Tchr 1986-94; Lafayette Pershing Schl Kndgtn Tchr 1994-; *ai:* Xmas Prgm Coord; Pupil Assistance Comm; NJEA, NEA, PGCP Tchrs Assn 1967-; Chptr 2 Block Grant; compiled Homework Tips Booklet; Initiated, Coordinated Holiste Scoring Writing Evaluations 4th-5th Grd Schl; *office:* Lafayette-Pershing Schl Shell Rd Penns Grove NJ 08069*

LAKE, JANICE JONES, Language Arts Teacher; *b:* Princeton, NC; *m:* William L. Sr.; *c:* William Jr., Jennifer; *ed:* Fayetteville St Univ (BA) Eng 1974; Salisbury St Univ (MA) Eng & Composition 1988; Attnd Washington Coll; *cr:* North Dorchester MS 7th Grd La Tchr 1974-; Sojourner Douglass Coll Eng Instr 1995-; *ai:* Schl Improvement Team; Discipline Comm; Judge for OM; MSTA 1974-; DE 1974-, Alt Bldg Rep; UMW 1986 VP; Zeta Phi Beta 1973-, Sec; Writing Consultant; Instr for Dimensions of Learning; *home:* 9211 Bayly Rd Cambridge Cambridge MD 21613*

LAKEFIELD, BRADLEY RONALD, Sci, Math & Computer Supvr; *b:* Passaic, NJ; *c:* Scott; *ed:* Montclair St Coll (BA) Comprehensive Sci 1968, (MA) Admin & Supervision 1980; 45 Credits Past MA; *cr:* WA Elem Schl Sci Tchr 1968-80; Franklin Elem Schl Sci Tchr 1981-84; Hawthorne HS Chem Tchr & Sci Supvr 1984-87, Supvr of Math, Sci & Comps 1987-; *ai:* Chem Sci League Team & Ecology Club Adv; Prins Supvrs Assn 1984-; NCTE; NCTM; NJ Sci Supvrs Assn; Assn of Math Tchrs of NJ; Hnr Soc of Phi Kappa Pi; Hawthorne Environmental Comm 1988-, Chrpsn; Passaic Cty Solid Waste Advy Comm, Ed Consultant 1991-; North Jersey Amer Chem Soc Edward J Merrill Awd Excl in HS Chem Tchng 1993; Book: Making the Grade in Science 1995; *office:* Hawthorne HS Parmelee Ave Hawthorne NJ 07506*

LAKEFIELD, PAMELA ANN (NOBEL), English Teacher; *b:* Hackensack, NJ; *c:* Scott Michael; *ed:* Montclair St Univ (BA) Scndry Eng Ed 1966; 9 Post Grad Credits; *cr:* Benjamin Franklin Jr HS Eng Tchr 1966-73; Wood-Ridge HS Eng Tchr 1980-82; Rockaway Valley Schl Eng Tchr 1983-86; Dumont HS Eng Tchr 1986-; Fairleigh Dickinson Univ Adjunct Hum Tchr 1992-95; Montclair St Univ Adj Tchr Ed Tchr 1995-; *ai:* Debate Coach; P A, Sports Announcers & Pub Speakers Adv; NEA, NJEA & BCEA 1966-; DEA 1986-; NCTE 1987-; NJCTE 1987-, Membership Chair 1989-91; NJNER 1995-; Hasbrouck Hghts Regionalization Comm 1979-81 & 1991-93; St Josephs Choir 1993-; *office:* Dumond HS 101 New Milford Ave Dumont NJ 07628

LAKES-FALES, MARTA, Voc Coord & Soc Stud Teacher; *b:* Cincinnati, OH; *m:* James F. Jr.; *c:* Jeffre, Jennifer, Jason; *ed:* Barat Coll (BA) His 1970; Xavier Univ (MED) Admin 1971; *cr:* Reading MS Soc Stud Tchr 1971-74; Great Oaks Joint Voc Schl Dist Soc Stud Tchr 1974-78; Turpin HS Voc Coord, Soc Stud Tchr 1978-; *ai:* Occupational Work Experience Coord Assn 1978-, Cncl Mem, Pres, Tchr of Yr SW OH; Cincinnati Art Museum 1993-, Docent; St John Soc Svc Ctr 1990-, Comm Fund Raising; Tchr of Yr; Martha Holden Jennings Fnd Fellow; *office:* Turpin HS 2650 Bartels Rd Cincinnati OH 45244*

LAKI, SAM L., Professor of Economics; *b:* Lanya, Sudan; *m:* Josephine Laura; *c:* Lomoro, Kujang, Lemi; *ed:* Univ of Khartoum (BS) Ag 1979; Reading Univ (MS) Ag Ec 1981; MI St (MA) Ec 1992; *cr:* Dept of Ag Evaluation Office 1978-80; Univ of Juba Adj Prof 1982; Ag Rsrch Corp Economist, Researcher 1983-85; Cntrl St Univ Prof of Ec 1993-; *ai:* AAUP, IWRA 1993-; AAEA 1991-; SSA 1990-; Flwshp Thomasn Fellow Intnl Food Security; Two Grants Rockefellor Ford; 1 Prize; Numerous Articles Pub; Conf Presentations; *office:* Central St Univ Intnl Ctr for Water Resources 207 Mc Lin Wilberforce OH 45384*

LAKTASH, SANDRA SMITH, Vocal Music Dir & Dept Chprsn; *b:* Akron, OH; *m:* Anthony C.; *c:* Michelle, Michael; *ed:* Kent St Univ (BSME) Music Vocal 1970; 24 Addl Hrs; *cr:* Kent St Univ Grad Asst 1970-73; Hyre MS Voc, Gen Music Tchr1977-; *ai:* Music Dept Chprsn; Stu Tchr Adv; Akron Tchrs Assn 1977-; Music Edctrs Natl Conf 1977-, Outstdng Prgrms Awd 1985; Ellet Women's Club 1990-, Spec Prgm Chair; Kids with Voices 1995-, Dir; Theodore J. Presser Fnd Awd Excl Vocal Category 1970; Semi-Finalist Wed Morning Musical Club Intnl Competition WA DC Vocal Category 1972; Schlsp Blossom Festival Schl, Kent St, Blossom Music Ctr 1970; Seasons OH Light Opera Co 1971-72; *office:* Hyre MS 2443 Wedgewood Dr Akron OH 44312

LALLI, BARBARA, Biology & Chemistry Teacher; *b:* Yonkers, NY; *m:* Amedeo; *c:* Rick, Jennifer Germain; *ed:* Hunter Coll of CUNY (BA) Zoology, Physiology 1964; Hunter Coll (MA) Biological Sci 1968; *cr:* Isaac E. Young Jr HS Sci Tchr 1964-66; Arlington HS Sci Tchr 1977-; *ai:* UFT 1977-; STANYS 1990-; *office:* Arlington HS-S Campus 110 Stringham Rd Lagrangeville NY 12540

LALLMAN, JAMES RICHARD, Physics & Mathematics Teacher; *b:* Erie, PA; *ed:* Gannon Univ (BS) Gen Sci, Math 1980; 18 Post Baccalaureate; 18 Grad Credits; *cr:* Cathedral Prep Math Tchr 1980-81; Elk Co Chrstn Sci, Math Tchr 1982-; *ai:* NHS Comm; NCEA 1985-; PSTA 1995-; Stu Achvmt in Physics Cert of Recognition 1990-95; *office:* Elk County Christian HS 600 Maurus St Saint Marys PA 15857

LALLOS, ANN M., First Grade Teacher; *b:* Mineola, NY; *m:* Robert; *c:* Laura, Maureen; *ed:* Queens Coll (BA) Elem Ed, Eng 1965; 30 Post Grad Credits; *cr:* PS 116 4th, 6th Grd Tchr 1965-67; Moriches Elem Schl 1st Grd Tchr 1975-; *ai:* PTO Cncl Playground Comm Former Mem; Cultural Arts Comm Former Chair; AFT, NYSUT 1965-; WFUT 1975-; Suffolk Rdng Cncl 1992-; Church Act; Parent-Schl Partnership Awd 1992; *office:* Moriches Elem Schl Montauk Hwy Moriches NY 11955

LALLY, DEBORAH PICOLLA, Middle School Counselor; *b:* Oneonta, NY; *m:* Thomas; *c:* Ryan, Evan; *ed:* SUNY at Oneonta (BS) Sci Ed 1987; SAGE Coll (MS) Cnslng, Guid 1992; *cr:* Colonie Cntrl Schls HS Sci Tchr 1987-91; Colonie Cntrl Schls 7-12th Grd Cnslr 1991-95; Vernon Verona Sherrill Schls 7-8th Grd Cnslr 1996; *ai:* Class Adv; Vlybl Coach; NYSCAD; NYSUT; Outstdng Achvmt in Guid SAGE Awd 1992; Tchr Appreciation Awd 1990; *office:* Vernon Verona Sherrill MS Rt 31 Verona NY 13478*

LALLY, JOANN ZAIKO, Co-Adj Instr of Surg Nrsng; *b:* Philadelphia, PA; *m:* James F.; *c:* James, Megan; *ed:* Philadelphia Gen Hos Schl of Nrsng (RN) Nrsng 1963; Post Basic Perioperative Nrsng Cert 1985, Holistic Nrsng Cert 1996; *cr:* MA Gen Hosp Staff Nurse 1963-64; Thomas Jefferson Univ Hosp Operating Room Staff Nurse 1964-74, Extracorporial Tech & Head Nurse 1974-85; DE Cty Comm Coll Co-Adj Fac, Surgical Tech & Peerioperative Nrsng 1985-; *ai:* Advy Bd; Surgical Tech Pgm; AORN 1987-, Delegate, Attendee Pres Awd 1995; AHNA 1995-, Delegate; H K Furness Lib 1992-, Vol Bd; *home:* 32 Todmorden Dr Wallingford PA 19086

LALLY, LISA M., Health & Physical Ed Teacher; *b:* Greenwich, CT; *ed:* Southern CT St Coll (BS) PE 1982; Adelphi Univ (MA) Hlth Ed 1989; *cr:* Miller Place HS Hlth & PE Tchr, Coach 1983-; *ai:* Stu Cncl Adv; Var Girls Bsktbl Coach; Womens Lacrosse Officiating; NYSUT, Miller Place TA 1983-; SCWBCA 1986-; AAHE 1989-; Eta Sigma Gamma 1988-; SCWBCA Coach of Yr 1994, 1995; *office:* Miller Place HS 15 Memorial Dr Miller Place NY 11764

LALONDE, JEROME V., Professor of Photography; *b:* Syracuse, NY; *ed:* Syracuse Univ (BA) Fine Arts 1988, (MS) Comm Photography 1992; Addl Post Grad Stud Dept of Fine Arts, Art & Music His; *cr:* Mohawk Vly Comm Coll Photography Asst Prof 1992-; *ai:* Photography Club Adv; Pub Relations Chm; MVCC Prof Assn 1992-; NYSUT, AFT 1992-; NPPA 1986-; ACT-SO 1994-, Judge, Photo Comp; Childrens Museum 1992-, Mentorship Prgm; Coll for Kids 1993-95, Guest Lecturer & Mentor; Fine Scale Model Magazine Pub 1994-95; Reviewer for Several Publications; *office:* Mohawk Valley Comm Coll 1101 Sherman Dr Utica NY 13501*

LALUNA, CAROL ANN, Second Grade Teacher; *b:* Brooklyn, NY; *ed:* St Johns Univ (BS) Elem Ed 1979, (MS) Rdng Specialist 1983; Courses in Whole Lang, Multicultural Ed, Prejudice Reduction, Conflict Resolution for Children & Adults; *cr:* St Gerard Majela 5th-8th Grd Math & Sci Tchr 1979-81; Our Lady of Peace Schl 1st Grd Tchr 1981-86; McVey Schl 1st-2nd Grd Tchr & Educl Advocate for Homeless 1986-; *ai:* Site-Based Mgmt Team Chprsn; Stu Cncl Adv; Educl Advocate for Homeless; Tchr Trainer A World of Difference; NY SUT 1986-; Kappa Delta Pi 1996; New Ground 1990-, Advy Bd; QCPA Pol 1992-, Vice-Chair; *office:* Mc Vey Elem Schl 2201 Devon St East Meadow NY 11554*

LA MACK-LUPO, REBECCA, School Counselor; *b:* Syracuse, NY; *c:* Bria Elizabeth, Eliott Francis; *ed:* St Univ Coll at Oswego (BA) Sociology, Soc Work 1977; St Univ Coll at Oneonta (MS) Cnslr Ed 1985; 27 Addl Grad Hrs Permanet Cert 1988; *cr:* Broome Cty Dept of Soc Svc Child Protective Caseworker 1978-82; NY St Dept of Labor Employment Security Claims Examiner 1982-85; Windsor Cntrl Schl Dist Schl Cnslr 1986-; *ai:* Yrbk Adv; Crisis Team; Windsor Tchrs Assn, NY St United Tchrs 1986-; Amer Cnslng Assn, Broome-Tioga Cnslrs Assn 1987-; Jr League of Binghamton 1990-93; Children & Yth Svcs Cncl 1992-; US Tennis Assn 1988-, League Player; Crime Victims Assistance Ctr 1990-, Hotline Vol; Downtown Singers 1985-; *office:* Windsor MS 213 Main St Windsor NY 13865

LAMADE, MARGARET SYLVIA, First Grade Teacher; *b:* Garfield, NJ; *ed:* Rowan Coll (BA) Elem Ed 1966; *cr:* Winslow Elem Schl First Grd Tchr 1966-; *ai:* First Grd Unit Ldr Spokesperson; Prgm Comm; NEA, NJEA, CCEA, VEA 1966-; Vineland Exch Club Edctr of Yr Awd 1992; *office:* Dr. John H. Winslow Elem Schl 1335 Magnolia Rd Vineland NJ 08360

LAMANNA, RICHARD G., Science Teacher; *ed:* Jersey City St Coll (BA) Ed 1966, (MA) Ed 1969; St Lawrence Univ NSF Grant 1970; Univ of Alabama at Huntsville 1989; *cr:* Paramus HS Honors Bio, Coll Prep Bio & General Sci Tchr 1966-; *ai:* Focus on Sci Newsletter 1992-95; NEA, NJEA 1966-; NJ Sci Tchrs Assn 1992-; William Paterson Coll Scholars Recognition Awd 1992; Mentoring Prgm 1994; *office:* Paramus HS 99 Century Rd Paramus NJ 07652

LAMAR, RONALD WILLIAM, Band Director; *ed:* Temple Univ (BM) Music Ed 1980; PA Dept of Ed (MEQ) Music Ed 1992; *ai:* Jazz, Marching & Concert Band; Chorus; PMEA 1982-; WPEA 1986-; DSEA 1986-; *office:* Penn Wood HS 100 Green Ave Lansdowne PA 19050

LAMARCHE, RUTH RICHARD, 7th Grade Mathematics Teacher; *b:* Cambridge, MA; *m:* Robert; *c:* Michelle, Lisa; *ed:* Univ of MA (BA) Elem Ed 1979; *cr:* Allenstown Elem 7th & 8th Grd Math Tchr 1979-83; Southside Jr HS 7th Grd Math Tchr 1984-; *ai:* Math Curr Comm; NEA 1984-; *office:* Southside Jr HS 140 S Jewett St Manchester NH 03103

LAMARRE, LEO E., Mathematics Teacher; *b:* Woonsocket, RI; *m:* Pauline A. Giard; *c:* Kristen, Gregory; *ed:* RI Coll (BA) Elem Math Ed 1976, (MED) Scndry Math Ed 1980; 4 Credit Hrs in Cmptr Sci; 3 Credit Hrs in Math Ed for Learning Disabled Stdnts; 1 Credit Hr in Career Ed, NSF Prgm of Integrating Math & Sci in Scndry Schls 9 Credits; Clsrm Implementation of NCTM Standers 3 Credits; *cr:* St Thomas Regnl Schl 6th-8th Grd Math & Sci Tchr 1976-78; Woonsocket Jr HS Math Tchr 1978-90; Woonsocket HS Math Tchr 1990-; Adult Edu Tchr; Former GED Tchr; *ai:* Past MathCounts Coach; Past Jr HS Math Club Adv; 9th Grd HS Math Team Vol Coach; Past Jr HS Math Competitions Coord; AFT Woonsocket Tchrs Guild 1978-; RI Math Tchrs Assn & Assn of Math Tchrs of New England 1988-; CT Assn of Math Tchrs 1992-; ASSN of Math Tchrs of MA 1994; NCTM 1995; Woonsocket Call Tchr of Yr; Woonsocket Jr HS Tchr of Yr; Woonsocket Jr HS Service to Youth Awd; Woonsocket Nom for Presidential Awd for Excl in Math & Sci Tchng; *office:* Woonsocket H S 777 Cass Ave Woonsocket RI 02895

LA MASTRO, LOUIS PAUL, Math, Comp & Science Teacher; *b:* Hoboken, NJ; *m:* Paula Pedulla; *c:* Lisa, Valerie; *ed:* Jersey City St Coll (BA) Math 1965, (MA) Rdng Specialist 1966, (MA) Math 1983; 50 Grad Credits Jersey City St Coll 1966-93; 15 Grad Credits Yeshiva Univ 1967-68; 6 Grad Credits City Univ of NY 1968-69, Cath Univ of Amer 1968; 3 Grad Credits St Peters Coll 1990-91; *cr:* North Bergen HS Math & Comp Sci Tchr 1966-; Jersey City St Coll Adj Prof, Math & Comp Sci Tchr 1972-90; *ai:* Stu Cncl, Yrbk, Class Adv; Bowling Coach; AFT 1966-; NCTM 1966-, Pub; Assn Math Tchr NJ 1970-; United Republican Club 1975-; Ft Lee Parking Auth 1985-, Commissioner; Ft Lee Planning Bd 1988-, Vice-Chm; Unico Natl 1990-; Zoning Bd Ft Lee 1995-, Sec; Contributor to Five Math Textbooks & Two Comp Sci Textbooks; Natl Sci Fndtn Grant; Coach of St Champ Bowling Team; Received Prin & Supvr Cert 1977; *office:* North Bergen HS 7417 Kennedy Blvd North Bergen NJ 07047*

LAMB, GERALD E., Mathematics Teacher; *b:* Addison, ME; *m:* Wendy Laurent; *c:* Jeremy, Timothy; *ed:* SUNY at Oswego (BA) Math 1974; Montclair St Coll (MA) Math 1979; Math, Math Ed, Admin Courses; 32 Addl Credit Hrs to Masters; *cr:* Emerson Jr Sr HS Math Tchr 1974-78; Verona HS Math Tchr 1978-89, Dept Chm 1987-89; Livingston HS Math Tchr 1989-; *ai:* Math Team; Competitions Adv; 1987 Tennis Coach of Yr St of NJ; Star Ledger; NEA, NJEA 17 Yrs; AMTNJ 10 Yrs; NCTM 12 Yrs, Speaker 1988-92; Church 1978-, Moderator 1992-, Head Deacon 1989-91;

Little League 1991-93, Coach 1991-95; Presidential Awd Winner 1989; Governors Tchrs Recognition Awd Winner 1988 (Verona); Woodrow Wilson Fellowship in Math 1987; Speaker at Several NCTM & AMTNJ Conferences 1988-; Gov Tchrs Rec Aw Win 1993 (Livngston; *office:* Livingston H S Robert Harp Dr Livingston NJ 07039

LAMB, JAMES THOMAS,III, HS Biology & Physics Tchr; *b:* Balimore, MD; *m:* Deborah Lynn Coulter; *c:* Patrick, Stephen, Caitlin, Brendon; *ed:* Loyola Coll of Baltimore (BS) Bio 1972; Univ of MD (DDS) Dental Surgeon 1976; Towson St Univ (MAT) Scndry Sci 1994; Attnd Walter Reed Hosp Var Courses 1976-78; Univ of NC Othognathic Theory 1977; Univ of PA Dental Ed 1993; Univ of CA Biogenetic Rsrch 1995; *cr:* US Army Dental Corp Capt, Dentist 1976-79; Private Dental Practice Owner, Practitioner 1979-93; Northwestern NS Bio Tchr 1993-94; Edgewood HS Blo, Phy Tchr 1994-; *ai:* Asst Ftbl, Head Lacrosse Coach; Sr Class Adv; SAT Cnslr; NEA, PDK 1994-; *office:* Edgewood HS 2415 Willoughby Beach Rd Edgewood MD 21040*

LAMB, JEANNE CUCUZZA, Family & Consumer Sci Teacher; *b:* Bradford, PA; *m:* Ralph R. Jr.; *c:* Colleen, Emily, Elizabeth; *ed:* Villa Maria Coll (BS) Home Ec Ed 1978; PA Cert; *cr:* North East HS Home Ec Tchr 1978-; *ai:* St, Local, Natl FHA; Sr Class Adv; Sr Magazine Sale; Wrestling Time Kpr; Lifesmarts Team Coach; NEA, PSEA, NEEA 1978-; AAFCS, PAFCS, NWPAFCS; North East Comm Fair Assn 1978-, Dir; Gannon Univ, Alumni Assn 1978-, VP 1994; FHA 1978-, PA Key Adv, Master Adv 1991, Adv of Yr 1990, 1994; Adv Mentor; Articles Pub; *office:* North East HS 1901 Freeport Rd North East PA 16428

LAMB, LARRY LEE, Instructor of Electronics Tech; *b:* Lancaster, OH; *ed:* OH Univ (BS) Electrical Engrng 1972, (MS) Electrical Engrng 1980; *cr:* OH Univ Instr 1985-; *ai:* Radar Endorsement Commercial Radio Telephone License; Advanced Class Amateur Radio License; *home:* 761 S Maple St Lancaster OH 43130

LAMB, LAWRENCE ROBERT, Guidance Counselor; *b:* St Paul, MN; *m:* Carole S. Fischer; *c:* Anthony, Andrew, Alexandra; *ed:* Bowling Green St Univ (BS) Eng Ed 1976; Univ of Dayton (MS) Schl Cnslng 1984; Addl 54 Credit Hrs; *cr:* Indian Riffle Jr HS Tutor, Eng Tchr 1976-83; Kettering Jr HS Eng, Gifted Tchr, OWA Coord, Ath Dir 1983-95; Van Buren Jr HS Guid Cnslr 1994-; Kettering Fairmont HS Guid Cnslr 1995-; *ai:* Career Chprsn; Coaching; NEA, OEA, KEA 1977-; *office:* Kettering Fairmont HS 3301 Shroyer Rd Kettering OH 45429

LAMB, RANDALL GLEN, Director of Bands; *b:* Dayton, OH; *m:* Denise Davis; *c:* Ryan; *ed:* Univ of Dayton (BM) Music Ed 1977; Morehead St Univ (MM) Music Ed 1980; *cr:* Carlisle HS Bands Dir 1977-79; Morehead St Univ Head Grad Asst 1979-80; Newark HS Bands Dir 1980-; *ai:* Marching Band, Jazz Ensemble Dir; OH Music Ed Assn 1977-, Dist Pres, Pres Elect; NEA 1977-; Amer Schl Band Dirs Assn 1994-; Phi Beta MU Band Dirs Honorary 1988-; Newark City Schls Levy Campaign Comm; Newark City Schl Tchr of Yr 1990; Newark Chamber Commerce Pride Builder Awd 1987-88; City of Newark Randall Lamb Day 1989; Nom OH Tchr of Yr 1991; *office:* Newark HS 314 Granville Rd Newark OH 43055

LAMB, SHANNON SCOTT, Biology & General Science Tchr; *b:* Minot, ND; *m:* Bradley John; *c:* Hannah Rose; *ed:* Defiance Coll (BA) Natural Systems 1990; *cr:* Kenton HS General Sci Tchr 1990-91; Stryker Local Schl Bio & General Sci Tchr 1993-; *ai:* Sci Fair Co-Chair; NEA, OEA 1990-; *office:* Stryker Local Schl PO Box 624 Stryker OH 43557

LAMB, WALLACE, 7th Grade Social Studies Tchr; *b:* North Tonawanda, NY; *ed:* St Univ Coll at Buffalo (BS) Elem Ed 1960, (MS) Scndry Ed 1964; Addl 60 Hrs Admin, Supervision; *cr:* Niagara Wheatfield Cntrl Schl Dist Tchr 1960-; *ai:* AFT 1979-; NYSUT 1960-, Field Rep for Negotiations 1970; NW Tchrs Assn 1960-, Pres, Chm of Salary, Negotiations; Tchr of Yr 1984-85; *office:* Niagara Wheatfield Sr HS 2292 Saunders Settlement Rd Sanborn NY 14132

LAMBERT, ANDREA AXILE, Home Economics Teacher; *b:* Providence, RI; *m:* Craig J.; *ed:* Univ of MA (BS) Family & Consumer Scis 1992; Currently Working Toward Masters in Guidance & Counseling at Providence Coll; *cr:* South Kingston HS Home Ec Tchr 1993-94; Smithfield HS Home Ec Tchr 1994-; *ai:* Frosh Class Adv.

LAMBERT, ARTHUR R., Teacher & Department Chairman; *b:* Philadelphia, PA; *m:* Elaine Tallerigo; *c:* Danielle, Torrey; *ed:* IN Univ of PA (BA) Art Ed 1965, (MS) Art Ed 1970; *cr:* Cntrl Cambria SD Elem Art Tchr 1965-67; Westmont Hilltop SD MS Tchr 1967-72; Windber Area SD HS Tchr 1972-; *ai:* Dept Chm Fine Arts, Music, Arts, Home Ec, PE, Tech; Stu Cncl, Jr & Sr Class, Art Club Advs; Var Track Asst Coach; NAEA; Windber Area Ed Assn 1972-, Bd Mem; Rotary 1985-, Pres, Sec; Eureka Coal Heritage Fnd 1993-, Bd Mem; Windber Improvement Assn 1993-95, Pres; Windber Centennial Comm 1992-, Chm; Assoc Artists of Pittsburgh Mem; Allied Artists of Johnstown; Somerset Historical Soc Demonstrator Papermaker; Marine Du Contricoeur Fr Marine Reinactor; *office:* Windber Area Schl Dist 2301 Graham Ave Windber PA 15963

LAMBERT, CHARLENE JANE, Spanish & French Teacher; *b:* Wilmington, DE; *m:* Cary; *c:* Melanie, Ashley, Meredith, Gregory; *ed:* Thiel Coll (BA) Fr; Cert in Span; 27 Credits Toward Masters in Fr; Studied in Spain, France & Costa Rica; *cr:* Oxford HS Fr Tchr 1986-88; Avon Grove MS Fr & Span Tchr 1988-92; Tatnall Fr & Span Tchr 1992-; *ai:* Frosh Class & Newspaper Adv; Girls Tennis Asst Coach; Prof Dev Comm Chm; Mentor Coord; Prsnl Comm; NAATSP, DECTFL 1992-; Schl Grant to Stud in Costa Rica 1993; Grant for Summer Stud in Puebla Mexico 1996; *office:* The Tatnall Schl 1501 Barley Mill Rd Wilmington DE 19807

LAMBERT, JANET PHILLIPS, Retired 4th Grade Teacher; *b:* Ironton, OH; *m:* Randy M.; *c:* Michael Zane; *ed:* OH Univ (BS) Elem Ed 1969, (MAEd) Elem Ed, Cmptr 1986; 6 Yrs of Coll; *cr:* Decatur-Washington Schls 2nd-3rd Grd Tchr 1964-66; Jefferson Local Schls 3rd Grd Tchr 1966-69; Dawson-Bryant Schls 4th, 6th Grd Tchr 1969-1994; *ai:* DBEA 1969-; OEA, NEA 1966-; Delta Kappa Gamma 1982-, Recording Sec, Treas.

LAMBERT, JAYNE PANETTA, Soc Stud & Sci Teacher; *b:* Philadelphia, PA; *m:* Joseph J. Sr.; *c:* Joseph Jr., Rannie Lambert Kloud, Ruth Lambert Mullin; *ed:* Immaculata Coll (BA) Eng, His 1959; Villanova Univ 6 Credit Hrs Scndry Ed 1960-62; Perm Cert 1962; *cr:* Ridley Schl Dist 8th Grd Eng Tchr 1959-62; Annunciation BUM 6-8 Grd Eng, His Tchr 1981-86; St Pius X 7-8th Grd Church His, Eng Tchr 1987-; *ai:* Stu Cncl Moderator 1988-; Forensics Moderator & Coach 1987-; Optimist Club Oratorical Contests 1987-; NCEA 1981-; DE Co Bd of Realtors 1981-; Middle States Evaluation Comm; *office:* Saint Pius X Schl 204 S Lawrence Rd Broomall PA 19008*

LAMBERT, JOAN WIRTZ, German Teacher; *b:* Norfolk, VA; *m:* Herbert Stanley Jr.; *c:* Stan, Chris; *ed:* WV Univ (BA) Ger & Eng Ed 1964, (MA) Ger & Eng 1969; *cr:* Mannington HS Eng Tchr 1964-65; Mountaineer HS Eng Tchr 1965-66; Northern HS Eng Tchr 1966-68; Southern HS Eng, Creative Writing & Ger I, II, III, IV Tchr 1968-; Garrett Comm Coll Eng, Ger Adjunct Prof 1970-89; *ai:* Ger Exch Prgm; Schl Newspaper; NEA 1964-; MSTA 1966-, Pub Relations Comm; GCTA 1966-, Sec; St Pauls United Meth Church 1966-; Garrett Choral Soc; McDonalds Ray Crock Outstanding Tchr Awd.

LAMBERT, NORMAND LEO,JR., HS Social Studies Teacher; *b:* Fall River, MA; *m:* Sharon Stanfield; *c:* Christina J., Jonathan E.; *ed:* Bridgewater St Coll (BS) Psych, Scndry Ed 1983; George Mason Univ at Fairfax (MA) Indstrl, Orgnl Psych 1990; *cr:* Groveton HS Soc Stud Tchr 1983-85; Friendly HS Soc Stud Tchr 1985-; *ai:* Stu Govt Adv 1985-90; Phi Alpha Theta, Kappa Delta Pi 1982-; *office:* Friendly HS 10000 Allentown Rd Fort Washington MD 20744

LAMBERT, R. MITCH, Chemistry Teacher; *b:* New Martensville, WV; *m:* Darlene Marie Wilson; *c:* Robert, Elizabeth; *ed:* Kent St Univ (BS) Chem 1988, (MA) Curr, Instruction 1995; *cr:* Columbiana Exempted Village HS Chem, Bio, Physics Tchr 1980-90; Manchester HS Chem Tchr 1990-92; Kent Roosevelt HS Chem Tchr 1992-; *ai:* Sr Class Adv 1996; Chess Club Co-Adv; KEA 1992-; *office:* Kent Roosevelt HS 1400 N Mantua St Kent OH 44240

LAMBERT, STEPHEN E., 7th Grade Mathematics Teacher; *b:* Boston, MA; *ed:* Salem St Coll (BS) Math Ed 1975; Lesley Coll at Cambridge (MS) Cmptrs in Ed 1985; 6 Cr Hrs Post-Grad Admin Prin, Supvr Cert; *cr:* St Agnes Schl Grd 7, 8 Math, Sci Tchr 1975-79; Ottoson Jr HS Grd 7, 8 Math Tchr 1979-90; Stoneham MS Grd 7 Math Tchr 1992-93; Lynnfield MS Grd 7 Math Tchr 1990-; *ai:* Math Team Coach; NEA, MTA 1979-; Arlington Ed Assn 1979-, Treas 1981-82; 3 Yr NSF Grant; *home:* 73 Everett St Arlington MA 02174*

LAMBERT, THOMAS J., Professor of Sociology; *b:* St Marys, PA; *m:* JoAnne; *c:* Richard Hoffman; *ed:* Univ of Pittsburgh (BA) Sociology 1968; New School of Soc Rsrch (MA) Socoiology 1970; Univ of CO NSF Stud Anthopology 9 Grad Credits; *cr:* Franciscan Univ Asst Prof of Sociology 1970-73; Sullivan Cty Comm Coll Sociology Prof 1973-; *ai:* Fac Adv Sociology, Philosophy Stud Club; Amer Acad of Arts & Sci 1975-; Amer Sociological Assn 1972-; NEA 1973-; Planning Bd 1980-; Edctr of Yr 1973; SUNY Chancellors Awd Excl in Tchng 1976; Who's Who Intnl Ec 1994; *office:* Sullivan County Comm Coll PO Box 4002 Loch Sheldrake NY 12759*

LAMBERTH, ANDREA M., AP English Teacher; *b:* Youngstown, OH; *m:* Rudy; *c:* Jesse; *ed:* Slippery Rock Univ (BS) Eng 1972; Trenton St Coll (MED) Eng 1978; Attnd Univ of the Arts, Univ of AK & Bloomsberg Univ; *cr:* Woodrow Wilson HS Eng Tchr 1972-79; Trenton St Coll Adjunct Prof 1993; Council Rock HS Eng Tchr 1979-; Asst Cood of Eng Dept 1994-; *ai:* CREA 1979-; Langhorne Planning Commission 1986-; Tchr of Yr 1979; Golden Apple Awd 1991; *office:* Council Rock HS 62 Swamp Rd Newtown PA 18940

LAMBORNE, JOAN CHERNUKA, Mathematics Tchr, Cmptrs Supvr; *b:* Philadelphia, PA; *ed:* LA Salle Univ (BA) Scndry Ed, Math 1976; Trenton St Coll (MED) Math Ed 1980; 18 Grad Credits Beyond MA; *cr:* Centennial Schl Dist 9th-10th Grd Math Tchr 1976-79; Delran HS Math Tchr, Supvr 1979-85; Egg Harbor Twp HS Math, Cmptrs Supvr 1985-; Atlantic Comm Coll Adjunct Tchr 1987-; *ai:* NCTM 1975-; Phi Delta Kappa 1989-; Natl Cncl Supvrs of Math 1992-; Textbook Reviewer; *office:* Egg Harbor Twp HS 24 High School Dr Egg Harbor Townshi NJ 08234

LAMBRECHT, CYNTHIA MARIE, English Teacher; *b:* Toledo, OH; *m:* Paul Andrew; *ed:* Univ of Toledo (MS) Admin 1992; *cr:* Whitmer HS Eng Tchr 1988-; *ai:* Club Adv; Vol Focus Chrstn Flwshp; Phi Delta Kappa 1991-, Newsletter Ed; NEA, OEA 1988-; Aldersgate Church 1990-; Ed Symposium 1993-; Sally May 1st Yr Outstdng Tchr Awd; *office:* Whitmer HS 5601 Clegg Dr Toledo OH 43613*

LAMBRIX, PATRICIA M., 9th Grade English Teacher; *b:* Buffalo, NY; *ed:* SUC at Oswego (BA) Sec Ed, Eng 1974; SUNY at Fredonia (MA) Eng 1982; Addl 60 Hrs Eng, Ed Buffalo St, Univ of Buffalo; *cr:* Lake Shore Cntrl Schls 9th Grd Eng Tchr 1974-76, 7th, 8th Grd Eng Tchr 1976-77, 11th, 12th Grd Eng Tchr 1977-78, 9th Grd Eng Tchr 1978-; *ai:* Privileges Comm; AFT, NYSUT 1977-; NYSEC, NCTE 1981-; ASCD 1984-; Kappa Delta Pi 1973-; LSCTA 1976-, Sec, VP, Pub Relations, Sick Bank Chair; Natl Writer's Project 1989-; Awd NYSUT Ldrshp Awd 1990, Eng Cncl Tchr of Excl 1993; Head Tchr Eng Dept 1979-94; Co-Wrote, Teach Course Team Tchng Other Tchrs; *office:* Lake Shore MS 8855 Erie Rd Angola NY 14006

LAMBROS, MARGO BOURDOSIS, Teacher; *b:* Washington, DC; *m:* Basil; *c:* Stacey Marie, Anne Jeanette; *ed:* Univ of MO at College Park (BA) His 1968; 30 Credit HRS Asian His, ED Courses; *cr:* Laurel Sr HS Tchr 1969-73; Atholton Sr HS Tchr 1982-83; Centennial HS Tchr 1983-; *ai:* Spon Drill Teams, Class of 91, 96; Fac Advy Cncl Mem, Chair; HCEA, MSTA, NEA 1985-; ASCD 1990-; St Demetrios Church 1975-, Parish Cncl, Sec, VP; Washington HS Fac Seminar; Participant Comm MD Hum Cncl; *office:* Centennial HS 4300 Centennial Ln Ellicott City MD 21042

LAMEYER, MATTHEW JON, Instr of Eng as a Second Lang; *b:* Grand Rapids, MI; *m:* Marguerite Ann de Haan; *ed:* Calvin Coll (BA) Eng 1991; 30 Addl Credit Hrs Univ of Southern MS at Hattiesburg; *cr:* Jiao Toug Univ TESL 1991-92; Admiral Farragut 9th-10th Grd Eng Tchr 1992-95; Tianjin CFE TESL 1995-; *ai:* Coaching Running Club; *office:* Tianjin Coll of Finance & Lang Tiaujin P.R China XX 00000

LAMISON, HELEN ELIZABETH, Spanish Teacher; *b:* Washington, DC; *m:* Jeffrey; *ed:* Maria Regina Coll (AA) Span 1976; LeMoyne Coll (BA) Span 1978; Colgate Univ (MAT) Span 1979; *cr:* Durgee Jr HS Span Tchr 1979-85; Baldwinsville HS Span Tchr 1985-88; Goshen HS Span Tchr 1988-; *ai:* Span Club & Class Adv; Renaissance Comm Recognition Ceremony Coord; HS Sunshine Club Rep; Span & Fr NHS Adv; Celestina Chapter; NYSAFLT 1979-; Tchr of Month; *office:* Goshen H S Scotchtown Ave Goshen NY 10924*

LAMKIN, MARCIA L., Frgn Lang Tchr & Dept Chair; *b:* Syracuse, NY; *ed:* Houghton Coll (BA) Fr, Eng 1974; Drew Univ (MPHIL) Eng Lit 1981; SUNY at Brockport (CAS) Ed Admin 1995; Penn St Latin Amer Lit; Brigham Young Univ Elem Ed; SUNY Coll at Brockport Elem Frgn Lang Methods; Daemen Coll Scndry Ed; *cr:* Damen Coll Dir, Comm Skills Ctr 1981-86; Franklinville Cntrl Schls Fr, Eng Writing Tchr 1986-87; Brockport Migrant Ed Project Asst Prin 1995; Oakfield-Alabama Cntrl Fr Lang, Eng Tchr 1987-; *ai:* Fr Club, Class of 96 Adv; Staff Dev Comm; MS Dev Team; ASCD; WNY Frgn Lang Tchrs; CBE Ind Stud Hum Grant 1994; Amer Women Amer Lives Hum Tchrs Inst Grant 1994; Jean-Paul Sartre Flwshp 1993; Rediscovering the Amers Grant Hum Tchrs Inst 1992; *home:* 101 Orchard Ave West Seneca NY 14224*

LAMMERS, HOLLY BIERMANN, Business Vocational Ed Teacher; *b:* Cincinnati, OH; *m:* Charles R.; *c:* Kari, Lauren; *ed:* Univ of Cincinnati (AS) Pre-Bus Ed 1974, (BS) Bus Ed 1976, (MED) Bus, Voc Ed 1977; 6 Post-Grad Quarter Hrs; 15 Post-Grad Semester Hrs Drake Univ; 5 Post-Grad Semester Hrs Seattle Pacific Univ; 1.5 Post-Grad Semester Hrs Miami of OH; *cr:* Forest Park HS Bus Tchr 1977-79; Diamond Oaks CDC Adult Ed Tchr Part-time 1983-84; Univ of Cincinnati Adj Instr Evening; Colerain HS Bus, Voc Ed Tchr 1979-; *ai:* Career Ctr Fair Coord; Career Ctr Recruitment; Stu Bookstore, Bus Profs Amer Adv; Delta Pi Epsilon 1979-; Bus Prof Amer 1980-, Adv; Delta Tau Kappa 1976-; Westminster Presbyn Church 1954-, Chrstn Ed, Centennial Planning Comms; Honorable Mention Insurance Educator of Yr 1993; *office:* Colerain HS Career Ctr 8801 Cheviot Rd Cincinnati OH 45251*

LAMMERT, PENNY J., Physics Teacher; *b:* Chicago, IL; *m:* Joseph M.; *ed:* Raymond Walters Coll U of Cinti (AA) 1975; Miami Univ (BA) Geology 1976; Univ of Cincinnati (MS) Geology 1980; Addl Work PHD Geology; *cr:* Ursuline Acad Earth Sci, Physics Instr 1978-; *ai:* Jr Engrng Tech Soc Coach; Adv VA Theater; NSTA 1980-; Scndry Ed Cncl of OH 1983-; Southern OH Section AAPT 1987-; AAPT; Greater Cincinnati Fnd Grantee; *office:* Ursuline Acad 5535 Pfeiffer Rd Cincinnati OH 45242*

LAMONCHA, CHARMAINE ELLEN (HAWKINS), Fifth Teacher; *b:* Salem, OH; *m:* Criss J.; *ed:* Kent St Univ (BS) Elem 1974; Math in Classroom at Ashland; Tchng Problem Solving a Team Planning, Collaboration at CEU; *cr:* Beaver Loca MS Fifth G 1974-; *ai:* Chrldng Adv; Girls Bsktbl Coach; NEA, OEA 1974- Kappa Gamma 1986-; Jennings Scholar 1990-91; *home:* 135 Columbiana OH 44408

LAMONTAGNE, DAVID LEO, Elementary Health Specialist; Bedford, MA; *m:* Donna Jean Moniz; *c:* Kathryn; *ed:* Norwich Un Hlth Ed 1987; 15 Credit Hrs Certfd Drug Addiction Csnlr; 9 Cre AIDS Prevention Ed Degree; *cr:* Univ of MA at Dartmouth Asst He Coach 1989-; US Marine Corps Sgt Platoon Ldr 1985-93; New Pub Schls 7th Grd Hlth Ed Tchr 1988-91, Elem Hlth Specialist 19 Asst Head Ftbl Coach NCAA; Resource Advs Chm MA Preventi Self-Esteem, Support Group Adv, Facilitator; NEA, MA Tchr Assn Natl Collegiate Ath Assn 1981-; New Bedford Edctr Assn Aca Schlshp 1983; Excl in Tchng Awd 1991; US Marine Corps 6000 C Medal 1993; *office:* New Bedford Pub Schl 455 County St New MA 02740*

LAMONTAGNE, PAUL LEO, Latin Teacher; *b:* Whitinsville, M Barbara Wells; *c:* David, Debra Le Blanc; *ed:* Providence Coll (BA Langs 1960; Worcester St Coll (ME) Ed 1965; World Langs Assu Coll; *cr:* Sutton HS Tchr, Coach Ath Dir 1960-; *ai:* STA, MA Tchr 1960-; MA Frgn Lang Assn 1965-; Natl Fed Intersch Ofcls Contrib Yr 1995; Worcester Umpires Assn Pres, Bill Wickman Meml 19 Hall of Fame 1980; Cntrl MA Field Hockey Ofcl of Yr 1989; SH Svc Awd 1993.*

LAMOREAUX, FRANK C., High School English Teacher; *b:* OH; *m:* Kelly Getz; *c:* Matthew, Jacob; *ed:* Heidelberg Coll (BA Hlth, PE 1980; Attnd Heidelberg Coll, Ashland Univ, Bowling G Univ; *cr:* Garfield Heights City Schls Eng Instr 1980-82; Sene Local Schls Eng, Hlth, PE Tchr 1982-84; Pioneer Joint Voc Sc Comms Tchr 1984-85; Seneca East Local Schls Eng Instr 1986- Class Adv; Head Bsbl Coach; Asst Ftbl Coach; Building Goals OEA, NEA 1980-; SEEA 1982-, VP, Bldg Rep; Attica Summer Ball 1995-; Little League Rep; BPOE 1985-; *office:* Seneca East HS 109 St Attica OH 44807*

LAMOREAUX, KATHLEEN WARNER, English Teacher; *b:* Da NY; *m:* David W.; *c:* Peter, Philip; *ed:* SUNY at Cortland (BA) Eler Fine Arts Conf 1970; Elmira Coll (MED) Rdng Specialist 1979; Cre Corning Comm Coll & Elmira Coll; Eng Cert 1984; *cr:* West Iron Cntrl Schl 1st Grd Tchr & Colebrook Schl Tchr 1970-72; Watkins G 7th-8th Grd Rdng Tchr 1979-84; Watkins Glen HS Scndry Eng Tchr *ai:* Girls Var Swim Team Coach 1985-; Jr Class Adv; Founding M Helpline; Lang Arts Curr Comm; WG Sports Booster Club; Ath C Eng Dept Coord; WG Fac Assn 1979-, Past VP; PTA 1979-; Delta Gamma 1987-; Southern Tier NY SCSOA 1995-, Swim Ofcl; St Espicopal Church 1957-, Jr Warden; American Red Cross 1973-, Summer Swim Pgm Dir; Yrbk Dedication Class of 1988; WGPTA Apperson Heart Edctr of Yr 1990-91; WG Booster Club Coach 1994-95; *office:* Watkins Glen HS 12th St Watkins Glen NY 14891

LAMORTE, DAVID S., Theater Arts Chairman; *b:* Chicago, IL; *m.* Dodge; *ed:* SUNY at Buffalo (BFA) Music Ed 1985, (BFA) Permormance 1985; Montclair St Univ (MA) Music Ed 1992; Credits; *cr:* Paulo Intermediate Schl Orch Tchr, Theater Arts Chair *ai:* Wide Orch, Marching Band, Symphony Orch, HS Band Conduct Music Assn Adjudicator, Festival Chair; AFT, UFT, NYSSMA, 1985-; *office:* Paulo Intermediate Schl 175 455 Huguenot Ave Staten NY 10312

LAMOS, SUSAN MARIE, Biology Teacher; *b:* Weymouth, M Daniel D.; *c:* Barbara, Benjamin; *ed:* Plymouth St (BS) Biologi 1982, (MED) Hlth Ed 1987; *cr:* Pembroke Acad Bio & Hlth Tchr *ai:* Class & Stu Senate Adv; Steering Comm Pembroke Compreh Stans; NEA 1982-; NHSTA 1982-, Bd of Dirs; EAP 1982-, Rep; Fndtn Biotechnology Equipment Grant; Tandy Scholar; *office:* Pe Acad 209 Academy Rd Pembroke NH 03275*

LAMOTHE, RONALD ROBERT, Social Studies Teacher & Co Fitchburg, MA; *m:* Barbara Davis; *c:* Lorene, Lon, Brian; *ed:* Bosto (BS) (EDM) Ed 1965, (CAGS), (ABD) Ed 1989; 60 Credits Plymo Fitchburg St, Univ of Cincinnati 1965-71; *cr:* Wrentham Schls 3-6 PE Tchr 1964-65; Plymouth Schls 7th, 8th Grd Soc Stud Tchr 1965-6 Coll His Instr 1967-68; Anna Maria Coll Pol Sci Instr 1970-71; Lun Schls 9-12th Grd Soc Stud Tchr 1967-95; *ai:* K-12 Summer Soc Stu Stud 1968; K-12 Summer Drug & Family Life Curr Stud 1970; K-1 Advy Cncl 1970-74; 5-12 Summer Career Ed Curr Stud 1977; K-12 Comm 1980-82; 9-12 Hlth Ed Comm 1980-92; 9-12 Soc Stud Summe Stud 1983; John Hancock Fellow 1986-87; Horace Mann Tchr 19 Blakeslee Fellow Clark Univ 1988; Groton Ctr for Arts, Local His F 1987; Groton Ctr for Arts Oral His Project 1988; k-12 Soc Stud 1988-89; Tchrs Ctr for Global Stud Clark Un;vBU Schl of Ed Stu Cn 1963-64; Plymouth Ed Assn VP 1966; Lunenburg Comm Cncl VP 19 Pres 1972-77; Lunenburg Ed Assn pres 1969-71; :eominster Jaycee 1972-74; MA Jaycees VP 1974-75, Regnl Dir 1976-78, Exec Dir 19 Notre Dame HS Ath Dir 1978-79; Stu Act, HS Philosophy Comm 1980-90; Lunenburg Constitutional Bicnetennial Commission 1986-87; Babe Ruth League Pres 1981-95; Lunenburg Citizens Schl VP 1971-95; Lib Trustees Chm 1992-93; NHS 1986-93; Clas 1967-78; Acad Decathalon 1988-93; Schl Newspaper Adv 1967-80; Govt Club 1985-95; Pub Speaking Club 1967-73; Stu Cncl 1965-67; & Asst Var Ftbl Coach 1965-95; 7th & 8th Grd Bsktbl Coach 19 Head Var Bsbl Coach 1982-95; Competitive Class Play Dir 19 1977-78, 1983, 1985, 1989; Drama Club 1965-67; Tchr of Yr 1968, Plymouth Jr HS 1966; Distngd Citizen Awd 1975; Clint Dunigan Aw Ten Regnl Dir in USA 1976; Yrb Dedication 1970, 1978, 1987; NHS of Yr 1984, Citizen of Yr 1989, 1994; Ftbl Hall of Fame Asst Coache 1991; Coach of Yr Babl 1987, 1989, 1994, 1995; *home:* PO Bo Lunenburg MA 01462*

LAMOTTA, VINCE J., Senior English Teacher; *b:* Brooklyn, N Mary; *c:* Vince; *ed:* St Johns (BA) Phil 1962, (MA) Phil 1965; Seto (MA) Sec Ed 1967; 15 Units Eng; *cr:* Don Bosco Prep Tchr 31 Yrs Chm 15 Yrs, Sr Dean 15 Yrs, Vice Prin 3 Yrs; *ai:* Debate Team Asst; 1965-; 25 Yrs of Svc Awd; Sr Dean; *office:* Don Bosco Prep Schl Franklin Tpke Ramsey NJ 07446

LAMOUR, GRACE BAXTER, Science Dept Chairman; *b:* New NY; *m:* Henry; *c:* Jacqueline, Hank, Tiffany; *ed:* Finch Coll (BS) Chem 1961; Fordham Univ (MS) Bio 1974; *cr:* Stevens Acad Bio, Tchr 1967-70; Xavier HS Sci Dept Chm 1970-; *ai:* Med Sci Oesteichthyes Soc, Sci Olympiad Moderator; NY Sci Hons So Journal, Engr Club; NYSSHS 1993- Bd of Governors; Sci Tchrs A NY, NY Bio Tchrs Assn, NSTA 1980-; East Side House Settlement Exec Ofcr; Winter Antiques Show 1994-, Catalogue, Advertising, Chm; *office:* Xavier HS 30 W 16th St New York NY 10011

LAMOUREUX, ARTHUR F.,JR., Director of Athletics; *b:* Boston, *m:* Maureen Guerin; *c:* Nicole D., Arthur; *ed:* Assumption Coll (BA 1967; Univ of Phoenix (MA) Orgnl Mgmt 1995; Attnd CT Coll & P Western Univ; Eastern CT St Eng Ed 1972; *cr:* St Bernard HS At 1967-; *ai:* Ath Dir; NTCE 1967-; NE Cncl Tchrs of Eng 1967-; CT

Eng 1967-; NIAAA 1976-; CAAD 1976-; K of C 1965-, DGK; Awd of Merit; Elks Club Hall of Fame; K of C Hall of Fame; *office:* ernard HS 1593 Norwich New London Tpke Uncasville CT 06382

UREUX, DENISE MARIE, Biology Teacher; *b:* Lowell, MA; *m:* Monique, Michael, Brian, David; *ed:* Emmanuel Coll (BA) Bio eorge Washington Univ (MAT) Ed 1972; Bridgewater St Coll Sci Ed 1985; Attnd Univ MA at Amherst, Univ MA at Dartmouth, Univ; *cr:* Normandin Jr HS Bio Tchr 1972-74; Apponequet Reg HS r 1984-; *ai:* EAFL 1984-; NEA 1984-; Middleboro Tennis Assn Good Sportsmanship Awd; *office:* Apponequet Reg HS 100 d Rd Lakeville MA 02347

E, ANN L. FLICK, Chemistry Teacher; *b:* Cincinnati, OH; *m:* L.; *c:* Cathy, Debbie; *ed:* Edgecliff Coll (BS) Natural Sci 1962; ame Univ (MS) Chem 1967; *cr:* St Ursala Acad Chem, Bio, Physics Tchr 1959-70; Mother of Mercy HS Chem & Physics Tchr 1970-76, chr 1988-; *ai:* JETS Teams & Sci Olympiad Coach; Big & Little Pgm Coord; Amer chemical Soc 1988-; *office:* Mother Of Mercy 36 Werk Rd Cincinnati OH 45211

E, JOHN LAWRENCE, Music Teacher; *b:* Kinnelon, NJ; *m:* Elaine *ed:* Hartt Schl of Music (BM) Music Ed 1979; Attnd Westminster Coll, Cntrl CT Univ & Univ of NH; *cr:* First Church of Christ st 1984-; Morgan Schl Choral Dir 1986-; Clinton Parks & ion Artistic Dir 1989-; *ai:* Musical Theatre Dir; Drama & Jazz Coach; ACDA 1990-; MENC, CMEA 1986-; CMEA Jr HS Chorus tor 1992; Clinton Choral Club Conductor 1986-; Intnl Chamber Festival; *home:* 12 Kenilworth Dr Clinton CT 06413

E, PHILIP ANTHONY, Biology & Chemistry Teacher; *b:* nati, OH; *m:* Laura Kuskowski; *c:* Kathryn Emma; *ed:* OH St Univ ology 1982, (BS) Sci Ed 1986; OSU 20 Hrs Post Grad Work; *cr:* Arlington HS Bio & Chem Tchr 1984-; *ai:* Acad Team & Sci Fair EA 1984-; NSTA 1984-; OSU Young Edctr Awd 1993; *office:* Upper on HS 1650 Ridgeview Rd Columbus OH 43221

E, RICHARD F., Vocal Music Director; *b:* New Castle, PA; *m:* Trickey; *c:* Christian T., Joshua F.; *ed:* Grove City Coll (BM) 1966; Temple Univ (MM) Music His & Lit 1974; Attnd Penn St West Chester Univ & SUNY at Fredonia; *cr:* New Castle Sr HS Dir 1966-67; Upper Perkiomen HS Vocal Music Dir 1967-; *ai:* 1980-, Newsletter Ed 1991-93; MENC & PMEA 1966-; Musikfest & Programming Comms 1988-; Choral Arts Soc of Upper men Valley, Founder, Artistic Dir & Conductor; PA-ACDA ire & Standards Comm Chm; Who's Who in the East Dist Nom; "St the YR" 1993; *office:* Upper Perkiomen H S 2 Walt Rd Pennsburg 73

ERELLI, ROBERT NICHOLAS, Social Studies Dept Chairman; wich, CT; *m:* Barbara Decarolis; *c:* Stacey; *ed:* Cntrl CT St Univ c Sci 1965, (MS) His 1970; Southern CT St Univ 6th Yr Admin & ision 1981; *cr:* Silas Deane Jr HS Tchr 1965-66; Montville HS Tchr 8; Dr C E Murphy Schl Asst Prin 1978-85, Prin 1985-89; Montville Stud Dept Chair, European & Amer His Tchr 1989-; *ai:* Statement ose Comm Chm; NEA 1989-; MEA 1968-; CEA 1989-.

ERT, SHERYL LEVINE, High School Math Teacher; *b:* New York Y; *m:* Howard M.; *c:* Craig L., Brian E., Elyse B.; *ed:* Boston Univ Math 1976; *cr:* Norwood HS Permanent Math Sub 1976; Canton HS nent Math Sub 1977; Brockton HS Math Tchr 1977-84; Sharon HS Tchr 1984-; *ai:* Steering Ten Yr Evaluation, Schlsp, Math Curr Swim Team Coach; Discipline Comm chrprsn; Helped write Sexual ment Policy; Helped form Gay-Straight Alliance Group; NEA, MTA STA 1984-, Bldg Rep; BEA 1977-84, Prin Advy Comm; Hertz y Schl 1985-, Bd; Natl Cancer Soc 1980-, Local Bd; Hadassah Nom Presidential Awd Excl Tchng Scndry Math 1989; Mentor New Invited by Houghton-Mifflin PUblishers Express Ideas Improve try Book; *office:* Sharon HS 180 Pond St Sharon MA 02067*

ING, GREGORY L., Spanish Teacher; *b:* Cincinnati, OH; *m:* Mary *c:* Rebecca; *ed:* Univ of Cincinnati (BA) Span 1988, (BS) Ed MA) Span & Latin Amer Lit 1991; Univ of OR Natl Endowment for Summer Inst 1995; Raymond Walters Coll Foreign Lang Insts 1993 5; Wright St Univ High Schl Span Prgm 1995; *cr:* Univ De nadura Guest Lecturer Foreign Lang Methods 1991; Univ Of nati Span Instr & Editorial Asst Estreno 1989-91; Elder HS Span & nics Tchr 1991-93; Saint Xavier HS AP Span Instr 1993-; *ai:* ur Radio Club & Span Club Moderator; Sr Retreat Adult Ldr; nes Accreditation Steering & Employee Benefits Comms Mem; P, OFLA 1993-; ACTFL 1996-; UC Amateur Radio Club 1980-, Pres tee; Saint Francis & Saint George Hospital 1978-, Vol; *office:* St HS 600 W North Bend Rd Cincinnati OH 45224*

ROPOULOS, PETER J., US & World History Teacher; *b:* Ipswich, : Joann Benirowski; *c:* Sarah, Katie; *ed:* St Anselm Coll (BA) His Salem St Coll (MAT) Amer Stud 1973; 48 Addl Credit Hrs; *cr:* dy Jr HS Soc Stud Tchr 1968-81; Higgins Jr HS Soc Stud Tchr 6; Peabody Veterans Meml HS US & World His Tchr 1986-; *ai:* AFT *office:* Peabody Veterans Memorial H S 485 Lowell St Peabody MA

UTH, JO ANN, English Teacher; *b:* Painesville, OH; *c:* Lindsey s, Dana Stearns; *ed:* OH St Univ (MS) Radio, TV 1972; 45 Credit r PHD in Ed Admin; *cr:* Braintree Jr HS Eng Tchr 1968-70; Braintree g Tchr 1970-71; Chardon HS Eng Tchr 1971-73; Bexley HS Eng Tchr *ai:* NEA; NCTE; Columbus Symphony Orch 1985-, Various s, Sec; Picnic With the Pops 1985-; Jr League of Columbus 1970-, s Offices Held; *office:* Bexley H S 326 S Cassingham Rd Bexley OH

AHAN, ROSEMARY BAK, Accounting Professor; *b:* Watervliet, : John; *c:* Glenn Hitchcock, Gregory Hitchcock, Susan Hitchcock, ohn, Michael, William, Dennis, Mary, Kerry; *ed:* Russell Sage Coll Bus Ed; SUNYA MS Permanent Cert 1970; Siena Coll 21 Cr Hrs g, Finance; *cr:* Windham-Ashland-Jewett Cntrl Schl Tchr 1963-65; Coll Tchr 1974-76; Mildred Elley Bus Schl Fac Supvr 1976-80; ectady Co Comm Coll Assoc Prof 1980-; *ai:* Prof Policies nations & Awds, Readmit Comms; Fac Assn Past Pres; NEA-NY IMA 1990-, VP Mbrshp, Mrktg; Church, Fund Raising Comm, gency Food Pantry Coord; *office:* Schenectady County Comm Coll 78 ngton Ave Schenectady NY 12305*

CASTER, JUDY MARIE (GARLAND), First Grade Teacher; *b:* delpha, PA; *c:* Jennifer Marie, Alisa Marie; *ed:* Bluefield St Coll (BS) Ed 1966; Rowan St Coll Grad Courses; *cr:* Belmont Elem Schl d Grd Tchr 1 Yr; Winslow Twp Schl #2 Kndgtn, First, Third Grd Tchr *ai:* NEA, Winslow Tchrs Assn 1967-; Nation Cncl of Negro Women South Jersey Chptr NCNW 1990-, Publicity Comm; Delta Sigma 1963-; Tchr of Yr Governor's Awd 1996; *office:* Winslow Twp Schl st Ave Cedar Brook NJ 08018

CASTER, MERLA SOZEK, English Teacher; *b:* Central Falls, RI; oward H.; *c:* Shannon, Abbey; *ed:* RI Coll (BA) Eng 1970, (MED) y Ed 1975; *cr:* North Cumberland MS Eng Tchr 1971-85; erland HS Eng Tchr 1985-; *ai:* Blue Ribbon Comm; Cumberland Assn 1970-, Exec Bd; NEA, RI Ed Assn 1970-; ARC Human Rights Comm, Alpha Delta Kappa 1990-; *home:* 280 Abbott Run Valley Rd Cumberland RI 02864*

LANCE, B. TIMOTHY, World His, Geog & Govt Teacher; *b:* Akron, OH; *m:* Teresa M. Pitts; *c:* Shawn, Katherine; *ed:* Univ of Akron (BA) Soc Studies 1971, (MA) His 1978; Attnd OH Wesleyan Univ, Kent St Univ & Syracuse Univ; *cr:* Brunswick HS Wrld His, AP European His, Wrld Geo & Amer Govt Tchr 1971-; *ai:* Faculty Advy, Handbook Chm & Exam in Svc Comms; Stu Govt Adv; Intramurals Bstkbl, vlybl & Ftbl; Debate Club Judge; Brunswick Ed Assn 1971-, Rep; OH Ed Assn, NEA & NEOTA 1971-; NOLPE 1992-; St Vincent DePaul 1993-; SHARE Prgm 1993-; Commentator & Lector 1968-; IDN Dstrbtr 1995-; 1992-93 Tchr of Yr; Sept 1993 Tchr of Month; *office:* Brunswick City Schls 3581 Center Rd Brunswick OH 44212*

LANCTOT, MICHELE MARIE, 6th-8th Grade Science Teacher; *b:* Manchester, NH; *c:* Kyle; *ed:* Notre Dame Coll (BA) Elem Ed 1983; *cr:* Saint Casimir Schl 6th Grd Tchr & 6th-8th Grd Sci Tchr 1983-; *ai:* NEA 1983-; NHSTA 1993-; *office:* St Casimir Schl 456 Union St Manchester NH 03103

LANDAS, NANCYANN HOCKING, English Dept Chair & Teacher; *b:* Warsaw, NY; *m:* Martin F.; *c:* Nyle, Tyler, Brandon, Marquelle; *ed:* Geneseo Coll (BS) Ed 1962; Potsdam Coll (MS) Ed, Eng 1967; Attnd Oswego Coll; *cr:* Niskayuna Cntrl Schl Elem Tchr 1962-63; Indian River Cntrl Schl Jr High Eng, HS Eng Tchr 1963-; *ai:* IREA Exec Cncl; ACIS Travael Abroad Chaperone; Amer Legion Oratorical, VFW Voice of Democracy Spon; NYS United Tchrs 1963-, Soc Pres; AFT, Exec Cncl; North Cntrl Rdng Cncl 1965-, Treas of Founding Org; Civic League, Chair, King & Queen Pageant; St Josephs Parish Cncl, Lector; Brownie Scout, Asst Ldr; Local Tchrs Newsletter Ed; Amer Legion Honoree; Natl Tchrs Educl Awd for Further Stud; *home:* 32546 Belile Rd Philadelphia NY 13673

LANDAU, SHARON ALTHA, Kindergarten Teacher; *b:* Berkeley Springs, WV; *m:* Glenn Charles; *c:* Stephen, Julie; *ed:* Messiah Coll (BA) Elem Ed 1974; 21 Credit Hrs at Bloomsburg Univ; *cr:* Susquehanna Valley Chrstn Acad 2nd-8th Grd Elem Tchr 1974-77; Sunbury Chrstn Acad Kndgtn Tchr 1983-; *office:* Sunbury Christian Acad RR 1 Box 226 Northumberland PA 17857

LANDEFELD, KYLE CARSON, HS Social Studies Teacher; *b:* Silver Spring, MD; *m:* Janet Lynne; *c:* Taylor Nicole; *ed:* Univ of MD (BS) Ed 1991; *cr:* Springbrook HS Soc Stud Tchr 1992-; *ai:* 9th Grd Transition Team; Girls JV Vlybl Coach; Boys Var Vlybl Coach; Peer Mediation Adv; SAT Test Coord; NEA 1992-; *office:* Springbrook HS 201 Valleybrook Dr Silver Spring MD 20901

LANDENBERGER, TIMOTHY HARRY, Tenth Grade Biology Teacher; *b:* Phila, PA; *c:* Hans, Lars; *ed:* Phila Comm Coll (AS) Chem 1971; Millersville St Coll (BS) Ed Bio 1978; PA St Univ (MEd); *cr:* Lee Tire & Rubber Quality Control 1978-79; Milton Hershey Schl Cross Cntry Coach 1979-87, Track Coach 1979-87, Summer Recreation Tchr 1980-89, Sci Instr 1979-; *ai:* Environmental Club; PEA, NEA 1994-; Sierra Club 1992-, Zero Population Growth 1991-; Fellow of Natl Writing Project; Bd Dirs Capital Area Writing Project; Tchr Excl Awd; Nom By Stdnts Thanks to Tchrs Awd Natl; IPAA Boys Class AA St Track Chapmion 1980-82, Cross Cntry 1984-85, ST Runnerups 1984; *office:* Milton Hershey Schl 300 Hotel Rd Senior Hall Hershey PA 17033*

LANDERMAN, DONNA, Instructor of Sociology; *b:* Hartford, CT; *ed:* Hartford Coll for Women (AA) Liberal Arts 1968; Univ of WI (BA) Sociology 1971; Univ of CT (MSW) Comm Org 1981; *cr:* Asnuntuck Comm Tech Coll Sociology Instr 1993-, Criminal Justice Coord 1995-; *ai:* Celebrating Diversity Comm Chair; Amer Sociological Assn 1993-; *office:* Asnuntuck Comm-Tech College 170 Elm St Enfield CT 06082

LANDERS, BERNARD JOSEPH,JR., Music Tchr & Dept Chprsn; *b:* Baltimore, MD; *m:* Gail; *ed:* Comm Coll of Balto (AA) Music 1971; Towson St Coll (BS) Music Ed 1973, (ME) Music Ed 1983; Tolson St Univ ME Music Ed 1983; *cr:* Actor, Entertainer Various Nightclubs, Colls, Concerts 1966-; Lindale Jr HS Music Tchr 1973-75; Guest Lecturer Various Colls, Univ, Schl Bds 1974-; Old Mill Sr HS Music Tchr 1975-; Songwriter, Recording Artist 1976-; Old Mill Sr HS Dept Chprsn of Music 1979-; Essex Comm Coll Nigh Guitar Instr 1986; Anne Arundel Cty Pub Schls Night Guitar Instr 1987; Guest Lecturer Working With Intensity 1994-; *ai:* Mid Sts Evaluation Comm 1978, 1988, 1990, 1992; Easter Seals 1990-94, Helping Hands 1995- Telethon; Released Album: Songs 1994; Maryland Musicians Union, Natl Fdn of Musicians 1976-83; Tchrs Assn of Anne Arundel Cty, MD St Tchrs Assn, NEA 1978-; SESAC Songwriting Licensing Org 1981-; Tree Pub Co 1983-86; R&R Pub Founder, Owner 1989-; Amer Songwriting Festival 7 Awds 1977-80; Jaycees Outstdng Yng Man of Amer 1978, 1983; Big Music Amer Songwriting Contest 1st Pl 1981; Letter from Governor Acknowledging Song: Chesapeake Heaven as an Excl Way to Promote MD 1989; MD Gen Assembly Recognition for Recovery From Accident & Writing Songs for Marylanders to Relate to 1994; Best Solo Entertainer Delmarva Area by Coconut Times Readers' Poll 1995; *home:* 1328 Vanderbilt Rd Bel Air MD 21014

LANDES, PHILIP B., Science Teacher; *b:* Sellersville, PA; *m:* Frances A.; *c:* Sonja Otto, Heidi, Bambi, Joseph, Isaac, Philip; *ed:* Moravian Coll (BA) Bio 1968; West Chester Univ (MED) Scndry Ed 1972; 12 Hrs Post Grad Ed; *cr:* West Chester Henderson HS Sci Tchr 1968-73; Indian Vly Jr HS Sci Tchr 1973-74; Indian Crest MS Sci Tchr 1974-89; Souderton Area HS Sci Tchr 1989-; *ai:* Photography Tech Souderton Area Schl Dist Pub Relations Prgm; SAEA, PSEA, NEA 1968-; PIAA Ofcl Sftbl & Bsbl 1990-; Northern Bucks Church Sftbl League 1979-, Pres, Scribe, VP; *office:* Souderton Area HS 41 N School Ln Souderton PA 18964

LANDIN, KEITH, Technology Teacher; *b:* New York City, NY; *m:* Judith Ann Suter; *ed:* SUNY at Oswego (BS) Tech Ed 1988; 21 Addl Credit Hrs Cntrl CT Univ; *cr:* Hampshire Regnl HS Tech Ed Tchr 1988-90; Sage Park MS Tech Ed Tchr 1990-; *ai:* Outdoor Adventures Club Adv; NEA 1988-; *office:* Sage Park MS 25 Sage Park Rd Windsor CT 06095*

LANDIS, CRAIG STEVEN, Fourth Grade Teacher; *b:* Allentown, PA; *m:* Donna L. Fogle; *c:* Jeremy A., Alison R.; *ed:* Millersville St Coll (BS) Elem Ed 1974, (MS) Elem Ed 1980; Western MD Coll Prin Cert 1989; *cr:* Red Lion Area Schl Dist 2-4th Grd Tchr 1975-; *ai:* NEA, PA St FA 1975-; Phi Delta Kappa 1992-; Consistory St Johns United Church Christ 1990-, Pre-Kndgtn Chm 1991-, Primary Sunday Schl Tchr 1986-; Outstanding Young Educator Red Lion Jaycees 1987; Outstanding Tchr Awd Southcentral PA Joint Cncl Schl Inmprovement 1988; *home:* 425 Bellevue Rd Red Lion PA 17356

LANDIS, ERIC NICHOLS, Civil Engineering Asst Prof; *b:* Milwaukee, WI; *m:* Janette Ann Geenen; *c:* Greta, Audrey; *ed:* Univ of WI at Madison (BS) Civil & Environmental Engrng 1985; Northwestern Univ (PHD) Civil Engrng 1993; *cr:* NW Engrng Consultants PC Staff Engr 1985-89; Northwestern Univ Research Asst 1989-94; Univ of ME Asst Prof 1994-; *ai:* ASCE, ACI; SEM 1992-; ASEE 1995-; US Dept of Ed Fellowship; Numerous Publications in Scientific & Tech Journals; *office:* Univ Of ME 5711 Boardman Hall Orono ME 04469

LANDIS, JOANN CLARK, Teacher; *b:* Sheffield, MA; *m:* Newton C. M.; *c:* Lauren Landis-Guzman; Lissa Landis-Bessette, Clark; *ed:* Greensboro Coll (BA) Spec Ed 1960; LA St Univ (MS) Speech Pathology 1962; Assn Montessori Intnl WA Montessori Inst Diploma Ages 6-12 1989-90; *cr:* Clinic Work Speech Pathology 1960-65; Montessori Schl of Rochester Tchr 1977-; *ai:* Assn Mantessori Intnl; Front Porch Theater Bd; Montessori Schl of Rochester Bd; *home:* 204 Hillary Ln Penfield NY 14526*

LANDIS, JOHN K., Assoc Prof of Comm Design; *b:* Philadelphia, PA; *c:* Alison, Steven; *ed:* Univ of DE (BA) Art 1965, (MA) Design 1969; Marywood Coll Cert of Completion of Grad Credits; Attnd PA St Univ, Westchester Unvi, Univ of Arts, Kutztown Univ; *cr:* Mortimer & Assoc Dir of Visual Comm 1967-70; Kutztown Univ Asso Prof 1970-; *ai:* Alumni Newsletter Ed & Art Dir; Cncl of ASsn of PA St Coll & Univ Fac Rep; Curator Continuring Comm Design Alumni Exhibitions; Supervise Campus Production of Printer Promotional Materials; Amer Inst of Graphic Arts 1984-; Assn of PA St Coll & Univ Faculties 1980-, Chprsn, Pub Relations Comm; Cert of Excl in Tchng & Designated a Commonwealth Tchng Fellow 1974-75; Assn of Non-Traditional Stdnts Awd 1989-90; Summer Courses in Austri 1991, 1993, 1995; Exch Taught at Buckinghamshire Coll 1995; *office:* Kutztown Univ Of PA Communication Design Dept Kutztown PA 19530

LANDIS, JON CHARLES, Chemistry Teacher; *b:* York, PA; *m:* Kimberly Susane; *c:* Kelsie Elizabeth, Zachary Charles; *ed:* PA St Univ (BS) Chem Ed 1992; Pursuing Masters in Chem Ed; *cr:* Red Land HS Chem Tchr 1992-; *ai:* Boys Fresh, Girls Jr Var Soccer & Quizz Bowl Adv Coach; Camelot 1992-; *office:* Red Land HS 560 Fishing Creek Rd Lewisberry PA 17339

LANDIS, LISA SHADOVITZ, Assistant Director; *b:* Boston, MA; *m:* Robert Stephen; *c:* Caleb Matthew; *ed:* Wheelock Coll (BS) Erly Chldhd Ed 1976; Curry Coll (MED)-With Distinction Ed 1993; Cert K-8; PC 101 Cmptr 1 Credit; 3 Credits 219 Photography, Career Voc Assessment Spec Needs Stdnts; *cr:* Temple Beth Elolim Nursery Schl Tchr of 3-4 Yr Olds 1976-77; Newton Corner Day Care Tchr of 2-5 Yr Olds 1977-78; Children's Ctr of Brookline, Greater Boston Tchr, Admin of 3-5 Yr Olds 1979-83; Wellesley Comm Children's Ctr Lead Tchr of 2 Yr Olds 1985-86; Learning Prep Schl Tchr of 2 Yr Olds, Supvr HS Spec Needs Stdnts in Trng 1986-87; Maimonides Tchr of Pre-Schoolers, Kindergarteners 1987-89; Lasell Child Stud Ctr Lead Tchr, Stu SUpvr 1989-; *ai:* Pact, Counsel Single Moms; Supervise Hnr, Stu Tchrs; Taught Prgm Mngmt Course, Stu Seminar; Admin Day Care Support Group, Newton Early Chldhd Assn 1989-; Lead Wkshps Early Chldhd Profs, Weekly Support Group Day Care Workers.*

LANDON, HOBART POWELL, 5th Grade Teacher; *b:* Amelia, OH; *m:* Rosemary Early Wine; *ed:* UC Cons of Music (BA) Radio-TV, Arts 1961; Thomas More Coll (BS) Elem Ed 1973; Xavier Univ (MED) Cons, Admin 1975; 30 Addl Hrs NKU; *cr:* Allison Street Schl 5th Grd Tchr 1973-; *ai:* Just Say No Club; NTA, OEA, NEA 1973-; Amer Radio Relay League 1958-, 25 Yr Pin; Erlanger Bapt Church 1980-; 4 Season Sports Cntry Club 1988-; PTA Lifetime Mem; *office:* Allison Street Schl 4300 Allison St Norwood OH 45212*

LANDON, JUDY ANN, General Music Teacher; *b:* Lorain, OH; *m:* Roger; *c:* Joseph, James, Patricia; *ed:* Mary Manse Coll (BM) Music 1968; Kent St Univ (ME) Higher Ed Admin 1986; *cr:* Custer Gen Music Tchr 1968-69; Western Reserve Local Gen Music Tchr 1969-71; Crestwood Schls Gen Music Tchr 1971-73; Streetsboro Schls Gen Music Tchr 1980-81; Ravenna Schls Gen Music Tchr 1981-; *ai:* NEA 1980-; *home:* 827 Stewart Rd Kent OH 44240*

LANDRY, DAVID E., French Teacher; *b:* Lewiston, ME; *m:* Martha E. Dolloff; *c:* Gerard D., Erika J.; *ed:* Univ of ME at Orono (BS) Fr 1977; *cr:* Boothbay Region HS Fr Tchr 1977-; *ai:* Fr Club Adv; JV & Var Girls Bsktbl, JV & Var Bsbl, Var Sftbl & JV Ftbl; MTA, NEA 1977-; Boothbay Region TA 1977-, Treas, VP, Pres, Grievance Officer, Negotiator; Phi Sigma Iota 1976-; Cmptr Tech & Renaissance Comms; *office:* Boothbay Region H S 156A Townsend Ave Boothbay Harbor ME 04538

LANDRY, JEAN E., Assistant Prof of Art; *b:* Worcester, MA; *c:* Corey Bourassa, Amy Bourassa, Kim Bourassa; *ed:* Plymouth St Coll (BA) Fine Arts 1972; Assumption Coll (MAT) Fine Arts 1984; Notre Dame Coll NH Tchr Cert K-12 1982; *cr:* Notre Dame Coll Art Asst Prof 12 Yrs; *ai:* Stu, Sr Art Show; NH Art Educators Assn 1986-, Chprsn Youth Art Month, Educator of Yr 1989; NH Art Assn 1983-; Scholastic Art Awds 1986-, Site Coord, Juror, Worker; NHAE Excl in Ed, Visual Arts Awd, Juror; NH Outstanding Art Educator 1989; Who's Who Amer Ed; Who's Who in East; *office:* Notre Dame Coll 2321 Elm St Manchester NH 03104*

LANDSMAN, ROBERT ERIC, Sci Rsrch, Bio & Psych Instr; *b:* Indiana, PA; *ed:* Rutgers Coll & Rutgers Univ (BA) Psych 1977; Fairleigh Dickinson Univ at Madison (MA) Psych 1980; Grad Schl, Univ Ctr of CUNY & American Museum of Natural His (MA) Biological Psych 1989, (MPHIL) Biotechs 1989, (PHD) Neuroscience 1990; Attnd Univ of HI at Manoa, Rutgers Inst of Animal Behavior at Newark, Univ of PR at Mayaguez, IN Univ at Bloomington, City Univ of NY, UCLA Schl of Med Brain Rsrch Inst & Dept of Anatomy & Cell Bio; *cr:* Glen Kirk Schl Tchr of Emotionally Disturbed & Neurologically Impaired Stdnts 1978-80; Fairleigh Dickinson Univ Tchr of Grad Statistics 1980; Montclair St Statistics, Experimental & Psychological Psych Instr 1980-82, Spcl Pgms Tchr for Academically Talented 1984-89; Kean St Coll Soc Psych Tchr 1980-84; IN Univ Gen Bio Lab Instr 1982; Hunter Coll Psych Adj Asst Prof 1985-92; Columbia Univ Psych Adj Asst Prof 1986-92; UCLA Statistics & Bio Psych Instr 1991; West Orange HS AP Bio Tchr 1992-93; *ai:* Sci Ed; Scientific Rsrch Coord; Scientific Rsrch Consultant; Mem Exec Comm for Regnl Jr Sci Symposium; Mem Review Bd at NJ Regnl Sci Fair; Midwestern Psychological Assn 1979-; Animal Behavior Soc 1982-; Amer Assn for Advancement of Sci 1985-; NY Acad of Sci 1985-; Sigma Xi 1988-; Soc for Neuroscience 1989-; Montclair Red Cross 1971-73, Yth Adv; Alpha Phi Omega Natl Svc 1974-77, Brother Delta Chptr; Rutgers Stdnts for Cerebral Palsy 1975-77, Pres & Founder; Concerned Stdnts for Cerebral Palsy Newspaper 1975-77, Founder & Ed in Chief; NJ Chptr Concerned Yth for Cerebral Palsy 1975-77, Co-Founder & VP; Equal Opportunity Fund Farleigh Dickinson 1978-80, Vol Tutor; Montclair St Univ Crises Drop In Ctr 1981-; Numerous Articles & Book Chptrs Pub; Numerous Scientific Paper Presentations; Grants: Rutgers Coll Rutgers Univ Deans Fund for Rsrch 1976, Farleigh Dickinson Univ Rsrch Grant-In-Aid 1979 & Deans Grant-In-Aid, Montclair St Coll Schl of Hum & Soc Sci Sloan Fund 1980 & Schl of Math & Natural Scis IM Rsrch 1981, Amer Museum of Natural His Theodore Roosevelt Memrl Rsrch 1983, Montclair St Coll Schl of Hum & Soc Scis IM Rsrch 1987, City Univ of NY Univ Ctr & Grad Schl NIMH Predoctoral Traineeship 1986-87, Montclair St Coll Fac Alumni Assn Grant-In-Aid Rsrch 1981 & 1988, Scientific Rsrch Soc Sigma Xi Grant-In-Aid of Rsrch 1988, City Univ of NY Grad Schl & Univ; *office:* Acad Advancement Sci & Tech 200 Hackensack Ave Hackensack NJ 07601*

LANDY-PEARCE, JUDITH HETMAN, 5th Grade Language Arts Tchr; *b:* Youngstown, OH; *m:* James F. Pearce; *c:* Maureen E. Landy; *ed:* Youngstown St (BA) K-Elem 1974, (MA) Rdng Supv 1982; Prin Cert 1985; Attnd Walsh Univ, Kent St, Ashland Univ, Univ of FL; *cr:* David Elem Schl Tutor 1976-78; Woodside Elem Schl 2nd Grd Tchr 1978-79, 3rd Grd Tchr 1979-92; Austintown MS 5th Grd Tchr 1992-; *ai:* Mahoning Cty Bd of Ed; Hlth Test Book, Course of Stud AIDS Comm; Written, Rdng Competency Course of Stud Comm; Back to Schl Comm 1983-86; Curr Cncl 1993-; Ongoing Report Card Revision; NEA, OEA, NEOEA 18 Yrs; AEA 18 Yrs, Electors Chprsn 4 Yrs, Uniserve 15 Yrs, Treas 1 Yr; IRA, OCIRA 15 Yrs; MUCIRA 15 Yrs, Bd of Dir, Pres; Delta Kappa Gamma 1980-, Chprsn Phoning Comm, Corresponding Sec; St Elizabeth Hosp 1982-83, Mental

Hlth Advy Comm; Mahoning Red Cross Bloodmobile 1985-; Eucharistic Minister 1983-; *office:* Austintown MS 5800 Mahoning Ave Austintown OH 44515*

LANE, AVA-LYNN SONSKY, Art Educator & Dept Chrmn; *b:* Laconia, NH; *m:* Dennis Elton; *c:* Britton Kyle; *ed:* Plymouth St Coll (BS) Art Ed, Soc Sci 1978; 31 Grad Credits Lesley Coll & UN H System Schl for Life Long Learning; *cr:* Freelance Consultant, Very Spec Art Educator 1976-78; Laconia Schl Dist Elem Spec Art 1978-79; Lane Studios Art Educator, Owner, Freelance 1978-91; Goffstown HS Art Educator 1979-, Art Dept Chair 1981-; Kaleidoscope Jewelry Designer,Owner; *ai:* Schl Improvement Comm; Art Club; Art Honors Mentor; Class of 95 Adv, Schl Pride & Moral, Prom; Self Study Stearing Comm for The New England Assn of Schls, Coll, Prin Search Comm; NEA 1978-; GEA 1979-; NHAE 1978-, Pres Elect, Pres, Past Pres Regnl VP 6 Yrs, Art Educator of Month 1988 & 1993; NAEA, NHSCD 1988-; NSCD 1989-; Londonderry Welcome Wagon 1986; Anna Lee Doll Soc 1985-; Night of Arts 1983-, Chprsn 13 Yrs; Friends of Ed; Publication 1992 Art Advocacy Booklet for NH Art Educators & Others Co-author with Janice Van Fleet Sponsored By NH Art Educators Assn; NH Art Educator of Month 1988 & 1993; NH Art Educator of the Yr 1993-94, Pres Elect NH Art Educators Assn 1993-94; NHAEA Pres 1994-95; NHAEA Past Pres 1995-; Art Edctr of Month 1988, 1993; Boston Globe Scholastic Art Awd Bd; *office:* Goffstown Area H S 27 Wallace Rd Goffstown NH 03045*

LANE, BARBARA T., English Teacher; *b:* Somerville, NJ; *ed:* Mt St Mary Coll (BA) Eng 1965; Villanova Univ (MA) Eng 1967; 43 Addl Credits; *cr:* Villanova Frosh Instr 1966-67; *ai:* Adv of Acad Team; Stu Cncl; Panther Pride Selection Comms; NHS Sel Comm; Jets Team Adv; BREA, NJEA, NEA & NCTE; *office:* Bridewater-Raritan HS PO Box 6569 Bridgewater NJ 08807

LANE, DAVID MICHAEL, Technology Education Teacher; *b:* Brockton, MA; *m:* Ann Miller; *c:* Jennifer, Kristen; *ed:* Fitchburg St Coll (BS) Ed 1968, (MS) Ed 1971; 20 Addl Credits; Licensed MA Real Estate Agent, Construction Supvr; *cr:* Uxbridge Pub Schls HS Tchr, Dir 1968-; *ai:* Local Access Television Dir, Studio Mgr; Yrbk, Newspaper Adv; JTPA Summer Prgm Dir; NEA 1972-; MA Tchr Assn 1968-; Uxbridge Tchr Assn 1968-, Pres, VP; TEAM 1970-; Andrews Tech Fnd, Dir; Alumni Recognition Awd 1993; Employee Excl Awds 1989, 1991; Pub Schls Svc Awds 1988, 1993; *office:* Uxbridge HS 62 Capron St Uxbridge MA 01569

LANE, ELLEN R., First Grade Teacher; *b:* Boston, MA; *ed:* Bridgewater St (BS) Elem Ed 1972; Various Credits; *cr:* Randolph Pub Schls K, 1, 3-4th Grd Tchr 1972-; *ai:* Randolph Tchrs Assoc 1972-, Elem Rep; Awded Apple Apple 1990, 1992.

LANE, GARY MICHAEL, English Teacher; *b:* Haverhill, MA; *ed:* Merrimach Coll (BA) Eng 1979; Univ of MA at Boston (MED) Eng Ed 1983; Univ of MA at Lowell (EDD) Eng, Lang Arts 1992; *cr:* Epping HS Eng Tchr 1979-92; Methuen HS Eng Tchr 1992-; *ai:* Project Awareness; MEA Bldg Rep; NCTE 1979-; NEATE 1990-; *office:* Methuen HS 1 Ranger Rd Methuen MA 01844

LANE, KATHY L., Media Generalist; *b:* New York City, NY; *c:* Sarah; *ed:* Univ of NH (BA) Eng Lit 1986; Univ of RI (MLis) Lib, Info Stud 1989; *cr:* Windham Ctr Schl Media Generalist 1986-89; Meml HS Media Generalist 1989-90; Woodbury MS Media Generalist 1990-; *ai:* Local Area Network Users, Facilitate TV Production Groups; Prof Dev Comm; Collaborative Team; Tech Comm; NEA, NH Ed Assn 1990-; NH Educl Media Assn 1989-, Schlsp, Tech Comms; ALA 1995-; Salem Ed Assn 1990-; Amer Assn Schl Librns 1995-; Alpha Delta Kappa 1992-, Publicity Chprsn; Phi Kappa Phi 1989-; Wkshp Presenter N. E. League of MS, NEA, Christa Mc Auliffe Tech Conventions; Article Pub; *office:* Woodbury MS 206 Main St Salem NH 03079

LANE, LINDA D., English Teacher; *b:* Glens Falls, NY; *m:* C. Thomas Ross; *c:* Chad T. Ross; *ed:* Hartwick Coll (BA) Eng Ed 1968; 33 Hrs Post Grad for Permanent NYS Tchng Cert; *cr:* Argyle Cntrl Eng Tchr 1969-70; Cambridge Cntrl Eng Tchr 1970-72; Argyle Cntrl Eng Tchr 1972-; *ai:* Drama Club Adv; *office:* Argyle Central Schl Sheridan St Argyle NY 12809

LANE, MELISSA ANN (KUNZE), High School Art Teacher; *b:* E Brunswick, NJ; *m:* Keith; *ed:* Trenton St Coll (BFA) Graphic Design 1991; *cr:* Chittick Elem Schl Instrl Aid 1992; Churchill Jr HS 8th-9th Grd Art Tchr 1992-93; East Brunswick HS 10th-12th Grd Art Tchr 1993-; *ai:* HS Art, Lit Magazine Club Adv; Natural Helpers Prgm; NEA, NJEA, AENJ 1992-; *office:* East Brunswick HS 380 Cranbury Rd East Brunswick NJ 08816*

LANE, MICHELE J., French Teacher; *b:* Paris, France; *ed:* Hunter Coll (MA) Fr 1968; City Univ of NY (PHD) Fr 1976; (MS) MS Ed & Counseling 1979; 15 Credit Hrs at FLCS; *cr:* Saint Saviour HS Chprsn Lang Dept 1965-76; Stony Brook Univ Fr Lecturer 1973-77; Allentown Coll Fr Asst Prof 1976-79; York Coll Fr Adjunct Asst Prof 1979-; Saint Saviour HS Lang Chprsn 1979-; *ai:* Fr Club Moderator 1979-; Fr Speaking Countries Yearly Trip Coord 1979-; Fac Dev, Recruitment & NHS Comms; Fr NHS Moderator; Amer Division of Fr Acad Palmes 1991-, Chevalier, Chevalier Knighted by Fr Govt; AATF 1979-; NYSAFLT 1986-92; PHD Alumni Assn 1978-, Bd of Dir; Young Amer Press 1993-95, Bd of Dir; Dowling Coll 1990-, Curr Dev Adv; ASCD 1992-; Taking Wkshp in Leadership Dev 1991-; Leadership Dev Grant 1991-; Howard Golding Borough Pres Brooklyn Outstanding Tchr Awd 1990; Video Paris Go Round Cable Casted Premiere 1990; Video Germany The Wall Breaking Through Aired on Television Since 1991; Video Monets Magic Garden Aired on Television since 1989; La Miseau Dous Loeuve d Chietien de Troyes Doctoral Dissertation 1976; *office:* St Saviour HS 588 6th St Brooklyn NY 11215*

LANE, RODGER LEE, Life Science Teacher; *b:* Kittanning, PA; *m:* Tina Marie Brochetti; *c:* Jacob, Joseph, Alexander; *ed:* Clarion Univ (BS) Scndry Ed Gen Sci 1986; 21 Post Grad Hrs Sci Ed; Wilks Coll 3 Post Grad Hrs Sci Ed; Slipper Rock Univ 3 Credits Drug & Alcohol Rehabilitation Prevention; *cr:* Leechburg Schl Dist Sub Tchr 1987; Armstrong Schl Dist Sub Tchr 1987; BASD Scndry Sci Tchr 1987-; *ai:* Soccer & Wrestling Coach; Comm Festival; Ath Fund-Raising Comm Vol; Mem Schlsp & Curr Cncl Comms; PSTA 1986-; PSEA 1987-; NEA 1987-; BEA 1987-; YMCA 1970-; Sci Dept Chm 1992-; Stu Favorite Tchr Runner-Up; New Tchr Mentor; Stu Tchng Pgms Participant; *home:* RR 3 Box 565 Kittanning PA 16201*

LANE, RONALD DALE, Special Education Teacher; *b:* Fort Leonard Wood, MO; *m:* Karen Thomas; *c:* Allison B.; *ed:* Univ of MD (BS) Bus Admin 1973, (MS) Ed 1992; *cr:* 3M Co Sales Rep 1973-77; Cartel Corp VP 1977-78; Metropolitan Bus Machines Inc Pres 1978-90; Springbrook HS Tchr 1992-; *ai:* Asst Ath Dir; Ftbl, Bsbl Coaching Staff; Silver Spring Chamber of Commerce 1978-90, Bd of Dir; Holy Cross Hosp Mens Guild 1980-89, Bd, Asst Treas; Calverton Rec Cncl 1985-, Pres, Cty Pres of Yr 1994; *office:* Springbrook HS 201 Valleybrook Dr Silver Spring MD 20904

LANE PIERCE, DOROTHY K., 6th Grade Teacher; *b:* Cooperstown, NY; *m:* J. Andrew; *c:* Karin Lane, Sarah Lane, Ryan Lane; *ed:* St Univ Coll at Oneonta (BA) Elem Ed & Fr 1969, (MS) Cnslr Ed 1981; *cr:* Margaretville Cntrl Schl Fr Tchr 1969-70; Northville Cntrl Schl 2nd Grd Tchr 1970-72; New Lebanon Cntrl Schl 2nd Grd Tchr 1972-74 Delaware Acad & Cntrl Schl Rdng Tchr & Sub 1974; Delaware Cty Infirmary Soc Worker 1981-83; Broome Developmental Svcs Soc Worker 1981-83 Chenango Forks Cntrl Schl Tchr for Gifted; Chenango Valley Cntrl Schl 6th Grd Tchr 1986-; *ai:* Bldg Ldrshp Team; Friendship Force of Greater Binhamton, Treas; Jr HS Ski Club Adv; Local Poetry & Choral Groups; Many Church Act; Rotary Exchange Host Parent; AFT & NEA 1969-; Binghamton Area Rdng Cncl 1988-, 2nd VP; *office:* Chenango Valley Cntrl Schls 1222 Arterial Hwy Binghamton NY 13901*

LANEY, SHELBY COY, Sixth Grade Teacher; *b:* Chambersburg, PA; *m:* Robert J.; *c:* Melissa J. Tobias, Jennifer Jo Tobias; *ed:* Shippensburg Univ (BA) Elem Ed 1966; Attnd Penn St 6 Credit Hrs, Univ of CO 10 Credit Hrs, Univ of PA 21 Credit Hrs, Univ of CA at Fullerton 6 Credit Hrs Masters Equivalency; *cr:* French Creek Elem 4th Grd Tchr 1966-68; Warwick Elem 5th Grd Tchr 1968-80; OJR MS 6th & 8th Grd Tchr 1980-; *ai:* Schl Newspaper; Schl Play; Schl Yrbk; NEA 1966-; PSEA 1966-; Roberts Ed Assn 1966-, Sec; UCC-St Pauls Church 1975-, Deacon; Pub 2 Childrens Books 1993; *home:* 25 Magnolia Dr Douglassville PA 19518*

LANFEAR, DEWAIN T., English Teacher; *ed:* Boston Coll (BA) Eng 1964; Long Island Univ (MS) Schl Admin 1986; 24 Eng Grad Stud Hrs; 24 Art Grad Stud Hrs; *cr:* US Army Transportation Corps Captain 1967-69; Levittown Pub Schls 7th-12th Grd Eng Tchr 1969-; *ai:* Cross Cntry & Bowling Coach; AFT 1969-; Local Tchr of Yr 1994-95.

LANFREY, JUDITH LEE (WINTERS), Literacy Specialist & Coord; *b:* Muncy Valley, PA; *m:* James F.; *c:* Jill Lynnette Stafford, Jody Lynne Lanfrey-Persson; *ed:* Lock Haven Univ (BSEd) Elem Ed 1965; Bloomsburg Univ (MSEd) Ed 1971; Univ of GA (EDD) Rdng Ed 1975; *cr:* Loyalsock Twp Schl Dist Elem Tchr 1963-66, Sub Tchr 1966-67; Council Rock Schl Dist Elem Tchr 1967-68, Literacy Specialist, Coord 1968-; *ai:* Lanfrey Ed Clinic Co-Owner, Dir, Clinician; NEA, PA St Ed Assn, IRA 1963-; Council Rock Ed Assn 1967-; Keyston St Rdng Assn 1963-, Bd Mem; Bucks Cty Cncl IRA 1967-, Bd Mem, Treas, Pres, Celebrate LIteracy Awd; PA Children's Book Cncl 1990-; IRA Publication; *home:* 35 S Chancellor St Newtown PA 18940

LANG, AMYE ROACHE, Team Ldr & MD Tomorrow Pgm; *b:* Dade City, FL; *m:* Kund Haraldo; *c:* Antony Dyon; *ed:* Talladega Coll (BA) Eng 1967; Johns Hopkins Univ (MS) Admin 1994; Post Grad Stud IL Inst of Tech, Univ of Puget Sound; Grad Stud Univ of the VI; *cr:* White Oak Jr High Eng Tchr 1976-77; Argyle Jr High Rdng Specialist 1977-78; Eastern MS Rdng Specialist 1978-92; Springbrook HS Team Ldr 1992-; *ai:* Breakfast Club Support Group Creator, Spon; Renaissance Leadership Comm; Mentor to Youth Prgm; MCABSE, NABSE 1976-, Pres Elect; MCEA, NEA 1976-; MAPE 1995-; Montgomery Cty Foster Parent Assn 1976-, 15 Yr Svc Awd; Rhema Chrstn Ctr 1986-, Choir Ministry; Montgomery Cty Rec Dept 1978-, Teen Club Coord, Yth Svc Awd; NAACP 1978-, Svc to Youth Awd; MCPS Educl Fnd Inc, Peer Mediation & Conflict Mgmt Grants; Constance Morella Congressional Awd; Cty Cncl Awd; *office:* Springbrook HS 201 Valleybrook Dr Silver Spring MD 20904

LANG, DEBORAH A., Technology Teacher; *b:* Lackawanna, NY; *ed:* SUNY at Buffalo (BSEd) Indstrl Arts Ed 1990; Dowling (MSEd) Spec Ed 1994; Coaching Cert; *cr:* Longwood CSD Tech Tchr 1990-; *ai:* Jr Var Chrldng Coach; Jr HS Sftbl Coach; STEA, NYSTEA, NYSUIT 1990-; *office:* Longwood Jr HS 198 Longwood Rd Middle Island NY 11953

LANG, ERICK JOEL, Music Teacher; *b:* Bethesda, MD; *m:* Staci Yeaman; *ed:* Longwood Coll (BME) Music Ed 1988; Peabody Conservatory of Music (MM) Music 1994; *cr:* Montgomery Cty Pub Schls Music Tchr 1988-; *ai:* Montgomery Cty Jr Honors Chorus; Anne Arundel Cty Junior Honors Chorus; Carroll Cty Junior Honors Chorus; NEA, MENC, MMEA 1988-; MD Music Ed Assn-Clinician; Natl Methodist Church Choir Dir Washington DC; *office:* Damascus HS 25921 Ridge Rd Damascus MD 20872

LANG, JAMES WILLIAM, Chem, Trig & Pre-Calculus Tchr; *b:* Kittanning, PA; *m:* Vickie M. Eastep; *c:* Angela Cravener, James, Brad, Holly, Christopher; *ed:* PA St Univ (BS) Chem 1969, IN Univ of PA (BS) Chem 1969; IN Univ of PA (MS) Chem 1970; 45 Addtl Credit Hrs in Math Cert; 30 Addtl Credit Hrs in Tchr Credentials; *cr:* Hollidaysburg Area Sr HS Chem Tchr 1970-76; PA Dept of AG Chemist 1976-89; Fairway Laboratories Water Test Lab Chemist 1989-93; West Greene HS Chem, Math Tchr 1990-; *ai:* Natl Chem Olympiad; Sci Olympiad; Certified 4-MAT Instr; NHS Comm; Upward Bound Tchr; PSEA, NEA 1970-; Amer Chemical Soc 1990-; PA Jr Acad of Sci 1970-, Judge, Spon Awd; Gideons of Greene Cty 1993-, Sec; Lions Club Schlsp Awd; Sr Awd for Perfec Scholastic Average; Book: Complexes of Molybdenum; Rsrch Decacoordinated Complexes of Molybdenum; *office:* West Greene HS RR 5 Box 36a Waynesburg PA 15370

LANG, JONATHAN, Psychology Professor; *b:* New York City, NY; *ed:* Adelphi Univ (BA) Psych 1969; Queens Coll, CUNY (MA) Physiological Psych 1972; The City Univ of NY (MA) Philosophy 1982, (PHD) Philosophy 1990, (MPhil) Dev Psych 1993; *cr:* Queens Coll Leccturer Psych 1972-76; Brooklyn Coll Adj Asst Prof Philosophy 1983-93; Stevens Inst of Tech Adj Asst Prof Philosophy 1990-; Boro Manhattan Comm Coll Asst Prof Soc Sci 1993-; *ai:* Soc Sci Dept Curr Comm;CUNY Grad Schl Research Comm, Intercultural Stud PHD Planning Comm; Prof Staff Congress 1993-; Amer Philo Assn 1982-; Amer Psych Assn 1995-; Sigma Xi Scientific Research Soc 1972-; CUNY Research Fnd 1993-, Dir, Bd of Dirs; CUNY GSUC Coll Assn 1982-84, Chprsn, Co-chair Bus Affairs 1992-93; Project Dir BMCC Project in Sci, Tech Soc; Aaron Diamond Fnd Planning Grant; Project Dir BMCC Project in Sci, Tech Soc Natl Sci Fnd Natl Endowment for Hum Grant; *office:* Borough of Manhattan Comm Coll Soc Sci Dept N604 199 Chambers St New York NY 10007

LANG, KATHY WEINAUG, 4th Grade Teacher; *b:* Olean, NY; *m:* Richard; *c:* Carrie, Amy Jo; *ed:* Fredonia (BA) Elem Ed 1974; St Bonaventure (MA) ATE 1978; Attnd S Hampton Coll; *cr:* Portville Central Elem Tchr 1974-; *ai:* Curr Dev; Assessment; Staff Dev; Tchr-toTchr Support Group; NYSYT 1974-; Conducted Wrkshp Affective Ed; *office:* Portville Central Schl Elm St Portville NY 14770*

LANG, LOUISE L., 7th Grade Teacher; *b:* Englewood, NJ; *m:* Jay G.; *c:* Paul, Linda Donner, Mark; *ed:* Kean Coll (BS) Georgian Court Coll (MA); NJ St SAC Cert; *cr:* Virgil Grissom Schl 2-6th Grd Tchr; Carl Sandburg HS 7th Grd Sci Tchr; *ai:* Shade Tree Com Manalapan Tup Chm 1991-; Monmouth Cty Shade Tree Commission; OBEA; NJEA; NEA; NJSTA; *office:* Carl Sandburg MS Rt 516 Old Bridge NJ 08857

LANG, PAUL, Social Studies Teacher; *b:* Ithaca, NY; *m:* Janet; *c:* Chris, Beth, Kirsten, Jeff; *ed:* Univ of Buffalo (BA) His, Ed 1970; Attnd SUNY Cortland, Elmira Coll, Coll of St Rose; *cr:* Dryden HS Tch, Coach 1970-; *ai:* Var Bsktbl, Bsbl Coach; Cornell 150's Ftbl Coach; NEA, DFA 1970-; Stonehedges Bd Dirs 1987-; Amer Legion-War Dad 1983-; Dept Chprsn; *office:* Dryden HS Freeville Rd Dryden NY 13053

LANG, SHARON SMITH, Fourth Grade Teacher; *b:* Huntington, WV; *m:* David D.; *c:* Kathryn M. Brock, Jennifer F. Johnson, Shelley R.; *ed:* Marshall Univ (BA) Elem Ed 1965; 20 Hrs Learning Disability; 12 Hrs Math Intrvntn; *cr:* Chesapeake Elem 3rd Grd 1965-66, 4th Grd 1966-68, & 1977-; *ai:* Elem At Risk Group Adv; K-4 Mentor for Tchrs; 4-H Adv 16 Yrs; Farm Bureau Cncl 9 Yrs; BYF Church Leader 3 Yrs, Pianist 25 Yrs; *office:* Chesapeake Elem 10183 CR 1 Chesapeake OH 45619

LANG, WILLIAM FREDERICK, Bus Law, Persnl Fin & Ec Tchr; *b:* Bad Homborg, W Germany; *m:* Carolyn R.; *c:* Kerry Jennifer, Diana Robinson; *ed:* Towson St Univ (BS) Bus, Pol Sci 1976; John Hopkins Univ (MS) Ec 1995; *cr:* C. Milton Wright HS Tchr 1985-; *ai:* Head Boys Vlybl, Swimming Coach; Cty Res Sftbl, Swim Teams; Harford Cty Young Republicans Spon; Harford Cty Crop Walk-A-Thon Chm Jarrettsville UMC 1973-88, Treas; Bel Air UMC 1988-, Stew Comm Chair, Admin Bd; *office:* C Milton Wright HS 1301 N F Green Rd Bel Air MD 21015

LANGAN, ANN KLIMAITIS, Senior English Teacher; *b:* Scran *m:* Michael Francis; *c:* Michael, Brian, Kathleen, James; *ed:* Ma Coll (BA) Eng 1968; Permanent PA Tchr Cert Eng 1972 & Bi Diocese of Scranton Grad 1995; *cr:* South Scranton Jr HS Er 1968-72; Scranton Tech Schl Bio Tchr 1974-76; Bishop Hannan Tchr 1988-; *ai:* EF Cnslr; Yrbk Moderator; NCEA & NCTE 1989 Rosary Folk Group 1990-; Ecumen Chorale 1995-; Natl Sci Fnd G 6 Grad Credits in Ecology at Univ of Scranton 1971-72; *office:* Hannan HS 330 Wyoming Ave Scranton PA 18503

LANGAN, MARTIN JOSEPH, Asst Prin & Physics Teac Brooklyn, NY; *m:* Sandra; *c:* Martin, Mary Beth; *ed:* Manhattan C Physics 1971; Pace Univ (MS) Admin 1978; Polytechnic Univ (M Sci 1980; *cr:* Brooklyn Tech HS Physics Tchr 1972-76; Erasmus Physics Tchr 1976-86, AP, Physics Tchr 1986-; *ai:* Sci Rsrch; S Gateway to Higher Ed Prgm; CSA 1986-; UFT 1973-, Tchr of Yr; U Reserves 1970-, Major; NYS Regents Schlsp; Governor's Comm Aw of Yr; Gateway to Higher Ed Grant; Core Curr Physics; Phys Sci La *office:* Erasmus Hall HS 911 Flatbush Ave Brooklyn NY 11226

LANGAN, PATRICIA, Social Studies Teacher; *b:* Rockville Cen *m:* Seamus Singleton; *ed:* St John's Univ (Ba) His 1993; Working in His; *cr:* Freeport HS Soc Stud Tchr 1994-; *ai:* Stu Mentor; Childr 1995-; Nassau Comm Band 1993-; Irish Northern Aid 1990-; Freeport HS S Brookside Ave Freeport NY 11520

LANGAN, ROBERT MICHAEL, Social Studies Teacher; *b:* Pitts *m:* Jannette Morgan; *ed:* Bucknell Univ (BS) Ed 1975, Wilkes Un Ed 1993; *cr:* Wyoming Area HS Sub, Soc Stud HS 1975-84; Lake HS Soc Stud Tchr 1985-; *ai:* Asst Var Ftbl Coach; NEA, PSEA 197 Citizenship Awd; *office:* Lake Lehman HS Market St Lehman PA

LANGDON, JOAN S., Computer Science Professor; *b:* Marion, Larry L.; *c:* Tomaysa, Yvonne Nichole, Yvette Gabrielle, Heather Danelle Sterling; *ed:* Hampton Univ (BA) Math 1973; Coll of WM (MA) Math Ed 1977, Old Dominion Univ (MS) Cmptr Sci 1985; Th Univ (PHD) Math 1989; *cr:* Rappahannock Comm Coll Instr 1 Hampton Univ Instr, Lecturer 1979-85; The Amer Univ Adj Fac 1 Bowie St Univ Prof 1989-; *ai:* AK Mu Adv; Fac Senate Chair; Review Sub-Comm; Cncl of Univ System Fac; Math, Sci Ed Chan Commission; Policy, Standards Comm; Catalog Comm Sec; ACM NCTM 1989-; IEEE 1992-; Summer Inst Engrng, Cmptr Applicatio NASA, Goddard Grant 1990-; Patricia Roberts Harris Fellow; Fo Awd; Bowie St Univ Admin Intern; *office:* Bowie St Univ 14000 Park Rd Bowie MD 20715

LANGDON, WILLIAM H., Social Studies Teacher; *b:* Philadelph *m:* Linda A. Dey; *c:* Lisa, Kim, William, Danielle; *ed:* West Che Univ (BS) Sec Ed, US His 1970; *cr:* Nottingham Jr HS 7th Grd Ge 1970-78; Nottingham MS 7th Grd Geog, 8th Grd US His Tchr 1 Nottingham HS US His, Amer Govt, Ec Tchr 1982-; *ai:* JV Bsbl NEA, NJEA, MCEA 1970-; NCSS 1995-; Natl & St Coaches Assoc Bsbl; Natl Fed & NJ St Interscholastic Coaches Assoc; Hamilton T Bsbl Assoc 1994-, Exec Bd, Candy Fund Raiser; Wkshp Facilita Staff Dev, Cooperative Learning; Cooperating Tchr 5 Times; Go Awd for Tchng Excl 1995; *office:* Nottingham HS 1055 Klock Hamilton NJ 08619*

LANGE, LINDA DIANE, Lang Arts & Reading Teacher; *b:* El Pa *m:* William; *c:* Stephanie X. Duffy; *ed:* Christian Coll (AA) Elem E Bradley Univ (BA) Elem Ed 1969; Trinity Coll; *cr:* Whittier Schl Tchr 1970-73; Marietta Schl System 2nd Grd Tchr 1976-79; Dwi Schl 1st & 3rd Grd Tchr 1977-79; St Columbia Schl Jr High Tchr *ai:* Patrol Ldr; Tchr Rep for Advy Bd; St Columbias Accreditation NCEA 1979-; Home & Schl Assoc; Andrews NCO Wives Club, Pre *office:* St Columba Schl 7800 Livingston Rd Oxon Hill MD 20745

LANGE, TIMOTHY P., Spanish Teacher; *b:* Albany, NY; *m:* Kimb Alyson; *ed:* Siena Coll (BA) Eng 1981; Univ of NY at Albany (MA 1987, (MS) Admin; *cr:* Columbia High Span Tchr 1981-; *ai:* Va Bsktbl & Var Golf Coach; NYSUT & AFT 1981-; Church Lector NYS Bsbl Umpires Assn 1988-; *office:* Columbia HS Luther R Greenbush NY 12061

LANGELLO, LAURA CIANCI, 7th & 8th Grd Choral Director; Britain, CT; *m:* Lawrence; *c:* Alyss Amanda; *ed:* CCSU (BS) Music Coll of Music (BS) Music 1979; *cr:* Hinsdale Elem Band & Choral Grd 1979-82; Bailey MS Band Dir, Choral Music Dir 1982-; N Comm Coll Music His Tchr 1983-; *ai:* Vocal Music, Marching Coach; CT St Fed of Tchrs 1982-; CMEA, MENC 1984-; *office:* Bai 106 Morgan Ln West Haven CT 06516*

LANGENHOP, LORI ARDS, High School Visual Arts Tchr; *b:* Na OH; *m:* Jerry; *c:* Callan, Laura; *ed:* Bowling Green St Univ (BFA) Grd Art 1979; Working Toward Masters in Art at Saint Francis Col Credit Hrs at Univ of TN; *cr:* Napoleon Area Schls 9th-12th Grd Arts Tchr 1979-; *ai:* Mentor Tchr; Renaissance Prgm Comm; Bld Bd; OAEA, NFA, OEA; *office:* Napoleon HS 701 Briarheath Dr Na OH 43545*

LANGENTHAL, SUZANNE A., 3rd Grade Teacher; *b:* New Yor NY; *m:* Howard; *c:* Sharon Parisl, Steven Langenthal, Jill Weism Paterson St Univ (BA) Elem Ed 1970; L I Univ (MS) Scndry Ed 1972 Spec Ed 1985; 15 Credits Weehawken Writing; 20 Credits Whole La St Francis Cath Schl 2nd Grd Tchr 1968; Deer Park Schls 4-6 Gr 1970; P S 115 3rd Grd Tchr 1985; Deer PK Schls 2-3 Grd Tchr 198 Drama Club; Multi Cult Comm; Whole Lang Rdng; NEA 1970-; Scouts 1952-, 10 Yr Pin.*

LANGER, MARIAN GONGOLA, Assistant Professor of Biolo Wheeling, WV; *m:* Henry L.; *c:* Noah L.; *ed:* West VA Univ (BA) Bi Univ of Pittsburgh (PHD) Anatomy & Cell Bio 1983; *cr:* Schl of Me Univ of Pittsburgh Acts in Anatomy Coord 1985-88; St Francis Co & Cadaver Lab Coord 1989-; Penn St Univ Anatomy P Physiology L 1991; St Francis Coll Asst Prof Bio 1992-; *ai:* Chair Stans & Adm Fac Dev, Mid Sts Stud Group, Safety, Ed Cahair & Registrar A Search Comms; St Joseph's Parish Catechist; Penn Cambria Sch Parent Vol; AAAS, Human Anatomy P Physiology Soc 1992-; PA Tchng Scholars, AAUW 1993-; St Joseph's Parish Cncl 1994-, Pres Hnr Soc Distngd Fac Awd; *office:* Saint Francis Coll Biology Dept L PA 15940*

LANGER, NORBERT JOSEPH,II, German Teacher; *b:* Brookly *m:* Marian Cruger; *ed:* Fordham Univ (BA) Philosphy, Ger 1971; U MA (MA) Ger 1973; Montclair St Coll ESL Cert 1992; 30 Credits B Masters in Ger & Scndry Ed-Pedagogy at Goethe Inst, Fordham Monmouth Coll & Montclair St Coll; *cr:* South Hadley HS Ger & Tchr 1974-75; Park Ridge HS Ger Tchr 1975-; *ai:* AFS Club Adv Amer Partnership Exch Prgm HS Coord; NJ AATG Ger Heritage F Stu Act Coord; AATG 1974-; NEA, NJEA, BCEA, PREA 1975-; St RC Church 1987-, Music Minister-Cantor; Fulbright Summer Fello to Germany 1979; NJ Governor's Tchr Recognition Awd 1986; G Montvale Bus Assn Tchr of Yr 1986; Park Ridge Borough Comm Sv

S Nom for Princeton Prize for Distinguished Scndry Schl Tchng JAATG Duden Awd for Outstanding Ger Tchng 1990; *office:* Park HS 2 Park Ave Park Ridge NJ 07656

ERAK, JACK, English & Theater Teacher; *b:* Utrecht, Netherlands; Leadbeter; *c:* Gretchen, Allison; *ed:* SUNY at Geneseo (BA) Eng MS) Scndry Ed, Eng 1974; Univ of Rochester 18 Addl Credit Hrs; field HS Eng, Theater Tchr 1972-; *ai:* Theatrical Productions, Soc Eng Co-Curricular Project Dir; AIDS Awareness Group Adkv; DS Ed Task Force Mem; AFT, NYSUT 1972-; Penfield Ed Assn Newsletter Ed; Rockefeller Brothers Fund Outstanding Arts or; Natl Endowment for Hum Grant; NY Ed Dept Outstanding Tchr; *office:* Penfield HS High School Dr Penfield NY 14526

FORD, LOUISE WATTS, Biology Teacher; *b:* Birmingham, AL; vard; *c:* Lisa; *ed:* Clark-Atlanta Univ (BS) Bio 1963; SUNY at (MS) Cnslr Ed 1974; *cr:* SUNY at Buffalo Rsrch Asst 1963-67; AB Rsrch Fnd Hlth Sci Dev Ctr Dir 1970-74; SUNY at Buffalo St ath, Sci Enrichment Prgm Tchr 1990-91; SUNY at Buffalo STEP d Bound Tchr, Dir 1992-94; Buffalo Pub Schls Sci Tchr 1967-; *ai:* omm; Friendship Bapt Church Schlsp Chprsn; NEA, Buffalo Tchr 57-; Friendship Bapt Church 1963-, Trustee; Iota Phi Lambda 1974-, es, Woman of Yr; Willowridge Civic Assn 1971-; WNY United Drugs 1993-; *office:* Mc Kinley HS 1500 Elmwood Ave Buffalo 207

LEY, CARMELLA MARY, Psychology Teacher; *b:* Woodbury, NJ; eland Pub Schls 3rd Grd Tchr 1992-93; Vineland HS South Psych 993-; *ai:* Spirit Club, Peer Ed, Project Grad Advs; Eating Disorder t Group Cnslr; NEA, NJEA, CCEA 1992-; Attnd NSF Conf 1995; Vineland HS 2880 E Chestnut Ave Vineland NJ 08360*

LEY, CATHERINE A. NIXON, Mathematics Educator; *b:* on, PA; *m:* Richard E.; *c:* Richard E. Jr., Brenda Robertson, Jeffrey nes D.; *ed:* Coll Misericordia (BS) Chem 1970; Rutgers Univ (MST) d; Bucknell Univ 6 Grad Credits; *cr:* Gate of Heaven Elem 6-8 Grd hr 1963; St Boniface Elem Sci Tchr, Bldg Sci Coord 1965-68; St HS 9-12 Grd Math, Sci Tchr 1968-71; Karamursel HS Math Tchr 2; Stuttgart HS 9-12 Grd Math Tchr 1972-73; Crossland HS Math 1987-90, 9-12 Grd Math, Sci Tchr 1981-, Math Coord 1995-, Instrl ec 1995-; *ai:* Acads Tutoring; Soc Comm Chprsn; PGCEA Bldg Rep; taff Dev Trainer; OEA 1971-72, Pres of Local in Turkey, Sustained or Performance; NEA 1973-, PGCEA Rep, Svc Awd; NCTM 1981-, rn Region Regnl Chair; ADK 1978-83 & 1994-; Pres 1980, Sec, Chaplain; Rose Hill Civic Assn 1979-, VP, Acting Pres; St Rose de Guild 1985-, Chaplain; Alexandria Toastmasters 1975-85, Pres, Sec, Sgt at Arms; NSF Grant to Bucknell Univ 1971, Rutgers Univ 5; MD St Math Tchr 1981; Semifinalist MD Presidential Awd 1986; ov Acad Summer, 1995; *office:* Crossland HS 6901 Temple Hills Rd Hills MD 20748*

LEY, DENISE BLANK, Mathematics Tchr & Dept Head; *b:* urg, MD; *m:* Thomas James; *c:* Tammi Brooke, Jason Thomas; *ed:* urg St Univ (BS) Elem Ed 1984; Masters Degree 1993; MD Math ed; *cr:* Bishop Walsh HS Math & Cmptr Tchr 1985-86; Northern MS d Math Tchr 1986-; *ai:* NCTM 1989-; Md St Tchrs Assn & NEA *home:* 10719 Catherine St NW Frostburg MD 21532

LEY, LESLIE M., Teacher & Coord of Gifted Ed; *b:* Portland, ME; id A.; *c:* Nicholas; *ed:* Univ of WI at Madison (BA) His 1978; Univ thern ME (MS) Gifted Ed 1989; Addl 18 Credit Hrs; *cr:* Freeport ept Interpeter for Hearing Impaired 1984-86; Minot Consolidated ng, Rdng 1986-87; Windham Schl Dept Soc Stud Tchr 1987-89; am Schl Dept Tchr, Coord of Gifted Ed 1989-; *ai:* Yth Lead Comm roup Adv; Bldg Dev Team Mem; Prof Dev Team Chprsn; Steering for Summer Tech Acad Mem; NAGC; NEA; MEA; WEA; MEGAT; dctrs of GAT, HS Mentor Prgm Svc Awds; Article Pub; *office:* am Schl Dept 228 Windham Ctr Rd Windham ME 04062

MAN, JACQUELINE CAPOZUCCA, Literature Teacher; *b:* -Barre, PA; *m:* William J.; *ed:* Marywood Coll (BA) Eng 1992; ng Toward Masters in Educl Counseling; *cr:* Seton Cath HS Tchr *ai:* Dispatch Correspondents; Adventure Club; Sr Class Moderator; ssistance Prgm; NCTE, Kappa Delta Phi 1992-; Natl Ski Patroller *office:* Seton Catholic HS 37 William St Pittston PA 18640

RALL, JAMES E., Business Education Teacher; *b:* Baltimore, MD; nda Abate; *c:* Nicholas, Caroline; *ed:* Gettysburg Coll (BA) Bus 1981; Johns Hopkins Univ Schl of Continuing Stud in Ec Ed; *cr:* Bus VP 1981-88; Liberty HS Tchr 1988-; *ai:* Var Lacrosse Coach; Connection Chm; NEA, MSTA 1988-; *office:* Liberty HS 5855 low Rd Eldersburg MD 21784

ER, CLIFFORD WAYNE, Eighth Grade Math Teacher; *b:* Ware, *d:* Worcester St Coll (BS) Math 1982; *cr:* Quaboag Reg J, Sr HS Tchr 1982-; *ai:* Class Adv 1987, 1990, 1995; Girls Var, Jr Var Bsktbl, Bsbl Coach; NCTM 1996; *office:* Quaboag Regional HS Old West field Rd Warren MA 01083*

ER, ROBERT GLENN, Biology Teacher; *b:* Altoona, PA; *ed:* Univ sburgh (BS) Scndry Ed, Bio 1991; Addl 3 Credit Hrs; *cr:* Northern rd HS Sub Tchr 1991-94; Cntrl HS Sub Tchr 1991-94; Hollidaysburg HS Sub Tchr 1991-94; Bishop Guilfoyle HS Bio Tchr 1994-; *ai:* Stu Moderator; NABT 1992-; *home:* 1281 Old Route 220 S Duncansville 635

GAN, JACK, Sixth Grade Teacher; *b:* Dorchester, PA; *m:* Gena *c:* Michelle, Sean, Kara; *ed:* Boston Coll (BA) His-Cum Laude Boston St (MED) Guidance 1974; 45 Credits Beyond Masters from s Insts; *cr:* Cunningham Jr HS 7th-9th Grd Tchr 1973-75; Charles S MS 6th & 7th Grd Tchr 1975-; *ai:* Milton HS Girls Sftbl Coach; Dir ramurals; Comm on Scheduling & Curr; NEA 1974-; MA Tchrs Assn, Tchrs Assn 1974-; NCSS 1974-; Canton Town Club 1987-; Canton ron Club 1992-, Exec Bd; Canton PTA 1980-; Co-Author Scndry Schl gnition Prgm-Flag of Excl Awd; *office:* Charles S Pierce MS 25 Gile ilton MA 02186

NG, THERESA KAUSEK, English Teacher; *b:* Cleveland, OH; *m:* ond Clark; *c:* Raymond; *ed:* Ursuline Coll (BA) Eng 1973; Cleveland iv 35 Hrs Toward MA; *cr:* North HS Eng Tchr 1973-; *ai:* Acad halon Asst Coach; Frosh Mentoring Prgm; Sunshine Comm; OWA, , NEOA, NEA 24 Yrs; Rock & Roll Hall of Fame 1995-; Museume tural His 1979-; Cleveland Philharmonic Orch Backer 1979-.

OK, MARGUERITE PANEPINTO, Substitute Teacher; *b:* ester, NY; *w:* Michael James (dec); *c:* Rachel, Leah; *ed:* St Catharine l (AS) 1964; Rosary Hill Coll (BA) Elem Ed, Eng 1966; Grad Courses eth Coll, Geneseo St Coll, Brockport St Coll; *cr:* Rochester City 3rd-4th Grd Tchr 1966-69; Northside Elem Schl 5th-6th Grd Tchr 75; St Rita's Schl Lang Arts Tchr, Team Ldr, Chprsn 7th-8th Grd 88; Northeastern Cath Jr HS Lang Arts Tchr, Team Ldr, Chprsn h Grd 1990-93; Our Lady Mercy HS Dev Alumnae Coord 1993-; *ai:* Yrbk, Newspaper Dir; Team Ldr; NEA 1966-75; Alumnae Bd Mercy 993-, Coord; Pultneyville Historical Soc 1981-; St Rita Schl Tchr of 88; Working on Book; *home:* 6994 Lake Ave Williamson NY 14589*

KAU, ALBERT JOHN, Mathematics Teacher; *b:* Nyack, NY; *m:* Ledogar; *ed:* Siena Coll (BS) Math 1963; Hofstra Univ (MS) Ed Stony Brook Univ (MALS) 1976; 15 Addl Credit Hrs Stonybrook; *cr:* US Army 1st Lieutenant 1964-66; Lindenhurst HS Math Tchr 1963-64, 1966-; *ai:* St James Church 6th Grd Rel Ed; AFT, TAL 1966-, Bldg Rep; NYSTM 1995-; Ed, Writer Textbooks; *home:* 9 Green Pl Centereach NY 11720*

LANNEVILLE, MADELEINE LAVOIE, Fourth Grade Teacher; *b:* Fall River, MA; *m:* Paul H. Jr.; *c:* Daniel, Michael, David; *ed:* Bridgewater St (BS) Elem Ed 1968; 18 Post Grad Hrs; *cr:* Chace St Schl 4th Grd Tchr 1968-; *ai:* Lang Arts, Thinking Skills, Parent Vol, POPSAT comms; MTA, NEA 1968-; Golden Apple Awd 1993-95; *office:* Chace Street Elem Schl 538 Chace St Somerset MA 02726

LANNIGAN, GERARD STEPHEN, Social Studies Teacher; *b:* Brooklyn, NY; *m:* Karen O'Neal; *ed:* SUNY at Stony Brook (BA) His 1970, (MA) His Ed 1975; 30 Related Credit Hrs in Ed; *cr:* RC Murphy Jr HS Soc Stud Tchr 1970-; SUNY Visiting Lecturer 1988-; *ai:* Substance Abuse & Sexual Harassment Task Force Dist Comms; Help Comm; Schl Sexual Harassment Task Force; NCSS 1980-; ASCD 1980-; Long Island Cncl on the Soc Stud 1980-; three Village Tchr of the Yr 1986; Golden Galleon Awd 1986; DAR Distngd Tchr of Amer His 1995-96; Numerous Articles Pub; *office:* Robert C Murphy Jr HS 351 Oxhead Rd Stony Brook NY 11790*

LANNING, DAVID E., History Teacher; *b:* Asbury Park, NY; *m:* Jo Ann; *c:* Benjamin, Daniel, Joseph; *ed:* Brockport St (MA) His 1969; 30 Credit Hrs Nazareth Coll at Brockport; *cr:* Fairport HS His Tchr 1969-; *ai:* Head Var Bsbl & Ftbl Coach; Fairport Ed Assn, NYSUT, NFICA 1969-; ABCA 1975-; Challenger Bsbl 1989-, Coach; Ftbl Coach of Yr Sec 5 Class A 1993-94.

LANSING, WARREN DONALD, Fifth Grade Teacher; *b:* Troy, NY; *ed:* Hudson Vly Comm Coll (AAS) Lbrl Arts 1970; Oswego St Coll (BA) Elem Ed 1972; Sage Evening Division; Saint Rose Evening Division; *cr:* Assn of Retarded Children Summer Adult Recreation Pgm Cnslr 1973-; Lansingburgh Schl System Tchr 1973-; *ai:* Choir Concert Assistance; DARE Pgm; Lansingburgh Tchrs Assn 1973-; NY St United Tchrs Assn 1973-; AFT 1973-; PTA Assn of Retarded Children 1973-; Brunswick Presbyn Church 1986-, Communicant Mem; Melrose Fire Dept 1993-, Honorary Mem; Awds: William Davey, PTA Life Mbrshp, PTA Natl Life Mbrshp, De Witt Clinton Masonic for the Lansing Family; Uncle Sam Citizen of Yr; *office:* Lansingburgh Schls 70 110th St Troy NY 12182

LANTOS, STEVE D., Teacher; *b:* Johnstown, PA; *ed:* Tufts Univ (MA) 1988; Univ of MI (BS) 1984; Manhattan Coll Chem Ed Coursework; *cr:* Brookline HS Tchr 1985-; *ai:* ACS 1989-, Chprsn HS Ed Comm; NE AST 1988-; MAST 1990-; *office:* Brookline HS 115 Greenough St Brookline MA 02146

LANTZ, DAVID J.,III, Vocal Music Director; *b:* Flemington, NJ; *m:* Martha; *c:* Trevor, Holly, Amy, David, Emily; *cr:* Morris Cath HS Dir of Music 1978-79; Knowlton Twp Elem K-6th Grd Music Tchr 1979-81; E Stroudsburg HS Dir of Vocal Music 1991-; *ai:* Musical Production & Show Choir Dir; Professional Musician; Menc 1991-; Local 577 AF of M 1975-; ACDA 1995-; Approximately 150 Choral Arrangements & Compositions Pub by Choral Publishers; *home:* HC 1 Box 444 Sciota PA 18354

LANTZ, THOMAS H., Admin Asst & English Instr; *b:* Altoona, PA; *m:* Ricki Burket; *c:* Thomas S., Bradley J.; *ed:* PA St Univ (BS) Ed Eng; IN U of PA (MS) Ed 1975; Admin Cert; *cr:* Claysburg-Kimmel HS Eng Tchr 1968-, Admin Asst 1993-; Penn St Altoona Campus Part-time Eng Instr 1990-; *ai:* Juniata Lodge F&AM, Vly of Altoona, Scottish Rite, Jaffa Temple Altoona 1977-; *office:* Claysburg-Kimmel Jr Sr HS Bedford St Claysburg PA 16625

LANTZER, JEFFREY D., Music Teacher; *b:* Lancaster, PA; *m:* Sharon Fischer; *c:* Elizabeth; *ed:* Mansfield St Coll (BS) Music Ed 1983; Mansfield Univ (MS) Music 1990; *cr:* Galeton Area Schl K-12 Music Tchr, Band, Choral Dir 1987-; *ai:* Vlybl Coach; Stu Assistance Prgm; Comm Drug, Alcohol Task Force; PMEA 1987-; Nom VP PMEA Dist #2; *home:* 133 Germania St Galeton PA 16922*

LANYON, SUSAN WARD, Fourth Grade Teacher; *b:* Fall River, MA; *m:* Kendall C.; *c:* Rebecca, Melissa, Jared; *ed:* Fitchburg St Coll (BS) Elem Ed 1972; 15 Credit Hrs Bridgewater St Coll, Lesley Coll; *cr:* Wiley Schl 1st, 2nd, 4th Grd Tchr 1972-; *ai:* Spelling Prgm, Success Through Accepting Responsibility Mentor Tchr; Fall River Educ Assn 1972-, Golden Apple Awds; MA Teach Assn, NEA 1972-; Deaconate First Cong Church 1968-, Chm; Prudential Comm Church 1992-, Chm; Bogle Street Women's Group 1991-, Vol; Apponequet Boosters Club 1992-, Vol; Tchng Excl Awd Aetna Co; 3 Time Nom Frank Lipis Awd; Eastern Edison Co Grant 1994; Earth Day Awd 1995; *office:* William J. Wiley Schl 2585 N Main St Fall River MA 02720*

LANZA, JOSEPH JOHN, Math & Computer Tchr; *b:* Mc Kees Rocks, PA; *m:* Donna Marie Kozak; *c:* Anthony, Jason; *ed:* IN Univ of PA (MED) Math Ed 1974; St Vincent Coll 15 Hrs of Cmptr Programming Courses; *cr:* Blairsville-Saltsburg Schl Bsktbl Coach 1969-78, Tchr, Math Dept Chair 1969-; Westmoreland Cty CC Instr 1986; Sylvan Learning Ctr Instr 1986-93; 8th Grd Lead Tchr; *ai:* Cmptr Club Spon; Mid Schl Advy, Math Portfolio, Scheduling, Math Comms; Chess Club Sec Inst Support Team; NEA, PSEA, BSEA 1969-; Latrobe Soccer Bossters 1993-; Latrobe Bsktbl Boosters 1994-; *home:* 1255 Maywood Ln Greensburg PA 15601*

LANZA, ROSARIA SALAMONE, Spanish Teacher; *b:* Manhattan, NY; *m:* John Jr.; *ed:* NY Univ (BA) Span Lang & LA Lit 1976, (MA) Frgn Lang Ed 1980; *cr:* St Raymond Acad Span Tchr 1976-82; St Joseph By the Sea Span Sub Tchr 1991; Msgr Farrell HS Span Tchr 1992-; *ai:* Usher Soc & Italian Club Moderator; Extracurricular Chaperone Coord; New Tchrs Mentor; Girl Scouts of Amer 1989-, Troop Ldr, Troop Organizer, Troop & Craft Consultant, Appreciation Pin; *office:* Msgr Farrell HS 2900 Amboy Rd Staten Island NY 10306*

LANZEL, HARRIS J., Instrumental Music Teacher; *b:* Saint Marys, PA; *m:* Judith Olskey; *c:* Sarah, Aaron; *ed:* Mansfield Univ of PA (BS) Music Ed 1968; Northwestern Univ of IL (MM) Music Ed 1972; *cr:* Clarion Univ Summer Clinic Instr 1974-92; Eisenhower HS Instrumental Music Dir 1968-; *ai:* Marching, Jazz Band Dir; PA Music Ed Assn 1968-, Dist 2 Pres, Citation of Excl 1990; PSEA, IAJE 1968-; ASBDA 1977-; Phi Beta Mu 1972-, Nu Chapter Pres 1996-; Warren Concert Assn 1982-, VP 1990-94; 40s Plus Big Band 1987-; Warren Civic Orch 1970-77; Numerous Wkshps & Clinics; Clinician & Lecturer at Ithaca Coll 1990; Eisenhower HS Yrbk Dedication 1990-91; Outstanding Warren Music Tchr by Philomel Club 1992; J Albert Loranger Sr Meml Awd for Excl in Tchng 1993; Numerous Guest Conducting Positions in PA, NY & NM; *office:* Eisenhower Middle HS RD 2 Russell PA 16345

LANZENDORFER, LINDA ANN YINGLING, First Grade Teacher; *b:* Puzzletown, PA; *m:* John Paul; *c:* John Leo, Michael Paul; *ed:* St Francis Coll (BS) Elem Ed 1971; 30 Credit Hrs PA St Univ; Stdnts Asst Prgm; Here's Looking at You 2000; *cr:* Hollidaysburg Cath Schl Second Grd Tchr 1972-75, First Grd Tchr 1975-77; Our Lady of Lourdes Third Grd Tchr 1977-78; St Patrick Schl Third Grd Tchr 1978-81, First Grd Tchr 1981-; *ai:* Instrl Support Team; Mentor; Schl Musicals; NCEA 1971-; Camp Together, Planning Comm, Support Group Ldr; *office:* St Patrick Schl PO Box 400 South St Newry PA 16665

LANZER, MARISA RANDALL, SLD Special Education Teacher; *b:* Alliance, OH; *m:* Curtis W.; *ed:* IN Univ (BA) Spcl Ed 1992; Bowling Green St Univ (BA) SLD & DH; *cr:* Marlington MS Resource Room Tchr & Tutor 1992-94, SLD Tchr & 8th Grd Inclusion 1994-95, SLD Tchr & 6th Grd Inclusion 1995-; Marlboro Migrant Ed 6th-8th Grd Tchr 1994; *ai:* Odyssey of Mind Coach 3 Yrs; Ski Club Adv 1 Yr; Union Ave United Meth Church 1981-; *office:* Marlington MS 10320 Moulin Ave NE Alliance OH 44601

LANZEROTTI, CAROL ANN, Kindergarten Teacher; *b:* Elizabeth, NJ; *m:* Charles; *c:* Lu Ann Wagner, Gerard; *ed:* William Paterson (BA) Elem Tchr 1971; *cr:* Columbus Sch 1st Grd Tcher 1971-75; Jefferson Schl Kndgtn Tchr 1975-; *ai:* NEA, BCEA, NJEA 1971-; Lyndhurst Ed Assn 1971-, Pres; Governors Tchr Recognition Awd 1988; *office:* Jefferson Schl 336 Lake Ave Lyndhurst NJ 07071

LAORIA, GAIL HENTZ, Business Chairperson; *b:* Jersey City, NJ; *m:* Paul; *ed:* Pace Univ (AAS) Secretarial Sci 1972; Montclair St Univ (BA) Bus Ed 1975, (MA) Bus Ed-Magna Cum Laude 1977; Rutgers Univ (EDD) Voc-Tech Ed 1984; *cr:* Union Cath HS Bus Dept Chprsn 1975-79; Roberts Walsh Bus Schl Dean 1979-89; H Frank Carey HS Bus Dept Chprsn 1989-; *ai:* FBLA Co-Adv; NY St Assn for Cmptrs & Tech; Fellowship at Montclaire St Univ; Awded NY St Distinguished Occupational Ed Tchr 1991; *office:* H Frank Carey HS 230 Poppy Ave Franklin Square NY 11010

LAPADULA, BONNIE WATSON, Teacher; *b:* Paris, France; *c:* Chris, Brent; *ed:* 33 Credit Hrs over MEQ Montgomery Cty Pub Schls, Trinity Coll; *cr:* Mayvale Elem Schl Tchr 1977-79; Highland View Elem Schl Tchr 1979-81; Woodfield Elem Schl Tchr 1981-91; Rosa Parks MS Tchr 1991-95; *ai:* Ski Club Spon; PTA Tchr Rep; Schl Dance, Parent Appreciation Comm Chprsn; NEA, MCEA 1977-; *office:* Rosa M Parks MS 19200 Olney Mill Rd Olney MD 20832*

LAPELLA, MARIA, Spanish Teacher; *b:* Camden, NJ; *ed:* Rutgers Univ (BA) Span 1977; Attnd Univ of Madrid 1974, Cert Computerized Travel 1989; *cr:* Berlitz Espana SA Eng Tchr 1977-79; Medford Twp Meml Schl Span Tchr 1979-80; Willingboro HS Span Tchr 1980-83; Moorestown HS Summer Schl Span Tchr 1990-93; Camden Cty Coll Span Instr 1992-95; Edgewood Regnl Sr, Jr HS Span Tchr 1983-; *ai:* Amer Assn of Tchrs of Span, Portuguese 1980-; Frgn Lang Edctrs of NJ 1983-; NJ Ed Assn 1980-; Lower Camden Cty Regnl Ed Assn 1983-; Players Place Condo Assn 1990-, Bd Dir; Employee of Marking Period Awd 1987; *office:* Edgewood Reg Sr HS 250 Cooper Folly Rd Atco NJ 08004*

LA PENNA, JANICE PIETRYCHA, Physical Education Teacher; *b:* Hartford, CT; *m:* Louis; *c:* Sophia; *ed:* Cntrl CT St Univ (BS) PE 1974, (MS) PE 1984; *cr:* Fred D Wish Schl PE Tchr 1974-79; Weaver HS PE Tchr 1981-95; Hartford Pub HS PE Tchr 1995-; *ai:* Girls Cross Cntry Coach 1982-; Girls Indoor Track Coach 1985-89; Girls Outdoor Asst Track Coach 1983-; AFT, CFT 1974-; SS Cyril & Methodius Schl Bd Mem 1995-, Elected Mem; SS Cyril & Methodius Home & Schl Assn 1993-, Treas; *office:* Hartford Pub HS 55 Forest St Hartford CT 06105

LAPERGOLA, DENISE MAUREEN, Third Grade Teacher; *b:* Philadelphia, PA; *ed:* Immaculate (BA) Elem Ed 1967; *ai:* Rel Ed to Pub Schl Children; NCEA 1985-; *office:* St Ephrem Schl 5300 Hulmeville Rd Bensalem PA 19020*

LAPERLE, MARGARET BERNADETTE, English Teacher; *b:* Berlin, NH; *m:* Steven; *c:* Andrew; *ed:* Univ of NH (BA) Eng Ed 1974; *cr:* Portsmouth HS 9 Grd Eng Tchr 1974-75; Berlin Jr HS 7-9 Grd Eng Tchr 1975-82; Berlin Sr HS 9, 10, 12 Grd Eng Tchr 1985-86; Berlin Jr HS 7-8 Grd Eng Tchr 1986-; *ai:* Dance Chaperone; NEA 1974-; *office:* Berlin Jr HS 200 State St Berlin NH 03570

LAPERRIERE, MICHELLE L., Instr of Drawing & Painting; *b:* Denver, CO; *ed:* Schl of the Art Inst of Chicago (BFA) Painting, Drawing 1984; MD Inst Coll of Art (MFA) Painting, Drawing 1989; Attnd Parsons Schl of Design at New York 1981-82, Univ of CO at Boulder 1978-79; *cr:* Schl 33 Art Ctr Instr 1988-91; Baltimore Schl for the Arts Instr 1989-93; Harford Comm Coll Adj Prof, Instr 1990-; MD Inst Coll of Art Instr 1990-; *ai:* Mentor Guide & Adv 1994-95; Mentoring Network; Coll Art Assn 1990-; Amer Assn of Univ Women 1994-; Exhibitions Goucher Coll 1995, Galerie Francoise; Residency Millay Colony for the Arts 1993, VT Studio Ctr 1986; Artists Grant, Mayor's Advy Cncl on Art, Cultural 1992; PUrchase Prize 1985-86; Alumni Exec Cncl 1994-; *office:* MD Inst Coll Of Art 1300 W Mount Royal Ave Baltimore MD 21217

LAPI, JANE ANZALONE, Cosmetology Teacher; *b:* Buffalo, NY; *m:* Anthony F.; *c:* Michael; *ed:* NY St Univ Coll at Buffalo (BS) Ed 1984, (MS) Voc Ed 1987, (MS) Exceptional Ed 1992; Intnl Dermal Inst Esthetician Cert; OPI Sculptured Nail Tech Instr Cert; *cr:* Suburban House of Beauty Owner, Stylist 1960-80; Natl Accred Comm Cos Arts Scis Accreditation Team Ldr 1988-90; Lackawanna Sr HS Cosmetology Tchr 1979-91; Erie I Boces Execptional Ed Tchr 1992-94, Cosmetology Tchr 1991-; *ai:* Stu Recruitment; W Seneca Yth Theatre Dir Makeup; Talent Show Dir 1986-88; Vocfest Publicity Comm; NYSUT 1979-; Natl Cosmetology Assoc 1960-; Lackawanna Women Tchrs Assn 1979-90, Sec; Inst for Learning Centered Ed 1995-; Assn Amer Univ Women 1990-, Flwshp; Pi Lambda Theta 1990-; Natl Hnr & Prof Assoc in Ed, Key Awd; Elanor Roosevelt Tchr Flwshp AAUW 1991-92; Erie I Tchr Cntr Mini Grant 1993; NY Ed Dept Grant Pivot Point Intnl Tchrs Symposium 1987; 1995 Tchr Ctr Summer Inst Grant; Who's Who in Amer Beauty 1989-90; *office:* Erie 1 BOCES Potter Rd Occptnl 705 Potters Rd West Seneca NY 14224*

LAPIDUS, K. NINON, Resource Room Teacher; *b:* Paramaribo, Suriname; *m:* Martin; *c:* Robin Schwab, Julie Rothbard, Amy Grady; *ed:* Brooklyn Coll (BA) Elem Ed 1954; Hofstra Univ (MA) Spec Ed 1977; 10 Post Grad Credit Adelphi, Brooklyn Coll, Hofstra Univ; 30 In-svc Credits; *cr:* Dutch Lane Schl Classroom Elem Ed Tchr 1954-58; Woodland Ave Schl Classroom Elem Ed Tchr 1962-63; Dutch Lane Schl Self Contained Spec Ed Tchr 1975-87; Old Cntry Rd Schl Resource Room Tchr, Spec Ed Evaluator 1987-; *ai:* Private Practice LD Specialist; Hicksville Congress of Tchrs 1954-; NEA; Hicksville Pub Schls Founders Day Honoree 1990; Hicksville Congress of Tchrs Honor 1994; *office:* Old Country Road Elem Schl 49 Rhodes Ln Hicksville NY 11801*

LAPIERRE, GEORGE OMER,JR., English Teacher; *b:* Haverhill, MA; *m:* Maureen B. Sulliva; *c:* Sean P., Bridgit E., Valgenti, Elisa, Nicole, George III, Jennifer; *ed:* Salem St (BA) Eng 1967; Lehigh Univ (MA) Medieval Eng 1972; Dept of Defense Radiological Control Technician Trng Portsmouth Naval Shipyard; *cr:* Lehigh Univ Tchng Asst 1968-70; Danvers HS Eng Instr 1970-82; Laconia HS Eng Instr 1982; Interlakes HS Eng Instr 1985-; *ai:* Newspaper Adv; Granite St Challenge Coach; NEA, 1970-; DTA, MTA 1970-82, Pres; ILEA, NHEA 1982-, Pres; *office:* Inter Lakes HS 1 Laker Ln Meredith NH 03253

LAPINSKI, DAVID J., Mathematics Teacher; *b:* Bedford Cty, PA; *ed:* Syracuse Univ (BS) Bio, Mechanical Engrng 1991; Kings Coll (BA) Math 1992; Masters in Ed Bloomsburg Univ 1994; *cr:* Coll Misericordia Math Tchr 1992-93; Coughlin HS Math Tchr 1993-; *ai:* Ftbl Coach 1991-; Sr Adv 1994-95; Prof Engr Soc 1991-; PA Tchrs of Math 1993-; *office:* James M Coughlin Sr HS 80 N Washington St Wilkes Barre PA 18701*

LAPINTA, LENNY, Music Teacher; *b:* Brooklyn, NY; *m:* Maria DaCosta; *c:* Melissa, Michael; *ed:* Nassau Comm Coll (AA) Music 1981; SUNY at Potsdam (BA) Music 1983; SUNY at Stonybrook (MS) Music 1987; 75 Post Masters Credits Music Tech; *cr:* Udall Rd MS Music Tchr 1983-; *ai:* Evaluation Comm; Prof Musician; AFT, NYSUT 1983-; WI Teach Assn 1983-, Mem Bd of Dirs, Grievance Comm; *office:* Udall Road MS 900 Udall Rd West Islip NY 11795

LAPLANCHE, JEAN-DAVID, French Teacher; *ed:* Heidelberg Coll (BA) Fr Lit, Ger 1974; Lake Erie Coll (MS) Fr, Ed 1988; Universite de Strasbourg Fr Lit 1972; John Carroll Univ; Cleveland St Univ; *cr:* Lakeland Comm Coll Fr Instr 1984; The Andrews Schl Fr Instr 1985-86; Brush HS Fr, Ger Tchr 1987-; Lake Erie Coll Fr Instr 1990-; *ai:* Canoes Film Festival Project; Motivation Techniques in Tchng Fr Wkshp Coord; Homestay Trips to Fr; NEA 1985-; SELTA 1986-; Grand River Kennel Club 1985-, Pres, VP, Sec; Midwest Afghan Hound Club 1980-, Sec; Articles Pub; Approved Judge by Amer Kennel Club; *home:* 8763 Marjory Dr Mentor OH 44060*

LAPOINTE, GARY JOSEPH, Heating, AC & Refrig Tchr; *b:* Holyoke, MA; *m:* Helen Marie Sbrega; *c:* Christopher, Ashley, James, Allison; *ed:* Springfield Tech Comm Coll (AS) Heat, Power, Air Conditioning Tech 1982; Voc Certfd MA; *cr:* Indstrl Heating Heat Technician 1982-85; West Springfield Schls Mechanic Foreman 1985-88; Tech Careers Inst Tchr 1988-90; Pathfinder Vo Tech HS Tchr 1990-; *ai:* NEA, MTA 1990-; *office:* Pathfinder Regnl Vo Tech HS Rt 181 Palmer MA 01069

LAPOINTE, LAURENCE ARTHUR, English Instructor; *b:* Jay, ME; *m:* Raechel Maxwell; *c:* Glen, Louise Atkinson, Paul, Mark; *ed:* Colby Coll (BA) Psych & Eng 1958; Univ of ME (MA) Eng 1969, (CAS) Guidance 1974; *cr:* Fort Kent Comm HS Eng Tchr 1958-60; Gardiner Area HS Eng Tchr 1960-91; Univ of ME at Augusta Eng Instr 1991-; *ai:* Accreditation Comm; AFT 1985-; NEA, MTA 1958-; GTA 1960-, Pres; Gardiner Federal Credit Union 1986-, Chm; Gardiner Tchr of Yr; Sanford Ctr Tchr of Yr; Pub Two Articles; Annenberg & CPB Grant; *home:* 35 Belmont Ave Randolph ME 04346

LA POINTE, STEPHEN MICHAEL, Social Studies & Language Tchr; *b:* Rumford, ME; *m:* Jeanne Brown; *c:* Tristan; *ed:* Univ of M at Farmington (BA) Elem Ed 1978, Spec Ed 1979; *cr:* Bangor Regnl Ctr Tchr 1978-79; Mountain Vly MS Lang, Soc St Tchr 1979-; *ai:* Var Ftbl, MS Boys Bsktbl, Var Bsbl Coach; Fin Comm 1990-; Recreation Bd 1991-; *home:* 2756 Isthmus Rd Rumford ME 04276*

LAPORTE, DANIEL B., Soc Stud Tchr & Dept Chprsn; *b:* New Kensington, PA; *m:* Phyllis; *c:* Elizabeth, Samuel, Jennifer; *ed:* Slippery Rock Univ (BA) Sociology 1970; St Vincent Coll (BS) Ed 1971; Duquesne Univ (MED) Counseling 1974; Slippery Rock Univ Sec Schl Counseling 1975; *cr:* Indiana Univ of PA Asst Prof Criminology 1972-78; Mars Area Schl Dist Tchr 1972-; Mid Western I U 4 Cnslr 1978-; Mars Area Schl Dist Soc Stud Dept Chair 1988-; *ai:* Sr Class Spon 1989-; NEA, PSEA 1972-; Mars Area Ed Assn 1972-, Welfare Comm Chair, Spec Svcs Comm; Grievance Chair; Butler Co Mental Hlth Assn 1990-, Pres, VP, Sec; East Butler Borough 1981-85, Councilman; Arnold Chamber of Commerce, Achvmt Awd; Mental Hlth Assn Trust Fund Bd of Trustees 1993-, Sec; Who's Who in Amer Ed; Who's Who in Amer; Who's Who in the World; *office:* Mars Area HS 520 Route 228 Mars PA 16046

LAPORTE, KAREN ANN, Chemistry Teacher; *b:* Astoria, NY; *m:* Angel M.; *ed:* SUNY at Cortland (BS) Bio-chem, Scndry Ed 1980; Western Ct St Univ (MA) Oceanography, Limnology 1989; *cr:* Holy Trinity HS Phys Sci Tchr 1980-81; New Fairfield HS Chem Tchr 1981-; *ai:* Frosh Class, Stdnts Against Drugs Adv; CEA, NEA 1981-; Conn Chem Tchrs Org, CHED ACS Division of Chem ED 1996; Delta Kappa Gamma 1988-, Mbrshp Chprsn; Gertrude Braun Recruitment Grant for Female Edctrs Completing Master's Degree; *office:* New Fairfield HS 54 Gillotti Rd New Fairfield CT 06812*

LAPORTE, VICKY GORDON, Teacher Assistant; *b:* Providence, RI; *m:* David LaPorte; *c:* David, Alexander; *ed:* RI Coll (BA) Eng for Sec Ed 1990; Classes at CCRI for Soc Stud Cert, ESL Endorsement; *cr:* Wm M. DAvies Jr Career & Tech Schl Sub, Asst Tchr 1990-; *ai:* Adv Voc Industrial Clubs of Amer; NEA 1993-; Voc Industrial Clubs of Amer 1991-, St Level Silver Medal in Extemporaneous Speech; *office:* Wm M. Davies Jr Career, Tech 50 Jenckes Hill Rd Lincoln RI 02865

LAPOSKI, STEPHEN, American Government Teacher; *b:* Hamilton, OH; *ed:* OH Univ (BS) Ed 1971; WV Univ, Univ of Dayton (MA) Secondary Admin 1980; *cr:* Buckeye Local Schl Dist Tchr 1971-72; Union Local Schl Dist Tchr 1972-; *ai:* Girls Var Bsktbl Coach; Negotiation Team for Contract Agreement; NEA, OEA 1971; ULACT, Pres, Building Rep, St Del 1972-; OHSBCA, Pres 1996-; OH HS Bsktbl Coaches Assn Awds 100 & 200 Wins; Dist 12 Bsktbl Coach of Yr; Coach OVAC OH-WV All Star Game 5 Times; Coord for OH First Vote Prgm; Coord for OH Supreme Court Cty Hearing; OH Citizenshiop Advocacy Seminar; *home:* 71053 Morr-Flushing Rd Flushing OH 43977

LAPP, RICHARD GORDON, Science Teacher of GATE; *b:* Toledo, OH; *m:* Susan Bolster; *ed:* Miami Univ at Oxford (BSEd) Comprehensive Sci 1968; Post Grad Work at Xavier Univ, Coll of Mount St Joseph & Univ of Cincinnati; Cert in GATE; *cr:* Fairfield Jr High 7th Grd General Sci Tchr 1968-71, 8th Grd Phys Sci Tchr 1972-79; Fairfield MS 6th-8th Grd Sci Tchr of GATE 1980-; *ai:* Photography & Rocket Club Spon; Liaison & Dist Sci Curr Comm; Invent Amer Spon & Coach; Young Inventors & Creators Comp Coach; FCTA 1968-, Bldg Rep & Pub Relations Comm Chair; OEA & NEA 1968-; OH Sci Cncl & NSTA 1980-; Wrote Career Ed Packets for OH St Dept of Ed 1991-92; Recognized for Success of Stdnts in Dist & St Sci Fair Comp, Invent Amer Comp & Young Inventors Comp; Nom for OH Tchr of Yr 1985; Designated Ambassador for Fairfield City Schls 1990-; Coaches Invent Amer OH St Winner 7th Grd 1991; Wrote Gifted Sci Curr for Fairfield City Schls 1985-86; Speaker at OH Consortium of Gifted Coords 1987; *home:* 900 Harrison Ave Hamilton OH 45013

LAPP, WANDA D. KING, 7th Grade Math Teacher; *b:* Coatesville, PA; *m:* Douglas M.; *c:* Douglas Benjamin; *ed:* West Chester Univ at PA (BSEd) Elem Ed & Math Concentration 1984; Masters Equivalency; *cr:* Octorara Intermediate Schl 7th Grd Math Tchr 1984-85, 7th-8th Grd Math Tchr 1987-; *ai:* Stu Cncl Adv 9 Yrs; Spring Variety Show Dir 9 Yrs; HS Auditorium Tech Dir 3 Yrs; Mentor Pgm 2 Yrs; NEA, PSEA & OAEA 1987-; Cochranville Fire Co 1988-, Fin Sec & Banquet Chprsn; *home:* RR 3 Box 312 Cochranville PA 19330

LAPSLEY, KRISTEN BETH, High School Science Teacher; *b:* Ridgewood, NJ; *ed:* Fairleigh Dickinson Univ (BS) Bio 1988; Attnd Univ of Medicine & Dentistry; *cr:* Fair Lawn HS Sci Tchr 1990-; *ai:* Asst Winter Track & Field & Asst Spring Track & Field Coach; NEA 1990-; NJEA 1990-; FLEA 1990-; *office:* Fair Lawn HS 14-00 Berdan Ave Fair Lawn NJ 07410

LARABEE, DAVE M., Physics & Mathematics Teacher; *b:* Cleveland, OH; *ed:* Bowling Green St Univ (BS) Phsycis & Math 1986, (Cert) Ed 1989; Univ of Toledo (MED) Ed 1993; *cr:* Bowling Green St Univ Instr 1989-90; St Francis HS Physics Tchr 1990-92; Ottawa Hills HS Physics & Math Tchr 1990-; *ai:* NCTM, OCTM & GTCTM 1989-; AAPT & OAPT 1990-; NEA, OEA & OHEA 1990-; Jennings Scholar 1994-95; Lucas Cty I Make A Difference Awd; *office:* Ottawa Hills Jr Sr HS 2532 Evergreen Rd Toledo OH 43606

LARAIA, ANN LEVESQUE, Third Grade Teacher; *b:* Madawaska, ME; *m:* Vincent James; *c:* Kathryn, Kristopher; *ed:* Univ of ME at Presque Isle (BS) Elem Ed 1977; *cr:* Teague Park Schl 2nd Grd Tchr 1978-90, 3rd Grd Tchr 1991-; *ai:* Gifted & Talented Project Explore Tchr; Young Author Tchr; Cooperating Tchr for Stu Tchrs; NEA, MEA 1978-; Outstanding Tchr Awd 1991; Speaker for the Pine Tree Burn Assoc 1995; *office:* Teague Park Elem Schl 59 Glenn St Caribou ME 04736*

LARAMEE, MAUREEN DOWNING, 8th Grade Teacher; *b:* Holyoke, MA; *m:* Robert Joseph; *c:* Bethany M., Robert A.; *ed:* Our Lady of the Elms Coll (BA) Sociology 1974; *cr:* Sacred Heart Schl 1st Grd Tchr 1975-79; Our Lady of Perpetual Help Schl 7th-8th Grd Tchr 1986-; *ai:* Yrbk Adv; NCTM; NCEA; *office:* Our Lady Of Perpetual Help Sch 261 Chestnut St Holyoke MA 01040

LARAMEE, PAULA WEBBER, 4th Grade Teacher; *b:* Fort Bragg, NC; *m:* Roger; *c:* Grace Lang-Michael, Lisa Herzig-Andrew; *ed:* RI Coll (BED) Elem Ed 1964; Gifted, Talented Cert; Diocese of Providence Rel Ed Cert; *cr:* Pied Piper Child Ctr Lib 1975-79; St Matthew Notre Dame Consolidated Schl 4-6th Grd Soc Stud, Eng Tchr, K-8th Grd Gifted, Talented Tchr 1983-94; Woodlawn Cath Reg Schl 4th Grd Tchr, 4-6th Grd Soc Stud Tchr 1994-; *ai:* Natl Geographic Soc, RI Geog Bee Schl Coord; NACST 1983-; RI TAWL; RI Geog Ed Alliance; AIM 1995-; *office:* Woodlawn Catholic Regional Sch 61 Hope St Pawtucket RI 02860*

LARDER, LINDA M., Physical Ed Instr & Coach; *b:* Penn Yan, NY; *ed:* SUNY Cortland (BSE) PE 1970; Attnd St Bonaventure & SUNY Cortland Post Grad; *cr:* Portville Central 7th-12th PE Instr Var Coach 1970-; *ai:* Var, JV Vlybl Coach; NYSUT 1970-; *office:* Portville Central Schl Elm St Portville NY 14770

LAREAU, SUSAN C., Second Grade Teacher; *b:* Syracuse, NY; *m:* Joseph; *c:* Meghan, Adam, Jesse; *ed:* William Paterson Coll (BA) Elem Ed 1968; 30 Grad Credits; *cr:* Spring Garden Schl Elem Tchr 25 Yrs; *ai:* Report Card Evaluation Schl Rep; Second Grd Chprsn; Schl Soc Comm Treas; NEA, NJ Ed Assn 1968-; Ed Assn of Nutley 1968-, Mbrshp Rep; *home:* 349 Hillside Ave Nutley NJ 07110

LARGENT, KATHLEEN KUCYK, English & Spanish Teacher; *b:* Akron, OH; *m:* Michael W.; *c:* Steven, Michael; *ed:* Kent St Univ (BSEd) Eng, Span Ed 1971, (MSEd) Rdng 1974; 12 Addl Misc Educl Course Hrs; *cr:* Claymont City Schls Eng, Span Tchr 1971-72; Lake Local Schls Eng, Span Tchr 1972-; *ai:* NEA 1971-; ECOEA 1972-; LLEA 1972-; OCTEL; OFLA; Jennings Scholar 1993; Canton Regnl Chamber of Commerce Tchr of Yr Nom 1995-.

LARIMORE, DORA TRADER, Math Teacher; *b:* Salisbury, MD; *m:* Lee; *c:* Kim Larimore Carey; *ed:* Salisbury ST (BS) Elem Ed 1973, (MED) Ed 1978; Addl 14 Credit Hrs 1978; *cr:* Berlin MS Math Tchr 23 Yrs; *ai:* Project Basic, TEN Modeline Hunter; Schl Improvement Team; Math Tutoring; NEA; MSTA; WCTA; Trinity United Meth Church 33 Yrs; Wicomico Cty Humane Sco 5 Yrs; Berlin MS Tchr of Yr; *office:* Berlin MS 309 Franklin Ave Berlin MD 21811

LARIVIERE, BLAIR J., Art Teacher; *b:* Gardner, MA; *m:* Susan H. Byron; *c:* Cristie A., David J.; *ed:* Clark Univ (BFA) Fine Arts 1968; Assumption Coll (MAT) Fine Arts 1971; *cr:* City of Gardner K-8th Grd Art Supvr 1968-82; Elm Street Schl Art Tchr 1982-93; Gardner HS Art Tchr 1993-; *ai:* GHS Art Club; Multicultural Festival Arts Comm; Arts Curr Comm Chair; GEA 1968-; NEA 1969-; MTA 1969-; NAEA 1994-; Ford Fndtn Grant; Worcester Art Musuem Outstdng Achvmt Awd; Pub Photo Claywork Book by Nibrosh; *office:* Gardner HS 200 Catherine St Gardner MA 01440*

LARKIN, FRANCES BOLLA, Special Education Teacher; *b:* Beverly, MA; *m:* Wilham J.; *ed:* Salem St Coll (BS) Elem Ed 1969; Boston Coll (MED) Spec Ed 1974; *cr:* Silver Lane Elem Schl 3 Grd Tchr 1969-72; Everett Pub Schls K-6 Spec Ed Tchr 1974-; *ai:* MTA, NEA 1974-, Bldg Rep; ETA, Exec Comm Treas; Everett Ride-A-Bike Retarded Citizens Coord 10 Yrs; *office:* Lafayette Elem Schl 115 Shute St Everett MA 02149

LARKIN, GAIL GRABER, Bus Ed Dept Chprsn; *b:* Philadelphia, PA; *m:* William T. Walukonis; *c:* Ted R.; *ed:* PA St Univ (BS) Bus Ed 1967; Widener Univ (MED) Grad & Adult Ed 1989; Post Grad 33 Credit Hrs Univ of Pittsburgh, Univ of DE & Shppensburg Univ; *cr:* Kensington HS Bus Tchr 1967-68; Churchill Area HS Bus Tchr 1968-70; Brandywine HS Bus Tchr 1970-78; Univ of DE Supvr, Bus Ed & Stud Tchr 1979-80; Goldey Beacom Acad Adv 1980-81; Padua Acad Dept Chair & Bus Ed Tchr 1982-83; Alexis I duPont HS Dept Chair & Bus Ed Tchr 1983-; *ai:* Tech Prep Liaison Comm; DO Coord; NEA 1967-; DSEA 1970-; BSA 1990-, Asst Scout Master, Comm Chprsn & Advance Chprsn, Cert of Recognition for Outstdng Svc; Receivied Funding for Comp Ctr Through a Grant Written by Me For Padua Acad; Excl Tchng Honorable Mention Univ of DE; *office:* Alexis I DuPont HS 50 Hillside Rd Greenville DE 19807*

LARKIN, JOAN MARY, 7th Grade Teacher; *b:* Kilgarvan Co Kerry, Ireland; *m:* Sean; *c:* Sheila, Shane; *ed:* Univ Coll at Galway (BA) Math 1976, (HDE) Ed 1977; *cr:* CBS Fr Tchr 1982-84; Presentation Convent Math Tchr 1984-87; St Barnabas Schl 7th Grd Tchr 1987-90; St Paul the Apostle 7th Grd Tchr 1990-; *ai:* Acad Coach for Math, Lang Arts Contests & Competitions; *office:* Saint Paul The Apostle Schl 77 Lee Ave Yonkers NY 10705

LARKIN, KIMBERLY MORTON, Spanish Teacher; *b:* Winthrop, MA; *m:* Gregg Joseph; *c:* Connor John, Shannon Kimberly; *ed:* Regis Coll (BA) Span 1985; Simmos Coll (MA) Ed 1990; *cr:* Memorial HS Span Tchr 1991-; *ai:* Prof Dev, Block Scheduling Comms; MEA Bldg Rep; Phi Delta Kappa 1992-; NEA 1991-.

LARKIN, PERRY, Guidance Counselor; *b:* Boston, MA; *m:* Janet Hogan; *c:* Matthew, Timothy, Brian; *ed:* Univ of MD (BA) Scndry Ed 1972; Univ of MA at Boston (MED) Schl Cnslng 1977; *cr:* Matignon HS Guid Cnslr 1977-85; Archbishop Williams Guid Cnslr 1985-; *ai:* Frosh Ftbl Coach; MA Schl Couns Assoc 1977-; Cath Schl Couns Assoc 1977-; St Jeromes Church 1979-, Euch Minister; *office:* Archbishop Williams HS 80 Independence Ave Braintree MA 02184

LARKO, MICHAEL J., Math Teacher; *b:* Wilkinsburg, PA; *m:* Marsha Lynn France; *c:* Karyn, Julie, Michael; *ed:* Edinboro Univ (BA) Scndry Ed 1964; Indiana Univ of PA Masters Equivalency Scndry Ed 1972; *cr:* Plum Jr HS Math Tchr 1964-69; Plum Sr HS Math Tchr 1969-; *ai:* Coach: Boys Vlybl 1973-90, 1992, Girls Vlybl 1975-82, Cross Cntry 1972-74; PSEA, NEA 1964-; PA Hall of Fame Vlybl Coach; *office:* Plum Sr HS 900 Elicker Rd Pittsburgh PA 15239

LARMOUTH, W. DAVID, Chemistry Teacher; *b:* Wilkes-barre, PA; *m:* Lois; *c:* Bartholomew, Megan; *ed:* Wilkes Univ (BS) Scndry Ed 1965; Univ of WY (MNS) Chem & Physics 1973; Attnd Insts on Energy; *cr:* Dundee Sci Tchr 1968-; *ai:* Discipline Comm; Masonic Lodge #123 1972-, Held Several Offices; GTO & Avanti Car Orgs; Grants to PA St Univ Nuclear Concepts & SUNY at Oswego Energy; *office:* Dundee Central Schl 55 Water St Dundee NY 14837

LAROCCA, FRED VINCENT, Retired Teacher; *b:* Arverne, NY; *m:* Patricia Murray; *c:* Fred, Katherine; *ed:* Montclair St Coll (BA) Soc Stud, Elem Ed 1958; Newark St Elem Ed; *cr:* Midland Schl 7th-8th Grd Tchr 1958-63; Burnett St Schl 5th-7th Grd Tchr 1963-69; Oak View Schl 5th-6th Grd Tchr 1969-95; *ai:* Past Safety Patrol Adv, Bsktbl Coach, Tchr-in-Charge; BEA 1969-, Rep; Essex Cty Ed Assn, NJEA, NEA 1969-.

LAROCHE, BARBARA HAWKEY, 2nd Grade Teacher; *b:* Celina, OH; *m:* David; *c:* Laura Stephens, Beth Ringelspaugh; Steven; *ed:* Wright St Univ (BA) Elem Ed 1976; Wright St Univ of Dayton, Portland Univ 150 Credit Hrs; *cr:* Ansonia Elem Schl 2nd Grd Tchr 1975-93, 3rd Grd Tchr 1993-95, 2nd Grd Tchr 1995-; *ai:* Cub Scout, Ldr; Montezuma Meth Church, Sunday Schl Tchr; Tchr of Yr by Fellow Tchrs; *office:* Ansonia Elem Schl PO Box 279 Ansonia OH 45303

LAROCHE, HELEN WIRMUSKY, Curriculum Coordina Bennington, VT; *c:* Michael, Matthew; *ed:* SUNY at Cortland (B Math 1975; SUNY at Plattsburgh (MSED) 1989, (SAS) Admin Ce 62 Credit Hrs Post Grad Work; *cr:* Queensbury Schl Dist 3rd G Curr Coord 1976-; *ai:* AFT, NYSUT 1976-; NCTM, ASCD 1987- Grants in Spec Ed, Math, Sci, Title I; Presented Wrkshps o Manipulatives; Pub Article in NYS MS Assn Journal; *office:* Que Elem Schl 431 Aviation Rd Queensbury NY 12804

LAROCK, ROBERT ALLEN,JR., Mathematics Teacher; *b:* Birm AL; *m:* Linda Rose; *c:* Brendan, Ajlan; *ed:* St Univ Coll at Plattsbu Scndry Math Ed 1968; Addl 33 Post Grad Credits; *cr:* Lake Pleasa Schl Jr HS Math Tchr 1968-69; Johnsburg Cntrl Schl HS Math Tch *ai:* Jr Class Adv; Discipline Comm; JCSTA 1969-, Treas; NYSUT *home:* 5 Robin Dr Warrensburg NY 12885

LAROCQUE, KATHLEEN CAMPBELL, Business Teach Pawtucket, RI; *m:* William Robert; *ed:* Johnson & Wales Univ (AS Sys Mngmt 1984, (BA) Tchr Ed 1986; RI Coll Working Towards Career, Technological Ed; *cr:* Block Island Schl Bus Tchr 1 Coventry Pub Schls Bus Tchr 1987-; *ai:* Prom Promise Adv; Co-Adv; AFT, RIBEA 1987-; *office:* Coventry HS 40 Reserv Coventry RI 02816*

LAROCQUE, KENNETH H., Provost; *b:* Chicopee, MA; *m.* Buchanan; *c:* Nicholas, Alexandra, Benjamin; *ed:* Harvard Coll (B 1975; Harvard Univ (MED) Ed 1981; *cr:* Charles River Acad Ma 1975-76; Rectory Schl Asst Head, Math Tchr 1976-80; Avon Ol Schl Provost, Dean, Math Tchr 1982-; *ai:* Coach Ftbl, Lacrosse, NACAC 1982-; NEACAC 1982-, Outstanding Cnslr; ESV 1982-; Avon Old Farms Schl 500 Old Farms Rd Avon CT 06001*

LAROSA, FRANCES DANIELA LOBASSO, 5th Grade Teac Manhattan, NY; *m:* Charles; *c:* Christopher, Tara; *ed:* Long Islan (BA) Elem Ed 1972; Richmond Coll (MA) Elem Ed 1976; 30 Cred Grad; *cr:* PS 176 Biling Resource Tchr 1974-75, Grd 5 & Tran Prgm Tchr 1977-79; PS 205 Grds 4 & 5 Tchr 1979-86, Multi Magnet, Art Tchr 1986-92, 5th Grd Tchr 1992-; *ai:* Art Club 1986- Org Adv & Supply Store Org 1989-92; UFT, NYSUT 1977-; D 1982-92; Wrote Curr for Project Equal Sponsored by Bd of Ed; *of* 205 6701 20th Ave Brooklyn NY 11204

LARRABEE, DEBORAH, 6th Grade Math Teacher; *b:* New York, Everett; *c:* Scott Harris, Glenn Harris, Dean Harris, Steve; *ed:* B (BS) Elem Ed 1953; U of Rochester Grad Credit; *cr:* Westbury S Grd Tchr 1953-55; Brighton Schls 4th & 6th Grd Tchr 1966-; *ai:* BT Brighton 21 Comm; Curr Cncl; Brighton Tchrs Assn 1966-, Pres NEA NY; St Task Force on Educl Reform; *office:* Twelve Corners M Elmwood Ave Rochester NY 14618

LARRABEE, NATHANIEL, Professor of Fine Arts; *b:* Hartford, Trinity Coll (BA) Art His-Cum Laude 1962; Boston Coll Schl of Fi (BFA) Painting-Hnrs 1964, (MFA) Painting 1966; Attnd Hartford A Univ of Hartford, Framingham St Coll; *cr:* Boston Univ Schl of Fi Instr 1967-69, Visiting Prof 1988-89; Wellesley Coll Asst Prof 1 Columbus Coll of Arts & Design Prof 1977-; *ai:* Curr, Visiting Accreditation, Exhibition Comms; Fac Cncl Rep, VP; Coll Art Assn Columbus Art League 1978-; OH Assn of Visual Artists 1990-94 Trustees; Grants, Flwshps Ford Fnd, Huber Fnd, Boston Univ Regnl Exhibitions Throughout US, Intnl; *office:* Columbus Coll Of Art & 107 N 9th St Columbus OH 43215

LARRABEE-BELL, GRETCHEN, Director of ESL Progra Portland, ME; *m:* Glenn S.; *c:* Enrique Espinetti; *ed:* Am Intnl Co Elem Ed 1977; The George Washington Univ (MA) Supervision 1982; 30 Credit Hrs Post Grad Stud in Rdng, Writing Process, Tech Linguistics, Early Chldhd Ed & Cognition & Learning; *cr:* Dept of D PI ESL Specialist 1986-88; ART Pgm Inst 1988-89; Dept of Def Seoul Korea ESL Specialist & K-1 Tchr 1989-92; Rivier Coll Early Instr 1992-94, Dir of ESL Pgms 1994-; *ai:* Amnesty Intnl & Intr Advs; Curr & Bicentennial Comms; Task Force 2.1; Intnl Rec TESOL 1982-; NAEYC 1992-; ASCD 1995-; Nashua Pub Schls 199 Tutor; Adult Svcs Adult Learning Ctr 1993-, ESL Tutor; Olympic Relay Team Comm 1996-; *office:* Rivier Coll 420 S Main St Nash 03060*

LARRAURI, ILEANA JAUME, Spanish Teacher; *b:* Oriente, Cu Pedro P.; *c:* Ileana, Nancy, Michael; *ed:* Montclair St Coll (BA) Spa *cr:* Middletown HS South Span Tchr 1985-; *ai:* Span Hnr Soc Adv; 1985-; MTEA 1985-; MCEA 1985-; NJEA 1985-; NEA 1985-; Ame of Tchrs of Span & Portuguese 1989-.

LARRIMORE, JOHN WAYNE, Guidance Counselor; *b:* Cheste MD; *m:* Diane Ray Sauger; *c:* Zachary, John, Christopher; *ed:* Fr St Coll (BA) Ed 1974; Loyola Coll (MS) Cnslng 1990; *cr:* Galena M & Cnslr 1975-90; Queen Annes Cty HS Cnslr 1990-; *ai:* Peer Cnslr & Adv; Boy Scout Ldr; Yth Soccer & Yth Bsbl Coach; Crisis Interv Team 1988-92, Dist Supvr, Mem of Yr; Calvery Asbury United Church 1963-; *office:* Queen Anne's County HS 125 Ruthsbu Centreville MD 21617

LARRIVEE, STEVEN E., Math & Comp Science Teacher; *b:* Provi RI; *ed:* Comm Coll of RI (AS) Mechanical Eng 1982; RI Coll (BA 1985, (MS) Instrl Tech 1991; *cr:* RI Coll Grad Asst 1986-87; Bidd HS Math & Comp Tchr 1988-; *ai:* Drama Club Adv; NCTM Biddleford Tchrs Assn 1988-, Sec; ME Tchrs Assn 1988-; MEA & 1988-; *office:* Biddeford HS Maplewood Ave Biddeford ME 04005

LARSEN, PAUL M., Assistant Professor of Biology; *b:* Evanston, Moira P.; *c:* Jens C., Rebecca L., Ethan P., Zachary M.; *ed:* Univ (BS) Zoology 1976, (MS) Zoology 1982, (PHD) Cell Bio 1987; *cr.* of MD Instr 1984-87, Rsrch Assoc 1987-93, Visiting Asst Prof 1989- Arundel Comm Coll Asst Prof 1994-; *ai:* Am Soc Cell Bio Microscopy Soc of Am 1986-; Phi Kappa Phi 1987-; Articles Pub; Anne Arundel Comm Coll 101 College Pky Arnold MD 21012*

LARSEN, PHYLLIS HAMILTON, 6th Grade Classroom Teach LaGro, IN; *m:* Ellis L.; *c:* David L., Stephen L., Eric L.; *ed:* Taylo (BSEd) Elem Ed 1959; Ball St UNiv (MED) Elem Ed 1968; Addl Pos Stud Amer Univ, Trinity Coll, Natl Coll; *cr:* New Castle Pub Schls 5 Tchr 1959-60; Dudley Twp Schls 1st-2nd Grd Tchr 1960-61; Mish Pub Schls Tchr 1961-63; Evanston PS Dist 65 Kndgtn Tchr 19 Montgomery Cty Schls 6th Grd Tchr 1977-; *ai:* Outdoor Ed Coord; Spon; Gifted Comm; NEA 1959-; NSTA 1976-; Kndgtn Tchrs Chprsn; Classroom Featured In Teacher Magazine 1977, Newspaper 1988, 1996; Outdoor Ed Tchr of Yr 1996; *office:* South Lake Elem 18201 Contour Rd Gaithersburg MD 20877

LARSON, DENNIS R., 7th-9th Grd Social Stud Tchr; *b:* Toledo, O Annarose Darr; *c:* Doug; *ed:* Bowling Green St Univ (BS) Soc Stud 30 Hrs Beyond Bachelors; *cr:* Danbury Jr HS Tchr 1963-; *ai:* Elks Jennings Scholar 1991-92.

LARSON, EINAR EVERT, Chemistry Teacher; *b:* Philipsburg, P Gloria Jean McDonald; *c:* Kristina, Karina, Jessica; *ed:* Clarion Univ Chem 1971; 61 Post Grad Credits; *cr:* Moshannon Valley HS Chem, Physical Sci Tchr 1971-; *ai:* NEA 1971-; MVEA 1971-, Pres, VP; 1971-; Flwshp From Dept Energy; NSF Grant; *office:* Moshannon & Sr HS RR 1 Box 314 Houtzdale PA 16651

ON, ELIZABETH WELLMAN, French Instructor; *b:* Cincinnati, : David Brice; *c:* D. Brice II, Eric William; *ed:* OH St Univ (BS) Ed, Span, Major Fr 1976, (MA) Ed, For Lang Ed 1979; (PHD) Ed, For .d 1987; *cr:* Thomas Worthington HS Fr Instr 1979-; *ai:* NEA 1979-; a Cum Laude Grad OSU 1976; Outstanding Tchr Awd Univ of go 1989, Denison Univ 1991; Tchr Most Effect on Stdnts 1988, 1990, & 1995; Phi Kappa Phi, Pi Lambda Theta, Alpha Lambda Delta; Thomas Worthington HS 300 W Dublin-Granville Rd Worthington 085

ON, PATRICIA M., English Teacher; *b:* Lexington, NC; *m:* Daniel Melissa Pillitiere, Daniel Jr., Matthew; *ed:* Univ of NC at Greensboro Eng 1975; Gannon Univ (MA) Ed 1989; *cr:* High Point Andrews HS chr, Tchr of Gifted & Debate Coach 1975-80; North Hills Chrstn Schl chr & Newspaper-Yrbk Adv 1981-83; Warren Cty Schl Dist Eng Tchr bate Coach 1987-; Performance Learning Systems Grad Ed Instr *ai:* NEA 1975-; PSEA, WCEA 1988-; PASCD 1989-; Lead Tchr *office:* Eisenhower HS RD 2 Russell PA 16345*

ON, PATRICIA MACKIL, Speech & Language Pathologist; *b:* stown, OH; *c:* Alina, Erik; *ed:* Kent St Univ (BS) Speech Patholgy Akron Univ (MS) Spcl Ed 1974; Macquarie Univ Spcl Ed 1980; Post Stud: Ashland Coll, Miami of OH, OH St Univ, Pontifical Coll at inum, Kent St; *cr:* Akron Pub Schls Speech Patholgist & LD Tutor 69; Six Pence Schl Speech Pathologist 1973-79; Southwest Licking Speech Pathologist 1981-; *ai:* Pataskala Performing Group-Choral ng 1992-93; NEA 1981-; OEA 1981-; SLEA; OSHA 1981-; COSHA League of Women Voters 1965-, Bd Mem, Unit Ofcr, Newsletter Ed; ept of Ed NET Grant; Kirkesville OH Rotary Grant; Herb Soc of Grant; Rotary Scholar to Sydney Australia; *home:* 405 Blenheim Rd bus OH 43214

'IGUE, DANNETTE ELIZABETH, Social Studies Teacher; *b:* e, AL; *m:* David Colin Menaker; *ed:* Mount Saint Mary's Coll (BA) 92; Soc Stud, Scndry Ed Cert 1993; *cr:* Sylvan Learning Ctr Tutor, 995; Frederick HS Soc Stud Tchr 1994-; *ai:* Act Sponsorship; SGA V, V Chrldng Coach; Stdnts Helping other People, Future Tchrs of Club Adv; MD St Tchrs Assn, Frederick Cty Tchrs Assn 1994-; Cath roup 1991-, Ldr; Recognized by German Historical Soc for Museum *office:* Frederick HS 650 Carroll Pky Frederick MD 21701*

FFA, NANCY FRITZ, Teacher & Math Dept Chprsn; *b:* LaPorte, : Francis V. Sr.; *c:* Anthony, Maria, Joanne; *ed:* Ball St Univ (BS) 1961; Attnd Syracuse Univ, Brockport St Tchrs Coll, George ngton Univ & Georgetown Univ; *cr:* West Irondequoit Schl System Tchr 1961-64; Acad Holy Cross Math Tchr 1982-95; Connelly Schl y Child Math Tchr & Dept Chprsn 1995-; *ai:* Acad Cncl; Homeroom NCTM, MCTM 1982-; Holy Cross Hospice 1989-; Natl Sci Fnd Governors Acad for Outstanding Math & Sci Tchrs; *office:* Connelly f Holy Child 9029 Bradley Blvd Potomac MD 20854

'EY, AUDREY LOIS (SHEFFER), Social Studies Teacher; *b:* n, MA; *ed:* Univ of MA at Amhert (BA) His 1970; Masters alency Various Univ; Masters of Scndry Counseling Kutztown Univ; almerton Area HS Sub Tchr 1970-84, Soc Stud Tchr 1984-94, nce Cnslr 1994-; *ai:* Trivia Club Adv; Track Asst, Helper; Strategic ng Steering Comm; NEA 1984-; Delta Kappa Gamma 1988-, Sec.

LA, JEFF A., Science Teacher; *b:* Stamford, CT; *m:* Debby R.; *ed:* d Heart Univ (MA) Sec Ed Sci 1987; *cr:* Westport Pub Schls Sci Tchr 89; Wilton Pub Schls Sci Tchr 1989-; *ai:* Weather Club Adv; Asst Norwalk MSBL Bsbl Team; NEA 1980-; *home:* 153 Lakeside Dr field CT 06877

LLE, CATHY L., Education Professor; *b:* Gloucester, MA; *m:* rd; *c:* Kristie, Kimberlee; *ed:* Plymouth St Coll (BS) Elem Ed, Rdng, 975; Univ of NH (MED) Ed, ECC 1985; Cert of Advance Grad Stud adership 21 Credits Earned; *cr:* Hudson Lib St Schl Fourth Grd Tchr 79; Hudson Meml MS Coord of Gifted & Talented Prgm 1979-83; CLL Adjunct Fac 1983-; River Coll Adjunct Fac 1989-; *ai:* ECE, Adv Bd; Hudson Schl Dist Kndgtn Implementation Comm; Odessey nd Coord NW Elem; Phi Delta Kappa 1980-; NAEYC 1990-; Assoc pervision and Curr Dev 1994-; Dir Stud Prgm & Self9Design degree dates Mentor; Success Practices in Ed Awd St Dept of Ed; guished Fac Awd 1994; *office:* Rivier Coll 420 S Main St Nashua NH

NE, TERELL PRINCE, Asst Professor of Psychology; *b:* Clark Phillipines; *ed:* Howard Uinv (BS) Psych 1990; Univ of DE (MA) 1993, (PHD) Psych 1995; *cr:* Univ of DE Research Fellow 1990-93, g Asst 1993-94, Prgm Cnslr 1990-95; St Mary's Coll of MD Asst Prof ; *ai:* Africana Stud; Institutional Review Bd; Acad Resources Comm, g Learning Group; Amer Psychological Assn, Amer Psychological 990-; Traffic Appeals Bd 1994-; Amer Psychological Assn Fellow 93; Univ of DE Fellow 1990-93; *office:* Saint Marys Coll Of MD of Psychology St Marys Cy MD 20686*

'ALA, MERRILY HANDELSMAN, Mathematics Teacher; *b:* ic, NJ; *m:* Faust A.; *c:* Larissa; *ed:* Montclair Univ (MA) Prsnl & Fairleigh Dickinson Univ (BS) Math Ed; 30 Credits Math & Prof *cr:* North Arlington HS Math Tchr 1973; Cedar Grove HS Math Tch 1980-; *ai:* PTA Fac Rep; Cedar Grove Ed Assn Bldg Rep; Schlsp n Mem; Class of 1996 Adv; NJEA 1968-; NEA 1968-; ECEA 1980-; A 1980-, VP; Delta Kappa Gamma 1985-, VP; Governors Tchr gnition Awd 1988; Tandy Corp Outstdng Tchr Awd 1994-95; *office:* Grove HS Rugby Rd Cedar Grove NJ 07009*

'ALA, PHILIP MICHAEL, Special Education Teacher; *b:* own, PA; *m:* Colleen Duddy; *c:* Nicole, Samantha, Gabrielle; *ed:* s Coll (BA) Spec Ed 1974; Marywood Coll (MS) Spec Ed 1975; Univ ranton (MS) Elem Sch Admin Prin Cert 1985; 30 Credit Hrs Wilkes Ed of Micro Cmptrs; *cr:* Luzerne Intermediate Unit White Haven Ctr Ed Tchr 1977-86, West Side Voc Tech Learning Support Tchr 1987-; IEA, PSEA 1977-; Luzerne Intermediate Ed Assn 1977-, Sec; *office:* Side Area Voc Tech Schl 75 Evans St Wilkes Barre PA 18704

EK, LESLIE SUE (COHEN), Spanish Teacher; *b:* Bronx, NY; *m:* ge M.; *c:* Rachel Rhoades; *ed:* Bronx Comm Coll (AA) Liberal Arts CUNY at City Coll (BA) Span, Fr 1967; SUNY at New Paltz (MS) gual & Spec Ed 1985; NYU 30 Credit Hrs Span Lit 1968; *cr:* Bronx n Coll Adjunct Lang Instr PT 1967-72; Mechanicstown Schl Sub & ev Tchr 1976-83; Acad Av Schl Itin Bilingual Tchr 1983-84; Chorley tin Biling ual Tchr 1983-84; T. Moon Schl Itin Bilingual Tchr -84; Middletown HS Span Tchr 1985-; *ai:* HS Bldg Rep Union -93; Schlsp Comm 1991-93; AFT, NYSUT 1968-; NYSFLT 1985-; gual Special Ed Grant 1984; *home:* RR 2 Box 64 New Hampton NY 8

H, MARGARET CLARE, Health & Physical Ed Teacher; *b:* Avon OH; *ed:* Notre Dame Coll (BA) Hlth & PE 1981; *cr:* St Augustine Hlth, PE Tchr 1981-83, 1993-; Regina HS Hlth, PE, AD Tchr -93; *ai:* JV Vlybl, Magnificat Swim Coach; *office:* St Augustine Acad 3 Lake Ave Lakewood OH 44107

HLEY, BARBARA REINER, Second Grade Teacher; *b:* Pottsville, *m:* William H. Jr.; *ed:* Millersville Univ (BSEd) Ed, Eng 1970; Trenton oll (MED) Ed 1978; Post Grad Work Villanova Univ Summer 1985 cal Thinking; *cr:* Southard Schl 1st Grd Tchr 1970-72; Howell Twp Step-Ahead Summer Prgm Tchr; Southard Schl 2nd Grd Tchr 1972-; *ai:* Past Staff Dev Comm; NEA 1970-; Howell Twp Ed Assn 1970-, Recording Sect-Past; Amer Assn of Univ Women 1989-, Pub Policy Chair, VP; Delta Phi Eta Past Mem 1970; *office:* Southard Schl Kent Rd & Lanes Mills Rd Howell NJ 07731

LASKEY, FRANCES POLLACK, English Teacher; *b:* Passaic, NJ; *m:* Richard A.; *ed:* William Paterson Coll (BA) Eng 1966; Addtl Stud Eng, Speech Arts, Cmptr Tech; *cr:* Clifton Pub Schls Eng Tchr 1966-; *ai:* Acad Awds Dinner Comm; Coach Acad Quiz Team; Clifton Tchrs Assn; Passaic Cty Ed Assn; NJEA; NEA; NCTE; *office:* Clifton H S 333 Colfax Ave Clifton NJ 07013

LASKOWSKI, ALLAN L.,JR., Teacher & Coach; *b:* Harrisburg, PA; *m:* Eloise R. Haag; *c:* Kara, Alana, John; *ed:* Millersville St Coll (BS) Comp Soc Stud & His 1965; CO St Univ Driver Ed 1972; TX Chrstn Univ Driver Ed 1974; Penn St Univ (MS) Driver Ed 1974; *cr:* Bermudian Springs HS Faculty Coach 1965-66; Eastern Lebanon HS Faculty Coach 1966-69; Williams Valley HS Faculty Coach 1969-; *ai:* Co-Dir Second Effort Bsktbl Camp; PA Forestry Assoc 1968-, Bd of Dir; Ned Smith Ctr Nature & Art 1995-; Trout Unlimited 1996-; Am Forestry Assoc 1968-; PA Forestry Conservation Awd St Championship; PA Tree Farm System St Championship; Eagle Scout Troop 147; ADTSEA Schlsp Awd 1972 & 1974; *office:* Williams Valley HS Rt 209 Tower City PA 17980

LASKY, MARSHA, Social Studies Chairperson; *b:* Brooklyn, NY; *m:* Stanley; *c:* Sean, Brian; *ed:* Brooklyn Coll (BA) His 1963, (MA) His & Soc Stud 1966; *cr:* Shellbank JHS 14 Soc Stud Tchr 1963-70; Long Island Schl for Gifted Soc Stud Chprsn 1985-; *ai:* News Bowl Adv; Stock Market Game Coord; Geography Bee Adv; Long Island Cncl for Soc Stud, NCSS 1986-; *office:* Long Island Schl For Gifted 165 Pidgeon Hill Rd Huntingtn Sta NY 11746

LASSEN, LOLITA WHITE, Foreign Language Dept Chair; *b:* New York City, NY; *m:* Jack A.; *ed:* Towson St Univ (BA) Span 1971; 60 Addl Credit Hrs; *cr:* Sudbrook Jr HS Span Tchr 1971-73; Parkville Jr HS Span Tchr 1973-74; Pine Grove MS Dept Chair 1974-90; Loch Raven HS Tchr 1990-94, Dept Chair, Tchr 1990-; *ai:* Sr Class Spon; Elem Span Prgm Taught by HS Stdnts Coord; Fac Cncl; Soc Comm; NEA, MSTA, TABCO 1971-; Ruxton Crossina Bd of Dirs 1991-; Outstdng Tchr MFLA 1986; Innovative Approach to Tchng Modern Langs Span Lang Prgm Recognition Bd Meeting; Highest Success Rate with Span AP Lang Scores in Cty 3 Yrs Recognition; *office:* Loch Raven HS 1212 Cowpens Ave Baltimore MD 21286*

LASSITER, ERNEST LEE, Journalism Professor; *b:* Durham, NC; *m:* Hannah Louise Edwards; *ed:* Tuskegee Univ (BS) Scndry Ed Eng 1959; Boston Univ (MS) Jrnlsm 1963; Morgan St Univ (EDD) Ed Admin, Ldrshp 1993; *cr:* Afro-Amer Newspapers Inc Copy Ed 1961-66; Baltimore News Amer Copy Ed 1966-71, Feature Ed, Wire Ed, Editorial Writer 1971-86; Coppin St Coll Jrnslm Assoc Prof 1986-; *ai:* Recruitment, Rentention, Budget, Frosh Advy Comms; Campus Newspaper Adv; NCEA 1993-; Phi Delta Kappa 1992-; *office:* Coppin State Coll 2500 W North Ave Baltimore MD 21216

LASTER, CAROLE ANN HURSEY, Assistant Principal; *b:* Bridgeton, NJ; *m:* Miles; *c:* Reginald Lamont, D'Andre Monare, Jana Camile; *ed:* Cumberland Cty Coll (AA) Lbrl Arts 1968; Rowan-Glassboro St Coll (BA) Sci, Math Ed 1969, (MA) Admin, Scndry Ed 1979; West Jersey Hosp Schl of Med Tech Cert 1957; *cr:* Bridgeton Jr HS Math, Sci Tchr 1969-77; Cumberland Regnl HS Math, Sci Tchr 1977-78, Subject Area Coord 1978-80, Dept Supvr 1980-82, Asst Prin 1982-; *ai:* African-Amer His Month Chrprsn; Affirmative Action Multi Equity Ofcr; Workers Right to Know Ofcr; Schls Restructing Comm; Band & Band Front Promoter; Natl & St Assn for Scndry Schl Prin 1982-; Alpha Kappa Alpha 1990-, Comm Svc 1988; Household of Ruth 1957-, Most Noble Governor of NJ Ldrshp; Cty Mental Hlth Bd 1992-; Bridgeton Bd of Ed 1983-92 VP 1 Yr; Focus on Teens 1988-, Exec Dir; Mt Zion AME Church 1970-, Treas, Head Steward; *office:* Cumberland Regional HS PO Box 5115 Bridgeton NJ 08302

LATCHFORD, MARY-MARGARET KARDIAN, Social Studies Teacher; *b:* Baltimore, MD; *m:* Paul Carroll; *c:* Kevin; *ed:* Univ of Baltimore (BS) Mrktg 1968; Coll of Notre Dame (BA) Comm 1987; Addl 30 Hrs Ldrshp Tchng; *cr:* Mercy HS Soc Stud Tchr 1991-; *ai:* Sr Team; Mid Sts Evaluation Comm Chair; Sr Slide Presentation Coord; Alumnae Affairs Asst Dir; NCEA 1991-; Marian House 1995-, Bd Mem; *office:* Mercy HS 1300 E Northern Pky Baltimore MD 21239

LATCHFORD, WAYNE H., Physics Teacher; *b:* Carlisle, PA; *m:* Janet Kieffer; *c:* Matthew, Shelby; *ed:* Shippensburg Univ (BA) Bio 1974; Attnd Susquehanna Univ Ed & Physics 39 Credits 1987, Bloomsburg Univ Biochemistry 6 Credits; 3 Addl Credits in Chem; *cr:* Boma Enterprises Tech Dir 1982-85; Middletown Area Sci Tchr 1985-87; West Snyder HS Sci Tchr 1987-91; Mifflinburg Area Physics Tchr 1991-; *ai:* Sci Club & NHS Adv; Natl Engrng Design Challenge Coach; PA Jr Acad of Sci Spon; AYSO Coach; AAPT, CPPTA 1988-; NSTA, PSTA 1986-; NEA, PSEA, MAEA 1985-; Freeburg BSA 1984-, Asst Scout Master; Emmanuel Luth Church 1977-, Church Cncl, Sunday Schl Tchr 1977-; Selinsgrove Soccer Parents 1993-, Fund Raising Comm; Susquehanna Ridge Runners 1990-; *office:* Mifflinburg Area HS 1st & Market Sts Mifflinburg PA 17844

LATELLA, JAMES J., English Teacher; *b:* PA; *m:* Annette Azzarello; *ed:* CA Univ of PA (BS) Eng 1963; Addl 40 Grad Hrs Penn St, CA Univ of PA; *cr:* Burgettstown JS HS Eng Tchr 1963-; *ai:* PSEA; NEA; *office:* Burgettstown Area Jr/Sr HS 99 Main St Burgettstown PA 15021

LATHAN, DEBORRAH ROUSE, 4th Grade Teacher; *b:* Erie, PA; *m:* Donald L.; *c:* Benjamin, Joshua, Amanda; *ed:* Thiel Coll (BA) Psych, El Ed 1975; SUNY at Geneseo (MS) Early Chldhd; *cr:* Mill Village Eelm Schl 1st, 3rd-4th Grd Tchr 1975-78; Wolcott Street Schl 4th Grd Tchr 1978-; *ai:* AFT 1975-; *office:* Wolcott Street Schl Wolcott St Le Roy NY 14482

LATHAN, LANCE EMERSON, History Teacher; *b:* Taunton, MA; *m:* Karen Elizabeth Zolnay; *ed:* Bates Coll (BA) His, Psych 1985; OH Univ (MS) Clinical Psych 1988; Addl 2 Yrs Post Masters Psych; *cr:* Berkshire Schl His Tchr 1990-94; Western Reserve Acad His Tchr 1994-; *ai:* Var Girls Bsktbl, JV Bsbl Coach; Admissions & coll Guid Comm; *office:* Western Reserve Acad 115 College St Hudson OH 44236*

LATHBURY, ALLEN FRANKLIN,JR., Science Teacher; *b:* Milford, DE; *m:* Kelly Jane Gray; *c:* Trent Allen-Madison; *ed:* Univ of DE (AS) Sci, MAth 1978; Salisbury St Coll Univ (BS) Sci, Math 1980; DE St Coll Univ (MED) Sci Ed 1992; Addl 36 Credit Hrs Undergrad & Post-Grad Stud, Accounting & Architectural Engineering; *cr:* A.J.'s Self-Employed Business 1980-; Sussex Cntrl HS Phys Sci, Physics & Chem Tchr 1991-; *ai:* Soph Class Adv; Instructional Materials Review Comm; Sci Olympiad; DSA, IREA, NSTA 1991-; Shriners 1982-; Lions Clubs 1984-.

LATHROP, CONSTANCE COOK, French Teacher; *b:* Washington, DC; *m:* Thomas A.; *c:* Aline Katherine; *ed:* UCLA (BA) Fr 1968; Universite de Bordeaux Cert Fr 1967; 36 Quarter Units Fr; Univ of Madrid Curso Intermedio Span; Univ of Delaware Span 6 Units, Interactive Lang Learning 4 Units; *cr:* Caravel Acad Fr Tchr 1982-87; Perryville HS Fr Tchr 1987-; *ai:* Club Intnl, Societe Houoraire de Francais Adv; FAC, TUST; NHS Fac Cncl Mem; Club Day Comm Chair; DECTFL, AATF 1982-; MSTA, CCCTA 1987-; Tchr of Week Cecil Whig; McDonald's Ray Kroc Jr. Tchr Achvmnt Awd; Article DECTFL Newspaper 1984, AATF Natl Bulletin 1989; Contribution to Langs of Thought Bette Hirsch Coll Entrance Exam Bd 1989; *office:* Perryville HS 1696 Perryville Rd Perryville MD 21903*

LATHROP, ROBERT D., Choral Director; *b:* Meshoppen, PA; *m:* Shirley M. Heller; *c:* Sarah, Cathleen; *ed:* Mansfield Univ (BS) Music Ed 1974; Marywood Coll (MED) Music Ed 1977; West Chester Univ 15 Credit Hrs; Cmptr Tech 15 Credit Hrs; *cr:* Pocono Mountain MS Gen Music Tchr 1974-86; Pocono Mountain Jr HS Choral Music Dir 1986-; *ai:* Natl Jr Hnr Soc, Stu Store Adv; Choral Ensembles Dir; New Tchrs Mentor; NEA, PSEA 1974-, Fac Rep, St Del; MENC, PMEA 1974-, Exec Comm Mem; ACDA 1993-; Wayne Choralaires 1990-, Dir; St Paul's Ev Luth Church 1975-, Choirs, Choir of Worship, Music Dirs; *office:* Pocono Mountain Jr HS PO Box 200 Swiftwater PA 18370

LATHROUM, MARCIA R., Guidance Chairperson; *b:* Baltimore, MD; *m:* Terry M.; *c:* Stephen Altshuler, Michael Altshuler, Jill Altshuler, Matthew; *ed:* Boston Univ (BS) Spec Ed 1968; Loyola Coll (MS) Guid Cnslng 1971; Addl Hrs Admin Supervision; *cr:* Ridge Schl Spec Ed Tchr 1968-73; Hillcrest Elem Schl Guid Cnslr 1973-81; Woodmoor Elem Schl Guid Cnslr 1981-82, 1984-87; Edmondson Hghts Maiden Choice Ctr Guid Cnslr 1982-84; Lansdoune HS Guid Cnslr 1987-89; Ouings Mills HS Guid Cnslr 1989-91; Landowne HS Guid Cnslr 1991-; *ai:* Mediation, Helper Peer Spon; BCACD 1971-; *office:* Lansdowne HS 3800 Hollins Ferry Rd Baltimore MD 21227

LATIMER, JAMES M., Physics Teacher; *b:* Hershey, PA; *m:* Denise E. Lang; *c:* James P.; *ed:* SUNY Maritime Coll (BS) Meteorology, Oceanography 1984; *cr:* Navitech Inc Marine Weather Forecaster 1984-86; SUNY-Maritime Coll Meteorology Adj Instr1986-88; Rancocas Vly Reg HS Physics Tchr 1988-; *ai:* Marching Band Ass't Dir; Physics Team Coach; Class Head, Peer Ldr, SADD Chapter Adv; Design 2000 Tech Comm; NJEA 1988-, Head Ass Rep; NJSTA 1988-; Cedar Brook Bible Church 1990-, Deacon; Tchr of Yr Nom 1990, 1991, 1995; WVU-NRAO Investigating the Universe Grant 1993; Presenter NJ St Sci Tchr Convention 1990, 1992, 1994-95, Earth Sci Conf 1991; *office:* Rancocas Valley Regional HS Jacksonville Rd & Ridgeway St Mount Holly NJ 08060

LATINI, GLORIA DEANNA, Spanish Tchr & Japanese Fac; *b:* Camden, NJ; *ed:* Rutgers Univ (BA) Frgn Lang 1968; Glassboro Rowan (MA) Ed, Supvr, Admin 1975; Rutgers Univ (EDS) Ed 1990; 100 Addl Credit Hrs; Certs in Span, Fr, Supervision, Prin, Chief Schl Admin; *cr:* Willingboro Meml Jr HS Span, Fr Tchr 1968-80; Willingboro HS Frgn Lang Supvr 1980-90, Span Tchr 1990-; *ai:* NEA, NJEA, WEA, Northeast Conf of Frgn Lang Tchrs 1968-; *office:* Willingboro HS Levitt Pkwy Willingboro NJ 08046

LATMAN, JOEL, United States History Teacher; *b:* Brooklyn, NY; *m:* Cheryl Hertz; *c:* Ken, Jason, Karen; *ed:* Eastern MT Coll (BSEd) Soc Stud Ed 1969; Eastern CT St (MSEd) Soc Stud Ed 1975; Attnd Stanford Univ, Univ of CA at Los Angeles, Wake Forest Univ, Univ of GA & KS Univ; *cr:* Montville HS US His & Law Tchr 27 Yrs; *ai:* Young Educators Soc Adv; Natl His Day Adv & Coord; Staff Dev & Standards Comms; NEA, CEA 1969-; NCSS 1980-, Citizenship Ed Comm; NCHE 1993-; Citizenship Ed Consortium, Prison Reform Bd 1990-; William Robertson Coe Fellowship; Natl Endowment for Hum Fellowship; Natl His Day Tchr of Yr; Celebration of Excl Awds; CT St His Day Tchr of Yr; *office:* Montville HS Old Colchester Rd Oakdale CT 06370*

LATNEY, CARLEEN MARIE LEWIS, English Teacher; *b:* Washington, DC; *m:* Gregory LaMont; *c:* Audra, Alyse, Alexis; *ed:* DC Tchrs Coll (BS) Eng 1974; Howard Univ (MED) Rdng 1977; Univ of DC (MLS) Lib Sci 1992; Attn Trinity Coll, Hampton Inst; *cr:* Shaw Jr High Eng Tchr 1980-81; Chamberlain Career Ctr Eng Tchr 1981-83; Coolidge Sr HS Eng Tchr 1983-94; McKinley Penn SHS Eng Tchr 1994-; *ai:* Jrnlsm, Honor Soc, Sr Class Spon; Media Ctr Comm Mem; Phi Delta Kappa 1990-; DC Cncl of Tchrs of Eng 1983-; WA Tchrs Union 1984-; Bd of City Educators Folger Shakespeare Lib 1995-; Alpha Kappa Alpha 1974-; Girls Scouts of Amer 1974-; Prof Dev Schl Fellow; Curr Writer for DC Pub Schls Pub; Chm Awd Outstanding Stu in Lib Sci; Intergenerataion Awd Svc to Comm; *office:* Mc Kinley-Penn Sr HS 2nd T St NE Washington DC 20002

LATOURELLE, SANDRA M. (RANKIN), Adjunct Professor of Biology; *b:* East Orange, NJ; *m:* Gary; *c:* William, Bonny Miraglia, Becky Folsom; *ed:* St Univ of NY at Plattsburgh (BS) Bio 1970, (MS) Bio 1976; W. H. Miner Inst (IVCBB) Molecular Bio 1989; 140 Addl Hrs; *cr:* Ausable Vly Cntrl Schl Bio Tchr 1971-95; Clinton Comm Coll Bio Instr 1983-; SUNY Bio Instr 1996; *ai:* Sci, Hlth, Math Dept Chprsn 8 Yrs; Girls Track Coack 2 Yrs; Boys Track, Field Coach 3 Yrs; AFT 1973-; STANYS 1971-; NABT 1992-, Outstdng Bio Tchr Awd 1995; NSTA 1990-; Town of Plattsburgh Zoning 1984-91, Chprsn; Clinton Cty Agricultural, Indstrl Soc 1979-, VP; Amer Heart Assn 1992-, Ed Dir, Cncl Mem; Clinton Cty Democrats 199, Co-Chprsn; Sigma Xi Rsrch Grant 1988, Northeastern Sci Tchr of Yr 1991; North Cntry Tchr Resource Ctr Grants 1990-91, 1994, 1996; Cornell Inst Bio Tchrs Grants 1992-94, 1996; Josephine Hopkins Grant 1995; ITV Master Tchr 1995-; *home:* 409 Rugar St Plattsburgh NY 12901*

LATSHA, TIMOTHY, High School Choral Director; *b:* Sunbury, PA; *m:* Jennifer E. Peters; *ed:* Mansfield Univ (BMME) Music Ed 1991; Marywood Coll Grad Stud; Orff & Kodaly Level One Certs; Voice Care Network; *cr:* Bloomsburg Area Schl Dist HS Choral Dir, K-5 Gen Music & Choral Tchr 1991-; *ai:* Catch 22, Amigos & No Bass Vocal Ensembles Dir; 4th-5th Grd Ensembles Dir; Bloomsburg Area Edctrs Assn & NEA 1991-; PMEA & MENC 1991-; ACDA 1993-, Regnl Coord; Bloomsburg Chrstn Missionary Alliance Church, Childrens Choir Dir 1994-; Penn St Stu Tchr Cooperating Tchr; *office:* Bloomsburg Area Schl Dist 1200 Railroad St Bloomsburg PA 17815*

LATTA, DEBRA LEE, Asst Principal; *b:* Allentown, PA; *m:* Stanley E.; *c:* Aimee, Erinn; *ed:* PA St Univ (BS) Scndry Ed, Eng, Fr 1979; Addl 30 Credits for MED in Curr, Instruction 1983, Exchange Stud for 4 Months to Univ of Strasborg in France for Fr Ed; Princ Cert 1995; *cr:* St Coll Area Schl Dist Fr Tchr, Substitute 1979, 10th Grd Eng Tchr 1979-80, 7th Grd Eng Tchr 1980-88, 8th Grd Eng Tchr 1988-95; Asst Prin 1995-; *ai:* Schl Dist Founder, Implementor Peer Mediation Prgm; Act Spon Spec Eng, Soc Stud; Contact Person Cntrl PA Jr High Spelling Bee, Adv; St Coll Area Ed Assn 1979-95, Pres, Past Pres, VP, Exec Cncl Mem, Fac Rep; PSEA 1979-, Exec Cncl, St Comm Intergroup Relations, Voting Del St Houses of Dels; NEA 1979-, Voting Del to Natl Conventions; Phi Delta Kappa Prof Educ 1990-; NCTE, AATF; YMCA, Instr 6 Yrs; St Coll Area Jaycees 1984-, Outstanding Young Educator Awd; St Coll Area Kiwanis, Local Schl Ldr of Builders Club; St Coll Area, Centre Comm Hospital Auxillary Bd; St Coll Nita-Nee Kennel Club, Sec; Samoyed Club of Amer; Nom Who's Who in East 1985; *office:* State College Jr HS 2180 School Dr State College PA 16803*

LATTA, EDWARD M.,JR., 5th Grade Teacher; *b:* Zanesville, OH; *c:* Brett, Cassie; *ed:* Wilmington Coll (BA) Elem Ed 1971; Wright St Univ (MA, Rdng, Admin; *cr:* Heywood Elem Schl 6th Grd Tchr 1975-91; Hook Elem Schl 5th Grd Tchr 1991-; *ai:* Amateur Radio Club Adv; Dist Tech Team; Bldg Tech Comm Chprsn; TCEA, OEA, NEA 1975-; Miami Cty Amateur Radio Club 1978-, Pres; Troy Strawberry Festival Comm 1992-; Nancy Currie Troy Schls Grant for Innovative Sci & Math Instruction; SW OH Educl Tech Ldrshp Awd; *office:* Hook Elem Schl 729 Trade Square W Troy OH 45373

LATTARI, NICHOLAS B., 9th & 12th Grd Soc Stud Tchr; *b:* Phila, PA; *m:* Georgeann; *c:* Nicholas, Christine; *ed:* John F. Kennedy (BA) Sociology

1969; *cr:* Cardinal O'Hara HS Soc Stud Tchr 27 Yrs, Ath Dir 6 Yrs; *ai:* Boys, Girls Sport Ath Dir 23 Yrs; *office:* Cardinal O'Hara HS 1701 S Sproul Rd Springfield PA 19064

LATTEN, JAMES EVERETT, HS Instrumental Music Teacher; *b:* Wellsville, NY; *m:* Darlene Nester; *c:* Bethany; *ed:* Mansfield Univ (BME) Music Ed, Percussion 1986; IN Univ Univ (MME) Music Ed, Conducting 1990; (PhD) Music Ed 2 Credits Eastman Schl of Music, 2 Credits Ithaca Coll; Begin PA St Univ 1996; *cr:* Penn Yan Acad HS Band Dir 1987-90; Homer Sr HS Band Dir Dist Percussion Lessons 1990-; *ai:* Marching Band; Indoor Color Guard; Theatre Orchestra; Indoor Marching Percussion Ensemble; Class of 2000 HS Steering, Instructional Tech Comms; NYS Schl Music Assn, Music Educators Natl Conf 1987-; NYS Band Dirs Assn 1990-; Percussive Art Soc 1983-; Articles Pub in NYS Schl Music News, NYS Band Dirs; HS Concert Band CD Released; *office:* Homer Central Schl 80 S West St Homer NY 13077*

LATTIMER, ROGER, High School Guidance Counselor; *b:* Goshen, NY; *m:* Debra Elliott; *c:* Shannon, Grey, Lindsey Allen, Jennifer, Roger; *ed:* SUNY at Cortland (BA) PE 1966, (mA) PE 1975; SUNY at Oneonta (MA) Schl Cnslng 1985; Grad Work SUNY at Buffalo 1974; *cr:* Brookfield Cntrl Schl PE Tchr & Coach 1966-77; Mt Markham HS Hlth & PE Tchr 1977-82, Schl Cnslr 1982-; *ai:* Soccer, Bsktbl & bsbl coach; *office:* Mt Markham HS Fairground Rd West Winfield NY 13491

LATTIMER, SANDY COX, Fifth Grade Teacher; *b:* Hackensack, NJ; *c:* Brian, Kevin; *ed:* Boston Coll (BA) Elem Ed 1969; Monmouth Coll Grad Stud; *cr:* Matawan Schls 5 Grd Tchr 1969-70; Wall Intermediate Schl Supplemental Tchr 1976-78; St Catharine's Schl 6 Grd Tchr 1978-80; Point Pleasant Meml Schl 8 Grd Tchr 1980-94; Nellie Bennett 4th & 5th Gr Tchr 1994-; *ai:* Stu Cncl, 8th Grd Adv; NEA, NJEA, Point Pleasant Ed Assn 1980-; Governor's Tchr Recognition Awd 1986; Tchr of Yr 1987; *home:* 2185 Terrace Pl Sea Girt NJ 08750*

LATTIMER, SARA VASTINE, 9th-12th Grd Spanish Teacher; *b:* Bloomsburg, PA; *m:* Barry Edward; *ed:* Susquehanna Univ (BA) Span 1976; Frostburg St Univ (MED) Scndry Admin & Supv 1984; *cr:* Ft Hill HS Scndry Span Tchr 1976-; *ai:* Mentor, Peer Mediation Coord; NEA & MSTA 1976-; MFLA; *office:* Fort Hill HS 500 Greenway Ave Cumberland MD 21502

LATTIMORE, KATHY LAMOREAUX, Adjunct English Instructor; *b:* Toledo, OH; *m:* Guy; *c:* Eugene Aarnio, Alexandria; *ed:* TX Tech Univ (BA) Eng 1970, (MA) Eng 1972; 21 Grad Hrs His, Ed; *cr:* Univ of MD Far East Division Adj Eng Instr 1973-75; DOD Predischarge Ed Prgm Lead Tchr 1973-75; SUNY at Plattsburgh Adj Eng Instr 1976-80; Clinton Comm Coll Adj Eng Instr 1976-80; TX Tech Univ Eng Instr 1980-89; TCCC Adj Eng Instr 1990-; SUNY at Cortland Adj Eng Instr 1990-; Broome Comm Coll Adj Eng Instr 1992-; *ai:* SUNY at Cortland Portfolio Comm, Amer Commitments Project; UUP 1990-; Articles Pub; *office:* Tompkins Cortland Comm Coll PO Box 139 Dryden NY 13053

LATULIP, DAVID ARTHUR, Sixth Grade Math Teacher; *b:* Seneca Falls, NY; *m:* Susan Jean Frarey; *c:* Corey Norton, Ryan; *ed:* Oswego St Univ 48 Grad Hrs; *cr:* St Mary's Schl 5th Grd Tchr 1972-74; Mexico MS 6th Grd Tchr 1974-; *ai:* JV Bsbl 1974-82, Var Girls Bsktbl 1979-91, Var Girls Soccer 1986-91, Boys JV Soccer 1992-94 Coach; NYSUT, AFT 1974-; Mexico Youth Soccer Bd 1992-; Mexico Tchrs Union 1989-, Pres, 1st VP, Union Ofcr; *home:* PO Box 683 Mexico NY 13114

LAU, PAMELA HAVEY, Assistant Professor of English; *b:* Mount Holly, NJ; *m:* Bradley Arnold; *ed:* Liberty Univ (BS) Eng, Jrnlsm 1991; CO St Univ (MS) Tech Jrnlsm 1994; *cr:* Gannett Newspapers Natl Ad Mgr 1990-91; CO Cntry Life Freelance Writer 1991-93; Sterling Coll Pres, Instr Exec Asst 1993-94; Lancaster Bible Coll Asst Prof 1994-; *ai:* Stu Newspaper Adv; Worship Team; SCA, NJEA 1994-; Pub Speaker; *office:* Lancaster Bible Coll 901 Eden Rd Lancaster PA 17601

LAUB, MARY L., Third Grade Teacher; *b:* Kutztown, PA; *m:* James H.; *ed:* Kutztown Univ (BS) Elem Ed 1973, (MED) Elem Ed 1976; Temple Univ (EDD) Ed 1993; Attnd Antioch Univ, Millersville Univ, West Chester Univ; *cr:* Greenwich Elem Schl Third Grd Tchr 1973-; Muhlenberg Coll Part Time Adj Prof 1994-; *ai:* Assessment, Math, Reading, Lang Arts Comms; Cooperating Tchr Kutztown Univ Stu Tchng Prgm, Prof Semester Prgm; NEA, PSEA, KATA 1973-, Sec, Publications Chprsn; Intnl Rdng Assn 1988-; Rdng Assn KSRA, TriCounty 1988-, VP; Kappa Delta Pi 1971-; Zion Union Church Maxatawny Consistory Sec; Pub Questionnaire; Doctoral Dissertation; *office:* Greenwich Lenhartsvle Elem Sch 1457 Krumsville Rd Lenhartsville PA 19534*

LAUB, ROBERT LEWIS, Guidance Counselor; *b:* Suffern, NY; *m:* Linda Webb; *c:* Phyllis Stookey, David; *ed:* SUNY at Fredonia (BA) ED 1967; Niagara Univ (MS) Ed 1971; *cr:* 95th St & H F Abate Schls Tchr 1967-78; North & South Jr HS Guidance Cnslr 1978-83; Lasalle HS Guidance Cnslr 1984-91; Niagara Falls HS Guidance Cnslr 1992-; *ai:* Niagara Falls Tchrs 1968-, Pres, Meritorious Svc 1994; NYSUT, AFT 1975-; Niagara Orleans Cnslrs Assn 1992-; Niagara Cty Youth Bd 1992-; Niagara Co Comm Coll Admissions Advy Bd 1990-; Niagara Labor Advy Bd United Way 1995-; P A L Schlsp Comm 1992-; *office:* Niagara Falls HS 1201 Pine Ave Niagara Falls NY 14301

LAUBACH, GERALD T., Adjunct Instructor; *b:* Danville, PA; *m:* Theresa V. Brown; *c:* Colleen, Colin; *ed:* Bloomsburg Univ (BS) Sec Ed Earth, Space Sci 1972; Penn St Univ (MED) Sec Ed Earth, Space Sci 1976; *cr:* Upper Dauphin Area Schl Dist 8th Grd Earth Sci Tchr 1972-77; South Middleton Schl Dist 9th Grd Earth Sci Tchr 1977-85; Dept Environmental Protection Air Quality Prgm Specialist 1985-; *office:* Harrisburg Area Comm Coll 3300 Cameron Street Rd Harrisburg PA 17110

LAUBAUGH, BONNIE KAY, Math Teacher; *b:* Akron, OH; *ed:* Univ of Akron (BA) Math, Scndry Ed 1978; 30 Post Grad Hrs in Math, Ed Courses OH St Univ; *cr:* Brecksville-Broadview Hts Schl Math Tchr 1978-95; *ai:* Hnr Soc Selection, Attendance Comms; Quality Cncl; NEA, BEA 1980-; Tchr of Yr 1993; Nom Presidential Awd for Excl in Sci, Math Tchng 1996; *office:* Brecksville-Broadview Hts HS 6376 Mill Rd Cleveland OH 44147*

LAUBAUGH, RONNIE, Mathematics Teacher; *b:* Barberton, OH; *m:* Cathy Huber; *c:* Brent, Megan; *ed:* Univ of Akron (BS) Ed 1969; 52 Grad Credit Hrs in Cmptrs; *cr:* Fairlawn Elem Tchr 1969-73; Firestone HS Head Wrestling Coach 1969-85, Tchr 1974-, Asst Ftbl Coach 1978-84, Ath Dir 1993-95; *ai:* Adv for Future Tchrs; Akron Ed Assn 1976-; Elected to Summit Cty Wrestling Coaches Hall of Fame; *office:* Firestone HS 333 Rampart Ave Akron OH 44313

LAUBENTHAL, NADINE RICH, First Grade Teacher; *b:* Toledo, OH; *m:* Dennis; *c:* Joseph, Michael, Steven; *ed:* Univ of Toledo (BA) Elem Ed 1966, (M) Elem Ed 1982; *cr:* Eagle Point Elem 2nd Grd Tchr 1966-69; Indian Hills Elem 6th Grd Tchr 1970-80, 1st Grd Tchr 1980-; *ai:* NEA, OH Ed Assn 1966-; *office:* Indian Hills Elem Schl 401 Glenwood Rd Rossford OH 43460

LAUBER, JENNIFER JO, Varsity Volleyball Coach; *b:* Dennison, OH; *m:* Patrick R.; *c:* Christian, Mackenzie; *ed:* Univ of Akron (BS) PE 1986; Grad Hrs 1995; *cr:* Green Local Schls PE & Adapted PE Tchr 1987-92, Var Vllybl Coach 1987-94; Tuscarawas Vly HS Var Vllybl Coach 1995-; *ai:* AAU Jr Olympic Vllybl Coach 1996-; Dist 4 Coaches Assn 1987-, Coach of the Yr 1989, 1992 & 1993; Wayne Cty Ath League 1987-, Coach of the Yr 1987 & 1994; OH HS Vllybl Coaches Assn 1988-, St Coaches Achievement Awd; Zoar United Church of Christ; Speaker OH Adapted PE Conf 1990, Wayne Cty Insvc 1991 & OH HPERD Conf Roundtable 1992; Franklin B Walter Outstdng Edctr Awd 1990; Outstdng Tchr Awd ECO SERC Region 1990; *home:* PO Box 408 Zoar OH 44697*

LAUCHER, DOUG M., Mathematics Teacher; *b:* Marion, OH; *m:* Pamala L.; *c:* Matt, Brad; *ed:* OH St Univ (BA) PE, Hlth, Math 1971; Attnd Bowling Green Univ, Ashland Coll; *cr:* Ridgedale Local Schls Math Tchr 1971-; *ai:* Past Bsktbl Coach; NEA, OEA, RTA 1971-; *office:* Ridgedale Jr Sr HS 3165 Hillman Ford Rd Morral OH 43337

LAUDENSLAGER, KEVIN WADE, French Teacher; *b:* Harrisburg, PA; *ed:* Penn St Univ (BA)-Magna Cum Laude 1985; *office:* Millersburg Area HS 799 Center St Millersburg PA 17061

LAUDER, KATHY BOWMAN, Librarian & Renaissance Coord; *b:* Muncie, IN; *m:* Stephen J.; *c:* David A. Gamble, Christopher W. Gamble; *ed:* Wilmington Coll (BA) Eng 1972; Drug Dependence Inst Yale Univ 1973; Univ of ME at Presque Isle, Post-Grad Theatrical Production; *cr:* Cntrl Aroostook HS Eng, Drama Tchr 1972-77; Sandy Spring Friends Schl Eng, Drama Tchr, Engl Dept Head 1977-87; Vassalboro Schl Dist Home-Schooling Tutor 1987-88; Winslow HS Lib Asst, Long-Term Fr Sub 1988-; Libr Supvr 1994; *ai:* Adv Yrbk 1988, Class 1990-92; Renaissance Coord 1991-; Film Editing Supvr 1989-; Achvmt Awds Comm 1992-; ME Tchrs Assn 1989-; Waterville Interfaith Cncl 1992-; Yrbk Dedications 1976, 1987, 1992; Commencement Address 1992; Articles Pub; Adaptations Performed 1986, 1994; *office:* Winslow HS 14 Danielson St Winslow ME 04901

LAUDER, THOMAS A., PE & Health Teacher; *b:* Worcester, MA; *m:* Susan O'Neil; *c:* Katherine, Andrew; *ed:* Univ of NH (BS) Recreation & PE 1978; Boston Univ (MED) Human Movement (PE) 1988; Wocester St Coll Grad Courses in Ed; Univ of MS Med Ctr Ath Trng Courses; *cr:* Auburn Pub Schls K-6th, K-3rd, 9-12th PE Tchr 1979-85, PE & Hlth Tchr 1993-; Leicester Pub Schls 4th-12th Grd PE Tchr 1985-93; *ai:* Head Ftbl Coach; IM St Hockey; NEA 1979-; MA Tchrs Assn 1979-; Auburn Edctrs Assoc 1979-; Natl Ftbl Fndtn & Hall of Fame 1990-; All Star Asst Ftbl Coach 1989, Head Coach 1993; *home:* 530 Pleasant St Leicester MA 01524

LAUDERMAN, SHARON GREEN, English Teacher; *b:* Lancaster, PA; *m:* Reid P.; *c:* Joseph, Kurt, Brian; *ed:* Bloomsburg Univ (BS) Scndry Ed Eng 1972; Penn St Univ (MA) Amer Stud 1992; Millersville Univ Cnslr Ed; *cr:* Bristol Twp Schl Dist Eng Tchr 1972-74; Donegal Schl Dist Eng Tchr 1976-; Elizabethtown Coll Adj Eng Instr 1989-91; *ai:* Donegal Key Club Adv; NEA 1976-; PSEA & DEA 1976-; NCTE & PCTE 1976-; Lititz Historical Fndtn 1990-; Linden Hall Bd of Trustees 1994-; PCTE Annual Convention Presenter 1994; *office:* Donegal HS Rt 772 Caller 304 Mount Joy PA 17552*

LAUDI, MARY ANNE GEMMA, Fifth Grade Teacher; *b:* Cleveland, OH; *ed:* Heidelberg Coll (BA) Elem Ed 1978; Baldwin-Wallace Coll (MAEd) Admin, Supervision 1982; 30 Addl Hrs; *cr:* Brooklyn City Schls Kndgtn Tchr 1978-79, 5 Grd Tchr 1979-; *ai:* Brunswick Ed Assn Rep; Admin Internship Pilot Prgm; Advy Cncl; Hlth Curr, Sci Book Review & Selection, Grd Reporting, Homework Guidelines Comms; Sci Fair Bldg Coord; Odyssey of Mind Coach; Delta Kappa Gamma 1989-; Phi Delta Kappa 1986-; Amer Assn of Univ Women; NEA 1978-; Heidelberg Women's Club of Cleveland 1979-; Tchr of Yr 1988-89; *office:* Hickory Ridge Elem Schl 4628 Hickory Ridge Ave Brunswick OH 44212

LAUERMAN, LINDA ROSE SANCHEZ, Guidance Counselor; *b:* Manhattan, NY; *m:* Edward James Jr.; *c:* Edward James III, Kevin John; *ed:* Trenton St Coll (BA) Eng 1972; Seton Hall Univ (MA) Cnslng 1977; Jersey City St Coll 6th Yr Level Spec Ed 1986; *cr:* Elizabeth HS Eng Tchr 1974-88, Dept Chprsn 1980-87, Guid Cnslr 1988-; *ai:* Union Cty Schl Cnslrs Assn, Natl Schl Cnslrs Assn 1977-; Scndry Schl Women's Club 1974-88; BSA 1987-, Asst Den Ldr, Advancement Chprsn; St Mary's Church 1994-, CCD Sub Tchr; *office:* Elizabeth HS 27 M L King Jr. Plaza Elizabeth NJ 07201

LAUFER, LORRAINE, English Teacher; *b:* Brooklyn, NY; *c:* Michael, Rebecca; *ed:* Pace Univ (BA) Eng 1971; St Univ of NY at New Paltz (MS) Ed 1978; Grad Stud in Eng Ed NY Univ 1971-72; *cr:* Webutuck Jr Sr HS Eng Tchr 1972-; *ai:* NY St United Tchrs 1972-, VP, Grievance Chprsn; Stanford Free Lib, Bd 5 Yrs, Pres 1 Yr; *office:* Webutuck Jr Sr HS Haight Rd Amenia NY 12501

LAUGHLIN, DEBORAH A., Spanish Teacher; *b:* Latrobe, PA; *m:* Patrick Alan; *ed:* Mercyhurst Coll (BA) Span 1975; Middlebury Coll (MA) Span Lang, Lit 1993; *cr:* Mercyhurst Prep Span Tchr 1978-88; Northeast HS Span Tchr 1988-90; Mercyhurst Prep Span Tchr 1990-; Mercyhurst Coll Span Tchr 1993; *ai:* Span club Adv; Mid St Curr Comm Chair; Tchr Intnl Baccalaureate Span Prgm; March of Dimes, Vol; Amer Heart Assn Vol; Articles Pub; Conducted Wkshp 1987-.

LAUGHLIN, DEBRA J., Marketing Education Coord; *b:* Dayton, OH; *m:* Michael G.; *c:* Sara, Matt; *ed:* Bowling Green St Univ (BS) Ed 1978; Univ of Dayton (MS) Schl Counseling 1985; Attnd Wright St Univ; *cr:* Middletown Schl Mrktg Ed Coord 1979-83; Centerville Schls Mrktg Ed Coord 1983-; *ai:* DECA Adv; Drug Core Team Mem; AVA, OVA; OMEA 1990-, Sec, OH Tchr of Yr Awd; NEA, OEA, CCTA 1983-; Western OH Ed Assn 1983-, Western OH Tchr of Yr Awd; South Metropolitan Optimists 1988-, VP, Optimist of Yr Awd; WTRC Swim Team Bd 1992-, Treas; Ashland Oil Golden Apple Awd; Excl in Ed Semifinalist; *office:* Centerville HS 500 E Franklin St Centerville OH 45459

LAUGHLIN, JEFFREY SCOTT, Second Grade Teacher; *b:* Portland, ME; *m:* Deborah H.; *ed:* Boston Univ (BA) Sociology & Eng 1969; Univ of Southern ME (MS) Admin EDU 1981; 15 Hrs Credit Beyond Masters Spec Courses; *cr:* Windham Primary Schl 2nd Grd Tchr 1976-; *ai:* Head Tchr for 16 Tchrs-Bldg Ldr; Bldg Dev Team Chprsn; Mem PET-TAT Team; Chprsn Team to Recertify Provisional Tchrs; NEA & MTA 1976-; Local PTA 1976-, Vol; Phi Delta Kappa 1979-, Historian, Plaque; Bronze Star Awd While in Military Service-Viet Nam; *home:* 28 Woodman Ave Saco ME 04072*

LAUGHLIN, SANDRA ELAINE, Mathematics Teacher & Dept Chm; *b:* Wilkinsburg, PA; *ed:* Indiana Univ of PA (BS) Math 1966; Post Grad Work Univ of Pittsburgh, Kent St Univ, Penn St; *cr:* Penn-Trafford HS Math Tchr 1966-; *ai:* Future Tchrs of Amer Spon; Penn-Trafford Ed Assn 1966-, Pres 1988-92; PSEA, NEA 1966-; NCTM 1992-; Cooperative Learning Trainer; Mentor Tchr for Interns Univ of Pittsburgh; NSF Grant to Kent St Univ; *office:* Penn Trafford HS Rt 130 Hamson City PA 15665

LAUGHMAN, DRUSILLA BELLE, Lang Arts & AP Eng Tchr; *b:* York, PA; *ed:* Wilkes Univ (BA) Eng 1974; Masters Equivalency 36 Hrs; *cr:* Tamaqua Area Schl Dist Eng Tchr 1976-; *ai:* NCTE 1980-; *office:* Tamaqua Area Sr HS Stadium Rd PO Box 90 Tamaqua PA 18252*

LAUGHTON, VIRGINIA HARRISON, 8th Grd Mathematics Teacher; *b:* Philadelpia, PA; *m:* Arthur Anderson; *ed:* Glocester Co Coll (AA) Early Chldhd 1973; Rowan Coll (BA) Early Chldhd, Elem Ed 1976; Plymouth St Coll (MED) Elem Ed 1985; NSF Grant SEA 5 Credits; NSF Grant Bridgewater St Coll 9 Credits; NSF Grant Hartford Trng in Math Standards; *cr:* Marie Katzenbach Schl for the Deaf Houseparent 1973-74; Gloucester Cty Coll Math Tutor 1974-76; Bankroft Schl Houseparent, Tchr 1976; Mira Flores Schl PE, Math & Eng Tchr 1976; Fairfield Twp Pub Schls Math Tchr 1976-77; Washington Twp Pub Schls 6-7th Grd Math Tchr 1977-85; Sandwich Pub Schls 8th Grd Math Tchr 1985-; *ai:* Boys Bsktbl Coach 1977, 1994; Girls BB Coach 1977; Swimming Coord 1978-80; Environmental Coord 1978, 1981; PEEC 2 Week Camping with 8t Intramurals 1984; Cmptr Club 1983-84; Stu Cncl 1986-91; Math Team Coach 1991-; Girls Soccer Coach 1993; Career Day Coord 1 NEA, NCTM 1976-; NJEA 1976-84; Sandwich EA 1985-, PRR Of Bldg Rep; Our Lady Queen of Peace Church 1967-85, 5th & HS CC May Queen Awd; St Davids Church 1985-; Tchr of Yr 1992; Natl Grants Oceanography, Chem & Physics, Math Standards.*

LAURATO, VINCENT I., Religious Ed Dept Chair & Tchr; *b:* Ne NY; *m:* Carol Sue Hoebermann; *c:* Christina, Carol Ann, Regi Fordham Univ (BA) Lbrl Arts 1971; St Joseph's Seminary (MA) R 1983; Post Grad 27 Credit Hrs Church His; *cr:* Ctr for Cath Lay Tchr 1984-; St Joseph's Seminary Permanent Deacon Formation Tc 1993-; Xavier HS Tchr 1989-, Rel Ed Dept Chair 1991-; *ai* Moderator; ASCD, Natl Assn of Stu Activity Advs 1995-; NCEA Woodlawn Taxpayers Assn 1971-; Tchr of Yr Awd 1992, 1995; Xavier HS 30 W 16th St New York NY 10011

LAURENCE, RONALD FREDERICK, AP & Honors Chemistry I New Plymouth, New Zealand; *ed:* Massey Univ (BS) Phys Che 1976, (BA) Math 1977; Working Toward MALS Sci; Tchng Diploma Church New Zealand; Grad Stud UNC; *cr:* Rath Keale Coll Tchr 1 Hotchkiss Schl Tchr 1988-; *ai:* Head of Boys Cross Cntry, Asst Coach; Acad Adv; Yrbk Dedication 1994; *office:* The Hotchkis Lakeville CT 06039*

LAURENZI, FRANCES PATRICIA HUNTER, Drama, Eng, Sp Hum Tchr; *b:* Memphis, TN; *m:* Ernest Sibley Jr.; *c:* Catherine B Mike, Gina, John, Joe, Francesca; *ed:* Memphis St Univ (BS) Eng, Drama 1962; Webster Univ at St Louis (MS) Eng, Speech, Drama 1 Hrs Art of Tchng, MS Belgium Maastrich, Oxford England, K Iceland; *cr:* Memphis-Tech HS Eng, Speech, Drama Tchr 1962 Agnes Acad Eng, Speech, Drama Tchr 1964-67; Bishop Byrne HS 1 Cristobal HS 1981-86; A.T. Mahan HS 1987-; *ai:* Intnl Thespian Founder, Spon; NEA, Federal Ed Assn 1987-; Rel CCD Tchr Eucharis Vol; Morale, Hospitality; Cath Choir Vol; VFW Dem Speech; Cancer Amer Diabeties United Way Fund Coord; Schl Adv Rep Textbook Selection; Stu Govt; Eng Dept Chair Odyssey of Min Keflavik Fire Dept Comm Fire Commercial Awds 1987-; Tchr 1992-93; United Kingdom West Dist DODDS; Yrbk Dedication 1992; Outstdng One Act Play England 1992; *office:* A T Mahon H 1003 Box 52 FPO AE 09728

LAURENZI, JOHN M., Varsity Wrestling Coach; *b:* Bronx, NY; Credits Cortland St Univ; *cr:* Laurenzi Contracting Owner Clarkstown Sr HS South Var Wrestling Coach 1989-; *ai:* Dir, Coac Wrestling Prgm; Rockland Cty Coaches Assn 1989-; NYS Sectio Wrestling Coaches Assn 1989-; Top 10 Ranking Comm 1992-, Chm; Comm 1995-, Chm; SOWCA Coach of Yr Rockland Cty 1993-95, One 1995; *office:* Clarkstown South HS 31 Demarest Mill Rd West NY 10994*

LAURI, ROSANN, Spanish, English & Jrnlsm Tchr; *b:* Wheeling, Gary William; *c:* Samantha; *ed:* West Liberty St Coll (BA) Eng, Spa WV Univ (MA) Instrl Comms 1990; 15 Hrs Cmptr Classes Robert Coll; 3 Hrs Andrews Univ; *cr:* Edison HS Eng, Span, Jrnlsm Tchr *ai:* Schl Newspaper Adv; LIterary Magazine Co-Adv; NEA, OEA, 1985-; Grant from Jefferson Cty Bd of Ed; Wrote Early Eng Asse Grant Given by OH Bd of Regents; *office:* Edison HS RR 1 B Richmond OH 43944

LAURIA, MARGARET MUNRO, English Teacher; *b:* Princeton, Peter F.; *c:* Kevin D. Pirko, Brian J. Pirko; *ed:* Tompkins-Cortland C Lbrl Arts 1977; SUC at Cortland (BA) Scndry Ed Eng 1980, (MS) Ed Eng 1984; NY St Permanent Cert Scndry Fr 1995; Post Grad S Cornell Univ; *cr:* Homer HS Eng Tchr 1979-80; Dryden Jr-Sr HS En 1980-; *ai:* Drama Club Asst Dir; Illusions Creative Writing Club Adv & NY NEA 1980-, Past VP; Dryden Schl Comm Tchr Awd 1994; Jr Sr HS Tchr of the Yr 1994; *office:* Dryden Jr Sr HS Dryden Cnt PO Box 88 Dryden NY 13053*

LAURIA, PETER F., US History, Govt & Ec Tchr; *b:* Brooklyn, Margaret Munro; *c:* Kevin Pirko, Brian Pirko; *ed:* SUNY Cortlan Geography 1969, (MAT) Scndry Soc Stud 1975; *cr:* Dryden Jr-Sr H Stud Tchr 1976-; *ai:* ACT & SAT Coach; Co-Curr Treas; NEA, Dryd Assn 1976-, Chief Negotiator; *office:* Dryden Jr-Sr HS Rt 38 B Dryden NY 13053*

LAURICH, JEAN, Principal; *b:* Philadelphia, PA; *ed:* Chestnut Hi (BS) Elem Ed 1981; Univ of Dayton (MA) Educl Admin; C Montessori Tchr Ed Elem Credential; *cr:* Saint Athanasius 3rd Gr 1973-75; Saint Michael 1st Grd Tchr 1977-81; Christ Our King 4 Tchr 1981-82; Immaculate Heart of Mary 4th Grd Tchr 1982-84; No Fontbonne Acad Jr Level Montessori 1984-90; Our Lady of the Valley Prin 1990-94; Norwood Fontbonne Acad Elem Prin 1994-; *ai:* Curr Facilities Comm Mem; NCEA 1978-, Speaker 1996; Amer Montessc 1985-; SSJ Commission for Justice, Pay Christi 1991-; Global Ed 1984-; *office:* Norwood Fontbonne Acad 8900 Norwood Ave Philad PA 19118

LAURIE, JUDITH ANN, Professor of Spanish; *b:* Lakewood, N Georgian Court Coll (BA) Span 1959; Rutgers Univ (MA) Span Lit 1960; Doctoral Stud Span 1960-68; Free Lance Translator Certfd Translators Assoc Span to Eng; *cr:* Jackson Meml HS Frgn Lang Dep 1964-67; Ocean Cty Coll Hum Prof 1966-; *ai:* Sigma Delta Mu Spc Northwest Region; NEA; FLENJ; ACTFL; AATSP; ATA; Outstdng Amer 1970; Outstdng Tchr FLENJ 1986, Coll Alumni Assn 1992; St Grant Dev Translating Higher Ed 1982-84; Pub Poetry; Pub Artic

LAURIELLO, GLADYS ANNE, Vocal Music Teacher; *b:* Wilmi DE; *m:* Anthony Joseph; *c:* Anthony, Jonathan; *ed:* Lyndhburg Coll Music 1972; Rowan Univ Admin Course Work 1995-; *cr:* Middle T Tchr 1978-; *ai:* Dir Concert Choir, Advanced Ensemble, Treble Musical; MENC, SJCDA 1978-; MTEA 1978-, Pres; NJEA, NEA Tchr of Yr; Governors Awd Outstdng Tchng 1991; *office:* Middle T 212 Bayberry Dr Cape May Court Hou NJ 08210

LAURO, SALVATORE, Spanish Teacher; *b:* Brooklyn, NY; *m:* Masiello; *c:* Livia; *ed:* St Francis Coll (BA) Latin Amer Stud Middlebury Coll (MA) Romance Langs 1976; Attnd Univ MA, Madrid; *cr:* St Gabriel's Schl 5-8th Grd Tchr 1972-75; Forgein Lan Eng Tchr 1975-76; Northfield-Mt Hermon Schl Span Tchr 19 Buckingham Browne & Nichols Schl Span Tchr 1980-82; Pascack Hi Span Tchr 1982-; *ai:* Soccer, Tennis Coach; Span Club & Newspaper Cmptr Tech Comm; Stu Assistance Counseling Program; NEA, TOFEL 1982-; Paramus Recreation 1993-; Bergen Passaic All Star Pres 1990; Lipton All Star Soccer Game Organizer 1993; CORE Chprsn; Help Organize Bergen Cty Soccer & Tennis Tournaments Member; Tchr of Yr Nom; Coach of Yr-Northern NJ.

LAUSCH, RONALD EUGENE, Fifth Grade Teacher; *b:* Lancaste *m:* Brenda Elise Shirk; *c:* John Michael; *ed:* Millersville Univ (BS) Ed 1969; Masters Lehigh Univ & Kutztown Univ Tech; *cr:* Marywoo Adj Instr; Pennridge Schl Dist 5th Grd Tchr 1969-; *ai:* PA St Ed NEA; Pennridge Ed Assn; Milford Twsp Lions Club; Pennridge Ja *office:* J M Grasse Elem Schl Pennridge Schl Dist 5th St Perkasie PA

'H, RONALD ROBERT, Latin & English Teacher; *b:* Lebanon, PA; inus Coll (BA) Philosophy, Religion 1972; Lancaster Theological ry (MAR) Biblical Theology 1976; Post Grad Stud Millersville A St Univ; Franklin, Marshall Coll Credit Hrs; *cr:* Cedar Crest HS ng Tchr 1972-; *ai:* Latin Club, NHS, Peer Mediators Adv; Mem of sistance Team; Episcopal Church Priest; Free, Accepted Masons; 'erit Badge Cnslr; *office:* Cedar Crest HS 115 E Evergreen Rd n PA 17042*

'ENHEISER, BRUCE ALLEN, Chemistry Teacher; *b:* Canton, Susan G. Black; *c:* Matthew, Mindy, Nathan; *ed:* Ashland Univ ath & Chem 1972; Kent St Univ (BSEd) Math & Chem 1976; *cr:* lle HS Math & Chem Tchr 1977-81; Jackson HS Chem Tchr 1983-, ot Chprsn 1995-; *ai:* Sci Fair Judge; NEA & OEA 1983-; SECO office: Jackson H S 7600 Fulton Dr Massillon OH 44646

ENHEISER, MARY JEAN CORDRAY, Social Studies & Math ; *b:* Defiance Cty, OH; *m:* George; *c:* Thomas E., Tamara Jo ; *ed:* Wright St Univ (BS) Elem Ed 1971, (MS) Elem Ed 1974; 2 rs Univ of Dayton; 6 1/3 Grad Hrs Bowling Green St Univ; 2 Grad Wayne Trace Local Schl 3rd-4th Grd Tchr 1967-69; Lincolnview Schl 5th, 7th-8th Grd Tchr 1969-73; Crestview Local Schl 2nd, Grd Tchr 1973-; *ai:* NEA, OEA 1967-; Crestview Ed Assn 1973-, Van Wert Order of Eastern Star 1972-; North Union United Meth 1962-, Sunday Schl Tchr; Crestview North Tchr of Yr 1977, 1982; Crestview Elem Schl 531 E Tully St Convoy OH 45832

'ENHEISER, RAY EUGENE, Vocal Music Teacher; *b:* Paris, OH; ine Marie Lingenhoel; *c:* Jo Ann Stagani, Mark, Kay; *ed:* Mt Union ME) Vocal Music 1962; Kent St Univ (MED) 1971; 9 Hrs OH Univ; nton HS Vocal Music Tchr 1962-93; Edison HS Vocal Music Tchr *ai:* Choir, Glee Club Musical Dir; Choir Dir Amer Music Abroad, Travels; OEA 1962-; ELEA 1968-; OMEA 1962-, Dist Pres; Club 1981-, Pres, Sec, Comm Svc Awd; *home:* PO Box 134 ndsville OH 43930*

'ER, JOANNE PICKELL, 1st Grade Teacher; *b:* Harrisburg, PA; *m:* L.; *c:* Donald L. Jr., Douglas, Jennifer; *ed:* West Chester St Coll Elem Ed 1962; Cert Credits Millersville St Coll; *cr:* er-Strasburg Schl Dist 2nd Grd Tchr 1962-64; Cntrl Dauphin Schl d Grd Tchr 1964-66; Susquehanna Twp Schl Dist 1st, 3rd Grd Tchr *ai:* Dist Soc Stud Comm; PSEA, NEA; Susquehanna Twp Ed Assn Mem, Contributing Ed; Estrelita Chptr; Progress Immanuel Presbyn , Former Deacon; *office:* Susquehanna Twp Schl Dist 3550 on Ave Harrisburg PA 17109

ALBERT, High School Mathematics Tchr; *b:* Bruchweiler, y; *m:* Linda Jean Yackee; *c:* Christopher Joseph, Andrea Jean, Mark ; *ed:* OH St Univ (BS) Math 1973; 9 Credit Hrs Univ of Findlay Programming; 20 Credit Hrs Bowling Green St Univ Cmptr Sci, 3 Hrs Hypercard; *cr:* Donnell Jr HS Math Tchr 1973-78; Findlay Sr h Tchr 1973-; *ai:* Boys Var Soccer Coach 1976-; NEA, OEA, FEA, 1973-; NSCAA, OSSCA 1979-, NW Dist Rep; Knights of ous 1982-, Advocate, Cncl Act Chair, Prgm Dir, Achvmt Awd, of Month; Educator of Month 1990; Coach of Yr 1980, 1994, 1995; Fame OH Scholastic Soccer Coaches Assn 1994-95; *office:* Findlay 200 Broad Ave Findlay OH 45840

JAMES LAWRENCE, Assoc Prof of Communication; *b:* nd, OH; *m:* Desmonde Jo Francik; *c:* Jessica, Derek, Jillian; *ed:* g Green St Univ (BS) Speech Ed 1971, (MA) Comm 1972, (PHD) 1975; *cr:* Bowling Green St Univ Asst Dean of Men 1975-76; Old on Univ Comm Asst Prof 1976-79; Marshall Univ Comm Asst Prof 4; Packard Elec Div of GM Sr Trng Consultant 1985-89; Slippery niv Comm Assoc Prof 1989-; *ai:* Alpha Sigma Phi Fac Adv; Dept omm; Dept Grad Schl, Continuous Improvment Coord; St System of Ed Rep; SCA 1974-; ABC 1994-, Tchng Methodologies, Concepts Blessed Sacrament Church 1985-; Stu Govt Assoc; Adv of Yr; Polisher's Awd for Outstdng Tchng; Exch Prof to S Korea; *office:* y Rock Univ Of PA Dept of Communication Slippery Rock PA

ON, LORRAINE MARIE, Art Teacher; *b:* Lynn, MA; *m:* Paul A.; , Stephen, Michelle Kane, Janice Caporale; *ed:* Art Inst of Boston 994; 3 Credit Gifted Child Course at N Adams St Coll; 3 Credit His edit Shakespeare & Short Story at Berkshire Comm Coll; Several ourses; *cr:* Childrens Art Berkshire Museum Art Tchr 1972-; re Comm Coll Sr Outreach Coll Art Tchr; Reg Art Area Schls Elem Child Courses; *ai:* Various Area Artists Adv; Berkshire Art Assn Sec, Recording Sec, Art Purchase Awd Williams Coll; Berkshire ican Assn; Womens Art Assn 1995-; Tyrigliam Art & Hand of Man es, Rep Art Work; Art Critique & News Articles The Cath Observer, per Written 1972-; Berkshire Writers Wkshp Poetry Pub 1994-95; f-Man & Tyriybam Galleries Art Work Shown; Particing Artist; 00 Poems Pub; Over 700 Newspaper Articles Pub; Countless es for Articles & Poems; *home:* 44 Pollock Ave Pittsfield MA 01201

ON, SALLY JOANNE, Science Teacher & Dept Chprsn; *b:* Malone, Brian Sydow; *ed:* SUNY at Plattsburg (BS) Ed, Sci 1984; SUNY nta (MS) Rdng 1989; 9 Credit Hrs Coaching; 3 Credit Meterology; Credits 1st Aid, CPR; Cert First Responder Course; PADI Scuba *cr:* Sharon Springs Cntrl Schl Sci Tchr 11 Yrs; *ai:* Vars Sftbl Coach; cl Adv; Ath Dir; NHS, Class Adv; Vlybl Coach; Sci Club Adv; Sci hair; Sci Fair Co-Chair; STANYS 1993-; NYSUT 1985-; Sharon s Rescue Squad 1987-, Treas; Explorer Post 17 1987-, Adv, William rgeon; Sharon Springs Yth Rec 1987-91, Life Guard; Who's Who Amer HS Tchrs.*

'EK, JOSEPH JAMES, Language Arts Teacher; *b:* St Albans, NY; bara Ruvolo; *c:* Justin; *ed:* Hofstra Univ (BA) Eng 1971, (MA) Eng Lit 1975; *cr:* Holy Family Schl Lang Arts Tchr 1984-; *ai:* Santa with Stdnts Elves Prison Ministry 1989-; Currently Writing, ng Third Movie Starring Stdnts; Guided, Edited Production 288 Novel Written 8th Graders; PDHP 1994-, Mandated Facilitator, er, Cert of Merit; NASAA 1992-; *office:* Holy Family Schl 7415 St Flushing NY 11366

.AS, SILVIA YOLANDA, Coordinator; *b:* Colon, Republic a; *c:* Allison Danielle, Amelia Dawn; *ed:* Brooklyn Coll (BA) Elem 9; Bank Street Coll of Educ Prins Inst (MS) Ldrshp in Ed Admin, ision 1995; *cr:* Jackie Robinson IS 320 Span Biling Tchr 11 Yrs; ngual Acad for Comm Svc Coord 1 Yr; *ai:* SBM, SDM Comm 1993-95; Multilingual Task Force 1994-; Emigrant After Schl Prgm adv; AFT 1984-; UFT 1984-, Del, Mem; Comm Bd 1994-, Ed Comm; Cncl Proclamation Women's His Month Comm Svc; Tchr of Yr

.ETTE, CINDY GREIDER, English Teacher; *b:* Waterbury, CT; *m:* D.; *c:* Brandon Moir, Sarah Greider; *ed:* St Joseph Coll (BA) Eng Southern CT St Univ (MA) Eng; 30 Addl Credits St Joseph Coll; *cr:* itney TVTS Summr Schl Eng Tchr 1985; Lyman Hall HS Eng Tchr *ai:* Stu Cncl Asst Adv; Stu Act Assessment Comm Chprsn; Admin ment Comm; Jr Class Adv; NEA, CEA, Wlfd EA, NCTE 1985-; Natl Stu Act Advs 1993-95; Jaycees 1986-91, VP, Statesman, Regnl-St Pub Speaking Competition Winner; Outstanding Young n of Amer 1991; Who's Who Among Amer Educators 1989-90, 1994-95; Completed Mentor Trng 1993; *office:* Lyman Hall HS 70 Pond Hill Rd Wallingford CT 06492*

LAVALLEY, DENNIS RALPH, Mathematics Teacher; *b:* Superior, WI; *m:* Seija Annikki Vuori; *c:* Minna Annikki, Mikko Ralph; *ed:* Hillsdale Coll (BS) Math 1964; Ball St Univ (MA) Admin 1972; 50 Plus Hrs Above Masters in Ed; *cr:* Bryant Jr HS Tchr & Coach 1964-66; Dept of Defense Schl Tchr & Coach 1966-; Dept of Defense Schl Upper Heyford England Tchr & Coach 1966-68; Dept of Defense Schl Wurzburg Germany Tchr & Coach 1968-70; Dept of Defense Schl Zweibrucleen Germany Tchr & Coach 1970-73; Dept of Defense Schl Karamusel Turkey Tchr & Coach 1973-75; Dept of Defense Schl Augsburg Germany Tchr 1975-; *ai:* Ftbl Head Coach; Math Dept Chprsn; NEA 1964-, Fac Rep; NTCM 1970-; Presenter at DODDs Wkshps on Block Scheduling & Tchng the 90-100 Minute Period; *home:* Cmr 456 Box 376 APO AE 09157*

LAVELLE, JAMES J., Teacher; *b:* Ashland, PA; *ed:* Bloomsburg PA St Coll (BS) His, Govt 1969; Trenton NJ St Coll (MA) Soc Stud 1972; Rutgers Univ (EDD) Labor Stud Ed 1984; *cr:* Mercer Cty Comm Coll Adj Prof 1972-; PA St Univ Adj Prof 1972-; Rutgers Univ Adj Prof 1972-; *ai:* Kappa Delta Pi 1969-; Natl Endowment For Hum Dickinson Coll, Emory Univ; Robert A. Taft Inst of Govt Grant Trenton St Coll; Univ of VA Walter & May Reutner Meml Scholar; *office:* Harry S Truman HS 3001 Green Ln Levittown PA 19057*

LAVENDER, RAMA LYNN, Business Ed & Comp Sci Teacher; *b:* Portsmouth, OH; *ed:* OH Univ (BSEd) Comprehensive Bus 1978; Attnd Univ of HI Scndry Ed, Univ of Dayton Higher Ed; *cr:* The OH Schl for the Deaf Bus Ed Tchr 1978; Minford Local Schls Bus Ed Tchr 1979-; *ai:* Yrbk Staff Past Adv; Tech 2000, Scioto Cty Stud & Textbook Adoption Comms; NEA 1979-; Minford Ed Assn 1979-; Scioto Cty Historical Soc 1994-, Vol; Yrbk Publication Big E Awd 1981; *office:* Minford HS 135 Falcon Rd Minford OH 45653

LAVER, CARLA (HAYNES), Fifth Grade Teacher; *b:* Toledo, OH; *m:* John Winfield; *c:* Julie Carlene Laver Sanford, John Charles, Jason Clifford; *ed:* Univ of Toledo (BS) Early Chldhd Ed, Elem Ed 1967; Cooperative Learning; Dunn & Dunn Learning Styles U of T; Arts Unlimited BGSU 1991-92, 1994-95; Montessori Dr. V. Fleege Xavier Univ; *ai:* Pilot Cmptr Prgm Team; Mentor Presch Tchr; Sci Resource Coord; Intervention Assistance 1995-; OEA 1967-, Life Mem; NWOEA 1967-, Planning Comm for NWOEA Day 6 Yrs; EEA 1967-, Sec; Delta Performing Arts Cncl 1990-; Trinity Luth Church, Several Comms; Presenter Four Cty Drug CAP Prgm & Martha Holden Jennings 1986; *office:* Lyons Elem Schl 518 N Adrian St Lyons OH 43533*

LA VERNE-LEWIS, ADRIENNE DENISE, Art Teacher; *b:* Philadelphia, PA; *m:* Arthur W. Jr.; *c:* Carmyn Teneil, Paris Tanay Adrienne; *ed:* Glassboro St Coll (BA) Art Ed 1974; Attnd Howard Univ; *cr:* Deptford Twp Bd Grds K-6 Elem Art Tchr 1975-76; Overbrook Sr HS Grds 9-12 Art Tchr 1976-, Adult Night Schl Art Instr 1991-92; *ai:* NJEA 1975-; First Bapt Church of Jericho Adult Church Choir 20 Yrs, Agabe Yth Cncl; Lead Soloist & Background Singer Bette Mc Cullough & Voices of Praise Recording Group; Soloist Many Prgms; *office:* Overbrook Sr HS Turnersville Rd Pine Hill NJ 08021

LAVERONI, BRYANA HANCOCK, Elem Physical Education Tchr; *b:* Kingston, NY; *m:* James John; *c:* Caitlin, Kersten; *ed:* SUNY Cortland (BSE) PE 1982, (MSE) PE 1986; *cr:* Little Friends Presch Tchr 1983-85; The Anderson Schl for Autistic Child PE Tchr 1986-87; Coxsackie-Athens Cntrl Schl PE Tchr 1987-; *ai:* JV, Var Girl's Vlybl Coach; AFT, NYSUT 1987-; NYSAHPERD 1985-; *office:* Coxsackie-Athens Elem Schl 24 Sunset Blvd Coxsackie NY 12051*

LAVERTY, J. PATRICK, Assistant Professor; *b:* Pittsburgh, PA; *m:* Karen Lynn; *c:* Patrick, Jonathan, Shawn, Ian, Michaela; *ed:* Duquesne Univ (BA) Ec 1973, (MBA) Finance 1977; Univ of Pittsburgh (PHD) Acad Computing 1993; Cert of Mgmt Accounting; *cr:* Robert Morris Coll Cmptr Information Scis Asst Prof 1975-; Univ of Pittsburgh Cmptr Sci Lecturer 1980-; Saint Vincents Coll Bus Admin Asst Prof 1980-84; *ai:* KPL Assocs Pres-Financial & Cmptr Consulting; *office:* Robert Morris Coll 5th & 6th Aves Pittsburgh PA 15219

LAVERY, KRISTEN HOLT, Chemistry Teacher; *b:* East Orange, NJ; *m:* James; *c:* Megan Connor; *ed:* Stockton St Coll (BS) Chem 1990; Univ of DE; Univ of HI Fast Prgm Trng; *cr:* Absegami HS Chem Tchr 1992-; *ai:* Tech & Goals 2000 Grant Comms; Dist Wide Tech Task Force; NJEA 1992-; ACS 1990-; Stockton St Coll Sci Fair Judge; *office:* Absegami HS 201 S Wrangleboro Rd Absecon NJ 08201

LAVIGNE, BARBARA TAVARES, 7th & 8th Grd Sci & Math Tchr; *b:* New Bedford, MA; *c:* Matthew O., Todd O., Melissa M.; *ed:* Univ of MA at Dartmouth (BS) Chem 1957; Credits for Cert Tchr; Update Subjects to be Taught 1984-87; 67 Credits Toward Masters; *cr:* Sacred Hearts Acad HS All Bio, Chem & Advanced Math Courses Tchr & Jr & Sr Fac Adv; Univ of MA at Dartmouth Basic Math Tchr & Visiting Lecturer Coll Now 1984-86, Chem Course Tchr & Visiting Lecturer Coll Now 1987-; Saint James-Saint John Schl 7th & 8th Grd Sci & Math Tchr 1987-; *ai:* Responsible for Planning & Managing the 7th & 8th Grd Annual Sci Fair; Schl Dances Chaperone; Regnl Sci Fair at Bristol Comm Coll Judg; NSTA 1990-, Summer Grant 1990; NCEA 1987-; Univ MA Alumni 1957-, Bd of Dirs 1989-95, Pioneers 1987-, Homecoming & Pioneers Weekend; Nom NSTA Excl in Tchng 1990, 1991 & 1996; Greater New Bedford Regnl Tech HS Excl in Tchng Awd 1992; NSF Summer Grant 1990; *office:* St James St John Schl 180 Orchard St New Bedford MA 02740

LAVIGNE, JOY TARALLO, Third Grade Teacher; *b:* S Amboy, NJ; *m:* Darren C.; *c:* Victoria Lynn; *ed:* Middlesex Cty Coll (AS)Early Chldhd Ed 1981; Monmouth Univ (BS) Elem, Early Chldhd Ed 1983; *cr:* South Amboy Elem Schl Tchr 1983-; *ai:* Pupil Assistance Comm; NJ Ed Assn, PTO 1983-; Friends of the Lib 1992-, VP; Yth Historical Awareness Prgm 1989-, Tchr; Tchr of Yr 1987-88; *office:* South Amboy Elem Schl 240 John St South Amboy NJ 08879*

LAVIGNE, KATHLEEN DOWD, Social Studies Dept Chprsn; *b:* Worcester, MA; *m:* Guy C. Truesdell; *c:* Meagan Moriarty; *ed:* Univ of MA (BA) Sociology 1960; Grad Work His, Sociology, Psych, PE, Coaching; *cr:* Grosvenor Neighborhood House Soc Worker 1960-62; Our Lady of Lourdes Schl Elem, Scndry Tchr 1969-73; Adult Ed GED Tchr 1973-78; South Kortright Cntrl Schl His, US His, Global Stud Tchr 1973-; *ai:* Modified Girls Bsktbl Coach; Var Sftbl Coach League & Sect Championships; NEA 1973-, Pres, Chair of Negotiations, Grievance; *office:* South Kortright Central Schl PO Box 113 South Kortright NY 13842

LAVINO, RICHARD GARY, Social Studies Teacher; *b:* New York City, NY; *m:* Mary Alice G.; *c:* Beth M., Alison M., Adam R.; *ed:* Marist Coll (BA) His 1967; Western CT Univ (MS) Soc Stud 1973; 18 Grad Credit Hrs African Stud New Paltz St Univ; *cr:* Yorktown HS Tchr 1967-; *ai:* NHS Comm Mem; Var Golf Coach; AFT 1974-; Curr Presenter at NY St Afro-Asian Conf; *office:* Yorktown HS 2727 Crompond Rd Yorktown Heights NY 10598*

LA VOICE, VICKIANN DESCHAMPS, HS Math & Science Teacher; *b:* Portsmouth, VA; *m:* George R.; *c:* Matthew, Damian; *ed:* Univ of Hartford (BSE) Interdisciplinary Engineering 1979; Rivier Coll (MBA) 1994; .; *cr:* Honeywell SSTD Quality Engr 1979-82; Wang Labs Inc Mfg Product Mgr 1983-90; Presentation of Mary Acad Math, Sci Tchr 1990-; *ai:* Curr Dev; Extra Curr Stencilling, Quilting; Yrbk Adv; NCEA 1990-; *office:* Presentation Of Mary Acad 209 Lawrence St Methuen MA 01844

LAVOIE, ALICE ANNA, 5th-8th Grade Religion Teacher; *b:* Ludlow, MA; *ed:* Catholic Tchrs Coll (BE) Ed 1962; *cr:* ND Cntrl Falls K-2nd Grd Tchr 1952-54; Saint Matthew 2nd-3rd & 6th Grd Tchr 1954-62; Saint James 6th Grd Tchr 1962-66; Saint Marie 3rd Grd Tchr 1971-75; Saint John the Bapt 5th-8th Grd Tchr 1975-; *ai:* Religion Dept Adv; Stu Field Trips Chperone; Tutoring; NCEA 1975-; Yearly Diocesan In-Svc Wkshps for Tchrs; Series of Lectures on New Cath Catechism of Cath Church; Silver Burdett Religion Wkshp; Cmptr Sci Wkshp; numerousa Other Wkshps; *office:* St John The Baptist Schl 217 Hubbard St Ludlow MA 01056

LAVOIE, PAUL A., Psychology Teacher; *b:* Worcester, MA; *ed:* Worcester St Coll (BA) Soc Stud & Fr 1969; Assumption Coll (MA) Guid & psych 1975; Anna Maria Coll Pursuing 2nd Masters Degree; *cr:* David Prouty HS Tchr 1970-; *ai:* AP Instr; Permanent Schlsp Comm; NEA 1970-; MTA 1970-; Spencer E. Brookfield Tchr 1970-; Amer Psychological Assn 1987-; Holder Little League 1990-, Coach; CRA Bsktbl 1993-, Coach; Yrbk Dedication 1975 & 1992; *office:* David Prouty HS 302 Main St Spencer MA 01562

LAW, BARBARA DOYLE, Child Care & Home Ec Teacher; *b:* Caro, MI; *m:* Jeffrey L.; *c:* Stephanie, J. P.; *ed:* Potomac St Coll of WVU (AA) Home Ec 1980; Fairmont St Coll (AAS) Child Care, Dev 1982, (BA) Home Ec Ed 1982; Hlth Cert; Maryland St Sci Alliance Fellows Prgm; *cr:* Kiddie Cntry Dev Learning Ctr Tchr 1983-84; Garrett Cty Head Start Asst Tchr 1985-86; Northern Garrett Cty HS Tchr 1987-; *ai:* VICA, FHA Adv; After Prom Comm; Blind Skier Guide Prgm, HS, Spec Olympics HS Coord; AFT 1989-; PTA 1993-; Deep Creek United Meth Church 1994-, Childrens Church Coord 1994; BPW 1992-; Spinning Interdisciplinary Svc Learning Webs; *office:* Northern Garrett Cty HS 96 Pride Pkwy Accident MD 21520

LAW, DAVID B., Associate Professor; *b:* Youngstown, OH; *ed:* Youngstown St Univ (BA) Eng 1975, (MBA) Acctng 1985; Cleveland St Univ (DBA) Acctng 1995; Scndry Tchng Cert Eng 1976 Youngstown St Univ; OH Cert of Pub Accountancy 1985; *cr:* Mahoning Cty Transitional Homes Behavior Tchng Consultant 1977-82; Youngstown St Univ Grad Asst 1982-84; Hill Barth & King CPAS Supvr 1985-89; Cleveland St Univ Grad Asst 1989-91; Youngstown St Univ Assoc Prof Acctng 1994-; *ai:* First Yr Stu Prgm Mentor; Co-Adv Alpha Tau Gamma; Amer Acctng Assn 1991-; OH Soc Certfd Pub Accountants 1985-; YSU Federal Credit Union 1994-, Bd of Dir; Alpha Tau Gamma Tchr of Yr Awd 1995; Awded Richard D. Irwin Fnd Doctoral Dissertation Flwshp 1993; Elected Beta Gamma Sigma 1991; Amer Inst Certfd Pub Accountants Elijah Watt Sells Awd High Distinction Achvmt CPA Exam 1985; *office:* Youngstown St Univ 410 Wick Ave Youngstown OH 44555

LAW, DAVID LAWRENCE, Asst Prof of Computer Science; *b:* Buffalo, NY; *m:* Catherine M. Sardina; *c:* Anthony, Stephen, Andrew; *ed:* Comm Coll of USAF (AAS) Electronics 1986; SUNY at Plattsburgh (BS) Cmptr Sci 1987; Canisius Coll (MS) Instructional Computing 1989; *cr:* Alfred St Coll Asst Prof 1989-; *ai:* Cmptr Club Adv; *office:* Alfred St Coll 221 Brown Hall Alfred NY 14802

LAW, GERALD H., Music Teacher; *b:* Oneonta, NY; *m:* Sarah Scranton; *c:* Robb, Gregory, Michael, Jason, Jeremy; *ed:* St Univ of NY at Potsdam Crane Schl of Music (BS) Music Ed 1966; Grad Stud at St Univ of NY at Oneonta; *cr:* Peace Corps Africa Agricultural Vol 1966-68; Richmondville Cntrl Schl Music Tchr 1969-76; Jefferson Cntrl Schl Music Tchr 1976-83; Schoharie Cntrl Schl Music Tchr 1983-; *ai:* Jr HS Stage Band & Flute Ensemble; HS Musical Dir; MENC, NYSSMA, NYSUT 1969-; SCMEA 1969-, Pres; Schoharie Tchrs Assn 1983-; Cobleskill Chamber Singers 1986-; Schoharie Cntrl Schl Tchr of Yr; Schoharie, Ulster, DE All Cty Music Festivals; *home:* RR 1 Box 35 Cobleskill NY 12043*

LAW, JUDITH ANN, Office Technology Professor; *b:* Reading, PA; *m:* Harry Gordon; *c:* Christopher; *ed:* Univ of Akron (MS) Post Scndry Ed 1975; *cr:* Howard Comm Coll Office Tech Prof 1975-; *office:* Howard Comm Coll 10901 Little Patuxent Pkwy Columbia MD 21044

LAW, MARY WILHELM, Second Grade Teacher; *b:* Pittsburgh, PA; *m:* Dennis Paul; *ed:* California Univ of PA (BS) Elem Ed 1971, (MS) Elem Ed 1975; *cr:* Maxwell Elem Schl 2nd Grd Tchr 1971-; *ai:* Girls Scouts Career Day Spon; NEA, PSEA, PTO 1971-; Amer Family Inst at Valley Forge Positive Tchng Awd1986; *home:* 219 Blackwood Dr Greensburg PA 15601*

LAW, NORMA PRATHER, Language Arts Teacher; *b:* Newark, OH; *m:* Charles Herbert; *ed:* OH St Univ (BS) Eng Ed 1966; Post Grad Courses Miami Univ of OH, Wright St Univ; *cr:* Marion City HS Eng Tchr 1966-69; Johnstown-Monroe Local HS Eng Tchr 1969-70; West Carrollton Sr HS Eng Tchr 1970-; *ai:* Lang Arts Dept Chprsn; Muse Machine Adv; Fac Wellness Comm; NEA, OEA 1966-; WCEA 1970-, Corresponding Sec, Past Pres; Edctr of Yr 1991-92; *office:* West Carrollton Sr HS 5833 Student St Dayton OH 45449*

LAWLER, ALICE S., English Department Chairman; *b:* Jersey City, NJ; *m:* John T.; *c:* Mary Kate, Sean, Robert; *ed:* Jersey City St Coll (BA) Eng 1972; Georgian Court (MA) Admin & Supvr (MA) 1990; Oxford Univ Shakespeare & Tudor Tradition Stud; *cr:* Acad of St Aloysius Eng Tchr 1968-70; St Rose HS Eng Tchr 1972-91, Eng Dept Chm 1991-; *ai:* Yrbk, Newspaper & Friends of Animals Club Moderator; NCTE 1972-; ASCD 1990-; Chinese Shar-Pei Club of Raritan Vly 1983-, Past Pres; Chinese Shar-Pei Club of Amer 1983-, Rescue Awd with John T Lawler 1993; Rider Univ Outstdng Tchr Awd 1990; Natl Endowment for Hum Grant 1995; Princeton Univ Stud of Tennyson & 19th Century Poets; Companion Grant Geraldine Dodge Fndtn 1995; Articles Pub; *office:* St Rose HS 607 7th Ave Belmar NJ 07719*

LAWLER, CHRISTOPHER, English Teacher; *b:* Maple Shade, NJ; *ed:* Glassboro St Coll (BA) Eng 1982; Rutgers Univ (MA) Eng 1996; *cr:* Washington Twp Schls Eng Tchr 1985-; *ai:* WTEA, GCEA & NEA 1985-; *office:* Washington Township H S Huffville Cross Keys Rd Sewell NJ 08080*

LAWLER, GLORIA ANN, Second Grade Teacher; *b:* Pittston, PA; *m:* William P.; *ed:* Wilkes Coll (BA) Eng, Elem Ed 1972; Masters Equivalency Cert PA St Univ; *cr:* Wyoming Area Schl Dist Tchr 1972-; *ai:* Long Range Planning, Math, Rdng Textbook Selection Comms; NEA, PSEA 1972-; WAEA 1972-, Treas, Exec Bd; WY Area Federal Credit Union 1979-, Bd of Dirs; Luzerne Cty Rdng, IRA 1991-; Lions Club Intnl quest Tchr; IMB-TLC Trng in Classroom Implementation; *office:* John F. Kennedy Elem School 58 Penn Ave Exeter PA 18643*

LAWLER, JOHN R.,JR., Science Teacher; *b:* Auburn, NY; *ed:* SUNY at Cobleskill (AAS) Fisheries & Wildlife Tech 1981; SUNY at Syracuse (BS) Forest Bio 1984; SUNY at Albany (MS) Sci Ed 1985; *cr:* SUNY ESF Wildlife Technician 1982; CANUSA Biological Technician 1983; NYS Dept Environ Cons Fisheries Technician 1984; Weedsport Cntrl Schl Sci Tchr & Coach 1985-; Yth Conservation Corp Group Ldr 1988; *ai:* Envirothon Adv; Environmental Club Adv; Var Boys & Girls Cross Cntry & Girls Var Track & Field Coach; STANAS 1985-; Cornell Coop Ext Environ Cncl 1991-; Weedsport Historical Run Comm 1994-, Dir; Drumlin Runners Club 1994-, Pres; Auburn YMCA Camp Comm 1995-; NY Conservation Tchr of Yr; Cayuga Cty Conservation Tchr of Yr; OHSL Coach of Yr.

LAWLER, JOSEPHINE LEVITE, Third Grade Teacher; *b:* Carbondale, PA; *m:* John J.; *c:* John, Patrick; *ed:* Marywood Coll (BS) Elem Ed 1975, (MED) Elem Ed 1981; *cr:* Washington Schl Third Grd Tchr 1976-78; Roosevelt Elem Fourth Grd Tchr 1975-76, Third Grd Tchr 1978-; *home:* 56 Laurel St Carbondale PA 18407

LAWLOR, DANA ROSE, Senior English Teacher; *b:* Cumberland, MD; *m:* Joseph J.; *c:* Jonathan; *ed:* Univ of DE (BA) Eng 1975, (MA) Eng 1978; Tech Prep, AP Trng; *cr:* DuPont Co Graphic Artist 1985-89; Mount Aloysius Coll Adj Fac 1990-91; Penn Cambria HS Sr Eng Tchr 1991-; *ai:* Renaissance Chprsn; NEA 1991-; Gethsemane UM Church 1990-, Yth Coord, Ed Chair; *office:* Penn Cambria HS 401 Linden Ave Cresson PA 16630

LAWLOR, ELLEN MORRISSEY, Substitute Teacher; *b:* Queens, NY; *m:* Gerard; *c:* Caitlin, Kevin; *ed:* St John's Univ (BS) Ed N-6 1981, (MS) Elem Ed 1986; *cr:* Most Precious Blood Second Grd Tchr 1981-86, Third Grd Tchr 1986-91, Learning Ctr 1991-93, Sub Tchr 1993-.

LAWLOR, JAMES W., HS Orchestra Dir & String Tchr; *b:* Amityville, NY; *m:* Marcia E.; *c:* Kate, Sean; *ed:* Nassau Comm Coll (AS) Music Ed 1971; SUNY at Fredonia (BM) Music Ed 1973; C. W. Post Coll (MS) Music Ed 1979; *cr:* Levittown Meml HS Orch, Jazz Band Dir 1974-76; Sayville HS Orch, Jazz Band Dir 1976-; *ai:* Jr Var Girls Soccer, MS Girls Asst Track Coach; NYSUT, Long Island String Assn 1974-; Sayville Tchrs Assn, Suffolk Cty Music Assn 1976-; Bayport Heritage Soc 1993-; BAFFA Symphony Orch 1996; All Conf, All NY St Soccer Team 1972; Who's Who of Coll Ath 1973; Inducted into SUNY Fredonia Ath Hall of Fame Soccer 1995; *office:* Sayville Pub Schls Greeley Ave Sayville NY 11782

LAWLOR, JANET SCHIAVONE, 6th Grade Teacher; *b:* Waterbury, CT; *m:* Andrew Michael; *c:* Brandon, Bryant; *ed:* Southern CT St Univ (BS) Ed 1969, (MS) Ed 1973; *cr:* Tyrrell Schl 5th Grd Tchr 1969-74; Comm Schl 5th Grd Tchr 1985-88; Long River MS 7th Grd Tchr 1988-91, 6th Grd Tchr 1991-; *ai:* NEA 1969-74, 1985-; *office:* Long River M S 38 Center St Prospect CT 06712

LAWLOR, SUSAN DUNPHY, Fifth Grade Teacher; *b:* Brockton, MA; *m:* Joseph; *c:* Ryan, Eve, Alison; *ed:* Solve Regina Univ (BA) Sociology, Psych 1968; Boston Coll (MA) Spec Ed of Multi-Handicapped 1973; Bridgewater St Coll Cert Schl Psych 1973; 33 Grad Credit Hrs Soc Systems & Children, Combatting Racism, MS Writing & Lit, Adolescent Psych, MS Math; Tchr Effectiveness Trng I & II, Understanding Tchng with Jon Safire, Cooperative Learning, Writing Process, Stress Mngmt Techniques; *cr:* Attleboro Pub Schls 2nd Grd Tchr 1968-70; Coventry R I Pub Schls 4th Grd Tchr 1970-71; Arlington Pub Schls 1-2 Grd Tchr 1971-72; Tyngsboro Pub Schls K-12 Dir Learning Disabilities 1973-75; Inst for Human Svcs K-8 Schl Psychologist 1975; Belmont Pub Schls 2-3 Grd Generic Spec Ed 1984-91; Cambridge Pub Schl 5-6 Grd Tchr 1992-; *ai:* Mentor Tchr Cambridge Pub Schls Mentoring Prgm; Founder, Ed Lit Journal; Environmental Stud; Cambridge Tchrs Assn; MA Tchrs Assn; St Eulalia's Church 1983-, Vol Local Hosp; *office:* Martin Luther King Jr Schl 100 Putnam Ave Cambridge MA 02139*

LAWLOR, TIMOTHY JAMES, 5th Grade Teacher; *b:* Danbury, CT; *m:* Kimberly; *c:* Caleb, Kelsey; *ed:* Keene St Coll (BS) Elem Ed 1987; *cr:* Mt Ceasar Schl Grd 4 Tchr 1987; Fuller Elem Schl Grds 2, 5 Tchr 1987-; *ai:* Odyssey of Mind Coord; Safety Patrol; Drama Club; Peer Mediation; Afterschl Sports; Mentor Tchr; NEA-NH 1996; Phi Mu Delta 1982-, KSC Pres; NH Odyssey of Mind 1994-, Regnl Dir; *office:* Fuller Elementary School 422 Elm St Keene NH 03431*

LAWNICZAK, JAMES HENRY, Technology Teacher; *b:* Buffalo, NY; *m:* Suzanne Barmasse; *ed:* Buffalo St coll (BA) Industrial Arts 1971, (MS) Industrial Arts 1973; *cr:* Depew HS Industrial Arts Tchr 1971-; *ai:* Photography Club; Dist Tech Comm; *office:* Depew HS 5201 Transit Rd Depew NY 14043

LAWRENCE, BARBARA R., French Teacher; *b:* Massena, NY; *ed:* SUNY at Potsdam (BA) Fr 1980; SUNY at Stony Brook (MA) Fr 1985; 75 Addl Credits; *cr:* Bellport MS HS Fr Tchr 1981-; *ai:* Fr Club Adv 1982-88; Second Lang Dept Chprsn 1990-92; SUNY at Potsdam Dept Scholar 1980; *office:* Bellport MS Kreamer St Bellport NY 11713

LAWRENCE, DONALD JEFFRIS,JR., Biology & Chemistry Teacher; *b:* Worcester, MA; *m:* Rose A. Sabourin; *c:* Juliet, Scott; *ed:* Fitchburg St Coll (BSEd) Bio, (MSEd) Sci Ed 1975; CAGS; *cr:* Oakmont Regnl HS Sci Tchr 1970-, Dean of Stud 1994, Vice Prin 1995; *ai:* Var Soccer & Bsktbl Coach; Stu Cncl Adv; Oakmont Tchrs Assn 1970-, Pres, VP, Treas, Exec Bd, Excl in Ed Awd; MA Bsktbl Coaches 1982-, Coach of Yr Awd; MTA & NEA 1970-; NSTA, MSCA, NSCAA & MASC, ASCD, NSSAA, MASSP; Saint Denis Church 1976-, Cncl Chair, Fin Comm; Saint Nicholas Soc 1990-, Pres; WAVE & Digital Equipment Corp Grants Chemecology; GE Star Tchr.

LAWRENCE, ELAINE M., HS Social Studies Teacher; *b:* Cobleskill, NY; *m:* Robert H.; *ed:* SUNY at Oneonta (BS) Scndry Ed, Soc Sci 1990; SUNY at Oneonta (MS) Scndry Ed Soc Sci 1995; *cr:* Oneonta City Schl Sub Tchr 1990-91; SUNY at Oneonta Asst Bsktbl Coach 1990-92; Charlotte Valley C S HS Soc Stud Tchr 1991-; *ai:* Yrbk Adv; Modified Bsktbl Coach; NCSS, ASCD 1990-; NYSUT 1991-; *office:* Charlotte Valley Central Schl Rt 23 Davenport NY 13750

LAWRENCE, KATHERINE A. (MANLEY), Eighth Grade Science Teacher; *b:* Troy, NY; *c:* Amy K.; *ed:* St Univ of NY at Oneonta (BS) N-9th Sci Ed 1976; St Univ of NY at New Platz (MS) 7th-12th Bio 1980; St Univ of NY St Ed Dept 7th-12th Earth Sci 1993; *cr:* J Watson Baily MS Sci Tchr 20 Yrs; *ai:* Schl Bookstore Adv; Awds Night & Moving Up Day Comm Chprsn; Ski Club Chaperone; Sci Tchrs Assn of NY St, NY St United Tchrs, AFT; Hurley Reformed Church 1979-, Deacon 1992-95; Hurley Little League 1995-, Sr Girls Coach; *office:* J Watson Bailey MS Merilina Ave Kingston NY 12401

LAWRENCE, KATHLEEN ROCKWELL, English Teacher; *b:* Brooklyn, NY; *ed:* Trinity Coll (BA) Eng 1967; Columbia Univ Tchrs Coll (MA) Eng 1968; Hunter Coll Admins Cert; *cr:* Harlem HS Eng Tchr 1968-71; City As Schl Tchr Coord 1971- 1983; Baruch Coll Adjunct & Eng Tchr 1984-89; Hunter HS Eng Tchr 1989-; *ai:* 7th Grd Adv; Fac Cncl; PEN 1988-; AFT, UFT; Novelist Maud Gone Atheneum 1986, The Last Room in Manhattan 1989; Paris Review Eds Essay Collection The Boys I Didn't Kiss 1990; Essays Pub in NY Times Mag, Vogue, MS, Poets & Writers, Antioch Review & Oxford; *office:* Hunter College HS 71 E 94th St New York NY 10128*

LAWRENCE, KIM CHONTOSH, 7th-12th Grd Math Tchr & Chair; *b:* Massena, NY; *m:* Timothy J.; *c:* Kendall Marie, Sean Timothy; *ed:* St Univ of NY at Potsdam (BA) Math & Scndry Ed 1980; St Univ of NY at Oswega (MA) Scndry Ed 1985, (CAS) Admin; *cr:* Pulaski Jr-Sr HS Math Tchr 1981-90, Math Tchr & Dept Chair 1990-; *ai:* NHS Adv; Oswego Cty Assessment Liaison; ASCD 1990-; AMTNYS, NCTM 1981-; *office:* Pulaski Jr-Sr HS 7250 Salina St Pulaski NY 13142

LAWRENCE, MICHAEL JOHN, Physics Teacher; *b:* Paterson, NJ; *m:* Katrinka Moore; *c:* Jamie; *ed:* NJIT (BS) Math 1972; Univ of FL (MAT) Math 1974; Rutgers Univ (MST) Physics 1979; Doctoral Candidate Sci Ed Rutgers Univ; *cr:* West Orange HS Physics Instr 1974-; *ai:* Sci League Physics Adv; NHS Selection Comm; Rank Class Comm; NJEA, NEA 1974-; AAPT 1976-; NY Downtown Yth Bsktbl Coach 1995-; St Level Winner PAESMT Awd 1994-95; Presidential Scholars Distngd Tchr 1993; Articles Pub 1994-95; Lead Tchr NSF Inst Video Assessments 1991-95; *home:* 139 Fulton St Rm 909 New York NY 10038

LAWRENCE, RUTH A. (SUTTON), Tchr of Severely Handicapped; *b:* Findlay, OH; *c:* Amy K., M. Joseph, Erin S.; *ed:* Univ of Findlay (MS) Spec Ed 1995; SBH Cert 28 Hrs Bowling Green St Univ 1994; *cr:* Washington Elem Sch 2nd-4th Grd Tchr 1985-90; Clinton-Washington Elem Schl SBH Tchr 1990-93; Tiffin MS SBH Tchr 1993-95; Columbian HS SBH Tchr, Resource Specialist 1995-; *ai:* CORE, IAT Chprsn, Coord; Spring Musical Properties Mistress; Phi Delta Kappa 1995-; Ritz Theatre 1987-, Vol, 1000 Hrs Svc Awd; Gen, Spec Ed Parent Support Groups, Speaker; *office:* Columbian HS 300 S Monroe St Tiffin OH 44883

LAWRENCE, SHARON LEE, Home Economics Teacher; *b:* Mc Keesport, PA; *m:* J. Richard; *c:* Ronald A. Massing, Shannon Marie, Jennifer Renee; *ed:* WV Wesleyan (BS) Home Ec 1969; Cmptr Trng; *cr:* Homeville Jr HS Home Ec Tchr 1969-77; West Mifflin Area HS Home Ec Tchr1 977-; West Mifflin Area MS Home Ec Tchr 1995-; *ai:* Schl Musical Costume, Prop Designer; AFT 1972-; *office:* West Mifflin Area Sr HS 91 Commonwealth Ave West Mifflin PA 15127*

LAWRENCE, SHAWN DANIEL, English Teacher; *b:* Akron, OH; *m:* Susan C. Broadhurst; *c:* Colleen, Denae, Connor; *ed:* Kent St Univ (BS) Ed, Eng 1989; 15 Addl Hrs; *cr:* Vly Forge HS Eng Tchr 1991-; *ai:* Morning Show Supvr; Grant for Upgrading Morning Show Equipment; *office:* Valley Forge HS 9999 Independence Blvd Parma OH 44130*

LAWRENCE, STEVEN RAYE, Vocal Music Director; *b:* Roanoke, VA; *ed:* Bridgewater Coll (BA) Music Ed 1980; Westminster Choir Coll Masters Music Ed 1986; Attnd Julliard Schl, Cambridge Univ at Cambridge England, Shenandoah Univ at Winchester; *cr:* Appomattox Cty HS Choral Dir 1981-84; St Bernards Episcopal Church Organist & Choirmaster 1984-; Newark Boys Chorus Assoc Dir of Music 1986-88; Bernards HS Dir of Vocal Music 1988-; *ai:* NEA 1988-; MENC 1981-; ACDA 1979-; Amer Guild of Organists 1978-; St Bernards, Artistic Dir Comm Concert Svcs Music; *office:* Bernards HS 25 Olcott Ave Bernardsville NJ 07924

LAWRENCE, SUSAN HUGHES, HS Mathematics Teacher; *b:* Bristol, PA; *m:* Jeffrey Lane; *ed:* West Chester Univ (BS) Math 1987; Trenton St Coll (MA) Counseling 1995; *cr:* Pennsburg Sch Dist Math Tchr 1988-; *ai:* Past Sports Nite Chrldrs, 9th Grd Chrldrs Coach; Past Yrbk Adv; Stu of Month Regulator; NEA, PSEA, NCTM 1988-; Kappa Delta Pi Honor Soc Exceptance; *office:* Medill Bair HS 608 S Olds Blvd Fairless Hills PA 19030*

LAWRENCE, VICTORIA HENCZ, Biology Instructor; *b:* Pittsburgh, PA; *m:* Tom S. Sr.; *c:* Tom Jr., Lorri Lynn, Amanda S.; *ed:* PA St Univ (AS) Arts, Letters, Sci 1987; CA Univ of PA (BS) Sec Ed Bio-Summa Cum Laude 1989; PA St Univ (MED) Hlth Ed 1993; Cert Aging, Hlth Ed PSU Grad Schl; *cr:* Allegheny Co Comm Coll Instr 1990-1995; Penn St Univ Instr 1995-; *ai:* Mc Keesport Coll Club 1993-; PA St Alumni Assn 1987-; Who's Who Among Coll, Univ 1988-89; Presidential Scholar CA Univ of PA; Scholars in Ed Awd Math, Sci PHEAA 1988-89; Patricia Klemens Meml Awd PSU 1986; Acad Alumni Schlsp Class 1992 PSU; *office:* Penn St Univ McKeesport Campus Univ Dr Rt 885 McKeesport PA 15132

LAWRENCE, VINNEDGE MOORE, Professor of Biology; *b:* Bangor, ME; *m:* Betty Jean Heinly; *c:* Malinda Robbin; *ed:* Miami Univ at Oxford (BS) Ed 1962, (MA) Zoology 1964; Purdue Univ 9PHD) Entomology 1968; *cr:* Xavier Univ Instr Bio 1964-65; WA & Jefferson Coll Asst Prof Bio 1968-72, Assoc Prof Bio 1973-86, Prof of Bio 1987-; *ai:* Nu Chptr Phi Sigma, Stu Active for the Enviroment Adv; Acad Status, Educl Planning Comms; AAUP 1967-, Treas; AAAS 1963-; AIBS 1962-; Assoc for Biol Lab Educ 1986-; PA Environ Defense Found 1991-, Trustee, Vic Chair for Western PA; Chartiers Creek Water Quality Improvement Corp 1990-, Dir, Treas; Sierra Club; The Nature Conservancy; The Wilderness Soc; Natl Defense Ed Act Title IV Flwshp 1965-68; NSF Instrl Equipment Grant 1974; 10 Articles Pub; *office:* Washington & Jefferson Coll 50 S Lincoln St Washington PA 15301

LAWRENCE, WILLIAM B., Science Department Chairman; *b:* Liberty, NY; *m:* Margaret; *c:* Sonya, Michael; *ed:* SUNY At Cortland (BA) Chem 1969; Union Coll (MS) Ed 1992; *cr:* Cairo-Durham Cntrl Schl Sci Instr 1970-; *ai:* NYSUT 1970-; STANYS 1975-; NSTA 1980-; Cairo-Durham Elks 1980-; Elected to Greene Cty Legislator Office 1980; Elected to Cairo Town Supvr Office 1988; Patent #5331075 Silicone Rsrch 1994; Patent #5432140 Silicone Rsrch 1995; *office:* Cairo Durham HS Rt 145 Cairo NY 12413

LAWSON, ALISA LYNNETTE, English Teacher; *b:* Lexington, KY; *ed:* KY St Univ (BA) Eng Ed 1989; OH St Univ (MS) Higher Ed & Stu Affairs 1994; Working Towards Prin Cert 7th-12th Grd; *cr:* Columbus Pub Schls Eng Tchr 1989-; *ai:* Home Instr Tutor; Young Scholars OSU Tutor; Cheerleading Asst Coach; NEA 1989-; Alpha Kappa Alpha 1987-; *office:* Independence HS 5175 E Refugee Rd Columbus OH 43232*

LAWSON, ANNAMAE, English Teacher; *b:* Pgh, PA; *m:* Robert Ross; *c:* Lydia, Jeffrey Ross, Pamela Orr; *ed:* Univ of Pgh (BA) Eng 1972, (MAT) Ed 1973; Attnd Allegheny Intermed Unit, Duquesne Univ; *cr:* Canevin HS Eng Tchr 1972-74; Northgate HS Eng Tchr 1974-; *ai:* NEA, NCTE, Pi Lambda Theta 1974-; Southminster Ringers 1974-, Tour Mgr; Church Schl Supt 1969-; MAC Grant; *office:* Northgate HS 589 Union Ave Pittsburgh PA 15202

LAWSON, CATHERINE ANN, French, Speech & Drama Teacher; *b:* Ashtabula, OH; *ed:* Ursuline Coll (BA) Fr 1971; *cr:* Assumption Schl 6th Grd Tchr 1971-74; St John HS Fr, Speech, Drama Tchr 1975-95; *ai:* Class Adv; Drama Dir, Adv; Fr Club; Local Comm Theaters Play Dir; Ashtabula Arts Ctr Yth Theater Classes Tchr; *office:* St John HS 3320 Station Ave Ashtabula OH 44004

LAWSON, DAVID A., Social Studies Teacher; *b:* Albany, NY; *m:* Lisa; *c:* Jennifer, Benjamin; *ed:* Queen's Univ at Kingston Ontario (BA) His 1979, (BED) Scndry Ed 1980; SVC at Potsdam (MS) Scndry Ed 1989; *cr:* South Jefferson HS Soc Stud Tchr 1984-88; Dover Jr Sr HS Soc Stud Rchr 1988-; *ai:* NYSUT, AFT 1982-; Phi Delta Kappa 1986-, 5 Yr Membership Awd; Amer Historians Organization 1992-; FFA Civic Citation 1987-88; *office:* Dover Jr/Sr HS Rt 22 PO Box 6311 Dover Plains NY 12522*

LAWSON, HOLLY JON, Associate Professor of Chem; *b:* Buffalo, NY; *m:* Jerry Keister; *c:* Colin Lawson-Keister, Patrick Lawson-Keister; *ed:* Alfred Univ (BS) Glass Sci 1982; SUNY at Buffalo (PHD) Inorganic Chem 1988; Post-Doctoral Stud Univ of Bristol; Inorganic Chem 1989; *cr:* SUNY at Fredonia Chem Fac 1989-; *ai:* Fredonia Chem Club Adv 1991-94; Coll Planning & Budget Comm 1993, Chair 1994; Coll Human Subjects Review Comm 1990-; Amer Chem Soc 1983-; Grants Funded Scholarly Incentive Awd 1996; Rsrch Corp 1993-; Prof Dev Awd 1992; Recent Publication; *office:* S U N Y Coll At Fredonia 201 Houghton Hall Fredonia NY 14063

LAWSON, JOE D., High School Algebra Teacher; *b:* Jellico, TN; *m:* Sophia; *c:* Jacob, Tessa; *ed:* Wright St Univ (BA) His, Math, Sociology 1974, (MA) His Ed 1981; *cr:* IN Vly MS 8th Grd Tchr 1974-75; Five Points Jr HS 8th Grd Tchr 1975-80; Fairborn HS Math Tchr 1980-; *ai:* FEA, OEA, NEA 1974-; *office:* Fairborn HS 900 E Dayton Yellow Springs Rd Fairborn OH 45324

LAWSON, JOYCE MUMMERY, Rdng Rcvry & Early Intrvn Tchr; *b:* Oneida, NY; *m:* Craig S.; *c:* Thomas G., Marc R.; *ed:* St Univ at Cortland (BS) Elem Ed, Eng 1966; St Univ at Oneonta (MS) Rdng 1984; 18 Hrs Rdng Recovery Tchr Trng; *cr:* Norwich City Schls First Grd Tchr 1966-91, Rdng Recovery, Remedial Tchr 1991-95, Rdng Recovery Intervention Spcialist 1995-; *ai:* Bldg Child Stu Team; Literacy L Stud Group; Mentor Intern Prgm; Kappa Delta Phi 1989-91; NEA Chen Vly Rdng Assn, NYSRA 1985-; N Amer Rdng Recovery Cnc Norwich Edctrs Org 1966-; Broad Street Meth Church 1987-; Cl Piecemakers Quilt Group 1990-; Town, Cntry Garden Club 1987-, S BSA Pack Comm; Nom Tchr of Yr 1967, 1995; *office:* Stanford Elem Schl Ridgeland Rd Norwich NY 13815*

LAWSON, JUDITH DAY, Secondary Mathematics Teacher; *b:* Pla NJ; *m:* Edward Niel; *c:* Kristin J., Timothy D.; *ed:* Cornell Un Sociology 1970; Univ of NH (MS) Math 1995; Summermath Holyoke 1987-88; *cr:* Groton Cntrl Schl Math Tchr 1970-73; Prude Co Mngmt 1973-86; Montclair Kimberly Acad Math Tchr 1986-89; Acad for Girls Math Tchr, Chair 1989-; *ai:* Class, SADD Adv; 1986-; AMTNYS 1989-; *office:* Albany Acad For Girls 140 Acad Albany NY 12208

LAWSON, PEGGY LICHT, 4th Grade Teacher; *b:* Bronxville, Reid; *c:* Craig, Jill; *ed:* Univ of NH (BA) Elem Ed 1964; Univ of Grad Credit Hrs; Trinity Coll of VT 3 Grad Credit Hrs; Johnson S Grad Credit Hrs; *cr:* Melrose Pub Schls Grd 3 Tchr 1964-76; Barr Schl Grd 1 Tchr 1968-68; Barre City Schls Grd 3 Tchr 1968-69 Basic Ed HS Drop Outs Tchr 1970-76; Barre Town Schl Grd 1984-86, Grd 4 Tchr 1986-; *ai:* Wellness Comm Chm; Cty Club of NEA 1984-; AAUW 1970-; First Presbyn Church 1968-, Jr, Sr Ch 1976-87; *home:* 235 Nuissl Rd Box 1930 Barre VT 05641*

LAWSON, TERRENCE BRUCE, Fourth Grade Teacher; *b:* Gree PA; *m:* Susan Cipra; *c:* Erin Nacole, Clinton Terrence; *ed:* Californ of PA (BS) Elem Ed 1973, (MS) Elem 1978; *cr:* Yougl Sch Dist Ele 1973-; *ai:* YEA, NEA 1973-; Madison UM Church 1962-, Com Ch

LAWTON, BONNIE WILLIAMS, Music & Strings Teac Meadville, PA; *w:* Willard C. (dec); *ed:* Mansfield St Univ (BS) Mu Violin 1967, (ME) Music Ed 1974; Austria, Certs Music His, Violi Violin Ped, Ithaca TalentEd; *cr:* Corning-Painted Post Schl Dist Tchr 1967-86; Auburn Enlarged City Schl Dist Music Tchr 198 Annual Spring Musical Dir 5 Yrs; Music Ed Natl Conf, Natl Sch Assn 1967-, Zone Rep to Newsletter; ASTA 1989-; NY St Unite 1967-; Auburn Chamber Orch 1986-, Concert Mistress; ACO Bd 1 Rep at Large; Delta Kappa Gamma; Sigma Alpha Iota; Theodore Awd; *office:* Auburn HS Lake Ave Ext Auburn NY 13021*

LAWTON, EVELYN NOELLE, Science Teacher; *b:* Berlin, Germ Raymond; *c:* Kristina, Kenneth, Kathryn; *ed:* St Univ Coll at Osweg Ed & Ger 1969; OH St Univ (MA) Ger 1970; 30 Addl Credit Hrs MA; *cr:* OH St Univ Grad Tchng Assoc 1970-71; Norton MS 8th Tchr 1971-83; N Franklin Elem Schl Kndgtn Tchr 1984-86; Westl Ger Tchr 1986-88, Sci Tchr 1986-; *ai:* Curr Comm Tchr Assn Rep of 1998 Adv; NEA 1971-; OEA 1971-; SWEA 1971-, Rep; PTA Down Syndrome Assoc of Cntrl OH 1981-, Founding Mem, Pres 19 OH St Univ Flwshp 1969; Dist Schl Bell Awd 1985 & 1990; PTA W HS Outstdng Edctr 1993; Honorary Hnr Soc Mem 1994; Voted H Sr Class of 1994; *office:* Westland HS 146 Galloway Rd Gallow 43119

LAWTON, HAROLYN C., Sixth Grade Teacher; *b:* Newark, Bernard W.; *c:* Jeffrey, Mark, Matthew; *ed:* Caldwell Coll (BA) Eng St Univ of NY at Albany (MS) Rdng 1988; Addl 4 Credit Hrs Masters; *cr:* Saint Vitos Elem Schl 3rd Grd Tchr 1965-68; Fram Elem Schls Poet-In-Residence 1977-79; Parsippany Schl System 7 Grd Bedside Tutor 1979-81; Sacred Heart Schl 7th Grd Tchr 1981-83 Clements Regnl Cath 6th Grd Tchr 1983-; *ai:* Explora Visions Mentor; Storytellers Club Dir; Challenges & Choices Enrichmen Coord; NCEA 1983-; Capital Dist Writing Project at St Univ of Albany; *office:* St Clement's Regional Cath Sch 231 Lake Ave S Springs NY 12866

LAWTON, PETER A., Psychology & Math Teacher; *b:* New Yor NY; *m:* Mildred Tarter; *c:* Thomas, Walter; *ed:* Fordham Univ (MS Psych 1960; Yeshiva Univ (MS) Math Ed 1965; NY Univ (PHD 1970; 9 Grad Credits Supervision & Admin; Beaver coll 3 Credits of Psych; *cr:* South Orangetown Cntrl Schl Dist Math Tchr 1959-, As 1969-76, Dean of Stdnts 1976-78, Math Dept Head 1990-91, Psyc 1994-; *ai:* Establish Adult Ed Prgm, AP Psych Prgm & Many Intensive Tchr Trng Prgm, Teach for Amer; Educl Assn of Orangeown 1968-, Founding, Bldg Rep; NY St Schl Bds Assn 19 1988-92; Rockland Cty Schl Bd Assn; NY St Schl Bds Assn; St Ag of Trustees; Yrbk Dedication 1965; Train Tchr Intersive Tchr Trng Train Tchr Teach of Amer USC 1990; *office:* South Orangetown Cnt 15 Dutch Hill Rd Orangeburg NY 10962*

LAWTON, THOMAS JOSEPH,V, Social Studies Teacher; *b:* Char WV; *ed:* Glassboro St Coll (BA) His 1989; NJ Tchr Cert in Elem Ed Working on Rel Cert for Diocese of Camden; *cr:* Washing Twp Sc Sub Tchr 1990; Clearview Regnl Dist Schl Sub Tchr 1990; St Cathe Siena Schl 6th-8th Math, Sci Tchr 1990-91; Notre Dame Regn 5th-8th Grd Soc Stud Tchr 1991-; *ai:* Stu Cncl Adv 1993-94; De Room Monitor 1995-; Soc Stud Curr Advy Panel; Sons of Union V of Amer Civil War 1992-, Chaplain; Marius H. Livingston Av Outstdng Schlsp in His.

LAX, BARBARA K., Professor of Biology; *b:* Pittsburgh, PA; *m:* G B.; *c:* Neil C.; *ed:* Univ of Pittsburgh (BS) Bio, (MAT), (PHD); *cr:* Coll Prof 1976-; *ai:* Bio Dept Chprsn; Internship Prgms Spon; A Soc; Natl Wildlife Fed; Western PA Conservancy; Grants for Veterin Ecological Experiences for HS Stdnts.*

LAYCHAK, LAWRENCE JOSEPH, Physics & Chemistry Teac McKeesport, PA; *m:* Kathleen; *c:* Mary Beth, Jayne Nicole; *ed:* U Pittsburg (BS) Physics & Math 1971; Tchng Cert 1974; 24 Hrs B Bachelors 1977; US Army Military Police-Field Intelligence 1971-7 Army Flight Trng at Fort Rucker 1972-73; *cr:* Pittsburgh Pub Sch Tchr; Mount Lebanon HS 9th Grd General Sci Tchr 1975; Church Physics, Chem & Astronomy Tchr 1976; Woodland Hills HS Geol Advanced Placement Physics Tchr; *ai:* Soccer & Track Coach; Club Spon; EDR & Physics for Elem Stdnts Comms; PSEA 1976-, Capitan, Pub Comm, Contract Negotiations Comm; NEA 1976-, Captain, Pub Comm; Police Athletic League 1994-95; Girls Sftb Coach; US Army Research & Devs Merit Citation for Work on Night Scopes, Military Strobe Lights for UHID Huey Attack Helic Optically Guided Automatic Weapons Firing Systems 1973; All Star Awd-Pittsburgh Post Gazette 1995; *office:* Woodland Hills Sr HS Greensburg Pike Pittsburgh PA 15221

LAYCOCK, ROBERT T., Professor of Accounting; *b:* Washingtor *ed:* George Washington Univ (MBA) Acctg 1968; CPA; *cr:* Montg Coll Prof 1967-; George Washington Univ Prof Lecturer 1987-; *ai:* F Phi Theta Kappa, Equestrian Club; AAUP 1967-; Amer Acctng Assn MD Assn CPAS 1972-; MD Soc Accountants 1990-; Washington Trails Assn 1979-, Treas; *office:* Montgomery Coll 51 Mannak Rockville MD 20850

LAYDEN, MARCIA ARLENE, Fifth Grade Teacher; *b:* Providenc *ed:* RI Coll (BS) Elem Ed 1970; Univ of RI (MA) Elem Ed 197 Westcott Annex 6th Grd Tchr 1970-71; Providence Street Schl 6t Tchr 1971-89; Greenbush Elem Schl 5th & 6th Grd Tchr 1989-; *ai:*

West Warwick Tchrs Alliance 1970-, Sec, Bldg Rep; Barker ıse 1988-, Bd Mem, Past Chprsn of Production Comm; Gifted & d 1989-93; St Systemic Initiative Leadership Team Mem 1993-95; Greenbush Elem Schl 127 Greenbush Rd West Warwick RI 02893

AN, DOUGLAS DINSMORE, English Teacher; *b:* Erie, PA; *m:* Ann Cooper; *c:* Scot; *ed:* Edinboro St Coll (BS) Comprehensive 72; Clarion St Coll (MS) Comm 1977; 30 Post Grad Credits Beyond s in Cmptr Applications for Educators & Tchng Methods; *cr:* d MS Lang Arts Tchr 1973-81; Fairview HS Eng Tchr 1981-93; d MS Rdng Tchr 1993-95; Fairview HS Comm Tchr 1995-; *ai:* PSEA 1973-; FEA 1973-, Pres; *office:* Fairview Schl Dist 7460 Rd Fairview PA 16415

AN, MARY JO FLETCHER, 6th Grade Teacher; *b:* Mt Vernon, David; *c:* Bret, Shannon; *ed:* Bowling Green St Univ (B S) DH Spcl lem Ed 1969; Post Grad Work at OH St Univ & Ashland Univ; *cr:* on City Schls Primary DH 1969-71; Northridge Local Schls 6th-8th g Arts Tchr & 6th Grd Tchr 1982-; *ai:* Just Say No Club Adv; Right Comm; Past Jr High Stu Cncl, Spelling Bee, Jr High Chrldr, Speech ry Contest & Talent Show Adv; Past Sci Fair Chm; NEA, OEA & 1982-; Highwater Congregational Church, Sunday Schl Tchr, VBS Choir Mem; Jennings Scholar; Dow Chem Outstndg Tchr; Mentor chr Dev Cncl; *home:* 2868 Lakefork Rd Utica OH 43080

E, ELLEN ROSE, Program Facilitator & Teacher; *b:* Cincinnati, Andrew S., Abigail R.; *ed:* Univ of CT (BS) Ed 1972, (BA) Eng Coll of Mt St Joseph (MA) Ed Rdng 1990; *cr:* CT Pub Schls Tchr 0; CT St Instr 1980-82; CT Pub Schls Tchr 1984-; Coll of Mt St Lecturer 1990-; CT Pub Schls Prgm Facilitator, Tchr 1994-; *ai:* Review Panel Mem; CT Fed of Tchrs 1984-; Monfort Heights Civic 995-, Trustee; Diesel Mechanics Voc Advy Comm NW Local Schls Mt St Joseph Ed Coll 1993-, Advy Bd; Lead Tchr Credentials; ent Distinguished Tchr Awd; Phi Beta Kappa 1970; *office:* nati Pub Schls 2601 Westwood Northern Blvd Cincinnati OH

ON, GENE ALAN, Learning Disabilities Teacher; *b:* Point ıt, WV; *m:* Teresa Neal; *c:* Derrick Ryne, Chelsea Nicole; *ed:* Univ Grande (BS) Hlth, PE 1984; Tchng Cert Learning Disabilities, or Disorders 1985; *cr:* Jackson HS Learning Disabilities Tchr *ai:* Boys Jr Var Bsktbl Head Coach; Boys Var Bsktbl Asst Coach; 1985-, Bldg Rep; OEA, NEA 1985-; OH HS Bsktbl Coaches Assn Jackson Elks Lodge #466 1990-; Franklin Vly Golf Course 1991-, Trustees; *office:* Jackson City Schools 21 Tropic St Jackson OH

ON, THEODORE GLENN, Agriculture Science Teacher; *b:* l, DE; *m:* Kathleen Bridget Arnott; *c:* Angela L., Teddy, Timothy; St Coll (BS) Plant Sci 1973, (BS) Gen Resource Mngmt 1973; PA v (MED) Voc Ed, Ag 1982; Univ of DE 20 Credit Hrs; DE Tech, Coll 6 Credit Hrs; CO St Univ 2 Credit Hrs; *cr:* Caesar Rodney HS r 1975-84, 1988-; DE St Coll Ext Cty Ag Agent 1984-88; *ai:* FFA nvirothon Team Coach; DVATA 1975-, Outstdng Ag Tchr; NVATA Regnl Sound-Off for Ag; OSEA, CREA, NEA 1976-; BSA 1985-, naster, Asst; Holy Cross Church; Outstdng Young Ag Tchr; NVATA Unlimited; Cty Agents Assn Regnl Svc to Yth Awd; Honorary St FFA Mem; *office:* Caesar Rodney HS 239 Old North Rd Camden ng DE 19934

ON, WALTER JOHN, Associate Principal; *b:* Milford, DE; *c:* Lisa, Amber; *ed:* WV Wesleyan (BS) Sci Ed 1965; Univ of DE Sci Ed 1977; Addl 65 Post Grad Credit Hrs in HS Admin; *cr:* Cntrl & 8th Grd Sci Tchr 1965-70; William Henry MS 6th Grd Sci Tchr 7; Dover HS Sci Tchr 1977-80, Chem Tchr 1980-93, Assoc Prin *ai:* NEA, DSEA, CEA 1965-93, VP 3 Yrs, Pres 2 Yrs, Negotiator; Schl Admin 1993-; BPOE Elks 1990-; *office:* Dover HS 1 Pat Lynn ver DE 19904*

R, BERNICE MARY (OBZUT), Secondary Mathematics Teacher; nandoah, PA; *m:* Mark E.; *ed:* Bloomsburg Univ (BS) Ed Scndry 970; Penn St Univ at Harrisburg Post Grd Stud; *cr:* Shenandoah Vly th Tchr 1970-72; Halifax Area HS Math Tchr 1972-; *ai:* Jr Class Adv Fnr Soc; Selection & Discipline Comm; Math Task Force Mem; 1970-, Sec 1986-; NEA, PSEA, 1970-; HEA 1970-, Treas 1978-79, 80-89; NCTM 1970; CPMA 1980-, Sec, 1986-; Amer Bus Womens 1978-, Sec 1982-83; Delta Kappa Gamma 1988-; Who's Who in Ed 1992; *office:* Halifax HS 3940 Peters Mountain Rd Halifax PA

RIS, NICOLE ELLEN, English Tchr & Guidance Cnslr; *b:* Staten NY; *ed:* Drew Univ (BA)E Eng 1969; Richmond Coll (MS) Sec Ed 976; St John's Univ (MS) Schl Guid, Cnslng 1994; 30 Credits Lbrl Vagner Coll; *cr:* IS 24 Eng Tchr 1973-76; Tottenville HS Eng Tchr, Cnslr 1977-; *ai:* Chrstn Flwshp Adv; Clinical Assoc; New Dorp Cntrl Assn, Little Theatre Group 1994-; *office:* Tottenville HS 100 Luten aten Island NY 10312

RO, DINA MARIE, Biology Teacher; *b:* Elizabeth, NJ; *ed:* Kean f NT (BA) Bio 1993; 4 Credit Hrs Princeton Univ Summer Prgm Electrophoresis Stud 1995; Tchr Cert; *cr:* Edison HS Bio Tchr 94; Kearny HS Bio Tchr 1994-; *ai:* Bio I Sci League Team Coach; Class Adv; Stdnts Against Vanishing Earth Adv; NEA, PTA 1994; ent of Good Guy, Good Gal Awd 1995; *office:* Kearny HS 336 Devon rny NJ 07032

ROFF, MICHAEL JONATHAN VIEIRA, High School Biology r; *b:* Berkeley, CA; *m:* Joan M. Viera; *c:* Emma; *ed:* San Francisco iv (BA) Lbrl Stud 1989; Univ of San Francisco Scndry Tchng ntial 1991; Univ of CA at Davis Lbrl Stud; Attnd Summer Sci Inst of CA at Irvine; *cr:* Dana Hills HS Bio Tchr 1991-93; Staples HS Bio 993-; *ai:* 4-Town Yth Conf Fac Adv, Organizer; NEA, Westport Ed CT Ed Assn 1995-; Stratford Parents Place 1995-, Advy Comm; Amer Liberties Union 1991-; Nom Going The Extra Mile 1995; *office:* s HS 70 North Ave Westport CT 06880*

RSKI, JOHN B., Soc Studies & Psychology Tchr; *b:* Syracuse, NY; sa, Katrine, Bethany; *ed:* SUNY at Oswego (BA) Scndry Ed 1969; Syracuse Univ Project Advance; *cr:* South Lewis Cntrl Schl Soc Stud 969; West Genesee HS Soc Stud, Psych, Pub Affairs Tchr 1969-; *ai:* iason, Shared Dec Making Comm; Curr Dev; NYSUT 1969-; WGTA Bldg Co-Pres, Pub Relations Chm; FRANYS 1990-; *office:* West ee Sr HS 5201 W Genesee St Camillus NY 13031

RWITZ, ROBERTA JOFF, Kindergarten Teacher; *b:* Paterson, NJ; ernard Joel; *c:* Jennifer Michele, Elyse Meredith, Ian Marc; *ed:* m Paterson Coll (BA) Kndgtn, Prim 1964, (MA) Elem Ed 1968; 55 Grad Credits; *cr:* Franklin Elem Schl Kndgtn Tchr 1964-70, First Grd 1973-74; Lincoln Mc Kenzie Elem Schl Kndgtn Tchr 1976-78, First chr 1982-83, Kndgtn Tchr 1983-; *ai:* NEA, NJ Ed Assn, Bergen Cty ssn 1964-; Assn Kndgtn Edctrs 1989-; St of NJ Governor's Awd 1985.

RE, MARY ANN, Junior High School Teacher; *b:* Ridgway, PA; *ed:* Marie Coll (BS) Elem Ed 1975; 24 Credit Hrs in Elem Ed at Clarion 3 Credit Hrs in PE at PA St Univ; *cr:* Saint Bernards Cath Schl h Grd Soc Stud & PE Tchr & 4th Grd Math & Religion Tchr 1975-76; of World Schl 6th-8th Grd Math & PE Tchr, 8th Grd Religion, Lit, ulary & Spelling Tchr, 1st-6th Grd PE Tchr & 6th Grd Religion Tchr 1976-; *ai:* Stu Cncl Adv; NCEA 1975-; PA Cncl Tchrs of Math 1988-; Laurel Rdng Cncl 1995-; Womens Internation Bowling Congress 1976-, High Single Game 198 1985 & 1987, Most Improved Bowler 1992; Saint Marys Clybl League 1978-; Erie Diocesan Tchr Svc Awd for 10, 15 & 20 Yrs of Svc; *office:* Queen Of The World Schl 134 Queens Rd Saint Marys PA 15857*

LAZUR, CAROLE GENNARO, English Teacher; *b:* Hazleton, PA; *m:* James E.; *c:* Kristen, Mark, Matthew, James; *ed:* Coll Misericordia (BA) Eng & Scndry Ed 1966; Grad Stud in Ed at Penn St & Marywood; *cr:* Pennsbury HS Eng Tchr 1966-68; Whitehall HS Eng Tchr 1968-69; Msgr Molino Elem Schl Eng Tchr 1979-82; Bishop Hafey HS Eng Tchr 1983-; *ai:* Schl Newspaper Golden Gazette, Lit Arts Magazine & Soph Class Adv; NCEA 1983-; Book Pub The Night Thoughts Dream Guide; *office:* Bishop Hafey Jr & Sr HS 1700 W 22nd St Hazleton PA 18201

LAZZARO, LINDA BERNACCHI, 8th Grade Mathematics Teacher; *b:* LaPorte, IN; *c:* Jennifer, Scott; *ed:* Indiana Univ of PA (BS) Scndry Math 1972; 35 Post Grad Credit Hrs; *cr:* Franklin Regnl Jr HS Math Tchr 24 Yrs, Dept Head 10 Yrs; *ai:* Mathcounts Team Coach; NCTM; Franklin Regnl Ed Assn; *office:* Franklin Regional Jr HS 4660 Old William Penn Hwy Murrysville PA 15668

LAZZARO, MARIA AMMERATA, Art Teacher; *b:* Jersey City, NJ; *c:* Joseph Anthony; *ed:* Jersey City St Coll (BA) Art 1974; Attnd St Peters Coll; *cr:* Lincoln HS Art Tchr 1975-; Freelance Art Work Design & Illustration 1975-; *ai:* Calligraphy, Banners, Murals & Genesis-Schl Lit Magazine; NEA, NJEA, HCEA & Art Eds of NJ 1975-; JCEA 1975-, Bldg Dir; Alahambra-Sultana 1980-92; Sayreville Little League Ladies Aux 1988-95; Chrstn Brothers Acad 1993-97.

LAZZINI, DENISE LAVAL, Kindergarten Teacher; *b:* Pittsburgh, PA; *m:* Ronald; *c:* Heather; *ed:* Edinboro St Coll (BS) Early Chldhd & Elem Ed 1974; Masters Equivalency; *cr:* South Fayette Elem Schl 1st Grd Tchr 1974-83, Kndgtn Tchr 1983-; *ai:* PA St Ed Assn 1974-; *home:* 1208 Oakridge Rd Mc Donald PA 15057

LEACH, JAMES GRANT, HS Chemistry Teacher; *b:* Pittsburgh, PA; *m:* Cynthia White; *c:* Johnathan, Elizabeth, Erin, Katherine; *ed:* Carnegie Mellon Univ (BS) Ec 1981; Temple Univ (MS) Ed 1993; *cr:* Cntrl HS Phys Sci Tchr 1986-87; DE Cty Chrstn Schl Chem Tchr 1987-; *ai:* Asst Wrestling Coach; Stu Senate Adv; NHS, Discipleship, Chapel & Spiritual Life Comms; NSTA 1996; *office:* Delaware County Christian Schl 462 Malin Rd Newtown Square PA 19073

LEACH, ROBERT HOMER, Social Studies Teacher; *b:* Glen Dale, WV; *m:* Bettisue Ober; *c:* Thaddeus, Timothy; *ed:* West Liberty St Coll (BA) Ed, Scndry 1965; Attnd Kent St Univ, Ashland Coll; *cr:* Marshall Cty Schls Tchr 1965-66; Sandy Valley Local Schls Tchr 1966-; *ai:* Stdnts Dean; Sr Class Adv; NEA, OEA 1966-; Sandy Valley Ed Assn 1966-, Pres, Chief Negotiator; Magnolia Lions Club 1967-, Pres; Stark Cty Regnl Planning 1980-, Pres; Village of Magnolia 1980-, Mayor; Magnolia United Meth 1968-,; Martha Holden Jennings Scholar; *home:* PO Box 331 Magnolia OH 44643

LEACH, TODD JOSEPH, Associate Prof of Business; *b:* Framingham, MA; *m:* Megumi Kondo; *ed:* MA Bay Comm Coll (AS) Bus 1981; Worcester St Coll (BS) Mngmt 1983; Bentley Coll (MBA) Orgnl Behavior 1985; *cr:* Overdoor Co Operations Mgr 1980-85; Lasell Coll Dir of Bus Prgms 1988-95, Assoc Prof 1986-; *ai:* Fac Marshal; Promotions Comm Chair; Yamawaki Exch Coord; Japan Soc of Boston 1990-; Intnl Ec Hnr Soc 1984-; In the Best Interest of the Children 1994-, Advy Bd; Dev 4 Yr Bus Prgm; Established Lasell Bus Advy Bd, Womens in Bus Club; Designed Mentor Club; Role in Sister Coll Relations; *home:* 59 Devens St Marlborough MA 01752

LEACHEY, JOHN D., Music Teacher; *b:* Plainfield, NJ; *m:* Lee Landini; *ed:* Westminster Choir Coll (BM) Music Ed 1990; Seton Hall Univ 9 Credits; *cr:* Hillsborough HS Music, Choral, Theory Tchr 1990-; *ai:* Schl Musical Dir; Tri-M Music Hnr Soc, Choral Cncl Adv; MENC 1988-; ACDA, NJEA, NEA 1991-; *office:* Hillsborough HS 466 Raider Blvd Belle Mead NJ 08502

LEACOCK, WILLIAM ANDREW, Physics Teacher; *b:* Hempstead, NY; *m:* Lorraine Patricia Thomas; *ed:* Clarkson Univ (BS) Industrial Engrng 1984; Hofstra Univ (MS) Scndry Ed & Sci 1990; *cr:* Estee Lauder Inc Industrial Engr, Production Supvr & Planning Analyst 1984-88; Bellmore-Merrick Cntrl HS Dist Physics Tchr 1990-; *ai:* Sci Research Mentor; Long Island Physics Tchrs Assn 1989-, VP; AAPT 1989-; Natl Eagle Scout Assn 1976-; Innovative Tchng with Telecommunications Awd NY-LI Division 1993; WNET-Texaco Natl Tchr Trng Inst Master Tchr 1995; US Dept of Energy Tchr Research Assoc 1993; Invent Amer Mentor Awd US Dept of Copyrights & Patents 1993; *office:* Mepham HS 2401 Camp Ave North Bellmore NY 11710*

LEADER, BRUCE ROBERT, Social Studies Teacher; *b:* Buffalo, NY; *ed:* St Univ of NY at Binghamton (BA) His & philosophy 1989; SUNY at Buffalo (MA) His 1991; *cr:* Starpoint Cntrl Schl Soc Stud Tchr 1991-; *ai:* Var Soccer & Scholastic Bowl Coach; Intramural Soccer Prgm; Shared Decision Comm; Debate Team; Bridges for Ed; AFT & NYSUT 1991-; Soccer Coach 1989; 1992 Sallie Mae 1st Yr Tchr Awd.

LEAF, JOSEPH EDWARD, Eng as a Second Lang Teacher; *b:* Upper Darby, PA; *m:* Monica Elizabeth; *c:* Edward, Brian; *ed:* Assumption Coll (BA) Fr 1973; West Chester Univ (MA) Tchng Eng Scndry Lang 1979; 30 Credit Hrs Cert; 15 Credit Hrs Chinese; 30 Credit Hrs Post-Grad; 10 Credit Hrs Liturgical Music; *cr:* Berlitz of Argentina Eng Scndry Lang Tchr 1974-75; Farmworkers Opportunities Eng Scndry Lang Tchr 1978-79; Norristown Area HS Adult Evening Pgm & Eng Scndry Lang Tchr 1979-85, Eng Scndry Lang, Fr & Eng Tchr 1979-; *ai:* Intercultural Club Adv; NEA 1979-; PSEA 1979-; TESOL Intnl 1980-; Penn TESOL-East 1985-, Scndry Level Rep & Publishers Rep; PA Summer Intensive Lang Pgm Grants 1988-92; Norristown British Exch Pgm; Numerous Articles Pub.*

LEAF, RICHARD A., Soc Stuid Dept Chprsn & Tchr; *b:* New York, NY; *ed:* Case Western Reserve Univ (BA) His 1970; Iona Coll (MS) Ed 1973; *cr:* Harrison HS Soc Stud Tchr 1970-71; Harrison Jr HS Soc Stud Tchr 1971-74; Louis M. Klein MS Soc Stud Tchr, Chair 1974-; *ai:* Spon, Coord 8th Grd Trip to Washington DC 1976-; Harrison Assn of Tchrs 1970-; Westchester Cty Soccer Ofcls Assn 1981-, Pres 1990-92; Section 1 Bsktbl Comm 1984-; *home:* 7 Lake St Apt 5J White Plains NY 10603*

LEAFE, FRANCIS WILLIAM, Physical Education Teacher; *b:* Manchester, NH; *m:* Denise Audrey Sponheimer; *c:* Jereme, Trevor, Brittany; *ed:* Plymouth St Coll (BS) PE 1976; Took Many Courses in Natl Guard Career, Honor Stu, Non-Commission Officer Course-Basic Advance, 10 Week Supply Sgt Schl; *cr:* Boston & Maine Railroad Foreman 1976-83; NH Army Natl Guard Unit Supply Sgt 1983-88; Woodsville HS & Haverhill Cooperative Schl PE Tchr 1988-; *ai:* Girls Var Soccer Coach 1987-; Girls Var Bsktbl Coach 1989-; NH Interscholastic Athletic Soccer Comm 1994-; NEA 1988-; Natl Soccer Coaches Assn, NH Soccer Coaches Assn 1987-; NH Bsktbl Coaches Assn 1989-; NH Natl Guard 1972-, 1st Sgt, Ret After 22 Yrs; Army Achvmt Awd for Outstanding Svc While Working as Btry C 2-197th FA Supply Sgt; NH Class M-S Girls Soccer Coach of Yr 1993 & 1994; *office:* Woodsville HS Hight St Woodsville NH 03785

LEAHAN, CHARLES J., Spanish Teacher; *b:* Phila, PA; *m:* Cindy Talucci; *c:* Caitrin, Maura; *ed:* West Chester St (BS) Sec Ed Span 1970; 36 Post Grad Credits Westchester & Villanovi; *cr:* Archbishop Kennedy HS Span Tchr 1970-94; Kennedy Kenrick Cath HS 1994-; *ai:* Asst Ftbl Coach Coatesville HS; *office:* Kennedy-Kenrick Cath HS 250 E Johnson Hwy Norristown PA 19401

LEAHEY, CHRISTOPHER THOMAS, Health & Physical Ed Teacher; *b:* Albany, NY; *ed:* Hudson Vly Comm Coll (AA) PE 1988; SUNY Coll at Cortland (BSE) PE 1990; Sage Grad Schl (MS) Hlth Ed 1996; *cr:* City of Rensselaer Exec Dir Yth Bureau 1990-94; Bishop Maginn HS 9-12 Grd Hlth Ed, PE Tchr 1990-; *ai:* Head JV Ftbl Coach; Asst Var Bsbl Coach; Stu Act Prgm Comm of Mid States Schl Evaluation Chm; Rensellaer Boys & Girls Club, Yth Bd 1995-, Bd Mem; *home:* 1801 9th St Rensselaer NY 12144*

LEAHY, KATHLEEN, Social Studies Teacher; *b:* Worcester, MA; *ed:* Westfield St (BA) His 1993; *cr:* Algonquin Regnl HS Soc Stud Tchr 1 Yr; *ai:* Soph Class Adv; Lower Schl Transition Team; Algonquin Regnl Tchrs Assn 1994-; *office:* Algonquin Reg HS 79 Bartlett St Northborough MA 01532*

LEAHY, WILLIAM LAWRENCE, Intro to Business Teacher; *b:* Batlmore, MD; *ed:* Loyola Coll (BA) Marketing 1991; 12 Credit Hrs Theology; *cr:* LaSalle College HS Bus Tchr, Lacrosse Coach 1992-; *ai:* Prof Indoor Lacrosse Player; *office:* Lasalle College HS 8605 Cheltenham Ave Glenside PA 19038

LEAP, BARBARA GOLIAN, Computer Coordinator; *b:* Johnstown, PA; *c:* Danielle, Garett; *ed:* Carlow Coll (BS) El Ed 1969; Penn St Univ of Pittsburgh (MS) Ed, Cmptrs 1989; *cr:* St Bede's Schl 2nd-4th Grd Tchr 1962-65; Conemaugh Vly Schl Dist 1st, 3rd, 5th Grd Elem Tchr 1969-94, Cmptr Coord 1994-; *ai:* Cmptr Club; Ed Cncl; Tech, Strategic Planning, Goals 2000 Comms; NEA 1969-, Treas 1976; IRA 1980-; PASCD 1991-; ASCD 1995-; AARP 1995-; Article Pub; Associateship Univ of Pittsburgh at Johnstown; Dev Curr Allegheny Indstrl Heritage Project; *office:* Conemaugh Vly Schl Dist 1451 Frankstown Rd Rd 1 Johnstown PA 15902*

LEAP, SUSAN K., 8th Grade Science Teacher; *b:* Altoona, PA; *ed:* PA St Univ (BS) Kndgtn, Elem Ed 1985; St Francis Coll (MED) Ed 1991; *cr:* St Aloysius Schl 4-6 Grd Sci Tchr 1986-89; Northern Cambria Cath Schl 5-8 Grd Sci Tchr 1989-90; St Michaels Schl 6-8 Grd Sci Tchr 1990-; *ai:* PA Jr Acad of Sci Adv, Judge 6 Yrs; Spelling Bee Adv 5 Yrs; Yrbk Adv, Ed 5 Yrs; Camp Instr 5 Yrs; Mentor 1 Yr; NCEA 1990-; *home:* 364 Wood St Lilly PA 15938*

LEAPLEY, PAMELA ANNE, First Grade Teacher; *b:* Middletown, OH; *m:* Steven F.; *c:* Steven Tad; *ed:* Univ of KY (BA) Elem Ed 1969; Wright St Univ (MS) Tchr Ldr 1994; *cr:* O. R. Edgington Elem Schl First Grd Tchr 1969-; *ai:* NEA 1969-; *home:* 313 Brownstone Dr Englewood OH 45322

LEAR, DEBRA KAY, Family & Consumer Sci Tchr; *b:* St Marys, OH; *m:* Lance L.; *c:* Kayla Jean; *ed:* Bowling Green St Univ (BS) Home Ec Ed 1978; *cr:* Ohio City-Liberty HS 7th-12th Grd Home Ec Tchr 1978-81; Urbana HS 9th-12th Grd Home Ec Tchr 1981-; *ai:* FHA, HERO Adv; NEA, OEA 1978-; AAFCS 1985-; Order of Eastern Star; Cert of Merit 1992; Awd of Merit 1991; *office:* Urbana HS 500 Washington Ave Urbana OH 43078

LEAR, JAMES P., Sci Dept Chm & Physics Tchr; *b:* West Lafayette, IN; *m:* Debra Kerr; *c:* LeAnne, Kaitlin, Jessica; *ed:* IN U of PA (BS) Bio 1974; Physics Cert 1993; *cr:* Cntrl Cath HS Physics, Bio & Ecology Tchr 1975-84; The Mercersburg Acad Physics Tchr 1984-85; St Paul Cathedral HS Physics, Bio & Sci Chair 1985-89; Oakland Cath HS Physics, Bio & Sci Chair 1989-; *ai:* Duquesne Univ Asst Track Coach; NCEA 1985-; GTE Gift Awd 1995; *office:* Oakland Catholic H S 144 N Craig St Pittsburgh PA 15213*

LEARN, NELSON R., HS Math Teacher; *b:* Berwick, PA; *m:* Bonnie J. Smith; *c:* Tenette Lanning, Radel Harding, Timothy, Christopher; *ed:* Bloomsburg Univ (BS) Scndry Math 1970; Addl Grad Courses Working Towards Supervisory Cert; *cr:* Berwick Area Schl Dist Math Tchr 1970-, Math Dept Chprsn 1993-95; *ai:* Advisory Comm; Project Retain; NEA & PA St Ed Assn 1970-; Berwick Area Ed Assn 1970-, Treas & VP; Berwick Area Ambulance Assn 1978-, Pres 1985, Treas 1988-, Bd of Dirs 1986-, Emergency Medical Technician 1984-; First Bapt Church 1989-, Bd of Chrstn Ed Chprsn 1991-4.

LEARY, ALINE LEBRUN, Language Arts & US His Teacher; *b:* Biddeford, ME; *m:* Merlin N.; *c:* Scott, Stephen, Michael; *ed:* Univ Southern ME (BS) Ed, Psych-Summa Cum Laude 1974; Grad Work; *cr:* Meml Jr HS Career Guid Cnslr 1975-77; Meml MS LA Tchr 1977-, His Tchr 1995-; *ai:* Lang Arts Curr Dev Comm; Home Schl Link Dev; SPTA 1975-, Exec Bd; MEA, NEA 1975-; So Portland Grant; *office:* Memorial Middle School 120 Wescott Rd South Portland ME 04106

LEARY, DONNA NAMISNIAK, Math Teacher; *b:* Auburn, NY; *m:* Stephen; *c:* Andrew; *ed:* Cayoga Comm Coll (AA) Lib Arts 1979; Oswego St Univ (BS) N-9 Ed 1981; Cortland St Univ (MS) Ed, Math Concentrate 1985; *cr:* East MS 7th-8th Grd Math 1981-; *ai:* Natl Jr Hnr Soc Adv; AFT NYSUT 1981-; *office:* East MS 159 Franklin St Auburn NY 13021

LEARY, EDWARD WILLIAM, Science Teacher; *b:* Rochester, NY; *m:* Lorraine C. Curry; *c:* Kristen A.; *ed:* St Univ of NY at Brockport (BS) Ed 1968, (MS) Earth Sci & Ed 1973; 24 Grad Hrs beyond Masters; *cr:* Rush Henrietta Cntrl Schls Tchr 1968-; *ai:* Mens & Womens Var Tennis Coach; Ski Club Adv; NYSUT 1968-; STANYS 1970-; *office:* Rush Henrietta Cntrl Schls 1799 Lehigh Station Rd Henrietta NY 14467*

LEARY, JOHN DANIEL, Spanish Teacher; *b:* Bethpage, NY; *m:* Kristine Drinkwater; *c:* Michael, Anna; *ed:* Univ of MD (BA) Span 1979; *cr:* Gaithersburg Hr High Span Tchr 1980-89; Redland MS Span Tchr 1989-91; Julius West MS Span Tchr 1991-92; Richard Montgomery HS Span & Comm Svc 1992-; *ai:* Comm Svc Club Spon; NEA 1979-; Kiwanis Club Awd in Recognition of Comm Svc 1992; MD St Svc Learning Fellow 1993; *office:* Richard Montgomery HS 250 Richard Montgomery Dr Rockville MD 20852

LEARY, LAWRENCE VINCENT, Fifth Grade Teacher; *b:* Teaneck, NJ; *c:* Brian, Erin, Megan; *ed:* Adelphi Univ (MA) Elem Ed 1974; 90 Credit Hrs Continuing Ed at St Univ of NY at Stony Brook; *cr:* Sound Beach Schl 4th-6th Grd Tchr 1972-; Miller Place Schls Effective Tchr Trng for Newly Hired Tchrs 1988-93; *ai:* Mock Trial Coord; Miller Place Tchrs Assn 1972-, Treas; Long Island Assn for AIDS Care 1990-, Vol; *office:* Sound Beach Schl 197 N Country Rd Miller Place NY 11764

LEARY, MARY DEBORAH OLDMAN, Spanish & Reading Teacher; *b:* Buffalo, NY; *m:* Daniel Fauls; *c:* Shane, Shannon, Skye, Sara; *ed:* Lake Erie Coll (BA) Span & Ed 1969; Allegheny (MED) Psych & Ed 1972; 35 Post Grad Hrs; *cr:* Roehm MS 7th & 8th Grd Span Tchr 1971-72; North Olmsted HS Span Tchr 1972-76; Magnificat HS Span Tchr 1976-78; Cleveland Schls Span Tchr 1988-; Upward Bound Rdng Tchr 1992-; *ai:* North Cntrl Chm; Curr Comm; AFT 1968-; MFL Assn 1972-; Tchr of Yr at Charles Elliot MS; *office:* John Marshall HS 3952 W 140th St Cleveland OH 44111*

LEASE, JOSEPH FRANCIS, Social Studies Teacher; *b:* Keyser, WV; *ed:* Frostburg St (BS) His 1972; Post Grad Stud; *cr:* Bishop Walsh Soc Stud Tchr 1974-, Stu Cncl Moderator 1979-83, Athletic Dir 1984-88, Ftbl Moderator 1983-95; *ai:* Asst Athletic Dir; Ftbl Moderator; Chess Club Adv; Distinguished Lasallian Educator of Baltimore Dist 1988-89; *office:* Bishop Walsh Schl 700 Bishop Walsh Rd Cumberland MD 21502

LEASE, KRISTINE RENEA LEWIS, Mathematics Teacher; *b:* Tiffin, OH; *m:* Perry; *ed:* Univ of Findlay (BA) Math 1990; *cr:* Carey HS Instr of Math 1990-; *ai:* Var Vllybl Coach; Prom & Jr Class Adv; NEA 1990-, VP; *office:* Carey HS 357 E South St Carey OH 43316

LEASE, ROBIN MEARS, Early Childhd Education Tchr; *b:* Massillon, OH; *m:* Courtney E.; *c:* Taylor, Brian; *ed:* Miami Univ (BS) Home Ec 1978; OSU (MS) Early Chldhd 1980; *cr:* Crestview MS Home Ec Tchr 1980-87; Fort Hayes Metro Schl Early Chldhd Tchr 1987-; *ai:* FHA, HERO Adv; Newspaper; NEA, OEA 1980-; NAEYC 1987-; TWIG 1985-, Pres; Sunday Schl Tchr 1990-95; Tchr of Yr; Good Apple Recepient; *office:* Ft Hayes Metropolitan Ed Ctr 546 Jack Gibbs Blvd Columbus OH 43215

LEATHEM, MARY TONITA ARMAO, Fourth Grade Teacher; *b:* Troy, NY; *m:* Joseph F.; *c:* Anne Brigid, Joseph, Anthony; *ed:* Maria Coll (AAS) Early Chldhd Ed 1972; Coll of St Rose (BA) Elem Ed, Eng 1974; Post-Grad Work; *cr:* Troy City Schl Dist Elem Tchr 1974-78; St Brigid Regnl Cath Schl Jr HS Eng, Lit Tchr 1986-89; Tamarac Elem Schl Fourth Grd Tchr 1990-; *ai:* Eighth Grd Adv; Strategic Action Comm; Sci Fair Coord Effective Schls; Brittonkill Tchrs Assn 1990-, Union Bldg Rep, Exec Bd; Ladies Ancient Order of Hibernians 1970-, Natl Chm of Cath Action; Math Grant Bittankill Educl Fnd; *office:* Tamarac Elem Schl RR 3 Box 200a Troy NY 12180*

LEATHERMAN, DAVID K., 5th Grade Teacher; *b:* Barberton, OH; *c:* Benjamin, Martin; *ed:* Bluffton Coll (BA) Sociology 1969; Univ of Akron (MA) Elem Admin 1976; Addl 40 Post Grad Hrs; *cr:* St Paul Schl 8th Grd Sci, Math Tchr 3 Yrs; Highland Elem Schl 4, 4-5, 5 Grd Tchr 23 Yrs; *ai:* Stow Tchr Assn 1972-, Bldg Rep; OEA, NEA 1972-; Who's Who 1991; *office:* Highland Elem Schl Stow City Schls 1843 Graham Rd Stow OH 44224

LEATHERS, STAN, High School Mathematics Tchr; *b:* Knoxville, PA; *m:* Betsy Boyd; *c:* Sandy, Zack, Meggie; *ed:* Lebanon Vly (BS) Math & Physics 1973; Penn St (MED) Ed 1990; Masters +45 Hrs; *cr:* Downingtown High Math Tchr 1973-82; Unionville High Math Tchr 1983-; *ai:* Ftbl, Wrestling & Tennis Coach; NEA 1973-; Coach of the Yr (5 Times); Yrbk Dedications (Twice); *office:* Unionville HS 750 Unionville Rd Kennett Square PA 19348*

LEAVER, ANN MCCARTHY, English Teacher; *b:* Salem, MA; *m:* William J.; *c:* William, Meghan; *ed:* Emmanuel Coll (BA) Eng 1974; Salem St Coll (MA) Amer Lit 1986; 21 Addl Credit Hrs; *cr:* Bigelow Jr HS 7th Grd Eng & Soc Stud Tchr 1974-75; Higgins Jr HS 7th-9th Grd Eng Tchr 1975-79; Marblehead HS 9th-12th Grd Eng Tchr 1979-; *ai:* MA Cncl of Tchr of Eng 1990-; NCTE 1994-; Univ of MA Flwshp in Expository Writing Inst 1978; Recipient of NBC Natl Tchrs Awd 1989; Presenter at Intnl Visual Lit Assns Natl Conf 1989; *office:* Marblehead HS Ducan Sleigh Sq Marblehead MA 01945*

LEAVITT, DUANE L., Chemistry Instructor; *b:* Portland, ME; *m:* Nancy J. Lowell; *c:* Garrett, Zachery; *ed:* Univ of ME at Orono (BS) Geological Sci 1968; Univ of So ME (MS) Ed Admin 1971; 60 Credit Hrs His, Cmptrs, Lang Arts; *cr:* Montello Jr HS Sci Tchr 1968-70; Univ of ME Lab Instr 1970-71; Leavitt Area HS Chem Instr 1971-90; ME Geological Survey Crest Project Dir 1990-91; Leavitt Area HS Chem Instr 1991-; *ai:* Sr, Jr Class Adv; TTA, MTA, NEA 1971-; MMSA 1990-, Bd of Dir; ME TAsk Force on Curr Reform 1991-95; Writer ME Educl Assessment Sci Section 1991-93; St Grant to Stud Nezinscot River; Articles Pub; *office:* Levitt Area HS RR 1 Box 1251 Turner ME 04282

LEAVITT, MONITA R., Project Explore Enrchmnt Tchr; *b:* Easton, PA; *m:* Larry; *c:* Tamara, Ryan; *ed:* Moravian Coll (BA) El Ed, Art 1971; Cntrl CT St Univ (MA) Spec Ed 1973; Attnd yale Univ, Wesleyan Univ, Southern CT St Univ; *cr:* CCSU Grad Asst Spec Ed 1971-72; Long Ln Correctional Inst Art Tchr 1972-73; Region 15 Schls K-8th Grd GATE Tchr 1973-; *ai:* Clubs Roats, Shoats, Kids to Kids Intnl Writing; Video Production Cable TV; ASCD; NEA; NAFSA; PDK; APPLE; Talents Unlimited; CEA; Roats, Shoats, Jane Goodall; Albert Schweitzer Intnl UN Symposium Planning Comm 1992-; Tchr of Yr 1993; Articles Pub; Presenter St, Natl Confs; Grants Ed, Video; CEA Video Awd 1993; Celebration of Excl Honorable Mention 1991; *office:* Rochambeau MS 100 Peter Rd Southbury CT 06488*

LEAVY, THOMAS A., Earth Science Prof Emeritus; *b:* Turkey City, PA; *m:* Joan; *c:* Meg Small; *ed:* Slippery Rock (BS) Ger; Penn St (MS) Geog 1962; Univ of Pittsburg (PHD) Higher Ed 1971; Allegheny-Clarion Vly Schl Tchr 1961-63; Glassboro St Coll Asst Prof 1963-64; California Univ of PA Prof 1964-79; Clarion Univ of PA Prof 1979-94; *cr:* Allegency-Clarion Valley Schl Sys Tchr 1961-63; Glansboro St Coll Asst Prof 1963-64; CA Univ of PA Prof 1964-79; Clarion Univ of PA Prof 1979-94; *home:* 128 S 8th Ave Clarion PA 16214

LEBARRON, THERESE ANN, HS Special Education Teacher; *b:* Albany, NY; *m:* A. Douglas Nevling; *c:* Kyle; *ed:* Marist Coll (BS) Juvenile Justice 1988; SUNY at New Paltz (MS) Spec Ed 1990; *cr:* Waverly Family Ctr Adult Ed Tchr 1990; Ripken Learning Ctr Adult Ed Tchr 1990-91; Baltimore Cty PS Spec Ed Tchr 1991-; *ai:* Spec Olympics Bowling Coach; Mentor; Cr of Friends Adv; NEA, NSTA 1994-; *office:* Owings Mills HS 124 Tollgate Rd Owings Mills MD 21117

LEBBING, DIANE M. (BUBLITZ), Business Technology Teacher; *b:* Trenton, NJ; *c:* Rick, Carla Young, Brad; *ed:* Rider Coll (BS) Accounting, Ed 1958; Jersey St Coll Cmptr Courses; *cr:* Steinert HS Bus Tchr 1958-59; Bound Brook HS Bus Tchr 1966-67; Montgomery HS Bus Tech Tchr 1968-; *ai:* MTEA Philanthropic Assn Treas, Schlsp Chm, Exec Bd; Cmptr Lab Monitor; MTEA 1968-, Sec, Treas; SCEA 1968-, Rep; NJEA, NEA 28 Yrs; Eastern Star; *office:* Montgomery HS Burnt Hill Rd Skillman NJ 08558

LEBEAU, GARY D., US History Teacher; *b:* Northampton, MA; *m:* Joanne Lee Sullivan; *c:* Kara, Matthew, Christopher; *ed:* Univ of MA (BA) Pol Sci 1969, (MED) Urban Admin 1975; Univ of CT (CAGS) Ed, Admin 1986; Cntrl Ct St Univ; *cr:* Worcester Alternative HS Tchr 1972-73; East Hartford HS Head Tchr 1973-87; East Hartford Drug Free Schls Drop-out, Prevention Coord 1987-91; East Hartford HS Coord, US His Tchr 1991-; *ai:* Leo Club Fac Adv; NEA 1973-, VP 1981-83, Pac Chair 1983-85; Lions Club 1985-, All Offices, Lion of the Yr 1986; Intercommunity Mental Hlth 1995-, Bd of Dirs; E Hartford Town Cncl 1989-91, Cnclr; St Legislator 1991-95, Vice Chm, Commerce Comm; Tchr of Yr 1979; *office:* East Hartford HS 869 Forbes St East Hartford CT 06118*

LE BLANC, GLORIRA JEAN (EICHORN), Latin Teacher; *b:* Buffalo, NY; *m:* Norman A. Jr.; *c:* Janelle A., Noelle A., Justin A.; *ed:* Canisius Coll (BA) Classical Lang 1970; Post Grad Ed; St Univ NY at Buffalo Post Grad Classics; *cr:* Southside Jr HS Latin Tchr 1972-77; Bennett HS Latin Tchr 1980-; *ai:* Alternative Assessment Comm; Intl Stud & Law Prgms; NEA, Buffalo Tchrs Fed 1972-; Amer Classical League 1994-; Salem Church Choir, Salem Bd of Chrstn Ed 1980-; Salem Vaction Bible Schl 1972-, Tchr, Assistant Supt; BA Summa Cum Laude Canisius Coll; Grad Assistantship St Univ of NY at Buffalo; *office:* Bennett HS 2885 Main St Buffalo NY 14214

LEBLANC, MARGE ADELINE, NH Grad Yth Job Specialist; *b:* College Point, NY; *c:* Jennifer Lint, Stephanie Lint; *ed:* Coll of Lifelong Learning (BS) Spcl Needs 1990; St Univ of NY Assoc Primary Ed 1970; Family Mediation; Crisis Intervention; *cr:* Kings Square Antiques Owner 1975-85; White Mts Schl Dist 36 Spcl Ed Tchr 1985-90, Chptr 1 Tchr 1990-93; NH Job Trng Cncl Yth Specialist 1993-; *ai:* Career Assn Adv; Stu Assistance Advy Bd; FHA Asst Adv; Schl to Work Region 3 Bd; Work Based Learning Comm; Alternative Schedule Comm; Crisis Intervention Team; Spcl Olympics 1975-, Coach Intnl Alpine; *office:* White Mountains Regional HS PO Box 338 Whitefield NH 03598

LEBLANC, MARY FLYNN, Dir of Rel Ed & Yth Ministry; *b:* Fitchburg, MA; *c:* Anthony, Matthew; *ed:* Fitchburg St Coll (BSEd) Ed 1962; SUNY Grad 20 Credit Hrs in Pol Sci 1966; Natl Ctr for Yth Ministry Dev Nationally Cert Yth Minister 1989; *cr:* Cntrl Schl Dist 5 Classroom Tchr 1962-69; Sub Tchr 1970-; Amer Intnl Schl Bd of Dirs 1976-78; MHT Schl Dir of Rel Ed & Yth Min 1984-; *ai:* Opening Speech at the Ath Banquet; Portland ME Diocesan Assn of Rel Ed Dirs 1985-; York-Cumberland Ctys Assn of Yth Ministers 1985-; Natl Assn of Yth Ministers 1989-; Recognition Awd for Svc Diocese of Portland 1989 & To Parish 1993; Thornton Acad Ftbl Mothers 1989-93; Taught Adult Wkshp at New England Yth Convention in Nashua NH 1991; *office:* Most Holy Trinity Parish Schl 271 Main St PO Box 310 Saco ME 04072*

LEBLANC, MARY HOYT, Second Grade Teacher; *b:* Catskill, NY; *ed:* St Univ at New Paltz (BS) Elem Ed 1967; Permanent Elem Ed Cert 30 Hrs; *cr:* Ostrander Elem Schl Second Grd Tchr 1967-; *ai:* Wallkill Tchrs Assn 1967-, Bldg Rep 2 1/2 Yrs; NYSUT 1967-; AFT 1975-; St Benedict's Rosary Altar Soc 1988-; Montgomery Nrsng Home 1988-, Vol, Svc Pins; St Charles' Sunday Schl Prgm 1996-, Asst Confirmation Tchr; Parents' Club 1987-94, Tchr Rep; *office:* Ostrander Elem Schl Viola Ave Wallkill NY 12589

LEBLANC, STEPHEN WALLACE, Language Arts & Soc Stud Tchr; *b:* Potsdam, NY; *ed:* SUC at Potsdam (BA) Eng, Scndry Ed 1970; Lawrence Univ (MED) Cnslng, Hum Dev 1993; 30 Grad Hrs SUC at Potsdam Elem Ed, Permanent Cert N, K-6 Scndry Eng 1975; *cr:* Berlin Cntrl Schl 8 & 9 Grd Eng Tchr 1970-71; Thousand Islands Clayton Elem Schl 5 & 6 Grd Lang Arts Tchr 1971-89; Thousand Islands MS Remedial Rdng, Math Tchr 1989-92; Thousand Islands Guardino Elem Schl 5 Grd Tchr 1993-; *ai:* Lang Arts Comm; NY St United Tchrs 1970-; NY St Rdng Assn 1976-, Conf Planning Comm 1982; Greater Thousand Islands Literacy Cncl 1976-, Treas, Pres; North Cntry Coordinating Cncl of Tchrs 1976-, Del-at-Large, Sec; Thousand Islands Tchrs Assn 1970-, Pres, Sec; Clayton Minor Thousand Islands Yth Hockey Assn 1980-, Sec, Tournament Dir, VP; Fan of Yr Awd 1872; Pres Awd 1991; Clayton Minor Hockey Hall of Fame 1993; Thousand Islands Craft Schl, Textile Museum 1984-, Bd of Trustees, Vol, Svc Awd 1991; Clayton Chamber of Comm 1995-; *home:* 508 Webb St # 14 Clayton NY 13624

LEBLANC, THERESE FECTEAU, Fourth Grade Teacher; *b:* Acushnet, MA; *m:* Claude A.; *c:* Diane James, Julie Medeiros, Margaret; *ed:* Rivier Coll (BA) Elem Ed 1966; Providence Coll 9 Credit Hrs; *cr:* Charles S. Ashley Schl Fourth, Fifth Grd Tchr 1966-68; St Anthony Schl Fourth, Fifth Grd Tchr 1979-84; St Mary's Schl Fourth Grd Tchr 1984-89, Fourth Grd Tchr 1993-; *ai:* NCEA 1979-; *office:* St Mary Schl 115 Illinois St New Bedford MA 02745

LEBO, ROBIN SNYDER, 4th, 5th & 6th Grade Teacher; *b:* Lewistown, PA; *m:* Phillip L.; *ed:* Bloomsburg Univ (BS) Elem Ed 1977, (MS) Rdng 1984; *cr:* Juniata Cty Schl Dist 2nd Grd Tchr 1977-78, 3rd Grd Tchr 1978-79, 4th, 5th & 6th Grd Tchr 1979-; *ai:* Power of Positive Stdnts Bldg Rep; NEA, PSEA 1978-; Delta Kappa Gamma Soc Intnl 1986-; Juniata Vly Drug & Alcohol Abuse Commission 1992-, Bd Mem; The Next Step Fnd 1994-, Bd Mem; *home:* RR 1 Box 192 Thompsontown PA 17094*

LEBRON, MIRIAM, 8th Grd Teacher; *b:* Mayaguez, PR; *c:* Ellie Sanchez, Eli Sanchez; *ed:* Jersey City St Coll (BA) Gen Elem 1971; *cr:* Shoe-Town Cashier 1968-69; Modern Home Stores Credit Clerk 1969-70; Cornelia F. Bradford Tchr 1971-; *ai:* Girl Scout Ldr; Treas Marist Mothers; Vol Coach; Math Tutor; NEA 1971-; JCEA 1971-; Tchr of Yr 1989; *office:* Cornelia F. Bradford PS #16 96 Sussex St Jersey City NJ 07302

LEBWOHL, EUGENE I., Co-Founding Dir & Sci Teacher; *b:* New York City, NY; *ed:* Bard Coll (BA) Environmental Stud 1974; Leslie Coll (MA) Environmental Stud 1987; Coll of New Rochelle Working on MS Educl Admin & Staff Dev; *cr:* Self-Employed Naturalist, Envrionmental Edctr 1974-77; BOCES Walkabout Prgm Dir, Sci Tchr 1977-; *ai:* Candreva Environmental Fnd 1980-, Pres; Copen Family Fund 1990-; Environmental Adv; Numerous Articles Pub; *office:* Boces Walkabout Program 200 BOCES Dr Yorktown Hts NY 10598

LECK, GLORIANNE M., Professor of Education; *b:* Lincoln Cty, WI; *ed:* Univ of WI Madison (BS) Philosophy, His1963, (MA) Educl Policy Stud 1966, (PHD) Educl Policy Stud 1968; Grad Stu Univ of PA 1965, Northwestern Univ 1966; Visiting Scholar NY Univ 1981-82; *cr:* WI StUniv Instr 1967-69; PA St Univ Asst Prof 1970-72, Philosopher, Home Ec Ed 1973-74; Youngstown St Univ Assoc Prof, Ed 1974-80, Full Prof, Ed 1980-; *ai:* Adv Gay, Lesbian Alliance; Grievance, Lib, Women's Stud Comms; Amer Educl Stud Assn 1978-, Pres 1989-90; Amer Educl Research Assn 1985-; NEA 1974-; Phi Delta Kappa 1977-; Human Relations Commission 1988-, Chair, 1995-; OutVoice 1992-, Chair 1994; Coalition for Soc Justice 1992-95; O.E.A. Holloways, Human, Civil Rights Commission Awd 1994; Articles Pub; *office:* Youngstown State University 410 Wick Ave Youngstown OH 44555

LECLAIR, PAUL JOSEPH, Professor of Fine Arts; *b:* Waterbury, CT; *m:* Cathleen Cooke; *c:* Helen-Marie, John, Mary, Paul Matthew; *ed:* Univ of CT (BA) Music Ed 1957, (MA) Music Ed 1960; Catholic Univ of Amer (PHD) Music 1973; *cr:* Watertown Pub Schls Jr High Music Tchr 1957-1960; Washington DC Pub Schl Band & Orch Dir 1960-70; St Michaels Coll Music & Fine Arts Tchr 1960-; *ai:* Wind & Jazz Ensembles; Papal-Vatican Recognition for Music for Humanity; Guest Conductor St Festivals; *office:* Saint Michaels Coll Winooski Park Colchester VT 05439*

LECOURS, DOROTHY ALICE, First Grade Teacher; *b:* Waterbury, CT; *ed:* Our Lady of the Elms (BA) Sociology 1969; Cntrl CT St Coll (MS) Rdng 1973; Western CT St Univ 6th Yr Rdng 1986; *cr:* B. W. Tinker Schl First Grade Teacher 1969-; *ai:* Dev STAR Self-Esteem Curr; WTA, CEA, NEA 1969-; 2nd Pl Awd 1994, 1st Pl Awd 1995 Drug Free Task Force Contest; *office:* B. W. Tinker Schl 809 Highland Ave Waterbury CT 06708

LECRONE, VIRGINIA STERNBERGH, Spanish Teacher; *b:* York, PA; *m:* Franklin N. Jr.; *c:* Marcia Howes, Isabel Reinert, Frank III, Benjamin; *ed:* Lake Erie Coll (BA) Span 1964; Early Chldhd Ed at Towson Univ; Attnd Univ of Madrid Spain; *cr:* Dallastown Area HS Eng Tchr 1964; North Hills Jr HS Span Sub Tchr 1967; Johns Hopkins Cooperative Nursery Tchr 1969-71; Delone Cath HS Span Tchr 1989-; *ai:* Frosh Class, Span Club Moderator; Wrestling Chrldrs Coach; Jr Retreats Tchr Vol; NCEA 1989-; Manheim Homemakers 1976-, Chprsn, Friendship; Spain, France, Mexico Educl Trips 1991-95; Svc Projects to Raise Funds for Comm Projects for Liver Transplant Patient, Child with Brain Tumors; *office:* Delone Catholic HS 140 S Oxford Ave Mc Sherrystown PA 17344*

LEDBETTER, RONALD EDWARD, Mathematics Teacher; *b:* Corbin, KY; *m:* Paula Janette Guthrie; *ed:* Allegheny Coll (BS) Physics 1989, (ME) Ed 1990; *cr:* John Hay HS Physics, Math Tchr 1989-90; South Side HS Math Tchr 1990-; *ai:* Math Counts; Var Wrestling; *office:* South Side HS 4949 St Rt 151 Hookstown PA 15050

LEDDY, JOHN JOSEPH, HS Band Director; *b:* Brooklyn, NY; *m:* Diane; *c:* James, Margaret; *ed:* SUNY at Potsdam (BM) Music Ed 1973; SUNY at Stony Brook (MA) Continuing Ed 1976; 75 Post Grd Hrs; *cr:* Connetquot Schls Elem Band Tchr 1973-93, HS Band Tchr 1994-; *ai:* NY Schl Music Assn; Instrumental Jazz Chprsn; Tri-M Music Hnr Soc Chprsn; 1973-; NYSSMA 1973-, Inst Jazz Chprsn; Suffolk Cty Music Edct Jazz Day Coord; PTA 1973-; *office:* Connetquot HS 190 7th St E NY 11716

LEDDY, STEPHANIE MIRANDA, English Department C Copigue, NY; *m:* Harold; *c:* John, Bethany; *ed:* Harper Coll St Uni (BA) Hum & Eng 1966; Cath Univ of Amer (MA) Scndry Eng 1 Newspaper & Lit Magazine Adv; Play & Renaissence Festi Sunshine Comm Chm; MD Scholastic Press Assn 1987-, Bd of D Writing Project 1990-; NEA 1987-; Dow Jones Ed Fund Schls MSPA Schlsp 1988; *office:* Catholic H S Of Baltimore 2800 Edis Baltimore MD 21213

LEDDY-SOKOL, MARIA NATALIE, Dean & History Tea Queens, NY; *c:* Danielle; *ed:* St Josephs (BA) His 1985; Queens C Soc Stud Ed 1996; Conflict Resolution Courses In Svc; Lit & Fordham; *cr:* St Johns Prep Soc Stud Tchr, Dean, Asst Summer S & Prin 1985-; *ai:* Retreat Ldr; Bsktbl & Sftbl Coach; Dram Chrldng; NCSS 1996-; 2 NEA Awds to Study Fr Revolu Enlightenment; *office:* Saint Johns Preparatory HS 2121 Cres Astoria NY 11105*

LEDIEU, SUSAN DAY, French Teacher; *b:* Boston, MA; *m:* Michel; *c:* Carolyn, Eric, Emilie; *ed:* Univ of CO (BA) Fr 1965; CA at Santa Barbara (MA) Fr 1967; Universite de Granable, Unive Paris; PA St Scndry Cert 1994; *cr:* Centre de Penscrgnement E Tchr 2 Yrs; Detroit Cty Day Schl Fr Tchr 6 Yrs; Villa Mana Acad 3 Yrs; *ai:* Moderator Fr Hnr Soc, Natl Fr Contest; Amer Assn Tc 1985-; US Figure Skating Assn 1990-, Local Competition Chprsn Villa Maria Acad Green Tree Malvern PA 19355*

LEDIOYT, SALLY SCHAEFFER, Sixth Grade Teacher; *b:* Bet PA; *c:* Jeff; *ed:* Doane Coll (BA) Elem Ed 1969; Western CT St Un Ed 1987; 50 Credit Hrs; *cr:* Prince George's Cty Pub Schls 2nd- Tchr 1970-72; Norwood Elem Schl 5th-6th Grd Tchr 1973-79 Woodcrest Schl ESL Tchr 1981-82; Haldane Elem Schl 6th G 1987-; *ai:* Soc Stud, Lib Comms; Peer Mediation Mentor; Adv Groups; NYSUT HFA 1987-, Trustee, Alternate Del; *office:* Haldar Schl 10 Craigside Dr Cold Spring NY 10516

LEDNUM, FLORENCE NASH, Biological Sciences Profe Abington, PA; *m:* C. Wendell; *c:* Dawn E. Rieken, Holly R. Rie Washington Coll (BS) Bio 1962; Univ of DE (MS) Bio, Physiolo, Bio 1964; Univ of MD (EDD) Ed, Curr, Instruction 1993; Grad Salisbury St Univ; *cr:* US Naval Oceanographic Office Bi Oceanographer 1964-69; Macqueen Gibbs Willis Schl of Nrsng A Physiology, Microbiology Instr 1969-82d; Wor-Wic Comm Coll As Biological Sci 1982-92; Cheasapeake Coll Prof Biol Sci, Dept H 1992-; *ai:* Curr Comm 1992-; Fac Assembly Rep to Coll Cncl 1993 Dept Chair 1994-; Assn Advancement Comm Coll Tchrs, Presenter; Trinity Cathedral 1977-, Ed, Pres 1977-82; ECW Pres 1977-82 Mem, Pastoral Care Comm 1983-85; Cursillo 1991-, Newsle Diocese of Easton; Waterfowl Festival Vol; Maritime Festival Vol; Tchng 1990; NSF Grant 1962-64; *office:* Chesapeake Coll PO Corner Rt 50 Wye Mills MD 21679*

LEDOUX, BRUCE, 6th Grade Teacher; *b:* New Britain, CT; *m:* Dunn; *c:* Sarah; *ed:* SCSU (BA Early Chldhd Ed 1976, (MA) Early Ed 1980; SCSU Educl Leadership 1996; *cr:* Marlborough Elem S Grd Tchr 8 Yrs, 4th Grd Tchr 10 Yrs, 6th Grd Tchr 2 Yrs; *ai:* NEA Pres, VP, Treas; *office:* Marlborough Elem Schl 25 School Dr Marlb CT 06447

LEDUC, VERONICA MARY, Vice Principal & Teacher; *b:* Wa CT; *c:* Jason, Nicole; *ed:* Regis Coll (BA) Chem 1971; Cntrl CT (MS) Sci 1987; Southern CT St Univ 6th Yr Admin 1992; *cr:* Notr Acad Math, Sci Tchr 1979-86; Thomaston HS Math, Sci Tchr 1 Thomaston MS Math, Sci Tchr 1989-93; Thomaston HS Vice Pr Physics, Pre Calculus Tchr 1993-; *ai:* Stu Asst Team; Dist Hlth Cn Discipline Comm; NEASS&C Reevaluation Comm Co-Chair; NE 1986-; CT Assn of Phys Tchrs; Girl Scouts of Amer 1983-; Thomaston HS 185 Branch Rd Thomaston CT 06787

LEDWITH, EDWARD J., Instrumental Music Teacher; *b:* Randol *m:* Lisa; *c:* Aaron, Jordan; *ed:* Johnson St Coll (BA) Music Ed 1 Credits Post-Grad Stud; *cr:* Brighton Elem Schl Instrumental Mus 1984-86; Whitingham Schl Music Tchr & Band Dir 1987-95; Aus Instrumental Music Tchr & Band Dir 1995-; *ai:* Jazz Band; Tech Music Educators Natl Conf 1987-; VT Music Educators Assn 198 VII VP; MA Music Educators Assn 1995-; MA Tchrs Assn 1995-; G R Austin MS 112 Howland Rd Lakeville MA 02347*

LEE, ALAN, Social Studies Supervisor; *b:* Irvington, NJ; *m:* Dia Montclair St Univ (BA) Psych 1974; Fairleigh Dickinson Univ Clinical Psych 1977; Soc Stud Tchng Cert 36 Credits 1983; Supe Cert 12 Grad Credits 1989; *cr:* St Francis Counseling Svc Psych 1980-81; Pinelands Regnl HS Soc Stud Tchr 1983-88, Soc Stud 1989-; *ai:* Curr, AP Coord; Coord Close Up 5 Day Govt Stu Washington DC; NJ Cncl for Soc Stud, NCSS 1994-; Amer Psych Assn 1995-; *office:* Pinelands Reg HS 565 Nugentown Rd Tucke 08087

LEE, ALFRED W.,SR., Social Science Teacher; *b:* Philadelphia, Cynthia L. Banks; *c:* Alfred, Jennifer, Lujuana; *ed:* Cheyney Un Scndry Soc Stud 1965; Temple Univ Grad Schl of Ed Curr & Glassboro St Coll Pub Relations; Career Acad Div of Famous Broad Announcer; Lincoln Tech Inst Radio & TV Rpr; *cr:* Strawberry M MS & HS Tchr 1965-; *ai:* SGA Adv 1968-75; Bowling Coach 19 Debate Team Adv 1982-92; Class of 1979 & 1982 Adv; AFT & PFT Bldg Rep; IB of TCW & H of A 1987-, Asst Shop Steward; Golde Comm Band 1987-, 3rd Trumpet; AARP; NAACP; USNR-R; Attendance 11 Yrs; *office:* Strawberry Mansion Mid/Sr HS 3133 Rid Suite 1 Philadelphia PA 19121

LEE, BARBARA ANN, Fifth Grade Teacher; *b:* Wheelersburg, Gary Michael; *c:* Julie Stewart Shonkwiler, Angela Stewart Turn Portsmouth Interstate Bus Coll (AS) Secretarial 1959; Shawnee S (AA) Ed 1978; OH Univ (BS) Ed-Summa Cum Laude 1979, (ME Supvr 1981; Univ of Dayton Post Grad Stud Ed 1984; *cr:* Portsmou Govt Clerk, Sec 1959-61; Minford Local Schls Ed Tchr 1979-; *ai:* Stu Tchrs & Univ Stdnts; NEA 1979-, Bldg Rep; Alpha Iota, Forme VP; Portsmouth Women's Tennis Assn, Publicity Chprsn; CTB Exemplary Tchng; *home:* 3115 Tick Ridge Rd Wheelersburg OH 4

LEE, BETTY A., HS Speech & Comm Instructor; *b:* Dayton, O Miami Univ (BS) Comm & Theatre 1975; Univ of Dayton (MS) Scn 1982; Miami Jacobs Bus Coll 2 Yrs Law Paralegal Cert 19 Miamisburg HS Radio Broadcasting Tchr 1975-88, Beginning Acti 1979-89, Comm Beginning & Advanced Tchr 1978-92, Comm & Tchr 1978-; *ai:* Speech Contests; NEA, OEA, Miamisburg Cla Tchrs Assn 1975-, Mem; Miami Univ Alumni 1975-; Exemplary Tc 1993; *office:* Miamisburg Sr HS 1860 Belvo Rd Miamisburg OH 4

LEE, CARLA ANTOINETTE, 4th Grade Teacher; *b:* Washington, Nisha Janelle, Tracee Alanna; *ed:* Stud Elem Ed at Westchester Univ *cr:* Morrison Elem 3rd & 4th Grd Tchr 1972-75; McCloskey Elem 4 Tchr 1976-; *ai:* Bldg & New Stan Comms; Soc Club & Kids Week

, Chm-Czar for Drug Prevention Ed; Drama Coach; PFT 1972-; 1994-; AFT; Wadsworth Concerned Neighbors Against Drugs 1991-; Ward Comm Person 1993- Asst Treas & Sec; Tchr of Excl Semi ist 1991; Drug Prevention Summer Pgm CLASP Pgm Grants ved; *office:* John F Mccloskey Elem Schl 8500 Pickering St ldelphia PA 19150*

CECIL LYNN, Science Teacher; *b:* Greeley, CO; *m:* Patricia Elaine ay; *c:* Joshua, Jennifer, Jeffrey; *ed:* Southern Coll (BA) Bio 1979; ws Univ (MAT) Bio 1986; *cr:* Broadview Acad Sci Tchr 1982-83; n St Acad Sci Tchr, Vice Prin 1983-90; Mile High Acad Sci Tchr 93; Highland View Schl Sci Chprsn 1993-; *ai:* Class Spon; ainment, Acad Stan Comm; NSTA 1979-; Zapatra Awd 1992; *office:* and View Acad 10100 Academy Dr Hagerstown MD 21740*

CLARENCE A., Principal; *b:* Grove City, PA; *m:* Susan J.; *ed:* Bapt Coll (AA) 1976, (BRE) Chrstn Day Schl 1978; Edinboro Univ (MED) Ed 1984; *cr:* Bethel Chrstn Schl of Erie Math & Comp Sci Tchr & pal 1978-; *ai:* Stu Cncl Adv; Sftbl, Soccer Coach; Sr Class Adv 1984, 1992; *office:* Bethel Chrstn Schl 1781 W 38th St Erie PA 16508

DAVID J., Sr HS Studies Teacher; *b:* Binghamton, NY; *m:* Susan c: Kevin, Justin; *ed:* Bloomsburg Univ (BS) Soc Ed, Soc Stud 1975; 54 Hrs; MEQ 1989; *cr:* Susquehanna Comm SD Sr HS Social Stud , Dept Chm 1993-; *ai:* Adv Jr Class, Chess Club; Former JV Bsktbl (14 Yrs); NEA, PSEA 1978-; NCSS 1989-; *office:* Susquehanna Schl Dist RD 3 Box 5A Susquehanna PA 18847

DIANE DONAHUE, English Teacher; *b:* Brooklyn, NY; *m:* Alan; Y Univ (BA); *cr:* Pinelands Regnl HS Tchr 1983-; *ai:* Class Adv; Cncl; Schlsp Comm; Eng Club; NCTE; Tchr of Yr Local PEA; *office:* ands Regional HS 565 Nugentown Rd Tuckerton NJ 08087*

DON FRANKLIN, Chemistry Teacher; *b:* Conway, SC; *m:* Erma s; *c:* Dawn M.; *ed:* SC St Univ (BS) Chem 1963; St Johns Coll (MS) 1975; Attnd Coastal Carolina Coll, Univ of DC, George Washington Bowie St Univ, Trinity Coll, Morris Coll; *cr:* Whittemore HS Chem 1963-67; Choppee HS Chem, Physics Tchr 1967-68; Rabaut Jr HS Sci Tchr 1968-93; Theodore Roosevelt HS Chem Tchr 1993-; *ai:* Ath ; Schl Chptr Advy Cncl; Tau Beta Mu Boys Club Adv; AFT, WTU, A 1969-; Metropolitan AME Church 1979-; Whittemore Alumni 1983-, Pres, Ldrshp Awd; DC Metro Fishermen Club 1980-, Pres, 3 Vater Tournament Awds; Together Black Mens Club 1989-, Founder, Ldrshp Awd; Capritz Fnd Grant St Johns Coll 1973-75; Awd ciation Commission Pub Hlth DC 1993; Outstdng Tchr 1984-87, ated Svc 1987 Awds Rabaut Jr HS; *office:* Theodore Roosevelt HS 13th St NW Washington DC 20011*

DONNA L. (DUGAN), Fourth Grade Teacher; *b:* Harrisburg, PA; *m:* d F.; *c:* Jonathan E.; *ed:* Millersville Univ (BS) Elem Ed 1969; Penn iv (MS) Elem Ed 1971; *cr:* Central Dauphin Schl Dist 5th Grd Tchr s, 4th Grd Tchr 12 Yrs; *ai:* Ftbl Parents Booster Club Pres; Parents Orchestras Treas; Wrestling Assn Mem; CD Tech, opementally Appropriate Practices Comm; NEA, PSEA 1969-; 1969-, Sec; IRA 1984-; Beta Sigma Phi 1969-, Pres, VP, Sec, Treas, f Yr; Capital Area Rdng Assn 1982-, Treas; Supermarket Investment 1984-, Treas; Cntrl Dauphin Investment Club 1987-; Distinguished wd Cntrl Dauphin Schl Dist; *office:* E H Phillips Elem Schl 100 ont Rd Harrisburg PA 17109

GORDON SUI-KWONG, Assistant Prof of Fine Arts; *b:* Hong China; *m:* Johanna Jun-Hoi; *ed:* Concordia Univ of Canada (BFA) Arts & Studio Art 1979; Cranbrook Acad of Art (MFA) Painting 1981; Abbott Coll of Canada Diploma Soc Scis, Urban & Regnl Planning *cr:* Columbus Coll of Art & Design Fine Arts Instr 1981-82; Asia ssion Limited Hong Kong Stage Designer 1982-83; Hong Kong echnic Univ Design Lecturer 1983-87; Columbus Coll of Art & n Fine Arts Asst Prof 1987-; *ai:* GL Design Art Dir; Visual Art Soc ng Kong 1982-, Chprsn 1986-87; Numerous One-Man & Group itions in Hong Kong, Canada, Germany, Taiwan & US of Amer; Columbus Coll Of Art & Design 107 N 9th St Columbus OH 43215

JAMES RAY, Criminal Justice Instructor; *b:* Steubenville, OH; *m:* Jo Pizi; *c:* Stacy, Amy; *ed:* West Liberty St (BA) Soc Sci 1972; Univ yton (MS) Cnslng 1978; *cr:* WV Supreme Ct Chief Probation Ofcr ; Belmont Tech Coll Instr 1994-; *ai:* WVAPO 1972-, Pres, Prob Ofcr 1995; APPA 1976-; Jaycees Young Ofcr of Yr 1973; US Attorney Gen Awd 1993; Whos Who Among Soc Workers 1993; *office:* Jefferson Coll 4000 Sunset Blvd Steubenville OH 43952

JOHN A., Reading Specialist; *b:* Wichita Falls, TX; *ed:* Wright St His Ed 1987, (MS) Rdng Specialist 1987; *cr:* Tecumseh Schls Rdng alist 1984-85; Milton Union Schl Rdng Specialist 1985-; Sinclair Coll Rdng Specialist 1988-; *ai:* Track & Field Coach; Dist Outstdng 1989; *office:* Milton-Union Schls 146 S Spring St West Milton OH

JULIE A., Fourth Grade Teacher; *b:* Augsburg, Germany; *ed:* East lsburg St Coll (BS) Elem Ed 1975; 90 Post Grad Credits West Chester Millersville Univ, Penn St Masters Equivalency 1982; *cr:* Dowington Schl Dist 4th Grd Tchr 1975-; *ai:* Downington Area Ed Assn Welfare, iations Comm; Dist Environmental Ed Com; NEA, PDEA, DAEA ; *office:* Uwchlan Hills Elem 50 Peck Rd Downingtown PA 19335

LARRY D., Social Studies Teacher; *b:* Van Wert, OH; *m:* Ann ine Etzler; *c:* Michael L. Jones, Kristine A. Jones; *ed:* Valparaiso BS) His, Eng 1970; Wright St Univ (MED) Ed 1976; GATE Studies Francis Coll, OH St Univ, Bowling Green St Univ; Admin at Univ of n; *cr:* Lincolnview Local Schls 5th Grd Tchr 1970-71; Coldwater e Schls 5th-6th Grd Tchr 1917-80; Mercer Cty Dept of Ed GATE 1980-86; Coldwater Schls 6th Grd Tchr 1986-95; *ai:* Curr Cncl; Advy Comm; 6th Grd Dept Chair; NEA 1970-; Coldwater Tchrs Assn , Pres, Treas; Kappa Delta Pi 1974-; Emmanuel Luth Church 1952-, of Congregation; Tech Scholar for Schl Dist; Martha Holden Jennings ar; *office:* Coldwater Elem Schl 310 N 2nd St Coldwater OH 45828*

LAURA, English Teacher; *b:* Sacramento, CA; *ed:* Beaver Coll (BA) 975; Ed Cert at Rutgers Univ 1987; *cr:* Edgewood Jr High 7th-9th ng Tchr 1987-94; Edgewood Sr High 10th-12th Grd Eng Tchr 1994-; AC Team; Peer Mediation Adv; NEA & NJEA 1987-; *office:* vood Sr HS 250 Cooper Folly Rd Atco NJ 08004

LINDA YVETTE, Teacher; *b:* Baltimore, MD; *c:* Marquette, Keena; ppin St Coll (BS) Early Chldhd Ed 1972; Towson St Univ (MS) Early d Ed 1979; *cr:* Harlem Park Elem Schl Tchr 1972-74; Graceland Park Schl Tchr 1974-89; Brehms Lane Elem Schl Tchr 1989-; *ai:* Blood ion Comm Chm; Schl Improvement Team; Balto Tchrs Union 1972-; g Loch Comm Assn 1984-, Sec, Pres; Faith United Bapt Church , Trustee; *office:* Brehms Lane Elem Schl 3536 Brehms Ln Baltimore 1213

MARGARET HEALEY, Eng as Second Lang Dept Chair; *b:* burgh, NY; *w:* DAvid C. Lee (dec); *c:* Rebecca Louise; *ed:* St ence Univ (BA) Eng Lit 1975; Univ of MA at Amherst (MED) ESL, 1982; In-Svc Courses Schl Intnl Trng World Learning, Russian Schl rwich Univ; *cr:* Tupperlake HS Scndry Schl Eng, Drama Tchr 77; Peace Corps ESL Tchr, Tchr Trainer 1977-79; Pulaski Acad y Schl Eng, Drama Tchr 1979-80; U Mass Writing TA 1981-82; ng Acad ESL Dept Chair, Intnl Stu Adv 1984-; *ai:* Acad, Attendance Comms; Intnl Club Adv; Intnl Day Dir; Drug, Alcohol Assessment Team 1985-90; TESOL 1982-; Church 1981-94, Choral Groups; ISAM Summer Wkshp Presenter; Terrific Tchrs Making Difference Awd 1993; Tchr of Yr 1990; *office:* Cushing Acad 39 School St Ashburnham MA 01430*

LEE, MARY ANN HAMLIN, Fr Tchr & Lang Dept Chair; *b:* Paris, France; *m:* Ronald S.; *c:* Elizabeth, Scott, Katherine; *ed:* SUNY at New Paltz (BA) Fr 1969; Colgate Univ (MAT) Fr 1982; Attnd Sorbonne Univ Fr Cert 1968; Univ of CT 30 Hrs; SUNY Upper Division 18 Hrs; Manhattan Coll AP French Literature; Pine Manor Coll Critical Thinking Trng; *cr:* Univ of CT Fr Grad Asst 1969-71; Clinton Cntrl Schl Fr Tchr 1971-, Lang Dept Chprsn 1975-; *ai:* Soph & France Trip Adv; Natl Fr Contest & Peer Tutors Coord; AATF & FLACNY 1971-; Level IV Textbook Co-Author; Critical Thinking Group Inservice Trng Tchr; *office:* Clinton Cntrl Schl 75 Chenango Ave Clinton NY 13323*

LEE, MICHAELEEN PEIPON, Chemistry Professor; *b:* New York City, NY; *m:* Walter; *c:* Charles, Michelle; *ed:* Univ of VA (BS) Chem 1967, (PHD) Bio Chem 1972; *cr:* Bucks Cty Comm Coll Chem Prof 1975-; *ai:* PAFT 1975-, 2 Yr Coll Chem Conf, Candidate for Chprsn; Amer Chem Soc; Soc of the Sigma XI; US Swimming Natl Championship Ofcl, Judged at Pan Pacific Games; PA Del Swim League Exec Comm; Stud Guide to Accompany Mortimers Introduction to Chem; *office:* Bucks County Comm Coll Swamp Road Newtown PA 18940

LEE, MILAGROS SANTONI, Spanish Teacher; *b:* Cabo Rojo, PR; *m:* Fredrick A.; *c:* Fredrick D., Linda M., Candice E.; *ed:* RUM Colegio de Agricu Hura of Artes Medunicas (BA) Hispanic Stud 1974; OH Univ (BA) 1986; Tchng Cert 1986; Grad Courses 1977; *cr:* OSESO Lang Tchr 1975-76; OH Univ TA Span Tchr 1977; Belpre City Schls Span Tchr 1986-89; Athens Cith Schls Span Tchr 1991-; *ai:* Span Club; Span Hnr Soc; BEA, AEA OEA, OFLA 1986-89, 1991-; Deans List 1986 OH Univ; *home:* 10822 State Route 550 Athens OH 45701

LEE, PATRICIA A., Spanish & French Teacher; *b:* Columbus, OH; *m:* James R.; *c:* Jim, Amy, Christopher; *ed:* OH St Univ (BS) Frgn Lang Ed 1975; Coll of Mount St Joseph (MA) Scndry Ed 1988; 15 Addl Hrs OH St Univ; *cr:* Groveport-Madison HS Span, Fr Tchr 1975-93; Pickerington HS Span, Fr Tchr 1993-; *ai:* PEA 1993-, Local Bldg Rep; OEA, NEA, OMLTA 1975-; Bland Stradley Meml Schlsp; FHA Hero, Ashland Oil Tchr Achvmt Awds; *office:* Pickerington HS 300 Opportunity Way Pickerington OH 43147*

LEE, PATRICK, Professor of Philosophy; *b:* Dallas, TX; *m:* Rita J. Brennan; *c:* Colleen, Bridget Munoz, Bernadette, Monica, Kevin, Thomas, Brendan, Theresa; *ed:* Univ of Dallas (BA) Philosophy 1974; Niagara Univ (MA) Philosophy 1977; Marquette Univ (PHD) Philosophy 1980; *cr:* Univ of St Thomas Assoc Prof 1981-92; Franciscan Univ Assoc Prof 1992-; *ai:* Amer Cath Philosophical Assn 1981-; Flwshp of Cath Scholars 1986-; Abortion & Unborn Human Life Book; 15 Articles Pub; *office:* Franciscan Univ - Steubenville Franciscan Way Steubenville OH 43952

LEE, PHYLLIS ANNE, Speech Communications Prof; *b:* Waterbury, CT; *c:* Joseph Lee Lovetere; *ed:* Univ of AZ (BA) Speech Arts-Hnrs 1972; Northeastern Univ (MED) Eng-Lang Arts Curr, Instruction 1983; *cr:* Cape Cod Comm Coll Adj Fac 1983-88, Acad Dev Ctr Writing Adv 1988-91, Assoc Prof 1988-; Univ of ME Summer Courses Instr 1991, 1993; *ai:* Speech Coord 1994-; Speech Arts Club Adv; Forensics Coach Tournaments Judge; Readers Theatre Dir; Lib Comm; Masters Degree Stu Practicum Adv Harvard Univ; Eastern Communication Assn; MA Tchrs Assn; MA Communication Assn; Natl Forensics Assn; Excl Tchng Awd 1995; Adv of Yr Awd Speech Arts Club 1995; Hum Scholar 1995; *office:* Cape Cod Comm Coll 2240 Iyanough Rd West Barnstable MA 02668

LEE, ROBIN L., Speech Pathologist; *b:* Boston, MA; *m:* Joseph D.; *ed:* Univ of MA at Amherst (BS) Comm Disorders 1987; Northeastern Univ (MS) Speech Pathology; *cr:* Dedham Pub Schls Speech Pathologist 1990-91; Boston Pub Schls Speech Pathologist 1991-; *ai:* Var Vlybl Coach Milton HS; Amer Speech-Hearing Assn 1989-; USAV Vlybl Coaches Assn 1996V; Mini Grant Multicultural Ed; *home:* 97 Campbell St Quincy MA 02169

LEE, TED J., Computer & Technology Coord; *b:* Mc Comb, OH; *m:* Mary Jane Feeham; *c:* Brian, Jeff; *ed:* Bowling Green Univ (BSEd) Indstrl Tech 1969; Univ of Datton; *cr:* Ada Exempted Schls Indstrl Tech Tchr 1969-88; Lima Tech Coll Night Class Instr 1980-; Ada Exempted Schls Ath Dir, Admin 1988-94, Cmptr, Tech Coord 1994-; *ai:* Adult Ed Cmptrs Supvr, Tchr; NEA, OEA, OTEA 1969-; OSU, Lima Tech Coll Instr Svc Awd; OHSBCA Svc Awd; *office:* Ada Exempted Village Schls 435 Grand St Ada OH 45810

LEE, THOMAS ALLEN, Social Studies Teacher; *b:* Bloomsburg, PA; *ed:* Washington & Jefferson Coll (BA) His & Ed 1982; 190 Addl Credit Hrs; Minor in Pol Sci; *cr:* Trinity Area Schl Dist Scndry Soc Stud Tchr 1983-; Dist Long Range Planning Comm; *ai:* Weight Room Coord; Jr HS Bsktbl Coach; Key Club Adv; NEA 1983-; NCSS 1985-; World Affairs Cncl of Pittsburgh; Richeyville Comm Church 1984-, Trustee; Washington & Jefferson Coll Scholar in Ed Awd 1982; *office:* Trinity Area Schl Dist Park Ave Washington PA 15301

LEE, WILLIAM JOSEPH, English Teacher; *b:* Boston, MA; *m:* Sharon Kelley; *c:* Chelsea, Alissa, Jacob, Samuel; *ed:* Knox Coll (BA) Eng & Writing 1990; *cr:* Londonderry HS Eng Tchr 1992-93; Kingswood Regnl HS Eng Tchr 1993-; *ai:* Ftbl & Track Coach; Peer Outreach; Weightlifting Coord; NEA 1993-; *office:* Kingswood Regional HS S Main St Wolfeboro NH 03894

LEE, WILLIAM R., Senior Instructor; *b:* Muskogee, OK; *c:* William R., Janet R. Doss, David E.; *ed:* wilberforce Univ (BS) Bio, Chem 1954; Shippensburg Univ (MS) Pub Admin 1976; 30 Post Grad Hrs Intnl Relations; *cr:* US Armed Forces 1955-84; Raytheon Corp Proposal Mgr 1985-90; Brighton HS Tchr 1991-; *ai:* Sr Class, Yrbk, Key Club Advs; Schl Site Cncl Co-Chair; Grad, Sr Honors Day Coords; AFT 1991; Kiwanis 1976-; Allston Brighton Aid & Hlth Group 1992-, Corporate Dir; Wilberforce Univ Alumni Assn Bd of Dirs 1986-, Asst Treas; *office:* Brighton HS 25 Warren St Brighton MA 02135

LEEDER, ROCHELLE LESLIE, Multi-Age Teacher; *b:* Brookline, MA; *m:* Ned Mc Sherry; *ed:* 45 Addl Credits Univ of Southern ME; *cr:* Berlin Pub Schls K Tchr 1977-78; MSAD #72 Spec Ed Tchr 1978-80, 1 Grd Tchr 1980-93, Multiage 1-2 Grd Tchr 1994-95, K-2 Tchr 1995-; *ai:* Tchr Ldr Assessing Reflecting Integrating Schl-Based Excl Prgm; Extended Tchr Ed Prgm, Staff Dev Comms; NEA 1978-; *home:* PO Box 332 Center Conway NH 03813*

LEEDS, BARBARA WEISBURST, English Teacher; *b:* New York, NY; *m:* Kenneth Joseph Simons; *ed:* Hofstra Univ (MA) Eng Ed 1970; 53 Addl Credit Hrs; *cr:* H.B. Thompson Jr HS Tchr 1963-81; Aufhauser Bros Mfg Corp VP 1981-86; Industrial Rod & Wire Inc VP 1981-86; Syosset HS Eng Tchr 1986-; *ai:* NCTE; NYSUT; Mentor in NYS Mentor Intern Pgm 1990-91; NOW 1974-; Save The Children Holocaust Museum Common Cause 1983-; Oxford Univ Tchrs Seminar Fellowship Finalist; Written Curricula for Coll Prepatory Courses & Reluctant Learners 7-9 Grds; NYSEC Eng Tchr of Excel 1994; *office:* Syosset HS South Woods Rd Syosset NY 11791

LEEDS, MICHAEL J., Language Arts Coordinator; *b:* New York City, NY; *m:* Sharon Wilson; *c:* Holden, Stacy, Elizabeth; *ed:* NY Univ (BS) Eng Ed 1966, (MS) Eng Ed 1967; Pace Univ (MS) Educl Supervision, Admin 1977; NY Univ 30 Post Grad Credits Guid, Admin 1969-70; *cr:* JHS 65 Eng Tchr 1966-80; IS 131 Eng, ESL Tchr 1980-88; IS 145 Lang Arts Coord 1988-, Desktop Publishing Specialist 1993-; *ai:* Lit, Art Magazine Adv; Ldrshp Comm Vice Chprsn; Gen Org Adv JHS 65; NYSED 1995-, Tchr of Yr; NCTE 1995-, Tchr of Excl Awd; UFT 1966-, Delegate; Knights of Pythias 1966-; E Meadow Lib 1972-; Kappa Phi Kappa 1963-, VP; Phi Delta Kappa 1977-; Dean's List NYU; Profiles NY Newsday, Queens Tribune, Jackson Heights News; Articles Pub; *office:* IS 145 Joseph Pulitzer 33-34 80th St Jackson Heights NY 11372*

LEEDY, JOYCE STRIMEL, Reading Teacher; *b:* Pittsburgh, PA; *m:* Ernest W.; *c:* Pamela Ohlinger, Stephen W.; *ed:* Malone Coll (BA) Elem Ed 1966; Attnd Dayton Univ, John Carroll Univ, Ashland Coll; *cr:* Hartford-Martin Schl Elem Tchr 1966-70; Baxter Elem Schl Elem Tchr 1980-95, Rdng Specialist Govt Prgms 1995-; *ai:* Rel Org Sr Yth Adv; Lang Arts Liaison; Tchr Mentor; Intervention Assistance Team; Canton Prof Educ Assn 1966-, Bldg Rep; OH Educ Ass, NEA 1966-; United Way; Lang Arts Grant; Ameritech-Canton Repository Feature Tchr; *home:* 4733 Preserve Dr NW Canton OH 44708*

LEEDY, KATHLEEN B., 10th Grade Health Instructor; *b:* Dartmouth, NH; *m:* Gregory A.; *c:* Jillian, Carley; *ed:* Shepherd Coll (BS) PE, Hlth 1983; 26 Credits Shippensburg Univ; *cr:* Greencastle-Antrim HSHlth, PE Tchr 10 Yrs; *ai:* PRIDE Adv; Strategic Planning Comm; Bsktbl Coach; SAT Team; PSEA, NEA 1987-; ASCD; G-A CARES 1994-, Sec 1995; *office:* Greencastle-Antrim HS 300 S Ridge Ave Greencastle PA 17225*

LEEGE, ROGER, Director of Computer Education; *b:* Rockville Centre, NY; *c:* Travis, Mason, Tracy; *ed:* Goddard Coll (BA) Ed 1971, (MA) Grad Prgm Fine Arts 1976; Post Grad Cmptr Sci Univ of Hartford; Tech Ed Cntrl Ct St Univ; *cr:* Tolland MS Tech Ed Tchr 1971-76, Tech Ed Dept Chair 1976-82; Tolland HS Cmptr Sci Dept Chair 1982-; Tolland Pub Schls Dir Cmptr Ed 1985-; *ai:* Newspaper Adv; Dist Techh Comm Chair; Cmptr Kids Summer Camp Prgm Dir; Tolland Ed Assn 1971-, Newsletter Ed, Negotiations Comm; NE 1971-; ISTE, CECA 1982-; Lib Friends 1991-, Tech Adv; Tolland Adult Ed 1985-, Instr; CT St Tchrs Talent Pool; Tchr of Yr; Tolland Commendation Sparkman Scholar; *office:* Tolland Pub Schls 1 Eagle Dr Tolland CT 06084*

LEEK, NATALIE ANN, Admns & Pub Relations Director; *b:* Cleveland, OH; *ed:* Cleveland Inst of Art (BFA) Fiber Arts 1990; Attnd Case Western Reserve Univ, Baldwin Wallace Coll; *cr:* Design Interface Graphic Designer 1987; Cleve Hlth Ed Museum Supvr, Art Dept, PR Asst 1987-90; Saint Joseph Acad Admissions & Pub Relations Dir, Above & Cmptr Graphic Design Instr 1993-; *ai:* All Admissions & Pub Relations Act; Moderator Acad Ambassadors, Schl Newspaper Design; Schl Graphic Designer; Natl Assn Female Exec 1995-; Acad Assn of Cath Admissions Dirs 1991-, Chprsn; *office:* Saint Joseph Acad 3430 Rocky River Dr Cleveland OH 44111

LEEK, RICHARD D., Social Studies Teacher; *b:* Philadelphia, PA; *m:* Cynthia; *ed:* Temple Univ (MA) Soc Stud Ed 1989; *cr:* Girard MS Tchr 1988-93, Prin 1993-94, Soc Stud Tchr 1994-; *ai:* Cross Cntry, Indoor & Outdoor Track & Field Coach; Stu Cncl Leadership Org Spon; Portfolio Assessment Comm CoChair; NCSS, ASCD 1988-; Seminar Ldr, Speaker Star Wars Defense Policy Freedom Fnd; Dev Interdisciplinary Model for Hum of Girard; Chprsn Philosophy, Objection Comm; *office:* Girard College HS 2101 S College Ave Philadelphia PA 19121

LEE-LOCKE, MAUREEN ELIZABETH, College Instructor; *b:* Boston, MA; *m:* Jonathan Locke; *c:* Brandon Locke, Reanna Locke; *ed:* Univ of NH (BS) Hotel, Restaurant Mngmt 1986; Cambridge Coll (MED) Ed 1994; *cr:* Ctr for Exec Ed Front Office Mgr 1987-88; Katharine Gibbs Schl Instr, Internship Coord 1988-; Middlesex Comm Coll Instr 1992-; ACE Shoppers Owner 1995-; *ai:* Katharine Gibbs Schl Hospitality Advy Bd, Fac Forum Pres, Lib Comm; Middlesex Comm Coll Travel Advy Bd; *home:* 86 School St Groveland MA 01834*

LEE-MAUGER, MARILYN, English Teacher; *b:* Camden, NJ; *ed:* Cedar Crest Coll (BA) Eng 1967; Univ of VA (MA) Eng 1969; Post Grad Temple Univ, Univ of PA, Rowan Coll, Exte Coll, Oxford univ, UK; *cr:* Haddonfield MS Eng Tchr 1969-77; Bottisham Village Coll Fulbright Exchange 1980-81; Camden Cty coll Eng Tchr 1984-86; Rutgers Univ Eng Tchr 1985-87; Haddonfield Meml HS Eng Tchr 1977-; *ai:* Teen Arts Supvr; Philadelphia Drama Guild Adv Bd; Walt Whitman Assn Bd of Dir; NEA, NJEA 1969-; Philadelphia Drama Guild Advy Bd 1992-95; NEH 1990, 1993 Seminar; NEH Tchr Scholar Awd 1994-95; Cooperative Learning Text; Articles Pub; *office:* Haddonfield Memorial HS 401 Kings Hwy E Haddonfield NJ 08033

LEEN, MARIE D. PAZOLA, French Teacher; *b:* Cambridge ; *m:* Edward M.; *c:* Elizabeth Nazar, Patricia A.; *ed:* Emmanuel (BA) Fr & Ed 1964; Attnd Univ of Reuues France, Middlebury Grad Schl, Wellesley Coll Fr Immersion Prgm; *cr:* Northeastern Univ Instr 1968; Addison Wesley Publishers Author Consultant 1983; Arlington Cath HS Foreign Lang Chprsn 1985-95; *ai:* Fr Club; Paris Trip Ldr 1988-; Fac Dev Comm; MA Foreign Lang Assn 1992-, Bd of Dirs; AATF 1988-; Tufts Univ Outstanding HS Tchr Awd 1992; *home:* 20 Colonial Rd Woburn MA 01801

LEENHEER, PATRICIA TRELL, Reading Teacher; *b:* Youngstown, OH; *ed:* Youngstown St Univ (BS) Elem Ed 1979, (MS) Elem Prin 1985; K-12 Rdng Cert 1979; *cr:* Holy Name Schl 4th-5th Grd Tchr 1979-85; Rayen Schl Rdng Tchr, ACT, SAT Preparation 1985-; *ai:* Sr Class Adv; Bsktbl Statistician; City Schls Proficiency Cncl; OEA, NEA 1985-; *office:* Rayen Schl 250 Benita Ave Youngstown OH 44504

LEEPER, JACQUELINE ELLIOTT, GATE Teacher; *b:* Pittsburgh, PA; *m:* Dennis P.; *ed:* Edinboro St Coll (BS) Elem Ed, Lib Sci 1969; Univ of CO (MA) Rdng 1972; Temple Univ (DED) Educl Ldrshp, Policy Stud 1996; Coursework, Personal Stud GATE Ed; *cr:* Cambridge Springs Elem Schl 4th Grd Tchr 1969-71; Bear Creek Elem Schl Librn 1972-75; *ai:* Strategic Planning Steering Comm; Tchr Mentor; Resource Partner; Tchr Trainer; PA Assn GATE Ed; GVEA; PSEA; NEA; Natl Staff Dev Cncl; ASCD; Wayne Presbyn Church 1987-, Elder, Chair Mission Comm; *office:* K. D. Markley Elem Schl 47 Church Rd Malvern PA 19355*

LEES, DOLORES R., 1st Grade Teacher; *b:* Apollo, PA; *m:* Robert J.; *c:* Robert E., William Matthew; *ed:* Indiana Univ of PA (BS) Elem 1969, (MEd) K-12 Rdng Specialist 1973; Comptometer Schl at Pittsburgh 1948; IN Univ Curr 3 Credits Towards Rdng Supvr; *cr:* Pittsburgh Plate Glass Co Sec 1 Yr; Sunnyside Schl Ad Hoc Comm Sr HS 2 Yrs, Head Tchr 13 Yrs, Stu Tchrs Supervisory Tchr 5 Yrs; N Apollo Schl Arin Mini-Grant Evaluator 2 Yrs, Mentor Tchr 1 Yr; *ai:* Kappa Delta Gamma Alpha Theta 1974-, Sec; NEA 1969-; PTA 1969-, Sec; Apollo Presbyn Church, Deacon; Phoebe Apperson Hearst Outstdng Edctr Awd Nom 1987; Tchr of Amer Nom 1989-90; *home:* 817 Moore Ave N Apollo PA 15673*

LEES, RICHARD L., Earth Sci Teacher & Supervisor; *b:* Jersey City, NJ; *m:* Irene Witer; *c:* Michael, Daniel, Jeremy; *ed:* Jersey City St Coll (BA) Sci 1963, (MA) Bio 1966; Franklin & Marshall (MA) Earth Sci 1973; 100 Credit Hrs Earth Scis; *cr:* LHS Tchr 1963-; *ai:* Rocket, Weather Clubs; NJESTA 1995-, Pres 1996; NJSSA 1988-; NJSTA 1965-; Earth Sci Tchrs Assn; Tchr of Yr; Project Atmosphere; AMS; NJ Agnet; Bulletin of AMS; Preprints 4 & 5th Symposium on Ed AMS; *office:* Lyndhurst HS Weart Ave Lyndurst NJ 07071

LEFAVIC, WENDY SMITH, 7th Grd Eng Tchr & Team Ldr; *b:* Lancaster, PA; *m:* Paul; *ed:* Immaculate Coll (BA) Eng 1990; Penn St Univ 24 Credit Hrs; Millersville Univ 6 Credit Hrs; *cr:* Lancaster Cath HS 11th-12th Grd

Eng Tchr 1990-91; Penn Manor Shcl Dist 7th Grd Eng Tchr 1991-; *ai:* Frosh Field Hockey Coach; Team Ldr; Hnr Soc & TV Studio Adv; Pub Relations Comm; PMEA 1991-; PSEA 1991-; NEA 1991-; *office:* Manor MS 2950 Charlestown Rd Lancaster PA 17603*

LEFCHAK, ARLENE HARRIS, High School Math Teacher; *b:* Scranton, PA; *m:* George; *c:* Jay, Russ, Nicole, Glenn; *ed:* Bloomsburg Univ (BS) Math 1963; Marywood Coll (MS) Math 1980; Addl 60 Grad Credits; *cr:* Binghamton HS Math Tchr 1964; Abington Heights Schl HS Math Tchr 1972-; *ai:* AHEA; NCPTM; NEA; PSEA; Sunday Schl Tchr 1972-, Nursery Caretaker; *home:* RR 6 Box 137D Tunkhannock PA 18657

LEFEVRE, DARLENE BARTUCCO, 7th Grade Reading Teacher; *b:* Southington, CT; *m:* Gerard Paul; *c:* John, James; *ed:* Cntrl CT St Univ (BS) Scndry Ed, Eng 1973; Attnd Anna Maria Coll; *cr:* Meml Boulevard Schl Grd 7 Lang Arts Tchr 1974-93; Chippens Hill MS Grd 7 Rdng Tchr 1993-; *ai:* Yrbk Adv; Lang Arts Curr; BFT, AFT 1974-; One Article Pub; *office:* Chippens Hill MS 551 Peacedale St Bristol CT 06010

LEFEVRE, JOSEPH WILLIAM, Associate Prof of Chemistry; *b:* Elkhart, IN; *m:* Linda Miraldi; *c:* Robert, David, Joanna; *ed:* DePauw Univ (BA) Pre-Med Sci 1975; Virginia Tech (PHD) Chem 1984; *cr:* Barrington Coll Asst Prof 1984-85; SUNY Oswego Asst Prof 1985-92; Virginia Tech Visiting Prof 1992-93; SUNY Oswego Assoc Prof 1992-; *ai:* Comms Chem Dept 1991-94, Equipment 1990-, Prsnl 1989-90, 1994-, Scholarly, Creative Act 1987-; Grad Cncl 1993-95; Amer Chem Soc 1985-; Phi Kappa Phi 1995-, Sigma Xi 1992-; Grants: NSF 1995, 1986, Fac Enhancement 1995, UUP Prof Dev, Quality Working Life 1993-94; Chancellors Awd Excl in Tchng 1994; 8 Publications Refereed Scientific Journals; *office:* S U N Y Coll At Oswego 220A Snygg Hall Oswego NY 13126

LEFF, JEANETTE BORBE, Reading & Language Arts Tchr; *b:* Palmerton, PA; *m:* Barton S.; *c:* Alan; *ed:* Shippensburg Univ (BS) Elem Ed 1969; *cr:* Susquehanna MS 6th Grd Soc Sci Tchr 1970-72; Glen Landing MS 6th-7th Grd Tchr 1972-; *ai:* 7th Grd Team Ldr; NEA, NJEA, GTEA 1972-; Town Watch 1994-; *office:* Glen Landing MS 85 Little Gloucester Rd Blackwood NJ 08012

LEFFLER, HAYDEN, Mathematics Teacher; *b:* Pottsville, PA; *m:* Carol Miller; *c:* Jane Lally, Joan Ruth, Lorrie Nichols; *ed:* West Chester Univ (BS) Math 1961; PA St Ed Dept Masters Equivalency in Ed 1988; 15 Additional Credits; *cr:* Downingtown Jr HS Math Tchr 1961-64; Downingtown Sr HS Math Tchr 1964-, Math Tchr & Dept Head 1968-; *ai:* 2 Yrs Jr High Bsbl & Ftbl Coach; 15 Yrs Sr High Asst Ftbl Coach; Dept Head 1968-; Downington Area Tchr Assn 1961-; PSEA 1961-, Mem; NEA 1961-, Mem; DAEA Mem; *office:* Downingtown Sr HS 445 Manor Ave Downingtown PA 19335

LEFFLER, JAMES TRACY, 7th-8th Grd Hlth & PE Teacher; *b:* Columbus, OH; *m:* V. Lyn; *c:* Megan Leah; *ed:* Otterbein Coll (BS) PE 1975; Coll of Mt St Joseph (MA) Ed 1989; Guidance & Cnslng; Tchng Effectiveness; Drug & Alcohol Cnslng; *cr:* Groveport Madison Schls Sixth Grd PE Tchr 1976-79, Seventh-Eighth Grd Hlth & PE Tchr 1980-; *ai:* MS Track & Ftbl; HS Wrestling; Prin Advy Comm; Outdoor Club Adv; Graveport Madison Local Ed Assn & AAHERD 1976-; *office:* Groveport Madison MS South 4400 Glendening Dr Groveport OH 43125

LEFFLER, LAURE JEANNE, Fourth Grade Teacher; *b:* Buffalo, NY; *ed:* St Univ Coll at Buffalo (BS) Elem Ed 1964, (MS) Elem Ed 1968; Numerous Credit Hrs In Svc; *cr:* N Tonawanda Pub Schls Third Grd Tchr 1964-69, First Grd Tchr 1969-74, Fourth Grd Tchr 1974-; *ai:* Stu Support, Shared Decision Making Team; Elem Concerns Comm; Mentor, Cadre Tchr; NTUT, NYSET 1964-, Corres Sec, Recognition 1982; NEA 1964-; Alpha Delta Kappa 1972-, VP, Pres; Phi Delta Kappa 1985-; Friends of Lib Bd 1990-, Pres; Lib Planning Comm 1996-; Beta Sigma Phi 1976-, Treas; Rel Ed Prgm Tchr of Yr; Recognized for Work in Peer Ldrshp Prgm; Helped Assemble Soc Stud Activity Book for Dist 4th Grds; *office:* Gilmore Elem Schl 789 Gilmore Ave North Tonawanda NY 14120*

LEFFLER, LINDA L., French Instructor; *b:* Mechanicsburg, PA; *m:* Walter G.; *c:* Jennifer; *ed:* 24 Post Grad Credits for PA Tchrs Cert; Undergrad l'Institut de Touraine; *cr:* Conemaugh Valley HS Fr Instr 1970-; *ai:* Fr Club Adv in Charge of Ed Foreign Travel; CVEA, PSEA & NEA; *office:* Conemaugh Valley Jr Sr HS 1342 Wm Penn Ave Johnstown PA 15906

LEFFLER, PAMELA SMITH, Anatomy & Physiology Teacher; *b:* San Francisco, CA; *m:* Michael Edmond; *c:* Jacqueline Ruth, Natalie Nancy; *ed:* Univ of MD (MS) Bio 1988; Toward MS Western MD Coll; *cr:* Paint Branch HS Tchr 1989-; *ai:* Pom, Jr Class Spon; Honors Comm; MSTA, NEA 1989-; Nom Montgomery Outstanding Sci Tchr Awd; *office:* Paint Branch HS 14121 Old Columbia Pike Burtonsville MD 20866

LEGAL, BARBARA L., Secondary Librarian; *b:* Corry, PA; *ed:* Edinboro St Coll (BS) Ed & Lib Sci 1970; Clarion St Coll (MS) Lib Sci 1975; Addl Credit Hrs in Gifted Pgm, Serialss, Mgmt, OCLC, Media Specialist Curr & Admin; *cr:* Buhl-Henderson Pub Lib Childrens Librn 1970-72; Jefferson Morgan Jr Sr HS Scndry Librn 1972-; *ai:* Lib Club; Interact Club; PSEA 1972-; NEA 1972-; JMPA 1972-, Sec; PA Schl Librns Assn 1974-; Greene Cty Historical Assn Life Mem; *office:* Jefferson-Morgan Jr Sr HS Greene St Jefferson PA 15344

LEGATES, GARY A., Latin & French Teacher; *b:* Wilmington, DE; *m:* Ninette O. Mellott; *ed:* Western MD (BA) Latin, Fr Ed 1974; PA St Univ (MA) Classics 1975; Addl 30 Hrs Western MD Coll; *cr:* Westminster HS Frgn Lang Tchr 1977-; *ai:* Guest Lecturer Western MD Coll; Latin, Fr Club Adv; Amer Classical League, Classical Assn of Atlantic Sts 1974-; Natl Assn of Blind Tchrs 1987-91, Sec, 1995-, 2nd VP; Westminster Bapt Church 1981-83, 1985-87, Deacon, Sunday Schl Tchr 1989-93; Amer Cncl of Blind 1988-92, Bd of Dirs; Alumni Assn MD Schl for Blind 1989-93, Pres; Nom Tchr of Yr 1995; Listed Among Who's Who in the East; Mid Sts Evaluation Comm Frgn Langs 1992-93; *office:* Westminster HS 1225 Washington Rd Westminster MD 21157*

LEGATH, JOHN GEORGE,JR., Jr High Guidance Cnslr; *b:* Northampton, PA; *m:* Linda Jane Miller; *ed:* Northampton Comm Coll (AA) Bus Admin 1975; East Stroudsburg St Univ (BA) Psych 1976; Kutztown Univ (MED) Scndry Counseling 1978; 24 Grad Credit Hrs Voc Ed Admin Courses; *cr:* Lehigh Cty Voc Tech Schl Cnslr & Co-op Coord 1977-89; Bangor Jr HS Guidance Cnslr 1989-; *ai:* Stu Assistance Prgm Team; Group Counseling Facilitator; NEA 1976-; PSEA 1976-, Bldg Rep; Northampton Youth Ath Assn 1966-, Pres, Life Membership Awd; Honorary Mem FFA; *office:* Bangor Area Jr HS RD 2 Box 2071 Bangor PA 18013

LEGENDRE, RENEE DENISE, 6th Grd Social Studies Teacher; *b:* New York City, NY; *ed:* DE St Univ (BS) Early Chldhd Ed 1976; Bank Street Coll of Ed (MS) Tchr Ed 1979; Long Island Univ (MS) Cnslng, Dev 1996; *cr:* Port Chester Head Start Head Tchr 1978-83; Virginia Road Schl 1-5th Grd Tchr 1983-91; Valhalla Schl Dist MS 6th Grd Tchr 1991-; *ai:* Whitney M. Young Soc Adv; Peer Ldrshp Prgm HS Adv; Peer Mediation Prgm MS Adv; NYS United Tchrs, Valhalla Tchrs Assn 1983-; Alpha Kappa Alpha 1984-, Pres, Pres Awd; FIRST 1993-, Bd Mem, Sec; Black Scholars of Westchester 1987-; NYS-PTA Jenkins Meml Awd; Whitney M. Young Jr Soc Unsung Hero Awd; *office:* Valhalla MS, HS 300 Columbus Ave Valhalla NY 10595

LEGERE, DAVID E., 8th Grade Science Teacher; *b:* Everett, MA; *m:* Mary Griffith; *ed:* Castleton St Coll (BS) Bio, Geology, Scndry Ed 1979; *cr:* Kambia, Sierra Leone Schl Bio, Math Tchr 1980-82; Fiji Schl Math Tchr 1983; Belfast Schl Sci, Math Tchr 1984-86; Bath MS Sci, Math, Writing Tchr 1986-; *ai:* Young Astronauts, Invent Amer, Sci Clubs; Track Coach; Physics, Ecology Confs; NEA, MEA 1982-; Hosp Vol, 100 Hrs Awd; Sci for Sci Tchrs Summer 1992; Grant Writing for Summer Sci Prgm 1994; *home:* 116 Flying Point Rd Freeport ME 04032

LEGG, KATHY JO, Business Teacher; *b:* Ironton, OH; *m:* James P.; *c:* Wendy Delawder, Jamie; *ed:* Morehead St Univ (BA) Bus Comp 1971; Attnd OH Univ & Univ of Dayton Post Grad Work; *cr:* Wheelersburg HS Bus Tchr 24 Yrs; *ai:* Soph Class, Jr-Sr Class Play, Majorette & Stu Cncl Spon; Girls Track Coach; Asst Band Dir; NEA; OEA; WEA; OBTA; Ashland Church; Coal Grove Band & Acad Boosters; Coal Grove Lions Club Wives Group; *home:* 115 Center St Coal Grove OH 45638

LEGGETT, SANDRA REBRES, Kindergarten Teacher; *b:* Steubenville, OH; *m:* Vance Jerry; *c:* Michael, Julie; *ed:* Univ of Steubenville (BS) Elem Ed 1979; *cr:* Jewett Elem First Grd Tchr 1979-84; Hopedale Elem Fifth Grd Tchr 1984-87, Third Grd Tchr 1987-89; Jewett Elem Kndgtn, Third Grd Tchr 1989-93; Hopedale Elem Kndgtn Tchr 1993-; *ai:* NEA, OEA, HHTA 1979-; Perrysville United Meth Church 1979-, Yth Dir, Fin Sec; Perrysville Emergency Svc 1982-, Emergency Medical Technician; Perrysville Fire Dept 1983-; Farm Bureau Advy Cncl 1981-, Sec; *office:* Hopedale Elem Schl PO Box 307 Hopedale OH 43988

LEGGETT, SHERYL L. (COX), Sixth Grade Teacher; *b:* Dover, OH; *m:* James Lewis; *c:* Susan, Sara, Nate; *ed:* Kent St Univ (BS) Ed 1970; *cr:* Tuscarawas Vly Schl Tchr 1965-66, 1968-69; Dover Schl Tchr 1970-71; Strasburg Schl Tchr 1986-; *ai:* Math Tournament; 6th Grd Camp.

LEGGIO, NANCY, Early Childhood Instructor; *b:* Brooklyn, NY; *ed:* NY Univ (BS) Early Chldhd, Elem Ed 1982; Bank Street Coll of Ed (MS) Early Chldhd Ldrshp 1988; *cr:* Families First Inc Early Chldhd Consultant 1989-; Kingsborough Comm Coll Early Chldhd Instr 1990-; Hostos Comm Coll Early Chldhd Instr 1992-; Bank Street Coll of Ed Early Chldhd Trainer, Consultant 1993-; *ai:* NAEYC 1982-; Edctrs for Soc Responsibility 1986-; Children's Book Cncl 1984-; Park Slope Comm Recycling Campaign 1992-; CDA Trng Prgm Outstdng Tchr Awd 1991, 1995; *home:* 455A 5th St Brooklyn NY 11215*

LEGO, PAMELA MORTON, Instructional Support Teacher; *b:* Erie, PA; *m:* Earl B.; *c:* Gretchen, Natalie, Erich; *ed:* Edinboro Univ, Millersville St Coll, IN Wesleyan Univ 33 Post Grad Stud Hrs; *cr:* Grandview Elem Learning Support & Elem Tchr 1975-86; Chestnut Hill 5th Grd Tchr 1987-89, 3rd Grd Tchr 1989-91, Instrl Support Tchr 1991-; *ai:* Prof Advy Cncl; Writing Curr Outcomes Based Ed Instrl Comm; Tchr Rep MEA; Strategic Planning Facilitator; NEA, PSEA & MEA 1995-; Advy Cncl 1995-; Outcomes Based Ed Dist Goals; *home:* 2803 Madeira Dr Erie PA 16506

LEGRAND, HENRI, Math, Sci & Computer Teacher; *b:* Gonaives, Haiti; *m:* Florence Hereaux; *c:* Christine, Alexandre; *ed:* City Coll of NY (BS) Ed 1978; NY Univ (MA) Fr Lit; Empire St Technological Inst Cert in Programming, Operation 1980; Lope Devega Cert in Span 1981; Julien Craan Cert in Acctg; Long Island Univ (MS) Instructional Tech 1996; *cr:* Joan of Arc Jr HS Bil Tchr 1982-88; AC Rowell Jr HS Bil Tchr 1988-; *ai:* AFT, UFT 1982-; *office:* Adam Clayton Powell Jr HS 509 W 129th St New York NY 10027

LEGROS, LIONEL, Science Teacher; *b:* Port-Au-Prince, Haiti; *m:* Jessie C.; *c:* Samora, Ayanna; *ed:* Columbia Univ (BA) His 1976; Long Island Univ (MS) Ed 1980; Attnd City Coll of NY, Coll of Mt St Vincent; *cr:* Joan of Arc Schl Tchr 1981-82; P-S 135 Schl Tchr 1982-84; IS 246 Schl Tchr 1984-; *ai:* Radio Station Broadcasting; UFT, AFT 1982-; Haitian Information Ctr 1982-, Founder, Many Awds; Articles Pub; *office:* IS 246 72 Veronica Pl Brooklyn NY 11226*

LEGTERS, CHRISTOPHER JAMES, 7th-8th Grd Math Teacher; *b:* Greenville, PA; *m:* Karen Louise Sum; *c:* Courtney, Kyle; *ed:* Grove City Coll (BA) Math, Scndry Ed 1989; Addl 13 Non-Grad Credit Hrs on MED Elem, MS Math; *cr:* Woodson MS 5-8 Grd Math, Cmptr Tchr 1990-92; Huston MS 7-8 Grd Math, Pre-Algebra Tchr 1992-; *ai:* 7th-8th Grd Boys Bsktbl Coach; IM Club Adv; NEA, NCTM 1990-; PSEA 1992-; *office:* Huston MS 1020 Puckety Church Rd Lower Burrell PA 15068

LEGTERS, JAMES R., Sixth Grade Teacher; *b:* Sharon, PA; *m:* Patricia Ann Herrick; *c:* Christopher, Steven, Jeffrey; *ed:* Edinboro Univ (BS) Scndry Soc Stud & Ed 1965, (MA) Elem Ed 1969; *cr:* Reynolds Schl Dist 5th Grd Tchr 1965-67, 6th Grd Tchr 1968-; *ai:* NEA, PSEA 1965-; Reynolds Ed Assn 1965-, Treas, Pace Dir, Pres, Negotiating Team; Mercer Cty Coord Cncl 1985-, Pace Team & Lobbyist; Jamestown Presbyn Church 1966-, Sunday Schl Tchr, Choir, Deacon, Trustee, Elder; SPEBSQSA Inc 1965-, Various Local Offices Held, Johnny Appleseed Dist Pres 1995-, 2nd Pl Quartet Champion Twice; *office:* Reynolds Schl Dist 531 Reynolds Rd Greenville PA 16125

LE HIR, MARIE-PIERRE, French Professor; *b:* France; *m:* Brooks J. Chapin; *c:* Louise Ann, Paul; *ed:* Freie Universisat at Berlin (MA) Linguistics 1979; Univ of IA (PHD) Fr Lit 1986; *cr:* Volkshochule Berlin Fr Tchr 1975-79; Windsor HS Fr & Ger Tchr 1980-81; Univ of IA Tchng Asst 1981-85; Case Western Reserve Univ Fr Prof 1986-; *ai:* Coll of Arts & Scis Exec Comm Mem; Fr Stud Prgm Dir; AATF, MLA 1987-; Women in Fr 1993-; Boulevard Elem Schl PTA; NEH Travel to Collection, Summer Inst Fellowship; One Book; Ten Articles; *office:* Case Western Reserve Univ Modern Lang & Lit 308 Guilford Cleveland OH 44106

LEHMAN, ANN MARIE NAZZARO, Art Department Chair & Teacher; *b:* Brooklyn, NY; *ed:* Fashion Inst of Tech (AAS) Textile Design 1963; St Univ at New Paltz (BS) Art Ed 1967; NY Univ (MA) Art Ed 1974; 60 Hrs Post Grad Credits Art His, Studio Art, Ed, Travel Stud; *cr:* Cannon Mills Inc Textile Designer 1963-65; Great Neck So Jr High Art Tchr 1967-81; Great Neck So Sr High Art Tchr & Dept Head 1981-; *ai:* Career Guidance; Schl Aesthetics; NYS Tchrs Assn, AFT 1967-; Great Neck Tchrs Assn 1967-, Scndry Dir; NAEA 1972-.

LEHMAN, DALLAS WAYNE, School Administrator; *b:* Wooster, OH; *m:* Nancy J.; *c:* Heidi, Mary, Kassey, Samantha; *ed:* OH St Univ (BSEd) Comprehensive Sci 1968; Akron Univ (MSEd) Ed Admin 1976; Addl Admin Coursework; *cr:* Greenhills-Forest Park Schls Chem & Physical Sci Tchr 1969-70; Massillon City Schls Sci Tchr & Asst Prin 1968 1970-79; Heritage Chrstn Schl Prin & Admin 1979-87; Real Life Chrstn Acad Sci Tchr & Admin 1987-; *ai:* Sci Club; Ftbl, & Bsktbl Coach; Bible Club; Missions Trips Coord & Chaperone; ACSI 1979-; *home:* 7733 Stonewood Dr NW North Canton OH 44720

LEHMAN, IRIS ELAINE, Social Studies Teacher; *b:* Columbus, OH; *ed:* Earlham Coll (BA) Sociology 1974; The Ohio St Univ (MA) Ed, Theory & Practice 1988; Am Currently ABD from OH St Univ in Educl Stud; *cr:* Alternative Schls Project Stu Tchr 1973-74; Hilliard HS Sub Tchr 1974-75; Hastings MS Tchr 1975-85; Upper Arlington HS Tchr 1985-; *ai:* Ed Fac Curr Magazine; Co-Adv Habitat for Humanity; Tech Team; Strategic Plan Comm on Ethical Behavior; NEA 1974-; NCSS 1975-; OEA; Upper Arlington Ed Assn; Tchr of Yr 1991-92; Ashland Tchr Achvmt Awd; Curr Dev CLASS Awd; Helen R. Dodge Fnd Flwshp; OH St Grad Acad Schlsp Rsrch Awd; *office:* Upper Arlington HS 1650 Ridgeview Rd Upper Arlington OH 43202

LEHMAN, MARSHA REYNOLDS, Art Teacher; *b:* Mc Keesport, PA; *m:* James; *c:* Maryelizabeth; *ed:* WV Wesleyan Coll (BA) Art 1971; Attnd Tyler Schl of Art, Univ of Arts, Indiana Univ of PA; *cr:* Mc Keesport Area Schl Dist Art Tchr 1971-73; Souderton Area Schl Dist Art Tchr 19 Upper Marion Area Schl Dist Art Tchr 1976-81; North Penn HS Ar 1989-; *ai:* Art Layout Adv Schl Lit Magazine; NEA; PSEA; NPEA; Equity Guild of Papermakers; One Man Show Artwork; *office:* North HS 1340 S Valley Forge Rd Lansdale PA 19446

LEHMAN, MARY-ALICE EABY, First Grade Teacher; *b:* Lancaste *m:* Ronald E.; *ed:* Millersville St Coll (BS) Elem Ed 1972; Temple (MED) Psych of Rdng 1977; *cr:* Leacock Elem Schl 1st Grd Tchr 19 Paradise Elem Schl 1st Grd Tchr 1987-; *ai:* Rdng, Hospitality & Portfolio Comms; Lancaster-Lebanon Intermediate Unit 13 Inter-S Performance Based Assessment-Writing Comm; *office:* Paradise Schl 3293 Lincoln Hwy E Paradise PA 17562

LEHMER, ELSIE JOYCE DURHAM, Contemp Amer & US Hist *b:* Baltimore, MD; *m:* Larry Gene; *ed:* Greenville Coll (BS) Pol Sci NY Univ (MA) Guid & Stu Prsnl; Towson St Univ 50 Hrs; *cr:* The Coll Dean of Women 1962-68; Franklin Jr High Tchr 1968-73; Ste Run Jr High Tchr 1973-78; Milford Mill HS Tchr 1978-83; Dulan Tchr 1983-; *ai:* Peer Cnslrs Co-Adv; Phi Delta Kappa 1985-; Dulaney HS 255 Padonia Rd Timonium MD 21093

LEHNER, RAYMOND ALBERT,SR., Chemistry & Biology Teac Auburn, MA; *m:* Dorothea Elizabeth Conway; *c:* Raymond Albe Karen Marie; *ed:* St Anselm Coll (AB) Chem, Bio 1952; Assumptio (MAT) Natural Scis 1974; 36 Addl Hrs Sci, Ed; *cr:* David Prouty HS Tchr 1969-; *ai:* Sr Class Adv; HS Mentor, Natl Sci Fnd Coord; A Advy Cncl Drug Free Schls; MA Tchrs Assn, NEA 1969-; Notary MA 1964-; *home:* 17 G French Rd Charlton MA 01507

LEHNER, RAYMOND ALBERT,JR., Science, Math & Physics T Worcester, MA; *m:* Gina Ann Chirchigno; *ed:* Worcester St Col Math, Physics, Cmptr Sci 1983; 21 Addl Credits; *cr:* North Quincy H Physics Tchr 1994-95; Southbridge HS Math, Sci, Physics Tchr 199 Class of 1999 Adv; Curr, Assessment Comms; Palms Ldrshp Experimental Aircraft Assn 1981-; Aircraft Owners & Pilots Assn NEA, MTA 1994-; Southbridge Ed Assn; Commercial Pilot 1984-; Flight, Ground Instr; *home:* 9 June St Auburn MA 01501

LEHRER, LYNNE HOLZAPFEL, Spanish Teacher; *b:* Sandusky, O Robert W.; *c:* Andrea, Daniel; *ed:* CT Coll for Women (BA) Pol Sci IN Univ (MA) Latin Amer His 1974; Attnd Case Western Reserve Doctoral Course Work Complete His; Attnd Yale Univ Frgn Lang In Dept of St Frgn Svc 1977-80; FL Comm Coll His Instr 1985-87; Ferna Beach HS His, Sociology Tchr 1985-86; Case Western Reserve Un Rsrch Asst 1987-92; Sandusky City Adult Ed Span Tchr 1994-95; St Cntrl Cath HS Span Tchr 1994-; *ai:* Cncl on Global Awareness; Frgn Dept Chprsn; Org Latin Amer Labor Historians 1987-; Equity in 1985-86, Regnl Rep; NEA 1985-87, Schl Rep; Phi Theta His Doctoral Honarary Soc; Girl Scouts of Amer 1986-, Regnl Ldr; Mer Round Museum 1987-, Advy Cncl; AAUW 1982-, Bd; Island Ed 19 Bd; Soc Policy His Doctoral Grant, Case Western Reserve; Article o Policy Formulation in Latin Amer; *office:* St Mary's Ctl Cath HS 4 Jefferson St Sandusky OH 44870

LEHRER, STEPHEN L., Mathematics Teacher; *b:* Providence, R Freda; *c:* Stacey, Andrew; *ed:* Brown Univ (SCB) Civil Engrng 197 Coll (MAT) Scndry Math 1973; Attnd Fairfield Univ, Rogers Willim & Univ of RI; *cr:* Bristol HS & Mt Hope HS Scndry Math Tchr 197 NEA 1973-; NCTM 1985-; RIMTA 1985-; *office:* Mt Hope HS Ch St Bristol RI 02809

LEHRHAUPT, KAREN KUECHENMEISTER, Social Studies T Detorit, MI; *m:* Michael; *c:* Gwen, David, Lisa Howard, Nancy Boga Amy (dec); *ed:* Hood Coll (BA) His 1964; Fairleigh DIckinson (MA) 1977; Monmouth Coll 45 Credits; *cr:* Mc Divitt Schl 6th Grade Elem 1968-1987; Salk MS Soc Stud Tchr 1987-88; Old Bridge HS Soc Stud 1988-; *ai:* NHS Adv; NEA, OBEA 1968-; Lib Bd 1981-1986, Eagleton Fellow in Pol Sci; Outward Bound Schlsp Recipient; *hom* Lakeridge Dr Matawan NJ 07747*

LEIB, BRUCE J., Amer Government & History Tchr; *b:* Hazleton, P Nancy Holz; *c:* Ryan, Christopher, Stephanie; *ed:* East Stroudsburg S Scndry Ed & Soc Stud 1974; Masters Equivalency; *cr:* Hazleton Are Stud Tchr 1974-77; Mullen HS Soc Stud Tchr 1977-85; Hazleton Are Stud Tchr 1985-; *ai:* Boys Bsktbl Head Coach Hazleton Area HS 11 Mullen HS 7 Yrs; NEA 1993-; Police Ath League 1978-, Bd of Dir; Ja Outstanding Young Educator 1987; *office:* Hazleton Area HS 1601 W St Hazleton PA 18201

LEIB, RONNIE R., English Teacher; *b:* New York, NY; *m:* Jay Robin J., Jeffrey A.; *ed:* Brown Univ (BA) Amer Lit 1964; Boston Un M) Scndry Eng 1966; *cr:* HS of Commerce 10th-12th Grd Eng 1966-67; Birchland Park MS 7th & 8th Grd Eng Tchr 1985-86; Longmeadow HS 9th-12th Grd Eng Tchr 1986-; *ai:* NEA 1985-; East Longmeadow HS 180 Maple St East Longmeadow MA 01025

LEIBACH, CHARLOTTE LEE, Science Teacher; *b:* Pittsburgh, P Joseph; *c:* Kevin, Kyle, Kimberly; *ed:* Allegheny Comm Coll (AA) 1976; Univ of Pittsburgh (BA) Elem Ed 1979, (MA) Spec Ed 1984; Theresa Schl Elem Sci Tchr 1979-; *ai:* PA Jr Acad of Sci Spon 17 Golden Apple Recipient 1995 Diocese of Pittsburgh; *office:* St Tere Avila Schl 800 Avila Ct Pittsburgh PA 15237

LEIBOWITZ, JODIE PLIMLEY, Former Spanish Teacher; *b:* King NY; *m:* David; *c:* Zachary, Joseph; *ed:* SUNY at New Paltz (BA) 1985; SUNY at Albany (MA) Span Ed 1987; Centro Biling Cuern Mexico; *cr:* Hudson Falls Cntrl Schls Span Tchr 1987-92; *ai:* Span Adv; NYSUT, NYSAFLT 1987-; *home:* 58 Mill Pond North Andove 01845

LEICHT, JOSEPH PETER, Mathematics Teacher & Coach; *b:* Jam NY; *m:* Susan Shutte; *c:* Stacey, Amy; *ed:* Montclair St Coll (BA) 1974; Montclair St Univ (MA) Admin & Supervision 1994; *cr:* Indian HS Math Tchr, Coach 1974-; *ai:* Head Boys Var Bsktbl Coach; Asst Sftbl Coach; Fall IM Adv; NJEA, NEA 1974-; Amer Ftbl Coaches Bergen Cty Bsbl Umpires Assn; Intnl Assn of Approved Bsktbl Ofc Coaches Assn Hall of Fame; Ridgewood News Bsktbl Coach of Yr Head Coach NJ North/South Bsktbl All-Star Classic 1992; *office:* I Hills HS 97 Yawpo Ave Oakland NJ 07436

LEICHT, LYNN M., Physical Education Teacher; *b:* Newcastle, P Ruth A. Latshaw; *ed:* Slippery Rock Univ (BS) Hlth & PE 1971; *cr:* Allegheny Schl Dist PE Tchr 1971-; *office:* North Allegheny School 200 Hillvue Ln Pittsburgh PA 15237

LEICHT-BOWERS, BARBARA A., Physical Education Teache Albany, NY; *m:* Louis W. Bowers; *ed:* Hudson Vly Comm Coll (AAS Arts 1967; St Univ at Brockport (BS) PE, Bio 1969, (MS) PE 1974; R Sage Coll (MS) Hlth 1978; *cr:* South Colonie Schls PE Tchr 1969-; & JV Boys Bowling Team, Var Girls Bowling Team, 7-8th Grd Sftbl Coach; AFT, NEA, NYSTA, So Colonie TA 1969-; Ladies Pro Bo Tour 1975-; Albany Women's Bowling Assn 1971-, VP, Hall of Fame NYS Women's Bowling Assn 1971-, Hall of Fame 1990; Natl Colle Bowling Champion 1969; WIBC Natl Singles Champion 1975; Comm of Yr 1987; Pub 1992.*

LEICHTMAN, SUE, Math Teacher; *b:* New York, NY; *m:* Charle Jason, Michael; *ed:* Queens Coll (BA) Elem Ed 1971; Hofstra Univ Scndry Math Ed 1975; 3 Credits Basic Programming Nassau Comm

›uth Side Jr HS MS Math Tchr 1971-75; Hebrew Acad 7-11 Grd Math 1983-; *ai:* NCMT 1996; *office:* Hebrew Acad Of Nassau Co 215 Oak ›iondale NY 11553

:HTNER, JACK, Dean; *m:* Francine Diamond; *c:* Jodi Pasette, Adam; ›ofstra Univ (BA) Ed 1968; Brooklyn Coll (MS) PE 1973; CW Post ›45 Credit Hrs; *cr:* Intermediate Schl 271 PE Tchr 1968-78; JHS 226 ›chr, Dean 1978-; *ai:* Singing in Band; UFT, AFT, AAHPER 1968-; ›: JHS 226 Virgil I Grissom 121-10 Rockaway Blvd S Ozone Park NY ›)*

:KLY, PORTIA ELAINE (SERGEANT), Science Teacher; *b:* Isleta, *m:* David William; *c:* Linda K., Darleen Ann, Janie Marie; *ed:* OH ›yan Univ (BA) Zoology Comprehensive Sci 1966; Ball St Univ (MS) ›975; Attnd John Carroll Univ, Univ of Akron, Case Western Reserve Kent St Univ OH St Univ; *cr:* New Philadelphia City Schls ›ptually Handicapped, Floating Tchr 1966-68; Lakewood City Schls ›chr 1968-, HS Sci Dept Chair 1978-90; *ai:* Watters Sci Seminar; Sci ›Organizer; NEA 1966-; OEA 1966-, Meeting Rep; LTA 1968-, ›sponding Sec, Membership Chprsn, Bldg Rep; AAAS; NABT; NSTA; ›land Regnl Cncl Sci Tchrs Bd; Cleveland Reg Assoc of Bio Tchrs; Kappa Gamma Intnl, Membership Chprsn; Natl Sci Fnd Acad Yr Inst; ›a Holden Jennings Scholar; *office:* Lakewood City Schls 14100 ›lin Blvd Lakewood OH 44107*

›HT, JON, Vocal Music Teacher; *b:* Kulpsville, PA; *ed:* Kings Coll Music Ed 1963; Temple Univ (MA) Elem Ed 1968; Over 60 Hrs; ›e Voice Lessons; *cr:* Ossing Elem Music Ed Tchr 1963; Lower ›d Elem 3rd Grd Tchr 1968-71, Vocal Music Tchr 1972-76; Souderton ›ocal Music Tchr 1977-96; EM Crouthamel Elem Vocal Music Tchr ›; *ai:* Zion Mennonite Church Music Dir; PA St Tchrs 1969-; PA ›: Edctrs 1977-; Army Commendation Medal; Army Security Agncy ›c Sec for Inspector Gen; *home:* PO Box 411 Kulpsville PA 19443

›HTON, ALISON JEAN CELONA, 12th Grade English Teacher; *b:* ›ville Centre, NY; *m:* Barry; *c:* Connor; *ed:* Bethany Coll (BA) Eng & ›983; St Johns (MA) Rdng 1985; *cr:* St Patricks PE & Eng Tchr ›85; Sewanhaka Eng Tchr 1985-; *ai:* Chieftain Newspaper & Dist ›snight Adv; Arrow Lit Magazine; NEA 1985-; SFT 1985-; Cath Yth ›975-, Coach; Coach of the Yr 1990; Nassau Cty Bsktbl Semi-Finalist

›HTON, HAROLD CLIFTON,JR., 7th Grade Social Studies Tchr; ›:hikawa, Japan; *m:* Dawn Johnson; *c:* Cassidy, Brock; *ed:* St Francis ›(BS) Elem 1975; Univ Southern ME (MS) Prof Tchr 1986; *cr:* ›nam MS 6th Grd Tchr 1976-82, 7th Grd Soc Stud Tchr 1982-; *ai:* ›nam Edctrs Assn 1975-, Pres; ME Tchrs Assn 1975-; NEA 1975-; Natl ›f Soccer Ofcls 1992-; *office:* Windham MS 408 Gray Rd Windham ›4062

BACH, LESLIE ANN, Telecommunications Teacher; *b:* Reading, › Jesse Tatum, Lara Rachel; *ed:* Temple Univ (BS) Comm, Radio, TV, ›1973, (MED) Educl Media 1975; Alvernia Coll Tchr Cert Eng, Comm Grad Courses in Ed Penn St, IN Weslyan Univ; *cr:* Penn St Media ›alist 1976-80; Lackawanna Cty Cultural Affairs Dir 1980-83; Reeser, ›ng, Resort Marketers Pub Relations Specialist 1983-87; ›ıonwealth of PA Governors Office Cultural Adv to Governor Exec ›987-93; Boyertown Area Sr HS Telecommunications Tchr 1993-; *ai:* › TV Adv; NEA, PSEA 1983-; PA Assn for Educl Comm & Tech ›; Boyertown Area Ed Assn; Society of Anthropology of Visual Comm; ›SA; United Nations Assn of Scranton Peace Ed Awd; Commendation ›wanna Cty Commission on Cultural Affairs; Article Pub; *office:* ›town Sr HS 4th & Monroe Sts Boyertown PA 19512

BERGER, GARY, Associate Professor of Finance; *b:* Philadelphia, ›: Gail Sanderson; *c:* Amanda, Luke; *ed:* Lehigh Univ (BA) Amer Stud Boston Univ (MBA) Fin 1976; OK St Univ (PHD) Bus Admin Fin *cr:* Franklin & Marshall Asst Prof 1980-84; Villanova Univ Asst Prof ›86; Millersville Univ Assoc Prof 1986-; *ai:* Cubmaster Pack 104; ›eim Soccer Club Asst Coach; Manheim Cntrl Fndtn Dir; *office:* ›sville Univ Of PA McComsey Hall Millersville PA 17551

ER, EVELYN JOAN, 4th Grade Teacher; *b:* Manhattan, NY; *ed:* ›n Univ (BS) Ed 1965; Stonybrook Univ (MA) Lbrl Stud; 60 Post Grad ›s; *cr:* Rolling Hills Schl Elem Tchr 1965-87; Mandracchia Sawmill ›nediate Tchr 1987-; *ai:* AFT; NYSUT; CTA; *office:* ›racchia-Sawmill Interm Sch New Hwy Commack NY 11787*

INGER, CAROL (LEVAN), Math Teacher; *b:* Reading, PA; *m:* E.; *ed:* Kutztown Univ (BS) Math 1967; 24 Credits; 6 Credits RACC; ›edits Marywood; *cr:* jTulpehocken HS 9th-12th Grd Math Tchr ›; *ai:* Misc Math Club Adv; SAT Review Comm; Mentor New Tchrs; PSEA, TEA 1967-, VP, Various Chairs, Tchr of Quarter; Berks Co Alliance 1986-; Woman's Club W Lawn 1981-, VP, 2nd VP, Various ›s; Consumer Panel 1985-; Co-Wrote Berks Co Planned Courses ›a I, Applied Math; *office:* Tulpehocken HS 430 New Schaeffertown ›rnville PA 19506*

O, PATRICIA WEST, Biology & Physiology Teacher; *b:* ›ngton, DC; *m:* John; *ed:* Wilson Coll (BS) Bio 1967; Univ of MD ›) Bio 1976; Post Grad Stud Marine Bio Bowdoin Coll 1977; *cr:* ›-Marine Dependents Schl Bio Tchr & Chprsn 1973-75; Prince ›es Cty Pub Schls Bio Tchr 1975-; *ai:* Fac Advy Comm; Space Shuttle Magnet Schl Tchr; MD Assn of Bio Tchrs, Outstanding Bio Tchr ›st 1985; AFT; Outstanding Microbiology Tchr Finalist; 2 Natl Sci ›Grants; Eisenhower Grant Environment; *home:* 3725 S St SE ›ngton DC 20020

, DONALD BRADLY, Senior Amer Government Teacher; *b:* Lima, ›: Virginia Basinger; *c:* Will, Jon, Katie, Sydney, Emily; *ed:* Bowling St Univ (BS) Comprehensive Soc Stud 1979; *cr:* Ottawa-Glandorf › Amer Govt & Soph World Geography Tchr 1979-; *ai:* Head Cross , Boys Var Track Coach; Sr Class Spirit Adv; NEA, OHEA, ›a-Glandorf Classroom Tchrs Assn 1979-; Ottawa-Glandorf Jaycees , Sec, Treas; IOOF Blanchard Lodge 1992-; Ottawa-Glandorf Ath ›ers 1979-; Stu Cncl Tchr of Yr 1993; Western Buckeye League Cross Coach of Yr 1985; *office:* Ottawa-Glandorf HS 630 Glendale Ave ›a OH 45875

VIRGINIA SUSAN, English Teacher; *b:* Lima, OH; *m:* D. Bradly; ›l, Jon, Katie, Sydney, Emily; *ed:* Bowling Green St Univ (BS) Eng ›80; Wright St Univ (MS) Tchr, Ldr 1993; *cr:* Putnam Co Schls Sub 1981-83; Ottawa-Glandorf HS Eng Tchr 1983-; *ai:* NEA, OEA, ›A 1983-; Tiny Titan's Mother's Club 1993-; Big Brothers, Big ›s, Former Bd Mem; Tchr of Yr 1986-87; *home:* 128 Spring St Ottawa ›5875

AWITZ, ANN GOLDEN, Humanities & Music Professor; *b:* ›ton, PA; *m:* Sheldon M.; *c:* Debra L. Taylor, David; *ed:* Marywood ›BM) Music Ed 1955; Penn St Univ (MA) Hum 1989; Eastman Schl ›sic 1951-53 68 Credits; Marywood Coll 6 Credits; West Chester Univ ›dits; *cr:* Stackpole Elem Schl Vocal Music Supvr 1967-69; Franklin ›arshall Coll Pianist in-Residence 1977-84; Harrisburg Area Comm ›Ium, Music Prof 1990-; Penn St Univ Adj Hum Prof 1992-; *ai:* Schl ›paper Adv; Lebanon Campus Cultural Acts; Coord Private Piano ›ction; Dir Stu Musical Productions; MTNA 1955-; PA Citizens for 1983-, Lanc Rep; PA Cncl of Arts 1979-, Perfoming Mem; Lanc ›ssah 1955-, VP Prgm; Jaycees 1955-, Bd Mem; Lanc Jewsih Comm Ctr 1970-, Bd Mem; Lanc Jewsih Family Svc 1995-; Temple Beth EL Sisterhood 1969-, VP Prgm; Classical Concert Pianist; Lancster Temple Beth EL Choir, Girl Scout Chorus 1976 Founder, Dir, Master Classes, Wkshps Unitarian Church; Artist in Residence Lancaster Pub Schls; Composer; Adjudicator; *home:* 48 Peach Ln Lancaster PA 17601*

LEISK, ELOISE CARLSON, Fifth Grade Teacher; *b:* St Peters, MN; *m:* Daniel G.; *c:* Judith, Joanne, Jeanette, Gary; *ed:* Tufts Univ (BA) Eng 1953; North Adams St Coll (MA) Elem Ed 1974; Post Grad Stud 36 Hrs N Adams St Coll; 9 Hrs Early Chldhd Berkshire Comm Coll; *cr:* Warren Schl First Grd Tchr 1953-54; Daniels Schl First Grd Tchr 1954-57; Highland Schl Pre Kndgtn Tchr 1973-85; William Schl Pre Kndgtn Tchr 1973-85; Pittsfield Pub Schls Sub Tchr 1975-85; Village Schl Title I Rdng Tchr 1985-86, Fourth Grd Tchr 1986-91; Plain Schl Fifth Grd Tchr 1991-; *ai:* Lang Arts Task Force; Recycling Comm; MA Tchrs Assn; MA Rdng Assn 1993-; NEA; Zion's Luth Church Choir; Class Awd US environmental Protection Agency's Ecology Poem & Poster Prgm 1991; Natl Historical Pictorial Map Contest 2nd Pl Dist 1991.

LEIST, NEIL E., Health & Physical Ed Tchr; *b:* Portsmouth, OH; *m:* Lillian; *c:* Doug, Dan, Drake, Drew, Lindsey, Leah; *ed:* Morehead St (BA) PE & Hlth 1985; *cr:* Eastern HS PE & Hlth Tchr 11 Yrs; *ai:* NEA 1985-; *office:* Eastern HS 1170 Tile Mill Rd Beaver OH 45613

LEITCH, AMELIA GRAZIANI, Fourth Grade Teacher; *b:* Pittsfield, MA; *m:* Charles N.; *c:* Cheryl; *ed:* North Adams St Coll (BS) Ed 1964; North Adams St Coll at North Adams (MED) 1969; Amer Intnl Coll Cert of Advanced Grad Stud 1985; *cr:* Cheshire Elem Schl 4 Grd Tchr 1964-; *ai:* Co-operating Tchr for Stdnts; Adams-Cheshire Regnl Schl Dist 1991; Lang Arts Curr Guid K-6; Dev Guide Comm; St Mary of The Assumption Tchr of Chrstn Doctrine; Horace Mann Grant; *office:* Cheshire Elem Schl 191 Church St Cheshire MA 01225*

LEITE, JOHN JOSEPH,SR., K-4th Grd Music Specialist; *b:* Manchester, NH; *m:* Melba Mac Leod; *c:* John Jr.; *ed:* Univ of Lowell-LSTC (BS) Music Ed 1959; Fitchburg St Coll (ME) Educl Tech 1989; Attnd MA Inst of Tech Ctr for Advanced Visual Stud; Berklee Coll of Music Music MIDI Tech & Jazz Theory-Arranging; *cr:* Milton Pub Schls Music Specialist 2 Yrs; Amer Fed of Musicians Prof Musician 20 Yrs; Chelmsford Pub Schls K-12th Grd Music Specialist & 9th-12th Grd Cmptr Music Tchr 16 Yrs; *ai:* Jazz Band Dir, NE Dist Jazz Mgr 1995-; Cntrl & NE Dist Adjudicator; Stow-Bolton Studio Low Brass Tchr; Merr Valley Musican #300 AFM 1955-, Pres; No Shore Musicans Assn #126 1980-, Performer; Framingham-Marlboro Musicians #393 1985-, Performer; AFT 1980-; MENC, Intnl Trombone Assn; Elks Lodge #2310 1971-; Lesley-Lowell Comm Cncl, Former Chm; Lowell Historic Preservation Commission, Former Arts Project Mgr; Prof Musician Northeast-Performed with all Major Artists Touring the NE; Lowell & Chelmsford Cultural Grants; MA Cultural Grants for HS-Collaboration with MIT & Ctr for Advanced Visual Stud; Fitchburg St Coll Merit Awd for Outstanding Achvmt-Ed Tech; *home:* 109 Carroll Pkwy Lowell MA 01851

LEITE, MARY ELLEN HUGHES, Spanish I & Journalism Teacher; *b:* Fremont, OH; *m:* Thomas H.; *c:* Paul A., Susan Batey; *ed:* Coll of Mt St Joseph (BA) Eng 1957; Bowling Green St Univ Grad Credits; *cr:* St Joseph Cntrl Cath Schl Tchr 1957-64, Tchr, PR Dir, Calendar Dir 1973-; *ai:* Weekly, Monthly, Yearly Schl Calendar; Svc Clubs Coord; NCEA 1970-; Cath Educl Dev Fund Bd 1995-; Outstdng Eductr of Yr 1980; Prin Appreciation Awd 1989-90; *office:* St Joseph Ctl Cath HS 702 Croghan St Fremont OH 43420

LEITERMAN, KENNETH JAY, 6th Grade Teacher; *b:* Brooklyn, NY; *m:* Florence Bella; *c:* Carey Wayne, Elisa Beth; *ed:* NYC Tech Coll (AAS) Dental Tech 1963; Long Island Univ (BA) Sociology, Anthropology 1968; Univ of NV at Las Vegas (MED) Curr, Instruction 1973; Adelphi Univ (MS) Spec Ed, Learning Disabilities 1980; Coll of Staten Island Sixth Yr Prof Cert Admin, Supervision 1991; *cr:* Matt Kelly Sixth Grd Ctr Tchr, Chm Math Dept 1972-77; John Faber Schl Tchr 6th Grd 1977-78; Moriah Schl of EnglewoodTchr 6th Grd 1978; Bd of Ed NYC Canarsie Yt h Ctr Site Coord 1979-84; PS 225 K Tchr 5th-6th Grds 1984-; United Lubavitch Yeshiva Part-time Tchr 6th Grd 1993-; *ai:* Head of Jr Police Prgm; Chess Club Adv; AFT 1979-; US Inc of Southern NV 1976-, Intern Cnslr; BSA 1978-, Asst Cub Master; Cert of Merit in Tchng; Awd of Merit in Ed 5th Grd Children; *home:* 38 Elson St Staten Island NY 10314

LEITH, ROBERT ALLAN, Retired Elementary Teacher; *b:* Braddock, PA; *ed:* IN St Tchrs Coll (BS) Elem 1962; PA St Univ (MS) Elem 1971; *cr:* North Braddock Pub Schls 4-6 Grd Soc Stud Tchr 1962-72; Gen Braddock Schl Dist 4-6 Grd Tchr 1972-81; Alleg Co Comm Coll GED Instr 1973; Woodland Hills Schl Dist 5 Grd Tchr 1981-94; *ai:* NEA, PSEA 1962-; Amer Family Assoc Awd Exceptioanl Tchrs Awd 1985; *home:* 3222 Cherry St West Mifflin PA 15122

LEITH, RONALD EDWARD, Sixth Grade Teacher; *b:* Pittsburgh, PA; *m:* Loraine Kitchen; *c:* Tracey Leith Bonidie, Lori, Ron Jr., Kelly; *ed:* Point Park Coll (BA) Elem 1972; Penn St Univ (MS) Elem 1990; *cr:* Swissvale Pub Schls 6th Grd Tchr 1972-81; Woodland Hills Schl Dist 6th Grd Tchr 1981-; *ai:* Head Bsbl Coach; NEA, PSEA 1972-; Amer Family Assn Excl Tchr Awd 1985; *home:* 2412 Columbia Ave Swissvale PA 15218

LEITH, VALORIE ANN (SCOTT), 5th Grade Teacher; *b:* Topeka, KS; *c:* Amber F., Erin M.; *ed:* SUNY at Cobleskill (AAS) Bus Admin 1974; SUCO at Oneonta (BS) Elem Ed 1989, (MS) Elem Ed 27 Credits 1996; *cr:* Middleburgh Cntrl 6th Grd Tchr 1989, 3rd Grd Tchr 1989-93, 5th Grd Tchr 1993-; *ai:* Var Vlybl Schoharie 4 yrs, Middleburgh 1 yr; Var Sftbl 2 Yrs Jr Var 1 Yr, Modified 3 Yrs; OM Coach 2 Yrs; Cheerleading 5 Yrs; OM Judge 1 Yr; MCS Tchrs Assoc 1989-; Village Bd Middleburgh 1994-, Trustee; *office:* Middleburgh Elem Schl RR 2 Box 78 Middleburgh NY 12122*

LEITMA, GRANT G., Psychology Professor; *b:* Washington, DC; *m:* Terry; *c:* Jordan, Marissa, Kimberly; *ed:* Columbia Union Coll (BA) Psych, His 1977; Cntrl MI Univ (MA) Dev Psych 1980, IL Inst of Tech (PHD) Experimental Psych 1987; *cr:* Columbia Union Coll Prof 1982-; *ai:* Lib Comm; Psi Chi Adv; Rank Review Comm Chair; Psyc of Tchng Conf; APA 1988-; Research Methods Orgaizational Mngmt Textbk; JFK Article; *office:* Columbia Union Coll 7600 Flower Ave Takoma Park MD 20912

LEITTEN, MICHELLE PRITCHARD, Mathematics Teacher; *b:* Rochester, NY; *m:* Matthew; *c:* Jessica, Megan; *ed:* SUNY at Fredonia (BS) Math 1986; SUNY at Geneseo (MA) Math Ed 1990; *cr:* Honeoye Cntrl Schl HS Math Tchr 1987-; *ai:* JV Vlbyl, Jr HS Bsktbl Coach; Class Adv 1994; NYS Assn Math Tchrs, NYSUT 1987-; *home:* 6893 Canadice Lake Rd Springwater NY 14560

LEITZEL, LOWELL LESLIE, French Teacher; *b:* Ephrata, PA; *ed:* Susquehanna Univ (BA) Fr 1976; Univ of PA at Millersville (MA) Fr 1986; *cr:* Southern Garrett HS Fr Tchr 1977-; *ai:* NHS, Asst Stu Cncl Adv; Fr Exch Prgm Coord; NEA, MD St Tchr Assn, Garrett CTA 1977-, Bldg Rep, VP; AATF 1982-; Oakland-Mt. Lake Park Lions Club 1995-; St. Marks Luth Church 1977-, Sec, Pres; Fulbright Exch Tchr Bourges France 1988-89; *home:* 803 Memorial Dr Oakland MD 21550

LEITZEL, WILLIAM EARL, 4th Grade Teacher; *b:* Hazleton, PA; *m:* Letitia Bleyzgis; *c:* Margaret, William, Matthew; *ed:* Bloomsburg Univ (BA) Elem Ed 1971; Temple Univ (MS) Ed 1975; *cr:* Tamaqua Area Elem Tchr 1971-; *ai:* Little League, Ftbl & Bsbl Coach; NEA 1971-; PSEA 1971-; Masonic Lodge 1973-; *office:* Tamaqua Area Rush Elem Schl RD 2 Meadow Ave Tamaqua PA 18252

LEIVERS, KATHLEEN A., Teacher; *b:* New London, CT; *m:* Robert; *c:* Courtney, Jenny, Bobby; *ed:* Eastern CT Univ (BS) 1971; Southern CT Univ 5th Yr (MS) Ed 1975; 6th Yr Admin 1985; *cr:* Groton Hghts 4th-5th Grd Tchr 1971-; *ai:* Groton Ed Assn; NEA; *office:* Groton Hghts Elem 244 Monument St Groton CT 06340*

LEKIC, ANITA MARIE, Elementary Education Teacher; *b:* Philadelphia, PA; *ed:* Holy Family Coll (BA) Span Lang, Elem Ed 1978; Saint Charles Seminary Rel Stud; *cr:* Saint Martin of Tours 6th Grd Tchr 1978-84; Holy Innocents Schl 7th Grd Tchr 1985-89; St Joan of Arc Schl 5th Grd Tchr 1989-; *ai:* Lang Arts, CYO, Walk-a-thon Coord; Spelling Bee Contest Moderator; Spec Ed Homebound Tutor; NCEA 1978-; *home:* 4342 Cottman Ave Philadelphia PA 19135

LEMALDI, JO ANN R., 5th Grade Teacher; *b:* Newark, NJ; *ed:* Seton Hall Univ (BS) Ed 1971; Montclair St (MA) Ed 1991; *cr:* West Orange Dist-Wide Instructional Skills Trainer 1985; Private Educl Consultant; West Orange Staff Dev Trainer, Elem Tchr; *ai:* Stu Cncl Fac Adv; Soc Affairs Comm Chprsn; Lang Arts Comm; NEA, WOEA 1971-; NJ Governor's Tchr Recognition Awd 1990; West Orange Tchr of Yr 1990.*

LEMANSKY, JANET R., Orchestra Director; *b:* Newark, NJ; *ed:* Douglass Coll (BA) Music Ed, Piano 1971; Columbia Univ (MA) Music Ed, Cello 1991; Grad Asst Montclair St Univ; Ulpan Schl for Hebrew; Brazilian Culture Stud; *cr:* Barringer HS String Specialist 1974; Elizabeth Elem Schl Band Dir 1975; Linden HS Orch Dir 1976-; Montclair St Univ Music Prep Division, Jazz & Rock Ensemble Dir, Orch Asst, Jazz Piano Instr 1995-; *ai:* Jazz 4 Teens Co-Founder; Latin Amer Festival Co-Chair; African-Amer Celebration Jazz Ensemble Dir; Linden-Montclair St Univ Music Prep Link Coord; NJEA, ASTA, NAJE, NJMEA 1971-; Latin Music Boys Harbor Performing Arts Ctr; Article Pub; *office:* Linden HS 121 W Saint Georges Ave Linden NJ 07036*

LEMASTERS, KAREN SUE (ABBOTT), Sixth Grade Teacher; *b:* Newark, OH; *m:* Stephen R.; *c:* Jennifer Zellar Shriner, J. Bradley Zellar; *ed:* Kent St Univ (BS) Elem Ed 1968; Ashland Univ (MS) Curr, Instruction 1990; Attnd OH Dominican, OH St Univ; *cr:* Maholm Elem Schl 6th Grd Tchr 1968; Cherry Vly Elem Schl 6th Grd Tchr 1968-70; Maholm Elem Schl 5th, 6th Grd Tchr 1970-87; Wilson MS 6th, 7th Grd Tchr, Tchr of Skills for Adolescence 1987-; *ai:* Math Curr, Soc Stud Comms; NEA, OEA 1968-; Several Church Affiliated Act Comm Wesleyan; *office:* Wilson MS 805 W Church St Newark OH 43055*

LEMAY, ALLEN BLAINE, Social Studies Teacher; *b:* Laconia, NH; *m:* Lorrie Ann Bailey; *c:* Joshua, Matthew, Cory; *ed:* Plymouth St Coll (BS) Soc Sci, Geog Minor 1977; Univ of VT 9 Grad Credit Hrs Geography; Salem St Coll 6 Grad Credit Hrs Geography; Boston Unv 4 Grad Credit Hrs Geography; *cr:* Merrimack HS Soc Stud Tchr 1981-; Plymouth St Coll Adjunct Geography Prof 1988-; Univ of NH Adjunct Geography Prof 1989-; Keene St Coll Adjunct Geography Prof 1989-91; *ai:* New England St Lawrence Valley Geographical Soc 1990-; NH Georgraphic Alliance Steering comm 1990-; Who's Who Among Stdnts in Amers Colls & Univs 1976-77; *office:* Merrimack HS 38 Mc Elwan St Merrimack NH 03054

LEMENILLE, STEVEN ROBERT, Social Studies Teacher; *b:* Jersey City, NJ; *m:* JoAnne C. Pozniak; *c:* Ross-Steven; *ed:* Jersey City St Coll (BA) Soc Stud Ed 1969; Admin & Supervision 16 Credits; His of Theatre 3 Credits; *cr:* Dow-Jones & Co News Asst 1963-69; Cntrl Bergon Fed Credit Union Account Exec 1987-89; Hackensack Pub Schls Soc Stud Tchr 1969-; *ai:* Adv Civics Enrichment Club; Drama Dir 1970-95; Outdoor Ed Pgrm Dir 1983-85; NEA 1969-; NJEA 1969-, Ldrshp Comm, RA Del; HEA 1969-, Pres, VP, Fac Rep; NCSS, NJCSS, NJGT 1969-, Mem; Jersey City Jaycees 1968-70, Mem, Miss Hudson Cty Pagaent Dir; NJ Credit Union League Dir; Republican Presidential Task Force 1985-, Charter Mem; Republican Natl Comm 1989-, Sustaining Mem; Distngd Svc Awd Hackensack Pub Schls 1991; Who's Who in Amer Colls & Univs 1968-69; Outstdng Young Men of Amer 1973; *office:* Hackensack MS 360 Union St Hackensack NJ 07601*

LEMINEN, WILLIAM RAFAEL, 5th Grade Teacher; *b:* Quincy, MA; *m:* Mary Ann; *c:* Kristen, William, Beth Ellen, Paul; *ed:* Massasoit CC (AA) 1968; Boston St Coll (BS) Elem Ed 1974; Cambridge Coll (MA) Integrated Stud 1989; Attnd Bridgewater St Coll 1975-81, Coll of Great Falls MT 1971-72; *cr:* Monatiquot Elem Schl Grd 5 Tchr 1974-83; Lakeside Schl Grd 5 Tchr 1983-; *ai:* Schl Safety Patrol Adv; Media Coord; Abington Music Parents VP; NEA 1974-, RA, Del; MTA 1974-, Del; BEA 1974-, Dir, Treas; *office:* Lakeside Schl Lakeside Dr Braintree MA 02184

LEMKE, MARILYN B., 3rd Grade Teacher; *b:* Berwyn, IL; *c:* Amy Levin, Michael Levin; *ed:* Univ of IL (BS) Elem Ed 1965; Marywood Coll (MS) Integrative Ed 1981; Addl 36 Grad Hrs Integrative Ed, Marywood Coll & Penn St Univ; *cr:* Prince Georges Cnty Schl Dist 3rd Grd, Sub Tchr 1967-70; Abington Schl Dist 4th, 5th Grd Tchr 1970-73; Restoration Nursery Schl Co-Dir, Tchr 1973-74; Cheltenham Twp Sch Dist K-4th Grd Tchr 1974-; *ai:* NEA, PSEA 1970-, CEA 1974-; *office:* Wyncote Elem Schl 333 Rices Mill Rd Wyncote PA 19095

LEMKE, SANDRA COSTANZA, K-4th Grade Music Teacher; *b:* Sewickley, PA; *m:* Richard; *ed:* Edinboro Univ of PA (BA) K-12 Grd Music Ed 1975; Manshall Univ of Huntington; *cr:* South Point Schl Dist Music Tchr 1976-78; Chesapeake Schl Dist Music Tchr 1978-; *ai:* Directed 3 Musicals; Talent Show Coord; Clarinet Instr; NEA, OEA 1984-; Amer Fed of Musicians 1976-; Paramount Arts Cncl 1988-, Rep Schl Dist; WV Symphony Orchestra 1980-, Clarinetist; Huntington Chamber Orchestra 1977-, Clarinetist; Huntington POPS Orchestra 1986-, Clarinetist; Martha Jennings Schlsp 1994-95; *home:* 6852 County Road 1 South Point OH 45680

LEMKE, WENDY (DABOLT), French Teacher; *b:* Buffalo, NY; *m:* Ronald J. Jr.; *ed:* SUNY at Geneseo (BA) Fr 1993; *cr:* Hamburg Jr HS Long Term Sub Tchr 1993-94; West Seneca East Sr HS Long Term Sub Tchr 1993-94; Hamburg Jr Sr HS Fr Tchr 1994-; *ai:* Yrbk Adv 1994-; Quebec Field Trip Chaperone; AFT 1995-; *office:* Hamburg Jr Sr HS 4111 Legion Dr Hamburg NY 14075

LEMLEY, BRUCE B., Kindergarten Teacher; *b:* Core, WV; *c:* Keith, Michael; *ed:* WV Univ (BS) Elem Ed 1970; 31 Grad, In Svc Credit Hrs; *cr:* Cntrl Greene Schl Dist Elem Tchr Elem Tchr 1971-; *ai:* NEA, PSEA 1972-; *office:* Perry Elem Schl PO Box 100 Mount Morris PA 15349

LEMMEY, WILLIAM, Social Studies Teacher; *b:* New York City, NY; *m:* Catherine; *c:* Karen, Ingrid; *ed:* Queens Coll (BA) 1966; Grad Ctr CUNY (PHD) HIs 1979; *cr:* Hicksville Jr HS Tchr 1966-87; Hicksville HS Tchr 1987-; *ai:* Natl His Day, Mock Trial Adv; Hicksville Fed of Tchrs 1979-, Pres; AFT 1976-; NCSS 1986-; United Comm Civic Assn 1993-, Bd of Dirs; William Adee Whitehead Awd; Best Article Pub; Co-Tchr of Yr 1995.

LEMONAKIS, STEVE FRANK, High School English Teacher; *b:* Leesburg, FL; *m:* Anita Sohn; *c:* Stephanie, James; *ed:* Towson St Univ (MS) Psych 1969, (MA) Scndry Ed Eng 1970; Loyola Coll (MED) Rdng Specialist 1975; 3 Addl Credits; Univ of MD 3 Credits; *cr:* Bester Elem Schl Rdng Specialist 1975-77; Clear Spring HS Eng Tchr 1977-83; Boonsboro HS Eng Tchr 1983-; *ai:* Acad Coach; Head Sftbl Coach 6 Yrs; Asst Soccer Coach 1 Yr; NEA 1983-; MSTA 1983-; WCTA Schl Rep 1989-91, Bd of Dir of Local Assn 1991-93.

LEMONCELLI, JOHN JOSEPH, Assoc Prof of Psych & Cnslng; *b:* Archbald, PA; *m:* Margaret A. Kolmansberger; *c:* Mark, Mauri; *ed:* Univ of Scranton (BA) Psych 1970, (MS) Counseling 1972; Temple Univ (EDD)

Adult Dev 1983; Amer Trng Acad Hypnosis Trng Cert; *cr:* Luzerne-Wyoming Co MHC Comm Svcs Dir 1973-83; G. D. Boriosi & Assoc Psych Intern 1983-87; Marywood Coll Assoc Prof 1987-; *ai:* Pres Pi Chapter Chi Sigma Iota; Marywood Counseling Assn Fac Mentor; Amer Couns Assn 1987-; Amer Psych Assn 1989-; PA Psych Assn 1984-; PA Counseling Assn 1983-; Amer Assn Pastoral Cnslrs 1991; Knights of Columbus 1984-; Diocese of Scranton Ed Commission 1990-, Exec Bd; Dept Hlth, Human Svcs Outstanding Committment to Children Awd; ERIC Articles Pub; Natl & Rgnl Pub; *office:* Marywood Coll Grad Schl of Arts & Sciences CHS Adams Ave Scranton PA 18509*

LEMPA, PATRICIA CAMPBELL, Sixth Grade Reading Teacher; *b:* Bayonne, NJ; *m:* Paul Richard; *c:* Paul Patrick, Meredith; *ed:* Jersey City St Coll (BA) Elem Ed 1967, (MS) Rdng Specialist 1970; 30 Credits Above Masters Sci & Cmptr Tech; *cr:* Bayonne Bd of Ed 3rd Grd Tchr 1967-70, 5th Grd Tchr 1976-94, 6th Grd Tchr 1994-; *ai:* Peer Mediation Adv; Family Tool & Tech Facilitator; Shared Decision Team Mem; NJEA 1967-; BTA 1967-; Govenors Tchr Recognition 1987; *office:* Midtown Community Schl 550 Avenue a Bayonne NJ 07002

LEMPA, ROBERT FRANCIS, Science Dept Chprsn & Teacher; *b:* Bayonne, NJ; *m:* Patricia Manzi; *c:* Nicole, Ryan, Douglas; *ed:* Rutgers Univ (BA) Bio 1976; Jersey City St (MA) Supervision; 30 Credits Beyond Masters; *cr:* Keyport HS Sci Tchr 1976-77; Manasquan HS Sci Dept Head & Sci Tchr 1977-; *ai:* Asst Ftbl, Asst Girls Bsktbl & Head Girls Track Coach; NJEA 1976-; NEA 1976-; MEA 1977-; Governors Tchr Recognition Awd 1992; Schl Ldr Awd Honorable Mention 1994; NJ Assn for Supervision & Curr Dev Outstdng Pgm Awd 1995; *office:* Manasquan HS Broad St Manasquan NJ 08736

LENAHAN, ALICE JEAN, Spanish Teacher; *b:* Suffern, NY; *ed:* Univ of Rochester Pol Sci, Span 1973; Union Univ (JD) Law 1976; Univ of Madrid Spain 16 Credit Hrs Hispanic Lit; *cr:* Antell Harris & Calleri Assoc Attorney 1977-80; Genesee Cty Asst Cty Attorney 1980-86; Port Jervis City Schl Dist Span Tchr 1987-; Orange Cty Comm Coll Adj Instr Span 1994-; *ai:* Mock Trial Team Adv; AFT, NYSTA 1987-; NYS, Amer Bar Assns 1977-; Cornell Univ Child Protective Svcs Merit Cert 1985; NY St Bar Assn Achvmt Certs 1990, 1993-94; *home:* RR 1 Box 240 Otisville NY 10963

LENART, AUDREY LYNN, Business Teacher; *b:* Torrington, CT; *ed:* NH Coll (AS) Admin Asst 1983, (BS) Bus Ed 1985; Cntrl CT St Univ (MS) Scndry Ed 1991; Univ of Hartford 6th Yr Guidance Cnslng; *cr:* Hall HS Adult Ed Tchr 1986-88; Housatonic Valley Regnl HS Adult Ed Tchr 1988-92, Bus Tchr 1986-; *ai:* Class Adv 7 Yrs; Chrldng Coach; Book & schl Store Adv; Frosh Advy Ldr; Sec Voc Arts Advy Cncl; Schl Improvement Comm; Adult Ed Tchr; Co-Chm Applied Ed Dept; CEA, CBEA, NEA 1986-; *office:* Housatonic Valley Reg HS 246 Warren Tpke Falls Village CT 06031

LENETT, LOIS HARRIOT, English Teacher; *b:* Brooklyn, NY; *m:* Stephen; *c:* Jarret; *ed:* Adelphi Univ (BA) Speech, Theatre 1964; Queens Coll (MS) Eng, Ed 1969; *cr:* Cardoza Hr JS Eng Tchr 1964; Valley Stream North HS Eng, Speech, Theatre Tchr 1965-; *ai:* NHS, Lit Magazine, Schl Newspaper Advs; AFT, NEA 1964-; PTA Life-Time Achvmt; Tuffs Tchr Who Makes A Difference; *office:* Valley Stream North HS 750 Herman Ave Franklin Square NY 11010*

LENETTI, ANGELO J., Industrial Arts Teacher; *b:* New Brunswick, NJ; *m:* Linda M. Garcia; *c:* Katherine Lynch, Angela, Linda DeVoe, Frank, CaraLynn; *ed:* Kean Coll (BA) Indstrl Ed 1973; Rutgers Univ Grad Schl of Ed (MA) Supervision 1977; *cr:* Perth Amby HS Indstrl Arts Tchr 1965-80; Spotswood HS Dept Supvr 1980-85; Elmwood Park Jr Sr HS Indstrl Arts Tchr, Eng, Soc Stud Dept Facilitator 1985-; Adult Ed Instr of Apprentices Tchr 1985-; *ai:* Tech Curr, Attendance Comms; NEA; TEANJ; Former Scoutmaster, Bd of Ed, Merit Badge Cnslr, PTA Pres; *office:* Memorial HS River Ave Elmwood Park NJ 07407*

LENGEL, GENA, Secondary English Teacher; *b:* NJ; *m:* Andrew; *c:* Peter; *ed:* Penn St Univ (BS) Ed 1990; Wilkes Univ (ME); *cr:* Lackawanna Trail HS Scndry Eng Tchr 1990-; *ai:* Asst Field Hockey Coach 1990-94; Adv Newspaper Club; PSEA 1990-; Dalton United Meth Church 1989-, Treas; Poetry pub in Blueline Poetry Journal, Anderie Poetry Press & Eng Journal; Bd Mem Northeastern PA Writing Cncl; *office:* Lackawanna Trail HS PO Box 85 Factoryville PA 18419

LENGEL, TRACI LAVON, Health & Physical Ed Teacher; *b:* Pine Grove, PA; *ed:* IN Univ of PA (BS) Hlth, PE 1993; Working Toward Masters East Stroudsburg Univ; *cr:* Pocono Mountain Schl Hlth, PE Tchr 1993-; *ai:* Var Asst Girls Bsktbl, JV Girls Sftbl Coach; *office:* Pocono Mtn Intermediate School PO Box 200 Swiftwater PA 18370

LENGLE, LARRY EDWARD, English Teacher; *b:* Newark, NJ; *m:* Maryann Saulle; *c:* Kurt, Christine, Scott; *ed:* Rutgers Univ (BA) Eng 1974; Jersey City St Univ (MA) Admin, Supervision 1983; 60 Credit Hrs; *cr:* Newton HS Eng Tchr 1974-; *ai:* NHS, Acad Bowl Team Adv; Newton Tchrs Assn, Sussex Cty Assn, NJ Educ Assn, NEA 1974-; Newton Presbyn Church, Elder; Old First Church 1944-, Elder, Clerk of Session; NJ Swimming Ofcls Assn, Certfd Ofcl; Natl Endowment of Arts Flwshp Univ of MD 1987; Dickens Seminar Grant 1988-93; *office:* Newton HS 44 Ryerson Ave Newton NJ 07860

LENGYEL, THERESE M., Science Teacher; *b:* Queens, NY; *m:* William C.; *c:* Jaimie, Jennifer; *ed:* SUNY at Stony Brook (BS) 1977; CW Post (MA) Genetics; *cr:* St John Bapt HS Tchr 1977-79; Southampton HS Tchr 1979-; *ai:* Outing Club & Class Adv; *office:* Southampton HS 141 Narrow Ln Southampton NY 11946

LENHART, ELIZABETH GIERHART, English Teacher; *b:* Pittsburgh, PA; *m:* Park William; *c:* Park, Todd; *ed:* PA St Univ (BA) Eng 1964, (MS) Ed 1995; OH Univ Schl of Jrnlsm; *cr:* Bethel Park HS Eng Tchr 1964-65; Upper St Clair HS Eng Tchr 1965-67; Hickory HS Eng, Jrnlsm Tchr 1984-; *ai:* Yrbk, Lit Mag Adv; NCTE, NEA 1964-; PA St Ed Assn 1984-; AAUW 1972-; Columbia Scholastic Press Assn, PA Press Jrnlsm Awds; *office:* Hickory HS 640 N Hermitage Rd Hermitage PA 16148

LENHART, JANICE KINTZ, Biology Teacher; *b:* Berks County, PA; *m:* Thomas A.; *c:* Todd, Natalie Lenhart Kovalusky; *ed:* Kutztown Univ (BS) Bio 1961, (MEd) Bio 1967; Post Grad Stud in Ed of 36 Credit Hrs 1982-84; *cr:* Boyertown Area Schls General Sci Tchr 1961-62; Fleetwood Area Schls Bio Advanced Bio Tchr 1962-69; Daniel Boone Schl Dist Bio, Anatomy, Physiology Tchr 1982-; *ai:* Cooperating Tchr for Stu Tchrs; Daniel Boon Ed Assn 1982-, Bldg Rep; PSEA, NEA, Amer Bio Tchrs 1961-; ASCD 1990-; *office:* Daniel Boone Jr Sr HS PO Box 450 Birdsboro PA 19508*

LENHOFF, MARGARET REES, German Teacher; *b:* Elkton, MD; *m:* Peter J.; *c:* Peter Joseph Jr.; *ed:* Westerm MD Coll (BA) Ger Ed 1974; Towson St Univ (MED) Scndry Ed 1984; Post Grad Credits in Tchng Skills & Learning Stud; *cr:* Elkton HS Ger Tchr 1974-95; Cecil Comm Coll Spcl Instr in Ger 1993-; *ai:* Chrldng Coach; CCCTA 1975-; NSTA 1975-; NEA 1975-; *office:* Elkton HS 110 James St Elkton MD 21921

LENICK, MARY ANN ANDERSON, High School Mathematics Tchr; *b:* Ridley Park, PA; *m:* Leo F.; *ed:* Immaculate Coll (BA) Math 1968; OH St Univ (MA) Math Ed 1973; Univ of SD (MA) Scndry Admin 1983, (EDD) Adult Ed 1985; Attnd Dakota Wesleyan Univ 1982, Old Westbury 1992 & Penn St 1993; *cr:* Cardinal Brennan HS Math Tchr 1968-76; Philadelphia Navy Yard Math Tchr 1976-77; Interboro HS Math Tchr 1977-79; Wood Schl Admin Asst & Tchr 1979-84; Schuylkill Haven HS Lead Tchr of Math 1986-; *ai:* Soph Class & NHS Adv; NEA, PEA, SHEA 1986-; *office:* Schuylkill Haven HS Main St Schuylkill Haven PA 17972*

LENK, CAROL ANN, Language Arts Dept Head; *b:* Cleveland, OH; *m:* Dennis; *c:* Gretchen, Steve; *ed:* Allegheny (BA) Eng, Speech 1968; BGSU (MA) Ed 1995; Attnd Ashland, Akron Univ, Walsh; *cr:* Medina Jr HS Eng Dept 1968-71; Medina HS Eng Dept 1977-; *ai:* Acad Challenge; Acad Decathlon; Amnesty Intnl; NEA, OEA 1968-; Phi Delta Kappa 1991-; NCTE 1977-; AAUW; YWCA; Distngd Svc Awd; Tchr of Month, Yr; *office:* Medina HS 777 E Union St Medina OH 44256*

LENK, THOMAS FREDERICK, Mathematics Supervisor; *b:* Jersey City, NJ; *m:* Judith Schick; *c:* Meredith, Thomas; *ed:* St Peters Coll (BS) Math 1966; Georgian Court Coll (MA) Supervision, Instruction Admin 1979; Grad Course Stevens Inst Tech; *cr:* N Plainfield HS Math Tchr 1967-71; Monmouth Regnl HS Math Tchr 1971-84, Math Supvr 1989-; Ocean Cty Coll Adjunct Asst Prof 1979-; *ai:* Gifted Ed Exec Comm Treas; NASSP, PSA 1989-; NJ Governors Demonstration Grant for Gifted Ed; Dwight D. Eisenhower Grant for Math & Sci 3 Yrs; Natl Sci Fnd Grant Calculator Use in Calculus; *office:* Monmouth Regional H S 535 Tinton Ave Tinton Falls NJ 07724

LENNON, DAVID JAMES, 7th-8th Grd Soc Studies Tchr; *b:* Adams, MA; *m:* Patricia Kleiner; *c:* David, Debra, Daniel; *ed:* North Adams St Coll (BA) Scndry Soc Stud, Elem 1965, (MS) Ed Admin 1973; 6 Addl Credit Hrs; *cr:* Readsboro Cntrl Schl 6th-8th Grd Tchr 1965-67; Liberty St Elem Schl 5th Grd Tchr 1967-72; Plunkett Intermediate Schl 5th Grd Tchr 1972-94; Adams MS 7th-8th Grd Soc Stud Tchr 1994-; *ai:* Adams-Cheshire Tchrs Assn 1972-; MA Tchrs Assn 1974-; NEA 1980-; *home:* 140 Maple Dr Rt 116 Adams MA 01220

LENON, MARYJANE, Economics Instructor; *b:* Fall River, MA; *c:* Jason; *ed:* Bryant Coll (BS) Ecs 1982; Univ of CT at Stores (MA) Ecs 1984, (PHD) Ecs 1989; *cr:* Providence Coll Chprsn 1986-; *ai:* Mission Statement Comm; AEA; Grant from Ctr for Real Estate, Urban Ecs Stud; *office:* Providence Coll Sullivan Hall #102 Providence RI 02918

LENOWICZ, STEPHEN, Social Studies Teacher; *b:* Queens, NY; *m:* Maureen Mc Call; *c:* Matthew, Mary Elizabeth, Melissa; *ed:* Hofstra Univ (BA) Soc Stud 1971, (MA) Ed 1975; 60 Addl Hrs; *cr:* West Islip HS Tchr, Coach 1971-; *ai:* JV Bsktbl, Wheatley Schl; Frosh Ftbl Coach; NYSUT, West Islip Tchrs Assn 1971-; Soc Stud LI Cncl; *office:* West Islip HS 1 Lions Path West Islip NY 11795

LENOX, DARRELL E., Language Arts Teacher; *b:* Columbus, OH; *m:* Cynthia Lee Wade; *c:* Andrew, Amanda, Benjamin, Daniel; *ed:* OH St Univ (BS) Eng 1989; Elem Tchng Cert; *cr:* Finland MS Lang Arts Tchr 1990-; *ai:* 8th Grd Boys Bsktbl Coach; Girls Track Coach; Bldg Curr Comm; Immanuel Bapt Church, Yth Group Spon; *home:* 1874 Little Water Dr Columbus OH 43223

LENOX, WILLIAM F., English & Pub Speaking Teacher; *b:* Newark, NJ; *m:* Sharon Mc Kenna; *c:* William Jr., Lauren; *ed:* Providence Coll (BA) His, Ed 1971; Univ of RI (MA) Comm Ed 1974; Attnd RI Coll; *cr:* Smithfield Jr HS Soc Stud, Eng Tchr 1972-80; Johnson & Wales Univ Eng Instr 1975; RI Dept of Corrections Prgm Coord 1978-81; Smithfield HS Eng, Pub Speaking Tchr 1980-; *ai:* NEA, Smithfield Ed Assn 1972-; Potterville Vol Fire Dept 1981-, Pres; Scituate Schlsp Comm; Yth Sports Coach; *office:* Smithfield HS 90 Pleasant View Ave Smithfield RI 02917

LENT, CLAIRE F. MC INTYRE, English Teacher; *b:* Jersey City, NJ; *m:* John D.; *c:* Thomas, Andrew, Jonathan, Laura, Stephen; *ed:* Anna Maria Coll (BA) Eng 1964; Worcester St (MED) Ed 1970; AP Eng at Taft Inst; *cr:* Maynard HS Eng Dept Chair 1970-72; Clinton HS Eng Tchr 1985-; *ai:* Drama Club; Frosh Class Adv; Schl Cncl; Acad Bowl Adv; MTA; NEA; NCTE; Impact Tchr of 1995; *office:* Clinton HS 80 Church St Clinton MA 01510*

LENT, LINDETTE IRENE, Asst Psychology Professor; *b:* Hahn, Germany; *ed:* Univ of Rochester (BA) Psych 1986; SUNY at Buffalo (ABD) Clinical Psych 1991; *cr:* SUNY at Buffalo Tchng Asst 1988-89; Millard Fillmore Coll Adj Fac 1990; SUNY at Buffalo Adj Fac 1990-92; Fingerlake Comm Coll Instr 1992-94; Schenectady Co Comm Coll Asst Prof 1994-; *ai:* Acad Adv; Planning, Fac & Staff Dev, Child Dev, Curr, EOP Adv Comm; Human Svcs Advy Bd; Schl Fdn; Human Svcs Prgm Review; Awd Dev Stud Fac Support; NEA 1990-; QUILTS 1996-; Undergraduate Minority Flwshp SUNY at Buffalo; SGA Elected, Honored Fac Advocate; *office:* Schenectady County Comm Coll 78 Washington Ave Schenectady NY 12305

LENTZ, EILEEN H., Substitute Teacher; *b:* Rexburg, ID; *m:* James E.; *c:* Derek E. Kathleen, Hamilton J.; *ed:* Ricks Coll (AS) Family 1974; Penn St at Harrisburg (BSE) Elem Ed 1989; Post Grad Math Their Way; BYU Ind Stud; *cr:* Williams Vly, Halifac, Millersburg SD Sub Tchr 1990-93; Upper Dauphin, Halifax, Millersburg SD Sub Tutor, Homebound Tutor 1990-; Halfiax Area Schl Dist 1st Grd Personal Dev 1992-93; Capital Area Head Start Tchr 1993-95; Upper Dauphin, Halifax, Millersburg SD Sub Tchr 1995-; *ai:* NEA 1992-; Church of Jesus Christ of Latter Day Saints Millersburg Branch of Relief Soc 1976-, Ed Cnslr; Girls Scouts of Amer 1984-, Daisy Ldr; BSA 1986-, Cub Scout Ldr, Cub Master, Comm Mem; Church, Choir Dir, Yth Ldr, Librn; Organized Halifax Area Sub Tchr Org; Amer Family Inst Gift of Time Awd.

LENZE, HERBERT BRENT, Fifth Grade Teacher; *b:* St Marys, PA; *ed:* Indiana Univ of PA (BS) Elem Ed 1967, (MS) Elem Ed 1971; *cr:* Ridgway Area Schl Dist Fifth Grd Tchr 1967-; *ai:* Band Boosters Treas; Ridgway Bsktbl Club Treas; PSEA, NEA 1967-; Ridgway Area Tchrs Assn 1967-, Treas; Ridgway Lion's Club 1971-, Treas, Lion of the Yr; St Marys Moose Club 1986-; *home:* 422 S Michael St Saint Marys PA 15857

LENZI, LINDA JEAN, Elem Tchr of Talented & Gifted; *b:* Monongahela, PA; *ed:* Univ of Steubenville (BA) Elem Ed 1970; Univ of Dayton (MS) Schl Admin 1974; OH St Validation Gifted Ed K-12; Attnd Univ of Cincinnati, Kent St Univ & Univ of Steubenville Gifted Course Work; *cr:* Indian Creek Schl Dist 5-6 Grd Tchr 1970-82, Elem Tchr of Gifted 1982-; Elizabeth Forward Schl Dist 2-5 Grd Rdng Tchr 1971-; *ai:* Gifted Ed Stud, Performing Arts Grant, Eisenhower Grant, OH Acad Competition Northeast Regnl Comms; TAG Sci Act Prgm; Co-Dir Grd 3 Sci Enrichment Prgm; TAG Parent Group; OH Valley Uniserv 1982-, Pres 1984-; Indian Creek Ed Assn 1970-, Pres 1980-84, Sec 1988-90, Neg Team 1982-; Delta Kappa Gamma 1983-, Schlsp Comm; OH Assn Gifted Children 1982-; Consortium Coord of Gifted 1993-; NEA, OEA, EOEA 1970-; Univ Women's Assoc 1994-; Who's Who of Amer Women; Assoc of Supervision and Curr Dev; Jefferson Co Democratic Party Exec Comm 1984-; OH Valley Labor Mngmt Cncl 1989-92; Natl Democratic Party 1995-; Indian Creek Labor Mgmt 1995-; Senator Campaign Comm 1995-; Co-Author 3 Jefferson Cty Schl Dist Grants 1988-89, 1993; Co-Author Material Gifted Children; Tchr Recognition Awd 1989; Venture Capital, Gftd Rsrch & Best Practices Grants; Natl Sci Assoc 1992, Natl Gftd Assoc 1995, OH Mega Conf 1994-95, OH Gftd Conf 1994-95, Martinsferry Schl Dist Inservice 1996, Jefferson Cty Ed Svc Cntr Inservice 1995-96 Co-Presenter; *home:* 2239 1/2 Cherry Ave Steubenville OH 43952

LENZI, SANDRA (HENRY), Learning Support Teacher; *b:* Sioux City, IA; *m:* Anthony J.; *ed:* IN Univ of PA (BS) Ed of Exceptional Child 1986; Post-Grad Stud Learning Disabilities Area; Credit Hrs Stu Assistance Team Work; *cr:* ARIN Intermediate Unit 28 Schl Learning Support Tchr 1986-95; Purchase Line HS learning Support Tchr 1995-; *ai:* Stu Assistance Team Mem; Sr Class Co-Adv; NEA, PSEA 1986-; ASCD
office: Purchase Line HS Rd 1 Box 374 Commodore PA 15729

LENZO, JOYCE BELT, Home Economics Teacher; *b:* Wheeling, W
Steve; *c:* Michael; *ed:* West Liberty St Coll (BA) Home Ec 1971;
Univ & Hood Coll (MS) Home Ec 1989; Health Cert In Progres
Southington Local Schls Home Ec Tchr, Dept Chr 1973-85; Frederi
Bd of Ed Home Ec Tchr, Dept Chair 1985-; *ai:* FHA Spon; NEA, M
FCTA 1985-, Bldg Rep; Am H Ec Assoc, MD H Ec Assoc 1986-;
OEA, NEOTA, TEC 1973-85, Cty Exec Bd Dist Pres, Exec Bd for St;
Delta Kappa 1993-; H Ec Comm 1973-85; Help with Needy, Homel
Regular Basis; Work on Local, St, Natl Level Pol Campaigns;
Outstanding Educator for Frederick Cty; Nom Outstndng Voc E
office: Brunswick HS 101 Cummings Dr Brunswick MD 21716*

LEOGRANDE, DENNIS MARTIN, String Instrument Teach
Paterson, NJ; *m:* Leslie Pickering; *ed:* William Paterson Coll (BA)
Ed 1968; NY Univ (MA) Music Ed 1972; 32 Addl Credit Hrs Beyon
Montclair Coll Supervisors Cert; *cr:* Pascock Hills & Pascade
7th-12 Grd String Instrument Tchr 1968-73; Ramapo & Indian
9th-12th Grd String Instrument Tchr 1973-76; Randolph Twp
7th-12th Grd String Instrument Tchr 1976-; *ai:* NJNEA, ASTA
NAMM 1994-; Books Pub; *home:* 18 Cadmus Pl Wayne NJ 07470

LEOGRANDE, VINCENT, English Teacher; *b:* Brooklyn, N
Katherine H.; *c:* Vincent Michael, Scott Joseph, Jennifer Marie, Kara
ed: SUNY at Albany (BA) Eng & Eng Ed 1968; SUNY at Stony
(MA) Hum & Lbrl Stud 1970; 90 Credits Beyond Masters; *cr:* Sa
HS-North Campus Eng Tchr 28 Yrs; Adelphi Univ Adj Prof Eng 197
Former Sr Class, Debate & Current Event Club, Poetry & Creative W
Club & Former Lit Magazine Adv; Poetry & Creative Writing Dra
Adv & Judge; Debate Coach; Chprsn of Several Comms; NYSUT
NEA 1968-; NCTE 1968-; St Louis DeMontford 1975-, Bishops A
Coord, Svc Awd; CYO 1975-, Coach Coord; Sachem Tchrs Assn,
Rep, VP, Negotiator, Textbook Curr Comms; Adelphi Univ P
Facilitator, Commentator, Guest Lecturer & Speaker, Tchr Exec C
Yrbk Dedications; Tchr of the Yr Awd; 25 Yr Awd.*

LEON, BLANCHE ALTCHILER, Retired Teacher; *b:* Bronx, N
Mark Altchiler, Robert Altchiler; *ed:* Univ of CT (BS) Sociology
New Paltz St Univ (MS) Ed 1959; 32 Addl Credits in Soc Work; 85 C
Inservice Credits in Ed; *cr:* New Rochelle Schl Dist 2nd Grd Tchr 19
Commack Schl Dist 2nd Grd Tchr 1959-61, Sub Tchr 1963-71; Mt
Schl Dist 3-4 Grd Tchr 1977-95; *ai:* Sunshine, Report Card Co
NYSUT, Mt Sinai Tchrs Assn 1977-; *home:* 119 Roe Ln Port Jefferso
11777

LEON, PAULA (HASSAY), Reading Specialist; *b:* Youngstown, O
Robert L.; *c:* Adrianne, Robert; *ed:* YSU (MS) Ed & Rdng Specialist
BS in Ed 1974; 3 Credit Hrs T-SAC Trng Drake Univ 1993; *cr:* Str
Schl System Elem Tchr 1973-78; Private Tutoring 1978-86; Southi
Schls Rdng Specialist 1986-; *ai:* Eng Festival Coord & Coach; BLAT
Mem; NEA, SEA & TARC 1986-; Womens Pharmaceutical Org
Pres, VP & Sec; Blessed Sacrament Church 1976-; Rdng Grant
Right-To-Read Awd; *home:* 3961 Welcker Dr NE Warren OH 44483*

LEONARD, ANNE MARIE, Business Teacher; *b:* New York, N
Donald F.; *c:* Suzanne, Keith; *ed:* St Univ of NY at Albany (BS) B
1967; Cntrl CT St Univ (MS) Bus Ed 1981; *cr:* Lakeland HS Bus Ed
1967-68; Windham HS Bus Ed Tchr 1968-69; Woodrow Wilson HS B
Tchr 1969-77; Parish Hill HS Bus Ed Tchr, Chprsn 1984-; *ai:* Q
Diversity Dist-Wide Comm; Curr, Instruction Comm NEASE; Sr Clas
1995; Schl Store Adv, Mgr; NEA, CEA 1984-; RDEEA 1984-, VP,
Delta Pi Epsilon; NHS, Bus Ed 1990; Windham Hills Healthcar
Liason Between Srs, Stdnts, Established Pen Pal, Visitation Prgm;
Prgm Supervise Stu Mem; Tchrs, Mentor New Tchrs; *office:* Paris
Jr-Sr HS 304 Parish Hill Rd Chaplin CT 06235*

LEONARD, BETTY LORRAINE, Primary Teacher; *b:* Woodsfield
w: Charles R. (dec); *c:* Joy Rise Gatten Cowdery, Jeffrey Nathan G
ed: OH Univ (BS) Elem Ed 1971; Post Grad Stud; *cr:* Newport
Primary Tchr 1966-; *ai:* OEA, NEA 1966-; FIEA 1966-, Bldg Rep;
710 Warren St Marietta OH 45750

LEONARD, BRUCE RAYMOND, Fifth Grade Teacher; *b:* Elizabeth
m: Phyllis Kasper; *ed:* Wagner Coll (BS) ELem Ed 1969; Seton Hall
(MA) Admin, Supervision 1974; *cr:* Schl Four 6th Grd Tchr 1970-80
Five Fourth Grd Tchr 1980-85; Schl Ten Fifth Grd Tchr 1985-; *ai:*
Mentor; Curr Comms; NEA, UCEA 1970-; LEA 1970-, Schl Rep
Yrs; Grant for Novel Stud in Lang Arts Prgm; BISED Grant for Stu
the Environment; *home:* 6 Litton Rd Flemington NJ 08822

LEONARD, CHARLES BROWN,JR., Dept of Biology Assoc Pr
Woodbury, NJ; *m:* Florence Jones; *c:* Charles B. III, Bruce J.; *ed:* R
Univ (AB) Natural Sci 1955; Univ of MD (MS) Biochemistry 1957, (
Biochemistry 1963; Diploma Bible Arlington Bapt Church Bible Inst
Cert Deaf Interpreter Prgm Western MD Coll 1983; *cr:* Univ of MD D
Schl Dept of Biochemistry Asst Prof 1963-69, Assoc Prof 1969-76
Dean Recruitment & Admissions 1975-84, Prof 1976-85, Prof &
1985-93; Gallaudet Univ Assoc Prof 1993-; *ai:* Bio Majors Acad
Departmental Rep Grant Writer Parsons Fnd, Sherman-Fairchild
Comm D Fac Grievance; Fac Mentor NASA Stdnts; Review Comm D
Govt & His Prgm; Human Anatomy & Physiology Soc 1993-; Amer
Advancement of Sci 1974-; Howard Comm Coll Bd of Trustees 1971-
The Alleluias Singing Group, Asst Dir & Singer; Nazarene Ch
Organist, Sunday Schl Tchr, Church Bd Sec 1983-93; Dictionary of
Biography 1971; Who's Who in East 1970; Amer Men & Women
1966; Christian B. & Mary F. Lindbeck Fnd Awd for Distngd Tchng
Univ of MD Bd of Regents Excl Tchng Awd; *home:* 9202 Furrow
Ellicott City MD 21042

LEONARD, FLORENCE COURTNEY, Assistant Principal; *b:* Tre
NJ; *m:* Henry L.; *c:* Guy, Carl, Celeste, Troy; *ed:* Treton St Coll (BS)
Ed 1968, (ME) Ed; Cert of Supervision; Cert of Prin, Supervisio
Harrison Elem Schl Tchr 1968-90; Parker Elem Schl Act Asst
1990-91; Jefferson Elem Schl Act Asst Prin 1991-92; Hedgepeth, Wil
MS Tchr, Disciplinarian 1993, Asst Prin 1993-; *ai:* NJPSA, NASSP
Governor's Tchr Recognition Prgm 1988-89; Tchr Contributor to Edi
Plans for Xerox Inter Dictionary 1973-; Who's Who of Amer W
1983-84.

LEONARD, FRANK D., Hawthorne Program Coord & Tchr; *b:* Bo
MA; *m:* Elizabeth A.; *c:* Kenneth, Sean, Mark; *ed:* Boston St Coll (B
1976; Grad Credit Hrs at Salem St Coll & Fitchburg St Coll; *cr:* E
Industry Mechanical Designer 1958-70; Salem HS Industrial Arts
1970-91, Hawthorne Pgm Coord 1991-; Salem St Coll Evening Au
Instr 1987-92; *ai:* hS Cncl; Ham Radio Club & Sr Show Adv; Assist
Extracurricular at HS; AFT 1970-; Ham Radio Operator 1989-;
Shore Repeator Assn 1992-; Grants Wrote for Industrial Arts, Altern
Ed & Hawthorne Pgm; *office:* Salem HS 77 Wilson Rd Salem MA 01

LEONARD, JANE ELDRIDGE, Special Education & LD Teach
Cincinnati, OH; *m:* Harry J.; *c:* Matthew A.; *ed:* Southern St Comm
(AA) Ed 1977; Morehead St Univ (BS) Home Ec 1979; Univ of D
(MS) Ed, Admin 1995; Spec Ed Cert LD BD 1986; 15 Hrs Phys Sc
OH Math & Sci; Discovery Project for Inquiry Methods; Cooper
Learning; *cr:* Southern Hills JVS Home Ec Resource Lib 1979-82; A
Cty, OH Vly Schls Spec Ed Tchr 1986-; *ai:* FLAC Corps Dir, Spon

Adv; Homecoming Dir; Tchr Inservice, Prof Dev Comm; NEA, OH sn 1986-; Sci Ed Cncl of OH 1995-; *office:* North Adams HS 355 way St Seaman OH 45679

ARD, JOAN F., English Teacher; *b:* Racine, WI; *m:* Salvatore e; *c:* Annie, Alex; *ed:* Univ of Wi (BS) Speech & Eng 1973; St Univ ny brook (MA) 1980; Oxford Univ Post Grad 6 Credits; *cr:* Girard Jr g Tchr 1974-75; Northport Eng Tchr 1975-; *ai:* Ind Film Studs Tchr; 1975-; NTCE 1990-; Pub Nonfiction Book of Essays-Tales From er Hell-My Life as a Mom; Freelance Writer for New York Times, s, Ladies Home Journal, Redbook, Parenting, Good Housekeeping &; *office:* Northport HS Elwood Rd Northport NY 11768

ARD, JULIE ANN, Physical Education Teacher; *b:* South town, RI; *ed:* Univ of RI (BS) Human Sci & Svcs & PE 1989; ence Cold Credit Hrs 1995; *cr:* North Kingstwon HS PE Tchr 1993-; st Vllybl Coach 1987-94; Head Field Hockey Coach 1989-; Jr High Coach 1990-; Frosh Co-Adv; Grad Comm; USFHA 1985-; RIFHCA Pres; NEA 1993-; RIAGWS 1995-, Sec 1995; RI Commission on n Title IX Awd; RI Field Hockey Southern Division Coach of the Yr; North Kingstown HS 150 Fairway Dr North Kingstown RI 02852

ARD, MICHAEL HEATON, English Teacher; *b:* Denver, CO; *m:* Altman Kelley; *c:* William, Anne, Katie, Kate, Abigail; *ed:* Harvard AB) Anthropology 1955; Stanford Univ (MBA) Bus Admin 1957; of So. Calif (MA) Eng 1962, (PHD) Eng 1967; *cr:* Univ of VT Instr, Prof 1964-71; Simon's Rock Eary Coll Instr 1971-73; Ethel Walker nstr 1973-; *ai:* Schl Newspaper Adv; Various Comms; NCTE 1970-; Club, Natl Audubon Soc 1985-; NDEA Flwshp Univ of VT Rsrch Natalie Galbraith Chair Hum; Book: A Critical Edition of Thomas ood's The Wise Woman of Hogsden; Articles Pub; *office:* Ethel r Schl 230 Bushy Hill Rd Simsbury CT 06070*

ARD, RICHARD, English Teacher; *b:* Biarritz, France; *ed:* Iona BA) Eng 1967; Fordham Univ (MA) Eng & Tchng 1968; Master +60 s; *cr:* Eastchester HS Eng Tchr 1968-72; Gorton HS Eng Tchr 1972-; Magazine Adv 20 Yrs; AFT 1968-; NYSUT 1968-; ETA 1972-; Delta Pi; Book: December; Tchr of Yr 1981 & 1990; *office:* ester HS 2 Stewart Pl Yonkers NY 10707

ARD, ROBERT E., Mathematics Teacher; *b:* Charleroi, PA; *m:* Celaschi; *c:* Amy, Brian, Michael; *ed:* CA Univ of PA (BS) Math Ed Western MD Coll (MED) Math Ed 1981; 30 Grad Credits; *cr:* omery Cty Pub Schls Math Tchr 1973-; Montgomery Coll Adj Prof *ai:* Math Team Coach; NEA 1973-; MSTA 1973-; MCEA 1973-; TA & MCMTA 1993-; Gymnastics Coach of the Yr 1979; *office:* rd Montgomery HS 250 Richard Montgomery Dr Rockville MD

ARD, SHARILYN ANNE, Third Grade Teacher; *b:* Oak Hill, OH; bert Edward; *c:* Meghan A., Alison N, Kirstin P.; *ed:* Rio Grande Coll Elem Ed 1986; *cr:* Wilton Elem Sci Tchr 1987-88; Allensville Elem Grd Sci & Math Tchr 1988-92; Hamden Elem Third Grd Tchr 1992-; fety Patrol Adv Allensville Elem; Right-to-Read Comm; NEA 1987-; 1987-, Bldg Rep; Kermis Jr Womens Club 1987-, Sec; Southern OH inigrant 1992 & 1995; *office:* Hamden Elem Church St Hamden OH

ARD, STANLEY S., Adjunct Prof of Percussion; *b:* Philadelphia, : Margaret Holman; *c:* Mark, Steven; *ed:* Eastman Schl of Music Performance 1954; Carnegie-Mellon Univ Grad Stud; *cr:* Pittsburgh hony Orch Prin Trumpet 1956-94; Carnegie-Mellon Univ Instr of ssion 1958-78; Duquesne Univ Prof of Percussion 1989-; *ai:* Ludwig Pub Co Percussion Ed; Amer Fed of Musicians 1948-; Percussive Soc 1963-; Pittsburgh Symphony Soloist for 2 World Premiers ani Concertos; Music Pub; Book: Pedal Technique for the Timpani; Duquesne Univ Pittsburgh PA 15282

ARD, VIOLET ELVA, 5th Grade Teacher; *b:* Taunton, MA; *ed:* chr Coll of Providence (BSEd) Ed 1967; Lesley Coll ME) 1992; Post Couses Bridgewater St Coll; Auna Maria Coll, U MA, RI Coll, urg St Coll; *cr:* Taunton Pub Lib Childrens Librn, Lib Asst 1956-62; Dame Schl Grd 4 Tchr 1962-66; Inst for Juvenile Guid Tchr, Head 966-69; St Clare Acad Jr HS Tchr 1969; Martin Schl 4-6 Grd Tchr *ai:* Negotiating Team-NAFT 1978-83, 1994-95; Bldg Rep 1973-74; MTA, NATA 1969-, Local Past Pres 1980-81; AFT, NAFT Past Pres cal 1982-83; Phi Delta Kappa 1996; AAUW, MSPCA, Friends of als, PETA 1970-; MA Horticultural Soc 1955-; MA Natl Audubon Old Colony Historical Soc 1990-; Museum of Fine Arts 1980-; Martin Schl 9 Landry Ave North Attlebo MA 02760*

ARDI, ANTHONY SALVATORE, Prof of Music & Coordinator; *b:* use, NY; *m:* Andrea G. Patrick; *c:* Christopher, Paula; *ed:* stown St Univ (BM) Music Ed 1971, (MM) Music Ed 1979; *cr:* Local Schls Instrumental Music Tchr 1971-78; Canfield Local Instrumental Music Tchr 1978-79; Youngstown St Univ Prof of , Coord of Jazz Stud, Inst of String Bass 1979-; *ai:* Jazz Soc Fac Adv; rous Comms; NEA, OMEA 1971-; Intnl Assn of Jazz Edctr 1976-, OH Unit; Jazz Edctr of Yr 1986; Distngd Prof 1991; *office:* stown St Univ 410 Wick Ave Youngstown OH 44555

ARDI, SUSAN CINOTTI, Kindergarten Teacher; *b:* Buffalo, NY; squale Jr.; *c:* Jennifer; *ed:* Buffalo St Coll (BS) Elem Ed 1973; Univ (MS) Elem Ed & Rdng 1977; 6 Credit Hrs Above Masters; *cr:* Dixie chls Kndgtn Tchr 1973-77; Cheektowago Cntrl Schls Rdng Specialist 86, Pre 1st & 3rd Grd Tchr 1986-90, Kndgtn Tchr 1990-; *ai:* Kndgtn Ldr; Dist Tech Planning Comm; Cheektowago Cntrl Tchrs Assn Exec Bd Rep; Phi Delta Kappan 1995-; Juvenile Diabetes Assn Bd Mem, Svc Awd; *office:* Cheektowage Cntrl Schls 3600 Union Rd towaga NY 14225

ARDI, THERESA M., High School Soc Stud Teacher; *b:* Auburn, *d:* Le Moyne Coll (BA) His 1987; Syracuse Univ (MS) Soc Stud Ed *cr:* West Genesee HS Soc Stud Tchr 1987-88; Weedsport Jr Sr HS tud Tchr 1988-; *ai:* JV Field Hockey & Modified Vllybl Coach; Sr Yrbk & Model Senate Adv; Big Brothers Big Sisters Bd of Dir ; Weedsport Free Lib Bd of Dir 1994-; *office:* Weedsport Cntrl Schl E Brutus St Weedsport NY 13166

ARDO, JENNIE (WALSH), 1st Grade Teacher; *b:* Catskill, NY; *m:* *c:* Kevin, Chad; *ed:* State Univ at Oneonta (BS) Ed 1972; Grad Work onta, New Paltz, Russel Sage Coll 33 Hrs in Ed; *cr:* Coxsackie Elem st Grd Tchr 1972-; *ai:* CATA 1972-; Hose Co #3 Ladies Auxiliary

ARDO, KRISTINE K., English Teacher; *b:* Sewickley, PA; *c:* y George III; *ed:* Slippery Rock St Coll (BS) Scndry Eng 1967; Univ tsburgh (MED) Lang Arts 1974; *cr:* Aliquippa Schl Dist Eng Tchr Fox Chapel Schl Dist Rdng Tchr 1967-68; Ctr Area Schl Dist Eng 968-69; Ambridge Area Schl Dist Eng Tchr 1969-; *ai:* PSEA & NEA ; *office:* Ambridge Area HS 909 Duss Ave Ambridge PA 15003*

NE, CLAUDIA A., Math Teacher; *b:* Boston, MA; *m:* Henry eguazza; *c:* Kristina Scuoteguazza, Nicole Scuoteguazza; *ed:* anuel Coll (BA) Math 1973; Clarkson Coll of Tech (MS) Math 19755; dl Hrs; *cr:* Hingham HS Math Tchr 1975-; *ai:* NCTM, NEA, MTA, 1975-; Blue Hill Montessori Bd 1991-94, Chm, Pres; Prescott Schl 1995-; Thesis Pub; *office:* Hingham Sr HS 41 Pleasant St Hingham 2043*

LEONE, MICHELE CASTALDO, Math Teacher & Dept Chprsn; *b:* Mineola, NY; *m:* James Blaise; *ed:* Hofstra Univ (BA) Math & Scndry Ed 1978, (MA) Math & Scndry Ed 1982; AB Inst Tchrs of AP Calculus; *cr:* Island Trees HS Summer Schl Asst Tchr 1976; Hempstead HS Asst Tchr 1977; Jerusalem Ave Jr HS Math Stu Tchr 1978; St Dominic HS Math Tchr & Chprsn 1978-, Comp Rm Suprvr 1987-; Nassau Comm Coll Adj Prof Math 1982-; *ai:* Math League Asst Adv; Comp Club; Math Pvt Tutor; NYS Assn of Math Tchrs 1980-; NCTM 1980-; Nassau Cty Math Tchrs Assn 1980-; ASCD 1980-; Kappa Mu Epsilon Thesis; Phi Theta Kappa; Arnold Naiman Awd; Matye Schlsp; *office:* Saint Dominic HS 110 Anstice St Oyster Bay NY 11771

LEONE, MORRIS ANTHONY, Language Arts Teacher; *b:* Lodi, NJ; *ed:* Jersey City St Coll (BA) Eng 1970; Kean Coll of NJ (MA) Hum 1978, (MA) Cnslr Ed 1991; Stud Toward CAC Rutgers Univ, John E. Runnels Hosp; *cr:* Joseph E. Soehl MS Eng Tchr 1970-85; Linden HS Eng Tchr 1985-88; Linden Voc-Tech Substance Awareness Coord 1988-91; Myles J. Mc MAnus MS Lang Arts Tchr 1991-; *ai:* Stu Cncl Adv; PTA; Comm Eighth Grd Grad Dinner Dance; Mentor Incoming Stdnts; Linden Ed Assoc 1970-, Bldg Rep 1995-; NJEA, NEA 1970-; Linden Jaycees 1978-82, Pres; Linden Bicentiennial Comm 1975-76, Chm; Linden Holloween Parade Comm 1974-77, Judge; NJ Cncl Tchrs of Eng 1975-; Recorded Record 1974; 1976 Outstdng Ldrs in El, Sec Ed; Presented Original Poetry on Radio Station 1972; *office:* Myles J. Mc Manus MS 300 Edgewood Rd Linden NJ 07036*

LEONE, PETER B., HS Social Studies Teacher; *b:* Rochester, NY; *m:* Cristine R. Rankin; *c:* Kellen, Lauren; *ed:* SUNY at Geneseo (BA) His 1988; SUNY at Brockport (MA) US His 1995; *cr:* Avon Cntrl Schl Soc Stud Tchr 1990-; *ai:* Girls Var Bsktbl Coach; PTA Fac Rep; NEA 1990-; 1995 Awd Excl in Scndry Schl Tchng Presented by Univ of Rochester; *home:* 274 River St Avon NY 14414

LEONE, SANDRA ELAINE, Business & Comp Ed Teacher; *b:* Weston, WV; *m:* Lewis N.; *c:* Benjamin; *ed:* Fairmont St Coll (BA) Bus Ed, 7-12 1971; Univ of Dayton (MS) Guidance Tchr 1981; Youngstown ST, Jefferson Tech Coll Credit Hrs Addl Knowledge in Tchng Field; Ashland Coll 1995; *cr:* WV Career Coll Bus Tchr 1972; Mingo HS Bus Tchr 1972-91; Indian Creek HS Bus Tchr 1992-; *ai:* NEA, OEA, ICEA 1972-; *office:* Indian Creek HS 200 Park Dr Wintersville OH 43952

LEONG, LAWRENCE, Social Studies Teacher; *b:* Singapore, Singapore; *m:* Lee L.; *c:* Kevin C., Davin M.; *ed:* Shelton Coll (BA) Philosophy 1966; Beaver Coll (MA) Ed 1974; *cr:* Lower Moreland HS Soc Stud Tchr 1968-; *ai:* Yrbk, World Affairs Cncl, Soph Class Adv; NEA 1968-; World Affairs Cncl of Philadelphia Bd of Dir 1975-76; Natl Sci Fnd Flwshp 1969-; *office:* Lower Moreland HS 555 Red Lion Rd Huntingdon Valley PA 19006

LEOPOLD, EUNICE ZIPPERMANN, Fine Arts Dept Chm, Choral Dir; *b:* Washington, DC; *m:* Martin L.; *c:* Susan, Steven, Judy; *ed:* Univ of MD at Coll Park (BS) Music Ed 1970; 40 Addl Credit Hrs; Gen Stud in Advanced Choral Conducting, Rdng, Spec Ed, Theater Mechanics, Choreography, Choral Lit, Group Dynamics; *cr:* Belt Jr HS Music Tchr 1970-71; Esperanza MS Music Tchr 1971-73; Leonardtown HS Choral Dir, Fine Arts Dept Chm 1984-; *ai:* Musical Dir; Curr, Final Exam Comms; Dir Vocal Jazz Ensemble, Mens Barbershop; Head of Stage & Lightening Crew; Auditorium Mgr; NEA, EASMC 1984-; MMEA 1984-, Southern Region Pres; Chm All-St T-Shirt Sales; MCEA 1984-, Chm Choral Festival, Chm Music Evaluation Comm; SMMC 1984-, Pres; ACDA 1990-, Treas; MD St Music Awd of Excl for Scndry Vocal Music; *office:* Leonardtown HS Rt 5 Box 49-3 Leonardtown MD 20650*

LEPAIN, CHERYL TURTURRO, Social Studies Depart Chair; *b:* Worcester, MA; *m:* Mark H.; *c:* Joshua, Amanda; *ed:* Bridgewater St Coll (BA) His 1970; Johns Hopkins Univ (MLA) Psych 1978; AP Psych; Analytical Writing Strategies 3 Credits; Substance Abuse Prevention 3 Credits; *cr:* Martin Spaulding HS Soc Stud Tchr 1970-71; St Joseph's Schl Soc Stud Tchr 1973; Notre Dame Prep Schl Soc Stud Tchr 1973-75; St Peter-Marian Cath HS Soc Stud Dept Chair, Tchr 1996; *ai:* SADD Adv; Post Prom Celebration Coord; APA 1992-; *office:* St Peter-Marian Cath HS 781 Grove St Worcester MA 01605*

LEPELLEY, TERESE LHOTA, Fourth Grade Teacher; *b:* Canton, OH; *m:* David Patrick; *c:* Emmalee Abigail, Mackenzie Joy; *ed:* Kent St Univ (BE) Elem Ed 1985 (MA) Rdng Specialization 1993; Conflict Mediation; Parenting for Ed; *cr:* Garfield Hts Bd of Ed Sub Tchr 1986-87; William Foster Elem Schl 3rd Grd Tchr 1987-88, 4th Grd Tchr 1988-; *ai:* Grd Level Chm; Safety Patrol Dir; IM Coord; Discipline Comm; Intervention Assistance Team; NEA, OH Ed Assn, Northeastern OH Ed Assn, Garfield Hghts Tchr Assn 1987-; *office:* William Foster Elem Schl 12801 Bangor Ave Garfield Hgts OH 44125*

LEPINE, MAURICE JOSEPH, Technology Education Teacher; *b:* Cazenovia, NY; *ed:* Oswego St Univ (BS) Indut Arts Ed 1984, (MS) Tech Ed 1989; *cr:* Whitesboro Jr HS Tech Tchr 1985-86; Theodore Durgee Jr HS Tech Tchr 1987-; *ai:* Yth Camp Prgm Dir Oswegatchie Camp; Coach Soccer, Bsbl, Track, Field, Bsktbl; Sci Olympiad Adv, Coach; Mem Baldwinsville Tech Ed Task Force; CNYTEA 1987-, Pres, VP, Outstdng Prgm 1994; NYSTEA, ITEA 1987-; NEA 1986-; Tech Stud Assn, Promotion Comm Oswegatchie Camp 1986-; Outstdng Tchr Awd Tech Club of Syracuse 1993-94; Tech Prgm of Yr CNYTEA 1994; Outstdng Adv of Yr NYS TSA 1995; Appreciation of Outstdng Svc NYS FFA; *office:* Theodore Durgee Jr HS 29 E Oneida St Baldwinsville NY 13027

LEPLEY, BONNIE ELIZABETH (RAPP), English Teacher; *b:* Reading, PA; *m:* James Richard Jr.; *c:* Amy, Megan, Jessica; *ed:* Susquehanna Univ (BA) Eng 1971; Attnd Bloomsburg Univ; *cr:* S. Williamsport Area Eng Tchr 1971-; *ai:* Dept Chm; Mentor; Pep Club Adv; SWAEA, PSEA, NEA 1971-; NCTE 1992-; Mazeppa Union Church 1984-, Youth Choir Dir; Sigma Kappa; *office:* South Williamsport Jr / Sr HS 700 Percy St Williamsport PA 17701

LEPORATI, DEBRA ANN, English Teacher; *ed:* SUNY at Oneonta (BS) Elem, Early Scndry Eng Ed 1985; SUNY at New Paltz (MS) Scndry Eng Ed 1988; *cr:* Warwick Vly MS 7-8 Grd Eng Tchr 1985-; *ai:* Club Adv Comm Environmentalists Org; AFT, NYSUT, WVTA, WV MS PTA 1985-; NY St Eng Cncl Edctr of Excl Awd; *office:* Warwick Valley MS PO Box 595 Warwick NY 10990*

LE PORE, MARY LUCILLE, Primary Teacher; *b:* Canton, OH; *ed:* St John Coll (BSE) Ed 1957; Marquette Univ (MED) Ed 1967; Post Grad Stud 15+ Credit Hrs; CEU for Participating in Wkshps to Up-Date Tchng Strategies; *cr:* Gesu Schl Primary Tchr 1949-53; St Stephen Demonstration Tchr for St John Coll Ed Dept 1953-55, 1960-63; Cath Univ of Amer Demonstration Tchr 1955-60, 1963-66; St Peter Primary Tchr 1979-94; *ai:* 17 Yrs Childrens Xmas Pageants Composed & Directed; Mission Coord to Aide the Poor; NCEA 1957-; NDEA 1991-; Numerous Articles Pub; Assisted in Revision of Primary Rel & Math Books; Presented Wkshps in Poetry, Art & Use of Functional Materials for Primary Tchrs.

LEPRE, ANTHONY, Professor of Mathematics; *b:* Morristown, NJ; *m:* Joyce Ann Sharo; *c:* David Anthony; *ed:* Fairleigh Dickinson Univ (BS) Math 1968; Drexel Univ (MS) 1970; Attnd Kutztown Univ; *cr:* Lehigh Carbon Comm Coll Math Instr 1970-76; Lehigh Carbon Comm Coll Asst Math Prof 1977-82; Lehigh Carbon Comm Coll Assoc Math Prof 1983-86; Lehigh Carbon comm Coll Math Prof 1987-; *ai:* Acad Standards, Basic Skills Comm; Act 101 Adv Bd; NEA, PSEA, LCCCEA 1972-; PSMATYC 1970-, Chprsn, Curr Comm; AMATYC 1991-; Lehigh Cty Authority Comm Adv Bd 1992-; George Elison Fac Awd 1991; Act 101 Service Awd 1992; Title III Grant, Educl Uses of Tech 1995-; *home:* 3911 Crestwood Dr Schnecksville PA 18078

LEPROHON, JOSEPH ARTHUR, Science Teacher; *b:* Biddeford, ME; *c:* David, Daniel, Jennifer, Matthew; *ed:* Suffolk Univ (BS) Bio & Chem 1969, (MA) Natural Sci 1972; Univ of MA at Lowell (MED) Admin & Supervision 1975; SEA 6 Cr Hrs; NSF New England Aquarium 12 Hrs & Terc Summer of 1995 Envir Sci 5 Hrs; *cr:* USFDA Asst Chemist 1962-66; Boston Latin Schl Sci Tchr 1970-81; Chelmsford HS Sci Tchr 1982-83; Tewksbury Memrl HS Sci Tchr 1983-; *ai:* Envirothon; Curr Comm; NSTA 1971-; MME & TTA 1983-; MAST 1985-; Middlesex Comm Coll 1980-, Night Schl Instr; Kelp Inc 1981-, VP & Treas; Biddeford HS Alumni Best Stu Awd Class of 1958; NSF Microbio 1972 Boston; Cruise Book at Sea Summer of 84 Newsletter Pub; *office:* Tewksbury Memorial HS 320 Pleasant St Tewksbury MA 01876*

LEPSCH, GEORGE W., Band Director & Music Coord; *b:* Mc Keesport, PA; *m:* Nancy Drabile; *ed:* Duquesen Univ (BS) Music Ed 1978, (MM) Music Performance 1986; *cr:* Mc Keesport Area Schl Dist Jr HS Orch, Elem Strings Tchr 1979-82; Serra Cath HS Music Dir 1983-86; East Allegheny Schl Dist Band Dir 1986-87; Serra Cath HS Music Dir 1987-90; Mc Keesport Area Schl Dist Band Dir, Music coord, MS Orch Tchr 1990-; *ai:* Marching, Pep Bands; Stage Adv; NEA, PSEA, MENC, PMEA 1979-; Natl Band Assn 1995-; Band PFCJ Class A Champion 1988-90, Band PFCJ Class AAA Champion 1992, TOB Chptr 8, Group 3 Champion 1994; *office:* Mc Keesport Area HS 1960 Eden Park Blvd Mc Keesport PA 15132

LERCH, ROCHELLE MOSAK, Elementary Teacher; *b:* Poking, Germany; *m:* Joseph B.; *c:* Jordan, Noah; *ed:* Brooklyn Coll (BA) Eng, Ed 1967; Kean Coll Schl Psych; *cr:* Elem Schl K-8 Grds Tchr 28 Yrs; *ai:* BSA Ldr; Bnai Brith; Vol Sr Citizens; Natl Cncl Jewish Hadassah Women; NEA, UFT 1967-; Jaycee-ettes 1967-71; *office:* Oak Ridge Heights Elem Sch 21 320 Inman Ave Colonia NJ 07067

LEREW, JASON D., Instrumental Music Teacher; *b:* Carlisle, PA; *m:* Christine Franconi; *ed:* West Chester Univ of PA (BS) Music Ed 1990; *cr:* Anne Arundel Cty Schl Dist Music Tchr 1990-91; Daniel Boone Schl Dist Instrumental Music Tchr 1991; Parkland Schl Dist Instrumental Music Tchr 1991-; *ai:* Marching, Jazz Band Dir; NEA, PA Music Edctrs Assn 1991-; Amer Fed of Musicians 1992-; Marine Band of Allentown 1992-, Clarinetist; Pi Kappa Lambda; *office:* Parkland HS 2675 PA Rt 309 Orefield PA 18069

LERI, RONALD LAWRENCE, Eng, Soc Stud & Jrnlsm Teacher; *b:* New York, NY; *m:* Patricia A. Hochswender; *c:* Alessandra C., Matthew D.; *ed:* NY Univ Washington Square Coll (BA) His 1969; NY Univ Grad Schl of Arts & Scis (MA) His 1971; 90 Addl Hrs His, Math Long Island Univ; *cr:* New York City Pub Schls Common Branches Tchr 1970-85; Greenville Cntrl Schl 6th Grd Tchr 1985-88; Windham-Ashland-Jewett Cntrl Schl Jr Sr HS Eng, Soc Stud, Jrnlsm Tchr 1988-; *ai:* Stu Cncl, Stu Newspaper Fac Adv; NHS Comm; NYSUT 1970-, Rep to Del; WAJ Tchrs Assn, Assembly 1975, Negotiator 1988; Town of Lexington 1990-92, Chm Planning Bd; Town of Windham 1987-88, Co-Chair Comm Playground Comm; Greene Room Players 1994-, Grant Writer Theatre Group; Articles Pub; *home:* PO Box 778 Hunter NY 12442*

LERNER, LOIS E. (LABOWITZ), Spanish Teacher; *b:* Brooklyn, NY; *m:* Richard; *c:* Jennifer, Alan, Joseph; *ed:* SUNY at Albany (BA) Span 1971; Attnd SUC at Geneseo; *cr:* Mont Pleasant HS Span, Fr Tchr 1972; ISD 34 Span Tchr 1972-74; Honeoye Cntrl HS Span, Fr Tchr 1975-78; ISD 34 Span Tchr 1982-85; Paulo ISD Span Tchr 1985-; *ai:* Choreographer Theatre Productions; UFT, NYSAFLT 1972-; AATSP 1989-; Curr Dev F L Dist 31; *office:* Paulo Intermediate Schl 455 Huguenot Ave Staten Island NY 10312

LEROUX, LYNNE ANNE SPELLMAN, First Grade Teacher; *b:* Washington, DC; *m:* Wayne Lawrence; *c:* Michael E., Kevin L.; *ed:* Univ of MD (BS) Elem Ed 1978; Cath Univ 6 Credit Hrs; Loyola Univ 6 Credit Hrs; *cr:* St. Peter's Fourth Grd Tchr 1983-88, First Grd Tchr 1988-; *ai:* Cub Scout Den Ldr; Steering Comm for Re-Accreditidation Process; NCEA 1983-; Tchr of the Week 1995 by Radio Zone; *office:* St Peter's Schl 2900 Sandy Spring Rd Olney MD 20832

LEROY, PAUL G., Math & English Teacher; *ed:* Vanderbilt Univ (BA) Eng Lit 1973; Johns Hopkins Univ (MLA) Lbrl Arts 1982; 6 Credit Hrs Jesus Coll & Cambridge Coll; 12 Credit Hrs Towson St Univ; 6 Credit Hrs Loyola Coll; *cr:* Sparrows Point HS Tchr 1976-; *ai:* Newspaper & Morning Announcements Adv; Schlrshp, NHS & 4 Period Lang Comms; SLOA 1986-; HARSOA 1991-, Interpreter; *office:* Sparrows Point HS 7400 N Point Rd Baltimore MD 21219*

LESAGE, PAUL EDWARD, Assoc Prof of Journalism & Lit; *b:* North Adams, MA; *m:* Sharon A.; *c:* Paul, Shauna, Chelsea, Dylan; *ed:* Norwich Univ (BA) Eng 1969; ID St Univ (MA) Eng 1971; Univ of MA at Amherst (PHD) Comm 1990; *cr:* ID St Univ Tchng Asst 1969-71; Southern UT St Univ Instr 1973-74; Berkshire Comm Coll Visiting Prof Adj 1993-; North Adams St Coll Assoc Prof 1981-; *ai:* Stu Newspaper Adv 1981-; Ath Cncl Chprsn, Who's Who Selection, Acad Appeals, Fac Selection Jrnlsm Chprsn Comms; Coll Media Adv 1989-; New England Collegiate Newspaper Assn 1986-, Past Adv; Capt Infantry US Army Reserve Ret 1985; Fac Incentive Awd Grant 1987; Eng, Comm Excl Acad Advising Awd 1990; *office:* North Adams St Coll 375 Church St North Adams MA 01247

LESERVIGET, ELIZABETH ANNE, French Teacher; *b:* New York City, NY; *ed:* Univ of WI (BA) Fr 1964; Hofstra Univ (MS) Fr, Sec Ed 1969; Univ of Caen Diploma Fr 1965; 10 Hrs Fr New York Univ 1986; *cr:* Berlitz Schl of Lang Tchr, Translator 1966-68; Gessler Publishing co Educl Dir, Ed 1984-86; Bronx HS of Sci Fr Tchr 1986-87; La Petuk Ecole Francaise Founder, Dir, Tchr 1987-90; Uniondale Pub Schl Fr Tchr 1971-84; L'Institution Ste Jeanned Arc Eng Tchr 1990-92; Margaretville Cntrl Schl Fr Tchr 1993-; *ai:* Sponsorship Fr Club, Stdnts to France; Private, Group Lessons; Margaretville Tchrs Assn 1993-; NEH, O'Connor Grants; Tchrs on Vol Svc Jerusalem Israel 1981; Publications: NE Conf Newsletter, Hispania Software Journal, Lang Assn Bulletin, NYS Lecturer, Mass Assn Frgn Lang Tchrs Conf; *home:* 10 Four Wheel Dr Willow NY 12495*

LESH, BRUCE ALLYN, Social Studies & History Tchr; *m:* Christine Louise Cassidy; *ed:* Salisbury St Univ (BA) His & Pol Sci 1992; Villanova Univ (MA) US His 1994; 9 Credit Hrs Post Masters in Ed; 3 Credit Towards PHD in Soc Stud Ed; *cr:* Milford Mill Acad His Tchr 1993-; *ai:* Class of 1997 Spon; Model Senate Schl Coord; Site-Based Mgmt Team; Intl Baccalaureate Tchr; Org of Amer Historians, Natl Cncl His Ed 1995-; MD Cncl for Soc Stud; NCSS; Participant Baltimore Cty Curr Inst; *office:* Milford Mill Acad 3800 Washington Ave Baltimore MD 21244*

LESH, MARY HAGSTROM, Third Grade Teacher; *c:* Lorri McNaughton, Scott, Angela Sneath, Heather Ulsh; *ed:* Penn St Univ (BA) Elem Ed 1977; Millersville Univ (MS) Elem Ed 1992; Math Their Way; *cr:* Susquenita Elem Schl 3rd Grd Tchr 1978-; *ai:* Soc & Earth Day Comms; Christmas Parent Vol Breakfast Chair; SEA, NEA 1977-; NB Civic Club 1984-, VP 1996, Pres 1994-95; Cty VP Civic Club, VP; Incarnation United Church Christ 1959-, 175th Anniversary Chprsn 1995; *office:* Susquenita Elem Schl 1725 Schoolhouse Rd Duncannon PA 17020

LESHEFSKY, AMY, Mathematics Teacher; *b:* Brooklyn, NY; *c:* Jay, Lynne Mitchell; *ed:* Brooklyn Coll (BS) Math Ed 1961; Adelphi Univ (MS) Math Ed 1978; *cr:* Winthrop JHS Math Tchr 1961-63; Springfield Gardens JHS Permanent Sub Tchr 1969; Valley Stream South HS Math Tchr 1970-;

ai: Math Hnr Soc Adv; Jr HS Math, Math Counts Adv, Coach; Nassau Cty Math Tchrs Assn 1994-; AMTNYS 1993, 1995; Assn Math Tchrs NY St; *office:* Valley Stream South Jr Sr HS 150 Jedwood Pl Valley Stream NY 11582*

LESHER, HUBERTA SHANHOLTZ, Retired Elem Tchr; *b:* Lemoyne, PA; *m:* James Edward; *ed:* Shippensburg St Coll (BS) ELem Ed 1957, (MS) Elem Ed 1966; *cr:* Silver Spring Elem Schl 4th Grd Tchr 1957-88; *ai:* NEA 1957-88; PSEA; *home:* 519 E Orange St Shippensburg PA 17257

LESHINSKI, TRINA VERNON, Sixth Grade Science Teacher; *b:* Fountain Springs, PA; *m:* John F. Sr.; *c:* John, Rusty, Michael; *ed:* Bloomsburg Univ (BS) Elem Ed 1973; Masters Equivalency 1985; *cr:* Mount Carmel Area Schl Dist 6th Grd Tchr 1974-; *ai:* Children for Environment Adv; PSEA 1973-; NEA; Northumberland Cty Environmental Tchr of Yr 1995; *home:* 6 Woodland Dr Mount Carmel PA 17851

LESHNOFF, SUSAN K., Art Teacher; *b:* Glen Ridge, NJ; *m:* Stephen; *c:* Jonathan, Jessica; *ed:* U of PA (BA) Art, His Tchr 1967; Phila Coll of Art (MA) Art Ed, Painting 1972; Columiba U (MED) Art Ed 1987, (EDD) Art Ed 1988; *cr:* The Baldwin Schl K-6, 7-9 Grd Art Tchr 1968-72; Essex Cty Coll Part-time Art Instr 1982-87; Montclair St Univ Ard Ed Prog Coord 1990-93; East Orange HS Art Tchr 1993-; *ai:* Natl Art Hnr Soc; ASCD 1992-; NEA, NJEA 1993-; Art Edctrs of NJ 1988-; NAEA 1987-; Phi Delta Kappa 1994-; Pub Articles; NE US Coord Crayola Team-Makers Art Ed Prgm for Children K-6 1993-94; Ed Assn Pride in Pub Ed Awd 1995; *office:* East Orange HS 34 N Walnut St East Orange NJ 07017*

LESHOCK, CAROL SARGENT, Learning Support Teacher; *b:* New Kensington, PA; *m:* Dennis; *c:* Leigh Ann, Christopher; *ed:* Slippery Rock St Coll (MED) Spec Ed Phys Handicapped, Elem Ed 1978; *cr:* Hempfied Area Schl Dist 7-9 Grd EMR, Second, Third Grd, Instrl Support, K-5 Grd Learning Support Tchr 1979-; *ai:* NEA, PSEA, Hempfield Area Ed Assn 1979-; Assistantship Slippery Rock St Coll Sp Ed Dept; *office:* Bovard Elem Schl RD 12 Box 75 Greensburg PA 15601*

LESHOR, ALAN WAYNE, Mathematics Teacher; *b:* Monongahela, PA; *m:* Lauren Jane Stockley; *c:* Scott, Brad; *ed:* Waynesburg Coll (BS) Math 1966; California Univ of PA (ME) Math 1973; *cr:* Monessen HS Math Tchr 1966-68; Mc Guffey HS Math Tchr 1968-; *ai:* NEA, PSEA 1966-; Mc Guffey EA 1968-; *office:* Mc Guffey H S 86 Mc Guffey Dr Claysville PA 15323

LESKO, VALERIE JURAN, Associate Professor of Nursing; *b:* Pittsburgh, PA; *m:* George M. Jr; *c:* Amanda, Monica; *ed:* LaRoche Coll (BSN) Nursing 1983, (MSN) Nursing 1989; Lilian S. Kaufmann Schl of Nursing Montefiore Hospital Nursing Diploma 1970; Univ of Pittsburgh 15 Post Grad Credits; *cr:* OH Valley Gen Hospital Critical Care Staff Nurse 1970-, Nursing Instr 1983-89; CCBC Assoc Prof of Nursing 1989-; *ai:* Phi Theta Kappa, Beta Alpha Upsilon Chapter Adv; Evaluation of Total Prgm (Nursing) Chprsn; PSEA, NEA 1989-; NLN, PLN 1991-, Nominating Chprsn Area 6; AACN 1986-; Sigma Theta Tau 1983-, Recording Sec; CCRN Cert; Whos Who in Amer Nursing, Amer Hlth Profs; *office:* Comm Coll Of Beaver County 1 Campus Dr Monaca PA 15061*

LESKOSKE, JOSEPH ANTHONY, Science Teacher; *b:* Syracuse, NY; *m:* Kathleen; *ed:* Northern MI Univ (BS) HPER 1971; SD St Univ (MS) HPER 1972; *cr:* Lyncourt Schl Tchr 1972-; *ai:* Audio Visual Coord; Sci Fair; Inclusion; AFT, NEA 1972-; STANYS 1980-; Tchr of Yr by Syracuse Univ 1994; *office:* Lyncourt Schl 2709 Court St Syracuse NY 13208

LESKOVICS, JOSEPH W., 8th Grade Mathematics Teacher; *b:* Paterson, NJ; *ed:* Paterson St Coll (BA) Elem 1964; William Paterson Coll (MA) Stu Prsnl Svcs 1978; *cr:* School #12 5th, 6th & 8th Grd Tchrs 1964-77; Schl #27 6th & 8th Grd Tchr 1978-; *ai:* Little League Coach 1977-79; NEA, NJEA, PEA, PCEA 1964-; Recreation Advy Cncl 1974-75; Vol Probation Cnslr 1978-85, Passaic Cty Cnslr of Yr 1981; Disabld Amer Vet US Army 1964-66; Gov's Tchr Rec Aw 1994; *office:* Public Schl 27 250 Richmond Ave Paterson NJ 07502*

LESKUSKY, VINCENT EDWARD, English Teacher; *b:* Pottstown, PA; *ed:* Ursinus Coll (BA) Eng 1990; MEQ Kutztown Univ Scndry Ed; *cr:* Pottstown Mercury News Ed 1990-91; Jimmy Boot Inc Comptroller 1991-92; Upper Perkiomen HS Eng Tchr 1992-; *ai:* Cross Cnty, Girls Track, Asst Wrestling Coach; NEA, PSEA, UPEA 1992-; Natl Fac 1994-; Trout Unlimited 1990-; Nature Conservancy 1991-; Natl Fac Hum Flwshp; *office:* Upper Perkiomen HS 2 Walt Rd Pennsburg PA 18073

LESLEY, MELLINEE K., Adjunct Professor; *b:* Fresno, CA; *m:* Ron Lile; *ed:* Univ of IA (BA) Eng 1988; NM St (MA) Eng 1990; Doctoral Candidate Univ of PA; *cr:* NM St Univ Tchng Asst 1988-90; El Paso Comm Coll & UTEP Lecturer 1990-93; Loretto Acad Tchr 1991-93; Philadelphia Coll of Textiles Adj Prof 1993-94; Univ of Penn Adj Prof 1995-; *ai:* TCTE 1991-; IRA 1996; AERA 1996; NMSU Tchng Assistantship; Univ of PA Rsrch Assistantship; *office:* Univ of PA 3700 Walnut Philadelphia PA 19104

LESLIE, GEORGE JEROME, Professor of Biology; *b:* Worcester, MA; *m:* Dorothy Early; *c:* Elizabeth, Jerome; *ed:* Coll of Holy Cross (AB) Bio 1968; Univ of Detroit (MS) Bio 1970; Westfield St Coll (MED) Ed 1979; Univ of MA at Amherst (EDD) Ed 1987; Zoology 12 Credit Hrs; *cr:* Springfield Tech Comm Coll Bio Dept Prof 1971-; *ai:* Bio Dept Curr Comm Chair; Founder-Dir STCC Annual Duffers Open Golf Tournment; NEA 1980-; MA Tchrs Assn 1980-, Faculty Rep; West Springfield Soccor Coach; Parent Comm of Pioneer Valley Aquatic Club 1985; Pres Fac Senate; STCC Prof Dev Grant Recipient; *office:* Springfield Tech Comm Coll 1 Armory Sq Springfield MA 01101

LESLIE, WILLIAM THOMAS, Biology & Computer Sci Tchr; *b:* Johnstown, PA; *m:* Judith R. Wieczorek; *c:* Christina, Timothy; *ed:* IN Univ of PA (BS) Bio 1966; Shippensburg Univ (MED) Bio Ed 1969; Shippensburg Univ Cmptr Sci 6; Cath Univ Adolescent Psych 3; Wilkes Coll Ed 6; *cr:* Gettysburg Sr HS Bio Tchr, Cmptr Sci Tchr 1966-; Gettsyburg Coll Adjunct Instr 1987-; Harrisburg Area Comm Coll Instr 1991-93; Penn St Univ Adjunct Instr 1991-; *ai:* Cmptr Resources Mgr; Ed Comm; Cmptr Club Adv; Band Booster Pres; NEA, PSEA, NABT 1966-, Gettysburg Ed Assn 1966-, VP 1 Yr, Pres 1 Yr; Natl Assn of Sci Tech & Soc 1988-; Educator of Yr Scholastic Magazine 1985; Tandy Tech Scholar Awd 1989; *office:* Gettysburg Sr H S Le Fever St Gettysburg PA 17325

LESSARD, JAN R., English Teacher; *b:* Dracut, MA; *m:* Ron; *c:* Jeffrey, Jodi; *ed:* Fitchburg St Tchrs Coll (BS) Eng, Psych 1973; *cr:* Greater Lowell Tech Voc Schl Eng Tchr 1978-79; Nashua High Eng Tchr 1979-; *ai:* Discipline Review Comm; Prin Search Team; Co-Facilitator Stu Assistance Prgm; NEATE, NCTE, AFT 1980-; Citizens for Discipline in Schls 1995-, Cub Scouts 1995-; PTO 1994-; *office:* Nashua Sr HS 36 Riverside Dr Nashua NH 03062

LESSEY, ROSLYN, English Teacher; *b:* New York, NY; *m:* Glenn J.; *ed:* Queens Coll (BA) Ed & Eng 1972, (MS) Ed 1974; 30 Credits Sociology, Psych, Philosophy & Spcl Ed; *cr:* Wm H Carr JHS 194 Eng Tchr 1982-; *ai:* AFT; NYSUT; UFT; *office:* William H Carr Jr HS 154-60 17th Ave Whitestone NY 11357

LESSLIE, DENNIS, Earth Science Teacher; *b:* Port Allegany, PA; *m:* Nancy; *c:* Jennifer, Brooke Loucks, Brant Loucks; *ed:* Clarion Univ of PA (BS) Sci 1969; Brockport St (MS) Ed 1985; St of NY (SDA) Admin 1988; PDIC Scuba Instr Trng; *cr:* Seward Pub Schls Sci Tchr 1969-70; Byron Bergen Cntrl Schl Sci Tchr 1970-; *ai:* Tchng Scuba Genesee Comm Coll; NYSTA 1970-; *office:* Byron-Bergen Central Schl 6917 W Bergen Rd Bergen NY 14416*

LESSOFF, STANLEY, Business Ed & Soc Stud Tchr; *b:* Boston, MA; *m:* Susan Geary; *c:* Robin Lessoff-Perry, Alan H.; *ed:* Northeastern Univ (BS) Acctng 1953; Attnd Univ of CT, Univ of MA, Bridgewater St Coll; *cr:* Pub Acctng 1953; Pvt Acctng 1973; New Bedford HS Bus Tchr 1974-81; Rockville HS Dept Head Bus Ed, Tchr 1981-; *ai:* FBLA Club Adv; CT Bus Ed Assn 1982-, Treas; Beta Mu Epsilon 1984-, VP, Rep Natl 6 Yrs; CEA, NEA, VEA 1981-; NBEA, NEBEH 1982-; BSA 1953-, Trng Chprsn Wood Badges; CT Sci Fair Assn 1990-, Treas; Adult Ed Comm, Cong B'Nai Israel; vernon Democratic Town Comm; *office:* Rockville HS 70 Loveland Hill Rd Vernon Rockville CT 06066*

LESTER, EVELYN COLE, Teacher of the Gifted; *b:* Pittsfield, MA; *m:* Robert P.; *c:* Andrew, Kathryn McCluskey, Sarah; *ed:* Univ of MA (BA) Ed & His 1961; Westfield St Coll (MED) Ed 1980; 15 Credits Beyond Masters; *cr:* Pittsfield Pub Schls Elem Tchr 1961-62; Springfield Pub Schls Elem Tchr 1962-63; Agawam Pub Schls Elem Tchr 1975-85, Tchr of Gifted 1985-; *ai:* Yrbk Adv; NEA 1975-; MTA 1975-; *office:* Agawam MS 68 Main St Agawam MA 01001

LESTER, FLORENCE THOMAS, Chem Teacher & Sci Dept Head; *b:* LaGrange, GA; *c:* Charles, Teresa D.; *ed:* Clark Atlanta Univ (BA) Bio 1966; Western KY Univ (MA) Ed 1968; Univ of CT (EDS) Prof Ed 1992; Attnd Morehead St Univ, GA St Univ at Atlanta; *cr:* DeKalb Cty Schl System Soc Worker, Cnslr 1970-72; Fort Vly St Univ Instr, Supvr of Practicum 1973-75; Avondale HS Sci Tchr 1981-86; Thomas Snell Weaver HS Sci, Chem Tchr, Head 1986-; *ai:* NHS Adv; Black Sisters United; Schedule, CAPT Comms; Acad Cncl Math, Sci; Scndry Coord City Sci Fair; Hartford Fed of Tchrs, AFT 1986-; Amer Voc Assn, Omicron Tau Theta, ASCD 1989-; CT Assn Sci Tchr 1994-; Wadworth Antheman Amstad 1994-; Natl Assn Negro B&P Women 1994-, 3rd VP: Urban League 1993-; Nom Presidential Excl Sci, Math Tchng Awd 1995-; CBIA Distngd Tchr; One of Authors in Learning Post 1991; *office:* Thomas Snell Weaver HS 415 Granby St Hartford CT 06112

LESTER, JO SUZANNE GREENBERG, Tchr of Substance Abuse Prvntn; *b:* Bronx, NY; *c:* Rachael Grace, Jackie; *ed:* Columbia Univ (BA) Psych of Rel 1986; 21 Credit Hrs Narcotic & Drug Rsrch Inst; 9 Credit Hrs Stu Tchng & Rdng NYS Regents Coll; *cr:* WFAS RAdio Invisible Dimension 1983-84, 1987; Alcott Montessori Schl Tchng Asst, Tchr 1983-85; Carmel NY Adult Ed Substance Abuse Prevention Intervention Tchr 1984-92; Schl Dist 11X Substance Abuse Prevention Tchr & Cnslr 1986-; *ai:* NY Jr Tennis League Coach 1993-; Liason; PS 96X Amer Chess Fnd; Pupil Prsnl Comm; Women's League for Israel 1980-, Fund Raiser; Ardsley PTA 1984-; Westchester GATE 1983-85, VP; Bronx Borough Press Advy Cncl 1987-94, Exec Bd; OASAS Inception, Alcohol & Drug Credential Cnslr; Pub Ghost Writer; *office:* Woodlawn Schl PS 19X 4318 Katonah Ave Bronx NY 10470*

LESTER, KRISTINE UETZ, Social Studies Teacher; *b:* Rochester, NY; *m:* Arnold W.; *c:* Vincent J., Joseph W.; *ed:* SUCO at Oswego (BS) Scndry Ed, Soc St 1971; SUNY at Brockport (MS) Elem Ed 1988; *cr:* Lifesaver-Beechnut Sales Rep 1975-83; Palmyra Macedon CSD Sub Tchr, Full-time Tchr 1986-.

LESTER, RICHARD REESE, Math Dept Chair; *b:* Pittsburgh, PA; *m:* Sandra Maria Siroky; *c:* Richard Jr., Jennifer, Krista, Lori; *ed:* CA St Univ (BS) Math 1966; Duquesne Univ (MA) Math 1972; Post-Grad Work Penn St Univ, Univ of Dayton; *cr:* Swissvale Area Schls Math Tchr 1966-81; Woodland Hills Schls Math Tchr, Dept Chair 1981-; *ai:* Mentor for New Math Tchrs; NCTM, PSEA, PCTM, NEA 1966-; Natl Sci Fnd Grant for Post-Grant Work at Univ of Dayton; *office:* Woodland Hills HS 2550 Greensburg Pike Pittsburgh PA 15221

LETAVEC, MONICA A. MALETA, First Grade Teacher; *b:* Grindstone, PA; *m:* Stephen A.; *c:* Stephen J., Sandra L.; *ed:* CA St Univ of PA (BS) Elem Ed 1963, (ME) Elem Ed 1966; Wright St Univ, Univ of Dayton 56 Credit Hrs; *cr:* Parklawn Primary Schl Second Grd Tchr 1963-66; Fairbrook elem Schl First Grd Tchr 1966-68; Oakview Elem Schl Kndgtn Tchr 1977-78; Kettering Moraine Schls 1977-; J. E. Prass Elem Schl Second Grd Tchr 1978-79; Rolling Fields Elem Schl Kndgtn Tchr 1979-80; Southdale Elem Schl Second Grd Tchr 1980-81; Beavertowne Elem Schls First Grd Tchr 1981-; *ai:* PTA Legislative, Staff Dev, Soc Comms; KEA, OEA, NEA, PTA 1977-; KOTA Awd 1992-93; Kettering Fnd Grant 1994-95; *office:* Beavertown Elem Schl 2700 Wilmington Ave Kettering OH 45419

LETKOVSKY, ANDREAS F., Architectural Instructor; *b:* New York, NY; *ed:* NY Inst of Tech (BAE) Architecture 1985; Univ of Palermo Post Grad Stud 1985; Inst Design & Construction Course Work 1991-94; *cr:* NY Inst of Tech Tchrs Asst 1983-85; Univ of Milano Polytechnico Prof 1987; Inst Design & Construction Asst Prof 1994-; Architect Andy Letkovsky Prin 1994-; *ai:* NY Inst of Tech Alumni Fed; Ed Grant NY Inst of Tech; NY Museum of Modern Art Personal Work Permanent Collection Status; Personal Work in Architecture Exhibited US & Europe; Amer Inst of Architects Awd with Mojo-Stumer Architects.

LETOURNEAU, CARLTON K., Biology Teacher; *b:* Potterville, PA; *m:* John S. Keeley-LeTourneau; *c:* D. Bruce Keeley; *ed:* Mansfield St Coll (BS) Sci, Math 1958; Elmira Coll (MS) Ed 1962; SUNY at Albany, SUNY at Oneonta, Elmira Coll, Bucknell Univ, Coll Ctr of Finger Lakes Post Grad Stud; *cr:* A. W. Booth Jr HS Sci Tchr 1958-75; Elmira Free Acad Bio Tchr 1975-; *ai:* NHS Adv; Tchr Admin Liaison Comm; Elmira Tchrs Assn Bldg Rep; NYS Sci Tchrs Assn 1960-, Southern Section Chm, Svc Awd 1994; NYS United Tchrs 1958-; NSTA 1960-; Elmira Tchrs Assn 1958-, Treas 1962-75, Ldrshp Awd 1992; AFT 1975-; NEA 1960-; CCSD Fed Credit Union 1970-, Dir 1972-, Treas 1993-; The Park Church 1962-, Care, Parish Ministry; Amer Field Svc 1982-, Treas 1988-; NSF Grants 1960, 1966, 1967, 1969; *home:* 9 Pinewood Cir Corning NY 14830*

LETOURNEAU, CAROL ANN, Title I Coord & Literacy Spec; *b:* Portland, ME; *ed:* Univ of Southern ME (BS) Elem Ed 1972; Boston Coll (MED) Literacy Specialist 1982; Summer Sessions Boston Univ, Univ of KS; Univ of ME Tech Courses; *cr:* Beatrice Rafferty Schl 4-8 Grd Lang Arts, Sci Tchr 1975-76; St Mary Schl 5-8 Lang Arts Tchr 1976-77; Ind Twp Schl Title I Coord, Literacy Spec, Tech Tchr, Tech Coord 1977-; *ai:* Ldrshp Team; Tech Comm Co-Chair; Parent-Schl Compact Federal Grant Writing; IRA 1989-; Diocesan Sisters of Mercy 1965-, Local Superior; St Ann Mission, Music Min 1979-, Dir; Natl Tekakwitha Conf, Assn Native Clergy-Rel 1985-; *home:* HC 78 Box 1 Princeton ME 04668

LETOURNEAU, DARLENE ANNE (LAUZIERE), Third Grade Teacher; *b:* Lewiston, ME; *m:* Raymond C.; *c:* Joel S. Parker, Tony, Dale; *ed:* Rivier Coll (BA) Elem Ed 1972; Univ of ME (MS) Prof Ed 1987; *cr:* St Peter Schl Kndgtn, 2 Grd Tchr 1972-74; McMahon Schl 3 Grd Tchr 1974-76; Jordan Elem Schl 4 Grd Tchr 1976-83; Martel Elem Schl 3 Grd Tchr 1983-; *ai:* Drug Free, Cmptr Comms; Adopt-A-Schl Busineses in Partnership with Ed; LTA, MEA 1983-; ASCD 1986-; *office:* Martel Schl 880 Lisbon St Lewiston ME 04240

LEU, MICHAEL R., Music Teacher; *b:* New Martinsville, WV; *m:* Lynne Lauffer; *c:* Jennifer, Jessica; *ed:* WV Univ (BM) Music Ed 1986; Duquesne Univ (MM) Music Performance 1988; *cr:* Meyersdale Area Schl Dist Asst Band Dir 1990; Ligonier Vly HS Band, Choral Dir 1990-; *ai:* Marching Band; NEA, PSEA, LVEA, MENC, PMEA 1990-; First Presbyn Church of Jeannette 1994-, Elder; Westmoreland Symphony Orch 1987-; Musical Composition Pub 1992; *office:* Ligonier Valley HS 40 Springer Rd Li PA 15658

LEUCHNER, LINDA DENISE (GAIDE), Advanced Placement Bi *b:* Brooklyn, NY; *m:* Paul G.; *c:* Lisa; *ed:* St Univ Coll at Buffalo (B & Ed 1974, (MS) Bio & Ed 1978; 30 Credit Hrs Schl Admin; *cr:* H Jr HS Sci Tchr 1974-78; Kenmore W Sr HS AP Bio Tchr 1982-; *ai:* Class Adv; Sci Olympiad Coach; NYSUT 1974-; Kenmore West 1982-; Natl Sci Olympiad Outstndng Coach Regnl Finals 1993.

LEUSCHNER, FREDERICK GRAHAM, Chemistry Teach Harrisburg, PA; *ed:* Bucknell Univ (BA) Chem 1985; *cr:* Ctrl Dauphi Jr High Algebra Tchr 1988-89; Swamra Jr High Phys Sci, Remedia Tchr 1989-92; Ctrl Dauphin HS Chem, Physics, Organic Chem Tchr *ai:* Head Cross Ctry, Indoor, Outdoor Track, Field Coach; Sci Fai Schl Safety Comm; NEA; PSEA; CDEA; ACS; AAAS; NSTA; PST 1989-; St Museum of PA 1988-, Vol; *office:* Central Dauphin HS Locust Ln Harrisburg PA 17109*

LEVANO, ROSEMARY RIENDEAU, English Dept Chairpers Brooklyn, NY; *m:* John; *c:* Michael; *ed:* Molloy Coll (BA) Eng & Ed Adelphi Univ (MA) Educl Theatre 1990; *cr:* Sewharaka Cntrl HS St Eng Tchr 1987; Sacred Heart Acad Eng Dept Chm & Dean of Disc 1988-; Bellmore-Merrick CHS Summer Eng Tchr 1989-91; *ai:* D Discipline; NCEA 1988-; NCTE 1988-; *office:* Sacred Heart Ac Cathedral Ave Hempstead NY 11550

LEVANTO, REGINA DZIALO, US History Teacher; *b:* Norwich, Charles F.; *ed:* Univ of CT (BA) His 1972, (MA) Ed 1976; Taft Sc Norwich Free Acad His Tchr 1972-; *ai:* CEA & NEA 1972-; NFA E 1972-, Sec 1980-93; *office:* Norwich Free Acad 305 Broadway Norw 06360

LEVASSEUR, DAWNA L., 8th Grade Eng & Lit Teacher; *b:* Lew ME; *ed:* Bates Coll (BA) Eng 1984; Credit Hrs in Curr, Tchng Excep Child & Wellness; *cr:* Lewiston Jr HS 8th Grd Eng & Lit Tchr, Tea 1984-; *ai:* Stu Cncl Co-Adv; Pride, Schl Improvement Comms; Tea LEA, MEA, NEA 1984-, Prof Image Awd 1992-93; Tchr of Month *office:* Lewiston Jr HS Central Ave Lewiston ME 04240

LEVASSEUR, DORIS LECUYER, Early Childhood Ed Profess New Bedford, MA; *m:* Michael S.; *c:* Brandon, Jessica; *ed:* Bristol Coll (AA) Elem Ed 1971; Univ MA at Dartmouth (BA) Multidiscip Stud 1980; Bridgewater St (MS) Early Chldhd Ed 1992; *cr:* Freetow Schl Kndgtn Tchr 1980-81; Creative Kids Preschl Owner & Dir 19 Fisher Coll Instr 1992-; *ai:* Disc Jockey Bus; NAEYC 1993-; *office:* Coll President Ave Fall River MA 02116

LEVEN, RAY, Spanish Teacher; *b:* Philadelphia, PA; *m:* B Adelman; *c:* Keith, Cindy; *ed:* Temple Univ (BA) Span 1696; Grat (BHL) Hebrew 1970; Temple Univ (MED) Scndry Ed 1971; Grat (MHL) Hebrew Lit 1977; Prins Cert 1984; Cert in Eng 1987; *cr:* Ol Eng as a Second Lang & Span Tchr 1969-86; JCHS of Gratz Coll H Lang Tchr 1977-; Cheltemham HS Span Tchr 1986-; *ai:* NEA, CEA SSBJ Syn 1978-, Educl Dir; Rockerfeller for Lang Fellow Cheltenham Fnd Grant Winner 1995; Family Ed Grant Rec in Conju with ACAJE in Phila 1992, 1993, 1994, & 1995; *office:* Cheltenha Carlton & Panther Rds Wyncote PA 19095*

LEVENS, BARBARA LYNN, English Teacher; *b:* Meadville, P James W.; *ed:* Edinboro Univ of PA (BS) Eng 1971, (MED) Speech, 1976; *cr:* Meadville Jr Sr HS Eng Tchr 1977-79; Maplewood Jr Sr H Tchr 1979-; *ai:* NHS Adv; Dist Eng, Comm, Rdng Curr Comm; Ne Mentor; Northwest Ldrshp Partcnt; NCTE 1980-; Delta Kappa 1988-, Pres 1994-; *office:* Maplewood Jr/Sr HS RD 1 Guys Mills PA

LEVENSON, MINA TERRY (ALTSHULER), Health, PE & S Teacher; *b:* Pittsburgh, PA; *m:* Michael H.; *c:* Jules, Ann; *ed:* U Pittsburgh (BS) Hlth, PE 1973; la Universidad de Salamanca (MA 1978; Univ of Pittsburgh (MS) Hlth, PE, Exercise Physiology 1986 Lit; Lit Translation; AP Inst Span; *cr:* Allderdice HS Span Tchr 19 Brashear HS Hlth, PE Tchr 1976-79; Allderdice HS Hlth, PE Tchr Span Tchr 1993-; *ai:* Ldrshp Prgm Coord; Parent Schl Comm Cncl; Team; Mediator; Vlybl Ofcl; Amer Coll of Sports Medicine 1973-; A 1995-; PFT; Allderdice Alumni Assn 1994-; Cerftd Exercise Spe *office:* Taylor Allderdice HS 2409 Shady Ave Pittsburgh PA 15217*

LEVENSTEIN, JEAN FRANCES,SSJ, Religious Studies Instruc Chester, PA; *ed:* Chestnut Hill Coll (BS) Ed 1965; St Charles Se (MA) Moral Theology 1977; *cr:* Abp Prendergast HS Rel Stud 1970-82; Little Flower HS Rel Stud Tchr 1982-83; Mt St Joseph Ac Stud Tchr 1984-; *ai:* Moderator SEA Stu Environmental Activist Network, NCEA 1970-; *office:* Mt St Joseph Acad 120 W Wissahick Flourtown PA 19031

LEVERETT, REBECCA SHUTTLEWORTH, Teacher of Gif Talented; *b:* Indianaola, MS; *m:* Carey Olan; *c:* Scott William, R Wallace; *ed:* Millsaps Coll (BA) Elem Ed 1971; Univ of TX at San A (MA) Educl Mid-Mngmt; Columbus Coll St GATE Cert 1988; Principalship St Cert 1981; *cr:* MS Private Schls Elem Tchr 19 North East ISD 1-3 Grd Tchr, K-5 GATE Tchr 1975-87; Fort Benning Tchr of 3rd, 1st Grd Gifted 1987-91; Washington Cty BOE P Challenge Tchr 1993-; *ai:* Odyssey of Mind Regnl Finals Judge; Teams Coach; Schl Improvement Team Sec; Author, Drama Children's Plays; Kappa Delta Epsilon 1971-, Sec; NEA, TX St Tchr Benning Ed Assn, Washington Cty Tchrs Assn 1975-; PTA 1971-, VP, Comm Chm, Lifetime TX Mbrshp, Terrific Tchr of TX; Natl Assn Chldren 1985-, Natl Convention Presenter 1990, 1994-95; Paramoun Church 1995-; MD Coalition of GATE 1996-; Northern Hills Elem T Yr 1983; TX St Convention for GATE Presenter 1987; *office:* Lincol Elem Schl 17545 Lincolnshire Rd Hagerstown MD 21740

LEVERICH, JOSEPH TERREL, Mathematics Teacher; *b:* New O LA; *ed:* Harvard Coll (AB) Math 1957; Harvard Univ (MA) Math Harvard Bus Schl DBA Prgm in Decision & Control 1967-72; *cr:* Sin Coll Asst Prof 1961-67; Brookline HS Math Instr 1972-; Mit Mites Math Instr 1992-; *ai:* Headmaster's Liaison Schl Govt; NEA 1975-; 1970-; WOS, COS 1974-; Hoar Fund Grant; *office:* Brookline H Greenough St Brookline MA 02146

LEVERICH, WILLIAM FRANCIS, HS English Teacher; *b:* Bro NY; *m:* Mary Steffann; *c:* Jean, Karen Baillie, Ellen Firkns, Gerard, *ed:* ST Johns Univ (BA) Eng 1960; Attnd Queens Coll at Jamaica, St Coll at Moraga, Georgetown Univ at Washington, Univ of NH at Du *cr:* Cntrl HS Eng Tchr 1963-67; Ward Melville HS Eng Tchr 1967-; Newspaper Adv 1968-71; Shakespeare Dramaturge 1982-; AFT & N 1965-; Cncl for Basic Ed 1980-; NYS Eng Cncl 1986-; Cntrl Suffolk Assn 1978-85, Outstdng Coaches Awd 1978-79; Natl Hum Fac F 1973-74; Ward Melville Outstdng Tchr Awd 1982, HS Tchr of Y 1989; Grant from Cncl for Basic Ed 1985; Eng Cncl Tchr of Exc 1986; Prof Achvmt 1987; *office:* Ward Melville Sr HS 380 Old To East Setauket NY 11733

LEVERING, NANCY STAHLER, 6th & 7th Grade Math Teach Davenport, IA; *m:* James D.; *c:* Amanda L., Sarah A., Matthew J.; *ed* of Findlay (BS) HPER 1972; 1-8 Elem Tchng Cert at OH Univ 19 Crooksville K-8 Schl Sub Tchr 1976-87; St Rose Schl 6th Grd 1987-93; Licking Heights MS 6th-7th Math Tchr 1993-; *ai:* Sci Oly 8th Grd Vlybl, MS Girls Track Coach; OEA, NEA 1992-; Venture C

; 1996; *office:* Licking Hghts MS 6539 Summit Rd SW Summit n OH 43073

ESQUE, MARIA RODRIGUES, English Teacher & Dept Head; *b:* dence, RI; *m:* Robert T.; *ed:* Univ of RI (BA) Soc Stud & Scndry Ed RI Coll (MA) Scndry Ed 1992; 9 Credits Eng; 12 Credits Psych; *cr:* ady of Litima HS Tchr 1975-; *ai:* Sr Class & Yrbk Adv; Drama Club NCEA 1980-; *office:* Our Lady Of Fatima HS 360 Market St Warren 885

ESQUE, SHIRLEY PISANI, Foreign Language Teacher; *b:* Beverly, *m:* Richard Joseph; *c:* Richard, Caren, Janice; *ed:* Boston Univ Schl beral Arts (AB) Romance Lang, Lit 1957, Schl of Ed (EDM) Ed 1958; Hrs at Salem St Coll, Northeast Consortium; Leslie Coll 3 Hrs; *cr:* rica Mem HS Span, Eng Tchr 1958-60; Brisco Jr HS Foreign Lang 1979-80; Mem MS Foreign Lang Tchr 1981-; *ai:* Girls Sftbl Coach ational League; Tutor Eng, Fr, Span, Latin; NEA 1979-; Phi Sigma 957-; Nom Golden Apple Awd 3 Times; *home:* 6 Leech St Beverly 1915*

ETT, COLLEEN ANN (COSTELLO), Speech & Language logist; *b:* Syracuse, NY; *m:* William Gregory; *c:* William Sean; *ed:* wood Coll (BS) Comm Disorders 1976; Ithaca Coll (MS) Speech logy 1977; *cr:* Somersville Schl Dist Speech, Lang Pathologist 1/2 ohn T. Roberts Schl Speech, Lang Pathologist 19 Yrs; *ai:* Schl ovement, Site Based, Chprsn of Action Teams; Bldg Comm; Chief Rep; Syracuse Tchrs Assoc 1978-, Chief Bldg Rep; NYSUT, AFT ; St Michael's Church 1993-, 5th Grd Religious Ed Tchr; *office:* John berts Schl 715 Glenwood Ave Syracuse NY 13207

, LARRY J., Am Government Teacher; *b:* Martins Ferry, OH; *ed:* OH (BA) Ed-Soc Stud 1970; Univ of Dayton (MS) Ed Admin 1975; *cr:* eye Local SD Educator 1970-; *ai:* Asst Ath Dir; NEA, OEA 1970-; ge Cncl 1989-; *office:* Buckeye Local HS Rd 2 Box 475 Rayland OH 3

, MARK, Mathematics Professor; *b:* Riga, Latvia; *m:* Olga Gelfand; ctoria, Nicole, Max, Eric, Kyra; *ed:* Latvian St Univ (BS) Math 1972; ant Inst (MS) Math 1976, (PHD) Math 1978; *cr:* Boston Univ Asst 1982-85; Boston Univ Assoc Prof 1985-91; Rensselaer Polytechnic ssoc Prof 1991-94, Prof 1994-; *ai:* Putnam Competition Coach; AMS; ; Jay Krakauer Meml Awd by NYU Alumni Assn for Best Thesis in al Sci; *office:* Rensselaer Polytechnic Inst Mathematical Sciences 110 8th St Troy NY 12180

IN, BETTE, Retired English Teacher; *b:* New York, NY; *ed:* Univ of Ann Arbor (BA) Eng; Attnd Coll St Elizabeth K-8, Convent Station -12 Eng; *cr:* St Vincent Martyr Schl Tchr Grd K-8 1970-94; Madison Schl Rdng Tchr 1974-75; *ai:* Eng Chprsn; Fac Coord Lit Magazine; Books Fnd, Discussion Ldr; NCEA.

IN, DEBBIE GANTMAN, Professor of Education; *b:* Philadelphia, : Jonah D.; *c:* Hope Wendy, Shira Jill; *ed:* Univ of PA (BS) Elem Ed Univ of Toledo (MED) Elem Curr 1972; Rdng Cert Beaver Coll 1981; Grad Credits St Joseph's Univ; *cr:* Pub Schl Tchng 1969-75; Comm Philadelphia Part-time Coll Tchng 1975-81; Montgomery Cty Comm Prof Ed; *ai:* AFT 1981-; NAEYC 1985-; Del Vly Ch Care Cncl 1990-; Lynne Lokoff Fnd 1990-, Honorary Bd; Presenter Numerous Confs; : Montgomery County Comm Coll 340 DeKalb Pike Blue Bell PA 2

IN, GAIL SUSAN, Fifth Grade Teacher; *b:* Brooklyn, NY; *ed:* St at Buffalo (BS) Spec Ed, Elem Ed 1965; Hofstra Univ (MS) Spec Ed 8 Credits Harvard Univ 1967; *cr:* Rhame Ave Schl Spec Ed Tchr -71, Elem Ed Tchr 1971-; *ai:* Lang Arts Curr, Soc Stud Curr Comms; chng Cooperating Tchr; Comm to Select Participants in Gifted Prgm; NYSUT, ERTA 1965-; *office:* Rhame Ave Schl 100 Rhame Ave East away NY 11518

IN, JACK, Sociology & Criminology Prof; *b:* New Orleans, LA; *m:* Lench; *c:* Michael, Bonnie Andrea; *ed:* Amer Intnl Coll (BA) logy 1963; Boston Univ (MS) Comm 1965, (PHD) Sociology 1968; Boston Univ Asst Prof 1968-70; Northeastern Univ Asst Prof -75, Assoc Prof 1975-80, Prof 1980-; *ai:* Dir of Prgm for Stud of nce, Soc Conflict; ASA 1965-; ESS 1970-, VP; NESA 1970-, Pres, er Awd; Spurwink Inst 1995-, Bd Dir; Joey Fournier Victim Svcs , Bd Dir; CASE Prof of Yr 1991-92; 18 Books; Numerous Articles, spaper Columns; Urban Law Inst Distngd Prof 1996; *office:* eastern Univ 500 Holmes Hall Boston MA 02115

IN, JENNIFER LYNNE, Remedial Math Teacher; *b:* Far Rockaway, *m:* Glenn; *ed:* Dowling Coll (BD) Elem Ed, Scndry Math 1991; *cr:* Babylon UFSD Sub Tchr, Var Chrldng Coach 1991-95; Deer Park Sub Tchr 1993-94; Massapequa UFSD Remedial Math Tchr 1994-; e Kids Cmptr Tchr 1995-; *ai:* Fashion Show Tchr Rep; 6th Grd Gym Girls Dance Adv; *office:* Fairfield Schl Massapequa Ave Massapequa 1758

IN, LAWRENCE ALAN, Science Teacher; *b:* Washington, DC; *ed:* of MD (BS) Hlth Ed 1970, (MS) Admin & Supervision 1985; 30 ts Beyond Masters in Ed Related Areas; *cr:* Montgomery Blair Sr HS 1970-80; Montgomery Cty Pub Schls Hlth Ed Tchr Specialist -82; Bethesda-Chevy Chase HS Tchr 1982-; ETS SAT & Achvmt Test Coord 1987-88; Bethesda Chevy Chase HS Adult Ed Coord 1987-; *ai:* Govt Adv; MCEA 1970-, Bldg Rep; MSTA & NEA 1970-; Prin Adult vening Prgm; Mid Sts Assn of Colls & Schls Visiting Team Mem; : Bethesda-Chevy Chase HS 4301 East-West Hwy Bethesda MD 4*

IN, RICHARD ALEXANDER, Professor of Biology; *b:* Hartford, : Amy Higgins; *c:* Rebecca Jane, Susan Levin Gadd, Sarah Ellen; *ed:* ard Coll (BA) Bio 1954; Univ of WA (MS) Genetics 1956, (MA) c Composition 1963; Univ of IA (PHD) Microbio 1968; *cr:* Univ of Lecturer 1956-63; Oberlin Coll Prof 1968-; *ai:* Sr Fac Assoc; HIV Ed n Chm; ASM 1968-; NASA Grant; Oberlin Coll Distngd Tchng Awd; OH Outstdng Tchng Awd; Numerous Articles Pub; *office:* Oberlin Kettering 119 Oberlin OH 44074

IN, ROBIN JACOBS, Mathematics Teacher; *b:* Camden, NJ; *m:* *c:* Lindsay, Shelby; *ed:* Glassboro St Coll (BA) Math 1971; Trenton oll (MA) Math 1975; *cr:* Cherry Hill HS West Math Tchr 1971-; *ai:* 1971-; Assn of Math Tchrs of NJ 1991-; *office:* Cherry Hill HS West el Ave Cherry Hill NJ 08002

IN, SUSAN B., Philosophy Professor; *b:* Buffalo, NY; *m:* Barry g; *ed:* Pomona Coll (BA) Philosophy 1984; Stanford Univ (PHD) osophy, Hum 1993; *cr:* Smith Coll Asst Prof of Philosophy 1993-; *ai:* er Philosphical, Philological Assn; Phi Beta Kappa 1984-; Ancient k Philosophy; Jean Picker Flwshp 1995-; Whiting Flwshp in Hum -92; Ancient Philosophy Pub; *office:* Smith Coll Dept of Philosophy hampton MA 01063

INDOFSKE, MATTHEW DAMIAN, Social Studies Teacher; *b:* awanna, NY; *m:* Deborah Hatala; *c:* Daniel; *ed:* Baldwin-Wallace Coll Criminal Justice 1983; Cleveland St Univ Tchrs Cert in prehensive Soc Stud 1989; Pursuing Master of Arts in His 20 Credit *cr:* Saint Edward HS Soc Stud Tchr 1990-; *ai:* Var Ftbl Coach 6 Yrs, nsive Coord 4 Yrs; Jr Var Wrestling Head Coach 5 Yrs; Cleveland Cncl World Affairs 1990-; OH Cncl for Soc Stud 1991-; Natl Cncl for Excl ritical Thinking 1993-; Staff Mem of 1992 St & Natl Championship Wrestling Team; Northeast OH Jr Achvmt Mgmt & Ec Simulating Excercise Tchr of Yr 1993 for Moderating JA Exec Decision Making Super Bowl Champions of 1993.

LEVINE, CAROL, First Grade Teacher; *b:* Brooklyn, NY; *m:* Robert G.; *c:* Susan Valentia, Karen Kagan; *ed:* Newark St Coll (BA) Gen Elem-cum laude 1971; Bank Street Coll (MS) Early Chldhd 1976; 30 Credit Hrs Post Grad Stud Marywood Coll 1978-90; *cr:* Tulsa Trail Pub Schl 2nd Grd Tchr 1971-74; Hudson Maxim Pub Schl 3rd Grd Tchr 1974-80, 2nd Grd Tchr 1981-85, 1st Grd Tchr 1986-; *ai:* Supt Liaison Comm; Dist Wide Textbook Evaluation; NEA 1971-, Mem; NJEA 1971-, Mem; Sussex Cty Ed Assn 1971-, Mem; Hopatcong Ed Assn 1971-, Bldg Rep; Juvenile Conf at Morris Cty 1989-; Morris Cty Hot Line 1994-; NJ St Grant Relevant Learning Through a Living Environment; Acknowledged Tchr of Influence Former Stdnts 1987 & 1992-93; Dist Mini Grant Bridging the Generaton gap 1988-; A for Kids Grant Puppet Magic 1989; A for Kids Grant Hopatcong A Learning Environment 1990; Hopatcong Tchr of Yr 1991-92; *office:* Hudson Maxim Elem Schl PO Box 1029 Hopatcong NJ 07843*

LEVINE, EVIE A., 11th-12th Grade English Tchr; *b:* Pittsburgh, PA; *ed:* Univ of Pittsburgh (BA) Eng Ed 1970; Columbia Univ, Tchrs Coll (MA) Eng Ed 1972; Addl 60 Credit Hrs Various Ed Courses; *cr:* North Hills HS Eng Tchr 1972-; *ai:* NEA 1972-; *office:* North Hills Sr HS 53 Rochester Rd Pittsburgh PA 15229

LEVINE, ILENE JOY ROSE, Scndry Schl Spanish Teacher; *b:* Passaic, NJ; *m:* Ira J.; *c:* Aaron D., Joshuea D., Michael, Ethan L.; *ed:* NY Univ (BS) Span 1965; Montclair St Coll (MA) Educl Psych 1985; *cr:* Fairlawn HS Span Tchr 1965-67 & 1982-; *ai:* Span Club, Womens Issues Club Adv; Boptones Asst; NHS Comm; NEA 1982-; NJEA 1982-; FLEA 1982-; *office:* Fair Lawn HS 14-00 Berdan Ave Fair Lawn NJ 07410

LEVINE, KATHLEEN ANN (HUEBNER), Former English Teacher; *b:* Sangley Point M B, Philippines; *m:* Randyll Lawrence; *c:* Rachel May; *ed:* OH St Univ (BS) Ed 1985; Working Toward Schl Cnslng Univ of Dayton; *cr:* Frazeysburg Jr HS Eng Tchr 1985-86; Milton Union HS Eng Tchr 1986-95; *ai:* NEA, OEA, MUEA 1986-; NCTE 1989-; Milton Union HS Awd of Merit 1989.

LEVINE, LEWIS, ESL Intensive Program Coord; *b:* Bronx, NY; *m:* Nellie T Justicia; *c:* Gabriel; *ed:* Harvard Coll (BA) Romance Lang & Lit 1974; Teachers Coll Columbia Univ (MA) Ed 1976; Fordham Univ at Lincoln Ctr ABD Lang, Literacy & Learning; *cr:* Hostos Comm Coll Rdng Pgm Coord 1980-86, ESL Intensiive Pgm Coord 1990-; *ai:* Upper Manhattan Naturalization Project Consultant; Coll Wide & Eng Dept Curr Comms; Fac Corps of Acad Adv; Outstdng Tchr 1995; Changing Times Toward An Integrated Approach To Reading Author 1985; *office:* City Univ Of NY Hostos Coll 500 Grand Concourse Bronx NY 10451

LEVINE, MARJORIE DAMASHEK, English Teacher; *b:* Brooklyn, NY; *m:* Ron D.; *c:* Jarrett Keith; *ed:* CUNY at Queens (BS) Drama, Theatre, Media Stud, Eng 1979, (MA) Eng, Creative Writing 1995; Trinity Repertory Conservatory Cert 1982; *cr:* Laguardia HS of Performing Arts Eng Tchr 1989; Jamaica HS Eng Tchr 1990; Beach Channel HS Eng Tchr 1991-; *ai:* Drama Club, Arista Adv; Multicultural Festival Stage Dir; Shakespeare Contest Coord; NYC Playwriting Contest Supvr; UFT 1989-; FTRA 1980-, Actor; Manhattan Theatre Club 1991-; HS Educl Ourtreach; Awded Stud Schlshp at Hebrew Univ on Holocaust Stud; Completed Symposium for Tchrs; Invited to Teach at Lincoln Ctr Inst; *office:* Beach Channel HS 100-00 Beach Channel Dr Far Rockaway NY 11694

LEVINE, MICHELE KAUFMAN, 6th Grade Teacher; *b:* New York, NY; *m:* Lawrence; *ed:* Lehman Coll (BA) Sociology & Ed 1975; Queens Coll (MS) Early Chldhd Ed 1980; 30 Grad Credit Hrs in Ed; *cr:* Lillian Wald Day Care Ctr Early Chldhd Tchr 1980-84; PS 61 Anna Howard Shaw 3rd, 5th-6th Grd Tchr 1984-94; PS 117 Briarwood Schl 6th Grd Tchr 1994-; *ai:* Instr for the Intensive Test Taking Pgm Spon by Dist; United Fed of Tchrs Wkshp Presenter; AFT 1984-; Grants: Sci, Learning Ctr Strategies for Early Chldhd Ed, Multicultural Curr & Parent Involvement; *home:* 24 Lace Ln Westbury NY 11590*

LEVINE, STEVEN BARRY, Physical Education Instructor; *b:* Dorchester, MA; *m:* Karen Ann Rochford; *c:* Ryan, Adam, Ashley; *ed:* Univ of MA at Amherst (BS) PE 1973; Leslie Coll Individualized Instruction; MA Martime Acad Sports Medicine Courses; *cr:* Tewksbury Pub Schls PE Instr 1973-; *ai:* Var Boys Soccer, Indoor Track & Field Coach; Boys Spring Track & Field Head Coach; Girls Indoor Track & Field Coach; Steering, Schl Accredidation Comms; NEA, TTA Tewksbury, MTA MA 1973-74; MA Soccer Coaches Assn 1976-, League Rep; MA Track & Field Coaches Assn 1987-; MA Referee Soccer Assn 1990-; Soccer, Track & Field Coach of Yr Awds; *office:* Tewksbury Memorial HS 320 Pleasant St Tewksbury MA 01876

LEVINS, MARY CLARE BAHRT, Middle School Science Teacher; *b:* Hazleton, PA; *m:* Peter J.; *c:* Kathryn Marie, Ruth Ann; *ed:* Coll of Mount Saint Vincent (BS) Bio 1967; Seton Hall Univ (MS) Bio & Virology 1972; Kean Coll (MAT) Scndry Ed & Sci 1974; *cr:* Holy Trinity HS Sci Tchr & Dept Chair 1967-72; Union Cath HS Sci Tchr & Dept Chair 1972-77; Saint Bartholomew Schl Sci Tchr & Dept Chair 1984-; Saint Agnes Schl Sci Tchr 1985-; Oak Knoll Schl Summer Sci Prgm Tchr 1993-; *ai:* Mid Sts Steering Comm; Sci Curr Comm, Chem, Engr Weeks & Sci Fair Co-Chair; NCEA 1984-, Nom Tchr of Yr; ACS 1993-; Girl Scouts 1981-, Ldr all Levels, Appreciation Awd; Coll Club 1993-; CASA 1986-; MADD 1985-; SADD 1985-, Appreciation Awd; Outstanding Ed Newark Archdiocese 1992; *office:* St Agnes Schl 342 Madison Hill Rd Clark NJ 07066*

LEVINSON, LYNN, High School Humanities Teacher; *b:* Providence, RI; *ed:* Univ of PA (BA) His 1988; Cornell Univ (JD) Law 1992; Grad Courses Georgetown Univ & George Washington Univ; *cr:* Maret Schl Hum Tchr 1992-; *ai:* 11th Grd Head; Model UN Team & Women at Maret Spon; Acad Team; Asst LaCrosse Coach; Sr Project Comm; NY Bar; *office:* Maret Schl 3000 Cathedral Ave NW Washington DC 20008

LEVITZ, PAUL, Professor; *b:* New York, NY; *m:* Wendy; *c:* Bryan, Kevin, Jonathan; *ed:* Hunter (MA) Rehabilitation Counseling 1969; New York Univ (PHD) Rehabilitation Counseling 1981; *cr:* CUNY Borough of Manhattan Comm Coll Prof 23 Yrs; *ai:* Pub in JARC; *office:* Borough Of Manhattan Comm Coll 199 Chambers St New York NY 10007

LEVKANICH, CYRIL, Reading Teacher; *b:* Cleveland, OH; *m:* Charlene Russo; *c:* Kristi; *ed:* John Carroll Univ (BA) His 1975; *cr:* Benedictine HS Rdng Tchr 1978-; *ai:* Var Cross-Cntry & Track Head Coach; Boys Cross-Cntry Coach of Yr 1995; *office:* Benedictine HS 2900 Martin Luther King Jr Dr Cleveland OH 44104

LEVO, ROGER A., Mathematics Teacher; *b:* Wilmington, OH; *m:* Linda; *ed:* Morehead St Univ (BA) Math 1983; Xavier Univ (MED) Math 1988; *cr:* Morehead St Univ Lab Instr & Tchrs Asst 1981-83, Math Instr 1983; Little Miami Schl Dist Tchr & Coach 1983-; *ai:* Golf Coach 1984-95; Acad Team Adv 1995-, Math Dept Chair 1986-88; NEA & OEA 1983-; CEAI 1985-; Amateur Radio 1974-, Gen License; FCA 1985-, Huddle Coach; Coach of the Yr 1991; Tchr of the Yr 1994; *office:* Little Miami HS 605 Welch Rd Morrow OH 45152*

LEVY, BONNIE L., 7th & 8th Grade Math Teacher; *b:* Kearny, NJ; *ed:* Douglass Coll (BA) Math 1972; Jersey City St Coll (MA) Prin, Supvr 1989; 11 Addl Credits; Montclair St 3 Credits; Bridgeport Univ 3 Credits; H&R Block Tax Schl Tax Preparation; *cr:* LIncoln Schl 7th-8th Grd Math Tchr 1972-; Bloomfield Adult Schl Math Tchr 1977; Livingston Saturday Enrichment Math Tchr 1981; H&R Block Tax Preparer 1981-; *ai:* Color Guard Adv 1974-; NEA, NJEA 1972-; *office:* Lincoln Schl 121 Beech St Kearny NJ 07032

LEVY, DENNIS IRA, Business Ed Dept Chm & Tchr; *b:* Staten Island, NY; *m:* Bonnie Dreyfus; *c:* Julie, Hollie; *ed:* Staten Island Comm Coll (AAS) Bus Admin 1967; Fairleigh Dickinson Univ (BS) Bus Ed 1969; Montclair St Univ (MA) Bus Ed 1972; Addl 40 Credits in Cmptrs, Voc Ed & Admin; *cr:* Hillside HS Bus Ed Tchr 1969-74; Bergen Comm Coll Adjunct Instr 1976-; Montclair St Univ Adjunct Instr 1982-85; Cresskill HS Bus Ed Dept Chm, Tchr & Coord of Co-op Work Study 1974-; *ai:* DECA & Schl Store Adv; Honor Soc Selection Comm Mem; NJBEA 1969-, Exec Bd Mem; NEA 1969-; NJMEA, CEA, NJCBEA 1974-; Delta Pi Epsilon 1972-; Whos Who in NJ Bus Ed; Several Articles Pub; NJ Standards for Excl in Bus Ed Comm; *office:* Cresskill HS 1 Lincoln Dr Cresskill NJ 07626*

LEVY, LEONARD HAROLD, 5th Grade Teacher; *b:* Paterson, NJ; *c:* Benjamin; *ed:* Fairleigh Dickinson Univ (BA) Elem Ed 1970; Attnd Naval schl of Music Washington DC 1963; *cr:* US Army Bandsman 1963-65; YM-YWHA Day Camp Asst Dir, Cnslr & Unit Head 1958-87; John A Forrest Elem Schl 5th & 6th Grd Tchr 1971-; *ai:* Self Esteem Comms; Lunchroom Duty Vol; Stu Cncl Adv; Math Comm 1993; Selected Tchr in Charge 1993; Vol for Mntly Chlngd; Fairlawn Ed Assn, Bergen City Ed Assn, NJEA & NEA 1971-; PTA 1971-, VP 1972-74; MFFA Hillsdale & MeadowWood Schl 1986-; Collalaborative Tchng Comm Mem 1993; Math Comm; Natl Cncl for Self Esteem 1993; John A Forrest Schl Tchr of Yr 1989; Tchr in Chrg 1993; Outstanding Classroom Tchr to Spec Ed 1993; 11 Day ITIP Course; PTA Outstndng Tchr Awd 1995.*

LEVY, LYNN, 6th Grd Rdng & Soc Stud Tchr; *b:* Palmerton, PA; *m:* Robert R.; *c:* Alyse; *ed:* Temple Univ (BS) Elem Ed 1968; Beaver Coll (MSEd) Ed 1977; Univ of PA Writing Project, Arts in Ed Prgm; *cr:* John Wister Schl Math Resource Tchr 1968-74; Schl Dist Phila Primary Skills Res Tchr 1974-76; A. Stearne Schl Checkpoint Tchr 1976-83; W. Meredith Schl 6th Grd Tchr 1983-; *ai:* Schl Garden Club Spon; Penn's Start Prgm Cooperating Tchr; Pennies for Park Drive Chprsn; IRA 1990-; PFT 1968-; Nom Rose Lindenbaum Awd; *office:* William Meredith Elem Schl 5th & Fitzwater Sts Philadelphia PA 19147

LEVY, MARY FITZGERALD, Social Studies Teacher; *b:* Newburgh, NY; *m:* Michael; *c:* Kara, Jill; *ed:* Mt St Mary Coll (BA) Scndry Ed, His 1975; SUNY at New Paltz (MS) Scndry Ed, His 1980; *cr:* St Mary Schl Soc Stud Tchr 1975-78; Highland Falls MS Soc Stud Tchr 1983-95; James I. O'Neill HS Soc Stud Tchr 1995-; *ai:* Dir Thanksgiving Dr; Co-Ldr Quiz Bowl Team 1990-; Comms Excl, Accountability; Internet Project; Tiorati Ldr 1989-93; Child Study Team 1985-93; AFT, Highland Falls Tchrs Assn, NYSUT 1983-; New Windsor Girls Sftbl 1991-93, Bd of Dir; St Joseph's Schl 1992-95, Bsktbl Coach, Chldng Coach 1988; S Jr HS PTA 1993-; *office:* James I O'Neill HS Rt 9W Highland Falls NY 10928

LEVY, MARY MARGARET, Physical Education Teacher; *b:* Spring Valley, NY; *w:* Vincent P. (dec); *c:* Erin Rebecca, Rachel Christina; *ed:* Univ of Bridgeport Arnold Coll (BA) PE 1970; Coll of New Rochelle (MS) Schl Admin & Staff Dev 1992; 60 Post Grad Credits Beyond Masters at New Rochelle, Rockland Tchrs Ctr in Staff Dev & Open Ed; *cr:* North Rockland HS PE Tchr 1996; *ai:* Key Club Adv & Fac Adv; Washingtonville HS Key Club Kiwanis Adv; AFT, NEA, NR Tchrs Assn, SPTA North Rockland 1970-; PTA Washingtonville 1982-; Spring Valley Kiwanis Club 1987-, 1st Woman in NY St; Chester Kiwanis Club 1992-, Newsletter Ed, Kiwanis Adv of Yr Awd 1994; Church, Choir 1974-, Soloist 1975; Track Coach of Yr 1975; Helped Form NY St Interscholastic Track for Women; Peer Facilitator & Coach; Class Adv 1970-74; *office:* North Rockland HS Hammond Rd Thiells NY 10984

LEVY, NANCY R., Education Professor; *b:* Chicago, IL; *m:* Harold L.; *c:* Ellen Davey, Susan; *ed:* Univ of Chicago (BA) Soc Sci 1958; Towson St Univ (MED) Rdng 1978; Johns Hopkins Univ (EDD) Spec Ed 1993; 12 Grad Credit Hrs Univ of Chicago Grad Schl of Ed 1962-63; *cr:* Homewood Pub Schls 5th Grd Tchr 1958-63; Bryn Mawr Schl k-12 Rdng Specialist Tchr 1977-81; Boys' Latin Schl HS Eng Tchr 1981-85; Garrison Forest Schl MS Eng Tchr 1985-91; Boys' Latin Schl MS Tchr 1993-94; Goucher Coll Ed Prof 1994-; *ai:* Baltimore Area Comm Stu Tchng Mem; Spec Ed Adv Comm Baltimore City Pub Schls; IRA 1979-; Orton Dyslexia Soc 1980-; Cncl for Learning disabilities, CEC 1990-; 3 Articles Pub; John Hopkins Univ Schlsps, Flwshps; Dodge Fnd, Goucher Coll Rsrch Grant; *office:* Goucher Coll 1021 Dulaney Valley Rd Baltimore MD 21204*

LEVY, RICHARD ANDREW, Spanish & ESL Teacher; *b:* New York City, NY; *m:* Geraldine Lisanit; *c:* Alessandra, Paul; *ed:* Herbert H. Lehman Coll (BA) Fr Lit 1974; Univ of Stony Brook (MA) TESOL Linguistics 1994; Span Cert; *cr:* Bellport Jr HS Span Tchr 1991-92; Copeogue Jr HS Span Tchr 1992-93; Hampton Bays Scndry Schl ESL Tchr 1994-; *ai:* Jr HS Bsbl Coach; Jazz Band; NYSAFLT; NYSIT; *office:* Hampton Bays Jr Sr HS 88 Argonne Rd Hampton Bays NY 11946*

LEVY, SHIRLEY YADGAROFF, Library Teacher; *b:* London, England; *m:* Robert; *c:* Andrew, Rani; *ed:* CCNY at New York (BS) Elem Ed 1956; 80 Credit Hrs Post Grad Stud at Hunter Coll; *cr:* PS 9 Second Grd Tchr 1956-62; PS 59 2-6 Grd Tchr 1975-83; PS 42 1-2 Grd Tchr, Lib Tchr 1983-; *ai:* UFT, AFT 1956-; NYC Lib Assn 1993-; *office:* PS 42 Benjamin Altman Schl 71 Hester St New York NY 10002

LEVY, STEVEN ELLIOT, Social Science Teacher; *b:* New York, NY; *m:* Eleanor Joseph; *c:* Felice, Neal, Traci, Deborah; *ed:* Hunter Coll (BA) His 1968; NYU (MA) His 1970; 24 Degree Credits Ed Amin; *cr:* JHS 120 Tchr 1968-71; JHS 141 Tchr 1971-85; Isaac Newton JHS Tchr 1985-; *ai:* AFT 1968-, Chapter Ldr; Dist Four Furniture Repair Prgm Dir; Career Ed Prgm Facilitator; *office:* Isaac Newton Jr HS E 116th St & FDR Dr New York NY 10029*

LEVY, SUSAN GAIL, Sixth Grade Teacher; *b:* New York, NY; *m:* Bryan; *c:* Amy, Barry, Michael; *ed:* The City Coll of NY (BS) Elem Ed 1971; 36 Cr-Masters Equivalency Millersville Univ; *cr:* San Diego City Schls Tchr, Supvr 1974-81; Hempfield Schl Dist Tchr 1990-; *ai:* NEA, PSEA 1990-; Jewish Ctr Yth 1989-, Adv; Jewish Comm Ctr, Dir 1991, Day Camp 1992, 1995; *office:* Mountville Elem Schl 120 College Ave Mountville PA 17554*

LEW, MAX, English Teacher; *b:* Paris, France; *m:* Vicky Zytnick; *c:* Nechama Goodman, Avi, Dov; *ed:* Yeshiva Coll (BA) Eng 1961; Hunter Coll (MA) Eng 1967; *cr:* Touro Coll Tchr 1977-81; Franklin D Roosevelt HS Tchr 1965-; *ai:* Assn Orthodox Jewish Tchrs 1965-, Akiva Clubs Dir, recognition Awd 1976; Supt of Brooklyn HS Awd 1991; Dist 20 Comm Schl Bd Awd 1996; *office:* Franklin Delano Roosevelt HS 5800 20th Ave Brooklyn NY 11204*

LEWANDOWSKI, AMY KOSNIK, Sixth Grade Teacher; *b:* Buffalo, NY; *c:* Todd; *ed:* St Univ Coll at Buffalo (BS) Ed 1972, (MS) Ed 1975; 7 Post Grad Credits; *cr:* Lincoln Elem Schl 4th-5th Grd Tchr 1972-81; Cayuga Heights Elem Schl 3rd, 5th Grd Tchr 1981-86; Depew MS 5th-6th Grd Tchr 1986-; *ai:* Bldg Comm 10 Yrs; Bldg Rep for Tchr Ed & Prof Standards Comm 13 Yrs; Depew Tchrs Org 1972-, Bldg Rep; NY St United Tchrs, AFT 1972-; *office:* Depew MS 5201 S Transit Rd Depew NY 14043

LEWANDOWSKI, MARY ANN HARRIS, Second Grade Teacher; *b:* Wilmington, DE; *m:* Albert S.; *c:* Benjamin, Mary; *ed:* Univ of DE (BS) Elem Ed 1968; 30 Grad Credits Elem Ed; *cr:* Brookside Schl 5th Grd Tchr

1968-72; Red Lion Chrstn Acad 2nd Grd Tchr 1981-; *ai:* Patriotic Comm; St Mark's United Meth Church 1975-, Chair Ed Comm, Childrens Coord; *office:* Red Lion Christian Acad 1400 Red Lion Rd Bear DE 19701

LEWBEL, SAMUEL ROBERT, 7th Grade Social Studies Tchr; *b:* New York City, NY; *ed:* Cntrl CT St Univ (BS) US His 1972, (MS) US His 1978; *cr:* Mc Gee MS Spec Ed Aide 1973-74; Rochambeou MS Tchr 1976-; New England League of MS Journal Ed 1992-; Quinnipiac Coll Adj 1993-; *ai:* Cross Cntry Coach, Boys Track Coach; His Day Contest Adv; New England League of MS 1989-, Publication Comm; Pomperacy Ed Assn 1976-, Bldg Rep; BSA 1987-, Cub Master, Asst Scout Master, Eagle Scout; Celebration of Excl CT St 3 Times; Region #15 Tchr of Yr 1986; CT Mid Level Edctr of Yr 1994; His Day Tchr of Merit 1994; *office:* Rochambeau MS 100 Peter Rd Southbury CT 06488

LEWELLEN, DALE ERIC, Band Director; *b:* Lancaster, OH; *m:* Eileen G. Maynard; *c:* Jeremy, Nathan, Matthew, Evan, Kathleen; *ed:* Kent St Univ (BM) Music Ed 1983; 4 Qtr Hrs Univ of Rio Grande; *cr:* Coshocton City Schls Band Dir 1984-86; Oak Hill Union Local Schls Band Dir 1986-; *ai:* Jr Beta Club Spon, Adv; NEA, OEA, OHUEA 1984-, Pres 1991-95; MENC 1984-; *office:* Oak Hill Union Local Schls 205 Western Ave Oak Hill OH 45656

LEWELLEN, SCOTT J., Earth & Environmental Sci Tchr; *b:* Jamestown, NY; *m:* Brenda; *c:* Carrie, Todd, Beck; *ed:* Dartmouth Coll (BA) Environmental Ed 1974; 49 Grad Hrs Various Inst; *cr:* Randolph Cntrl Schl Sci Tchr 1974-79; Bankers Trust Mgmt 1979-80; Bemus Point Cntrl Schl Sci Tchr 1981-; *ai:* JV Bsbl Coach; Battle of Bus Ldr; Various HS Comms; NEA 1981-; Chautauqua Cty Environmental Mgmt Cncl 1992-, EPA Region 2 Ed & Media Awd; Bemus Pt U Meth Church; *office:* Maple Grove Jr Sr HS Dutch Hollow Rd Bemus Point NY 14712

LEWICKI, KATHARINE WACH, Mathematics Teacher; *b:* Chicago, IL; *m:* Robert J.; *c:* Ben, Ann; *ed:* OH St Univ (BSEd) Eng & Elem Ed 1976; OH St Univ MSEd) Early & Mid Chldhd with a Math Major 1991; *cr:* Gahanna MS East Tchr 1988-; *ai:* Mathcounts Coach; Drama Club Coach; NCTM 1988-; OCTM 1990-, Outstanding Classroom Tchr 1991; Mathcounts Team in Top 10 the Last 5 Yrs in a Row; 100 Percent of my Stdnts have Passed the 9th Grd Proficiency Test on Their First Try; *office:* Gahanna MS-EAST 730 Clotts Rd Gahanna OH 43230*

LEWIN, DEBRA ANN, HS Mathematics Teacher; *b:* New York City, NY; *ed:* SUNY at Stony Brook (BS) Math 1979; Pace Univ (MBA) Corporate Financial Mgmt 1987; Coll of New Rochelle (MS) Schl Admin & Supervision 1990; *cr:* George Washington HS Math Tchr 1979-83; Evander Childs HS 1983-85; Doubleday & Co Financial Analyst 1985-87; Sullivan & Cromwell Sr Financial Analyst 1987-88; Evander Childs HS Math Tchr 1988-94; Jane Addams Voc HS Pgm Chair & HS Math Tchr 1994-; *ai:* Dir of Honor Schl & Arista; Selection Comm for In-House Coll Schlsp Awds & Comm HS Math Curr Mem; ASCD 1991-; NYC Tchrs Ed Assn 1989-; Standing Comm on Math 1991-, Sec; NYC Tchrs of Math 1988-; Presenter at NYCTM Convention 1993; *office:* Jane Addams Voc HS 900 Tinton Ave Bronx NY 10456*

LEWIN, MICHAEL R., Prof of Piano & Artistic Dir; *b:* Brooklyn, NY; *m:* Dora Present; *ed:* Juilliard Schl (BM) Piano 1977, (MM) Piano 1978; *cr:* Whitman Coll Johnston Visiting Prof 1986-87; Boston Conservatory Prof of Piano, Boston Conservatory Chamber Players 1988-; *ai:* World-wide Concert Tours; Recordings; Liszt Competition Winner 1986; Beethoven Flwshp 1983; MD Intnl Competition 1982; NEA Solo Recitalists Grant; Rockefeller Schlsp; *office:* Boston Conservatory of Music 8 The Fenway Boston MA 02215

LEWIS, ALLISON, Group Teacher; *b:* New York, NY; *c:* Khyla Veneaut Machuca; *ed:* LaGuardia Comm Coll (AS) Mental Hlth 1987-89; 110 Credits Pursing BA Clinical Psych Old Westbury Coll; *cr:* Bathgate Comm Ctr Asst Tchr 1986-88; Claremont Comm Ctr Asst Tchr 1989; Lucille Murray CDC Group Tchr 1990-; *ai:* Choir Dir; St Barnabas Hosp Vol 1986; Most Valueable Tchr Awd Spec Ed Dept; Sidewalk Theatre Dealing with Homeless Children; HS Stu Mentor, Receive Awd; *home:* 125 W 228th St Apt 11F Bronx NY 10463

LEWIS, BRIAN SALVATORE, French Teacher; *b:* Lima, PA; *ed:* St Joseph's Univ (BS) Fr 1992; Univ of PA (MSEd) Scndry Ed 1993; *cr:* Haddon Twp HS All Levels Fr Tchr 1993-; *ai:* Fr Club; HIV, AIDS Awareness Ctr; Dir Annual One-Act Plays; Ind Stud Tchr; AATF 1993-; Alliance Francaise 1995-; Commended Courier Post Delegation Ldr People to People Stu Exch Prgm, HIV, Aids Ctr Elizabeth Taylor Aids Fnd; *office:* Hadden Township High School 406 Memorial Ave Westmont NJ 08108

LEWIS, CARLA KOTAS, Third & Fourth Grade Teacher; *b:* Friend, NE; *m:* Henry; *c:* Trevor, Tyler; *ed:* Univ of NE (BA) Elem Ed, Spec Ed 1974; Univ of VT (MA) Rdng, Lang 1985; 15 Credit Hrs St Michael's; Univ of VT, Trinity, Goddard, VT Coll; *cr:* Sub Tchr, Tutor, Spec Ed Aide 1974-78; Fayston Elem Schl 3-5 Primary Grds Tchr 1978-; *ai:* Curr Comm; Local Standards Bd 4 Yrs; VT Tchrs Assn, NEA 1978-; ASCD 1995-; Washington West Dist Tchrs of Yr 1988; Finalist VT Tchr of Yr 1996; *office:* Fayston Elem Schl German Flats Rd Fayston VT 05673*

LEWIS, CAROL CYNTHIA CURTIS, Jr High English Teacher; *b:* Odgensburg, NY; *m:* William G.; *c:* Cynthia C. Miller, Will V., Sherrill L., Heather Lewis-Hoover, Kevin C.; *ed:* Syracuse Univ (BA) Eng 1981; SUNY at Cortland (MS) Rdng 1985; 15 Credit Hrs; Mohawk Vly Comm Coll Assoc Lbrl Arts 1977; *cr:* Brookfield Cntrl Schl Sub Tchr 1974-81; Mt Markham Cntrl Schl Sub Tchr 1974-81; Edmeston Cntrl Schl 4th Grd Tchr 1981-82, Jr High Eng Tchr 1982-; *ai:* Jr Class Adv; Field Hockey Ofcl; NYSUT 1986-; Ed Tchrs Assoc 1991-; Peet Hook Theatre Group, Past Bd Mem; BSA 10 Yrs; St Andrews Church 1959-; Order of Eastern Star 1960-, Star Pts; Utica Bd of Field Hockey Ofcls 1974-, Pres; NY Bd of Field Hockey Ofcls 1988-, Sec; Leonardsville Meth Church 1990-, Assoc Mbrshp, Layspeaker; Edmeston Comm Schl Org Tchr of Yr Awd 1994; *home:* PO Box 34 Leonardsville NY 13364*

LEWIS, CAROL D., Band Director; *b:* Norfolk, VA; *c:* Eric, Robert; *ed:* Temple Univ (BM)(BMED) Flute Performance 1969, (MMED) Ed 1977; Combs Coll of Music (DMA) Flute Performance, Composition 1987; Real Estate Sales License 1973; Estititian St CA 1980; *cr:* Camden City Schls Dept Head, Band Dir 1969-79; Camden Cty Coll, Rowan Coll, Moravian Coll Flute Instr 1969-93; LCC Spec Ed Music Therapy 1981-87; Edgewood Schls Choir, Band Dir 1987-; *ai:* Jazz Band; Brass Ensemble; Flute Choir; NEA, NJEA, Local Musicians 77 1969-; Musicians Local 802 1988-; NARAS 1990-; Amer Assn Music Copyists Flute Soc; Camden Cty Cultural, Heritage Commission 1995-, Commissioner; Numerous Performances, Music Preparations; Consulting Producer Singing City CHoir, Duke Ellington Orch 1995; *office:* Edgewood Sr HS 250 Cooper's Folly Rd Atco NJ 08004*

LEWIS, CAROL HAWISHER, First Grade Teacher; *b:* Lima, OH; *m:* George Joseph; *c:* John Alan, Timothy Gene; *ed:* OH Northern Univ (BS) El Ed 1969; Cert Lima Schl of Practical Nursing 1959; Licensed Practical Nurse St of Oh; Addl Credit Hrs Schl Counseling; *cr:* St Ritas Medical Ctr Practical Nurse 1960-75; United Local El Schl 1st Grd Tchr 1969-; *ai:* Vol Prison Worker, Help Train Vols, Facilitator for Bible Seminars, Write Bible Lessons for Seminars, Help at Haflway House; NEA 1969-, Mem; Church 1941-, Tchr; Martha Holden Jennings Scholar; *home:* 3720 S Kemp Rd Cridersville OH 45806

LEWIS, CAROL (RUPP), Kindergarten Teacher; *b:* Greensburg, PA; *m:* Terrence D.; *c:* Terrence Jr., Kristen; *ed:* Grove City Coll (BA) Elem Ed 1970; Attnd Ball St Univ, Penn St Univ, CA Univ of PA; *cr:* Hempfield Schl Dist 4th Grd Tchr 1970-71; Centerville Schl Dist 6th Grd Tchr 1971-72; Head Start of Westmoreland Cty Supvr, Tchr 1977; Holy Cross Schl Kndgtn, 4th-5th Grd Tchr 1978-; *ai:* Chess Club; Bell Choir; NCEA 1978-; St Luke's Luth Church 1985-, Choir Dir; *home:* 606 Delaware Ave Scottdale PA 15683*

LEWIS, CHERYL LYNN, 4th-6th Grd Gftd Support Tchr; *b:* Charleroi, PA; *m:* Gary Michael; *c:* Zachary, Lewis; *ed:* CA Univ of PA (BS) Elem Ed 1970; Post Grad Credits Millersville St Coll; *cr:* Marion Elem Schl Art 1970-76; Rostraver Elem Schl Self Contained 6th Grd 1976-82; Marion Elem Schl Self Containes 5-6th Grd Tchr 1982-93, 4th-6th Grd Gifted Support Tchr 1993-; *ai:* AFT 1988-93; NEA 1970-88; Roscoe Boro Cncl 1988-, Councilperson; Elder Presbyn Chrch 1994-; *office:* Marion Elem Schl 500 Perry Ave Belle Vernon PA 15012

LEWIS, CYNDI M., Chemistry Teacher; *b:* Springfield, OH; *m:* Krut; *c:* Ryan; *cr:* Kettering Fairmont Chem Tchr 1993-; *office:* Kettering Fairmont HS 3301 Shroyer Rd Kettering OH 45429

LEWIS, DALE J., Secondary Social Studies Tchr; *b:* Erie, PA; *m:* Donna M. Colley; *ed:* Gannon Univ (BA) Soc Sci 1982; Completing (MA) in Curr & Instruction; *cr:* St Patrick Elem PE Instr 1982-89; Academy HS Sco Stud Tchr 1999-91; Erie East HS Soc Stud Tchr 1991-92; Fairview HS Soc Stud Tchr 1992-; *ai:* Extra Curr Act Dir; Asst Ftbl Coach; NEA, PA St Ed Assn, Fairview Ed Assn 1990-; PA St Geographic Alliance 1991-; PA St Ath Dir Assn, Dist 10 Ath Dir Assn 1994-; *office:* Fairview HS 7460 Mccray Rd Fairview PA 16415

LEWIS, DEBORAH LEE, Third Grade Teacher; *b:* Baltimore, MD; *m:* Manuel A. Jr.; *c:* Shannan Dawn; *ed:* Univ of Baltimore (BA) Elem Ed 1973; Towson St, Hopkins Univ 30 Credit Hrs Ed MA Equiv; *cr:* Charlesmont Elem Schl 3rd Grd Tchr 1973-; *ai:* Exec Bd; Multicultural Laison; Grd Chprsn; Soc Comm; NEA 1973-; Galilee Bapt Church 1959-, Choir; Balto Cty Chamber of Commerce Awd of Excl in Ed; Maryland Tchr of Yr Recognition Awd; *home:* 7233 Orth Rd Baltimore MD 21219

LEWIS, DONNA CHATLAND, 9th-12th Grd English Teacher; *b:* Port Huron, MI; *m:* Dennis J.; *c:* Norman, Deena; *ed:* SUNY (BA) Eng, Ed 1971; SUNY at Potsdam (MA) Ed, Specializing Rd 1978; *cr:* Notre Dame Schl 3, 5, 7-8 Grd Tchr 1972-80; Brushton-Moira Cntrl Schl 9-12 Grd Eng Tchr 1981; Malone Cntrl Schl 9-12 Grd Eng Tchr 1983-; North Cntry Comm Coll Dev Composition 1995; *ai:* Eng & Travel Club Adv; Franklin Acad Schl Improvement Comm; AFT, NYSUT 1983-; *office:* Malone Cntrl Schls Malone NY 12953

LEWIS, EVELYN ELLIOTT, Art Teacher; *b:* Utica, NY; *c:* Orion, Jasmine, Maya; *ed:* Alfred Univ Coll of Ceramics (BFA) Photography, Art Ed 1971; Alfred Leairwsitg Grad Schl (MSEd) Art Ed 1972; Coll of St Rose 6 Hrs Grad Level 1976; SUNY at Geneseo 6 Hrs Grad Level 1975-76; *cr:* Mt Lake Terr Jr High 7-9th Grd Art Tchr 1973-75; Dansville Sr HS 9-12th Grd Art Tchr 1975-; *ai:* Class of 1998 Adv; Natl Art Honor Soc; Jr Prom; Sr Ball; Spirit Week for Homecoming; AFT 1975-; Dansville Tchrs Assn 1975-, Newsletter Ed; NYS Art Tchr Assn 1980-, Bldg Rep, Negotiator; NAEA 1980-; NYSUT, Rep; *office:* Dansville Sr HS N Main St Dansville NY 14437

LEWIS, GREGORY W. J., Rel & Soc Studies Dept Chair; *b:* Rochester, NY; *m:* Jennifer Pepi; *c:* Zoe Skye; *ed:* NY Univ (BA) His of Rel 1973, (MA) Rel Ed 1975; Pratt Inst (MS) Information Mngmt 1981; *cr:* Masters Schl Media Specialist 1979-81; Mt St Joseph Acad Rel Tchr 1981-; *ai:* Mediation Team, Soc Justice Club Moderator; Core Mediation Prgm Dir; MA Bar Fnd Grants 1989-92; Mayor's Neighborhood Safety Grant 1994; *home:* 3 Bayou St Winthrop MA 02152*

LEWIS, HOPE GERSHEN, 5th Grade GATE Pgm Teacher; *b:* New York City, NY; *m:* Leon D.; *c:* Stacey N., Scott D.; *ed:* Hunter Coll (BA) Anthropology 1966; The Coll of New Rochelle Curr Dev for the Potentially Gifted, Culturally Different I, II, Implementing Differentiated Curr for the Culturally Different-Potentially Gifted; Lehman Coll Writing Practice Theory; Dominican Coll Cmptr Programming for Edctrs; *cr:* CB 132 K-2 Grd Early Chldhd Tchr 1966-71; PS 31 5th Grd GATE Pgm Tchr 1981-; *ai:* Chess Club Adv; Values Ed Prgm Chprsn; Cmptr Comm; Alternative Assessment Stud Group; UFT, AFT 1966-; Tchr Writer; *office:* PS 31 William Lloyd Garrison 425 Grand Concourse Bronx NY 10451*

LEWIS, JANE (INGRAM), Soc Studies Teacher; *b:* New York City, NY; *m:* John Lewis Jr.; *c:* John, Diane; *ed:* SUNY at New Paltz (BA) Ed 1962; Iona Coll (MS) His, Ed 1984; Post Grad Plus 60 Credit Hrs at Coll of New Rochelle, Iona, Long Island Univ, Hunter Coll; *cr:* Wh Plains Pub Schls Elem Tchr 1962-76; Clarkstown Schl Dist Jr HS Soc Stud Tchr 1979-83, Sr HS Soc Stud, Global Stud, Amer His, Govt, Ec Tchr 1983-; *ai:* Interact, Soph Class Adv; Fund-Raising Activity Ldr; Clarkstown Tchr Assn 1980-, Schl Rep; AFT; Rockl Co SS Tchrs Assn 1986-; New City Lib 1986-, Group Recognition; Catskill Lib Assn Gifts Comm, Fund Raising; Arethusa Alum Assn 1962-, Pres 1989-91; New City Rotary Club Recognition Awd; *office:* Clarkstown HS North Congers Rd New City NY 10956

LEWIS, JENNIFER E., Special Education Teacher; *b:* Hartford, CT; *ed:* Smith Coll (BA) His 1989; Univ of CT (MA) Ed 1991; *cr:* W. Johnston MS Resource Tchr 1 Yr; Univ of CT Grad Asst 1 Yr; *ai:* Yrbk Club Adv; NEA, Phi Delta Kappa 1991-; Yth Stud Ctr 1991-, Vol Tutor; Publication Stu Handbook Univ of CT; *office:* Vernon Ctr MS 777 Hartford Tpke Vernon Rockville CT 06066

LEWIS, JOAN CAROL, Chemistry Teacher; *b:* Dayton, OH; *ed:* Eastern KY Univ (BS) Chem & Math 1982, (MA) Chem Ed 1983; Inst for Chemical Ed at Univ of CA at Berkeley 1987; *cr:* Bellevue HS Chem Tchr 1983-91; Roger Bacon HS Chem Tchr 1991-; *ai:* Acad Team Coach; Taking Responsibility for the Earth Everyday Recycling Club Spon; NSTA 1982-; NEA 1985-; ACS 1991-; Northern KY Univ Woodrow Wilson Fellowship 1990-91, 1993; Presented Fire Safety Wkshp for Northern KY Firefighters; Inst for Chemical Ed Tchng Tips & Demonstrations at KAPS Convention; PTA Tchr of Yr Awd 1987; The Drackett Co. Internship; Presenter of "How to Start a Chem Shadowing Prgm" 1993; *office:* Roger Bacon HS 4320 Vine St Cincinnati OH 45217*

LEWIS, JOANNE, Fifth Grade Teacher; *b:* Pittsburgh, PA; *m:* William R.; *c:* Linda Ritsig, Michael, Jessica; *ed:* Clarion Univ (AA) Habilitative Services 1980; Clarion Univ (BS) Spec Ed 1981; Slippery Rock Univ (MS) Ed 1984; *cr:* Franklin Area Schl Dist Elem, Spec Ed Mixed Category Tchr 1981-86, 5th Grd Tchr 1986-; *ai:* Lead Tchr; Instructional Support Team; NEA 1981-, IPD Chprsn, Building Rep, Staff Dev Comm Chprsn; PA Dept of Ed Tech Grant Recipient; Mentor Tchr; *office:* Victory Elem Schl R D 1 Georgetown Rd Harrisville PA 16038*

LEWIS, JOANNE, Business Education Teacher; *b:* Springfield, VT; *ed:* Trinity Coll of VT (BS) Bus Admin, (BA) Scndry Ed 1993; 6 Addl Credits; *cr:* Bariatrix Intl Admin Asst 1993; Danville Schl HS Bus Tchr 1993-; VT Army Natl Guard Gen 1990-; *ai:* Adv FBLA, Jr Class, Upward Bound; NEA 1993-, Sec; VT Army Natl Guard 1990-, Sgt, Natl Defense, Ldrshp, Achvmt Awds; *office:* Danville Schl PO Box 176 Danville VT 05828*

LEWIS, JOHN EDWARD, Mathematics Teacher; *b:* Boston, MA; *m:* Judith Ann Kent; *c:* Anne Marie Wilmot, David; *ed:* SUNY at Plattsburgh (BS) Math Ed 1965; Grad Stud at Cornell Univ, Mt Holyoke Coll; *cr:* Van Wyck Jr HS Math Tchr 1965-68; John Jay HS Math Tchr 1969-84; Roy C. Ketcham HS Math HS 1984-; *ai:* Track, Field Coach 1966-; Cross Coach 1986-94; Wappingers Congress of Tchrs, AFT 1970-, VP 1971-76; Assn of Math Tchrs of NY St 1980-; BPOE 1991-; K of C Westchester, Rockland, Dutchess Track Coaches Assn 1985-, Exec C Richard Lacey Coaches Awd for Distngd Svc 1995; *home:* 26 Fenm Wappingers Falls NY 12590

LEWIS, JUDY OUELLETTE, 8th Grd Language Arts Teach Rutland, VT; *m:* David; *c:* Jennifer, Heather, Lindsay; *ed:* Plymouth S (BS) Ed 1972; Post Grad Stud Univ of Mass at Lowell, Boston Univ of NH; *cr:* Allenstown Elem Schl 5th Grd Tchr 1973-84; Armand D Schl 7th-8th Grd Eng 1985-87; Rundlett Jr HS 8th Grd Lang Arts *ai:* NEA 1973-; NH Tchrs Eng Assn 1991-; Chubb Life Amer Fellow *office:* Rundlett Jr HS 10 Conant Park Dr Concord NH 03301

LEWIS, JULIA ANN, Physical Education Teacher; *b:* Columbus, O Bowling Green St Univ (BS) Ed 1979; Kent St Univ (MA) Sports 1984, (EDS) Educl Admin 1994; *cr:* Tallmadge Recreation Dept 1975-79; Akron Pub Schls PE Tchr 1979-82, 1984-; Kent St Univ Gra 1983-84; *ai:* Ath Dir; Girls Bsktbl Coach; Discipline Review Comm Ldrshp Team; PE, Hlth Dept Chprsn; AAHPERD 1975-; Jr League Ctr for Marine Conservation, World Wildlife Fund, Sierra Club, Peace 1991-; *office:* Akron East Sr HS 80 Brittain Rd Akron OH 44

LEWIS, KAREN JEAN, Sixth Grade Teacher; *b:* Lancaster, PA Millersville Univ (BS) Elem Ed 1990, (MED) Elem Ed 1995; *cr:* Esh Elem Schl Sixth Grd Tchr 1991-; *ai:* NEA, PSEA 1991-; Penn Mar Assn 1991-, VP; *office:* Eshleman Elem Schl 545 Leaman Ave Mille PA 17551

LEWIS, KATHLEEN ANN (MYERS), English Teache Independence, MO; *m:* William; *c:* Cassandra; *ed:* MO Western S Eng 1980; 15 Credit Hrs TX Women's Univ 1984; Attnd North TX S *cr:* Westfield HS Eng 10 Tchr, Girls' Bsktbl 1981-83; Escuela Ame Eng 1986-87, Curr Coord 1987-89; Lincoln Intl Schl AP Eng, Boys, HS Bsktbl; *ai:* NHS Adv; HS Boys, Girls Bsktbl Coach; Jr Class NASSP 1992-; NHS 1973-; John Greif Eng Awd, MO Outstdng Co Major 1980; *office:* Lincoln Intl Schl Kathmandu Ls Dept Of Washington DC 20521*

LEWIS, NANCY F., Prof of English & Coordinator; *b:* Perth Ambo *m:* Ralph David; *c:* Rebecca L. Alexander, Rachael L. Ide; *ed:* Tren Coll (BA) Eng 1958; Hunter Coll (MA) Eng Lit 1964; *cr:* Woodbrid Eng Tchr 1958-59; Colton-Pierrepont Anhal Schl Schl Librn, Eng 1959-60; Nations Bus Magazine Merchandising Mgr 1963-65; Bri HS Schl Librn, Eng Tchr 1965-68; North Shore Comm Coll Eng Coord, Hnrs Prgm 1970-; *ai:* Hnrs Prgm Coord; Organized Alpha L Chptr of Pi Theta Kappa, Adv; NEA; Citation Outstdng Perf 1988; N Excl Awd Intnl Conf Tchng Excl 1993; NSCC Prof Growth Recog Awds; *office:* North Shore Comm Coll 1 Ferncroft Rd Danvers MA 0

LEWIS, NED L., Music Teacher; *b:* Shreveport, LA; *ed:* Fisk Univ Music Ed 1974; Univ of MI (MM) Organ Performance 1976; S Choral Music Cert Hampton Univ; *cr:* Tuskegee Univ Univ Organis 1976-79; Mount Gilead Bapt Church Minister of Music 1980-83; C Hill Cluster Schl Music Tchr 1983-92; Dunbar Sr HS Music Tchr, Dir 1992-; *ai:* Choral Dir; Concert Choir; WA Tchrs Union Theodore Presser Awd; Ranckham Schl of Grad Stud Flwshp, Univ Campus; WA Post Outstdng Tchr Awd Finalist; *office:* Dunbar HS D Fine Arts 1301 New Jersey Ave NW Washington DC 20001*

LEWIS, PAMELA ANNE, French Teacher; *b:* Jamaica, NY; *ed:* NY (BA) Fr 1975, (MA) Fr Lit 1977; *cr:* Francis Xavier HS Fr & Ge 1978-81; Sacred Heart Acad Fr & Eng Tchr 1981-83; Museum of M Art Admin Asst & Drawings Dept 1983-86; Metropolitan Museum Admin Asst & Stu & Tchr Prgms Dept 1986-89; Hunter Coll HS F 1989-; *ai:* African-amer Cultural Soc, Polyglot Foreign langs Mag Programming Comm-11th Grd Prgm Adv; AFT 1989-.

LEWIS, PATTY L., English & History Teacher; *b:* Lima, OH; *m:* W R.; *c:* Steven, Andrew; *ed:* Wilmington Coll (BA) His, Eng 1967; 30 Hrs Grad Work Ashland Coll; *cr:* Blanchester HS Eng, His Tchr 19 Teays Vly HS Eng, HIs Tchr 1974-77; South Central HS Eng, His 1977-86; Granville HS Eng, His Tchr 1986-; *ai:* Stu Cncl Adv; So Dept Chair; Prins Advy Comm; Revie Evaluation Supts Comm; OEA, Local Tchr Org 1974-, Sec, VP, Pres; Greenwich Lib Bd; Gree Ladies Historical Soc; Ashville Jr Women's Club; Martha Holden Jen Scholar; *office:* Granville HS 248 New Burg St Granville OH 43023

LEWIS, PHILIP, Second Grade Teacher; *b:* Lynn, MA; *m:* Shery Westfield St Coll (BSE) Elem Ed 1975; *cr:* Southampton Rd Schl 3r Tchr 1986-87, 1st Grd Tchr 1987-88, 2nd & 3rd Grd Tchr 1988-91, 2r Tchr 1991-; *ai:* Schl Improvement Cncl Mem 1987-90; Schl Cncl 1994-; NEA 1985-; MA Tchr Assn 1985-; Westfield Ed Assn 1985-, Bd Mem; *office:* Southampton Road Schl 330 Southampton Rd We MA 01085

LEWIS, RICHARD A., Mathematics Teacher; *b:* Freeport, N Lorraine M. Murphy; *c:* Kevin, Brian, Michele Kimbrell; *ed:* St U NY at Albany (BS) Math 1961; Adelphi Univ (MS) Math Ed 1969; St Univ of NY, Hofstra Univ, Westminster Coll, PA St Univ; *cr:* W Floyd Schl Dist Math Tchr 1961-75, math Dept Chm 1969-74, Math 1974-78, Asst HS Prin 1978-82; clarion Arch Schl Dist Scndry 1982-92, Math Tchr 1992-; *ai:* NCTM 1961-; NEA, PSEA 1992- Inst; *office:* Clarion Area Jr Sr HS 219 Liberty St Clarion PA 16214

LEWIS, ROBERT ALAN, Industrial Language Teacher; *b:* New C PA; *m:* Cathleen L. Taylor; *c:* Robert T., Margaret J. Suit, Ann L. Su CA Univ of PA (BA) Industrial Arts 1970; Westminster Coll (M Scndry Ed 1975; *cr:* Ellwood City Area Schls Tchr 26 1-2 Yrs; *ai:* Fac Sound Mgr; NEA, PSEA, EAEA 1970-, Chief Negotiator; *office:* El City Area Schls 501 Crescent Ave Ellwood City PA 16117

LEWIS, ROBERT ANTHONY,JR., Civics & US History Tc Connellsville, PA; *ed:* IN Univ of Penna (BS) Scndry Soc Sci Ed Univ of Pittsburgh MA Pgm in His; *cr:* Taylor Allderdice HS Civics His Tchr 1991-; *ai:* Stu Ldrshp Pgm Adv; Pittsburgh Fed of Tchrs Pub in Journal of Amer His 1994; *office:* Taylor Allderdice HS 2409 Ave Pittsburgh PA 15217*

LEWIS, ROBERT DAVID, Science Dept Chprsn & Tchr; *b:* Pitts PA; *ed:* IN Univ of PA (BS) Scndry Earth & Space Sci 1976; U Rochester (MS) Scndry Sci Ed 1980; *cr:* Wayland-Cohocton Cntr Earth Sci Tchr 1976-; *ai:* Astronomy Club; Natl Sci Olympiad Asst C NEA 1976-; United Meth Church 1976-; Tchr of the Yr 1980; Genese Regnl Tchr of the Yr 1980; *office:* Wayland-Cohocton Cntrl Schl Route 63 Wayland NY 14572

LEWIS, ROBERT K., Band & Drama Teacher; *b:* Farmville, VA; *m:* A.; *c:* Adam, Joshua, Mark; *ed:* Salisbury St Coll (BS) Music Ed 19 Laurel Schl Dist HS Band & Drama Dir, MS Gen Music Tchr 198 Marching Band; Leo Club & Drama Club Adv; NEA 1987-; DMEA MNEC 1987-; SCMEA 1987-; Lions Club 1994-, Project Chm; Laurel Sr HS 1133 S Central Ave Laurel DE 19956

LEWIS, ROWENA LOUISE, 8th Grade Language Arts Tchr; *b:* B Bow, OK; *m:* Clarence W.; *c:* Riccardo, Clarence III, Khalisha; Langston Univ Elem Ed 1969; *cr:* Dowagiac Schls 6th Grd Tchr 19 Akron Pub Schls 6th Grd Tchr 1973-83, 7th Grd Tchr 1983-93, 8t

1993-; *ai:* 7th-8th Grds Girls Sftbl, Vlybl Coach; Act Supvr; Akron ssn 1973-; *office:* Riedinger MS 77 W Thornton St Akron OH 44311

IS, SHARON LOWE, Peer Mediation Teacher; *b:* Salisbury, MD; *m:* R.; *c:* Brad LeFevre, Rod, Brad; *ed:* Univ of MD (BA) Eng 1973, (MA) 975; Attnd Johns Hopkins Univ, Bowie St Univ; *cr:* Prince George's ng Tchr 1973-84; Prince George's Guid Cnslr 1984-94; Eleanor evelt HS Peer Mediation Coord 1994-; *ai:* Stdnts Against Violence on; NEA, MSTA 1973-; Discoveries in Gardening 1989-, Treas; BSA , Sec; *office:* Eleanor Roosevelt HS 7601 Hanover Pky Greenbelt MD

IS, STEPHEN ROBERT, Art Teacher; *b:* Danville, PA; *m:* Sally e Burge; *c:* Michelle R., Stephanie A.; *ed:* Millersville St Coll (BS) d 1971; *cr:* Eastern Lancaster Cty Schl Dist Art Tchr 1971-; Cecil n Coll Guest Artist, Set Designer 1986; *ai:* Past Garden Spot rming Arts Artistic Dir 1978-92; NEA, PSEA, ELCEA 1971-; Arts & Magazine 1973; *office:* Eastern Lancaster County Schl PO Box 609 Holland PA 17557

IS, VALERIE MAE, Principal & Kindergarten Tchr; *b:* Brooklyn, *d:* A&T St Univ (BS) Early Chldhd Ed 1981; City Coll (MS) Rdng *cr:* Childs Meml Chrstn Acad Prin 2 Yrs, Kndgtn Tchr 15 Yrs; *ai:* h Choir; Capt Womens Day Group at Church; Tchr of Yr; *office:* s Memorial Chrstn Acad 1763 Amsterdam Ave New York NY 10031*

IS, WAYNE AUSTIN, 5th & 6th Grade PE Teacher; *b:* Rockville r, NY; *m:* Deborah A. Smith; *c:* Kimberly K.; *ed:* Dutchess Comm Art Ed 1970; SUNY at Brockport (BS) PE 1972; 15 Credit Hrs Grad PE; *cr:* Truman Elem Schl PE Tchr 1973-89; Eisenhower Elem Schl chr 1989-90; Sayreville MS 5th, 6th Grd PE Tchr 1990-; *ai:* nastic Mgr & Instr Middlesex Gymnastic Acad 1979-96; Schl ctions 1973-; Truman Schl Gymnastics Team 5 Yrs; Dev, IM After Schl Kids Fit for Life Club 1991-; Dev Recreation Hockey League 1995-; , NEA 1973-; Governors Tchr Recognition Awd 1986; Ed, Review Bd rnal of Tchng in PE 1980-83 One Article Pub; *office:* Sayreville MS ngton Rd Parlin NJ 08859

IS, WILLIAM F., Associate Professor of Mrktg; *b:* Jackson, MI; *m:* hy M.; *c:* Kathering M., Kevin F.; *ed:* Jackson Comm Coll (AGS) Ed, 961; Spring Arbor Coll (BA) Ec, Bus 1967; MI St Univ (MBA) Mrktg Univ of Cincinnati (PHD) Mrktg 1976; *cr:* Xavier Univ Asst Mrktg 973-76; Miami Univ Asst Mrktg Prof 1976-79; Univ of Dayton Assoc Prof 1980-; *ai:* Fac Adv; Stu Amer Mrktg Club; Amer Mrktg Assn ; Acad of Mrktg Sci 0964-, Dev VP; Southern Mrktg Assn 1973-; Pub es in Acad Journals; *office:* Univ Of Dayton Dept of Mgmt, Mrktg n OH 45469

ISSOHN, ROBERT LOUIS, Frgn Lang & Driver Ed Teacher; *b:* a, Colombia; *m:* Gloria B. Cohen; *c:* Joshua, Alexis, Michelle; *ed:* Island Univ (MS) Cmptr Tech 1995; Emporia St Univ (BS) Span, Ger, 1966; HIV, AIDS, Defensive Driving Instr; *cr:* Irvington HS Tchr 67; Paramus HS Tchr 1967-68; Hackensack HS Span, Driver Ed, Driver Ed, Ger Tchr 1969-; *ai:* Tchr Mentor; SADD Adv; Peer ation Certfd Adv; Sexual Harassment Panel Trained Mem; Tchr ing Tchrs; HEA, BCEA, NJEA, NEA 1967-; Rochelle Park Fire Dept 92, Batallion Chief, Life Saving Medal of Valor; Rochelle Park Fire ctor 1986-92, Fire Ofcl; Rochelle Park Municipal Alliance Comm st Alcohol, Drug Abuse 1989-, Pres; Bergen Cty Juvenile Fire ntion Prgm Edctr 1987-; Red Cross 1996; *office:* Hackensack HS 1st Beech Sts Hackensack NJ 07601*

IT, PHOEBE PLATT, Resource Room Teacher; *b:* New York, NY; ward; *c:* Jennifer Lewit Pearlman, Peter; *ed:* Mills Coll of Ed (BS) Ed 1962; Hofstra Univ (MS) Spec Ed 1975, (MS) Cnslng, Guid 1982; ib Schl 112 Kndgtn Tchr 1962-63; Pine Avenue Elem Schl Kndgtn 1963-64; Cuttermill Schl Individual Dev Class Tchr 1975; Lakeville ndividual Dev Class Tchr 1975-91, Resource Room Tchr 1992-; *ai:* Curr Group Chprsn 1993-95; Bldg Level Team; Tchr Selection ; Mentor Tchr; Presentations to Parent Groups; AFT; Great Neck Assn; Roslyn Cntry Club Civic Assn; *office:* Lakeville Schl 4727 n Ave Great Neck NY 11020*

ON, CANDACE YOUNG, Substance Abuse Prvntion Tchr; *b:* ke, MA; *m:* James B.; *c:* James, Katie, Casey; *ed:* Univ of MA (BA) 73; Westfield St Coll MS in Psych Concentrating in Guid; *cr:* Kelly Schl Tchr 1974-89; Lynch MS Substance Abuse Tchr & Mediation 1989-; *ai:* Violence Task Force Chm; Holyoke Tchrs GESA & ict Resolution & Mediation Trainer; PAC Co-Chm; NEA 1974-; MTA ; HTA 1974-; *office:* John Lynch MS 1575 Northampton St Holyoke 1040

ORF, JANET RUTH, Language Arts Teacher; *b:* Edgewater, MD; enn C.; *c:* Jennifer C.; *ed:* Towson St (BA) Eng 1973; Master's alency 15 Credits Univ of MD, 15 Credits MDSE 1977; *cr:* Mac r MS Lang Arts Tchr 1973-94; *ai:* Tabernacle 1978-, Sunday Schl Nursery Coord; *office:* Mac Arthur MS Rockenbach Rd Fort Meade 0755

SHON, DEBORAH L., Vocal Music Teacher; *b:* Williamsport, PA; rsey Shore Area Schl Dist Elem Music Tchr 1978-80; Easton Area Dist Scndry Vocal Music Tchr 1980-; *ai:* Chorale Dir; Bd of Dirs nee Little Theater; Annual Musicals Choreographer, Costumer & Coach; Cntrl Morarian Church Choir 1980-, Soloist; *office:* Shawnee nediate Schl 610 Northampton St Easton PA 18042

UREUX, DONALD CHRISTOPHER, Schl Counselor & 5th Grd *b:* Rowsell, NM; *m:* Kelly Ann; *c:* Jessie; *ed:* Univ of ME at Portland m (BS) Elem Ed; Univ of So ME (MS) Elem Cnslng 1987; 18 Addl r: Yarmouth Intermediate Schl 4th Grd Tchr 1978-87; Harrison MS rd Tchr 1987-; Rowe Schl Cnslr 1993-; *ai:* 5th Grd through JV Bsktbl ; Var Sftbl; SAT Coord; YTA Negotiations Team 1991; NEA 1978-;), ACA 1993-; Trout Unlimited 1983-, Bd of Dir; *office:* Rowe Schl son MS 8 Portland St Yarmouth ME 04096*

UREUX, JAMES MICHAEL, Admissions & Pub Relations Dir; *b:* River, MA; *m:* Ann Henry; *c:* Matthew, Erin; *ed:* RI Coll (BS) Early d Ed 1978, (BS) Spcl Ed Neurologically Impaired 1978; *cr:* Governor chl Self-Contained Tchr of LD 1978-82; Saints Peter & Paul Schl h Grd Tchr 1982-86; Bishop Connolly HS Soc Stud Tchr 1986-94, n Svc Dir 1987-91, Admissions & Pub Relations Dir 1991-; *ai:* olly Choral Group Guitarist 1987-; Yrbk Moderator 1988-93; Schl ographer 1988-; Schl Newsletter Publisher 1991-; Amnesty Intnl rator 1994-; NCEA 1982-; *office:* Bishop Connolly HS 373 Elsbree l River MA 02720

ILLER, LORRAINE DEANE, French Teacher; *b:* Titusville, PA; *m:* l A.; *c:* Erica; *ed:* Westminster Coll (BA) Fr 1978; Middlesburg Coll Fr 1984; *cr:* Cranberry Area Jr-Sr HS Fr Tchr 1979-; *ai:* Order of astern Star 1977-, Organist; Second Presbyn Church 1994-, Choir; : Cranberry Area Jr-Sr HS 1 Education Dr Seneca PA 16346

ICTORIA BLANCA, Spanish Teacher; *b:* Lima, Peru; *ed:* Queens BA) Span, Ed 1984, (MS) Span, Ed 1988; 30 Addl Credits; *cr:* Police etic League Inc Asst Dir 1983; Benjamin Cardozo HS Educl Asst Newtown HS Span Tchr 1985-; *ai:* Asst to Prgm Officer; Span Club Multi-Cultural, HIV, Schl Improvement Comms; Sr Spon Show Adv; P 1991-; AFT, NYSUT, UFT 1985-; *office:* Newtown HS 48-01 90th nhurst NY 11373*

LIAMOS, JANE BAINES, Business Instructor; *b:* Manchester, NH; *m:* Basil S.; *c:* Pamela J. Guidoboni, William J.; *ed:* Plymouth St Coll (BED) Bus Ed 1961; NH Coll (MS) Bus Ed; *cr:* Mt St Mary HS Bus Instr 1979-92; NH Tech Coll Bus Instr 1992-95; Castle Coll Bus Instr & Internship Coord 1995-; *ai:* Admissions Comm; Curr Comm; Stu Affairs Comm; NE Assoc for Cooperative Ed & Field Experience 1996; Mt St Mary Yrbk Dedication 1989; Mt St Mary Sv Awd 1992.

LIAO, ALEXANDER, Science & Psychology Teacher; *b:* Teipei, Taiwan; *m:* Carmelita Ortiz; *ed:* City Coll of NY (BS) Bio 1968; Queens Coll (MS) Sci Ed 1974; *cr:* Haaren HS Sci Tchr 9 Yrs; Park West HS Sci Tchr 13 Yrs; Bayard Rustin Schl for the Hum Sci & Psych Tchr 4 Yrs; *office:* Bayard Rustin Schl for the Hum 351 W 18th St New York NY 10011

LIAPES, PETER CHARLES, HS History Teacher; *b:* New Bruns, NJ; *m:* Catherine Ricci; *c:* Joanna, Leslie-Anne; *ed:* Cook Coll, Rutgers Univ (BA) His 1978; Rutgers Univ Grad Schl (MA) Ancient His 1984; Tchng Cert; *cr:* Wagner Coll Part Time Adjunct 1983; Hun Schl of Princeton His Tchr 1984-85; West Milford HS His Tchr 1985-; *ai:* Adv "The Historical Simulation Club"; NEA 1985-.

LIBBY, CHERI A., Prof of Management & Mktg; *b:* Bangor, ME; *ed:* Husson Coll (BS) Bus Admin 1969; Univ of Hartford (MBA) Mrktg 1979; Dale Carnegie Inst; *cr:* Univ of Hartford Instr 1979-80; Manpower Inc Dist Mgr 1980-82; Alta Enterprises Founder, Pres 1982-92; Asnuntuck CTC Prof 1982-; Comm of Terra Lux Dir 1987-; *ai:* Persons with Disabilities Chair Campus Comm; Instrl Excl Comm; Learning Disabilities Chair; Acad Skills Ctr Advy Bd; Yrbk Adv; Literacy Vol 1994-, Tutor, Mrktg Consultant; REACH 1982-, Vol, Mrktg Consultant; Several Articles Pub; *office:* Asnuntuck Comm Tech Coll 170 Elm St Enfield CT 06082

LIBBY, KARA MILEY, Social Studies Teacher & Coord; *b:* Washington, DC; *m:* Gordon Spencer III; *ed:* St Marys Coll of MD (BA) Ec, Bus 1985; Trinity Coll (MA) Admin, Supervision 1991; *cr:* Longfields Elem Schl Instrl Aid 1985; Longfields Elem Schl Cmptr Lab Operator 1986-89; Fairmont Heights Schl Classroom Tchr 1989-; *ai:* Awds Comm; Future Tchrs Mentor; Crisis Intervention Team Mem; Mock Trial Coord; SGA Spon; Peer Mentor Coach; Black His Month Coord; Black Trivial Pursuits Coach; NHS Fac Comm; Girls Bsktbl Clock Mgr; NASSP, NEA, PGCEA 1989-; PGCSS 1985-, Area Rep 1995-; MDCSS, NCSS 1991-; First Bapt Church 1987-, Financial Sec Asst; Smithsonian 1994, Advy Bd; Prince George Comm Coll 1994-, Civil War Summer Ctr Appreciation Awd; 9th Grd Curr Guide Writing L-S-N Gov; Dana Kusfman Outstdng Soc Stud Edctrs Awd 1995; Ray Kroc Tchr Achvmt Awd 1994; Outstdng Contribution & Committment to SGA 1995; Conducted Schl Improvement Classroom Mngmt Discipline, CivilWar, Cmptr Softwarefor MD Test Citizenship Skills Wkshp; *office:* Fairmont Heights HS 1401 Nye St Capitol Heights MD 20743

LIBENSON, LOIS JANE (AARONSON), Third Grade Teacher; *b:* Winthrop, MA; *m:* Michael; *c:* Laurie Dawn Yablon, Shari Rotman; *ed:* Suffolk Univ (BSEd) Elem Ed 1969, (MAEd) Elem Ed 1976; 15 Post-Grad Credits Framingham St Coll, Fitchburg St Coll, Lesley Coll; *cr:* Temple Emanual Schl Early ChldhdDept Dir 1969-74; Boston Coll Sci Instr 1993-94; Dover Pub Schls Elem Tchr 1974-; *ai:* 3rd Grd Space Sci Tchr; Sci, Tech Comms; MA Tchrs Assn 1976-, Tchr of Yr 1995; NTA 1976-; Natl Space Soc 1996-; Cambridge Symphony 1988-, Violin; Natl Sci Grant 1987-88; Awded Dover-Sherborn Educ Fnd Grants; Candidate Cosmonaut Trng Educator Space Prgm 1992; Author Several Articles; Space Trng Speaker; Rotary Awd 1992; Tchr of Yr Awd Dover-Sherborn Schl System 1995; *office:* Caryl Schl Farm St Dover MA 02030*

LIBER, MARILYN SPAHLINGER, Fifth Grade Teacher; *b:* Warren, OH; *m:* Loyd W.; *c:* Christy Liber Boone, Jeffrey B.; *ed:* Kent St Univ (BS) Ed 1972; Attending Ashland Univ, Curr; *cr:* Newton Falls Schls Kndgtn Tchr 1972, Grd 1 Tchr 1973-83, Grd 5 Tchr 1984-, Var Vlybl Coach Grds 7-12 1993-; *ai:* Co-Coord Land Lab Environmental Learning Ctr; AFT 1994-; Meth Church Choir 1972-; Dev On Site Environmental Land Lab 52 Acres 1994-96 EPA Educl Grant; Bill Penn Meml Conservation Awd Trumbull Soil, Water Conservation Dists 1995-96; *office:* Newton Falls Exempted Vlg Schl Rt 1 Box 909 Milton Blvd Newton Falls OH 44444

LIBERATO, PAMELA DIANE HOWARD, Spanish Teacher; *b:* New Kensington, PA; *m:* Nick; *c:* Alyssa, Angela; *ed:* Edinboro Univ (BS) Span, Eng, Ger; Addl Classes Ger, Eng; *cr:* Comm Coll of Allegheny Cty Conversational Span, Ger Tchr 1980-81; Greater Works Acad Span, Ger, Eng Tchr 1981-87; Leechburg Area HS Span Tchr 1987-; *ai:* Span Club; Apples Lang Edctrs Soc, Amer Assn of Tchrs of Span & Portugese, PA St Modern Lang Assn 1990-; NEA, LEA 1988-; Pittsburgh City Wide Choir 1989-; Back-Up Choir for Natl Recording Artists Choir 1990-; Kappa Delta Phi 1975-; Frgn Lang Dept Stu Rep 1974-; Deans List; Escorted Stdnts to W Germany 1985; Judenburg Austria Yth Group Svc, Music Team 1984; Melk Austria Music Team 1983; Brazil, Bolivia, Peru, Colmbia Continental Music Team 1982; Bitburg, Trier W Germany Teen Challenge Worker 1978; Worked in Kinderhom Children's Orphanage 1975; *office:* Leechburg Area HS 215 1st St Leechburg PA 15656*

LIBERATORE, ANTHONY A., Science Teacher; *b:* Waynesboro, PA; *m:* Bonnie Gail Booze; *c:* Amy Lou, Gerald; *ed:* CA Univ of PA (BS) Scndry Ed & Bio 1971; Millersville Univ of PA (MED) Scndry Ed & Bio 1979; Comprehensive Spcl Ed Cert; Environmental Sci Cert; FAST I, II, III; *cr:* North Hartford HS Bio & Earth Sci Tchr 1971-74; Bethel Park HS Bio & Environmental Sci Tchr 1974-81, Dean of Stdnts & Sci Tchr 1982-85, Sci Tchr 1991-; Independence HS Spcl Ed & Sci Tchr 1985-91; *ai:* AFT 1974-; Caron MacMillian Hockey 1992-, Fee Scheduler; Pub Article; *office:* Bethel Park High School 309 Church Rd Bethel Park PA 15102

LIBERATORE, MARGARET MARY, Fifth Grade Teacher; *b:* Lakewood, OH; *ed:* Univ of Toledo (BED) Elem Ed 1987; 45 Credit Hrs Cnslng; *cr:* Miami Cntry Day Schl First Grd Tchr 1988-89; Bay MS Fifth Grd Tchr 1989-; *ai:* Town Cncl Adv; Jr Var, Var Asst Girls Bsktbl Coach; 7th-8th Grd Girls Track Coach; NEA 1989-; OH HS Bsktbl Coaches Assn 1995-; PTA 1990-; Nom Crystal Apple Tchrs Awds; *office:* Bay Village MS 27725 Wolf Rd Bay Village OH 44140

LIBERATORE, MELODY LEGGETT, English & Speech Teacher; *b:* Uhrichsville, OH; *m:* Robert Carl; *ed:* Kent St Univ (BFA) Theatre Speech Ed 1973; Kent St Univ Tchng Cert Rdng 1987; *cr:* New Philadelphia Schls 7th-12th Grd Sub 1972-73; New Philadelphia Jr High 7th-8th Grd Eng Tchr 1976-88; New Philadelphia HS HS Eng Tchr 1988-; KSU Tuscarawas Campus Eng 10000 Tchr 1990-91; New Philadelphia HS HS Speech Tchr 1991-; *ai:* Eng Dept Head; Grd Card Comm; NEA 1976-; Alpha Psi Omega 1972; Music Stud Club & Tuscarawas Philharmonic Chorus 1980-; Canton Symphony Chorus 1992-; Little Theatre of Tusarawas Cty, Dir; OH Outdoor Historical Drama Assn 1970-; Medelssola Chorus Eur Tour 1995; Soloist NC Symp 1996; Kent St Tuscarawas Campus Advy Bd Svc Awd; Com Theatre Assn Outstanding Actress; Martha Holden Jennings Lecture Series Scholar Awd; Pub Article; *office:* New Philadelphia Schl 343 Ray Ave NW New Philadelphia OH 44663*

LIBERI, RICHARD, Math Department Chairperson; *b:* Philadelphia, PA; *m:* Veronica M.; *c:* Jacqueline, Cynthia, Karen; *ed:* Villanova Univ (BS) Math 1964, (MA) Math 1968; Penn St Univ Extra Grad Credits; *cr:* Springfield HS Math Tchr 1964-68; Harriton HS Math Dept Chprsn 1969-; Villanova Univ Univ Lecturer 1985-; *ai:* Math League; AAUP 1985-; NEA, NCTM 1964-; Speaker Regnl & Natl NCTM Conf; Speaker at Intnl Collegiate Conf of Tech Twice; *office:* Harriton HS 600 N Ithan Ave Bryn Mawr PA 19010

LIBERMAN, ROSETTE BELLE, English Teacher; *b:* Tabriz, Iran; *c:* Gregory Heyworth; *ed:* Barnard Coll (BA) His & Govt 1958; Vassar Coll (MA) Fr Lit & Lang 1973; Univ of Bridgeport (EDD) Ed Mgmt 1987; Tchng Certs: Eng, Fr, Soc Stud; Intermediate Admin Cert; Eng Lit & Psych Post Grad Stud; *cr:* Sloan Kettering Inst & Cornell Schl of Med Sci Asst Dean of Admissions 1958-60; Plainville JHS Eng & Soc Stud Tchr 1964-65; Sharon Ctr Schl Eng & Soc Stud Tchr 1965-66; Nanny Nursery Schl Founder & Dir 1968-73; Dutchess Day Schl Fr & Eng Tchr 1973-78; NW CT Pub Svcs Ed 1974-79; Cromwell HS Eng Tchr 1978-79; New Haven Hebrew Day Schl Prin 1979-85; A Better Chance Pgm Resident Dir 1985-86; Yale Univ Disabilities Svcs Asst Dir 1985-88; Amity Regnl Schl Dist Eng Tchr 1985-; *ai:* Lit Magazine Adv; Shoreline Fndtn for Folk Lit & Art Inc 1984-86, Exec Dir; CEA 1985-; CT Tchng Prof Adv Cncl 1989-90; Nolpe Dissertation Awd for Outstdng Schlsp in Ed Law 1987; Essay, Guide & Article Pub; *office:* Amity Regnl Schl Dist Luke Hill Rd Bethany CT 06524

LIBERTI, LORRAINE NANCY, Sixth Grade Teacher; *b:* Brooklyn, NY; *ed:* St John's Univ (BA) Speech Pathology 1979; Univ of VA (MED) Speech Pathology 1981; *cr:* Rhame Avenue Schl Speech Tchr 1981-85, Elem Tchr 1985-; *ai:* Site-Based Mngmt Team; Spec Ed PTA 1981-, Lifetime Mem; Rhame Ave PTA 1985-; NYSUT 1981-; IRA; NSTA; Delta Kappa Gamma; *office:* Rhame Avenue Elem Schl 100 Rhame Ave East Rockaway NY 11518

LIBERTONE, CARL ANTHONY, English Teacher; *b:* Syracuse, NY; *m:* Cheryl Ann Paussa; *c:* Robert, Holli; *ed:* Syracuse Univ (BA) Eng, Eng Ed 1983, (MS) Eng Ed 1989; *cr:* Phoenix Cntrl Schls 7-10 Grd Eng Tchr 1983-84; Bryant & Stratton Bus Schl Eng Tchr, Post Sec 1983-84; Baldwinsville Cntrl Schls 8-9 Grd Eng Tchr 1984-85; Phoenix Cntrl Schls 10-12 Grd Eng Tchr 1985-; Onondaga Com Coll 9-10 Grd HS Summer Schl Tchr 1995; *ai:* Sr Class, Newspaper, Prom Comm Sr Class Trip Adv; Schl Improvement Team Mem; AFT 1985-; Solvay Tigers Yth, Ath Club 1993-, Trustee 1994-95, 2nd VP 1996; Video Review's Syracuse New Times Mid 1980's; *home:* 612 Abell Ave Solvay NY 13209

LIBORDI, FRANCIS ANDREW, Amer His & Govt Teacher; *b:* Hornell, NY; *ed:* Alfred SUNY (AAS) Hum 1984; Alfred Univ (BA) Amer His 1986; Elmira Coll (MA) Amer His 1991; *cr:* Hornell HS His Tchr 1987-; *ai:* Asst Var Ftbl Coach; Comm Svc Coord; BPOE #364 1989-; Marine Corps League 1979-; Presidential Schlsp Awd; *office:* Hornell HS 14 Allen St Hornell NY 14843

LIBUDA, LINDA JOHNSON, Fourth-Fifth Grade Teacher; *b:* St Johnsbury, VT; *m:* Gerald M.; *ed:* Univ of VT (BSEd) Elem Ed 1970; 30 Addl Credit Hrs; *cr:* Winooski Schl Dist Tchr 1970-; *ai:* Sci Comm; Parent Tchr Org; Delta Kappa Gamma 1992-; Lake Champlain Regnl Chamber of Comm, Ed Comm; Project Asst, Bd Mem; Outstdng Tchr Awd Univ of VT 1994-95; *office:* John F. Kennedy Elem Schl 70 Normand St Winooski VT 05404*

LICATA, ANN MANZO, Education Professor; *b:* Brooklyn, NY; *m:* Guy T.; *c:* Thomas, Stephen, Therese Paff; *ed:* Mt St Mary Coll (BA) 1970; NY Univ (MA) 1975; Fordham Univ (PHD) Lang, Literacy, Learning 1992; *cr:* Newburgh Enlarged City Schl Dist Rdng Tchr 1970-92; Mt St Mary Coll Asst Prof Ed 1992-; *ai:* NYSUT 1970-; NCTE, IRA, ACEI, ASCD 1992-; Kappa Delta Pi; *office:* Mount Saint Mary Coll 330 Powell Ave Newburgh NY 12550

LICATA, FRANK M., English Teacher; *b:* Kingston, PA; *m:* Karen Rinko; *c:* Kerri E., Amy L., Kylie J.; *ed:* Kings Coll (BA) Eng 1974; Coll Misericordia (ME) Ed 1987; Instrl Support Team Trng; *cr:* Crestwood HS Eng Tchr 1975-; *ai:* 8th Grd Class Adv; Fac Advy & NHS Comm; NEA 1974-; PSEA 1974-; CEA 1974-; *office:* Crestwood HS 281 S Mountain Blvd Mountain Top PA 18707

LICATA, MARCIA L., Spanish Teacher; *b:* Pittsburgh, PA; *m:* Jeff; *c:* Lauren, Kelly; *ed:* Univ of Pittsburgh (BA) Scndry Ed Span 1977; Univ of Valencia in Spain 18 Credit Hrs 1977-80; Univ of PA & Penn St Univ 30 Post Grad Credits Toward (MA) 1989-; *cr:* Mt Lebanon Jr & Sr HS Span Tchr 1978-; *ai:* Co-Spon of Natl Span Exam; Foreign Lang Club Spon at Elem Level 6 Yrs; PA St Modern Lang Assn, Amer Assn of Tchrs of Span & Portuguese, Amer Cncl of Tchrs of Foreign Langs, Mt Lebanon Ed Assn, PA St Ed Assn, NEA & Amer Foreign Lang Assn 1980-; St George Church Cncl; Yth Adv; Outstanding Achvmt & Creative Tchng Nom Johns Hopkins Univ; 3-Time Nom Thanks to Tchrs; Gift of Time Awd; *office:* Mt Lebanon Jr HS 7 Horsman Dr Pittsburgh PA 15228

LICHI, DONALD ALLEN, VP, Dir of Ed & Professor; *b:* Akron, OH; *m:* Marcia Shiltz; *c:* Anthony, Adam, Anne Marie; *ed:* Nyack Coll (BS) Ed 1980; Univ of Akron (MS) Counseling 1984, (PHD) Psych 1993; 1 Yr Post Masters Marriage & Family Counseling & Schl Admin; *cr:* Chapel Hill Chrstn Schl Tchr & Cnslr 1980-92; Private Practice Psych Cnslr 1985-92; Univ of Akron Adjunct Prof 1986-92; Emerge Ministries-Ashland Seminary Dir of Ed 1992-; *ai:* masters Degree Interns Supvr; Amer Psychological Assn, Amer Ed Research Assn 1993-; Amer Assns of Chrstn Cnslrs 1996; Cuyahoga Valley Chrstn Acad 1994-, Bd of Trustees; Stow Alliance Fellowship 1980-, Bd of Elders-Governing Bd; Book Chapter In Press Gospel Publishing House 1996; Paper Presentation MMPI Missionaries IN Februrary 1996; Paper Presentation 30th Annual Symposium on MMPI Saint Petersburg FL 1995; Paper Presentation AERA Annual Convention Atlanta GA 1994; Pub Speaker at seminars & Retreats; *office:* Emerge Ministries Inc 900 Mull Ave Akron OH 44313*

LICHT, STEVE LEONARD, Physical Education Teacher; *b:* Brooklyn, NY; *m:* Sharon Lazarus; *c:* Melissa, Matthew; *ed:* Kent St Univ (BS) Hlth, PE 1967, (MED) Schl Cnslng 1968; Hofstra Univ CAS Schl Admin 1983; 60 Grad Credits; *cr:* Plainedge Elem Schl PE Tchr 1968-76; Plainedge MS PE Tchr, Wrestling, Ftbl Coach 1976-85; Plainedge HS PE Tchr, Wrestling, Ftbl Coach 1985-92; Plainedge Elem Schl PE Tchr, Wrestling Ofcl 1992-; *ai:* Vol Ftbl Coach; Schwarting Schl Strategic Planning Action Team; AFT, NYSUT, PFT 1968-; AAHPER&D 1967-; NYSAHPER&D 1970-; Phi Epsilon Kappa 1966-, Past Pres; Cong B'Nai Israel 1983-, Chm of Bd, VP, Fund Rsg; Mini Grant Adapted PE Curr; NYS Grant Elem Schl Curr; Contributor to Planning & Producing Audiovisual Materials; *office:* Plainedge Public Schl Stewart & Boundary Aves Bethpage NY 11714

LICHTENSTEIN, JUDITH ARKIN, Dental Health Teacher; *b:* New York City, NY; *c:* Russell B., Abbey M.; *ed:* NYC Comm Coll (AAS) Dental Hygiene 1969; 32 Credits Ed, Spec Ed; *cr:* Tottenville HS Tchr 1983-; *ai:* Tops Coord 3 Yrs; Trng Opportunity Prgm; NYSHOEA 1994-; AFT 1983-; NYS Registered Dental Hygienists 1969-, Registered D H; Natl Cncl Jewish Women 1975-77, VP, Cert; Wrote NYS Dental Curr; *office:* Tottenville HS 100 Luten Ave Staten Island NY 10312

LICHTMAN, PHYLLIS, Asst Principal; *b:* NY; *m:* Irving; *c:* Steven, Robert, David; *ed:* Brooklyn Coll (BA) 1965; Adelphi Univ (BS) 1984; Queens Coll CUNY (PD) Admin, Super 1995; *cr:* PS 60 Q Tchr 1976-; PS 56 Q Asst Prin 1996-; *ai:* AFT 1964-; Impact II Awd; Metlife Flwshp.*

LICKLIDER, PATRICIA M., English Professor; *b:* New Haven, CT; *m:* Roy E.; *c:* Virginia; *ed:* Regis Coll (BA) Eng 1965; Columbia Univ (MA) His of Eng Lang 1966, (PHD) Eng & Comparative Lit 1971; *cr:* Yeshiva Coll Adj Instr 1969-70; John Jay Coll Assoc Prof 1970-; *ai:* Dept Prsnl; Budget Comm; Acad Adv; Univ Task Force on Assessment; NCTE 1974-;

CCCC 1974-; St Peters Church 1985-, Scheduler; Woodrow Wilson & Columbia Univ Flwshp; Articles Pub; *office:* John Jay Coll of Crmnl Justice 445 W 59th St Ofc New York NY 10019

LIDDICK, DAVID E., Math Teacher; *b:* Lock Haven, PA; *m:* Carol Day; *c:* Brandon, Caleb, Gavin; *ed:* Lock Haven Univ (BS) Ed, Math 1966; *cr:* Lock Haven HS Math Tchr 1966-; *office:* Lock Haven HS 301 W Church St Lock Haven PA 17745

LIDDY, MARY ANN, School Counselor; *b:* Philadelphia, PA; *ed:* Georgian Ct Coll (BA) Elem Ed 1968; Trenton St Coll (MA) Ed 1974; Rowan Coll Schl Cnslr Cert 1993; Fordham Univ, Rutgers Univ Admin Cert Courses; Ctr for Applied Psych 6 Credits Play Therapy; *cr:* Schl Tchr 1960-69; St Joseph Prin 1969-75; St Matthew Prin 1975-88; Star of Sea Schl Tchr 1988-92, Cnslr 1993-; *ai:* Rainbows Prgm Facilitator; Build Esteem in Stdnts Today Prgm Coord; NCEA 1968-; ACA, CACA 1995-; St Vincent De Paul Soc, Diocese of Metuchen Schl Task Force Recognitions; Today's Cath Tchr Prin of Yr Honorable Mention; Mercy Ministry Cnslng Prgm Grant; *office:* Our Lady Star Of Sea Schl 15 N California Ave Atlantic City NJ 08401

LIDMAN, MONICA VON HAEFEN, Sixth Grade Teacher; *b:* Akron, OH; *m:* Jeremy; *ed:* Miami Univ (BA) Elem Ed 1989; Xavier Univ (MS) Elem Ed 1993; *cr:* Liberty Jr Schl Sixth Grd Tchr 1989-90; Union Elem Schl Sixth Grd Tchr 1990-94; Cherokee Elem Schl Sixth Grd Tchr 1994-; *office:* Cherokee Elem Schl 5435 Kyles-Station Rd Hamilton OH 45011

LIEBCHEN, ROSARITA LORETTA, History Teacher; *b:* Philadelphia, PA; *ed:* Holy Family Coll (BA) Elem Ed 1971; Temple Univ (MED) Sec Ed in Soc Stud 1979; 7 Grad Credits; Attnd Philadelphia Coll of Textiles & Sci, LaSalle Univ; *cr:* Our Lady of Calvary Grd Schl 4th & 6th Grd Tchr 1960-62; St John Cantius Grd Schl 7th & 8th Grd Tchr 1962-68; St Stanislaus Grd Schl 5th-6th, 7th-8th Grd Tchr 1968-73; St Hubert HS Soc Stud Tchr 1973-; *ai:* NCEA 1973-; CRT 1973-, Corres Sec, Del; Article Pub 1975.

LIEBENBERG, ROBIN BROWN, English Teacher; *b:* Miami, FL; *m:* George; *c:* Brandon Kahn, Lauren Kahn, Amanda; *ed:* Coll of William & Mary (BA) Psych 1976; 30 Grad Hrs in Ed; *cr:* Manor HS Tchr 1976-79; Glen Burnie St HS Tchr 1979-83; Henderson HS Tchr 1984-85; Monmouth Regnl HS Tchr 1985-; *ai:* Images Adv; Mid Sts Steering Comm; Futures Acad Team Coach; FPS of NJ Coach; Regnl Reporter; NCTE Writing Achvmt Awds, Adv, Coach; Schl Based Planning Comm; NEA, NCTE 1976-; FPS of NJ 1993-, Outstdng Coach Certs 1994-95-; Eastern VA Writing Inst at William & Mary Flwshp 1977; NJ Governor's Tchng Grant 1987, Writing Competency Prgm; Who's Who 1990; Star-Ledger Distngd Tchr 1994; *office:* Monmouth Regional HS 1 Norman J Field Way Tinton Falls NJ 07724*

LIEBER, MARLA KAY BUSCH, Family & Consumer Sci Teacher; *b:* Chillicothe, OH; *m:* Michael Bert; *c:* Molly, Matthew; *ed:* Otterbein Coll (BA) Voc Home Ec 1977; Wright St Univ (MED) Tchr Ldr Ed 1993; Addl 4 Post Grad Stud Cred Hrs; *cr:* Houston HS Voc Home Ec Tchr 1977-78; Fairlawn HS Voc Home Ec Tchr 1978-91; Sidney HS Family & Consumer Sci Tchr 1991-; *ai:* FHA/HERO Adv for 18 Yrs; OEA, NEA 1977-, Sec; 1st United Meth Church 1978-; Dorena Circle 1987-, Sec, Treas; Master Adv FHA; Mentor Adv FHA; Copeland Grant; *office:* Sidney HS 1215 Campbell Rd Sidney OH 45365*

LIEBER, R. OKUAKI, English Professor; *b:* Tokyo, Japan; *c:* Mara Rose; *ed:* Coll of William & Mary (BS) Bio 1976; Columbia Univ (MFA) Creative Writing 1983; Attnd Ctr for Modern Psychoanalytic Stud; *cr:* John Jay Coll Adj Asst Prof 1984-89; Borough of Manhattan CC Adj Asst Prof 1989-; Nassau Comm Coll Asst Prof 1990-; *ai:* Assoc Ed; Fac Adv for Creative Writing Club; NYSUT 1990-; ACA 1990-; SMP 1992-; Articles Pub; *office:* Nassau Comm Coll 1 Education Dr Garden City NY 11530

LIEBERMAN, ARLENE, Vocal Music Tchr & Chorus Dir; *b:* Brooklyn, NY; *ed:* Brooklyn Coll (BA) Music Ed 1959; NY Univ Post Grad Stud; *cr:* Winthrop Jr HS Music Tchr 1959-66; Erasmus Hall HS Music Tchr 1966-73; Talent Unlimited HS Music Tchr 1973-; *ai:* NYC Outstanding Tchr of Yr Cert 1987; Chorus Performances for NYC Mayors, Senator, & Pres Clinton; *office:* Talent Unlimited HS 300 E 68th St New York NY 10021

LIEBERMAN, RICHARD ROBERT, High School Government Teacher; *b:* Cleveland, OH; *m:* Linda Kaye Jordan; *c:* Jeffrey, Lauren, Michael, Sara; *ed:* Kent St Univ (BA) His, Govt 1972; Post Grad Hrs Univ of Akron, Coll of Mount St Joseph; *cr:* Cuyahoga Falls HS Tchr POD World His 1975-; Akron Pub Schls GED, Able Instr 1977-; Cuyahoga Falls HS HS Track Coack Asst 1993-95, Asst HS Ftbl Coach 1993-, HS Track Coach, Head 1995-; *ai:* Head HS Track, Asst HS Ftbl Coach; NEA, OEA, CFEA, NEOEA 1984; *office:* Cuyahoga Falls HS 2300 4th St Cuyahoga Falls OH 44221

LIEBMANN, DAVID W., Assistant to the Director; *b:* Atlanta, GA; *ed:* Middlebury Coll (BA) Environmental Stud 1991; Attnd Bread Loaf Schl of Eng; *cr:* The ME Coast Semester Asst to Dir 1991-; *ai:* Fly Fishing, Kayaking, Outdoor Skills Adv; Klingerstein Summer Fellow Columbia Univ; *office:* Chewonki Foundation RR 2 Box 1200 Wiscasset ME 04578

LIEBOWITZ, S. JAY, Assoc Prof of Org Behavior; *b:* New York City, NY; *m:* Jayne Arlene Berlinger; *c:* Jason, Jared; *ed:* SUNY at Cortland (BA) Psych 1975; Univ of TN (PHD) Ind-Org Psych 1983; Certfd SHRM, HRCI as Prof in Human Resources; *cr:* TN Vly Authority Prsnl Analyst; Oak Ridge Nat Lab Researcher; Wilson Learning Trainer, Consultant; Duquesne Univ Prof; *ai:* Pittsburgh Prsnl Bd Mem; SHRM, Fac Adv; Acad of Mngmt; IRRA; Beth Samuel Jewish Ctr, 2nd VP; Several Articles Pub; *office:* Duquesne Univ School of Business 600 Forbes Ave Pittsburgh PA 15282

LIENAU, MARK W., Science Teacher; *b:* Tarrytown, NY; *m:* Frances Zittel; *c:* Donald, Rebecca; *ed:* Johnson St Coll (BS) Environmental Sci 1984; 20 Credit Hrs Univ of VT, Trinity Coll, Coll of Atlantic; *cr:* Johnson St Coll Upward Bound Sci Instr 1983-87, 1995; Canaan Meml HS Sci Instr 1985-; *ai:* NEA 1985-, Negotiations; NSTA 1988-; VSTA 1990-; Town of Norton VT 1988-, Selectman, Moderator; 7 Articles Pub; NSTA Natl Convention 1995-; NSTA Reg Conventions 1993-94; VSTA St Convention 1993-93; NABT Natl Convention 1993; *office:* Canaan Meml HS 1 School St Canaan VT 05903*

LIGGETT, JANET GOUDIE, Biology Teacher; *b:* New Brunswick, NJ; *m:* William R.; *c:* Megan, Matthew; *ed:* Keene St Coll (BS) Chem & Bio 1984; *cr:* Monadnock Regnl HS Chem Tchr 1984; Avon Pub HS Bio Tchr 1984-85; Choate Rosemary Hall Summer Bio & Chem Tchr 1985, 1986 & 1987; West Morris Cntrl HS Bio Tchr 1985-; *ai:* Acad of Sci Adv; NEA 1984-; NJEA 1985-; MASA 1988-; BTNJ 1990-; *office:* West Morris Central HS 4 Bridges Rd Chester NJ 07930

LIGHT, MARCY BRADLEY, English Teacher; *b:* New Britain, CT; *m:* Randall; *ed:* Central CT St Univ (BA) Comm 1987; St Joseph Coll Post Grad Stud in Ed; *cr:* John Wallace MS Writing Tutor 1992-93; Mary Immaculate Acad Eng Tchr 1993-; *ai:* Newspaper Staff, Stu Book Club Adv; Horizons Gifted & Talented Prgm Dir; NCTE 1993-; Article Pub in Eng Journal 1995; *office:* Mary Immaculate Acad 370 Osgood Ave New Britain CT 06053

LIGHT, NANCY G., High School English Teacher; *b:* Elmira, NY; *m:* Gary E.; *c:* Garner, Julie, Erik; *ed:* Cortland St Univ (BS) Ed, Eng 1961; Buffalo St Univ (MS) Eng Ed 1967; 9 Post Grad Credits Canisius Coll at Buffalo; *cr:* Kenmore Schl Dist Elem Tchr 1961; Clarence Jr HS Eng Tchr 1964-65; Clarence Sr HS Eng Tchr, Regular Sub 1967-89; Clarence HS Eng Tchr 1989-; *ai:* AFT, NYS Eng Cncl, NCTE 1989-; Clarence Tchrs Assn 1989-, Exec Bd Mem; Assn of Prof Women Writers 1993-; Yng Life Comm 1990-; Clarence United Meth Church 1963-; 2 Articles Pub; Western NY Writing Project Fellow; Edctr of Excel Awd NYSEC 1995; Kappa Delta Pi; *office:* Clarence HS 9625 Main St Clarence NY 14031

LIGHTCAP, GEORGE ALLEN,JR., English Teacher; *b:* Easton, PA; *ed:* McKendree Coll (BA) Speech Comm, Drama 1976; Univ of SW LA His; MA Eng Prgm at The Bread Loaf Schl of Eng Middlebury Coll VT; *cr:* Delcambre HS 7-8 Grd Soc Stud Tchr 1979-83; Glen Meadow MS 8th Grd Eng Tchr 1984-92; 6th Grd Lang Arts Tchr 1992-; *ai:* Dir & Founder Glen Meadow MS & Lounsberry Hollow MS Drama Club 1984-90; NJEA 1984-, Rep 8 Yrs; NY & NJ Trail Conf1992-; Trail Maintainer & Shelter Caretaker for Appalachian Trail 1987-; Overseer Appalachian Trail Pochuck Mountain 1992-; *office:* Glen Meadow M S Rt 517 & Sammis Rd Vernon NJ 07462

LIGHTCAP, PATRICIA TAPPE, Fourth Grade Teacher; *b:* New Ulm, MN; *m:* Jonathan; *c:* Adam, Megan; *ed:* Northern IL Univ (BS) Elem Ed 1971; Kean Coll Math Ed Cert; *cr:* Livingston Schl 6th Grd Tchr 1980-81; Westfield HS Basic Skills, Math Tchr 1981-82; Abraham Clark HS Basic Skills, Math Tchr 1983-84; Harrison Schl 4th Grd Tchr 1984-; *ai:* Climate, Discipline, Thoughtful Comms; Asst to Prin; NEA, NJEA 1979-; *office:* Harrison Schl 310 Harrison Ave Roselle NJ 07203

LIGHTELL, LYN FREEMAN, Coordinator & Tchr Gifted Svcs; *b:* Ashtabula, OH; *m:* Don; *c:* Megan, Josh; *ed:* Kent St Univ (BS) Ed 1973, (MED) Gifted 1991; *cr:* Coshocton City Schls Elem Tchr 18 Yrs, Coord & Gifted Tchr 4 Yrs; *ai:* Quiz Team Adv; Odyssey of the Mind Pgm Coord; Region VI Governing Bd Mem; NEA & OEA 1973-; COCG & GCCO 1992-; OACG 1995-; Roscoe Village Found 1991-; Friends of the Park 1993-94; Phi Delta Kappa Outstdng Edctr Awd 1987.

LIGHTNER, LINDA LINGENFELTER, Communications Teacher; *b:* Altoona, PA; *m:* Larry B.; *c:* Brent, Kevin; *ed:* PA St Univ (BA) Ed 1969; Grad Cert; *cr:* Stanford Schl Dist Tchr 1969-71; Spring Cove Schl Dist Tchr 1971-77, 1985-; Blair Cty Drugs & Alcohol Asst Pub Relations Specialist 1984-86; Omiya City Schls Asst Supv of Eng 1988-89; *ai:* NHS Bd Mem; NEA 1969-; PSEA 1971-; SCEA 1971-; GFWC 1975-, Intnl Affairs; Blue Knob Ski Assn 1995-; PA Tchr Rep to Omiya Saitama Japan 1988-89; *office:* Central HS Rd 2 Martinsburg PA 16662

LIGHTY, MICHELLE MC COWAN, Spanish Teacher; *b:* Wilmington, DE; *m:* Todd Christopher; *c:* Trevor A., Hannah K., Aidan E., Tessa E.; *ed:* Penn St Univ (BA) Span 1982; Nazareth Coll (MS) Ed 1989; SUNY at Brockport Tchr Cert in Sec Span 1985; *cr:* Penfield HS Span Tchr 1985-90; APW HS Span Tchr 1990-; *ai:* Span Club Adv; NYSUT, NYSAFLT 1985-; Dewitt Comm Church 1991-; Who's Who in Amer Ed 1994; *office:* Altmar Parish Williamstwn HS Co Rt 22 Parish NY 13131*

LIGON, SAMUEL W., Assistant Professor of English; *b:* Baltimore, MD; *m:* Kimberly Mitchell; *ed:* Univ of IL (BA) Eng, Rhetoric 1985; Univ of NH (MA) Eng, Writing 1989; *cr:* Univ of NH Instr 1989-90; Univ of Lowell Instr 1990-91; Oakland Univ Spec Lecturer 1991-92; Suffolk Comm Coll Asst Eng Prof 1992-; *ai:* Fac Adv to Lit Magazine; AFT 1992-; Pub Short Stories; *office:* Suffolk Comm Coll 533 College Rd Selden NY 11784*

LIGONS, FRANK JOSEPH, Music Teacher & Chorus Dir; *b:* Pittsburgh, PA; *m:* Margaret Louise Baker; *c:* Frank Douglas, Frank Marra, Marcie B. Marie; *ed:* Duquesne Univ Schl of Music (BA) Sci of Music 1962; *cr:* Conroy Jr HS Music Tchr, Chorus 1962-67; Langley HS Music Tchr, Chorus Dir 1967-74; Greenway MS Music Tchr 1974-84; Concord-Burgwin-Mifflin Elem Schls MUsic Itinerant & Choral Dir 1984-; *ai:* Choral & Performance Dir; AFT, PFT 1968-; Freedom Fnd; Valley Forge Awd; Natl Tchr Awd 1992; *office:* Mifflin Elem Schl 1290 Mifflin Rd Pittsburgh PA 15207

LIGUORI, PATRICIA BLAUVELT, Third Grade Teacher; *b:* Hackensack, NJ; *m:* John F.; *ed:* Wittenberg Univ (BA) Elem Ed & Art Ed 1974; 30 Paterson Equivalency Credits; *cr:* High Mountain Schl 7th Grd Tchr 1974-75; Paterson Schl 27 Compensatory Ed & Math Tchr 1976-78, 3rd Grd Tchr 1978-81, 1983-, 5th Grd Tchr 1981-83; *ai:* NJEA & NEA 1974-; PEA & PCEA 1976-; Governors Tchr Recognition Awd 1990; *office:* PS 27 250 Richmond Ave Paterson NJ 07502

LIGUORI, RICHARD, Fifth Grade Teacher; *b:* Brooklyn, NY; *m:* Giulia Gualiardi; *c:* Riccardo, Martina, Maria; *ed:* Hofstra Univ (BS) Elem Ed 1967; Stonybrook (MA) Liberal Stud 1973; Hofstra Univ (MA) Amer Lit & Eng 1974; Post Coll 8 Credits Math Problem Solving in Elem Schls; *cr:* East Street Schl 5th Grd Tchr 1967-68; Park Ave Intermediate Schl 5th-6th Grd Tchr 1968-75; Dryden Street Schl 5th-6th Grd Tchr 1975-82; Drexel Ave Schl 5th-6th Grd Tchr 1982-91; Westbury MS 6th Grd Tchr 1991-93; Drexel Ave Schl 5th Grd Tchr 1993-; *ai:* Chess Club; Math Olympiads; Stock Mrkt Game; Westbury Tchrs Assn 1968-, Bldg Rep; Math Olympiads Achieved Outstanding Levels Twice; Stock Market Game Top Ten Finish in Our Division; Top Three Schl; Manhattan Chess Clb Trnmnt 1995; *home:* 24 Squirrel Ln Levittown NY 11756

LIHVARCHIK, WILLIAM EDWARD, Spanish Teacher; *b:* Spangler, PA; *ed:* Lock Haven St Coll (BS) Span 1970; Millersville St Coll Masters Equiv Span 1976; 21 Credits Univ of Valencia Spain; 8 Credits Univ of Guadalajara Mexico; *cr:* Fairfield Schl Dist Span Tchr 1970-93; Harrisburg Area Comm Coll Span Tchr & Adult Ed 1991; Conewago Valley Schl Dist Span Tchr 1993-; Harrisburg ACC Adj Prof 1996; *ai:* Span Club Adv 1970-94; Class of 1975, 1981, 1988 & 1992 Adv; Sports Boys-Girls Bsktbl Scorekeeper, Ticket Seller, Starter-Timer for Cross Cntry Team & Track Helper; PSEA & NEA 1970-' CVEA 1993-; Ukrainian Youth for Christ 1986-87, Convention Del; St Johns Luth Church 1992-, Translator for Sister Parish in El Salvador; PA Tchr of Yr Finalist 1988; Mentor for Adams Cty Induction for New Tchrs 1990-91; Prin Advy Comm 1975-87, 1994-95 for NOHS; *office:* Conewago Valley Schl Dist 130 Berlin Rd New Oxford PA 17350

LIJEWSKI, DORI JEAN, Science Teacher; *b:* Pittsburgh, PA; *m:* David R.; *c:* Dana, Devon, Daniel; *ed:* Edinboro St Coll (BS) Bio 1974; Duquesne Univ (MS) Bio Ed 1978; *cr:* Saint Louise de Marillac Schl 7th-8th Grd Sci Tchr 1976-; *ai:* PA Jr Acad of Sci Spon; NCEA 1986-; Soc of Analytical Chemists Tchr of Yr 1980; Thanks to Tchrs Nom 1990, 1991, 1993 & 1994; Golden Apple Awd 1995; *office:* Saint Louise de Marillac Schl 310 McMurray Rd Pittsburgh PA 15241

LILIE, GERALDINE MAROTTA, Sixth Grade Teacher; *b:* Brooklyn, NY; *m:* Martin M.; *c:* Steven, Julia Altman,Barbara Neary, David; *ed:* St John's Univ (BS) Elem Ed 1963; Adelphi Univ (MA) Ed 1972; *cr:* Connetquot Elem Schl 3rd Grd Tchr 1963-69; Ron Kon Koma Jr HS 6th Grd Rdng Tchr 1972-82; Sycamore Ave Elem Schl 3-4th Grd Tchr 1982-90; Idle Hour Elem Schl Ungraded Elem Classes 1969-72, 6th Grd Tchr 1990-; *ai:* Schl Fair Organizer; Schl Newspaper, Math a Thon Spon; NEA, NY St Tchrs Assn 1963-; Connetquot Tchrs Assn 1969-; Cold Spring Hills Civic Assn 1984-; *office:* Idle Hour Elem Schl Idle Hour Blvd Oakdale NY 11769

LILL, KATHLEEN GARGANO, First Grade Teacher; *b:* Philadelphia, PA; *m:* James F.; *c:* James K., Brian D.; *ed:* Holy Family Coll (BA) Elem Ed 1989; Addl Credit Hrs Rel Stud St Charles Seininary, Gwynedd-Mercy Coll; *cr:* Our Lady of Angels Second Grd Tchr 1967-69; Almond & Westmoreland Recreation Facility Dir of Pre Schl Prgm 1972-76; St Hilarys of Poitiers First Grd Tchr 1982-; *ai:* Parish, Schl Cncl; 1982-; *office:* Saint Hilary Of Poitiers Schl 820 Susquehanna Rd Ryd 19046

LILLEY, ARTHUR H., Math, Science & PE Teacher; *b:* Hartford, C Johnson St Coll (BA) Ed 1982; *cr:* Wolcott Elem Schl Tchr 1982-; Grd Bsktbl, L L Softbl, Cty Sftbl Coach.

LILLEY, PATRICIA ANNE, Stu Assistance Cnslr & Coord; *b:* Ne NJ; *ed:* Stockton St Coll (BA) Soc Stud 1980; Georgian Cour Substance Abuse Cert 1992; Rutgers Schl of Soc Work Candidate 19 Friendly's Ice Cream Restaurant Night Mgr 1970-82; Manchester Tw Soc Stud Tchr 1981-88, Stu Assistance Cnslr 1988-; *ai:* Peer Ed Ocean Cty Stu Assistance Cnslrs, Coords Chprsn; OC Domestic Vi Comm; OC Childrens' Sub-Comm; Active Parenting Facilitator; AS 1989-, Ocean Cty Chair; NCADD 1994-; NALSAP, NACA 1990-; Manchester Township HS 101 S Colonial Dr Lakehurst NJ 08733

LILLI, NICK J., Track & Football Coach; *b:* Bellevue, OH; *m:* Ka Birkholz; *c:* Scott, Nicole Strunk, Dominique, Jamie; *ed:* Heidelber (BS) Ed 1973; *cr:* Bellevue HS Asst Var Ftbl Coach 1984-95, Boys Coach 1988-95; *home:* 603 Kilbourne St Bellevue OH 44811

LILLIE, MICHAEL WAYNE,II, Math & Science Coordinator; *b:* OH; *m:* Elisabeth Stewart; *c:* Michael Stewart; *ed:* Kent St Univ Commnctn 1989; Univ of AK (MA) Scndry Ed 1992; Working on Ed Degree; *cr:* Akron Pub Schls Lang Arts Sub Tchr 1989-90, Tchr Pgm 1992; Univ of Akron Grad Asst Ed Fndtns 1991-92, Upward Bou & S Coord 1993-; *ai:* OAEOPP Legislation & Ed Comm Chair 2 Yr Tchrs Assn 1989-; NCEOA 1993-, OH St Coord for Policy Ser OAEOPP 1993-, Comm Chair; TRIO Pgms Natl Stu Rep 1987; Ou Upward Bound Alumni Awd 1996; *home:* 1732 DeLia Ave Akron OH

LILLIS, CAROL A., Asst Professor of Nursing; *b:* Washington, D John M.; *c:* Scott, Brad, Stephen, Brian; *ed:* Villanova Univ (BS) 1964; Univ of DE (MS) Nrsng 1979; *cr:* Hosp of U of PA F-T, P-T Nurse 1964-77; Univ of De Asst Nsg Prof 1979-81; DCCC Assoc Nsg 1981-; *ai:* Nrsng Club Fac Mentor; NEA, Sigma Theta Tau 1979- League for Nsg 1984-; Neighborhood Civic Assn 1973-, Street Rep 1973-; Parent Org; Co-Author Fundamentals of Nursing The Art & Sc of Nursing Care; *office:* Delaware Cnty Comm Coll 901 S Media Li Media PA 19063

LILLIS, DE LOURDES, Retired Grade School Teacher; *b:* Ki Ireland; *ed:* Loyola Univ at New Orleans (BSEd) 1960; London C Music (AA) Piano 1968; Carysfort Trng Coll Primary Ed Natl Tchr Credit Hrs Loyola Univ at New Orleans Piano Stud 1962, Limerick In Trng Coll Speech, Drama 1958; *cr:* Nenagh Primary Schl Asst 1946-57; Nativity BVM Elem Schl Asst Tchr 1957-63; St James Sch Tchr 1963-91; Nenagh Primary Schl Remedial Tchr 1995-; *ai:* T Vietnamese Stdnts Eng 1991-94.

LILLO, MICHAEL A., Chemistry Teacher; *b:* Las Vegas, NV; *m:* Jean Moll; *c:* Bronson Michael, Brennyn Joy; *ed:* Malone Coll (BA) C His 1986; Ashland Univ (BA) LD Tutor, (MED) Curr, Instruction (MBA) Admin 1996; Western Reserve HS LD Tutor 1987-89; Willa Chem Tchr 1989-; *cr:* Western Reserve HS LD Tutor 1987-89; Willa Chem Tchr 1989-; *ai:* Boys Bsktbl Coach; YMCA Bsktbl Coord; OEA, 1987-; WEA 1989-; *office:* Willard HS 123 W Whisler Dr W OH 44890*

LILLY, ELLEN (MOTTER), Former Teacher; *b:* Mansfield, O Gordon Keith Jr.; *c:* Ariel Marie, Tyler Gordon; *ed:* Grace Coll (BS) Ed 1982; *cr:* Mansfield Chrstn Schl Fifth Grd Tchr 1982-90.

LILLY, LAURA PEEBLES, Sixth Grade Teacher; *b:* Cincinnati, O Matthew F.; *ed:* Bowling Green St U (BSEd) Elem Ed 1986; Xavier (MAEd) Cnslng 1993; *cr:* Maddux Elem Schl 4th Grd Tchr 1986-8 Grd Tchr 1987-; *ai:* Stu Cncl Adv; Good Apple & Hall Monitor C NEA; OEA; NCTE; Friend of Children Awd PTA; *office:* Maddux Schl 943 Rosetree Ln Cincinnati OH 45230*

LIM, TECK-KAH, Physics Professor; *b:* Malacca, Malaysia Nyok-Kheng Liew; *c:* Kian-Tat, Al-Li; *ed:* Univ of Adelaide Australia (BSC) Mathematical Physics-Hnrs 1964, (PHD) Mathem Physics 1968; *cr:* Univ of Malaya Lecturer 1968; FL St Univ Rsrch 1968-70; Drexel Univ Asst Prof 1970-75, Assoc Prof 1975-82, Prof 1 *ai:* Hong Kong Stdnts Assn Fac Adv; Malaysian Stdnts Assn Fac Badminton Club Fac Adv; Amer Phys Soc 1970-, Flwshp 1988; L Merion Aquatic Club, Pres; Alexander Von Humboldt Stiftung F 1980-81; NSF Grants 1979-92; Rsrch Fnd 1977-78; *office:* Drexel Ur And Chestnut Street Philadelphia PA 19104*

LIMA, SALLY MURPHY, Elem & Scndry Ed Professor; *b:* Philadel PA; *m:* Robert F. Jr.; *c:* Mark X., Keith E., Michele B., Debra C Rosemont Coll (AB) Chem 1962; Penn St Univ (MA) Ed Theory, F 1984, (PHD) Ed Theory, Pol 1990; *cr:* Rohm & Haas Co Inc Rsrch Ch 1962-64; Our Lady of Victory Schl Tchr 1979-90; Lock Haven Univ Prof 1990-; *ai:* Fac Prof Dev Comm Treas; Gen Ed Comm; Frosh Yr C Spring Convocation Comm; Elem Prof Semester Team Ldr; Soph Por Comm; Life Experience Comm; NCTM 1991-; PA Soc Tchng Sch 1993-; ASCD, APSCUF 1990-; Cntrl Intermediate Unit 1992-, Prof Bd; Keystone Cntrl Schl Dist 1993-, Prof Dev Bd; Hammermill E Grant Consultant; Lock Haven Presidential Initiative Grant; 2 F System of Higher Ed Grants; Numerous Tchr Trng Presentations; Lock Haven Univ Lock Haven PA 17745

LIMBACH, GARY ROBERT, Mathematics Teacher; *b:* Columbus, *m:* Joyce McRoberts; *c:* Alison, Elisabeth; *ed:* OH St Univ (BS) Ma 1971, (MA) Math Ed 1979; 10 Semester Hrs Post Grad Stud; *cr:* Gah Lincoln Jr HS Math Tchr 1971-75; Gahanna Lincoln HS Math Tchr Columbus St Comm Coll Part-Time Math Instr 1986-; *ai:* Renais Comm Chprsn; NEA, OEA & GJEA 1979-; NCTM 1990-; OH MA 1992-; *office:* Gahanna Lincoln HS 140 S Hamilton Rd GAHANNA 43230

LIMBERG, PATRICIA BAIDEME, Math Teacher; *b:* Westfield, N Bruce E.; *c:* Annika, Jared; *ed:* Fredonia St Univ Coll (BA) Scndry S 1969; SUNY Coll at Fredonia (MSEd) Scndry Ed 1986; Cert Scndry Post Grad Stud Mid Level Sci, Math Integration NSF, Clinical Supervision; *cr:* Jamestown Pub Schls Tchr 1969-; *ai:* Team Ldr; NYEA, Jamestown Tchrs Assn 1969-; Assn of Math Tchrs of Women's Club of Jamestown, Pres, Treas; WCA Hosp Auxillary; Jefferson MS 195 Martin Rd Jamestown NY 14701

LIMES, TERRI L., Vocal Music & String Teacher; *b:* Lewistown, PA Mansfield Univ (BS) Music Ed 1978; Elmira Coll (MS) Ed 1984; *cr:* Elem Schl & Davis Jr HS Instrumental Music & Vocal Music Tchr 197 Broadway Jr HS Vocal Music Tchr 1981-86; Southside HS Vocal M Tchr 1986-; *ai:* Frosh Jazz Ensemble Dir; Class of 1993 Adv; Class of Adv; NEA, MENC & NYSSMA 1978-; Local Music & Theater *office:* Southside H S 777 S Main St Elmira NY 14904

LIMOLI, DENISE WARNER, Assistant Prof of Dance; *b:* Meriden, *m:* Michael D.; *c:* Christopher, Francesca; *ed:* Full Schlsp to B Theatre Schl 1969-70, Jacobs Pillow Dance Festival 1965-67, Sc Hartford Ballet 1967-69; *cr:* Amer Ballet Theatre Ballerina 197 Nutmeg Ballet Master Tchr, Regisseur 1970-; NC Schl of Arts Ballet 1991-92; Skidmore Coll Ballet Fac 1992-; Ballet Master for Num Ballet Cos 1979-; *ai:* Closely Involved with Arts in Ed; Saratoga Cty

Bethesda Episcopal Church Sunday Schl Tchr, Yth Ldr; Amer Guild sical Artists 1965-, Honorary Withdrawal; Screen Actors Guild Amer Fed of Television & Radio Artists 1972-; Dance Comm 1992-; Integrity 1994-; Teach Pedagogy Courses for Ballet Tchrs, Stdnts; Skidmore Coll N Broadway Saratoga Springs NY 12866

:N-BING, Professor; *ed:* Johns Hopkins Univ (PHD) Math 1982; *cr:* of Toledo Prof; *ai:* Amer Mathematical Soc 1978-; Tchng cement Awd 1995; *office:* Univ Of Toledo 2801 W Bancroft St OH 43606

BERRY, RICHARD, Math Teacher; *b:* East Rush, PA; *m:* Shirley ian; *c:* Gregory, Scott, Laura L. Hurley, R. Justin Mc Neill, Rebecca :ill; *ed:* St Coll at Lock Haven (BS) Math 1963; Kean Coll (MA) Ed 1992; *cr:* Madison Twp HS Math Tchr 1963-; *ai:* Pub Address ncer Sporting Events; Marking Period Coord; Tchrs Sunshine Club Magazine & Picture Adv; NEA, NJEA 1963-; Middletown Twp Ed 1964-; BSA 1980-, Institutional Rep; *office:* Middletown HS North dall Rd Middletown NJ 07748

BERRY, ROBIN LEE, Music Teacher; *b:* Troy, PA; *m:* Patricia McDowell; *c:* Whitney, Christopher; *ed:* Mansfield Univ (BM) Music 32; Ithaca Coll (MM) Conducting 1986; *cr:* Maine-Endwell Sr HS Music 1987-; Binghamton Univ Adj Low Brass Instr 1990-92; Ithaca onductor 1993-94; Broome Comm Coll Adj Low Brass Instr 1993-; arching Band; Jazz Band; Symphonic Band; Wind Ensemble; Music Team Dist-Wide Comm; HS Scheduling Comm; MENC 1982-; NEA NYSUT 1984-; NYSSMA 1984-, Certfd Adjudicator, Nationally ered Music Edctr Awd; ASBDA Stanbury Awd for Young Band Dirs In-Demand Guest Conductor in NY & PA; *office:* Maine Endwell Sr 0 Farm To Market Rd Endicott NY 13760*

UGH, KATHY MORGAN, Physics Teacher; *b:* Philadelphia, PA; *m:* *c:* Allison, Patrick, Christopher; *ed:* Immaculate Coll (BA) Physics, 1970; Univ of PA, PA St Master Equivalency; *cr:* Sleighton Farm or Girls Part-time Remedial Math Tchr 1968-73; Springfield Sr HS s Tchr 1970-74; Downingtown Sr HS Physics Tchr 1987-; *ai:* DHS & Schl Assn Fac Rep; Long Range Planning, Living Arts Comms; Ec Advy Bd; One on One Staff; Stu Asst Staff; NEA 1970-74; PSEA Malvern Swim Assn Sec 6 Yrs; Immaculate Coll Bd of Governors; ci Fnd Grant; Mechanical Universe HS Adaptation Wkshp; *office:* ngtown Sr HS 445 Manor Ave Downingtown PA 19335

OLN, MARK JOSEPH, English Teacher; *b:* Brockton, MA; *ed:* ewater St Coll (BA) Eng 1973, (MED) Rdng 1978; New England Schl v (MD) Law 1992; Bridgewater St Coll (CAGS) Educl Ldrshp 1996; ndwich HS Tchr 1974-75; Quincy Coll Prof 1992-95; Brockton HS chr 1975-; *ai:* NHS Chm; Lit Review Adv; NCTE 1973-; Amer Rdng 1978-; Amer Bar Assn 1992-; St Anne's Church 1992-; Brockton HS 993-; Schl Comm Citation Lit Review; Tchr Recognition Stonehill *office:* Brockton HS 470 Forest Ave Brockton MA 02401

OLN, TAUNYA PURRINGTON, English Teacher; *b:* Keene, NH; nes; *c:* Zachary, Olivia, Allura; *ed:* Keene St Coll (BA) Eng & ED Critical Skills Inst at Antioch New England; *cr:* Fall Mountain Regnl g Tchr 1990-; *ai:* NHS & SADD Adv; NEA 1991-; NHTE 1992-; Fall Mountain Reg HS RR 1 Box 89 Alstead NH 03602*

, DIANNE, High School English Teacher; *b:* Needham, MA; *ed:* St Coll (BA) Theatre 1985, (MA) 1986 Eng; Cmptrs for Edctrs, Coop ass; *cr:* Nokomis Regnl HS Eng Tchr 1989-; *ai:* Asst Dir Nokomis a Clb; NCTE 1994-; Article Published 1995; *office:* Nokomis nal HS RR 2 Box 4800 Newport ME 04953*

, ELEANOR RADZWILL, Math Coordinator; *b:* Norwood, MA; *m:* J.; *ed:* Boston Coll (BS) Ed 1959, (MA) Math 1962; 30 Hrs Harvard fication Grad Prgm; *cr:* Millekin HS Math Tchr 1961-62; Huntington ath Tchr 1963-64; Walpole HS Math Tchr 19865-68, Math Dept Chm 32; Walpole Schl System Math Coord 1982-; *ai:* NCTM 1961-; 1992-; ATLAM 1970-, Bd Dirs, Sec; NEA; MTA; ATMIM; Intuitive Prgm; *office:* Walpole HS 257 Common St Walpole MA 02081

JOAN K., Third Grade Teacher; *b:* Proctor, VT; *ed:* Castleton St BS) Elem Ed 1971; Coll of St Joseph the Provider (MAEd) Elem Ed Post-Grad Work Univ of VT; *cr:* Clarendon Elem Schl Grds 3 & 4 971-; *ai:* Univ of VT Tchr of Yr Rutland South Supervisory Union *office:* Clarendon Elem Schl PO Box 7 North Clarendon VT 05759

BERG, CHARLES AARON, Science & Math Teacher; *b:* Concord, Pamela Jean Hunsberger; *c:* Haley Ariel; *ed:* The Kings Coll (BS) 91; *cr:* Chrstn Heritage Schl PE Tchr, Coach 1991-94; The New nent Chrstn Schl Sci, Math Tchr 1994-; *ai:* Var Soccer Coach; Boys sktbl, Bsbl Coach; Class Adv; AAHPERD 1991-.

BERG, PATRICIA LYNN, Assistant Professor; *b:* Worcester, MA; chard John; *c:* Cailey Anne; *ed:* Univ of NJ (BA) Yth Drama, (BS) Ed 1977; Emerson Coll (MA) Theatre Ed 1981; NY Univ (PHD) Theatre 1994; *cr:* Colby-Sawyer Coll Asst Prof 1984-88; Grafton chls Fac 1988-90; Plymouth St Coll Asst Prof 1990-; *ai:* Educl re Collaborative, Kearsarge Arts Theatre For Children Artistic Dir; d Stud, Continuing Ed, Schlsp Comms; NETC, Children's Theatre Bd Moss Hart; AACD; AATE; NJ Dev Disabilities Grant; Moss Hart Awd; Dev, Produced Numerous Educl Theatre Productions; *office:* outh St Coll Rounds 030 Education Dept Plymouth NH 03264*

EKE, WILLIAM A., Professor & Department Chair; *b:* Pasadena, Tara Elyssa; *c:* Lisa; *ed:* San Diego St (AB) Soc Sci 1968, (MA) ci 1970; Claremont Grad Schl (PHD) Govt 1978; *cr:* UC Irvine 76; OR St Univ 1977; Boston Univ; Metropolitan Coll; Univ of MA 983-; *ai:* MTA 1983-, Exec Bd MSP; Articles Pub; *office:* Univ Of t Lowell 1 University Ave Lowell MA 01854

EMANN, THOMAS, Music Teacher & Band Director; *b:* New York, Genevieve Gilbert; *c:* Hans, Erik; *ed:* St Univ of NY at Fredonia Music Ed 1964; Ithaca Coll (MS) Music Ed 1969; *cr:* Westhill Cntrl Music Tchr, Band Dir 1964-; Syracuse Symphony orch Prin Tuba 75; Westhill Cntrl Schls Dept Ldr 1979-; *ai:* Onondaga Cty Music s Assn Exec Bd; Onondaga Cty Music Edctrs Wind ensemble Gen Site Based Mngmt Team; Guest Conductor Music Festivals; NY St l Tchrs, Music Edctrs Natl Conf 1964-; Onondaga Cty Music Edctrs 1964-, Pres, VP, Treas; Local 78 A F of Musicians 1965-; Natl Band 1978-; Free & Accepted Masons Morningstar Lodge #524 1980-; ing HS Tchr 1995; Syracuse Symphony Yth Orch Founder; *home:* Arizona Way Marcellus NY 13108*

EN-BURNS, MARJORIE, Biology Teacher; *b:* South Amboy, NJ; an Burns; *c:* Kyle, Caroline; *ed:* Univ of VT (BS) Botany & Psych Trenton St Coll Tchng Cert; *cr:* Princeton HS Bio Tchr 1987-; *ai:* NJSTA, NJEA & PREA 1987-; NJ League of Women Voters; PTO; ing; *office:* Princeton HS 151 Moore St Princeton NJ 08540

ENMAIER, RACHEL MARY, Asst Mgr of Tele-Ministry Dept; *b:* napolis, IN; *ed:* Marian (BA) Ed 1962; Post Grad Stud St Xavier, Ball Parochial Schls Primary Tchr 34 Yrs; *ai:* Cmptr Dir; Archdiocese of nnati Curr Guide; Coached Kickball; Parent Tchr Club; Ed nission; Prin Awd; *home:* 355 Grand Ave Apt 16 Cincinnati OH 45205

ER, ELAINE B., Ret Vocal Music Tchr, Dept Chm; *b:* Jamestown, Lester W. (dec); *c:* Marshal W., Marsden W., Michele E. Mc Bride, N.; *ed:* Houghton Coll (BM) Applied Piano 1958; Syracuse Univ (MS) Soc Work, Mental Hlth 1986; Cooperative Classroom Mngmt, Blueprints for Learning 1992; Collaborative Comm Skills 1990; Project Intervention 1988; Effective Tchng, Schl Drug Prevention Prgm 1986; Rape Crisis Intervention 1984; Stress Mngmt 1982; Didactic, Experiential Learning 155 Hrs; Group Treatment with Trainer 55 Hrs; Learning & Peer Group Classes 60 Hrs; Supervision 30 Hrs; 50 Post Grad Credits 1968-84; *cr:* Phelps-Clifton Springs Schl Dist Music Tchr 1969-95; Renaissance Group Home for Girls Soc Worker, Cnslr 1986-89; Comm Cnslng Ctr Staff Soc Worker 1989-94; Coll of St. Rose, Long Island Univ NYSUT & IRI Graduate Courses Prgms Instr 1990-; *ai:* Church Organist, Choir Dir; Handbell Choir; Teach Pvt Piano Lessons; NYSSMA, NYSUT 1967-; NASW 1986-; Classical Concert Group Intnl Tour Pianist; Transactional Analysis, Stress Mngmt, Chorus Adult Ed Tchr; Neuro-Linguistic Programming, Transactional Analysis, Gestalt Advanced Trng Co-Ldr; Fred Waring Music Wkshps Accompanist; *home:* 158 Latonka Dr Mercer PA 16137*

LINDER, LOUISE P., 5th-6th Grade Teacher; *b:* Bridgeport, CT; *ed:* Ctrl CT St (BS) Elem Ed 1973; Univ of Bridgeport (MS) Ed 1976; Addl 30 Credits Ed Classes; *cr:* Birdseye Schl 4th Grd Tchr 1973-82; Stratford Acad 5th-6th Grd Tchr 1982-; *ai:* Quality Circles, Effective Schl Comms; Stu Asst Team; Schl Play Production Asst Dir 14 Yrs; Schl Imprvmnt Comm; Stratford Ed Assn, CT Ed Assn, NEA 1973-; Covenant Church of Easton, Life Mem, Chrstn Ed, Financial Sec, Adult Family Ministry; *office:* Stratford Acad 719 Birdseye Stratford CT 06497

LINDER, RAYMOND A., Math Teacher; *b:* Tarentum, PA; *m:* Ann; *c:* Jeffrey, Gregory; *ed:* Hamilton Coll (BA) Math 1969; Brockport (MA) Math 1975; *cr:* Webster Sr HS Math Tchr 1969-; Monroe Comm Coll Adjunct Assoc Prof 1978-; *ai:* AFT, NEA, NYSUT 1969-; Excl in Scndry Tchng Awd 1994.

LINDIA, FRANCESCO M., Italian Teacher; *b:* Cosenza, Italy; *m:* Lucrezia Gioia; *c:* Fabio, Melissa; *ed:* Lehman Coll (BA) Italian 1974; Hunter Coll (MA) Italian 1976; 60 Grad Credits Past Masters in Ed, Comparative Lit Coll of New Rochelle, Manhattanville Coll; *cr:* Cathedral Prep Seminary Italian & Latin Tchr 1975-80; Eastchester HS Italian Tchr 1980-; *ai:* Italian Club & Natl Italian Hnr Soc Adv; Conducted Tours of Italy; Established an Exch Prgm; Natl Soccer Referee 1985-91, Coll Referee to Present; NYSAFLT, AATI 1980-; ATI 1981-, Trustee; Sons of Italy 1988-, Trustee, Man of Yr 1993; Multinational, Comparative Ed Schlsps 1992, 1995; Impact II Prgm 1994-95; Italian Regents Examination Comm; *office:* Eastchester HS 580 White Plains Rd Eastchester NY 10707

LINDO, MARCUS WILLIAM, Social Studies Teacher; *b:* Washington, DC; *m:* Rose Waters; *c:* Marcus II, Maury; *ed:* Atlantic Union Coll (BA) His, Rel 1979; Howard Univ (MDIV) Ethics, Religious Ed 1982; Harvard Univ (MTH) Ethics 1984; *cr:* Dupont Park SDA Schl Rel 1986-88; Martin L. King Jr Acad Ctr Soc Stud Tchr 1988-92; Eleanor Roosevelt HS Soc Stud Tchr 1992, 1995-; *ai:* Benjamin E. Mays Flwshp 1980-82; Outstdng Young Man of Yr 1982; Wayne Swanson Meml Schlsp 1978; *office:* Eleanor Roosevelt HS 7601 Hanover Pkwy Greenbelt MD 20770

LINDON, JAMES ALLEN, English Teacher; *b:* Gnadenhutten, OH; *c:* Amanda; *ed:* The Defiance Coll (BS) Eng 1975; Kent St Univ (MED) Rdng Specialist 1985; 42 Addl Hrs; OH Wesleyan 16 Hrs; *cr:* Tinora HS Eng Tchr 1975-83; Newcomerston HS Eng, Speech Tchr 1983-88; Tuscarawas Vly HS Lang Arts Tchr 1988-; Kent St Univ Eng Instr 1989-; *ai:* Sr Class Adv; Stu Tchr Mentor; NCTE, OCTELA, IRA 1975; OCIRA; NEA; OEA; TVTA; Phi Delta Kappa; Masons 1993-; BPOE 1983-; Book: The Pen Is In My Hand Now What; Articles Pub; Phi Delta Kappa Educl Writing Grant; *office:* Tuscarawas Vly HS 2637 Tuscarawas Vly Rd Zoarville OH 44656*

LINENDOLL, STEWART DANA, Mathematics Teacher; *b:* Troy, NY; *m:* Anne Blakeborough; *c:* Heather, Heath, Jessica; *ed:* Hudson Valley Comm Coll (AS) Math Sci 1967; St Univ of NY at Albany (BS) Math 1971; *cr:* Schoharie Cntrl Math Tchr 1970-72; Watervliet HS Math Tchr 1972-; *ai:* Math Club; Class of 1976 Adv; Natural Helpers; Hlth Ed Advy Comm; Cross Cntry Ski Coach; Watervliet Tchrs Assn 1970-; Altamont Lib, Pres 1972-74 & 1989-, Outstanding Trustee Awd; PTA, Local Pres, Area Circulation Coord; New Games & Cooperative Play Wkshp Presentor at Many Schls; *office:* Watervliet Jr Sr HS Wiswall Ave Watervliet NY 12189

LINGENFELDER, JANE FRANCES, Second Grade Teacher; *b:* Toledo, OH; *m:* Thomas P.; *c:* Ross, Brooke; *ed:* (BS) Elem Ed 1976; (MS) Instruction & Curr 1990; *ai:* Head Tchr; Young Writers Wkshp; Inservice Chprsn; Strategic Planning Comm 1992; EEA, NEA 1976-; *home:* 663 Deer Run Perrysburg OH 43551

LINGENFELTER, CAROLINE F., Fifth Grade Teacher; *b:* Philipsburg, PA; *ed:* Lock Haven Univ (BS) Elem Ed 1964; Penn St Univ (MED) Ed 1972; *cr:* Philipsburg Osceola Schl Tchr 3 Yrs; West Branch Acrea Schl Tchr 29 Yrs; *ai:* Curr Advy Cncl; Career Awareness, Dev; NEA, PSEA 1964-; WBEA 1964-, Treas; AAL 1964-, VP; *office:* West Branch Area Schl Rd 2 Box 194 Morrisdale PA 16858

LINGENFELTER, THOMAS PAYNE, Science Student Tchng Supvr; *b:* Punxsutawney, PA; *m:* Beverly Ann Hoffman; *c:* Sheilah, Tom; *ed:* Indiana Univ of PA (BS) Bio 1960; St Bonaventur Univ (MS) Scndry Schl Admin 1965; 72 Grad Hrs; *cr:* Bradford Area Schls Sci Tchr 1961-64; Southwestern Cntrl Schls Sci Dept Chair, Tchr 1965-94; SUC at Fredonia Sci Stu Tchng Supvr 1995-; *ai:* AAUP 1996; NEA 1961-; *home:* 16 Glenwood Ave Lakewood NY 14750

LINGENFETTER, WILLIAM M., Fifth Grade Teacher; *b:* Mahaffey, PA; *m:* Betty W.; *ed:* Hobe Sound Bible Coll (BA) Soc Stud 1985; *cr:* Soldier Chrstn Acad Tchr 1985-88; Clinton Chrstn Schl Tchr 1989-; *ai:* Yrbk Jrnlsm Tchr; Yrbk Adv; Amer Assn of Chrstn Schl 1989-; Chesapeake Lighthouse HOA 1994-95, Pres; Bible Bapt Church 1989-, Tchr & Sunday Schl Ldr; *home:* 8874 Chesapeake Lighthouse Dr North Beach MD 20714*

LINGO, FELTON,SR., Health, PE Teacher & Coach; *b:* Gordon, GA; *m:* Patricia Everston; *c:* Norman, Linda Olivarez, Felton Jr., Eric, Jonathan, Derrick, Dwayne, Calvin, Debrea Boyce; *ed:* DE St Univ (BS) Hlth, PE 1962; Rowan Coll Cert; William Paterson Coll; *cr:* Fairfield Twp Schl Tchr 1962-64; Bridgeton Bd of Ed Tchr, Coach 1964-; *ai:* Head Girls Bsktbl, Asst Sftbl Coach; Pupil Asst Comm; So Jersey Coaches Assn 1974-, Coach of Yr; NEA 1962-; NJ Ed Assn 1962-, Hum Relations; Cumb Ed Assn 1962-, Hum Relations Comm; Brigeton Ed Assn 1962-, AR; Bridgeton Jaycees 1968-, Inter VP, Outstdng Young Man, Outstdng Spoke Comm Svc; Bridgeton Amer Union 1990-, Vice-Chm, Comm Svc; NJ Commission Civic Rights 1985-, Chm; Omega Man of Yr 1994; Cumberland Cty Black Hall of Fame Awd Fnd 1988; Martin L. King Acad Comm Yth Awd 1992; Natl Bus League Minority Issues Advocate of Yr 1994; Mansfield M. Finney Achvmt Awd Ed 1980; NJ Assn of Bl Edctrs Outstdng Bl Ed of Yr 1985; United Bl Clergy Assn Appreciation Awd 1980; *office:* Bridgeton HS 111 West Ave Bridgeton NJ 08302

LINGRUEN, REX C., Physical Education Teacher; *b:* Akron, OH; *m:* Kaye Palte; *c:* Brooke, Brandi, Blake; *ed:* OH Northern Univ (BA) Hlth, PE 1972; *cr:* North Union Schls Jr HS Tchr 1 Yr; Liberty Ctr Schls Tchr, Coach 23 Yrs; *ai:* Head Ftbl Coach 11 Yrs; Head Wrestling Coach 20 Yrs; Jr HS Track Coach 15 Yrs; NEA 23 Yrs; OEA 23 Yrs; OH Ftbl Coaches 11 Yrs; OH Wrestling Coaches 20 Yrs; League Coach of Yr; Natl Ftbl Fnd Awd; *home:* 102 Lincoln St Liberty Center OH 43532

LINHART, THOMAS M.,SR., Social Studies Teacher; *b:* Buffalo, NY; *m:* Barbara A. Manning; *c:* Lisa, Courtney, Thomas Jr.; *ed:* Canisius Coll (BA) Amer His 1970, (MS) Ed 1973; Attnd Niagara Univ, SUNY Coll at Buffalo & Harvard Univ; *cr:* Lockport City Schls Soc Stud Tchr 1972-88; Spencerport Cntrl Schls Soc Stud Tchr 1988-; *ai:* Sr Class Adv; Peer Mediator & Peer Listener Adv & Trainer; Comm Svc Internship Coord; AFT, NYSUT & STA 1972-; NCSS 1980-; ASCD 1985-; BSA 1990-, Asst Scoutmaster; Excl in Scndry Ed Awd 1989 Univ of Rochester; *office:* Spencerport HS 2707 Spencerport Rd Spencerport NY 14559*

LINIAK-BODWELL, MARY ANN, Vocal & Music Teacher; *b:* Hartford, CT; *m:* Donald S. Bodwell; *c:* Taylor; *ed:* Keene St Coll (BM) Music, Vocal 1974; Wesleyan Univ (MALS) Fine Arts 1985; *cr:* Free Lance Choral Conductor 1990-; Free Lance Concert Artist Soprano Soloist 1976-; East Lyme Pub Schls Vocal Music Dir, Music Theory Tchr 1974-; *ai:* Dir Musical Theater Act; Vocal Extra Curr Ensembles; Natl Assn of Tchrs of Singing 1984-, Clinician; Amer Choral Dir Assn 1986-; CT Music Edctrs Assn, Clinician, Guest Conductor for Festivals, Music Tech Comm; CT Ed Assn 1974-; Eastern CT Symphony Young Artist Awd 1976; Featured Great Artist Vocal with Harford Symphony, Lincoln-Cntr Out-of-Doors, New Music Amer Intnl, Cardiff Intnl Festival, Wales Natl Sr Symphony; Recording Artist, Premiers of New Solo Vocal Works; Guest Conductor Choral New England, Europe; *office:* East Lyme HS 30 Chesterfield Rd East Lyme CT 06333*

LINK, LOIS E., 1st Grade Teacher; *b:* Perry, NY; *c:* John C., Daniel, Lynne; *ed:* Geneseo St (BS) Elem Ed 1959; *ai:* Rdg Club, Testing Comm; NEA 1959-, VP; WY Cty Env Comm; *home:* 7166 Swyers Rd Castile NY 14427*

LINLEY, MARCIA GUEST, English Teacher; *b:* Toledo, OH; *m:* Michael S.; *c:* Trish, Jenny; *ed:* OH St Univ (BS) Scndry Ed, Comprehen Comm 1977; Cert Coursework Spec Ed 1981; Writing Classes Wright St Univ; *cr:* Franklin Co Prgm for Mentally Retarded Asst Tchr 1977-78; Learning Unlimited Dramatics Tchr 1978-79; Hilliard HS L D Tutor 1980-85, Eng Tchr 1985-; *ai:* Asst Var Tennis Coach; Past Yrbk, Chrldng, Soph Class Adv; Past Prom Asst Adv; Past Hnr Soc, Prins Adv Comms; NEA, OEA, HEA, 1980-; NCTE 1982-; Greater Columbus Tennis Assn 1988-; Olympic Tennis 1989-, 4.0 Singles Champion; OH Tennis Coaches Assn 1990-; Linworth United Meth 1980-; Short Story Pub; *office:* Hilliard HS 5100 Davidson Rd Hilliard OH 43026

LINN, TERRY ANN NOFFSINGER, Mathematics Teacher; *b:* Ft Belvoir, VA; *m:* Joseph Earl; *c:* Steven Orders, Renee, Tara, Joe; *ed:* East Carolina Univ (BS) Math 1972; Addl Hrs; *cr:* Various HS 1972-76; Charles Carroll MS Math Tchr, Dept Chair 1977-80; Eleanor Roosevelt HS Math Tchr 1980-; *ai:* Var Men, Women Swim Team Coach; NCTM, NEA 1972-; MD Cncl of Tchrs of Math 1977-; MAA 1990-; Presidential Math Excl Awd Finalist 1991; Insvc Instr; *office:* Eleanor Roosevelt HS 7601 Hanover Pky Greenbelt MD 20770

LINNENBOM, SUE ANNE KNOWLES, Coord of Gifted Support; *b:* New Castle, PA; *m:* Victor John Jr.; *c:* Victor Andrew; *ed:* Westminster Coll (BA) Speech, Eng, Scndry Ed 1971, (MA) Rdng Specialist, Ed 1972; Post Grad Rdng Supvr Univ of Pittsburgh; Credit Hrs Carlow Coll; *cr:* Westminster Coll Rdng Grad Asst 1971-72; Butler Area Jr HS Eng Tchr, Rdng Specialist 1972-73; Alston Jr HS Eng Tchr, Rdng Specialist 1973-74; Trident Tech Coll Coord Lrng Lab 1974-76; Penn St Univ Rdng, Writing Lab Coord, Instr Rdng, Eng 1977-89; Blackhawk HS Coord Gifted Support, Rdng Specialist, Eng Tchr 1989-; *ai:* Gifted Support Musical, Plays Adv; Club Adv; Acad Games Coach; Kappa Delta Pi 1971-; IRA 1972-; NCTE 1976-; NEA 1990-; Beaver Cty Comm Skills Consortium 1980-, Co-Chprsn; Beaver Cty Enrichment Consortium 1995-; Articled Pub; *office:* Blackhawk HS 500 Blackhawk Rd Beaver Falls PA 15010

LINNER, DONALD, Business Professor; *b:* New York, NY; *ed:* Cntrl CT St Univ (BS) Acctng Ed 1961; Tchrs Coll Columbia Univ (MA) Bus Ed 1964; Seton Hall Univ (MBA) Acctng 1974; Tchr Coll Columbia Univ Prof Diploma Supervision of Bus Ed 1968; Word Processing; 3 Credits Auditing; 3 Credits Wills Trusts & Estates; *cr:* Brien Mc Mahon HS Bus Ed Tchr 1961-68; Essex Cty Coll Instr, Asst Prof, Assoc Prof, Prof 1968-, Chair, Bus Division 1987-92; *ai:* Bus Division Curr Comm; Fac Alliance for Ed 1989-95; NEA 1957-; Delta Pi Epsilon 1963-, Tau Chptr Pres 1967; NBEA, Eastern Bus Ed Assn 1958-, Exhibitis Chprsn 1992; Intnl Soc for Bus Ed; Grant Implement Cmptr Learning Lab 1986; Stock Market Investments Practice Set Pub 1987; Presenter Eastern Bus Ed Assn Convention Session Bus Law 1987; *office:* Essex County Coll 303 University Ave Newark NJ 07102

LINSENBIGLER, DAVID ALLEN, Math Teacher; *b:* Clearfield, PA; *m:* Elizabeth Tubbs; *c:* Casey; *ed:* Clarion St Coll (BS) Math & Drivers Ed 1973; Masters Equivalency Plus 9 Credit Hrs; *cr:* Curwensville JSHS Math Instr 1973-.

LINSLEY, CHRISTINE LOUISE, Assoc Prof of Sociology; *b:* Liverpool, England; *m:* Colin; *c:* Alexandra Pope, Rachel; *ed:* Essex Univ (BSC) Sociology 1982; Univ of IL at Urbana (MA) Sociology 1984; London Schl of Ec & Pol Sci (PHD) Soc Sci, Admin 1993; *cr:* Univ of WI at Milwaukee Instr 1985-87; St John Fisher Assoc Prof 1987-; *ai:* Values Comm; Fac Dev; Bursery at London Schl of Ec; 2 Summer Grants; 1 Article Pub; *office:* Saint John Fisher Coll 3690 East Ave Rochester NY 14618

LINTERMOST, RANDY LEE, Social Studies Teacher; *b:* Van Wert, OH; *m:* Jane Ann Borden; *c:* Jeffrey, Kasey; *ed:* Defiance Coll (BS) Scndry Ed 1974; Univ of Toledo (MA) Scndry Ed 1989; Addl Coursework in Admin & Supervision; *cr:* Pike-Delta-York Schls Soc Stud Tchr 1974-; *ai:* Var Ftbl Asst Coach; Frosh Bsktbl Coach; His Day Coord; nEA 1974-; *office:* Pike-Delta-York HS 605 Taylor St Delta OH 43515

LINTHICUM, ERLENA CLAUDETTE, Sixth Grade Teacher; *b:* Chestertown, MD; *m:* Frederick; *ed:* Bowie St Univ (BS) Elem Ed 1962; Temple Univ Elem Ed 1964-68; Univ of MD Stu Tchr Rdng; Prince Georges Comm Coll Sci 1989-93; *cr:* Garnett Elem Schl 6th Grd Tchr 1962-68; Barnaby Manor Elem Schl 6th Grd Tchr 1968-; *ai:* Tutorial Prgm After Schl; 5th & 6th Grd Level Cluster Chprsn; 6th Grd Tchr Grd Level Chprsn; Prince Georges Cty 27 Yrs; MD St Tchrs Assn 33 Yrs; NEA 33 Yrs; Cancer Assn Fundraiser; Henryland Garnett Schl 15 Yrs, Hall of Fame Awd; Bowie St Univ 25 Yrs; Asbury United Meth Church 33 Yrs; PTO of Barnaby Manor 27 Yrs, Appreciation Awd; Outstanding Elem Tchrs of Amer 1972; Outstanding Tchr of Appreciation by Prince Georges Bd of Ed; Cert of Recognition for 20 Yrs Svc Prince Georges Cty 1989; *home:* 12900 Applecross Dr Clinton MD 20735

LINTON, BARBARA ANN, Religious Studies & Psych Tchr; *b:* Louisville, KY; *ed:* St Mary of the Woods (BA) Soc Stud 1960; La Salle Univ (MA) Rel Ed 1976; Indiana Univ (MS) Adult Ed 1976; *cr:* Notre Dame HS Campus & Peer Ministry Dir 1983-86; Shrine of St Joseph Rel Ed Dir 1986-88; Stamford Cath HS Rel Stud Tchr 1988-91; Sacred Heart Acad Rel Stud, Psych Tchr 1991-; *ai:* Sr Class Adv; Comm Svc Prgm Coord; Liturey Retreat Coord; NCEA 1991-; Delta Kappa Gamma 1978-; Bread for the World, Amnesty Intnl, Oxfam Amer, Pax Christi, Network 1990-; NSF Chem Grant; *office:* Sacred Heart Acad 200 Strawberry Hill Ave Stamford CT 06902*

LINTON, DEBORAH J., Mathematics Teacher; *b:* Lancaster, PA; *m:* Samuel C.; *c:* Maura, James; *ed:* Univ of PA (BS) Math Ed 1974; Penn St Univ 15 Credits Spcl Ed; Millersville Univ 9 Credits Math Ed; *cr:* Mitchell-Main Line Day Schl Math Tchr 1974-77; Garden Spot HS Math Tchr 1978-; *ai:* Sr High NHS Adv; NEA 1977-; PSEA 1977-; ELCEA

1977-; NCTM 1985-; VFW Ladies Auxiliary 1983-; *home:* 66 Peach Ln Ronks PA 17572

LION, RITA GLEASON, Retired Teacher; *b:* West Chester, PA; *m:* Frank J.; *ed:* Immaculata Coll (BA) Sci 1954; West Chester Coll (BS) Ed 1955; Masters Equivelancy 1992; Attnd St Joseph's Univ, Penn St Univ, Drexel Univ; *cr:* Downingtown Jr HS Sci Tchr 1955-; *ai:* PSEA; *home:* 410 W Lafayette St West Chester PA 19380

LIOZZI, BRUCE NICHOLAS, 5th Grade Teacher; *b:* Staten Island, NY; *m:* Elizabeth Michaelson; *c:* Stephen; *ed:* Wagner Coll (BS) Elem Ed 1964; Richmond Coll CUNY (MS) Elem Ed 1969; Prof Cert Admin; *cr:* Mt Pleasant Elem Schl 4th Grd Tchr 1964-66; PS 10 Mount Loretto 6th-12th Grd Tchr of Emotionally Handicapped 1966-72; PS 3 Pleasant Plains Schl 3-5th Grd Tchr 1972-; *ai:* UFT 1970-; *office:* PS 3 Pleasant Plains 80 S Goff Ave Staten Island NY 10309

LIPCHEK, JOHN JOSEPH, Social Studies Teacher; *b:* Pittsburgh, PA; *ed:* Univ of Pittsburgh (BA) Hum Ed 1989; Working Towards Masters; *cr:* Pottstown MS Long-Term Sub Tchr 1990-91; Pittsburgh Pub Schls Sub Tchr 1991-93; Avonworth Jr Sr HS Soc Stud Tchr 1993-; *ai:* Stu Assistance Team; PSEA 1993-; NCSS 1995-; PA Army Natl Guard 1985-95, 1st Lt, Inf Ofcr, Natl Defense Svc, Res Comp Achvmt Medals; *office:* Avonworth Jr Sr HS 250 Josephs Ln Pittsburgh PA 15237

LIPECKY, MARILYN, Physics Teacher; *b:* Punxsutawney, PA; *m:* Garret; *ed:* IVP (BS) PE 1967; Attnd Gettysburg Coll, Worcester Polytechnic Inst, Hamilton Coll; *cr:* Mars Schl Dist Physics Tchr 1967-70; Greater Latrobe Physics Tchr 1970-; *ai:* AAPT 1970-; NSF & Bridges Project Grants; *office:* Greater Latrobe Sr HS Country Club Rd Latrobe PA 15650

LIPELES, ENID SINGER, Schl Dept Chair & Chem Teacher; *b:* New York City, NY; *m:* Ralph; *c:* Brett, Charles, Jenny; *ed:* Hunter Coll (AB) 1963; Univ of Bridgeport (MS) 1969; Sacred Heart 18 Credits Intermediate Admin Cert 1994; 30 Grad Credits; *cr:* Paul D Schreiber HS Chem Hnrs, Coll Prep & Gen Tchr 1963-65; Masuk HS Chem I & II Hnrs & Coll Prep Tchr 1965-; Sacred Heart Univ Adj Instr & Gen Chem Tchr 1987-93; *ai:* MEA, CEA & NEA 1965-; Amer Chemical Soc 1967-70, 1977-; Monroe Ed Assn Prof Rights & Responsibilities Comm Chprsn 1975-79, 1981-84, 1986-94; CT Sci Tchrs Assn 1975-; New England Assn of Chem Tchrs Asst Treas & Registrar 1980, Wkshps Chm 1981, NEACT Newsletter Ed 1981-89, 1991-94, Hospitality Chm 1985, Exhibits Chm 1987; Kappa Delta Gamma; Amer Field Svc 1965-, Pres 1971-77 & Treas 1982-94; Monroe Tennis Assn 1975-, Womens Singles & Doubles Round Robins Dir 1978-88, Yth Round Robin Dir 1980-82 & Pres 1982-87, 1991-94; Monroe Jewish Womens Club 1976-, Pres 1978-82, 1990-94; Monroe League of Women Voters 1980-, League Newsletter Ed 1983-93 & Co-Pres 1994-; Monroe Park & Recreation Commission Appointed Town Ofcr 1979-89 & Vice-Chm 1982-89; Zoning; Numerous Articles Pub; Awds: Amer Chemical Soc Schlsp 1978 & 1987, Monroe Tchr of Yr 1990-91, CT Tchr of Yr Finalist 1991, CT Assn of Stu Cncl Adv of Yr 1991-92, Outstdng CT HS Sci Tchr 1995-96, Chemical Manufacturers Assn Catalyst Regnl Level; Grants: Talented & Gifted Pgm for 5th Graders to Learn Chem 1989-90, Urban & Suburban CES Mini-Grant for Exch Stu Visitation 1990, CT Sci Tchrs Assn 1994; Tishiba Fndtn Amer 1994 & 1995; *office:* Masuk HS 1014 Monroe Tpke Monroe CT 06468

LIPIANO, JAMES JOSEPH, Visual Arts Teacher; *b:* Easton, PA; *c:* Victoria; *ed:* Amer Univ (BA) Art 1970; 45 Credit Hrs Post Grad Stud; *cr:* Gwynn Park Jr HS Visual Arts Tchr 1972-80; Francis Scott Key MS Visual Arts Tchr 1980-87; Thomas G Pullen Arts Magnet Schl Visual Arts Tchr 1987-; *ai:* Dept Chprsn; Stage Crew, Set Design Club Spon; Natl Jr Art Honor Soc Spon; Tech Dir Schl Productions; NEA, MSTA 1976-; NAEA, MAEA 1984-; Smithsonian Assn 1990-, Prince Georgian on Camera 1985-; Outstndng Edctr Awd; Excl Educ Awd; Governors Citation; AAA Natl Schl Traffic Safety Pub Svc Awd; Citizens Concerned for Cleaner Cty Pub Svc Awd; WA Metropolitan Area Transit Authority Pub Svc Awd; *office:* Thomas Pullen Arts Magnet Schl 700 Brightseat Rd Landover MD 20785

LIPINSKI, JOHN JOSEPH, Junior High School Teacher; *b:* Cleveland, OH; *m:* Peg; *c:* Michelle, Allison, Matthew; *ed:* Cleveland St Univ (BA) El Ed 1976; *cr:* St Stanislaus Jr HS Tchr Math, Religion 1976-78; Sts Peter & Paul Jr HS Tchr Soc Stud 1978-85; St Monica Jr HS Tchr Math, Rel 1985-; *ai:* Trinity HS Ftbl, Bsbl Coach; *office:* St Monica Schl 13633 Rockside Rd Garfield Hgts OH 44125

LIPKIN, ROSEMARY A., 4th-5th Grade Math & Sci Tchr; *b:* Huntington LI, NY; *m:* Robert J.; *c:* Jamie, Jodie; *ed:* Adelphi Univ (MS) Elem Ed 1974; 60+ Hrs from Various Univs & Prof Orgs; *cr:* Greatneck Road Elem Kndgtn 3rd Grd Tchr 1968-78, 4th & 5th Grd Sci & Math Tchr 1978-; *ai:* Dist Level Comm for Sci & Math; Copragie Tchr Assn 1984-, VP; Western Suffolk Tchr Ctr 1988-, Sec & Treas; Natl Sci Assn 1990-; 1994 Mini Grant Awd Winner; *office:* Great Neck Road Elem Schl 1400 Great Neck Rd Copiague NY 11726

LIPKIN-WEEKS, MARLA, Architectural Specialist; *b:* New York, NY; *m:* Paul Weeks; *c:* Rebecca; *ed:* Cooper Union Schl of Art & Architecture (BFA) Fine Arts 1973; Hunter Coll (MA) Fine Arts 1976; Schl of Visual Arts Post Baccalaureate Ed Cert 1989; *cr:* Creative Learning Comm Schl Art Tchr 1988-89; Wm H. Carr Jr HS Arch Tchr 1990-; *ai:* Yrbk Art Dir; AFT, UFT 1988-; Flwshps Michael Karolyi Fnd Vence France 1974, Edna St. Vincent Nullay Colony for Fine Arts Austerlitz NY 1985, 1987, Summer Inst at the Brooklyn Museum NY 1992, The Sappling Prgm, The NY Botanical Gardens 1995; *office:* William H Carr Jr HS 154-60 17th Ave Whitestone NY 11357

LIPP, ALAN, Mathematics Department Head; *b:* Brooklyn, NY; *m:* Edith Chamberlain; *c:* Kathryn; *ed:* Polytechnic Inst of Brooklyn (MS) Math 1970; Univ of MA (EDD) Math Ed 1989; *cr:* Baldwin Schl of NY Math Tchr 1965-72; Williston Northampton Schl Math Dept Chair & Dir of Acad Computing 1975-; Univ of MA Instr 1979-81; Mount Holyoke Coll Smmr math & Cmptr Coord 1983-; *ai:* Math Team Adv; NCTM 1966-; MAA 1988-; Articles Pub in Multimedia Schls, The Math Tchr, The Computing Tchr, Journal of Comp Sci in Ed, The New England Math Journal; *office:* The Williston Northampton Schl 19 Payson Ave Easthampton MA 01027*

LIPPER, DENISE FRANCES, Elem Kdg Tchr; *b:* Brockton, MA; *m:* Kevin P.; *c:* Adriann, Adam; *ed:* Bridgewater St Coll (BS) Elem Ed 1973; Post Grad Stud Early ChldhdBehavioral Techniques, Dev Task Forces, Lit Based Curr, New Curr Dev; *cr:* Brockton Pub Schls K-5th Grd Tchr 1973-; *ai:* Supt Tchrs Advy Cncl; Early Chldhd Task Force; MTA, NEA, BEA 1973-; Girl Scouts 1984-87; *office:* Brookfield Elem Schl 135 Jon Dr Brockton MA 02402

LIPPERT, ROBERT LEE, Assistant Professor of Finance; *b:* Cincinatti, OH; *m:* Nora Alston Flynn; *ed:* Xavier Univ (BS) Finance 1985; Univ of SC (PHD) Finance 1992; *cr:* Rutgers Univ Asst Prof of Finance 1992-; *ai:* Finance Soc & Phi Kappa Sigma-Gamma Omicron Adv; Stu Affairs, Fac Composition & Dev Comms; Financial Mgmt Assn 1990-; Multinational Finance Soc 1995-, VP of Membership; Southern Finance Assn 1993-; Schl of Bus Excl in Tchng Awd 1992-93, 1994-95; Schl of Bus Research Grant 1992-96; Research Cncl Grant 1994; *office:* Rutgers Univ School of Business Camden NJ 08102

LIPPIATT, NANCY MILLER, Teacher of Gifted & Talented; *b:* Youngstown, OH; *m:* Roger Alan; *ed:* Youngstown St Univ (BSEd) Elem Ed 1966, (MAEd) Ed Curr; *cr:* Canfield Local Schls Tchr 1966-; *ai:* Power of the Pen Coach; NEA 1966-; OH Ed Assoc 1966-; Canfield Ed Assoc 1966-, VP, Negotiation Team; Friends Church 1973-; Delta Kappa Gamma 1989-; *home:* 7530 W Garfield Rd Salem OH 44460

LIPPMAN, LINDA VERRICO, Sixth Grade Teacher; *b:* New York City, NY; *m:* Stephen D.; *c:* Keri, Deena, Jill; *ed:* Hofstra Univ (BA) Sociology 1971; Dowling Coll (MS) Ed 1984; 30 Post Grad Credits; *cr:* Hebrew Acad 4th Grd & Cmptr Tchr 1984-85; North Shore Montessori 2nd Grd Tchr 1985-86; Brentwood Schls Permanent Sub Tchr 1986-87; Islip MS 6th Grd Tchr 1987-; *ai:* Builders Club Adv; Advy & Writing Comms; ITA 1987-; NYSUT 1984-; Homeowners Assn 1978-80, Pres; Spiked Shoe Club 1993-, VP; Glencoe Math Snapshot; Inter-Cty Grants; Spec Olympics; *office:* Islip MS 215 Main St Islip NY 11751

LIPPO, FELICE DIDIA, Kindergarten Teacher; *b:* Brooklyn, NY; *ed:* Hunter Coll (BA) Ed, Early Chldhd 1970; Brooklyn Coll (MS) Rdng 1974; 30 Grad, In-Svc Credits Early Chldhd Ed, Arts, Crafts, Sci, Human Relations, Spec Ed; *cr:* Pub Schl 58K Kndgtn-2nd Grd Tchr 1970-; *ai:* AFT, NEA, UFT 1970-.

LIPPS, RAYMOND, Mathematics Teacher; *b:* Clinton, TN; *c:* Stephen, Stephanie, Jason; *ed:* Univ of Cincinnati (BS) Math 1967, (MED) Cnslng 1972; *cr:* Cincinnati Pub Schls Math Tchr 1966-68; North Coll Hill HS Math Dept Chm 1968-70; Campbell Jr HS Math Tchr, Dept Chair 1970-77; Western Hills HS Dept Chm 1977-; *ai:* Lead Tchr Cinti Publ Schls; Univ of Cincinnati Math Competition Supvr; Math Curr Cncl 1992-, Schl Rep; AFT, CFT 1974-; NCTM 1980-; Fraternal Order of Eagles 1982-; Olympian Yth Club 1977-, Bd of Dirs, Civic Svc Awd; Independent Order of Forresters 1971-; *office:* Western Hills HS 2144 Ferguson Rd Cincinnati OH 45238

LIPPY, MARTHA J., Kindergarten Teacher; *b:* Hanover, PA; *m:* Harry W.; *c:* Michele A., Harry S.; *ed:* Shippensburg Univ (BS) Elem Ed 1966; Ship Millersville Univ (MS) Elem Ed 1975; 18 Addl Credit Staff Dev Ctr in Southwestern Schl Dist; *cr:* Manheim Elem Schl 1st Grd TChr 1966-70; W. Manheim Elem Schl 3rd Grd Tchr 1975-76; Barosville Elem Schl K Tchr 1976-92; West Manheim Elem Schl K Tchr 1992-; *ai:* Spirit Comm; Safety Comm Rep; Liason Comm Chprsn SW Ed Assn; NEA, PSEA 1966-; SWEA 1966-, Sec, Pres; St Mark Luth Church Congregational Cncl 1994-, VP; Hanover String Quartet 1976-, Play Cello; Tchr of Yr SW SChl Dist 1986; *office:* West Manheim Elem Schl 2412 Baltimore Pike Hanover PA 17331*

LIPSCHUTZ, BETTY LOWE, Second Grade Teacher; *b:* Bedford Cty, PA; *m:* Barry; *c:* Benjamin; *ed:* Messiah Coll (BS) Soc Scis 1969; Shippensburg Univ (MA) Elem Ed 1972; 30 Addl Hrs; *cr:* Upper Allen Schl Dist Elem Tchr; Line Mountain Schl Dist Elem Tchr; Dover Area Schl Dist Elem Tchr 1970-; *ai:* Lang Arts, Math, Soc Stud, Art Task Force, Gifted Prgm, Stu Recognition, Creative Writing Projects Comms; NH Ed Assn, PA Ed Assn 1970-; Dover Area Ed Assn 1970-, Bldg Rep; York Little Theater 1972-, Producer, Actress, Vol, Supporting Mem, Stage Mgr, Costume Designer; Agricultural & Indstrl Museum of York 1990-, Vol, Vol Awd; Cancer Soc, Heart Assn, Easter Seals 1980-, Vol; Good Bears of World 1995-, Honorary Mem; Church, Choir, Soloist; WSCS, Past Pres; Creator of Project 2000; Created Comm Ed Prgms; Article Pub; *office:* Dover Area Schl Dist 109 E Canal Rd Dover PA 17315*

LIPSETT, KATHLEEN E., French Teacher; *b:* Rochester, PA; *m:* William; *c:* Matthew, Alison; *ed:* Penn St Univ (BA) Fr 1972; *cr:* Cntrl Dauphin Schl Dist Fr Tchr 1973-; *ai:* Fr Club; NEA, PSEA 1973-; *office:* Central Dauphin HS 4600 Locust Ln Harrisburg PA 17109

LIPSKI, JEAN JOHNSON, Secondary English Teacher; *b:* Kingston, PA; *m:* Philip Joseph; *c:* Lauren, Jaime, Michael; *ed:* Wilkes Coll (BA) Eng Ed, Soc 1978; Master's Equiv Plus 21 Credits; *cr:* Lake-Lehman HS Scndry Eng Tchr 1978-; *ai:* Field Hockey Coach; Schl Play, Sr Class Night Theatre Dir; SAP Mem; Support Groups Facilitator; Lake-Lehman Ed Assn 1978-; Lehman UM Church 1956-, Sunday Schl Tchr, Children's Choir Dir, Choir Mem; *office:* Lake Lehman HS Market St Lehman PA 18627

LIPTAK, MARY ANN ELIZABETH, Dean Acad Affairs; *b:* Trenton, NJ; *ed:* Rider Coll (BA) Fr, Eng 1966, (MA) Ed Admin 1988; Also Attnd Trenton St Coll, St Francis Coll at Loretto PA; *cr:* St Anthony's HS Fr, Span Tchr 1966-71; Notre Dame HS Fr, Eng Tchr 1971-, Asst Prin 1988-90, Eng Chm, Acad Dean 1990-; *ai:* Learning Styles Prgm, Stu Tchng with Local Colls, AP Coord; Local & St Grant Writer; Engl Dept Chprsn; NCEA 1966-; NCTE 1981-; PHi Delta Kappa 1991-; ASCD Assoc; *office:* Notre Dame HS 601 Lawrence Rd Lawrenceville NJ 08648*

LISAC, GARY EDWARD, Computer & Mathematics Teacher; *b:* Sharon, PA; *m:* Cynthia Williams; *c:* Joshua, Jacob; *ed:* Waynesburg Coll (BS) Math 1974; PA St Dept of Ed (MEQ) Ed 1989; Attnd Geneseo St Univ, E Stroudsburg Univ, St Bonaventure Univ, Penn St Univ & Univ of Pittsburgh 30 Credit Hrs; *cr:* Oswayo Valley Schl Dist Math & Cmptr Tchr 1974-90; Academia Alianza Americana in Quito Ecuador Math & Cmptr Tchr 1987-88; *ai:* Tech Comm Mem; NEA & PSEA 1974-; Faith Bible Church 1978-, Bd of Trustees; *home:* 281 Pleasant Acres Dr Portville NY 14770*

LISANDRELLI, ELAINE SLIVINSKI, English Teacher; *b:* Pittston, PA; *m:* Carl A.; *ed:* Marywood (BA) Scndry Ed Eng 1973, (MS) Scndry Cnslng 1976; 75 Credits Beyond MS; *cr:* North Pocono 7th Grd Eng Tchr 1973-; Marywood Coll Part-Time Fac 1986-; *ai:* Lit Magazine; Team DE; PSEA 1973-; SCBWI 1990-; NCTE 1996; Co-Authored: Study Skills Workout, Levels G & H Easy Writer; Articles Pub; Books: Maya Angelou- More Than a Poet, Senator Bob Dole; *office:* North Pocono MS Church St Moscow PA 18444*

LISCO, JOHN FITZGERALD, Recreation Professor; *b:* Denver, CO; *m:* Sherryl Lynn Harsh; *c:* Holly Celeste; *ed:* Mesa St Coll (BS) Geology 1988; Memphis St Univ (MS) Recreation 1990; Univ of Memphis (EDD) Higher & Adult Ed 1994; *cr:* Univ of Memphis Instr 1992-94; Univ of ME at Presque Isle Asst Prof 1994-; *ai:* Park Ranger Trng Pgm Dir; Natl Park Svc Seasonal Park Ranger; Parks & Recreation Club Co-Adv; Impact Mrktg Comm; ANPR 1988-; NRPA 1996; Spcl Achvmt Awd From: Pub Svc, NPS, USFWS, USFS; Articles Pub; *office:* Univ Of ME At Presque Isle 181 Main St Presque Isle ME 04769

LISHACK, JOHN H., Math Teacher; *b:* Pittsburgh, PA; *m:* Nancy Jean DiClemente; *ed:* IN Univ of PA (BSEd) Scndry Math 1975; Robert Morris Coll (M5BA) Admin 1985; 11 Credits beyond Masters; *cr:* Northgate Schl Dist Scndry Math Tchr 1976-77; South Fayette Schl Dist Scndry Math Tchr 1978; Canon Mc Millan Schl Dist Scndry Math Tchr 1978-81; Shaler Area Schl Dist Scndry Math Tchr 1982-; *ai:* 7th-9th Grd Girls Sftbl Coach; Advy Comm; NEA, PSEA 1978-; Stu Nom for Gift of Time Awd 1992; *office:* Shaler Area HS 381 Wible Run Rd Pittsburgh PA 15209

LISHACK, NANCY DICLEMENTE, Business Teacher; *b:* Pittsburgh, PA; *m:* John H.; *ed:* Robert Morris Coll (BS) Bus Admin 1977, (MS) Bus Ed 1982; Addl 37 Credits; Mrktg Cert Univ of Pittsburgh 1988; *cr:* Cornell Educl Ctr Bus Tchr 1977-79; Comm Coll of Allegheny Cty Bus Instr 1977-88, 1995; North Allegheny Intermediate HS Bus Tchr, Coord of Gifted Prgm 1987-88; *ai:* NEA, NAFT 1977-; Tri-St Bus Assn 1977-; Mid Sts Assn Colls, Schls 1984-, Visiting Team; Christa Mc Auliffe Awd; NY Stock Exchs Teach the Tchrs Prgm; Chprsn Educl Prgm, Evaluation of Self Stud; *office:* North Allegheny Interm Sch 350 Cumberland Rd Pittsburgh PA 15237

LISI, RICHARD ROLAND, Electronics Teacher; *b:* Westfield, MA; *m:* Carolyn J. Lutt-Lisi; *c:* Dominic, Cristina, Erica; *ed:* Eastern KY Univ (AA) Drafting, Design Tech 1969, (BS) Applied Arts, Sci 1971; Univ (MA) PE, Recreation 1986; Parks, Recreation; Univ of Ci Natural Sci Field Stud; *cr:* Cutter Jr HS World of Construction Tch Finney Town HS Woods, Metals, Drafting Tchr 1972-73; Princet Electronics, Cmptr Aided Design, Drivers Ed Tchr 1973 Environmental Club, Explorer Scouts Adv; Structure, Act, Disc Alternative Ed Comms; NEA 1972-; SWOTEA 1973-, Dist Rep; 1975-, HS Rep; PACE 1972-, Fac Rep; Explorer Scouts 1973-78, A Horn, Father of Yr Awds; Cinti Audibon, Sierra Club 1986-; Natl Res Defens Cncl 1993-; Assoc Producer 2 Made-For-TV After Schl Chi Productions; Article Pub; *home:* 3363 Shadow Ridge Dr Lovela 45140*

LISICA, GARY CHARLES, Science Teacher; *b:* Sewickley, P Slippery Rock Univ (MS) Ed 1990; Working on Masters at Westr Coll; Scndry Prin Cert 16 Hrs; *cr:* Seneca Valley Jr HS Tchr 1990-; *a* Club Spon; NEA 1990-; PSEA 1990-; SVEA 1990-; *home:* RR 3 S Rock PA 16057

LISKA, CYNTHIA, Second Grade Teacher; *b:* Johnstown, PA; *m:* *c:* Ryan; *ed:* Univ of Pittsburgh (BS) Elem Ed 1973; Post Grad Cred Conemaugh Twp Schl Dist 2nd Grd Tchr 1977-; *ai:* NEA, PSEA, C 1977-; St David's Lutheran Church, Kidschoir Dir, Church Cncl; Conemaugh Twp Primary Schl Front St Jerome PA 15937

LISNIK, DONNA BELL, Mathematics Teacher; *b:* Presque Isle, John; *c:* John Jr., Eric, Allison; *ed:* Westbrook Coll (AS) Dental H 1967; Univ of ME at Presque Isle (BA) His 1986, (BS) Math Ed 19 Presque Isle HS Math Tchr 1987-; *ai:* Sr Class of 1996 Adv; NCTM PITA 1987-, Exec Bd Mem; MTA, NEA 1987-; ME Presidential Aw Tchng 1994; *office:* Presque Isle HS 16 Fort St Presque Isle ME 04

LISSNER, ELLEN SOPRANO, 8th Grd Math & Computer T Newark, NJ; *m:* Robert; *c:* David, Patricia Ann; *ed:* Jersey City (BA) Elem Ed 1968; Addl 30 Credits Cmptr; *cr:* Bridgewater Ele 8th Grd Rdng Tchr 1977-78; Tewksbury Elem Schl Sub Tchr 1978 Elizabeth Schl Math Tchr 1981-86; Long Hill Bd of Ed Algebra, Cmptrs Tchr 1986-; *ai:* Cmptr Club, Booster Club Adv; Curr Comm; 1986-, Pres, VP; NJ Math Tchrs; NEA 1986-; Jr Women's Club 197 St Chm; Woman's Club of Tewksbury 1980-86, VP; Tewksbury Bd 1983-; Govenor's Awd Outstdng Tchr; Courier News Outstdng, Inno Math Prgm; *office:* Central MS 90 Central Ave Stirling NJ 07980

LIST, GEORGE, Department Chair; *b:* Philadelphia, PA; *m:* Car Young; *c:* Matthew, Shannon, William; *ed:* Carnegie-Mellon Univ 1971; Univ of DE (MEE) 1976; Univ of PA (PHD) 1984; *cr:* Ren Polytechnic Inst Asst Prof 1984-90, Assoc Prof 1990-, Dept Chair *ai:* ITE & Chi Epsilon Stu Chapters Adv; IEEE 1970-; ASCE 1984- Hazardous Material Transport Comm; TRB 1978-, Chm, Inte Freight Transport Comm; Saint Georges Episcopal Church, Orga Choirmaster; BSA Troop 6, Asst Scoutmaster; R K Dental Awd; Re Grants From NSF, USDOT, DOE & Numerous Other Agencies; Nu Journal Articles & Book Chapters.

LISTER, DAWN SHEETZ, Social Studies Teacher; *b:* Washingto *m:* Paul Richard; *ed:* Salisbury St Univ (BA) His, Ed 1992; 15 Cre Towards MED Soc Stud Ed Univ of MD-CP; *cr:* Calvert HS Soc Stu 1993-; *ai:* Stu Govt, Class of 1996, Mock Trial Adv; NEA, MSTA 1993-; *office:* Calvert HS 600 Dares Beach Rd Prince Frederick MD

LISZKA, JOSEPH JOHN, Math Teacher; *b:* Carnegie, PA; *m.* Schoket; *c:* Melissa Carpenter, Jason, Michael, Julie, Margo; *ed:* Univ (BS) Biological Sci 1962; *cr:* Hammonton HS Math Tchr 19 Randolph Jr HS Math Tchr 1967-79; Winston Churchill HS Mat 1979-; *ai:* AFT 1970-; *office:* Winston Churchill HS 11300 Gainsb Rd Potomac MD 20854

L'ITALIEN, ANNE, HS Art Teacher; *b:* Buffalo, NY; *ed:* Heidelber (BA) Art Ed 1980; Attnd BGSU Coll; *cr:* Seneca East Schls Scnd Tchr 1980; *ai:* Yrbk Production Adv; Choreographer Swing Ch Musical; Course of Stud Comm; OAEA 1985-; OEA 1980-, U Building Rep; Philalethean Soc 1977-, Adv; Tiffin Ritz Players Theatre 1982-, Pres, Gus Awd; *home:* 310 Sycamore St Tiffin OH 4

LITAVISH, FRANK T., Science Teacher; *b:* Spangler, PA; *m:* Suzar Maloney; *c:* Jennifer, Leanne, Rebecca, Frank M.; *ed:* Slippery R Univ (BS) Elem Ed 1977; Penn St Grad Prgm; *cr:* Northern Cambri Dist Sci Tchr 1977-; *ai:* Ftbl, Boys, Girls Track, Field Coach; NEA, 1977-; Natl Wild Turkey Fed 1978-; PA Game Commission 1990- Wildlife Permit; Moss Creek, Patchinville Sportsmen 1977-; Camb Conservation Tchr of Yr; Design, Implementation Wildlife Curr; Northern Cambria Schl Dist 600 Joseph St Barnesboro PA 15714

LITCHFIELD, BETH JOHNSON, Kindergarten Teacher; *b:* Elmir *m:* Robert W.; *c:* James R., Julie A.; *ed:* Endicott Jr. Coll (AS) Early 1964; Elmira Coll (BS) Ed 1969, (MS) Elem Ed 1972; Mark Twain SCT Boces Inservice Trng Classroom Mngmt & Tchng Strategi Beecher Elem Schl Kndgtn Tchr 1966-79; Broadway Elem Schl K Tchr 1980-; *ai:* Concert Choir Parents Support Group; SHS Booste Cmptr Comm Broadway Elem Schl; ETA, NEA, NYSUT 1966-; Ch Rdng Cncl 1980-; *office:* Broadway Elem Schl 1000 Broadway St NY 14904*

LITCHKO, JOSEPH MICHAEL, 7th & 8th Grade Teacher; *b:* As PA; *ed:* Bloomsburg Univ of PA (BS) Elem Ed 1974; Addl 24 Hrs; Univ of PA 3 Hrs; Cntrl Susquehanna Inter Univ 16 3 Hrs; *cr:* Assur BVM Schl 7-8th Grd Tchr 1976-85; Holy Spirit Schl 7-8th Grd Tchr *ai:* NCEA 1976-; Assumption BVM Parish Cncl 1993-, Pres; N Frederick F. Noel Distinguished Svc Awd for Diocese of Harrisburg *home:* 1221 Scott St Kulpmont PA 17834

LITEVICH, JOHN A.,JR., HS Social Studies Teacher; *b:* Newpor *m:* Ghislaine R. Ferland; *c:* John III, Larry M., Gary A., Kathleen Keene St (BED) Soc Sci 1966; Southern CT (MS) Soc Sci 1973; 6t Specialist 1985; 5 Yrs CEUs; *cr:* Amity Jr HS Soc Stud & Eng 1966-72; Guilford HS Soc Stud Tchr 1977-; *ai:* Environmental Team; Boys & Girls Tennis Teams; NEA, CEA 1966-; GEA 1977 Saybrook Raquet Club 1990-, Bd of Dirs; Guilford Bright Ideas Awd CT Celebration of Excl 1987; *office:* Guilford HS New Engla Guilford CT 06437

LITTER, KIMBERLY RILEY, Clerical Services Instruct Chillicothe, OH; *m:* Joseph; *c:* Maggie Alice, Riley Jo; *ed:* OH S (BA) Bus Ed 1981; Ashland Univ MA Curr & Instruction Pendir Chillicothe HS Bus Instr 1981-82; Pickaway-Ross JVC Clerical S 1982-; *ai:* Bus Profs of Amer Adv; OBTA; OVA; Bourneville Chrstn *office:* Pickaway Ross Co Jt Voc Schl 895 Crouse Chapel Rd Chil OH 45601

LITTLE, BARBARA BROWN, Psych & Education Assoc Pr Elizabeth, NJ; *w:* James Saxon (dec); *c:* Barbara Faith Little And James Stuart, Allison Sue, Jonathan Scott; *ed:* Trenton St Coll (BS) Ed 1958; Thcrs Coll at Columbia Univ (MA) Educl Psych 1964; S of NY Higher Ed; *cr:* Cranford Bd of Ed 6th Grd Tchr 1958-60; Pla Bd of Ed 5th Grd Tchr, Spec Ed Instr 1965-70; Villa Maria Coll Assoc Prof 1971-74; Canisius Coll Ed Asst Prof 1974-78; Medaill Elem Ed Asst Prof 1978-80; Villa Maria Coll Psych Assoc Prof 198 Mid Sts Steering Comm; Fac Senate, Assn, PS 18 Vol; Pi Lambda 1985-, Prgm, Schlsp Co-Chair; APA Tchng Unit 1992-; BSA Ldr 19

Cnslr; Cub Scout Ldr 1973-74; Soc Justice Comm 1995-, Vol; *home:* ler Dr Orchard Park NY 14127*

LE, DENNIS ROBERT, Adjunct Faculty; *b:* York, PA; *m:* Sandra ier; *c:* Alexis, Robert, Caitlyn; *ed:* Juniata Coll (BS) Bio 1974; St n Hosp Schl for Respiratory Therapy Cert 1977; *cr:* St Joseph Hosp Care Asst Dir, Adj Fac Resp Care Prgm 1978-85; Comm Gen Hosp Care Dir 1985-87; Sacred Heart Hosp Resp Care Dir, Clinical Instr Care Prgm 1987-90; Lehigh Carbon Comm Coll Prgm Coord, Resp Prgm 1990-95; Palmerton Hosp Resp Care Dir, Clinical Instr 1995-; uth Parkland Yth Assn Bsktbl & Sftbl Coach; Amer Assn for Resp 1975-; PSEA, NEA 1990-95; *office:* Palmerton Hosp 135 Lafayette almerton PA 18071

LE, JANET MARIE, French Teacher; *b:* Pittsburgh, PA; *ed:* Clarion (BA) Fr 1970; Millersville Univ (MA) Fr 197; Attnd Univ of ourgh, Univ of Grenoble, Univ of Santandem, CA Univ of PA; *cr:* ffey HS Fr Tchr 1970-95; *ai:* Fr Club Spon; *office:* McGuffey HS 86 ffey Dr Claysville PA 15323

LE, JOANN BUCK, HS Eng & Creative Writing Tchr; *b:* Stamford, *:* James; *c:* Callan; *ed:* Bowling Green St Univ (BS) Jrnlsm 1983; ta St Univ (MS) Eng Ed 1994; *cr:* Sidney Cntrl Schl Tchr 1988-89; n Cntrl Schl Tchr 1989-95; *ai:* 9th Grd Adv; Mentor Prgm; atives to violence Prgm; Open House Comm; NEA 1989-, Local Sec; 1987-; Catskill Area Tchrs of Eng; HS Alumni Assn, Sec.*

LE, JOHN ALBERT, High School Science Teacher; *b:* Boston, MA; thanne M.; *ed:* St Anselm Coll (BA) Bio 1982; Lyndon St Coll (MST) *cr:* Richford Jr, Sr HS Bio, Chem, Physics, Environmental Sci Tchr ; *ai:* Canoebuilder's Club Founder, Adv 1993-; NEA, VEA, RTA , VP 1988-; Town Recreation Ctr 1993-, Bd Mem; Excl in Voc Tech Commissioners Awd 1992; Schl Dist HS Tchr of Yr, VT Outstdng Awd 1995; *office:* Richford Jr-Sr HS 1 Corliss Hts Richford VT *

LE, MARCY HALL, Jr High & Elem Title I Tchr; *b:* Wellsboro, PA; n D. Little III; *c:* Johnna, Max; *ed:* Mansfield Univ (BSEd) Elem Ed Rdng Specialist 1984; *cr:* Cowanesque Valley HS Title I Tchr 9 Yrs; u Assistance Team Chprsn; Peer Helper Adv; NEA, PSEA, NTEA ; Westfield Bapt Church 1972-, Sec, Treas of Diaconate Bd; *office:* nesque Vly Jr Sr HS Rt 49 Westfield PA 16950

LE, SHERYL G., Social Studies Teacher; *b:* St Joseph, MO; *m:* el B.; *c:* Jeremy, Andrea; *ed:* IN Univ (BA) Govt 1965; NY Univ) Ed 1968; Grad Courses in His, Ed at Univ of VA, Univ of Southern *r:* JHS #45 1967-69; Ballou HS 1969-72; R. W. Traip Acad Soc Stud 1983-; *ai:* NHS Adv; Soc Stud Curr Chair K-12; NCSS 1986-; *office:* Traip Acad HS 12 Williams Ave Kittery ME 03904*

LEFIELD, LAWRENCE EBEN, Fourth Grade Teacher; *b:* Belfast, *ed:* Farmington St Coll (BS) Elem Ed 1967; Univ of ME Extension es; Creative Inst; *cr:* Waterville Pub Schl System Fourth Grd Tchr ; *ai:* Stu Cncl Adv 2 Yrs; Team Ldr 6 Yrs; System-Wide Tech Comm ; NEA, ME Tchrs Assn, Waterville Tchrs Assn 1967-; Fac Cert Awd Bd of Ed 1985; *office:* Albert S Hall Schl 27 Pleasant St Waterville 4901*

LEFIELD, ROBERT E., Assistant Principal; *b:* Waltham, MA; *m:* een Adams; *c:* Timothy, Adam; *ed:* Bates Coll (BA) His 1975; ewater St Coll (MED) Admin 1987; *cr:* Norwell HS Soc Stud Tchr 93; South Kingstown HS Asst Prin 1993-; *ai:* Track & Field, Cross Coach; NEA 1975-; NASSP 1993-; MA Track Coach of Yr 1984, & 1992; MA Track Coaches Hall of Fame; *office:* South Kingstown 5 Columbia St Wakefield RI 02879

LEFIELD, VIRGINIA LUCAS, Adjunct Professor; *b:* New swick, NJ; *m:* Ronald George; *c:* Thomas; *ed:* Queen Coll (AB) Lit, n, Hist 1964; Univ of ME (MA) Hist 1974, (EDD) Soc Stud 1981; es Bus, Law, Acctng; *cr:* Husson Coll Instr 1972-81; Pub Svcs -Goddard-NASA Asst Mgr Ed, Mgr Tchr Resource 1986; Amtrak Comm Svcs 1990-94; Capitol Coll Adjunct Prof 1988-; *home:* 6509 e St Lanham MD 20706*

IN, ELAINE DIAMONSTEIN, GATE Teacher; *b:* Newport News, *:* Joseph; *c:* Sharon Litvin Schramm, Ruth; *ed:* Wright St Univ (MA) Ed, (MA) GATE Ed 1981; OH Ctr for Law Related Ed; Sinclair Coll egal Classes; *cr:* Magruder Schl Tchr 1956-57; Hillel Acad Kndgtn 1965-79; Wright St Univ Instr 1979-87; Northmont City Schls GATE 1979-; *ai:* Odyssey of the Mind Coach; Governing Bd; Dist Coord; r Club; Young Authors, Right to Read, Soc Stud Curr Comms; OH GATE 1980-, Dist Rep, Bd; NEA; Hadassah 1958-, Bd; Presenter l Conf GATE 1991, 1993, 1995; *office:* Northmont City Schls 702 t St Englewood OH 45322*

WHILER, MARY GRAVES, Third Grade Teacher; *b:* Vallejo, CA; *m:* drow W.; *c:* Joshua; *ed:* Long Beach City Coll (AA) Speech; CA St at Long Beach (BA) Speech, Grad Work Elem Ed; 45 Addl Hrs; *cr:* Elem Schl Tchr 1969-70; Tabor Elem Schl Tchr 1970-80; Littleton Schl Tchr 1980-; *ai:* Citizens Ad Hoc Budget Advy Comm sn 1995-; Hackellstown Bd of Ed 1989-92; Curr Comm Chprsn; Stu Policy Comm; Pub Relations; Various Comm 1992-; Dist Instrl Cncl, ppany 1994-; Bldg Instrl Cncl, Parsippany 1995-; Titanic Intnl Inc -; Hacketstown Recreation Comm 1989-; Hacketstown Pool Comm -; Personel Comm Rec Comm 1989-; NJ Governors Tchr Awd 1993; Geog Olypiad 3rd Place Winner 1992, First Place for Third Grd 1993; Hnrs for Geog 1991; *office:* Littleton Elem Schl Brooklawn Dr Morris s NJ 07840*

Z, CLAUDIA, Science Teacher; *b:* Cleveland, OH; *m:* Robert M.; *c:* n A.; *ed:* Purdue Univ (BS) Bio, Chem Ed 1979; Ashland Univ (MED) Instr 1994; *cr:* Univ of Canterbury Lab Instr 1981; Laurel Schl Life, Sci Tchr 1982-85; Lomond Elem Schl Sci Specialist 1988; Mentor Schls Phys Sci Tchr 1990-; *ai:* Eighth Grd Interdisciplinary Team Ldr; ructuring Comm; NEA, OEA 1990-; ASCD 1993-; Natl Endowment Grant Recipient; OH St Outstdng Edctr Talent Pool, Sharing Effective ices Seminar Cleveland St Univ 1995; Two Time Presenter Coalition ntial Schls Forum 1994-95; Plain Dealer Crystal Apple Awd 1996; *e:* Mentor Ridge Jr HS 7860 Johnnycake Ridge Rd Mentor OH 44060*

ZINGER, MARY JUDE,CSJ, Retired Teacher; *b:* Johnstown, PA; *ed:* ow Coll (BA) Ed 1950; *cr:* Cath Schls of PA Primary Tchr 1993-85; Schls of OH Primary Tchr 1932-85; Cath Charities of Brooklyn Art Summers 1978-81; Pub Schl of KY Art Tchr 1986-87; *ai:* Cath Schl nals Author Plays, Poetry 1970-95; Comm Ldrshp: Adult Armchair Ed 1970; GED Tchr Awd 1990.*

EZEY, MARLEN DODSZUWEIT, Communication Arts Professor; Philadelphia, PA; *m:* Fred; *c:* Amy Carpenter, Julie; *ed:* East udsburg Univ (BS) Eng & Scndry Ed 1963; Univ of PA (AM) British r Lit 1965; Temple Univ (PHD) Mass Media & Comm 1995; *cr:* Upper eland Sr HS Eng Tchr 1964-67; Cheyney Univ Prof of Eng 1967-87, of Speech & Communication Arts 1984-; *ai:* Fac Senate Recorder; l Affairs Advy Cncl; Communication Arts Prgm Coord; APSCUF -; PA Jrnlsm Educators 1994-; Women of ELCA 1970-, Pres 1996; Aid Friends 1980-; Over 70 Articles in Montgomery Cty PA Record spaper; Dissertation; *office:* Cheyney Univ Of PA RR 4 Cheyney PA 9

LIVINGSTON, DAVID G., Fifth Grade Teacher; *b:* North Tonawanda, NY; *m:* Janet Pifer; *c:* David, John, Jillian, Kathryn; *ed:* Buffalo St Coll (BS) Ed 1971, (MS) Ed 1975; Univ of Buffalo (EDA) Admin 1985; *cr:* Springville-Griffith Inst Asst Prin 1 Yr; Niagara-Wheatfield Cntrl Schls Tchr 25 Yrs; *ai:* 5th Grd Annual WA Trip Adv 1973-; AFT 1971-; Sci Tchrs Assn of NY St 1995-; NY St Sci Mentors 1994-; Youngstown Recreation 1985-; Eisenhower Grant Awd 1993-95; *office:* Niagara-Wheatfield Cntrl Schls 6839 Errick Rd North Tonawanda NY 14120

LIVINGSTON, JEAN MARIE, Math Teacher; *b:* Upper Darby, PA; *m:* John W.; *c:* Jennifer; *ed:* West Chester Univ (BS) Elem Ed 1972, (BA) Math 1974; 38 Grad Credits; *cr:* Interboro Schl Dist Math Tchr 23 Yrs.

LIVINGSTON, JOHN WILLIAM, Amer History & Govt Tchr; *b:* Chester, PA; *m:* Jean Marie Fagan; *c:* Jennifer; *ed:* Univ of WI (BS) His & Bio 1972; 30 Post Grad Credits; *cr:* Interboro Jr HS His 1973-84; Tinicum MS His 1982-84; Prospect Park HS Bio 1984-87; High Schl His 1987-; *ai:* Girls Var Bsktbl Coach 1986-, Boys 9th Grd Bsktbl Coach 1973-78; *office:* Interboro HS 16th & Amosland Rd Prospect Park PA 19076*

LIVINGSTON, KIMBERLY ANN, English Teacher; *b:* Columbia, SC; *c:* Chase; *ed:* Univ of SC (BA) Scndry Ed, Eng 1990; *cr:* Keenan HS Eng Tchr; *ai:* Stu Newspaper Adv; NEA 1995-; *office:* Caesar Rodney HS 239 Old North Rd Camden Wyoming DE 19934

LIVINGSTONE, JUDITH PIERCE, Biological Sciences Teacher; *b:* Boston, MA; *m:* John King; *c:* Lara Lee, Paul, John; *ed:* Wellesley Coll (BA) Zoology & Physiology 1959; Harvard Univ (MAT) Scndry Sci Tchng 1961; 3 Credit Hrs Historical Geology; *cr:* Wilson Jr HS 7th & 8th Grd Sci Tchr 1960; McCall Jr HS General & Earth Sci Tchr 1960-65; Rogers Hall Bio, Chem & General Sci Tchr 1967-70; DePaul HS Sci Dept Chm & Biological Scis Tchr 1977-; *ai:* NJ Sci League Coord; Standing Curr Comm; Natl Sci Supvrs Assn 1982-; NJ Wellesley Club 1970-, In Charge of Wellesley Book Awd; Pacquenac Tennis Club 1970-, In Charge Jr Prgm; Jacksonville Chapel 1985-, Choir Officer; NJ Harvard Club 1990-, Interviewer; *office:* De Paul Diocesan HS 1512 Alps Rd Wayne NJ 07470*

LIVOTI, STEPHEN JOSEPH, World Studies Teacher; *b:* Tiffin, OH; *m:* Kathryn Butdorf; *c:* Kara, Anthony; *ed:* BGSU (BS) Geography & Compr SS 1978; Attnd Tiffin Univ, Heidelberg Coll, Toledo Univ; *cr:* Lakota Jr HS 7th Grd SS Tchr 1978-; *ai:* Head Var Track Coach Men & Womens Teams; NEA, Lakota Ed Assn 1978-, Building Rep; Elks 1981-, Trustee; Luth Church Mem; 1991 Dist 6 Track Coach of Yr OH; Nom Ashland Tchr Awds; *home:* 496 Hedges St Tiffin OH 44883

LIVRONE, ROBERT G., Chemistry Teacher; *b:* New Kensington, PA; *ed:* PA St Univ (BS) Scndry Ed 1978; Univ of Pittsburgh (MED) Gifted Ed 1984; *cr:* Gateway HS Chem Tchr 1979-80; Plum HS Chem Tchr 1980; Bethel Park HS Chem Tchr 1980-81; Freeport HS Chem Tchr 1981-; *ai:* HS Asst Track Coach; NSTA & NEA 1978-; PA Interscholastic Athletic Assn 1987-, Track & Field Ofcl; USA Track & Field 1989-, Track & Field Ofcl; Amateur Radio Emergency Srv; *office:* Freeport HS PO Drawer H Freeport PA 16229

LIZOTTE, THOMAS P., Band Director; *b:* Marlboro, MA; *ed:* Univ of MA (BA) Music Ed 1986, (MA) Music Ed 1991; Post Grad Stud in Wind Conducting at Ithaca Coll; *cr:* Norwood HS Asst Dir of Bands 1986-88; Bloomfield HS Dir of Bands 1991-92; Norwood HS Dir of Bands 1992-94; Biddeford HS Dir of Bands 1991-; *ai:* Exec Bd ME Band Dir Assn; MMEA; Fine Arts Dept Head; MMEA 1995-; IAJE, Dist Chm; NESBA & MICA 1986-, Exec Bds; *office:* Biddeford HS 25 Maplewood Ave Biddeford ME 04005*

LLARULL, MARCELO, Professor of Math; *ed:* SUNY at Stony Brook (MA) Math 1987, (PHD) Math 1988; *cr:* Univ of PA Hans Radamacher Instr 1988-90; William Paterson Coll Asst Prof 1990-; *ai:* Math Club, Frosh Adv; Math Awareness Week Coord; Fac Mentor; Share Time to Save Minds Prgm; AMP; Inst For Tech in Math Undergrad Curr Comm; Implementation of Tech into Curr; AMS 1982-; MAA, AFT 1990-; NYAS 1993-; NSF 1989; Ctr for Research Grant 1994-95; Achievers Cr Awd 1995; Articles in Prof Journals, 1 Book & Lab Manuals; *office:* William Paterson Coll 300 Pompton Rd Wayne NJ 07470*

LLEWELLYN, A. JAMES,III, Technology Coordinator; *b:* Youngstown, OH; *ed:* Youngstown St Univ (BSEd) Elem Ed 1970; *cr:* Norwalk-La-Mirada 6th Grd Tchr 1970-72; So Euclid-Lyndhurst Schls 6th Grd Tchr 1972-90, Math & Tech Resource Tchr 1990-95, Tech Coord 1995-; *ai:* Educl Comp Consortium of OH Chair; ECCO 1986-, Chair & Vice Chair; NCTM 1986-; ISTE 1990-; *office:* So Euclid-Lyndhurst City Schls 1825 S Green Rd South Euclid OH 44121*

LLEWELLYN, MARVIN THOMPSON, Algebra & Trigonometry Teacher; *b:* Lonaconing, MD; *m:* Lesta Louise Eichhorn; *c:* David W., Lori B., Kevin S.; *ed:* Frostburg St Coll (BS) Math 1958, (MED) 1967; *cr:* West Frederick Jr HS Math Tchr 1958-59; Fort Hill HS Math Tchr 1959-61; Vly HS Math Tchr 1961-86; Westmar HS Math Tchr 1986-; *ai:* NEA 1983-; MSTA 1980-; Allegany Cty Tchrs Assn 1980-; *home:* 81 E Main St Lonaconing MD 21539

LLOYD, BARBARA SHIREY, 7th Grade English Teacher; *b:* Connellsville, PA; *m:* Scott; *c:* Gareth; *ed:* Penn St Univ (BS) Scndry Ed, Eng 1974; *cr:* Connellsville Area Schls 7-9, 12 Grd Eng Tchr 21 Yrs; *ai:* NEA, PSEA, CAEA, NCTE 1974-; *office:* Connellsville Area Jr HS West 215 Falls Ave Connellsville PA 15425

LLOYD, BRENDA S. (WILLING), Mathematics Teacher; *b:* Pottstown, PA; *m:* Mark S.; *c:* Kimberly M; *ed:* Bloomsburg Univ (BSEd) Scndry Math Ed 1989; Millersville Univ (MEd) Math 1995; *cr:* Pennridge HS Math Tchr 1989-90; Wyomissing HS Math Tchr 1990; Exeter Twp HS Math Tchr 1991-92; Solanco HS Math Tchr 1992-; *ai:* Class of 1997 Adv; Prom Promise Coord; NCTM 1991-; NEA & PSEA 1989-; St Paul Luth Church 1993-, Sunday Schl Asst Supt; *office:* Solanco HS 585 Solanco Rd Quarryville PA 17566

LLOYD, CAROL LANNON, Pre-K Teacher; *b:* Cumberland, MD; *m:* William Leroy; *c:* W. Kevin, Krista Jo; *ed:* Frostburg St Univ Advanced Prof Cert Early Chldhd 1975; *cr:* West Side Elem Schl First & Second Grd Tchr 1960-62; Kndgtn Ctr Kndgtn Tchr 1970-75; Parkside Elem Schl Kndgtn, First Grd, Pre-Kndgtn Tchr 1975-; Frostburg St Univ Cooperating Tchr 17 Yrs; *ai:* NEA, MSTA 1960-; Kingsley United Meth Church 46 Yrs, Adult Choir Dir 25 Yrs; *office:* Allegany Cty Bd of Ed Washington St Cumberland MD 21502

LLOYD, LINUEL PARKER,III, Lecturer in Business Admin; *b:* Lakewood, NJ; *m:* Barbara Ann Ginolfi; *c:* Brian, Michele; *ed:* Rowan Univ (BA) His 1976; Rutgers Univ Grad Schl of Mngmt (MBA) Mrktg 1986; Soc Stud Cert; Ocean Cty Coll Acctng, Bus Law; Georgian Court Coll Schl Law; Amer Mrktg Assn Edctrs Mrktg Conf Boston, 1993, Washington DC 1995; *cr:* Toms River Intermediate East Soc Stud Tchr 1978-88; Toms River HS South His Tchr 1988-94; Georgian Court Coll Mrktg Instr 1987-; Toms River HS South Soc Stud Suvr 1994-; Toms River HS East Soc Stud Supvr 1994-; Toms River HS North Soc Stud Supvr 1994-; *ai:* Admin, Supervisory Cncl Trustee Comm; Regnl Schls Hall of Fame Trustee Comm; Amer Mrktg Assn, World Future Soc 1991-; NJ Prins & Supervisory Assn 1994-; ASCD 1995-; Toms River Yacht Club 1995-; Spokesperson for Dover Twp Neighborhood Group 1990-; WWII Commemoration Comm 1994-95; Steering Comm Scndry Schls Mid Sts Assn Chprsn; Professionally Certfd Mrktg Instr Assn of Collegiate Bus Schls, Prgms; *office:* Georgian Court Coll 900 Lakewood Ave Lakewood NJ 08701

LLOYD, MALINDA MAURIE, English Teacher; *b:* Elko, NV; *m:* Ronald Lynn; *c:* Michelle Andersen, Jennifer Christensen; *ed:* Brigham Young Univ (BA) Eng, Ger 1968; Johns Hopkins Univ (MA) Writing 1995; *cr:* People's Schl 1 Eng, Ger Tchr 1971-74; Roosevelt HS Eng, Ger, Drama Tchr 1976-84; Rockville HS Eng Tchr 1984-86; Sherwood HS Eng Tchr 1986-; *ai:* Yrbk Adv; Morale, Summer Rdng, Curr Comms; MTA 1984-; NEA 1976-; Victorian Lyric Opera Co 1991-, Bd Mem at Large; Tchr of Yr 1991; Novel in Publication; Poetry Pub Various Lit Journals; *office:* Sherwood HS 300 Olney Sandy Spring Rd Sandy Spring MD 20860

LLOYD, MIRIAM, Eighth Grade Teacher; *b:* Wilkes Barre, PA; *ed:* Saint Joseph Coll for Women (BA) Eng 1966; Brooklyn Coll (MA) Amer Lit 1970; 150 Credit Hrs Diocese of Brooklyn; *cr:* Saint Clare Schl 4th Grd Tchr 1954-57; Saint Ann 1st Grd Tchr 1957-61; Saint Francis DeSales 1st Grd Tchr 1961-62; Holy Child Jesus 5th Grd Tchr 1962-64; Saint Athanasius 6th Grd Tchr; Saint Rose of Lima 8th Grd Tchr 1966-; *ai:* Lang Arts Coord; AAA Crossing Guards Spon; Spelling Bee & Speech Contest Coord; Diocese of Brooklyn 1954-, Outstanding Tchr Awd 1992; NCEA 1966-; NCTE 1970-85; Brooklyn Rdng Cncl 1970-86; Dutch Kills Comm Assn 1975-; *office:* St Rose Of Lima Schl 259 Parkville Ave Brooklyn NY 11230

LLOYD, THOMAS HOWARD, Asst Professor of Marketing; *b:* Olympia, WA; *ed:* Dutchess Comm Coll (AAS) Retail Bus Mgt 1965; Long Island Univ (BS) Mrktg 1968, (MBA) Mrktg 1970; 12 Credit Hrs Toward Cert Scndry Ed; *cr:* Westchester Comm Coll Asst Prof of Mrktng, Retail Bus Mngmt 23 Yrs; *ai:* Mrktg Ret Bus Mgt Chprsn, Dept Comm; Alpha Beta Gamma Adv; Solidarity Day Comm; NY St Assn of 2 Yr Colls Inc 1980, Historian Coord of Campus Reps, Outstndng Campus Rep Awd; AFT; New Hackensack Fire Co 1963-, Recording Sec, Life Mbrshp; Rhinebeck NY Masons 1991-, Master, Ldrshp Awd 1995; Cyprus Temple Shriners 1992-, Band Mem, Cyprus Potentates Citation 1993; Distinguished Alumnus Awd Dutchess Comm Coll 1991; Outstndng Svc Awd from Alpha Beta Gamma 1985; *office:* Westchester Comm Coll 75 Grasslands Rd Valhalla NY 10595

LLOYD, WILFRED, English Teacher; *b:* Bath NB, Canada; *ed:* Central MI Univ (BA) Eng 1968; Fitchburg St Coll (MS) Eng 1977; *cr:* Ravenna HS Tchr 1966; Buenna Vista HS Tchr 1967-; Greenville Pub Schls Tchr 1968; Manchester Pub Schls Tchr 1969-; *ai:* Lit Magazine; NEA 1966-, Bldg Rep; *home:* 141 Middle St Apt 1 Manchester NH 03101*

LO, SIMON, Chinese Teacher; *b:* Hong Kong; *ed:* Natl ChengKung Univ (BA) Frgn Langs, Lit 1987; NY Univ (MA) Ed 1992; *cr:* Echo Intnl Lang Ctr ESL, Chinese Tchr 1986-88; Chinese-Amer Planning Cncl ESL Tchr 1988-90; Ft Hamilton HS ESL, Chinese Tchr 1990-; *ai:* United Fed of Tchrs 1990-; Fed Grants from Title VII; Book Pub; *home:* 10821 63rd Dr Forest Hills NY 11375

LOBALBO, GINA M., Business Teacher; *b:* Amsterdam, NY; *ed:* Siena Coll (BS) Mrktg, Mngmt, Bus Ed 1992; SUNY at Albany (MS) Educl Tech 1994; *cr:* Mayfield HS Bus Tchr 1992-; *ai:* HS Bldg Level Team Minutes Keeper; BMEA, BTA, AFT 1992-; *office:* Mayfield HS School St Mayfield NY 12117

LOBAUGH, DONNA PASCARELLA, 6th Grade Teacher; *b:* Pittsburgh, PA; *m:* Ross O.; *ed:* WV Univ (BA) Elem Ed 1972; Univ of Pittsburgh (MS) Elem Ed 1976; Cmptr Courses; Mrktg Positive Images Disney World; Tchr Effectiveness Trng; Assertive Discipline; Succeeding with the Difficult Stdnts; Self-Esteen for Edctrs; Dealing with Disruptions, Hostility & Excesses; *cr:* Renton Elem Schl 4th Grd Tchr 1973-87; Regency Park Elem Schl 6th Grd Tchr 1987-; *ai:* Soc Stud Comm Chprsn; Annual Washington DC Field Trip Spon; Sexual Harrassment Policy Comm; Christmas Play Dir; Stu Tchrs Cooperative Tchr; Instrl Support Tchr Team; PTA; NEA; PSEA; Gift of Time Tribute; *home:* 3409 Lashan Dr Murrysville PA 15668

LOBELL, KATY WOLITZKY, Spanish Teacher; *b:* Rochester, NY; *m:* David; *ed:* Skidmore Coll (BA) Span & Govt 1991; Univ of WI at Madison (MA) Latin Amer & Iberian Stud 1992; Nazareth Coll Completion of Ed Courses for Tchr Cert 1995; *cr:* Our Lady of Mercy HS Span Tchr 1993-; *ai:* Father-Daughter Dinner Dance; Spain Trip; Stress Release Club; Authentic Assessment Comm; NYSAFLT, FLATRA 1993-; Phi Beta Kappa 1991-; Phi Sigma Iota 1990-.

LOBO, FRANCIS X., Prof of Biological Science; *b:* Aden, Yemen; *c:* Anthony L., Francis M., Glyndwr P.; *ed:* Univ of Bombay (BS) Microbiology 1947, (MS) Microbiology 1950; Institutum Divi Thomae (PHD) Experimental Med, Bio 1959; Certfd Natl Registry Microbiologists Amer Acad Microbiology Specialist Pub Hlth, Med Lab; *cr:* Marywood Coll Biological Sci Prof 1960-; Argonne Natl Lab Resident Rsrch Assoc 1968-69; St Jude Children's Hosp Rsrch Participant 1970; Thomas Jefferson Univ Microbiology visiting Prof 1982; *ai:* Clinical Microbiology Consultant; OSHA Trng Prgm; Hnrs Advy Bd; Rsrch Review Comm; Amer Soc for Microbiology 1962-; Natl Registry of Microbiologists 1965-; Register PA Biologists 1993-; Gifted Prgm Scranton Schl Dist 1990-, Mentor; Amer Red Cross 1990-, AIDS Instr; Ldrs in Amer Sci, Amer Men & Women of Sci 1975-; Who's Who in Amer Ed 1975-; Evaluation Tms Mem PA Dept of Ed; Introductory Manual Microbiology; Indian, Canadian Patents Production Citric Acid; Dir Clinical Micribiology Lab; *office:* Marywood Coll 2300 Adams Ave Scranton PA 18509

LOBODA, CATHERINE NICOLOFF, Russian & Drama Teacher; *b:* Lorain, OH; *c:* Larissa, Raisa, Luke; *ed:* Kent St Univ (BS) Speech, Theatre, Russian 1974; Post Grad Cert in Elem Ed, Rdng, Eng, Jrnlsm; *cr:* Best Beginnings Presch Tchr of 4 Yr Olds 1984-86; Amherst Schls Eng, Rdng, Drama, Russian Tchr 1986-; *ai:* Nord Jr HS Drama Dir; Amer Cncl Tchrs of Russian 1994-; US Swimming 1985-, Age Group, Zone Age Group, Sr Chair; Hudson Music Assn 1990-, Band Pres; Grant Enriching the Curr 1989; *office:* Amherst Steele HS 450 Washington St Amherst OH 44001*

LOBOZZO, DIANA ANDREOPOULOS, Hlth Occupations Tchr & Coord; *b:* Greensburg, PA; *m:* Paul; *c:* Christopher, Alexander; *ed:* Fairleigh Dickinson Univ (BS) Nrsng 1975, (BS) Hlth Ed, Schl Nrsng 1979; Grad Courses Montclair St Univ; Tchr, Coord Cooperative Ed; *cr:* Abraham Clark HS Tchr Coord, Hlth Occupations 1979-; Union Cty Coll Consultant Curr, Hlth Occupations; *ai:* Liaison Comm Chprsn, Tchr, Admin; Care Comm, Hall of Fame, Union Hosp Schlsp Comm, Hlth Careers Wkshps Chprsn; NJ Ed Assn, Roselle Ed Assn 1979-; Jr League of Montclair 1983-, Exec Sec; Jr League Intnl 1983-, Exec Sec; Mental Hlth Res Ctr 1995-, Pub Relations; Governor's Recognition Awd Tchr of Yr 1995-; Jr League Vol of Yr for the Comm 1993; *office:* Abraham Clark HS 122 E 6th Ave Roselle NJ 07203

LOBRON, JOHN RICHARD, Spanish & Social Studies Tchr; *ed:* Temple Univ (BA) His 1989, (EDM) Ed 1996; *ai:* Soc Awareness Club; *office:* Philadelphia HS For Girls 1400 W Olney Ave Philadelphia PA 19141

LOCALIO, WILLIAM, Guidance Counselor; *b:* New York, NY; *c:* Jessica Stites; *ed:* Univ of Rochester (BA) His 1968; Smith Coll (MAT) His 1975; Univ of Rochester (MA) Counseling Psych 1984; *cr:* Stoneleigh-Burnham Schl His Tchr 1974-77; Hamden Hall Schl His Tchr 1978-84; Mansfield MS Guidance Cnslr 1985-86; Rham HS Guidance Cnslr 1986-; *ai:* Explorers Club Adv; NEA 1985-, Sec of Local; *office:* Rham HS 67 Rham Rd Hebron CT 06248

LOCASCIO, STEVEN ANDREW, Mathematics Teacher; *b:* Massapequa, NY; *m:* Cheryl Ann; *ed:* St Vincent Coll (BA) Math 1975; IN Univ of PA (MED) Math 1980; St Vincent Coll (MA) Theology 1996; *cr:* Greater Latrobe Schl Dist Math Tchr 1975-; *ai:* Asst Bsbl Coach; Greater Latrobe Ed Assn 1975-, Fac Rep; NEA 1975-; *office:* Greater Latrobe Sr HS 131 Country Club Rd Latrobe PA 15650

LOCASTRO, WILLIAM A., 7th Grade Science Teacher; *b:* Auburn, NY; *m:* Kathleen Graney; *c:* Todd, Scott, Marc; *ed:* Cayuga Comm Coll (AS) Sci 1969; SUNY at Oswego (BS) Bio 1971; Post Grad Stud; *cr:* West MS 7th-8th Grd Sci Tchr 1971-83; East MS 7th Grd Sci Tchr 1983-; *ai:* Natl Jr Hnr Soc Comm; Stu Govt Org Adv; *office:* East MS 159 Franklin St Auburn NY 13021

LOCH, DALE ANN A., Instructional Support Teacher; *b:* Easton, PA; *c:* Katherine D., Daniel T.; *ed:* Bloomsburg Univ (BS) Elem Ed 1972; East Stroudsburg Univ (MED) Prof, Sec Stud 1995; *cr:* Wilson Area Schl Dist Third Grd Tchr 1986-94, Instrl Support Tchr 1994-; *ai:* Wilson Area Ed Assn 1986-; *office:* Williams Township Elem Schl 2660 Morgan Hill Rd Easton PA 18042*

LOCH, JANIS BEAVER, Sixth Grade Teacher; *b:* Marion, OH; *m:* Nicholas G.; *c:* Rachel E., Jonathan E.; *ed:* Bowling Green St Univ (BS) Elem Ed, Learning, Behav Disorders 1975, (MED) Rdng 1979; 36 Semester Hrs Univ of Toledo Elem Ed; *cr:* Cory-Rawson Schls 1st-3rd Grd Learning Disabilities Tchr 1975-76; Springfield Local Schls 1st-3rd Grd Learning Disabilities Tchr 1976-79; Washington Local Schls 1st-6th Learning Disabilities Tchr 1979-83, 5th-6th Grd Tchr 1983-; *ai:* OEA, NEA 1975-; *office:* Meadowvale Elem Schl 2755 Edgebrook Dr Toledo OH 43613

LOCKARD, KAREN OBERHEIM, English Teacher; *b:* Lock Haven, PA; *m:* David; *c:* Katherine, Adam; *ed:* Susquehanna Univ (BA) Eng 1977; Georgetown Univ 30 Credits Lbrl Stud Prgm; *cr:* Joppatowne Jr, Sr HS Lang Arts Tchr 1977-78; Magnolia MS Lang Arts Tchr 1978-79; North Bethesda Jr HS Eng Tchr 1979-81; Walt Whitman HS Eng Tchr 1981-82; Bethesda Chevy Chase HS Eng Tchr 1982-91; Springbrook HS Eng Tchr 1992-; *ai:* Renaissance Dir; MCEA 1980-; NCEA 1978-; Co-Author Book: Falling Grades 1992; *office:* Springbrook HS 201 Valleybrook Dr Silver Spring MD 20904*

LOCKARD, LYNN FAHRINGER, Third Grade Teacher; *b:* Easton, PA; *m:* Richard James; *c:* Keith, Kristen; *ed:* Trenton St Coll (BA) Kndgtn & Primary Ed 1969; "Instructional Theory into Practice" NJ St Dept of Ed Acad for Advancement of Tchng & Mgmt 1985; Early Chldhd Inst at NJ St Dept of Ed HSPT Inst 1990-91; *cr:* Harmony Pub Schls 1st-2nd Grd Tchr 1969-71; Bloomsbury Elem Schl Kndgtn & 3rd Grd Tchr 1980-; *ai:* Yrbk Adv; Bd Fac Liaison, Lib & Schl Lunch Comms; Curr Dev; Comm-Schl Connection Comm; PTA; Cheering Adv, Drama Costumes Coord, PTO, Cooperative Tchr With Stu Tchr; Binney and Smith Tchr Think Tank; Huderton Cty Ed 2001 Core Member-Authentic Learning Component; NEA & NJEA 1980-; Bloomsbury Ed Assn 1980-, Sec; Member of Phillipsburg Riverview Org; Bloomsbury Tchr of Yr 1991; *office:* Bloomsbury Elem Schl 20 Main St Box 375 Bloomsbury NJ 08804

LOCKART, DAVID R., District Music Dept Chairman; *b:* Seattle, WA; *m:* Linda Caldwell; *c:* Jason, Heather; *ed:* Westminster Choir Coll (BM) Music Ed 1978; Univ of IL (MM) Choral Music 1980; Supervisory Cert Trenton St Coll; Post Grad Stud Westminster Choir Coll; *cr:* North Hunterdon HS Music Tchr 1980-90, Music Dept Chm 1990-; *ai:* Intnl Concert Tours England, Scotland, Austria, Germany, Italy Ldr; Musical Dir; MENC 1980-; NJMEA 1980-, Choral Procedures Cmmt; ACDA 1990-; AP Music Theory Recognition Awd 1995; NJ ACDA Choral Festival, Chamber Singers, Superior & Top 10 in St 1995; *office:* North Hunterdon HS 1445 State Route 31 Annandale NJ 08801

LOCKERBY, ROBERT WILLIAM, 8th Grade Social Studies Tchr; *b:* Portland, OR; *m:* Susan Marie Mc Nulty; *c:* Courtney, Meghan, David; *ed:* Elon Coll (BS) PE 1980; Working Towards MA; *cr:* Bellows Falls MS 7-8 Grd Tchr 1981-; *ai:* Coaching: Var Ftbl, Alpine Ski Team, JV, Amer Legion Bsbl; Geog Bee Team; Fund Raising; Team Ldrs; Stu Act; NEA 1981-; Improvement Assn, Little League Bd 1995-; VT Amer Legion Bsbl Ldrshp Awd; *office:* Bellows Falls MS 11-17 School St Bellows Falls VT 05101

LOCKHART, CLEO SIMONS, Third Grade Teacher; *b:* Norfolk, VA; *m:* Anthony Brown; *c:* Anthony B. II; *ed:* Univ of Akron (BA) Elem ED 1985; Booker T. Washington Gen, Voc 1978; Managing Elem Schl Classroom; Basics of Cmptrs; EEI; Clarisworks; *cr:* Shiloh Day Care Kndgtn Tchrs Aide 1979-80; Norton Homes Daycare Prgm Supv 1982; Amer Elem Ed Instruc Asst 1-6 Grd Tutor 1986-87; Akron Bd of Ed Elem Tchr 1987-; *ai:* Yth Awareness Prgm Coord; Black His Prgms Coord; Career Ed Liason; Chprsn Prgm, Soc Comm; New Hope Bapt Children Easter Prgm Comm 1994; Akron Ed Assn 1986-; PTA 1986-, Liason; Bldg Ldrshp Team 1994-, Chprsn; FBLA 1977-, VP; Debutonte Widow Org 1979-, Comm Mem; Little League Ftbl, Bsktbl 1986-, Team Mem; Zeta Alpha Outstdng Scholastic Achvmt Awd; Deans List Univ of Akron; Excl Tchng Awd Robinson Elem Schl; Nom Outstdng Edctr 1990-94; One in a Million Tchr Awd Essiex Drill Team 1994; *office:* Portage Path Schl of Tech 55 S Portage Path Akron OH 44303*

LOCKHART, KIMBERLY A., English Teacher; *b:* Huntington, WV; *m:* Vincent T.; *ed:* Rio Grande Univ (BS) Comm 1987; Wright ST Univ MED) Ed 1995; *cr:* Springfield South HS Eng Tchr 1987-; *ai:* Soph Booster Adv; Lang Arts Comm; Spirit Bd Mem; NCTE 1994-; *office:* Springfield South HS 700 S Limestone St Springfield OH 45505

LOCKSHISS, DOLORES E., English & Art History Tchr; *b:* Kankakee, IL; *c:* Dean (dec), Scott; *ed:* Univ of WI at Oshkosh (BA) Liberal Arts 1965; Manhattanville (MA) Ed, Eng 1985; Western CT Univ at Danbury Eng Cert 1981; *cr:* Brewster Cntrl Schls Spec Ed Tchr 1981-82; John F. Kennedy Cath HS Eng 9 & Art His Tchr 1985-; *ai:* Excalibor Lit Mag & Adv Jr-Sr Prom & SAT Course Adv; *office:* John F. Kennedy Cath HS Rt 138 S Somers NY 10589*

LOCKWOOD, ANNE MC GRATH, Retired Elem Teacher; *b:* Rochester, NY; *m:* Donald F.; *c:* Donna Glover, Gail A., Steven G., Gregory M., Michelle M.; *ed:* SUNY at Brockport (BS) Hlth, PE 1949; 30 Addl Hrs Cert Elem Ed N-6 SUNY at Geneseo, St Rose Coll; *cr:* Letchworth Cntrl PE Tchr 1956-60, 4th & 5th Grd Elem Ed Tchr 1979-90; *ai:* NYS Ret Assn 1990-; WY Cty Ret Tchrs Assn 1990-, Trustee; *home:* 11 Beechwood Ave P.O. Box 143 Castile NY 14427

LOCKWOOD, DEBORAH E., Literature Teacher; *b:* Tamaqua, PA; *m:* William D. Nutt; *ed:* Mansfield St Coll (BS) Elem Ed 1974; Open Court Rdng Prgm Cert Fairfield Univ; *cr:* Fayette Elem Schl Remedial Rdng Tchr 1974-75; Liberty Schl Third, Sixth, Eighth Grd Eng, Fifth Grd, Sixth-Eighth Grd Lit Tchr 1976-; *ai:* Dist Spelling Bee Organizer, Pronouncer; NEA; Dover Little Theatre 1989-, Plays, Casting Comm; NJ Governors Tchr Recognition Awd 1991; *office:* Liberty Schl Rt 46 Great Meadows NJ 07838*

LOCKWOOD, JOANNE SMITH, Lecturer of Mathematics; *b:* Quebec City PQ, Canada; *m:* Bryce M. Jr.; *c:* Daren M., Keith M.; *ed:* St Lawrence Univ (BA) Eng 1968; Plymouth St Coll (MBA) Bus 1980, (BA) Math 1985; *cr:* Houghton Mifflin Co Ed 1969-86, Author of Math Texts 1986-; New Hampshire Schl Tchr 1974-76, 1980-81; Plymouth St Coll Lecturer of Math 1988-; *ai:* MAA; AMATYC; TAA; Textbooks: Beginning Algebra with Applications, Intermediate Algebra with Application, Bus Math, Introductory Algebra with Basic Math, Algebra with Trigonometryfor Coll Stdnts, Prealgebra, Algebra for Coll Stdnts: A Functions Approach, A Review of Geometry, Algebra: Introductory & Intermediate; *office:* Plymouth St Coll Plymouth NH 03264

LOCKYER, GEORGE EDMOND, Professor Emeritus; *b:* Broadalbin, NY; *m:* Mary Lou Jones; *c:* Christine, Jeffrey, Jennifer Lockyer MacClean; *ed:* Univ of Denver (BS) Math 1962; Post Grad 12 Hrs; Grad 15 Hrs; *cr:* Lowell Technological Inst Math Instr 1965-72; Stone & Webster Engr Co Sr Engr Matls, NDT 1972-76; Gen Electric Co Mgr Materials, NDT 1976-79; Schenectady Co Comm Coll Prof 1979-93; *ai:* Ret; Amer Soc for Nondestructive Testing 1962-, Dir, Chm, Tech Achvmt Awd, Fellow 1988; Tech Articles Pub; *home:* 60 Bridge St Broadalbin NY 12025*

LOCONTE, MICHAEL ANTHONY, Industrial Technology Teacher; *b:* Newark, NJ; *ed:* Kean Coll (BA) Industrial Tech 1977; *cr:* South Plainfield HS Tchr 1977-; *ai:* Fishing Club; Electronics Club Adv; South Plainfield Ed Assn 1977-; NJEA 1977-; Halcyon Park Enviromental Comm 1991-, Pres; Bloomfield Elks 1994-, Esteemed Lecturing Knight; Outstdng Industrial Arts Tchr of the Yr 1989; *office:* South Plainfield HS 200 Lake St South Plainfield NJ 07080

LOCONTO, TERESA CARMEN, English & Law Teacher; *b:* Southridge, MA; *ed:* Clark Univ (BA) Eng, Soc Stud 1973; Amer Intnl Coll (MED) Spec Ed 1981, (CAGS) Ed, Admin 1985; Western New England Schl of Law (JD) Law 1992; *cr:* Southbridge HS Eng, Law Tchr 1974-; *ai:* Schl Cncl; Words not Weapows Adv, Peer Mediation; NEA, MTA 1974-; Southbridge Ed Assn 1974, VP; MA Bar Assn Amer Bar Assn; Pub Article 1992; *office:* Southbridge HS 25 Cole Ave Southbridge MA 01550*

LOCOPO, MARIA GRAZIA GIUGNO, First Grade Teacher; *b:* Laurana, Italy; *m:* Antonio; *c:* James; *ed:* Adelphi Univ (BS) Elem Ed 1972, (MA) Early Chldhd 1974; 30 Post Grad Credits Brooklyn Coll; 6 Post Grad Credits Adelphi Univ; 3 Post Grad Credits LIU; About 45 Inservice Credits; *cr:* Garden City Elem Schls Sub Tchr 1972-78; Locust Schl First Grd Tchr 1978-79; Stewart Schl 5th Grd Permanent Sub Tchr 1979-81; Homestead & Stratford Schls First, 3rd Grd Sub Tchr 1981-83; Homestead Schl First Grd Tchr 1983-; *ai:* Dist Advy Comm; Site Base Team; AFT, NYSUt, Garden City Tchr Assn 1978-; Delta Kappa Gamma 1992-, VP; Italian Culture of LI Soc 1984-, VP; Tchr of The Yr 1988; *office:* Homestead Primary Schl 2 Homestead Ave Garden City NY 11530*

LODANOSKY, FRANCIS ANTHONY, Math Teacher; *b:* Mahonoy City, PA; *m:* Theresa V. Zotcavage; *c:* Frank, Michael; *ed:* Bloomsburg St Coll (BS) Scndry Ed Math 1965; Beaver Coll (MA) Ed Math Core 1976; Addl 30 Credit Hrs; *cr:* W. G. Harding Jr HS Math Tchr 1965-75, Dept Head 1973-75; W. B. Saul HS Math Tchr 1975-; *ai:* Intramural Golf Coach; PFT 1965-; NSF Grant Univ of IL 1968, Drexel Univ 1974; *office:* W B Saul Agricultural Schl 7100 Henry Ave Philadelphia PA 19128

LODER, M. AYAKO, Fourth Grade Teacher; *b:* Manzanar, CA; *m:* Daniel III; *c:* Janiffer, Daniel P.; *ed:* Glassboro Coll (BA) Elem Ed; Rowan Coll (MA) Learning Disabilities 1996; *cr:* Bridgeton Pub Schls Elem Tchr 1982-; *ai:* Alpha Delta Kappa; NJEA, BEA 1982-; *office:* Indian Ave Elem Schl 399 Indian Ave Bridgeton NJ 08302

LOEB, NINA (BEN), Mathematics Teacher; *b:* Munich, Germany; *m:* Joel S.; *c:* Karen, Wayne, Marc; *ed:* Brooklyn Coll (BA) Math 1971; Coll of SI (MS) Math 1987; 6th Yr Cert Supervision & Admin 1989; *cr:* IS 246 Math Tchr 1971-74; New Dorp HS Math Tchr 1983-88; McKee HS Math Tchr 1988-92; Tottenville HS Math Tchr 1992-; *ai:* Regents Marking Comm; Tutor; AFT, UFT 1971-; Schlsp from Empire St; *office:* Tottenville HS 100 Luten Ave Staten Island NY 10312*

LOEBEN, PRISCILLA SUZANNE, Physical Sci & Honors Bio Tchr; *b:* Philadelphia, PA; *m:* Arthur F. Jr.; *c:* Alexander VanderKleut, Adrienne L. Beyer; *ed:* Kutztown Univ (BSEd) Bio 1969, (MS) Curr & Instruction of Scndry Ed 1991; 45 Credit Hrs Post Grad Stud; *cr:* Northwest Jr HS Bio, Hlth tchr 1969; Souderton Area HS Bio Tchr 1969-73; Boyertown Sr HS Bio Tchr 1980-81; Boyertown Jr HS East Ctr Phys Sci, Bio Hnrs Tchr 1982-; *ai:* Svc Learning Coord; Strategic Planning Cncl; Sci Olympiad Coach; Recycling Coord; PSEA, NEA, Montgomery Cty Sci Tchrs Assn 1969-; Boyertown Ed Assn 1982-; Boyertown Schl Dist Tchr of Yr 1992; Article Pub; *office:* Boyertown Jr HS # 305 2020 Big Rd Gilbertsville PA 19525

LOECHLE, SUSAN D., English Teacher; *b:* Cincinnati, OH; *m:* Paul R.; *c:* Eric, Anne; *ed:* Edgecliff Coll (BA) Eng 1970; *cr:* Notre Dame Acad Eng Tchr 1970-73; St Ursula Acad Eng Tchr 1989-; *ai:* Stu Fac Advy Bd; Stu Spotlight Comm; Soph Class Moderator; NCTE 1990-; Presenter Ursuline Educators North Amer Conf; *office:* Saint Ursula Acad 1339 E Mc Millan St Cincinnati OH 45206

LOEFFEL, JOHN WILLIAM, Eng & Wstrn Civilization Tchr; *b:* Ashtabula, OH; *m:* Janie Katherine Laine; *c:* Jennifer, Amanda, John, Erika; *ed:* Kent St Univ (BSEd) Eng 1972; Post Grad Work at Edinboro St Univ; *cr:* Madison HS Eng & His Tchr 1973-; *ai:* NEA, OH Ed Assn 1973-; Madison Ed Assn 1973-, 1 Time VP; *office:* Madison HS 3100 Burns Rd Madison OH 44057

LOEFFLER, CYNTHIA GALE ROBINSON, Biology Teacher; *b:* Lockport, NY; *m:* Warren H. Jr.; *c:* Cristin; *ed:* St Univ of NY at Fredonia (BS) Bio Ed 1971; 41 Grad Credits at Various Pub & Private Colls & Univs; *cr:* Rush-Henrietta Cntrl Schl Dist Sci & Bio Tchr 25 Yrs; *ai:* Rush-Henriettas Educators Assn; NYS United Tchrs 1971-; AFT-CIO 1971-; Fairport Historical Soc; Asbury First United Meth Church; Natl Sci Fnd; Designed an Approved NYS Bio Varience; Dev of Co-Tchng Prgm for Regular & Spec Ed Stdnts; Writer of Project Landscape Ecology Artists Relation to Nature-Ecology Unit; *office:* Rush-Henrietta Sr HS 1799 Lehigh Station Rd Henrietta NY 14467

LOEFFLER, JULIA COWAN, HS Social Studies Teacher; *b:* Wilmington, NC; *m:* William Lawrence; *c:* Jeffrey L., John E.; *ed:* Queens Coll (MS) Scndry Ed, Soc Stud 1994; Miller Motte Bus Coll 30 Credit Hrs Bus Admin; Univ of NC at Wilmington Acctng; Post Grad Ed Stud 30 Credits; *cr:* Forest Hills HS Soc Stud Tchr 6 Yrs; *ai:* Amer His, Movie Club; New Tchr Mentor 1993-; AFT, UFT, NYSUT 1990-; UFT Grant; Phi Alpha Theta 1989; Hnrs Grad; NASD License; *office:* Forest Hills HS 67-01 110th St Forest Hills NY 11375*

LOESCHNER, RICHARD JOSEPH, HS Math Teacher; *b:* Queens, NY; *m:* Annemarie Maresca; *c:* Richard, Christopher; *ed:* Stonybrook Univ (BA) Math 1985, (MS) Math 1996; *cr:* LaSalle Military Acad HS Math Tchr 1984-90; Holy Trinity Diocesan HS Math Tchr 1993-; *ai:* Bsktbl & Bsbl Coach; NCMT 1984-; LaSalle Military Acad Tchr of the Yr 1989; *office:* Holy Trinity Diocesan HS 98 Cherry Ln Hicksville NY 11801*

LOEWEN, MARVIN E., Chemistry Teacher; *b:* Alton, IA; *m:* Sally Sorenson; *c:* Jonathon, Christopher; *ed:* St Univ of SD (BA) Chem, Math 1963; Adelphi Univ (MS) Chem 1968; Attnd Yale Univ, Manhattan Coll, SD Schl of Tech, Hofstra Univ, C. W. Post; *cr:* West Jr HS Math Tchr 1963-64; Bellport HS Chem Tchr 1964-; Suffolk Cty Comm Coll Chem Prof 1980-; Bellport HS Sci Chm 1989-94; *ai:* Stdnts for Environmental Quality Adv; NYSUT 1970-; Bellport Tchrs Assn 1964-, VP; Suffolk Cty Sci Tchrs 1980-; Suffolk Cty Sci Tchr of Yr 1987; RITEC Outstdng Sci Tchng Awd; *office:* Bellport HS Beaver Dam Rd Brookhaven NY 11719*

LOEWEN, PHILIP JON, Band Director; *b:* Bellefonte, PA; *m:* Joan Dixon; *c:* Benjamin, Matthew; *ed:* Penn St (BS) Music Ed 1980; Post Grad Credits Westchester Univ; *cr:* South Middleton MS Band Dir 1982; Newport HS Band Dir 1982-85; Southern Huntingdon Cty HS Band Dir 1985-; *ai:* PSEA & NEA; PMEA & MENC; AFM; *office:* Huntingdon Cty Jr Sr HS RR 1 Box 1124 Three Springs PA 17264

LOFRUMENTO, DEBRA ELAINE, Kindergarten Teacher; *b:* Re PA; *m:* Christian; *c:* Kristin; *ed:* Kutztown Univ (BA) Elem Ed 1974, Elem Ed 1976; *cr:* Reading Schl Dist Second, Third, Split Grds ESEA I Rdng Tchr 1974-83; Riverside Elem Schl Kndgtn Tchr 1983-; *ai:* His Interpreter Vol; St Thomas UCC Choir, Handbell Choir; Ring Foster Parent Berks Cty Children, Yth Svcs; NEA 1974-; First Church of Christ, Deacon, Elder; Co-Operating Tchr, Stu Aide Prgm Dist Mentor; Advanced Instructional Methods Trainer; Dist Kndgtn, Soc Stud, Parenting Acad Comms; Co-operating Tchr of Kutztown *office:* Reading School Dist 1400 Centre Ave Reading PA 19601*

LOFTON, SAMUEL C.,JR., Dept Chair & Soc Stud Tchr; *b:* M Ferry, OH; *m:* Della A; *c:* Samuel III, Lori; *ed:* OH Univ (BSEd) Ed 1966; Kent St (MED) His 1974; *cr:* North Ridgeville Schls Tchr 19 Berea City Schls Tchr 1967-; *ai:* Stu Cncl Adv 1970-93; OH Ed 1966-; Berea Ed Assn 1966-; Jennings Scholar Awd 1975; All OH St Adv 1984; Berea Schl Curr Writing Team; OH PTA Lifetime Mem Reader AP Test US His 1995 & 1996; *office:* Midpark HS 7000 Pa Cleveland OH 44130

LOFTUS, PAMELA ANN, Mathematics Teacher; *b:* Roxborough, P Muhlenberg Coll (BS) Math 1991; *cr:* Upper Merion HS Math 1991-92; Conestoga HS Math Tchr 1992-94; Downington Sr HS Mat 1994-; *ai:* Lacrosse Coach; NEA 1994-; NCTM 1991-; Downingtown Sr HS 445 Manor Ave Downingtown PA 19335*

LOGALBO, MARGARET THERESA (KING), English Instruct Utica, NY; *m:* Paul P.; *c:* Christine, Alicia, Mary; *ed:* Utica C Syracuse Univ (BA) Eng 1971; SUNY Cortland (MS) Eng, Ed 197 Oris Kany Cntrl HS Eng Tchr 1971-76; Cato-Meridian HS Eng 1976-77; Binghamton Univ Adj Instr 1988-92; Broome Comm Co Instr 1979-; *ai:* Union Rep Fac Assn; Written Expression, Cumminic About Ideas, Values Comm; NCTE, NEA 1970-; Vestal Democratic 1980-, Comm Person; Our Lady of Sorrows 1977-, Pres Parish 1989-90, Sec 1988-89, Mem 1987-88, Eucharistic Minister, L Workshops: How Safe Are You in Classroom 1993, Writing Across 1989-91; Initiated Tchrs Support Group 1987-88; Natl Masters Seminar Schlsp 1987; Pub Article 1991; *office:* Broome Comm Co Box 1017 Binghamton NY 13902*

LOGAN, CATHY D., Professor; *b:* Sunbury, PA; *ed:* McCann Schl (ASB) Court Reporting 1971; *cr:* Freelance Reporter 1971-73; Cn Bus Schl Tchr 1972-73, Chprsn of Court Reporting Division 1973-78 to the Dean 1978-79, Dir of Stu Svcs 1980-88 Instr, Prof 1988-; *ai:* N 1971-, Mem of BASE; PCRA 1971-; Bus Assoc of the Yr; Co-Aut Book: Technology; Articles Pub.

LOGAN, CLIFFORD ROBINSON, American History Teache Dubois, PA; *m:* Penelope E. Isaly; *c:* Bridget E. Miller, Eugene J., Je R., Rebecca R.; *cr:* Butler Jr HS Tchr 1962-, Gifted Prgm Supvr 197 Yrbk Adv; NEA 1965-; *home:* 542 S Benbrook Rd Butler PA 16001

LOGAN, EILEEN EGERT, Nursing Teacher; *b:* Brooklyn, N Allison, Kathleen; *ed:* SUNY at Downstate (BS) Nursing 1974; Seton Univ (MSN) Nursing 1981; Natl Bd of Pediatric Nurse Practitioners Cert 1982; *cr:* Interfaith Med Ctr Pediatric Nurse Practitioner 198 Lafayette HS Nursing Tchr 1989-; *ai:* Sr Grd Adv; Coord Pub Svc NYS; Nurse Aide Evaluator; Tutor Residential Hlth Care Fac Exam; 1989-; Sigma Theta Tau, NYSNA 1982-; Robert Wood Johnson Fellov Seton Hall Univ 1980-81; *office:* Lafayette HS 2630 Benson Ave Bro NY 11214

LOGAN, GWENDOLYN RUNNELS, Science Teacher; *b:* Houston *ed:* Huston-Tillotson Coll (BS) Chem 1966; Towson St Univ (MA) S Ed 1991; Continuing Ed Credits Trinity Coll 1988-, Marymount Coll UDC 1993; *cr:* Conoco Oil Co Chemist 1966-69; Baltimore City Sch Tchr 1969-72; Baltimore Cnty Schls Sci Tchr 1972-75; Stauffer Che Safety Engr Trainee 1975-76; Coolidge HS Sci Tchr 1988-; *ai* Accelerator Dist of Columbia Pub Schls; Sci Chprsn; NSTA 1991- Delta Kappa 1992-; NEA 1993-; Genentech Access Fellow 1995; Na Medicine Fellow 1995; Flwshp Howard Univ Schl of Medicine Flwshp Rsrch Division Howard Univ Schl of Medicine 1993; *o* Coolidge Sr HS 5th Tuckerman St NW Washington DC 20011

LOGAN, LYNN JOHNSTONE, High School Guidance Counsel Kearney, NJ; *c:* Matthew; *ed:* Ocean Cty Coll (AS) Commercial Art Montclair St (BA) Fine Art Ed 1977; Kean Coll (MA) Stu Personnel 1982; Jersey City St +30 Prin, Admin, Supervision 1985; Attnd East Univ; *cr:* Brick Twp HS Art Tchr 1977-92, Guidance Cnslr 1993-; *a* Proficiency Test, Rotary Youth Leadership Awds & Girls St Amer L Coord; Interact Club; NJEA, OCCEA, NEA 1977-; BTEA 1977-, Exe OCPGA 1993-; Outstanding Art Tchr Awd 1984; Photographs Pub; *o* Brick Township HS 346 Chambersbridge Rd Brick NJ 08723

LOGAN, MADELYN ESPOSITO, Natural Sciences Prof & Chai Taylor, PA; *c:* Kelly Ann, Kristy Ann; *ed:* Wilkes Univ (BA) Bio Northeastern Univ (MED) 1969; *cr:* Merck Inc Rsrch Asst 1965-6 Shore Comm Coll Tchng 1966-71, 1974-; *ai:* Phi Theta Kappa Distance Learning, Title III Comms; St Phi Theta Kappa Bd Preparati Dept Labs Policy; Assessment Act; NSTA 1986-; MTA 1984-; A 1994-; NISOD Tchng Awd for Tchng Excl 1995; *office:* Northshore C Coll Ferncroft Rd Danvers MA 01923

LOGES, BRIAN T., Art Teacher; *b:* Dayton, OH; *ed:* Univ of Dayton Art Ed 1976; Prof Cert 1979; *cr:* Studebaker Jr High Art Tchr 197 Wayne HS Art Tchr 1992-; *ai:* Studebaker Jr High Spcl Tchr Awd Tchr of the Month Dec 1981, Tchr of the Yr 1982-83, Tchr of the M 1985 & Spcl Tchr Awd for Outstdng Artistic Contributions 1987; *o* Wayne HS 5400 Chambersburg Rd Huber Heights OH 45424

LOGSDON, JOHN WAYNE, First Grade Teacher; *b:* Cumberland, *m:* Carol; *c:* Kirsten, Christopher; *ed:* Frostburg St Univ (BS) Chldhd, Elem 1990; 6 Hrs Towards Masters in Admin, Supervision; *c* John Neuman Tchr 1981-87; Bishop Walsh Schl Tchr 1987-88; Alle Cty Bd of Ed Tchr 1990-; *ai:* Coach Cross Cntry Ft Hill HS, Bsbl HS; Allegany Cty Tchrs Assn, NEA, MD St Tchrs Assn 1990-; Knigh Columbus, Alhambra 1990-; Eagles 1995-; Nom Allegany Cty Tchr 1994-; *office:* Northeast Elem Schl 11001 Forest Ave NE Cumberland 21502*

LOGSDON, MARGE, English Teacher; *b:* Pittsburgh, PA; *ed:* Slip Rock Univ (BS) Eng Ed 1969; Duquesne Univ (MLA) Liberal Arts Univ of Pittsburgh 60 Credits Towards PHD; *cr:* Sacred Heart HS Bsktbl Coach 1969-84, Eng Tchr 1969-89; Indiana Univ of PA Asst B Coach 1985-86; Oakland Cath HS Eng Tchr 1989-; *ai:* Lit Maga Moderator; Western PA Tchr of Eng 1993-; Advy Cncls Poetry F 1993-; NEH Shakespeare Grant IUP 1988; All-Star Tchr Awd 1991; Pittsburgh Admin Intern 1992; Bsktbl Coach of Yr 1989; Duquesne Excl Tchng Awd 1993; Eng Dept Chairwoman 1991; St Vincents Coll Tchng Recognition 1991; herff-Jones Yrbk Gold Awd 1987-88, 1991 Diocese of Pittsburgh & Carlow Coll Regnl Ctr for Prof Growth Pr 1992; AAAA Girls St Bsktbl Championship Head Coach 1989; Rand Macon Women's Coll Significant Tchr Awd 1987; Wellesley Coll Ex Tchng 1987; Duquesne Univ Tchng Assistantship in Eng 1982.

STON, STEPHEN KENNETH, Title I Math Teacher; *b:* East pool, OH; *c:* Mike, Willie, Jessica; *ed:* Shepherd Coll (BA) Elem Ed Univ of Dayton (MA) Elem Ed 1984; Inst of Childrens Lit Grad; *cr:* as 12 Yr Schl Grd 5 Tchr 1975-76; Wellsville Local Schls Grd 6 Tchr, I Math Tchr 1978-; *ai:* Drug Free Schls Coord; Just Say No Club Coached Bsbl; Wellsville Local Tchrs Assn 1978-, VP; DEA, NEA ; *home:* 17339 Crews Rd Wellsville OH 43968

UE, JAMES W., Accounting Professor; *b:* Philadelphia, PA; *m:* aret Ann Brooks; *c:* Kelly, Christine, Brian, Andrew; *ed:* Boston Coll Acctng 1981; Widener Univ (MS) Taxation 1990; Currently DED St Univ; *cr:* Arthur Andersen & Co Staff Auditor 1981-83; Nu-car ers Inc Sr Accountany 1983-85; Peirce Jr Coll Acctng Prof 1985-91; ll Chem Senses Ctr Acctng Mgr 1991-93; Saint Francis Coll Acctng 1993-; *ai:* Acctng Club, SIgma Beta, Delta Adv; Chair Cmptr Dev, Acad Standing, Stu Affairs Comm; AICPA 1984-; IMA 1995-; AYSO ; Stu Govt Assn Outstdng Edctr Awd 1995; Hnr Soc Distngd Fac Awd st; *office:* Saint Francis Coll Loretto PA 15940

UE, ROBERT EMMET, Science Teacher; *b:* Wilkes Barre, PA; *m:* Ann Campbell; *c:* Patricia E., Robert J.; *ed:* Bloomsburg Univ (BS) 67; Post Grad Work Hofstra Univ, St Univ at Stony Brook & Adelphi *cr:* Lindenhurst Jr High Tchr 1967-81; Lindenhurst Sr High Tchr -; *ai:* Lacrosse Coach; AFT 1967-; Lacrosse Coachs Assn 1972-, n of Yr 1994; Lindenhurst Tchrs Assn 1967-; PTA 1967-; Suffolk Cty osse Jr Var Coach of Yr 1994; *office:* Lindenhurst Sr HS 300 Charles ndenhurst NY 11757

NES, MAGALY LOPEZ, Social Studies Teacher; *b:* Havana, Cuba; obert C.; *c:* Robert, Melissa; *ed:* St Joseph's Coll (BA) His 1966; NY (MA) His 1967; 12 Credits St John's Univ Law Schl; 9 Credits In-Svc ses; *cr:* Clara Barton HS Soc Stud Tchr 4 Yrs; St Andrew Avellino Schl , Lang Arts Tchr 4 Yrs; St Luke's Schl Soc Stud Tchr, Coord 9 Yrs; ub Relations Comm; Natl Geographic Competition Schl Coord; NCEA ; BSA 1978-, Cncl Trng Chm, Troop Positions; Girl Scouts 1979-, n Ldr, 10 Yr Pin; Silver Beaver St George Dist Awd of Merit; *office:* ke Schl 16-01 150th Pl Flushing NY 11357*

R, ANNE MARGARET, Math & Computer Teacher; *b:* Johnstown, *m:* Douglas W.; *c:* Gage D.; *ed:* Univ of Pittsburgh at Johnstown (BS) , Sec Ed 1986; Addl 24 Credit Hrs; Cmptr Specialist Cert; *cr:* North HS Tchr 1986-; *ai:* Stu Cncl Adv; Jr Magazine Sales; Colorguard Instr; , NEA 1986-; Vlybl Leaue 1984-; *office:* North Star HS 400 Ohio St ell PA 15531*

RIUS, LINDA (ROSENZWEIG), English Teacher; *b:* Racine, WI; even; *c:* Joshua, Sarah; *ed:* Northwestern Univ (BA) Comparative Lit Columbia Univ Tchrs Coll (MA) Tchng of Eng 1969; *cr:* Jr HS 43 Tchr 1969-71; Friends Acad Eng Tchr 1985-92; North Shore HS Eng 1992-; *ai:* NHS Adv; Site-Based Decision Making Comm; NCTE -; Comm Ed Prgm Bd 1995-; *office:* North Shore HS 450 Glen Cove Glen Head NY 11545

AI, LARRY P., Agri-Business & Science Tchr; *b:* Dayton, OH; *m:* Ann Bertram; *c:* Chris Scanlan, Michelle Williams, Susan Farr, Rick , Brad, Amy Toops; *ed:* OH St Univ (BS) Ag Ed 1970, (MS) Ag Ed Notre Dame, OH St Univ, Wittenberg Univ 25 Hrs; *cr:* Northwestern Schls Agri Bus Tchr, Voc Dept Head 1967-89; Ehove Career Ctr Ag Tchr 1989-90; Keystone Local Schls Ag Bus, Ag Sci Tchr 1990-; *ai:* St Judging, Pub Speaking Teams Coach; Parliamentary Procedure ; Adv FFA, FFA Alumni, Natl FFA; Dairy Foods, FFA Poultry ms; Natl FFA Tchr Rep Contests, Awds; AVA, OVA, OVATA, NVATA -; OEA; NEA; Keystone Local EA; Alpha Gamma Sigma; OH St Univ; FFA Alumni Assn; Keystone PTA; Natl FFA Almni; St Vincent De Paul ch; Elks Lodge #465; United Polish Club; Friends of Black River; in Cty Natl Rsource Comm; Avon Lake Republican Club; North eville Republican Club; Lorain Cty Republican Club; Elyria blican Club; Cooperation Tchr for Stu Tchrs OH St 1970-88; OH Agri 1989, OH Voc 1985, OH Ag 1984 Tchr of Yr; Honorary Amer FFA ee 1976, 1994; Citizen of Yr Granges Lorain Cty; Natl Regnl Ag er 1977; *home:* 625 Song Bird St Elyria OH 44035

KEN, CAROLYN FIEGL, Vocal Music Teacher; *b:* Lockport, NY; erry William; *c:* Patrick, Mary, Margaret; *ed:* Ithaca Coll (BM) Music 976; Attnd SUNY at Fredonia, Potsdam, Buffalo, Temple Univ; *cr:* e Jr HS Vocal Music Tchr 1976-77; Dansville Cntlr Vocal Music Tchr -85; Clarence Jr High Vocal Music Tchr 1985-88; Grand Island Sr Vocal Music Tchr 1993-; *ai:* Madrigals; Womens Ensemble; HS cal; NYSSMA 1976-; Genesee Vly Music Tchr 1977-85, Pres & VP; MEA 1985-; GITA 1993-; Genesee Vly All Cty Chorus Guest luctor; *office:* Grand Island HS 1100 Ransom Rd Grand Island NY 2

LAR-SCHMIDT, JULIE, Art Teacher; *b:* Evanston, IL; *m:* David ; *ed:* Miami Univ (BS) K-12 Art Ed 1979, (MA) Art Ed K-12 1993; West Carrollton Jr HS 7-9th Grd Art Tchr 1979-89; West Carrollton Sr 10-12 Grd Art Tchr 1989-; *ai:* NEA, OAEA 1979-; WCEA 1979-, shp Chprsn; WCEF Grant 1987, 1995; OAC Grant 1992, 1995; ificant Tchr Awd 1979-95; *office:* West Carrollton H S 5833 Student Carrollton OH 45449*

O, CIRCE M., Spanish Teacher; *b:* Matauzas, Cuba; *m:* Eduardo C.; rank P. Laucerica, Pedro P. Laucerica; *ed:* City Coll of NY (MS) Ed 3; Superior Pedagogical Inst Cuba His Professorship 1977; Educl rovement Inst Cuba HS Tchr His 1972; City Coll Schl Admin 15 dits 1994-95; NYSUT Cooperative Learning Exceptional Stdnts Rose's 9 Credits 1995; NYU Leadership Inst 3 Credits Schl of Ed 1995; *cr:* Soc Stud Tchr, Supvr, Prin 1960-70; Matanzas Educl Broadcasting ns Coord 1970-74; Agrotechnical Inst Alvaro Reynoso His Prof 4-77; Superior Pedagogical Inst Juan Marinello His Prof 1977-80; PS 3 Span Biling Tchr 1987-88; IS #195 Roberto Clemente Span Biling 1988-; *ai:* PDL Prgm 1991-, Resident Tchr; UFT 1987-; Exemplary Awd 1994-95; Awd Excellent Svc Prof Dev Lab 1994; Cert reciation Excl Peer Collabortion Prof Dev Lab 1993-94; Recognition Awd Dedication, Commitment to Staff, Stdnts, Parents 1992; Awd Svc dnts 1991; *office:* IS 195 Roberto Clemente 625 W 133rd St New York 10027

MAGISTRO, KATHLEEN CROWLEY, Science Teacher; *b:* Bourne, ; *c:* Peter, Justin; *ed:* Adelphi Univ (BA) Bio 1973; Univ of Pittsburgh) Exercise Physiology 1981; *cr:* Pittsburgh Pub Schls Sci Tchr; sburgh Northgate Schl Sci Tchr; Cardozo HS Math Sci Tchr 1984-87; al Park Meml Schl Sci Tchr 1987-; *ai:* 7th Grd Adv; Great Neck North ol Coach, Lacrosse Coach; NEA 1985-; NSTA; Amer Bro Tchr; York Bio & Earth Sci Grant; Ithaca Coll Cmptrs & Sci Grant; SUNY chase Chem Grant; SUNY Old Westbury Neurobiology Grant.

MAGLIO, ALEXANDER A., 7th Grade Science Teacher; *b:* Holyoke, ; *m:* Ellen K. Coughlin; *c:* Michael A.; *ed:* Univ of Lowell (BS) Hlth 1987; North Adams St Coll (MED) Scndry Sci 1993; 33 Addl Hrs; *cr:* Cntrl Schl 7th Grd Sci Tchr 1987-; *ai:* Tchr Trainer Cooperative rning; Lee Ed Assn 1987-, Pres; Pi Lambda Theta; *office:* Lee Central 122 High St Lee MA 01238

MANNO, DOMENIC, English Teacher & Soccer Coach; *b:* Boston, ; *m:* Jane Fleming; *c:* Domenic S., Jessica E., Gregory W.; *ed:* Salem Coll (BSEd) Soc Stud 1961; Boston St Univ (MSEd) Eng 1971, (CAGS) dio, Visual 1985; Salem St Coll Scndry Level Rdng Cert; *cr:* Revere HS Eng Tchr 9171-; *ai:* Var Soccer Coach 21 Yrs; Newspaper Adv 10 Yrs; Revere Tchrs Assn 1971-; Elk 1989-; Wrote Interdisciplinary Course Curr 11th Grd Hnrs US His, Amer Lit; Helped Restructure Eng, Soc Stud Curr; *office:* Revere HS 101 School St Revere MA 02151

LOMAS, JEREMY RICHARD, Elem Gifted Education Teacher; *b:* Philadelphia, PA; *m:* Savona; *c:* Walter; *ed:* Bloomsburg Univ (BS) Elem Ed 1966; Trenton St Coll (MA) Elem Ed; 18 Hrs Philadelphia Coll of Arts; 12 Hrs Temple Univ; 6 Hrs Penn St; *cr:* Butler Elem Schl 6th Grd Tchr 1966-71; Pine Run Elem Schl 5th-6th Grd Tchr 1971-83; Doyle Elem Schl Elem Gifted Prgm Tchr 1983-; *ai:* Schl Store Adv; Spec Events Planning, Discipline Code Planning Comms; NEA, PSEA 1968-; Cntrl Bucks Ed Assn 1968-, Treas; Rocky Meadows Homeowners Assn 1990-, Pres; Camp Curiostiy 1990-, Dir; Moreys Camp 1996-, Advy Cncl; *home:* 110 Rocky Ct S Chalfont PA 18914

LOMBARD, MICHAEL S., Fourth Grade Teacher; *b:* Bridgeport, CT; *ed:* Sacred Heart Univ (BA) His, Elem Ed 1973; Univ of Bridgeport (MS) Elem Ed 1975; Emergency Med Technician 1979-89; *cr:* Jane Ryan Schl Fourth Grd Tchr 1973-; *ai:* Stu Assistance Team; NEA, CEA 1973-; TEA 1973-, Exec Bd, VP; *office:* Jane Ryan Elem Schl 190 Park Ln Trumbull CT 06611

LOMBARDI, DONNA BALL, Third Grade Teacher; *b:* Albany, NY; *m:* Gary L.; *ed:* Coll of Mt St Vincent (BA) Eng 1970; Russell Sage Coll (MA) El Ed 1973; Various In-Service Courses; *cr:* Boght Hills Schl 1st Grd Tchr 1970-73, 3rd Grd Tchr 1973-; *ai:* Prof, Dist Wkshp, Gifted, Grievance, Pol Action, Lang Arts Steering, Dist Mentor Comms; Pilot Comm for Portfolio Assessment; NYSUT, AFT 1970-; Vol; Saratoga Performing Arts Ctr; Proctors Theater; Math Mini Grant Elem Ed.

LOMBARDI, JUDITH ANN TOMCZUK, Art Teacher; *b:* Elizabeth, NJ; *m:* Thomas; *c:* Joshua; *ed:* Kean Coll (BA) Fine Arts 1967, (MA) Fine Arts Supervision 1982; *cr:* Carteret Schls 3-8 Grd Elem Arts Tchr 1967-84, 9-12 Grd HS Tchr 1984-; *ai:* Lit Magazine Reflections Club Spon, Adv 1995-; Coord of Annual Dist Art Show 1988, VFW Patriotism Poster Contest 1992; NEA, NJAEA, CEA 1967-; Oak Tree Presbyn Womens Assn 1990-, Co-Pres; VFW Ladies Auxillary 1993-; *home:* 10 Clemmens Ct Edison NJ 08820*

LOMBARDI, MARGARET RIZZUTI, Chemistry Teacher; *b:* Waterbury, CT; *c:* Judith Ann, James; *ed:* Univ of CT (BA) Chem 1957; Cornell Univ (MST) Chem 1965; Yale Univ 6 Credit Hrs; *cr:* Crosby HS Chem Tchr 1957-62; Our Lady of Lourdes HS Chem Tchr 1963-64; Poughkeepsie HS Chem Tchr 1978-79; Arlington HS Chem Tchr 1984-; *ai:* AFT, NYSTA & STANYS 1984-; NSF Grant Yale Univ 1959; NSF Grant Cornell Univ 1962-63; *office:* Arlington HS Rt 55 Lagrangeville NY 12540

LOMBARDO, PAUL ANTHONY, Math Teacher; *b:* Cleveland, OH; *ed:* OH St Univ (BS) Scndry Math Ed 1992; Attending Cleveland St Univ; *cr:* Maui HS Math Tchr, Ftbl Coach 1992-93; Mayfield HS Math Tchr, Sftbl Coach 1993-; *ai:* Notre Dame Cathedral Latin HS Ftbl Coach 1993-; Girls Sftbl 1993-95; Big Brothers, Big Sisters Club Adv 1994-95; OMCTM, NCTM 1992-, MEA 1993-; Mayfield Alumni Assn 1987-, Soc Dir 1995; *office:* Mayfield H S 6116 Wilson Mills Rd Mayfield Hts OH 44143

LOMBARDOZZI, PATRICK ENRICO, Social Studies Teacher; *b:* Media, PA; *m:* Lisa Ann Clifton; *ed:* Millersville Univ (BA) Soc Stud Ed 1992; Attnd Univ of DE, Wilmington Coll; *cr:* Wilmington HS Soc Stud Tchr 1992-95; A. I. duPont HS Soc Stud Tchr 1995-; *ai:* Ftbl, Tennis Coach; Phi Kappa Sigma 1989-, Acad VP, VP, Pres; *office:* A. I. duPont HS 50 Hillside Rd Greenville DE 19807

LOMIS, LOIS M., Business Teacher; *b:* Philadelphia, PA; *m:* Charles; *ed:* Temple Univ (BS) Bus Ed 1968; Master's Equiv Bus Ed 1974; *cr:* Olney HS Bus Tchr 1968-70; West Springfield HS Bus Tchr 1970-73; Roxborough HS Bus Tchr 1973-74; Univ City HS Bus Tchr 1974-84; Overbrook HS Bus Tchr 1984-; *ai:* Hlth Acad, Bus Inst Tutor; Philadelpha Fed of Tchrs 1973-; *office:* Overbrook HS 59th St & Lancaster Ave Philadelphia PA 19131

LOMPERIS, TIMOTHY JOHN, Associate Prof of Pol Science; *b:* Guntur, India; *m:* Ana Maria Turner; *c:* Kristina Maria, John Scott; *ed:* Augustana Coll (BA) Pol Sci & His 1969; Johns Hopkins Univ Schl of Adv Intnl Stud (MA) Intnl Affairs 1975; Duke Univ (MA) Pol Sci 1978, (PHD) Pol Sci 1981; Woodrow Wilson Ctr for Intnl Scholars Fellow 1988-89; Ctr for Intnl Affairs Harvard Univ Post Doctoral Flwshp 1985-86; *cr:* LA St Univ Asst Prof of Pol Sci 1980-84; Duke Univ Asst Prof of Pol Sci 1984-94; US Military Acad Assoc Prof of Pol Sci 1994-; *ai:* Amer Pol Sci Assn 1984-; Helen Dwight Reid Awd APSA Best Dissertation in Intnl Relats 1982; Books Pub: From Peoples War To Peoples Rule 1996, Reading The Wind 1987, The War Everyone Lost And Won 1984 & 1993; Hindu Influence On Greek Philosophy 1984; *home:* 5 Peterson Rd Monroe NY 10950*

LONAKER, LINDA SUE, 5th Grade Math & History Tchr; *b:* Cincinnati, OH; *ed:* Franklin Coll of IN (BS) Elem Ed 1971; 21 Hrs Post Grad, Several Hrs CEU'S; Attnd Findlay Coll; *cr:* Bethel-Tate Schl Dist 5th Grd Tchr 24 Yrs; *ai:* Tutoring; Honor Roll, Tiger Paw, Tchr Evaluation, Soc Stud, Math Curr Comms; Intervention Asst Team; NEA 1972-; Bethel Tate Tchrs Assn 1972-, Bldg Rep; *office:* Bethel-Tate MS 150 Fossyl Dr Bethel OH 45106

LONDON, DAVID EDWIN, Mathematics Teacher; *b:* Punxsutawney, PA; *m:* Mary Catherine Mc Cullough; *c:* Sarah C.; *ed:* Penn St Univ (BS) Scndry Math Ed 1986; 24 Credit Hrs Grad; *cr:* Redbank Valley HS Math Tchr 1986-; *ai:* Stu Cncl Adv; Jr HS Bsktbl, Var Bsbl Head Coach; Goals 2000 Schl Improvement Comm Chair; NEA, PA Ed assn 1984-; Fed League Bsbl 1982-, Pres; Trout Unlimited 1982-92, Dir; *office:* Redbank Valley HS 920 Broad St New Bethlehem PA 16242*

LONDON, DOUGLAS, Principal; *b:* New York, NY; *m:* Kathy Kilroy; *c:* Kevin, Katie, Lindsay; *ed:* Kenyon Coll (BA) Eng 1974; Univ of MD (MA) Eng 1983, (PHD) Eng; Univ of VT (MA) Eng; Johns Hopkins (MED) Admin, Supervision; 75 Addl Hrs; *cr:* Bullis Schl 11th-12th Grd Prin 1977-; *ai:* Var Soccer Coach; Admissions, Long Range Planning Comms; Curr Comm Chair; NCTE, NSCAA 1988-; NAIS 1980-; Tchr of Yr 1986; All-Met Coach of Yr 1993; *office:* The Bullis Schl 10601 Falls Rd Potomac MD 20854*

LONDON, SUSANNE ABRAMS, English & Alternative Ed Tchr; *b:* Hartford, CT; *m:* Marshall; *c:* Rebecca, Linda, Saul, Sara, Naomi, Danny, Rachel; *ed:* Univ of VT (BA) Eng 1954; Addl 60 Hrs in Eng, Psych, Ed; *cr:* Champlain Valley Union HS Eng Tchr 1975-91, Life Prgm Tchr 1991-; *ai:* Ind Stud in Creative Writing; Sr Grad Challenge Adv; VTNEA, NEA 1975-; Poetry Soc of VT 1968-; NCTE 1978-; Acad of Amer Poets; Tchr of Yr; VT Tchr of Week; *office:* Champlain Valley Union HS RR 2 Box 160 Hinesburg VT 05461

LONDRAVILLE, CHARLES WILLIAM, Physical Ed & Health Teacher; *b:* Springfield, IL; *ed:* Univ of MA (BS) PE, Hlth 1974; *cr:* Chicopee Schl Dept PE, Hlth Tchr 1974-; *ai:* Hockey, Sftbl, Field Hockey Coach; Curr Writer Chicopee Schls; Time & Learning Comm; CEA, MTA, NEA 1974-; C-Tape West 1994-; Ready Set Go Conf 1996-, Coord; Elks 1976-; *office:* Chicopee Comprehensive HS Montgomery St Chicopee MA 01020

LONERGAN, SANTINA PALMERI, Social Studies Teacher; *b:* Pittston, PA; *m:* J. Brian; *c:* Brian, Lynn, Christopher; *ed:* Marywood Coll (BA) His 1967, (MS) His 1971; *cr:* Pittston Area Schl Scndry Tchr 1968-; *ai:* Stu Cncl Moderator; Stu of Month Comm Co-Chair; AFT 1971-; Lozerne Cty Cncl of Soc Stud Tchrs 1968-; Marywood Coll Alumni Assn 1969-, VP, Sr M. Denis Donegan Vol Awd; Scranton Prep Parents Club 1984-, Pres 1990-91; Loyola Club 1991-; One-Day Jeopardy Champion 1992.

LONES, STEVE ALAN, Physical Education Teacher; *b:* Montpelier, OH; *ed:* Rio Grande Univ (BS) PE, Hlth, Sci 1980; *cr:* Our Lady of Lourdes Schl PE Tchr 1980-96; *ai:* Track Coach; Ath Coord; NEA 1986-; *office:* Our Lady Of Lourdes Schl 5835 Glenway Ave Cincinnati OH 45238*

LONG, ANDREW, Business Education Teacher; *b:* Plainfield, NJ; *m:* Valerie Fyson; *c:* Andrew, Valerie Jane, Elizabeth Richards; *ed:* St Univ of NY at Albany (BA) Bus Ed 1977; 39 Addl Hrs; *cr:* Shenendehowa HS Bus Tchr, Bsbl & Soccer Coach & Class Adv 1977-; *ai:* Jr Var Soccer Coach; VFW & Amer Legion 1975-; 20 Yr Air Force Veteran; Muscular Dystrophy Assn 1979-, vol, Vol of Yr 1991.*

LONG, ANNE WILLIAMS, Fourth Grade Teacher; *b:* Syracuse, NY; *m:* Robert Arthur; *c:* Gregory Christopher; *ed:* SUNY at Potsdam (BA) Elem Ed 1965; 1 Addl Credits Masters Equivalency; *cr:* DeForest Union HS Dist 4th Grd Tchr 1966-67; Edmonton Pub Schl Dist 3rd Grd Tchr 1967-69; Wyalusing Area Schl Dist 3rd-4th Grd Tchr 1970-, Sub Tchr 1971-78; *ai:* Area Ed Assn Soc Comm Chair; NEA 1969-70, 1978-; PSEA, WAEA 1978-; PA Geographic Soc 1992-, Distinguished Tchr Awd 1992; Delta Kappa Gamma 1984-; Central Bradford Cty United Way 1979-95, Campaign Chm, Bd; Amer Assn of Univ Women 1970-, Pres 1973-75, 1991-93, Outstanding Woman of Yr 1995; Childrens Cultural Prgm Trust 1975-92, Dir; Jaycees 1978-, Pres; BSA 1979-90, Bd; Towanda Area Schl Bd Dir 1987-95; Bradford Cty Vo-Tech Bd 1987-89; Whos Who Amer Ed 1994-95; *office:* Wyalusing Elem Schl RR 4 Box 8 Wyalusing PA 18853

LONG, BRUCE JOHN, Retired Guidance Counselor; *b:* Brooklyn, NY; *m:* Lisa Marino; *c:* Allie, Chelsea, Vicky DeVean, Chris, Cathy Goldbas, Bruce; *ed:* SUNY at Brockport (BS) Ed 1957; Hofstra Univ (MS) Eng Ed 1962; 45 Addl Credits Eng, Cnslr Ed; *cr:* Weeks Rd Elem Schl PE Tchr 1957-59; North Babylon Jr HS Eng Tchr 1959-67; North Babylon HS Eng Tchr 1967-85, Guid Cnslr 1985-95; *ai:* Coached Var Golf, Track; Chess, Debate, Creative Writing Club Adv; AFT; NCTE 1968-; NBTO 1957-; West Suffolk Cnslrs Assn; Babylon Lib; Honored as Fac Speaker by Class of 1983; *home:* 350 Fire Island Ave Babylon NY 11702

LONG, CAROLE KULPON, Business Teacher; *b:* York, PA; *m:* Michael C.; *c:* Gretchen; *ed:* York Coll of PA (BS) Bus Ed 1975; Penn St Univ; *cr:* Kennard-Dale HS Bus Tchr 1976-; *ai:* NEA, PSEA 1976-; Amer Shire Horse Assn 1994-; PA Draft Horse & Mule Assn, MD Draft Horse & Mule Assn 1993-.

LONG, CRAIG SHERIDAN, English Teacher; *b:* Harrisburg, PA; *m:* Wendy Lynn Orange; *c:* Derek Thomas, Christa Noel; *ed:* Grove City Coll (BA) Lit, Comm Arts 1977; IN Univ of PA (MA) Eng; *cr:* IN Area Schl Dist Eng Tchr 1977-89; Hollidaysburg Area Schl Dist Eng Tchr 1989-; *ai:* Bsktbl Coach; Weightroom Supvr; Lit Magazine Adv; *office:* Hollidaysburg Area Jr HS 501 Hart St Hollidaysburg PA 16648*

LONG, DANIEL M., Music Teacher & Band Director; *b:* East Meadows, NY; *m:* Jody E.; *c:* Crescenda, Daniel, Erika; *ed:* Wilkes Univ (BA) Music Ed 1984; Marywood Coll (MA) Music Ed 1991; *cr:* David Brearley Regnl HS Music Tchr, Band Dir 1984-86; Greene Cntrl HS Music Tchr, Band Dir 1986-88; Chenango Vly Sr HS Music Tchr, Band Dir 1988-91; Daniel Boone Jr Sr HS Music Tchr, Band Dir 1991-; *ai:* Jr-Sr HS Stage Band, Stage Crew, Marching Band, Percussion Ensemble, Jr-Sr HS Concert Band Dir; NEA, PMEA 1991-; MEBC 1991-, VP; MENC 1984-; BSA 1996, Ldr; Guest Conductor NY, PA, Amer Music Abroad in Europe 1995-; Sighted for Excl in Tchng; *office:* Daniel Boone Jr Sr HS 501 Chestnut St Birdsboro PA 19508*

LONG, DAVID M., Health & Phys Ed Teacher; *b:* Pittsburgh, PA; *m:* Christine Marie Mathews; *c:* David M., Anne E., Mary Colleen, Kelly C., Michael L., Joseph M.; *ed:* Univ of Dayton (BS) Hlth, PE 1974; 17 Credits Masters Prgm Hlth, PE, Recr Ed Univ of Pittsburgh; *cr:* St Ann's Schl K-8 Hlth, PE Tchr, Bsktbl Coach 1974-88; North Cath HS Asst Var Bsktbl Coach 1981-; Holy Spirit Schl K-8 Grd Hlth, PE Tchr, Bsktbl Coach 1988-; *ai:* Coach JV, Var Boys Bsktbl, Asst Var Boys Bsktbl Coach North Cath HS; Adv JV, Var Boys CYO Bsktbl; NEA; *office:* Holy Spirit Schl 100 Howard St Pittsburgh PA 15209

LONG, DOLORES GRAYSON, Retired 2nd Grade Teacher; *b:* New Kensington, PA; *m:* Herbert; *c:* Jonathan, Melinda Long Slaughter; *ed:* Stephens Coll (AA) Aviation 1948; Kent St Univ (BS) Ed 1971; *cr:* Belle Stone Elem Schl 2nd Grd Tchr 1972-73; Allen Elem Schl 3rd GrdTchr 1973-74; Clarendon Elem Schl 2nd Grd Tchr 1974-89; *ai:* NEA 1972-89.

LONG, DONNA JEAN, Retired English Teacher; *b:* Toledo, OH; *ed:* Univ of Toledo (BE) Scndry Ed 1964, (ME) Admin, Supervision 1979; Addl 17 Hrs; *cr:* Woodward HS Eng Tchr 1964-66; Oakdale Jr HS Lang Arts Tchr 1966-67; Scott HS Eng Tchr 1968-78; Rogers HS Eng Tchr 1978-94; *ai:* Former Youth to Youth Adv; Newspaper Adv; Dance Team Adv; Speech, Essay Contest Coord; Toledo Fed of Tchrs 1964- Retired Member; Eng Tchr Hall of Fame 1983; Rampage Fac Spirit Awd 1988; Spec Svc Awd 1983: Honored Tchr Tpg 1995.

LONG, JAMES DEWITT, German Teacher; *b:* Dayton, OH; *m:* Valerie Browne; *c:* Martha, Jamie; *ed:* Wright St Univ (BSE) Ger 1970; Post Grad Stud at Wright St Univ, Univ ov Dayton, Univ of Cincinnati Conservatory of Music & Schiller Univ in Heidelberg Germany; Portland St Univ; *cr:* Northmont Sr HS Ger Tchr 1970-; *ai:* Englewood United Meth Church Organist 1972-; AATG, OH Ed Assn & OH Mod Lang Tchrs Assn 1970-; NFSG Natl Tchr Adv Awd 1974; Northmont Jaycees Young Educator of Yr Awd 1974; Whos Who in Religion 1992-93; *office:* Northmont Sr HS 4916 National Rd Clayton OH 45315*

LONG, JAMES RICHARD, Physical Education Instructor; *b:* Pittsburg, PA; *m:* Lisa Piccione; *c:* Christopher, Gina, Tony; *ed:* OH St Univ (BS) PE 1979, (MA) Adapted PE 1980; *cr:* Upper Arlington Schls Adapted PE Instr 1980-87; Tremont Elem Schl PE Instr 1987-93; Upper Arlington Schls Adapted PE Instr 1993-94; Tremont Elem Schl PE Instr 1994-; *ai:* IM, Patrol, Jump Rope Club Supvr; Dist Safety Rep; North Cntrl Accreditation Comm; Jump Rope for Heart Coord; NEA, OEA 1980-; OAHPER & D 1980-, Adapted PE Chprsn 1983; OSU Prof Dev Schl 1990-; Ruffed Grouse Soc 1985-, Chptr Pres 1990-95; Tchr of Yr 1988; Upper Arlington Civic Assn Golden Apple Awd 1994; OH St Univ Cooperating Tchr Awd; Cntrl OH Tchrs Assoc PE Inservice Day Presenter; *home:* 4057 Ridgewood Dr Hilliard OH 43026*

LONG, JAY EDWARDS, Professor of English; *b:* Sweet Valley, PA; *m:* Mary Ruth Shoop; *c:* Brent, Brenda Santoli; *ed:* Bloomsburg Univ (BS) Bus Ed 1959, (MED) Bus Ed 1964; Temple Univ (EDD) Bus Ed 1989; Baptist Bible Coll Theological Stud; Univ of Scranton Eng Ed; *cr:* Selinsgrove Area HS Bus Ed Tchr 1959-63; Penn Manor HS Bus & Eng Tchr 1963-70; Bapt Bible Coll Asst Prof of Eng 1970-73; Mehoopany Bapt Church Pastor 1972-82; Bapt Bible Coll Prof of Eng & Bus Communication 1982-; *ai:* Fac Evaluation Comm; Curr Assessment Comm; NCTE 1982-; NBEA, EBEA 1983-; PBEA 1984-; ASCD 1985-; Delta Pi Epsilon 1986-, Historian; Comm Assn 1982-, Treas; Cert for Pub Svc From Amer Red Cross & March of Dimes; 2 Books Pub; Numerous Articles in Family Periodicals & Prof Journals; Numerous Articles for Local Newspapers; *office:* Bapt Bible Coll of PA 538 Venard Rd Clarks Summit PA 18411

LONG, JOHN SHERMAN, Music Dir & Cross Cntry Coach; *b:* Columbus, OH; *m:* Judy Ann; *c:* Jim, Jennifer; *ed:* Capital Univ (BME) Music Ed; OH St Univ (MS) Music Ed; Addl Hrs Choral Music Ashland

Univ, Ed Walsh Coll; *cr:* Pickerington HS Vocal Music Dir, Cross Cntry Coach 1974-; *ai:* Chorale; Spring Musical Asst Dir; OH Music Ed Assn 1974-, Pres 1994-, Dist VP; MENC 1974-; ACDA 1974-; NEA, OEA; Columbus Swiss Singers 1977-, Dir; Ath, Music Boosters; HS Choir Honors Natl Festivals, Disney World; *office:* Pickerington HS 300 Opportunity Way Pickerington OH 43147*

LONG, JOHN TEES,JR., Sixth Grade Math & Sci Tchr; *b:* Philadelphia, PA; *m:* Marilyn Elizabeth DiLemmo; *ed:* Grove City Coll (AB) Pol Sci 1968; Penn St Univ (MA) Scndry Ed 1989; 30 Addl Hrs; Temple Univ MA Eq Elem Ed 1974; *cr:* UPPER Dublin Twp Schl Dist Educator 1968-; *ai:* Boys Tennis Team Coach 1986-; NEA, PSEA, UDEA 1968-; *office:* Sandy Run MS 520 Twining Rd Dresher PA 19025

LONG, KATHARINE MAE (HARTEUSTINE), Math Teacher & Supervisor; *b:* Pottstown, PA; *m:* Jere D.; *c:* Matthew, Elissa; *ed:* Millersville Univ (BED) Math 1961; West Chester Univ (MED) Math 1964; *cr:* Pottstown Jr HS Math Tchr 1961-64; Pottstown HS Math Tchr, Dept Chprsn 1964-66; Warwick HS Tchr, Dept Chair 1966-67; Ephrata Jr HS Tchr, Dept Chair, Math Supvr 1970-; Ephrata MS Tchr, Dept Chair, Math Supvr 1970-; *ai:* Greenhouse Club; Tessellations Club; PCTM, EAEA 1970-; PSEA 1961-; NEA, NCTM 1965-; NCSM 1989-; IU 13 Math Consortium 1987-, Mid Schl Chprsn; Mid Schl Math Consultant Wkshp Presenter; St Mid Schl Conventions, PA Cncl Tchrs of Math Presenter, Rgnl NCTM Presenter, Elem Math Wkshps Presenter.

LONG, KENWYN JUDITH, Research Physicist; *b:* Chicago, IL; *m:* John Gelski; *c:* Kristen, Nikolett; *ed:* ND St Univ (BS) Physics 1972; Cleveland St Univ 8 Grad Credit Hrs Mechanical Engrng; *cr:* Univ of DE Tchng Asst 1974-75; IITRI-ECAC Electronics Engr 1976-80; Severn Schl Physics Instr 1980-81; NTIA-Dept of Commerce Electronics Engr 1982-86; NASA-Lewis Rsrch Ctr Rsrch Physicist 1986-; *ai:* Westlake Schls Citizen's Advy Comm; Participant Natl Engrs Week; Westlake, North Olmsted Pub Schls HS Sci, Math Tutor; Inst of Electrical, Electronics Engrs 1983-; Amer Chemical Soc 1995-; Articles Pub; NASA Group Achvmt Awds.

LONG, LARRY EUGENE, High School Principal; *b:* Lima, OH; *c:* Chris, Jenni, Cori; *ed:* Bluffton Coll (BA) Hlth, PE, Basic Bus, Typing & Bookkeeping 1972; Bowling Green St Univ (MA) Educl Admin, Supervision 1976; Wm. Howard Taft Univ Doctoral Candidate, Supt Cert 1991; *cr:* Willard HS Bus Tchr, Ath Dir, Asst Prin, Dir of Ath, Act & Attendance 1972-93; Napoleon HS 9-12 Grd Principal 1993-; *ai:* Cntrl Elem PTG, Auditing Comm; Northwest Dist Ath Bd 1994-, VP; NASSP, Past Mem; Willard Ed Assn, Past Treas; Northwest OH Ath Admins Assn & Exec Comm, Past Mem; OH HS Ath Admin Assn, Past Mem; Natl Interscholastic Ath Admins Assn, Past Mem; Northwest Dist Ath Bd 1992-, Ath Dir Rep; Willard City Cncl, Ward, At-large Rep; Assisted with Red Cross, United Fund, United Way, Amer Cancer Soc, Diabetes Fnd, Napoleon Rotary & Elks; OH Assn of Scndry Schl Admin, Act & Ath Comms; United Meth Church, Active Mem; Northwest OH Ath Admin of Yr Awd 1989; OH Ath Admin of Yr Awd 1989; Taught Summer Wkshp Admin of Ath 1992; Nom Outstdng Young Man of Yr; *office:* Napoleon HS 701 Briarheath Dr Napoleon OH 43545

LONG, LEONARD KARL, Asst Prof & Head Soccer Coach; *b:* Doylestown, PA; *m:* Maribeth Hanna; *c:* Patrick, Kathleen, Erin; *ed:* Lock Haven Univ (BS) HPER 1975; Trenton St Coll (MS) HPE 1976; 12 Grad Hrs Old Dominion Univ Recreation; 6 Grad Hrs Trenton St Coll Recreation; *cr:* VA Wesleyan Coll Head Soccer, Tennis Instr 1978-84; Lock Haven Univ Asst Prof, Head Soccer Coach 1984-; *ai:* Head Soccer Coach; Chm Dept Evaluation Comm; Various Search Comms; Natl Soccer Coaches Assn 1978-, Pres Div II, Coach of Yr 4 Times; PA Parks & Rec Assn; PA St Soccer Coaches 1984-, Pres, Coach of Yr 3 Times; Lock Haven City Parks Stud 1995-; 5-6 Major Recreation Projects; LHU Soccer Team Comm Svc Awd; *office:* Lock Haven Univ Thomas Fieldhouse Lock Haven PA 17745

LONG, MARIBETH HANNA, Assistant Professor; *b:* Lock Haven, PA; *m:* Leonard Karl; *c:* Patrick, Kathleen, Erin; *ed:* Lock Haven St Coll (BS) Scndry Ed & His 1978; Old Dominion Univ (MS) Cnslr Ed 1981; 4 Credit Hrs PA St Univ; 3 Credit Hrs Lock Haven Univ & IN Univ of PA; *cr:* VA Wesleyan Coll Acting Dean of Stdnts 1981-82, Dir of Career Dev 1982-84; Lock Haven Univ of PA Instr & Tutorial Coord 1987-89, Instr & Cnslr 1989-92, Asst Prof 1992-; *ai:* Frosh Yr Experience Comm Lock Haven Univ; Enrollment Mgmt Team Lock Haven Univ; Enrollment Mgmt Comm Lock Haven Univ; Comm Advy Bd Lock Haven Univ; Phi Delta Kappa 1987-, Pres; Amer Assn Univ Women 1988-; Natl Acad Advising Assn 1994-; Lioness Club 1990-; Lock Haven Cath Home & Schl Assn 1990-; Natl Bd Cert Cnslr 1990; Grant from Lock Haven Univ Assessment Comm to Assess Frosh Seminar 1993; *office:* Lock Haven Univ Bentley Hall Fairview St Lock Haven PA 17745

LONG, PATRICIA BURKE, French & Spanish Teacher; *b:* Drexil Hill, PA; *w:* Duane Robert (dec); *ed:* Bloomsburg Univ (BA) Fr 1983, (BS) Bus Admin Acctng 1987; Completed Scndry Ed Pgm 1986; 36 Credit Hrs Univ Paul Valerie through West Chester Univ; *cr:* Northwest Area Jr & Sr High Fr Tchr 1987-88; St Josephs HS Fr & Eng Tchr 1988-90; Newark Acad Fr Tchr 1992-93; The Albany Acad Fr & Span Tchr 1993-; *ai:* Fac Affairs Comm, Sec; Asst Comm Svc Pgm Coord; Prof Dev Comm; AATF 1993-; Cert du Francais Commercial 1984, Paris; *office:* Albany Acad 135 Academy Rd Albany NY 12208*

LONG, PETER GREGORY, Third Grade Teacher; *b:* Bethlehem, PA; *m:* Regina Ann Oswald; *c:* Dana, Rachel; *ed:* Kutztown St Coll (BED) Elem 1974, (MED) Elem 1979; *cr:* Swain Cntry Day Schl 3-6 Grd Tchr, 3-12th Grd Gym Tchr 1974-75; ASA Packer Schl 5th-6th Grd Tchr 1975; Buchanan Schl 3rd Grd Tchr 1976; Miller Heights Schl 3rd Grd Tchr 1976-; *ai:* Sci Fair Dir; Liason for Schl with Hughes BASD, Lehigh Univ Enrichment Prgm; NEA, PSEA, BEA, Schl Rep 10 Yrs; Freidens Luth Church, Cncl VP 5 Yrs, Sunday Church Schl Tchr, Chrstn Ed Dir; *office:* Miller Heights Elem Schl 3605 Allen St Bethlehem PA 18017

LONG, RAE HOLLAND, 2nd Grade Teacher; *b:* Pawtucket, RI; *m:* Donald R.; *ed:* Coll of Our Lady of the Elms (BA) Sociology 1965; RI Coll (EdM) Elem Ed 1973; *cr:* Pawtucket RI Schl Dept 1st Grd Tchr 1965-66; Fairfax Cty VA 1st Grd Tchr 1966-67; East Providence RI 1st & 2nd Grd Tchr 1967-; *ai:* Our Lady of the Elms Alumnae 1965-, Sec, Treas & St Fundraiser; NEA, NEARI & EPEA 1967-, PR&R Comm Sec; Elem Tchr of Month 1991.

LONG, RANDALL DAVID, Eighth Grade Reading Teacher; *b:* Altoona, PA; *m:* Karin Wagner; *c:* Erin; *ed:* Lock Haven Univ (BS) Elem Ed 1972; Penn St Univ (MEd) Educl Admin 1989; Prin Cert Scndry Elem 1990; *cr:* Bellwood Antis Area Sixth Grd Tchr 1972-75; Altoona Area Sixth Grd Tchr 1975-81, Eighth Grd Tchr 1982-; *ai:* Ath Dir; Co Chm Adv Comm Scndry Schls; SOS Comm; Scndry Schl Strategic Planning Comm; Pi Lambda Theta; Alpha Kappa; PSU; Outstanding Coll Stdnts of America; *home:* 5720 California Ave Altoona PA 16602*

LONG, RYAN JON, Social Studies Teacher; *b:* Bellefonte, PA; *ed:* Shippensburg Univ (BSEd) His 1991; 15 Post Grad Credit Hrs; *cr:* State Coll Area Soc Stud Tchr 1993-; *ai:* Asst Ftbl, Track & Field Coach; NEA, PSEA, SCEA 1995-; NCCS 1989-; Elk 1995-; *office:* State College Area HS 650 Westerly Pkwy State College PA 16801

LONG, SANDRA M. KUBE, Social Studies Teacher; *b:* Winston Salem, NC; *ed:* Antioch Coll (BA) Psych 1974; Lesley Coll, 45 Credit Hrs, 1993; *cr:* Boston Pub Schls Tchr 1975-; *ai:* AFT 1978-; Boston Tchrs Union 1975-; MA Civil Liberties Union 1994-, Steering Comm; Notre Dame Ed Ctr 1993-, Educl Consultant, Bd Mem; *office:* Hyde Park HS 655 Metropolitan Ave Hyde Park MA 02136*

LONG, SUSAN J., Transitional First Grd Tchr; *b:* Carlisle, PA; *m:* Robert R.; *c:* Christine, Amanda; *ed:* Shippensburg Univ (BS) Elem Ed 1968, (MA) Elem Ed 1970; 16 Addl Hrs; *cr:* Dover Area Schl Dist Third Grd Tchr 1968-69, 1975-76, First Grd Tchr 1969-71, 1976-88, T-1 Tchr 1988-; *ai:* Site Based Mngmt Team; PSEA, NEA 1968-; IRA; Eastern Star; United Church of Christ Cherub Choir Dir 1975-; Dover Schl Dist Grant; First Capital Compact Grant.

LONG, SUSIE HUNTER, Mathematics Teacher; *b:* Bridgeport, CT; *m:* Robert T.; *c:* Robert T., Robin M., Kevin J.; *ed:* Southern CT St Univ (BS) Scndry Ed 1963; Univ of Bridgeport (MS) Ed 1974; Mentor & Cooperating Tchr Trng 1988; DEI 1990; *cr:* Wooster Jr HS Math Tchr 1963-65; Albert Leonard Jr HS Math Tchr 1965-68; Wooster Jr HS Math Tchr 1971-81; Stratford HS Math Tchr 1981-, Mentor 1994-; *ai:* Math Advancement Club Adv; Multicultural Comm; Math Dept Asst Chprsn; SEA, CEA & NEA 1971-; NCTM & ATOMIC 1989-; NAACP 1981-; *office:* Stratford H S 45 N Parade Ave Stratford CT 06497*

LONG, VERYL DEWEY,SR., Health & Phys Ed Teacher; *b:* Washington, PA; *m:* Shirley M.; *c:* Veryl Jr., Lee, Bryan; *ed:* IA St Univ (BA) Hlth & PE 1966; Penn St Univ (MS) Ed 1973; *cr:* Jersey City YMCA PE Dir 2 1/2 Yrs; Ferris HS Tchr 1 1/2 Yrs; Pittsburgh Pub Schl Tchr 26 Yrs; *ai:* Wrestling Coach; USAF Reserves; PIAA-PA Wrestling Ofcl; AFT Tchr Union, Pittsburgh Fed Union 1970-; NCAA Natl Wrestling Champion 1965; PA St Wrestling Coaches Hall of Fame 1987; Pittsburgh City Wrestling Champion 1990; *office:* Carrick HS 125 Parkfield St Pittsburgh PA 15210

LONGENECKER, CHARLES BRUBAKER, High School Biology Teacher; *b:* Manheim, PA; *m:* Barbara Rutt; *c:* Jo Ann, Fred, Kenton, Lynn; *ed:* Cornell Univ (MS) Bio 1960; Attnd IN Univ, Millersville Univ; *cr:* Lancaster Mennonite HS Bio Tchr 1958-63; Eastern Mennonite Coll Asst Prif of Bio 1963-64; Lancaster Mennonite HS Bio Tchr 1964-; *home:* 730 Maple Grove Rd New Holland PA 17557*

LONGENECKER, DENNIS LEE, HS Mathematics Teacher; *b:* Lancaster, PA; *m:* Anita Louise Gurney; *c:* Maia Autumn, Molly Mae; *ed:* PA St Univ (BS) Mineral Ec 1971; Univ of Scranton (MS) Scndry Ed & Math Emphasis 1992; Millersville Univ Scndry Ed Math Tchng Cert 1976; Supervisory Cert in Math 1992; *cr:* Malibu Educl Inst Math & Sci Tchr 1971-74; East Stroudsburg HS Math Tchr 1976-86; Honesdale HS Math Tchr 1986-; *ai:* Field Hockey Head Coach; Scholastic Bowl Adv; LCCC Adult Ed Tchr; NEA 1974-; PSEA 1974-; NCTM 1976-; Jr Miss Sftbl 1987-, Coach; *office:* Honesdale HS 459 Terrace St Honesdale PA 18431

LONGMORE, PAULETTE, English Professor; *b:* Jamaica, West India; *m:* Edward; *c:* Karja, Kamilyn; *ed:* Setan Hall Univ (MA) Scndry Ed 1992; Univ of West Indies (BA) Modern Langs 1995; 15 Addl Hrs; Church Tchrs Coll Lang, Lit Diploma 1980; *cr:* St Elizabeth Tech HS Eng, Span Tchr 1980-86; Essex Cty Coll Eng Tchr 1990-91; Hazel Ave Schl Biling Ed Tchr 1991-92; Essex Cty Coll Eng Instr 1992-; *ai:* Essex Cty Dept of Hum Tutoring Liaisoin; Cir K Club Adv; Renaisance Project Cntrl HS Mentor; Hospitality Comm Co-Chair; Testing, Schlsp, Stu Reconit & Retention, Curr Comms; Kappa Delta Pi Xi Gamma 1992-; NJ Coll Eng Assn 1994-; Essex Cty Coll Fac Assn 1992-; 1st Church of Newark 1987-, Asst Church Clerk, Guest Sec, Pub Relations Consulted, Voc Bible Sch, Asst Youth Ldr; Seton Hall Univ Biling Flwshp 1990-92; UWI John Mills Schlsp 1982-85; Church Tchrs Coll Tchr of Yr 1980; Church Tchrs Coll Best Math, Rdng, Span Tchr 1980; *office:* Essex County Coll 303 University Ave Newark NJ 07102*

LONGNECKER, JAMES EDWARD, Physical Education Professor; *b:* Dayton, OH; *m:* Jean V.; *c:* Barbara Jean, Beth Lynn, Karen Jill Lapcevie, Kelly Susan; *ed:* Bowling Green St Univ (BS) Hlth, PE, Rec 1954; Miami Univ (MED) Ed 1957; *cr:* Miami Univ Var, Asst Frosh Swimming Coach 1956-57; Grove City Coll PE Prof 1957-; *ai:* Swimming, Diving, Track & Field Coach; Dir Blue Dolphin Swim Camp; Coll Swimming Coaches of Amer 1957-, Master Coach Awd 1977, Distngd Coach Awd 1987, 40 Yr Awd 1997; Tower Church, Deacon, Clerk of Session, Elder, Trustee; PAC Conf 17 Coach of Yr Awds Swimming, Track; Distngd Coaching Awd Bowling Green St Univ; *home:* 612 Ridgeway Ave Grove City PA 16127

LONGNECKER, RANDY LEWIS, Social Studies Teacher; *b:* Hagerstown, MD; *m:* Laurel Stephens; *c:* Stephen J.; *ed:* Hagerstown Jr Coll (AA) Ed 1988; Shippensburg Univ 9BA) Psych, Soc Stud 1990; 12 Credits Towards MA Guid, Cnslng Frostburg St Univ; *cr:* Wayensboro Sr HS Soc Stud Tchr 1992-; *ai:* Head 9th Grd Ftbl Coach; Ath Hall of Hnr Comm; Gideon Intnl 1995-; Grace Brethren Church 1975-, Tchr; Outstdng Stu Tchr Nom 1990; Outstdng Airman of Month 1980-81; *office:* Waynesboro Area Sr H S 550 E 2nd St Waynesboro PA 17268*

LONGO, DEREK DANIEL, American Studies Teacher; *b:* Endicott, NY; *m:* Constance M. Roscoe; *c:* Megan E., Derek J.; *ed:* Bloomsburg Univ (BS) Soc Sci 1973; 60 Grad Hrs; *cr:* Council Rock HS His & Soc Sci Tchr, Pgm for Acad Gifted & Talented 1973-; *ai:* PA Free Interprise Club Adv; Natl Cncl of His in Ed 1990-; Golden Apple Awd by Fellow Tchrs; Designed Several Class Simulation Act; *office:* Council Rock HS 62 Swamp Rd Newtown PA 18940*

LONGO, MARY TASSIELLI, Fourth Grade Teacher; *b:* Newark, NJ; *m:* Donald; *c:* Donald Jr., Joanne Longo Fagan, Peter, MaryJean; *ed:* Coll of St Elizabeth (BA) Fr & Span 1951; Newark St Coll Elem Cert 1952; Montreal Univ Grad Stud Fr; *cr:* Belleville Schl System 4th Grd Tchr 1951-55, Kndgtn Tchr 1956, 4th Grd Tchr 1956-58, 6th Grd Tchr 1958-60; Long Hill Twp Schl System 3rd & 4th Grd Tchr 1960-; *ai:* All Schl Cncl Chprsn; NJEA 1951-; NEA 1951-; Long Hill Twp Tchrs Assn 1960-, VP; Outstdng Tchrs of Amer 1972; NJ Governors Outstdng Tchr Awd 1987-88; *home:* 13 Ellers Dr Chatham NJ 07928*

LONGO, PATRICIA M., Physical Education Teacher; *b:* Bayonne, NJ; *ed:* Kean Coll of NJ (BA) Hlth, PE 1973; Jersey City St Coll (MA) Admin, Supervision 1988; Driver Ed Cert 1979; Admin, Supervision Cert 1988; Kean Coll of NJ 8 Credit Hrs; *cr:* Bayonne Bd of Ed PE Tchr 1973-; St Aloyious HS Driver Ed Tchr 1983087; Holy Family Acad Summer Schl PE Tchr 1988-; *ai:* Kean Coll of NJ Asst Sftbl Coach 1973-77, Asst Bsktbl Coach 1974-77; St Peter's Coll Head Sftbl Coach 1977-84; Holy Family Acad Head Bsktbl Coach 1977-; Head Girls Vlybl Coach 1984-, Head Boys Vlybl Coach 1989-; C. J. Murphy Jr Girls Bsktbl League Prgm Dir 1990-; Bob Hurley's Bsktbl Camp Girls Section Dir 1990-; Outstdng Female Aths Org, Started 1995-; NJ Ed Assn, Bayonne Tchrs Assn 1973-; NJSIAA, Bsktbl Ofcl 1972-84, Examiner; NJSIAA, Vlybl Ofcl1994-; Hudson Cty Vlybl Coaches Assn, Treas 1985-; NJ Interscho lastic Coaches Assn, Active Mem 1994-; NJSIAA NJ St Interscholastic Ath Assn; North NJ Cath Girls Bsktbl League 1977-85, Treas; New Spirit of Bayonne 1994-; Outstdng Coll Aths of Amer 1973; NJ Interscholastic Coaches Assn, Hall of Fame Inducted 1990; Holy Family Acad Attained 300 Career wins as Bsktbl Coach 1994; Bayonne Bd of Ed Resolution for Coaching 1990; Named Bsktbl Coach of Yr 1985-89; *office:* Bayonne HS 669 Avenue A House 1 Bayonne NJ 07002

LONGO, VITO ANTHONY, French Teacher; *b:* Aliquippa, PA; *ed:* Geneva Coll (BS) Fr, Math 1958; Millersville St (MA) Fr 1971; Attnd Bucknell Univ, OH St Univ, Institut Natl Des Scis Appliquees Lyon France; *cr:* Hopewell Area Schl Dist Tchr, Dept Chair 1958-; *ai:* NEA, PSEA, HEA 1958-, Pres, V Pres, Treas; PSMLA, MLA; AATF, ACTFL; BC Pres; Lions Club, King Lion; MPIC; Sons of Columbus Lib Ethnic NDEA Grants 1964, 1966; 1 of PA's 10 Most Outstanding Tchrs Outstanding Scndry Educator 1975; Thanks to Tchrs Nom 1991-92; 1021 Duke St Aliquippa PA 15001*

LONGSTRETH, DEBORA CAROL, English Teacher; *b:* Wayne PA; *m:* Jerry; *c:* Scott, Nathan; *ed:* Washington Jefferson Coll (BA Psych 1990; Credit Hrs Intermediate Unit; *cr:* Waynesburg Cntrl H Tchr 1990-; *ai:* Frosh, Jr Class Adv; Prom Adv; NEA, PSEA 1990- 1985-, Cnslr for Merit Badges 1992; North Ten Mile Church 1978-, Tchr, Bd Mem; *office:* Waynesburg Central HS RR 2 Box 39 Wayne PA 15370*

LONGSWORTH, ELLEN LOUISE, Art History Prof & Dept Chr Auburn, IN; *m:* Joseph Nicholas Teta; *ed:* Mount Holyoke Coll (BA His, Studio 1971; Univ of Chicago (MA) Art His, Italian Renais 1976; Boston Univ (PHD) Art His, Italian Renaissance 1987; Amherst Coll 1969-70, John Herron Art Inst 1969; *cr:* Bradford Col Art Adj Prof 1975-80; Univ of Lowell Art His Adj Prof 1981-82; B Univ Art, Art His Visiting Lecturer 1982-83, 1984-85, 1988, 1991; B Copll Art His Adj Prof 1984-85; Merrimack Coll Asst Prof 1985-90; Prof 1990-95; Art His Prof 1995-, Art His Dept Chair 1993-; *ai:* Appeals Comms; Colleague Promotion Advocate; AAUW 1993-; Art Soc 1987-; Renaissnace Soc of Amer 1993-, Session Chair Renaissance Sculpture Symposium 1988-; Winnekenni Fnd Inc Mbrshp Comm Chair 1991-92; Isabella Stewart Gardner Mu Internship 1979-80;; Boston Univ Grad Assistantship, Samuel H. Rsrch Grant 1980, 1986, Tchng Flwshps 1980-82, 1985; Grad Dissertation Schlsp 1987; Merrimack Coll Fac Dev Grants 19 1992-93, 1995; Boston Univ Appreciation Cert 1991; Who's Who of Women; Articles Pub; *office:* Merrimack Coll Turnpike Rd North An MA 01845

LONGWARE, ALTA JO, Technology Teacher; *b:* Elizabethtown, N Erie Comm Coll (AAS) Mngmt Engrng 1979; St Univ at Buffalo Indstrl Tech 1982; St Univ At Plattsburgh (MS) Instruction, Curr NYS Tchng Cert 1990; *cr:* Fisher Price Toys Indstrl Engrng 1979-8 Sport Products Production Supvr 1982-86; Denton Publica Composition Supvr 1986-89; AuSable Vly Schl Tech Tchr 1991 Patriot Yrbk Consultant; Staff Dev, Shared Decision Making Comm; Tech Edctrs 1991-; NYS Tech Edctrs 1990-; AARCH 1992-, Elizabet Zoning, Rediscover Elizabethtown 1996; Eisenhower Excl in Tchng NYSEG Energy Grant; *office:* Ausable Vly Mid HS 1490 R Clintonville NY 12924

LONGWORTH, PATRICIA ENFIELD, 6th Grade Teacher; *b:* Angeles, CA; *m:* Robert J.; *c:* Eric Brown, Tad Brown; *ed:* San Jose St (BA) Ed 1963; Antioch New England (MED) Ed 1988; Course W Keene St Coll, Lesley Coll, Plymouth St, Notre Dame Coll & Fr Pierce; *cr:* Alhambra Cty Schls 6th Grd & Kndgtn Tchr 1963-67; L Beach Schl Dist Created Gifted & Talented Pgm 1974-78; Mont V Coop Kndgtn Tchr 1978-82; North River Schl 3rd & 5th Grd Tchr 19 Conval Schl Dist Gifted Pgm Tchr & 6th Grd Tchr 1986-; *ai:* CVEA Schl Fund Raising & Back to Schl Night Comms; NEA 1963-; NH Assn 1986-; Conval Tchrs Assn 1986-; Amherst Outting Club 197 Mem; Amherst Bapt Church 1985-, Comm Chprsn; *home:* 17 Ravi Amherst NH 03031

LONSERT, LORI MAZZONE, Head Girls Cross Country Coac Dayton, OH; *m:* Mark D.; *c:* Patrick, Reece, Joseph; *ed:* Miami Univ PE, Math 1979; Univ of Dayton (MA) Cnslng 1990; *cr:* Watts MS Tchr 1981-83; Centerville HS Math Tchr 1983-87, Asst Girls Track C 1983-, Head Girls Cross Cntry Coach 1987-; *ai:* Girls Head Cross C Asst Track Coach; *office:* Centerville HS 500 E Franklin St Centervill 45459

LOOMIS, DONALD AUSTIN, Business Professor; *b:* Greenville, P Peggy Joyce Bollard; *c:* Melanie Loomis Alston, Kevin D.; *ed:* Thie (BS) Bus Ed-Cum Laude 1960; Kent St Univ (MS) Bus 1968; *cr:* Win Exempted Village Schls HS Tchr 1960-67; Kent St Univ Grad Tchng 1967-68; Butler Cty Comm Coll Bus Prof 1968-; *ai:* Mid Sts Accredi Comm; NEA & PSEA 1994-; Meth Church, Mission Work, Disaster R Team; Butler Cty Comm Coll Outstdng Fac Mem 1993; Butler Chamb Commerce Outstdng Coll Tchr 1994; Butler Cty Comm Coll Outstdn Adv 1995; Article Pub; *office:* Butler County Comm Coll Oak Campus Butler PA 16001

LOOMIS, JEFFREY PAUL, Vice Principal & Math Teacher; *b:* Al NY; *m:* Elizabeth Ann Daniels; *ed:* Siena Coll (BA) Math 1990; *cr:* James Inst Tchr, Coach 1989-90; Saint Gregory's Schl Upper Schl Tchr, Coach 1991-94; La Salle Inst Vice Prin, Tchr 1994-; *ai:* IA 1987-; *office:* La Salle Inst 174 Williams Rd Troy NY 12180*

LOONAM, JOHN P., English & Humanities Teacher; *b:* New York, *m:* Maria A. Mottola; *c:* John J., Joseph P.; *ed:* SUNY at Albany (BA Sci, Eng 1980; City Coll CUNY (MA) Creative Writing 1987; Nineteen Credits Beyong Masters Pursuing PHD Eng; *cr:* A. P. Rand HS Eng Tchr 1984-87; Westside Alternative HS Eng Tchr, Core 1987-92; Hum HS Eng Tchr 1992-; *ai:* Debate Team Coach; Re Portfolio Comm; Fiction & Non-Fiction Pub; *office:* Bayard Rustin H Hum 351 W 18th St New York NY 10011

LOONEY, KATHLEEN MC CARTHY, English Teacher; *b:* Broc MA; *m:* Robert E. Jr.; *c:* Christopher, Brendan; *ed:* Univ of MA at Am (BA) Eng 1967; *cr:* Rockland HS Eng Tchr 1967-; *ai:* NEA, MTA, 1967-; *office:* Rockland HS Mac Kinlay Way Rockland MA 02370

LOOSEMORE, MARIE KATHLEEN, Mathematics Teacher; *b:* Mil MA; *m:* William J.; *c:* Mary-Sarah Stuart; *ed:* Worcester St Coll Math, Ed 1970, (MED) Counseling 1989; Worcester Polytechnic Graphing Calculators 1993; *cr:* Westboro Jr HS Math Tchr 197 Auburn HS Math Tchr 1984-; *ai:* Stdnts for the Environment Adv; N AEA; NCTM; Chamber of Commerce Excl in Ed Awd; *office:* Auburn 99 Auburn St Auburn MA 01501

LOPES, JOHN F., Retired Teacher; *b:* Honolulu, HI; *m:* Janet Momit Johnnye L. Tamaru, Jamie L. Folk, Jeffrey; *ed:* Univ of HI (BA) Ele 1954; One Semester of 5th Yr Completed; *ai:* Montgomery Cty Ed A NEA 1979-; *home:* 812 Kenbrook Dr Silver Spring MD 20902

LOPES, KATHLEEN M., Mathematics Teacher; *b:* Proctor, VT Raymond E.; *ed:* Castleton St Coll (BS) Bus Ed 1974; 44 Grad Credi in Tech, Math & Bus; *cr:* Rutland Area Voc-Tech Ctr Clerical Occupa Instr 1974-77; Chittenden Bank Branch Mgr 1977-83; Rutland HS Tchr 1983-; *ai:* Chm Attendance Comm; Cooperating Tchr for Stu NEA, NCTM 1986-; Church Cncl 1990-, Sec; Chm NEASC, PSA Ste Comm; Chm Schlrsp Comm; Rutland Region 20,20; Rutland Pub S Mission Statement; CCD Tchr; *office:* Rutland HS 22 Stratton Rd Rut VT 05701*

LOPES, PATRICIA AIRES, Spanish Teacher; *b:* Danbury, CT; *m:* Jo Dion; *ed:* Western CT St Univ (BS) Span 1971; Southern CT St Univ (Span Lit 1983; *cr:* New Fairfield HS Tchr 1971-; *ai:* Class Adv 1979, 1 1993; Prins Advy, Attendance Comms; NEASAC Sterring Co Danbury-Gouveia Sister Cty Prgm; COLT 1992-; AATSP 1994-; Son Portugal Schlsp Comm 1991-, VP, Pres; *office:* New Fairfield HS Gillotti Rd New Fairfield CT 06812*

ES, PATRICIA RUFOLO, Social Studies Teacher; *b:* Newark, NJ; *w:* ony (dec); *c:* Tricia Ann; *ed:* Jersey City St Coll (BA) Elem Ed 1964; nn Street Schl 7th Grd Tchr 7 Yrs, 8th Grd Tchr 20 Yrs, 8th Grd Lang Tchr 1 Yr; 8th Grd Soc Stud Tchr 3 Yrs; *ai:* Tchr Adv Schl Biling paper; in Charge of NIE Prgm; Optimist Club Chair; AFT 1971-; : 26 Webster Ave Kearny NJ 07032

ES, RAYMOND EDWARD, Science Teacher; *b:* Springfield, MA; *m:* een Mary Sule; *ed:* Western New England Coll (BS) Chem 1978; 44 Credits Ed, Cmptr, Sci; *cr:* Longmeadow HS Sci Tchr 1979-80; nd HS Sci Tchr 1980-; *ai:* Attendance, Eisenhower, Selection, Stu, p Comms; NHS; NEA 1981-; NSTA 1983-; *office:* Rutland HS 22 on Rd Rutland VT 05701*

ES, REGINA MARIA, Retired Music Teacher & Dir; *b:* West ham, MA; *ed:* Boston U (BM) Music Ed 1956; U of Rochester (MM) : Ed 1963; U of IL Schl of Music EDD Candicate Music Ed; His, sophy, Psych Bridgewater Coll; *cr:* New Lebanon Pub Schls Music 1956-61; Fair Lawn HS Choral, Musicals Dir 1961-64; Norton Pub Music Tchr 1964-67, Bridgewater Coll Lecturer 1966; Fitchburg Coll c, Master Tchr Trng Sch 1967-68; Norton Pub Schls Music Tchr, r 1968-70; Ashland Schls Music Tchr, Musicals Dir 19790-91; *ai:* 1956-; MTA 1965-; AEA 1970-91; MENC 1956-91; Mu Phi Epsilon -; AARP 1991-; Arts Assn 1980-, Founder, Bd Sec; Pianist on ɔean Concert tours 1968-73; Accompanist for Mem Vienna Orch; St of Yr Nom; *home:* 85 Middleboro Rd East Freetown MA 02717

EZ, BONNIE J., Fourth Grade Teacher; *b:* Walton, NY; *m:* Hernan *d:* Roberts Wesleyan Col (BA) Eng 1971; Edinboro Univ Elem Cert Cmptr Ed ITEC 6 Cr Hrs; Elem Ed Conf 1 Cr Hr; *cr:* Pleasant Elem Fourth Grd Tchr 1971-; *ai:* Jr Amer Red Cross; Amer Heart Assoc; , PSEA, WCEA 1978-; Coll Club 1972-; Assn for Retarded Citizens 991; *home:* 120 N Parker St Warren PA 16365

EZ, ELBA I., Bilingual Spec Ed Teacher; *b:* Fajardo, Puerto Rico; *c:* za, Rafael, Christian; *ed:* Univ of PR (BA) PE 1979; Inter Amer Univ Spec Ed-Magna Cum Laude 1992; 6 Credit Hrs Gaining & taining Stu Cooperation, Succeeding With Difficult Stdnts; *cr:* PR of Ed PE & Spec Ed Tchr 1979-91; Cleveland Bd of Ed Spec Ed Tchr -; *ai:* Girls Sftbl Team & Little League Coach; Liga Atletica Policiaca; 1991-; Phi Delta Kappa 1989-, Sec; Little League of Fajardo 1986-, h of Yr Awd; Walking Club 1991-, Pres; Cert of Excl in Developing, uating & Involving Parents in the IEP Process 1995; PR Tchr of Yr ; *home:* 1514 Winchester Ave Lakewood OH 44107*

EZ, LYNN BRILLI, Kindergarten Teacher; *b:* Brooklyn, NY; *c:* , Rhiana, Marisa; *ed:* SUNY at Oneonta (BA) Elem Ed 1970; SUNY onybrook (MA) Ed 1975; *cr:* Lynwood Ave Schl 1st Grd Tchr 1970-90, gtn Tchr 1990-; *ai:* NYSUT, AFL-CIO 1970-; *office:* Lynwood Avenue Schl 50 Linwood Ave Farmingdale NY 11738

EZ, MARIANNE O'KEEFE, Sixth Grade Teacher; *b:* Sandusky, OH; illiam Timothy, Daniel (dec), Richard, Dawn Marie; *ed:* D'Youville (BS) Elem Ed 1986; Buffalo St Tchrs Coll (MS) Ed, Rdg 1992; erative Learning Instr, Trainer Coll of St Rose at Albany 1987-; *cr:* esan Schls Tchr 1952-55; #37, 73, 67, 29, 33 Southside Elem Schls Temporary Assignments Tchrs 1976-85; Buffalo Pub Schls Various ions 1956-69; Southside Elem Schl 6 Grd Tchr 1986-; *ai:* Site Based mt Team Chm; Richmond Speaking Rdng Den Coopera; Soc Stud m; BTF 1955-, Bldg Comm; NEA 1955-; IRA 1993-, Rdg onstration, convention; Socl Stud WNY Mbrshp, Presenter; Hockey ı, Clarence Girls Natl Champion, Coach, Mgr; PTA 1977-82, Schl 29 South Buffalo Advy Comm, Co-Chm, Founder; South Buffalo Comm Bd Mem; Hockey, Bsbl, Ftbl, Bsktbl 1955-78, Servicing Children & ts Sport Teams, Placques; 2 Grants Acad Achvmt D'Youville Coll; as List Pub Sr Achvmt 1986; Buffalo Tchr of Yr Awd 1992; *home:* 24 aria St Buffalo NY 14220

EZ, PHYLLIS RUNDIO, Seventh Grade Teacher; *b:* Atlantic City, *n:* Rafael Lopez; *c:* Andrew; *ed:* Stockton St Coll (BA) His & Ed 1983; :h & Early Chldhd Cert; Elem Cert; 7-12 Soc Stud Cert; 3 Post Grad its Rowan Coll; *cr:* Holy Spirit HS 9th-12th Grd Tchr 1984; Saint ent de Paul 7th & 8th Grd Tchr 1984-89; Weymouth Twp Elem Schl 8th Grd Tchr 1989-; *ai:* CORE & SAC Team; NEA, NPRC 1989-; Tchr eography Awd 1991; *office:* Weymouth Twp Elem Schl PO Box 231 othy NJ 08317

EZ, SANDY MANCUSO, HS Physical Education Teacher; *b:* gston, NY; *m:* William A.; *ed:* SUNY at Cortland (BA) PE 1981; SUNY ew Paltz (MS) Ed 1986; *cr:* Kingston HS PE Tchr 1982-; *ai:* Girls Var bl Coach; AVCA 1993-; Coach of Yr 1986, 1989, 1992 & 1995; *office:* gston HS 403 Broadway Kingston NY 12401

EZ, TERESITA (MARTINEZ), Spanish Teacher; *b:* Havana, Cuba; scar; *c:* David, Teresita; *ed:* Bernard M. Barsch Coll (BA) Span, Ed ; NY Univ (MA) Span, Latin Amer Lit 1992; 20 Credits US Intl Univ; redits Cert Glassboro St Coll; 3 Credits St Peter's Coll; *cr:* Alcoholics nymous Span Translator 1977-78; Irving Trust Co Intl Dept Adm Asst 9-81; Oak Knoll MS Span Tchr 1989-90; WiliamstownHS Span Tchr 9-90; Cher ry Hill HS West Span Tchr 1991-; Columbia Univ, Columbia olastic Press Assoc Judge 1994-; AP Eeader ETS, Span Tchr 1993-; *ai:* C-Frgn Lang, Mjulticultural Comms; Adv Span Honor Soc, Visions ; NEA 1991-; AATSPNJ 1991-, Pres, Natl Span Exam Coord VP; NJ 1991-, Flenjawd 1995 Outstdng Contribution to FL Ed; *office:* ry Hill HS West Chapel Ave Cherry Hill NJ 08002

EZ-ESPINA, GIL J., Visual Art & Photography Instr; *b:* Artemisa, a; *ed:* Jersey City St Coll (BFA) Fine Arts 1972; *cr:* Bloomfield MS al Art Tchr 1975-76; Bloomfield HS Visual Art Tchr 1972-75, Visual Photography Tchr 1977-; *ai:* Chess Club Team Adv 1972-; NEA 1972-; side Cultural Ctr 1982-89, Trustee; 200 Minor Awds Art, Photography , Intnl Levels; Articles, Photographs, Paintings Pub; *office:* Bloomfield 160 Broad St Bloomfield NJ 07003

PRESTI, CATHERINE, Allied Health Instructor; *b:* Johnstown, PA; Duquesne Univ (BS) Nrsng 1973; IN Univ of PA (MS) Nrsng Sci 1987; cy Hosp Schl of Nrsng Diploma RN Nrsng 1964; Voc Certs Level I & 994; *cr:* Case Western Univ Clinical Rsrch RN 1965-67; St Anns Hosp nt ICU Head Nurse 1967-69; Lee Hosp Med-Surgical Nrsng RN 9-70; Pgh Mercy Med-Surgical Nrsng RN 1970-73; Farmingham Union of Nrsng Med Surgical Instr 1973-75; Mercy Hosp Ed Dir 1977-90; nstown Sr High Wrote & Implemented Allied Hlth Pgm 1990-; *ai:* NEA -; Amer Heart Assn 1978-, Affiliate Fac CPR; Wrote Pgm Guidelines Allied Hlth Sci Tech for St of PA Dept of Ed; Mercy Hosp Wellness ; *office:* Greater Johnstown Sr HS 222 Central Ave Johnstown PA 02*

PRESTI, MARILYN WARCHOL, English Teacher; *b:* Hackensack, *m:* Charles; *c:* Adam, Kevin; *ed:* Seton Hall Univ (BS) Scndry Ed, Eng 3; Kean Coll (MA) Lbrl Stud 1979; *cr:* Lodi HS Eng Tchr 1973-; *ai:* Advy Comm; NHS Adv; Hnrs Fac; NEA, NJEA, BCEA 1973-; LEA 3-, Sec; Maywood Yth Ath Assn 1985-; Governor's Tchr Awd 1992; ntoring 1995-; *office:* Lodi HS 99 Putnam St Lodi NJ 07644

PRESTO, CHARLES THOMAS, Associate Professor of Psych; *b:* imore, MD; *m:* Colleen Larkin; *c:* C. Patrick, Kevin; *ed:* La Salle Univ) Bio 1969; Loyola Coll (MA) Psych 1982; Howard Univ (PHD) Psych 7; Licensed in Clinical Psych St of MD 1989; *cr:* Calvert Hall Coll HS Chair & Sci Dept 1969-80; Loyola Coll Assoc Prof of Psych 1986-; *ai:* Mulicultural Affairs & Whos Who Among Amer Coll Stdnts Selection Comm; Mens Weekend Retreat Coord; Amer Psych Assn 1987-; Balto Psych Assn 1987-; AAUP 1992-; SIECUS 1995-; Advy Bd Calvert Hall Coll HS 1990-; Order of the Sons of Italy 1993-; Distngd Tchr of the Yr Awd 1992; 6 Articles Pub; *office:* Loyola Coll IN MD 4501 N Charles St Baltimore MD 21210*

LORCH, LISA STOTT, Sixth Grade Teacher; *b:* Erie, PA; *m:* David C.; *c:* Zachary D.; *ed:* Cedar Crest Coll (BA) Psych, Ed 1980; Southern CT St Univ (MS) Spec Ed 1983; *cr:* Deverux Glenholme Schl Tchr 1980-83; R.F.K. Lancaster Schl Tchr 1983-86; ILES 6th Grd Tchr 1986-; *office:* Inter-Lakes Elem Schl 21 Laker Ln Meredith NH 03253

LORCHAK, JOHN JOSEPH, AP American Government Teacher; *b:* Coaldale, PA; *ed:* Kutztown Univ (BS) Scndry Ed 1992, (MS) Ed, Scndry Ed Soc Stud 1995; *cr:* Mehlenberg Sr HS AP Amer Govt 1994-; *ai:* Jr HS Ftbl, Wrestling, Bsbl Coach; NEA, MEA 1994-; Lit Cncl 1993-; *office:* Muhlenberg Sr HS Sharp Ave & Frances St Laureldale PA 19605

LORD, ANNA COUGHLIN, First Grade Teacher; *b:* Rockland, ME; *m:* Roger G.; *c:* Andrew, Jennifer L. Frazer, Gregory, Karen; *ed:* Univ of ME at Machias (BS) Ed 1963; *cr:* Vernon Elem Schl 1st Grd Tchr 1963-66, 2nd Grd Tchr 1967; St Bernard Schl Title I Tcher 1974, 1st Grd Tchr 1974-; *ai:* NCEA 1974-; Tolland Soccer Club 1976-, Sec 1980-84, Svc Awd 1982; Schl Bd of Ed 1976-80, Tchr Rep; Spec Olympic Vol 1986-87.

LORD, JOHN R., English Supervisor & Teacher; *b:* Newark, NJ; *m:* Loretta Sheila; *c:* Jeffrey, Michael, Holly Dunn; *ed:* Montclair St Coll (BA) Eng 1965, (MA) Eng 1969; Jersey City St Coll Supvr's Cert; Kean Coll of NJ Prin's Cert; Georgian Court Coll; *cr:* Manasquan HS 9-12th Grd Eng Tchr 1965-67; Ocean Twp HS at Oakhurst 9-12 Grd Eng Tchr 1967-80; Twp of Ocean Intermediate Schl 8th Grd Eng Tchr 1980-85; Keyport Pub Schls K-12 Grd Eng Supvr 1986-89; TWP of Ocean Pub Schls 7-12 Grd Eng Supvr 1989-; *ai:* NJPSA 1986-; NCTE 1965-; Elks 1989-, Sec 1992-93; *home:* 10 Devon Ct Ocean NJ 07712

LORD, N. JANE, English Teacher; *b:* Gloucester, MA; *m:* David John Corbett; *c:* Amy Paige; *ed:* Univ of NH (BA) Fr 1969, (MST) Eng 1976; 30 Post Grad Credit Eng & Ed; *cr:* Parkside Jr HS Fr & Eng Tchr 1971-82; Cntrl HS Eng Tchr 1982-; *ai:* NEA 1971-; NCTE 1995-; Manchester Literacy Portfolio Project Mem; UNH Rsrch Project 1993; *office:* Central HS 207 Lowell St Manchester NH 03104

LORD, RICHARD NEWELL,JR., Biology Teacher; *b:* Ft Fairfield, ME; *m:* Marcia E. Valliere; *c:* Andrew; *ed:* Univ of ME (BS) Bacteriology 1965, (MED) Scndry Life Sci 1971; Univ of Southern ME Human Genetics Inst 1981, Immunology Inst 1990; Cold Spring Harbor Lab DNA Sci Inst 1989; Infectious Diseases, Montanta St Univ 1995; *cr:* Presque Isle HS Chem Tchr 1965-66, Bio Tchr 1966-; *ai:* NHS Adv; Curr Advy Comm; NEA, ME Ed Assn 1965-; NABT 1965-, Outstanding Bio Tchr ME 1975, 1994; NSTA 1970-, Gustav Ohaus Awd; ME Sci Tchrs Assn 1980-; Assn of Presidential Awardees in Sci Tchng 1986-; Bethany Bapt Church 1980-94, Bd of Dir, Pres, VP; Outstanding Hi-Y Adv; Friend of Yth Awd Hi-Y; Presidential Awd for Excl in Sci Tchng 1986; First Pl A&E Network Natl Tchr Grant Competition 1991; Crystal Apple Awd Timer Warner Cable 1993-95; Discovery Ntwk Tchr Recognition Awd 1995; Tandy Tech Scholar 1995; *office:* Presque Isle HS 16 Fort St Presque Isle ME 04769*

LORENZ, IRMA VELA, ESL Teacher & Coordinator; *b:* Brooklyn, NY; *m:* Herbert J.; *c:* Diane Louise, Eric Herbert; *ed:* Trenton St Coll (BA) Elem 1963, (MED) Urban Ed 1976; 40 Post Grad Credits; *cr:* Burlington Co Spec Svcs Migrant Ed, Cty Coord 1976-79; Burlington Cty Coll Fin Aid Cnslr 1979-81; Burlington Twp Schls Second Grd Tchr 1981-84, ESL Tchr 1984-; *ai:* Multicultural Acts Coord; Young Schl Co-Chair Statewide Advy Bd Biling, ESL Ed; Delta Kappa Gamma 1990-; Kappa Delta Pi 1980-; Burl Twp Ed Assn 1964-, VP, Pres 1993-; NJ TESOLIBE 1986-, Pres 1995-; ABCO Fed Credit Union 1970-, Pres Bd of Dirs 1995-; South Jersey Track & Field Assn 1988-, Sec 1992-; Burlington Twp Tchr of Yr Young Schl 1986; NJ Dept of Ed Exemplary Prgm Awd 1987; Sensitivity Comm Mem Statewide Testing Prgm; *office:* Burlington Township HS PO Box 428 Burlington NJ 08016*

LORENZ, JUDITH ANNE, Fourth Grade Teacher; *b:* Washington, DC; *m:* Edward B.; *c:* Leigh Anne Lorenz Mayo, Michael E.; *ed:* Towson Univ (BS) Ed 1960; Western MD Coll Masters Equivalent; *cr:* Happy Acres Elem Schl 1st Grd Tchr 1960-61; Loch Raven Elem Schl 1st Grd Tchr 1961-62; Fifth Dist Elem Schl 1-4 Grd Tchr 1971-; *ai:* Soc Welfare, Values, Schl Based Mngmt Teams; Tchr Mentoring; Stu Tchr Supervision; TABCO 1971-, Rep, Meritorious Svc 1995; MSTA 1971-; *office:* 5th District Elem Schl Mt Carmel Rd Upperco MD 21155

LORENZEN, LOUIS OTTO, Full Prof of Fine Arts; *b:* Akron, OH; *m:* Veronica Ann DeCarulis; *c:* Michelle Melody Ruitt, Teresa Ann Hopkins, Lisette Marie Jackson, Anthony Frederick, Nicholas Joseph; *ed:* Bowling Green St Univ (BS) Art Ed 1959; Bridewater St Coll (MED) Ed Admin 1964; Assumption Coll (MAT) Fine Arts 1970; Syracuse Univ (MFA) Illustration 1982; Harvard Summer Schl 4 Credit Hrs 1965; *cr:* Bluffton Pub Schl Grd 1-12 Art Tchr 1959; Ed Rsrch Comm of Greater Cleveland Illustrator 1959; Dept of Corrections Eng Tchr 1960-61; Old Rochester Regnl Sch Dist Sp Ed Tchr 1961-62; New Bedford Pub Schl Eng Tchr 1962-63; New Bedford Voc HS Eng Tchr 1963-65; Fitchburg St Coll Art Prof 1968-; *ai:* Comm to Hire Ftbl Coach Chrprsn; Summer Schl Extension Wkshp Ldr; Hnrs Adv Hnrs Stu Prgm; MTA 1970-; Phi Delta Kappa 1980-; MA Art Ed Assn 1968-, Exec Office, Pres 1985-89; NAEA 1968-, Ethics Comm Chair 1985, Cert of Appreciation; Intnl Soc of Ed Through Art; NEA 1970-, Life Mem; Amnesty Intnl 1985-; Numerous Shows of Work; Who's Who of East 1993-94; Who's Who in Amer Ed 1996-; Distngd Svc Awd Twice; Pres Medal 1994; *home:* 37 Elm Hill Ave Leominster MA 01453*

LORENZO, SUSAN M., Health & Physical Ed Teacher; *b:* Jersey City, NJ; *ed:* Seton Hall Univ (BS) Hlth & PE 1982; *cr:* Kawameeh MS Hlth & PE Tchr 1983-; *ai:* Asst Var Bsktbl 1983-, Head Var Vlybl 1989-, 8th Grd Field Hockey 1984-88 Coach; NJAHPERD 1983-; A Plus for Kids Grant 1995; *office:* Kawameeh MS 490 David Ter Union NJ 07083

LORENZONI, BARBARA, Resource Center Teacher; *b:* New York City, NY; *m:* Frank P.; *c:* Eric, Marta Loeb; *ed:* Hunter Coll (BA) Psych 1960; William Paterson Coll (ME) Rdng 1971; Cert as Tchr of the Handicapped, Rdng Specialist & Pre Schl Tchr; 60+ Credits Beyond masters; *cr:* Bristol Learning Disabilities Tchr 1971-72; Kinnelon Supplemental Instr 1972-91, Resource Ctr Tchr 1991-; *ai:* MCEA 1972-; NJEA 1972-; NEA 1972-; Article Pub; Govenors Tchr Recognition Awd 1989-90.

LORENZONI, VIVIAN MARIA, Fourth Grade Teacher; *b:* Boston, MA; *ed:* St Coll at Boston (BS) Elem Ed 1962; Boston Coll (MED) Rdng 1967; 17 Addl Credits; *cr:* Thomas A. Edison Elem Schl Fourth Grd Tchr 1962-66; James A. Garfield Schl Fourth Grd Tchr 1966-; *ai:* AFT 1967-, 25 Yr Awd; *office:* James A. Garfield Schl 95 Beechcroft St Boston MA 02135

LORETI, DANIEL, Health & Physical Ed Teacher; *b:* Italy; *m:* Regina Ann Nargi; *c:* Brandon Joseph; *ed:* Slippery Rock Univ (BS) Hlth, PE 1981; Rider Univ (MA) Guid Cnslng 1995; 9 Post Grad Hrs Seton Hall Univ; *cr:* Wardlaw Hartridge Schl Hlth, PE Tch 1981-87; Reading-Fleming MS Hlth, PE Tchr, Ath Coord 1987-; *ai:* Fall IM, Girls Var Bsktbl Coach; NJAHPERD, JOPERD 1981-; NJ Coaches Assn 1995-; *office:* Reading Fleming MS 50 Court St Flemington NJ 08822

LORGAN, THOMAS PATRICK, Secondary English Teacher; *b:* Chester, NY; *m:* Patrica Zawaski; *c:* Jason, Justin; *ed:* Plattsburgh St (BS) Scndry Eng 1965, (MS) Scndry Eng 1969; Attnd Univ of NH & Iona Univ Post Grad Stud; *cr:* Warwick Hs Boys Soccer Coach 1966-, Athl Dir 1982-88, Scndry Eng Tchr 1965-; Boys Bsbl Asst Coach 1967-77; Soph and Jr Class Adv; *ai:* WVTA Schlsp Comm; Var Sftbl Coach 1995-; Warwick Valley Tchrs Assn & NYSTA 1965-; Youth Soccer 1982-88, Founder & Dir; Orange Cty Soccer Offcls Chris Chasis Awd; Orange Cty Interscholastic Athl Assn Soccer Coach of Yr; *home:* 189 N Route 94 Warwick NY 10990

LORGE, BARBARA CASH, Soc Stud Dept Chair & Teacher; *b:* Batavia, NY; *w:* Benjamin P. (dec); *c:* Daniel, Sarah, Abigail; *ed:* Wells Coll (BA) His 1963; Boston Univ (MED) Ed 1964; Univ of Rochester 6 Credit Hrs; Clark Univ 1 Course Audited; *cr:* South Jr HS Soc Stud Tchr 1964-67; Dept of Defense Soc Stud Tchr 1967-69; USAF Base at Zaragosa Soc Stud Tchr 1969-70; West Boulston Schl Long Term Sub Soc Stud Tchr 1986; Quabbin Regnl HS Soc Stud Tchr 1988-, Dept Chair 1995-; *ai:* Class of 95 Adv 1991-95; HS Cabinet 1995-; QRTA, MTA, NEA, NCSS 1988-; Paxton Schl Comm 1980-88, Vice Chprsn, Svc Awd; First Congretional Church 1974-, Sr Deaconess; Friends of Richards Meml Lib 1975-; *office:* Quabbin Regnl HS South St Barre MA 01005

LORIA, MARIE GRILLI, Frgn Lang Teacher & Dept Head; *b:* Acquaviva Delle Fo, Italy; *m:* Vincent; *c:* Marisa, Sabrina; *ed:* Hofstra Univ (BA) Span, Italian, Scndry Ed 1871, (MA) Spal Lit 1976; C. W. Post Coll (PD) Admin 1996; Post Grad Stud NY Univ, Isituto Universitario Orientale, Univ of Florence, Univ of Madrid; *cr:* Suiole Medie e Ginnasio Antonio Giordano Eng Tchr 1968-69; Vly Stream HS Tchr, Dept Head 1971-; Hofstra Univ Italian Instr 1987; *ai:* Organizing Frgn Lang Week March; Poetry Competition; NYSUT, AATI 1971-; NYSAFLT 1975-; Phi Delta Kappa 1995-; Friends of Mineola Lib 1990-; Book: Italian for Communication; Grant Govt Italy Open AIACE Schl in Vly Stream NY; Italian Dept Flwshp for PHD; *office:* Vly Stream North HS 750 Herman Ave Franklin Square NY 11010

LO RICCCO, MICHAEL P., Business Educator; *b:* Jersey City, NJ; *m:* Heather Di Sciascio-Lo Ricco; *ed:* Trenton St Coll (BS) Bus Ed 1992; *cr:* Hopewell Vly Cntrl HS Bus Edctr 1992; *ai:* JV Girls Soccer Coach 1993-; Tech Comm; Fac Senate; Block Scheduling Visitation Team; Curr Cncl; NJBEA 1992-; *office:* Hopewell Valley Cntrl HS 259 Pennington-Titusville Rd Pennington NJ 08534

LORINCHAK, MARIANNE SCHMID, Latin Teacher; *b:* Cleveland, OH; *m:* Edmund Paul; *ed:* Millersville Univ (BS) Latin, Span 1968; Univ of MN (MA) Latin 1971; Cours de Vacances Universite De Neuchatel Switzerland Under Grad Courses Fr, Classical Civilization, Art, Mythology 1982; *cr:* Columbia Jr Sr HS Latin, Span Tchr 1968-69; Westinghouse HS Latin, Span Tchr 1971-83; Schenley HS Latin, Span Tchr 1983-87; Westinghouse HS Latin, Span Tchr 1987-90; Gateway Sr HS Latin Tchr 1990-; *ai:* Jr Classical League Spon, St Championships 1993-95; Amer Classical League 1968-; PA Classical Assn 1971-, Newsletter Ed; Classical Assn of Pittsburgh & Vicinity 1972-, Pres 1990-; Classical Assn of Atlantic Sts 1976-, Regnl Rep for Western PA 1992-; Textbook Series Numerous Wkshps, Pub Materials; Univ of Pittburgh Schl of Ed All Star Edctr Awd 1995; *office:* Gateway Sr HS 2629 Mosside Blvd Monroeville PA 15146

LORO, LAUREN MARGUERITE, Instrumental Music Director; *b:* New Haven, CT; *ed:* Western CT St Coll (BS) Music Ed 1970; Univ of Bridgeport (MS) Music Ed 1977; *cr:* Sleeping Giant Jr HS Instrumental Music Dir 1970-77; Hamden HS Instrumental Music Dir 1977-; *ai:* Hamden HS Concert, Dance & Marching Band & Orch Dir; Hamden Theatre Dept & Summer Theatre Music Dir; Michael J Whalen Jr HS Theatre Dept Music Dir 1975-84; Sleeping Giant Jr HS Theatre Dept Music Dir 1972-83; Quinnipiac Coll Music Dir 1980; South Regnl MS Band Dir 1994; Prof Devlpmt Chrpsn 1994-; Dist Prof Devlpmt Co Chair 1995-; CT Music Educators Assn 1975-; Whos Who in Amer Ed 1992, 1994-95; *office:* Hamden H S 2040 Dixwell Ave Hamden CT 06514

LORTON, BARBARA FERGUSON, Teacher of Gifted & Talented; *b:* Sidney, OH; *c:* Mark, Beth Wagner; *ed:* Miami Univ (BA) Elem Ed 1962; Attnd Kent St Univ, Cleveland St, Loyola; *cr:* Massillan Schls 2nd Grd Tchr 1962-69; Streetsboro Schls Rdng Resource 1980-81; Calvert Co Schls 4, 5th Grd Tchr 1981-95; *ai:* Appeal Nature Trail Club; Good News Laison; Cellist for HS Musicals, Pgrms; CCP Prof Group of Tchrs Playing Baroque Music for Schl Functions; NEA, MSTA 1981-; CEA 1981-, Bldg Rep; St Andrews Church 1987-, Vestry Soc Comm, Sub Organist Chldrns Choir Dir; Girls Scouts 1975-, Ldr, Order of Green Angel; Calvert Chamber Players 1989-, Cellist; VA Natl Med Musical Group Cellist, Soloist 1988-; Cleveland Orchestra Chorus 1970-81; Soloist, Chamber Chorale; St Maries Musical 1981-, Soloist; Beach Schl Nature Trail Grants; Schlsp Audubon to Enviromental Studies Prgm Muscangos Bay ME.

LORUSSO, STEPHEN MICHAEL, Assistant Prof of Biology; *b:* Philadelphia, PA; *m:* Denise T. Esposito; *c:* Jennifer, Daniel, Nancy, Madeline; *ed:* Temple Univ (BA) Psych 1978, (MA) Psych 1980, (PHD) Exercise Physiology 1989; *cr:* Coll Misericordia Asst Prof of Bio 1992-; *ai:* AAAS 1992-; NY Acad of Sci 1993-; Human Anatomy & Physiology Soc 1992-; Luzerne Cty Sci Tchrs Assn 1993-; Pub & Presented Papers on Cardiovascular Physiology; Univ of PA Dept of Anatomy Post-Doctoral Trng Grant 1989-92; *office:* Coll Misericordia 301 Lake St Dallas PA 18612

LORUSSO, TINA MARIE ELENA, Music Teacher & Choral Dir; *b:* Newport, RI; *ed:* Naugatuck Vly Comm Tech Coll (AS) Acctng 1977, (AA) Mngmt 1978; Univ of Bridgeport (BS) Music Ed 1981, (BM) Conducting 1981; Univ of Miami (MM) Choral Conducting 1983; *cr:* Paleerm Schl Chorus, Gen Music, Theatre Tchr 1981-83; Ponus Ridge MS Chorus, Gen Music Tchr 1983-84; Bristol Schls Music His, Theory Tchr, Choral Dir 1985-86; New Fairfield HS Music Theory Tchr, Vocal Dir 1986-89; Teikyo-Post Univ Music His Tchr 1995-; Naugatuck Vly Comm-Tech Coll Music Theory, His, Jazz, Vocal Tchr 1992-; Holy Cross HS Choral Dir 1989-; *ai:* Jazz Chori Dir; Stu Recital Coord; Musical Theatre Music Dir; MENC, CMEA, IAJE 1983-; ACDA 1981-; AGO 1986-, Treas, Registrar; AFM 1973-; Waterburg Chorale 1990-; Accompanist, Singer; Laurel Music Camp 1985-, Accompanist, Bd; Who's Who in Entertainment 1989-; Roy T. D'Arcy Musican of Yr 1977; Asst Dir US National Chourse 1988-91; *home:* 24 Blueridge Dr # 5 Waterbury CT 06704

LOSI, CAROLANN SLOANE, Jr HS Mathematics Teacher; *b:* Brooklyn, NY; *m:* Michael; *ed:* NY Univ (BS) Math Ed 1990; Brooklyn Coll (MS) Math Ed 1993; *cr:* IS 162 New York City Bd of Ed Math Tchr 1990-; *office:* IS 162 Willoughby 1390 Willoughby Ave Brooklyn NY 11237

LOSIEWICZ, DEBRA REED, 2nd Grade Teacher; *b:* Danville, PA; *m:* Paul B.; *c:* Sean (dec), Matthew; *ed:* Bloomsburg Univ (BS) Elem Ed 1973; Post-Grad Stud; *cr:* Lincoln Schl 2nd, 4th & 6th Grd Tchr 1973-75; Stevens Schl 2nd Grd Tchr 1975-79; Shamokin Elem 2nd Grd Tchr 1979-; *ai:* PSEA, NEA & SEA 1973-; The Compassionate Friends 1990-; Fall Sports Club Mem & Track & Field Booster 1995-; *home:* 2038 Stetler Dr Coal Township PA 17866

LOSIEWICZS, PAUL B., Middle School Teacher; *b:* Shamokin, PA; *m:* Debra Reed; *c:* Sean (dec), Matthew; *ed:* Slippery Rock St Coll (BA) Elem Ed 1974; Attnd Bucknell Univ, Penn St Univ, Bloomsburg Univ; *cr:* Shamokin Area Schl Dist MS Tchr 1974-; *ai:* Var Club, Class Adv; Head Golf, Head Womens Track & Field, 7th Grd Bsktbl Coach; Shamokin Ed

Assn, PSEA, NEA 1974-; PA Track, Field Coaches 1993-; Lions Club 1979-86, Sec; Shamokin Housing Auth 1980-88, Chm; Northumberland Cty Planning Commission 1982-84, Vice Chm; Coach of Yr Golf 1993-95, Track 1995; *home:* 2038 Stetler Dr Coal Township PA 17866

LOTH, BONNIE JEAN, Math & Science Teacher; *b:* Altoona, PA; *m:* David Robert; *c:* William Robert, Marsha Ann; *ed:* Saint Francis Coll (BA) Math 1977; 24 Post Grad Stud Credits; *cr:* Spring Cove Jr HS Math & Sci Tchr 1979-81; Spring Cove MS Math & Sci Tchr 1990-; *ai:* Odyssey of Mind Coord & Coach; Memory Book Adv; Math Chprsn; NEA & PSEA 1990-; Band Parents 1994-; Rel Stud Tchr 1987-.*

LOTKA, EDWINA ROSE, Retired Teacher; *b:* Philadelphia, PA; *m:* James L.; *c:* James, Catherine, John, Marirose; *ed:* Manor Jr Coll (AA) Lbrl Arts 1960; Gwynedd Mercy Coll (BS) Elem Ed 1987; *cr:* St Matthew Schl 4th Grd Tchr 1960-65; St Charles Borromeo 4th Grd Tchr 1982-89, 8th Grd Tchr 1989-93; *ai:* NCEA 1982-; *home:* 1041 Old Ln Drexel Hill PA 19026*

LOTT, JOYCE GREENBERG, English Teacher; *b:* Atlantic City, NJ; *m:* Gary C.; *c:* Elizabeth Greenberg, Suzanne Greenberg, Larry Greenberg; *ed:* Douglass Coll (BA) Eng 1976; Rutgers Univ (MA) Eng 1979; 21 Addl Credit Hrs; *ai:* Reorganization, Structuring Comm; NEA; NJEA; NCTE; Stories Pub 1994; Eng Journal 1991, 1994; Educl Ldrshp 1995; Speaker NCTE 1992-93, 1995; CCCC'S Speaker 1996; *office:* S Brunswick HS Major Rd Monmouth Junction NJ 08852

LOTZ, DIANNE VANALESTI, Teacher of the Handicapped; *b:* Jamacia, NY; *m:* Richard William; *c:* Christopher, David; *ed:* Duquesne Univ (BS) Early Chldhd, Elem Ed 1973; Hofstra Univ (MS) Spec Ed 1976; Nova Southeastern (EDD) Ed 1993; Learning Disabilities, Tchr, Consultant Internship Rutgers Univ 1994; 15 Credit Hrs Doctoral Level Spec Ed Univ of Pittsburgh 1981-83; *cr:* Freeport Pub Schls 1st Grd Gen Ed Tchr 1973-79; Southvue Child Learning Ctr Dir, Owner 1983-84; Brookdale Comm Coll Adj Fac Rdng Dept 1994-; Marlboro Twp Pub Schls Tchr of Handicapped 1985-; *ai:* Supt Advy Comm 1996; Phi Delta Kappa 1992-, Historian 1994-96, VP Mbrshp 1996-; CEC 1990, 1990-; ASCD 1991-; NEA 1985-; NJ Ed Assn 1985-, Bldg Del; Marlboro Meadows Homeowners Assn 1985-, Pres, Founder; Citizens Advy Comm 1989-; Stratford Manor Neighborhood Watch Prgm 1983-84; *office:* Marlboro MS 355 County Rd Rt 520 Marlboro NJ 07746*

LOTZ, LUCILLE TUCKER, 4th Grade Teacher; *b:* Baltimore, MD; *m:* Donald H.; *c:* Christopher D., Stephanie Lotz Wasson; *ed:* WMC (BSEd) Home Ec 1962; Addl 33 Hrs Elem Ed; *cr:* Sudbrook Jr HS Home Ec Tchr 1962065; Pikesville Sr HS Home Ec Tchr 1965-66; Liberty HS Home Ec Tchr 1981; Freedom Elem Schl 3rd-4th Grds Tchr 1981-; *ai:* Cty Discipline Comm; Sit Team; PTA Ex Bd; NEA, MSTA, CCEA 1981-; Bell Choir; *office:* Freedom Elem Schl 5626 Sykesville Rd Sykesville MD 21784

LOTZ, ROBIN ELIZABETH (PALMER), Spanish Teacher; *b:* Canton, OH; *m:* William H.; *c:* Brandi E. Korzan; *ed:* Malone Coll (BA) Span, Fr 1976; Post Grad Malone Coll, Kent St Univ; *cr:* Sandy Valley Schls Sp, Fr Tchr 1977-; *ai:* Foreign Lang Club, SV Travel Club Adv; OFLA, NEA, OEA 1977-; EMT-A Quad Ambulance Dist 1978-83; Sandy Valley Tchr of Yr 1980; *office:* Sandy Valley HS 5362 St Rt 183 NE Magnolia OH 44643*

LOUCKS, JUDY ALLEN, 1st-2nd Grades Multiage Tchr; *b:* Schenectady, NY; *m:* James; *ed:* SUNY at New Paltz (BS) K-2nd, 9th-12th Ed 1966; SUNY at Albany (MS) Scndry Eng Ed 1968, (MS) Developmental Rdng 1983; Russell Sage at Troy 6 Credits; SUNY at Oneonta 12 Credits; *cr:* Elementary Ed 5th, 3rd, 2nd, 1st, Kndgtn, Multiage 1st-2nd Grd Tchr 1966-; *ai:* Curr Advy, Soc Stud Coret Comm; Math Cabinet; NUSUT 1966-; Niskayuna Tchr Assoc 1968-; Niskayuna Day Care Bd; Schdy Jr League; Ec Cncl Russell Sage Coll 1st Grd Ec Awd; *office:* Nisleayuna Schl System Dexter Rd Schenectady NY 12309

LOUDER, DAVID EDWARD, English Teacher; *b:* Windber, PA; *m:* Ethel M. Mong; *c:* Dana Lynn, David Eugene, Dyan Marie; *ed:* Clarion St Coll (BS) Comprehensive Eng, Rdng 1968, (MED) Elem Ed 1972; *cr:* US Navy F&G2 Fire Control Technician 1960-64; Clarion-Limestone Area Schls Tchr 1968-; *ai:* Clarion-Limestone Ed Assn 1972-; PSEA, NEA 1972-, Bldg Rep, Negiotiator; *office:* Clarion-Limestone HS Box 205 Strattanville PA 16258

LOUDERBACK, CAROL FAWLEY, English & Latin Teacher; *b:* Hillsboro, OH; *m:* Donald D.; *c:* David, Jill Carter, Kevin; *ed:* Morehead St Univ (BA) Eng & Latin 1968; Miami Univ (MA) Ed 1979; *cr:* Western Brown HS Eng, Latin, Speech & Drama Tchr 1968-73; Lynchburg-Clay HS Eng & Latin Tchr 1974-; *ai:* Soph Class & Latin Club Adv; *office:* Lynchburg-Clay HS 8250 State Route 134 Lynchburg OH 45142

LOUGHEED DESSERT, KATHRYN ISOBEL, Fifth Grade Teacher; *b:* Cornwall ON, Canada; *m:* Steven Edward; *c:* William, Andre; *ed:* Univ of TN at Chattanooga (BS) Elem & Early Chldhd Ed 1982; Credit Hrs; *cr:* Mary Anne Garber Elem Schl Kndgtn Tchr 1983-86; Westside Elem Schl Kndgtn Tchr 1986-88; White Sulphur Elem Schl 1st Grd Tchr 1988-91; St Vincent de Paul Schl 2nd, 5th, 7th Grd Tchr 1991-; *ai:* Writer's Wkshp Coord; Coach Fun Olympics; NAEYC, NEA 1982-; IRA, ASCD 1991-; Children Attnetion Deficit Disorder 1989-, Founder & Pres, Outstdng Coord Awd; Young Authors 1992-, Schl Rep; Arts in Schls 1989-, Schl Rep; Articles Pub; Tchr of Yr White Sulphur Elem; Outstdng Young Women of Amer Awd 1992; *home:* 133 Lakeview Heights Dr Howard OH 43028*

LOUGHLIN, JUDY BUCHHOLZ, Kindergarten Teacher; *b:* Wellsville, NY; *m:* Bob M.; *c:* Patrick, Jennifer; *ed:* Certfd ELIC Tutor; Numerous Courses Behavior, Themes, Tchng, Cmptrs 28 Yrs; *cr:* Whitesville Cntrl Schl Third Grd Tchr 1966-, Second Grd Tchr 1966-, Kndgtn Tchr 1966-; *ai:* 11th Grd Adv; 5-8th Grd Girls Bsktbl Asst Coach; Schl Improvement; Credit Union Rep; ACTA 1968-80, Treas; AAUW Ed Coord; Delta Kappa Gamma 1992-, Treas; NEA 1996-; Comm Vol; *office:* Whitesville Central Schl 692 Main St Whitesville NY 14897

LOUGHLIN, THOMAS WILLIAM, Associate Professor of Acting; *b:* New York City, NY; *m:* Ann Marie Margagliotti; *c:* Jenna Marie, Brian Thomas, Eric Robert; *ed:* SUNY College at Oswego (BA) Theatre, Eng 1974; Univ of NE at Lincoln (MFA) Theatre, Acting 1982; NY Univ Tisch Schl of Arts-Actor Trng Prgm; SUNY at Stonybrook Scndry Ed; *cr:* Southeast COmm COll Fairbury Comm Instr 1982-86; Genesee Comm Coll Speech, Theatre Asst Prof 1986-88; SUNY Coll at Fredonia Acting Assoc Prof 1988-; *ai:* Performing Arts Co Adv; Sub-Comm for Improvement of Under-Grad Instruction Chprsn; United Univ Profs 1988-; Amer Coll Theatre Festival 1974-, Respondent; Newman Center 1988-; Guest Dir, Prin Actor WI Shakespeare Festival; Freelance Prof Actor in Buffalo; *office:* State Univ College at Fredonia Dept Theatre Arts 212 Rockefeller Arts Ctr Fredonia NY 14063*

LOUGHNER, HELEN L., Chemistry Teacher; *b:* Greensburg, PA; *ed:* Penn St Univ (BS) Pre-Medicine 1976; Univ of Pittsburgh (MED) Sci Ed 1980, (PHD) Instrl Sci 1987; *cr:* Penn-Trafford HS Chem Tchr 1978-; *ai:* Chess Club Spon; Coord of Chem Competitions; Amer Chemical Soc; Kevin Bums Awd; Pride Awd Winn; Outstdng Tchr in Penn-Trafford Schl Dist; Recipient of Four Spechoscopy Soc of Pittsburg HS Equipment Grants; All Star Edctr; St Vincents Coll Tchr Recognition Awd; Numerous Publications; *office:* Penn Trafford HS PO Box 366 Harrison City PA 15636

LOUGHRAN, PATRICIA ANN, Spanish Teacher; *b:* Abington, PA; *ed:* Cabrini Coll (BA) Span 1993; Enrolled in the Master of Foreign Lang Ed Prgm at Temple Univ; *cr:* Tamanend MS Span Tchr 1993-; *ai:* Comm Svc, Svc Learning Coord; NJHS Adv; Character Bldng & Foreign Exchange Comm; CBEA, PSEA & NEA 1993-; Bucks Cty Assn of Foreign Lang Tchrs 1995-; 3 Yrs Mini Grant Learn & Serve Amer Svc Learning; *office:* Tamanend MS 1492 Stuckert Rd Warrington PA 18976

LOUGHRIDGE, ROBERT LELAND, English & Computer Sci Teacher; *b:* Corning, NY; *m:* Victoria Kolcun; *c:* Jennifer Balonek, Pamela, Jeffrey; *ed:* Alfred Univ (BA) Eng 1965; SUNY at Brockport (MA) Eng 1969; Addl Major Cmptr Sci; *cr:* Bryon-Bergen Cntrl Schl Tchr 1966-; Genesee Comm Coll Adj Fac 1981-; *ai:* Compact for Learning, Dist Tech, HS Steering Comms; Cmptr Coord; Chess Club Adv; AFT, NYSUT 1966-; NYSCATE 1986-; NY Eng Cncl 1975-; NCTE 1974-; Rochester Schl for the Deaf; *office:* Byron-Bergen Central Schl 6917 W Bergen Rd Bergen NY 14416

LOUGHRIGE, ROBERT ASHLEY, Music Dept Chairman; *b:* Muskegon, MI; *m:* Patricia Ann Joyner; *c:* Claire, Maria Loughrige-Pascua; *ed:* OH Northern U (BS) Music Ed 1966; Miami U (MA) Music Ed 1973; FL St U 3 Yrs Undergrad Work Music; *cr:* Botkins HS Band Dir 1966-69; Wright St U Jazz, His, Instr 1985-90; Celina Sr HS Dept Chair, Symphonic, Jazz Bands Dir 1969-; *ai:* Pep, Jazz, Marching Bands, Pat Orch for Musicals; NEA, OEA, MENC, OMEA 1966-; ASBDA 1994-; Adjudicator Music Contests OH, KY, IN; Originator OMEA Dist III Hons Jazz Band; *home:* 1002 Harbor Point Dr Celina OH 45822

LOUK, MARJORIE A. CIRULLO, 8th Grade Tchr & Private Tutor; *b:* Clarksburg, WV; *w:* John W. Jr. (dec); *c:* Gregory, Tammy Halasa, Cerafina Gotto; *ed:* Univ of Akron (BS) Elem Ed 1969, (MS) Admin & Supervision 1977; Post-Grad Classes 1980-; *cr:* St Vincent-St Mary 6th Grd Tchr 1960-62; Sawyerwood 1st Grd 1962-63; Tallmadge Schls 4th & 6th-8th Grd & Asst Prin 1964-, Dir Tallmadge Stu Ctr; *ai:* Affiliated with Portage Lakes Career Ctr; Track Coach 1 Yr; Stu Cncl Adv 10 Yrs; Pep Club Adv 2 Yrs; Work with Stdnts Before & After Schl; Mid Schl Tchrs Assn 1987-; Pi Lambda Theta 1989-, Above Average Grds at Univ of Akron; Tallmadge Our Lady of Victory Cath Church, EM 6 Yrs; Tallmadge Tchr of Yr; Worked with Insight Pgms, DARE Pgms, & Stdnts of Divorced Parents; *office:* Tallmadge MS 76 North Ave Tallmadge OH 44278

LOURENCO, DOLORES NOBREGA, English Teacher; *b:* Cumberland, RI; *m:* Leonidio S.; *c:* Lori Ann Lourenco Collins; *ed:* Bryant Coll (BS) Secretarial Sci 1961, (BBED) Bus Ed 1970; Boston Univ (MED) Ed 1972; RI Coll 6 Credit Hrs; Providence Coll 9 Credit Hrs; Suffolk Univ 9 Credit Hrs; *cr:* St of RI Employment Security Dept Labor Relations Bd Stenographic Reporter 1961-69; Cumberland HS Bus Tchr 1970-86, Eng Tchr 1986-; *ai:* Delta Pi Epsilon 1972-; Alpha Delta Kappa 1990-, Chaplain, Recording Sec; CTA, NEA 1970-; RI Eng Tchrs 1986-; Natl Eng Tchrs 1996; Portuguese Women Assn 1991-, First Lady of Portugal Dinner Co-Chm 1993; Portuguese Cultural Assn 1974-; Bryant Coll Key Honor Soc; *home:* 6 Ursa Way Cumberland RI 02864

LOURENSO, FAYE, Asst Prof of Graphic Design; *b:* LeMars, IA; *m:* A.; *c:* Fara, Lauren; *ed:* Mankato St Univ (BS) Art Ed 1972; SUNY at Stony Brook (MALS) 1988; Long Island Univ C W Post Campus (MA) Studio Arts 1991, (MS) Cmptrs in Ed 1993; *cr:* Searles Graphic Inc Industry Position 1975-88; Suffolk Comm Coll Asst Prof 1988-; *ai:* Publications Co-Dir; Art Club Co-Adv; Asst Dept Chair; AFT 1988-; GDEA; *office:* Suffolk Cty Comm Coll 2 Speonk Riverhead Rd Riverhead NY 11901

LOUZONIS, HELENA P., Science Teacher; *b:* Johannesburg, South Africa; *m:* John A.; *c:* Timothy, Daniel, Maggie, Catherine; *ed:* Anna Maria Coll (BS) Bio; Worcester Polytechnic Inst (MNS) Natural Sci; *cr:* St Peter-Marian HS Sci Tchr 1980-82; St Marys HS Sci Tchr 1982-92; Athol HS Sci Tchr 1992-; *ai:* Soccer Coach; Worcester Yth; Girls Teams; MAST 1990-; Delta Kappa Gamma 1988-, Mbrshp Chair.

LOVATO, VANESSA LYNN, Nursing Professor; *b:* Frederick, MD; *m:* Robert S. Turner; *c:* Laura E. Turner; *ed:* Frederick Comm Coll (AD) Nrsng 1976; Univ MD at Balto Co (BS) Nrsng 1984, (MSN) Nrsng 1987; *cr:* Suburban Hosp Staff Nurse 1976-77; Frederick Meml Hosp Staff & Charge Nurse 1977-83; Frederick Comm Coll Nursing Prof 1987-; *ai:* Adv Sr Nrsng Stdnts; Nrsng, Coll Curr Comm; AORN 1977-, Treas; Sigma Theta Tau 1986-; N-OADN 1991-; Univ & Nrsng Alumni Assn 1987-, ANA 1986-; Amer Med Assn Alliance Inc, PTA 1992-; *office:* Frederick Comm Coll 7932 Opossumtown Pike Frederick MD 21702*

LOVE, ADELLE LODZIA, ESL Teacher; *b:* New York, NY; *m:* Robert James; *c:* Robert S., Jessica L.; *ed:* Elms Coll (BA) Sociology 1966, (MAT) Eng as 2nd Lang 1990; *cr:* Chicopee Pub Schls Elem Tchr 1966-68, Bilingual Tutor & Adult Ed 1980-88, ESL Tchr 1988-; *ai:* MABE 1988-; MATSOL 1988-; St Vincent de Paul 1975-, VP; Polish Jr League 1975-; Chicopee Housing Authority 1984-, Pres & VP; Whos Who in Amer Ed; *office:* Chicopee HS 650 Front St Chicopee MA 01013

LOVE, ALYCE ANN (SALOMONE), Spanish Teacher; *b:* Perth Amboy, NJ; *m:* John T.; *c:* Erin B., Corey T., Kyle W.; *ed:* Glassboro St Coll (BA) Span 1972; 30 Grad Credits; *cr:* Port Jervis HS Span Tchr 1972-73; Buena Regnl HS Span Tchr 1974-75; Arthur Rann MS Span Tchr 1986-; *ai:* Absegami HS PTSA Project Grad Co-Chair; Schlsp Comm; Absegami Soccer Booster Club Schlsp Comm; Cologne Arthur Rann & Absegami PTA-PTSA; Frgn Lang Proficiency Coaching; ACEGT Consortium; NEA, NJEA 1988-; *office:* Arthur Rann MS 8th Ave Absecon NJ 08201

LOVE, ANNAMARIE MOSCHELLA, 9th-12th Grd Math Tchr & Chair; *b:* Bethpage, NY; *m:* Alfred G. III; *c:* Alfred G. IV, Adam W.; *ed:* St Leo Coll (BA) Math & Ed 1976; Attnd Cecil Comm Coll & Univ of DE; *cr:* Taunton HS Math Tchr 1977-78; Cecil Cty Pub Schls Math Tchr 1978-80; St Elizabeth HS Math Tchr & Chprsn 1987-; *ai:* Math Dept Chprsn; Jr Class, Pep Club, Ring Mass & Math League Moderator; Acad Cncl; Diocesan Math Task Force Rep; NCTM 1990-; DCTM 1990-; Nrsng Mothers Inc 1979-, Regnl Ldr, 1st VP & Pres; Greater Elkton Jaycees 1988-, Sec, Treas, St Dir, Jays PM, Pres, OYF PM & First Timers PM, Pres of Yr, Comm Svc PM of the Yr & Lifetime MD Jaycee; *office:* St Elizabeth HS 1500 Cedar St Wilmington DE 19805

LOVE, BETSY JAY, 2nd Grade Teacher; *b:* Clearfield, PA; *m:* Robert L.; *c:* Michael, Elizabeth; *ed:* Lock Haven Univ (BS) Elem Ed 1966; IN Univ (MED) Elem 1970; Addl Post Grad Courses; *cr:* Leonard Grd Schl Grd 1 Tchr 26 Yrs, Grd 2 Tchr 2 Yrs; *ai:* PSEA, NEA 1966-; United Meth Church, Bd Discipleship; *home:* 113 W Pauline Dr Clearfield PA 16830*

LOVE, MARY JOYCE, Retired Elementary Schl Tchr; *b:* Cordele, GA; *m:* D. Goodloe; *c:* Marth Marie Hale; *ed:* Andrew Jr Coll (BA) Elem Ed 1957; GA Southern (BS) Elem Ed 1959; Scarritt Coll Chrstn Workers (MA) Chrstn Ed 1960; George Peabody Coll of Vanderbilt (MA) Spec Ed 1961; *cr:* Haven Elem Schl Tchr Bl & Part Sighted 1963-65; Haven Jr HS Tchr BL & Part Sighted 1963-65; Antioch Schl 5 & 6 Grds Tchr 1969-70; Waynsboro Area Schls Kndgtn, 1st Grd Tchr 1974-87; *ai:* NEA, PSEA 1974- Life Mem; Phi Theta Kappa 1957; Finalist for PA Tchr of Yr 1986-87; Outstdng Edctr of Yr Shippensburg Univ Chptr Phi Delta Kappa 1986-87; Articles Pub 1989, 1991, 1994; *home:* 315 Tri Hill Rd York PA 17403

LOVE, SHERRI LEE (WRIGHT), 6th-8th Grade Teacher; *b:* El Paso, TX; *m:* Scott Miller; *c:* Jason C., Chris R. B.; *ed:* Concord Coll (BSE) K-12 Art 1972; Grad Stud WVU at Marshall, OSU, Otterbien; *cr:* Jackson Cty Schl K-12 Grd Art Tchr 10 Yrs; OH Sub Tchng K-12 Grd Art Tchr 1 1/2 Yrs; OH Curr, Dev K-12 Grd Art Tchr 1 Yr; Westerville City Schl K-12 Grd Art Tchr 10 Yrs; *ai:* Newspaper Spon; PTSA Ofcr, Reflections Dir; Written, Illustrated Spon; Stewart Scholar; CCAD Scholastic Arts
Exhibition; Westerville Dist Art Show Dir; Jr Women's Club 1975-82,
Best Unit for Youth Dev; OAEA 1986-, Presenter, Youth Art Month;
1986-; PTSA 1986-, Tchr of Yr 1994; Columbus Museum 1989-, Bd
Regr; Exhibit Presenter at STRS St of OH Supt Awd 1995; Article
PTSA Tchr of YR 1995; *office:* Walnut Springs MS 888 E Walr
Westerville OH 43081*

LOVE, SUSAN SMYTH, Nurse Educator; *b:* Buffalo, NY; *c:* A
Aaron; *ed:* St Univ of NY Coll of Tech (BS) Nursing 1980; Syracuse
(MS) Nursing 1989; Saint Joseph Hospital SON Diploma Nursing
cr: Strong Memorial Hospital Registered Nurse Staff 1975-76; Livin
Cty Infirmary Registered Nurse Staff & Supvr 1976-78; Little
Hospital Registered Nurse Staff & Charge Nurse 1979-81; Saint Eliz
Hospital SON Nurse Educator 1981-; *ai:* Sunshine Fund, Spiritualit
& Peer Review Comm Chprsn; Admissions, Fac Dev, Prof Practice C
Lib, Comm Based Experience Comm Mem; Jr Junction Chief Car
NYSNA 1981-, Union Rep SON; PNCNY, Treas 1982-84, Bd 198
Barnfest FOTA 1995-; PTA, PTG 1992-; Girl Scouts of Amer 199
office: Saint Elizabeth Hosp Sch Nurs 2215 Genesee St Utica NY 1

LOVE, WESLEY ALAN, Physics Teacher; *b:* Bellefonte, PA; *m:* Pa
Ann; *c:* Julie Michelle, Christopher James; *ed:* Gordon Coll (BA) Ph
1971; SUNY at New Paltz (MA) Scndry physics 1979; *cr:* Valley Cnt
Sci Tchr 23 Yrs; *office:* Valley Central HS 1175 Rt 17 K Montgomer
12549*

LOVECCHIO, JOSEPH ANTHONY, Instrumental Music Directo
Berwick, PA; *m:* Alice Bright; *c:* Joseph Jr., Maria, Michael; *ed:* Pe
Univ (BS) Music Ed 1974; Trenton St Coll (MA) Music 1979; Addl
Masters Music, Admin Credits Penn St Univ, West Chester Univ, Villa
Univ, Vander Cook Coll; *cr:* Centennial Schl Dist Elem Inst M
Specialist 1975-89; WT HS Instrum Music Dir 1989-; *ai:* Marching
Dir; Swing n Panther Jazz Band Dir; Symphonic Wind Enxemble, Cc
Band, Orch Dir; Pit Orch Dir for Musical Theatre Production; NEA, P
CEA 1975-; MENC; PMEA; BCMEA; Natl Band Assn; Intnl Jazz Ed
Warminster Symphony Orch Music Dir, Prin Conductor; *office:* Wi
Tennent HS 333 Centennial Rd Warminster PA 18974

LOVECE, MONICA KUMP, Spanish Teacher; *b:* Bayshore, N
Gregory; *c:* Mark, Tyler; *ed:* Dowling Coll (BA) Foreign Lang 1978;
of Madrid Span Convers & Grammer 1978; SUNY at Stony Brook
MALS 1985; *cr:* Center Moriches UFSD Span Tchr 1980-; *ai:* Hold
Time & Makeup Time for Span Classes; Crisis Prevention Prgm; Sch
Handbook; NYSUT, NYSFLTA 1980-; Sylvan Ave PTA 1992-; *o*
Center Moriches HS 311 Frowein Rd Center Moriches NY 11934

LOVEJOY, DAWN DE WOLF, Biology Teacher; *b:* Gettysburg, PA
William; *c:* Allison, Geoffrey, Matthew; *ed:* Immaculata Coll (BA) E
Chem 1982; Addl 9 Credit Hrs; West Chester Univ 6 Credit Hrs; Ca
Coll Tchr Cert; *cr:* Villa Maria Acad Bio Tchr 1983-93; Gwynedd-M
Coll Adj Lecturer 1984-86; Immaculata Coll Adj Lecturer 1987-; Sh
Schl Bio Tchr 1993-; *ai:* Activities Coord; NABT; NSTA; 61st NY
War Re-Enactor Unit 1994; Commonwealth Partnership Bio Initia
Summer Rsrch Flwshp Amer Soc of Cell Bio; Summer Rsrch At W
Hole Marine Biological Funded by Howard Hughes Med In
Administered by Ursinus Coll; *office:* Shipley Schl 814 Yarrow St
Mawr PA 19010

LOVELACE, JUANITA FAYE (MURRAY), LPC High Sc
Counselor; *b:* Winchester, KY; *m:* William N.; *c:* William, David; *ed:*
St Univ (BSEd) Elem & MS Ed 1965; Xavier Univ (MED) Guid
Attnd Mt St Joseph; *cr:* Rockdale Elem Lang Arts Tchr 1965-68; Taft
Math & Sci Tchr 1968-71; Princeton HS Guid Cnslr 1971-; *ai:* Coun
Coll & Inner City Stdnts; Black Stu, Jr & Sr Adv; Mentorship to Cr
Guid Dept Head; OEA 1970-; NEA 1970-; OACAC 1975-, Princeton
Rep.*

LOVELAND, WILLIAM P., Fourth Grade Teacher; *b:* Elmira, NY
Amy Jo Strong; *ed:* SUNY at Geneseo (BS) Elem Ed 1986; Elmira
(MS) Rdng 1989; *cr:* Dundee Elem Schl Sixth Grd Tchr 1986-87, F
Grd Tchr 1987-; *ai:* Girls Bsktbl Coach1998-92; Co Adv Elem Stu
1994-; DCS Elem Sci Comm 1995-; DCS Elem Honor Roll Comm 1
NYSUT 1986-; Dundee Tchrs Assn 1986-, Treas; Parent Advy Cncl 1
home: 16 Myrtle Ave Penn Yan NY 14527*

LOVELESS, CAROL MILLER, 3rd Grade Teacher; *b:* Baltimore,
c: Joseph S. III, Donna L.; *ed:* Towson St Univ (BS) Elem Ed 196
Credit Hrs Beyond BS; *cr:* Federalsburg Elem Schl 1st Grd Tchr 196
1967-69; Denton Elem Schl 1st Grd Tchr 1970-91, 3rd Grd Tchr 1991
Tutoring; Schl Improvement Team; Grd Group Chm; Mentor Tc
Times); Supervising Tchr for 3 Stu Tchrs; NEA 1963-; MSTA 1963-; C
1963-, Fac Rep & Treas 2 Yrs; Alpha Delta Kappa Iota Chptr 1972-,
Treas & Recording Sec; St & Cty Tchr of the Yr Awds Nom; *office:* De
Elem Schl 303 Sharp Rd Denton MD 21629

LOVELETTE, ROXANNE PICTON, 10th Grade English Teache
Sunbury, PA; *m:* Timothy M.; *c:* Andrea, Genna; *ed:* Comm Coll o
(AA) Gen Ed 1982; Trinity Coll (BA) Scndry Ed, Eng & Soc Stud 1
27 Credit Hrs; *cr:* Enosburg Falls HS Soc Stud Tchr 1985-94, Eng
1985-; *ai:* Jr Class & Prom Adv; IST Coord; FNERB Mem; NCTE 1989
NEA 1986-, Pres; Holocaust Stud Grant; At Risk Pgm Grant; *of*
Enosburg Falls Jr-Sr HS School St Box 417 Enosburg Falls VT 05450

LOVELL, ELIZABETH HELEN (CORBISSERO), High School
Teacher; *b:* Akron, OH; *m:* Timothy P.; *ed:* Kent St Univ (MAT) Scndr
1990, (BS) Applied Math 1987; *cr:* Archbishop Hoban HS Math
1991-; *ai:* Sr Class Moderator; Ski Club Adv; Acad Challenge Re
NCTM, OCTM 1989-; GAMES 1991-; *office:* Archbishop Hoban HS
Elbon Ave Akron OH 44306

LOVELL, MATTHEW S., Music Teacher; *b:* Hamilton, OH; *m:* Mary
M. Lovell; *c:* Katherine, Samantha; *ed:* UNH (BA) Zoology 1977, (
Music Ed 1979; SUNY at Binghamton (MA) Music 1984; 25 Post
Credit Hrs; *cr:* Ticonderoga Pub Schls Music Tchr 1980-82; Burlingtor
Music Tchr 1985-; *ai:* Marching & Jazz Bands; Summer Band Ca
MENC, BEA & MMEA 1985-; Cuttyhunk Yacht Club 1960-; MA A
Prsntr 1995-; Disney Tchr of the Yr Nom; Panalist at Dartmouth C
Marching Band Performed at Disney World 1987, 1989, 1991 & 1
Chapter II Block Grant Music Theory & Tech Lab; *office:* Burlington
123 Cambridge St Burlington MA 01803

LOVELLO, SAMUEL JOSEPH, Social Studies Teacher & Coach
Reading, PA; *m:* Paula L.; *c:* Kristi, Joseph; *ed:* Lees McRae Coll (AA
1969; Kutztown Univ (BS) Ed 1974; Attnd NC St, Penn St, Univ of
cr: Reading Schl Dist 6th Grd Tchr 1974-76; Brandywine Heights
Dist 6th Grd Tchr & Wrestling Coach 1977-; *ai:* Wrestling Coach; BH
1977-; Berks Cty Coaches Assn 1977-, Treas, Outstdng Coach 5 Tir
Dist III Wrestling Coach 1977-, Rep, Outstdng Coach 2 Times; *of*
Brandywine Hgts Schl Dist 200 Weiss St Topton PA 19562*

LOVELOCK, PATRICIA MC DERMOTT, Language Arts Coordina
b: New York, NY; *m:* Robert J.; *c:* Kerry Jude Bazany; *ed:* Fordham U
Schl of Ed (BA) Pre-Law 1970; *cr:* St Nicholas of Tolentine Eng T
1970-75; St Denis Lang Arts Coord 1979-; St Columba Lang Arts Co
1979-; *ai:* Coord Confirmation Prgm; Recording Sec, Fac; *office:* S
Denis-Saint Columba Schl Rt 82 Hopewell Jct NY 12533

LOVERING, JOHN HENRY, Enrichment Coordinator & Tchr; *b:* Ke
NH; *m:* Mealnie Virginia Mattson; *c:* Kimberly Anne, Amy Theresa;

of NH (BA) Bio 1969, (MST) Bio Ed 1977; Salem St Coll vision, Evaluation 9 Hrs; Univ of Ct GATE Prgm 6 Hrs; *cr:* Spaulding Tchr 1969-70; Epping HS Bio Tchr 1970-73; Triton Regnl Jr-Sr HS hr 1973-87, Enrichment Coord 1987-; *ai:* Amateur Radio Club, Kids ck Puppet Troupe, Television Media Adv; Renaissance Prgm Coord; 1973-; Triton Tchrs Assn 1973-, VP 2x; NEA 1969-; Amer Red Cross Disaster Comm Speicalist; Amer Radio Relay League 1990-, Vol ner; Antique Wireless Assnn 1995-; Port City Amateur Radio Club Bd of Trustees, 1991 Amateur of Yr; Publ Three Articles 1982-87; GATE Grants 1987-89; Co-Founded MA Odyssey of Mind Prgm.*

RING, JUDITH HOLLIE (WHITTEMORE), Sixth Grade er; *b:* Boston, MA; *m:* Howard D.; *c:* Kristen Spaulding, Michael; *ed:* ngham St Coll (BS) Elem Ed 1964; 45 Addl Credit Hrs UVM, St el's Coll; *cr:* Page Schl 5th Grd Tchr 1964-67; Northfield Elem Schl h Grd Tchr 1971-77; Hartford HS Voc Child Care Svcs Tchr 1977-78; rd MS 6th Grd Tchr 1978-; *ai:* Math Curr, Sunshine Comms; Chrldng ; NEA 1971-; NCTM 1995-; VT Tchrs 1971-; *office:* Hartford Mem Highland Ave White River Juncti VT 05001*

RSO, PAMELA OLSEN, Mathematics Teacher; *b:* Rockville Ctr, : Peter Joseph; *c:* Peter, Steven; *ed:* SUNY Cortland (BS) Math Ed Grad Stud NY Inst of Tech, Coll of St Rose; *cr:* Massapequa SD #23 Tchr 1979-81; Warwick Vly SD Math Tchr 1986-; *ai:* anizational Comm; NYSUT, AFT 1986-; Warwick Schl Sports 1994-; Tchr 1990-92; Warwick United Soccer 1994-; *office:* Warwick Valley Box 595 Warwick NY 10990*

TT, CYRIL, Interim Principal; *b:* Cork, Ireland; *ed:* Univ Coll at (BED) Psych & Math 1978; Diploma in Catechetical Stud; Cert in Abuse Prevention; Diploma in PE; *cr:* Ireland Schls 7th Grd Tchr 85; St Philip Neri Schl 8th Grd Tchr 1988-95, Interim Prin 1995-; *ai:* Schl Prgm Dir; Regents Math Prgm Dir; Cath Fed of Tchrs 1988-; St Philip Neri Schl 3031 Grand Concourse New York NY 10468*

TT, SHIRLEY J. COSTON, Span & Frgn Lang Survey Tchr; *b:* nbus, OH; *c:* Sonja R., Nicole J.; *ed:* OH St Univ (BS) Span 1965; Estate; Hermeneutics; His of Pentecost; Drug & Alcohol Counseling; in Ed; Coursework at CA Universidad Interamericana, Saltillo o; *cr:* Columbus City Schl System Tchr 1965-70, 1972,73, 1981-84; moor MS Tchr 1985-; *ai:* 8th Grd Team Ldr; 8th Grd Spring otion Chprsn; Chair Multi Cultural Comm; Foreign Lang Survey Curr e Comm-Columbus City Schls; CEA, OEA, NEA 1967-; Living Faith olic Church 1992-; Taught Elem Span at 28 Schls 1966-68; Tchr of vd 2 Yrs; Initiated Foreign Lang Pgrm, North Adult HS, Columbus Started AYUDO; on Comm Which Prepared the Foreign Lang Oral ssment for Columbus City Schls; *office:* Southmoor MS 1201 Moler olumbus OH 43207*

ZIO, PAUL WILLIAM, Dept of His, Eco, Pol Prof; *b:* Brooklyn, *m:* Christine Marie smith; *c:* Robbie, Thomas; *ed:* SUNY at ngdale (AAS) Aerospace 1965; Hofstra Univ (BA) His 1967, (MA) His 1969; Post Grad Stud SUNY at Stonybrook, Hofstra; *cr:* Stevens His, Eng Instr 1968-70; SUNY at Farmindale Amer His Prof 1970-, al Arts Dept Chm 1984-95; *ai:* Var Men, Women Bowling 1983-92, Golf 1983-, Coach; Liberal Arts Honor Soc Adv; Liberal Arts Club; Band; Alumni Assn Bd of Dirs; Field Stdy Class Cord; 2 Publications *office:* SUNY Farmingdale Thompson Hall Farmingdale NY 11735*

LEY, BARBARA S., Special Education Teacher; *b:* Portland, OR; *m:* k D.; *c:* Shawn P., Seth M., Samuel E.; *ed:* Univ of ME at Presque BS) Elem, Spec Ed 1976; Univ of ME at Farmington (BS) Home Ec, Chldhd 1974; 12 Credit Hrs Univ of ME at Orono MA Prgm in Spec ansition Svc; *cr:* MSAD #1 Schl HS Schl Home Ec Tchr 1980-83; Baxter Aroostook Outreach Schl Itinerate Tchr of the Dean 1989-90; D #27 Schl HS Home Ec Tchr 1990-94; MSAD #27 Schl Jr HS Spec chr 1994-; *ai:* Future Ed Planning Comm; Transition Grant Comm; Language Club Adv; Winter Carnival Coach; NEA 1980-; NAD 1982-; ern ArooStook Parent of Dean 1982-, Pres, Currently Sec; Northern of Handicapped 1985-, Pres; Bd of Dirs Extension Assn 1993-, Sec; of Rel Ed 1974-, DRE for 3 Yrs; LeLeche League Intl 1984-; Tchr of Month 1992; Adv to All Star Gold Medal ME Rep to Future makers of Amer Natl Convention 1993; 100% Nutra Sweet Awd er 1994; Pub in SPIN 1986; Pub in Of Cradles & Careers; *office:* D #27 Eagle Lake Elem Schl PO Box 190 Eagle Lake ME 04739*

RICH-GIL, PATRICIA, ESL Teacher; *b:* Jersey City, NJ; *m:* avo; *ed:* Douglass Coll (BA) Span 1969; Fairleigh Dickinson Univ) ESL, Span 1970; 20 Credit Hrs in Related Areas; *cr:* River Edge Schl 3rd-6th Grd Span Tchr 1969-71; Union City Robert Waters Schl Tchr 1971-86; Emerson HS ESL Tchr 1986-; *ai:* NEA, NJEA, HCEA, A, NJTESOL 1971-; Union City Day Care Bd 1986-93, VP, Treas; : Emerson HS 318 18th St Union City NJ 07087

, CHARLES MALCOLM, Biology Teacher; *b:* Lynn, MA; *ed:* on Coll (BS) Ed, Bio 1967; Salem St Coll (MA) Scndry Ed 1972; 60 t Hrs in Various Scientific, Ed Fields; *cr:* Malden HS Bio Tchr 29 Yrs; NEA 1967-; AAAS 1992-; NEERS 1991-; Participated in Boston or Rsrch Project with Dr. Howard Weiss; *office:* Malden HS 77 Salem alden MA 02148*

, SHARON RUTH, First Grade Teacher; *b:* Altoona, PA; *m:* James Nancy Moran, Steven; *ed:* Kent St Univ (BS) Early Chldhd 1965; OH niv (MS) Early Mid Chldhd 1983; 30 Quarter Hrs After Masters; OH Recovery Prgm 1989-90; *cr:* Maple Heights Schls Kndgtn Tchr -66; Garfield Heights Schls Kndgtn Tchr 1968; Bedford Schls First Tchr 1968-69; Newark Schls First Grd Tchr 1970-; *ai:* NEA 1968-; St H Venture Capital Writing Team; *office:* William E Miller Elem Schl Granville Rd Newark OH 43055*

VE, CAROL MC BURNEY, HS Humanities & Bible Teacher; *b:* Los les, CA; *m:* Duncan; *c:* James, Nora, Joanna, Everett; *ed:* Reformed oyn Theological Seminary Cert Missions Stud 1969; *cr:* n-Economy Schls Fifth Grd Tchr 1967-68; Alliance Chrstn Schl Vol 1980-86; The Chrstn Acad Sub Tchr 1986-89; Trinity Chrstn Schl time Sub Tchr 1991-94, HS Tchr 1994-; *ai:* Drama Production Asst; Bd Comm; Act Sponsorship; Church 1993-, Adult Ed Comm; *office:* ty Christian Schl 299 Ridge Ave Pittsburgh PA 15221

VE, CATHARINE M., 9th Grade Civics Teacher; *b:* Hamilton, OH; effery D.; *c:* Niki, Derek; *ed:* Lawrence Univ (BA) His 1967; *cr:* eld Jr HS Civics Tchr 1988-; *ai:* Hnr Soc, Adopt A Schl, Optimist ch Club, Builders Club Adv; NEA, OEA, Local 1988-; *office:* Garfield S 250 N Fair Ave Hamilton OH 45011

VE, GREGORY MARK, Professor of Comp ACC Division; *b:* Bel Air, *m:* Jennifer Ann Larsen; *c:* Joshua, Jonathan, Josiah; *ed:* Towson St (BS) Bus 1988; *cr:* Nestle Food Dist Mgr 1988-92; Cntrl PA Bus Schl 1992-; *ai:* Adv Campus Chrstn Flwshp, Star Dot Star Club; New enant Flwshp 1991-, Elder; *office:* Central PA Bus School Campus on ge Hill Summerdale PA 17093

VE, JAMES LAWRENCE, Business Teacher; *b:* Pittsburgh, PA; *m:* n Smith; *c:* Jennifer, Renae, Anglina; *ed:* Eastern KY Univ (BS) Bus 970; Xavier Univ (MED) PE 1974; 6 Credit Hrs Comp Sci; *cr:* Little ni Schls PE, Hlth & 1st Aid Tchr 1969-74, PE Hlth & bus Ed Tchr -85; Moore Haven Local Schls Acct 1 & 2, Typing & Bus Ed Tchr -76; Chincoteage HS Rdng, Acctng & Bus Ed Tchr 1976-78; Pittsburgh Pub Schls Bus Instr, Comp App, Acctng 1, Law & Ec Tchr 1991-; *ai:* Asst Var Ftbl & Asst Var Sftbl Coach; Ldrshp Adv; Pep Club; NEA 1976-; PSAT 1991-; AFT 1993-; Perry Ath Assn 1965-; Numerous Poems Pub; Making a Difference Awd; Moore Haven Tchr of the Yr; *home:* 3915 Winshire St Pittsburgh PA 15212*

LOWE, JAMES SCOTT, History Teacher; *b:* Altoona, PA; *m:* Donna Kay Bennett; *ed:* IN Univ of PA (BS) Soc Stud Ed 1989; 24 Credits Toward Degree in Educl Psych; *cr:* Altoona HS Tchr 7 Yrs; *ai:* NEA 1989-; APIC 1995-; 3 Grants for Creative Tchng Projects; PA Lead Tchr; Presented Many Confs on Variety of Topics; *office:* Altoona Area HS 1415 6th Ave Altoona PA 16602

LOWE, MARTA NESTOR, Resource Center Teacher; *b:* Trenton, NJ; *c:* Lindsay Ayn, Molly Lynch; *ed:* Trenton St Coll (BS) Ed, Early Chldhd 1972, (MED) Ed, Dev, Handicapped, Spec Ed 1975; *cr:* Chesterfield Twp Schl Spec Ed Tchr 1973-; Mercer Cty Comm Coll Adj Fac 1993-; *ai:* Stu Variety Show Tchr Adv; Hamilton Aquatic Club USS, YMCA Swim Coach; Chesterfield Twp Ed Assn, NJEA, NEA 1973-; Sons & Daughters of Erin 1986-; NJ Governors Tchrs Recognition Awd 1988; *office:* Chesterfield Twp Schl 295 Bordentown Chesterfld Rd Trenton NJ 08620*

LOWE, NANCY L. (GORDINIER), High School Math Teacher; *b:* Watertown, NY; *m:* Andrew I.; *c:* Shari, Daniel; *ed:* SUNY at Oswego (BA) Scndry Math Ed 1973; 30 Grad Hrs; *cr:* Watertown City Schls 8th Grd Math Tchr 1971; Lowville Acad, Cntrl Schl 7th-9th Grd Math Tchr 1981-85; South Jefferson Cntrl Schl 7th-12th Grd Math Tchr 1985-; *ai:* Coord Peer Tutoring Prgm; NYSUT, AFT 1971-; South Jefferson Tchrs Assn 1985-; Tandy Tchr; *office:* South Jefferson Central Schl Box 10 Adams NY 13605

LOWE, RALPH G., English Teacher & Dept Head; *b:* Smithville, OH; *m:* Judy Ann King; *c:* Jamie Ashbaugh, Tami Carter, Scott; *ed:* Ashland Univ (BS) Bio Sci 1965; Mt St Joseph (MA) Ed 1986; *cr:* Southeast Local Schls Tchr & Coach 1965-68; West Holmes Local Schls Tchr & Coach 1968-80; Loudonville-Perrysville Tchr & Coach 1980-; *ai:* Adv Power of the Pen Writing Coach; Ftbl Coach; NEA, OEA 29 Yrs; LPEA 14 Yrs; *office:* Loudonville-Perrysville Schls 155 W Third St Perrysville OH 44864*

LOWE, SHIRLEY GERNHARDT, Latin Teacher; *b:* Phillipsburg, NJ; *m:* John Stephen; *c:* J. Michael; *ed:* Montclair St Coll (BA) Latin, Ed 1967; Trinity Coll (MA) Latin Lit, Classical Civ 1976; Attnd Tufts Univ, Amer Acad, Rutgers Univ; *cr:* Bernards HS Latin, Eng Tchr 1967-73; Wayland MS Latin, Eng Tchr 1973-, Foreign Lang Curr Ldr 1978-94; *ai:* Staff Dev Comm System Wide; Amer Cncl on Tchng Foreing Langs 1195-, Exec Cncl; CANE 1973-, Editorial Bd of Newsletter, Coulter Schlsp 1992; MAFLA 1976-, Pres 1989; NEA 1967-; MTA CAM, ACL, ACTFL; Lib Bd of Church 1993-, Chair 1994-; Earthwatch 1992-, Tchr Flwshp 1993; NEH Inst Fifth Century Athens, The World of Homer' 1990-91, The Words of Renaissance 1995; Consultant Ecce Romani Text Series 1980's; Pub NECN, J; *office:* Wayland MS 201 Main St Wayland MA 01778

LOWE, TERENCE A., Mathematics Teacher; *b:* Peterbrough, NH; *m:* Joan Ferris; *c:* Zachary, Sarah; *ed:* Dartmouth Coll (AB) Math 1964; Wesleyan Univ (MAT) Math 1966; Amer Univ; *cr:* Greenwich HS Math Tchr 1966-, Math Dept Chair 1982-88, Stu Act Sr Tchr 1988-91; *ai:* Boys Water Polo, Swimming Coaches; ANEA, NISCA 1966-; NCTM 1976-; Natl HS Swimming Coach of Yr 1985; Distinguished Tchr Awd 1990; NFL Tchr of Yr 1995; *office:* Greenwich HS 10 Hillside Rd Greenwich CT 06830

LOWENSTEIN, KAREN LYNNE, Spanish & AP Lit Teacher; *b:* Philadelphia, PA; *ed:* Rutgers Coll, Univ (BA) Span, Ed 1992; Middlebury Coll (MA) Span Lang, Lit 1995; *cr:* J. P. Stevens HS Span Tchr 1992-94; Edison HS Span, AP Lit Tchr 1995-; *ai:* AATSP, FLENJ 1992-; Northeast Conf Awd; *office:* Edison HS Blvd of Eagles Edison NJ 08817*

LOWER, CONRAD H.,IV, French Teacher; *b:* Philadelphia, PA; *ed:* Dickinson Coll (BA) Fr Ed 1989; West Chester Coll (MA) Fr Lit 1994; Fr & Ec at Universite Des Sciences Sciales; *cr:* Strath Haven Mid & HS Fr Tchr 1990-; *ai:* Stu Cncl Spon 1991-; Tennis Var Coach 1990-92; AATF 1993-, Exec Cncl; PSEA 1990-, Bldg Rep, Workload; AATF Schlrsp Grant 1994; Co-Arthur of MS Fr Text.*

LOWER, CONRAD H.,III, English Teacher & Admin Asst; *b:* Philadelphia, PA; *m:* Mary Elizabeth Fink; *c:* Conrad H. IV, Jannell Blythe; *ed:* Muskingum Coll (BA) His & Eng 1962; Temple Univ (MED) Admin 1967; *cr:* Euclid Schl Dist His & Eng Tchr 1962-63; Upper Dublin Schl Dist His & Eng Tchr 1963-76, Eng Dept Chm 1977-92, Admin Asst & Eng Tchr 1993-; *ai:* Bsbl Coach 1967-95; NEA 1963-; PCTE 1970-; ASCD 1975-; *office:* Sandy Run MS 520 Twining Rd Dresher PA 19025

LOWER, JEAN BIGGS, Retired Elementary Teacher; *b:* Coshocton, OH; *w:* Francis (dec); *c:* Debrah Kay Kleypas, Brooke; *ed:* Muskingum Coll (BS) Ed 1967; Attnd OSU; Post Grad Audited 2 Courses Cmptrs & Art Ed; *cr:* West Lafayette Elem Schl First Grd Tchr 1962-66; Coshocton-Lincoln Schl 2nd Grd Tchr 1966-72; Etna Elem Schl First Grd Tchr 1974-87; *ai:* NEA 1962-, Permanent Mbrshp; OEA 1962-, EOTA 1966-72; COTA 1974-; ORTA 1987-; AAUW 1970-, Local Branch Pres; *home:* 1811 Sawgrass Dr Reynoldsburg OH 43068

LOWERY, CLARK C., English Teacher; *b:* Providence, RI; *m:* Elizabeth Crabb; *c:* Steven, Deborah; *ed:* RI Coll (EDB) Eng 1965, (MAT) Eng 1968; 27 Addl Grad Credit Hrs; *cr:* Riverside Jr HS Eng, Fr Tchr 1965-80; East Providence Sr HS Eng Tchr 1980-; *ai:* Asst Coach Men's, Women's Track, Field; NEA 1965-; EPEA 1965-, Pres 1972; EPTCU 1965-, Pres 1973; USA Track, Field 1972-, New England Distngd Svc Awd 1995; *office:* East Providence Sr HS 2000 Pawtucket Ave East Providence RI 02914

LOWERY, NANCY D., Spanish Teacher & Dept Chprsn; *b:* Mc Allen, TX; *m:* John C. Jr.; *c:* Mark, T. Trent, Michele Mc Clure; *ed:* SUNY at Cortland (BA) K-9 Ed, K-12 Span 1972; 30 Addl Hrs Ithaca Coll, Cornell, SUNY at Cortland, Madrid Spain, Mexico City; *cr:* Dryden Cntrl HS Span Tchr 1972-; *ai:* Foreign Lang Dept Chprsn; Span Club Adv; Dist Planning cncl; Schlshp Comm; NEA, NYSAFLT 1974-; *home:* 2981 N Triphammer Rd Lansing NY 14882

LOWREY, JOYCE ANN, Education Professor; *b:* Meadville, PA; *ed:* Villa Maria Coll (BS) Elem Ed 1973; IN Univ of PA (MED) Spec Ed 1978; 6 Undergrad Hrs, 21 Grad Hrs Cnslng; *cr:* Villa Maria Coll Campus Schl Dir, Tchr Perpetual Dev Ctr 1978-81; Villa Maria Elem Schl Learning Disabilties Tchr 1981-85; Villa Maria Coll Dir LD Stdnts Prgm, Asst Prof Schl of Ed 19860-; Gannon Univ Dir LD Stdnts Prgm, Asst Prof Schl of Ed 1986-; *ai:* Bicentennial Childrens Lit Experience for Elem Stdnts Chair; Retention Task Force; Sigma Sigma Sigma Adv; Tchng, Learning Enhancement Advy Bd; Learning Disabilities Assn of Amer 1971-, Natl Bd of Dir 1994; L'Arche Erie 1987-, Sec; Learning Disabilities Assn of PA 1971-, Prof Advy Bd, Pres; Villa Maria Ctr 1993-, Bd of Dir; Books for Kids 1994-, Bd of Dir; Inst for Stdnts with LD 1990-, Advy Bd; Learning Disabilities of Erie Cty 1971-, Advocate; Pub Articles; Apple Polishing Awd Sigma Sigma Sigma; Barbara Bush Letter of Acclamation for work with Learning Disables; EACLD Awd; *office:* Gannon Univ University Square Erie PA 16541*

LOWRY, CHIEKO, Japanese Language Teacher; *b:* Yonago-shi, Japan; *m:* Raymond F. III; *c:* Naomi, Emily, Meg; *ed:* Tokyo Womens Chrstn Univ (BA) Eng 1969; Western Coll for Women Eng 1970-71; Bowling Green St Univ Japanese 1988-89; Univ of Toledo Ed 1990-; *cr:* Nippon Electric Co Translator & Interpreter 1971-72; Joshi Gakuin Jr & Sr HS Eng Tchr 1972-74; Univ of Toledo Japanese Instr 1982-88; Bowling Green St Univ Japanese Instr 1989; E L Bowsher HS Japanese Tchr 1988-; *ai:* Japanese Club Adv; Valedictorians Honoree; *office:* E L Bowsher HS 3548 S Detroit Ave Toledo OH 43614

LOWRY, JOAN HEANEY, Kindergarten Teacher; *b:* Flushing, NY; *m:* John R.; *c:* John R. II, James R., Joseph R.; *ed:* St Univ of NY at Cortland (BS) Elem Ed 1957; St Univ of NY at Stonybrook (MA) Liberal Stud 1976; 64 Credit Hrs Beyond Masters; *cr:* Plainview-Old Bethpage Schl Dist Kndgtn & 5th Grd Tchr 1957-59; Kindley Air Force Base 5th Grd Tchr 1959-60; Big Springs 4th Grd Tchr 1960-61; Yokota Air Force Base Japan 3rd Grd Tchr 1964-66; Miller Pl UFSD Kndgtn Tchr 1972-; *ai:* NYSTA 1972-; NEA 1957-; Miller Place Tchrs Assn 1972-; Plainview-Old Bethpage Tchrs Assn 1957-, Chm of Intnl Relations Comm; Miller Place-Mount Sinai Historical Soc; Rel Ed Tchr; Cub Scout Ldr; PTO 1957-, VP in Japan; Instr Magazine Article; *home:* PO Box 747 Miller Place NY 11764*

LOWTHER, MARTHA H., Mathematics Teacher; *b:* Pittsburgh, PA; *m:* William M.; *c:* Betsy, Andrew; *ed:* U of DE (BA) Math 1971, (MED) Scndry Math 1993; *cr:* St Elizabeth HS Math Tchr 1970-77; The Tatnall Schl Math Tchr 1983-; *ai:* Dir Stud; NCTM, DCTM 1985-; Pub in NCTM; *office:* The Tatnall Schl 1501 Barley Mill Rd Wilmington DE 19807

LOY, JENNIFER AMOLE, English Teacher; *b:* Chillicothe, OH; *m:* Dean; *c:* Stephanie, Nicole; *ed:* Wright St Univ (BS) Speech & Theatre 1978; Eng & Rdng Certs; *cr:* Mississinawa Vly Schls Tchr 1978-; *ai:* Future Edctrs of Amer; MVCTC 1978-, Sec; VOD Tchr of Yr; *office:* Mississinawa Valley HS 1469 St Rt 47 Union City OH 45390

LOY, STEVEN A., Headmaster & English Teacher; *b:* Los Angeles, CA; *m:* Philomena C.; *c:* Matthew, Christopher, Eric; *ed:* Princeton (BA) Eng 1974; Stanford (MA) Ed 1975; UCLA (EDD) Ed 1980; *cr:* Brentwood Schl Asst Head of Schl 1976-82; Dunn Schl Head of Schl 1982-92; Rutgers Prep Schl Head of Schl 1992-; *office:* Rutgers Preparatory Schl 1345 Easton Ave Somerset NJ 08873

LOY, SUSAN SINCLAIR, Teacher of Gifted & Language; *b:* Washington, DC; *w:* Donald E. (dec); *c:* Nancy Marie Loy-Jackson, Debra Sue Loy-Canini; *ed:* OH Univ (BSEd) Span, His, & Pol Sci 1958; Dayton Univ (MED) Tchr Ed & Gifted Ed 1987; Attnd OH Univ, Univ of Maryland, Coll of Mount St Joseph; *cr:* Groveport-Madison Jr & Sr HS Amer His & Span 1959-60; Fairfield Cty Jr Sr HS Sub Tchr 1967-74; Bloom & Carroll Jr HS Tchr of Gifted, Rdng & Eng 1974-; *ai:* Pi Lambda Theta 1958-; NEA, OEA, & BCEA 1975-, Bldg Rep; Fairfield Heritage Assn 1970-; OH Historical Assn 1975-; 1st Eng Luth Church 1991-, Church Cncl, Educl Comm Chprsn; Martha Holden Jennings Scholar; Ashland Tchr of the Yr Nom; *office:* Bloom Carroll HS 69 N Beaver St Carroll OH 43112*

LOYST, BEVERLY WOODS, Social Studies Teacher; *b:* Carthage, NY; *c:* Richard, Kim Butts, Abdrewm, Kevin; *ed:* St Lawrence Univ (BA) Fr, Eng 1952; SUNY at Buffalo (MED) Elem Ed; Attnd Middlebury Coll, Colgate Univ; *cr:* St Vincent DePaul Schl 16 Yrs; *office:* St Vincent Depaul Schl Rice Rd & Seneca St Spring Brook NY 14140

LOZA, LEONARD ANTONY, Physical Science Teacher; *b:* Brooklyn, NY; *ed:* Orange Cty Comm Coll (AA) Bio 1970; SUNY at New Paltz (BA) Bio 1978, (MA) Ed 1981; *cr:* Middletown Cntrl Schls Tchr 1980-82; Poughkeepsie City Schls Tchr 1983-; *ai:* Vlg of New Paltz Planning Bd Chm 1994-95, Tree Commission 6 Yrs; Mid Hudson Suba Assn 1993-, VP, Search & Rescue; Ecological Evaluation of Whaley Lake Grant Dept of Bio Vassar Coll 1977; *office:* Poughkeepsie City Schls 55 College Ave Poughkeepsie NY 12603

LOZO, ELLEN CYBUCH, Fourth Grade Teacher; *b:* Jersey City, NJ; *m:* William Robert; *c:* Sheryl Lynn, Buckley; *ed:* Jersey City St Coll (BA) Elem Ed 1974; 15 Credits Grad Courses Jersey City St Coll, Monmouth Coll; *cr:* Fairfield Schls Tchr; Winston Churchill Elem Schl 4-5 Grd Tchr, Adlai E. Stevenson Elem Schl 4 Grd Tchr 22 Yrs; *ai:* NEA, NJEA, ECEA, FEA 1974-.

LUBANOVIC, THOMAS FRANCIS, Professor of Civil Engineering; *b:* Wilkingsburg, PA; *m:* Linda Ellen Vilsack; *ed:* CCAC Boyce Campus (AS) Civil Engrng 1976; Point Park Coll (BS) Civil Engrng 1979; Univ of Pittsburg (MS) Civil Engrng 1983; Grad Stud PA St Univ; *cr:* Epic Metals Corp Drafting Technician 1972-75; Overly Mfg Co Project Desing Engr 1975-79; Westinghouse Co Structural Engr 1979-81; Comm Coll of Allegheny Co Engrng Prof 1981-; *ai:* Golf, Bowling Coach; Engrng Club Adv; PA Soc of Surveyors, PA Soc of Engrs 1992-; Croation Fraternal Union 1980-; PA, ME, WV PRof Engr; PA, WV Prof Land Surveyor; *office:* Comm Coll of Allegheny 595 Beatty Rd Monroeville PA 15146

LUBAR, PHYLLIS L., Speech & Language Pathologist; *b:* New Haven, CT; *m:* Edward; *c:* Emily Berman; *ed:* Syracuse Univ (BS) Speech Pathology 1969; Boston Univ (MED) Speech, Lang 1971; 30 Addl Credit Hrs Job, Career Courses; *cr:* Brockton Pub Schls Speech, Lang Pathologist 1969-71; Spaulding Rehab Hosp Speech, Lang Pathologist 1971-75; Learing Prep Schl Speech, Lang Pathologist 1977-84; Needham Pub Schls Speech, Lang Pathologist 1984-; *ai:* Schl Cncl; Parent Cnslng Groups; Self Assessment Comm; Amer Speech, Lang, Hearing Assn 1969-; NEA, MA Tchrs Assn 1984-; Grants Provide Parent Groups, 3 Credit Course Inclusion to Tchrs; Ed Speech, Lang Text.

LUBECK, ANNE LINDENBAUM, Third Grade Teacher; *b:* New York City, NY; *m:* C. David; *c:* Susan, Robert; *ed:* Trenton St (BSEd) K-8 Elem Grd Tchr 1972; Trenton St Coll (MA) Rdng 1974; Supvrs Cert, Rdng Specialist 1975; *cr:* Beverly Elem Schl Title I Tchr 1973-76; Willingboro Elem Schls Title I, Basic Skills, 1st, 5th, 3rd Grd Tchr 1974-; *ai:* Stu Cncl Schl Store Adv; Peer Mediation; Advy Cncl; Planning Comm; Teacher Liason PTO; NEA 1973-; AAUW; Bd Outstdng Will Stdnts 1987-; Yth Achvmt 1987-; Human Relations 1983-86; Tchr of Yr Awd 1993-94; AT Grant Peer Mediation; *office:* Martin Luther King Elem Schl 157 Northampton Dr Willingboro NJ 08046*

LUBIN, CHERYL BETH, Adj Prof of Speech & Theater; *b:* Los Angeles, CA; *ed:* Vassar Coll (BA) His 1986; Tulane Law Schl (JD) Law 1989; Post-Grad Stud: Dramatic Writing & Performance, The New Schl; *cr:* John Jay Coll Adj Prof 1992-; Stern Coll Adj Prof 1993-; *ai:* Debate Club Fac Adv; Theatrical Dir; NY Bar Assn 1990-; Intnl Womens Writing Guild 1995-; Taught Courtroom Commnctn, Media & Crime, Argumentation & Debate at John Jay Coll; Taught Courtroom Drama & Film at Stern Coll; *office:* City Univ Of NY John Jay Coll 445 W 59th St Ofc New York NY 10019

LUBINGER, JOSEPH DAVID, American History Teacher; *b:* Charlotte, NC; *m:* Diane Marie Lenzotti; *c:* Jillian; *ed:* Cleveland St Univ (BA) Sociology 1978, (MED) Curr & Instruction 1993; Tchng Cert Comprehensive Soc Stud 1987; Kent St Univ, Drake Univ 7 Credit Hrs; *cr:* Beachwood HS Soc Stud, Amer & World His Tchr 1988-89; Taylor Acad Soc Stud, Amer & World Geog Tchr 1989-90; Shaker Hts Soc Stud, Amer & World His Tchr 1990-93; Brecksville-Broadview Hts HS Soc Stud, Amer His & Sociology Tchr 1993-; *ai:* Sr Class Adv; Asst Var Bsbl Coach; Fac Mgr; Natl Geog Alliance 1990-; NEA, OEA & BEA 1993-; OH HS Bsbl Coaches Assn 1995-; *office:* Brecksville-Broadview Hts HS 6376 Mill Rd Cleveland OH 44147

LUBINSKY, HIUDY DEBORAH, Prof & Chair of Speech Dept; *b:* Brooklyn, NY; *m:* Menachem Y.; *c:* Tzippy Fettmah, Meiri, Tzviya; *ed:* Brooklyn Coll (BA) Speech Pathology 1975, (MS) Speech Pathology 1980; ASHA Cert Accredited Courses; Sign Langc; *cr:* OHEL Group Homes

Supervising Speech Therapist 1979-89; Al Pi Darleo Speech Therapist 1991; Pvt Practice Speech Pathologist 1982-; XIYC Bd of Ed Ind Speech Provider 1992-; Touro Coll Prof, Chair Speech Dept 1991-; *ai:* Stu Cnslr; Lecturer; Seminars; ASHA, NYSHLA, NYS Speech Lic 1982-; Tchr, Speech & Hearing Handicapped Lic 1975-; Outstdng Svc Awd OHEL Family Svcs & Children's Home; *home:* 1042 E 23rd St Brooklyn NY 11210

LUBRECHT, KAREN EMLEY, Math & Computer Science Tchr; *b:* Easton, PA; *c:* Clint, Chad; *ed:* Susquehanna Univ (BA) Physics 1970; Masters Equival Ed 1991; 19 Addl Hrs; *cr:* Camden City Schls Math Tchr 1970-72; Red Lion HS Physics Tchr 1981-82; Cntrl Daydain Schl Dlst Math Tchr 1984-87; E. Stroudsburg HS Math & Tech Tchr 1987-; Lafayette Coll Part-time Physics Lab Instr 1989; *ai:* Dist Tech, Supts Advy Comms; NPCTM, Mbrshp Chair; NCTM; PCTM; APS; AAPT; NEA; PSEA; ESEA; Atomic, Molecular & Optical Physics Div of APS; Coopers Battery B Civil War Reinactment Group 1995-, Sec; AAUW; Delegate, Speaker to 1st US, Russia Joint Conf on Ed 1994; *office:* E Stroudsburg HS N Courtland St East Stroudsburg PA 18301

LUBY, THOMAS AQUINAS,JR., Radiolgc Tech Prof & Dept Head; *b:* Baltimore, MD; *m:* Kathryn; *c:* Thomas III, Kristen; *ed:* Univ of MD (BS) Radiologic Tech 1976; Univ of Baltimore (MBA) Bus, Fin 1988; *cr:* Children's Hosp Natl Med Ctr Imaging Mgr 1983-87; Fallston Gen Hosp Imaging Dir 1987-91; Anne Arundel Comm Coll Dept Head 1991-; *ai:* Class Adv Radiologic Tech Club; Instruction, Discipline, Compensation, Curr Comm; ASRT 1983-; MSRT 1976-; AES 1994-; *office:* Anne Arundel Comm Coll 101 College Pky Arnold MD 21012

LUCABAUGH, NATHAN JOHN, 8th Grade Language Arts Tchr; *b:* Hanover, PA; *m:* Susan Miller; *c:* Abram M., Alison S.; *ed:* Salem Coll (BS) Eng, PE 1968; Western MD 24 Credit Hrs; *cr:* New Oxford MS Lang Arts Tchr 1971-; *ai:* Fly Tying Club Adv; *home:* 1448 Abbottstown Pike Hanover PA 17331

LUCANIK, KAREN M., Pub Speaking, Drama & Eng Tchr; *b:* St Marys, PA; *ed:* Univ of Pittsburgh at Johnstown (BA) Scndry Ed Comm; Various Govt, Comm Courses; *cr:* St Marys Area HS Pub Speaking, Drama, Eng Tchr 1981-; St Marys MS Eng Tchr 1983-90; Polley Real Estate Schl Instr 1987-; *ai:* Drama, Gymnastics Coach; Aerobic Instr, Competitor, Club Adv; Jr Class Adv; Nom Tchr of Yr; *office:* St Marys Area HS 977 S Saint Marys Rd Saint Marys PA 15857

LUCARELLI, JOHN A., Assoc Professor of English; *b:* Elmira, NY; *m:* Nancy J. Moore; *c:* David; *ed:* St Bonaventure Univ (BA) Eng 1963, (MA) Eng 1967; Univ of Pittsburgh (PHD) Medieval Lit 1971; 6 Grad Credits Linguistics, Lit Criticism at NY St Univ Geneseo 1964-65; Post Doctoral Work Italian Lang, Culture Dante Alighieri Inst Florence Italy 1987; *cr:* Letchworth Cntrl Schl 10th, 12th Grd Eng Tchr 1963-65; Allegany HS 9th Grd Eng Tchr 1965-67; CCAC-Allegheny Campus Eng Composition, Lit Tchr 1969-; *ai:* Alpha Mu Theta Adv; Phi Theta Kappa Intnl Hon Soc; AFT 1972-84, Campus VP 1975-77; Western PA Symposium on World Lit 1975-, Advy Bd; Jane Austin Soc of N Amer 1993-, Dickens Flwshp 1994-; Western PA Historical Soc 1987-; Carnegie Museum of Art, Natural His 1980-; Pittsburgh Jazz Soc 1989-; Societa Dante Alighieri 1986-, Treas; Articles Pub; *office:* Comm Coll Algny Co Algny Cmps 808 Ridge Ave Pittsburgh PA 15212

LUCARELLI, ROSEMARY, Lang Arts & Frgn Lang Teacher; *b:* Passaic, NJ; *m:* Mario; *c:* Nicole, Michael; *ed:* Fairleigh Dickinson Univ (BA) Fr 1968; *cr:* Woodrow Wilson Jr HS 8-9 Grd Fr, Eng Tchr 1969-78; Woodrow Wilson MS 8 Grd Lang Arts, For Lang Tchr 1986-; *ai:* Natl Jr Hnr Soc Adv; NEA, NJEA 1969-78; Clifton Tchrs Assoc; Passaic Cty Tchrs Assoc; Natl Assoc of Stu Activity Advs; *office:* Woodrow Wilson MS 1400 Van Houten Ave Clifton NJ 07013

LUCAS, BERNIE A.,JR., Fourth Grade Teacher; *b:* Bangor, ME; *m:* Catherine M. Goodwin; *ed:* Univ of ME at Presque Isle (BS) Elem Ed 1975; Univ of ME at Orono (MED) Elem Ed 1980; *cr:* Helen Hunt 4th Grd Tchr 1975-80, 1984-; Lewis Stairs Grd 4-5th Grd Tchr 1980-83; Herbert Gray Grd 3rd-4th Grd Tchr 1983-84; *ai:* Cooperating Tchr for Stu Tchrs; Prof Preparation Team Bldg Rep; Old Town Math Curr Comm; Old Town Assn 1975-; ME Tchr Assn 1975-; Natl Ed Assn 1975-; Phi Kappa Phi Honor Soc 1981-; Contributor to ME Stud Curr Project Title IV 1979; Contributor to Instr & Tchr 1982; Contributor to Tchng Tips from Kodak 1983; *office:* Helen Hunt Schl 47 S Brunswick St Old Town ME 04468

LUCAS, CONSTANCE SANTARIELLO, HS French & Spanish Teacher; *b:* Uniontown, PA; *m:* Donald G.; *c:* Christina Angela Mascia; *ed:* Univ of Dayton (BS) Scndry Ed, Fr Span 1965; Duquesne Univ, Penn St Extension (MEQ) Scndry Ed, Span 1971-72; *cr:* Anne Arundel Cty Schls Fr Span HS Tchr 1965-66; Sto Rox Jr Sr HS Fr Span HS Tchr 1966-; *ai:* Lang Club Adv; Frgn Trip Coord, Cnslr; NHS Comm for Review & Selection; PA St Ed Assn, SREA Local Tchrs Assn, NEA 1966-; Pittsburgh Post Gazette & U of Pittsburgh All Star Edctr 1994; *office:* Sto-Rox Jr-Sr HS 1105 Valley St Mc Kees Rocks PA 15136*

LUCAS, CYNTHIA SEKEL, Mathematics Teacher; *b:* Cambridge, OH; *m:* Randy; *ed:* OH Univ (BSEd) Elem Ed 1991; *cr:* Roseville MS 7th-8th Grd Math Tchr 1991-; *ai:* Bsktbl, Vlybl Coach; Math Counts Adv; NEA, OEA 1992-; NCTM 1991-; *office:* Roseville MS 76 W Athens Rd Roseville OH 43777*

LUCAS, DAVID MIGUEL, Professor of Spanish & Speech; *b:* Seymour, IN; *c:* Jason, Jessica, Jordan; *ed:* KY Chrstn Coll (BA) Comm 1973, (BA) Theology 1924; Marshall Univ (MA) Comm 1976; OH Univ (PHD) Intnl Rel 1996; Cert ESL Trng, Cross Cultural Trainer; Intnl Negotiations Seminar WA DC; *cr:* OE Inc CEO 1971-90; Marshall Univ Asst Prof 1976-78; OH Univ Prof 1990-96; *ai:* Fac Adv Los Amigos Intnl Alumni Coord; Phi Beta Delta 1995-, Int Relations; Latin Amer Assn 1993-; *office:* OH Univ 1804 Liberty Ave Ironton OH 45638*

LUCAS, EILEEN, Special Education Teacher; *b:* Cairo, WV; *m:* Robert Terry; *c:* Joshua, Jesse, Justin; *ed:* OSU (BA) Early Child Dev 1970, (MS) Spec Ed 1972; Cert LD, BD Classroom Dayton U 1988; *cr:* Waterown 3rd-4th Grd Tchr 1967-68; Franklin Co Prgm for Mentally Retarded 9-12 Yr Olds Tchr 1970-73; Marietta Jr HS Rdng, Sci, Eng, Spec Ed Tchr 1992-; Frontier HS Rdng, Sci, Eng, Spec Ed Tchr 1992-; *ai:* Stu Cncl Adv; NHS Comm Nominations; NEA 1976-; Demcher Bapt Church 1978-, Sunday Schl Tchr; Project Youthdead Marierta Coll.*

LUCAS, GAY LYNN, Sixth Grade Teacher; *b:* Pittsburgh, PA; *m:* Daniel George; *c:* Craig Daniel, Jack Adair; *ed:* Kent St Univ (BS) Elem Ed 1965; Grad Work Baldwin Wallace Coll, John Carroll Univ, FL St Univ; *cr:* Edith Whitney Elem Schl Sixth Grd Tchr 21 Yrs; *ai:* Rdng Club Adv; Fac Rep to Supt; Staff-Comm Relations Rep; Tech, Prins Advy Comms; OEA, NEA, NEOEO 1975-; PTA 1969-; Ath Booster; Women's League; North Cntrl Assn of Colls, Schls Evaluation Comm 1987-88; Martha Holden Jennings Scholar 1987-88; Strongsville Tchr of Yr 1989-90; OH Congress of Parents, Tchrs Honorary Life Mem; Ashland Oil Co Inc Golden Apple Achiever Awd 1992, 1995; Honorable Mention Cleveland Plain Dealer Crystal Apple Awd 1995.

LUCAS, HARRY D., English Teacher; *b:* Mahonoy City, PA; *ed:* The PA St Univ (BS) Scndry Ed, Eng 1984; Kutztown Univ (MED) Curr, Instruction 1990; *cr:* St Clair Area HS Eng Tchr 1984-85; Pottsville Area HS Eng Tchr 1985-86; Tamaqua Area HS Eng Tchr 1987-89; N Schuylkill Jr Sr HS Eng Tchr 1986-87, 1989-; *ai:* Schl Play Dir; Co-Adv Class 1994; Stu Cncl Adv; PSEA, NEA 1984-; Mahonoy City Lib 1990-, Dir; BPO Elks #695 1981-; Who's Who in Amer Ed 1992, 1993; *office:* North Schuylkill Jr Sr HS RR #2 Box 47 Ashland PA 17921

LUCAS, LAWRENCE ARTHUR, High School Music Teacher; *b:* Ft Knox, KY; *m:* Sheree Hutter; *ed:* Carnegie Melion Univ (BFA) Music-Trumpet Performance 1992, (BS) Indstrl Mngmt 1992; Addl Music Ed Cert, Minor in Instrumental Conducting; Duquesne Univ Orff Methods Level I Cert; *cr:* North Hills HS Priv Music Instr, Music Asst 1989-93; East Allegheny HS Band Dir, Music Tchr 1993; Peters Twp HS Band Dir, Music Tchr 1993-95, Music Dept Facilitator, Band Dir, Music Tchr 1996; *ai:* Marching Band, Pep Band Dir; Music Dept Facilitator, Grad Project Comm; Amer Fed of Tchrs, PA Music Ed Assoc, MENC 1993-; *office:* Peters Twp HS 264 E Mcmurray Rd Mc Murray PA 15317*

LUCAS, LOUIS RALPH, Adjunct Asst Prof; *b:* New York, NY; *ed:* City Coll of NY (BS) Bio 1979; Tulane Univ (PHD) Neurobiology 1993; Laboratory of Neuroendocrinology BS Mc Ewen 1993-; *cr:* NYS Psychiatric Inst Rsrch Scientist I 1980-83; NOVO Diagnostic Systems Rsrch Assoc 1983-85; Columbia Univ Staff Assoc 1985-86; NYS Psychiatric Inst Rsrch Scientist II 1986-88; *ai:* Soc for Neuroscience 1988-; Rockefeller Univ Postdoctoral Flwshp; Natl Insts of Drug Abuse Dir's Travel Awd 1995; Coll of Problems with Drugs Dependence Meeting; *office:* Borough Of Manhattan Comm Coll 199 Chambers St New York NY 10007

LUCAS, MELBA, Dance Teacher; *b:* Washington, DC; *ed:* Amer Univ (BA) Performing Arts, Dance 1978; Univ of DC (MA) Adult Ed 1983; Continuing Stud Dance, Hum, Other Interrelated Art Forms at The Smithsonian Inst, Knock on Wood Studios, Kathy Harty Gray Modern Dance, Ethel Butler Modern Dance; *cr:* Ellington Schl of Arts Tchr 15 Yrs; DC Art Works Artistic Dir 3 Yrs; Jones-Haywood Schl of Ballet Tchr 4 Yrs; Largo HS Tchr 2 Yrs; *ai:* Dev Dance Ensemble; PGCEA, NEA 1994-; Kennedy Ctr 1983-, Dance Consultant; Suitland VPA 1993-, Dance Consultant; Jones-Haywood Schl 1990-, Dance Consultant; Danced Professionally with Jason Taylor Dance Theatre, Cacho's African Drummers & Dancers, Numerous Musical Theatre Productions; Dev Curr Dance His Ellington Schl for Arts DC Pub Schls; *home:* 301 G St SW Apt 316 Washington DC 20024

LUCAS, PAMELA HOWE, Fourth Grade Teacher; *b:* Pittsburgh, PA; *m:* Roy Dean; *c:* Tanja, Aaron; *ed:* Capital Univ (BA) Art Ed 1971; Working on Master of Lang Arts, Recertified Elem Ed 1981 OH St Univ; Completing Rdng Speciality Cert; *cr:* Whitehall City Schls Math, Sci 8th Grd Tchr 1981-, All Subjects 4th Grd Tchr 1981-; *ai:* Peer Mediation Bldg Coord; Whitehall Citywide Mediation Cncl, Advy Bd; Grant Admin Basic Schl Planning Bd; OEA, NEA, Whitehall Ed Assn 1995-; Amer Red Cross 1985-, Site Bloodmobile Coord; Columbus Lit Cncl 1987-, Past Tutor; Gideons Intnl Auxilary 1986-, Chaplain, VP; PTA 1976-, Past Pres; Whitehall Citizen of Yr 1990; Edctr of Yr 1986; WCMH-TV4 Golden Apple Awd Tchr of Month 1993; *office:* Etna Road Elem Schl 4531 Etna Rd Columbus OH 43213*

LUCAS, PAUL, Assoc Prof of European History; *b:* New York, NY; *c:* Jonathan, Jennifer; *ed:* Bradeis Univ (BA) European His 1955, (MA) European His 1957, (PHD) European His 1963; *cr:* WA St Univ at St Louis Ass't Assoc Prof 1959-69; Clark Univ Assoc Prof 1969-; *ai:* Amer Historical Assn 1960-; Various Articles; *office:* Clark Univ 950 Main St Worcester MA 01610*

LUCAS, RENEE SUE, Biology Teacher; *b:* Marion, OH; *ed:* OH Wesleyan Univ (BA) Pre-Prof Zollogy 1991; Post-Degree Prgm Sci Ed OH St Univ; *cr:* Bishop Ready HS Bio Tchr 1993-; *ai:* Asst Track, Cross Cntry Coach; Soph Class Adv; Yth to Yth Moderator; SECO, NSTA 1992-; Presented Swap Shop Discussion 1995; Papers at Assn for Chemoreception Sci 1991-93; COSEN Summer Schlr; *office:* Bishop Ready HS 707 Salisbury Rd Columbus OH 43204*

LUCAS, SHEILA WHITE, English & Reading Teacher; *b:* Washington, DC; *m:* Edrick a.; *c:* Tyrone, Paul; *ed:* DC Tchrs Coll (BS) Speech Correction 1976; Trinity Coll 12 Credit Hrs Rdng; *cr:* DC Pub Schls Eng Tchr 1976-83; St Phillip The Apostle Eng Tchr 1984-86; St John Bapt de la Salle Eng Tchr 1986-; *ai:* Safety Patrol Spon; Pub Relations Comm; 8th Grd adv; *office:* St Johns Military HS 5704 Sargent Rd Hyattsville MD 20782*

LUCAS, THEODORE ALAN, Chemistry Teacher; *b:* Chambersburg, PA; *m:* Denise Naugle; *c:* Brenton T., Bradley S.; *ed:* Shippensburg Univ (BS) Chem 1967, (MS) Chem 1970; *cr:* S Huntington Cty HS Chem & Physics Tchr 1967-68; James Buchanan HS Chem Tchr 1968-; Penn St Chem Lecturer; *ai:* Audio-Visual Dir; Cmptr Consultant; NEA, PSEA & Tuscrora Ed Assn 1967-; Local Model Aircraft Assn 1980-, Treas; Church Choir 1980-, Baritone; *office:* James Buchanan HS 4773 Ft Loudon Rd Mercersburg PA 17236

LUCAS, WADE E., 7th-8th Grd Math Teacher; *b:* Barnesville, OH; *m:* Teresa Randell; *c:* Nicole, Jenna, Zachery; *ed:* OH Univ (BS) Elem Ed 1986; Ashland Univ (MS) Admin 1996; *cr:* Coshocton HS 5th Grd Tchr 1986-87; Mt Vernon MS 6th Grd Tchr 1988-89; Coshocton HS 7-8 Grd His, Math Tchr 1989-; *ai:* Head Ftbl, Track Coach; Key Club Adv; 8th Grd Washington DC Trip Dir; CCEA, NEA 1986-; Grace United Meth Church 1987-; Coach of Yr Eastern Dist, Region II 1994; Coach of South Squadon OH; *office:* Coshocton HS 1205 Cambridge Rd Coshocton OH 43812

LUCCIOLA, PATRICIA ANN, Secondary School Art Teacher; *b:* Providence, RI; *ed:* RI Coll (BS) K-12 Art Ed 1980; RI Schl of Design (MAT) Ed, Painting 1985; Tchr Inst; Post-Grad Stud RI Coll; *cr:* North Providence Schl Dept Grd K-8 Grd Art Tchr 1980-88, Grd 9-12 Scndry Art Tchr 1988-; *ai:* Trng Prgm for NE Regnl Coalition for Drug-Free Schls Sponsored by US Dept of Ed 1990; Art Club 1988-90; Super Teams Ltd Substance Abuse Drug Prevention Prgm 1988-93; Special Art Projects Coord 1987-; Co-Chair Annual RIAEA Art Tchrs Exhibition 1985-; NEA 1979-80; RI Art Ed Assn 1983-, Corresponding Sec 1987-92; NAEA 1979-80, 1993-; RI Regnl Advy Comm Regnl Scholastics Art Awds 1987-91; Boosters Assn 1990-; Substance Abuse Prevention Task Force 1990-, Sec 1991-94; Champlain Grant 1987-88; Key to Town 1989; Cert of Appreciation & Dedication Schl Dept 1988-90; Resolution of Congratulations Town Cncl for Presiddntial Awd Drug Free Schls 1990; *office:* North Providence HS 1828 Mineral Spring Ave North Providence RI 02904*

LUCE, AMY E., 11th & 12th Grade English Tchr; *b:* Erie, PA; *m:* Gregory; *ed:* Penn St Univ at Univ Pk (BS) Scndry Ed, Eng 1986; 36 Credits; *cr:* Villa Maria Elem Schl Grds 6-8 Eng Tchr 1986-93; Fairview HS Grds 11-12 Eng Tchr 1993-; *ai:* Former Lit Magazine Adv, Acad Decathlon Coach; Northwest PA Writing Project 1989-; PSEA, NEA, NCTE, NW PA Cncl Tchrs of Eng 1993-; St Mark Church 1994-, Catechist, Lector, Musician; Conf Presenter Northwest PA Writing Project 1990-; PA Dept Ed Writing Assessment Scorer Statewide Exam 1995; Mentor Tchr 1990-93; Initiated & Instituted Mandatory Summer Rdng Prgm Hnrs Stdnts 1993; *office:* Fairview HS 7460 Mccray Rd Fairview PA 16415*

LUCE, ANNE CRANDALL, Psychology Professor; *b:* Brockport, NY; *m:* Ronald; *c:* Sommer Donovan, Shannon Donovan, Jonathan; *ed:* Cornell Univ (BS) Psych 1970; SUNY at Buffalo (PHD) Dev Psych 1975; *cr:* Jamestown Comm Coll Prof 1974-; *ai:* Phi Theta Kappa Co-Adv; Phi Kappa Phi, Natl Sci Fnd Flwshps; Outstdng Women of Amer; Excl in Tchg Fac Awd; *office:* Jamestown Comm Coll 525 Falconer St Jamestow 14701

LUCE, DEBORA REYNOLDS, Fourth Grade Teacher; *b:* Wh AFB, MO; *m:* David; *c:* Joel; *ed:* Univ of ME (BS) Elem Ed 19 Portland Schl Dept Tchr Asst 1978-79; Windham Schl Dept Clas Tchr 1979-; *ai:* Cmptr Comm; Staff Cmptr Dev; Dirigo Day Educators Rep; BSA Adv; MEA Assn 1979-; Windham Boosters Gifted & Talented Grant; Technology Grant AIM 1996; Manchester-Arlington Schl 709 Roosevelt Trl Windham ME 04062

LUCE, JEFFREY ROGER, Mathematics Teacher; *b:* Garfield H OH; *ed:* Northwestern Univ (BS) Math 1989; 22 Credit Hrs Kent S Sports Admin; *cr:* Hoffman Estates HS Math Tchr & Girls Soccer 1989-90; Hillcrest HS Math Tchr & Boys Cross Cntry & Track 19 Norton HS Math Tchr & Girls Bsktbl Boys Track & Acad Challeng 1991-93; Breckville Brdvw Hts HS Math Tchr, 8th Grd Boys Bsktbl Girls HS Track Coach 1994-; *ai:* Head Var Boys Track Coach; Challenge Team Adv; Fac Advy Comm Mem; Scoreboard Operator f Games; PA Announcer for Bsktbl Games; NEA 1989-; *home:* Berkshire Dr Macedonia OH 44056*

LUCE, JULIA M., French & German Teacher; *b:* Westwood, N Daniel; *c:* Christian, Patrick; *ed:* Montclair St Univ (BA) Fr, Ger Summer Stud Laval Univ 1983; NJ Alternate Route to Ed for Tchn 1986-87; *cr:* Compagnie Francaise de Forges et Fonderies Biling Admin Asst 1984-86; Park Ridge HS Fr, Ger Tchr 1986-; *ai:* Co-Di Park Ridge High Schl Pageant; Organize Annual Intnl Dinner Frgn Stdnts; NEA 1986-; AATF 1987-; Lakeside Choraliers 1987-; Congregational Church of Park Ridge 1975-; *office:* Park Ridge HS Ave Park Ridge NJ 07656

LUCERNE, MARY JOYCE DAVIDSON, Second Grade Teach Trenton, NJ; *c:* Robert, John, David; *ed:* St Francis Coll at Loretto Elem Ed 1962; Attnd Immaculate Coll, West Chester St Univ; *cr:* C Jt Schl Dist 1st, 2nd 3rd Grd Tchr 1962-63; Coatesville Area Cath Sc Grd Tchr 1981-82, Kndgtn Tchr 1982-83, 2nd Grd Tchr 1983-95; GED Instr 1990-95; *ai:* Mission Coord; NCEA 1981; Jr Womans 1964-81, Ways, Means Chm; Visiting Team Mem for Assembly of Schls of Mid Sts Assn of Colls, Schls; *office:* Coatesville Area Cath Sch 605 E Lincoln Hwy Coatesville PA 19320

LUCEY, JEANNETTE,IHM, Eighth Grade Teacher; *b:* Easton, P Immaculata Coll (BA) His 1970; Villanova Univ (MA) His 197 Suburban Philadelphia Cath Schls 1st Grd & 8th Grd Tchr 1962-72 of Philadelphia Cath Schls 8th Grd Tchr 1972-; *ai:* Math Club Ad Club Adv; Geography Club Adv; Schl Peace Awd Comm; Dev Co-Di Trying to Eliminate Pollution Adv; NSTA, NCEA; Anheuser Environmental Awd A Pledge & A Promise Natl 2nd Place 1995; Saint Francis De Sales Schl 917 S 47th St Philadelphia PA 19143

LUCHANSKY, BARBARA PILECKI, HS English Instructo Middletown, CT; *m:* Richard J.; *c:* Adam; *ed:* Cntrl CT St Univ (MS) 1990; *cr:* St Mary Home Prgm Dir 1972-77; Consolidated Schl Permanent Sub Tchr, Tutor 1977-78; E. C. Goodwin Tech Schl HS Instr 1978-; *ai:* Fitness Club; Peer Coaching; Mentor Prgm; Co Resolution Comm; Class, Yrbk Adv; AFT, SVFT, NCTE 1978-, Me Jerome's Parish Cncl 1989-, Mem; Tchr of Yr 1989; Pub Article *office:* E.C. Goodwin Technical Schl 735 Slater Rd New Britain CT

LUCHT, CHERYL ADAMS, Reading & English Teacher; *b:* Ironton, *m:* Gary R.; *c:* Jeffrey, Kirsten, Gregory; *ed:* Grove City Coll (AB) 1968; Grad Credit Hrs At Edinboro Univ, Gannon Univ; *cr:* Meml Reading, Eng Tchr 1968-71; Gridley MS Eng Permanent Sub 1980-81; Luther Meml Schl Rdng, Eng Tchr 1982-; *ai:* Newspaper Wkshps; Parent Tchrs League 1982-, Pres 1982; NCTE Intermitten Prison Wardens Auxiliary 1978-Pres 1984-86; Elmwood Presbyn C Session; *office:* Luther Memorial Learning Ctr 220 W 11th St Eri 16501

LUCHT, SONITA TEISE, Mathematics Teacher; *b:* Lakewood, O Todd; *ed:* OH St Univ (BS) Math Ed 1992; *cr:* Parma City Schls Math 1992-; *ai:* Stu Cncl & Soph Class Adv; Var Swim Coach; NEA, PEA NCTM 1991-; Navy Marine Corps Relief Soc 1995-, Vol; *office:* Parr H S 6285 W 54th St Parma OH 44129

LUCIANI, BRIAN THOMAS, History Teacher; *b:* Union, NJ; *m:* Ba Ann Luciani; *c:* Brian Taylor, Jameson Reid; *ed:* Slippery Rock (BSA) Soc Stud 1989; *ai:* Var Wrestling; Asst Var Sftbl, Ftbl; Var Cntry; NJEA 1989-; Irvington Ed Assn 1989-, Rep; Essex Cty Co Assn 1990-; Essex Cty Cross Cntry Coach of Yr 1994; *office:* Irvingto Springfield Ave Irvington NJ 07111

LUCIANI, LIA ANNE (AZZATO), Fourth Grade Teacher; *b:* St M PA; *m:* Frank A.; *c:* Kevin Carter, Marc Carter, Gina, Teresa; *ed:* Edin Univ (BS) Elem Ed 1970; 29 Credit Hrs; *cr:* St Michael Schl 2nd Grd 1970-71, 1st Grd Tchr 1971-91, 5th Grd Tchr 1991-94, 4th Grd Tchr 1 *ai:* NCEA; Thiel Coll Womens Club; St Michael Tchr of Yr 1984 & *office:* Saint Michaels Schl 80 N High St Greenville PA 16125

LUCIANO, GUY E., Social Studies Teacher; *b:* New York, NY Catherine Ruffo; *c:* Mike, Chris, Kathy; *ed:* C. W. Post Coll (BA) His 30 Credit Hrs in Ed; *cr:* St Ignatious Loyola Schl Tchr 1969-71; Se MS Tchr 1971-; *ai:* Team Ldr; Ftbl, Boys & Girls Bsktbl, Track C MCTA 1971-, SBT Rep; LICSS 1990-; *office:* Selden MS 22 Jefferson Centereach NY 11720*

LUCIANO, LAWRENCE PATRICK, English Teacher; *b:* Cleveland, *ed:* Cleveland St Univ (BA) Eng 1993, (MA) Ed 1996; *cr:* Mentor Rid High Tchr 1993-; *ai:* 7th & 8th Grd Ftbl, 8th Grd Girls Bsktbl & Pow Pen Writing Coach; OEA 1993-; NEA 1993-; Mentor Tchr Assn 19 Sallie Mae First Yr Tchr Awd; *office:* Mentor Ridge Jr High Johnnycake Ridge Rd Mentor OH 44060*

LUCIER, EDWARD GERARD, English Teacher; *b:* Bristol, CT; *m:* Ilene Kline; *c:* Terry, Troy; *ed:* Cntrl CT St Univ (BS) Eng 1968, (Psych 1971; CA St at Northridge (ADM) Schl Adm 1986; Addl 65 Cr CA Luth, Univ of CA at Santa Barbara, CA at St Northridge, Penn S Wesleyan; *cr:* J. F. Kennedy Jr HS Eng Tchr 1968-70; Dodd Jr HS Eng. Tchr 1972-75; Mesa Union Schl Lang Arts Tchr, Asst Prin 1976-86; V Vly Sr HS Eng Tchr 1987-88; Wallenpaupack Area HS Eng Tchr 1992- Schl Newspaper Co-Adv; NEA 1968-; PSEA 1992-; CA Distngd Recognition 1985-86; Natl Distngd Schl Recognition 1986-87; *of* Wallenpaupack Area HS HC 6 Box 6075 Hawley PA 18428*

LUCIER, EDWARD H., Professor of Biology; *b:* Worcester, MA Carol A. Lucier-Reynolds; *c:* Lynn Slapik, Nancy Sanko, Karen Bercu *ed:* St Coll at Worcester (BSEd) Elem Ed 1957; Colgate Univ (MA) 1966; Attnd St Coll at Framingham MA, Coll of the Holy Cross, Uni CA at Berkeley, Becker Coll at Worcester, Worcester Poly Tech & M Marine Lab at Sarasota; *cr:* Saint Clair Shores 6th Grd Tchr 1957 Leicester Pub Schls Advanced Placement Bio Tchr 1959-65; Becker Prof, Dept Chair & Sci Tchr 1965-; *ai:* NJCAA Region XXI Sec & T 20 Yrs; AFT 1972-.

LUCK, ROBBIN LYNN, Physical Education & Hlth Tchr; *b:* Wasing C.H., OH; *ed:* Univ of Rio Grande (BS) PE 1987; Xavier Univ (M Sport Admin 1994; Attnd Drake Univ 3 Credit Hrs & Wright St Un Credit Hrs; *cr:* Univ of Rio Grande Asst Coach 1987-88; White Oak Tchr & Coach 1988-; *ai:* Var Girls Bsktbl Coach; Var Sftbl Co

PERD & OAHPERD 1987-; NASSM 1994; Various Church Groups ; *office:* Whiteoak HS 1100 Northview Dr #3G Mowrystown OH 5*

KENBILL, BARBARA MILLER, Family & Consumer Sci Tchr; *b:* onard Wood, MO; *m:* Rodney C.; *c:* Judith, Sarah; *cr:* Tamaqua Area Jr HS Home Arts Tchr 1986-94; Tri-Vly HS Family, Consumer Sci 1994-.

KENBILL, STANLEY M., MS Physical Education Teacher; *b:* ville, PA; *m:* Linda K. Augustine; *c:* Traci Lyn Luckenbill Falco, Rodd topher; *ed:* East Stroudsburg St Coll (BS) Hlth, PE 1969; Penn St Masters Equivalency 1973; *cr:* Schuylkill Haven HS Hlth, PE Tchr 71; Whitehall Coplay Schl Dist Driver Ed, Hlth, PE Tchr 1971-; *ai:* Ftbl Coach; Head Sftbl Coach; NEA, PSEA 1969-; *home:* 4321 on Way Whitehall PA 18052

OT, MARY ALICE A., 6th-8th Grade Teacher; *b:* Pittsburgh, PA; *ed:* esne Univ (BS) Ed 1972; Post-Grad Courses 27 Hrs Penn St Univ, esne Univ; Stu Assistance Prgm Trng St Francis Med Ctr; *cr:* St sius Schl 6-8 Grd Tchr 1972-; *ai:* Safety Patrol Supvr; PA Jr Acad of pon; Stu Assistance Prgm Team Mem; Sci Fair Coord; NCEA 1972-; S Assn 1994-; Nom Miriam Farrell, Golden Apple, KDKA Thanks to Awds; *office:* St Aloysius Schl 3614 Mount Troy Rd Pittsburgh PA 2

Y, ELLEN LOUISE GOWEN, Third Grade Teacher; *b:* Augusta, *m:* John W.; *c:* Abigail; *ed:* Univ of Southern ME (BS) Elem Ed 1983; , Math Inservice, Grad Rdng Courses; *cr:* Scarborough Schls Sub 1983; SAD #6 Chptr I Rdng Asst 1983-84, 1 Grd Asst Tchr 1984-85, 1 Tchr 1985-; *ai:* Stu Assistance Team Coord; Staff Dev; NEA, MEA -; SVTA 1985-, Bldg Rep; Fanfare Concert Band 1987-; *office:* Edna y Elem Schl Rt 114 Box 177 Sebago Lake ME 04075*

GATE, JUDITH, Bus Ed & Tech Prep Coord; *b:* Manchester, NH; *m:* ; *c:* Jeffrey, Jonathan, Jenna; *ed:* Plymouth St Coll (BED) Bus Ed ; Worcester St Coll (MED) HS Admin 1986; *ai:* Bus Profs of Amer Tech Prep, Schl to Work Coord; NEA; MBEA; NEBEA; Delta Pi on; Outstdng Tchr of Yr 1994-96; Employee of Month 1992; *office:* borough HS 461 Bolton St Marlborough MA 01752

INGTON, JIM, High School Math Teacher; *b:* Endicott, NY; *m:* ia Fisher; *c:* Melinda, Tamara, Sara; *ed:* SUNY at Potsdam (BA) ry Ed & Math 1972; BA+30 in Ed 1976; *cr:* Massena Schl Dist Math 1973-78; Garanda Schl Dist Math Tchr 1978-; Peak Learning Systems onsultant 1994-; *ai:* Coach: Var Soccer, Bsbl & Golf; Frosh & Sr Class Schl Improvement Team; K-12th Math Comm; GTA 1978-, VP, Treas; NYS 1980-; NCTM 1985-; Gananda Tchr of the Yr 1981; Univ of ester Excl in Tchng (Twice); Peak Learning Systems Inc Natl Ed ultant; Co-Authored: Quick Tips & Strategies for Teachers & The ormance Learning and Assessment Toolbox; *office:* Gananda Central HS 1500 Day Spring Rdg Walworth NY 14568*

LUM, DANIEL SPENCER, Social Studies & Comm Tchr; *b:* mbus, OH; *m:* Mary Ellen Dobberstein; *c:* David, Stephen; *ed:* Capital (BA) Ed, Soc Stud & Speech 1974; Attnd Lutheran Theological nary, IN Univ & OH St Univ; *cr:* Upper Arlington HS Tchr, Coach & 1975-; *ai:* Youth-in-Govt Adv; Ath Trainer; Debate Coach; Stu Cncl Bsktbl, Track & Field & Cross Country Coach; Bldg Planning Team; Cncl; Seeking Educl Equity & Diversity; ASCD 1990-; NEA, OEA & A 1975-; OH Voc Assn 1994, Presenter; Intnl City Mgmt Assn 1984-, enter; Atonement Luth Church, Pres, Head Elder; HBA, Bd; Delaware Schls Consultant; Worthington City Schls Consultant; Coll Bd sultant & AP Reader; EACH, Curr Comm Chair; Civic Assn Golden e Awd; Ashland Tchr Achvmt Nom; Pub "Advanced Placement, US & Politics; 3 Articles on Assessment in Horizon; Who's Who in Amer Tchr of Yr; *office:* Upper Arlington HS 1650 Ridgeview Rd Columbus 43221*

MAN, KAREN LEE, Second Grade Teacher; *b:* Drexel Hill, PA; *ed:* Stroudsburg Univ Elem & Spec Ed 1975; West Chester Univ (MED) g 1989; *cr:* Ridley Schl Dist 1st-5th Grd Tchr 1975-; Eddystone Elem Grd Tchr 1994-; *ai:* Mentor; Instructional Support Team; Intramurals; ., REA, PSEA 1975-; *office:* Eddystone Elem Schl 9th & Simpson Sts ystone PA 19022

WIG, ANN O., Ninth Grade English Teacher; *b:* Carbondale, PA; *m:* es D.; *c:* Meghan, Kevin; *ed:* SUNY at Binghamton (BA) His 1978, T) Tchng 1979; *cr:* Johnson City Schls Sub Tchr 1979-80; uehanna Valley Schls Eng Tchr 1980-; *ai:* Frosh Class Adv; Schl rovement Team & Observation Task Force Mem; NEA 1980-, Bldg ; Our Lady of Sorrows Church 1960-, Chprsn, Family Festival Comm; e: Susquehanna Valley Jr HS 1040 Conklin Rd Conklin NY 13748*

DWIG, EDMUND BRUCE, Biology & Physics Teacher; *b:* Cortland, *m:* Marcia Clemens; *c:* John Edmund; *ed:* SUNY at Cortland (BS) Bio 5, (MSEd) Bio 1989; PA St Univ Nuclear Concepts 6 Hrs; *cr:* Tompkins tland Comm Coll Summer Regnl Bio Instr 1986, 1989; SUNY at tland Adjunct Instr 1988; DeRuyter Cntrl Schls HS Sci Tchr 1985-; *ai:* -AIDS Regnl Turnkey Trainer; Marine Sci, Environmental Sci Coord; Cncl Co Adv; NEA-NY 1985-, Vice Pres 6 Yrs; Natl Wild Turkey Fed 3-; NRA 1985-; Town Councilman 1994-; NSF Atomic Optics SUNY ortland 1989; Penn St Nuclear Physics Grant; *office:* De Ruyter Central 711 Railroad St De Ruyter NY 13052

DWIG, MARJORIE, HS Mathematics Teacher; *b:* Staten Island, NY; Lawrence; *c:* Kristin, Dean; *ed:* Coll of Staten Island (BA) Ed & Math 5; *cr:* Manufacturers Hanover Trust Co Intnl Adjuster 1970-72; ning Inst Tchr & Part-Time Tutor 1980-86; Msr Farrell HS Tchr 1986-.

DWIG, MARK ANDREW, Special Education Teacher; *b:* Jersey City, *m:* Kelly Ann; *c:* Andrew P., Zachariah J.; *ed:* Kean Coll of NJ (BA) ech, Hearing 1985; Union Cty Coll at Cranford Cert in Paramedicine; Roselle Bd of Ed Spec Ed 1986-; JFK Med Ctr Paramedic 1991-; *ai:* ne Tutor; NEA 1986-; NSTA 1996; Woodbridge Emergency Squad 4-, Honorary Mem; Best Practices Awd 1995 NJ Dept of Ed; *office:* Elem Schl 1100 Warren St Roselle NJ 07203*

DWIG, RICHARD E., Health & Physical Ed Teacher; *b:* Lima, OH; *m:* th Sherer; *c:* Nicole Brown, Carey Brown; *ed:* West Chester Univ (MS) 2th Hlth & PE, Driver Ed 1971; 12 Grad Credit Hrs William Paterson Admin; Project Adventure; *cr:* Manchester Regnl HS Tchr 1971-; m Ldr for Bus, Industrial Arts & PE Depts 1988-; *ai:* Past Ftbl & estling Coach; Girls Vllybl Coach; Class, IM, & Phys Fitness Team ; Steering Comm for Schls Preparation for Mid Sts Evaluation; NEA 1-; Manchester Ed Assn 1971-, VP 1974-76; NJ Ed Assn 1971-; ASCD 5-; Assisted Schl to Obtain Grant from Municipal Alliance to Start ject Adventure in PE Dept; Grant From Fndtn of Girls & Women in orts to be Put into the Girls Sports Pgm at Manchester; *office:* nchester Regional HS 70 Church St Haledon NJ 07508

DWIG, SHEILA JAMES, Vocal Music Teacher; *b:* Philadelphia, PA; James F.; *c:* Joshua, Rachel; *ed:* Bowling Green St Univ (BM) Music Choral 1976, (MM) Music Performance, Voice 1980; Further Stud With ert Shaw, Ann Howard Jones, Paul E. Oakley, Weston Noble; *cr:* North walton HS Vocal Music Tchr 1979-82; Buckeye HS Vocal Music Tchr 2-84; Priv Tchr 1979-89; Medina HS Vocal Music Tchr 1990-; *ai:* Block eduling Rsrch Comm; MENC, OMEA 1979-; ACDA 1990-; OMEA All Choir Housing Chair, All St Choir Regnl Chair, Competition Selection Comm, Adjudicator, All St Choir Selection Comm; NEOEA Wkshp Presenter; *home:* 1121 Waterbury Dr Medina OH 44256*

LUDWIG, STEVEN M., Seventh & Eighth Grade Teacher; *b:* Jersey City, NJ; *m:* Susan DeCaro; *ed:* Montclair St Coll (BA) Lang Arts 1976; 21 Addl Hrs; *cr:* North Bergen Schl System Eng, Math, Soc Stud, HS Eng, Rdng Tchr 1976-; *ai:* Tchrs Contract Negotiating Team; North Bergen Fed Tchrs 1978-, VP; NBFT 1978-, Union Bldg Rep; Comm on Pol in Ed; Tchr of Yr; NJ Governor's Tchr Recognition Prgm; *home:* 227 Forest Rd Fort Lee NJ 07024

LUDWIN, ROBERT A., Math & Computers Teacher; *b:* Garfield Hts, OH; *ed:* Miami of OH (BS) Ed 1974; John Carroll (MBA) Bus 1983; Kent St Comp Sci; Wabash Coll Bus Ed; *cr:* Lake Cath HS Math, Comp, Soc Stud & Bus Tchr 1974-86; Marysville HS Math & Comp Tchr 1986-; *ai:* Var Golf & 9th Grd Girls Bsktbl Coach; NEA 1986-; NCTM 1992-; OCTM 1992-; OHSGOLFCA 1976-; IAABO 1982-; COBOA 1986-; Kent St NSF Summer Flwshp 2 Yrs; OH Insurance Inst-Miami of OH; *office:* Marysville HS 800 Amrine Mill Rd Marysville OH 43040

LUEBKE, JENNIFER WEIGANDT, 9th-12th Grd English Teacher; *b:* Sidney, OH; *m:* Larry P.; *c:* Jordyn N., Justin M.; *ed:* Bowling Green St Univ (BS) Eng 1984; Coll of Mt St Joseph (MA) Ed 1989; Schl Cnslng; *cr:* Sidney HS 9-12 Grd Eng Tchr 1984-; *ai:* Frosh Class Adv; NEA, OEA, NCTE 1984-; *office:* Sidney HS 1215 Campbell Rd Sidney OH 45365*

LUEDDE, SUSAN KNOWLTON, Math Teacher; *b:* St Louis, MO; *m:* Christopher Shryock; *c:* Carrie Marie, Shawn Fullerton; *ed:* Univ of KS (BS) Math 1973; *cr:* Chartier Vly HS Full Time Math Sub 1973-74; St Pauls Cathedral HS Math Tchr, Sr, Yrbk & Newspaper Moderator 1974-76; Bridgeport Spaulding Schls Sub Tchr 1979-80; Toledo Cntrl Cath HS Math Tchr & Dept Chair 1986-; *ai:* Sr Class Moderator, Yrbk & Newspaper Adv 1974-76; Yth to Yth Adv 1987-89; NHS Adv 1989-92; Math Dept Chair 1990-95; NCTM 1993-; Toledo Museum of Art; Maumee Vly Historical Soc; Toledo Zoo Soc; Episcopal Church Women; *office:* Toledo Cntrl Cath HS 2550 Cherry St Toledo OH 43608

LUEHMAN, CYNTHIE BRYANT, Nursing Professor; *b:* Dansville, NY; *m:* William Randall; *c:* Marlee, Kari; *ed:* Alfred Univ (BS) Nrsng 1970; SUNY at Buffalo (MS) Nrsng 1985; *cr:* Overlook Hosp Staff & Head Nurse 1970-71; Livingston Cty Pub Hlth Nurse 1972-74; Noyes Memrl Hosp Infection Control Coord & Staff Nurse 1976-85; Alfred Univ Nrsng Instr 1984-86; SUNY Nrsng Prof 1985-95; *ai:* Acad Integrity Comm Chair; Sigma Theta Tau 1980-, VP; Dalton Meth Church 1987-, PPR Comm & Worship Comm; SUNY at Buffalo Schl of Nrsng Grad Stud Excl in Nrsng Rsrch 1985; SUNY Alfred Alumni Tchr of the Yr 1988; Nurse of Distinction Nom 1993; SUNY Chancellors Awd Excl in Tchng 1995; NYS Assoc of 2 Yr Colls Tchr of the Yr 1995; *office:* Alfred St Coll 230 Allied Hlth Alfred NY 14802

LUEHRMANN, ROSA PATRICIA (LARREA-PEREZ), Spanish Teacher; *b:* Tacna, Peru; *m:* Michael J.; *ed:* Univ of Jose Jimenez-Borja (BA) Chem, Biological Scis 1985; *cr:* Colegio Victor Mayuri HS Sci Tchr 1986-88; Colegio Santa Ana HS Sci Tchr 1989-93; St Xavier HS Span Tchr 1994-; *ai:* Span NHS; Summer Mission Trips; *office:* St Xavier HS 600 W North Bend Rd Cincinnati OH 45224

LUERS, BETH HURLEY, Professor of Social Sciences; *b:* Baltimore, MD; *m:* Bob; *c:* Scott, Ann; *ed:* Frostburg St Coll (BA) Fr 1973; Frostburg St Univ (MA) Modern Hum, His 1989; *cr:* US Peace Corps TEFL Tchr 1974-75; ELS Lang Ctr TESL Tchr 1976-79; Amer Lang Acad TESL Tchr 1981-82; Garrett Comm Coll Dev Stud Supvr, Soc Scis Prof 1986-; *ai:* Curr, MD Womens Commissions Hall of Fame Comms; Phi Theta Kappa Adv; Org of Amer Historians 1994-; Historic Preservation 1994-; Focus on Excl Awd Outstdng Tchr 1989; Worked Archaeological Dig in Israel 1989; *office:* Garrett Comm Coll 687 Mosser Rd Mc Henry MD 21541

LUERSMAN, ROGER JOHN, Sixth Grade Sci & Lang Tchr; *b:* Ft Jennings, OH; *m:* Nora Lynn Lehmkuhle; *c:* Jeffery, Melissa, Christopher, Gregory; *ed:* Bowling Green St Univ (BS) Ed, Bio 1972; Univ of Dayton (MS) Ed, Admin 1982; OH St Univ Elem Ed Cert; *cr:* Allen-East Local Schls HS Bio & Earth Sci Tchr 1972-73; Kalida Local Schls Jr High & 6th Grd Sci & Lang Tchr 1974-; *ai:* 8th Grd Boys Bsktbl Coach 1974-; SAY Soccer Coach, Referee & Admin 1979-; B-Team Little League Bsbl 1993-; NEA & OEA 1993-; SAY Soccer-Putnam Cty 1979-, Pres & VP; Red Cross 1989-; Parish Cncl-St Michael Cath Church 1994-; *office:* Kalida Local Schls 208 N 4th St Box 358 Kalida OH 45853

LUFF, MARILYN K. ARCURI, 5th Grade Math & Sci Teacher; *b:* Utica, NY; *m:* Kenneth W.; *ed:* SUNY at Oswego (BS) Elem Ed 1978; Long Island Univ (MS) Elem Ed & Tech 1993; *cr:* Kemble Schl Kndgtn Tchr 1978-79; Lincoln Schl 3rd-4th & 6th Grd Tchr 1982-91, 6th Grd Rdng & Lang Arts Tchr 1991-94, 5th Grd Math & Sci Tchr 1994-; ICS Schl 5th-6th Grd Tchr 1983; *ai:* Future Tchrs Club & Drama Club Adv 1988; Chess Club Adv 1989; Dist DARE Coord 1989-; Stock Market Club & Inventors Club Adv 1990-; Curr Comm; NJEA 1984-; NJIRA 1986-; ASCD 1992-; NCTM 1993-; Elem Schl Consortium 1994-; NJ Governors Awd for Excl in Tchng 1994; *home:* 3233 Pine View Dr Walworth NY 14568*

LUFT, GARY LEE, Math Teacher; *b:* Reading, PA; *m:* Peggy Reese; *ed:* Penn St at Harrisburg (BS) Math Sci 1993; 24 Grad Credits at Millersville Univ; *cr:* Penn Manor Schl Dist HS Math Tchr 1993-; *ai:* Jr High Bsktbl Coach; Serteen Club, Class Adv; NEA, PSEA 1993-; NCTM 1992-; *office:* Penn Manor HS PO Box 1001 Millersville PA 17551

LUFT, MICHAEL, Dean of Students; *b:* Mc Keesport, PA; *m:* Bonnie Ann Grilli; *c:* Michael, Melissa; *ed:* CA Univ of PA (BA) Elem Ed 1973; Duquesne Univ (MED) Scndry Guid 1986; Prin Cert 1996; Masters Equivalency in Theology; Catechist Cert in Diocese of Pittsburgh; *cr:* St Elizabeth HS Classroom Tchr 1976-83; Mon Vly Cath Schl Classroom Tchr 1983-84; Lawrenceville Cath Schl Classroom Tchr 1984-86; Serra Cath HS Classroom Tchr 1986-92, Dean of Stdnts 1992-; *ai:* Campus Minister; Mid Sts Comm Chprsn; Retreat Coord; Core Team Mem; Assist in Dev Office; Liturgy Planning Comm; Best Tchr Awd 1995; *office:* Serra Catholic HS 200 Hershey Dr Mc Keesport PA 15132

LUGANO, MICHAEL RAYMOND, 4th Grade Teacher; *b:* New York, NY; *ed:* Herbert H. Lehman Coll (BA) Psych 1975, (MS) Elem Ed, Rdng 1981; 15 Credits GATE, Spec Ed, Admin; *cr:* PS 105 Elem Schl Tchr 1977-; *ai:* Pathways for Yth Camp Dir 1980-; AFT 1977-; Kappa Delta Pi 1981-; Dist II Expo Awd Dedication to Children Tchng Sci 1988-89; Recognition Dedication Children CSD II 1990-93; *office:* PS 105 725 Brady Ave Bronx NY 10462*

LUGINBUHL, ANN, Resource Room Teacher; *b:* Fort Bragg, NC; *m:* Christopher Guida; *c:* Sophia Guida, William Guida; *ed:* Middlebury Coll (BA) Pol Sci 1981; Spec, Gifted Ed Credit Hrs; *cr:* Peace Corps Vol 1981-83; Middlebury Elem Schl Grd 3, 4 Tchr 1983-84; Charlotte Elem Schl Resource Room Tchr 1985-88; Robbinston Elem Schl Resource Room Tchr 1985-87; Charlotte Elem Schl Resource Room Tchr 1994-; *ai:* Newspaper, Eighth Grd Adv; NEA, MEA, CEA 1994-; *office:* Charlotte Elem Schl Rte 214 Pembroke ME 04666

LUGO, EMIL J., Foreign Language Teacher; *b:* New York, NY; *m:* Yvette Corsino-Lugo; *c:* Karl Philip, Cynthia M.; *ed:* St John's Univ (BA) Soc Sci 1968; Fordham Univ (MA) Modern European His 1976; Addl 60 Credits Various NY Insts; *cr:* Stuyvesant HS Soc Stud Tchr 1968-71; Automotive HS Soc Stud Tchr 1971-72; Washington Irving HS Soc Stud Tchr 1973-76; Stuyvesant HS Soc Stud, Japanese, Span Lang Tchr 1976-; *ai:* Stu Exch Prgms to Japan Schl Coord; Japanese Animation Club Fac Adv; AFT, UFT 1968-; ATSS 1970-, Exec Bd 1973-75; NYSAFLT, ATJ, NEASTJ 1988-; NYS Summer Modern Chinese His Grant 1969; Fulbright Summer Grant, Japan 1985; Articles Pub; *office:* Stuyvesant HS 345 Chambers St New York NY 10282

LUIDHARDT, BETTIE MEISTER, 6th Grade Teacher; *b:* Bucyrus, OH; *m:* Gene; *c:* Beth Eileen; *ed:* Wittenberg Univ (BA) Elem Ed 1970; Ohio St Univ (MA) Early, Mid Chldhd Ed 1979; 30 Addl Hrs; *cr:* Saginaw City Schls 6th Grd Tchr 1970-71; Wynford Schls 4th Grd Tchr 1971-78; Colonel Crawford Schls 6th Grd Tchr 1982-; *ai:* Sci Fair Comm; Sci Curr; NEA, OEA 1972-; CCEA 1972-, Pres, Treas; OCTELA; OH Sci Tchrs; Bus & Prof Women 1975-, Pres Dist Dir, Young Career Woman, Woman of Yr; 4-H Adv 1972-; Doll Club 1990-, Sec; Presenter Wkshps for Tchr Insvc; *office:* Colonel Crawford Schls St Rt 602 North Robinson OH 44856

LUIDHARDT, DONNA ADORNETTI, Second Grade Teacher; *b:* Cleveland, OH; *m:* Donald; *c:* Laurie, Julie, Kristi; *ed:* Bowling Green St Univ (BS) Elem Ed 1968; 30 Grad Hrs from Univ of Toledo, FL St Univ & Drake Univ; *cr:* Mayfield City Schls 2nd Grd Tchr 1968-69; Bowling Green City Schls 3rd Grd Tchr 1969-70, 2nd Grd Tchr 1987-; *ai:* NEA, OEA, BGEA 1987-; PEO Chapter AA 1989-, Guard; *office:* Coneaut Elem Schl 542 Haskins Rd Bowling Green OH 43402

LUKAS, ANN MARIE, Home Ec & Child Care Teacher; *b:* Scranton, PA; *m:* Chester C.; *c:* David, Diane Mustra, Karen Holdren; *ed:* Douglass Coll (BS) Home Ec 1972; Rairleigh Dickinson Univ (MA) Human Dev 1982; Rutgers Univ St Cert Psych 1978; Kean Coll St Cert Supervision 1980; Trenton St St Cert Early Chldhd 1983; *cr:* North Hunterdon Reg HS Home Ec Tchr 1972-82; Voorhees HS Child Dev Tchr 1982-; *ai:* Futre Home Makers of Amer, Home Ec Adv; Related Occupations FHA HERO; Ski Club Chaperone; Amer Assn of Family & Consumer Sci 1972-, Home Ec Tchr of Yr 1985; NAEYS 1983-; NJEA, NEA 1972-; Phi Theta Kappa 1969; Nancy Higginson Dorr Future Tchr Awd 1972; *home:* 1116 Cambridge Ln Bridgewater NJ 08807

LUKAS, CHERYL A., Graphic Arts Technology Prof; *b:* Worcester, MA; *ed:* MA Coll of Art (BFA) Design, Illustration; Amer Intnl Coll (MED) Scndry Ed 1995; *cr:* Springfield Tech Comm Coll Div Cont Ed Graphic Arts Instr 1983-, Graphic Arts Tech Prof 1985-; *ai:* Prof Dev Chair 1994, Acad Cmptr Advising Comm; Graphic Arts Tech Adv; Macintosh Cmptr Consultant, Techician; NEA, MA Teach Assn, MA Const Comm Coll 1985-; Vly Interface Macintosh User Group 1995-, VP, Newsletter Ed; Springfield Tech Commission 1996-, Comm Mem; Fdn Incentive Grant 1988; Employee of Month 1994; Engrng Techs Div Distngd Svc Awd 1994; *office:* Springfield Tech Comm Coll 1 Armory Sq Springfield MA 01105

LUKAS, EDWARD MICHAEL, Sociology & Psych Teacher; *b:* Kingston, PA; *m:* Carol A. Johnson; *c:* Cherrie, Carl, Craig (dec); *ed:* King's Coll (BA) Sociology 1966; Scrantin Univ (MS) Scndry Admin 1973; *cr:* Wilkes Coll Part-time Night Adult Class Instr 2 Yrs; King's Coll Ftbl Coach 1 Yr; Wilkes Coll Ftbl Coach 8 Yrs; Crestwood Schl Dist Tchr 30 Yrs; *ai:* Asst Dean of Discipline; PSEA, NEA 1966-; NSCA 1970-; Tchr of Yr 1988; Book Being Recognized by Publisher; *office:* Crestwood Schl Dist 281 S Mountain Blvd Mountain Top PA 18707*

LUKASIAK, ROBERT F., Mathematics Teacher; *b:* Revere, MA; *m:* Donna Lee; *c:* Evan, Emily; *ed:* St Anselm Coll (BA) Psych 1983; 30 Credit Hrs in Math; Univ of NH Masters Prgm; *cr:* Notre Dame Coll Math Instr 1987-; Math Tchr 1982-; Math Dept Chair 1992-93; *ai:* Var Boys & Girls Cross Cntry Coach; Awd NH Tchng Flwshp 1994-95; NEA, NEANH & GEA 1983-; NHATMNE 1985-; NCTM 1993-; *office:* Goffstown H S 27 Wallace Rd Goffstown NH 03045

LUKASIK, JOHN PETER, School Psychologist; *b:* Scranton, PA; *ed:* Webster Univ (MA) Cnslng Svcs 1982; Univ of Scranton (MS) Cnslr Ed 1990; Marywood Coll Schl Psych Cert 1993; *cr:* Childrens Svc Ctr Psychotherapist 1989-90; Cath Yth Ctr Ath Dir 1990-91; Bishop Hannan HS Guid Cnslr 1991-93, Schl Psych 1993-; *ai:* Stu Act Dir; Stu Cncl Moderator; Amer Cnslng Assn 1990-; Amer Psychological Assn 1991-; Natl Assn Schl Psych 1992-; NCEA 1992-; Big Brothers Big Sisters 1990-, Bd of Advs, Appreciation Cert; *office:* Bishop Hannan HS 330 Wyoming Ave Scranton PA 18503

LUKASKIEWICZ, ROBERT PAUL, Theology Teacher; *b:* Holyoke, MA; *m:* Julie S.; *ed:* Syracuse Univ (BA) Eng 1992; Villanova Univ (MA) Theology 1994; *cr:* St Mark's HS Theology Tchr, Coach 1994-; *ai:* Winter, Spring Track, Field Coach; Fin Aid Coord; Theata Alpha Kappa 1991-; NCEA 1995-; Sallie Mae First Class Tchr of Yr Nom; *office:* St Mark's HS Pike Creek Rd Wilmington DE 19808

LUKASZEWSKI, ANGELA CIGNA, Physics Teacher; *b:* New York City, NY; *m:* Chester Paul II; *c:* Chester Paul III, Chadwick Joseph; *ed:* Hofstra Univ (BA) Physics 1969; Adelphi Univ (MA) Sec Ed 1973; Masters Candidate Comp Sci 15 Cr Hrs; MA Plus 40 Credit Hrs; *cr:* Bayshore HS Physics Tchr 1969-70; Syosset HS Physics Tchr 1970-76; Hofstra Univ Adj Asst Prof of Physics 1974-; Syosset HS Physics Tchr 1986-; *ai:* STANYS 1974-, Nominating Comm Ch; AAPT 1969; SCSTA 1994-, Pres & Newsletter Ed; Stanys Annual Conf Comm Chr 1994-; Nassau Sci Exploration Day Comm 1979-, Chm 1989-; SCSTA Sci Material & Textbook Comm 1975-, Chm 1983-; LI Chap of March of Dimes 1984-89, Bd of Dir; Hlth Prof Advy Comm of LI 1982-89; Sci Tchrs of NYS Svc Awd 1991; Sci Talent Search Sci Svc Washington DC Awd 1992; NY Sci Talent Search Vassar Coll Awd 1992; Amer Nuclear Soc Long Island Section Awd 1992; *office:* Syosset HS S Woods Rd Syosset NY 11791

LUKAVITCH, JOSEPH EDWARD, Social Studies Teacher; *b:* Plymouth, PA; *m:* Ella M. Maier; *c:* Ella Karassik, Joseph E., Christopher J.; *ed:* Wilkes Univ (BS) His, Govt, Sec Ed 1964; Univ of Scranton (MS) His, Ed 1970; PA Cncl for Ec Ed; *cr:* Plymouth HS Soc Stud Tchr 1964-66; Wyoming Valley West HS Soc Stud Tchr 1966-; *ai:* PIAA Track & Field Official; Cross Cntry, Track & Field, Winter Track 1975-90 Coaches; PA His Day Competition; Track Club, Stud Cncl, Schl Newspaper, Envrnmntl Clb Adv; PA Interscholastic Ath Assn 1967-; NEA, PA St Ed Assn 1964-; WY Valley West Ed Assn 1966-; Natl Fed Interscholastic Officials Assn 1987-; Plymouth Borough Zoning Bd 1976-80, Sec; Plymouth Borough Cncl 1981-85, Chm 1985; Track & Field Coach of Yr 1986, 1990; Cross Country Coach of Yr 1990; *office:* Wyoming Valley West HS Wadham St Plymouth PA 18651

LUKEHART, BARBARA J. BRADY, Soc Studies Tchr & Dept Chair; *b:* New York, NY; *m:* Cichard C.; *c:* Matthew, Katie, Benjamin; *ed:* IN Univ of PA (BA) His 1979, (MA) His 1980, (BS) Ed 1981; *cr:* IN Area Jr High Permanent Sub Soc St 1982-84; Smethport Jr & Sr High Soc Stud Tchr 1984-86; Mt Carmel High Soc Stud Tchr 1986-; *ai:* Stu Govt, Jr & Prom Adv; Acad Cncl; Admissions & Curr Comm; MASSP 1989-; NASSP 1989-; Schl Nom for the Archdiocesan Awd for Tchng Excl; *office:* Our Lady Of Mt Carmel HS 1706 Old Eastern Ave Baltimore MD 21221

LUKEN, ROBERT DALE, English Instructor; *b:* Greensburg, IN; *ed:* Ball St Univ (BS) Scndry Ed 1971, (MA) Eng 1978; Post Masters OH St Univ; *cr:* Jac-Cen-Del HS Eng Instr 1971-85; Bamberg Amer HS Eng Instr 1985-; *ai:* Schl Advy Comm; Cross Cntry, Drama, Asst Soccer, Acad Games Coach; Sr Class Adv; Former Ath Dir; STARS Renaissance, Outdoor Ed Spon; NEA, Overseas Ed Assn 1992-; PTA 1990-; Lambda Iota Tau 1970-; Knights of Columbus 1987-; Knights of St John's 1993-; Lions Intnl 1988-; *office:* Bamberg HS 279th Bsb Unit 27535 APO AE 09139*

LUKS, KENNETH ROBERT, Secondary School English Tchr; *b:* Jersey City, NJ; *m:* Rachel Brown; *c:* Rebecca, Jeremy, Trevor; *ed:* Hobart Coll (BA) Eng 1972; Brown Univ (MA) Eng 1974; *cr:* Verona HS Eng Tchr 1974-; *ai:* Class, Radio Station Adv; Drama Asst; NEA 1974-; Phi Beta Kappa 1972-; Chief Union Negotiator; St Tchng Awd 1987; Yrbk Dedications; Univ of Chicago Tchng Awd; *office:* Verona HS 151 Fairview Ave Verona NJ 07044*

LULAY, DONNA PATRICE, Language Arts & Soc Stud Tchr; *b:* Oceanside, NY; *ed:* Hofstra Univ (BA) Amer Lit 1980, (MA) British & Amer Lit 1985, (MS) Elem Ed 1987; *cr:* PS 114 6th Grd Classroom Tchr 1988-89; IS 211 6th Grd Eng, Soc Stud, Rdng, Lang Arts Tchr 1989-; Coll of New Rochelle Adj Fac, Writing Skills 1994; *ai:* Curr Writing Act; Drug Free Schls; Cooperative Learning; Interdisciplinary Theme Units; Give Wkshps in Bringing Geog Back into Classroom; NYSUT, UFT 1988-; NY Geographic Alliance 1994-; Winning Class for NYC Women's His Month Contest1989; *office:* IS 211 John Wilson 1001 E 100th St Brooklyn NY 11236

LUM, STACY B., Fifth Grade Teacher; *b:* Butler, PA; *ed:* Univ of DE (BA) Ec, Ed 1985; City Coll of NY (MS) Math 1987; Addl 69 Credit Hrs; *cr:* Viola Elem Schl First Grd Tchr 1986-87; Montebello Elem Schl Fifth Grd Tchr 1987-; *ai:* Conducted Comptr Trng Courses for Tchrs; Charter Mem Compact Learning, Schl Discipline Comm; Peer Mediation Adv; Dist Sci Mapping Comm; Dist & Site Based Tech Comm; Advised Stu Design New Schl Logo; Schl Videographer; After Schl Homework, Sci Club; Tchrs as Readers 2 Yrs; Ramapo Tchrs Assn, AFT,; NY St Tchrs Union 10 Yrs; Dist Wide Sixth Grade Teen Ctr Dir 3 Yrs; Drug Abuse Resistance Ed, Act Nights Sixth Graders; Participated in Design of Dist Sci Curr; Dev NY St Writing PEP Test Variance for Fifth Graders.

LUMLEY, JAYNE PEFFER, Third Grade Teacher; *b:* Connellsville, PA; *m:* Paul A. Sr.; *c:* Paul Jr., Amanda, Rebecca; *ed:* CA Univ of PA (BS) Elem Ed 1977; Widener Univ, St Josephs Univ, Drexel Univ, West Chester Univ Post Grad Stud; *cr:* Penn-Delco Schl Dist Elem Tchr 1978-; *ai:* PSEA, NEA 1978-; DE Co DAR 1979-; Proud Awd 1995; Positive Tchng Tribute Amer Family Inst; *office:* Pennell Elem Schl Pennell & Weir Rds Aston PA 19014

LUNA, BARBARA JABOUR, Fourth Grade Teacher; *b:* Mineola, NY; *m:* Vincent; *c:* Tracey Johnson, Kristin, Kerri; *ed:* Hofstra Univ (BS) Elem Ed 1968, (MS) Rdng 1972; Coll of New Rochelle (SAS) Schl Admin Sup 1993; Addl 50 Credit Hrs Effective Classroom Strategies, Gifted Ed; *cr:* Miller Place UFSD 4th, 4-6 Tchr of Gifted 1979-89; Mid East Suffolk Tchr Ctr Asst Dir 1989-91; Huntington UFSD 6th Grd Tchr, Ctr Dir 1991-94; Harborfields CSD 4th Grd Tchr 1994-; *ai:* Stu Cncl, Odyssey of Mind Adv; Sunshine, Lang Arts Collaborative, Rdng Olympics Comm; AFT, NYSUT 1979-; Assoc Prof LIU, Coll of St Rose; Adj Prof Dowling Coll.*

LUNARIO, ROSS ANTHONY, Mathematics Teacher; *b:* Bronx, NY; *c:* Tony; *ed:* City Coll of NY (BS) Math 1972, (MA) Math Ed 1981; *cr:* Our Savior Schl Math Tchr 1972; Holy Rosary Schl Math & Sci Tchr 1973-77; Cardinal Spellman HS Math Tchr 1977-80; Montclair HS Math Tchr 1980-; *ai:* NJ Math League Contest Supvr 6 Yrs; MEA, NEA & NJEA 1981-; Research Paper Voted for Symposium during Master Degree Work 1981; Montclair Pub Schls Josh & Judy Weston Awd for Excl in Tchng 1992 & Nom Again 1993; *office:* Montclair HS 100 Chestnut St Montclair NJ 07042

LUND, CARROL GAGLIARDI, Speech Pathologist; *b:* Harwick, PA; *m:* Robert E.; *c:* Marcjana, Anton; *ed:* Carlow Coll (BS) Hearing, Speech Pathology 1966; Boston Univ (MEd) Lang Pathology 1967; Attnd Univ of Pittsburgh, Univ of CT; *cr:* Prv Practice Speech Pathologist 1972-; Guilford Pub Schls Speech Pathologist 1979-84; Regnl Schl Dist #4 Speech Pathologist 1984-85; Guilford Pub Schls Speech Pathologist 1985-; *ai:* Prof Dev Comm Shoreline Speech Pathologists; NEA, CT Ed Assn 1979-; Guilford Ed Assn 1979-, Spec Svcs Rep; Amer Speech Lang Hearing 1967-; St George Parish 1973-, Rel Ed Tchr; VNA-Madison 1986-, Prof Advy Comm; VNA-Guilford 1986-, Prof Advy Comm; VNA-Branford 1994-, Prof Advy Bd; Homestead West Homeowners Assn 1971-, Pres; *office:* Guilford Pub Schls New England Rd Guilford CT 06437*

LUNDQUIST, MONA ELIZABETH, Guidance Counselor; *b:* New York City, NY; *ed:* Hartwick Coll (BA) Eng 1990; Long Island Univ-C W Post (MS) Cnslng 1994, (PHD) Ed Admin 1995; *cr:* Chapel of the Redeemer Schl 7th-8th Grd Tchr 1990-91; Nassau Luth Schl 5th Grd Tchr 1991-93; Carle Place HS 9th-12th Grd Guid Cnslr 1994-; *ai:* Newspaper Adv; NY Cnslng Assn 1994-; Chi Sigma Iota 1994-; AFT 1994-; *office:* Carle Place High School 168 Cherry Ln Carle Place NY 11514

LUNDY, DEBRA LYNN (HOWELL), Language Arts Teacher; *b:* Peoria, IL; *m:* Jonathan F.; *c:* Jennifer, Julia, Gregory; *ed:* Bob Jones Univ (BS) Speech Ed 1976; Madonna Coll at Livonia 4 Sem Hrs 1989; Ashland Univ 9 Sem Hrs 1984-85; Akron Univ 3 Credit Hrs 1981; OH St Univ at Columbus 6 Credit Hrs 1991; *cr:* Heritage Chrstn Schl Jr HS Lang Arts Tchr 1976-80; Ashland Univ Acad HS Lang Arts Tchr 1982-85, AD Asst in Admissions 1985-86; Agape Chrstn Acad Jr Sr HS Lang Arts Tchr 1989-90; Riverside HS Jr Sr HS Lang Arts Tchr 1990-; *ai:* Jr, Sr Class Play Dir; Discipline Comm Chprsn; Career Ed Bldg Rep; Tech Prep Comm; 8th Grd Class Adv; Chrstn Flwshp Church 1991-, Tchr, Small Group Ldr; Outstdng Tchr of Month 1995; *office:* Riverside HS 200 Moore St PO Box 190 De Graff OH 43318*

LUNDY, RENWICK P., HS Math & Science Teacher; *b:* Quakertown, PA; *m:* Nancy Marie Wengert; *c:* Renwick II, Kent; *ed:* Mansfield St Coll (BA) Math 1975; 12 Stud Credits Open Bible Inst; *cr:* Cumberland Valley Chrstn Schl HS Math & Sci Tchr 1978-; *ai:* Shippensburg Band 1988-, Trustee; Outstanding Young Men of Amer 1980 & 1984; KCEA Prof Recognition Cert 1986 & 1988; Tandy Outstanding Tchr Awd 1991-92 & 1993-94; *home:* 1184 Gayman Rd Chambersburg PA 17201

LUNKO, GINNY WEIR, 5th Grade Teacher; *b:* Brooklyn, NY; *m:* Greg B.; *c:* Allison, Maclean; *ed:* Univ of Pittsburgh at Johnstown (BS) Psych 1981, (BS) Elem Ed 1984; Masters Degree Equivalency in Ed 1995; *cr:* Our Mother of Sorrows 7th & 8th Grd Tchr 1986-90; Roxbury Elem Schl 5th Grd Tchr 1990-; *ai:* Legal Adv to In-School Ct; Adv to Constitutional Convention; NEA & PSEA 1990-, Fac Rep; *office:* Roxbury Elem Schl 111 Sell St Johnstown PA 15905*

LUNSFORD, SHIRLEY BADGER, Communication Skills Asst Prof; *b:* New Castle, PA; *c:* Brian Hall, Elliott Hall; *ed:* Clarion Univ (BS) Eng, Lib Sci 1963; Univ of Pittsburgh (MLS) Lib Sci 1967; Univ of Akron (MS) Ed, Rdng 1977; *cr:* Mohawk Area Schls Librn 1963-67; OH Univ Lib Librn 1968-71; OH St Univ Agricultural Tech Inst Asst Prof, Comm Skills 1976-; *ai:* Phi Theta Kappa Intnl Hnr Soc Fac Adv 10 Yrs; Wayne Cty Cncl Intnl Rdng Assn 1977-, Past Pres; OH Coll Cncl Intnl Rdng Assn 1980-, Past Pres; IRA 1976-; Natl Assn Dev Ed 1980-; First Presb Church 1982-, Deacon; Beacon House, Vol; Beta Phi Mu Intnl Lib Sci Hnr Soc; Presentation Rdng, Writing at Educl Conf; *office:* OH St Univ Agri Tech Inst 1328 Dover Rd Wooster OH 44691

LUNT, DAWN WEIDMAN, HS Math Teacher; *b:* Dansville, NY; *m:* Broderick; *c:* Ashley Elizabeth, Kelsey Anne; *ed:* SUC at Brockport (BA) Math 1978, (MS) Scndry Math 1983; 3 Credit Hrs Math Inst; *cr:* Rochester City Schls Scndry Math Tchr 1979-; *ai:* Bldg Comm 1994-; Class Adv 1983-86; Instrl Cncl; AFT, NYSUT 1979-; Rochester Tchrs Assn 1979-, Bldg Rep Alternate; Lake Shore Ladies Assn 1987-; Pub Several Editorials; Yrbk Dedication 1986; Grad Summa Cum Laude 1983; *home:* 5 Newcomb Dr Hilton NY 14468*

LUNTZ, MYRON, Physics Professor; *b:* Brooklyn, NY; *m:* n; *c:* Barbara Weiler, Jonathan; *ed:* CCNY (BS) Physics 1962; UCONN (MS) Physics 1964, (PHD) Physics 1968; *cr:* Aarhus U Visiting Scientist 1968-69; SUNY Coll at Fredonia Prof of Physics 1969-; U DE Visiting Assoc Prof 1975-76; *ai:* Fredonia Soc Physics Stdnts Fac Adv; Sigma Pi Sigma; Educl Dev Prgm Fac; Holography Rsrch Coord; Numerous Standing & Ad Hoc Coll & Dept Comms; APS, Am Assn Physics Tchrs 1968-; Phi Kappa Phi 1966-; Republican Natl Comm, Natl Republican Senatorial Comm 1994-; Three SUNY Summer Fac Rsrch Flwshps; Corp Rsrch Grant Lord Corp; Exemplary Svc Awd of EDP; Numerous Articles Pub; *office:* S U N Y Coll At Fredonia Physics Dept Fredonia NY 14063*

LUONGO, LINDA, English Teacher; *b:* Providence, RI; *m:* Thomas; *c:* Alysha; *ed:* Rhode Island Coll (BA) Eng 1972, (MAT) 1975; 45 Credit Hrs Beyond Masters at Providence coll; *cr:* Johnston HS Eng Tchr 24 yrs; *office:* Johnston Sr HS 345 Cherry Hill Rd Johnston RI 02919

LUPE, JOHN RICHARD,JR., Professor; *b:* Niskayuna, NY; *m:* Janet Bielinski; *c:* John, Angela; *ed:* Hudson Vly Comm Coll (AAS) Elect Eng Tech 1967; St Univ of NY at Albany (BA) His, Physics 1973, (MS) Educl Comm 1976; 65 Grad Hrs; *cr:* Gen Dynamics Corp Elect Drafting 1967-68; Hudson Vly Comm Coll Prof of Elect, Construction & Maintenance Dept 1968-; Allstate Design & Dev Elect Drafting 1974; Graphic Techniques Elect Design 1980; *ai:* Fac Assn 1968-; Pop Warner Ftbl, Coach 1982-83; Adult Womens Sftbl, Mgr 1979-93; Capital Dist Womens Sftbl League, Sec 1991-93; *office:* Hudson Valley Comm Coll 80 Vandenburgh Ave Troy NY 12180

LUPICA, ANTHONY, Italian Teacher; *b:* Cleveland, OH; *ed:* Bowling Green St Univ of OH (BA) Italian, Span 1973; IN Univ (MA) Italian 1976; *cr:* West Orange HS Italian Tchr 3 Yrs; Nutley HS Italian Tchr 1 Yr; Seton Hall Prep Schl Italian Tchr 16 Yrs; *ai:* Italian Club; Soccer Coach; UNICO Natl 1978-, Chptr Pres; VITA 1985-, Pres; Salvature Caprio Awd; *office:* Seton Hall Prep Schl 120 Northfield Ave West Orange NJ 07052

LUPINACCI, S. CLAIRE (NEWELL), Third Grade Teacher; *b:* Bay St Louis, MS; *m:* James Vincent; *c:* Rebecca, Kevin; *ed:* LA St Univ (BA) Elem Ed 1965; PA St Univ MA Equivalency Ed; *cr:* New Orleans Pub Schls Third Grd Tchr 1965-66; Moon Area Schls Third, First Grd Tchr 1966-; *ai:* Stu Cncl Co-Spon; Adopt A Hwy Helped Establish; NEA; PSEA; Bldg Rep 1989-91; *home:* 119 Wyngate Rd Moon Twp PA 15108

LURENZ, MICHAEL LEIBERT, Middle School Teacher; *b:* Sidney, NY; *ed:* Hartwick Coll (BA) Eng 1980; Shippensburg Univ (MA) Eng 1984; Doctoral Candidate ABD Binghampton Univ; *cr:* Shippenburg Univ Learning Assistance Ctr Tutor 1981-84; Binghampton Univ Tchng Asst & Adj 1984-89; Hartwick Coll Adj Asst Prof 1992-93; St James MS Eng & Lit Tchr 1993-; *ai:* Odyssey of the Mind Adv, Coach; Barbershop Harmony Club; NCEA 1993-; Phi Mu Alpha 1996, Treas, Pres; BSA 1980-, Asst Scoutmaster, Comm Chair; SPEBSQSA 1981-, Chptr Pres; Poetry Pub; *home:* RR 2 Box 1365 Afton NY 13730

LURZ, KIMBERLY JULIANO, High School Math Teacher; *b:* Orange, NJ; *m:* Robert; *ed:* NC St Univ (BS) Math Ed 1990; 18 Credits Towards Masters Montclair St Univ; *cr:* Belleville HS Math Tchr 1990-91; Hanover Park HS Math Tchr 1991-; Newark Acad Math Tchr 1993-; *ai:* Class of 1996 Adv; Negotiations Comm; NEA 1991-; Tchr of Yr 1994-95; CIESE Project; *office:* Hanover Park HS 63 Mount Pleasant Ave East Hanover NJ 07936

LUSH, MARK, HS Social Studies Teacher; *b:* Wilkensburg, PA; *m:* Brenda Claire Gehly; *c:* Jesse Clay, Casey Aaron; *ed:* CO St Univ (BS) Bus Admin 1982; Univ of NH Grad Schl; *cr:* Kingswood HS Soc Stud Tchr 1987-; *ai:* NH NEA, NHCSS 1987-; Sidetracked Railroad Soc 1993-, Treas; Served as Cooperating Tchr for 2 Stu Tchrs; DECA All-Star Bsktbl Team; *office:* Kingswood Regional HS S Main St Wolfeboro NH 03894*

LUSHER, JOHN HENRY, Social Studies Teacher; *b:* Painesville, OH; *m:* Cathy Breech; *c:* Charles Brandon; *ed:* Univ of Rio Grande (BS) Elem Ed 1979; Univ of Dayton (MS) Educl Admin 1985; *cr:* Hannan Trace Elem Tchr & Coach 1978-, Head Tchr 1991-92; *ai:* 7th-12th Grd Boys & Girls Bsktbl Coach 17 Yrs; NEA; SVAC Coach of Yr 1989-90; OH SE Dist Coach of Yr 1990-91; Gallia Cty Tchr of Yr 1992; Hannan Trace HS Act Coord 1989-90; *home:* 9442 State Route 218 Crown City OH 45623

LUSHINSKY, MARIE DANIELS, English Teacher; *b:* Youngstown, OH; *c:* Todd, Amy; *ed:* Youngstown St Univ (BS) Ed Rdng, Eng 1989; Youngstown St Univ 45 Credit Hrs; *cr:* Brookfield HS Soph Eng Tchr 1989-90; Sebring Mckinley HS Eng, Mythology & Shakespeare Tchr 1991-; *ai:* Jr Class Adv 4 Yrs; NHS Comm; ONTASC Drug, Alcohol Intrvention Team Mem; Youngstown St Eng Festival Schl Chrprsn & Presentor; NCTE Conventions 1989-1995; Hiram Coll Wkshp; Multi-Cultural Diversity in Ed; NCTE 1989; Kappa Delta Pi 1989; Gamma Delta Pi 1989; Intnl Rdng Assoc 1989; OH Chapter Rdng Assoc 1989; Sebring Local Ed Assoc 1991; Mahoning Cty Lang Arts Team 1995-; Youngstown Playhouse 1983, 1996; Mahoning Cty Historical Assoc 1987, 1996; EECAP Team Mem; Jewish Comm Ctr Wkshp Holocaust Presentor; Who's Who Among Amer Univ & Coll 1989; Chamber of Commerce Tchr of the Month 1994; *office:* Sebring McKinley HS 225 E Indiana Ave Sebring OH 44672

LUSK, TABITHA PRICE, Art Teacher; *b:* Chillicothe, OH; *m:* Shad Matthew; *c:* Dillon Matthew; *ed:* OH Univ (BA) Art Ed 1990; BA & 5 Yr Degree; *cr:* Adena Local Schls K-6th & 9-12th Art Tchr 1991-92, K-3rd & 9-12th 1993-; *ai:* 8th Grd Vllybl Coach; Adena Ed Assoc 1993-,Soc Chprsn; OH Art Ed Assoc 1994-; Tchr of the Yr 1994; *office:* Adena HS 167 W High St Frankfort OH 45628*

LUSSEN, RICHARD E., History & Social Sciences Tchr; *b:* Ravenna, OH; *m:* Laurel Austin; *c:* Katharine, Andrew, Caitlin Thompson, Megan Thompson, Lea Emery; *ed:* Yale Univ (BA) His 1969; Columbia Univ Tchrs Coll (MA) Comm 1975; Univ of MA (MS) Geography 1996; *cr:* New Canaan HS Tchr 1969-78; Ted Bates & Young & Rebicam Advertising Account Exec 1978-81; Saint Georges Schl Tchr 1981-85; Northfield Mount Hermon Schl His & Soc Scis Tchr & Dept Head 1985-; *ai:* Bsktbl Coach; Farm Prgm Asst; Dormitory Duty; AAG 1992-; NMH Independence Masters Grant for Foreign Stud; *office:* Northfield Mt Hermon Schl 206 Main St Northfield MA 01360

LUSSIER, BARBARA KERANS, Science Teacher; *b:* Staten Island, NY; *m:* Roger; *c:* Tamah, Craig, David Chad; *ed:* Notre Dame Coll (BA) Bio 1963; Wagner Coll (MS) Ed 1971; 30 Addl Credits Montclair Univ, NJ Inst of Tech; *cr:* Bertha Dreyfus JHS SCi Tchr 1963-67; Lafayette Twp Schl Sci Tchr 1977-81; Frankford Twp Schl Sci Tchr 1981-; *ai:* Middle Level Task Force; NJ Sci Tchrs Assn 1977-; Natl Middle Level Sci Tchrs Assn 1991-; Our Lady of Lake Roman Cath Church 1971-; NSF Grant Stud Oceanography; JCPL Energy, Environmental Grant; NJBISEC Grant Schering-Plough; *office:* Frankford Township Schl PO Box 430 Branchville NJ 07826

LUSSIER, DIANE MARIE, 5th & 6th Grd Science Teacher; *b:* Woonsocket, RI; *m:* Roger L.; *c:* Denise, Lise, Michelle Lawrence; *ed:* RI Coll (BA) Elem Ed & Fr 1968; *cr:* St Denis-St Columba Tchr 1983-; *ai:* Sci Fair Comm; *office:* St Denis-St Columba Elem Schl Rt 82 Box 368 Hopewell Junction NY 12533

LUSSIER, RUTH E., Retired Teacher; *b:* Providence, RI; *w:* Alf (dec); *c:* Gary, Joseph, Suzanne, Marie; *ed:* RI Coll (EDB) Elem Ed Attnd Univ of RI; *cr:* Charlestown Elem Schl 3-6 Grd Tchr 1957-9 Classroom Vol; Rdng, Math Tutor; Retired Tchr Org; NEARI Washington Cty Retired Tchrs 1990-, Prgm Chmn 1990-94, VP 19 Pres 1995-; *home:* 1580 Shermantown Rd Saunderstown RI 02874

LUSTER, JUDY ANN, English Teacher; *b:* Charles City, IA; *ed:* Hawk Jr Coll (AA) Theatre 1965; Drake Univ (BFA) Theatre 1967 of CT (MA) Theatre 1971; Northwestern Univ Fellowship, Fairfiel Grad Stud; *cr:* Carlisle Elem 5th Grd Tchr 1967-68; Staples HS 1969-; *ai:* Curr Cncl; Tchr Ldr Grant-Writing; Readers Theatre; V Presenter; Yrbk Adv; CT Wrtng Proj Consultant; WEA, NEA, CEA NCTE; CCTE; Westport Tchr of Yr 1989; Drake U Outstanding Sr W 1967; Black Hawk Jr Coll 1 of 12 Outstanding Sophs 1965; CO Ou Bound 1982; *office:* Staples HS 70 North Ave Westport CT 06880*

LUSTGARTEN, ANN WAKEFIELD, 5th Grade Teacher; *b:* Boston *m:* Richard; *c:* Robin; *ed:* Garland Jr Coll (AS) Nursery, Kndgtn Ed Unif of Bridgeport (BS) Elem Ed 1969; Wm Paterson Coll (MA) El 1993; *ai:* Pi Lambda Theta 1993-; Girl Scouts 1953-, Dist Chair; 1980-, Pres; *office:* Radburn Elem Schl 18-00 Radburn Rd Fair Law 07410

LUSTIC, THERESE DURKIN, English Teacher; *b:* Cleveland, O Gary; *ed:* Ursuline Coll (BA) Eng 1966; (MA) Eng 1984; Carnegie-Mellon, Duke U, Ashland Coll, John Carroll Univ, Ke LaSalle Univ, UCSD; *cr:* Nazareth Acad Tchr 1968-76; Ursuline Col 1978-80; Magnificat Schl Tchr 1980-85; Beaumont Schl Tchr 198 Hudso HS Tchr 1989-; *ai:* Acad Decathlon Adv; Dist Long Planning; Mentor Tchr; Curr Writing; North Cntrl Comm Chair; OEA; HEA; NCTE; OCTELA; ASCD; Cath Life Tech, Comm Co-C Ursuline Coll, Class Rep; Providence House, Vol; Distngd Tchr; Outstdng Edctr Denison Univ; Outstdng Tchr Richmond Univ; *o* Hudson HS 2500 Hudson Aurora Rd Hudson OH 44236*

LUTE, CHARLES EDWARD, Music Teacher & Dept Chairma Greensburg, PA; *m:* Marianne Hanson; *c:* Brianne, Jenna; *ed:* Un Edinboro (BS) Music Ed 1974, (MS) Music Ed 1979; *cr:* Tech HS Tchr 1974-83; Academy HS Music Tchr 1983-92; Central HS Music 1992-; *ai:* Marching, Jazz Bands; Schl of Visual & Performing Ar Class Adv; Schl Variety Show; AVA; MENC 1980-; PA Fed of C Judges 1981-; NY Fed Contest Judges 1982-; Erie Playhouse 1979-, Dir; Lake Shore Marching Band 1985-, Pres; Bands of Amer Grand Class A Champions 1991; Tchr of Yr 1992; *home:* 2576 Corvette Dr PA 16510

LUTERAN, IDA CERULLO, English Teacher; *b:* Newark, N Michael J.; *c:* Andrea, Michael; *ed:* Caldwell Coll (BA) Fr 1972; NY (MA) Fr 1974; Seton Hall Univ Cert Media Specialist 1993; Jersey C Cert Eng 1975; *cr:* Saddle Brook HS Eng, Fr Tchr 1974-; *ai:* Interact Co-Adv; EMANJ 1994-; NJEA, BEA 1974-; Women in His Soc Svc 1995; *office:* Saddle Brook HS 355 Mayhill St Saddle Brook NJ 076

LUTES, CAROLE LINN, 7th Grade English Teacher; *b:* Paso Ro CA; *c:* Erica Lynn, Devin; *ed:* Univ of IL (BS) Spcl Ed & Elem Ed Cntrl CT St Univ (MS) Rdng & Lang Arts 1993; 6th Yr South CT St 3 Credit Hrs; *cr:* Dist #105 2nd & 7th Grd Tchr 1964-68; Pekin C Schls 3rd Grd Tchr 1968-69; Dodd MS 7th-8th Grd Lang Arts & Soc Tchr 1986-; *ai:* Liaison Bd of Ed; Flex Act Spon; Tech Grant; Team Lang Arts Comm; Stu Asst Team; 2-35 Club; NCTE 1980-; NEA 1986- Cncl Tchr of Eng 1987-; CT Ed Assoc 1987-; ASCD 1990-; Jr Leag Greater Waterbury 1978-, VP & Sustainer; YMCA 1981-86, Bd of Alpha Delta Kappa 1989-; Copper Vly Club, Bd of Dirs; Tchr of Yr 1 *office:* Dodd MS 100 Park Pl Cheshire CT 06410*

LUTHER, C. DAVID, Bio & Envrmntl Sci Plant Tchr; *b:* Cambridge, *m:* Catherine Bradbury; *c:* Andrew, Douglas; *ed:* Boston St Coll (BSEd Earth Sci 1969, (MED) Ed Natural Sci 1973, (CAGS) Media 1 Northeastern Univ Cert Graphic Design 1994; 85 Masters Credit Hrs Palmer Schls Math Sci Tchr 1969-70; Burlington Schls Bio Tchr 197 Bio Tchr & Interdisciplinary Coord 1993-; Middlesex Comm Photography Instr 1981-90; *ai:* Sci Olympiad Team Coach; 18 Te Factathlon IM Acad Quiz Bowl Adv; NEA 1969-; MTA 1969-; Burlin Ed Assn 1970-, Past Pres; Waltham Yth Soccer Assn 1986-, Coach; Gr 2 Boston Univ Natl Sci Fndtn Summer for Bio Work; 2 MA Horace M for Interdisciplinary Projects Macro Photography & Bio; *of* Burlington HS 123 Cambridge St Burlington MA 01803

LUTHY, NANCY MORRIS, Mathematics Teacher; *b:* Newark, NJ James Eugene; *c:* Christopher, James Mangiafico, Melissa Gandor, St Mangiafico; *ed:* Muskingum Coll (BA) Math Ed 1963; Marietta (MALL) Lib Arts 1979; 30 Addl Hrs Discrete Math, Graphing Calcul in Precalculus, Alternative Assessment & Cooperative Learning; Hanover Park Reg HS Dist Math Tchr 1963-65; Ridge HS Math 1965-67; Marietta Jr HS Math Tchr 1974-76; Marietta HS Math 1976-; *ai:* Emergency Exit & Discipline Comms; Staff Soc Comm Ch Mentor; EPAC; MEA 1974-, Pres Elect, Pres 1994-; OEA & NEA 19 OCTM 1974-, Past Dist Dir, Outstanding Tchr SE; ADK 1979-, Past First Bapt Church 1981-, Adult Sunday Schl Tchr; WITS 1988-, Instr; 1983-, Vol; Caring Tch 1991-; Martha Holden Jennings Sch Outstanding Tchr 4 Times NHS; Martha Holden Jennings Grant Recip Dist Team OH Dept of Ed; *home:* 114 Rauch Dr Marietta OH 45750*

LUTON, BRYAN, Math Teacher; *b:* Akron, OH; *ed:* Kent St Univ Math 1969; *cr:* Springfield Local Schls Math Tchr 1969-; *ai:* Yth Christ Campus Life Club Ldr; 27 Yrs Perfect Attendance; *office:* Sp Hill Jr HS 660 Lessig Ave Akron OH 44312*

LUTTE, CAROLE ANNE, Instrumental Teacher; *b:* Allentown, PA; West Chester Univ (BS) Music Ed 1985, (MM) Music Ed 1994; Allentown Schl Dist Instrumental Dir 1985-86; Easton Area Instrumental Dir 1986-89; Easton Area HS Instrumental Dir 1989-; Marching, Jazz, Bsktbl Pep Band; All-City Elem Band-Orch; Pit, St Orchestra; NEA, MENC 1985-; NSOA 1987-, Sec 2 Yrs; PMEA Dist 1985-, VP 1 Yr, Pres 1993-95, VP 1995-; Allentown Municipal Ba Royalaires Dance Band 1980-, Allentown Symphony Orch 1985-; *off* Easton Area H S 2601 William Penn Hwy Easton PA 18042

LUTZ, JEANNE, Second Grade Teacher; *b:* Brooklyn, NY; *ed:* Ade Univ (MS) El Ed 1975; 75 Addl Credits; *cr:* Waverly Ave Schl Second Tchr 1973-; *ai:* PTA Liaison; AFT, NYSUT 1973-; SCTA 1973-, Bldg R *office:* Waverly Avenue Elem Schl 1111 Waverly Ave Holtsville NY 11

LUTZ, RICHARD J., Gifted Support Teacher; *b:* Sewickley, PA; Cheryl Lynn Johnson; *ed:* Edinboro Univ of PA (BA) Scndry Eng Ed 19 St Bonaventure Univ (MED) Ed 1980; *cr:* Bradford Area Pub Schls Vari Scndry Tchng Assignments 1972-; *ai:* HS Bowl Coach; Internet Co NED, PA St Ed Assn 1972-; Bradford Area Ed Assn 1972-, H Negotiator; *office:* Bradford Area Sr HS 81 Interstate Pkwy Bradford 16701

LUTZ, RONALD L., Mathematics Teacher; *b:* Bernville, PA; *m:* Linda Frazer; *c:* Steven M., Susan L. Painton; *ed:* Kutztown St Coll (BS) M 1965; 54 Credits; *cr:* Conrad Weiser HS Math Tchr 1965-; *ai:* Sr Cl Berks Cty Math Test Advs; Var Golf Coach; Math Dept Chm; NEA, PS CWEA 1965-; Lions Club 1990-, VP; *office:* Conrad Weiser Jr/Sr HS 3 E Penn Ave Robesonia PA 19551

Z, SHARON FIGINSKI, English & Theater Arts Teacher; *b:* nore, MD; *m:* Robert D. Jr.; *c:* Rachel Anne, Brett, Jonathan; *ed:* on St Univ (BS) Eng, Scndry Ed 1971; Univ of MD & Western MD Ed 1980; Post Grad Courses Eng, Drama, Tchng of Honors; *cr:* Old MS 8-9th Grd Eng Tchr 6 Months; Arbutus Jr HS 8-9th Grd Eng Tchr ; Owings Mills Jr, Sr HS 9-12th Grd Eng, Drama Tchr 6 Yrs, Owings Sr HS 9-12th Grd Eng, Drama Tchr 11 Yrs; *ai:* Fall Drama iction, Spring Musical Dir; Kids on Block Prgm Spon; Svc Learing, p Comm; Morning Announcement Coord; Old St Pauls Parish 1986-, ch Schl Dir; Articles Pub; *office:* Owings Mills Sr HS 124 S Tollgate wings Mills MD 21117*

Z, STEVEN CRAIG, Ger, Speech, Drama & Eng Tchr; *b:* Grand ds, MI; *m:* Judith Hope; *c:* Matthew, Ryan; *ed:* Western MI Univ (BA) Eng 1970, (MA) Eng Ger 1978; 30 Credit Hrs Beyond Masters ding Course Work in Admin; Counseling, Curr Design; MS odologies; Ger, Eng; *cr:* Belvidere HS 9-12th Grd Ger, Eng, Speech -75; Hillside Jr HS 7-9th Grd Ger, Eng 1975-79; Kalamazoo Valley n Coll Inst Ger Part-Time 1977-78; Brussels Amer Schl 6-12th Grd Eng, Speech, Drama 1979-94; Wuerzburg MS Ger, Eng, Speech 1994-; IS & HS Stu Cncl Spon; Var Cross Cntry Coach; Child Case Study, Comms, NJHS Comm; Chess & Drama Clb Spon; Overseas Ed Assn -; NEA 1971-; Brussels Educl Assn 1992-, Treas; Brussels Amer Schl) 1979-; Brussels Boosters Club 1979-; Brussels Sports Assn 1979-, h, Umpire, Referee; Amer Theatre Co of Brussels 1979-, Actor, Set gn, Publicity; Waerzburg Mid PTSA; Sustained Superior Svc Awd; n Svc Awd Contribution to NATO Comm; Spec Act Awd for oting Ger, Amer Relations; Spec Awd for Coordinating BENELUX Stu Cncl; Numerous Certs of Appreciation from PTSO, Boosters Club, sels Sports Assn; *office:* Wuerzburg MS Cmr #475 Box 215 APO AE 6*

Z, WILLIAM D.,JR., Fourth Grade Teacher; *b:* Towanda, PA; *m:* leen A. Stoneking; *c:* Zechariah, Mariah; *ed:* Mansfield Uni (BS) Ed 1985; Elmira Coll & Penn St Univ Post Grad Stud; *cr:* Scio Cntrl s Kndgtn Tchr 1985-89; Wyalusing Area Schls 4th Grd Tchr 1989-; *ai:* Var Bsktbl & Vllybl Coach; NEA 1989-; PSEA 1989-, Local Pres; ntrim Bapt Church 1994-; NTL Vllybl Coach of the Yr 1994; *home:* RR x 84 Wyalusing PA 18853*

Z, WILLIAM HARRY, Fourth Grade Teacher; *b:* Hershey, PA; *m:* h Morris; *c:* Kathleen, William R., Jennifer; *ed:* Elizabethtown Coll Ed) Elem Ed 1965; Shippensburg Univ (MS) Rdng 1969; *cr:* Donegal Schl Dist 5th Grd Tchr 1 Yr; Lower Dauphin Schl Dist 4th Grd Tchr rs; *ai:* PSEA 1965-; NEA 1965-; Lower Dauphin Ed Assn 1966-, Pres; y Two Schl Bd 1987-, VP; Dauphin Cty Tech Schl Bd 1994-; *office:* er Dauphin Schl Dist Rd 2 Box 3210 Grantville PA 17028

TON, RICHARD NEIL, Assoc Prof of Human Studies; *b:* Lima, ; *m:* Melissa Vandiver Thomas; *c:* Jared, Maya, India; *ed:* Univ of x (PHD) Antrhopology 1978; *ai:* Intnl Voluntary Svcs; Bd of Dirs; an Stud Chair; The Book of Chumayel & The Yucatec Maya Book of nsel 1539-1 1539-1638 Pub 1995; British Acad Research Fellow 1979; vard Fellowship in Pre-Columbian Stud 1981.

BEN, SHARON PATRICIA (LOVE), Choral Dir & Music Dept r; *b:* West Reading, PA; *m:* William; *c:* Nathaniel, Trevor; *ed:* Lebanon Coll (BS) Music Ed 1981; Attnd Millersville Univ, West Chester Univ d Stud; *cr:* Oxford Area Schl Dist Elem Music Tchr 1982-86; missing Area Schl Dist Music Edctr 1986, Jr-Sr HS Choral Dir 1990-, ic Dept Chair 1995-; *ai:* HS Select Chorale, Jr HS Var Singers Choral Drama Club Musical Dir; Prof, Steering Comm; NEA 1981-, Bldg , MENC, PA Music Ed Assn, Amer Guild of Organists 1981-; Amer ral Dir Assn 1994-; Wyomissing Jaycees 1987-89; Minister of Music sman Mem UCC 1986-; MS Soc 1992-; PA Tchr of Yr Nom 1987; ord Citizen of Yr 1985; *office:* Wyomissing Area Schl Dist 630 Evans Wyomissing PA 19610*

ON, EILEEN OXLEY, Fifth Grade Teacher; *b:* Camden, NJ; *m:* mas M. Jr.; *ed:* Glassboro St Coll (BA) Ed 1977; *cr:* M E Costello Schl 5th Grd Tchr 1977-; *ai:* Site Based Planning Comm; 5th Grd Chprsn; itor 1st Yr Tchr; Gloucester City Ed Assn 1977-, Mbrshp Chair, Soc ir; NJEA, NEA 1977-; Governors Recognition Awd 1987; *office:* M E tello Schl Joy & Cumberland Sts Gloucester City NJ 08030

DON, FRANCES T. MACCHIA, Biology & Chemistry Teacher; *b:* th Boston, MA; *m:* Thomas K.; *c:* Maria Lyndon Barnes, Julie Lydon erman, Thomas K. Jr., Stephanie A.; *ed:* Emmanuel Coll (BA) Bio 6; Boston Coll (MS) Bio 1958; 18 hrs Chem 1980; Univ of MA at herst 3 Hrs Bio 1977; Univ of Boston 9 hrs Chem 1990, 1992-94; 3 Hrs 980; *cr:* MA General Hospital Researcher 1956-57; Jimmy Fund cer Fnd Researcher 1958-59; Bridgewater HS Sci, Bio & Chem Tchr 9-60; Boston Pub Schls Sci, Bio & Chem Tchr 1960-62 & 1973-; *ai:* C 1959-; *office:* South Boston HS 95 G St South Boston MA 02127

KE, SHERMAN E.,JR., Music Department Program Coord; *b:* Buffalo, *m:* Barbara Jill LiVecchi; *c:* Abigail, Ryan; *ed:* St Univ of NY at sdam (BM) Ed 1973; St Univ of NY Coll at Buffalo (MA) Ed 1979; 6 il Hrs; St Univ of NY Coll at Fredonia 10 Hrs; Eastman Schl of Music mpet Stud; *cr:* Grand Island Cntrl Schls HS Band Dir 19 Yrs, Elem rumental Tchr 4 Yrs, Dist Music Coord 15 Yrs; *ai:* Grds 4 & 5 Elem d; Grds 9-12 HS Jazz Ensemble; MENC 1973-; NYSSMA 1973-, Exec cl 1984-87; ECMEA 1973-, Marching Bands St Chm 1980, Bd of Dirs 5-77, Childrens Ministry Dir; Chrstn Fnd Performing Arts 1986-, Sec, t of Appreciation 1993; Victory Chrstn Ctr 1989-, Yth Ldr, Children's nistry Dir, Outstdng Ministry 1991; 19 Consecutive A Ratings Grand nd HS Concert Wind Ensemble, Intnl Competition Silver Medallions shington DC 1981, MontreaL Quebec 1984, 1988; Band Performed VP ckefeller 1977; Feature Article Pub; *office:* Grand Island Cntrl Schl Dist 0 Ransom Rd Grand Island NY 14072*

KINS, LAVERN BROOKS, Owner & Manager; *b:* Hazel Green, KY; Mark Elvin, Keith Douglas; *ed:* Lee's St Coll (AS) Elem Ed 1951; tern KY St Univ (BS) Elem Ed 1958; *cr:* Pine Ridge Elem Schl 2nd-3rd l Tchr 1 Yr; Carlisle Elem Schl 2nd, 4th Grd Tchr 11 Yrs; Vly View Elem l 2nd Grd Tchr 23 Yrs; *ai:* NEA, OEA, SWOTA 1953-; Retired Tchrs 93-; Sunday Schl Tchr; Amer Heart Fund, Amer Cancer Soc Vols 10 Yrs; urch Quilting Circle; Brownies 1990-, Ldr; Boy Scouts of OH 1975-, nored Mem; *home:* 7852 Franklin Trenton Rd Carlisle OH 45005

LE, ANITA ARGUST, HS Mathematics Teacher; *b:* Scranton, PA; *m:* adford H.; *c:* Jenneth, Matthew; *ed:* PA St Univ (BS) Soc Stud 1964, ED) Ed 1966; Attnd Boston Coll, NYC Coll of Insurance, Univ of MA; Toms River HS North Math Tchr 1980-85; Chelmsford HS Math Tchr 35-86; Nashoba Vly HS Math Tchr 1986-93; Nashua HS Math Tchr 93-; *ai:* Putting the Pieces Together Quilt Project Facilitator; NCTM 35-; AFT, ATMNE-NH 1993-; First United Bapt Church 1985-, Tchr; bitat for Humanity 1992-; Gov Merrill Citation, Proclamation; esidential Awd for Excl in Math Tchng Nom 1996; *office:* Nashua Sr HS Riverside Dr Nashua NH 03062*

LE, DONALD LEE, Chairman of PE Department; *b:* E Liverpool, OH; Barbara Ann Lyons; *c:* Amy, David, Michael; *ed:* Muskingum Coll (BA) 1971; Miami Univ of OH (MED) Ed, PE 1972; IN Univ of PA (DEd) gher Ed Admin 1989; *cr:* Grove City Coll PE Dept Chm, Assoc Prof 72-; *ai:* Soccer, Bsbl Coach; Housing Group Adv; Curr, Instruction, ntinuing Evaluation Comms; Stu Act Sub-Comm Chair; NCAA 1972-; Amer Alliance for Hlth, PE Recreation, Dance 1995-; Grove City Youth Soccer 1977-, Founder; YMCA Advy Bd 1991-93; Bsktbl Boosters 1984-, Pres; Florence E. MacKenzie Comm Svc Awd; *office:* Grove City Coll 100 Campus Dr Grove City PA 16127

LYLE, JOHN W.,JR., Assistant Principal; *b:* Providence, RI; *m:* Lori A. Martin; *ed:* Barrington Coll (BA) His, Soc Stud 1974; Providence Coll (MED) Ed Admin 1978; Suffolk Univ Schl of Law (MD) Law 1992; *cr:* Lincoln HS Dept Chair, Soc Stud 1992-95, Tchr 1994-, Asst Prin 1995-; *ai:* NAASP, RTASP, ASCO 1995-; RI Senate 1981-87, 1991-95, Senator; Blackstone Vly Tourism Cncl 1984-, Bd Dirs; Cumb-Linc Boys, Girls 1984-, Trustee; NETUA 1985-, 1st Vice-Pres; Distngd Alumnus; Close Up Awd; Articles Pub; *office:* Lincoln HS 135 Old River Rd Lincoln RI 02865*

LYLE, KRISTINE KRECKEL, Middle School Teacher; *b:* St Marys, PA; *m:* Brent Edward; *c:* Brooke, Brandon; *ed:* Mansfield Univ of PA (BSEd) Home Ec 1973; Masters Equivalency 1983; Edinboro Univ of PA Elem Ed Cert 1987; *cr:* East Forest HS Home Ec Tchr 1974-79; St Marys HS Home Ec Tchr 1979-90; St Mary MS Math & Rdng Tchr 1991-; *office:* Saint Marys Area MS 977 S St Marys Rd St Marys PA 15854*

LYLE, LISA MARIE, Asst Dir of Residence Life; *b:* Rochester, NY; *ed:* The PA St Univ (BS) Human Dev & Family Stud 1989; Gannon Univ (MS) Psych, Stu Prsnl 1991; *cr:* The PA St Univ Resident Asst 1986-89; Gannon Univ Resident Dir 1989-91; Fairleigh Dickinson Univ Resident Dir 1991-94, Asst Dir of Residence Life, Frosh Seminar Facilitator 1994-; *ai:* Univ Crime Bd Co-Creator, Mem; Univ Auxillary Svcs Bd, Sec, Mem; Ferguson Recreation Ctr Programming Bd, Mem; NASPA, ACPA 1989-; *office:* Fairleigh Dickinson Univ 285 Madison Ave Madison NJ 07940

LYLE, PAMELA BONACE, Fifth Grade Teacher; *b:* Warren, PA; *m:* Gregory Scott; *c:* Brendan Scott; *ed:* Edinboro St Coll (BS) Elem Ed, Erly Childhood 1974; Elem Ed Crly Childhood Equiv Edinboro, Penn St Univ 1980; *cr:* Home St Elem 4th Grd Tchr 1975; Lander Elem k-4th Grd Tchr 1975-80; Market St Elem 2nd Grd Tchr 1980; Mc Clintock Elem Kndgtn Tchr 1980-86; Beaty Warren MS 6th Grd Tchr 1986-95, 5th Grd 1995-; *ai:* Yrbk Co-Editor 1993-94; GED Instr 1987-90; Team Ldr; Cooperative Lrng Network; TESA Prgm; Peer Coaching Participant; NEA, PSEA, WCEA 1975-; Jr Woman's of Warren 1987-93, Pres 1991-92; Coll Club of Warren; First Presbyn Church, Deacon 1991-92; Warren Co Amber Cancer Society, Co Chair Gourmet Tasting Fundraiser 1992; Bus, Prof Women's Club 1983-85; Alpha Gamma Delta 1972-, Panhellenic Officer 1973-74; *office:* Beaty Warren MS 2 E 3rd Ave Warren PA 16365*

LYMAN, RICHARD BURR, English Teacher; *b:* Holden, MA; *m:* Janice Lynn Cable; *c:* Russell Burr, Jeffrey Ray; *ed:* Yankton Coll (BA) Eng Ed 1968; Plymouth St Coll (MED) Scndry Ed 1980; 30 Addl Credits; *cr:* Plymouth Regnl HS Eng Tchr 1968-; *ai:* Ski Coach 25 Yrs; Jr HS Bsktbl Coach; Jr Var Bsbl Coach; NEA-NH 1968-, Local Pres; Little League, Coach; Babe Ruth Bsbl, Coach; Ski Patrole; Manchester Union Leader Ski Coach of Yr Awd; *office:* Plymouth Regional HS Old Ward Bridge Rd Plymouth NH 03264

LYNAM, JAMES RICHARD, Computer Science Teacher; *b:* Oil City, PA; *c:* Benjamin, James; *ed:* Clarion Univ (BS) Bio, Gen Sci 1968; 48 Post Grad Hrs Bio, Cmptr Sci; *cr:* West Middlesex HS Bio, Cmptr Sci Tchr 1968-; *ai:* NHS, Soph Class Adv; Dist Cmptr Coord; NEA, PSEA 1968-; PA-OH Radio Control Soc 1990-, Sec, Treas; Most Respected Tchr 1989, 1995; Article Pub; *office:* West Middlesex HS 3591 Sharon Rd West Middlesex PA 16159*

LYNAM, JOLENE M., Teacher & Facilitator of GATE; *b:* Marshall, MI; *c:* Elizabeth, John; *ed:* Cntrl MI Univ (BS) Pol Sci 1963; MI St Univ (MS) His 1965; Cert in Bus; *cr:* Birmingham HS Tchr 1963-66; East Lansing HS Tchr 1966-70; Fairport HS Tchr, Facilitator 1974-; *ai:* Pol Action Club; Fairport Ed Assn Pub Relations, Dist Standards Comms; AFT, NYSUT 1976-; Frgn Policy Assn 1984-; Article Pub; Tchr of Yr 1984; *office:* Fairport HS 1358 Ayrault Rd Fairport NY 14450*

LYNAUGH, BARBARA J., French Teacher; *b:* Gloversville, NY; *ed:* St Univ of NY at Albany (BA) Fr 1968, (MA) Advanced Classroom Tchng 1971, (MS) Educl Admin 1994; 27 Grad Hrs in Fr & Eng as Second Lang; *cr:* Sarartoga Springs Jr HS Fr Tchr 1968-; *ai:* AFT, NYSUT SSTA 1968-; Pub CR Bravo A Foreign Lang Game in Fr, Span, Ger & Eng 1986; Pub CR Do-Re-Mi En Francais-A Cassette of 10 Original Fr Songs Used for Instruction 1990; *office:* Saratoga Springs Jr HS W Circular St Saratoga Springs NY 12866

LYNCH, BILLIE S., English Teacher; *b:* Warren, OH; *m:* Lawrence L.; *c:* Douglas S., William K., David L.; *ed:* Bethany Coll (BA) Eng 1967; Kent St (MA) Eng 1980; *cr:* Peters Twp HS Eng Tchr 1967-69; Austintown Fitch HS Eng Tchr 1969-; *ai:* NCTE 1970-; AAUW; Bethany Coll Alumni 1968-, Pres; Bd of Dirs-Chrstn Church in OH 1982-88; *home:* 7180 Knauf Rd Canfield OH 44406

LYNCH, DEBRA MACZYNSKI, Science Teacher; *b:* Schenectady, NY; *m:* Jerry C.; *ed:* Hudson Valley Comm Coll (AS) Early Chldhd Ed 1979; Coll of St Rose (BS) Elem & Scndry Ed 1981; Russell Sage Coll (MS) Hlth Ed 1986; Attnd Schenectady Comm Coll; 18 Post Grad Credit Hours; *cr:* W H Lynch MS Sci Tchr 1981-; *ai:* Comp Tech Comm; Dept Environmental Conser Campership Spon; NYSUT 1981-; ATA 1981-; NSTA 1985-; Earth Island Inst 1989-; ASPCA 1990-; Natl Audubon Activist 1991-; Cooperative Learning Wkshp Presenter 1992; *office:* Lynch MS Coolidge Rd Amsterdam NY 12010*

LYNCH, DIANE F., Biology Teacher; *b:* New York, NY; *m:* Patrick; *c:* Sean, Brian; *ed:* St Johns Univ (BS) Ed, Bio 1967, (MS) Bio & Protozoology 1969; 60 Addl Credit Hrs; *cr:* Mineola HS Bio Tchr 1969-; *ai:* NYSUT, NEA & AFT 1969-; Delta Zeta 1966-; *home:* 22 Linden Ave Floral Park NY 11001

LYNCH, DONNA RIMMER, Social Studies Teacher; *b:* Philadelphia, PA; *c:* Kelly, Kevin; *ed:* Glassboro St Coll (BA) Ed 1968; St Univ at Albany (MS) Ed 1990; Addl 30 Credit Hrs in Soc Sci Courses Including Pub Policy, Sociology, Pysch, His, Govt; *cr:* Chews Landing Elem Schl Fifth Grd Tchr 1968-69; Martin Luther King Jr Elem Schl Fifth Grd Tchr 1969-74; Shenendehowa HS Soc Stud Tchr 1984-; Syracuse Univ Adj Prof 1992-; *ai:* Crew Club, Stu Comm Vol Adv; AFT 1984-; STA 1984-, Rep; CDCSS 1984-, Newsletter Ed; PTSA 1984-, Legislative Liaison; Captain 1988-; Learn N Serve Amer Grant; G E STARS Awd; Testified at Congressional Hearings; Child Labor Consultant to ABC Nightline; Task Force on Child Labor Laws; Consultant to Newsweek; *office:* Shenendehowa HS 970 Route 146 Clifton Park NY 12065

LYNCH, DOROTHY L., Guidance Counselor; *b:* Brooklyn, NY; *ed:* Adelphi Univ (BA) Sociology 1974; St Johns Univ (MS) Cnslr Ed 1977; Permanent Cert-Schl Dist Admin; Provisional Cert-Schl Admin & Supervision; 61 Credits Beyond Masters; *cr:* Garden City Jr HS Guidance Cnslr 1977-78; Baldwin Jr HS Guidance Cnslr 1979-; *ai:* Var Sftbl Coach at Oceanside HS 10 Yrs; Vlybl Ofcl at Nassau Cty 9 Yrs; Nassau Cnslrs Assn 1993-; NYSUT 1977-; NEA 1977-; Nassau Cty Sftbl Coaches Assn 1979-, Pres, Coach of Yr Awd; *home:* 120 Morris Ave Apt A-8 Rockville Centre NY 11570

LYNCH, EDWARD JOSEPH, Hlth & Alternative Prgm Supvr; *b:* Flushing Queens, NY; *ed:* East Stroudsburg Univ (BA) Hlth Ed 1991; Working on Masters of Ed in Hlth, PE; *cr:* USAF Life Support Specialist 1983-87; Pocono Mt HS Hlth, In Schl Alternative Prgm Supvr 1991-; East Stroudsburg Univ Upward Bound, Hlth Instr 1991-; *ai:* Boys Var Tennis Coach 1991-; Supervise Hlth Club; PSEA, NEA, US Tennis Assn 1991-; Air Force Achvmt Medal 1987; Magna Cum Laude ESU 1991; Family Inst Awd 1995; Dr Kingsbury Awd 1995; *office:* Pocono Mtn Intermediate School PO Box 200 Swiftwater PA 18370*

LYNCH, EDWARD RICHARD,JR., 7th Grade English Teacher; *b:* Winchester, MA; *m:* Maureen Cogan; *c:* Colleen, Restivo, Michael, Katie; *ed:* Boston St Coll (BA) Eng Ed 1969; Cambridge Coll (MED) Ed 1992; Grad Courses; Holding a Masters with 30+ Credit Hrs; *cr:* Kennedy MS Eng Tchr 1969-; *ai:* NEA 1969-; MTA 1969-; WTA 1969- VP 1970-71; Copyrighted Masters Project Thesis 7th Grd Eng Lets Get Physical; *office:* Woburn Public Schools Middle St Woburn MA 01801

LYNCH, HARRY EDWARD, Band Director & Music Teacher; *b:* Brooklyn, NY; *m:* Gail D VonBurg; *c:* Jason, Amanda; *ed:* SUNY at Potsdam (BS) Music Ed 1971; SUNY at New Paltz (MA) Ed 1978; *cr:* Chester NY General Music 1974-75; Wappingers Central Schl Band Dir, Tchr 1975-93; *ai:* Jazz Ensemble, Musical Dir for Musicals, Sound Adv; NYSUT 1975-; NYSSMA 1971-; DCMEA 1974-, Treas 4 Yrs; *office:* Roy C. Ketcham HS 99 Myers Corners Rd Wappingers Falls NY 12590*

LYNCH, JAMES R., American History Teacher; *b:* New York City, NY; *m:* Barbara Ann Amorose; *c:* Christopher, Debra, Timothy, James Jr.; *ed:* Hofstra Univ (BA) His 1965; Long Island Univ (MS) Admin 1990; SDA Cert in Admin 1991; 45 Addl Credit Hrs Admin, Supervision; *cr:* West Babylon HS Soc Stud Tchr 1965-, Dean of Stdnts 1988-, Var Bsktbl coach 1972-, Prin Summer Schl 1995-; *ai:* Comm Chm of Excelsior Self-Stud, 9th Grd Transitional, REACH, Mentor Prgm; Dir 100 Prgm for At-Risk Stdnts; AFT, NEA, West Babylon Tchrs 1965-; West Babylon Coaches 1965-, Pres, Coach of Yr 6 Times; Suffolk Cty Coaches 1968-, VP, Coach of Yr, Long Island Coach of Yr; Little League of Islips 1970-, Bd of Dir; Assoc for Quality & Participation of Long Island, Guest Speaker Wkshps in NE; Tchr of Yr 1995; *office:* West Babylon HS 500 Great East Neck Rd Babylon NY 11704

LYNCH, JANE CATHERINE, Retired Teacher; *b:* Jersey City, NJ; *ed:* Saint Elizabeth Convent (BS) Ed 1946; *cr:* 1st Grd Tchr 58 Yrs; *ai:* Missions Moderator.

LYNCH, JEAN M., Religion Teacher; *ed:* Molloy Coll (BS) Ed 1965; St John Univ (MA) Theology 1991; Immaculate Conception Seminary Advanced Cert Spirituality 1996; *cr:* Bowling Green Elem Schl 3rd Grd Tchr 1965-70; St Joseph's Elem Schl Garden City 7th & 8th Grd Tchr 1985-90; Mary Louise Acad Religion Tchr 1991-; *ai:* NEA, NCEA; *office:* Mary Louis Acad 17621 Wexford Ter Jamaica NY 11432

LYNCH, JOSEPH FRANCIS, English Teacher; *b:* Philadelphia, PA; *m:* Margaret Judge; *c:* Brian, Chris, Tom; *ed:* La Salle Univ (BA) Eng 1965; Villanova Univ (MA) Eng 1973; *cr:* La Salle HS Eng Tchr 1965-70; Geo Washington HS Eng Tchr 1970-; Villanova Univ Adj Eng Prof 1989-; Chestnut Hill Coll Adj Eng Prof 1996; *ai:* Coord Cities-in-Schls 1992-94; AFT 1970-; Semi-Finalist Phila Tchr of Yr 1994; *office:* George Washington HS Verree & Bustleton Ave Philadelphia PA 19116

LYNCH, KAREN LAWRENSEN, Spanish Teacher; *b:* Jackson Heights, NY; *m:* Timothy J.; *ed:* St Univ of NY at Plattsburgh (BS) Bus Admin 1986; St Univ of NY at Albany (MA) Span 1988; *cr:* Schalmont Cntrl Schls 7th-12th Grd Span Tchr 1988-; *ai:* Ski Club Adv; Modified Girls Soccer Coach; NYSAFLT 1988-; *office:* Schalmont HS 2 Sabre Dr Schenectady NY 12306

LYNCH, LISA DECKTOR, French Teacher; *b:* Wilmington, DE; *m:* Robert; *ed:* American Univ (BA) Fr 1970; Univ of MD Univ Coll (MA) Intnl Mngmt 1995; *cr:* Berlitz Schl Eng Tchr 1971-73; Inlingua Schl Eng Tchr 1980-82; Capitol Coll Eng Tchr 1982-84; Montgomery Cty Pub Schls Fr Tchr 1985-; *ai:* NEA 1985-.

LYNCH, MARK THOMAS, Asst Professor of Social Work; *b:* Johnstown, PA; *m:* Deborah Kay Stoker; *c:* Jennifer, Caitlin; *ed:* CA St Coll (BA) Sociology, Psych 1975; WV Univ (MSW) Soc Work 1977; 12 Credits Toward PHD in Soc Work Prgm Univ of Pittsburgh; 15 Credits Toward PsyD in Psych Prgm IN Univ of PA; *cr:* Southern Highland CMHC Staff Dev Dir, Soc Worker 1977-78; Concord Coll Instr 1978; Osborne Partial Hospitalization Prgm Team Ldr, Psychiatric Soc Worker 1978-86; Conemaugh Cnslng Assocs Psychotherapist, Consultant 1986-92; Saint Francis Coll Asst Prof, Field Instr 1992-; *ai:* Girls Elem Bsktbl Coach; Sr Peer Cnslr Edctr; Soc Work Club Adv; Cncl of Soc Work Edctrs 1992-; Natl Assn Soc Workers 1978-; Western PA Partial Hospitalization Assn 1979-86, Pres; Act 101 Bd 1993-, Diversity Comm Chair; Clinical Soc Work Practice Diplomate; NASW Registry of Soc Workers; Acad of Certfd Soc Workers; PA Recreational Therapy Assn 1991, PA Occupational Therapy Assn 1984 Presenter; *office:* Saint Francis Coll Raymond 109 Loretto PA 15940

LYNCH, MARTHA MILLER, Third Grade Teacher; *b:* Peoria, IL; *m:* Albert Vanstory Jr.; *c:* Albert V. III, David Wayne; *ed:* Duke Univ (BA) Elem Ed 1954; 30 Credit Hrs; *cr:* Lincroft Elem Schl Tchr 1976-95; *ai:* NEA, NJEA, MTEA 1976-; Withcombe Grant; Tchr of Yr; Governor's Awd; *office:* Lincroft Elem Schl 729 Newman Springs Rd Lincroft NJ 07738

LYNCH, MARYANN YANNOTTY, English Tchr & Dept Chair; *b:* Butler, PA; *m:* Richard W.; *c:* Peter; *ed:* Carlow Coll (BA) Eng 1977; Duquesne Univ (MA) Eng 1979; Post Masters Credits in Eng, Ed; *cr:* Duquesne Univ Tchng Asst 1977-78, Tchng Fellow 1979-80; Canevin HS Eng Tchr 1980-81; Cntrl Cath HS Chair Dept of Eng 1981-; Carlow Coll Writing Instr 1982-86; *ai:* NHS Moderator; Peer Tutoring Coord; Acad Cncl; Stu Affairs Cncl Fac Rep; ASCD 1992-; NCTE 1980-; WPCTE 1990-; *office:* Pittsburgh Central Cath Schl 4720 5th Ave Pittsburgh PA 15213

LYNCH, MARY DIANE, Seventh & Eighth Grade Teacher; *b:* Brooklyn, NY; *m:* Robert John; *c:* Daniel, Louise; *ed:* Hunter Coll (BA) Anthropology, Ed 1972; City Univ of NY (MS) Elem Ed 1977; NYS Cert 7-9 Grd Sci, Soc Stud, K-6 Grd; *cr:* St Anthony Third-Fourth Grd Math, Soc Stud, Sci Tchr 1973-78; St Thomas of Canterbury Seventh-Eighth Grd Lang Arts Lit, Soc Stud Tchr 1988-; *ai:* Soc Action, Grad Dinner, Dance Schl Coord; Cornwall Cntrl Dist Bd of Ed 1995-, Trustee; AIDS Advy Cncl 1995-; Awded NY Cncl for the Hum Inst 1995; Awded SUNY at Oneonta Cntrl Hudson Utilities 1993; *office:* St Thomas Of Canterbury Schl 336 Hudson St Cornwall-On-Hud NY 12520

LYNCH, MICHAEL P., 7th & 8th Grade Math Teacher; *b:* Bayonne, NJ; *m:* Barbara Bielen; *c:* Todd, Stephanie; *ed:* Jersey City St Coll (BA) Elem Ed 1970, (MA) Stu Prsnl Svcs 1983; *cr:* M J Donohoe #4 5th Grd Tchr 1970-80, 6th Grd Tchr 1980-83, 8th Grd Tchr 1983-95, 7th Grd Tchr 1995-; Elem Coord of After Schl Pgms 1983-; *ai:* Elem Act Coord 13 Yrs; Girls Bsktbl; Chrldng; Vllybl; Chess; Pub Speaking; NEA 1970-; NJEA 1970-; ASA 1974-, Sftbl Umpire; Fed of HS 1977-, Bsbl & Sftbl Umpire, 1991-, Vllybl Ofcl; 1st Tchr of the Yr Awd; Governors Tchr Recognition Pgm 1986; *office:* Mary J Donohoe Elem Schl 4 E 5th St Bayonne NJ 07002

LYNCH, NANCY ELLEN, Mathematics Teacher; *b:* Lewiston, ME; *m:* Kenny E.; *c:* Brian, Kenny; *ed:* Pensacola Chrstn Coll (BS) Math Ed 1985, (MS) Educl Admin 1987; *cr:* Paris Chrstn Acad Math Tchr 1987-; *ai:* Stu Cnsl Adv; Math Team Coord; ACSI 1991-.

LYNCH, NEIL SAMUEL, 9th-12th Grd ESL & TBE Teacher; *b:* Lawrence, MA; *m:* Margaret Rita Holland; *c:* Kristin, Sarah, Shawn; *ed:* Merrimack Coll (BA) Eng 1973; Lesley Coll (MED) Moderate Spec Needs 1992; Facing His & Ourselves Inst 2 Credit Hrs, U Mass Lowell ESL Stud 6 Credit Hrs; Fitchburg St Coll Biling SPED Stud 5 Credit Hrs; *cr:* St

Augustine Schl Grd 7-8 Tchr 1973-78; Natl Park Svc Park Ranger 1977-78; Gen Electric Co Various Positions 1978-90; Methven HS ESL, TBE 9-12 Grd Tchr 1990-; *ai:* Moderator of Asian Club; ESL, TBE Guid Cnslr; NEA 192-; MTA 1991-; MABE 1992-, HS Tchr of Yr 1993; Natl Parks & Conservation Assn 1984-, Parkwatcher; Lawrence City Cncl 1988-91; Lawrence Redev Authority 1992-; St Augustine Schl Bd 1992-; A. B. Bruce Schl PTO 1986-88, Pres; MA Biling HS Tchr of Yr Awd 1993; Numerous Articles Pub; *office:* Methuen HS 1 Ranger Rd Methuen MA 01844*

LYNCH, PATRICIA A. (HENIGIN), English Teacher; *b:* Queens, NY; *m:* Joseph L.; *c:* Stefanie, Elizabeth, Nathaniel; *ed:* Mount St Joseph Coll (BA) Ed 1965; Breadloaf Middlebury Coll (MA) Eng 1972; 9 Grad Credits Eng Simmons Coll; *cr:* St James Schl Eng Tchr 1965-67; Prout Meml HS Eng Tchr 1967-70; Notre Dame Schl Eng Tchr 1970-72; Grover Cleveland Jr HS Eng Tchr 1972-73; Northwest Cath HS Eng Tchr 1989-; *ai:* Newspaper; Poetry Club; Sharing The Faith Fac Comm; MLA, NCEA 1989-; NCTE 1995-; Mark Twain Meml 1989-; Hill Stead Museum 1995-; Smithsonian Inst 1980-; Natl Endowment for Arts Grant Simmons Coll 1969; Retreat Movement Presenter; Poetry Pub, Awd.

LYNCH, PATRICIA O'NEAL, 7th Grade Social Studies Tchr; *b:* Binghamton, NY; *m:* Gerard B.; *c:* Timothy, Matthew, Kathryn; *ed:* SUNY at Cortland (BS) Scndry Soc Stud 1964, (MS) Scndry Soc Stud 1969; *cr:* Binghamton Schl Dist 7th Grd Soc Stud Tchr 1964-67; Maine Endwell HS 11th Grd Amer His Tchr 1968-69; Binghamton Schl Dist 7th Grd Soc Stud Tchr 1969-70; Susquehanna Vly Schl Dist 7th-8th, 11th Grd Soc Stud Tchr 1986-; *ai:* Stu Cncl Adv; NEA, NYSUS 1964-; Binghamton Yth Symphony 1982-, Bd of Dirs, Pres; Parish Cncl St Patrick's 1990-; Regnl Pastoral Cncl 1992-.

LYNCH, PETER, Math, Sci Instr & Dept Chprsn; *b:* Cambridge, MA; *m:* Jessica Maria Jansen-Lynch; *c:* Ian Jacob, Micah William; *ed:* Univ of NC at Chapel Hill (BS) Zoology 1981; Univ of RI (MS) Zoology 1985; Univ of MA at Lowell (EDM) Curr & Instruction 198; 10 Hrs Univ of MD; 3 Hrs Each at Johnson St Coll, Univ of ME at Orono & Univ of VT; *cr:* Univ of RI Grad Labs Instr 1983-84; Haverhill HS Sci Tchr 1986-88; Fair Haven Union HS Sci Tchr 1988-95, Math & Sci Chprsn 1995-; *ai:* Nature Club & Ind Sci Adv; Summer Bio Field Apprenticeships Hong Kong Dir; Pi Lambda Theta, NSTA 1986-; Coker Awd for Excl in Undergraduate Research at Univ of NC at Chapel Hill 1981; Honors Thesis at Univ of NC at Chapel Hill 1981; Masters Thesis at Univ of RI 1985; Addison-Rutland Supervisory Union Bd Awd for Excl in Tchng 1994; Grantee Hong Kong Field Apprenticeships 7300 Dollars 1995; Nom Presidential Awd for Excl in Sci Tchng 1996; *office:* Fair Haven Dist 16 Union HS 33 Mechanic St Fair Haven VT 05743*

LYNCH, ROBERT JOSEPH, Social Studies Teacher; *b:* Jersey City, NJ; *m:* Denise L. Bolden; *c:* Erin, Suzanne, Jennifer; *ed:* Saint Edwards Univ (BA) Soc Sci 1972; George Mason Univ (MED) Admin 1980; Attnd P G Comm Coll, George Washington Univ, Bowie St Univ, Charles Cty Comm Coll Post Grad Credits; *cr:* Shugert Jr HS Tchr & Coach 1974-82; James Madison Jr HS Tchr & Coach 1982-83; Forestville Sr HS Tchr & Coach 1983-85; Friendly Sr HS Tchr 1985-; *ai:* Soc Comm; Mid Sts Evaluation Comm; NEA 1976-78; NAIFA 1990-, Metro Chapter Sec; Mount Vernon Athletic Youth Assn 1990-, Coach; *office:* Friendly HS 10000 Allentown Rd Fort Washington MD 20744

LYNCH, ROBERT VINCENT, Sixth Grade Teacher; *b:* Darby, PA; *m:* Eileen Virginia Harter; *c:* Jennifer; *ed:* West Chester Univ (BS) Elem Ed 1971; Villanova Univ (MS) Elem Admin 1985; *cr:* Hillcrest Elem 5th & 6th Grd Tchr 1971-81; Beverly Hills MS 6th Grd Tchr 1981-; *ai:* Team Ldr; PSEA, NEA 1971-; *office:* Beverly Hills MS 1400 Garrett Rd Upper Darby PA 19082

LYNCH, STEPHEN M., Architectural Drafting Teacher; *b:* New York City, NY; *m:* Mary Elizabeth Mc Carthy; *c:* Stephen J., Jerome P., Elizabeth M.; *ed:* Iona Coll (BA) His 1961; Columbia Univ Grad Schl of Arch & Planning (MA) Arch 1974; *cr:* US Marine Corps Comm Ofcr, Captain 1961-66; Jr HS 143 Soc Stud Tchr 1967-85; NYC Transit Authority Asst Architect 1978-80; Bronx HS of Sci Arch Drafting Tchr 1985-; *ai:* Irish, Korean Clubs Moderator; Math, Sci Summer Inst Tchr Stuyvesant HS; AFT, UFT 1966-, Union Rep; NYC Tech Ed Assn 1986-; VFW 1992-; William Kinne Fellows Summer Schlsp 1973; *office:* Bronx HS Of Science 75 W 205th St Bronx NY 10468

LYNCH, TERESA DAY, 2nd Grade Teacher; *b:* Portland, ME; *m:* John Patrick; *c:* John Jr., Jennifer, Christopher; *ed:* Sacred Heart Coll (AA) Elem Ed 1966; Mary Mount Coll (BA) Elem Ed 1976; Univ of ME (MA) Elem Ed 1990; *cr:* Dr. Charles C. Knowlton Schl 2nd Grd Tchr 1990-; *ai:* Quality of Main Street Bd 1995-; Hancock Cty Auditorium 1980-, Bd of Trustee; Black House Historic Preservation 1980-, Trustee; Ellsworth Historical Soc Mem; St Joseph's Woman Cncl Mem; *office:* Dr. Charles C. Knowlton Schl 126 State St Ellsworth ME 04605

LYNCH, VICTORIA EVONE, 5th & 6th Grade Teacher; *b:* Zion Hill Portland, West Indies; *c:* Jaceta Fevrier; *ed:* West Indies Coll (BS) Natural Sci 1978; Diploma Gen Sci 1976; Thirty Credit Hrs Grad Stud Andrews Univ; *cr:* Montserrat Comm Schl Prin, Tchr 1978-81; Bermuda Inst Seventh Grd Tchr 1981-85; William Parker HS Sci, Multigrade Tchr 1986-87; Trinity Temple Acad Fifth-Seventh Grd, 6th-8th Grd Sci Tchr 1987-; *ai:* Children's Choir Dir; Sci Fair Coord; Outdoor Environmental Schl Staff; NJEA 1987-; ASCD 1989-; *home:* 75 Summit Ave Newark NJ 07112*

LYNCH KILLORAN, SUSAN, 5th Grade Teacher; *ed:* NY St Univ Coll at Oswego (MS) Ed 1992; *cr:* Salem Hyde Elem 5th Grd Tchr 1988 & 1994-, 6th Grd Tchr 1988-89; 4th Grd Inclusive Tchr 1989-94; *office:* Salem Hyde Elem Schl 450 Durston Ave Syracuse NY 13203

LYND, ANN FRANCES, Basic Skill Reading & Art Tchr; *b:* Suffern, NY; *m:* Edward John III; *c:* Eddie IV; *ed:* Burlington Comm Coll (AA) Ed Major 1970; William Paterson Coll (BA) Elem Elem 1972; Trenton St Coll (ME) Rdng Specialist 1980; *cr:* Southampton Twp Schl 2 5th Grd Tchr 1972-91; Southampton Twp Schl 1 Basic Skills Rdng Instr, Art Tchr 1991-; *ai:* NJEA 1972-; Art Edctrs of NJ 1991; West Jersey Rdng Cncl 1980; PTA Vincentown 1972-, Tabernacle 1987-; *office:* Southampton Twp Schl 1 26 Pleasant St Vincentown NJ 08088

LYND, JOHN C., Retired Social Studies Teacher; *b:* Rochester, NY; *m:* Judith Simonet; *ed:* St John Fisher Coll (BA) His 1962; Univ of Rochester (MA) His 1967; Sophia Univ at Tokyo; NDEA India Syracuse Univ; SUNY at Cortland; NDEA Latin Amer; SUNYat Potsdam; East-West Ctr HI; NDEA Univ of Rochester; *cr:* Ben Franklin HS Soc Stud Tchr 1962-70; Churchville Chili HS Global Stud Tchr 1970-95; *ai:* Intnl Stu Adv; Global Stud Curr Comm; NEA; NY STA; CCEA; NCSS; NYSCSS; RACSS; Asia, Japan Socs; Rochester Intnl Friendship Cncl, Bd of Dirs; Parks Meigs Neighborhood Assn, Bd of Dirs; Kirkhaven 1985-95, Eucharistic Minister, Vol of Yr 1995; Rochester Area Soc Stud Tchr of Yr; NY St Tchr of Yr; Churchville Chili Tchr of Yr; *home:* 51 Brighton St Rochester NY 14607

LYNES, DANIEL PAUL, Mathematics Tchr & Dept Chm; *b:* Greenfield, MA; *m:* Karen Frances Lamoureaux; *c:* Jeffrey; *ed:* Providence Coll (BA) Math 1964; Boston Coll (MA) Math 1972; 15 Addl Hrs; *cr:* Ludlow HS Math Tchr 1964-76, Math Dept Head 1976-; *ai:* Math Team Adv; NCTM 1982-; Math West 1990-; MA Tchrs Assn 1964-; Empire One Running Club 1982-, Past Pres; NSF Grant Toward Masters Degree; *office:* Ludlow Sr HS 500 Chapin St Ludlow MA 01056

LYNES, MARTHA A., Physics Teacher; *b:* Buffalo, NY; *m:* Gregory; *c:* David Curry, John Curry Lynes, Stephen Curry Lynes; *ed:* William Smith Coll (BA) Physics 1955; IA St Univ (MS) Physics 1958; Anna Maria Coll (MS) Cnslng Psych 1978; Boston & Framington St 12 Grad Credits; Newton Coll Sacred Heart 6 Hrs; Harvard 6 Hrs; Univ of MA at Boston 6 Hrs; CO Univ 6 Hrs; *cr:* IA St Univ Physics Instr 1958-59, Physics Rsrch 1959-62; Lincoln Pub Schls 8th Grd Phys Sci Tchr 1971-74; Algonquin Reg HS Phys Sci, Math & Physics 1974-; *ai:* Lowell Regnl Physics Alliance Steering, Upper Schl Curr & Tech & Schl to Look Comm; Sci Team Coach 1988-95; Physics Team Coach 1988-; Sigma Xi 1958-; ARTA Local MTA St NEA 1974-; New England Section AAPT & Natl AA PT 1988-, Phys Olympics Co-Chair; League of Woman Voters 1967-69; New England Historic Genealogical Soc 1981-, Life Mem; Square Dance Club 1985-, Sec, Presidential Awd; Wellesley Bapt Church 1989-, Trustee & Deaconess; Article Pub 1958; APS Mtg in New Orleans 1987; Grantee for Global Lab Funding Classroom Connection Internet; Tufts Univ Micro-Comp Based Lab Pilot Schl; Participate in Micro-Observatory Summer Wkshp; *office:* Algonquin Reg HS 79 Bartlett St Northborough MA 01532

LYNN, ANNE MARIE AGNES, Sixth Grade Teacher; *b:* Pottsville, PA; *ed:* Bucks Cty Comm Coll (AA) Ed 1974; West Chester Univ (BS) Elem Ed 1976; Trenton St Coll (MA) Elem Ed 1983; *cr:* Queen of the Universe Schl 4th-5th Grd Tchr 1977-87; Saint Ephrem Schl 5th-6th Grd Tchr 1987-; *ai:* Peer Coaching Team; Cmptr Coord; NCEA 1978-; Contributed Sci Unit Plans for DE Vly Coll, Bucks Cty Intermediate Unit No 22; Conducted Sci Wkshps for Tchrs; *home:* 59 Cobalt Ridge Dr N Levittown PA 19057

LYNN, BILLY R., Dramatic Productions Promoter; *b:* Dothan, AL; *m:* Allie E. Branch; *ed:* Tuskegee Univ (BS) Lang Arts Ed 1984; Pepsico Trng Ctr Cert Basic Mngmt 1995; Correspondence Course Cmptr Programming; MC Graw-Hill Educl Systems; Home Schl Curr Rsrch Ind Schl of Joy; *cr:* NJ Inst of Tech Eng Tutor, Mentor 1981-83; Tuskegee Inst HS Eng Tchr 1983-84; St Anthony HS Gen Bio Tchr 1984-85; St Rocco Schl Eng, Rndng Tchr 1985-89, 1990-; *ai:* NEA 1983-, Gen Mem; Reuben Dyes Comm Awd 1980; Deans List Tuskegee Univ 1984; Musical Score.*

LYNN, DEBORAH ANN, Physical Education Teacher; *b:* Cleveland, OH; *ed:* Towson St Univ (BS) PE & Tchr Ed 1994; *cr:* Harford Cty Pub Schls PE Tchr 1994-; *ai:* Head Vllybl, Asst Bsktbl & Asst Sftbl Coach; 9th Grd Transition Comm; MHPERD 1992-; Mem at Large; Outstdng St Major of MD; *office:* Edgewood HS 2415 Willoughby Beach Rd Edgewood MD 21040

LYNN, DONALD R.,JR., Health & Physical Ed Teacher; *b:* Connellsville, PA; *m:* Indy M. Wasnak; *c:* Jeff, Tracey, Jennie; *ed:* Baldwin Wallace Coll (BA) Hlth & PE 1963; Kent St Univ (MED) Hlth & PE 1966; *cr:* Berea HS Tchr & Coach 1963-68; Connellsville Jr HS W Tchr & Coach 1968-; *ai:* Dept chprsn; Coached Ftbl, Wrestling, Swim & Bsbl; Amer Shorthorn Breeders Assn 1995-; *office:* Connellsville Jr HS West 215 Falls Ave Connellsville PA 15425

LYNN, GARY S., Assoc Prof of Mngmt Engrng; *b:* Hammond, IN; *m:* Nancy Louise Schell; *c:* Ashley Rose; *ed:* Vanderbilt Univ (BE) Mechanical Engrng 1980; J. L. Kellogg Grad Schl (MM) Mrktg 1984; Rensselaer Polytechnic Inst (PHD) Mrktg Emerging Technologies 1993; *cr:* Gen Electric Tech Design, Mrktg Specialist 1980-82; Sunrise Med Market Dev Dir 1984-85; The Innovation Rsrch Inst Pres, Founder 1986-90; *ai:* Amer Soc for Engrng Mngmt New Product, Process Team Co-Chm; Amer Mrktg Assn Tech, Mrktg Spec Interest Group Co-Chm; AMA 1994-; ASEM 1995-; PDMA 1993-; Rubbermaid Innovation Mrktg Fellow; Book Authored From Concept to Market; Idea Log; Co-Authored Innopreneurship, Breaking Through Bureaucracy; Several Articles, Monographs Pub; *office:* Stevens Institute of Tech Castle Point On The Hudson Hoboken NJ 07030

LYNN, NANCY CHAMBERLAIN, Chemistry Teacher; *b:* Hartford, CT; *m:* John D.; *c:* Mary E. Anderson, John D. Jr., Michael J., Karen L. Darantiere; *ed:* Rosemont Coll (BA) Chem 1963; Attnd Moravian Coll 1963-65, PA St Univ 1967, Allentown Coll 1981, 1985; Lehigh Univ Educl Tech Lecturer 1985-; *cr:* Liberty HS Math, Sci Tchr 1963-64; Southern Kehigh HS Sci Longterm Sub Tchr 1974-79; Bethlehem Cath HS Phys Sci, Chem Tchr 1979-; *ai:* Stu Cncl Moderator; Scholastic Scrimmage Team Adv; PA Jr Acad of Sci Awd; NCEA 1965-; Teachem 1980-; St Joseph Church 1970-, Parish Cncl; Yth Group Adv 1970-; Eisenhower Math, Sci Prgm Grants Grad Stud Allentown Coll; Pub Cmptr Manual; *office:* Bethlehem Catholic HS 2133 Madison Ave Bethlehem PA 18017*

LYNN, PEGGY LEE (SKIBO), Kindergarten Teacher; *b:* Fayette City, PA; *m:* George K. Jr.; *c:* Kristopher Matthew, Ashue Marie; *ed:* CA St Coll (BA) Elem Ed 1970; CA Univ (MS) Elem Ed 1975; *cr:* Dr. Robert F. Nicely Elem Schl Kdg Tchr 1970-; *ai:* PSEA, NEA, GSEA 1970-; United Meth Church 1960-, Chrstn Ed Dir; *office:* Dr Robert F Nicely Elem Schl 55 Mclaughlin Dr Greensburg PA 15601

LYNN, SARA HORTON, Fifth Grade Teacher; *b:* Elizabeth, NJ; *c:* Jeffrey Howard, Tracey Lynn Coudriet; *ed:* CA (BA) Rdng 1977; Addtl 21 Hrs Elem Cert, 31 Hrs Continuing Ed; *cr:* Elyria Schl Dist Jr HS Soc Stud 1962-63; Connellsville Schl Rdng Clinic 1970-80, Elem Classroom Tchr 1980-; *ai:* PSEA 1970-, CAEA 1970-, Bldg Rep Amer Ed; Solid Rock Church 1990-; *home:* RR 1 Box 21A Vanderbilt PA 15486

LYON, CHERYL D., English Teacher; *b:* Boston, MA; *m:* Bert R.; *c:* Michael Kaplin; *ed:* Univ of MA (BA) Eng 1971; William Paterson Coll (MA) Rdng 1977; Long Island Univ (MS) Lib Sci 1988; *cr:* Ramapo Central Schl Dist Eng Tchr 23 Yrs; *ai:* Poetry Club Adv; HS Climate Comm Mem; AFT, NYSUT 1973-; *office:* Suffern HS Viola Rd Suffern NY 10901

LYON, DARLENE L., German Teacher; *b:* Detroit, MI; *m:* Philip J.; *ed:* Oakland Univ (BA) Ger 1987; Univ of SC (MAT) Ger 1992; Addl Course Work at Kent St & Ashland Univ; *cr:* Univ of SC Summer Schl Instr 1992; Concordia Lang Villages Summer Schl Tchr 1993-95; Elyria HS Tchr 1994-; *ai:* Ger Club Adv; Awds Ceremony Comm; AATG 1990-; Delta Phi Alpha 1991-; Natl Arbor Day Fnd 1990-; *office:* Elyria HS 311 6th St Elyria OH 44035

LYON, KENNETH ALBERT, Geology, Anatomy & Psych Tchr; *b:* Mineola LI, NY; *m:* Susan Allison Hart; *ed:* Pfeiffer Coll (BS) Hlth & PE 1965; Southern CT St Univ (MS) Bio 1974; *cr:* Milford Acad Bio Tchr 1965-72; Manchester Comm Coll Anatomy & Physiology Tchr 1974-76; Greenwich HS Bio Tchr 1976-; Sacred Heart Univv Adj Instr 1993-95; *ai:* Suzi Hart & Mike Makarewicz to SHNA Fac Co-Adv; NEA & GEA 1976-; CSTA, NSTA 1976-; CESTA, NAGT 1985-; Greenwich Distngd Tchrs Awd for Exc in Tchng 1988; CT Ed Assn Prudence Crandall Memrl Awd for Distngd Human Svc 1989; *office:* Greenwich HS 10 Hillside Rd Greenwich CT 06830*

LYON, MICHAEL EUGENE, HS Mathematics Teacher; *b:* Piqua, OH; *m:* June Leatherwood; *c:* John, Daniel; *ed:* Bowling Green St Univ (BA) Math 1973; (MA) Guidance & Counseling 1981; 20 Credit hrs in Admin; *cr:* N Baltimore Schls 7th & 8th Grd Math Tchr 1975-95, HS Math Tchr 1995-; *ai:* Soph Class Adv; NEA 1975-; OEA 1975-, Treas & VP; NBEA; Ohio Math Teachers; Church of Good Shepherd 1992-, Elder; *office:* North Baltimore HS 123 S 2nd St North Baltimore OH 45872*

LYONS, BONNIE SPENCER, Third Grade Teacher; *b:* Hoboken, NJ; *m:* George A.; *c:* Erin, George M.; *ed:* Newark St Coll (BA) Elem Ed 1967; *cr:* Thomas Edison 1st Grd Tchr 1967-68; Bernards Twp Bd of Ed Kndgtn Tchr 1968-69; Plainfield Pub Schls 1st Grd Tchr 1969-70; Mt View Schl 2nd Grd Tchr 1974-78, 5th Grd Tchr 1978-82, 3rd Grd Tchr 1982 NEA, NJEA 1967-; MCCOE, EAMO 1974-; Dodge Flwshp Grant to Stud Marine Sci, Dev Third Grd unit of Stud 1990; *office:* Mc View Schl Cloverhill Dr Flanders NJ 07836*

LYONS, DANIEL L., Sociology Professor; *b:* Brooklyn, NY; *m:* Smith; *c:* Cathlin, Daniel, Matthew; *ed:* Univ of Notre Dame Sociology 1961, (MA) Sociology 1964; NYU Grad Credits Ed & Sc St Johns Univ Grad Credits Sociology; *cr:* Fordham Univ Instr 19 William Paterson Coll Instr 1968-71; Passaic Cty Comm Coll Prof *ai:* Promotions Comm; Fac Review Comm; PCCFA Exec Comm; NJEA; PCTA 1971-; PCCFA 1971-, VP, Pres; Evas Kitchen & She Pgms 1991-, Bd VP, Bd of Dirs; *office:* Passaic County Comm College Blvd Paterson NJ 07505

LYONS, JOANNE COPPOLA, Second Grade Teacher; *b:* Spring MA; *m:* Richard Cooper; *c:* Matthew C., Michael J.; *ed:* Our Lady Elms (BA) Math 1967; *cr:* Hampden Elem Schl Third Grd Schl 19 Bowie Memorial Schl Third Grd Tchr 1969-74; Patrick E. Bowe Second Grd Tchr 1974-83; Lambert Lavoie Schl Second Grd Tchr *ai:* NEA, MTA 1967-; Womens Comm Club 1974-, Sec; *office:* La Lavoie Schl 99 Kendall St Chicopee MA 01020

LYONS, JOHN LOUIS, History Teacher; *b:* Greenfield, MA; *m:* H Montgomery Felton; *c:* Rachel Kathleen, Madeline Andersor Middlebury Coll (BA) His 1982; Georgetown Univ (MA) His 1989 Robertson Coe Fellowship SUNY Stony Brook 1991 & Stanford 1992; Freedom Fnd Fellowship 1993; *cr:* Northfield Mt Hermon Sch Tchr 1983-85; St Andrew Schl His Dept Chair 1985-95; Groton Sch Tchr 1995-; *ai:* Head Ftbl & JV Ice Hockey Coach; Dormatory Paren of Amer His 1987-; Wm Robertson Coe Fellowship Awd 1991-92; Fre Fnd Fellowship Awd 1993; *office:* Groton School Box 991 Groto 01450*

LYONS, JOHN S., Technology Teacher; *b:* Irwin RD, PA; *m:* Mar Albright; *c:* Barry V., Eric T., Armel T.; *ed:* CA Univ of PA (BS) I Arts 1960, (MED) Indstrl Arts 1972; *cr:* West Mifflin Area Schls IA 1960-65; Yough Schl Dist IA Tchr 1965-; *ai:* PSEA 1960-' YEA, 1965-; Sewickley Presby Church, Elder; *office:* Yough Sr HS 99 Lc Rd Herimine PA 15642

LYONS, MARY LAW, 7th Grd Language Arts Teacher; *b:* Rumford *m:* Robert L.; *c:* Amy Adrienne, Kate Victoria; *ed:* Saint Josephs C North Windham (BA) Ed 1970; Attnd Univ of NH & & Univ of M Credit Hrs Each; *cr:* Pollard Schl 3rd Grd Tchr 1970-75; Massabesic 7th & 8th Grd Lang Arts Tchr 1988-; *ai:* NEA 1970-; ME Ed Massabesic Tchrs Assn 1988-; World Learning Exch 1991-, Stu C *home:* PO Box 97 Sebago Lake ME 04075

LYONS, MICHAEL P., 5th Grade Teacher; *b:* Cold Spring, N Teresa; *c:* Michael Jr., Hilary; *ed:* Findlay Coll (BS) Elem Ed Western CT St Univ (MS) Elm Ed 1989; *cr:* Holy Name of Mary 4t Tchr 1980-84; Wappingers Cntrl Schls 4th & 5th Grd Tchr 1986-; *ai:* 1986-; Wappingers Congress of Tchrs 1986-, Exec Bd Mem; Wappingers 1986-; *office:* Sheafe Rd Elem Schl 145 Sheafe Rd Wappi Falls NY 12590

LYONS, THOMAS TOLMAN, History Instructor; *b:* Stoneham, M Eleanor F.; *c:* John, Kathleen Fanikos, David, Joseph; *ed:* Harvard (AB) His 1957; Harvard Grad Schl of Ed (MAT) His 1958; Ha Summer Schl 1958 & 1964; *cr:* Mt Hermon Schl His Tchr 1958-63; Ph Acad His Tchr 1963-68 & 1969-; Dartmouth His Dept 1968-90; *ai* Newspaper Faculty Adv 1973-; Ftbl Coach 1958-68; Bsbl Coach 195 Various Comms; Org of Amer Historians 1960-; New England His Assn 1960-, Kidger Awd; Amer Historical Assn 1983-; Various Gra Fellowships; Author of Numerous Books, Presntl Power in the Era of Deal 1963, Realism & Idealism in Wilson's Peace Pgm 1965, Black Lc in Amer His 1971, The Supreme Court & Individual Right Comtemporary Soc 1975, Reconstruction & Peace Problem 1968, Expansion of Federal Union (1801-1848) 1975, After Hiroshima: Ame Since (1945) 1979; Created Andover His Qualifying Test 198 Developed Experimental Urban Stud Prgm 1968-77; Stanford 1963 Fellowship; Wesleyan Univ Soc Sci Fellowship 1960; Harvard Distngd Scndry Schl Tchng Awd 1966; *office:* Phillips Acad S. Ma Andover MA 01810

LYTLE, CONNIE SUE, Second Grade Teacher; *b:* Warren, OH; *ed:* St Univ (BA) Elem Ed 1970, (MEd) Rdng Specialization 1975; *cr:* L Ave Elem Schl Second Grd Tchr 1970-; *ai:* Stu Cncl Adv 1970-; Warren Ed Assns, NEA 1970-; Martha Holden Jennings Scholar 197 *office:* Laird Avenue Elem Schl 565 Laird Ave SE Warren OH 44484

LYTLE, JANE, English Teacher; *b:* New York, NY; *ed:* Hunter Coll Eng 1964, (MA) Theatre 1973; Studied Lit at City Coll, Columbia U The New Schl, NYU; Studied Art at Schl of Visual Arts & Parsons William W. Niles Jr HS 118 Eng Tchr 1964-71; Adlai E. Stevenson HS Tchr 1971-79; Auxiliary Svcs for HS GED Course Preparer 1979 Aviation HS Eng Tchr 1985-90; Brooklyn Tech HS Eng Tchr 1990-; UFT 1964-, Brooklyn Tech Chptr Comm; MEA 1971-; NEH Grant 1 *office:* Brooklyn Tech HS 29 Fort Greene Pl Brooklyn NY 11217*

LYTLE, PATRICIA A., Mathematics Teacher; *b:* Warwick, RI; *m:* Jo Jr.; *c:* John P. III, Christopher F., Marissa L.; *ed:* RI Coll (BA) M Scndry Ed 1976; Providence Coll (MAT) Math 1996; 50 Addl Credits of RI, Comm Coll of RI & Brown Univ; *cr:* Lockwood Jr HS Math 1978-79; Alarich Jr HS Math Tchr 1979-86; Winman Jr HS Math 1986-89; Toll Gate HS Math Tchr 1989-; *ai:* FAC, CAP, CAST A Comms; NEASC Accred Tm Mem; AFT, WTU, RIMTA, ATMNE 19 CPAM; Apponaug Girls Sftbl 1987-, Coach; Presidential Awd of Excl Math Tchng 1993-94; Natl Presdntl Awd 1994; Gov Fellow, AT & T T Tech Inst 1995; *office:* Tollgate HS 575 Centerville Rd Warwick RI 028

LYVER, JULIE CECILIA, Eighth Grade Teacher; *b:* Somerville, N *ed:* Emmanue Coll (BA) Elem Ed 1960; Salem St Coll (MA) Elem Ed 1 Cmptr, Rel, Math Courses; Flexible Packaging Ed Fnd; *cr:* St Lawrence 4 Grd Tchr, Jr HS Tchr 17 Yrs, 5 Grd Tchr 4 Yrs, Prin 8 Yrs; H Redeemer East Boston 6 Grd Tchr 4 Yrs, Jr HS Tchr 11 Yrs; *ai:* Dru Alcohol Abuse Coord for Schl; NCEA.

M

MAACK, NANCY (PAPE), French Teacher; *b:* Woodbury, NJ; *m:* Cha L.; *c:* Nathan B., Esther C., Katherine S.; *ed:* Douglass Coll, Rutgers U

:ussian Lang, Lit 1974; *cr:* Bethany Luth Schl Math, Rdng Tchr,)87-91; Mercer Chrstn Acad Fr Tchr 1991-; *office:* Mercer Christian)015 Pennington Rd W Trenton NJ 08628

, ROBERT ARTHUR, Band & Orchestra Director; *b:* Lincoln, NE; :resa Marie Shevlin; *c:* Brian Philip, Shannon Leigh, Brandon :l, Sean Patrick; *ed:* Univ of NE at Lincoln (BMEd) Music Ed 1983; :v of PA (MM) Music 1985; *cr:* Ft Scott Comm Coll Music Tchr 6; Prince Georges Cty Pub Schl Band Dir 1986-88; Harrisburg City ist Music Tchr & Band Dir 1988-90; Shippensburg Schl Dist Band Dir 1990-; *ai:* Jazz Ensemble Dir; NEA 1985-; MENC 1985-; BSA Den Ldr; *office:* Shippensburg Area Sr HS 317 N Morris St nsburg PA 17257

:T, JOANNA KETT, Jr High Science Teacher; *b:* Philadelphia, PA; g T.; *ed:* Pillsbury Coll (BS) Scndry Ed 1993; *cr:* Calvary Bapt Schl Tchr 1993-95; House of Fabrics Asst Mgr 1993-95; *ai:* Var Chrldr Sunday Schl Class Outreach Coord; *office:* Calvary Baptist Schl Valley Forge Rd Lansdale PA 19446

, LINDA JEAN, Teacher of the Gifted; *b:* Bradford, PA; *c:* Kerryn, *d:* Edinboro Univ of PA (BS) Art Ed 1969, (MED) Art His 1974; 51 Irs Tech & Enrichment; *cr:* Fort Le Boeuf Schl Dist Elem Art Tchr '1; Crawford Cty Schl for Exceptional Children Art Tchr 1978-80; 'est Schl Dist Elem Art Tchr 1980-81, 1st, 5th Grd Remedial Math 982-85, Tchr of Gifted 1985-; *ai:* Hi Q Acad Competition Judge; PSEA 1980-; Penncrest Area Ed Assn 1980-, Pres, VP; Cambridge Pub Lib 1978-, Pres, Bd of Dirs, VP, Sec; Cam-Sac Math Women's 979-, Treas, Sec; *office:* Penncrest Schl Dist RD 1 Townville PA

SSEN, DENISE E., His, Eng, Span & Ger Teacher; *b:* Endicott, NY;)b Jones Univ (BA) Ger 1972, (MS) Admin Ed 1980; *cr:* Westside Schl Tchr 1972-75; Tioga Ctr Chrstn Schl Tchr 1975-, Prin 1979-82; iid; Tutor; Help Organize Events; Lahore Bible Inst, Pakistan Bd; Assn of Chrstn Schls, Tchng Cert; Tioga Ctr Bapt Church, Sunday 'chr, Choir Mem, Schl Bd, Missionary, Music Comms; *office:* Tioga rristian Schl PO Box 244 Halsey Vly Rd Tioga Center NY 13845

', CAROL DOROTHY, Social Studies Teacher; *b:* Jersey City, NJ; ncent Jr.; *c:* Scott C., Stacey A. Recanati; *ed:* William Paterson Coll Elem Ed 1976; *cr:* South Hackensack Meml Schl Tchr 20 Yrs; *ai:* Adv ncl, Safety Patrol, Eighth Grd Act; Soc Stud Five Yr Plan Chprsn; , NEA, NJ Cncl for Soc Stud 1976-; Ed Assn of S Hackensack 1976-, VP, Treas, Sec; NJ Cncl of Int Rdng 1990-; *office:* South Hackensack Schl 1 Dyer Ave South Hackensack NJ 07606

ZAOUI, ABBES, French & Arabic Professor; *b:* Jendouba, Tunisia; ia; *ed:* Univ of Tunis (BA) Fr Lit 1977, (MS) Fr Lit 1978; Univ of nce (PHD) Fr Lit, Linguistics 1982; Univ of Tunis Prof 1982-89; oin Coll Prof 1990-91; Colby Coll Prof 1991-92; Ramapo Coll Prof, ir 1992-93; Lincoln Univ Prof 1993-; *cr:* Lang Lab Dir; Lang Tchng Placement Exams Coord; *ai:* MLA, AATF 1990-; ACTFL 1995-; es Pub; *office:* Lincoln Univ Dept Of Langs Lincoln Universit PA

RY, MYRA CUMMINGS, Biology Teacher; *b:* Exeter, NH; *m:* Dell; iint Lawrence Univ (BA) Bio & Ed 1991, (MS) Ed 1996; 3 Credits of vice Cmptr Trng; *cr:* Indian River HS Bio Tchr 1992-; Jefferson 1 Coll Adjunct Bio Instr 1993-; *ai:* Discipline Comm; Peer Mediation; Rep; Soph Class Adv; Var Vlybl & Sftbl Asst Coach; Effective Schl Mem; Indian River Tchrs Assn 1992-, Soc Chair; NYSUT 1992-; Beta Beta 1989-, Univ Pres; Integral Part of Team that Wrote & mented a Variance to NYS Regents Exam; Project Learning Tree ed Presenter, Presenter at Early Chldhd Prof Conf Falling For Kids; Aids Wkshp Participant; Completion of Effective Tchng Wkshps; : Indian River HS Rte 11 Philadelphia NY 13673*

ADINO, RITAMARIE FRASCA, Teacher & Specialist; *b:* Boston, *m:* Anthony; *c:* Caitlin, Vittoria; *ed:* Boston Coll (BA) Elem Ed 1976,) Elem Ed, GATE 1982; *cr:* Summer St Schl Sixth Grd Tchr 1976-77; r Schl Third Grd Tchr 1977-78; Huckleberry Hill Schl Sixth Grd Tchr -80; Lynnfield MS Acad Talented Specialist, Tchr 1980-; *ai:* Odyssey : Mind Spon, Coach; 8th Grd Team Mass Bar Assn Mock Trial iament; Educl Trust Tchr Rep; LTA, MTA 1976-; MAAIP Pub Svc 1991; LET Grant 1990-92; *office:* Lynnfield MS 505 Main St field MA 01940*

'ALUSH, JEAN CONAHAN, Fifth Grade Teacher; *b:* Summit Hill, *n:* Michael J. Sr.; *c:* Michael Jr., Barry; *ed:* Jersey City St Coll (BA) Ed 1977; *cr:* Our Lady of the Assumption Schl Kndgtn Tchr 1971-73, Grd Tchr 1973-78, Fifth Grd Tchr 1978-; *ai:* Rdng Coord; NCEA -; BSA 1965-, Bayonne Pack 27 Den Mother, Sec, Fleur-de-Lis Awd; diocese of Newark Outstdng Edctr 1992-93; *office:* Our Lady Of The mption Sch 101 W 23rd St Bayonne NJ 07002

:ALUSO, JOSEPH THOMAS, English Teacher; *b:* New York City, *m:* Rosa DiGiacomantonio; *c:* Lorenzo, Olivia; *ed:* Montclair St Univ Eng 1970; Rutgers Univ (MA) Eng 1981; Grad Work Montclair St, of CA; *cr:* Montclair HS Eng Tchr 1970-; *ai:* Boys Gymnastics Coach 'rs; NJEA, NEA 1970-; Montclair Ed Assn 1970-, Pres 6 Yrs; Star :er Tchr Awd 1991; NJ Governor Tchrs Awd; *office:* Montclair HS 100 itnut St Montclair NJ 07042

:ANKA, WILLIAM JOHN, Assoc Prof of Chemistry & Math; *b:* rson, NJ; *ed:* William Paterson Coll (BA) Bio, Chem 1972; Seton Hall (MS) Bio 1974; Rutgers Univ (PHD) Phys Chem 1981; *cr:* Boston Chem Instr 1981-82; Regis Coll Asst Prof Chem 1982-86; Long Island Asst Prof Chem 1986-87; Elms Coll Assoc Prof Chem, Math 1987-; Various Standing, Ad Hoc Comms; Fac Dev, Governance Comms; ia Xi 1974-; Amer Chemical Soc 1987-; Pittsburgh Conf Grant 1986; Recipient of MA Higher Ed PALMS Grant 1994; *office:* Elms Coll 291 ngfield St Chicopee MA 01013*

C ARTHUR, JOHN WILLAND, Social Studies Teacher; *b:* Watham, ; *m:* Marie Daileanes; *c:* Anne Marie, John Willand Jr.; *ed:* Plymouth 'oll (BED) Soc Stud 1962; Rivier Coll (MED) Scndry Ed 1976; *cr:* rne HS Soc Stud Tchrs 1962-65; Salem HS Soc Stud Tchr 1965-; *ai:* k Adv 1966-; NEA & NHEA 1962-; SEA 1965-; Univ of NH NDEA it 6 Post-Grad Credits; Univ of Santa Clara Natl Sci Grant 9 Post-Grad its; Numerous Yrbk Awds; Amer Eagle Awd; *office:* Salem H S 44 emonty Dr Salem NH 03079

C ARTHUR, LINDA S., Learning Support Teacher; *b:* Pittsburgh, PA; Edward; *ed:* Bloomsburg St Univ (BS) Spec Ed 1979; Attnd ppensburg Univ, IN Univ of PA, Allegheny Cty Comm Coll; *cr:* icarora Intermediate Unit Emotional, Learning Support Tchr 1979-81; IN Intermediate Unit Emotional, Learning Support Tchr 1981-85; New ghton Area Schl Dist Learning Support Tchr 1985-; *ai:* Strategic nning Comm; New Brighton Ed Assn 1985-, Pres; PSEA, NEA 1985-; 1985-; *office:* New Brighton Area MS 901 Penn Ave New Brighton PA 66

CAULAY, WILLIAM ANDREW, Science Teacher; *b:* Oneida, NY; *m:* y Anne Dougherty; *c:* Michael, Matthew; *ed:* Cornell Univ (BS) Sci Ed 9; Syracuse Univ (MS) Sci Ed 1987; Attnd SUNY Coll of ironmental Sci, Forestry at Syracuse SUNY Cortland; *cr:* Mynderse id Sci Tchr 1969-70; Fayetteville-Manlius Schl Sci Tchr 1970-; *ai:* Ftbl, l Coach; AFT, NYSUT 1969-; NYSTA 1995-; Town Manlius Environmental Cncl 10 Yrs; *office:* Wellwood MS S Manlius St Fayetteville NY 13066

MACAULEY, FRANCIS JOHN, Professor of Criminal Justice; *b:* New Haven, CT; *m:* Mary Ann Johnson; *c:* Sharon Perakis, Francis J. Jr., Donna Triolo, Gregory; *ed:* Youngstown Univ St Univ (BS) Bus 1961, (BS) Bus Admin 1961; Univ of Baltimore (LLB) Law 1968, (JD) Law 1968; George Washington Univ Postdoctoral Stud in Hlth Care Admin 1974; *cr:* US Army Post Adjutant 1965-67; Crownsville St Hospital Prsnl Dir 1968-70; Coppin St Coll VP of Bus & Finance 1970-72, Prof of Criminal Justice 1972-; *ai:* Law Schl Admissions Comm Chm; Chm of Pres Comms on Equal Employment & Criminal Justice; US Army Reserves 1961-, Legal Adv, Army Accommodations Medal; Amer Bar Assn 1970-, Criminal Justice Comm; Amer Correctional Assn, Conf Presenter; USAA 1966-; Moose 1994-; Optimists; Hickory Ridge Assn, Bd Mem; Abbey Homes Inc, Bd Mem; Anne Arundel Assisted Living Assn, Bd Mem; US Army Reserves Ret LtCol; Distinguished Prof Awd; MD Acad of Criminal Justice Profs Pres; *office:* Coppin St Coll 2500 W North Ave Baltimore MD 21216*

MACAUSLAND, MARY BARDSLEY, Asst Professor of Accounting; *b:* Sellersville, PA; *m:* D. Stuart; *c:* Sarah, Sean; *ed:* Temple Univ (BBA) Acctng 1990; St Josephs Univ (MBA) Bus 1993; *cr:* Rdng Area Comm Coll Asst Prof 1991-; *ai:* TACTYC 1993-, Regnl Rep; ALCPA 1995-; *office:* Reading Area Comm Coll 2nd & Penn Sts Reading PA 19603

MACBETH, DANIELLE MONIQUE, Philosophy Professor; *b:* Edmonton, Canada; *ed:* Univ of Alberta (BSC) Biochemistry 1977; Mc Gill Univ (BA) Philosophy & Rel Stud 1980; Univ of Pittsburgh (PHD) Philosophy 1988; *cr:* Univ of HI Lecturer 1986-89; Haverford Coll Asst Prof of Philosophy 1989-; *ai:* Amer Philosophical Assn; Amer Assn of Univ Women; Articles Pub in Philosophy & Phenomenotogical Rsrch, Philosophical Stud, Journal of Philosophical Rsrch, Journal for the Theory of Soc Behavior; *office:* Haverford Coll 370 Lancaster Ave Haverford PA 19041

MAC BETH, JAN, English Department Chair; *b:* Newport, RI; *ed:* Wilson Coll (BA) Eng 1961; York Univ (MA) Eng 1969; Working Towards PHD Brown Univ; *cr:* Walnut Hill Schl Chair Eng Dept 1961-63, 1965-66, 1976-; *office:* Walnut Hill Schl 12 Highland St Natick MA 01760

MAC BURNEY, ANDREA EOMME, French & Spanish Teacher; *b:* New York City, NY; *w:* Lee (dec); *ed:* Coll of New Rochelle (BA) Fr, Span 1951; Tchrs Coll, Columbia Univ (MA) Tchng of Fr, Span 1955; 32 Hrs Faculty of Pol Sci, 15 Hrs of Philosphy, 16 Hrs Ger, Italian, Russian; Univ Laval PQ 18 Hrs; Univ of Mexico 4 Hrs; Univ De Gladalajara 8 Hrs; Hofstr a Univ 3 Hrs Admin; Alliance Francaisede NY 6 Hrs; In-Svc Courses of G. C.; *cr:* Tchrs Coll Psych Fnds Sec 1951-55; Garden City Pub Schls Fr, Span Tchr 1955-, Lang Dept Chprsn 1957-; *ai:* Dept Comms, Act Rep; NYSUT, NEA 1960-; LILT, FLACS 1980-; HYSAFLT; GCTA 1955-; Tchrs Coll of Columbia Univ Franklin Baker Awd 1955; Nom Fridel, Otto Eberspacher Awd for Excl Tchng Modern European Lang at Johns Hopkins Univ 1993; Coll of New Rochelle Magna Cum Laude 1951, Fr Hnrs 1951; *office:* Garden City MS Cherry Valley Ave Garden City South NY 11530

MAC BURNEY, CHRISTINE CLEAVELAND, English Teacher; *b:* Summit, NJ; *m:* Michael Griffith; *ed:* Gordon Coll (BS) Elem Ed-Summa Cum Laude 1965; Post Grad Work Fairleigh Dickinson Univ, IN Univ, Kean Coll; *cr:* New Providence Bd of Ed Grd 1 Tchr 1965-68, Grd 4 Tchr 1969-80, Eng Tchr 1980-; *ai:* Writing Club Adv; Teen Arts Coord; Writing Comm; Multi-Generational Act Club; NEA, NJEA 1965-; NCTE 1982-; LHC Sr Choir 1969; Governor's Tchr Awd 1990; Articles Pub; NJ His, Geog Grant; *office:* New Providence MS 35 Pioneer Dr New Providence NJ 07974

MACCARONI, GARY, Curriculum Coord & Rel Teacher; *b:* Trenton, NJ; *ed:* Trenton St Coll (BA) Pol Sci 1986; Princeton Theological Seminary (MA) Rel Ed 1992; Attnd Boston Coll; *cr:* Covenant House Under 21 Yth Specialist 1989; Mc Corristin Cath HS Tchr 1986-87, 1989=90; Rider Univ Assoc Dir, Cath Campus Ministry 1990-93; Msgr Donovan HS Curr Coord, Rel Stud Dept 1994-; *ai:* Moderator Philosophy Club; Asst Var Soccer Coach; Soc of Chrstn Philosophers 1986-, NCTA 1992-; *office:* Msgr Donovan HS 711 Hooper Ave Toms River NJ 08753*

MAC CRACKEN, CYNTHIA DIMON, Instrumental Music Teacher; *b:* Towanda, PA; *m:* Durward K.; *c:* Christopher, Shaylyn; *ed:* Mansfield St Coll (BS) Music Ed 1978, (MS) Music Ed 1982; *cr:* Charlotte Valley Itinerant Mucis Tchr 1978-79; Morris Itinerant Music Tchr 1978-79; Cherry Valley Itinerant Music Tchr 1979-80; Springfield Itinerant Music Tchr 1979-80; Morris Itinerant Music Tchr 1979-80; Cherry Valley Itinerant Music Tchr 1980-81; Springfield Itinerant Music Tchr 1980-81; Gilboa-Conesville Itinerant Music Tchr 1981-82; Andes Itinerant Music Tchr 1981-82; Gilboa-Conesville Cntrl Schl Instrumental, Vocal Music Tchr 1982-90; Charlotte Valley Ctnrl Schl Instrumental Music Tchr 1990-; *ai:* Marching Band; Colorguard; HS, Elem Choruses, HS Musical Accompanist; NY St United Tchrs 1978-; DE Cty Music Tchrs Assn 1978-79, 1982-; Cty Music Festival Site Chprsn 1993, Sr Chorus Chprsn 1982; Otsego Cty Music Tchrs Assn Sec 1979-82;Davenport Comm Choi r Accompanist 1990-; Charlotte Valley Presbyn Parish Organist, Choir Dir 1984-; Charlotte Valley Bldg Leadership Team Chprsn 1993-; Jr HS All City Band Chr 1995; BOCES Tchr of Month 1982.

MAC CURTAIN, WILLIAM PATRICK, AP English Teacher; *b:* Boston, MA; *m:* Denise Ahern; *ed:* Boston St (BS) Ed, (MED) Scndry Rdng 1974; *cr:* Cathedral High 12th Grd Eng Tchr 1973-75; Wareham High A P Eng Tchr 1975-; *ai:* Newspaper Adv; Literacy Comm; NEA 1975-; PCEA 1975-; Horace Mann Grant 1988; *office:* Wareham HS 1 Viking Way Wareham MA 02571*

MAC DANIEL, ELIZABETH JO, Assistant Professor of English; *b:* Connersville, IN; *m:* Gregory H. Clark; *c:* Jennifer L. Stealey, Rachel C. Stealey; *ed:* OH St Univ (BA) Eng 1982; Rice Univ (MA) Eng, Medieval Lit 1984; OH St Univ (PHD) Eng, Folklore 1989; *cr:* OH St Univ Lecturer 1989-90; Otterbein Coll Lecturer 1990; Clarion Univ Asst Prof of Eng 1990-; *ai:* Eng Dept Curr Comm Chair 1990-; IRB; Alternate Del to APSCUF Legislative Assembly; Grad Fac Comm; Am Folklore Soc, Modern Lang Soc 1987-; Popular Culture Soc; Amer Culture Soc; Arts, Sci Fac Rsrch Grants; *office:* Clarion Univ Of PA 266 Carlson Clarion PA 16214

MACDAVITT, CHARLOTTE ANN, 1st-2nd Grade Teacher; *b:* Lynn, MA; *ed:* St Coll at Salem (BA) Elem Ed 1956; Curry Coll Cert to Teach Learning Disabled Stu; *cr:* Harrington Elem Schl 2nd Grd Tchr 1956-60; Cyrus Dallin Schl 2nd Grd Tchr 1960-93; Castile Chrstn Acad 1st-2nd Grd Tchr 1995-; *ai:* Tchr Vol; Schl Adv; NEA, MTA 1956-93; Christa McAuliffe Awd; Most Memorable Tchr Awd; Church Outreach Prgms for Children, Teens, Mentally Disabled Vol.

MACDONALD, DEBRA J., English Teacher; *b:* Ridgewood, NJ; *ed:* Castleton Coll (BA) Lit, Scndry Ed 1993; *cr:* Long Trail Schl Eng Tchr 1993-; *ai:* Adv Mix of Stdnts; Girls Sftbl Coach; *home:* RR 1 Box 365A East Dorset VT 05253*

MAC DONALD, JANE ABBOTT, Fourth Grade Teacher; *b:* Winchester, MA; *c:* Katie Ann; *ed:* Mt St Mary Coll (BA) Elem Ed 1968; 15 Addl Hrs; *cr:* Billerica Schl 3rd Grd Tchr 1968-74; Edward Fenn Schl 4th Grd Tchr 1974-; *ai:* Math Curr Coord; Report Card, Enrichment Comm; NEA 1968-; Bd of Dirs N Conway Pub Lib 1995-; *home:* PO Box 194 Glen NH 03838*

MAC DONNELL, BRENDAN JUDE, Assistant Principal; *b:* Springfield, MA; *m:* Claire A. Sullivan; *c:* Maryanne, Brendan Jr., Martin, John, Patrick, Matthew, Eileen, Kathleen; *ed:* Fairfield Univ (BA) Philosophy, Sociology 1961; Westfield St Coll (MED) Supervision 1969; 30 Hrs Beyond Masters in Math, Rdng, Gen Ed Courses Holy Cross Coll, AIC, Elms Coll, Westfield St; *cr:* Bondsville Elem Schl 5-8 Grd Tchr 1962-73; Three Rivers Elem Schl 5-8 Grd Tchr 1973-91; Converse MS 7-8 Grd Tchr 1991-93, Asst Prin 1993-; *ai:* Palmer Tchrs Assn 1962-, Pres 23 Yrs; MA Tchrs Assn, NEA 1962-; Natl Sci Fnd Grant for Math Courses; *office:* Converse MS 24 Converse St Palmer MA 01069

MAC DOUGALL, JOHN, Professor of Sociology; *b:* Oxford, England; *m:* Marilyn Martha Pallys; *c:* Peter Donald, Jessica Ruth; *ed:* Oxford Univ (BA) Ec 1962; Harvard Univ (PHD) Sociology 1975; Cornell Univ 1966-68 Work Towards MS in Ag Ec; *cr:* Wesleyan Univ Inst & Asst Prof Sociology 1973-76; Univ of MS at Lowell Asst & Assoc Prof & Prof Sociology 1976-; *ai:* Co-Dir of Peace & Conflict Stud Inst; Amer Sociological Assn 1975-, Mem of Cncl Section on Peace & War; Numerous Books & Articles Pub; 3 Pub Svc Grants Univ MA at Lowell; Univ of MA at Lowell Awd for Svc Learning 1995; Fac Semester at Sea 1987; *office:* Univ Of MA At Lowell South Campus 1 University Ave Lowell MA 01854

MACDOUGALL, SUSAN MURPHY, Sixth Grade English Teacher; *b:* Brighton, MA; *m:* Bruce A.; *c:* Gregory, Bradley; *ed:* Salem St Coll (BS) Elem Ed 1972, (MED) Rdng 1976; *cr:* Searles Schl 4th Grd Tchr 1972-74; Tenney Mid 6th Grd Tchr 1974-89; Comprehensive Grammar 6th Grd Tchr 1989-,Soc Stud & Rdng; *ai:* Stu Cncl Adv 1982-88; Greater Lawrence Merrimack Valley Leadership 1985-88; Tchr of GATE 1988-93; Asertive Discipline Comm 1993-95; Peer Mediation Adv & Tchr 1995-; ADHD Adv/Parent Group; Methuen Ed Assn & NEA 1972-;Boy Scouts of America; Friends of Methuen Youth Ctr 1993-95; BSA Food Dr N Essex Cncl Chm 1987-91;Catechist 1994-; *office:* Comprehensive Grammar Schl 100 Howe St Methuen MA 01844

MACDOWELL, JAMES WILBERT, Building Construction Teacher; *b:* Cleveland, OH; *m:* Patricia A. Heller; *ed:* Miami Univ (BA) Rel 1973; Cleveland St Univ Elem Ed Cert 1975; Kent St Univ Voc Ed Cert 1994; *cr:* Cleveland Pub Schls ABLE, GED & ESL Tchr 1993-94, Bldg Construction Tchr 1994-; *ai:* Union Del; Voc Club Adv; AFT & CTU 1993-; IECC 1995-; NATIE 1995-; *office:* Max S Hayes Vocational High 4600 Detroit Ave Cleveland OH 44102*

MACE, CATHY BONAR, Vocal Music Teacher; *b:* Wheeling, WV; *m:* David A.; *c:* Amanda, Alex; *ed:* WV Univ (BM) Music Ed 1977; 34 Post Grad Hrs; *cr:* Edison Jr HS Vocal Music Tchr 1980-89; Ft Frye HS Vocal Music & Piano Tchr 1990-; *ai:* Girls Ensemble & Childrens Patch the Pirate Club Choir Dir; NHS Selection Comm; Soph Class Adv; Church Pianist & Accompanist; Gospel Bapt Ladies Trio Mem; OH Music Edctrs Assoc 1990-; Arranged & Coordinated Act for Bringing the USAF Band to Parkersburg WV to Perform with the Edison Jr High Choirs 1989; Selected as Dir of Music for WV Rhododendron Girls St 1993; *office:* Fort Frye HS PO Box 68 5th St Beverly OH 45715

MACE, JOAN RODRIAN, Retired Professor of Aviation; *b:* Columbus, OH; *c:* Mark Nolan, Patrick Alan, Michael Todd; *ed:* OH Univ (AA) Applied Sci 1970, (BA) Aviation 1978; *cr:* OH Univ Flight Instr 1963-85, Chair Aviation Dept 1985-94; *ai:* Judge Natl Intercollegiate Flying Meets; Univ Aviation Assn, Bd of Dir; OH Educl Assn; Natl Assn of Flight Instrs; Natl Intercollegiate Flying Assn; Amer Legion Auxiliary; Ninety Nines Womens Intnl Pilots Assn; Prof Emerita of Aviation; Flight Instr of Yr; Aviation Merit Awd Aviation OH Univ; *home:* 33 Charles St Athens OH 45701

MACE, ROGER D., Physical Education; *b:* Logan, OH; *m:* Mary Beth McVey; *ed:* OH Univ (BA) PE 1988-89; Drivers Ed 1988-89; Attnd Grad Classes OH Univ & Walsh Univ; *cr:* Logan HS PE Tchr, Drivers Ed Tchr, First Aid Tchr, Ath Trng Tchr & Coach 1988-; *ai:* Bsbl & Bsktbl Asst Var Coach; Reserve Boys Bsktbl Coach; Jr Class Adv; Masonic Lodge Delta #207 1987-; *office:* Logan Sr HS 50 North St Logan OH 43138*

MACERA, ROSARIA, Orchestra Director; *b:* Philadelphia, PA; *ed:* The New Schl of Music (BM) Violin Performance 1986; Univ of DE 6 Grad Credits; Villanova Univ 10 Continuing Ed Credits; *cr:* Episcopal Acad Violin Instr 1986-88; Univ of DE Part-time Music Ed Fac 1993; Chrstn Schl Dist 7-12th Orch Dir 1988-; *ai:* Orch Performances; String Quartet Concerts; Music Ed Curr Comm; NEA, Chrstn EA 1991-; MENC, DMEA 1989-, DE All-St Orch Chair; HS Commencement Honored Tchr 1992; Philadelphia Orch Ed Advy Cncl; DE Symphony Prof Violinist; Newark Symphony Prof Violinist & Concertmaster; *office:* Newark HS E Delaware Ave Newark DE 19711

MAC FARLAND, FRANCES C., Chemistry Teacher; *b:* Albany, NY; *ed:* Coll of St Rose (BS) Chem 1969; Syracuse Univ (MS) Chem Ed 1972; *cr:* St Patrick's HS Chem, Physics Tchr 1969-75: Sisters of St Joseph Prsnl Dir 1980-83; Cath Cntrl HS Physics, Chem Tchr 1976-80, Chem Tchr 1984-; *ai:* Com Svc Club Moderator; Faith Formation, Curr Comms; Moderator Class 1999; Bd Dirs Joseph's House, Shelter 1988-, Pres; Casda Master Tchr Seminar; *office:* Catholic Central HS 625 7th Ave Troy NY 12182

MAC GILFREY, JUNE DENISE, Physical Education Teacher; *b:* Albany, NY; *ed:* Hudson Valley Comm Coll (AA) Lbrl Arts, PE 1977; St Univ Coll at Brockport (BS) PE 1979; St Univ of NY at Albany (MS) Curr 1989; *cr:* Averill Park Cntrl Schls PE Tchr Grds 6-8 10 Yrs; *ai:* Girls Modified Soccer; Boys Modified Bsktbl; girls Var Sftbl; *office:* Averill Park Cntrl Schls 333 NY 351 Averill Park NY 12018

MAC GILLIVRAY, SANDRA J., Bus Ed Office Admin & Instr; *b:* Bridgeport, CT; *m:* Peter E.; *c:* Peter L., Courtney P.; *ed:* Univ of CT (BS) Scndry Ed 1968; Univ of VT (MED) Ed 1987; 30 Hrs Bus, Ed, Cmptrs; *cr:* Springfield Adult Ed Instr 1968-92; Comm Coll of VT Instr, Group Cnslr 1970-78; Springfield Schl Dist Instr 1976-; *ai:* Regnl Schl-to-Work Initiative; Stu Assistance Prgm; Adv Class, FBLA; Tennis Coach; Restructuring, NEASC Steering Comms; Coord Tech Ctr Evaluation; NEA, VT Voc ssn, New England Bus Ed Assn 1977-; VT Bus Tchrs Assn 1977-, Pres; Southeast Cncl on Arts 1985-, Chair; Chamber Commerce 1990-; Spfld Hosp Auxiliary 1970-, Comm Chair; Grant Writer Southeast Cncl on Arts; *office:* Springfield HS, Tech Ctr 303 South St Springfield VT 05156*

MAC GREGOR, CATHERINE LOUISE, MS Science & Math Teacher; *b:* White Plains, NY; *m:* Donald A.; *c:* Christopher, David, Robert; *ed:* Allegheny Coll (BS) Bio 1967, (MAT) Ed 1970; Art Courses Mercyhurst Coll; Sci Courses Edinboro Univ, Ganon Univ; *cr:* Ludlow 4th Grd Tchr 1967-69; Richard Byrd 5th Grd Tchr 1969-71; Luther Meml Learning Ctr MS Sci, Math Tchr, K-8 Grd Art Tchr 1980-; *ai:* 8th Grd Class Spon; Founder & Dir White Swan Art Camp 1978-96, White Swan Sci Camp 1992-96; PA Jr Acad of Sci Adv, Spon 1984-96; Priv Schl; Jr League of Erie 1974-, Various Comm, Sustainer of Yr, Chm Major Fundraising 3 Yrs; Erie Cty Dental Aux 1973-, Pres Etc; White Swan Civic Ctr 1981-, Yth Chm Prgms; Copyright Several Art Pieces; *office:* Luther Memorial Learning Ctr 220 W 11th St Erie PA 16501*

MACHADO, JOAN MARIE, Spanish & French Teacher; *b:* Fall River, MA; *ed:* Bristol Comm Coll (AA) Lbrl Arts 1984; Bridgewater St Coll (BA) Span 1987; RI Coll (MAT) Span 1991; 6 Credit Hrs Grad RI Coll Fr; 6 Credit Hrs Univ of MA at Dartmouth Portugese; *cr:* Sargent Ctr Day Schl Biling Aide & Span Tchr 1988-89; West Warwick JFD Jr High Span & Fr Tchr 1991-94; West Warwick HS Span & Fr Tchr 1994-; *ai:* West Warwick

Tchrs Assn 1991-; *office:* West Warwick HS Webster Knight Dr West Warwick RI 02893

MAC HAFFIE, BARBARA J., Assoc Prof of History & Rlgn; *b:* Philadelphia, PA; *m:* Fraser G.; *ed:* The Coll of Wooster (BA) Rel 1971; Univ of Edinburgh (BD) His of Christianity 1974, (PHD) His of Christianity 1977; *cr:* Princeton Theological Seminary Reference Librn 1988-90; Cleveland St Univ Visiting Asst Prof of Rel 1991-93; Marietta Coll Rel Lecturer 1983-87, His & Rel Asst Prof 1987-93, His & Rel Assoc Prof 1993-; *ai:* His, Pol Sci & Rel Dept Chair; Amer Acad of Rel, Ame Soc of Church His 1977-; Scottish Church His Soc 1980-; Phi Beta Kappa 1970-, VP; Alpha Lambda Delta, Phi Alpha Theta 1988-; Omicron Delta Kappa 1993-; Books Pub 1986, 1992; *office:* Marietta Coll Marietta OH 45750

MACHEK, KIMBERLY FERNBERG, Business Education Teacher; *b:* Kittanning, PA; *c:* Lauren; *ed:* Youngstown St Univ (BS) Comprehensive Bus Ed 1991; *cr:* Fauquier Cty Schls Bus Ed 1991-93; Corry Area HS Bus Ed 1993-; *ai:* Chrldng Adv; Discipline, Strategic Planning Comms; NEA 1991-; PBEA 1993-; *office:* Corry Area HS 534 E Pleasant St Corry PA 16407

MACHEMER, PAUL AUBREY, Mathematics Teacher; *b:* Bryn Mawr, PA; *m:* Pamela E. Rea; *c:* Robert, Kate; *ed:* Amherst Coll (AB) Math 1969; Harvard Univ (MEd) Schl Admin 1978; Attnd Soccer Schl; *cr:* George Schl Math Tchr 1969-71; Continuation Schl Math, W I His, Eng, Sci Tchr 1971-73; George Schl Dept Chm 7 Yrs, Math Tchr, Soccer, Tennis, Bsbl Coach 1973-; *ai:* Var Soccer, Tennis Coach; NSCAA, PSCA 1985-; SPSCA 1985-, Pres Twice; *office:* George Schl PO Box 4000 Newtown PA 18940

MACHER, RICHARD ALAN, Social Studies Teacher; *b:* Rockville Centre, NY; *m:* Cecilia; *c:* Richard, Jodie; *ed:* IL Coll (BA) Soc Stud & His 1968; SUNY at Stony Brook (MA) Amer His 1973; *cr:* Iles Schl Tchr 1968; Malverne Pub Schls Tchr 1968-; Mineola Summer Schl Tchr 1977-; *ai:* Boys Soccer Coach; Homebound Stu Tutor; NEA 1968-; NYSUT 1968-; Malverne Tchrs Assn 1968-; *office:* Malverne Schl Dist Ocean Ave Malverne NY 11565

MACHINCHICK, JOAN W., Kindergarten Teacher; *b:* Glen Lyon, PA; *m:* George J.; *c:* Jane M., Thomas J., Maureen M. Gibson, Ann C. Gensel; *ed:* Marywood Coll (BM) Music Ed 1952, (MS) Ed 1962; 6 Grad Credits Cath Univ of Amer; 6 Grad Credits NY Univ; 3 Grad Credits Wilkes Univ; *cr:* Bristol Boro Pub Schls K-12 Grd Music Supvr 1952-55; Dept of Army Civ Employee 1957-58 Music Tchr 1957-58; Bd of Cooperative Ed Music Tchr 1955-57, 1959-60; St Marys & Holy Trinity Schl Music Tchr, Organist 1955-57, 1959-60; Pope John Paul II Schl Kndgtn Tchr 1982-; *ai:* Holy Chldhd Assn Mission Coord; Organist & Coord Childrens Liturgies; Mid Sts Evaluation Steering Comm Chprsn; NCEA 1985-; Marywood Coll Alumnae Assn; Pope John Paul II Home & Schl Assn; Friends of Mill Meml Lib; Kings Coll Century Club; PHEAA Grant Wilkes Univ; Rdng Buddies; Orbit 2000 Diocesan Schls Grant Author, Writer; *home:* 16 W Washington St Nanticoke PA 18634*

MACHOSKY, CLAIRE JOHNSON, Supervisor & Soc Studies Tchr; *b:* Brooklyn, NY; *w:* Adrian Peter (dec); *c:* Brenda E., Dwayne F., Gwendalyn I.; *ed:* Adelphi Univ (BA) His, Govt 1962; LI Univ (MS) Ed Admin 1987; Hofstra Univ 6 Credits; Queens Coll 18 Credits; Freedom Fnd 4 Credits; *cr:* Woodmere MS Tchr, Co-Curricula Adv 1971-, Dept Ch, Tchr, Peer Coach 1991-95, Grd Level Sup, Dept Ch, Tchr 1995-; *ai:* Coord Natl His Day, Yorker Act; Administer Soc Stud Olympiad, Natl Geography Bee; Chair Curr, Parent Comms; Hewlett Woodmere Adm & Sup Assn 1991-, Comm Chairs; PTA 1965-, Cncl Pres, Honorary Life Mbrshp; LICSS 1987-, Presenter, Facilitator; NCSS 1991-; Wantagh Preservation Soc 1985-; Delta Delta Delta 1961-, Alum Dist Ofcr; St Williams Church Choir 1993-; DAV Flwshp, Freedom Fnd; Canadian Govt Flwshp St Lawrence Univ; Presidential Classroom; Founder Summer Recreation Prgm; *office:* Woodmere MS 1170 Peninsula Blvd Hewlett NY 11557*

MACIE, MARY JONES, Substitute Teacher; *b:* Oswego, NY; *m:* Edward J.; *c:* Joseph P., Andrew J.; *ed:* SUCO (BS) Elem Ed 1966; Johns Hopkins Univ (MED) Communicative Disorders 1979; Practical Bible Trng Schl 1962; Univ ND Linguistics 1967; *cr:* North Bay Schl Kndgtn Tchr 1966-68; Newburg Schl 1 Grd Tchr 1968-69; W Windsor Schl Spec Ed Tchr 1969-70; Arlington Bapt Presch, Day Care Tchr 1974-76; Grace Bible Bapt Kndgtn Tchr 1976-78; Faith Bible Church Acad Elem Supvr 1980-92, Kndgtn Tchr 1994-95; *ai:* Intnl Stu Conventions for Schl of Tomorrow Story Telling Judge; *home:* 5829 Forest Hill Rd Elkridge MD 21227

MACIEJEWSKI, JAMES JOHN, Social Studies Teacher; *b:* Buffalo, NY; *m:* Elizabeth Pacifico; *c:* Jennifer, James; *ed:* SUNY at Buffalo (BA) His 1969; 30 Post Grad Hrs; *cr:* PS 1 Soc Stud Tchr 1969-76; PS 45 Soc Stud Tchr 1976-; *ai:* Schl Trip, Spelling Bee Coord; Head Union Del; Supervise Hnr Guard; Started Safety Patrol, Hnr Soc; NEA 1969-; Exploer Hockey League, Coach, Coach of Yr 1980-; *office:* PS 45 141 Hoyt St Buffalo NY 14213

MACIK, PATRICIA ANN, English Teacher; *b:* McKeesport, PA; *ed:* CA Univ (BSEd) Eng 1963; 12 Hrs Eng Grad Work; *cr:* EF Jr HS Eng Tchr 1963-70; EF Sr HS Eng Tchr 1970-, Eng Dept Chprsn 1986-91; *ai:* AFT 1970-; Best Sr Tchr Female 1988-92, 93-95; All Star Educator 1990 Univ of Pittsburgh & Pgh Press Excl Tchng; *office:* Elizabeth Forward Sr HS 1000 Weigle's Hill Rd Elizabeth PA 15037

MACINTYRE, RUBY L., English & Latin Teacher; *b:* Barre, VT; *m:* James III; *c:* James Wesley, Jeffrey Martin, Helen Elizabeth; *ed:* Westminster Coll (BA) Eng, Latin, Ed 1963; Miscellaneous Courses; *cr:* St Johnsbury Jr HS Eng Tchr 1963-64; Longmeadow HS Eng Tchr 1964-66; Buckingham Jr HS Eng Tchr 1966-67; Essex HS Eng, Latin Tchr 1984-; *ai:* Schl Cncl; Frosh Collaborative; NEA 1984-; CANE 1984-, St Rep; UCC 1964-; *office:* Essex HS 2 Educational Dr Essex Junction VT 05452

MACIOCE, CATHERINE ANN, Math Teacher; *b:* Columbus, OH; *m:* Frank; *c:* Anthony, Christine; *ed:* OH St Univ (MA) Math Ed 1985; Miami Univ (BS) Elem Ed 1991; 18 Addl Quarter Hrs in Math, Ed; *cr:* St Agatha Schl 6-8 Grd Math Tchr 1986-; *ai:* Stu Cncl, Mathcounts Adv; Schl Math Chprsn; NCTM 1991-; Nom OCTM & COCTM Tchr of Yr 1995; *office:* St Agatha Schl 2767 Andover Rd Columbus OH 43221*

MACIONE, PAULA KIRBY, Chemistry Instructor; *b:* Medford, MA; *m:* Peter J.; *c:* Justin; *ed:* Regis Coll (BA) Chem 1958; Univ of MA (MED) Guid 1961; Univ of NM NSF Grant Radiation Chem 1963; 53 Credit Hrs Beyond MED Univ of Lowell, Rivier Coll, Fitchburg St Coll 1963-94; *cr:* MA Inst of Tech Radiation Safety Tech 1958-59; Burlington HS Chem Instr 1959-; *ai:* Safety In the Lab Comm; MA Tchrs Ed Assn 1959-; Burlington Edctrs Assn 1959-, VP 1961-65; NEA; New England Assn of Chem Tchrs 1989-; Regis Coll Alumnae 1958-, Pres, VP, Class Reporter; Veridames of Providence Coll 1991-; Campfire Ldr, Bluejays 1978-82; Internship Lakey Clinic doing on the Job Lab Trng; *office:* Burlington HS 123 Cambridge St Burlington MA 01803

MACK, JANET SHAFFER, Music Teacher; *b:* Hamlin, PA; *m:* Barry Vincent; *c:* B. Scott; *ed:* Marywood Coll (BM) Music Ed 1965; Penn St 12 Addl Hrs; East Stroudsburg 6 Addl Hrs; Marywood Coll 6 Credit Hrs; Westminster Choir Coll 6 Credit Hrs; *cr:* Edgewater Elem Schl Elem Music Tchr 1965-66; Bethlehem Schl Dist Elem Music Tchr 1966-69; Watts MS Music Tchr 1978-79; Bethleham Schl Dist MS, HS Music Tchr 1980-; *ai:* Dir of Les Chanteurs; MENC 1985-; PSEA, BEA 1980-; *office:* Freedom HS 3149 Chester Ave Bethlehem PA 18017

MACK, RICHARD CLARENCE, History Teacher; *b:* Akron, OH; *m:* Shelley McCowin; *c:* Al, Benjamin, Louis; *ed:* Univ of Akron (BA) Ed 1975, (MA) His 1980; John Carroll Univ Inst for Soviet & Eastern European Stud; Oberlin Univ Soviet Stud; *cr:* Univ of Akron Grad Asst 1976-78; Strongsville City Schls Tchr 1978-; *ai:* Stu Cncl Adv 1979-90, 1995-; 8th Grd Boys Track Coach 1985-; NEA 1978-; Lions Club 1984-, Treas; Indian Guides 1988-, Chief 4 Yrs; Yth Sports 1992-, Bsktbl, Bsbl, & Soccer Coach; Benevolence Bd at Church 1993-95, Chm; Cleveland Plain Dealer Crystal Apple Awd 1991; Strongsville Optimist Achvmt in Ed Awd 1992; Phi Alpha Theta His Honorary; *office:* Albion Jr HS 11109 Webster Rd Strongsville OH 44136

MACK, ROBERT D., Senior Marine Instr; *b:* Uhrichsville, OH; *m:* Ruth I.; *c:* Robert Jr., Kellie Bailey; *ed:* Kent St Univ (BA) 1985; *cr:* USMC MSG 20 Yrs; Beaver Local HS Sr Mar Instr 24 Yrs; *ai:* Rifle Team Head Coach; Drill Team & Color Head; Cadet Club Adv; Amer Leg 1974-; VFW 1982-; Mason 1974-, 32 Deg.

MACK, SHARON LESLIE, First Grade Teacher; *b:* Johnstown, PA; *m:* David C.; *c:* Lesley Simmons, Tracey Sisitki; *ed:* IN Univ of PA (BS) Elem Ed 1971, (MED) Elem Ed 1979; *cr:* United Elem Schl First Grd Tchr 1971-; *ai:* Lang Arts, Rdng Comms; NEA, PSEA, VEA 1971-; *home:* RR 2 Box 183 New Florence PA 15944

MACK, TIMOTHY ALAN, Middle School ESL Teacher; *b:* Cleveland, OH; *m:* Dawn Kessler; *c:* Danny, Kevin; *ed:* OH St Univ (BS) Elem Ed 1983; Univ of CO (MA) Educl Tech 1986; K-12 Tchng Eng to Speakers of other Langs Cert 1995, Scndry Sci Cert 1983, Working on Gen Supervisory Cert OH St Univ; *cr:* Aurora Pub Schls MS Math, Sci, Eng Tchr 1983-88; Worthington Pub Schls MS 7th Grd Math Tchr 1988-91, MS ESL Tchr 1991-; *ai:* NEA 1983-; OCTELA 1991-; Northwest Chapel Church; Indian Guides; Presented LAU Conf 1994 Tech in the Classroom, 1995 Tchr as Researcher; *office:* Worthington Pub Schls 752 High St Worthington OH 43085

MACKAIN, CHERYL LYNN, English Teacher; *b:* Bay City, MI; *c:* Jesse Stuart; *ed:* Christ Coll at Irvine (BA) Eng & Ed 1991; *cr:* Concordia Luth HS Eng Tchr 1991-93; Luth HS East Eng Tchr 1993-; *ai:* Chrldng Coach; *office:* Lutheran HS East 3565 Mayfield Rd Cleveland OH 44118*

MACKAR, THOMAS P., Health, Phys Ed Tchr & Coach; *b:* Cleveland, OH; *m:* Bonnie Campbell; *c:* Christopher, Douglas; *ed:* Cleveland St Univ (BSEd) Hlth & PE 1972, (MED) Human Performance, Sport Psych 1980; 45 Addl Hrs; *cr:* Cleveland Cath Bd of Ed PE Tchr 1972-73; Mentor HS Hlth & PE Tchr, Boys Var Soccer Coach 1973-; *ai:* Hlth & PE Curr Comms; Mentor Tchrs Assn, NEA, OEA 1973-; Natl Ath Trainers Assn 1968-, Ret; OH Scholastic Soccer Coaches Assn 1973-, St Rep; Natl Soccer Coaches Assn 1973-; Mentor Soccer Club 1976-, Clinician; Mentor Sftbl Assn 1984-, Clinican; Natl Yth Sport Coaches Assn 1988-, Clinician; Mentor Schls Excl in Tchng Awd 1984; 14 Soccer Coach of Yr Awds; St of OH Boys Soccer Coach of Yr 1990; Coach of Boys Division I St Champions 1994; Inducted into OH Scholastic Soccer Coaches Hall of Fame 1996; *office:* Mentor HS 6477 Center St Mentor OH 44060

MAC KENTHUN, CAROLE,RSM. Jr HS Lang Arts Teacher; *b:* Trenton, NJ; *ed:* Georgian Court Coll (BA) Elem Ed 1968; Trenton St Coll (MED) Elem Ed 1976; *cr:* St Mary Acad Primary Tchr 1968-72, 1975-83; St Mary Schl Fourth Grd Tchr 1972-73; Sacred Heart Schl 3rd, 4th Grd Tchr 1973-75; St Matthias Schl Mid Grd, Jr HS Tchr 1983-93; St Catharine Schl Lang Arts, Rel Tchr 1993-; *ai:* Jr HS Prayer Group Moderator; Pub Schl Stdnts Rel Tchr; Liturgical Comm Parish, Schl Mem; Kappa Delta Pi 1976-; NCEA 1968-; Mercy Elem Ed Assn 1986-; Authored 13 Rel Ed Books, 5 Books on Cath Saints; Authored Early Chldhd, Vocabulary, Primary Lang Arts Books; Outstdng Edctr Awd Diocese of Metuchen 1991; Hosted Rel Ed Cable TV Show 5 Yrs; Presentor Wkshps Lang Arts, Rel Ideas; Elizabeth Ann Seton Awd Svc Girl Scouts; Miriam Joseph Farrell Awd NCEA 1986; *home:* 211 Essex Ave Spring Lake NJ 07762

MAC KENZIE, MALCOLM IAN, English Teacher; *ed:* Univ of Toronto (BA) 1975; Drake Univ (MST) Ed 1978; *ai:* Town Italy 1984-95, Councilman, Suprvsr 1996-; *office:* Marcus Whitman Cntrl Schl Baldwin Rd Rushville NY 14544*

MAC KEOWN, MARJORIE GABRIEL, English Teacher & Dept Chair; *b:* Delaware, OH; *m:* Graeme J.; *c:* Jack, Christopher; *ed:* Muskingum Coll (BA) Eng 1963; Wright St (MS) Ed 1992; Post Grad of Cmptrs at Univ of Dayton; *cr:* Tecumseh HS 9-12 Grd Eng Tchr, Dept Chair; Madison HS 10-12 Grd Eng Tchr; University City HS 10 Grd Eng Tchr; Marion City Schls 9, 11 Grd Eng Tchr; *ai:* Clark Cty Exemplary Writers, Curr Comms; NCTE 1978-; OCTELA 1984-, Exec Bd, WOCTELA Rrp; WOCTELA 1984-, Pres, HS Rep; NEA, OEA, TEA 1963-, Rep; Church, Group Ldr, Tchr; Martha Holden-Jennings Scholar 1992-93; Ed Fnd Grant; Clark Cty Grant; *office:* Tecumseh HS 9830 W National Rd New Carlisle OH 45344*

MACKEY, JAMIE CRYAN, Fourth Grade Teacher; *b:* Toledo, OH; *m:* Richard E.; *c:* Emily C., Lindsay E.; *ed:* OH St Univ (BS) Elem Ed 1970; Westminster Coll (MA) Scndry Cnslng 1975; Penn St Univ Ag 1994; *cr:* Laurel Elem Schl 3-4th Grd Tchr 1970-; *ai:* NEA, PSEA 1970-; Laural Ed Assn 1970-, Hall Rep; KDKA-TV Univ of Pittsburgh Thanks to Tchrs Awd; A Gift of Time Awd Recepient 1993; *office:* Laurel Elem Schl Rd 4 Box 52 New Castle PA 16101

MACKEY, JOELLE ENRICO, Social Studies Teacher; *b:* Brooklyn, NY; *m:* Kirk W.; *ed:* CW Post Univ (MS) Soc Stud Ed 1994; 9 Credits at St Johns Univ, Prof Diploma Admin; *cr:* Elmont Memorial HS Soc Stud Tchr 1993-; *ai:* Class of 1998 Adv; Jr Var Sftbl Coach; NEA 1993-; *office:* Elmont Memorial HS 555 Ridge Rd Elmont NY 11003

MACKEY, JOSEPH LEONARD, Social Studies Curr Coord; *b:* Boston, MA; *m:* Catherine Marie Saccone; *c:* Kathleen T., Michael J., Alison M.; *ed:* MA Coll of Art (BFA) Art Ed 1977; Regis Coll (MA) Spec Ed 1981; Boston St Coll 84 Credits His, Eng, Art 1971-74; Vesper George Schl of Art 36 Credits Art Illustration 1969-70; Northeast Regnl Ctr for Drug Free Schls US Dept of Ed 15 Credits; *cr:* Boston St Coll Asst to Registrar, Fac Svcs 1971-74; Melrose Pub Schls Tchr 1977-91; Emmanuel Coll Supvr 1981-; Univ of NH Adjunct Fac, Tchr 1993-; Kenneth Jr, Sr HS Curr Coord, Soc Stud, Art, Music 1992-; *ai:* Curr Comm K-12; Art Club; Principals Cabinet; Scholastic Arts Awd; Plymouth Friends of the Arts; NEA, MA Tchrs Assn 1977-; MEA, NAEA 1977-, Del; MA Art Alunmi Assn 1977-; NCSS; ASCD; Melrose Schl Comm 1990-, Chair Spec Ed, Vice Chair, Legislation; MA Assn Schl Comms 1990-; Schl Based Improvement Project 1992-, Rep; Horace Mann Grant 1988-89; MCA Assoc Schlsp 1976-77; Christa Mc Auliff Tchr of Yr; Girl Scouts of Amer 1986-87; Super Team Drug Free Schls 1988; American Mutal Show 1979, 1980; One Man Show 1980-81; Stu Exhibit MA Art 1975; Scholastic Arts Awds 1966-67; *office:* Kennett Jr/Sr HS 118 Main St Conway NH 03818*

MACKEY, SHARON LEIB, Computer Literacy Teacher; *b:* Passaic, NJ; *m:* Raymond L.; *c:* Keith E.; *ed:* Cedar Crest Coll (BA) Eng Lit-Cum Laude 1964; Attnd Rowan Coll; *cr:* Emmaus Jr HS Grd 8 Eng Tchr 1964-65; Somers Point Grd 7-8 SS, Eng Tchr 1965-67; Campbell Soup Co Records Analyst 1967-68; Waterford Twp Schls Grd 5-6 Basic Skills, GATE, Cmptr Lit Tchr 1971-; *ai:* NJ Math League Contest Spon; Regnl Tech Comm; Regnl Curr Dev Cmptr Ed Local Rep; NEA, NJEA 1971-; Waterford Twp Ed Assn 1971-, Pres 1987-95; Ducks Unlimited; Dist Tchr of Yr; Freedom Fnd Seminar Schlsp 2 Times; St Champion Jaycette Pub Speaking Awd 1970; *office:* Waterford Township Schl Old White Horse Pike Waterford Works NJ 08089*

MACKEY, SUNNI AUERHAHN, Fifth Grade Teacher; *b:* Mar NY; *m:* Steven P.; *ed:* SUNYC at New Paltz (BA) Psych 1973, (MS Ed 1977; *cr:* Plattekill Elem Schl 2nd Grd Tchr 1973-77, 4th G 1978-80, 5th Grd Tchr 1981-; *ai:* Shared Decision Team; NY St Tchrs 1973-; Wallkill Tchrs Assn 1973-, Past VP, Past Recordin AFT; Co-Author Written Comm, Lang Arts Curr Wallkill Cntrl *office:* Plattekill Elem Schl Rt 32 S Plattekill NY 12568

MACKIE, DIANE DEROSIER, English & American Stud T Springfield, MA; *m:* James B.; *c:* Gavin, Alexander; *ed:* Wheat (BA) Amer His, Lit 1979; Springfield Coll (MED) Eng Ed 19d85; 16 Hrs Amer Civilization Brown Univ; *cr:* Cathedral HS Soc Stu 1980-82d; Springfield Coll ESL Tchr 1982-86; MA Career Dev In Tchr 1986-87; Springfield Cntrl HS Eng Tchr 1987-; *ai:* Schl C Decision Making Team; Attendance Improvement Comm; NEA NCTE 1990-; Trinity Church Trustee, Vice Chair; Invited Chines Coach Syncronized Swimming, Teach Eng 1985, 1986; *office:* Spri Cntrl HS 1840 Roosevelt Ave Springfield MA 01109

MACKIE, J. ALEXANDER,III, Earth Science Teacher; *b:* Philad PA; *m:* Jill Fisher; *c:* Amber, Ashley, Alexandra, Lydia; *ed:* OH W Univ (BA) Botany 1976; Villanova Univ (BS) 1979; Boston Coll (M Ed Marine Sci 1986; Bio Tchr Cert; Attnd Shoals Marine Lab of Univ, Union Coll; *cr:* Chapin Schl Gen Sci & Marine Sci 1979-84; Acad Earth Sci & Marine Sci 1985-92; Schoharie Cntrl HS Earth Ecology 1993-; *ai:* Natl Marine Edctrs Assn 1985-; Schoharie Tch 1993-; Sci Tchrs of NY St 1995-; Mohawk Vly Field Hockey U Assn; Princetown Reformed Church 1994-; Acadia Natl Park ME Ecology Summer Pgm Marine Ecolgy Tchr 1986-95; *office:* Sch Cntrl HS Main St Schoharie NY 12157

MACKIEWICZ, BARBARA B., Religious Studies Teacher; *b:* Rive NY; *ed:* Brentwood Coll (BS) Ed 1971; Fordham Univ (MS) Rel S 1978; St John's Univ 24 Grad Credits Sociology 1973-75; *cr:* Holy of Jesus Schl 1-4 Grd Tchr 1971-75; Our Lady of Perpetual H 9-12 Grd Rel Stud Tchr 1975-88; Bishop Kearney HS Guid Cnslr 19 Stella Maris HS 10-11 Grd Rel Stud Tchr 1990-; *ai:* Moderate Lit NCEA; Cert, Recognition Exemplary Efforts in Support Cath Ed 19 Yrs Tchng; *office:* Stella Maris HS Beach 112th St Rockaway Pa 11694

MAC KINNEL, SHARON RUDDEN, Kindergarten Teacher; *b* Haven, CT; *m:* Douglas Scott; *c:* Kyle, Abby; *ed:* SCSU (MS) Rdng Attnd SCSU 1978; *cr:* Branford Bd of Ed 2nd-3rd Grd Tchr 1978-7 Grd Tchr 1979-80; Indian Neck & Tisko Schls Kndgtn Tchr 198 Branfords 350th Birthday Schl Rep; NEA; 1978-; *office:* Mary R Elem Schl 118 Damascus Rd Branford CT 06405

MACKINTOSH, KATHY KESPER, 4th Grade Teacher; *b:* New City, NY; *m:* Richard Donald; *ed:* Glassboro St Coll (BA) Elem Ed William Paterson, Monclair St, Ryder, Jersey City St Post Grad C *cr:* Roosevelt Elem Schl 3rd-4th Grd Tchr 1970-; *ai:* Stu Cncl Adv Goals Comm; Shakespeare Production Asst; REEA, BCEA 1970-; NEA; First Dog Trng Club of NNJ Inc 1987-, VP, Trng Dir, Spons Good Citizen Awds to Pub; Course Grant on Weather From Monclai of Yr 1991; Stu Tchr Mentor 1994-95; Sci Fair Coord; *office:* Roo Elem Schl 711 Summit Ave River Edge NJ 07661

MACKLE, ELIZABETH, Mathematics Teacher; *b:* Oak Park, I Bernard; *ed:* Ocean Cty Coll (AA) Bus 1980; Georgian Court Coll Math 1983; 16 Credits Grad Stud Alchohol, Substance Abuse Cnslr Toms River HS North Math Tchr 1983-; *ai:* NJEA 1994-; *office:* River HS North Old Freehold Rd Toms River NJ 08753

MACKLIN, FRANCIS ANTHONY, English Professor; *b:* Philade PA; *m:* Judith Ann Baker; *c:* Steven, Stacy; *ed:* Villanova Univ (BA 1960, (MA) Eng 1963; *cr:* Univ of Dayton Instr 1962-66, Ass 1966-72, Assoc Prof 1972-; Univ of CA at Santa Barbara 198 Supervised Ind Stud; Books: Palestra, Beyond Justice; Numerous J Articles; *office:* Univ Of Dayton 300 College Park Ave Dayton OH

MACKOWSKI, GREG JOHN, HS Social Studies Teacher; *b:* Bro NY; *m:* Valerie Saas; *c:* Chris, Vincent, Matt; *ed:* Hudson Vly CC Lbrl Arts 1966; Oneonta St (BA) Ed 1968; 30 Addl Hrs His, Ed; *cr* Plain Cntrl HS Soc Stud Tchr 1968-74; Chatham Cntrl HS Soc Stud 1974-; *ai:* Golf Coach; Strategic Planning Comm; NYSTA 1968-86; 1986-, VP 1986, Dist Rep 1987-89; Elks 1979-; Ghent Rod & Gun *office:* Chatham Cntrl HS 50 Woodbridge Ave Chatham NY 12037

MACKRELL, KEVIN FRANCIS, Social Studies Teacher; *b:* Ni Falls, NY; *m:* Susan Morris; *c:* Christopher, Kate, Lauren, Ryan, Zac *ed:* SUNY at Buffalo (BA) His 1969, (MA) Ed 1975; *cr:* Gaskill Jr 8-9th Grd Soc Stud Tchr 4 Yrs; LaSalle Sr HS 9-11th Grd Soc Stud T Yrs; CYP 2 Yrs; Trott Voc 2 Yrs; LaSalle Jr, MS 15 Yrs; *ai:* Var Ftbl, Tennis, Soccer Coach; Stu Cncl, Yrbk Adv; AFT, NYSUT 1970-, Bldg *office:* La Salle MS 76th St & Buffalo Ave Niagara Falls NY 14304

MACKSOUD, RICHARD CHARLES, 4th Grade Teacher; *b:* Attle MA; *ed:* RI Coll (BS) Elem Ed 1976, (MED) Elem Admin 1980; U RI MS Cert 1986; *cr:* St Raymond's Schl 5-8 Grd Soc Stud Tchr 197 Richmond Schl 6th Grd Tchr 1980-89; Chariho MS 6th Grd Tchr 198 Hope Vly Schl 4th Grd Tchr 1990-; *ai:* Soccer, Girls Sftbl, Little L Bsbl, Instrl Bsktbl Coach; NEA 1980-; *office:* Hope Valley Elem Schl St Hope Valley RI 02832

MAC LEAN, BRUCE EDWARD, Social Studies Teacher; *b:* Wengm MA; *m:* Margaret Dodd; *c:* Alexander; *ed:* Univ of MA at Amherst His 1975; Univ of VT (MA) Russian & E European His 1986; Ad Credits Beyond Masters; *cr:* Anglo-Amer Schl His Tchr 1976-78; Schl Aberdeen His Tchr 1976-78; Oxbow HS His Tchr 1978-80; Amer Sotia Class, PE Tchr 1980-82; Amer Schl Warsaw Class, PE Tchr 198 Oxbow HS His Tchr 1982-; *ai:* Admin, Advy Team; Responsible for His, & Eng Dept Chprsn; Local Chptr NEA 1978-, Pres, VP; Bus Com Peachem Congregational Church 1994-; Trustee Peacham Lib 1993-, Fulbright Scholar to Egypt & Israel 1991; *office:* Oxbow HS Rt 5 Bra VT 05033*

MAC LEAN, JOHN V., English Teacher; *b:* New York, NY; *m:* darragh; *c:* Cora, Caitlin, Emma, Sarah; *ed:* Fordham Univ (BA) Eng Oxford Univ (BA) Eng 1972; Univ of SC (JD) Law 1977; Attnd Yale of Drama, Univ of MA, SUNY, CUNY; *cr:* Bruke Cath HS Eng 1979-83; Woodlands HS Eng Tchr 1986-; *ai:* Breadloaf Writers, England Stu Jrnlsm Confs; Newspaper Adv 1991-95; Mock Trial C 1986-93; Drama Dir 1988-; *office:* Woodlands HS 475 W Hartsdale Hartsdale NY 10530

MAC LEAN, KENNETH IAIN, High School Band Director Dumbarton, Scotland; *c:* James C.; *ed:* Jersey City St Coll (BA) Musi 1982, (MA) Music Ed 1990; Temple Univ 9 Hrs; Villanova Univ 3 Kean Coll 3 Hrs; St Peters Coll 3 Hrs; West Chester Univ 6 Hrs Hasbrouck Heights Jr-Sr HS Instrumental Music Dir 1982-84; Red Regnl HS Music Tchr 1984-; *ai:* Band Dir; Stu Svc Comm; Sr Musicals Dir; MENC 1984-, Nationally Registered Music Edctr; All S Band Dir Assn 1984-, Pres 1986-87; Natl Judges Assn 1982-, Music Ch 1989-; Drum Corps Assoc 1989-, Brass Caption Chm 1989-; Shore Ch Ctr Church 1990-, Music Ministry; Panel Evaluate Drum, Bugle Corps Naval Acad, Air Force Acad, Coast Guard Acad; Instr NBC Macys All 'orps; *office:* Red Bank Regional HS 101 Ridge Rd Little Silver NJ

EOD, DANIEL COLE, Physical Ed Tchr & Act Dir; *b:* Beverly, ; Joanne Elizabeth Gee; *ed:* Springfield Coll (BS) PE 1987; *cr:* Schl Dept Sub Tchr & in Schl Suspension Supvr 1987-88;)qunquit Comm Schl Dist PE Tchr & Act Dir 1988-; *ai:* Wells HS ar Bsktbl Coach; Soccer Coach; Archeticural Stud, Transportation, Prin Search & Home Schl Comm Involvement Comms; Bldg ship Team; NEA 1989-; Wells Ogunquit Tchrs Assn 1989-, Bldg Rep 5; Southern York Act Assn 1989-, Pres 1993-95; MTA; *home:* 39 Mill Dr Kennebunk ME 04043

EOD, DONALD WILLIAM, English & Public Speaking Tchr; *b:* vay, Scotland; *m:* Terry Plaskon; *c:* Heather, Robert; *ed:* Fairleigh son Univ (BS) Ed 1964; Seton Hall Univ (MA) Eng Lit 1968; Kean NJ (MA) Admin, Supervision 1977; Grad NY Schl Broadcasting, acing; *cr:* Hawthorne HS Eng, Pub Speaking Tchr 1964-; Ramapo djunct Prof 1980-84; *ai:* Curr Comm; Past Asst, Head Soccer Coach Adv; NEA, NJEA 1964-; HTA 1964-, VP; NCTE 1994-; Pub s Magazines; *office:* Hawthorne HS Parmelee Ave Hawthorne NJ

EOD, ELIZABETH DONOVAN, Science Teacher; *b:* Rochester, Charles D.; *c:* Thomas D., John D.; *ed:* Univ of DE (BA) Bio 1984; gton Coll (MA) Psych 1992; *cr:* Rising Sun HS Sci Tchr 1986-88; ty HS Sci Tchr 1988-; *ai:* Sr Class Adv 4 Yrs; KCTA, NEA 1988-; Kent County HS Lambs Meadow Rd Worton MD 21678*

EOD, EVA-MARIE CUNSOLO, English Teacher; *b:* Queens, NY; id B.; *c:* Heather L., John Alex; *ed:* Eastern Nazarene Coll Eng; *cr:* hrstn Acad 7-12th Grd Vol Eng Tchr 1991-95; *ai:* SR Class Adv; f Chrstn Schl Intnl Creative Writing Local Coord; ACSI 1991-; Paris Christian Acad PO Box 282 South Paris ME 04281

EOD, HEIDI HIGHMARK, Third Grade Teacher; *b:* Youngstown, Devon, Cameron H.; *cr:* Kimberton Waldorf Schl Work, Farm Prgm 980-84; Class Tchr 1984-; *office:* Kimberton Waldorf Schl West Stars Rd Kimberton PA 19343

EOD, LEAH MINEMIER, Mathematics Teacher; *b:* Dansville, Donald; *c:* Donald Jr., Robert, Hannah; *ed:* Cornell Univ (AB) 978, (MS) Math Ed 1983; Post-Grad Syracuse Univ, St Univ Coll at o; Attnd St Univ Coll at Geneseo; *cr:* Livonia MS Math Tchr 1; Cornell Univ Math Lecturer 1981-83; Oswego HS Math Tchr *ai:* Alternative Scheduling Comm; NYS United Tchrs 1985-; o Classroom Tchrs Assn 1985-, 1st VP, Nom Tchr of Yr; Twins & s Mothers Club of CNY 1991-, Pres; Ed Syracuse Univ Project e Calculus Text; *office:* Oswego HS 2 Buccaneer Blvd Oswego NY

MAHON, TIMOTHY, Instructor of Chemistry; *ed:* Rutgers Univ Chem 1982; Purdue Univ (PHD) Analytical Chem 1989; *cr:* Spex ies Chemist 1982-84; IBM Analytical Chem 1989-93; Orange Cty Coll Tchr 1993-; *ai:* ACS 1990-; ASMS 1990-; 8 Papers in ved Journals; 1 Patent; *office:* Orange County Comm Coll 115 South dletown NY 10940

MILLAN, DONALD HUGH, Fifth Grade Teacher; *b:* Rochester, Catherine Gates; *c:* Sara Catharine, Margaret Anne; *ed:* Univ of r (BA) Sociology 1967; SUNY at Geneseo (MS) Ed 1970; *cr:* rt Cntrl Schls Elem Tchr 1968-; *ai:* Ski Club, Stu Govt, Sci Fair Adv; T 1981-; FEA 1968-; Fishers Fire Dept 1981-, Commissioner; Natl trol 1988-, Ski Patroller of Yr 1992; *office:* Northside Schl 181 on Rd Fairport NY 14450

MBER, KATHLEEN G., Business Teacher; *b:* Dansville, NY; *m:* L.; *c:* Ronald E.; *ed:* St Bonaventure Univ (BS) Ec 1979, (MS) Ed *cr:* Radio Shack Retail Mgr; Canaseraga Cntrl Schl Bus Tchr; *ai:* Stu Cncl & Schl Store Adv; NEA-Canaseraga Assn 1988-, Local *office:* Canaseraga Central Schl E Main St Canaseraga NY 14822*

OMBER, SANDRA L., Physical Education Teacher; *b:* Troy, NY; JNY at Brockport (BS) PE 1968; Attnd Ithaca Coll, SUNY at o, SUNY at Potsdam, Azusa Pacific Coll; *cr:* Franklin Acad PE Tchr *ai:* Var Swimming Coach; NYSAPHERD 1968-, Pres AWPENYS ern Zone; AAPHERD, NYSUT, AFT 1968-; ASCA: SCANYS; , 25 Yrs Svc Awd; NYSCA, Century Club Awd; NFICA; Past n 10 Chm Swimming, Track & Field; *office:* Franklin Acad State St e NY 12953

PHEE, DANIEL R., Science Teacher; *b:* Ft Monmouth, NJ; *m:* ret Ryan; *c:* Katie, Daniel, Matthew; *ed:* Stockton St Coll (BS) Bio 39 Grad Credits Jersey City St Coll; US Coast Guard Master ns License; *cr:* St John Vianney HS Sci Tchr 1986; Manchester Twp i Tchr 1986-; *ai:* Head Var Bsbl, Asst Var Ftbl Coach; Sci Club Adv; 1986-; Legacy, GLOBE Grants; NJ Governors Grant for Excl pant; *office:* Manchester Township HS 101 S Colonial Dr Lakehurst 733

PHERSON, DANIEL CRAIG, Elementary Band Director; *b:* mbo, Ceylon; *m:* Susan Mancuso; *c:* Katie, Brian; *ed:* SUC at Fredonia s) Ed, Music 1981; Youngstown St Univ (MMus) Perf, Music 1985; Cert Classroom K-6; *cr:* Brockport Cntrl Schls Instrument Music 982-84; Greece Cntrl Schls Band Dir 1984-; *ai:* Self Esteem Comm air; Announcers-Guardians of Flag Adv; NEA 1982-; NYSBDA ; ITA 1978-; GTA 1984-; Numerous Articles Pub; *office:* Brookside Schl 1144 Long Pond Rd Rochester NY 14626

QUESTON, CAROLE BEAUMONT, French & Spanish Tchr; *b:* ester, MA; *m:* Harold; *c:* Brittany, Callie; *ed:* Nasson Coll (BA) Fr Attnd Centre Sico Pedagogique at Paris, Universite De Caen, rsite De Nice, Worcester St Coll, Westfield St Coll, Framingham St Post Grad Stud; *cr:* Lee HS Fr, Span Tchr 1974-80; Houghton Schl Fr 1980-82; Hudson HS Fr, Span Tchr 1982-; *ai:* Mentor Prgm; *office:* on HS 69 Brigham St Hudson MA 01749

RI, JULIE ILLICK, Director of Bands; *b:* Edison, NJ; *m:* Richard; ebanon Vly Coll (BS) Music Ed 1986; *cr:* Lodi HS Dir of Bands ; *ai:* Marching, Concert & Jazz Band; Fac Advy Comm; NEA, NJEA, & LEA 1986-; MENC, NJMEA & MEBCI 1986-; 1st Presbyn h 1982-, Deacon; *office:* Lodi HS 99 Putnam St Lodi NJ 07644*

UGA, NADINE LEAVY, Music Teacher; *b:* Pittsburgh, PA; *m:* e M.; *c:* Kristen, Justin; *ed:* IN Univ of PA (BS) Music Ed 1968; esne Univ (MA) Music Ed 1971; St Vincent Coll Elem Cert; *cr:* Penn Schl Dist Music Tchr 1968-80; Norwin Schl Dist Music Tchr 1989-; horus; NEA 1989-; PSEA 1989-; DEMENC 1990-; St Johns Choir , Accompanist; *office:* Norwin Sr HS & MS East 251 Mcmahon Dr Huntingdon PA 15642

URA, MICHAEL PETER, PE Teacher & Ath & PE Dir; *b:* ville, NY; *m:* Mary Ann Race; *c:* Michael, Adam, Ethan; *ed:* Norwich (BS) PE 1975, (MSEd) PE, Ath Admin 1976; *cr:* Granville Cntrl Schl chr, Ath Dir 1976-; Adirondack Comm Coll Prof of PE 1994-; *ai:* Ath Ftbl Coach; Wasaren League Sec, Treas; Amer Ftbl Coaches Assn ; NY St Ath Admin Assn 1990-; NY St Ftbl Coaches Assn 1994-; ; 29 E Main St Granville NY 12832

WILLIAMS, ELIZABETH ULRICKSON, Science Teacher; *b:* and, ME; *m:* Joseph C.; *c:* Jennifer, Melissa; *ed:* Univ of ME (BSEd) Bio 1966; 45 Addl Hrs; 30 Hrs at MS Level; *cr:* David Brearly Reg HS Sci Tchr 1967-68; Bell Telephone Lab Sr Tech Aide Biophysics Rsrch 1968-70; Ctr for Comm Dental Hlth Edctrs 1978-79; SAD #6 Sci Tchr 1983-; *ai:* Envirothon Coach; Ldrshp Cncl; NEA, ME Ed Assoc; Saco Vly Tchrs Assoc 1984-; ME Sci Tchrs Assoc 1991-; Gulf of ME Marine Ed Assoc 1991-; ME Environment Edctrs Assn 1993-; Howard Hughes Med Inst Tchrs Scholar 1995; Outstdng Tchr York Cty Soil & Water Cons Dist 1992, ME Assn of Conservation Dist 1993; *office:* Bonny Eagle HS 700 Saco Rd Standish ME 04084

MAC WILLIAMS, MARK WHEELER, Visiting Professor; *b:* Albany, NY; *m:* Diane Jefchak; *c:* Zoe, Zia, Ziven, Zel; *ed:* Syracuse Univ (BA) Rel Stud 1974; Indiana Univ (MA) Rel Stud 1980; Univ of Chicago (PHD) Rel Stud 1990; *cr:* Nanzen Cath Girls Schl Eng Instr 1980; Univ of Chicago Divinity Schl Editorial Asst, His of Rels Tchr 1984-86; Univ of TN at Knoxville Lecturer, Dept of Rel Stud Tchr 1986; Bethany Coll Asst Prof of Rel Stud 1989-95; Bucknell Univ Visit Prof Rel Dept 1995-; *ai:* Project Dir; NEH Regnl Inst Japanese Culture Through Lit 1995-; Amer Acad of Rel, Assn of Asian Stud 1988-; AAS Comm 1994-; Fulbright-Hayes Flwshp; Univ of Tsukuba Japan 1987; Charlotte W. Newcombe Dissertation Flwshp 1988; Jr Fellow Inst Advanced Stud Rel 1988; *home:* 103 Main St Bethany WV 26032*

MACY, DRUSILLA, English Teacher; *b:* Montclair, NJ; *ed:* Ottawa Univ (BA) Eng 1969; Univ of VT (MAT) Eng 1985; Dartmouth CANE Inst; *cr:* Mount Anthony Union Jr HS Eng Tchr 1969-72; Spaulding Graded MS Eng Tchr 1973-88; Spaulding HS Eng Tchr 1988-; *ai:* Poetry Club; Drama Production Musical Dir; Assist Team; VT Philharmonic Orch 1973-, Violinist; Tuesday Poets 1975-, Poet; Poetry Soc VT 1976-, Poet; Bartholdy Ensemble 1989-, Violinist; Montpelier Chamber Orch Soc 1995-, Violinist, Concertmaster Awd; Grad Schl UVM Full Schlsp & Flwshp Awd 1984-85; Sabbatical 1984-85; Outstdng Tchr Awd 1982; Arthur Wallace Peace Awd 1982; Norwich Univ Adj Prof 1989-; *office:* Spaulding HS 155 Ayers St Barre VT 05641*

MACY, RICHARD COLE, Professor of Mechanical Tech; *b:* Port Jefferson, NY; *m:* Vivian Governale; *c:* Robin, Lauren Calvano, Ellen Macy-Flint; *ed:* Suffolk Comm Coll (AAS) Mechanical Tech 1968; NY Inst of Tech (BS) Mechanical Engrng 1972; SUNY at Stony Brook (MS) Electrical Scis 1975; 18 Credits in Environmental Engrng; *cr:* Fairchild Engine Div Drafter 1957-60; Deutsch Relays Inc Designer 1961-67; Suffolk Comm Coll Prof 1967-; *ai:* Multimedia, Coll Personnel Comms; NYSUT 1967-; VATEA 1994, CETA 1979, VEA 1977 Grants; *office:* Suffolk Comm Coll 533 College Rd Selden NY 11784

MACY, THOMAS LAWRENCE, Humanities Teacher; *b:* Chicago, IL; *m:* Abby Parker Warner; *ed:* Antioch Univ (BA) Human Dev 1978; Wesleyan Univ Eng Lit; *cr:* Saint Dunstans Epis Schl 6th Grd Tchr 1978-80; Rye Cntry Day Schl Hum Tchr 1980-85; Maret Schl Hum Tchr, Dean of Grd 5, Asst Head of MS 1985-; *ai:* Organize & Execute 6 Outings Per Yr with Stdnts; 2 Overnight Outings Include WV & New York City; Organize Stdnts to Participate in a Geography Bee; City Tavern Club 1988-; Nantucket Yacht Club 1985-; Friends of Nobska Inc 1980-; *office:* The Maret Schl 3000 Cathedral Ave NW Washington DC 20008

MADAMA, PAMELA ANN, English Teacher; *b:* Cincinnati, OH; *ed:* Miami Univ (BA) Eng Ed 1990; Working on Masters Schl Admin Univ of Cincinnati; *cr:* William Henry Harrison HS Eng Tchr 6 Yrs; *ai:* Var Girls Soccer Coach 4 Yrs; Yrbk 3 Yrs, Jr Class 2 Yrs Adv; 9th Grd Transition Comm; Prin Team; Ed Admin Schlsp; Renaissance Festival Grant; *office:* Wm Henry Harrison HS 9860 West Rd Harrison OH 45030*

MADAR, ROBERT JOSEPH, Mechanical Engineering Instr; *b:* McKeesport, PA; *m:* Martha Ann Proco; *ed:* Univ of Pittsburgh (BS) Mechanical Engnrng 1970, (MBA) Bus Admin 1974; Grad Coursework Mech Engrng; *cr:* Peoples Natural Gas Co Design Engr 1970-75; LaRoche Coll Instr 1974-77; Triangle Inst of Tech Instr 1975-82; PA St Univ Instr 1982-; *ai:* Tech Adv Comm Parkway West Vo-Tech Schl; ASMR ME Club Adv; ASMR 1970-; ASRE 1984-; Writing Across the Curr; Tchng via Pictorial; *office:* PA St Univ N Kensington Cmps 3550 7th Street Rd New Kensington PA 15068

MADARAS, LAWRENCE HIGGINS, Prof of His & Political Sci; *b:* Bayonne, NJ; *m:* Margaret Cullen; *c:* Lawrence Jr., Sean, Stephen; *ed:* Holy Cross (BA) Eng 1959; NY Univ (MA) His 1961, (PHD) His 1964; *cr:* Spring Hill Coll His Instr, Asst Prof 1964-68; Coppin St Coll Asst His Prof 1969-70; Howard Comm Coll Assoc, Full His Prof 1970-; *ai:* OAH 1966-70 1995-; CCSSA 1972-76; Natl Endowment for Hum Fellowship 1973; NEH Seminar 1977-78; Comm Coll Soc Sci Assn 1972-75, Bd Mem; Co-Author & Ed of Taking Sides Amer His; Fulbright-Hays Fellow in Taiwan Summer 1966; *office:* Howard Comm Coll 10901 Little Patuxent Pkwy Columbia MD 21044

MADARAS, PAUL MICHAEL, Gifted Program Coordinator; *b:* Wall, PA; *m:* Donna L.; *ed:* CA St Coll (BSEd) Elem Ed 1969; Master's Equivalency Univ of Pittsburgh, Penn St Univ 1978; *cr:* Churchill Area Schl Dist 6th Grd Tchr 1969-77, Gifted Prgm Coord 1978-81; Woodland Hills Schl Dist Gifted Prgm Coord 1981-; *ai:* Head Track, Field 7-9 Grd, Head Cross Cntry 7-8 Grd Coach; NEA, PSEA 1969-; WHEA 1981-; F&AM 1984-, Past Master; Shrine, Scottish Rite 1985-; PA Air Natl Guard 1972-, First Sergeant; Triple Creek Acres Water Auth 1991-, Bd of Dir; Turkey Trot Run-a-Thon 1987-, Co-Organizer; *office:* Woodland Hills Schl Dist 2430 Greensburg Pike Pittsburgh PA 15221

MADDEN, GRACE WILSON, 5th Grd Lang & Soc Stud Tchr; *b:* Canton, OH; *c:* Christopher; *ed:* Malone Coll (BS) Elem Ed 1968; Ashland Univ (MED) Curr, Instruction 1981; Attnd Ashland Univ, Salem St Coll, Akron Univ, Kent St Univ; *cr:* Trump Elem Schl 2nd Grd Tchr 1963-67; North Industry Elem Schl 1st, 3rd & 5th Grd Tchr 1967-85; Prairie Coll Elem Sch 3rd, 5th Grd, Tchr of Gifted 1985-; *ai:* Canton Local Writers Bdlg Coord; Mini Park Project; Coord, Co-Dev Mystery Minds; New Tchr Mentor; Stark Cty Soc Stud, Local Lang Arts, Local Gifted Comm; OH Arts Ed Assn 1995; Canton Local Tchrs Assn 1968-, Ed Newsletter, OCOEA Outstdng Newsletter, Bldg & EPAC Rep, TEPS & Schlsp Comms; OH Ed Assn, NEA 1968-; Democratic Women's Club 1990-, Act Coord; Alpha Gamma Delta 1961-, Mbrshp Recruitment Adv; Boston Artist's Summer Festival 1991-, Coord Childrens Art; Dueber United Meth Church 1965-, Chm Chrstn Bd of Ed, Sunday Schl Supt, Sunday Schl Tchr; Martha Holen Jennings Scholar 1993-94, Educl Grant; OH Arts Ed Assn St Convention Presenter; Grd 6 Soc Stud OH Profiency Test Curr Writer; *office:* Prairie College Elem Schl 3021 Prairie College Rd SW Canton OH 44706*

MADDEN, JOHN F., Religious Studies Chairperson; *b:* New Brunswick, NJ; *m:* Cynthia Meyer; *c:* Kateri, Paige; *ed:* Univ of Dayton (BA) Religious Stud 1986; 15 Credit Hrs Scndry Admin & Supervision at Rutgers Grad Schl of Ed; *cr:* Saint Joseph HS Rel Stud Chprsn 1987-; *ai:* Var Track Asst Coach; Frosh & Soph Stu Cncl Asst Moderator; Frosh Assistance Prgm Dir; NCEA 1991-; Sigma Nu 1984-, Chaplain; Saint Gabriels Roman Cath Church 1991-; *office:* Saint Joseph HS 145 Plainfield Rd Metuchen NJ 08840*

MADDEN, KATHLEEN J. (RAYMOND), Retired Teacher; *b:* Manchester, NH; *m:* Edward J.; *c:* Kathleen I., Thomas, Sheryl Madden Estrada, David, Kenneth; *ed:* Boston St Coll (BSEd) K-8 Ed 1967; Attnd Boston Coll, Univ of AK, Univ of NH; *cr:* Elem Schls 4-6 Grd Tchr 1967-90; MS 6 Grd Lang Arts Tchr 1990-94; *ai:* NOW Schl; NEA 1967-; MA Tchrs Assn 1967-, Convention Del 1970; Westwood Tchrs Assn 1967-, Past VP, Exec Bd, Sec; Presentor at NEA Convention 1993 Lang Arts.*

MADDEN, MARJORIE E., Reading Coord of Basic Skills; *b:* Houston, TX; *m:* Michael Paul; *c:* Michael, Melissa, Lisa, Christopher, David; *ed:* Coll of William & Mary (BA) Elem Ed 1968; Glassboro St Coll (MA) Rdng 1975; Univ of PA Working on PHD; *cr:* Lee Hall Schl 2d Grd Tchr 1968-69; Cntrl Schl 4th Grd Tchr 1969-72; Elizabeth Haddon 2nd Grd Tchr 1972-75; Camden Cty Coll Rdng, Writing Instr 1985-88; Rowan Coll of NJ Rdng Courses to Elem Ed Majors, Basic Skills 1988-; *ai:* Mentor; EOF Fac Liason Prgm; AFT 1988-; NJEA 1996; IRA 1996; Coll Rdng Lang Assoc 1996; NJ Rdng Assoc 1990-, VP; All Coll Grant for Learning Comm 1995-; NJRA Newsletter; Pub Articles.

MADDEN, PATRICIA ANNE, 4th Grade Teacher; *b:* Philadephia, PA; *ed:* Chestnut Hill Coll (BS) Ed 1980; Beaver Coll (MED) Ed 1989; *cr:* St Rose Schl 4th Grd Tchr 1980-86; St Hugh Schl 6th Grd Tchr 1986-90; Norwood-Fontbonne Acad Prin 1990-94; Blessed Katharine Drexel Schl 4th Grd Tchr 1994-95; Corpus Christi Schl 4th Grd Tchr 1995-; *ai:* Schl Outreach, Svc Character Ed Comm Dir; NCEA 1980-; Sisters of St Joseph Justice Commission 1990-; Distinguished Cath Edctr, Who's Who in Amer Colls 1989; *home:* 900 Sumneytown Pk Lansdale PA 19446

MADDOX, CHARLES E., Mathematics Teacher; *b:* Washington, DC; *m:* Dawn L. Withers; *c:* Andrew, Michael; *ed:* Univ of MD (BS) Math, PE 1970; 45 Addl Hrs Ed; *cr:* Walter Mill Jr HS PE Tchr 1970-75, Elem PE 1975-85; Largo HS Math Tchr 1985-; *ai:* Ftbl Coach Walter Mill Jr 1970-75, Crossland HS 1977; NA, NSTA, PGCEA 1970-; PE Hnr Frat; Pub Poet; Cmptr Enrichment Developer; *office:* Largo HS 505 Largo Rd Upper Marlboro MD 20774*

MADDOX-HAFER, MARJORIE, Associate Professor of English; *b:* Columbus, OH; *m:* Gary Hafer; *ed:* Wheaton Coll (BA) Eng 1981; Univ of Louisville (MA) Eng With Creative Thesis 1985; Cornell Univ (MFA) Creative Writing & Poetry 1989; *cr:* Univ of Louisville Eng Instr 1982-85; The Cobb Group Ed 1984-86; Cornell Univ Eng Instr 1987-89; Lock Haven Univ Assoc Prof of Eng 1990-; *ai:* Rdng Series Coord; Lit Journal Adv; Univ Comms; Sigma Tau Delta, Adv; AWP, MLA 1985-; United Luth Church 1990-; Saint James Episcopal Church 1995-; Sandstone Natl Book Awd Winner 1994; Bread Loaf Scholar; VA Ctr for Creative Arts Fellow; Painted Bride Quarterly Chapbook Winner; Over 200 Poetry & Fiction Publications in Natl Lit Journals; Seattle Reviews Bentley Prize for Poetry; Acad of Amer Poets Prize; PA Grant for Poetry; Cornells Chasen Awd for Poetry; *office:* Lock Haven Univ Dept Of Hpe Lock Haven PA 17745

MADE, VIENA CEBALLOS, Spanish Teacher; *b:* Santo Domingo, Dominican Rpblc; *m:* Fausto; *c:* Leybin, Thania, Jose; *ed:* Lehman Coll (BA) Span 1993; Hunter Coll (MA) Span Pending Yr; *cr:* Lehman HS Span Tchr 1993-; *ai:* AATSP 1994-; *home:* 2049 Watson Ave Bronx NY 10472

MADER, DOUGLAS PAUL, Mathematics Teacher; *b:* Celina, OH; *ed:* Thomas More Coll (BA) Math 1989; 35 Hrs Schl Admin Univ of Dayton; *cr:* Villa Madonna Acad Tchr, Ath Dir 1988-90; Celina City Schls Math Tchr 1992-; *ai:* Head Vlybl Coach; NEA, CEA 1992-; *office:* Celina City Schls 715 E Wayne St Celina OH 45822*

MADERIA, THOMAS JOSEPH,SR., Guidance Cnslr & Ftbl Coach; *b:* Johnstown, PA; *m:* Jennifer C. Lusardi; *c:* Thomas Joseph III, Taylor Anne; *ed:* Mount Union Coll (BA) Phys Ed & His 1980; WV Univ (MS) Sports & Ed Admin 1988; *cr:* St Edwards HS Asst Ftbl & His Tchr 1980-81; Mount Union Coll Asst Ftbl Coach & PE Instr 1982-85; West Virginia Univ Grad Asst Ftbl Coach 1986-88; US Naval Acad Asst Ftbl Coach & PE Instr 1989-91; Holy Cross HS Guidance Cnslr 1992-; *ai:* Ftbl Head Coach; Track Asst Coach; Amer Ftbl Coaches Assn 1982-; Burlington Cty Times Coach of Yr 1992; Philadelphia Inquirer Coach of Yr 1992; Trenton Times Coach Of Yr 1994; *office:* Holy Cross HS 5035 Route 130 Delran NJ 08075

MADISON, CHRISTINE M., Biology & General Science Tchr; *b:* Johnstown, PA; *m:* Brian G.; *ed:* Univ of Pittsburg at Johnstown (BS) Bio, Sci Ed 1989; *cr:* Ferndale Area Sci Tchr 1990-; *ai:* Math, Sci Dept Chprsn; Scholastic Quiz Acad Team Coach; NEA, PSEA, FAEA 1990-; *office:* Ferndale Area HS 600 Harlan Ave Johnstown PA 15905

MADISON, ELLEN L., English Teacher; *b:* Westerly, RI; *ed:* RI Coll (BA) Eng 1967; NY Univ (MA) Eng 1969; Univ of RI (PHD) Eng 1986; Attnd UCONN, Univ of MS, St Univ of NY; *cr:* Mystic Jr HS Eng Tchr 1969-70; Ledyard HS Eng Tchr 1970-; *ai:* NHS Adv; Discipline Comm Tchrs; LEA 1969-, Sec, Alternate for Tchr of Yr; NEA, CEA 1969-; Westerly Pub Lib 1990-, Bd of Trustees, Sec, VP, Pres; Bed & Breakfasts of Mystic Coast & Cntry 1993-, Parliamentarian; South Cty RI Bed & Breakfasts; Woody Hill Bed & Breakfast 1973-, Owner, Operator; South Cty Tourism Outstanding Bed & Breakfast; Several Articles on Bed & Breakfasts Pub; Certified Food Handler, Mentor & Cooperating Tchr; *home:* 149 S Woody Hill Rd Westerly RI 02891*

MADONIA, ANTHONY JOSEPH, Spanish Teacher; *b:* Rome, NY; *m:* Anne Marie Nigro; *c:* Matthew; *ed:* St Univ at Albany (BA) Span 1971; Syracuse Univ (MS) Span 1977; *cr:* Onondaga Comm Coll Adjunct Span Instr 1980-; Macellus HS Span Tchr 1971-; *ai:* AFT 1974-; NY St Assn of Foreign Lang Tchrs 1972-; NY St Regents Comm in Span Consultant 1984-88 & Item Writer 1984-; *office:* Marcellus Sr H S Reed Pkwy Marcellus NY 13108

MADONNA, SUE SCHNEIDER, Physical Education Teacher; *b:* Neptune, NJ; *m:* Louis A. Jr.; *c:* Jeffrey; *ed:* Montclair St Coll (BS) PE 1968, (BS) Hlth 1968; *cr:* Tinton Falls MS PE Tchr 1968-; *ai:* Stu Cncl Co-Adv; Safety Patrol & Svc Squad Adv; Hall Patrol Co-Adv; Girls Track Coach; Fac Cncl; NEA, NJ Ed Assn 1968-; Tinton Falls Ed Assn 1968-, Bldg Rep; *office:* Tinton Falls MS 674 Tinton Ave Eatontown NJ 07724*

MADONNA, WILLIAM A., Horticulture & Biology Teacher; *b:* Providence, RI; *ed:* Univ of RI (BS) Horticulture, Bio 1968; Addl Credits in Bio from RI Coll; *cr:* Ferri MS Sci Tchr 1968-75; Johnston HS Horticulture, Bio, Gen Sci Tchr 1975-; *ai:* Teens for Life; AFT 1968-; *office:* Johnston Sr HS 345 Cherry Hill Rd Johnston RI 02910

MADORE, DAVID JOSEPH, Business Education Teacher; *b:* Van Buren, ME; *ed:* Univ of ME at Machias (BS) Bus Ed & Bus Admin 1977; 12 Credits in Cmptr Tech at Northern ME Tech Coll; 3 Credits in Introduction to Criminology at Univ of ME at Fort Kent; 3 Credits in Cmptr Tech for Educators at Casco Bay Coll; Critical Skills Inst at Univ of ME; *cr:* Peoples Heritage Bank Part-Time Teller 1973-; Van Buren Adult Ed Cmptr Keyboarding Tchr 1979-95; Van Buren Dist Scndry Schl Bus Ed Tchr 1977-; *ai:* Van Buren Dollars for Scholars Treas; Discipline, Recertification & Project Respect Comms; NEA 1977-; Bus Ed Assn of ME 1977-, Region A Recorder; Van Buren Ed Assn 1977-, Pres, Treas, Sec; ME Tchrs Assn 1977-; Saint Bruno-Saint Remi Bazaar 1978-, Treas; Van Buren Chamber of Commerce 1990-, Treas; Van Buren Budget Comm 1991-; Van Buren Centennial Comm 1981, Fund Raiser Chprsn; *office:* Van Buren Dist Secondary Schl 321 Main St Van Buren ME 04785

MADRACK, DEBORAH FIALKO, Third Grade Teacher; *b:* Pittston, PA; *ed:* Wilkes Univ (BA) Psych 1973; Masters Equivalency 1991; *cr:* Wyoming Area Schl 1st Grd Tchr 1973-74, 3rd Grd Tchr 1974-; *ai:* Act 178 Prof Dev Induction Comm; WAEA, PSEA, NEA 1973-; Wyo Area Credit Union 1975-, Exec Bd 1993-; Girls Scouts of Amer 1973-78, Brownie Ldr; Project Learn, Partnership Between Pub Schl Presenter 1991; *home:* 73 Willow St Plymouth PA 18651

MAELIA, LYNN JONES, Chemistry Professor; *b:* Wilkes-Barre, PA; *m:* William T.; *c:* William E., Thomas P.; *ed:* Wilkes Coll (BS) Chem 1980; SUNY at Stony Brook (PHD) Chem 1985; Brookhaven Natl Labs Post-Doctoral Position 1985; *cr:* Orange Cty Comm Coll Instr 1991-92; Penn St Cooperative Extension Instr 1990-92; Univ of Scranton Instr 1992-93; Mt St Mary Coll Asst Prof 1993-; *ai:* ACS Stu Affiliate Chptr Adv; Acad Stans & Fac Dev Comm Chair; Amer Chemical Soc 1980-; CUR 1993-; PTA 1990-; *office:* Mount Saint Mary Coll 330 Powell Ave Newburgh NY 12550

MAENZA, LEONARD FRANCIS, History Teacher; *b:* White Plains, NY; *ed:* Univ of Dayton (BS) Soc Stud 1969; Wright St Univ (MED) Soc Stud 1974; Advanced Placement Clinics at Butler Univ & Univ of Cincinnati; *cr:* Vandalia-Butler HS Soc Stud Tchr 1969-; *ai:* Soccer & Tennis Coach; Class & Jr Cncl on World Affairs Adv; NEA, OEA & VBEA 1969-; NCSS 1986-; Ctr for Tchng Resources MAZER Corp 1990-, Editorial Bd; Univ of Dayton Tchr of Yr Awd 1990; *office:* Vandalia-Butler HS 600 S Dixie Dr Vandalia OH 45377*

MAESTRANZI, PATRICIA LUKAS, 6th Grade Teacher; *b:* Morristown, NJ; *m:* John L.; *c:* Elizabeth, Stephen; *ed:* St Johns Univ (BA) Eng 1973; Northeastern Univ (MED) Rdng 1978; 3 Credit Hrs; 6 Post Grad Credits; *cr:* St Margarets Schl 5th Grd Tchr 1973-75; Woodbury MS Rdng Tchr 1976-91, 8th Grd Tchr 1991-93, 6th Grd Tchr 1993-; *ai:* Yrbk Adv; Prof Dev Comm Rep; NH Ed Assn 1976-; Delta Kappa Gamma Soc 1990-; Blanchard MS Parent Tchr Assn 1994-, Sec; Blanchard MS Schl Cncl 1994-, Rep; Presenter of New England League of Mid Schls Conf; *office:* Woodbury MS 206 Main St Salem NH 03079*

MAFFEI, STEPHANIE, Mathematics Teacher; *b:* Brooklyn, NY; *ed:* Binghamton Univ (BA) Math 1993, (MAT) Math Ed 1994; *cr:* Saint John Villa Acad Math Tchr 1994-; *ai:* NCTM 1994-; *office:* St John Villa Acad 26 Landis Ave Staten Island NY 10305

MAFFIA, GENNARO JOSEPH, Assoc Prof & Chem Eng Dept Chm; *b:* Brooklyn, NY; *m:* Nancy L.; *c:* Margaret, Katharine, Timothy; *ed:* Manhattan Coll (BCHE) Chemical Engineering 1972, (MCHE) Chemical Engineering 1973; NY Univ (MBA) Ec 1977; Dartmouth Coll (DE) Chemical Eng 1988; *cr:* Lummus Co Sr Engr 1973-79; Arco Chemical Co Tech Dev Mgr 1979-91; Widener Univ Assoc Prof & Chm 1992-; *ai:* Safety Officer; Promotion & Tenure, Grad Curr Comms; AICHE 1981-, Local Chm 1982-83; ACS 1981-; AAUP 1988-; ASEE 1992-; Jr Achvmt 1988-, Adv; CCD 1983-, Tchr; 6 Patents; 40 Tech Articles & Presentations; Contributions to 2 Books; 4 Industrial Grants; 2 Govt Grants; *office:* Widener Univ 1 University Pl Chester PA 19013*

MAFFIA, LUCY MENNONA, Retired Elementary Teacher; *b:* Long Island City, NY; *m:* Alfred John; *c:* Maria Mazurek, Michael; *ed:* St John's Univ (BS) Elem Ed 1958; *cr:* St Rita's Schl 5th Grd Tchr 1958-59; Cayuga Schl Sub Tchr 1967-70, 2nd, 4th-6th Grd Tchr 1970-91; *ai:* NYSTA, AFT 1970-; SRTA, WSRTA 1991-.

MAGALHAES, SUZANA JOAO, Medical Radiography Professor; *b:* Ludlow, MA; *m:* Luis; *c:* Stephanie Ann; *ed:* Springfield Tech Comm Coll (AS) Radiology Tech 1981; Cert Achvmt Mgmt Orientation Prgm; Conflict Mgmt; Introduction to Role of Clinical Instr; *cr:* Baystate Medical Ctr Staff Radiologic Technologist 1981-87, Sr Staff Radiologic Technologist OR 1987-88, Mammography Portable Tech 1988-91; Springfield Tech Comm Coll Part-Time Clinical Instr, Clinical Coord Prof 1991-; *ai:* Radiology Continue Ed, Research Comms; Stu Radiolgy Club Adv; MA Soc Radiography, Assn of Educators Radiologic Sci 1991-; *home:* 62 Truby St Granby MA 01033*

MAGARITY, BARBARA V., School Counselor; *b:* Philadelphia, PA; *c:* Jacqueline, Brad; *ed:* Temple Univ (BA) Psych 1978, (MED) Scndry Schl Cnslng 1980; Post-Grad Trng in Family Therapy; *cr:* Eisenhower Jr HS Schl Cnslr 1980; North Penn Jr HS Cnslr 1981-83; Montgomery Co Intermediate Unit Schl Cnslr 1983-86; North Penn HS Cnslr 1986-; *ai:* Team Mothers Support Group; NEA, PA Schl Cnslrs Assn 1980-; Montgomery Cty Cnslng Assn 1980-, Pres, Cnslr of Yr 1993; Homeless Projects; Korean Amer Assn Eng Tutor; Dev K-12 Comprehensive Dev Guid Curr; *office:* North Penn HS 1340 Valley Forge Rd Lansdale PA 19446

MAGEE, MICHAEL JOSEPH, MS Guidance Counselor & Coach; *b:* Rockville Centre, NY; *m:* Anuradha Sharma; *c:* Kali; *ed:* Hofstra Univ (BA) Librl Arts 1988, (MS) Schl Cnslng 1990; *cr:* Woodland MS Guid Cnslr 1990-, Coach 1989-; *ai:* 7th & 8th Grd Ftbl, 8th Grd Bsktbl & Var Lacrosse Coach.

MAGEE, MOLLIE PATRICK, Proficiency Skills Teacher; *b:* Manchester, KY; *m:* Mark Alan; *c:* Matthew; *ed:* Morehead St Univ (BA) Learning, Behavior Dis K-12, Elem Ed 1-8 1978; Wright St Univ (MA) Rdng Specialist K-12 1983; Cmptr Instruction Microsoft Word, Excel, Advanced Word; Time Mngmt; *cr:* Kitty Hawk Elem Schl 3-6, LD, Reg Tchr 1978-83; Menlo Park Elem Schl 1&6 Grd Tchr 1983-88; Weisenhorn MS 6-7 Grd Intervention Specialist 1988-89, 7 Grd Eng Tchr 1989-92; Studebaker MS 8th Grd Proficiency Skills Tchr 1992-; *ai:* Pro Musician; Chrstn Music Minister; Studebaker Stu Bible Study, Hnr Soc Adv; Renaissance Comm; Fac Cncl; Ginghamsburg United Meth Church 1985-; OH Environmental Ed Grant; Prof Sound Recording CD, Cassettes; Ed Writer Son Reign Ministries; *home:* 6919 Rushleigh Rd Englewood OH 45322*

MAGG, ROBERT, Head Coach; *b:* New York City, NY; *m:* Mary Polak; *c:* Alexander, Cynthia; *ed:* Polytechnic Univ (BS) Physics 1962; Univ of Santa Clara (MBA) Bus 1966; AT&T Mngmt Trng Prgm; *cr:* AT&T Rsrch Admin Dir 1978-82, Mgr 1982-84, Software Dev Dir 1984-89; *ai:* Pennsbury HS Mens Var Swimming Coach; Head Coach; Lower Makefield Swim Team Head Coach; Amer Swim Coaches Assn 1992-, USS Level 3; US Swimming Assn 1989-; North Andover YMCA Capital Budget Chm, Fundraiser; Boy Club, Coach, Achvmt Awd; *office:* Pennsbury Aquatic Club 948 Princess Dr Yardley PA 19067

MAGGI, KAREN CARMICK, Amer History & Government Tchr; *b:* Wilkes Barre, PA; *m:* James W.; *c:* Brian J., Mark J.; *ed:* West Chester St Univ (BA) Scndry Ed, Soc Stud 1974; SUNY at Stony Brook (MA) Lib Stud; *cr:* Islip HS 11th-12th Grd Soc Stud Tchr; Bayport-Blue Point Jr HS 7th-8th Grd Soc Stud Tchr; William Paca Jr HS 8th Grd Soc Stud Tchr; Bayport-Blue Point HS 11th-12th Grd Soc Stud Tchr; *ai:* Gen Org Adv; Schl Improvement, Renaissance Teams; NYSUT 1974-; *office:* Bayport Blue Point HS 200 Snedecor Ave Bayport NY 11705

MAGGIO, JO-ANN, Religion Teacher; *b:* Manhattan, NY; *ed:* St Josephs Coll (BA) Ed, Speech, Psych 1975; St Johns Univ (MS) Ed 1977; 33 Hrs Theology Seminary of Immaculate Conception; *cr:* Most Holy Trinity Elem Schl Religion, Soc Stud, Lang Arts Tchr 1977-82; St Charles Borromeo Religion, Soc Stud, Lang Arts Tchr 1982-94; Holy Trinity HS Frosh & Jr Religion Tchr 1984-; *ai:* Stdnt Cncl Moderator; Bowling, Badminton Coach; Chm Fac Advy Cncl; LFA 1984-; NYS Speech Assn 1975-; NCEA, Phi Delta Kappa 1977-; Eucharistic Minister 1977-; Campaign Local Assembly Woman 1991-; Lector 1970-; Assistantship; *office:* Holy Trinity HS 98 Cherry Ln Hicksville NY 11801

MAGGIO, JOSEPH PAUL, Mathematics Teacher; *b:* Butler, NJ; *m:* Katherine Brieger; *c:* Paul, Steven; *ed:* Rutgers Univ (BA) Math 1972; William Paterson Coll (MA) Ed 1981; *cr:* Warren Hill Regnl HS Math Tchr 1972-74; Prudential Insurance Co Insurance Statistician 1974-79; Vernon Twp HS Math Tchr 1979-; *ai:* Boys, Girls Head Tennis Coach; NEA, NJEA 1979-; Pine Island NY Recreation Comm 1985-, Dir; Sussex Cty Girls Tennis Coach of Yr 1993; *office:* Vernon Township HS PO Box 800 Vernon NJ 07462

MAGGIO, RAYMOND PATRICK, Religion Teacher; *b:* Baltimore, MD; *m:* LuAnn Steiger; *c:* Nicholas; *ed:* Univ of MD at Balto Cty (BA) Rel Stud 1974; Chrstn Bible Coll & Seminary (MS) Theology 1995; *cr:* Mt St Joseph HS Tchr, Coach, Ath Dir & Dept Chair 1974-, Tchr 1993-; *ai:* Mothers Club & Frosh Class Moderator; Var Bsktbl Asst Coach; NCEA 1974-; *office:* Mount St Joseph HS 4403 Frederick Ave Baltimore MD 21229

MAGGIO, WILLIAM CHARLES, Retired HS Art Teacher; *b:* Buffalo, NY; *m:* Carol A. Sole; *c:* Bill, Burt, Joe, John; *ed:* St Univ Coll at Buffalo (BS) Art Ed 1960; St Univ Coll at Buffalo (MS) Art Ed 1963; Post Grad Work in Supervision; *cr:* Wilson Schl Dist Art Tchr 1960-61; Buffalo Schls Art Tchr 1961-69; Grand Island HS Art Tchr 1969-95; Full Time Artist; *ai:* Yrbk Adv; Acting Dept Chm; GITA, AFT, NYSUT 1970-; AF of M 1955-; Gr Isl Jaycees, Outstanding Young Educator Awd 1972; Personal Art Work Exhibited Locally, Natl Competition; 1 Man Shows; Many Private Collections; Gr Isl Chamber of Commerce Citizen of Yr Awd 1987.

MAGGIORE, MARY ISTANISH, Family & Consumer Sci Tchr; *b:* Greensburg, PA; *m:* Nicholas A.; *c:* John, Michelle; *ed:* Indiana Univ of PA (BS) Home Ec 1970; 39 Grad Credits Ed, Home Ec Penn St Univ, Indiana Univ of PA, Seton Hill Coll; *cr:* Greater Latrobe Jr HS Home Ec Tchr 1972-90; Greater Latrobe Sr HS Family, Consumer Sci Tchr 1990-; Greater Latrobe Schl Dist Dept Head 1994-; *ai:* Wildcats for Kids; NEA, PSEA 1976-; Saint Vincent Coll Great Tchr Recognition Prgm 1991; Fac Recognition Awd 1987-88; *home:* 1249 Maywood Ln Greensburg PA 15601

MAGIER, THOMAS GEORGE, Language Arts & Amer His Tchr; *b:* Wadsworth, OH; *m:* Julie Anne Himes; *c:* Jacob, Nicole; *ed:* Bluffton Coll (BA) Eng, His 1976; 35 Hrs Post Grad; *cr:* Holgate Local Schls Tchr 1976-77; Buckeye Local Schls Tchr 1977-95; *ai:* Spelling Bee, Bookbowl Adv; Wrestling Asst; Cty Spelling Bee Judge; AFT 1993-; Local Sftbl Assn 1977-, Dir; St Jude's Rsrch Hosp Chprsn; Ride-for-Life Bike-a-Thon 10 Yrs; *office:* Buckeye Jr HS 3024 Columbia Rd Medina OH 44256

MAGIERA, JACQUELINE ARRIGENNA, Consultant Teacher; *b:* Rochester, NY; *m:* John Scott; *c:* Kellen James, Connor Patrick; *ed:* SUNY at Geneseo (BA) Elem Ed 1988, (MS) Spec Ed 1990; *cr:* York Cntrl Schl Elem, Spec Ed Tchr 1985-; *ai:* Jr, Sr Class Adv; St Lucy's Parish, Church Schl Tchr; *office:* York Central Schl PO Box 102 Rt 3 Retsof NY 14539

MAGIN, JOAN HELMAN, Social Studies Teacher; *b:* New York City, NY; *m:* Ed; *c:* Suzanne, Jonathan, Robert; *ed:* SUNY at Albany (BA) Soc Stud Ed 1975; Univ of MD (MA) Amer Stud 1977; *cr:* Northwestern HS Soc Stud Tchr 1976-77; Eleanor Roosevelt HS Soc Stud Tchr 1977-; *ai:* Helping Stdnts with Soc Sci, Museum Internships; NCSS; Girl Scouts 1992-, Troop Leader; *office:* Eleanor Roosevelt HS 7601 Hanover Pky Greenbelt MD 20770*

MAGINN, JOHN PATRICK, Mathematics Teacher; *b:* Indianapolis, IN; *m:* Jolinda McMahon; *c:* Christine Inskeep, Laurie Evans, Brian, Keith; *ed:* Univ of Cincinnati (BSEd) His & Govt 1968; Xavier Univ (MED) Guidance 1972; *cr:* Bridgetown Jr HS Math Tchr 1968-; *ai:* Talenttown Light Crew Asst Head; Peer Mediation Adv; OEA, NEA, Oak Hills Ed Assn 1968-; Oak Hills Educator of Yr 1992.

MAGLIETTO, TINA MARIE, Asst Prof of Criminal Justice; *b:* Buffalo, NY; *ed:* Erie Comm Coll (AAS) Criminal Justice 1979; Buffalo St Coll (BS) Criminal Justice 1981, (MS) Criminal Justice 1990; NYS Tchr Cert; NYS Certfd Gen Topics Security Guard Instr; Amer Red Cross CPR Certfd Instr; *cr:* Erie Comm Coll Campus Saftey Security 1982-91, Asst Prof 1989-; Niagara West Boces Instr 1991-; *ai:* Instr for 2 Yr Pub-Pvt Security Occupations; *home:* 107 Claremont Ave Buffalo NY 14222

MAGLIO, MARY BETH HETHERINGTON (EVANS), Second Grade Teacher; *b:* West Chester, PA; *m:* John Michael Jr.; *c:* Stephen Robert, Elizabeth Anne; *ed:* West Chester St Coll (BS) Elem 1973; Addl 36 Hrs Post Grad Masters Equivalency; *cr:* Coles Elem Schl 4th Grd Tchr 1973-74; Glen Acres Elem Schl Tchr 1974-91; Exton Elem Schl Tchr 1991-; *ai:* NEA 1973-; PSEA 1974-; WCAEA 1974-, Bldg Rep; Moms Club 1994-; *office:* Exton Elem Schl 829 Paoli Pike West Chester PA 19380

MAGLIONE, MARY, Pre K Teacher; *b:* Philadelphia, PA; *ed:* LaSalle Coll (BA) Psych 1981; 24 Credit Hrs Towards MA; *cr:* Holy Name Schl 1st Grd Tchr 1981-83; St Jerome Schl 1st Grd Tchr 1983-90, 7th Grd Tchr 1990-95, Pre K Tchr 1995-; *ai:* Cath Schls Week; Crisis Mgmt Comm; Leukemia & Amer Cancer Soc; Bone Marrow & Phessis Donor; Summer Schl Dir; NEA 1981-; St Jerome Summer Schl 1983-, Dir; Walkathon Comm 1987-; Stu Cncl Dir 1992-94; Eucharistic Minister 1990-; Mid Sts Comm; Holy Name Schl Rdng Asst Coord; Guest Speaker Alpha House; Parish Cookbook Coord; Leukemia Fund Raiser Dir 1996; *office:* St Jerome Schl 3031 Stamford St Philadelphia PA 19136*

MAGOWAN, JOY GLAZE, High School English Teacher; *b:* Chadron, NE; *c:* Marni; *ed:* Univ of NE (BS) Eng Ed 1970; AZ St Univ (MA) Eng 1984; IN Univ Writing; San Diego St Univ AVID Methodologies; U of CA at Berkeley Writing; Eng as Second Lang; *cr:* Fairbanks North Star Borough Eng As 2nd Lang Tchr 1980-83; AZ St Univ Eng Instr 1983-85; Baumholder Amer HS Eng & Eng as 2nd Lang Tchr 1985-92, 12th Grd Eng, AP & Hnrs Eng Tchr 1992-; Univ of MD Eng Instr 1986-; *ai:* NHS; British Lit 12th Grd Stud Trip; Schlsp Comm; SAT Preparation; NEA 1980-; Overseas Ed 1985-; *office:* Baumholder American HS Cmr 405 Box 1282 APO AE 09034*

MAGRAM, ELYSE CAREN (MADNICK), Mathematics Teacher; *b:* Brooklyn, NY; *m:* Eugene; *c:* Pamela Leanne, Lawrence Perry; *ed:* Queens Coll (BS) Math 1962, (MSE) Math Ed 1965; SUNY at Stony Brook (MS) Applied Math, OP Research 1994; Princeton Univ Fractals and Chaos Symposium; Rutgers Univ Discrete Math Leadership; *cr:* Martin Van Buren HS Math Tchr 2 Yrs; Springfield Gardens HS Math Tchr 3 Yrs, Acting Chm 2 Yrs; Smithtown HS Math Tchr 22 Yrs; *ai:* Math Team Coach; Curr Writer; Frequent Wkshp Giver; Question Writer for Suffolk Cty Meets; AMTNYS 1990-, Sr High Del; NCTM, Suffolk Cty Math Tchr 1990-; MAA 1993-; TX Instruments, Speaker at Natl Conf, Wkshp Ldr; NY St Tech Ed Network, Network Mentor; Tandy Scholars Awd; Tandy Scholars Hon Mention Awd; Suffolk Cty Math Tchrs Assn Outstanding Tchr; Pub in UFT; Pub 3 Times in Discrete Mathematics.

MAGRINO, JEAN N., 5th Grade Homeroom Teacher; *b:* Brooklyn, NY; *m:* John; *c:* Jeanmarie, Daniel, John Jr.; *ed:* Fordham Univ (BS) Early Chldhd 1963; Mt St Vincent Eng 2 Yrs; Post Grad Stud in Learning Disabilities; Catechist Formation Pgm; *cr:* Creative Play Group 4 Yr Olds Tchr 1971-74; St Augustine Kndgtn Tchr 1974-85, 3rd-6th Grd Tchr 1985-95, Lang Arts Tchr 5th-8th Gra 1995-; *ai:* Stu Cncl Moderator; Mid States Accreditation Steering Comm Person; Fed of Cath Tchrs 1974-; *office:* St Augustine Schl 114 S Main St New City NY 10956

MAGROGAN, HEATHER MICHELE, Guidance Counselor; *b:* Baltimore, MD; *ed:* Loyola Coll (BA) Psych 1994; Completed 33 Credit Hrs Towards Masters Degree in Clinical Psych; *cr:* Loyola Coll Resident Asst 1991-93; Inst of Notre Dame Guid Cnslr 1994-; *ai:* Chrldng Coach; Organize Ski Trip; Teach Stud Skills Course; *office:* Institute Of Notre Dame 901 N Aisquith St Baltimore MD 21202

MAGUIRE, JACK, English & Humanities Teacher; *b:* Philadelphia, PA; *m:* Kim Gower; *c:* Neal, Craig, Brendan, Meghan; *ed:* LaSalle Univ (BA) His & Eng 1969; St Josephs Univ (MS) Rdng 1991; 12 Hrs Grad Ed Marywood Coll; *cr:* Cardinal OHara HS Eng Dept 1969-1992, De 1989-1990; Upper Darby HS Eng Dept 1992-; *ai:* NEA 1992- Upper Darby HS Lansdowne Ave & School Ln Upper Darby PA 1

MAGUIRE, JAMES P., Guidance Counselor; *b:* Kearney, NJ; *m* Della Fera; *c:* Kelly, Patrick; *ed:* Jersey City St Coll (BA) Elem E Georgian Ct Coll (MA) Curr Planning & Supervision 1985; Personal Svcs Cert; NJ Prin Cert; *cr:* Walnut St Elem Schl 5th G 1977-78; Toms River South HS Basic Skills Tchr 1978-92; Toms Ri HS Guid Cnslr 1992-; *ai:* Former Girls Var Soccer & Strength Co Ed Assoc 1977-; NJ Girls Soccer Coach of the Yr 1982; *office:* Tom East Schl Raider Way Toms River NJ 08753

MAGUIRE, KATHLEEN THERESA, Assistant Pastor; *b:* Bric PA; *ed:* Immaculata Coll (BA) Elem 1978; Theology; St Charles Se *cr:* Parish Schls Sixth Grd Tchr 25 Yrs, Primary Grd Tchr 10 Yrs; *ai* Visiting; *home:* 45 Harrop Pl Trenton NJ 08618

MAGUIRE, KIM G., English Teacher; *b:* Lowell, MA; *m:* Jack; Ori, Jonathan Ori; *ed:* Shippensburg St Coll (BS) Eng & Comn Cabrini Coll (MS) Ed 1991; St Josephs Univ 30 Hrs toward Mast Admin; *cr:* Atlantic Richfield Co Mrktg Mgr 8 Yrs; Upper Darby Tchr 5 Yrs; *ai:* NHS Adv; NEA 1990-; *office:* Upper Darby HS Lansdowne Ave Upper Darby PA 19082

MAGUIRE, MARGARET BRANSFIELD, Second Grade Teac Philadelphia, PA; *m:* Michael J.; *c:* Jeanmarie, Sheilah Meg Immaculata Coll (BA) Eng, Ed 1969; *cr:* Our Lady of Vly Sc 1969-70; St Michael's Presch Tchr 1983-86; SS Philip & James Sc 1986-; *ai:* Art Coord; NCEA 1986-; IRA 1995-; Girl Scouts of Amer Ldr; *office:* SS Philip & James Schl Rt 30 & Ship Rd Exton PA 19

MAGUIRE, MICHAEL J., Latin Teacher; *b:* Boston, MA; *ed:* Univ (BA) Classical Lang, Lit 1993; Univ of MA at Boston M Boston Latin Acad Latin Tchr 1994-; *ai:* Drama Club Dir; Classic of NE 1993-; AFT 1994-; BSA 1996, Asst Scoutmaster.

MAGULAK, MARY JANE, Third Grade Teacher; *b:* Plainfield, Peter M. Jr.; *c:* Peter J.; *ed:* Univ of Bridgeport (BS) Elem Ed 19 Piscataway Twp Elem Ed 1968-; Grandview Schl, Grd 1-4 Tch Market Schl Grd 1-4 Tchr; Dwight D. Eisenhower Schl Grd 1-4 T Yrs; *ai:* Schl Pupil Assistance, Multicultural Celebration, Pc Comms; Piscataway Ed Assn 1968-, Former Fac Rep; Middlese Assn 1968-; NSEA, NEA 1970-; *office:* Dwight D Eisenhower El 360 Stelton Rd Piscataway NJ 08854

MAGYAR, SALLY FABER, Fifth Grade Teacher; *b:* Harrisburg, Stephen W.; *ed:* Shippensburg Univ (BS) Elem Ed 1964; Credits Masters Equivalency Degree in Elem Ed Penn St Univ, Millersvill Bloomsburg Univ; *cr:* Cameron Elem Schl 1st Grd Tchr 19 Harrisburg Elem Schl 1st Grd Tchr 1964-66, Rdng Tchr, Elem Sp 1966-67; Millersburg Area Schl 5th Grd Tchr 1973-; *ai:* Curr 1990-; Mentor Tchr 1995-; NEA, PSEA, MEA 1964-; Dauphin Do Club 1986-; Grace United Meth Church 1957-, Pastor Parish Rel Trustees, Pioneer Club Ldr; Outstdng Elem Tchrs of Amer 1973; Lenkerville Elem Schl S Market St Millersburg PA 17061

MAGYAR, VINCENT J., History & Sociology Teacher; *b:* Beth PA; *m:* Patricia Consorto; *c:* Christine, Vincent Jr., Andrew; *ed:* PA S (BS) Scndry Ed 1968; West Chester Univ (MA) His 1976; 40 Pos Credits; *cr:* Charles H. Boehm HS US His Tchr, Dept Chair 19 Medill Bair HS US His Tchr 1990-93; Pennsbury HS AP US His, Soc Tchr 1993-; *ai:* Pennsbury Ed Assn 1968-, VP; PA St Ed Assn 1968 NEA 1968-, Del; NCSS 1976-; Pennsbury Ath Assn 1988-, Coach; Pennsbury HS 705 Hood Blvd Fairless Hills PA 19030

MAHADY, PATRICIA ANNE, Fifth Grade Teacher; *b:* Buffalo, N Martin F.; *c:* Craig, Michael, Timothy; *ed:* Buffalo St Coll (BSEd Ed 1972, (MSEd) Elem Ed 1976; *cr:* Union East Elem Schl First Gr 1972-74; Drake Schl Fifth Grd Tchr 1985-; *ai:* Math, Soc Stud C AFT, North Tonawanda United Tchrs 1985-.

MAHAJAN, Y. LAL, Assoc Prof of Econ & Fin; *b:* India; *m:* Pir Tony, Jeffrey, David, Paul; *ed:* Univ of Chicago (MA) Econ 1971; No IL Univ (PHD) Econ 1976; Rutgers Univ (PHD) Fin 1995; *cr:* Northe Univ Asst Prof 1976-79; Monmouth Univ Assoc Prof 1979-; *ai:* Asst Soccer Club; AEA 1976-; ASA, AEA 1978-; JSCI 1980-; Articles *office:* Monmouth Univ Cedar & Norwood Ave West Long Bran 07764

MAHALA, MICHAEL J.,JR., US Cultures Teacher; *b:* Coldale, F Paula Marie Polambo; *c:* Theresa, Matthew, Timothy; *ed:* Bloomsb Univ (BS) Scndry Ed, Soc Stud 1973; Kutztown St Univ (MEd) Ed Life Underwriting Trng Cncl Grad 1975; *cr:* Southern Lehigh HS So Tchr 1975-; *ai:* Head Rifle Coach 1988-; JV Sftbl Coach 1980-; SLEA 1976-; Natl Rifel Assn 1982-, Life Mem; Ducks Unlimited Natl Wildlife Fed 1984-, Life Mem; *office:* Southern Lehigh HS 5775 St Center Valley PA 18036

MAHALSKY, BRADLEY P., Environmental Teacher; *b:* Taylor, PA Mansfield St Coll (BS) Scndry Ed, His 1971, (BS) Scndry Ed, Bio Univ of Scranton (MS) Scndry Schl Admin 1978; *cr:* WY Area MS Sci Tchr 1976-79; WY Area HS BSCS Bio, Environmental Sci 1979-90; WY Area Scndry Ctr Chm of Sci Dept 1982-89, AP Bio, B Bio, Environ Sci Tchr 1990-93, Environmental Sci Tchr 1993-; *ai:* Raising Coord; WY Area Schl Dist Recyling Coord; PSEA, WAEA PSTA 1991-; West Pittson Park, Rec Bd 1975, Dir; Greater Pittston Waster Mngmt Bd 1985-; St Johns Lodge 1974-; West Pittson Fire Ambulance 1967-; PSTA Grant for Advvanced Sci Stud; Howard H Fnd Grant Molecular Bio, Neuroscience Stud; Co-Author EMF Cou Stud Spon by PA Power & Light; *office:* Wyoming Area Secondar Memorial Ave Exeter PA 18643*

MAHAN, NANCY L., French Teacher; *b:* Natrona Heights, PA; *e* Union Coll (BA) Span, Fr 1973; Kent St Univ (MA) Fr 1976; *cr:* Ma HS Fr, Span Tchr 1976-; *ai:* NEA 1976-; Fulbright Exch Tchr to F 1987-88; *office:* Marietta HS 208 Davis Ave Marietta OH 45750

MAHAN, PATRICIA HORVATH, Sixth Grade Teacher; *b:* Cleve OH; *m:* Francis B.; *c:* Sarah L.; *ed:* Miami Univ (BS) Elem Ed Nazareth Coll (MS) Ed 1975; 52 Credit Hrs Above Masters Degre Ada & Lima OH Schls 1st & 4th Grd Tchr 1965-69; West Ave Schl 4 5th Grd Tchr 1969-83; Dudley Schl 3rd Grd Tchr 1983-89; Northside 3rd-5th Grd Tchr 1989-94; Martha Brown MS 6th Grd Tchr 1994- Comm & Schl Relations; Character Ed Task Force; AFT 1969-; NY 1969-; Fairport Ed Assoc 1969-, Bldg Rep, Comm Relations & S Comm; Rochester Alumnae of Gamma Phi Beta 1969-, Pres & T Province I Alumnae Svc Awd; Gamma Phi Beta Intnl 1992-, Provinc Dir; *office:* Martha Brown MS 665 Ayrault Rd Fairport NY 14450*

MAHANY, ROBERT JAMES, Business Education Teacher; *b:* Bu NY; *m:* Kathleen Flett; *c:* Robert D.; *ed:* Hartwick Coll (BA) Bus 1981; Canisius Coll (MS) Educl Admin 1992; *cr:* Lake Shore Cntrl Bus Ed Tchr 1987-; *ai:* Boys Var Soccer & Girls Var Track Coach; NS 1984-, Advanced Natl Diploma 1995; *office:* Lake Shore Cntrl Sr HS Beach Rd Angola NY 14220*

MAHEADY, LAWRENCE JOSEPH, Professor Dept of Educatio Wilkes-Barre, PA; *m:* Bethany Carlson; *c:* Jason Carlson, Joshua, Cor *ed:* King's Coll (BA) Psych 1974; Univ of West FL (MA) Schl Psych f Pittsburgh (PHD) Spec Ed 1981; *cr:* SUNY Coll at Fredonia Asst. of 1981-85, 1989-; MI St Univ Assoc Prof 1986-89; *ai:* Fac Adv Delta Pi; Fac Advs Co-Ed Vlybl; Chair Prgm Planning, vement of Undergraduate Instruction Comms; Fac Cncl; Planning & ; Steering Comm Educl Reform; CEC 1978-; Assn for Behavior sis 1981-, Research Awds 1984-86; Tchr Ed Division 1989-; Dunkirk oc 1983-, VP, Bd of Dirs; Parish Cncl 1991-; 52 Journal Pubs; ing Stdnts with Behavior Disorders Textbook; 5 Chapters in Edited oks; 6 Funded Educl Grants; *office:* S U N Y Coll At Fredonia ia NY 14063*

ER, ANTINA STORNELLI, Homeroom & Science Teacher; *b:* , NY; *m:* Robert James; *c:* Brendan; *ed:* SUNY at Buffalo (BS) Sci 1969; Iona Coll (MS) Bio 1978; Syracuse Univ 6 Credit Hrs in gy 1970; Purdue Univ 24 Credit Hrs in Bio 1973; *cr:* Solvay HS Gen Bio Tchr 1969-71; St Lawrence Schl 6th-8th Grd Gen Sci Tchr 73; Sacred Heart Bio & Advanced Sr Bio Tchr 1973-75; Blindbrook -4th Grd Sci Enrichment Tchr 1975-76; St Gabriel 6th-8th Grd Sci 989-; *ai:* Sr Cnslr Chappaqua Town Camp; Co-Founder of Parent rt for Gifted Ed; Adv to Acad Olympics Team; Sci Fair Coord; Regnl ir Judge; NSTA 1990-; NEA; Selected as an Inspirational Tchr by r Stdnts Awded from Fordham Prepatory Acad 1995; Mini Grant for on Ed from Dist Archdiocese of NY; *office:* St Gabriel Schl 590 W St Bronx NY 10463

ER, JEANNE ELIZABETH, Religious Education Teacher; *b:* t, MI; *ed:* John Carroll Univ (BA) Rel Stud 1981; Comm ention, Drug & ALcohol Prevention; Intervention-Adelphi, Drug & ol Prevention, DARE; *cr:* St Vincent-St Mary HS Rel Ed Tchr 84; St Thomas Aquinas HS Rel Ed Tchr 1985-; *ai:* Soph Class Adv; Comm; Spon Drama, Ski Club; NCEA 1985-; Tchr of Month 1991, Toys for Tots, Vietnam Vets Class Project; *office:* Saint Thomas as HS 2121 Reno Dr Louisville OH 44641

ER, JUDITH ADAMS, AP Coll Engl Tchr & Dept Chrmn; *b:* n, NY; *m:* Edward T.; *c:* Alison K. Murphy; *ed:* Coll of Saint Rose Eng 1971, SUNY at New Paltz (MS) Ed 1977; *cr:* Our Lady of es HS 9-12th Grd Eng Tchr, Dean of Women 1994-; *ai:* Yrbk Adv; line Advy Bd; Tonw of Fishkill NY Parks Comm 1989-, Comm Mem; Our Lady-Lourdes HS 29 N Hamilton St Poughkeepsie NY 12601

ER, JUDITH KEENAN, Science Teacher; *b:* Passaic, NJ; *m:* John Susan; *ed:* Mount Saint Agnes Coll (BA) Bio, Scndry Ed 1968; City f NY (MS) ED 1990; 60 Addl Grad Hrs Sci, Ed; *cr:* Fulton HS Sci 968-70; Pearl River MS Sci Tchr 1970-83; Pearl River HS Sci Tchr ; *ai:* Dist Rdng Comm; AFT, NY St United Tchrs 1970-; Pearl River Assn 1970-, Rep; NABT 1985-; Sci Tchrs Assn NY 1983-; *office:* River HS 275 E Central Ave Pearl River NY 10965

ER, MARGARET K., Life Science Teacher; *b:* Cincinnati, OH; *ed:* n Coll (BS) Bio 1967; Ball St Univ (MAE) Bio Ed 1973; *cr:* Stephen lin HS Sci Dept Chair & Life Sci Tchr 1968-77; Our Lady of Angels ci Dept Chair & Life Sci Tchr 1980-84; Roger Bacon HS Sci Dept & Life Sci Tchr 1985-; *office:* Roger Bacon HS 4320 Vine St nnati OH 45217

ER, PAUL L., Chemistry & Earth Science Tchr; *b:* Albany, NY; *m:* Klaja; *c:* Emily, Adam; *ed:* Plattsburgh St NY (BS Chemical Ed Albany St NY (MS) Chemical Ed 1981; 30 Addl Credit Hrs; 3 Credit Coll of St Rose; 4 Credit Hrs PA St Univ; 3 Credit Hrs Union Coll; 3 t Hrs Oneonta St; *cr:* Maple Hill HS Sci Tchr 1975-; *ai:* Ski Club 7th-8th Grd Sftbl Coach; STANYS 1989-; AFT, NYSUT 1975-; u Bsbl Assn 1987-94, Sec; BSA 1993-, Troop Comm; Amer Museum al His 1991-; *office:* Maple Hill HS 1216 Maple Hill Rd Castleton On o NY 12033

ER, R. WILLIAM, 6th Grade Math Teacher; *b:* Flushing, NY; *m:* e; *c:* Kelly, Steve, Jeff; *ed:* St Univ of NY at Fredonia (BA) Ed 1970, Ed 1974; 9 Credit Hrs in Admin; *cr:* Westfield Acad & Central Schl rd General Tchr 1970-80, 5th Grd Math Tchr 1980-89, 6th Grd Math 1989-; *ai:* Babe Ruth Bsbl Coach; Chautauqua Babe Ruth 14-15 tar Coach; Westfield Tchrs Assn 1970-; NEA-NY 1970-; Chautauqua Fine Chiefs Assn 1981-; SWNY Vil Firemans' Assn 1983-; Brocton Co 1976-92, Chief 1983-84; Brocton Portland L L 1982-89, VP 1989; tauqua Babe Ruth League VP 1992-; Elected Village of Brocton ee 1988; Re-Elected Trustee 1990, 1992; *office:* Westfield Acad & al Schl E Main St Westfield NY 14787

ER, ROBERT E., 4th Grade Teacher; *b:* Camden, NJ; *m:* Rose er; *c:* Kelly, Randy; *ed:* Temple Univ (BS) Elem Ed 1972; Masters 30 Credits Elem Ed & Admin at Glassboro; *cr:* Cinnaminson 3rd-8th Grd 24 Yrs; Title I Dir & Summer Schl Tchr 1974-82; *ai:* Started MS Track Written Numerous Curr Guides; Textbook Selection Comm; NEA -; NJEA 1972-; CEA 1972-; NJ Governors Tchr Recognition Awd; *e:* Cinnaminson School Dist Bd of Ed Rt 130 Cinnaminson NJ 08077

ILER, PHILIP HENRY, Mathematics & Cmpter Sci Prof; *b:* Boston, *m:* Marguerite Aline St Jean; *ed:* Assumption Coll (BA) Modern s 1968; Univ of FL (MAT) Math 1976; Univ of MA at Lowell 18 Grad its Cmptr Sci; *cr:* US Navy Electronic Simulators 1968-72; Henry CC Instr 1977-81; Public Svc of NH Programmer 1981-82; Middlesex Prof 1982-; *ai:* Campus Chapter of Fac Union Pres; MAA 1977-; ATYC 1978-; NCTM 1988-; Author 5 Math Texts; *office:* Middlesex m Coll Springs Road Bedford MA 01730*

HON, COLLEEN COCHRANE, Chairperson & Tchr of Classics; *b:* eland, OH; *m:* Edward James; *c:* David Edward, Michael James; *ed:* St Univ (BS) Speech, Eng, Latin 1958; Cleveland St Univ (MED) 1979; *cr:* Parma Sr HS Eng, Latin Tchr 1958-61; Vly Forge HS -time Eng Tchr 196-70; Midpark HS Eng, Latin Tchr 1978-78; St tius HS Eng, Latin Tchr 1978-, Classics Chprsn 1985-; *ai:* Latin ring Prgm Moderator; Grd Schl Latin Prgm Coord; Midwest Classical 1979-, Hildesheim Awd to Dept; OH Ed Assn, Cleveland Diocesan Lang 1979-; *office:* Saint Ignatius H S 1911 W 30th St Cleveland OH 3*

HON, MARY ENDERS, K-6th Grd Art Teacher; *b:* Middlesex, NJ; *m:* ert F.; *ed:* Kean Coll (BA) Fine Art Ed 1970; William Paterson Coll) Ceramics 1989; 30 Credits 1990-91; Old Church Cultural Ctr 1993; J. Honiss Schl Art Tchr 1970-; *ai:* Multi Cultural Comm; NJEA, PTA 0-; AENJ 1980-; Artist's Network 1992-; DEA 1970-, Fac Rep; sades Guild of Spinners, Weavers 1995-; Art Work Pictured NJ thly Magazine 1978, Newark Museum 1995; Invitational Exhibits; ls for Hungry 1993; *office:* Lovell J Honiss Schl Depew St Dumont NJ 28*

HON, ROBERT JOSEPH,JR., Science Teacher; *b:* Baltimore, MD; Loyola Coll (BS) Bio 1975; Attnd Towson St Univ, Univ of ME, muda Biological Station Rsrch; *cr:* Mc Donogh Schl Upper Schl Sci r 1976-; *ai:* Ftbl Coach; Martial Art Club; 9th Grd Adv; Schlsp Review, & Conduct Comms; SAT Test Ctr Supvr; NSTA, NABT, MABT 1985-; *e:* Mc Donogh Schl PO Box 380 8600 Mc Donogh Rd Owings Mills 21117

HONEY, GERALDINE WILLIAMSON, Eng Tchr & Tech Theatre ; *b:* Long Branch, NJ; *m:* John; *c:* Nicole L., Laura A. Gail E.; *ed:* gner Coll (BA) Speech, Theatre, Eng 1979; Guid, Cnslng, Cmptr rses; *cr:* Middletown HS North Tchr, Tech Dir 1981-; *ai:* Thespian Soc Adv; Tech Dir Fall Play; Renaissance Comm Fair; Spring Musical; Childrens Theatre; MTEA 1981-, Bldg Rep; NJEA 1981-; STANJ 1989-, Governors Tchr of Yr 1994; Intnl Renaissance Fair Consortium Grant; Governors Recg Awd 1989-90; *office:* Middletown HS North 63 Tindall Rd Middletown NJ 07748

MAHONEY, HELEN SCHWARTZ, 7th & 8th Grade English Tchr; *b:* NYC, NY; *m:* W. Bryan; *ed:* Aurora Coll (BS) Bio 1965; Attnd Northern IL Univ, Cntrl CT St Coll; *cr:* Oswego Jr HS 7th Grd Eng Tchr 1965-69; John Winthrop MS 7th, 8th Grd Eng Tchr 1969-; *ai:* IM Coach; NEA, CEA, Local Regnl Dist #4 Tchrs Assn 1969-; Tchr of Yr 1984; *office:* John Winthrop MS Warsaw St Deep River CT 06417

MAHONEY, JOSEPH FRANCIS, Math Teacher; *b:* Rockville Center, NY; *ed:* Ithaca Coll (BA) Math 1993; 18 Credit Hrs at Western CT St Univ; Expected MA Scndry Curr; *cr:* Mahopac HS Math Tchr 1993-; *ai:* Head Var Wrestling, Head Jr Var Lacrosse Coach; NCTM 1992-; NYSUT 1993-; *office:* Mahopac HS 421 Baldwin Place Rd Mahopac NY 10541

MAHONEY, LYNDA RADULICH, Guidance Counselor; *b:* Jersey City, NJ; *m:* Harold J. III; *c:* Brian, Alison, Scott, David; *ed:* Jersey City St Coll (BA) Speech Correction 1973, (MA) Counseling 1990; K-12th Grd Eng Cert; *cr:* St Michael HS Eng Tchr 1974-76; James J. Ferris HS Eng Tchr 1976-96; Dickinson HS Guidance Cnslr 1996-; *ai:* Yrbk, Literary Magazine, Class, Sr Prom Adv; NEA, NJEA, JCEA 1976-; North Shore League 1993-, Sec 1993-95, Pres 1995-97; 1995 Tchr of Yr Recognition Prgm St, Cty Candidate; *office:* William Dickinson HS 2 Palisade Ave Jersey City NJ 07306

MAHONEY, MARY HAWES, Teacher & Literature Comm Chm; *b:* Boston, MA; *c:* Brendan, Stacy, Brian; *ed:* Boston Coll (BA) Ed 1968, (MED) Curr & Instruction 1994; *cr:* Ephraim Curtis MS Tchr 15 Yrs; Fowler Jr HS Tchr 1 Yr; *ai:* Soccer Coach; Schl Cncl Elected Mem; Staff Courses Prof Developer; Presenter at New England League of MS Conf; MTA & NEA 1981-; Sudbury Ed Assn 1981-, Exec Bd; NCTE Conf Recorder; 2 Grants to Dev Gender Curr & Sexual Harassment Curr; Piloted NEA Hurting or Flirting Curr; *office:* Ephraim Curtis MS 12 Pratts Mill Rd Sudbury MA 01776

MAHONEY, MARYKAY ANNE, Assoc Prof of English Dept; *b:* Pittsfield, MA; *ed:* Coll of St Rose (BA) Eng 1971; Boston Coll (MA) Eng 1973; Univ of KS (PHD) Eng 1983; *cr:* Boston Coll Tchng Fellow 1971-73; Wayne St Coll Instr 1979-81; Univ of KS Grad Tchng Asst 1973-79, 1981-83; U MA at Boston Adj Lecturer 1983-88; Boston Coll Adj Lecturer 1984-86; Merrimack Coll Asst Prof, Assoc Prof 1987-; *ai:* AAUP 1990-, Ofcr, St Conf Exec Comm; Articles Pub; *office:* Merrimack Coll 315 Turnpike St North Andover MA 01845

MAHONEY, MICHAEL EDWARD, English Teacher; *b:* New York, NY; *m:* Janet Minges; *c:* Brian, Darren; *ed:* Fordham Univ (BA) Eng Lit 1971; CUNY Lehman Coll (MA) Eng 1977; SUNY at New Paltz (CAS) Ed Admin 1985; *cr:* Walter Panas HS Eng Tchr 1971-, Project Images Dir 1985-91; Westchester Comm Coll Adjunct Prof 1986; Lakeland Schl Dist Summer Schl Prin 1987-90; Pale Univ Instr 1988-; *ai:* Project Turnkey Staff Dev Founding Mem; AFT 1971-, Bldg Rep; NYS Eng Cncl 1980-, Mem; ASCD, NCTE 1985-, Mem; Mahopac Sports Assn 1981-86, Coach; NY St Eng Cncl Tchr of Excl 1990; Zenith Data Corp Master of Innovation Awd 1992; Article Pub 1991; *office:* Walter Panas HS 300 Croton Ave Cortlandt Manor NY 10566*

MAHONEY, MICHAEL JOSEPH, 8th Grade English Teacher; *b:* Boston, MA; *m:* Dawn M. Mead; *c:* Sam R.; *ed:* Boston Coll (BA) MS Ed 1990; 45 Addl Credit Hrs Amer Lit Framingham St Coll; *cr:* Pennichuk Jr High 8th Grd Eng Tchr 1991-; *ai:* Nashua HS JV Bsbl Coach; Head Vlybl Coach; AFT 1992-; NEA 1991-; Mem Weymouth Youth Cncl 1984-86; Received Commendation from Spec Needs Dept Coord 1994; *office:* Pennichuk Jr HS 207 Manchester St Nashua NH 03060

MAHONY, ELIZABETH, High School Mathematics Tchr; *b:* New York, NY; *m:* Michael; *c:* Lorraine, John; *ed:* Herbert H Lehman Coll (BA) Math-Summa Cum Laude 1975; IN Univ (MA) Math 1979; Post Grad Stud; *cr:* IBM APL Programmer 1979-81; Archbishop Stepinac HS Math Tchr 1981-89; Rye Neck HS Math Tchr 1989-; *ai:* REEF Club & Math Club Adv; Asst Jr & Sr Class Adv; NY Chptr of Phi Beta Kappa 1975-; NCTM 1981-; MAA 1989-; PT SA & Readers Digest Grants for Work with Graphing Calculators; Outstdng Tchr Recognition From Tufts Univ, Kohl Ed Fndtn; *office:* Rye Neck HS 300 Hornidge Rd Mamaroneck NY 10543*

MAHOSKY, HENRY J.,JR., Science Teacher; *b:* Beaver Falls, PA; *m:* Nancy Lynne Melani; *ed:* Geneva Coll (BS) Physics 1971; Slippery Rock St Coll (MED) Physics 1975; Tech Electronics Allegheny Tech Inst 1965; Harvard Project Physics St Univ Coll of Arts & Sci 1972; Enviro Sci Penn St 1975; Attnd Univ of Pittsburgh 1978, IN Univ of PA 1987; *cr:* US Navy Weapons Control Technician 1966-69; Duquesne Light Tour Guide at Shipping Port 1970; New Brighton Area Schls Tchr 1971-; *ai:* Cmptr Club Adv; Boys Tennis Coach; HS Physics Tea Assn 1985-; Independence Marsh Cncl 1995-, Bd; Intnl Alliance of Theatrical & Stage Employees 1969-, Sec; Beaver Co Conservation Dist 1974-, Conservation Edctr of Yr 1978; Pittsburgh Hunting & Fishing Club 1990-, Sec; FCC Lic; NSF Grants for PSSC Physics, Cmptr Interfacing, Cmptr Tech, Environmental Ed; *office:* New Brighton Area Sr HS 3200 43rd St New Brighton PA 15066*

MAHOSKY, NANCY MELANI, Math, Cmptr Tchr & Coord; *b:* Pittsburgh, PA; *m:* Henry J. Jr.; *ed:* IN Univ of PA (BS) Math 1973; Duquesne Univ (MS) Scndry Ed 1977; *cr:* Blackhawk HS Tchr 1973-; *ai:* Cmptr Room Mgr; Cmptr Club, Young Women's Tech Club Spon; NEA 1973-; Natl Sci Fnd Grant 1986; Cmptr Equity Expert Project Grant 1991; Nom for PA Excl in Math Tchng Awd, KDKA Thanks for Tchrs Awd; *office:* Blackhawk H S 500 Blackhawk Rd Beaver Falls PA 15010

MAHTESIAN, VALERIE ANN, Computer Teacher; *b:* Brockton, MA; *m:* Kenneth; *c:* Cassandra; *ed:* Bridgewater St Coll (BS) Cmptr Sci 1982; Cambridge Coll (MS) Ed 1994; 15 Grad Credits at Fitchburg St Coll; *cr:* Southeastern Tech Dental Asst 1980-81; Cmptr Options Inc Programmer 1982-85; Silver Lake HS Tchr 1985-; *ai:* March Carnival Adv 1988-; Sr Class Adv 1987-94; Stu Cncl Adv 1988; Yrbk Adv 1986-87; NEA, PCEA, MTA 1985-; *office:* Silver Lake Reg HS-Kingston 132 Pembroke St Kingston MA 02364

MAHUNIK, PETER WILLIAM, Business Teacher & Chair; *b:* Auburn, NY; *ed:* Cayuga Comm Coll (AS) Bus Admin 1986; SUNY at Oswego (BS) Voc Tech Ed 1990, (MS) Voc Tech Ed 1995; *cr:* Otselic Vly Cntrl Schl Bus Tchr & Chair 1990-; *ai:* JV Bsktbl Coach 1990-92; Var Soccer Coach 1990-93; Var Sftbl Coach 1992; Stu Cncl Adv 1992-; Ski Club Adv 1995-; Class of 1996 Adv; NYSAT 1990-; NASAA 1992-; Polish Falcons of Amer 1980-; Amer Legion Post 973 1992-, Assoc Mem; Yrbk Dedication 1994; *office:* Otselic Vly Cntrl Schl Maple Ave PO Box 161 South Otselic NY 13155

MAIA, PHILIP C., Spanish Teacher & Track Coach; *b:* Porto Moniz, Portugal; *m:* Patricia Gaffney; *c:* Alyssa Rose; *ed:* Univ of MA at Lowell (BA) Ed, Span 1982, (MEd) Rdng, Lang 1983; *cr:* Lowell HS Foreign Lang Tchr, Coach 1984-; *ai:* Track, Cross-Cntry Coach; MA Track Coaches Assn, Mem; AFT, NEA, Mem; Parker Fnd Grant 1992; *office:* Lowell HS 50 Fr Morrissette Blvd Lowell MA 01852

MAIBERGER, MERRY PORTER, History & Science Teacher; *b:* New York City, NY; *m:* Donald P.; *c:* Todd P., Michele P., Patrick G.; *ed:* Newton Coll of Sacred Heart (BA) His 1966; LA St Univ at New Orleans (MA) His 1969; NY Univ 6 Addl Credits; Univ of MD Credits Toward PHD; *cr:* Cath Univ Admin Asst to Housing Dir 1968-69; Town & Cntry Day Schl Preschl Tchr 1969-70; Christ Episcopal Schl Upper Schl Coord, Seventh-Eighth His & Sci Instr 1985-; *ai:* Sci Fair Coord; 7th-8th Grd Speech Coach; Parents Cncl Rep 1988-92; Phi Alpha Theta 1965-; Assn Ind MD Schls 1991-; Christ Episcopal's Comm Svc for Natl Cathedral Flowr Mart 1995-, Chprsn; Master Tchrs E. E. Ford Fellow, Assn of Ind MD Schls 1995.

MAIELLA, DANIEL JOSEPH, Retired 4th-8th Grd Teacher; *b:* Newark, NJ; *m:* Gail; *c:* Randy, Scott De Vito, Melissa Cocuzza, Brett; *ed:* Rugers (BA) His, Pol Sci 1965; Montclair St (MA) Sociology 1980; *cr:* Allamuchy Elem Schl Tchr 1966-94; *ai:* Former Drama Club, Chess Club Adv; Sftbl, Bsktbl, Soccer Coach; Ofcl Sftbl, Bsktbl, Soccer; Stu Cncl Adv; Safety Patrol Adv; Washington DC Trip; Curr Writer; C ommencement Exercise Coord; AEA, NJEA, NEA, WCEA 1966-, Pres, Leg Rep, Negotiation Chm; Assn Supervision, Curr Dev 1989-; St of NJ Govt Tchr Recognition Awd 1988; Acad Advancement of Tchng & Mngmt; Instrl Theory Practice Prgm 1987; *home:* 2 Sunset Lake Rd Blairstown NJ 07825

MAIER, ANNE CECILIA, HS English Tchr & Dept Chprsn; *b:* Wilmington, DE; *m:* Robert G.; *c:* Julia, Christopher; *ed:* SUNY at Geneseo (BA) Eng 1975; SUNY at Brockport (MA) Eng 1982; Univ of Nottingham 6 Post Grad Credit Hrs; *cr:* Schl of Christ the King 7th-8th Grd Eng Tchr 1975-82; Our Lady of Mercy HS 9th-12th Eng Tchr 1982-, Dept Chair 1988-; *ai:* Dept Chprsn; Steering Comm Chprsn for Mid States Evaluation of Schl; NY St Regnets Test Comm; NCTE 1984-; Univ of Rochester's Excl in Tchng Awd 1994; *office:* Our Lady Of Mercy HS 1437 Blossom Rd Rochester NY 14610*

MAIER, BRENDA SWITZER, Art Teacher; *b:* Lewistown, PA; *m:* Kevin Maier; *c:* Natalie; *ed:* IN Univ of PA (BS) Art Ed 1974; NY Univ (MA) Studio Art 1981; Coll of St Rose 1996; Long Island Univ 1995; Syracuse Univ 1994; *cr:* Morrisville-Eaton Schls 1-6 Grd Art Tchr 1974-89; BOCES Drawing for Adult Ed 1981-82; Cazenovia Coll Adj Instr 1986-90; Eagle Hill MS 5-8 Grd Tchr 1989-; *ai:* Scholastic Art Competition; Everson Museum Winter Festival; Syrcuse Univ Art Ed Show; Cntrl Nysata Wkshp; NAEA 1995-; NYSUT 1989-; Cazenovia Preservation Co 1992-; Stdnts Won Top Awd Imagination Celebration 1992-93; Gold, Silver Key Winners at Scholastic Arts Competition 1992-94, 1994-95; 2 Top Awds Everson Museum Comp 1995; *office:* Eagle Hill MS 4645 Enders Rd Manlius NY 13104

MAIER, CYNTHIA FOLLSTEADT, Third Grade Teacher; *b:* Pittsburgh, PA; *m:* Donald R.; *c:* Stacy Vogel, Dawn; *ed:* Slippery Rock Univ (BS) Elem Ed 1964; Post Grad Work; *cr:* Wilmington Area Schls 3rd Grd Tchr 1964-65; Butler Area Schls 4th Grd Tchr 1965-71; St Luke Luth Schl 2nd-3rd Grd Tchr 1984-.

MAIER, JOANNE LUCILLE, Biology & Physiology Teacher; *b:* Ithaca, NY; *m:* Daniel J.; *c:* Brennan M., Craig A.; *ed:* Cornell Univ (BS) Bio 1970; The Univ at Albany (MS) Advanced Classroom Tchng of Bio 1975; *cr:* Guilderland Cntrl HS Bio & Physiology Tchr 1970-; *ai:* AFT 1970-; NEA 1970-; NYSUT 1970-; Guilderland Tchrs Assn 1970-; PTSA 1970-, Rep, Exec Bd 1989-.

MAIER, SUZANNE CAHOON, Professor of Dental Hygiene; *b:* Sodus, NY; *m:* Lawrence R.; *c:* Carolyn, Kristin; *ed:* Broome Comm Coll (AAS) Dental Hygiene 1965; Boston Univ (BS) Ed 1969; SUNY at Binghamton (MS) Advanced Tech 1975; Attnd Univ of NC Schl of Dentistry Radiology Inst; St Univ of NY at Binghamton Creativity & Physics Courses; *cr:* Broome Comm Coll Dental Hygiene Educator, Prof 1969-; *ai:* Prof Dev, Math, Sci, Tech General Ed, Dept Curr, Dept Infection Control Comms; Amer Dental Hygienst Assn 1963-; Sigma Phi Alpha DH Honor Soc 1965-; NEA 1969-; Acad of Oral Maxillofacial Radiology 1991-; Cornell Cooperative Extension, Town of Maine Recreation Comm 1990-; Girl Scout Ldr 1989-; Maine Elem Schl for Rdng Improvement Vol 1991-; Pub Art of Tchng Campus Prof Dev Publication; Written DH Instrumentation & Dental Radiography Instructional Manuals, Exposure to Radiation & Infection Control Policy Manuals.

MAILLE, LORRAINE R., Guid Cnslr & Admissions Dir; *b:* Lowell, MA; *ed:* Rivier Coll (BA) Sociology; Assumption Coll (MA) Psych, Guid 1970, (CAGS) Psych, Cnslng 1974; *cr:* Univ of MA Guid Cnslr, Spec Acad Svcs Dept 1978-88; Lowell Cath HS Guid Cnslr, Admissions Dir 1989-; *ai:* Shades of Essence Adv; Peer Cnslr Trng; Career Day Planner; Multicultural Day Co-Adv; Amer Cnslng Assn 1975-; *office:* Lowell Catholic HS 530 Stevens St Lowell MA 01851

MAIN, DALE CARBONE, Health & Physical Ed Teacher; *b:* New York City, NY; *c:* Jason, Matthew, Allison; *ed:* Baldwin Wallace Coll (BA) Hlth, PE 1975; Adelphi Univ (MA) Adaptive PE 1979; *cr:* Hempstead HS Tchr 1975-77; JHS 189 Queens Tchr 1977-79; JHS 185 Queens Tchr 1981-; *ai:* Stu Act Adv; UFT 1981-; Cub Scouts, BSA 1982-; PTA 1981-; Angela Zirpiades Awd; *office:* Edward Bleeker Jr HS 185 147-26 25th Dr Flushing NY 11354*

MAINE, RICHARD WAYNE, History, Gov & Economics Tchr; *b:* Paola, KS; *m:* Debra Ann Farrell; *c:* Ashley, Seth, Kayla, Drew; *ed:* TN Temple Univ (BS) Hlth & Physical 1984; 9 Addl Credit Hrs in Scndry Ed at Emporia KS; Completed Worldwide Trng at Summitt Ministries 1995; *cr:* Mc Callie Priv Boys Prep Schl Asst Coach 1985-87; Trinity Bapt Schl Tchr, Asst Admin, Coach 1987-89; Willo-Hill Chrstn Schl Tchr Coach 1989-; *ai:* Jr HS Soccer, Var Boys Bsktbl, Head Track Coach; Civics Club Adv; Intervention Team; ACSI 1992-; Willo-Hill Bapt Church 1989-, Deacon, Deaf Bible Tchr 1994-, Children's Church Dir 1989-; *office:* Willo-Hill Christian Schl 4200 State Route 306 Willoughby OH 44094

MAINES, DONNA JEANNE, English Teacher; *b:* Suffern, NY; *m:* Robert James; *c:* Amanda J., Richard A.; *ed:* St Univ Coll at Brockport (BS) Elem & Early Scndry 1974; St Univ Coll at New Paltz (MS) Elem 1977; Post Grad Bucknell Univ; *cr:* West Road Elem Schl 6th Grd Lang Arts & Soc Stud Tchr 1974-75; Jersey Shore Jr High Eng Tchr 1977-; *ai:* Awds Comm Chprsn; Jersey Shore Elem Wrestling, Admin Bd Mem; Jersey Shore Area Ed Assn, PA St Ed Assn, NEA 1977-; Pine Creek Valley Rec Assn 1994-, Sec, Treas; First United Meth Church 1976-, Sec, Bd of Trustees; *office:* Jersey Shore Area Jr HS 601 Thompson St Jersey Shore PA 17740

MAINES, MARIANNE L., Assistant Principal; *b:* Rochester, NY; *m:* John A.; *c:* Lauren, Matthew, Mark, John; *ed:* Nazareth Coll (BA) Eng Lit 1965; Canisius Coll Grad Stud Cmptr Ed; *cr:* Christ the King Schl 6th Grd Tchr 1968-69; Rochester City Schls 1970-73; St Therese Sch 6-8th Grd Tchr 1975-78; SS Peter & Paul Schl Asst Prin 1982-; *ai:* After Schl Prgm Dir; Cath Schl Admin of Amer; NCEA; SS Peter & Paul Church, Parish Cncl; Schl Bd; Deaman Coll Tchr of Yr Nom; Rel Educator of Yr Blfo Dicese; *office:* SS Peter & Paul Schl 5480 Main St Williamsville NY 14221*

MAINHART, DAVID ALAN, Teacher of the Gifted; *b:* Butler, PA; *m:* Karen E. Decker; *c:* andrew, Erika, Stefan, Matthew, James; *ed:* Indiana Univ of PA (BS) Ger 1970; Philipps Univ Germany 1 Yr Abroad; Villanova Univ Grad Work; West Chester Univ Eng Cert; Beaver Coll Natl Endowment for Hum Inst 1986; *cr:* Methacton Schl Dist Ger Tchr 1970-, Eng Tchr 1980-, Tchr of Gifted 1985-, Dept Chair Gifted Ed 1985-; *ai:* Acad Pentathlon Adv; Arcola News Journal Co-Spon; ASCD 1988-; Challenger Fnd Grant 1987-88; *home:* 809 Mill Grove Dr Audubon PA 19403*

MAINIERO, RAYMOND, HS Biology Teacher; *b:* Portchester, NY; *m:* Alice Burrows; *c:* Patricia, JoAnne, Michael, James; *ed:* Fordham Univ (BS) Bio 1961; Addl 64 Credits Western CT Univ, Bridgeport Univ, Vassar Univ, Cortland SUNY; *cr:* Amer Machine, Foundry Bio Engr 2 Yrs; Francise for Telephone Answering Machines 2 Yrs; Carmel Cntrl Schl Dist Earth Sci, Bio, Meteorology, Astronomy, 21st Century Sci Tchr 33 Yrs; *ai:* 15 Yrs Ftbl, Girls, Boys Tennis, Sking Club; Sr Class Adv 5 Yrs; NYSAT 1966-; US Marine Corp 1953-56, Sargent; Eastern Paralyzed Veterans Assn 1987-; Yrbk Dedication 1979, 1987.

MAINOLFI, ANN, Drama Teacher; *b:* Wilkes Barre, PA; *m:* Ferdinand G.; *c:* Michael, Marianne Cromwell, Thomas, Matthew, Eileen Slaughter; *ed:* Mt St Agnes (BA) Sci 1955; Towson St (BA) Theatre 1989; *cr:* Mercy Hosp Med Technologist 1955-63; Seton HS Drama Dir 1976-79; Roland Park Cty Schl Drama Tchr, Dir of Shows 1979-; *ai:* Spon Thespian Troupe; Established Entire Curr Drama; MD Drama Assn 1978-81, VP 3 Yrs, 1981-86 Pres 6 Yrs; Educl Theatre Assn 1991-; Vagabonds, Bd of Dirs 5 Yrs.*

MAINS, ROBERT LOUIS, Middle School Computer Teacher; *b:* New Eagle, PA; *m:* Laura Thwaites; *c:* Jacob Barton; *ed:* Grad Stu William Paterson Univ Learning Technologies Prgm; *cr:* Dover MS Math, Cmptr Tchr 1981-; *ai:* Schl Ldrshp Tm; Yrbk Staff Adv; Play Dir; HS Musical Set Designer; NEA 1981-; Kappa Delta Pi 1980-; *office:* Dover MS 302 E Mc Farlan St Dover NJ 07801

MAINS, TIM O., Teacher & Center Director; *b:* Indianapolis, IN; *ed:* Ball St Univ (BS) Sociology & World His 1971; SUNY at Brockport (MS) Cnslng 1975; 30 Credit Hrs Univ of Rochester Cnslng; *cr:* Greece Arcadia HS Soc Stud Tchr & Curr Ldr 1971-81, Schl Cnslr 1982-91; Greece Athena Jr High 7th Grd Soc Stud Tchr 1981-81; Greece Athena HS Schl Cnslr 1991-95; Greece Cntlr Schls Tchr & Ctr Dir 1995-; *ai:* NHS Adv 1993-95; Ed Tech Advy Comm 1990-; NEA NY 1971-; Amer Cnslng Assoc 1978-; ASCD 1983-; Greece Tchr Ctr 1989-, Policy Bd Chair 1993-95; Rochester City Cncl 1986-, City Cncl Mem at Large, Whos Who in Local Govt Ofcls; Action for a Better Comm 1989-, Bd Mem; Isaiah House Hospice 1991-, Bd Mem; Active Parenting Natl Trainer; Outstdng Young Mem of Amer 1979; *office:* Greece Cntrl Schls 1790 Lattan Rd Rochester NY 14612

MAIO, GUY JOSEPH, Math Teacher; *b:* Brooklyn, NY; *m:* Madelene (Pugliese); *c:* Rachel, Ryan; *ed:* Queens Coll at Flushing (BA) Ec 1970; C. W. Post Coll (BS) Marine Sci 1981; *cr:* St Pauls Schl Math, Sci tchr 5-7th Grd 1970-71; Hackley Schl Math, Sci Tchr 7-9th Grd 1971-76; Holy Trinity HS Sci Tchr 1976-77; Bellport MS Math Tchr 7-8th Grds 1977-; *ai:* Chess Club Adv; After Schl Homework Help Stdnts Supvr; NCTM 1979-; PAL Hockey 1978-, Coach, 1st & 2nd Pl.

MAIO, JAMES ALBERT, Technology & Drafting Teacher; *b:* Wilmington, DE; *m:* Candice R. Johnson; *c:* James; *ed:* William PA Coll (BA) Industrial Arts 1969; Univ of DE Trade & Industry Cert 1975; St of DE Tech Ed Cert 1994-; *cr:* Christiana HS Electronics Tchr 1970-71; Clow Corp Product Designer 1971-79; Newark HS Architecture, Drafting, CAD Tchr 1973-; DE Tech Comm Coll Drafting Instr 1980-83; *ai:* Amer with Disabilities Act Comm Mem; Mid Sts Cert for Schl Facilities; Asst Ath Dir; NEA, Fac Rep DE St Ed Assn 1973-; DE Tech Ed Assn 1995-; Babe Ruth Bsbl League 1984-, Coach; BSA 1983-, Comm Mem; Natl Awd for Product Design; Tchr of Yr 1986-87; *office:* Newark HS 750 E Delaware Ave Newark DE 19711

MAIORANO, BETTY BRADLEY, Math Teacher; *b:* Providence, RI; *m:* Stephen Albert; *c:* Catherine Carey, Jaclyn Mary, Lyndsey Ann, Ashley Elizabeth; *ed:* Anna Maria Coll (BA) Elem Ed 1973; Westfield St (MA) Math 1978; 9 Credits Rhode Island Coll; *cr:* Providence Schls Long Term Sub Tchr 1973-75; White Brook MS Sub Tchr 1975-76; White Brook MS Math Tchr 1976-; *ai:* Church Comm Svc; Girls Sftbl Team Scorekeeper; NEA, MTA, EEA 1976-; Notre Dame Immaculate Conception PTL 1984-; *office:* White Brook MS 200 Park St Easthampton MA 01027

MAIRE, FRANK H., Fifth Grade Teacher; *b:* Cleveland, OH; *m:* Connie Lyn Stacy; *c:* Michael Roe Burge, Nicole Allison Burge; *ed:* Cleveland St Univ (BS) Elem Ed 1984; Ashland Univ (MA) Curr 1989; Drake Univ 12 Semester Hrs; John Carrol Univ of Steubenville 6 Semester Hrs; *cr:* Euclid Pub Schls 1st Grd Tchr 1984-86; South Cntrl Intermediate 4th Grd Tchr 1987-88; Collins Western Reserve MS 5th Grd Tchr 1988-; *ai:* Head Bsbl, Asst Ftbl, Girls Tennis, JV Bsktbl, 8th Grd Ftbl Coach; OEA, NEA 1984-; WRTA 1988-; Using Cooperative Learning & Hands-On Experimentation to Teach Sci Concepts Book Pub; *office:* Collins Western Reserve MS 3841 US Rt 20 E Collins OH 44826*

MAISANO, ALAN A., Social Science Dept Chprsn; *b:* Newark, NJ; *ed:* Rutgers Univ (BA) His, Ed 1975; CA St Univ (MA) Hum, His 1990; Seton Hall Univ Grad Schl of Ed 12 Credits in Educl Admin, Supervision 1981-82; *cr:* Kearny HS Stdnt Tchr 1975; Queen of Peace HS Soc Sci Dept Chm, Tchr 1975-; *ai:* NCSS, Amer Historical Assn 1975-; NCEA 1980-; Queen of Peace Peace Quest 1984, Co-Founder, Co-Moderator; Rutgers Univ Nancy Higginson Dorr Awd Most Outstanding Stdnt Tchr 1975; Phi Beta Kappa; Edward H. Zabreskie Awd Most Outstanding Historian; Phi Alpha Theta; Artical Pub CA St 1981; Dstngshd La Sallion Ed Aw 1994-95; Phi Kappa Phi; *office:* Queen of Peace HS 191 Rutherford PL North Arlington NJ 07032

MAISANO, ANNA C., Foreign Language Teacher; *b:* Hackensack, NJ; *ed:* Rutgers Coll (BA) Italian & Fr 1978, (MA) Italian 1982; 30 Hrs Span for Span Cert; 12 Hrs Admin for Supvr Cert; *cr:* Berlitz Translation Svcs Natl Project Coord 1983-84; CPT Corp System Support Rep 1984-87; Floral Park Meml HS Tchr of Italian 1987-89; Summit Solutions Inc Regnl Trng Coord 1989-90; Middletown HS North Tchr of Italian 1990-; *ai:* Renaissance Festival Coord; Italian Honor Soc-Club Adv; MLA, AATI 1980-; FLENJ, ITA, NYC 1990-; Italian-Amer Club of Middletown 1990-, Sec 1993-; Saint Vincent de Paul Soc 1995-, Vol; Beechwoods Condo Assn 1995-, Sec; Consortium Grant of 12000 Dollars for Renaissance Festival Awded by Middletown Twp Ed Fnd 1995; NEH Summer Tchr Insts Leonardo 1992, Figaro 1993; Phi Beta Kappa & Phi Sigma Iota; *office:* Middletown HS North 63 Tindall Rd Middletown NJ 07748

MAISCH, CHRISTIAN JOAQUIN, Assistant Professor; *b:* Lima, Peru; *ed:* OH Dominican Coll (BA) Pol Sci 1977; The Amer Univ (MA) Intnl Stud 1978, (PHD) Intnl Relations 1981; *cr:* Inter-Amer Dev Bank Prof Staff 1982-88; The Amer Univ Asst Prof of Comparative, Regnl Stud 1988-; *ai:* Fac Cncl Washington Semester Prgm Vice Chair; Soc for Historians of Amer Forsign Relations 1994-; Intnl Stud Assn 1984-; Mid Atlantic Cncl of Latin Amer Stud 1996-; Book A Juridical and Historical Analysis of the Anglo-Areentine Dispute Over the Falkland Malvinas Islands 1995; *office:* American Univ Schl of Intnl Service 4400 Massachusetts Ave NW Washington DC 20016

MAISEL, HARVEY MICHAEL, Fifth Grade Teacher; *b:* Bronx, NY; *ed:* Hunter Coll in Bronx (BA) Pol Sci 1969; Lehman Coll in Bronx (MS) Media in Ed 1975; 30 Addl Credit Hrs; *cr:* PS 150 Tchr 1969-72; PS 47 Tchr 1972-75; PS 76 Tchr 1975-76; PS 119 Tchr 1976-; *ai:* St Jude's Math a Thon Adv; The Constitution Works at Fed Hall Facilitator; Math Consultant; Acad Math Challenge SC Schls; UFT 1969-; AFT 1972-; Papec Tchr of Yr 1993; *office:* PS 119 1075 Pugsley Ave Bronx NY 10472*

MAISONET, TITO MANUEL, Physical Education Teacher; *b:* New York, NY; *c:* Tiffany; *ed:* Augustana Coll (BA) PE 1976; 23 Semester Units Cal St Univ at Los Angeles, PE, Admin; 10 Semester Units East Stroudsburg St Univ PE, Admin; 18 Semester Units Mt St Mary Coll Spec Ed; *cr:* Bd Cooperative Educl Svcs Walden Schl Spec Ed Tchr 1974-75; Westchester Luth Schl Span Tchr 1975-76; Mira Costa HS PE Tchr, Coach 1976-80; Gardnertown, Horizons ElemSchl PE Tchr, Coach 1987-92; Cornwall Cntrl HS PE Tchr, Coach 1994-; *ai:* Coach Head Var Ftbl, Asst Var, Head Jr Var Girls Bsktbl; NY St United Tchrs, AFT 1987-; Soccer of Yr 1989; *office:* Cornwall Central HS 122 Main St Cornwall NY 12518

MAISTROS, HARRY CONSTANTINE, Art Department Chair; *b:* Baltimore, MD; *ed:* MD Inst Coll of Art (BFA) Art Ed, Design 1966; (MFA) Art Ed 1972; Credited Inservice Supervision, Dimensions of Learning, Spec Ed, Ed That is Multicultural, Tech Ed, Cmptr Graphics, Implementing Art His, A P Portfolio Assessment; *cr:* Overlea HS Art Instr 1966-69; Deep Creek Jr, Sr HS Art Dept Chair 1969-78; Franklin HS Art Dept Chair 1978-; MD Inst Coll of Art Cont Stud YPS Instr 1987-; *ai:* Arts & Tech Completer, Implementation Model 1995-; Ed That is Multi-Cultural, Schl Liaison 1995-; GATE Resource Comm, Ofc of Art 1994-; Yrbk Adv 1979-92; NEA, NAEC 1966-; MD St Tchrs Assn 1966-; MD Art Ed Assn 1970-; Phi Beta Sigma 1984-; Baltimore Museum of Art 1970-; Walter's Art Gallery 1980-; United Chios Soc of Baltimore 1973-, Sec; Congratulatory Citation, House of Dels, Natl Art Hnr Soc, Natl Fnd for Advancement in Arts, Arts Recog & Talent 1990; Columbia Press Silver Crown Yrbk Winner 1988-92; Second Congressional Arts Competition Coord, Host 1988; Dept of Curr & Instr Presentor 1993; *home:* 645 Stoney Spring Dr Baltimore MD 21210*

MAITE, JENNIFER EVANS, Mathematics Teacher; *b:* Massillon, OH; *m:* Anthony D.; *c:* Kyle; *ed:* OH St Univ (BS) Math Ed 1990, (MA) Math 1993; 1 Credit Hr Great Seal Comp Trng OH Univ at Chillicothe; *cr:* OH St Univ Tchng Asst 1991-93; Circleville HS Math Tchr 1993-; *ai:* Odyssey of the Mind Club & Math Club Adv; OSU & CTM 1989-90, Publicity Chprsn; *office:* Circleville HS 380 Clark Dr Circleville OH 43113*

MAITLAND, WILLIAM D., English Teacher; *b:* Elizabeth, NJ; *m:* Judith Lynne Leinbach; *c:* Andrew, James; *ed:* Mansfield St Univ (BSE) Eng 1972; Elmira Coll (MSE) Eng 1975; *cr:* Broadway Jr HS Eng Tchr 1972-79; Southside HS Eng Tchr 1979-; *ai:* Class Adv 1987-88, 1996; Elmira Tchrs Assn, Negotiator 1989-92, Chief Negotiator 1992-94; NY St United Tchrs 1972-; AFT 1975-; NCTE 1980-; Order of Eagles Aux Tchr of Yr 1988; NY St United Tchrs Leadership Awd 1994; *home:* PO Box 113 Pine City NY 14871*

MAJCHER, PATRICIA ANN, Art Teacher; *b:* Pittsburgh, PA; *m:* Robert J.; *c:* Heather Baker, Kristen, Adam, Megan; *ed:* IN Univ of PA (BS) Art Ed 1966; Seton Hill Coll Elem Ed, K-8 1982; Addl Hrs IN Univ of Penna Art Ed1989; *cr:* Canon Mc Millan Schl Dist Art Tchr 1966-67; Hempstead Area Schl Dist Art Tchr 1980-; *ai:* Hnrs Art Club; Stu Cncl; HAEA, SSEA, NEA 1966-; Church Ed, Tchr; *office:* Harrold MS RR 6 Box 75 Greensburg PA 15601*

MAJER, JOHN M., Psychology Adjunct Professor; *b:* Elmhurst, IL; *ed:* Anne Arundel Comm coll (AA) Gen Stud 1989; Bowie St Univ (BS) Psych 1990; Bowie St Univ (MA) Cnslng Psych 1993; 9 Grad Credit Hrs Amer Univ 1990-91; *cr:* New Life Addiction Cnslng Svcs Consultant, Cnslr 1992-94; Hope House Inc Case Mgr, Primary Care Therapist 1993-95; Anne Arundel Comm Coll Psych Adj Prof 1993-; Johns Hopkins Hosp Psychiatric Addiction Therapist 1995-; *ai:* Anne Arundel Cty Substance Abuse Treatment Cncl 1993-; Substance Abuse Initiative Comm 1995-; Viktor Frankl Inst of Logotherapy 1991-; Psi Chi 1989-; Article Pub 1992; *office:* Anne Arundel Comm Coll Division of Social Sciences 101 College Pkwy Arnold MD 21012

MAJEWSKI, CHERYL S., Business Education Teacher; *b:* Gloversville, NY; *m:* Michael R.; *c:* Marc, Melissa; *ed:* D'Youville Coll (BS) Bus Ed 1971; Permanent Cert Bus Ed 30 Grad Hrs; *cr:* Broadalbin-Perth HS Bus Ed Tchr 1971-; *ai:* Broadalbin-Perth Tchrs Assn, NYSUT 1971-; *office:* Broadalbin Perth HS Extension Bridge St Broadalbin NY 12025

MAJEWSKI, DIANNE CALASCIBETTI, Social Studies & Relgion Tchr; *b:* Cleveland, OH; *m:* Walter G.; *c:* Melissa; *ed:* Kent St Univ (BA) 1970; Baldwin Wallace Coll 25 Hrs Towards Masters; *cr:* St Monic Schl Tchr 1970-72; St Ambrose Schl Tchr 1973-79; Berea St Mary Schl Tchr 1979-85; Mansfield St Mary Schl Tchr 1985-; *ai:* Stu Cncl Moderator; Soc Stud Ldrshp Cncl; Quiz Bowl Chm; Scheduling Coord; Eighth Grd Class Trip Chm; Jr HS Level Coord; Rel Ldrshp Cncl; OASC 1993-; Star Tchr Awd 1994; *office:* St Mary Schl 1630 Ashland Rd Mansfield OH 44905*

MAJIKAS, VINCENT J., 9th Grade Phys Science Tchr; *b:* Ashland, PA; *m:* Janet Tazik; *c:* Amy, Derek, Vincent Jr.; *ed:* Bloomsburg U (BS) Bio Ed 1968; Trenton St (MS) Comprehensive Sci 1972; Penn St Post Grad Credits in Ed; *cr:* Ben Franklin JHS Earth Sci Tchr 1968-72; Neil Armstrong JHS Phys Sci Tchr 1972-79, 1981-; Delhaas HS Bio & Chem Tchr 1980-81; *ai:* Wrestling Coach 1972-95; Instrl Fly Fishing Club Adv; PSEA 1968-; NEA 1968-; SPBSQSA 1980-83; Knights of Columbus 1981-; *home:* 71 Martha Dr Levittown PA 19054

MAJOR, CARICELLA, Music Teacher; *b:* Brooklyn, NY; *ed:* Georgian Court Coll (BA) Music Ed 1982; *cr:* Calvary Bapt Church Organist, Minister of Music 1982-; Orange Bd of Ed Music Tchr 1984-90; Twp of Ocean Bd of Ed Music Tchr 1991-; *ai:* Performing Arts Dept Musical Dir; NEA 1984-; *office:* Twp of Ocean Intermediate Schl 1200 W Park Ave Asbury Park NJ 07712

MAJOY, PETER WILLIAM, English Teacher; *b:* Jamaica, NY; *m:* Theresa Cook; *c:* Sean, Brian, Christopher, Jennifer; *ed:* St Johns Univ (BA) Philosophy 1966, (MA) Theology 1968; W CT St Coll (MS) Eng Ed 1973; 30 Credit Hrs Admin & Supervision; *cr:* Holmdel HS Eng Tchr 1973-78; Tewksbury HS Eng Tchr 1978-81; McKelvie Schl 7th & 8th Grd Eng Tchr 1981-83; Dedham HS Eng Tchr 1983-86; Nashua HS Eng Tchr 1987-; *ai:* TEAM SNTAS; AFT 1987-; Princetons Distinguished Scndry Schl Tchr Awd Nom 1976; Teach Grad Course Rivier Coll; Books Doorways To Learning 1993 & Riding the Crocodile, Flying the Peach Pit.*

MAKALUSKY, MARIPAT MACDONALD, English Teacher; *b:* Pittston, PA; *w:* Joseph (dec); *c:* Jean, Joseph, Kerry, Lynn, Michael; *ed:* Coll Misericordia (BA) Soc Stud & Eng 1964, (MS) Organizational Mgmt 1991, (MS) Ed 1993; Wilkes Univ Chemical Dependency for Educators, Stu Asst Trng; *cr:* Woodbridge Twp Tchr 1964-68; Franklin Twp Schls Tchr & Sr Class Moderator 1969-72; Our Lady of Lourdes Tchr 1987-88; Bishop OReilly Tchr 1988-; McCann Schl of Bus Instr 1989; *ai:* Faith Team Alternate, Stu Asst Team; Past Experience Yrbk Co-Adv, Asst Soccer Coach; SDACT 1988-; Rdng Cncl; Lambda Iota Tau 1964-; Poem Pub Poetry Anthology; Woodrow Wilson Candidate in Coll; Project Learn Presenter Ethical Issues in Curr; *home:* 1521 Shoemaker Ave West PA 18644

MAKAR, BARBARA ELAINE, Business Education Teacher; *b:* Berwick, PA; *ed:* Bloomsburg Univ (BS) Bus Ed 1965; PA St Univ (MED) Bus Ed 1968; Attnd CO St Univ, UT St Univ, Rider Coll, PA St Univ; *cr:* Williamson Jr Sr HS Bus Ed Tchr 1965-66; Palmerton Area HS Bus Ed Tchr 1966-68; Plymouth Whitemarsh Schl Bus Ed Tchr 1970-; *ai:* PE Yth in Ed; Stu Mentor Prgm; Local PEW Spon; NEA, NBEA, PSEA 1965-; CEA 1970-, Sec; PBEA, SPBEA 1965-, Sec; Amer Cancer Soc 1990-, Survivor Medalion, Unit Pres; Literacy Cncl 1995-; NCATE Cnslr 1996; ACS Survival Speak, Medation Holder; NEA Prof Stans, Practices; PSEA Intnl Ed Comm; *office:* Plymouth Whitemarsh HS 109 Germantown Pike Plymouth Meeting PA 19462*

MAKAR, NADIA EISSA, College Industry Liaison; *b:* Cairo, Eg Boshra Makar; *c:* Ralph, Roger; *ed:* St Peters Coll (BA) Math, Phys 1969, (MA) Admin 1981; Moscow Univ Cert 1964; Attnd Brow Hope Coll; *cr:* Hudson Cath HS Chem Tchr 1970-72, Dept Chair 1 Union City Bd of Ed Sci Specialist, Gifted Prgm 1979-81, Math, Tchr 1982-89, Coll Coord, Industry Tchr 1989-95, Coll, Industry 1995-; *ai:* Mu Alpha Theta, Math Club Moderator; Scholars Coord; Bergen Chem, Pres, Treas, Am Chem Reg; NY Amer Chem Sc Nichols; NCTM, AMTNJ 1981-, Mem at Large; NSTA 1971-; N Supvrs Assn 1973-; Jersey City Bd of Ed 1989-94; Jersey City BPW Pres, VP; NJ BPW 1975-, Sec, Woman of Yr; NJ Mental Hlth Assn, NJ Bisec 1981-, Pres, Most Valuable; Math Excl Presidentia Governors Awd; Hudson Cty Tchr of Yr; Outstanding Scndry Educa Amer; *office:* Union Hill HS 3808 Hudson Ave Union City NJ 070

MAKARY, FRANK J., Social Studies Teacher; *b:* Bethlehem, Alverta Pealer; *c:* Ross, Jennifer; *ed:* E Stroudsburg St Coll (BA) E 1964; Kutztown St Coll (MED) 1968; *cr:* Whitehall-Coplay Elem Tchr 1964-71; Whitehall-Coplay MS 7th-8th Grd Tchr 1971-86; Wh HS Soc Stud Tchr 1986-; *ai:* Pol Discussion Club; NEA, PSEA & 1964-, Fac Rep.

MAKEE, LINDA MEREDITH, French Teacher; *b:* Cleveland, James E. Sr.; *c:* James E. Jr., Michael D., Randall M., Meredith Denison Univ (BA) Eng 1964; Attnd Kent St Univ, CWRU, Clevel Am Universite a Paris; *cr:* SE Lyndhurst Bd of Ed Fr & Eng Tchr 19 Mentor Bd of Ed Fr & Eng Tchr 1985-86; SE Lyndhurst Bd of Ed & Gifted Ed Tchr, Coord Gifted Ed 1987-; *ai:* NHS Adv; Strategic Pl Comm Chm; Stu Tchr Mentor; NEA 1986-; Kappa Kappa Gamma Pres; PTA 1970-, Pres; Denison Alum Organ 1964-, Pres; Messia Church Cncl 1965-, VP; *office:* Charles F Brush HS 4875 Glen Cleveland OH 44124*

MAKELA, MARIA MARTHA, Art History Professor; *b:* Miami, Neal Benezra; *c:* Ava; *ed:* Stetson Univ (BS) Math, Hum 1977; Univ (MA) Art His 1981; Stanford Univ (PHD) Art His 1987; Gra Freie Univ at West Berlin Germany; *cr:* Drake Univ Lecturer Stanford Univ Lecturer 1984; Schl of Art Inst of Chicago Visiting As 1986-91; MD Inst Coll of Art Prof 1993-; Walker Art Ctr Guest C 1994-; *ai:* Ger Stud Assn; Coll Art Assn; Amer Assn of Univ W Grants: Natl Endowment for Hum, Flwshp for Coll Tchrs, Ind S 1994-95; Alexander Von Humboldt Fnd 1991-92, Fulbright Post-D 1990, Kress Fnd 1984 Flwshps; Stanford Hum Ctr Fellow 1982-84; The Munich Secession: Art & Artists in Turn-of-the-Century Munic Photomontages of Hannah Hoch; Articles, Catalog Essays; *office:* M Coll Of Art 1300 W Mount Royal Ave Baltimore MD 21217

MAKI, BRUCE LAWRENCE, Retired Teacher; *b:* Albany, NY; *m:* Witkowski; *c:* Kristin, Bruce; *ed:* HVCC (AA) PE 1968; *cr:* Niskayu Bsbl, Ftbl Coach 1988-95; *ai:* Directed Bsbl Camp, Clinics; Coache Bsktbl, Little League, Babe Ruth Bsbl; Schl Ath Act Supervision Elks 1991-, Chm Yth Comms; *home:* 154 Benjamin St Schenecta 12303

MAKOWER, ESTHER ROTHMAN, 9th-12th Grade Biology Teac Lakewood, NJ; *m:* Jordan; *c:* Joshua, David, Jennifer; *ed:* Hunter Co Human Physiology 1960; Univ of MA (MA) Zoology & Genetics 1 Credits at OR St Univ, 3 Credits at Saint Thomas Aquinas; Addl 3 C *cr:* Univ of MA Grad Tchng Asst 1960-63; Westport Schl Dist Home Tchr 1965-68; Rockland Comm Coll Anatomy, Physiology & Bi 1973-84; Pearl River Bio Tchr 1978-81; Nanuet Schl Dist Bio 1982-84; Nyack Schl Dist Bio Tchr 1984-; *ai:* Sci Hnr Soc Ad Olympiad Team Coach; Sci Tchrs of NY 1978-, Outstanding Bio Tch 1993; NSTA, NABT & NYSUT 1978-; Nyack Tchrs Assn 1984-, Bld AFT & NEA 1978-; *office:* Nyack Sr HS 361 Christian Herald Rd NY 10960*

MAKOWSKI, ELAINE ROMAN, First Grade Teacher; *b:* Wilkes PA; *m:* Thomas E.; *c:* Paul Thomas; *ed:* Coll Misericordia (BS) El 1970; Masters Equivelency 60 Addl Credit Hrs PA St Univ; *cr:* Nanticoke Area Schl 1st, Third Grd Tchr 26 Yrs; *ai:* Head Tchr; GN PSEA, NEA 1970-.

MAKRAVITZ, CAROL, Vice Prin & Advanced Bio Tch Wilkes-Barre, PA; *ed:* Marillac Coll (BS) Bio 1970-; Fordham (M 1972, (PHD) Bio 1975; Marywood Coll (MSEd) Schl Ldrshp 1996; Bishop O'Reilly HS 316 N Maple Ave Kingston PA 18704

MAKRIDES, MARY ANGELA POPE, First Grade Teache Fitzgerald, GA; *m:* Nicholas Sr.; *c:* Nicholas S. Jr., Kathryn F. Gaffne GA St Coll for Women (BS) Elem Ed 1959; Cleveland St, U Pittsburgh Post Grad Work; *cr:* Cedar Hill Bapt Chrstn Schl First Grd 1966-68; J. Arthur Duff Schl Second Grd Tchr 1968-89; Newlonsburg First Grd Tchr 1989-; *ai:* Penn St, Duquesne Univs Stu Tchrs Coope Tchr; New First Grd Tchrs Mentor; FREA, PSEA, NEA 1968-; Gi Intnl Auxiliary 1969-; *home:* 15 Bel Aire Rd Delmont PA 15626

MALACHOWSKI, ANN MARY, Elem Art Coordinator; *b:* Chelsea *ed:* MS Coll of Art (BS) Art Ed 1970; Lesley Coll (MED) Tech, Curr Fitchburg St Coll Cert Fine Arts Dir 1990; *cr:* Norwood Pub Schls Ar 1970-, Elem Art Coord 1974-; Fitchburg St Coll Adjunct Fac 1991-9 Tech, Curr Frameworks, Interdisciplinary Comms; Arts Frameworks Group; MDAE 1989-, Pres; MAEA 1990-, Cncl Mem; Alpha Upsil 1990-, Past Sec; ASCD, MASSCUE 1990-; MAAE 1994-; NAEA, MTA, NTA 1970-; Polish Falcons of Amer 1970-, Dist Financial Bronze Legion of Honor; Educator of Yr MA Art 1995; Natl A Presentations 1994-95; Conf Presentations MA Art Ed 1990-94; Norwood Pub Schls 100 Westover Pkwy Norwood MA 02062

MALADY, KEVIN JOHN, Science Teacher; *b:* Providence, RI; *m:* B.; *c:* Deirdee, Siobhan, Richard, Joseph; *ed:* Univ of Miami (BS 1977; Bowdin Summer Session on Tchng the Gifted & Talented Ecolo Physiology & Summer Session on Spectroscopy; *cr:* Oakgrove-Cobur Tchr 1977-78, Sci Dept Chm 1978-79; Lawrence Jr HS Sci Tchr 197 Lawrence HS Sci Tchr 1980-; *ai:* Regnl Gifted & Talented Sci Gaming Club; Stu Assistance Team; Sci Olympiad Coach & Pres 1990; ME Tchrs Assn, ME Sci Tchrs & NSTA 1980-; Toh Moh No 1980-, Chief Karate Instr; Cub Scout Pack 238 1992-, Treas; Nom to Awd for Sci Tchng 1995; Fac of Yr 1995; *office:* Lawrence HS Scho Fairfield ME 04937

MALAFRONTE, RAFFAELE JOSEPH, English Teacher; *b:* Broo NY; *ed:* Cathedral Coll (BA) Eng 1979; Brooklyn Coll (MA) Eng 198 St Rose of Lima Math Tchr 1979-82; St Edmund HS Eng Tchr 1982 Yrbk Moderator; JV Sftbl, Var Swimming Coach; NCEA 1979-; C Outstanding Contribution to Ed from St Francis Coll; *office:* St Edmu S 2747 Ocean Ave Brooklyn NY 11229

MALAMAS, KIMBERLY ALLGRIM, Former Teacher's Aide; *b:* Ste Marie, MI; *m:* Nickolas John; *c:* Yanni; *ed:* St Univ of NY C Buffalo (BS) Spec, Elem Ed 1991; *cr:* Holland Cntrl HS Tchrs 1991-94; *ai:* Co-Adv Stu Cncl; Var Chrldng, Jr Var Field Hockey Co

MALANOWSKI, CHARLENE, Mathematics Teacher; *b:* Holyoke, *ed:* Mt Holyoke Coll (BA) Math 1980; Univ MA at Amherst (MED 1987; 30 Addl Credits; *cr:* Lynch Jr HS Math Tchr 1980-82; Peck J Math Tchr 1982-88; Holyoke HS Math Tchr 1988-; Dean Voc Math

2; *ai:* Math Club Adv; MTA 1980-; *office:* Holyoke HS 500 Beech oke MA 01040

QISI, ANDREW P., Guidance Counselor; *b:* Gloversville, NY; *m:* Guarnier; *c:* Ann Marie, Gina Leigh, Kristia Michelle; *ed:* MVCC a (AAS) Mech Tech 1966; Utica Coll (BA) Math 1970; SUC at (MS) Dist Admin 1991; SUC at Oneonta Perm, St Cert SDA Schl dmin 1991; *cr:* GE Co Elec Design Engr 1966-68; Gloversville d Schl Dist 1970-85; Gloversville Guid Cnslr 1985-; *ai:* NYSUT Knights of Columbus 1990-; *home:* 173 1st Ave Gloversville NY

RA, ANTHONY IGNAZIO, 7th Grd US History Tchr; *b:* Newark, Monmouth Univ (AA) Ed 1966, (BA) Pol Sci 1968, (MAT) Ed Addl Credits; *cr:* Sayreville MS Tchr 1970-; *ai:* Mt Wachusett CC amp Instr; Chicago Cubs Scout 1986-; Toronto Blue Jays Assoc 1980-84; TX Rangers Assoc Scout 1985-86; Var Bsbl Coach 8; Champs Cty 1975, Conf 1976; NYC Marathon 13 Yrs; NEA, MCEA, SEA 1970-; HS Reunion Comm, NY Pro Bsbl Hot Stove 1984-; St Bernadette's Youth Group 1978-88, Adv; Eucharistic er 1980-; Knights of Columbus 1983-; Amecigo Vespucci Soc 1992-; Comm 1990-; John Honey Russell Awd Bsbl Ed 1989; Amer Assn of sbl Coaches Quartership Digest; *office:* Sayreville MS 800 gton Rd Parlin NJ 08859

SZCZYK, MARK SCOTT, HS Social Studies Teacher; *b:* yn, NY; *m:* Lisa Barletta; *c:* Joanna Lynne; *ed:* St John's Univ (BA) 39, (MA) His 1991; 45 Credits Towards Doctoral Degree in Modern His; *cr:* St John's Univ Grad Asst 1989-91; St John the Bapt DHS ud Tchr 1991-92; St Francis Preparatory Soc Stud Tchr 1992-93; n HS Soc Stud Tchr 1993-; *ai:* Moderator St John the Bapt Citizen uad 1991-92; Stu Tchng Against Racism Club 1991-92; Moderator n Stu Cncl & Ctzn Bee Team 1993-94; Babylon Cross Cntry Coach Track Coach 1993-; Babylon Oratorical Club Coach 1995-; NYSUT, sland Soc Stud Cncl 1993-; Amer His Assn 1990-; Babylon PTSA St John's Univ Doctoral Fellowship 1992-, Scholastic Excl Schlsp 9; 2 Articles Pub on Amer Foreign Policy; Commncmnt Spkr on HS; *office:* Babylon Jr-Sr HS 50 Railroad Ave Babylon NY

TESTA, BETSY A., Health & Physical Ed Teacher; *b:* Berwick, Joseph; *c:* Andrea; *ed:* Penn St Univ (BS) Hlth, PE 1982; *cr:* k Area Sr HS Tchr 13 Yrs; *ai:* Field Hockey Coach 1982-95; NEA, 1982-; *office:* Berwick Area Sr HS 1100 Fowler Ave Berwick PA

COLM, JEFFERY J., Economics & Civics Teacher; *b:* Kitchner ON, a; *m:* Kathleen Trainor; *ed:* Univ of Ottawa (BA) His 1991; Plymouth (MED) Ed 1994; *cr:* Farmington HS Ec & Civics Tchr; *ai:* Jr Var oach; Class of 1999 Adv; Outreach Ski Prgm Coord; NHCSS, NEA Fnd for Tchng Ec Wkshp Summer 1995; *home:* PO Box 43 Strafford 884

COLM, RUTH LAMB, Retired Art Teacher; *b:* Springfield, VT; *m:* Cameron; *c:* Leslie Favini, Bradley; *ed:* Boston Univ (BS) Art Ed *cr:* Sutton-Oxford Schls Gr 1-Hi Sch Art Tchr 1953-54; oro-Troy Schls Gr 1-Hi Sch Art Tchr 1954-56; Ayer Schls Gr 1-6 Art 967-81; Marlow Elem Schl K-6 Grd Art Tchr 1982-93; *ai:* Good Camp Craft Tchr 1982-95; Good News Club Tchr 1983-; NEA; Nat Assn.

ET, MARK WILLIAM, Chemistry Teacher; *b:* Johnstonn, PA; *m:* tha Diane; *ed:* Univ of Pittsburgh (BS) Sec Ed Chem 1990; Penn St ED) Tchng & Curr; *cr:* Halifax Area SD Chem Tchr 1990-91; enita SD Chem Tchr 1991-92; West Shore Schl Dist Chem Tchr *ai:* Debate Co-Coach; NEA 1990-94; ASCD 1995-; 2 Yr Research Research Corp for Chem Research; *office:* West Shore Schl Dist e & Warwick Rds Camp Hill PA 17011

ECKI, ANNETTE HAGY, High School Science Teacher; *b:* g, NY; *m:* David J.; *c:* Alex; *ed:* Corning Comm Coll (AS) Engrng 84; SUNY at Binghamton (BS) Chem 1987, (MA) Chem 1989; SUC tland (MAT) Scndry Ed 1990; *cr:* SUNY Lab Asst 1987, Tchng Asst 89; Ithaca, Dryden, Cortland Schls Sub Tchr 1989; Ithaca HS term Sub Tchr 1989-90; Baldwinville Cntrl Schls Sci Tchr 1990-; *ai:* ympied, Sci Fair Adv; NY St Regents Empire St Challenger Flwshp hr 1989-90; Deans List at Corning Comm Coll; *office:* C W Baker E Oneida St Baldwinsville NY 13027

ES, COLETTE T., French Teacher; *b:* Metz, France; *w:* William R. *c:* Bettina, Kevin, William; *ed:* AL A&M (BS) Fr 1976; Auburn Univ Coll Tchng 1981; Linquistics 8 Hrs; *cr:* J. O. Johnson HS Fr-Russian 1974-76; Auburn Univ Instr Fr, Russian 1978080; Caddo Parish et HS Fr-Russian Tchr 1980-86; SHAPE Amer HS Fr Tchr 1990-; *ai:* Spon; OEA 1990-; AATF 1980-; Pi Delta Phi 1979-; Alpha CappaMu ; Edctr of Distinction LA 1982; Distngd Tchr White House aission on Presidential Schls 1984; *office:* Shape American HS Cmr ox 0005 APO AE 09708*

ETTE, JOHN, Special Education Teacher; *b:* Nashua, NH; *ed:* Wachusett Comm Col (AS) Mental Hlth 1976; Fitchburg St Col (BS) Ed, Spec Ed 1979; Enrolled MED Prgm Univ of VT Integration ator; *cr:* Spec Needs Educ Collaborative Lang Based Pgrm Tchr 80; Ashby Elem Schl K-6 Grd Resource Room Tchr 1980-81; Ashby Schl 6 Gr Classroom Tchr 1981-95; W. Rutland Schl K-5 Resource Tchr 1995-; *ai:* AES Newspaper Adv 1983-87; Chprsn Lang Arts n N Middlesex Reg Schl 1987-88; Odyssey of Mind Judge 1989-90; Nature's Classroom AES 1981-95; NEA, MTA 1980-; VTA 1995-; amental Action to Conserve Energy 1992-93, Instrumental in Creating ogy Curr for AES; Recycling Prgm AES 1992-95, Coord; Flwshp to d UVM MA Integration Facilitator; Awded Apple Cmptr for Use in m for Winning Essay Contest; *office:* West Rutland Schl 9 Bennett pperell MA 01463

EVRIS, THEODORE, Instrumental Music Teacher; *b:* Bayonne, NJ; ersey City St Coll (BA) Music Ed 1968, (MA) Music Ed 1972; *cr:* nne Bd of Ed Instrumental Music Tchr 1967-; *ai:* Performer in Annual Stu, Alumni Recital; 8th Grd Fac Adv; Music Dept Fac Adv; uctor & Dir Vroom Schl Orch, BHS String Ensemble, BHS Orch nble; BTA, NJEA 1967-; Musicians Union Local 248 1980-; Amer g Tchrs Assn 1985-; Jersey City St Coll Orch 1964-; N Jersey armonic 1980-; Bergen Philharmonic Orch 1985-; Bayonne Comm 1994-; Governors Tchr of Yr Awd 1990; *office:* Bayonne HS 29th St e A Bayonne NJ 07002

EY, JAMES ANDREW, HS Social Studies Teacher; *b:* Bucyrus, OH; anette Rader; *c:* Susan, Ryan; *ed:* Findlay Coll (BA) His & Pol Sci Bowling Green St Univ (MS) Admin 1979; Univ of Dayton 15 Credit Walsh Coll 6 Credit Hrs; *cr:* Ottoville Local Schl HS His Tchr 1971-; r Golf Coach 1975-95; OH Golf Coaches Hall of Fame; Ath Dir; NEA -; OEA 1971-, Local Pres 1984; Amer Legion 1983-; Cleveland ns Backer 1993-; Elks #54 1994-; *home:* 111 Weger Ave Elida OH

EY, MICHAEL BENJAMIN, Social Studies Chairman; *b:* Dayton, *m:* Ida McIntosh; *c:* Michael A., Zachary Benjamin; *ed:* Wright St (BS) Soc Stud Comp 1970, (MA) His 1979; Post Grad Wright St Univ -85 in His, Cmptrs, Anthropology, Econ; Archaeology & Museums 45 Quarters Hrs; *cr:* Xenia HS Soc Stud Tchr 1970-; *ai:* Steering Comm; N Centrl Assn Co-Chair; NEA 1970-; Phi Delta Kappa, OH Cncl for Soc Stud 1985-; Phi Alpha Theta 1971-; Martha Holden Jennings Fnd Schlr 1980-81; Catherine Greene Chapter of DAR Tchr of Yr 1983; Nom Western OH Ed Assn 1983-; Tchr of Yr 1987; *office:* Xenia H S 303 Kinsey Rd Xenia OH 45385

MALFER, THOMAS WAYNE, HS Mathematics Teacher; *b:* Johnstown, PA; *ed:* IN Univ of PA (BS) Math 1969; Masters Equivalency; *cr:* Greater Johnstown Schl Dist Math Tchr 1969-; *ai:* Chess Club Adv; NEA 1969-; PSEA 1969-; GJEA 1969-; *office:* Greater Johnstown HS 222 Central Ave Johnstown PA 15904

MALHAME, EUGENE G.,JR., Asst Prin & Soc Studies Tchr; *b:* Brooklyn, NY; *m:* Rosemary Elizabeth Simpson; *c:* Kara, Brianne; *ed:* St Anselm's Coll (BA) His 1971; Georgian Court Coll (MA) Admin, Supervision, Curr 1981; NJ Certs Soc Stud K-12, Prin & Supvr; Non-Pub Schl Prsnl Orientation HS Core Team 25 Addl Hrs; *cr:* St Mary's Regnl HS Asst Prin, Dean of Discipline, Soc Stud Dept Chm, Soc Stud Tchr 25 Yrs; *ai:* Discipline, Curr Comm, Core Team, Alumni; NJ Scndry Schl Tchrs Assn 1975-; NJ Soc Stud Cncl NCEA 1980-; ASCD 1989-; Shore Ofcls Soccer Assn 1973-89, Chm Prof Stans Comm; *office:* St Mary's Regnl HS 310 Augusta St South Amboy NJ 08879

MALIA, MARY, Fourth Grade Teacher; *b:* Scranton, PA; *ed:* Marywood Coll (BS) Home Ec, Ed 1960; 45 Addl Hrs; PA St Univ; Univ of Scranton 12 Addl Hrs; *cr:* Northeastern Hosp Dietitian 1960-63; Wilkes Barre Gen Hosp Dietitian 1963-65; Moses Taylor Hosp Dietitian 1965-70; Lackawanna Trail Schl Dist Elem Tchr 1970-; *ai:* Crisis Comm; After Schl Tutoring Prgm; PA St Ed Assn 1960-, Exec Comm; Lackawanna Trail Ed Assn 1960-, Pres; PA Cncl Tchrs of Math 1980-, Hospitality Comm for Annual Conf; Amer Red Cross 1960-, Vol; Women's Guild 1960-, Publicity Sec; Amer Cancer Soc 1985-, Vol; Prof Dev Coord; Schl Improvement Prgm Evaluator; PRIMES Prgm Coord; *office:* Lackawanna Trail Schl Dist Box 85 College Ave Factoryville PA 18419*

MALIANI, DIANE GUADAGNINO, English Teacher; *b:* Rochester, NY; *m:* Robert P. Sr.; *c:* David Samuel, Marianna-Hope; *ed:* Nazareth Coll of Rochester (BA) Eng, Ed 1970; Attnd Syracuse Univ 30 Hrs 1979, SUNY at Binghamton 30 Hrs 1970-71; Completed Grad Stud; *cr:* Whitesboro Cntrl Schl 9-12th Grd Tchr 1971-; *ai:* Goals 2000 Cadre; Group A Participant; Mediation Team; Accredited Mediator; NYSUT, AFT, WTA 1971-.

MALICAN, WILLIAM V., Teacher & Coach; *b:* Liverpool, NY; *ed:* Canisius Coll (BA) Amer His 1970; Purdue Univ (MA) Amer Stud 1972; Suny at Buffalo (MA) Ed 1978; 30 Grad Hrs Voc Ed, Admin & Drivers Ed; *cr:* Purdue Univ Tchng Asst 1971-72; Buffalo NY Tchr & Coach 1973-75; Hamburg Hs Tchr & Coach 1975-; *ai:* Cross Cntry, Indoor & Outdoor Track Head Coach; Hamburg TA 1975-, Bldg Rep, Retired Del; Nysut, AFT 1975-; Phi Delta Kappa 1985-; Amer Red Cross 1969-, Water Safety, Life Guard Instr; Empire St Games 1979-,Western Region Staff; NYS PHSAA 1989-, Section Chm; Western NY Coach on Yr Track 1983, 1987-88, 1990-91; Erie Cty Conf 20 Yr Svc Awd; *office:* Hamburg Sr HS 4111 Legion Dr Hamburg NY 14075*

MALIN, SUE A. MC CARTHY, Professor of Music; *b:* Lockport, NY; *m:* Denis R.; *ed:* IN Univ of PA (BS) Music Ed 1972; MI St Univ (MM) Music 1982; Penn St Univ (DED) Music Ed 1993; 3 Grad Credits Westminster Choir Coll; *cr:* Loyalsock Schl Dist Elem General Music Tchr 1972-74; East Grand Rapids Pub Schls Elem & MS Music Tchr 1974-83; Lock Haven Univ Prof of Music 1983-; *ai:* Tau Beta Sigma Honory Band Sorority Adv; General Ed Comm; Phi Kappa Phi Schlrsp Comm; Flutist & Classical Performer; Jazz Vocalist; Adv to Phi Sigma Pi Scholastic Frat; Music Educators Natl Conf 1972-; Phi Kappa Phi; Pi Kappa Lambda 1982-; PA Music Educators Assn 1983-; Lock Haven Music Club 1983-; Prof Jazz Singer; Classical Flutist; Pub Music Ed in Journal of Research, Music Educators Journal & Best of Elem Music; *office:* Lock Haven Univ 243 Sloan Fine Arts Center Lock Haven PA 17745*

MALINAK, ROBERT CHARLES, 5th Grade Teacher; *b:* Buffalo, NY; *m:* Donna Elizabeth Colwell; *c:* Aicia Marie; *ed:* Cntrl CT St Coll (BS) Elem Ed 1969; Seton Hall Univ (MS) Admin & Supervision 1975; 32 Credit Hrs Seton Hall Univ, Jersey City St Coll Cmptr Ed; *cr:* Wilson Schl 2-6 Grds Tchr 1970-; *ai:* Tech, Long Range Planning Comms; NEA 1970-; Caldwell-W Caldwell Ed Assn 1970-, Bldg Rep; Civil War Reenactment Group 15th NJ Vol Infantry 1985-; *office:* Wilson Elem Schl 71 Orton Rd West Caldwell NJ 07006

MALINAR, BRANKA MARIE (FRIGAN), Intervention Specialist; *b:* Popovec Croatia, OH; *m:* Jerry; *c:* Drina Irwin, Mirna, Vesna Elbert, Nada Rogers; *ed:* Baldwin-Wallace (BS) Elem Ed 1973; Cleveland St Univ (MA) Curr 1989; Cmptr Sci; Gifted Ed; *cr:* North Ridgeville City Schls Elem Tchr 1973-80, Gifted Ed Intervention Specialist 1980-; *ai:* Cmptr Coord; Young Authors; NEA 1973-; Phi Delta Kappa 1990-; Croatian Heritage 1984-, Pres; Museum, Lib, Librn; Educl Grants; *home:* 9037 Root Rd North Ridgeville OH 44039

MALINCONICO, ROSE G., Chem & Forensic Sci Teacher; *b:* Brooklyn, NY; *c:* Sharon Policano; *ed:* Brooklyn Coll (BA) Bio, Scndry Ed 1965; Hofstra Univ (MA) Scndry Ed, Sci 1977; 80 Post Grad Credits; *cr:* NY City Schls Jr. HS Sci Tchr 1964-66, Sub Tchr 1973-77; Long Beach Schls Bio, Earth Sci, Chem Tchr 1977-; *ai:* Stu Relations Comm; Sci Club, Sr Class Adv; AFT, NYSUT, ACS, NSTA 1977-; NYCCT 1995-; NSTA Grants; ICE Grant; Organized Stu Presentation for Elem Schls on Moon Rocks; *office:* Long Beach HS 322 Lagoon Dr W Long Beach NY 11561*

MALINOWSKI, CHARLES JOHN, Science Teacher; *b:* Dupont, PA; *m:* Janice Peaslee; *c:* Jon; *ed:* Lock Haven Univ (BS) Ed 1956; *cr:* BSA Dist Exec 1956-73; Industry Tool Designer 1973-87; Springfield HS Tchr 1987-; *ai:* Mth, Sci & Tech Lab; NEA 1987-; VT Sci Tchrs 1991-; *office:* Springfield HS 303 South St Springfield VT 05156

MALINOWSKI, JEAN L., Math Teacher; *b:* Passaic, NJ; *m:* Paul; *c:* Jason, Michael; *ed:* William Paterson Coll of NJ (BA) Applied Math with Cert 1990; Montclair St Coll; *cr:* First Natl Bank of NJ Teller, Cmptr Dept 1975-80; Lakeland St Bank Teller, Platform Asst 1980-90; Vernon Twp HS Math Tchr 1990-; *ai:* Soph Class Adv; AMTNJ 1990-, Publicity; Nom Presidential Awd Excl in Math Tchng; *office:* Vernon Township HS PO Box 800 Vernon NJ 07462*

MALKEVITCH, JOSEPH, Mathematics Professor; *b:* Brooklyn, NY; *m:* Nina Greenberg; *c:* Benjamin, Alexander; *ed:* Queens Coll at Flushing (BS) Math 1963; Univ of WI at Madison (MS) Math 1965, (PHD) Math 1969; *cr:* City Univ of NY York Coll Prof 1968-; *ai:* Math Club; Undergraduate Research; MAA 1963-; NY Acad of Scis 1970-, Math Section Chair; NY Acad of Scis Fellow; Phi Beta Kappa; Co-Author 2 Books Graphs, Models & Finite Math & For all Practical Purposes; Co-Ed 3 Books; Author Monograph; *office:* City Univ Of NY York Coll Math Dept Jamaica NY 11451*

MALLEN, JANET GREENE, 7th-8th Grade English Teacher; *b:* New York City, NY; *m:* Richard A.; *c:* Brett, Alexis; *ed:* Queens Coll (BA) Eng 1967; Hofstra Univ (MA) Scndry Ed 1971; Addl 75 Credits, 45 Grad, 30 In-Svc; *cr:* Udall Rd Jr HS Eng Tchr 1967-71; Harry B. Thompson MS Super Sub Tchr 1 Yr, Eng Tchr 1987-; *ai:* Yrbk Adv; Sunshine Club; Moving Up Comm 8th Grd; Awds Comm 7th Grd Team Liason; NYSUT, NCTE 1987-; Long Island Lang Arts Cncl 1995-; Hauppauge Bd of Ed 1984-89, VP; HYO Soccer, Bsbl 1980-89, Sec; *office:* H B Thompson MS 98 Ann Dr Syosset NY 11791*

MALLERY, BARBARA LOU BELLE, 5th-6th Grade Teacher; *b:* Baltimore, MD; *m:* Robert Ford; *c:* Marjorie J. Lotz, Robert Louis; *ed:* Towson Univ (BS) Ed 1952; Syracuse Univ Spec Ed Cert 1957; Univ of CT Gifted Cert 1980; Hebrew Univ 1993; Univ of MD Theatre; Johns Hopkins Rdng; Loyola Coll Psych; *cr:* Essex Tchr in Charge 1952-57; Villa Cresta Schl Tchr 1964-77; Dundalk HS GED Tchr 1970-80; Middlesex Schl Tchr 1978-93; Torah Inst Tchr 1993-; *ai:* NEA 1965-; MSTA 1965-, Del; BCTA 1965-, Rep; Articles & Poems Pub; *home:* 2900 Alden Rd Baltimore MD 21234*

MALLETTE, KRISTINE MARIE, French Teacher; *b:* Hornell, NY; *ed:* SUNY at Potsdam (BA) Fr 1985, (MS) Instrl Tech & Media Mgmt 1992; *cr:* Beaver River Cntrl Fr Tchr 1985-; *ai:* Fr Club & Sr Class Adv; After-Schl Tutorial Supvr; Choral Lang Coach; NYSUT 1985-; NYSAFLT 1995-; Presbyn Church 1987-, Choir Dir & Organist; *office:* Beaver River Central Schl PO Box 179 Artz Rd Beaver Falls NY 13305*

MALLIA, PAUL PATRICK, Math Tchr & Coach; *b:* Hartford, CT; *m:* Sharon Lund; *c:* Jim, Jill, Kim; *ed:* CCSU (BA) Math 1971, (ME) Ed 1978; *cr:* Newington HS Tchr, Coach 1971-; *ai:* Var Girls Soccer, Var Boys Ice Hockey Coach; NEA, CEA 1971-; Exch Club 1979-, Pres, Presidential Awd; Soccer Coach of Yr 1987; Soccer Coaching Awd 1985; *home:* 799 New Britain Ave Farmington CT 06032*

MALLORY, KATHLEEN CLAIRE, Principal; *b:* Toronto Ontario, Canada; *ed:* Univ of Toronto (BA) Pol Sci 1971; Univ of New Brunswick (BED) Scnd Ed 1972; Pensacola Chrstn Coll (MS) Educl Admin 1984; *cr:* Fredericton HS His Tchr 1972-76; Brunswick St Bapt Church Chrstn Ed Dir 1976-78; Heritage Acad Tchr, Prin 1978-; *office:* Heritage Acad 12215 Walnut Pt W Hagerstown MD 21740*

MALLOY, THOMAS PAUL, English Teacher; *b:* Binghamton, NY; *m:* Margaret Creagh; *c:* Maureen E.; *ed:* SUNY at Geneseo (BS) Ed, Eng 1968; SUC at Cortland 30 Credit Hrs Eng, Ed; *cr:* Susquehanna Vly Jr HS Eng Tchr 1967-; *ai:* Dist Spelling Bee Coord; NEA, AFT 1967-; SVTA 1967-, Pres, VP, Chief Negotiator, Grievance Chm; *office:* Susquehanna Valley Jr HS Box 225 1048 Conklin Rd Conklin NY 13748*

MALLOZZI, MARY ANN HOFFMAN, Third Grade Teacher; *b:* Maspeth, NY; *m:* John S.; *c:* John Jr., Michael; *ed:* St John's Univ (BS) Elem Ed 1963, (MS) Elem Ed 1964; 30 Addl Credits; *cr:* PS 113 Elem Ed Tchr 1964-; *ai:* New Rochelle Theatre Works 1991-, Bd of Dirs; *office:* PS 113 Isaac Chauncey Schl 87-21 79th Ave Glendale NY 11385

MALLY, NANCY GAIL, Language Arts Teacher; *b:* Hartford, CT; *m:* Paul G.; *c:* Charles Paul, Scott David, Kevin Richard; *ed:* OH St Univ (BA) Eng Ed 1970; Coll of Mount St Joseph (MA) Ed 1988; Post Grad Courses; *cr:* River Vly HS 7-11th Grd Lang Arts Tchr 1970-; *ai:* Class, Chrldng, Jr HS Yrbk Adv; Asst Dir; Schl Musicals; RVTA 1970-, Sec; COTA, NEA 1970-; Phi Delta Kappa 1988-; Presbyn Church 1985-, Deacon 3 Yrs; United Way 1970-, Yth Coord for Marion Cty, Yth Ldrshp; Hnr Soc Awded Tchr of Yr 1982-83; NCTE Convention Presentor 1993; Statewide Portfolio Conf Ldr 1995; *office:* River Valley HS 1267 Columbus Sandusky Rd N Marion OH 43302

MALMBURG, CHARLES JOSEPH, Engineering Professor; *b:* Dunkirk, NY; *ed:* Univ of MA (BS) Industrial Engr 1977; GA Tech (MS) Industrial Engr 1978, (PHD) Industrial Engr 1981; *cr:* VA Tech Asst Prof 1982-85; Rensselaer Polytechnic Inst Asst Prof 1985-88, Assoc Prof 1988-95, Prof 1995-; *ai:* Alpha Pi Mu Adv; DSEJ Dept Assoc Chair; Grad Prgm Dir; IIE 1978-; INFORMS, IEEE 1982-; 100 Journal Articles & Other Publications; Sponsored Research; *office:* Rensselaer Polytechnic Inst 110 8th St Troy NY 12180

MALOBICKY, JOHN JOSEPH, Computer Science Teacher; *b:* Natrona Heights, PA; *m:* Dr. Roberta Bock; *c:* John III; *ed:* Univ of NC (AB) His 1966; Univ of Pittsburgh (BS) Scndry Ed 1972, (MED) Ed 1977, (PHD) Ed 1986; *cr:* Blaw Knox Steel Open Hearth Supvr 1966-73; South Butler Cty Schl Dist Cmptr Sci Tchr 1973-; *ai:* Sugar Loaf Hill Homeowners 1988-, Pres 1995-; Ftbl Coach-Offensive Line & Defensive Coord 1974-78; Dissertation-Programming Processes of Scndry Stdnts-Planning Activity, Strategy Selection & Error Production; Coll in HS Prgm Meritorious Svc Awd From Univ of Pittsburgh; *office:* Knoch Jr & Sr HS Knoch Rd Saxonburg PA 16056

MALOFF, RICHARD M., Science Teacher; *b:* Syracuse, NY; *ed:* SUC at Buffalo (BA) Lib Arts Sociology 1969; Hunter Coll Scndry Ed Sci 1977; Brooklyn Coll 12 Credit Hrs; Attnd Brooklyn Law Schl; *cr:* J117K Frances Scott Key JHS Sci Tchr 1972-87; J22M Gustave Straubenmuller JHS Sci Tchr 1987-; *ai:* Involved in Jr HS Restructuring; Bank St Coll Model; Gifted & Talented Pgm; AFT & UFT 1972-; Beth Israel Med Ctr 1985-, Vol; Mint Schls Johnson City Pgm Magnet Grant; *office:* Gustave Straubenmuller Jr HS 111 Columbia St New York NY 10002

MALONE, BARBARA MARSHALL, Second Grade Teacher; *b:* Middletown, CT; *m:* Vincent P.; *c:* Elizabeth, Jennifer; *ed:* Cntrl CT St U (BS) Elem Ed 1961, (MS) Rdng 1981; *cr:* Spencer Schl 2 Grd Tchr 1961-63; VanBuren Moody Schl 2 Grd Tchr 1978-; *office:* Van Buren Moody Elem Schl 300 Country Club Rd Middletown CT 06457

MALONE, CAROL J., English Teacher; *b:* Baltimore, MD; *ed:* Univ of SC (MA) Eng 1971; Loyola Coll (MS) Psych 1988; *cr:* Maryvale Schl Tchr 1971-79, 1987-; Catonsville Comm Coll Tchr 1979-87; *ai:* Lit Magazine; NCTE; NCTA; *office:* Maryvale Prep Schl 11300 Falls Rd Brooklandville MD 21022

MALONE, GEORGE MANUEL, Pastor; *b:* Marion, OH; *m:* Helen Peterson; *c:* Paul Matthew, Andrew Michael; *ed:* Circleville Bible Coll (THB) Theology 1979; Wesley Biblical Seminary 1984-84; *cr:* Faith Chrstn SChl 5trh Grd Tchr 1990-92, His Tchr 1990-94; *ai:* Geog Bee Chm 1992-94; Boys' PE Tchr 1990-92; Ellet-Suffield Clergy Group 1994-; Akron Area Nazarene Minister Assn 1994-, Treas; DAR His Tchr of Yr 1994; *home:* 444 Dennison Ave Akron OH 44312

MALONE, KENNETH R., Mathematics Teacher; *b:* Passaic, NJ; *ed:* Montclair St Univ (BA) Math 1967, (MA) Math 1973; 30 Grad Credits Supvr & Prin Certs; *cr:* Passaic Vly HS Math Tchr 1967-; *ai:* Chm Andrew Hackes Schlsp, Math Awd Marcliff Schlsp; NEA, NJEA, PVEA, NCTM 1967-; Grace Church 1965-, Chm Bd Deacons, Elders; Exemplary Edctr 1985-90; Tchr of Yr 1989; Governor's Tchr Recognition Awd 1995; *office:* Passaic Valley HS East Main St Little Falls NJ 07424

MALONE, LAURENCE JOSEPH, Associate Prof of Economics; *b:* Troy, NY; *m:* Eva Trelease Davidson; *c:* Luke; *ed:* Purchase Coll (BA) Ec 1979; New Schl for Soc Research (PHD) Ec 1991; *cr:* Hartwick Coll Assoc Prof of Ec 1985-; *ai:* Fac Cncl; Ec Dept Chair; AEA, EHA 1985-; Bunn Awd for Tchng Excl; CDS Intnl Grant; Co-Ed The Essential Adam Smith WW Norton 1986; *office:* Hartwick Coll Bresee Hall Oneonta NY 13820

MALONE, LOIS LUKE, Adjunct Prof & Dir Stu Svcs; *b:* Franklin, NJ; *c:* Robin Wendy; *ed:* Douglass Coll (BA) Eng 1967; Rutgers Univ Schl of Law (JD) Law 1975; *cr:* Division Youth & Family Svcs Soc Worker 1967-69; Torii Army Ed Ctr Dir, Tchr 1969-71; Private Law Practice Attorney 1976-84; St Vincent Martyr Schl Tchr 1986-87; Mt St Dominic Acad Tchr 1987-89; Fairleigh Dickinson Univ Adjunct Prof, Dir Stu Svcs 1989-; *ai:* Ath Acad Review, Charter Day Schlsp, Martin Luther King Jr. Schlsp Comm; Natl Acad Advising Assn 1992-, Omicron Delta Kappa

1996-, Adv; NJ Bar Assn 1976-; Natl Bone Marrow Drive Organizer 1991-; Awded Life-Time Membership Omicron Delta Kappa Natl Leadership Soc Outstanding Contributions to Stdnts & Svc; *office:* Fairleigh Dickinson Univ 285 Madison Ave Madison NJ 07940*

MALONE, MARJORIE ANN, 5th Grade Elementary Teacher; *b:* Oswego, NY; *m:* Timothy C.; *c:* Margaret A. Knopp, Emily A. Knopp; *ed:* SUNY at Oswego (BS) Elem Ed 1984, (MS) Rdng 1989; *cr:* Minetto Elem Schl 5th & 6th Grd Tchr 1984-; *ai:* AFT 1984-, NYSUT 1984-; NYS Tchrs Retirement 1984-; OCTA 1984-; Oswego YMCA 1992-; Minetto Home & Schl 1991-; Minetto PreSchool Coop 1991-; *office:* Minetto Elem Schl Granby Rd Oswego NY 13126

MALONE, PATRICIA BULICEK, Reading Recovery Teacher; *b:* Cleveland, OH; *m:* Donald Anthony; *c:* Donald Jr., Michael Earle, Melissa Terra; *ed:* Lake Eric Coll (BS) Elem 1978; Rdng Cert; Post Grad; CTE Cleveland St Univ; Rdng Recovery Cert Cleveland St; *cr:* Thomas Jefferson Schl Grd 4 Tchr 1979-80; Upson Schl Grd 2 Tchr 1980-81; Willoughby Rdng Specialist 1981-82; Eastlake Schl Rdng Specialist 1981-82; Roosevelt Schl Grd 2 Tchr 1982-95, Rdng Recovery Tchr 1995-; *ai:* Conflict Mediation Coord; Stu Cncl Adv; PTA Liaison; NEA, IRA, OEA 1979-; ETA 1979-, Schl Rep, Outstdng Edctr; Kiwanis; Outstdng Tchr of Yr Euclid Cncl PTA 1990; Outstdng Tchr of Yr Euclid Tchrs Assn 1992; *office:* Roosevelt Elem Schl 551 E 200th St Cleveland OH 44119

MALONE, THOMAS EDWARD, Social Studies & Speech Tchr; *b:* Toledo, OH; *m:* Susan Ann Dariano; *c:* Casey, Brendan, Garrett; *ed:* Univ of Toledo (BA) Lbrl Arts 1973, (MA) Amer His 1980; 24 Hrs Scndry Ed; *cr:* Univ of Toledo Grad Asst 1979-80; St John's Jesuit Tchr, Admin 1980-; Lourdes Coll Part-time Instr 1992-; *ai:* Fall Play Dir; Bookstore Mgr; Father's Club Moderator; NCEA 1980-; Phi Alpha Theta; *office:* St John's Jesuit HS 5901 Airport Hwy Toledo OH 43615*

MALONE, THOMAS MICHAEL, English Teacher; *b:* Holyoke, MA; *m:* Darcia Jones; *c:* Meghan; *ed:* Univ of MA (BA) Eng 1970; Amer Intnl Coll (MAT) Ed, Eng; Univ of MA 18 Credit Hrs Toward CAGS; *cr:* Somers HS Tchr of Eng 1970-; *ai:* NHS Adv; Eng Curr Team Ldr; Mentor Tchr St of CT Cert for First Yr Tchr; Co-Operatus Tchr St of CT Cert for Stu Tchr; Somers Educ Assn, NEA 1975-; Granby MA Bd of Assessors 1983-91 MA Certfd Assesor, Elective Office Chm of Bd 1985, 1988; Commencement Speaker by Invitation of Class of 1994, 1980; Mentor Tchr 1990-; *office:* Somers HS Ninth District Rd Somers CT 06071*

MALONEY, CHERYL RYAN, History Teacher; *b:* Springfield, MA; *m:* Paul J. Jr.; *c:* Patrick, Christine; *ed:* Mount Holyoke (BA) His 1973; Boston Coll (MA) His 1993; Univ of Ma at Amherst 18 Credits Grad Schl of Ed; Northestern Univ Eng Grad Work; Univ of Chicago Pub Course; *cr:* So Hadley HS His Tchr 1073-79; Rand Mc Nally Publishing Editor, Soc Stud Tchr 1979-83; Ed Dev Co Consultant, Curr 1984-85; Weston Pub Schls His Tchr 1985-; *ai:* Asian Stu Unionv, MA Stu Govt Day Adv; Human Relations Facilitator; NEA, MTA 1973-79, 1985-; MA Cncl Soc Stud 1973-79, 1985-; Western Cultural Diversity Comm Mem; Rhomba Comm 1995-; Mt Holyoke Awareness Pres; Advanced Placement Fac Consultant; *office:* Weston HS 444 Wellesley St Weston MA 02193

MALONEY, DIANE BERNEBURG, Associate Professor; *b:* Pittsburgh, PA; *m:* Robert D.; *c:* Heather Kochen, Stephanie Kochen; *ed:* OH Northern Univ (BS) Acctng 1983; Ashland Univ (MBA) 1990; *cr:* Northwestern Coll Assoc Prof 1983-91; Lima Tech Coll Assoc Prof 1991-; *ai:* IMA 1989-; OH Soc of CPAs 1991-; AICPA 1991-; *office:* Lima Tech Coll 4240 Campus Dr Lima OH 45804

MALONEY, EILEEN KATHRYN, Eng Teacher & Department Chair; *b:* Buffalo, NY; *ed:* Canisius Coll (BA) Elem Ed 1974; Univ at Buffalo (MA) Scndry Eng Ed 1983; Admin Courses; Learning Styles Course; Western NY Writing Project; *cr:* St Agatha's Schl 5-8 Grd Tchr 1974-78; St Benedict's Schl 6-8 Grd Sci, Hlth Tchr 1978-80; Buffalo Acad of the Sacred Heart Schl 9-12 Grd Eng Tchr 1980-; *ai:* Dept Head; Mid Sts Schl Planning Team; Sr Class, Newspaper, Lit Magazine Moderator; Canisius Coll Cooperating Tchr for Stu Tchrs; Design Team for Schls Long Range Planning; NEA, NCEA 1974-; NCTE 1980-; Kolbe Cath Schl Bd 1995-, Ed Comm; Western NY Writing Project Bd 1994-; Rel Educator of Yr 1975; Co-Author Tchng Material; Mid Sts Evaluation Teams 4 Visitations 1985-; *office:* Buffalo Acad Of Sacred Heart 3860 Main St Buffalo NY 14226*

MALONEY, ELLIOTT CHARLES,OSB, Religious Studies Dept Chair; *b:* Pittsburgh, PA; *ed:* St Vincent Coll (BA) Philosophy 1968; Pontifical Atheneum of St Anselim Rowe (STL) Theology 1972; Fordham Univ (PHD) New Testament Studies 1979; *cr:* St Vincent Coll Asst Prof & Full Prof 1978-, Chprsn Rel Stud Dept 1986-; *ai:* Campus Landscaping Consultant; Vocalist; CBA, SBL 1972-; Book: Semitic Interference in Marcan Syntax; Articles 1986; *office:* Saint Vincents Coll & Sem 300 Fraser Purchase Rd Latrobe PA 15650*

MALONEY, KEVIN EDWARD, Guidance Counselor; *b:* Woonsocket, RI; *m:* Paula H. Powers; *c:* Brian, Kristen; *ed:* Worcester St Coll (BSEd) Soc Stud 1968; Univ of HI (MED) Ed Psych 1973; Attnd Brown Univ; *cr:* US Navy Admin 1968-73; Blackstone-Millville Reg HS Guid Cnslr 1974-; *ai:* Boy's Cross Cntry Natl Record Holders Longest Winning Streak, Track & Field Coach; NEA 1974-; MA Schl Cnslrs Assn; *office:* Blackstone-Millville Regnl HS 175 Lincoln St Blackstone MA 01504

MALONEY, MARY THERESA, English Teacher; *b:* Warren, OH; *ed:* Hiram Coll (BA) Eng-Cum Laude 1993; Youngstown St Univ (MA) Eng 1996; Prof Writing, Editing Cert; Graphics Design Internship; *cr:* Howland HS Eng Tutor 1994-95; Warren City Schls ABLE Tchr 1993-; Ursuline HS 10th-11th Grd Eng Tchr 1993-; *ai:* SADD Adv; Audio, Visual Coord; Speech Team Debate Judge; NCTE, OAACE, ABLE 1995-; OEA, NEA 1993-; Kappa Delta Pi 1993-; *office:* Ursuline HS 750 Wick Ave Youngstown OH 44505*

MALONEY, MAUREEN MURPHY, Instructor of Psychology; *b:* Jamaica Queens, NY; *m:* Paul K.; *c:* Jennifer Maloney Seka, Paula, Edward Paul; *ed:* Holy Name Hosp Schl of Nrsng (RN) Neurosurgery 1962; Sacred Heart Univ (BS) Psych 1982; Fairfield Univ (MA) Applied Psych 1986; 3 Hrs Univ of Hartford; *cr:* Neurological Inst Columbia Presbyn Hosp Head Nurse 1962-65; Silver Hill Psychiatric Hosp Staff Psychiatric Nurse, Tchr 1992-93; Housatonic C&T Coll Asst Prof of Psych 1993-; *ai:* Drug, Alcohol Rehabilitation Prgm Liaison; Tchng Partnership; NHS 1958-, Acad Hnrs Awd; Sigma Lambda 1980-82, Dean's List 1980-82, 1986; Amer Psych Assn; Amer Psych Soc; Norwalk Symphony Trustee 12 Yrs; Mayor's Awd 1986; *office:* Housatonic Comm-Tech College 510 Barnum Ave Bridgeport CT 06608*

MALONEY, MELONEY, Rel, Global & Soc Stud Teacher; *b:* Great Neck, NY; *ed:* Marywood Coll (BA) Soc Stud 1964, (MA) Cnslng 1988; Univ of Notre Dame (MA) European His 1969; Attnd Dequesne Univ, Hofstra; *cr:* IHM Sisters Vocation Dir 1983-89; Holy Cross HS Tchr, Dir of Peace & Justice Ctr 1989-94; Our Lady of Guadalupe Parish Dir, Summer Migrant Prgm 1989-; Aquinas HS Tchr 1994-; *ai:* Amnesty Intnl Club; Tutoring Prgm; ESL Tutor; Pax Christi 1986-, Nom Peace Awd; Interracial Comm of Dist 6 Bronx 1995-; Comm Bd; Serve Amer, Svc to Migrants Grants;

MALONEY, MIRIAM GARY, Eng Dept Chprsn & Teacher; *b:* Philadelphia, PA; *m:* Francis E.; *ed:* La Salle Coll (BA) Eng 1974; Temple Univ (MSE) Eng Ed 1978; *cr:* Bishop Mc Devitt HS Eng Tchr 1975-, Eng Dept Chair 1985-; *ai:* Mrktg Comm; Forensics Co-Moderator; Sr Prom Moderator; NCTE 1978-; ASCD 1990-; *office:* Bishop Mc Devitt HS 125 Royal Ave Wyncote PA 19095

MALONEY, PHYLLIS A. MIRAGLIA, Social Studies Teacher; *b:* Philadelphia, PA; *m:* Edward John; *c:* Edward J. Jr., Mary Regina, Joseph J., Theresa Ann; *ed:* Univ of PA (BS) Sociology 1973, (MA) Comprehensive Soc Sci 1975, (PHD) Ldrshp Admin 1985; Post Grad Stud Harvard Univ, Villanova Univ; *cr:* St Maria Goretti HS Soc Stud Chair 1973-83; Guynedd-Mercy Coll Adj Prof Allied Hlth 1983-88; Univ of PA Adj Prof Grad Ed 1983-89; Villanova Univ Adj Prof His 1983-93; *ai:* AFT, NEA, AAUP, ASCS, PDK, NCSS, PCSS 1973-; Lindback 1988-; Haverford Civic League for Women 1990-; Var Articles Pub; Collegiate Press Advy Bd.

MALONEY, SYLVIA ROMANOSKI, Mathematics Chair; *b:* Wilkes-Barre, PA; *c:* Julianne Maloney Clifford; *ed:* Coll Misericordia (BS) Chem & Math 1961; WA coll (MA) Psych 1974; Cert Supervision & Scndry Schl Prin; *cr:* Iselin Jr High Tchr 1961-64; Elkton Jr & Sr High Tchr 1964-66; Chestertown High Tchr 1969-71; Kent Cty High Tchr 1971-, Math Tchr & Chair 1989-; *ai:* Drama Dir & Producer 1982-; NEA, MSTA & KCTA 1971-; NCTM & MCTM 1980-; ASCD 1992-; Friends of Kent Cty Lib 1975-, Past Pres; Chestertown Tea Party 1979-; Church Hill Theatre 1985-, Awd for Direction; St Task Force for Grad Requirements 1983; Asst Dir Gifted & Talented Summer Ctr 1984-89; Governors Acad for Math & Sci 1990; Phillips Exeter Conf for Math & Tech; MD Arts Cncl Grant; *office:* Kent Co HS 25301 Lambs Meadow Rd Worton MD 21678

MALOY, JAMES W., Physics Teacher; *b:* Washington, PA; *m:* Sharon Kaye Stutler; *c:* J.R.; *ed:* Washington & Jefferson Coll (BA) Chem 1966; WV Univ 48 Credits Chem; CA Univ of PA 18 Credits Math Cert; Univ of Pittsburgh 6 Credits Cmptr; Cert in Chem & Physics; *cr:* WV Univ Grad Asst, Part Time Instr 1966-72; Wash & Jeff Instr 1973-76; Industrial Exp Sales, Instruments & Cmptr 1976-87; Chantien Houston HS Physics Tchr 1987-88; Beth-center HS Physics Tchr 1988-; *ai:* PA Jr Acad of Sci, Spon & Region 8 Dir; Stud Cncl Spon; Girls Soccer Coach; Soc of Analytical Chem 1972-, Spectroscopy Soc of Pittsburgh 1973-, W. PA Sec AM Asso of Physics Tchr 1987-, Sec Treas; PSEA 1987-; Strategic Planning Comm 1993-; Master Tchr WQED Natl Tchr Trng Inst; New Valley Consortium 3 Grants; Spectroscopy Soc of Pittsburgh 2 Grants; Schl to Work Fellowship; Optical Soc of Amer 2 Grants; *office:* Bethlehem Ctr Sr HS 179 Crawford Rd Fredericktown PA 15333*

MALSEED, ZORIANA KAWKA, Associate Prof of Physiology; *b:* Stryj, Ukraine; *m:* Roger T.; *c:* Mark, Natalie; *ed:* Philadelphia Coll of Pharmacy & Sci (BS) Pharmacy 1966, (MS) Pharmacology 1970-, (PHD) Pharmacology 1973; *cr:* Univ of PA Lecturer 1971-72, Instr 1972-73, Asst Prof 1973-74, Assoc Prof 1974-; *ai:* Undergraduate Adv; Doctoral Admissions, Prsnl, Undergraduate Curr Comm; NY Acad of Scis 1978-; Amer Assn for Advancement of Sci 1976-; Ukrainian Educl & Cultural Assn 1980-; Lindback Awd Distngd Tchng 1981; Honorary MA Outstdng Young Women of Amer 1974; Rsrch Fellow Amer Fnd Pharmaceutical Ed 1966-72; *office:* Univ Of PA NEB-Guardian Dr Philadelphia PA 19104

MALSON, MARY ANNE LEE, Fourth Grade Teacher; *b:* White Plains, NY; *m:* Barry K.; *ed:* St Univ Coll at Potsdam (BA) Elem Ed 1969; Attnd Coll of New Rochelle, Manhattanville Coll, Iona Coll; *cr:* Haverstraw Elem 4th Grd Tchr 1969-71; West Haverstraw Elem 4th Grd tchr 1971-; *ai:* North Rockland Schl Dist Tech Cncl, Soc Stud Comm; Awds, Assemblies Comm; NY St United Tchrs, AFT 1969-; Trinit United Meth Church 1954-, Trustee, Chprsn, Pastor, Parish Relations Comm, Sunday Schl Tchr; The Voices of Trinity Choir Chaplain; *office:* West Haverstraw Elem Schl Blauvelt Ave West Haverstraw NY 10993*

MALSTROM, KATHLEEN ANNE, French Teacher; *b:* Baltimore, MD; *ed:* Coll of Notre Dame of MD (BA) Fr 1965; Middlebury Coll (MA) Fr 1973; Ger 16 Hrs; Arabic 12 Hrs; *cr:* Elem Schls Tchr 1949-64; Archbishop Keough HS Fr Tchr, Dept Chair 1969-79; Notre Dame Prep HS Fr Tchr 1980-85; Saint Maria Goretti HS Prin, Fr Tchr 1985-87; Seton Keough HS Dept Chair, Fr Tchr 1988-; *ai:* Acad Cncl; Fr Club; Frosh Adv; MD FL Assn, AATF 1974-; Schl Sisters of Notre Dame 1949-, Rome Intnl Educl Conf Del 1985, 1987; Tchr of Yr 1995; *office:* Seton Keough HS 1201 S Caton Ave Baltimore MD 21227

MALTACEA, JOSEPH PAUL, 11th Grade Health Educator; *b:* Somerville, MA; *m:* Carole Ann Baumgart; *c:* Michelle An Bishop, Jennifer Marie; *ed:* Boston St Coll (BS) PE 1973; Univ of MA at Boston (MSED) Scndry Admn 1980; Attnd Tufts Univ; *cr:* Joyce Jr HS Physical Sci Tchr 1973-85; Woburn HS Hlth Ed 1986-; *ai:* Boys, Girls Cross Cntry Coach 6 Yrs; Indoor, Outdoor Head Track Coach 23 Yrs; Peer Ldr Adv 4 Yrs; SADD Adv, Peer Mediation Coord; NEA, MTA 1973-; MA St Track Coll 1973-95, Division I Coach of Yr Girls Indoor Track; Domestic Violence Task Force; Chrprsn of Hlth Dept; *office:* Woburn Sr HS 88 Montvale Ave Woburn MA 01801*

MALTESE, RALPH, High School Teacher; *b:* Bronx, NY; *m:* Polley Ott; *c:* Christine, Rebecca, Meredith, James; *ed:* Villanova Univ (BS) Ed 1968; IN Univ at Bloomington (MA) Eng 1970; Temple Univ, Penn St Univ, Beaver Coll 36 Credit Hrs; *cr:* Ridgefield Memrl HS Tchr 1969; Abington Schl Dist Tchr 1970-; *ai:* Dist Comms; NEA 1970-; AEA; Natl Endowment for Hum Grant 1986; 2 Articles Pub; *office:* Abington Schl Dist Highland Ave Abington PA 19001*

MALYUK, ANNE MYERS, 5th & 6th Grade Teacher; *b:* Franklin, PA; *m:* John R.; *c:* Scott J. Green; *ed:* Slippery Rock Univ (BS) Elem Spec Ed 1972; Edinboro Uni (MS) Elem 1976; *cr:* Clymer Cntrl Schl 3rd-6th Grd Tchr 1972-; *ai:* NEA 1972-; *office:* Clymer Central Schl PO Box 580 Main St Clymer NY 14724

MAMAKAS, MARIA, High School Mathematics Tchr; *b:* Nassau, Bahamas; *ed:* Youngstown St Univ (BS) Scndry Ed 1992; *cr:* Rayen HS Math Tchr 1993-; *ai:* Adv Math Club, Jr Class, Pep Club; Honor Roll Comm.

MAMAKOS-WERNER, CYNTHIA ANN LASH, English Tchr & Admin Asst; *b:* Hamburg, Germany; *m:* William Thomas Werner; *c:* Dean, Lauren; *ed:* Seton Hall Univ (BS) Sec Ed, Eng 1984, (MA) Psych Stud 1991; Post Grad Stud Schl & Comm Psych; *cr:* Eastside HS Eng Tchr 11 Yrs; *ai:* NJEA, NCTE 1984-; APA 1991-; Future Tchrs Amer Grant; *office:* Eastside HS 150 Park Ave Paterson NJ 07501*

MAMANA, LISA ANN, English Teacher; *b:* Easton, PA; *ed:* Penn St Univ (BA) Eng 1989, (MED) Eng Ed 1995; *cr:* Bishop Hafey HS Eng Tchr 1992-93; Abington Heights HS Eng Tchr 1993-; *ai:* Soph Class, Book Club Adv; Stu Support Team; *office:* Abington Hghts HS 401 W Grove St Clarks Summit PA 18411*

MAMONE, DENISE BRISSON, French Teacher; *b:* Berlin, NH; *m:* Joseph G.; *ed:* Univ of NH (BA) Fr Lit 1970; Addl Work Art His, Scndry Ed; *cr:* Sunapee Cntrl Schl Fr Tchr 1970-71; Milford MS Fr Tchr 1972-; *ai:* AATF, NHATFL 1971-; *office:* Milford MS 33 Osgood Rd Milford NH 03055*

MANARD, BELINDA MC GINNIS, Language Art Curriculum Spclst; *b:* Dennison, OH; *m:* Robert S.; *c:* Makenzie; *ed:* Miami Univ of OH (BS) Eng, Theater 1971; Coll of Mt St Joseph (MED) 1986; 32 Hrs Kent St Univ, Ashland Univ, Malone Coll, Akron Univ; *cr:* Cloverleaf HS Speech & Debate Tchr 1975-76; Mc Kinley Sr HS Eng Tchr, Eng Dept Chair, Testing Coord 1977-; Kent St Stark Branch Eng Prof 1989-91; *ai:* NHS, Lit Magazine, Story Telling Team Adv; Proficiency Test Tutor; Mentor Tchr; Curr Cncl; Prep Trainer; NCTE 1977-, Ctr of Excl Coord; OCTELA CPEA1977-; 5 Time Impact II Grant Winner; CPEA Tchr of Y *office:* Mc Kinley Sr HS 2323 17th St NW Canton OH 44708

MANASCO, GARY WAYNE, Science & PE Teacher; *b:* Bellevue, Brenda M. Stoldt; *c:* Jonathon, Alison; *ed:* Univ of North AL (BS His 1977; Bowling Green St Univ Sci; *cr:* South Cntrl HS PE Tch Seneca East HS Sci & PE Tchr 1990-; *ai:* Bsktbl Coach 6 Yrs; Fa Yrs; NEA, OEA, SEEA, Natl Sci Tchrs Assn 1990-; Stu AL E 1976-77, St Pres; Stu Natl Ed Assn 1976-, Natl Ex Comm; B Kiwanis 1981-87, Pres.*

MANBECK, MARGARET A. (SPITTIER), Biology Teacher; *b* Reading, PA; *m:* Dennis J.; *c:* Kate Elizabeth, Beth Aileen, Ryan *ed:* Kutztown Univ (BS) Ed, Bio, Gen Sci 1973; Temple Univ (M 1977; Penn St Univ 44 Post Grad Credits; *cr:* Rdng Schl Dist Jr Sci Tchr 1973-74; Wilson Schl Dist Jr HS Gen Sci Tchr 1974-81; El Dist 6th Grd Life Sci Tchr 1985-91; Conrad Weiser Schl Di Advanced Bio Tchr 1991-; *ai:* Stu Assistance Team; Stu Cnc Requirement Comm; NEA, NSTA, PSTA 1973-; Berks Cty Pub Ed Tchr of Yr 1992; Prose to Poetry Sci Classroom Wkshp; Cord Applied Tech; TESA Ldr; *office:* Conrad Weiser Area Schl Dist 347 Ave Robesonia PA 19551*

MANBECK, SANDRA POTTS, Mathematics Teacher; *b:* Pine Gro *m:* Richard D.; *c:* Kristen Manbeck Kaufman, Kent; *ed:* Susquehan (AB) Math & Bio 1965; Addl 27 Hrs of Credit in Ed Wilkes Uni Prgm; *cr:* Williams Vly Schls math Tchr 1965-66; Line Mountai Math Tchr 1984; Pine Grove Area Schls Math, Cmptr, Sci Tchr 19 Chrldng Coach; NEA, PSEA, PGEA 1984-; *office:* Pine Grove A School St Pine Grove PA 17963

MANCHESTER, LINDA GODFREY, First Grade Teacher; *b:* Uti *m:* Mark A.; *c:* Megan; *ed:* SUNY at Geneseo (BS) Elem Ed, Music Grad Credits Russell Sage, SUNY at Oswego, SUNY at Cortla Central Sq Cntrl Schl Elem Music Tchr 1969-72; Averill Park Cn Elem Music Tchr 1972-75; Madison Cntrl Schl 1st-3rd Grd Mus 1975-; *ai:* NEA, NYSUT 1969-; Madison Tchr Assn 1975-; Easte 1988-; Church Choir Dir, Organist 1985-; *office:* Madison Central 20 Madison NY 13402*

MANCHESTER, MARK ALLISON, Professor of Mathematics; Berlin, NY; *m:* Linda Jean Godfrey; *c:* Megan; *ed:* SUNY at Osweg Secondary Ed Math 1970, (MA) 1972; SUNY Inst of Tech (MS) Cm 1991; *cr:* SUNY at Oswego Grad Asst 1970-72; North Colonie Cn Math Tchr 1972-75; SUNY at Morrisonville Instr, Asst, Asso 1975-93, Prof 1993-; *ai:* NCTM, NYSMATYC 1976-; Article Pub; SUNY at Morrisville Rt 20 Morrisville NY 13408

MANCHESTER, SIDNEY RONALD, Health & PE Teacher; *b:* Er *m:* Martha Lynn; *c:* Bethany, Brooke; *ed:* Slippery Rock Univ (B 1976; Addl 24 Credit Hrs; *cr:* Corry YMCA Recreation Dir 1 Yr; C McLane HS Tchr 20 Yrs; *ai:* Var Bsbl & Jr Var Girls Bsktbl Coach, PSEA 1976-; Fairview Presbyn Church 1980-, Elder & Youth Grou Giant Eagle Golden Apple Awd-Tchr of Week; Bsbl Coach of Yr; General Mc Lane HS 11771 Edinboro Rd Edinboro PA 16412

MANCINELLI, ANGELA, English Teacher; *b:* Montclair, NJ; *m. c:* Dennis Sasso; *ed:* Fairleigh Dickinson (BA) Eng Ed 1971; Jerse St (MA) Basic & Urban Ed 1985; 30 Addl Credit Hrs Supvr 19 Archbishop Walsh HS Eng Tchr 1971-84; Hillside HS Eng Tchr 19 9th Grd Acad Team Ldr; Acad Decathlon Coord, Coach; Pa Adoption Prgm Coord; Schl Paper Ed; Eng Dept Curr Ldr; NEA, 1985-; ASCD 1987-; NJ Governors Tchr Recognition Awd 1995; Hillside HS 1085 Liberty Ave Hillside NJ 07205*

MANCINELLI, JOSEPH A., 7th & 8th Grade Math Teach Monongahela, PA; *m:* Cynthia Jo McCathren; *c:* Meghan E., Meli *ed:* CA Univ of PA Math, Scndry Ed (BS) 1973, (MED) 1981; 24 in Accounting; *cr:* Finley Jr HS Math Tchr 1974-86; Ringgold HS Tchr 1986-92; CA Univ of PA Part-Time Instr 1989-92; Univ of Pitt Evaluator for Quasar 1992-95; Finley MS Math Instr 1992-; *ai:* REA 1973-; Westmoreland Gymnastics Parents Club 1995-; *office:* Finl Rt 88 Finleyville PA 15332

MANCINELLI, KATHLEEN ELIZABETH, Fifth Grade Teach New Eagle, PA; *ed:* California Univ of PA (BS) Elem 1975, (MED 1980; Attnd Univ of Pittsburgh 1982-83, Westmoreland Comm Coll *cr:* Ginger Hill Schl 2nd Grd Tchr 1977-81; Roosevelt Schl 5th Gr 1981-82; Elrama Schl 2nd Grd Tchr 1982-83; Monongahela Elem Grd Tchr 1983-85; Ginger Hill 5th Grd Tchr 1985-87; Gastonville Ctr 5th Grd Tchr 1987-; *ai:* PSEA 1977; NEA 1977-; Delta Kappa G 1985-, Numerous Offices Held; Monongahela Area Historical Soc United Way Team Player 1987-; March of Dimes Walkathon Monongahela Area Revitalization Corp 1994-; Pittsburgh Press W Contest Winner 1986; Walking Magazines 1994 Walking Amer Cont Place Winner; Featured Story in Pittsburgh Post-Gazette on Ja Cultural Experience 1993; Tchr Exch Prgm in Omiya City Japan Nom for Natl PTA Awd for Outstanding Educator 1990; Nom for T to Tchrs Excl Awds 1991; Chosen to Participate in Colonial Stud Wk Williamsburg VA 1992; Taught Adult Basic Ed & Eng as a Secon Classes 1985-93; Adventures in Intnl Ed Instr 1990; Accompaniment for Spring Musical 1986, Choreographer 1988; G Mon-Valley Acad All Sports Symposium Instr 1991; Spec Presentation for Spring Musical 1987; *home:* 18 Prosperi Monongahela PA 15063*

MANCINI, MARY ANN, Relgn, Math, Eng & Rdng Tchr; *b:* Newar *m:* Nicholas; *c:* Joseph, Lynda; *ed:* Newark St Tchrs Coll (BA) Sp 1969; Attndng Kean Coll for Master Degree for Admin & Super Enrolled at Archdiocese of Newark in Future Schl Ldrs Pgm; *cr:* Eli Pub Schl Spec Ed Tchr 1969-78; St Mary's Elem Schl Tchr 1981-, 6 Grd Math, 8th Grd Homeroom Tchr; *ai:* Roselle Cath Mother's Club; Chprsn; St Mary's Parish Cncl 1996-, Eucharistic Minister; *offi* Mary Assumption Elem Schl 237 S Broad St Elizabeth NJ 07202

MANCINI, MICHELLE LAQUAY, Social Studies Teacher; *b:* Utica *c:* Temperance Puffer, Goldie Puffer, Ian; *ed:* Mohawk Valley Comr (AA) Lbrl Arts; Univ of CA at Riverside (BS) Anthropology 1988; E St Coll (MA) Cultural Stud 1995; *cr:* Univ of CA at Riverside Lab Asst 1985-88; Utica City Schl Dist Soc Stud Tchr 1988-; *ai:* Num Articles Pub; *office:* Utica City School Dist 13 Elizabeth St Utic 13501

MANCINI, RICHARD GUY, 5th Grade Teacher; *b:* Canton, O Sherry Moushey; *c:* Jennifer, Damon; *ed:* Kent St (BS) Ed 1971; Univ (MS) Ed Admin 1974; Akron Univ 35 Hrs Towards PHD; *cr:* C City Tchr 26 Yrs; *ai:* CPEA 1971-; OEA 1971-; NEA 1971-; Phi Kappan 1980-; Jennings Scholar Outstdng Tchng Awd; PTA Tchr of *office:* Worley Elem Schl 1340 23rd St NW Canton OH 44709*

MANCIVALANO, JOSEPH CHARLES, Soc Studies Tchr & Chprsn; *b:* Pittsfield, MA; *m:* Gail Ruisseaux; *c:* Johanna, Mitche Berkshire Comm COll (AA) Lbrl Arts 1967; Westfield St Coll (BA 1969; RI Coll (MAT) His 1972; *cr:* The Brooklyn Schl Soc Stud 1969-71; Lenox Schl System Soc Stud Tchr 1973-81; St Mary's Sc 5 Tchr 1983-85; St Joseph Cntrl HS Soc Studi Tchr, Dept Chprsn

Alpha Theta His Conf Adv; NCSS, ASCD, MASCD, NCEA 1983-; St Joseph Central HS 22 Maplewood Ave Pittsfield MA 01201

USO, ANN KICEY, Retired Teacher; *b:* Jersey City, NJ; *m:* Joseph; ey City St Coll (BS) Ed 1939; *cr:* Union City Schls Sub Tchr ; RCA-Harrison Posting Inv, IBM 1943-58; Washington Schl First ar 1958-83; *ai:* NEA, NJEA, PTA 1958-; Hudson Cty Ret Ed Assn *home:* 406 Gregory Ave Weehawken NJ 07087

USO, BARBARA RICE, Physics Teacher; *b:* Johnson City, NY; *m:* ; *ed:* Penn St Univ (BS) Indstrl Engrng 1988; West Chester Univ Scndry Ed 1994; *cr:* Bensalem HS Physics Tchr 1991-92; Lower HS Physics Tchr 1992-93; Conestoga HS Physics Tchr 1993-; *ai:* s, Sci Club Adv; Adopt-A-Grandparent, Stage Crew Asst Spon; Tchr 1995-; Cooperating Tchr for Stu Tchr Prgm 1994-95; NEA AAPT 1990-; Arranged Donation of Sun Workstation to HS 1995-; d AT&T Grant for WWW Comms, Joint Project with Conestoga & Univ 1996; *office:* Conestoga HS 200 Irish Rd Berwyn PA 19312*

USO, CONSTANCE JOAN (BARONE), Fifth Grade Teacher; *b:* n, NY; *m:* Ronald; *c:* Ronald, Karen, Andrea; *ed:* Queens Coll (BA) 1973, (MS) Lang Arts 1976; 30 Inservice Credits; *cr:* Elmont Schl b Tchr 1973-76; Lee Ave Schl 5th Grd Tchr 1987-; *ai:* Behavior cation Prgm Chm; NEA, HCT 1987-; *office:* Lee Avenue Elem Schl n Ave Hicksville NY 11801

USO, ELISA ALVAREZ, Nursing Professor; *b:* Rockville Ctr, NY; chael James; *c:* Tiffany, Andrea; *ed:* Adelphi Univ (BA) Bio, d 1975; SUNY at Farmingdale (AS) Nrsng 1984; SUNY at Stony (BS) Nrsng 1986, (MS) Nrsng, Neonatology 1988; NCC Cert al Nrsng 1994; Resolve through Share Bereavement Cnslr 1988; Hi eonatal Assessment 3 Credits 1994; *cr:* Nassau Cty Med Cntr Head 984-94; Suffolk Comm Coll Nrsng Prof 1991-; *ai:* Acad Standards Chprsn 1993-; Coll Wide Acad Standards Comm; Mid States ation; Tchng Excl; Tchng Consultant; Search Comm Hlth Scis Fac; 1992-; NYSNA 1988-, Alternate Del; NANN, AWHONN 1986-; Cty Perinatal Coalition 1988-, Consultant; Minority, Mentor Mentor; Summer Internship 1994-, Coord; NAPARE 1988-, ement Cnslr; VATEA Grant 1995; Master Tchr Awd 1994, 1992; rgical Nrsng Reviewer Text 1994; Fellow of Nightingale Soc 1988; 1996; Commencement Speaker 1995; *office:* Suffolk Community 01 Crooked Hill Rd Brentwood NY 11717*

USO, GAIL BAIER, Second Grade Teacher; *b:* Cambridge, OH; ke; *c:* Keith, Tony; *ed:* Mt Vernon Nazarene Coll (BA) Elem Ed Credit Hrs Akron Univ; 16 Credit Hrs Ashland Univ; 3 Credit Hrs Univ; *cr:* West Holmes Local Schls 1st Grd Tchr 1979-83, 5th Grd 988-89, 2nd Grd Tchr 1989-; *ai:* West Holmes Ed Assn 1979-; Millersburg Elem Schl 430 E Jackson St Millersburg OH 44654*

USO, THERESA A., Fourth Grade Teacher; *b:* Oswego, NY; *ed:* th Coll of Rochester (BA) Soc Sci 1972, (MS) Elem Ed 1975; 60+ Hrs Dist Inservice Courses; *cr:* Brooks Hill Schl 3rd Grd Tchr 9, 5th Grd Tchr 1979-81, 3rd Grd Tchr 1981-82, 4th Grd Tchr 4, 5th Grd Tchr 1994-95, 4th Grd Tchr 1995-; *ai:* Core Team; GATE ing Comm; Supvr Homework Club; AFT, NYSUT, FEA 1972-; ster Area Rdng Cncl 1989-; Homeowners Assn 1996, Bd of Dir, Highland Hosp 1986-; Big Brother, Big Sisters 1995-; *office:* Brooks em Schl 181 Hulburt Rd Fairport NY 14450

USO, TONI-MARIE MENDES, Assistant Principal; *b:* Ludlow, ; Salvatore; *c:* Jason; *ed:* Elms (BA) Math 1974; Westfield St Coll Scndry Admin 1992, (CAGS) Scndry Admin 1996; *cr:* Notra-Dame ulate Conception 5th-8th Grd Math & Sci Tchr 1974-75; Cathedral th Tchr 1975-78; Ludlow HS Math Tchr 1978-95, Asst Prin 1995-; ss of 1982, 1986, 1991, 1999 Adv; Ludlow Curr Comm; LEA, NEA, 978-; NCTM 1990-; ASSP 1992-; Saint Marys Guild 1980-, Pres & *fice:* Ludlow Sr HS 500 Chapin St Ludlow MA 01056*

ALAKIS, STRATOS JOHN, High School Choral Director; *b:* New NY; *m:* Suzanne Marie Miller; *c:* Christopher John; *ed:* Fordham BA)(Byzantine Stud, Fine Arts 1984; Maryknoll Schl of Theology Theology, Rel Ed 1985; NJ Supvr Cert 1995; NJ Alternate Rt Tchng lem Ed, K-12th Grd Music Ed 1987; *cr:* Bergenfield Pub Schls HS Skills Tchr 1986-87, Elem Music Ed, Instrumental Tchr 1987-91, MS Ed, Choral Tchr 1991-94, HS Mus Ed, Choral, Instr Tchr 1994-; *ai:* HS Vocal, Ensemble, Madrigal Choirs; Asst Band Dir; Marching, rt Bands; HS Acads Comm; NEA, NJEA, BEA 1986-; MENC, A 1987-; St Antony Orthodox Church 1985-, Chanter, Music Dir; NJ ony Orch Master Tchr 1994; Conductor MS Festival Chorus 1995; Bergenfield HS 80 S Prospect Ave Bergenfield NJ 07621*

DEL, JOHN PAUL, Vocational Welding Teacher; *b:* Philipsburg, PA; St Univ Voc 1988; *cr:* Clearfield Co Vo-Tech Schl Welding Tchr 12 *ai:* VICA Adv; NEA 1985-, Mem-at-Large; AWS 1985-; *office:* ield Cty Voc Tech Schl RR 1 Box 5 Clearfield PA 16830

DEL, MICHAEL R., Business Professor; *b:* New York, NY; *m:* s; *ed:* Queensborough Comm Coll (AS) Bus Admin 1975; Queens BA) Acctng & Ec 1977; NY Inst of Tech (MBA) Mgmt & Mkrtng Salem Schl for Ministry 3 Yr Pgm Biblical Stud; Dir Mrktng Assn Inst; *cr:* Coll of Staten Island Bus Instr 1985-92; Kings Coll VP ng, Dept Chair & Asst Prof 1985-94; Housatomic Comm Tech Coll nstr 1992-; Intercessor Schl for Ministry Dean 1995-; *ai:* Amer g Assn; Natl Soc for Trng & Dev; St Michaels Seminary 1994-, e; *office:* Housatonic Comm-Tech College 510 Barnum Ave eport CT 06608*

DEL, VERONICA H., Adjunct Professor of Law; *b:* NY City, NY; UNY New Paltz (BA) Ed 1976; Pace Univ Schl of Law (JD) Law Hunter Schl of Soc Work, Coursework; *cr:* Bronx Cnty Dist Attorney Asst Dist Attorney 1987-92; Quirk, Bakalor Attorney 1992-94; mployed 1994-; *ai:* NY St Bar Assn; Bronx Bar Assn; *office:* City Of NY John Jay Coll 899 10th Ave New York NY 10019

DELL, CHARLOTTE C., Professor of Psychology; *b:* New York, *n:* Norman H. Michaels; *c:* Jacob, Amanda; *ed:* Brooklyn Coll (BA) 1967; Columbia Univ (MA) Psych 1969, (PHD) Psych 1973; *cr:* of NH Research Assoc & Instr 1972-78; Univ of MA at Lowell Psych 978-; *ai:* Dept Chair; Psych Club & Psi Chi Adv; APA; EPA 1972-; Outstanding Tchr Awd; Odyssey of Mind 1993-, Coach; Numerous es in Prof Journals; *office:* Univ Of MA At Lowell 1 University Ave ll MA 01854

DELL, OLGA KARMAN, Spanish Professor; *b:* Havana, Cuba; *c:* niel, Carla Brown; *ed:* CT Coll (BA) Span 1966; Harvard Univ (PHD) Amer Lit 1976; *cr:* Simmons Coll Asst Prof 1969-70; Nichols Schl 1976-79; D'Youville Coll Prof 1980-; *ai:* Mentoring Prgm, Comm s Dir; Western NY Hispanics & Friends 1985-, Pres, VP; Herman lo Advy Bd 1990-; Pub Poetry Books, Articles; Governor NYS nics of Distinction Awd 1994; Natl Conf of Chrstns & Jews Arts, y Awd 1996; *office:* D'Youville Coll 320 Porter Ave Buffalo NY 14201

DELL, RAYMOND ANDREW, Band & Orchestra Director; *b:* Monte, PA; *m:* Catherine Hopko; *c:* Zachariah, Jacob; *ed:* Grove City BS) Music Ed 1985; Grad Credits PA St Univ, Gannon Univ, IN Univ , Carlow Coll, Wilkes Univ; *cr:* Philipsburg-Osceola Schl Dist HS Choral Dir 1986-89; Clearfield Area Schl Dist HS Band, Orch Dir ; *ai:* HS Marching Band, Jazz Ensemble, Stage Band Dir; NEA, PSEA, CEA, MENC, PMEA 1986-; Natl Band Assn, IAJE 1989-; Who's Who in Music; Outstanding Young Men of Amer; *office:* Clearfield Area HS PO Box 910 Clearfield PA 16830

MANDEVILLE, THOMAS ROBERT, Assoc Professor of Social Sci; *b:* Port Huron, MI; *m:* Alison Marie Nowak; *c:* Elizabeth, Constance; *ed:* Eastern MI Univ (BS) Cum Laude Pol Sci, His 1983; Bowling Green St Univ (MA) Pol Sci 1986; Wayne St 20 Grad Credits Ed; *cr:* Bowling Green St Univ Adjunct 1987-88; Macomb Comm Coll Adjunct 1989-90; St Clair Cty Comm Coll Adjunct 1989-90; Clinton Comm Coll Soc Sci Asst Prof 1990-; *ai:* NY St Senate Interns Campus Liason Officer; Truman ScholarsFac Rep; Planning & Curr Comms; Fac Stu Assoc Bd; Native Amer Clb & Stu Fshng Clb Adv; NEA 1990-; North Cty Vietnam Veterans Assn 1990-; Mc Cellan Grant Local His; Two Fed Grant Lake Champlain Basin Prgm; S Lk Champlain Trust Rvltnry War Grant; *office:* Clinton Comm Coll Lakeshore Rd Rt 9 S Plattsburgh NY 12901

MANDIBERG, JUDITH SUSAN, Eng & Creative Writing Teacher; *b:* Brooklyn, NY; *ed:* Brooklyn Coll (BA) His, Pol Sci 1970; Coll of Staten Island (MS) Scndry Ed 1974; Brooklyn Coll (MS) Admin, Supervision 1989; Eng, Ed, Photography, Photojournalism Courses; *cr:* IS 296K Schl Soc Stud Tchr 1971; IS 302K Schl Eng, Soc Stud Tchr 1971-76; IS 126 Schl Eng 1976-77; O. W. Holmes Jr HS Writing Specialist, Eng Tchr, New Tchr Trng 1977-91; Wm. Mc Kinley IS 259 Schl Eng, Creative Writing Tchr 1991-; *ai:* 6th Grd Coord Supts Creative Writing Prgm; Fundraising Act; Coord Penpal Prgm; NCTE; NY St Tchr Eng; NYC St Tchrs Eng; UFT, AFT; PTA; Wrote Writing Schls Curr; Eng, Creative Writing Act Grants; Cool Schl Awd 1995; Judi Mandiberg Cool Schl Awd Svc, Humanitarianism; *office:* JHS 259 William Mckinley 7301 Fort Hamilton Pky Brooklyn NY 11228*

MANDLOWITZ, LINDA D., 6th Grade Teacher; *b:* Bronx, NY; *m:* Gerald S.; *c:* David, Tracy; *ed:* Penn St Univ (BS) Elem Ed 1963; Masters Equivalency 1992 Penn St Univ, St Joseph's Univ; *cr:* Schuylkill Schl 6th Grd Tchr 1963-66; East Pikeland Schl 4th, 6th Grd Tchr 1977-87; Schuylkill Schl 6th Grd Tchr 1987-92; Phoenixville Area MS 6th Grd Tchr 1992-; *ai:* Class Plays, Musicals 10 Yrs; Core MS Transition; Prins, Soc Stud Comm; Breakfast Club; NEA, PSEA, PAEA 1977-; Forge Theatre 1977-, Pres, Sec, Best Dir, Actress; Bna Jacob Sisterhood 1963-, Pres, VP; United Synagogue Yth Adv; Parenting Inst Tchr Awd 1984.

MANEGGIA, PETER,JR., Softball & Volleyball Coach; *b:* Andover, CT; *m:* Donalyn Wolmer; *ed:* NH Coll (BS) Human Svc Admin 1988; Elem Ed Cert Prgm Eastern CT St Univ; *cr:* Amer Intnl Coll Asst Coach 1991; *ai:* Vlybl Asst Coach 1992-; Sftbl Head Coach 1996; Griswold Sftbl Head Coach 1994-95; NSCA 1994-; CIAC 1993-; Championships Sftbl Camps Cnslr 1992-; *home:* 11 Riverview Rd Mansfield Center CT 06250

MANERCHIA, THOMAS EVANS, Biology Teacher; *b:* Chester, PA; *ed:* St Josephs Coll (BS) Bio 1965; Villanova Univ (MSS) Scndry Sci 1978; Univ of DE (MC) Cnslng 1981; Cmptr Prgmng, Drawing, Watercolor, Instrumental Music, Psych, His of Sci; *cr:* Archmere Acad Bio Tchr 1965-; *ai:* Asst Dir of Ath; NABT; NSTA; DABT, Bd of Dir; NSF Grant Biotech; Woodrown Wilson Natl Flwshp; Fac Consultant ETS AP Bio Reader; AP Recognition Awd; Outstdng Tchr Tandy Tech; *office:* Archmere Acad 3600 Philadelphia Pike Claymont DE 19703

MANES, ELIZABETH JOAN, Math Teacher; *b:* Berlin, Germany; *m:* Antoni Paul; *c:* Michael, Matthew; *ed:* West Chester Univ (BSEd) Math Ed 1970; Temple Univ (MSEd) Math Ed 1974; 30 Addl Credits in Cmptr Tech, Ed; *cr:* Bristol Twp Schls 7-12 Grd Math Tchr 1970-; *ai:* Bristol Twp Math Curr Cmmm for Jr High, HS; NEA, PSEA 1970-; NCTM 1993-; BCCTM 1987-; Book Reviewer for Algebra 1 an Integrated Approach; *office:* Harry S Truman Schl 3001 Green Ln Levittown PA 19057*

MANETTA, LOUIS, High School Music Teacher; *b:* Malden, MA; *m:* Janet Louise Pratt; *c:* Cris, Steven, Paul, Michael; *ed:* Univ of Lowell (BM) Composition 1972, (BME) Music Ed 1972; *cr:* North Middlesex Regnl HS Music Tchr 1972-; *ai:* Choral Dir; MMEA 1985-; NEA 1972-; MA Cable Television Commissions Annual Best Performing Arts Prgm Awd; *office:* North Middlesex Regional HS Main St Townsend MA 01469

MANFREDI, JOAN M., Third Grade Teacher; *b:* Brooklyn, NY; *m:* John J.; *c:* Ruth, Mary Joan; *ed:* St John's Univ (BS) Elem Ed 1961; Lehman Coll (MS) Rdng 1990; 30 Credits Awded to Stud Lang Based Classrooms, Sci, Math, Rdng; *cr:* Seaford Harbor Schl Third Grd Tchr 1961-68; Katonah-Lewisboro Schl Dist Sub Tchr 1978-85; PS 205A Third Grd Tchr 1985-; *ai:* Advy Comm; AFT, UFT 1985-; US Pony Club Inc 1980-, Dist Commissioner; United Nations Rights of Child Convention Guest Speaker 1990; NY Bronx Zoo Congo Gorilla Forest Ground Breaking Ceremony Keynote Address 1995; NY St Martin Luther King Arts Festival Second Place 1990; Lehman Coll Fnd Schlsp 1989-90; Grants: NSF Tchng of Math Lehman Coll 1991; Dwight D. Eisenhower Rdng in Content Areas Math & Sci Lehman Coll 1990, Sci Inquiry Skills Manhattan Coll 1990; City Coll of NY Fnds Arithmetic, Ind Stud; Ctr for Stud Chldhd Ed Dev Lang Based Classrooms Lehman Coll 1989; *office:* PS 205A 2475 Southern Blvd Bronx NY 10458*

MANFREDO, CHRISTINE A., English Teacher & Dept Chprsn; *b:* Brooklyn, NY; *m:* Randall R.; *ed:* William Paterson Coll (BA) Eng, Ed 1976; NY Univ (MA) Eng 1978; *cr:* Port Jervis HS Eng Tchr, Chprsn 1978-; *ai:* Effective Schls, Renaissance Comms; NCTE; *office:* Port Jervis HS Rt 209 Port Jervis NY 12771

MANFREDO, PATRICK J., Business Education Teacher; *b:* Utica, NY; *m:* Betty Joy; *ed:* Syracuse Univ (BS) Accounting 1966, (MS) Counseling Psych 1973; 18 Post Grad Hrs Toward a Doctorate in Bus Admin; *cr:* General Electric Cost Analyst F111 Govt Project 1966-67; Westmoreland Cntrl Schl Bus Ed Tchr 1967-; *ai:* Yrbk Financial & Class Adv; Model Schls Rep; NYSUT & Westmoreland Tchrs Assn 1967-; *office:* Westmoreland Cntrl Schl Rt 233 Westmoreland NY 13490

MANGANELLO, DENNIS CARMINE, Social Studies, Lang Arts Tchr; *b:* Bronx, NY; *ed:* Herbert H. Lehman Coll (BA) His 1974; Fordham Univ (MST) Curr, Tchng 1981; Coll of New Rochelle (SAS/SDA) Schl Admin, Supervision 1988; NY Archdiocese Catechist Formation Prgm Levels 1 1989, Level 2 1990; *cr:* Holy Rosary Schl 7th-8th Grd Tchr 1981-; *ai:* HS Liaison; Grad Moderator; Grd level Coord; Phi Delta Kappa, NCEA 1981-; Cert Appreciation Educl Svcs by John Cardinal O'Connor 1986; *office:* Holy Rosary Schl 1500 Arnow Ave Bronx NY 10469

MANGANIELLO, ANN M., Music Teacher & Dept Chprsn; *b:* Pittston, PA; *ed:* Marywood Coll (BM) Music, Piano 1977, (MA) Music Ed 1983; LIU Cert Completion Microsoft Works; PMEA Ldrshp Conf 1989, 1991-92, 1994-95; LUI Completion Desktop Publishing 1991; West Chester Univ Musicin Motion 1992; Mt St Marys Rel Music 1991; *cr:* St Cecilia Church Organist, Choir Dir 1976-; Bishop Hoban HS Music Tchr, Dept Chprsn 1977-; *ai:* 2+2 Singers Vocalist; Piano, Voice, Organ Instr; Liturgical Music Dir; Color Guard Moderator; Chorus Dir; Select Ensemble; Musical Dir; Future Hobanite, Curr Inst, Anniversary Comm; PMEA; Curr Inst Dist Chair; PA Music Ed Assn 1977-, Curr Inst Dist Chair; Natl Pastoral Musicians 1977-, Mus Dir 125th Anniversary Choir, 250 Voice Adult Choir; Natl Guild of Piano Tchrs 1980-; NCEA 1980-; Chrstn Womens Soc 1995-; Liturgy Comm 1982, Chm; Charitable Org Contributor; Article Pub; Outstdng Young Women of Amer 1991; Host Dir All-St Jazz Festival 1993; Music Dir 125th Diocesan Anniversary Stu Liturgy, 300 Voice Stu Choir; *home:* 1921 Scarboro Ave Exeter PA 18643*

MANGANO, CHRISTINA C., Language Arts & Reading Tchr; *b:* New York City, NY; *m:* Bernard; *c:* Aleia; *ed:* Boston Coll (BA) Elem & Spcl Ed 1988; St Peters Coll (MS) Ed Admin & Supvr 1991; 12 Credit Hrs Fordham Univ; *cr:* Immaculate Conception Pre-Kndgtn Head Start Tchr 1989-90; Cliffside Park PS 4 7th-8th Grd Tchr 1990-; *ai:* Knowledgte Bowl Coach; NEA & NJEA 1990-; NCTE 1991-; Fatima Of NJ 1983-, Bd of Dir, Dir of camp; Interreligious Flwshp for Homeless 1991-, Yth Dir; Boston Coll Alumni Club 1992-, Pres; On Eagles Wings 1993-, Mem; Whos Who Among Amer Edctrs; Outstdng Coll Stdnts of Amer; *office:* Elem Schl 4 279 Columbia Ave Cliffside Park NJ 07010*

MANGANO, VINCENT, HS Mathematics Teacher; *b:* Brooklyn, NY; *m:* Sara Fiore; *c:* Thomas, Ann Marie; *ed:* C. W. Post (BS) Math 1978; SUNY at Stony Brook (MA) Math ed 1981; NATA Cert Ath Trainer 1978; *cr:* Southampton HS Math Tchr 1978-; Southampton Coll Adjunct Prof Ath Trainer 1979-; *ai:* Head Bsbl 1980-85, Head Ftbl 1986- Coach; Head Ath Trainer 1986-; Var Club Adv 1987-; NATA, EATA 1978-; Suffolk Cty Ftbl Coaches Assn 1986-, Coach of Yr 1989, 1992, 1993; *office:* Southampton HS 141 Narrow Ln Southampton NY 11968*

MANGELS, ROSALIE DIGIOVANNA, English Teacher; *b:* NYC, NY; *m:* George; *c:* George Jr., Paul, John, Kristin; *ed:* Regis Coll (BA) Eng 1963; Hofstra Univ (MS) Eng, Sec Ed 1967; 60 Addl Credits Long Island Univ, Coll of St Rose; *cr:* East Windor HS Eng Tchr 1963-64; Roslyn HS Eng, Hlth Tchr 1965-71, West Islip HS Eng Tchr 1972-; *ai:* Class Adv 1985-88; 1990, 1992-; Kickline Coach 1976-90; Soc Comm 1994-; Sunshine Comm 1989-; West Islip Tchrs Assn 1974-; NY SUT 1966-; *office:* West Islip HS Lions Path West Islip NY 11795

MANGIAFICO, SALVATORE A., French Teacher; *b:* Siracusa Sicily, Italy; *m:* Roberta Losi; *c:* Hongjoon, Michael, Julie; *ed:* Univ of CT (BA) Fr, Italian 1973, (MA) Comparative Lit 1977; Diplome D'Etudes Francaises 2d Degree Univ of Rouen in France 1972; *cr:* Bloomfield HS Fr, Italian Tchr 1973-74; BUlkeley HS Eng Tchr 1981-88, Fr Tchr 1988-; *ai:* Tae Kwon Do Instr; AFT 1978-, Union Schl Comm; CT Mentor, Cooperating Tchr; Phi Kappa Phi; Phi Beta Kappa; *office:* Bulkeley HS 300 Wethersfield Ave Hartford CT 06114*

MANGIALETTI, NANCY E., Third Grade Teacher; *b:* Mt Vernon, NY; *ed:* Cortland St U of NY (BS) Elem Ed 1971; BinghamtonUniv (MS) Rdng Ed 1984; 45 Addl Credit Hrs; *cr:* George F. Johnson El Schl 5th Grd Tchr 1971-79, 2nd Grd Tchr 1979-80; Ann G. Mc Guinness 5th Grd Tchr 1980-84; Thomas J. Watson Sr Schl 5th Grd Tchr 1984-88, 3rd Grd Tchr 1988-; *ai:* Southern Tier Inst Arts ind Ed Bldg Coord; Prins Advy Cncl; 3rd Grd Level Co-Chair 1993-95; 5th Grd Level Chair 1985, 1988; Phi Delta Kappa 1982-, VP-Mbrshp; BP Chptr Delta Kappa Gamma, Co-Ed Yrbk; Binghamton Area Rdng Cncl 1978-, Newsletter Ed; IRA 1980-; NYSRA 1978-; PTA, Life Mbrshp Awd; Endicott Tchrs Assn 1971-, Bldg Sr Rep; NYSUT, AFT 1971-; Prof Ed Grad Org 1980-84, Pres 1983-84, VP 1982; Endicott Tchr Ctr Policy Bd 1988-95; Presenter 3 Times NYSRA Conf, IRA Natl 1984; *office:* Thomas J Watson Elem Schl Watson Dr Endicott NY 13760

MANGINI, JOHN JOSEPH, Sixth Grade Teacher; *b:* Saratoga Spgs, NY; *m:* Vivian; *c:* John, Christopher, Jeffrey; *ed:* Siena Coll (BA) Ec 1963; Coll of St Rose (MA) Ed 1970; Stud at Skidmore Coll, Mater Christi, Shenendehowa Staff Dev; *cr:* Mechanicville HS Tchr 1959-60; Cohoes Schl 4 Elem Tchr 1963-65; Chango Elem Tchr 1970-93; Acadia Elem Tchr 1993-; *ai:* Comms: Math, Decision Making, Soc Stud, Discipline, Soc Act & Tech; Stu Cncl Fac Advy; AFT & NEA 1970-; NYSUT 1970-; Shen Tchr Assn 1970-; Knights of Columbus 1963-, Fin Sec; Tech Grant Soc Stud; *office:* Shenendehowa Cntrl Schls 970 Route 146 Clifton Park NY 12065

MANGINI, ROSANNE CAMPANELLA, Retired Teacher; *b:* New York, NY; *m:* Robert J.; *c:* Robert B., Susanne Mangini Shaw; *ed:* St John's Univ (BS) Elem Ed 1965; Attnd Queen's Coll 1965-67, Syracuse Univ 1980, Emmanuel Coll 1982; *cr:* P S #123 5th-6th Grd Tchr 1965-67; St Margaret's Schl 7th-8th Grd Tchr 1977-; *ai:* Organizer, Moderator Stu Tutoring Prgm 1985-88, Stu Svc League 1986-89; Moderator, Chaperone Dance Comm 1977-95; NCEA 1977-95; Pearl River Environmental Assn 1978-83, Treas; St Margaret's CCD of Rel Prgm Coord; Estates of Pearl River Bd of Mgrs 1990-95, Pres 1991-94; *home:* 21 Mendolia Ct Pearl River NY 10965

MANGINO, DEBORAH LUNDIN, Physical Education Teacher; *b:* New Brunswick, NJ; *m:* Gary Anthony; *ed:* Glassboro St Coll (BA) PE, Hlth, Dance Ed Minor 1985; *cr:* East Brunswick HS PE Tchr, Var Coach 1985-; *ai:* Co-Ed Chrldng; Natural Helpers Adv; NJ Ed Assn 1985-; AAHPERD 1996; AFFA 1994-; IDEA 1993-; Golden Apple Tchr Awd 1994-95; Grant; *office:* East Brunswick HS 380 Cranbury Rd East Brunswick NJ 08816*

MANGIONE, MICHAEL, Social Studies Teacher; *b:* New York City, NY; *m:* Sherrie Mc Kinley; *ed:* Eastern CT St Univ (MS) Human Relations 1969; St John's Univ (BA) Soc Sci, Ed 1988; *cr:* Portland Soc Stud Tchr 1973-76; St Joseph Schl Soc Stud Tchr 1978-; *ai:* Stu Cncl Moderator; NCEA 1978-; CT Cncl For Soc Stud 1980-; *office:* St Joseph Schl 41 West St Vernon Rockville CT 06066

MANGO, MICHAEL,JR., Spanish Teacher; *b:* Newark, NJ; *m:* Maria C. Christoford; *c:* Michael, Matthew, Christopher, Daniel, Jason; *ed:* Rutgers Univ (BA Span, Italian 1965; Kean Coll Ed MA Equivalency 35 Credits; *cr:* Union HS Span, Italian Tchr 1965-; *ai:* Span Club, Class Advs; NEA, NJEA, VTEA 1965-; *office:* Union HS N 3rd St Union NJ 07083

MANIACI, JOSEPH DAVID, Social Studies Instructor; *b:* Pittsburgh, PA; *m:* Diana Marie Schee-Maniaci; *c:* Alexandra Maniaci Gordon, Philip; *ed:* Adelphi Univ (BA) Ed 1970; Dowling Coll MS Ed 1973; *cr:* Connetquot HS European His 1970; Ronkonkoma JHS US His 1970-l Dowling Coll Bsktbl Coach 1980-85; St Francis Coll Asst Bsktbl Coach 1985-88; CW PostColl Asst Bsktbl Coach 1988-90; St Joseph's Coll Bsktbl Coach 1991-; *ai:* Yorker, Conservation Clubs; Security Watch; Bldng Reporter; Quarterly Ed; Sports Inf at Dowling Coll & St Josephs Coll; AFT CTA 1970-; NABC 1989-; NAIA, SID 1980-86; Letter of Commendation, Swedish Bsktbl Fed; Big Apple Conf Coach of yr 1985; NAIA-SID Bsktbl Media Guide & Game Prgm Awds; *office:* Ronkonkoma Jr HS 501 Peconic St Ronkonkoma NY 11779

MANIERY, NICK ANGELO, Head Football Coach; *b:* Rutland, VT; *m:* Cheryl Ann; *c:* Kimberly, Kayla, Dominick; *ed:* Castle St Coll (BS) Exercise Tech 1984; *cr:* The Spa Mgr 1983-90; USPS Rural Carrier 1990-; *ai:* Head Ftbl Coach; Wt Trng CoachH; Natl Strength Assn 1985-; Natl Ftbl Hall of Fame 1994-; Mill River Booster Club 1993; Mill River Ftbl Club 1991; *home:* Meadowcrest Rd Box 161-F N Clarendon VT 05759

MANIFRANG, MARK ANDREW, Social Studies Teacher; *b:* New Castle, PA; *m:* Nancy Orlando; *c:* Jason, Brandon; *ed:* Westminister Coll (BA) His, Govt 1972, (BA) Soc Stud 1991; 36 Post Grad Hrs in His; *cr:* Union Area Schls Soc Stud Tchr 1974-; *ai:* Asst Var Bsktbl, Bsbl Coach; Pub Relation Comm PSEA; UEA, PSEA, NEA 1974-; Union Booster 1974-; Union Ath Assn 1984-; *office:* Union Area Mid HS 2106 Camden Ave New Castle PA 16101

MANINGO, SHERYL L., Social Studies Teacher; *b:* Bay Shore, NY; *m:* Raymond Rothamel; *c:* Elisabeth Le Merle; *ed:* Susquehanna Univ (BA) His, Ed 1978; Plattsburgh St Univ of NY (MS), (CAS) Schl Guid Cnslng 1994; 53 Hrs Scndry Ed, Environmental Ed Bowling Green St Univ 1978-79; *cr:* Smithtown Cntrl Schl Dist Learning Ctr Aide & Soc Stud Tchr 1980-82; Pok-O-Mac Cready Outdoor Ed Ctr Instr & Dir 1982-84; Au

Sable Vly Cntrl Schl Dist Soc Stud Tchr 1984-; *ai:* SADD & Yth to Yth Adv; Shared Decision Making Comm Schl Improvement; Cooperating Tchr for Stu Tchrs; NYSUT 1984-; AVTA; Willsboro Congregational Church 1983-, Deaocn, Steward, Edctr of Yr 1995; Ti Yth to Yth 1990-, Pres, Adult Vol, Outstdng Svc; Outstdng Cnslng Grad Stu Awd SUNY at Plattsburgh 1995; Phi Alpha Theta; Pi Gamma Mu; Phi Kappa Phi; Grad Rsrch Assistantship Bowling Green St Univ 1978-79; *office:* Ausable Valley Middle HS 1490 Rt 9 N Clintonville NY 12924*

MANION, WILLIAM PAUL, English Teacher; *b:* Rochester, NY; *c:* Kevin C.; *ed:* St Vincent Coll (BA) Eng 1968; Bowie St Coll (MEd) Admin 1975; Addl Post Grad Stud at Univ of MD; *cr:* Samuel Ogle Jr High Eng Tchr 1968-69; Laurel Jr High Dept Chprsn & Eng Tchr 1970-77; Eleanor Roosevelt High Eng Tchr 1977-; *ai:* NEA, MSTA & PGCEA 1968-; Natl Youth Sports Coaches Assn 1992-; *office:* Eleanor Roosevelt HS 7601 Hanover Pkwy Greenbelt MD 20770

MANISCALCO, ANTHONY JOSEPH, Political Science Lecturer; *b:* Brooklyn, NY; *ed:* (BA) Pol Sci, Philosphy-Cum Laude 1989; (BA) Regents Schlsp; (BA) Assembly Internship Prgm; CUNY Grad Ctr Doctoral Cand Pol Sci; *cr:* Kingsborough Comm Coll Grants Coord 1991-93; CUNY Cntrl Office Research Assoc 1991-95; CUNY Internship Prgm Asst Coord 1995-; *ai:* PSC 1990-, Mem; Urban Revitalization SAGE Pub; *office:* City Univ Of NY John Jay Coll 445 W 59th St Ofc New York NY 10019

MANISERO, ROBERT MICHAEL, English Teacher; *b:* Gwinn, MI; *m:* Loretta Cristino; *c:* Robert, Nicholas; *ed:* Columbia Coll (BA) Eng Lit 1987; Brooklyn Coll (MA) Eng Ed 1993; *cr:* Bishop Kearney HS Eng Tchr 1987-; St Francis Coll Evening Summer Admin 1990-91, 1994; *ai:* Speech Team Coach; Sr Yr Moderator; NCTE 1987-; Knights of Columbus 1995-; *office:* Bishop Kearney HS 2202-60th St Brooklyn NY 11204

MANKIS, STACEY RENEE, Language Arts Teacher; *b:* Jamestown, NY; *ed:* Kent St Univ (BS) Comm II 1994; *cr:* Avon Lake HS Lang Arts, Eng Tchr 1994-; *ai:* Chrldng Coach; Pep Club Adv; Renaissance Comm; NEA, OEA 1994-; *office:* Avon Lake HS 175 Avon Belden Rd Avon Lake OH 44012*

MANKOWSKI, DANIEL CHRISTOPHER, English Teacher & Drama Dir; *b:* Philadelphia, PA; *m:* Julia Witman; *ed:* St Joseph's Univ (AB) Eng 1968, (MA) Ed 1972; Villanova Univ (MA) Theatre 1989; *cr:* Pennsbury HS Tchr, Drama Dir 1968-; *ai:* Dramatics; Yrbk, Bus Adv; Pennsbury Ed Assn, PA St Ed Assn, NEA 1968; Drama Critic, Judge West Chester Univ Theatre Festival, Bucks Cty Playhouse Theatre Festival; *office:* Pennsbury Sr HS 705 Hood Blvd Fairless Hills PA 19030

MANKOWSKI, DIANA YINGST, Mathematics Teacher; *b:* Weirton, WV; *m:* Joseph A.; *ed:* WV Univ (BA) Math 1986, (MA) Ed 1991; Addl Credit Hrs at OH Univ & Ashland Univ; *cr:* WV Univ Instr 1988-91; Westover Jr HS Tchr 1988-91; Kent St Univ at East Liverpool Instr 1991-92; Belmont Tech Coll Instr 1991-92; Steubenville HS Tchr 1992-; *ai:* NEA, OEA, SEA 1992-, Bldg Rep; NCTM, OCTM 1992-; *office:* Steubenville HS 420 N 4th St Steubenville OH 43952*

MANLEY, SARA JANINE, Spanish Teacher; *b:* Grafton, WV; *m:* Paul Baktaki; *ed:* Davis & Elkins Coll (BA) Span & Fr 1974; WV Univ (MA) Frgn Lang Ed 1979; Univ Simon Bolivar Hispanic Culture 1977-78; St Lawrence Univ 30 Hrs Towards Masters Ed Admin; *cr:* Grafton Sr HS Span & Fr Tchr 1975-77, 1978-80; Instituto Venezolano Americano ESL Tchr 1977-78; Charleston Cath HS Span Tchr 1980-82; Parishville-Hopkinton Cntrl Span & Fr Tchr 1982-; *ai:* Frgn Lang Club Adv; Span Homestays Coord; HS Stans Comm; NHS Advy Bd; NYSAFLT 1983-, Bd of Dir, Sec; AATSP 1989-, Newsletter Ed; NYSAFLT Tchr Incentive Grant; Pub Article on Alternative Scheduling.*

MANN, GEORGE WYATT, Guidance Counselor; *b:* Ossining, NY; *m:* Linda Melton; *c:* Bashon, Dwayne; *ed:* Cntrl St Univ (BS) Ed, Ind Arts 1967; Hunter Coll (MS) Guid, Cnslng 1973; *cr:* Milwaukee City Schls Machine Shop Instr 1967-68; Katonah-Lewisboro SD Indstrl Arts Instr 1968-77, Cnslr 1977-; *ai:* 9th Grd Bsbl Coach; NEA 1968-; WCSD Bd Ed, Pres 1990-93; Omega Psi Phi 1968-; Natl Black Child Dev Inst 1989-; Afro-Amer Mens Group 1995-; *office:* John Jay Sr HS Rt 121-124 Cross River NY 10518

MANN, KATHLEEN COMEDY, Fourth Grade Teacher; *b:* Canonsburg, PA; *m:* M. Nicholas; *c:* Luther Roberts; *ed:* Hiram Scott Coll (BA) Music Ed 1970; Trenton St Univ Urban Stud; Trinity Coll Ed, Admin; *cr:* Plainfield Pub Schls Elem Tchr 1974-86; Holy Trinity Elem Schl 4th Grd Tchr 1986-; *ai:* 1-4 Grd Dept Chprsn; Multicultural, Multiple Intelligences Applications Comms; NEA; NCEA; ASCD; Natl Black Child Dev Inst; Simpson Hamline United Meth Church, Gospel Choir, Alter Guild.*

MANN, MARY E., Former English Teacher; *b:* Dover, OH; *c:* Elizabeth, Steve, Susan; *ed:* Kent St Univ (BA) Eng 1972; Addl Coursework in Cmptr, Eng, Tech Prep Eng; *cr:* Galion HS Eng Tchr 1972-74; *ai:* Stu Cncl Adv 1992-94; Galion Tchrs Assn 1972-74; New Philadelphia Tchrs Assn, OEA, NEA 1991-; Quaker Fnd Grant 2 Yrs.

MANN, SUSAN LYNN, Sixth Grade Teacher; *b:* Brooklyn, NY; *m:* Barry Stuart; *c:* Jason; *ed:* Queens Coll (BA) Elem Ed 1967; Long Island Univ (MS) Elem Ed, Gifted & Talented Ed 1991; *cr:* PS 147 4th Grd Tchr 1967-70, 5th Grd Tchr 1975-76; PS 37 5th Grd Tchr 1977-87; PS 129 6th Grd Tchr 1988-; *ai:* Schl Geog Bee Organizer & Host; 6th Grd Fund Raising Act Adv Supv 6th Grd Visits Nrsng Homes & Nursery Schl; Interscholattic Math League Adv; Scenery Dir for 6th Grd Performance; GATE Distngd Performance Awd Grad Division Long Island Univ; *office:* PS 129 Patricia A Larkin 128-02 7th Ave College Point NY 11356

MANNARA, JOSEPH FREDERICK, Science Teacher; *b:* Rome, Italy; *m:* Tracy Graff; *ed:* Syracuse Univ (BA) Arts, Sci 1989, (BS) Ed Sci 1990; Working on MS Sci Ed Cortland St Univing; *cr:* West Genesee HS Sci Tchr 1990-; *ai:* Bsbl Coach; Strategic Planning Comm; Blind Men & Criers Assn 1996; *office:* West Genesee HS 5201 W Genesee St Camillus NY 13031*

MANNARINO, THOMAS A., 8th Grade History Teacher; *b:* Uniontown, PA; *m:* Laura C.; *c:* Jack; *ed:* OH St (BS) Acctng 1983, (MA) Ed 1988; *cr:* Arthur Young & Co Accountant 1983-84; Cardinal Foods Co Accountant 1984-88; Wedgewood MS Tchr 1988-; *ai:* NEA, OEA, CEA 1988-; *office:* Wedgewood MS 3771 Eakin Rd Columbus OH 43228*

MANNEY, LAURIE WILLIAMS, Third Grade Teacher; *b:* Meshoppen, PA; *m:* Craig Aaron; *c:* Joshua, Timothy, Rebecca; *ed:* West Chester St Coll (BS) Elem Ed 1974; 28 Credit Hrs; *cr:* Wyalusing Area Schl Dist 3rd Grd Tchr 1974-; Camptown Elem 3rd Grd Tchr & Head Tchr 1994-; *ai:* NEA, PSEA & WAEA 1974-; Delta Kappa Gamma 1986-; Wyalusing United Meth Church, Choir, Sunday Schl Tchr, Jr Choir Ldr; *office:* Camptown Elem Schl RR 1 Box 41 Wyalusing PA 18853

MANNI, KAREN BERTOLOTTI, Business Teacher & Dept Chprsn; *b:* Washington, PA; *m:* John Elio Jr.; *c:* Jessica, Katie; *ed:* IN Univ of PA (BS) Bus Ed 1977; California PA 24 Addl Credits Intermediate Unit I; WVU 3 Addl Credits Cmptr Literacy; *cr:* McGuffey HS Bus Tchr 1980-; *ai:* Stu Cncl Spon, Hosting Dist IV PA Conf 1992; Commercial Club Spon; McGuffey Ed Assn 1980-; Tri-State Bus Assn 1980-; *home:* 174 North St Atlasburg PA 15004

MANNIELLO, ANDREW FRANCIS, Mathematics Teacher; *b:* New York, NY; *ed:* St Francis Coll (BA) Math, Philosophy 1966; Fordham Univ (MA) Philosophy 1968, (PHD) Philosophy 1974; St John's Univ, Queens Coll Post Grad Stud in Math; *cr:* Fordham Univ Adjunct Instr 1968-69; St Anthony's HS Math Tchr, Acad Dean 1974-79; Cardinal Hayes HS Math Tchr 1979-80; St Francis Prep HS Math Tchr 1980-; *ai:* Girls Var Tennis Asst Coach & Moderator; NCEA, CACE 1991-; Franciscans 1993-; Natl Defense Ed Act Title IV Grad Stud Fellowship; *office:* Saint Francis Prep Schl 6100 Francis Lewis Blvd Fresh Meadows NY 11365

MANNING, BARBARA, English & Communications Tchr; *b:* Boston, MA; *ed:* Merrimack Coll (BA) Eng, Ed, ESL 1971; Cambridge Coll (MEd) Ed 1990; *cr:* China Trade Museum Educl Tour, Interpretor 1977-83; BU-Chelsea Partnership Schl Eng, Ed 1983-90; Arlington Cath HS Eng, Comm Tchr 1991-; TNT Wkshp Innovator, Pub Speaker 1987-; *ai:* Oratory, Asst Girls Tennis Coach; Curr Comm; AFT 1975-; NEA 1985-; SALT 1990-, Soc Accelerated Learning; Lucretia Crocker Flwshp Finalist 1987; Poetry Pub 1989, 1995; TNT Ancillary Educl Manual 1987; Kiwanis Tchr of Yr 1989; AMA Auxiliary Women's Congress Hlth Awd 1988 TNT Prgm 1988; *home:* 3166 Lake Pine Way S Tarpon Springs FL 34689*

MANNING, BERTHA NASH, Mathematics Teacher; *b:* Mobridge, SD; *m:* Stephen Orr III; *c:* Stephen Neal, Bryce Adam; *ed:* AR St Univ (BSE) Math 1964; MI St Univ (MA) Curr, Instruction 1982; Addl 30 Hrs Univ of MD Tchng, Univ of S FL Mid Level Stud, Boston Univ Math, Tech for Tchrs; *cr:* Rapid Valley Schls 7-8 Grd Math, Sci Tchr 1965-67; Keflavik HS 7-12 Grd Math, Sci Tchr 1968-69; Roper Jr HS 7-9 Grd Math Tchr 1973-77; Lakenheath Amer MS 7 Grd Math Tchr 1980-; *ai:* Rain Forest Team Ldr; Schl Coordinating Cncl; Natl Jr Hnr Soc Spon; Stu Cncl; Math Counts; Ldrshp Trng; Earth Squad; Schl Act Fund Mem; Spon Overnight Field Trip to Scotland; SDEA, OEA, FEA, NEA 1965-; NCTM 1980-; World Wide Fund for Nature 1987-; Alpha Omicron Pi 1962-; Kappa Delta Pi 1963-; Exceptional Tchr Awd 1985-95; Dodds Sustained Superior Awd 1985, 1987, 1989-92, 1994-95; Family Svcs Vol of Yr 1971; Dept of Defense Dependent Schls Overseas; *office:* Lakenheath Amer MS Unit 5185 Box 55 Dodds CCSM APO AE 09461*

MANNING, DIANA GALLO, High School Religion Teacher; *b:* Jersey City, NJ; *m:* Robert; *c:* Michele, Marc, Corinne; *ed:* Georgian Ct Coll (BA) Theology 1989; Seton Hall Univ (MA) Theology 1996; *cr:* St Rose HS Tchr 1989-; *ai:* Sr Seminar; Soph Retreats; NCEA 1989-; Pay Christi 1995-; Alpha Theta Kappa.

MANNING, ELIZABETH A., 4th Grade Teacher; *b:* Boston, MA; *ed:* RI Coll (MAT) Elem Educ 1979; Cert MA Gen Hosp Specific Lang Disability; *cr:* Holy Name Schl Tchr 1974-85; Rocky Hill Schl Summer Rdng Clinic tutor 1983-86; North Providence Schl Dept Sub Tchr 1985-89, Tchr 1989-; *ai:* AFT 1986-; Orton Dyslexia Soc 1983-, Treas Local Bd; PTO Greystone Sch 1988-; Friends of Cran Lib; Nomination for Tchr of Yr Awd Cath Schls; Sci Fair Coord 1984-85; Sci Fair Judge.*

MANNING, GRETA SORGENFREI, Biology Teacher; *b:* Columbus, OH; *m:* David Scott; *c:* Abigail; *ed:* Bowling Green St Univ (BA) Bio 1989; OH St Univ (MSEd) Sci Ed 1994; *cr:* Bowling Green St Univ Tchng Asst 1988-89; Westerville City Schls Sci Tchr 1989-; *ai:* OH Wildlife Rsrch Class Instr; NEA 1989-; *office:* Westerville South HS 303 S Otterbein Ave Westerville OH 43081*

MANNING, JACQUELINE JEAN, General & Vocal Music Teacher; *b:* Bristol, PA; *m:* Daniel G.; *c:* Daniel M.; *ed:* Westminster Choir Coll (BA) Music Ed 1979; *cr:* East Brunswick Bd of Ed Elem Gen & Vocal Music Tchr 1979-89; Hamilton Twp Bd of Ed Gen & Vocal Music Tchr 1989-; St James Episcopal Church Organist & Choir Dir 1976-; *ai:* Private Piano Tchr; NEA, NJEA, MENC 1976-; Nom for NJ Governors Awd for Outstdng Tchr; *office:* Richard C Crockett MS 2631 Kuser Rd Robbinsville NJ 08691

MANNING, JAMES MICHAEL, Middle School Mathematics Tchr; *b:* Providence, RI; *ed:* Univ of RI (BA) Math, Scndry Ed 1983; 42 Addl Credit Hrs RI Coll & Providence Coll for Cert; *cr:* Roger Williams MS Math Tchr 1990-; *ai:* Shea HS Asst Ftbl Coach 1990-; Barrington HS Frosh Girls Bsktbl Coach 1990-; *office:* Roger Williams MS 278 Thurbers Ave Providence RI 02905

MANNING, JAMES MICHAEL, Assoc Prof Exercise Physiology; *b:* Easthampton, MA; *ed:* Niagara Univ (BS) PE 1970; IN St Univ (MS) Ath Trng 1977; Univ of MD (PHD) Exercise Physiology 1981; Post Doctoral Trng Bowman Gray Schl of Med at Winston-Salem; *cr:* Fall Mountain Schl Dist PE Tchr 1973-76; Univ of MD Asst Instr 1979-81; US Sports Acad Asst Prof 1981-84; William Paterson Coll Assoc Prof 1984-; *ai:* Coord Exercise Physiology Prgm; Institutional Review Bd; Curr, Retention & Tenure, Search, Research Comm; Cohort Analysis; Dept Cncl; Reviewer for CHOICE; Amer Coll of Sports Med 1977-; Natl Ath Trainers Assn 1976-; Amer Assn Clinical Chem 1990-; Amer Heart Assn 1991-, Arteriosclerosis Cncl; Sr Flwshp Natl Rsrch Svc Awd NIH-NHLBI, Amer Heart Assn, William Paterson Coll Summer Grants; Putting Stdnts First Awd; Amer Coll of Sports Fellow; Numerous Articles Pub; *office:* William Paterson Coll 300 Pompton Rd Wayne NJ 07470

MANNING, NANCY J., Asst Prof of Political Sci; *b:* North Canton, OH; *m:* Eric Fenstermaker; *c:* Evan; *ed:* OH St Univ (BS) Landscape Horticulture 1972, (MS) Landscape Horticulture 1978; Univ of MI (PHD) Natural Resource Policy 1991; *cr:* OH Univ Asst Prof 1993-; *ai:* Environmental Stud Cert Prgm Dir; Masters of Sci Environmental Stud Prgm Asst Dir; Soc Prof Dispute Resolutions 1994-; Articles Pub; Grant OH Commission Dispute Resolutions & Conflict Mngmt, OH Environmental Protection Agency; *office:* OH Univ Bentley Hall Athens OH 45701

MANNING, SCOTT EDWARD, Biology & Science Teacher; *b:* S Williamsport, PA; *ed:* Working on Grad Degree Penn St Univ; *cr:* S Williansport Area Schl Dist Bio & Gen Sci Tchr 1993-; *ai:* Sr Class & Key Club Adv; Curr Stratigic Planning Comm; NEA & PSEA 1993-; NSTA 1993-; NABT 1993-; *office:* S Williamsport Area Jr Sr HS 700 Percy St South Williamsport PA 17701

MANNINGHAM, CHERYL A., International Studies Teacher; *b:* Cleveland, OH; *c:* Justin Gibson; *ed:* Spelllman Coll (BA) Eng His, Theatre 1981; Cleveland St Univ Comm; Baldwin Wallace Coll MS Cert; *cr:* Grady HS His Tchr 1981-85; Roosevelt HS His Tchr 1985-89; Martin L. King L. P. S. HS Intnl Stud Tchr 1993-; *ai:* Stu Govt, Precious Stones, Dream Team, Soph Adv; Choir Dir; Cleveland Tchrs Union 1989-; Prof Black Edctrs 1986-; Prayer Warrior 1995-, Singer of Yr; Naomi Cir 1996, VP; Shiloh Bapt Church 1959-; Gospel Choir 1989-, Sargent at Arm; GA Oratorical Excl Awd; Co-Tchr of Yr 1996.

MANNINO, GRACE ZUMMO, Foreign Language Teacher; *b:* Italy; *m:* Vincent; *c:* Frank; *ed:* Hunter Coll (BA) Italian 1969, (MA) Italian 1972; SUNY at Stony Brook (DA) Italian 1983; *cr:* Bishop MC Donald HS Span Tchr 1969-71; Holy Trinity HS Span Tchr 1971-72; Brentwood HS Span, Italian, Fr Tchr 1972-; Suffolk Comm Coll Span, Italian, Fr Adj Prof 1986-; SUNY Italian Lecturer 1990-; *ai:* HS Italian Club, Intnl Night Adv; Staff, Stu of Month Comm Chprsn; Ed Amer Assoc Tchr of Ital Newsletter; AATI Natl 1975-, Exec Bd; AATI 1977-, Pres 2 Terms, Sec; Long Island Lang TE 1984-, VP; NYSAFLT 1987-; NY St Regents Examination 1990-, Consultant, Contributor; MCES Schlsp Siena Multinatoinal, Comparative Ed; AATI Travel Stud Grant; Numerous Articles Pub; AATI Rep Natl Frgn Lang Stan; *office:* Brentwood HS 1st & 5th Ave Brentwood NY 11717

MANNINO, LAURIE SUE, Social Studies Teacher; *b:* Washington, DC; *m:* Alfred Paul; *c:* Christopher, Timothy; *ed:* Westfield St Coll (BA) His-Summa Cum Laude 1991; Attnd Boston Conservatory of Music, Harvard Univ & Western MD Coll; *cr:* Quince Orchard HS Tchr 1! Class of 1997 Spon; Mentoring Prgm; NEA 1992-; NCSS 1991-; N for Soc Stud 1995-; Org of Amer Historians 1991-; *office:* Quince HS 15800 Quince Orchard Rd Gaithersburg MD 20878*

MANNINO, LOUIS ANTHONY, Mathematics Teacher; *b:* New CT; *m:* Avis Marie Cotter; *c:* Marcus; *ed:* Fort Hays St Univ (BS) 1965, (MS) Elem Ed 1966; KS Univ, George Washington Univ P Credits; Montgomery Coll Math Credits; *cr:* KS City Pub Schls E 5 Tchr 1966-69; Montgomery Cty Pub Schls Elem Grd 6 Tchr Montgomery Coll GATE Instr, Saturday Discovery Prgm 1991-93, Math Instr for Adults 1993-95; Montgomery Cty Pub Schls 7-8th G 1979-; *ai:* Math Textbook Evaluation, GATE Comm; Team Tchng 17 Yrs; Laison Spokesperson Instr Metric System; Outdoor Ed Chm MCEA 1969-, 25 Yrs Svc Awd; MSTA, NEA 1969-; Pine Crest El PTA 1971-72, First VP; Outstdng Edctr Awd 1991; Fort Hays St U Tchr Awd 1971; Outstdng Tchr Awd 1968; Stoney Point Elem PT Ldr in Coll 1965; Scholastic Schlsp 1965; Ath Schlsp 1959; Rocketry Prgm 3 Yrs; Goddard Space Ctr Model Rockets Launche 10404 Drumm Ave Kensington MD 20895*

MANNION, BARBARA A., Social Studies Teacher; *b:* New Ha *m:* John J.; *c:* Kate, John, Timothy, Kelly; *ed:* Albertus Magnus C His 1970-; Southern Ct St Univ (MS) Ed 1974; *cr:* Joseph Melillo 1971-; *ai:* NEA, CEA, EHEA 1971-; Sacred Heart Acad Mothe 1995-; *office:* Joseph Melillo MS 67 Hudson St East Haven CT 06

MANNION, FRANCES CHASE, English Teacher; *b:* St Louis, Anthony F.; *c:* Anthony Paul, Stephen, Elizabeth, Mary; *ed:* India of PA (BS) Eng, Rdng 1968; Univ of Pittsburgh (MED) Sec Ed, Er California Univ of PA Rdng Specialist Cert; *cr:* Bethel Park Schl Eng, Rdng Tchr 1968-74; Faith Comm Chrstn Schl Eng Tchr 1 Hillcrest Chrstn Schl MS Tchr 1989-92; Bethel Park Schl Dist E 1993-; *ai:* AFT 1993-; *office:* Bethel Park Sr HS 309 Church Rd Park PA 15102

MANNO, BARBARA CHEPEY, Second Grade Classroom Tea Perth Amboy, NJ; *m:* Ralph; *c:* Jeffrey, Lise Gega, Steven, Christop Kean Coll at Union (BA) Elem Ed; Rdng, Presch, Handicapped Ce Grad Stud Rdng, Spec Ed 24 Credits; *cr:* Roselle Pub Schl S 1972-75, Tchr of Handicapped 1975-83, First Grd Tchr 1983-86, Grd Tchr 1986-; *ai:* Dist Rep Affirmative Action Comm; Discipli Climate Comms; Lit Vol of Amer, Tutor-Trainer, Peer Vol Tchr; Rd Assn; NEA 1975-; St Joseph Mission 1983-, Organist; Inter-Fai Svcs, Organist, Choir Dir; Roselle Bd of Ed Tchr of Yr Awd; Sci A 2nd Place Dist Fairs; Kids In Nature's Defense Humanitarian Awd

MANNO, CHRISTOPHER MICHAEL, Mathematics Teac Brooklyn, NY; *m:* Melissa Ann Borgia; *ed:* Trenton St Coll (BA 1990, (MED) Math 1993; 12 Credit Hrs Supvrs Cert; Masters Ldrshp; *cr:* Hillsborough HS Math Tchr 1990-, Head Cross Cntry 1990-, Head Track & Field Coach 1995-, Head Swimming Coach *ai:* NCTM 1990-; AMTNJ 1990-; NJEA 1990-; NEA 1990-; Hillst Twp Ed Assn 1990-; Cntrl NJ Coach of Yr 1994-95; *office:* Hillst HS Raider Blvd Belle Mead NJ 08502*

MANOLI, CHERYL ELLEN, HS Mathematics Teacher; *b:* Frami MA; *ed:* Boston Univ (BS) Math 1968, (MED) Math Ed 1972; Bos (MA) Math 1976, (CAES) Educl Rsrch 1987; *cr:* North Quincy H Tchr 1968-; QPS Summer Inst for Gifted Stdnts Asst Dir 1992-; N Coll Instr 1992-; *ai:* Calculus Team Coach; South Shore Alliance P Comm; NCTM 1984-; Pi Lambda Theta 1982-; MTA, NEA 197 Grant 1972-75; *office:* North Quincy HS 316 Hancock St North Qui 02171

MANOLOFF, BRETT A., High School Science Teacher; *b:* Cle OH; *ed:* Wittenberg Univ (BA) Earth Sci 1994; *cr:* Amesbury HS S 1994-; *ai:* Soph Class Adv; Project PALMS; Frosh Boys Bsktb Coach; Sci, Tech Curr Facilitator; Track, Field Judge; *office:* Amest 5 Highland St Amesbury MA 01913

MANOS, MICHELE BONINI, Second Grade Teacher; *b:* New Yo *m:* James; *ed:* ST John's Univ (BS) Elem Ed 1967; C.W. Post (MS Ed 1976; *cr:* ThaKew-Forest Schl Second Grd Tchr 1967-; *ai.* Humane Ed Soc; PETA; Natl Wildlife Fed; Bide-A-Wee Assn; Kew-Forest Schl 11917 Union Tpke Flushing NY 11375

MANOS, TED PETER, United States History Teacher; *b:* Indiana, Barbara Galanis; *c:* Peter, Elias; *ed:* Indiana Univ of Pa (BSED) S 1962; *cr:* Union Area HS Geog Tchr 1962-64; Atlantic City HS Tchr 1964-; *ai:* NJ Governors Awd for Outstndng Tchr; AP B Outstndng AP Tchr Eastern Region.

MANSEAU, LANI,DC, Old Testament Teacher; *b:* Honolulu, Dominican Coll of San Rafael (BA) Amer Stud 1963; Univ of Dayto Stud 1979; 15 Grad Credit Hrs in Theology; Flwshp-Eastern Coll Credits in Amer Stud; *cr:* St Christine Schl Jr High Tchr 1966-69; Seton Schl Jr High Tchr 1969-79; Our Lady Queen oif Peace Schl Tchr 1979-82; St Patrick Schl Jr High Tchr 1982-83; Elizabeth Se Tchr, Rel Dept Chair 1983-; *ai:* Acad, Liturgy, Discipline Comm Assn of Cath Schls 1966-; Flwshp Eastern Coll; *office:* Elizabeth Se 5715 Emerson St Bladensburg MD 20710

MANSELL, DARREL, English Professor; *b:* Canton, OH; *m:* A Saviane; *c:* Benjamin; *ed:* Oberlin Coll (BA) Eng Lit 1956; Yal (PHD) Eng Lit 1963; Dartmouth Coll (MA) (Hon) 1975; Fulbright Pembroke Coll 1961-62; *cr:* Dartmouth Coll Instr 1962-64, As 1964-68, Assoc Prof 1968-74, Prof 1974-; *ai:* Jane Austen Soc Fo Patron; Northeast Victorian Lit Soc; Soc for Lit & Sci; Phi Beta 1956-; Author Novels of Jane Austen, Articles; *office:* Dartmou Hanover NH 03755

MANSER, RICHARD L., History Teacher; *b:* Philadelphia, PA; *m* Carson; *c:* Christopher, Jonathan; *ed:* Penn St Univ (BA) His 1965 His 1967; Temple Univ (PHD) His 1987; *cr:* Villanova Univ Adj H 1988-89; Coll of St Francis Adj His Prof 1993-, Upper Merion Area Tchr 1966-; *ai:* Upper Merion Area Ed Assn Negotiating Comm; An Assoc 1966-; Organ Amer Historians 1980-; Natl Cncl Hist Ed 199 of Historians Amer Frgn Relations 1987-; Martin Luther King Day 1990-; Myles J. Brennan Meml Schlsp Comm 1985-, Trustee; Phi Theta Natl His Honorary 1966; Who's Who in Amer Ed 1992-; B Awd; *office:* Upper Merion Area HS 435 Crossfield Rd King Of Prus 19406

MANSER, WILLIAM E., Technology Educator; *b:* Springfield, M Peg Mitchell; *c:* Meg, Erich; *ed:* Fitchburg St (BS) Industrial Arts E (MED) Tech Ed 1979; IBM Comp Ed 1984, Apple Comp Mgmt Trn & Compaq Dealer Authorization Trng 1986; *cr:* Hudson HS Tech 1974-84; IBM, Apple & Compaq Comp Sales Mgr & Dealer 19 Grafton MS Tech Ed Dir 1987-91; Oakmont Reg HS Tech Ed D 1992-95; Overlook MS Tech Edctr 1995-; *ai:* Jr Engrng Tech Soc; Educl & Math, Sci, Tech Comm; NEA & MA Tchers 1974-; World Soc 1989-; MA CUE 1992-; MA Sci Tchrs; MA RP Fndtn 1981 WAVE 1991-, Sec; NSF Grant Project 1991; Modular Tech Ed Trnr; Overlook MS 10 Oakmont Dr Ashburnham MA 01430*

MANSFIELD, CAROL PAULIE, Special Education Teach Pittsburgh, PA; *m:* John M.; *c:* Todd, Jacqueline, Scott; *ed:* Bingh Univ (MSEd) Spec Ed 1981; *cr:* Vestal Cntrl Schls Sub Tchr 19

hanna Vly HS Resource Room Tchr 1981-; *ai:* Spirit Club, Peer Ldr, resentation Adv; Project Team Prevenative Prgms; Peer Tutor, Sr Luncheon Coord; Spring Revue Co-Chmn; NEA 1981-, Tchr Ctr elta Kappa; Boome Cty Self-Esteem Cncl 1992-; Drug Free Schls PTA Life Mem; Grants Tchr Ctr Mini, Broome Tioga Exemplary NY St Pub Television Mini; Susquehanna Vly Cntrl Schl Dist 1 Svc Awd 1984-85; Natl Cncl Self-Esteem Enhancement Awd 1993; Hero Olympic Torch Bearer 1996; *office:* Susquehanna Valley Sr HS onklin Rd Conklin NY 13748*

FIELD, ELLEN K., 9th Grade English Teacher; *b:* New York, NY; U Schl of Ed (BS) Eng, Math 1969, (MS) Comm, Media 1971; Post ourses Guid, MS Initiative, Voc Rehab; *cr:* Harriet Beecher Stowe Eng Tchr, Media Specialist 1970-85; Frederick Douglass IS 10 rogrammer Eng, Media 1985-91; Tourd Coll Adj Prof Professional 1-95; Rachel Carson IS 237 Eng, Cmptr Tchr, Schl Programmer *ai:* Schl Programmer; Svc Monitor Squad Adv; Writing Comm for MS Initiative Prgm; Staff Dev Wkshps; UFT, NYSUT, NCTE 1970-; II Grant for Dev of Schl Radio Station; Book Basic English Skills; Rachel Carson IS 237 4621 Colden St Flushing NY 11355*

FIELD, ELYSE DENAT, Second Grade Teacher; *b:* New York, NY; l R.; *c:* William, Michael, Alice M. Zech, Sara Mc Laughlin; *ed:* at New Paltz (BS) Elem Ed 1966, (MS) Elem Ed 1970; *cr:* Titusville Schl Primay Tchr 1966-73; La Grange Elem Schl Primary Tchr *ai:* NYSUT; ATA 1966-; BLT 1995-; Temple Beth-El Sisterhood

FIELD, MARCI WILLIAMS, Elem Phy Ed Teacher & Coach; *b:* rgh, PA; *m:* Michael E.; *c:* Jenna Lee; *ed:* Slippery Rock Univ of PA lth, PE 1985; SUNY at Brockport (MS) PE 1994; *cr:* Pine Vly Cntrl 987; Westfield Acad, Cntrl Schls Elem PE Tchr 1988-; *ai:* Var Boys , Competitive Chrldng, Girls Track Coach; Dance Team Dir, grapher; Field Day Dir; NEA, Westfield Tchrs Assn 1988-; NY St E, Recreation, Dance Assn 1989-; Natl Chrldng Coaches Assn; qua Cty Chrldng Coaches Assn; Buffalo Jills NFL Chrldr 1988-, n, Rookie of Yr 1988, Captain of Yr 1989; Universal Chrldrs Assn 8, Camp Dir; Soccer Coach of Yr 1991; Chautauqua Cty Chrldng s Awd 1993; *office:* Westfield Acad & Central Schls E Main St eld NY 14787*

FIELD, MARY ELLEN E., English Chair; *b:* Queens, NY; *ed:* at Stony Brook (BA) Eng 1980; Dowling Coll (MS) Sec Ed 1987; ttan Coll (SAS) Admin 1992; *cr:* LSMA 7th-12th Grd Asst Prin & chr 1985-93; Comsewogue HS Dir Alt Schl 1993-94; OLMA Eng 994-95; Riverhead HS Eng Dept Chair 1995-; *ai:* Curr Review Task Chair 1988-89; Mercy Collaborative Comm 1994-95; Curr Comm NCTE 1985-; LILAC 1990-; Kappa Delta Pi 1987; *office:* Riverhead) Harrison Ave Riverhead NY 11901

SKE, BRIAN KENNETH, Mathematics Department Chm; *b:* Staten NY; *m:* Carolyn Blomquist; *c:* Erik; *ed:* Wagner Coll (BS) Math Stevens Inst of Tech (MS) Math 1976; *cr:* Staten Island Acad Math 977-82, Chair 1979-82; Msgr Mc Clancy HS Math Tchr 1982-83; Island Acad Math Tchr, Chm 1983-; *ai:* 7th-8th Grd Bsktbl, Var Tennis Team Coach; 7-12th Grd Schedule; Coll Cnslr; Curr Comm; 1985-; Woodrow Wilson Flwshp 1985; AP Calculus Reader 1991-; Staten Island Acad 715 Todt Hill Rd Staten Island NY 10304*

SPEAKER, JANET BECHTEL, Asst Prof of Political Science; *b:* gton, KS; *ed:* Univ of SC (MA) Intnl Stud 1981; Univ of DE (PHD) i 1990; Military His Fellow at US Military Acad 1993-94; ROTC ry His Flwshp; *cr:* Univ of DE Instr 1990-92; Cheyney Univ Asst 992-; *ai:* Soc, Behavioral Sci Dept Internship Coord; APSA 1990-; 992-; *office:* Cheyney Univ Of PA PO Box 169 Cheyney PA 19319

TELL, NORA MARGARET, English Teacher; *b:* Ellenville, NY; st Grad Work Eng, Ed, Cmptr Tech; *cr:* Little Brown Publish Co Asst v Dept 6 Yrs; Andover Inst of Bus Eng Tchr 1969-70; B-R Regnl HS chr 1970-; *ai:* Staff Cmptr Instruction; Comm Night Schl Cmptr Tech Triathlete; Poet; Journalist; *office:* Bridgewater Raynham Reg HS ount Prospect St Bridgewater MA 02324*

TELLA, ROSE M., English & Spanish Teacher; *b:* Pittsburgh, PA; quesne Univ (BS) Scndry Ed, Span, Eng 1990, (MS) Rdng & Lang 995; *cr:* Central Cath HS Span, Eng Tchr 1992-; *ai:* Drama Club.

THARAM, MYTHILI, Assistant Professor of Math; *b:* Seergazhi, nadu India; *c:* Subbiah; *ed:* Queen Mary's Coll (BS) Math 1964; ency Coll (MSC) Math 1966; Univ of Madras India (MPhil) Math St Univ of NY at Buffalo (MA) Math 1986, (MS) Cmptr Sci 1988; Cmptr Sci 1993; *cr:* Madras Govt Coll Asst Prof, Prof 1966-83; d Fillmore Coll Instr 1988, 1990-92; St Univ of NY Visiting Lecturer 92; John Jay Coll of Criminals Justice Instr 1992-93, Asst Prof 1993-; CM 1991-; IEEE, PSC CUNY, NYSUI, AFT 1993-; AARP 1995-; PSC Y Rsrch Awd Grant 1994-95; Co-Author Eberlein Papers, Chptr; John Jay Coll Criminal Justice The City Univ of NY 445 W 59th St York NY 10019

TINEO, JOSEPH LOUIS, Italian Teacher; *b:* Englewood, NJ; *m:* yn E.; *c:* Kathryn Teresa, Joseph Louis, Lisa Marie, Mary Elizabeth; utgers Univ (BA) Italian 1967, (MA) Italian 1972; Montclair Univ Cert; *cr:* Princeton HS Italian, Span Tchr 1967-69; Dumont HS n, Span Tchr 1969-; *ai:* Italian Hnr Soc Adv; NEA, NJEA, BCEA ; DEA 1969-; FLE NJ 1967-, Outstdng Contribution to Frgn Lang Ed Knights of Columbus 1973-, Grand Knight; St Philip the Apostle Name Soc 1987-; Phi Beta Kappa 1967-; NDEA Schlsp 1966-67; ght Schlsp 1987, 1991; Tchr of Yr 1987; Rsrch Grant; *home:* 71 ridge Ave Saddle Brook NJ 07663

TINI, NOREEN F., School Counselor; *b:* Exton, PA; *m:* Terry kle; *c:* Alexandra Arbuckle, Blair Arbuckle, Danielle Arbuckle; *ed:* of AZ (BA) Biling, Elem Ed 1978; West Chester Univ (MED) Cnslng 18 Hrs GATE Cert Univ of South ME; Addl 69 Grad Hrs; *cr:* Drexel Schl Biling Tchr 1978-81; Wetzel Elem Schl 5th Grd Tchr 1981-83; Elem Schl GATE Tchr 1983-91; Wetzel Elem Schl Cnslr 1991-; *ai:* Mngmt, Transdisiplinary Team, Placement Comm Chprsn; nrichment Team; Mental Hlth Steering Comm; Schl Improvement n 3 Yrs Co-Chair; Installation Adv Comm Chprsn 3 Yrs; Dist ADA, D Comm; NEA 1978-, PDK 1994-; FEA, BAEA, ACA, ASCD 1991-; C 1984-; European Branch ACA 1995-; ASCA 1990-; PTSA 1981-; rior, Performance Awds 1983, 1985-94; Dept of Army Svc Awd; r Ed, Spec Projects Grant St of AZ 1978-79; NCA Accreditaion Team 1989; *office:* Wetzel Elem Schl Unit 23815 APO AE 09034*

U, FRANKLYN, Assoc Professor of Marketing; *b:* Kumasi, Ghana; argaret Mensa; *c:* Kwame, Nana Amponsem; *ed:* Univ of Ghana) Mgmt 1977; NY Univ (MBA) Finance 1981, (PHD) Mktg & Intl Bus *cr:* NY St Univ Instr 1986-88; Loyola Coll Asst Prof 1988-93; an St Univ Assoc Prof 1993-; *ai:* Intl Bus Club Adv; Acad of Intl Bus ; Amer Mktg Assoc 1989-; Assoc for Global Bus 1989-; Acad of Mktg 991-; Beta Gamma Sigma; Mu Kappa Tau; Numerous Journals Pub; Morgan St Univ 1700 E Cold Spring Ln Baltimore MD 21239

UEL, ANDREA DEJOHN, French Teacher; *b:* Meadville, PA; *c:* J. topher, Gina M. Chatfield, Michael; *ed:* Edinboro Univ (BS) Scndry r 1969, (MED) Rdng 1986; *cr:* Conneaut Lake HS Fr Tchr 1969-70; bridge Springs HS Fr Tchr Part-Time 1981-86; Segertown HS Fr Tchr Part-Time 1981-86; Penncrest Schl Dist Elem & HS Remedial Rdng Tchr 1986-91; Saegertown HA Fr Tchr 1991-; *ai:* Fr Club, Fr Choir Spons; PSEA, PAEA, NEA 1981-; *office:* Saegertown Jr-Sr HS 18079 Mook Rd Saegertown PA 16433

MANUEL, EMMA J., Teacher; *b:* McNeil, AR; *c:* Cassandra, Cedric; *ed:* Cntrl St Univ (BS) Elem Ed & Spec Ed 1971; Wright St Univ (MED) Curr & Supervision 1989; *cr:* Dayton Bd of Ed Tchr 1966-, Roth Day Camp Sr Camp Cnslr 1976-78, Home Instruction Instr 1992-; *ai:* Sr Class Adv; Jr Achvmt, Convocation & Staff-Admin Comms; Alpha Kappa Alpha 1989-; Dayton Schl Toastmasters 1990-; NEA 1971-; DEA 1971-; NAACP 1992-; St Timothy Bapt Church 1991-, Sec, Bldg Fund Comm; *office:* Dunbar HS 2222 Richley Dr Dayton OH 45408*

MANUEL, THOMAS GEORGE, German & French Teacher; *b:* Woburn, MA; *m:* Jane Paula Kroll; *c:* Kristine (Wilson), Korin; *ed:* Union Coll (BA) Fr & Ger 1969; Millersville Univ (MA) Ger 1979; *cr:* Coventry HS Fr & Ger Tchr 1969-77; RB Jr HS Ger Tchr 1977-79; Stuttgart HS Fr & Ger Tchr 1979-81; Munish HS Fr & Ger Tchr 1981-92; Patch HS Fr & Ger Tchr 1992-; *ai:* Class Spon; Girls Var Soccer Coach; Stud Fac Lunch Comm; Fac Comm for HHS & Extracurricular Assignments Chprsn; FEA 1977-, FRS Recording Section; AATG; HS Ath Booster 1979-; Soccer Ofcls Assn 1986-; NYSCA 1993-; Coaching 5 Dodds European Small Schls Girls Soccer Championship Teams 1985-92; Tchr of the Yr Munich HS 1986 & 1992; Master Thesis Pub 1979; *office:* Patch American HS Unit 30401 Box 2991 APO AE 09131

MANY, RUTH ROSE, Kindergarten Teacher; *b:* Oneonta, NY; *m:* Floyd B.; *c:* Dana, Janet Many Mc Hugh, Neal, Elaine Many Starheim, Rena Many Davis; *ed:* St Univ at Potsdam (BS) Music 1949; St Univ at Oneonta (BA) Ed N-9 1975; *cr:* East Greenbush Cntrl Schl Instrumental, Vocal Tchr Grd 1-6 1950-51; South Kortright Cntrl Schl Kndgtn Tchr 1972-91; *ai:* Church Pianist 15 Yrs; Intnl Farm Youth Exch 1949; *home:* RR 1 Box 152 Hobart NY 13788

MANZ, SHERYL LYNN, Guidance Counselor; *b:* Brooklyn, NY; *m:* Paul Stephen; *c:* Katie, Lisa; *ed:* SUNY at Geneseo (BA) Eng, Scndry Ed 1980; SUNY at New Paltz (MA) Rdng K-12 1986; CW Post (MS) Cnslng 1992; *cr:* Monticello HS Eng Tchr 1981-92, Guid Cnslr 1992-; *ai:* Interact, Sr Class Adv; *office:* Monticello HS Port Jervis Rd Monticello NY 12701

MANZELLA, LINDA RUSIGNUOLO, Mathematics Teacher; *b:* Newark, NJ; *m:* Ronald; *c:* Carrie Lynn, Ronald; *ed:* Montclair St Coll (BA) Math 1971; *cr:* Bloomfield MS Tchr 1971-; *ai:* Natl Jr Hnr Soc Adv; NEA 1971-; Tchr of Yr Awd 1994; *home:* 133 Jockey Hollow Way Union NJ 07083

MANZI, SUSAN LILLIAN, Kindergarten Teacher; *b:* Worcester, MA; *ed:* Worcester St Coll (BS) Elem Ed 1970, (MA) Elem Ed 1974; 60 Addl Credits; *cr:* Roosevelt Schl Grd 2 Tchr 1970-71; Belmont St Schl Kndgtn Tchr 1971-79, Grd 1 Tchr 1980-85, Kndgtn Tchr 1986-; *ai:* Early Chldhd Resource Ctr Advy Cncl; Books & Beyond, Belmont's Best Comms; Educl Assn of Worcester, MA Tchr Assn 1970-; NEA 1970-, Whole Lang Assoc; Horace Mann Tchr Grants 1988-89; Nom Worcester's Tchr of Yr 1993; *office:* Belmont St Comm Schl 170 Belmont St Worcester MA 01605*

MAPES, THOMAS CARL, Occptnl Work Adjstmnt Tchr; *b:* Mansfield, OH; *m:* Valerie Kay Brooks; *c:* Holly, Levi; *ed:* OH Univ (BSEd) Ed 1969; Attnd Ashland Coll, Xavier Univ, LaVerne Coll & OH St Univ; *cr:* OH St Reformatory Tchr 1969-72; Mansfield Opportunites Industrialization Ctr Tutor 1969-72; Mansfield Neighborhood Youth Corps Tutor 1979-81; Mansfield City Schls Tchr 1972-; *ai:* OWA Club Adv; PALS Bsbl Coach; Owner of Paullin Sealcoating Bus; NEA, OEA, MSEA 1972-, Negotiations Team; Moose Lodge 341 1991-, Mem; St Marys Parish 1985-, Mem; OWA 5 Yr Achvmt Awd; Awd for Yrs Successful Soccer Coaching Madison S Soccer; Prof Certs in Comprehensvie Soc Studs, Developmentally Handicapped & Voc Ed; Honored by Stdnts in in Local Newspaper & TV 1993; *office:* Mansfield City Schls 53 W 4th St Mansfield OH 44902

MAPPES, GORDON H., Social Studies Teacher; *b:* Auburn, NY; *m:* Linda Brewster; *c:* Carrie, Jessica; *ed:* Utica Coll of Syracuse Univ (BA) His 1972; 42 Addl Grad Hrs in Ed & His; *cr:* Stockbridge Valley CS Soc Stud Tchr 1972-; *ai:* Stu Cncl, Jr Class, NHS Adv; NEA-NY 1972-, Pres 4 Yrs; Oneida Area Day Care Bd 1976-, Pres 2 Yrs; Madison Co Schl Emp Fed Credit Union 1974-.

MARADEI, WILLIAM F., Physical Sci & Algebra Teacher; *b:* Winthrop, MA; *m:* Mary C. Pizzano; *c:* Billy, Mark; *ed:* Boston St Coll (BS) Hlth, PE 1977; 21 Hrs Career Ed at U MA at Boston; *cr:* St Dominic Savio HS Tchr, Frosh Dean, Head Ftbl Coach 1977-93; Austin Prep Schl Tchr, Head Ftbl Coach 1993-; *ai:* Lacrosse Asst Coach; Head Hockey Coach Savio Prep; Natl Cath Ed Assn 1977-; MA Ftbl Coaches Assn 1979-, Coach of Yr; Northshore Rec, Soc Cntr 1971-, Dir; Boston Globe, Boston Herald Coach of Yr Ftbl; *office:* Austin Prep Schl 101 Willow St Reading MA 01867

MARADEN, DAVID E., English Teacher; *b:* Pittsburgh, PA; *m:* Joann Cannon; *c:* Kara, Michael; *ed:* Edinboro St Coll (BS) Eng 1970, (MED) Rdng Specialist 1976; 36 Hrs Post-Grad Stud; *cr:* Acad HS Eng Tchr 1970-72; Woodrow Wilson Jr HS Eng Tchr 1972-75; New Direction Ctr Eng Tchr, Rdng Specialist 1975-79; Woodrow Wilson MS Rdng Tchr 1979-93; Strong Vincent HS Eng Tchr 1993-; *ai:* NEA, PSEA, EEA 1972-; League Urban Scholars 1994-; PTSA; St Life Mem PA PTA; Tchr of Yr Commendation 1986; *office:* Strong Vincent HS 1330 W 8th St Erie PA 16502*

MARANDOLA, DAVID C., Social Studies Teacher; *b:* Providence, RI; *m:* Elvira A. Ambrosino; *c:* Tamatha Ann, Michelle Marie; *ed:* Providence Coll (BA) His 1969, (MA) Amer His 1972; 30 Credit Hrs in Scndry Admin; 30 Credit Hrs in Math; *cr:* Providence Coll Grad Flwshp 1970-71; Johnston Pub Schls Soc Stud Tchr 1971-83; Johnson & Wales Coll His Instr 1980-84; Johnston Pub Schls US His, Western Civ Instr 1983-90, Asst Prin 1990-93, US His, Western Civ Instr 1993-; *ai:* Track, Cross Cntry Coach 1979-85; Schl Improvement Team 1990-93; Sftbl Coach 1981-88; Act Dir 1992-93; AFT 1971-, Bldg Rep; JFT 1971-; Johnston Recreation, Cranston Recreation, Sftbl Coach; *office:* Johnston Sr HS 345 Cherry Hill Rd Johnston RI 02920

MARANDOS, LYNDA L., First Grade Teacher; *b:* Syracuse, NY; *m:* Cosmos E.; *c:* Tara K., Tory C.; *ed:* Keene St Coll (BED) Elem Ed 1971; Lesley Coll (MED) Curr Dev Fine Arts 1995; *cr:* Charlotte Ave Schl 1 Grd Tchr 1971-72; Main Dunstable Schl 1 Grd Tchr 1972-74; Amherst Street Schl 2 Grd Tchr 1976-77; Bicentennial Schl 1 Grd Tchr 1977-; *ai:* Dist Wide Report Card, Field Trip, Character Ed, Prof Dev Procedures; Nashua Tchr Assn 1981-; Walnut Hill 1994-, VP Bd of Dir; *office:* Bicentennial Elem Schl 296 E Dunstable Rd Nashua NH 03062

MARASCO, FLOYD C.,JR., Instr of Math & Computer Sci; *b:* Washington, PA; *m:* Sonya Jean Sinclair; *c:* Debbie, Angela; *ed:* CA Univ of PA (BSEd) Scndry Math 1974, (MED) Scndry Math 1977; *cr:* Monessen Schl Dist Math Instr 1975-76; McGuffey Schl Dist Math, Cmptr Sci Instr 1976-; Adult Evening Schl Inst 1983-86; *ai:* Chm Fac Curr Comm; Fac Adv of NHS; Fac Spon Peer Tutoring Prgm; Fac Coach Math Competition Team; Fac Facilitator of Satellite Ed Prgm; Ftbl Gatekeeper 1976-; Bsktbl Official Clock Operator 1976-; Fac Senate 1995-; Grading Policy Comm 1987-; PSEA, NEA 1975-; NCTM 1995-; Local Church In Washington PA 1965-, Pres 1975-80; Presbyn Church 1983-, Elder 1986; Sunday Schl Tchr 1972-; Church Dartball Team; Gift of Time Tribute Amer Family Inst 1991; All-Star Educators Awd Univ of Pittsburgh & Pittsburgh Post Gazette 1993; Rookie Tchr of Yr 1976; *office:* McGuffey HS 86 McGuffey Dr Claysville PA 15323

MARASCO, MICHELE RENEE (MALONE), Mathematics Teacher; *b:* Altoona, PA; *m:* Thomas Vincent; *c:* Seth Vincent; *ed:* IN Univ of PA (BS) Applied Math 1989; Tchng Cert Scndry Ed in Math 1991; Statistics Ed in Quantitative Lit SEQual Wkshp; T-I Calculator Wkshp; *cr:* Tyrone Area Schl Dist Math Tchr 1991-; *ai:* Prom Co-Adv; NEA 1992-; *office:* Tyrone Area Jr Sr HS Clay Avenue Ext Tyrone PA 16686

MARASHIO, NANCY FEENEY, Eng Prof & Gen Ed Dept Chair; *b:* Claremont, NH; *m:* Paul; *ed:* Keene St Coll (BED) Eng 1964; Boston Coll (MA) Eng 1970; Wesleyan Univ (CAS) Lbrl Stud 1977; Attnd George Washington Univ, AZ St Univ, Teyts Univ, Georgetown Univ, Univ of NH, Dartmouth Coll; *cr:* Aloise HS Eng Tchr 1964-; Newfound Regnl HS Eng Tchr 1964-; Salem HS Eng Tchr 1964-; Haverhill HS Eng Tchr 1964-; Sanborn Regnl HS Eng Tchr 1964-; Windham Ctr Schl 7th-8th Grd Eng Tchr; Mascoma Regnl HS Eng Tchr, Hum Dept Chair; NH Comm Tech Coll Prof, Chair Gen Ed Dept 1986-, Intering Acad Dean 1996; *ai:* Advy Team; System Eng Fac Facilitator; System Core Comm Chair; Pedsgogy Comm; Claremont Rep to Cntrl Fac Senate; NCTE 1970-; New Eng Assn Tchr of Eng 1964-; NH Assn Tchr of Eng 1970-, Bd Mem; Phi Delta Kappa; Assn Gen Heberd Stud; NH Lakes Assn 1994-, Dir; John Hay Natl Worldlife Regnl 1988-, Commssing; Upper Valley Lake Sunapee Regnl Planning Commission & Newbury Planning B, Past Chair, NH Hum Cncl, Past Chair; Articles Pub; Presenter Inst for Tchng Excl, Northeast Regnl Conf on Eng 2 Yr Coll, NHATE Confs; *office:* NH Comm Tech Coll 1 College Dr Claremont NH 03743

MARATOS, NIKI, English Teacher; *b:* Bronx, NY; *m:* Nikolaos Stefanakis; *ed:* Deree Coll Amer Coll of Greece (BA) Engl 1991; Queens Coll (MA) Eng 1994; *cr:* Archbishop Iakovos HS Eng Tchr 1991-; *ai:* Jrnlsm Tchr; Drama Club Adv; Nwsp Adv; NCTE 1993-; Curr Dev 1994-; Arts & Scis Valedictorian 1991; 2 Poems Pub; *office:* Archbishop Iakovos HS 84-35 152nd St Jamaica NY 11432

MARAZITA, GERALDINE GARTIG, English Teacher & Dept Chair; *b:* New York City, NY; *m:* Anthony J.; *c:* Mark Anthony; *ed:* Good Counsel Coll (BA) Eng 1967; Fordham Univ (MA) Eng 1968; 36 Post-Grad Eng Hrs 1968-92; Iona Coll Credit Hrs; *cr:* PS #5 Yonkers Schl Eng Tchr 1968-69; Burroughs Jr HS Eng Tchr, Eng Dept Chair 1969-78; Walt Whitman MS Eng Tchr, Eng Dept Chair 1978-83; Roosevelt HS Eng Tchr, Team Communicator 1983-84; PS #5 Schl Eng Tchr 1984-85; PS #32 Schl Eng Tchr 1985-86; Burroughs Jr HS Eng Tchr, Eng Dept Chair 1986-; *ai:* Co-Chair Schl Improvement Plan, Ed 2000 Steering, Dist Lit, Innovations, Eng Curr, Federal Grant Writing, English Consultant Model, Co-Spon Sunshine, President'S Ed Awds, Gearing Up for Jr High Comm; Staff Outreach, Rsrch, Vistation, Magnet Dev Sub-Comm; NY St Turnkey Trainer Eng, Lang Arts; Tchr Support, Mentor Comm; Congruence Team; Co-Adv Natl Jr Hnr Soc; Facilitator of Dist & Eng Dept Wkshps; Co-Spon Washington DC Grad Trip; Bus & Fin House Advy Bd; Coord Stu Awds; Kappa Gamma Pi, NCTE, NY St Eng Cncl 1967-; Kappa Delta Pi, Yonkers Fed of Tchrs 1968-; Westchester Cncl Eng Edctrs 1987-, Treas 1987-90, Sec 1990-; Natl Assn Stu Act Advs, Natl Chptr Natl Jr Hnr Soc, Childrens Intnl 1987-; ASCD 1990-; IRA 1994-; March of Dimes Rep 1980-; United Way 1968-; PTSA 1967-, VP 22 Yrs; Home Schl Assn Immaculate Conception Schl 1995-; Fordham Univ HEA Flwshp; Tchr of Yr 1989-1900; Tchr Hall of Fame; Merit & Excl in Tchng 1989-90; Recognition Awd Excl in Tchng, Commitment to Stu, Outstdng Achvmt Excl Tchng Profession, Outstdng Svc to Stdnts; Hnr & Appreciation Awd; Eng Dept Appreciation Awd; Exc; Awd Tchng Eng; Flagship Acad Coach Awd; 14 Curr Enrichment Innovation Grants; Innovator Awds 1986-95; 4 Be A Model Awds; Honorary Lifetime Mbrshp NY St Congress of Parents & Tchrs; Article Pub; Curr Guide Comm; You're #1 Awd of Excl; *office:* Burroughs Jr HS 150 Rockland Ave Yonkers NY 10705

MARBLE, PATRICIA ANN, English Teacher; *b:* Boston, MA; *ed:* Boston St Coll (BA) Eng 1974; St Marys Univ at Winona 9 Grad Credits; *cr:* St Margarets Elem Eng Tchr 1974-76; St Patricks HS Theology Tchr 1976-77; Cardinal Spellman HS Eng Tchr 1977-; *ai:* Newspaper, Lit Magazine; NCEA 1974-; BATA, NCTE 1977-; South Shores AIDS Project 1990-; Golden Apple Awd 3 Yrs in a Row; Natl Endowment for the Hum Grant; *office:* Cardinal Spellman HS 738 Court St Brockton MA 02402

MARBOT, DAVID S., Agriculture Teacher; *b:* Troy, NY; *m:* Robin Reed; *c:* Brandon, Alex, Bryan, Garrett; *ed:* Cobleskill Coll (AAS) Dairy Sci 1982; Cornell Univ (BS) Ed 1984, (MS) Arts & Tchng 1994; *cr:* Edmaral Farms Herd Mgr 1984-89; Schoharie Cntrl Schl Ag Tchr 1989-; *ai:* FFA, Sr Class Adv; Peer Mediation Shared Decision Making, Bldg Planning Team; ATANY 1989-, Region Rep 1989-72; NVATA 1991-; Local 4-H 1971-, Natl Medal, Club Ldr 1995; Holstein Assn 1971, Natl DJM; Distngd Svc Awd NY Assn of FFA; PDCA & Holstein Assn Certfd Dairy Judge; Coach 2nd Team Nation Hoard's Dairyman Contest; *office:* Schoharie Central Schl Main St Schoharie NY 12157

MARCANO, ANA M., Social Studies Teacher; *b:* Cidra, PR; *c:* Ana Katiria Salazar; *ed:* Univ of PR (BA) His & Eng as Second Lang 1960; City Coll of New York City (MS) Biling Ed-Span & Eng 1970; *cr:* Cidra HS Eng as Second Lang & His Tchr 1960-71; New York City Commission on Human Rights Investigator 1972-73; IS 52 Biling & Soc Stud Tchr 1972-; *ai:* Bsktbl Team Parent; *office:* I S 52 Schl 650 Academy St New York NY 10040*

MARCANTE, JOHN PAUL, Reading Specialist & Coach; *b:* Allentown, PA; *m:* Lynda Ketner; *c:* Anthony, Jason; *ed:* East Stroudsburg Univ (BS) Elem Ed 1981; Kutztown Univ (MED) Rdng Specialist 1988; *cr:* Allentown Schl Dist 6th Grd Tchr 1983-85; Northampton Area Schl Dist Rdng Specialist 1985-95; Parkland Schl Dist Rdng Specialist 1995-; *ai:* Asst Ftbl Coach; Weight Trng, Strength, Conditioning Coach; Asbury United Meth Church 1993-, Ed Ministry Team; *office:* Parkland HS 2675 Rt 309 Orefield PA 18069

MARCARELLI, GREGORY NICHOLAS, Mgmt & Mrktg Dept Chairman; *b:* Suffern, NY; *m:* Deborah Ann Burden; *c:* Rebekah, Josiah; *ed:* Mercy Coll (BS) Bus Admin 1985; Pace Univ 30 Credit Hrs Ed; *cr:* The Westchester Bus Inst Instr, Chm 1985-; *ai:* Past Club Adv 1985-90; WCBEA 1985-; Tchr of Yr Awd 1989; *office:* Westchester Bus Inst 325 Central Ave White Plains NY 10606

MARCELLO, CLAUDIA ORSINI, Vocational Agriculture Ed Tchr; *b:* Opelieka, AL; *m:* Peter Wallace; *c:* Otto Guithrie; *ed:* Univ of CT (BS) Animal Sci 1986; Southern CT ST Univ Working Toward MS 6th Yr; UIONN 60 Addl Credit Hrs; *cr:* Millbrook Riding Ctr Barn Mgr 1986-87; Cntrl Vet Hosp Vet Tech 1987-89; Yale Med Schl Asst Researcher 1989; Cheshire Vet Hosp Vet Tech 1989-90; *ai:* FFA Dairy Showmanship; Horsejudging; CEA, WEA, NEA 1991-; CVATA 1990-, Recording Sec; HSEA 1980-, Num Ribbons & St Awds; AHSA, CHJA 1994-; *home:* 808 Wadsworth St Middletown CT 06457

MARCELT, DENISE MARIE, Soc Stud & History Teacher; *b:* Hamtramck, MI; *ed:* Wayne St Univ (BS) elem Ed 1974; 10 Post Grad Hrs Ed 1983-84; Youngstown St Univ His & Geog 27 Grad Hrs 1987-92; Miami Univ Geology 3 Grad Hrs 1994; *cr:* Detroit Area Schl Dist Sub Tchr All Grds 1975-77; Detroit Pub Schls Sub Tchr All Grds 1979-80; St jude Parish Schl 7th-8th Sub Tchr 1981-84; St Aloysius Schl 5th-6th Grd & 5th-8th Grd SS & His Tchr 1985-; *ai:* Natl Geographic Geog Bee Spon & Coord; Schl Club Together We Grow Spon; SS Textbook & Right to Read Comms;

Natl Cath Edctrs Assn 1986-; Habitat for Humanity 1992-, Comm Chair & Pres; Wayne St Univ Bd of Governors 1973-74 & Grad Prof 1983-84 Schlsps; Martha Jennings Grant 1989; *office:* St Aloysius Elem Schl 335 W 5th St East Liverpool OH 43920

MARCH, CATHLEEN C., Reading Specialist; *b:* Port Jervis, NY; *c:* Elizabeth Leeds, Brian Austin, Matthew Austin, Melinda Austin; *ed:* Edinboro Univ at PA (BS) Ed 1964; SUNY at Buffalo (MS) Rdng 1978, (ABDPHD) Ed, Rdng; *cr:* Warren Pub Schls Spec Ed Tchr 1964; Lockport Pub Schls Rdng Specialist 1964-66; Starpoint Cntrl Schls Rdng Specialist 1976-78; Canisius Coll Adj Prof; *ai:* Niagara Frontier Rdng Cncl Ed Spotlight 5 Yrs, IRA; Intnl Rdng Assn NY St Rdng Assn 1974-; Niagara Frontier Rdng Cncl 1974-, VP, Pres Elect; NCTE 1991-; Assn for Supervision & Curr Dev 1992-; Lockport Pub Lib Vol Storyteller; Educator of Excl NY St Rdng Cncl; Who's Who in Amer Ed; Who's Who in the World.

MARCH, LESLIE SUSAN, Acad Dean & English Teacher; *b:* Reading, PA; *ed:* Ursinus Coll (BA) Eng 1964; Univ of DE (MA) Eng 1975, (PHD) Eng 1993; Amer Stud Flwshp 1974; NEH Bronte Seminar 1994; *cr:* Linden Hall Schl Head Eng Dept 1968-77; Ursinas Coll Assoc Dean Stu Life, Union Dir, Eng Lecturer, Sr Symposium Tutor 1977-83; Harrisburg Acad Dean, Eng Tchr 1983-; *ai:* NHS Spon; Intshp Prgm Dir; NAIS 1983-; NCTE 1984-; St Stephens Episcopal Cathedral 1983-, Lay Reader, Ed Comm; NEH Summer Seminar; Am Stud Flwshp; Pub Poem; *office:* Harrisburg Acad 10 Erford Rd Wormleysburg PA 17043*

MARCHAL, MICHAEL HUBERT, English Teacher; *b:* Sidney, OH; *ed:* Xavier Univ (AB) Eng 1966; Fordham Univ (MA) Philosophy 1968, (PHD) Philosophy 1969; *cr:* Covington Latin Schl Eng & Latin Tchr 1970-74; St Xavier HS Eng & Latin Tchr 1974-; *ai:* Act Moderator; Speakers Bureau & Sr Retreat Follow-Up; Retreat Bd, N Cntrl Reevaluation & Scheduling Comms; NCEA 1974-; NCTE 1984-; Neighborhood Assn 1970-, Comm Work; Aids Vols 1990-, Outreach & Ed; 2 Books; Numerous Articles; Esp for the NCTE; *office:* St Xavier HS 600 W North Bend Rd Cincinnati OH 45224*

MARCHAND, JEAN-LOUIS G., Psych & Sociology Professor; *b:* Mondoubleau, France; *m:* Sylvie Zeman; *c:* Valerie, Jon-David; *ed:* Columbia Union Coll (BA) Sociology 1973; Univ of MD at C. P. (MA) Sociology 1975; Univ of Md at A. B. Soc Welfare 1986; Washington Schl of Psychiatry Family Therapy Cert; *cr:* Washington Adventist Hosp Dir Mental Hlth Prgm 1076-79; Midshore Parent Aide Exec Dir 1979-83; Chesapeake Coll Prof 1984-; *ai:* Admin Cncl Fac Rep; Curr Comm; Hnrs Prgm Fac; Coord Human Svcs 1990-94; NASW 1986-; Forum for Stud of Film 1989-; Washington Schl of Psychiatry 1984; Avalon Fnd 1991-, Consultant; Dept of Soc Svcs Bd Mem 1985-90; Dev Hnr Prgm; Dev Human Svcs Prgm of Stud; *office:* Chesapeake Coll PO Box 8 Wye Mills MD 21679*

MARCHAND, SHARON E., Mathematics Teacher; *b:* Fall River, MA; *c:* Rebecca; *ed:* Rhode Island Coll (BS) Elem Ed 1974; 15 Grad Credits in Ed; *cr:* Somerset Schl Dept Sub Tchr 1974-87; Fall River Schl Dept Eng & Soc Stud Tchr 1987-88, Sci Tchr 1988-92, 6th-7th Grd Math Tchr 1992-; *ai:* Tutoring Prgm; Yrbk Adv; NEA 1989-; Teen Topics Prgm; Grant to Create Stained Glass Window for Schl as Interdisciplinary Project; *home:* 3269 Riverside Ave Somerset MA 02726

MARCHBANK, TAMMY JO, Teacher of Multihandicapped; *b:* Canton, OH; *ed:* St Francis Coll (BS) Mild, Moderate, Severe, Profound Retarded 1982; Kent St Univ (MED) Gen Supervision 1993; *cr:* Goodwill Rehabilitation Tchr, Case Mgr 1982-83; Stark Cty Bd of Ed Tchr of Multihandicapped 1983-; *ai:* Stark Pub Spec Olympics Coord; CEC 1978-88, Pres, St VP, Outstdng Ldrshp St Francis Coll Chptr; NEA 1983-86; Assoc for Retarded Citizens 1982-, Sec, Vol of Yr 1987; Pilot Club of Canton 1982-, Pres, VP, Sec, Treas, Pilot of the Yr 1983, 1988; The Arc Weekend Camp 1983-, Dir; Tchr of Yr Finalist Greater Canton Chamber of Commerce 1990; Named as 1 of 20 Most Interesting People in Stark Cty by Stark Magazine 1990; *home:* 3712 Grunder Ave NW Canton OH 44709*

MARCHELL, CAROL ANNE (RODENBACH), Science Dept Head Teacher; *b:* Brooklyn, NY; *m:* Richard M.; *c:* Richard II, Amy; *ed:* Hartwick Coll (BA) Bio 1968; Long Island Univ (MA) Bio 1972; Dutchess Comm Coll (AA) Registered Nurse 1977; *cr:* Wappingers Jr HS 7th Grd Sci Tchr 1968-69; Roy C. Ketcham HS Gen Sci, Applied Bio, Gen Bio, Regents Bio Tchr, Sci Dept Tchr-in-Charge 1969-; *ai:* USFHA Field Hockey Referee; NYSUT 1968-; AFT; Zion Episcopal Church 1980-, Licensed Lay Reader; Book Review Pub; Taconic Ind Practice Assn Sci Ed Prgm Grant 1996; *office:* Roy C Ketcham H S 99 Myers Corners Rd Wappingers Falls NY 12590

MARCHESANI, LOUIS F., Science Tchr & Asst Ath Dir; *b:* Union City, NJ; *ed:* Rutgers Coll of Pharmacy (BS) Pharmacy 1959; Montclair St Coll (MS) Admin, Supervision; Addl 32 Credits Montclair St Coll, Monmouth Coll, Seton Hall Univ; *cr:* Meml HS Sci Tchr 1961-, Asst Ath Dir 1987-; *ai:* Stu Cncl Adv; Mid Atlantic Sts, Stu Act Chprsn; NEA 1961-, NEA Resolutions; NJ Ed Assn 1961-, Del Assembly; Hudson Cty EA 1961-; West NY EA 1961-, Past Pres; Elected to Union Cty Bd of Ed, VP 13 Yrs; *office:* Memorial HS 5501 Park Ave West New York NJ 07093

MARCHESE, FRED V., Fine Arts Teacher; *b:* Harrisburg, PA; *m:* Carole; *c:* Carl; *ed:* Pratt Inst (BS) Art Tchrs Ed 1965; NY Univ (MA) Fine Arts & Ed 1966; Brooklyn Coll (MFA) Theatre & Design 1975; *cr:* Ft Hamilton HS Fine Arts Tchr 1966-76; Kingsborough Comm Coll & Sheepshead Bay Adult Ed Painting & Drawing Instr 1966-86; Beach Channel HS Fine Arts Tchr 1976-88; BN Cardozo HS Fine Arts Tchr 1988-; *ai:* Cardozo Art Club & Advertising Club NY Adv; Planning Comm; VFT 1982-, Asst Chptr Ldr; Actors Equity 1986-; Kingsborough Comm Chorus 1986-; Grants: Advertising Club NY, Canon Camera, Teenage Performing Arts Wkshp, Human Relations Wkshp; Arts Act: Theatrical Designs for Actors Playhouse, Golden Fleece Musical Theatre, Manhatten Theatre Club; Exhibitions for Bay Ridge Arts Cncl & NY St Festival Photo Exhibit; *office:* Benjamin N Cardozo HS 5700 223rd St Bayside NY 11364*

MARCHETTI, EILEEN MARIE, Spanish Teacher; *b:* New Philadelphia, PA; *ed:* Millersville Univ (BS) Span 1977; 30 Credits Eng Cert East Stroudsburg Univ; 9 Grad Credits Nicholls St Univ; *cr:* Easton Schl Dist Span Tchr 1978-79; North Hunterdon Regnl Schl Dist span Tchr 1980; Shenandoah Schl Dist Span Tchr 1980-; *ai:* NEA, PSEA 1978-; *office:* Shenandoah Vly Schl Dist Stadium Rd Shenandoah PA 17976

MARCHETTI, KATHLEEN ROSE (BIRONI), Spanish Teacher; *b:* New Britain, CT; *m:* Ronald Sr.; *c:* Ronald Jr., James; *ed:* CCSU (BS) Span 1979, (BS) Eng 1980, (BS) TESOL 1980, (MS) Span 1986; Post-Grad Stu in Scndry Ed; *cr:* Wethersfield HS Span Tchr 1979-80; St Louis Univ Eng as a Second Lang Tchr 1979; Newington HS Span, Eng Tchr 1980-; *ai:* Frgn Lang Comm; Modern Lang Assn, NEA 1980-; Assn of Eng Tchrs of CT 1979-; *office:* Newington HS 605 Willard Ave Newington CT 06111*

MARCHETTI, RICK, Guidance Counselor; *b:* Hazleton, PA; *m:* Marcy; *ed:* East Stroudsburg St Coll (BS) Sec Ed 1972; Univ of Scranton (MS) Sec Guid 1980; Post Grad Stud Wilkes Univ; *cr:* Hazleton HS Tchr 1973-75; D. A. Harman Jr HS Tchr 1976-83; Freeland HS Cnslr 1984-92; Hazleton Area HS Cnslr 1993-; *ai:* Key Club Adv; NEA, PSEA 1975-; PA Schl Cnslrs Assn 1983-; Kiwanis 1994-; *office:* Hazleton Area HS 1601 W 23rd St Hazleton PA 18201*

MARCHETTI, VIVIAN ANNETTE (FROMENT), Second Grade Teacher; *b:* Prov, RI; *m:* Domenic; *ed:* RI Coll (BA) Elem Ed 1972, (MA) Elem Ed 1976; Attnd URI, Prov Coll; *cr:* Harris Schl 2 Grd Tchr 1973-93; Kendrick Ave Schl 2 Grd Tchr 1993-94; Pothier 2 Grd Tchr 1994-; *ai:* SIT; Yrbk; AFT 1973-; RI Kennel Club 1976-, VP, Bd, Pres, Treas; Yankee Siberian Husky Club 1976-, Treas, Bd; Siberian Husky of Amer 1990-; *office:* Pothier Elem Schl 1044 Social St Woonsocket RI 02895

MARCHITELLI, ANITA MARIE, Assoc Prof of PE & Recreation; *b:* Washington, DC; *ed:* Univ of MD (BS) PE 1971; GAllaudet Univ (EDS) Admin, Supervision 1971; Univ of MD (MA) PE 1974; *cr:* Univ of MD Grad Asst 1972-74; Gallaudet Univ Assoc Prof PE, Recreation 1974-; *ai:* Tennis Coach; Child Dev Cncl; Evaluation Comms; Amer Alliance of Hlth, PE, Rec 1974-, Life Mem; ARFA 1995-, Life Mem; Natl Recreation & Parks Assn 1990-; Tchr of Yr Awd, Alpha Sigma Pi, Dedication, Appreciation 20 Yrs Svc awd Staff on Children's Instrl Summer Prgm, 20 Yr Svc Awd 1994; Svc, Appreciation Awd 15 Yrs Coaching field Hockey 1990; *office:* Gallaudet Univ Physical Education Dept 800 Florida Ave NE Washington DC 20002*

MARCHITELLI, MARGUERITE MELUSO, First Grade Teacher; *b:* Jersey City, NJ; *m:* Louis Francis; *c:* David G., Lauren T.; *ed:* Jersey City St (BA) Gen Elem 1971; *cr:* Jersey City Bd of Ed Tchr 1971-; *ai:* NEA, NJEA & JCEA 1971-; HCEA; Girl Scouts 1987-92, Troop Ldr; *office:* Martin Luther King Jr #11 Schl 886 Bergen Ave Jersey City NJ 07306*

MARCHIZZA, MICHAEL JOSEPH, AP Biology Teacher; *b:* Springfield, IL; *ed:* Southern IL Univ (BA) Bio 1974; Sci Ed Univ of MD; DNA Sci Georgetown Univ; *cr:* Largo HS Bio Tech Instr, Tchr 22 Yrs; *ai:* Biotechnology, Sci Fair Coord; Class Spon; AFT 1990-; NABT 1978-; Governor's Acad Math & Sci; Outstdng Edctr PE Cty Spirit Awds; *office:* Largo HS 505 Largo Rd Largo MD 20772

MARCHLEWSKI, JOSEPH HAROLD, Life Science Instructor; *b:* Natrona Hgts, PA; *m:* Kerry E. Wilson; *c:* Lindsey, Bruce; *ed:* Edinboro Univ (BS) Ed Bio 1969; *cr:* Plum Borough Schl Dist Instr 1969-; *ai:* Wrestling, Womens Vlybl Coaches; NEA, PSEA 1969-; Pittsburgh Wrestle Referee 1976-; *office:* A E O Block Jr HS 440 Presque Isle Dr Pittsburgh PA 15239

MARCIAL, LAURENCE GABRIEL, Sociology & US History Teacher; *b:* Port Jervis, NY; *m:* Christine Marie Witkowski; *c:* Dominique Theresa; *ed:* Boston Coll (BA) Pol Sci 1989; East Stroudsburg Univ PA Tchg Cert 1993; 30 Grad Credits Towards MEd in Pol Sci; SAP Trng 3 Credits; *cr:* Port Jervis City Schl Dist Sub Tchr, Wrestling Coach 1989-93; NY St Dept of Correction Biling, Eng as 2nd Lang Tchr 1993; East Stroudsburg Area Schl Dist Soc Stud Tchr, Adv 1994-; *ai:* Jr HS Wrestling Coach 1994-95; Stu Govt, Ski Club Adv 1995-; Stu Assistance Cnslr 1995-; NEA, PSEA 1993-; NASSP 1994-; Boston Coll Grant, Scholarship; ESU Grad Fellowship 1993; *office:* East Stroudsburg HS N Courtland St East Stroudsburg PA 18301*

MARCIANO, CHARLES, English Teacher; *b:* New York City, NY; *m:* Barbara; *c:* Frank, Matthew; *ed:* Glassboro St Coll (BA) Eng Ed 1971, (MA) Eng Ed 1975; *cr:* Overbrook Jr High Eng Tchr 1971-78; Overbrook Sr High Eng Tchr, Dept Chair, 1978-; *ai:* Var Bsktbl Coach; Phi Delta Kappa 1977-; *office:* Overbrook Sr HS Turnersville Rd Pine Hill NJ 08021

MARCINKIEWICZ, MARIAN FILKOSKI, First Grade Teacher; *b:* Hadley, MA; *c:* Mark, Heidi; *ed:* Univ of MA (BA) Pol Sci, Ed 1963; Southern CT St Coll (MA) Elem Ed 1984; *cr:* Maple St Schl 6th Grd Tchr 1963-65; Ryerson Schl 1st Grd Tchr 1979-; *ai:* Cooperating Tchr; CEA 1979-; Madison Proud; *office:* Kathleen H Ryerson Elem Schl 982 Durham Rd Madison CT 06443

MARCINKO, THOMAS JOHN, Science Teacher & Dept Chair; *b:* Philipsburg, PA; *m:* Diane M. Belko; *c:* Jennifer, Ryan, Michael; *ed:* Clarion St Univ (BS) Bio, Med Tech 1977; Penn St Univ 31 Addl Credits; *cr:* Moshannon Valley HS Sci Tchr 1977-94, Sci Dept Chair 1985-; *ai:* Enviro-Thon, Class Adv, Comm Service Coord; MVEA 1977-, VP 2 Yrs; PSEA, NEA 15 Yrs; Trout Unlimited 7 Yrs; *office:* Moshannon Valley HS RD 1 Box 314 Houtzdale PA 16651

MARCINOWSKI, JANE STUART, Fourth Grade Teacher; *b:* Ellwood City, PA; *m:* John E.; *ed:* Edinboro Univ (BS) Art Ed 1970, (MED) Art Ed 1976; CA Univ of PA Prof Elem Ed Cert 1985; Univ of Pittsburgh TESA, Inquiring Schls Trng; *cr:* Clairton Schl Dist Elem Art Tchr 1970-84, Fourth Grd Tchr 1985-; *ai:* NEA, PSEA 1970-; Clairton Ed Assn, Treas 1986-89, Negotiating Team 1993-, Exec Comm 1986-95; *home:* 218 Grouse Dr Elizabeth PA 15037

MARCO, GREGORY DAVID, Science Department Chair; *b:* Bath, ME; *m:* Catherine Gnibus; *c:* Sarah, Andrew; *ed:* Colby Coll (BA) Chem, Bio 1983; Univ of ME (MEd) Sci Ed 1986; Grad Stud: Biochemistry OH St Univ 1983-85, Sci Wesleyan Univ 1992-; *cr:* Cony HS Sci Tchr 1986-87; Mt Ararat Schl Sci Tchr 1987-89; Westminster Schl Sci Tchr, Dept Chair 1989-; *ai:* Var Bsktbl, Golf Coach; Dormitory Supvr; Acad Prgm, Sci Renovation, Major Plant Budget Comms; NSTA 1987-; AAAS 1995-; ASCD 1994-; Swayze Fac Awd 1995; *office:* Westminster Schl 995 Hopmeadow St Simsbury CT 06070*

MARCO, SANDERS M., Fifth Grade Teacher; *b:* New York City, NY; *ed:* City Coll of NY (BA) Acctng 1968; Post Grad Stud; Attnd Fordham Univ, St Johns Univ; *cr:* PS 186 Manhattan Cluster in Sci & SS, 4th Grd Classroom Tchr 1968-76; PS 153 Manhattan 4th Grd Classroom Tchr 1976-87; PS 115 Manhattan 4th-5th Grd Classroom Tchr 1987-; *ai:* AFT 1968-; UFT 1968-; Diagnostic Prescriptive Arithmatic Pgm 1978-79; Original GATES Pgm NYC 1980-86; Group Head 9-10 Yr Olds Summer Day Camp 1981-91; Original UFT Sponsored Mentor Intern Pgm 1986-87; Primary Promoting Success Bd of Ed Pgm 1992-; *office:* PS 115 Manhattan Humboldt Schl 586 W 177th St New York NY 10033*

MARCOALDI, JOSEPH JOHN, Junior High School Teacher; *b:* Canton, OH; *m:* Patricia McCarty; *c:* Julie, Joey; *ed:* Walsh Coll (BA) Ed 1968; 154 Hrs; *cr:* Waynesburg Elem 5th Grd Tchr 1968-70; Sandy Valley Jr Sr HS 7-8 Grd Tchr 1970-; *ai:* Lori Sickafoose Awd Dir; Ftbl Coach 17 Yrs, Bsktbl Coach 8 Yrs; NEA, OEA, ECOEA 1968-; SVEA 1968-, Pres 1987-88; St Anthony's Church 1946, Parish Cncl 1987-90, 1992-94; Canton Sftbl Assn 1975-; Little Cardinal Ftbl Pres 1991-94; Little Cardinal Bsktbl Dir 1990-; Marth Holden Jennings Awd; Greater Canton Tchr of Yr Nomination; Sandy Valley Jr HS Tchr of Yr 4 Times; Ashland Oil Tchr Achievement Nomination; *home:* PO Box 202 East Sparta OH 44626

MARCONI, VICTORIA, Store Mgr & Retired Teacher; *b:* St Marys, PA; *ed:* Villanova Coll (BA) Early Chldhd, Elem 1956; Attnd Mercy Hurst Coll, St Vincent's Coll; *cr:* Presch Aid 1987-90; Kndgtn Aid 1992-93; Gift Shop Dir 1994-; *ai:* Adult Vols Dir.

MARCOTTE, CHUCK, History Teacher; *b:* Pawtucket, RI; *m:* Michele; *ed:* Providence Coll (BA) His 1976, (MA) His 1989; Ed Cert 1977; Post-Grad Courses; Presently Pursuing Intermidate Admins Cert; *cr:* Killingly HS His Tchr 1979-; *ai:* Asst Dir Dramatic Arts-Norwick Free Acad; NEA 1979-.

MARCOUX, CAROL GEE, Special Education Teacher; *b:* Lewiston, ME; *m:* Larry; *ed:* Univ of ME at Farmington (BS) Spec Ed & elem Ed 1982; Univ Southern ME (MS) Ed Admin 1992; Grad Stud in Educl Research; *cr:* Lewiston HS Tchr 1983-; *ai:* Co-Adv Class of 1999; Support Team Mem; Mentoring for New Tchrs; NEA, ME Tchrs Assn, Lewiston Educators Assn 1983-; Prof Image & Golden Apple Awds; *office:* Lewiston HS 1[illegible] Ave Lewiston ME 04240*

MARCOUX, JOEY ALBERT, 7th Grade Math & Science T[illegible] Pittsfield, ME; *m:* Andrea Marie Pasco; *c:* Lauren Elizabeth, E[illegible] Paige Anne; *ed:* Colby Coll (BA) Psych 1986; *cr:* Lawrence Jr HS 7 Math, Sci Tchr 1986-; *ai:* HS Var Sftbl, Jr HS Girls Bsktbl Coache[illegible] Card Club Adv; NEA 1993-; Cntrl ME Sftbl Coach of Yr 1993; Lawrence Jr HS 7 School St Fairfield ME 04937

MARCOUX, MARC PAUL, Physics & Chemistry Teacher; *b:* Wat[illegible] ME; *m:* Corrina King; *c:* Scott, Sarah, Jacob, Clayton; *ed:* Univ of Orono (BS) Bio 1986; *cr:* Lawrence HS Physics & Chem Tchr 19[illegible] Spring Track Asst Coach; Acts 29 Adv; First Bapt Church 1994-, D[illegible] *office:* Lawrence HS School St Fairfield ME 04937

MARCOUX, PHILIP JAMES, Sci, Math & Tech Coord & T[illegible] Rochester, NH; *m:* Kathleen Hull; *c:* Christopher, Timothy; *ed:* U[illegible] ME at Farmington (BS) Bio 1974; Univ of Southern ME (MS) Cla[illegible] Tchr & Sci 1980; 15 Credit Hrs Above Masters in Global Ed & I[illegible] Sensing; *cr:* Georges Valley HS Bio Tchr & Dept Head 1974-; Univ at Augusta Lab Instr Bio 101 & Bio 102 1980-; *ai:* Soccer Ofcl; B[illegible] Bsktbl Coach; Var Sftbl Coach 3 Yrs; Boys Var Bsbl Coach 17 Yrs & NEA 1974-; Gulf of ME Marine Ed Assn 1974-, Bd of Dirs; NSTA Bd of Dir; Natl Bio Tchrs Assn 1990-; GAIA Grant; Title II Grant; Awd for Outstdng Math, Sci & Tech Tchr Semi-Finalist; *office:* C[illegible] Valley HS PO Box 192 Valley St Thomaston ME 04861*

MARCUM, MARY SEEKINS, Fourth Grade Teacher; *b:* Jamestow[illegible] *m:* Victor J.; *c:* Christopher, Erica; *ed:* Thiel Coll (BA) Elem Ed, Hi[illegible] St Bonaventure Univ (MS) Elem Ed, Rdng 1995; Grad Stud Marshal[illegible] *cr:* Arnold Ave Elem Schl Tchr 1976-77; St Cecelia Schl Tchr 1978[illegible] Peter & Paul Schl Elem Tchr 1985-; *ai:* Intermediate Rdng Level Tchr Rep Fin Comm; Yrbk Adv; NCEA; Natl Fuel Educl Advy Sunday Schl Tchr; Rel Educator of Yr; *office:* SS Peter & Paul Sc[illegible] N Main St Jamestown NY 14701

MARCUS, JOAN ISABEL (CUSHING), Adj Instr of French & E[illegible] *b:* Floral Park, NY; *m:* Bernard A.; *c:* Paul, Forrest, Justine Jones-[illegible] *ed:* St Lawrence Univ (BA) Fr 1966; Colgate Univ (MA) Fr 1967; G[illegible] Comm Coll (AAS) Acctng 1991; 42 Grad Hrs Eng, Now Working on for Master's Degree in Eng SUNY at Brockport; *cr:* Cooperstown Jr Tchr 1966-67; South Orangetown MS Fr Tchr 1967-68; Albion HS F[illegible] 1968-69; Genesee Comm Coll Fr, Eng Instr 1980-; *ai:* Environe[illegible] Mgmt Cncl; Genesee Cty Mental Hlth Assn, Treas; Sigma Tau Delta Brockport.*

MARCUS, PETER, English Teacher; *b:* Binghamton, NY; *m:* Cor[illegible] Gabe; *ed:* St U of NY (BA) Eng, Math 1972, (MA) Eng 1976; Pos[illegible] Stud Eng, Math; *cr:* Gilbertsville HS 7-12 Grd Eng Tchr 19[illegible] Binghamton Division Yth 3-12 Grd Math, Eng Tchr 19[illegible] Morrisville-Eaton HS 10-12 Grd Eng Tchr 1977-80; Utica City HS Grd Eng Tchr 1980-; *ai:* SAT Prep Instr; AFT 1973-; Short Fictio[illegible] *office:* T. R. Proctor Sr HS Hilton Ave Utica NY 13501

MARDER, LORI RAND, Fourth Grade Teacher; *b:* Manhassett, [illegible] Cary; *ed:* Aldelphi Univ (MS) Elem Ed 1989; 30 Credit Hrs [illegible] Classes Elem Ed; *cr:* Phyllis Wheatley Elem 6th Grd Tchr 1984-85; [illegible] Tchr 1985-92, Alternative Learning Styles Tchr 1992-95, Tchr 199[illegible] AFT 1984-; *office:* PS 158 400 Ashford St Brooklyn NY 11207

MARE, ROSETTE JACQUELINE, French & Spanish Teach[illegible] Saigon, So Vietnam; *c:* Alexander Webster, Andrew Webster, Webster; *ed:* Hofstra Univ (BS) Fr 1971, (MA) Ed 1973; Pace Uni[illegible] Educl Admin 1991; Attending St Univ at Stony Brook Working [illegible] Doctorate in Second Lang Ed; *cr:* Herricks Schl Dist Tchr 197[illegible] Co-Adv Human Relations Club; AFT, NYSUT 1971-; LILT 1990-[illegible] 1993-, Fundraising Chprsn; Medal of Excl on the Stud of Educl [illegible] 1991 from Pace Univ; *home:* PO Box 114 Albertson NY 11507*

MARECKI, LORETTA JOAN, Accounting & Computer Teach[illegible] Bayonne, NJ; *ed:* Montclair Univ (BA) Bus Ed 1963; Seton Hal[illegible] (MA) Scndry Ed 1967; 3 Credits PE Ithaca Coll 1972; Cmptr Prgm Zoeb Inst 1994; *cr:* Holy Rosary Acad HS Acctng, Cmptr Tchr 19[illegible] Cmptr, Acctng Dept Chprsn; Stu Govt Co-Moderator; Attendanc[illegible] Bsktbl Statistician; Curr, Schl Scheduling Comms; Scndry Schl Tchr 1988-; NJBEA 1964-; *office:* Holy Rosary Acad HS 1509 Bergenli[illegible] Union City NJ 07087*

MARGITAY-BALOGH, CLAUDIA ELIZABETH, High School E[illegible] Teacher; *b:* Bridgeport, CT; *m:* Joseph Felix; *c:* Justin; *ed:* Univ (BA) Eng & Ed 1967; Univ of Bridgeport (MA) Lit 1980; Univ of F[illegible] 6th Yr Related Stud 1989; *cr:* Staples HS 9th-12th Grad Eng Tchr 19[illegible] Fairfield Woods MS 7th & 8th Grd Eng Tchr 1972-82; Ludlane HS 9t[illegible] Grd Eng Tchr 1983-87; Fairfield HS 9th-11th Grd Eng Tchr 198[illegible] Yrbk Adv 1990-; NEA 1967-; CEA 1967-; FEA 1972-; AHHA [illegible] Comm; Univ of Bpt Hungarian Schlsp Comm; *home:* 60 Tyr[illegible] Stratford CT 06497

MARGOLIS, BRUCE E., Student Assistance Counselor; *b:* Bingh[illegible] NY; *ed:* St Univ of NY at Albany (BA) Psych 1981, (MSW) Soc W[illegible] 1988; *cr:* Unity House Residence Cnslr 1982-84; Ellis Hosp Psyc[illegible] Caseworker 1984-86; Hope House Inc Out-pt Substance Abuse 1989-; Troy HS Stu Assistance Cnslr 1988-; *ai:* Peer Ldrshp Prgm [illegible] Re-Evaluation Cnslng Comm 1989-, Tchr; Comm Svc Awd Rensselu[illegible] Rape Crisis Prgm 1993; *office:* Troy HS 1950 Burdett Ave Troy NY

MARGOLIS, IDA MOSKOWITZ, Psychology & AP History T[illegible] Stuttgart, Germany; *m:* Jeffrey Allen; *c:* Jamibeth; *ed:* Temple Univ His 1970; Glassboro St Coll (MA) Stu Prsnl 1975; Grad Stud at [illegible] Coll & Rider Coll; Supvrs Cert; *cr:* Ocean City HS Psych & His 1971-; Richard Stockton Coll Adj Ed 1989-; *ai:* Founded Ocean C[illegible] Psych Club; New Tchr Orientation & Study Skills Comm Chairs; So[illegible] Curr Comm; NEA 1971-; NSEA 1971-; OCEA 1971-, Bldg Rep; Phi Kappa 1987-, Rsrch Rep & Svc Key Awd; NJ Cncl of the Soc Stud, Sunshine Fndtn; Presenter of NJEA Convention & Cape May Cty Inservice Article Pub in NJEA Review & NJ Cncl of the Soc Newsletter; *office:* Ocean City HS 6th & Atlantic Aves Ocean C[illegible] 08226*

MARGOLIS, JUDITH MARCUS, Guidance Counselor; *b:* Jersey[illegible] NJ; *m:* Leonard; *c:* Gregory, Marc; *ed:* Douglas Coll (BA) Span Ed Montclair St Univ (MA) Cnslng 1990; *cr:* Fairlawn HS Span Tchr 19[illegible] Dumont HS Guid Cnslr 1990-91; Northern Vly Old Tappan Guid 1991-; *ai:* Peer Mediation Coord; Pupil Assistance, Multicultura[illegible] Advy & Average Stu Comms; NJ Ed Assn 1967-; NEA 1967-; N[illegible] Helpers 1994-; Natl Assn of Mediation in Ed; Fair Lawn Jewish Ctr Bd Mem, Sec; Article Pub; Phi Delta Kappa; *office:* Northern Valley HS 160 Central Ave Old Tappan NJ 07675*

MARGRAF, DAVID JON, Social Studies Teacher; *b:* New Castle, [illegible] Susan Mason; *c:* Haley, Alexander; *ed:* Westminster Coll (BA) His Edinboro Coll (MA) His 1982; *cr:* Westlake MS Soc Stud Tchr 197[illegible] MS Girls Bsktbl, Jr Var Girls Sftbl Coach; Asst Ath Dir; PA St Ed NEA 1977-; Millcreek Twp Schl Dist Employee of Month 1995; [illegible] Westlake MS 4330 W Lake Rd Erie PA 16505

MARGRAF, MARY E. (LUTZ), Third Grade Teacher; *b:* Tiffin, [illegible] Natalie, Nicole; *ed:* Heidelberg Coll (BA) ELem Ed 1982; Ashlan[illegible] (MA) Ed 1988; 9 Addl Hrs; *cr:* Clinton Schl 3rd Grd Tchr 1983-84; [illegible]

rd Grd Tchr 1984-; *ai:* Rdng, Math, Sci Textbook Comm; Sci Curr : TEA, NEA, OEA 1983-; Cooperating Tchr for Stu Tchrs; *home:* estwood Dr Tiffin OH 44883

GREY, RONALD F., Secondary Mathematics Teacher; *b:* Syracuse, · Catherine; *c:* Sam; *ed:* Oswego St (BA) Math Ed 1970; Syracuse MS) Ed 1975; Admin Courses; *cr:* H. W. Smith MS Tchr 1970-75; nger HS Tchr 1975-85; Adm for Challenge Prgm Admin 1985-90; ran HS Tchr 1990-; *ai:* Bsktbl Coach; NCMT 1990-; *office:* Corcoran 9 Glenwood Ave Syracuse NY 13207

GULIS, GRETA SCHWARTZ, Spanish Teacher; *b:* Newark, NJ; *m:* *c:* Alan, Megan; *ed:* Univ of Northern IA (BA) Eng, Span 1968; *cr:* ssex Regnl HS Eng Tchr 1968-71; Howell HS Eng, Span Tchr 1983-; an Club, CARE Svc Club Advs; Renaissance Comm; FLENT 1984-; Tchr of Yr 1994-96; Tchr of Month 1995; Wkshp Presenter FLENJ St Meeting; Co-Chap Exchange Prgm Russia 1993; Mid St Visiting ating Comm 1992; *office:* Howell HS Squankum-Yellowbrook Rd ngdale NJ 07727*

ANI, MELODY ANDRIELLO, English Teacher; *b:* Syracuse, NY; rio A.; *c:* Jeremy A., Aubrey G.; *ed:* SUNY at Geneseo (BA) Eng Syracuse Univ (MS) SS Ed 1991; 21 Hrs Towards Cert of Advanced n Educl Admin; *cr:* Corcoran Schl 9-12 Grd Eng Tchr 1984-; *ai:* Lit ine; Improvement, Self Esteem Comms; SAT Verbal Preparation Syr Tchrs Assn, Rep; AFT, NYSUT, 1984-; NCTE 1995-; ASCD *office:* Corcoran HS 919 Glenwood Ave Syracuse NY 13207

ANI, TERRI, Nursing Professor; *b:* New York, NY; *m:* Walter; *c:* w James; *ed:* Kings Cty Hosp Ctr Schl of Nrsng (RN) 1968; St s Coll (BS) Hlth Care Admin 1978; Univ Of MA (MS) Nrsng 1987; uth Nassau Comm Hosp Staff & Head Nurse & Nrsng Care Coord 78; Providence Hosp Critical Care Coord 1978-79; Holyoke Comm rsng Instr 1980-82; Univ of MA Nrsng Tchng Asst 1983-85; STCC Nrsng Asst Prof, Assoc Prof & Prof 1985-; *ai:* Williston Northampton arents Assn; Holy Cross Parish 9th Grd CCD Tchr; MA Tchrs Assn Hawthorne Svcs 1987-, Bd of Dir; Authored 11 Nrsng Ed Software 1992-; STCC Anthony Scibelli Endowed Chair 1994; NISOD Excl in Awd 1994; *office:* Springfield Tech Comm Coll 5 Armory Sq field MA 01105

INACCI, ERIC A., Mathematics Teacher; *b:* Wheeling, WV; *m:* Lisa ttern; *c:* Jeremy Vermillion; *ed:* Miami Univ (BS) Math Ed 1993; ng Toward Bachelors in Math Ed at OH St Univ Grad Schl; *cr:* ngton Court House HS Math Tchr 1993-; *ai:* Var Ftbl Asst Coach; mans Club Adv; NCTM, OCTM 1991-; Washington Ed Assn 1993-; Univ Alumni Assn 1993-; *office:* Washington Court House Sr HS Willard St Washngtn Ct Hse OH 43160*

INACCIO, MICHAEL ANTHONY, Adjunct Instr & Paralegal Pgm; nx, NY; *m:* JoAnn DeMasi; *c:* Jennifer, Alexis, Amanda; *ed:* Colgate BA) His 1973; Saint Johns Univ (JD) Law 1976; *cr:* Dist Attorney nx Cty Asst Dist Attorney 1976-85; Culleton, Marinacci & Foglia r 1985-; Berkeley Coll Adjunct Instr 1992-; *ai:* Amer Bar Assn, NY r Assn 1973-; Bronx Cty Bar Assn 1985-; Kiwanis 1987-, Pres, guished Mem Awd; *office:* Culleton, Marinaccio & Foglia 245 Main ite Plains NY 10601

INARI, MELISSA M., Spanish Teacher; *b:* Trenton, NJ; *ed:* in & Marshall Coll (BA) Romance Langs 1992; Middlebury Coll MA 1996; *cr:* Notre Dame High Frgn Lang Tchr 1992-; *ai:* Peer Ldrshp n Hnr Soc Moderator.

INARO, ROBERT JOSEPH, 7th-8th Grd Lang Arts Teacher; *b:* , NY; *m:* Rita Nicolella; *c:* Robert, Nina; *ed:* Queens Coll (BA) ean His 1970, (MS) Scndry Ed 1973; New Schl for Soc Rsrch (MA) Stud 1982; *cr:* David Farragut Jr HS 44 Soc Stud Tchr 1970-73; ne Hansberry IS 167 SS-LA Rdng Tchr 1973-88; Robert H. Goddard 202 LA Tchr 1988-; *ai:* UFT, AFT 1970-; NY Alliance for Pub Schls f Commendation 1985; *office:* Robert H. Goddard Jr HS 202 138-30 ette St Ozone Park NY 11417

INARO, VINCENT PAUL, 5th Grade Sci Specialty Tchr; *b:* eld, MA; *ed:* St Anselm Coll (BA) Bio 1970; *cr:* Crane & Co Paper ech 1970-72; Notre Dame Schl Sci Tchr 1972-75; St Marks Schl Sci 1975-78; Sacred Heart Schl Sci Tchr 1978-; *ai:* Jump Rope for Heart ; Var Soccer & Sftbl Coach; NCEA 1970-; Knights of Columbus ; Pittsfield Youth Commission 1990-, Comm Person; Cath Youth ni 1992-, Sec; CYC Svc Soc Adv; CYC Vol of Yr 1981-82; CYC of Yr 1993; Tim Shepard Awd for Lifesaving Effort 1990; Exec Dir lic Youth Cntr; *home:* 94 Elaine Dr Pittsfield MA 01201

INELLI, ELIZABETH A. O'NEILL, 8th Grade Teacher; *b:* lelphia, PA; *c:* Michele Lee, Ron Jr.; *ed:* St Joseph Univ Elem Ed; ost Blessed Sacrament Schl 2nd-3rd Grd Tchr 1960-63; Annunciation Schl 3rd & 6th Grd Tchr 1963-70; Our Lady of Peace Schl 4th Grd 1970-72; St Irenaeus Raphael Schl 3rd Grd Tchr 1981-82; Our Lady arity Schl 6th Grd Tchr 1982-91; St Alice Schl 7th-8th Grd Tchr ; *ai:* Chrldng Coach Our Lady of Charity Schl; Math Coord; NCEA; : St Alice Schl Copley Rd & Sansom St Upper Darby PA 19082

INELLI, PHILIP JOSEPH, Religious Studies Teacher; *b:* Bronx, : Elizabeth Kafka; *c:* Peter, Reid; *ed:* St John's Univ (BA) Theology (MA) Theology 1988; *cr:* Yth Fous Asst Dir 1988-91; *ai:* JV Sftbl ı; Pax Christi 1985-.

INELLO, ELIZABETH A., Guidance Cnslr & Coll Coord; *b:* rk, NJ; *ed:* Trenton St Coll (BA) Elem Ed, Psych 1969; Seton Hall (MA) Cnslng, Spec Svcs 1973; 6 Credits Cnslng Internship Prgm; City St 3 Credits Career Guid Inst; *cr:* Fourteenth Ave Elem Schl 1969-74; West Orange Family Yth Svc Personal Cnslr 1973-76; ont-Runyon Elem Schl Guid Cnslr 1974-77; Univ HS Guid Cnslr 78; East Side HS Guid Cnslr, Coll Coord 1978-; *ai:* Amer Schl Cnslrs NJ Prof Guid, Cnslng Assn 1975-; NJ Schl Cnslr Assn, Essex Cty Guid Assn 1978-; Newark Prnsl, Guid Assn 1980-; *office:* East Side 38 Van Buren St Newark NJ 07105

INI, JAMES THOMAS, Spanish Teacher; *b:* New York, NY; *m:* aret J.; *c:* Tracey, Jimmy; *ed:* Iona Coll (BA) Span 1965; Richmond at NY (MSEd) Span 1972; Fordham Univ 1967-68; 10 Credit Hrs Univ 1974-75; *cr:* Msgr Farrell HS Span Tchr 1965-70; Bishop Keaney HS Tchr 1970-72; Bishop Hendricken HS Span Tchr 1972-75; Notre Bishop Gibbons HS Asst Prin 1975-76; *ai:* Chair Frgn Lang Dept; Club Moderator; NCEA 1991-; ASCD 1991-; AATSP 1995-; ACTFL; ssn Our Lady Star of the Sea Bd Mem 1992-95; Stamford Cath Regnl System 1994-; Assn of New England Colls & HS 5 Yrs; Bd of Ed ford CT Regnl Schl System; *office:* Trinity Catholic HS 926 Newfield Stamford CT 06905

INNIE, FRANCES BROADWAY, 3rd Grade Teacher; *b:* Princeton, : Sydni Alexis Craig, Julian Jay Craig; *ed:* WV St Coll (BA) Elem Ed , Trenton St Coll (MS) Rdng Specialist 1981, (MS) Supervisory ee 1981; *ai:* Refusal Skills Prgm; Parent Adv for NJ Orators; Audio al Coord; Rdng Book Club for Women; Asst Gymnastic Coach -73; Bsktbl Coach 3 Yrs; NEA, NJEA 1965-; Princeton Regnl Ed Assn ; Alpha Kappa Alpha 1962-, 25 Yr Mem Awd; NAACP 1969-; Tutor ung Achievers of Princeton 1995; Greater Princeton Division of Amer Assn Bd Mem; Multi Cultural Involvement Comm & Amer Heart ; Mentor for New Tchr 1995-; Woman of Yr Mt Pisgah AME Church; Jump for Heart Coord; Outstdng Edctr in Princeton Reg Schls; *office:* Community Park Schl 372 Witherspoon St Princeton Twp NJ 08540*

MARINO, BERNICE BOGDEN, High School Guidance Counselor; *b:* Warren, OH; *m:* Dominic Anthony; *c:* Molly; *ed:* Youngstown St U (BA) Latin & Eng 1962; Westminster Coll (MS) Guid 1967; *cr:* Champion HS Latin & Eng Tchr 1962-63; Howland HS Latin & Eng Tchr 1964-, Guid Cnslr 1995-; North Rd Intermed Guid & Elem Tchr 1994-95; Howland Springs Primary Guid & Elem Tchr 1994-95; *ai:* Jr Class; Girls Tennis; Prom; NEA 1962-; OEA; NEOEA; HCTA, Pub Relations Chair; Warren Area Bd of Realtors 1993-, Pub Relations Chair; Feature Tchr 1991; Distngd Tchr Awd 1991; White Horse Comm on Ed.

MARINO, BETSY MARIE, Special Education Teacher; *b:* Holyoke, MA; *m:* Stephen C.; *c:* Donald, Stephen, Kathleen; *ed:* Westfield St Coll (BSE) Elem Ed K-8th Grd 1971, (MED) Moderate Spec Needs 1987; Amer Intnl Coll 3 Post-Grad Credit Hrs in Linquistics 1994; *cr:* Stanley Kozial Elem Schl 1st Grd Tchr 1971-78; East St Schl & Chap St Schl Long Term Sub Tchr 1982-87; Veterans Park Schl K-6th Grd Tchr & Resource Room 1987-; Anna Maria Coll Adjunct Prof; *ai:* Mentor Tchr; 766 Bldg Coord; Ludlow Tchrs Assn 1987-; Confraternity of Chrstn Doctrine, Tchr, Piux 10th Awd; Stewardship Appeal 1978-, Steward & Captain, Cert of Svc; Loaves & Fishes 1990-, Server; Wkshp & Seminar Presenter; Courses & Wkshps on Story Grammar Marker, Phonemic Awareness & Integrated Rdng Strategies; Contributor to Dev of The Story Grammar Marker Manuel Describing the Use of an Ed Tool to Dev Narrative Skills Dev by Mary Ellen Rooney-Moreau & Patented & Sold Through Discourse Skills Production; *office:* Veterans Park Elem Sch 486 Chapin St Ludlow MA 01056*

MARINO, DIANE, Second Grade Teacher; *b:* Brooklyn, NY; *ed:* Queens Coll (BA) Early Chldhd Ed 1981; St John's Univ (MS) Spec Ed 1984; Queens Coll Prof Diploma Schl Admin, Supervision 1990; *cr:* St Sylvester's Grammar Schl Kndgtn Tchr 1981-84; George Gershwin Jr HS Resource Room Tchr 1984-86; PS 108 Second Grd Tchr 1986-87; PS 100 Second Grd Tchr 1987-; *ai:* SAT, Rdng, Math Tutor; PS 100 United Fed of Tchrs 1984-, Sec; *office:* PS 100 Queens Dist 27 Schl 111-11 118th St Jamaica NY 11420*

MARINO, JAMES IVOR, American History Teacher; *b:* Queens, NY; *m:* Sandra Joan Stefanco; *c:* Kirby; *ed:* Coll of William & Mary (BA) His 1975; Kean Coll (MA) Supervision Admin 1984; Amer Military Univ Military Sci; Trenton St Coll Ed 6 Credit Hrs; *cr:* Rahway Jr HS Amer His Tchr 1977-86; Hopatcong HS Amer His Tchr 1986-; *ai:* Newspaper Adv; Hackettstown HS Ftbl Coach; NJEA 1977-, Negotiation Team; Article Pub; *home:* 515 W Plane St Hackettstown NJ 07840

MARINO, JANET ZIDOW, Spanish Teacher; *b:* Buffalo, NY; *m:* Michael; *c:* Lisa A., Jason P.; *ed:* SUNY at Buffalo (BA) Span 1966; Grad Work in Span; *cr:* Kenmore West Sr HS Span Tchr 1966-75; Hoover Jr HS Span Tchr 1976-81; Kenmore East Sr HS Span Tchr 1981-; *ai:* Senate Fac Rep; Book Chairman; ACRES Exch Adv; AFT, NYSUT, WNYFLEC & KE PTA; *office:* Kenmore East Sr HS 350 Fries Rd Tonawanda NY 14150*

MARINO, JOSEPH ANTHONY,JR., Greek Mythology & Drama Tchr; *b:* Warren, OH; *m:* Susan Repasky; *c:* Kim, Joey, Jane; *ed:* Youngstown St Univ (BA) Eng 1975, (MS) Sec Admin 1978; 15 Semester Hrs Curr Dev; 10 Semester Hrs Driver Trng; *cr:* Princeton Jr HS Eng, Rdng Tchr 1975; Fitch HS Eng, Rdng, Media, Mythology Tchr 1975-; *ai:* Girls Tennis Coach; Annual Christmas Show Writer, Dir, Producer, Actor; RDE Gftd Instr; NEA, OEA, AEA 1975-; USTA, USPTR 1983-; Only HS Tchr Invited to Teach YSU's Gov's Gifted & Talented Inst; NHS Tchr of Yr 1983; Favorite Tchr 1982-88; Certified Tennis Tchng Prof; *home:* 322 Genesee Ave NE Warren OH 44483

MARINO, LINDA CAROL, Math Teacher; *b:* Queens, NY; *ed:* Staten Is Comm Coll (AA) Lbrl Arts 1970; Richmond Coll (BA) Psych Early Chldhd 1972; Coll of Staten Is (MS) Ed, Math 1980; *cr:* St Patricks Schl Tchr, Early Chldhd 1972-82; St Joseph By The Sea HS Math Tchr 1982-; *ai:* Math Resource Tchr 1982-; NCEA 1982-; Federation of Cath Tchrs 1982; Sigma 1986-; S. I. Inst of Arts, Sci 1995-; S. I. Historical Soc, Commanders Club Disabled Vets, S. I. 200 1990-; *office:* St Joseph By The Sea HS 51-50 Hylan Blvd Staten Island NY 10312

MARINO, MICHAEL GERARD, Art Teacher; *ed:* NY Inst of Tech (BFA) Art Ed 1983; St Univ of NY at Stony Brook (MA) Art Ed 1994; *cr:* Half Hollow Hills Asst Tchr 1985-87, Art Tchr 1987-92; Elwood Pub Schls Art Tchr 1992-; *ai:* Art & Gallery Club; Var Wrestling; JV Ftbl; MS Track; Musical Sets Dir; AFL, CIO & AFT 1985-; NY St TRS 1985-; HHHTA & EIA 1986-; NY Inst of Tech Gold Medal Awd for Tchr Ed Excl 1983; *office:* John H Glenn Schl 478 Elwood Rd East Northport NY 11731

MARINO, PAMELA, Prof of Office Info Systems; *b:* Houston, TX; *ed:* Baruch Coll (BS) Bus Ed 1972, (MS) Bus Tchr Ed 1975; NY Univ (PHD) Office Info Systems 1992; *cr:* New Utrecht HS Bus Ed Tchr 1972-75; Wood Tobe-Coburn Schl Prgm Admin, Cooperative Ed Tchr 1977-85; Baruch Coll Educl Computing Prof 1985-95; Pace Univ Office Information Systems Prof 1995-; *ai:* Office Information Systems Club Adv; Educl Cmptr Policy Comm; Frosh Seminar Fac Ldr; Bus Ed Assoc of Metropolitan NY 1972-, Pres, Outstdng Bus Ed 1993; Office Systems Rsrch Assoc 1985-, Editorial Bd; Delta Pi Epsilon, Alpha Chptr 1981-, Manuscript Reviewer; NBEA 1972-; NY Acad of Pub Ed 1994-; Soroptimist Int'l 1991-, Corresponding Sec'y, Outstdng Career Woman 1991; Paul Lomax Awd; Outstdng Schlsp, Ldrshp Doctoral Stud NYU 1992; Rsrch Mini-Grant Awd Office Systems Rsrch Assoc 1991; Refereed Articles 1993, 1995; *office:* Pace Univ 1 Pace Plaza New York NY 10038

MARINO, PAUL M., Asst Professor of Education; *b:* Hazleton, PA; *m:* Joan; *c:* Kristen, Jeffrey, Jonathan; *ed:* PA St (PHD) Curr, Instruction 1976; *ai:* Phi Delta Kappa 1974-; ASCD 1976-; *office:* Delaware Valley Coll 700 E Butler Ave Doylestown PA 18901*

MARINO, PHILIP A., 6th Grade Teacher; *b:* New York City, NY; *m:* Patricia Ford; *c:* Karam, Philip, David; *ed:* Iona Coll (BA) Philosophy 1968; Queens coll (MS) Philosophy 1970; Tehman Coll (MS) Ed 1974; *cr:* St Athamasius Schl 6th-8th Grd Tchr 1968-73; New City Elem Schl 4th Grd Tchr 1973-81; 6th Grd Tchr 1981-; *ai:* Sci Curr Comm Writer; Critical Thinking Skills Comm Writer; MS Transition Comm; AFT 1973-; NYSUT 1973-; Ordained Permanent Deacon Cath 1984-; Chaplin Local Fire Dept 1985-; Chaplin Vietnam Veterans 1988-; *office:* Link Elem Schl 51 Red Hill Rd New City NY 10956*

MARINO, ROSARIE SEMENZA, English Teacher & Dept Chprsn; *b:* Taylor, PA; *c:* Lisa Marino Franklin, Linda, Luanne; *ed:* East Stroudsburg (BS) Eng & Scndry Ed; Marywood Coll (MS) Ed 1971; *cr:* Bishop Hannan HS Tchr 1979-; *ai:* Sr Class Adv; Eng Dept Chair; ASCD; NCTE; SDACT; NCEA.

MARINO, SALVATORE ANTHONY, Mathematics Teacher; *b:* Manhattan, NY; *m:* Faye Carol DiPeri; *c:* Thomas, Stacey; *ed:* St Francis Coll (BS) Math 1972; Hofstra Univ (MA) Natural Sci 1976; Coaching Cert Adelphi Univ Track, Field; Theological Stud Diaconate Diocese Rockville Centre Huntington Seminary; *cr:* Cathedral Prep Seminary Math Tchr, Coll Guid Cnslr 1973-; Blessed Sacrament Parish Vly Stream Deacon 1994-; *ai:* Track Coach 1973-93; Cath Schls Ath Assn Svc Awd 20 Yrs Svc Track, Field Diocese of Brooklyn; NYCCSSC 1990-; Natl Endowment Awd Stony Brook Univ 1995; Natl Endowment for Hum; *office:* Cathedral Prep Sem 56-25 92nd St Elmhurst NY 11373

MARINO, SUZANNE MARIE, Mathematics Teacher; *b:* Rochester, NY; *m:* Joseph E.; *c:* Michael, Marc; *ed:* SUNY Brockport (BS) Math 1972, (MS) Math 1990; *cr:* De Sales HS MATH Tchr 1972-73; Marcus Whitman Schl Math Tchr 1973-84; Mynderse Acad Math Tchr, Dept Chair 1984-; Adj Finger Lakes Comm Coll Math Prof 1984-; *ai:* Math Dept Chair; Math Portfolio Comm; Cmptr Rep BOCES; AMTNYS 1986-, Dist Rep; *home:* 142 Slosson Ln Geneva NY 14456*

MARINO, VINCENT L., Mathematics Teacher; *b:* New York, NY; *ed:* Hunter Coll (BA) Math 1970, (MA) Math 1973; *cr:* Cathedral HS Math Tchr 1970-; *ai:* Schl Bazaar, Soc Comm Chm; *office:* Cathedral HS 350 E 56th St New York NY 10022

MARINOS, PATRICIA A., Social Studies Teacher; *b:* Boston, MA; *c:* Christopher; *ed:* Boston St Coll (BSEd) His 1960, (MED) Ed 1963; Tufts Univ (MA) European His 1972; Boston Museum of Fine Arts Schl; 15 Credits Photography; Grad Credit Courses in Psych at Bridge Water St Coll & Univ of MA Boston; *cr:* Central Jr HS Social Studies Tchr 1960-67; Weymouth HS Soc Stud Tchr 1967-; Staff Mem Coll Acad Tch 1985-91; GATE Prgm Asst Coord 1989-91; *ai:* Adv Weymouth High Chapter Natl Honor Soc Faculty Senate; Schl Based Mgmt; Pub Relations Coord; Weymouth Tchrs Assn, MA Tchrs Assn & NEA 1960-; Eastern Psychological Assn; Amer Psychological Assn; Weymouth Town Meeting Mem 1988-; Weymouth Fair Housing Comm 1991-; Natl Sci Fnd Grant Seminar Participant Psych; Boston Univ Summers 1980-81; Beaver Coll PA 1992, 1994 Summer; Eastern Psychological Assn Symposium Speaker 1993 Convention Washington DC; *office:* Weymouth HS 1051 Commercial St Weymouth MA 02189

MARIOS, GERTRUDE A., Language Arts Teacher; *b:* Troy, NY; *m:* Robert L.; *c:* Judith Barrett, Robert, Janet Smith, Joli Mc Kay; *ed:* St Univ of NY at Albany (BA) Scndry Tchng Eng 1956, (MA) Scndry Tchng Eng 1961; Russell Sage Coll at Troy Cert Elem Degree 1972; *cr:* Mechanicville HS Soph Lang Arts 1956-61; Cohoes Schl System Sub 1962-63, 1977, 1988-90; Waterford-Halfmoon HS Adult Ed, Speech Tchr 1965-66; St Marie's Elem Cath Lang Arts Jr HS Tchr 1972-73; Pvt Day Care Nursery Tchr 1974-77; St Augustine's Cath Schl 4th Grd Tchr 1977-87; St Agnes Jr HS Cohoes Lang Arts Tchr 1991-; *ai:* Play Productions, Yrbk, Newspaper Adv; Orgnize Theater Trips; After Schl Club Supvr; Accompanist for Choir, Musical Groups; Mechanicville Tchr Assoc; NY St Tchr Assoc; PTA; Cohes Cath Schls Exec Bd; Cohoes Cnslng & CAre Bd of Trustees; Cohoes Lib Bd of Trustees; Parish Cncl of Sacred Heart Church; Umbudsman Drug Ed Cert; Civil Defense Cncl; News Articles Pub; Entire Class Awded by WMHT Learning Channel 17; *office:* Cohoes Catholic Sch-St Agnes 45 Johnston Ave Cohoes NY 12047

MARK, ANN MARIEA, Mathematics Teacher; *b:* Pt Fortin, Trinidad; *ed:* Univ of the West Indies (BSE) Math 1988; Sanfernando Technicia Inst Chem, Physics & Bio Diploma 1979; Corinth Tchrs Coll Math Diploma 1981; York Coll Bookkeeping Cert 1991; *cr:* Bethlehem Bapt Acad Math Tchr 1989-; Hope for Yth Cnslr 1995-; *ai:* Girls Net Ball Coach; Sunday Schl Tchr; *office:* Bethlehem Baptist Acad # 84 1962 Linden Blvd Brooklyn NY 11207

MARK, ELLEN S., Spanish Teacher; *b:* Hanover, NH; *c:* Philip E., Nathan C., Lisa J. Chaga, Jonathan B.; *ed:* Gordon Coll (BA) Bible & Greek 1957; Temple Univ (MA) Span Lit 1973; West Chester Univ 24 Credit Hrs Toward MED; *cr:* The Chrstn Acad Span Tchr & Dept Head 1966-77; Padua Acad Span Tchr 1991-; Neumann Coll Instr 1991-; *ai:* Club Mexico; DECTFL 1991-; AATSP 1992-; Designed & Teach Wkshp at St Francis Hosp, Span for Hlth Care Profs; *office:* Padua Acad 905 N Broom St Wilmington DE 19806

MARK, ESTELLE IDA, Extended Projects Program Tchr; *b:* Udevalla, Sweden; *m:* H. Mic Horbaly; *ed:* Cuyahoga Comm Coll (AA) 1971; OH St Univ (BA) Pub Recreation 1973, MA Spec Ed 1977; 45 Addl Post Grad Work Hrs Rdng Ed, Childrens Lit, Gifted Ed; *cr:* Central OH Adolescent Ctr Act Therapist 1973-76; Centre Schl LB, DB Tchr 1976-78; Worthington Campus Schl SBH Tchr, Rdng Coord 1978-88; Brookside & Sutter Park Schls EPP Tchr 1986-; *ai:* Worthington Soc Stud Comm 1995-; Worthington Staff Dev 1986-89; SWEPP; PTA; NEA 1978-; OH Assn Gifted Children 1992-; Nat Assn Gifted Children 1990-; US Holocaust Mem Museum 1990-; Save the Manatee Club 1988; FL Audubon Soc 1991-; Honorarium Rosemont Ctr Presentation Childrens Lit Based Curr 1986; *office:* Brookside Elem Schl 6700 Mcvey Blvd Columbus OH 43235

MARK, JAMES D., Director of Instrumental Music; *b:* Lancaster, PA; *m:* Susan Chopek; *c:* Douglas James; *ed:* West Chester Univ (BS) Music Ed 1986; Grad Stud Rowan Coll; *cr:* Millville Meml HS Instrumental Music Tchr 1986-92; Millville Sr HS Instrumental Music Dir 1993-; *ai:* Marching Band; Jazz Ensemble; Wind Ensemble Co-Curricular Contract Comm; NEA, NJEA, MENC, NJMEA, SJBODA 1986-; Millville Elks Lodge 1993-, Chaplain; *office:* Millville Sr HS 200 Wade Blvd Millville NJ 08332

MARKEL, DONALD L., Instrumental Music Teacher; *b:* Seweckley, PA; *m:* Marsha; *c:* Harmony, Adam; *ed:* Clarion Univ of PA (BS) Music Ed 1975; Attnd OH St Univ, Kent St Univ, IN Univ of PA, Gannon Coll, Penn St Univ, Shippensburg Univ; *cr:* Elk Cty Chrstn HS Instrumental & Vocal Music 1975-79; Claysburg-Kimmel HS Instrumental Music 1979-; *ai:* Marching Band; Jazz Ensemble; Tchr Mentor; PSEA 1979-; PMEA 1975-, Cty Rep; MENC 1975-; Cubmaster BSA 1992-95.

MARKELL, LINDA BETH, History Teacher; *b:* Boston, MA; *m:* Philip; *c:* Andrew, Joseph, Robert; *ed:* Connecticut Coll (BA) His 1961; Harvard Grad Schl Ed, Radcliffe Grad Schl Arts, Sci (MAT) Ed, His 1962; *cr:* Arlington HS Soc Stud Tchr 1962-65; Brookline HS Soc Stud Tchr 1965-; *ai:* Cadence Schl Newspaper Adv 1993-95; Amer Cncl Learned Societies 1992-, Tchr, Fellow; Amer Stud Assn 1994-; Wellerley Schlsp Fnd 1986-, Trustee; Natl Endowment for Hum Grant; Flwshp World His, World Civilizations Inst at Harvard Univ Natl Resource Ctr for Russian, East European & Cntrl Asian Stud; Silence The Evolution of Democracy and the Women's Movement in the History of the United States Pub 1994; Reappointed Assoc in Ed Harvard Grad Schl of Ed1993-94; Panelist Amer Stud Conf 1993; Natl Grant Amer Cncl of Learned Societies, Tchr Fellow 1992-93; Participation Natl Ctr on Effective Scndry Schls Univ of WI Prgm for Curr Implemntation & Evaluation 1980-90; Summer Wkshp & Acad Yr Curr Creation & Implementation; Brookline Liaison Harvard Schl of Ed Project for Suburban, Urban Schls 1970-80; Trustee Wellesley Schlsp Fnd 1987-; *office:* Brookline HS 115 Greenough St Brookline MA 02146*

MARKER, RITA MAXWELL, Spanish Teacher; *b:* Peoria, IL; *m:* Timothy; *c:* Patrick, Daniel; *ed:* OH St Univ (BS) Span 1971, (MA) Counseling 1977; Addl 6 Hrs at Univ of Cincinnati in Span Lit, 3 Hrs at Xavier Univ in Ed & 3 Hrs in Cmptr Sci; *cr:* Upper Arlington HS Span Tchr 1971-72; Greenhills-Forest Park HS Span Tchr 1973-76; Worthington City Schls Span Tchr 1977-; *ai:* Span NHS Co-Spon; Bldg Design & Planning Teams Facilitator; NEA, OEA 1971-; WEA; Phi Delta Kappa 1977-; Translated Comic Book into Span; *office:* Worthington Kilbourne HS 1499 Hard Rd Columbus OH 43235*

MARKETOS, GEORGE B., Mathematics Professor; *b:* Akron, OH; *m:* Susan Marie Erickson; *c:* Dann, Jill, Sara; *ed:* Unif of Akron (MA) Math 1971; *cr:* Bolich Jr HS Math Tchr 1969070; Firestone Tire & Rubber Co QA Engr, Indstrl Engr 1970-72; Rockwell Intl Indstrl Engr 1973-74; Univ of Cincinnati Math Prof 1974-; *ai:* Math Assn of Amer 1985-; Akron Twp Transportation Comm 1993-; Pub Radio Station WUXU Com Adv Bd 1975, Chair; Coll UCCAS Tchr of Yr Awd 1988; Nom A. B. Cohen Excl in

Tchng Awd 1987; *office:* Univ Of Cincinnati 2220 Victory Pky Cincinnati OH 45221

MARKEY, DIANE LOUISE, 8th Grd Science Teacher; *b:* York, PA; *c:* Tammy Lynn; *ed:* York Jr Coll (AA) Sec ed 1965; Millersville st Univ (BS) Sec Ed 1967; Shippensburg St (MED) Sec Ed 1981; 15 Post Grad Hrs; *cr:* Spring Grove Schl Dist Bio Tchr 1967-68; South Eastern Schl Dist Gen Sci Tchr 1969-; *ai:* PA Sci Tchrs Assoc, Delta Kappa Gamma 1993-; Philadelphia Electric Mini Grant for Ecohome Project; Lincoln Intermediate Unit Mimi Grant for Environmental Sci; *home:* 324 Ruth Dr York PA 17403

MARKHAM, BARBARA NICCOLO, Social Studies Instr & Chprsn; *b:* West Chester, PA; *m:* James; *ed:* Villanova Univ (BA) His 1977, (BS) Ed 1978; Univ of DE (MA) Amer His 1988; Attnd Universitaire Grammont at Tours France, Smith Coll, Univ of MA & Temple Univ; *cr:* Padua Acad Tchr 1978-, Chprsn 1990-; *ai:* NHS Adv; NCSS 1988-; DE Cncl for Soc Stud 1978-, Sec, Tchr & Historian Awds; DE Theatre Co 1995-, Ed Advy Bd; Natl Endowment for Hum 1 Seminar, 3 Insts & 1 Hum Focus Grants; Textbook Reviewer; Wrkshp Presenter-NCSS Org for Amer Historians; *office:* Padua Acad 905 N Broom St Wilmington DE 19806*

MARKHAM, CHRISTINE L., English Dept Chairperson; *b:* Schenectady, NY; *m:* Thomas C.; *c:* Jennifer; *ed:* SUNY at Plattsburgh (BA) Scndry Ed 1971; Iona Coll (MA) Eng 1975; SUNY at New Paltz (CAS) Scndry Admin 1986; NYC Writing Project Literacy Lehan Coll; Tech, Cmptr Tech, Long Island U; *cr:* Clarkstown HS North Eng Tchr 1971-, Eng Dept Chair 1986-; *ai:* Adv Asian Club, Yrbk 7 Yrs, Humar Magazine; Var Sftbl Coach 7 Yrs; Mid Sts Evaluation Chprsn; Russia for Exch Prgm; Instituted Environmentalist Club; NCTE 1975-; Superv, Curric Dev Assoc 1986-, Sftbl Coach of Yr 1976; NYS Eng Cncl 1990-; Clarkstown Teach Assoc 1971-; Broadacres Golf Club 1985-, Ladies League Pres; Clarkstown PTSA 1971-, Lifetime Mem Awd 1986; Nanuet PTSA 1982-; Rockland Bus, Prof Women, Blanche Mulder Schlsp; Mid Hudson Schls Bd Assoc Tchng Excl Awd 1993; SUNY at New Platz Adjunct Prof; Schl of Tchr Ed Blanche Mulder Women Schlsp Awd 1987; *office:* Clarkstown HS North 50 Congers Rd New City NY 10956

MARKHAM, JOHN THOMAS, Social Science Dept Instructor; *b:* Fitchburg, MA; *m:* Catherine Marashio; *c:* Colleen; *ed:* Mount Wachusett Comm Coll (AS) Mental Hlth Tech 1975; Anna Marie Coll (BA) Soc Work 1981; Boston Coll (MSW) Clinical Soc Work 1985; Attnd Kantor Family Inst 1987; *cr:* Lunenburg Family Therapy Pvt Practice Clinical Soc Worker 1981-; Lipton Mental Hlth Ctr Clinical Soc Worker 1987-; Mount Wachusett Comm Coll Part-time Fac 1988-; *ai:* Natl Assn of Soc Workers, Clinical Soc Diplomate, Register, lualified Clinical Soc Worker; *office:* Mount Wachusett Comm Coll 444 Green St Gardner MA 01440

MARKHAM, MARYALICE BRIDGET, Third Grade Teacher; *b:* Bay Shore, NY; *ed:* Sacred Heart (BA) Ed, Math 1971; Adelpi (MA) Ed 1975; Dowling Coll 75 Credit Hrs 1990; *cr:* Bank St Schl Sixth Grd Tchr 1971-72; Wenonah Elem Schl Second Grd Tchr 1972-75, First Grd Tchr 1975-82, Third Grd Tchr 1982-; *ai:* Author Visitation Prgm; Hobby & Math Club; SCTA, NYSUT, AFT 1972-; Cath Daughters of Amers 1977-, Fin Sec, First Vice Regent, Second Vice Regent, Regent, Msgr Nolan Awd 1996.

MARKIEWICZ, JOHN H., Library Director; *b:* Webster, MA; *ed:* Worcester Jr Coll (AA) Lbrl Arts 1963; Clark Univ (BS) His 1966; *cr:* St Joseph Schl 7-8 Grd Soc Stud Tchr 1966-94, Lib Dir 1994-; *ai:* Webster Schl Comm, MA Assn of Schl Comm Inc 1969-87, 1990-; Calvin Coolidge Meml Fnd 1986-; MA Schl Lib Media Assn 1994-; BSA Troop 173 Asst SM 1977-; *office:* St Joseph Elem Schl 47 Whitcomb St Webster MA 01570

MARKIN, ESTA B., English Teacher; *b:* Jersey City, NJ; *c:* Kyle Dara Sofman; *ed:* Syracuse Univ (BA) Eng 1965; Fairleigh Dickinson Univ (MAT) Eng 1966; Post Grad Developmental Rdng at Temple Univ; *cr:* Fairleigh Dickinson Univ Eng Instr 1965-66; Abington Schls Eng Tchr 1966-70; Lowell Univ Eng Instr 1973-77; Lasell Jr Coll Eng Instr 1975-77; Brandes Univ Eng & Hum Instr 1975-86; Newton South HS Eng Tchr 1983-; Leave of Abs Stud at Berkley CA & Tuscany Italy; *ai:* Lit & Art Magazine Adv 3 Yrs; Schl Climate Comm Chm; Human Differences Comm Mem 2 Yrs; Union Rep 4 Yrs; NTA 1983, Schl Rep; MTA 1983; NEH Grant 1989, Creative Rdng & Writing, Vol of Poetry; *office:* Newton South HS 140 Brandeis Rd Newton Center MA 02159*

MARKLE, DAVID E., High School Vocal Music Dir; *b:* Cleveland, OH; *m:* Mary Healey; *c:* Andrea Thompson, Kyle, Kristen; *ed:* OH St Univ (BME) Voice, Piano 1978; 20 Addl Hrs; *cr:* West Jefferson HS Band & Choir Dir 1978-82; Westland HS Choir Dir 1982-85; Midpark HS Choir Dir 1985-; *ai:* Show Choir; Men's Chorus; Women's Chorus; Vocal Ensembles; MENC, OMEA, Phi Kappa Phi, Pi Kappa Lambda 1978-; OMEA Adjudicator 1983-; Organized & Presented Cmptr, Music Seminar OMEA Conf in Cleveland 1990; Asst Dir All St Chorus 1985; Chm Dist XV South, Band, Choir Contest 1982-85; *office:* Midpark HS 7000 Paula Dr Cleveland OH 44130*

MARKO, DALE F., Assistant Professor of Chem; *b:* Pittsburgh, PA; *ed:* PA St Univ (BS) Chemical Engrng 1980; Northwestern Univ (PHD) Organic Chem 1987; Post-Doctoral Fellow Univ of UT 1985-86; *cr:* Coll of St Rose Asst Prof of Chem 1986-92; Siena Coll Asst Prof of Chem 1992-; *ai:* Chem Club Adv; Bd of Instruction; Amer Chem Soc 1981; Sigma XI 1983-; St Tchrs Assn of NY 1994-; NSF Grant 1995; Pub Stud Guide Environmental Perspective 1995; *office:* Siena Coll 515 London Rd Loudonville NY 12211

MARKO-DEVORE, DEBORAH, Choir Director; *b:* Cleveland, OH; *m:* Richard; *c:* Rebecca; *ed:* WV Univ (BS) Music Ed & Applied Music 1976; Kent St Univ (MM) Music Ed 1983, (PHD) Music Ed 1989; *cr:* Geneva Area City Schls Instrumental Music 1977-83; Revere Local Schls Vocal Music 1985-; *ai:* Asst Dir of Marching Band; OH Music Ed Assn 1977-; Music Educators Natl Conf 1977-; Amer Choral Dir Assn; OEA, NEA 1977-; *office:* Revere HS 3420 Everett Rd Richfield OH 44286*

MARKOE, DONALD JOHN, Teacher; *b:* Staten Island, NY; *m:* Andrea; *c:* Lauren; *ed:* SUNY at Cortland (BS) Ed 1985; Western CT Univ (MS) Curr, Instruction 1989; *cr:* Mahopac MS Tchr 1985-; *ai:* Boys Var Bsktbl Coach 1992-; *office:* Mahopac MS Baldwin Place Rd Mahopac NY 10541*

MARKOFF, KAREN LOUISE (AUNGLER), Asst Prin & Special Ed Dir; *b:* Syracuse, NY; *m:* Richard; *c:* Erin, Jon, Philip; *ed:* SUNY at Buffalo (BA) Eng 1973; Syracuse Univ (MS) Eng Ed 1979, (CAS) Ed Admin 1995; *cr:* Williamsville North HS Eng Tchr 1974; West Genesee CSD Eng Tchr 1974-80; Onondaga Comm Coll Adj Instr 1980-85; Lafayette Jr Sr HS Eng Tchr, Lang Arts Coord 1985-95, Asst Prin, Dir of Spec Ed 1995-; *ai:* Shared Decision Making, Restructuring Team; Stans of Excl Comm; Crisis Intervention Team; Schl Admin Assn of NYS, NASSP 1995-; ASCD 1990-; NEA 1985-91; NUSUT Affiliate 1991-, Pres; NCTE 1974-95; St Joseph's Church 1985-; Comm Connections 1995-; Comm Cncl 1991-95; Lafayette Republican Club 1993-; Legislature Grant Great Kids & Lift Prgms; Class Awd LCHS 1995; *office:* La Fayette Jr Sr HS Rt 11 N La Fayette NY 13084*

MARKOT, MICHAEL, Mathematics Teacher; *b:* Indianapolis, IN; *m:* Linda Virtue; *c:* Jonathan Virtue; *ed:* Cornell Univ (BA) Math 1974; Rutgers Univ (MEd) Math Ed 1975; Several Extra Credit Hrs; *cr:* East Brunswick HS Math Tchr 1975-; *ai:* Fac Cncl; NCTM, AMTNJ 1993-; *office:* East Brunswick HS 380 Cranbury Rd E Brunswick NJ 08816

MARKOVICH, DEBRA ANN, High Schl Social Studies Tchr; *b:* Youngstown, OH; *ed:* Youngstown St Univ (BS) Elem Ed 1974; Kent St Univ (MED) Gifted 1-12 Grd 1976, (EDS) Gifted 1-12 Grd 1978; *cr:* Youngstown City Schls 2nd Grd Tchr 1974-75; Struthers City Schls 2nd, 6th, 8th Grd Tchr 1975-, Grd 9-11 Soc Stud Tchr 1985-, 9th Grd His, Geog Tchr 1996; *ai:* Voice of Democracy Contest; His Day Adv St winner; NEA, OEA 1985-; Fed of Tchrs 1974-85; Mahoing Cty Landlords 1992-, Friends of Lib 1985-; OH Soc Stu Tchr of Yr 1988; *home:* 2388 Shetland Ln Poland OH 44514*

MARKOWITZ, MARJORIE DANNEN, 7th Grade English Teacher; *b:* Manhattan, NY; *m:* Mark J.; *c:* Leanne, Kaitlyn; *ed:* St Univ Coll at New Paltz (BA) Ed-Summa Cum Laude 1974; 30 Grad Credits; 6 Grad Hrs Weslyan Univ Grad Summer Schl for Tchrs 1975; *cr:* John Jay Sr HS 9th & 10th Grd Eng Tchr 1974-77; Wappingers Jr HS 9th Grd Eng Tchr 1977-81 & 1983-85; VanWyck Jr HS 7th & 8th Grd Eng Tchr 1987-88, 7th Grd Eng Tchr 1988-; *ai:* WCT 1974-; NYSUT 1974-; Holy Trinity Childrens Chorus 1988-, Co Dir; Taught Adult Ed Classes in Creative Writing; Folk Guitar, Drama & Schl Newspaper Advs; Project Adventure Team; Taught Alternative HS; *office:* Van Wyck Jr HS Hillside Lake Rd Wappingers Falls NY 12590

MARKOWITZ, MARK J., English Teacher; *b:* Mitchell Field ARB, NY; *m:* Marjorie Dannen; *c:* Leanne, Kaitlyn; *ed:* St Univ Coll at Oneonta (BA) Lit 1974; 39 Grad Hrs St Univ at New Paltz; *cr:* St Patrick's Military Acad Grds 7-8 Eng, Math, Sci Tchr 1974-78; Most Precious Blood Schl Grds 6-8 Lang Arts, Rdng Tchr 1978-80; Wappinger Cntrl Schls Grds 7, 9-12 Eng Tchr 1980-; *office:* Roy C Ketcham HS 99 Myers Corners Rd Wappingers Falls NY 12590

MARKOWITZ, MICHAEL DAVID, Music Teacher; *b:* Newport News, VA; *m:* Sara F.; *c:* Robert, Maura; *ed:* IN Univ of PA (BS) Music Ed 1970; George WA Univ (MA) Scndry Schl Admin, Super 1975; Attnd Towson St Univ, Johns Hopkins Univ; *cr:* Severna Park Jr HS Music Tchr 1970-74; Severn River Jr HS Music Tchr 1974-80; MacArthur MS Music Tchr 1980-; *ai:* String Orch; Jazz Ensemble; NEA 1970-, Natl Del; MSTA 1970-, St Del; Tchrs Assoc of AA Co 1970-, Assoc Rep; MENC 1970-; Handel Choir of Baltimore 1970-; BSA 1984-, Troop Comm, Vice-Chair, Jewish Comm on Scouting, Shofar Awd; *office:* MacArthur MS 3500 Rockenbach Rd Fort Meade MD 20755

MARKOWSKI, PATRICIA ALLWEIN, Mathematics Teacher; *b:* Lebanon, PA; *m:* Michael P.; *c:* Paul, Andrew; *ed:* George Mason Univ (MS) Math; Coll Misericordia (BS) Math; *cr:* Hospital Assn of PA Research Assoc 1982-86; Trinity HS Math Tchr 1986-; *ai:* Yrbk Adv; PA Cncl of Tchrs of Math; NSF Grant Through Mount Saint Marys in Emmittsburg MD Math Stud; *office:* Trinity HS 3601 Simpson Ferry Rd Camp Hill PA 17011

MARKS, BRIAN, Art Teacher; *b:* Gallipolis, OH; *m:* Dawn Calloway; *ed:* Rio Grande Coll (AA) Art Emphasis 1983; OH Univ (BA) Art Ed; 3 Addl Hrs Adobe Photoshop, Quark X-Press on MAC; *cr:* Scioto Vly Schls Elem & HS Art Tchr 1990-91; Western Local Schls Elem & HS Art Tchr 1991-; *ai:* Art Curr Dev Comm; Annual Art Show; OAEA 1990-; Golden Key NHS 1989-; Church of Christ & Chrstn Union 1996; Jackson Merchants Assn 1993-; Pub Cartoon City Map of Jackson OH 1992; Pub Map of Franklin Vly Golf Course 1980-81; *office:* Western Local Schls 12599 SR 124 Piketon OH 45661

MARKS, JOEL HOWARD, Professor of Philosophy; *b:* New York City, NY; *ed:* Cornell Univ (BA) Psych 1972; Univ of CT (MA) Philosophy 1978, (PHD) Philosophy 1982; *cr:* Portland Schl of Art Instr of Psych 1973-75; St John Fisher Coll Asst Prof 1982-83; Univ of New Haven Asst, Assoc, Full Prof 1984-; *ai:* Symposium Series Ethics in Workplace Coord; Radio Show Host; Occasional Ethics Newspaper Columnist; Amer Philosophical Assn; Amer Assn of Philosophy Tchrs; Soc for Asian and Comparative Philosophy; Editor 3 Books 1986, 1992, 1995; *office:* Univ Of New Haven 300 Orange Ave West Haven CT 06516

MARKS, KAREN CECELIA, 7th-8th Grade Science Teacher; *b:* Akron, OH; *m:* David Charles; *c:* Tammy Marks Brizzi, David E.; *ed:* Barry Coll (BS) Ed 1978; *cr:* St Augustines Sch 3rd Grd Tchr 1962-64; St Joseph Schl 3rd Grd Tchr 1964-65; Our Lady Queen of Martyrs K-8th Grd Tchr 1965-84; St Francis DeSales Schl 7th-8th Grd Tchr 1985-; *ai:* Sci Fair Coord; NCEA 1985-; *office:* St Francis De Sales Schl 4009 Manchester Rd Akron OH 44319*

MARKS, NORA MARALEA, Dir of Vocal Music; *b:* Tarentum, PA; *m:* Carr Bishop; *c:* Matthew John Jacobs, Donna Marie Jacobs; *ed:* Temple Univ (BS) Music Ed 1961, (MS) Music Ed 1981; 17 Grad Credits Temple Univ; Hofstra Univ 15 Grad Credits; Westminster Choir Coll 3 Grad Credits; *cr:* Upper Perkiomen HS Vocal Music Tchr 1961-67; Valley Stream HS Vocal Music Tchr 1973-79; Gettysburg Area Schls Vocal Music Tchr 1979-; *ai:* Choral Dir Jr Sr HS Chorus, Concert Choir; 50's Swing Choir; HS Musicals Vocal Coach; Amer Choral Dirs Assn 1983-; MENC 1979-; NEA 1981-; Adams Cty Music Educators Assn 1979-; PA Rural Letter Carriers Aux 1984-, St Sec 1993-; Berkshire Music Ctr MA Schlsp 1963; Who's Who in Music, Musicians; *office:* Gettysburg Area Schl Dist Lefever St Gettysburg PA 17325

MARKS, PENNY ECKSTINE, Spanish Teacher; *b:* Hagerstown, MD; *m:* Richard D.; *c:* Scott, Chris, Lee, Todd, Heidi; *ed:* Shippensburg St Tchrs Coll (BS) Span & Eng 1969; Grad Stud at Millersville Univ; Various US Pgms Affiliated with Universidad de Valencia & Other Pgms Offered in Spain; *cr:* Greencastle-Antrim MS Span Tchr & Frgn Lang Dept Chair 1969-; *ai:* GAEA 1969-, Sec; PSEA, NEA 1969-; Young Life Exec Cncl, Sec.

MARKS, RANDALL J., Vocal Director; *b:* Lebanon, PA; *m:* Dawn M.; *ed:* West Chester Univ (BS) Music Ed 1974, (MM) Music Ed 1986; *cr:* Cedar Crest MS Vocal Dir 1974-75; Eastern Lebanon Cty HS Band & Vocal Dir 1975-88; Cedar Crest HS Vocal Dir 1988-; *ai:* HS & Womens Chorus, Concert & Show Choir Dir; PSEA, NEA 1974-; PMEA 1974-, Cty Rep 1991-; ACDA 1988-; Phi Mu Alpha 1971-; Youth Christ Bd 1976-82; *office:* Cornwall Lebanon Schl Dist 105 East Evergreen Rd Lebanon PA 17042*

MARKS, ROBERT GALE, Vocal Music Director; *b:* Yorktown Heights, NY; *m:* Karen Lavaughn Ullman; *c:* Kimberly; *ed:* Heidelberg Coll (BM) Music Ed 1977; *cr:* Caldwell Exempted Village Schls K-12th Grd Vocal Music Tchr 1977-81; Cambridge City Schls Sub Tchr 1981-83; Rolling Hills Local Schls K-6th Grd Vocal Music Tchr 1983-84; Cambridge City Schls Jr & Sr HS Vocal Music Dir 1984-; *ai:* Drama Club Musicals Music Dir; MENC & OH Music Ed Assn 1977-, Dist IX Pres 1992-94, VP 1994-; NEA & OEA 1977-; ACDA & OCDA; AGEHR; Cambridge Ed Assn; First United Meth Church of Cambridge, Music Dir 1981-; *office:* Cambridge HS 1201 Clairmont Ave Cambridge OH 43725*

MARKS, RONALD PAUL, Teacher & Athletic Director; *b:* Freedom, ME; *m:* Jewell Gifford; *c:* Ellen, John, James, Jeffrey; *ed:* Univ of ME at Orono (BA) PE 1962; 30 Addl Hrs PE, Ath Admin; *cr:* Sherman HS Tchr, Ath Dir 1962-67; Katahdin HS Tchr, Ath Dir 1967-68; Foxcroft Acad Tchr, Ath Dir 1968-69; Schenck HS Tchr, Ath Dir 1969-; *ai:* Ath Dir; Coach Boys Bsktbl 20 Yrs, Girls Soccer 16 Yrs; NEA, ME Tchrs Assn 1962-; AAHPERD 1968-; ME Ath Dir Assn 1970-; Elks Club 1984-; ME Hall of Fame 1988-; IAABO Ofcls 1964-, Exec Bd, 25 Yrs Svc; Vol Recreation Dept Summer Prgms; Natl Ath Dir of Yr Nom 1988-; ME Coaches Assn Bsktbl Coach of Yr 1971, 1976; ME Soccer Coach of Yr 1988, 1990, 1004; Bsktbl Coach 5 St Championships; Soccer Coach 4 St Championships.

MARKWORTH, WAYNE, Band Director; *b:* Chicago, IL; *m:* Tam Andrew; *ed:* IN Univ (BMusEd) Music Ed 1969; Northwester (MMusic) Music Ed 1977; *cr:* Madison HS Band Dir 1969-70; Cen HS Band Dir 1970-; *ai:* Marching Band, Jazz Ensemble Dir; M Sound Engr; NEA, OEA, CCTA 1970-; MENC, OMEA 1969-; IAJE Montgomery Co Exl Tchng Awd 1992; *office:* Centerville HS Franklin St Centerville OH 45459

MARLER, ANN-FRANCES TESTA, English & Publications Teac Canonsburg, PA; *m:* Scott Warren; *c:* Adrienne; *ed:* Flagler Coll (B & Ed of Hearing Impaired 1985; *cr:* Crescent City HS Eng II & C Writing Tchr 1985-86; RIRIE Elem Schl Chapter I & Mirgrant Work 1986-87; Various Schls in ID & PA Daily & Long Term Sub 19 Burgettstown Area Jr-sr HS 7th, 10th & 12th Grd Eng & Publicatio 1993-; *ai:* Yrbk Spon; Steering Comm Grad Requirements Comm; Interview Mentor Tchr; Discipline Comm; 7th Grd PA Project; S Bee Judge; Drama Production Audition Evaluator & Back Stage NEA, PSEA, BAEA 1993-; Educl Advy Cncl HS Rep; Crescent Ci of Month; *home:* 216 Walker Rd Burgettstown PA 15021

MARLOVITS, KENNETH WILLIAM, Social Studies Teach Pittsburgh, PA; *ed:* Penn St Univ (BS) Scndry Ed 1992; 3 Cre Wesleyan Univ; 4 Credits PA Dept of Ed; *cr:* Blackhawk Area Sc HS Soc Stud Tchr 1993-; *ai:* Girls Golf Coach; Jr High Wrestling PSEA 1993-; NEA 1993-; Lions Club Intnl 1995-; Gift of Time Awd; *office:* Blackhawk HS 500 Blackhawk Rd Beaver Falls PA 15

MARLOW, GEORGETTE FREEMAN, English Teacher; *b:* Hun AL; *m:* David A.; *c:* David G., William J.; *ed:* IN Univ (BA) Eng Univ of Cincinnati Rdng Cert, Grad Drama Stud; Miami Univ Gr MED Prgm Curr, Tchr Ldrshp; *cr:* Goshen HS 9-10 Grd Honors Er 1973-77; Merry Jr HS 7-8 Grd Eng Tchr 1978-80; Schwab Jr HS Grd Eng Tchr 1980-81; Roberts Jr HS 7, 8, 9AA Grd Eng Tchr 19 Western Hills HS 11AA-12AP Eng Tchr 1988-; *ai:* Daisy Chair Thespian Troupe Spons; Cum Laude Comm; Fall Play Dir; NCTE Credentialed Cincinnati Pub Schls Lead Tchr; Lead Tchr ir Appointed Dist Consulting Tchr in Eng; *office:* Western Hills H Ferguson Rd Cincinnati OH 45238

MARLOWE, BRUCE ALAN, Education Professor; *b:* New York, N Pam Rush; *c:* Rachel; *ed:* Union Coll (BA) Philosophy 1983; Cat (MA) Ed 1986, PhD) Educl Psych 1991; *cr:* Ctr for Unique Learne 1983-85; Chelsea Schl Tchr 1985-88; William Stixrud & Assoc T Diagnostician 1988-92; Johnson St Coll Prof 1992-; *ai:* Variety o Comms; ASCD; Orton Dyslexia Soc; CEC; JSC Child Dev Ctr 19 Mem; Prof Dev Grant; Speaker at Variety of Natl Confs; Article Pub; PO Box 166 Johnson VT 05656*

MARLOWE, JAMIE E., Prof of Radiation Physics; *b:* Conway, Joanne Margaret Saunders; *c:* Jamie Jr., Lisa Ann; *ed:* Miami Dade Coll (AS) Radiologic Tech 1973; Ottawa Univ (BA) Hlth Care, 1982; Nova Univ (MBA) Bus Admin 1984, (EDD) Higher Ed 1991; Nuclear Weapons Schl Nuclear Hazards 1983; US Army Environ Hygeine Agency Nuclear Med Sci 1983-86; Univ of TX X-Ray F 1984; US Army Acad of Hlth Sci X-Ray Survey Techniques 198 Ridge TN Radiation Emergency Assistance Course 1993; *cr:* K Clinic Staff Radiologic Technologist 1964-66; Jackson Meml Hos Radiologic Technologist 1964-66; Doctors Hosp Asst Chief Radiology 1966-69; Palm Springs Gen Hosp Tech Dir Radiology 19 Broward Med Ctr Asst Tech Dir Radiology 1971-72; Jameson Mem Asst Tech Dir Radiology, Dir Nuclear Med 1973-74; Univ Hosp Spain Nuclear Med Technologist 1974-75; Southwest Comm Hosp Tech Radiology 1975-76; Lee Meml Hosp Surgical, Portable Techn 1976-78; Ft Myers Comm Hosp Asst Tech Dir Radiology 1978-80 Dir Radiology 1980-83; US Army Nuclear Med Sci Ofcr 1983-86; S Hlth Physicist 1986; Miami Dade Comm Coll Fac Prof Rad P 1986-93; Dade Co Med Examiner Hlth Physicist 1993-; Palm Beach Coll Adj Prof Rad Physics 1992; *ai:* Rsrch Post Mortem Arteriogra Demonstrate Massive Subarachnoid Hemmorrage Due to Vertebral Laceration; Amer Soc Rad Tech, Amer Reg Rad Tech 1964-; MD S Tech 1993-; Book Pub Textbook of Surgical Radiology; *office:* Arundel Comm Coll 101 College Pky Arnold MD 21012

MARMAROU, STEPHANIE, Spanish Teacher; *b:* Reading, P. Albright Coll (BA) Span 1988; Millersville Univ (MA) Span 19 Instituto Cultural Guadalajara Mexico; *cr:* Rdng Area Comm Co 1988; Holy Name HS Tchr 1990-; *ai:* Asst Ath Dir; Prom, Jr Class Recruitment Comm; AATSP 1994-; *office:* Holy Name HS Wyomissing Blvd Reading PA 19611*

MARMON, JEFFREY D., Guidance Counselor; *b:* Philadelphia, P Villanna Univ (MA) Admin 1972, (MA) Guid Cnslng 1978; *cr:* Ne HS Tchr 1969-71; Abington HS Tchr 1971-81, Cnslr 1981-; *ai:* PIA Bsktbl, Bsbl Ofcl; USPTR Regnl Tennis Pro; NEA, USPTR, PSEA Tennis Around Town Pub 1986; *office:* Abington Sr HS 900 Highlar Abington PA 19001

MARNIK, ELIA D., Asst Prin & Rdng Specialist; *b:* Winchester, M Michael P.; *c:* Ralph, Robert, Alicia; *ed:* Newton Coll (LIB) Psych Boston Coll (MED) Elem Ed 1966; Univ of Lowell (CAGS) Admin *cr:* Joshua Eaton Schl Rdng Specialist Tchr 1983-, Asst Prin 1988 IRA; MA Rdng Assn; Rdng Lib Trustees 1970-, Chm; St Bd Commissioners 1995-; *office:* Joshua Eaton Elem Schl 365 Summe Reading MA 01867

MAROLD, MARY ANN SULLIVAN, Acting Supervising Vice P Waterbury, CT; *m:* Donald; *c:* Rebecca; *ed:* Cntrl CT St Univ (BS) Ed 1972, (MS) Lang Arts 1976; 6th Yr Degree Admin, Supervision *cr:* Walsh Magnet Schl Acting Supervising Vice Prin 2 Yrs; Tinke Tchng Vice Prin 6 Yrs, First Grd Tchr 22 Yrs; *ai:* ASCD 1989-; Nau Cncl of Cath Women 1972-, Pres, Sec; Tinker PTO 1972-; Walsh 1994-; Tinker Schl Tchr of Yr 1988; *office:* Walsh Magnet Schl 29 St Waterbury CT 06704

MARONA, REBECCA, Sixth Grade Reading Teacher; *b:* Worcester *m:* Robert R.; *ed:* Worcester St Tchrs Coll (BSEd) Eng 1965; Worce Coll (MSEd) Rdng 1975; 6 Credits Post Grad Stud Univ of Riverside; *cr:* Oxford Cntrl Jr HS 8 Grd Rdng Tchr 1965-67; Riversi Jr HS 7-8 Grd Eng Tchr 1967-68; Alvord Elem Schl 6 Grd Tchr 19 Southbridge Elem Schls 4 Grd Tchr 1971-86, 6 Grd Tchr 1986-; *ai:* Club Asst Dir, Supvr 1986-95; Curr, Internation Day Comms; Rdng T Dancercize Club, Activity; NEA, MTA, SEA, MA Rdng Assn 1971- 1995-; Brookfield Comm Club 1986-, Exec Bd, MC at Cntry Fair; F of the Lib 1986-95, Patron; MA Cultural Cncl for the Arts, Rep; MA Lottery Comm, Brookfield Rep; Brookfield Rent Control Bd; Horace Grant; Grant for Excl 1996; Safety Awd 10 Yrs; *office:* Mary E Wells 82 Marcy St Southbridge MA 01550

MARONI, MARY ANN PRATT, Jr HS Lang Arts & Math Tc Worcester, MA; *m:* John A.; *c:* JoAnne Lavin, Suzanne Jackson; *ed* Path Jr Coll (AS) Secretarial Sci 1960; N Adams St Coll (BA) Math 75 Hrs Beyond Bachelors Degree; *cr:* Sprague Electric Co Sec 19 Clarksburg Elem Schl Jr HS Tchr 1968-; *ai:* McManan Voc & Te Sftbl Var Coach, Jr Var Soccer Coach; Jr Olympic Sftbl & Bsktbl C Clarksburg Tchrs Assn 1968-, Pres; MTA & NEA 1968-; NCTM; N Schl Governance Cncl 1994-, Sec; Humane Educator of Yr 1989;

988; *office:* Clarksburg Elem Schl W Cross Rds Clarksburg MA

ON, DAVID JAMES, Band Director; *b:* Cleveland, OH; *m:* *c:* Wendy, Michael, Dustin; *ed:* Bowling Green St Univ (BME) Ed 1977; McNeese St Univ (MM) Music Ed 1981; *cr:* Merryville nd Dir 1978-81; Princeton HS Band Dir 1981-; *ai:* Marching, onic Band Dir; Structure & Org Comm; OMEA, MENC 1977-; 1989-; Faith Comm United Meth Church, Handbell Choir Dir; 812 S Monticello Dr West Chester OH 45069

TTOLI, VINCENT, Foreign Language Tchr; *b:* New Haven, CT; alind; *c:* Vincent Jr., Maria; *ed:* Providence (BA) Hum 1966; Univ PHD) Fr Complit 1974; *cr:* Milford Bd of Ed Lang Dept 1971-; *ai:* ub Moderator; NEA; MLA; Rockefeller Fellow; Natl Defense Art *office:* Joseph A Foran HS 80 Foran Rd Milford CT 06460

USCH, ORRIN WESLEY, Mathematics Teacher; *b:* Cleveland, Christine Dudley; *c:* Wade Allan; *ed:* Kent St Univ (BS) Elem Ed MA) Admin 1969; Schl Law 3 Hrs; Elem Ed Math, Manipulatives 3 : Silver Lake Elem Schl 7th Grd Sci, Math Tchr 1965-69; Roberts Grd Math Tchr 1969-; *ai:* Var Boys, Girls Bsktbl Coach 31 Yrs; Var Ftbl Coach 30 Yrs; CFEA Tchr Union 1965-75, Rep; Quest , Facilitator; Martha Holden Jennings Scholar; Project Impact Thinking Seminar; Bldg Tchr of Yr Twice; System Wide Tchr of ; *office:* Roberts MS 3333 Charles St Cuyahoga Falls OH 44221*

ZZI, SANDY LORETTA FALCONE, Kndgtn & Reading ry Tchr; *b:* Bangor, PA; *c:* Christopher, Gina, Tricia; *ed:* East sburg Univ (BS) Elem 1965; 36 Hrs Beyond BS; Rdng Recovery 996; *cr:* Bangor Area Schl Dist Kndgtn 1982-, Rdng Recovery *ai:* PSEA, NEA, BAEA 1982-; *office:* 5 Points Elem Schl 363 Five & Richmond Rd Bangor PA 18013*

UARDT, KATHARINE TURLEY, Advanced Placement Bio Instr; York, NY; *m:* Robert James; *c:* Katharine Marquardt Bost, Jennifer, ; *ed:* St Josephs Coll (BA) Bio & Scndry Ed 1968; SUNY at Albany Bio 1974; *cr:* Newtown HS Bio Instr 1968; Niskayuna HS Bio Instr 0; Indian Lake Schl AP Bio Instr 1973-76; Warrensburg Cntrl AP tr 1976-; *ai:* Yrbk Adv; Distance Learning Comm; Tchr Mentor; Decision Making Team Facilitator; NYSUIT 1968-; NEA 1968-; sburg Teach Assn 1976-, VP & Sec; Lake George Bus & Prof s Assn 1988-, Schlrshp & Fashion Show Model Chair; Golub Awd g Tchr 1990, 1993 & 1995; *office:* Warrensburg Central Schl 1 St Warrensburg NY 12885

UART, JOSEPH MATTHEW, English Teacher; *b:* Philadelphia, Donna Davis; *c:* Vincent, David, Caitlin; *ed:* LaSalle Coll (BA) Eng Villanova Univ (MA) Lbrl Stud 1989; *cr:* Bishop Eustace Prep Eng 969-, Eng Dept Chprsn 1985-87, Dean of Stdnts 1987-92; *ai:* Drama loderator; Yrbk Co-Moderator; NCTE 1980-; St Joans Church Choir Alumni Excalibur Awd; Admin Unsung Hero; *office:* Bishop e Prep Schl Rt 70 Pennsauken NJ 08109

QUES, ALICE JEANNE, Math Teacher; *b:* Hannibal, MO; *ed:* Coll of Phila (AGS) Gen 1974; Temple Univ (BS) Math Scndry Ed Widener Univ 30 Grad Credits; *cr:* Peirce Coll Part-time Instr 1984-; Flower HS Math Tchr 1986-; *ai:* Math, Bowling Moderator 4 Yrs; SAT Prep Course; NCTM, ATMOPAV 1990-; *office:* Little Flower S 10th & Lycoming Sts Philadelphia PA 19140*

QUETTE, DAVID WAYNE, Math Teacher; *b:* Danville, PA; *m:* Carrico; *c:* Daniel, Joy, Anne, Paige; *ed:* Penn St Univ (AA) Forest 969; TN Temple Univ (BS) Scndry Ed 1975; Liberty Univ Schl of ng Learning 18 Post Grad Hrs; Pensacola Chrstn Coll 18 Post Grad : Cumberland Valley Chrstn Schl Math Tchr 1975-77; Chapel Chrstn Math Tchr, Asst Admin 1977-; *ai:* Keystone Chrstn Ed Assn 1978-, f Yr; Limerick Chapel 1977-, Deacon; Promoted to Asst Admin in *office:* Chapel Christian Acad 378 W Ridge Pike Royersford PA

, ELIZABETH TIMMERMAN, 1st Grade Teacher; *b:* Dryden, Donald L.; *c:* Peter R., John H.; *ed:* Cornell Univ (BS) Early Chldhd Cortland St Tchrs (MS) Elem Ed 1978; Ithaca Coll & Brighamton Grad Courses; *cr:* Union Ctr Elem 1st Grd Tchr 1965-77; Homer Elem Kndgtn Tchr 1978-95, 1st Grd Tchr 1996-; *ai:* Delta Kappa a 1968-, Past Treas; Beta Iota; Church Childrens Choir Dir; *office:* Brink Elem Schl 3618 Briar Ln Endicott NY 13760

, WILLIAM MITCHELL, Fifth Grade Teacher; *b:* Buffalo, NY; ncy Pembridge; *c:* Heather, Christy; *ed:* Heidelberg Coll (BA) Elem 68; Cleveland St (MA) Elem Admin 1974; 30 Addl Credit Hrs; in Wallace 2 Lee Canter Discipline Courses; Cleveland St Asthetic ness Art for Classroom; *cr:* Westlake City Schls Fifth Grd Tchr *ai:* MS Ski Club; NEA, OEA, WTA 1968-, Bldg Rep; PTA 1968-, Rep, Lifetime Mem; *office:* Holly Lane Elem Schl 3057 Holly Ln and OH 44145

RA, MICHAEL H., History Teacher; *b:* Providence, RI; *m:* Maria rmisano; *c:* Matthew; *ed:* Colby Coll (BA) His 1986; Providence Coll His 1993; *cr:* Barrington HS His Tchr 1986-89; Salzburg Intnl ratory Schl His Tchr 1989-90; Portsmouth HS His Tchr 1990-; *ai:* sty Intnl Coord; RI Soc Stud Assn 1990-; *office:* Portsmouth HS tion Ln Portsmouth RI 02871

RATTA, TERRI WALLS, History & Psychology Teacher; *b:* n, OH; *m:* Wendell L.; *c:* Matthew, Ashley; *ed:* OH St Univ (BSEd) rehensive Soc Stud 1974; Wright St Univ (MED) Ed 1992; *cr:* a City Schls His Tchr 1974-; *ai:* Soc Stud Dept Chm; Fac Admin Tech Comm Rep; OH Soc Stud Cncl; Urbana Classroom Tchrs, OH ssns, NEA 1974-; Phi Delta Kappa 1992-; 1st Presbyn Church, n, Elder; Champaign Cty Soc Stud Tchr of Yr 1983; Selected to OH Cncl Holocaust Stud in Germany 1990; *office:* Urbana HS 500 ngton Ave Urbana OH 43078

RIOTT, SALIMA SILER, Soc Work & Mental Hlth Prof; *b:* nore, MD; *c:* Terrez Siler Marriott Thompson, Patrice Kenyatha Siler; organ St Coll (BS) Physics 1964; Univ of MD (MSW) Soc Work Howard Univ (DSW) Soc Work 1988; Bowie St Coll Grad Schl 24 s; *cr:* Baltimore City Pub Schls Sci & Math Tchr 1964-65; NY City Velfare Soc Worker 1965-68; Baltimore City Soc Svcs Soc Worker 72; Morgan St Univ Soc Work & Mental Hlth Prof 1972-; MD Gen nbly Del 1990-; *ai:* Pol Partcipation & Ldrshp Activists Adv; AAUP ; Natl Black Womens Hlth Project 1984-, Bd Chair 1993-94, Ldrshp; Rainbow Coalition 1984-, Bd Sec 1994-; Flemming Fellow; ective on US Policy Toward Southern Africa Ed; Delta Sigma Theta egacy; *home:* 4515 Homer Ave Baltimore MD 21215

RO, JUDITH, 10th Grade Social Studies Tchr; *b:* Bayport, NY; *m:* D'Agostino; *ed:* The Univ of Albany (MA) Scndry Ed & Soc Stud Newport Univ at Salve Regina (BA) His; *cr:* St Gregory Schl 6th-8th Soc Stud Tchr 1983-85; The Ursaline Schl 10th Grd Soc Stud Tchr ; *ai:* Environmental & His Club Adv; WSSC 1985-; Bronx Zoo 1990-, NY Natural His 1991-, Mem; *office:* The Ursaline Schl 1354 North lew Rochelle NY 10804*

RONE, DANIEL SCOTT, Business Administration Prof; *b:* klyn, NY; *m:* Portia Terrone; *c:* Jamie; *ed:* Queens Coll (BA) Ec 1972; nst of Tech (MBA) Mgmt 1975; NY Univ (PHD) Bus Ed 1989; *cr:* anty Inst Instr 1978-81; Adelphi Inst Instr 1982-85; Coll of Saint Elizabeth Asst Prof 1986-87; St Univ of NY at Farmingdale Assoc Prof 1987-; *ai:* Industrial Tech Prgm Club Adv; APICS 1991-, Dir of Cert Prgms; ASQC 1991-; NAIT 1992-; *office:* S U N Y Coll Of Tech At Frmgdl Whitman Hall Farmingdale NY 11735

MARRONE, JOSEPH ROBERT,JR., Industrial Education Teacher; *b:* Staten Island, NY; *m:* Marie Precopio; *c:* Jocelyn; *ed:* Brookdale Com Coll (AA) Hum 1973; Glassboro St (BA) Indstrl Arts 1975; *cr:* Jamesburg HS Indstrl Arts Tchr 1975-78; Wall HS Indstrl Arts Tchr 1978-; *ai:* Adv Flwshp Chrstn Ath; NJEA, WTEA, NEA 1975-; *office:* Wall HS 18th Ave & New Bedford Rd Wall NJ 07719

MARROTTA, CATHERINE AIELLO, Business Professor; *b:* Utica, NY; *m:* Reid Albert; *c:* Alexis, Matthew; *ed:* Herkimer Cty Comm Coll (AAS) Sec Sci 1974; SUNY Coll of Tech at Utica-Rome (BS) Voc Ed 1981; SUNY at Oswego (MS) Voc Ed 1987; Spencer's Bus Schl Cert Court Reporting 1977; 6 Post Grad & 3 Under Grad Credits; *cr:* Drs Hatfield, Locke & Rinehart 1977-78; Childrens Hospital 1978-79; Martin Murphy Court Reporting Agency 1979; Herkimer Cty Comm Coll 1981-; *ai:* Fine Arts, Court Reporting Advising & Registration Comm; NYS Assn for Women in Higher Ed, NYSUT & Office Tech Sec Educators Cuny-Suny; Amer Cancer Soc 1989-91; Pop Warner Boosters Club 1994-; Cath Charities 1996; Asst Pop Warner Cheerleading Coach 1994-; Frosh Sec of Yr; Outstanding Young Women of Amer Awd; *office:* Herkimer County Comm Coll 100 Reservoir Rd Herkimer NY 13350

MARRYAT, JENNIFER STEPHENS, English Teacher; *b:* Ancon Canal Zone, Panama; *m:* Glenn H.; *ed:* Univ of MD (BA) Eng 1992; *cr:* Eleanor Roosevelt HS Eng Tchr 1992-; *ai:* Minority Achvmt Prgm Eng Coord; Teach AP Eng; NEA 1992-; Kappa Delta Pi 1992-, Ed Hnr Soc; Sigma Tau Delta 1992-, Eng Hnr Soc; *office:* Eleanor Roosevelt HS 7601 Hanover Pky Greenbelt MD 20770

MARSCHALL, CLAUDIA ANN, English & Theater Arts Teacher; *b:* Buffalo, NY; *ed:* SUNY at Binghamton (BA) Eng 1973; SUNY Coll at Buffalo (MSEd) Scndry Eng Ed 1978; Post Grad Stud Univ of WA at Seattle in Tchng of Rdng, Drama Ed; *cr:* Kensington HS Eng, Dramatics Tchr 1978; Buffalo Acad for Visual & Performing Arts Eng, Theatre Arts Tchr 1978-; *ai:* Theatre Stu Govt Adv; NCTE 1989-; AATE 1992-; NYSTEA 1995-; Buffalo News Books for Kids Drive Steering Comm; *office:* Buffalo Acad Vsl/Perf Arts 333 Clinton St Buffalo NY 14204

MARSDEN, CARL L., 9th-11th Grd History Teacher; *b:* Philadelphia, PA; *w:* Theresa (dec); *cr:* Vineland Meml Jr HS Tchr 1957-58; Cntrl Jr HS Tchr 1960-61; Atlantic City HS Tchr 1961-92; Tracki Hebrew Acad Tchr 1992-; *ai:* NEA, NJEA 1960-; *office:* Trocki Hebrew Acad of Atlantic 6814 Black Horse Pike Egg Harbor Townshi NJ 08234

MARSEILLE, CAROLYN G., Math Teacher; *b:* Brooklyn, NY; *ed:* Univ of Rochester (BS) Psych, Math 1991, (MA) Ed 1993; Admin Courses; *cr:* Uniondale HS Math Tchr 1992-; *ai:* Stu Cncl, Chrldr Adv; Sr Class Coord; Uniondale Tchr Assn, NCTM 1992-; LVA Nassau Cty Inc 1995-, Vol; Uniondale Coalition of Prof; *office:* Uniondale HS 933 Goodrich St Uniondale NY 11510

MARSH, CATHERINE REGAN, Lit Tchr & Rdng Specialist; *b:* East Orange, NJ; *m:* Michael F.; *c:* E. Anne Seiler, Robert J.; *ed:* Miami Univ of OH (BS) Elem Ed 1963; Beaver Coll (MED) Ed 1977; Rdng Specialist Cert 1979; *cr:* Greece Schl Dist 2nd Grd Tchr 1963-67; Pittsford Schl Dist 4th Grd Tchr 1969-72; Wissahickon Schl Dist 4th Grd Tchr 1973-75, 6th Grd Tchr 1975-80, MS Rdng Specialist 1980-; *ai:* Bsktbl, Sftbl & Field Hockey Coach; NEA, PSEA, WEA 1973-; *office:* Wissahickon MS 500 Houston Rd Ambler PA 19002

MARSH, DAVID CHARLES, Physical Education Teacher; *b:* Groton, CT; *m:* Diana Lynn McCollough; *c:* David Jr., Deanna, Melissa; *ed:* Springfield Coll (BS) PE 1976; Univ of RI (MS) PE 1986; *cr:* Groton Pub Schls PE Tchr 1977-; *ai:* Girls Sftbl Coach; NEA 1977-; Articles Pub Tchng Elem PE, Great Act Newspaper, Operation New Kid; *office:* Robert E Fitch MS 61 Fort Hill Rd Groton CT 06340*

MARSH, DONALD A., History Teacher; *b:* Warren, OH; *m:* Mary Ann Bevacqua; *c:* Donald, Andrew; *ed:* Geneva Coll (BA) His 1974; Youngstown St Univ (MA) Admin 1978; *cr:* Grand Vly Schl Tchr 1975-; *ai:* Ashtabula Cty Course of Stud Comm; Soph Class Adv; AFT; OFT; GV Ed Assn; OHSAA Registered Track Ofcl 1976-, Astabula Cty Ofcl of Yr 1995; *office:* Grand Valley HS 44 N School St Orwell OH 44076

MARSH, DONALD H., Jr High Science Tchr; *b:* Cambridge, NY; *m:* Karen M. Nowak; *c:* Brian, Christopher; *ed:* St Univ of NY at Plattsburgh (BS) Bio & Ed 1974; Over 40 Grad Hrs from Russell Sage Coll, Coll of Saint Rose & North Adams St; *cr:* South Glens Falls Cntrl Jr HS Sci Tchr 1974-75; New Lebanon Cntrl Jr HS Sci Tchr 1976-; *ai:* NEA, NYSUT 1976-.

MARSH, JAMES H., Health Education Teacher; *b:* Gloversville, NY; *m:* Theresa P. Greek; *c:* Ian, Sara, Amanda; *ed:* SUNY at Cortland (BA) Hlth Ed 1983, (MS) Hlth Ed 1990; *cr:* Tryon Schl Hlth Tchr 1983; Corcoran HS Hlth, OLC Tchr 1984-; *ai:* Girls Var Bsktbl Coach 1996; Golf Instr; NEA, NYSUT, ESMUT 1983-; NY St Girls Bsktbl Champions, 40th Annual Schlshp Awds Honored Guest, Speaker 1993; NY St Coach of Yr 1993; Coord of OLC Pgm 1993-; *office:* Corcoran HS Occupational Learning Ctr 919 Glenwood Ave Syracuse NY 13207

MARSH, KAREN JANE (SANFORD), First Grade Teacher; *b:* Massillon, OH; *m:* Douglas W.; *c:* Lindsay, Geoffrey; *ed:* Akron Univ (BA) Elem Ed 1979; Ashland Univ (MS) Curr & Instruction 1989; *cr:* Watson Kndgtn & 1st Grd Tchr 1979-85; Genoa Kndgtn Tchr 1986-87; Watson 1st Grd Tchr 1988-; *ai:* Soc Stud, Math, Cmptr Comms; NEA, OEA, PCTA 1979-; NMTA 1994-; Faith Luth Church 1989-, Bd of Chrstn Ed; Perry HS Top 25 Outstanding Educator 1995; Nom for Cantons Tchr of Yr 1995; Integrating Manipulatives into 1st Grd Curr; *office:* Watson Elem Schl 515 Marion Ave NE Massillon OH 44646*

MARSH, KIMBERLY ANN HELLER, Nursing Instructor; *b:* Clearfield, PA; *ed:* PA St Univ (BS) Nrsng 1977; 3 Credits Hlth Ed Toward Doctorate; MS in Nrsng 1996; *cr:* Rush Presbyn St Lukes Med Ctr Staff, Dialysis Nurse 1977-80; Quality Care, Home Hlth Agencies Pvt Duty Nurse in Homes 1980-84; Cntrl PA Schl of Nrsng Instr 1984-89; Clearfield Co Voc Tech Schl Nrsng Instr 1987-89; Lock Haven Univ Nrsng Instr 1990-; *ai:* Curr, Fac Org, Tenure, Evaluation, Schlsp Comms; Follow-Up Comm Chprsn; Stu Adv; Amer Nurses Assn, PA Nurses Assn 1989-; Assn of PA St Coll & Univ Faculties 1990-; *office:* Lock Haven Univ 119 Byer St Clearfield PA 16830

MARSH, MARY FRANCES, Family & Consumer Sci Teacher; *b:* Black Lick Twp, PA; *m:* Donald R.; *c:* Gregory D., Gretchen A.; *ed:* IN Univ of PA (BS) Home Ec Ed 1980, (MS) Home Ec Ed 1982; Robert Morris Coll Secretarial Sci 1963; *cr:* McNaughton Oil Co Sec 1957-61; Syntron Co Sec 1963; Amer Red Cross Sec 1963-65; Farmers Bank & Trust Co Sec 1965-68; Purchase Line Schl Dist Tchr 1984-; *ai:* FHA Adv; IUP Home Ec Alumni Pres & VP; Church Womens Orgs; PSEA & NEA; Certfd in Family & Consumer Scis; Grants; *office:* Purchase Line HS Rd 1 Box 374 Commodore PA 15729

MARSH, MELINDA RAY, Choral Dir & Gifted Prgm Coord; *b:* Joliet, IL; *m:* Truman Bruce; *c:* Michael; *ed:* Kalamazoo Coll (BA) Music, German 1965; Univ of DE (MED) Curr Dev 1980; Attnd Westminster Choir Coll, MI St Univ, Univ of DE; *cr:* Custer HS Choir, Drama, German Tchr 1965-69; Caesar Rodney HS Orch, Choir, German 1969-79, Choir, Gifted Coord 1980-; Drama 1970-78; *ai:* Acad Bowl Team, Odyessey of Mind Teams, Forensic Coach; Show Choir Dir; Music Dept, Dist Fine Arts Chair; Dist Curr Cabinet Mem; ASCD 1980-; MENC DMEA 1969-, All St Chorus Chm, Music Educator of Yr 1994; DE Alliance Arts in Ed 1992-; Amer Choral Dir Assn 1980-, DE Pres, US Rep to Germany 1990, Gt Britain Wales 1992-; Member of Del St Comm of Visual & Perf Arts 1994-; Dover Arts Cncl 1992-; DE Arts Cncl 1980-89, Vice Chair 1986; Delta Kappa Gamma 1984-, Pres Zeta, Keynote Speaker St Convention; Who's Who in the East; Who's Who in Ed; Intnl Bio; Natl Creativity Assn Presenter; Tchr of Yr 1986; *office:* Caesar Rodney HS 239 Old North Rd Camden-Wyoming DE 19934

MARSH, RITA MAHONEY, Kindergarten Teacher; *b:* Springfield, OH; *m:* James; *c:* Christine, Michelle, Pamela; *ed:* OH Dominican Coll (BS) Elem Ed 1970; Wright St Univ (MA) Early Chldhd Ed 1985; *cr:* St Mary schl Primary Tchr 1970-77; St Bernard Schl Kndgtn Tchr 1981-; *ai:* Vlybl, Sftbl Coach in Cath Yth Sports Org; Bowling League Sec, Treas; Mother of Twins Club Sec, Treas; NCEA 1970-; Jaycees 1970-80; Miami Vly Cath Tchrs Outstdng Tchr Awd; *office:* St Bernard Schl 800 Lagonda Ave Springfield OH 45503

MARSH, ROBERT ANDREW, Mathematics Teacher; *b:* New Britain, CT; *m:* Doreen Marie Errede; *c:* Melissa, Jason; *ed:* Wesleyan Univ (BA) Psych 1974; Trinity Coll (MA) Ed 1983; Tchr Cert Math; *cr:* Assumption Schl Math Tchr 1976-80; Maloney HS Math Tchr 1980-; *ai:* NHS Fac Bd; Denis Gannon Schlsp Comm; Upward Bound Tchng Staff; AFT 1980-; *office:* Maloney HS 121 Gravel St Meriden CT 06450

MARSH, THERESA PATRICIA GREEK, 7th Grd Language Arts Teacher; *b:* Jamaica, NY; *m:* James H.; *c:* Ian James, Sara Theresa, Amanda Nichole; *ed:* SUNY at Cortland (BA, BA) Elem Ed, Scndry Eng 1983, (MS) Rdng 1989; Tryon Schl Rdng, Eng Tchr 1983-84; Pine Grove Jr HS Pupil Prsnl Adv 1989-90, Excellerated Eng Tchr 1992-, Eng Tchr 1984-; *cr:* Tryon Schl Reading, Eng Tchr 1983-84; Pine Grove Jr High Pupil Personell Adv 1989-90, Excellerated Eng 1992-; *ai:* NEA, NYSUT, ESMUT 1983-; *office:* Pine Grove Jr HS 6320 Fremont Rd East Syracuse NY 13057

MARSH, TOM, History Teacher; *b:* Fitchburg, MA; *ed:* Fitchburg St Coll (BS) His 1981; Worcester St Coll (MS) Human Svc Mngmt 1986; City Univ of NY (JD) Law 1992; *cr:* Comm Treatment Ctr Cnslr 1985-89; City Univ of NY Legal Intern 1989-92; New York City Bd of Ed Tchr 1992-; *ai:* Trip Coord; Yrbk Adv; Tchr of Month Awd; UFT 1993-; Queens Lesbian & Gay Pride Comm 1991-; YMCA Flushing 1994-.

MARSHALL, BARBARA UNDERCOFLER, Second Grade Teacher; *b:* Clearfield, PA; *m:* Gary L.; *c:* Brian, Susan; *ed:* Clarion Univ (BS) Elem 1970, (MED) Elem 1972; *cr:* Glen Richey Schl 2nd Grd Tchr 1970-72; Plymptonville Schl 1st Grd Tchr 1972-91; Third Ward Elem Schl 2nd Grd Tchr 1991-; *ai:* PSEA, CEA 1970-; *office:* Third Ward Elem Schl PO Box 710 Clearfield PA 16830

MARSHALL, BRUCE THOMAS, Physical Education Teacher; *b:* Fort Erie, Ontario Canada; *m:* Joan Graham; *c:* Steven Pearson, James; *ed:* Springfield Coll (BSC) PE 1958, (MSC) PE, Admin 1962; Northeastern Univ Hotel & Resort Mngmt; *cr:* Rosemere Schl System Dir, PE Instr 1958-61; Springfield Coll Asst Ftbl, Strength Coach; 1961-62; Dean Jr Coll PE Instr 1962-66; Montreal Aluettes CFL Asst Line Coach Trng Camp 1964; Philips Exeter Acad PE Instr 1966-68; Carlisle Pub Schls Dir, PE Instr 1968-69; Chelmsford HS PE Instr 1969-; Nashoba Vly Ski Area Skiing Instr 1981-; *ai:* Ski Club; Boy's LaCrosse, Girls' Field Hockey Ofcls; Eastern Pro Ski Inst Assn, Natl Pro Ski Inst Assn 1982-; New England Off Assn; MA Tchrs Union; Masonic Lodge 1962-; Ski Instr of Yr Nashoba Vly Ski Area 1991; *home:* 524 Westford St Lowell MA 01851

MARSHALL, CHARLES DONALD, Science Teacher; *b:* Bellefonte, PA; *m:* Janice Hall; *c:* John; *ed:* PA St (BS) Bio, Scndry Ed 1967, (MED) Bio Sci 1974; Post Grad Credit Hrs; *cr:* St Coll Area Schls Sci Tchr 1968-; *ai:* Hunting & Fishing Club; Archery Instr; NRA Hunter Trapper Ed; Phi Delta Kappa 1974-; Article Pub; *office:* Park Forest MS 2180 School Dr State College PA 16803

MARSHALL, CHERYL WRIGHT, First Grade Teacher; *b:* Phila, PA; *m:* Wilson; *c:* Meredith; *ed:* Comm Coll of Phila (AA) Elem Ed 1972; Temple Univ (BS) ELem Ed 1974; 30 Credits Post Grad Stud; *cr:* Bache-Martin Schl Tchr 1974-77; Fell Elem Schl Tchr 1977-78; Bache-Martin Schl Tchr 1978-; *ai:* United Way Combined Campaign Ldr; Phila Fed of Tchr Bldg, Hlth, Welfare, Ldrshp Comms; AFT, PFT 1974-; NAACP 1991-; Nom Tchr of the Yr; TESA, ECRI Certs; *office:* Bache Martin Elem Schl 22nd & Brown Sts Philadelphia PA 19130*

MARSHALL, CYNTHIA L., Associate Professor; *b:* Ellwood City, PA; *m:* William H. Smith; *ed:* Slippery Rock Univ (BS) Eng 1978, (MA) Eng 1980; Univ of Pittsburgh (PHD) Ed 1987; *cr:* Slippery Rock Univ Grad Asst1978-80; Comm Coll of Butler Cty Adj Prof 1987-90; Comm Coll of Beaver Cty Assoc Prof 1990-; *ai:* Phi Theta Kappa Fac Adv; Coll Fnd Dir; Stu Magazine Emerge Fac Ed; NEA, MLA, NCET, PSEA 1990-; Native Amer Profs 1993-; PA Writers Assn 1987-; Numerous Articles Pub; *office:* Comm Coll Of Beaver County 1 Campus Dr Monaca PA 15061*

MARSHALL, EDWARD P., Physical Education Teacher; *b:* Waterville, ME; *m:* Cathy Worcester; *c:* Edward II, Benjamin, Meghan; *ed:* Univ of ME at Presque Isle (BS) Hlth PE 1974; 15 Hrs Ath Train; *ai:* Girls Soccer, Sftbl Coach; VP ME St Soccer Coaches Assn; NEA, ME St Ath Assn, ME St Coaches Assn 1974-; ME St Coach of Yr Soccer 1986, 1992; NAIA Womens Coach of Yr Dist 5 1990; *office:* Madawaska HS 7th Ave Madawaska ME 04756

MARSHALL, GRAYSON BERNARD, Retired 6th Grade Teacher; *b:* Washington, DC; *m:* Marie Celine Howell; *c:* Grayson Jr., Terri L.; *ed:* Univ of DC (BS) Elem Ed 1970; Trinity Coll (MA) Admin, Supervision 1981; *cr:* LaSalle Elem Schl 4th-6th Grd Tchr 1969-94, Head Tchr 1990-94; *ai:* WA Tchrs Union 1969-, Bldg Rep; Phi Delta Kappa 1985-, Treas; Kappa Alpha Psi 1952-, Records Keeper, Pledge Dean; Urban League; NAACP; CYO.

MARSHALL, GREGORY JAMES, Pastor; *b:* Warren, OH; *m:* Lori Maria Lorentzen; *ed:* Liberty Univ (AA) Rel 1990, (BS) Yth Ministries 1990, (MA) Rel 1994; *cr:* Third Ave Chrstn Church Yth Pastor 1989-90; Howland Chrstn Schl HS Tchr, Yth Pastor 1990-92; New Life Bapt Church Assoc Pastor 1992-; *ai:* Soccer Coach; Bible Study Spon; *home:* 511 Meek St Sharon PA 16146

MARSHALL, JAMES ALAN, Biology & Wilderness Teacher; *b:* Detroit, MI; *c:* Kevin, Keith, Craig; *ed:* Cornell Univ (BS) Landscape Architecture 1967; St Univ of NY at Buffalo (MED) Scndry Sci Ed 1973; 14 Hrs Scndry Ed Univ of AZ; *cr:* USAF Titan II Missle Engineering Officer 1967-71, 803 C Civil Engineering Squadron Landscape Architecture Project Officer; Clarence Cntrl Schls Bio & Wilderness Tchr 1971-; *ai:* Wilderness Wise Club Adv; Town of Amherst Soccer Coach 9 Yrs; Natl Inst Cert in Engineering Technologies 1970-, Assoc Engineering Technician; NY St Adopt-A-Hwy 1992-; Amer Red Cross Vol Instr 1988-; First Runner UP as NY States Outstanding Young Educator 1975; *office:* Clarence Cntrl Schls 9625 Main St Clarence NY 14031*

MARSHALL, JAMES HILTON, HS Social Studies Teacher; *b:* Fort Lee, Canada; *m:* Virginia L.; *c:* Thomas, Debra Fenton; *ed:* Springfield Coll (BS) Soc Stud 1961; Univ of CT (MA) Pol Sci 1963, (PHD) Pol Sci 1971;

cr: Glastonbury High Tchr 1964-; *ai:* Bolton Bd of Ed 1976-, Chm; 21st Century NWSP Tchr of the Year.

MARSHALL, JAMES JAY, Chemistry Teacher; *b:* Jersey Shore, PA; *m:* LuAnne Martin; *c:* Carly, Daniel; *ed:* Bloomsburg St Coll (BS) Scndry Ed 1982; West Chester Univ (MS) Chem 1996; *cr:* Wilson HS Chem Tchr 1982-84; Daniel Boone HS Chem Tchr 1984-; *ai:* PSEA, NEA 1982-; DBEA 1984-; ACS 1995-; PSDC 1992-; *office:* Daniel Boone Jr Sr HS 501 Chestnut St Birdsboro PA 19508

MARSHALL, JOHNNIE B., Band Conductor; *b:* Pickens, MS; *m:* Gladys; *c:* Johnnie B. Jr., Shawn Desmond; *ed:* Jackson St Univ (BS) Music 1962; Univ of MI (MM) Music 1963; Attnd Columbia Univ, Fairfield Univ, Coll of St Rose, Montclair St Coll; Post Grad Stud; *cr:* MS Vly St Univ Brasswind Instr 1963-64; Nichols HS Band Conductor 1964-68; South Orangetown MS Band Conductor & Instrumental Music 1968-89; Tappan Zee HS Band Conductor & Instrumental Music 1985-; Cottage Ln Elem Schl Band Conductor 1989-; *ai:* Jazz Soc; Multi-Cultural Coalition; Band Club; Music Edctrs Natl Conf 1963-; NY St United Tchrs 1968-; NY St Schl Music Assn 1968-; AFT 1968-; Natl Band Assn 1973-; Kappa Alpha Psi 1959-68; Rockland Cty Sewer Commission 1980-85, 1994-; Rockland Cty Bd of Realtors 1986-; NY St Assn of Realtors 1986-; Natl Assn of Realtors 1986-; Rockland Cty Pub Svc Awd for Sewer Commission; Lincoln Ctr Inst; *office:* Tappan Zee HS 15 Dutch Hill Rd Orangeburg NY 10962*

MARSHALL, ROBERT DALE, HS Mathematics Teacher; *b:* Dover, OH; *m:* Rhonda Lee Jonus; *c:* Gregory Adam, Eric Robert; *ed:* Kent St Univ (BS) Math 1977, (MA) Math 1981; Project Teach; Cmptrs in Ed; *cr:* Malvern HS General Math, Chem, Industrial Arts Tchr 1977-78, Jr HS Math Tchr 1978-84, HS Math Tchr 1984-; *ai:* NHS Fac Cncl; NEA 1977-, Bldg Rep; NHS Tchr of Yr 1985-86, 1989-90, 1994-95; Jennings Scholar Martha Holden Jennings Fnd 1990-91; *office:* Malvern HS 401 W Main St Malvern OH 44644*

MARSHALL, ROBERT HULINGS, Physics Teacher; *b:* Pittsburgh, PA; *m:* Susan J. Washington; *c:* Tracy, Jennifer; *ed:* Loyola Coll (MS) Ed 1977; *cr:* Greenspring MS Tchr 1973-85; Baltimore Schl for the Arts Tchr 1985-; *ai:* Sr Class Adv; AFT 1975-; Author Textbooks: Basic Steps to Basic, Investigating Our World, Matter, Motion and Machines, Physical Science; *office:* Baltimore Schl For The Arts 712 Cathedral St Baltimore MD 21201

MARSHALL, RUBY JEAN (SMITH), Life Science Teacher; *b:* Birmingham, AL; *m:* Oliver Jr.; *c:* Robbin Kimberly Marshall Williams, Carol Joyce; *ed:* Wilberforce Univ (BS) Bio & Comprehensive Sci 1961; Rutgers Univ (MS) Educl Theory & Supervision 1983; Glassboro St Coll Tchr of Sci Cert 1962-65; Prin & Supervisory Cert 1983; Addl 30 Credit Hrs Past masters Degree; *cr:* Samuel Miller Schl Third Grd Tchr 1961-64; Hattie Brit, Parkway Schls Third Grd Tchr 1966-70; Rutgers Univ Assoc Prof 1982-91; William W. Allen III MS Life Sci Tchr 1971-; *ai:* Elocutionist, Singing, Sewing, Quilting, Gardening, Hosp Vol, Creative Play Directing, Ecology Field Trip Supvr & Organizer, Pro-bono Tutoring; NEA, NJ Ed Assn 1961-; Moorestown Ed Assn 1971-; NJ Sci Tchrs Assn; Wilberforce Univ Alumni 1961-, Sec; Rutgers Univ Alumni 1983-; Delta Sigma Theta 1959-, Sec; Sigma Omega; Kappa Delta Pi; *home:* 603 Flynn Ave Moorestown NJ 08057*

MARSHALL, SHERON EVANS, Mathematics Teacher; *b:* Memphis, TN; *m:* Walter J.; *c:* M. Katherine, Tim; *ed:* Univ of Memphis (BS) Math 1971; Credit Hrs from Old Dominion, William & Mary, IN Wesleyan, Carlow & Coll of St Rose; *cr:* Tabb Intermediate Math Tchr 1971-77; Seven Sorrows Cath Schl Math Tchr 1977-79; Lower Dauphin HS Math Tchr 1992-; *ai:* After Schl Tutor Pgm; Grad Project Comm; PSEA 1992-; NEA 1992-; ELD 1992-; Cncl of Cath Women 1978-, Treas & VP; *office:* Lower Dauphin Sr HS 201 S Hanover St Hummelstown PA 17036

MARSHALL, VICTORIA L., Third Grade Teacher; *b:* Decatur, IL; *m:* Rex W.; *c:* Brannon, Adam; *ed:* Univ of NC at Greensboro (BA) Elem Ed-Cum Laude 1971; 30 Grad Hrs Univ of Akron; *cr:* Parkwood Elem Schl 4th, 5th Grd Tchr 1971-72; Lane Elem Schl 1st, 2nd, 3rd, 5th Grd 1972-80; Rimer Elem Schl 1st Grd 1980-81; Bettes Elem Schl 3rd Grd 1981-; *ai:* AEA 1972-; Nom Tchr of Yr 1983-84; *office:* Bettes Elem Schl 1333 Betana Ave Akron OH 44310

MARSICANO, HELEN WYSOCKI, Math Teacher; *b:* Forest City, PA; *m:* James F.; *c:* James, John, Michael; *ed:* Marywood Coll (BA) Chem, Math 1957; Univ of Scranton 18 Credits Ed 1960-62, Wilkes Coll 3 Grad Credits Cmptr Literacy 1985; *cr:* E. I. DuPont DeNemours & Co Quality Control Chemist 1957-58; Forest City Regnl Schl Dist Sub, Part-time Tchr 1963-73, Math Tchr 1973-; *ai:* NEA, Pa St Ed Assn, Forest City Regnl Ed Assn 1973-; *office:* Forest City Regnl HS 100 Susquehanna St Forest City PA 18421

MARSICANO, MADELINE, 6th Grade Teacher; *b:* Brooklyn, NY; *ed:* Queens Coll (BA) Antropology-Sociology 1964; Bank St Coll of Ed (MS) Ed 1976; Manhattan Coll Cnslng Post Grad Stud; *cr:* PS 43X Jonas Bronck Clearpool Family Schl Tchr 1966-; *ai:* Hnr Roll Soc Coord; Schl Wide Projects Grd Rep; Astronomy Club Adv; Contributed Lit Pieces, Suggested Lesson Plans Curr Instrl; Pub Books Stars And Stripes, Stripes 1990-91; *office:* PS 43X Jonas Bronck Clearpool 165 Brown Pl Bronx NY 10454*

MARSLEY, KATHLEEN, HS Social Studies Teacher; *b:* Sewickley, PA; *m:* A. James; *c:* Jami, Jonathan; *ed:* PA St Univ (BA) Sec Ed 1970; St Univ Coll at Buffalo (MS) Soc Stud Ed 1984; Addl 12 Credits; Mc Gill Univ at Montreal 6 Credits; *cr:* Williamsville North HS Soc Stud Tchr 1970-75; Williamsville East HS Soc Stud Tchr 1975-90; Williamsville South HS Soc Stud Tchr 1990-; *ai:* Summer Schl Revision & Course Proposal Selection Comms; Pilot Prgm for 9th Grd Curr; Presenter NY St Cncl for Soc Stud Conf 1994; Reader Advanced Placement Govt & Politics Exam 1994, Curr Cncl; NCSS 1978-, Voting Del to Natl Convention 1991; NY St Cncl for Soc Stud 1978-; Amherst Skating Club 1991-, Bylaws Comm; Ira Spirawk Awd; NY St Scndry Soc Stud Tchr of Yr Nom; Runner-Up Crista Mc Auliffe Fellowship; *office:* Williamsville South HS 5950 Main St Williamsville NY 14221*

MARSTEINER, CAROL O'BRIEN, Mathematics Teacher; *b:* Lyons, NY; *m:* Edward L.; *c:* Stacy, Edward II; *ed:* SUNY at Oswego (BS) Sec Ed, Math 1972; Addl 30 Grad Hrs; 16 Credit Hrs of Prof Stud; *cr:* Desales HS Math Tchr 1977-89; Lyons HS Math Tchr 1989-; Syracuse Univ Adjunct Prof of Calculus 1992-; *ai:* JV Girls Tennis COach; Soph Class Adv; Prin Advy Comm; Curr Cncl Chprsn; Peer Observation Comm; AMTNYS 1990-; NYSUT, LTA 1989-; Church Lector; Univ of Rochester, Lyons Tchr Assn Tchr of Yr; Lyons Stu Cncl Tchr of Momth; Clarkson Inspirational HS Tchr 1995; Lyons HS Yrbk Dedication 1995; *office:* Lyons Jr Sr HS 10 Clyde Rd Lyons NY 14489*

MARSTELLAR, JAY EDWARD, 8th Grade Math Teacher; *b:* Grove City, PA; *m:* Vicky Linn Munnell; *c:* Jay Jr., Bret, Kristin; *ed:* Slippery Rock Coll (BS) Ed, Math 1972; Slippery Rock Univ (MS) Guid & Counsel 1976; *cr:* Lakeview Schl Dist Math Tchr 1972-; *ai:* 8th Grd Team Ldr; PSEA, NEA 1972-; Lakeview Ed Assn 1972-, Chprsn; WFMJ TV Class Act Awd 1994; *home:* 30 Grant St Fredonia PA 16124

MARSTELLER, JEAN N. W., Spanish Teacher; *b:* Allentown, PA; *m:* Craig A.; *c:* Brooke A., Ashleigh M.; *ed:* Maravian Coll (BA) Span, Ger 1979; Master's Equivalency Ed 1993; *cr:* Allentown Cntrl Cath Schl Span Tchr 1979-80; Whitehall HS Span Tchr 1980-; *ai:* Span NHS, Class of 1995 Adv; Chrldr Coach 1981-91; Span Club Adv 1979-85; AATSP 1984-; PSEA 1980-; NEA; Western Salsburg UCC 1994-, Sunday Schl Tchr; *office:* Whitehall HS 3800 Mechanicsville Rd Whitehall PA 18052*

MARTEL, DAVID H., US History Teacher; *b:* Lewiston, ME; *ed:* Univ of ME at Farmington (BS) His 1975; *cr:* Lewiston Jr HS Grd 8 US His Tchr 1977-; *ai:* NEA, ME Ed Assn, Lew Ed Assn 1977-; Trout Unlimited 1982-, Pres; *office:* Lewiston MS 65 Central Ave Lewiston ME 04240

MARTELLARO, MATTHEW JOSEPH, 7th-8th Grade Math & Sci Tchr; *b:* Brooklyn, NY; *m:* Jean Graber; *c:* Nicholas James, Sarah Elise, Camille Giuliana; *ed:* CA St Univ at Northridge (BA) Geo Earth Sci 1984; His Soc Stud Tchng Credential, +50 Hrs & Math Minor; *ai:* Guitar Players Exploratory Class; NEA 1985-; Los Angeles Mayors Awd for Excl in Ed Pgm 1988; Los Angeles USD Awd for Excl in Tchng 1990.

MARTELLO, CAROLYN A., English Teacher; *b:* Worcester, MA; *m:* John V.; *ed:* Worcester St Coll (BA) Eng 1974, (MED) Rdng 1978; Tchr Corps Univ of MA 15 Hrs; Worc Pub Schl Staff Dev 45 Cr Over Masters; *cr:* Doherty High Eng Tchr; Worc E MS 1974-85; North HS 1985-95; *ai:* Soph Class, Stu Cncl, Ski Club & Newspaper 1995- Adv; SAT Verbal Coach; Mentor Coord at North High 1994-95; NEA, MTA & EAW 1976-; Horace Mann Grant Recipient For Interdisciplinary Tchng; Recipient of Yrbk Dedication North HS 1994.*

MARTELLO, JAMES LAWRENCE, English Teacher; *b:* Manchester, CT; *m:* Gail Marshall; *c:* Gregg, Jennifer; *ed:* Wesleyan Univ (BA) Classics Latin 1969; Univ of CT (MA) Eng, Ed 1978; *cr:* Robinson Schl Tchr, Coach 1969-72; Vernon Ctr MS Tchr, Coach 1972-76; Rockville HS Tchr, Coach 1976-; *ai:* Girls Bsktbl Coach 1977-; NEA 1973-; Conn HS Coaches Assoc 1977-; Vernon Little League Brd 1982-85; *office:* Rockville HS 70 Loveland Hill Rd Vernon Rockville CT 06066

MARTENSEN, KATHY PINELLA, Mathematics Teacher; *b:* Teaneck, NJ; *m:* Karl O.; *ed:* Upsala Coll (BA) Math 1969; 3 Credits Jersey Cite St Coll; 6 Credits Kean Coll; 15 Credits Fairleigh Dickinson Univ; 6 Addl Credits; *cr:* Dumont HS Math Tchr 1969-; Montclair St Univ Ed Dept Clinical Adj 1994-j; *ai:* Mu Alpha Theta Adv; Media Advy Comm; NEA, NJ Ed Assn, Bergen Cty Ed Assn 1969-; Dumont Ed Assn 1969-, Corr Sec, Treas; NCTM, NJ Assn of Math Tchrs 1974-; NJ Network for Ed 1994-; Outstdng Tchng Governor's Awd; *office:* Dumont HS 101 New Milford Ave Dumont NJ 07628

MARTHY, KATHLEEN MILLET, Resource Room Teacher; *b:* Troy, NY; *m:* Peter F.; *c:* Stephen, Andrew, David; *ed:* Coll of St Rose (BS) Spec Ed & Elem Ed 1982, (MS) Spec Ed for Learning Disabilities 1984; *cr:* Schl 12 Troy NY Spec Ed Tchr 1984-85; Carroll Hill Elem Schl Resource Room Tchr 1985-92; Doyle MS 6th Grd Inclusion Tchr 1992-93; Carroll Hill Elem Schl Resource Room Tchr 1993-; *ai:* Child Stud Team Chm; Troy Tchrs Assn 1984-; *office:* Carroll Hill Elem Schl 112 Delaware Ave Troy NY 12180

MARTI, CAROLINE LINDELL, Third Grade Teacher; *b:* Jamestown, NY; *m:* Steven C.; *c:* S. Todd, Julia Lynn; *ed:* Edinboro Univ of PA (BA) Elem Ed 1970; 31 Addl Hrs; *cr:* Allegheny Vly Elem Schl Third Grd Tchr 1970-83; South Street Elem Schl Third Grd Tchr 1983-; *ai:* IRA 1993-; NEA, PSEA 1970-; Grants Planning & Directing Local His Camp 1992-94; *home:* 27 Gibson St Warren PA 16365*

MARTI, SUSAN KAY, Jr HS Health Teacher; *b:* Wauseon, OH; *m:* M. F.; *c:* Adrienne Mills, Lindsay, Nathan; *ed:* Eastern KY Univ (BS) PE 1972; Fitchburg St Coll Eng Certification, Grad Stud; *cr:* Nashoba Comm Hosp Vol Svcs Dir 1989; North Middlesex Regnl HSOral Interpretor 1989-92; Montachusett Reg Voc Tech Schl Eng Tchr 1993; Tyngsborough Jr Sr HS Hlth Tchr 1993-; *ai:* SADD Adv; Hlth Advy Comm; Little League Sftbl Coach 7 Yrs; NEA, MA Tchrs Assn, Tynsborough Tchrs Assn 1993-; Little League, Past Sec; Prins Awd 1995; *office:* Tyngsborough Jr Sr HS 36 Norris Rd Tyngsboro MA 01879

MARTIN, ANTHONY J., Computer Science Teacher; *b:* Carbondale, PA; *m:* Jane; *c:* Andrew, Rebecca; *ed:* Mount St Marys (BS) Math Ed 1973; Marywood (MS) Math Ed 1980; Hood Coll Post Grad Stud; *cr:* Frederick HS Math, Cmptr Sci Tchr 1973-; *ai:* Club Adv, Coach; Optimist Intnl 1975-, Pres, Outstdng Pres; *office:* Frederick HS 650 Carroll Pky Frederick MD 21701

MARTIN, ARLENE PATRICIA (LUCAS), Home Economics Teacher; *b:* Queens, NY; *m:* John; *c:* Lindsay, Kelly; *ed:* Mansfield Univ (BS) K-12 Home Ec Ed 1972; Jersey City St Coll (MA) Urban Ed, Admin, Supervision 1988; *cr:* West Morris Cntrl HS Home Ec Tchr 1972-78; Vernon Twp HS Home Ec Tchr 1980-, Home Ec Dept Coord 1988-; *ai:* NJEA 1972-; VTEA 1980-; HOME Awd 1992; NJ St Dept of Ed, Consumer, Homemaking Ed for Home Ec Dept Awd 1994; *office:* Vernon Township HS Rt 565 PO Box 800 Vernon NJ 07462

MARTIN, BERNARD FRANCIS, Latin Teacher; *b:* Bayonne, NJ; *m:* Sharon E. Jones; *ed:* Seton Hall Univ (BA) Classical Langs & Eng 1964; Jersey City St Coll (MA) Rdng Ed 1967, (MA) Eng 1969; 6 Grad Credit ESL Montclair Coll; *cr:* Hoboken Schls Eng, Rdng & Latin Tchr 1964-; A J Demarest MS Rdng Tchr 1964-; *ai:* NEA 1964-; NJEA 1964-; HTA 1964-; Hoboken Elks Lodge 74 1980-; Maxwell House Educl Grant; *office:* Hoboken HS 9th St & Clinton St Hoboken NJ 07030

MARTIN, CAROL TOWNE, Physical Education Teacher; *b:* Silver Creek, NY; *m:* Lawrence Edward; *c:* Kelly, Keith; *ed:* St Univ of NY at Brockport (BS) Hlth, PE 1961; St Univ of NY at Buffalo (EDM) Hlth, PE, Rec 1967; Schl Admin, Supvr 1986; 36.5 Grad Inservice Credits; *cr:* Lake Shore Cntrl Schl 9-12 Grd PE Tchr 4 Yrs; Victor Cntrl Schl 9-12 Grd PE Tchr 30 Yrs, Dist PE Coord 7 Yrs, Dept Chair; *ai:* Girls Ldr's Club; Dollars for Scholars Comm; Victor Tchrs Assn 1965-; NYSUT, NYSHPERD 1961-; Delta Kappa Gamma; Recipient Univ of Rochester Awd for Excl Scndry Schl Tchng 1994; *office:* Victor Cntrl Schl High St Victor NY 14564*

MARTIN, CAROLYN WILLIAMSON, Retired Teacher; *b:* SC; *c:* Derrick R.; *ed:* Claflin Univ (BS) Bio, Gen Sci 1963; City Univ (MA) Ed 1973; 60 Hrs Ed; *cr:* NYC Bd of Ed Schl Tchr, Early Chldhd Coord, Staff Dev; *ai:* Tchr Trainer; Parent-Stu Coord; UFT, AFT, NY Tchr 1966-; Alpha Kappa 1961-, Pres; L I Focus of Links Inc 1994-; NAACP; PTA Svc Awd Dist; Tutorial Svc Awd; Rebuilding PS 65 Lib Awd; Outstdng Tchr Awd BOCES; *home:* 6 Executive Ct Dix Hills NY 11746*

MARTIN, COLLEEN LOUISE, German Teacher; *b:* Ipswich, MA; *ed:* Univ MA at Amherst (BA) Ger 1988; Boston Univ (MAT) Modern Frgn Langs 1993; Univ of CT 1 Credit Ger; Salem St Coll 6 Credits Span; *cr:* Cntrl HS Ger Tchr 1993-; *ai:* Ger Amer Partnership Prgm Coord; Cntrl Vision News Adv; Intnl Hnr Soc Induction Ceremony; Delta Epsilan Phi Adv; AATG, NEA 1993-; ACTFL 1996; Trinity Congregational Church 1980-; Goetue Inst Schlsp for Stud in Hamburg Germany 1995; *home:* 2 Overlook Ave Gloucester MA 01930

MARTIN, CRAIG RONALD, English Department Chair; *b:* Elizabeth, NJ; *ed:* Seton Hall Univ (BS) Eng 1970, (MA) Admin 1976; Kean Coll (MALS) Lit 1988; *cr:* Edison Jr HS Eng Tchr 1970-71; St Mary's HS Eng Tchr 1972-73; Somersett Hills Schl Tchr, Cnslr 1974-75; St Joseph's HS Eng Tchr, Dept Chair 1976-; *ai:* Drama Production Liason; Var Club Moderator; Robert Frost Lit Contest Moderator; NJEA, NCTE, NCEA 1976-; ASCD 1994-; Geraldine Dodge Fnd 1992-; Seton Hall 4 Yr Undergrad Schlsp, Grant Grad Schl; Who's Who Among Amer Ed 1987-88; Who's Who Among Human Svc Profs 1988-89; *office:* St Joseph's HS 145 Plainfield Rd Metuchen NJ 08840*

MARTIN, CYNTHIA LATURNER, 2nd Grade Teacher; *b:* Cle OH; *m:* L. Chris; *c:* Robin; *ed:* DePauw Univ (BS) Elem Ed 196 Grad Stud Rdng OH St Univ, Heidelburg Coll & Ashland Coll; *cr:* E Vly Schls 1st Grd Tchr 1969-75; Col Crawford Schls 2nd & 5th G 1983-; *ai:* NEA 1983-; OEA 1983-; CCEA 1983-; First United Met Choir Dir & Organist; CCIRA 1983-, Sec; Outstdng Young E Delaware Cty.

MARTIN, CYNTHIA WELTY, Business Teacher; *b:* Gettysburg, Shippensburg St Univ (BS) Ed, Bus 1974; Mount St Marys Coll Acctng 1985; Frederick Comm Coll Cmptr Sci, Acctng; Univ Transfer Hrs for MBA: Hood Coll Credits Acctng; *cr:* Fairchild S Electronics Various Admin Secretarial Positions 1974-78; Alexandr Various Admin Secretarial Positions 1974-78; Frederick Mem Various Admin Secretarial Positions 1974-78; Frederick Cty Pub Sc 1978-; *ai:* Dept of Bus Chprsn; Tech, PTSA Advy Comms; Cmp Co-Adv; FCTA 1978-, Chm, Budget Comm; NEA 1978-; *office:* Fr HS 650 Carroll Pky Frederick MD 21702*

MARTIN, DANIEL G., Instrumental Music Teacher; *b:* Oneonta, Kathleen Leahy; *ed:* Ithaca Coll (BM) Music Ed 1981; Univ of N (MM) Music Performance 1991; *cr:* Laurens Cntrl Schl Instru Music 1987-; *ai:* Jazz Ensemble; Marching Band; Coaching Instru Ensembles Brass Quintet, Saxophone Quartet; NYSUT 1987-; Winn Ensemble Competition 1993-94; Berklee Coll Jazz Festival; Whitney Achvmnt Awd 1993-95; Sherburne Band PageantBes 1993-95; Frank Miller Outstdng Dir Sherburne Band Pageant; *home* Box 217F Otego NY 13825

MARTIN, DANIEL ROBERT, His & Soc Stud Dept Chprsn; *b:* La PA; *ed:* Millersville Univ of PA (BS) Soc Stud 1985, (MA) Amer Hi *cr:* Lancaster Cath HS Soc Stud Tchr 1989-; *ai:* Schl Newspaper, UN Club & Citizen Bee Adv; Asst Ftbl Coach; NCEA 1990-; NCSS NEH Summer Seminars for Tchrs 1994; *office:* Lancaster Catholic Juliette Ave Lancaster PA 17601

MARTIN, DAVID IRVIN, Eng Tchr & Dept Chprsn; *b:* Pittsburgh, Donna M.; *ed:* Kutztown Univ (BSEd) Eng, Speech & Theatre Lancaster Theo Sem (MAR) Human Dev 1976; *cr:* Bradford Area Tchr 1971-72; Catasauqua Area HS Eng Tchr 1972-73; Wyomissin HS Eng Tchr 1977-; *ai:* Dist Calendar & Handbook Ed; Colloqu NEA, PSEA, WAEA & NCTE 1977-; *office:* Wyomissing Area Evans Ave Wyomissing PA 19610

MARTIN, DEBORAH EILEEN, 6th Grade Teacher; *b:* Bethesd *ed:* St Louis Univ (BA) Eng 1969; *cr:* Wolfson SHS 10th Grd En 1969-70; Stanton SHS 10th-11th Grd Eng Tchr 1970-71; B Sacrament Schl 6th-8th Grd His Tchr 1971-76; Dunblane Schl 3rd-8 Eng, His, Homeroom Tchr 1976-82; Immaculata MS 7th-8th Grd Tc 1982-85; Sidwell Friends Schl 6th Grd Eng, Math, His Tchr 198 Tutor Inner City HS Stdnts in DC; NEA 1990-; Tchr of Yr; Du Wkshp 1995; *office:* Sidwell Friends Schl 3825 Wisconsin A Washington DC 20016*

MARTIN, DIANE (NEVILLE), Science Dept Chm & Bio Teacher; River, MA; *m:* Joseph M.; *c:* Jeffrey, Christine; *ed:* Bridgewater (BA) Bio 1971; Lesley Coll (MED) Curr 1993; 15 Addl Hrs Tech, Norton HS Tchr, Dept Chm 1971-; Newbury Coll Visiting L 1994-95; *ai:* System Wide Steering, Prof Dev Comm; K-12 Sc PALMS; Curr Frameworks; NEA, MTA 1971-; SEMASS 1990-; Kappa Gamma 1974-, Pres, 1st VP; Tounton HS Parent Group 1990 *office:* Norton HS 66 W Main St Norton MA 02766

MARTIN, DOUGLAS G., Television Production Teacher; *b:* Roc PA; *m:* Linda Ruth Steiner; *ed:* Grove City Coll (BA) Comm Arts Slippery Rock Univ Scndry Tchr Cert 1989; Working on MS Degree Morris Coll Comm, Information Systems; *cr:* Eastern Inst of Comm Broadcasting Instr 1983-85; Parajax Productions Freelance Videog 1984-86; KDKA-TV Studio Technician 1984-89; Fox Chapel Are Dist Television Production Tchr 1989-; *ai:* Video Club; Auditorium Stage Crew; Western PA Television & Video Tchrs Consortium 199 of Dir; PSEA, NEA 1989-; Kiwanis 1995-; Article Pub; All Star Edct CNN Newsource Awd for Excl in Jrnlsm Ed; *office:* Fox Chapel Are Dist 611 Field Club Rd Pittsburgh PA 15238

MARTIN, DOUGLAS PETER, Social Studies Teacher; *b:* Trento *m:* Lois Ciavaglia; *c:* Peter, Amy; *ed:* Trenton St Coll (BA) His 1971, Soc Stud 1972; Rider Univ 30 Credit Hrs, Supervisors & Admin Ce Reynolds Jr HS Soc Stud Tchr 1972-76; Hamilton HS East Soc Stu 1976-; *ai:* Cross Cty, Indoor Winter Track, Outdoor Spring Track NEA, NJEA 1972-; *office:* Hamilton High School E 2900 Klockr Trenton NJ 08690*

MARTIN, EMILY L., Spanish Teacher; *b:* Warren, OH; *m:* John M *ed:* OH Univ (BA) Span, Bus Admin 1984; Bowling Green St Univ Span 1987, (ME) Bus Ed 1988; Attnd Univ of Madrid 1990, U Findlay 1995; *cr:* Bowling Green St Univ Grad Asst, Part-time 1985-88; Defiance HS Span Tchr 1988-; *ai:* Span Club Adv; DCE Lang Stdnts Overseas Travel Dir, Spon; Frgn Lang Festival Partic OFLA 1990-93; NEA 1988-, Sec; Delta Sigma Pi 1987-; Ashlar Golden Apple Awd 1994-95; *office:* Defiance HS 1755 Palmer Dr De OH 43512*

MARTIN, GENE MICHAEL, Fourth Grade Teacher; *b:* New Roc NY; *m:* Sherry; *c:* Michael; *ed:* Mount Saint Mary's Coll (BS) E 1969; Coll of New Rochelle (MS) Elem Ed 1974; 12 Addl Hrs; *cr* Rochelle Cath 4, 5, 6, 7, 8 Grd Tchr 1969-83; Garrison Union Fre 5-6 Grd Tchr 1983-85; Webutuck Cntrl 3 Grd Tchr 1985-86; Sheafe 2, 3, 4 Grd Tchr 1986-; *ai:* Weather Project Club Moderator; Little L Bsbl Coach 1986-; Wappingers Congress of Tchrs 1986-, Jr Bldg Hudson Valley Parent Magazine Tchr of Month 1995; Fund W Project Mini-Grant Awd; *home:* 11 4 Winds Dr Poughkeepsie NY 1

MARTIN, GEORGE A., Fifth Grade Teacher; *b:* Belle Vernon, P Barbara; *c:* Mark, G. Adam, Brad; *ed:* CA (MS) Elem 1967; *cr:* Eliz Forward Sch Dist 6th Grd Tchr 1967-82, Environmental Tchr 1982-9 Grd Tchr 1992-; *ai:* PSEA, NEA, EFEA 1967-.

MARTIN, GILDA SALVIO, Spanish Teacher; *b:* New Britain, C Robert W. X.; *c:* William X. II, Garth; *ed:* Saint Joseph Coll (BA) Span 1952; Attnd Wesleyan Univ 1956; *cr:* New Milford HS Span & Tchr 1952-56; Wilton Jr-Sr HS Fr & Eng Tchr 1956-57; New Milfo Span & Eng Tchr 1957-58; Pettibone Schl Span Tchr 1963-66; Cante Schl Fr & Span Tchr 1966-; Dept Chm 1992-95; *ai:* Canterbury L Adv & Founder; Comm Svcs Supvr; Jr & Sr Prom; Annual Carnation Peace Corps Prgm; Cultural Awareness; New Milford Historical Soc 1st Woman Pres 1984-87; New Milford Trust for Historic Preserv Past Mem; New Milford Hospital Auxiliary; Kappa Gamma Pi NH Women Awd for Excl in Tchng Univ of Chicago; 1st Woman Tchr o Canterbury Schl; *office:* Canterbury Schl 103 Aspetuck Ave New M CT 06776*

MARTIN, HARLAN S., Retired Math Teacher; *b:* Saranac Lake, N Gloria C. Horan; *c:* Kendra, Kara; *ed:* St Univ at Potsdam (BS) Math (MS) Math 1967; *cr:* LaFargeville Cntrl Schl Math, Sci Tchr Syracuse Cntrl Tech HS Math Tchr 1963; Corfu-East pembroke Cntr Jr HS Math Tchr 1963-64; Heuvelton Cntrl Schl Sr HS Math Tchr 196 euvelton Tchrs Assn, AFT, NYSUT 1964-; NYS Ret Tchrs Assn

IN, JAMES DAVID, Mathematics Department Chair; *b:* burg, PA; *ed:* Mt St Marys Coll (BS) Math 1969; 30 Hrs Post Grad *r:* St Maria Goretti HS Math Tchr 1969- & Math Dept Chm 1975-; cer & Sftbl Coach; Math Competitions; Bsktbl Statistician; Goretti Camp Coach; Natl Anthem Singer at all Basketball Games; Math Coach; St Cecilia Choral Soc 2 Yrs; Christs Reformed Church Choir St. Maria Goretti Athletic Assn; Wstrn MD Lightning Asst Coach; town Chamber of Commerce Excel in Ed Awd 1990; Potomac Grant for Cmptrs in Classroom 1987; Franklin Life Insurance Co Awd for Soccer Coaching 1987; Recognized for Excellence in ng by Emmitsburg HS Alumni Assn; 233 Wins in 21 Yrs of Coaching *office:* Saint Maria Goretti H S 1535 Oak Hill Ave Hagerstown MD

IN, JAMES EDWIN, Driver Education Teacher; *b:* Altoona, PA; borah; *c:* James, Justin, Jennifer; *ed:* Lycoming Coll (BA) Eng 1972-; Cred Hrs Towards Cert; IN Univ Cert Drivers Ed; 12 Creds; *cr:* ger IGA Clerk & Stock 1965-67; Altoona Mirror Newspaper sing 1967-73; Clearfield Schl Dist Tchr 1972-; PA Motorcycle Pgm Site Coor & Instr 1987-; *ai:* PA Assn for Safety Ed 1987-, Dir; Clearfield Ed Assn 1972-, Exec Comm; PA St Ed Assn; NEA; Clearfield Area Sr High PO Box 910 Clearfield PA 16830

IN, JANE M., Third Grade Teacher; *b:* Bergen Cty, NJ; *ed:* Jersey Coll (BA) Elem Ed 1972, (MA) Supervision & Admin 1992; *cr:* rgh Elem Schl 3rd Grd Tchr 1973-; *ai:* NEA 1973-; NJ Governors 993.

IN, JANET H., Grad & Undergrad Ed Supvr; *b:* Springfield, MA; ward Wright; *c:* Jane Barberio, Edward W. Jr, Diana Ganley, Jill *ed:* Boston Univ (BS) Retailing 1953, (MED) Ed 1962; 3 Credit nptr Course Bentley Coll; 3 Credit Hrs Learning Disabilities Regis *r:* St Dominics Acad Second Grd Tchr 1955-57; Wellesley Pub Schls , Third Grd Tchr 1957-89, K-2 Grd Elem Aide 1989-93, Asst Librn 3; Simmon Coll Schl of Ed Supvr 1993-; *ai:* Cooperating Tchr for Wheelock & Boston Coll; Wellesley Tchr Assn 1960-, Sec of Assn; hr Assn, NEA 1960-; Wellesley Choral Soc 1991-, Mbrshp; Vol Wellesley Hosp 1960-; Judge for DAR Schlsp 1994-95.

IN, JEFFREY STEPHEN, Music Teacher; *b:* Oak Lawn, IL; *ed:* est MO St Univ (BS) Music 1989; 7 Addl Hrs Grad Stud; *cr:* Crane hls Music Tchr 1990-92; Brunswick HS Music Tchr 1992-; *ai:* ng Band Dir; NEA, MSTA, FCTA 1992-; *office:* Brunswick HS 101 ngs Dr Brunswick MD 21716

IN, JOANNY JONES, Guidance Counselor; *b:* Fairmont, WV; *m:* s E.; *c:* Jeffrey; *ed:* Univ of MD (BS) Home Ec 1969; Frostburg St MED) Guid & Cnslng 1987; Boston Univ, Univ of NH 12 Credit Hrs; r 1972-74; Pentucket HS Tchr 1974-76; Northern HS Tchr 1978-87, 988-; *ai:* Peer Cnslr Adv; MD Stu Assistance Team; Chm of Crisis AFT 1978-; GA Co Cnslrs Assn 1992-; MD Stu Assistance Pgm Prof 995-; MD 4-H All Stars 1968-; Exec Bd BSA Troop 29 1990-; Co Womens Commission Comm 1992-.

IN, JOHN CHARLES, Social Studies Teacher; *b:* Norristown, PA; y Martha Bisbing; *c:* Mary Elizabeth Newbegin, Audra Linnea, John *ed:* West Chester St (BS) His 1961; Temple Univ (MA) Amer His Prins Cert 27 Credits; Grad His Credits; 30 Addl Credits; *cr:* own Area Schl Dist 7th Grd Sci Tchr 1 Yr; Plymouth-Whitemarsh Tchr 33 Yrs; *ai:* World Affairs Club; Colonial Ed Assn 1963-, Tchr Nom; PA St Ed Assn, NEA 1962-; *office:* Plymouth-Whitemarsh HS ntown Pike Plymouth Meet PA 19462

IN, JOHN DAVID, Director of Admissions; *b:* Holyoke, MA; *m:* Brennan; *c:* Conor, Patrick, Ryan; *ed:* Tufts U (BA) His 1974; Yale New Testament 1977; AIC (MED) Scndry Ed 1977; *cr:* Tabor Acad hr & Chaplain 1977-81; Peddie Schl Chaplain, His Tchr & Dir of sions 1981-91; Sewickley Acad His & Philosophy Tchr & Dir of sions 1991-; *ai:* Var CC Adv; *office:* Sewickley Acad 315 Academy wickley PA 15143

IN, JOLENE HOHENADEL, Math Teacher & Dept Chair; *b:* ter, PA; *m:* John Robert; *c:* Jordan Robert; *ed:* Millersville Univ Math Ed 1971, (MED) Math 1975; 60 Math & Cmptr Sci Credits; Supvr Cert; *cr:* Columbia HS Math Tchr 1971-; *ai:* NEA, PSEA, 971-; NCTM, PCTM 1983-;ASCD 1995-; *office:* Columbia HS 901 le Pike Columbia PA 17512*

IN, JOYCE MARIE, Fourth Grade Teacher; *b:* Boston, MA; *m:* n B.; *c:* Kelly; *ed:* Bridgewater St Coll (MSEd) Elem Ed 1992; ng CAGS Degree; *cr:* H B Burkland 4th Grd Tchr 1984-85, 6th Grd 985-86, 4th Grd Tchr 1986-92, 4th Grd Tchr 1993-; Lincoln D Lynch Sp Ed Tchr 1992-93; *ai:* Middleboro Ed 1985-, Treas; PCEA; Organ Donation Bank 1994-; MADD 1994-; MTA Prof Grants; MA Career Ctr; *office:* Henry B Burkland Schl 41 Mayflower Ave boro MA 02346*

IN, JUDITH ANN, Business Teacher; *b:* York, PA; *m:* Stanley W. Mason, Cody; *ed:* Shippensburg St (BS) Ed Bus 1982; Shippensburg MED) Bus 1987; 45 Credits Above Masters; *cr:* Northeastern HS hr 4 Yrs; South Western HS Bus Tchr 8 Yrs; *ai:* FBLA Adv; Musical ty Dir; PSEA, NEA & SWEA; *office:* South Western Sr HS 200 an Rd Hanover PA 17331

IN, JUDITH KLEIN, 5th Grade Teacher; *b:* Newark, NJ; *m:* James Seton Hall Univ (BS) Ed 1966, (MA) Rdng 1969; Post Grad Stud; ods Road Schl 1st Grd Tchr 1966-69, 2nd Grd Tchr 1969-72, 4th Grd 972-86; Triangle Schl 4th Grd Tchr 1986-87, 5th Grd Tchr 1987-; EA, NSEA, SCEA 1966-; Hillsborough Ed Assn 1966-, Exec Bd 4; Hillsborough Pub Lib Bd of Trustees 1989-91, VP 1990, Pres *office:* Triangle Schl 156 S Triangle Rd Somerville NJ 08876

IN, JULIE A., Biology Teacher; *b:* Cincinnati, OH; *ed:* Denison BS) Bio 1992; Earlham Coll Acceleration Prgm; *cr:* St Mark's Schl hr 1992-; St Paul's Schl Ecology Tchr ASP 1995; *ai:* Girls Var , JV Bsktbl Coach; 8 Stdnts, Sr Class Adv; Dorm Head; Stu ance Team; Fearing Club Pres; Residential Curr Comm; Bd of es-Dev Fac Rep; New England Prep Schl Womens Soccer Assn Treas; The Kidder Fac Prize Recognize, Hnr Outstdng Work of Fac

IN, KAREN A., English Teacher; *b:* Boston, MA; *ed:* St Coll at water (BA) Eng 1969; Boston Univ (MED) Eng 1975; 30 Addl Hrs; Inst Frgn Stud 1974; Yeats Intnl Summer Schl 1977; Intern MTA ative Action Trng Prgm 1980-81; *cr:* Plymouth North HS Eng Tchr *ai:* NEA, MTA 1969-; MCTE 1995-; Delta Kappa Gamma 1977-; South Rivers Watershed Assns 1996; Duxbury Rural, Historical Soc Pub Article 1981; *office:* Plymouth North HS 41 Obery St Plymouth 360

IN, KATHLEEN PODLESNY, Sixth Grade Teacher; *b:* Hazleton, Timothy John; *ed:* Frostburg St Univ (BS) Early Chldhd, Elem Ed Bowie St Univ (MS) Rdng Ed 1996; *cr:* Northern MS 6th Grd Tchr *ai:* Chrldng Adv; NEA 1988-; *office:* Northern MS 2954 yville Rd Owings MD 20736

MARTIN, KATHRINE OVERLY, Music Teacher; *b:* Anderson, SC; *m:* LeRoy E.; *c:* Caitlin Joy, Elizabeth Marie; *ed:* Bob Jones Univ (BS) Music Ed 1988; *ai:* Acad Choir, Band Dir; Rdng Comm Orch 1994-, French Horn; *home:* PO Box 85 Bowmansville PA 17507

MARTIN, KENT ADAM, Instrumental Music Teacher; *b:* Altoona, PA; *m:* Margaret Sharp; *ed:* PA St Univ (MS) Music Ed 1978; Addl 30 Credits Post-Grad in Ed Admin; *cr:* Self Employed Prof Musician 1978-87; Altoona Area Schl Dist Instrumental Music Tchr 1987-; Penn St Univ Lecturer in Music 1992-; Altoona Symphony Orch Performer 1993-; *ai:* Marching, Concert Bands; Jazz Ensemble, Orch; NEA 1987-; PMEA, MENC 1990-, Outstanding Music Tchr 1992-93; *office:* Keith Jr HS 1318 19th Ave Altoona PA 16602*

MARTIN, LINDA CICCHETTI, English Teacher; *b:* Brockton, MA; *m:* Joseph; *c:* Kevin, Elizabeth, Brian; *ed:* Bridgewater St Coll (BA) Eng 1970; Cambridge Coll (MED) Intergrated Stud 1995; *cr:* West Jr High Eng Tchr 1970-74; Brockton Area Pvt Industry Cncl GED Prep Tchr 1990-91; Williams Jr High Eng Tchr 1991-; *ai:* Bldg Based Support Team; BREA 1991-; MTA 1991-; NEA 1991-; *office:* Williams Jr HS 200 South St Bridgewater MA 02324

MARTIN, MARCELLA TABISZ, High School Guidance Counselor; *b:* Newark, NJ; *m:* James J.; *c:* Julia; *ed:* Trenton St Coll (BS) Eng Ed 1970, (MED) Stu Prsnl Svcs 1976; 32 Credit Hrs Supvr, Guid Dir Certs; *cr:* Iselin MS Eng Tchr 1970-77; John F. Kennedy Meml HS Guid Cnslr 1977-; *ai:* NEA, WTEA 1977-; Middlesex Cty Prsnl, Guid Assn 1977-, Sec; *office:* John F Kennedy Memorial H S Washington Ave Iselin NJ 08830

MARTIN, MARGARET RUSSELL, Biology Teacher; *b:* Elwood, IN; *m:* Donald; *ed:* IN St Univ (BS) Bio 1965; Univ of Dayton (MS) Cnslng 1986; Attnd Miami Univ of Oxford, OH St Univ at Columbus; *cr:* Danville City Schls Bio Tchr 1966-70; Kettering City Schls Bio Tchr 1970-; *ai:* Sci Club Adv; Sci Olympiad Coach; NEA, OEA 1970-; Dayton Montgomery Co Excl Tchng Awd 1991-92; *office:* Kettering Fairmont HS 3301 Shroyer Rd Kettering OH 45429*

MARTIN, MARIE T., Guidance Counselor; *b:* Perth Amboy, NJ; *ed:* Douglass Coll (AB) Span 1965; Rutgers Grad Schl of Ed (EDM) Guid, Cnslng 1968; LaSalle Univ Working Towards PHD in Theocentric Cnslng; 63 Credits in Biling, Bicultural Ed, ESL, Admin, Supervision Jersey City St, Kean Coll; *cr:* New Brunswick HS Span Tchr 1965-85, Guid Cnslr 1985-; *ai:* Schlsp, Attendance Appeals Comms; Crisis Intervention Team; Guidelights Ed; NEA, NJEA, MCEA, NBEA 1965-; MCPGA 1985-, Sec, VP, Pres; MC Guid Cncl 1987-, Sec, VP; Tchr of Yr 1984; Cnslr of Yr 1993; Articles Pub 1981-85; Author: The ABC's of Self Esteem: An Instructional Guide for Parents; *office:* New Brunswick HS 1125 Livingston Ave New Brunswick NJ 08901*

MARTIN, MARTHA SMITH, Enrichment Teacher; *b:* New York, NY; *m:* Thomas E.; *c:* Chistian A., Stacey Fowler; *ed:* SUNY at Old Westbury (BS) Elem Ed 1987; C W Post (MS) Ed 1992; 60 Addl Credits Beyond Masters; *cr:* Jonas Salk MS 6th Grd Tchr 1987-93; Wisdom Lane MS Enrichment Tchr 1993-; *ai:* Environmental Ed Club; Supreme Court & Math Adv; PTA & SEPTA 1975-, Unit & Cncl Pres, Honorary Life & Distngd Svc; AFT, NYSUT & LUT 1987-, Bldg Rep, Friends of Ed; NCTM 1987-; Tchr Ctr 1987-, Policy Bd Chair; Schl Bd 1983-86, Pres; Yth Direction Cncl 1973-86, Trustee; *office:* Wisdom Lane MS Center Ln Levittown NY 11756

MARTIN, MARTINE KENT, Career Awareness Teacher; *b:* Perkasie, PA; *m:* Edward King Sr.; *c:* Lauren, Edward Jr.; *ed:* Bowie St Univ (BS) Early Chldhd Ed 1974; Bowling Green St Univ (MED) Ed, Rdng Specialist 1975; 30 Credit Hrs of In Svc Classes; *cr:* Bowie St Univ Rdng Specialist 1975-76; Pyle Int Schl Rdng Specialist 1976-88; Wootton HS Eng, Rdng Tchr 1988-91; Seneca Vly HS Career Tchr 1991-; *ai:* Minority Achvmt Prgm Adv; Black His, Scholastic Ach Test Comms; NEA, MSTA, MT Cty Tchrs Ed Assn 1976-; Seneca Comm Church 1994-, Steward Bd; Coordinated, Designed, Implemented a Career Course for 9th Grds CATAPULT; *home:* 11232 Valley Bend Dr Germantown MD 20876

MARTIN, MARY ANN, Retired Teacher; *b:* Keene, NH; *ed:* Keene St Coll (BED) Soc Stud, Eng 1957; Post Stud Soc Stud, Eng; *cr:* Hinsdale Elem Schl Tchr 1957-59; Hinsdale HS Tchr 1961-95, Chm Soc Stud Dept 1985-95; *ai:* Drama Club; Yrbk 1961-69; Chrldrs 1960; AFT, NEA 20 Yrs; NH Cncl Soc Stud; Local Hosp, Vol.

MARTIN, MARY G., Social Studies Chair & Teacher; *b:* Delhi, NY; *ed:* Elmira Coll (BA) Soc Stud 1966; Addl 30 Hrs of Grad Stud at St Univ Coll at Oneonta; *cr:* Greene Cntrl Schl Tchr 1966-; *ai:* Key Club; Jr Class; Phi Delta Kappa 1993-; Barrons Review Course Series-Lets Review Global Stud; Barrons Regents Review Global Stud; *office:* Greene HS 40 S Canal St Greene NY 13778

MARTIN, MARY HARKNETT, Nursing Instructor; *b:* Rockville Centre, NY; *m:* Edward J.; *c:* Timothy J.; *ed:* Niagara Univ (BS) Nursing 1976; Russell Sage Coll (MS) Nursing 1990; *cr:* Pennsylvania Hospital Med, Surg Staff Nurse 1976-78; Albany Medical Ctr Hosp ICU Staff Nurse 1978-79; Samaritan Hospital ICCU Staff Nurse 1979-84; Samaritan Hospital Schl of Nursing Fac 1984-; Regents Coll Nursing Examiner Clincial Performance 1994-; *ai:* Chair Media Comm 1990-95, Nursing IV 1990-93, 1995-; Sigma Theta Tau 1991-; Kids Castle Bd Dir 1993-, VP; *office:* Samaritan Hosp Schl Of Nursing 2215 Burdett Ave Troy NY 12180

MARTIN, MICHAEL JAMES, Health & Physical Ed Teacher; *b:* Fremont, OH; *m:* Kim Ellen; *c:* Justin, Jared; *ed:* The Defiance Coll (BA) Hlth & PE 1984; Attnd Univ of Toledo, Bowling Green St Univ, Drake Univ & Ashland Univ; *cr:* Clyde-Green Springs Hlth & PE Tchr 1985-; *ai:* Var Ftbl Asst; Head Boys & Girls Var Track; AAHPERD 1986-; Lions Club 1989-; *office:* Clyde Sr HS 1015 Race St Clyde OH 43410

MARTIN, MICHAEL THOMAS, Dir of Adm & Rel Stud Tchr; *b:* Baltimore, MD; *ed:* St Hyacirth Coll at Saminaly (BA) Philosophy 1984; Pontifical Theological Fac of St Bonaventure at Rome (STB) Theology 1988; Boston Coll (MED) Ed Admin 1993; *cr:* St Francis HS Rel, His Tchr 1984-85, Rel Tchr, Dir of Admin 1989-94; Archbishop HS Rel Tchr, Dir of Admin 1994-; *ai:* Stu Govt Monderator; Asst Var Bsktbl Coach; Booster Club Moderator; NECA 1989-; *office:* Archbishop Curley HS 3701 Sinclair Ln Baltimore MD 21213

MARTIN, NANCY JOSEPH, French Teacher; *b:* South Bend, IN; *m:* Brett E.; *c:* Scott, Amy; *ed:* Clarion St Coll (BS) Eng, Fr 1973; Post Grad Credits UC Berkeley, UC Hayword, Clarion Univ; *cr:* Carlynton HS Eng, Fr Tchr 1988-; *ai:* Ski Club Spon; NCTE; *office:* Carlynton Schl Dist 435 Kings Hwy Carnegie PA 15106

MARTIN, NEOKLIS JOHN, History Teacher; *b:* Derby, CT; *m:* Eileen Krause; *c:* Neoklis Jr., Christine; *ed:* Sacred Heart Univ (BA) Eng 1970; Univ of Bridgeport (MS) Scndry Ed 1979; Southern CT St Univ 6th Yr Admin, Supervision 1986; *cr:* East Side MS 7th-8th Grd Tchr 1970-81; Park City Magnet Schl 7th-8th Grd Tchr 1981-; *ai:* 8th Grd Working Together Club Fac Adv; Safety Patrol Coord; Stu Assistance Team; 8th Grd Field Trip Coord; NEA, CEA, BEA 1973-; Seymour Jaycees 1973-77, Sec, Jaycee of Month 4 Times; Derby Fire Dept 1980-87, 2nd Lieutenant, 1st Lieutenant, Captain; Vly Umpires Assn 1978-, Pres; Governors Yth Action Conf 1982; United Way RYSAP; Project Bus 10 Yr Awd; Bridgeport Area Fnd Safety Patrol Grant; *office:* Park City Magnet Schl 1526 Chopsey Hill Rd Bridgeport CT 06606

MARTIN, PATRICIA SUE, Language Arts Teacher; *b:* Newark, OH; *m:* Donald Paul; *c:* Charity Mc Farland, Amber Clements, Trisha Brighton; *ed:* OH St Univ (BS) Ed 1974; Ashlnd Univ, OH St Univ Grad Work; *cr:* Northridge Local Schl Dist 2nd Grd Tchr 1974-76, 4th Grd Tchr 1976-82, 6th-8th Grd Tchr 1982-92, 7th Grd Tchr 1992-; *ai:* Quiz Bowl, Writing Team Coach; Fac Team Ldr; PTO; NEA; OH Educ Assn; Eng Tchrs' Groups; Chrstn Flwshp Church; Dow Tchr of Yr; *office:* Northridge MS PO Box 68 College St Alexandria OH 43001

MARTIN, PAULA DEPASQUALE, English Teacher; *b:* Cambridge, MA; *m:* George Kenneth Jr.; *c:* Joseph; *ed:* Boston Coll (BA) Fr, Ed 1972; Attnd Univ of Lyon 1 Yr; Harvard Univ Extension, Northeastern Univ Eng; *cr:* Medford HS Fr Tchr 1972-81, Fr & Eng Tchr 1982-88, Eng Tchr 1988-; *ai:* Medford Tchrs Assn, NEA, MA TA 1972-; *office:* Medford HS 489 Winthrop St Medford MA 02155*

MARTIN, PETER JOHN, Professor of Music; *b:* Evanston, IL; *ed:* Northern IL Univ (BS) Music Ed 1971; Wichita St Univ (MME) Music Ed 1973; Northwestern Univ (PHD) Music Ed 1983; *cr:* Southeast MO St Univ Instr of Music 1973-74; Transylvania Univ Asst Prof of Music 1974-80; Univ of Southern ME Prof of Music 1980-; *ai:* Conductor Portland Symphony Yth Wind Ensemble; Coll Band Dirs Natl Assn 1973-, St Chair; Natl Band Assn 1973-, St Chptr Adv; Assn of Concert Bands 1980-, St Chair & Natl Rsrch Chair; Whos who in Music; Intnl Whos Who in Music; Univ of Southern ME Fac Performance & Fac Achvmt Awds; *office:* Univ Of Southern Maine Music Dept Corthell Hall 37 College Ave Gorham ME 04038*

MARTIN, PHILIP KEITH, Music Teacher; *b:* Fairfield, CA; *m:* Sherry Clark; *c:* David P., Kenneth A.; *ed:* Keene St Coll (BM) Music Ed 1976; Univ of NH (MM) Music Ed 1983; *cr:* Belmont Jr Sr HS Music Tchr 1976-83; Gilford MS HS Music Tchr 1983-85; Londonderry HS Music Tchr 1985-94; Concord HS Music Tchr 1994-; *ai:* Band, Choral, Jazz, Pep Band, Marching Band, Orch Dir; MENC 1973-, AS Band Chair; NHMEA 1973-, Pres; NEA 1976-; Londonderry HS Tchr of Yr 1988, Hall of Fame Inductee 1990; *home:* 191 Greeley St Manchester NH 03102

MARTIN, R. RUSSELL, Photography & Art Teacher; *b:* Clinton, NY; *m:* Marcia Martin; *ed:* St Univ of NY Coll at Brockport (BS) Art & Elem Ed 1972; St Univ of NY Coll at New Paltz (MFA) Photography 1975; St Univ of NY Coll at New Paltz (CAS) Schl Bus Admin 1991; *cr:* St Univ of NY Coll at New Paltz Grad Tchng Asst 1973-74; Fairleigh Dickinson Univ Adj Art Instr 1975-80; Mercy Coll Adj Art Instr 1978-79; Bloomfield Coll Adj Art Instr 1979-81; Schl Dist of Orange & Maplewood Scndry Art & Photo Tchr 1981-83; Bergen Comm Coll Adj Art Instr 1984-85; Secaucus Pub Schls Scndry Art & Photography Tchr 1985-86; Wappingers Cntrl Sch & Roy Ketchum HS Art & Photo Tchr 1988-; *ai:* NY St United Tchrs 1988-; NY St Art Tchrs Assn 1989-; Excl in Art Tchng Scholastic Art Competition 1991-95; *office:* Roy C Ketcham HS 99 Myers Corners Rd Wappingers Falls NY 12590

MARTIN, REGINA BRADY, Junior High Science Teacher; *b:* Springfield, MA; *m:* Stephen; *c:* Justin, Conor; *ed:* Holyoke Comm Coll (AS) Sci 1973; Univ of MA (BS) Microbio 1975; Westfield St Coll (MS) Bio; Post Grad Courses in Immunology & Ed; *cr:* Deerfield Acad Sci Lab Dir 1980-83; Holy Name Schl Jr High Sci 1985-; *ai:* Sci Dept Chprsn; Stu Cncl Dir; NEA 1984-; NSTA 1984-; *home:* 21 Parkview Dr Feeding Hills MA 01030

MARTIN, RICHARD EMORY, Music Teacher & Band Director; *b:* Danville, PA; *m:* Cecile Stiner; *c:* Cyril Alexander; *ed:* Temple Univ (BME) Music 1974; Ithaca Coll (MM) 1984; Bloomsburg Univ of PA Cert Credits; *cr:* Southern Columbia Schls Band Dir 1974-75; Benton Area Schls Music Tchr, Band Dir 1975-; *ai:* Jazz, Marching, Jr, Elem Band; Band Front; Schl Music Conductor; Grad Adv;Chm Staff Dev, Act 178 Comm; PMEA, MENC 1974-, PMEA Dist 8 Curr Chair; Intnl Horn Soc 1981-; BAEA, PSEA, NEA 1976-; Natl Band Assn 1975-; Catawissa Military Band 1966-, Dir 1974-; Bloomsburg Univ Orch 1977-, Prin Horn; Sacred Chorale 1980-, Mem; Benton Chrstn Church Choir 1976-, Dir; Benton Zoning Hearing Bd 1995-, Mem; PMEA Dist 8 Curr Instruction Chair; PMEA St Bd; Guest Conductor Danville Legion Band, Bradford Sullivan Cty Jr Band; Temple Univ Pres Scholar; *office:* Benton Area HS RR 2 Park Ct Box 8 Benton PA 17814

MARTIN, RICHARD JOHN GEORGE, Civics Teacher; *b:* Providence, RI; *m:* Nina Marie Brown; *c:* Kellan, Simone; *ed:* Univ of RI (BA) Ed, His 1979; *cr:* Lincoln Jr Sr HS Soc Stud Tchr 1979-80; Project New Pride Schl Soc Stud, Rdng Tchr 1980-84; Martin Jr HS Soc Stud Tchr 1984-; *ai:* NEA 1979-; EPNEA 1985-; Tchr of Month 1991; Dev an African-Amer Elective Course; Pilot Team Copesnican Model; *office:* Edward R. Martin Jr HS 111 Brown St E Providence RI 02914*

MARTIN, RICHARD NEAL, Sixth Grade Teacher; *b:* Pittsburgh, PA; *m:* Linda Ritchings; *c:* Jeremy, Ericka; *ed:* OH Univ (BBA) Bus, Mngmt 1968; Lehigh Univ (MED) Elem Ed 1977; *cr:* Pleasant Vly Schl Dist 5th-6th Grd Tchr 1977-; *ai:* Church Bd; Sunday Schl Tchr; Former Wrestling Coach; PVEA 1977-; *office:* John C. Mills Schl Brodheadsville PA 18322

MARTIN, RICHARD THOMAS, English Department Chair; *b:* Providence, RI; *m:* Dale Evans; *c:* Justin, Alisha; *ed:* Univ of RI (BA) Eng 1971; Masters Equivalency; *cr:* Burrillville HS Tchr 1972-; Various Pubs Freelance Writer 1976-; Greyledge Review Magazine Asst Editor 1977-82; Newspaper Sports Editor, Feature Writer 1981-91; Burrillville Eng Chair 1984-1993; Columnist, Feature Writer; *ai:* Bsktbl Referee; Curr, Lang Arts Comms; Newspaper, Schl Mag Adv 1991-; Girls Var Bsktbl 1980-87, Vllybl 1982-86 Coach; New England Press Assn 1989-; NEA 1972-, HS Rep 3 Yrs; NCTE 1972-; RICTE 1975-; Woonsocket CALL Coach of Yr 1982; RI Sportsmanship Awd 1988; RI Press Assn 1st Place Feature Writing 1987, 2nd Place 1986, 1984; New England Press Assn 2nd Place Feature Writing 1988; Consultant Scott, Foresman: America Reads; Eng Chm; Editor; Tchr of Yr 1993; *office:* Burrillville H S 425 East Ave Harrisville RI 02830

MARTIN, ROBERT A.,JR., Assoc Prof Criminal Justice; *b:* Milford, CT; *m:* Maureen Martin; *ed:* Nathaniel Hawthorne Coll (AA), (BA) His, Pol Sci & Criminal Justice 1975 & 1976; St Univ of NY at Albany (MA) Criminal Justice 1979; St Univ of NY at Buffalo (JD) Law 1983; Coursework Toward PHD Criminal Justice; *cr:* Fulton Cty Asst Dist Attorney 1984-86, Asst Pub Defender 1988-89, Pub Defender 1989-90; Fulton Montgomery Comm Coll Prof of Criminal Justice 1990-; *ai:* Criminal Justice Club Adv; NYS Certified Police Instr; Fulton Cty NY Bar Assn 1984-; NEA 1990-; Citizens in Comm Svc 1984-, Bd of Dirs; *office:* Fulton Montgomery Comm Coll 2805 St Hwy 67 Johnstown NY 12095

MARTIN, ROBERT ANDREW, Business Education Teacher; *b:* Somers, NY; *ed:* Marist Coll (BS) Bus & Mrktg 1987; Pace Univ (MS) Ed; *cr:* George Fisher MS Stu Tchr 1990; John F Kennedy Cath HS Bus Ed Tchr 1991-; *ai:* Var Girls Soccer, Var Boys Soccer & Jr Var Girls Bsktbl Coach; *office:* John F Kennedy Cath HS 54 Route 138 Somers NY 10589

MARTIN, ROBERT J., Social Studies Teacher; *b:* Providence, RI; *ed:* Providence Coll (BA) Eng, His & Ed 1990, (MA) His 1992, (MED) Admin & Curr 1996; Certified in Eng & Soc Stud; *cr:* Smithfield HS Eng Tchr 1989-90; Classical HS Eng & Soc Stud Tchr 1990-, Intern Prin 1995-; *ai:* Class of 1995, Model Legislative & Comm Svc Explorers Post Adv; AFT, RI Soc Stud Assn, NCSS, NCTE 1990-; US Army, Officer; RI Pilots Assn 1990-, FAA Certified Pilot; Knights of Columbus 1986-, Grand Knight; Elks Club 1989-, St Officer; Whos Who in Tchng 1993, 1994 & 1995; *office:* Classical HS 770 Westminster St Providence RI 02903

MARTIN, ROBIN MARIE, High School Mathematics Tchr; *b:* Alexandria Bay, NY; *m:* Stephen Scott; *c:* Travis Scott, Shawn Matthew; *ed:* Plattsburgh Coll (BA) Ed Elem 1982; Potsdam Coll (MS) Ed 1989; Jefferson Comm Coll Extension Math 7-9 1989; Addl 12 Credit Hrs Math; *cr:* Alexandria Cntrl Schl HS Math Tchr 12 Yrs; *ai:* Jr Class Adv 8 Yrs; Figure Skating Coach 1982-; Mentor Ldr 1994-; Golf Coach 1994-; PACe 1995-; Historical Soc 1988-; *office:* Alexandria Central Schl 34 Bolton Ave Alexandria Bay NY 13607

MARTIN, ROSEMARY ELIZABETH, English Teacher; *b:* Bridgeport, CT; *m:* Reynold F.; *c:* Jeremy, Geoffrey, Torey; *ed:* Univ of Bridgeport (BS) Eng, Ed 1971; Southern CT St Univ (MS) Schl Cnslng 1993; 30 Crd Hrs Educ Media at Univ of Fairfield 1980; *cr:* Joel Barlow HS Eng Tchr 1971-76; Flood MS; Wooster MS; Johnson MS; Stratford HS; Bunnell HS 1977-; *ai:* Drama Club; Diversity Comm; Stratford Educ Assn, CT Educ Assn, NEA 1971-; Sister Cities Chorus 1993-; Episcopal Church Women 1976-; St Marks Players 1985-; Band Parents 1991-; Homework Hotline Project Coord 1990-94; Celebration of Excl Awd 1991; *office:* F. Scott Bunnell HS 1 Bulldog Blvd Stratford CT 06497*

MARTIN, ROY EDWARD, Science Teacher; *b:* Toledo, OH; *m:* Cathay M. McHenry; *c:* Jeffrey, Jennifer; *ed:* Univ of Toledo (BED) Comp Hlth & PE 1969, (MED) Sci Ed 1973; *cr:* Devilbiss HS Sci Tchr 1969-91; Start HS Sci Tchr 1991-; *ai:* AFT 1969-; OFT 1969-; TFT 1969-, DHS Bldg Comm; *office:* Start HS 2100 Tremainsville Rd Toledo OH 43613

MARTIN, SAMUEL RAYMOND, Band Dir & Dist Dept Crair; *b:* Lancaster, PA; *m:* Carol Koshuta; *c:* Adam, Ross, Ethan; *ed:* Shenandoah Coll & Conservatory of Music (BME) Music Ed 1975; Northwestern Univ (MM) Performance Major 1977; 15 Credit Hrs in Gen Ed; *cr:* Prairie City Schl Dist 1st-12th Grd Music Tchr 1977-78; Carlisle HS Asst Band Dir 1978-79; Middletown Area HS Band Dir, Music Dept Chprsn, Instrumental Music Tchr 1979-; *ai:* Marching Band; Jazz Club; Band Front Clubs; MENC, PMEA 1979-; DCMEA 1979-, Pres; NBA; Bainbridge Band 1993-, Soloist Awd; *office:* Middletown Area HS 1155 N Union St Middletown PA 17057

MARTIN, STEFAN, Asst Professor of English; *b:* Baltimore, MD; *ed:* WV Univ (BA) Eng 1975; Univ of Chicago (MAT) Eng 1976; Univ of MD (PHD) Linguistics 1992; *cr:* Randallstown HS Eng Tchr 1976-85; Univ of MD Writing Coord 1986-91; St Marys Coll Asst Eng Prof 1991-; *ai:* Gen Ed Assessment & Writing Comms; Linguistic Soc of Amer 1992-; NCTE 1992-; *office:* Saint Marys Coll Of MD Dept of Eng St Marys Cy MD 20686

MARTIN, SUSAN M., Librarian; *b:* Lancaster, PA; *ed:* Millersville Univ (BS) Educl Media 1976; Villanova Univ (MS) Lib Sci 1982; *cr:* Lancaster Cath HS Lbrn 1978-; *ai:* Stu Cncl Adv; ALA 1995-, PSLA 1978-; *office:* Lancaster Catholic HS 650 Juliette Ave Lancaster PA 17601

MARTIN, TERRY MICHAEL, Principal; *b:* Mt Pleasant, PA; *m:* Linda Zerbe; *c:* Nathan; *ed:* Clarion St Coll (BS) Ed 1967; Univ of Pittsburgh (MS) Ed 1972; 39 Addl Credits Past Masters; *cr:* Fraser Pub Schls Tchr 1967-68; Norwin Schl Dist 4th-6th Grd Tchr 1968-95; PA Ave Schl Prin 1995-; *ai:* NEA & PSEA 1967-; NCTM & PCTM 1991-; NAESP 1995-; United Meth Church 1970-; Hempfield Area Schl Dir 1983-91, Pres 1990-91; *office:* PA Avenue Elementary 1015 PA Ave Irwin PA 15642

MARTIN, URSULA MARINO, Mathematics Teacher & Dept Rep; *b:* Yonkers, NY; *m:* Robert F. Mart; *c:* Robert, Lynda; *ed:* Coll of Mt St Vincent (BS) Math 1962; Fordham Univ (MS) Math 1970; 60 Addl Credits Cmptrs, Ed Woodrow Wilson Inst; *cr:* Albert Leonard JHS Math Tchr 1962-65; Walt Whittman JHS Math Tchr 1965-70; Charles E. Gordon HS Math Tchr, Dept Rep 1989-; *ai:* Math League, Sr Class Adv; NCTM 1980-; Natl Sci Fnd Schlsp; Woodrow Wilson In-Svc Grant; Innovators Awd; *office:* Charles E. Gorton HS 100 Shonnard Pl Yonkers NY 10703

MARTIN, WILLIAM LOUIS, History Tchr & Dept Chprsn; *b:* Cumberland, MD; *m:* Sandra S. Fairgrive; *c:* Jonathan W.; *ed:* Frostburg St Univ (BS) Soc Stud, His 1963, (MS) Soc Stud 1975; *cr:* Westmar HS Tchr 1966-74; *ai:* Dept Chprsn; Stu Cncl & Mock Trial Adv; AFT 1968-; Kemp Lodge 154 AF & AM 1966-, Sec; Corriganville Light & Improvement Assn 1993-, Sec; Phi Eta Sigma Cert for Acad Excl 1993-95; *home:* PO Box 142 Corriganville MD 21524

MARTINEAU, IRENE MARGUERITE, Religion & Language Arts Tchr; *b:* Salem, MA; *ed:* Anna Maria Coll of Paxton (BS) Ed, Eng & Fr 1970; Boston Coll (MS) Educl Admin 1986; Over 30 Credit Hrs in Hlth, Span, Sociology, His of Lowell at Univ of Lowell, Middlesex Comm Coll & Salem St; *cr:* Saint Joseph HS Sr Adv & Tchr 1970-81; Saint Louis Acad Sr Adv & Tchr 1981-86, Prin 1986-91; Saint Louis Jr HS Prin & Tchr 1991-95; Saint Louis Schl Religion, Lang Arts & Span Tchr 1995-; *ai:* Natl MS Assn 1991-; NCEA 1985-; Drama Club Dir of 14 Plays; Woman of Yr Nom by Saint Louis Veterans Inc & Recognized by St & City of Lowell MA; *home:* 85 Boisvert St Lowell MA 01850

MARTINELL, JUDITH SEBER, Kindergarten Classroom Teacher; *b:* Newton, NJ; *m:* Ronald James; *c:* Christine Peterson, Matthew; *ed:* East Stroudsvburg Univ (BA) Elem Ed 1964; Marywood Coll, Wilkes Coll 30 Grad Credits Ed; *cr:* Belvidere Schl Dist Tchr 1964-65; Pleasant Palley Schl Dist Tchr 1965-67; Pocono Mountain Schl Dist Tchr 1980-; *ai:* Past Girl Scout Ldr 1964-67, Asst Ldr 1973-79; NEA, PSEA, PMEA 1964, 1980-; *office:* Tannersville Learning Ctr PO Box 200 Swiftwater PA 18370

MARTINELLI, JACK B., Health & Physical Ed Teacher; *b:* Quincy, MA; *m:* Joanne M. Sullivan; *c:* Kristy, Jacqui, Brian; *ed:* Northeastern Univ (BS) Hlth, PE, Gen Sci 1968; Credit Hrs Soc Scis, Sports Philosophy, AIDS Ed; *cr:* Norwood HS Hlth, PE Tchr, Coaching 1968-82; Foxboro HS Hlth, PE Tchr, Head Ftbl Coach 1983-86; *ai:* Peer Ldrshp; Fitness Prgm; NEA 1968-; MA St Coaches Assn 1968-, Coach of Yr 1987-88, 1991; Yth Ftbl, Bsbl; Nom Tchr of Yr by Natl Ftbl League; *office:* Foxborough HS 120 South St Foxboro MA 02035

MARTINELLI, JEANNE ANN, 4th Grade Teacher; *b:* Salem, OH; *ed:* Mount Union Coll (BA) Elem Ed 1971; Westminster Coll (MA) Elem Ed 1977; Akron Univ, Youngstown St Univ Post Grad Courses; *cr:* B. L. Miller Elem Schl Tchr 25 Yrs; *ai:* New Tchr Mentor; NEA, OEA 1971-; Sebring EA 1971-, Treas; NCTM 1992-; Tchr of Yr 1972, 1989; Martha Holden Jennings Scholar 1972; Career Dev Ctr Grant 1986; *office:* B L Miller Elem Schl 506 W Virginia Ave Sebring OH 44672*

MARTINES-CAPPELLINI, CHARLOTTE, Associate Professor of English; *b:* Jamestown, NY; *m:* John Albert Jr.; *ed:* Jamestown Comm Coll (AA) Hum 1969; St Univ Coll at Brockport (BA) Eng 1971; St Unv Coll at Fredonia (MA) Eng 1974; 12 Credit Hrs; St Bonaventure Univ 3 Credit Hrs; Empire St Coll 3 Credit Hrs Post Grad; *cr:* Jamestown Comm Coll Stu Learning Lab Dir 1975-80; Cattaraugus Campus of Jamestown Comm Coll Eng Prof 1980-; *ai:* Multi-Cultural Programming & Grad Comms; Comm Coll Tchr Preparation Pgm; Natl Endowment of Hum Summer Flwhsp at Univ of MA at Amherst; *office:* Jamestown Comm Coll Cattaragus Cty Campus N Barry St Olean NY 14760*

MARTINETTI, RAYMOND F., Professor of Psychology; *b:* New York, NY; *m:* Rose Ann; *ed:* City Coll of City Univ of NY (BS) Psych, Chem 1968; Fordham Univ (MA) Psych 1970, (PHD) Experimental Psych 1974; *cr:* Marywood Coll Psych Prof; *ai:* Statistical Research Consultant; Book Reviewer; Stu Adv; Sr Research Psychologist; APA, Psi Chi 1973-; Marywood Coll 1973-, Prof, CMFC Medal; Numerous Scholarly Publications; Cognitive Assessment Device Pub; *office:* Marywood Coll 2300 Adams Ave Scranton PA 18509

MARTINEZ, INEZ, Professor of English; *b:* Albuquerque, NM; *ed:* St Louis Univ (BS) Eng 1964, (MA) Eng 1965; Univ WI at Madison (PHD) Eng 1979; *cr:* Sacred Heart Univ Instr 1965-66; Kingsborough Comm Coll Instr 1970-73, Asst Prof 1974-79, Assoc Prof 1980-88, Prof, Women's Stud Co-Dir 1989-; *ai:* Environmental Comm Chair; Senator to CUNY Senate; Coll Cncl Del at Large; MLA 1970-; Poets, Writers 1990-; Jung Inst 1976-90; City Univ Scholar's Incentive Fiction Awd 1988-89; NY Fnd for the Arts Fiction Flwshp 1987; PSC Fiction Summer Grant 1987; Kent Fellow 1967-70; *office:* Kingsborough Community Coll 2001 Oriental Blvd Brooklyn NY 11235

MARTINEZ-STRUBBE, ELIZABETH, Tchr of the Talented & Gifted; *b:* Bridgeport, CT; *m:* Leopold; *ed:* Sacred Heart Univ (BA) Span & Elem Ed 1974; Univ of Bridgeport (MS) Elem Ed 1979; Univ of CT 1989 Confratute for Gifted Tchrs; Southern CT St Univ 24 Credits in Admin & Supervision; 6 Credits Beyond Masters; *cr:* Elias Howe Schl 3rd-5th Grd Classroom Tchr 1974-89, Tchr of Biling Talented & Gifted 1989-; *ai:* SAT Mem; Schls Action Plan Comm; Comm for the Annual Anti-Drug Parade; NEA 1974-; CEA 1974-; Padua House 1994-, Treas; Grant for The Arts Come to Howe; *office:* Elias Howe Elem Schl 287 Clinton Ave Bridgeport CT 06605

MARTIN-FORTIN, JANE, Mathematics Teacher; *b:* New Bedford, MA; *m:* Henry G.; *c:* Ross, Kirby; *ed:* Stonehill Coll (BA) Math 1974; Bridgewater St Coll & Univ of Southern ME Post Grad Stud; *cr:* St Marys Schl 7th & 8th Grd Math & Sci Tchr 1974-75; Fairhaven HS Math Tchr 1975-80; Dartmouth HS Math Tchr 1980-; *ai:* MTA 1975-; NEA 1975-; DEA 1980-; *office:* Dartmouth H S 366 Slocum Rd North Dartmouth MA 02747

MARTINI, JAMES A., Instrumental Music Teacher; *b:* Bloomsburg, PA; *m:* Michelle L. Button; *ed:* Mansfield Univ of PA (BM) Music Ed 1985; Attnd Bowling Green St Univ, Penn St Univ, Wilkes Univ Grd Credits; *cr:* Bald Eagle-Nittany HS Instrumental Music Tchr 1989-92; Bowling Green St Univ Grad Asst Instrumental Methods 1992-93; East Stroudsburg Area Sr HS Instrumental Music Tchr & Band Dir 1993-; *ai:* Marching Band; Jazz Ensemble; Musical Dir; MENC & PMEA 1986-; NEA & PSEA 1987-; Natl Band Assn 1994-; BSA 1994-, Cnslr; Pocono Lively Arts 1995-, Musical Dir; *office:* E Stroudsburg HS 279 N Courtland St East Stroudsburg PA 18301

MARTINI, JUDITH A., Theology & English Teacher; *b:* Hazleton, PA; *ed:* A.S. Luzerne C. Coll (AS) Rec & PE 1980; King's Coll (BA) Mass Comm, Theatre, Theology 1990; Univ of Scranton (MS) Scndry Ed 1994; 32 Hrs Eng, Theatre, Theology; 32 Hrs Drama, Dance; *cr:* United Rehab Svcs Soc Worker; Bishop O'Reilly HS Theology Tchr 1990-91; Bishop Hafey HS Theology, Eng, Theatre Tchr 1991-; *ai:* Players, Drama Club, Ski Club, Soph Class Moderator; NCEA 1991-; Jaycees 1985-, Jr Miss St Awd Prgm; Article Pub; Choreography, Drama, Photography Awds; Miss Amer Judge; *office:* Bishop Hafey HS 1700 W 22nd St Hazleton PA 18201

MARTINO, JOHN JAMES, Mathematics Instructor; *b:* Drexel Hill, PA; *m:* Carolyn Hunt; *ed:* Ursinus Coll (BS) Math 1987; Eastern Coll (MS) Ed 1996; *cr:* Stella Maris Schl Math Tchr 1989-92; Girard Coll Math Tchr 1992-; *ai:* Monsignor Bonner HS Ftbl Asst Coach; Girard Coll Girls Var Bsktbl Asst Coach, Girls Var Track & Field Head Coach; NCTM 1987-; PFT 1992-; Girard Coll Tchr of Yr 1994, 1995; *office:* Girard Coll 2101 S College Ave Philadelphia PA 19121

MARTINO-AVELLA, MARGHERITA, 3rd Grade Teacher; *b:* Melbourne, Australia; *m:* Rocco; *c:* Leonardo, Marco; *ed:* Kean Coll of NJ (BA) Early Chldhd Ed 1986; Working on Masters Prgm Cnslr Ed; *cr:* Christopher Columbus Schl #15 3rd Grd Tchr 1986-; *ai:* NEA 1986-; 1991 Child Assault Prevention; Americanism Awd 1992; *office:* Christopher Columbus Schl #15 511 3rd Ave Elizabeth NJ 07202*

MARTINS, PAUL WILLIAM, Social Studies Dept Chairman; *b:* Cleveland, OH; *m:* Donna; *c:* Timothy, Daniel; *ed:* Kent St Univ (BED) Soc Stud 1972, (MED) Soc Stud 1978, (MA) Pol Sci 1980; *cr:* Schaaf Jr HS Tchr 1972-82, Valley Forge HS Tchr 1982-93; Parma HS Dept Chm 1993-; *ai:* Var Tennis Coach; NEA, OEA, NEORA, Parma Ed Assn 1972-; Robt. A. Taft Inst of Govt 1976, 1982; OH Dept of Ed 1991-92, Consultant; Lake Erie League Tennis, Coach of Yr 1994; OH Tennis Coaches Assn, 100 Career Victories 1994; *office:* Parma Sr H S 6285 W 54th St Parma OH 44129

MARTONE, RALPH ANTHONY, Physics Teacher; *b:* New Castle, PA; *m:* Denise Elaine Heminger; *c:* Michael, Matthew; *ed:* PA St Univ (BS) Bun Admin 1981; Westminster Coll (BS) Physics 1989; Environmental Ed Stud Univ of IN; 28 Hrs ME; *cr:* Butler Sr HS Phys Sci, Earth-Space Tchr 1989-92; Shenango Area HS Physics Tchr 1992-; *ai:* Conservation Club; Jr Class, Newspaper Adv; Prof Dev, Strategic Planning Curr; PA Game Commission; NEA 1989-, Local Sec; PSTA 1989-, Presenters Awd; APTA 1989-, Tech Awd; Hunters Ed Instrs 1989-, Lawrence Cty rep; Safari Club Internation 1989-, Tchr Essay & Rocky Mountain Trip Awds; Shenango Ath Assn 1985-, League Pres; LCSFY 1991-, VP; Pub Curr on STS; *office:* Shenango Area HS 2550 Ellwood Rd New Castle PA 16101*

MARTORANA, BARBARA JOAN, English Teacher; *b:* New York City, NY; *ed:* St Johns Univ (BA) Eng, Ed 1970, (MS) Eng, Ed 1972; LIU CW Post Advanced Cert Cmptrs Ed 1988, NYS Schl Admin Supvr 1989, NYS Schl Dist Admin 1990; *cr:* St Martin of Tours 7-8 Grd Eng, Rel Tchr, Guid, Lang Arts Coord 1970-77; Oceanside Jr HS Eng Tchr 1977-78; Freeport HS Eng Tchr 1979-; *ai:* ASCD 1989-; NCTE 1969-; Long Island Writing Proj 1992-, Steering comm; Conf on Eng Ed NCTE 1990-; Seaford Republican Club 1975-; Co-Author Writing Competency Practice 1980, Writing Competency Practice Revised & Expanded 1989; Marques Who's Who in Amer Ed 1996-67; *office:* Freeport HS 50 S Brookside Ave Freeport NY 11520*

MARTS, DIANE MARIE, Fifth Grade Inclusion Teacher; *b:* Buffalo, NY; *m:* Robert D.; *c:* Lisa Freeborn, Tara Freeborn, Tracy Dunbar, Carrie, Becky; *ed:* D'Youville Coll (BA) Elem Ed 1964; 16 Addl Hrs; *cr:* Maryvale Schl Tchr 1964-66; Kenmore Schl Tchr 1966-68; Lancaster Schl Tchr 1971-; *ai:* Inclusion Tchr Working Collaboratively BOCES Spec Ed Tchr; NYS Rdng Conf Concord Wkshp; PDS Partnership W Buffalo St Coll 1995lo St Coll; AFT 1964-; LCTA 1971-; Church, Team Ldr Yth Group, Confirmation; *home:* 4983 Burlbrook Dr Orchard Park NY 14127

MARTTER, STEVEN BUTLER, Social Studies Teacher; *b:* Akron, OH; *c:* Phillip, Sarah; *ed:* Univ of Akron (BA) Scndry Ed, Soc Stud Comp 1990; *cr:* Archbishop Hoban HS His Tchr 1989-92; Akron Pub Schls Soc Stud Tchr 1992-; *ai:* Ftbl Coach; Archbishop Hoban HS Tchr of Yr 1990-91, 1991-92; *home:* 2239 Broad Blvd Apt 5 Cuyahoga Falls OH 44223

MARTUCCI, ANTHONY ROBERT, Social Studies Teacher; *b:* Jersey City, NJ; *m:* Lillian Patricia Magee; *c:* Robert, David, Karyl Lynn, Peter, Anthony; *ed:* St Peter's Coll (BS) His 1964; *ai:* Gftd & Tlntd Curr Comm, Social Stuies Comm; HTEA 1968-, Negotiation Chm & Treas 1970-74; MCEA, NJEA, NEA 1968-; *office:* Howell MS 501 Squankum Yellowbrook Rd Farmingdale NJ 07727*

MARTUCCI, JOSEPH JOHN, Assistant Athletic Director; *b:* Newark, NJ; *m:* Patricia Pocsaji; *c:* Joseph, Melissa; *ed:* Univ of CT (BS) PE, Hlth 1972; Kean Coll (MA) Schl Admin 1980; 18 Credits Jersey City St Coll; *cr:* Marlboro Elem Jr HI Hlth, PE Tchr 1972-73; Matawan Rgnl Schls PE Tchr, Asst Ath Dir 1973-; *ai:* Head Ftbl, Asst Wrestling Coach; NJFICA, MCDA 1984-; NEA, NJEA 1972-; MRTA 1973-; Maroon & Steel Club 1984-; Matawan Italian Amer Club 1972-, Man of Yr 1985; Ftbl (Yr 1988; *office:* Matawan Regnl HS Atlantic Ave Matawan NJ 07

MARTUCCI, PATRICIA POCSAJI, Guidance Counselor; *b* Amboy, NJ; *m:* Joseph; *c:* Joseph, Melissa; *ed:* Monmouth Coll (B Ed 1972; Kean coll (MA) Schl Admin 1982; Attnd Kean Coll 3 Jersey City St 57 Credits, Georgian Ct 6 Credits; *cr:* Keansburg El Tchr 1972-88; Keansburg HS Soc Stud Tchr 1988-93; Keansburg G Counselor 1993-; *ai:* Girls Cross Cntry Coach; His & Govt Cl Cheerleading Coach; NEA, NJEA, KTA 1972-; NCSA; *office:* Ke Elementary 142 Port Monmouth Rd Keansburg NJ 07734*

MARTUCCI, RAYNA WEINGART, 7th-8th Grd Language Arts Princeton, NJ; *m:* Gregory R.; *c:* Gregory Joseph; *ed:* Newark St C Elem Ed 1969; Kean Coll (MS) Rdng; 6 Hrs Urban Stud Rutgers Ur Supvr, Prin; *cr:* Perth Amboy Schl #10 4th Grd Tchr 1968-78; Sa Shull Schl 6th Grd Tchr 1978-79; William C. Mc Ginnis 7th-8th G Art Tchr 1979-; *ai:* AFT 1968-95; NJEA, NEA 1995-; Linder 1983-95, Pres 3 Yrs; Cath Comm Svcs 1979-89, Fundraising Chair Bus, Prof Women 1978-90, Sec Schlsp Fund; Italian Amer Ladies Fundraising; Governor's Tchr Recognition Recipient 1982; Tch 1988; NJ Schl Bds Assn 100 Club; *office:* Perth Amboy Bd of Barracks St Perth Amboy NJ 08861*

MARTY, DAVID LEE, Mathematics Teacher; *b:* Salem, OH; *m* Hurd; *c:* Caleb, Joshua, Leah; *ed:* Bowling Green St Univ (BS) Ma (MS) Guidance & Counseling 1995; *cr:* Clyde HS Math Tchr 19 Var Ftbl Asst Coach; Math Dept Chair; Chrstn Educators Assn Intn Prayer Chm; Fremont Grace Brethren Church 1992-.

MARTY, GEORGE A., Algebra & Calculus Teacher; *b:* Bridgep *m:* Amy Kennon; *c:* Michelle; *ed:* OH Univ (BSED) 1976; Wheelir Coll (MASMED) 1990; *cr:* Bridgeport HS Jr High Math Tchr 1 Algebra, Calculus Tchr 1979-; *ai:* Var Boys Bskbl Coach; NEA Outstanding Young Men of Amer 1992; *office:* Bridgeport HS 501 St Bridgeport OH 43912

MARTZ, BEVERLY DOBOS, English Teacher; *b:* Youngstown, Michele Hodge; *ed:* Youngstown St Univ (BA) Eng 1984, (MA) En Addl Post Grad Work in Ed Admin; *cr:* Struthers HS Tchr Youngstown St Univ Adjunct Fac 1990-91; Struthers HS Dep 1993-95; *ai:* Newspaper Adv; Youngstown St Univ Eng Festival; O Phi Kappa Phi 1984-; Mahoning Cty Lang Arts 1994-, Liaison; Re 1976-, Vol; Presenter at 1st Annual Mahoning Cty Lang Arts Barbara Brothers Writing Awd for Tchrs 1985 & 1986; Who's Who Colls & Univs 1984; *office:* Struthers HS 111 Euclid Ave Strut 44471

MARTZ, HOMER B., Automotive Technology Teacher; *b:* Cum MD; *m:* Kelly Ann Riley; *ed:* Allegany Comm Coll (AA) Automoti 1982; Univ of MD (T&I) Industry 1992; *cr:* Northern HS Automoti Tchr 1989-; *ai:* Emergency Medical Svcs Club Adv; AFT 1991-; N Rescue Squad 1990-, Paramedic, Lieutenant; Star of Life Awd fr Inst of Emergency Medical Svcs; *office:* Northern Garrett Cty S Pride Pkwy Accident MD 21520

MARTZ, KELLY ANN (RILEY), English II Teacher; *b:* Cum MD; *m:* Homer B. Jr.; *ed:* Potomac St Coll (AA) Bus Admi Shepherd Coll (BA) Scndry Ed, Eng, LA 1991; *cr:* Broadford El Media Asst 1991-92; Northern MS Level IV, CPA 1992-93; N Garrett HS Eng I, II Tchr, Yrbk 1993-; *ai:* Chrldng Coach; Jr. Clas Prom Club Adv; AFT 1994-; Collegiate Chrldng Coach of Yr 1994; Northern Garrett HS 86 Pride Pkwy Accident MD 21520*

MARTZ, ROCCO ANTHONY, Eighth Grade Teacher; *b:* Queens, Christine; *c:* David; *ed:* Nyack Coll (BA) Ed 1982; Coll of New R MA Admin Pgm; *cr:* St Jerome Schl 3rd, 5th, 7-8th Grd Tchr 19 Coord of Religious Ed St Jerome Parish Bronx NY; United Fed Ca 1981-; NCEA 1985-; *office:* Saint Jerome Schl 222 Alexander Av NY 10454

MARTZALL, DEBORAH WEAVER, Art Teacher; *b:* Lancaster, Shannon, Megan; *ed:* Millersville Univ (BS) Art Ed 1973; *cr:* Lancaster Co Schl Dist Art Tchr 1973; Elizabethtown Area Schl Tchr 1973-; Lancaster Preparatory Schl Part-time Art Tchr 1986 Co-Direct Support Group Stdnts Serving on Supts Advy Cncl; Am Univ Women; *home:* 807 Centerville Rd Lancaster PA 17601

MARULLO, ANNETTE, Fourth Grade Teacher; *b:* Rome, NY; *c* *ed:* (MS) Elem Ed & Curr Elem Ed 1977; Insvcs: The Writing F Microsoft Works, Local His, Math Their Way; *cr:* Maple West E Grd Remedial Math Tchr 1972-74; Rome City Schls 5th Grd R Math Tchr 1974-77; McConnellsville Schl 4th Grd Tchr 1977-; Cncl Adv; Tchr in Charge; AYSO Soccer Asst Coach; NYSUT Camden Tchrs Assn, Sec, Negotiator & Bldg Rep; AFT 1972- Omega 1985-, Pres, Sec & Treas; *office:* Mc Connellsville Schl R Connellsville NY 13401

MARUSAK, ROBERT, Math & Reading Teacher; *b:* Carnegie, Michele D.; *ed:* CA St Coll (BA) Elem 1964; Univ of Pittsburg Elem; *cr:* Nixon Elem Schl 4th-5th Grd Tchr 1964-89; Heidelber Schl 4th Grd Tchr 1989-93; Chartiers Vly MS 6th Grd Tchr 1993- Math Club Spon; NEA 1964; AFT 1981; Pub Book Friendship fo 1988; *office:* Chartiers Valley Schl Dist 50 Thoms Run Rd Bridge 15017

MARUSZCZAK, JOSEPH PETER, Chemistry Teacher; *b:* Sprin MA; *m:* Diane Mercurio; *c:* Alison; *ed:* Providence Coll (BA) Chem MED Scndry Admin Candidate; *cr:* Ponaganset HS Sci & Che 1990-; *ai:* Class Adv; Co-Chair Schl Improvement Team; Co Scheduling Comm; NEA 1990-; NSTA 1990-; ASCD 1993-; RI Alzh Assoc 1993-; RI Sci Frameworks Comm, Mem; New England A Schls & Colls, Mem & Accreditation Visiting Comm; *office:* Pon HS 137 Anan Wade Rd North Scituate RI 02857

MARVELLE, JOHN DAVID, Associate Prof & Chrmn of Attleboro, MA; *m:* Elise Manning; *c:* Melissa, Kimberly, Christopher; *ed:* Bridgewater St Coll (BA) His 1972, (MED) Spec E Univ of MA at Amherst (EDD) Ed 1990; *cr:* Mansfield Pub Sch 1972-76; Project SPOKE Collaborative Project Dir 1976-84; Apple Inc Consultant 1984-90; Bridgewater St Coll Prof of Ed 1990-; *ai:* Coordinating Comm; Phi Delta Kappa 1978-; Awded Numerous Gr Areas of Tech & Early Chldhd Spec Ed; *office:* Bridgewater St C Hall Bridgewater MA 02325

MARVIN, ANGELA (MEAD), Third Grade Teacher; *b:* Long Beac *m:* Douglas B.; *c:* Mariangela, Teriangela; *ed:* Saint Marys Coll Dame (BA) Philisophy 1969; Duquesne Univ (MA) Theology (MSEd) Elem Ed 1991; *cr:* Resurrection Schl 4th Grd Tchr 19 Southside Cath HS 9th & 10th Grd Religion Tchr 1971-72; Resur Schl 6th & 7th Grd Sci Tchr 1974, 3rd Grd Tchr 1986-; *ai:* M Productions for Performances at Schl, Sr Citizen Homes & Civi Choreographer; Organized White Ribbon Campaign; Fed of Pitt Diocesan Tchrs 1989-, Rep; Amer Family Assn, Pittsburgh Co Against Pornography; Parish, Pro-Life Group Sec, March for Life Bus Capt; *office:* Resurrection Schl 1100 Creedmore Ave Pittsbu 15226

MARVIN, DANIEL, American Cultures Teacher; *b:* E. Stroudsbu *m:* Colleen Gillespie; *c:* Joshua, Aaron, Gabrielle, Danielle, Abiga

Stroudsburg Univ (BS) Scndry Ed; Colonial Northampton ediate 20, 30 Credit Hrs; *cr:* Pocono Mountain Schl Amer Cultures 990-; *ai:* Ftbl Coach; Speech, Debate; Weight Lifting Trng; PMEA Sunday Schl Tchr 1995-; Article Pub; *office:* Pocono Mountain Schl hool House Rd Swiftwater PA 18370

IN, JAMES A., Mathematics Tchr & Dept Chair; *b:* Meadville, Beverly A. Bergholtz; *c:* Timothy, Tracy, Toby; *ed:* Edinboro Univ ath, Sci 1956; Allegheny Coll (MA) Math Ed 1967; Post Grad Work Coll & Univ of Pittsburgh; *cr:* Meadville HS Tchr 1958-59; dge Springs HS Tchr & Dept Chair 1959-81; Saegertown HS Tchr Chair 1981-; *ai:* JETS Team Adv; Jr Class Adv; Fac Admin Bd; Act mm; NCTM 1989-; PSEA, NEA 1957-; Masonic Lodge 234 1986-, Yr; Church Cncl 4 Yrs; Natl Sci Fnd Summer Inst 1961-62; Natl Sci r 1970-71; Acad Excl Edinboro Univ 1989; *home:* RR 3 Saegertown 33

IN, JAMES PAUL, Drama Teacher; *b:* Lansing, MI; *ed:* Univ of IL mpaign-Urbana (BA) Drama 1975; Trinity Univ of San Antonio Drama, Playwriting 1979; *cr:* Dallas Theater Ctr Co Mem 1976-83; re Arts Ctr Drama Tchr 1984-; *ai:* Summer Camp Dir 1989-; ists Guild 1980-, Full & Active Mem Awd; Actors Equity 1985-; n 7 Plays, Produced Professionally; Several Play Adaptations; Fillmore Arts Ctr 35th & S Streets NW Washington DC 20007

IN, JOHN D., Retired Teacher; *b:* Buffalo, NY; *ed:* St Univ of NY Buffalo (BS) Ed 1961, (MS) Ed 1963; Univ of Bridgeport Grad 968; Univ of Buffalo PHD Candidate; *cr:* Sweet Home HS Tchr 4; *ai:* Pub Poet.

, KENNETH ALLAN, Chemistry Professor; *b:* Chicago, IL; *m:* en G.; *c:* Nicholas C.; *ed:* San Diego St Univ (BS) Chem 1968; Univ at Berkeley (PHD) Phys Chem 1973; Attnd Univ of Edinburgh ad, Worcester Fndtn for Experimental Bio; *cr:* Dartmouth Coll Asst 977-84; Dartmouth Med Schl Adj Prof 1977-84; Univ of MA Asst 985-87, Assoc Prof 1987-89, Full Prof 1989-; *ai:* Ctr for Intelligent erials & Biochem PHD Pgm Dir; Sigma Xi Natl Collegiate Honor mer Chemical Soc 1977-; Amer Soc Cell Bio 1977-; Amer Assn of i 1979-; Amer Soc Biochem & Mol Bio 1979-; Materials Rsrch Soc Union Concerted Scientists 1980-; Natural Resources Defense Cncl Francesfower NH Conservation Commission 1990-92, Decision Muscular Dystrophy Assn of Amer Post Doctoral Flwshp 1974-76; rants 1978-81, 1982-84; NIH Area Grant 1988-91; Army Rsrch Univ Instrumentation Grant 1991-95; 7 Patents Awded; 6 Book Pub; Numerous Articles Pub; *office:* Univ Of MA At Lowell 1 sity Ave Lowell MA 01854

ELLI, CAMERON L., English Teacher; *b:* San Francisco, CA; *m:* *c:* Michael; *ed:* Bates Coll (BA) Eng 1975; Bridgewater St Coll Cnslng 1981; Univ of MA at Amherst (CAGS) Ed 1993; *cr:* ith Carver Schls Eng Tchr 1977-83; Fisher Coll Adj Instr 1984-91; HS Guid Cnslr 1988-90, Eng Tchr 1990-; *ai:* Environmental Adv; MTA 1977-; NCTE ASCD 1990-; Pub Article; *office:* Carver HS S w Rd Carver MA 02330*

CIALE, HENRY WILLIAM,JR., Psych & World Cultures Tchr; *b:* rgh, PA; *m:* Ellen Haug; *c:* Nickolas, Kelsey; *ed:* Indiana Univ of SEd) Soc Stud 1970; Duquesne Univ (MA) His 1976; 61 Post Grad Hrs; In Svc Credits; *cr:* North Hills Schl Dist Psych & Soc Stud Tchr Ftbl Asst Coach 1972-86, Track Coach 1978-; Pine-Richland Schl kbl Head Coach 1986-94; Avonworth Schl Dist Ftbl Asst Coach *ai:* Intensive Schedule Electives Comm; NEA, PSEA, NHEA 1970-, c Rep 3 Yrs; NCSS; PA Cncl for Soc Stud; Western PA Cncl for Soc Mid Sts Cncl for Soc Stud; PA Scholastic Ftbl Coaches Assn; Natl hletic Coaches Assn; Tchrs of Psych in Scndry Schls-HS Affiliate; Psych Assn; North Hills Kiwanis 1970-80; North Hills Jaycees 9; Pine Twp Parks & Recreation Comm 1990-, Co-Chm; Agenda For motion of Ed Excl Mem at Duquesne Univ; 1 of 4 Tchrs Chosen to Interdisciplinary Connections Prgm at North Hils HS Top Sophs; or the Tchr Excl Awd Through The Pittsburgh Fnd 1995; *office:* Hills Sr HS 53 Rochester Rd Pittsburgh PA 15229

L, JAN C., Second Grade Teacher; *b:* Baltimore, MD; *m:* Ray; *c:* Karin; *ed:* Towson St Univ (BS) Early Chldhd Ed 1963; Montgomery ab Schls Inservice Prgm Master's Equivalency, Addlt 30 More ; *cr:* Frankfurt Dependent Schls Kndgtn Tchr 1963-64; Baltimore ub Schl 2 Grd Tchr 1964-66; Spackenskill Union Free Schl 2 Grd 967-68; Monthgomery Cty Pub Schls K-3 Grd Schl 1976-; *ai:* NEA MCEA 1980-; Nom for WA Post's Agnes Meyer Outstdng Tchr Awd *office:* Darnestown Elem Schl 15030 Turkey Foot Rd Gaithersburg 878

ARO, BRET L., Band Director & Music Teacher; *b:* Lansdale, PA; onica E. Ferraro; *c:* Angelina; *ed:* West Chester Univ (BS) Music Ed Master's Equivalency 1992; *cr:* WA Twp MS Band Dir 1980-83; Penn Jr HS Band Dir 1983-84; Downingtown Schl Dist Jr HS Band 85-89; Souderton HS Band Dir 1989-93; Methacton HS Band Dir *ai:* Dir of Marching, Concert, Jazz Bands, Pit Orch; PMEA, MENC Methacton Ed Assn 1993-; Cavalcade Indoor Drill Assn 1994-, Pres; Methacton Sr High 1001 Kriebel Mill Rd Norristown PA 19408*

AVAGE, LINDA MARIE, Asst Prof of Organic Chemistry; *b:* c City, NJ; *ed:* Georgian Ct Coll (BS) Chem, Ed 1972; Seton Hall MS) Chem 1984, (PHD) Organic Chem 1987; *cr:* Pius X Regnl HS pt Chair, Tchr 1972-82; Seton Hall Univ Tchng Asst, Adjunct Prof 7; Temple Univ Visiting Asst Prof 1988-92; Beaver Coll Asst Prof *ai:* Fac Sec; Retention Mgmt Comm Mem; Cafeteria Benefits ng; Stu Amer Chemical Soc Affiliate Co-Adv; Adv; Research Mentor Amer Chemical Soc 1988-; Philadelphia Organic Chemists 1988-, DE Valley Scic Cncl 1994-; G. W. Carver Sci Fair 1993-; Fac Dev Intellectual Inquiry Awd; Outstanding Tchr Asst Awd; Author; Beaver Coll 450 S Easton Rd Glenside PA 19038

CIA, CHERYL A., 5th-8th Grade Teacher; *b:* Uniontown, PA; *m:* it A. Jr.; *c:* Matthew P.; *ed:* Indiana Univ of PA (BS) Elem Ed 1981, Math 1986; TEI at St Vincent Coll; *cr:* Conn-Area Cath Schl Tchr Sylvan Learning Ctr Math Tch 1987-91; *ai:* Tutor; NCEA 1981-; RR 2 Box 240X Connellsville PA 15425

CIADRELLI, GARY JOHN, Mechanical Engrng Tech Prof; *b:* eld, MA; *m:* Carol O'Brien; *c:* Meghan, Michael; *ed:* Western New nd Coll (BS) Mechanical Engrng 1975; Rennselaer Polytechnic Inst Mechanical Engrng 1975; *cr:* Natl Bank Book Co Manufacturing 975-77; Amer Bosch Corp Sr Engr 1977-84; Hamilton Stan Sr Engr 87; Springfield Tech Comm Coll Mechanical Engrng Tech Prof *ai:* Mechanical Engrng Tech Dept Chm; ASME 1975-; Dept of Ed ne Tool Advanced Skills Trng Grant; Natl Sci Fnd Machine Tool ced Skills Trng Educl Resources Grant; Outstanding Fac Mem Awd *office:* Springfield Tech Comm Coll 1 Armory Square Springfield 1105

CIANGELO, STEPHEN VINCENT, Social Studies Teacher; *b:* , NY; *m:* Elizabeth Travers; *c:* Jennifer, Jeffrey; *ed:* Iona Coll (BA) 970, (MSEd) Ed 1973; 45 Addl Credits; *cr:* Sagamore Jr HS Track 1971-82, Tchr 1970-; *ai:* Sachem Cntrl Tchrs Assn 1970-, VP 5; Grant Mid Suffolk Tchr Ctr for Stud on Vietnam War; *home:* 75 Ln Medford NY 11763*

MASCIOLA, DOUGLAS ANTHONY, Administrative Assistant; *b:* McKees Rocks, PA; *m:* Janet Abercrombie; *ed:* Bethany Coll (BA) Hlth & PE 1969; Carnegie Mellon Univ (MPM) Pub Mgmt 1993; Duquesne Univ Interdisciplinary Doctoral Prgm for Educ Ldrs, Currently Completing Doctoral Dissertation 60 Credit Hrs; *cr:* Washington Schl Dist Tchr 1969-90, Admin Asst 1990-; *ai:* Curr Cncl Chair; Act 178 Staff Dev Chair; Federal Prgms Coord; ASCD, PASCD 1990-; Phi Delta Kappa 1993-; PSBA 1990-; Cntrl Washington Bus Dist, Washington Schl Comm Coalition; Presenting Dist Initiatives in Stu Achvmt, Motivation, Adv-Advisee Prgms, Strategic Planning & Alternative Assessment to Schl Dists Univs & Prof Orgs; *office:* Washington HS 201 Allison Ave Washington PA 15301

MASCOLL, SHIRLEY E., Science Instructor; *b:* New York, NY; *c:* Stefan, Cameron; *ed:* SUNY at New Paltz (BS), (MS) Sci Ed 1966, 1968; Tchrs Coll at Columbia Univ (EDD) Sci & Hlth Ed 1975; CCNY Hlth Ed; *cr:* Fordham Univ PT Instr Tutorial Pgm 1976-77; Tchrs Coll at Columbia Univ PT Instr 1977-79; Nanuet Pub Schls Sci Instr 1966-; *ai:* Team Ldr; Coord of Personalized Ed Plans; Tchrs & Admin Liaison; Coordinate Comm Involvement with Specific Grd Level Functions; NYSUT 1966-; STANYS 1970-; Clarkstown Gridiron Club 1990-; Jack & Jill of Amer 1991-, Exec Bd, Corresponding Sec; Dissertation Pub; Voter Registration; Comm Tutoring Svc; *office:* A MacArthur Barr MS 143 Church St Nanuet NY 10954*

MASER, MARGARET FRACE, French Teacher; *b:* Pittsburgh, PA; *m:* Richard R.; *c:* Laura Mills, Richard; *ed:* IN Univ of PA (BSEd) Span & Fr 1963; Credit Hrs at OH St 1964, Penn St 1970, IUP 1989 & Millersville Univ 1992 & 1995; *cr:* Penn Hills Schl Dist Span & Fr Tchr 1963-65; Penn Hall Acad Span & Fr Tchr 1967-70; Shaler Area Schl Dist Span & Fr Tchr 1978-; *ai:* Fr Hnr Soc Spon; AATF; PSEA & NEA; Shaler Area Ed Assoc; AFLA; *office:* Shaler Area Sr HS 381 Wible Run Rd Pittsburgh PA 15209

MASET, ELISABETH BETHEL, Lecturer; *b:* Prescott, AZ; *m:* Alvin J.; *c:* Caroline Sciandra, Renee, Dawn Metzler, Alicia; *ed:* Dutchess Comm Coll (AA) Liberal Arts, Hum 1982; Vassar Coll (AB) Pol Sci 1984; City Univ of NY (MA) Intnl Relations 1988; Completed All Credits for PHD 1994; *cr:* Dutchess Comm Coll Lecturer 1987-; *ai:* Freelance Research FDR Pres Lib; PHD Dissertation Presentation; Mid Hudson Consortium for Gender Equity; NEA 1990-; AAWCC 1994-; AAUW 1995; Sheridan Awd for Acad Excl; Tchng Awd for Non-Traditional Stu Assn; *home:* 4 New Rd Fishkill NY 12524*

MASIELLO, JOHN J., Social Studies Teacher; *b:* Matawan, NJ; *ed:* Villanova Univ (BA) Ec 1972; Rutgers Univ (MBA) Fin 1984; Grad & Post Grad Credits; *cr:* Matawan Reg HS Soc Stud Tchr 1974-; Brookdale Comm Coll Adj Ec Instr 1988-; *ai:* NHS Adv; Acad Challenge Team Coach; Schl Climate, SRA Scoring Comms; Fed Challenge Team Adv; Voter Registration Coord; NEA 1974-; NY Fed Ed Advy Bd 1995-; Cert of Excl Awd 1995; *office:* Matawan Regional HS 450 Atlantic Ave Matawan NJ 07747

MASIN, PATRICIA CAROL, Physical Education Teacher; *b:* Newark, NJ; *ed:* Springfield Coll (BS) PE 1973; *cr:* Battin HS PE Tchr 1973-77; Elizabeth HS PE Tchr 1977-, PE Dept Chprsn 1987-94, Peer Ldrshp Tchr 1993-; *ai:* Asst Girls Track Coach; Amer Ed Week Comm; Elizabeth, Union Cty, NJ Ed Assns 1973-; NEA 1973-; Guest Speaker NJ Tchrs Convention 1984; Outstanding Tchr Awd 1994; *office:* Elizabeth HS 600 Pearl St Elizabeth NJ 07202

MASKELL, KATHLEEN M., 9th-10th Grd Rdng Specialist; *b:* Baltimore, MD; *ed:* Towson St Univ (BS) Mass Comm 1984; MD St Cert Elem, MS 1994; Archdiocese of Baltimore Youth Ministry Cert; Preliminary Catechist Cert; *cr:* Holy Rosary Schl 3rd Grd Self-Contained Tchr 1987-90, 8th Grd Homeroom Tchr 1990-95; Archbishop Curley HS 1995-; *ai:* Safety Patrol; Stu Cncl, Fr Club Moderator; Grad Coord; Nwspr Moderator; Campus Ministry; Blck Friars; Thtr Grp; NCEA 1987-; Tchr of Yr 1993-; *office:* Archbishop Curley HS 3701 Sinclair Ln Baltimore MD 21213*

MASKOW, BRIAN DAVID, Director of Bands; *b:* Cleveland, OH; *m:* Laura Havir; *ed:* Bowling Green St Univ (BM) Music Ed 1977; Northwestern Univ (MM) Music Ed 1988; Attnd St Univ of NY at Buffalo, Univ of Akron, Duquesne Univ; *cr:* Parma City Schls Band, Music Tchr 1978-82; Highland Local Schls Band, Music Tchr 1982-83; Lakewood City Schls Bank & Music Tchr 1983-; *ai:* Marching Band, Jazz Band, Musical Pit Orch Dir; NEA, OEA, LTA, MENC, OMEA 1978-; IAJE, NBA 1983-; North Royalton United Meth Church 1978-; YMCA 1995-; Music Flwshp Northwestern Univ 1985; *office:* Lakewood HS 14100 Franklin Blvd Lakewood OH 44107*

MASLEY, SUE VERI, Sr HS Art Teacher; *b:* Rochester, PA; *m:* Jerry; *c:* Michael, Michelle; *ed:* Edinboro Univ (BS) Art Ed 1977; 24 Grad Credit Hrs; *cr:* Beaver Falls Schl Dist Art Tchr 1979; Hopewell Schl Dist Elem Art Tchr 1984-86, Sr High Art Tchr 1990-; Aliquippa Schl Dist Jr High Art Tchr 1986-90; *ai:* Scarab Art Club Spon; Dreamscapes Lit Arts Club; Strategic Planning Comm; NEA & PSEA 1984-; NAEA 1986-; PA Coalition for the Arts 1990-; *office:* Hopewell Sr HS 1215 Longvue Ave Aliquippa PA 15001

MASON, ADRIANA FERDMAN, Bilingual Mathematics Teacher; *b:* Buenos Aires, Argentina; *m:* Joel; *c:* Debra, Zachary; *ed:* Univ of Buenos Hills (BA, MBA) Acctng 1970, (CPA) Acctng 1971; New York Univ (MBA) Bus Admin 1972; Adelphi Univ (MA) Biling Ed 1996; Brooklyn Coll Ed; *cr:* Manhattan Reading Inst Tchr 1986-91; F.D.R. HS Tchr 1991-; *ai:* NABE, SABE 1995-; Hebrew Acad of Five Towns & Rdng 1977-, Rec Sec; PTA 1977-, Treas.

MASON, AGATHA JOHNSON, Nursing Teacher & Counselor; *b:* New York, NY; *w:* Jerome (dec); *c:* Michael; *ed:* NY Univ (BS) Nursing Ed 1969; Queens Coll (MS) Cnslr Ed 1976; Misericordia Hospital Schl of Nursing Diploma 1956; *cr:* USAF General Duty Nurse 1957-61; Metropolitan Hospital Operating Room Head Nurse 1961-63; Queens Hospital Ctr Operating Room Instr 1963-78; NYC Bd of Ed Tchr 1980-; *ai:* AFT 1980-; Delta Sigma Theta 1978-; *office:* Hillcrest HS 160-05 Highland Ave Jamaica NY 11432*

MASON, DAVID GEORGE, Math Teacher; *b:* Putnam, CT; *m:* Sandra Bernier; *c:* Darcy, Lindsey, Chris; *ed:* Univ CT (BA) Math Ed 1975, (MS) Math Ed 1978; *cr:* Fitch Jr HS Math Tchr 1975-76; Brooklyn Jr HS Math Tchr 1976-79; Kennett Jr HS Math Tchr 1979-; *ai:* Outing Club Adv; Grad Comm; NEA 1975-; CEA 1980-; NHEA 1980-; Local Boy Scouts; Local Sports Teams; *office:* Kennett Jr HS 126 Main St Conway NH 03818

MASON, GARRY R.,II, Physics & Chemistry Teacher; *b:* New Martinsville, WV; *ed:* Grove City Coll (BS) Chem Engrng 1982; Attnd Slippery Rock Univ Tchng Cert Physics & Chem 1985; Attnd Robert Morris Coll Working Towards (MBA); *cr:* Shaler Area HS Chem Tchr 1985-87; Hopewell Area HS Physics & Chem Tchr 1987-; *ai:* Odyssey of Mind, Class of 1996 Spon, Class of 1997 Spon; NEA & PSEA 1987-, Hopewell Area Ed Assn 1987-, Treas; *office:* Hopewell Area Schls 1215 Longvue Ave Aliquippa PA 15001

MASON, JANE ELLISON, Fifth Grade Teacher; *b:* Boston, MA; *m:* William Scott; *c:* Melissa N.; *ed:* Lesley Coll (BS) Elem Ed 1970, (MElEd) Elem Ed 1984; 30 Credit Hrs Beyond Masters; *cr:* David M Mindess 5th Grd Tchr 1970-; Boston Coll Stu Tchr Supvr 1975-76; David M Mindess Team Ldr 1992-; *ai:* Yrbk & Stu Cncl Adv; Peer Mediator Coach-Ldr; NEA, MTA, AEA 1970-; Temple Beth Torah, Ed Comm 1982-88, Co-Chair; Thanks to Tchrs Excl Awd 1990; Jiffy Lube Salute to Excl Awd 1993, 1994 & 1995; Horace Mann Scholar 1988; Ashland Ed Fnd 1996; *office:* David M Mindess MS 90 Concord St Ashland MA 01721*

MASON, JOHN GROUARD, Asst Prof of Pol Sci; *b:* New York, NY; *m:* Catherine Michele Coufleau; *c:* Julia DeForest, Jonathan Loving; *ed:* NYU Wash Sq Coll (BA) His 1972; NYU GSAS (MA) Pol Sci 1977; CUNY Queens Coll (MA) Sociology 1989; CUNY Grad Ctr (MPhil) Sociology 1991, (PHD) Sociology 1993; L'Ecole des Hautes Etudes En Sci Soc Paris 1985; Rsrch Intern, Fndtn Pour les Etudes de la Defense Nationale Paris 1984-85; *cr:* Queens Coll Adj Instr Sociology 1985-92; Michael Harriston Ctr Rsrch Fellow 1990-92; BMCC Adj Instr 1989-92; William Paterson Coll of NJ Asst Prof 1992-; *ai:* All Coll Commencement Comm Chair; NHS Co-Chair; Frosh Seminar Coord; Socialist Scholars Conf 1983-, Organizing Comm; Amer Pol Sci Assn 1986-; NYU Ctr for European Stud 1991-, Visiting Scholar, Wkshp Chair, European Security; Democratic Socialists of Amer 1981-, Intl Affairs Comm; PTA Lab Schl 1994-; WBAI Pacifica, Producer, Pub Affairs Dept; NY Soc Democratic Forum, Advy Bd Mem; Author: French Security Policy in a Disarming World; Co-Ed Les Syndicats Francais et Americains; Bourse Chateaubriand Flwshp 1984-85; Joseph Benseman Dissertation Awd 1989.

MASON, JOSE, Associate Prof of Mathematics; *b:* Caracas, Venezuela; *m:* Bonnie S. MacMillan; *c:* Carlos, Esteban, Eva; *ed:* Universidad Cntrl De Venezuela (Lic) Math 1965; Grad Pgm SUNY at Buffalo; *cr:* Universidad Cntrl Prof Asistente 1969-71, 1973-76; Universidad De Oriente Prof Asistente 1971-72; Communite Coll of Phila Assoc Prof 1976-; *ai:* Task Force for Dev Ed; Scientific Reasuring Dimension Comm; AFT 1976-; Math Assn of Amer 1990-; Amer Assn for Supervision & Curr Dev 1990-; NSF Grant Pre-Calculus II Book, Mathematica Universitaria; Stud Govt, Bilingual Pgm, Coucilio de Organizaciones Hispanas, awds; Participated in First Hispanic Symposium on Increasing Participation in Sci, Engr & Tech Careers; *office:* Comm Coll Of Philadelphia 1700 Spring Garden St Philadelphia PA 19126*

MASON, PAMELA L., Special Ed Department Chair; *b:* Fairfield, OH; *c:* Gregory, Kimberly; *ed:* Lynchburg (BA) Elem Ed 1973; Loyola (MED) Spec Ed 1977; Johns Hopkins Cert Admin 1995; *cr:* Relay Elem Schl Classroom Spec Ed Tchr 1980-82; Howard Co Schl of Tech Teen Parenting Tchr 1985-86; Atholton HS Spec Ed Tchr 1987-95, Dept Chair 1995-; *ai:* ARD, Schl Improvement Team, Stu Support Team, Social, Inclusion, Administrative Sub Comms; Block Scheduling Comm Chprsn; NEA, MSTA, HCEA 1987-, Bd of Dir; NASSP; Teen Parenting, Transition from Teen Parenting Grants; *office:* Atholton HS 6520 Freetown Rd Columbia MD 21044*

MASON, REBECCA S., Instrumental Music Teacher; *b:* Knoxville, TN; *ed:* St Univ of NY at Fredonia (BA) Music Ed 1967; Columbia Univ (MA) Conducting 1977; 30 Post Grad Credits from Montclair St, St Univ of NY at New Paltz & E Ramapo Tchrs Ctr; *cr:* Kakiat Jr High Instrumental Music Tchr & Dept Liaison 1967-95; Ramapo HS Instr Music 1995; *ai:* Jr HS All Dist Band Asst Conductor; NYSTA, NEA, NYSSMA & MENC 1967-; PTA Life Membership; Assorted placques & letters; PTA Cert of Merit; Bd of Ed & Stdnts; *office:* E Ramapo Cent Schl Dist 105 S Madison Ave Spring Valley NY 10970

MASONE, MARLEEN DADDIO, Jr High Math Teacher; *b:* Rockville Ctr, NY; *m:* Robert E.; *c:* Christopher, Nicole; *ed:* Suny New Paltz (BS) Math 1972; Adelphi Univ (MA) Tchng 1977; Long Island Univ (PD) Ed Admin 1992; 38 Addl Credit Hrs; *cr:* Long Beach Cath Schl 2nd Grd Tchr 1972-74; Longwood MS 7-8 Grd Math Tchr 1975-85; Longwood Jr HS 8-9 Grd Math Tchr 1985-; *ai:* Phi Delta Kappa 1990-; Mini Grant Tchr Mentor Prgms; *office:* Longwood Jr HS 198 Longwood Rd Middle Island NY 11953

MASONE, SALLY, High School Spanish Teacher; *b:* Trenton, NJ; *m:* Vincent B.; *ed:* Wilkes Coll (BA) Span, Fr, Ed 1968; Montclair St, Seton Hall, Westchester St Frng Lang, Ed Master's Equivalency 1979; Ibero-Americana Univ at Mexico City 12 Credits Conversational Span, Grammar 1966-67; Cty Coll of Morris 18 Credits Ger 1977-79; *cr:* Boonton HS Span Tchr 1968-70; Hopatcong HS Span, Fr Tchr 1970-72; Jefferson Twp HS Span Tchr 1972-; *ai:* Span Hnr Soc; Frgn Lang Competitions Stdnts Trainer; Stu Tchr Trng 1995; NJEA, NEA, MCCEA 1968-; JTEA 1972-; Extensive Travel Throughout Span-Speaking Areas; *office:* Jefferson Township HS Weldon Rd Oak Ridge NJ 07438

MASON-GRELL, BARBARA, Business Teacher; *b:* Yonkers, NY; *m:* Einar; *c:* Christopher Mason, Gordon Mason, Gregory Mason; *ed:* NY Inst of Tech (BS) Bus Mngmt-Magna Cum Laude 1977, (MBA) Fin-Graduated with Distinction 1982; Touro Coll (JD) Law 1989; *cr:* Bermuda Trade Dev Bd Admin Asst 1951-54; Kudner Advertising Agency Admin Asst, Copywriter 1955-58; Katherine Gibbs Schl Instr 1976-77; Half Hollow Hills HS East Bus Tchr 1977-; SUNY at Farmingdale Adj Prof 1979-83; Suffolk Comm Coll Adj Instr 1983-85; Sole Practioner Real Property Law 1989-; *ai:* DECA, Schl Store Adv; Supvrs Bldg Asst; Schl Based Mngmt Comm; Dept NYSUT Rep; NYSUT 1977-, Bldg Rep; Suffolk Cty Bar Assn 1988-, Real Property Comm; NY St Bar Assn 1988-, Labor & Employment Comm; Amer Bar Assn 1988-, Gen Practice Comm; Babylon Beautification Soc 1985-; Deans List; *office:* Half Hollow Hills HS East 50 Vanderbilt Pky Dix Hills NY 11746

MASONIS, KATHLEEN TODD, Former English Teacher; *b:* Washington, DC; *m:* William Talbott; *c:* Alexander, Elizabeth; *ed:* Univ of MD (BA) Latin 1981; *cr:* Immaculata Preparatory Schl Latin Tchr 1982-85; Immaculata Coll HS Latin & His Tchr 1985-91; Acad of Holy Cross Eng & Latin Tchr 1991-95; *ai:* NHS Adv.

MASS, ANTHONY J., His, Psych & Sociology Tchr; *b:* Oregon, OH; *m:* Elizabeth Bergman; *c:* Anthony II, Aaron, Austin, Allison, Abigail; *ed:* Univ of Toledo (BS) Soc Stud 1977; Heidelberg Coll (MA) Ed 1996; *cr:* Walbridge St Jerome 7th Grd Tchr 1977-81; Huron St Peter Schl 8th Grd Tchr 1981-85; Calvert HS Tchr, AD, Coach 1985-; *ai:* Head Bsktbl Coach; *office:* Calvert HS 152 Madison St Tiffin OH 44883*

MASSA, FRANK, Math Teacher; *b:* Patchogue, NY; *m:* Deana Wilton; *c:* Madeline; *ed:* SUNY at Oneonta (BA) Math Ed 1983; SUNY at Stony Brook (MA) Math Ed 1987; 6 Credits Schl Dist Admin Prgm; *cr:* William Floyd SD Math Tchr 1983-87; Mattituck Cutchogue SD Math Tchr 1987-; *ai:* Jr HS, Var Vlybl Coach; Negotiations Comm; NY St United Tchrs 1983-; *office:* Mattituck-Cutchogue SD Main Rd Mattituck NY 11952*

MASSA, KAREN, English Teacher; *b:* Orange, NJ; *ed:* AZ St Univ (BS) Advertising 1982; Montclair St Univ Tchr Cert Scndry Eng 1993; 35 Addl Hrs in Critical Thinking; *cr:* Media Buying Svcs Intl Media Buyer 1982-86; Power 96 FM Radio Account Exec 1986-88; WDFX FM Radio Sr Account Exec 1988-90; Parsippany HS Eng Tchr 1993-; *ai:* Schl Newspaper, Stu Cncl Adv; NJEA, NCTE 1993-; ASCD 1995-; *office:* Parsippany HS 309 Baldwin Rd Parsippany NJ 07034

MASSAGLIA, GARY JOHN, Biology & Earth Science Tchr; *b:* Philipsburg, PA; *ed:* Lock Haven St Coll (BA) Natural Sci & Bio 1983; Lock Haven Univ (BS) Scndry Ed Bio & General Sci 1987; Clarion Univ of PA (MEd) Sci Ed 1992; 9 Credit Hrs Gannon Univ; 15 Credit Hrs Clarion Univ of PA; 21 Credit Hrs Puquene Univ of PA, Toward (MEd) Admin & Supervsn; *cr:* Elk Cty Chrstn HS Bio-Earth Sci Tchr 1987-, Sci Dept Chm 1993; *ai:* Rotary Interact 1988-, Chprsn 1991; NHS Selection Comm 1988-; Stud Assistance Prgm 1988-; Yrbk Photographer 1991-;

Human Anatomy & Physiology, Mosby Yrbk Textbook Reviewer 1994; Mid St Chrprsn Steering Comm 1995-; NSTA 1988-; PSTA 1991-; NABT 1989-; ASCD 1994-; AAAS 1995-; HAPS 1995-; NY Acad of Sci 1995-; Amer Red Cross 1982-; Reliance Fire Company 1977-; St Marys Rotary Clb 1988-; St Marys Rotary Club Bd of Dir 1990; *office:* Elk County Christian H S 600 Maurus St Saint Marys PA 15857*

MASSAR, BARBARA CAROLINE, Asst Prof of Bus Management; *b:* Brooklyn, NY; *ed:* Fairleigh Dickinson Univ (BA) Mrktg, Psych 1977; Iona Coll (MBA) Fin 1982; Grad Courses in Multimedia Cmptr Intnl Mrktg SUNY at New Paltz; *cr:* BBDO Advertising Inc Rsrch Account Mgr 1979-85; Avon Products Inc Rsrch Assoc 1985-87; Sterling Pharmaceutical Inc Market Rsrch Mgr 1987-89; Orange Comm Coll Asst Prof 1989-; *ai:* Bus Stdnts Club Founder, Adv; Fac & Staff Dev, Various Dept Comms; Book Selection, eg Adv; Assn of Mrktg Edctrs 1995-; Co-Club of Yr Awded to Bus Club; *office:* Orange County Comm Coll 115 South St Middletown NY 10940

MASSARELLI, GREGORY A., HS Mathematics Teacher; *b:* New Philadelphia, OH; *m:* Susan Davis; *ed:* Denison Univ (BA) Math 1976; OH St Univ (MA) Guid, Cnslng 1981; Natl Sci Fnd Summer Inst Math Kent St Univ 1989-90; *cr:* Pickerington HS Math Tchr, Frosh Bsktbl Coach 1976-77; Watkins Meml HS Math Tchr, Asst Bsktbl Coach 1977-90, Math Tchr, Head Boys Bsktbl Coach 1990-; *ai:* NEA, OEA, SLEA 1976-, Schlsp Chm; OCTM 1985-; Knights of Columbus 1994-; St Pius X Cath Church 1977-, Lector, Communion Distributor; *office:* Watkins Memorial HS 8868 Watkins Rd SW Pataskala OH 43062

MASSARO, CATHERINE JEANNE, Spanish Teacher; *b:* Jamaica, NY; *ed:* St Univ Coll at Oneonta (BA) Scndry Ed, Span 1976; St Univ of NY at Stony Brook (MA) Lbrl Stud 1981; *cr:* Smithtown Cntrl Schl Dist Span Tchr 1979-92; Three Village Schl Dist Span Tchr 1992-; *ai:* Chrldng Adv 1982-92; Five Stu Trips to Spain Co-Coord; Stony Brook Univ Wind Ensemble Clarinetist; NYSAFLT 1976-.

MASSARO, THERESA BRUNO, Biology Teacher; *b:* New Kensington, PA; *m:* Warren Jr.; *ed:* Univ of Pittsburgh (BS) Bio 1959; IN Univ of PA (MS) Psychological Cnslng 1966; 1 Semester Post Grad Study Advanced Bio Penn St 1992; *cr:* Valley HS Sci, Bio Tchr 1965-95; *ai:* NEA, PSEA, NKAEA 1965-; Hosp Auxiliary 1993-; Alle-Kiski Vly Concert Assn 1993-, Bd of Dir; *office:* Valley HS 703 Stevenson Blvd New Kensington PA 15068

MASSE, ANN WALKER, English Teacher; *b:* Boston, MA; *c:* Susan Elisabeth Masse Woodyatt, David Charles, Leslie Ann; *ed:* Vassar Coll (AB) Eng 1948; Fitchburg St Coll (BS) Ed 1964, (MA) Ed 1968; Middleburry Coll (MA) Eng 1972; Katharine Gibbs Cert Bus 1949; Mt Wachosett Comm Coll 8 Bus, Cmptr courses 1979-87; *cr:* Eisenhower Personal Staff Writer, Researcher 1952; Bus Week Magazine Pub Relations, Assoc Ed 1952-56; Fitchburg Pub Schls Tchr, Dept Head, Curr Ldr 1964-83; Twin City Chrstn Schl Eng Tchr, Scndry Tchr 1983-87, 1994-; *ai:* Grant Writer; MACS, MA Assn of Chrstn Schls 1994-; *office:* Twin City Christian Schl 194 Electric Ave Lunenburg MA 01462

MASSEY, JANET F., Assistant Professor; *b:* Philadelphia, PA; *ed:* St Joseph's Univ (BS) Acctng 1979, (MBA) Fin 1983; *cr:* Neumann Coll Asst Prof 1987-; *ai:* Bus Club Adv; VITA site Coord; AAUP 1995-; PICPA, AICPA, NAA 1983-; *office:* Neumann Coll Concord Rd Aston PA 19014

MASSEY, PATRICIA FARRY, Librarian; *b:* Newark, NJ; *m:* Denis Barry; *c:* Paul F., Sean P., Brian J., Megan E.; *ed:* Caldwell Coll (BA) Art Ed 1970; Seton Hall Univ (MA) Ed 1975; Rutgers Univ Information, Lib Stud; Newark St Coll 9 Credits Lib Sci 1971; Caldwell Coll 12 Credits Lib Sci 1972-73; *cr:* 18th Ave Schl Librn 1970-76; Wilson Ave Schl Librn 1976-82; South Plainfield HS Librn 1989-92; South Plainfield MS Librn 1992-93; South Plainfield HS Librn 1993-; *ai:* Infolink Regnl Interlibrary Loan Voting Rep; Information Ctr Cncl; NJEA; NEA; ALA 1992-; EMANJ, EMAMC 1989-; South Plainfield Pub Lib 1992-, Lib Bd Trustee; Edison PTA, PTO Schlsp comm 1979-, Sec; Internet Grant NJ HS Media Ctrs; *office:* South Plainfield HS 200 Lake St South Plainfield NJ 07080

MASSEY, SUZANNE KNOX, Mathematics Teacher; *b:* Salisbury, MD; *c:* Laura Elizabeth, Leann Knox; *ed:* Salisbury St Univ (BS) Math 1968; Post Grad Stud; *cr:* Wicomico HS Math Tchr 1968-75; James M. Bennett HS Math Tchr 1993-; *ai:* Var Math Team Adv; NEA; MS St Tchrs Assn; Wic Cty Tchrs Assn; MD Cncl Tchrs of Math; MCTM; Ayres United Meth Church; *home:* 34000 Rounds Rd Pittsville MD 21850

MASSEY, VERONICA, Prof of Eng as a Second Lang; *b:* Norwich, CT; *ed:* Albertus Magnus Coll (BA) Fr 1964; Univ of Rochester (MA) Fr Lit 1969; Columbia Univ (PHD) Fr Lit 1983; Jersey City St Coll Post Grad Stud in Tchng of Eng to Speakers of Other Langs 1976; *cr:* Dracut Jr HS Fr Tchr 1964-67; Jersey City St Coll Fr Instr 1968-78, Asst Prof of ESL 1978-88, Assoc Prof of ESL 1988-94, ESL Prof 1994-; *ai:* Prsnl, Policy Comms ESL Prgm; TESOL, NYSTESOL 1984-; Univ of Rochester Tuition Waiver Awd 1968.

MASSI, CAROL-ANNE REESE, Secondary Mathematics Teacher; *b:* Tamaqua, PA; *m:* Paul; *c:* Karyn; *ed:* Gettysburg Coll (BA) Math 1962; Trenton St Coll (MA) Math 1962; La Salle 3 Credit AP Course; *cr:* Hamilton HS West Math Tchr 1963-66; N Burlington Cty Regnl HS Math Tchr 1966-; *ai:* Math Team Adv; Pupil Assistance Comm; Stu Staff Recognition Comm; Stu of Month Comm; Middle Sts Visiting Comm; NEA, NJEA 1963-; BCEA, NBCRTA 1966-; Band Parents Bd 4 Yrs; Chm of Phone Comm 1989-93; NHS Master Tchr of Yr 1986-87; NHS Honorary Member 1990; NJ Governors Tchrs Awd 1995-; *office:* Northern Burlington Reg HS 160 Mansfield Rd E Columbus NJ 08022*

MASSICOTTE, BARBARA S., 7th & 8th Grd Mathematics Tchr; *b:* Port Chester, NY; *c:* Heather Marie, Kelly Elizabeth; *ed:* Keene St Coll (BA) Psych 1971, Elem Ed 1977; Antioch New England Grad Schl (MED) Fnds in Ed 1992; Coll of William & Mary His; Credit Hrs Notre Dame Coll, UC Berkeley, Keene St Coll; *cr:* Alstead Primary Sdchl 4 Grd Tchr 1977-83; Vilas Schl 6 Grd Tchr 1983-94, 7-8 Grd Math & Algebra I Tchr 1994-; *ai:* Wellness Comm; Math Assessment Curr Stud; Math Team Coach; 7th Grd Adv; NEA, Fall Mt Tchrs Assn 1977-, Past Bldg Rep, Past Pres; NH ATMNE, NCTM 1993-; Delta Kappa Gamma 1988-, 2nd VP, Mbrshp Chm; Equals Prgm in NH Dir 1993-; Master Tchr Natl Tchr Trng Inst 1994; NH Partners in Ed Awd Outstdng Vol, Tchr Team 1993-; *home:* 59 Maple Ave Apt 92 Keene NH 03431

MASSICOTTE, JOY M., First Grade Teacher; *b:* Bridgeport, CT; *ed:* Southern CT St Coll (BS) Early Chldhd Ed 1979; Southern CT St Univ (MA) Rdng 1986; Sixth Yr Admin 1989; *cr:* St Raphaels Schl 6th-7th Grd Tchr 1979-80; Grasmere Nursery Schl Thcr of 4 Yr Olds 1980-81; St Anns Schl 3rd Grd Tchr 1981-85; Franklin Schl 1st-3rd Grd Tchr 1985-; *ai:* Mini Course Prgm Dir; Active Authors Club Ldr; Soc Stud Curr Comm; Drama Club Adv & Dir; ASA, PDK, ASCD 1989-; SEA, NEA 1985-; St Lawrence CCD Prgm 1994-, 7th-8th Grd Instr; Whos Who Among Young Profs; Spec Recognition Certs for Mentor, Cooperating Tchr; Tchr of Yr Finalist; *office:* Franklin Elem Schl 1895 Barnum Ave Stratford CT 06497*

MASSIE, ANNETTE ALBAN, Third Grade Teacher; *b:* Ironton, OH; *m:* Larry K.; *ed:* OH Univ (BS) Elem Ed 1978, (MS) Elem Ed 1981; *cr:* Ironton City Schls Tchr 18 Yrs; *ai:* Distance Learning Tchr; Tech Team Co-Chair; OH Univ Stu Tchr Trainer; Sci Day Presenter; OEA 1978-; SECO 1991-, Presenter; Nazarene Church, Childrens Church Dir; Governors Trailblazer, OH Best Practice, Ashland Oil Golden Apple Awds; Ameritech Superschool Presenter; Martha Holding Jennings Scholar; *office:* Whitwell Elem 2213 S 4th St Ironton OH 45638*

MASSIE, BYRON KENT, Teacher of Learning Disabled; *b:* Dayton, OH; *ed:* Capitol Univ (BA) Soc Stud 1992; Univ of Dayton Ed Admin; *cr:* Tecumseh HS Tchr of Learning Disabled 1992-; *ai:* Var Ftbl Team Offensive Coord; Power Lifting, JV Bsbl Coaches; NEA, OH Ed Assn, Tecumseh Ed Assn 1992-; N Cntrl Comm 1993-; Liaison 1992-.

MASSIMI, MARIA G., Foreign Lang Teacher & Liaison; *b:* New Rochelle, NY; *m:* Frank; *c:* Robert, Stephen; *ed:* Marymount Coll (BA) Fr Lit; Columbia Univ (MA) Curr Dev 1975; Coll of New Rochelle (MSEd) Admin 1993; Attnd Fordham Univ, Iona Coll, Tchrs Ctr; *cr:* Westlake MS Fr Tchr; Westlake HS, MS Fr & Italian Tchr, Dept Liaison; Westchester Comm Coll Advanced Ital Tchr 1993-95; *ai:* AFS Club, Fr Club, Italian Club Adv; Natl Schlsp Comm; Schl Exchs; European Field Trips; Exam Comm; ACTFL; NYSTAFLT; AATL; AFT; AIFS, Awd; Historical Soc 1976-, Pres; Newcomers Club 1976-, Pres; Womens Club 1980-, Mbrshp Chprsn; Lit Magazine Grant; Sardinia Exch; Pilot Proficiency Comm; Consultant to Regents; Dev WHS Course Catalogue; Dev Frgn Lang Curr Guidebook; Historical Soc Past Pres & Mem Bd of Trustees; *office:* Westlake HS MS Westlake Dr Thornwood NY 10594

MASSOUD, DONALD PETER, Guidance Counselor; *b:* Fall River, MA; *m:* Donna Rizzo; *c:* Alexandra, Jonathan; *ed:* Bridgewater St Coll (BS) Ed 1967, (MED) Guid 1968; Vanderbilt Univ Inst in Eng as 2nd Lang 1969; *cr:* Fall River Pub Schls Eng as 2nd Lang Tchr 1968-72, Elem Guid Cnslr 1972-82, HS Guid Cnslr 1982-, HS Guid Cnlsr in Charge 1994-; *ai:* Stu Asst Team; Girls Bsktbl Ofcl Scorer; Curr Revision Comm; MA Schl Cnslr Assn 1972-; Fall River Admin Assn 1972-, Past Sec; Fall River Jr Twilight Bsbl League 1961-, Bd of Dirs, 2 Svc Awds; Cath Church 1993-, Ordained Deacon; Bentley Coll Excl in Cnslng Awd 1990; MA Army Natl Guard Ed Awd 1993; Local Newspaper Golden Apple Awd 1994; *office:* Durfee HS 360 Elsbree St Fall River MA 02720

MASSUCCI-FERRANTE, CAROL A., 9th-11th Grd Italian Teacher; *b:* Brooklyn, NY; *m:* John B. Ferrante; *ed:* Queens Coll (BA) Italian, Span, Lit 1984, (MA) Italian Lit 1988; Rutgers Univ PHD Candidate; Working Toward Admin, Supervision Cert Coll of New Rochelle; *cr:* Christ the King HS Italian Tchr 1984-89, 1990-; Rutgers Univ Italian Instr 1990; *ai:* ASCD 1995-; MLA 1990-; MCES Schlsp 1988; *office:* Christ The King Regional HS 68-02 Metropolitan Ave Middle Village NY 11379*

MAST, RUBY BAIER, Retired Math Teacher; *b:* Cincinnati, OH; *m:* Daniel Lynn; *ed:* Univ of Cincinnati (BSEd) Math 1963; Attnd Wittenberg Univ, Wright St Univ & Univ of Dayton Post Grad Stud; *cr:* Cincinnati Pub Schls Math Tchr 1963-64; Northwestern Local Schls Math Tchr 1964-78; Clark Co Bd of Ed Coord of GATE 1979-80; Northwestern Local Schls Math Tchr 1980-94; *ai:* Task Force & Magazine Fund Comms; NEA, OEA & COTA 1980-94; Northwestern Tchrs Assn 1980-94, Negotiations Team; Northwestern Outstanding Tchr of Yr Awd 1972-73; Educl Excl Awd 1993; Hnry Mem Northwestern Natl Hnr Soc 1995; *home:* 4241 Willowdale Rd Springfield OH 45502

MAST, SUSAN PLANCEY, Sixth Grade Teacher; *b:* Camden, NJ; *m:* Gordon Richard Oesterle; *c:* Christine, Patricia; *ed:* Monmouth Univ (BA) Elem Ed 1966; Kean Coll Masters Prgm Equivalency 12 Addl Credits; *cr:* Meadowbrook Elem Schl Fifth Grd Tchr 1966-72, Sixth Grd Tchr 1972-73; Vanamassa Schl Second Grd Tchr 1973-74; Oakhurst Schl Second Grd Tchr 1974-75; Meadowbrook Elem Schl Spec Ed Tchr 1975-84; Margaret L. Vetter Elem Schl Third Grd Tchr 1984-89, Sixth Grd Tchr 1989-; *ai:* Yrbk; Sixth Grd Newspaper; Eatontown Tchrs Assn 1966-, Sec; NJEA, NEA 1966-; NCTM 1984-; Greater Shore Band 1966-, Bd Mem; Tchr of Yr; NJ Math Curr Framework.

MASTANDREA, DIANE MARIE, Spanish & Latin Teacher; *b:* Boston, MA; *ed:* Westfield St Coll (BA) Span Ed 1977; Harvard Univ Latin, Northeastern Univ Cmptr Sci Attnd; *cr:* Norwood Jr HS Span Tchr 1979-83; North Middlesex Reg HS Span Tchr 1984-; *ai:* Cultural Arts & NHS Comms; Schl Cncl; Bldg Rep; K-12 Lang Com; Ma Fla 1979-; Kappa Delta Pi 1976-; NEA & MTA 1979-; Friends of the Lib 1993-; Townsend Historical Soc; *home:* 40 Fitchburg Rd Apt 334 Townsend MA 01469

MASTANDREA, MARY T., Drama & English Teacher; *b:* Norwood, MA; *ed:* Stonehill Coll (BA) Eng Lit 1978; Emerson Coll (MA) Theatre Arts 1987; 18 Credit Hrs Critical, Creative Thinking Univ of MA at Boston; *cr:* Canton Summer Theatre Dir, Bd Chair 1976-84; Canton HS Dir 1979-88; Huntington Theatre Co Tchr Advy Cncl 1984-; Brookline HS Tchr, Dir 1987-; *ai:* Dir Afterschool Productions; Fac Liason Drama Soc; At Risk Comm; Seminar Ldr Huntington Theatre Yount Critics Inst; NCTE 1992-; Huntington Theatre Tchr Advy Cncl 1989-; NETC; Masspirg 1991-; WGBM 1992-; NEH Summer Shakespeare Tchng Inst 1991-92, Seminar 1994; Terrific Tchrs Making Difference Awd 1992; Pub Stud & Curr Guides Huntington Theatre Co; *office:* Brookline HS 115 Greenough St Brookline MA 02146*

MASTAS, SANDRA M., 4th Grade Teacher; *b:* Lowell, MA; *m:* Gary N.; *ed:* Lowell St Coll (BS) Elem Ed 1971; Northeastern Univ (MED) Ed 1975; *cr:* New Searles Elem 5th Grd Tchr 1971-; *ai:* AFT 1971-; NCMT; Philoptoches Soc 1978-; *home:* 146 Jewett St Lowell MA 01850

MASTERS, EILEEN DIMON, Vice Principal; *b:* Brooklyn, NY; *c:* Mary, Brian, Mark, John; *ed:* Ladycliff Coll (BA) Eng 1959; St John's Univ (MS) Elem Ed 1963; Loyola Coll Sp Ed; Trinity Coll Sp Ed, Admin; *cr:* North Babylon Pub Schl Kndgtn, 1st Grd Tchr 1959-62; St Bernard's Schl Kndgtn, 2nd Grd Tchr 1974-80; St John the Bapt Schl 1st Grd Resource, 2nd, 1-7 Grd Tchr 1980-95; Howard Comm Coll Part-time Cnslng Asst 1985-88; St Pius X Regnl Schl Vice Prin 1995-; *ai:* Mid Atlantic States Evaluation Comm; Gifted Prgm; Children Are People Prgm; NCEA 1974-; Drug Prevention, Drug Free Schls 1992-, Montgomery Cty Comm Partnership SSTART Awd 1993-94; Outstdng Young Women of MD Awd.*

MASTERS, ELIZABETH MC MARTIN, Secondary English Teacher; *b:* Ogdensburg, NY; *m:* William A.; *c:* Vickie Bartholomew, David, Daniel, Valerie Kelly; *ed:* Houghton Coll (BA) Eng, Bible 1951; SUNY at Potsdam (MS) Eng 1970; 21 Hrs Counseling, Admin St Lawrence Univ; Attnd Wesley Theological Seminary; *cr:* Frenchburgh HS Latin, Eng Tchr 1 Yr; Heuvelton Cntrl Sub Tchr 3 Yrs; Madrid-Waddington Cntrl Sub Tchr 3 Yrs, Music Tchr 1/2 Yr; Lisbon Cntrl Schl Scndry Eng Tchr 28 Yrs; *ai:* Forensic Club; Jr Class, Yrbk Adv; Oratorical Contests; Play Dir; Splng Bee; 4-H; NYSUT, AFT 1967-; Lisbon Tchrs Assn 1967-, Pres, VP, Negotiations; NYSEC; NCTE; ASCD; Delta Kappa Gamma Epsilon 1985-, Recording Sec; United Meth Church 1983-, Pastor; Local Part-time Pastor; NYC Grange; Order of Eastern Stars; Pomono Grange Citizen of Yr; Amer Legion Svc Awd; Dewitt Clinton Masonic Comm Svc Awd; *home:* 1585 W Lake Rd Heuvelton NY 13654*

MASTERS, MAUREEN MC GREAL, Remedial Mathematics Teacher; *b:* White Plains, NY; *m:* Stephen D.; *c:* Stephen, Meghan; *ed:* Pace Univ (BS) Math 1961; 6 Credit Hrs Each Columbia Univ, Syracuse Univ, Coll of New Rochelle, Long Island Univ; 12 Credit Hrs CCNY; 10 Credit Hrs Western CT St; *cr:* Tarrytown Pub Schls MS Math Tchr 1962-67; Eisenhower Sr HS Math Tchr 1967-69; Tarrytown Pub Schls MS, HS Math Tchr 1969-72, 1974-75, 1977-78, 1981-; *ai:* Bldg Site, Sick Bank Comm Tchr Rep; Tarrytown Tchr Assn 1962-, Bldg Rep; NYSUT, AFT 1981-; Amer Assn of Univ Women 1970-; PTA 1990-; NSF Grant; Tandy Tech Scholars; Outstdng Tchr Awd; *office:* Tarrytown Pub Schls 210 N Broadway Tarrytown NY 10591*

MASTERS, SHEHREVER, Honors Phys & Anat Teacher; *b:* K Pakistan; *m:* Barbara Anne; *c:* Trevor Earl; *ed:* OH St Univ (B Zoology 1978; Bowling Green St Univ (MS) Bio, Genetics 198 Tchng Cert Bio, Chem, Comprehensive General Sci; *cr:* R. S. Rog Honors Chem, Physics, Gen Sci Tchr 1987-88; Univ of Toledo Com Coll Anatomy, Physiology, Bio Tchr 1987-91; E. L. Bowsher H Honors General Sci Tchr 1988-89; A. Devilbiss HS General Sc 1990-91; E. L. Bowsher HS Honors Anatomy, Physiology, Environmental Sci, Gen Sci Tchr 1991-; *ai:* TFT, AFT Sub Tchrs C Negotiation Comm 1990-91; Environmental Sci Book Selection 1991-92; Schl Bldg Comm 1992-93; Cogitators Order Adv; AF 1987-; *office:* E. L. Bowsher HS 3548 S Detroit ave Toledo OH 43

MASTERSON, ROBERT PATRICK, 6th Grade Math Teach Taunton, MA; *m:* Dianne Johnson; *c:* Jeffrey Patrick, Benjamin Arth Providence Coll (BA) Soc Sci 1968; Bridgewater St Coll Grad St HopewellSchl 5th Grd Self Contained Tchr 1968-69; Brewster Ele 5th Grd Self Contained Tchr 1969-73; Nauset Regnl MS 6th Grd Tea 1973-; *ai:* Girl's Sftbl Coach 1986-; Cape Cod Soccer Ofcls Ass 1991-94; IAABO Bd #154 Bsktbl Ofcls, Lower Cape Rep 1988- 1968-; Nauset Ed Assn 1969-; MA Bsktbl Coaches Assn 1976-88 Dist Rep 1986-88, Asst Coach of Yr 1983; Bldg Comm 1987-94; Nauset MS Eldredge Pkwy Orleans MA 02653

MASTERSON, ROSEMARY AUSTIN, 7th-8th Grade Soc Stud T *b:* Albany, NY; *m:* Peter J. III; *c:* Peter, Kevin; *ed:* Coll of Saint Ros Soc Stud 1974; 30 Credits Permanent Cert from SUNY at Albany, Sage Coll at Troy; *cr:* Knickerbacker MS Soc Stud Tchr 1982-; Mentoring Prgm, Cooperating Tchr; AFT 1982-; PTA 1982-; Jr NH of Yr 1986.

MASTERSON, SANDRA KREUTER, High School English Teac Buffalo, NY; *m:* Edward; *c:* Erin; *ed:* Daemen Coll (BA) Eng Canisius Coll (MS) Eng 1970; 30 Credit Hrs in Cnslng; *cr:* Buffa Schls Stu Tchr 1967; West Seneca East MS Eng Tchr 1967-68; West East HS Eng Tchr 1967-68; West Seneca East HS Eng Tchr 1969-7 Seneca West HS Eng Tchr 1972-; *ai:* Annual Shaw Festival Fie Co-Chm; Tech Comm; YMCA, Various Chairs, Comms; Buffalo S Club, Various Chairs, Comms; Daemen Coll Bd of Governors, Tre Elect; Arabian Horse Registry of Amer 1996; Red Cross Certfd Lecturer 1996; *office:* West Seneca West Sr HS 3330 Seneca S Seneca NY 14224*

MASTERSON, WILLIAM,JR., Director of Dev & English T Trenton, NJ; *m:* Elaine D.; *c:* Mark, Gregory, Nancy; *ed:* St Joseph Psych 1960; Trenton St (MA) Eng Ed 1968; *cr:* St John Neumann H 1961-64; Archbishop Wood HS Tchr, Dept Head, Dir of Dev Delaware Vly Coll Adj Eng Tchr 1981-; *ai:* Mid Sts Steering, Comm; ACT 1965-; NCEA 1961-; *office:* Archbishop Wood HS 65 Rd Warminster PA 18974

MASTOROVICH, MELISSA LYNNE, Nursing Instructor; *b:* pitt PA; *ed:* Univ of Pittsburgh (BSN) Nrsng 1988; Duquesne Univ Nrsng Ed 1994; *cr:* Childrens Hosp of Pittsburgh Staff Nurse 198 Vly Gen Hosp SON Nrsng Instr 1989-; STAT Nrsng Cons Psychiatric Nurse Consultant 1989-; Comm Coll of Alleq Co Nrsn 1992-; *ai:* Natl Leage for Nrsng Self Study comm; ANA 1988-; S INSNA 1986-, Honorary Mem; NLN 1990-; Sigma Theta Tou Rsrch Contributer to Good Thinking; Test Taking Problem Solving & Study for Nrsng Stdnts; *office:* Community Coll 595 Beatty Rd Monroevi 15146

MASTRANGELO, ANGELA M., Former Music Educat Philadelphia, PA; *ed:* Immaculata Coll (BA) Theology, Music 197 Chester Univ (MM) Music Ed 1983; 18 Addl Credits; Schl Psych C Diocesan Elem Schls Grd Tchr 1967-72, Elem Music Ed Tchr 19 Diocesan Scndry Schls HS Music Ed Tchr 1978-91; St Maria Gor Music Edctr 1991-95; St Christopher's Hosp for Children Psych 1995-; *ai:* Orch; Archdiocesan Band Festivals; NCEA, PMEA NASP 1994-; ACA, AAC 1993-; Scndry Schl Comm IHM 1984-93.

MASTRANGELO, DEAN ROSS, Choral Music Director; *b:* Wash PA; *m:* Lisa Gill; *ed:* Clarion Univ (BS) Music Ed 1991; *cr:* Burget Jr, Sr HS Choral Music Dir 1993-; *ai:* NEA, PSEA, MENC 1993 Song Copyrighted & Recorded; *home:* 17 OHare Rd Canonsburg PA

MASTRANGELO, LAURA M., Biology Instructor; *b:* Jackson H NY; *m:* Paul Gudewicz; *c:* Jason, Nicholas, Emily; *ed:* Siena Coll (1985; Albany Med Coll (PHD) Physiology & Cell Bio 1991; *cr:* Med Coll Post Doctoral Fellow 1991-92; SUNY at Albany Post D Fellow 1992-93; HVCC Instr 1993-; *ai:* NABT 1995-; NIH & Po Doctoral Fellow; Articles Pub; *office:* Hudson Valley Comm C Vandenburgh Ave Troy NY 12180

MASTRIAN, ANTHONY P., Biology Teacher; *b:* Sharon, PA; *m:* McEntire; *c:* Anthony Jr., Nicholas; *ed:* Edinboro St Coll (BS) Scnd Bio 1974; Westminster Coll (MED) Cnlsr Ed 1977, Elem Ed 19 Hickory HS Tchr 1975-; *ai:* Cross Cntry Coach; Boys Bsktbl Asst Schl Quality Cr; NEA, Hermitage Ed Assn 1975-; *office:* Hermitag Dist 640 N Hermitage Rd Hermitage PA 16148

MASTRO, CHRISTOPHER PAUL, Senior High English Teac Schenectady, NY; *m:* Linda Condon; *ed:* St Michael's Coll (BA) Eng Winooski VT (MA) Eng, Ed 1969; *cr:* Mohonosen HS 10, 12 Grd En 1969-71; Voorheesville HS 9 Grd Eng, 11 Grd Regents Eng Tchr 197 NY United Tchrs 1969-; Golub Tchr Recognition in Excl Tchr Awd Commencement Speaker 1986.

MASTROG, ROSEMARIE BRINDLE, Fifth Grade Teacher; *b:* Er *m:* Ronald; *c:* Greg; *ed:* Mercyhurst Coll (BS) Elem Ed 1962; Ed Univ (MED) Elem Ed 1967; Mercyhurst Coll Amer Sign Lang; Gannon Univ; *cr:* Greene Twp Elem Schl 3-6 Grd Tchr 1962-71; East Campus 3 Grd Tchr 1971-72; Harbor Creek Jr HS 7-8 Grd Rdn 1974-80; Klein Elem Schl 4-5 Grd Tchr 1980-; *ai:* NEA, PSEA WEA 1962-71; HCEA 1974-; Lawrence Park Bus, Prof Assn 1989-9 Taft Tchr 1991; *office:* Klein Elem Schl 5325 E Lake Rd Erie PA 1

MASTROIANNI, JOHN FRANK, Director of Bands; *b:* Bridgepo *ed:* Univ of Bridgeport (BS) Music Ed 1982, (BM) Jazz Stud 198 Univ (MA) Jazz Performance & Composition 1987; Doctorate Can *cr:* Cntrl HS Dir of Bands 1982-89; Univ of Bridgeport Concert Ba 1986; NY Univ Applied Saxophone Tchr 1987-90; New Canaan HS Bands 1989-; *ai:* Jr Class Adv; NCEA 1989-; MENC 1980-; IAJE Young Peoples Symphony 1992-, Conductor; Recordings Cookin Burners Stash Records, The Time Being Jazz Alliance Records, Ve New England Jazz Ensemble; Performances at Festivals in US & E *office:* New Canaan HS 11 Farm Rd New Canaan CT 06840

MASTRONARDI, ELAINE MARIE, Art Teacher; *b:* Springfield *ed:* Holyoke Comm Coll (AA) Arts & Scis 1981; Univ of MA at Ar (BA) Art His 1983; Elms Coll (MAT) Ed 1993; *cr:* Bay Ban Operations Supvr 1985-87; Cathedral HS Art Tchr 1987-; Wad Atheneum Conservation Intern 1994-;Anna Maria Coll Adj Prof Springfield Col l Adj Fac 1995-; *ai:* MAEA, NAEA 1995-; NCEA Naurison Schlsp; *office:* Cathedral HS 260 Surrey Rd Springfiel 01118*

MASTROPOALO, ROSEMARIE SORRENTINO, Latin T Technology Coord; *b:* Neward, NJ; *m:* James B.; *c:* James J., Antho

:k J.; *ed:* Douglas Coll (BA) Classical Civilization 1968; Iona Coll mptr Ed 1989; 45 Addl Hrs; *cr:* Nutley HS Latin, Fr, Italian Tchr ; Gino's Inc Office Mgr, Admin Asst 1979-81; Marriott Corp Legal :c 1981-83; Northern Highlands Regnl HS Latin, Fr Tchr, Tech 983-; *ai:* Yrbk, Coll Bd Test Ctr Supvr; Ldrshp Team; NEA, NJEA, NJ Classical Assn 1983-; Mid-Atlantic Classical Assn 1985-; Northern Highlands Reg HS 298 Hillside Ave Allendale NJ 07401

', SUE ELLEN, Secondary Social Studies Tchr; *b:* Detroit, MI; *m:* ; *c:* Joshua, Jason; *ed:* Univ of CO (BA) Pol Sci 1971; Wayne St IA) His 1980; *cr:* Clawson Schl Dist Soc Stud Tchr 1972-79; Troy st Soc Stud Tchr 1979-88; North Penn Schl Dist Soc Stud Tchr *ai:* Acad Decathlon Team Adv; NEA 1972-; Amer Assn of Univ 1988-, Branch VP; *office:* North Penn HS 1340 Valley Forge e PA 19446

CCI, JUDITH DOROTHY, Guidance & Tech Facilitator; *b:* p, MA; *ed:* Salem St Coll (BS) Math & Sci Ed 1969, (MED) Guid 1971; Lesley Coll (MED) Tech & Comp 1991; Post Grad Work In Tech at Various Insts; *cr:* Augustine J Belmonte Saugus MS Sci 969-75, Guid Cnslr 1975-81, Math Tchr 1981-83, Comp Tchr , Guid & Tech Facilitator 1989-; Fisher Coll Adj Instr 1981-; *ai:* North Regnl Alliance & Pgm Improvement Cncl Chprsn; MS s Adv; Saugus Edctrs Assn Negotiator; SEA 1969-, Negotiator; MA slrs Assn 1995-; Commle 1995-; Winthrop Town Meeting Mem ; Pub Dept of Ed Career Awareness Pgm; Natl Tchrs of Math & ants; *office:* Augustine Belmonte Saugus MS Dow St Saugus MA

LLO, BEVERLY MARINO, Sixth Grade Teacher; *b:* Newark, NJ; nine; *c:* Christopher, Scott; *ed:* Newark St Coll (BA) Elem Ed 1964; oll of NJ (MA) Rdng Specialist 1977; *cr:* Roosevelt Schl Sixth Grd 64-73; Franklin MS 7th Grd Math Tchr 1985-87; Yawtachaw Elem Grd Tchr 1988-; *ai:* Stu Cncl Adv; NEA 1964-; Ed Assn of Nutley Acad Booster Club 1983-; *office:* Yantacaw Elem Schl 20 Yantacaw y NJ 07110

UCCI, KIPP RALPH, German & Russian Teacher; *b:* Vineland, Wake Forest Univ (BA) Ger 1973; Middlebury Coll (MA) Russian *r:* Gateway Regnl Schl Ger, Russian Tchr 1977-; *ai:* Ger Russian uman Relations Comm; World Affairs Cncl; AATG, NJEA 1977-; 989-; Christ Church 1975-; Grant Stud Pushkin Inst 1987-88; NEA 1993; *office:* Gateway Regional HS Egg Harbor Rd Woodbury NJ 08097*

RAZZO, THOMAS, Social Studies & Bus Ed Supvr; *b:* Hoboken, Barbara Ann Bonaguaro; *c:* Ida-Marie, Dina, Samantha; *ed:* St Coll (BA) Soc Stud 1972; Jersey City St Coll (MA) Stu Prsnl, Guid ; CA Coast Univ (EDD) Educl Admin 1991; Monmouth Coll Grad 1978; *cr:* Hackensack MS Tchr 1972; Ridgefield HS Tchr 1973; Schls Tchr 1973-81; Cliffside Pk HS Tchr, Supvr 1973-; *ai:* Rotary y & Girl of Yr; Chprsn Dist Soc Stud Curr Revision; Mid Sts Soc nal Exam Comm; Cliffside Park Supvrs Assn, NEA, NJ Ed Assn, Cty Cncl Soc Stud, NJ Prins & Supvrs Assn 1980-; Palisades Park atic 1983-, Trustee, Mr Democrat 1990; Bergen Cty Juvenile Conf 980-, Chm; Palisades Park Bd of Ed 1984-88, 1995-, Pres, Trustee; nael's Parish Cncl 1978-, Greeter; Palisades Park Swim Clumb Mgr; Honored by Temple Israel for Holocaust Work; *home:* 33 E d Ter Palisades Park NJ 07650*

RESE, JAMES D., Spanish Teacher; *b:* Mount Holly, NJ; *m:* L. Iasilli; *c:* Christine Ann, Claudia Frances Metcalf; *ed:* LaSalle A) Span Ed 1961; Theological Stud Diploma St Francis Seminary 5 Credits Monmouth Coll; *cr:* Trenton Cath Boys HS Span, Eng 61-62; Rancocas Vly Regnl HS Span Tchr 1962-; *ai:* Natl Span c, Natl Span Exam Adv; NJEA, NEA 1962-; AATSP, ACTFL 1992-; of Columbus 1958-; Grand Marshall for Homecoming Parade; Rancocas Valley Regional HS Jacksonville Rd & Ridgeway St Holly NJ 08060*

IA, DUANE ALLAN, Sociology Professor; *b:* Grafton, ND; *m:* A. Sessing-Matcha; *c:* Lisa, Annie; *ed:* Minot St Coll (BA) Soc Sci D St Univ (MA) Soc Sci, Sociology 1980; Purdue Univ (PHD) gy 1985; *cr:* Univ of FL Soc Sci Asst Prof 1986-91; Siena Coll gy Asst Prof 1991-; *ai:* Fac Handbook, Women & Minority Stud , Amer Sociological Assn, Eastern Sociological Soc 1991-; Books b: The Sociology of Aging, Medical Sociology; Article Pub; *office:* oll 515 Loudon Rd Loudonville NY 12211

HETT, ROBERT KENNETH, Director of Bands; *b:* Pittsburg, PA; lyn Joan; *c:* Robert III, Elizabeth Ann; *ed:* Duquesne Univ (BA) d 1962, (MM) Music Ed 1966; *cr:* Seneca Valley Schl Dist Dir of 962-; *ai:* Marching Band; PMEA & MENC 1962-; IJEA 1984-; JC ding Young Man of Yr 1975; Zelienople Distinguished Service Awd est-i-val Outstanding Contribution to Musical Excl Awd 1991 & ift of Time Awd 1991 & 1994; Numerous Articles for Music Ed s & Magazines; Performed as Professional Player for Various Big cts; *office:* Seneca Valley Sr H S 124 Seneca School Rd Harmony 37

ER, ANITA K., English Teacher & Dept Chair; *b:* New York, NY; es L.; *c:* Lisa M., Amy L., Sara A.; *ed:* Washington Coll (BA) Eng 3; 33 Plus Post Grad Credits Univ MD, Towson St Univ, Western l; *cr:* Thomas Pullen Schl Eng Tchr 1984-; *ai:* Adv Natl Jr Honor t Magazine; Eng Dept Chprsn; Mem Schl-Based Instructional n Making Effective Schls Comm; NCTE 1995-; ASCD; NEA, PGCEA 1984-; Washington Post Ed Grant;Outstanding Educator y & City of Bowie; Co-Author Lit Connection; *office:* Pullen & Perf Arts Schl 700 Brightseat Rd Landover MD 20785

ER, G. DIRK, Associate Prof of Bus & Ec; *b:* Summit, NJ; *m:* Joan Robertson; *c:* Noelle Elizabeth; *ed:* Pfeiffer Coll (BS) Math 1985; niv (MS) Ec 1990, (PHD) Ec 1991; *cr:* FL St Univ Instr, Grad Asst ; Goucher Coll Ec Asst Prof 1991-93; Grove City Coll Bus, Ec Prof 1993-; *ai:* Asst Mens Golf Coach; Entrepreneur Adv; Amer Ec 91-; Contemporary Ec & Bus 1993-; Tower Presbyn Church 1993-, Book Ed & Freedom; Numerous Articles, Prof Presentations; *office:* City Coll Box 2694 Grove City PA 16127

RNA, LINDA S., Assoc Professor of Spanish; *b:* Milwaukee, WI; mas J. Newman; *c:* Bryan; *ed:* Univ of WI at Madison (MA) Span PHD) Span 1980; *cr:* Trenton St Coll Adj Prof of Span 1983-88; on Univ Lecturer of Span 1986-88; Rider Univ Asst, Assoc Prof of 988-; *ai:* Lbrl Arts & Sci Acad Policy Comm Chprsn; Mid Sts t Sub Comm Chprsn; Baccalaureate Hnrs Prgm; Hnr Key Soc; Advisement Comm; AAUP, MLA 1983-; NEMLA 1984-, Chprsn of ous Sessions at Annual Conf; U of WI at Madison Vilas Travel 1977; Rider Univ Summer Rsrch Grant 1992; Articles & Book on 19th-20th Century Span Lit in E.G. Span Review, Hispanofila; poranea & Modern Lang Stud; *office:* Rider Univ Dept of Foreign 083 Lawrenceville Rd Lawrenceville NJ 08648

RNA MC CLOSKEY, CAROLYN DAY, Physical Education & chr; *b:* Honolulu, HI; *m:* William B.; *c:* Marisa Materna, Mike ; *ed:* OR St Univ (BS) PE 1962; Boston Univ (EDM) Ed Human 82; Addl 30 Credit Hrs Post Masters in Mid Level Ed; *cr:* Bell HS d PE, Hlth Tchr 1962-65; Zama MS 7-8th Grd PE Tchr 1971-73; Elem Schl K-5 Grd PE Tchr 1973-76; Stuttgart Jr HS 7-9 Grd PE Tchr 1976-77; Ansloach HS 7-12 Grd PE, Sr HS Hlth Tchr 1978-84; Hanau MS 6-8th Grd PE, Hlth Tchr 1986-; *ai:* Ath, IM Dir; Positive Rewards Prgm Chair; Comm Svc Group Spon; Edctrs Day Planning Comm; 6-8th Grd Cross Cntry, Track, Bowling Coach; Mid Level Trng Ctr; NEA 1986-, Fac Rep; Natl MS Assn 1989-; AAHPERD 1986-; EAHPERD 1993-, Sec; PDK 1996-; Walt Disney Co PE & Hlth Tchr of Yr1991; Profile of Tchng 1992; Selected to Present Beyond Condoms, Tchng Sexuality Across the Curr at NMSA Natl Convention; *office:* Hanau MS Cmr 470 Box 7429 APO AE 09165*

MATES, DONA, Retired Teacher; *b:* Walpole, NH; *c:* Heather, Matthew; *ed:* UNH (BA) Psych, Sociology 1951; 30 Credit Hrs Ed; *cr:* Fall Mtn Schl Tchr 25 Yrs; *ai:* NEA-R 1975-; Charlestown Lib, Bd of Trustees; Charlestown Cemetery, Bd of Trustees; Tchr of Yr 1992; *home:* Olcott Ln Charlestown NH 03603

MATESIC, CHARLES THOMAS,JR., Eighth Grade Math Teacher; *b:* Pittsburg, PA; *m:* Beverly Jo Clayton; *c:* Amy, Lori; *ed:* IN Univ of PA (BS) Math Scndry 1971; Univ of Pittsburgh (MED) Math Scndry 1974; *cr:* Penn Hills Schl Dist Math Tchr 1971-; *ai:* PHEA, PSEA & NEA 1971-; MCWP; Penn Hills Scndry Tchr of the Yr 1986-87; All Star Educator; *office:* John H. Linton MS 250 Aster St Pittsburgh PA 15235

MATEYAK, JOHN AARON, Earth & Space Science Teacher; *b:* Coaldale, PA; *m:* Karen Rother; *c:* John, Maria Dunaway, Heather; *ed:* Kutztown St Coll (BS) Geog, Earth, Space Sci 1971; 25 Hrs for Permanent Cert; *cr:* St Clair Area Schl Dist 9th Grd Earth, Space Sci Tchr 1971-86; Tamaqua Area Schl Dist 9th Grd Earth, Space Sci Tchr 1986-; *ai:* Sci Dept Chm; NEA, PSEA 1971-; St Clair Ed Assoc 1971-86, Pres, Treas; Tamaqua Ed Assoc 1986-; *office:* Tamaqua Area Schl Dist 90 Stadium Hill Rd Tamaqua PA 18252

MATHER, FRANCES TWOHIG, Chemistry Teacher; *b:* Dedham, MA; *m:* Ian H.; *c:* Stephen, Elizabeth; *ed:* Smith Coll (BA) Biological Sci 1972; Purdue Univ (MS) Cell Bio 1974; *cr:* Suitland HS Tchr Bio, Chem, E Sci 1984-87; Potomac HS Chem Tchr, Dept Chm 1987-92; Duval HS Chem Tchr 1992-; *ai:* NSTA 1985; MAST 1985; PGCEA 1984; Mellon Grant; *office:* Duval HS 9880 Good Luck Rd Lanham Seabrook MD 20706

MATHESON, SUSAN E., Tchr of Elem Gifted Students; *b:* Detroit, MI; *c:* James Lothian, David Lothian, Scott Lothian, Matthew Lothian; *ed:* Western MI Univ (BA) Eng, Sci 1963; 30 Grad Credits in Ed Lehigh Univ, Millersville Univ, IU 20; *cr:* Hart Schl Dist 5th Grd Tchr; Portage Pub Schls 4th Grd Tchr; Richland Schl Dist 4th-5th Grd Tchr; Key West-Monroe Co Schl 3rd Grd, Tchr of Elem Gifted; Bethlehem Area Schl Dist Tchr of Elem Gifted; *ai:* Math 24 Club Spon, St Runner-up 1995; Knowledge Master Open Coach St Winner 1995; NEA 1966-; Environmental Stud Florida Keys Grant1976; Tchr of Yr Awd 1975; *office:* Bethlehem Area Schl Dist 1516 Sycamore Bethlehem PA 18017

MATHEWS, EDWARD WILLIAM,JR., Special Education Teacher; *b:* Media, PA; *m:* Barbara Beletti; *c:* Edward III, Brittany; *ed:* Mansfield Univ (BS) Spec Ed 1981; Widener Univ (MA) Ed, Schl Soc Work 1988; 16 Post-Grad Credits; *cr:* Pinelands Regnl HS Resource Room Tchr 1981; Chichester MS Learning Support, Life Skills 1981-; *ai:* Head Coach MS Wrestling, Vlybl; IM Instr; NEA, PSEA, CEA 1981-; Southeastern PA Wrestling Ofcls Chptr 1978-, Pres, VP, Exec Comm; Greater Chester Vly Little League Coach 1995-; *office:* Chichester MS PO Box 2100 Boothwyn PA 19061

MATHEWS, GEORGEANNE, English Teacher; *b:* New Castle, PA; *m:* Don; *c:* Meghan; *ed:* Baldwin-Wallace Coll (BA) Eng 1990; *cr:* Trinity HS Eng Tchr 1990-; *ai:* NHS Moderator; Soph Retreat Team; NCTE 1991-; *office:* Trinity HS 12425 Granger Rd Cleveland OH 44125

MATHEWS, GEORGIANN ELIZABETH, Spanish, French & Hlth Teacher; *b:* West Point, NY; *m:* Robert B.; *c:* Michael, Nicole, James; *ed:* Western Ky Univ (BS) PE, Hlth, Span 1971; Eastern KY Univ 12 Grad Credits PE; North Cntrl Tech Coll 1 1/2 Yrs Nrsng Schl; Ashland Univ 22 Grad Credits Span; *cr:* Athens Elem Schl PE Tchr 1971-75; St Peters HS PE Tchr, Coach 1976-77, Span Tchr 1983-85; Ontario MS Span, Hlth Cultures, Fren Tchr 1985-; *ai:* Asst Ath Dir; MS Frgn Lang Prgm Grds 4-6; MS Restructing Network, Venture Capital Grant Writing Comms; AFT, OFT 1985-; OFLA; BSA Comm 1993-, Treas; Nom 1996 Channel Tchr of Yr; Sigma Delta; Sigma Delta Pi; *office:* Ontario MS 3560 Park Ave W Mansfield OH 44906*

MATHEWS, JANETTE ADAMS, Mathematics Teacher; *b:* Ithaca, NY; *m:* Lou; *c:* Heather, Shawn; *ed:* Univ of Rochester (BA) Math 1971; SUNY at Buffalo (MS) Scndry Ed, Math 1976; *cr:* Lewiston Porter Schl Math Tchr 1971-; *ai:* Class Adv; Crisis, Mid Sts Evaluation Teams; Hnr Soc Advy Cncl; Hnrs Comm; Lewiston Porter United Tchrs 1971-; St Bernard's RC Church, Schl Vol Instr; *office:* Lewiston Porter HS 4061 Creek Rd Youngstown NY 14174

MATHEWS, KATHRYN MEYERSON, 3rd-5th Grd Choral Music Tchr; *b:* Poughkeepsie, NY; *m:* Kenneth J. Jr.; *ed:* Cath Univ (BM) Music Performance 1988; Mannes Coll of Music (MM) Music Performance 1990; Credits for Tchr Cert City Univ of NY, Queens Coll; *cr:* Holy Name Schl Music Tchr 1989-91; St Catharine Acad Music, Drama Tchr 1992-; Brookside Elem Choral Music Tchr; *ai:* Choral Dir; Drama Moderator; Multicultural Comm; MENC 1993-; Manhattan Chamber Orch Bassoonist, Several Recordings; Pub in Journal of Conductors' Guild; *office:* Brookside Elem 2285 Broad St Yorktown Hts NY 10598*

MATHEWS, KENNETH JOSEPH, Assistant Principal; *b:* Livingston, NJ; *m:* Kathryn Meyerson-Mathews; *ed:* Cath Univ of Amer (BA) Eng Lit 1988; NY Univ (MA) Eng Lit 1992; *cr:* St Catharine Acad Eng Tchr 1990-; *office:* Saint Catherine Acad 2250 Williamsbridge Rd Bronx NY 10469*

MATHEWS, LINDA ROTH, First Grade Teacher; *b:* New Haven, CT; *m:* William John; *c:* Shannon Martinello, William B.; *ed:* Southern CT St Univ (MS) Early Chldhd 1987; *cr:* Alma E. Pagels First Grd Tchr 12 Yrs, Third Grd Tchr 1 Yr; Forest Schl Sixth Grd Tchr 1 Yr; *ai:* Aquarium Club Marine Bio; Cadre Tchr Responsive Classroom; PTA; West Haven Fed of Tchrs, Asst Steward 2 Yrs; NEA 1982-; Saxon Publications Tchr Author Math I; CT St Tchr of Yr 1991; *office:* Alma E. Pagels Schl 26 Benham Hill Rd West Haven CT 06516

MATHEWS, WILLIAM PHILIP, Associate Prof of Counselor; *b:* Buffalo, NY; *ed:* Sunny Plattsburgh (BA) Sociology 1976; Suny Albany (MSCAS) Cnslng Psych 1979, (MS) Ed Admin 1986; *cr:* Columbia-Greene Comm Coll Cnslr 1979-; *ai:* Var Bstkbl Coach 1981-84; Lead Trainer Trng, Orgnl Dev Group 1994-; SUNY CDO 1980-; *office:* Columbia Greene Comm Coll 4400 Route 23 Hudson NY 12534

MATHEWS, WILLIAM ROBERT, Choral Director; *b:* Elizabeth, NJ; *m:* Cynthia Zimansky; *c:* Gregory, Timothy, Jillian; *ed:* Montclair St Coll (BA) Music 1975; Amer Guild of Organists (AAGO) Music, Organ 1989; *cr:* Edison Jr HS Choral Dir 1976-88; Westfield HS Choral Dir 1988-; *ai:* JV Sftbl Coach; Stu of Month Comm; NEA 1976-; AGO 1986-, AAGO Awd; *office:* Westfield Sr HS 550 Dorian Rd Westfield NJ 07090

MATHEY, LEE EDWARD, HS Math Teacher; *b:* Dover, OH; *m:* Kathleen Ann Wartluft; *c:* Jessica, Michael, Maggie, Kyle; *ed:* Kent St Univ (BS) Math 1978; 3 Qtr Hrs at Dayton Univ & Coll of Mount St Joseph; *cr:* North Union Local HS Math Tchr 1978-93; *ai:* JV Bsktbl Coach 1980-; NCTM 1978-; NEA & OEA 1978-, Treas; *office:* North Union HS 401 N Franklin St Richwood OH 43344

MATHIAS, CINDY, Third Grade Teacher; *b:* Coshocton, OH; *m:* Gene; *c:* Darcy; *ed:* OH St (BS) Elem Ed 1973; *cr:* Keene Elem 1st-3rd Grd Tchr 1973-; *ai:* River View EA 1973-, VP, Treas; OEA, NEA 1973-; Canal Lewisville Recreation, VP; Coshocton Soccer Org, Referee, Coach; *home:* 25033 Township Road 192 Coshocton OH 43812

MATHIAS, STEPHEN ARTHUR, Social Studies Teacher; *b:* Columbus, OH; *ed:* OH St Univ (BA) Ec 1987, (BS) Soc Stud Ed 1989; Univ of Dayton (MS) Scndry Ed 1994; *cr:* Lancaster City Schls Soc Stud Tchr 1987-; *ai:* Tech, Set Plays Dir; Musicals Voice Dir; European, World Trip Ldr; Scuba Club; Forensics; Natl Current Events League; Past Builders Club; Schl Comms; NEA, LEA, OEA 1989-; OH St Univ Alumni Club 1987-; TBDBITL Marching Band Alumni Club, Bd of Governors; *office:* Lancaster HS 1312 Granville Pike Lancaster OH 43130*

MATHIS, LOUPHELIA BROWN, Science Coordinator & Chprsn; *b:* Lumpkin, GA; *m:* Douglas; *c:* Douglas, Staci; *ed:* Knoxville Coll (BS) Gen Sci 1962; Loyola Coll (MS) Sci Ed 1992; *cr:* Avalon Elem Schl 5 Grd Tchr 1980-82; Benjamin Foulois MS 8th Grd Sci Tchr, Sci Chprsn 1982-86; Thurgood Marshall MS 8th Grd Sci Tchr, Sci Chprsn 1987-95, Sci Coord, Sci Chprsn, Sci Mentoring Tchr 1995-; *ai:* Sci Fair Coord; Sci Bowl; PGCEA, MSTA, NEA 1980-; MSBT 1987-; Alpha Kappa Alpha 1962-; Ebinezzer AME Church 1985; Outstdng Sci Tchr 1992; *office:* Thurgood Marshall MS 4909 Brinkley Rd Temple Hills MD 20748*

MATHISON, DOROTHY ELAINE, Adj Prof of Liberal Arts & Ed; *b:* St Mary Jamaica, West Indies; *m:* Clenton C.; *ed:* Mills Coll of Ed (BS) Elem Ed; Long Island Univ (MS) Early Chldhd, Elem Ed 1973; Univ of Sarasota (EDD) Curr Dev, Evaluation 1977; Long Island Univ Prof Diploma, Ed Admin, Sup 1990; Attnd Bank St Coll of Ed 1972, Shortwood Tchrs Coll 1965; *cr:* Comm Schl Dist 19 Dir of Comm Arts, SS, Libs 2 Yrs; Comm Schl Dist 15 Chptr I Prgms Coord 2 Yrs, Staff Dev 4 Yrs; Touro Coll Adj Prof 11 Yrs; Long Island Adv C oll Adj Prof 3 Yrs; *ai:* Amer Assn of Univ Women, Comm Mem; Amer Automobile Club; WI Shortwood Trs Alumnae 1990-; AFT, NEA, UFT 1973-; NCTE 1980-, Comm Mem; IRA 1986-; Amer Library Assn 1973-; Amer Assn of Univ Women, Comm Mem; Bapt church Comms; Comm Organ & Dev Spon; Comm Svc Awd, Coalition Commitment Awd 1977; *office:* Medgar Evers Coll Bedford Ave Brooklyn NY 11225*

MATHURA, CLYDE BRADMAN, Assoc Prof, Applied Psych Chm; *b:* Port of Spain, Trinidad; *c:* Bradman, Kiran; *ed:* Univ of Miami (BA) Psych-Cum Laude 1970; Univ of NE at Lincoln (MS) Psych 1973, (PHD) Medical Psych 1975; Hilton Head Island Clinical Neuropsychology; Harvard Univ Behavioral Medicine, Psychophamacology; *cr:* Howard Univ Asst Prof Dept of Psych 1975-80; Howard Univ Medical Coll Dir, Rsrch, Dept of Psych 1980-90; Coppin St Coll Assoc Prof 1990-, Dept Applied Psych, Rehab Cncl Chm 1995-; *ai:* Caribbean Assn Consultant; Planning, Chairs Comms; NIH Review Comms, Epert Rsrch Consultant; APA Eastern Psych Assn, Soc of Neuroscience 1970-; Numerous Scientific Articles Pub; *office:* Coppin St Coll 2500 W North Ave Baltimore MD 21216*

MATLACK, HARRY VERNON,JR., High School Chemistry Teacher; *b:* Camden, NJ; *m:* Daphne R. Cody; *c:* Harry W.; *ed:* Rutgers Univ (BS) Forestry 1974, (MS) Plant Pathology 1982; *cr:* Calvary Bapt Chrstn Schl Learning Ctr Supvr, 6-8 Grd Tchr 1983-84; Cumberland Chrstn Schl 7-12 Grd Sci, Math Tchr 1984-88; Pleasantville HS Bio Tchr 1988-89; Oakcrest HS Chem Tchr 1989-; *ai:* Tech Comm; Chrstn & Missionary Alliance Church 1984-, Bd Mem, Trustee, Missionary Treas; *office:* Oakcrest HS 1824 Vienna Ave Mays Landing NJ 08330

MATLIN, STEPHEN, English Teacher; *b:* New York, NY; *m:* Randye Frank; *c:* Aliza; *ed:* Saint Johns Coll at Annapolis (BA) Liberal Arts 1963; CCNY (MA) Eng Lit 1970; Completed Course Work for PhD at NY Univ 42 Credits; *cr:* Borough of Manhattan Comm Coll Instr 1971-74; HS of Graphic Arts Tchr 1977-; *ai:* Chess Club; Developed Advanced Placement Course; UFT 1978-; *office:* Graphic Communication Arts HS 439 W 49th St New York NY 10019

MATLOCK, HERMAN BRADLEY, Secondary Music Teacher; *b:* Ogden, UT; *m:* Yolanda Danko; *c:* Med, Brock, Curt, Lincoln; *ed:* Indian St Univ (BS) Mus Ed 1967; Valparaiso Univ (Mlas) Music 1972; 10 Hrs Eastman Schl of Music; *cr:* Hobart HS Band Dir 1968-77; Plattsburgh St Univ Jazz, Band, Brass, Theory Tchr 1977-86; Crane Schl of Music Jazz, Theory Tchr 1986-87; Franklin Acad Band Dir 1987-; *ai:* Sporting Events; Schl Improvement Comm; Various Comm Work; MFT, MENC 1987-; Lions Club 1988-; Pub Svc Performances; TV, Recording; *home:* 30 Franklin St Malone NY 12953

MATOLYAK, JOHN, Physics Professor; *b:* Johnstown, PA; *c:* Dmitri, Alexander; *ed:* St Francis Coll (BS) Math 1963; Toledo Univ (MS) Physics 1966; West VA Univ (PHD) Physics 1975; *cr:* NASA Rsrch Physicist 1963, 1981-82; Night Vision Lab Rsrch Physicist 1985; IN Univ of PA Physics Prof 1966-; *ai:* Orthodox Chrstn Flwshp Fac Adv; AM Phys Soc 1973-; AAUP 1989-; Numerous Articles Pub; Rsrch Grants; *office:* Indiana Univ Of PA Physics Dept Indiana PA 15705*

MATONE, VIRGINIA ELAINE, Art Instructor; *b:* Pittsburgh, PA; *ed:* Edinboro Univ (BS) Art Ed 1968; 26 credits; *ai:* Stu Cncl & Stu Store Spon; Head of Art Dept Chprsn; PSEA.

MATOS, WILFREDO, EOP Counselor; *b:* Cidra, PR; *ed:* Univ of SC (BA) Psych & Sociology 1986; Webster Univ (MA) Bus Mgmt 1989; Started Grad Work Towards PHD in Higher Ed Admin; *cr:* US Marine Corp Admin Chief 1981-88; Beaufort Tech Inst Upward Bound Cnslr 1988-89; St Univ At Plattsburg Admissions Adv & Minority Recruiter 1989-90; Alfred Univ EOP Cnslr 1990-92; St Univ at Cortland EOP Acad Cnslr 1992-; *ai:* Chrstn Yth Bsktbl Team Coach; Sigma Delta Pi 1992-; Phi Sigma Iota 1992-; Natl Tutoring Assn 1993-, Mem of Ethics & Standards Comm; NCBI Cert Trainer; Assemblies of God Church 1992-, Yth Dir; Cortland Cty Comm Credit Union 1995-, Bd of Dir; Mem SUNYCAP; SC Cncl of Spcl Pgms; *office:* S U N Y Coll At Cortland PO Box 2000 Cortland NY 13045*

MATRA, SUSAN FLEISCHHAUER, Spanish Teacher; *b:* Mt Kisco, NY; *m:* Angelo; *c:* Peter Jason; *ed:* St Lawrence Univ (BA) Span 1971; Middlebury Coll (MA) Span 1972; Attnd C W Post, Westchester Comm Coll; Inservice Credits; *cr:* Brewster HS Span Tchr, Dept Liaison 1972-; *ai:* Fac Cncl; Quality Schls Comm; Organized 9 Frgn Trips; NYSUT, NYSAFLT, Brewster Tchrs Assn 1972-; *office:* Brewster HS Foggintown Rd Brewster NY 10509*

MATSINGER, ELIZABETH ANN, Third Grade Teacher; *b:* Bethlehem, PA; *m:* Charles M.; *c:* Julie Travis, Michael, Bryan; *ed:* Millersville St Coll (BS) Elem Ed 1978; *cr:* Friends Schl First Grd Tchr 1976-80; Chews Elem Schl Third Grd Tchr 1981-; *ai:* NEA, NJEA 1981-; *office:* Chews Elem Schl 600 Somerdale Chews Landing Rd Blackwood NJ 08012

MATSON, JEFFREY C., History Dept Chair; *b:* Stuttgart, W Germany; *m:* Wendy Ann Stout; *c:* Alexandra, Mercedes; *ed:* Georgetown Univ (BA) His, Philosophy 1978; Univ of Chicago (MA) European His 1979; PHD Cand 1979-81; *cr:* Gill-St Bernard Schl His Tchr 1981-85; Red Bank Cath Schl His Tchr 1985-90; Monmouth Univ Adj Prof His 1988-; CBA Chair His 1990-; *ai:* Var Boys, Girls Soccer; *office:* Christian Brothers Acad 850 Newman Springs Rd Lincroft NJ 07738*

MATT, LUCILLE INSERRA, French Teacher; *b:* Utica, NY; *m:* Robert W.; *c:* Ryan R., Craig A.; *ed:* SUNY at Potsdam (BA) Fr Scndry Ed 1973;

Syracuse Univ (MS) Clinical Rdng 1977; Attnd Univ de Poitiers Diplome des Etudes 1971-72, Francaises; SUC at North Adams 12 Credit Hrs Spec Ed 1978; *cr:* St Johnsville Cntrl HS Fr Tchr 1973-77; Berkshire Cntrl Schls Rdng Tchr 1977-81; Union Endicott Cntrl Schls Rdng Tchr 1981-83; Grand Island Cntrl Schls Rdng, Fr 1983-85; Whitesboro Cntrl Schls Fr Tchr 1985-; *ai:* Site Based Team 1993-; Tchr Ctr Policy Bd 1988-95; Intnl Club Adv; Head Chaperone Bi-Annual Trips to France, Canada; Effective Schls Dist Team Chprsn 1987-92; Dimensions of Learning Cadre Team; NYSAFLT 1974-; NEA, AFT 1973-; New Hartford Knights Swim Bd 1993-, Sec; Welcome Wagon of Utica 1985-, Sec; Prof d'Honneur Awded by AAFLT; *home:* 3 Hubbardton Rd New Hartford NY 13413

MATTE, JOSEPH DOMINIC, English Teacher; *b:* Holyoke, MA; *ed:* St Michaels Coll (BA) Eng 1993; Bay Path Coll 1995; *cr:* Holyoke Cath HS Eng Tchr 1993-; *ai:* Frosh Class Adv; Quiz Team Coach; *office:* Holyoke Catholic HS 91 Chestnut St Holyoke MA 01040

MATTER, DAVID LEROY, Practical Arts Curr Coord; *b:* Harrisburg, PA; *m:* Cynthia A. Chubb; *c:* Daniel, Grant; *ed:* Bloomsburg Univ (BS) Acctng, (MED) Ed; Attnd Bucknell Univ; *cr:* Loyalsock Sr HS Scndry Bus Ed Tchr 23 Yrs; *ai:* Class Adv; Long Range Planning Comm; Stu Asst Team; PSEA 1973-, Treas; NEA 1973-; Don Leader Scouts 1995-, Treas; Jaycees Outstdng Young Edctr Awd; Penn Coll Scholars Recognition Awd; Yrbk Dedication; *office:* Loyalsock Township HS 1801 Loyalsock Dr Williamsport PA 17701

MATTERN, BONNIE STORM, 3rd Grade Teacher; *b:* Baltimore, MD; *m:* Jim; *c:* James, Andrew, Meredith; *ed:* BS +30 Grad Credits; *cr:* Cherry Hill Elem Schl Early Admissions Tchr 1974-76; Avalon Elem Schl basics Skills Tchr 1976-77; Davenport Schl 3rd & 4th Grd Tchr 1983-; *ai:* IM Instr; Hospitality Comm; NJEA 1983-; Cntry Shore Womens Club 1987-, Trustee; Governors Tchr Recognition Recipient 1990; *home:* 706 Breckley Rd Marmora NJ 08223*

MATTHAEI, JOAN ANN MC CULLOUGH, Kindergarten Teacher; *b:* Brooklyn, NY; *m:* Justus; *c:* Justus, George, Joseph, Paul, Ann; *ed:* Marymount Coll (BA) Ec 1953; 30 Credit Hrs St John's Univ Ed, Fordham Univ Ed; *cr:* PS 104 5th Grd Tchr 1951-58; PS 20 3rd Grd Tchr 1958-59; St Patrick's Schl Kndgtn Tchr 1975-77; Corpus Christi Schl Kndgtn Tchr 1977-; *ai:* Lang Arts Curr Coord Early Chldhd, Primary Grds; Tchr Rep Regnl Planning Bd; NCEA 1977-; *home:* 153 Loines Ave E Merrick NY 11566

MATTHES, M. KRISTIN, Rel & Integrated Math Teacher; *b:* Orlando, FL; *ed:* Bowling Green St Univ (BA) Ed 1989, (MED) Ed 1994; *cr:* St Mary's Schl Jr HS tchr 1889-92; Ladyfield Schl 6th Grd Tchr 1992-93; Notre Dame Acad Rel, Math 1994-; *ai:* Stu Cncl Moderator; Pep Club Moderator; Cntrl City Tutoring Outreach Moderator; NDEA 1991-; NCTM, NCEA 1989-; *office:* Notre Dame Acad 3535 W Sylvania Ave Toledo OH 43623

MATTHEWS, ADAM LEE, Mathematics Teacher; *b:* Columbus, OH; *m:* Karen Lynn Matthews; *c:* Brittany; *ed:* Oh St Univ (BS) Math Ed 1985; 9 Credit Hrs Xavier Univ; 3 Credit Hrs Ashland Univ; *cr:* West Jefferson Local Schls Math Tchr 1985-88; Marion City Schls Math Tchr 1988-; *ai:* ABLE Instr; Monty Python Club Adv; NEA 1985-; OH Math Tchrs 1988-; *home:* 557 Mawyer Dr Worthington OH 43085*

MATTHEWS, ARTHUR CLAY, Social Studies Teacher; *b:* Baltimore, MD; *m:* Nancy Elizabeth Watson; *c:* James, Jennifer; *ed:* Messiah Coll (BA) His, Soc Stud Ed 1979; The Johns Hopkins Univ (MS) Ec Ed 1988; *cr:* Westminster HS Soc Stud Tchr 1980-; *ai:* Club Adv Stdnts for Christ, Young Repulican Club; Carroll Cty Cncl for Soc Stud 1988-, Treas; Chrstn Edctrs Assoc 1994-; Maryland Chrysalis 1990-, Asst Lay Dir.

MATTHEWS, BARBARA WARD, English Teacher; *b:* Boston, MA; *m:* Edward; *ed:* Boston Coll (BA) Eng 1967; Post-Grad Stud; *cr:* Curtis Jr HS Tchr of Eng 1967-68; Waltham HS Tchr of Eng 1969-; *ai:* Steering Comm Mem for Cert & Accreditation; Corporating Tchr for Stu Tchr; Writing Across the Curr Wkshp; NEA 1969-; MTA 1969-; WEA 1969-; Lecture Scenes for Stu Tchrs at Framingham St Coll; Novel Ideas on All Quiet on the Western Front; Articles Pub; Schl Cncl Grant 1994-95; City of Choice Tchr Awd 1995; *office:* Waltham HS 617 Lexington St Waltham MA 02154

MATTHEWS, CHARLES, Basic Skills Teacher; *b:* Hoboken, NJ; *m:* Janice Stolte; *c:* Trace Poggioli; *ed:* St Peter's Coll (BA) Elem Ed, Eng 1976; 36 Post Grad Hrs; Jersey City St Drivers Ed; *cr:* Joseph F. Brandt Grammar Schl 8-9 Grd Comp Ed Tchr 1977-78; T. G. Connors Grammar Schl 7th Grd Tchr 1979-85; Hoboken HS 10-11th Grd Basic Skills Tchr 1986-; *ai:* Frosh, JV, Asst Var Bsktbl Coach 11 Yrs; Class Club Adv 1989-92; Head Var Bsbl Coach, 4 Cty, 3 St Championships, Top 10 Ranking for 10 Weeks USA Today 1991; NEA, NJEA, Hoboken Tchrs Assoc 1976-; Hoboken Elks Club 1984-; Proclamation for Winning St Sectional Championships from NJ Assembly 1990, 1994; Proclamation from City 1990, 1992, 1994.

MATTHEWS, DAVID GERALD, High School Band Director; *b:* Greensburg, PA; *m:* Darlene Hudack; *c:* David Jr., Anne, Stephen, Alison; *ed:* Duquesne Univ (BSME) Music Ed 1973; Univ of Pittsburgh Elem Cert 1984; St of PA Masters Equivalency 1993; 9 Addl Credits 1994; California Univ of PA 3 Credits 1995; *cr:* Pittsburgh Pub Schls Band Dir 1973-77; Pvt Music Instr Woodwinds Tchr 1977-80; Keystone Oaks Schl Dist Music Tchr 1980-; *ai:* Symphony, Jazz, Marching Bands; PA Music Ed Assn 1986-, Hnrs Band Chm; NHEA, NEA 1980-; North Hills Symphony Band Performed at PMEA St In-Svc Conf 1995, William Revelli Awd 1994; *office:* North Hills Sr HS 53 Rochester Rd Pittsburgh PA 15229*

MATTHEWS, DONALD FRANK, History Teacher; *b:* Pittsburgh, PA; *m:* Sharon Nixon; *c:* Lauretta; *ed:* Edinboro Univ (BS) Scndry Ed, His 1990; Univ of Pittsburgh (MA) His-Summa Cum Laud 1993; Univ of Pittsburgh Doctoral Prgm; *cr:* Comm Coll of Allegheny Co Instr 1986-88; Northgate HS Tchr 1990-, Asst Princ 1993-94; Carlow Coll Asst Prof 1995-; *ai:* NEA 1990-; Gift of Time Ed Awd for Excl; AP Natl His Reader; Pub Novelist & Magazine Writer; *office:* Northgate HS 589 Union Ave Pittsburgh PA 15202

MATTHEWS, ELAINE HARDY, Health & Physical Ed Teacher; *b:* Baltimore, MD; *m:* Leroy W.; *c:* Kimberly A., Kevin L.; *ed:* Howard Univ (BS) PE; George Washington Univ (MA) Hlth Ed 1968; Cnslng Courses; *cr:* Dunbar HS Hlth, PE Tchr 1966-; *ai:* Girls Var Vlybl, Asst Var Stfbl Coach; WA Tchrs Union 1969-; DC Coaches Assn 1980-; NAFE 1994-; Vlybl Coach of Yr DCCIA, Natl Regnl 1994; *office:* Dunbar HS 1301 New Jersey Ave NW Washington DC 20001

MATTHEWS, JAMES M., Asst Prof of Civil Engineering; *b:* Kavali, India; *ed:* Sri Venkateswara Univ (BS) Civil Engrng 1979; Univ of CA at Berkeley (MS) Civil Engrng 1988, (Doctorate) Civil Engrng 1989; Registered Prof Engr; *cr:* Univ of CA Asst Rsrch Engr 1989-90, Transportation Engr 1990-91; Temple Univ Asst Prof of Civil Engrng 1991-; *ai:* Natl Soc Prof Engr Stu Chptr Fac Adv; Amer Soc of Civil Engrs & Amer Soc for Testing & Materials Natl Comms; Natl Soc Prof Engrs 1991-, Rsrch Comm Mem, Top Spon of Yr 1994; Philadelphia Club of Engrs 1991-, Vice Chair of Young Engrs Forum, DE Young Engr of Yr 1993; Amer Soc of Civil Engrs Philadelphia Transportation Engr of Yr 1994; Temple Univ Coll of Engrng Alumni Assn Outstdng Fac Awd 1995; Numerous Articles Pub; *office:* Temple Univ Coll of Engineering 12th & Norris St Philadelphia PA 19122

MATTHEWS, JEFFREY J., Lang & Social Sciences Teacher; *b:* Akron, OH; *m:* Pamela J. Hicks; *c:* Nichole, J. Scott; *ed:* Univof Akron (BS) Elem Ed 1975; Attnd Malone Coll; *cr:* Waterloo Schls 5th Grd Tchr 1975-85, 7th-8th Grd Tchr 1985-89, Gifted, Talented Coord 1989-93, 5th Grd Tchr 1993-; *ai:* Schl Magazine; Stu Cncl; NEA 1975-; OEA, WEA 1975-, Rep; OH Assn for Gifted 1989-; Waterloo Acad Boosters 1989-, Pres; Tallmadge Bsbl Assn 1989-, Mgr, Bd Mem; Tallmadge Little League 1986-, Mgr; BSA 1983-86, Troop Ldr; Tallmadge Ath Boosters 1989-, Fields Comm; Cleveland Plain Dealer Crystal Apple Awd; Tallmadge Express Sports Writing; *office:* Waterloo Local Schls 1776 State Rt 44 PO Box 216 Randolph OH 44265

MATTHEWS, JUANITA FRANKLIN, Retired First Grade Teacher; *b:* Darlington, SC; *m:* George E.; *c:* Melanie Simon, Valerie Larkins, Tracie A.; *ed:* Univ of TX at El Paso (BS) Ed 1978; Attnd Lesley Coll Grad Schl, Hampton Univ; *cr:* US Army AK Rel Ed Dir 1970-72; Ysleta ISD First Grd Tchr 1978-; *ai:* Staffing Comm; NEA, Ysleta Tchrs Assn 1978-; IRA 1984-; Letter of Commendation US Army AK Dir of Rel Ed; Ysleta ISD Tchr of Yr 1991-92; Ysleta Tchrs Assn Excl in Ed Awd 1991-92.

MATTHEWS, KENNETH HARRY, Music & Band Director; *b:* West Chester, PA; *m:* Kay Beaverson; *c:* Andrew, Lauren; *ed:* IN Univ of PA (BS) Music Ed 1968; Penn St (MMEd) Music Ed 1972; Post Grad Stud Millersville Univ, Villinova Univ & West Chester Univ; *cr:* Cntrl York Schl Dist Music Instr 1968-; *ai:* Band Dir; Asst Marching Band; Stage Band; Fife & Drum Corps; Christmas Brass; Stage Coord; NEA & PSEA 1968-; MENC & PMEA 1968-; NBA 1972-, Former St Chair; BSA 1994-; *office:* Cntrl York MS 1950 N Hills Rd York PA 17402*

MATTHEWS, LINDA ESTOK, High School Mathematics Tchr; *b:* Taylor, PA; *m:* John C.; *c:* John C. Jr.; *ed:* Bloomsburg Univ (BS) Elem Ed 1971; Marywood Coll (MS) Math Ed 1974; *cr:* Riverside Elem Schl 1st Grd Tchr 1971-75; Emma C. Attales Schl Math Tchr 1975-80; Egg Harbor Twp HS Math Tchr 1986-; *ai:* NJEA 1975-; NEA 1971; Lesson Suggestion Vignette Printed; *office:* Egg Harbor Twp HS 24 High School Dr Egg Harbor Townshi NJ 08234*

MATTHEWS, MAUREEN T., Third Grade Teacher; *b:* Malden, MA; *ed:* Salem St Coll (BS) Elem Ed 1967; Lesley Coll (MED) Curr, Dev 1994; *cr:* Holmes Schl 4th Grd Tchr 1967-75, 5th Grd Tchr 1975-78, 3rd Grd Tchr 1978-; *ai:* Malden Tchrs Assn, MA Tchrs Assn, NEA 1967-.

MATTHEWS, PATRICIA DONOVAN, 8th Grd Language Arts Teacher; *b:* Westfield, MA; *m:* Richard; *c:* Elizabeth Matthews Sitnik, Lisa; *ed:* Coll of St Scholastica (BA) His 1963; 18 Credits Cert in Eng Westfield St Coll 1981-82; *cr:* St Mary's Cntrl Cath HS Tchr His, Eng, PE 1963-64; Chicopee HS Tchr His 1964-68; North MS Tchr Soc Stud 1974-81; Westfield MS Tchr Lang Arts 1981-; *ai:* Drama Club; Shakespeare Festival Adv for Production of Play; Western MA Writing Project Contact Person for Writing Magazine; NCTE 1982-; WEA, MTA, NEA 1974-; MA Cncl of Tchrs of Eng 1995-; United Ostomy Assn 1993-; *office:* Westfield MS 30 W Silver St Westfield MA 01085

MATTHEWS, SARAH C., Fourth Grade Teacher; *b:* Waynesburg, PA; *ed:* Indiana Univ of PA (BS) Elem Ed 1975; WV Univ (MA) Ed Admin 1982; *cr:* Wilsonburg Elem Schl 4-6 Grds Tchr; Whiteley Elem Schl 3-4 Grds Tchr 1983-90; East Franklin Elem Schl Grd 4 Tchr 1990-; *ai:* Cntrl Greene In-Svc Cncl Treas; Dist Strategic Planning Comm; Dist New Bldg Transition Team; NEA 1975-; PSEA 1983-; Kappa Delta Pi 1981-; Phi Delta Kappa 1974-; ASCD 1985-; NCTM 1993-; Soc Svc League of Waynesburg 1987-; *office:* East Franklin Elem Sch 300 North St Waynesburg PA 15370

MATTHEWS, TERENCE S., 9th Grade Guid Cnslr & Ath Dir; *b:* Jersey City, NJ; *m:* Jacqueline Pirozzi; *c:* Liam; *ed:* Rutgers Coll (BA) Eng 1985; St Peter's Coll (MA) Ed 1995; 3 Hrs Each ADD Seminar, Cnslng; *cr:* Hudson Cath HS Eng Tchr 1985-94, Guid Cnslr 1995-, Ath Dir 1995-; *ai:* Coach Var Swim, Asst Track, Field; NCEA 1985-; *office:* Hudson Catholic Regional HS 790 Bergen Ave Jersey City NJ 07306*

MATTHEWS, WENDY MURPHY, Mathematics Teacher; *b:* Harrisburg, PA; *m:* Thomas; *c:* Mark, Stephen; *ed:* Penn St Univ (BS) Math 1981; Fairleigh Dickinson Univ Ed; Centenary Coll Ed; Grad Stud at Montclair St Coll; *cr:* Sparta HS Math Tchr 1988-89; West Morrison Mendham HS Math Tchr 1989-; *ai:* Soccer, Track Coach; Winter Chrldng Adv; NJEA 1988-; WMREA 1989-; Tri Aths 1991-; Good Samaritans 1996; *office:* West Morris Mendham HS E Main St Mendham NJ 07945

MATTHIESEN, STEVEN, English as Second Lang Tchr; *b:* Baltimore, MD; *m:* Guadalupe Aviles-Valle; *c:* Stephanie Nicole; *ed:* High Point Coll (AB) Span Lit 1970; Southern IL Univ (MA) Span Lit 1973, (MA) Eng as Frgn Lang 1973; Attnd Loyola Coll, Georgetown Univ; *cr:* Prince George's Cty Bd of Ed Eng as Second Lang 1974-; Catonsville Comm Coll Eng as Second Lang 1993-; Johns Hopkins Univ Eng As Second Lang Instr Summer Prgm 1995-; *ai:* Intnl Club; Mexican Exch Prgm; Baltimore Area Tchrs of Eng to Speakers of Other Langs 1980-, Pres; US-China Educl Ventures 1988-, Exec Bd; Fulbright Tchr Exch Prgm Awd 1990; Books: Newbury House to EFL Preparation Kit, Essential Words for the TOEFL; *home:* 6124 Wheatland Rd Baltimore MD 21228

MATTICOLA, BRIAN MICHAEL, Instrumental Music Teacher; *b:* Ashtabula, OH; *m:* Jill B.; *ed:* OH St Univ (BME) Music 1992; Pre-Law, Music at Youngstown St Univ; 20 Hrs Grad Schl Educl Admin at OH St Univ; *cr:* Franklin Alternative MS Instrumental Music Tchr 1992-; *ai:* Newspaper Co-Adv; Bldg Instrl Team; NEA, OH EA 1992-; Columbus Ed Assn 1992-; OMEA 1991-; *home:* 723 S Pearl St Columbus OH 43206*

MATTINGLY, CATHERINE SCHULZ, English Teacher; *b:* New York City, NY; *m:* George E.; *c:* Virginia, Kate; *ed:* Trinity Coll (BA) Pol Sci 1962; Completed Course Work in Liberal Stud Masters Prgm at Georgetown Univ; *cr:* Good Housekeeping Magazine Ed 1962-68; Educl Testing Svc Ed 1968-73; Georgetown Visitation Eng Fac 1983-, Eng Dept Chair 1988-93; *ai:* Great Books Spon; NCTE 1990-; NEH Summer Inst 1994; Agnes Meyer Distinguished Tchr Awd 1992; Named Most Influential Tchr by 2 Presidential Scholars 1989, 1994; *office:* Georgetown Visitation Prp Schl 1524 35th St NW Washington DC 20007*

MATTINGLY, KATHRYN CECELIA, Math Teacher; *b:* Cumberland, MD; *ed:* Bellarmine-Ursuline Coll (BA) Sociology 1970; Frostburg St Univ (MED) Ed 1987; *cr:* St Peter, Paul Schl MS Math Tchr 1970-80; St John Neumann Schl MS Math Tchr 1980-85; Bishop Walsh MS HS Math Tchr 1985-; *ai:* MS Stu Cncl, Math Club Moderator; NCTM 1980-; Womens Golf Assn of Cumberland Cty Club 1989-, Treas 1994-96; Ursufine Assoc, Euchaustic Minister of Cumberland Nrsng Home 1985-; *office:* Bishop Walsh Schl 700 Bishop Walsh Rd Cumberland MD 21502

MATTIS, RONALD EUGENE, Associate Professor of Engrng; *b:* Kane, PA; *m:* Angela Maria Asp; *c:* Natasha Lynn; *ed:* PA St Univ (BS) Nuclear Engrng 1978; Univ of MI (MS) Nuclear Engrng 1980; PA St Univ (PHD) Nuclear Engrng 1991; *cr:* Sandia Natl Labs MTS 1980-83; Cornell Univ Grad Research Asst 1983-85; Univ of Pittsburgh Asst Prof of Engrng 1985-93; Sandia Natl Labs Summer Fac 1992; Univ of Pittsburgh Assoc Prof of Engrng 1994-; *ai:* Acad Tech, Tenure, Univ Assessment Comms; Amer Nuclear Soc 1990-, Grad Schlsp; Kane Comm Hospital Bd 1994-; Kane Area Schl Dist 1987-88, Schl Dir; WC Foster Fellows Visiting Schlrs Prgm US Arms Control & Disarmament Agency Finalist 1995-96; PA St Grad Fellowship; Univ of MI Engrng Coll Grad Fellow; Articles in Nuclear Sci & Engrng Journal of Optical Soc of Amer Journal of Applied *office:* Univ Of Pittsburgh At Bradford 300 Campus Dr Bradford P

MATTIUCCI, CHRIS MEUCCI, Kindergarten Teacher; *b:* Uni PA; *m:* Fredrick; *c:* Tiffany, Charles; *ed:* CA St Coll (BA) Eler Chldhd 1971; West VA Univ (MA) Classroom Tchng 1975; *cr:* Primary Schl Kndgtn Tchr 1971-72; John Street Kndgtn Tchr Hutchingson Elem Schl First Grd Tchr 1974-82, Third Grd Tchr Hutchinson Schl Half Day Kndgtn Prgm 1982-83; Hatfield Schl F Kndgtn Prgm 1982-82; *ai:* Chrldng Parent Helper; Tchr Spon; P Stdnts; NEA, PSEA 1974-; CA Univ Alumni 1971-; Uniontown C 1974-79; Weekly Rdr Summer Giveaway Winner 1978; *office:* Elem Schl 370 Derrick Ave Uniontown PA 15401*

MATTRAW, GAIL E., Director & PE Teacher; *b:* Watertown, SUNY at Brockport (BS) PE 1973; St Lawrence Univ (MED) Educ 1990; Cert Schl Admin, Supvr 1990; Cert Advanced Stud in Educ 1992; *cr:* Hermon DeKalb Cntrl Schl K-12 Grd PE Tchr 1973-, Aths 1984-; *ai:* Aths Dir; Stu Ath Assn Adv; Section X Aths El Comm; AFT, NYS United Tchrs Assn 1973-; NYS Ath Admin Ass Northern Ath Conf Ath Admin Assn 1984-; Educl Karate Inst *office:* Hermon-De Kalb Central Schl 709 E DeKalb Rd De Kalb NY 13630

MATTSON, PAULA JO J., English & Science Teacher; *b:* Dover, Stephen; *c:* Cherith, Sharon Rose; *ed:* Bob Jones Univ (BS) His, Er 1 Yr Art Ed Univ of ME; *cr:* Tabernacle Christian Schl HS Tchr Victory Christian Schl HS Tchr 1991-; *ai:* Church Outreach P Class Spon; Class Trip Spon.

MATTSON, VERONICA WHARTON, Science Teacher; *b:* Phila PA; *m:* David C.; *ed:* Working on BS Bio PA St Univ; *cr:* Multip Sub Tchr 1987-88, 1990-92; Children's Hosp of Pittsburgh Rsr 1988-90; West Mifflin HS 9th Grd Sci Tchr 1992-; *ai:* Bio Club; P Stu Assistance Prgm; Career & Acad Passport Dev Team; US Partnership; NSTA, NABT 1993-; NAFT-PAFT 1992-; WPBTA Docent Cncl Pittsburgh Zoo 1989-, Bd Mem; Greater Pittsburgh Cncl 1989-90; Western Penn Conservancy 1993-; Mon Vly Ed Cor Great Idea Grants; Summer Schlsp CATCMB Cath Univ; Cont Author Rsrch Children's Hosp; *office:* W Mifflin Area Commonwealth Ave West Mifflin PA 15122*

MATTY, JEFFREY ALAN, Japanese Teacher; *b:* Monongahela, Junko Yamamoto; *ed:* Washington & Jefferson (BA) Bio 1986; Pittsburgh (MA) East Asian Stud 1989; Cert in K-12 Japanese; C Mellon Univ Masters Pub Mgmt Stu; *cr:* Ritsumeikan Univ at Kyo Eng Instr 1989-91; South Fayette Jr-Sr HS 7-12th Grd Japane 1992-95; *ai:* Asst Ftbl, Head Jr High Bsktbl & Var Girls Sftbl Coac 1992-; PSEA 1992-; ACTFL; *office:* South Fayette Jr Sr HS 2 Oakdale Rd Mc Donald PA 15057*

MATURO, WILLIAM DONALD, Sixth Grade Teacher; *b:* New CT; *m:* Diane Joan; *ed:* Southern CT St Univ (BS) Elem Ed 196 Upper Elem Ed 1971; 6th Yr Degree Admin 1974; *cr:* Darcey Sch Grd Tchr 1969-71; Highland Schl 2nd-4th, 6th Grd Tchr 1971-, Le 1974-76; *ai:* Nature's Classroom 1980-95; Prin Advy Comm 1995- Adoption, Lang Arts Revision Comms; EAC 1969-, Bldg Rep; CEA Prof Rights, Responsibilities; NEA 1969-; 1st Cong Church Moderator, Deacon; Temple Lodge AF & AM 1983-, Master; CT Chevaliers 1970-, Grand Commander; Cheshire Comm Theater 199 Crew; Book: History of Temple Lodge, Cheshire 1990; *home:* 29 E Cheshire CT 06410

MATUS, BERNARD T., Director of Science & Tech; *b:* New Yo NY; *m:* Nancy Leavitt; *c:* Lisa, David; *ed:* Tchrs Coll at Columb (MA) Sci Ed 1963; Yeshiva Univ (BA) Bio & Chem 1961; Prof D Sci Supervision 1969; *cr:* Easton Jr HS Asst Prin 1974-76; Pen Arg Prin 1976-77; E Hills MS Sci Tchr & Team Ldr 1977-81; Easton A Dist Sci Coord 1991-95, Dir of Sci & Tech 1995-; *ai:* Chprsn Initiative in Any Schl Dist; Chprsn of Strategic Planning Comm 1990-; ASCD 1991-; Weller Hlth Ctr Bd of Dirs 1994-, Dir; Outs Sci Tchr Awd Bethlehem Schl Dist 1988; Pub Article in PA Journal-Alternative Ed Prgms 1975; Cited for Exemplary Sci Prgm Directory of Sci Ed Opportunites & Resources in PA; *office:* East Schl Dist 811 Northampton St Easton PA 18042*

MATUSH, STEPHEN J., Title I Reading Teacher; *b:* Monessen, Matthew, Nicholas; *ed:* East Stroudsburg St Coll (BS) Elem E Marywood Coll (MS) Hum Stud 1977; Addl 50 Credit Hrs to I Instruction; *cr:* Pennsbury Schl Dist 5-6 Grd Tchr 1972-79; Spri Schl Dist 2-5 Grd Tchr 1979-95, Title I Rdng Tchr 1995-; *ai:* Park Schl Ski Prgm Coord; Springfield Town Recreation Bsbl, Bsktbl, Coach; NEA 1872-; Springfield Tchrs Assn 1979-, Pres; Park Stre PTA 1979-, Pres; Eisenhower Grants to Improve Sci Instruction; *h* Wcfr Dr Springfield VT 05156

MATUSZEWSKI, ANNE CUNNINGHAM, Language Arts Teac Pittsburgh, PA; *m:* Leonard J.; *c:* Michael, Kate; *ed:* Duquesn (BSEd) Scndry Eng 1969, (MED) Scndry Guid & Cnslng 19 Assessment Prgm Trng; *cr:* Freeport Area HS Eng Tchr 1969-76 Hills Cnslng & Tutoring Ctr Tutor, Eng Tchr, SAT 1978-83; St E Schl 8th Grd Lang Arts Tchr 1983-; *ai:* Stu Cncl, Newspaper, Vide Moderator; SAP Team Coord; NCEA 1983-; Federation of Pgh D Tchrs 1990-; Mid St Evaluation Comm; *office:* St Bernard Sc Washington Rd Pittsburgh PA 15216

MATZ, KARIS HORNER, Fifth Grade Teacher; *b:* Fostoria, C Gerald Eugene; *c:* Joshua; *ed:* Bowling Green St Univ (BA) Elem E *cr:* Fostoria City Schls 5th Grd Tchr 1962-64; North St Paul Map Schls 5th Grd Tchr 1964-71; Fostoria City Schls 5th Grd Tchr 19 Chm of Pub Relations Comm for Elem Bldg; Delat Kappa Gamma *office:* Fostoria City Schls 129 Elm St Fostoria OH 44830

MATZNER, BARBARA J., English Teacher; *b:* New York City, Gad; *c:* Jennifer, Daniel; *ed:* CCNY (BA) Eng Ed 1965, (MA) En Brooklyn Coll (PD) Admin Supvr 1988; *cr:* NY City Bd of E 1965-71; Deer Park Schls Tchr 1976-83; IS 320 Tchr 1983-86; L Coll Adjunct 1990-; Bayside HS Eng Tchr & Conflict Resolution 1986-; *ai:* Lit Art Magazine Adv; Dean; UFT 1965-; Distinguishe Awd Genesseo; *office:* Bayside HS 32-24 Corporal Kennedy St B NY 11361

MAUCH, JEFFREY DAVID, 9th Grade English Teacher; *b:* Young OH; *m:* Wendy Dee; *c:* Kathryn D., Abbey Lou, Sophie Nico Bowling Green St Univ (BSEd) Ed, Eng 1984; 30 Addl Hrs Gu Counseling; *cr:* Chardon HS Scndry Eng Tchr 1984-85; Greenevi Scndry Eng Tchr 1985-86; Kettering Jr HS Scndry Eng Tchr Kettering Fairmont HS 1995-; *ai:* Boys Track, 8th Grd Bsktbl, 7th G Coach; Drug, Alcohol Intervention Team; NEO, OEA 1984-; KCTA, 1986-; Tchr of Yr; Super Tchrs Are Rewarded; *office:* Kettering Jr H Glengary Dr Kettering OH 45420

MAUCK, SUSAN REIDER, English Teacher; *b:* Harrisburg, Charles J.; *c:* Sara, Adele; *ed:* Millersville Univ (BS) Eng 1978; P Univ Rdng Specialist Cert 1981; East Stousburg Univ MA Eq 19 Conestoga Vly 12th Grd Eng Tchr 1978-79; Donegal 9th-11th G Tchr 1979-81; Littlestown HS 9th-10th Grd Eng Tchr 1986-; *ai:* Newspape, Arts Magazine Adv; Musical Asst Dir; Stu Assistance

SEA, LEA 1986-; Delta Kappa Gamma 1995-; Order of Eastern 85-; St Pauls Luth Church 1990-, Yth Dir; *office:* Littlestown HS Myrtle St Littlestown PA 17340

ANS, JAYNE ELLEN, Assoc Prof of Sociology; *b:* Kansas City, Robert H.; *c:* Grace Maugans Scherzer; *ed:* Wichita St Univ (BA) gy 1983, (MA) Sociology 1988, SUNY at Buffalo (PHD) Sociology *r:* Alfred Univ; Alfred St Coll Adj Prof of Sociology 1989-92; Univ Dir Lrng Ctr 1992-93; Houghton Coll Assoc Prof Sociology, nily Stud 1991-; *ai:* Stu Dev Cncl Fac Rep; Christian Womens Fac)-chair, Sexual Har, Interview Comm; Coord Soc Prog, Family Stud Planning Bd 1996 Ctr Chrstn Women Ldrshp Conf; ASA, CSA NYSSA 1995-; Books: Aging Parents Ambivalent Baby Boomers; Review Jr of Socl, Evolutionary Systems; *office:* Houghton Coll on NY 14744

ER, CYNTHIA CARROLL, English Teacher; *b:* Pottstown, PA; rence Joseph; *c:* Joshua, Jordan, Caitlin; *ed:* Shippensburg Univ ndry Eng 1978; Villanova Univ (MA) Ed 1995; PA St Univ 12 Hrs; roudsburg Univ 9 Hrs; *cr:* Boyertown Area Schl Dist Eng Tchr *ai:* Sr Class Play Dir; Eng Curr Comm; NCTE; NEA; PSEA; BAEA.

HAN, JOSEPH A., French & Spanish Teacher; *b:* Pittston, PA; *m:* ettengill; *c:* Michelle Grace, Renee Perkins; *ed:* Kings Coll (BA) ; Binghamton Univ (MS) Fr 1974; NEA Schlsp 1966, Endowment *r:* Blue Ridge Schl Dist Eng, Fr Tchr 1958-62; Binghamton Schl g, Fr, Span 1962-; *ai:* Fac Mgr; NEA 1958-; Police Ath League Bd of Dir; Sister Cities Exchange La Teste France 1992-, Comm tu Exchange.

LE, RANDY S., History Teacher; *b:* Quakertown, PA; *m:* Valerie Cncl Rock Schl Dist His Tchr 1978-; *ai:* Bsktbl 2 Yrs, Winter Track Spring Track 14 Yrs, Boys Soccer 17 Yrs, Girls Soccer 3 Yrs Coach; Holland Jr HS 400 E Holland Rd Holland PA 18966

, PATRICIA FURLONG, Fifth & Sixth Grade Teacher; *b:* wn, PA; *m:* Donald B.; *c:* Tara; *ed:* PA St Univ (BS) Elem Ed 1968; nemaugh Valley Schl Dist 5th & 6th Grd Tchr 1968-; *ai:* NEA, CVEA 1968-; Amer Legion Auxiliary 1990-.

CHARLES BRYCE, Social Studies Teacher; *b:* Millville, NJ; *m:* ; *c:* Brittany; *ed:* Glassboro St Coll (BA) Soc Stud 1968; Fairleigh on (MA) Human Dev; *cr:* Millville Sr HS Soc Stud Tchr 1968-; *ai:* Cumberland Cty Cncl of Ed Assn 1968-; NJEA 1968-, Urban Ed Millville Ed Assn 1968-, Pres; NCSS; *office:* Millville Sr HS 200 lvd Millville NJ 08332

LER, BETTE FRASER, Sixth Grade Teacher; *b:* Clinton, IA; *m:* an; *c:* Tricia, Matthew, Scott; *ed:* OH St Univ (BS) Elem Ed 1966; leville Schl 5th Grd Tchr 1966-67; Lancaster Schl 5th Grd Tchr); Pataskala Schl 5th Grd Tchr 1969-71; Rushville Schl 6th Grd 71-73; Lancaster EastSchl 6th Grd Tchr 1984-; Lancaster South ptr Rdng Tchr 1984-; *ai:* Schl Newspaper; NEA; OEA, LEA 1986-; Yth Choir Dir; Jennings Scholar.

UCCI, ANTHONY SEBASTIAN, English & Humanities or; *b:* Hartford, CT; *m:* Janet Elaine Tormay; *c:* Jacqueline A., A.; *ed:* Charter Oak St Coll (BA) Eng 1987; Wesleyan Univ) Hum 1989; *cr:* Univ of Hartford Eng Prof 1987-91; Univ of CT of 1989-92; Three Rivers Comm Coll Eng Prof 1992-; *ai:* Fine Arts Festival Coord; Theatre Dir; Reader, Performer of Lit Work; The Guild 1983-; AFT 1992-; Pub Novel Discovery of Luminous Being *ome:* PO Box 975 Norwich CT 06360

ER, ALICE ANN, Kindergarten Teacher; *b:* Somerset, PA; *ed:* IN PA (BS) Elem Ed 1966; Univ of Pittsburgh (MED) Rdng 1973; pecialist Cert 1973; *cr:* Bedford Area Schls 1st Grd Tchr 1966-67; Ridge Elem SCh 1st Grd Tchr 1967-69; Somerset Area Schls Rdng ist, Resource Specialist 1969-73; Patroiot St El Schl Kndgtn Tchr *ai:* PSEA, NEA 1966-; SAEA 1967-; Delta Kappa Gamma 1973-, al Alpha Delta, St Schlsp Twice; KSRA 1990-; Conducted Wkshps d Start Somerset Cty; *office:* Patriot Street Elem Schl 209 W Patriot erset PA 15501*

ER, CINDY DAVENPORT, First Grade Teacher; *b:* Dover, OH; *m:* Ray; *c:* Tiffany Joy; *ed:* Mt Vernon Nazarene Coll (BA) Elem Ed 8 Grad Hrs Otterbein & Ashland Univ; *cr:* Centerburg Elem Kndgtn 79-91, First Grd Tchr 1991-; *ai:* Centerburg Tchr Assn 1979-, Bldg Centerburg Church of Christ Ast Dir Jr Choir 1995-; *office:* burg Elem School 207 S Preston St Centerburg OH 43011

ER, FRANK HAYES,III, Bus Tchr & Vice Prin for Discp; *b:* lphia, PA; *ed:* Salem Comm Coll (AS) Information Processing Wilmington Coll (BS) Bus Mngmt 1992; Working Toward MED in nin; *ai:* Stage Crew Adv; Golf Coach; Discipline, Attendance, Prin Comms; NJEA 1994-; Knights of Columbus 1995-, Lecturer; *office:* s HS 350 Georgetown Rd Penns Grove NJ 08069

ER, KATHLEEN L., 7th Grade Teacher; *b:* Johnstown, PA; *m:* J.; *c:* Kara, Kassie Jo, Kip; *ed:* Univ of PA at Johnstown (BS) Elem 5; IU 8 Credits in Ed, Grad Credits in Ed; *cr:* St Joseph Schl 3rd t Grd Tchr 1985-87, 4th Grd Tchr 1988-89; Local Pub Schl Dists ir 1991-93; St Joseph Schl 7th Grd Tchr 1993-; *ai:* Var Girls Bsktbl Coach; Rdng Competition Team, Celebrate Diversity Adv; NCEA Portage Area Historical Soc 1993-; St Joseph Ath Assn 1985-.

ER, KEVIN MICHAEL, Music Teacher; *b:* Altoona, PA; *m:* Karen issell; *c:* Kevin, Kari, Katelyn; *ed:* Edinboro Univ of PA (BS) Music 6; Masters Equivalency; *cr:* Sacred Heart Elem Schl Music Tchr); South Fayette Jr, Sr HS Music Tchr, Choral Dir 1979-; *ai:* Schl ement Comm; Stu Assistance Team; Broadway Musical, Show, Choir Dir; PSEA, MENC 1979-; PASAP 1993-; ACDA 1996-; 42 W Manilla Ave Pittsburgh PA 15220*

ER, MARY D'URSO, Frgn Lang Dept Chr & Span Tchr; *b:* lphia, PA; *m:* Frank H. Jr.; *c:* Frank H. III, Lawrence N., Stephanie Glassboro St Coll (BA) Eng 1986; *cr:* St James Grammar Schl Third hr 1980-83, Seventh Grd Tchr 1983-85; St James HS Span Tchr *ai:* SADD, Yrbk, Jr Class Moderator; NJ-SCTO 1985-; NJ FLTA Tchr of Yr 1994-95; *office:* St James HS 350 Georgetown Rd Penns NJ 08069

O, ANTHONY F., Chemistry Teacher; *b:* Brooklyn, NY; *m:* Eileen; ooklyn Coll (BS) Chem 1969; Tchrs Coll Columbia Univ (MA) tion 1978, (EDM) Neuroscience, Ed 1990; *cr:* NYU Med Ctr t 1969-71; IS 293 Sci Tchr 1972-79; Tottenville HS Chem Tchr 4; Fort Hamilton HS Chem Tchr 1984-; *ai:* Peer Tutoring Prgm Tchr Mentor Prgm Mentor; UFT 1972-; Orton Soc 1994-; *office:* amilton H S 8301 Shore Rd Brooklyn NY 11209

O, JEAN CRANSTOUN, Orchestra Director; *b:* Trenton, NJ; *m:* andolph; *c:* Gabriella, Eric, Alexander; *ed:* Univ of IA (BM) Music Trenton St Coll (MA) Conducting Music 1990; *cr:* Grinnell Newburg Orch 4-12th grds 1975-77; West Windsor-Plainsboro Schls High Schl ir; *ai:* String Quartert; NEA, NJEA, MENC, ASTA, NSOA 1978-; West Windsor-Plainsboro H S 346 Clarksville Rd Princeton Jct NJ

O, NICOLE MARIE, Psychology Professor; *b:* Poughkeepsie, NY; rist Coll (MA) Cnslng, Psych 1991, (MACAS) Schl Psych 1993; dvanced Stud Schl Psych; *cr:* Poughkeepsie Children's Home Psychometrician 1991-; Marist Coll Prof 1993-; Mt St Marys Coll Prof 1994-; Spockenkill Schl Dist Schl Psychologist 1996; *ai:* NY Chapter Natl Assocs Schl Psychologists 1993-; Amer Psychological Assn 1990-; Grad Awd Psych; *office:* Mount St Marys Coll 330 Powell Ave Newburgh NY 12550

MAUST, MADELEINE SCHMIDT, Ctr Leader & Speech Therapist; *b:* Ridley Park, PA; *m:* Russell Jr.; *ed:* PA St Univ (BS) Speech Pathology 1973; West Chester Univ (MA) Speech Pathology 1978; Spec Ed Supervisory Cert; Elem & Scndry Prins Cert; *cr:* Cardinal O'Hara HS Speech Therapist 1973-; *ai:* ASHA 1978-; NEA, PSEA 1990-; Awd of Excl from Employer 1995; *office:* Delaware Cty Intermediate Unit 6th & Olive Sts Media PA 19063

MAUTONE, ROBERT JOSEPH, Psychology Teacher; *b:* Newark, NJ; *m:* Midge Fiore; *c:* Anthony; *ed:* Kean Coll of NJ (BA) Spec Ed 1984, (MA) Cnslng 1995; 42 Post-Grad Credits Supervision, Cnslng, Psych; *cr:* Arlington Ave HS Tchr of Handicapped 1984-86; Belleville MS Tchr of Handicapped 1986-87; Elizabeth HS Tchr of Handicapped 1987-89, Tchr of Psych 1989-; *ai:* Wrestling Coach; NEA; NJ Cnslng Assoc; *office:* Elizabeth HS 600 Pearl St Elizabeth NJ 07202

MAUW, STEPHEN DAVID, 7th-12th Grd Fr & Span Tchr; *b:* Rome, Italy; *m:* Heather L. Werth; *c:* Zachary; *ed:* Houghton Coll (BA) Fr 1990; SUNY Geneseo (MS) Scndry Ed 1995; *cr:* Letchworth Cntrl Schl Fr & Span Tchr 1990-95; Geneseo Cntrl Schl Fr & Span Tchr 1995-; *ai:* Frgn Lang Club Adv; Travel Club Asst Adv; Bldg Planning Team Mem; Vol Womens Soccer Asst Coach; NYSUT 1995-; WY Free Lib Bd 1995-, Trustee; *office:* Geneseo Central Schl 4050 Avon Rd Geneseo NY 14454

MAVER, ROBERT EDWARD, High School Math Teacher; *b:* Willoughby, OH; *m:* Lisa Ann Jarc; *ed:* OH Univ (BS) Math 1987; St Joseph Univ Post Grad Tchrs Cert 1990; Baldwin-Wallace Coll 5 Credit Hrs; *cr:* Lakewood HS Math Tchr, Ftbl, Head Sftbl Coach 1991-; *ai:* Frosh Class Adv; NEA, Lakewood TA, OH EA 1991-; 1994 Coach of Yr; *office:* Lakewood HS 14100 Franklin Blvd Lakewood OH 44107*

MAXON, JENNIFER PAGE, English Teacher; *b:* Arlington, MA; *ed:* Holy Cross Coll (BA) Eng 1990; *cr:* St Michael Anthony Dev Dir 1990-93, Eng Tchr & Land Dir of Admissions 1993-; *ai:* Var Bsktbl Coach; Ambassador Club Moderator; Career Day Coord; *office:* Saint Michael Acad 425 W 33rd St New York NY 10001

MAXTON, WAYNE CHARLES, 7th Grade Language Arts Tchr; *b:* Dayton, OH; *m:* Mary G.; *c:* Patrick W., Mary R.; *ed:* Miami Univ (BSEd) Eng, Hlth, PE 1967, (MED) Guid, Cnslng 1972; 30 Credit Hrs Post Masters Stud; *cr:* West Carrollton Jr HS Eng, Lang Arts Tchr 1968-; *ai:* West Carrollton Ed Assn, OH Ed Assn, NEA 1968-; Significant Tchr Awd; West Carrollton Sr HS High Significant Tchr Awd; *office:* W Carrollton Jr HS 424 E Main St West Carrollton OH 45449

MAXWELL, BRIAN, Assistant Professor; *b:* Marlette, MI; *m:* Andrea McAllister; *c:* Brandon, Travis, Alyssa, Evan; *ed:* Cornerstone Coll (BA) Speech & Drama 1985; Calvin Coll (BS) Scndry Ed 1985; Bowling Green St Univ (MA) Theatre 1986; Baptist Bible Seminary (MMin) Communication 1994; NY Univ Currently 9 Hrs Toward a PHD Educl Theatre; *cr:* Baptist Bible Coll Asst Prof 1986-; *ai:* Drama Dept Dir-Direct 2 Main Stage Plays Each Yr; Worship & Drama; CITA 1988-, Regnl Rep & Trustee; *office:* Bapt Bible Coll 538 Venard Rd Clarks Summit PA 18411

MAXWELL, CYNTHIA, Sixth Grade Teacher; *b:* Buffalo, NY; *ed:* St Univ Coll of NY at Buffalo (BA) Elem Ed 1963, (MS) Eng, Amer Lit 1972; 10 Credit Hrs Arts in Eng, Amer Lit; *cr:* Schl 36 Sixth Grd Tchr 1963-70; Olmstad 56 Sixth Grd Tchr 1971-; *ai:* Trustee Bd St Luke Amer Church, Ruby C. Smith Schlsp Comm Church Sec; Intermediate Oratorical Contest Adv; NEA 1975-; NAACP 1975-; Poem Pub; *office:* F. L. Olmsted Schl for GT 716 W Delavan Ave Buffalo NY 14222

MAXWELL, DAVID A., Prof of Law & Criminal Justice; *m:* Jane V. Brown; *c:* David Jr., Daniel, Elizabeth; *ed:* Univ of Miami (BBA) Bus 1954, (JD) Law 1965; John Jay Coll (MA) Criminal Justice 1977; *cr:* FBI Special Agent 1955-80; Univ of New Haven Law, Crim Justice Prof 1980-; *ai:* Dept Criminal Justice Chair; ACJS, CT Police Chiefs Assn 1980-; ACIS 1979-; IACP 1970-; BSA Exec Bd Cncl, Silver Beaver; Corporate Security Admin, Mngmt Private Security Law; *office:* Univ Of New Haven 300 Orange Ave West Haven CT 06516

MAXWELL, IRENE, English Teacher & Chairperson; *b:* Buffalo, NY; *m:* Charles W.; *c:* Geoffrey; *ed:* Rosary Hill Coll (BA) Eng; St Univ of NY at Buffalo (MA) Hum; *cr:* Lancaster HS Eng Tchr; *ai:* Bldg Planning Team; NYSUT; *office:* Lancaster HS 1 Forton Dr Lancaster NY 14086*

MAXWELL, MARILYN, English Teacher; *b:* Brooklyn, NY; *ed:* Bucknell Univ (BA) Philosophy 1969; NY Univ (MA) Philosophy 1973; HOfstra Univ (MSE) Eng, Ed 1975; NY Univ (MPhil) Eng, Amer Lit 1991, (PHD) Eng, Amer Lit 1994; *cr:* Great Neck Jr HS Sub, Eng Tchr; Long Beach Jr HS Sub, Eng Tchr; Hewlett HS Tenured Eng Tchr 1979-; Hofstra Univ Asst Adjunct Eng Prof 1994-; *ai:* Lit Magazine, Book of Month Club, Russian Exch Co-Advs; AADP; MLA; Lit Tchr Awd; NEH Harvard Summer Fellowship; Two Articles Pub; *office:* George W Hewlett HS 60 Everit Ave Hewlett NY 11557

MAXY, LEONORA B., Social Studies Teacher; *b:* St Louis du Nord, Haiti; *ed:* Normal Superior Schl (BA) Ed 1964; Long Island Univ (MS) Ed 1977; C. W. Post of Long Island Univ (EA) Ed 1979; NY Univ (PHD) Higher Ed 1983; *cr:* Cours Clasiques d'Haiti Schl Tchr, Admin 1964-65; Ecole Kimbanquiste Schl Soc Stud Tchr 1965-69; Ecole Secondaire d'Alma Schl Soc Stud Tchr 1969-70; Bd of Ed Temporary Per Diem 1978-85; Erasmus Hall HS Soc Stud Tchr 1985-; *ai:* Doctorate Assn of NY Edctrs 1979-; *office:* Campus School of Sci & Math 911 Flatbush Ave Brooklyn NY 11226

MAY, JOANNE, Resource Room Teacher; *b:* Queens, NY; *m:* Robert Scott; *c:* Christopher, Lauren Walerski, Andrea, Danielle, Matthew Walerski; *ed:* Trenton St Coll (MS) Spec Ed 1979, (BS) Elem, Early Child 1981; *cr:* Hamilton High West Resource Room Tchr 1979-80; Steinert HS Resource Room Tchr 1980-81; Grice MS Self Contained Tchr 1981-83; Hamilton High West Resource Room Tchr 1983-; *ai:* Career Explores Post 706, Craft Show Adv; Momouth Cty ACLD 1978-; NJEA, HTEA 1979-; Stdnts with ADD Parent Group 1995-; BSA 1986-, Adv, Natl Quality Adv; *office:* Hamilton High West 2720 S Clinton Ave Trenton NJ 08610*

MAY, JOSEPH ANTHONY, Social Studies Teacher; *b:* Providence, RI; *m:* Patricia M.; *c:* Gregory, Katlyn; *ed:* Marietta Coll (BA) His & Pol Sci 1969; RI Coll (MA) Ed & His 1973; 28 Credits Beyond Masters at Providence Coll & Univ of RI; *cr:* Westrn Hills MS Soc Stud Tchr & Team Ldr 1969-; Comm Coll of RI Instr, Natl Youth Sports Prgm 1981-88; The Scarlet Knights Bsktbl Schl Pres & Owner 1993-; *ai:* West Greenwich HS Boys Bsktbl Head Coach; Univ of RI Womens Bsktbl Head Coach; Comm Coll of RI Womens Head Bsktbl Coach; AFT 1969-; NEA; Exeter-West Greenwhich Recreation League 1992-, Bd of Dir, Honorary Chm; RI Red Cross 1977-, Bd of Dir; Little League, Babe Ruth 1980-84, All-Star Coach; Providence Coll Former Womens Bsktbl Asst Coach; Pub 5 Articles in Coaching Magazines Such As Scholastic Coach, The Athletic Journal & The Bsktbl Clinic; Class C-2 RI Coach of Yr 1996; *office:* Western Hills MS 400 Phenix Ave Cranston RI 02920*

MAY, MARIANNE LYONS, Spanish Teacher; *b:* Bronx, NY; *m:* James; *c:* Michael; *ed:* SUNY at Geneseo (BA) Elem Ed 1987; SUNY at Brockport (MS) Elem Ed 1988; 27 Credit Hrs in Span & Permanent Cert; *cr:* Rochester Cath Diocese Span Tchr 1988-89, Kndgtn Tchr 1989-91; Pavilion Cntrl Schls Span Tchr 1991-95; *ai:* Soph Class Adv; Comm Intervention Team; NYSUT & AFT 1991-; Alpha Phi Omega 1987-; Tchr of Yr 1993-94; *office:* Pavilion Central Schl Big Tree Rd Pavilion NY 14525

MAY, MARNIE ROETHER, English Teacher; *b:* Dayton, OH; *m:* Jeffrey M.; *c:* Caroline; *ed:* OH Univ (BA) Comm Comp 1987; Northern KY Univ (MED) Ed 1993; *cr:* Northwest HS Eng Tchr 1987-94; Sycamore HS Eng Tchr 1994-; *ai:* Drama, Speech Team; NCTE 1995-; *office:* Sycamore HS 7400 Cornell Rd Cincinnati OH 45242

MAY, PATRICK JOSEPH, Instructor of Geog & History; *b:* Sandusky, OH; *m:* Patti Marie Ference; *ed:* Bowling Green St Univ (BLS) Liberal Stud 1986, (MA) Geog 1990; Currently Pursuing PHD in Geog at Univ of MD; *cr:* Coppin St Coll Instr Dept of His & Geog 1990-; *ai:* Honors Stu Mentor; Acad Adv; Assoc of Amer Geographers 1990-; NCSS 1991-; NEH HBCU Fac Flwshp 1995-; *office:* Coppin St Coll 2500 W North Ave Baltimore MD 21206

MAY, TODD WHITLOW, PE & Science Teacher; *b:* Danville, PA; *m:* Shawn L. Dexter; *c:* Kelsey Deanna, Kyle Allen Richard; *ed:* Liberty Univ (BS) PE 1985; *cr:* Wintersville Chrstn Acad Sci Tchr 1985-86; Central Bapt Chrstn Acad Sci Tchr 1986-88; Twin Tiers Bapt High PE & Sci Tchr 1988-; *ai:* Soph Class Adv; Sci Fair Coord; *home:* 1356 Breesport Rd Lot 7 Erin NY 14838

MAYDAK, DAWNA M., High School English Teacher; *b:* McKeesport, PA; *ed:* Indiana Unvi of PA (BSEd) Eng & Speech 1967; Univ of Pittsburgh (MED) Eng & Composition 1971; *cr:* West Mifflin Area HS Scndry Eng Tchr 1967-; *ai:* AFT 1974-; Natl League of Amer Pen Women 1985-; 1st Book of Poetry Because the Death of a Rose, T S Eliot Awd; Postscripts Illustrated Poetry Post Cards; 10 Poems in Poetry Chapbook; Over 100 Pub Poems; Honors & Awds at 20 Poetry Competitions.

MAYER, BARBARA SUTCLIFFE, Mathematics Teacher; *b:* Staten Island, NY; *m:* George H.; *c:* Allyson J.; *ed:* St Univ Coll at Oswego (BA) Math, Scndry Ed 1975; Glassboro St Coll at Glassboro 30 Credit Hrs; *cr:* Beck MS 7th Grd Math Tchr 1975-79; Taconic Hills Cntrl Schl 9-12th Grd Remedial Math Tchr 1979-82; Ichabod Crane Cntrl Schl 8th Grd Math Tchr 1985-; *ai:* Team Ldr; Math Curr, Acceleration Comm; AFT 1975-; NYSUT 1979-; ICTA 1985-; Kinderkrafters 1981-, Chairwoman Sec, Treas; Girl Scouts 1987-, Daisy Troop Ldr 1 Yr; *office:* Ichabod Crane Cntrl Schl Rt 9 Valatie NY 12184

MAYER, GEORGE MARTIN, Chemistry Teacher; *b:* Buffalo, NY; *m:* Barbara Ann Mosier; *c:* Katherine, Andrew, Benjamin; *ed:* Williams Coll (BA) Psych 1963; Univ of NH (MST) Chem 1969; Attnd Duke Univ 1978, Canisius Coll 1990, 1993; *cr:* St Paul's Schl Chem Tchr 1963-69; Nichols Schl Chem Tchr 1969-93; St Pauls Schl Advanced Stud Prgm Summer Advanced Chem Tchr 1980-88; *ai:* Womens Var Tennis Coach; Cum Laude Society; Nichols Fac Assn Chrm; Chrm of Youth Ministries Comm at Calvary Epscpl Church; Calvary Episcopal Church 1969-; Enrichment Funds Comm Chrm; Concord St Prison, Hospital Summer Ministry; Sunday Schl Tchr; Youth Group Vol; *office:* The Nichols Schl 1250 Amherst St Buffalo NY 14216*

MAYER, JENNIFER ANN, High School Teacher; *b:* Wilmington, DE; *ed:* Univ of DE (BS) ECDE 1994; *cr:* Southern HS Tchr, Child Care Dir 1994-; *ai:* Jr Class, Fashion Show, Homecoming Adv; Hospitality Mem; Sftbl; Balt Tchrs Union 1994-; MAEYC 1996-; Sftbl Awd; *office:* Southern Sr HS 70 1100 Covington St Baltimore MD 21230*

MAYER, SUZANNE M., Adjunct Prof of Psychology; *b:* Philadelphia, PA; *ed:* Immaculata Coll (BA) Eng 1970; Villanova UNiv (MS) Experimental Psych 1975; Neuman Coll (MS) Pastoral Cnslng 1990; Loyola (PHD) Pastoral Cnslng 1993; *cr:* Allentown Cntrl Cath HS Eng Tchr 1978-80; Lourdes Regnl HS Eng Tchr, Dept Chair 1980-83; Villa Maria Acad Eng Tchr, Cnslr 1983-90; Immaculata Coll, Neuman Coll,St Charles Seminary Pysch, Pastoral Cnslng Adj Prof 1993-; *ai:* IHM Congregation Task Force for Mental Hlth Issues Liason 1993-; Pastoral Cnslr; Amer Assn of Pastoral Cnslrs, Natl Bd of Cert Cnslrs 1993-; Pub Celebrating the Woman You Are 1995, Numerous Articles.*

MAYER, WENDY ROWLAND, High School Math Teacher; *b:* Rochester, NY; *m:* Michael F.; *c:* Brett M., Lindsay M., Alex D.; *ed:* SUC at Brockport (BS) Math & Scndry Ed 1973; Post Grad Stud; *cr:* Rush Henrietta Cntrl Schls MS Math Tchr 1974; Byron Bergen Cntrl Schls MS Math Tchr 1974-81, HS Math Tchr 1992-; *ai:* Mentor; Soph Class Adv; NYSUT; AFT; *office:* Byron Bergen Central Schl 6917 W Bergen Rd Bergen NY 14416

MAYES, SAMUEL WILLIAM, Instrumental Music Director; *b:* Lock Haven, PA; *m:* Kimberly Dawn Fye; *c:* Lindsay Dawn; *ed:* IN Univ of PA (BS) Music Ed 1977, (MA) Music Ed 1979; *cr:* Coventry Local Schls Dir of Instrumental Music 1979-82; Wadsworth City Schls Dir of Instrumental Music 1982-; *ai:* Curr Dev Comm; Bsktbl Pep Band Adv; Dir Pit Orch for Schl Musical; N Cntrl Assn Evaluator; NEA, OEA, WEA, CEA, MENC, OMEA, Natl Band Assn & Intnl Trombone Assn 1979-; Phi Mu Alph Sinfonia 1974-, Ed Dir; *office:* Wadsworth City Schls 625 Broad St Wadsworth OH 44281*

MAYFIELD, DAVID WAYNE, Geometry & Physics Teacher; *b:* Springfield, MO; *ed:* Evangel Coll (BS) Math, Physics 1972; Frostburg St Univ (MS) Admin & Supervision 1981; *cr:* Southern Garrett HS Math, Physics Tchr 1972-; *ai:* Local Stu Cncl Adv 24 Yrs; Regnl Adv Stu Cncl 2 Yrs; Asst Ath Dir 13 Yrs; NEA 1972-, Local Treas 1 Yr; MD Tchrs of Math 1990-; Southern Ath Boosters 1980-, Citizen of Yr; *office:* Southern Garrett HS 345 Oak St Oakland MD 21550

MAYFIELD, DOLORES CAMILLE (KING), Social Studies Teacher; *b:* Akron, OH; *m:* Carl; *ed:* Univ of Akron (BSE) Eng, Ancient His 1970; Rel Certfd; *cr:* Erie Island Elem Schl Stu Tchr 1969; Soc Stud, Lit, Eng Tchr 1970-; *ai:* Initiated Stu Cncl; Church Related Work Comms; Began Geog Bee; Natl Geog Bee Coord; NEOCA; *office:* St Paul Schl 1580 Brown St Akron OH 44301

MAYFIELD, WALTER PATTON, Professor of English; *b:* Alexander City, AL; *ed:* Univ of AL (BS) Bio 1956; Rensselaer Polytechnic Inst (MS) Tech Writing 1959; Attnd Harvard Grad Schl of Ed; 92d St Y Poetry Ctr; *cr:* Western New England Coll Adj Prof Eng 1969-73; Tuskegee Univ Visiting Prof Eng 1991; Springfield Coll Adj Prof Eng 1973-75, 1995-; Springfield Tech Comm Coll Prof Eng 1967-; *ai:* Editorial Adv Bd; Collegiate Press; MA Tchrs Assn 1975-; MA Bd Regnl Comm Colls Fac Ofcr; One Man Show of Work; Numerous Stories Recorded; *office:* Sprinfield Tech Comm Coll One Armory Square Springfield MA 01105

MAYHER, CATHERINE A., English Teacher; *b:* Teaneck, NJ; *ed:* Trenton St Coll (BA) Speech Comm, Theatre, Eng 1979; Rutgers Univ (MED) Educl Admin 1988; *cr:* Burlington Cty Inst of Tech Eng Tchr 1979-85; Cherokee HS Eng Tchr 1985-; *ai:* Lenape Dist TV Show Host; Girls Bsktbl Statistician; NJEA 1979-; NCTE; Haddonfield Plays, Players 1990-, Plays Comm; *office:* Cherokee HS Willow Bend Rd Marlton NJ 08053

MAYHEW, RACHEL I., Mathematics Teacher; *b:* Bridgeton, NJ; *c:* Jeremy Sammons; *ed:* Glassboro St Coll (BA) Math & Scndry Ed 1972; *cr:* Bridgeton HS Math Tchr 1972-; *ai:* Peer Group Connection Adv; NEA 1972-; NJEA 1972-; CCEA 1972-; BEA 1972, AR; *office:* Bridgeton HS 111 N West Ave Bridgeton NJ 08302

MAY-LESH, LOIS M., Fine Arts & Jewelry Teacher; *b:* Jersey City, NJ; *m:* WalterLesh; *c:* Mark W.; *ed:* Seton Hill Coll (BA) Art, Ed 1969; Wm Paterson Coll (MA) Textiles, Jewelry 1979; *cr:* Pequannock Twp HS Art Tchr 1971-84; Gill St Bernard's Upper Schl 7-12th Grd Art Tchr 1994-95; James Caldwell HS Art, Jewelry Tchr 1996; *ai:* Art Club; Lit Magazine Adv; Gallery Dir.

MAYNARD, BARBARA BURNS, Physical Education Teacher; *b:* Burlington, VT; *m:* Stuart A.; *c:* Merrie-Beth, Stephen, Megan; *ed:* Univ of VT (BSEd) PE 1975, (MSEd) PE, Cmptrs 1992; *cr:* Harwood Union HS PE Tchr, Coach 1977-; *ai:* Var Field Hockey, Var Sftbl Coach; AAHPERD 1984-; NEA, VEA 1977-; VT Field Hockey Coaches Assn 1980-, Sec, Treas 1980-; Harwood Boosters 1977-; *office:* Harwood Dist 19 Union HS RD 1 Box 790 Moretown VT 05660

MAYNARD, DEAN CLARK, Elementary Principal; *b:* Corry, PA; *ed:* Gannon & Edinboro (MS) Elem Ed 1990; Edinboro Univ (MS) Ed Admin 1992; Westminster Coll Letter of Eligibility 1995; *cr:* Corry Schl Dist 5th-6th Grd Tchr 1985-91, 1st Grd Tchr 1991-92, Prin & Coord of Spcl Projects 1992-; *ai:* Cty 4-H Chm; Fair Dir; Cert Horse Judge; PDK 1990-; ASCD 1994-; *office:* Corry Area Schl Dist 426 Wright St Corry PA 16407*

MAYNARD, E. PAUL, 8th Grd Hlth Tchr & Swim Coach; *b:* Niagara Falls, NY; *m:* Marie; *c:* Kelly, Eddie, David; *ed:* Univ of WY (BS) PE 1969; Univ of Buffalo (BS) Hlth 1972, (MED) PE 1974; *cr:* Miami Springs HS PE Tchr, Swim Coach 1969-70; Niagara Falls Bd of Ed Hlth Tchr, Swim Coach 1970-; *ai:* Boys, Girls Var Swim Coach 26 Yrs; Frosh Ftbl Coach 2 Yrs; Schl Comms; Natl Interscholastic Swim Coaches Assn 1980-; Amer Swim Coaches Assn 1974-; Amer Red Cross 1970-; White Water Swim Club 1985-, Pres, Coach; Have Produced Numerous St Level Swimmers & HS Swimming All Amer; Named Niagara Frontier Girls Swimming Coach of Yr; *office:* Niagara MS 607 Walnut Ave Niagara Falls NY 14302

MAYNARD, JOHN ROGERS, Professor of English; *b:* Williamsville, NY; *c:* Alex; *ed:* Harvard Coll (BA) His, Lit 1963; Harvard Univ (PHD) Eng 1970; *cr:* Harvard Univ Asst Prof 1969-74; NY Univ Asst-Full Prof 1974-, Dept Chair 1983-; *ai:* Undergraduate Eng Colloquium Adv; Henry James Assoc Dir; MLA 1969-; Concord Squaro Assn 1971-74; Browning Inst 1986-, Bd Dir; NEH, Guggenheim Flwshp; Wilson Prize; Books: Browning's Youth, Charlotte Bronte and Sexuality, Victorian Discourses on Sexuality and Religion; Co-Ed 1991; *office:* NY Univ 19 University Pl New York NY 10003

MAYNARD, JULIE ANN (BERGER), Computer Tchr & Network Admin; *b:* Lima, OH; *c:* Amanda, Robby, Ronnie; *ed:* OH St Univ (BA) Elem Ed 1989; Network Typology Univ of Findlay 1995; *cr:* Continental Local Schl 5th Grd Tchr 1989-90, 6th Grd Tchr 1990-91, 4th Grd Tchr 1991-94, 7th Grd Math Tchr, Network Admin 1994-95, Cmptr Tchr, 7th Grd Math Tchr, Network Admin 1994-95, Cmptr Tchr, Network Admin, Tech Coord 1995-; *ai:* Tech Comm Chrpsn; Supts Advy, Total Quality Mngmt, Putnam Cty Advy Tech Comms; Newspaper Staff Co-Adv; Putnam Co Dist Tech Dev Team; NEA 1989-; Putnam Cty Tech Trailblazing Awd, Tech Grants; *home:* 7426 Old State Route 224 Ottawa OH 45875

MAYNARD, LESLIE BEEBE, Eighth Grade Science Teacher; *b:* Boonton, NJ; *m:* Richard J.; *ed:* Cook Coll Rutgers Univ (BS) Natural Resource Mngmt 1984; Kean Coll (MA) Earth Sci Ed 1991; 60 Addl Credits in Ed & Nat Scis; *cr:* Christopher Columbus MS Sci Tchr 1984-93; Wisdom Lane MS Sci Tchr 1993-; *ai:* 7th Grd Ecology Club Adv; Tech Comm for Staff Dev; Attnd After Schl Functions; Phi Delta Kappa 1995-; Natl Parks & Conservation Assn, Natl Wildlife Fed 1979-; Natl Geographic Soc 1971-; Seasonal Natl Park Ranger; Trng Manual Pub 1990; *office:* Wisdom Lane MS Center Ln Levittown NY 11756

MAYNARD, SCOTT DAVID, History Teacher; *b:* Honolulu, HI; *c:* Corbin Joseph; *ed:* St Michaels Coll (BA) His Scndry Cert 1991; 9 Grad Credits; MS Cert; *cr:* Campbell Home Co-op His, Eng & PE Tchr 1991-92; Cranston East His Tchr 1995-; *ai:* Girls Var Soccer Head Coach; Frosh Class & Ski Club Adv; CTA 1995-; NEA 1995-; Phi Alpha Theta 1990-; Eagle Scouts; *office:* Cranston Sr HS East 899 Park Ave Cranston RI 02910

MAYNER, EDITH, Teacher of Gifted & Talented; *b:* Roselle, NJ; *ed:* Wilberforce Univ (BS) Elem Ed 1961; Kean Coll 36 Credits; Trenton St 3 Credits; Rider 2 Credits; *cr:* Lincoln Schl 2nd Grd Tchr 1961-80, 4th Grd Tchr 1980-86; Polk Schl GATE Tchr 1986-; Harrison Schl GATE Tchr 1986-; *ai:* Wee Deliver in Schl Postal Svc, Writing Club Adv; Ride Prgm; REA 1961-, Treas, Sec; NEA 1961-; Gifted Tchrs Assn 1989; YWCA 1976-, Pres, Bd of Dir; Roselle Sr Citizen Bd of Dir 1980-, Sec; NAACP 1961-; Alpha Kappa Alpha 1957-, Pres; Tchr of Yr Lincoln Schl 1987; Clean Comm Awd 1995; *office:* Polk Elem Schl 1100 Warren St Roselle NJ 07203*

MAYO, ANGELA RODRIGUEZ, Math Tchr; *b:* Las Villas, Cuba; *m:* Ruben; *c:* Elizabeth; *ed:* St Peter's Coll (BS) Math 1974; Jersey City St (MA) Math Ed 1978, (MA) Biling-Bicultural Ed 1986; *cr:* Union Hill HS Math Tchr 1976-77; Emerson HS Math Tchr 1977-; Essex Cty Comm Coll Adj Math Tchr 1981-; *ai:* Span Club Adv; NEA, NJEA, UCEA 1976-; Circulo de Cultura Panamericano; Governor's Tchr Recognition Prgm; Tchr of Yr 1992; *office:* Emerson HS 318 18th St Union City NJ 07087*

MAYO, JAMES BRENT, Mathematics Teacher; *b:* Huntington, WV; *m:* Julia Gail Wilgus; *c:* Sarah, Anna; *ed:* Muskingum Coll (BA) Math 1977; Univ of Dayton (MA) Admin 1989; Post Grad Stud Prin Cert; *cr:* Chesapeake HS 9th-12th Grd Math Tchr 1977-79; Paul Blazer HS 9th Grd Math Tchr 1979-80; Chesapeake HS 9th-12th Grd Math Tchr 1981-; *ai:* OEA & NEA 1989-; MAA 1993-; *office:* Chesapeake HS 10183 County Rd 1 Chesapeake OH 45619

MAYO, KATHLEEN ANNE, 8th Grade English Teacher; *b:* New York, NY; *ed:* Hartwick Coll (BA) Eng 1990; Oneonta St Univ (MA) Eng Lit 1994; Credit Hrs Portfolio Assessment; *cr:* Fallsburg CSD Scndry Eng Tchr 1991-; *ai:* Girls Var Bskbl Coach 1991-92; JV Girls Sftbl Asst Coach 1992-93; JV Bsktbl & Head Bsktbl Coach; Jr Class Adv; Co-Chair of Decorum Comm; Fallsburg Tchrs Assn 1991-, Corresponding Sec; AFT 1991-; NYSUT 1991-; Grant Writing Portfolio for Grd Eight; *office:* Fallsburgh Jr Sr HS PO Box Ah Brickman Rd Fallsburg NY 12733*

MAYO, MICHAEL ALLEN, Marketing Professor; *b:* St Louis, MO; *m:* M. Murray; *ed:* Univ of MO at St Louis (BA) Psych 1976; Kent St Univ (MBA) Bus Mngmt 1979, (PHD) Psych 1984; *cr:* Cleveland Psychiatric Inst Bus Admin 1982-84; Kent St Univ Asst Prof Mrktg 1985-; *ai:* Assoc Dir Ctr for Intnl & Comparative Prgms; Acad of Intnl Bus 1995-; Amer Mrktg Assn 1991-; Mortar Bd Soc; Beut Paper Awd 1993 Amer Mrktg Assn; *office:* Kent St Univ Dept of Marketing Kent OH 44242

MAYO, MICHAEL JAMES, Business Teacher; *b:* Enfield, CT; *ed:* Bryant Coll (BS) Accounting 1984; Cntrl CT St Univ Cert Bus Ed 1990; Currently working on Masters in Scndry Ed; *cr:* Somers HS Bus Tchr 1991-; *ai:* Jr, Sr Var Show, Big Brothers, Sisters Adv; Jr Class Co-Adv; Town of Enfield Recreation Soccer Coach; *office:* Somers HS Ninth District Rd Somers CT 06071

MAYO, PATRICIA A., Teacher; *b:* St Louis, MO; *c:* Brandon Maurice; *ed:* Cntrl St Univ (BA) Bus Ed 1971; Bever Coll (MS) Scndry Ed 1976; Penn St Tchng & Learning; Lee Cartor Assertive Discipline; Temple Univ Cmptr Courses; Shippensburg Univi Schl to Work Prgm; *cr:* Penn Treaty Jr HS Tchr 1973-85; Germantown HS Tchr 1985-88; Strawberry Mansion HS Tchr 1989-; *ai:* FBLA Adv; Coalition of Essential Schls, Re Learning Chprsn; Cmptr Technologist; Mapping Rsrch; Family Group Facilitator, Trainer; Cmptr Lead Tchr; SAPP Team; PFT 1971-; AFT 1973-; Alpha Kappa Alpha 1971-; *office:* Strawberry Mansion HS Ste 1 3133 Ridge Ave Philadelphia PA 19121

MAYORAK, MARY ANN WUKOVITZ, Fifth Grade Teacher; *b:* Nazareth, PA; *m:* Robert John; *c:* Robert Paul; *ed:* East Stroudsburg Univ (BS) Elem Ed 1963; Kutztown Univ 15 Credits Elem Ed; *cr:* Floyd R. Shafer Schl Fifth Grd Tchr 1963-; *ai:* NEA, PSEA, Nazareth Area Ed Assn 1963-; Awd Outstdng Utilization of Prgm Places in the News WNYE TV Channel 25 NY 1972; Book: Call It Nautilus 1989; Nom Howard Klopp Exemplary Tchr Awd Cedar Crest Coll 1991; Nomination PA Tchr of Yr 1993; Jelly Bean Portrait of Pres Reagan Done by Stdnts Featured in Smithsonian, Book: To The Pres, Folk Portraits, in Reagan's Presidential Lib 1994; *office:* Floyd R Shafer Elem Sch 49 S Liberty St Nazareth PA 18064

MAYOTTE, GAIL ANNE, Principal; *b:* Lowell, MA; *ed:* Univ of Lowell (BS) Hlth Ed 1983; Boston Coll (ME) Admin 1991; *cr:* Assumption Schl Jr High Math & Sci Tchr 1984-85; St Paul School Jr High Math & Sci Tchr 1986-87; Sacred Heart Schl Jr High Math & Sci Tchr 1987-92; St Louis Elem School Prin 1993-; *ai:* NCEA 1984; AESPA 1993; Article Pub in Tchng K-8 & ScienceScope & Ideas Pub in Today's Catholic Tchr One Article Has Been Accepted For Publication, for Learning; *office:* Saint Louis Elem Schl 77 Boisvert St Lowell MA 01850

MAYS, KRISTIN LEE (COOK), Mathematics Teacher; *b:* Gallipolis, OH; *m:* Michael Reed; *c:* Corey Dane; *ed:* Rio Grande Coll (MS) Math 1988; Univ of Dayton (ME) Educl Admin; Post-Grad Hrs Prins Cert; *cr:* Fairborn HS Math Tchr 1988-; *ai:* Peer Mediation Adv; NEA, OEA 1988-; ASCD 1995-; Martha Holden Jennings Scholars Prgm; *office:* Fairborn HS 900 E Dayton Yellow Springs Rd Fairborn OH 45324

MAYS, LONA J., Language Arts Teacher; *b:* Zanesville, OH; *m:* Tom L.; *c:* Greg, Jeff, Todd, Kelly Ehrmer; *ed:* Kent St Univ (BA) Elem Ed 1991; 6 Credit Hrs; Ashland Univ; *cr:* Superior Brand Meats Order Desk 1968-71, Sec 1971-, Production Coord; John R Lea MS 7th-8th Grd Lang Arts 1991-; *ai:* Schl Newspaper Adv; Writing Team Coach; Spelling Bee Coord; Southeast Local Ed Assn 1991-, Bldg Rep, Co-Pres; OEA, NEA, NCTE & IRA 1991-; Venture Planning Comm, Sec & Treas; Schl Improvement Curr Comm 1995-; Co-Writer for Venture Grant; 1 of 200 Applicants to Attnd Holocaust Museum 1995; *office:* John R Lea MS 9130 Dover Rd Apple Creek OH 44606*

MAYS, PAT L., French Teacher; *b:* Holden, WV; *ed:* Rio Grande Coll (BS) Commnctn 1976; OH Univ Fr; *cr:* Belmont Casket Co Liner 1969; Reston Slacks Seamstress 1969-73; Adult Ed Instr 1973-76; Gallia Cty Schls Eng, Drama, Speech, Jrnlsm & Fr Tchr 1996; *ai:* Yrbk Adv; NEA 1975-; GCLEA 1976-; OEA 1976-; *office:* River Valley HS 1482 Little Kyger Rd Cheshire OH 45620

MAYWALT, JOANN JOHNS, Culinary Arts Instructor; *b:* Milwaukee, WI; *m:* Frederick J.; *ed:* Cntrl New England Coll of Tech (BS) Engrng 1977; Post Grad Stud Worcester St Coll, Univ of MA at Boston; *cr:* Bay Path Reg HS Culinary Arts Instr 9 Yrs; Spencer, E. Brookfield Reg Schls Food Svc Dir 2 Yrs; Grafton Job Corps Ctr Culinary, Food Svc Dir 5 Yrs; Our Lady of Mercy Ctr Culinary Arts Instr 2 Yrs; *ai:* MA Tchr Assn 1987-; Luther Church of Amer Young Women of Yr.*

MAZA, NORMAN JOHN, Instrumental Music Teacher; *b:* Binghamton, NY; *m:* Mary Ann Cassamatis; *c:* Jennifer Anne, Kathryn Diane; *ed:* IN Univ of PA (BS) Music Ed 1975; Northwestern Univ (MS) Music Ed 1979; Attnd Lehigh Univ Stud in Cmptr Programming, Penn St Univ Stud in Continuing Ed, Wilkes Univ Educl Ldrshp; *cr:* North Pocono MS Instrumental Music, Dir of Orch 1975-83; Cntrl Unite Meth Church Dir of Music, Chancel, Folk Choir Dir 1978-; Wallenpaupack Area MS Instrumental Music, Dir of Bands 1983-; *ai:* All Extracurricula Band Act, Jazz Band, Brass Ensemble; Stage Crew Adv 1/2 Time; Summer Band Dir; Recent Mid Sts Assn Co-Chair for Evaluation; NEA, PA Music Edctrs Assn, MENC 1975-; Masonic Lodge #218; Wayne Choralaires Dir; Cntrl United Meth Church Dir of Music, Admin Bd; *office:* Wallenpaupack Area MS HC 6 Box 6071 Hawley PA 18428

MAZANEC, POLLY HIMES, Medical & Surgical Nrsng Instr; *b:* Pittsfield, MA; *m:* Daniel John; *c:* Daniel C., Brian, Gregory, Sarah; *ed:* Univ of Rochester (BSN) Nrsng 1975; Case Western Reserve Univ (MSN) Nrsng 1983; Cert Nrsng Specialty OCN; *cr:* Univ Hosps Clinical Nurse Specialist 1 Yr; Cleveland Clinic Staff Nurse 3 Yrs; Ursuline Coll Div of Nrsng Instr 2 Yrs; *ai:* Acad Assessment, Curr Evaluation Comm; Oncology Nrsng Soc, Cleveland Chptr ONS 1979-; SGMA Theta Tau 1982-, Fac Adv; Hospice SIG 1995-; Prentiss Fnd Grant to Advance Oncology Nrsng Ed; Mary Redding Eckel Awd Caring & Clinical Excl in Nrsng; *office:* Ursuline Coll 2550 Lander Rd Pepper Pike OH 44124

MAZANEK, PATRICK, Sixth Grade Teacher; *b:* Natrona Heights, PA; *m:* Patricia Shannahan; *c:* Erin, Melanie; *ed:* IN Univ of PA (BS) Elem Ed 1973, (MED) Elem Ed 1982; *cr:* North Washington 6th Grd Tchr 1973-; *ai:* Kiski Area Ed Assn 1973-, Pres; PSEA, NEA 1973-; Vandergrift Fire Dept #1 1978-, Various Offices Held; Kiski Area HS Sr Class Elem Tchr of Yr 1980, 1987-88 & 1993; *home:* 806 McKinley Ave East Vandergrift PA 15629

MAZARESE, CARLO, Italian & Literature Teacher; *b:* Sicily, Italy; *m:* Patricia Ann Mc Donald; *ed:* SUNY at Stony Brook (BA) Italian, Span 1974, (MA) Italian Lit 1982; *cr:* Deer Park Pub Schls Italian Tchr 1974-78; Garden City Pub Schls Italian Tchr 1978-; SUNY Adj Instr 1982-; *ai:* Var Boys Soccer Coach; Adv Italian Club, Italian Lang Lit Magazine; NYSUT, AFT, AATI Natl 1978-; AATI Long Island 1978-, Pres 1984-86, Svc Awd; Soc Italian Culture 1980; Natl Soccer Coaches Assn 1986-; Nassau Cty Soccer Coaches Assn 1986-, Pres 1989-90; Coach of Yr 1989; Long Island Jr Soccer League Exceptional Srs Coach Svc Awd 1995; *office:* Garden City HS 170 Rockaway Ave Garden City NY 11530*

MAZELLA, MICHAEL A.,JR., Principal; *b:* Staten Island, NY; *m:* Pamela Smith; *c:* Julie Ann, Michael Joseph, Jessica Ann; *ed:* Richmond Coll (MS) Ed 1974; St John Univ (BA) Soc Stud 1969; Manhattan Coll Admin; *cr:* St Ann 7-8 Grd Tchr 1969-86, Prin 1986-; *ai:* Var Boys Bsktbl Coach; Summer Bsktbl Clinic Elem Children; Lunchtime Classes for Coop; Religion Organizer Father-Son, Mother-Daughter Bsktbl Games; Yrbk Chm; Knights of Columbus; CYO Exec Bd; Awds Distinguished Grd 1991, Maurice Wollin 1984, Jack Anglin Meml Trophy-CYO Anuual; Outstanding Elem Tchr Amer 1975; *office:* Saint Ann Schl 125 Cromwell Ave Staten Island NY 10304

MAZELLA, PAMELA SMITH, Mathematics Teacher; *b:* Staten Island, NY; *m:* Micheal A. Jr.; *c:* Julie Mazella Touhey, Michael J., Jessica; *ed:* Notre Dame Coll (BS) Elem Ed 1969; Wagner Coll (MS) Elem Ed 1979; 15 Credits Above Masters in Rel Ed; *cr:* Sacred Heart Schl 6th Grd Tchr 1969-70; St Ann Schl Remedial Rdng Tchr 1981-85; St Charles Schl 5th-6th Grd Tchr 1985-; *ai:* Lunch Duty Coord; Speaker for New 5th-6th Grd Tchrs at Dist Orientation; Parish Renewal Team 1992-, Exec Bd; Fed of Cath Schl Parents 1991-, Parish Schl Rep, Svc Awd; *home:* 156 Winchester Ave Staten Island NY 10312

MAZEN, REBECCA ANN, Science Teacher; *b:* Wareham, MA; *m:* Kenneth S.; *c:* Joshua, Daniel, Ricky; *ed:* Colby-Sawyer Coll (BS) Med Tech 1981; Beaver Coll (MED) Scndry Ed 1993; 12 Post Grad Credit Hrs; *cr:* Cardeza Fnd Rsrch Technician 1981-83; Abington Meml Hosp Lab Coord 1982-93; Germantown Acad Sub Sci Tchr 1993; Cheltenham HS Sci Tchr 1993-; *ai:* Sci Fair Mentor, Judge; Stu Assistance Prgm; S Adv; NSTA, ASM 1993-; MCSTA 1993-, Bd; ASCP 1982-; Chel Fnd Grant; PA Commonwealth Biotechnology Wkshp; Beaver C Tchr of Yr 1993; *office:* Cheltenham HS 500 Rices Mill Rd Wyn 19095

MAZEN, TOBY, Mathematics Teacher; *b:* Bronx, NY; *m:* Sam Emanuel; *ed:* Hunter Coll (BA) Math, Sociology 1967, (MA) M 1970; Stud Sabbatical SUNY Purchase Calculus, Cognitive Manhattan Ctr for Advanced Psychoanalytic Stud 21 Credits; *cr:* HS Math Tchr 1967-71; De Witt Clinton HS Math Tchr 1971-72, 1 Jane Addams Voc HS Math Tchr 1976-77; De Witt Clinton HS Ma 1977-79; Harry Struman HS Math Tchr 1979-; *ai:* 9th Grd Ori Project Welcome Tchr; 7 Homeroom Classes Grd Adv; UFT 1967- 1987-, Advy Comm; *office:* Harry S. Truman HS 750 Baychester Av NY 10475*

MAZER, KEN R., Mathematics Teacher; *b:* Cleveland, OH; *m:* Bubnick; *c:* John Kaniecki, Jennifer Kaniecki; *ed:* Cleveland St Ur Math 1969, (MA) Math 1979; *cr:* Wickliffe MS Math Tchr 1969-; L Comm Coll Math Tchr 1993-; *ai:* Mathcounts Coach; OEA, NEA Wickliffe Ed Assn 1975-, VP; NCTM, NEOCTM, OCTM, ECCTM; Assn 1981-, Regnl Rep; Mathcounts 1991-; *office:* Wickliffe MS Euclid Ave Wickliffe OH 44092

MAZEROSKI, RONALD FRANKLIN, Associate Dean of Stude *b:* Cadiz, OH; *m:* Barbara Joan Benson; *c:* Jenna, Brenae; *ed:* Mu Coll (BA) His, Comm 1979; OH St Univ (MA) Higher Ed Admin Credit Hrs in Real Estate; *cr:* Muskingum Coll Asst Dir of Pub R 1979-82, Bsbl Coach 1982-95, Assoc Dean of Stu Life 1983-; *a* Adv; NACA, OASPA 1983-; Cadiz Alumni Schlsp Comm Mem, Diamond Club Mem; NACA Great Lakes Research Grant on Lea 1989; OH Ath Conf Coach of Yr 1990; *office:* Muskingum C Stormont St New Concord OH 43762

MAZUR, DANIEL F., Social Studies Educator; *b:* Cleveland, Pamela M. Newman; *ed:* Cleveland St Univ (BA) Soc Stud & E Working Toward Masters in Ed with Ed Cmptr Usage Specialty; *cr* HS Soc Stud Educator & Tech Coord 1993-; *ai:* Soph Class & C Club Moderator; Fac & Admin Advy Comm; Cleveland Cncl o Affairs 1990-; Natl Archaeological Soc 1991-; *office:* Padua Fra High School 6740 State Rd Parma OH 44134

MAZUR, MARCIA LYNN, Health Teacher; *b:* Toledo, OH; *m:* R Molly; *ed:* Univ of Toledo (BED) PE & Hlth 1974; Grad Cl Bowling Green St Univ; *cr:* Eastwood Local Schls Tchr 1975-; *ai.* NEA 1975-; Delta Kappa Gamma 1995-; MS Assn 1993-; Girl Sco 1995-; *office:* Eastwood MS 4800 Sugar Ridge Pemberville OH 4

MAZUREK, JOHN MICHAEL, American History Teacher; *b:* R PA; *m:* Cyndi Oshnack; *c:* Michelle; *ed:* California Univ of PA (BS) Ed 1970; PA Cert 28 Credits; *cr:* Laurel Highlands Schl Dist 8th G His Tchr 1970-; *ai:* NEA, PSEA, LHEA 1970-; *office:* Laurel Hi Jr HS Hookton Ave Uniontown PA 15401*

MAZUREK, KATHLEEN HARTZ, Business Education Tea Connellsville, PA; *m:* Edward Richard; *c:* Matthew E.; *ed:* Univ of (BS) Bus Ed 1980; 21 Grad Credits; *cr:* Jeannette Schl Dist B 1980-; *ai:* FBLA Spon; Dept Chprsn; NEA, PSEA 1980-; JTEA 19 *office:* Jeannette Schl Dist PO Box 418 Florida Ave Jeannette PA

MAZUREK, MALENA MARIE, Biology Teacher; *b:* Ford City, Clarion Univ of PA (BA) Ed, Bio, Gen Sci 1989, (MA) Sci Ed 1 Abraxas HS Sci Tchr 1989-90; Keystone HS Sci Tchr 1990-91; E Forward HS Sci Tchr 1992-; *ai:* Ski Club, Stu Cncl Spon; Fac Advy Peer Mediation Trng; EFEA, PSTA 1992-; *office:* Elizabeth Forwar 1000 Weigle'S Hill Rd Elizabeth PA 15037

MAZZA, DONALD, Instrumental Music Teacher; *b:* Canonsburg, Nancy Kunkle; *c:* Matthew, Susan; *ed:* IN Univ of PA (BS) Music E Duquesne Univ (MS) Music Ed 1974; *cr:* Bentworth HS Band Dir 1 Bentworth MS Band Dir 1989-; *ai:* Concert, Stage Band, Stdnt Cn Natl Hon Soc Adv; NEA, PSEA, MENC, PMEA 1970-; Bentwor Assoc, Pres 1992-; BSA, Scoutmaster 3 Yrs, Dist Commissioner Scouter 1982-; H. C. Frick Fnd Schlsp; BSA Dist Awd Merit, Wood *office:* Bentworth M S Pine St Ellsworth PA 15331

MAZZA, JOHN MICHAEL, Spcl Education & History Tchr; *b:* N City, NY; *m:* Joann Bodycott; *c:* Joseph, Allison, Brian; *ed:* Manhat (BS) PE 1975; Coll of New Rochelle (MS) Spec Ed 1984; 30 Addl Admin; 50 Credits Bus Admin WCC; *cr:* Mamin HS Tchr 1975- Med Coll Tchr 1978-80; Rye HS Tchr, Coach 1980-; *ai:* Coa Skiing, Wrestling, Soccer, LaCrosse; WC Socl St 1988-; AFT, NCA *office:* Rye City Schls 324 Midland Ave Rye NY 10580

MAZZA, MICHELLE-ANNE, Science & Social Studies T Providence, RI; *ed:* Roger Williams Univ (BA) Art, His 1979; (MED) Instrl Tech 1981, (CAGS) Instrl Tech 1983; Cert Gra Educator GATE RI; Working MAT Degree Environmental Ed; *cr:* Part-time Educl Comm Instr 1981-84; St Elizabeth Schl MS S 1985-95; St Mary Acad Sci, Soc Stud Tchr 1995-; *ai:* MS Sci 1989-94; Local Newspaper Publicity Asst; RISSA, NSTA 199 Scouts of USA 1975-, Distngd Photography; Authored Mid Grd Ha Schl System 1994; *office:* St Mary's Acad-Bayview 3070 Pawtuc Riverside RI 02809*

MAZZAFERRO, JOHN JACK, Biology Teacher; *b:* Rome, Maryann Dublanica; *c:* Lora Mazzaferro Nunez; *ed:* SUNY at (BS) Scndry Ed 1965, (MS) Scndry Ed 1970; 90 Addl Credit Hrs; *cr* Free Acad Bio Tchr 1965-; *ai:* Sci Tchr Coord; Yrbk Adv; Rom Assn; AFT; NYSTA; Rome Common Cncl 1980-, Pres; Old Erie A Soc 1980-, Treas; Loyal Order of Moose; Knights of Columbus; Cty Environment Cncl; NYS Tchrs Retirement; NSF Grants; *office* Free Acad 500 Turin St Rome NY 13440*

MAZZARELLA, FRED A., 7th Grade Math & Science Tchr; *b:* PA; *m:* Karen Semko; *c:* Jason, Jarett, Jeffrey; *ed:* Saint Francis C Elem Ed 1976; Attnd Univ of UT, Millersville 12 Credits, IN Credits, Univ of Pittsburgh at Johnstown 8 Credits; *cr:* Cntrl Cambr & Sci Tchr 1986-; *ai:* Jr HS Ftbl Coach; NEA, PSEA 1986-; Little Coach; *office:* Central Cambria MS 208 Schoolhouse Rd Ebensb 15931*

MAZZARELLA, MICHAEL LYNN, Eighth Grade Science T Colver, PA; *m:* Maryanne McAlister; *c:* Zachary; *ed:* St Francis C Gen Sci & Bio Scndry Ed 1979; 33 Grad Hrs; *cr:* Cntrl Cambria Tchr 1979-; *ai:* Jr HS Ftbl Coach; PSEA 1979-; NEA 1979-; CCEA *office:* Central Cambria MS 205 Highland Ave Ebensburg PA 1593

MAZZARELLA, MIMI FETTA, English Teacher; *b:* New York, Steven Goldman; *c:* Joe, Mike; *ed:* C W Post Univ (BA) Eng Ed W Post Grad Schl (MS) Eng Ed 1995; 33 Credits Eng Ed 1972, 15 1995; *cr:* Sewanhakah HS Eng Tchr 1972; Syosset HS Hum Tchr 1 Lawrence Rd JHS Eng Tchr 1988-91; Uniondale HS Eng Tchr 19 Magazine Club & JHS Newspaper Adv; PTSA 1972-; UTA & AFT NYS Eng Cncl 1993- Tchr of Excl 1993; PTA 1983-, Pres; 1 E Numerous Articles Pub; Lecturer 1995 NYS Eng Cncl; Numerou Lectures; *office:* Uniondale HS 933 Goodrich St Uniondale NY 11.

ZARELLI, DOLORES M., First Grade Teacher; *b:* Milford, MA; orth Adams St Coll (BS) Ed 1972; Lesley Coll (MED) Creative Arts rr 1993; 30 Addl Hrs; *cr:* Town of Milford Schl Grd 1 Tchr 23 Yrs; Amer Cancer Soc Vol; Oil & Watercolor Painting; Walking & rcise; MTA 1974-; *office:* Woodland Elem Schl N Vine St Milford MA 7

ZARESE, MAUREEN ANN, Health Educator; *b:* New York, NY; *m:* ael L.; *c:* Lauren, Adrienne; *ed:* Brooklyn Coll (BS) Hlth Ed 1969, Hlth Ed 1972; Substance Awareness Coord Cert; *cr:* St Joseph by the HS Hlth, PE Tchr, Dept Chair 1969-73; Montclair St Coll Instr -76; St Barnabas Medical Ctr Instr 1979-88; Westfield HS Tchr, Stu stance Cnslr, Substance Awareness Coord 1988-; *ai:* Peer Helper ; Project Grad; Sr Class Adv; Cross-Age Drug Awareness Tchng Club; 1988-; Amer Coll of Childbirth Educators 1983-, NJ Tchr Trng Coord; Heart Assn 1991-, VP; Westfield YMCA Steering Comm 1984-, Pres; field PTO 1978-, Pres; Northern NJ ASPO, Lamaze 1983-, Pres; Tchr ; Peer Mediation Grant; Friend of Youth Awd; *home:* 330 Benson Pl field NJ 07090*

ZARISI, LISA JO, Assistant Principal; *b:* Brooklyn, NY; *m:* Kurt A. der; *ed:* Bernard M. Baruch Coll at NY (BS) Bus Ed-Magna Cum 1982; Rider Coll at Lawrenceville (MA) Bus Ed-with Distinction Coll of Staten Island 6th Yr Cert Admin/Supervision 1988; *cr:* lin D. Roosevelt HS Bus Ed Tchr 1982-90, Bus Ed, Tech, Art Music Prin; *ai:* Bus Ed Assn of Metropolitan NY 1979-; NBEA, Eastern Bus ssn 1987-; Assn for Asst Prins Secretarial Stud 1990-; Columbia Univ Coll Bus Ed Consultant; Delta Pi Epsilon Natl Honorary in Bus Ed ; *office:* Franklin D. Roosevelt HS 5800 20th- Ave Brooklyn NY 4

ZELLA, ANTHONY JOHN, Professor of English; *b:* Elizabeth, NJ; Seton Hall Univ (BA) Eng 1962; Columbia Univ (MA) Eng, arative Lit 1964, (PHD) Eng, Comparative Lit 1970; *cr:* Hunter Coll rer 1968; William Paterson Coll Asst Prof 1968-76, Asst Dept Chair -72, Assoc Prof 1976-84, Coord, Hum Media Ctr 1979-, Hum Asst 1980-86, Prof 1984-, Eng Dept Chair 1988-94; *ai:* AFT 1968-; MLA; James Soc 1981-; Numerous Articles Pub; *office:* William Paterson 300 Pompton Rd Wayne NJ 07470

ZELLA, BERNICE BONGIORNO, Spanish & Italian Teacher; *b:* PA; *m:* Julius P.; *c:* Michael, Marc; *ed:* Penn St Univ (BA) Span 1960; Pa (MS) Span, Italian 1971; 41 Grad Hrs Gannon Univ, Cntrl Ct Univ, Univ, Univ of Rome Italy, Gonzaga Univ in Florence Italy, YO St Univ, and Univ; *cr:* Strong Vincent HS 10-12 Grd Italian Tchr 1960-61, -72; Grover Cleveland Elem Schl Tchr, FLES Prgm 1961-62; evelt Jr HS Ital & Span Tchr 1962-70; YO St Univ Italian Instr -81; Austintown Fitch HS Span, Italian Tchr 1982-83, 1985-86; dman HS Italian, Span Tchr 1986-; *ai:* Textbook Selection Comm; n Club; NEA 1960-; OEA 1982-; BEA 1986-; AATSP; Youngstown n Schl Bd 1992-, Schl Bd Mem; Hwy Tabernacle 1985-, Advy Bd n Ed; Fulbright Hays Grant; Natl Defense Ed Grants 2 Yrs; Class Act Outstanding Tchr 1991; Consultant Ginn & Co Textbook Materials ; Translator of Materials; *office:* Boardman HS 7777 Glenwood Ave dman OH 44512*

ZEO, CHERYL ANN, Second Grade Teacher; *b:* Providence, RI; *ed:* (AEd) Early Elem, Spec Ed 1975; Annhurst Coll (BA) Elem Ed, Spec 977; Lesley Coll (MED) Elem Ed, Spec Ed 1982; Bryant Coll Cmptr *r:* Cranston Presch Ctr Tchrs Aide 1975-77; Meeting Street Schl Spec chr 1977-82; Plainville Pub Schls Spec Ed Tchr 1982-89, Second Grd 1989-; *ai:* Tech Coord 1995-; PEA 1982-, VP 1986-88, Sec 1992-94; 1982-; Plainville PTO 1982-, VP 1995-, After Schl Cmptr Enrichment & 2 1992-93; Horace Mann Grant After Schl Enrichment 1987-88, Cmptr Trng 1988-89; PLANOW Grant A Dinosauer Hunt 1994; : Plainville Pub Schl 68 Messenger St Plainville MA 02762

ZEO, FRANK ARTHUR, Professor of Saxophone; *b:* Atlantic City, Benjamin, Joseph, Kelly, Kristen, Kami; *ed:* West Chester Univ (BS) Ed 1981; Temple Univ (MM) Music Performance 1985; *cr:* sbury Schl Dist Instrumental Music Tchr 1986-; Temple Univ phone Instr, Jazz Band Dir 1992-; Bucks Cty Comm Coll Clarinet Instr ; Univ of Arts Small Jazz Ensemble Dir, Saxophone Instr 1995-; *ai:* MENC 1986-; Amer Fed Musicians 1977-; IAJE 1987-; Outstdng g Men of Amer 1986; Soloist Competition Winner 1984; West Chester Soloist Competition Winner 1981.*

ZEO, MICHAEL JOSEPH,JR., Social Studies Teacher; *b:* Buffalo, *n:* Betty Teresa Armstrong; *c:* Madelyn E.; *ed:* Charles Co Comm Coll Gen Stud 1979; Salisbury St Univ (BA) His 1981; George WA Univ, ern MD Coll for Masters Equivalent; *cr:* Matthew Henson MS Soc Tchr 1981-; *ai:* Soc Stud Dept Chprsn; Stu Cncl Adv; Schl ovement Team; MD SchlPPerformance Prgm Comm; The Madrigal & Ladies Coord; NEA, MD St Teach Assn, Ed Assn of Charles Cty ; Historical Soc Charles Co 1978-, Pres; Southern MD Concert Band , Pres; Sons of Amer Revolution 1986-, Registrar; Charles Co sm Advy Bd 1987-, Chm; Charles Co Heritage Comm 1993-, Pres; Pub Book: The Simmons & Welch Family of Charles Co; 1983 US al Historical Soc Outstdng Tchr, Historian; 1981 MD ST ives-Archival Intern; 1990 Charles Co Bd of Ed Outstdng Soc Stud 1995 Port Tobacco DAR Outstdng His Tchr; *office:* Matthew Henson 535 Livingston Rd Indian Head MD 20640*

ZERLE, ROBERT S., Biology Teacher; *b:* Bridgeport, PA; *m:* Carol Mosser; *c:* Lauralyn, Brett; *ed:* Kutztown St Univ (BS) Ed Bio 1967; nova Univ (MED) Scndry Guid-Hnrs 1975; 90 Grad Credits Beyond Gannon Univ, Penn St Univ, Wilkes Coll, Millersville St Univ, ensburg St Univ; *cr:* Norristown Area Schl Dist 7th Grd Life Sci Tchr -71; Upper Merion Area Schl Dist 10th Grd Bio Tchr 1971-, 12th Grd culture Tchr 1976-82, 12th Grd Ecology Tchr 1982-94, 10th-12th Grd Tech Tchr 1984-86; *ai:* Past Ftbl, Bsbl & Bsktbl Coach 1982; NAEA -71; NEA 1967-; PSEA 1967-; UMAEA 1967-; Pikeville Wildlife ; Victor Emmanual Italian-Amer Club 1986-; Dev 2 HS Courses ogy & Horticulture; *office:* Upper Merion Area HS 435 Crossfield Rd Of Prussia PA 19406*

ZI, JOAN M. LOTZ, Senior High English Teacher; *b:* Buffalo, NY; obert C.; *ed:* St Univ Coll at Buffalo (BS) Scndry Eng Ed 1968, (MS) ry Eng Ed 1972; *cr:* Reszel Jr High Eng Tchr 1970-88; North wanda Sr HS Eng Tchr 1988-; *ai:* NYSUT & NTUT; Buffalo Friends mstead Parks 1988-; *office:* North Tonawanda Sr HS 405 Meadow Dr Tonawanda NY 14120*

ZIE, REBECCA ROSS, English Teacher; *b:* Conneaut, OH; *m:* J.; *c:* Maria Kindberg, Elizabeth Tonkin, Emily; *ed:* Youngstown (BSEd) Eng 1965; SUNY at Fredonia (MSEd) Eng 1981; *cr:* Madison ng Tchr 1965-66; Madison Tchr 1966-67; Jamestown Jr HS Eng Tchr -68; Southwestern HS Eng Tchr 1979-; *ai:* Speech Coach; NEA & NY 1979-; Southwestern Tchrs Assn 1979-, 1st VP, Pres, Curr Chprsn; s Peter & Paul RC Church 1967-; Jamestown Projects Group 1969-; : Southwestern Cntrl HS 600 Hunt Rd Jamestown NY 14701

ZIO, ROBERT JOSEPH, Math Teacher & Dept Chair; *b:* Wilm, DE; Univ fo DE (BA) Math 1970, (MED) Math 1976; *cr:* Claymont HS Tchr 1971-77; Salesianum HS Math Tchr, Dept Chair 1978-; Widener Adj Math Prof 1981-; *ai:* Var Golf Coach; Frosh Math League Moderator; NCTM 1990-; DCTM 1971-; NCEA 1978-; Distgnd Svc Awd for Tchng Excl; *home:* 4 Bavarian Ln Wilmington DE 19810*

MAZZOCCO, DIANE KENSICKI, English Teacher; *b:* Cleveland, OH; *c:* Marco Angelo; *ed:* OH St Univ (BS) Span, Eng 1966; Northern IL Univ (MS) Rdng Specialization 1973; Univ MA at Amherst 21 Hrs Towards Masters ESL; San Francisco St Univ, Univ CA at Berkeley 25 Hrs Eng, Span, Ital; *cr:* Claremont Jr HS Span Tchr 1966-69; IL Yth Ctr Tchr 1070-73; Haines Jr HS Eng Tchr 1973-76; Ceta Skills Ctr Tchr 1977; White Brook MS Rdng Tchr 1977-79; holyoke Street Schl LA Coord, Rdng Tchr 1979-84; Greenfield MS Rdng Tchr 1984-85; Ludlow HS Eng Tchr 1985-; *ai:* Fac Cncl; Pilot Mentoring Prgm; NEA, MTA 1977-; LEA 1985-; NECTE 1994-; Pi Lambda Theta 1965-; *office:* Ludlow Sr HS 500 Chapin St Ludlow MA 01056

MAZZOLA, MICHAEL, Instructor & Dept Chairperson; *b:* Willmantic, CT; *ed:* Univ of Bridgeport (BS) Art 1971; Cntrl CT St Univ (MS) Art 1980; Attnd Boston Univ, Univ of CT, Eastern CT St Univ, Univ of Hartford; *cr:* Windham HS Instr 1971-, Dept Chprsn 1984-; *ai:* Educl & Staff Dev Comm; Mural Projects; Exhibiting Artist in Cape Cod Gallery; Free-Lance Artist; Lecturer for Comm Historical & Art Groups; CAEA 1971-; AFT 1975-, VP; NAEA 1976-; William Benton Museum of Art 1980-; Metropolitan Museum of Art; Wadsworth Athenleum; Smithsonian; Staff Mem of the Yr 1982; Tchr of the Yr System Wide 1986; Tchr of the Yr St of CT Nom; *office:* Windham HS 355 High St Willimantic CT 06226

MAZZOLA, SAL, Instrumental Music Teacher; *b:* New York, NY; *c:* Anthony, Daniel, Lauren; *ed:* Lehman Coll (BA) Music Ed 1985; Pace Univ (MS) Ed, Admin & Comp Sci 1993; Attnd Manhattan Schl of Music; *cr:* Saint Dominic Schl Music Tchr & Admin Intern 1978-85; IS 192 Instrumental Music Tchr 1985-; *ai:* Bronx-Borough Wide Band Conductor; Elvis the Legend Lives Concert Tour Musical Dir; Various Musical Artist Arranger, Conductor & Producer; AFT & UFT 1985-; MENC 1985-; AFM 1990-; NYCMTA 1994-; BMI 1995-; *office:* Piagentini/Jones I S 192 Schl 650 Hollywood Ave Bronx NY 10465

MAZZONI, THERESA BAGNELL, Third Grade Teacher; *b:* Philadelphia, PA; *c:* Christopher; *ed:* Villa Maria Coll, Gannon Univ (BS) Elem Ed 1969; *cr:* Our Lady Star of the Sea 3rd Grd Tchr 1985-; *ai:* Choir Dir; Mid Sts Evaluation Steering Comm Chm; NCEA 1986-; *office:* Our Lady Star Of Sea Schl 15 N California Ave Atlantic City NJ 08401

MBAYE, FATOU NDENE, French Professor; *b:* Saint-Louis, West Africa; *ed:* Cntrl St Univ (BA) Pol Sci 1989; OH St Univ (MS) Fr 1992; PHD Candidate Fr; 25 Hrs Masters Ed; 30 Hrs Tchng Cert; *cr:* Kenwood Elem Schl Tchrs Aid 1990-91; OH St Univ Grad Tchng Asst 1990-92, Rsrch Asst 1991-92; Cntrl St Univ Fr, Wolof Prof 1992-; *ai:* African Stud Assn 1993-; Miami Vly Lang Tchrs Assn, African Lit Assn 1992-; Middfest Intnl 1995-, Chair Rel Comm, Recognition Awd; Francoph Afr Rsrch, African Lang Tchr Assn 1993-; OH Assn Afric Stud, Grad Stu Mentor 1995-; OH St Univ Ldrshp Awd 1992; Up & Coming Awd 1995; Cold Cord 1989; Dean's List 1987-89; *office:* Central St Univ 1400 Brush Row Wilberforce OH 45384*

MCABEE, MARNA WILSON, First Grade Teacher; *b:* Marion, IN; *m:* Russell DeWayne; *c:* Cynthia McAbee Chapman, Todd Michael; *ed:* Midway Jr Coll (AA) Elem Ed 1962; Univ of KY (BA) Elem Ed 1965; Ball St Univ (MA) Elem Ed 1979; Sign Lang; AMIS Univ of Dayton; *cr:* St Peter Elem 2nd Grd Tchr 1963-68, 1st Grd Tchr 1968-83; West Elem 1st Grd Tchr 1983-90; Sharpsburg Elem 1st Grd Tchr 1990-; *ai:* Grade Level Chprsn 1990-; FREA 1969-, Bldg Rep; OEA, NEA 1963-; Village Players 1965-68, Treas; BPW 1963-70; *office:* Sharpsburg Elem 2454 Sharpsburg Rd Fort Recovery OH 45846

MC ADAM, JOHN J., Social Studies Teacher; *b:* Malden, MA; *m:* Christine White; *c:* Sean; *ed:* Salem St Coll (BS) Ed 1974, (MED) Admin 1979; Attnd Boston St Coll, Univ MA at Boston, Lincoln-Filene Ctr, Tufts Univ; *cr:* Medford HS Tchr 1974-; *ai:* Ath Dept Spec Projects; Medford Tchrs Assn, MA Tchrs Assn, NEA 1974-; Mustangs Hall of Fame 1990-, Treas; *office:* Medford HS 489 Winthrop St Medford MA 02155

MC ADAMS, THOMAS ROBERT,SR., Third Grade Teacher; *b:* Bronx, NY; *m:* Isabel Popoli; *c:* Thomas Jr., Kevin J.; *ed:* SUNY Coll at New Paltz (BS) Elem Ed 1968, (MS) Elem Ed 1973; Prof Diploma Educl Admin 1979; Schl Bus Admin, Dist Admin 1982; *cr:* Ben Franklin Elem Sch Fifth Grd Tchr 1968-89, Acting Asst Prin 1976-78, Head Tchr 1985-87; George Washington Elem Sch Head Tchr 1989-92; Van Cortlandtville Elem Sch Fifth Grd Tchr 1992-95; Ben Franklin Elem Third Grd Tchr 1995-; *ai:* Rocketry, Track & Field, Hockey, Detective, Chess & Drama; Fishkill Correctional Facility Educator Adult Basic Ed; Drug Ed, Discipline Comms; AFT 1969-; ALAC 1989-92, Treas 1990-92; Scholastic Essay Competition; Authored Soc Stud, Sci Curr Guides; *office:* Benjamin Franklin Elem 3477 Kamhi Dr Yorktown Hts NY 10598*

MC AFEE, DIANE ELAINE (STOUDT), Eng & Creative Writing Teacher; *b:* Palmerton, PA; *m:* Neville Delmarr; *c:* Heather Elaine, Erica Lynn Young, N. Dayne; *ed:* Muhlenberg Coll (BA) Eng 1965; Masters Equivalency Eng 1990; 40 Credits Wilkes Univ, Bloomsburg Univ, PA St Univ; *cr:* Rock Glen Jr HS Classroom Tchr 1966-92; West Hazelton Jr HS Classroom Tchr 1992-; *ai:* Yrbk, Spelling Bee, Drama Club Spon, Adv; Lit Magazine; Hazleton Area Educ Assn 1966-, Fac Rep; PSEA, NEA 1966-, St Race Relations Comm, St & Natl Tchr Conventions Del; Nuremberg Comm Players 1968-, Bd of Dirs, Sec, Theatre Dir, Actress; Emmanuel UCC Nuremberg 1970-, Organist, Choral Dir; Hazleton Area Poetry Writing Awds; Nom PA Tchr of Yr; *office:* West Hazleton Jr HS 325 North St West Hazleton PA 18201

MCAFEE, TRACY L., Assoc Prof of Speech & Theatre; *b:* Marion, OH; *m:* Susan K.; *c:* Ami, Jonathan, Timothy, Monica; *ed:* Baldwin-Wallace Coll (BA) Speech Commnctn 1983; The OH St Univ (MA) Speech & Theatre Ed 1987; Masters Plus 45 Credit Hrs; *cr:* Harding HS Bus & Drama Tchr 1983-88; Manchester Coll Adj Fac & Admissions Cnslr 1988-89; Northern VA Comm Coll Instr 1989-91; WA Comm Coll Assoc Prof Speech & Theatre 1991-; *ai:* Phi Theta Kappa & Chrstn Flwshp Co-Adv; Drama Club Adv; Fac Evaluation Comm Mem; Facilitator for OH Great Tchrs Seminars; SCA 1983-; OSCA 1983-; BSA 1969-, Trng Chair; VITA 1996-, Site Coord; Washington Cty Pub Lib 1996-, Bd of Trustees; Outstndng Tchr Awd Washington St Comm Coll 1994; *office:* Washington State Comm Coll 710 Colegate Dr Marietta OH 45750*

MCALEER, FRANCES D., Supervisor of Gifted Programs; *b:* Philadelphia, PA; *c:* Michael Thomas, Mark Thomas; *ed:* West Chester Univ (BS) Elem Ed 1968; Temple Univ (MED) Lang Arts 1971; Duquesne Univ (MED) Admin 1982; *cr:* Hatboro Horsham Tchr 1968-69; Schaumburg SD Tchr 1970-76; Keystone Oaks SD Tchr of Gifted 1976-89, Supvr of Gifted 1989-; *ai:* K-12 Odyssey of the Mind; Acad Events; Stock Mrkt; NEA, KOEA & PSEA 1976-; PA Assoc for Gifted Ed 1976-, Pres, Tchr of Yr Awd 1988; Numerous Books & Articles Pub; Instr at Duquesne Univ & TX A&M; Presenter at World, Natl, St & Local Confs; Inservice Course Instr for 10 Yrs; *home:* 321 Lorlita Ln Pittsburgh PA 15241*

MC ALEXANDER, NANCY KEELY, Third Grade Teacher; *b:* Bisbee, AZ; *m:* Don E.; *ed:* OH Northern Univ (BSEd) Ed 1968; Attnd Miami Univ, Univ of Dayton, Wright St Univ, Drake Univ; *cr:* Wapakoneta Schls Grd 1 Tchr 1968; Tipp City Ex Vil Schl 3rd-4th Grd Tchr 1968-; *ai:* Delta Kappa Gamma 1995-; Comm Minded Women 1971-, VP, Pres; Tipp, Monroe Historical Soc 1983-, Worked on Founding Comm; TWIGS 1992-, Comm Chm, Several Comms; Campfire Girls Ldr; *home:* 614 Barbara Dr Tipp City OH 45371*

MC ALILEY, FRANCES WRIGHT, 8th Grd Comm & Lit Teacher; *b:* Philadelphia, PA; *c:* Dwayne, Ira, Lauren; *ed:* Cheyney Univ (BS) Elem Ed 1959; Temple Univ 10 Credits Cnslng; *cr:* Arthur Elem Schl 3rd-4th Grd Tchr 1959-63; Kinsey Elem Schl 6th Grd Tchr 1963-65; Ferguson Elem Schl 6th Grd Tchr 1966-68; Hartranft Elem Schl 6th Grd Tchr 1965-66; East Norriton MS 6-8 Grd Tchr 1981-; *ai:* 8th Grd Chprsn; Cooperative Tchr for Stu Tchr; EANA, PSEA, NEA 1981-; Fed Women's Club 1964-76, Fine Arts, Prgm, Project Chprsn; Whitpain Twp Park, Rec Bd 1970-75, Rec Chr; Montgomery Co Speaker's Bureau 1972-73; Amer Red Cross Bd Wissahickon Branch Sec Bd, Chprsn Jr Red Cross; Lower Providence Bapt Church 1978-, Chprsn Chrstn Ed; Ministry of Coll Stdnts Dir; Vacation Bible Schl Chprsn; Headstart Curr, Recreation Vols, Preschl Helps for Parents, Creative Worship Handbooks; Rel, Secular Plays, Musical Adaptations; Pub Articles; Wissahickon Ed Assn Layman 1972; Gift of Time Tribute Amer Family Inst at Vly Forge PA 1990; *home:* 1545 Clearview Ave Blue Bell PA 19422*

MC ALINEY, EILEEN MC KEON, 7th & 8th Grade Math Teacher; *b:* Poughkeepsie, NY; *m:* Daniel P.; *ed:* Mount St Mary Coll (BA) Math 1989; 15 Hrs SUNY at New Paltz Math, Scndry Ed; *cr:* St Denis, St Columba 7th, 8th Grd Math Tchr 90-; *ai:* Drama Club Fac Adv, Producer; NCEA 1990-; *office:* St Denis, St Columba Schl Rt 82 Hopewell Junction NY 12533

MCALISTER, HORACE BERNARD, High School Mathematics Tchr; *b:* New York, NY; *ed:* York Coll (BS) Math 1978; NY Univ (MS) Math 1982; City Coll (MS) Ed Admin & Supvr 1989; 45 Credits in Undergraduate Bio; *cr:* Boys & Girls HS Math Tchr 2 Yrs; Bronx Regnl HS Math Tchr 6 Yrs; Prospect Heights HS Math Tchr 9 Yrs; NY City Tech Coll Math Adjunct Lect 13 Yrs; *ai:* Regents Math Tutoring; UFT 1978-; *office:* Prospect Heights HS 883 Classon Ave Brooklyn NY 11225*

MC ALISTER, SUSAN JEAN (OWEN), Elementary Vocal Music Teacher; *b:* Norwalk, CT; *m:* John David; *c:* Kathleen, Matthew, Patrick, Amy; *ed:* Westminster Choir Coll (BA) Music Ed 1976; Georgian Court Coll Spec Ed Cert 1988; *cr:* Middletown Twp Schl Elem Vocal Music Tchr 1976-; *ai:* Adv Kids for Kids 4-H Club; Ldr All Saints Yth Group; MTEA, NJEA 1976-; ADK 1995-; *office:* Harmony Elem Schl Tindal Rd Middletown NJ 07748*

MC ALLISTER, ELIZABETH HEVIA, Ed Opportuity Program Cnslr; *b:* Bayamon, PR; *m:* Robert J.; *ed:* Seton Hall Univ (BA) Music, Comm 1984; Rutgers Univ (MSW) Soc Work 1994; Alcohol & Substance Abuse Cert; Mental Hlth Clinican Licensed; *cr:* Tour US, Mexico, Japan Vocalist 1972-76; Meth Hosp Soc Worker 1976-80; Univ Hosp Soc Worker 1980-86; Hackensack Medical Ctr Soc Worker 1986-87; Rutgers Univ Soc Worker, Clinician 1987-; *ai:* Adv PR Org Cuban, Span Club; Sexual Assault Comm; Latino Caucas Fac, Staff; Cultural Resource Initiative Comm; AAUP 1987-; Natl Org for Soc Workers of Amer 1991-; Hispanic Assoc for Higher Ed, Cultural Comm; Awardee 1996; Newark Museum Aspira of NJ, Advy Bd; Dir Hispanic Images Project Grant; NJ Comm Awd; *office:* Rutgers St Univ At Newark Conklin Hall 175 University Ave Newark NJ 07102*

MC ALLISTER, FRANCIS THEODORE, Professor of Forestry; *b:* Lowell, MA; *m:* Cecilia Lucia Cielinski; *c:* Amanda, Alexander; *ed:* Univ of MA (BS) Wood Sci, Tech 1970, (MS) Wood Sci, Tech 1972; Post Stud Wood Sci Coll Environmental Sci, Forestry at Syracuse 1976-78; Cert Lincoln Elec Welding Schl 1991; *cr:* SUNY At Morrissville Asst Prof Wood Sci 1973-76; City of Oneida City Forester 1979; Paul Smith's Coll Arts, Sci Forestry Prof 1980-; *ai:* Acad Adv; Campus Saw Mill Facility; Dry Kiln, Welding, Small Engines Shops; Amer Welding Soc 1991-; New England Kiln Drying Assn 1985-; 2 Grants NY St Voc Ed Trng; *office:* Paul Smiths Coll Of Arts & Sci Paul Smiths NY 12970

MCALLISTER, RONALD J., Professor of Sociology; *b:* Andover, MA; *m:* Judith Delaney; *ed:* Merrimac Coll (BA) Soc Sci 1966; Duke Univ (MA) Sociology 1968, (PHD) Sociology 1971; *cr:* CA Dept of Mental Hygiene Research Specialist 1970-73; Univ of CA Asst Prof 1971-77; Northeastern Univ Assoc Prof 1977-90, Full Prof 1990-; *ai:* Assn for Sociology of Religion; Ethnic Stud Network; Articles, Chapters; *office:* Northeastern Univ 360 Huntington Ave Boston MA 02115

MC ALOON, JAMES DAYTON, Psychology & Sociology Tchr; *b:* Potsdam, NY; *m:* Helen Rae; *c:* Megan Colleen, Sean Alexander; *ed:* Murray St Univ (BA) His, Eng 1970; Chapman Coll (MA) Ed Admin 1978; Attnd Univ of MD Ger; Boston Univ Intnl Relations; East Carolina Univ Geo, His; Boston Univ Ed; Charleston Southern Eng; *cr:* Iraklion Schl Tchr 1971-72; Signonella Schl Tchr 1972-73; Karlsruhe Amer HS Tchr, Coach 1973-77; Osterholz Amer HS Tchr, Coach 1978-83; Bonn Amer HS Soc Stud Tchr, Coach 1983-; *ai:* Tennis, Ladies Bsktbl, Boys Asst Bsktbl Coach, MS Bsktbl Coach, Instr; Eighth Grd Adv; Schl Placement, Publicity Comm; Federal Ed Assn, NEA 1973-; Bonn Cath Church, Parish Cncl; Benenor Ftbl Coach of Yr 1986; Commencement Speaker Sr Class 1982; uropean Bsktbl Championship 1993; *office:* Bonn American HS AmEmbassy Bonn PSC 117 Box 390 APO AE 09080

MC ANANEY, MICHAEL C., English Teacher; *b:* Syracuse, NY; *c:* Jessica, Brian, Kerri; *ed:* Hobart Coll (BA) Eng 1974, (BA) Pol Sci 1974; SUNY at Cortland 30 Grad Hrs; SUNY at Oswego 15 Grd Hrs; *cr:* Bishop Ludden HS Eng Tchr 1974-79; Liverpool HS Eng Tchr 1979-; *ai:* Creative Writing, Magic Club Adv; 10th, 11th Eng Dept Curr Comm; NYSUT, United Fac Liverpool Tchrs Assn 1980-; NCAA Lacrosse Ofcl 1989-; Poetry Book Second Guessing; VP Comstock Writers Group Article Pub; *office:* Liverpool HS 4338 Wetzel Rd Liverpool NY 13090

MC ANDREW, EILEEN, Mathematics Teacher; *b:* Scranton, PA; *ed:* Marywood Coll (BS) Math 1958, (MS) Scndry Ed 1963; 20 Credits Continuing Ed Units; *cr:* Middletown HS North Tchr 1958-; *ai:* NEA, NJEA, Monmouth Cty Ed Assn 1958-; Middleton Twp Ed Assn 1958-, Bldg Rep 20 Yrs; Monmouth Civic Chorus 1965-; Natl Sci Fnd Grant; *office:* Middletown HS North 63 Tindall Rd Middletown NJ 07748

MC ANDREWS, SUE SWIER, Business Education Teacher; *b:* Jersey City, NJ; *m:* Gerard; *ed:* Montclair St Univ (BS) Bus Ed 1983; *cr:* Cranford HS Bus Ed Tchr 1983-85; Bogota HS Bus Ed Tchr 1985-91; Wallington HS Bus Ed Tchr 1991-; *ai:* Asst Vlybl Coach; NJEA, NEA, NJBEA 1983-; WEA 1991-; Ladies Auxilary ELKS 1987-, Pres, Sec; *office:* Wallington HS 234 Main Ave Wallington NJ 07057*

MC ANENY, SALLY, Science Teacher; *b:* Johnstown, PA; *ed:* PA St Univ (BS) Scndry Ed; IN Univ of PA (MS) Bio; *cr:* North Point Jr HS Sci Tchr; Montgomery Hills Jr HS Sci Tchr; Ridgeview Jr HS Sci Tchr; Gaithersburg HS Sci Tchr; *ai:* Frosh Orientation; NEA; Tchr of Yr 1992; *office:* Gaithersburg HS 314 S Frederick Ave Gaithersburg MD 20877*

MC ANINCH, JOSEPH W., Guidance Counselor; *b:* Natrona Hghts, PA; *m:* Ruth Burkey; *c:* Kelli, Cale; *ed:* IN Univ of PA (BED) Spec Ed 1967, (MED) Guid Cnslng 1971; Credits in Supervision of Spec Ed; *cr:* Highlands HS Tchr, Cnslr 1967-; *ai:* NEA, PSEA, NEA, NRA 1967-; Teh Freedom Ctr Gift of Time Tribute 1991; *office:* Highlands HS Idaho & Pacific Aves Natrona Heights PA 15065

MC ARDLE, MAUREEN (MC CAULEY), Spanish & French Teacher; *b:* Pittsburgh, PA; *m:* Bernard T.; *ed:* Grove City Coll (BA) Span, Fr 1978; Univ of Pittsburgh (MBA) Fin 1986; Prof Yr Tchr Cert 1991; *cr:* Fisher Body Division Gen Motors Accountant 1978-82; PPG Industries Inc Mgr, Internal Auditing 1982-90; Shaler Area HS Span, Fr Tchr 1991-93; Hempfield Area HS Span, Fr Tchr 1993-; *ai:* AATSP 1995-; NEA 1991-; *office:* Hempfield Area Sr HS Rd 6 Box 77 Greensburg PA 15601

MCARTHUR, JOHN G. M., Associate Professor of Music; *b:* Kingston Jamaica, West Indies; *ed:* Manhattan Schl of Music (BM) Piano Performance 1980, (MM) Piano Performance 1982 & (DMA) Piano Performance 1986; *cr:* Manhattan Schl of Music Staff 1983-85; Nyack Coll Fac 1984-, Chm Div of Performing Arts & Comm 1994-; *ai:* Concert Pianist Solo Engagement & Other Performances; *office:* Nyack Coll 1 South Blvd Nyack NY 10960

MC ARTHUR, KAYE IVES, English Teacher; *b:* Pittsburgh, PA; *m:* Kenneth C. Jr.; *c:* Matthew, Kirsten; *ed:* Coll of Lake Cty (AS) Math, Chem 1980, (AA) Eng 1980; Trenton St Coll (BA) Psych 1986, (BA) Eng 1986, (MAT) Ed 1988; *cr:* Council Rock HS Eng Tchr 1989-; *ai:* PSEA-NEA 1989-; Phi Kappa Phi 1986-; Kappa Delta Pi 1988; *office:* Council Rock HS 62 Swamp Rd Newtown PA 18940

MC AULAY, ROBERT ERNEST, Associate Prof of Sociology; *b:* Albuquerque, NM; *m:* Ann Elizabeth Davis; *c:* Sara, Jeffrey; *ed:* The Univ of NM (BA) Sociology 1970, (MA) Sociology 1975; WA Univ at St Louis (PHD) Sociology 1978; *cr:* Vassar Coll Asst Prof 1978-86, Assoc Prof 1986-; *ai:* ASA 1975-; Soc for Soc Stud & Sci 1980-; HBES 1995-; Reviews & Articles Pub; Papers Presented at Prof Meetings ASA & 4S; *office:* Vassar Coll Raymond Ave Poughkeepsie NY 12601

MC AULEY, EDWARD J., Social Studies Teacher; *b:* Bridgeport, CT; *w:* Suzanne Pepin (dec); *c:* Anne Marie, Edward III, Daniel; *ed:* St Bonaventure Univ (BA) His 1969; Fairfield Univ (MA) Amer Stud 1974; Southern Ct St Univ Cert of Advanced Stud Admin, Supervision 1988; *cr:* Trumbull HS Soc Stud Tchr 1969-; *ai:* Stu Cncl Adv; Mock Trail Contest Adv; Yale Model Congress Adv; His Day Adv; Speech Contest Adv; Variety of Curr Revision Comms; Participated in 3 NEASC Evaluations; Natl, CT, Trumbull Ed Assn 1969-; St James Church Music Ministry 1980-; Adv Yale Model Congress Team to first Pl Finish 1985; Adv Natl His Day Studnts to Natls 1989; Outstndg Tchr Recognition; *office:* Trumbull HS 72 Strobel Rd Trumbull CT 06611*

MC BATH, SUZANNE BURKE, Health & Home Economics Tchr; *b:* Auburn, NY; *m:* Stephen R.; *c:* Stephen A., Ryan A.; *ed:* Auburn Comm Coll (AAS) Lib Arts 1973; Syracuse Univ (BS) Home Ec Ed-Cum Laude 1975; Potsdam St (MS) Ed 1986; *cr:* Fabius Pompey CS Home Ec Tchr 1976-77; BOCES Oswego Cty Interpreter, Tutor, Aide for Deaf Stdnts 1977-78; BOCES Oswego Cty Consumer Edctr for Adults 1978-79; Edwards-Knox Cntrl Schl Hlth, Home Ec Tchr 1982-; *ai:* Class of 1988 Adv 1985-88; Planning Team 2 Yrs; Alpha Team 1995; NEA 1984-; Omicron Nu 1988-; Offered Full Assistantship at SU in Grad Work; Wrote Grant & Served as Chair DFSCA 1987-93; *office:* Edwards-Knox Central Schl PO Box 630 Russell NY 13684

MC BEE, ANDREW AVERY DIGGES, English & Drama Teacher; *b:* Baltimore, MD; *m:* Emily Biscoe; *c:* Ian A., James E.; *ed:* NY Univ (BA) Eng, Fr 1977; Towson St Univ (MS) Prof Writing 1994; *cr:* Eagle Hill Schl Lang Arts Tchr 1979-80; Mc Lean Schl of MD Eng, Fr, Soc Stud Tchr 1980-85; Park Schl 5th Grd, Comm, Outdoor Ed Tchr 1985-90; Aberdeen HS Eng, Drama Tchr 1990-; *ai:* Drama Club, Intnl Thespian Soc Spon; Dir Schl Plays; NEA 1990-; Numerous Articles Pub; *office:* Aberdeen H S 251 Paradise Rd Aberdeen MD 21001

MC BRIDE, DARRIN GERARD, High School Science Teacher; *b:* Rochester, NY; *ed:* SUNY at Albany (BS) Bio 1989; SUNY at Brockport (MS) Scndry Sci Ed 1992; *cr:* Gates-Chili HS Tchr 1993-; *ai:* Sci Olympiad Adv; *office:* Gates Chili HS 910 Wegman Rd Rochester NY 14624*

MC BRIDE, JAMES A., Mathematics Teacher; *b:* Clearfield, PA; *m:* Patricia Brown; *c:* Kate, Kevin; *ed:* Lock Haven Coll (BS) Math Ed 1963; Buffalo St (MS) Ed 1986; 60 Addl Hrs; *cr:* Lake Shore Cntrl Math Tchr 1963-; *ai:* Bible Club; Sr Class Adv; FCA; AFT, NEA 1963-; *office:* Lake Shore Cntrl Schl 959 Beach Rd Angola NY 14006

MCBRIDE, JOHN DANIEL, Alternative Program Teacher; *b:* Baltimore, MD; *m:* Laura Jean; *c:* Macklin James, Ryley Stephen, Shaena Naomi; *ed:* Frostburg St Univ (BS) Poly Sci, Soc Sci & Scndry Ed 1990; 15 Hrs toward MED; 78 Hrs at Garrett Comm Coll; *cr:* Vision Quest Current Events Tchr 1992; Garrett Cty Bd of Ed Alternative Pgm Tchr 1992-; *ai:* Svc Club Bsktbl League Referee; Outdoor Adventure; NEA 1993-; *office:* Garrett Cty Bd of Ed 40 S 4th St Oakland MD 21550

MC BRIDE, JOSEPH THOMAS, English Teacher & Track Coach; *b:* Hoboken, NJ; *m:* Donna Bongiovanni; *c:* Meredith C., Joseph A.; *ed:* Seton Hall Univ (BS) Scndry Ed Soc Stud 1974; Schl for Intnl Trng (MAT) ESL 1986; Addl Hrs Japanese; Attnd Montclair St Coll Linguistics; *cr:* Nishi Machi Intnl Schl Engl Tchr 1976-78; Kearny HS Eng, Drama Tchr, Asst Track Coach 1979-81; Queen of Peace HS Eng Tchr, Head Track Coach 1986-89; Cedar Grove HS Eng, Drama Tchr, Head Track Coach 1989-95; Cedar Grove HS Eng Tch 1996- Cedar Grove B O E ESL Coord K-12 1996-; *ai:* Head Coach Boys Track & Field; Drama Coach; Dir Schl Theater; Intnl Stdnts Club Adv; NEA, CGEA, NJTFOA, Essex Cty Coaches Assn 1989-; Livingston Youth Soccer 1989-, Coach 5 Yrs; Favorite Male Tchr 1991 & 1992; Undefeated Track Season 9-0 1991; Coached 2 Individual NJ 400M Champions 1988-1990.*

MCBRIDE, KATHY (ANDRES), 7th Grd Social Studies Teacher; *b:* Oil City, PA; *m:* Dana P.; *c:* Alan M.; *ed:* Slippery Rock Univ (BS) Scndry Ed, Comprehensive Soc Stud 1975; Permanent Cert Post-Grad Stud PA Dept of Ed 1979; *cr:* Oil City Area Schl Dist Soc Stud Tchr 1975-; *ai:* Stu Assistance Prgm Core Team Mem 1992-; Natl Geography Bee Schl Coord 1995-; Music Club Adv; Awds Assembly Calligrapher; NEA, PA St Ed Assn, Oil City Area Ed Assn 1975-; Slippery Rock Alumni Assn 1996; PA Geographic Alliance 1992-; Polish Women's Alliance 1960-, Del Natl Conventions; Saint Stephen Schl Parent Vol 1994-; Assumption B. V. M. Church 1953-; Article Pub; *office:* Oil City Area Schl Dist 69 Spring St Oil City PA 16301*

MCBRIDE, MARY THERESE, Jr High English Teacher; *b:* Cleveland, OH; *ed:* Notre Dame Coll (BA) Ed 1979; John Carroll Coll (MA) Eng 1981; Post Grad Work Univ of Dayton & Notre Dame; *cr:* John Carroll Univ Eng Tchng Asst 1979-81; St Paschal Baylon Schl Jr High Eng Tchr 1981-; Notre Dame Coll Part Time Writing Instr 1985-; *ai:* Newspaper Moderator; Power of Pen Writing Tournament Coach & Judge; Sign Lang Liturgical Gesture Coach; Liturgical Music Ministry Ldr; NEA 1981-; NCTE 1981-; OCTELA 1981-; NCEA 1981-; Cleveland Cath Deaf Apostolate 1978-; Fed of Cath Comm Svcs 1978-, Vol of Yr Awd 1978; Spon NCTE Promising Young Writers Pgm Natl Acvmt Awd 1991; Spon Scholastic Writing Awds Natl 3rd Pl Awd 1993; *office:* St Paschal Baylon Schl 5360 Wilson Mills Rd Highland Heights OH 44143

MC BRIDE, SANDRA MARIE, Business Department Chprsn; *b:* Providence, RI; *m:* Peter; *c:* Mark; *ed:* Bryant Coll (BS) Bus Ed 1971; Providence Coll (MED) Admin 1976; *cr:* East Providence HS Tchr 1971-, Bus Dept Chprsn 1987-; *ai:* FBLA Adv; Rhode Island Bus Edctrs Assn 1971-, Treas, Mbrshp Chprsn, Educator of Yr Awd; NEA 1971-; Mc Guire Schl PTA 1986-, Treas; LaSalle Acad Parent's Org 1994-, Soc Comm & Fashon Show Chprsn; *office:* East Providence Sr HS 2000 Pawtucket Ave East Providence RI 02914

MCBRIEN, ALAN F., Spanish Teacher; *b:* Staten Island, NY; *m:* Blanca Quintana; *ed:* SUNY at Albany (BA) Span & Ed 1968, (MA) Span Lit 1974; 15 Hrs of Educl Admin at SUNY-Albany; *cr:* Staley Jr HS Span Tchr 1968-69; Draper HS Span Tchr 1969-72; Columbia HS Span Tchr 1972-73; Scarsdale HS Span Tchr 1973-; *ai:* Span Club Adv; Sr Options Mentor; AFT & NYSUT 1973-; Several Curr Dev Grants During Summer to Dev AP Curr & Spec Ed Skills Curr; *office:* Scarsdale HS 1057 Post Rd Scarsdale NY 10583

MC BRINN, LAURIE MARY, AP English Tchr & Dept Chprsn; *b:* Philadelphia, PA; *m:* Thomas J. Guiniven; *c:* Molly; *ed:* LaSalle (BA) Classical Lang 1975; Villanova Univ (MA) Classical Lang 1977; Temple Univ (MED) Scndry Ed 1981; *cr:* Archbishop Ryan HS Girls Latin Tchr 1977; Lenape HS Latin Tchr 1977-78; Springfield HS Latin Tchr 1978-79; Villa Joseph Marie HS Latin, Eng Tchr 1979-89, AP Eng Tchr 1992-, Eng Dept Chprsn 1986-89, 1994-; *ai:* NHS, Ldrs Club, Villa's Lit Magazine Adv; American Classical League, Phi Kappa Phi; *office:* Villa Joseph Marie HS 1180 Holland Rd Holland PA 18966

MCBROOM, MARCIA LEANNE, Soc Stud Scndry Tchr & Coord; *b:* New York, NY; *c:* Jeremy Hosea Landess, Gregory Benjamin Landess; *ed:* Hunter (BA) Cultural Anthropology 1973; Currently a James Madison Fellow at NY Univ; Attnd NY Theological Seminary, Brooklyn Coll, Staten Island Univ; Constitution Course at Amer Univ; *cr:* Comm Church of NY Rel Ed Dir 1975-85; Manhattan Comprehensive Night & Day HS COSA Tchr 1990-; *ai:* Stu Govt Class Fac Adv; Stu Affairs Coord; Currently Advising Stdnts on HIV-AIDS & Stu Philanthropy Svc Projects; Working on Stu Trip to Africa; Rel Ed Assn 1980-, Bd Mem Advy Cncl; United Fed of Tchrs 1990-, Del Tchr of Yr for Borough of Manhattan 1994; NY Metro Comm for UNICEF 1980-, Bd Mem; Comm Bd #6 Man 1985-90, Bd Mem Started First Human Rights Comm in His of NYC; for Our Childrens Sake Inc 1987-, Pres, Founder; James Madison Flwshp; Spoke Before 2 Different United Nations Comms; Numerous Articles Pub; *office:* Manhattan Comp Night & Day HS 240 2nd Ave New York NY 10003

MC BRYAN, BRIAN ANTHONY, Hlth & Physical Education Tchr; *b:* Danville, PA; *m:* Cynthia Susan Gass; *c:* Laura, Matthew; *ed:* Lock Haven Univ (BS) Hlth, PE 1980; Permanent Certs; *cr:* Milton Schl Dist Hlth, PE Instr, Coaching 14 Yrs; *ai:* Coach Head Track 1982-87, Asst Ftbl 1981-83; Ftbl Coach Susquehanna Univ 1985-91, Bucknell Univ 1992, Bloomsburg Univ 1993-; NEA 1980-; *office:* Milton Schl Dist 700 Mahoning St Milton PA 17847

MC CABE, BRIAN J., Professor of Human Services; *b:* Jersey City, NJ; *m:* Gail Groark; *c:* Jessica, Libby, Carrie; *ed:* Siena Coll (BS) Ec 1968; St Univ of NY at Albany (MSW) Soc Work 1972; *cr:* Albany Cath Family Svcs Soc Worker 1973-74; LaSAlle Schl for Boys Soc Worker 1974-76; Private Practice Soc Worker 1986-; Hudson Vly Comm Coll Prof 1976-; *ai:* Hum Svcs Club, Minorities in Field of Alcholism Adv; Nasw 1972-; Chem Dependency Cnslng Prgm; *office:* Hudson Valley Comm Coll 80 Vandenburgh Ave Troy NY 12180

MCCABE, CAROLYN CARLEY, English Teacher; *b:* Winchester, MA; *m:* Michael F.; *ed:* Univ of ME (BA) Eng 1968; Boston Univ (MED) Rdng 1969; 48 Addl Credit Hrs His, Womens Stud, Schl to Work, Writing, Critical Skills, Character & Citzenship; *cr:* Marshwood HS Eng & Rdng Tchr 1969-73; Spaulding HS Eng Tchr 1976-; *ai:* NEA 1994-; 1979 Charter Participant in Exeter Writing Project; 1988 NEH & CBE Grant for Ind Stud; *office:* Spaulding H S N Wakefield St Rochester NH 03867

MCCABE, CHARLES JOSEPH, History Teacher; *b:* Cambridge, MA; *m:* Elizabeth Dever; *c:* Sean, Michael, Charles, Colin, Matthew, Meaghan; *ed:* MI State (BA) His 1954; Boston St (MED) Ed 1957; Attnd Boston Univ 1949-50, Boston Coll 1964, Harvard 1965, P G Smith 1967, Tufts 1970-71; Masters Plus 54; *cr:* Raymond NH Pub Schls Tchr 1954-55; Westwood Pub Schls Tchr 1955-56; Dwight & Lewenberg Tchr 1957-58; England & France Tchr 1958-61; Rockland Tchr 1961-63; Boston Latin Schl Tchr 1964-; *ai:* Former Bsbl, Ftbl, & Hockey Coach; AFT 1963-, Exec Bd; AFSCME 1970-; AmVets 1970-; Amer Legion 1970-, Trustee; DAV 1970-; K of C 1970-, Trustee; Smith & Tufts NDEA Grants (3 Times); *office:* Boston Latin Schl 78 Avenue Louis Pasteur Boston MA 02115

MC CABE, GEORGE C.,JR., Social Studies Curr Coord; *b:* Brockton, MA; *m:* Cheryl Jackson; *c:* Shawn, Shannon, Brian, Kevin, Jeremy; *ed:* Bridgewater St Coll (BA) His 1970, (MAT) Tchng 1976; Addl 15 Hrs Beyong Masters; *cr:* East Bridgewater HS Tchr 1970-83; East Bridgewater HS Soc Stud Coord 1983-; *ai:* Key Club Adv; Track & Field Coach; Stu Senate Adv; Cross Cntry Coach; EB Tchrs Assn, MTA, NEA 1970-; E Bridgewater Pub Lib 1991-, Trustee; E Bridgewater Schl Cncl 1993-; E Bridgewater Historical Soc 1985-; Plymouth Cty Tchrs Assn Citation Awd.*

MC CABE, JOHN JOSEPH, Chair of Modern & Clscl Langs; *b:* Philadelphia, PA; *ed:* Allentown Coll (BA) Fr 1971; Cath Univ (MA) Fr 1973; Villanova Univ (MA) Ed 1989; 30 Addl Credits in Fr & Comparative Lit at Cath Univ of America & Institut Catholique De Paris; *cr:* Allentown Coll Fr Instr 1975-76; Northeast Cath HS Fr & Span Instr 1976-77; Mt St Joseph Acad Fr Instr 1977-94; Bucks Cty Comm Coll Fr Instr 1985-; Abington Friends Schl Fr & Span Instr 1994-, Chair Mod & Clascl Lang 1994-, Interim Dir of Upper Schl 1995-; *ai:* Fr Club Moderator; Fr Honor Soc; Stu Exch; Staff Dev Comm Chm; Curr Comm Mem; Upper & All Schl Curr Comm; AATF 1977-; ASCD 1989-; MLA 1971-; AATSP 1995-; St Joachim Parish Liturgy Commission 1976-, Chm 5 Yrs; Mid Sts Visiting Comms 1982, 1987 & 1992; Experiment in Intnl Living 1984 Kappa Delta 1989; Univ of PA NEH Summer Seminar for Scndry Tchrs 1986; Rotary Wkshp for Amer & Fr Tchrs Summer 1985; *office:* Mount Saint Joseph Academy Wissahickon & Stenton Aves Flourtown PA 19031

MC CABE, LYNN JOHNSON, Fifth Grade Teacher; *b:* Putnam, CT; *m:* David Hilaire; *c:* Deborah Lynn Jones, Alexander Johnston IV, Matthew, Mark, Michael, Claire Rogers; *ed:* Lasell Jr Coll (AA) Interior Design 1957; Towson St Univ (BS) Elem Ed 1974, (MED) Elem, GATE 1976; 60 Addl Credits Math & Cmptrs Western MD Coll; *cr:* Lutherville Elem Schl Fourth Grd Tchr 1974-81; Towson St Univ Adj Fac Math Instr 1977-84; Prettyboy Elem Schl Fifth-Sixth Grd Tchr 1981-; *ai:* Olympics of Mind Coach; NEA 1974-; *office:* Prettyboy Elem Schl 19810 Middletown Rd Freeland MD 21053

MC CABE, MARION LOUISE, English Teacher; *b:* Providence, RI; *m:* Francis P.; *c:* Brenna, Meaghan; *ed:* Univ of RI (BA) Ed, Eng 1976; 36 Credits Beyond Bachelors Degree; *cr:* Mt Pleasant HS Eng Tchr 1990-; *ai:* Certfd as Tchr to Tchr Mentor; AFT 1990-; *office:* Mt Pleasant HS 434 Mount Pleasant Ave Providence RI 02908*

MC CABE, SHANNON MARIE, English Teacher; *b:* Levittown, PA; *ed:* Penn St Univ (BS) Scndry Ed, Eng 1993; *cr:* William Tennent HS Stu Tchr 1993; Pittsburgh Pub Schls Sub Tchr 1993-94; Allderdice HS Eng Tchr 1994-95; Avonworth HS Tchr of GATE, Eng 1995-; *ai:* NHS, Jr High Newspaper Spons; Girl Soccer Asst Coach; Jr Great Books Ldr; Future Problem Solving Adv; Sr Project Comms; Natl Assn of Stu Act Advs 1995-; *office:* Avonworth HS Joseph's Ln Pittsburgh PA 15237*

MCCABE, WILLIAM F., English Teacher; *b:* Jersey City, NJ; *m:* Anne; *c:* Bill, Sheila, Kevin, Siobhan; *ed:* Siena Coll (BA) Eng 1965; Univ of MD (MA) Amer Stud 1967; 60 Hrs Beyond Masters; *cr:* R C Ketcham HS Eng Tchr 1967-69; John Jay HS Eng Tchr 1967-; *ai:* AFT 1971-; NCTE 1987-; *office:* John Jay HS Rt 52 Hopewell Jct NY 12533

MC CAFFERTY, KATHLEEN, English Teacher; *b:* Cleveland, OH; *ed:* Notre Coll of OH (BA) Eng, Drama & Fr 1964; IN Univ (MA) Eng Lit 1975; TX Southern Univ Eng Lit; Cleveland St Univ Integration of the Arts; *cr:* Regina HS Tchr 1964-68; Notre Dame Acad Tchr 1968-71, 1978-81; Clearwater Cntrl Cath HS Tchr 1971-73; Notre Dame Coll Dir of Admissions 1973-78; Regina HS Tchr 1981-; *ai:* Dir of D Regent Schl Paper Adv; Mentorship Prog Coord; Multiple Intelligenc Chprsn; Cleveland Theater Conf 1964-, Coord, 25 Yr Svc Awd; 1964-; NCEA 1981-, Tchr of the Yr 1996; Diocesan Arts Awareness Coord; Diocesan Natural Family Planning 1981-, Chprsn; Grants: Le Coll of CUNY 1984, Ind Stud NEH 1985, & NEH at Oxford Univ NFP Curr for HS Rel Tchr; *home:* 1857 S Green Rd South Euclid OH

MCCAFFERY, MICHAEL SEAN, Elementary Teacher; *b:* Oswego *m:* Laura; *c:* Sean; *ed:* Fredonia St Univ (BA) Sociology 1985; LeM Coll Elem Ed Cert 1993; *cr:* Gillette Road MS 6th Grd Elem Tchr; *ai:* Var Soccer Coach 6th Yr; Girls Jr Var Coach 3rd Yr; Olympic Dev Boys Soccer Coach 3rd Yr; NY St United Tchrs 1995-; Natl S Coaches Assn of Amer 1993-; *office:* Gillette Road MS Gillette Rd C NY 13039

MC CAFFREY, JANE, First Grade Teacher; *b:* Westfield, MA; *ed:* Coll (BA) His 1966; Lesley Coll (MED) Elem Ed 1991; *cr:* F. J. Dutile First Grd Tchr 30 Yrs; *ai:* Site Cncl; Billerica Assessment Comm; Bil FT, AFT 1973-.

MC CAFFREY, JOAN MAGUIRE, Social Studies Teacher; *b:* New City, NY; *m:* James; *c:* John, Jennifer; *ed:* Hofstra Univ (BA) His SUNY at Stony Brook (MA) Librl Stud 1969; *cr:* Half Hollow Hills Soc Stud Tchr 1967-76; Miller Place HS Soc Stud Tchr 1982 Renaissance, Schl Improvement Team; NEA, NYSU, LI Cncl Soc 1982-; PTO, Ath Booster Club 1982-; *office:* Miller Place HS 15 Mem Dr Miller Place NY 11764

MCCAFFREY, LORAINE HOSPOD, Fourth Grade Teacher; *b:* B NY; *m:* Raymond F.; *ed:* SUNY at New Paltz (BS) Elem Ed 1970; Grad Stud; SUNY at Albany Programming, Cmptr Use; *cr:* Roeliff-J Cntrl Sub Tchr 1966-70; Northville Cntrl Schl Third Grd Tchr 197 Wells Cntrl Schl Fourth Grd Tchr 1972-; *ai:* NYSUT 1970-, Sec; 1970-, Sec; NCTM 1993-; NMAI 1993-; Outstdng Svc Awd 1991-92

MC CAFFREY, MARGARET COSTIN, Fourth Grade Teache Bronx, NY; *m:* Frank; *c:* Francis; *ed:* Coll Misericordia (BS) Ed Hofstra Univ (MS) Ed 1973; *cr:* John F. Kennedy Elem Schl 3rd Grd 1969-83, 2nd Grd Tchr 1984-86, 3rd Grd Tchr 1987-89, 4th Grd 1990-; *ai:* East Islip TA, AFT, NYSUT 1969-; *office:* John F Ken Elem Schl 94 Woodland Dr East Islip NY 11730

MCCAFFREY, MARY CARROLL C., Bio Tchr & Sci Dept Chprs Philadelphia, PA; *ed:* Chestnut Hill Coll (BA) Bio 1974; Villanova (MS) Bio 1980; San Francisco St Univ Molecular Bio; Montgomery Intermediate Unit Cmptr Courses; Ball St Univ Genetics; Tufts Genetics; *cr:* Phila Archdioces 4th-8th Grd Tchr 1965-74; Holy F Acad Sci Tchr 1974-81; Mount Saint Joseph Acad Sci Tchr 1981-; *a* Sci Research Projects Coord; Sci Club Moderator; Curr Comm; Aca NABT 1974-, Outstanding Bio Tchr 1988; Montgomery Cty Sci Tchr 1981-, Pres, Exec Bd, Outstanding Sci Tchr 1989; PJAS 1981-, Genetic Network 1978-, Mentor Tchr, DE Vly Sci Cncl Outstndng Sci 1995; NASA & NSTA SSIP 1981-, Regnl Dir, Outstanding Space 1989; Ball St Univ & Univ of KS Med Ctr NSF Grants; Articles P Amer Journal of Human Genetics April 1989 & Cath Lib World Dece 1987, January 1988 & February 1988; *office:* Mount Saint Joseph Aca W Wissahickon Ave Flourtown PA 19031*

MC CAFFREY, SUSAN WARRINGTON, English Teacher Philadelphia, PA; *c:* Michael, Katherine; *ed:* Beaver Coll (BA) En 1966; IUP Cert Scndry Eng 16 Grad Credits 1974; *cr:* Arin IU #28 1979-87; IUP Instr 1988-89; IN Area Schl Eng Tchr 1989-; *ai:* Pub for Drama Production; Conflict Resolution Comm; Portfolio Group; Trainer; Lang Arts Comm; Induction Prgm; NCTE 1991-; NEA 1 Friends of Lib 1993-; *office:* Indiana Area Jr HS 245 N 5th St Indiar 15701*

MC CAHILL, DENNIS F., Director of Construction Pgms; *b:* Mone PA; *m:* Julia L.; *c:* Colleen, Michael, Sean, Kevin; *ed:* US Naval Acad Engrng 1962; Tulane Univ (MS) Civil Engrng 1965; Univ of MD (Civil Engrng 1990; *cr:* US Navy CEC Ofcr 1962-82; US Naval Acad Prof 1983-85; Univ of MD Fac Rsrch Asst 1986-90; Cath Univ of Ame Construction Prgms 1990-; *ai:* Construction Mngmt Grad P Construction Undergrad Concentration; ASCE 1991-; Assn Build Contractors 1991-, Stu Chptr Adv; Numerous Articles Pub; Bronze with Combat V Construction Co Commander with Seabees in Viet *office:* The Catholic Univ Of America Dept of Civil Engine Washington DC 20064

MC CALEB, JUNE NICHOLAS, Second Grade Teacher; *b:* Loga PA; *m:* Perry Albert; *c:* Carla, Earl; *ed:* Lock Haven Univ (BS) Ed *cr:* Sugar Vly Elem Schl Tchr 1963-; *ai:* NEA, PSEA 1963-; IRA 1 *office:* Sugar Vly Elem Schl RR 2 Box 10 Loganton PA 17747

MC CALISTER, WATSON C., Ret Dist Curriculum Coord; *b:* Dror N Ireland; *m:* Gail A.; *c:* Craig, Tara Dlybon, Drew, Beth; *ed:* Brock SUC (BS) Ed, His 1956; Buffalo SUC (MS) Admin 1964; Certs HS Dist Schl Admin, Supervision; *cr:* Lewiston-Porter Schl 6th Grd 1958-1970, Elem Prin 1970-75, 6th Grd His Tchr 1975-91, Dist C Coord 1991-95; *ai:* Consultant to Dist Curr Coordination, Comprehe Assessment Reports; NYSUT, LP Tchr of Yr; Youngstown Recreat C 1989, Chm; Youngstown Lions Club 1965-, Pres 2, Sec'y, Lion o Niagara Pioneer Soccer L 1970-, Bd, Eastern Regnl Vol of Yr; M Youngstown NY 1975-79; LaSalle Lodge F&AM 1985-; Co-Author, P Vista of Niagara Falls Power Auth, an Educl Resource Booklet; Lion, Democrat of Yr; Mem Brocport SUC Sports Hall of Fame; US All-A Soccer Team 1954.

MCCALL, DAVID NELSON, Counselor; *b:* Pittsburgh, PA; *m:* Pat Ann; *c:* Jeremy, Matthew, Daniel; *ed:* Morehead Univ KY (BS) Hlth & Rec 1965, (MA) Scndry Ed & Counseling 1966; Act Advs Cert Te Univ; Lay Ldrs Instr in United Meth Church 1st Trng; NASSP Act Trng; Renaissance Educator; CA Univ of PA Prins Letter 1986; *cr:* Local Schls Sci Tchr 1966-67; Somerset Area HS Cnslr 1967-96; Alle Comm Coll Site Dir & Instr 1989-; *ai:* Boys Track Coach Record 186- Stu Cncl Adv; Twice Host of St Conf; Co-Dir Somerset Youth Corp Dem Youth Group; NEA 1967-; PSEA 1967-; PASC 1972-, St Adv; NA 1975-, Dir Summer Leadership Wkshp; PSCA 1968-; ACC Fnd 1 Chm; ACC Advy Comm 1992-, Chm; Habitat for 1992-, Exec Comm; Day Ministries 1991-, Exec Comm; Coach of Yr 3 Times; Somerset Cnslr Pres; Dir Jr HS- MS Natl Wkshp; Dir Track Clinic Uni Pittsburgh; *home:* 364 W Race St Somerset PA 15501*

MC CALL, DONALD CHARLES, Soc Stud Tchr & For Lang Supv Doylestown, PA; *m:* Mary Lyon; *c:* Scott, Mindi; *ed:* Eastern Baptist (BA) His 1965; Glassboro St Coll (MA) Counseling 1973; *cr:* Woods HS Soc Stud Tchr 1965-71; Gloucester Cty Coll W Civil Ins Admissions Cnslr 1971-76; Arthur P Schalick HS Guidance Dir, Soc & Foreign Lang Supvr & Dept Chm 1976-; *ai:* 9th Grd Tchrs Coord; 8th Grd Bsktbl Coach; 8th Grd Stdnts Entering HS Cnslr; Track Offi NJ Prins & Supvrs Assn 1983-; NCSS 1989-; NJ Cncl for the Soc 1983-; Treas of Pittsgrove Supvr Assoc 1990-; Natl Cncl for SCL 1983-; *office:* A P Schalick H S Rd 1 Centerton Rd Elmer NJ 08318

MC CALL, H. GALE (BRINN), French & Latin Teacher; *b:* Boston, *m:* Arthur J.; *c:* Charles, Michelynn; *ed:* St Univ of NY at Albany (BA

, Syracuse Univ (MS) Frgn Lang Ed 1982; Doctoral Courses; *cr:* ett Jr HS Fr Tchr 1966; Zogg MS Fr Tchr 1966-68; Liverpool HS Fr 1969-75; West Genesee HS Fr, Latin Tchr 1976-; *ai:* Frgn Lang Club; Sr Class Adv 1986; Chaperone Stdnts to Europe; ATLAS 1991-, VP; S 1988-, Prgm Chm; NYSAFLT 1988-; Optimist Club 1990-, Pres; winsville Ambulance Corps 1974-, Awded Life Mbrshp; BSA Troop 80-, Treas; Parish Cncl 1981-, Pres; Rotary Schlsp to Study in France; Tchr of Yr; *office:* West Genesee HS 5201 W Genesee St Camillus 3031

CALL, JENNIFER ANN, Instructor of Office Tech Dept; *b:* New York NY; *ed:* Westchester Comm Coll (AAS) Secretarial Sci 1970; Pace (BBA) Ed 1972; Coll of New Rochelle (MS) Spec Ed, Emotional icaps 1979; *cr:* Dobbs Ferry HS Scndry Ed Tchr 1979-92; Westchester Inst Adj Instr 1992-; Westchester Comm Coll Adj Instr 1993-94; son Ort Tech Inst Dept Coord, Instr 1994-; *ai:* NBEA 1979-.*

CALL, MARLENE, Biology & Chemistry Professor; *b:* Pittsburgh, *n:* Dale Dean; *ed:* Univ of MO at K. C. (BA) Bio 1965; Pittsburg St (MS) Bio, Chem 1970; PA St Univ (PHD) Hlth, Human Dev 1984; Grad Auburn Univ 1975-76, Univ of KS 1977; *cr:* Avila Coll Prof -83; IN Univ of PA Prof 1983-84; Comm Coll of Allegheny Cty Prof -; Carlow Coll Prof 1988-; *ai:* Minority Mentor Curr Adv; Women's Instr; Nrsng Recruitment, Lab, Adj, Sci Coalition for Pittsburgh d; Bio Club Spon; NSTA Rep; AFT, NSTA 1984-; PAACE 1990-; ACS -; MENSA 1978-; Twp Environmental Cncl 1995-; PAACE, NSTA enter; AIDS Ed, Hlth Ed Journal; Ford Fnd, NSF Grant Recipient; CDC ; *office:* Comm Coll Algny Co Algny Cmps 808 Ridge Ave Pittsburgh 5212*

CALLA, JACQUELYN LEE, First Grade Teacher; *b:* Abington, PA; West Chester St Coll (BS) Ed 1970, (MED) Elem Ed 1974; 30 Addl its; *cr:* Lionville Elem Schl Second Grd Tchr 1970-79, Kndgtn Tchr -80; West Bradford Elem Schl Second Grd Tchr 1980-81; Lionville Schl Kndgtn Tchr 1982-83, First Grd Tchr 1983-; *ai:* Early Chldhd Force Parent Involvement Comm; NEA 1970-, RA Del 1982-; PA St Assn 1970-, Chprsn Ldrshp Dev Comm, Sec Southeastern Region; ningtown Area Ed Assn 1970-, VP, Pres, Fac Rep; Delta Kappa Gamma -, Sec; Chester Cty Alum Chptr Delta Zeta, Sec; Keystone Federal t Union 1995-, Ambassador; Parenting Inst Tchr Inspiration Awd ; Amer Family Inst Vly Forge Awd of Hnr 1985, Gift of Time Tribute ; *home:* 245 Smallwood Ct West Chester PA 19380

CALLEY, BARBARA VAGLIA, Honors Eng & Speed Rdng Tchr; *b:* on, PA; *m:* Bruce W.; *ed:* Slippery Rock Univ (BS) Eng & Soc Stud ; Attnd Pitt, PA St 32 Credits Post Grad in Eng, Rdng & Cmptrs; *cr:* ory Twp Jr HS Eng Tchr 1961-63; Shaler Area HS Eng Tchr 1963-; *ai:* mencement Coord; Sign Lang Instr; Natl Honor Spon; *office:* Shaler Sr HS 1800 Mount Royal Blvd Glenshaw PA 15116*

CALLISTER, ELIZABETH RENEE, CP Biology Teacher; *b:* leston, WV; *ed:* OH St Univ (BS) Gen Sci Ed 1990; Howard Hughes ical Inst Summer Bio Class; *cr:* Marysville MS Earth Sci Tchr -91; Kenton Sr HS Gen Sci Tchr 1991-92, Coll Prep Bio Tchr 1992-; sst Band Dir; Asst Coach of JRTC Rifle Team; NEA, OH Sci Educ 1991-; NBT 1993-; OSU Alumni Assn 1990-; TBDBITL Alumni Assn -; Upsilon Pi Upsilon 1989-; OH EPA Grant Review Bd; KHS sion Team; Natl Sci Fnd Research Grants, Paleobotany; St of OH Ldr omorrow Awds; *office:* Kenton Sr HS 200 Harding Ave Kenton OH 6

CALLOPS, MARY KRISKA, Fourth Grade Teacher; *b:* Akron, OH; avid A. (dec); *c:* Maryann Mc Callops REchner, David G., James S.; Univ of Akron (BS) Elem Ed 1971, (MS) Elem Ed, Sci 1978; *cr:* on Elem Schl 4th Grd Tchr 24 Yrs; *ai:* Boys Fifth Grd Bsktbl, Girls Hockey, Interschl 3rd-5th Grd Sftbl Coach; NEA, OCEA 1972-, ion Chm; CFEA 1972-, Bldg Rep, Good Apple Awd; AARP 1988-; a Kappa Gamma; Tchr of Month; PTA Tchr of Yr; *home:* 2561 wood Dr Cuyahoga Falls OH 44221

CALLUM PETERS, YVONNE VERONICA, Adjunct Professor; *b:* ana, South America; *c:* Brian Mc Callum, Lester Mc Callum, Roger Mc am, Dionne Mc Callum; *ed:* Univ of Guyana (BA) Eng, Fr 1979, Tchrs Columbia Univ (EDD) Adult, Higher Ed 1996; Univ of Guyana Dip 982; Post Grad Stud Brooklyn Coll 1986-89; *cr:* Queens Coll Dept r 1979-84; Caribbean Examinations Examiner 1981-84; John Hus avian Schl Prin 1988-92; Educl Planning Inst Educl Coord 1989-90; t Johns Church Every Mem Campaign, Chrstn Ed Comm; AMer Assn er Ed, NY Assn of Dev Edctrs 1990-; ABE 1990-, Comm Mem; ST s Episcopal 1984-, Vestry, Sunday Schl Co-Chair; Tchrs Coll Minority rsp 1993-.

CALMON, DONALD A., English & Drama Teacher; *b:* Pittsburgh, *n:* Sherrilyn Louise; *c:* Paige Louise, Andrew Donald; *ed:* Edinboro St (BS) Eng 1965; Slippery Rock Univ 6 Hrs; Gannon Univ 26 Hrs; *cr:* George Jr Republic Eng Tchr 1 Yr; Northwestern Schl Dist Eng Tchr & a Coach 29 Yrs; *ai:* 1970, 1974, 1989, 1993 Class Adv; Play Dir; na Club, Intnl Thespian Soc Adv; Bsktbl Scorekeeper; Ftbl PA ouncer; PSEA & NEA 1966-, Pres 1974, Treas 1975-89; Erie Cty Sch Fd & Cr Un 1967-, Pres 1982-89; Grace United Meth Church 1970-, Various Comms; Scottish Rite Masons, Consitory, Zem-Zem Shrine -; Perfect Attendance Awds; Eng Summer Wkshp Gannon Univ; Eng Developer Erie Cty Voc-Tech Schl; *office:* Northwestern Sr HS 200 than Way Albion PA 16401

CALMONT, VERONICA J., Mathematics Tchr & Dept Chair; *b:* ington, PA; *m:* Donald B.; *c:* Elizabeth, Pamela; *ed:* IN Univ of PA Math 1968; Attnd Penn St & West VA Univ Masters Equivalency; *cr:* er Area Jr-Sr HS Math Tchr 1968-69; Fort Cherry Jr-Sr HS Math Tchr -; *ai:* Stu Cncl Adv; NEA & PSEA 1968-; FCEA 1969-; *office:* Fort rry HS 110 Ft Cherry Rd Mc Donald PA 15057

CANN, BRIAN JOHN, English & Journalism Teacher; *b:* Fall River, *m:* Kathleen Blake; *ed:* Boston Coll (BA) Eng & Theater 1984; Univ I (MA) Jrnlsm 1987; Tchr Cert Univ of MA at Dartmouth; CAGS, Ed p & Management, Fitchburg St Coll; *cr:* Naval Ed & Trng Ctr vision Production Specialist 1988-89; Joseph Case HS Tchr 1989-; *ai:* Newspaper & NHS Adv; Co-Dir Theatre Co; NEA & MTA 1989-; MA na Festival St Championship Winner 1993; Dir of Fall River Little atre; *office:* Joseph Case HS 70 School St Swansea MA 02777

CANN, CAROLYN L., Fourth Grade Teacher; *b:* Terre Haute, IN; *m:* es H.; *c:* Julie L. Seitz, Christine S.; *ed:* Univ of FL (BSEd) 1967; *cr:* lick Elem Schl Fifth Grd Tchr 1967-69; Fairfield City Schls Sub Tchr -80, 1981-82; Morgan Elem Schl Fourth Grd Tchr 1983-; *ai:* Sci Task e; Soc Stud Task Force; NEA, Ross Ed Assn 1989-; *office:* Morgan n Schl 3427 Chapel Rd Hamilton OH 45013

CANN, DOROTHY GANGI, Fifth Grade Teacher; *b:* Passaic, NJ; *m:* ert Neal; *c:* Jennifer, Jeffrey; *ed:* Paterson St Coll (BA) Elem 1969; *cr:* on Schl #15 3rd-5th Grd Tchr 1969-; *ai:* Bldg Sci Coord 1983-; Bldg to Admin 1995-; NJEA, Clifton Tchrs Assn, NEA 1969-; Governor's Recognition Awd 1994; *office:* Schl #15 700 Gregory Ave Clifton NJ 1

CANN, HARRISON F., Span Tchr & Intnl Stu Coord; *b:* New York NY; *m:* Rebecca Downey; *c:* Kelly Ann, Theodore F.; *ed:* Williams (BA) Eng 1960; Middleburg Coll (MA) Span 1966; *cr:* Trinity Pawling Schl Eng Tchr 1960-62; Northfield Mt Hermon Schl Span Tchr, Chm MLD, Dir Intnl Prgms 1962-76; Schl Yr Abroad Exec Dir, Resident Dir Barcelona Spain 1976-93; Phillips Acad Span Tchr, Intnl Stu Coord 1993-; *ai:* Intnl Club, Intntl Stdnts Adv; Lacrosse Coach; Multicultural Affairs Comm; AATSP 1994-; *office:* Phillips Acad 180 Main St Andover MA 01810

MC CANN, JAMES E., 11th-12th Grd English Teacher; *b:* Tucson, AZ; *m:* Helen Boucher; *c:* Christopher J., Ryan P.; *ed:* Univ of New England (BA) Eng, His 1967; Voc Exploration, Rdng, Tech Writing, Cmptr Tech Courses; *cr:* Wolcott HS Eng Tchr 1967-70; Biddeford HS Eng Tchr 1970-; *ai:* Retired Track Coach; JMG Adv; La Kermese Festival Comm 1990-95; Voc Ed Book Contributor; Working on Tech Writing Manual; Dev Articulation Agreement with Local Colls for Credit Acceptance; Global Stud Class Dev Curr; *office:* Biddeford HS Maplewood Ave Biddeford ME 04005

MC CANN, JOHN A., Physics Instructor; *b:* Chambersburg, PA; *m:* Barbara Burrell; *c:* Kathleen, Meghan; *ed:* Shippensburg St Coll (BSEd) Physics, Math 1981; Shippensburg Univ of PA (MSEd) Math 1984; *cr:* East Juniata HS Sci Tchr 1981-82; PA St Univ Mont Alto Campus Part-time Physics Instr 1984-; Waynesboro Area HS Physics Tchr 1982-; *ai:* All-Schl Stu Production Set Construction Stage Mgr; Waynesboro Area Educ Assn 1982-, Treas Schlsp Fund; Pub Book 1988; Tchr of Yr 1989; *office:* Waynesboro Area Schl Dist 550 E Second Waynesboro PA 17268

MCCANN, LINDA H., Business Education Curr Coord; *b:* Brockton, MA; *m:* James; *c:* John, Elise; *ed:* Barrington Coll (BS) Bus Ed 1973; Bridgewater St Coll (MED) Schl Admin 1996; *cr:* Whitman-Hanson Regnl HS Bus Ed Tchr 1973-, Chprsn Bus Ed Dept 1990-95, Curr Coord for Bus Ed, Marketing, Family & Consumer Sci Depts 1995-; *ai:* 1992 & 1996 Classes Co-Adv; NEA, MA Tchrs Assn 1973-; Whiteman-Hanson Ed Assn 1973-, Exec Bd Negotiations, PR & R; Whitman-Hanson Bus & Prof Assn 1991-; Hall of Fame; Tchr of Yr 1991; *office:* Whitman Hanson Regional HS 600 Franklin St Whitman MA 02382

MC CANN, MAUREEN, Health & Physical Ed Teacher; *b:* Newark, NJ; *ed:* Kean Coll (BA) Hlth, PE 1984; *cr:* Manchester Twp HS Hlth, PE Tchr 1985-; *ai:* Var Sftbl, Sub-Var Field Hockey Coach; NJEA, MTEA 1985-; NASO 1995-; NJSIAA Girls Bsktbl Ofcl of Yr 1995; *office:* Manchester Township HS 101 S Colonial Dr Lakehurst NJ 08733*

MC CANN, MICHAEL R., Social Studies Teacher; *b:* Salamanca, NY; *m:* Cynthia Ann Donnelly; *c:* Joel, David; *ed:* Univ of Notre Dame (BA) His 1970; St Bonaventure Univ (MA) His 1974; 12 Grad Hrs Ed, His Courses; *cr:* Portville Cntrl Schl Soc Stud Tchr 1970-; *ai:* NHS Adv; Cty Govt Internship Liason Tchr; NYSUT, AFT 1970-, Treas; NYS Cncl Soc Stud 1970-; Alleghany-Cattaraugus Soc Stud Cncl 1990-, VP; Portville Outstdng Edctr of Yr 1987; Phoebe Apperson Hearst Awd Nom; *office:* Portville Central Schl Elm St Portville NY 14770

MCCANN, PATRICIA MARIE,RSM, Associate Professor; *b:* Hazleton, PA; *ed:* Coll Misericordia (BS) Elem Ed 1969; Univ of Scranton (MS) Elem Ed 1975; Lehigh Univ (EdD) Tchr Ed 1991; Permanent Cert in Elem Admin & Physical & Mental Handicaps; *cr:* Immaculate Conception 2nd Grd Tchr 1969-75; Holy Child Schl Prin 1975-80; Honesdale Cath Prin 1980-85; *ai:* Class Adv; Coll Senate; Curriculum Comm; Mercy El Ed Network 1985-; Assn of Supervision & curr 1986-; Tchr of the Yr Coll Misericordia 1989; Preventing Schl Failure 1995.*

MC CANN, REBECCA DOWNEY, Spanish Teacher; *b:* Erie, PA; *m:* Harrison F.; *c:* Kelly, Theodore; *ed:* Lake Erie Coll (BA) Span 1964; Middlebury Coll (MA) Span 1966; *cr:* Northfield Mt Hermon Span Tchr, Dept Chair 1966-76; Brooks Schl Span Tchr 1976-77; Phillips Acad Span Tchr, Dept Chair 1978-; *ai:* Track Coach; AATSP 1978-; Co-Authored Grammar Review Text; *office:* Phillips Acad S. Main St Andover MA 01810

MC CANN, RICHARD R.,JR., Social Studies Tchr & Dept Chm; *b:* Baltimore, MD; *m:* Sandra Howry; *c:* Justin, Sean; *ed:* Millersville Univ (BS) Soc Stud, Sec Ed 1975, (MA) Sec Ed, His 1980; 45 Addl Credits; *cr:* Hershey HS Tchr, Soc Stud Dept Chm 1975-; *ai:* Yth & Govt Club Adv; NCSS; NEA; PSEA; HEA, Pres; ASCD; BSA 1994-, Cub Scout Ldr; Palmyra First United Meth 1985-, Mission Commission Chm, Admin Cncl; *office:* Hershey HS PO Box 898 Homestead Rd Hershey PA 17033

MC CANNEY, TERRA BAKER, Spanish Teacher; *b:* Galion, OH; *m:* Thomas Owen; *c:* Andrea, Mark; *ed:* Otterbein Coll (BA) Span, Home Ec 1968; OH St Univ Grad Masters Program; Columbus St Comm Coll Landscape Architecture; *cr:* Buckeye Cntrl HS Span, Home Ec Tchr 1968-74; Big Walnut HS Span Tchr 1984-96; *ai:* Span Club; Spon Stu Tutoring Elem Schls; Trips to Mexico; Advanced Placement Curr Dev Tchr; Prins Advy Comm; Adv Natl Span Hnr Soc; OEA, NEA, Tchrs of Span, Portuguese 1968-; Ed Assn 1984-; Sunbury United Meth Church 1975-; Delaware Cty Humane Soc 1993-, Bd; Leaders Scndry Ed; Who Who's 1990; Golden Eagle Awd; *home:* 3044 Carters Corner Rd Sunbury OH 43074*

MCCARDELL, KIMBERLY KILBY, Health & Physical Ed Teacher; *b:* Jennersville, PA; *m:* Allen Randolph; *c:* Randi Ruthanna; *ed:* West Chester Univ (BS) Hlth & PE 1985; Working Towards Masters in Hlth & PE; Grad courses at Penn St Univ in Cnclng; *cr:* Padua Acad Hlth & PE Tchr 1986; Oxford Intermediate Schl Hlth & PE Tchr 1986-89; Oxford Area HS Hlth & PE Tchr 1989-; *ai:* Sr Class Adv; Amer Alliance of Hlth, PE & Recreation 1985-; First Bapt Church of Oxford 1986-, Supt of Sunday Schl; *office:* Oxford Area HS 301 S 5th St Oxford PA 19363*

MCCARRELL, DEANNA TRIVELLI, Business Teacher; *b:* Frankfurt, Germany; *m:* G. Bernard; *c:* Christopher; *ed:* Kent St Univ (BS) Bus Ed 1981, (ME) Schl Counseling 1990; Cert Schl Cnslr 1996; *cr:* Ravenna HS Bus Tchr 1982-; *ai:* Mem Dist Steering Comm; Co-Dir North Cntrl Assn Evaluation; Adv Bus Profs of Amer; NEA 1982-; North Eastern OH Ed Assn 1982-; Natl Counseling Assn 1995-; United Meth Church 1993-, Dir Daycare Bd; *office:* Ravenna HS 345 E Main St Ravenna OH 44266

MCCARRICK, MARYBETH DUFFY, Music Teacher; *b:* Philadelphia, PA; *m:* Timothy P.; *ed:* Chestnut Hill Coll (BS) Music Ed 1984; 24 Credits Toward Masters in Music Ed at West Chester Univ; *cr:* Holy Souls Schl General Music Tchr; Hallahan HS String Tchr 1984-88; Archdiocese of Philadelphia Saturday & Summer Schl for the Arts Music Tchr 1988-92; West Cath HS Music Tchr & Fine Arts Dept Chprsn 1988-; *ai:* Orch Conductor; Jazz Band Dir; String & Chamber Music Ensembles; MENC 1980-; NSOA 1988-; Archdiocesan Curr Comm 1990-; Archdiocesan All Cath Orch 1993-, Host.

MC CARRICK, TIMOTHY, Music Director; *b:* Bryn Mawr, PA; *m:* Marybeth Duffy; *ed:* West Chester Univ (BM) Music Performance, Violin 1986; Master of Music Prgm; Immaculata Coll St Cert Ed 1996; *cr:* Malvern Prep Schl Dir of Music 1991-; *ai:* Advy; Cmptr Club; All Performing Ensembles; MENC, PMEA 1991-; ASTA, NSOA 1993-; Fine Arts Curr; Comm of Archdiocese Philadelphia 1993-; Conductor Philadelphia All Cath Orch 1993-; *office:* Malvern Prep Schl For Boys 418 S Warren Ave Malvern PA 19355*

MC CARTAN, PATRICIA PETERS, Mathematics Teacher; *b:* Buffalo, NY; *m:* Clifford A.; *c:* Daniel P., Michael E.; *ed:* Rosary Hill Coll (BA) Math 1961; Canisius Coll (MS) Scndry Ed 1983; 3 Credit Hrs Trocaire Coll; 6 Credit Hrs SUNY at Brockport; *cr:* Mount Mercy Acad Math Tchr 1980-86; Trocaire Coll Math Instr 1984-95; St Francis HS Math Tchr 1986-89; St Mary's HS Math Tchr 1989-; *ai:* Frosh Class Co-Moderator; Math Club Moderator; Schlsp Comm; NCTM 1990-; AMTNYS 1983-; BSA 1982-, Troop Chprsn; Amer Red Cross 1987-, Disaster Vol; Rel Edctr of Yr 1982, 1992; Natl Cath Comm on Scouting St George Emblem; *office:* St Marys HS 142 Laverack Ave Lancaster NY 14086

MCCARTHY, CARMEN CARRASQUILLO, Spanish Teacher; *b:* Cayey, PR; *m:* Arthur M.; *c:* Michelle; *ed:* Univ of PR (BA) Hum 1972, (MLS) Lib Scis 1974; Eastern Nazarene Coll Tchr Cert 1989; Simmons Coll Doctor of Arts Prgm Lib Admin; *cr:* Boston Pub Lib Adults Librn 1975-81; Univ of PR Humacao Coll Librn 1982-83; Univ of PR Carolina Coll Lib Dir 1984-86; Boston Pub Schls Span Tchr 1987; Pingree Schl Span Tchr 1988-92; Lincoln Sudbury Reg HS Span Tchr 1992-; *ai:* Stu, Club SHARE Adv; Tchr Mentor; Adv Comm; Departamental Curr Prgm; Tech Ctr Lang Dept; MTA, NEA, MAFLA 1990-; *office:* Lincoln Sudbury Reg HS 390 Lincoln Rd Sudbury MA 01776*

MC CARTHY, COLLEEN, Fifth Grade Teacher; *b:* Neward, NJ; *ed:* Coll of St Elizabeth (BA) Elem Ed 1983; *cr:* Clifton Avenue Schl Fifth Grd Tchr 1983-93, Third Grd Tchr 1993-94, Fifth Grd Tchr 1994-; *ai:* NEA, NJEA 1983-; Lakenood Ed Assn 1983-, Assn Rep; *office:* Clifton Ave Grade Schl 625 Clifton Ave Lakewood NJ 08701

MC CARTHY, DESMOND FERGUS, Assistant Professor of English; *b:* Boston, MA; *ed:* Framingham St Coll (BA) Eng 1981; Brandeis Univ (MA) Eng 1984, (PHD) Eng 1992; *cr:* Brandeis Univ Lecturer 1987-88; Simmons Coll Part-time Instr 1989-91; Northeastern Univ Part-time Instr 1990; Framingham St Coll Eng Asst Prof 1991-; *ai:* Independent Stu Newspaper Adv; CMA 1994-; MLA 1988-; MTA 1991-; Completing Revisions on a Book: Reconstructing The Family in Contemporary American Fiction 1997; *office:* Framingham St Coll # 2000 100 State St Framingham MA 01701*

MC CARTHY, ELAINE M., Sixth Grade Teacher; *b:* Boston, MA; *ed:* New England Conservatory of Music (BME) Voice 1970; Boston St Coll (MED) Elem Ed 1977; Attnd Boston Univ Ethno-Musicology 1976, Trinity Coll Irish Stud 1981, Univ Coll of Dublin Irish Stud 1983, Univ Coll of Cork Irish Stud 1985, Longy Schl of Music Opera 1996; *cr:* North East Conservatory Comm Svc Dept Theory, Voice Tchr 1970-74; Leonard Elem Schl K-6 Grd Music, Choral Arts Tchr 1970-75; St Joseph's Indian Schl 1-8 Grd Vol Music Tchr 1975-76; Linden Elem Schl K-6 Grd Music, Choral Arts Tchr 1977-80; Glenwood Elem Schl 4-6 Grd Tchr 1980-; *ai:* Concert Classical Vocal Soloist; Children's Operettas, Musical Plays Dir 1978-; NEA 1972-; Shattuck Hosp Chaplaincy 1989-, Cantor, Soloist, Vol; Schl Tchr of Yr, Nom MA Tchr of Yr 1993; Article Pub 1992; *office:* Glenwood Elem Schl 145 Glenwood St Malden MA 02148

MC CARTHY, GLENN ANTHONY, 8th Grd Teacher & Asst Prin; *b:* New York, NY; *m:* Elizabeth Mascellino; *ed:* Iona Coll (BA) Psych 1973; Immaculate Conception Seminary 30 Credits in Grad Theology Prgm, Cert; Level I, II Rel Ed Cert by the Archdiocese of NY; *cr:* Lincoln Hall Schl House Parent, Cnslr 1973-75; Our Lady of Fatima Schl Eighth Grd Tchr 1975-76; St. Gabriel Schl Seventh-Eighth Grd Tchr 1976-, Asst Prin 1987-; St. Gabriel Schl of Rel Ed Dir of Rel Ed 1994-; *ai:* Head Coach JV Bsktbl Team; Asst Var Girls Bsktbl Team; Math Club Supvr; NCEA 1975-; Parish Schl Planning Bd 1986-; South Riverdale Bsbl League 1980-92, Commissioner; Journal Dedication for 10 Yrs of Schl Svc 1986; *office:* St Gabriel Schl 590 W 235th St Bronx NY 10463

MC CARTHY, GLORIA ANNA, First Grade Teacher; *b:* Buffalo, NY; *m:* Dennis J. Jr.; *c:* Dennis J. III; *ed:* Buffalo St Coll (BS) Elem Ed 1974, (MS) Elem Ed 1976; Post Grad Credits Univ of Buffalo EEd; *cr:* Cntry Parkway ELem Schl K-4th, 5th Grd Tchr 1074-78; Dodge Elem Schl 1st, 2nd, 3rd Grd Tchr 1978-; *ai:* Mentor for Former Stu, Beginning Tchrs; Alpah Delta Kappa 1992-; WTA, NYST 1974-; Natl Pen Women of Amer 1985-, Washington Liaison; Western NY St Elem Tchr of Yr 1988; Several Books Pub; *office:* Dodge Elem Schl 1900 Dodge Rd East Amherst NY 14051*

MC CARTHY, IRENE NEWSTAD, Prof of Accounting & Taxation; *b:* Brooklyn, NY; *c:* Christine; *ed:* Baruch Coll (BBA) Acctng, Ed 1955; City Coll (MS) Ed, Acctng 1958; NY Univ (PHD) Acctng, Higher Ed 1993; Certified Pub Accountant 1976; Addnl Hrs Prof Ed; *cr:* Bay Ridge HS Acctng Tchr 1957-59; Coll of Staten Island Asst Prof 1967-69; St John's Univ Prof 1975-, Assoc Dean 1981-86; *ai:* Ctr for Tchng, Learning Assoc Dir; Pastors Mngmt Prgm; Univ Hnrs, Tchr Scholar Awds Comms; Task Force; AACSB Reaccreditation; NY St Soc of CPA's 1978-, Treas, Dir, Chptr Pres; Fnd Acc Ed 1984-88, Trustee; Amer Inst of CPA's 1978-, Cncl Mem; Amer Acctng Assn 1970-; NYS Bd for Pub Accountancy 1993-, Chair, Ed Comm; Mandatory Continuing Ed Stud Comm 1986-90; Kappa Delta Pi; Beta Gamma Sigma; Delta P Epsilon; Delta Kappa Gamma; Beta Alpha Psi; Tchr of Yr Awds 1977-78, 1989-90; Bus Rsrch Inst Grant 2 Yrs; Paul S. Lomax Bus Ed Awd; *office:* Saint Johns Univ 300 Howard Ave Staten Island NY 10301*

MC CARTHY, JOAN KANE, History Teacher; *b:* Philadelphia, PA; *m:* F. Desmond; *c:* Brendan, Justine; *ed:* Immaculata Coll (BA) Ec 1975; Trinity Coll (MED) Geog 1991; Cmptr Programming USDA; Comparative Politics, AP Curr LaSalle Univ; Archaeology Ancient Nubia Smithsonian; *cr:* Woodrow Wilson HS His Tchr, Chprsn 1981-91; Immaculata Prep Schl His Tchr 1985-86; Georgetown Visitation PrepSchl His Tchr 1991-; *ai:* Model UN Moderator; Tech Comm Fac; Level Meeting Co-Chair; NCGE 1990-; NGS 1996; Hillwood Museum 1993-, Fac Consultant; AP Rdr; Amer Express Geog Competition Tchr Awd; *office:* Georgetown Visitation Prep Sch 1524 35th St NW Washington DC 20007

MCCARTHY, JOSEPH F., HS Computer Science Teacher; *b:* Lynn, MA; *m:* Elaine T. LeBlanc; *c:* Sean, Ryan, Evan; *ed:* Salem St Coll (BS) Geography & Earth Sci 1977; Fitchburg St Coll (MED) Cmptr Tech 1992; *cr:* Dartmouth HS Sci Tchr 1977-82; Dartmouth MS Math & Cmptr Tchr 1982-87; Dartmouth HS Cmptr Sci Tchr 1987-; *ai:* Indoor Track Head Coach 1985-; Univ of MA at Dartmouth Cross Cntry Asst Coach 1985-; Prof Dev Comm 1993-; NEA, DEA 1977-; Greater New Bedford Track Club 1979-, Pres 1981-82; Indoor Track Asst Coach 1979-84; Outdoor Track Asst Coach 1980-86 & Head Coach 1987-1995; *home:* 8 Middlewood Dr Acushnet MA 02743

MC CARTHY, JULIE, Fifth Grade Teacher; *b:* Concord, MA; *ed:* Westbrook Jr Coll (AA) Elem Ed 1962; Univ of Bridgeport (BS) Elem Ed 1964; Attnd Lesley Coll, Boston Coll; *cr:* Stow Pub Schls 2nd-5th Grd Tchr 1964-; Dept of Defense Office of Dependent Schls 2nd Grd Tchr 1982-84; *ai:* NEA, MTA, STA 1964-; Acton Planning Bd; Acton Conservation Commisoner; Minute Man Arc For Human Svc, Bd of Dir; Grant to Dev Understanding of Broad Range of Disabilities for Elem Stu; *office:* Center Schl 403 Great Rd Stow MA 01775

MC CARTHY, KATHLEEN ANN, Science Teacher; *b:* New York, NY; *ed:* Fordham Univ (BS) Bio 1988, (MSEd) Bio 1991; City Coll of NY (MA) Environmental Ed 1996; *cr:* Clarkstown HS North Tchr 1988-; *ai:* Chaos Schl Sci Magazine Adv; Shared Decision Making Team; Yrbk Adv 1988-94; Clarkstown Tchrs Assn, AFT, STANYS 1988-; Sigma Xi 1991-; *office:* Clarkstown HS North 151 Congers Rd New City NY 10956

MCCARTHY, KENNETH, Eighth Grade Science Teacher; *b:* Cincinnati, OH; *m:* Leanne Hemmelgarn; *ed:* Wright St Univ (BA) Biological Sci 1986, (MED) Classroom Tchng 1989; 50 Credit Hrs as Doctural Stu in Sci Ed & Educl Tech; *cr:* Bellefontaine MS Sci Tchr 1988-90; Harrison Jr HS Sci Tchr 1990-, Sci Dept Head 1992-95; *ai:* Boys Var Soccer Coach; NEA, NSTA, Sci Educators Cncl of OH 1988-; Soc of Cell Biologists Fellowship

1994; Martha Holden Jenning Scholar 1992; Jennings Grant Awd 1994 & 1995; *home:* 8171 Timberjack Way West Chester OH 45069*

MC CARTHY, KEVIN F., Sixth Grade Teacher; *b:* Medford, MA; *m:* Teddi; *c:* Keith, Kristin, Kevin; *ed:* UMASS at Boston (BS) Elem Ed 1974; UMASS at Lowell (MA) Curr, Instruction 1978; Post Grad Work at Salem St, Fitchburg St; *cr:* Kittredge Schl Grd 5 Tchr 1974-83; North Andover MS Grd 6-7 Tchr 1983-; *ai:* Girls Soccer Coach JV 1983-86, Var 1987-; NEA, MTA 1974-; Eastern MA Girls Soccer Coaches Assn 1987-; Natl Soccer Coaches Assn 1988-; Cape Ann League coach of Yr 1990, 1993-95; *office:* North Andover MS 495 Main St North Andover MA 01845*

MC CARTHY, KEVIN MICHAEL, Special Ed & Head Ftbl Coach; *b:* Brooklyn, NY; *m:* Laura Blydenburgh; *c:* Kyle; *ed:* Dowling Coll (BA) Spec Ed 1979, (MS) Ed 1982, (PDA) Ed Admin 1994; *cr:* Cntrl Islip Learning Ctr Spec Ed Tchr BOCES II 1979-81; Longwood Cntrl Schls Spec Ed Tchr 1981-; *ai:* HS Head Ftbl Coach 1992-; Var Asst Coach 1984-85, 1991; Sayville HS Var Asst Coach, Defensive Coord 1988-90, Jr Var Ftbl Coach 1982-83; William Floyd Schl Dist Var Asst Coach 1986-87; HS Head Sftbl Coach 1982-88; AFT, NEA 1979-; ASCD 1994-; SCFCA 1983-; NFFCHF 1995-; Dists Behavior Mngmt Handbook Coord; Behavior Mngmt Curr Author; Taught Inservice Wkshps; Div I Coach of Yr 1995, 1993, 1992; Suffolk Cty Coach of Yr 1993; Rutgers Trophy Winner 1993; Have Coached Teams to Many Championships; *home:* 31 Hampton St Sayville NY 11782*

MC CARTHY, KEVIN MICHAEL, Social Studies Dept Chprsn; *b:* Malden, MA; *m:* Eileen M. Kirk; *c:* Brian, Michael; *ed:* Univ of MA at Amherst (BA) US His 1980; Univ of MA at Boston (MED) Cnslng 1987; Univ of MA at Amherst Tchr Cert 1988; Univ of Dayton OH Stud in Philosophy, Theology 1982; *cr:* St Frances House Cnslng Supvr 1984-87; Cathedral HS Soc Stud Tchr 1988-91, Soc Stud Dept Chair 1991-; *ai:* Amnesty Intnl Club Adv; NCSS 1992-; ASCD 1995-; NCEA 1988-; Paxchrist USA 1988-; *office:* Cathedral HS 260 Surrey Rd Springfield MA 01118

MC CARTHY, LISA MITCHELL, Secondary History Teacher; *b:* Philadelphia, PA; *m:* William G.; *c:* Kathleen Grace; *ed:* Rosemont Coll (BA) Pol Sci 1984; Villanova Univ (MA) His 1993; Immacultata Coll His Ed Cert 1986; Foreign Policy Rsrch Inst; *cr:* Bishop Eustace Prep Schl Soc Stud Tchr 1986-; *ai:* Current Events Club 1994-; Debate Coach 1986-93; NCEA 1990-; World Affairs Cncl of Philadelphia 1989-; *office:* Bishop Eustace Prep Schl Rt 70 Pennsauken NJ 08109*

MC CARTHY, MARY C., Middle School Math Teacher; *b:* Sicily, Italy; *m:* Charles; *c:* Linda, Michael; *ed:* Seton Hall Univ (BS) Math Ed 1973; *cr:* Holmdel HS Math Tchr 1973-74; Rutgers Prep Schl Summer Schl Math Instr 1990-93; Montgomery MS Math Tchr 1974-88; John Witherspoon MS Princeton Reg Schls Math Tchr 1994-; *ai:* Math Co-Adv; Site Cncl; NJEA, NEA 1973-; PREA, NCTM, AMTNJ 1994-; *office:* John Witherspoon MS 217 Walnut Ln Princeton NJ 08540

MC CARTHY, MARY-THERESA, Professor of French; *b:* Plainfield, NJ; *ed:* Georgian Ct Coll (BA) Fr 1957; Laval Univ (MA) Fr 1965; Rutgers Univ (PHD) Fr 1972; Sorbonne DES Fr 1967; Cath Inst of Paris DEF Fr 1967; *cr:* Holy Spirit HS Fr Tchr 1957-59; Georgian Ct Coll Fr Prof 1959-; *ai:* Dir Autumn Semester in Quebec; Alliance Francaise Liaison; MLA 1960-; AATF 1970-; ALTA 1980-; Inst of Sisters of Mercy of Amers; Sr Fulbright Schlshp Univ of Paris; NEH Flwshps Univ of Chicago, Univ of CA at Santa Cruz, Harvard Univ, Princeton Univ; Articles Pub; *office:* Georgian Court Coll 900 Lakewood Ave Lakewood NJ 08701

MC CARTHY, MICHAEL JAMES, High School Science Teacher; *b:* Cleveland, OH; *m:* Susan Weinacht; *c:* Patrick; *ed:* Kent St Univ (BS) Scndry Ed, Sci 1973, (MED) Scndry Admin 1975; 17 Hrs Scndry Admin; *cr:* Memorial Jr HS Sci Tchr 1973-78; Sheffield MS Prin 1978-82; West Geauga HS Asst Prin 1982-91, Sci Tchr 1991-; *ai:* Sci Task Force Comm; Discipline Comm; T & G Flying Club 1995-, Private Pilot; Educator of Yr 1979; *office:* West Geauga HS 13401 Chillicothe Rd Chesterland OH 44026

MC CARTHY, MOLLY, Physical Education Teacher; *b:* Rochester, NY; *ed:* St Univ of NY at Cortland (BS) Ed 1982; Nazareth Coll (MS) Ed 1988; Addl 6 Hrs in Hlth Ed at Univ of TN; *cr:* Cornwall HS PE Tchr & Coach 1983-84; Hannibal Elem Schl PE Tchr & Coach 1984-85; North Rose-Wolcott PE Tchr & Coach 1985-93; Fairport Cntrl Schls PE Tchr 1993-; *ai:* Fairport HS Girls Var Soccer Coach; Fairport HS Girls Var & 3rd-5th Grd Girls Soccer Kicks for Kids Prgm Dir; NSCAA 1986-; NYSAHPERD, NEA 1983-; Monroe Cty Sportsmanship Awd Var Soccer 1994; Wayne Cty Sportsmanship Awds Var Soccer 1991, Var Sftbl 1993; *office:* Martha Brown MS 665 Ayrault Rd Fairport NY 14450*

MCCARTHY, RITA A., Technology Dept Chprsn & Tchr; *b:* Danbury, CT; *ed:* Central CT St Univ (BS) Accounting, Bus Ed 1970; Univ of New Haven (MBA) Bus Admin 1992; *cr:* Holy Cross HS Bus Tchr 1970-; *ai:* CT Bus Educators 1969-; NCEA 1970-; Womens Emergency, Treas; Shelter of Waterburg Inc 1988-; Organized a Team for Making Strides for Breast Cancer 1995; *office:* Holy Cross HS 587 Oronoke Rd Waterbury CT 06708

MC CARTHY, STEPHEN CHARLES, English Teacher; *b:* New York, NY; *m:* Maureen Finnerty; *c:* Cynthia Klein, Christina T., Cherylyn M., Jonathan G.; *ed:* Montclair St Coll (BA) Eng, Tchr Ed 1972; Seton Hall Univ (MA) Admin, Supervision 1975; 30 Addl Credits Curr, Ed; *cr:* Morris Hills HS Eng Tchr 1972; Parsippany HS Eng Tchr 1972-; *ai:* Girls, Boys Tennis Coach; NEA 1972-; *office:* Parsippany HS 309 Baldwin Rd Parsippany NJ 07054

MC CARTHY, THERESA M., 6th Grade Teacher; *b:* Bronx, NY; *ed:* Coll of New Rochelle (BA) Psych; Archdiocese of NY Dept of Ed Levels One & Two Cert Cath Schl Catechist; Post Grad Brooklyn Coll; *cr:* St Augustine Schl 3rd, 4th Grd Tchr 1960-64; Our Lady of Refuge 3rd Grd Tchr 1964-65; St Athanasius Schl 4th, 5th Grd Tchr 1965-70; St Francis Xavier Schl 5th, 6th Grd Tchr 1970-; *ai:* Fed of Cath Tchrs 1960-, Union Del; NCEA, Past Mem; *office:* St Francis Xavier Schl 1711 Haight Ave Bronx NY 10461

MC CARTHY-PASCUZZO, LORETTA MARIE, Math, History Teacher & Coach; *b:* Bryn Mawr, PA; *m:* Michael J. Pascuzzo; *c:* Tess; *ed:* St Francis (BS) Ed, His 1971; *ai:* Track, Cross Ctry Coach; 6th Grd Field Trips Fund Raising; PTA Exec Bd; WEA 1971-, Various Awds, Tchr of Month; NJEA 1971-; *office:* Hawthorne Elem Schl Hampshire Ln Willingboro NJ 08046*

MC CARTNEY, KATHLEEN TANSEY, 5th Grade Teacher; *b:* Toledo, OH; *m:* Robert F.; *c:* Donna, Katie; *ed:* Siena Hghts Coll (BSEd) Sociology 1971; *cr:* St Clement Schl 6th Grd Tchr 1971-81; Sacred Heart Schl 5th Grd Tchr 1988-; *ai:* OH Catholic Ed Assn 1971-; Heart Beat 1993-, Cnslr; *office:* Sacred Heart Schl 500 Smith Rd Fremont OH 43420

MCCARTNEY, LORRIE KAY, High School Art Teacher; *b:* Milford, DE; *m:* John Thomas Jr.; *c:* J. Taylor; *ed:* DE St Coll (BA) Art Ed 1983; 30 Credit Hrs; *cr:* Lake Forest Schl Dist Gifted & Talented Tchr 1987-88; Lake Forest High Art Tchr 1988-; *ai:* Art Club & SGA Adv; Acad Advy Cncl; Fine Arts Dept Chprsn; Attendance Comm; Tchr Advy Cncl for Winterthur Museum & Mentor; NEA 1987-; LFEA 1987-; *office:* Lake Forest HS 5407 Killens Pond Rd Felton DE 19943

MC CARTY, MARGARET MARIE, English Teacher; *b:* Cincinnati, OH; *ed:* Marywood Coll (AB) Eng 1967; LeHigh Univ (MA) Scndry Ed 1969; *cr:* Nitschmann Jr HS Eng Tchr 1967-82; Freedom HS Eng Tchr 1982-; *ai:* 1992 Class Adv; 1987 Class Adv; NHS Adv 1991-95; NEA, AAUW 1967-93; NCTE 1982-; Our Lady of Hungary Regnl Schl Bd 1989-92, VP 1989-90, Pres 1990-92; Allentown Dioecse Schl Bd 1977-83, Pres 1982-83; Cntrl Cath HS Advy Bd 1995-; *home:* 737 Front St Catasauqua PA 18032

MC CARTY, ROSANNE M., Eng, Rdng & Study Skills Tchr; *b:* Bethlehem, PA; *ed:* Kutztown Univ (BSEd) Comprehensive Eng 1966; Penn St Univ M Equiv Eng 1972; IRI Regnl Trng Courses; *cr:* Easton Jr HS Rdng, Eng Tchr 1966-73; R. E. Strayer MS Eng, Rdng, Study Skills Tchr 1973-; *ai:* Yrbk Photographer; OCEA 1973-, Bldg Rep 1995-; NEA, PSEA 1966-; *office:* Richard E Strayer MS 349 S 9th St Quakertown PA 18951

MC CARVILLE, ALMA N., English Teacher; *b:* Millville, NJ; *m:* Thomas J.; *c:* Lisa Martine, Laura, Susan; *ed:* Glassboro St (BA) Eng 1964, (MA) Rdng 1975; *cr:* Vineland HS Eng Tchr 1965-70; Edgarton Mem Schl Rdng Specialist 1973-79; Buena Reg HS Eng Tchr 1979-; *ai:* NHS Adv; Evaluation Comm Block Scheduling Chprsn; Drama Club Presentation Asst Dir; Shakespeare Festival Coord; NEA, NJEA 1964-; BREA 1979-, Area Rep; ADK 1994-; Jaycee-ettes 1968-75, Pres; Lib Bd Chprsn Bldg New Lib; Tchr of Yr 1991-92; NJ Pride in Ed Grant Shakespeare Festival; *office:* Buena Regional HS Weymouth Rd Buena NJ 08310*

MCCASLIN, ELAINE NEIDLINGER, Elementary Teacher; *b:* Sidney, NY; *m:* Timothy D.; *c:* Mason, Luke; *ed:* Oral Roberts Univ (BS) Elem Ed 1975; SUNY at Oneonta (MS) Elem Ed 1986; *cr:* First Chrstn Assembly Acad 4th Grd Tchr 1975-77; Bainbridge-Guilford CS Sub 1985-86; New Life Chrstn Schl Elem Tchr 1983-84, 1987-; *ai:* Booster Club; Campbell's Soup Label Chm; St Jude Math-a-Thon Chm; Booster Club 1992-, Treas; *home:* RR 1 Box 319 Eaton NY 13334

MCCASLIN, GARY RAY, Sixth Grade Teacher; *b:* Grove City, PA; *m:* Marguerite Mamounis; *c:* Brent; *ed:* Edinboro St (BS) Elem Ed 1969; Westminster Coll (ME) Curr, Surpervision 1972; Elem Admin Cert 1976; *cr:* West Middlesex Schl Dist 6th Grd Tchr 1969-, Acting Prin 1984-85; *ai:* Past Asst Bsbl Coach, Schl Store Dir, 6th Grd Overnight Field Trip Coord; WMEA 1969-, IPD, Sick Bank Comm; PSEA, NEA 1969-; *office:* West Middlesex Schl Dist Sharon-New Castle Rd W Middlesex PA 16159

MC CASLIN, RODNEY KIMBEL, History Teacher; *b:* Norfolk, VA; *m:* Mary Elizabeth; *c:* Robert Bruce, Sarah Elizabeth, Andrew Calum; *ed:* Univ of MD at College Park (BA) British Hist 1986; 30 Credit Hrs in World & Scottish His; *cr:* Centennial HS His Tchr 1986-; *ai:* Television Coll Bowl Team Spon; Celtic Stud Club Spon, Adv; NEA 1986-; St Andrew Soc of Baltimore 1976-, Historian; Clan Buchanan Soc, Robert Burns Soc of Annapolis 1976-; *office:* Centennial HS 4300 Centennial Ln Ellicott City MD 21042

MC CASLIN, SHARI K., French & English Teacher; *b:* Cleveland, OH; *m:* Paul E.; *c:* Anne, Eric; *ed:* Muskingum Coll (BA) Fr, Eng 1985; Attnd Univ Francois Rabelais, Univ of Hartford, Coll of Mt St Joseph, Walsh Univ; *cr:* Pymatuning Vly HS Fr, Eng Tchr 1985-; *ai:* Track, Field Coach; NEA, OEA, PVEA 1985-; PVEA 1985-, Pres, Grievance Chair; Mahoning Vly Track Ofcls, OH Assn of Track & Cross Cntry Coaches 1985-; *office:* Pymatuning Valley HS 5571 Rt 6 West Andover OH 44003*

MCCAULEY, GARY LEE, Counselor; *b:* Seattle, WA; *m:* Sandra Kay Salstrom; *c:* Christy Marie, Carey Lynn; *ed:* Western WA U (BAEd) PE 1967; Boston Univ (MED) Guid & Cnslng 1977; 30 Post Grad Hrs; *cr:* London Cntrl HS PE Tchr 1969-73; Ansbach HS Schl Cnslr & PE Tchr 1973-79, Schl Cnslr 1984-; White Pass HS Schl Cnslr 1979-80; Tumwater MS Schl Cnslr 1980-84; *ai:* Var Vllybl Coach; Renaissence Comm 1995-96; Career Ftbl Coach 14 Yrs; Bsktbl Coach 5 Yrs; Soccer Coach 10 Yrs; Cross Cntry 3 Yrs; Track & Field 6 Yrs; Overseas Ed Assn 1984-; Natl Assn of Coll Admin Cnslrs 1992-; Ansbach Comm Chapel 1984-, Chapel Bd; *home:* Cmr 454 Box 2469 APO AE 09250*

MC CAULEY, JOHN A., Fourth Grade Teacher; *b:* Sayre, PA; *m:* Cynthia Kissel; *c:* John, Adam; *ed:* Bloomsburg St Coll (BS) Elem Ed 1977; Cert Credits Elmira Coll, Mansfield Univ; *cr:* Athens Area Schls Sub Tchr 1978-80; Bradford Cty Alternative Schl Tchr 1980-85; She Shequin-Ulster Elem Schl 4th Grd Tchr 1985-; *ai:* Head Coach Winter Track, Boys Spring Track, Field Teams; Asst Coach, Defensive Ftbl Team; Athens Area Ed Assn, PA St Ed Assn, NEA 1985-; BPO Elks 1977-; PA Ftbl Coaches Assn 1985-; *home:* 101 Lake St Sayre PA 18840

MC CAULEY, JOSEPH H.,III, Math & Science Teacher; *b:* Boston, MA; *m:* Julie A. Toran; *c:* Meaghan, Colleen, Brenna; *ed:* Clark Univ (BA) Math 1976; *cr:* Falmouth HS Math & Sci Tchr 1977-; *ai:* JV Soccer & Bsbl Coach; NCTM 1993-; MTA 1977-; NEA; Distinguished Tchr White House Commission on Presidential Scholars; Distinguished Tchr Tandy Excl in Tech Awd; Distinguished Tchr Optical Soc of Amer; *office:* Falmouth HS 874 Gifford St Falmouth MA 02540

MC CAULEY, MICHAEL ROBERT, Admin Assistant & Band Dir; *b:* Allentown, PA; *m:* Veronica Yandrisovitz; *c:* Elizabeth, Kathryn; *ed:* Lebanon Valley Coll (BS) Music Ed 1976; East Stroudsburg Univ (MS) Ed 1993; Continued Ed PA Prin Cert; *cr:* Bethlehem Cath HS Band Dir, Adm Asst 1976-; *ai:* Music Merit Badge Cnslr; Musical Dir Schl Plays; Tuition, Bldg Schedulint Coord; Concert, Marching, Jazz Band Dir; Music Chprsn; PMEA 1976-; AFM 1972-; Allentown Diocesan Lay Tchrs Assn 1980-; Knights Columbus 1970-; Holy Family Club 1991-; *office:* Bethlehem Catholic HS 2133 Madison Ave Bethlehem PA 18017*

MCCAULEY, ROBERT JAMES, Mathematics & Music Teacher; *b:* Manhattan, NY; *ed:* Marist Coll (BA) Math 1970; Rutgers Univ (MED) Math Ed 1973; St John's Univ Post Grad Stud; *cr:* Roselle Catholic HS Math Tchr 1969-70; Archbishop Molloy HS Math & Music Tchr 1970-; *ai:* NY St Textbook Coord; Coll Bd Supvr; Schl Play, Stage Band Asst Dir; Schl Drama Clb Moderator; NCEA 1970-, Tchr Assoc; Assn of Tchrs of Math NYC 1993-; Marist Coll Magna Cum Laude Grad; Educl Testing Svc Appreciation Cert; 25 Yrs Serv Awd Molloy HS; *office:* Archbishop Molloy Schl 83-53 Manton St Briarwood NY 11435*

MCCAULEY, W. KEITH, Secondary School Counselor; *b:* Indiana, PA; *ed:* Westminster Coll (BA) His & Ed 1968; Edinboro Univ (MED) Scndry Schl Counseling 1972; Attnd IN Univ, Bowling Green St Univ, Stonehill Coll, Harvard Univ; *cr:* Madison Local Schls Tchr 1968-72; Brunswick City Schls Cnslr 1972-75; North Cntrl Local Schls Cnslr 1975-86; Manchester Local Schls Cnslr 1986-; *ai:* Acad Challenge, Chess Club, Sr Class Adv; Manchester Ed Assn 1990-, Pres; OH Assn of Schl Cnslr 1987-, Chm of Natl Coll Fairs; NEA 1990-; Barberton Citizens Hospital 1990-, Chm Cotillion Ball; Masonic Lodge 1971-; Republican Party 1968-; Presbyn Church 1960-; Outstanding Northeastern OH Cnslr; Westminster Coll Outstanding Alumni Svc Awd 1994; Marion Ctr Area HS Hall of Fame Awd 1995; Grad Commencement Speaker 1995; *home:* 5900 Stuckey Rd Creston OH 44217*

MC CAVITT, CAROL A., Social Studies Teacher; *b:* New York City, NY; *m:* Jerome N.; *c:* Jerome C., Chandra; *ed:* Queens Coll (MA) His, Ed 1974; Full Doctoral Schlsp Carnegie Mellon Univ 1981; *cr:* Garden City Jr HS Soc Stud Tchr 1970-71; Garden City Sr HS Soc Stud Tchr 1971-; *ai:* Discipline Comm; Site Based Team; Dist Action Comm; Garden City Tchr Assn 1971-; Citizens Campaign for Environment 1989-; Civic Assn of Copiague 1990-; Crt Apptd Spec Advocate for Children in Foster Care; Recognition Long Term Svc Bldg Rep Garden City Tchrs Assn; Middle St Evaluation Team; *office:* Garden City HS Merillon Ave Garden Cit[illegible] 11530*

MC CAWLEY, WILLIAM PETER, Biology Teacher; *b:* Brooklyn[illegible] *m:* Joyce Gail Smith; *c:* Lisa Joy Mc Cawley, Lori Jill Huyler, Amy Payne, Angela Marie, William Adam; *ed:* Mansfield St Coll (BS) E[illegible] 1967; 30 Hrs Post Grad Penn St Univ; *cr:* Cowanesque Vly HS Bio[illegible] 29 Yrs; *ai:* Lead Tchr; Instrl Support Team; 4 Period Day Chair, Bd P[illegible] Review Comms; Northern Tioga Ed 1967-, Bldg Rep; PSEA, NEA 1[illegible] United Meth Church 1988-, Trustee, Pastor Parish Relations Comm; *o[illegible]* Cowanesque Valley HS Rt 49 Old Fairgrounds Rd Westfield PA 1695[illegible]

MCCLAFFERTY, JAMES JOSEPH, Math Department Chair & Tc[illegible] Shenandoah, PA; *m:* Eva Marie Hemerick; *c:* Kevin, Brian; *ed:* PEN[illegible] Univ (BS) Math Ed 1974; PA Dept of Ed (MEQ) Ed 1982; Attnd Kutz[illegible] Univ, Marywood Coll; *cr:* Weatherly HS Math Tchr 1974-, Math Chprsn 1988-; *ai:* T Ball Coach 1990-; Little League Coach 1993-; Bsktbl Coach 1995-; NEA, PSEA 1974-; Weatherly Ed Assn 1974-, VP; Shenandoah Planning Comm 1974-76; *home:* RR 2 Box 487 Ring[illegible] PA 17967

MC CLAIN, PATRICIA MARIE, Intermediate Teacher; *b:* Detroit[illegible] *ed:* Bowling Green St Univ (BS) Elem Ed 1986, (MS) Elem Ed [illegible] Ursuline Coll Admin Cert; *cr:* St Joseph 4th Grd Tchr 1986; Chris[illegible] King 1st Grd Tchr 1986-87; Lial Schl Primary, Intermediate Tchr 198[illegible] St Mary's Intermediate Tchr 1993-; *ai:* Cmptr Club Adv; Yth Group[illegible] IRA 1987-; NCTM 1993-; Double ARC 1992-; *office:* St Mary's Sch[illegible] Page Toledo OH 43620*

MCCLAIN, RUTH A., English Teacher; *b:* St Louis, MO; *ed:* Green[illegible] Coll (BS) Ed 1966; OH Univ (BS) Eng 1980; *cr:* Christian Union[illegible] 7th-8th Grd Tchr 1962-64; Coffeen Jr High 7th-8th Grd Tchr 196[illegible] Papua K-12th Grd Self Conatined Tchr 1970-76; Paint Valley Local [illegible] Eng Tchr 1976-; *ai:* CORE Team; Prof, Tech Dev Staff; Track C[illegible] NCTE 1980-, SLATE Liaison, Natl Standing Comm Against Censor[illegible] OH Cncl Tchrs of Eng 1980-, Exec Dir, Out ELA Ed 1992; Southea[illegible] OH Cncl of Tchrs of Eng 1980-, Pres, Censorship Chair, SLATE, J[illegible] Hazel Davis Awd; Lib Book Series 1992-, Presenter; Church Youth Le[illegible] Blood Donor; Hazen Fellow; Tchr of Yr 3 Times; OCTELA Censo[illegible] Chair; Jennings Scholar, Grant Recipent; Golden Apple Awd; Pub W[illegible] Lit Awd 1992; Phi Delta Kappa Tchr of Yr; *home:* 1069 Edgewoo[illegible] Chillicothe OH 45601*

MCCLAIN, THERESA HOWARD, English Teacher; *b:* Orange, T[illegible] Marion Lee; *c:* Amy Jo, Derrick; *ed:* SWTSU (BA) 1994; TX A&m (M[illegible] 1979; 4 Addl Hrs Wright St Univ, 9hrs Grad credit; 6 Addl HS OH Wr[illegible] Project; NEA; *cr:* Judson HS Eng & Jrnlsm Tchr 1974-79; Greenon H[illegible] Grd Eng Tchr 1980-81; Sinclair Comm Coll Dev Eng Tchr 198[illegible] Greenon HS 9th Grd Eng Tchr 1982-83; Garne MS Rdng Tchr 198[illegible] Univ of TX San Antonio Writing Instr 1984-88; Southwest HS 9th Grd Tchr 1984- 88; Greenon HS Schl 10th & 12th Grd Eng Tchr 1989-; Mad River Green Tchrs Assn 1989-; Outstanding Young Woman in [illegible] 1975; Books Pub Never Too Late 1988 & Forever After 1990; Artic[illegible] Catholic Digest 1994; Article in Amer Colletables 1995; *office:* Gre[illegible] HS 3950 S Tecumseh Rd Springfield OH 45502

MC CLARAN, WILLIAM B., Law Enforcement Tech Teacher; *b:* G[illegible] Rapids, MI; *m:* Mary Force; *c:* William, Lynn Moriarty, Patricia Ande[illegible] *ed:* MI St Univ (BS) Police Adm 1963; Univ of Southern ME (MED[illegible] 1977; Columbia Pacific Univ (PHD) Criminal Justice 1987; *cr:* G[illegible] Rapids MI Police Ofcr 1957-63; Fed Bureau of Narcotics Fed Na[illegible] Agent 1963-66; Harvey IL Police Dept Chief of Police 1966-68; Be[illegible] Harbor MI PD Chief of Police 1968-72; Portland ME Police Dept Chi[illegible] Police 1972-78; Southern ME Tech Coll Tchr 1978-; *ai:* Dir Frgn [illegible] Prgm; Campus Disciplinary Comm; Adv Criminal Justice Club; ME T[illegible] Assn 1978-; ME Plice Chiefs Assn 1988-; Int'l Assn Chiefs of Police 1[illegible] B. H. Kiwanis Club 1968-, Citizen of Yr 1969; Law Day, Outstdng [illegible] Awds; Law Enforcement Commendation; *office:* Southern ME Tech [illegible] Fort Road S Portland ME 04106

MC CLARNON, WILLIAM FRANCIS, Social Studies Teache[illegible] Pittsburg, PA; *m:* Karen Vargo; *c:* Ryan E., Jacob A.; *ed:* Lafayette [illegible] (BA) His, Scndry Ed 1988; Univ of Pittsburg 12 Cr; *cr:* Gladstone [illegible] 6-7th Grd World Cultures Tchr 1989-91, Milliones MS 6th Grd W[illegible] Cultures Tchr 1989-91; Butler Cnty Area Vo-Tech Schl Beha[illegible] Modification Tchr, Spec Needs Aide 1991-93; Kiski Area Schl Dist 9-[illegible] Grd Soc Stud Tchr 1993-; *ai:* Asst Var Ftbl Coach 1994-; Wester[illegible] Writing Project 1993; Portfolio Pilot Comm 1995-; NEA, PSEA, K[illegible] 1993-; Luth Yth & Family Svcs Support Staff 1996; *office:* Kiski Are[illegible] 200 Poplar St Vandergrift PA 15690

MCCLARY, KENT LEE, Fourth Grade Teacher; *b:* Toledo, OH; *m:* [illegible] K. Everhart; *ed:* Bowling Green St Univ (BA) Elem & Spec Ed 1980, [illegible] Elem Admin & Supervision 1984; Arts Unlimited 20 Hrs; OH Histo[illegible] Sites 3 Hrs; *cr:* Kenwood Elem Schl Spec Ed LD Tchr 1980-85, 4th Tchr 1985-; *ai:* Ocean Quest 4th Grd Prgm Dir; Zimmerman Schl Li[illegible] His Prgm, Jr Great Books, Sherlock Holmes Rdng Club Ldr; Stu Cncl [illegible] NEA, OEA, BGEA 1980-; Bowling Green Rotary 1994-; Outstan[illegible] Young Educator; Outstanding Alumni Awd Spec Ed; *office:* Kenwood [illegible] Schl 710 Kenwood Ave Bowling Green OH 43402*

MC CLAY, RANDALL ELLIOT, Chemistry & Physics Teacher[illegible] Portsmouth, OH; *m:* Regina Gayle Mossbarger; *c:* Aaron; *ed:* OH [illegible] (BS) Chem Ed 1991; Project Discovery; *cr:* Vly HS Tchr 1991-; *ai:* T[illegible] Coach; Quiz Team Adv; Sci Ed Cncl OH 1993-; Eisenhower Grants; *of[illegible]* Valley HS PO Box 888 Lucasville OH 45648*

MC CLEARY, CHERYL MARIE, Second Grade Teacher; [illegible] Waynesboro, PA; *m:* Denton L.; *c:* Marc; *ed:* Hagerstown Jr Coll [illegible] 1969; Messiah Coll (BA) Elem Ed 1972; Shippensburg St (MED) Elem 1976; *cr:* Guilford Hills Elem Schl 2nd Grd Tchr 1973-78; Cumberland Chrstn Schl 2nd Grd Tchr 1985-87; Victory Chrstn Schl 2nd Grd [illegible] 1987-; *ai:* Lower Elem Coord.

MCCLEARY, JEAN WAGNER, HS Physical Ed & Health Tchr [illegible] Clarion, PA; *m:* Ray; *ed:* Credit Hrs Gannon Univ at Erie; *cr:* Brook[illegible] Schl Dist Scndry PE & Hlth Tchr 1993-; *ai:* Sftbl Club Adv; 7th-9th [illegible] Bsktbl Coach; Bsktbl Club Adv; 9th-12th Grds Sftbl Asst Coach; [illegible] Bsktbl Coach; NEA, PSEA 5 Yrs; YMCA 1 Yr; Outcome Based Wellness & Fitness Comm 1 yr; Hunger Station Golf Mem 1 Yr; *home:* 1 Box 51-B Tionesta PA 16353

MCCLEARY, LOUISE SHARPS, First Grade Teacher; *b:* Baltim[illegible] MD; *m:* Ralph A.; *c:* Karl J.; *ed:* Coppin St Coll (BS) Elem Ed 1960; A[illegible] Oakwood Coll 1985, Columbia Union Coll 1986, Coppin St Univ 1995; Collington Square Elem #97 Primary Grd Tchr 1960-70, Demonstra[illegible] Tchr, Tchr 1966-70; Robert E. Poole MS #56 Primary Grd Tchr 1[illegible] Edgecombe Circle Elem #62 Supervising Tchr, Tchr 1971-72; Baltimo[illegible] Acad Primary Grd Tchr 1972-; *ai:* Curr Comm Allegheny E Con[illegible] Seventh Day Adventist 1982-85; Book Review Comm Columbia U[illegible] Conf of Seventh Day Adventist 1987-89; Yrbk Comm, Ed 1976-1988-89; Annual Fund Raising Coord 1983-93; Vision 2000 Co[illegible] Columbia Union Conf of Seventh Day Adventist 1990-93; Tchr of Allegheny E Conf of Seventh Day Adventist 1987; Thomas & Violet Za[illegible] Excl in Tchng Awd 1992; *home:* 1011 Evesham Ave Baltimore MD 21[illegible]

MCCLELLAN, ANETTE, Fourth-Twelfth Grade Supvr; *b:* Mannh[illegible] Germany; *m:* William E.; *c:* Michelle R., Markus; *ed:* Freedom Univ [illegible] rstn Ed 1987; 2 Yr Trade Schl Specializing in Hospital Aid 1972; 3 hl of Nursing RN 1973-76; NJ Ocean Cty Coll Psychiatric Course cr: Calvery Acad HS Monitor 1983-84; New Life Chrstn Acad 2th Grd Supvr 1986-; *ai:* Art, Gym, Home Ec, Stu Convention, 'aisers, Ger; First Assembly of God 1985-, Tchr; *office:* New Life tian Acad 2 Drift Rd Fryeburg ME 04037*

LELLAN, SYLVIA J., Special Needs Teacher; *b:* Little Falls, NY; rry L.; *c:* Brian P. Smith, Kevin J. Smith; *ed:* SUNY at Albany (BA) 967; Attnd Kent St, Ashland Univ, Walsh Univ; *cr:* Mogadore HS Eng 1969-76; Kirby HS Eng Tchr 1983-84; Mogadore HS Tchr of LD ; *ai:* MEA, OEA 1984-; NEA 1969-; *office:* Mogadore HS 130 S land Ave Mogadore OH 44260

LELLAN, WESLEY RUSSELL, Social Studies Teacher; *b:* uver BC, Canada; *m:* Cecilia V.; *c:* Miranda Mitchell; *ed:* Univ of BS) Elem Ed, Speech 1971, (MS) Admin & Planning 1973, (CAS) Ed *ai:* Instrl Support Team 12 Yrs; Chair, Mem Local Relicensing Bd 4 Phi Delta Kappa 1984-, Pres & Sec VT Chptr; NEA 1984-, Local ance Chprsn; *office:* Milton Jr Sr HS 17 Rebecca Lander Dr Milton 5468*

LELLAND, JAMES WARREN, Biology Teacher; *b:* East land, OH; *m:* Carol Lutz; *c:* Amanda, Megan; *ed:* Kent St Univ (BS) 1964; Bridgewater St Coll (MED) Admin 1972; Grad Courses ting in Guid Cert; Post Grad Courses in Cmptr Sci; *cr:* Bay Village Sci Tchr 1964-65; Ravenna HS Bio Tchr 1965-66; Barnstable HS Bio Dean 1966-; *ai:* MA Tchrs Assn 1966-; Phi Delta Kappa; OH ological Soc Awd; 1980 Tchr of Yr.

LELLAND, TERRY, Visual Communications Teacher; *b:* Grove PA; *m:* Rhonda Palmer; *c:* Jodi, Jason; *ed:* CA Univ (BS) Industrial 1968; Slippery Rock Univ (MS) Guidance, Counseling 1972; minster Coll (MS) Admin 1975; Univ of WY Grad Stud; *cr:* Grove HS Tchr 1968-; *ai:* Sr Class, Ski Club Adv; PSEA; NEA; Wildlife ervation Officer PA Game Commission; Owner Laurel Lane Bed & fast; *home:* 1305 S Center Street Ext Grove City PA 16127

LENNEN, KAREN FERN, Science Teacher; *b:* Philadelphia, PA; eorge; *c:* Lindsey, Evan; *ed:* Penn St (BS) Bio Ed 1977; Temple Univ Sci Ed 1982, (MS) Curr Inst 1982; *cr:* Cecilian Acad Sci Tchr -79; Merion Mercy Acad Sci Tchr 1979-84, Dept Head 1986-; *ai:* disciplinary Comm; Svc Act Mercy Tutor; Sci Club; Early Interventin Drugs & Alcohol; Black His Month, Sr Appreciation Day Vol; NSTA ; NCEA 1979-; Andorra Civic Assn 1994-, Block Capt; YMCA 1986-, cise Instr 1986-; Leverington Pres 1990-, Spec Events Costumes, ren's Sermons; Nom Natl Sci Sci Tchr Awd 1995; *office:* Merion y Acad 515 Montgomery Ave Merion Station PA 19066*

LINTOCK, EDNA SPRUNG, Mathematics Teacher; *b:* Endicott, *m:* Thomas Allen; *c:* Wendy, Kristi; *ed:* Bloomsburg St (BS) Math, Ed 45 Credits Accounting; 9 Credits Early Chldhd Ed; 15 Credits Post *cr:* Berwick Area Schls Tchr 1972-82; St Joseph Schl Tchr 1982-86; ick Area Schls Tchr 1986-; *ai:* Mentor Tchr; Instr to Parents; NEA, , BAEA 1988-; Civic Club; *home:* 600 E 4 1/2 St Berwick PA 18603*

LINTOCK, ELIZABETH BEVERIDGE, Third Grade Teacher; *b:* o, OH; *m:* Paul; *c:* Amy, Christoper; *ed:* Kent St Univ (BS) Elem Ed Ashland Univ Grad Stud; *cr:* Shiloh Elem Schl Remedial Rdng Tchr -74, Third Grd Tchr 1974-76, Remedial Rdng Tchr 1977-81, Second Tchr 1981-86, Third Grd Tchr 1987-; *ai:* Music Boosters; NEA, OEA ; PEA 1972-, Sec; First Presbyn Church 1972-, Elder; Chrstn Alliance ch 1993-; Plymouth Historical Soc; *home:* 51 North St Plymouth OH 5

LINTOCK, MARY E., Mathematics Teacher; *b:* Buffalo, NY; *m:* h L. Scarpace; *ed:* SUNY at Buffalo (BS) Math, Fr 1973, (MS) Elem 987; SUNY at Fredonia (SDA) Educl Admin 1991; *cr:* Buffalo City Math, Fr Tchr 1975-83; Frontier Cntrl Schl Dist Math Tchr 1983-, Dev Asst 1991-92, Dept Chair 1993-94; *ai:* AMTNYS 1987-; AFT ; PDK, NCTM, ASCD 1993-; Amer Diabetes Assn; Extensive erative Learning Trng; Cooperative Learning Presenter.

LINTOCK, PAUL N., English Teacher; *b:* Ravenna, OH; *m:* Beth; *c:* topher, Amy; *ed:* Kent St Univ (BSEd) Eng 1970; *cr:* Streetsboro City 8th Grd Speech & Eng Tchr 1970-71; Shiloh MS 7th-8th Grd Tchr -; *ai:* Track Coach 17 Yrs; Bskbl Coach 9 Yrs; OEA 1970-; NEA -; *home:* 51 North St Plymouth OH 44865

LOREY, MARK J., Mathematics & Science Teacher; *b:* Southfield, *ed:* Hillsdale Coll (BS) Math & Physics 1990; Univ of Notre Dame Physics 1993; *cr:* Immaculate Conception Acad Math & Sci Tchr -; *ai:* 9th-12th Grd Boys Bsktbl Coach; JETS TEAMS Coach; *office:* aculate Conception Acad 4510 Floral Norwood OH 45212

LOSKEY, DIANE L., Professor of Flute; *b:* Ravenna, OH; *ed:* al Univ Conservatory of Music (BM) Flute Performance 1981; Univ ncinnati Conservatory of Music (MM) Flute Performance 1983; IN 3 Yrs Doctoral Pgm Flute Performance; *cr:* Kenyon Coll Instr of Flute -87; Northeast MO St Univ Prof of Flute 1987-91; IN Univ Assoc Instr -91; Kent St Univ Prof of Flute 1991-; *ai:* Natl Flute Assn 1991-, ap Coord for Natl Convention 1994-; Pi Kappa Lambda 1993-; Phi Delta 1995-; *office:* Kent St Univ HA Glauser Schl of Music Kent OH 2

CLOSKEY, DONNA WEAVER, Management Professor; *m:* George; niv of DE (BS) Fin, MIS 1990; Widener Univ (MBA) Fin, MIS 1992; atnl Bus Stu Assn Fac Adv; Outstdng Undergraduate Tchng Awd 1995; *e:* Widener Univ 1 University Pl Chester PA 19013

CLOSKEY, MARGARET R., Math Teacher; *b:* Philadelphia, PA; *m:* oh A.; *c:* Kevin, Patrick, Julie; *ed:* Loyola Univ (BS) Math 1973; St les Seimary Scripture 1995; West Chester Univ Math, PA St Univ Ed Grad Credits; *cr:* St Bernadette's Tchr 1974-78; PA Inst of Tech Tchr -88; Rosemont Schl of Holy Child Tchr, Math Chair 1989-; *ai:* Yrbk erator; Math Club Coach; NCTM; Annunciation Ath Bd, Sec; Girl t Ldr 1974-95; *office:* Rosemont Schl Of Holy Child 1344 gomery Ave Rosemont PA 19010

CLOSKEY, MARY ANN, English Teacher; *b:* Pittsburgh, PA; *m:* S.; *c:* Sean, Ryan, Colleen; *ed:* Duquesne Univ (BSEd) Eng & Ed , (MSEd) Eng & Ed 1972; *cr:* Carlynton Schl Dist Lang Arts Tchr -70; Mt Lebanon Schl Dist Eng Tchr 1970-; *ai:* NEA 1969-; *office:* ebanon Sr H S 155 Cochran Rd Pittsburgh PA 15228

CLOSKEY, MILDRED CRAGO, Adjunct English Teacher; *b:* Ross nty, OH; *w:* Dale (dec); *ed:* Capital Univ (BSED) Elem Ed 1952; Univ ayton (MSED) Ed, Soc Stud, Eng 1967; Credit Hrs Scndry Ed nington Coll, Miami Univ; *cr:* Dayton City Schls Elem Schl, Scndry 1952-69; Hillsboro City Schls Eng, Soc Stud Tchr 1969-82; Southern omm Coll Adj Eng Prof;1985-; *office:* Southern St Comm Coll 200 art Ave Hillsboro OH 45133

CLOSKEY, ROBERT JAY, United States Government Tchr; *b:* isburg, PA; *c:* Kimberly, David; *ed:* Shippensburg Univ (BS) Ed, Bio, Stud 1961, (MS) Soc Sci 1967; Penn St Univ; *cr:* Lower Paxton Jr HS His, Civics Tchr 1961-79; Cntrl Dauphin East Jr HS Civics Tchr -93; Cntrl Dauphin HS US Govt Tchr 1993-; *ai:* Class 1998 Adv; ling, Asst Track & Field Coaches; Act 178, Fac Advy, Pol Action ms; Sports Card Club Adv; NEA, PA St Ed Assn 1961-; Cntrl Dauphin Ed Assn 1961-, VP; Rutherford Lions Club 1966-, Pres, VP; Rutherford VFW 1963-; Amer Cancer Soc, Vol; Amer Heart Assn, Vol; Elected Del Republican Natl Convention 1992; Choosen by Amer Historical Assn Represent Eastern St at Constitutional Conf in Phila; Classes Awded 3 Freedoms Fnd Awds, 3 PA Senate Citations, Textbook Consultant for Scott Foresman Co Civics Text Civics for Amer; *office:* Central Dauphin HS 4600 Locust Ln Harrisburg PA 17109

MC CLOUD, SCOTT G., Journalism Teacher; *b:* Windber, PA; *m:* F. Carol Pauley; *ed:* Univ of Pittsburgh (BA) Eng 1967; 24 Credit Hrs; *cr:* WCRD Radio On-Air Personality 1963-80; WJAC, WKYE Sports Dir, News Announcer 1980-; Greater Johnstown Schl Dist Tchr, Admin 1967-; *ai:* Newspaper, Yrbk Advs; Owns 4 Radio Stations, States 2nd Most Powerful FM radio Station; NEA, PSEA, GJEA 1967-, Bldg Rep; PSBA 1993-; Comm Fnd Greater Johnstown 1993-, Publication Dir; Richland Schl Bd 1993-; Exch Club 1964-66; Polish Natl Alliance 1994-; Newspaper, Yrbk Natl 1st Place Awds 3 Yrs; Herff Jones Natl Merit Awd; 4th Place Natl Jrnlsm Tchr of Yr Awd; *office:* Greater Johnstown HS 222 Central Ave Johnstown PA 15902

MC CLURE, GORDON ARAD, Administrator; *b:* Centralia, IL; *m:* Kristina Kay; *ed:* Eastern IL Univ (BM) Music 1985; Bowling Green St Univ (MM) Music Ed 1987; *cr:* St John's HS Music Dir 1987-95; Calvary Christian Schl 1995-; *ai:* Bd Youth for Christ; Bd Mem Crisis Prgncy Center; Music Educators Natl Conf 1985-; OH Music Ed Assn 1985-; Natl Cath Band Dirs Assn 1993-; Outstanding Tchr Awd Univ Chicago 1991-; Nom Outstanding Music Alumni BGSU 1992; Outstanding Tchng Asst BGSU 1987; George Westcott Band Awd Eastern IL Univ 1985; *office:* Calvary Christian School 5025 Glendale Toledo OH 43614

MC CLURE, NANCY SCOTT, Seventh Grade Reading Teacher; *b:* Berwick, PA; *m:* Harry L.; *c:* Katherine Keller, Tamara Dluzeski, Nancy Hall, Allison Cross; *ed:* Bloomsburg Univ (BS) Eng, Elem Ed 1972; *cr:* Garrison Elem Schl 4th Grd Tchr 1968-70; 14th St Elen Schl 4th-5th Grd Tchr 1971-80; Orange St Elem Schl 6th Grd Tchr 1980-89; Berwick Area MS 7th Grd Tchr 1989-; *home:* PO Box 96 Benton PA 17814

MCCLURE, PATRICIA CROWLEY, Prof of Acctng Fin & Statistic; *b:* Springfield, MA; *m:* Bruce A.; *c:* Kristen, Kari, Kenneth; *ed:* Amer Intnl Coll (BSBA) Acctng 1975, (MBA) Bus 1980; *cr:* Price Waterhouse & Co Auditor 1975-78; Western New England Coll Instr of Acctng 1979-82; Aetna Life & Casualty Sr EDP Internal Auditor 1981-82; Exec Tax Svc Asst Office Mgr 1982-83; Springfield Tech Comm Coll Dept of Bus Prof 1983-; *ai:* Enfield Soccer Club, Div Mgr, Equipment Mgr, Coach; Schlsp Awds Comm Chprsn; NEA, MTA 1983-; Amer Acctng Assn 1980-; MA Assn of Acctng Profs 1987-; Make-A-Wish Fnd 1989-; CT St Legislative 1980-, Campaign Treas; St of CT Certfd Pub Accountant 1977-; *office:* Springfield Tech Comm Coll 1 Armory Sq Springfield MA 01105

MCCLURE, ROBERT LEE, Physics Teacher; *b:* Chambersburg, PA; *m:* Lori A. Stull; *c:* Robbin; *ed:* Shippensburg Univ (BSEd) Physics & Math 1988, (MSEd) Cmptr Ed 1994; *cr:* Big Spring HS Physics Tchr 1988-; *ai:* Sr Class Adv; NEA, PSEA & BSEA 1988-; Tandy Tech Scholar; *home:* 11 Howard Ave Shippensburg PA 17257

MCCLURKEN, SANDRA LEA, Teacher of ESL & Comp Tech; *b:* Philadelphia, PA; *ed:* Temple Univ (BA) Fr & Span 1976, (MBA) Intnl Bs 1982; Philadelphia Coll of Textiles & Sci (MS) Instrl Tech 1996; *cr:* Schl Dist of Philadelphia ESOL Tchr 1986-; *ai:* PFT 1986-; *office:* Horace Furness HS 3rd & Mifflin Sts Philadelphia PA 19148

MC CLUSKEY, LAURA ANN, Science Teacher & Dept Lead; *b:* Montclair, NJ; *c:* Jennifer; *ed:* William Paterson Coll (BA) Envivonmental Stu 1982; Montclair St Univ (MA) Environmental Ed 1990; 27 Credits Grad Schl Ed Stud William Paterson Coll 1984-86; *cr:* Hawthorne HS Sci Tchr 1986-90; Cntrl MS Sci Tchr, Sci Dept Head 1990-; *ai:* Adv Ecology Club; New Jersey Sci Tchrs Assn 1986-, Exec Bd; Alliance for NJ Environmental Ed 1989-, Advy Bd; Environmental Adv Comm 1994-, Bd Mem; Govenor's Tchr Recognition Awd 1990; Tchr as Researchers Prgm 1992, Mini-Grant 1993 Parsippany Bd of Ed; Educl Wkshp Presenter NJSTA, NSTA Confs 1989-; *office:* Central MS RR 46 Parsippany NJ 07054*

MC COACH, ROGER FREDERICK, Mathematics Professor; *b:* Warwick, NY; *ed:* Clarkson Univ (BS) Chem Engrng 1970; SUNY at Stony Brook (MA) Math 1975; NY Univ (PHD) Math Ed 1989; *cr:* Cty Coll of Morris Math Prof 1975-; *ai:* Phi Theta Kappa 1986-; NEA, NJEA 1975-; MAA 1989-; COMAP 1993-; AMATYC 1990-; MATYCNJ 1980-; Who's Who in NJ 1992; Pub Books: A Supplement For Calculus I, A Supplement For Precalculus, An Introduction To DERIVE-Precalculus, An Introduction To DERIVE-Caculus; *office:* County Coll Of Morris A304 Randolph NJ 07869

MC COLLAR, WANDA ARLENE, AP Eng Cmpstn & TV Prod Tchr; *b:* Syracuse, NY; *w:* Robert (dec); *c:* Kaylene Bushaw, Kim Mc Collar Schiller, Sean; *ed:* Northern CO Univ (BA) Eng, For Lang 1954; Boston Univ (EDM) Psych 1984, (EDM) Educl Tech 1989; Broadcast Jrnlsm, Emerson Coll, Maastricht, Netherlands; Lotus Notes Telecommunication Among AP Eng Classes World Wide; *cr:* Hardin Jr High 8th Grd Eng Tchr 1955-57; Montana Sr High 10th Grd Eng Tchr 1955-57; San Juan Baudista Elem 6th-7th Grd Tchr 1958-59; Ro hardin Jr High Span Tchr 1959-63; Ni6 C Kinnick HS 10th Grd Eng, Speech, Span Tchr 1967-70; Heidelberg HS 10th Grd Eng, Speech, AP Eng, TV Production Tchr 1972-; *ai:* Eng Dept Chprsn; Schl Advy, Schl Improvement Steering Comms; NHS Fac Cncl; Writing Consultant for Do DDS Tchrs; NEA 1955-, Frs in Past Local; NCTE; Natl Defense Ed Act Fellowship in Span 1964; Presidential Scholars Cert of Excl in Ed 1984.*

MC COLLOM, BURTON L., Lang Arts Tchr & Theatre Dir; *b:* Hamilton, OH; *m:* Michelle; *ed:* Wilmington Coll (BA) Eng, Theatre 1967; Xavier Univ (MED) Spec Ed 1970; *cr:* Talawanda City Schls Tchr, Drama Dir 1968-76; Finneytown Local Schls Tchr, Drama Dir 1976-; *ai:* Theatre Dir; NCTE 1986-; NEA, OEA, FEA 1976-; Theatre Awd Wilmington Coll 1967; Natl Ctr of Excl NCTE 1986; Friend of Ed NSPRA 1990; *office:* Finneytown Local Schls 8916 Fontainebleau Ter Cincinnati OH 45231

MCCOLLUM, DELORES LARHEINE, Secondary Social Studies Tchr; *b:* Ann Arbor, MI; *ed:* Spelman Coll (BA) His & Scndry Ed 1973; Cleveland St Univ (MA) His 1977; *cr:* James Ford Rhodes HS Soc Stud Tchr 1973-77; Joseph M Gallager Jr HS Soc Stud Tchr 1977-81; AB Hart Jr HS Soc Stud Tchr 1981-82; Martin Luther King Jr HS Soc Stud Tchr 1982-86; John Hay HS Soc Stud Tchr 1986-; *ai:* "Bridge Builders" Project with Cleveland Hghts HS; "Bus Tomorrow" Career Awareness Project 1992-93; "Windows Oral His Project" 1991-92; "The People Kaleidoscope Carnival" I & II 1990-92; Co-Adv JHS Class of 1996; AFT & Cncls for the Soc Stud 1973-; Fulbright Alumni Assn 1984-; African Amer Archives Auxiliary 1994-, Trustee; Cleveland Spelman Alumnae Assn 1977-, VP & Treas, Appreciation Plaque; Antioch Bapt Church Bd of Trustees 1994-, Vice Chm 1995, Chm 1996; Cleveland Spelman Alumnae Assn, Pres 1995-; Great Lakes region Natl Alumnae Assn of Spelman Coll, Delegate 1994-; Martha Holden Jennings Tchr Grant Awd 1985, 1992 & 1994; Armonk Inst Scholar 1992; Outstanding Young Woman of Amer 1980 & 1984; Fulbright Scholar to Israel 1984; Armonk Scholar to Germany; Cong Citation Dec 2 1994; Prtcpnt Holocaust Sum Sem for US Tchrs; *home:* 4266 E 170th Pl Cleveland OH 44128

MC COLLUM, JOHN HATCHER, English Teacher & Dean; *b:* Winooski, VT; *ed:* Columbia Univ Tchrs' Coll (ABD); Johnson St Coll (BA) Eng Lit 1971; Univ of VT (MEd) Stu Prsnl, Cnslng 1973; Attnd Die Sprache Schule at Hamburg Germany, Univ of MD at Baltimore, Univ of West Indies; *cr:* Univ of VE Cnslr, Lecturer 1977-83; Univ of DE Hnrs Prgm Asst Dir, Dean of Stdnts 1980-83; Friends Cntrl Schl Tchr, Dean 1983-, Dept Head 1983-93; *ai:* Newspaper, Prom, Stu Advy, AIDS Awareness, Cmptr Lab, Curr, Awds, Assembly, Tech, Diversity Comms; NCHC 1984-; NAIS, AATE 1986-; Deleware Cty AIDS Network 1993-, Bd of Dirs; Philadelphia Theatre Caravan 1994-, Bd of Dirs; Article Pub.*

MC COLOUGH, MARY CLARE RYCHLEWSKI, Art Teacher; *b:* Toledo, OH; *m:* Jerry R.; *c:* Brittney, Joshua, Kristen; *ed:* Univ of Toledo (BE) Art Ed 1991; 28 Qtr Hrs towards Masters; *cr:* OC Federal Credit Union Clerk 1984-86; Southview HS Art Tchr 1991-; *ai:* Basic Stud Skills Instr; Art Club Co-Adv; United Way, Outcomes Accreditation-Basic Stud Skills Comms; Proficiency Wrtng Tutor; Phi Kappa Phi, Phi Lambda Theta 1991-; OH Ed Assn, NWOAE 1989-; Toledo Botanical Gardens; Spectrum Gallery; Common Space Ctr for Creativity; *office:* Sylvania Southview HS 7225 Sylvania Ave Sylvania OH 43560*

MC COMBS, BRIAN JOSEPH, Math Teacher; *b:* Ravenna, OH; *m:* Michele Grunenwald; *c:* Katherine Elizabeth; *ed:* (BA) Math, Scndry Ed 1990; 15 Hrs Toward Masters as Math Clinician; *cr:* Kent Roosevelt HS Bsktbl, Bsbl Coach 1988-91; Tallmadge HS Bsktbl Coach 1987-88; Nordonia HS Math Tchr, Girls Bsktbl Coach 1991-; *ai:* Var Girls Bsktbl & Sftbl Coach; NEA, Nord Hills Ed Assn, NCTM, OCTM 1991-; Knights of Col 1986-; *office:* Nordonia HS 8006 S Bedford Ave Macedonia OH 44056*

MCCOMMONS, BRENDA PERKINS, 5th Grade Teacher; *b:* Middletown, OH; *c:* Thorpe; *ed:* Miami Univ (BS) Elem Ed 1988; 9 Credit Hrs Admin & Supervision; *cr:* Doty House Behavior Modification 1985-86; Head Start Asst Tchr 1986-89; Middletown City Schls Tchr 1989-; *ai:* Sci Fair & Spelling Bee Comm; Asst Bsktbl Coach; OEA & NEA 1989-, Bldg Rep; Bldg Lead Team 1989-93; Eastern Star 1995-; Acceptance into Childrens Acad of Lit; *office:* Mc Kinley Elem Schl 1210 S Verity Pky Middletown OH 45044*

MCCOMSEY, OLIVER JAMES,JR., 7th Grade Geography Teacher; *b:* Reading, PA; *m:* Kathleen Villforth; *c:* Kelly Jo, Erin Janel; *ed:* Kutztown Univ (BS) Soc Stud 1973; Attnd Western MD, Penn St, Wilkes Coll, Millersville; *cr:* Tolpehocken HS 12th Grd Problems of Democracy Tchr 1973-74; Spring Ridge MS 7th & 8th Grd Soc Stud Tchr 1975-79; Daniel Boone 7th Grd Geog Tchr 1979-; *ai:* Coach: Girls Track, Boys & Girls Cross Cntry; Mentor; NEA & PSEA 1975-; PA Geographic Alliance 1990-, St Steering Comm; Natl Cncl for Geographic Ed 1995-, Tchr of the Yr 1995.

MC CONNELL, JOAN (BASILIO), Spanish Teacher; *b:* West Chester, PA; *m:* Raymond F. Jr.; *c:* Matthew R., Brian R.; *ed:* West Chester Univ (BS) Ed, Span 1975, (MA) Span 1980; *cr:* Bishop Shanahan HS Span Tchr 1975-83; Sussex Cntrl Jr HS Span, Soc Stud Tchr 1985-86; West Chester East Schl Span Tchr 1986-88; Delaware Cty Comm Coll Co-Adj Span Prof 1986-87; East St Mark's HS Span Tchr 1988-; *ai:* Soph Class Adv; Frgn Travel Chaperone; AATSP 1975-; *office:* St Mark's HS Pike Creek Rd Wilmington DE 19808*

MC CONNELL, KAREN SIMS, French & Spanish Teacher; *b:* Hutchinson, KS; *m:* George T. Jr.; *c:* Michael Austin; *ed:* LA St Univ (BA) Fr 1967; Debutante Prgm at Univ of Caen France 1964-65; 12 Credits MD Accreditation at Univ of MD; 12 Credits Accreditation at Jacksonville St Univ; *cr:* Bishop Kenny HS Tchr 1969-70; Andover Sr HS Tchr 1980-82; Severna Park Sr HS Tchr 1990-; *ai:* Class of 95 Spon 1992-95; Frgn Lang Club Spon 1982-90; AATF 1982-; MD Frgn Lang Assn 1982-, VP; *office:* Severna Park Sr HS 60 Robinson Rd Severna Park MD 21146

MC CONNELL, LEON MARY,IHM, Tutoring Program Teacher; *b:* Altoona, PA; *ed:* Marywood Coll(BA) Elem Ed, Soc Stud 1950; Theology; *ai:* Dominic Savio Classroom, Yth Group Act Adv; Oratorical Contests Coach; Tchr of Yr 1994; Distinction in Tchng Awd 1995; *home:* 2300 Adams Ave Scranton PA 18509

MC CONNELL, LINDA KAY, 7th Grd Lang Arts & Math Tchr; *b:* Hoisington, KS; *ed:* Phillips Univ (BS) Scndry Ed, Lang Arts 1979; Univ of ME at Orono (MED) Rdng, Lit 1987; Support Group Cert; Numerous Cmptr Classes; *cr:* Newport Elem Schl Assoc Tchr 1980-82, Migrant Tchr 1982-86, 6th Grd Tchr 1986-87, 5th Grd Tchr 1987-90; Weatherbee Schl 6th Grd Tchr 1990-91, 7th Grd Lang Arts, Math Tchr 1991-94; Reeds Brook MS 7th Grd Lang Arts, Math Tchr 1994-; *ai:* Assn Rep; Coord; Dist Inservice, Accreditation Comm; Negotiations Team; NEA, ME Ed Assn 1986-; Tchrs Assn 1990-, Bldg Rep; Natl MS Assn 1995-; Delta Kappa Gamma 1991-; PTO 1990-; *office:* Reeds Brook MS 28 A Main Rd S Hampden ME 04444*

MC CONNELL, LOIS NAYLOR, Retired First Grade Teacher; *b:* Norristown, PA; *m:* J. Russell; *c:* Martha Walker; *ed:* West Chester Univ (BS) Elem Ed 1956; Attnd Temple Univ, Merrywood Coll; *cr:* Norristown Areas Schl Dist 2nd Grd Then 1st Grd Tchr 1956-64; Metacton Schl Dist Rdng Tchr 1972-75, K-1st Grd Tchr 1975-93; Church Presch 3 Yr Old Class Tchr 1993-95; *ai:* PSEA, NEA 1956-, Ret; Cty Ret Tchrs 1993-; Church Womens Group 1950-, Guild Pres 1995, Comm Charimanships; Garden Club 1965-; Order of Eastern Star 1958-; Cooperating Tchr for Stdnts From Several Colls; Awd Cabrini Coll for Outstdng Assistance with Their Studing Tchng Prgm.

MC CONNELL, RONALD CHARLES, English & Reading Teacher; *b:* Dover, OH; *m:* Donna Marie Uptegraph; *c:* Lora N.; *ed:* Kent St Univ (BSEd) Eng 1969; Rdng Cert K-12 Walsh Coll; *cr:* Tusc Cntrl Cath HS Tchr & Adv 1969-74; IN Valley HS Tchr & Adv 1974-; *ai:* Class, Yrbk, NHS Adv; EECAP Co Dir; Voice of Democracy Adv; Moose Lodge # 707 1987-, Jr Gov 3 Yrs; Bd of Dir Tuscarawas Schls Credit Union 4 Yrs; Media Now Grant Recipient; *office:* Indian Valley H S 253 S Walnut St Box 130 Gnadenhutten OH 44629

MCCONNELL, STEVE, Professor of Theatre Arts; *b:* London, England; *m:* Jaret Johnson; *ed:* Allegheny Coll (BA) Ec 1972-; Brandeis Univ (MFA) Acting 1980; *cr:* The Boston Conservatory Prof of Theatre 1981-; *ai:* dir & Tchr Walnut Hill Summer Schl; Acting Tchr Lyric Stage; Actor & Dir Boston Theatres; Actors Equity Assn 1985-; *office:* The Boston Conservatory 8 The Fenway Boston MA 02215

MC CONNELL, THOMAS STEVEN, 7th-12th Grade Science Teacher; *b:* Syracuse, NY; *m:* Janet B. Fuller; *c:* Shannon, Valerie; *ed:* SUNY at New Paltz (BS) Scndry Ed Bio 1969; Addl 36 Credit Hrs SUNY at Oswego; *cr:* Gillette Rd MS Sci Dept Chprsn 1986-91, Sci Tchr 1969-; *ai:* NY St United Tchrs, NEA, Sci Tchrs Assn of NY St 1959-; NSTA 1979-; Sigma Tau Gamma 1966-; Sons of Amer Legion 1992-; Natl Sci Fnd Grant 1973; *office:* Gillette Road MS 6150 S Bay Rd Cicero NY 13039

MC CONNELL, TIMOTHY JOHN, Head Basketball Coach; *b:* Pittsburgh, PA; *m:* Shelly Lupica; *c:* Timothy John Jr.; *ed:* Waynesburg Coll (BA) Eng, Comm 1987; 6 Credits Canisius Coll 1988; *ai:* Head Bsktbl Coach; *home:* 105 Chambers Ln Canonsburg PA 15317

MC CONVILLE, GARRY OWEN, Fourth & Fifth Grade Teacher; *b:* Manchester, CT; *m:* Debra Jean Lavech; *ed:* Southern CT St Univ (BS) Elem Ed 1985; Grad Lbrl Stud Prgm Wesleyan Univ 27 Credit Hrs; Coll Prof Stud Univ of New England 3 Credit Hrs; Natl Outdoor Ldrshp Schl; North Cascades Mountaineering; *cr:* Abraham Pierson Schl 4th-5th Grd Integrated Day Prgm 1985-; *ai:* Sci, Invention Convention Coord; Odyssey of Mind Adv; CEA, NEA, NSTA 1985-; Grange P of H 46 1967-; Applachian Mountain Club 1985-; MS Horticultural Soc 1994-; Applachian Trail Conf 1983-; CT St Tchr of Yr Semi-Finalist 1994; Clinton Tchr of Yr 1994; *office:* Abraham Pierson Schl 75 E Main St Clinton CT 06413*

MC CONVILLE, MELISSA ANN, Middle School Math Teacher; *b:* New Kensington, PA; *ed:* St Vincent Coll (BA) Math, Scndry Ed 1991, Elem Ed 1993; Tchrs Enhancement Inst 1995; *cr:* St John Neumann Regnl Elem Schl MS Math, Sixth Grd Tchr 1993-; *ai:* Aftermath Peer Tutoring; Stu Cncl Spon; NCTM 1990-; PA Cncl of Tchr of Math 1995-; Math Cncl Western PA 1994-; *office:* St John Neumann Regnl Elem Sch 250 44th St Pittsburgh PA 15201

MC COOL, CONNIE MC AFEE, Second Grade Teacher; *b:* Bethlehem, PA; *m:* Henry; *ed:* East Stroudsburg Univ (BS) Elem Ed 1968; St Joseph's Univ (MS) Elem Ed 1993; Addl Post Grad Stud East Stroudsburg Univ; *cr:* Pleasant Vly Schl Dist First Grd Tchr 1968-69; Stroudsburg Area Schl Dist Second Grd Tchr 1969-; *ai:* PTO Coord Hamilton Schl Parent Vol Prgm; Co-operating Tchr for East Stroudsburg Univ Stu Tchrs; Schl Dist negotiations Team; Curr, Report Card Comm; SA Edctrs Assn 1969-, Past Bldg Rep; PSEA, NEA 1968-; Delta Kappa Gamma Intnl PHI Chptr 1982-, Pres 1988-90; Monroe Cncl of Republican Women 1996; PA Outstdng Tchr Awd 1981; Stroudsburg Schl Dist 25 Yrs Svc Awd 1994; East Stroudsburg SPSEA Awd 1993; Co-authored Integrated Thematic Unit for Grd 2; Article Pub; *office:* Hamilton Elem Schl HC 1 Box 218 Sciota PA 18354*

MC COOL, DEBORAH (BUTLER), Science Teacher; *b:* Johnstown, PA; *c:* Bryan Spiker, Jeffrey Spiker, Eric Spiker, Sean; *ed:* Univ of Pittsburgh (BS) Bio 1974; St Francis Coll at Loretto (MED) Ed 1990; Clarion Univ Cmptrs Phys Sci; Univ of Pittsburg (post-bacculaureatte); *cr:* Penn Cambria HS Sci Tchr 1984-; Mount Aloysius Coll Sci Instr 1990-; *ai:* Sci Olympiad Team Coach; Penn Cambria Ed Assn, NEA, PSEA 1984-; CNtrl Penna Assn Chem Tchrs 1989-; Educ Division Am Chem Soc 1991-; Natl Sci Tchr Assn 1984-; Amer Assn for the Advancement of Sci 1993-; Spectroscopic Soc Pittsburgh Equipment Grants 1986-87, 1990, 1991; St Grant Hands On Sci Wkshps; Marquis Who's Who in Amer; *office:* Penn Cambria HS 401 Linden Ave Cresson PA 16630*

MC COOL-HENNESSY, ALYSIA GRACE, English & Journalism Teacher; *b:* Salisbury, MD; *m:* Christopher Anthony; *ed:* Swarthmore Coll (BA) Eng Lit 1994; *cr:* High Point HS Eng, Jrnlsm Tchr 1994-; *ai:* Multicultural, Schlsp, Philosophy, Stu Act Comms; Newspaper Spon; JV Sftbl Coach; NAET 1995-; NEA 1994-; Friends of Montgomery Cty Libs 1994-; MENSA 1980-; Smithsonian Assocs 1985-; MD Scholastic Press Assn 1995-, Bd of Trustees; Sallie Mae New Tchr Awd Nom; Regis Boyle Jrnlsm Awd; *office:* High Point HS 3601 Powder Mill Dr Beltsville MD 20705*

MC CORD, DONALD EUGENE, Soc Stud & Photography Tchr; *b:* Rew, PA; *w:* Elizabeth M. Godden (dec); *c:* Gretchen, Alan; *ed:* Clarion Univ of PA (BS) Soc Stud 1955; Grad Comm 1973, Soc Stud 1969, Ec 1964; *cr:* USAF, USAFR 1946-1955; Fredonia-Delaware HS Tchr 1955-57; Clarion Chamber of Commerce Exec Sec 1957-60; Clarion Area Jr Sr HS Tchr 1960-93; Sub Tchr CAJSHS 1993-; *ai:* Soc Stud Dept Chm; Nwspr, Yrbk & Safety Adv; Clarion Area Ed Assn 1960-, Treas; PSEA, NEA 1960-93; Clarion Borough Cncl, Councilman; Cntrl Cty Ambulance Svc, Bd, Emergency Medical Tech; Clarion Borough Recreation Bd; Clarion Planning-Zoning Commission; Clarion Free Lib Bd, Pres; Clarion C of C; EPDA, NDEA Title XI & General Electric Fellowship Grants.

MC CORD, JENNIFER REVIS, English & Speech Teacher; *b:* Dayton, OH; *m:* Howard Laurence; *c:* Susannah Leigh, Julia Eden, Wyatt Asher, Eva Ariella Siobhan; *ed:* Wright St Univ (BS) Ed, Eng 1971; Bowling Green St Univ (MA) Eng 1976; 55 Addl Semester Hrs; *cr:* Mt Health HS Eng Tchr 1971-73; Bowling Green St Univ Eng Instr 1980-84; Otsego HS Eng, Speech Tchr 1985-; *ai:* Creative Writing Club Adv; Pub Lit Magazine; Adv Film Stud Club, Drama Club; OH Edctrs Assn 1985-; NEA 1971-; Vol Cnslr LINK 1978-79; OH Arts Cncl Grants, Summer Media Wkshp; Wood Cty Bd of Ed Grants; Pub Poems, Rsrch Asst; *office:* Otsego HS Tontogany Creek Rd Tontogany OH 43565*

MC CORKLE, ROBERT, Algebra & Calculus Teacher; *b:* Sutersville, PA; *ed:* CA Univ of PA (BS) Math 1963; IN Univ of PA (MED) Math 1967; Attnd Saint Vincent Coll, Univ of Pittsburgh, Drew Univ; *cr:* Glassport Schl Dist Math Tchr 1963-67; Norwin Schl Dist Math Tchr 1968-; *ai:* Math Club Spon; AP Calculus; NCTM 1961-; Sutersville Moose Lodge 1964-; Westmoreland Ski Club 1990-; *office:* Norwin Sr H S 251 Mcmahon Dr Irwin PA 15642

MCCORMACK, ARLENE SMITH, Dept Sociology Chairperson; *b:* Somerville, MA; *c:* Theodore, Jennifer Miranda; *ed:* Boston Univ (BA) & (MA) Sociology 1981, (PHD) Sociology 1983; *cr:* U Mass Lowell Asst Prof 1984-88, Assoc Prof 1988-90, Prof 1990-; *ai:* Amer Sociological Soc 1984-; NEA 1984-; Numerous Journals Pub; *office:* Univ Of MA At Lowell 1 University Ave Lowell MA 01854

MCCORMACK, GAIL G., Medical Careers Pgm Coord; *b:* New Haven, CT; *w:* Dennis (dec); *c:* Catherine Krokus, Christine Bryson; *ed:* Grace-New Haven (RN) Nrsng 1950; SCSU (BS) Hlth Ed 1978; CCSU (MS) Scndry Ed & Nrsng Ed 1980; SCSU 6th Yr Admin 1983; *cr:* Mass Gen Staff ICU 1958-59; Yale New Haven 1959-61; Veterans Memrl Med Ctr Part-Time Staff CCU 1962-67; Wallington Pub Schls Schl Nurse 1967-75, Med Careers Coord 1975-; *ai:* Industrial Voc Club Adv; GNH-Alumni 1958-; NEA, CEA, WEA 1975-; Phi Delta Kappa 1983-; Quinnipiac Chamber 1985-, Dir; Veterans Memrl Med Ctr 1992-, Govenor; Staff Mem of Month; *office:* Wallingford Pub Schls Hope Hill Rd Wallingford CT 06492

MC CORMACK, JANE E., Social Studies Teacher; *b:* Newark, NJ; *m:* Brian; *c:* Moira, Katherine; *ed:* Montclair St Univ (BA) Soc Stud 1967; Monmouth Univ (MA) 1983; Post Grad Supervisory Cert; *cr:* Freehold Regnl HS Dist 27 Yrs; *ai:* Life Discussion Peer Cnslng; NEA; NJEA; NJCSS; *office:* Marlboro HS 95 N Main St Marlboro NJ 07746*

MC CORMACK, JOHN A., English & Writing Skills Tchr; *b:* New York, NY; *m:* Graciela; *c:* Suzanne; *ed:* Iona Coll (BA) Span; OH St Univ (MA) Frgn Lang Ed 1972; Soc Stud, Eng, Span Certs NY St; *cr:* Ramapo Sr HS Span Tchr 1972-73; Spring Valley Sr HS Span Tchr 1973-76; Chestnut Ridge Jr HS Eng, Writing Skills Tchr 1976-; *ai:* NYSUT, NEA 1972-; Golden Apple Awd from Channel 13 Learning Link; *office:* Chestnut Ridge Jr HS 892 Chestnut Ridge Rd Chestnut Ridge NY 10977

MC CORMACK, LOUISE SAMAHA, Associate Professor; *b:* Plymouth, NH; *m:* Phillip Gene; *c:* Brenten, Devin-Jean; *ed:* Plymouth St Coll (BA) Hlth, PE 1972; OH St Univ (MA) 1973; Boston Univ (EDD) Human Movement 1985; *cr:* Brooklyn Coll Instr 1973-76; Merrimack HS Tchr 1977-79; Plymouth St Coll Assoc Prof 1980-; *ai:* Governor's Cncl on Sport, Fitness Schl Subcomm; HPER Club Adv; AAHPERD 1973-, Inspirational Awd; NHAHPERD 1980-, VP PE, Hlth, Rec, Merit Awd; Plymouth St Coll EDies Nom; *office:* Plymouth St Coll Draper & Maynard Plymouth NH 03264

MCCORMACK, MICHAEL DAVID, 8th Grade Earth Science Tchr; *b:* Natrona Heights, PA; *ed:* CA St Univ (BA) Geog & Earth Sci 1968; Penn St 30+ Credit Hrs; Attnd Towson St at MD, Slippery Rock Univ; *cr:* Clarksville MS Tchr 1969-70; Deer Lakes Tchr 1970-; *ai:* Jr High Vllybl & Ftbl, JV Bsbl & Yth Ftbl Coach; Bd of Dirs; NEA 1970-; PSEA 1970-; DLEA 1970-; *home:* 809 Jefferson Ave Natrona Heights PA 15065

MC CORMACK, SANDRA J., Special Education Teacher; *b:* Huntington, NY; *m:* Thomas; *ed:* Dowling Coll (BA) Spec Ed 1978; Long Island Univ CW Post Ctr (MS) Spec Ed 1980; 45 Addl Credits; *cr:* Wenonah Elem Schl Tchr Asst, Sub Tchr 1978-80, Spec Ed Tchr 1980-; *ai:* Spec Olympics; *office:* Wenonah Elem Schl 251 Hudson Ave Lake Grove NY 11755

MC CORMICK, AMY D., Math & Science Teacher; *b:* Wilkinsburg, PA; *m:* Edward; *ed:* Clarion Univ (BS) Math, Gen Sci Ed 1978; Post Grad Work Penn St, Westmoreland IU; *cr:* Harrold Jr HS Tchr 1978-; Harrold MS Tchr 1978-; *office:* Harrold MS RR 6 Box 75 Greensburg PA 15601

MCCORMICK, ANNE MARIE, Chemistry Teacher; *b:* Rochester, NY; *m:* Guy Gordon; *c:* Guy Albert, Kiel Harrison; *ed:* Trenton St Coll (BS) Chem 1994; *cr:* Jackson Meml HS Chem Tchr 1994-; *ai:* Intensive Scheduling Evaluation Comm Chprsn; Grant Comm; Sci League; Amer Chemical Soc 1993-; *office:* Jackson Memorial HS 101 Don Connor Blvd Jackson NJ 08527

MC CORMICK, CHRISTINE JOANN, Spanish Teacher; *b:* Santa Barbara, CA; *c:* John; *ed:* Montgomery Coll (AA) Ed 1970; Univ of MD (BA) Ed 1972; Simmons Coll (MA) Bus 1984; *cr:* Mc Call Jr HS Span Tchr 1974-81; Currituck Co HS Span Tchr 1984-85; First Colonial HS Span Tchr 1985-87; Seneca Valley HS Span Tchr 1987-; *ai:* Span Club, Natl Span Hon Soc Spon; Attendance Dean 9th Grd; NEA 1987-; AATSP 1987-, Best Chapter Act; St Rose of Lima 1987-, CCD Tchr, Breadbaker; Peer Tchr Inservice Hispanic Arts; Pacesetter Pilot 1994-95; Natl Span Exam Spon; *office:* Seneca Valley HS 12700 Middlebrook Rd Germantown MD 20874*

MC CORMICK, EDWARD, English & Social Studies Tchr; *b:* Pittsburgh, PA; *m:* Amy D. Dinning; *ed:* St Vincent Coll (BA) Eng, Soc Stud 1979; Attnd Univ of Pittsburgh, Millersville St; *cr:* Hempfield Area Schl Dist Tchr 1979-; Westmoreland Cty Comm Coll Summer Prgm Tchr 1989-92; *ai:* Yrbk; Jr HS Wrestling Coach; Drama Club; Var Girls Soccer Head Coach; Tutor; JV Boys Soccer; NEA, PSEA, HAEA 1979-; Greater Greensburgh Jaycees 1985-, VP; St Vincent Alumni Cncl 1991-, VP; Bearcat Ath Club 1979-, Pres; *office:* Harrold MS RR 6 Box 75 Greensburg PA 15601

MCCORMICK, KIMBERLY ANN, Sixth Grade Teacher; *b:* New Castle, PA; *m:* Rodney W.; *c:* Kaycee, Nicolette; *ed:* Slippery Rock Univ (BS) Elem Ed 1987; Westminster Coll (MS) Ed with Rdng Specializaton 1992; *cr:* Shenango Elem Schl 1st Grd Tchr 1988; New Bedford Elem Schl 1st Grd Tchr 1988-89; New Wilmington Elem Schl 6th Grd Tchr 1989-92; Wilmington MS 6th Grd Tchr 1992-; *ai:* 6th Grd Team Ldr 1993-; German Fun Fest Activity Spon; 6th Grd Parent Newsletter Adv; NEA, PSEA, Lawrence Cty Rdng Assn 1988-; Wilmington Area Tchrs, Pub Relations Rep; Articles Pub by Instr & Good Apple Magazines; Awded Sallie Mae 1st Yr Tchr Awd; *office:* Wilmington MS 400 Wood St New Wilmington PA 16142*

MC CORMICK, LINDA MC CARTHY, Fourth Grade Teacher; *b:* Springfield, MA; *m:* Jeffrey L.; *c:* Meaghan, Jeffrey Jr.; *ed:* Univ of MA (BA) Ed 1970, (MED) Ed 1971; Addl 15 Credit Hrs CAGS Ed 1972; *cr:* Pelham Elem Schl Sixth Grd Tchr 1970; Marks Meadow Schl 2-3rd, 4-6th Grd Team Tchr 1970-72; Union Schl Fifth Grd Tchr 1972-75; Longmeadow Schls 2-6th Grd Tchr 1975-; *ai:* Longmeadow Prof Dev, System-wide Soc Stud Comms; Longmeadow Ed Assn, MA Tchrs Assn 1975-; NEA 1970-; Springfield Jr League 1977-, Provisional, Nom Chrprsn, Bus Mgr; Longmeadow His Soc 1995-, Bd of Dirs; *office:* Ctr Elem Schl 837 Longmeadow St Longmeadow MA 01106

MC CORMICK, MARJORIE LYNN, 10th Grade English Teacher; *b:* Sewickley, PA; *m:* Dennis M. Pepper; *c:* Karissa; *ed:* Kutztown St Coll (BS) Scndry Ed 1976; 40 Credits Latin Univ of Scranton; *cr:* Upper Perkiomen HS Sub, LTS Tchr 1977-90; Tamoqua Area HS Latin, Eng Tchr 1992-94, Eng Tchr 1994-; *ai:* Newspaper Adv 1994-95; NEA, PSEA, Tamaqua Ed Assn 1992-; *office:* Tamaqua Area HS Stadium Hill Rd Tamaqua PA 18252

MCCORMICK, MARK, Law Professor; *b:* Sullivan, IN; *ed:* Davidson Coll (BA) Fr 1980; NY Univ (JD) Law 1984; *cr:* Peirce Coll Assoc Prof, Paralegal Stud Pgm Asst Coord 1986-93; Comm Coll of Philadelphia Assoc Prof & Paralegal Stud Curr Coord 1993; *ai:* Amer Bar Assn 1987-; PA Bar Assn 1987-; Philadelphia Bar Assn 1987-; Amer Assn for Paralegal Ed 1987-; William J Hamilton Awd for Enhancing Acad Excl at Peirce Coll 1991; *office:* Comm Coll Of Philadelphia 1700 Spring Garden St Philadelphia PA 19130

MC CORMICK, RICHARD JOSEPH, Theology & English Teacher; *b:* Boston, MA; *ed:* Don Bosco Coll (BA) Philosophy 1965; Pontifical Josephinum Coll (MA) Theology 1970; Boston Coll (MA) Ed 1975; Summer Inst in Soc Stud 1966; *cr:* Salesian Preparatory Schl Rel Act Dir, Tchr 1970-75; Salesian Jr Seminary Dir, Tchr 1975-80; Vocation Dir, Provincial Superior 1980-91; Don Bosco Technical HS Dir 1991-95; *ai:* Stu Cncl Moderator; Sch Bd Chprsn; NCEA 1965-; Amer Tchrs of Eng Assn 1970-; Mayor's Recognition for Achvmt Cup Boston 1991; *office:* Don Bosco Tech HS 300 Tremont St Boston MA 02116*

MC COSHAM, JOYCE L., Counselor; *b:* Cincinnati, OH; *w:* William D. (dec); *c:* Colleen Hamberg, Kyle Hellman; *ed:* Univ of Cincinnati (BS) Hlth, PE 1948, (MED) Guid, Cnslng, Admin, Supervision 1972; Xavier Univ 36 Post Grad Hrs; *cr:* North Coll Hill Schls Hlth, PE Tchr 1948-52; Cincinnati Recreation Commission Water Safety Instruct 1948-74; Mercy HS PE Tchr, Asst Prin, Ath Dir, Coach, Chair 1952-92; Edge Cliff Coll PE, Hlth Tchr, Chair 1959-74; Oak Hills HS Cnslr 1992-; *ai:* Schlsp Prgm Dir; A-Da-9-12 Cnslr; NEA, OEA, OHEA 1992-; OCA, NCA 1972-; GCCA 1972-, Pres, VP, Mary Corre Foster Outstdng Cnslr 1994; Kappa Delta Phi 1972-, Outstdng Edctr 1972; AHPER, OAHPER 1948-; Mercy Ath Hall of Fame Outstdng Coach 1987; Cincinnati Archdiocese Outstdng Svc 1992; Greater Cincinnati Guid Assn Outstdng Svc 1994; Mercy HS Svc 1992; *office:* Oak Hills HS 3200 Ebenezer Rd Cincinnati OH 45248

MC COY, ANN-MARIE ALOSKY, High School Biology Teacher; *b:* Cambridge, MA; *m:* John F. Jr.; *c:* Jayme Ann, Elizabeth Marie; *ed:* Merrimack Coll (BA) Bio 1970; River Coll (MS) Bio 1990; *cr:* Keith Hall Schl Bio Tchr 1970-73; Goffstown HS Bio Tchr 1989-; *ai:* Marine Bio Floating Lab Coord; Class of 1998 Adv; NABT 1992-; NSTA 1990-; NEA 1989-; Wright Ctr Interdisciplinary Tchr, Scholar Flwshp at Tuft's Univ; *office:* Goffstown HS 27 Wallace Rd Goffstown NH 03045

MC COY, CHARLIE LORENZO, Associate Naval Science Instr; *b:* Norfolk, VA; *m:* Uldanelis Sanchez; *c:* U. Chaletta, Charlie L. II; *ed:* No VA Comm Coll (AAS) Bus Mngmt 1982; Park Coll (BS) Mngmt 1989; Chaminade Coll of Honolulu 4.5 Sem Hrs; Univ of MD Far East Division 12 Sem Hrs; GWU Wash DC 18 Sem Hrs; Mngmt Dev for Supvrs Managerial Ethics; *cr:* US Marine Corps Manpower Mngmt MGYSGT 30 Yrs; Northern HS Assoc Naval Sci Instr 1 Yr; Calvert HS Assoc Naval Sci Instr 8 Yrs; *ai:* Competition Drill Team; Competition Color Guard; FRA 1994-; MC League 1953-; Medals: Navy Commendation, Navy Achvmt, Meritorious Svc; Navy League Awd for Spec Merit; Gen Commission of Chaplians, Armed Forces Prsnl Appreciation Certs; BSA Dist Awd of Merit, Silver Beaver Awd; *office:* Calvert HS 600 Dares Beach Rd Prince Frederick MD 20678*

MC COY, DANIEL, Spanish Teacher; *b:* Camden, NJ; *m:* Carolyn M *c:* Daniel S., David J.; *ed:* Rutgers Univ (BA) Span 1967; Univ of DE Span 1969; NJ Supvr Scndry Ed Glassboro St Coll; *cr:* Penns Gro Span Tchr 1971-, Dept Chair 1974-78, 1987-; *ai:* Grad Comm; Tennis Club; Hall of Fame Selection Comm; Foreign Lag Educators 1972-; NJEA, NEA 1971-; Bethel Bible Church 1964-90, Pres Bd First Bapt Church 1991-; Bd Mem; Pianist; *office:* Penns Grove H Harding Hwy Carneys Point NJ 08069

MC COY, DEBORAH FAYE, HS Social Studies Teacher; *b:* Akron *m:* Daniel Keith; *c:* Dawn, Donna; *ed:* Univ of Akron (BA) Scndry E Stud 1987; 30 Addl Credit Hrs; *cr:* Stow-Munroe Falls HS Tchr 198 Mentorship, Hlth & Wellness Comms; Close-Up Club Adv; STA, OEA, NEOEA 1988-; *office:* Stow-Munroe Falls HS 3227 E Graha Stow OH 44224*

MCCOY, DEBRA ANN, Fifth Grade Teacher; *b:* New York City, N Richard; *c:* Katie, Nathaniel; *ed:* Albany St Univ (BA) Speech Path & Audiology 1970; Binghamton Univ 12 Addl Credits Elem Tchr S 30 Addl Credits Cert; Cortland St Ocll & Ithaca Coll Attnd; *cr:* Sprin Pub Schls Speech Therapist 1970-71; Vestal Cntrl Schls Elem Tchr *ai:* NEA NY & Vestal Tchrs Assn 1972-; *office:* Glenwood Elem Jones Rd Vestal NY 13850

MC COY, ELLA MARIE, Seventh Grade Social Stud Tchr; *b:* Cinci OH; *m:* Douglas; *c:* Tabarc D.; *ed:* Miami Univ (BS) Comp Soc Stud Xavier Univ (MED) His 1973; Attnd Univ of Cincinnati; *cr:* Cincinna Schls Tchr 1976-73; Princeton City Schls Tchr 1974-; *ai:* Pep Schl; Selection Comm; Comm Ctr Adv Elem, Jr HS Drill Team; NEA, SW OEA 1968-; PACE 1974-; NASSP Dept of Stu Act 1994-.

MC COY, LYNN MARIE, Choir Director; *b:* Hartford, CT; *m:* Way *c:* Dane; *ed:* Heidelberg Coll (BM) K-12 Spec, Music 1979; Addl Bowling Green St Univ, 3 Hrs Drake Univ, 2 Hrs Heidelberg Co Millcreek-West Unity Schls LD Tchr, Tutor 1979-82; Margaretta Schls 7-12 Grd Vocal Music Tchr 1983-; *ai:* Marching Band Asst; Music; Show Choir; Bible Stud Cnslr; MENC, OMEA, OED 1979-; A 1984-; Holy Angels Church Folk Group 1983-; Towne & Cntry T Orch 1982; *office:* Margaretta Local Schls 306 S Washington St Ca OH 44824

MC COY, MARISA GORI, Retired English Teacher; *b:* Brookline, *m:* Roger; *c:* Christopher, Ariane; *ed:* Bryn Mawr Coll (AB) His o Amer His 1958; Grad Work at Harvard Schl of Ed, Middlebury-Brea Schl of Eng, Boston Univ, Southern CT St Coll; *cr:* Shady Hill Apprentice Tchr 1958-59; Lincoln-Sudbury Regnl HS Engl Tchr 19 North Haven HS Eng Tchr 2962-63; Wellesley HS Eng, Hum Tchr 19 *ai:* Acad Decathlon Team Coach; MA Tchrs Assn 1976-; Wellesley Meetings 1976-95; Metro Svc Awd; Most Influential Tchr Recogni From MIT, 1 Univ of Chicago.

MC COY, MARY GROVE, Chemistry Associate Professor; *b:* Colu OH; *m:* John J.; *c:* Michael, Timothy, Rebecca; *ed:* Coll of Wooster Chem 1965; Univ of Cincinnati (PHD) Chem; Ed Courses OH St 1964; Ger Lang Inst of European Stud 1965; *cr:* Univ of PA Postdo Fellow 1971-73, Rsrch Assoc 1975; Haverford Coll, Bryn Mawr C Joseph's Univ, Neuman Coll Part-time Chem Adj Instr 1975-89; PA S Chem Instr 2 Yrs; Neuman Coll Asst, Assoc Prof 1990-; *ai:* Pre-Med Comms Fac Dev 3 Yrs, Diversity Enrichment 1995-; Core Curr Task 3 Yrs; Sigma Xi, Amer Chemical Soc 1969-; Nether Providence Ath Coach Girls Soccer Teams 1985-93; Tri Cty Girls Soccer League 1986-90, Referee Rep 1991-92; Co-Author Articles Pub; *office:* Neu Coll Concord Rd Aston PA 19041

MC COY, RAY ARTHUR, Senior High Biology Teacher; *b:* Carlisle *m:* Sandra L.; *c:* Erin E. Mc Coy Madson, Megan L.; *ed:* WV Univ Animal Sci 1966; Univ of Cincinnat (MEDC) Scndry Ed 1969; Ur Pittsburgh (MED) Scndry Schl Admin 1976; 15 Credit Hrs; 10 Cred Penn St; 6 Credit Hrs Ball St Univ; *cr:* Cincinnati Pub Schl Sci 1976-70; Mt Lebanon HS Bio Tchr 1970-, Coord of Adult Educ 1 Summer Schl Prin 1992-; *ai:* Ski Club Spon; NABT; NSTA; NSF Gr Genetics; *office:* Mt Lebanon Sr H S 155 Cochran Rd Pittsburgh PA

MCCOY, ROBERT A., Government & Amer His Teacher; *b:* Broo NY; *m:* Andrea; *c:* Robert, Jon; *ed:* Adelphi Univ (BA) Pol Sci 1969, Pol Sci 1970; 7 Hrs Post Grad Stud; *cr:* East Islip HS Tchr 1968-; *ai:* 1969-; NYSUT 1969-; LICSS 1986-; Tchr of Yr 1991; *office:* East Isl Redmen St East Islip NY 11730

MCCOY, SAMUEL AARON, Department of Science Chairma Napoleon, OH; *m:* Denese J. Bortel; *c:* Leland, Aaron, Jeremy Bowling Green St Univ (BS) Bio 1956, (MA) Physiology 1961; Attn St Univ & Univ of Toledo; *cr:* Maumee Valley Cntry Day Schl Sci Chair 1957-; *ai:* Track & Field Head Coach; Ind Stud & Research S Natl Assn Bio Tchrs 1970-; OH Acad of Sci, Batelle-Acker Awd; Grants 1966-68; *office:* Maumee Vly Country Day Schl 1715 S Rey Rd Toledo OH 43614

MCCRACKEN, BRUCE R., Chrstn Ed Chm & Yth Ministr Philadelphia, PA; *m:* Karen A. Palmer; *c:* Ryan, Ross; *ed:* Taylor (BA) Rel & Chrstn Ed 1974; Trinity Evangelical Divinity Schl Chrstn Ed 1983, (EDD) Chrstn Ed 1993; *cr:* Evangelical Covenant C Pastor of Yth Ministries 1974-79; Manoa Presbyn Church Pastor o Ministries 1979-82; Lancaster Bible Coll Chair of CE 1983-; *ai:* Adv; Impact Adv; NAPCE 1983-; YMCA Bd 1985-87; Numerous Ar Pub; Chptr Pub; *office:* Lancaster Bible Coll 901 Eden Rd Lancaste 17601*

MC CRACKEN, DOROTHY KNEPP, Fourth Grade Teache Schenectady, NY; *m:* Joseph Alfred; *c:* Joseph Alfred II, David Lee Ball St Univ (BS) Elem Ed 1969; Attnd Penn St Univ, Clarian Univ New Castle Elem Schl Kndgtn Tchr Sem II 1969; Middletown Elem Third Grd Tchr 1969-70; Penn-Grampian Elem Schl Kndgtn, First, T Fourth Grd Tchr 1970-89; Curwensville Elem Schl Fourth Grd Tchr 1 *ai:* PA St Math Assessment Comm Grd Five; Charter Mem CESTA; I Sci Comm; CAEA 1970-, Negotiating Comm; PSTA, NEA 1970-; Kappa Gamma 1992-; Fed Bus Prof 1970-, St Pres, St Treas; Women's Inc St Comm Chm; Grampian Days Comm, Outstdng Citizen Awd; Outstdng Svc Comm 1987; Featured in News Article; Went Soviet U Citizen Ambassador Team Prof Women 1989; *office:* Curwensville Schl 650 Beech St Curwensville PA 16833*

MC CRADY, WILLIAM F., English & Special Ed Teacher; *b:* Pittsb PA; *m:* Sylvia Thorn; *c:* Amber; *ed:* Duke Univ (BA) 1971, (MAT) Ed 1972; 41 Hrs Rdng, Supervision, Spec Ed; *cr:* Southside HS Eng 1971-72; Kennedy HS Eng, Spec Ed Tchr 1972-77, 1981-89; Argyle Rdng Specialist 1977-80; Walter Johnson HS Spec Ed, Rdng, Eng 1980-81, 1989-; *ai:* Stu Newspaper Adv; Debate Team, Forensics Coach; NEA 1980-; Cty Debate League 1991-, Pres; Cty Forensics Le 1989-, Treas; Univ of KS HS Tchr Recognition Awd 1991; Colu Scholastic Press Assn Bd of Judges 1993-; *office:* Walter Johnson HS Rock Spring Dr Bethesda MD 20814*

MC CRAE, LINDA R., German & Latin Teacher; *b:* Reading, PA Richard D.; *c:* Sean Christoph, Patrick Michael Richard Reed; *ed:* Alb Coll (BA) Ger-Cum Laude 1967; Kutztown Univ (MED) Ger 1969; W Coll 3 Grad Credits; Goddard Coll 6 Grad Credits; FL St 3 Grad Cre *cr:* Reading Area Comm Coll Ger Instr 1971-72; Albright Coll Ed Lec

-76; Alvernia Coll Ger Instr 1995; Muhlenberg Schl Dist Ger, Latin, ology, Eng Tchr 1967-; *ai:* Co-Adv Acad Challenge Team; Gifted Ed Force; HS Intensive Scheduling, Strategic Planning Comms; Instrl er Ldr for Frgn Langs; AATG 1992-; FLASH 1990-; MEA, PSEA, 1967-; Delta Phi Alpha 1966-; Phi Delta Sigma 1967-, Treas 1970-75; nissing Schl Dist Strategic Planning; Book: Latina Vivit! A Guide to Latin Classes 1995; European Travel Correspondent Reading Eagle s 1989-90; Creator Etymology Enrichment Course Grd 5 1990-91; : Muhlenberg Sr HS Sharp Ave Frances St Reading PA 19605*

CRAVE, LINDA, English Teacher; *b:* Providence, RI; *m:* Gil; *c:* on; *ed:* Univ of RI (BA) Eng & Scndry Ed 1971; RI Coll (MAT) Eng 30 Credit Hrs in His Life Cert; *cr:* Johnston HS Eng Tchr 1971-; NE of Tech Adjunct Fac Eng 1989-90; *ai:* AFT 1971-; *office:* Johnston HS Cherry Hill Rd Johnston RI 02919

CRAY, JERLINE F., Mathematics Teacher; *b:* Georgetown, SC; *m:* ; *c:* Shakisha, Lavelle; *ed:* Claflin Coll (BS) Math 1970; NJ Inst of (MS) Applied Math 1975; Montclair St Coll Project Thistle 1985; Coll Supervision Cert 1989; *cr:* Bankers Trust Reconciliation Dept oyee 1970-71; Newark Bd of Ed Math Tchr 1971-; Rutgers Univ Coll Consortium Prgm Math Tchr 1986-95; *ai:* Math Club Adv; Schl l Planning Team; NEA; NJEA; NCTM; NAME; Church Trustee Bd; ionary Bd; Newark City Outstdng Commitment, Educl Excl gnition 1993; *office:* Central HS 100 Summit St Newark NJ 07103

CREE, JOYCE WINN, Technology Teacher; *b:* Jersey City, NJ; *m:* lph Jr.; *c:* Sharmaine, Clyde, Rozlyn; *ed:* Montclair St Coll (BA) n Sci, Disorders 1978; *cr:* Our Lady of the Vly 4th Grd Tchr 1985-88; vood Schl 6th Grd Tchr, Tech 1988-; *ai:* Stu Cncl, Panasonic KWN Tutor; Soc Stud, Publishing, Fine Arts Curr Comm; NEA, EOEA, A 1988-; *office:* Elmwood Schl 181 Elmwood Ave East Orange NJ 8*

CREERY, BARBARA LYPKA, Small Bus Learning Comm Coord; iladelphia, PA; *c:* Allyson Marie; *ed:* Chestnut Hill Coll (BA) His ; Villanova Univ (MA) Scndry Ed 1976; Phila Coll Textiles, Sci (MS) r Ed 1992; Penn St Univ 30 Post Grad Credits Spec Ed 1980; *cr:* aried Jr HS Soc Stud Tchr 1975-80; Phila Comm Coll SAT Coord -85; Germantown HS Tchr 1980-94, Bus SLC Corrd, Proj Invest -; *ai:* Trips, Events: Grant Writing; Insurance, Coord Proj Invest Pgm , NAIW 1992-, Rookie of Yr, St Dir Asst; Spencer Educl Fnd Inc ts; Nom Tchr of Yr; Ind Agents of Amer; Natl Proj Invest; Amer Assn ging Gen Agents Achvmnt Awd; *office:* Germantown HS Germantown Philadelphia PA 19144*

CRONE, ROBERT MARTIN, English Teacher; *b:* Buffalo, NY; *m:* Orzell; *c:* Caitlin, Benjamin; *ed:* SUNY at Buffalo (BA) Eng 1980, Ed 1988; Working Toward Second Degree Masters Schl Cnslng; *cr:* wanda Schls Eng Tchr 1980-81; Liverpool Schls Eng Tchr 1981-; *ai:* 1980-; NCTE 1984-; *office:* Soule Road MS 8340 Soule Rd Liverpool 3090*

CUE, ANNE E., English & Language Arts Tchr; *b:* Philadelphia, PA; Benton; *c:* David, Lisa, Darren; *ed:* Beaver Coll (BA) Eng 1964; l Penn St; Masters Equivalency Temple Univ; *cr:* Indian Valley MS & Lang Arts Tchr 1964-68 & 1980-; *ai:* Newspaper; Honor Soc; Tchr or; NEA, PSEA, NASSP & NCTE 1980-; *office:* Indian Valley MS 130 e Ave Harleysville PA 19438

CUE, HAROLD LEWIS, Mathematics Teacher; *b:* Youngstown, OH; Cynthia Lynn Calvin; *c:* Keesha, Kaylin; *ed:* Youngstown St Univ d) Math 1978; *cr:* Austintown Schls,th Grd Math, HS Math Tchr -; *ai:* Jr High Track, Bsktbl Coach; NEA, OEA, NEOEA, AEA 1978-; nford Ruritan 1980-; *office:* Austintown Fitch HS 4560 Falcon Dr intown OH 44515

CUE, JEREMY T., Soc Stud, Sci & Religion Tchr; *b:* NY City, NY; inda Hansen; *c:* Jeremy Jr., Michael, Andrew, Brian, Erik; *ed:* NY Inst ch (BS) Criminal Justice 1978; *cr:* US Army PFC, MP Conp Germany -60; NYPD Police Ofcr 1963-83; St Mel's Schl Soc Stud Tchr 1983-; Merit Badge Cnslr BSA; Civil War Round Table Nassao Chptr; Cath s Assn 1983-; PBA NYPD 1963- Honor Legion 1972-; *home:* 25 flower Rd Levittown NY 11756

CUE, LOIS WILMOTT, Second Grade Teacher; *b:* Jersey City, NJ; ohn; *c:* Catherine, Christopher; *ed:* Trenton St Coll (BA) Elem Ed , (MA) Supervision, Admin 1989; *cr:* Hanover Twp Bd of Ed 2 Grd 1967-71; Toms River Bd of Ed 2 Grd Tchr 1984-; *ai:* Trenton St Coll nni Assn Pres; NEA, NJEA 1984-; TREA 1984-, Bldg Rep; Shore Area an's Club 1990-, Treas; AAUW 1990-; *home:* 975 Cedar Grove Rd s River NJ 08753*

CUE, MARTIN JOSEPH, Television Production Teacher; *b:* West ford, CT; *m:* Angela Jane; *c:* Kelley, Matthew; *ed:* Boston Univ (BS) m 1981; Tchr Cert in Ed 1990-92; *cr:* Rollins Cablevision News Dir -84; Bradgate Assoc Video Production Mgr 1984-87; Jordan Marsh Co ucer, Video 1987-90; Salem HS Television Production Tchr 1990-; *ai:* o Yrbk Adv, Producer; Voice Over Talent-CTV 30; NEA 1990-; Int Assn 1987-91; Derry Recreation 1995-, Girls Bsktbl Coach; Holy s Parish 1993-, Vol, Fundraising; Gold Cr Partnership Awd St of NH -94; FL Dept of Citrus Video Production Honorable Mention 1992; sta McAuliffe Tech Conf Presenter 1995; *office:* Salem HS 44 emonty Dr Salem NH 03079

CULLEN, WENDY HOWELL, Associate Professor of Biology; *b:* xville Center, NY; *m:* Phillip James; *c:* Michael, Evan; *ed:* OH St Univ Zoology 1974, (MS) Zoology 1978, (DVM) Veterinary Medicine ; *cr:* Columbus St Comm Coll Adj Instr 1978-87; OH St Univ Lecturer -80; Columbus St Comm Coll Asst Prof 1987-94, Assoc Prof 1994-; Biological Scis Dept Lead Instr; DE Cty 4H Prgm Equine Adv; Small nal, Equine Veterinarian; Institutional Animal Care, Use Comm; T, AAAS 1987-; PVMA, AVMA 1993-; PTA Westerville Schls 1985-, at Large, Sec, VP, Pres; DE Cty 4H Club Ldr; NSF Grant Incorp of imedia Sci Curr; Coord DOE, Eisenhower Grants Sci MS at Risk ts; Authored Numerous Books; Excl Awd Veterinary Emergency icine; Semi-Finalist Distngd Tchng Awd; *office:* Columbus St Comm 550 E Spring St Columbus OH 43216*

CULLEY, FRANK J., Physics Teacher; *b:* Philadelphia, PA; *m:* ifer Lynn; *c:* Galileo; *ed:* Rutgers Univ (BA) Physics 1989; *cr:* Delsea l HS Physics Tchr 1989-; *ai:* Ed, Stu of Month, Tech Comms; NEA -; Rsrch Corp Grant 1992-93; *office:* Delsea Regional HS kwoodtown Rd Franklinville NJ 08322

CULLIN, FRANCIS MATTHEW, Eighth Grd Math & Algebra Tchr; altimore, MD; *m:* Peggy Shifflett; *c:* Erin E., Tara M., Megan A.; *ed:* tern MD Coll (BA) Scndry Ed 1981; Masters Equivalence 1987; *cr:* nsville Comm Coll Math Instr 1982-84; Westminster West MS Math, ebra 1 Instr 1985-; *ai:* Liberty HS Boys Var Soccer 1980-84, Girls JV cer 1985, Var Tennis 1983-85; Boys JV Soccer 1986-; Var Tennis 3-85; Var Tennis 1986-; Scheduling Comm 1993-; Schl Improvement n 1995-; NEA, CCEA 1986-; MCTM 1992-; Carroll Cty Tchr of Yr 1994, Tennis Coach of Yr 1989-90; *office:* Westminster West MS 60 nroe St Westminster MD 21157*

CULLOCH, CAROLE OLKOWSKI, Soc Stud & Economics cher; *b:* Johnson City, NY; *m:* Bert; *c:* Jason, Michael; *ed:* St Univ of Coll at Potsdam (BA) Anthropology, Scndry Ed 1971; 12 Hrs Grad Schl Ed Binghamton Univ; 10 Hrs Grad Schl Ed Ithaca Coll; 8 Hrs Grad Schl Ed SUNY at Cortland; *cr:* Liverpool Cntrl Schls MS 7-8th Grd Soc Stud Tchr 1971-72; Jennie F. Snapp MS 7th Grd Soc Stud Tchr 1972-76; Union-Endicott HS 9th Grd Soc Stud, 10th Grd World His, 11th Grd Amer His, 12th Grd Environmental Issues, Ec Tchr 1976-; *ai:* Yth Environmental Soc Adv; Transition Team Comm; NYSUT, AFT 1972-; NY St Cncl for Soc Stud, Southern Tier Cncl for Soc Stud 1974-; PTA 1975-, Life Mem Awd; *office:* Union Endicott HS 1200 E Main St Endicott NY 13760

MC CULLOUGH, DIANE SUSAN (STONER), Latin Teacher; *b:* Columbia, PA; *m:* Chester C.; *c:* Jeremy, David, Steven; *ed:* Millersville Univ (BS) Scndry Ed Latin 1974; Latin Grad Classes, Ed Courses 24 Credit Hrs; *cr:* Schl Dist of Lancaster 7-12 Latin Tchr 1984-; *ai:* Schl Yrbk, NHS, Jr Class Adv; NEA, PSEA, Lancaster Ed Assn 1986-; Capitol Area Classics Assn 1984-, VP 1993-94, Pres 1994-95; *office:* Mc Caskey HS 445 N Reservoir St Lancaster PA 17602

MCCULLOUGH, GEORGE HEATH, Biology Tchr & Sci Dept Chm; *b:* Toledo, OH; *m:* Kristin Louise Peterson; *c:* Elizabeth, Katherine; *ed:* OH St Univ (BS) Bio 1975; Univ of Toledo (ME) Counseling & Guidance; *cr:* US Navy 2nd Class Quartermaster 1967-71; Davis Boat Works Ships Carpenter 1974-75; Eisenhower Jr HS Sci Tchr 1976-85; Clay HS Bio Tchr & Dept Chair 1985-; *ai:* Girls Bsktbl Coach; Fac Advy Comm; AFT 1976-; Treas of Local 1080; North Cape Yacht Club 1964-, Commodore; First Saint John Luth Church 1985-; US Sailing 1980-, Regnl Trng Officer; Post Grad Masters Wkshps on Environmental Issues; Jenning Scholar; *office:* Clay HS 5665 Seaman St Oregon OH 43616*

MCCULLOUGH, JAMES JOSEPH, Social Studies Teacher; *b:* Philadelphia, PA; *m:* Carole Ann Minissale; *c:* Karen, Suzanne, Kim, Tricia, Jimmy; *ed:* LaSalle Univ (BA) Soc Stud Ed 1975; Trenton St Coll (MED) Pol Sci 1981; *cr:* St Katherine of Siena Soc Stud Tchr 1975-79; St Martin of Tours Soc Stud Tchr 1979-83; Holy Ghost Prep Soc Stud Tchr 1983-; *ai:* CAFE Moderator; Audio-Visual Dir; NEA 1975-; *office:* Holy Ghost Prep Schl 2429 Bristol Pike Bensalem PA 19020

MC CULLOUGH, JOHN ROBERT, Elementary Education Instr; *b:* Franklin, PA; *m:* Leeann Hart; *c:* Corey Benjamin, Shawn William; *ed:* Clarion Univ of PA (BS) Math 1984, (MED) Sci Ed 1986; 38 Credits Elem Ed Doctoral Candidate Indiana Univ of PA; *cr:* Cranberry Area Jr-Sr HS Math, Cmptr Sci Tchr 1984-89; PA STEP, ITEC Tech, Math Coord 1989-93; Clarion Univ Elem Ed Instr 1991-; *ai:* Schlsp Comm; World Wide Web Univ Comm; Tech Comm Chair; Cmptr Lab Coord; Strategic Planning Comm; Tech Comm; Kappa Delta Pi 1994-; Twice Chosen Fac Spon by Stu Aths; 1 Paper for NCTE, AVLA; *office:* Clarion Univ Of PA 113 Stevens Hall Clarion PA 16214

MC CULLOUGH, JOSEPH, Third Grade Teacher; *b:* Somerville, NJ; *m:* Patricia McDonnell; *c:* Bethany, Holly; *ed:* Bloomsburg St Coll (BA) Elem Ed 1974, (MS) Elem Ed 1976; Bucknell Univ Admin Cert; *cr:* Benton Elem Schl 3rd Grd Tchr 1974-; *ai:* Kids Helping Kids Coord; BAEA 1974-, Past Pres; PSEA 1974-; NEA 1974-; YMCA 1992-, Bd; CYE Tchr; *office:* Benton Area Elem Schl R R 2 Park St Benton PA 17814

MC CULLOUGH, MARSHA MC CRAE, Business Education Teacher; *b:* Brooklyn, NY; *c:* Alexis, Robert Jr., Kevin; *ed:* Herbert H. Lehman Coll (BA) Acctng 1981, (MS) Ed 1994; *cr:* Robert Fiance Bus Inst Acctng Tchr 1982-84; A. Phillip Randolph HS Acctng Tchr 1984-87, 1992-; *ai:* Chrldng Team Adv; Delta Pi Epsilon 1994-; *office:* A Philip Randolph HS 135th St & Convent Ave New York NY 10031

MC CULLOUGH, MARY JO MEYER, Former 4th Grade Teacher; *b:* Cincinnati, OH; *m:* Michael; *c:* Michael Patrick, Conor Joseph; *ed:* Univ of Cincinnati (BS) Elem Ed 1988; *cr:* St James Elem Schl 4th Grd Tchr 1988-92; *ai:* 5-7th Grd Girls Vlybl Coach 1988-93; Curr Fair Comm 1990-93; *home:* 6051 LaGrange Ln Cincinnati OH 45239

MC CULLOUGH, PHYLLIS A., Mediation Specialist; *b:* Raleigh, NC; *ed:* Shaw Univ (BA) Ed, Art 1969; Bowie St Univ (MA) Ed 1976; Courses in Conflict Resolution, Peer Mediation, Recognizing Gang Symbols, Gang Violence, Math Inst; *cr:* Nottoway Cty Schl Tchr 1969-70; City of Raleigh Art Dir 1970; Prince Georges Co Pub Schls Elem Tchr, Scnry Tchr, Mediation Specialist 1970-; *ai:* Men of Madison; Stomping Ambassadors of Madison; Yrbk Spon; Peer Mediators, Field Trip, Spec Project Coord; PGCEA 1970-, Fac Rep, Outstdng Svc 1983; MSTA, NEA 1970-; PTA 1970-, Exec Bd Mem, Tchr of Yr; Tchr of Yr Nottoway Cty 1969; Outstdng Elem Tchrs of Amer 1973; PTA Tchr of Yr 1974-77, 1987-88; Ldrshp Awd Environmental Ed 1983; Pan Hellenic Cncl Awd 1991; P G Co Cncl of PTAS 1987; Outstdng Edctr City of Bowie 1987, PG Co Pub Schls 1988; Congressional Awd of Recognition; Senate of Maryland Awd 1987; State of Maryland Govenor's Awd 1987.*

MCCUMBER, LINDA M., Science Teacher; *b:* Plattsburgh, NY; *m:* John R.; *c:* Aryn L., Jerielle N.; *ed:* Northeastern Univ (BS) Hlth Sci 1986; CA St Univ (MA) Hum 1996; CVPH Schl of Radiologic Tech 1980; Meth Hosp of Radiation Therapy Tech 1981; Univ of MA Bio Inst Grad 1995; *cr:* Univ of MD Hosp Sr Radiation Therapist 1988-90; MD Gen Cancer Ctr Chief Radiation Therapist 1990-92; Clinical Radiologists Radiation Oncology Supvr of Radiation Oncology 1992-94; Frederick Cty Bd Ed Middletown High Sci Tchr 1994-; *ai:* Womens Bsktbl Asst Coach at Hood Coll; Field Hockey Head Coach; Publications Review, Cline Good Samaritan Awd & Peer Mediation Comm; Amer Soc of Radiologic Tech 1978-; MD Soc of Radiologic Tech 1988-; NEA & Frederick Cty Tchrs Assn 1994-; MtAiry Yth Ath Assn Soccer & Bsktbl Coach; Linganore Area Yth Ath Assn Soccer & Bsktbl Coach; Middletown Vly Ath League Bsktbl Coach; CVPH Awd for Clinical Excl; Magna Cum Laude Northeastern Univ; Howard Cty PTA VP Waterloo Elem Schl; *office:* Middletown HS 200 High St Middletown MD 21769*

MC CUNE, ALEX, Reading Recovery Teacher; *b:* Dayton, OH; *ed:* Miami Univ (BSEd) Elem Ed 1975, (MED) Remedial, Diagnostic 1976; 45 Addl Hrs Rdng Recovery Trng; *cr:* Mc Guffey Lab Schl Grad Asst, Primary Unit 1975-76; Canterbury Schl Dir of Admissions, Rdng 1976-77; Montgomery Schl 2nd, 4th Grd Tchr 1977-89; Symmes Schl 4th Grd Tchr, Rdng Recovery 1989-; *ai:* Rdng Recovery Cncl 1996; Jennings Scholar; *office:* Symnes Elementary Schl 11820 Enyart Rd Loveland OH 45140

MCCUNE, MARION EVANS, Soc Stud Dept Chair & Tchr; *b:* Utica, NY; *m:* Thomas E.; *c:* Jennifer, John, Jessica; *ed:* Utica Coll (BA) Soc Stud 1989; Elmira Coll (MS) Soc Stud 1994; *cr:* Rome Cath Jr Sr High Soc Stud Tchr 1990-92, Dept Chair 1992-; *ai:* Adv to Key Club; Adv to Stud Cncl; Kappa Delta Pi 1975-; Natl Asso of Stud Actvy Adv; St Leos Ministry 1990-, Family Life Lay Minister; St Leos Parish Cncl 1990-; *home:* 9630 Powell Rd Holland Patent NY 13354

MC CUNE, RHONDA N., English & Art Teacher; *b:* Indianapolis, IN; *m:* Steven W.; *c:* Jason, Matthew; *ed:* Univ of MA (BA) Art 1977; Univ of NH (MAT) Eng Ed 1979; *cr:* Salem HS Eng Tchr 1979-; *ai:* Outgoing Club Adv Diverse Unity; COPE Team Drug Assessment; Cooperating Tchr; Stu Intern; New Tchr Mentor Soc Stud Dept; NEA 1979-; Bd Mem, Comm Chprsn Salem Chptr Dollars for Scholars; *office:* Salem HS 44 Geremonty Dr Salem NH 03079

MC CURDY, INDIA H., English Teacher; *b:* Brooklyn, NY; *ed:* Brooklyn Coll (BA) Linguistic Sci 1985; Univ of NH (MST) Eng 1994; Attnd Northwester Univ Medill Schl of Jrnlsm; *cr:* Benjamin Banneker Schl 1st Grd Tchr 1986; Walt Whitman IS 7th Grd Shop, Eng Tchr 1986-87; Brooklyn Tech HS Eng Tchr 1987-, 12th Grd Jrnslm Tchr 1990-94; *ai:* NY City, Natl Writing Projects 1991-; NCTE 1996; *office:* Brooklyn Tech HS 29 Fort Greene Pl Brooklyn NY 11217

MC CURDY, JANET L. (BIBZA), Speech & Language Therapist; *b:* Natrona Hghts, PA; *m:* Jeffrey L.; *c:* Melissa, Brian; *ed:* Indiana Univ of PA (BS) Speech Pathology, Audiology 1973, (MED) Speech Pathology, Audiology 1980; *cr:* Pittsburgh Diocese Speech, Lang Therapist 1974-75; Allegheny I U Speech, Lang Therapist 1975-78; Easter Seal Soc Speech, Lang Therapist 1978-80; Valley Comm Svcs Speech, Lang Therapist 1980-82; Seneca Vly Schl Dist Speech, Lang Therapist; Highlands Schl Dist Speech, Lang Therapist 1992-; *ai:* Var Swim Meets Announcer; Parent Involvement Prgm, Schlsp Comms; 24 Relay Challenge Team Participants Chprsn; PTO Past Pres; Band Parents Booster; PA Speech & Hearing Assn, Highlands Ed Assn, NEA, PSEA 1974-; Highlands Area Soccer Club 1990-, Registrar, Tops Soccer Prgm Founder 1994; Faith Luth Church 1952-, Chrstn Ed Coord, Ldr of Openings, Day Camp Coord; Pittsburgh Dioceses Conducted Total Comm Wkshp; *home:* 3242 Rambler Dr Natrona Heights PA 15065*

MC CURTY, BRUCE KEVIN, Science Teacher; *b:* Glen Cove, NY; *m:* Lourdes Pagan; *c:* Joshua, Jesus; *ed:* SUNY at Farmingdale (AS) Med Tech 1979; SUNY at Old Westbury (BS) Hlth Admin 1981; Hofstra Univ (MA) Hlth Care Admin 1983, (MS) Scndry Ed 1987; *cr:* Amityville HS Bio Tchr 1987-88; Hofstra Univ Bio, Chem Tchr 1987-; Hempstead HS Bio, Biling Sci Tchr 1988-; *ai:* AFT 1988-; NY St Registry of Med Tech 1979-; Fair Housing Bd 1993-, Bd Trustee; Grad Acad Excl Schlsp; *home:* 6 Burns Ave Glen Cove NY 11542

MC CUTCHEON, CATHERINE JORGENSEN, Physical Education Teacher; *b:* Cleveland, OH; *m:* Ronald; *c:* Sevim Tsardoulias; Karin Pavlovic; *ed:* St Olaf Coll (BA) Hlth, PE 1965; Kent St Univ (MED) Ed 1996; Attnd Portland St Univ, Univ of Oslo, Cleveland St Univ; *cr:* Cleveland City Schls Tchr 1965; Peace Corps Vol 1965-67; Cleveland City Schls Tchr 1968; Lakewood City Schls Tchr 1979-; *ai:* Frgn Exch Club; Ldrshp Comm; NEA, OEA, OPHERD 1965-; Northeast OH Returned Vol Assn 1985-, Sec, Pres; OH Norsemen 1993-, Trustee; Westside Irish Amer Club 1992-; AFS 1972-94; Beyond War Awd; Jennings Scholar; Conf Presenter on Global Ed; *office:* Lakewood HS 14100 Franklin Blvd Lakewood OH 44107

MC CUTCHEON, JEANNINE E., Chemistry Teacher; *b:* Natrona Hghts, PA; *m:* David A.; *ed:* Univ of Pitt at Johnstown (BA) Chem Ed 1988; 25 Addl Credits Physics, Ed; *cr:* United HS Chem, Gen Sci Tchr 1988-89; King George HS Chem, Physics Tchr 1989-90; Deer Lakes HS Chem Tchr 1990-; *ai:* Sci Club Spon; New Tchr Mentor; NEA, PSEA 1990-; *office:* Deer Lakes Jr Sr HS PO Box 10 Russellton PA 15076

MC CUTCHEON, MAUREEN C., Educational Consultant; *b:* Cleveland, OH; *c:* Kelly, J. Casey, Katherine; *ed:* St John Ursuline Coll (BSN) Nrsng 1955; Kent St Univ (MS) Ed 1986; *cr:* Lakewood Schl System Diversified Med Occupations Tchr 1987-93; Careers Consultant; *ai:* Career Ed Dev Prgm Wkshps; Publications: Exploring Health Careers 1993, Care of the Patient with Common Medical-Surgical Conditions 1970, Care of the Maternity Patient with Diana Vietor 1971; Lakewood Schls Ed Excl Awd 1993; Kent St Univ Acad Achvmts 1986; Cleveland Hosp Cncl Achvmt Awd 1979; *home:* 1171 Fernwood Dr Westlake OH 44145

MCDANEL, JOANNE EMILO, Elementary Principal; *b:* Youngstown, OH; *m:* Charles; *c:* Christopher, Diana; *ed:* Youngstown St (BS), (MS); 18 Grad Hrs Spcl Ed; Walsh Coll 3 Hrs Human Relations; *cr:* Youngstown City Elem Tchr 1963-71, LD Tutor 1972-74; Struthers City LD Tutor 1972-74, Elem Tchr 1974-87, Elem Prin 1987-; *ai:* NAESP & OAESA 1987-; IRA 1987-; Poland Band Booster 1985-; Poland All Sports Boosters 1985-; Delta Kappa Gamma 1988-, Various Comms; Struthers Tchr of the Yr; *office:* Struthers City Schls 230 E Manor Ave Struthers OH 44471

MC DANIEL, SUSAN HEARTH, Special Education Teacher; *b:* Berea, OH; *m:* Richard W.; *c:* Scott, Alexander, Andrew, Timothy; *ed:* VA Commonwealth Univ (BS) His, Ed 1973, (MED) Spec Ed 1975; Post Grad Studies Ashland Univ, Bowling Green St Univ, Butler Univ; *cr:* Goochland Jr HS Spec Ed Tchr 1975-80; Eastwood Elem Schl Spec Ed Tchr 1981-82; Prospect Elem Schl Spec Ed Tchr 1982-83; Langston MS Spec Ed Tchr 1984-; *ai:* Cmptr Tech Coord; Odyssey of the Mind Coach; Site Mngmt Comm; Oberline Schls Dist Site Mngmt Comm; NEA, OH Ed Assn, CEC 1981-; Oberlin Ed Assn 1981-, Pres 1993-95, First VP 1995-; Sec, Treas 1991-93; Oberlin Schls Fnd Grant; Howard Hughes Fnd Grant 1995-; *office:* Langston MS 150 N Pleasant St Oberlin OH 44074

MCDERMOND, JAY E., Asst Prof of Chrstn Ministries; *b:* Harrisburg, PA; *m:* Wanda Thuma; *c:* Malcolm I. D., Duncan A. S.; *ed:* Messiah Coll (BA) Bible 1976; Mennonite Biblical Seminary (MDiv) New Testament Stud 1979; Univ of Durham (MLitt) New Testament Stud 1989; Attnd Univ of Tubingen 1984 & Currently Pittsburgh Theological Seminary D Min Prgm; *cr:* Sunderland Polytechnic Part-Time Instr 1984-86; Messiah Coll Asst Prof of New Testament 1987-94; Daystar Univ Visiting Prof & Dept Chair 1992-93; Messiah Coll Asst Prof of Chrstn Ministries 1994-; *ai:* Advising & Stu Dev Comms; Coll Review Bd Chprsn; Campus Ministries Comm; Residence Dir; Adv to Various Classes; Soc of Biblical Lit 1977-; Acad of Homiletics 1994-; Brethren in Christ Historical Soc 1985-; Messiah Coll Curr Grant 1994; Messiah Coll Schlsp Grant 1992; Outstanding Bible Stu Mennonite Biblical Seminary 1979; Various Scholarly Articles, Book Reviews, Popular Articles & Sermons; *office:* Messiah Coll Grantham PA 17027

MC DERMOTT, CYNTHIA B., English & Study Skills Teacher; *b:* Philadelphia, PA; *ed:* La Salle Univ (BA) Comm 1986, (MA) Ed, Eng 1990; *cr:* Annunciation BVM Schl 5th-6th Grd Tchr 1990-91; Thomas MS 7th-8th Grd Rdng Tchr 1991-92; Christiana HS 9th Grd Eng, Jrnlsm Tchr, Newspaper Adv 1992-95; Clearview Regnl Jr HS 7th-8th Grd Stud Skills, Eng Tchr 1995-; *ai:* NEA 1992-; NJEA 1995-; Poetry Pub.*

MC DERMOTT, GEORGE J., AP American History Teacher; *b:* Pottstown, PA; *m:* Judith Baraldi; *c:* Melissa, Sara, Matthew; *ed:* West Chester Univ (BS) Sec Ed, Soc Stud 1974, (MED) Rdng 1978; Northern VA Law Schl 1981-82 27 Quarter Hrs; *cr:* Brookhaven Jr High His Tchr 1974-78; Northly Jr High His Tchr, Rdng Specialist 1978-83; Sun Valley HS His Tchr, Rdng Specialist 1983-86; East HS Amer His Tchr 1986-; *ai:* Frmr Head Boys Bsktbl Coach, Intramural Dir; PSEA, NEA 1974-, Bldg Rep 1977; Article in Coaching Clinic 1974; *home:* 407 Christian Dr Wallingford PA 19086

MC DERMOTT, JAMES E., Eng Tchr & Dept Head; *b:* Worcester, MA; *m:* Margaret E.; *c:* Kelli L., James J.; *ed:* Coll of the Holy Cross (BA) Eng 1969; Clark Univ (MA) Eng 1975, (EDD) Ed 1994; *cr:* Burncoat MS Eng, Rdng, Drama Tchr 1969-78; South High Comm Eng Tchr 1978-, Eng Dept Head 1992-; Worcester Pub Schls K-12 ELA Liaison 1994-; *ai:* Bsbl, Drama Coach; NCTE, MCTE, ASCD; MA St Tchr of Yr 1988; Worcester City Tchr of YR 1987; Cntrl MS Bsbl Coach of Yr 1984-85, 1989; *office:* South High Comm Schl 170 Apricot St Worcester MA 01603*

MCDERMOTT, KATE GLASS, Life Sci Teacher & Team Ldr; *b:* Buffalo, NY; *m:* William John; *c:* Sean P., Patrick K.; *ed:* D'Youville Coll (BS) Elem Ed 1965; SUNY at New Paltz (MS) Bio & Gen Sci 1988; 15 Credit Hrs SUNY at Fredonia; 30 Credit Hrs Coll of New Rochelle; 8 Credit Hrs Long Island Univ & Coll of St Rose; *cr:* Pub Schl #3 1st Grd Tchr 1966-67; Westfield Acad & Cntrl Schl 3rd Grd Tchr 1967-69; Immaculate Conception Schl Comps & 5th-7th Grd Sci Tchr 1978-85; Havestraw MS 7th Grd Life Sci Tchr 1985-; *ai:* HMS Sunshine Fund & Stu Schlsp Fund

1986-; SIPT Comm Mem & Team Ldr 1993-; NRCSD 1993-; NYSUT Effective Tchr Pgm Instr 1992-; NRTA 1985-, Bldg Rep; NYSUT 1986-, Del & Teller 1990, Svc Awd; AFT 1986-, Del; New City Jaycees 1969-, Pres of Local, Svc Awd; Democratic Comm 1970-78; NYS Jaycees 1972-, Spokette Chm, Outstdng 1st Yr St Pt; Stony Pt Fire Commissioner 1974-80; NY Zoological Soc 1978-; NYSUT 1st Pl Awds for Articles Written (Twice); AFT 1st Pl Best News Story & Best Feature Story Awds 1995; *home:* 40 Old Route 9W Tomkins Cove NY 10986*

MC DERMOTT, KATHLEEN, US History Teacher; *b:* Fair Lawn, NJ; *m:* Kevin Walter; *ed:* Univ of MA at Amherst (BA) Pol Sci, His & Ed 1990; Attnd Harvard Inst on Civic Ed; Montclair Univ Working on (MA) Amer His; *cr:* Westwood HS His Tchr 1991-92; West Milford Twp HS His Tchr 1992-; *ai:* JV Tennis & Frosh Sftbl Coach; Asst Girls Track Coach; Model UN, His Club & Unity 2000 Club Adv; NJCHE 1992-, Bd of Dirs; Article Pub; Passaic Cty Prosecutors Grant for Unity 2000 1994-96; *office:* West Milford Twp HS 67 Highlander Dr West Milford NJ 07480*

MC DERMOTT, KIM MARIE, Special Education Teacher; *b:* Newark, NJ; *ed:* Kean Coll NJ (BA) Spec Ed 1984; Post Grad Stud Drug & Alcohol Stud, Soc Work & Early Chldhd Ed; *cr:* AAMH Cnslr 1983-87; Washington Acad Tchr 1987-88; Riverside Schl Tchr 1989-90; Overbrook HS Tchr 1991-; *ai:* Pupil Assistance Comm; AID Awareness Club Adv; Soccer, Chrldng Coach; NEA, NJEA 1990-; NSCAA 1995-; AIDS Coalition of Southern NJ 1991-; Teens Networking Together of Reality House 1994-, Adv; *office:* Overbrook High School 1200 Turnerville Rd Pine Hill NJ 08021

MC DERMOTT, MAUREEN LAWRENCE, English Teacher; *b:* Philadelphia, PA; *ed:* Immaculate (AB) Eng 1974-78; West Chester Univ (MA) Eng 1982-86; Attnd Nordham Univ; *cr:* PA Hs Speech League Dist Chair 1994; Phila Cath Forensic League 1990-92, Pres; Natl Cath Forensic League VP 1992-; *ai:* Speech; Debate; Jr Prom; NHS; NCEA; Keeper of Flame Mont Cty Tchr Awd 1993; Marquis Who's Who 1995; *home:* 370 Old Lincoln Hwy Malvern PA 19355

MC DERMOTT, MICHAEL STEPHEN, Seventh & Eighth Grade Teacher; *b:* Euclid, OH; *ed:* Concordia Tchrs Coll (BSEd) Elem Ed 1977; *cr:* St Paul's Luth Church & Schl Fifth Grd Tchr, Band Dir 1977-86; West Park Luth Schl Fifth-Eighth Grd Tchr, Music Dir 1986-; *ai:* 2-8 Grd Marching Band Dir; Music Dir Write Two Schl Prgms; Luth Ed Assn 1977-; Tchr of Week TV Channel 3 Interview 1991; Outstdng Young Men of Amer 1983; *home:* 12520 Edgewater Dr Apt 1602 Lakewood OH 44107

MC DERMOTT, THOMAS EDWARD, Health Teacher; *b:* Bangor, ME; *m:* Kathleen Perry; *c:* Corrie, Tracy; *ed:* Univ of MA at Amherst (BA) Hlth, PE 1976; Bridgewater St (MS) Hlth Ed; *cr:* Fall River Schl Sub Tchr 1976-77; Somerset Schl Sub Tchr 1977-78; Dartmouth HS Hlth Tchr 1978-; *ai:* Head Ftbl & Bsbl Coaches; Asst Drama Adv; NEA, MTA 1978-79; Natl Ftbl Coaches Assn 1986-; MA Bsbl Coaches Assn, Amer Bsbl Coaches Assn 1984-; *office:* Dartmouth HS 366 Slocum Rd North Dartmouth MA 02747*

MCDEVITT, JANE F., 3rd Grade Teacher; *b:* Philadelphia, PA; *ed:* West Chester Univ (BS) Ed 1968; Drexel Univ (MS) Lib Sci 1972; 45 Credit Hrs Post Grad Stud in Elem Ed; *cr:* Marple Newton Schl Dist Tchr 27 Yrs, Elem Librn 1 Yr; *ai:* Various Comms; Mentor; NEA 1968-; PSEA 1968-; Alpha Delta Kappa 1995-.

MC DEVITT, MEG CALLAHAN, Mathematics Teacher; *b:* Delaware County, PA; *m:* Michael; *ed:* Villanora Univ (BSME) Mechanical Engrng 1986; Penn St Univ (MS) Trng, Instrl Dev; Scndry Math Cert 1989; 15 Credit Hrs; *cr:* Boeing Helicopter Co Tool, Production Planning Engr 1986-87; Springfield Schl Math Tchr 1989-90; Peco Energy Co Nuclear Division Trnr 1990-93; Springfield Schl Math Tchr 1993-; *ai:* NEA, PSEA 1993-; *office:* Springfield HS 49 W Leamy Ave Springfield PA 19064

MCDIVITT, GREGORY THRASHER, Health & Physical Ed Teacher; *b:* Ravenna, OH; *m:* Susan Carol Greene; *c:* Amy Jo, Julie Beth, Gregory Todd; *ed:* OH Univ (BA) PE & Hlth 1970, (MS) PE & Ed Admin 1971; *cr:* CNA ins Co Mrktg 1979-81; Hartford Ins Group Mrktg 1981-83; Insurance Affiliates Account Exec 1983-85; Cuyahoga Vly Chrstn Acad PE & Hlth Tchr 1985-; *ai:* Head Bsktbl Coach; *office:* Cuyahoga Valley Chrstn Acad 4687 Wyoga Lake Rd Cuyahoga Falls OH 44224

MCDONALD, AMY E., High School Science Teacher; *b:* Philadelphia, PA; *m:* Thomas F.; *ed:* St Joseph's Univ (BS) Physics 1990; Univ of PA Post-Grad Bio; Holy Family Coll Post-Grad Bio & Chem; Pursuing Physics Grad Degree & Tchng Cert; *cr:* Univ of PA Rsrcher 1990-92; Archbishop Prendergast HS Sci Tchr 1993-; *ai:* Schl Newspaper Moderator; Environmental Club Moderator; ACT 1993-; NCEA 1993-; Soc of Physics Tchrs 1996-; Article Pub on Orthopaedic Rsrch 1991; *office:* Archbishop Prendergast HS 401 N Lansdowne Ave Drexel Hill PA 19026

MC DONALD, ANN BRUBAKER, 6th-8th Grade Teacher; *b:* New York, NY; *m:* John J.; *c:* John F., Peter B., Kathryn Ann; *ed:* Mary Mount Coll at Tarrytown (BA) Eng, Ed, Psych 1960; CCNY 18 Credits Ed 1962-65; Fairfield Univ 9 Credits Guid, Cnslng 1980-82; *cr:* Rolando Park Schl 2nd Grd Tchr 1960-61; Daniel Webster Schl 2nd-3rd Grd Tchr 1961-63; Our Lady of Fatima Schl 6-8th Grd Tchr 1982-; *ai:* Stu Cncl, Yrbk Moderator; Adv Publicity; Elem Stu Asst Team; Jr Achvmt; NCEA 1982-; Natl Geographic Alliance, ATOMIC Math 1988-; Natl Assn of Stu Act Advs 1990-; Lacrosse Assn 1982-94; Wilton Family Y 1988-92, Bd of Dirs; Democratic Town Comm 1990-92; *office:* Our Lady Of Fatima Schl 225 Danbury Rd Wilton CT 06897

MC DONALD, CAROL CONKLE, Accounting & Computer Teacher; *b:* Akron, OH; *m:* Gary Brian; *ed:* Kent St Univ (BS) Comprehensive Bus Ed 1965; 40 Hrs in Drug Cnslng, Awareness; 20 Hrs in Vo-Tech Ed; *cr:* Revere HS Bus Tchr 1965; Cuyahoga Falls HS Bus Tchr, Bus Dept Chprsn 1965-; *ai:* Chrldng Spon; Drug Prgm Facilitator; NEA, OEA, CFEA 1965-; Jr League 1965-; CARE 1982-; Golden Apple Awd 1994; *office:* Cuyahoga Falls HS 2300 4th St Cuyahoga Falls OH 44221

MCDONALD, CHERYL ANN, Marine Biology Instructor; *b:* Newark, NJ; *ed:* Rutgers St Univ (BA) Biological Scis 1982; Cook Coll NJ Tchng Cert; *cr:* NJ Marine Scis Consortium Asst Station Biologist 1983; Marine Acad of Sci & Tech Marine Bio Instr 1983-; Natl Park Svc Ranger 1984-; *ai:* NEA 1983-; NJEA 1983-, Pres & Bldg Rep; Tchr of Yr 1992; Whos Who 1992; *office:* Marine Acad Of Sci & Tech Bldg 305 Sandy Hook NJ 07732

MCDONALD, CYNTHIA KUTHAN, Business Education Teacher; *b:* Akron, OH; *m:* John B.; *c:* Meghan, Molly, Michelle; *ed:* Univ of Akron (AAS) Secretarial Sci 1975, (BS) Bus Ed 1989; Cmptr Data Processing Cert; *cr:* Portage Lakes Career Ctr Bus Ed Instr 1977-89; Coventry HS Bus Ed Tchr & Cmptr Coord 1989-; *ai:* Jr Class Adv; Fac Cncl; OH Bus Tchrs Assn & Akron Area Bus Tchrs Assn 10 Yrs; OH Soc for Tech Ed, Coventry Ed Assn, OH Ed Assn & NEA 5 Yrs; TWIGS Childrens Hosp 1 Yr; Manchester PTA 2 Yrs, Sec; *office:* Coventry HS 3257 Cormany Rd Akron OH 44319

MCDONALD, DIANE MURPHY, Tchr of Gifted & Talented; *b:* Bangor, ME; *m:* Stephen Thomas; *c:* William, Stephen, John, Michael; *ed:* St Joseph Coll (BA) Child Stud 1966; Brooklyn Coll (MS) Early Chldhd Ed 1971; Attnd Long Island Univ, Fordham Univ; *cr:* PS 133 Kndgtn Tchr 1966-69; PS 69 3rd & 4th Grd Tchr 1985-; *ai:* Math Curr Comm; Grd Ldr 3 Yrs; Swimming Ofcl; PSAL HS Girls; SI Rdng Assn 1985-; NCTM 1995-; Wild Acre Lakes Swim Team Bd 1982-, Pres; Com Schl Dist 31 QUIPP Newsletter; Tchng Math Through Lit Presenter; Rdng Assn Symposium 1995; *office:* PS 69 Daniel Tompkins 144 Keating Pl Staten Island NY 10314

MCDONALD, GREGORY SCOTT, Mathematics Teacher; *b:* Philadelphia, PA; *m:* Sandra Lauren Willis; *c:* John Paul; *ed:* William Paterson Coll (SEC) Math 1987; Montclair St Univ MED Ed 1997; *cr:* Manchester Regnl Tchr 1983; Don Bosco Prep Tchr & Coach 1984-89; Northern Highlands Tchr & Coach 1989-; *ai:* Head Girls Soccer, Asst Wrestling & Asst Bsbl Coach; CORE Team Chair; Highlands Ldrshp Team Mem; NJEA 1989-; NHEA 1989-, Exec Bd; *office:* Northern Highlands Reg HS Hillside Ave Allendale NJ 07401

MC DONALD, JACQUELINE ANN, French Teacher; *b:* Pittsburgh, PA; *ed:* Chatham Coll (BA) Fr, Scndry Ed 1986; Bryn Mawr Coll (MA) Fr Lit 1988; *cr:* Dorseyville Jr HS Fr Tchr 8th Grd 1990-91; Mars Area HS Fr Tchr 9th-12th Grd 1990-91; Lang Ctr ESL, Fr Tchr 1991-92; Mount Alvernia HS Fr, Italian Tchr 9th-12th Grd 1992-; *ai:* Fr Club, NHS Spon; AATF 1988-; Alliance Francaise 1992-; *office:* Mt Alvernia HS 146 Hawthorne Rd Pittsburgh PA 15209

MC DONALD, JAMES ANTHONY, Professor of Mathmatics; *b:* Springfield, MA; *m:* Diane E.; *c:* Megan, Brian; *ed:* Univ of MA (BS) Math 1967; Amer Intnl Coll (MA) Ed, Physics 1969; 25 Credit Hrs Univ of MA, Amer Intnl Coll, Advanced Math, Statistics, Cmptrs; *cr:* Springfield Tech Comm Coll Prof of Math 1968-; Western New England Coll Lecturer in Math 1981-; Spring Coll Adj Prof of Math 1991-; *ai:* Math Dept Chair 1987-90; Title III Math Coord 1987-90; Div of Continuing Ed Math Coord 1984-; Math Rep To Tech Prep Consortium; Nynex New England Math Coord; Assessment Comm; Offer Cmptr Wkshps for HS Tchrs; Amer Math Assn 1980-; NEA, MTA 1976-; AMATYC 1996; New England Math Assn of Tow Yr Colls 1996; Northern Educl Svc 1969-70; Pres Awd for Outstdng Svc 1992; Outstdng Fac Mem Awd 1992; Math, Sci Ed 1989-90; *home:* 1414 Parker St Springfield MA 01129*

MC DONALD, JAMES THOMAS, US History Teacher; *b:* Manhattan, NY; *m:* Patricia A.; *c:* Michele, Kelly Morra, Joseph; *ed:* Fordham Univ (BS) His 1963; Montclair St Univ (MA) Soc Sci 1971; Addl 30 Grad Hrs Educl Admin, Supervision; *cr:* Queen of Peace HS Soc Stud Tchr 1963-65; Rosell Park HS Soc Stud Chprsn 1965-84, Asst Prin 1984-91; Immaculata HS Soc Stud Tchr 1991-93; Bishop Stang HS Soc Stud Tchr 1993-; *ai:* Debate Coach; MA Cncl of Soc Stud 1994-; NASSP 1986-; NCEA 1994-; Knights of Columbus 1958-; Holy Name Soc 1968-, Pres; Fulbright Grant Rsrch Africa 1979; Freedom Fnd Grant 1981-; Tchr of Yr 1978; *office:* Bishop Stang HS 500 Slocum Rd North Dartmouth MA 02747

MC DONALD, JANE RUSSELL, Mathematics Teacher; *b:* Forest Hills, NY; *c:* Christopher; *ed:* Univ of NH (BA) Math 1965; Cambridge Coll (MS) Ed 1991; *cr:* Lynnfield Jr HS Math Tchr 1967-71; Dunn MS Math Tchr 1985-; *ai:* NEA, DTA 1985-; *home:* 126 Merrimac St Unit 34 Newburyport MA 01950

MC DONALD, JOHN WILLIAM, Dean of Students; *b:* Bath, NY; *m:* Cindy Jane Richards; *c:* Jessica; *ed:* Lycoming Coll (BA) Math 1972; Magna Cum Laude; 30 Addl Post Grad Credits; *cr:* Hollidaysburg Area Jr HS Math Tchr 1972-93, Dean of Stdnts 1993-94; *ai:* Bsbl Head Coach; Stu Asst Prgm; PASAP & NASSAD 1988-; NCTM 1972-.

MC DONALD, MARY KATHRYNE, German Teacher; *b:* Washington, DC; *ed:* Western MD Coll (BA) Ger 1983; 36 Credit Hrs Post Grad Stud in Dimensions of Learning, Multiple Intelligences, Cooperative Learning, Discipline with Dignity, PLS, Germanic Stud; *cr:* Frederick Co Pub Schls Frgn Lang Tchr 1983-88; Glen Construction Co Inc Admin Asst 1988-91; Frederick Co Pub Schls Ger Tchr 1991-; *ai:* Ger Club Adv; Cadre Team 1995-; Frgn Exch Stdnts Mentor; Phi Beta Kappa 1983-; Lambda Iota Tau 1981-; Christmas in April Mont Co 1990-, Bd of Dirs, Sec, Project Day Vol; Natl Endowment for Hum Grant 1995; Nom Tchr of Yr Frederick Co 1995; *office:* Governor Thomas Johnson HS 1501 N Market St Frederick MD 21701*

MCDONALD, MICHELE, Special Education Teacher; *b:* Altoona, PA; *m:* Kevin; *ed:* Bloomsburg Univ (BS) Spcl Ed K-12th 1985, (MS) Mental Retardation 1986; *cr:* NJ-ARC Group Home Asst Mgr 1987; MCARP, NJ-ARC Camp Dir 1988-; Manchester Regnl HS Spcl Ed Tchr 1986-; *ai:* Class of 1998 Adv; Girls JV Bsktbl Asst Coach 1988-91; Mid Sts Comm; Lib Comm; Spcl Ed Curr Comm; NJEA 1986-; MEA 1986-.

MCDONALD, NANCY E., AP Amer & European His Tchr; *b:* Scranton, PA; *ed:* Marywood Coll (BA) His 1962, (MA) His 1967; 21 Post Grad Hrs in Applied Voice Music; *cr:* West Scranton HS Tchr 34 Yrs; *ai:* Scranton Fed of Tchrs 1962-, 2nd VP & Exec Comm; AFT & PAFT 1962-, Negotiating Comm; Phi Alpha Theta 1965-; Lackawanna Historical Soc 1962-; St Mary-Mt Carmel Cantor & Choir 1970-93; Marywood Alumna Soc; Singers Guild of Scranton 1974-; Cathedral Cantor & Choir 1993-; PA Prof Stans & Practices Comm Appointed by Gov Thornburgh 5 Yrs; Book: If You Can Play Scranton; Finalist PA Tchr of Yr 1983.

MC DONALD, STUART CAMERON, Earth Science Teacher; *b:* Rochester, NY; *m:* Lisa Carr Buckshaw; *ed:* SUNY Coll of Environmental Sci & Forestry at Syracuse (BS) Resources Mngmt 1989; SUNY at Brockport (MS) Scndry Sci Ed 1993; *cr:* Penfield Cntrl Schl Dist Earth Sci Tchr 1990-; *ai:* HS Shared Decision Making Team; Class Adv; Scheduling, Performance Stands Comm; Natural Helpers; NYSUT, Penfield Ed Assn, Sci Tchrs Assn NY St 1990-; Assn of Adirondack Scout Camps 1995-; *office:* Penfield HS 25 High School Dr Penfield NY 14526

MCDONALD, VICTORIA CORINE, Latin Teacher; *b:* Scranton, PA; *c:* Alexandra Terranella, Neil Neyman; *ed:* Marywood Coll (BA) Comprehensive Eng & Latin 1967, (MS) Classics Ed 1973; Harvard Writing Inst at Keystone Writing in Process; PA Writing Assessment Evaluator & Scorer 2 Yrs; Collins Writing Inst; *cr:* South Scranton Jr HS Rdng & Eng Tchr 1968-74; East Scranton Jr HS Rdng & Eng Tchr 1974-79; Scranton Tech HS Eng Tchr 1979-88; Scranton Cntrl HS Eng, Rdng & Latin Tchr 1988-90; Scranton HS SAT Preparatory, Eng, Jrnlsm & Latin Tchr 1990-; *ai:* Latin Club; Jr Classical League; NEA 1981-; Amer Classical League 1993-; Friends of Scranton Pub Lib 1979-85, VP & Pres; Saint Pauls Prison Guild 1984-85, Publicity Dir, Creative Writing Tchr at Local Prison; Harvard Writing Inst Grant; Scranton HS Newspaper Moderator 1990-93; *office:* Scranton HS 723 Adams Ave Scranton PA 18510*

MCDONALD, VIRGINIA FIORITO, Teacher of Gifted & Talented; *b:* Pittsburgh, PA; *c:* Kristin, Sean; *ed:* Trenton St Coll (BS) Elem Ed & Early Chldhd 1983; Kean Coll (MS) Mastery of Tchng 1996; *cr:* Marlboro Elem Schl Tchr 1983-; *ai:* KAPOW Environment Group Adv; Kappa Delta Pi 1982-; NEA 1983-; *office:* Marlboro Elem Schl 100 School Rd W Marlboro NJ 07746

MC DONNELL, DARBY UNGER, 8th Grade Science Teacher; *b:* Danville, PA; *m:* Thomas A.; *ed:* Bloomsburg Univ (BS) Earth, Environmental Sci 1983; 24 Addl Credits Elem Ed; *cr:* Mifflinburg Area Schl Dist Sci Tchr 1983-89; Merck Pharmaceuticals Biotech Lab Technician 1992; Danville Area Schl Dist Sci Tchr 1989-; *ai:* Sci Olympiad Co-Coach; Prof Dev Strategic Planning Comm; NEA, PSEA 1983-; Danville Area EA 1989-, Sec, Comm Chprsn; Susquehanna Univ Holocaust Consortium 1993-; First Tchr Intern Biotechnology, Microbiology at Merck & Co Pharmaceuticals; *office:* Danville MS 120 Northumberland St Danville PA 17821

MC DONNELL, MARY EASTMAN, Lang Arts & Soc Stud Tc
Chicago, IL; *m:* William Joseph; *c:* Sean F., Brendan D.; *ed:* Loyola
(BA) Sociology 1969; St Univ of NY at Cortland (MSEd) Rdng 1995;
of IL at Chicago 16 QH Math Ed 1975; *cr:* Peace Corps Eng Tchr 19
Transfiguration 7-8 Lang Arts, Soc Stud Tchr 1970-77; St Mary's S
Grd Lang Arts, Soc Sci Tchr 1985-95; *ai:* Lang Arts, Soc Stud Ch
League 1978-85; Mary Free Bed Guild, Grand Rapids Art Mu
1978-85 Bd of Dir; ABC Inc 1986-, Bd of Dir; Kirkland Art Ctr 199
of Dir; Tchr of Yr Diocese of Syracuse 1994; NSF Schlsp 1975; *offi*
Mary's Schl 5 Prospect St Clinton NY 13323*

MC DONNELL, THOMAS ALLEN, History Teacher; *b:* Philade
PA; *m:* Darbara Unger; *ed:* Bloomsburg St Coll (BSEd) Soc Stud
(MEd) His, Ed 1981; SUPV Ed 1982; *cr:* Annville Cleona Schls SS
1977-80; Bloomsburg Univ Instr 1983; Berwick Area Schls SS
1980-89, Staff Dev Facilitator 1987-90, HS His Tchr 1989-
Cooperating Tchr Bloomsburg Univ & King's Coll; Mentor Tchr;
PSEA 1977-; BAEA 1980-, Chief Negotiator, Pres; Columbia Monto
St Club 1992-, Bd; Article Pub; *office:* Berwick Area HS 1100 Fowle
Berwick PA 18603*

MCDONOUGH, CAROLE FADDEN, English Teacher; *b:* Lowell,
m: Brian L.; *c:* Geoffrey E., Gregory S.; *ed:* Univ of MA Lowell (BA
1963; Salem St Coll (MA) Eng 1974; CAGS; *cr:* Lowell HS Eng
1963-95; *ai:* MFT 1963-; AFT 1963-; Article Pub in Eng Journal;
61 Van Greenby Rd Lowell MA 01851

MC DONOUGH, JAMES RICHARD, English Teacher; *b:* New
NY; *m:* Mary Elizabeth Molesworth; *c:* Anne, Jesse Molesworth; *ed:*
of MD (BA) Eng 1976, (BA) Ed 1978; Western MD Coll (MLA) Li
Arts 1990;Ph.D. Eng; *cr:* Frederick HS Eng Tchr 1978-87; Gov Th
Johnson HS Eng Tchr 1987-; *ai:* Speech, Debate Dir; Natl Fed of Ins
Speech & Debate 1990-; Ray A. Kroc Tchr Achvmt Mc Donald's
Chamber of Comm Tchr Recog Awd 1995; *home:* 802 N Mark
Frederick MD 21701*

MC DONOUGH, JOANN M., Teacher of Gifted & Talented; *b:* J
City, NJ; *m:* Thomas; *c:* Tara, Thomas-Jon; *ed:* William Paterson Coll
Elem Ed 1971; *cr:* West NY Schl System 1-8 Gifted & Talented
1971-; *ai:* Cheerleading, Bstkbl Coach Horace Mann Schl;
Improvement Team Chprsn; NJEA 1971-; North Bergen Bsbl Ladies
1984-, Sec, Plack; *office:* Public Schl #4 317 66th St West New Yo
07093*

MCDONOUGH, JOSEPH PETER, Mathematics Teacher; *b:* Broo
NY; *m:* Maryellen; *c:* Thomas, Maeve; *ed:* Manhattan Coll (BS)
1968; Hofstra Univ (MA) Scndry Ed 1974; 45 Credits; *cr:* Peace
Nepal 1969-71; Sewanhaka Dist Tchr 1971-; *ai:* Math Team; SFT
NCTM 1990-; CYO 1995-; Fullbright Exch Tchr; Tchr of the Yr;
Elmont Memorial HS 555 Ridge Rd Elmont NY 11003*

MC DONOUGH, LYNETTE CAFARO, History & Women's St
Tchr; *b:* Glen Cove, NY; *ed:* Lehigh Univ (BA) Govt 1990; Univ
(MA) Pol & Feminist Philosophy 1991; 24 Credit Hrs PHD Pol Philos
Fordham Univ; *cr:* Preston HS Tchr 1993-; *ai:* NHS Tutoring; Prom C
Sr Class Adv; Natl Endowment for Hum 1995; *office:* Preston HS
Schurz Ave Bronx NY 10465*

MCDONOUGH, PAUL FRANCIS, Social Sci Tchr & Dept Hea
Boston, MA; *m:* Ann Marie Doherly; *c:* Maureen, Meghan; *ed:* St Fr
Coll (BA) His & Sociology 1973; Univ of Southern ME (MS) Scnd
1974, (MS) Schl Admin 1993; *cr:* St Andres Schl Soc Stud Tchr 197
Kennebunk HS Soc Stud Tchr 1979-80; Biddeford HS Soc Stud
1980-; *ai:* Soc Sci Dept Head; Boys Bsktbl Head Coach; Bidd
Historical Soc 1992-; Local His & Ath Awd Banquets Pub Spe
Engagements; *office:* Biddeford HS Maplewood Ave Biddeford ME

MCDONOUGH, SHAWN P., Computer Educator; *b:* Metheun, MA
Catherine Cronin; *c:* Patrick, Kelsie; *ed:* Saint Amelm Coll (BA) Bu
Math, Cmptr 1983; 15 Addl Hrs; Youth Minister Cert; *cr:* Raymon
Cmptr Educator 13 Yrs; *ai:* Class Adv Frosh, Soph, Jr, Sr 8 Yrs; Stdnt
Adv 2 Yrs; Yrbk Adv 4 Yrs; NEA 1983-; NHSTE 1990-; Scndry
Accreditation; Saint Joseph Parish 1987-, Cncl, Youth Minister, Ea
Cross; Raymond HS Tchr of Yr; Desktop Publishing Awd 1993
Co-Chr Accreditation Comm; *office:* Raymond HS 45 Harriman Hi
Raymond NH 03077*

MC DONOUGH, SUSAN, English Teacher; *b:* Wakefield, MA; *m:*
Brian; *ed:* Salem St Coll (BA) Eng 1971, (MA) Eng 1980; 30 Addl C
Hrs; *cr:* Nashua Pub Schls Eng Tchr 1971-73; Wakefield Pub Schls
Tchr 1976-; *ai:* Chapter Amnesty Intnl Adv; Co-Adv Soc Awareness
Study Skills Comm; Fac Cncl; Mntr Coord; Lynnfield HS Cncl Mem;
Univ Cooperating Tchr; Wakefield Tchrs Assn 1976-; NEA & MCTE
Sister Org 1986-; Founding Fellow John F. Kennedy Lib; Presenter
Conf MA Cncl for Exceptional Children 1993; *office:* Wakefield H
Farm St Wakefield MA 01880

MC DONOUGH, THERESA CANDLEORO, Fifth Grade Teache
Jersey City, NJ; *m:* Anthony; *c:* Edward Joseph; *ed:* Jersey City Tchrs
(BA) Kndgtn, Primary 1961; Addl Hrs Educl Psych, Rdng Fundamen
ai: PTA Schlsp Comm 8 Yrs; George Bate Fund for Stu Loans 6 Yrs;
Assn 1961-; Ridgefield Park Ed Assn 1966-, Pride Comm 1995; Pla
Bd 1988-, Sec; Tchr of Yr Grant 1986; *home:* 359 Teaneck Rd Ridge
Park NJ 07660

MC DOUGAL, ALISON LANE, Spanish Teacher; *b:* Potsdam, NY
Joshua Distenfeld; *ed:* SUNY at Cortland (BA) Span, Scndry Ed
Nazareth Coll (MS) Scndry Ed 1995; Attnd Univ of Salamanca Spain
Geneva City Schl Dist 7-8th Grd Span Tchr 1992-; *ai:* Intnl, Span
Adv; Curr, Scheduling, Prin Liason Comm; Tchrs Assn Union Rep; Ge
Tchrs Assn 1992-, Rep; NY St Assn of Frgn Lang Tchrs, Frgn Lang
of Cntrl NY 1988-; WAFFLE 1992-; *office:* Geneva MS 63 Pulten
Geneva NY 14456*

MCDOUGAL, DIANE BATEMAN, Asst Professor of Nursing; *b:* Sh
PA; *m:* Robert; *ed:* Penn St Univ (BSN) Nrsng 1970; Univ of Pitts
(MNEd) Nrsng Ed 1977; Presbyn-Univ Hosp Diploma Nrsng 1965
Magee-Womens Hosp Staff Nurse 1965-70; Univ of Pittsburgh
1970-72; Presbyn-Univ Hosp Clinical Specialist 1972-79; Mercy
Asst Exec Dir 1979-82; Youngstown St Univ Asst Prof 1982-; *ai:*
Chptr of Sigma Theta Tau Intnl Pres; Eta Chptr of Sigma Theta Tau 19
NEA 1982-; OEA 1982-; Amer Assn Critical Care Nurses
Presbyn-Univ Hosp Nrsng Alumnae 1970-, Bd of Dir; Colleg Club 19
office: Youngstown St Univ 410 Wick Ave Youngstown OH 44555*

MC DOUGALD-CAMPBELL, RITA A., English Teacher; *b:* Coates
PA; *m:* Leonard R.; *c:* Leonard; *ed:* Boston Univ (BS) Pub Relations
(EDM) System Dev, Adaptation 1978; Southern Ct St Univ Eng Cert
Ed 1989; Univ of Lancaster Bronte Sisters Seminar; Inst Tchng, Learn
CT Hum Cncl Seminars Wesleyan Univ 1993-95; CT Lit Univ at
Haven 1995; *cr:* Boston Univ Asst Dir Admissn 1975-76, Acad
1976-78; Univ of Bridgeport Dir, Transfer Admissions 1979-80; S
Cntrl Comm Coll Eng Instr 1989-90; Wilbur Cross HS Eng Tchr 1990-
New Have City-Wide Eng curr Dev Comm; Trumbull Lang Arts Curr A
Bd; AFT, CCTE, NCTE 1990-; Trumbull Newcomers 1994-, Theatre C
Article CCTE Journal 1996; *office:* Wilbur Cross HS 181 Mitchell Dr
Haven CT 06511*

DOUGALL, DUNCAN C., Assoc Professor of Business; *b:* Chelsea, *m:* Shirley Kimball; *c:* Christal A., Brian D., Jamie K., Jesse S., Piper lexander B.; *ed:* Amherst Coll (BA) Fine Arts 1965; Harvard (MBA) (DBA) Operations Mngmt 1986; *cr:* Gen Motors Materials Foreman -68; Rockwell Intnl Plant Mgr, Product Mgr 1971-75; Plymouth St Asst Prof 1976-80, Assoc Prof 1992-; Boston Univ Assoc Prof -88; Rochester Shoe Tree Pres 1988-92; *ai:* Small Bus Inst Dir; OMA; C; Campton Historical Soc 1988-, Bd Mem; Boston Univ Schl of nt Broderick Prize for Distinguished Tchng 1987; *office:* Plymouth Coll Soc Sci Dept Hyde 109 Plymouth NH 03264*

DOUGLE, SHARON, 7th-8th Grd Math Teacher; *m:* Wayne; *ed:* Y at Old Westbury (BA) Math Ed; C. W. Post Long Island Univ (MS) *i:* Stu Cncl Adv; AFT, UFT 1991-; NCTM 1994-.

DOWELL, DAVID W., MS English & Soc Studies Tchr; *b:* Sandusky, *m:* Deborah D.; *c:* Christine, Chad; *ed:* Bowling Green St Univ (BS) Ed 1973, (MS) Educl Admin 1980; 25 Hrs Gifted Ed, Cooperative ning, Elem Sci & Soc Stud at Univ of Toledo, Ashland Univ, Bowling n St Univ, Baldwin-Wallace Coll; *cr:* Margaretta Local Schls Unit C 1973-74; Perkins Schls 3, 6 Grd Tchr 1974-85, MS Eng & Soc Stud 1986-; *ai:* Adv Stu Cncl, Lang Arts Team, Meeting of Minds Teams; , OEA, PEA 1974- Bldg Rep 1977-80; Phi Delta Kappa 1981-, Pres -93; OH Gifted Children Assn 1986-; Sandusky Elks #285 1978-, nist; Martha Holding Jennings Fnd Scholar 1991-92; *office:* Perkins 700 South Ave Sandusky OH 44870*

DOWELL, ROBIN LYNN (DORSEY), Computer & Business her; *b:* Cumberland, MD; *m:* Michael L.; *c:* Cameron Fraley, Tyler y; *ed:* Potomac St Coll (AAS) Exec Sec Sci 1983; Fairmont St Coll Bus Ed 1984; WV Univ (MS) Ed 1986; Cert Admin, Supervision sburg St Univ; Addl Courses Cert Early Chldhd Ed; *cr:* FCI gantown Kennedy Ctr Bus Tchr 1985-86; Allegany Cty Ctr for Career ch Ed Data Processing Tchr 1986-95; Potomac St Coll Part-time Bus 1986-; Westmar HS Cmptr, Bus Tchr 1995-; *ai:* Stdnts Helping Other le Adv; FBLA Adv 9 Yrs; Various Acad, Soc Comms; MSTA, NEA -; Xi Gamma Tau 1987-, Sec, Soc Chprsn, Svc Chprsn, Girl of Yr; mption Parish Ladies Guild 1996-; Named Allegany Cty Career Ctrs of Yr; *home:* 1465 Terri St Keyser WV 26726

DOWELL, STEPHEN A., In School Suspension Supvr; *b:* Drexel PA; *m:* Debra A.; *c:* Casey, Kevin; *ed:* Millersville Univ (BS) Scndry 972; Post-Grad Millersville, Shippensburg, Temple, Penn St; *cr:* hester Jr HS Eng Tchr 1972-73; Lower Paxton Jr HS Eng Tchr -79; Linglestown Jr HS Eng Tchr 1979-90, In Schl Suspen Super -; *ai:* Stock Market Game, Jr Natl Honor Soc Adv; NEA 1972-; ees Outstanding Young Educator Awd; NIE Schslp, Grant; *office:* lestown Jr HS 1200 N Mountain Rd Harrisburg PA 17112*

EACHERN, JOAN E., Second Grade Teacher; *b:* Wayburn, MA; *m:* ert; *ed:* 15 Grad Credit Hrs; *cr:* Rel Order Tchr 4 Yrs; *ai:* NTA 1969-; 1969; *office:* Shamrock Mem Elem Schl Eastern Ave Woburn MA 1

ELFISH, DONALD ALBERT, Geography & US History Teacher; *b:* berland, MD; *ed:* Frostburg St Coll (BS) Soc Sci, Scndry Ed 1973, Ed Scndry Admin 1981; *cr:* Gwynn Park MS Seventh Grd Geog Tchr -87; Lord Baltimore MS Seventh Grd Geog, Eighth Grd US His Tchr -; *ai:* FAC; Schl Evaluation, Magnet Uniform, Chose Current Prin, i Cultural Comms; Dept Chair Soc Stud; NEA, MSTA, PGCEA 1973-; : 1300 Army Navy Dr Apt 930 Arlington VA 22202*

ELFISH, SHAWNEE LEE, Social Studies Teacher; *b:* Cumberland, *m:* Gregory; *c:* Meagan; *ed:* Allegany Comm Coll (AA) Gen Stud ; Frostburg St Univ (BS) Scndry Soc Stud 1991, (MS) Ed Guid & ng 1995; *cr:* ACBOE Tchr Asst 1989-91; Allegany Comm Coll Tech Coord 1991-93; Oldtown Schl Tchr 1993-; *ai:* Bowling Coach, Ski Adv; Prom Adv; NEA 1991-; Phi Delta Kappa 1995-; Thrasher iage Museum 1995-; Tchr of the Yr Nominee 1993; Ray A Kroc Awd ; *office:* Oldtown HS Main St Oldtown MD 21555

ELHANEY, BARBARA GANGONE, Physical Education Teacher; *b:* burgh, PA; *m:* James G. Jr.; *c:* James Joseph, Sean Patrick; *ed:* pery Rock Univ (BSEd) Hlth & PE 1963; *cr:* Charties Valley Schl Dist & PE Tchr 1963-64; Butler Area Schl Dist Hlth, PE & Swim Tchr -; *ai:* Club Adv; Intramural Bowling; Water Aerobics for Schl Dist loyees Tchr; Strategic Planning Comm Mem; BEA, PSEA, NEA -; Jr Womens Club of Butler 1972-78, Ways & Means Co Chm; Spec npics Aquatics; Coach of Yr; SRU Cooperating Tchrs Wkshp Cert; *e:* Butler Area Schl Dist 151 Fairground Hill Rd Butler PA 16001*

ELHANEY, GAYLE GRIM, 5th Grade Elementary Teacher; *b:* hington, PA; *m:* Harry B.; *c:* Michael, Peggy Baker, Sue Sedlitsky; *ed:* Univ of PA (BS) Elem Ed 1971; Addl Cert K-12 Grd Lib Sci 1987; *cr:* Guffey Schl Dist 4th Grd Tchr 1971-75, 5th-6th Grd Tchr 1975-78, 3rd Tchr 1978-81, 4th-5th Grd Tchr 1981-; *ai:* NEA 1971-; MEA 1971-, Rep; *office:* Mc Guffey Intermediate Schl 119 Main St Claysville PA 23

ELHATTAN, GLENN RICHARD, Chemistry Professor; *b:* Knox, *m:* Mary F.; *c:* Brenda Sturtz, Dianne Abrams, David, Curtis; *ed:* on ST Coll (BS) Chem 1956; Western Reserve Univ (MS) Chem 1963; pf Pittsburgh (PHD) Sci Ed 1973; *cr:* Rocky Grove HS Chem Tchr -68; Clarion Univ Chem Prof 1968-; *ai:* Campus Schlsp Comm Chm; otr, Hnrs Comms; Amer Chem Soc 1968-; Assoc PA St Coll Univ Facs -; PA Sci Tchrs Assn 1975-; Distngd Fac Awd 1994; *office:* Clarion Of PA Venango Campus 1801 W First St Oil City PA 16301

ELHATTAN, JOHN T., Mathematics Teacher; *b:* Oil City, PA; *m:* en Havrilko; *c:* James, Jennifer; *ed:* Clarion Univ (BA) Math 1968; Post Credits Kutztown, Penn St; *cr:* Exeter Schl Dist Jr HS Tchr, Dept d 1968-; *ai:* Var Golf Coach; NEA, PSEA, ETEA 1971-; *home:* 201 Ave Sinking Spring PA 19608

ELHENY, MICHAEL F., 6th Grade Science Teacher; *b:* Rushford, *m:* Martha K. Burr; *c:* Melinda; *ed:* St Univ Coll at Fredonia (BS) n Ed 1975, (MS) Elem Ed 1980; Cmptr Programming; Cooperative ning; *cr:* St Univ Coll Research, Grad Asst 1975-76; Falconer Cntrl ls Elem Tchr 1976-85, 6th Grd Tchr 1985-; *ai:* Tech Comm; Labor ations Comm Co-Chair; Falconer Ed Assn Exec Comm; NY St United rs, AFT 1976-, Rep Assembly Del; FEA Tchrs Assn 1976-, Ex Pres, sidential Asst; Roger Tory Peterson Inst 1992-, Prgm Instr, Pioneer of borne Project; Employee of Month 1993; Numerous Articles Pub; *ce:* Falconer Cntrl Schls East Ave Falconer NY 14733

ELHENY, WADE L., Secondary Social Studies Tchr; *b:* Pittsburgh, *m:* Megan Placzek; *ed:* Comm Coll of Allegheny Cty (AA) Hum 1988; Univ of PA (BA) His-Summa Cum Laude 1990; Duquesne Univ (MS) 1994; *cr:* Valuation Engrs Inc Appraiser 1991-93; Mt Nazareth Learning Summer Day Camp Supvr 1993-94; IN Area Sr HS Ec, US His, Soc d Tchr 1994-; *ai:* Asst Ftbl, Asst Track & Field, Asst Bsbl Coach; ensics League Coach; Mock Trial, Chess Club Adv; NEA 1994-; PCSS 3-; PAC-TE Outstdng Stu Tchr Awd 1994; Duquesne Univ Cert of Excl d in Ed 1994; Provost Scholars Awd 1990; *office:* Indiana Area Sr HS N 5th St Indiana PA 15701

ELROY, BETTY HOUGENDOBLER, Vocal Music Teacher; *b:* nton, OH; *m:* William E.; *c:* Natelie R., Jeffrey D., Michele L., Rhonda *ed:* Capital Univ (BS) Ed, Elem, Music 1967; *cr:* Elgin Local Schls 4th Grd Tchr 1967-68, Elem Music Tchr 1975-92, HS, JHS Vocal Music Tchr 1992-; *ai:* Elgin Energizers Show Choir; HS Musical Production; NEA, OEA, COTA 1967-; MENC, OMEA 1975-; Church Choir 1955-, Dir 1974-; *office:* Elgin Local Schls 1239 Keener Rd S Marion OH 43302

MC ELROY, CATHY, English Teacher; *b:* Seneca Falls, NY; *ed:* SUNY at Albany (BA) Eng 1970, (MA) Eng 1972; 30 Hrs Effective Tchng, Cnslng, Co-operative Learning; *cr:* Shaker HS Eng Tchr 1972-79; Salem Cntrl Schl Eng Tchr 1979-80; Cambridge Cntrl Schl Eng Tchr 1980-; *ai:* Hnr Soc Comm; AFT 1972-; Fac Assn, Sec 5 Yrs; Highland Quilters Svc, Interest Org 1990-, Sec; Honorary Mem NHS; AP Eng Tchr; Dev Grd 12, AP Curr; *office:* Cambridge Central Schl 24 S Park St Cambridge NY 12816*

MC ELROY, ELLEN M., High School Math Teacher; *b:* Natrona Hghts, PA; *m:* Kevin; *c:* Megan, Caitlyn, Kevin; *ed:* IN Univ of PA (BA) Elem Ed 1976; Hofstra Univ (MS) Rdng 1987; Attnd Nassau Comm Coll, East Stroudsburg Univ; *cr:* Cathedral Schl Tchr 1977-80; Rhodes Schl Tchr 1980-81; Long Beach HS Tchr 1981-; *ai:* Girl Scouts, Ldr; *office:* Long Beach HS 322 Lagoon Dr W Long Beach NY 11561

MC ELROY, HUGH J., Ceramics & Photography Prof; *b:* New York City, NY; *c:* Sean, Natascha Jenna; *ed:* St Univ at Farmindale (AA) Advertising 1958; Hofstra Univ (BA) Fine Arts, Ed 1964; St Univ at New Paltz (MA) Ceramics, Photography 1968; Univ San Miguel (MFA) Ceramics, Photography; Attnd New Schl of Soc Rsrch, Parsons Schl of Design; *cr:* Suffolk Comm Coll Art Prof 6 Yrs; Adelphi Univ Art Prof 25 Yrs; Roslyn HS Artist, Tchr 31 Yrs; *ai:* Camping, Scuba Diving, Sailing Clubs; Yrbk Adv; Alternative Schl Tchr; AAUP 20 Yrs; NEA 25 Yrs; BSA 1950-62, Asst Scout Master, Eagle Scout; Fullbright Schlsp, Exch London; Art Shows New York City, Long Island, West Coast; One Man Shows New York City; Showing, Selling Work; *home:* 114 Hallett Ave Port Jefferson NY 11777*

MC ELROY, JAMES EDWARD,JR., Biology & Chemistry Teacher; *b:* Mt Pleasant, PA; *m:* Linda G. Martin; *c:* Steven J., Erin E.; *ed:* Berry Coll (BS) Bio, Chem 1969; Attnd Univ of Richmond, Univ of VA, Coll of William & Mary, Univ of Pittsburg Ed Credits; *cr:* City of Richmond Pub Schls Classroom Tchr 1970-73; Chestnut Ridge Schl Dist Classroom Tchr 1973-; *ai:* PA Jr Acad of Sci Adv; NEA, PASES, Chestnut Ridge Ed Assn 1973-; *office:* Chestnut Ridge Sr HS R R 1 Box 79 A New Paris PA 15554

MCELROY, KEVIN P., HS Social Studies Teacher; *b:* White Plains, NY; *m:* Ellen Freehling; *c:* Megan, Caitlyn, Kevin Glenn; *ed:* C. W. Post at Liv (MA) Spec Ed 1981; 14 Addl Credit Hrs Post Grad; *cr:* Longbeach HS Soc Stud Tchr 1978-85; W. C. Mepham HS Soc Stud 1986-; *ai:* Head Ftbl 1986-, Head bsktbl 1985-92, JV Sftbl 1985- Coach; 9th Grd Team Comm; NYSUT 1978-; Nassau Cty Ftbl Coaches Assn, Sec; 1993, 1994 Ftbl Coach Yr Conf II; *office:* W. C. Mephan HS Camp Ave Bellmore NY 11710*

MC ELROY, RICHARD LEE, Social Studies Teacher; *b:* Smithfield, OH; *m:* Pamela; *c:* Matthew, Rachael, Luke; *ed:* Kent St Univ (BA) Soc Stud 1969, (MS) Ed 1975; Post-Grad Stud Univ of Akron; *cr:* Stow HS 1970-72; North Canton City Schls 1972-; *ai:* Coach Track, Ftbl, Bsktbl; Stu Cncl Adv; NEA, OEA 1970-; OH Cncl Sco Stud 1972-; North Canton Ed Assn, Rep; Councilman 2 Terms; Jaycee Intl Senator; Mason; Citizen of Yr; Author 6 Books; Magazine Ed; *office:* North Canton MS 200 Charlotte St North Canton OH 44720

MC ELWEE, HELEN REID, Retired Elementary Teacher; *b:* Portage, OH; *m:* Leonard; *c:* Michele Roush, Michael; *ed:* OH Northern Univ (BA) Elem Ed-High Distinction 1961; Bowling Green St Univ (MA) Ed 1973; *cr:* Horace Mann Schl Elem Tchr 1961-93; *ai:* Delta Kappa Gamma 1966-, 2nd VP, Schlsp 1972; Phi Delta Kappa 1975; LEA 1961-, Sec; OEA, NEA 1961-; Jennings Scholar 1970-71; Golden Apple Awd; Tchrs Touch Lives Awd 1990 Lima Ed Assn; *home:* 130 Seriff Dr Lima OH 45807

MC ENANY, SHAWN ARTHUR, Religious Studies Teacher; *b:* Lowell, MA; *ed:* Providence Coll (BA) His 1984; St Michael's Coll (MA) Theology 1993; Rhode Island Coll Intro to Rehab Svcs; Brothers of the Sacred Heart Novitiate 1982-83; *cr:* Mt St Charles Acad Rel Stud, Soc Stud Tchr 1984-86; St Dominic RHS Rel Stud Tchr, Campus Minister 1986-87; Tri-Hab Inc Cnslr 1988-89; Bishop Guertin HS Rel Stud Tchr 1990-; *ai:* BG Key Club Moderator; Soph Class Co-Moderator; Campus Ministry Team; Music Ministry; Mission Drive Coord; Natl Assembly of Rel Brothers 1990-; Nashua Kiwanis 1992-; *office:* Bishop Guertin HS 194 Lund Rd Nashua NH 03060

MCENROE, MARYANN, English as a Second Lang Tchr; *b:* Jersey City, NJ; *w:* Richard (dec); *c:* Shannon, Kyle, Tara; *ed:* Jersey City St Coll (BA) Art Ed Cert K-12 1968; 34 Post Grad Credits; Jersey City St Coll Cert Elem Preschl 1983; Montclaire Univ Cert ESL 1992; *cr:* Union City Roosvelt Ann ESL Tchr 1984-86; Jersey City #6 Schl 2nd Grd Tchr 1987-88; Secaucus MS-HS Art Tchr 1988-90, ESL Tchr 1990-95; *ai:* New Beginnings Club Adv; Jr Prom Comm; Detention Supvr; NEA 1983-; NJEA 1983-; SEA 1988-; *office:* Secaucus Mid & HS Mill Ridge Rd Secaucus NJ 07094*

MC ENTEE, MARCILLE,IHM, English Teacher; *b:* Ankara, Turkey; *ed:* Immaculata Coll (BA) Theology 1984, (BA) Eng 1984; Villanova Univ (MA) Eng 1990; *cr:* Holy Trinity Elem Schl 5th-8th Grd Tchr 1970-72; St Matthew Schl 5th-8th Grd Eng & Soc Stud Tchr 1972-73; Our Lady of Grace Schl 7th & 8th Grd Eng & Sci Tchr 1974-79; St Gabriel Schl 8th Grd Eng & Rdng Tchr 1979-85; Villa Maria Acad 9th & 10th Grd Eng Tchr 1985-91; Little Flower HS 12th Grd Eng Tchr 1991-; *ai:* Stage Crew & Liturgical Dance Troupe Moderator; Yrbk 1985-91; NCTE 1985-; NCEA 1970-; Villa Maria Acad NCTE Cept of Excl 1984; Co-Author Voyages in 7th & 8th Grd Eng 1984; Co-Ed Magnificat Poetry Journal 1972-; *office:* Little Flower HS 10th & Lycombing St Philadelphia PA 19140*

MCENTEE, MARYLIN M., 11th-12th Grades Math Teacher; *b:* Brooklyn, NY; *m:* Peter F.; *c:* Gary O., Brian P., Diane E., Karen D., Constance G., Kathleen A.; *ed:* Hofstra Univ (BA) His & Math 1974, (MA) Math Ed 1984; *cr:* Lincoln Arens Jr High Soc Stud Tchr 1975-77; Holy Trinity Diocecan HS Math Tchr 1977-; *office:* Holy Trinity HS 98 Cherry Ln Hicksville NY 11801

MC EVOY, KEVIN THOMAS, High School History Teacher; *b:* Perth Amboy, NJ; *m:* Donna Lynn Schwartz; *c:* Blaine Thomas; *ed:* Seton Hall Univ (BS) His, Scndry Ed 1976; *cr:* Hammarskjold Jr HS His Tchr 1977-84; East Brunswick HS His Tchr 1984-; East Brunswick HS Vietnam War His Tchr 1992-; *ai:* Head Track Coach 19 Yrs; Conf Coach of Yr 1984 & 1987; 21 Conf Indiv Champs; 4 Team Champs; 2 St Champs; 1 Eastern St Champ; East Brunswick Ed Assn 1977-, Pub Awareness Comm Chair; Friendly Sons of the Shelleigh 1988-, Thanksgiving Baskets Chair; Nat Train Collectors Assn 1995-; *office:* East Brunswick HS 360 Cranbury Rd E Brunswick NJ 08816

MCEWAN, JOHN FRANCIS, Principal; *b:* Brockton, MA; *m:* Margaret Sperandio; *c:* Heather, Christopher, Julie; *ed:* Stonehill Coll (BA) Eng 1972; Bridgewater St Coll (MED) Guidence 1976; Univ of MA at Amherst (EDD) Leadership 1992; CAGS Amin 1985; *cr:* Cardinal Spellman HS Eng Tchr & Dept Head 1972-77; Silver Lake Regnl HS Eng Tchr 1977-83, Asst Prin & Housemaster 1983-91, Prin 1991-; *ai:* Schl Career Prgms; Renaissence Prgm; Restructuring Act; NASSP 1983-; MSSAA 1983-; ASCD 1991-; Parish Cncl 1991-, Chprsn; Eucharotic Minister, CCD Tchr 1991-; Presentation on Donahue 1996; Speaking Prgm Throughout Cntry on Renaissance, School Career & Restructuring; *office:* Silver Lake Regional HS 132 Pembroke St Kingston MA 02364*

MCFADDEN, CHARLES ANNICE, 6th-8th Grd Mathematics Tchr; *b:* Jersey City, NJ; *ed:* Chestnut Hill Coll (BS) Elem Ed 1969; Fairleigh Dickinson Univ (MA) Human Dev 1978; 18 Credits Math at Montclair St; *cr:* Olph K-8th Grd Prin 1974-80; Saint Peter Schl 8th Grd Tchr 1980-82; Saint Catharine Schl 8th Grd Tchr 1982-87; Saint Joseph Schl 7th & 8th Grd Tchr 1987-88; Saint Ambrose Schl 6th-8th Grd Tchr 1988-; *ai:* Math Coord K-8th Grd; Stu Cncl Adv; Mid Sts Evaluation Chprsn; Soc Justice Walkathon Annual Coord; NCEA 1958-; Pax Christi USA, Amnesty Intnl 1986-; Bread for the World 1985-; Network-Soc Justice Lobby 1985-; SSJ Financial Advy Bd 1985-86; Ozanam Shelter 1989-93, Vol; Natl Sci Fnd Grant Math 1970-73; NJ Tchr of Yr Nom 1986; Tchr of Yr Saint Ambrose 1993; *office:* St Ambrose Schl 81 Throckmorton Ln Old Bridge NJ 08857

MCFADDEN, DEBORAH WITT, Special Education Teacher; *b:* Cincinnati, OH; *m:* Edward; *c:* Erin; *ed:* Univ of Dayton (BA) Elem & Spcl Ed 1980; Post-Grad Stud Rowan Coll at Glassboro St; *cr:* CR Coblentz Elem K-5th Grd Spcl Ed Tchr 1980-83; Gibbsboro Schls K-8th Grd Spcl Ed Tchr 1983-87; Washington Twp HS 11th-12th Grd Spcl Ed Tchr 1987-; *ai:* The Interact Club Adv; NEA 1980-; NJEA 1983-; Washington Twp Ed Assn 1987-; Rotary Club 1995-.

MC FADDEN, KATHRYN SUSKO, Fifth Grade Language Arts Tchr; *b:* Palmerton, PA; *c:* Francine Confer, Suzanne, Peter; *ed:* East Stroudsburg Univ (BS) Elem Ed 1973; 36 Credit Hrs PA Prof Cert Elem Ed; *cr:* St Joseph's Elem Schl 2 Grd Tchr 1968-69; Jim Thorpe Area Schl Dist 7-8 Grd Remedial Math Tchr 1976-86, 5 Grd Lang Arts Tchr 1986-; *ai:* Majorette, Flag Team, Colorguard Coach; Jim Thorpe Ed Assn, PA Ed Assn, NEA 1986-; Carbon Cty Environmental Ed Ctr Garden Project & Wkshp Asst 1995-; NHS; Joseph Weiss Meml Schlsp; Deans List; Who's Who in Amer Ed 1987-88, 1989-90, 1992-93; *office:* Jim Thorpe Area Schl Dist 150 W 10th St Jim Thorpe PA 18229

MC FADDEN, PAUL EDWARD, Math Teacher; *b:* Washington, DC; *m:* Mary Katherine Gouveia; *c:* Anthony Jarrod, April Danae; *ed:* US Merchant Marine Acad (BS) Marine Transportation 1992; Attnd Bowie St Coll Masters Ed Prgm; *cr:* MC Caffery, Whitener Inc Analyst Defense Contractor 1992-93; PG Cty Pub Schls Permanent Sub Tchr 1993-94, Music Tchr 1994-; *ai:* Omega Alpha Psi Mentoring Prgm Spon 1994-; Black Stu Assn Spon 1994-; NEA 1995-; Kappa Alpha Psi 1996; Founded Omega Alpha Psi Mentoring Prgm 1994; Svc Awds for Mentoring 1994-95; *office:* Eleanor Roosevelt HS 7601 Hanover Pky Greenbelt MD 20770

MC FADDEN, YVONE, French Teacher; *b:* Hereford, England; *m:* John Paul; *ed:* West Chester Univ (BS) Fr 1971; NY Univ (MS) Fr 1990; Attnd Sorbonne in Paris France; *cr:* East Jr HS Fr Tchr 1973-78; Downingtown Sr HS Fr Tchr 1980-; *ai:* Fr Club Spon; Take Stdnts to France on Schl Trips; AATF 1980-; *office:* Downingtown Sr HS 445 Manor Ave Downingtown PA 19335

MCFALL, MARVIN EDWARD, Data Processing Instructor; *b:* Muskogee, OK; *m:* Lois E.; *c:* Kimberly Bettencourt, Lois Gomes, Holly; *ed:* Bristol Comm Coll (BA) Bus 1978; Fitchburg St Coll Voc Courses; *cr:* US Navy Personelman 1965-69; Hemingway Transportation DP Operator, Mgr; Bank of Boston DP Supvr; GNBRVTHS DP Instr 1986-; *ai:* US Navy Prsnl 1965-69; Hemingway Transportation DP Operator, Mgr 1970-82; Bank of Boston DP Supvr 1982-85; GNBRUTHS DP Instr 1986-; VICA Adv; Commnctn Comm Mem; MA Voc Assn 1992-; *office:* Greater New Bedford Reg Voc HS 1121 Ashley Blvd New Bedford MA 02745*

MC FARLAND, ANNA MUNTEAN, 7th Grd Social Stud Teacher; *b:* Martins Ferry, OH; *m:* Thomas Joseph; *c:* Daniel David, Timothy Brian, Thomas Patrick; *ed:* OH Univ (BS) Ed 1964; *cr:* North Elem Schl 4th Grd Tchr 1960-61, 5th Grd Eng, Soc Stud Tchr 1962-66; Hilltop Elem Schl 4th Grd Eng, Soc Stud Tchr 1979-94; Elm MS 7th Grd Soc Stud Tchr 1994-; *ai:* MFEA 1960-61; OEA 1962-66; NEA 1979-; *home:* 54084 Highview Rd Martins Ferry OH 43935

MC FARLAND, BRUCE EDWARD, Band Director; *b:* Canton, NY; *m:* Paula Ruth; *c:* Rebecca, Ruth, Sarah, Paul; *ed:* Ithaca Coll (BM) Music Ed 1981, (MM) Music Performance 1989; Univ of TX at Austin 3 Credits; Eastman Schl of Music 4 Credits; SUNY at Brockport 9 Credits; *cr:* Hays Consolidated ISD MS Band Dir, Asst HS Dir 1981-83; Parishville-Hopkinton Cntrl Schls Instrumental Music Tchr 1983-85; Ukarumpa HS Music Dir, MS & HS Choir 1985-87; Ithaca Coll Tchng Asst 1987-89; Gates Chili HS Band Dir, Marching & Jazz Band Dir, Instrumental Lesson Tchr 1989-; *ai:* Jazz Band, Aspects of Marching Band, Aspects of Band; NY St Schl Music Assn, Moroe Cty Schl Assn, MENC 1989-; GCTA, NYSUT, AFT; Westside Bapt Church 1990-, Choir Dir; Chrstn Svc Brigade 1995-, TC Ldr; 8th Grd Band 1st Div 1983; Outstdng Color Guard 1982; 1st Place Spencerport Firemen's Parade, Caledonia Firemen's Parade 1994; 2nd Place Painted Post Colonial Days Parade, 1st Place Spencerport Firemen's Parade, 1st Mendan Firemen's Parade 1995; Invitation Rochester Lilac Festival Parade 1991-95; Band Clinician 1995; *office:* Gates Chili HS 910 Wegman Rd Rochester NY 14624*

MCFARLAND, DEBORAH SCOTT, Administrator; *b:* Washington, DC; *m:* Calvin G. Jr.; *c:* Calvin G. III; *ed:* Bowie St Univ (BS) Elem Ed 1969; George Washington Univ (MA) Spcl Ed 1977; 36 Credit Hrs Scndry Admin Supervision Cert; *cr:* Elem Schls Tchr 1970-82; Northwestern HS Tchr 1981-82; Laurel HS Tchr & Admin 1982-83, 1986-; MS Tchr 1983-86; *ai:* Pom Pon Coach; Majorettes; Class Adv; Black Male Achvmt & 9th Grd Team Coord; PGCEA 1970-, Bldg Rep; MSTA 1970-, St Del; NEA 1970-, Del; Francis Fuchs Awd for Outstdng Spcl Edctr; *office:* Laurel HS 8000 Cherry Ln Laurel MD 20707*

MCFARLAND, JAMES RUSSELL, Physical Education Teacher; *b:* New Castle, PA; *m:* Joanne Dudek; *ed:* Taylor Univ (BS) Soc Scis 1977; Slippery Rock St Univ & Youngstown St Univ (BS) Hlth & PE 1982; Post Grad Work; *cr:* Wilmington Area HS Hlth, PE & Soc Scis Tchr 1977-92; Wilmington Area MS PE Tchr 1992-; *ai:* Girls Vlybl, Track & Field Head Coach; NEA, PSEA, WAEA 1977-; 1st Bapt Church 1986-, Deacon; PA Vlybl Coaches Assn 1980-; PA Track & Field Coaches Assn 1995-; Coach of Yr Awds; *office:* Wilmington Area MS 400 Wood St New Wilmington PA 16142*

MC FARLAND, JEAN RAMSAY, 7th & 8th Grd Lang Arts Tchr; *b:* Canton, OH; *c:* Elizabeth Soden, Victoria Prince, Anne; *ed:* Frostburg St Univ (BS) Ed 1956; *cr:* Annapolis Pub Schl Third Grd Tchr 1956-59; Ipswich Pub Schl Fourth Grd Tchr 1959-60; St Paul Schl Fifth Grd Tchr 1980-87, 7th, 8th Grd Lang Arts Tchr 1987-; *ai:* Mid Sts Accreditation Sub-Comm Chprsn; Lang Arts Coord; NCEA 1980-; *office:* St Paul Schl 250 James St Burlington NJ 08016

MCFARLAND, KATHY LYNN, High School English Teacher; *b:* Columbus, OH; *m:* Daniel Wade; *ed:* NC St (BA) Communication 1991; OH Dominican Cert Scndry Ed 1993; *cr:* Dublin Coffman HS Tchr 2 Yrs; *ai:* Boys & Girls Swim Team Coach; Yrbk Adv; Dublin Educators Assn, OH Educators Assn 1995-; *office:* Dublin Coffman HS 6780 Coffman Rd Dublin OH 43017*

MCFARLAND, PAULA WIISE, French Teacher; *b:* Florence, SC; *m:* James Stephen; *c:* Kelly, Matthew, Jeffrey; *ed:* Agnes Scott Coll (BA) Fr 1972; Oberlin Coll Stud Abroad 1971; Univ of WI at Whitewater Grad Stud Abroad 1994; *cr:* Severn Schl Tutoring, Fr, Span & Latin Tchr & Fresh Dean 1986-; *ai:* Fr & Z Club & Comm Svc Adv; AATF 1990-; AA Tchrs of Span & Porteguese 1989-; Tchr of Yr Awd 1991; Anne Arundel Cty Awd for Exel in Ed 1995; *office:* Severn Schl Water St Severna Park MD 21146

MC FARLAND, S. DIANE, Asst Prof of Communication; *b:* Clinton, TN; *c:* Kevin Moore; *ed:* SUNY at Buffalo (BA) Geog 1976, (MA) Geog 1982, (PHD) Comm 1996; *cr:* SUNY at Buffalo Adj Prof 1990-92; Youngstown St Univ Asst Prof 1992-; *ai:* SCA, Visually Impaired Advs; ICA 1989-; SCA 1990-; ECA 1993-, Sec to Voices of Diversity Division; Phi Beta Delta 1995-; Smith, Murphy Awd Outstdng Fac Commitment; ICA Grad Stu Tchng Awd; *office:* Youngstown St Univ Dept of Comm & Theatre Youngstown OH 44555*

MC FERRAN, MARTHA, Social Studies Teacher; *b:* Baltimore, MD; *ed:* Kalamazoo Coll (BA) Pol Sci 1978; Ohio St Univ (MA) Soc Stud Ed 1988; *cr:* Ohio St Univ Grad Asst 1987-89; Sterling MS Tchr 1989-94; Independence HS Tchr 1994-; *ai:* Prof Dev Comm; Globeplotters; NEA, OEA, CEA 1989-, Bldg Rep; OH Cncl Soc Stud 1989-; Phi Delta Kappa; Sister City Project 1988-; Grants for Stu Trips to El Salvador; Finalist for Intnl Edctr; *office:* Independence HS 5175 Refugee HS Columbus OH 43214

MCFETRIDGE, JANET S., French Teacher; *b:* Ft Benning, GA; *m:* Clarke C. Herdic; *c:* Colin, Caitrin, Connor; *ed:* OR St Univ (BA) Fr 1974; Univ of OR (MA) Fr Ed 1981; Attnd SUNY at Plattsburgh, Univ de Poitiers; *cr:* Corvallis HS Fr Tchr 1974-78; Huron Coll Skills Center Asst Dir 1978-80; SUNY at Plattsburg Asst Dir EOP 1980-84; Northeastern Clinton Cntrl Schl Fr Tchr 1984-; *ai:* Fr Club Adv; Future Tchrs Adv; AFT, NY St Tchr, NCCS Tchrs Assn 1984-; NYSFLT; North Cntry Youth Hockey 1984-, Pres 1991-94; Champlain Village Planning Bd Chprsn; Who's Who Among Young Amer Women; *office:* Northeastern Clintn Cntrl Schl Rt 276 Champlain NY 12919*

MC GARRIGLE, MAUREEN E., English Teacher; *b:* Manchester, NH; *ed:* Merrimack Coll (BA) Eng Ed 1971; Rivier Coll (MED) Scndry Ed 1979; Rdng, Gifted Ed; Univ of Galway Ireland; *cr:* Three Rivers Schl Eng Tchr 1971-; *ai:* Site Supvr For Stu Tchrs; Bldg Team Rep; Coord of Annual Schl Spelling Bee; NEA, NHEA 1971-; Alpha Delta Kappa 1993-; Presenter Annual Schl Dist Wkshp, Colleague on Interdisciplinary Tchng Strategies; Voted Tchr of Yr by Colleagues 1984; *office:* Three Rivers Schl 243 Academy Rd Pembroke NH 03275

MC GARRITY, MICHAEL PATRICK, English Teacher; *b:* Connellsville, PA; *m:* Jane E. Showalter; *ed:* Edinsboro Univ of PA (BSEd) Scndry Eng 1975; Cert CA Univ of PA, IN Univ of PA, Penn St Fayette Campus; Enrolled MA at WV Univ; *cr:* Connellsville Area Sr HS Tchr 1975-; *ai:* Organizing, Writing AP Eng Lang, Composition Course; Schl Yr Organizing E-Mail Mentorship Prgm for AP Stu; NEA 1975-, Bldg Rep, Gray Hair Awd; Pub Twice Poetry; *office:* Connellsville Area Sr HS 201 Falcon Dr Connellsville PA 15425*

MC GARRY, CATHERINE ANN, Art Teacher; *b:* New Haven, CT; *ed:* Southern CT St Univ (BS) Art Ed 1979, (MA) Art Ed 1989; Prof Diploma of Advanced Grad Stud Admin & Supervision 1991; *cr:* East Haven HS Rdng Aid 1979-83, Art Tchr 1985-; *ai:* Art Club Adv; Renaissance Comm; CEA, NEA 1985-; Flood & Erosion Comm 1995-; Appreciation Awd 1992; Svc Awd 1991; *office:* East Haven HS 200 Tyler St East Haven CT 06512

MCGARRY, MICHAEL F., Band Director; *b:* Philadelphia, PA; *m:* Michell Ann O'Donnell; *c:* Michael J., Conner M.; *ed:* Temple Univ (BME) Music Ed 1982; Trenton St Coll (ME) Educl Admin 1983; Scndry Principals Cert 1993; Elem Principals Cert 1993; K-12th Grd Music Supvrs Cert 1995; *cr:* Pennsbury Schl Dist Band Dir 1988-; *ai:* NEA 1988-; Prof Musician; 1st Chair Bassist Temple Univ Orch 1980-82; *office:* Pennwood MS 1523 Makefield Rd Morrisville PA 19067

MCGARVEY, BARBARA GAFFNEY, Third Grade Teacher; *b:* Harrisburg, PA; *m:* Frederick John; *ed:* Shippensburg Univ (BS) Elem Ed 1976; Masters Degree Equivalency; *cr:* Lower Dauphin Schl Dist 1st Grd Tchr 1976-85, 3rd Grd Tchr 1985-87 & 1988-, 1st Grd Team Tchr 1987-88; *ai:* PSEA & NEA; Trinity United Meth 1968-, Church, Soc & Spiritual Growth Comms; *office:* Lower Dauphin Schl Dist 291 E Main St Hummelstown PA 17036

MC GARY, JEFFREY O., Communication Arts Teacher; *b:* Harrisburg, PA; *m:* Cynthia Pike; *c:* Patrick, Brad; *ed:* Lebanon Vly Coll (BA) Eng 1975; Attnd Millersville Univ, Penn St Univ at Lancaster; *cr:* Wheatland Jr HS Comm Arts Tchr 1975-; *ai:* Asst Track Coach; Schl Newspaper, Schl Lit Magazine Adv; Chr MS Transition Comm; Lancaster Ed Assn; NEA; NCTE; *office:* Wheatland Jr HS 919 Hamilton Park Dr Lancaster PA 17603

MC GAURAN, KATHLEEN, Fifth Grade Teacher; *b:* Long Island, NY; *ed:* Queens Coll (BS) Eng, Ed; Lehman Coll (MA) Fr Lit; Sorbonne France Diploma Fr Lang, Culture; 20 Credit Hrs Sci Chem, Bio Fordham Univ; 18 Credit Hrs Sci Astronomy, Span Lehman Coll; *cr:* PS 207 4th, 6th Grd Tchr; Joan of Arc Jr HS 7th-8th Grd Eng Tchr; PS 173 1st-2nd Grd Tchr; The Mott Hall Schl 5th Grd Tchr; *ai:* Ec; Algebra; Fr; UFT; AFT; Fr Biling License; Tchr of Eng Cert; Spec Ed License; *office:* The Mott Hall Schl 131st & Convent Ave New York NY 10027

MC GEE, ANNE FOXWORTH, Math Teacher; *b:* Tampa, FL; *m:* Stephen Larry; *c:* Stephen Larry Jr., Russ Derek; *ed:* Univ of South FL (BA) Soc Sci 1964; Scndry Math; Chrstn Schl Admin; *cr:* Sligh Jr HS Math Tchr 1964-65; East Bay HS Math Tchr 1965-67; Auburndale Jr HS Math Tchr 1968-69; Westwood Jr HS Math Tchr 1974-75; East Liverpool Chrstn Schl Math Tchr 1977-88, HS Prin 1988-94, Math Tchr 1994-; *ai:* Spon OH Math League HS Math Contests; First United Meth Church 1978-, Chm Cncl on Ministries; *home:* 49235 N Meadowbrook Cir East Liverpool OH 43920

MC GEE, MICHAEL PATRICK, PE Tchr & Hd Boys Bsktbl Coach; *b:* Waterville, ME; *m:* Kathy; *c:* Jaime, Michaella, Haley; *ed:* Clark Univ (BA) His, Soc 1982; Univ of ME at Farmington Working Towards Masters; *cr:* Lawrence HS Tchr, Coach 1982-; *ai:* Head Boys Bsktbl Coach; KVAC 1985-, Pres 1990-91, Coach of Yr 1986-94; PAL 1982-; Coach of Yr 1986, 1989-90, 1993-94; St Champions 1990, 1994; Alumni Awd 1992; *office:* Lawrence HS School St Fairfield ME 04937

MC GEE, PATRICIA ELLEN O'NEILL, 7th-8th Grd Language Arts Tchr; *b:* Brooklyn, NY; *m:* Gregory Marck; *c:* Taylor Mairead, Trevor Christopher; *ed:* Siena Coll at Loudonville NY (BA) Eng, Scndry Ed 1990; *ai:* Ski Club Adv 1991-95; Chrldng Coach 1992-95; 8th Grd Adv 1993-95; Lang Arts Coord 1993-; Schl Level Planning Team; Pub Prsnl Comm; Norwood Ed Assn 1991-; Book Making Mini Grant 1992; *office:* Norwood Public Schl 177 Summit St Norwood NJ 07648*

MC GEE, PETER O., 8th Grade History Teacher; *b:* Middletown, CT; *m:* Ruth Hughes; *c:* Whitney; *ed:* Univ of New Haven (BA) His 1971; Suffolk Univ (MA) Ed 1974; *cr:* Mc Kelvie MS 8th Grd Tchr 1975-; *ai:* Track, Cross Country Coach; 8th Grd Class, Yrbk Adv; Curr Dev, Tchrs Negotiations Comms; NEA 1975-; NCSS 1990-; NH Cncl Soc Stud; Fight Against Breast Cancer 1994-, Organizer; Tri Cty Track League 1980-, Pres; *office:* Mc Kelvie MS 108 Liberty Hill Rd Bedford NH 03110

MCGEE, ROBERT M., 9th Grd Math Tchr & Dept Chair; *b:* Philadelphia, PA; *ed:* Shippensburg Univ (BS) Math Ed 1987; Philadelphia Coll of Textile & Sci (MS) Comp Sci Ed 1990; *cr:* Carl Sandberg MS Math Tchr 1987-; *ai:* Sftbl Coach; Dept Chprsn; AFT 1987-, Bldg Rep; NCTM 1993-; *office:* Carl Sandburg MS 30 Harmony Rd Levittown PA 19056

MC GEEHAN, PAUL T., English Teacher; *b:* Philadelphia, PA; *m:* Margaret Mc Laughlin; *c:* Colleen, Maureen, Patrick; *ed:* La Salle Univ (BA) Pre-Law 1968; *cr:* Archbishop John Carroll HS Eng Tchr 1968-, Var Bsbl Coach 1975-86; *ai:* Bsbl Camp Dir; NACST 1968-, Sr Del; Non-Resident Taxpayer Assn 1991-, Exec Bd; Main Line Times Coach of Yr 1980 & 1982; *office:* Archbishop Carroll HS 211 Matsonford Rd Radnor PA 19087

MCGEEHIN, ROSEANN EROH, Mathematics Teacher; *b:* Hazleton, PA; *m:* Patrick Andrew; *ed:* Kutztown Univ (BS) Scndry Ed & Math 1976; Univ of MD (MED) Admin, Supervision & Curr 1982; *cr:* Banneker Jr HS Math Tchr 1977-84; Magruder HS Math Tchr 1984-; *ai:* NEA & MSTA 1984-; NCTM & Mont Co Math Tchrs Assn 1989-; Ed of Montgomery Cty Curr & Corresponding Book Pub by Montgomery Cty Called Principles of Geometry & Algebra; *home:* 4821 Great Oak Rd Rockville MD 20853

MC GHEE, MIKE, 7th Grade Teacher; *b:* St Louis, MO; *m:* Janice L. Miessler; *c:* Micah, Kevin, Travis; *ed:* Concordia Tchrs Coll (BA) Elem Ed 1966, (MA) Elem Ed 1973; *cr:* St John Luth Schl Tchr, Soccer Coach, Art Dir 1966-; *ai:* Luth Ed Assn 1966-; *office:* St John Lutheran Schl 655 Wayne Ave Defiance OH 43512

MC GHEE, R. FAYE MC CALLUM, Choral Music Teacher; *b:* Durham, NC; *m:* William Lee; *c:* William Talmadge, Daniel Joseph; *ed:* Winston-Salem St Univ (BS) Music Ed 1968; Bowie St Univ (MA) Scndry Ed 1978; *cr:* Carter G Woodson HS Cty Choral, Gen Music Tchr 1968-70; Bel Alton MS Choral, Gen Music Tchr 1970-77; Piccowaxen MS Choral, Gen Music Tchr 1977-79; Lackey HS Choral, Piano Tchr 1979-; *ai:* NEA 1968-; MSTA, EACC 1970-; Delta Sigma Theta 1965-; Lane CME Church 1971-, Chrstn Ed Dir, Outstdng Ofcr; *home:* 303 Serena St Kettering MD 20774

MCGILL, THOMAS A., Industrial Arts Teacher; *b:* Columbus, OH; *m:* Sally K. Morgan; *c:* Carrie, Kellie; *ed:* OH St Univ (BS) Ed 1965, (MA) His 1986; *cr:* US Army Officer 1965-68; Columbus Pub Schls Tchr 1968-78; Echenrode Furniture Customer Svc 1978-81; Alder Local Schls Tchr 1981-; *ai:* Christmas Toy Project for Handicapped Children; NEA, OEA, JAEA 1981-; Masons 1965-; Scottish Rite; Shrine; Amer Legion; HS Yrbk Dedication; *office:* Jonathan Alder HS 6440 Kilbury Huber Rd Plain City OH 43064

MC GILLIN, WILLIAM PATRICK, Social Studies Teacher; *b:* Amsterdam, NY; *m:* Karen Niski; *ed:* SUNY at Albany (BA) Soc Stud Ed 1989; The Coll of Saint Rose (MS) Scndry Ed 1995; *cr:* Lynch MS 8th Grd Soc Stud Tchr 1991-; *ai:* Boys Bsbl, Ftbl Coach; Schl Discipline Comm; AFT 1991-; *office:* Lynch MS Coolidge Rd Amsterdam NY 12010

MC GINLEY, MARY MALONEY, Jr Sr HS English Teacher; *b:* Wilkes-Barre, PA; *m:* Timothy M.; *c:* Michael John, Erin Mary; *ed:* Kings Coll (BA) Eng 1974; Lehigh Univ (MS) Rdng 1978; 60 Addl Credit Hrs; *cr:* Meyers HS Rdng, Eng Tchr 1978-86; Coughlin HS Eng Tchr 1986-89; Elmer L. Meyers Jr Sr HS Eng Tchr 1989-; *ai:* Past Field Hockey Coach, Tennis Coach, Chrldr Adv; Awds Comm; PSEA 1978-; Church Lector; *office:* Elmer L Meyers Jr Sr HS 341 Carey Ave Wilkes Barre PA 18702*

MCGINN, RONALD BRIAN, Social Studies Teacher; *b:* Elizabeth, NJ; *m:* Harumi Miyabayashi; *ed:* St Josephs Univ (bA) Politics 1983; Cabrini Coll (MED) Scndry Ed 1992; 3 Grad Credits PA Cert; *cr:* Little flower Cath HS Soc Stud Tchr 1993-; *ai:* Asian Club & World Affairs-Model UN Club Moderator; 9th Grd Study Skills Curr Comm Chprsn; ACT 1993-; *office:* Little Flower HS 1000 W Lycoming St Philadelphia PA 19140

MC GINNIS, PAUL F., Director of Guidance; *b:* Paterson, NJ; *ed:* Montclair St Univ (BA) His 1980; Addl Hrs Rutgers Univ Soc Work; Elizabeth Gen Med Ctr; *cr:* Queen of Peace HS Soc Stud Tchr 1980-95, Soc Stud Dept Chprsn 1985-90, Dir of Guid 1995-; *ai:* Var Bowling Coach; Ski Club, Soc Stud Club, Jr Class Moderator; Power Lifting Coach Asst; Berger Cty Prof Cnslng Assn 1995-; NJ Cnslrs Assn 1995-; Outstdng Edctr Awd 1994; Century Club Ath Awd; *office:* Queen Of Peace HS 191 Rutherford Pl North Arlington NJ 07031

MC GINNIS, R. CHUCK, Chem & Physics Tchr, Ath Dir; *b:* Springdale, PA; *m:* Carol J. Redman; *c:* Robert, Daniel, Patrick; *ed:* Slippery Rock St (BS) Geology 1973; Bowie St (MED) Guid 1978; Attnd Trinity Coll; *cr:* Kenmoor Jr HS Sci Tchr 1973-79; Largo HS Sci Tchr 1979-; *ai:* Ath Dir; MSTA 1979-; MSADA 1994-; BSA 1978-, Asst Scoutmaster, Wood Badge; Pepco Outstdng Sci Tchr 1993; *office:* Largo HS 605 Largo Rd Largo MD 20774*

MCGINNIS, ROBERT J., Social Studies Teacher; *b:* Honesdale, PA; *m:* Patricia Solversen; *c:* Richard, James; *ed:* Mainland Inst Masters Equivalency Humanistic Ed 1980; *cr:* Wallenpaupack Schl Dist 7th Grd Soc Stud Tchr 1974-; *ai:* 5th-6th Grd Biddy Bsktbl Commissioner; 4th-6th Grd Babe Ruth Bsbl Coach; WAEA, NEA, PSEA 1974-; *office:* Wallenpaupack Area MS HC 6 Box 6071 Hawley PA 18428

MC GINNIS, SAM, 6th-7th Grade Mathematics Tchr; *b:* Springfield, OH; *m:* Jackie Brooks; *c:* Lori, Sara; *ed:* Cedarville Coll (BA) PE 1976; Wright St Univ Elem Ed 1982; Univ of Dayton Grad Courses in Admin; *cr:* Miami View Elem 6th-7th Grd Math Tchr 1976-; *ai:* MS Girls Bsktbl; Math Dept Chprsn 1994-; Nom Cty Tchr of Yr; *office:* Miami View Elem Schl 230 Clifton Rd South Charleston OH 45368

MC GINNIS, STEVEN CHRISTOPHER, High School English Teacher; *b:* Ft George E Meade, MD; *m:* Debra Irene Veazey; *c:* Christopher, Rebecca; *ed:* OH Univ (BA) Eng, Ed 1976, (MS) Higher Ed 1981; OH Peace Ofcrs Trng 375 Hrs 1983; *cr:* Eastern HS Cmptr Eng Tchr 1977-; Shawnee St Park Summer Seasonal Ranger 1981-; Shawnee St Univ Eng, Cmptrs Tchr 1992-; *ai:* Newspaper Adv; Eastern Local Tchrs Assn 1978-, Contract Negotiator; OH Ed Assn 1978-, Rep; Scioto Cty Sheriff's Dept 1983-, Spec Deputy; Scioto Cty Dive Team 1989-, Top Tender; OH Military Reserve 1990-, 1st Lt; Chptr II Grant; *office:* Eastern HS 1170 Tile Mill Rd Beaver OH 45613

MCGINNIS, THOMAS JAMES, French & Spanish Teacher; *b:* Hartford, CT; *m:* Cheryl Hannum; *ed:* Central CT St Univ (BS) Intl Mgmt 1988; Middlebury Coll (MA) Fr 1993; Working Towards Masters in Span; Cert Span 1994; *cr:* Middletown HS Fr, Span Tchr 1991-93; Hale Ray HS Fr, Span Tchr 1993-; *ai:* Multi-Cultural & Diversity Club Adv; Natl Collegiate Foreign Lang Honor Soc 1985-, Mem; AATF 1990-, Mem; NEA, COLT 1991-, Mem; Excl in Lang Stud Awd 1986; Svc Awd from Career Svcs Office 1994; *office:* Nathan Hale-Ray HS 15 School Dr Moodus CT 06469*

MC GINTY, LINDA WAGY, Retired English Teacher; *b:* Warren, OH; *m:* P. Gerald; *c:* Anthony; *ed:* Bowling Green St Univ (BA) Eng, Art 1964, (BS) Ed 1965; Kent St Univ (MA) Eng 1984; *cr:* Greenbriar Jr HS Eng Tchr 1965-67; Parma Sr HS Eng Tchr 1967-68; Normandy HS Eng Tchr, Yrbk Adv 1968-95; *ai:* Yrbk Adv 26 Yrs; Parma Ed Assn; OH Ed Assn; NEA; NCTE; GCCTE; Chi Omega Alumnae; Authored Yrbk Textbook; Outstdng Tchrs Plain Dealer Crystal Apple Awd 1995.

MCGINTY, REGIS WILLIAM, Social Studies Teacher; *b:* Pittsburgh, PA; *m:* Karen A.; *ed:* St Univ of NY at Buffalo (BA) Pol Sci 1988; Kent St Univ (BS) Scndry Ed 1991; 3 Credit Hrs Towards Masters in Counseling at Univ of Akron; *cr:* Saint Henry Schl 6th Grd Tchr 1992-93; Saint Vincent-Saint Mary HS Soc Stud Tchr 1993-; *ai:* Cross Cntry & Track & Field Coach; Urban Tchrs Project; *office:* Saint Vincent-Saint Mary Schl 15 N Maple St Akron OH 44303

MC GIRR, BERNADETTE BERWICK, Eighth Grade Teacher; *b:* Elizabeth, NJ; *m:* Douglas Paul; *c:* Christopher F., Stephen, Denise, David; *ed:* Fairleigh Dickinson Univ (BS) Elem Ed 1967; Southern CT St Univ (MS) Elem Ed 1993; *cr:* Cranbury Elem Schl 5th, 6th Grd Team Tchr 1967-70; Moran Jr HS 7th, 8th Grd Sci Tchr 1970-72; St Joseph Elem Schl 8th Grd Tchr 1990-; *ai:* Schl Sci Fair Organizer; Stu Cncl Adv; Sci Coord; Talent Show Adv; *home:* 19 Sheffield Rd North Haven CT 06

MCGLADE, CAROL POWELL, Second Grade Teacher; *b:* Philade PA; *m:* Michael A.; *c:* Kelsey; *ed:* East Stroudsburg Univ (BS) Ele 1978; 36 Addl Hrs for Cert at Marywood Coll, Villanova Univ & In *cr:* Calais Schl Emotionally Disturbed Children Tchrs Aide 197 Manoa Elem Kndgtn Tchr 1979-80; Lynnewood Elem Kndgtn 1980-81; Chestnutwold Elem Kndgtn & Second Grd Tchr 198 Lynnewood Elem Second Grd Tchr 1984-; *ai:* NEA & HTEA 1980-; *o* Lynwood Elem Schl 1400 Lawrence Rd Havertown PA 19083

MC GLEN, NANCY E., Professor of Political Science; *b:* Oswego *m:* Joseph Gadawski; *c:* Joseph Gadowski; *ed:* Ithaca Coll (BA) Po 1969; Univ of Rochester (MA) Pol Sci 1972, (PHD) Pol Sci 1975 SUNY at Buffalo Asst Prof 1973-80; Niagara Univ Asst Prof 198 Assoc Prof 1982-88, Prof, Soc Sci Prgm Dir 1988-; *ai:* Pi Sigma A Moderator; Soc Sci Prgm Dir; Northeast Pol Sci Assn 1990-, VP, 1996; NY St Pol Sci Assn, Pres 1992; BPW 1983-, Pres; Pub Books States of Women in Foreign Policy 1995, Women, Politics & Ame Society 1995, Women and Foreign Policy, The Insiders 1993, Wor Rights, The Smizzle for Equiality in the 19th & 20th Centuries *office:* Niagara Univ Timon Hall Niagara University NY 14109*

MCGLEW, KATHLEEN MCFEATERS, Television Produc Teacher; *b:* Detroit, MI; *m:* Donald B.; *c:* Kara, Michelle, Jennifer; *ed* St Univ (BS) Eng 1969, (MA) Educl Media 1974; 30 Hrs Post-Grad in TV & Film Production, Classical Lit & Curr Dev; *cr:* Worthington Schl Eng Tchr 1970-74; Potomac HS Eng Tchr 1977-80; Eleanor Roos HS Eng Tchr & Studio Dir 1981-94, TV Productions 1991-; *ai:* TV S Dir & Producer; Video Club Spon; NEA 1977-; Amer Women in Rad Broadcasting 1995-; Women in Film & Video 1996-; United Cerebral 1985-90, Exec Bd of Dir, Svc Awd; Assn for Retarded Citizens 1 Shakespeare Theatre of Wash DC 1990-, Guild Mem; Actress in Educ Series; *office:* Eleanor Roosevelt HS 7601 Hanover Pky Greenbelt 20770

MCGLINN, MARGUERITE MULLIGAN, 9th & 11th Grade En Tchr; *b:* Bryn Mawr, PA; *m:* Thomas; *c:* Christine, Heather, John Immaculata Coll (AB) Eng 1966; Villanova Univ (MA) Eng 1972; Chester Univ PA Writing Project 5 Credits; Univ of PA Philade Writing Project 3 Credits; Univ of IA Summer Writing Courses Haverford HS Eng Tfchr 1966-70; Villanova Univ Grad Tchng 1970-72; Mount Saint Joseph Acad Eng Tchr & Dept Chair 1983-; *ai* & Lit Magazine Moderator; NCTE 1983-; AAUW 1992-; Jane Austen 1988-; 2 Short Articles, 1 Long Article, 1 Short Story & 1 Class Strategy Article Pub in Eng Journal & NCTE Book Notes Plus; T Story Pub in Los Angeles Times; Attnd Breadloaf Writers Conf; Art & Magazine & Stdnts have Won NCTE Natl Writing Contest 2nd pl Fi & Honorable Mention Essay Awds; *office:* Mt St Joseph Academy 12 Wissahickon Ave Flourtown PA 19031*

MCGLONE, KATHY JEAN, Biology Teacher; *b:* Columbus, OH; *ed* Univ (BS) Botany & Field Bio 1980; Oh St Univ Cert in Ed 1984; Wor Toward MSES in Land Planning; *cr:* River HS Biological Scis Tchr 12 *ai:* Vlybl & Track Coach; Sr Class, Quiz Team & Sci Club Adv.*

MC GLYNN, AUDREY ELIZABETH, Junior High Teacher; *b:* York, NY; *ed:* Dominican Coll (BA) Ed 1965; Manhattan Coll (MS) Ad Ed; Fordham Univ Theology; Math in Mind's Eye; 50 Credit Hrs; *c* Pius Schl First Grd Tchr 1965-68; St Martin de Porres Sixth Grd 1968-71; St Luke Schl Eighth Grd Tchr 1971-72; St Frances of Rome Seventh, Eighth Grd 1972-88; St Mary Academy Seventh-Eighth Grd 1988-; *ai:* Math Tutorial Prgm; Dance Chair; AFT 1966-; NEA, NC DeLasalle Grant; *office:* St Mary Acad 222 Central Ave Dover NH 03

MC GLYNN, MICHELE HANNI, Retired Teacher; *b:* St Louis, MC Frank; *c:* Kate, Michael, Maggie, Joe, Mary, John; *ed:* St Cloud St (BA) Fr 1976; Catechetical Course for Archdiocese of Baltimore Visitation Acad 5-6th Grd Rel, Fr Tchr 1993-95.

MC GLYNN, SEAN E., Science Teacher; *b:* Syracuse, NY; Binghamton Univ (BS) Bio 1987; Syracuse Univ (MS) Sci Ed 1989; St Coll of Environmental Sci, Forestry (MS) Env, For Bio 1990; *cr:* Liver Cntrl Schls Homebound Instr, Sub 1990; East Syracuse Minoa Cntrl S Sci Tchr 1990-; *ai:* Sci Olympiad Coach; Ski Club Adv; Educl Tech Co STANYS 1992-; Extensive Curr Dev Chem, Bio; *office:* Syracuse-Minoa HS 6400 Fremont Rd East Syracuse NY 13057

MC GOEY, ROSEMARY ANN, Fifth Grd Teacher & Asst Prin; *b:* Rochelle, NY; *ed:* Good Counsel Coll at White Plains (BA) His 1966; A Southampton Coll; *cr:* Holy Family Schl Sixth Grd Tchr 1966-68; Lady of Mercy 5-8th Grd Tchr 1968-; *ai:* NCEA 1968-; Southw Property Owners Assn 1965-, Sec; *office:* Our Lady of Mercy Schl M Rd Cutchogue NY 11935

MC GOLDRICK, ELLEN TERESE, Sixth Grade Teacher; *b:* Scran PA; *ed:* Marywood Coll (BA) Elem Ed 1972; Univ of Scranton (MA) 1980; *cr:* James Madison Elem Schl Sixth Grd Tchr 1972-73; Ge Bancroft Elem Schl Fifth Grd Tchr 1973-79; North Scranton Intermec Schl Sixth Grd Tchr 1979-88; East Scranton Intermediate Schl Sixth Tchr 1988-; *ai:* NEA, PSEA 1982-; *office:* East Scranton Interm Schl Quincy Ave Scranton PA 18510

MC GONIGLE, PATRICIA, English Teacher & Dept Coord; *b:* Eve MA; *c:* Seamus; *ed:* Boston St Coll (BA) Eng 1970; Boston Coll (MA) 1989; 44 Credit Hrs Eng; 8 Credit Hrs Global Perspectives Framingha Coll; *cr:* Hopkinton MS HS Tchr 1972-, Eng Dept Coord 1994-; *ai:* N HTA 1972-; Distinctive Merit 1994; Cert of Achvmt 1993; Salute from of Ed 1995; *office:* Hopkinton HS Hayden Rowe St Hopkinton MA 0

MC GORRY, EUGENE COLEMAN, Social Studies Teacher; Allentown, PA; *m:* Susan Yacapsin; *ed:* Kutztown Univ (BS) Ed Soc 1984; East Stroudsburg Univ (MED) His 1993; Prin Certification 1996; *cr:* Jim Thorpe Area Schl Dist Soc Stud Tchr 1983; Tamaqua A Schl dist Soc Stud Tchr 1983-; Pocono Mountain Schl Dist Soc Stud 1984-; *ai:* Wrestling Coach 1984-1993; NPSEA; NEA Flwshp Roose Inst 1990; *office:* Pocono Mountain Schl Dist PO Box 200 Swiftwate 18370

MC GORRY, MARIAN ELIZABETH, Assoc Prof of Office Admir Philadelphia, PA; *ed:* Comm Coll of Philadelphia (AAS) Secretarial 1975; Temple Univ (BS) Bus Ed 1978, (MED) Bus Ed 1983; *cr:* Bucks Comm Coll Part-time Instr 1981-82; Comm of Coll of Philadel Part-time Instr 1980-84, Instrl Aid 1976-84, Asst Prof 1984-90, Assoc 1990-; *ai:* Co-Coord Office Admin Hnr Soc; Acad Adv; Coord Fac Gathering; NBEA, PBEA 1982-; Delta Pi Epsilon 1983-, Pres Alpha 1988-90, VP, Prgm Chair, Newsletter Ed; Friends of Fluehr Park at E Hall 1990-, Corresponding Sec; *office:* Comm Coll Of Philadelphia 1 Spring Garden St Philadelphia PA 19130

MCGORY, DARLENE KAY, Third Grade Teacher; *b:* Sandusky, OH Blake Stephen; *c:* Bradley, Elizabeth; *ed:* Bowling Green St Univ (Elem Ed 1981; Ashland Univ (MS) Curr & Dev 1995; *cr:* Perkins Pub S 3rd Grd Tchr 1985-; *ai:* Math Enrichment & Curr Comms; Grant to F Parents & Children Commnctn.*

MC GOULDRICK, FRANCIS JOSEPH, Mathematics Tchr & D Chair; *b:* Allentown, PA; *m:* Theresa Marton; *c:* Kevin, Taryn, Ste Jeffrey; *ed:* Kutztown Univ (BS) Sec Ed Math 1973; Addl 36 Cre

76; Lehigh Univ 12 Credits 1986-; Allentown Coll 6 Credits 1989-90; llentown Cntrl Cath Math Tchr 1973-, Dept Chair 1987-; *ai:* nural Sports Dir; Math Club Moderator; Math Team Competition Jr HS Enrichment Coord; Scholastic Scrimmage Coach; Acad Bowl ; PCTM, NCTM 1973-; Allentown Diocesan Teach Assoc 1976-, Pres 84, 1990-92, Treas 1976-81, 1985-89, VP 1989-90; Local Schl Bd , VP 2 Yrs; Church Wrestling Coach 1981-; League Commissionar; : Allentown Central Catholic HS 301 N 4th St Allentown PA 18102

GOVERN, HELEN, Guidance Counselor; *b:* New York, NY; *ed:* Coll unt Saint Vincent (BA) His, Ed 1965; Hunter Coll (MS) Spec Ed Cert Credits Schl Admin & Supvr; *cr:* St Peter's Schl Prin 1976-82; of Mount Saint Vincent Acad Advisement Dir 1982-91; St Catharine Guid Cnslr 1991-; *ai:* NCEA 1975-; Westchester Putnam Rockland g Assn 1991-; Higher Ed Opportunity Awd.

OVERN, LYNN ARCHAMBAULT, Chemistry Teacher; *b:* socket, RI; *m:* Michael Joseph; *c:* Kerri Lynn, Michael Joseph; *ed:* BA) Gen Sci & Scndry Ed 1972; URI (MA) Scndry Ed & Sci 1976; oonsocket Jr High Sci Tchr 1972-74; North Kingstown High Chem 1974-; *ai:* Astronomy Club Adv; Vllybl & Tennis Coach; ISS; Grad n; Affirmative Action Comm; PTSO; NEA 1974-, VP, St Del; NSTA ; NECTA 1980-; NOACC Grant for 10-Day Rsrch Trip; Brown Univ for Sci Ed; *office:* North Kingstown H S 100 Fairway North stown RI 02852*

GOVERN, MARYCAROL W., Nursing Professor; *b:* Bryn Mawr, *m:* Thomas D.; *c:* Megan, Julie; *ed:* Gwynedd-Mercy Coll (ADN) 1965, Villanova Univ (BSN) Nrsng 1968, (MSN) Nrsng Ed 1986; le Univ (PHD) Educl Psych 1995; *cr:* Lankenau Hosp Staff, Charge 1965-68; Presbyn U of P Med Clinical Instr 1968-78; Lankenau Staff, Charge Nurse 1973-80; Villanova Univ Asst Prof Coll of NUR ; *ai:* Sigma Theta Tau 1967-, Excl in Nsg Ed; SE PA League for 1984-, Dir; Natl League of Nrsng 1984-; PA-Amer Nurses Assn; ed Research, Pub Articles on Topics Related to Nursing Ed, Cognitive Critical Thinking; *office:* Villanova Univ College of Nursing 800 E aster Ave Villanova PA 19085

GOVERN, TERRENCE MICHAEL, High School English Teacher; iladelphia, PA; *m:* Eileen F.; *c:* Timothy; *ed:* Saint Josephs Univ (BA) 1970; West Chester Univ (MA) Eng 1979; Peace Corps Trng in ec, Tchng Eng as a Foreign Lang & African Stud; *cr:* CEG Divo Ivory Eng Lang Tchr 1970-71, 1971-72; Drexel Hill Jr HS Eng Tchr -81; Drexel Hill MS Eng Tchr 1981-84; Upper Darby Sr HS Eng Tchr ; *ai:* Creative Writing Tchr; Cntrl League Writing Contest Adv; NEA, , UDEA 1974-, Rep; Natl Assn of Returned Peace Corps Vols 1995-; r Darby Twp Tercentennial Cert for Contribution to Celebration 1984; of Citizen Svc Governors Office of Citizen Svc Penn Serve 1988; Natl for the Achvmt in the Arts 1990; *office:* Upper Darby HS 601 N lowne Ave Upper Darby PA 19082

GOVERN, TERRY E., Fourth Grade Teacher; *b:* Buffalo, NY; *m:* ie Barrows; *c:* Michael, Geoffrey; *ed:* Buffalo St (BS) Elem Ed 1966, Supervision of Instruction 1970; St Univ of NY at Buffalo (EDM) Specialist 1975; *cr:* Smallwood Dr Elem Schl Grd 4 & 5 Tchr 1966-; ist Math Comm, Sci Mentor; Amherst Ed Assn, AFT, NYSUT 1966-; Rdng Assn 1975-; *office:* Smallwood Drive Elem Schl 300 Smallwood mherst NY 14226

GOWAN, BRENDAN JOHN, English Teacher & Band Dir; *b:* Long h, NY; *ed:* Fordham Univ (BA) Eng 1991; Lehman Coll MS in EN Complete With Completion of Thesis, 3 Credits; *cr:* Roosevelt HS Stu hing 1991; Holy Trinity Grammar Schl Summer Schl Tchr 1991; nas HS Eng Tchr, Marching Band Dir 1991-; *ai:* Marching Band Dir; n Instr; Spring Musical, Christmas Concert; UFT, NCTE 1991-; *office:* nas High School 685 E 182nd St Bronx NY 10457*

GOWAN, JAMES P., Chemistry Teacher; *b:* Brooklyn, NY; *m:* Gloria; mes, Michael, David; *ed:* Suffolk Cty Comm Coll (AA) Sci 1964; ner Coll (BS) Bio, Chem 1967; SUNY Stony Brook (MALS) Sci Ed ; Attnd St Bonaventure Univ, Adelphi Univ, Queens Coll, hampton Coll, SUNY Farmingdale; C.W. Post Educl Admin; *cr:* ort HS Sci Tchr 1967-; *ai:* Boys Var Bsktbl Coach; Suffolk Cty Bsktbl hes Assn 1970-, Pres, VP; Bellport Tchr Assn 1967-; Treas, Bldg Rep; ort Coaches Assn 1975-, Pres, VP; Hedges Creek Civic Assn 1985-, South Cntry Alliance 1985-, Exec Cncl; NSF Inst Ecology, Physics ns Coll; NSF Inst Sci Curr SUNY Stony Brook; Bsktbl Coach of Yr lk Cty 1985, Daily News 1985, Var 1980, 1982, 1985-86, JV 1976-77; *e:* Bellport HS Beaver Dam Rd Brookhaven NY 11719

GOWAN, TERESA M., English Teacher; *b:* Sligo, Ireland; *ed:* Miami (BSEd) Eng 1973, (MED) Diagnostic & Remedial Ed 1975; OH ing Project Curr & Supervision; *cr:* Cath Cntrl Elem Schl 7-8 Grd Eng 1973-74; Badin HS 9, 11 Grd Eng Tchr, Dean of Girls 1974-90; on Jr HS 8-9 Grd Eng Tchr 1990-; *ai:* Dist Lang Arts Curr; Champion p Team; NEA 1990-; NCTE; Nom Martha Holden Jennings Master Awd; Hamilton Comm Fnd Grant Excl in Ed; *office:* Wilson Jr HS 714 n Ave Hamilton OH 45013

GOWAN, WILLIAM ELLIS, Mathematics Teacher; *b:* Binghamton, *m:* Susan Foley; *c:* William J., Matthew P.; *ed:* Binghamton Univ (BA) 1974, (MAT) Math 1976; Princeton Univ Chaos & Fractal posium; Colgate Univ Pascal Programming 3 Grad Credits; *cr:* hamton North HS Math Tchr 1976-81; Binghamton HS Math Tchr -; Chenango Forks Schl Dist Astronomy, Archaeology Tchr 1986-93; Math Club Co-Adv; Intnl Baccalaureate Planning, Dist Outcomes ms; Binghamton Tchrs Assn, NEA-NY 1976-; Pub Article 1978; *e:* Binghamton HS 31 Main St Binghamton NY 13905

GRAIME, JUDITH M., French Teacher; *b:* Cleveland, OH; *m:* neth; *c:* Lindsay, Emily; *ed:* Wittenberg Univ (BA) Fr 1971; Boston (MA) Fr 1973; Span Cert Requirements 1975-77; *cr:* Weeks Jr HS Fr 1976-80; Newton South HS Fr Tchr 1980-; *ai:* Tchr Group Ldr Fr 1996; Cooperating Tchr Wellesley Coll Stu 1995; MAFLA 1980-; *e:* Newton South HS 140 Brandeis Rd Newton Center MA 02159*

GRANE, BRIDGET ELIZABETH, Third Grade Teacher; *b:* ford, CT; *ed:* Emmanuel Coll (BSE) Elem Ed 1982; Lehman Coll (MS) y Chldhd Ed 1991; Tutor; CCD Tchr; Spec Olympic Vol; Tchng, Lrng m Chrprsn; Sci Comm; unit Coord; *cr:* Hartford Cty Sub Tchr 1982-83; Family Schl Grd 2 Tchr 1983-86; Cathedral Regnl Schl Grd 3 Tchr -87; Japan-Amer Learning Ctr Part-time Tutor; Holy Family Schl Grd hr 1987-; *ai:* Tutor; CCD Tchr; Spec Olympics Vol; Tchng, Learning m Chprsn; Sci Comm; Unit Coord Grd K-3; ACEI 1991-; Fed of Cath s 1990-; United Prof Horsemans Schlsp Awd; Project Seminar.*

GRATH, BILL MICHAEL, 8th Grd American History Tchr; *b:* adelphia, PA; *m:* Lisa Anderson; *c:* Austin, Cullin; *ed:* Kutztown Univ Ed) Soc Stud 1979; Wilkes Coll (MSEd) Ed 1993; *cr:* Kutztown Univ Ftbl Coach 1979-81; Kutztown HS Asst Ftbl Coach 1990-93; twood Area MS Acad Challenge, Jr HS Bsktbl Coach 1988-95; ztown Jr HS Bsktbl Coach 1995-; *ai:* NEA, FEA 1988-; Kutztown Area Org 1990-, Coach; Kutztown Univ Ftbl Alumni 1979-; Mentor Tchr -; *office:* Fleetwood MS 407 N Richmond St Fleetwood PA 19522

GRATH, GERALD, HS Social Studies Teacher; *b:* Philadelphia, PA; Laura Catharine Wahn; *c:* Jack, Allison Margaret; *ed:* West Chester (BS) Sociology, US His 1988; Addl Courses Towards BS in His, Ed; Cert by USPTA as Prof Tennis Instr; *cr:* Great Vly HS Soc Stud Tchr 1993-; *ai:* Stu cncl, Interest Club Adv; Fac Club Pres; NEA, PSEA, GVEA 1993-; *office:* Great Valley HS Rts 29 & 401 Malvern PA 19355

MC GRATH, JEAN, 1st Grade Teacher; *b:* Boston, MA; *m:* John R.; *c:* Debra Ann, John R. Jr., Mark Patrick; *ed:* Lesley Coll (BS) Ed 1955; *cr:* Goodyear Schl 1955-57; Walter Scherra Schl 1965-68; Hosmer Schl 1968-69; Gates Schl 1969-; *ai:* PTO 1971-; Kndgtn Orientation Comm 1971-; Acton Tchr Assn 1968-; NEA, MA Tchrs 1967-; *home:* 53 Concord St Maynard MA 01754

MC GRATH, JOSEPH THOMAS, Social Studies Teacher; *b:* Brooklyn, NY; *m:* Nancy G. Hanley; *c:* Craig, Caitlyn; *ed:* St Francis Coll (BS) Bus Mngmt 1983; City Univ of NY (MS) Spec Ed 996; 33 Credit Hrs Ed Brooklyn Coll; *cr:* Natl Financial Svcs Stock Loan Rep 1983-85; Drexel Burnham Lambert Govt Securities Rep 1985-90; IS 303 Schl Soc Stud Tchr 1990-; *ai:* Debate Team Adv; United Fed of Tchrs 1990-; Knights of Columbus 1980-; Great Kills Little League 1993-, Coach; Staten Island Pee Wee Ftbl League 1992-, Coach; *office:* Intermediate Schl 303 501 West Ave Brooklyn NY 11224

MC GRATH, MARY GORDON, Mathematics Teacher; *b:* Long Island, NY; *c:* Gordon; *ed:* Kutztown Univ (BS) Elem Ed 1975, (ME) 1980; Contiuned Ed Cert in Math; *cr:* St Joseph's Schl Second Grd Tchr 1977-79; Assumption Schl Math Tchr 1979-81; Bayley Ellard HS Math Tchr 1981-83; Valleyview Schl Math Tchr 1985-; *ai:* Cross-Cntry Coach; Chrldng Coach; Tchr of Yr 1994; *office:* Valleyview MS 320 Diamond Spring Rd Denville NJ 07834*

MCGRATH, MICHAEL BERNARD, English Teacher; *b:* Pittsburgh, PA; *m:* Patricia Anne Howard; *ed:* Duquesne Univ (BA) Eng 1971, (MA) Eng 1973; Rdng Specialist Cert; *cr:* Equibank Pub Relations Staff 1973-75; Cntrl Cath Eng Tchr 1975-; *ai:* Fac Cncl of NHS Chm; Parents Newsletter Coord; NCTE 1975-; Braun Jeffery Ath Assn 1989-, Sec; St Bonaventure Ath Assn 1992-; Duquesne Univ Tchng Assistantship; Univ of Pgh Apple for the Tchr Awd; *office:* Central Catholic HS 4720 5th Ave Pittsburgh PA 15213

MC GRATH, PATRICIA LOUZAN, Mathematics Teacher; *b:* Pittsburgh, PA; *c:* Jennifer, James, Joseph; *ed:* Boston Coll (BA) Math 1970; 32 Post Grad Hrs Math; *cr:* Scituale Pub Schls First Grd Tchr 1970-75; The Pinwhale Women's Apparel Owner 1976-89; Avon Pub Schls Math Tchr 1989-; *ai:* Adv Class of 1997; Asst Adv Class of 1996; Natl Jr Hnr Soc Selection Comm; NEA, MTA 1970-; AEA 1989-; *office:* Avon HS W Main St Avon MA 02322

MCGRATH, SUSAN J., English, Science & Math Tchr; *b:* West Lawn, PA; *m:* Evan M.; *cr:* Accomack Cty Schls 2nd Grd Tchr 1988-89; Wilson Schl Dist Hum Tchr 1989-90; Wyndcroft Schl Eng, Sci & Math Tchr 1990-93; Linden Hall Schl for Girls Eng, Sci & Math Tchr 1993-; *ai:* Var Girls Bsktbl & Var Sftbl Coach; MS Stu Cncl, MS Yrbk & Sr Class Adv; *office:* Linden Hall Schl For Girls 212 E Main St Lititz PA 17543*

MCGRATH, WILLIAM PAUL, Social Stud Tchr & Dept Chair; *b:* Plant City, FL; *ed:* Univ of FL (BA) Pol Sci & His 1966, (MED) Curr 1967; Addl 50 Post Grad Hrs; *cr:* Lakewood HS Tchr & Dept Chair 1967-71; Kaiserslautern Amer HS Tchr & Dept Chair 1971-82; Ramstein Amer HS Tchr & Dept Chair 1982-; *ai:* NHS; NEA 1982-; Amer Psychological Assn 1990-; Stratford Hall Seminar; *home:* PSC Box 3 Box 183 APO AE 09094

MC GRATH THORPE, ELLEN HUNT, Social Studies & Psych Teacher; *b:* Paterson, NJ; *m:* Edward A.; *ed:* Georgian Court Coll (BA) Hist, Eng 1968; Montclair St Coll (MA) Soc Stud 1971; Addl Studs for Psych in NJ, NY & OH 60 Credits; *cr:* Middle Rd Schl 8th Grd Tchr 1968-69; Middletown HS Soc Stud & Psych Tchr 1969-; *ai:* APA, MOCPA; NEA, NJEA, MCEA 1968-; MTEA 1969-; *office:* Middletown HS North 63 Tindall Rd Middletown NJ 07748*

MCGRAW, DAVID C., Science Teacher; *b:* Norwalk, CT; *m:* Jane Good; *c:* Erin Beth, Kara Lynn; *ed:* OH Univ (BGS) Environmental Bio 1974, (MS) Plant Ecology 1977; Syracuse Univ (MS) Sci Tchng 1981; *cr:* Montpelier HS Tchr 1981-; *ai:* Stu Cncl Adv; NEA & NSTA 1981-; Ctr for Image Proc in Ed 1992-; VT Christa McAuliffe Fellowship 1994; IBM Grant of Scanning Electron Microscope for Schl; *office:* Montpelier HS 5 High School Dr Montpelier VT 05602*

MC GRAW, JOSEPH ALLEN, Social Science Teacher; *b:* Charleston, WV; *m:* Ann L.; *c:* Jessica L., J. Scott, Rori, Rusty, Ryan; *ed:* St Peterburg Coll (AA) Ed 1984; Univ of South FL (BS) Ed 1986; *cr:* Shorecrest Prepartory Schl Tchr 1982-85; Northest HS Soc Stud Tchr 1985-87; Williamstown HS Soc Stud Tchr 1987-88; Mapleton HS Soc Stud Tchr 1989-; *ai:* Stu Adv; Bsbl Coach; NEA 1988-; OEA 1990-; MTA 1991-, VP; *office:* Mapleton HS 635 Co Rd 801 Ashland OH 44805*

MC GRAW, KELLY, Guidance Counselor; *b:* Albany, NY; *ed:* Hartwick Coll (BA) Mngmt 1990; Coll of Saint Rose (MSEd) Schl Cnslng 1994; *cr:* Bishop Maginn HS Guid Cnslr 1994-; *ai:* Svc Corps Moderator; JV Girls Bsktbl Coach; CDCA 1994-; *office:* Bishop Maginn HS 99 Slingerland St Albany NY 12202

MCGRAW, MICHAEL LEO, 8th Grd Social Studies Tchr; *b:* Ithaca, NY; *m:* Josephine; *c:* Michele, Thomas; *ed:* Saint Francis Coll (BA) His 1967; Cortland St Univ (MA) His Ed 1974; *cr:* Saint Francis Prep HS Soc Stud tchr 1968-69; Port Byron Cntrl Jr HS Soc Stud Tchr 1970; Jordan Elbridge Cntrl Jr HS Soc Stud Tchr 1971-74; Saratoga Springs Cntrl Jr HS Soc Stud Tchr 1974-; *ai:* Ftbl, Bsktbl & Bsbl Coach; NYSTEA 1967-; *office:* Saratoga Springs Jr HS Circular St Saratoga Springs NY 12866*

MC GREGOR, DIANE AGNES, English & Writing Teacher; *b:* Cuba, NY; *m:* Glenn Herbert; *c:* Matthew, Tanya Lee Mc Gregor Cepek; *ed:* Muskingum Coll (BA) Eng 1972; Univ of Dayton (MS) Guid 1987; Grad Hrs OH St Univ at Newark; *cr:* Newark City Schls Sub Tchr 1972-78; Sheridan HS Eng Tchr 1978-88; Newark HS Eng Tchr 1988-; *ai:* NHS Comm; Soc Comm Co-Chair; Newark Org Tchrs Eng 1976-, Dir 1988-91; Newark Tchrs Assn 1988-; OEA, NEA 1978-; First United Meth Church 1973-, Many, Various; Received Grant St of OH 1980; *office:* Newark HS 314 Granville St Newark OH 43055

MCGREGOR, PAMELA RAE (WALTENBAUGH), AP Chemistry Teacher; *b:* Natrona Heights, PA; *m:* Robert John; *c:* Amanda, Cassandra (dec); *ed:* IN Univ of PA (BS) Chem Ed 1977; Baldwin-Wallace Coll (MEd) Ed & Supervision 1992; Admin Degree Ed 1993; 27 Addl Credit Hrs in Various Areas; *cr:* Monessen HS 11th Grd Chem & 9th & 12th Grd Phys Sci Tchr 1977-83; Uniontown Area HS Chem, A P Chem & Phys Sci Tchr 1983-87; St Edward HS Hnrs Chem & Chem Tchr 1987-88; E C Labs Inc Inorganic Lab Mgr 1990; St Ignatius HS AP Chem, Chem & Physics Tchr 1990-; *ai:* CARE Team; CLC Ldr; North Cntrl Assoc 1994-, Chprsn Completing OE Process; Meth Womans Assoc 1996; Vacation Bible Schl, Chprsn; Denison Coll Outstdng HS Tchr Awd 1993; *office:* Saint Ignatius H S 1911 W 30th St Cleveland OH 44113

MCGREW, JOHN D., Emeritus Professor; *b:* Washington, PA; *m:* Kim Sanford; *c:* Sarah, Virginia Dodo, Robert, Duncan; *ed:* MIT (BSCHE) Chem Engr 1951; Washington & Jefferson (BA) Chem 1956; One Yr Grad Work; *cr:* Union Carbide Corp Dir to Data Processing 1952-83; Marietta Coll Asst Prof Comp Sci 1985-95; *ai:* TBTT 1950-; Assn Comp Mach 1987-; ODK 1994-; Kiwanis 1969-; Betsey Mills 1985-, Bd; Ser Corps Ret Ex, Chm, Gold Card; Outstndng Prof by the Stu Body 1985 & 1995; *office:* Marietta Coll 306 Mills Hall Marietta OH 45750

MCGRIFF, BONNIE MARIE, Spanish & French Teacher; *b:* Brookville, OH; *m:* Alan Wayne; *c:* Ashley Nicole, Benjamin Alan; *ed:* Wright St (BSEd) Span & Fr 1987, (MAEd) Tchr Ldr 1992; 3 Credit Hrs Stu Psych; *cr:* Wright St, Beavercreek, Troy Elem & Enrichment Tchr 1987-92; Esther Dennis MS Span & Fr Tchr 1987-; Sinclair Coll Span Conversation Tchr 1995; *ai:* 7th Grd Tchrs Team Ldr 5 Yrs; Odyssey of Mind Team Coach 3 Yrs; Former Asst Chrldng Coach 2 Yrs; NTA 1987-; Wright St Span Soc 1987-, Lifetime Mem Awd; Ashland Tchr of Yr Nom; *office:* Esther Dennis MS 5120 N Dixie Dr Dayton OH 45414

MC GROARTY, CYNTHIA MARION, Vocal Music Teacher; *b:* Trenton, NJ; *m:* Daniel P.; *c:* Colin T., Ryan J.; *ed:* Ithaca Coll (BA) Vocal Performance 1973, (BA) Music Ed 1974; St Univ of NY at Stonybrook (MA) Lbrl Stud 1978; 75 Addl Credits; *cr:* Edith L. Slocum Elem Schl Vocal Music Tchr 1975-80; Oakdale-Bohemia Rd Jr HS Vocal Music Tchr 1980-86; Connetquot HS Vocal Music Tchr 1986-90; Ronkonkoma Jr HS Vocal Music Tchr 1990-; *ai:* Show Choir Major Musical Presentation Dir; Suffolk Cty Music Edctrs Assn, NYSSMA, MENC 1975-.*

MC GROARTY, PATRICK P., Mathematics Teacher; *b:* Co Oonegal, Ireland; *m:* Maureen; *c:* John, Maura; *ed:* Maynooth Co Kildare Ireland (BSC) Math, Mathematical Physics 1987; St Patricks Coll (MS) Math 1988; *cr:* Our Lady of Mercy Schl Third Grd Tchr 1989-90, Gym, Rel Tchr 1991-93; St Josephs HS Math Tchr 1993-; *ai:* Soccer Coach; NCEA 1989-; *office:* St Joseph's HS 145 Plainfield Ave Metuchen NJ 08840

MC GROERTY, PHYLLIS MURRAY, First Grade Teacher; *b:* Chester, PA; *m:* Harry J.; *c:* Michael, Sharon Height, Thomas, Kevin, Mary Mc Donald, Phyllis Hennessy, Harry, Helen Wright, John, Jeanette Hildwind; *ed:* Neumann (BA) Soc Sci-Magna Cum Laude 1976; 24 Addl Credits West Chester U, St Joseph's U; *cr:* St Thomas the Apostle Schl Tchr 26 Yrs; *ai:* Rdng Coord; NCEA, M. Joseph Farrell Awd Distngd Tchng.

MC GROTTY, KIRK THOMAS, Chemistry Teacher; *b:* Philadelphia, PA; *m:* MaryAnn M. Cocron; *ed:* Univ of Miami (BA) Chem 1988; Temple Univ (MED) Ed 1990; *cr:* Penncrest HS Chem Tchr 1988-89; Interboro HS Chem Tchr, Track, Cross Cntry Coach 1989-; *ai:* Head Boys, Girls Cross Cntry, Winter Track, Field, Boys Spring Track, Field Coach; IEA, PSEA, NEA 1989-; DE Cty Track Coaches Assn 1989-, Del-Val League Rep; NSTA 1994-; Greater Phila Track Coaches Assn 1989-, Del-Val League Rep; Cross Cntry Team 2 League Championships, 4 Sportsmanships Awds; Track Team 1 Sportsmanship Awd; Cross Cntry Coach of Yr 1994-95; *home:* 3650 Geryville Pike Green Lane PA 18054

MC GUCKIN, DEBORAH ANNE, Sixth Grade Teacher; *b:* Hornell, NY; *ed:* Wesley Coll (AA) Elem Ed 1972; WV Wesleyan Coll (BA) Elem Ed 1974; Elmira Coll (MS) Ed 1978; 15 Addl Hrs Ed; *cr:* Hornell Schl Dist Fifth Grd Tchr 1974-79; Metcalf Elem Schl Sixth Grd Tchr 1980-; *ai:* Site Based Strategic Planning, Curr Advy, Cmptr Comms; NEA 1974-; Exeter W Greenwich Tchrs Assn 1980-, VP, Bldg Rep, Negotiating Team; *office:* Metcalf Elem Schl 30 Nooseneck Hill Rd Exeter RI 02822

MC GUINN, PATRICK JAMES, HS Govt & History Teacher; *b:* New York, NY; *ed:* Franklin & Marshall Coll (BA) Govt, His 1993; Attnd London Schl of Ec & Pol Sci Jr Yr; *cr:* Inst for Strategy Dev Rsrch Analyst 1993-94; Queen Anne Schl HS Govt Tchr 1994-; *ai:* Coll, Model Congress, Acad, Hnr Cncl Adv; Primary Class Spon; Head MS Lacrosse, Asst Upper Schl Lacrosse Coach; Phi Kappa Tau 1990-; Maret Schl Alumni Cncl 1995-; *office:* Queen Anne Schl 14111 Oak Grove Rd Upper Marlboro MD 20774

MCGUINN, REX ALEXANDER, English Instructor; *b:* Hendersonville, NC; *m:* Margaret Regis; *ed:* St Andrews Pres Coll (BA) Philisophy & Rel 1973; UNC at Chapel Hill (MS) Eng 1974, PHD Renaissance Lit 1980; Whitemore Coll & Oregon St Festival NEH Seminar; *cr:* UNC at Chapel Hill Instr 1979-80; Moses Brown Schl Eng Instr & Dept Head 1980-87; Brown Univ Mentor & MAT Prog 1989-90, PEA Eng Instr 1987-; *ai:* JV Boys Bsktbl; Poetry Magazine; NCTE 1980-; Habitat for Hum 1993-, Bd Mem; Book of Poems: Landing on Minneapolis 1992; Numerous Poems Pub; *office:* Phillips Exeter Acad 20 Main St MSC 81372 Exeter NH 03833

MC GUINNESS, JOHN EDWARD, Music & Math Teacher; *b:* Astoria, NY; *m:* Kathleen A. Mc Ginn; *c:* John; *ed:* Iona Coll (BS) Math 1971; *cr:* St Agnes HS Math Tchr 1972-74; St Francis Prep HS Chem Tchr 1975-77; Mater Christi HS Math Tchr 1979-82; Mc Clancy HS Music, Math, Physics, Chem Tchr, Fine Arts Dept Coord 1988-; *ai:* Schl Band Dir; Golf Coach; *home:* 5022 47th St Woodside NY 11377*

MC GUIRE, CAROL BROWN, Mathematics Teacher; *b:* Baldwin, NY; *m:* John J.; *c:* Kevin J., Cara L., Erin M.; *ed:* Hofstra Univ (BA) Math 1965; St Univ of NY at Stony Brook (MA) 1983; *cr:* Berner HS Math Tchr 1965-68; West Islip HS Math Tchr 1979-; *ai:* Mathlete Adv, Mentor; NYSUT 1965-; *office:* West Islip HS Higbie Lane West Islip NY 11795*

MC GUIRE, CHARLES ROBERT, 7th Grade Social Studies Tchr; *b:* Brooklyn, NY; *m:* Christina Susan Chekan; *ed:* William Paterson Coll (BA) His 1974; Boston St Coll (MA) His 1977; NY Univ 16 Credit Hrs in His; *cr:* Cty Coll of Morris Adjunct Assoc Prof of His 1979-; Eisenhower MS 7th & 8th Grd Enrichment Tchr 1980-; *ai:* NEA 1977-; NJEA 1977-; *office:* Eisenhower MS 47 Eyland Ave Succasunna NJ 07876

MC GUIRE, CHRISTINA SUSAN CHEKAN, High School English Teacher; *b:* Hackensack, NJ; *m:* Charles R.; *ed:* Boston St Coll (BA) Eng 1979; Lehigh Univ (MA) Eng 1991; *cr:* Warren Hills Regnl HS Eng Tchr 1979-; *ai:* SEED Rdng Group; NJEA 1981-; NEA 1981-; *office:* Warren Hills Regional HS Jackson Valley Rd Washington NJ 07882

MCGUIRE, JAMES WILLIAM, Social Studies Teacher; *b:* New Haven, CT; *m:* Janice L. Cooper; *c:* Conor; *ed:* Univ of PA (BA) Sociology 1982, (MS) Ed 1983; Montclair St Supervision Cert 1994; *cr:* Parkway Gamma Pgm Soc Stud Tchr 1982-83; St Cecilias HS Soc Stud Tchr 1983-84; NVRHS at Demarest Soc Stud Tchr 1984-94; NVRHS at Old Tappan Soc Stud Tchr 1994-; *ai:* Var Ftbl Asst Coach; Weight Room Supvr; NEA 1984-; NJEA 1984-; NVEA 1984-, Grievance & Constitution Comm; *office:* Northern Valley Regnl HS Central Ave Old Tappan NJ 07675*

MC GUIRE, KATHLEEN KOCIS, English & Art Teacher; *b:* Passaic, NJ; *m:* Joseph; *c:* Anne Paris, Maureen; *ed:* Georgian Court Coll (BA) Eng 1962; Montclair St Univ Art Ed Cert 1992, Printmaking Post Grad Ind Stud; *cr:* Clifton Pub Schls Eng Tchr 1962-68; St Andrew Schl Art Tchr 1979-81; Our Lady of Holy Angels Schl Eng, Art Tchr 1981-; *ai:* Schl Lit Magazine; Mid Sts Chm 1990-91; Mid Sts Evaluation Comm 1994-95; NCTE 1986-; NAEA, NJAEA 1990-; Fac Advy Cncl 1986-, VP; *office:* Our Lady Of Holy Angels Schl 471 Main St Little Falls NJ 07424*

MC GUIRE, MARIE MARRA, Guidance Department Chairman; *b:* Jersey City, NJ; *w:* Joseph (dec); *ed:* Montclair St Univ (BA) Span, Ed 1954; Wm Paterson Coll (MA) Stu Personnel Svcs 1969; Attnd Seton Hall, Kean Coll, Wm Paterson Coll, Jersey City St Addl 32 Credit Hrs; *cr:* Memorial Schl 7th Grd Tchr 1957-60; South End Schl 8th Grd Tchr 1960-69; Cedar Grove HS Guid Cnslr 1969-; *ai:* PA Squad; NHS; Delta Kappa Gamma Soc 1970-, St Pres; Essex Cty Guid Assn 1970-, NEA, NJEA 1954-; Cath Daughters of Amer 1955-, Regent Schlsp Chm; Jaycees, Rotary, Panther Pride, Schl Assn Svc Awds; *office:* Cedar Grove HS Rugby Rd Cedar Grove NJ 07009

MC GUIRE, MARK SEAN, Biology Teacher; *b:* Findlay, OH; *m:* Cindy Jean Wood; *c:* Bevin, Megan, Jarrid, Eric; *ed:* Findlay Coll (BS) Hlth, PE 1976; Addl 25 Hrs Bio OH St Univ, 25 Hrs Physics & Marine Bio Bowling Green St Univ; *cr:* Marion Cath HS Hlth, PE, Bio Tchr 1977-79; Richwood

North Union HS Sci Tchr, Ftbl, Wrestling Coach 1979-81; Marion River Vly HS Bio Tchr, Wrestling Coach 1981-; *ai:* Head Wrestling Coach; Sci Dept Head; Sci Club Head; *office:* Marion River Vly HS 1267 Columbus Sandusky Rd N Marion OH 43302

MC GUIRE, NANCY KING, Third Grade Teacher; *b:* Bellefontaine, OH; *m:* Nicholas; *c:* Anicia, Michael, Peter, Nichole, Christy, Thomas, Mamie, Molly; *ed:* Miami Univ (BS) Elem Ed 1970; Credit Hrs Univ of Dayton, Wright St Univ, Fresno St Coll; *cr:* Graham Local Schl 3rd Grd Tchr 1970-71; Benjamin Logan Schl 3rd Grd Tchr 1988-; *ai:* OEA 1970-; BLEA 1996-, Bldg Rep; 4-H Club 1958-, Adv; Logan Cty Ed Fnd Grant 4 Yrs; *home:* 4149 State Route 287 West Liberty OH 43357

MCGUIRE, SCOTT ALLEN, Biology Teacher; *b:* Pittsburgh, PA; *ed:* IN Univ of PA (BS) Natural Sci & Math 1990; (BS) Bio Ed 1993; 3 Cr Tchr Enhancement Inst; *cr:* Greater Latrobe HS Bio Tchr 1993-; Latrobe Chamber of Commerce Prep GED Instr 1995; *ai:* Comm: Block Scheduling, Capstone, Voc-Tech Awareness & Plant Curr; Greater Latrobe Ed Assn 1995-; *home:* PO Box 61 Nicktown PA 15762

MC GUIRE, WILLIAM F., MS Social Studies Teacher; *b:* Massena, NY; *ed:* Clinton Comm Coll (AAS) Lbrl Arts 1974; SUNY (BS) Ed 1976; SUNY at Potsdam (MS) Ed 1991; *cr:* Massena Cntrl Schls Soc Tchr 1982-84; Ogdensburg City Schls 6th-8th Grd Soc Tchr 1984-; *ai:* AFT 1975-; St Lawerence Cncl Soc Stud 1995-; BSA Troop Ldr 29 Yrs; *office:* Ogdensburg City Schls 1100 State St Ogdensburg NY 13669

MC GUIRE, WILLIAM JAMES, Social Studies Teacher; *b:* Perth Amboy, NJ; *m:* Norma Joy Weisbrot; *c:* Sean; *ed:* Jersey City St Coll (BA) Soc Sci 1967, (MA) Mod European His 1970; Univ of AR (PHD) Mod European His 1992; *cr:* Woodbridge HS Soc Stuc Tchr 1968-; *ai:* Phi Delta Kappa 1968-; NJEA 1980-; Woodbridge Twnshp Educ Assn 1980-; Cape May Cnty Hist & Genealogical Soc 1988-; AR Alumni Assn 1992-; A Friend To The Prisoner Dissertation; *office:* Woodbridge HS Kelly St Woodbridge NJ 07095

MCGURRIN, SANDRA HRAPSKY, Mathematics Teacher; *b:* Chester, PA; *m:* John J.; *c:* Kris; *ed:* Kutztown Univ (BS) Math 1966; Temple Univ (MS) Ed 1973; *cr:* Raub Jr HS Math Tchr 1966-80; William Allen HS Math Tchr 1980-; *ai:* NEA & AEA 1966-; NCTM 1966-; Lioness 1989-, 2nd VP; Allentown Women Tchrs 1966-, Sec; Hope Church Cncl 1986-; *office:* William Allen HS 17th & Turner St Allentown PA 18104

MC HALE, BARBARA MAJEWSKI, English Teacher; *b:* Philadelphia, PA; *m:* Jerome C. Jr.; *c:* Kateryn, Daniel; *ed:* Immaculata Coll (BA) Eng, Scndry Ed 1972; West Chester Univ (MA) Eng 1981; 12 Credit Hrs; *cr:* Marple Newtown Schl Dist 7-10 Grd Eng Tchr 1974-; *ai:* PSEA, MNEA 1974-; *office:* Marple Newtown Sr HS 120 Media Line Rd Newtown Square PA 19073

MC HALE, GERALDINE, Math Teacher & Dept Chair; *b:* New York, NY; *m:* Thomas; *c:* Sean, Patrick; *ed:* Fordham Univ (BS) Math 1969; *cr:* St Cecilia HS Math Tchr 1969-77; St Philip the Apostle Math Tchr 1977-94; Queen of Peace HS Math Tchr 1994-; *ai:* Math Dept Chprsn; NCTM; ASCD; NJTM; *office:* Queen Of Peace HS 191 Rutherford Pl North Arlington NJ 07031

MC HALE, JAMES F., 8th Grade Teacher; *b:* Phila, PA; *ed:* St Joseph's Univ at Philadelphia (BS); *cr:* Stella Maris Schl 5th-8th Grd Math Tchr 1988-; Winnet South Philadelphia Comm Ctr Evening Prgm Staff 1992-; *ai:* Sftb;, Vlybl Coach; Ath Dir; CYO Treas; Safety, Mathletes Moderator; *office:* Stella Maris Schl 814 Bigler St Philadelphia PA 19148

MC HALE, THOMASINA T., Sixth Grade Teacher; *b:* Carbondale, PA; *m:* Patrick; *c:* Micah, Tim, Zachary; *ed:* Marywood Coll (BA) Spec, Elem Ed 1973; Post Grad Stud; Continuing Ed Credits NEIU #19; *cr:* Carbondale Area Schl Dist Elem Tchr 21 Yrs; *ai:* Spirit, Pride Comm Co-Founder; NEA, PSEA 1973-; CATA 1973-, Sec, Chm of Ethics Comm; Carbondale Area Booster Assn Founding Mem 2 Yrs; *office:* Carbondale Elem Schl Brooklyn St Carbondale PA 18407

MC HENRY, CATALINA MARIA, Spcl Education Dept Chairman; *b:* Asuncion, Paraguay; *m:* Gary Eric; *c:* Frank, Caline; *ed:* Duquesne Univ (BS) Elem, Sp Ed 1975; Univ of South AL (MA) Spec Ed 1976; Univ of MD 30 Credit Hrs Admin; *cr:* Old Mill HS Tchr 1977-83; Franklin HS Tchr, Dept Chair 1984-; *ai:* NHS Adv; Svc Learning Coord; NASSP 1993-; Meals on Wheels 1982-, Coord; Reisterstown Comm Tchr of Yr 1993-94; *office:* Franklin High School 12000 Reisterstown Rd Reisterstown MD 21136

MCHENRY, JAY ROBERT, Earth, Life Sci & Cmptr Tchr; *b:* Nantecoke, PA; *m:* Susan E. Keller; *c:* Christi, Mikelanne, Jayson; *ed:* Bloomsburg Univ (BS) Bio, Earth Sci 1979, 1981; *cr:* US Army Sgt 1971-74; Becthel Construction Quality Control Engr 1979-83; *ai:* Sftbl Coach; Stu Cncl, Archery Club, Class Adv; NEA, PSEA 1979-; *office:* Benton Area Schl Dist RR 2 Park St Box 8 Benton PA 17814*

MCHENRY, LINDA BUPP, 5th Grade Teacher; *b:* Wooster, OH; *c:* Beth, Sarah, Mark; *ed:* Ashland Univ (BSEd) Elem Ed 1972; Kndgtn & Comp Sci Certs; *cr:* Oak St Schl 6th Grd Tchr 1972-75, Kndgtn Tchr 1975-86, 5th Grd Tchr 1986-; *ai:* Young Mothers & Math Curr Comms; Heartland Comm for Math; EAO 1972-, Soc Comm & Schl Rep; OEA 1972-; NEA 1972-; United Church of Christ 1964-, Worship Comm, Yth Act & Mission Trip; Oak St Schl & Orville City Schls Tchr of the Yr 1986-87; *office:* Oak Street Elem Schl 209 W Oak St Orrville OH 44667

MC HENRY, NADINE K., Education Professor; *b:* Philadelphia, PA; *m:* Arthur S. Jr.; *c:* Arthur III, Joseph; *ed:* PA St Univ (BS) Early Chldhd, Elem Ed 1977; Beaver Coll (MA) Ed, Concentration Environmental Stud 1981; Temple Univ (EDD) Curr Theory, Dev 1993; *cr:* St Marys Schl 1st Grd Tchr 1977-78; Rosemont Schl of Holy Child 2nd Grd Tchr, Sci Specialist 1978-84; Rosemont Coll Ed Fac Tchr 1984-86; Schuylkill Ctr for Environmental Ed Naturalist, Consultant 1982-; Nuemann Coll Ed Prof 1994-; *ai:* Prof Ed Soc; NSTA, PSTA, Natl Convention Comm Chair; ASCO; Amer Nature Stud Soc; Garnet Vly Schl Dist Concord Advy Cncl 1993-; *office:* Neumann Coll Concord Rd Aston PA 19014

MC HOME, JENNIFER L., Spanish Teacher; *b:* Winooski, VT; *m:* Agustin A. Diaz; *c:* Sara Luisa, Nicolas Alexander; *ed:* SUNY at Potsdam (BA) Span, Scndry Ed-Cum Laude 1991; *cr:* The Children's Hour Day Care Ctr 1987; Easter Seals Achvmt Ctr Art Dir 1987-88; Camp Allen Nature Dir 1990-91; Hopkinton HS 7th-12th Grd Span Tchr 1991-; *ai:* Jr Class Adv; Costa Rican Exch Prgm Coord; Nutrition, Scheduling Comms; EJHS Peer Cnslr; Organize Latin Amer Fiestas; NEA, NATFL, NHATFL, NATSP 1991-; Kappa Delta Pi; Word of Life Chrstn Flwshp 1995-, Cert of Appreciation, Children's Ministries Vol; Potsdam St Univ Ed Dept Scholar; Potsdam Coll Collaborative Project Presenter 1990; Translator; *office:* Hopkinton HS 297 Park Ave Contoocook NH 03229*

MCHUGH, CATHERINE B. (NOONAN), 7th Grd Language Arts Tchr; *b:* Long Isl City, NY; *m:* James; *c:* Jim Jr., Joy; *ed:* Hunter Coll City Univ of NY (BA) Eng 1969; Salem St Coll (MA) Amer Lit 1978; 45 Hrs in Tchng Related Courses; *cr:* Methuen System 7th Grd Eng Tchr 1970; Cntrl Jr High 1970-75; Tenney Mid 1978-; *ai:* NEA; *office:* Tenney MS 75 Pleasant St Methuen MA 01844*

MCHUGH, KEVIN CLADER, English Teacher & Dept Chprsn; *b:* Bryn Mawr, PA; *m:* Christine Beckman; *c:* Kathryn, Brendan; *ed:* Univ of Detroit (AB) Eng, His 1970; Univ of Windsor at Canada (MA) Eng 1972; Attnd Univ Coll Dublin Ireland; Post Grad Stud Tchng Writing, Ed, Supvr Miami Univ; OH Univ Jrnlsm; *cr:* Georgetown Preparatory Schl Eng Tchr 1973-77; St Ignatius HS Eng Tchr 1977-78; Cuyohoga Comm Coll Part-time Composition Instr 1977-78; Finneytown HS Eng Tchr, Dept Chprsn 1978-; CT Coll of Mortuary Sci Part-time Composition Instr 1981-85; *ai:* Conf of Ldrshp 1980-, Sec, Mem at Large, Plague for Svc 1990; OEA, NEA, FEA 1978-; NCTE 1974-; NCTE 1974-; OH Cncl of Tchrs of Eng, Lang Arts 1978-; Ancient Order of Hibernians 1994-, VP; PTA 1978-, Past Exec VP; Finneytown Educl Fnd 1986-; OH Writing Project Fellow 1960; NCTE CEL Pub Schls Univs Presenter; Reviewer Textbooks; Num Articles, Poetry; Delphi Study Mem; CTE Standards Comm; SWOEA COnf Key Note Specker 1985; Chprsn of Dept Recognized NCTE as Ctr of Excl 1985-86; *office:* Finneytown HS 8916 Fontainebleau Ter Cincinnati OH 45231*

MCHUGH, PHILIP GEORGE, 5th-8th Grd Mathematics Tchr; *b:* Catskill, NY; *ed:* Pace Univ (BBA) Bus Admin 1971; Working Toward Masters at New York Inst of Tech; *cr:* Brookhaven Natl Lab Budget Analyst 1975-83; Pub Schl 51 7th & 8th Grd Math Tchr 1985-86; Our Lady of the Miraculous Medal 7th & 8th Grd Math Tchr 1986-89; Most Holy Trinity Schl 5th-8th Grd Math & 6th Grd Math, Religion & Rdng Tchr 1989-; *ai:* Math League; *office:* Most Holy Trinity Schl 140 Montrose Ave Brooklyn NY 11206*

MC HUGH, ROBERT J., History Teacher; *b:* Abington, PA; *m:* Kathleen Fatzinger; *c:* Joshua L.; *ed:* LaSalle Univ (BA) His 1981; Beaver Coll (MED) Ed 1989; *cr:* Queen of Peace Grd 5-8 Tchr 1984-88; Gwynedd Mercy Acad Math Tchr 1988-90; Saucon Vly HS His Tchr 1991-; *ai:* Instrl Support Team; NEA, PSEA 1991-; Civil War Round Table Eastern PA 1991-; Coalition on Pol Assassinations, Citizens for Truth Kennedy Assassinations 1994-; Lincoln Flwshp of PA Tchr Schlsp Civil War Inst 1995; Natl Park Svc Licensed Battlefield Guide Gettysburg Natl Military Park 1986; *office:* Saucon Valley Sr HS 2100 Polk Valley Rd Hellertown PA 18055*

MCHUGH, WILLIAM P.,JR., Chemistry Teacher; *b:* Breckenridge, TX; *m:* Linda E. Davis; *c:* Maryann, Cynthia; *ed:* St Michaels Coll (AB) Bio 1967; Salem St Coll (MED) Ed & Scndry 1968; 36 Credit Hrs; *cr:* Hamilton jr HS Sci Tchr 1968-69; Lynn Eng HS Bio & Chem Tchr 1969-; *ai:* AAAS 1970-; *office:* Lynn English HS 50 Goodridge St Lynn MA 01902

MC ILVAINE, KAREN BARBARA, HS English Teacher; *b:* Wadsworth, OH; *ed:* Kent St Univ (BA) Comm 1969; Walsh Univ Tchr Cert 1990; *cr:* WKBF TV Promotion Supvr 1969-71; WJER RAdio Continuity Dir, Traffic Mgr 1973-89; Dover HS Eng, Hum, Yrbk, Rdng Tchr 1991-; *ai:* Variety Show, Yrbk Adv; Prin Advy Comm; Publicity Comm Chair; NEA, DEA 1992-; St John's United Church of Christ 1950-, Yth Adv, Drama Coord; *office:* Dover HS 520 N Walnut St Dover OH 44622

MCILWAIN, ELIZABTH PALICKI, Junior English Teacher; *b:* Toledo, OH; *m:* Craig Moore; *c:* Grace, George; *ed:* Univ of Toledo (BE) Eng 1988; *cr:* Four Cty JVS Jr Eng 1988-91; Springfield HS Jr Eng 1991-; *ai:* Stud Govt Adv, Devil's Advct Adv; NCTE 1986-; OCTELA 1988-; OEA & SEA, Sec; NCTE Achvmt Awds Writing Judge 1991 & 1993; *office:* Springfield Sr HS 1470 S McCord Holland OH 43528*

MC INERNEY, KEVIN JAMES, Chemistry Teacher; *b:* Elmira, NY; *m:* Judith A. Strausbaugh; *c:* Sean, Megan, Patrick, Daniel; *ed:* St Bonaventure Univ (BS) Chem 1968; Elmira Coll (MSEd) Ed 1972; *cr:* Horseheads HS Chem Tchr 1968-; Elmira Coll Adj Fac, Chem Tchr 1986-; Corning Comm Coll Adj Fac, Chem Tchr 1985-; *ai:* NYSPHAA, USSF Soccer Referee; STANYS 1976-; BSA 1985-, Scoutmaster 1986-89; *office:* Horseheads HS 401 Fletcher St Horseheads NY 14845

MC INERNEY, PATRICIA COYNE, Reading & English Teacher; *b:* Philadelphia, PA; *c:* Patrick, Mary; *ed:* Immaculata Coll (BA) El Ed 1974; Villanova Univ (MA) El Ed 1981; *cr:* St Francis de Sales 1st Grd Tchr 1974-79; Girard Coll 5th Grd Tchr 1981-83, 6th, 7th Grd Tchr 1983-; *ai:* 6th Grd Adv & Coord; Curr, Tchr Evaluation Comms; Phili FT, AFT 1981-; Home & Schl 1988-; *office:* Girard Coll 2101 S College Ave Philadelphia PA 19121

MC INERNY, JOSEPH C., Fifth Grade Teacher; *b:* Pittsburgh, PA; *c:* Jason; *ed:* Duquesne Univ (BA) Lit 1969; Boston Coll (MA) Ed Philosophy 1972; Grad Hrs Harvard Univ, Univ of VA, Boston Univ, Miami of OH, Boston Coll; *cr:* Fitton Schl 4-6 Grd Tchr 1969-72; McCarthy-Towne Schl 4-5 Grd Tchr 1972-; *ai:* Schl, System Wide Curr Dev; Admin Comms; NSTA; NSCC; NCTM; Boston Japan Soc; NSTA Elem Sci Intnl Cncl Exemplary Sci Tchng Awd 1981; NSTA OHAUS Awd 1982; NEH Inst Philosophy in Elem Schls Ft Worth TX 1985; NEH Aeneid Inst Miami Univ of OH 1985; NCSS JISEA Japan Travel Fellowship 1983; Jefferson Fnd, Univ of VA Stratford Fellow 1987; Edgerton Project, MIT 1993-; Pres Awd for Math & Sci Tchng 1992; Founder of Michael McInerney, Donald McKenzie Foundation for Math and Sci Tchng 1995-.*

MC INTIRE, GERALD ALLEN, Associate Professor of Finance; *b:* San Diego, CA; *m:* Donna J. Premo; *c:* Cara Leigh White, Gerald A. Mc Intire Jr.; *ed:* San Diego St Univ (BA) Ec 1956; AR St Univ (MBA) Fin 1967; Coll Fin Planning at Denver Certfd Financial Planner 1982; *cr:* USAF Major Ret 1957-77; Grove City Coll Assoc Prof of Fin 1977-; *ai:* Stu Bus Honorary, Fin Mngmt Assn Adv; Rotary Intnl, Pres; *office:* Grove City Coll Dept Business Administration 100 Campus Dr Grove City PA 16127

MC INTIRE, JACK LOUIS,JR., US History & Government Tchr; *b:* Erie, PA; *m:* Rhoda Dorcas; *c:* Renee Leigh, Jack Hunter, Joseph Tyler; *ed:* Edinboro Univ of PA (BS) Scndry Soc Stud 1973, (MA) His 1978; 6 Addl Hrs; *cr:* J. S. Wilson MS Civics Tchr 1973-75; Mc Dowell Intermediate HS World Cultures, Ec Tchr 1975-95; MC Dowell HS US His, US Govt Tchr, Dept Chair 1995-; *ai:* Ath Trainer; Mc Dowell Clock Corp Founder, Club Adv; 9-12 Grds Soc Stud Dept Chair; Mid St Steering, Svc Learning Grant Comms; Mill Creek Ed Assn 1973-, Bldg Rep; PA St Ed Assn, NEA 1972-; PA Cncl of SS; Ft Le Boeuf Fnd 1993-, Fin Chm; Millcreek Hall of Flame 1995-; *office:* Mc Dowell HS 3580 W 38th St Erie PA 16506

MCINTIRE, JEAN MORSE, Vocal Music Teacher; *b:* Bangor, ME; *m:* David Reese; *c:* Brian, Beth; *ed:* Eastern Coll at St Davids (BA) Music Ed 1971; Masters Equivalency; *cr:* Marple Newtown Schl Dist Music Tchr 1971-76; Manoa Presbyn Church Early Ed Tchr 1981-86; Haverford Schl Dist Music Tchr 1988-; *ai:* Direct 3 Church Choirs; Vol for Heart Assoc & Amer Cancer Soc; Sing in Chrstn Artists Singers Choral Group; Asst Dir Chrstn Artists Singers; NEA 1988-; PSEA 1988-; *home:* 509 Furlong Ave Havertown PA 19083

MC INTOSH, DONNA D., Human Services Instructor; *b:* Gouverneur, NY; *m:* Allan Hewitt Jr.; *ed:* Jefferson Comm Coll (AA) Liberal Arts 1979; BUffalo St Coll (BSW) Soc Work 1981; St Univ of NY at Albany (MSW) Soc Work 1985; *cr:* Equinox Inc Assoc Exec Dir 1985-92; Mental Hlth Assn Exec Dir 1992-95; Hudson Valley Comm Coll Human Svcs Fac 1990-; Siena Coll 1995-; *ai:* NY St Mental Hlth Assn 1996-, Bd Mem; Empire St Coalition on Youth, Family Svcs 1985-, Sec, Pres; Pueblo House 1992-95, Bd Mem; *office:* Hudson Valley Community Coll 80 Vandenburgh Ave Troy NY 12180

MC INTOSH, EDWARD LEON, Anatomy, Physiology & Bio Tchr; *b:* Fairfax, SC; *ed:* Hampton Inst (BA) Bio1981; Hampton Univ (MA) Ed, Bio 1985; Attnd Univ of MD, Trinity Coll, IN Univ, Columbia Union Coll; *cr:* All Saints HS Tchr 1983-86; Charles E. Smith 1986-91; *ai:* Dir Minority Access to Rsrch Careers 1990-; Mentor Prgm; Track & Forensic Coaches; NEA, Mont Co Educl Assn, MD St Tchrs Assn 1990-; WA Acad of Sci 1993-, Tchr of Yr; Beta Kappa Chi 1981-, Honor Soc; NSF F 1983-85; Inst for Advanced Stud in Aging & Immunology 1994-; Na of Hlth Summer Tchng Flwshp; *home:* 3402 Halloway S Upper Ma MD 20772*

MC INTOSH, NANCY ZIEGENFUS, Ceramics Art Teacher; *b:* PA; *m:* Richard J.; *ed:* PA St Univ (BA) Art Ed 1974; Columbia Visua Coll (MFA) Studio Ceramics 1983; 7 Hrs Scranton Univ; 3 Hrs Tyle of Arts; *cr:* Penn Traford HS Artist in Residence 1977-78; Capito Intermediate Schl Artist in Residence 1978-79; The Clay Studio Re Mem 1979-80; Montgomery Cty Pub Schl Tchr 1984-; *ai:* Ceramic Columbia Art Ctr Tchr; MSTA, NEA 1984-; PA Guild of Craftsmen The Clay Studio 1979-; PA Cncl of Arts Grants 1977-80; Hbg Art Fe Penn Museum Best of Show 1979; Stdnts Partnership Co-Coordinating Tchr; *office:* Bethesda-Chevy Chase HS 4301 E Hwy Bethesda MD 20814*

MCINTOSH, WAYNE V., Political Science Professor; *b:* Charlotte *m:* Cynthia L. Cates; *c:* Lea, Jesse, Emma; *ed:* Univ of SC (BA) P 1973; Wichita St Univ (MA) Pol Sci 1974; Washington Univ at St (PHD) Pol Sci 1981; *cr:* TX A&M Univ Asst Prof 1981-83; Univ o Assoc Prof 1983-; *ai:* Stu Internship Spon; Univ, Coll, Dept, Stu Comms; APSA 1983-; MWPSA 1990-; 2 Tchng Fellowships, Awds; Pub; Articles Pub; *office:* Univ Of Maryland Dept of Govt & Politics Tydings Hall College Park MD 20742*

MC INTOSH-MOORE, VIOLET HENRIETTA, Principal; *b:* Gre West Indies; *c:* Lystra Mc Intosh, Fernette, Danielle; *ed:* Brooklyn (BA) Ed 1983; 30 Credit Hrs in Ed; Univ of Cambridge Ed Cert 195 Technologist Manhattan Med Asst, Sc 1958; *cr:* Dover Govt Secon 1953-57; Hanson Place Elem Schl Second Asst 1969-73; Carmel C Schl Prin 1983-; *ai:* Lit Club; CAMPO 1992-; Carmel SDA C Pathfinder Dir, Yth Ldr, Bible Instr; Oxford's Who's Who the Elite Re of Extraordinary Profs 1992; The World's Who's Who of Women Biographical Ctr Cambridge England; *home:* 103 Jean Ave Hempstea 11550

MC INTYRE, DIANA MC INTYR, English Teacher; *b:* Marianna *m:* Levi H.; *ed:* FSU (BA) Eng; Nova Univ (MS) Rdng 1985; *ai:* NCTE, NSYUT 1986-; *office:* Lawrence Road Jr HS 50 Lawren Hempstead NY 11706

MC INTYRE, DINA HELENE, 7th Grd Social Studies Teach Greensburg, PA; *m:* John Douglas; *ed:* Duquesne Univ (BS) Elem, Sp 1987; Salisbury St Univ (MS) Pub Schl Admin 1996; *cr:* Worcester C Schls Tchr 1987-91; Seaford Schl Dist Tchr 1991-; *ai:* Conflict Resol Peer Mediation Prgm Adv; *office:* Seaford MS 500 E Stein Hwy Se DE 19973

MC INTYRE, ELIZABETH J., Math & Computer Teache Philadelphia, PA; *ed:* St Joseph's (BS) Elem Ed 1970; Penn St Un Credit Hrs, Cert; *cr:* St Madeline-St Rose 5th Grd Tchr 1968-80, 7t Tchr 1980-91, PE, Cmptr Tchr 1991-94, Hnrs Math, Cmptr Tchr 199 Newspaper Adv; Math Club Moderator; Sftbl Coach; CYO Dir; 1970-; *office:* Saint Madeline Saint Rose Schl Tome & Rodgers Sts R Park PA 19078

MCINTYRE, JANE ELIZABETH, Second Grade Teacher; *b:* Balti MD; *ed:* Muskingum Coll (BA) Elem Ed 1984; Univ of Akron (MA) 1988; Credit Hrs Kent St Univ, Ashland Univ; *cr:* East Muskingum 2nd-4th Grd Tchr 1984-87; Univ of Akron Grad Asst 1987-88; Stow Schls 5th Grd Tchr 1988-95, 2nd Grd Tchr 1995-; *ai:* Served 3 Y Dist-Wide Comm; Stow Tchrs Assn 1988-, Bldg Rep; OEA & NEA 1 Phi Delta Kappa 1991-, Fndtns Rep; *office:* Highland Elem Schl Stow Schls 1843 Graham Rd Stow OH 44224*

MCINTYRE, JERRY L., Mathematics Teacher; *b:* Corry, PA; *m:* Jud Darnofall; *c:* Jennifer, Jaimie; *ed:* Edinboro St Coll (BA) Math Edinboro Univ (MSEd) Math; Cleveland Engrs Soc 12 Hrs; *cr:* Ma HS Tchr, Coach & Adv 1966-; *ai:* Wrestling, Track, Ftbl & Swim C SR Class Adv; NEA, OEA, NEOTA & MEA 1966-, Salary & Be Comms; YMCA 1975-, Bd Mem, Bd Mem of Yr; *office:* Madison HS Burns Rd Madison OH 44057

MCINTYRE, PAUL DOUGLAS, Biology Teacher; *b:* Canton, OH Walsh Univ (BS) Bio, Comprehensive Sci 1993; Miami Univ Recomb DNA Tech 3 Credit Hrs; Kent St Univ Voc Educ Cert 11 Credit Hrs North Canton Hoover HS Bio, Chem, Voc Ed Tchr 1993-; *ai:* Boys B Var Asst, JV Coach; Tech Comm; NEO, OEA 1993-; OHSBCA 1986- Blast Project NASA; *office:* Hoover HS South 605 Fair Oaks SW Canton OH 44720*

MCINTYRE, RICHARD A., Music Teacher; *b:* Trenton, NJ; *m:* Step Newgarde; *c:* Gerald, Daniel; *ed:* Boston Conservatory (BM) Musi 1977; Trenton St Coll (MA) Musical Composition 1996; *cr:* Middle Union HS Music Tchr 1977-80; Bridgewater Raritan Schl Dist Music 1980-82; Hackettstown Schl Dist Music Tchr 1983; North Hunte Voorhees Regnl HS Music Tchr 1983-; *ai:* Asst Marching Band Musical Dir; VHS Theatre Advy Bd; NEA, NJEA 1980-; CJMEA, M 1977-; Ed Advy Cncl Philadelphia Orchestra 1995-97; Dir of Music Presbyn Church Bloomsbury NJ 1983-; Performing Keyboard & Voc *office:* Voorhees HS 256 County Road 513 Glen Gardner NJ 08826

MC INTYRE, RICHARD EARL, High School English Teache Niagara Falls, NY; *m:* Linda Ellen Knapp; *c:* Laurel Anna; *ed:* St Univ at Buffalo (BED) Scndry Ed 1969; Elmira Coll (MED) Scndry Eng 1974; Cornell Univ, Alfred Univ NYS Permanent Cert Schl Counse Attnd Ithaca Coll; *cr:* Watkins Glen MS Tech Tchr 1969-73; Watkins HS Tech Drawing Tchr 1973-84, 9-12 Grd Eng Tchr 1985-; Newfiel 10-12 Grd Tchr 1985; *ai:* Summer Driver Ed Tchr; Watkins Glen Assn, AFT 1969-; Watkins Glen Lib Trustees 1978-82, VP, Sec; *of* Watkins Glen HS 12th St Watkins Glen NY 14891

MC INTYRE, VALERIE LUMPKIN, Fifth Grade Teacher; *b:* Brook NY; *ed:* Brooklyn Coll (BA) Eng, Lang Arts 1972, (MS) Ed 1976; 30 C Hrs; *cr:* PS 243 Schl 3rd Grd Tchr 1972-76; PS 321 Schl 5th Grd 1977-81; PS 39 Schl 5th, 6th Grd Tchr 1981-; *ai:* Math Clinic; AFT, 1972-; NAACP 1994-.

MC ISAAC, JAMES JOSEPH,JR., Science Teacher; *b:* Norwood, *m:* Ann Marie Dempsey; *c:* Katherine A., Maureen E.; *ed:* Towson St (BS) Bio 1978; St Univ Coll at Buffalo (MSEd) Bio 1983; Canisus C Buffalo 12 Grad Credits 1985-89; SUNY at Fredonia 18 Grad Cr 1992-95; *cr:* US Army Medic 1972-75; Nardin Acad Sci Tchr, C 1979-85; Trocaire Coll Sci Evening Lecturer 1984-; Holland Cntrl S Sci Tchr 1985-; *ai:* NEA 1985-; NSTA 1979-; Amherst Girls Sftbl 1990-, Coach, Asst Coach; Papers Presented at 2 NSTA Natl Conven 1986, 1989; Founding Mem Bio Interaction Group Canisus Coll; *hom* Scarbora Dr Williamsville NY 14221

MC JILTON, THOMAS STEVEN, Eighth Grade Science Teache Syracuse, NY; *m:* Sabrina T.; *c:* Kaitlyn, Thomas, Tyler; *ed:* St Univ of at Alfred (AAS) Animal Sci 1976; Univ of GA (BS) Animal Sci, Ed 1 Syracuse Univ (MS) Sci Ed 1993; Tchng at Le Moyne COll 25 Ed Oswego St Univ 6 Post Grad Hrs; Syracuse Univ 31 Post Grad Hrs West Genesee HS Term Sub 1986-88; North yracuse Jr HS 8th Grd Sci 1988-; *ai:* Var Swimming, Sftbl Coach; Event Coach Adv; Sci Olym Team; Frosh Bsktbl Coach; Natl Sci Educators Assn, AFT, NYS STANYS 1988-; Boat, US 1980-, Amer Red Cross 1974-; Awds for ment in Nationally Ranked Sci Olympipad Team; Cable in the room Awd 1994; *office:* North Syracuse Jr HS 5353 W Taft Rd North use NY 13212*

AIG, COLIN PIERSOL, High School English Teacher; *b:* ington, DC; *m:* Courtney Sarah Messer; *ed:* Keene St Coll (BA) Eng ; Univ of MA (MFA) Eng 1993; 30 Hrs Post Bachelors Tch Ed Prgm ; *cr:* Brunswick HS Eng Tchr 1988-90; Black River HS Eng Tchr -; *ai:* Jr Class; Stu Cncl Co-Adv; Prof Dev Comm; AWP, Hemingway 993-; NCTE 1988-; Pub Poetry & Reviews; *office:* Black River HS 43 St Ludlow VT 05149

KAIN, LISA MECKSTROTH, Former Math Teacher; *b:* Lima, OH; avid W.; *c:* Nathan, Anna; *ed:* Asbury Coll (BS) His, Math 1982; *cr:* urn Jr HS Math Tchr 1982-84; White Oak Jr Hs Math Tchr 1984-87; Schl Yaounde Math Tchr 1987-90; Cincinnati Hills Chrstn Acad Tchr 1990-91.

KAY, CHARLES O., High School English Teacher; *b:* Bellville, NJ; arol Ann Elizabeth; *c:* Connor, Dylan; *ed:* Trenton St Coll (BA) Eng ; Montclair St Univ (MA) Eng 1996; Attnd Oxford Univ England ner Stud Prgm; *cr:* Vernon Twsp HS Eng Tchr 1983-; *ai:* Head Girls er, Asst Sftbl Coach; NJEA 1982-; NEH Grant 1994; NJ Excl Tchng 1995; *home:* 34 Walnut St Sussex NJ 07461

KAY, DAVID WILLIAM, 6th Grade Teacher; *b:* Dunoon, scotland; *c:* ssa, David; *ed:* St Univ Coll at Buffalo (BS) Elem Ed 1970, (MS) Elem 973; *cr:* Tonawanda Pub Schls Tchr, Coach Boys Soccer Var 1970-; *ai:* h Boys Soccer Var 1970-; Coach Girls Bsktbl Jr Var 1983-85; AFT -; Tonawanda Ed Assn 1970-, vP; Alderman City of Tonawanda -92; Cncl Pres of City 1992-94; Tonawanda Soccer Club 1982-, h.

KAY, DONALD EDWARD, Chemistry & Physics Teacher; *b:* DC; Margaret C.; *c:* Laura, Douglas, Linda, David; *ed:* Univ of CA at eley (BS) Chem 1960; Univ of IL (PhD) Organic Chem 1966; *cr:* Amer amid Co Research Chemist 1966-82; Timothy Chrstn HS Tchr 1983-; r Class Adv; Amer Chemical Society 1963-; NSTA 1989-; Hydewood Bapt Church 1974-, Organist 1973-; *office:* Timothy Christian H S Ethel Rd Piscataway NJ 08854

KAY, JAMES J., Foreign Language Teacher; *b:* Philadelphia, PA; *m:* L. Kibele; *ed:* La Salle Univ (BA) Ger 1964; NDEA Inst for anced Stud in Russian, Dartmouth Coll; *cr:* West Philadelphia Cath HS Lang Tchr 1965-; *ai:* Band Moderator 1965-70; Soccer Moderator -75; Talent Show Coord 1990-93; Soc Comm Chprsn 1993-; AATG -; Knights of Columbus 1986-, Dist Deputy & Grand Knight; Distngd Sallian Edctr 1991-92; *office:* West Philadelphia Catholic HS 4501 stnut St Philadelphia PA 19139

KAY, ROBERT FRANCIS, Business Education Teacher; *b:* Bangor, *m:* Janice Leach; *c:* Allyson Marie; *ed:* Univ of ME at Machias (BS) Ed 1971; *cr:* Wilmington HS Bus Ed Tchr 1971-74; Lisbon HS Bus Ed 1974-84; Oxford Hills HS Bus Ed Tchr 1985-; *ai:* NEA 1971-; MTA -; OHHTA 1984-; *office:* Oxford Hills HS Main St South Paris ME 1

KAY, SHAWN WILLIAM, Ornamental Horticulture Tchr; *b:* adelphia, PA; *m:* Sharon; *c:* Shawn Robert, Sheena; *ed:* DE Vly Coll Orn Hort Landscape 1980; Glassbord St Coll Tchng Stud; Flying hman Air Svc Pilot Instrument; *cr:* Gaudio's Garden Ctr Asst Store 1980-81; CCVTS Pennsauken Orn Hort Tchr 1981-; *ai:* FFA Club ; PA Flower Show Chprsn Pennsauken; YMCA Bsktbl Coach; NEA, A 1981-; FFA 1981-, Adv; Lectures Horticultural Soc South Jersey, anic Gardening Soc; *office:* Camden Co Voc Tech-Pennsauken 6008 wning Rd Merchantville NJ 08109*

KAY, WILLIAM L., Sixth Grade Teacher; *b:* Pittsburgh, PA; *m:* marie; *c:* Billy, Megan; *ed:* Slippery Rock Univ (BS) Resource Mngmt ; Temple Univ (MS) Educl Admin 1995; Prin Cert; Post Bacc Elem Ed ; *cr:* French Creek St Park Ranger 1989; Wilson Schl Dist Sixth Grd 1989-; Woods, Water & Wildlife Environmental Edctr 1991-; Sinking ngs Elem Schl Staff Ldr 1993-; *ai:* Character Ed, Assessment, Strategic ning Comms; Homework Club; Sci Fair Spon; Phi Delta Kappa 1995-; Wilson Fed of Tchrs 1994-; Immanuel United Church of Christ 1990-, con, Elder; Natl Rifle Assn 1990-; Hawk Mountain Sanctuary Assn ; PA Fed of Sportsmen 1995-; DER Environmental Classroom Awds -; *office:* Sinking Spring Elem Schl 630 Vester Pl Sinking Spring PA 08

KEAN, KEITH JOSEPH, Asst Professor of Psychology; *b:* Salem, *ed:* Seton Hall Univ (BA) Psych 1983, (MA) Cnslng 1986, (PHD) ing Psych 1990; *cr:* OH Univ Statistics Instr 1989-91; Muskingum Coll Prof Psych 1991-; *ai:* Numberous Articles Pub; *office:* Muskingum New Concord OH 43762

KEATING, THOMAS FRANCIS, Ec, Govt & Global Stud Tchr; *b:* falo, NY; *m:* Linda Varecka; *c:* Todd, Colleen; *ed:* SUC at Buffalo (BS) 1973, (MS) Ed 1976; SUNY at Buffalo (MA) Ec 1980; 12 Credits in cl Admin; *cr:* Letchworth Cntrl Tchr 1973-74; Bishop Timon HS Tchr 4-75; West Seneca Cntrl Tchr 1975-; *ai:* Conference Day Comm; CSIP; , NYSUT 1975-; West Seneca TA 1975-, Bldg Rep, Newsletter Ed; er Legion 1990-; Evans Youth Bsbl 1983-, Pres; Won 19 Awds West eca TA Newsletter Ed NY St United Tchrs Jrnlsm Competition; *office:* st Seneca West Sr HS 3330 Seneca St West Seneca NY 14224*

KECHNIE, CLAIRE COLLINS, Fourth Grade Teacher; *b:* Boston, *m:* Paul Douglas Sr.; *c:* Christa, Debra, Paul Jr., Michael; *ed:* Boston (BA) Ed1969; Cambridge Coll (MED) Ed 1994; 60 Credit Hrs; *cr:* m Schl Kndgtn Tchr 1969-70, Kndgtn, 3rd Grd Tchr 1977-81; Wheelock 4th Grd Tchr 1981-85; Dale St Schl 4th, 5th Grd Tchr 1985-; *ai:* Grd el Ldr; Curr Cncl; Medfield Tchrs Assn 1977-, VP; Mass Tchrs Assn, A 1977-; *office:* Dale St Schl 45 Adams St Medfield MA 02052

KEDY, JOHN WILLIAM, Mathematics Dept Chm & Tchr; *b:* gara Falls, NY; *ed:* SUC at Fredonia (BS) Math 1971; Binghamton Univ S) Cmptr Sci 1989; *cr:* Desales HS Math Tchr 1972-73; Seton Cath rl HS Math, Cmptr Sci Tchr 1973-; *ai:* Asst Bsktbl, Head Boys & Girls nis Coach; Amer Math Tchrs of NY St 1993-; *office:* Seton Catholic ntral HS 70 Seminary Ave Binghamton NY 13905

KEE, BARBARA JO SNYDER, Librarian & Media Director; *b:* ron, OH; *m:* Don M.; *c:* Melissa Jo; *ed:* Kent St Univ (BS) Ed, Soc Stud, 1964; Univ of Akron (MS) Ed 1968; *cr:* Norton HS Librn 1964-74; eetsboro HS Librn, Media Dir 1978-; *ai:* NHS Adv; NEA, OEA 1964-; eetsboro Ed Assn 1978-, Sec, 1st VP; OELMA 1978-; Delta Kappa mma, 1st VP; Portage Cty, Summit Cty Lib Assns 1974; Book Reviewer, de; *office:* Streetsboro HS 1900 Annalane Dr Streetsboro OH 44241

KEE, ELAINE LANG, Prof of Foreign Ed & French; *b:* Casablanca, nch Morocco; *m:* Darrell D.; *c:* Bryan V., Russell W.; *ed:* Wright St iv (BA) Fr Lit 1972; OH St Univ (MA) Fr Lit 1973, (PHD) Frgn Lang 1980; Office Audio-Visuel de L'Universite de Poitiers 1990-91; On-Site d of Schls Pre K-12 in Paris 1995; *cr:* OH St Univ Tchng, Rsrch Asst 72-79; SUNY Coll at Buffalo Asst Prof of Frgn Lang Ed, Fr 1980-84; ole Francaise Curr Dev 1984-85; SUNY Coll at Buffalo Prof of Frgn ng Ed, Fr 1985-; *ai:* Ed of NYSAFLT; Schlsp Comm Chprsn; Higher Ed mm Co-Chprsn; Phi Delta Kappa 1982-; ACTFL, AATF 1980-; SAFLT 1985-, Consultant to Bd; Numerous Conf Presentations, kshpr; Co-Authored Several Books; 3 Time Recipient of Grants Fr Govt; Ruth E Wasley Distngd Tchr Awd 1993; *office:* S U N Y Coll At Buffalo 1300 Elmwood Ave Buffalo NY 14222*

MC KEE, ERIKA L., Vocal Music Teacher; *b:* Coudersport, PA; *m:* Christopher A.; *ed:* Clarion Univ of PA (BS) Music Ed 1989; Bowling Green St Univ (MM) Music Ed 1996; South Western Prof Dev Credits; *cr:* Clarion HS Stu Tchr 1989; Bowling Green St Univ Piano Grad Assist 1989-91; South Western HS Vocal Music Tchr 1991-; *ai:* Show Choir Dir; Schl Store, Stud Cncl, Choral Booster Org Adv; Musical Vocal Dir; HS Dedication, Tchr of Yr Comms; Music Edctrs Natl Conf, PA Music Edctrs Assn 1986-; Amer Choral Dirs Assn 1995-, Bd Dirs; NEA 1991-; NASSP, PASC 1992-; Tchr of Yr 1995, Finalist 1994; Articles Pub; Grad Assistantship Bowling Green St Univ 1989-91; *office:* South Western HS 200 Bowman Rd Hanover PA 17331*

MC KEE, FRANK XAVIER, English & Humanities Teacher; *b:* Philadelphia, PA; *m:* Ellen Brandt; *c:* Erin M., Kristin M., Rachel M.; *ed:* LaSalle Coll (BA) Eng 1972; Villanova Univ (MA) Eng 1975, (MA) Educl Admin 1977; Lehigh Univ Post Masters Admin 1978-70; Temple Univ Cmptr Assisted Writing 1988-90; *cr:* Lower Moreland HS Eng, Hum Tchr 1988-, Eng Dept Chm 1976-88; Northeast Cath HS Eng Tchr 1972-76; LaSalle Univ Adj Ed Fac 1986-92; *ai:* Womens Track, Field Head Coach 1988-; Acad Decathlon Adv 1993-95; Sr Class Spon 1980-89; NEA 1976-; PA Track, Field Coaches Assn 1988-; PA Dist 1 Steering Comm 1993-; Natl Assn Scndry Schl Prins 1990-; Fullbright Fellow 1986; Schl is Cool Outstand Tchr Awd 1995; Natl Endowment Arts Awd Recipient 1985, 1988; Cornell Univ Younger Schlrs Tchr Recognitoin 1989; Franklin & Marshall Coll Outstdng Tchr Awd 1984; Univ of Chicago Tchr Recognition Awd 1981; *office:* Lower Moreland HS 555 Red Lion Rd Huntingdon Valley PA 19006*

MC KEE, PATRICIA GIRGENTI, High School Counselor; *ed:* North Adams St Coll (BS) Elem Ed 1965; SUNY at Albany (MS) Counseling 1973; *cr:* Van Buren Moody Schl Fourth Grd Tchr 1965-66; Niskayuna Cntrl Schls Sub 1971-75; Iroquois MS Cnslr 1975-91; Niskayuna HS Cnslr 1991-; *ai:* NTA Schlsp Comm; PTO; Banana Splits; AFT, NTA, NYSUT, Capitol Dist Counseling Assn, NYSACAD 1976-; GE Star Awd 1993; Scholars Recognition Prgm Awd 1993; *office:* Niskayuna HS 1626 Balltown Rd Niskayuna NY 12309

MC KEEVER, GARY W., Instrumental Music & Band Dir; *b:* Mc Keesport, PA; *m:* Linda L. Lamont; *ed:* Duquesne Univ (BS) Music Ed 1974, (MA) Music Ed 1986; Univ of NC at Chapel Hill Jazz Improvisation 1986; Vandercook Coll of Music Marching Band, Auxillary, Percussion 1978-79; *cr:* Mon Vly Cath HS Marching, Concert, Stage Band, HS Choir Dir, Dept Chprsn 1974-80; Elizabeth Forward Schl Dist Instrumental Music Tchr, Marching, Symphonic, Concert Band, Jazz, Wind Ensemble, Brass Choir Dir 1980-; *ai:* PA Music Ed Assn, MENC 1974; Intern Assocot Jazz Edctrs 1982-; Comm Chorus 1990-; Outstdng Jazz Edctr Schlsp Awd 1986-89; *office:* Elizabeth Forward Sr HS 1000 Weigle'S Hill Rd Elizabeth PA 15037

MC KELVEY, JILL HATCHER, Social Studies Teacher; *b:* Bellefontaine, OH; *m:* William G. Jr.; *c:* Mathew Ryan; *ed:* Univ of Dayton (BS) Comprehensive Soc Stud 1986; *cr:* Benjamin Logan HS Soc Stud Tchr 1986-; *ai:* Mock Trial, Yrbk, Ski Club Adv; Venture Capital Grant, Restructuring Steering Comms; Sftbl, Vlybl Asst Coach; NEA 1986-, UniServ, Bldg Rep; OCSS 1987-; *office:* Benjamin Logan HS 6609 State Route 47 E Bellefontaine OH 43311

MCKELVEY, MARIE NUYIANES, Math Teacher; *b:* Philadelphia, PA; *m:* Daniel; *c:* Lena Marie, Melanie, Danny; *ed:* Penn St Univ (BS) Math Ed 1974; Beaver Coll (MS) Math Ed 1978; Wilkes Coll, Clarion Univ 30 Addl Credits Beyond MA; *cr:* Tamanend Mid Math Tchr 1974-87; Holicong MS Math Tchr 1987-; *ai:* Peer Tutoring Prgm Adv; Buckingham Ath Assn Travel Soccer Asst Coach; NEA, CBEA, PSEA 1974-; NCTM 1994-; *office:* Holicong MS PO Box 426 Buckingham PA 18912*

MC KELVEY, MAXWELL GEORGE, 4th Grade Science Teacher; *b:* Salisbury, MD; *m:* Pat Ard; *c:* Kevin, Tammy Whitelock; *ed:* Lee Coll (BA) Elem Ed 1969; Salisbury St Univ (MA) Elem Ed 1977; *cr:* Glen Ave Schl 5th Grd Math Tchr 1970-81, 1984-93; Willards Schl 3rd Grd Tchr 1981-82; East Salisbury Schl 4th Grd Tchr 1982-83; Pittsville Schl 4th Grd Tchr 1993-; *ai:* NEA 1969-; WCEA, MSTA 1970-; *office:* Pittsville Elem-MS 34404 Old Ocean City Rd Pittsville MD 21850

MCKENNA, BARBARA KOSIBA, Mathematics Teacher; *b:* Homestead, PA; *m:* Edward J.; *c:* Lauren; *ed:* Indiana Univ of PA (BS) Math, Scndry Ed 1968; West Chester Univ 30 Hrs Post Grad Work; *cr:* North Jr HS Math Tchr 1968-73; East Jr HS Math Tchr 1973-78; East Sr HS Math Tchr 1978-; *ai:* Schl Staff, Admin Comms; NEA, PSEA 1980-; SAT Tutoring Prgm Facilitator.

MC KENNA, CHRISTINE ANN, Secondary Mathematics Teacher; *b:* Rochester, PA; *m:* John Matthew; *c:* Ian Matthew, Geoffrey Joseph; *ed:* Edinboro St Univ (BS) Scndry Ed, Math 1973, (MED) Math 1975; *cr:* Beaver Cty Schls Sub Tchr 1976-77; Hopewell Sr HS Math Tchr 1977-79; South Fayette Jr Sr HS Math Tchr 1979-81; Quigley Cath HS Math Tchr 1981-; *ai:* Class Moderator 12 Yrs; PA Math League Spon; Class of 1996 Moderator; NCTM 1973-; NCEA 1981-; Edinboro Univ Grad Asst; Teach Calculus for Univ of Pittsburgh Coll in HS Prgm; La Roche Coll SCHOLARS Prgm Pre-Calculus Tchr; *office:* Quigley Cath HS 200 Quigley Dr Baden PA 15005

MC KENNA, GREER K., English Teacher; *b:* Brooklyn, NY; *m:* Matthew P.; *c:* Maureen Herman, Daniel M., Kathryn B.; *ed:* Molloy Coll (BA) Eng 1965; Rdng Tchr Trenton St Coll 1984; *cr:* Bishop Reilly HS Eng Tchr 1965-66; North Plainfield HS Eng Tchr 1966-67; Hunterdon Cntrl HS Title One Basic Skills 1981-84; Immaculata HS Eng Tchr 1984-; *ai:* Acad Team, Parent's Newsletter Adv; NTE, NJTE 1985-96; St Magdalen's Church 1972-, Minister, Lector; Carnegie Mellon Grant Advanced Placement Eng; Natl Endowment Humanities Flwshp; Geraldine Dodge Flwshp; NJ Inst Humanities Flwshp; Rutger's Univ "Educ of Women" Awd; *office:* Immaculata HS 240 Mountain Ave Somerville NJ 07060*

MCKENNA, JOSEPH ANTHONY, Religion Teacher; *b:* Bronx, NY; *m:* Christine Pestrak; *c:* Timmy, Heather, Jennifer, Katie; *ed:* Fordham Univ (BA) Eng 1980; St Johns Univ (MA) Theology 1986; 6 Credits Family Life Ministry Richard Stockton St; *cr:* Msgr McClancy HS Rel Tchr 1983-88; Gloucester Cath HS Rel Tchr 1992-; *ai:* Forensics Coach, Religion Dept Chprsn; Sr Moderator; Wash Twp Recreation 1992-, Coach Bsktbl, Bsbl & Soccer; *office:* Gloucester Catholic HS 333 Ridgeway St Gloucester City NJ 08030

MCKENNA, KATHLEEN MARIE, Assistant Professor; *b:* Rome, NY; *c:* Danielle McKenna Falcon; *ed:* LeMoyne Coll (BA) Fr 1981; Georgetown Univ (JD-MSFS) Law & Intnl Relations 1988; *cr:* Univ of MD-European Division Tchr 1989-92; Broome Comm Coll Asst Prof & Affirmative Action Officer 1993-; *ai:* Affirmative Action Comm Chair; Dialogue on Race Relations Mem; Common Hour Presenter; Amer Bar Assn 1989-; NEA 1993-; Unitarian-Universalist Congregation Task Force Against Racism, Sunday Schl Tchr 1993-; *office:* Broome Comm Coll PO Box 1017 Binghamton NY 13902

MCKENNA, LAURENCE MARK, English Teacher; *b:* Philadelphia, PA; *m:* Kathleen Leister; *c:* Tim, Colleen, Shaun, Shane; *ed:* Millersville St Coll (BS) Eng & Spcl Ed 1973; Univ of VA (MED) Spcl Ed 1974; *cr:* Keystone Learning Ctr Tchr 1974-75; Radnor HS Eng & Spcl Ed Tchr 1975-; *ai:* Class Adv; 9th Grd Girls Bsktbl Coach; NEA 1974-; Won Bucks Fever Play Festival Competition; Wrote & Produced 6 Musical Comedies; *office:* Radnor HS 130 King Of Prussia Rd Radnor PA 19087

MC KENNA, MARYANN VERONICA, Asst Prof of Nursing; *b:* Wilmington, DE; *ed:* Univ of PA (BSN) Nrsng 1969, (MSN) Nrsng 1974; Certfd Emergency Nrsng 1986-; *cr:* Lankenau Hosp Emergency Dept Nurse 1977-94; Delaware Co Comm Coll Asst Prof 1989-; *ai:* Nurses Week Prgm, Distngd Nrsng Alumni Comm Chprsn; NLN, NEA 1989-; RN-CLEX Item Writer 1993; Publication Reviewer; *office:* Delaware Cnty Comm Coll 901 S Media Line Rd Media PA 19063

MC KENNA, RICHARD E., Advanced Biology Teacher; *b:* Plainfield, NJ; *m:* Gail J. Looker; *c:* Douglas E., Joanna G. Bartholomew Jr, Jennifer L M; *ed:* Columbia Univ (AB) Bio 1962; Rutgers Univ (MED) Scndry Ed 1969; Kean Coll Supvr Cert Scndry Ed 1992; *cr:* N Plainfield HS Bio & Advanced Tchr 1963-; *ai:* Renaissance Prgm Coord; Head Coach Cross Cntry; Asst Coach Boys Track & Field; N Plainfield Ed Assn 1963- Past Pres Treas; NJEA, NEA, NABT & NJSSTA 1963-; BSA 1950-, Asst Scoutmaster Dist Awd of Merit; Dev a set of Modern Bio Overhead Transparency Masters for Coll Entrance Book Co in 1964; *office:* North Plainfield HS 34 Wilson Ave North Plainfield NJ 07060

MC KENNA, RICHARD THOMAS, High School English Teacher; *b:* Canastota, NY; *c:* Richard D., Timothy D.; *ed:* Jefferson Comm Coll (AA) Liberal Arts 1968; St Univ of NY At Oneonta (BA) Fr 1970; Post-Grad St Univ of NY at Oswego, St Univ of NY at Oneonta; *cr:* Morrisville Eaton Jr-Sr High Fr & Eng Tchr 1970-73; Walton Cntrl Schl Eng & Fr Tchr 1974-75; Jamesville-DeWitt Cntrl Eng Tchr 1975-77; Camden Cntrl Mid & HS Eng Tchr 1977-; *ai:* NY St United Tchrs, AFT 1970-; Camden Tchrs Assn 1977-; Amer Legion Post 230 1981-, Sergeant-at-Arms 1985; Notre Dame Club of Mohawk Valley 1990-; Ancient Order of Hibernians in Amer; *home:* 111 Primo Ave Sherrill NY 13461

MC KENNA, SHANNON M., French & Spanish Teacher; *b:* Chicago, IL; *ed:* Dunbarton Coll (BA) Fr-Cum Laude 1965; Villanova Univ (MA) Scndry Ed 1978; Cert of Rel Stud 18 Hrs St Charles Seminary 1992; Attnd Laval Univ 1964; PA Cert Fr Immaculata Coll; Ursinus Coll; PA Cert Span; *cr:* US Govt Joint Publications Research Svc Ed, Translater 1965-66; Archbishop Carroll HS Fr Tchr 1967-72; J. W. Hallahan Cath HS Fr Tchr 1972-78; Bishop Mc Devitt HS Fr, Span Tchr 1978-; *ai:* Schl Newspaper Adv; Schl Trip to Italy Chaperone; Recruitment Publication; Montgomery Cty Office of Children & Youth 1991-, Past Foster Parent; Parish Rel Instr 1990-; Fr Govt Grant Inst de Tourraine 1970; Kappa Delta Pi 1978; Excl in Test Dev Archdiocesan Foreign Lang Curr Comm 1985; Phi Sigma Iota 1995; *office:* Bishop Mc Devitt HS 125 Royal Ave Wyncote PA 19095

MC KENNEY, BETTY VALENTINE, English & Journalism Teacher; *b:* Flat Lick, KY; *m:* Jack T.; *ed:* Union Coll (BA) Eng 1970; Northern KY Univ (MA) Ed 1986; Attnd Xavier Univ, Marquette Univ, Miami Univ, Berea Coll; *cr:* Pierce Elem Schl Tchr 1970-71; New Richmond HS Eng, Jrnlsm Tchr 1972-; *ai:* Schl Newspaper Adv; Curr Design, Dev; Mentor Tchr; Schl Ed Assn; Pub Relations Prgm Dir; New Richmond, OH Ed Assns; Southwestern OH Ed Assn, Pub Relations Comm; NEA; NCTE; OH Schls Jrnlsm Assn, Bd of Dir; Jrnlsm Ed Assn; OH Eng, Lang Arts Tchrs Cncl; Southwest Hills Uniserv Cncl, VP; Dist, St, Natl Prof Assn Convention Del; Schl Newspaper Awds; Clermont Cty Tchr of Yr 1993; Newspaper Fund Jrnlsm Fellowship; Presented Wkshps; Press Assn Judge; Natl Ptry Cont 3rd Pl; 6 Cty Tchr Ldr Pgm Participant; Ashland Tchr Achvmt Awds Pgm; *office:* New Richmond HS 1131 Bethel New Richmond Rd New Richmond OH 45157

MC KENNEY, JAY ANTHONY, Third Grade Teacher; *b:* Ft Fairfield, ME; *c:* Shaina Lee, Steven Micah Marr; *ed:* Univ of ME at Presque Isle (BS) Elem Ed 1988; *cr:* Harvest Schl 6th-8th Grd Rdng, Writing Tchr 1988-90; Ft Fairfield Elem Schl 3rd Grd Tchr 1988-; Project Explore 2nd-3rd Grd Sci, 6th-9th Grd Drums Tchr 1990-95; SAD #20 Adult Ed Sci Tchr 1994-; *ai:* Pvt Drum Lessons 13 Yrs; Young Astronauts 1990-; Welfare Comm 1988-; MEA, FFTA, NEA 1988-; *office:* Ft Fairfield Elem Schl 80 Brunswick Ave Fort Fairfield ME 04742

MC KENNEY, KAREN A., High School Counselor; *b:* Schenectady, NY; *ed:* SUNY at Brockport (BS) Psych, Elem Ed 1973; Univ of NH (MED) Cnslr Ed 1975; SUNY at Albany (MS) Cnslng Psych 1979, (EDS) Cnslng, Psych 1979; *cr:* St Anne Inst Child Care Worker 1973-74; Farmington HS Cnslr 1975-76; Hoosic Vly HS Cnslr 1976-79; Scotia-Glenville HS Cnslr 1979-; *ai:* Tchrs Org 1979-, Bldg Rep; NYSUT, Capitol Dist Cnslrs Assn 1979-; Consultation Ctr 1992-, Bd Mem; Ballston Lake Emergency Squad 1986-95, EMT-I, Bd Mem, Past VP; *office:* Scotia-Glenville HS 1 Tartan Way Scotia NY 12302*

MC KENNY, DIANE MARIE, English Teacher; *b:* Cheyenne, WY; *m:* Donald A.; *ed:* Wright St Univ (BS) Ed 1992; *cr:* Walter E. Stebbins HS Eng Tchr 1994-; *ai:* Ketting Fairmont HS Jr Var Vlybl Coach, Western OH League Champions 1993-95; NEA 1993-; *office:* Walter E Stebbins HS 1900 Harshman Rd Dayton OH 45424

MC KENZIE, THOMAS WILLIAM, GATE Teacher; *b:* Pittsburgh, PA; *m:* Julie Ann Cuccarese; *c:* Matthew, Korri Inderlied, Scott; *ed:* Edinboro Univ (BS) Art Ed; Attnd Penn St; *cr:* Port Allegany Schl Art Tchr 1968-69; Montour Schl Art Dept Chprsn 1977-80, Tchr of Art, Gifted 1969-; *ai:* Raccoon Boys Club Coach; NEA, PSEA 1968-; Montour Ed Assn 1969-; Raccoon Boys Club 1996 Bd Mem; Montour Ed Fdn Grant; Articles Pub; *home:* 151 Maplehurst Dr Aliquippa PA 15001

MC KENZIE, WILMA TEEL, Sixth Grade Lang Arts Tchr; *b:* Floyd, VA; *m:* Joseph Arthur; *c:* Deborah Pitts, Jeffrey, Jennifer Whitestone; *ed:* Radford Coll (BA) PE, Hlth 1956; Xavier Coll Elem Ed 1974; Miami Univ Elem Ed 1973; *cr:* Andrew Lewis HS PE, Hlth Tchr 1956-57; East Hartford HS PE, Bio Tchr 1957-58; Lebanon Cty Schls Self-Contained Fifth Grd Tchr, 5th Grd Sci Math, Soc St Tchr 3 Yrs, 5th Grd Sci, Math, Spelling Tchr 1 Yr, 6th Grd Lang Arts Tchr 2 Yrs; *ai:* Judge Odyssey of Mind Competition; SOS, PAT GATE, Playgound, Chm Soc Comms; Spelling Bee; NEA, OEA, LEA 1988-; *home:* 208 E Orchard Ave Lebanon OH 45036

MC KEOWN, SANDRA L. (ROWLEY), Sixth Grade Teacher; *b:* Lower Merion Twp, PA; *m:* James F.; *ed:* Millersville Univ (BS) Ed 1989; St Joseph's Univ (MS) Rdng 1995; *cr:* Mc Call Schl 6th Grd Tchr 1989-; *ai:* Schl Newspaper, Yrbk Adv; IRA 1995-; *office:* Mc Call Elem Schl 6th Delancey St Philadelphia PA 19106*

MC KERNAN, ANNE T., Social Studies Teacher; *b:* Hartford, CT; *ed:* Fordham Univ (BA) Pol Sci 1985; Trinity Coll (MPP,MA) Pub Policy 1989; *cr:* William H. Hall HS Soc Stud Tchr 1985-86; Newington HS Soc Stud Tchr 1986-; *ai:* Model United Nations Adv; Vlybl, Bsktbl, Sftbl Coach; CT Ed Assn, NEA 1985-; Newington Tchr Assn 1986-; St Patrick,St Anthony Church 1995-; *home:* 102 Talcott Forest Rd Farmington CT 06032*

MC KERNAN, WILLIAM HENRY, Physical Science Teacher; *b:* New Haven, CT; *m:* Patricia Vanacore; *c:* Brian, Kathleen, Shannon; *ed:* Southern CT St Coll (BS) Scndry Ed, Earth Sci 1975, (MS) Scndry Ed, Earth Sci 1980; Post-Grad Stud Fairfield Univ, Cntrl CT St Univ; *cr:* DePaolo MS Earth Sci Tchr 1975-94, Phys Sci Tchr 1994-; *ai:* Girls Bsktbl Coach; Natl Jr Honor Soc Adv; Quality Plus Comm; NEA; CEA; SEA; CT Sci Tchrs Assn; CT Earth Sci Tchrs Assn; Intnl Assn Approved Bsktbl Ofcls Bd 6 1980-; Tchr of Yr 1985; CT St Dept Ed Best Assessor 1990-; *office:* Joseph A Depaolo MS 385 Pleasant St Southington CT 06489*

MC KEY, DAN E., 6th Grade Teacher; *b:* Bloomington, IL; *m:* Penny Jane Miller; *c:* Brett, Bryce; *ed:* Taylor Univ (BS) Ed 1981; Ashland Univ (MS) Educl Admin 1995; *cr:* Walnut Creek Elem Schl 6th Grd Tchr 1981-; *ai:* Dist Chess Adv; Yth Bsktbl Coach; Berlin First Bapt 1981-; Received Approximately 20 Grants for Schl; *home:* PO Box 91 Berlin OH 44610

MC KIBBIN, MARTIN HOWARD, AP US History Teacher; *b:* San Antanio, TX; *m:* Leila; *c:* Suzanne, Mayoni, Lisa Smith, Gina Ripton; *ed:* Bucknell (BA) His 1952; Western MD (ME) Ed 1968; 8 Credit Hrs Harvard; *cr:* Westtown Schl Tchr 1953-54; Calvent Hall Schl Tchr 1954-57; Mc Donogh Schl Tchr 1957-; *ai:* Bsbl, Ftbl, Bsktbl Coach; AHA 1980-; Horn Fnd; MD His DAR Tchr of Yr 1952; Editor of What If? & Exploring the Path Not Taken in Amer His; *office:* Mc Donogh Schl PO Box 380 Owings Mills MD 21117

MC KIERNAN, PEGGY ANN, Mathematics Teacher; *b:* Bronx, NY; *ed:* Manhattan Coll (BS) Math 1992; Working Toward MS in Spec Ed; *cr:* Cardinal Spellman HS Math Tchr 1992-; Mount Saint Michael Acad Math, Cmptr Tchr 1993-94; *ai:* JV Chrldng Coach; Emerald Soc Moderator; NY St Math Tchrs Assn 1994-; *home:* 420 E 238th St Bronx NY 10470

MC KILLOP, DAVID J., Soc Stud Teacher & Adj Instr; *b:* Riverhead, NY; *m:* Alice; *c:* David, Alexandra; *ed:* C.W. Post (MA) Schl Admin; SUNY at Cortland (BA) Scndry Soc Stud Ed 1982; 45 Post Grad Credits; *cr:* Riverhead HS Tchr 1982-; Boces I Summer Schl Prin 1987-89; Riverhead HS Var Ftbl Head Coach 1989-93; *office:* Riverhead Cntrl Schl Dist 700 Harrison Ave Riverhead NY 11901

MCKINLEY, JOANNE MAY, English Teacher; *b:* Washington, DC; *m:* Reginald W.; *ed:* Madison Coll (BS) Eng 1964; Bowie St Univ Masters Equivalent 1977; *cr:* Falls Church HS Eng Tchr 1964-68; Bowie HS Eng Tchr 1968-; *ai:* Tchr Rep to PTSA; Prince Geos Cty Ed & MD Tchrs Assn 1968-; NEA 1964-; Yrbk Dedication 1992; Outstanding Educator 1992-93; *office:* Bowie HS 15200 Annapolis Rd Bowie MD 20715

MCKINNEY, CHESTER EDWARD, Science Teacher; *b:* Piqua, OH; *m:* Mary Tumbush; *c:* William, John; *ed:* Univ of Dayton (BS) Pre-Med 1967, (MS) Educl Admin 1984; Addl Studies; *cr:* Houston HS Sci Tchr 1966-; *ai:* OEA 1966-; WOEA 1966-; NEA; Hardin-Houston Ed Assn 1969-, Pres; West Cntrl OH Ftbl Ofcls Assn 1969-, Pres & VP; West Cntrl Oh Track Ofcls Assn 1975-, Charter Mem & VP; OH Track, Field & Cross Cntry Ofcls Assn 1990-; Shelby Cty Jr Fair Sale Comm 1994-, VP; *office:* Houston Jr Sr HS 5300 Houston Rd Houston OH 45333

MC KINNEY, HEATHER RUTH, English & History Teacher; *b:* Bozeman, MT; *m:* Richard B.; *c:* Richard, Brian, Kirk, Eric; *ed:* 3 Post Grad Credits Tchr Effectiveness Trng, Italian Renaissance Art; *cr:* Naperville HS Eng Tchr 1966-67; MacArthur Schl Co-Founder, Prin 1974-86; Montrose Schl Asst Head, Tchr 1986-92, Tchr, Adv 1992-; *ai:* Adv Character Formation Prgm; *office:* Montrose Schl 45 E Central St Natick MA 02026

MC KINNEY, LYNDA R., Public Relations Professor; *b:* Boston, MA; *m:* David Ashe; *c:* Stephen J., Michael J.; *ed:* Boston Coll (BA) Comm 1984; *cr:* William Donoghue Org Writer, Ed 1984-85; Hill, Holliday, Connors, Cosmopulos Inc Account Exec, Supvr 1985-88; Ingalls, Quinn & Johnson Group Mgr, VP 1988-93; Boston Coll Fac 1990-; Mc Kinney Pub Relations Pres 1993-; *ai:* Bell Ringer Awds 1987, 1992-93; *office:* Boston Coll Chestnut Hill MA 02167*

MC KINNEY, NANCY LOBAUGH, Social Studies Teacher; *b:* New Kensington, PA; *m:* Ronald C.; *c:* Jeffrey, Kevin; *ed:* IN Univ of PA (BS) Home Ec, Soc Stud 1961; Post Grad Work Bowling Green St Univ; *cr:* Butler Area Schls Jr High Home Ec Tchr 1961-62; Bellevue HS His & Eng Tchr 1962-63; Butler Evening Schl Adult Ed Tchr 1963-75; Butler Jr HS Homemanagement Tchr 1964-67; Butler Sr HS Home Ec Tchr 1982-83; Butler Intermediate HS Soc Stud Tchr 1983-; *ai:* Butler Ed Assn, NEA, PSEA 1982-; Phi Mu Alumni, Omicron Phi 1957-; *office:* Butler Intermediate HS 551 Fairground Hill Butler PA 16001

MC KINNEY, RANDALL LYNN, US History & Government Tchr; *b:* Irvine, KY; *m:* Shari Lynn Powers; *c:* Cory Lynn; *ed:* Miami Univ (BS) Ed 1989; *cr:* Twin Vly Local Schls US His, US Ec 1989-90; Eaton City Schls Jobs for Dayton Grads 1991-92; Northmont City Schls Jobs for Dayton Grads 1992-93; Eaton City Schls US His, US Ec 1993-; *ai:* Var Men's Cross Cntry Head Coach; Var Asst Men's Bsktbl Coach; 7th, 8th Grd Boys Track Coach; Soc Stud Proficiency Intervention Coord for Civics; OCSS 1986-; NEA, ECTA 1989-; OHSAA Bsktbl Coach 1985-; OHSAA Track, Field Coaches 1984-, X-C Dist Coach of Yr 1990; Optimist Club 1985-; *office:* Eaton City Schl Dist 307 N Cherry St Eaton OH 45320

MC KINNEY, WILLIAM SAMUEL, English Teacher; *b:* Bronx, NY; *m:* Denise Pisano; *c:* Marissa, Matthew; *ed:* Iona Coll (BA) Eng 1966, (MS) Eng 1973; *cr:* St John Vianney Schl 8th Grd Tchr 1966-68; Longfellow MS 8th Grd Eng Tchr 1968-76; Charles E. Gorton HS 9-12 Grd Eng Tchr 1976-; *ai:* Newspaper, Lit Magazine Advs; Yonkers Fed of Tchrs 1968-, Bldg Rep; Westchester Cncl Eng Ed 1976-; Eastchester Democratic Comm 1986-, Dist Ldr; Tuckahoe After Schl Care Inc 1994-, Sec; Tuckahoe PTA 1988-, Chprsn, Spec Ed; *office:* Charles E Gorton HS 100 Shonnard Yonkers NY 10703

MC KINNEY, WM. LYNN, Professor of Ed & Human Svc; *b:* Marshalltown, IA; *c:* Megan B., Andrew S.; *ed:* Cornell Coll (BA) His 1965; Univ of Denver (MA) Ed 1968; Univ of Chicago (PHD) Ed 1973; IN Univ Public Admin Cert 1983; *cr:* Univ of RI Prof of Ed 1972-; Hum Svc Prgm Dir 1984-, Co-Dir Ed 1995-; *ai:* Natl Org of Hum Svc Ed 1984-, VP for Conf, Lenore Mc Neer, Miriam Clubok Awds; New England Org for Hum Svc Ed 1983-; Vols in Action 1984-, Pres; RI Coalition Against Domestic Violence 1994-, Bd Mem; Sunrise Housing Corp 1994-, Bd Mem; Articles Pub; *office:* Univ Of RI Kingston RI 02881

MC KINNON, LENNELLE DOUGHERTY, English Teacher; *b:* Big Stone Gap, VA; *m:* Bernard; *c:* Michael Andrew, Cathy Anne Morrison, Christina Lee Cooper; *ed:* St Lawrence Univ (BA) Eng 1958; Hofstra Univ (MSEd) Ed, Eng 1964; Queens Coll 6 Hrs; SUNY at Potsdam 6 Hrs; *cr:* Oceanside HS Eng Tchr Grds 11-12 1958-60; Edwards-Knox C S Eng Tchr Grds 10-12 1965-; *ai:* NHS Adv; Drama Dir; NEA, NYEA 1960-; EKCS TA 1960-, Past Pres 3X, Past Sec, Past Treas; Canton Hosp Guild 1982-, Bd; St Law Golf & Cntry Club 1970-, Past Pres Women's Assn, Tournament Chair, Six Woman Team Mem; Delta Delta Delta 1964-, Advy Bd; Beta House Corp 1964-, Past Pres of Beta House Corp; Delta Kappa Gamma 1973-, Past VP & Pres; Stud Grant 1989 From Delta Kappa Gamma; Sabbatical Leave 1989 to Stud Educl Incentives Being Offered to Average Stdnts Scndry Schls.

MC KINNON, MARGARET CONNOR, English Teacher; *b:* Springfield, MA; *ed:* Sprinfield Tech Comm Coll (AA) Lbrl Arts 1987; Smith Coll (BA) Eng 1990, (MAT) Eng 1991; Our Lady of Elms Coll 3 Credit Courses Span for Thcrs; *cr:* Roger L. Putnam Voc & Tech HS Eng Tchr 1991-; Springfield Pub Schls Adult Ed Prgm at R. L. Putnam Voc Tech HS Eng Tchr 1996; *ai:* Drill Team Adv; Springfield U Mass Minority Achvmt Prgm Tutor; Acad Standards Comm; MTA, NEA, NCTE 1992-; *office:* Roger L. Putnam Voc & Tech HS 1300 State St Springfield MA 01109

MCKINNON, ROBERT JOHN, Vocal Music Director; *b:* Queens, NY; *m:* Susan; *c:* Rachel; *ed:* Long Island Univ CW Post Ctr (BFA) Music Ed 1978; Aaron Copeland Schl of Music (MS) Music Ed 1983; 30 Addl Credit Hrs in Music Stud; *cr:* Elmont Memrl HS Vocal Music Tchr 1979-81; H Frank Carey HS Vocal Music Tchr 1981-88; New Hyde Park Memrl HS Vocal Music Tchr 1988-; *ai:* Dir Chamber Singers; Nassau Music Edctrs Assoc 1979-; Amer Choral Dirs Assoc 1979-; Several Articles Pub; *office:* New Hyde Park Memorial JR HS 500 Leonard Blvd New Hyde Park NY 11040

MC KIRAHAN, DONNA BROWNING, Cosmetology Instructor; *b:* Zanesville, OH; *c:* Staci Lynn Heller, Gwyn Dee Griffths, Jeff; *ed:* Attnd OH Univ at Zanesville, OH St Univ; *cr:* Mid-East OH Voc Schl Dist Cosmetology Instr 13 Yrs; Boutique Beauty Salon Part-time Cosmetologist 1 Yr; The Image Boutique Owner, Operator 15 Yrs; Donna's Beauty Salon Owner, Operator 14 Yrs; *ai:* VICA Past Adv 4 Yrs; OEA, NEA, OVCTA, OVA, NVA 1984-; Natl VICA 1986-; New Concord Emer Med Svc 1976-, Sec, Treas; *home:* 12955 Longview Ln New Concord OH 43762*

MC KISSOCK, SCOTT HARDY, Bio & Adv Physiology Tchr; *b:* Meadville, PA; *m:* Cindy J. Proper; *c:* Ryan; *ed:* Edinboro Univ of PA (BA) Bio 1973, (MA) Ed 1976; 15 Addl Hrs; *cr:* Camb Spgs HS Tchr 1974-; *ai:* Coaching BB, Ftbl 15 Yrs; Ath Dir 5 Yrs; Mentor Tchr; NEA 1974-; Camb Spgs Borough Cncl 4 Yrs; Jaycees Started Little Gridders Prgm in Comm; Masonic Org Past Master; *office:* Cambridge Springs HS Venango Ave Cambridge Springs PA 16403

MC KNACK, JAYNE WOODS, Guidance Counselor; *b:* Waterbury, CT; *ed:* Coll of St Elizabeth (BA) Fr 1961; Fairfield Univ (MA) Guid 1966; Admin & Supervision Cert Southern CT St Univ; Cert in 4-MAT Trng; *cr:* Naugatuck HS Fr Tchr, Guid Cnslr 1961-; *ai:* Past Drama Coach, Class Adv; NEA 1961-; CEA; NTL; *office:* Naugatuck HS 543 Rubber Ave Naugatuck CT 06770

MCKNIGHT, TIMOTHY LEE, Social Studies Teacher; *b:* Amsterdam, NY; *m:* Theresa Giardino; *c:* Kelly; *ed:* Univ of VT (BA) Ed 1975; Grad Credits at Coll of St Rose & Albany St; *cr:* Mayfield HS Soc Stud Tchr 1975-76; Amsterdam Elem Schl Tchr 1976-80; Amsterdam Schl Dist Tchr of Gifted & Talented 1980-90; Lynch MS Soc Stud Tchr 1991-; *ai:* Track Coach; Cmptr, Soc Stud & Compact for Learning Comms; Former Tennis Coach; Asst Ftbl Coach 1978-; AFT, NYSUT 1975-; Amsterdam Tchr Assn 1976-, Soc Chm; United Presbyn Church, Deacon; Irish Amer Club; Dev Dist Gifted & Talented Prgm 1981; Received 2 IBM Cmptrs for Schl Through IBM Essay Contest 1990; *office:* Lynch MS 11 Liberty St Amsterdam NY 12010

MC KOAN, THOMAS FRANCIS, Fifth Grade Teacher; *b:* Concord, NH; *m:* Debra Ann; *ed:* St Anselms Coll (BA) Eng 1968; *cr:* Rumford Schl 5th-6th Grd Tchr 1974-; *ai:* Elem Bsktbl, Hockey Coach; Photography Club Adv; NEA, CEA 1974-; Appalachiam Mountain Club 1985-; Amer Legion 1987-; NH Presidential Distinguished Tchr Awd 1995.

MCLANE, DARIA MARIE (MUZI), 6th Grade Teacher; *b:* Scranton, PA; *m:* Leo C.; *c:* Mary M. McLane-Cassidy, Patrick L.; *ed:* Bloomsburg Univ (BS) Elem Ed 1968; Post Grad Stud at Wilkes Univ & Marywood Coll; *cr:* Old Forge Elem Schl 1st Grd Tchr 1980-86, Tchr of Gifted 1987-92, 6th Grd Tchr 1993-; *ai:* Sr Class Adv 1987-; Elem Comp Lab Coord 1990-; Young Authors Day Adv Elem 1989-; NEA 1979-; OFEA 1979-, Elem Bldg Comm 1996; St Josephs Auxiliary 1987-, Booth Chair Summer Festival; Friends of the Taylor Pub Lib 1990-91; ITEC Grant Writing Team Mem Elem Comp Lab 1989-90.

MC LANE, ROBERT T., Mathematics & Science Teacher; *b:* Pittsburgh, PA; *m:* Janet M.; *c:* Ryan, Brendan, Darren, Shannon; *ed:* Univ of Notre Dame (BSME) Mechanical Engineering 1970; Duquesne Univ (MAT) Scndry Ed 1972; Carlow Coll Post Grad Stud; *cr:* Quigley Cath HS Math & Sci Tchr 1971-; *ai:* PA Jr Acad of Sci St Judge; Acad Bowl Team Adv; Elem Schl Battle of Wits Coord; High Q Team Spon; Baden Lions Stu of Month Comm; Stu Cncl Moderator; Tandy Technology Scholars; Saint Francis College Outstanding Secondary Tchr Recognition; NCEA 1971-; Schl Sci & Math Assn 1971-; NCTM; Red Rage Wrestling Club 1988-, Asst Coach 1990-; Knights of Equity 1976-, Lector 1978-80; St Athanasius Athletic Assn 1985-; *office:* Quigley Catholic H S Franklin Road Ext Baden PA 15005

MC LAREN, HARRIET KAYE, Chemistry Teacher; *b:* Ambridge, PA; *m:* Gerald E.; *c:* Robert, Deborah; *ed:* Edinboro Univ of PA (BS) Scndry Ed Chem 1971, (MS) Scndry Ed Chem 1974; 9 Credit Hrs at Gannon Univ; Endorsement on Cert in Environmental Sci From Mercyhurt Coll; *cr:* Rochester HS Stu Tchr 1970; Tech Meml HS Sci Tchr 1971; Gen Mc Lane HS Chem Tchr 1971-; *ai:* Cooperating Tchr, Stu Tchrs; Gen Mc Lane Ed Assn, PA St Ed Assn, NEA 1971-; CSHS Boosters Club 1995-, Pres; *office:* General Mclane HS 11761 Edinboro Rd Edinboro PA 16412*

MC LAREN, JOHN R., Health Teacher; *b:* Butler, PA; *m:* Betty Jo Reed; *c:* Kristen A., Kelly L. Mc Laren-Olin; *ed:* Slippery Rock Univ (BS) Hlth, PE 1970; Attnd Slippery Rock Univ, Edinboro Univ; *cr:* Highland Schl Dist Hlth, PE Tchr 1970-71; Girard Jr, Sr HS Hlth, PE Tchr 1971-; *ai:* Coaching; AFT 1972-; Northwestern Schl Dist Bsktbl, Girard Jaycees CoachingCoaching Awds; *office:* Girard HS 1135 Lake St Girard PA 16417

MCLAREN, MARTHA GOODE, Eighth Grade Science Teacher; *b:* Baltimore, MD; *m:* Clyde W. Sr.; *c:* Clyde Jr., Terri P. Soward, Ryan Z. Hinrichs; *ed:* Western MD Coll (BA) Bio & Scndry Ed 1966; Shippensburg Univ Masters Equivalency Ed 1987; 24 Assorted Hrs of Other Grad Classes; *cr:* Baltimore Cty Bio Tchr 1966-68; Gettysburg Coll Sci Lab Instr 1968-84; James Gettys Elem 3rd Grd Tchr 1984-85; Gettysburg MS 8th Grd Sci 1985-; *ai:* Sr HS Band Front Adv; Knowledge Masters Coach; Mind Mania, MS Comm & Sci Dept Chair; Dist Cmptr Comm; PA Sci Tchrs Assn, NEA, Gettysburg Area Ed Assn 1985-; Soc for the Prevention of Cruelty to Animals 1980-; Soup Kitchen Bd 1994-; Keefauver Grant; Dist Mini-Grant; Outstanding Scndry Tchr Awd; Ed for Global Warming Curr; MCTP Visiting Comm; *office:* Gettysburg MS Lefever St Gettysburg PA 17325

MC LAUD, CARLA A., Mathematics Teacher; *b:* White Plains, NY; *m:* Eric S.; *c:* Julie, Eric M.; *ed:* SUNY at Albany (BS) Math 1982, (BA) Psych 1982; SUNY at New Paltz (MS) Ed 1987; *cr:* Perry Cntrl Schls Math Tchr 1982-83; Pine Bush Cntrl Schls Math Tchr 1983-; *ai:* NHS Adv 1992-95; Extra-Class Eligibility Chprsn 1992-; *office:* Pine Bush Cntrl Schls Rt 302 Pine Bush NY 12566*

MC LAUGHLIN, BRIAN, High School History Teacher; *b:* South Amboy, NJ; *ed:* Grad Schl of Newark, Rutgers Univ His 9 Credit Hrs; St PetersColl Admin & Supervision 15 Credit Hrs; *cr:* Woodbridge Schl Dist Sub, Replacement Tchr 1987-90; Berkeley Coll of Bus Admissions, Career Cnslr 1990-91; Roselle Cath HS Amer & World His Tchr 1992-; *ai:* Club Adv Environmental, His Club; Young Democrats, Republicans, Independents; *office:* Roselle Catholic HS 1 Raritan Rd Roselle NJ 07203*

MC LAUGHLIN, CHARLES JOHN, Social Studies Tchr & Attorney; *b:* Lancaster, PA; *m:* Barbara Clark; *c:* Maura, Kristen; *ed:* St Joseph's Univ (BA) Amer His 1966; Widence Univ (JD) Law 1995; Addl 18 Post Grad Credits Univ of DE, 30 Post Grad Credits; *cr:* Bishop Eustace Prep Schl Tchr 1967-69; Monsignor Bonner HS Tchr 1969-87; Malvern Prep Schl Tchr 1987-; *ai:* 7th Grd Bsktbl Coach; Producer of 8th Grd Video; PA Bar Assn, NJ Bar Assn, Chester Cty Bar Assn 1995-; Amer Jurisprudence Awd; *office:* Malvern Prep Schl 418 S Warren Ave Malvern PA 19355*

MC LAUGHLIN, CLAUDIA, Lang Dept Head & Span Teacher; *b:* St Louis, MO; *ed:* Cath Univ (AB) Fr 1965; John Hopkins Univ (MED) Scndry Ed 1976; Cath Univ (MA) Span 1984; *cr:* Severn Schl Tchr 1976-; *ai:* Span Club; Model OAS Delegation; AATSP 1987-; Kellogg Mexico US Project; *office:* Severn Schl 201 Water St Severna Park MD 21146*

MCLAUGHLIN, DEBORAH BELL, K-4th Grade Reading Teach Montreal, Canada; *m:* R. Mitchell; *c:* Courtney, Cameron; *ed:* Potsd Univ (BA) Psych 1981; Geneseo St Univ (MS) Rdng; *cr:* Moravia Schl 2nd Grd Tchr 1981-82; Letchworth Cntrl Schl 1st Grd Tchr 198 Rdng Tchr 1995-; *ai:* Grd Level Rep; Project Read Treas; Rdng Clu PDK 1986-, VP for Mbrshp; SPCA 1982-; *office:* Letchworth Cntr 5550 School Rd Gainesville NY 14066

MC LAUGHLIN, DONNA C. LORDEN, US History & Psych Te *b:* Medford, MA; *m:* Michael E.; *c:* Michael Jr., Matthew, Erin; *ed* Enrolled in Prgm Cambridge Coll; *cr:* Acad of Notre Dame Tc Seminar 21st Century Issue 1983-; *ai:* Sr Class Adv; Fac Laiso Comm; NCEA 1983-; *office:* Acad of Notre Dame 180 Middlese Tyngsboro MA 01879

MCLAUGHLIN, JAMES A., Fourth Grade Teacher; *b:* Summervill *m:* Nancy Greenwood; *c:* Molly Warner; *ed:* Clarion St Coll (BS) El 1963, (MS) Elem Math 1971; *cr:* Brockway Area Schls Fifth Grd 1963-64, Sixth Grd Tchr 1964-86, Fourth Grd Tchr 1986-; *ai:* Gir Sftbl, Boys Elem Bsktbl Coach; PSEA, NEA 1963-; Brookville E Assn 1964-; Brookville Elem Tchr of Yr 1982-83; *home:* RR 4 Bo Brookville PA 15825

MCLAUGHLIN, JAMES LEE, Vocal Music Director; *b:* Hillsboro *ed:* OH Univ (BFA) Music Ed 1968; Post Grad Stud at Westminster Coll & OH St Univ; *cr:* Grover Cleveland Jr HS Vocal Music Dir 196 Zanesville HS Vocal Music Dir 1990-; *ai:* MENC & OCDA 1968-; OEA & NEA 1968-; OMEA 1968-, Adjudicator, Dist 9 Pres; Cntrl T United Meth Church, Music Dir; Thursday Music Club 1978-, Zanesville Civic Chorus 1978-, Conductor; Jennings Scholar Optimist Boys Choir Dir; Zanesville Chamber Orch Dir; *office:* Zane City Schls 1701 Blue Ave Zanesville OH 43701

MCLAUGHLIN, JAMES MARTIN, Amer & European His Teach Pittsburgh, PA; *m:* Vickie L.; *ed:* IN Univ of PA (BS) Soc Stud 1973; St Univ Masters Equivalency; *cr:* Franklin Regnl Advanced Place Amer & European His Tchr 1973-; *ai:* Caring Team & Cty-Wide Stu F Spon; Soc Stud Dept Head; NEA 1973-; *office:* Franklin Regional S 3200 School Rd Murrysville PA 15668

MC LAUGHLIN, JOHN GROVER, Math Chair; *b:* Franklin, PA Eleanor Kersting; *c:* Jonathan, Douglas, Shannon; *ed:* Duquesne Univ Music Ed 1969, (MS) Music Ed 1971; Math Credit Hrs Towson St, Lo Univ; *cr:* Monongahelee HS Music Tchr 1969-72; Golden Ring J Music Tchr 1973-76; Milford Mill HS Music, Math Tchr 1977-85; Ov HS Math Tchr 1986-; *ai:* Voice of the Falcons; NCTM 1984-; Catons Meth Church Choir 1977-; Dir Ctr for Math, Sci & Tech; *office:* Ov HS 5401 Kenwood Ave Baltimore MD 21206

MCLAUGHLIN, JOHN LAWRENCE,III, English Teacher; *b:* Sa MA; *ed:* Salem St Coll (BA) Eng 1966; Cambridge Coll (MED) Integ Stud 1991; *cr:* Danvers Pub Schls Tchr 1966-; Salem St Coll North Consortium for Staff Dev & Tchr 1993-; *ai:* Dunn MS Team Ldr; Dar Tchrs Assn 1966-; MA Tchrs assn 1967-; NEA 1967-; *office:* Dunn M Cabot Rd Danvers MA 01923

MCLAUGHLIN, JUDITH SWEET, English Teacher; *b:* Cleveland, *m:* Robert E.; *c:* Megan Jones, Kate, Patrick; *ed:* Ursuline Coll (BA) 1959; John Carroll Univ (MA) Eng 1981; 60 Credit Hrs; *cr:* Euclid HS Tchr 1959-63 & 1978-; *ai:* Drama Coach; OEA, NEA & ETA 1959-; N 1959-, Writing Contest Coord; *home:* 286 E 260th St Euclid OH 441

MCLAUGHLIN, LISA MARIE, Social Studies Teacher; *b:* Toms R NJ; *ed:* Georgian Court Coll (BA) His & Ed 1993; *cr:* Toms River HS S Sub Tchr 1993-94; Jackson Memrl HS World His & Cultures Tchr 1994 *ai:* Color Guard Adv; Jr Class Co Adv; PTA Jackson 1994-; NEA 19 NJEA 1994-; Kappa Delta Pi; Delta Tau Kappa; Phi Alpha Theta; *of* Jackson Memorial HS 101 Don Connor Blvd Jackson NJ 08527*

MCLAUGHLIN, MICHAEL PATRICK, Theology Teacher; Cleveland, OH; *ed:* Quincy Coll (BA) Commnctn 1989; John Carroll (MA) Theology 1996; *cr:* St Ingatius HS Theology Tchr 1991-, Var So Coach 1991-; *ai:* Var Soccer Coach; Environmental Club Modera Amnesty Intnl Adv; *office:* Saint Ignatius H S 1911 W 30th St Clevel OH 44113

MCLAUGHLIN, PAUL FRANCIS, Principal; *b:* Cincinnati, OH Rebecca Abshear; *c:* Erin, Sean; *ed:* Xavier Univ (BA) His & Govt 1 (MED) Ed 1976; Post Grad Math & Statistics Work at Univ of Cincinn Admin Cert; *cr:* Saint Andrew Schl Sci Tchr 1975-86; Saint Aloy Gonzaga Schl Sci & Eng Tchr 1987-89; Saint William Schl Math & Tchr 1989-94; Our Mother of Sorrows Schl Prin 1994-; *ai:* NCEA, N AACD; Catechetical Ldr; *office:* Our Mother Of Sorrows Schl 7 Eastlawn Dr Cincinnati OH 45237*

MCLAUGHLIN, ROSEMARY KATRRYN, English Teacher; Pittsburgh, PA; *m:* William J.; *c:* Molly, Barry; *ed:* Univ of Pittsburg (Eng Ed 1970, (MAT) Eng Ed 1974; 12 Credit Hrs in Spec Ed; Homestead Jr HS Eng Tchr 1970-71; Oliver HS Eng Tchr & Dept C 1971-93; Pittsburgh Pub Schls Acting Eng Supvr 1990-91; Mount Leba HS Eng Tchr 1993-; *ai:* Lit Magazine; AFT 1971-83; PSEA 1993-; Co Svc Appalachia Workcamp 3 Yrs; Art & Eng Grant 1974; Tchrs M Grants 1983, 1989; Write Bi-Monthly Article for North Hills News Rec About Ed & Teenagers; *office:* Mt Lebanon Sr H S 155 Cochran Pittsburgh PA 15228

MC LAUGHLIN, VIRGINIA L., Kindergarten Teacher; *b:* Baysh NY; *m:* Gerard J. Avolio; *c:* Alison Avolio, Marcus Avolio; *ed:* SU Oneonta (BS) Elem Ed 1973; SUNY at Stony Brook (MALS) Lbrl S 1978; 16 Addl Hrs; *cr:* Blue Point Schl Kndgtn, 2nd-3rd Grd Tchr 19 *ai:* Grandperson's Day Comm Chair; Parents as Rdng Partners Co Peercoaching Team; NYSUT 1973-; Bayport Blue Point TA 1973-, B Rep, Elem VP, Recording Sec; Girl Scouts 1991-, Ldr, Asst Ldr; *home* Lacy Ct Blue Point NY 11715

MC LAUGHLIN, WILLIAM FRANCIS, 6th-8th Grade Tech Teacher Brooklyn, NY; *m:* Ernestine; *ed:* Staten Island Comm (AAS) Electro 1967; City Coll NYC (BSEd) Indstrl Arts 1970, (MSEd) Ed 1975; Add Credits 1993; *cr:* Winthrop Jr HS Indstrl Arts Instr 1972-75; N Afterschool Ctr Arts, Crafts Instr, Supvr 1972-75; BOCES II GATE Robotics Instr 1987-89; Bellport MS Tech Tchr; *ai:* Tech Club A Renaissance Core Comm; Dist Wide Tech Task Force; Suffolk Cty T Tchr Assn 1986-; NY St Tech Ed Assn.

MC LAUGHLIN, WILLIAM FRANCIS, English Teacher; Wilmington, DE; *m:* Toni; *c:* Christopher; *ed:* St Thomas of Villanova (B Eng 1966; Wilmington Coll (MS) Ed 1996; Univ of DE 15 Grad Cred *cr:* St Mark's HS Eng Tchr 1973-74; Concord HS Eng Tchr, Dept C 1975-; *ai:* Eng Dept Chm; NCTE, NSGS 1975-; DATE 1975-, Tchr of Tchr of Yr 1996; *office:* Concord HS 2501 Ebright Rd Wilmington 19810

MCLAUGHLIN, WILLIAM JOHN,JR., Associate Professor; *b:* Sara Lake, NY; *m:* Lorraine Larkins; *c:* Kerry Ann, Timothy Michael; *ed:* Univ of NY at Plattsburg (BA) Speech Comm 1977, (MA) Mgmt Leadership 1987; Univ of AR 36 Grad Hrs 1979; *cr:* Paul Smiths Coll In 1980-87, Asst Prof 1987-92, Assoc Prof 1992-; *ai:* Prof Standar Judiciary Comms 1990-; Soph Class & Foreign Stdnts Club A Intramural Sports; NBEA 1994-; Saranac Lake Little League Bsbl 198

Coach, Champions 1995; Adv of Yr Paul Smiths Coll 1992; *office:* Smiths Coll Of Arts & Sci Paul Smiths NY 12970*

LAUGHLIN BRUEGGER, RUTH E., Fifth Grade Teacher; *b:* on, OH; *m:* Elam G.; *c:* Scott, Sharon Dubler; *ed:* Ashland Univ (BS) 1972; Bowling Green St Univ (MS) Ed 1982; Miami Univ ronmental Sci Elem Tchrs Geology Field Station; *cr:* Avon Lake Pub Tchr 1972-; *ai:* Fifth Grd Level Chprsn; Safety Patrol Supvr; Avon Ed Assn, Northeastern OH Ed Assn, NEA 1972-; Eisenhower Fnd t; *office:* Troy Intermediate Schl 237 Belmar Blvd Avon Lake OH 2

LAUGHLIN-SMITH, DAVE, Intermediate Math Teacher; *b:* Wilkes , PA; *m:* Carolyn G.; *c:* Macee, John; *ed:* E Stroudsburg (BS) Soc Stud -76; Wilkes Univ (MSEd) Gen Ed 1988; Univ of Scranton (MS) Adm, El Principalship 1989; Elem Cert; Temple Univ Doctoral Stud; *cr:* -Lehman SD Elem Tchr 1979-; *ai:* Strategic Planning Comm; NEA -, Grievance Chair; PSEA 1986-; PTA, Life Mem; Upward Bound nni Assn 1992-, VP; Doctoral Flwshp Temple; Outstdng Grad Schl in U of Scranton; *office:* Lake Noxen Elem Schl RR 3 Box 270 eys Lake PA 18618*

LEAN, ELIZABETH BOORSE, Science Teacher; *b:* Cleveland, OH; ll, Brad; *ed:* Miami Univ (BA) Bio 1966; Univ of Dayton (MED) Ed ; 3 Grad Hrs Barrie Univ; 3 Grad Hrs MI St Univ; 6 Grad Hrs Miami , Field Geology & Environmental Sci for Tchrs; Tropical Rainforest oral Reef Ecology Belize 1993; 6 Grad Hrs Chem & Phys Miami Univ; Wilder Jr Hs Sci Tchr 1980-; *ai:* Coord Dist 1 NEED Project for 1992-; Olympiad; Event Captain Sci Olympiad 1993-, Coach 86-89; Wilder Jr NEED Team St Wnrs 1994 & 1995, Natl Fnlst 1994, Natl Wnr 1995; ., OEA 1980-; SECO 1983-; NSTA 1989; Piqua Ed Fnd Distinguished xemplary Service in Ed Awd, Grant to Implement the Word Game & Sci; WY Wkshp Environmental Sci Lead Tchr; OH NEED Project Lead 3 Yrs; Piqua Cty Schls Tchr of Yr 1995; State of OH TOY Fnlst; tndng Tchr Greater Miami Vlly by Eng & Sci; Hall of Fame; Bd of tees; *office:* Wilder Jr H S 1120 Nicklin Ave Piqua OH 45356

LEAN, JAMES DOUGLAS, High School Mathematics Tchr; *b:* alo, NY; *m:* Maija Karlson; *c:* Brian, Marissa; *ed:* SUNY at Brockport Scndry Math 1969; 48 Hrs Ed, Math, Cnslng; *cr:* Gates Chili Cntrl s HS Math Tchr 1969-; *ai:* Boys Var Soccer & Hockey Coaches 17 Yrs; SUT 1969-; NYSMTA 1989-; NSCAA 1980-; Section V Class A Soccer ch of Yr 1986, 1992, Hockey Coach of Yr 1991, 1994; *home:* 21 Barn llow Ln Rochester NY 14624

LEAN, NANCY, 7th-8th Grd Biling & ESL Tchr; *b:* Guantanamo nte, Cuba; *m:* Gladstone George; *c:* Gladstone George II, Joseph rge; *ed:* Georgian Ct Coll (BA) Span 1975, (ELEM) Elem Ed 1975; gers Univ (MS) Cncl Psych 1985; Biling Cert 1983; ESL Cert 1983; Bil 975; *cr:* Lakewood Bd of Ed ESL Tchr 1975-76; New Brunswick Bd d 3rd Grd Biling Tchr 1976-78; Lakewood Bd of Ed Biling, ESL Tchr -; *ai:* Adv LEP Tex, Span Club; Funraiser, Attendance Comm; AAUW -; NJEA, LEA 1976-; Adult Com Ed 1976-, Outstdng Tchr Awd; Jack of Amer 1985-; Tutorial Svcs 1977-, Tchr; Tchr of Yr 1993; *home:* 620 ceton Ave Lakewood NJ 08701

LENNAN, HELEN M., Dance Teacher & Owner; *b:* Nairobi Kenya, Africa; *m:* James Gallagher; *c:* Carol; *ed:* Grad Grandison Coll 3 Yr g Ballet, Jazz, Tam Modern, Ballroom, Acting, Singing 1970; *cr:* Les tre Des Jennes Ballet Dept Dir 1972-77; Coune Studio Ballet Dept Dir 8-84; Dance Design Schl Tchr 1984-; *ai:* Hudson Vly Dance Theatre stic Dir; Royal Acad of Dancing 1970-, Registered Tchr, Intermediate mination; Choreographer Several New BAllets; *office:* Dance Design Box 750 291 Main St Cornwall NY 12518

LENNAN-SMITH, NANCY, Social Science Teacher; *b:* Garfield atn, ME; *m:* Parker R. Smith; *c:* Jodi Smith Bolduc; *ed:* Univ of ME) Behavorial Sci 1978; 33 Credit Hrs in Art Working Toward BA; *cr:* ningham MS Migrant Tchr 8 Yrs; *ai:* Asst Drama Dir; Close-Up Adv; A, MTA 1978-; Who's Who in Univ; *home:* 12 3rd St Presque Isle ME 59

LENON, VONDA LYNN (KEELERE), Science Teacher; *b:* tabula, OH; *m:* Hal; *ed:* Hiram Coll (BA) Bio 1981; SUNY Brockport) Sci Ed 1992; *cr:* Aquinas Inst Sci Tchr 1988-, Sci Dept Chair 1992-; Ski Club; Sci Tutors; NY St Bio Major; NABT 1993-; *office:* Aquinas 1127 Dewey Ave Rochester NY 14613

LEOD, JOANNE SLIWINSKI, 4th Grade Teacher; *b:* Troy, NY; *w:* ert N. (dec); *c:* Deborah Halpin, Robert J., Patricia O'Brien; *ed:* SUNY Fredonia (BS) Music Ed 1961; Coll of Saint Rose (MS) Ed 1968; ltisensory Techniques for Tchng Rdng, Writing, Spelling 5 CEU; ssell Sage Coll Mngmt & Leadership Skills for Women 6 CEU; dership & Jr Great Books Prgms; *cr:* Saint Gregory's Schl Tchr 1969-, ad of Lower Schl 1978-83 & 1986-95; Asst Head 1995-; *ai:* Arts Comm; of Trustees Fac Rep; Headmaster Comm Search; Discipline, Advy, r, Salary Schedule& Benefits Comms; CAIS & NYSAIS Confs; Mentor, aluator Tchr; Dean of Stdnts 1990-92; Accmpnst at Our Lady of Fatima urch; Kappa Delta Pi 1959-; ASCD 1989-; CRISA 1994-; *office:* St egorys Schl For Boys Old Niskayuna Rd Loudonville NY 12211*

LEOD, JULIA MARIE, Third Grade Teacher; *b:* Cleveland, OH; *c:* hleen, Kenneth, Erik; *ed:* Bowling Green St Univ (BS) Elem Ed 1974; Grad Hrs Ed; *cr:* North Madison Elem Schl Second Grd Tchr 1974-84, rd Grd Tchr 1985-; *ai:* Elem Math Comm 1995-; Title I Summer Rdng mp Tchr 1994-; Tchr Ldr People to People HS Ambassador Prgm 1975; A, OEA 1974-, Soc Comm; MEA 1974-, Local Bldg Rep; Cub Scouts 9-, Wolf, Bear, Weblo Den Ldr, Comm Mem, 6 Yr Pin, Webelos Den Medal & Square Knot; Nom Lubrizol Corp Lake Cty Sci Tchr of Yr d 1993; OAESA Hall of Fame Schl Staff Mem 1994-95; Lakelana Area Sci, Math Awd 1991-92; *office:* North Madison Elem Schl 6735 N ge Rd Madison OH 44057*

CLEOD, MAUREEN C., Assoc Prof Criminal Justice; *b:* Chicago, IL; Frederick Kitzrow; *c:* Ryne, Andrew; *ed:* Mundelein Coll (BA) Soc Sci 75; Univ at Albany (MA) Criminal Justice 1977, (PHD) Criminal Justice 33; *cr:* Stockton St Coll Asst Prof 1983-84; Hindelang Criminal Justice search Ctr Principle Investigator 1984-87; NYS Division of Parole searcher 1987-88; Russell Sage Coll Assoc Prof 1988-; *ai:* Acad of minal Justice Scis; Amer Soc of Criminology; Criminal Justice ucators Assn of NYS, Regnl VP; Bethlehem Youth Court 1996, Citizens vy Bd; Court Referred Vol Prgm of Rensselaer Co 1990-, Advy Comm air; Victim-Offender Mediation Prgm of Columbia & Greene Ctys 93-, Treas & Bd of Dirs; Articles Pub in the Following Journals Journal Criminal Justice Ed, Sage Colls Magazine, Criminal Justice, Judicature, minal Law Bulletin, Journal of Criminal Justice, Criminology, Justice arterly & Crime & Delinquency; *office:* Russell Sage Coll At Troy 45 rry St Troy NY 12180

C LIMANS, JEFFREY PAUL, English Teacher; *b:* St Paul, MN; *m:* ristine; *c:* Ashley, Blake; *ed:* Buffalo St (BA) Eng Ed 1972, (MA) Eng 1979; *cr:* Hamburg Cntrl Schl Eng Tchr 1972-.

CMACKIN, WILLIAM J., Economics Teacher; *b:* Philadelphia, PA; *m:* san; *c:* Molly, Kevin; *ed:* Cert & Post Grad Courses in Mrktg at Saint sephs Univ; *cr:* West Cath HS Tchr, Admin, Coach & Moderator 1966-; Sigma Phi Epsilon Alumni 1966-; Assn of Cath Tchrs 1970-; Amer ktg Assn 1966-; Glenside Youth Athletic Assn 1990-; Overbrook Soc Club 1985-; Mid Sts Fac Comm Chm 1995; *office:* West Catholic H S 4501 Chestnut St Philadelphia PA 19139

MCMAHON, CHRISTINA MARIE, Biology & Ocean Studies Tchr; *b:* Rochester, NY; *ed:* SUNY at Cortland (BS) Bio Ed 1990; SUNY at Potsdam (MS) Bio & Sci Ed 1994; Boston Univ 128 Credit Hrs Bio Tech; *cr:* Malone MS 7th Grd Sci Tchr 1990-91; Lowville HS 8th & 9th Grd Sci Tchr 1991-92; Pine Bush HS 9th-11th Grd Sci Tchr 1992-93; Gloucester HS 9th-12th Grd Sci Tchr 1993-; *ai:* Class of 1997, Yrbk & Ecology Club Adv; NABT 1994-; MA Senate Awd of Excl in Sci Tchng; MA House of Rep Awd of Excl in Sci Tchng; *home:* 4 Wiley St Gloucester MA 01930*

MC MAHON, JOE, 8th Grade Teacher; *b:* New York, NY; *ed:* Marist Coll (BA) Math 1970; Univ of Notre Dame (MA) Ed 1976; *cr:* St Casimir Schl Tchr 1973-74; Whitney Young Street Acad Tchr 1975-87; John Adams HS Tchr 1987-89; St Anthony Schl Tchr 1989-; *ai:* Coach Ftbl, Bsktbl, Bsbl, Track; *office:* St Anthony Schl 1395 Nepperhan Ave Yonkers NY 10703

MC MAHON, KENNETH J., Fourth Grade Teacher; *b:* Brooklyn, NY; *m:* Lorraine S. Lyon; *c:* Dawn, Debra, Dianne; *ed:* St Univ of NY at Stony Brook (BA) His Ed 1965; Hofstra Univ (MS) Elem Ed 1966; St Univ of NY at Stony Brook (MA/LS) Lbrl Stud 1971; Addl 45 Hrs to Enhance Tchng Skills; *cr:* Harborfields CSD 6th Grd Tchr 1966-67; Connetquet CSD 3-6 Grd Sci Specialist Tchr 1967-; *ai:* Connetquet Tchr Ctr Chprsn 6 Yrs; Connetquot Tchrs Assn VP 25 Yrs; Bldg Sci Mentor of NY St ESPET 8 Yrs; Site Based Mngmt Dist Steering Comm; Connetquot Tchrs Assn 1967-, VP; AFT 1967-, Del; NYSUT 1967-, Del; NSF Inst for Elem Sci Grant; *office:* John Pearl Elem Schl 1070 Smithtown Ave Bohemia NY 11716*

MC MAHON, MARGARET (MIANO), 4th Grade Teacher; *b:* Salem, MA; *m:* Thomas V.; *ed:* Salem St Coll (BS) Elem Ed 1981; Salem State (MEd) 1995; *cr:* Our Lady of Grace 5th Grd Tchr 1981-83; Our Lady of The Assumption 4th Grd Tchr 1983-; *ai:* Self Stud Co-Chprsn 1993-; Stu Cncl Adv 1992-93; Math Coord 1993-; *office:* Our Lady The Assumption Schl 40 Grove St Lynnfield MA 01940

MC MAHON, PATRICIA A. CARROLL, Assistant Professor of Spanish; *b:* Weehawken, NJ; *m:* Francis Xavier; *c:* Jennifer, Scott; *ed:* Mt St Agnes coll (BA) Span 1967; Fairleigh Dickinson U (MAT) Span Ed 1972; Rutgers Univ (MA) Span Lit 1992; Working on PHD Span, Womens Stud; MI St Univ Frgn Stud in Spain 1966; Frgn Lang Inst Mexico 1971; *cr:* Buffalo Sminars for Girls Span Tchr 1967-68; Iberian Press Biling Receptionist 1969; Holy Angels Acad Span Tchr 1970-73; Westfield HS Span Tchr 1973-77; Georgian Ct Coll Span Asst Prof 1981-; *ai:* Moderator Sigma Delta Pi; Admissions Comm; Acting Dir of Admissions 1995; Campus Connection Liaison Ofcr; Spon Womens His Month Representing Hispanic Women; Modern Lang Assoc 1987-; FLENJ; Womens His Month Comm 1990-; St Anthony Claret Misson for Span Speakers, Vol; Nom Sigma Iota Phi; Mercy Coll Hnr Soc; Asst Prof 1993; *office:* Georgian Court Coll Lakewood Ave Lakewood NJ 08701

MC MAHON, ROBERT HUGH, History Teacher; *b:* Camden, NJ; *m:* Diane; *c:* Tara, Shanna; *ed:* Glassboro St Coll (BA) His, Eng 1970; 30 Hrs Post Grad; *cr:* Gateway Regnl HS His Tchr 1970-72; Matawan Ave MS Soc Stud Tchr 1973-86; Matawan Regnl HS His, Eng Tchr 1986-; *ai:* AFT 1973-; NEA, NJEA 1988-; MRTA; Intnl Assn of Approved Bsktbl Ofcls 1980-; *office:* Matawan Regional HS Atlantic Ave Matawan NJ 07747*

MC MAHON, SABINA LEIGH, Mathematics Teacher; *b:* Huntington, NY; *m:* William; *c:* Quinn, Colin; *ed:* Colgate Univ (BA) Eng 1984; Tchrs Coll (MA) Math 1987; Columbia Univ (MA) Math 1987; *cr:* Nightingale Bamford Schl Math Dept Head 1984-90; Northfield Mount Hermon Schl Math Tchr 1991-; *ai:* Var Gymnastics Coach; Dormitory Head; *office:* Northfield Mount Hermon Schl 206 Main St Northfield MA 01360

MC MAHON, TERENCE THOMAS, Social Studies Teacher; *b:* New York, NY; *m:* Dianne E. Prorok; *c:* Kevin, Timothy, Colleen Coate, Erin; *ed:* Canisius Coll (BA) His 1963, (MA) His Ed 1965, (MS) Cnslr Ed 1970; SUNY at Buffalo Rdng 1970-75; *cr:* Cardinal O'Hara HS Soc Stud Tchr 1963-65; Orchard Park HS Guid Cnslr 1967-80, Soc Stud Tchr 1980-; *ai:* Girls, Boys Var Tennis Coach; NYSJT 1965-; HYSPHSSAA 1965-, Coach of Yr 1980, 1986, 1990, 1994; Nativity of Our Lord Parish 1977-, Parish Cncl 1984; *office:* Orchard Park HS 4040 Baker Rd Orchard Park NY 14127*

MCMAHON, WILLIAM E., English Teacher; *b:* Middletown, CT; *m:* Jacqueline DeBari; *c:* Michelle Dabrowski, Sean; *ed:* Univ of CT (BA) Eng 1958; Univ of Hartford (ME) Ed 1962; Wesleyan (MA) Studio Arts 1987; Attnd Univ of MA, St Josephs Coll; *cr:* Rocky Hill HS Eng & Photography Tchr 1962-, Eng Dept Head 1968-89; *ai:* Lit Magazine Adv; Girls Track Coach; NEA 1962-; CEA 1962-; RHTA 1962-; U Conn Alumni Awd for Excl in Tchng; Numerous Poems Pub; Essex Art Assn Sculpture Awds (Twice); *home:* 180 Prospect St Middletown CT 06457*

MC MAHON, WILLIAM EDWARD, Social Science Teacher; *b:* Fall River, MA; *m:* Annie France Sloan; *c:* William Jr., Stephanie, Rachel; *ed:* St Michael's Coll (BA) Govt 1963; Attnd Boston Coll, Univ of MA at Amherst, Univ of MA at Dartmouth Post Grad Stud; *cr:* B.M.C. Durfee HS Soc Sci Tchr 1971-; *ai:* NEA, MTA, FREA 1971-; Vietnam Veteran of Amer 1991-; USAF Former Captain, Viet Nam Combat Fighter Pilot Awd Distinguished Flying Cross, Air Medal 11 Oak Leaf Clusters; Golden Appled Awd by Fall River Nerald News 1993; *office:* Durfee HS 360 Elsbree St Fall River MA 02720

MC MAKEN, ROSE ANN, Sixth-Seventh Grd Math Teacher; *b:* Detroit, MI; *m:* R. Tracy Jr.; *c:* Jennifer, Jeffrey, Elizabeth; *ed:* Wright St Univ (BS) Elem Ed 1987; Grad Stud Univ of Dayton; *cr:* Covington MS Tchr 1988-; *ai:* Curr & Instructional Cncl; OEA, NEA, CEA, NCTM, OCTM, WSACTM 1988-; 4-H Club Premier Livestock 1990-, Adv; Miami Co Livestock Comm Sec; MCPP; Natl Deans List; Coached Sci Olympiad Team to St Finals 1988-92; *office:* Covington MS 25 Grant St Covington OH 45318

MCMANN, MARY ELIZABETH, Assoc Prof of Counseling Dept; *b:* Potsdam, NY; *ed:* St Lawrence Univ (BA) Govt & His 1976; Colgate Univ (MAT) Tchng 1980; St Univ of NY at Albany (MS) & (CAS) Cnslng Psych 1981; Syracuse Univ PHD Ed 1996; *cr:* SUNY Inst Of Tech Cnslr 1981-82; Hamilton Coll Cnslr & Asst Dir of Career Planning-Placement 1982-83; Onondaga Comm Coll Assoc Prof & Cnslng 1983-; *ai:* Fin Aid Advy Comm; Co-Chair of Mid Sts Coll Comm on Stu Svcs; Scholastic Stan Comm; Co-Developer of HS Transitions Course; NY St Fed of Tchrs 1983-; AFT 1983-; Schls of Character Task Force 1989-92; Hospice Of Cntrl NY 1995-, Fundraising; NISOD Excl Awd; Univ of TX at Austin Ctr Comm Coll Ldrshp; Outstdng Frosh Advocate from Univ of SC at Columbia Ctr for Frosh Yr Experience; Bd of Trustees Recognition Awd from Onondaga Comm Coll; *office:* Onondaga Comm Coll Rt 173 C-209 Syracuse NY 13215

MCMANUS, COLLETTE GARTNER, 7th & 8th Grade Science Tchr; *b:* Hackensack, NJ; *m:* Warren Edward Jr.; *c:* Melissa, Megan, Michele; *ed:* Caldwell Coll (BA) Elem Ed 1971; Fairleigh Dickinson Univ Sci Inst for Elem Schl Tchrs 1971; *cr:* Navesink Schl 5th Grd Tchr 1971-72; St Leo the Great Schl 7th-8th Grd Sci Tchr 1985-; *ai:* Fac Rep to PTA; Asst Dir Schl Play; Curr Coord for Sci; Sci Fair Adv & Organizers; NCEA 1985-; *office:* St Leo The Great Schl 550 Newman Springs Rd Lincroft NJ 07738

MC MANUS, JEFFREY SCOTT, Science Teacher; *b:* Dayton, OH; *m:* Ann Pelc; *ed:* Univ of Dayton (BA) Chem 1992; Working Towards MED; *cr:* Fairmont HS Sci Tchr 1993-; *ai:* Sci Olympiad Coach; Kettering Outstdng Tchr Awd 1995.

MC MANUS, MARY HAIRSTON, English Professor; *b:* Danville, VA; *m:* Booker; *c:* Philip T., Kenneth A.; *ed:* VA St Univ (BA) Eng 1958, (MA) Eng 1967; Univ of MD at College Park (PHD) Eng Lang, Lit 1992; Attnd Univ of NC at Chapel Hill, Southern IL Univ at Edwardsville, Cambridge Univ; *cr:* VA St Univ Instr 1965-70; Fayetteville St Univ Instr 1975-78; Venice-Lincoln Tech Ctr Instr 1978-83; Bowie St Univ Asst Prof & Hnrs Prgm Dir 1984-; *ai:* Sigma Tau Delta Co-Fac Adv; Fac Senate; Founders Day, Inaugural, Commencement Comms; Modern Lang Assn 1988-; Coll Lang Assn, IVCTE 1987-; Mid Atlantic Writers Assn 1992-, Newsletter Co-Ed; Alpha Kappa Alpha 1969-; Chums Inc 1982-, Pres; Kiwanis 1995-; Natl Endowment for Hum Flwshp; Who's Who in Ed 1989-; Outstdng Edctrs Awd PG Co Fire Dept; *office:* Bowie St Univ 14000 Jericho Park Rd Bowie MD 20715

MC MANUS, PAUL M., Curriculum Specialist; *b:* Fall River, MA; *m:* Teresa M. Houlihan; *c:* Paul A., Erin A.; *ed:* Bridgewater St Coll (BSE) His 1964; Providence Coll (MA) Amer His 1968; 12 Credit Hrs Boston Coll; 6 Credit Hrs RI Coll; 30 Credit Hrs Bridgewater St Coll; *cr:* Somerset HS Soc Stud Tchr 1964-, Dept Chm 1968-94; Bridgewater St Coll Instr 1972-74; Bristol Comm Coll Instr 1969-; Curr Specialist 1994-; *ai:* Critical Thinking Skills Comm Co-Chm; NCSS; MA Cncl Soc Stud; New England His Tchrs Assn; Souhteastern Cncl Soc Stud; ASCD; Natl Assn Realtors; MA Realtors Assn; NEA; MA Tchrs Assn; Somerset Tchrs Assn; Rep John F. Quinn Comm Co-Chm; St Mary's Parish Lector, Eucharistic Minister; Robert A. Taft Fellow RI Coll 1975; Brown Univ Fellow 1986; *office:* Somerset Pub Schls Grandview Ave Somerset MA 02726

MC MEANS, JAN, Gifted Support Tchr & Consult; *b:* New Kensington, PA; *m:* Larry; *c:* Ian; *ed:* IN Univ of PA (BA) Elem Ed 1974; Penn St Univ of PA Permanent Cert 1977; *cr:* Freeport Area Schl Dist Elem Tchr 1974-79; Buffalo Elem Schl Gifted Support Tchr & Consultant 1979-; *ai:* Action Team for Strategic Plan & Environmental Ctr Comms; 24 Game Schl Coord; NEA, PSEA & AEA 1974-; PAGE 1980-; All Star Edctr Awd 1995; *office:* Buffalo Elem Schl 500 Sarver Rd Sarver PA 16055*

MCMEEKIN, JANE MARGARET, Social Studies Teacher; *b:* Topeka, KS; *m:* Donald Ray; *ed:* Otterbein Coll (BA) His, Govt 1969; OH St Univ Post Grad Stud; *cr:* Westerville South HS Soc Stud Tchr 1972-; *ai:* Peer Mediation Adv; Westerville Ed Assn, OH Ed Assn, NEA 1972-; NCSS 1972-90, 1995-; *office:* Westerville South HS 303 S Otterbein Ave Westerville OH 43081

MC MENAMIN, MARGARET MARY, Assoc Professor & Prgm Coord; *b:* NYC, NY; *ed:* Temple Univ (BS) Phys Therapy 1979; Univ of Scranton (MS) Human Resources 1985; Lehigh Univ Ed Leadership; *cr:* LCCC Instr 1984-86; Good Shepherd Clinical Dir 1986-90; LCCC Assoc Prof, Coord 1990-, Intern Dean 1994-95; *ai:* Allentown Cntrl Cath HS Bsktbl Asst Coach; NEA; Amer PTA 1978-, Stat Treas; *office:* Lehigh Carbon Comm Coll 4525 Education Park Dr Schnecksville PA 18078

MCMILLAN, MARY DONATACCIO, HS Home Economics Teacher; *b:* Akron, OH; *c:* Jeral, Jacqueline; *ed:* Univ of Akron (BS) Home Ec Ed 1973; *cr:* Brunswick HS Home Ec Tchr 1973-79; Cuyahoga Falls Schl System Sub Tchr 1980-90; Cuyahoga Falls HS Home Ec Tchr 1987-88; Archbishop Hoban HS Home Ec Tchr 1993-; *ai:* Summer Schl Coord; Lending Hand to Stu Cncl Spon Dance; Akron Home Ec Tchrs 1993-95; *office:* Archbishop Hoban HS 400 Elbon Ave Akron OH 44306

MC MILLAN, SUSAN ALEXANDER, Math Teacher; *b:* Oceanside, NY; *m:* Marty; *c:* Cody; *ed:* Adelphi Univ (BS) PE 1980, (MS) Math 1988; 15 Credits above MS at Ctr for Integrated Tchr Ed; *cr:* Massapequa Pub Schls 7th Grd Math Tchr 1985-; *ai:* Massapoqua Fed of Tchrs, NYSUT 1985-.

MCMILLEN, LORETTA RYAN, Communications Arts Teacher; *b:* Staten Island, NY; *m:* Harlow; *c:* Ryan, Lauren; *ed:* Brooklyn Coll (BA) Eng 1965; Coll of Staten Island (MA) Eng, Ed 1970; *cr:* Paulo IS 75 Comm Arts Tchr 10 Yrs; Bernstein IS 7 Comm Arts Tchr 9 Yrs; *ai:* Newspaper, Debate Team Adv; Publications Coord; UFT 1965-; SI Historial Soc Conf House Assn 1969-, Past Mem; Wrote, Edited Cookbook Hisorical Soc Vol Post; *office:* Paulo Intermediate Schl 75 455 Huguenot Ave Staten Island NY 10312

MCMILLIN, KATHARINE E., Physics Teacher; *b:* Philadelphia, PA; *m:* Larry; *c:* Mark, Timothy; *ed:* Iowa St Univ (BS) Physics & Ger 1969, (MS) Physics 1971; Stud in Comp Sci Ed; *cr:* Suitland HS Phys Sci Tchr 1972-73; Gwynn Park HS Physics & Math Tchr 1973-79; NASA Comp Programmer 1979-85; Friendly High Physics & AP Physiics 1991-; *ai:* Math Team Spon; Equity 2000; Math & Sci Liaison; Physics Outcomes Curr Comm; Stud Tchr Supvr; PGCEA, NEA & MSTA 1972-; AAPT 1995-; Clinton Boys & Girls Club 1985-; Maryland Choral Soc 1978-; Pepco Outstdng Tchr Awd 1994; Carnegie-Mellon Fellow 1985; *office:* Friendly HS 10000 Allentown Rd Fort Washington MD 20744*

MC MILLION, LAURA LANE, 9th Grade English Teacher; *b:* Manila, Philippines; *m:* Gaither Landern; *c:* David; *ed:* Concord Coll (BS) Eng, Span 1963; Univ of Dayton (MS) Schl Cnslng 1989; 4 Qtrs Schl Cnslng Youngstown St Univ; 1.8 CEUS Applied Comm Jefferson Comm Coll; *cr:* Barboursville HS Tchr 1963-66; Steubenville HS Tchr 1966-; *ai:* ACT, SAT Tutor; ABLE, GED Tchr; Steubenville Ed Assn, OEA, NEA 1966-; OARCE 1995-; *office:* Steubenville HS 420 N 4th St Steubenville OH 43952*

MC MILLON, DELORES NI, 8th Grd American History Tchr; *b:* Jackson, MS; *m:* Roosevelt; *c:* Keith R., Angelique D.; *ed:* Jackson St Univ (BS) Soc Sci 1960; Ball St Univ (MS) Guid, Cnslng 1981; 1 Credit Hr African Amer Stud; 3 Credit Hrs MS Acad; 1 Credit Hr Death & Dying; *cr:* Corinth Elem Schl 4th Grd Music Tchr 1960-61; Coleman HS 7th-8th Grd Soc Stud Tchr 1961-67; Lakenheath Amer HS 10th-11th Grd Soc Stud Tchr 1967-68; Peachbelt Mental Hlth Clinic Adolescent Cnslr 1974-77; Ramstein Jr HS 8th Grd Tchr, Cnslr 1979-; *ai:* Prins Advy Comm; Overseas Ed Assn, NEA 1983-; Alpha Kappa Alpha 1959-, Treas; *home:* PSC Box 2 Box 7987 APO AE 09012*

MC MONIGLE, FRANCIS MARIE,SND, Art Teacher; *b:* Havertown, PA; *ed:* Trinity Coll (BA) Ed 1958; Drexel Univ (MS) Art, Home Ec 1965; Notre Dame IN 9 Grad Credits; MD Fine Arts Ins 15 Grad Hrs; Simmons Coll 6 Grad Credits; Seton Hill Coll 15 Grad Hrs; Marymount Coll & Credits; *cr:* Villa Julie Coll Art Dept Chair, Home Ec Chair, Guid 1952-62; Notre Dame HS Art Dept Chair 1962-66; Notre DameAcad Art Dept Chair 1966-67; Kennedy Ins Handicap ped Ch Art Dept Chair, Arts & Craft Tchr 1968-72; Archbishop Ryan HS Art Dept Chair, Home Ec Chair 1972-73; Bishop Ireton HS Art Instr, Fine Arts Dept Chair 1973-85; Padua Acad Art Instr, Fine Arts Dept Chair 1985-; *ai:* Arts & Crafts Prgm for Mentally Handicapped Children; NCEA, NEA, Notre Dame Ed Soc 1962-; DE Fnd Yth in Art 1985-; Designed Ofcl Seal or MD Assn of Colls, Catonsville Comm Coll; *office:* Padua Acad 905 N Broom St Wilmington DE 19806

MC MULLEN, DOUGLAS D., Automotive Mechanics Instr; *b:* Stamford, NY; *m:* Vicki D. Collins; *c:* Matthew D., Lucas D., Cassandra D.; *cr:* SUNY Instr, Automotive Mechanic's 1993-; *ai:* NcOC Advy Comm Auto Mechanics; NACAT 1995-; NIASE 1978-, Master Cert; BSA 1993-, Chprsn Den Ldr; *office:* S U N Y Coll Of Tech At Delhi 106 Sanford Hall Delhi NY 13753

MC MULLEN, TIMOTHY DANIEL, Elem Physical Ed Teacher; *b:* Batavia, NY; *m:* Marcia Ann Mc Keon; *c:* Jamie, Corky; *ed:* Ithaca Coll

(BA) PE 1980; Geneseo SUNY (MA) Elem Ed 1985; *cr:* York Cntrl Schl PE Tchr, Coach 1981-82; Letchworth Cntrl Schl PE Tchr, Coach 1982-; *ai:* Asst Var Ftbl Coach; Head Var Bsktbl Coach; JV Bsbl Coach; Var Club Adv; Bsktbl Coaches of NYS 1989-; NEA, NY Tchrs Assn 1982-; United Church of Christ 1993-, Bd of Elders, Sunday Schl Tchr; Coach of Yr 1994, Bsktbl, Section V; *office:* Letchworth Cntrl Schl 5550 School Rd Gainesville NY 14066

MCMULLEN, TIMOTHY MICHAEL, Honors Ec Instr; *b:* Baltimore, MD; *m:* Mary T.; *c:* Erin, Tim, Eddie; *ed:* Towson St (BA) Sec Ed 1970, (MA) Soc Stud 1974; *cr:* Arundel Jr HS His Tchr 1970-71; Brooklyn Park Sr HS His Tchr 1971-81; Brodneck His & Ec Tchr 1981-; *ai:* Asst Ath Dir; Asst Bsbl Coach; Tchrs Assn of Anne Arundel Cty; MSTA; NEA; Natl Reader APUSH Exam 1995 & 1996; Ath Dir of Yr Balto Sunpaper; Tchr of Yr Nom 1990 & 1996; *office:* Broadneck Sr HS 1265 Green Holly Dr Annapolis MD 21401*

MC MULLIN, MARCIA TURTZO, Biology Teacher; *b:* Bethelhem, PA; *m:* William C.; *c:* Kimberly, Melody, Jim, Linda M. Smith, Greg, Tony; *ed:* Centenary Coll for Women (AA) Bio 1968; West Chester St Univ (BS) Bio 1970; DPI at Harrisburg M Eq Bio 1978; 32 Credits Cmptr Ed Daytona Beach Comm Coll, Jt univ Cntrl Fl; Marine Rsrch DE Bay Marine Scis Consortium, R. V. Annandale, Cheney St Univ; *cr:* Phoenixville Sr HS Bio Tchr 1971-, Ecology Tchr 1988-91; *ai:* Coach JV Girls Bstkbl 1971-72, YMCA Swim 1973-76; Girls Track Asst Coach 1977-83; SUN Club; Adv Class of 1974, Soph Class of 1994; PSEA 1970-; NEA; YMCA; Girl Scouts of Amer; Human Genetic Rsrch Dr W. Tesize West Chester Univ; NASA Rsrch Team Investigate Effects Marine Waste, Disposal Nuclear Waste Washington Canyon, Gulf Stream, Atlantic O; Pub Article; Three Yrs Diving Rsrch Bermuda Bilogical Soc; *office:* Phoenixville Area HS Gay & City Line Ave Phoenixville PA 19460

MC MURRAY, PEGGY HARRISON, 2nd Grade Teacher; *b:* Lockport, NY; *m:* Lorne A.; *c:* Bradley Ryan, Andrew Benjamin; *ed:* SUNY at Brockport (BS) Psych 1982, (MS) Elem Ed 1984; Video Courses St Peters, Univ of AK, George Washington Univ, Drake Univ; Credit Hrs West MI, Chapman; *cr:* Barker Cntrl Schl 3rd Grd Tchr 1985-87, 2nd Grd Tchr 1987-; *ai:* Math, Negotiating Comm; Grd Cncl Mem; Video Course Approval Comm Chair; NYSUT, AFT, NYSC, TE 1995-; Meth Church 1973-; Barker Cntrl Alumni 1979-; Tech NY St Cncl of Sschl Supt Presenter; NYNEX Grant; Oratorical Contests for Optomists Club Judge; 4-H, FFA; NYSC, TE Conf Presenter; *office:* Barker Central Schl 1628 Quaker Rd Barker NY 14012

MCMURTRY, EMMA LEE ELIZABETH, Social Studies Teacher; *b:* Bellevue, PA; *m:* John F.; *c:* James M., Melanie, John M.; *ed:* Westminster Coll (BA) Soc Stud 1953; Univ of Pittsburgh (MS) Elem Ed 1955; Advanced Work on Ed Admin; *cr:* Knoxville 3rd Grd Tchr 1955-56; Avalon 6th Grd Tchr 1956-61; Washington 3rd & 4th Grd Tchr 1963-64, 3rd-8th Grd Tchr 1966-87, 11th & 12th Grd Amer Govt & Amer His Tchr 1987-; *ai:* NEA 1956-, Life Mem; PSEA 1956-; WEA 1963-; Church of the Convenant 1961-; Bradford House 1980-, Former Pres; Applied for NASA Tchr in Space Pgm 1986; DAR Tchr of the Yr for Washington Cty & St of PA 1990; League of Women Voters Svc Awd 1993; PA Cncl for the Soc Stud Scndry Tchr of the Yr for the St of PA 1994; *office:* Washington Schl Dist 201 Allison Ave Washington PA 15301

MC NABB, EDWARD JOSEPH,JR., US History Teacher; *b:* Boston, MA; *c:* Amy, Moira, Teddy; *ed:* Boston St Univ (BS) His 1969; Univ of MA (MED) Ed 1992; Attnd Fitchburg St, US Army Schl of Aviation; *cr:* J. F. Kennedy Schl Grd 6 Tchr 1972-76; Charles Taylor Schl Asst Prin 1976-81; Eng HS His Tchr 1984-; *ai:* Nazzaro Yth Ctr Bd Mem; Friends of Copps Hill VP; Scituate Beach Assoc Pres; Boston Tchrs Union 1972-; Amer Legion #316 1976-; *office:* English HS 144 Mcbride St Jamaica Plain MA 02130

MCNABB, NANCY GREIN, School Nurse; *b:* Englewood, NJ; *c:* Matthew; *ed:* Englewood Cliffs Coll (AA) Lbrl Arts 1968; Felician Coll (AAS) Nrsng 1973; Caldwell Coll (BA) Psych 1987; Certfd Coronary Care, Critical Care & Remotiational Therepy; Teen Pregnancy Nutrition Edctr; Quest; *cr:* Newton Mem Hosp Rehabilitation Nurse 1981-83; NJ DYFS Grant Coord 1985-87; Kittatinny Reg HS Schl Nurse 1988-; Camp Nejeda Hlth Ctr Dir 1991-; *ai:* Schl With a Heart Rep; Baby on Bd Edctr; Child Stud Team & JDA Mem; Remotivation Therapist; Amer Red Cross 1976-; NEA 1988-; ADA 1988-, Med Comm; Wrote Manuals for Head Trauma Inst & Nurses Aide Trng; *office:* Kittatinny Regnl HS Rd 10 Box 10255 Newton NJ 07860*

MC NAIR, ERICK DONNELL, Anatomy & Hnrs Gen Bio Teacher; *b:* Bethesda, MD; *c:* Erick Jr.; *ed:* Howard Univ (BS) Bio 1984; Case Western Univ (BS) Cardiovas Perfusion 1989; Howard Univ (MS) Physiology 1993; Fairfax Hosp Schl of Cardiovascular Tech 1985; *cr:* Fairfax Hosp Assoc Instr 1985-88; The WA Hosp Cnt Instr 1990-93; Archbishop Carroll HS Instr 1992-; *ai:* Cardiovascular Credentialing Int 1985-; Amer Bd of Cardiovascular Perfusion 1988-; 3 Pub Articles.

MC NALLY, ARDETH D., Third Grade Teacher; *b:* Brooklyn, NY; *m:* Michael Alan; *c:* Kelli Lyn Mc Nally Lorey; *ed:* St Univ of NY at Oswego (BS) Ed 1965; Long Island Univ at Southampton (MS) Ed 1980; 75 Addl Credits; *cr:* Bellew Schl 4th Grd Tchr 1965-67; Westbrook Schl 3rd Grd Tchr 1970-; *ai:* PTA; NYSUT 1970-; AFT; West Islip Tchrs Assn 1965-67, 1970-; Honorary Life Mem NY St Congress of Parents & Tchrs; *office:* Westbrook Elem Schl Higbie Ln West Islip NY 11795

MCNALLY, EDWARD JAMES, 5th Grade Teacher; *b:* Port Jefferson, NY; *m:* Carol Ann Wischhusen; *c:* Christopher, Brian; *ed:* Dowling Coll (BA) Ed 1973; Adelphi Univ (MS) Ed 1975; Post Grad Work Univ of AK; *cr:* Longwood Dist 3rd, 4th, 5th Grd Tchr 1973-; *ai:* Photo-Journal Club Adv; Middle Island Tchrs Assn & NYSUT 1973-; St Pauls Lutheran Church 1980-, Cncl Mem 1987-89, 1989-90, 1990, 1991, Soup Kitchen Dir 1989-; BSA Comm Chm 1987-91; NYS PTA, Life Mem Awd 1990; *office:* Coram Schl 61 Coram Mt Sinai Rd Coram NY 11727

MCNALLY, EILEEN (O'DONNELL), 4th Grade Teacher; *b:* New York City, NY; *m:* John K.; *c:* Michael, Kenneth; *ed:* Jersey City St Coll (BA) Elem Ed 1967; Presch, Nursery Schl Cert From Kean Coll; *cr:* Jersey City P512, 22 1st, 4th Grd Tchr 1968-71; Packanack Lake Presch Tchr of 2 Yr Olds 1984-86; St Rose of Lima Acad 4th Grd Tchr 1986-; *ai:* Mid Sts Strategic Action Plan Coord; NCEA 1986-; Our Lady of Mt Carmel Ed Cncl 1989-93; *office:* St Rose Of Lima Acad 316 Ridgedale Ave East Hanover NJ 07936

MC NALLY, MARGARET CLARKE, Second Grade Teacher; *b:* Auburn, NY; *m:* James E.; *c:* Wendy R. Marks, Joel A., Lindy M. Drapikowski; *ed:* Oswego St Tchrs Coll Elem Ed 1970; 48 Other Grad Hrs; *cr:* K. C. H. Elem Schl 2nd Grd Tchr 1970-; *ai:* NYSUT 1970-; Altar Rosary Soc Craft Club.

MCNAMARA, BRIAN J., Sixth Grade Teacher; *b:* Staten Island, NY; *m:* Judith Tarallo; *c:* Kate Lynn, Evan; *ed:* Wagner Coll (BS) Elem Ed 1970, (MED) Elem Ed 1972; *cr:* Willowbrook Schl Classroom Tchr 1970-74; Wildwood Schl Classroom Tchr 1976-; *ai:* Coaching Girls Bsktbl, Boys Soccer & Boys Bsbl Leagues; MA Tchrs Assoc 1976-; Amherst Tchrs Assoc 1976-, Pres 1982-83; NEA 1976-.

MC NAMARA, CATHERINE VIRGINIA (HUDDY), Reading & Language Arts Tchr; *b:* Brooklyn, NY; *m:* Michael J.; *c:* Maureen Sager, Dawn Sager, Edward Sager; *ed:* St John's Univ (BS) Eng 1960; Coll of New Rochelle (MS) Gifted Ed; William Paterson Coll LDTC Cert Learning Disab; Brooklyn Coll 4 Hrs Grad Schl; Queens Coll 6 Hrs Grad Schl; *cr:* Long Beach Jr HS Eng Tchr 1961-63; NY City Bd of Ed Elem Tchr 1963-65; Martin J. Ryerson MS 8th Grd Tchr, Lang Arts Rdng 1975-; Japanese Amer Soc Tutor 1989-91; *ai:* Mind & Spirit Lit Moderator 4 Yrs; IM Pupil Assistance Comm; Great Books Trust Moderator; Yrbk Moderator 2 Yrs; NJEA 1975-; Ringwood Ed Assn 1975-, Pres 3 Yrs, Rep Cncl 7 Yrs, NEA 1973; NCTE 1985-87; US Olympic Torch Carrier 1996, Comm Hero; Ringwood Gifted Ed Prgm Selection & Dev Prgm; Rdng & Spelling Materials Comm; Ringwood PTO Grant.*

MC NAMARA, DAVID L., Chemistry Teacher; *b:* Arlington, MA; *c:* Joseph; *ed:* Stonehill Coll (BS) Bio, Chem 1965; Northeastern Univ (MED) Ed 1969; 60 Credits Beyond Masters Degree; *cr:* Avon HS Tchr 1966-68; Concord-Carlisle Regnl HS Tchr 1968-; *ai:* SADD Adv; NEA, MTA 1966-; Concord-Carlisle Tchr Assn 1968-; Meritorious Tchr Awd; *office:* Concord-Carlisle Regnl HS 500 Walden St Concord MA 01742

MC NAMARA, DENNIS BOWEN, High School Mathematics Tchr; *b:* Providence, RI; *m:* Deborah A. Sperduti; *c:* Michael, Eric; *ed:* RI Coll (BA) Math 1971; Providence Coll (MED) Scndry Admin 1993; Post Grad stud; Enrolled in Courses Obtain Supts Cert; *cr:* Aldrich Jr HS Math Tchr 1971-72; Winman Jr HS Math Tchr 1972-93; Toll Gate HS Math Tchr 1993-; *ai:* Schl Improvement Team; AFT, RIMTA 1971-; NCTM 1993-; *office:* Toll Gate HS 575 Centerville Rd Warwick RI 02886*

MC NAMARA, DENNIS JAMES, Biology Teacher; *b:* Princeton, NJ; *m:* Teresa Jean Mc Clain; *c:* Dawn Jean, Brian James; *ed:* Monmouth Univ (BS) Bio 1969, (MA) Scndry Adv Scis 1974; Prin Supvrs Cert 1981; *cr:* Middletown HS North Bio Tchr 1968-, Sci Dept Coord 1993-94; *ai:* Stu Cncl Adv; Cooperating Tchr; Tchr Mentor; NJ Sci Symposium Exec Comm; NEA, NJEA, MTEA 1969-; NSF Grant Chem for Bio Tchrs 1972; Govt Tchr Recognition Awd 1995; *office:* Middletown HS North 63 Tindall Rd Middletown NJ 07748*

MCNAMARA, ROBERT P., Social Studies Teacher; *b:* Webster, MA; *m:* Janice Pfeiffer; *c:* Jeffrey, Shawn; *ed:* Worcester St (BS) Scndry Ed 1972, (MEd) Educl Admin 1982; 42 Grad level Courses; 90 Hrs Masters; *cr:* Epson NH Cntrl Schl 7th & 8th Grd Sci & Soc Stud Tchr 1972-73; Bay Path Reg Voc Tech HS 9th-12th Grd Soc Stud Tchr 1973-; *ai:* Accreditation Co-Chprsn; Mentor Pgm & Inclusion Tchr; Stu Govt Day Adv; Grad Comm Co-Chair; Bay Path Educl Reform Comm; NEA 1973-; MA Tchr Assn 1973-; BPTA 1973-, Bd of Dirs; MA Voc Assn 1990-; Dudley Little League 1985-92, Coach; Awds: Cntrl MA Soccer Referees Sportsmanship, Colossial Ath League Coach of Yr (Twice), Twenty First Century Tchr of Yr Auburn Chamber of Commerce Tchr of Yr; Sr Yrbk Dedications (Twice; *office:* Bay Path Regional Vo Tech Schl 57 Old Muggett Hill Rd Charlton MA 01507*

MCNAMEE, JARI G., Life Studies Teacher; *b:* Laconia, NH; *m:* William J. McNamee; *c:* Robert McNamee, Kristin, Ashley; *ed:* Keene St Coll (BS) Home Ec 1978; Working Towards MA in ELem Ed; *cr:* Concord HS 10th-12th Grd Life Stud Tchr 1978-84, 9th-12th Grd Tchr, Dept Chprsn 1984-92, 10th-12th Grd Tchr 1992-; *ai:* NEA 1978-; NHVA 1992-; TOPSS, APA 1993-; Consumer & Familty Sci Federal Grant 1988-92; NH Pub Trust Peer Mediation 1994-95; *office:* Concord HS 170 Warren St Concord NH 03301

MCNAMEE, JOYCE MARIE, Prof & Dept Chair of Chrstn Ed; *b:* Waterloo, IA; *ed:* Bapt Bible Coll of PA (BRE) Rel Ed 1957; SUNY at Cortland (MS) Elem Ed 1963; Attnd Univ of Northern IA, Univ of Akron, Marywood Coll; *cr:* Immanuel Bapt Church Dir of Chrstn Ed 1959-60; Northfield Bapt Church Dir of Chrstn Ed 1962-64; Syracuse St Schl Tchr 1960-62; Bapt Chrstn Schl Tchr 1964-76; Bapt Bible Coll Prof 1976-; *ai:* NCTE 1990-; IFCST 1994-; *office:* Bapt Bible Coll & Sem 538 Venard Rd PO Box 800 Clarks Summit PA 18411

MC NANEY, PATRICIA BARBARA, Teacher; *b:* Rochester, NY; *m:* William F.; *c:* Irene E. Steele; *ed:* Nazareth Coll of Rochester (BA) Eng Ed 1973; Cornell Univ (AAS) Indstrl Labor Relations 1975; Nazareth Coll of Rochester (MS) Eng Ed 1976; Advanced Coursework; Staff Dev Courses; *cr:* Monroe Comm Coll Assoc Prof Eng Adj 14 Yrs; Greece Cntrl Schl Dist Eng Tchr 19 Yrs; *ai:* Bldg Prof Support, Bldg Budget Comm; Genesee Valley Supervision & Curr Dev Bd Mem 1980-; NCTE 1970-; NY St Cncl of Eng, NY St Rdng Cncl 1973-; Lit Vol 3 Yrs; Phi Delta Kappa 1990-; Polands Govt Dept of Ed Cert of Tchng Excl 1993; Taught South China Univ 1986; Tchng Position UNESCO Kosciuszko Fnd 1993; *office:* Greece Athena HS 800 Long Pond Rd Rochester NY 14612

MC NATT, JODY LYNN, English & Drama Teacher; *b:* Cleveland, OH; *m:* Richard; *c:* Emily Regan; *ed:* Grove City Coll (BA) Eng, Comm Arts, Scndry Ed 1991; Working on MA Eng John Carroll Univ; *cr:* Chagrin Falls HS Eng, Drama Tchr 1991-; *ai:* Drama Dir; Thespian Club Adv; Spring Musical Dir; Var Vlybl Coach; NEA, OEA 1992-; OH Theater Assoc 1994-; Co-Dev Mentoring Prgm; Drama Dept Grants; *office:* Chagrin Falls HS 400 E Washington St Chagrin Falls OH 44022*

MCNEAL, KAY D., Elementary Librarian; *b:* Sayre, PA; *m:* Marshall; *c:* Stacie Anderson, Nicole Anderson, Kevin, Traci; *ed:* Mansfield Univ (BS) Lib Sci 1969; Elmira Coll; *cr:* Troy Area Schl Dist Librn & Tech 25 Yrs; *ai:* TAEA 1969-, Pres, Sec; PSEA, NEA 1969-; Freedom to Learn; *office:* W R Croman Elem Schl 250 Canton St Troy PA 16947

MCNEAL, PHYLLIS ELAINE, English Teacher; *b:* Emporia, KS; *m:* Bruce A. Marks; *c:* Anthony Marks, Allen Marks; *ed:* Univ of KS (BA) Eng & Fr 1984; Mansfield Univ Ed Cert 1987; *cr:* Coll du Capouchine Eng Lang Tchng Asst 1984-85; Wyalusing HS Eng Tchr 1987-; *ai:* Schlsp Challenge; Peer Tutoring; NEA 1987-; PSEA 1987-; Mellon AP Flwshp Awd.

MCNEELY, KENNETH PATRICK, Mathematics Teacher; *b:* Graves Cty, KY; *m:* Enrichetta Favero; *c:* Clifton, John, Kenneth W., Cheri; *ed:* Murray St Univ (BS) Math 1963; Ball St Univ (MA) Cnslng 1979; *cr:* Benton Harbor Math Tchr 1960-61; Berrien Springs Math Tchr; Cassopolis Math Tchr; Hillsdale Math Tchr; Aviano Math Tchr 1974-; *ai:* Ftbl & Bsktbl Coach; Ath Dir; AFT; NEA.

MC NEIL, RACHEL EADDY, English Teacher; *b:* Zebulon, NC; *m:* Leo; *c:* Derek Carl, Kimberly Chirawn, Kelly Jarrod; *ed:* St Augustines Coll (BA) Eng 1971; Salisbury St Univ (MED) Ed 1985; *cr:* John Graham HS Eng Tchr 1971-72; Charles City HS Eng Tchr 1972-74; Washington HS Eng Tchr 1975-; *ai:* Sr Spon, Sunshine, Pub Relations & Guidance Advisory Comms; TESA & Wellness Teams; Eng Dept Chprsn; NEA 1971-; TASCO 1975-; Delta Kappa Gamma 1987-; Human Relations Awd 1990; Perfect Attendance Awd; *home:* 7636 Fentral Ave Salisbury MD 21801*

MC NEILL, ANNE H., Mathematics Teacher; *b:* Lackaghmore Offaly, Ireland; *w:* Alexander (dec); *c:* Elizabeth; *ed:* Neuman Coll at Aston (BA) Eng; Long Island Univ Brooklyn Campus (MS) Ed, Math 1986; 39 Credits Brooklyn Coll; 6 Credits St Michaels Coll; *cr:* St Raphael Elem Schl Grd 4, 7 Tchr 1961-71; Our Lady of Assumption Elem Schl Grd 7, 8 Tchr 1971-74; Gen Paper Goods Cost Accountant Asst 1974-75; St Savior Elem Schl Grd 8 Tchr 1975-79; Franklin D. Roosevelt HS Math Tchr 1986-; *office:* Franklin D. Roosevelt HS 5800 20th Ave Brooklyn NY 11204

MC NELLY, CHARLES WESLEY, Music Teacher; *b:* Sidney, OH; *ed:* Olivet Nazarene Univ (BS) Music Ed 1964; 30 Hrs Toward MA OH St Univ 1980-81; *cr:* Heberle Elem Schl Music Tchr 1965-70; Manhattan Pub Schls 19 Elem Tchr 1970-72; Elizabeth Pub Schls Elem Schl Music Tchr 1972-; Victor Mravlag Elem Schl #21 Elem Schl Music Tchr 1981-; *ai:* Schl Chorus; Union Cty Educ Assn; NEA, NJ Educ Assn, Elizabeth Educ 1972-; MENC; St of NJ Governor's Tchr Recognition Awd 1990; Victor Mravlag Elem Schl 21 132 Shelley Ave Elizabeth NJ 07208

MC NERNEY, MICHAEL KENNETH, Sixth Grade Teache Bayonne, NJ; *m:* Renee Mazzucola; *c:* Christopher, Megan; *ed:* Jerse St Coll (BA) Elem Ed 1978; Commonwealth Excl in Sci Tchng Al 1992; Natl Sci Resources Ctr Elem SCi Ldrshp Inst 1993; *cr:* Madiso Dist 6th Grd Tchr 1978-85; Montgomery Elem Schl 5th Grd Tchr 198 North Wales Elem Schl 5th Grd Tchr 1992-94, 6th Grd Tchr 1994 Merck Inst for Sci Ed Advy Comm 1992-95, Summer Ldrshp Inst NEA, PSEA, North PA Ed Assn 1987-; NSTA 1996; Montgomery S Assn 1991-, Coach; Hatfield Little League 1993-, Coach, Mgr; Cub S 1994-, Webelo Ldr; *office:* North Wales Elem Schl 201 Summit St Wales PA 19454

MC NICHOLAS, EUGENE F., 7th-8th Grade Science Teache Brooklyn, NY; *m:* Barbara Steen; *ed:* Ramapo Coll (BS) Bio, Ed Working Toward Masters in Elem Sci Ed at Fairleigh Dickenson Un Ramsey HS Bio Tchr 1989-90; Chancellor Acad 8th Grd Sci Tchr 199 Hardyston Twp Schl 7th-8th Grd Sci Tchr 1991-; *ai:* Stu Cncl Adv; Sftbl Coach; Community Affairs Comm; Sci Curr Chm; NSTA 199 Sci Tchrs Assn 1989-, North Regnl VP; Dodge Fnd, HPTA, IKE C 1995-96; BET Fnd Participant 1995; *office:* Hardyston Twp Elem Sc State Route 23 Franklin NJ 07416*

MC NIFF, MARIE PAULA, Literature Tchr, NHS Moderator; *b:* Bo MA; *ed:* Emmanuel Coll (BA) Ed, Eng, Fr 1958, (MA) Ed 1967; Sale Coll Rsrch Methods in Ed, Amer Short Story Courses 6 Credits 196 St Mary's Elem Tchr 1947-52; Notre Dame, Missionary, Scndry 1953-67; St Mary's Scndry Tchr 1968-69; Julie Cntry Day Jr HS 1970-75; St Charles Jr HS Tchr 1975-83; Acad of Notre Dame HS 1984-; *ai:* Japanese Conversation Club Moderator, Tchr; Alumnae, Missions Moderator; Lit Club; NEA; NEASC; NCEA; NASSP; AHA 6 *office:* Acad Of Notre Dame HS 180 Middlesex Rd Tyngsboro MA 0

MC NIFF, ROSEMARY LINDEN, English & Media Arts Teache New York, NY; *m:* Thomas James; *c:* Megan, Sean; *ed:* SUNY at S Brook (BA) Eng 1970; 6 Credit Hrs Montclair St Coll Rdng; 6 Credi St Elizabeth Coll Tech; *cr:* Cresskill HS 8th Grd Eng Tchr 1971-7 Milford Twp HS 9-12 Grd Eng Tchr 1977-80, 7-12 Grd Arts, Media 1992-; *ai:* NEA 1971-; Lindy Lake Assn 1975-, Bd of Governors 198 Charles E. Schaefer PHD Writing Asst; Numerous Articles Pub; *o* West Milford Twp HS 67 Highlander Dr West Milford NJ 07480

MC NULTY, CAROL DANOWSKI, Fourth Grade Teacher Wilkes-Barre, PA; *m:* Dennis Michael Jr.; *c:* Brandon Dennis; *ed:* Misericordia (BS) Elem 1973; Grad Credits for Masters Equivalen Wilkes Univ, Marywood Coll, PA St Univ; 54 Addl Credits; *cr:* W Schl Third Grd Tchr 1973-74; S&S Meml Schl Kndgtn Tchr 197 Calvin Schl Fourth Grd Tchr 1974-89; Edward Mackin Elem Schl F Grd Tchr 1991-; *ai:* Math-a-thon Co-Coord St Jude Children's C Rsrch Hosp; Coord of Anthology of Poetry, Natl Library of Poetry; Arts Comm; Wilkes-Barre Area Ed Assn, PSEA, NEA 1973-; PTA 1 Golden Poet Awd 1990; Caring Hearth Awd 1993; Amer Poetry Publication 1993; Poet Laureate Awd; Numerous Poems Pub; *of* Edward Mackin Elem Schl # 27 13 Hillard St Wilkes Barre PA 18702

MC NULTY, CINDY, English & History Teacher; *b:* Patton, PA Duquesne Univ (BSEd) Eng 1976, (MLS) Liberal Stud 1993; *cr:* Sa Heart HS Eng Tchr 1977-89; Oakland Cath HS Eng Tchr 1989-92, E His Tchr 1994-; Canevin HS Eng Tchr 1992-93; Cntrl HS Eng 1993-94; *ai:* Flwshps: Natl Endowment for the Humanities Fulbright-Hays Group Project to Namibia & Botswana 1995; *of* Oakland Catholic HS 144 N Craig St Pittsburgh PA 15213

MC NULTY, EUGENE P., Biology & Health Teacher; *b:* Bingham NY; *m:* Kathryn Rachow; *c:* Stacy, Kevin; *ed:* SUNY at Buffalo (BA) 1968; Elmira Coll (MS) Bio 1971; SUNY at Cortland (MS) Hlth 1985 East Aurora HS Chem Tchr 1968-69; Thomas A. Edison HS Bio, Hlth 1969-; *ai:* Class of 1999, Ski Club, Key Club Adv; Yrbk Co-Photograp Fac, Union Exec Cncl; Bldg Leadership Team; Retirement Del; NYSF 1985-; Kiwanis 1988-; Key Club Dist, Comm Svc Project Awds 1993.

MCNULTY, KEVIN MICHAEL, Religious Education Chprsn; *b:* York, NY; *m:* Cathleen Moore; *c:* Maureen, Thomas; *ed:* Iona Coll (Rel Stud & His 1982; Fordham Univ (MA) His 1988; Iona Coll (MS) E Admin 1994; *cr:* Rice HS Theology & His Tchr 1984-88; Chrstn Brot Acad Theology & His Tchr 1988-91; Bergen Cath HS Rel Ed Chair 19 *ai:* Stu Govt & Habitat for Humanity Moderator; Lacrosse Coach; N 1991-; ASCD 1992-; NASSP 1991-; Saint Marys Adult Ed 1995-, Co Personhood; Presenter at NCEA Convention 1996; *office:* Bergen Cath HS 1040 Oradell Ave Oradell NJ 07649*

MC NULTY, MARY (MCLAREN), Mathematics Dept Chairman Providence, RI; *c:* Ian Andrew, Colin Joseph; *ed:* RI Coll (BS) Math 1 Brown Univ (MAT) Math 1968; Attnd Univ of CA at Berkeley; Har Univ & Univ of RI; *cr:* Intnl Tchng Fellowship Victoria Australia 1972 East Greenwich HS Math Tchr 1968-72 & 1974-86, Math Dept Chm 19 *ai:* Math Team Coach; NEA 1968-; NCTM 1985-; RIMTA 19 Saunderstown Yacht Club 1978-, Soc Chm 2 Yrs; Christ the King Ch 1974-; Presidential Awd for Exc in Sci & Math Tchng 1987; Distinguis Tchr Awd 1988; Co-Prin Investigation of RI Calculus Consortium Mo Project; *office:* East Greenwich H S 300 Avenger Dr East Greenwich 02818*

MC NULTY, ROWENA CATHERINE, Special Education Teacher Staten Island, NY; *m:* Vincent Baglivo; *c:* Liam Mc Nulty Baglivo; Boston Coll (BA) Elem Ed 1982; CUNY at Staten Island (MS) Spec 1986; *cr:* St Patrick's Schl Kndgtn Tchr 1 Yr; SFSU Presch Tchr 1 Yr 97 Readiness Tchr 5 Yrs; ERIC NJ St Dept of Ed Mgr 2 Yrs; Hopatc HS Spec Ed Tchr 6 Yrs; Hopatcong HS Spec Ed Tchr 6 Yrs; *ai:* Dist-W Environmental Club Founder, Adv 5 Yrs; Project Adventure Facilita Adventure Based Cnclng; NEA 1990-; ANJEE 1992-, Advy Bd; N 1988-; Green Team 1990-, Dir; Project Wild, Acquatic Wild, NJ Audo WET 1995-, Facilitator; Tchr of Yr: Hopatcong Boro Schls & Sussex 1995; Geraldine Dodge Summer Opportunity Awd 1993; Grants: San Pharmaceutical 1991, Mennin Co 1992, Warner-Lambert 1995; *off* Hopatcong HS PO Box 1029 Hopatcong NJ 07843*

MCNUTT, BARBARA SPONSELLER, Tchr of Dvlpmntlly Handicap Tiffin, OH; *m:* Jeffrey Alan; *ed:* Bowling Green St Univ (BA) Spec 1991; Findlay Univ 30 Hrs Post Grad; *cr:* Fremont Jr HS 7th-9th Grd T of Developmentally Handicapped 1991-; *ai:* Homebound Instr; Schl Tu *office:* Fremont Jr HS 501 Croghan St Fremont OH 43420

MC NUTT, HELEN ELIZABETH, 4th-6th Grade Math Teacher; Philadelphia, PA; *m:* Thomas I.; *c:* Scott, Mark, Thomas D., Christoph *ed:* West Chester Univ (BS) Elem Ed 1965; Temple Univ (MED) Math Math, Cmptr Sci; *cr:* Phila Pub Schls Tchr 1965-88; Cncl Rock Sch T Math Cmptr K-6 1988-; *ai:* Schl Shows; AFT, PFT 1965-88, Bldg R NEA, CREA 1988-, IPD Rep; Bucks Cty Democratic, Asst Chair, 1 Assembly; Awd for Work CYO Org in Doylestown; *office:* Goodnoe E Schl 298 Frost Ln Newtown PA 18940*

MC NUTT, ROBERT SCOTT, AP US History Teacher; *b:* Jersey C NJ; *m:* Joan Bochniak; *c:* Brian, Bradley, Robert; *ed:* St Peter's Coll (B Soc Stud, His 1970; Jersey City St Coll (MA) Urban Admin 1995;

City Bd of Ed Tchr, Legal Professions Magnet Coord 1987-; ai: Trial Team, Scholastic Bowl Team Tchr, Coach; Explorer Post Adv; NEA, NJEA, Natl Cncl Soc Stud Tchrs 1987-; Jersey City Schl Dist of Yr 1995-; Hudson Cty Tchr of Yr 1995-; office: Lincoln HS 60 ent Ave Jersey City NJ 07304*

UTT, THOMAS IGNATIUS, English Teacher; b: Philadelphia, PA; len McFadden; c: Scott, Mark, Thomas, Christopher; ed: St Charles nary (BA) Philosophy 1958; St Josephs Univ (MA) Ed 1969; cr: p McDevitt HS Tchr 1960-; ai: NCEA 1980-; NCTE 1980-; AFTRA ; SAG 1989-; AEA 1990-; Doylestown Bourough, Councilman.

ARLAND, MARY PATRICIA, 4th Grade Teacher; b: Greenville, d: Edinboro Univ (BS) Elem Ed 1983; Certified Elem Librn; Addl 29 Credits; cr: Saint Michael Schl Tchr 1985-; ai: Girls Bsktbl Coach; Mem; Message & Svc Comm; Liturgy & Worship Comm; NCEA ; Tchr of Yr Awd 1991; Thanks to Tchrs Awd Nom 1993; home: PO 247 Jamestown PA 16134*

PHAUL, MARY F., Mathematics Teacher; b: Charleroi, PA; m: Wade Maralee Csellar, Katherine Csellar; ed: Carlow Coll (BA) Math 15 Credits Western MD Coll Ed Math; 9 Credits Cmptr Courses; cr: is Scott Key Jr HS Tchr 1970-73; Piccowaxen MS Tchr 1981-87; ce Mc Donough HS Tchr 1987-; ai: Math Team, MD Math League NEA, MSTA, EACC, MD Cncl of Tchrs of Math 1981-; office: ice J. Mc Donough HS 7165 Marshall Corner Rd Pomfret MD 20675

HEE, LAWRENCE JOSEPH, 7th-8th Grade Soc Stud Teacher; b: Weymouth, MA; m: Doreen C.; c: Megan D.; ed: Blassboro St Coll Elem Ed 1975, (MA) Schl Admin 1981; cr: Gibbsboro Schl Dist th Grd Lang Arts Tchr 1975-76; Barrington Schl Dist 5th Grd Tchr -94, 7th-8th Grd Soc Stud Tchr 1995-; ai: Stu Cncl Adv; Outdoor Ed Dir; NJ Ed Assn 1975-, Pres & Treas; NJ Governors Tchr Recognition 1988; Runner-Up Outstdng Naval Reservist 1989; Meritorious Svc al for 29 Yrs Svc; office: Woodland Schl School Ln Barrington NJ 7

PHERON, JOHN W., 7th-8th Grd Language Arts Tchr; b: Lima, OH; Marilyn M. Klotz; c: John T., Melissa M.; ed: OH St (BSEd) Elem Ed ; Wright St (MED) Elem Admin 1971; cr: Lima St Hospital Lit Tchr -69, Soc Sci Curr 1970-71; Lima Pub Schls 6th Grd Tchr 1969-70, e Schl Coord 1971-72; Northeastern Local Schls Elem Prin 1972-73; n East Local Schls Lang Arts, His & 6th Grd Tchr 1973-; ai: NCTE -.

PHERSON, IONIE M., Jr High Mathematics Teacher; b: Jamaica, Indies; m: Errol W.; c: Errol II, Tamiko, Lor-Ren; ed: York Coll (BS) Admin 1985; Queens Coll (MS) Ed 1993; Arts, African Stud, Span; cr: nical Bank Shift Supvr 1976-93; Bd of Ed Math Tchr 1986-; ai: Girl at Troop Ldr; After Schl, Saturdays Tutorial; AFT, UFT 1987-; inated, Run Summer Camp; office: Linden MS 109-89 204th St Saint ns NY 11412

PHERSON, SANDRA S., English Teacher & Dept Chprsn; b: inatti, OH; ed: WV Univ (BS) Scndry Ed, Fr, Eng 1966; Attnd Univ of at Riverside, Penn St Univ, Univ of HI; cr: Mc Clure Jr HS 7th Grd Eng 1966-82; Mc Keesports Area Sr HS AP Amer Lit, Creative Writing, Lit Tchr 1982-; ai: NHS Selection Comm; NEA, PSEA, NCTE 1966-; at Idea Grant Children's Lit, Oral His an Intergenerational Experience; e: Mc Keesport Area Sr HS 1960 Eden Park Blvd Mc Keesport PA 32*

PIKE, JAMES I., Chemistry Tchr; b: Indianapolis, IN; m: Karlyn K.; Michael, Mathew, Sean; ed: Bowling Green St (BS) Cmptr Sci 1971; St acis Coll (MS) Guid 1980; cr: Maumee HS Tchr 1971-72; Edgerton HS 1972-95; ai: Ath Dir; Track Ofcl; NEA, OHSAA; Lions; Masons; n Men.

PIKE, KARLYN KORSGAARD, German & French Teacher; b: veland, OH; m: James Isaac; c: Michael, Matthew, Sean; ed: Bowling en SU (BS) Ger & Fr 1972; Attnd Westminster Coll, NEH Ger Summer Univ of OR; NEH Inst; cr: Edgerton Local Schls Substitute Tchr 2-85; Hicksville HS Ger & Fr Tchr 1985-; ai: Foreign Lang Club; vel Abroad Prgm; NEA, OEA, HEA, OFLA AATG 1985-; NEH Grant Summer Inst 1989, 1993; OH Northern Wkshp for Fr 1986, Ger 1987; ce: Hicksville HS Smith & Main Hicksville OH 43526

QUADE, RICHARD JOHN, Coordinator; b: Columbus, OH; ed: tern KY Univ (AS) Drafting, Design 1979, (BS) Ed Indstrl Arts 1980; Univ Working Toward MS Ath Admin; cr: Bullen Jr HS Printing, fting, Woods Tchr 1980-81; Liberty Union-Thurston Schls Indstrl Arts r 1981-84, Occupational Work Experience Coord 1984-; ai: Big thers, Big Sisters 1983-; Lions Club 1990-; Jennings Scholar Awd; ce: Liberty Union HS 500 Washington St Baltimore OH 43105

QUAID, BARBARA MOLINE, PE & Aquatics Teacher; b: Pittsburgh, m: Quentin James; ed: Slippery Rock St Coll (BS) Hlth, PE & reation 1971; cr: Highlands Schl Dist PE & Aquatics Tchr 1971-; ai: etter Idea Spon; Anti-Drug & Alcohol Org; Amer Alliance for Hlth, PE, reation & Dance 1982-; PSEA, NEA 1971-; office: Highlands HS Idaho Pacific Ave Natrona Heights PA 15065

QUEEN, KEVIN MICHAEL, Math Teacher; b: Methven, MA; m: en Ann Pelleren; c: Meaghan E., Colin P.; ed: Univ of NH (BS) Admin 77; Rivier Coll (MBA) Bus Admin 1990; Math & Ed Credits 1980-82; Salem HS Math Tchr 1980-84; Timberlane Regnl HS Math Tchr 1984-; Bsbl Var Coach 1984-; AFT 1992-; NH Bsbl Coaches Assn 1988-; Amer gion Bsbl 1989-; Plaistow NH Amer Legion Awd for Svc to Youth 1991; wlett Packard Calculus Grant Recipient 1995; office: Timberlane gional HS 36 Greenough Rd Plaistow NH 03865

QUILKIN, RITA NOEL, Spanish Teacher & Grd Advisor; b: nidad, West Indies; m: George; c: Janine, Carlton, Camille; ed: ooklyn Coll (BA) Span 1967; NY Univ (MA) TESOL 1979; Long Island iv (MS) Guid 1993; 36 Post Grad Credits in Span; cr: Bushwick HS an Tchr 1968-70; South Shore HS Span Tchr 1972-93; Tottenville HS an Tchr, Grd Adv 1993-; ai: Young Peoples Flwshp Adv; UFT, AFT 58-; Frgn Lang Tchrs Assn 1972-; St Pauls Episcopal Church, 1994-, stry Mem; office: Tottenville HS 100 Luten Ave Staten Island NY 10312

CQUISTON, DAVID M., High School History Teacher; b: Darby, PA; Joanne C.; ed: Villanova Univ (BS) Sec Ed & His 1971, (MA) His 1972; Villanova Univ Grad Asst 1971-72; Nativity BVM Schl His Tchr 73-74; St James HS Eng Tchr 1974-76; Bishop Shanahan HS His Tchr 76-; ai: Stu Cncl Moderator; Comm Relations Dir; Assn Cath Tchrs 74-, Area VP; office: Bishop Shanahan HS 103 N Everhart Ave West ester PA 19380

C QUISTON, JOSEPH E., Cmptr Newtworking Tech Instr; b: iladelphia, PA; m: Nancy E. Carroll; c: Melissa, Amanda; ed: PA Inst of ch (AST) Electronic Engr Design 1984; Neumann Coll (BS) Lbrl Stud, M 1995; cr: PA Inst of Tech Cmptr Svcs Dir, Fac 1985-; allingford-Swarthmore Fac 1987-93; ai: Middle Sts Subcommittees on ad Prgms, Curricula, Lib, Learning Resource Ctr; home: 527 S Old ttletown Rd Media PA 19063

C RAE, MICHAEL R., High School Math Instructor; b: Beverly, MA; Pamela S.; c: Heather, Alvaro, Chris; ed: Springfield Coll (BS) Hlth, 1977; cr: US Peace Corps Vol Tchr 1978-80; Zuni Pub Schls PE, Hlth chr 1980-81; De Matha Cath HS Math Tchr 1981-86; Northwestern HS Math Tchr 1986-94; Eleanor Roosevelt HS Math Tchr 1994-; ai: Former HS Wrestling, Soccer, Currently Boys, Girls Club Wrestling, Sftbl Coach; NCTM, MCTM, PGCEA 1981-; Outstdng HS Math Tchr St of MD 1990-91; office: Eleanor Roosevelt H S 7601 Hanover Pky Greenbelt MD 20770*

MC SHANE, HELEN RAMSEY, Sixth Grade Teacher; b: Bremerton, WA; ed: Barnard Coll (BA) Geology 1949; NY Univ (MA) Ed 1951; cr: PS 104 3-8 Grds Tchr 1950-; office: PS 104K 9115 5th Ave Brooklyn NY 11209

MC SHANE, JOHN BERNARD,JR., English Department Chairman; b: Rutland, VT; m: Nance Mack; c: John Bernard III, Kathryn Lara; ed: Univ of VT (BA) Ger 1970;Castleton State Coll (MAEd) 1994; Attnd Castleton St Coll & Coll of St Joseph; Addl Stud; cr: Proctor HS Eng Dept Chm 1970-75; Castleton St Coll Adjunct Faculty 1973-; Green Mountain Coll Adjunct Faculty; Mill River Union HS Eng Dept Chm 1988-92; ai: SADD Asst Adv; Pub Schl Stu Act Approval Comm Chm; Pub Schl Lib & Media Approval Comm; AFT 1972-, St Pres 1975-76, Honorary Lifetime Mem Awd; Mill River Tchrs Assn 1983-, VP 1989-; NCTE 1989-; Rotary Club; Poultney Mens Club; Sporting Alliance for VT Environment 1986-, VP 1990; Poultney Fish & Game Club 1980-, Co-Pres 1989-90; Poultney Justice of the Peace & Mem of Poultney Bd of Schl Dirs, Planning Commission & Bd of Civil Authority; office: Mill River Union H S Middle Rd N Clarendon VT 05759

MC SHERRY, SUSAN DEE, Eng Tchr & Stu Assistance Adv; b: Dayton, OH; c: Anne Dee; ed: OH Univ (BSC) Comm 1972; Post Grad Stud Wright St Univ Eng; Univ of Dayton Stu Assistance; cr: Kettering Fairmont HS Eng Tchr 24 Yrs, Stu Assistance Adv 12 Yrs; ai: Safe Emotional & Phys Environment Comm Chm 1995-; North Cntrl Evaluation Comm Co-Chm 1988; Steering, North Cntrl Evaluation Comms 1995-; KEA, OEA, NEA 1972-; Pub Svc Trng Staff & Comm Mems Intervention for Stdnts with Emotional, Substance Issues; office: Kettering Fairmont HS 3301 Shroyer Rd Kettering OH 45429

MCSOLEY, CATHERINE DITORO, 6th Grade Teacher; b: Providence, RI; m: Charles; c: Shannon Gray, Derek Gray, Jared; ed: RI Coll (BS) Elem Ed 1968, (EDM) Elem Ed 1972; Post-masters 30 Hrs; cr: Pawt Schl Dept 5th Grd Elem Tchr 1968-72; S Kingsten Schl Dept 6th Grd Elem Tchr 1979-; ai: AFT 1968-72; NEA 1979-; office: Peace Dale Elem Schl 109 Kersey Rd Wakefield RI 02883*

MC SWAIN, PATRICK EDWARD, 6th-8th Grade Band Director; b: Baltimore, MD; ed: Towson St Univ (BS) Music Ed 1989; 12 Addl Credits Music Ed; 20 Credits Cert Prof Cooking, Baking Baltimore Intnl Culinary Coll; cr: Patuxent Vly MS Band Dir 1989-; ai: Bakers Club Baltimore Intnl Culinary Coll; Prof Percussionist, Drummer Various Bands; Howard Cty Edctrs Assn 1989-; MD Music Edctrs Assn, MENC 1991-; Grace Comm Church Percussionist, Music, Worship Group; home: 5209 Garmouth Rd Baltimore MD 21229

MC SWEENEY, BRIAN THOMAS, Theology Teacher; b: New York, NY; ed: Georgetown Univ (BS) Fin, Bus Admin 1979; Hagan Schl Iona Coll (MBA) Fin 1984; St Josephs Seminary (MA) (MDiv) Moral Theology 1988; cr: Our Lady of Lourdes HS Vice Prin 1991-93; Kennedy Cath HS Rel Dept 1993-; ai: Stdnts for Life; Drama Club; Comm Svc; Chess Club; Knights of Columbus 1988-; Ancient Order of Hibernians 1995-; office: Kennedy Cath HS 54 Route 138 Somers NY 10589

MCSWEENEY, DINA LUCARELLI, Fifth Grade Teacher; b: University Hgts, OH; m: Jeffrey M.; c: Ryan Jeffrey; ed: Cleveland St Univ (BA) Elem Ed 1989, (MA) Rdng & Ed 1993; cr: Thoreau Park Elem 5th Grd Tchr 1989-; ai: IRA 1989-93; NEA 1989-; ADK 1990-; PTA Lifetime Mbrshp Awd; Currently on Grant Writing Team to Receive a Venture Capital Grant; Cleveland St Univ Outstdng Stu Tchr Awd; office: Thoreau Park Elem Schl 5401 W 54th St Parma OH 44129*

MCSWEENEY, TERENCE JAMES, Jr HS Social Studies Teacher; b: Buffalo, NY; m: Sandra M.; c: A & Z; ed: Bucknall Univ (BA) Intnl Relations & Ec 1980; New Schl for Soc Rsrch MA Pgm 36 Credit Hrs Earned in Pol Sci 1986-87; Attnd Univ of VA; Cath Univ 24 Credit Hrs in Scndry Ed; cr: Warren Cty Pub Schls HS Soc Stud Tchr 1989-93; Amherst Regnl Schls Jr HS Soc Stud Tchr 1993-; ai: Former Spon for Acad Teams, VA Model Assembly & Principles & Concerns Comm; Assn for Supervision & Curr Dev; NCSS; MA Tchrs Assn; Western MA Geog Alliance; office: Amherst Regional Jr HS 170 Chestnut St Amherst MA 01002

MC TAGUE, THOMAS HUGH, Prof of Alcohol & Drug Abuse; b: Calais, ME; m: Merwyn Elizabeth Murray; c: Kenneth, Michael, Dorothy Mc Tague LaFont, Terry (dec), James, Thomas; ed: Univ of MW (BA) Zoology 1952; Univ of MO (DDS) Dental Surgery 1956; NH Tech Inst (AA) Mental Hlth 1979; Unif of AZ (MS) Addiction Stud 1982; Tufts Univ Dental Refresher Course 1964; Univ Of AK 3 Credits Law, Ethics, Tannana Comm Coll 3 Credits Case Mngmt 1984; cr: Gen Dentistry Pvt Practice 1956-77; US Navy, Univ AZ, NASAP, DASAP Prgm, Facilitator, Tasking Admn 1982-83; Native Amer Assoc AK Cnclr 1983-84; Seaborne Hosp NH Cnslr 1986-88; NH Tech Inst Prof of Alcohol, Drug Cnslng Prgm 1988-; ai: Acad Adv Alcohol, Drug Cnslng Stdnts; Sigma Nu; Delta Sigma Delta; Thea Nu Epsilon; Amer, ME, MA, NH Dental Assn; Acad Schlsp; Stdnt Rsrch Asst; Retraining Navy Facilitators, Contributor US Navy Alcohol, Drug Revised Mannual; office: NH Tech Inst 11 Institute Dr Concord NH 03301

MCTAMNEY, AASE MARIE, English Teacher; b: Arendal, Norway; c: Melissa, John, Marianna, Raymond, Judith, Machnee, Jesse; ed: Clemson Univ (BA) Eng 1972, (MA) Eng 1978; cr: Trenton St Coll Adjunct Instr 1979-83; Kings Acad Eng Tchr 1983-; Burlington Cty Coll Adjunct Instr 1984-; ai: Yrbk & Jr Cheerleading Adv; Fall Festival & Fundraising Chm; office: Kings Acad 131 E Main St Wrightstown NJ 08562

MC TIGHE, JANET NICKERSON, School Counselor; b: Wellsville, NY; m: Vincent; c: Eric, Kyra; ed: SUNY Coll at Oneonta (BS) Home Ec Ed 1973; SUNY at Albany (MS) Curr, Instruction 1976; Coll of St Rose (MS) Schl Cnslng 1990; cr: Ballston Lake Jr HS Home Ec Tchr 1973-88; Gowana Jr HS Schl Cnslr 1989-; ai: Adv to Builders Club; Honrary Life Mem NY St Congress of Parents, Tchrs; office: Gowana Jr HS 970 Route 146 Clifton Park NY 12065

MC VEIGH-SCHULTZ, JANE, Third Grade Teacher; b: Philadelphia, PA; m: David; c: Josh, Jody; ed: Univ of ND (BS) Ed 1972; Post Grad Stud Northeastern Univ Writing, Poetry; Studied with poet Stephen Dunn During Sabbatical 1991-92; Arrist Tchrs Inst Adv Poetry Stud; cr: Ft Totten Indian Reservation Head Start Prgm Tchr 1972-73; Patura Farm Schl K-1-2 Grd Tchr 1973-74; Daybrook Inst K-3rd Grd Tchr 1974-79; Abington Friends Schl 3rd, 4th Grd Tchr 1979-; ai: Schl Curr Comm; Penn Start Prgm; Poetry Wkshps; NCTE 1985-, Studying Childs Work Grant 1987; Articles Lang Arts; Poetry Pub Beloit Poetry Journal; Contract to Write Book on Sharing Poetry with Children; office: Abington Friends Schl 575 Washington Ln Jenkintown PA 19046*

MCVERRY, MARY K., English Teacher; b: Hartford, CT; ed: Annhurst (BA) Eng 1969; SCSU (MS) Counseling 1988; 30 Grad Hrs Eng; Currently in 6th Pgm Cnslng; cr: Torrington HS Tchr 1969-; ai: Class of 1999 Adv; Drama Dir; Thespian Troupe #611 Adv; BEST Prgm; Close Up Prgm & Lit Magazine Adv; Shared Ldrshp Team; Public Relations Comm Chm; NEA, CEA, TEA & NCTE; Title IVC NJ Writing Project I & III; HS Tchr Awd; office: Torrington HS Major Besse Dr Torrington CT 06790

MC VEY, MARILYN, Sr High School English Teacher; b: New Kensington, PA; m: James Thomas; c: Heather, Geoffrey; ed: CA Univ of PA (BA) Eng 1969; Eng & Soc Stud Cert; 9 Credit Hrs Toward MA Eng; cr: St Johns HS Eng Tchr 1970-74; Frazier Eng & Psych Tchr 1977-; ai: NEA, PSEA 1977-; FEA 1977-, Pres 1994-; Cty Ed Assn, Pres 1994-; NCTE 1995-; Articles Pub; office: Frazier Schls Box 302 Constitution St Perryopolis PA 15473

MC VEY, MARJORIE WHITE, Retired Business Teacher; b: Nelsonville, OH; m: Jack; c: Kristy Mc Vey Walter, Mary Beth Mc Vey Mace; ed: OH Univ (BSEd) Bus Ed 1958; cr: Starr-Washington HS Bus Tchr 1958-73; Logan HS Bus Tchr 1973-74; Tri-Cty Voc Schl Bus Tchr 1974-94; ai: Bus Profs of Amer Class Adv; OEA; NEA; Ret Tchrs of OH 2 Yrs; Ret Hocking Co Tchrs 1 Yr; Union Furnace United Meth Church, OH Eastern Stars 25 Yrs.

MC VICKER, BARBARA J., Italian & Amer Lit Teacher; b: New Castle, PA; ed: Youngstown St Univ (AB) Italian, Eng 1978; Westminster Coll (MED) Admin 1988; Elem, Sec Prin Cert 1989; cr: Ursuline HS Italian, Amer Lit Tchr 1979-; ai: Italian Club Moderator; Lady Irish Golf Coach; Handbook Revision, NHS Selection Comms; OH Cath Ed Assn 1979-; Amer Assn Tchrs of Italian; ASCD; Phi Delta Kappa; NCTE; office: Ursuline HS 750 Wick Ave Youngstown OH 44505

MC VICKER, JEANETTE, English Professor; b: Gary, IN; ed: Purdue Univ (BA) Eng 1981; SUNY at Binghamton (MA) Philosophy 1986, (PHD) Comparative Lit 1988; cr: SUNY at Fredonia Asst Prof of Eng 1988-; ai: Women's Stu Union Adv; Women's His Month Planning Comm; UUP 1988-, Affirmative Action 1993-94, Nuala Drescher Rsrch Leave Awd 1994; Modern Lang Assn 1988-; VA Woolf Soc 1990-; Fulbright Flwshp to Teach in Romania 1991-92; Assoc Ed; office: S U N Y Coll At Fredonia English Dept Fenton Hall 277 Fredonia NY 14063

MC VICKER, RICHARD JOHN, Fifth Grade Teacher; b: Pittsburgh, PA; m: Linda Janssen; ed: Point Park Coll (BA) Elem Ed 1975; Attnd CA St Coll, Univ of Pittsburgh, Slippery Rock, Univ of Pittsburgh's Lab Schl at Pymatuning, Univ of Akron, Penn St; cr: J&L Steel Millwright 1963-66; Penn-Central Railroad Foreman, Gen Foreman 1966-71; Fort Cherry Schl Dist Tchr, Coach 1975-; ai: Women's Cross Cntry Coach; Elem Sci Dept Chprsn; Sci Olympiad Co-Chair; PSTA 1978-; NEA 1976-; WCRRA, RRCA 1986-; PTA 1975-; Rails to Trails 1989-; WTAE Tchr of Yr Nom; Presidential Tchng Awd; PA Sci Tchr of Yr Runner-up; Numerous Articles Pub; NSF Grants; home: 161 Pennsylvania Ave Bridgeville PA 15017*

MC WHERTER, KIMBERLY RUPERT, Chemistry Teacher; b: Latrobe, PA; m: Richard; c: Nathaniel, Ian; ed: Univ of Pittsburgh (BS) Biological Sci 1979; CA Univ of PA Chem Cert 1989; IN Univ of PA Master Eq Sci Ed 1993; Attnd PA St Univ, Gannon Univ, Carlow Coll, Millersville St Coll; cr: Greater Latrobe Schl Dist Phys Sci Tchr 1980; Derry Area Schl Dist Bio Tchr 1980-81, Phys Sci Tchr 1981-83, Chem Tchr 1988-; ai: Sci Olympiad-Chem Coach; BRIDGES Tchr Partner; Curr, Review, Grad Proj Comms; PSEA, NEA 1980-; ACS Chem Ed 1993-; PSTA, NSTA 1988-; Spectroscopy Soc 1989-; United Meth Church 1970-, PPRC-Chprsn; Red Cross, Vol; Am Heart Assn, Vol; Equipment Grant Spectrospcopy Soc of Pgh; Kievin Burns Awd Outstdng Sci Tchng 1995; office: Derry Area HS Rd 1 Box 169 Derry PA 15627

MC WHIRR, ALBERT H., Industrial Ed & Tech Teacher; b: Burlington Cty, NJ; m: Andrea B. Homa; c: Matthew, Patricia; ed: Montclair St Univ (BA) Indstrl Ed 1970, (MA) Indstrl Ed, Tech 1976; Cert Cooperative Indstrl Ed 1976; Addl 30 Hrs Beyond MA; cr: Dumont Bd of Ed Tchr 1970-; Jersey City St Coll Prof 1993-; ai: NIEA, NEA, BCEA 1970-; DEA, NTCIFCA 1976-, Schlsp Chm; Knights of Columbus 1992-; USATF; North Jersey Masters Runners Club 1991-; NJ Cooperative Ed Assn Coord of Yr 1992, 1994; Catechist of Yr Diocese of Newark NJ 1994; office: Dumont HS 101 New Milford Ave Dumont NJ 07628*

MCWHORTER, JANE BRILL, Coordinator of College Graphic; b: Brooklyn, NY; m: John MacGruer; ed: Schl of Visual Arts (BFA) Graphic Design 1989; cr: Blue Sky Productions Owner & Designer 1979-; Berkshire Comm Coll Coord of Coll Graphics 1985-; Berkshire House Publishers Book Designer 1990-; ai: MTA 1985-; office: Berkshire Comm Coll 1350 West St Pittsfield MA 01201

MCWILLIAMS, CHRISTOPHER J., Video Production Teacher; b: Philadelphia, PA; m: Cristine Wetzler; ed: Temple Univ (BA) Comm 1987; Cabrini Coll (M.Ed.) 1996; Temple Univ Video Operations 1986-87; Visual Innovations House Ed 1987-89; Colonial Schl Dist Tchr & Admin 1989-; cr: Var Soccer Head Coach; ai: Colonial Admin Supvr Ed Assn, Intnl TV Assn 1989-; office: Plymouth-Whitemarsh HS Germantown Pike Plymouth Meet PA 19462*

MC WILLIAMS, LANA LOUMEDA (BREDEMEIER), English & Journalism Teacher; b: Lincoln, NE; m: Richard Hoye; c: Sean Frederick, Melissa Noelle; ed: Univ of NE at Lincoln (AB) Journalism 1967; Univ of NE at Kearney (BAEd) Ed 1968; Various Courses Eng, Ed Univ of MD, Jacksonville Univ, Univ of San Diego, UC Berkeley Extension; cr: Richland Ctr HS Eng, Jrnlsm Tchr 1969-72; Los Angeles Comm Coll Adult Ed Tchr 1976-80; Bitburg Amer HS Eng, Jrnlsm Tchr, Eng Dept Chm 1983-; ai: Yrbk Adv; Eng Dept, Act Fund Cncl Chms; Sr Class Spon; Eifel Ed Assn, NEA 1983-; home: PSC Box 118 Box 464 APO AE 09137

MC WILLIAMS, MARIE CHARLOTTE, Spanish Teacher; b: Philadelphia, PA; ed: Chestnut Hill Coll (BA) Span 1970; Millersville Univ (MA) Span; Univ of Madrid Summer Prgm Post Scndry 1971; cr: John Carroll HS Span Tchr 1969-79, Foreign Lang Dept Head 1974-79; Mount Saint Joseph Acad Span Tchr & Foreign Lang Dept Head 1979-; ai: Acad Bd Chprsn; Curr Comm; Tech Comm; Span Honor Soc Moderator; AATSP, NCEA 1970-; PSMLA 1990-; MLAPV 1980-; ACTFL 1995-; PASE 1993-; office: Mt St Joseph Academy 120 W Wissahickon Ave Flourtown PA 19031

MC WILLIAMS, PAUL H., Third Grade Teacher; b: Geneva, NY; ed: SUNY at Geneseo (BS) El Ed 1962; SUNY at Buffalo (MS) El Ed 1980; Univ of Roch 6 Grad Hrs; Buff St 14 Grad Hrs; Canisius Coll 3 Grad Hrs; Drake Univ 3 Grad Hrs; cr: Gorham Cntrl Schl 2nd & 6th Grd Tchr 1962-66; Lincoln Schl 4th-5th Grd Tchr 1966-80; Cayuga Heights 3rd-4th Grd Tchr 1981-; ai: NYSUT 1961-; Depew Tchrs Organi 1966-, Bldg Rep; NEA, AFT 1970-; Dev Summer Enrichment Prog Sci & Math-Chktg Schls Educator of Yr Depew 1973-74; office: Cayuga Heights Elem Schl 1780 Como Park Blvd Depew NY 14043

MC WREATH, CYNTHIA LOUISE, Eighth Grade English Teacher; b: Doylestown, PA; ed: CA St Coll (BS) Scndry Ed 1971; Post Grad Stud CA Univ of PA 34 Credits; Presidential Scholar; cr: Burgettstown Schl Dist Eng Tchr 1971-; ai: 8th Grd Class Spon; 8th Grd Project, Natl Jr Hnr Soc Comms; NEA, PA St Ed Assn 1971-; NCTE 1972-; Gift of Time Tribute 1996; PTA Cert of Appreciation 1990, 1992; office: Burgettstown Area HS 99 Main St Burgettstown PA 15021

MEACCI, KATHY ZAJACKOWSKI, Science Dept Chair & Teacher; b: Sewickley, PA; m: William C.; c: Julie, Katie; ed: Clarion St Univ (BA) Bio 1970; Univ of Pittsburgh (MS) Curr & Supervision 1976; Attnd PA St Univ, Bethany Coll, WV Univ; cr: Moon MS Life Sci Tchr 1970-; ai: MS Sci Fair, Moon Ed Assn Pub Relations & Moon Ed Assn Moon Relay for Life Chprsn; NEA 1970-; NSTA 1970-; PSEA 1970-; office: Moon MS 1407 Beers School Rd Coraopolis PA 15108

MEACHEM, KEVIN J., Social Studies Teacher; *b:* Schenectady, NY; *m:* Laura Campagna; *c:* Rachel; *ed:* Siena Coll (BA) Amer Stud 1983; SUNY at Albany (MA) Amer His 1994; *cr:* Notre Dame Bishop Gibbons HS Soc Stud Tchr 1983-88; Schalmont HS Soc Stud Tchr 1988-; *ai:* Var Vllybl Coach; Audio-Visual Coord; Helped Develope NY St Validated Pgm for Eng & Soc Stud; *office:* Schalmont HS 1 Sabre Dr Schenectady NY 12306

MEAD, ANN TUROWSKI, Music Specialist; *b:* Chicago, IL; *m:* Kevin; *c:* Francesca, Brendan; *ed:* Duquesne Univ (BS) Music Ed 1971; SUNY at Fredonia (MM) Performance 1974; *cr:* Warren Cty Schl Dist Music Specialist Tchr 1971-80; Gannon Univ Adult Ed, Music-Intro Tchr 1990; St Joseph Schl Music Specialist Tchr 1985-; Private Studio Instr; *ai:* Warren Cty Summer Music Schl Coord; Private Studio Instruction; Struthers Lib Theatre Co-Chair, Prof of Summer Playhouse, Trustee; Warren concert Assn, 1st VP; Philomel Club 1974-; Assn of Coll Women; Harry A. Logan Jr Fnd Grant 1990-; Struthers Lib Theatre Co-Written Grants; Vol of The Yr 1993; *office:* St Joseph Schl 608 Pennsylvania Ave W Warren PA 16365*

MEAD, ELDON LEROY, 9th Grade Science Teacher; *b:* Woodward, OK; *m:* Mary Ann Spomer; *c:* Brenton Carl, Dusten Drew, Adina Larson; *ed:* Northwestern St Coll (BA) Ed 1970; Natl Louis Univ (MA) Ed 1990; 18 Hrs Post Grad Earth Sci, Field Stud; Avid Trng; *cr:* Dusten HS Sci Tchr, Bsktbl Coach 1971-74; Siloam Springs Jr HS Sci Tchr 1974-78; Baumholder Amer HS Sci Tchr, Cross Cntry Coach 1978-86; Ramstein Jr HS 9th Grd Sci Tchr 1986-; *ai:* Sci Dept Chprsn; Schl Improvement Process Co-Chprsn; Schl Safety, Discipline Comm; NEA 1970-; FEA 1978-; FBLA 1995-; Natl Sci Fnd Grant Earth Sci OK St Univ 1970-71; Natl Sci Fnd Grant Chem OK Univ 1973; AVID Trng 1995; *home:* PSC Box 2 Box 5336 APO AE 09012

MEAD, G. MICHAEL, Mathematics Teacher; *b:* Arlington, MA; *ed:* Assumption Coll (BA) Math, Psych 1990; Worcester Polytechnic Inst (MM) Math 1996; Anna Maria Coll 3 Credits; *cr:* Saint John's HS Math Tchr 1990-; *ai:* Hockey Coach; Intramural Sports Dir; NCTM 1991-; NCEA 1990-; *office:* Saint John's HS 378 Main St Shrewsbury MA 01545*

MEAD, KEVIN R., Music Teacher; *b:* Buffalo, NY; *m:* Nadia Ostapczuk; *c:* Nicole Elisabeth; *ed:* SUNY Fredonia (MS) Music Ed 1982; SUNY Brockport (MA) Liberal Stud 1988; *cr:* Kendall Cntrl Schl Music Tchr 1983-86; Lyndonville Cntrl Schl Music Tchr 1986-87; Churchill-Chili Cntrl Schl Music Tchr 1987-; *ai:* MS Musical Dir; Juggling Intramurals Instr; Jr HS Dev Steering Comm; NEA 1983-; MENC 1982-; Monroe Cty Schl Music Assn 1992-, Percussion Coord; Greater Rochester Music Educators Wind Band 1990-; NY St Cncl of Arts Grant; *office:* Churchville-Chili Cntrl Schls 139 Fairbanks Rd Churchville NY 14428

MEAD, MORGAN NOYES, Dean of Students & Eng Tchr; *b:* Bennington, VT; *ed:* Williams Coll (BA) Eng 1973; Univ of MA (MA) Eng 1986; *office:* Buckingham Browne Nichols Schl 80 Gerrys Landing Rd Cambridge MA 02138

MEAD, MORRIS C., Assoc Prof & Curr Coordinator; *b:* Cortland, NY; *m:* C. Jeanne Brady; *c:* Kim Mead-Colegrove, Michael; *ed:* SUNY at Morrisville (AAS) Horticulture 1962; Alfred Univ (BS) Bus Admin 1973, (MS) Ed 1980; *cr:* Alfred St Coll Instr, Curr Coord 1963-82, Asst Prof Dept Chair 1982-90, Assoc Prof Curr Coord 1990-; *ai:* Ed Fnd Bd of Dir; Niagara Intnl Assoc of FTD Bd Mem; Hortus Club Adv; Soc of Amer Florists 1990-; Interior Plantscape Assn 1985-.

MEAD, PAMELA ANN, Earth Sci & Biology Teacher; *b:* Syracuse, NY; *ed:* SUNY at Geneseo (BS) Elem Ed, Sci 1984; SUNY at Cortland (MS) Sci Ed 1989; Addl Hrs Paleoclimate, Oceanography, Historical Geology; *cr:* Fulton Jr HS Life Sci Tchr 1984-85; Jordan Elbridge Cntrl Schl Earth Sci, Bio Tchr 1985-; *ai:* Girls Bsktbl Scorekeeper; Natl Ski Patrol 1985-, Regnl Adv, Patrol Dir, Instr Trainor, Outstdng Patroller Awd.

MEADE, FRANCIS J., Business Education Teacher; *b:* Ashland, PA; *m:* Joan Sasso; *c:* Timothy, Maria, Teresa; *ed:* Bloomsburg Univ (BS) Accounting & Bus Ed 1967; Villanova Univ (MA) Scndry Schl Admin 1972; Prins Cert in Scndry Schl Admin 1979; Attnd PA St Univ, Temple Univ, Univ of Cntrl FL, Univ of AK, IN Wesleyan Univ; *cr:* Downingtown Area Sr HS Bus Ed Tchr 1967-77; Lionville Jr HS Bus Ed Tchr 1977-; *ai:* NEA 1967-; PSEA 1967-, Bldg Rep; DAEA 1967-, Bldg Rep; Knights of Columbus 1975-, Financial Sec; *office:* Lionville Jr HS 50 Devon Dr Downingtown PA 19335

MEADE, JAMIE LESTER, English, French & Speech Tchr; *b:* Huntington, WV; *m:* James M.; *c:* Wyatt; *ed:* Morehead St Univ (BA) Fr 1987; *ai:* Fr Club; NEO 1987-; *office:* South Point HS 302 High St South Point OH 45680

MEADE, ROSEMARY, Chemistry & Physics Teacher; *b:* Orange, NJ; *m:* Shawn T.; *c:* Shawn II, Ryan; *ed:* Alfred Univ (BA) Chem 1985; *cr:* Edison Bd of Ed Chem Tchr 1986-89; Wood Bridge Bd of Ed Chem & Physics Tchr 1989-; *ai:* Stu Cncl & Soph Class Adv; NEA, MEA, WETA, NJEA 1989-; Received Eco-Lab Grant for Excl in Ed 1993, 1995; *office:* Colonia HS East St Colonia NJ 07067

MEADE, SCOTT A., History Teacher; *b:* Pittsburgh, PA; *ed:* Univ of Pittsburgh (BS) Psych 1993, (MAT) Scndry Soc Stud 1994; *cr:* Carrick HS 9th Grd Civics Tchr 1993-94; Steel Vly HS 9th Grd His Tchr 1994-95, Summer Schl Dean of Stdnts 1995, 6th, 7th Grd His Tchr 1995-; *ai:* Asst Soccer, Var Asst Hockey Coaches; Var Club Spon; PA St Ed Assn, NEA, Steel Vly Ed Assn 1996; World Affairs Cncl of Pittsburgh 1993-; *office:* Steel Valley HS 3113 Main St Munhall PA 15120

MEADER, BARBARA TOWER, Math Teacher; *b:* Gowanda, NY; *m:* W. John; *c:* Julie Meader Jones, Matthew; *ed:* Univ of MI (BA) Math 1967; Canisius Coll (MS) Scndry Ed 1987; *cr:* Abington HS North Campus Math Tchr 1967-68; Trumbull HS Math Tchr 1968-73; Lake Shore Cntrl Schl HS Math Tchr 1973-74; Holland Cntrl Schl HS & MS Math Tchr 1987-; *ai:* Bldg Level Team Comm; Report Card Comm; Transportation Comm; NEA 1987-.

MEAGHER, LINDA DARYL, Humanities Professor; *b:* Lynn, MA; *m:* Edward; *ed:* Salem St Coll (BS) Eng, Ed 1976; Suffolk Univ (MED) Ed 1979; Univ of MA at Lowell 24 Credit Hrs Post Grad Stud; *cr:* Hudson Schl Dist Lang Arts Tchr 1977-78; Reading Pub Schls Chptr 1 Specialist 1978-79; Univ of Lowell Eng, Rdng Instr 1979-84; Lawrence Pub Schls Prgm Specialist 1984-88; Middlesex Comm Coll Hum Prof 1988-; *ai:* Adults Returning to Schl Club Adv; Acad Stans Comm; IRA; MA Rdng Assn; Pi Lambda Theta; Rails-to-Trails; Co-Author: Mastering Study Skills: A Student Guide 1988, Handbook on College Teaching 1993, Connections: Reading Skills and College Success 1996; Natl & Intnl Speaker Rdng, Stud Skills 1981-94; *office:* Middlesex Comm Coll Springs Road Bedford MA 01730*

MEAGHER, SUSAN LIVINGSTON, English Teacher; *b:* Brooklyn, NY; *m:* Robert V.; *c:* Matthew; *ed:* SUNY at Stony Brook (MA) Lbrl Stud, Ed 1991; *cr:* Islip HS Eng Tchr 1986-; *ai:* Stu Cncl, Marching Band Adv; Parent Tchr Stu Assn; Islip Tchrs Assn, NYSUT, AFT 1986-; Natl Assn Stu Act Adv 1995-; Bus Advy Cncl 1996-; Tchr of Month 1994-95; *office:* Islip HS 2508 Union Blvd Islip NY 11751

MEALY, GINGER ZITO, Coop Work Experience Coord; *b:* New London, CT; *m:* Thomas J.; *ed:* Cntrl St Univ (BS) Mrktg Ed & Bus Ed 1980, (MS) Organizational Mgmt 1990; Tchng Cert for Cooperative Work Experience; *cr:* South Windsor HS Bus Tchr 1981-82, Cooperative Work Experience Tchr 1983-; *ai:* NEA 1981-; CEA 1981-; CT Assn of Cooperative Work Experience Coords 1983-, Region III VP, Outstdng Coord; *office:* South Windsor HS 161 Nevers Rd South Windsor CT 06074

MEALY, MARSHA HOFF, Math Teacher; *b:* Youngstown, OH; *m:* Larry E.; *c:* Amy, Scott; *ed:* Younstown St Univ (BA) Math 1972, (MS) Ed 1991; *cr:* Trumbull Cty Schls Substitute 1972 & 1985; Howland Schls Math Tchr 1972-75; Crestview HS Math Tchr 1985-; *ai:* Prom Adv Jr Class; NHS Comm; Columbian Mentor Prgm; Math Curr Comm; NEA 1972-75, 1985-; NCTM 1991-; Ohio Cncl Tchrs of Math 1986-; Northeastern OH Cncl Tchrs of Math 1986-; YMCA Vol; Bsktbl Boosters; *office:* Crestview H S 44100 Crestview Rd Columbiana OH 44408

MEARES, LORRAINE POLISEO, Mathematics & Computer Teacher; *b:* New York City, NY; *m:* Robert Brainard; *c:* Anna Michele Rossi, Jennifer Lynn Rossi; *ed:* CUNY Hunter Coll (BA) Math 1967; Fairleigh Dickinson Univ (MA) Psych 1977; Addl 30 Plus Credits in Ed Admin at Montclair St Univ; Currently Hold Prin & Supervisory Certs; *cr:* North Rockland HS Math Tchr 1976-77; Verona HS Math Tchr 1977-; *ai:* NJ Assn of Realtors 1987-; Verona Educl Assn Past Chief Negotiator; *office:* Verona HS 151 Fairview Ave Verona NJ 07044

MECAGNI, CAROL, High School Art Teacher; *b:* Quincy, MA; *m:* Philip P.; *c:* Chiara, Giordana, Anna; *ed:* MA Coll of Art (BFA) Painting, Illustrating 1965; Southern IL Univ (MFA) Painting, Printmaking 1967; Tchng Credits Bridgewater St Coll; Ed Fitchburg St Coll; Papermaking, Basketry, Pottery, Printmaking, Dying; *cr:* Southern IL Univ Art Instr; Boston Pub Schls Art Tchr Spec Needs; Haystack Schl Crafts Weaving Instr; Braintree Pub Schls Art Tchr Elem; Summer Arts Children Dir, Instr 1985-95; Artist, Weaver, Painter Commissions, Sales 1967-; *ai:* Adv Schl Art Club, Animal Rights Club; Dir Stage Sets Drama Club, Exhibits, Art Show; Liason Art Tchrs; Juror Art All St, Art Month Reflexions; Boston Seven, Boston Artists Assn; St, Natl Art Tchrs Assn; Local St, NEA; West Suburban Creative Arts; Hop Arts Cncl, Past Pres, Pass Grant Goord; Hop Parent Support Assn, Past Pres, Chair Prgm Coord; Hop, Southboro Art Assn, Past Pres, Charter Mem; St John's Yth Group, Ldr, Weekend Retreats, Wkshps; Artist Prof Tapestry Weaver, Painter, Work Shown Museums, Galleries, Exhibits; Work Pub; *office:* Hopkinton Mid HS Hayden Rowe St Hopkinton MA 01748

MECCA, JOSEPH MATTHEW, Mathematics Teacher; *b:* Scranton, PA; *ed:* East Stroudsburg St Coll (BS) Math Ed 1969; Math Ed from Wilkes Coll & Penn St Univ; *cr:* Dunmore HS Math Tchr 1969-; *ai:* Bsbl Coach; Announcer for Bsktbl Team; Advanced Placement Adv; NCTM, PaCTM, PCTM 1969-; St Anthonys Playground Assn 1964-; Tchr of Yr Awd 1972; Tandy Math Tchr Awd 1991.

MECCARIELLO, GERALD P., 11th Grade Chemistry Teacher; *b:* Schenectady, NY; *m:* Margaret G. Lawyer; *c:* Paul, Clare; *ed:* SUNY at Cortland (BS) Bio 1983; Syracuse Univ (MSEd) Sci Ed 1986; Neurophysiology SUNY at Albany; Trng in Use of Electronic Mail BOCES; *cr:* NYS Hlth Dept Rsrch Asst 1982-84; SUNY at Albany Lab Instr 1985; Solvay HS Gen Sci Tchr 1985-87; Cato Meridian HS Chem Tchr 1987-; OCM BOCES E-Mail Trng Sub Tchr 1996-; *ai:* Modified Track Coach; Outdoor Club Adv; NHS Comm; Natl Chem Week; Hockey Coach; AFT 1987-; Sci Tchr Assn NY 1987-, Syracuse Area Rep; NSTA 1987-; Amer Chem Soc 1987-; Rotary Club of Cato 1994-, Sec; Articles Pub; OCM BOCES Read Out 1994; Blood 1986,67 6 1568-1577; Blood 1983, 62 252a; *office:* Cato Meridian HS Rt 370 Box 100 Cato NY 13033*

MECHERLY, GEORGE JOSEPH, Eng Dept Chair & Tchr; *b:* Philadelphia, PA; *m:* Anne Finnesey; *ed:* LaSalle Univ (BS) Acctng 1966; Temple Univ (MA) Eng 1969, (PHD) Eng 1977; LaSalle Univ Scndry Eng Cert 1975; *cr:* Roman Catholic HS Tchr 1966-; LaSalle Univ Tchr, Adj 1977-, Head Men's Tennis Coach 1990-95; *ai:* Asst Tennis Coach; NCEA, NACST 1966-; Cncl for Basic Stud Grant; *office:* Roman Catholic HS 301 N Broad St Philadelphia PA 19107*

MECHLEY, DONNA KATHMAN, Algebra & Geometry Teacher; *b:* Cincinnati, OH; *m:* Ted; *ed:* Xavier Univ (BA) PE, Hlth 1993; *cr:* Turpin HS Tchr, Vlybl Coach 1993-; *ai:* Var Girls Vlybl, Reserve Girls Bsktbl Coach; Var Boys Vlybl Coach at St Xavier HS; 4 Yr Div I Coll Vlybl Player; 1 Yr Div I Coll Bsktbl Player; *office:* Turpin HS 2650 Bartels Rd Cincinnati OH 45244

MECHLING, KENNETH R., Prof of Bio & Science Ed; *b:* Ford City, PA; *m:* Dorothy J. Bower; *c:* Ken C., Kelly Anne, Amy, Kristine, Andrew; *ed:* IN Univ of PA (BS) Bio, Gen Sci 1960, (MED) Bio 1964; MI St Univ (PHD) Sci Ed 1970; Post Grad Univ CA at Berkeley, Univ CO at Boulder; *cr:* Ford City HS Sci Tchr 1960-65; US Army Lieutenant 1961-62; Clarion Univ Prof of Sci 1966-; PA St Univ Adj Prof of Ed 1991-; *ai:* Consultant in Sci Ed to US Dept of Denfense Dependents, Intnl Schls; St, Natl Sci Ed Projects Dir; NSTA 1962-, Bd of Dirs, Out Svc Awd; PA Sci Tchrs Assn 1960-, Pres, Bd of Dirs, Hnrs Fellow; Cncl of El Sci Int'l 1966-, Pres, Bd of Dir, Out Ldrshp Awd; Schl Sci Svcs Inc 1982-, Pres; PA Sci Tchr Ed Prgm 1983-95, Dir; Info Tech Ed or Commonwealth 1984-93, Dir; Clarion Borough Cncl 1976-82, Pres; Natl Sci Supv Assn Presidential Awd for Outstdng Svc; IN Univ of PA Citation for Achvmt; Kappa Delta Pi Distinguished Scholar Awd; 4 Books, 50 Journal Articles Pub; *office:* Clarion Univ Of PA Clarion PA 16214

MECKEY, MARYLYNNE LEARISH, English Teacher; *b:* Clearfield, PA; *m:* Timothy; *c:* Matthew, Kurt; *ed:* Clarion Univ of PA (BS) Scndry Ed & Eng 1979; Post Grad Stud in Rdng Prgm; *cr:* Clearfield Schls Scndry Eng Tchr 1979-; *ai:* Lang Arts Comm; Soph Class Adv; Reader for St Assessment; Jr Class Adv; NEA & Clearfield Ed Assn 1979-; Anti-Racism Group 1991-; NON Social Org 1985-; United Meth Women; *office:* Clearfield Area HS PO Box 910 Clearfield PA 16830

MECKLEY, JAMES WILLIAM,III, Band Director; *b:* York, PA; *m:* Brenda Papastrat; *ed:* Mansfield Univ (BS) Music Ed 1971; Attnd Ithaca Coll 33 Post Grad Hrs, Elmira Coll 3 Post Grad Hrs; *cr:* Haverling Jr-Sr HS Band Dir 1971-81; Cntrl Music Supply Sales Rep 1981-87; Corning East HS Band Dir 1987-; *ai:* NY St Schl Music 1973-, Zone 15 Rep; NYSUT 1971-; Steuben Cty Music Tchrs Assn 1971-, Pres 1979 & 1989; Southern Tier All Star Jazz Band 1984-, Lead Alto Sax; Guest Conductor All Cty & Area All St Bands in NY & PA; Solo Festival Adjudicator 1975-; *office:* Corning East HS 201 Cantigny St Corning NY 14830*

MECKLEY, ROD L., Music Teacher; *b:* York, PA; *m:* Melissa A. Shutter; *c:* Ethan; *ed:* West Chester Univ (BS) Music Ed 1990; 17 Credit Hrs Towson St Univ; *ai:* Marching Band; Jazz Ensemble; Fac Advy, Discipline Comm; NEA 1992-; MENC 1992-; PMEA; *office:* William Penn Sr HS 101 W College Ave York PA 17403*

MEDEIROS, DAVID, English Teacher & Athletic Dir; *b:* New Bedford, MA; *m:* Mary Beth Bourget; *c:* Sarah, Matthew; *ed:* Univ of MA at Dartmouth (BA) His 1969; Bridgewater St Coll & Framingham St Coll Post Grad Courses; *cr:* Hastins Jr HS Eng & His Tchr 1969-78; Fairhaven HS Asst Ftbl Coach 1969-82, Eng Tchr 1979-, Ath Dir 1993-; Old Rochester Reg HS Asst Ftbl Coach 1986-87; GNB Voc Tech HS Asst Ftbl Coach 1990-91; *ai:* Head Girls Track Coach 1979-; Peer Ldrshp Adv; NEA, MTA & FEA 1969-; MA St Track Ofcls Assn 1986-; MA Scndry Schls Ath Dirs Assn 1993-; Certfd Ath Admin 1994-; *office:* Fairhaven HS 1-2 Huttleston Ave Fairhaven MA 02719

MEDEIROS, RICHARD ALAN, Sixth Grade Teacher; *b:* New Bedford, MA; *m:* Eileen Kincaid; *c:* Curtis, Noel, Erin; *ed:* Univ of MA (BA) Elem Ed 1970; 15 Credit Hrs Univ of MA at Dartmouth; *cr:* Charles S. Ashley Schl Sixth Grd Tchr 1971-; New Bedford HS Adult Ed Tchr, Summe Math Tchr; Parker Schl Summer Elem Math, Rdng Tchr; *ai:* IM Ath Performing Arts 1988-, Yrbk Co-Chprsns; Schl Advy, Schl Improv Cncls; Multimedia Coord; Book Store Adv; NEA, MTA, NBEA Greater New Bedford Little League, Coach 8 Yrs, 6 Championships Bedford High Band Booster 1989-, Parent Adv 1991-92, VP 1992-93 1993-94; Recommendation for MA Tchr of Yr 1991; Writing P Autograph Writing Project; *office:* Charles S Ashley Schl 122 Rochar St New Bedford MA 02745*

MEDFORD, GAIL STEWART, Asst Prof of Spch Comm & Thtre; *b* Orleans, LA; *m:* Rodney H.; *c:* Rodney Andrew, Bryon; *ed:* Xavier (BA) Comm Arts 1976; Univ of SC (MA) Theatre Arts 1982; Univ o (PHD) Pub Comm, Theatre 1994; *cr:* Univ of AR Instr 1980-83; H Univ Lecturor 1987-88; St Philip's Comm Coll Instr 1991-93; Bov Univ Asst Prof 1994-; *ai:* Forensics Dir; Univ & Dept Curr Comms Dir St Anthony's Grd Schl Comm Arts Group; NADSA 1988-; SCA Doctoral Fellow; Articles Pub; *office:* Bowie St Univ De Communications Jericho Rd Bowie MD 20715*

MEDINGER, JOSEPH CHRISTOPHER, High School Gui Counselor; *b:* Ironton, OH; *m:* Mary Janet Payton; *c:* Nick J., Christ R.; *ed:* OH Univ (BSEd) Biological Sci Comprehensive 1970; Xavier (MED) Guid, Cnslng 1972; Attnd Morehead St Univ, Marshall Univ Univ; *cr:* Ironton St Joseph HS Sci Tchr, Coach 1970-72; Ironton HS Cnslr, Tchr 1972-; OH Univ Part-time Cnslr 1973-; *ai:* Past Class, F Tchrs of Amer Adv; Past Bsbl, Ftbl Coach; NEA, OEA, IEA 1985- Schl Cnslrs Assn 1972-; United Commercial Travelers 1975-; Knigh Columbus 1968-, Grand Knight, Knight of Yr; *office:* Ironton HS 1 7th St Ironton OH 45638

MEDNITSKY, ADRIA, English Teacher; *b:* Hazleton, PA; *ed:* Ride (BA) Eng 1968; Attnd Temple Univ & Penn St Univ Masters Equiva Plus 36 Credits; *cr:* Upper Dublin Sr HS Eng Tchr 28 Yrs; *ai:* Lit Mag Natl & St 1st Pl Awds; Scholastic Writing Natl Competition; PTO Rep; NEA & PSEA 1968-; UDEA 1968-, Sec 1993-95, Rep Cncl 1 Liaison Bldg Rep 25 Yrs; *office:* Upper Dublin H S 800 Loch Alsh Ave Washington PA 19034

MEDVE, JOSEPH E., Science Teacher; *b:* Daisytown, PA; *c:* Joe K CA Univ (BED) Bio 1962, (MED) Bio 1968; 40 Credit Hrs at Pen Washington & Jefferson Coll, Bethany Coll, WV Univ; *cr:* Bentv Schls Sci Tchr 1984; *ai:* NEA, PSEA, BEA 1962-; NSF; *office:* Bentv MS 89 Pine St Ellsworth PA 15331

MEDVED, BERNARD, Social Studies Teacher; *b:* McKeesport, P Cathy J. Crawford; *c:* Lauren, Michael; *ed:* CA Univ of PA (BS) Sc Soc Stud 1973; Cert in Elem Ed; Post Grad Stud for MS; *cr:* Charleroi HS Scndry Soc Stud Tchr 23 Yrs; *ai:* Newspaper Adv; Soc Stud Ch PSEA 1974-; NEA 1974-; PIAA Bsktbl Ofcl 1983-; *office:* Charleroi HS Fecsen Dr Charleroi PA 15022

MEDWIN, MARIA CARMEN, French & Spanish Teacher; *b:* Sn TX; *m:* Thomas A. Sr.; *c:* Tommy; *ed:* Coll of Notre Dame of MD (B & Span 1973; Towson St Univ (MA) Ed; 15 In Svc Credit Courses Hereford HS Fr & Span Tchr 6 Yrs; Hanover Pub Schls Fr & Span T Yr; Woodlawn MS Fr & Span Tchr 4 Yrs; Hereford MS Fr & Span T Yrs; *ai:* Frgn Lang Club; Comm Team Ldr; NEA 1973-; Natl Org of of Fr 1990-.

MEE, MICHAEL FRANCIS, English Teacher; *b:* Johnson City, NY LeMoyne Coll (AB) Eng, Philosophy 1969; Harvard Univ (EDM) Ed SUNY, Univ at CT, Bennington Coll 36 Hrs Eng; *cr:* Vestal HS Eng 1970-71, 1981-; African Rd Jr HS Eng Tchr 1971-76; Cntrl Jr HS Eng 1976-81; *ai:* NEA 1970-; Harvard Fac Club 1993-; White H Distinguished Tchr 1986; Articles Pub; *office:* Vestal Sr HS Woodlawn Vestal NY 13850

MEEHAN, BARBARA AILEEN, Guidance Counselor; *b:* White Pl NY; *ed:* Manhattanville Coll (BA) Eng 1969; St Michael's Coll (Counseling 1977; Issues in Schl Reform Univ of MA; *cr:* Milford HS Tchr 1969-70; Northfield Jr-Sr HS Eng Tchr 1970-74; Norwich Admissions Cnslr 1974-75; Milton Jr-Sr HS Guidance Cnslr 1976-79; Rochester Regnl Guidance Cnslr 1979-; *ai:* Schl Cncl Fac Instructional Cncl; Bldg Based Support Team; Girls Bsktbl Timekee Schlsp Comm; ORPEA, MTA, MSCA 1979-; NEA 1978-; DKG 1989 Essay Contest Chm; *office:* Old Rochester Regional HS 135 Marion Mattapoisett MA 02739

MEEHAN, CHARLES GEORGE,JR., Mathematics Teacher; *b:* Cl Chase, MD; *m:* Kathy Louise Wilson; *c:* Sean; *ed:* Franklin & Mars Coll (AB) Math 1969; *cr:* St James Schl Tchr 1969-; *ai:* Ath Dir; Ftbl, Coach; Sr Master; Hnrs Cncl; Rotary 1991-; *office:* Saint James Schl S James MD 21781*

MEEHAN, DAVID, Social Studies Teacher; *b:* Wilkes-Barre, PA; *ed:* U of Scranton (BS) Scndry Ed 1991; Coll Misericordia (MS) Ed 1994; Elmer L. Meyers HS Soc Stud Tchr 1992-; *ai:* SADD Adv; N Wilkes-Barre Area Ed Assn, PA St Ed Assn 1994-; United Way of Wyom Vly 1995-, Dist Rep; Fine Arts Fiesta 1991-, Chprsn; Educl Staff Coord; Performance-Based Assessment Seminar Instr; Mid Sts Evalua Team; Cultural Diversity Resource Tchr; *office:* Elmer L Meyers Jr Sr 341 Carey Ave Wilkes Barre PA 18702*

MEEHAN, DAVID PAUL, Arts & Humanities Teacher; *b:* Methuen, *ed:* New England Schl of Art (AA) Fine Arts, Painting 1973; Univ of (BFA) Art Ed 1976; Classical Assn of New England Hum Stud Dartmo Coll; Lesley Coll at Cambridge Curr, Instruction, Creative Arts in Learn 12 Credits Towards MED; *cr:* Lawrence HS Art Dept Lead Tchr 1976-; Acad Olympics; Art Adv; AFT 1976-; Essex Cty Green Belt Assn 19 MA Trustees of Reservations 1986-; MA Audubon Soc 1988-; Lawre Planning Bd; Essex Art Ctr Bd of Dirs; Arts for Lawrence 1989-, Bd M Lawrence Design Review Bd 1984-90; Greater Lawrence Ed Collaborative 1988-; Lawrence Cultural Cncl 1983-89; Classical Assn New England 1994-; Edctr of Yr 21st Century Educl Journal 1995; Bos Museum of Fine Arts Natl Endowment for Arts, Hum Classical Collect Curr Consultant 1989-90; Univ of MA Lawrence Arts Extension Consultant 1987-88; MA Cncl of Cultural Affairs Grant Pub Histori Walking Tours; *office:* Lawrence HS 233 Haverhill St Lawrence MA 01

MEEHAN, DENNIS JOSEPH, Social Studies Teacher; *b:* New York C NY; *m:* Dorothy Whelan; *c:* Edwin, Christopher, Julie; *ed:* Iona Coll (B Ec, His 1965, (MSEd) Soc Stud 1972; 60 Addl Credit Hrs; Attnd CC Manhattan Coll, Yonkers Tchrs Inst; *cr:* Hawthorne Jr HS Soc Stud T 1968-72; Yonkers HS Soc Stud Tchr 1972-86; Mark Twain Jr HS Soc S Tchr 1986-89; Charles Gorton HS Soc Stud Tchr 1989-; *ai:* Learn Dimensions Specialist; Ed 2000 Sub-Comm; Century Hnrs Tchr; HS Vl Bsktbl, Sftbl Ofcl; NYSUT, YFT, West Cncl Soc Stud Tchrs 1968-; Ministry 1985-, Bd Mem; Scarsdale STEP Prgm 1984-, Bd Mem; Dist Grd Curr Writer; Hitachi Travel Prgm 2nd Place Awd; 25 Yrs Svc Yonkers Schl Children Awd; *office:* Charles Gorton HS 100 Shonnard Yonkers NY 10583

MEEHAN, DUANE, Biology Teacher; *b:* Philadelphia, PA; *m:* Eil Kelly; *ed:* La Salle Coll (BA) Ger 1968; Temple Univ (MED) Educl Me 1972; Attnd Gwynedd Menca Coll, Chestnut Hill Coll, La Salle Univ; Cinnaminson Twp Bd of Ed Ger Tchr 1968-82, F L Dept Coord 1970- Schl Dist of Philadelphia Bio Tchr 1992-; *ai:* Discipline Comm Chm; S

& Comp Ldr; AFT 1992-; PASTA 1992-; *office:* M L King HS Stenton Haines St Philadelphia PA 19138

HAN, JANET LOUISE, Art Dept Chprsn & Teacher; *b:* Tarrytown, *d:* Good Counsel Coll (BA) Math 1965; Notre Dame Univ (MA) Art); *cr:* Preston HS Art, Math Tchr 1965-67; J. F. Kennedy HS Math, chr 1967-8`, Art Dept Chprsn, Tchr 1967-; *ai:* NY St Indoor Track, Coord 1981-; Cross Cntry Secttion I Exec Comm; Head Coach Boys, Indoor, Spring Track & Field; NAE Assn, NCEA, NYSATA 1967-; hester ROckland Dutchess Track, FIeld Coaches Assn; Natl Fed nes & Officials 25 Yr Awd; Univ of RI Schlsp Seminar Exceptional ; Dick Lacy Awd Conspicuous Svc to Yth of Sect I; Garnett hester Coach of Yr Awds; *office:* John F Kennedy Cath HS 54 Route omers NY 10589

HAN, KERRY F., English & Social Studies Tchr; *b:* Northampton, *m:* Donna L. Miemiec; *c:* Darrell, Darren; *ed:* Westfield St Coll (BA) Soc Stud 1968; Univ of ME (MED) Eng Ed 1976; Doctoral Stu Univ A at Amherst; *cr:* Gateway Regnl HS Asst Prin, Eng Tchr 1968-92; er Vly Reg Schl Soc Stud, Eng 1992-; *ai:* Model Congress; Sr Class NEA, MTA 1968-; Author of The Collaborative Social Studies room Book; Interdisciplinary Strategies for Eng & Soc St Book; NEH aps William Faulkner The Regnl & The Mysthic, Eugene O'Neill & r Miller Amer Playrights; *home:* 22 Grandview St Northampton MA)*

HAN, TERENCE P., Business Education Instructor; *b:* New Castle, *d:* Youngstown St Univ (BS) Ed 1989; Univ of Pittsburgh Grad Stud; ox Chapel Area Schl Dist Tchr 1990-; *ai:* Stu Cncl Adv; Schl paper & Publisher of Kidsburgh Press; *office:* Fox Chapel Area HS ield Club Rd Pittsburgh PA 15238

K, GARY DEE, Amer His, Psych & Ec Teacher; *b:* Baton Rouge, LA; eborah Applegett; *c:* Cassandra Dawn Meek Widney, Adam Todd; *ed:* eese St Univ (BA) Soc Stud Ed 1965; Wright St Univ (MED) Scndry ipalship 1974; 24 Quarter Hrs Psych; 12 Post Grad Hrs Educl Admin; rs Cmptrs & Acctng Edison St Comm Coll; *cr:* Tangipahoa Parish 7th Grd Tchr 1966; Piqua City Schls Bus, Soc Stud Tchr 1966-; *ai:* OEA, NEA 1966-; ASCD 1995-; OCSS 1990-; Piqua Bapt Church -, Moderator, Charister, Sunday Schl Tchr; *home:* 322 Pinewood Ave OH 45356

K, GARY EDWIN, Prof of Management & Chair; *b:* Columbus, OH; argaret Rose Wyatt; *c:* Barbra Allyn Carr, Courtney Kristine Christie, y Jane, Wyatt Anton; *ed:* Fenn Coll (BS) Math 1963; Casewestern rve Univ (PHD) Statistics 1970; Nondegree Grad Work Math Univ of *cr:* John Carroll Univ Asst Prof, Mngmt 1969-71; Univ of Akron Prof, mt 1971-; *ai:* Mentoring, CBA Operations, Curr Comms; Amer Stat 1991-; ASQC 1985-; Amer Pwdr Met Inst 1986-; Grad Tchng Flwshp RU 1965-69; Textbooks Pub; 3 Chptrs Pub; Numerous Articles Pub; t Cleveland Fnd 1987; *office:* Univ Of Akron Dept of Management 302 atel Mall Akron OH 44325

EK, KATHY L., Math Teacher; *b:* Norwich, NY; *m:* Ronald A.; *c:* , Jared; *ed:* SUNY at Oneonta (BA) Ed, Math, Eng 1970; Post-Grad SUNY at Albany; *cr:* Norwich City Schls Tchr 1970-; *ai:* Math m; NEO, NEA-NY, NEA 1970-; Presenter AMTNYS Conf Toronto ; Grant Catskill Regnl Tchr Ctr; Attnd Woodrow Wilson Insts; *office:* wich MS Midland Dr Norwich NY 13815

EK, SUSAN HUDOCK, Sixth Grade Teacher; *b:* Allentown, PA; *c:* n Czwartacky, Michael, Kevin; *ed:* IN Univ at Kokomo (BS) Elem Ed ; Lehigh Univ (ME) Spec Ed 1983; Attn Ball St Univ; *cr:* Dodds Base s Madrid Spain Kndgtn Tchr, Hahn AFB Germany 4th-6th Grd Tchr; evue Elem Schl Rdng Tchr; Macanaquah MS Spec Ed Tchr; Dodds Schls Hainerberg Elem Wiesbaden Germany 4th-5th Grd Tchr, erberg MS 6th Grd Tchr; Bethleham Area Schl Dist Spec Ed, Sixth Tchr; *ai:* Stu Assistance Prgm; Team Ldr Acad Team; IM Sports Spon; er Schls Prgm Wiesbaden Germany; NEA, BEA 1980-; *office:* East s MS 2005 Chester Ave Bethlehem PA 18017

EKINS, OLGA JEAN ZITMAN, Former Teacher; *b:* Flushing, NY; ames P.; *c:* Bethany, Jesse, Joanna, Rebecca, Joseph, Naomi; *ed:* Kings (BS) Elem Ed 1983; 21 Addl Credits Earyl Chldhd William Paterson ; *cr:* Parkway Chrstn Acad Grade 1 Tchr 1984; Flushing Chrstn Schl de 2 1984-85; New Hyde Park Bapt Church Nursery Schl 1992-93; *ai:* ffern Presbyn Church Grds 2-3 Sunday Schl Tchr; *home:* 600 Eagle ey Rd Tuxedo Park NY 10987

EKS, MARILYN (MOFFAT), Quest, Hlth & Teen Tchrs Tchr; *b:* a, OH; *m:* Charles; *c:* Amy Marie Meeks Arrambide; *ed:* OH Univ (BS) & Hlth 1966; Marietta Coll (MD) MALL & Leadership 1994; *cr:* Lima HS Hlth, PE, Marriage & Family Living Tchr 1966-72; Marietta City 's LD Tutor 1977-80, Hlth, Quest, Teen Tchrs Tchr 1981-; *ai:* Past Lima Cheerleaders & Girls Bsktbl Coach 1966-70, Var Cheerleader Adv -87, Var Girls Tennis Coach 1981-91, Var Boys Tennis Coach 1988-92; Cheerleader Adv 1995-; LEA, OEA, NEA 1966-72; MEA, OEA, NEA 1-; Teen Pregnancy Bd, Drug Intervention Bd, Drug Core 1985-, Bd; UW 1981-; Project Youth Lead 1994-; Outstanding Ed 1993; Martha dren Jennings Tchng Awd 1992; Honor Ed 1988, 1990, 1994; Most uential Tchr 1988-95; *office:* Marietta City Schools 701 3rd St Marietta 45750*

ESE, CYNTHIA EKBLAD, Music & Theater Teacher; *b:* Fort Collins, ; *m:* William Eric; *c:* Jessica Krystyn; *ed:* CO St Univ (BA) Music Ed ; *cr:* Schl of Weston Tchr 1976-78; Bement Schl Tchr 1978-80; neleigh-Burnham Schl 1980-; *ai:* Dir & Producer All Schl Musical, ect Choir & Drama Coach; Shea Theater 1991-, Bd Mem, Past Sec; ena Civic Theater 1978-84, Bd Mem, Past Sec.

GAHAN, LARRY E., Physics & Astronomy Instructor; *b:* East Keesport, PA; *m:* Susanna G. Luther; *c:* Amy; *ed:* CA St Univ (BSED) nprehensive Sci 1963; Cornell Univ (MST Astronomy 1970; Geology St Univ; Cmptr Sci Univ of Pittsburgh; Radio Astronomy at NRAO eenbank WV Univ; Particle Physics Westminister Coll; Calculus Penn Univ; Astronomy IN Univ PA; *cr:* Penn Hills Schl Dist Astronomy, ysics, Sci Inst Tchr 1963-; Buhl Planetarium Sky Show & Staff Lecturer 58-87; *ai:* NEA, PSEA, PHEA 1963-; Cornell Alumni Admissions nbassadors Network 1986, Group Chair; Lead Tchr HS INitiative mputational Sci at Pittsburgh Supercomputing Ctr; NASA Lunar Sample Project, Tchr in Space Project; *office:* Penn Hills Sr HS 12200 Garland Pittsburgh PA 15235

EGALE, LYDIA, Vocal Music & Theory Teacher; *b:* Bayonne, NJ; *m:* briel; *ed:* Jersey City St Coll (BA) Music Ed 1985; 6 Addl Credits; *cr:* Paul's Schl Rdng, Eng, Music Tchr 1983-87; John M. Bailey Schl Elem usic Tchr 1987-90; Mary J. Donohoe Schl Elem Music Tchr 1987-90; yonne HS Vocal Music Tchr 1991-; *ai:* Accidental Club Adv; NJEA no Judicator; Free Lance Accompanist; Schola Cantorum 1994-; Church ganist; Princetonian Finalist 1994; Lebowitz Tchng Excl Awd Class of 95 Nom; Tchr of Month 1994; Governor's Tchr of Yr 1992; *office:* yonne HS 29th St & Ave A Bayonne NJ 07002*

EGELLO, BRENDA J., Earth Science Teacher; *b:* Middletown, NY; *m:* ward; *ed:* St Univ of NY at Albany (BS) Earth Sci Ed 1987; St Univ of ' at New Paztz (MS) Geology Ed 1993; 30 Hrs Past Masters; *cr:* Pine sh CSD 8th Grd Sci Tchr 1987-88; Goshen CSD Earth Sci Tchr 1988-; Class of 1996 Co Adv; Bsktbl, Track Coach 1987-93; STANYS 1990-; NYSUT 1988-; Empire St Challenger Schlsp; *office:* Goshen Central HS Scotchtown Ave Goshen NY 10924

MEHALICK, WAYNE, Biology Teacher; *b:* Elizabeth, NJ; *m:* Lucille Origoni; *c:* Erica; *ed:* DE Vly Coll (BS) Horticulture 1970; Kean Coll (MA) Admin Supervision 1988; 30 Addl Hrs; *cr:* Linden HS Bio Tchr 1972-; *ai:* Head Girls Var Soccer, Indoor, Outdoor Track Field Coach; NEA, NJEA 1972-; Natl Fed Coaches Assn 1985-; Union Cty Track Coaches Assn 1982-, Pres; Union Cty Girls Soccer Coach of Yr 1995; Track Coach of Yr 1993-94; Gator Aid Natl Coaches Who Care Awd 1993; Franklin Life, Scholastic Coach Magazine Coaching Awd 1987; Pub Women's Coaching Clinic Magazine 1979; *office:* Linden HS 121 W Saint Georges Ave Linden NJ 07036

MEHL, THOMAS R., Social Studies Teacher; *b:* Wheeling, WV; *m:* Deborah Jo Braham; *c:* Zachary T.; *ed:* OH Univ (BS) Ed 1974; *cr:* Union Local HS Soc Stud Tchr 1983-; *ai:* Adv Close Up Washington DC Prgm 1993-, Stu Cncl 1984-89; Jr HS Girls Bsktbl Coach 1983-89; NEA 1983-; OEA 1983-, Outstanding Treas 1990-92; Union Local ACT 1983-, Treas; *office:* Union Local HS 66859 Belmont-Morristown Rd Belmont OH 43718

MEHLEISEN, PATRICIA ANN (RELIHAN), Fifth Grade Teacher; *b:* Albany, NY; *m:* William Frederick Sr.; *c:* William F. Jr., Daniel Francis; *ed:* Rosary Hill Coll (BS) Elem Ed 1969; Russell Sage Coll (MS) Tchng the Mentally Retarded 1973; *cr:* Giffen Elem Schl 4th Grd Tchr 1969-70; Schl #10 2nd-3rd Grd Tchr 1970-74; Philip Schuyler Elem Schl 3rd, 5th-6th, Academically Talented 5th Grd Tchr 1974-; *ai:* Fac Sunshine Fund, Soc Comm Chprsn; Discipline, Budget, Sci Text Selection, Hnr Roll Comms; After Schl Cmptr Club; Albany Pub Schl Tchrs Assn, NY St Tchrs Assn, AFT, NEA 1969-; Chrstn Brothers Acad Mothers Assn 1989-, Class VP; Chrstn Brothers Acad Academic Cncl 1995-; North Colonie Yth Bsbl Ladies Auxiliary 1986-; Albany City PTA Life Mbrshp Awd; *office:* Philip Schuyler Elem Schl 141 Western Ave Albany NY 12203

MEHLMAN, LESLEY LUNIN, Latin Teacher; *b:* Boston, MA; *m:* Edwin S; *c:* Jeffrey, Brian, Erik; *ed:* Mount Holyoke Coll (AB) Latin 1959; Bureau Jewish Ed 1981-84; Hebrew Univ in Jerusalem 1984; Univ of RI, RI Coll 1984-85, 1990-93, 1996-; *cr:* Pennsauken HS Latin Tchr 1959-61; Newport News Schl System Eng, Hist Tchr 1961-62; Jewish Family Svc Outreach Cnslr to Elderly 1974-81; Temple Habonim Religious Schl Tchr 1981-84; Lincoln HS Latin Tchr 1984-85; East Greenwich HS Latin Tchr 1985-; *ai:* NHS Adv 1993-; Coord Schl Peer Tutoring Prgm; NEA 1984-; Amer Classical League 1985-; New England Classical Assn 1985-; RI Foreign Lang Assn 1985-; RI Classical Assn 1993; Fellowship to Hebrew Univ 1984; Ed Methods Honored by Tufts Univ as Inspirational Tchr 1992; Honored by East Greenwich Schl System Schl Comm 1992; Foreign Lang Tchng 1993; Natl Foreign Lang Exams Nations; *office:* East Greenwich HS Avenger Dr East Greenwich RI 02818*

MEHRHOF, EDWARD J., US History AP & Regents Tchr; *b:* Newark, NJ; *m:* Lorie D.; *c:* Ian, Brienne; *ed:* SUNY at New Paltz (BA) 7-12 Soc Stud 1986, (MS) Ed, His 1988; *cr:* Washingtonville HS Tchr 1986-; *ai:* Travel Group Ldr for Stu Tours in Europe; AFT, NYSUT, Washingtonville Tchrs Assn 1986-; *office:* Washingtonville HS 54 W Main St Washingtonville NY 10992

MEHUS, HELEN ANN (BENCIC), Family & Consumer Sci Teacher; *b:* Indiana, PA; *m:* Bruce G.; *c:* Brian B., Melanie A.; *ed:* IN Univ of PA (BS) Home Ec Ed 1969, (MS) Home Ec Ed 1973; *cr:* IN Sr HS Home Ec Tchr 1971-78, 1987-88; IN Univ of PA Instr Consumer Svcs 1988-90; IN Jr HS Home Ec Tchr 1990-91; IN Sr HS Family & Consumer Sci Tchr 1991-; *ai:* Strategic Planning; Grad Requirements; IN Area Ed Assn, PA St Ed Assn, NEA 1990-; Alpha Delta Kappa 1993-, Schlsp Chm; Red Line Club 1995-; IN Yth Hockey Assn 1988-; Acad Excl Grant; *office:* Indiana Sr HS 450 N 5th St Indiana PA 15701

MEIBERS, LAWRENCE JOHN, Mathematics Teacher; *b:* Cincinnati, OH; *m:* Christine Souders; *c:* Mark, Lynn; *ed:* Miami (BS) Math 1971; Xavier (MED) Admin 1976; Attnd Univ of Cincinnati 1966-67; *ai:* 9th Grd Bsktbl Coach 1971-72; 10th Grd Bsktbl Coach 1972-74; Jr Var Bsktbl Coach 1974-77; Var Bsktbl Coach 1977-83; OEA & NEA 1971-; Sons of Amer Legion 1990-; *home:* 5876 Butler Warren Rd Mason OH 45040*

MEICHSNER, KERRY T., History Teacher; *b:* Easton, PA; *m:* Kathryn M. Vreeland; *c:* Keith Morrison, Kimberly Holthaus, Kathleen Baugher; *ed:* Montclair St Univ (BA) His 1963; Attnd Trenton St Univ, Montclair St Univ, Drew Univ, Fairleigh Dickinson Univ; *cr:* Oxford Cntrl Schl Sci, PE Tchr 1963-65; Millburn HS His Tchr 1967-; *ai:* Interact Club Adv; CORETEAM; Bowling, Ftbl, Bsbl Coach; NEA, NJEA 1963-; Millburn Ed Assn 1967-, Legislative Liaison 1983; Shade Treen Comm 1978-80, Chm, Svc Commendation 1980; Emergency Squad 1963-67, Cert of Merit 1965; WA Ath Assn 1970-71, Pres; Mansfield #36 F&AM 1963-, Historian 1970-72, 25 Yr Awd 1988; Amer Legion WA Post #103, Honorary Life Mem 1987; Millburn Rotary Club 1988-, Honorary Life Mem 1991; *home:* 166 Cregar Rd High Bridge NJ 08829

MEIER, CARL W., Social Studies Department Head; *b:* Syracuse, NY; *m:* Carolyn Johnson; *c:* William, Richard; *ed:* Hamilton Coll (BA) Philosophy 1964; Syracuse Univ (MSSC) His 1978; *cr:* Duxbury Schls Tchr 1966-, Soc Stud Dept Head 1978-, Curr Cncl Chair 1990-; *ai:* NCSS 1966-; ASCD 1978-; *office:* Duxbury Jr Sr HS 130 St George St Duxbury MA 02332

MEIER, JANINE JOHN, Physics & Computer Sci Teacher; *b:* Grove City, PA; *ed:* PA St Univ (BS) Environmental Resource Mngmt 1978; Slippery Rock Univ (BS) Physics 1982; *cr:* I. C. Norcom HS Physics, Sci Tchr 1984-85; Slippery Rock Area HS Physics, Sci Tchr 1986-; *ai:* Svc Learning Mentoring Corps Spon; Kids That Care Steering Comm; Western PA Amer Assn Physics Tchrs, NEA 1986-; Advy Cncl Family Svc Corps Butler Cty 1996; *office:* Slippery Rock HS 201 Kiester Rd Slippery Rock PA 16057

MEIER, KELLY A., 1st Grade Teacher; *b:* Concord, NH; *m:* Gene C.; *c:* Jason, Monica; *ed:* Keene St Coll (BSEd) Elem Ed 1984; *cr:* Inter-Lakes Elem 1st Grd Tchr 1984-; *ai:* Inter-Lakes Ed Assn 1984-, Bldg Rep 1986-90; *office:* Inter-Lakes Elem Schl 21 Laker Ln Meredith NH 03253*

MEIERING, JUDITH ANN, Social Studies Dept Chprsn; *b:* Cincinnati, OH; *ed:* Univ of Cincinnati (BS) Ed, His 1969, (MED) His, Psych 1972; Xavier Univ Philosophy, Psych Post Grad Work; *cr:* Gamble Jr HS Psych, His, Eng Tchr 1969-75; Cincinnati Pub Schls Tchr Specialist Rsrch Dept 1975-76; Walnut Hills HS Tchr His Dept 1976-; Cincinnati Pub Schl Consulting Tchr 1991-93; Walnut Hills HS Dept Chm 1994-; *ai:* North Cntrl Review Steering, Tech, Fin Comms; Hnrs Team Ldr; AFT, Cinti Fed of Tchrs 1973-; NCSS, Amer Psychological Assn 1993-; Lead Tchr Appt 1991; Hebrew Union Coll Natl Conf Speaker; *office:* Walnut Hills HS 3250 Victory Pkwy Cincinnati OH 45207*

MEIGS, HELEN YABLONSKI, Russian Teacher; *b:* Mexico, NY; *m:* Lee E.; *c:* Kristina, Robert; *ed:* Syracuse Univ (BA) Russian Lang 1968, (MA) Russlan Lang, Lit 1971; Post Masters Work Univ of Pittsburgh, Bryn Mawr Coll, Pedogogical Univ; *cr:* Pittsburgh Pub Schls Tchr 1985-; *ai:* Russian Club, SLAVA Honorary Spon; Ldrshp Club Fac Asst; Schl Safety, Discipline Comm Chprsn; Schl Cabinet; Facilitator GATE Stdnts; ACTR, AATSEEL 1988-; AFT 1985-; Parent Schl Comm Cncl 1994-; NEH Summer Insts Russian Lang; US, USSR Tchr Exch; *office:* Taylor Allderdice HS 2409 Shady Ave Pittsburgh PA 15217*

MEILLIER, MARC PHILIP, Art Teacher; *b:* Yeadon, PA; *m:* Penny Lee; *c:* Justin, Ethan, Ryan, Andrew; *ed:* Glassboro St Coll (BA) Art Ed 1977; *cr:* Cherry Hill East HS Art Tchr 1978; Cherry Hill West HS Art Tchr 1979; Oaklyn Pub Schl Art Tchr 1980-93; Clayton HS MS Art, Vidoe Productions, GATE Tchr 1993-; *ai:* GATE; Art Club; PAC Comm; Stu Cncl; Schl Store; Horticulture; Yrbk Adv; Audio Visual Coord; NEA, NJEA 1978-; Tchr of Yr 1989-90, 1995-96.

MEINERT, ROBIN VAN METER, 2nd Grade Teacher; *b:* Washington Ct H, OH; *m:* Walter T. Jr.; *c:* Zachary Wayne, Megan Elizabeth; *ed:* Morehead St Univ (BA) Elem Ed 1979; Attnd Miami Univ & Ashland Univ; *cr:* Belle Aire Elem Schl 2nd Grd Teacher 1979-81, 1987-; 3rd Grd Tchr 1981-85, 4th Grd Tchr 1985-87; *ai:* Dist Lang Arts Comm; Dist Comp Tech Comm; Delta Kappa Gamma 1993-; Grace United Meth Church 1969-; Helped Implement Effective Schls Grant & Venture Capital Grant; *office:* Belle Aire Elem Schl 1120 High St Washington Court H OH 43160

MEINKING, TERRY, Athletic & Facilities Director; *b:* Cincinnati, OH; *m:* Kathy; *c:* Joe, Jennifer, Jake, Jessica; *ed:* Xavier Univ (BS) Span, PE, Hlth, Ed 1972; Grad Schl; *cr:* St Francis Seminary Schl Tchr, Coach 1971-72; St Anthony Elem Schl Tchr, Coach 1973-74; Purcell Marian HS Admin, Coach 1974-; *ai:* Head Var Wrestling Coach; OHS Wrestling Coaches Assn 1975-; SW OH Wrestling Coaches Assn 1975-, Pres, Coach of Yr 2 Times; Natl Wr Coach Assn 1979-; Norwood Knights of Columbus 1986-; St Cecilia Boosters 1981-; *office:* Purcell Marian HS 2935 Hackberry St Cincinnati OH 45206

MEINZER, HARRY VALENTINE, Retired Art Dept Coord & Tchr; *b:* Rahway, NJ; *ed:* Kutztown Univ (BS) Art Ed 1954; *cr:* Lower Paxton Jr HS Art Tchr 1954-56; Battin HS Art Tchr 1957-58; Hanover Park HS Coord, Tchr 1958-90; *ai:* Yrbk, Natl Art Hnrs Soc Adv; Hanover Pk Ed Assn 1968-, Pres 1964; Art Edctrs of NJ 1968-, Pres, VP 1968-70, Distngd Svc; NAEA, VA 1958-, Eastern Region Scndry Dir, Cert; NEA, NVEA 1958-; Sons of Amer Revolution 1954-; F&AM #147 1964-; NH Antiquarian Soc 1995-; Hopkinton Rotary Club 1996-; Pub Article; East Hanover Jaycees Outstdng Edctr 1973, Merit Tchr HPHS 1970, 1973, 1976, Natl Art Ed Scndry Tchr of Yr Eastern Region 1985, NAEA Marion Quinn Dix Ldrshp 1990, Art Edctrs of NJ Distngd Svc 1975, Bd of Ed Svc to Schl & Comm 1984, Outstdng Scndry Edctr of Amer 1973, Nom Princeton Univ Excl Tchng 1972 Awds; *home:* 1645 Hopkinton Rd Hopkinton NH 03229

MEISEL, HARRIET KAPLAN, Second Grade Teacher; *b:* Waterbury, CT; *m:* Harry A.; *c:* Mitchell B. Kaplan, Sherry K. Solomon; *ed:* Cntrl CT St Univ (BS) Elem Ed 1956, (MS) Elem Ed 1973; St Joseph's Coll 30 Credits Educl Philosophy & Issues; *cr:* Webster Schl 1st Grd Tchr 1966-75; Carrington Schl 1st Grd Tchr 1975-79; Chase Schl Biling Tchr 1979-80; Barnard Schl 2nd Grd Tchr 1980-; *ai:* City-Wide Lang Arts Curr Task Force; City-Wide Rdng Assessment, Math Textbook Selection & Curr Review Comms; Mentor for Intern Enrolled in Grad Prgm at Univ of Bridgeport, Partners in Ed; Waterbury Tchrs Assn 1966-, Schl Rep; CT Educ Assn, NEA 1966; Beth-El Synagogue Sisterhood 1957-; Waterbury Heb Free Loan Assn 1975-, Bd of Dirs; Ridgewood Club 1965-, Sec, Bd of Dirs; Nom Twice for Outstdng Alumnus Awd at Cntrl CT St Univ; *home:* 49 Currier Way Cheshire CT 06410

MEISSNER, JAMES J.,SR., Mathematics Asst Professor; *b:* Meadville, PA; *m:* Mary Kathleen Moran; *c:* James, Richard, Christine Herbstritt, Patricia Fair; *ed:* Slippery Rock Univ (BS) Math 1960; Attnd Penn St Univ, OH Univ, Case-Western Reserve Univ, Baldwin-Wallace Coll; *cr:* Butler Area Scndry Schls Math Instr 1960-64, St Fidelis coll & Seminary Math Instr 1964-80, Slippery Rock Univ Math Instr 1980-81; Butler Cty Comm coll Math Instr 1981-; *ai:* Bsktbl, Soccer, Tennis Team Coach; BC3EA 1992-, Treas, Pres 1994-; PSEA 1992-; NEA 1992-; Summit Twp Parks & Recreatio 1975-, Chm; Outstanding Fac Awd 1987-88, 1990-91; Outstanding Educator Awd in Higher Ed 1987-88; Butler Cty Chamber of Comm; *office:* Butler County Community Coll College Dr Oak Hills Butler PA 16001*

MEISSNER, JANET ANDERSON, Mathematics Lecturer; *b:* Jamestown, NY; *m:* Leonard R.; *c:* Jill, Andrew; *ed:* SUNY at Fredonia (BS) Math Ed 1972, (MS) Math Ed 1976; *cr:* Fredonia HS Math Tchr 1972-73; Eathan Allen Furniture Cmptr Prgmr 1973-75; Fredonia Coll Math Lecturer 1977-; *home:* 4484 Canterbury Dr Mayville NY 14757

MEISSNER, JOHN CHARLES,III, Teacher of the Gifted; *b:* Detroit, MI; *m:* Marcia Kyle; *c:* John IV, Daniel, Christy; *ed:* William Tyndale C (BRE) Soc Sci 1970; Eastern MI Univ (MA) Scndry, Elem Ed 1972; Rdng Specialist 1972; Attnd Univ of PA, PA St Univ; *cr:* Washington Elem Tchr 1972-74; Stewart MS Tchr 1974-84; East Norriton MS Tchr of Gifted Ed 1984-; *ai:* Drama, Mural Clubs, Newspaper, TV Crew Spon; Stage Crew Mgr;Sci Olympiad Judge; NEA, PSEA 1972-; S Coventry Chester Co 1986-92, Zoning Officer; Historical Review 1990-92, Comm; Boys Club Chrstn Svc Brigade; Exeter Bible Church Choir; PA Renaissance Faire Star Chamber; *office:* East Norriton MS 330 Roland Dr Norristown PA 19401

MEISSNER, LEONARD ROBERT, Vocal Music Director; *b:* West Seneca, NY; *m:* Janet Anderson; *c:* Jill, Andrew; *ed:* SUC at Fredonia (BA) Vocal Music Ed 1972; *cr:* Chautauqua Cntrl Voc Music Dir 1972-; *ai:* 24 Elem Musicals; Cty Music Festival Coord 24 Yrs; Sr Band, Choir Trip Co-Coord; NEA 1972-, Assn Pres 1 Yr; Mayville United Meth Church 1976-, Organist, Choir Dir; *office:* Chautauqua Cntrl Schl State Rd Chautauqua NY 14722

MEITL, CLAIRE WAGNER, Sixth Grade English Teacher; *b:* Chicago, IL; *m:* John F.; *c:* Jodi Lynn, Michael John; *ed:* Univ of IL (AB) LAS, Eng 1969; Johns Hopkins Univ (MSE) Spec Ed 1989; *cr:* Lincoln Jr HS 7th Grd Eng Tchr 1971-73; Christ The King Schl 7th Grd Eng Tchr 1979-80; Lanphier HS Eng Tchr 1980; Dunloggin MS Eng Tchr 1981-; *ai:* Memory Book Spon; NEA 1981-; NCTE 1970-; MCTLA 1990-; *office:* Dunloggin MS 9129 Northfield Rd Ellicott City MD 21042*

MEKLUS, RUTH ANN, 1st Grade Teacher; *b:* Cleveland, OH; *ed:* Bowling Green St Univ (BS) LD-DB Elem Ed 1980; Kent St Univ (MED) Specific Learning Disabilties 1986; Addl Credit Hrs Ashland Univ, Univ of Akron, Kent St Univ; *cr:* Arrowhead Primary Schl Learning Disabilities K-4th Grd Tchr 1980-91, 1st Grd Tchr 1991-; *ai:* NEA, OEA 1980-; BP Amer Excl Ec Ed Honorable Mention Grd K-4; Joint Cncl on Ec Ed, Intnl Paper Co Fnd; Honorable Mention Open Competition Tchng of Ec; Natl Awds Prgm Abstract Pub; *office:* Arrowhead Primary Schl 1600 Raleigh Blvd Copley OH 44321

MELAMPY, RONALD F., Vocal Music Director; *b:* Lebanon, OH; *m:* Joy Wendling; *c:* Ron, Kim, Jon, Shara; *ed:* Coll Coservator of Music Univ of Cincinnati (BS) Music Ed 1959; George Washington U (MS) Intnl Affairs 1973; US Naval War Coll 1972-73; Defense Lang Inst 1977; *cr:* Lakota HS Vocal Music Dir 1959-61; US Navy Various 1961-88; Little Miami Schls Vocal Music Dir 1990-; *ai:* OMEA 1990-; ACDA 1995-; *office:* Little Miami Schls 605 Welch Rd Morrow OH 45152*

MELBOURNE, BERTRAM LLOYD, Department of Religion Chair; *b:* St James, Jamaica; *m:* Cavel Beckford; *c:* Yolande, Maurice, Launice; *ed:* West Indies Coll (BTH) Theology 1968; Andrews Univ (MA) Religion 1976, (PHD) Biblical Stud 1986; *cr:* Savanna La Mar HS Vice Prin, Bible Tchr 1968-70; West Jamacia Conf Of SDA Pastor Evanglist, Youth Ed Dir 1970-78; West Indies Coll Asst Prof, Chair Tech Dept 1978-82; Columbia Union Coll Assoc Prof 1985-90, Chair Dept Religion & Division Religion & Soc Sci 1990-; *ai:* Biblical Research Comm Mem; Fac Dev Chair; West Indies Alumni Assoc Pres, VP; Wheaton Pathfinder Club; Soc of Biblical Lit 1986-; Amer Acad of Religion 1986-; Amer Assoc of Higher Ed 1993-; Adventist Soc for Rel Stud 1986-; ASCD 1984-; Natl Assoc of Rel Prof 1995-; Andrews Univ Seminary Stud Bd 1992-; West Indies Coll Alumni

Assoc Washington Chapel 1985-, Disinguished Alumnus Awd; Book Pub to Understand Disciples in Synoptic Perspective, Beginners Guide to New Testament Greek; Journals, Magazine Articles, Book Reviews; Zappara Awd Excl Tchng; Distinguished Leadership Awd; *office:* Columbia Union Coll 7600 Flower Ave Takoma Park MD 20912*

MELBOURNE, CAVEL ANDREA (BECKFORD), Junior High School Teacher; *b:* Jamaica, West Indies; *m:* Bertram; *c:* Yolande, Maurice, Launice; *ed:* West Indies Coll at Jamaica (BA) His 1982; Andrews Univ (MA) His 1984; *cr:* Jamaica Elem & Jr Scndry Schls Tchr 1969-74; Harrison HS Tchr 1974-78; West Indies Coll HS Tchr 1978-81; John Nevins Andrews Schl Jr HS Tchr 1986-; Columbia Union Coll Adj Tchr 1991, 1995-; *ai:* Potomac Conf Curr Comm; Multicultural Comm Chair; NCSS; *home:* 8121 Lockney Ave Takoma Park MD 20912

MELCHING, SUSAN BUNDSCHUH, Teacher of Gifted & Talented; *b:* Fremont, OH; *m:* Jeffery D.; *c:* Molly, Ted; *ed:* Miami Univ (BA) Ed 1972; Bowling Green S Univ (MA) Ed 1976; 15 Addl Grad Hrs; *cr:* Perkins Schls 6th-8th Grd Tchr 1972-78, 7th-8th Grd Tchr 1979-82, 3rd-6th Grd Gifted, Talented Tchr 1985-; *ai:* Schl Advy Cncl; St Peter Schl Huron Church Lector; OEA 1972-, Bldg Rep; NEA 1972-; Phi Delta Kappa 1993-; St Grant 1978; Organized 2 6th Grd Expedition Trips; *office:* Perkins Schls E Bogart Rd Sandusky OH 44870*

MELDROM, CAROL SZACIK, Third Grade Teacher; *b:* Keene, NH; *ed:* Univ of NH (BA) His 1965; 70 Plus Post Grad Credit Hrs; *cr:* Rhinebeck Cntrl Schl Elem Tchr 1965-; *ai:* Mid Hudson Tchrs Ctr Policy Bd; Elem Math Curr Comm; Rhinebeck Tchrs Assn 1965-, Current VP; AFT 1965-; NY St United Tchrs 1965-, Dist Rep; Star Lib Bd 1984-88; Rhinebeck Zoning Bd of Appeals 1988-90; 2 Area Fund Grants for Prof Dev From Partnership for Ed in Dutchess Cty NY.*

MELDRUM, JOAN LESLIE (MATTHEWS), K-12th Grd Tchr of Gifted Ed; *b:* Bay Village, OH; *m:* James Michael; *c:* Matthew, Julie, David; *ed:* IN Univ of PA (BS) Spec Ed 1974, (MED) Ed 1977; *cr:* Ebensburg IU 08 Life Skills Tchr 1974-83; Scranton IU 19 Emotional Support Tchr 1983-84; Canon-Mc Millan Schl Dist Learning Support Tchr 1988-89; Washington Schl Dist Emotional Support Thcr 1989-90, Gifted Ed Tchr 1990-; *ai:* HS Acad Team Coach; History Day Team Spon; CERDEC Corp, Washington Schl Liaison; Comm Coalition; Odyssey of Mind Teams Coord; Washington Ed Assn 1989-; NEA 1974-; KDKA, Westinghouse, Giant Eagle Thanks to Tchrs Awd 1994; *office:* Washington HS 201 Allison Ave Washington PA 15301

MELFI, PATRICIA S., Early Childhood Education Dir; *b:* Columbus, OH; *m:* Rudy C.; *c:* Mitch, Eric, Amy Stahr, Nanci Stradley; *ed:* OH St Univ (BS) Home Ec Ed 1992; Univ Toledo 5 Hrs; *cr:* DE Joint Voc Schl Early Chldhd Ed Dir 1992-; *ai:* Stud Asst Pgm; FHA; HERO; Prof Dev; Kappa Omicron Mu 1990-; Phi Upsilon Omicron 1990-; OUA & AVA 1992-; NEA 1992-; Courtesy Car Memrl Tourn 1979-; Human Ecology Prof Awd; William & Nellie Draut Schlsp; Kappa Omicron Nu Sr Scholar; AHEA Non Traditional Awd; *office:* Delaware Joint Voc Schl 1610 State Route 521 Delaware OH 43015*

MELGAARD, GAIL APPLE, 7th-8th Grd Lang Arts Teacher; *b:* Gratis, OH; *m:* Wayne K.; *c:* Carol Howard, Matthew, Brandon; *ed:* Miami Univ (BS) Eng 1967; Univ of Dayton (MS) Interdisciplinary Stud 1981; *cr:* Wheeling HS Eng Tchr 1967-69; Madison HS Eng Tchr 1969-71; Springboro HS Eng Tchr 1973-75; Bennett Jr HS Eng Tchr 1975-76; Wilder Jr HS Eng Tchr 1977-; *ai:* Spelling Bee; PEA, OEA & NEA 1977-; *home:* 480 E Loy Rd Piqua OH 45356

MELICHAREK, MILAN PAUL, High School Art Teacher; *b:* Coaldale, PA; *c:* Lori, Michael; *ed:* Kutztown Univ (BS) Art 1973; St of PA (MS) Art Ed; *cr:* USAF Security Police 1965-67, Security Police Instr 1967-68; Northwestern Lehigh HS Art Tchr 1973-; *ai:* Hnrs Allentown Art Museum Mbrshp Show 1978, Gallery in the Park Best of Show 1983, Bethlehem Art Show Best of Show 1986, People Choice Awd, Muhlenberg Art Ctr 1988, 1990, NJ Festival of the Arts 1st Pl in Watercolor 1989, Scenic River Days Art Festival 3rd Place in Painting 1989, Midwest Watercolor Soc Show Honorable Mention 1989, PA Watercolor Soc Keystone Medallion Awd 1989; PA Watercolor Soc 1989-, Keystone Awd 1990; Submitted Work Allentown Art Show 1978, Lehigh Art Alliance Shows 1987, 1988, 1989, 1990, 1991, Mayfair Juried Exhibition 1988-91, 1993, Midwest Watercolor Soc Show 1989, PA Watercolor Soc Show 1989-1992, Northeast US Watercolor Show 1991, PA Watercolor Soc Calendar 1995 Issue; *office:* Northwestern Lehigh HS 6493 Route 309 New Tripoli PA 18066

MELINK, MICHAEL CHRISTOPHER, 8th Grade American His Teacher; *b:* Cincinnati, OH; *m:* Meri Beth Bagnoli; *c:* Joshua; *ed:* OH St Univ (BA) Soc Stud Ed 1987; Currently Working on Masters in Schl Cnslng at Capital Univ Through Dayton Univ; *cr:* Gahanna-Jefferson City Schls Educl Aide SBH Classroom 1987-88, Sub Tchr 1988-89, 8th Grd Amer His Tchr 1989-; *ai:* Wrestling, & Cross Cntry Head Coach; Soc Stud Dept Chprson; OEA 1989-; NEA 1989-; GJEA 1989-; ST Matthews Church 1992-.

MELLACE, EDITH SLOVSHEK, Mathematics Teacher & Tutor; *b:* Far Rockaway, NY; *m:* Richard; *c:* Liz, Carolyn; *ed:* SUNY at Cortland (BS) Elem Ed 1960; Adelphi Univ (MA) Math & Ed 1989; *cr:* USFD 15 3rd Grd Tchr 1960-61, 4th Grd Tchr 1961-64; Vly Stream Cntrl HS Math Tutor & Tchr 1980-; *ai:* RCT Math Comm; Tchr SAT & PSAT Prep Courses; Math III R Variance Course Comm Writer; NEA, NYSTA 1980-; VSTA 1980-; NCTM 1990-; Jenkins Memrl Schlsp; NY St Regents Schlsp; Kappa Delta Pi; *office:* Valley Stream Central HS 135 Fletcher Ave Valley Stream NY 11580

MELLON, VINCENT G., Physics Teacher; *b:* Potsdam, NY; *m:* Linda Denuel; *c:* Bryan, Jeff, Danielle; *ed:* Mohawk Vly C. C. (AS) Engrng Sci 1967; SUNY at Potsdam (BA) Physics 1970; 39 Grad Hrs Physics, Ed; 18 Under Grad Cmptr Programing; *cr:* Madison Oneida BOCES Summer Section 1990-95; Camden HS Physics, Sci Tchr 1970-; *ai:* Sr Class Adv; AFT, NYSUT 1970-; AYSO, Little League 1991-, Coach; City League T-Ball 1995-, Coach; *office:* Camden H S Oswego St Camden NY 13316

MELLOR, COLLEEN KELLY, HS English Teacher; *b:* Providence, RI; *c:* Kerry Leigh, Amanda Jean; *ed:* URI (BA) His, Eng, Fr 1967; 40 Addl Hrs RIC, PC; *cr:* Park View Jr HS Soc Stud, Eng Tchr 1967-71; Hugh B. Bain Jr HS Eng Tchr 1971-90; Cranston East HS Jrnlsm, Eng Tchr 1990-; *ai:* Adv Schl Newspaper; AFT; Schl Paper Won Second Pl in St for Best Feature Story; *office:* Cranston Sr HS East 899 Park Ave Cranston RI 02910

MELLOTT, SONYA DESHONG, Language Arts Teacher; *b:* Saluvia, PA; *m:* Phillip D.; *c:* Craig P., Monica F. Richendrfer; *ed:* Bloomsburg Univ (BS) Eng & Lang Arts 1987; Wilkes Univ (MS) Ed 1995; *cr:* Mid-St Literacy Cncl Pgrm Coord 1987; Mifflinburg Area HS Lang Arts Tchr 1988; Penns Valley Area HS Lang Arts Tchr 1989; West Snyder HS Lang Arts Tchr 1990-; *ai:* Adv to Class of 1998; Schl Newspaper Adv at Mt Peek; PSEA, NEA, NCTE 1987-; PCTE 1989-; *office:* West Snyder HS RR 1 Box 292 Beaver Springs PA 17812

MELNICK, ANDREW DIMITRY, 6th Grade Teacher; *b:* Cambridge, MA; *ed:* Univ of NM (BS) Bio 1969; 50+ Grad Credits; *cr:* Nathaniel H Wixon MS 6th-8th Grd Tchr 1971-; *ai:* Former Coach Girls Bskbl; NEA 1972-; MA Tchrs Assn 1972-; The Register Best Tchr Awd 1995; *office:* Nathaniel H Wixon MS 901 Route 134 South Dennis MA 02660

MELNICK, MICHAEL J., High School Business Teacher; *b:* Scranton, PA; *m:* Lois; *c:* Michael, Linda Krehel, Robert, Thomas; *ed:* Univ of Scranton (BS) Scndry Ed 1960, (MS) Ed 1967; Cooperative Ed Cert Temple Univ 1987; *cr:* Flanders Schl Eng Tchr 1960-61; St Patrick's HS Bus Tchr 1961-63; Lackawanna Trail HS Bus, Eng Tchr 1963-72; West Scranton HS Bus Tchr, Cooperative Ed Coord 1972-; *ai:* Schl Treas; Cooperative Ed Adv; Jr HS Track Coach; Bus Curr Comm; SFT; PA Cooperative Ed Assn; Northeast PA Cooperative Ed Assn; PIAA Ftbl, Bsktbl, Track Ofcl, Pres, VP, Rules Interpreter; Scranton City Cncl, Pres 4 Terms; Scranton Area Sports Hall of Fame; *office:* West Scranton H S 1201 Luzerne St Scranton PA 18504

MELNICK, RICHARD ANDREW, French & English Teacher; *b:* Darby, PA; *ed:* CA Univ of PA (BS) Fr 1966; WV Univ (MA) Ed & Fr 1975; Post Grad Stud; *cr:* West Allegheny Sr HS Fr & Eng Tchr 1966-; Frgn Lang Dept Chair 1990-; *ai:* European Trip Spon; NEA, PSEA 1966-; Wilkinsburg Stamp Club 1976-; *office:* West Allegheny HS W Allegheny Rd Imperial PA 15126

MELO, CHELSA A., Third Grade Teacher; *b:* New York City, NY; *ed:* St Univ of NY at New Paltz (BS) Ed 1961, (MS) Ed 1961; *cr:* Irving Elem Schl 1-5 Grd Tchr 1961-63; Grandview Elem Schl 1-5 Grd Tchr 1963-; *ai:* Mentoring Prgm; Spec Ed Comm; NYSUT 1961-; Catskill Tchrs Assn 1961-, Sec 1980-90; Albany Area Rdng Cncl; Columbia-Greene Rdng Cncl; Ladies Aux Palenville Fire Dept; Alumni Asssn St Univ of New Paltz 1961-; *office:* Grandview Elem Schl 10 Grandview Ave Catskill NY 12414

MELON, RUTH BERNADETTE, English & Social Studies Tchr; *b:* Orange, NJ; *m:* Ira M.; *c:* Rebecca, David; *ed:* Rutgers Univ of NJ (BA) Eng 1969; Princeton Univ Tchr Preparation Inst Scndry Ed 1969; Centenary Coll Elem Ed 1981; UVA Summer Insts for Tchrs Multicultural Stud 193-94; *cr:* Copeland MS Tchr 1969-; *ai:* NJEA, NEA 1969-; Mt Olive Human Relations Comm 1993-; NJ Governor's Tchr Recognition Awd 1990; *office:* Copeland MS 100 W Lakeshore Dr Rockaway NJ 07866

MELONE, FRANK TALBOT, Middle School Teacher; *b:* Copaigue, NY; *c:* John Talbot, Luke Campbell, Lea Ame; *ed:* Univ of Bridgeport (BS) Ed, Sociology 1962, (MS) Cnslng 1963; Hofstra Univ (MS) Admin 1970; Stony Brook Univ (MA) Lbrl Stud 1976; *cr:* Univ of Bridgeport Ed Dept Instr 1962-63; Central Blvd Schl Fifth-Sixth Grd Tchr 1963-90; John F. Kennedy MS Summer Schl Prin 1970-, Lang Arts, Math Tchr 1990-; *ai:* Bethpage HS Wrestling 1965-85; Bethpage Jr HS Lacrosse 1973-75; Northport HS Winter Track 1989-91; Bethpage Cong Tchrs 1968-, Bldg Rep; PTA 1965-; SEPTA 1970-; CYO 1985-89, Coach; Cub Scouts 1982-84, Scout Master; Little League 1984-87, Coach; Huntington Soccer Club 1981-83, Coach; Univ of Bridgeport Dean's List 1961-62, Flwshp 1962-63.

MELROY, DEBRA PETSKO, Kindergarten Teacher; *b:* Washington, DC; *m:* Douglas W.; *c:* Torey, Chad; *ed:* Lynchburg Coll (BA) Elem Ed 1973; *cr:* Flocktown Elem Schl 3rd Grd Tchr 1975, 1st Grd Tchr 1975-77; Bells Elem Schl 3rd Grd Tchr 1989-90, Kndgtn Tchr 1990-91; Grenloch Terr Early Chldhd Ctr Kndgtn Tchr 1991-; *ai:* Co-Chair Sunshine Comm; NJEA 1989-; GCAKE, NJAKE 1991-; *home:* 122 Wilson Rd Turnersville NJ 08012

MELTZER, MICHAEL ROBERT, Physics & AP Physics Teacher; *b:* Syracuse, NY; *m:* Sandra L. Ellison; *c:* Dawn E., David C., Steven A.; *ed:* Syracuse Univ (BS) Sci Ed 1963, (MS) Sci 1964, (MS) Ed 1974; Amateur Radio License; *cr:* East Syracuse HS Physics Tchr 1964-65; East Syracuse, Minoa Cntrl HS Physics Tchr 1965-; *ai:* Jr Engrng, Tech Soc, Ham Radio Club Adv; Instrl Improvement, Stu of Month, Prin Advy, Stu Handbook, Achvmt Awds, Summer Schl, Block Schedule, Plagiarism, Schl Improvement, Character, Assessment Comms; Sick Leave Bank Chm; East Syracuse United Tchrs 1964-; Radio Amateurs of Greater Syracuse 1956-, Pres 1984-88; Amer Optical Soc 1 of 100 Most Outstdng Tchrs on NY St 1987; NHS Tchr of Yr 1988; Excl Tchng Awd 1992; NY St Regents Examination Item Writing Comm 6 Yrs; NY St Regents Exam Evaluation Comm 6 Yrs; Physics Regents Curr Revision Comm 3 Yrs; Articles Pub; *office:* E Syracuse Minoa Ctl HS 6400 Fremont Rd East Syracuse NY 13057

MELUCCI, CAROL A., Business Education Teacher; *b:* Brooklyn, NY; *ed:* Hunter Coll (BA) Bus Ed 1972, (MA) Bus Ed 1975; Coll of Staten Island Admin & Supervision Cert 1986; *cr:* Clara Barton HS Tchr 1972-78; New Dorp HS Tchr & Grd Adv 1984-89; Curtis HS Tchr & Grd Adv 1989-; *ai:* Pre-Cooperative Ed Coord; Tchr Trng in Comps; Schlsp Comm; Schl-Based Support Team; BEA 1972-; *office:* Curtis HS 105 Hamilton Ave Staten Island NY 10301

MELUSKY, JOSEPH, Prof & Chair of His & Pol Sci; *b:* Pottsville, PA; *m:* Marie Belecanech; *c:* Michael, Jessica; *ed:* West Chestern St Coll (BA) Pol Sci 1975; Univ of DE (MA) Pol Sci 1978, (PHD) Pol Sci 1983; Visiting Scholar 1987-88, 1995, Univ of MI 1987; Attnd Asheville Inst od Gen Ed 1992, Acad Ldrshp Inst, Carnegie Mellon Univ 1991; *cr:* Univ of DE Lecturer 1979-80; St Francis Coll Fac Mem 1980-, Dean of Gen Ed 1993-94, Prof & Chair 1992-; *ai:* Pre-Law Adv 1980-; Co-Chair Gen Ed Task Force, Comm 1991-94; Fac Senate Pres 1985-87, VP 1984-84, 1990-92; Amer Pol Sci Assn 1980-; Northeastern Pol Sci Assn 1985-, Exec Dir, Dir of Employment Svcs; PA Pol Sci Assn 1980-, Pres, VP 1994-; Second VP 1992-94; PA Amer Legion HS Oratorical Contest on US Constitution Judge 1991-93, 1995; Pi Sigma Alpha 1976-; Pi Gamma MU 1974-; Books: The Bill of Rights: Our Written Legacy 1993, To Preserve These Rights: The Bill of Rights 1791-91 1991, The Constitution: Our Written Legacy 1991; St Francis Coll Natl Alumni Assn Dist Fac Awd 1995; Swatsworth Fac Merit Awd 1990; Hnr Sco Outstdng Fac Citation 1983; *office:* Saint Francis Coll Loretto PA 15940

MELVIN, NOREEN M., World Language Teacher; *b:* Brookline, MA; *ed:* Emmanuel Coll (AB) Fr 1965; Emmanuel Coll at Boston, Sorbonne at Paris (MA) Contemporary Fr Lit 1967; *cr:* Beebe Jr HS Fr Tchr 1967-81; Malden HS Fr, Span Tchr 1981-; *ai:* HS Cncl; Curr Frameworks Comm; NEA, MTA, MEA, MAFLA 1971-; Irish Dance Tchrs Assn of North Amer 1974-, NE Region Treas 1987-, NE Honoree 1993; Spirit & Pride Awd 1994; *office:* Malden HS 77 Salem St Malden MA 02148

MENAPACE, LAWRENCE WILLIAM, Assoc Professor of Chemistry; *b:* Brooklyn, NY; *m:* Eileen Mary; *c:* Barbara LaPilusa, James I.; *ed:* St Peters Coll (BS) Chem 1960; Univ of New Hampshire (PHD) Organic Chem 1964; *cr:* Marist Coll Assoc Prof 1968-95; *ai:* Amer Chem Soc 1960-; Marist Coll Comm Svc Awd; *office:* Marist Coll 82 North Dr Poughkeepsie NY 12603

MENARD, BARBARA CHANDLER, Mathematics Teacher; *b:* Oakland, CA; *m:* Maxime III; *c:* Tami Rashel, Shannon Anne; *ed:* USIU CA Western Univ (BA) Math 1969, (MA) Ed 1971; Addl Post Grad Stud; Coll of the Holy Cross 3 Credits, UCSD 12 Credits; *cr:* Bell Jr HS Math Tchr 1969-72; Poway Unified Twin Peaks MS Math Tchr 1972-78; Burrillville HS Math Tchr 1978-; *ai:* Class of 1994 & SADD Adv; Prins Advisory Comm; Former Tennis Coach; Var Hockey Team Acad Progress Monitor; Cheerleading Asst Coach, Acad Eligibilty Comm., Clothes Closet for Needy; NEA 1978-; NCTM, ASCD; Burrillville Org for Substance Abuse Prevention 1988-, Treas 3 Yrs; Burrillville Arts Festival 1980-; RI St Sci Fair 1988-, Judge 1988-; RI Governors Comm for Youth Alcohol & Substance Abuse Prevention 3 Yrs; NSF Grants; Whos Who in RI, RI PRESDNTL Awd for Math & Sci; *office:* Burrillville H S 425 East Ave Harrisville RI 02830

MENCONI, RALPH JOSEPH,II, Eng Dpt Chm, Sr Mstr & Ec Tchr; *b:* Bronxville, NY; *ed:* Hamilton Coll (BA) Lbrl Arts 1970; Attnd Middlebury Coll, Georgetown Univ, Northeastern Univ; *cr:* Putney Rdng Inst Tchr 1970-71; Salisbury Schl Fac, Admin 1971-; *ai:* Yrbk Adv; Archivist; Fac Sec; Scndry Schl Archivists Assn 1992-; Lib of Congress Assn Assoc Mem; *office:* Salisbury Schl 251 Canaan Rd Salisbury CT 06

MENDAK, MIRTA MENDEZ, ESL Teacher; *b:* Lorain, OH; *m:* M.; *ed:* Lorain Cty Comm Coll (AA) Bus 1985; Univ of Findlay Biling Bus Ed 1988; Ashland Univ Pursuing Masters in Rdng Lorain Admiral King HS Bus Tchr 1988-91, 1992-93, 1994-95; Long MS ESL Tchr 1991-92, 1993-94; Lorain MS ESL Tchr 1995-; *ai:* Ed Assn, OH Ed Assn, NEA 1988-; *home:* 125 Graybark Ln Amher 44001

MENDELLO, JAMES PETER, French Teacher & Dept Chairm Paterson, NJ; *ed:* Montclair St Coll (BA) Fr Lit, Eur His 1980; W Paterson Coll (MElEd) Elem Ed, Soc Sts 1987; St Mary's Sem & (MDiv) Theology 1993; Mexican-Amer Cultural Ctr Span Lang C Achvmt 1992; *cr:* Immac Heart of Mary Schl Tchr 1982-88; St Mar Tchr, Dept Chair 1993-; *ai:* Drama Club, Frgn Lang Club Adv; Lit NCEA 1993-; *office:* St Mary-Assumption H S 237 S Broad St Eli NJ 07022*

MENDELSON, ROBERTA KLEIN, English Teacher; *b:* New York NY; *m:* Fred S.; *c:* Michal; *ed:* Fairleigh Dickinson Univ (BA) Lehman Coll (MA) Eng 1996; Cert of Completion in Acting Amer A Dramatic Arts; *ai:* Shakespeare Recitation Competition Coord; Eng Curr Revision Comm; *office:* Brooklyn Technical HS 29 Fort Gre Brooklyn NY 11217*

MENDELSON, SHERRY MARLENE, First Grade Teacher; *b:* Bro NY; *ed:* Queens Coll (BA) Elem Ed K-6 1971, (MS) Rdng Prgm K-12 65 Addl Credits Elem Ed 1977-; *cr:* Half Hollow Hills HS Rdng Tchr Tulakes Elem Schl Fourth & Sixth Grd Tchr 1981-83; Matzke Elem Fourth-Fifth Grd Tchr 1983-85; Candlewood Jr HS Rdng Tchr 1985 Kennedy Schl First Grd Tchr 1985-; *ai:* Bldg Rep, Tchr Assistance Co NYSUT, AFT 1980-; Great Neck Tchrs Assn 1985-; *office:* John F Ke Schl 1a Grassfield Rd Great Neck NY 11024

MENDELSON, SUSAN COEN, Counselor; *b:* Cleveland, OH; Robert; *ed:* Carleton Coll (BA) Sociology 1971; Univ of Pittsburgh (Scndry Ed 1974, (MSW) Hlth & Mental Hlth 1983; Post-Grad W Carnegie-Mellon Univ, Duquesne Univ & Indiana Univ of PA Cleveland Hghts HS Soc Stud Tchr 1971-72; Penn Hills HS Cnslr & Tchr 1972-86; Univ of Pittsburgh Schl of Medicine Part-Time Instr Peters Twp HS Cnslr 1986-; *ai:* Stu Svcs Dept Facili Washington-Green Cty Cnslrs Assn 1986-, Sec, Past Pres; PA Schl C Assn 1986-; Allegheny Cty Cnslrs Assn 1983-; PA Assn of Scndry S Coll Admission Cnslrs 1986-; Ntnl Assn of Coll Admisn Cnslrs De Beta Kappa 1971-; Soc Networks & Mental Htlh; Beverly Hills: SAG 1985; Columbia Tchr Coll Book Prize for Excl in Ed; PA HS Cnslr Yr 1996; *office:* Peters Township HS 246 E Mc Murray Rd Mc Murr 15317

MENDENHALL, JACK LEONARDO,JR., Biology Teache Rochester, PA; *m:* Veronica; *c:* Todd; *ed:* Geneva Coll (BS) Bio & Pre 1967; Univ of Pittsburgh (MED) Ed 1972; *cr:* Aliquippa Area Schls Sci Tchr 1967-69; Beaver Cty Comm Coll Bio Tchr 1972-90; Hop Area Schls Bio Tchr 1969-; *ai:* Hlth Careers Club Co-Spon; Improvement Comm; Dist Envir Pgm Coord; Strategic Planning C NEA, AEA, HEA & PSEA 1967-; Hopewell Twp Park Bd 1982-, Dir; 1980-, Sec; Aliquippa Area Citizen of Yr; Hopewell Twp Citizen Field & Stream Sportsman Awd; Buhl Sci Ctr Tchr awd; Beaver Conservationist of Yr Awd; *home:* 4312 Beverly Dr Aliquippa PA 15

MENDENHALL, WARNER D., Professor; *b:* Savannah, GA; *m:* Lepley; *c:* Warner, David, Blair, Mary; *ed:* Davidson (BS) Chem Duke Univ (MA) Pol Sci 1960; Kent St Univ (PHD) Pol Sci 1982; C Hrs Rutgers St Univ, Walsh Univ, Univ of Akron; *cr:* Caswell Cty Prin 1959-60; Grove City Coll Asst Prof 1960-66; Kent St Univ Assoc 1966-72; Univ of Akron Wayne Coll Prof 1972-; *ai:* Distngd Stu Distngd Prof Comm; Fac Well Being, Budget Comm; Natl Alcoholism, Drug Abuse Cnslr; OH Assn of Alcohol, Drug Abuse C Rotary Intnl 1972-; Ed Co-Dependency Issues in Treatment.*

MENDENHALL, WILLIAM L.,III, Chemistry Teacher; *b:* West Ch PA; *m:* Susan J.; *ed:* Messiah Coll (BS) Chem 1991; West Chester (MED) Chem Ed 1995; *cr:* Avon Grove HS Chem Tchr 199 Coatesville Area Sr HS Chem Tchr 1993-; *ai:* JV Sftbl Coach; Assess Comm; NEA, PSEA 1991-; Brandywine Tract & Conservation Club 1 Natl Eagle Scout Assn 1987-; *office:* Coatesville Area Sr HS 14 Lincoln Hwy Coatesville PA 19320

MENDEZ, GLORIA ELAINE, Math Teacher; *b:* Manchester, Jam *m:* Trevor; *c:* Michelle, Trevor, Steven; *ed:* Western Carolina Univ (Math, Mid Grd Ed 1980; Jamaica West Indies Diploma Elem Ed 1 Attnd Bethlehem TC; *cr:* Min of Ed Tchr 1965-69; Belair Schls Tchr, Coord 1970-84; Grace Chrstn Ed Ctr Tchr, Vice Prin 1984-86; St Comm Chrstn Schl Math Tchr 1986-; *ai:* Sunday Schl Tchr, Supt; Ch Elder, Soc Comm; Yth Adv; Prof Dev Wkshps; *office:* Saint Paul C Chrstn Schl 819 Schenck Ave Brooklyn NY 11207

MENDEZ, KENNETH BERNARDO, Music Teacher; *b:* Brooklyn, *m:* Maria Teresa Suarez; *c:* Kristyn, Daniel, Elizabeth; *ed:* NY Univ (Elem Ed 1990; 30 Credits Ed Admin; *cr:* PS 130M K-6th Grd 1985-90, ESL Tchr 1990-93, Admin Asst 1990-; *ai:* Disc Jo Entertainer, Camp Dir; AFT 1985-; *office:* PS 130M 143 Baxter St York NY 10013*

MENDEZ-CATLIN, LOIS MARIE, Dev Skills, Stu Life Asst Prof; Albans, NY; *m:* Lionel Catlin; *c:* Sean Blane; *ed:* CT Coll (BA) Eng 1980; Columbia Univ Educl Psych 1982; Tchrs Coll (MED) (EDD) Hig Adult Ed 1995; CT Coll HS Tchr Cert 1980; Long Island Univ & C. W. Cmptr Ed Tech Prof Diploma 1989; *cr:* CUNY Adj Instr 1981-87; Ade Univ HEOP Assoc Dir 1986-89; Queens Coll Asst to Dean of St 1989-91; Borough of Manhattan Comm Coll Asst Prof 1989-; *ai:* Natl of Hispanic, Latino Stud 1996, St Chprsn; AAHE Hispanic Caucus; Delta Kappa; Kappa Delta Pi; Beacon Parents Assn 1993-, Pres; Imo Eletia Carr Schlsp 1991-, Trustee, Chprsn; Faculty Voices Co Contributor; Natl Assn of Hispanic, Latino Stud Conf Proceed Publication; *home:* 4406 Manayunk Ave Philadelphia PA 19128*

MENDLER, PEGGY-ANN BRUSH, Second Grade Teacher; *b:* Brook NY; *m:* James A.; *c:* J. Christopher, Matthew Joseph, Jeanne-Marie; *ed* John's Univ (BS) Ed 1962; Queens Coll of the City of NY (MS) Ed 19 60 Addl Post Grad Credit Hrs; *cr:* Massapequa NY Bd of Ed Tchr 1962- Bergenfield Bd of Ed Sub Tchr 1969-72; Bergenfield NJ Bd of Ed T 1979-; *ai:* Multicultural, Family Life, Values Comms; Bergenfield T Assn 1979-, Schl Rep; Bergen Cty Tchrs Assn, NJEA, NEA 19 Westwood Bd of Ed 1974-79, Trustee, Comms Chm; Our Lady of G Counsel, Choir Mem 1978-, Sunday Schl CCD Tchr 1968-; Bergenfiel Women's Club 1968-75, Treas, VP; NJ Tchr of Yr 1994; *home:* 9 Elf Ct Hillsdale NJ 07642*

MENDOSA, DORIS KURSCHEID, Eighth Grade English Teacher; Lindlar, Germany; *ed:* Howard Univ at DC (BA) Sociology-Anthropol 1965, (MAT) Ed 1972; 72 Addl Credit Hrs Bowie St Coll, Trinity Col Wash DC, Univ of MD, Westminster Coll; *cr:* Lyndon Hill Elem 5th Tchr 1972-73; Matthew Henson Elem 5th Grd Tchr 1973-84, Chprsn 19 Langley Park Mc Cormick Elem 4th-5th Grd Tchr 1984-88; Bucklodge 7th-8th Grd Eng Tchr 1988-, Writing Resource Tchr Mentor 1994-95;

paper Spon 1994-; Schl Based Supervisory Team Ldr Univ of MD, e Heo Ctys Scndry Prof Dev Cntr PDC 1994-95; PECEA, MSTA, 1972-; ASCD 1992-; MAACIE, IASCE 1990-; *office:* Buck Lodge MS Buck Lodge Rd Hyattsville MD 20783*

EELY, JAMES CLYDE, 9th-11th Grd Biology Teacher; *b:* sutawney, PA; *m:* Deborah E.; *c:* Joel, Matthew, Cassie; *ed:* Penn St Bio 1971, (MED) Ed 1973; Cnslng IN Univ of PA 1986-; 27 Credit *:r:* Ambler Jr HS Life Sci Tchr, Sftbl Coach 1971-72; Great Vly HS Phys Sci Tchr 1972-73; Punxsutawney Sr HS Bio Tchr, Stu Govt Adv -; *ai:* Bsbl Coach 1986-94; PSEAA, NEA 1971-; Elks 1986-; *office:* sutawney Area Sr HS N Findley St Punxsutawney PA 15767

EFEE, SELITHA MEACHAM, French Teacher; *b:* Aiken, SC; *m:* ael Aaron; *c:* Sonja Renee, Michael Everett; *ed:* Hampton Inst (BS) 63; Attnd NDEA Summer Lang Inst, Howard Univ Summer Lang Inst, of MD Baltimore cty Ed Courses, Loyola Univ, Coppin St Univ; *cr:* Glen Jr HS Fr Tchr 1963-78; Northwestern HS Fr Tchr, Dept Chair -; *ai:* Foreign Lang Club, NHS Spon; Class of 1990 Adv; Schlsp, Grad ns; BTU, AFT 1975-; MFLA 1979-, Outstanding Tchr 1991; NAACP -; Mt Pisgah AME Church 1977-, Steward 1980, VP, Lay Org; Delta a Theta Inc 1962-; Experiment in Intnl Living France 1963; Tchr of 984; *home:* 5643 Settler Pl Columbia MD 21044

IGES, ROBERT LEE, Business Teacher; *b:* Turbotville, PA; *m:* R. Stroup; *c:* Stephen R. L., Christian H. P.; *ed:* Penn St Univ (BS) Bus in 1960; Bloomsburg Univ Ed, Bus 1962; Univ of AL Mrktg; *cr:* ming Cty Schls Spec Svc Tchr 1962-65; Bethlehem Area Schls Bus 1965-71; Shikellamy Area Schls Bus Tchr 1971-; *ai:* Past Spon of stment Clubs; NEA, PSEA 1962-; SEA 1971-; Muncy Recreation mission; Muncy Creek Twp Park Comm, Historical Soc, Bsbl Assn :h; Church Orgs; Geneological Publications Contributor.*

NHORN, NORMAN W., Fifth Grade Teacher; *b:* Meyersdale, PA; *m:* L. Bush; *c:* Katherine, Nathan, Emily; *ed:* Shippensburg Univ (BS) l Ed 1977; Grad Credits; *cr:* Shade Cntrl Cty Schls 4th Grd Tchr -81; Berling Brothersvalley Schls 3rd, 5th-6th Grd Tchr 1981-; *ai:* Fac ms; NEA 1977-; BBEA 1981-, Treas; AGEHR 1984-, PA St Rep; ng Fife & Drum Corps 1975-, VP; Berlin Area Historical Soc 1977-, Berlin Brethren Church 1967-, Minister of Music; Outstdng Young of Amer 1987; *home:* 811 Main St Berlin PA 15530

NICHIELLO, JOHN, English Teacher; *b:* Scranton, PA; *m:* Kay; *c:* , David; *ed:* Penn St (BA) Lang Arts 1964; OK St (MED) Lang Arts ; *cr:* North Penn HS Tchr 1964-67; Oklahoma City Pub Schls Tchr -69; Methacton HS Tchr 1969-; Montgomery Cty Comm Coll Instr -; *ai:* Grad Dir; NEA 1964-; PSEA 1964-; Zoning Hearing Bd 1990-, Sec; *office:* Methacton Sr High 1001 Kriebel Mill Rd Norristown PA)3

NKE-FISH, SARAH FRANCES, Hum & Comm Magnet Pgm Coord; herokee, IA; *m:* F. Donald; *c:* Sean, Michelle; *ed:* Univ of Northern IA) Speech Theatre Tchng & Radio Television Broadcasting 1979; The r Univ (MA) Film & Video 1992; *cr:* Dowling HS Speech & Drama & Dir 1981-84; The Hum & Commnctn Magnet Pgm Television & n Production Tchr 1986-92, Coord 1993-; Amer Univ Adj Prof 1995-; GATE Supts Advy & Prof Dev Comms; Educl Extravaganza; NEA 5-; MCAASP 1992-; PEO 1979-; Presenter at NABT Nashville 1991, A Boston 1992 & ASCD Convention San Francisco; CINE Awds for umentaries if You Change Your Mind & Remotely Science; Presidential ironmental Yth Awd for Documentary, Trash What a Waste; *office:* ern MS 300 University Blvd E Silver Spring MD 20901

NKES, MARSHA ANN, Fourth Grade Teacher; *b:* Brooklyn, NY; *m:* ry M.; *c:* Howard, Madeline Weiss; *ed:* Brooklyn Coll (BA) Ed & Lit 1, (MA) Ed & Rdng 1979; 46 Credits Above Masters; Varied Prof rses in His & Lit; *cr:* PS 182 Brooklyn 4th Grd Tchr 1961-64; Sub Tchr arious NYC Elem & Scndry Schls 1967-76; PS 27 Rdng Tchr 1976-77; 189 3rd-8th Grd Tchr 1977-; *ai:* VFT, AFT 1981-; Howard Beach Judea 1979-, Sisterhood Bd; Temple Judea 1973-79, Pres of Sisterhood, Youth up Ldr, Bd Mem, Svc Awd 1978 & 1979; *office:* PS 189 Bilingual Ctr 0 E New York Ave Brooklyn NY 11212

NNA, ELIZABETH JONES, Basic Skills Teacher; *b:* Camden, NJ; *m:* holas R. Jr.; *ed:* Glassboro St Coll (BA) Elem Ed 1964; Temple Univ ED) Ed 1967; Penn Literacy Course Univ of PA; *cr:* Wilkins Schl 4th Tchr 4 Yrs, 3rd Grd Tchr 23 Yrs, Basic Skills Tchr 5 Yrs, Head Tchr; Pupil Assistance Comm Chm; Maple Shade Ed Assn, Burlington Cty Ed sn, NJ Ed Assn, NEA 1964-; PTA 1964-; Rodale Inst, Nature nservancy 1993-; Burlington Cnty Historical Soc 1990-; Tchr of Yr; *ne:* 31 E 2nd St Moorestown NJ 08057

NNA, LARRY K., Assistant Professor of History; *b:* Poughkeepsie, ; *ed:* Columbia Univ (BA) His 1980, (MA) His 1982, (MPhil) His 1985, D) His 1991; *cr:* Tufts Univ Adj Instr of His 1986-92; Manhattan Coll Instr of His 1988-89; NC St Univ Adj Instr of His 1988-89; Fordham v Adj Instr of His 1989; SUNY Asst Prof of His 1991-; *ai:* Southern torical Assn 1991-; Org of Amer Historians 1991-; SHEAR 1992-; umbia Univ Amer Civilization Seminar 1993-; Grants: Mellon Rsrch vshp 1994-95, UUP Rsrch Awa 1994; Book Pub The Origins of Modern rts 1982-40 1995; Articles Pub; Conf Papers; *office:* St Univ of NY at rmingdale 224 Thompson Hall Melville Rd Farmingdale NY 11735

NNEFEE, SUSAN L., Fifth Grade Teacher; *b:* Cleveland, OH; *c:* ky James Jr.; *ed:* Cleveland St Univ (BA) Ed 1978, (MS) Ed, Rdng 96; *cr:* Cleveland Job Corps Math Tchr 1978-79; Cleveland Bd of Ed K-8 l Tchr 1979-; Summer Yth Employment Remedial Tchr 1989-; Salvation my Tutor 1994-; *ai:* Drug Liaison; Aerobics Exercise; Adv Stu Tchrs; Tutor Mentor; TEEMS Lead Tchr Math; AFT 1979-; Sickle Cell Assn 95-, Bd of Trustees; Emanual Bapt Church 1995-; *office:* Miles Park m Schl 4090 E 93rd St Cleveland OH 44105*

ENON, KONTHATH KUNHIRAMA, English Teacher; *b:* Rangoon, rma; *m:* Meryl Blau; *ed:* Travancore Univ (BA) Ec, His, Pol Sci 1953; adras Univ (MA) Eng, Lang, Lit 1957; NY Univ (MA) Eng Ed 1969; *cr:* ima Mata Natl Coll Eng Tutor 1953-54; Madras Med Coll Asst Eng cturer 1958-60; Govt Sec Schl Ambo & Debra Berhan Eng Tchr 1960-61; nana Natl Coll Eng Tchr 1961-63; Choate Rosemary Hall Dept Head 77-82, Eng Tchr 1964-; *ai:* Comm Svc Prgm, Interfaith Group Comm; m Laude Soc; Choate Rosemary Hall Chptr 1983-; Johannes Van raalen Awd 1988; Charles Rice Chair Eng Awded Trustees of Schl 1989; me: 101 Hotchkiss Grove Rd Unit 16 Branford CT 06405

ENSHEL, DENNY, Professor of Business Admin; *b:* Gowanda, NY; *m:* nja Hwang; *c:* Sonya Pero, Sonia Bovo, Sondra, Samuel; *ed:* Univ of ffalo (BA) US His 1971; Syracuse Univ (JD) Law 1978; Fredonia St Coll Hrs Grad Work Pol Sci; Buffalo St Coll 21 Hrs Grad Work Stu Prsnl lmin; Univ of MD 30 hrs Undergraduate Work; *cr:* Bryant & Stratton Bus st Bus Law Instr 1979-82; Erie Comm Coll Bus Admin Prof 1979-; agara Univ Bus Law Instr 1980-82; *ai:* Bus Club Adv 1979-81; Asst restling Coach 1979-80; NEA 1979-; Erie Cty Bar Assn, NYS Bar Assn 85-; Gowanda Cntrl Schl Bd of Ed 1992-93; *home:* 24 Caroline Rd PO ox 67 Gowanda NY 14070

ENSING, TERESA MARIE, Geology Professor; *b:* Rochester, NY; *m:* nter Faure; *ed:* Monroe Comm Coll (AS) Geology, Math 1978; SUNY Geneseo (BA) Geology 1980; OH St Univ (MS) Geology 1982, (PHD) eology 1987; *cr:* Shell Oil Co Geologist Mineral Exploration Dept 1982; OH St Univ Byrd Polar Rsrch Assoc 1987-88; Wittenberg Univ Visiting Asst Prof 1988-90; Oh St Univ at Marion Asst Prof 1990-; *ai:* Acad Affairs, Curr Comm, Prairie Advy Comms; Reviewer of Proposals for NSF & NASA; Geological Soc of Amer; Geochemical Soc; Intnl Assn of Geochemistry & Cosmochemistry; Sigma XI; SUNY Geneseo Alumni Advy Cncl; Sci Fair Judge; NSF Grants for Antarctic Rsrch; Articles Pub; Antarctic Svc Medal; Outstndg Young Woman in Amer 1991.

MENTZER, DEBORA GRILEY, Spanish Teacher; *b:* Coshocton, OH; *m:* Gene S.; *c:* Gregory; *ed:* Denison Univ (BA) Span 1982; *cr:* Crooksville HS Span Tchr 1984-; Hocking Coll Span Instr 1993; *ai:* Tchr Advy Bd; Delta Kappa Gamma 1989-; *office:* Crooksville HS 4075 Ceramic Way Crooksville OH 43731

MENTZER, GENE STEPHEN, Science Teacher; *b:* Carlisle, PA; *m:* Debora R. Griley; *c:* Gregory; *ed:* Kent St Univ (BSEd) Soc Stud & Biological Sci 1973; Attnd OH Univ Aviation Sci, Muskingum Coll Earth Sci & Geology; *cr:* Austintown Fitch HS Tchr 1975-76; New Lexington HS Sci Tchr 1977-; *ai:* Stu Cncl Adv; AFT 1980-, Bldg Rep 3 Yrs; Sci Ed Cncl of OH 1985-; New Lexington Jaycees, Pres, Jaycee of Yr 1989-90; New Lexington Elks Lodge #509 1990-, Schlsp Comm; *home:* 300 Delaware Dr Crooksville OH 43731

MENTZER, JAYNE MARIE, Former Director & Coach; *b:* Morehead City, NC; *m:* Brian C.; *c:* Cannon, Morgan; *ed:* Bob Jones Univ (AS) Child Care 1985; Voice, Piano; *cr:* LaPetite Acad Tchr 1982-83; Atlantic Shores Bapt Schl Asst Dir 1986-87; LaPetite Acad Dir 1988-89; Riverdale Bapt Schl Cheer Coach 1994-95; *ai:* Riverdale Bapt Church 1994-.

MENTZER, MARSHA LEE (RHODES), English Teacher; *b:* Altoona, PA; *m:* Ronald Lee; *c:* Rebecca, Jonathan; *ed:* Shippensburg Univ (BS) Scndry Eng Ed 1976, (MED) Eng Ed 1980; *cr:* Carlisle HS Eng Tchr 1976-; *ai:* Strategic Planning Steering, Stu Assessment & Prins Advy Comms; Club Adv; Curr Comm; CAEA 1976-, Newsletter Ed; PSEA, NEA, NCTE 1976-; First Luth Church, Comm Mem, Tchr; *office:* Carlisle HS 623 W Penn St Carlisle PA 17013

MENTZER, PATRICIA GABLE, 6th-8th Grade Reading Teacher; *b:* York, PA; *m:* Ray G.; *c:* Eric R.; *ed:* Shippensburg Univ (BS) Elem Ed 1959; Peabody Tchrs Coll Post Grad Stud; *cr:* Hawaii Area Schl Dist First Grd Tchr 1959-61; Norfolk Area Schl Dist First Grd Tchr 1962-63; Nashville Area Schl Dist First Grd Tchr 1964-65; Dallastown Area Schl Dist 3-6 Grd Tchr 1978-82; Schl Dist of City NY 6-8 Grd Tchr, Comm Arts Dept Chm 1986-; *ai:* Adv Newspaper, Lit Magazine; Lang Arts Dept Chm; NEA, PSEA 1978-; YCEA 1986-; Delta Kappa Gamma 1992-; Welcome Wagon 1967-, Pres; Young Women's Club; Outstanding Young Woman of Amer 1971; *office:* Edgar Fahs Smith MS 701 Texas Ave York PA 17404

MENZEL, SUSAN MAGEE, 4th Grade Teacher; *b:* Philadelphia, PA; *m:* Kenneth; *c:* Kenny; *ed:* West Chester U (BA) Elem Ed 1972; 30 Grad Credits Rowan Coll; *cr:* Stoy Schl 4 Grd Tchr 1972-80, 2 Grd Tchr 1980-82; Edison Schl 4 Grd Tchr 1983-; *ai:* Peer Coaching Tutor 1994; Arbor Day Coord 1992-; NEA, PTA 1972-; Babe Ruth Bsbl, Vol 1992-; Little League Mom, Coord 1984-92; Tchr of Yr 1992; Mentor Tchr 1994; *office:* Thomas A Edison Elem Schl 205 Melrose Ave Collingswood NJ 08108

MENZIES, THOMAS JAMES, Math Teacher; *b:* McKeesport, PA; *m:* Marcia Gene Railingshafer; *ed:* IN Univ of PA (BA) Math 1973; Washington & Jefferson Coll (MS) Math 1979; 18 Credit Hrs Cmptrs Penn St; *cr:* Ft Cherry Sr HS Math & Cmptr Tchr 1974-88; Elizabeth Forward HS Math Tchr 1988-; *ai:* Math Club; Overnight Engr Creative Project Field Trip; PSEA, NEA 1974-; PA Achvmt Excl PA St Senator Albert Belan; KDKA Recipient Partners in Ed; *home:* 203 Walnut Rd Mc Donald PA 15057

MEOLI, PATRICIA ANN SETARIANO, English Teacher; *b:* Brooklyn, NY; *m:* Peter; *c:* Anthony, Michael; *ed:* Ulster Cty Comm Coll (AAS) Liberal Arts 1968; St Univ Coll at New Paltz (BA) Eng 1970, (MS) Admin 1990; *cr:* Ellenville Cntrl Schl Eng Tchr 1970-72; Fallsburg Cntrl Schl Eng Tchr 1984; Rondout Valley Cntrl Schl Eng Tchr 1984-; *ai:* AFT 1970-; RUTF 1984-; Ulster Cty Rdng Cncl 1977-80, Sec; Rondout Valley Tchrs Schlsp Comm; NHS Comm; *office:* Rondout Valley Cntrl Schl Kyserike Rd Accord NY 12404

MERCADANTE, JAMES N., Art Teacher; *b:* Paterson, NJ; *m:* Donna Ruggiano; *ed:* Monmouth Univ (BS) Art Ed 1970; Newaric Schl of Fine & Industrial Arts Cert Commercial Art 1966; Montclair St Univ 32 Grad Credit Hrs; *cr:* Passaic Valley Regnl HS Art Tchr 1970-; Cty coll of Morris Adj Prof of Fine Arts 1988-84; *ai:* Yrbk; Schl Newspaper; PVEA 1970-, Treas, Exec Comm; NEA 1970-; NJEA 1970-; AENJ 1970-; Natl Trust for Historic Preservation 1980-; PVHS Tchr of the Yr; NJ Governors Recognition Grant; Recognized for My Efforts by Cleveland Inst of Art, The Ctr of Creative Stud & MD Inst Of Art; NJ St Panel for Proficiencies in the Arts; Merit Art Schlsps Awded to My Stdnts; *office:* Passaic Vly Regnl HS East Main St Little Falls NJ 07424

MERCALDE, AMY L., English Teacher; *b:* Pittsburgh, PA; *ed:* PA St Univ (BA) Eng 1971, (BS) Scndry Ed 1971; CA St Univ 12 Credit Hrs; Univ of Pittsburgh 18 Credit Hrs; *cr:* Thomas Jefferson HS Sr Eng, Creative Writing Tchr 1971-; *ai:* HS Literary Magazie, Bible Club Spon; AFT, NCTE 1971-; ACUPET 1994-.*

MERCALDO, DAVID, Teacher; *b:* Brooklyn, NY; *m:* Linda Ann; *c:* Isaac, Christy, Rachel, Amy; *ed:* Central Bible Coll (BA) Ed 1967; Richmond Coll (MS) Elem Ed 1970; OK St Univ (PD) Admin 1985; Columbia Pacific Univ (PHD) Neuro-Psych 1996; Post Grad Stud Central St Univ, Langston Univ; *cr:* NY City Pub Schls Tchr 1968-73; Long Island Schls Tchr, Prin 1973-78; Boces-Westchester Schl Supervision 1978-81; Tulsa Pub Schls Prin 1981-86; Summit Schl Asst Dir 1986-88; NY City Pub Schls Tchr, Adj Asst Prof 1989-; *ai:* UFT 1968-; SI Rdng Assn 1993-; Phi Beta Kappa 1996-; Parkinsons Soc 1976-77, Bd Chm; Pub Television TV Show 1996-; CBS TV TV Show 1984-87; Outstdng Young Men Amer 1975; Pub OK Mid Schl Assn Journal, Admin Magazine, Rainbows Magazine, Syndicated Column Lets Talk About Kids; *home:* 414 Pendale St Staten Island NY 10306

MERCED, JOSE, Medical Tech & Biology Teacher; *b:* Brooklyn, NY; *m:* Lisa Muniz; *c:* Lori, Rebecca; *ed:* City Univ of NY (BS) Med Tech 1988; NY Univ (MA) Scndry Ed 1995; *cr:* US Army Power Generation Equip Repair Specalist 1977-84; Schwartz Chemical Technician 1984-86; Meth Hosp Med Technologist 1986-88; John Dewey HS Sci Tchr 1988-; *ai:* Hlth Occupations Stdnts of Amer 1989, Aspira 1988-89 Adv; Coord Hlth Careers Prgm; Flwshp Brookhaven Natl Lab 1994, Columbia Univ 1995-97; Tchr of Yr 1993; Amer Med Assn Med Soc Cty of Kings Inc; Pres NY City Chapter HOSA; *office:* John Dewey HS 50 Avenue X Brooklyn NY 11223

MERCER, SCOTT DEMING, History Teacher; *b:* Canton, OH; *m:* Connie S. Young; *c:* Eric, Kristi Lee, Scott, Thomas; *ed:* Mount Union Coll (BA) His 1975; 15 Hrs Towards Masters in Ed; *cr:* Jackson HS His Tchr 1978-; *office:* Jackson HS 7600 Fulton Dr NW Massillon OH 44646

MERCER, WILLIAM JAMES,JR., Orchestra Director; *b:* Syracuse, NY; *m:* Margret Pols; *ed:* Ithaca Coll (BM) Music Ed 1987, (MM) Conducting 1992; *cr:* Auburn Enlarged City Schl Dist Orch Tchr 1987-88; West Genesee Cntrl Dist HS Orch Dir 1988-; *ai:* HS String Quartet Instr; Syracuse Musical Theater Tech Dir; ASTA, NYSSMA, MENC 1988-; Ontario Cty All Cty Festival, Southeastern MA Regnl Festival 1994, NYSSMA All St Festival 1995 Guest Conductor; *office:* West Genesee HS 5201 W Genesee St Camillus NY 13031*

MERCIER, LINDA, Frgn Lang Dept Chair & Fr Tchr; *b:* Montreal Quebec, Canada; *m:* Mark Andrew Trimble; *c:* Alexander; *ed:* Mc Gill Univ (BA) Tchng Fr as Second Lang 1989; CA St Univ in San Bernardino (MA) Scndry Ed 1993; Millersville Univ Supervisory Cert 1996; Lang Dev Specialist Cert; *cr:* San Jacinto HS Fr & ESL Tchr 1991-93; Oak Park Schl Dist Fr Tchr 1992-93; Elizabethtown Coll Adj Proj of FR 1993-94; Conestoga Vly Schl Dist Frgn Lang Dept Chair, Fr Tchr 1994-; Franklin & Marshall Coll Adj Prof of Fr 1996-; *ai:* Above & Beyond, HS Grad Project Comms; PSMLA 1993-; Best Tchr Awd; *office:* Conestoga Vly Schl Dist 2110 Horseshoe Rd Lancaster PA 17601*

MERCIER, MEGHAN SULLIVAN, High School Religion Teacher; *b:* Livingston, NJ; *m:* Adrian G. II; *ed:* Chestnut Hill Coll (BS) Psych 1992; Fordham Univ 3 Credit Hrs Theology; *cr:* Mt St Joseph Acad Rel Tchr 1992-94; Holy Family Acad Rel Tchr 1994-; *ai:* NEA 1992-; Rainbows Intnl 1995-, Cnslr; *office:* Holy Family Acad 239 Avenue A Bayonne NJ 07002

MERCURIO, VICTOR DONALD, English Teacher; *b:* Warwick, RI; *m:* Brenda; *ed:* Boston Coll (BA) Eng 1989; Providence Coll (MED) Admin 1995; 3 Addl Credit Hrs; *cr:* Winman Jr HS Eng Tchr 1989-93; Aldrich Jr HS Eng Tchr 1993-94; Pilgrim HS Eng Tchr 1994-; *ai:* Toll Gate HS Boys Var Soccer Coach; Warwick Tchrs Union 1989-; NCTE 1990-; *office:* Pilgrim HS 111 Pilgrim Pky Warwick RI 02888

MERDIAN, PATRICIA DERMOTTA, Lang Arts Tchr & Dept Chprsn; *b:* McKeesport, PA; *m:* Francis Jay; *c:* Brian J.; *ed:* CA Univ of PA (BS) Comprehensive Eng 1967, (MA) Eng, Fine Arts 1986; Admin 21 Hrs; Advanced Placement Curr 9 Hrs Carnegie Mellon Univ; *cr:* Yough HS Tchr, Dept Chprsn 1967-; *ai:* Newspaper Spon; Staff Dev Comm; Curr Cncl; Yough Ed Assn 1967-, Sec; PA St Ed Assn, NEA 1967-; St Edward Schl Advy Bd 1995-; St Edward Church 1986-, Lector; Awds Staff Dev Svc, St Vincent Coll Great Tchr Recognition, Univ of Chicago Outstanding Tchr, Seton Hill Coll Great Tchr Recognition; *office:* Yough Sr HS 99 Lowber Rd Herminie PA 15637*

MEREDITH, DIANE AVENIA, HS English Teacher, Dept Chair; *b:* Gt Barrington, MA; *m:* William D. Jr.; *c:* John, William, Patrick; *ed:* St Univ Coll at Oneonta (BS) Scndry Eng Ed 1977; 36 Grd Hrs; *cr:* Walton Cntrl Schl Jr, Sr HS ENg Tchr 1977-, Dept Chair 1985-; *ai:* Essential Elements of Effective Tchng Lead Tchr Trainer; Yrbk Adv; Speech Coach; WTA 1977-, Sec, VP; Delta Kappa Gamma 1987-94; William B. Ogden Free Lib Bd of Trustees 1993-, Sec; United Meth Church 1979-, Lay Ldr, Admin Bd Chair; *office:* Walton Cntrl Schl 47-49 Stockton Ave Walton NY 13856

MERENDA, MERILYN WENSLEY, Communications Professor; *b:* Rochester, NY; *m:* John; *c:* John, Marly; *ed:* St Univ Coll of NY at Oswego (BA) Speech & Theater 1969; Long Island Univ at C. W. Post (MA) Speech Arts 1980; 12 Credit Hrs Stony Brook Univ; 6 Credit Hrs Albany Univ; 7 Credit Hrs Suffolk Comm Coll; 9 Credit Hrs; *cr:* Patchogue-Medford HS Speech, Drama, Eng Tchr 1969-72; Suffolk Cty Comm Coll Comm Prof 1981-; Hazeltine Corp Comm Consultant 1985-88; King Features Syndicate Comm Consultant 1985-88; NY Metropolitan Transportation Authority Comm Consultant 1990; *ai:* Pres's Kitchen Cabinet Comm; Intercultural Assn Adv; Encourage Appreciatoin of Diversity Comm Former Chair; Show Dir, Producer; Suffolk Comm Coll Fac Assn, AFT, NYSUT 1981-; India Soc at Stony Brook 1995-; Natl Tchng Excl Awd 1989; Who Made a Difference Tchng Awd 1989; Book: Speech Communication and Theater Arts 1979; *office:* Suffolk Cty Comm Coll Crooked Hill Road Brentwood NY 11717*

MERICLE, DANA R. (FRIESS), Sixth Grade Teacher; *b:* Camden, NJ; *m:* Scott D.; *c:* Alyssa Lee, Ashlee Paige; *ed:* Upsala Coll (BA) Sociology, Elem Ed 1980; Rowan Coll NJ (MA) Elem Admin 1988; Whitehall Elem Schl Third Grd Tchr 1980-81; Radix Elem Schl Third Grd Tchr 1981-87, Sixth Grd Tchr 1987-; *cr:* Whitehall Elem Schl 3rd Grd Tchr 1980-81; Radix Elem Schl 3rd Grd Tchr 1981-87, 6th Grd Tchr 1987-; *ai:* Advisor of Act, Safety Patrol, Schl Yrbk, PA System, Fish Patrol, Walking Biography Prgm, AVA Club, Peer Mediation, Stu Cncl, Stdnts at Risk Comm; AFT 1982-; Delta Kappa Gamma 1989-; Phi Delta Kappa 1990-; NJ Governor's Tchr Recognition Prgm Tchr Of Yr 1989; *home:* 50 Olympia Ln Sicklerville NJ 08081*

MERKEL, MATTHEW STEPHEN, Rel & Philosophy Tchr & Chprsn; *b:* Silver Spring, MD; *m:* Audra Rodway; *ed:* Bapt Bible Coll (BS) Bible 1992; Regent Univ at VA Beach MFA Prgm Comm, Theatre Arts Fall 1996; *cr:* Ross Corners Chrstn Acad Rel Tchr, Coll Guid 1993-; *ai:* Var Girls Soccer Coach 3 Yrs; Chapel Comm Dir 2 Yrs; Drama Dept, Jr HS Bsktbl Coach, Guid, Coll Entrance 1 Yr; Sr Class Adv; Lacrosse Team Defense Coach; ACSI 1993-; Mid-Atlantic Chrst Schls Assn 1995-; Ross Corners Bapt Church 1992-, Yth Dir 1992-95; WNBF Radio Tchr of Month 1994; *office:* Ross Corners Christian Acad 2101 Owego Rd Vestal NY 13850

MERKER, GAIL EMILIA ESQUIVEL, Parent Dev-Congruence Teacher; *b:* Almirante, Panama Cn Am; *c:* Michael, Maya; *ed:* Univ of MA (BA) Span Lit 1968; Richmond Coll (MS) Scndry Ed & Span Lit 1972; City Coll of NY 24 Credit Hrs Admin-Educl; *cr:* Prall Jr HS Rdng & Span Tchr 1969-70; IS 70M Span & Biling Tchr 1970-86; PS 14Q Biling Span Tchr 1986-94; PS 81Q Parent Developer 1994-95; PS 14Q Parent Developer & Congruence Tchr 1995-; *ai:* Asst Prin & Elem Prin Licenses NYC 1995; *office:* PS 14Q The Fairview School 107-01 Otis Ave Corona NY 11368

MERKLE, WILLIAM GOTTHILF, History & Mathematics Teacher; *b:* Portchester, NY; *m:* Kimberly; *c:* Alayna, Meaghan; *ed:* Quinnipiac Coll (ASN) Nursing & Sociology 1983; Pace Univ (BSN) Nursing 1988; Pensacola Chrstn (MS) Scndry Ed 1994; *cr:* West Woods Chrstn Acad Tchr 1988-; *ai:* Girls Bsktbl Coach; Stu Leadership Adv; *office:* West Woods Christian Acad 165 Hillfield Rd Hamden CT 06518

MERKLEY, ROBERT B., Math Teacher; *b:* Rochester, NY; *m:* Margaret Mae Reed-Merkley; *c:* Charles, Lauren; *ed:* Roberts Wesleyan Coll (BS) Music Ed 1972; West Chester Univ (MM) Musid Ed 1979; Albright Coll Math Cert Prgm 30 Hrs 1986; *cr:* Boyertown Area Schl Dist Music Tchr 1972-87, Math Tchr 1987-; *ai:* After Schl Tutoring Prgm; NEA, PSEA 1972-, Local Exec Bd; NCTM 1987-; *office:* Boyertown Jr HS-WEST 200 S Madison St Boyertown PA 19512

MERLAU, DONNA A., Social Studies Teacher; *b:* Rochester, NY; *m:* Volney Paul Burgess; *c:* Volney Jeremy Burgess; *ed:* SUC at Geneseo (BA) His, Scndry Ed 1978; Syracuse Univ (MS) Soc Stud Ed 1983; 18 Grad Hrs Syracuse Univ; Univ of Toronto Fr Summer Lang Prgm; *cr:* Holy Apostles, Holy Family Schl Tchr 1979-80; Holy Rosary Schl Tchr 1980-82, 1984-86; Syracuse Univ Grad Asst 1982-84; Union Schl Tchr 1986-87; Onondaga Cntrl Schl Tchr 1988-; *ai:* NHS, Natl Jr Honor Soc; NCSS 1988-, Textbook Comm 1988-90; Kappa Delta Pi 1978-; Phi Delta Kappa 1983-; Cntrl NY Cncl Soc Stud 1990-; NY St Geog Alliance 1993-; Soc Stud Dept Chair 1990-92; ILI Sponsored by Natl Geog Soc 1994; Reg Liason for NY St Geog Alliance 1995; *office:* Onondaga Central Jr/Sr HS 4479 S Onondaga Rd Nedrow NY 13120*

MERLUZZI, DEBORAH JOSEPHINE, First & Second Grade Teacher; *b:* Syracuse, NY; *ed:* Nazareth Coll (BS) Applied Music, Piano 1973, (MS) Ed 1975; Eastman Schl of Music Post Grad Work; *cr:* Rochester Piano Entertainment Prof Performer; Holiday Inn Corp Prof Performer 1975-82; LeClub Intnl Prof Piano 1982-83; Syracuse City Schls Elem Tchr 1983-95;

ai: Webster Schl Internal Facilitator, Cambridge Mgmt Trng 1993-95; 5 Yr Stategic, Site Based Plan 1995-98; Mini Olympics Participant, Spon 1990-93; Study Skills Comm; AFT 1983-; Syracuse CYO Summer Camp 1970-, Music, Drama Dir; Stud Skills Pilot Cert of Completion 1986-87; Supt of Schls Cert of Appreciation 1985-86; Pub Study Skills Across the Curricula 1987; *office:* Webster Elem Schl 500 Wadsworth St Syracuse NY 13208*

MERMAGEN, GEORGE T., HS English Teacher; *b:* Rochester, NY; *c:* Erik, Kristen, Leif; *ed:* Boston Univ (AB) Amer Lang, Lit 1966; Post Grad Hrs SUC at Geneseo, Univ of Rochester, Nazareth Coll; *cr:* Mc Quaid Jesuit Prep Schl Eng Tchr 1966-71; Honeoye Falls-Lime Cntrl Schl Eng Tchr 1972-; *ai:* NHS Comm; AFt 1972-; *office:* Honeoye Falls-Lima Cntrl Schl 83 East St Honeoye Falls NY 14472

MEROLLA, MICHAEL BERNARD, High School Music Teacher; *b:* Roslyn, NY; *ed:* Queens Coll CUNY Aaron Copland Schl of Music (BA) Music Ed 1977, (MS) Music Ed 1980; *cr:* William Floyd Schl Dist Music Tchr 1977-; Dowling Coll Music Adj Lecturer 1990-92; *ai:* Local Chptr Music Hnr Soc Spon; NY St Music Tchrs Assn 1985-, Pres, Treas, Dist Chprsn; MTNA 1985-, Natl Rep; SCMEA 1977-, Cty Treas; MENC 1977-; Queens Coll Choral Soc Awd, Music Dept Joseph Machlis Awd 1977; Tchr of Yr Awd 1994; Queens Coll Summa Cum Laude Grad; *office:* William Floyd HS 240 Mastic Beach Rd Mastic Beach NY 11951

MEROW, CRAIG BANKS, Math Coord & Physics Teacher; *b:* Philadelphia, PA; *m:* Donna June Snyder; *c:* Rebecca, Katharine; *ed:* Temple Univ (BA) Geology 1973, (MED) Sci Ed 1975; Universidad Nacional Federico Villarreal at Lima (EDD) Math Ed 1990; Cornel Univ Fellow; Attnd Univ of PA, Univ of Waterloo at Ontario, Villanova Univ; *cr:* Sun Vly HS Sci Tchr 1973-77; Germantown Acad Math Dept Chair 1978-86; Delaware Vly HS K-12 Math Coord, Physics Tchr 1986-; *ai:* Mu Alpha Theta, NHS, Adv; Cross Cntry, Track Coach; Prin Advy Cncl; Acad Stans, Curr, Sr Project Comm; Stu-Fac Senate; Math Assoc of Amer, NCTM 1983-; Best Editorial in a Scholarly Journal Awded by Soc of Natl Assn Publications; Presidential Awd Excl Sci, Math Tchng St Level; Educl Ldrshp Awd Colonial Northampton IU 20; Germantown Acad Bd of Trustees Outstdng Tchr Awd; Numerous Articles Pub; *office:* Delaware Valley HS HC 77 Box 379c Milford PA 18337

MERRELL, SIS SULLIVAN, Third Grade Teacher; *b:* Syracuse, NY; *m:* David; *c:* Jill, A. J.; *ed:* Syracuse Univ (BS) Presch Ed 1967, (MS) Elem Ed 1971; *cr:* Guardian Angels Cath Elem Sch 3rd Grd Tchr 1967-69; Adirondack Cntrl Schl Kndgtn Tchr 1969-71; VVS 2nd Grd Tchr 1971-86, 3rd Grd Tchr 1986-; *ai:* Bowling Coach; Parents at Band; Canastota Childrens Comm Theatre; VVS Comms; VVSTA 1971-; NYSUT 1969-; Canatota Canaltown 1967-77, VP, Pres; *home:* RR 1 Box 196A2 Canastota NY 13032

MERRIAM, DONNA BRIDGES, Latin Teacher; *b:* Barre, VT; *m:* Richard Dean; *c:* Patrick, Rick; *cr:* Montpelier HS Latin Tchr 1965-69; Lamoille Union HS Latin Tchr 1978-; *ai:* Block Scheduling Comm; Fac & Staff Team; Amer Classical League 1978-; Classical Asst of New England 1978-; VT Classical Lang Asst 1978-; Dir of Reading Is Fundamental Program; Morrisville Womens Club 1978-; *office:* Lamoille Union HS PO Box 304 Hyde Park VT 05655

MERRILL, ARTHUR M., Secondary English Teacher; *b:* Callicoon, NY; *m:* Mary Patricia Stafford; *c:* Brooke Allyson, Ryan Stafford; *ed:* SUNY at Oneonta (BS) Scndry Eng Ed 1972; 30 Grad Credit Hrs to Complete Permanent Cert; *cr:* South Glens Falls CS HS Eng Tchr 1972-81; Downsville Cntrl HS Eng Tchr 1981-; *ai:* Adv Class of 99; Dir Drama Club; NEA 1981-; DTA 1981; Colchester Town Bd 1988-, Councilman; Downsville Antenna 1985-, Pres; Downsville Fire Dept 1983-; Co-Ed People and Places Remembered Bicentennial Book of Local His 1992; *office:* Downsville Central Schl PO Box J Maple Ave Downsville NY 13755

MERRILL, DAVID ROYCE, Science Tchr & Head Ftbl Coach; *b:* Cumberland, MD; *m:* Debra Ann Drew; *ed:* Univ of Pittsburgh (BA) Geog, Chem 1967; Frostburg St Coll Advanced Prof Cert 1987; *ai:* Former Asst Ftbl Coach 26 Yrs; NEA 1988-; *office:* Alleghany HS 616 Sedgwick St Cumberland MD 21502

MERRILL, JOHN ARTHUR, Amer, US & World History Tchr; *b:* Laconia, NH; *m:* Anne Lockwood Copeland; *c:* Keristen, Tyler James, Casey Jean; *ed:* Marshall Univ (BA) Hst, Soc Stud, Ed 1972, (MA) US Hst, Colonial Period 1975; Credit Hrs Schl Admin, Historical Rsrch Methodology; *cr:* St Joseph's Elem Jr HS Sci, Soc Stud 6-8 Grd Tchr 1972-75; Lower Cape May HS Amer His, World His Tchr, Soc Stud Super, Chprsn 1975-; *ai:* Track & Field, Weightlifting Coach; Cmptr Applications, Scheduling, Credit Restoration, Black His Comm; NEA 1975-; LCMR Ed Assn 1975-, Bldg Rep, Pres; Phi Alpha Theta 1972-; Author: Ye Last Whaling Village of Portsmouth NJ, Vagrancy and Social Legislation in Stuart England; 2 Yrs Weekly Article Author; Tchr of Yr Univ of Chicago; Keynote Speaker Black His Month Cape May Cty; Rsrch Publication Author; *office:* Lower Cape May Reg HS 687 Route 9 Cape May NJ 08204*

MERRILL, MARY MURRAY, Education Consultant; *b:* Bangor, ME; *m:* Richard C.; *c:* Dean M., Beth Merrill-Bulawa; *ed:* Univ of ME (BS) Ed 1957; SUNY at Albany & Plattsburgh 30 Plus Credit Hrs; Russell Sage 3 Credit Hrs; *cr:* North East Schl 3rd Grd Tchr 1957-58; South Hill Schl 2nd Grd Tchr 1958-59; Glens Falls NY 2nd & 3rd Grd Tchr 1966-70, 1972-94; *ai:* BOCES Planning Comm Adirondack Conf; NYSUT; NY Retired Tchrs; Glens Falls Home Bd of Dirs; Iroquois Rdng Cncl, Sec; Fort House Museum Trustee; Adirondack Pipes & Drums; Chapman Historical Museum Ed Comm; PTA Founders Day Awd 1980-81; Tchr of the Yr 1981-82; Eisenhower Grant 1994-95; Dev Childrens Pgms Local His.*

MERRILL, NORMAN W., English & Latin Teacher; *b:* New York, NY; *m:* Jeanne Wile; *c:* Norman II, Richard; *ed:* Univ of VT (BA) Classics-Magna Cum Laude 1969; Univ of CT (PHD) Classics 1975; *cr:* Rumsey Hall Schl Dir of Stud, Chair Eng & Latin 1976-86; Berkshire Schl Eng & Latin Tchr 1986-; *ai:* Coach Thirds Soccer & Hockey; Amer Philologal Assn 1969-; CANE 1976-; Vergilian Soc 1980-; Hemingway Soc 1985-; Pub in New England Journal of Pub Poetymology; *office:* Berkshire Schl 245 N Undermountain Rd Sheffield MA 01257*

MERRILL, SUZANNE PESEZ, English Teacher & Dept Chair; *b:* Glens Falls, NY; *m:* Robert; *c:* Elizabeth, Robert John, Kathleen; *ed:* Marymount Coll (BA) Eng 1967; Univ of VT 6 Grad Hrs; Russell Sage 6 Grad Hrs; SUNY at Plattsburg 9 Grad Hrs; Union Coll 6 Grad Hrs; Attnd St Rose; *cr:* Oliver W. Winch Jr HS Eng Tchr 1967-74; S Adirondack Educl Ctr HS Equivalency Tchr 1977-83; Queensbury MS Eng Tchr 1983-84; Queensbury HS Eng Tchr 1985-; *ai:* Crisis Comm; Issues Group Ldr; NCTE, NYSUIT 1985-; NY St Eng Cncl 1994-; Queensbury PTSA 1985-; NEH Flwshp Joseph Conrad Novels Union Coll 1993; Outstdng Capital Region Tchr 1995; Vision '68 Fine Arts Prgm Grant NY St at St Rose Coll; *office:* Queensbury HS 409 Aviation Rd Queensbury NY 12804

MERRILL, THEODORE JOHN, Cmptr Assisted Drafting Instr; *b:* Portland, ME; *m:* Twanetta; *c:* Alicia M., Kevin P., Katherine A.; *ed:* Cntrl CT St Univ (BS) Indstrl Arts Ed 1972, (MS) Indstrl Tech Ed 1980; 24 Credits Toward 6th Yr Tech Ed; *cr:* Fairfield HS Indstrl Tech, Machining, Animation, Design Instr 1972-; *ai:* Boys Soccer, Jr Var Bsbl Coach; Model Railroad Club; Drafting Club; Extra Pay Compensation Comm; NEA, CEA, FEA, NEITEA, CTEA 1972-; CT Soccer Coaches Assn 1982-; Auto Desk Ed Grants 1980, 1994; CT Ind Arts Achvmt Awd 1986; CCSU Outstdng Alumni Awd Nom 1993; *office:* Fairfield HS 755 Melville Ave Fairfield CT 06432

MERRIOTT, CHARLES RONALD, ROTC Aerospace Science Instr; *b:* Vinita, OK; *m:* Laura Jane; *c:* Scott, Angie, Jon, Jason; *ed:* OK St Univ (BS) Aerospace Stud 1967; Troy St Univ (MS) Guid, Cnslng 1975; Air Command, Staff Coll 1980, Air War Coll 1985 Maxwell AFB 1980; Natl Security Mngmt Course Washington DC 1981; *cr:* USAF Pilot 1967-92, Plans Ofcr 1980-85, US Dept of St Aviation Adv 1985-89, Air Force Liaison Commander, Civil Air Patrol 1989-92; Millcreek Schl Dist Aerospace Sci Instr 1993-; *ai:* ROTC Drill, Colorguard, Vlybl Teams Spon, Comm Svc Weekly Projects; Retired Ofcrs ASsn 1993-; Phi Kappa Tau 1967-; ROTC Advy Comm 1994-, Chm; Legion of Merit; 2 Distngd Flying Cross; 4 Meritorious Svc, Defense Meritorious Svc, 7 Air, Joint Svc Commendation, USAF Commendation, Armed Forces Expeditionary, Vietman Svc, Campaign Medals; Vietnam Gallantry Cross with Device; *office:* Mc Dowell HS 3320 Caughey Rd Erie PA 16506

MERRITT, JODI ANN, Montessori Teacher; *b:* Plymouth, MI; *ed:* Schoolcroft Coll (AA) 1977; Xavier Univ (MED) Gifted Ed, Montessori Ed 1980; *cr:* Sands Montessori Schl Tchr 1980-; *ai:* Cmptr Coord; Team Ldr; CFT, AFT 1980-; Amer Montessori Soc 1978-; *office:* Sands Montessori Elem Schl 940 Poplar St Cincinnati OH 45214

MERRITT, JUDITH PSCHIRER, Fifth Grade Teacher; *b:* Pittsburgh, PA; *m:* Lloyd W.; *c:* Richard Boland Jr., David Boland, Lori, Lisa; *ed:* Indiana Univ of PA (BS) Elem Ed 1963; PA St Univ (MS) Elem Ed 1976; 50 Addl Grad Credits; *cr:* Millvale Boro Schl Dist 7th-8th Grd Tchr 1963-68; Shaler Area Schl Dist 5th-6th Grd Tchr 1968-; *ai:* Adv, Spon 5th Grd Stock Market Club; Curr Support Tchr Math, Sci, Hlth 1995-; NEA, PSEA 1963-; Shaler Area Ed Assn 1968-, Bldg Rep 1984, Mem-at-Large 1985-88; Connoquenessing Cntry Club 1990-; Peoples Natural Gas Co Tchr Advy Panel 1990-92; Golf Club of Amelia Island 1991-; Carlow Coll 1985, Eisenhower PA Dept of Ed 1995, Duquesne Univ Comm Alliance 1992-94, Fulbright-Hayes Attnd Budapest Univ Ec Sci Grants; Teach Tchr Achvmt Awd NY Stock Exch 1993; *home:* 2107 Coventry Dr Allison Park PA 15101*

MERRITT, MARLENE JANNETTE, Youth Coordinator; *b:* Baltimore, MD; *c:* Otis IV, Jannette; *ed:* Catonsville Comm Coll 65 Credit Hrs in Bus Admin; Coastal Carolina Comm Coll 23 Credit Hrs; MDs Tomorrow 1993; Dale Carnegie Courses 1995; *cr:* Office of Employment & Dev Employment Specialist 2 Yrs, Job Coord 2 Yrs, Youth Coord 2 Yrs; *ai:* Career Adv for Commonwealth Yth Svcs; Womens Support Group for a Better Tomorrow; *office:* Walbrook HS 2000 Edgewood St Baltimore MD 21216

MERRITT, RONALD J., Science Chairperson; *b:* Westfield, MA; *m:* Ann S. Strickland; *c:* Randolph J., Brett A.; *ed:* Univ of CT (BE) Sci Ed 1964; Westfield St Coll (MEd) Schl Admin 1969; Masters Plus 50 Hours at AZ St Univ, Sonoma St Univ; Addl Work at Springfield Coll & Smith Coll; *cr:* Longmeadow HS Sci Tchr 1964-1988, Sci Chprsn 1989-; *ai:* Sci Team; NEA, MTA 1964-; NSTA 1988-; Western MA Sci Supvrs 1989-, Former Pres; Appalachian Mt Club 1970-, Local Chair; Town Schl Comm 1974-80, Chair & Mem; Town Moderator 1980-; 3 NSF Grants in 1970s; Wrote Nature Trail Guide; *office:* Longmeadow HS 95 Grassy Gutter Rd Longmeadow MA 01106

MERRIWEATHER, BARBARA CHRISTINE, Sixth Grade Teacher; *b:* Philadelphia, PA; *m:* Frank Washington; *ed:* Cheyney Univ (BA) Elem Ed 1969; Beaver Coll (MAH) Hum 1989; 42 Addl Hrs PA St, Marywood, Larkenau; 20 Addl Hrs Inservice Courses; *cr:* Watson T. Comly Elem Schl 1-5 Grd Tchr 1969-90; CCA Baldi MS 6th Grd Tchr 1990-; *ai:* Beta Club Co-Chprsn; New Stans For PA Schl Dist; Internet for African Amer Stud; Natl Archives for Thomas Jefferson Curr Writer; CHAIN Cluster Writing Team; Black Women's Ed Alliance 1983-, Pres, VP, Mem Chair, Merit of Excl, Ldrshp Awds; PA Fed of Black Bus & Prof Org 1984-, Pres, VP, Pub Chair, City of Philadelphia Citation; Alpha Kappa Alpha 1995-; Frank Washington Schl Fund 1993-, Coord, Consultant; Pepsi FWSF Cele Golf Tour 1989-, Consultant; Cheyney Univ Reunion Comm 1988-, Chprsn Germantown HS Alumni Assn 1986-, VP, 75th Anniv Chprsn, Outstdng Achvmt Awd; Rose Lindenbaum Tchr of Yr Awd 1990; Cncl for Basic Ed Flwshp Ind Stud in Hum 1988; PA Senate Citation for Outstdng Svc 1995; Holy Family Coll Cert of Achvmt 1995; Who's Who in Black Amer 1988-; *office:* CCA Baldi MS Verree Rd & Alburger Ave Philadelphia PA 19115*

MERRYMAN, ROBERT EARL, History Teacher; *b:* Ocean City, NJ; *m:* Patricia; *c:* Robert Jr.; *ed:* Rowan Coll (BA) Soc Stud 1961; BA +12 Credit Hrs; *cr:* Mid Twp HS Tchr 1962-; *ai:* Discipline Comm; Chaperone-Security-Bsktbl Games; NEA 1962-; NJEA 1962-; MTEA 1962-, Negotiating Team; Schl Plaque 35 Yrs of Svc; Introduced Black His Stud to Curr; Introduced Overseas Travel Club; Chm Soc Stud 2 Yrs; *office:* Middle Twp HS 212 Bayberry Dr Cape May Court Hou NJ 08210*

MERSHMAN, DOROTHY A. (FISHER), Diversified Cooperative Coord; *b:* Lima, OH; *m:* Thomas G.; *c:* John, Anne; *ed:* St Ritas Schl of Nrsng (Diploma) Nrsng 1971; The Defiance Coll (BS) RN Completion 1986; Univ of Dayton (MS) Schl Cnslng Ed 1992; Univ of Toledo Voc Tchr Ed & Cert; *cr:* St Ritas Med Ctr Pediatrics Staff Nurse 1971-74, Asst Head Nurse Pediatrics 1974-77, Infection Control Nurse 1977-84; Lima Sr HS Diversified Hlth Occupations Instr 1984-87, DCHO Coord 1987-; *ai:* VICA Adv; Blood Donor Day Chprsn; Voc Ed Week Comm Mem; LEA, OEA & NEA 1985-; OVA, AVA & Hlth Occ Div 1985-, Sec; DCT & DCHO Northwest OH 1985-; Altar Rosary Soc 1972-, Pres; Mercy Home Hlth Care 1985-, Adv Comm; Iota Lambda Sigma 1988-; WIVE Club 1995-; New Tchrs Mentor; OVA Convention Presenter; *office:* Lima Sr HS 600 S Pierce St Lima OH 45804

MERSHON, LUCRETIA WHITACRE, Language Arts Teacher; *b:* Mariemont, OH; *m:* Robert Michael; *ed:* Univ of Dayton (BA) Eng 1968; Wright St Univ (MS) Ed 1983; Grad Hrs in Rdng & Writing; *cr:* Butlervill Elem 4th Grd Tchr 1969; Little Miami Jr Hgh 7th-8th Grd Tchr 1969-; *ai:* Yrbk Adv; Jr NHS Adv; Lit Club Adv; OEA, NEA 1969-; LMTA 1969-, Sec; PDK 1992-; 1994 Project Excl Winner; *office:* Little Miami HS 605 Welch Rd Morrow OH 45152

MERSHON, ROBERT MICHAEL, Social Studies Teacher; *b:* Dayton, OH; *m:* Lucretia Whitacre; *ed:* Univ of Dayton (BA) His, Pol Sci 1967; Wright St Univ (MS) Ed 1983; *cr:* Little Miami Jr, Sr HS Soc Stud Tchr 1967-; *ai:* Yrbk Adv; OEA, NEA, LMTA 1967-; PDK 1966-; Soc Stud Dept Chprsn; *office:* Little Miami HS 605 Welch Rd Morrow OH 45152

MERSKY, MARTIN, Assistant Principal; *b:* Philadelphia, PA; *m:* Deborah Cohen; *c:* Samuel, Andrew, Rebecca; *ed:* West Chester Univ (BS) Scndry Ed, Soc Sci 1970; Beaver Coll (MED) Scndry Ed; Prin Cert K-12 Beaver Coll; *cr:* Springfield Twp SD Tchr, Coach 1970-86; Enfield MS Asst Prin 1986-92; Springfield HS Ath Dir 1986-92, Asst Prin 1992-; *ai:* Spartan Serve Comm Svc Org, Peer Tutoring Prgm, Conflict Resolution Peer Mediator Trng Prgm Spon; NASSP, PA Assn of Scndry Schl Prins, Natl Assn of Ath Admin 1986-; Cert of Merit PA St Ath Dir Assn; Cert of Achvmt NASSP; *office:* Springfield HS 1801 E Paper Mill Rd Erdenheim PA 19038

MERTZ, LARRY A., Art Teacher; *b:* Greenville, PA; *m:* Susan J. Thomas; *c:* Larry Jr., Heidi, Stefanie, Michael; *ed:* Edinboro St Coll (BS) Art Ed 1969; Attnd Edinboro; PITT; IUP; *cr:* North Clarion Area Schls Art Tchr 1969-71; Pittsburgh Pub Schls Art Tchr 1971-; *ai:* Boys Sftbl, Girls Bsktbl & Wrestling MS Coach; AFT 1971-; *office:* Knoxville MS Cha Grimes St Pittsburgh PA 15210

MERTZ, MARY BETH DANKO, Seventh Grade Teacher; *b:* Alle PA; *m:* Craig S.; *ed:* Kutztown St Coll (BS) Elem Ed 1975; *cr:* St Schl 6th Grd Tchr 1975-83; Christ the King Schl 7th Grd Tchr 198 Yrbk Photographer; Stu Cncl Adv; Sci Curr Coord; Allentown Dioce Tchrs Assn, Schl Union Rep; *office:* Christ The King Schl 22 S Coplay PA 18037

MESCAN, MARY ANN, 6th-8th Grade Teacher; *b:* Cleveland, OH; John Coll of Cleveland (BSE) Elem Ed 1963; *cr:* Our Lady of Angels Schl 7th-8th Grd Tchr 1963-78; St Luke Elem Schl 6th-8th Grd Tchr *ai:* Asst Prin; Eucharistic Minister; Admin Team; Schl Futuring Confirmation Preparation Team; Moderator for 8th Grd Svc to St F Hunger Ctr; NCEA 1963-; Cleveland Diocese Rel Ed Awd; *home:* Madison Ave Lakewood OH 44107

MESCHUTT, LISA BUMP, Secondary Science Teacher; *b:* Oneonta *m:* Randall; *c:* Alexander, Jonathan; *ed:* SUNY at Oneonta (BA) Eart Sec Ed, Anthropology 1992; 26 Addl Hrs Rdng Ed; *cr:* Charlotte Vly Schl Sec Sci Tchr 1992-; *ai:* Brain Game, Prom Comm, 7th Grd Class *office:* Charlotte Valley Central Schl Rt 23 Davenport NY 13750

MESERVE, DANIEL SCOTT, Social Studies Teacher; *b:* Washir DC; *m:* Danielle LaCroix; *ed:* Tufts Univ (BA) His 1991, (MAT) Ed *cr:* Winnisquam Regnl HS Soc Stud Tchr 1992-; *ai:* Var Bstkbl, JV MS Soccer Coach; Frosh Adv; Schl to Work Comm; Co-Dir Yth F Prgm; NEA, NH Tchrs Assn 1992-; Cntrl NH Ed Corsortium Tchr 1993-94; *office:* Winnisquam Regional HS 367 W Main St Tilto 03276

MESING, MARGARET L., English Teacher; *b:* Coraopolis, PA Edinboro Univ (BA) Eng 1973, (ME) 1993; Bowling St Univ, Gannon Millersville Univ; *cr:* Beaty Warren MS 7th-9th Grd Eng Tchr 1973 Peer Tutoring; Past Cheerleading Adv, Jr HS Girls Bsktbl & HS Girls Coach, Drama Club; Team Ldr; OBE; Video Production Adv; NEA; & WCEA 1973-; Delta Kappa Gamma; St Johns Luth Church; *office:* Warren MS E 3rd Ave Warren PA 16365

MESSEMER, JOHN FRANCIS, 6th Grade Teacher; *b:* White Plains *m:* Cindi Kulas; *ed:* Moravian Coll (BA) Bus, Ciminial Justice Western CT Univ (MA) His 1991; Fairfield Univ, Western CT, Coll Rose, Coll of New Rochelle 60 Post Grad Hrs; *cr:* White Plains HS Asst, Wrestling, Ftbl, Track Coach 1984-87; Pearl River HS Soc Stud 1987-88; Westchester Comm Coll Ftbl Coach 1987-91; Westlake M Stud Tchr 1987-94, 6th Grd Tchr 1994-; *ai:* Head Var Wrestling, MS Coach; 5th-6th Grd Intramural Wrestling Coord; NYSUT 1985-; Wres Conf C Coach of Yr 1995-; *office:* Westlake MS Westlake Dr Thorn NY 10594

MESSERLY, JOHN G., Asst Professor of Philosophy; *b:* St Louis, *m:* Jane Clancy; *c:* John B., Katie, Anne; *ed:* Univ MO St Louis Philosophy 1985; St Louis Univ (MA) Philosophy 1990, (PHD) Philos 1992; *cr:* St Louis Univ Instr 1987-92; Ursuline Coll Asst Prof 1992- Philosophy Club Spon; Acad Policy Comm; Coll Org Comms; Philosophical Assn 1991-; Introduction Ethical Theories Book; Pi Conception Evolution Book; Numerous Articles; *office:* Ursuline 2550 Lander Rd Pepper Pike OH 44124

MESSERLY, MARILOU BERES, French Teacher; *b:* Cleveland, OH John; *c:* Sam, Emily; *ed:* OH St Univ (BA) Fr 1979; Cleveland St Tchng Cert 1989-; *cr:* Padua Franciscan HS Tchr 1990-; *ai:* Sr Adv; 1985-; *office:* Padua Franciscan HS 6740 State Rd Parma OH 44134*

MESSERSMITH, ELAINE COOPER, Family & Consumer Sci Tchr; *b:* Middletown, PA; *m:* Paul R.; *c:* Lori Elaine Messersmith-Bra Kate Liesl; *ed:* Drexel Univ (BS) Home Ec Ed 1959; Masters Equiva Plus 45 Post Grad Credits; *cr:* Annville Cleona Schl Dist 7-12 Grd H Ec Tchr 1959-60; Northern Lebanon Schl Dist 7-12 Grd Home Ec 1961-62; Cornwall Lebanon Schl Dist HS Home Ec Tchr 1962-92, Family, Consumer Sci Tchr 1992-; *ai:* Class Adv 1964, 1971, 1990; The Arts Club Adv 1974-93; Fall Play Dir 1979-; Spring Musical Dir 1985- Gretna Playhouse Summers 1983-85, Asst Costumer; AHEA, PHEA 19 NEA, PSEA, CLEA 1962-, Bldg Rep; Lebanon Comm Theatre 1976- Mem, Dir; St Andrews Presby 1974-, Choir, Bell Choir; Bucks Playhouse Best Dir 1991, 1993; Outstdng Tchr Awd 1988; Dist Awd Dedication 1994; *home:* 20 E Poplar St Lebanon PA 17042

MESSETT, DENNIS MARTIN, Principal; *b:* Sharon, PA; *m:* Patti J. Grath; *c:* Lance, Dax; *ed:* Slippery Rock (BS) Elem 1966, (MS) Elem 1 Westminster Prin Cert Elem Admin 1972; *cr:* Farrell Schls 6 Grd 1966-72, Elem Prin 1972-83; Bortner Tours Sales 1983-88; Middlesex Schls Elem Prin 1989-; *ai:* BSA Charter Rep; Kiwanis 19 Pres, Pres Awd; *office:* West Middlesex Area Schls 3591 Sharon Rd Middlesex PA 16159

MESSICK, EDWARD BURTON, Pre Algebra & Math Teacher Millsboro, DE; *m:* Barbara Tanner; *ed:* Univ of DE at Newark (BS) E Ed 1979; 26 Credit Hrs Applied to Scndry Math Cert; 19 Credit Hrs in Svc; *cr:* Stubbs Elem Schl 6th Grd Math Team Tchr 1978-79; Su Cntrl MS 7th-9th Grd Eng & Math Tchr 1979-91, 6th Grd Math 1991-93, 8th Grd Math Tchr 1993-; *ai:* Grd Level Team Ldr; Builders C Kiwanis Intnl Schl Spon; Math League Contest Coach 1994-95; Ski C Spon for Fac in Bldg; Wrestling, Ftbl, Track Coach; NEA 1979-; DE C Math Tchrs; Kiwanis Club 1995-; Amer Legion 1994-; PTA 1982-; Mem of the Month; Stu-Tchr of Graduating Class Univ of DE Nom.*

MESSICK, LINDA LOPES, 6th Grade English Teacher; *b:* Exeter, *c:* Lindsay, Elizabeth; *ed:* James Madison Univ (BS) Elem Ed 1969; Grad Stud Penn St Univ, West Chester Univ & St Josephs Univ to Acq 36 Post Grad Credits Masters Equiv; *cr:* Lynnbrook Elem 4th Grd 1969-70; Barkley Elem 4th Grd Tchr 1970-74; East Pikeland Elem 6th Tchr 1986-92; Phoenixville Area MS 6th Grd Tchr 1992-; *ai:* Natl Spell Bee Schl Adv; Dist Performance Evaluation & Prin Advy Comm; Ac Comm Chm; NEA 1969-74 & 1986-; PSEA 1970-74 & 1986; PA 1970-74 & 1986-, VP; *office:* Phoenixville Area MS 1330 S Main Phoenixville PA 19460

MESSIER, DAVID CHARLES, Principal; *b:* Manchester, NH; *ed:* Anselm Coll (BA) Eng 1969; Fitchbur St Coll (MA) Ed Admin 19 (CAGS) Ed & Voc 1982; *cr:* West HS Tchr 1969-82; Manchester Cham of Commerce Govt Affairs 1982-84; Southside Jr High Tchr 1984-88, P 1988-; *ai:* Chair Manchester Staff Dev Comm; NH Dept of Ed; Prof S Bd; Governors Task Force on Spcl Ed; NEA 1969-, Treas-Local; Teams 1988-, Past Pres; St Vincent de Paul Soc 1983-, Pres; NH Dept of Ed P Standards Bd Governor; Task Force on Spcl Ed; *office:* Southside Jr 140 S Jewett St Manchester NH 03103

MESSIER, TIMOTHY JAY, Mid Level Soc Stud Tchr; *b:* Lancaster, N *ed:* Univ of VT (BS) Soc Sci, Ed 1990; *cr:* VT Tech Coll Admissions Cr 1990-91; Lamoille Union HS Tchr 1991-; *ai:* Mid Level Team Ldr; Bsk Coach; NEA 1991-; Tchr of Yr 1992-93; *office:* Lamoille Union HS Rt Hyde Park VT 05655*

MESSINA, ALBERT LAWRENCE, 8th Grade English Teacher; Brooklyn, NY; *m:* Elaine Nielsen; *c:* Gregory, Christopher, Jennifer; *ed:* Univ of NY at Oyster Bay (BA) Eng 1962; Attnd St Univ of NY at Genes Hofstra Univ, C.W. Post, Univ of Rome, Italy; *cr:* Island Trees HS E Tchr 1962-64; New Hyde Park HS Eng Tchr 1964-68; HS of the Vir

; Eng Tchr 1968-71; Mineola MS Eng Tchr 1971-; *ai:* Rel Ed Tchr Immaculate Parish 1984-, Pius X Medal; *home:* 72 S Howells Point llport NY 11713*

INA, ANTHONY JAMES, Jr Level Cnslr, Hum Antmy Tchr; *b:* urgh, PA; *m:* Beatriz Esteban; *ed:* Duquesne Univ (BS) Music Ed Indiana Univ of PA 60 Credits 1967-70; Jersey City St Coll 16 s 1986-89; U of ID 3 Cr; Brigham Young U 2 Cr 1995; Hudson Cty n Coll 6 Cr 1993; *cr:* St Aloysius Grammar Schl 8th Grd Tchr 85; Ivy League Schl Music, Sci Tchr 1991-92; St Mary HS Bio Tchr, 91, Anatomy, Jr Level Cnslr 1992-; *ai:* Gospel Choir, Peer Mediation rator; Yrbk Adv; Stu Svc Prgm Coord; *office:* Saint Mary HS 209 3rd sey City NJ 07302

SING, PATRICA, Spanish Teacher; *b:* Passaic, NJ; *m:* Steven; *c:* er, Allison, Sean; *ed:* Keene Coll (BA) Elem Ed 1970; SUNY at y (MA) Span Tchng 1993; Hudson Vly Comm Coll 6 Hrs Fr; *cr:* n Schl 3rd Grd Tchr 1970-73; Ballston Spa MS Span Tchr 1987-; *ai:* ch Coord; NYSAFLT 1988-; NYSUT 1987-; *office:* Ballston Spa MS Rd Ballston Spa NY 12020

SMER, RISE MARIE, Fifth Grade Teacher; *b:* New York City, NY; aymond J. III; *c:* Rochelle, Raymond, Rafaela; *ed:* St Univ of NY at and (BA) Elem Ed & Eng 1968; 30 Credit Hrs for NY St Permanent Cert; Wordprocessing, Data Base-Learn to Choose Enrichment *cr:* Savona Cntrl Schl 6th Grd Tchr 1968-70; Camden MS 5th & 6th Tchr 1970-91; McConnellsville Elem Schl 5th Grd Tchr 1991-; *ai:* Sci d; Tech Comm Mem; NYSUT 1968-; AFL-CIO 1970-; Camden Tchrs 1970-, Sec 1974, Negotiator 1976; Hillsboro Bapt Church 1978-, Sec; Kappa Gamma 1991-, Stationer Chprsn; Amer Legion Auxiliary -; Elem Sci Strategies Inservice Model Schls-Cmptr Spreadsheet; rs of Commendation for Act as Mem of CMS Soc Stud Tchrs; Summer atical Leave St Univ of NY at Oswego; *office:* McConnellsville Elem 8654 St Rt 13 Blossvale NY 13308*

SNER, CAROL, Sixth Grade Teacher; *b:* Florence, PA; *m:* George; lippery Rock Univ (BS) Elem Ed 1963; Duquesne Univ (MA) Elem 967; *cr:* Hopewell Area Schl Dist 6th Grd Tchr 1963-; *ai:* NEA 1963-; 1963-; HEA 1963-, Bldg Rep; *office:* Hopewell Jr HS 2121 Brodhead liquippa PA 15001

SNER, DIANE L. (STRAITS), Retired Third Grade Teacher; *b:* and, OH; *m:* Jack; *c:* Jeffrey, Jacqueline Mc Cauley; *ed:* Ashland Coll Elem Ed 1965, (MS) Curr & Instruction 1978; Attnd Kent St Univ 3 Cmptr Sci, Child Abuse Classes; *cr:* Savannah Schl Fifth Grd Tchr -61; Hayesville Elem Schl Third Grd Tchr 1965-90; *ai:* OH Ret Tchrs 1990-, Treas; OH Ed Assn 1959-; Delta Kappa Gamma 1989-, Past Hillsdale Tchrs Assn 1965-, Past VP; Ashland Samaritan Hosp 1990-, Guide, Messenger Vol; Luth Communion 1960-, Deacon; Luth Church , OH Synod Outreach Comm; AARP 1993-; Ashland Historical Soc, and Symphony League 1994-; Martha Holden Jennings Scholar -90; Nom for Tchr of Yr Twice; Amer Poetry Press Poem; *home:* 804 nty Road 1775 Ashland OH 44805

SSORE, JOSEPH ANTHONY, English Teacher; *b:* Vineland, NJ; *m:* rly Jean Colla; *c:* Gia, Cara, Tessa; *ed:* East TN St Univ (BA) Eng ; *cr:* Marshall Jr HS Eng Tchr & Coach 1978-80; James Wood HS Tchr -86; Cumberland Regnl Tchr 1986-; *ai:* Ftbl Asst Coach; NEA 1978-; A; Dist Tchr of Yr 1993; Cumberland Cty Tchr of Yr 1993; Pub A ollection 50 Yrs Later South Jersey Magazine; *office:* Cumberland Reg PO Box 5115 Silver Lake Rd Seabrook NJ 08302

TCALF, ELAINE KRAUSHAAR, English Teacher; *b:* Syracuse, NY; erald M.; *c:* Paul, Ellen, Mark; *ed:* St Univ of NY at Brockport (BS) Ed 1968; St Univ of NY Permanent Cert 1975; *cr:* Liverpool Cntrl s Eng Tchr 1969-70; Carthage Cntrl Schls Eng Tchr 1968-69, 1979-; Schl Newspaper Adv; Stu Tchr Spon; Mentor; Curr Cncl; Outcome ed Ed Comm; AFT, NYSUT, Carthage Tchrs Assn 1979-; *office:* hage Cntrl HS 36500 NYS Rt 26 Carthage NY 13619

TCALF, MIKE, HS Social Studies Teacher; *b:* Wareham, MA; *m:* y Lee Merrill; *c:* Chase G., Keyes M.; *ed:* Colby Coll (AB) Amer His ; Univ of AR (MA) Intnl Relations 1974; *cr:* Van Buren HS Soc Sci 1968-69; US Air Force Medevac Pilot 1969-74; Hazen Union Schl Sci Tchr, Adj Instr Amer Govt 1974-; St of VT St Senator 1989-94; *ai:* se Up; People to People; Class Adv; VT NEA 1975-; Town of ensboro Selectman 1983-; VT St Senate 1989-94, St Senator, Vice ir of Appropriations Comm; Northeast Kingdom Adult Basic Ed, Sec'y 1-; Northeaster VT Dev Assn 1976-; NASA Tchr in Space Natl Finalist 5-86; Jimmy Doolittle Awd Air Force Assn 1986; NHS Tchr of Yr 1983; k Dedication 1981; *office:* Hazen Union Schl N Main St Hardwick VT 43*

TCALF, ROSAMOND SMITH, Retired Fifth Grade Teacher; *b:* bile, AL; *m:* Robert; *c:* Charles, R. Michael; *ed:* St Lawrence Univ (BA) , Sociology 1957; Keene St Coll (MED) Elem Ed 1974; 52 Addl Credits se St, Castleton; *cr:* Springfield Pub Schls 5th Grd Tchr 1974-95; *ai:* A 1974-; Charlestown Women's Club 1970-, VP, Sec; Charlestown ngregational Church 1967-, Diaconate; Old Ft #4, Bd of Trustees.

TEER, MARVIN G., English Teacher; *b:* Sayre, PA; *m:* Maxine sley; *c:* Melissa Souto, Michael; *ed:* Mansfield Univ (BS) Speech, ama, Eng 1967; 36 Credit Hrs Post Grad Stud; *cr:* Wyalusing Vly HS g Tchr 1967-, Eng Dept Chprsn 1980-; *ai:* Stu Cncl Adv; Discipline, Stu Month Comms; Mentor New Tchrs; WAEA, PSEA, NEA 1967-; alusing Twp Supvr 1981-, Chm of Bd; Wyalusing Rainbow Club 1989-; tern Bradford Cty COG 1991-, Treas; Wyalusing United Meth Church 1-; Sunday Schl Supt,Sr Choir Dir; Wyalusin Ambulance Inc 1993-, ; Vallian Yrbk Dedication 1990; *home:* RR 2 Box 298 Wyalusing PA 53

TIVIER, ANTOINETTE POIRIER, Asst Prof of Dental Assisting; *b:* mford, ME; *m:* Mark Cyr; *ed:* Univ of ME at Oreno (BS) Child Dev 1; Univ of Southern ME Learning Disabilities Cert, Grad Level Ed urses; Certfd Dental Asst Cert; 100 Continuing Ed Credit Hrs in Dental sisting; *cr:* Rumford Schl Dept Learning Disabilities Tchr 1982-87; rious Pvt Practice Dental Offices Certfd Dental Asst 1987-94; NH Tech t Asst Prof Dental Assisting 1994-; *ai:* NH Dental Assists Assn, Amer ntal Assists Assn 1991-; *office:* NH Tech Inst 11 Institute Dr Concord 03301

ETRICK, KATHERINE DUNTON, Biology Teacher; *b:* Ft Walton ach, FL; *m:* John Joseph; *c:* Jody Ann, Aaron James; *ed:* Penn St Univ S) Environmental Resource Mgmt 1978; Kutztown Univ Tchng Cert ndry Ed Sci 1988; Temple Univ 6 Hrs Grad Ed Ldrshp; *cr:* Yth nservation Corps Environmental Learning Coord 1977-78; Soc Security min Claims Authorizer 1979-81; Pocono Mountain Jr HS Earth & Space i Tchr 1989-90; Northwestern Lehigh HS Sci Dept Head & Bio Tchr 90-; *ai:* Stu Cncl; Stdnts for Environmental Action; Stu Forum; Ski Club; u Assistance Team; Curr Review Cncl; Restructuring, Assessment, -Extra Curr & Grad Comms; NSTA 1989-; NEA 1989-; PSTA 1994-; ABT 1996; LeHigh Valley Sci Curr Cncl 1993-; Presidential Awd for Excl Sci Tchng 1995; Outstdng Conservation Tchr for LeHigh Cnty 1994; utstdng & Dedicated Svc Awd for Northwestern HS 1993; *office:* orthwestern Lehigh HS 6493 Route 309 New Tripoli PA 18066

ETRINKO, PAUL WALTER, Tchr & Social Stud Dept Chair; *b:* New rk, NY; *m:* Janis L. Richardson; *c:* Jeannine, Michelle; *ed:* St John's Univ (BS) Elem Ed 1969; Morgan St Univ (MS) Elem Ed 1977; 3 Addtl Hrs Rdng; 3 Addtl Hrs Spec Ed; 1 Addtl Hr Ed Mngmt; *cr:* West Annapolis ELem Schl 6th Grd Tchr 1970-76; George Fox MS 6th, 7th, 8th Grd Tchr 1976-, Soc Stud Dept Chair 1980-; *ai:* Archbishop Spalding Asst Girls Bsktbl Coach 1986-93; Arthur Slade Commissoner of Girls Bsktbl 1986-93; NEA 1978-; Greater Glen Burnie Jr Sports League 1977-; Anne Arundel Co PSTA Tchr of Month; *office:* George Fox MS 7922 Outing Ave Pasadena MD 21122*

METROPOLIS, ANDREW MURRAY, Social Studies Teacher; *b:* Salem, MA; *m:* Elaine Toleos; *c:* Ted, Georgia; *ed:* Salem St Coll (BS) Soc Stud 1969, (MAT) His 1970; 60 Hrs Beyond Masters; *cr:* Peabody Veterans Meml HS Tchr 1970-93, 1995-, Dept Chm 1993-95; *ai:* Fac Advy Bd; Comm Svc Prgm; JROTC Comm; AFT 1970-; George Peabody House 1988-, Adv; Holocaust Ctr; Peabody Historical Soc 1970-78, VP 1975-78; Bicentennial Commission; Navy Life Awd; Local Historian; Hall of Fame Comm; *office:* Peabody Veterans Memorial HS 485 Lowell St Peabody MA 01960

METROPOULOS, ADAM PETER, Chemistry Teacher; *b:* Saginaw, MI; *m:* Elizabeth DeLollis; *ed:* Saginaw Valley St Univ (BS) Chem 1986; Univ of NH (MST) Chem & Ed 1990; Hellenic Coll Theology; *cr:* Dow Chemical Co Technologist 1982-86; Univ of NH Chem Lab Instr 1986-90; Dover HS Chem Tchr 1989-90; Stearns HS Chem Tchr 1990-; *ai:* Track & Math Teams Coach; NEA, ME Sci Tchrs Assn 1990-; NSTA 1993-; AHEPA 1982-; Millinocket Players 1990-; Chem Ed-Natl Symposium Research Paper; Whos Who in Colls & Univs; Whos Who in HS; *home:* 40 Elm St Millinocket ME 04462

METTHE, ESTHER (GRILLO), 8th Grade English Teacher; *b:* Lawrence, MA; *m:* Raymond A.; *c:* David Eric, Joseph Raymond, Anne Metthe Mc Donough; *ed:* Salem St Coll (BS) Elem Ed 1975; MA Coll of Art at Boston Art Ed 1960-72; 45 Credit Hrs Boston Univ; Fitchburg St Coll, Lesley Coll, Salem St Coll, Northern Essec Comm Coll, In-Svc Haverhill Pub Schls; *cr:* Winter Street Schl Grd 4 Tchr 1975-77; Walnut Square Schl 3rd, 4th Grd Tchr 1977-78; Burnham Schl 3rd Grd Tchr 1978-79; C D Hunking MS 6th, 7th Grd Sci Tchr 3 Yrs, 8th Grd Lang Arts Tchr 1979-; *ai:* Acad Bowl; Class Yrbk Adv; Drama Productions, Choral Presentations, Schl Fairs, Numerous Other Act Asst; Haverhill Ed Assn, MA Tchrs Assn, NEA, NCTE 1975-; St Rita's Cath Church; Tchr of Yr Nom; Textbook, Curr Comms; Schl-Based Mngmt, Cooperative Learning, Process Writing Projects; Comprehensive Hlth Grant Dept of Ed; *office:* Caleb Dustin Hunking Mdl Sch Winchester St Haverhill MA 01835*

METZ, CAROL ANN, Mathematics Asst Professor; *b:* Binghamton, NY; *m:* Gary; *c:* Jennifer, Heather; *ed:* Cortland St (BS) Ed, Math 1973; Manhattanville (MAT) Ed 1986; *cr:* Yonkers Pub Schl Tchr 1973-80; Westchester Comm Coll Asst Math Prof 1981-; *ai:* Placement, Disabled, Handicapped Comms; PTA 1984-, VP; *office:* Westchester Comm Coll 75 Grasslands Rd Valhalla NY 10595*

METZ, CONSTANCE B., French Teacher; *b:* Boston, MA; *m:* Steven B.; *c:* Adrew, Rebecca, James; *ed:* Simmons Coll (BS) Ed 1961; Univ of IL (MA) Fr 1962; Middleburg Fr Summer SChl 1962; St Michael's Coll Prins Licensure; *cr:* Ketchikan HS Fr, Eng Tchr 1962-64; Laurel Schl for Girls Fr Tchr 1964-67; John F. Ross HS Fr, Eng Tchr 1967-70; Champlain Vly Union HS Eng, Fr Tchr 1974-95, Fr Tchr, Admin 1995-; *ai:* Stu Cncl; VT Frgn Lang Assn 1972-; Univ of VT Cncl 1992-94; UVM, NHS Tchr of Yr Awds.*

METZ, ELINOR DASCHBACH, Teacher; *b:* Pittsburgh, PA; *c:* Kathryn, Paula, Brad; *ed:* Seton Hill Coll (BA) Psych 1965; Cath Univ of Amer (MA) Cnslng 1990; 40+ Post Masters Credits Cnslng & Ed; *cr:* Allegheny Cty Juvenile Detention Home Tchr 1965-66; Allegheny Cty Office of Ec Opportunity Admin Asst & Comm Coord 1966-71; Montgomery Cty Pub Schls Scndry & Advanced Placement Psych Tchr & Peer Cnslng 1982-; Affiliated Comm Cnlsrs Part Time Therapist 1990-; *ai:* Class & Big Brother & Big Sister Spon; MD Stu Asst Pgm; Fac Comm; NHS; MCEA, NEA & MTA 1982-; APA 1984-; ACA 1988-; PTSA 1982-; GSA 1982-86, Camp Cert Ldr; BSA 1986-88, Den Ldr; St Soc Stud Conf Presenter; Article Pub 1993; *home:* 13 Orchard Way S Rockville MD 20854*

METZ, ELIZABETH ANN, Third Grade Teacher; *b:* Cincinnati, OH; *ed:* Univ of Cincinnati (BAEd) Elem Ed 1982; 20 Post Grad Hrs; *cr:* Ben Tillman Elem Schl 3rd Grd Tchr 1983-84; Nativity Schl 3rd Grd Tchr 1985-93; St Clement Schl 3rd Grd Tchr 1993-; *ai:* Intervention Asst Team Mem; Exemplary Edctr Awd 1989; *office:* St Clement Schl 4534 Vine St St Bernard OH 45217

METZ, JAMES DAVID, 8th Grade Social Studies Tchr; *b:* Pittsburgh, PA; *m:* Donna Lyn Caldwell; *c:* Cynthia Lyn, Alison, James Jr.; *ed:* Davis & Elkins Coll (BA) His, Ed 1976; 18 Credits Cmptr Sci 6 Credits Ath Admin Slipper Rock, IN Univ of PA, Butler Comm Coll; *cr:* Butler Cath Schls Soc Stud Tchr 1977-86; Slippery Rock Park Mgr 1980-85; Moniteau HS Soc Stud Tchr 1986-; *ai:* Ath Dir 1990-; Ftbl Coach 1987-95; Natl Jr Hnr Soc Adv 1988-89; Track Coach 1987-88; NEA, PA St Ed Assn 1986-; Moniteau Ed Assn 1986-, Pres; PA St Ath Assn 1991-; Alpha Phi Omega 1974-, Historian; Phi Alpha Theta 1974-, VP; Mentor Tchr 1993-94; Dept Chair 1993-94; Gift of Time 1994; Grad Cum Laude 1976, Deans List 1975Davis & Elkins Coll; *home:* PO Box 211 West Sunbury PA 16061*

METZ, KENNETH ALAN, Associate Professor of Physics; *b:* Cincinnati, OH; *m:* Mary A. Bill; *c:* John D.; *ed:* Xavier Univ (BS) Physics 1966, (MS) Physics 1969; (MBA) Functional Mngmt 1973; 33 Credit Hrs Univ of Cincinnati Grad Level Information Systems; *cr:* RCA Production Engr 1966-70; Univ of Cincinnati Assoc Prof of Physics 1970-, Assoc Dean of Acad Affairs 1980-91; *ai:* Coll of Applied Sci FacChair; Alpha Pi Omega Adv; Lib Advy Comm; Amateur Radio Station Trustee; AAPT, Natl Prof Concerns Comm Mem; Amer Soc of Engrng Edctrs; AAUP; Sigma Pi Sigma; BSA 1955-, Asst Scout Master, Meritorious Svc; Sierra Club 1987-; Amateur Radio Operator 1964-, Extra Class License, Vol Examiner; Novell Certfd Network Engr; *office:* Univ Of Cincinnati 2220 Victory Pky Cincinnati OH 45206

METZ, MARY LOU DIETRICK, Mathematics Teacher; *b:* Philipsburg, PA; *c:* Jason, Erin; *ed:* Indiana Univ of PA (BS) Math Ed 1976; Frostburg Univ (MED) Cnslng 1980; 60 Grad Credits Toward MEd; *cr:* Rockwood HS Math Tchr 1976-; *ai:* NHS Adv; Prof Dev Comm; Coll in HS Instr; Mentor Tchr; NEA, PSEA, REA, NCTM, PCTM 1976-; Laurel Highlands Math Alliance 1990- PR Chair; St Peters Church 1976-; Somerset Soccer Boosters 1993-, PR Chair; Somerset PTA 1985-, PR Chair; Somerset Comm Band 1988-; Pres Awd for Excl in Math Tchng 1993; Hardesty Awd 1980; PA Higher Ed AA Tech Grants; Who's Who in Amer Ed; *office:* Rockwood Area HS Somerset Ave Rockwood PA 15557

METZ, NANCY J., Instruction Specialist; *b:* Ridley Park, PA; *c:* Melissa Di Marzio; *ed:* West Chester Univ (BS) Math 1966; Az St Univ (MS) Math 1973; 50 Addl Grad Credits; *cr:* Boeing Aircraft Corp Engr Asst 1965-67; Takoma Park Jr HS Math Tchr 1970-72; Rockville HS Math Tchr 1973-89; Watkins Mill HS Math, Resource Tchr 1989-95; *ai:* Montgomery Cty Math Tchrs Assn 1973-, Pres; MD St Tchrs Assn, NEA, NCTM 1973-; Women in Ed 1989-, Treas; IBM Tchr Recognition Awd; *office:* Montgomery Cty Pub Schls 850 Hungerford Dr Rockville MD 20850*

METZ, ROBERT J., Business Department Chairman; *b:* Buffalo, NY; *ed:* Niagara Cty Comm Coll (AAS) Accounting 1968; St Univ of NY at Albany (BS) Bus, Ed 1970; Canisius Coll (MS) Ed 1976; Mngmt of Defense Acqusition Contracts; Govt Contract Law; US Navy Supply Corps Grads; *cr:* Springville-Griffith Inst Bus Dept Tchr 1970-84, Bus Dept Chm 1984-; *ai:* Fac Advy, Tech Comm; Griffith Inst Fac Assn 1970-, Treas, PAC Mem; NYSUT, AFT 1970-; US Navy Reserve 1970-95, Commanding & Admin Officer; Authored 3 Voc Ed Act Grants; Distinguished Occupational Ed Tchr Awd NY St Region 10 1990; Cert of Achvmt Outstanding Western NY Occupational Ed Tchr 1991; *home:* 92 Forest Ave Springville NY 14141*

METZ, SHERYL FELICIA, Fourth Grade Teacher; *b:* Brooklyn, NY; *m:* Stephen; *c:* Jared, Brandon; *ed:* Brooklyn Coll (BA) Ed-Cum Laude 1971, (MS) Ed 1974; Trained in Great Books Lit Prgm & Madeline Hunter Strategies; *cr:* Brooklyn PS 75 Sixth Grd Tchr 1972-74, Music Tchr 1974-75; PS 384 Fifth Grd Tchr 1975-76, Third Grd Tchr 1977-78; PS 269 Fifth Grd Tchr 1983-84, Art Tchr 1984-87; Cntrl Schl 4th, 5th Grd Tchr 1987-; Robertsville Schl 4th, 5th Grd Tchr 1987-; *ai:* PTA Liaison 4 Yrs; NEA 1987-; *office:* Robertsville Elem Schl 36 Menzel Ln Morganville NJ 07751*

METZE, CHARLES LEVI,II, Literature Professor; *b:* Columbia, SC; *m:* Anne Marie Augusitne Sissoko; *c:* Charles III; *ed:* Northeastern St Univ (BA),(MA) Eng, Speech, Jrnlsm 1980, 1984; *cr:* Ecole Normal Superieure Prof Eng 1984-86; Allen Univ Prof Eng 1986-90; Howard Univ Lit Prof 1991-; *ai:* Clubs Eng 1984, Drama 1986; Frosh Orientation Comm Chair 1987, 1988; Founders Day Comm Co-Chprsn 1988; Gen Ed Comm 1991-93; Judiciary Comm 1995-; SC Flwshp 1989; Natl Endowment for Hum Flwshp 1990; Pres Awd Outstdng Svc 1987, 1988, 1989; African Methodism SC, Ed-in-Chief 1987; *office:* Howard Univ 2400 6th St NW Washington DC 20059

METZENDORF, VIRGINIA MELLON, 5th Grade Teacher; *b:* Kew Gardens, NY; *m:* Edward J. Jr.; *ed:* C W Post (BA) Elem Ed 1972, (MS) Elem Ed 1979; 60 Post Grad Credit Hrs; *cr:* Blue Point Schl Kndgtn Tchr 1972-76, First Grd Tchr 1976-83, 3rd Grd Tchr 1983-91, 5th Grd Tchr 1991-; *ai:* Improvement Team; NYSUT, Bayport Blue Point Tchrs Assn 1972-; Blue Point PTA 1990-; Blue Point PTO 1985-, Tchr Rep; Tchr of the Month September 1989, November 1990, February 1992, March 1994.

METZGER, JAMES D., Industrial Technology Teacher; *b:* Gnadenhutten, OH; *m:* Brenda; *ed:* Bowling Green St Univ (BA) Industrial Tech 1981; Grad Stud at Baldwin Wallace Coll, Dayton Univ & OH St Univ; *cr:* North Union HS Industrial Tech Tchr 1981-; *ai:* Tech Stu Assn Adv; Girls Var Track Coach; North Union Ed Assn 1995-; OH Ed Assn & NEA 1981-93, 1994-; Intnl Tech Ed Assn 1981-; Natl Arbor Day Fnd; Claridon United Meth Church, Bd of Trustees; Buckeye Joint Voc Schl Hydraulics Unit Dev; OH Initiation of Industrial Techs Curr; OH Inst of Engrng & Employability Skills Cluster for Tech Prep Model; OH St Hand Blown Solo Glass Exhibition at Fine Arts Gallery; *office:* North Union HS 401 N Franklin Richwood OH 43344*

METZGER, JANICE KOMAREK, Art Teacher; *b:* New York, NY; *m:* Michael L.; *c:* Gretchen Grove, Timothy, Eric, Kristine; *ed:* SUNY Coll at Buffalo (BS) Art Ed 1960; Montclair St Coll (MA) Fine Arts 1970; Post Grad Work at Seton Hall, Albany St, RI Schl of Design in Fine Arts; *cr:* Massena Cntrl HS 7-12 Grd Art Tchr 1960-63; Troy HS 9-12 Grd Art Tchr 1964-65; Kawameeh Jr HS 7-9 Grd Art Tchr 1967-69; Madison HS 9-12 Grd Art Tchr 1980-81; Union Cty Reg HS 9-12 Grd Art Tchr 1981-; *ai:* Teen Arts Festival Coord; Art Club Adv; Asst Testing Supvr Ranking Comm; NAEA 1990-; Art Ed of NJ, AFT 1980-; Natl Assn of Women Artists 1989-; Assn Artists of NJ 1982-; Lit Vols of Amer 1992-; Marie Walsh Sharpe Art Fnd Tchr, Artist Awd; Geraldine R. Dodge Fnd Artist, Edctr Awd; Hnrs Seminar RI Schl of Design; Summer Six Prgm Skidmore Coll Flwshp; *office:* Jonathan Dayton Reg HS 139 Mountain Ave Springfield NJ 07081

METZGER, JUDITH A., 5th Grade Teacher; *b:* Dayton, OH; *m:* Douglas L.; *c:* Jennifer; *ed:* Univ of Dayton (BS) Elem Ed & Spcl Ed 1985, (MS) Schl Cnslng 1994; *cr:* Springboro Comm Schls LD Tutor 1985-86, 5th Grd Tchr 1986-; *ai:* Inclusion Pgm; Intervention Asst Team; Grd Level Lang Arts Curr Comm; OEA & NEA 1985-; Springsboro Comm Schls Tchr Grant Recipient 1992-93; 1995 Project Excl Awd Recipient Warren Cty; Martha Holden Jennings Scholar 1995-; *office:* Clearcreek Elem Schl 750 S Main St Springboro OH 45066

METZGER, MARYLOU SCHOPPE, Math Teacher; *b:* Philadelphia, PA; *m:* Patrick F.; *c:* Sara, Andrew, Gerald; *ed:* Temple Univ (BA) Math 1972, (MED) Math Ed 1975; *cr:* Bishop Mc Devitt HS Math Tchr 1988-90; Archbishop Ryan HS Math Tchr 1990-91; Father Judge HS Math Tchr 1991-92; Bucks Cty Comm Coll Adj Math Tchr 1984-94; Conwell-Egan Cath HS Math Tchr 1992-; *ai:* NHS Moderator 1994-; Archdiocese Curr Comm 1993-; ATMOPAV, PCTM 1990-; *office:* Conwell-Egan Cath HS 611 Wistar Rd Fairless Hills PA 19030

METZGER, RONALD JOHN, Mathematics Instructor; *b:* Williamsport, PA; *m:* Ellie Winn Way; *ed:* Penn St Univ (BS) Scndry Ed & Math 1971, (MS) Math Ed 1990; Presently in Doctoral Pgm; *cr:* Shippensburg Univ Math Instr 1990; Lock Haven Univ Math Instr 1991-; *ai:* PCTM 1991-; NCTM 1992-; *home:* 117 Palmer Ave Mill Hall PA 17751

METZGER, STEPHANIE NEFF, Special Services Coordinator; *b:* Circleville, OH; *m:* Charles Eric; *c:* Kalie, Addison; *ed:* OH Univ (BS) Elem Ed 1977; OH St Univ (MA) Schl Psych 1983; Capital Univ SLD Cert in Ed; *cr:* Westfall Local Schl Dist 1st Grd Tchr 1977-81; Franklin Cty Schls Intern Schl Psychologist 1983-84; Pickaway Cty Schls Psychologist 1984-94, Spec Svcs Coord 1994-; *ai:* NASP, CEC 1983-; *office:* Pickaway County Board Of Ed 139 W Franklin St Circleville OH 43113*

METZIDAKIS, PHILIP, Spanish Professor; *b:* Springfield, MA; *m:* Pauline Jansizian; *c:* Philip Avedis, Penelope Metzidakis Barnett; *ed:* Yale (PHD) Span 1960; Diploma Romance Philology 1955; *cr:* Yale Univ Asst to Instruction 1958-60; Mills Coll Asst, Assoc Prof 1960-68; Trinity Coll Visiting Prof 1967-77; Swarthmore Coll Prof 1968-; *ai:* MLA 1959-; Rsrch Grants Yale, Mills, Swarthmore; Natl Endowment For Hum Grant.

METZLER, MARION GISH, Fourth Grade Teacher; *b:* Lancaster, PA; *m:* Eric F.; *c:* Gregory S., Christopher E., Jessica L. Bair; *ed:* Millersville Univ (BS) Elem Ed 1969; Masters Equivalency; *cr:* Manheim Cntrl Schl Dist 4th Grd Tchr 1986-; *ai:* Active Mem PTO; Theme Day Comm; NEA, PSEA 1987-; MCEA 1987-, Bldg Rep; Gift of Time Awd.

METZLER, THOMAS JAMES, English Teacher; *b:* Providence, RI; *m:* Anne Hake; *c:* Jeffrey, Michael; *cr:* J. P. Stevens HS Eng Tchr 1972-73; Bloomfield MS Eng Tchr 1973-; *ai:* Frosh Bsbl Coach 1979-84; NEA, NJEA 1972-; BEA 1973-; *office:* Bloomfield MS 60 Huck Rd Bloomfield NJ 07003

MEUNIER, CAROL ANN, 8th Grd Math & Alegebra Tchr; *b:* Canton, OH; *m:* Edward P.; *ed:* Akron Univ (BA) Ed, Math & His 1972; Grad Hrs Ashland Coll; *cr:* Taft MS 7th Grd Math Tchr 1972-78, 8th Grd Math, Algebra Tchr, Math Team Ldr 1978-; *ai:* 8th Grd Field Trip Adv; Awds Prgm Organizer; Mathletes Team Organizer, Coach; PLTA Tchrs Assn 1972-; GCCTM 1990-; Taft Tchr Recognition Awd 1982; Twice Nom Myrtle Miller Outstdng Tchr Awd; Taft Tchr Recognition 1995; *office:* R A Taft MS 3829 Guilford Ave NW Canton OH 44718

MEUSER, DIANE, Associate Professor of Math; *b:* Huntington, NY; *ed:* SUNY at Albany (BA) Math 1975; Johns Hopkins Univ (PHD) Math 1980; *cr:* Boston Univ Math Assoc Prof 1980-; *ai:* Undergrad Dormitory Fac Resident; Undergrad Math Assn Adv; Amer Math Soc 1980-; NSF Postdoctoral Rsrch Fellow Harvard Univ 1984-86; Princeton Inst for

Advanced Stud 1988-89; *office:* Boston Univ Mathematics Dept 111 Cummington St Boston MA 02215

MEUTE, DANA RAE, English Teacher; *b:* Pittsburgh, PA; *ed:* Grove City Coll (BA) Lit, Scndry Ed 1987; Slippery Rock Univ of PA (MA) Eng Lit; *cr:* Butler Area Sr HS Eng Tchr 1989-; *ai:* Speech, Debate Team Coach 1989-93; Prom Adv 1990-; NHS Co-Adv 1993-94; NEA, NCTE 1989-; *office:* Butler Area Sr HS 165 New Castle Rd Butler PA 16001*

MEYER, ANN ELIZABETH, English Teacher; *b:* Concord, NH; *m:* Albert J.; *c:* Alison; *ed:* Univ of NH (BA) Eng 1967; *cr:* Stamford HS Tchr 2 Yrs; Beverly HIlls Schl Tchr 7 Yrs; Alvrine HS Tchr 2 Yrs; *ai:* NHS; Odyssey of the Mind; Hum Curr; AFT 1984-; *office:* Alvirne HS Derry Rd Hudson NH 03051

MEYER, BARBARA JEAN, Kindergarten Teacher; *b:* Xenia, OH; *m:* Paul Edward; *c:* Jonathan D., Jason H.; *ed:* Bowling Green Univ (BS) Elem Ed 1974; Wright St Univ (MED) Rdng Spec 1978; 36 Addl Hrs; *cr:* Kettering City Schls Tchr 1974-95; *ai:* Centerville Ftbl Mother's Club; Prin Advy; NEA, OEA, KTCA, PTA 1974-; Holden Jennings Scholar; Kettering Fnd Grant; *office:* John F Kennedy Elem Schl 5030 Polen Dr Dayton OH 45440*

MEYER, BRIAN JOSEPH, Music Teacher; *b:* Cincinnati, OH; *ed:* UC Coll Conservatory of Music (BM) Music Ed 1994; *cr:* West Union HS Music Tchr 1994-; *ai:* Marching, Pep, Steel Band; Prof Steeldrum Ensemble; OMEA 1995-; *office:* West Union HS 201 W South St West Union OH 45693

MEYER, CARLIN, Professor of Law; *b:* Chicago, IL; *c:* Molly Jacobs-Meyer; *ed:* Harvard Univ (BA) Pol Sci 1970; Rutgers Univ Schl of Law (JD) Law 1974; Yale Univ Schl of Law (LLM) Law 1988; *cr:* Gladstein Meyer & Reif Partner 1975-77; DC37, AFSCME Asst Gen Counsel 1977-81; NY St Dept of Law Civil Rights Bureau Asst Gen Counsel 1981-82, Labor Bureau Chief 1982-87; NY Law Schl Law Prof 1988-; *ai:* Amer Assn of Law Schls 1988-; Natl Lawyers Guild 1970-, NYC Chptr Pres 1980-82; Assn of the Bar of NYC 1991-94, Civil Rights Comm, Legislative Liaison; NY City Commission on the Status of Women 1992-; Articles Pub; *office:* NY Law School 57 Worth St New York NY 10013

MEYER, DALE ANTHONY, Spanish & French Teacher; *b:* Coldwater, OH; *ed:* Univ of Dayton (BS) Span, Scndry Ed 1974; Wright St Univ (MS) Principalship, Curr & Supervision 1984; Have Taken Courses Inservice & Attnd Foreign Lang Confs Beyond My Masters Degree; *cr:* Minster HS Span & Eng Tchr 1976-79; St Henry HS Span & Eng Tchr 1980-85; Lima Cntrl Cath HS Span Tchr 1985-91; Wapakoneta HS Span & Fr Tchr 1991-; *ai:* NEA, OH Ed Assn & OH Foreign Lang Assn 1976-; Wapakoneta Ed Assn 1991-; Minster Bd of Ed 1986-, Pres; Minster Civic Assn & Minster Historial Soc 1985-; Minster Alumni Band 1976-; Wapakoneta Exec Bd 1991-; Kappa Delta Pi Honor Soc in Ed; Fund Raiser for The Heart Fund; *office:* Wapakoneta City Schls 1 W Redskin Trl Wapakoneta OH 45895*

MEYER, DANIEL LUTHER, High School Science Teacher; *b:* New York City, NY; *m:* Marilyn Evelyn Coon; *c:* Luther, Bonnie Sue, Trudi, Lynn, Roman; *ed:* SUNY at Albany (BA) Sci Ed 1954; Rutgers Univ (MA) Microbiology 1961, (PHD) Microbiology 1965; Attnd John Hopkins Univ & Univ of MD; *cr:* Mexico Acad & Cntrl Schl Sci Tchr 1954-56; Baltimore Cty Schl Sci Tchr 1956-58; Edison HS Sci Tchr 1958-59; SUNY at Geneseo Microbio Prof 1965-76; Earlville Assembly of God Church Pastor 1976-82; Kings Acad Sci Tchr 1982-; *ai:* Assemblies of God, Licensed Minister; St Univ of NY Rsrch Grants; *office:* King's Acad 131 E Main St Wrightstown NJ 08562

MEYER, DONALD PAUL, Hlth, Physical Education Tchr; *b:* Rochester, NY; *m:* Sharon Keilman; *c:* Mark, Robyn; *ed:* Springfield Coll (BS) PE 1965; Oswego NY, Ithaca NY, Cortland NY Grad Stud; *cr:* Penn Yan CSD PE Tchr, Coach 1965-85, Hlth, PE, Ath Dir 1985-; *ai:* Hlth, PE Admin; Directs Interscholastic Prgm Twenty Var Offerings, JV, Frosh, Mod Lead up Prgms; Responsible for Stu, Employee Wellness Events, Comm Recreation Opportunities; Natl Ath Admins V Ath Adm; Schl Admins, Amer Assn HPE R, Dance; NYS Coachs Assn; NYS Ath Admins; NYS Assn Hth, PE Rec, Dance; Penn Yan Lions Club 1985-, Outstdng Svc 1993; *office:* Penn Yan Cntrl Schl Dist 305 Court St Penn Yan NY 14527

MEYER, DONNA BOWSER, Third Grade Teacher; *b:* Indiana, PA; *m:* Edward; *c:* Andrea; *ed:* Indiana Univ of PA (BSEd) Elem Ed 1971; 32 Grad Credits; *cr:* United Schl Dist Third Grd Tchr 1971-; *ai:* NEA, PSEA 1971-; Girl Scouts of Amer 1992-, Troop Ldr; IN Garden Club; Grace United Meth Church; *office:* United Elem Schl PO Box 168 Armagh PA 15920

MEYER, DORIS BROWER, English Teacher; *b:* Paterson, NJ; *m:* John; *c:* John J., Janice Cendana, Suzanne; *ed:* The Kings Coll (BA) Eng Ed 1962; William Peterson Coll (MA) Eng 1991; Supvrs Cert; *cr:* Ramapo & Indian Hills Regnl HS Eng Tchr 1962-66; Benjamin Franklin Jr HS Eng Tchr & Writing Centea 1983-86; Montclair St Univ Clinical Adj Fac 1988-; Hasbrouck Hghts HS Eng Tchr 1986-; *ai:* Yrbk Adv; Steering Comm; Moonachie & Woodridge Goals 2000 Local Improvement Panel; HHEA 1986-, VP & Bldg Rep; Pi Lambda Theta Honor Soc 1993-; BCEA & NJEA; Mem of Montclair St Univ Task Force on the Renewal Of Schls & Tchr Ed in Collaboration with John Goodlad & the Ctr for Educl Renewal 1993-94; *office:* Hasbrouck Heights Jr Sr HS 365 Boulevard Hasbrouck Heights NJ 07604

MEYER, GARY STEPHEN, Mathematics Teacher; *b:* Newark, NJ; *m:* Lois; *c:* Holli, Kenny, David; *ed:* Montclair St (BA) Math Ed 1965; Kean Coll (MA) Math Ed 1969; *cr:* Dover HS Tchr, Supvr 1965-; *ai:* NJPSA 1992-; *office:* Dover HS 100 Grace St Dover NJ 07801*

MEYER, GEORGE R., Leadership Teacher; *b:* Pittsburgh, PA; *m:* Ruth Ellen Mc Elfish; *c:* Sheri Leigh, Erin Michelle; *ed:* CA Univ of PA (BS) Soc Sci 1967, (MED) Soc Sci 1972; Numerous Confs LdrshpEd; *cr:* Bethel Park Schl Dist Act Dir 1978-85; Bethel Park Sr HS Soc Sci Tchr 1967-77, Tchr, Act Coord 1986-; *ai:* Stu Govt Assoc; Homecoming; Bethel Park Fed of Tchr AFT 1969-, VP, Svc Awd; Natl Asso of Stu Cncls 1970-, Chm, Bd of Dir, Svc Awd; Natl Asso of Stu Act Advs 1970-; Caring Team for Children 1991-, Svc; Luth Church 1942-, Summer Camp Dir; Dir PA Assoc of Stu Cncls Summer Ldrshp Dev Prgm, Natl Asso of Stu Cncls Natl Conf 1985, PA Asso of Stu Cncls St Conf 1980; *office:* Bethel Park Sr HS 309 Church Rd Bethel Park PA 15102

MEYER, GLENN WILLIAM, Science Teacher; *b:* Kingston, NY; *m:* Susan L.; *c:* Amethyst; *ed:* Morrisville Ag & Tech Coll (AAS) Animal Sci 1978; Cornell Univ (BS) Bio 1980; St Univ of NY at New Paltz (MS) Scndry Bio Ed 1984; Addl 24 Credit Hrs Beyond MS in Earth Sci & Cmptrs in Ed; *cr:* Cornell Univ Belmont Race Track Drug Testing Lab 1980-81; MJM Jr HS Sci Tchr 1983; Marlboro Cntrl Schls Sci Tchr 1983-; *ai:* Sr Enrichment Prgm Club Adv; Sci Coord & Chprsn; STANYS 1983-; 1350 dollar Grant from Area Fund of Orange Cty for Videomicroscopy 1992; NY Regents Exam Item Writer 1986, 1987, 1889, 1996; Selected for VISION Summer Prgm 1991; Natl Assessment of Educl Progress Cert of Appreciation 1995; *office:* Marlboro Central HS 50 Cross Rd Marlboro NY 12542

MEYER, HAROLYN, English Teacher; *b:* New York, NY; *m:* Albert; *c:* Amanda; *ed:* St Univ at Oneonta (BA) Eng 1967; St Univ at Stony Brook (MA) Lib Stud 1984; *cr:* Corning-Painted Post West HS Eng Tchr 1967-69; Lindenhurst HS Eng Tchr 1970-; *ai:* Family Svc League 1994-, Cnslr; NDEA Grant Summer 1968; *office:* Lindenhurst HS 300 Charles St Lindenhurst NY 11757

MEYER, JOHN ROBERT, For Lang Chair & Span Instr; *b:* Cincinnati, OH; *m:* Betty Baumgartner; *c:* Matthew, Katherine; *ed:* (BA) Span 1973; Xavier Univ (MED) Ed 1976; *cr:* Newport Cath HS Span Inst 1973-79; St Xavier HS Foreign Lang Chair & Span Instr 1979-; *ai:* Foreign Lang Honor Soc; OFLA, AATSP 1979-; *office:* St Xavier HS 600 N Bend Rd Cincinnati OH 45224

MEYER, JOSHUA LEE, Teacher of Gftd & Tlntd Pgm; *b:* Philadelphia, PA; *m:* Norma; *c:* Adam, Ranaan; *ed:* Glassboro St Coll (BA) Elem Ed 1977, (MA) Elem Ed 1982; Prin, Supvr Cert 1985; *cr:* Winslow Elem Schl #3 Kndgtn Tchr 1976-84, Fourth Grd Tchr 1985-; *ai:* Just Say No Club Organizer; Publicity, Synagogue Youth Group Coord; Schl Newspaper; Bsktbl Coach; NEA 1977-; Blood Drive, Chm 1990-; Synagogue Bd of Dirs 1980-, Dir 4 Yrs, Pres 2 Yrs, Cert; *home:* 40 Bells Lake Dr Turnersville NJ 08012*

MEYER, JUDITH WILLARD, Fourth Grade Teacher; *b:* Camden, NJ; *m:* Richard T.; *c:* Joshua, Jonathan; *ed:* Seton Hall Univ (BS) Elem Ed 1969; *cr:* Montrose Elem Schl Primary Tchr 1969-76; Verona Bd of Ed Supplemental Tchr 1977-79; William Mason Elem 4th Grd Tchr 1985-; *ai:* Verona 5th Downers Ftbl Treas; Verona Sports Booster; NEA 1969-; Montville Tchrs Assn 1985-, Schl Rep; Former Home & Schl Pres; NJ Governors Tchr Recognition Awd 1990; BET Real World Grant Recipient 1996; Senator Bill Bradley Geography Awareness Recognition Prgm Cert of Commendation 1992; A Plus Grant for Kids Cmptrs & Classrooms Perfect Tchr 1990; *office:* William Mason Elem Schl 5 Shawnee Trl Montville NJ 07045

MEYER, MARY ALICE (GODDARD), First Grade Teacher; *b:* Steubenville, OH; *m:* Samuel A.; *c:* Steven, Sheryl Meyer Kratsas; *ed:* Coll of Steubenville (BS) Elem Ed 1964; Dayton Univ (MA) Educl Admin 1978; Addl 15 Post Grad Hrs Ed Admin; *cr:* Knoxville Schl Kndgtn Tchr 1963-64; Steubenville City Schls Kndgtn Tchr 1964-65; Knoxville Elem Schl First Grd Tchr 1965-; *ai:* OEA, NEA 1965-; ELEA 1966-; Jefferson Cty Grant 1987-88; Natl Grant 1985; St of OH Tchr Grant 1979; *home:* RR 2 Box 1B Toronto OH 43964*

MEYER, MARYANN WALSH, Tchr of the Gifted & Talented; *b:* Orange, NJ; *m:* William George; *c:* Ralph Perrella, Dawn Perrella, Michael Perrella; *ed:* Seton Hall Univ (BS) Elem Ed 1972; *cr:* St Johns Schl Second Grd Tchr 1972-73; Central Schl 6th Grd Tchr 1981; Haywood Ave Schl 6th Grd Tchr 1981-83; Prime Cmptr Distributor Admin 1983-87; Green Hills Schl GATE Tchr 1988-; *ai:* Summer Schl Coord, Tchr; Stu Asst Team Mem; NJEA, NEA 1981-; GTEA 1988-, VP; Good Shepherd Church 1984-, CCD Tchr; *office:* Green Hills Schl PO Box 14 Mackerly Rd Greendell NJ 07839

MEYER, MICHELLE MONICA MONNIN, Admission Counselor; *b:* Springfield, OH; *m:* Michael Peter Monnin; *ed:* John Caroll Univ (BA) Eng & Rel Stud 1984; Xavier Univ (MED) Schl & Agency Cnslng 1992; *cr:* Case Western Reserve Univ Admission Cnslr 1984-85; Jesuit Retreat House Pub Relations Coord 1986-87; St Xavier HS Eng Tchr 1988-89; Roger Bacon HS Eng Tchr & Admission Cnslr 1991-; *ai:* Ambassadors Moderator; Evening for Excl Benefit Auction Comm Mem; NCEA 1992-; Intnl Enneagram Assn 1995-; Certfd Tchr & Presenter of Enneagram Personality Theory Wkshps; *office:* Roger Bacon HS 4320 Vine St Cincinnati OH 45216

MEYER, NANCY E., Speech & English Teacher; *b:* Cincinnati, OH; *c:* Shannon R., Emily J., Amy E.; *ed:* Coll of Wooster (BA) Eng & Speech 1970; Univ of Dayton (MS) Ed 1994; *cr:* Cornell Heights Elem Schl Lang Arts Tchr 1970-71; Orville Wright MS Lang Arts Tchr 1971-74; Bus Office Work, Sales & Presch Tchr 1974-89; Xenia HS Speech & Eng Tchr 1989-90; Wayne HS Speech & Eng Tchr 1990-; *ai:* Schl Newspaper Club Adv; Mentor for New Tchrs; NEA, OEA 1970-74 & 1989-, Bldg Rep; Girl Scouts 20 yr Mem, Scout, Troop Ldr; *office:* Wayne HS 5400 Chambersburg Rd Dayton OH 45424*

MEYER, NORMA WEINTRAUB, Music Teacher & Orch Director; *b:* Philadelphia, PA; *m:* Joshua Lee; *c:* Adam, Ranaan; *ed:* Philadelphia Musical Acad (BSME) Piano Performance 1968; Temple Univ (MA Music) Piano Performance 1970; Grad Credits Working Toward K-12 Music Tchrs Cert Philadelphia Musical Acad, Glassboro St Coll; Grad Credits Working Toward Supvrs Cert Rowan Coll; *cr:* Pvt Piano Instr 1965-; Vare Elem Schl K-8 Grd Music Tchr 1974-78; Washington Twp MS Orch, Chorus Dir 1985-89; Washington Twp HS Orch Dir 1987-90; Chestnut Ridge MS Orch Dir 1990-; *ai:* Orch Dir; All Schl Musical Co-Dir; MENC 1985-; ASTA 1985-, Dir; NSOA; ASCD; ARTS for Every Kid Grant; Tchr of Yr 1995; *office:* Chestnut Ridge MS 641 Hurffville Crosskeys Rd Sewell NJ 08081*

MEYER, SYLVIA ADEY, Soc Stud Tchr & Honors Coord; *b:* Lebanon, PA; *m:* Lloyd Edward; *c:* David, Allen, E. Kathryn Meyer-Jeffers, Jane Meyer-Mc Clellan; *ed:* Millersville Univ (BS) Soc Stud-summa Cum Laude 1979, (ME) Soc Stud 1984; 61 Credit Hrs Beyond Masters; *cr:* Milton Hershey Schl Sec 1954-55; Cedar Crest HS Soc Stud Tchr 1979-, Honors Coord 1989-; Lebanon Valley Coll Adj Prof 1995; *ai:* NHS Adv; Career Comm Mem; NEA, PSEA & CLEA 1979-; Lebanon Cty Educl Honor Soc 1989-; Delta Kappa Gamma 1990-; UCC Church 1948-, Consistory Mem 1990-92, Choir 1958-70 & 94; Comm Chorus 1970-72; Outstanding Millersville Stu 1978 & 1979; His Awd; Whos Who Among Amer Women 1986-; Freedoms Fnd Awds 1988 & 1989; *office:* Cedar Crest H S 115 E Evergreen Rd Lebanon PA 17042

MEYER, WADE KENNETH, HS Language Arts Instructor; *b:* Middletown, CT; *m:* Sandra Michelle LaBatt; *c:* Christopher; *ed:* Wittenberg Univ (BA) Eng Ed 1986; Wright St Univ (MEd) Tchr & Leadership 1993; *cr:* Chillicothe City Schls Lang Arts Instr 1986-91; Indian Lake Local Schls Lang Arts Instr 1991-; *ai:* Dir of Drama; Career Ed Rep; Cty Wide Lang Arts Curr Comm; ILEA, OEA & NEA 1991-, Treas; First Luth Church 1994-, Congregation Cncl; *office:* Indian Lake Local Schls 6210 State Rt 235 N Lewistown OH 43333*

MEYERHUBER, LISA WALKER, Teacher of Gifted; *b:* Winchester, MA; *m:* Carl I. Jr.; *c:* Eric, Stephen, Daniel; *ed:* Colby Coll (BA) Philosophy, Eng 1962; 36 Hrs Univ of CA; 6 Hrs Penn St; *cr:* ARIN IV #28 Tchr of Gifted 1979-; *ai:* PSEA, NEA 1979-; ARIN Ed Assn 1979-, 1982-84; Progressive Wkshp Armstrong Co 1987-, Bd.

MEYERL, GARY T., Campus Minister, Religion Tchr; *b:* Hartford, CT; *m:* Amy Hoffman; *c:* Jordan Marie; *ed:* Loyola Coll (BA) Theology 1986; *cr:* Cardinal Gibbons HS Rel Tchr, Coach 1986-87; Mount St Joseph HS Coord of Comm Svc 1987-89; Sacred Heart Cath Church Yth Ministry Coord 1989-92; Calvert Hall Coll HS Campus Minister, Rel Tchr 1992-; *ai:* JV Tennis Coach; Var Bsktbl, Juggling Club Moderator; Co-Coord of Comm Svc; Dir Archdiocese of Baltimores HS Ldrshp Inst; Assn of Archdioceson Prof Yth Ministers 1989-, For God & Yth Awd; Pub Curr; *office:* Calvert Hall Coll HS 8102 Lasalle Rd Baltimore MD 21286

MEYERS, ANN E., Math Teacher; *b:* Dayton, OH; *ed:* Univ of Dayton (BSEd) Math 1980; *cr:* Chaminade-Julienne HS ALg, Geometry Tchr, Math Dept Chprsn 1981-93; *ai:* HS Vlybl Coach; NCTM, NCEA, OCTM 1981-; OHSVBCA 1986-, Past Pres, Treas; *office:* Chaminade-Julienne HS 505 S Ludlow St Dayton OH 45402

MEYERS, DEBBIE BOETZ, Lang Arts Teacher; *b:* Montpelier, OH; *m:* Richard A.; *c:* Craig, Dustin; *ed:* Univ Toledo (BA) Elem Ed 1985; *cr:* Superior MS Grd 8 Lang Arts Tchr 1985-; *ai:* NEA 1985-; OH Child Conservation League 1985-94, Sec 1 Yr, VP 1 Yr, Pres 1 Yr; *office:* Superior MS 10-034 St Rte 576 Montpelier OH 43543

MEYERS, GARY PHILLIP, Biology Teacher; *b:* Holsopple, P Dolores Alice Davis; *c:* Matthew; *ed:* IN Univ of PA (BS) Sci 19 Johnstown HS Bio Tchr 33 Yrs; *home:* PO Box 202 Davidsville PA

MEYERS, KAREN HALL, Second Grade Teacher; *b:* Damariscott *m:* James E.; *c:* Jessica Jane; *ed:* Farmington St Coll (BS) Spcl Ed & Ed 1966; Critical Skills Pgm; Support & Mentor Trng; *cr:* Towpat Spcl Ed Tchr 1966-68; Avon Schl Spcl Ed Tchr 1968-71; Consolidated Schl 2nd Grd Tchr 1971-; *ai:* Lang Arts Curr & Uni Governance Comms; Support & Mentor Team Mem; MEA 1971- 1971-; BTA 1974-, Pres; Amer Cancer Soc 1970-, Reach to Recove *office:* Bristol Consolidated Schl HC 62 Box 200 Pemaquid ME 04

MEYERS, MAUREEN MC DONNELL, English Teacher; *b:* B NY; *m:* Peter J.; *c:* John; *ed:* State Univ of NY at Buffalo (BA) Eng Grad Stud Ed; *cr:* Lancaster Aurora MS & HS 7-9th Grd Eng Tchr 19 Silver Creek HS 10th, 12th Grd Eng & Publications Tchr 19 Lancaster Aurora MS 8th Grd Eng Tchr 1989-; *ai:* Lang Arts Dept LCTA 1974-; Hamburg Cntrl PTA 1992-; S S Peter & Paul Churc Beta Kappa; BA Summa Cum Laude; Eng Dept Honors with H Distinction; *office:* Aurora MS 148 Aurora St Lancaster NY 14086

MEYERS, NADINE, Kindergarten Teacher; *b:* Jersey City, N Samuel; *ed:* St Peter's Coll (BS) Philosphy, Fine Arts 1970; Lehma of the City Univ of NY (MS) Elem Ed 1974; Azusa Pacific Coll Credits; La Guardia Coll of the City Univ of NY Visual Arts Pr Credits; *cr:* US Army Ed Svc Specialist 5th Grd Sci Tchr 1976-77; Kndgtn, 3rd, 2nd, 4th Grd Rdng, 6th, Grds 1, 2 Tchr 1986-; *ai:* Kndgt Ldr 1986-; UFT Grd Rep 1986-; UFT, NEA 1970-; Chrohn's and C Fnd, Irvington Inst for Immunological Rsrch 1977-; Tchr of Yr 1986; Newspaper Excl Awd 1978; Dean List 1993-94 La Guardia Coll C Parents Assn Recognition of Tchng Excl 1991-92; Outstdng Atten Awd 1970-; *office:* PS 36 Unionport 1070 Castle Hill Ave Bron 10472*

MEYERS, SANDY SUE, High School Spanish & Eng Tchr; *b:* Se WA; *m:* John F. III; *c:* Sherry L.; *ed:* NM Highlands Univ (BA) Eng Attnd Univ of OK, Univ of Dayton, Morehead St Univ; *cr:* Maysvil Span, Eng Tchr 1969-70; Manchester HS Span, Eng Tchr 1970-; *ai:* D Club; Cheerleading Spon; Schl Improvement, Prom Comms; Span GED, Drivers Trng Instr; NEA 1969-; OEA 1970-; OCTELA 1994-; M Holden Jennings Scholar; Excl Tchr Awd; Ashland Tchrs Awd 2 Christa McAuliffie Tchr Nom; OH Tchr of Yr Nom; Golden A Achiever Awd; Wrote 2 Grants; *office:* Manchester HS 309 E 9 Manchester OH 45144

MEYERS, WILLIAM ANGOVE, 5th Grade Science Teache Hazleton, PA; *m:* Mary Jo Griffith; *c:* Anne Thomas, Jill Jenkins, M Gotthardt; *ed:* Penn St (BS) Forestry 1950, (MS) Wildlife Mngmt Bloomsburg Univ (BA) Ed 1962; *cr:* Amer Chem Co Plant Researc 1951-56; Cornell Univ Instr 1957; Amer Electric Power Co Chief Fo 1958-60; Hazleton Area Schl Sci Tchr 1960-; *ai:* NEA 1960-; Ma Lodge 1947-; *office:* Valley Elem Schl 100 Rock Glen Rd Sugarlo 18249

MEYRICK, BARBARA ANN (APPLEBY), Health & PE Teache Huntingdon, PA; *m:* David L. Jr.; *c:* David III, Christopher; *ed:* W Ch Coll (BS) Hlth, PE 1974; Rowan Coll (MA) Health, PE 1987, (MA) E Supervision 1992; *cr:* Buena Regnl HS Hlth, PE Tchr 22 Yrs; *ai:* St Adv; Var Field Hockey Coach; NEA, NJEA 1974-; NJ Assn of Stu C 1992-, Fac Adv on Local & St Levels, 3 Yr Honor HS; Cooperating for Stu Tchrs from Rowan Coll; *home:* RR 24 Box 125 Harding Richland NJ 08350*

MEZZACAPPA, ROSE ANN MONTALBANO, 4th Grade Teache Staten Island, NY; *m:* Nicholas J.; *c:* Steven, Nicole; *ed:* St John's (BS) Elem Ed 1971; City Univ of NY (MS) Elem Ed 1973; 30 Grad Cr in Ed, Cmptr Sci; *cr:* Holy Rosary Schl 2, 4-6 Grd Tchr 1971-76, 198 39R 4-5 Grd Tchr 1986-; *ai:* Fac Consultative Comm; Schl Based M Comm; Parent Ed Wkshps Spon; AFT, UFT 1986-; Alumni Assn St J Univ 1971-; Alumni Coll of Staten Island; NYC Dist 31 Soc Stud, B His, Women in His Awds; NYC Pub Lib Parent Ed Grant; *office:* Pub 39R Sand & Mc Farland Ave Staten Island NY 10305*

MIANULLI, SUSAN IMPRESS, Choral Music Director; *b:* Empor PA; *m:* Alan Williams; *c:* Molly Jeong; *ed:* Penn St Univ (BS) Musi 1970, (MFA) Vocal Performance 1972; Certfd McClosky Voice Thera 1981; *cr:* OH Univ Dept of Theatre Vocal Performance 1973-74; N Shore Comm Coll Inst Voice 1977-84; Juniata Coll Instr Voice 198 Nashoba Regnl HS Dir, Choral Music 1994-; *ai:* Dir Two Madr Chamber, Show Choirs; Menc 1994-; ACDA 1995-; MIVT 1982-, Foun Mem; NATS 1982-, St Adjudicator PA & MA; Outstdng Young Wome Amer 1981; Grant Nat Endow for Arts to Teach Singing to Acting St OH Univ 1973-74; Schlsp Stu Temple Music Festival at Ambler 1 *office:* Nashoba Regional HS 12 Green Rd Bolton MA 01740*

MICCHELLE, PATRICIA ANN GUIDER, 6th-8th Grade Rea Teacher; *b:* Newark, NJ; *m:* Charles Anthony; *c:* Craig Anthony, Lisa R *ed:* Seton Hall Univ (BS) Ed 1964; Western CT St Univ (MS) Rdng 1 *cr:* Franklin Schl 6th Grd Tchr 1964-65; Williams Schl 1st Grd Team 1968-69; St Lawrence O'Toole 1st, 2nd, Kndgtn, Nursery Schl 1978-82; St Patrick's Schl 6th-8th Grd Rdng Tchr 1982-; *ai:* Self Team; Vol Local Hosp; Co-Organizer Annual Church Christmas Fair Lambda Theta 1985-; Westchester Read Cncl 1986-.

MICELI, CAROL JEAN J., Business Teacher; *b:* Lockport, NY; *m:* Scott; *ed:* Niagara Cty Comm Coll (AAS) Exec Secretarial Sci 1984; at Buffalo (BS) Bus Ed 1989; Nazareth Coll of Rochester (MS) Bus 1991; Cooperative Work Experience Coord Cert 1991; *cr:* SUC at Buf Career Ctr Stu Asst 1987-88; Froehler & Assoc Exec Sec 1989; Univ Rochester Exec Sec 1990; Jamestown HS Bus Tchr 1990-; *ai:* Girls Track Goach 1995; Class Adv 1993; FBLA Adv 1990-93; Dist Tech Co 1994-; NYSC & TE 1994-; NBEA 1992-; NYSBTA 1989-; CCBTA 19 CEL 1995-; Amer Red Cross Sixer Club 1987-; 2 Prof Journal Articles P *office:* Jamestown HS 350 E 2nd St Jamestown NY 14701

MICELI, ELAINE MARIE, French & Spanish Teacher; *b:* Cambri MA; *ed:* Salem St Coll (BA) Fr 1976; Cambridge Coll MED Degree July 1994; *cr:* Matignon HS Guidance Sec 1976-77; Mount Alvernia Fr, Span Tchr 1977-82; Archbishop Williams HS Fr, Span Tchr 1982 Matignon HS Fr, Span Tchr 1985-; *ai:* Stu Cncl Moderator; Trip Co BATA Rep; Exec Bd Rcdng Sec; NEA 1977-; MAFLA 1982-; AA AATSP 1985-; *office:* Matignon HS 1 Matignon Rd Cambridge MA 02

MICELI, LEONARD, Western Heritage Teacher; *b:* Somerville, MA; Patricia J.; *c:* Mark, Linda, Laura, Patricia, Leonard; *ed:* Boston Univ Ed 1958, (EDM) Ed 1959; Addl Stud at Univ of MA at Boston; Newburyport HS Govt Tchr 1959-61; N Quincy HS His Tchr 1961-; Tchr Adv for 2 Stdnts; Prof Dev Prgm Pre-Practicum Mentor; N Qui HS Interpersonal Conflicts Mediator; NEA & MTA 1962-; Quincy Ed A 1962-, Bldg Rep; *office:* North Quincy H S 316 Hancock St Quincy 02169

MICELI, VIRGINIA COLFORD, 7th Grade Science Teacher; *b:* Jers City, NJ; *m:* Frank A.; *ed:* Jersey City St Coll (BA) Earth Sci & Ed 19 15 Credit Hrs Comp Sci 1995; *cr:* Firemens Insurance Co Typist 1966- Western Electric Co Typist 1968-70; West Essex Jr High Sci Tchr 1976- 1978-; Edison Jr High Sci Tchr 1977-78; *ai:* Fac Adv Comm; NJEA 197

976-; West Essex Ed Assn 1976-77, Exec Bd 1978-; West Orange Ed 977-78; NJST 1978-86; *office:* West Essex Jr HS W Greenbrook Rd Caldwell NJ 07004

AEL, BARBARA JOAN (PIERSON), Counselor; *b:* York, PA; *m:* E.; *c:* James, Joshua; *ed:* Penn St Univ (BS) Bus Ed 1974, (MED) Ed 1977; Temple Univ 6 Credits; West Chester Univ 12 Credits; Penn at Vly Campus 18 Credits; Ursinus Coll 3 Credits; CCIU 5 Credits; vernor Mifflin Schl Dist Bus Ed Tchr 1974-75; Twin Vly Schl Dist l Tchr & Coach 1975-76; Wilson Schl Dist 7th-10th Grd Cnslr & 1977-79; Owen J Roberts MS 6th-8th Grd Cnslr 1979-; *ai:* Strategic ng Comm; PEP Comm Chprsn; Peer Pals Pgm; NEA & PSEA 1974-; 1977-; Phi Delta Kappa 1977-; NBCC 1981-; Elverson United Meth 1983-, Crop Walk Chair; Stu Tchr Alumni Network-Berks Campus t Univ 1991-, Chprsn; Penn St Univ Alumni Bd of Dir Sec 1981-90; Walk Recruiter 1988-95; PA St Cnslrs Conf Presenter 1996; *office:* J Roberts MS 881 Ridge Rd Pottstown PA 19465*

AEL, DAVID E., Health & PE Teacher; *b:* Williamsport, PA; *m:* a Joan Pierson; *c:* Erin, James, Joshua; *ed:* E Stroudsburg Univ (BS) PE 1969; W Chester Univ (MED) Hlth & PE 1972; 30 Post Grad Penn St Univ; *cr:* N Coventry Elem SchlPE Tchr 1969-81; Owen erts MS Hlth, Swimming, PE Tchr 1981-; *ai:* Boys & Girls Cross Girls Track Head Coach; PIAA Dist I Cross Cntry Comm; NEA, 1969-; Greater Phil Track & Field Coachs Assn 1970-, Outstdng Svc PA Track Coachs Assn 1980-; *office:* Owen J. Roberts MS 881 Ridge ttstown PA 19465

AEL, ROBERT ERLKING, Distinguished Svc Prof of Eng; *b:* son, IN; *m:* Elizabeth Kidder; *c:* Alexandra Michael Collins, Patrick *ed:* IN Univ (BA) Eng Lit 1950, (MAT) Eng Lit 1952, PHD) Eng Lit *cr:* OH Univ Eng Instr 1961-63; St Lawrence Univ Asst Eng Prof 57; Reed Coll Asst Prof 1967-70; Lewis & Clark Coll Visiting Prof 71; Mankato St Univ Assoc Prof 1971-73; Nathaniel Haethorne Coll 86; Notre Dame Coll 1987-; *ai:* Grace Episcopal Church, Eucharistic Minister; Folger Shakespeare Lib Fellow; Natl Endowment for nities Grant; Outstanding Tchr Awd St Lawrence Univ 1967; anding Tchr Awd Lewis, Clark 1971; Outstanding Tchr Awd niel Hawthorne Coll 1976-77; Outstndg Tchr Notre Dame Coll 1995; Notre Dame Coll 2321 Elm St Manchester NH 03104

AELIAN, MELVA STRONG, English Teacher; *b:* Springfield, *n:* Gerald L.; *c:* Michelle, Matthew, Eric, Theresa; *ed:* Elms Coll Eng 1969; Univ of MA (MED) Ed 1994; 30 Addl Credit Hrs CAGS; olyoke HS Eng Tchr 1965-; *ai:* Schl Newspaper Adv; Schl Lit zine Adv; NEA, MA Tchrs Assn, Holyoke Tchrs Assn 1965-; Holyoke Dev Sch 1989-, Site Coord; Pub Articles; *office:* Holyoke HS 500 St Holyoke MA 01040

AELS, CATHERINE ANN, Religious Studies Teacher; *b:* New City, NY; *ed:* SUNY at Stony Brook (BA) Philosophy 1972; Fordham (MS) Rel Ed 1976; John XXIII Inst for Eastern Chrstn Stud 21 Grad s; *cr:* Mater Christi HS Religion Tchr 1972-75; Msgr Scanlan HS on Tchr 1977-85; St Paul the Apostle Ch Rel Ed Dir 1985-86; The Louis Acad Religion Tchr 1986-; *ai:* Facilitator of Rap Group; A, REA 1986-; Cert in Spiritual Direction; St Francis Coll anding Tchr Awd; Articles Pub in Momentum & The Cord; *office:* The Louis Acad 176-21 Wexford Terr Jamaica NY 11432

HAELS, FRANK J., Physics Teacher; *b:* Wilkes-Barre, PA; *m:* es Swiderski; *c:* Kristi, Adam; *ed:* Wilkes Coll (BA) Math 1970; ton Univ (MS) Scndry Admin 1976; *cr:* J.M. Coughlin HS Tchr 26 *ai:* Mid Sts Evaluation & Self Stu 1996-, Chprsn; WBAEA, PSEA, 1970-; Knights of Columbus 1992-, Chanchellor; *office:* J.M. hlin HS 80 N Washington St Wilkes Barre PA 18701

HAELS, HERBERT, Musical Theatre Dept Chair; *b:* New York City, *n:* Patricia; *c:* Kristin S., Kadyn S.; *ed:* Acting Studio with Master Jeff Cory & Leonard Nimoy 3 Yrs; *cr:* BOCES Cultural Arts Ctr nt Drama, Musical Theatre & Audtion, Dept Coord 1975-; *ai:* Own Events Bus HPM Entertainment Inc; Producing Corp & Private ts for Universal Pictures, Spalding Worldwide, Gitano, TG MAXX & Israel; SAG 1960-; AEA 1954-; SSDC 1970-; AFTRA 1965-; Served ue Ribbon Panel for Tony Awds; Film Credits as Performer; Broadway its for Performer & Asst Choreographer; Commercial Credits with 200 Products.

HAELS, PATRICIA G., Musical Theatre Teacher; *b:* Riverside, CA; erbert; *c:* Kristin, Kadyn; *cr:* Boces Cultural Arts Ctr Tchr 1976-; *ai:* Bus HPM Entertainment Inc; Produce Corporate, Private Events; rs Equity Assn 1963-; Amer Fed of Television, Radio Artists 1960-; rmer Broadway, Television Credits; *office:* Boces Cultural Arts Ctr Cold Spring Rd Syosset NY 11791

HAELSON, BARRY LEONARD, 5th Grade Teacher; *b:* delphia, PA; *m:* Francine R. Schwartz; *c:* Jason, Danielle; *ed:* Lasalle (BS) Mrktg 1967; Temple Univ (MS) Ed 1971; Pierce Bus Coll ounting; *cr:* Stokley Elem Schl 2nd, 4th, 6th Grd Tchr 1967-71; ck Elem Schl 6th Grd, Sci Tchr 1972-80; Finletter Schl 2nd Grd Tchr ; Hopkinson Schl 3rd,-6th Grd Tchr 1982-83; Pollock Elem Schl 5th Tchr 1984-; *ai:* 4th-5th Grd Sports, Math Remediation Prgms; Sci Fair; Grd Grad Ceremonies; PFT 1967-; Wrote Booklet; *home:* 8138 Lister iladelphia PA 19152

HAELSON, WENDY DEEGAN, Chemistry & Physics Teacher; *b:* y, CT; *m:* Christian H.; *c:* Benjamin, Andrew; *ed:* Univ of CT (BS) macy 1980; Southern CT St Univ 6th Yr Sci Ed 1996; Wesleyan Univ Ed *cr:* CVS Pharmacy Pharmacist 1980-90; Career HS Chem Tchr -93; Seymour HS Chem & Physics Tchr 1993-; *ai:* Curr & Instruction m; NEA, NSTA 1993-; CT Pharmaceutical Assn 1980-; Nomination Sci Tchr of Yr; Seymour HS Unsung Hero Awd 1995; *office:* Seymour 2 Botsford Rd Seymour CT 06483

CHAL, SUSAN LYNN (CASTELLUCCIO), Media Production net Coord; *b:* Newark, NJ; *m:* James Richard; *c:* James, Lauren; *ed:* re Coll of Art & Design (BS) Art Ed 1974; George Washington Univ) Art Therapy 1976; 50 Addl Hrs; Addl Courses in Media Production, Spec Ed, Math, Sci Completed; *cr:* Natl Insts of Hlth Pediatric Art rapist, Psych Technician 1976-77; Montgomery Cty Pub Schls rrelated Arts Prgm, Grant Coord 1978-79, Art Specialist 1979-80; st Knolls Elem Schl Art Tchr 1980-82; Cresthaven Elem Schl Art Tchr)-82; Forest Knolls Elem Schl Art Tchr 1982-85, Comm Arts Magnet n, Media Production Coord 1985-; *ai:* Tchr Spon Radio Show 1985-, anese Sister Schl Project Mutusai ES 1986-, Global Ed Club 1994-; Bus Partnership Coord 1990-; Supts Advy Comm for Ed of GATE Yth ntgomery Cty Pub Schls; GATE, Rdng, Writings of the Month, Cultural , Parent Involvement Comms; In-Svc Staff; St Andrew Apostle Schl, Scouts Vol; Tchr Adv; NEA; Montgomery Cty Ed Assn; PTA; Cty, St, Educl Confs & Tchr In-Svcs Presenter; 3 Washington Post Ed Grants; Assn of Partners in Ed Natl Conf Co-Presenter 1995; Tchr Adv for evision Series 1995, Stdnts Using Internet for VP Al Gore's Visit 1995; ng Demonstration & Interview WRC-NBC 1993; Tchr Adv entennial Media Project KIDSNET 1991-92, TIPS for Raising Kids w 1990-92; Natl Geographic Soc GTV Video Festival Co-Recipient l; First Lady Barbara Bush Natl Assn of Broadcasters & KIDSNET's & Books Campaign 1990, Natl Assn of Cable Programmers Conf 1990 Co-Presenter; *office:* Forest Knolls Elem Schl 10830 Eastwood Ave Silver Spring MD 20901

MICHALEC, DANIEL JOHN, Retired Language Arts Teacher; *b:* Akron, OH; *m:* Mary Lou Maier; *c:* Christy Ann, Cortney Ann; *ed:* Kent St Univ (BS) Eng 1968; Univ of Akron (MS) Scndry Schl Admin 1980; Univ of Akron Schl of Law (JD) Law 1989; *cr:* Sill MS Tchr, Coach 26 Yrs; Gallager, Sharp, Fulton & Norman Law Firm Cleveland Assoc Attorney 1 Yr; Sill MS Tchr 26 Yrs; Attorney in Private Practice 6 Yrs; *ai:* Boys Var Tennis Coach 17 Yrs; 9th Grd Ftbl Coach 15 Yrs; Var Ftbl Asst Coach 2 Yrs; Amer Bar Assn, OH Bar Assn, Akron Bar Assn 1989-.

MICHALENICZ, CATHERINE M., Fourth Grade Teacher; *b:* Brooklyn, NY; *ed:* Orange Cty Comm Coll (AAS) Soc Sci 1973; SUNY at Cortland (BS) Elem Ed 1975; SUNY at New Paltz (MS) Early Chldhd Ed 1981; *cr:* Goshen Area Day Care Head Tchr, Asst Dir 1976-79; Harriman Coll Campus Schl Dir 1979-81; WOC Headstart Tchr, Ed Coord 1982-86; Port Jervis City Schls Elem Tchr 1986-; *ai:* Super Kids Adv 4 Yrs; Adult Ed Tchr GED Instr 6 Yrs; AFT, NYSUT 1986-; Port Jervis Tchr Assn 1986-, Bldg Rep; Port Jervis Yth Ctr 1985-, Vol Tutor; *office:* Anna S Kuhl Elem Schl Rt 209 Box 1104 Port Jervis NY 12771

MICHALEWICH, RICHARD PAUL,SR., 7th Grade Math Teacher; *b:* Fall River, MA; *m:* Judith C. Ciesla; *c:* Richard P. Jr., Jennifer Lyn; *ed:* Bridgewater St Coll (BSEd) Earth Sci 1962, (MED) 1964; 84 Credits Math & Sci IL Inst of Tech, NY St Univ, Univ of MA, Wesleyan Univ, Eastern Nazarene, Bridgewater St, RI Coll, Southeastern Univ of MA, Boston Coll, Boston St Coll, Portland St Coll; *cr:* Henry Lord Jr HS 8-9 Grd Math & Sci Tchr 1962-68; Somerset Jr HS Cmptr Coord 1982-93, Math Dept Chair & Tchr 1968-94; 7th Grade Math Tchr 1994-; *ai:* Cmptr Club Adv; CML Math Meet Coord; Jr HS Math Curr Comm; Co-Chair Elem Math Comm; HS Math Comm; Grant Writer; MCET Liaison Satellite Comm; Jr HS Adv Cmptr Task Force; Cmptr Resource Troubleshoot, Internet Group; Prjct ERR Sci Fair Jdge; NEA, MTA 1962-, Life Mem; Somerset Tchrs 1968-, Treas 2 Yrs; ASCD 1983-; NCTM 1980-; MASSCUE 1989-94; Knights of Columbus 1966-; NSF, DDE & Horace Mann Grants; Eastern Edison Energy Grant 1993; Who's Who in Amer Ed 1989; Tchr of Yr 1991; *office:* Somerset Jr HS 1141 Brayton Ave Somerset MA 02726*

MICHALOWSKY, DONNA MARIE (DONAHUE), Seventh & Eighth Grade Teacher; *b:* Pittsburgh, PA; *m:* Robert W.; *ed:* Edinboro Univ (BS) Elem Ed 1972; Attnd Duquesne Univ 18 Credits, Carlow Coll 2 Credits & Allegheny Intermediate Univ 6 Credits; *cr:* St Wendelin Schl 7th & 8th Grd Tchr 1973-95; Bishop John McDowell Reg Schl 7th & 8th Grd Tchr, Lang Arts 1995-; *ai:* Past Stu Cncl & Schl Newspaper Adv, Girls Var Bsktbl Coach, Spelling Bee & Service Safety Patrol Moderator; *home:* 123 Hickory Heights Dr Bridgeville PA 15017

MICHAUD, DAVID RAYMOND, Business Teacher; *b:* East Millinocket, ME; *m:* Joan; *c:* Kelly, Kerry, Jennifer; *ed:* (BS) Bus Ed 1968; *cr:* Lee Acad Bus Tchr 1968-74; Schenck HS Bus Tchr 1974-; *ai:* Wolverine's Den Club Adv; GATE Adv; Goals 2000 Participant; NEA, MTA 1968-; EMTA 1974-, Bldg Rep; *office:* Schenck HS 41 North St East Millinocket ME 04430

MICHAUD, LEONA FOURNIER, French & Spanish Teacher; *b:* Nashua, NH; *m:* Benoit; *ed:* Rivier Coll (BA) Fr 1969; Clark Univ (MAT) Fr 1972; Attnd Nashua Bus Coll Diploma Bus Adm 1961, OH St Univ-France, Univ of NH, Middlebury Coll, Laval Univ; *cr:* Phaneuf Press Full Charge Bookkeeper 1957-65; Nashua Schl Dept Tchr 1971-; *ai:* Natl Jr Honor Soc Adv; Pennichuck NE NYNEX Partnership Co-Coord; AATF 1968-; MaFLA 1980-; NHATFL 1972-, Pres 3 Yrs; Act FANE 1980-, Dir 8 Yrs; ADK Mu Chapter 1991-, Pledge 2 Yr; Gilbert Lang F 1984-, Dir 7 Yrs; Nashua Coll Club 1971-, Treas 13 Yrs; AATF Quebec Govt Schlsp Laval 1980; *office:* Pennichuck Jr H S 207 Manchester St Nashua NH 03060

MICHAUD, PATRICIA OUELLETTE, Fourth Grade Teacher; *b:* Edmundston NB, Canada; *m:* Guy R.; *c:* Jonathan; *ed:* Ft Kent St Tchrs Coll (BA) Elem Ed 1966; *cr:* Madawaska Schl Dept 1 Grd Tchr 1961-65; LImestone Schl Dept 2 Grd Tchr 1966-67; Orono Schl Dept 3 Grd Tchr 1968-70; Van Buren Schl Dept 3,4 Grd Tchr 1965-68, 1974-; *ai:* Drama, Speech Adv; GATE Comm; Odyssey of Mind Judge; PTA 1987-; *home:* 367 Main St Van Buren ME 04785

MICHEL, MARY T., Guidance Director; *b:* Morristown, NJ; *m:* Joseph G.; *c:* Shaun, Maureen, Beth; *ed:* Coll of Notre Dame (AB) Eng, Art 1969; West Chester St Univ (MED) Guidance & Counseling 1973; Drug & Alcohol Cert; *cr:* Neumann Coll Admissions Cnslr 1969-71; Coll of Notre Dame Asst Dir of Guidance 1971-72; Delaware Cty Intermediate Unit Guidance Cnslr 1973-75; Villa Joseph Marie HS Dir of Guidance 1993-; *ai:* Peer Cnslrs Adv Chm; Admin Advy Comm; Fac Mem-Stu Advocate to Schl Disciplinary Review Bd; PA Schl Cnslrs Assn 1973-; Bucks Co Cnslrs Assn 1993-; *office:* Villa Joseph Marie HS 1180 Holland Rd Holland PA 18966*

MICHEL-MOYER, EDNA R., Associate Professor of Nursing; *b:* Balt, MD; *c:* Ronald J. Moyer; *ed:* Comm Coll of Balt (AA) Gen Ed 1975; Univ of MD (BSN) Nrsng 1977, (MS) Nrsng Ed 1981; George Washington Univ (MSN) Nurse Practitioner 1995; Sinai Schl of Nrsng Diploma-RN Nrsng 1972; *cr:* Sinai Hosp RN Staff, Asst Head Nurse 1970-81; Northwest Hosp Ctr RN Staff 1982-; Catonsville Comm Coll Assoc Prof of Nrsng 1981-; *ai:* Wkshp Sponsorship; Tech-Prep Org Speaker; Natl League of Nrsng 1994-; Nurse Practitioner Assn 1995-; Outstdng Tchr of Yr 1989.*

MICHELONE, ROGER A., Agriculture Coordinator; *b:* Williamsburg, PA; *m:* Rachel Royer; *c:* Sara Elizabeth, Samelyse Rachelle; *ed:* WI St Univ (BS) Ag 1965; PA St Univ Masters Equivalency 1971; Voc Ed Supvr Cert; Cooperative Ed Coord Cert; Voc Admin Dir; *cr:* Bellwood-Antis HS Ag Tchr 1965; Western Montgomery Co AVTS Ag Tchr 1965-87; Walter Biddle Saul HS Ag Tchr, Coord 1987-; *ai:* Adult Farms Assn, FFA Adv; AFT 1975-; PVATA 1965-, 25 Yr Awd; NEA 1965-; FFA 1955-; Lions 1986, 10 Yr Pin; Honorary St Farmer Degree; *office:* Walter Biddle Saul HS 7100 Henry & Cinnaminson Sts Philadelphia PA 19126

MICHELS, JAMES ROBERT, 9th Grade English Teacher; *b:* Clinton, IA; *m:* Mary Kay Rancourt; *c:* Molly, Maureen, James, Megan, Melissa; *ed:* John Carroll Univ (BA) Eng 1969, (MA) Eng 1972; *cr:* Cathedral Latin HS Eng Tchr 1969-71; Mentor Meml Jr HS Eng Tchr 1971-; *ai:* Fac Cncl; Redesigning Curr & Procedure Comms; Past Coach Bsktbl & Track 12 Yrs; NEA & Mentor Tchrs Assn 1979-; Painesville City Citizens Advy Bd 1992-93; Several Local Tchrs Awds; Sportswriter for Newspaper; Writing Awds Local, St & Natl Levels; OH Sports Writer of Yr 1990 by OH Assn of Intercollegiate Cross Cntry Track Coaches; *office:* Mentor Memorial Jr HS 8979 Mentor Ave Mentor OH 44060*

MICHELSON, ROSELLEN BERLIN, French & Spanish Teacher; *b:* East Orange, NJ; *m:* Jeffrey E.; *c:* Evan Samuel, Heather Leigh; *ed:* George Washington Univ (BA) Scndry Ed 1972; Attnd Georgetown Univ, La Sorbonne Univ at Paris France; *cr:* Woodson HS Fr, Span Tchr 1972-73; Millburn Jr HS Fr Tchr 1973-74; Morris Hills HS Fr, Span Tchr 1974-79; Roxbury HS Fr, Span Tchr 1988-; *ai:* Fr Club Activity, Fr NHS Advs; ITIP Instructional Prgm Comm; NJE, NEA 1973-; Morris Cty Democratic Org 1992-, Cty Comm; Princeton Univ Dstngshd Tchr Awd for Roxbury HS; Lorillard Dstrbtrs Ctznshp Awd;Princeton Univ Nmntn Comm; *office:* Roxbury HS 1 Bryant Dr Succasunna NJ 07876

MICHELSON, SUSAN S., Spanish Teacher; *b:* Worcester, MA; *m:* Steven Michelson; *c:* Joshua, Zachary; *ed:* Boston Univ (BS) Span, Scndry Ed 1970, (MED) Span, Scndry Ed 1971; *cr:* Coconut Creek HS Span, Eng Tchr 1971-72; Univ Schl Span, Fr Tchr 1972-73; Landsdowne MS Span, Fr Tchr 1973-74; Nashoba Regnl HS Span, Fr Tchr 1974-81; Acton-Boxborough Regnl HS Span Tchr 1991-; *ai:* NEA 1971-81, 1991-; AATSP, MAFLA 1991-; MA Tchrs Assn 1971-81, 1991-.

MICHENER, LORI ANN, Assistant Professor; *b:* Columbia, PA; *ed:* Lock Haven Univ (BS) Hlth Sci 1984; Univ of VA (MED) Ath Trnng 1985; SUNY at Buffalo (BS) Phys Therapy 1988; 40 Addl Credits PHD Orthopedic Phys Therapy; *cr:* Lock Haven Univ Asst Prof 1988-; Nova Care Staff Phys Therapist 1989-93; Hahnemann Univ Tchng Asst 1995-; *ai:* Ath Trng Club Adv; Stu Ath Comm; Physican Asst Prgm Dev; NCAA Fac Ath Rep; Gender Issues Comm; Hlth Sci Dept Evaluations Comm Chprsn; Hlth Sci Dept Search Comm; Phi Delta Kappa 1995-; Amer Phys Therapist Assn 1986-; Natl Ath Trainers Assn 1984-; PA Ath Trainers Assn 1986-, Chprsn Convention Comm; Fac Dev Grant Lock Haven Univ 1993; PA St System Fac Prof Dev Grant 1994; PA St System Fac Prof Dev Grant 1991; *office:* Lock Haven Univ 115 Himes Hall Lock Haven PA 17745*

MICHETTI, JEAN ANN, Science Teacher; *b:* Bronx, NY; *ed:* SUNY at New Paltz (BS) Elem Ed N-6, Soc Stud 7-9 1987, (MS) Elem Ed N-6, Cmptrs, Tech 1996; Cert Identifying, Reporting, Child Abuse, Maltreatment; *cr:* St Josephs Schl of the Archdiocese of NY 5th-8th Grd Sci Tchr 1988-; *ai:* Sci Fair Coord; Sci Curr Officer; Mentor; NYS Invention Convention Coach; Earth Week Act Supvr; Sci Fair Judge; Chess Club Adv; Amer Assn for Advancement of Sci; Rhineck Choral Soc 1988-, 2nd Soprano; CCD 1982-, Tchr; Collecting Food, Clothes for Poor 1988-; ICE Inst Grant to Stud Chem Univ of Northern CO; Project Learning Tree Facilitator; Inservice Developing Integrated Act Inquiry Skills Tchng Environmental Sci; *office:* St Joseph's Schl North Ave Millbrook NY 12545*

MICHEWICZ, NANCY CAROL, Mathematics Teacher; *b:* Reading, PA; *m:* Peter S.; *c:* Jennifer, Jonathan; *ed:* Immaculata Coll (BA) Math 1974; Wilkes Univ (MS) Ed 1992; *cr:* Spring-Ford Schl Dist Math Tchr 1974-; *ai:* Acad Team Coach; NEA 1974-; NCTM 1987-; *office:* Spring-Ford HS Lower Lewis Rd Royersford PA 19468*

MICHIELLI-PENDL, JEAN, Science Teacher; *b:* Savannah, GA; *m:* Douglas; *c:* Jessica, Christopher, Jonathan; *ed:* St Univ at Fredonia (BS) Elem Ed 1972; ESL Linguistics 1978; *cr:* School #3 ESL Tchr 1972-76, 5th Grd Tchr 1978-91; School #4 5th Grd Tchr 1976-78; Dunkirk MS Sci Tchr 1991-; *ai:* Rel Ed Instr; Eucharistic Minister; Church Choir; Inservice & Chptr I Comms; NYSUT Assn 1972-; TESOL 1972-; Team Pub Relations 1992-; Jaycees 1974-; 4-H 1985-; Presentor at Natl TESOL Convention Metrics Fac Instr; *office:* Dunkirk MS 525 Eagle St Dunkirk NY 14048

MICHIELS, LEO PAUL, Chemistry Professor; *b:* Detroit, MI; *ed:* Manhattan Coll (AB) Chem 1953, (MA) Math 1959; Univ of Detroit (MS) Chem 1964, (PHD) Chem 1968; Attnd Buttimer Inst, St Mary's of CA; *cr:* Christian Brothers Acad Math, Sci Tchr 1953-59; St Joseph HS Math, Sci Tchr 1959-64; De La Salle Collegiate HS Chair of Math, Sci 1964-74; Manhattan Coll Assoc Prof of Chem 1974-; Univ of Touhouse Visiting Rsrch Asst 1985; CA Inst of Tech Visiting Rsrch Asst 1986; *ai:* Moderator Manhattan Coll Singers; Amer Chem Soc 1975-; Sigma Xi 1972-, Sec, Treas; Brother of Chrstn Schls 1947-, Dir 1968, 1974; L.P. Michiels Inorganica Clinica Acta 100 (211-218) 1985, J Chem Ed 63, 806-7 1985, 60 154 (1983), 59, 157 (1982); NSF Cause Grant 1979-82; *office:* Manhattan Coll 4513 Manhattan Coll Pkwy Riverdale NY 10471

MICHITSCH, TIMOTHY M., Chef & Instructor; *b:* Bristol, CT; *c:* Alecia, Michael; *ed:* Culinary Inst of Amer (AA) Culinary Arts 1984; Kent St Univ Ed Tchng Cert 1988; Ashland Univ Food Mngmt 1989; Zona Spray Cooking Schl Pastry Classes 1984; *cr:* Oakwood Cntry Club Exec Chef 1986-87; Lorain Cty JVS Chef, Instr 1987-; Swamp Club Chef 1993-94; Players on Madison Server 1994-; *ai:* Culinary Team Coach, Adv; Voc Yth Club Coord; OH FHA-HERO Resource Dev Endowment Bd; FHA-HERO Skill Event Comm; NEA, OEA 1987-, Pacesetter; OVA, AVA 1989-, New Prof; ACF-Cleveland 1993-, Culinry Edctr; OH Cncl Hotel Restaurant Industry Ed 1988-; Culinary Inst of Amer 1984-; Lorain Cty JVS Tchrs Assn 1988-, Sec; OH FHA-HERO Resource Dev Endowment 1991-, Co-Chprsn; Lorain Cty JVS Advy Comm 1988-, Chprsn; OH St Fair Recipes Pub; Certfd Applied Food Svc Sanitation Instr; Nom Voc Tchr of Yr 1990-92; Kent St Univ 2nd Plce Lab Demonstration Contest; *office:* Lorain Cty Joint Voc Schl 15181 State Route 58 Oberlin OH 44074

MICHNEY, KAREN M., Theology Teacher; *b:* Cleveland, OH; *ed:* Wilmington Coll (BA) Elem Ed, Rel, Philosphy 1987; John Carroll Univ (MA) Rel Stud 1989; *cr:* Trinity HS Theology Tchr 1989-91; St Joseph Acad Theology Tchr 1991-; John Carroll Univ Adj Fac, Rel Stud Dept 1995-; *ai:* Theology Dept Chair; Reatreat Dir; Natl Cath Edctrs Assn 1989-; Amer Assn of Univ Women 1995-; Ctr Women & Rel 1990-; Congregation of St Joseph 1995-, Co-Mem; 2 Articles Pub; *office:* Saint Joseph Acad 3430 Rocky River Dr Cleveland OH 44111

MICKA, PAULA B., Foreign Lang Dept Chprsn; *b:* Cambridge, MA; *m:* John; *c:* John, Beth; *ed:* Hood Coll (BA) Fr & Span 1963; Johns Hopkins Univ (MS) Admin & Suervision 1990; Attnd Univ of MD, Loyola, Antioch Univ; *cr:* Arundel Sr HS Fr Tchr & Dept Chair 1963-69; Mount Hebron HS Span Tchr 1976-77; Centennial HS Fr & Span Tchr 1977-80; Howard Comm Coll fr Tchr 1980-85; chair 1980-; Oakland Mills HS Fr Tchr, Dept Chair 1980-; *ai:* Schl Improvement & Foreign Travel Comms; NEA, MSTA, HCEA 1976-; AATF 1977-; Homeowners Assn 1991-, VP; Federal Credit Union 1976-, Mem, Bd of Dirs; Amer Cancer Soc 1986-; Pub Foreign Travel Handbook & Eric Abstracts; Grant in Paris Video Exploration; Chamber of Commerce Outstanding Tchr of Yr 1987; MD Foreign Lang Assn Tchr of Yr 1989; *office:* Oakland Mills HS 9410 Kilimanjaro Rd Columbia MD 21045*

MICKEWICZ, WILLIAM D., Science & Math Teacher; *b:* Manchester CT ; *ed:* Univ of CT (BA) Chem 1973, (MS) Chem 1975; 60 Addl Hrs Cntrl CT St Univ, Weslyan Univ; *cr:* Simsbury HS Sci, Math Tchr 1975-; *ai:* Pimms Vanguard Fellow 1984; *office:* Simsbury HS 34 Farms Village Rd Simsbury CT 06070

MICKLOS, CHARLES RICHARD, Sixth Grade Teacher; *b:* Dover, DE; *ed:* Univ of MD at Coll Park (BA) His 1969; Loyola Coll (MED) Rdng 1982; Univ of MD Balto Co Tchng Cert Ed 1971; *cr:* Samuel Coleridge Taylor Elem Schl Fifth Grd Tchr 1971-72; West Meade Elem Schl Sixth Grd Tchr 1972-; *ai:* Sci Club; Soc Comm; NEA, MSTA, TAAAC 1972-; Catonsville Presbyn Church 1983-, Deacon; Edctr of Month 1989; Agnes Meyer Outstdng Tchr Awd 1990; Animal Collection Guidebook; *office:* West Meade Elem Schl 7722 Ray St Fort Meade MD 20755

MICSKY, GREGG PATRICK, Industrial Arts & Tech Ed Tchr; *b:* Greenville, PA; *m:* April Knapp; *ed:* CA Univ of PA (BS) Industrial Arts & Tech Ed 1988; *cr:* Ft League Schl Dist Tchr 1988-91; Reynolds Schl Dist Tchr 1992-93; Neshannoch Schl Dist Industrial Arts & Tech Ed Tchr 1993-; *ai:* PSEA 1988-; TEAP 1994-; *office:* Neshannock Twp Schl Dist 301 Mitchell Rd New Castle PA 16105

MIDDLETON, GLORIA JEAN, Fifth Grade Teacher; *b:* Charleston, SC; *ed:* Voorhees Coll (BS) Elem Ed 1972; 18 Credit Hrs Lehman Coll; *cr:* Millie Hill Elem Schl Tchr 1972-77; R. D. Schroder Elem Schl Tchr 1977-85; Jefferson Elem Schl Tchr 1986-; *ai:* Coach Little League Schl Bstkbl; Site Base Mgmt Team; NEA 1972-; *home:* 73 Tussle Ln Scotch Plains NJ 07076

MIDDLETON, MARY, English Department Chairman; *b:* Lackawana, NY; *ed:* OH St Univ (BS) Elem Ed 1965; Attnd Univ of Akron; Cleveland St Univ 40 Hrs Eng; *cr:* Columbus Schls Tchr 1966-68; Brooklyn Schls Tchr 1968-; *ai:* Acad Challenge; Eng Honorary; Lit Magazine; Group Ldr CARE Prgm; Mentor to Incoming Tchrs; Brooklyn Ed Assn 1968-, Sec; NEA 1968-; OEA 1968-; NEOTA 1968-; OCTELA 1988-; AAUW 1995-; Democratic Club 1988-; NE OH Writing Project & Flwshp; Who's Who in Ed 1989-90, 1992-93; Who's Who in Amer Women 1995-96; *home:* 7127 Bayberry Cir North Olmsted OH 44070*

MIDDLETON, ROBERT CAREY, Chemistry Teacher; *b:* Bronx, NY; *m:* Mary P. Hahn; *c:* Robert J., Timothy P., Andrew C.; *ed:* Concordia Tchrs Coll (BS) Ed 1971; Fordham Univ (MS) Sci Ed 1976; Attnd NJ Inst of Tech, Monmouth Coll, William Paterson Coll; *cr:* Our Saviour Luth Schl Sci & Math Tchr 1971-79; West Orange HS Chem Tchr 1979-; *ai:* NJ Sci League; Chem Teams Adv; NJEA 1979-; WOEA 1979-; NJSTA 1979-; Roxbury Little League 1991-, Mgr & Coach; Good Shepherd Luth Church 1991-, Treas; Roxbury Yth Ice Hockey 1992-, Coach; Tchr in Industry Pgm 1990; Presented by Amer Chemical Soc Edward J Merrill Awd for Excl in HS Chem Tchng 1990; NJ Bus Industry & Scndry Ed Consortium; *office:* West Orange HS 51 Conforti Ave West Orange NJ 07052

MIDDLETON, STEVEN A., Science Teacher; *b:* Orange, NJ; *m:* Carol Puckett; *c:* Dwayne, Andrea; *ed:* Fairleigh Dickinson Univ (BA) Physics Ed 1978; NJ Inst of Tech (MS) Applied Sci 1985; Jersey City St Coll Advanced Credits; *cr:* Pilar Inc Chem Lab Technician 1971-78; Orange HS Sci Tchr 1978-88; Mt Olive HS Sci Tchr 1988-; *office:* Mount Olive HS Corey Rd Flanders NJ 07836

MIDDLETON, SUZANNE MARIE (SWIS), Math Teacher; *b:* Cincinnati, OH; *m:* John D.; *c:* Allison M., John A.; *ed:* Coll Mt St Joseph on the OH (BA) Math 1958; 36 Grad Credits Math OH St Univ; 6 Grad Credits Math, Philosophy Queens Coll; *cr:* Dodd Jr HS Math Tchr 1969-75; Baldwin Jr HS Math Tchr 1979-88; Washington HS Math Tchr 1989-; *ai:* SHOP Adv; Stu Assistance, Schl Improvement Teams; Scndry Advy Cnsl; Selection Comm Var Club; Tasco, Mysta, NEA 1989-, Local, St, Natl Unions; NCTM, MD St Cncl 1990-; Amer Legion Aux 1994-; Moose Lodge Aux 1996; Tchr of Yr 1992, 1993; Tandy Co Outstdng Tchr Awd 1992; Lifetime Mbrshp NY St PTA Outstdng Contributions to Yth; Outstdng Tchr Awd 1987; *office:* Washington H S 10902 Old Princess Anne Rd Princess Anne MD 21853*

MIED, JUDITH MAUDE, Biology & PE Teacher; *b:* Baltimore, MD; *m:* Paul Anthony; *c:* Joshua Paul, Rebecca Maude, Anna Marie; *ed:* Villa Julie Coll (AA) Med Asst 1970; Towson St Univ (BS) PE 1973; Repeated Coaching Clinics Vlybl 4 Clincs, Bsktbl 2 Clinics; CPR Tchr Cert Course 1994; *cr:* Harpers Choice MS PE Tchr, IM Coord 1973-78; Carroll Chrstn Schls Tchr, Coach 1988-; *ai:* Sci Chm; Coach Var, JV, Jr HS Vlybl, Sftbl, Jr HS Bsktbl; MAHPER 1990-91; MACS 1988-; Liberty Bapt Church 1981-, Music Dir 5 Yrs; Koinonia 1990-, Dir; *office:* Carroll Chrstn Schls 550 Baltimore Blvd Westminster MD 21157*

MIEDANER, CHERYL PALUCCI, Social Studies Teacher; *b:* Syracuse, NY; *m:* Anthony; *c:* Nina Palucci, Rachel Palucci, Paul Palucci, Allison; *ed:* LeMoyne Coll (BA) His 1990; Cortland Coll (MS) Scndry Soc Stud 1995; *cr:* NY St Div for Yth Tchr 1990-91; P. V. Moore HS Soc Stud Tchr 1991-; *ai:* Stu Cncl Adv; AFT, NYSCSS 1990-; *home:* 7390 Liffey Ln Liverpool NY 13088

MIEKINA, CAROL BRANSTROM, 6th Grade Teacher; *b:* Jamestown, NY; *m:* Gilbert A.; *ed:* North Park Coll (BA) Fr 1967; St Univ of NY at Fredonia (MS) Dev Rdng 1972; 16 Credit Hrs Post Grad SUNY at Fredonia; *cr:* Des Plaines Elem Schls 4th Grd Tchr 1967-68; Southwestern Cntrl MS 6th Grd Tchr 1968-; *ai:* NEA, NYEA, Southwestern Tchrs Assn 1968-; Family Svc of Jamestown; Comm Music Project.

MIEKINA, GILBERT ANTHONY, Social Studies Teacher; *b:* Chicago, IL; *m:* Carol Branstrom; *ed:* Northwestern Univ (BA) His 1965, (MAT) His 1967; 60 Credit Hrs St Univ of NY at Fredonia; *cr:* ME East HS Soc Stud Tchr 1965-68; Southwestern Cntrl HS Soc Stud Tchr 1968-; *ai:* Legislative Intern Prgm Dir; Mock Trial, HS Bowl Team Coach; NEA 1965-; NYEA 1968-; Southwestern Tchrs Assn 1968-, Pres; Rsrch, Planning Bd 1991-, Bd Mem; Cty Legislator 1981-85, 1991-.

MIELE, BONNIE MC PARTLAND, Science & Health Teacher; *b:* Paterson, NJ; *c:* Marrya, Janine; *ed:* Seton Hall Univ (BS) Elem Ed 1972; Jersey City St Sci 4 Credit Hrs; William Paterson Coll at Wayne Sci 7 Credit Hrs; Lesley Coll Math 3 Credit Hrs; *cr:* Paterson Bd of Ed K-8 Grd, GATE, Sci Tchr 1972-; Passaic Cty Comm Coll Sci Project Awareness Tchr 1990-, Homework Helper Coord 1993-; *ai:* Sci Coord; PEA 1972-, Bldg Rep; Paterson Midget League 1987-, Sec Exec Bd, Girls Sftbl Coach 1988-; Paterson 200 Educl Comm Coord; St Bonaventures 1986-, Sec; MHCA 1992-, Exec Bd; Governors Tchr Recognition Awd 1990-91; *office:* Paterson Bd of Ed 33 Church St Paterson NJ 07501

MIERZEJEWSKI, MARK MICHAEL, Science Teacher; *b:* Wallingford, CT; *m:* Elizabeth Ann Jeffrey; *c:* Timothy, Sharon, Laura; *ed:* Univ of Lowell (BS) Meteorology 1983, Sacred Heart U (MA) Ed 1990; Central Ct St Univ Post Grad Sci; *cr:* Kennedy HS Sci Tchr 1987-; *ai:* Weather Forecasting Club Adv; Tech Prep, Meteorology & Astronomy Curr Dev; NEA, CEA 1987; CSTA 1988; CESTA 1988; Received Grant for Computer & Weather Satellite.*

MIGAL, LEWIS, Social Studies Dept Chairman; *b:* Taylor, PA; *m:* Joan Capozza; *c:* Christine Walker, Michele; *ed:* Wilkes Univ (BS) Scndry Ed 1964; Temple Univ (MS) Scndry Ed 1969; Univ of Scranton 15 Credit Hrs; Univ of AK 13 Credit Hrs; Marywood Coll 3 Credit Hrs; *cr:* Riverside Jr Sr HS Tchr & Dept Chm 1965-; *ai:* Grad Project & Curr Revision Comms; NEA, PSEA, REA 1964-; ASCD 1985-; PCSS 1980-; NCSS 1980-; *home:* 309 Bridge St Old Forge PA 18518

MIGLIARINI, CHERYL S., Advanced Physics Teacher; *b:* Columbus, OH; *m:* Brian; *ed:* Radford Coll (BS) Soc Sci 1971; Towson St Univ (BS) Bio 1981; Physics Cert Western MD Coll 1987; *cr:* Stemmers Run Jr HS Sci Tchr 1981-82; Woodlawn MS Sci Tchr 1982-87; Franklin MS Sci Tchr 1987-93; Hereford HS Physics, Anatomy Tchr 1993-; *ai:* Adv NHS, Safe; Fac Cncl Rep; ENvironmental Stu Comm; NEA, TABCO, MSTA 1981-; ASCD 1990-; Monton Garden Club 1995-, Recording Sec; *office:* Hereford HS 17301 York Rd Parkton MD 21120

MIGNEAULT, DEBORAH R., Social Studies Teacher; *b:* Nashua, NH; *ed:* Rivier Coll (BA) His, Scndry Ed 1976; Georgetown Univ (MA) 20th Century Amer 1980; Rivier Coll (MED) Schl Admin 1984; Attnd Keene St Coll, Northeastern Univ, Univ of NH, Univ of Lowell Amer Constitutional His Inst, Univ of ME at Orono; *cr:* Nashua Sr HS Soc Stud Tchr 1977-; *ai:* Soph, Jr, Sr Class Adv 1977-92, Sr Class Adv 10 Yrs; Schl Coord for United Way Yth Day of Caring; Boys, Girls Club Duck Race; AFT 1977-; Nashua Tchrs Union 1977-, VP, Pres 1991-95; Fulbright Tchr Exch Prgm Nom for NH Tchr of Yr 1990; Exch Club Book of Golden Deeds Awd 1990; *office:* Nashua Sr HS 36 Riverside Dr Nashua NH 03062

MIGNERY, MICHAEL E., Secondary Social Studies Tchr; *b:* Hamilton, OH; *m:* Mary Jo; *c:* Ben, Sarah, Mark, Ann, Katie; *ed:* Miami Univ (BS) Ed 1970, (MAT) Geography 1972; Attnd Xavier Univ; *cr:* Miami Univ Tchng Asst 1974; Roosevelt JHS Soc Stud Tchr 1974-76; Edgewood HS Soc Stud Tchr 1976-; *ai:* Hum Dept Chm; Prin Cabinet; Edgewood Tchrs Assn 1975-, VP; Right to Life 1979-, Pres; Knights of Columbus 1982-, Trustee; Labor Local 534 1968-; Farm Bureau 1986-; OH Trustees Assn 1986-; Hanover Twp Trustee; City Hamilton Family of Yr 1994; OH Univ Scholar Tchr Awd; *office:* Edgewood HS 5005 Oxford State Rd Trenton OH 45067*

MIHALIK, CHRISTOPHER STEVEN, World His & Psychology Tchr; *b:* Wilmington, OH; *m:* Deborah White; *c:* Emily, Matthew; *ed:* Otterbein Coll (BA) Ed & His 1979; Morehead St Univ (MA) Scndry Ed 1983; *cr:* East Clinton MS Soc Stud Tchr 1979-81; Little Miami HS World His & Psych Tchr 1982-; *ai:* Soc Stud Dept Attendance Ofcr; St Model Coord; NEA 1984-; OEA 1984-; LMTA 1984-, Pres 1986; Sons of the Amer Legion 1992-, Squadron Commander 1992-; *office:* Little Miami HS 605 Welch Rd Morrow OH 45152

MIHALIK, MICHELLE RENEE (BRINKLEY), Substitute Teacher; *b:* Aiken, SC; *m:* Matthew James; *ed:* Bowling Green St Univ (BS) Fr Ed 1993; *cr:* Toledo Chrstn Schls Fr, Eng Tchr 1992-95; Beavercreek Pub Schls Sub Tchr 1995-; Cedar Cliff Pub Schls Sub Tchr 1995-; *home:* 2219 E Whipp Rd Kettering OH 45440*

MIHALKO, AUDREY MURPHY, Physical Education Teacher; *b:* Winsor NS, Canada; *m:* James E.; *c:* Randall, Geoff, Brian, Jaime; *ed:* Ithaca (BS) PE 1970; 9 Grad Hrs in Spcl Ed; 21 Grad Hrs in Ed; *cr:* Lowville ACCA Schl PE Tchr 1970-71; Adirondack Cntrl Schl PE Tchr 1971-; *ai:* Girls Ath Assoc Adv; Life Guard Trng Instr; AYSO Coach; AFT 1971-; NY St United Tchrs 1971-; Sec Three Assn of PE Prof 1992-; Red Cross Instr 1968-; Amer Yth Soccer Org 1985-, Chm & Registrar; *office:* Adirondack Cntrl Schl 8181 Star Rt #294 Boonville NY 13309*

MIHALOS, MARIE S. DENESSI, Gifted Support Teacher; *b:* Wilkes-Barre, PA; *m:* Emanuel W.; *c:* Emanuel W. II; *ed:* Wilkes Univ (BA) Sociology 1970, (MS) Elem Ed 1973; Luzerne Intermediate Unit 45 Post Master Credit Hrs; *cr:* Wilkes-Barre Area Schl Dist Tchr 1970-; *ai:* Schl Self Stud Comm for Mid Atlantic St; Trival Pursuit Club; Book Selection Comm; WBAEA, PSEA, NEA 1970-; NOIAW 1990-93; USTA 1980-90; *office:* Kistler Schl 301 Old River Rd Wilkes Barre Towns PA 18702

MIHELBERGEL, ROBERT CHARLES, English Teacher; *b:* Buffalo, NY; *m:* Sharon Conk; *c:* Eric, Leah; *ed:* Niagara Cty Comm Coll (AA) Liberal Arts 1969; SUNY Coll at Buffalo (BSEd) Scndry Ed & Eng 1971; St Univ of NY Buffalo (MSEd) Ed & Eng 1975; *cr:* Cheektowaga Central Jr & Sr HS Eng Tchr 1971-; *ai:* Mem Promotional Review Comm, Crisis Comm, Effective Schl Comm; Drama Club Adv 1972-74; Field Trip Assembly & ASARC Comm; PET Prgm With SUNY Coll of Buffalo; Schl Improvement Team Comm; NYSUT, AFT, CCTA 1971-, Exec Bd 1980; US Navy 1963-69, Honorable Discharge HM2 1969; St Pauls Cath Church 1972-; Most Memorable Tchr Awd 1990; Sr Class Adv 1979 & 1984; Ecology & Conservation Club Adv 1980 & 1982; Chm Eng Curr Comm 1978; Adv Literary Magazine 1977; *office:* Cheektowaga Central H S 3600 Union Rd Cheektowaga NY 14225*

MIHOCIK, NANCY SCHMIDT, French Teacher; *b:* Lakewood, OH; *m:* John R.; *ed:* Univ of MI (AB) Fr 1969, (AM) Comparative Lit 1973; *cr:* Rocky River Jr HS Fr Tchr 1969-72; Rock River HS Fr, Eng, & Amer His Tchr 1973-; *ai:* Key Club Adv; RRTA 1969-, Grievance Chair 1975-80; OEA & NEA 1969-; MLA 1969-; AATF 1969-; Comm Challenge 1984-, Pres 1989-91; Delta Kappa Gamma 1991-; Rocky River Kiwanis Club 1994-; Rocky River Ed Fndtn Grant; Cox Cable Citizen Spotlight Awd; SW Conf Bsktbl Coach of the Yr 1981; Ashland Oil Apple Recipient; *office:* Rocky River HS 20951 Detroit Rd Cleveland OH 44116

MIKE, VALERIE W., Spanish Teacher; *b:* Philadelphia, PA; *m:* Anthony G.; *c:* Andrew James, Rachel Marie; *ed:* Moravian Coll (BA) Span 1979; 24 Credit Hrs; *cr:* Corning-Painted Post Schl Dist Span Tchr 1979-87; Lewisburg Schl Dist Span Tchr 1987-; *ai:* Adv Natl Span Honor Soc, Span Club; Quality Ed, Schl Improvement Comms; Frgn Lang Dept Liaison to Admin; AATSP 1987-, Sec, Treas 4 Hrs; NEA 1987-.*

MIKELL, LINDA JANARO, Tchr of Learning Disabilities; *b:* Yonkers, NY; *m:* Edward; *c:* Theresa Castellone, Jennifer, Timothy; *ed:* Hofstra Univ (BS) Music Ed 1964, (MS) Spec Ed 1976; 80 Post Grad, Insvc Hrs; *cr:* Baldwin Pub Schls Music Tchr 1964-65; Spackenkill Schl Dist Music Tchr 1965-66; AHRC Brookville Schl Music Tchr 1968-70; Connetquot Cntrl Schl Dist Tchr of Learning Disabilities 1977-; Dowling Coll Adj Asst Prof of Ed 1986-95; *ai:* Global Vols; Connetquot Tchrs Assn 1978-; Phi Delta Kappa 1986-; Unitarian Universalist Flwshp of Stony Brook 1981-; PTA Tchr of Yr 1989; *office:* Idle Hour Schl Ocean Ave Bohemia NY 11769

MIKES, LUCINE, Mathematics & Drafting Teacher; *b:* Cleveland, OH; *ed:* Ursuline Coll (BS) Chem 1958; Univ of Detroit (MS) Chem 1963; Attnd John Carroll Univ, Wayne St Univ & Kent St Univ; *cr:* Marymount HS Chem & Math Chprsn 1966; Immaculata Coll Chem & Math Instr 1967-68; Ursuline Coll Physics & Math Instr 1968-72; Trinity HS Chem, Math & Drafting Tchr 1972-; *ai:* Ministry Team; Amer Chem Assn 1958-; NEA, NCEA 1973-; Natl Sci Fnd Grant; *office:* Trinity HS 12425 Granger Rd Garfield Heights OH 44125

MIKLOICHE, ANTHONY MICHAEL, Vocational Agriculture Teacher; *b:* Carbondale, PA; *m:* Patricia Jane Palko; *c:* Sarah; *ed:* St Univ of NY (AAS) Horticulture 1963; Penn St Univ Ag Ed 1976; Masters Equivalency in Voc Ed; *cr:* Lackawanna Cty Area Voc Tech Schl Horticulture Instr 1973-88; Monroe Cty Area Voc Tech Schl Floriculture & Landscaping Instr 1988-95; *ai:* FFA Adv 22 Yrs; PVATA 1974-; AFT 1974-88; NEA 1988-; Penn St Univ Dept of Agricultural Ed Advy Comm 2 Terms, Cooperating Tchr for Stu Tchrs.*

MIKOVICH, THEODORE, Sixth Grade Teacher; *b:* Nesquehoning, PA; *m:* Joanne Marouchoc; *c:* Gregory, Christopher; *ed:* East Stroudsburg Univ (MED) Elem 1969; *cr:* Salisbury Twp Schl Dist Tchr 1967-; *ai:* Stu Asst Pgm Team; Group Support Facilitator; NEA, PSEA, SEA 1967-; *office:* Salisbury MS 3301 Devonshire Rd Allentown PA 18103

MIKSZA, SUSAN ROBICHAUD, Asst Superintendent of Schls; *b:* Winchendon, MA; *ed:* Kean Coll of NJ (BA) Elem Ed 1971, (MA) Early Chldhd 1980; Kearn Coll Admin & Supvn MA 30 Hrs 1981; *cr:* Elizabeth BOE Tchr Grd 1st-5th 1971-81, Prin 1981-86; Clark Bd of Ed Prin 1986-84, Asst Supt 1994-; *ai:* NEA & NJEA 1971-, Exec Comm; NAESP 1981-; Phi Betta Kappa 1985-; ASCD 1986-; Co-Author Tchng Children to Love Themselves 1992; *office:* Clark Bd of Ed Schindler Rd Clark NJ 07066

MIKULA, JAMES E., English, Theater & Film Tchr; *b:* Uniontown, PA; *ed:* St Vincent Coll (BA) Eng 1968; PA State Univ (MA) Eng 1970; *cr:* Greater Latrobe Sr HS Eng Tchr 1968-; *ai:* Drama Dir; NEA 1968-; Valley Players of Ligonier 1970-, Pres 1990-92; NEA Flwshp Shakespeare 1984; *office:* Greater Latrobe Sr HS Country Club Rd Latrobe PA 15650

MIKULAK, DAVID THOMAS, English Teacher; *b:* Hartford, CT; *ed:* Cntrl CT St Coll (BS) Eng, Theatre 1972, (MS) Supervision, Curr 1979; St Trng as Tchr Assessor & Mentor Cert Prgms; *cr:* Guilford HS Eng Tchr 1973-; *ai:* Cooperating Tchr to Stu from Yale Univ; Task Force on Certified Staff Evaluation Dist Comm; NEA, CEA, GEA 1973-; CT Hum Cncl 1988-; CT St Dept of Ed Dist Facilitator, Consultant, Assessor, Mentor; Recognized for Excl by Tufto Univ & MIT 1992-93; *office:* Guilford HS New England Rd Guilford CT 06437*

MIKULSKI, JOHN MICHAEL,JR., Instrumental Music Teacher; *b:* Buffalo, NY; *m:* Marguerite Denton; *c:* John F., Richard M., Andrew R.; *ed:* Shenandoah Conservatory of Music (BME) Music Ed 1979; St Univ of NY at Buffalo (MA) Music Ed 1987; Cert Clarinet Performance 1979; *cr:* Saint Gregory the Great Schl K-8th Grd General Music Tchr 1979-81; Oakfield-Alabama Cntrl Schl 7th-12th Grd Instrumental Mus[illegible] 1981-; *ai:* Sr Class Adv; NY St Schl Music Assn Adjudicator; [illegible] Valley Judging Assn Marching Judge; Music Educators Natl Conf, [illegible] WY Music Educators, AFT NYSUT, Oakfiled-Alabama Tchrs Assn[illegible] Intnl Clarinet Assn 1980-; *home:* 1129 Boncliff Dr Alden NY 140[illegible]

MILAN, GODFREY, Biling Program English Teacher; *b:* Bronx, [illegible] SUNY Coll at Brockport (BS) Eng 1990, (MS) Creative Writing, En[illegible] *cr:* East HS Eng, Biling Ed Tchr 1990-; *ai:* Org Latin-Amer Stdnts, [illegible] Adv; Peer Mediation, Wellness Comms; Natural Helpers; Sch[illegible] Planning Team; AFT, UFT 1990-, Bldg Rep; NYS Assn Biling[illegible] 1992-, Awd Comm; Biling Ed Cncl 199k4-, Tchr Liason; Hispanic Coalition 1993-, Stakeholder; Guest Speaker Urban Educl Issues Coll at Brockport, Nazareth Coll; *office:* East HS 1801 Mai[illegible] Rochester NY 14609*

MILANO, STEPHEN PAUL, Health & Physical Ed Tchr; *b:* Cant[illegible] *m:* Paula Ginella; *c:* Rocco, Anthony; *ed:* OH Univ (BSES) Hlth, P[illegible] 1980; Ashland Univ (MS) Educ Admin; *cr:* Malvern HS Hlth, [illegible] 1982-92; Glen Oak HS Hlth, PE Tchr 1992-; *ai:* Asst Ftbl Var; S[illegible] Coach; NEA, OEA, OHSFCA 1982-; *home:* 3195 Knollridge [illegible] Canton OH 44721

MILCETICH, CHRISTINE ANN, AP Physics & Chemistry Teac[illegible] Alliance, OH; *ed:* Walsh Univ (BS) Bio, Compre Sci 1988; Attn[illegible] Western Reserve Univ, Univ of Akron Physics Grad Work; Attn[illegible] Highlands Univ, Ashland Univ Grad Course Work; *cr:* Beaumont [illegible] Physics, Physics, Hon Physics 1990-92; St Thomas Aquinas Hs H[illegible] Bio 1992-93; Akron Firestone HS AP Physics, Hnrs Chem, Gen Che[illegible] Chem & Physics 1993-; *ai:* Head Vlybl Coach 1994-; Women in S[illegible] 1994-; Ath Dir 1995-; Yrbk Adv 1990-92; JV Sftbl Coach 1993; Sv[illegible] Adv 1990-92; Clown Minstry Adv 1991-92; NSTA, SECO, Phi[illegible] Kappa 1995-; OS-AAPT 1992-; Loyal Cath Benevolent Assn [illegible] Outstdng Young Women in Amer; Impact II Grant; SEPF Grant; Ldrshp Dev Prgm; *office:* Firestone HS 333 Rampart Ave Akr[illegible] 44313*

MILCH, SHARON KARP, English Teacher; *b:* Springfield, MA; [illegible] *ed:* Univ of MA (BA) Eng 1970; Fairleigh Dickinson (MA) Huma[illegible] 1979; Univ of Chicago 6 Credits Lib Sci; Attnd Bard Coll, U[illegible] Hartford, Wm Paterson Coll; *cr:* River Dell Schls Eng Tchr 1978-; [illegible] Magazine, Frosh Class & Creative Writing Club Adv; Curr Cncl; [illegible] NJEA 1978-; NCTE 1978-; Governors Tchr of the Yr Nom 1994; En[illegible] Chm 1995-; *home:* 10-79 Plymouth Dr Fair Lawn NJ 07410*

MILES, DAVID LEE, Electronics Technology Tchr; *b:* Michigan Ci[illegible] *m:* Stephanie Lynn Livingston; *ed:* Attnd Aviation Electronics C[illegible] Schl, Advanced Electronics Class C-7 Schl, NASA Soldering & Tra[illegible] Receive Schls, TV Servicing Schl; Cmptr Upgrading & Repair; W[illegible] Towards BA in Voc Ed Southern IL Univ; *cr:* US Navy Aviation Elect[illegible] Technician 1984-91; ATSC NASA Satellite Comm Technician 19[illegible] Wicomico Applied Tech Ctr Electronics Tech Tchr 1994-; *ai:* VICA[illegible] Local Comm Colls Electronics Curr Dev Mem; NEA 1994-; Goodwil[illegible] Church, Yth Sunday Schl Tchr; Restructured a Failing Electronics [illegible] into a Highly Successful & Popular Career Choice for Stdnts; [illegible] Wicomico Applied Tech Ctr 607 Morris St Salisbury MD 21801*

MILES, HAROLD L.,JR., Admin Asst & Economics Teacher; *b:* [illegible] Spring, MD; *m:* Betty Jane Culler; *c:* Sandra, Steven; *ed:* Frostburg S[illegible] His, Soc Stud 1963; Shippensburg St (MED) Soc Stud 1967; *cr:* Boo[illegible] MS Eng, Soc Stud Tchr 1963-68; Yaninacocha Mission Schl HS H[illegible] Tchr 1969-73; Heritage Acad HS Eng Tchr 1973-75; Yaninacocha M[illegible] Schl HS His Tchr 1975-76; Heritage Acad Talent Dev, Admin Asst, [illegible] 1976-; Bible Cont Issues; *ai:* Sr Class Adv; Girls Var Bsktbl [illegible] 1992-95; AARP 1991-; CCAGW 1992-1994; Church Bd Chm 2[illegible] Accreditation & Stans Comm MD Assoc of Chrstn Schls; Evalu[illegible] Teams AACS & US Dept of Ed; Cert of Appreciation Dedicated Prom[illegible] of Acad Excl & Leadership; Phi Eta Sigma Frostburg St Univ; [illegible] Heritage Acad 12215 Walnut Point Rd W Hagerstown MD 21740

MILES, JOAN BAKO, Business Education Teacher; *b:* Warren, O[illegible] Brian, Allyson; *ed:* Youngstown St Univ (BSEd) Bus Ed 1964; K[illegible] Univ (MSEd) Bus Ed 1971; Working Toward Masters in eng; *cr:* McD[illegible] HS Bus Ed Tchr 1964-; *ai:* NHS Adv; Var & Jr Var Cheerleading [illegible] Youngstown St Univ Eng Festival; Leadership Comm; NEA, OH Ed [illegible] NEOEA, McDonald Ed Assn 1964-; McDonald Village Progress C[illegible] 1990-; McDonald Comm Chest 1993-; Beta Sigma Phi 1966-, Pres, W[illegible] of Yr Awd; Trumbull Cty Mentor Prgm; Martha Holden Jennings Sc[illegible] 1975-76; *office:* Mc Donald HS 600 Iowa Ave Mc Donald OH 44437

MILES, LILLIAN E., Fifth Grade Teacher; *b:* Philadelphia, PA; *m:* [illegible] Jr.; *c:* E. B. III; *ed:* Cheyney St Univ (BS) Elem Ed 1966; Temple [illegible] (MED) Elem Ed 1970; *cr:* William Dick Elem Schl Tchr 1966-73; P[illegible] Hall Elem Schl Tchr 1973-; *ai:* Stu Cncl Spon; AFT 1970-; NABSE 1[illegible] *office:* Prince Hall Elem Schl Gratz St & Godfrey Ave Philadelphi[illegible] 19141

MILES, PATRICIA BAILEY, Sixth Grade Teacher; *b:* Akron, O[illegible] Richard C.; *c:* Sarah J., Joel B.; *ed:* Kent St Univ (BS) Elem Ed 1967; [illegible] Ashland Univ; *cr:* Melrose Elem Schl Sixth Grd Tchr 1967-; *ai:* Stu [illegible] Adv; WEA, OEA, NEA 1967-; *office:* Melrose Elem Schl 1641 Suns[illegible] Wooster OH 44691

MILES, ROBERT C., 9th-12th Grade English Instr; *b:* Mamaroneck, [illegible] *m:* Donna Marie Francini; *c:* Joshua, Brandon; *ed:* Cntrl CT St Univ [illegible] Eng 1970, (MA) Eng 1972; Addl 33 Hrs Post Grad Stud; *cr:* Cntrl C[illegible] Univ Eng Instr & Adjunct Staff 1970-72; US Marine Corps Capt 197[illegible] Mattatuck Comm Coll Eng Instr & Adjunct Staff 1975-77; Cntrl C[illegible] Univ Eng Instr & Adjunct Staff 1976-; Portland HS Eng Instr 1976-[illegible] Writers Guild Adv; Non-Performing Stu Comm; NEA 1976-, Mem; E[illegible] Assn of Portland 1976-, Exec Bd Mem; AAUP 1988-, Mem; Berlin L[illegible] League 1991-, Coach; Berlin Recreational Bsktbl Prgm 1993-, Co[illegible] Grad Tchng Assistantship; The Cadger Novella; *office:* Portland H[illegible] High St Portland CT 06480

MILES, SANDRA LOREE, Drama, Eng & Span Teacher; *b:* Hagerst[illegible] MD; *ed:* Pensacola Chrstn Coll (BA) Speech 1990; *cr:* Pensacola C[illegible] Coll Health Ctr Aide 1987-90; Citibank Customer Svc Specialist 199[illegible] Heritage Acad Tchr 1991-; *ai:* Drama Coach; *office:* Heritage Acad 1[illegible] Walnut Point Rd W Hagerstown MD 21740

MILEWSKI, MARY CLARE, Reading & Religion Teacher; *b:* B[illegible] NY; *ed:* Our Lady of Elms at Chicope (BA) Ed, His 1967; CCSU [illegible] Admin, Supervision 1977; *cr:* New Britain Sacred Heart Tchr 1955-5[illegible] Marys Tchr 1959-62; North Bergen Sacred Heart Tchr 1962-64; [illegible] Britain Sacred Heart Prin 1964-65; St Marys Prin 1965-69; Our Lad[illegible] Czestochowa Tchr 1969-70; St Pauls Jr HS Prin 1970-86; North Be[illegible] Sacred Heart Prin 1986-87; St Marys Tchr 1987-; *ai:* Stu Cncl Adv; *off*[illegible] St. Mary's Schl South & Charles Sts Ware MA 01082

MILEY, CHARLES EDWARD, Art Teacher; *b:* Ravenna, OH; *c:* Jenn[illegible] A., Phillip C.; *ed:* Kent St Univ (BS) Art Ed 1965; Rutgers Univ [illegible] Painting 1976; Pratt Graphics Cntr 45 Hrs Printmaking 1986; *cr:* U[illegible] Peace Corps Vol 1967-69; Summer Arts Inst Instr 1980-90; Manha[illegible] Graphic Ctr Instr, NJ Printmaking Cncl Instr 1986-; NJ Ctr for Visual [illegible] Instr 1988- Newark Museum 1990-; *ai:* Set DEsign Adv; Theater Musi[illegible] NEA 1966-; WEA 1970-, VP; AENJ 1970-; NJCVA 1994-; MGC 1985-; Print Cncl 1986-, Art Dir; GAAMC 1992-; NJ Cncl Arts Paint[illegible] king Fellowship; Governor's Tchr Awd; NJ Arts Fnd Master Tchr *fice:* Franklin HS 415 Francis St Somerset NJ 08873

, CONNIE LYNN, Vocal & General Music Teacher; *b:* Dayton, Campbellsville Coll (BM) Music Ed 1986; Miscellaneous Credit Child Psych, Discipline; *cr:* Black River Local Schls Vocal, Music 987-; *ai:* MS Stu Cncl, Natl Jr Honor Soc Adv; MENC, OMEA, EA 1987-; BRTA 1987-, Pres; OH Assn of Stu Cncls 1988-, Exec l Level Coord; Local Awd of Appreciation Winner 1991-94; *office:* River MS 233 Cty Rd 40 Sullivan OH 44880

ELLO, BRENDA S., Business Education Teacher; *b:* East ol, OH; *m:* Bruce J.; *ed:* Univ of South FL (BA) Bus Ed 1993; *cr:* Area HS Tchr 1993-94; Western Beaver HS Tchr 1993-; *ai:* Girls 'lybl, Girls Head Sftbl Coach; Bus Club Co-spon; NEA 1993-; Western Beaver HS 216 Engle Rd Industry PA 15052

ELLO, FRANK C., Middle School Math Teacher; *b:* Buffalo, NY; a Tresmond; *c:* Anthony, Lori, Katie Rose; *ed:* Buffalo St Coll (BS) Ed 1971; Canisius Coll (MS) Guidance Ed 1976; *cr:* West Seneca chl MS Math Tchr 1972-; *ai:* Jigsaw Puzzle & 8th Grd Class Adv; Γ, WSTA 1972-; *office:* West Seneca East MS 1445 Center Rd West NY 14224

SCHER, JOAN F., Foreign Language Dept Chprsn; *b:* New York, Joseph; *c:* Jay, Jennifer; *ed:* Loch Haven Univ (BSEd) Fr & Ed Middlebury Coll (MA) Fr 1968; Univ De Besancon Cert d'Etudes Fr C W Post Univ Prof Diploma Educl Admin 1983; *cr:* Dawnwood Jr Tchr 1965-67; Longwood HS & Jr HS Fr & Span Tchr 1967-; ood HS Foreign Lang Dept Chprsn 1993-; *ai:* Long Island Lang 1980-, VP; NYS Assn Foreign Lang Tchrs 1970-; Phi Delta Suffolk Chapter 1980-, Pres; *office:* Longwood Sr HS 100 ood Rd Middle Island NY 11953

MAN, PAUL ALAN, English Teacher; *b:* Brooklyn, NY; *m:* ne Kalzmarek; *c:* Rebecca, Jesse, Caitlyn; *ed:* City Coll of NY (BA) 71; Hunter Coll (MS) Ed 1976; Rutgus Univ (PHD) His 1994; *cr:* NYC Schls Spec Ed Tchr 1972-87; Rutgus Univ His Instr 1980-87; od HS Eng Tchr 1987-; *ai:* Newspaper Adv; AFT 1975-; Book PM Deal in Jrnlsm; *office:* Midwood HS Bedford Ave at Glenwood Rd yn NY 11210

AN, MARIANN SENNA, English Teacher; *b:* Ridgewood, NJ; *m:* v Paul; *c:* Jason, Kimberly; *ed:* Corning Comm Coll (AS) Liberal 987; Elmira Coll (BS) Eng & Ed 1989, (MS) Eng 1994; *cr:* Cntry Asst Mgr 1972-75; Urban Natl Bank Head Teller 1975-78; Bradford Schl HS Eng Tchr 1989-; *ai:* Acad All-Star Adv; Bldg Leadership Sr Class Adv; 1988 Class Adv; Eng Chrpsn; NEA 1989-; Kappa Pi 1988; Sports Booster Club 1991-; NHS Honorary Mem; Stu Cncl Awd 1991-92; *office:* Bradford Central Schl Rt 226 Bradford NY

AR, JOHN ALLAN, Physical Ed Teacher & Coach; *b:* Jersey City, Meghan, Scott, Michael; *ed:* Montclair St Coll (BA) Hlth, PE 1971; Hall Univ (MA) Admin, Supervision 1981; Course Work in Ath NY Univ; *cr:* Roosevelt Schl PE Tchr 1972-; Kearny Pub Schls Coach 1972-; *ai:* IM Dir Roosevelt Schl Girls Bsktbl Prgm; Supvr of Kearny; Dir of Schls Indoor Soccer Prgms & Tournaments; NEA, KEA 1972-; Natl Soccer Coaches Assn 1972-, Regnl Rep; Chprsn ion Top 20 Team Poll; Regnl All Amer Comm; Town of Kearney ation Advy Bd; NJ Soccer Coaches Assn Pres, St Coach of Yr; Regnl Bd of Dir; Thistle F. C. Coach Field Coord, Bd of Dir, League Select Coach; Natl HS Coach of Yr 1994; Coaching Awds by St Assembly, eeholders, Local Town Govt.

AR, JUDY LYNN, English Teacher; *b:* New Castle, PA; *m:* Thomas Jayme, Jolene; *ed:* Clarion St Univ (BS) Comm Arts, Eng Speech 1981; 6 Semester Units Eng; CA St Univ at San Bernardino 45 er Units Ed; *cr:* Oil City Sr HS Eng Tchr 1 Yr; Beaumont Jr HS Eng, n, Drama, Chorus Tchr 7 Yrs; Cranberry Jr HS Eng Tchr 1/2 Yr; ille Sr HS Eng, Comm Tchr 5 Yrs; *ai:* Stu Cncl Adv; Video ancement Coach; NEA 1990-; TEA 1991-; YWCA Bd 1995-; Titus er Theatre 1991-; Pub 5 One Act Plays; Local, St Eng Conventions er; Nom Tchr of Yr 1988, Stu Cncl Adv of Yr 1995; *office:* Titusville 302 E Walnut St Titusville PA 16354*

ER, A. BRAD, Mathematics & History Teacher; *b:* Fairmont, WV; atilda Jane Hulsey; *c:* Benjamin, Daniel, Samuel, Hannah; *ed:* tta Coll (BA) Elem Ed 1985; *cr:* Lawrence Elem Schl 5-8 Grd Math, His Tchr 1985-; *ai:* 8th Grd Class Adv; Head Tchr; Jr HS Bsktbl n; Math Textbook Selection, Washington Cty Eisenhower Math ng Comms; NEA, OEA 1985-; OH Farm Bureau, OH Cattlemen's 1985-; Amer Blonde'd Aqwitaine Assn 1990-; *office:* Lawrence Elem Rt 5 Marietta OH 45750*

ER, ALBERTO, Dir of Contracted Intnl Ed; *b:* Lima, Peru; *m:* Dina *c:* Oliver, Andrea, Stefan; *ed:* Universidad Nacional Mayor de San os (BA) Soc Sci 1976; Binghampton Univ (MA) Anthropology 1979,) Anthropology 1986; *cr:* Broome Comm Coll CAPS Dir 1986-90, Dir ntracted Intnl Ed & CASS Pgm 1990-; *ai:* Broome Comm Coll Spcl ations Comm Mem; NY St United Tchr 1988-; AFT 1988-; Amer Soc uality Control 1993-; Fulbright Schlsp; *office:* Broome Comm Coll ox 1017 Binghamton NY 13902

ER, ALICIA JO, Math & Reading Title I Teacher; *b:* Cleveland, *ed:* Kent St Univ (BS) Elem Ed 1991; Pursuing Master of Ed; *cr:* ield Lake City Schls Sub Tchr 1991-; Clearview Local Schl Dist , Rdng Title I Tchr 1995-; *ai:* Brookside HS Majorette & Flag Adv; : Vincent Elem Schl 2303 N Ridge Rd Lorain OH 44055

LER, ALISON ANN (CAMPBELL), Biology Teacher; *b:* New York NY; *m:* Richard H.; *c:* Gwen E., Marsha L., Elizabeth A.; *ed:* SUNY ttsburgh (BS) Ed, Scndry, Bio 1973; SUNY at Albany (MS) Ed Comm , Syracuse Univ Project Advance SUPA; Cornell Univ-Cornell Inst for 'chrs; *cr:* Shenandehowa Cntrl Schl Bio Tchr 1973-; The Diet Wkshp 1978-; Syracuse Univ Adjunct Instr 1993-; *ai:* Prin Selection, HS Org anning, At-Risk Stud Ed, HS Reconfiguration, Shared Decision ng, ODYSSEY Team Intergarated Schl of Choice Comms; *office:* endehowa HS 970 Rt 146 Clifton Park NY 12065

LER, ALLIE F., Asst Professor of Accounting; *b:* Portage, WI; *ed:* of WI at Milwaukee (BA) Eng 1976, (MS) Acctng 1979; AZ St Univ) Acctng 1986; *cr:* Temple Univ Asst Prof 1986-89; Rutgers Univ at den Asst Prof 1989-; *office:* Rutgers St Univ At Camden School of ness 406 Penn St Camden NJ 08102

LER, ANGELA, English Teacher; *b:* Brooklyn, NY; *c:* Kevin; *ed:* klyn Coll (BA) Eng, Sec Ed 1991; City Coll (MA) Eng, Sec Ed 1996; oys & Girls HS Eng Tchr 1991-; Medgar Evers Coll Adj Prof 1993-95; AFT 1992-; Video Series Effective Tchng; *home:* 231 Decatur St klyn NY 11233

LER, ANTHONY C., English Teacher; *b:* Buffalo, NY; *m:* Sondra; *c:* stopher Jason, Anthony Jr., Justin; *ed:* Canisius Coll (MS) Eng Ed ; *cr:* Starpoint Cntrl HS Tchr 1970-; *ai:* Jr HS Stu Cncl Adv; vation Comm; Drama Club; NYSUT, NEA 1970-; NA; *office:* point Cntrl HS 4363 Mapleton Rd Lockport NY 14094

LER, BARBARA J., Elementary Vocal Teacher; *b:* Hornell, NY; *m:* ary; *c:* Michelle A. Feltham, Michael Duke; *ed:* Fredonia St Univ (BS) Music Ed 1966; Certified in Elem Ed from Geneseo St Univ 1972; 37 Post Grad Hrs; *cr:* Jamestown Pub Schls K-6th Grd Music Tchr 1966-68; Greenwood Cntrl Schl Music & Kndgtn Tchr 1968-72; Sub Tchr Many Yrs; York Cntrl Schl Tchr of Gifted Ed 1980-91, K-6th Grd Music Tchr 1991-; *ai:* Musicals Dir; NYSUT 1981-; Genesee Valley Music Tchrs Assnn; MENC 1991-; PTA 1985-; *office:* York Central Schl Rt 63 Retsof NY 14539

MILLER, BETH ANN, Guidance Counselor; *b:* Tyrone, PA; *ed:* Grace Coll (BS) Psych 1986; Penn St Univ (MED) Scndry Cnslr Ed 1988; *cr:* Comm Ed Ctr ABE-General Ed Diploma Cnslr 1988-89; Mount Aloysius Coll Career Cnslr 1989-90; Hollidaysburg Sr HS Guidance Cnslr 1990; Gettysburg HS Guidance Cnslr 1990-; *ai:* Schl Improvement Team; Advanced Placement Coord; Stu Asst Team Facilitator; PA Schl Cnslrs Assn 1989-; *office:* Gettysburg HS Lefever St Gettysburg PA 17325

MILLER, BETH LONGWELL, Seventh Grd Language Arts Tchr; *b:* Pittsburgh, PA; *m:* John V. III; *c:* Maureen, Michelle; *ed:* PA St Univ (BA) Eng, Ed 1987; Millersville Univ (MS) ELem Ed 1993; 6 Credits Lee Canter Grad Stud; *cr:* Rochester Area Schl Dist Eleventh Grd Eng Tchr 1988; Elizabethtown Area Schl Dist Seventh Grd Lang Arts 1988; *ai:* Publisher's, Teamworkers Club Spon; Elizabethtown Area Ed Assn, NEA 1988-; Phi Beta Kappa; *office:* Elizabethtown Area MS 600 E High St Elizabethtown PA 17022*

MILLER, BETH REICHARD, English Teacher; *b:* York, PA; *m:* Mark Anthony; *c:* Jared; *ed:* Elizabethtown Coll (BA) Eng 1976; St of PA Masters Equiv 1992; Addl 4 Credits; *cr:* South Western HS Eng Tchr 1976-77; Dallastown HS Eng Tchr 1977-; *ai:* Southwestern Chrldng Coach 1 Yr; Asst Chrldng Coach 1 Yr; Dram Dir 8 Yrs; Swimming, Track, Field Ofcl 5 Yrs; Phi Delta Kappa, High Lib 1993-; NCTE 1976-; Elizabethtown Coll Auxiliary Mem 1986-, Bd Mem; DAEA 1977-, Schlsp Comm Chprsn; St Pauls UCC 1960-, Sunday Schl Tchr; Stu Assistance Team 1993-, 11-12 Grd Team 1 Yr, 9-10 Grd Team 2 Yrs; Gift of Time Tchng Awd; *office:* Dallastown Area Sr HS 700 New School Ln Dallastown PA 17313

MILLER, B. RENE, English Teacher; *b:* Hamilton, OH; *ed:* Miami Univ of OH (BA) Scndry Eng 1973, (MED) Rdng 1981; 18 Addl Hrs Grad Courses; *cr:* Hopewell Jr Schl Lang Arts Tchr 1973-78, Rdng Specialist 1979-81; Lakota HS Eng Tchr 1982-; *ai:* Sr Class Spon; Lakota Ed Assn 1973-; NEA 1975-; NCTE 1985-; NASAA 1990-; Habitat for Humanity & Hamilton-Fairfield Arts Cncl 1993-; *office:* Lukota HS 5050 Tylersville Rd West Chester OH 45069*

MILLER, BRETT R., Environmental & Life Sci Tchr; *b:* Reading, PA; *m:* Joan L. Schroeder; *c:* Ben, Kate; *ed:* West Chester Univ (BA) Bio 1982; Eastern IL Univ (BS) Ed 1987; *cr:* Solanco HS Life Sci Tchr 1987-; *ai:* Head Sftbl, Soccer Coach; Discipline, Tech Comms; *office:* Solanco HS 585 Solanco Rd Quarryville PA 17566

MILLER, BRIAN DOUGLAS, Biology Teacher; *b:* Indianapolis, IN; *m:* Tamara Sue Mc Kinley; *c:* Aaron, Allison; *ed:* Berea Coll (BA) Bio 1980; Xavier Univ (MED) Scndry Rd 1989; Post-Grad Stud Univ of Cincinnati; *cr:* Rdng MS Sci Tchr 1982-84; Deer Park HS Bio Tchr 1984-; *ai:* Sci Course of Stu Comm; NEA 1982-; NABT 1989-; Acad Excl Awd; Jennings Scholar; Mentor Tchr; Article Pub; *office:* Deer Park Jr Sr HS 8351 Plainfield Rd Cincinnati OH 45236

MILLER, BRUCE, Math Teacher; *b:* Brooklyn, NY; *m:* Arlene; *c:* Beth, Stephanie; *ed:* Brooklyn Coll (BS) Math 1969; *cr:* Jr HS 51 Math Tchr 1969-70; Jr HS 263 Math Tchr 1970-72; South Shore HS Math Tchr 1972-; *ai:* Tchr of the Yr 1986; PTA Awd 1992; *office:* South Shore HS 6565 Flatlands Ave Brooklyn NY 11236

MILLER, BRUCE WAYNE, Math Teacher; *b:* Allentown, PA; *ed:* PA St Univ (BS) Scndry Ed 1972; Kutztown St Univ (MED) Math 1976; *cr:* East Hills MS Math Tchr 1972-; *ai:* Asst to Choral Music Dir; Adv to Stage, Lighting Crew; NEA, PSEA, BEA 1972-; NCTM 1972-75, 1995-; *home:* 2290 Honeysuckle Rd Allentown PA 18103

MILLER, CAROL ANN, Spanish & Reading Teacher; *b:* Butler, PA; *ed:* Slippery Rock Univ (BS) Triple Major Span, Eng, Rdng 1970, (MED) Eng 1973; 18 Credit Hrs Towards Rdng Specialist Cert; *cr:* Laurel Schl Dist Chprsn Lang Dept, Span, Rdng Tchr 1970-; *ai:* Yrbk Adv 1993-, Chprsn 1971-; Yrbk Adv 1987-1990; Chrldr Adv 1973-89; Stu Cncl Adv 1971-74; NEA, PSEA 1970-; Laurel Educ Assoc 1970-, Treas 1993-; Worth Township 1995-, Auditor; Worth Grante 1964-; St John's United Meth Church Organist, Choir Dir; Gift of Time Tribute 1994; *office:* Laurel Schl Dist R D 4 Box 30 New Castle PA 16101

MILLER, CAROL DEE, Third Grade Teacher; *b:* Burlington, VT; *ed:* Amer Intnl Coll (BS) Elem Ed 1965; Inter Amer Univ (MS) Cnslng 1971; Project TEACH 1990; *cr:* Springfield Pub Schls Second Grd TChr 1964-65; Ramey Air Force Base Second Grd Tchr 1966-68; Springfield Pub Schls Second Grd Tchr 1968-69; Ramey Air Force Base Second Grd Tchr 1969-71; Miramar Schl Second-Third Grd Comm Tchr 1971-72; Brunton Schl Third Grd Tchr 1972-; *ai:* Springfield Ed Assn, MA Ed Assn, NEA 1972-; Who's Who Among Stdnts in Amer Colls & Univs 1965; *office:* Brunton Schl 1801 Parker St Springfield MA 01128

MILLER, CAROLE FOTI, French Teacher; *b:* Greensburg, PA; *m:* John Allen; *c:* Nicole Miller Wassil, Henry A.; *ed:* Westminster Coll (BA) Fr 1964; 24 Post Grad Hrs; *cr:* Fox Chapel 7th-8th Grd Fr Tchr 1964-65; Hickory Sr HS Fr & Span Tchr 1965-71; Hermitage Elem Span & Fr Tchr 1978-85; Sharpsville HS Span Tchr 1983-86; Grove City HS Fr & Span Tchr 1986-; *ai:* Fr Club Adv; 1st Yr Tchrs Mentor; Chaperone Groups to France & Quebec; NEA, PSEA, Local Ed Assn 1964-; PSMLA 1983-; AATF 1990-; Coll Womens Assn 1970-, Treas; Article Pub; *office:* Grove City Area Sr HS 511 Highland Ave Grove City PA 16127

MILLER, CHARLENE MARIE, 8th Grd History & Reading Tchr; *b:* Painesville, OH; *m:* Robert Allen; *c:* Dawn Marie, Bryan Allen; *ed:* Lake Erie Coll (BS) 1-8 Elem Ed 1986; 30 Addl Hrs; *cr:* Chardon Schls Sub Tchr 1986-87; Madison Schls Sub Tchr 1986-87; Ledgemont Schls Sub Tchr 1986-87, 5th-8th Grd Tchr 1987-; *ai:* Stu Cncl, Yrbk Adv 1990-93; 6th Grd Camp; 5th-8th Grd Class Play; MS Bldg Rep, Math Tutor; OEA, NEA, LEA 1987-; *office:* Ledgemont MS 16200 Burrows Rd Thompson OH 44086

MILLER, CHARLES FREDERICK, Writing Teacher; *b:* Pontiac, MI; *m:* Robbin Ann; *c:* Joshau Charles, Jesse William; *ed:* Asbury Coll (BA) Eng Lit 1976; Asbury Theological Seminary (MDIV) Cnslng, Biblical Lang 1981; 42 Credit Hrs 1981-82; KY, OH Tchng Certs; *cr:* Fayette Cty Pub Schls Scndry Sub Tchr 1982-83; Toledo Chrstn Schl HS Eng, Bible Tchr 1983-95; Stoutzenberger Coll Part-time Writing Tchr 1995-; *ai:* Aritcles Pub; Supvr Assoc of Chrstn Schls Missions Exchange 1994; *home:* 721 Colima Dr Toledo OH 43609*

MILLER, CHRISTIAN O., 6th Grade Math Teacher; *b:* New Haven, CT; *m:* Elizabeth Cook; *c:* Carole Bishop, Christian; *ed:* Bates Coll (BA) Ec 1959; Western CT St Univ (MA) Ed 1974; Southern CT St Univ 6th Yr Admin 1980; Addl 36 Credit Hrs; *cr:* Katonah-Lewisboro Schl Dist 4th Grd Tchr 1970-83, 6th Grd Tchr 1983-; *ai:* Schl-Based Compact Team Chm; Math Club Adv; NEA 1970-; Conn Radio Information Svc 1995-, Vol Reader; Danbury Westerners 1995-, Bd of Dir; *office:* John Jay MS Rte 121 Katonah NY 10536*

MILLER, CYNTHIA MOONEY, English Teacher; *b:* Cincinnati, OH; *m:* Bart E.; *ed:* OH Wesleyan Univ (BA) Eng, Hum 1976; Post Grad Work in Amer, British Poetry; *cr:* Buckeye Vly HS Eng Tchr 1977-92; Torah Acad Eng Tchr 1993-; *ai:* Drama Club, Newspaper Adv; Act Coord; *office:* Torah Acad Wynnewood & Argyle Rds Ardmore PA 19003

MILLER, DAVE K., Composition & Philosophy Tchr; *b:* Youngstown, OH; *ed:* Bowling Green St Univ (BA) His 1961, (BS) His & Pol Sci 1961, (MA) His 1964; Writing Pgms; *cr:* Genoa HS Tchr 1962-; *ai:* Var Boys Track Coach; Sr Class & Key Club Adv; NEA 1962-; OAT-CCC 1980-; NCTE 1986-; AFT 1992-; OFT 1992-; GAEA; Kiwanis 1965-; *home:* PO Box 44 Williston OH 43468

MILLER, DAVID THOMAS, Math Teacher; *b:* Corning, NY; *m:* Sharon Ellison; *c:* Kyle D., Katy E.; *ed:* Corning Comm Coll (AS) Lbrl Arts 1971; Cortland St (BS) Math 1974; Elmira coll (MS) Ed 1977; Drivers Ed Cert Cortland St, Ithaca Coll; Elem Ed Cert; *cr:* ST Patrick's Jr HS 7-8 Grd Math Tchr 1974-78; Bradford Centrl Schl 7-8 Grd Math Tchr 1978-81; Campbell Cntrl Schl 7, 11 Grd Math Tchr 1981-92; Campbell-Savona Cntrl Schl 7, 11 Grd Math Tchr 1992-; *ai:* Sr Class Adv; Hon Pass, Perfect Attendance, NHS Selection Comms; 7th Grd MS Team; Odyssey of Mind Coach; Negotation Team CSTA; CSTA 1986-, Past Pres; NY Assn of Math Tchrs; Elks Club 1991-; Wrote Math Course Specifically Designed for Workforce; *home:* 11 Katie Ln Painted Post NY 14870

MILLER, DEBRA ANN (BUNKER), Moderate Special Needs Teacher; *b:* Attleboro, NH; *m:* William A. Jr.; *c:* Kelly, Kimberly, William; *ed:* Bridgewater St (BS) Spec Ed 1978; *cr:* St Mary's Sacred Heart Kndgtn Tchr 1979-80; Attleboro Pub Schls MSN Tchr 1981-86; Plymouth Pub Schls MSN Tchr 1986-; *ai:* NEA, MTA 1979-; CEC; Learning Disabilities Network.*

MILLER, DENNIS EUGENE, 6th Grade Teacher; *b:* Lock Haven, PA; *m:* Linda Carol Munro; *c:* Joelle Lingenfelter, Duane, Brad; *ed:* Lock Haven Univ (BS) Elem Ed 1965; Attnd Rowan Univ, Rider Univ, Monmouth Coll; *cr:* Vineland Bd of Ed Tchr 1985-; *ai:* Wrestling Coach; Dept Chprsn; NEA 1965-; NJEA 1965-; VEA 1965-; CCEA 1965-; 1st Meth Church 1970-, Bd Mem; Region 8 Outstdng Coach of Yr 1985; A C Press South Jersey Coach of the Decade 1990; Governors Outstdng Tchr Awd; Exch Club Outstdng Tchr Awd; South Jersey Wrestling Hall of Fame; Recognized By NJ St Congress for Tchng & Coaching Accomplishments; *office:* Memorial MS 424 S Main Rd Vineland NJ 08360

MILLER, DIANE LIN, Spanish Teacher; *b:* Ashtabula, OH; *m:* Larry E.; *c:* Brett, Maria; *ed:* Hiram Coll (BA) Span 1970; Attnd Youngstown St Univ; *cr:* Grand Vly Local Schl Span Tchr 1970-71; Southington Local Schl Span Tchr 1973-76; Mc Donald Local Schl Span Tchr 1987-; *ai:* OFLA, NEA 1987-; *office:* Mc Donald HS 600 Iowa Ave Mc Donald OH 44437

MILLER, DIANE MARIE, Teacher of Gifted Students; *b:* Franklin, PA; *m:* John Dale; *c:* Kelly Miller Martin, Carrie, Adam; *ed:* Indiana Univ of PA (BS) Music Ed 1969; 36 Grad Credits from 5 Univs Masters Equivalence; *cr:* Carrington Jr HS Music Tchr 1969-71; Intermediate Univ #9 Tchr of Gifted Stdnts 1990-; *ai:* Model UN, Debate Competition, Sci Olympiad Coach; NEA, PSEA 1994-; Curr Pub; *office:* Intermediate Unit #9 Schl 119 Mechanic St Smethport PA 16749*

MILLER, DOLORES OSTERMAN, Chem Teacher & Sci Chairperson; *b:* Hesperia, MI; *m:* Patrick M.; *c:* Mary Stein, Brenda Power, Suzanne Phillips, P. Michael; *ed:* MI St Univ (BA) Chem Ed 1959; St Univ of NY at Buffalo (MS) Chem 1971; *cr:* Lansing Pub Schls Tchr 1959-60; Wayne Pub Schls Tchr 1961-62; Holt Pub Schls Tchr 1963-66; Alden Pub Schls Tchr 1967-; *ai:* Chem Turnkey Trainer; Sci Olympiad Coach; Presenter of Chem Tchng Confs; NSTA 1989-; NYSNT 1967-; STANYS 1970-, Sec, Svc Awd 1995; ACS 1988-; Outreach Grant; Master Tchr Flwshp 1990-; Chemmatters Magazine Contest 1986-, Winner; ACS Western NY Distngd Sci Tchr of Yr 1987; Articles Pub; *office:* Alden Cntrl HS 13190 Park St Alden NY 14004*

MILLER, DONALD JAMES, German Teacher; *b:* Allentown, PA; *m:* Shirley L. Rineer; *ed:* Gettysburg Coll (BA) Ger 1970; Attnd Shippensburg Univ, Wilkes Univ; *cr:* Elizibethtown Area HS Ger Tchr 1970-; *ai:* Foreign Lang Dept Chair 1993-94; AATG 1970-, PSMLA 1970-, EAEA, PSEA, NEA 1970-; Ashara Lodge 398 FTAM 1978-; *office:* Elizabethtown HS 600 E High St Elizabethtown PA 17022

MILLER, DOROTHY FARRIS, Tchr of Missionary Children; *b:* Waynesville, MO; *m:* David Lee; *ed:* Southwest Bapt Univ (BA) Elem Ed 1975; Grad Hrs Univ of MO, Drury Coll, Univ of AK at Fairbanks; *cr:* Independence Chrstn Schl 4th Grd Tchr 1975-78; Raymondville R-7 4th-5th Grd Tchr 1978-95; Bapt Mission of Kigoma 2-6th Grd Tchr 1995-; *ai:* Elem Newsletter Spon; Coach.

MILLER, DOUGLAS, Health & PE Teacher; *b:* Canton, OH; *ed:* Malone Coll (BA) Sociology 1977; Ashland Univ (MS) Sports Sci 1988; 15 Hrs Beyond Masters; *cr:* Canton Cntrl Cath HS World His, Sociology, Hlth & PE Tchr 1979-; *ai:* Boys Bsktbl & Bsbl Head Coach; OH HS Athletic Assn; OH HS Bsktbl Coaches Assn; OH HS Bsbl Coaches Assn; Amer Bsbl Coaches Assn; Natl HS Bsbl Coaches Assn; *office:* Canton Cntrl Cath HS 4824 Tuscarawas St W Canton OH 44708

MILLER, DUANE R., Biology Teacher; *b:* Greensburg, PA; *ed:* California Univ of PA (BS) Bio 1974; Attnd Loyola Univ at Baltimore; *cr:* Broad Run HS Bio Tchr 1974-77; Hempfield Area Schl Dist Bio Tchr 1980-83; Joppatowne HS Earth, Space Tchr 1983-87; Hempfield Area Schl Dist Bio Tchr 1987-; *ai:* PSEA 1980-; NEA 1974-; *office:* Hempfield Area Sr HS Rd 6 Box 77 Greensburg PA 15601

MILLER, DWIGHT, Earth Science Teacher; *b:* Bellefontaine, OH; *m:* Virginia Peck; *c:* Brian, Marissa; *ed:* Ball St Univ (BS) Earth Sci 1969; Wright St Univ (MS); 9 Hrs Univ of Dayton, 3 Hrs OH St Univ; *cr:* Tecumseh Local Schls Tchr 1969-; *ai:* Boys Head Track Coach; Inservice Comm; Ed Assn Rep; OEA, NEA, TEA 1969-; Natl Geographs 1970-; OH Geographic Alliance 1989-; Ex-Jaycee; Jaycee of Yr; *home:* 16 Bellaire Dr Tipp City OH 45371*

MILLER, EDWARD JOHN, Science & Mathematics Teacher; *b:* Batu Gajah Fed, Malaya States; *m:* Carol Rose; *c:* Sharon Ann; *ed:* Monmouth Univ (BS) Scndry Ed-Chem 1963; Union Coll (MST) Chem 1967; NSF Yr Prgm Rutgers Univ Geology 1967 10 credits; NSF Summer Prgms Bowdoin Coll 1971 & 1973 10 Credits; NSF Summer Prgm 1980 & 1982 6 Credits; Supvrs Cert 1983 12 Credits; *cr:* Shore Regnl HS Chem Tchr 1963-84, Sci Dept Chm & Chem Tchr 1984-; Sci & Math Supvr & Chem Tchr 1991-; Sci, Math & Tech Supvr & Chem Tchr 1995-; *ai:* Mem Conflict Resolution Comm; Chm Strategic Planning Comms- Math, Sci & Tech Curr; Cultural Awareness Club Adv; NEA, MCE, SREE 1963-, VP SREA; NSTA, NJSTA 1963-; NJP, SA 1984-; ASCD 1990-; Lions Club 1985-, VP, Pres; Shore Soccer Ofcls Assn 1964-, VP, Elected to Hall of Fame; Oceanport Boro Cncl 1990-, Cncl Pres; NSF Prgms Grants; Several AFCEA Grants for Schl Sci & Tech Depts; *office:* Shore Regional HS St Hwy 36 West Long Branch NJ 07764*

MILLER, ELDO JAMES, Music Director; *b:* Red Lake, Ontario; *m:* Dorcas Luella Beiler; *c:* Anthony James, Caroline Elizabeth, Rachel Christine; *ed:* William Jewell Coll (AB) Oxbridge & Music 1992; *cr:* Wahbon Bay Acad Music & Eng Tchr 1983-85; Faith Chrstn Schl Prin 1985-86; Terre Hill Mennonite Schl Music Dir 1992-; *ai:* Dir of Mennoitee Heritage Chorale; Dir of Homeschl Chldrns Choir; Rockville Mennonite Church 1990-, Worship Ldr; *office:* Terre Hill Mennonite HS 1416 Union Grove Rd Terre Hill PA 17581

MILLER, ELLEN M., Health & PE Tchr; *b:* Houston, TX; *m:* Dale; *c:* Korin, Holly; *ed:* Bethany Coll (BA) Hlth & PE 1970; Masters Equivalency; *cr:* Manville Intermediate PE Tchr 1970-80; Selinsgrove

Schl Dist Sub, Coach & Tchr 1981-; *ai:* JV Field Hockey Coach 1982-; Jr High Field Hockey Coach 1981-86; Peer Leadership Pgm 1990-; SAP Mem; IST Team; PSAHPERD & PASAP 1994-; Church Choir 1986-92; *office:* Selinsgrove Area H S N Broad St Selinsgrove PA 17870

MILLER, ERIKA VITTUR, German & French Teacher; *b:* Bressanone, Italy; *m:* Andrew K.; *c:* Christina T., Alex A.; *ed:* Millersville Univ (BS) Ger, Fr 1989; 30 Grad Credits Towards MA in Ger; *cr:* Lancaster Waldorf Schl Elem Ger Tchr 1983-85; Pequea Valley HS Ger, Fr Tchr 1990-93; McCaskey HS Ger, Fr 1993-; Millersville Univ Grad Asst Summer 1995; *ai:* AIS Club Co-Adv; Extracurricular Italian Class Inst; AATG, AATI, NEA 1990-; *office:* Mc Caskey Sr HS Lehigh & Reservoir Rd Lancaster PA 17602*

MILLER, ERNEST JOHN,FSC, History & Religion Teacher; *b:* New Orleans, LA; *ed:* Loyola Univ (BA) Pol Sci 1991; George Washington Univ (MA) Intnl Affairs 1993; LaSalle Univ (MA) Ed 1995; Addl 12 Hrs Rel Stud; *cr:* LaSalle Coll HS His, Rel Tchr 1993-94; West Philadelphia Cath HS His, Rel Tchr 1994-; *ai:* Forensics Moderator; NCEA 1993-; Nasaa 1996; *office:* West Philadelphia Cath HS 4501 Chestnut St Philadelphia PA 19139

MILLER, EUGENIA HODGE, Magnet Facilitator; *b:* CLEVELAND, OH; *c:* Brian James; *ed:* Bowling Green St Univ (BA) Elem Ed 1960; Coll of New Rochelle (MA) Comm 1987; Iona Coll Elem Admin Cert NYS 1992; *cr:* Woodland Elem Schl 2nd Grd Tchr 1964-66; Stephenson Schl 1st Grd Tchr 1967-68; Barnard Schl 1st Grd Tchr 1970-81; Columbus Schl 1st Grd Tchr 1981-82; Webster Schl 2nd Grd Tchr 1982-90, Magnet Facilitator 1991-; *ai:* Curr Dir Kiafrika Taalimu Shule; Adv, Star Serve; Natl Assn Black Schl Educators 1983-; AFT 1969-; Westchester Alliance Black Schl Educ 1990-, Corr Sec; New Rochelle Day Nursery 1993-, Bd Mem; African Amer Advy Bd 1992-, Bd Mem; NAACP, Exl in Ed Awd; *office:* Daniel Webster Hum Magnet 95 Glenmore Dr New Rochelle NY 10801*

MILLER, EVAN KIMBALL, English Teacher; *b:* Pittsburg, PA; *ed:* CA Univ of PA (BSEd) Elem Ed 1966; Univ of Pittsburgh (MED) Elem Ed 1970; *cr:* Gladstone Elem Schl Lang Art Tchr 1968-75; Gladstone MS Lang Tchr 1975-92; Schenley HS 10-12 Grd Eng Tchr 1992-; *ai:* Crosswood Puzzle Club; AFT, PAFT, PFT 1967-; NCTE 1991-; Friends of Carnegie Library 1995-, Vol; Pittsburgh Lit Cncl 1987-, Tutor; Frick Fnd Schlsp; HS Tchr Ctr Replacement Tchr; Comm Coll of Allegheny Cty Rdng, Stud Skills Instr; *office:* Schenley HS 4410 Bigelow Blvd Pittsburgh PA 15213*

MILLER, G. DANE, 10th Grade Health & Ath Dir; *b:* Valley Forge, PA; *m:* Chiro Disney; *c:* Kai, Brooks, Dane; *ed:* East Stroudsburg Univ (BS) Hlth, PE Ed 1976; Post Grad Stud in Eductl Ldrshp; *cr:* World Book Childcraft Sales Mgr 1976-79; St Chem Mfg Sales Mgr 1980-84; Miller Municipal Supply Owner 1984-93; Daniel Boone SD Hlth, Ath Dir 1993-; *ai:* Asst Var Wrestling, JH Girls Soccer Coach; NEA, PSEA, DBEA, PA St Ath Dirs Assn 1993-; Schuykill Vly SD 1991-95, SChl Bd Mem; Leesport Ath Assn 1987-, Pres 1991-95; Numerous Articles Pub; PIAA Dist 3 Exec Cncl; *office:* Daniel Boone Jr Sr HS PO Box 450 Birdsboro PA 19508*

MILLER, G. JAMES,III, Music Director; *b:* Manhattan, NY; *m:* Karen R. Purzycki; *c:* Kirk, Michaela; *ed:* William Paterson Coll (BS) Music Ed 1983; Columbia Univ at TC (MA) Music Ed 1985; *cr:* Kinnelon Pub Schls Dir of HS, MS Bands 1983-86; Frank Scott Bunnell HS Dir of Music 1986-; Fairfield Univ Adj Prof in Percussion 1995-; *ai:* Marching, Jazz Band Dir; Select Choir Dir; Percussion Ensemble Dir; Ski Club Adv; NEA 1983-; CEA 1986-; MENC 1979-; Music, Exercises Pub; William Paterson Coll Outstdng Sr in Music; Stratford Tchr of Yr Finalist; Music Writer for 5 Time World Champion Percussion Section; *office:* Frank Scott Bunnell HS 1 Bulldog Blvd Stratford CT 06497

MILLER, GARY LEE, Title I Math Teacher; *b:* Altoona, PA; *m:* JoAnn Walker; *c:* Brent James, Courtney Leigh, Garrett Michael; *ed:* Clarion St Coll (BS) Elem Ed 1972; Grad Credits Penn St Univ, Clarion St Coll, Indiana Univ of PA; *cr:* West Branch Elem Schl Tchr 1973-; *ai:* Sr HS Head Wrestling, Asst Sftbl Coach; Ski Club Adv; PSEA, NEA 1973-; *home:* RR 1 Box 646 Morrisdale PA 16858

MILLER, GERALD H., Guidance Counselor; *b:* Lancaster, PA; *m:* Evelyn Mae Stokes; *c:* Donald, David, Kimberly Ann Schubert; *ed:* Franklin & Marshall Coll (AB) Philosophy 1955; Drew Univ MDiv) Theology 1958; Lehigh Univ (MED) Guid 1972; 30 Addl Credit Hrs; *cr:* United Meth Church Pastor 1954-70; Pleasant Valley SD Guid Cnslr 1971-; *ai:* Ftbl Run Chains; Bsktbl Scorebook; Track Announce Meets; NEA 1972-; PSCA 1973-; UMC Effort 1970-, Assoc Pastor; YFC Campus Life 1980-, Chm of Bd; Organized & Coord Chemical Free Grad All-Night Party 1988; *home:* PO Box 154 Effort PA 18330

MILLER, GREG A., Sixth Grade Math Teacher; *b:* Warren, OH; *m:* Sheryl Babics; *c:* Lindsy, Chelsea; *ed:* Kent St (BS) Elem Ed 1981; Kent St Univ (ME) Gifted Ed 1993; 3 Credit Hrs Cmptr Programing LaVerne Univ; 6 Quarter Hrs Calculas Youngstown St Univ; 3 Quarter Hrs Statistics Cleveland St Univ; *cr:* Fremont Jr HS Seventh, Eighth Grd Math Tchr 1982-84; JRW Jr HS Seventh Grd Math Tchr 1984-85; Hale Road Elem Sixth Grd Self Contained Tchr 1985-89; Auburn MS Sixth Grd Math Tchr 1989-; *ai:* Outdoor Ed Dir for Painesville Twp; *office:* Auburn MS 6700 Auburn Rd Painesville OH 44077

MILLER, GRETCHEN MARIA, Math Teacher & Computer Coord; *b:* Cincinnati, OH; *m:* William C.; *ed:* Univ of Cincinnati (BS) Scndry Ed Math 1972, (MA) Math Ed 1989; *cr:* Anderson MS Math Tchr 1972-73; Turpin MS Math Tchr 1973-83; Turpin HS Math, Cmptr Tchr 1983-; *ai:* Cmptr Coord; NEA, OEA, Forest Hills Tchrs Assn 1972-; Natl Cncl of Tchrs of Math, OH Cncl of Tchrs of Math 1971-; Intnl Soc for Tech in Ed 1983-; Amer Med Assn Alliance 1987-; *office:* Turpin HS 2650 Bartels Rd Cincinnati OH 45244

MILLER, HAZEL H., Retired 4th Grade Teacher; *b:* Cardington, OH; *m:* Robert P. Jr.; *ed:* Malone Coll (BS) Elem Ed 1964; Post Grad Stud Bowling Green, OH St Univ; *cr:* Perry Local Schls 5th Grd Tchr 1964-71; Cardington Lincoln Schls 4th Grd Tchr 1971-95; *ai:* OEA, NEA, Cardington Lincoln Fac Assn, Sec MCIRA; Morrow Cty IRA, Treas CLFA; OH Cncl IRA; Right to Read Training; Jennings Scholar Capital Univ; *home:* 2436 State Route 61 Marengo OH 43334

MILLER, HEATHER SMITH, Sixth Grade Teacher; *b:* Amarillo, TX; *m:* Norman R. Jr.; *c:* Mackenzie; *ed:* Kent St Univ (BS) Elem Ed 1984, (MED) Math Ed 1988; Doctoral Candidate; *cr:* U. L. Light MS 8th Grd Rdng, Hlth Tchr 1984-85, 7th Grd Rdng, Math Tchr 1985-86; Highland MS 6th Grd Tchr 1986-Mid Schl VP; *ai:* Barberton Ed Assn; Audio Visual Materials Coord; NEA, OEA 1984-, BEA Mid Schl VP; PTA 1993-; Akron, KSU Internship Prgm 1983-84; PTA Nom Educator of Yr 1993-94; EQUALS Conf Participant 1992-93; Chosen to Represent Dist in OH Sponsored Wkshp 1989-91; Partcpnt Summit Tech Acad; *office:* Highland MS 1152 Bellview Ave Barberton OH 44203*

MILLER, IRMA JEAN, Teacher; *b:* Altoona, PA; *m:* Robert E.; *c:* Michael, Jason, Crystal, Matthew; *ed:* Math, Sci Classes; Wkshps; *cr:* St Mary's Schl Tchr 1980-; Altoona Vo-Tech Adult Algebra Tchr 1990-; *ai:* Mathcounts Coach; Jr Acad of Sci Adv; Grad Supvr; Dept of Environmental Resources Grant; Penelec Grants for Energy Awareness 2 Yrs; *office:* Saint Marys Schl 1400 4th Ave Altoona PA 16602

MILLER, J. RICHARD, Learning Support Teacher; *b:* Danville, PA; *ed:* Shippensburg St Coll (BA) Soc Sci 1966; Bloomsburg St Coll (MED) Spec Ed 1978; *cr:* Shamokin Area Schl Dist Spec Ed Tchr 1967-; *ai:* Shamokin Area Educ Assn, PA St Educ Assn, NEA 1967-; Shamokin Lodge F&AM, Shamokin Commendry No 77 DR, Shamokin Cncl No 68 R&S MM, Shamokin RA Chptr No 264 1973-; *home:* 34 Hemlock Ln Elysburg PA 17824

MILLER, JACQUELINE I., Counselor; *b:* Pittsburgh, PA; *c:* Lauren, Randall; *ed:* Univ of Pittsburgh (BS) Psych, Ed 1966; Fairleigh Dickinson Univ (MS) Human Dev 1980; *cr:* St of PA Rehabilitation Cnslr 1966-69; Cty of Atlantic Hlth Edctr 1974-75; Egg Harbor Twp Bd of Ed Tchr 1975-84, Cnslr 1984-; *ai:* NEA, NJEA, EHTEA 1975-, Sunshine Chm; Cape Atlantic Cumberland Guid Assn 1984-, Bd Mem, Cnslr of Yr Awd 1990; Contact 1988-, Bd Support Worker; Juvenile Conf Comm 1987-92; Cape Atlantic Transplant Support 1992-, Founder; Total Living Ctr 1995-, Bd; *office:* Egg Harbor Twp MS 4034 Fernwood Ave Egg Harbor Townshi NJ 08234*

MILLER, JACQUELINE MARIE, 6th Grd Teacher; *b:* Johnson City, NY; *m:* Tim; *ed:* Broome Comm Coll (AA) Lbrl Arts 1986; St Univ Coll at Cortland (MS) Curr & Instruction 1993, (BS) Elem Ed 1988; *cr:* Vestal Cntrl Schls 6th Grd Tchr 1989-; *ai:* Sci Curr Task Force; Bldg Planning Team Chprsn; Stu Cncl Adv; Conflict Resolution Comm; Vestal Tchrs Assoc, NEA-NY1989-; Cmptr & Software for Sci Classroom Mini-Grant 1995; *office:* Vestal MS 620 S Benita Blvd Vestal NY 13850*

MILLER, JACQUELINE WILSON, First Grade Teacher; *b:* Pittsburgh, PA; *m:* Bruce D.; *ed:* CA Univ of PA (BA) Elem Early Chldhd 1993; *cr:* Creative Adventure Learning Ctr Kndgtn Tchr 1993-94; Moon Schl Dist Sub & Vllybl Coach 1994-95, 1st Grd Tchr & Vllybl Coach 1995-; *ai:* HS Vllybl Coach; Read-In Night & Math Night Comm; PSEA 1995-.

MILLER, JAMES L., Music Tchr, Band & Choral Dir; *b:* New Kensington, PA; *m:* Joylyn A.; *c:* Saralyn, Jameyan; *ed:* Vly Forge Military Jr Coll (AA) Lib Arts 1971; Duquesne Univ (BSME) Music Ed 1973; WV Univ (MM) Fr Horn Performance 1979; *cr:* Martins Ferry SD K-12 Grd Music Tchr 1984-85; Mingo Cty SD 7-12 Grd Music Tchr 1985-87; Jamestown SD K-12 Grd Muisc Tchr 1987-; *ai:* Dir of Bands Thiel Coll, Drama Club; Mercer Cty HS, JH Cty Band Coord; Artist in Residence Thiel Coll; Greenville Area Comm Theater; PSEA 1987-, Pres; AF of M 1975-.

MILLER, JANET DILBONE, Track & Field Coach; *b:* Wauseon, OH; *m:* Kevin K.; *c:* Jordon A., Taylor A., Paxson D.; *ed:* Bowling Green St Univ (BS) Hlth Ed K-12th 1988; *cr:* Edgerton HS Track Coach 1986; Archbold HS Trach Coach 1989-92; Stryker HS Track Coach 1994-; *ai:* NW Dist Ofcls Assn, OH HS Track Coaches Assn 1989-; US Women Track Coaches Assn, US Track Coaches Assn 1996-; OH HS Coaches Hall of Fame Nom; Coached Only Ath to Win 1600, 3200 M 4 Yrs OH HS His; 2nd, 5th, 8th pl Natl Meets Coach; *home:* 202 E Holland St Archbold OH 43502

MILLER, JOSEPH A., Mathematics Teacher; *b:* Waterbury, CT; *m:* Nina DeVito; *c:* Bryan, Kelly; *ed:* Sacred Heart Univ (BS) Math 1973; Wesleyan Univ (MALS) Math 1993; *cr:* Richard C. Lee HS Math Tchr 1976-78; H. C. Wilcox Tech Schl Math Tchr 1979-; Teikyo Post Univ Adj Math Instr 1995-; *ai:* Chess Club Adv; AFT 1976-; CT Cap Upward Bd 1990-; BSA 1987-91, Cub Master, Camp Cnslr; Recreational Math Column 1980-84; *office:* Horace C. Wilcox Tech Schl Oregon Rd Meriden CT 06451

MILLER, JOSEPH MICHAEL, Secondary Level Sci Teacher; *b:* Poughkeepsie, NY; *m:* Bernadette Schiller; *c:* Erica C., Erin M., Michaela C., Coleen R., Clare K., Sarakate, Luke M., Molly R.; *ed:* Marist Coll (BA) Bio 1967; St Johns Univ (MS) Bio 1969; *cr:* Suffern HS Chem, Bio Tchr 1973-; *ai:* Ramapo Tchr Assn, AFT 1973-; JDF 1986-, Walk Chm; *office:* Suffern HS Viola Rd Suffern NY 10901

MILLER, JOYCE ANN, Religion & Art Teacher; *b:* Philadelphia, PA; *ed:* Chestnut Hill Coll (BA) Art Studio 1984; Pursuing MA in Ed, Cert in Art K-12th Grd Beaver Coll; *cr:* St Rose HS Art Tchr 1986-87; Notre Dame HS Art Tchr 1987-88; Our Lady of Ransom 5th Grd Tchr 1990; Nazareth Acad HS Relgion, Art Tchr 1991-; *ai:* LIFE Club Co-Moderator; NCEA 1987-; Natl Right to Life 1991-; Amer Life League 1992-; Chrstn Coalition 1993-; Concerned Women for Amer 1994-; *office:* Nazareth Acad HS 4001 Grant Ave Philadelphia PA 19114

MILLER, JOYCE SUSAN, English Teacher; *b:* Pittsburg, PA; *ed:* OH Univ (BSEd) 7-12 Eng 1974; Duquesne Univ (ME) K-12 Rdng 1981; *cr:* Latimer MS Rdng Tchr 1975-80; David B OLiver HS Eng Tchr 1981-; *ai:* Teenage Parents Conf Prof Spon 1980; Law Magnet Adv 1984-86; Asst Sftbl Coach 1994; Olivers Enviromental, Fishing Club Adv 1994-95; PFT, PAFT, AFT, Local 400 1975-; AMF, AFL-CIO; Congressional Israeli Rsrch Paper Ed 1986; JCC Little League Asst Coach 1993-; Eng, Rdng Tutor 1984-; Pilot Tchr, Syllabus Examination Project Pgh Pub Schls 1993; *office:* David B Oliver HS 2323 Brighton Rd Pittsburgh PA 15212*

MILLER, JUDITH ANN, Sixth Grade Teacher; *b:* Worcester, MA; *ed:* Framingham St Coll (BSE) Elem Ed 1979; 10 Post-Grad Hrs; *cr:* Franklin Jr HS Grd 7-8 Math Tchr 1979-80; Whitinsville Chrstn Schl Grd 6 Tchr 1980-89, 1992-, Grd 5-6 Combination Class Tchr 1989-92; *ai:* Elem Cmptr Coord; MS, Cmptr Comms; Girl Scouts of Amer 1964-75, 1985-; MA Soc of Mayflower Descendants 1995-; Blackstone Vly Chamber of Commer Grant 1995; 1 Article Pub; *office:* Whitinsville Christian Schl 279 Linwood Ave Whitinsville MA 01588

MILLER, JUDITH W., Second Grade Teacher; *b:* Coreopolis, PA; *m:* William G.; *c:* Christy M. Hunsberger, Matthew W.; *ed:* Duquesne Univ (BS) Elem Ed 1966; *cr:* Butler Elem Schl 1st Grd Tchr 1966-67; Florence City Schls 4th Grd Tchr 1967-68; Trinity Schls Kndgtn, 2nd Grd Tchr 1973-; *ai:* PSEA 1973-; Alpha Delta Kappa 1990-, VP.

MILLER, JUDITH WOODWARD, German Teacher; *b:* Williamsport, PA; *m:* Terry John; *c:* Brian, Michelle; *ed:* Gettysburg Coll (BA) Ger 1970; Villanova Univ 12 Post Grad Credits; Trenton St Univ 12 Post Grad Credits; Georgian Court Coll ESL Cert; *cr:* Lower Moreland MS Ger Tchr 1970-76; Freehold Regnl Adult Schl Ger Tchr 1979-81; Grace Rogers & Kreps MS Ger Tchr 1988-93; Hightstown HS Ger Tchr 1990-; *ai:* Ger Club Adv; Ger Exch Coord; FLENJ 1990-; NEA 1970-76, 1988-; First Presbyn Church 1978-, Elder, Tchr; FPC Nursery Schl 1979-, Bd of Dir; Girl Scouts 1985-90, Troop Ldr, Svc Awd; *office:* Hightstown HS 25 Leshin Ln Hightstown NJ 08520

MILLER, JULIA ELLEN, High School Counselor; *b:* Hamilton, OH; *m:* Philip D. Cline; *ed:* Miami Univ (BSEd) Soc Stud Compre 1973; Xavier Univ (MED) Guid, Cnslng 1975; Addl Hrs Xavier Univ, OH St Univ Masters; 60 Hrs Grad Stud Areas of Grief, Bereavement, Juvenile Justice, Group Guid, Curr; Supvr Cert Curr; Drivers Ed Cert; *cr:* Hamilton Badin Cnslr, Rel Tchr 1974-75; Westerville South HS Cnslr 1975-76; Walnut Springs Jr HS Cnslr 1976-79; Westerville South HS Cnslr 1979-; *ai:* Ath Dir For Fin Asst; Gate Security, Ticket Mngmt; NEA, OEA 1977-, Bldg Rep, Tchr of Yr Nom; Westerville Ed Assn Rept to Natl Convention; *office:* Westerville South HS 303 S Otterbein Ave Westerville OH 43081

MILLER, JULIE, Instrumental Music Teacher; *b:* Utica, NY; *ed:* LeMoyne Coll (BS) Bus Admin 1982; Onondaga Comm Coll (AS) Music 1987; Syracuse Univ (MS) Music Ed 1989; *cr:* Clifton-Fine Cntrl Schl 6th-12th Instrumental, Gen Music Tchr 1990-91; Bradford Cntrl Schl 7th-12th Instrumental Music Tchr 1991-93; Poland Cntrl Schl 7th-12th Instrumental Music Tchr 1993-; *ai:* Marching Band, Musical Dir; Color Guard, Drama Club, Jazz Band Adv; MENC, NYSSMA 1989-; NYSUT 1990-; St Joseph-St. Patrick Church Choir 1993-; Coll Fight Song Composer; NHS Honorary Fac Mem 1992-93; Tchr of Yr 1990-91; *office:* Poland Central Schl Rt 8 Poland NY 13431*

MILLER, KAREN WALSH, Special Education Teacher; *b:* New *m:* Robert Edward; *c:* Lisa, Kristin, Rose-Marie, Tara; *ed:* Kean C Spec Ed, Early Chldhd Ed 1966; *cr:* Evergreen Schl Kndgtn Tchr *ai:* Spec Ed Coord & Comm; WEA Del Assembly; NEA, NJEA WEA 1987-; LD Assn 1995-; St Helen's Eucharistic 1986-, Min Helen's CCD 1978-.*

MILLER, KAREN KAY DROPPERS, Advanced Placement Eng Cleveland, OH; *m:* Duane F.; *c:* Dana Carl, Dawn; *ed:* Case Reserve Univ (BA) Speech Comm & Eng 1964, (MA) Speech Com Attnd WA St Univ in Speech, Drake Univ in Eng, Baldwin- Wall in Eng & Ec; *cr:* Fairview HS Eng & Speech Tchr 1964-71 Franciscan HS Advanced Placement Eng II & Amer Lit II Tchr 19 Lit Magazine; Advanced Placement Curr Co-Dir; NCTE 1964-; Schl, Church Vacation Schl, Supt; Church, Magazine Ed; 2 NDEA *office:* Padua Franciscan H S 6740 State Rd Parma OH 44134*

MILLER, KATHLEEN ELLEN, Asst Professor of Sociol Springville, NY; *ed:* SUNY at Buffalo (BA) Sociology 1987 Sociology 1991, (PHD) Sociology 1995; *cr:* SUNY Schl Lectur Tchr 1991-93; Monroe Comm Coll Adj Instr 1993; SUNY Coll F Adj Instr 1994-95; SUNY Coll Geneseo Asst Prof 1995-; *ai:* Sociological Assn 1988-; Eden Emergeny Squad 1989-, Trng Capta Article Pub 1994; Who's Who Among Stdnts in Amer Univ & Co Woodburn Flwshp 1987-91; ASA Hnrs Prgm 1987; Phi Beta Kapp Natl Merit Scholar 1982; *office:* SUNY Coll at Geneseo 1 Coll Cr C NY 14454

MILLER, KATHLEEN KENYON, Instrumental Music Teac Westerly, RI; *m:* Joseph B.; *c:* Randall, Tamatha; *ed:* Alfred Un Music Ed 1969; 36 Credit Hrs from Univ of RI, RI Coll, Comm Co *cr:* Chariho Regnl Schl Dist Music Tchr 1969-70; First Bapt Organist 1992-; Pawcatuck SDB Church Organist 1977-; Chariho Schl Dist Music Tchr 1978-; *ai:* Band Adv; Chariho Music Booste MENC; RI Music Edctrs Assn; NEA RI; *office:* Chariho Reg Switch Rd Wood River Junctio RI 02894

MILLER, KATHRYN SWENSON, Head Counselor; *b:* Altoona, Irven G. Jr.; *c:* Patrice, Kate, Matthew; *ed:* Cardinal Stritch Co Home Ec 1969; Attnd Monmouth Univ & St Peters Coll; *cr:* Keansb Schls Tchr 1969-91, Substance Awareness Coord 1991-94, Hea Substance Awareness Coord 1994-; *ai:* Club Adv; Dist Advy Com Ed Assn 1969-; NEA 1969-; ASAANJ 1991-; Amer Cnslng Assn 199 Delta Kappa 1994-; Numerous Grants; *office:* Keansburg HS 14 Monmouth Rd Keansburg NJ 07734

MILLER, KEITH D., 5th & 6th Grade Teacher; *b:* Defiance, (Kathleen; *c:* Jeremy, Jennifer, Randy; *ed:* Univ of Toledo (BE) E 1975; Attnd Bowling Green Univ & OH St Univ; *cr:* Willard Ci Head Tchr 1975-; *ai:* Jr High 7th-8th Grd IM Dir of Bsktbl; OEA NEA 1975-; NCOEA 1975; Richmond Parent-Tchr Group, Pres; Ric Schl Bldg, Head Tchr; Willard Ed Assn, Pres, VP, & Bldg Rep; Acad Booster Club, Pres; Willard Youth Bsbl, Pres; Willard YMCA Pgm Coord & Coach; Willard Little League, 1974 Coach; Appleseed Bsbl, Bd of Ed & Trustee; Willard City Schl Good Appl Winner; Nom for Ashland Oil Outstdng Edctr Awd; Nom for Cleveland Outstndg Tchr Awd; *office:* Richmond Elem Sch Sectionline Rd Willard OH 44890*

MILLER, KEITH ROBERT, Sixth Grade Teacher; *b:* Sharon, Rosalyn Walker; *c:* Zachariah, Nathaniel; *ed:* Clarion Univ of PA Elem Ed 1974; Post Grad Stud Slippery Rock Univ of PA; *cr:* Lak Schl Dist 6th Grd Tchr 1974-; *ai:* PSEA, NEA; *office:* Lakeview Sc 2482 Mercer St Stoneboro PA 16153

MILLER, KEVIN ERIC, Science Teacher; *b:* Huntington, WV; *m* Marie Goecke; *c:* Karley; *ed:* Northwest MO St Univ (BS) Bus 1983, (BS) Scndry Ed 1988; 9 Credit Hrs MBA; 9 Credit Hrs M Georgetown HS Sci Tchr Jr HS 1989-92; Ripley HS Sci Tchr 1994-

MILLER, KIMBERLIE WITZBERGER, 7th-8th Grd Sci & Hlth *b:* Akron, OH; *m:* Michael Alan; *c:* Jamie, Katie; *ed:* Bluffton Col Elem Ed 1980; Marietta Coll 6 Grad Hrs; WV Univ 3 Grad Hrs; Drak 3 Grad Hrs; *cr:* Taft MS 7th & 8th Grd Lang Arts Tchr 1980-82; Parker MS 6th & 7th Grd Lang Arts Tchr 1982-83; Cedar Grove Ele Grd Tchr 1983-89; Kanawha Elem 5th & 6th Grd Tchr 1989-90; V Elem Schl 7th & 8th Grd Sci Tchr 1990-; *ai:* YES Club 1991-; Stu Adv 1990-94; NEA 1980-; WLA 1990-; *home:* RR 2 Box 102 Marie 45750

MILLER, KIMBERLY PIETSCH, Language Arts Teacher; *b:* Liverpool, OH; *m:* Mark William; *c:* Joshua William; *ed:* OH St Uni Eng Ed 1989; Univ of Cincinnati (MED) Ed Admin 1993; *cr:* Cinc Pub Schl 7th Rdng, Eng Tchr 1989-91; Southwest Local Schl Dist 8th Arts Tchr 1991-; *ai:* ASCD 1991-; Phi Delta Kappa 1994-, Historian 1991-; Martha Holden Jennings Grant 1993-95; Southwest Local Grant 1993-94; Sallie Mae First Yr Tchng Awd; *office:* Southwest Schl Dist 230 S Elm St Harrison OH 45030*

MILLER, KIRK A., Phys Sci & Geology Tchr; *b:* Detroit, MI; *e* Technological Univ (BS) Geology 1984, (MS) Mineral Ec 1986; Cert Sci & Math 1987; 45 Addl Credit Hrs; *cr:* Notre Dame Coll V Prof 1988; Manchester Schl System Night Schl Tchr 1988-89, Su Schl Tchr 1989-90; Goffstown HS Tchr 1987-; *ai:* Co-Adv Stu Cncl, STEM; Cls Adv 4 Yrs; NSTA, NHSTA, NEA, GEA 1987-; Tchr of Yr *office:* Goffstown HS 27 Wallace Rd Goffstown NH 03045*

MILLER, KIRK EDWARD, Instrumental Music Teacher; *b:* Pittsb PA; *m:* Kyong Suk C.; *c:* Diane E., Sarah E.; *ed:* Potsdam Coll (B Music Ed 1986; Nazareth Coll (MS) Ed 1989; *cr:* BOCES Instrum Music Tchr 1989-91; Cuba-Rushford Schls Instrumantal Music 1991-; *ai:* NY St Schl Music Assn 1990-; *office:* Cuba Rushford C Schl 15 Elm St Cuba NY 14727

MILLER, LARRY KENT, Instrumental Music Teacher; *b:* Huntin WV; *m:* Terry Gail Burns; *c:* Matthew Montgomery, Jeremy Ross Marshall Univ (BA) Music Ed 1980; *cr:* Buffalo MS Gen Music 1983-84; Ceredo-Kenova HS Instrumental Music Tchr 198 Chesapeake HS Instrumental Music Tchr 1988-; *ai:* Tech Coord, Sy Admin; Video Specialist; MS Yrbk; NEA, OEA 1988-; MENC 1 Pace-Setter Grant; *office:* Chesapeake HS 10181 Cty Rd 1 Chesapeak 45619

MILLER, LEONARD M., English & Drama Teacher; *b:* Cambridge, *ed:* North Adams St Coll (BA) Eng 1972; Rivier Coll (MAT) Eng 199 Alvirne HS Eng Tchr 1972-79, 1986-; *ai:* Class Act Drama Soc 1 Frosh Class Adv 1990-; Stu Group Therapy Sessions Co-Facellator Schl Therapist 1993-; Hudson Fed of Tchrs 1972-, VP 1993-94; NCTE 1972-; NEATE 1990-; NEH Flwshp 1987 TX A&M; NEH Fl 1992 CT Coll; *office:* Alvirne HS 200 Derry Rd Hudson NH 03051

MILLER, LEONISA FLORESCA, Science Teacher; *b:* Ma Philippines; *m:* Philip; *ed:* Univ of the East (BA) Bio 1970; Centro Es Univ (MS) Bio 1978; Brooklyn Coll Credit Hrs Spcl Ed; Comp Lit Credit Hrs; Bronx Zoo Trng; *cr:* Juan Sumulong Memrl Schl HS Sci 1970-74; Jose Rizal Coll HS Sci Tchr 1974-81; Jakusko Scndry Sch Sci Tchr 1981-86; St Margaret of Cortona JH Sci Tchr 1986-; *ai:* Participants for Acad Olympics Coach; Jose Rizal Coll Voted Outstdng

-ordham Prep Schl Awded an Inspirational Tchr; *office:* Saint ›et Of Cortona Schl 452 W 260th St Bronx NY 10471

ER, LILYAN ZACCARIA, English & Theatre Arts Teacher; *b:* ›wken, NJ; *m:* Anthony; *c:* Scott, Christian; *ed:* Notre Dame Coll ›ng, Theatre, Speech Arts 1965; Montclair Univ (MA) Theatre Arts ›ersey City St Univ, Rutgers Univ 30 Post Grad Hrs; *cr:* Bergen Cty ›ech HS Eng, Theatre Dir 1966-69; Ridgefield Meml HS Eng, ›, Speech Arts Tchr, Theatre Dir 1969-; *ai:* Valedictorians, ›orian Speech Coach; Schl Plays, Variety Show, Drama Competition ›Yrs; Educl Theatre Assn 1990-; Ridgefield Tchrs Assn 1969-, VP; ›965-; NJ Governors Tchr Recognition Prgm Tchr of Yr 1991; Vision ›Star Tchr Awd 1995.*

ER, LINDA AZIZA, Vocal Music Teacher; *b:* New York, NY; *c:* ›n; *ed:* Manhattan Schl of Music (BA) Music Theory 1971, (MA) ›Ed 1972; *cr:* Jr HS 263 Vocal Music Tchr 9 Yrs; West Angeles Chrstn ›Vocal Music Tchr 1 Yr; Prof Performing Arts Schl Vocal Music, ›Tchr 6 Yrs; *ai:* Henry St Music Settlement Choral Wkshp Tchr; NY ›Choir Rehearsal Pianist; Universal Ctr of Eternal Truth Church ›; UFT 1971-; Former Musical Dir, Pianist for Natalie Cole; Choir ›med at Vatican for the Pope 1995; Successful Song Writer, ›ser; *office:* Prof Performing Arts Schl 328 W 48th St New York NY

ER, LINDA CLARK, First Grade Teacher; *b:* Keyser, WV; *m:* John ›April Lynne, Paula Rene; *ed:* Frostburg St Univ (BS) Elem Ed 1969, ›Ed 1975; Facilitator of a Whole Lang Approach; *cr:* Parkside Elem ›irst Grd Tchr 1969-71; Midland Elem Schl First Grd Tchr 1971-75; ›'s Creek Elem Schl First Grd Tchr 1975-76; Barton Elem Schl First ›hr 1976-; *ai:* Tutor Coord; Testing Coord; Chm of Tchr Assistance ›Mem of Schl Improvement Team; Tchr in Charge; NEA, MSTA, ›ny Cty Tchrs Assn 1969-; Cath Daughters of the America's 1986-, ›; ADK 1990-; *office:* Barton Elem Schl 19808 New Geo Creek Rd ›arton MD 21521

ER, LINDA GALE, Special Education Teacher; *b:* Springfield, MA; ›ll of Our Lady of the Elms (BA) Eng, Elem Ed 1976; Westfield St ›MED) Spec Ed 1985; Amer Intnl Coll (CAGS) Human Resource Dev ›BEST Co-operating Tchr, Mentor Prgm St of CT; Amer Stud Prgm ›of MA; *cr:* Noah Webster Elem Schl Fourth Grade Tchr 1978-79; ›aszko Jr HS 7-8 Grd Rdng, 7 Grd Math, Eng Tchr 1979-82; Enfield ›12 Grd Eng, Spec Ed Tchr 1982-; Amer Intnl Coll Adj Instr Human ›ces Summer 1995; *ai:* Class, Newspaper Advs; Weightlifting Club ›iv; Variety Show Co-Dir 1995; Enfield Tchrs Assn 1979-, Head Bldg ›990-94; Safe Grad 1995-; Natl Endowment for Hum Summer Grant ›of Whitman & Dickinson 1989, Myths of Amherst 1990, The ›es 1992; Natl Endowment for Hum Ind Stud Grant Andy Worhol A ›of Vacuity 1993.*

ER, LINDA GUTHRIE, Home Economics Teacher; *b:* Burbank, ›: William R. (dec); *c:* Megan, Richard, Erin; *ed:* SUNY at Oneonta ›Home Ec Ed 1971; Russell Sage Grad Work; *cr:* Lansingburgh Cntrl ›Home Ec Tchr 1971-; *ai:* NYS Regents Question Writer; 8th Grd ›Comm; NYSUT, AFT, LTA 1971-; St George's Church 1992-; *office:* ›ngburgh Cntrl Schls 320 7th Ave Troy NY 12182

ER, LINDA KAUFMAN, Third Grade Teacher; *b:* Williamsport, ›William Richard Jr.; *c:* Michael David, Nathan Douglas; *ed:* Lock ›St (BS) Elem Ed 1971; *cr:* WA Elem Schl K-1st Grd Tchr 1971-76; ›ah Luth Church Presch Tchr 1982-; Cntrl Elem Schl 1st, 3rd, 6th Grd ›996; *ai:* NEA 1988-; Messiah Luth Church; Nursery Schl Bd; *office:* ›al Elem Schl 555 W Mountain Ave Williamsport PA 17701

ER, LINDA ROSE, Adaptive PE Teacher; *b:* El Paso, TX; *ed:* RI ›BS) PE 1987; APE; Hlth; PE; *cr:* Cranston Schl System APE Tchr ›88; Beckwith Schl APE Tchr 1988-, Girl's Bsktbl Coach 1988-; *ai:* ›irls Bsktbl Coach; 4th-8th Grd IM Soccer, Bsktbl Prgms; 5th-8th Grd ›ports' Prgms; Elem Spec Olympics Coach; MAHPERD 1988-; ›socket Women's Bsktbl Assn 1985-, Sec; *office:* Beckwith Schl 2700 ›nal Rd N Dighton MA 02764

ER, LUCINDA BELLOWS, Health & Physical Ed Teacher; *b:* ›ta, NY; *m:* Joseph W.; *c:* Tiffany Nicole, Brittany Michelle; *ed:* ›mer Co Comm Coll (AS) PE 1973; SUC at Cortland (BS) PE 1975; ›Cert PE, Hlth 1980; *cr:* Mt Upton Cntrl Schl PE, Hlth Tchr 1975-88; ›Berlin Cntrl Schl PE, Hlth Tchr 1988-; *ai:* Adv for SADD, Stdnts ›st Substance Abuse, HIV, AIDS Peer Edctrs, Soph Class; Sftbl ›; Chprsn Hlth Advy Comm; Governor's Cert of Merit Hlth Educ Awds ›NYS 1992; Tchr of Yr Awd 1994; Nom NYS Tchr of Yr Awd 1995; ›New Berling Cntrl Schl 1 School St New Berlin NY 13411

ER, MARIANNE GIORDANO, Fourth Grade Teacher; *b:* New ›, CT; *ed:* Southern CT (BS) Intermediate, Upper Ed 1972; Univ of ›eport (MS) Elem Ed 1975; *cr:* Colonial Park Schl 3-6th Grd Tchr ›80; Seth G. Haley Schl 4-5th Grd Tchr 1980-; *ai:* Vlybl Coach; Talent ›s Comm Chprsn; West Haven Fed of Tchrs 1972-, Elem VP; Colonial ›PTA 1972-80, Tchr Rep, Sec; PTA 1980-, Tchr Rep, VP; Summer ›er Wkshp 1991-93, Bus Mgr; Orange Players Comm Theater 1990-, ›Tchr of Yr Nom 1990-91; *office:* Seth G Haley Elem Schl 148 South ›est Haven CT 06516

ER, MARK A., English Teacher; *b:* Bellefontaine, OH; *m:* Teresa ›onnell; *ed:* OH St Univ (BS) Eng 1981; Working Towards Masters at ›and Univ; *cr:* Northwestern HS Eng Tchr 1981-82; Sylvania HS Eng ›1982-85; Lincoln HS Eng Tchr 1985-; *ai:* NEA, OEA, GJEA 1980-; ›rticles Pub in Film Journals 1988-; Author of Book 1995; Contributed ›ters to 3 Pub Books 1995-; *office:* Gahanna Lincoln HS 140 S ›lton Gahanna OH 43230

ER, MARK CARLTON, Assistant Professor of Govt; *b:* Delaware, ›*ed:* OH Northern Univ (BA) Pol Sci & Pub Admin 1980; George ›ington Univ (JD) Law 1983; OH St Univ (PHD) Amer Politics 1990; ›S Rep John Seiberling Legislative Asst 1983-86; Clark Univ Asst Prof ›ovt 1990-; Boston Univ Washington Pgm Visiting Asst Prof 1992-94; ›cester Polytechnic Inst Adj Asst Prof 1993-95; *ai:* Pre-Law Advy ›m Chair; Undergrad Acad Bd; Ath hall of Fame & Fin Aid Comms; ›of Columbia Bar 1983-; Amer Pol Sci Assn 1987-; Law & Soc Assn ›-; OH St Univ Grad Flwshp 1986; Clark Univ Tchr of Yr 1994; Book: ›High Priests of American Politics 1995; Congressional Flw with ›tor Paul Wellstone 1995; *office:* Clark Univ 950 Main St Worcester ›01610

ER, MARTIN STEPHEN, History Teacher; *b:* New York, NY; *m:* ›eline; *c:* David, Colin; *ed:* Syracuse Univ (BA) Pol Sci 1966; CUNY ›Schl (PHD) Pol Sci 1982; *cr:* Stockton St Coll Pol Sci Instr 1971-73; ›Coll Instr Pol 1976-79; Blair Acad His Chm, Tchr 1980-95; *ai:* Blair ›ew Ed; Soc of Skeptics Lecture Forum Adv; Head Cross Cntry, Track ›ch; NJ Assoc of Independent Schls Mc Clellan Flwshp; E. Bosle ›anding Tchr, Brooks Hoffman Awds; Howard Fund Grants; *home:* Park ›lairstown NJ 07825*

ER, MARY E., 3rd Grade Teacher; *b:* Mt Holly, NJ; *m:* James A. Jr.; ›Chestnut Hill Coll (BS) El Ed, Montessori 1977; *cr:* Mt Holly Twp ›c Skills Tchr 1977-80; Pemberton Twp Basic Skills Tchr 1980-81; ›nong Twp Talented, Gifted Tchr 1981-82; Mt Holly Twp Kndgtn Tchr ›2-83, 1st Grd Tchr 1983-84, 4th Grd Tchr 1985-86, 7th-8th Grd Rdng, ›Tchr 1986-92, 2nd Grd Tchr 1992-95, 3rd Grd Tchr 1995-; *ai:* NJEA, NEA 1977-; PTO 1978-, S J Rdng Assoc 1988-; Vol Spec Olympics, S J Aids Fnd, Church Orgs; Nom Tchr of Yr, Most Outstdng Tchr in US.

MILLER, MARY RICE, 4th Grade Teacher; *b:* Wilton, WI; *m:* Charles; *c:* Karen, Diane, Barbara, Andrew, Richard; *ed:* Univ of WI at Oshkosh (MS) His & Eng 1956; M of Ed MS Equiv Eng Lit 1976 New Paltz St Univ Coll; Spcl Ed Stud Northern IL Univ at DeKalb; *cr:* Westwood & Chicago Heights Jr Highs Eng & His 1960-68; East Ramapa Schl Dist Tchr 1970-76; St Augustine Cath Schl 1976-; *ai:* Spcl Olympics, NYS & BOCES Rockland Co Adv; East End Spcl Players Inc Bd Mem; AFT 1959-; FCT 1976-, Del; League of Women Voters 1960-90, Park Forest Lib Bd 1964-66; St Chm on Juvenile Correction 1965-68; Assn of Retarded Children VP & Sec 1973-90; Assn of Univ Women; Assn of Retared Children Vol Awd; Recognition of Svc Confraternity Of Chrstn Doctrine; Chrstn Formation Stud Schlsp 2 Yrs.

MILLER, MARY JANE, English Teacher; *b:* Clarion, PA; *ed:* IN Univ of PA (MS) Eng 1970; *cr:* Dubois HS Eng Tchr 1962-63; Clarion Area Schl Eng, Hnrs, AP Eng Tchr 1963-; *ai:* CAEA, PSEA, NEA 1963-; *office:* Clarion Area Jr Sr HS 219 Liberty St Clarion PA 16214

MILLER, MAXINE KLINK, Assistant Principal; *b:* Meyersdale, PA; *m:* Jeffery Todd; *ed:* Frostburg St Coll (BS) Elem Ed 1984, (MED) Admin, Supervision 1986; Frostburg St Univ (MED) Curriculum, Instruction 1990; MD Assessment Ctr Prgm 1995; Numerous Local, Regnl, Natl Prof Confs; Ireland Travel Stud 1990; *cr:* Southern HS Math Tchr 1985-88; Accident Elem Schl 4-5 Grd Tchr 1988-92; Southern HS Math Tchr 1992-93, Asst Prin 1993-; *ai:* Staff Dev Comm Chprsn; Schl Improvement Team Sec; MFT's Coord; Tri-St Chptr Phi Delta Kappa 1986-, Sec 1988-89, Treas 1987-88; NCTM 1986-; ASCD 1987-; NASSP 1993-; Joyful Noise Child Care 1993-, Bd of Trustees, Sec 1995-; Ruth Enlow Libs 1994-, Bd of Dirs; AAUW 1985-; Rotary Intnl Group Stud Exch to Germany 1992; Curr, Instr Hnr Grad FSU 1991; Supervised Tchr Interns FSU; Co-Dir FSU Children's Lit Festival 1985; James A. Graham Ed Hnr Grad 1985; Elem Ed Dept Hnrs 1985; Phi Eta Sigma Dist Sr 1985; John Allison Outstdng Sr 1985; Gen Ed Hnrs & Summa Cum Laude; *office:* Southern HS 345 Oakland Dr Oakland MD 21550

MILLER, MICHAEL, Mathematics Teacher; *b:* New York, NY; *m:* Jeri Prinkey; *c:* Matthew; *ed:* SUNY at Purchase (BA) Math, Ed 1989; Western CT St (MS) Earth, Space & Enviromental Sci 1994; *cr:* Haldane HS Math Tchr 1989-; *ai:* Head Track Coach 1989-; *office:* Haldane Cntrl Schls Craigside Dr Cold Spring NY 10516

MILLER, MICHAEL ALLEN, Health & Language Arts Tchr; *b:* Cincinnati, OH; *m:* Lori Ann Mergard; *c:* Jacob Clay; *ed:* Morehead St Univ (BA) Elem Ed 1989; Working on Masters Degree Educl Admin Xavier Univ; *cr:* Batavia Jr Sr HS 7th Grd Intervention Tchr 1989-90, 7th Grd Math, Lang Arts, OH His Tchr 1990-93; Batavia Elem Schl 5th Grd Tchr 1993-94; Batavia Jr Sr HS 7th Grd Hlth, 7-8th Grd Lang Arts, 8th Grd Keyboarding Tchr, Bus Driver 1994-; *ai:* NHS, Peer Cnslng Spon; Pub Relations Coord 7-12 Grds; NEA, OEA 1989-; Batavia Prof EA 1989-, Sec, Mem-at-Large; OCTELA 1994-; Sigma Alpha Epsilon Alumni 1989-; Batavia Alumni Assn 1994-; Nom Clermont Cty Tchr of Yr 1994; Articles Pub; *office:* Batavia Jr Sr HS 800 Bauer Ave Batavia OH 45103*

MILLER, MICHAEL CHARLES, 8th Grade English Teacher; *b:* Lancaster, PA; *m:* Janis L. Shultz; *c:* Andrew M., Jennifer L., Stephanie R.; *ed:* Millersville St (BS) Sec Ed Eng 1980; Millersville Univ Master Equivalent 1992; *cr:* Ephrata MS 8th Grd Eng Tchr 1985-; *ai:* Stu Cncl & Boston Club Adv; Asst Boys Soccer & Head Girls Soccer Coach; Costumes Dir; PSEA & NEA 1985-; EAEA 1985-; PA Soccer Coaches Assoc 1990-; *home:* 1124 Martin Ave Ephrata PA 17522

MILLER, MICHAEL EDWARD, History Teacher; *b:* Manila, Philippines; *ed:* Univ of MO at Columbia (BA) Honors Pol Sci 1986, (MA) Pol Sci 1988; Univ of IA at Iowa City Ed Grad Hrs; *cr:* Peoria Mannal HS Soc Stud Tchr 1990-92; Trotwood-Madison HS His Tchr 1992-; *ai:* Head Soccer & Sftbl Coach; NCAA & NPSL Referee; NEA 1990-; G. Ellsworth Huggins Fellow 1986 & 1988; univ of MS Univ Scholar 1986 & 1988; *home:* 302 Oldham Way Englewood OH 45322

MILLER, MICHAEL LEE, Art Teacher; *b:* Coatesville, PA; *ed:* Kutztown Univ (BFA) Comm Design 1989; Tchrs Cert 1992; *cr:* Leaman Assocs Graphic Artist 1988-90; Allen Designs Custom Woodworker 1990-94; Wyomissing HS Art Tchr 1992-93; Conrad Weiser HS Art Tchr 1994-; *ai:* Art Club Adv; NAEA 1992-; NEA 1994-; Mayfair Sculpture in the Park Grant 1995; *office:* Conrad Weiser Jr Sr HS 347 E Penn Ave Robesonia PA 19551

MILLER, MICHAEL M., Religion Teacher; *b:* N Tonawanda, NY; *ed:* St Hyacinth Seminary (BA) Philosophy; St Bonaventures Franciscan Stud; *cr:* St Francis HS Tchr 1992-93; Archbishop Curley HS Tchr 1993-; *ai:* Franciscan Yth Org; Choir; IM Duckpin Bowling League; *office:* Archbishop Curley HS 3701 Sinclair Ln Baltimore MD 21213

MILLER, MILTON MAXWELL, Sixth Grade Teacher; *b:* Altoona, PA; *m:* Cynthia Kay Leipold; *c:* Russ, Melanie; *ed:* PA St Univ (BA) Elem Ed 1972, (MED) Curr, Instruction 1976; Univ of Pittsburgh at Johnstown 1984-85 Grad Stud ITEC-Cmptr Tech; *cr:* Hollidaysburg Area Schl Dist Elem Tchr 1972-; *ai:* Coach Girls, Boys Var Tennis; PAs RCRC Awd for Utilization of Cmptr Tech in Classroom; *home:* 114 25th Ave Altoona PA 16601

MILLER, M. SAMMYE, Professor of American History; *b:* Philadelphia, PA; *m:* Gloria Jean Sellman; *c:* Tanisha U. Sellman-Miller; *ed:* DE St Univ (BA) His 1968; Trinity Coll (MAT) His 1970; Cath Univ of Amer (PHD) His 1977; Post Doctoral Stud Stanford Univ; *cr:* Bowie St Univ His Dept Chm 1975-84; Natl Endowment for Hum Historian Admin 1979-80; Assn for Stud of Afro-Amer Life & Hist Exec Dir 1983-84; Bowie St Univ Prof; *ai:* ASALH 1970, CEO; NCSS; Org of Amer Historians; Knights of Columbus; Kappa Alpha Psi 1965-; Kappa Delta Pi; Phi Alpha Theta; Bd Trustees Scholar Cath Univ; Penfield Fellow; Natl Rsrch Achvmt Awd 1984; Knights of Columbus Fellow; *office:* Bowie St Univ Dept of History & Govt 14000 Jericho Park Rd Bowie MD 20715

MILLER, NADINE C., Social Science Teacher; *b:* PA; *ed:* Millersville Univ (BS) Soc Sci 1967; Westminster Coll (MS) Scndry Ed 1971; Educl Admin Degree Western MD Coll; *cr:* Dallastown Area Sr HS Soc Sci Tchr 1967-; *ai:* NEA, PSEA, DAEA 1967-, PR Chair, Bldg Rep; VNA Hospice 1988-, Vol; *office:* Dallastown Area Sr HS 700 New School Ln Dallastown PA 17313

MILLER, NANCY HILL, Sixth Grade Teacher; *b:* Philadelphia, PA; *m:* Robert L.; *c:* Mary Frances Fresta, Rob; *ed:* Gwynedd Mercy Coll (BS) Elem Ed-Cum Laude 1983; Permanent Cert Theology; *cr:* St Francis Xavier Schl Tchr 1963-70; St Francis of Assisi Tchr, Coord 1974-77; St John the Baptist Tchr, Coord 1977-, CCD Dir 1991-; *ai:* Area Undergraduate Tchrs Mentor; Vol Tutoring; NCEA 1977-; Home & Schl Bd 1982-, Fac Rep; Immaculata Coll Parents Guild Bd 1987-91.

MILLER, NANCY S., Music Teacher; *b:* Aliquippa, PA; *m:* Carl E. II; *c:* Brendan; *ed:* 24 Post Grad Credit Hrs; *cr:* Hopewell Schl Dist Sub Tchr 8 Yrs, Elem Music Tchr 10 Yrs; *ai:* PA Life Schlshp PTA Awd; Phoebe Hearst Tchr Awd; *home:* 115 Jennylynn Dr Aliquippa PA 15001

MILLER, PAM VAN DE WEGHE, Mathematics Department Chair; *b:* Teaneck, NJ; *m:* Robert W.; *c:* Kimberly, R. Troy; *ed:* Trenton St Coll (BA) Math 1974; Montclair St Univ (MS) Math 1995; Supvr Cert; *cr:* Ewing Twp HS Math Tchr 1974-77; New Milford HS Math Tchr 1978-, Math Chair 1994-; *ai:* HS Treas; NEA, NCTM 1974-; *office:* New Milford HS 1 Snyder Cir New Milford NJ 07646

MILLER, PAMELA BLEVINS, Music Teacher; *b:* Arlington, VA; *m:* David James; *c:* Dustin C., Corey A., Cassandra I.; *ed:* Univ of VT (BS) Music Ed 1979, (MS) Tchr Ed; *cr:* Hinesburg Elem Schl Music Tchr 1980-; *ai:* Drama Music Dir; NEA, VT Ed Assn, VMEA, MENC 1980-; CSEA 1980-, Unit Pres; Vermont Winds 1980-; *office:* Hinesburg Elem Schl Box 1800 Hinesburg VT 05461

MILLER, PATRICIA FIELD, English & Reading Teacher; *b:* Mexico City, Mexico; *m:* Keith Michael; *c:* Todd, Marc, Carrie; *ed:* Bowling Green Univ (BS) Eng 1970; Kent St Univ (MA) Rdng 1984; Hrs Focusing on Integration of Curr & Portfolio Assessment & Talented & Gifted Instruction at Ashland, Cleveland St & Notre Dam Univs; *cr:* Eber Jr HS Eng Tchr 1970-71; Chardon MS Eng Tchr 1971-75, Eng & Rdng Tchr 1982-; *ai:* Eng Dept Chprsn; 8th Grd Power of Pen Coach; Competenency Testing Facilitator; Curr Revision Comm; Textbook Adoption; NEOEA 1990-; OEA, NEA 1970-; Rebel Mothers Club 1990-, After Prom Coord; W E Levy Comm 1990-; Chardon Levy Comm 1982-; Chardon Local Schl Tchr Awd 1990; Ashland Golden Apple Awd 1995; *office:* Chardon MS 424 North St Chardon OH 44024

MILLER, PATTY MC LAUGHLIN, K & Title 1 Rdng Recovery Tchr; *b:* Charleston, WV; *m:* Stanley F.; *c:* Shannon, Jonathan; *ed:* Mount Vernon Nazarene Coll (BA) Elem Ed 1978; Post Grad Stud Child Dev, Writing Process, Observing Young Readers, Transitions to Literacy, Rdng Recovery Trng, early Literacy Learning; *cr:* Fredericktown Local Schls Stu Intern 1977-78; Highland Local Schls Kndgtn Tchr 1978-80; Fredericktown Local Schls 1st Grd Tchr 1980-91, 1st Grd, Rdng Recovery Tchr 1991-95, Kndgtn, Rdng Recovery Tchr 1995-; *ai:* Knox Cty Young Authors Chprsn 1994-; Right to Read Week Comm 1990-; Grant Writing Team 1990-; HS Drill Team Adv 1983-85; NEA, OEA, FEA 1981-, Amer Ed Week Chprsn; IRA, OCIRA, KVIRA 1989-; NCTE 1989-; NAEYC, OAEYC, KAEYC 1992-; Church of the Nazarene 1974-, Supt of Ed; North Cntrl OH SERRC Parent Advy Cncl 1995-, Sec; Delta Kappa Gamma Mbrshp; Martha Holden Jennings Grant; Eisenhower Mini Grant for Sci, Math; Bd of Ed Exemplary Svc Awd; Tchr of The Yr Nom; *office:* Fredericktown Primary Schl 124 High St Fredericktown OH 43019

MILLER, PAULA KAY, Cooperative Work Tchr; *b:* Houston, TX; *ed:* Univ of Houston (BS) Human Dev & Consumer Scis 1980, (MS) Occupational Ed 1985; 36 Hrs in Guidance & Counseling Toward Masters at Northwestern St Univ at Natchitoches; *cr:* Alvin HS Voc Home Ec Tchr 1980-88, Single Parent Prgm Coord 1985-88; Kinnick HS Japan Home Ec Tchr 1988-94, Cooperative Work Experience Tchr & Practical Arts Dept Chair 1994-; *ai:* Schl Improvement Process-North Cntrl Accrediation Visit, Practical Arts Dept & Installation Advy Comm Chair; Schl Advy Comm; NEA 1988-; Amer Schl Cnslrs 1995-; Awded 50000 Dollars Federal Grant for 3 Consecutive Yrs for Designing, Implementing, Running & Evaluating Single Parent Prgm at Alvin TX; *office:* Nile C Kinnick HS PSC Box 473 Box 95 FPO AP 96349*

MILLER, PAULINE SRSEN, 2nd Grade Teacher; *b:* Cleveland, OH; *m:* William; *c:* Matt, Tim; *ed:* Cleveland St (BS) Elem Ed 1975; *cr:* St Christine 1st Grd Tchr 1975-78, 2nd Grd Tchr 1979-; *ai:* Sacramental Prgms, Rainbowq For Gods Children Facilitator Coord; Choir Dir; PSR Tchr; NCEA 1975-; Alice & Patric McGinty Fnd; *office:* St Christine Schl 860 E 222nd St Euclid OH 44123*

MILLER, PHILIP CARL, Algebra II Teacher; *b:* Pittsburgh, PA; *m:* Daira Englehart Miller; *c:* Jessica, Matthew, Nathaniel; *ed:* Millersville Univ (BS) Math 1976; Duquesne Univ Master Equivalency Elem Ed 1990; *cr:* Plum Boro Schl Dist Scndry Math Tchr 1978-; *ai:* Liaison Comm; New Tchr Mentor Prgm; NEA, PSEA 1978-; *office:* Plum Sr HS 900 Elicker Rd Pittsburgh PA 15239

MILLER, ROBERT E., Fr & Computer Lab Title I Tchr; *b:* Northampton, MA; *m:* Priscilla Alden Tracy; *c:* Scott, Brett, Stacey; *ed:* Westfield St Coll (BSEd) Ed 1966; MT St Univ (MED) Ed 1974; *cr:* De Berry Schl Tchr 1967-68; Warner Schl Tchr 1968-95; *ai:* MTA; NEA; *office:* Warner Elem Schl 493 Parker St Springfield MA 01129

MILLER, ROBERT LEE, Fifth Grade Teacher; *b:* Canton, OH; *m:* Suzanne Perdue; *c:* Melissa, Michelle; *ed:* Malone Coll (BS) Elem Ed 1968; Kent St (ME) 1974; *cr:* Canton Local Bd of Ed Tchr 1969-; *ai:* NEA 1968-; *office:* Canton Local Bd of Ed 4526 Ridge Ave SE Canton OH 44707

MILLER, ROBERT THOMAS, Math Dept Chm & Teacher; *b:* Hazelton, PA; *m:* Evelyn M. Yanick; *c:* Stephanie M., Tracey A.; *ed:* Bloomsburg Univ (BS) Math 1960; Univ of SC (MM) Math 1971; 72 Grad Credits Beyond MS at Wilkes Univ, Temple Univ Kent St Univ, Penn St Univ & Lehigh Univ; *cr:* Hazelton Area HS Math Tchr 1960-, Math Dept Chair 1981-; *ai:* NHS Adv; Stu Cncl adv 15 Yrs; Asst Boys Bsktbl Coach 17 Yrs; HAFT, PFT & AFT 1963-, Treas; Luzerne Cty Math Tchrs 1966-; Hazelton Schl 1960-, VP; Employees Credit Union Bd of Trustees; NSF Grant 1970-71; Outstndg Tchr Awd 1994; *office:* Hazleton Area HS 1601 W 23rd St Hazleton PA 18201*

MILLER, ROBERT WAYNE, Band Director; *b:* Philadelphia, PA; *m:* Judith Lynn Bodenheimer; *c:* Arielle Sara; *ed:* Univ of MD at College Pk (BS) Music Ed 1981, (BS) Psych 1981, (MED) Music Ed 1986; *cr:* Howard HS Band Dir 1981-85; Hammond MS Band Dir 1985-; *ai:* Jazz Ensemble Dir; MENC, NEA, Intnl Assn Jazz Edctrs 1981-; Columbia Concert Band 1989-, Dir; Columbia Concert Band Jazz Ensemble 1989-, Dir; Edctr Recognition Awd Howard Cty Chamber of Congress 1990; *office:* Hammond MS 8110 Aladdin Dr Laurel MD 20723*

MILLER, ROBERT WAYNE, High School Art Teacher; *b:* Jamestown, NY; *m:* Cynthia Lou Sample; *c:* Nicole, Nichelle, Nirissa; *ed:* Alfred Univ (BFA) Fine Arts 1979; Syracuse Univ (MFA) Ceramics 1984; *cr:* Baldwinsville Schls Art Tchr 1979-; NYSSSA Instr 1980; Syracuse Univ Art Prof 1983-84; *ai:* Future Artist Club Adv; Weight Room Coach; Stu Support Team Comm; NEA, NYSATA 1979-; NY St Fair Sculpture 1st Place 1984, 2nd Pl 1986, 1st Place 1992, Best of Show 1987; *office:* Baldwinsville Schl Dist 29 E Oneida St Baldwinsville NY 13027

MILLER, ROSALYN ANN (WALKER), French & German Tchr; *b:* Franklin, PA; *m:* Keith; *c:* Zachariah, Nathaniel; *ed:* Clarion Univ (BS) Fr, Ger 1975; Slippery Rock Univ (MED) Guid, Cnslng 1977; *cr:* Vly Grove Schl Dist Fr, Ger, Guid Tchr 1975-; *ai:* Vly Grove Ed Assn, PSEA, NEA 1975-.

MILLER, SANDRA SHULINOFF, Music Teacher; *b:* New York City, NY; *m:* Ernest N.; *c:* Kelly, Kristy; *ed:* Hunter Coll (BS) Music 1964, (MA) Music 1966; *cr:* Featherbed Lane Presbyn Church Organist, Choir Dir 1959-67; Inwood JHS Music Tchr 1964-71; Pomona JHS Music Tchr 1971-74; New Hempstead Presbyn Church Organist, Choir Dir 1975-; Pomona JHS Music Tchr 1986-; *ai:* Jr All-Cty Music Festival; AFT 1964-; NEA 1971-; *office:* Pomona Jr H S Pomona Rd Suffern NY 10901

MILLER, SHARON LABUZ, 1st Grade Teacher; *b:* Utica, NY; *m:* Harry J.; *c:* Katherine C.; *ed:* SUC at Oswego (BA) Eng Elem Ed 1973; SUC at Cortland (MS) Elem Ed Curr 1978; *cr:* Chadwicks Union Free Schl 2nd Grd Tchr 1973-84; Sauquoit Vly Cntrl Schl 2nd Grd Tchr 1984-91, 1st Grd Tchr 1993-; *ai:* Sci Comm; Fac Advy Cncl; AFT 1973-; NYSUT 1973-; St Lukes Hosp Guild 1978-; *office:* Sauquoit Vly Cntrl Schl Oneida St Sauquoit NY 13456

MILLER, SHARON WIATROWSKI, Spanish Teacher; *b:* Buffalo, NY; *m:* James D. Jr.; *c:* Jay, Alex; *ed:* Edinboro Univ of PA (BS) Span 1978, (BS) Fr 1978, (BS) Eng 1984; *cr:* Titusville Area Schls Span, Fr Tchr 18 Yrs; *ai:* PSEA, NEA 1978-.

MILLER, SHERYL LEE (BABICS), Library & Media Specialist; *b:* Grove City, PA; *m:* Greg A.; *c:* Chelsea; *ed:* Clarion Univ (MS) Lib Sci 1975, (BS) Lib Sci 1980; Post Grad Work Lib Sci; *cr:* Painesville Twp Schls Elem Lib Coord 1975-78; John R. Williams Jr HS Lib Media Specialist 1978-95; Riverside Complex Lib Media Specialist 1995-; *ai:* Venture Capital Grant Comm; Library Aides, Audio Visual Aides Adv; Delta Kappa Gamma 1993-, Prof Growth Chair; PTEA, OEA 1975-; OELMA; Beta Phi Mu; Perry Womens League 1980-85, Sec; Morley Friends of Lib 1980-84; Martha Holden Jennings Scholar; PSLA Stu Recognition Awd; Received Excl Ed Grant; *office:* Riverside Complex HS 585 Riverside Dr Painesville OH 44077

MILLER, SHIRLEY BASSETT, Retired Elementary School Tchr; *b:* Passaic, NJ; *m:* Seymour H.; *c:* Reva Morowitz, Mark, Debra; *ed:* Newark St Coll (BA) Eng-Magna Cum Laude 1969; *cr:* Edith Bogert Schl 3rd Grd Tchr 15 Yrs, 4th Grd Tchr 5 Yrs, 5th Grd Tchr 5 Yrs; *ai:* Former Mem Tchr, Bd of Ed Negotiations Comm; NEA, NJEA 1969-; Bnai Brith 1953-; Hadassah 1970-; ORT 1954-, Sec; Governor's Tchr Recognition Cert from Jim Florio 1992; *home:* 632 Iroquois St Oradell NJ 07649

MILLER, SHIRLEY HUBER, Retired String Tchr & Orch Dir; *b:* Lancaster, PA; *m:* Arley Keener; *ed:* Lebanon Vly Coll (BS) Music Ed 1963; Penn St Univ (MA) Hum 1982; North Park Coll Summer 1965; Univ Ctr Summer 1970-71; *cr:* Manheim Twp Elem & Jr HS Instr of Strings & Orch 1963-64; Wentworth Elem & Hr HS Instr of Vocal Music & Choirs 1964-65; Parkview Elem & Jr HS Instr of Gen Music & Strings 1965-69; Cumberland Vly Schl Instr of Strings & Orch 1970-95; Tchr of Pvt Violin & Viola Lessons 1970-82; *ai:* Tchr At Summer Music Camp Messiah Coll 1981-90; Carlisle Arts Magnet Schl Dev Comm 1991-; Free Lance Violin, Viola; Mem String Quartet; Coached Stdnts in Strollup Strings & Quartets; Comm for Adjudication Festivals in PMEA 1986-88; Cumberland Cty Music 1970-95, Sec 1976-80; PMEA, MENC, AFM, SAI, ASTA, NEA, PSEA 1970-95; Natl Schl Orch Assn 1970-95, Sec of St 1986-90; Amer Assn of Univ Women 1975-, Cultural Chair; Harrisburg Symphony 1970-82, Prin Violinist II; Amer Yth Symphony Bd for 2 Yrs; Little Orch of Hbg Bd for 2 Yrs; Harrisburg Symph Bd for 2 Yrs; Guest Conductor for Elem, Jr, Sr HS Orchs; *home:* 440 Brentwater Rd Camp Hill PA 17011*

MILLER, SUE BOWERS, Sixth Grade Teacher; *b:* Monroe, NC; *m:* Darrell T.; *c:* Matthew, Justin; *ed:* Wingate Coll (AA) Lbrl Arts 1969; Univ of NC at Greensboro (BS) Elem Ed 1971; Radford Coll Post Grad Courses Child Psych; *cr:* Rankin Elem Schl Second Grd Tchr 1971-72; Baywood Elem Schl First-Second Grd Tchr 1972-79; Severn Chrstn Schl Supvr 4-8 1979-84; Granite Bapt Church Schl First, Sixth Grd Tchr 1982-, Elem Coord 1993-95; *ai:* Outstdng Young Edctr Awd 1977; *office:* Granite Baptist Schl 7823 Oakwood Rd Glen Burnie MD 21061

MILLER, SUSAN DAWSON, Mathematics Teacher; *b:* Princeton, NJ; *m:* Ted W.; *c:* Jennifer Stettler, Richard Stettler; *ed:* Mansfield St Coll (BS) Math Ed 1969; Univ of DE (MED) Natural Scis 1972; Goldey Beacom Coll (BA) Acctg 1986; 60 Addl Credit Hrs; *cr:* Shue MS Math Tchr 1969-74, 1978-79; Christiana HS Math Tchr 1980-81; Alfred I. Dupont HS Math Tchr 1981-82; Caravel Acad Math Tchr 1982-84; Christiana HS Math Tchr 1985-87; Gauger MS Math Tchr 1987-90; Newark HS Math Tchr 1990-; *ai:* Christina Schl Dist Math Stans Implementaion Comm; Warranty Prgm; NCTM, DCTM, NEA, CEA 1969-; *office:* Newark HS E Delaware Ave Newark DE 19711*

MILLER, SUSAN E., Cnslr & Stu Assistance Coord; *b:* Fountain Springs, PA; *c:* Shannon, Ryan; *ed:* Mansfield Univ (BS) Home Ec 1968; Kutztown Univ (MA) Counseling 1972; Courses in Stu Assistance, Crisis Prevention Inst, Conflict Resolution; *cr:* Harrison Morton Home Ec Tchr 10 Yrs; William Allen HS Cnslr 6 Yrs; *ai:* Parenting Classes Tchr; Safety Comm Chm; NEA 1968-, VP; PA Stu Assistance Bd 1990-; Lehigh Carbon Cnslrs 1992-, Outstanding Cnslr; Lehigh Cty Delta Zeta Alumnae Assn 1969-, Pres, Many Awd; Allentown Womens Tchr 1992-; Tchr Support Facilitator; *office:* William Allen HS 126 N 17th St Allentown PA 18104

MILLER, SUSAN G. (THOMAS), French & Spanish Teacher; *b:* Newark, NJ; *m:* Paul A.; *c:* Michelle A.; *ed:* Upsala Coll (BA) Fr 1967; Montclair St Coll Fr & Ed 16 Grad Credits 1967-69; Monmouth Coll Ed 8 Grad Credits 1969-70; Brookdale Comm Coll & Monmouth Coll Span 27 Credits 1974-77; *cr:* Bayshore Jr HS Fr Tchr 1968-70, Fr & Ger Tchr 1970-77; Bayshore Jr HS & MS FL Dept Coord 1970-95; Bayshore MS Fr & Span Tchr 1978-; *ai:* NEA, NJEA, MCEA & MJEA 1968-; FLENJ 1970-; *office:* Bayshore MS 36 Leonardville Rd Leonardo NJ 07737

MILLER, SUSAN LEPLEY, Spanish Teacher; *b:* Indiana, PA; *m:* Harold K. Jr.; *c:* Evan; *ed:* IN U of PA (BED) Span Lang & Lit 1972, (MA) Span Lang & Lit 1976; 30 Credit Hrs Beyond Masters; *cr:* IN Area Jr HS Span Tchr 1973-81; IN Area Sr HS Span Tchr 1981-; *ai:* Span Exch Pgm & Club 1984-; NEA, PSEA & IAEA 1973-, Fac Rep; APPLES 1990-; ACTFL 1990-; *office:* Indiana Sr HS 450 N 5th St Indiana PA 15701

MILLER, SUSAN STEGGERT, Math Teacher & Dept Chprsn; *b:* Philadelphia, PA; *m:* Joseph T. Sr.; *c:* Joseph Jr., Stephanie, Melissa, Jeff; *ed:* Neumann Coll Aston (BA) Elem Ed 1985; Learning Disabled Child Summer Course 3 Credits 1987; *cr:* St George Tchr 1970-73, 1979-81; St Robert Tchr 1977-78; St Francis of Assisi Tchr 1983-; *ai:* Yrbk, Math Club Moderator 6 Yrs; Math Competitions Dir 7 Yrs; Mathcounts Coach 6 Yrs; Chair Math Dept; Math Competitions 8 yrs; Hnrs Math Pgm Dir, Tchr 3 Yrs; NCEA 11 yrs; NCTM 2 yrs; Prospect Park Youth Club 15 Yrs; St Gabriel Schl Parish Cncl 1 Yr; Selected by Peers as Distinguished Cath Educators Awd Candidate 1987; *office:* St Francis of Assisi Schl 112 Saxer Ave Springfield PA 19064

MILLER, TERESA CELADON, Second Grade Teacher; *b:* Glens Falls, NY; *m:* Doug; *c:* Melissa; *ed:* Trinity Coll (BA) Elem Ed, Human Svcs 1974; 31 Grad Hrs in Elem Ed, Rdng SUNY 1978; *cr:* Queensbury Elem Schl First Grd Tchr 1976-89, Second Grd Tchr 1989-; *ai:* Wellness Comm Chprsn; Lang Arts, Math, Soc Skills, Placement Comms; NYSUT, AFT 1976-; Cancer Soc 1980-, Work on Fund Raisers; *home:* 4 Stone Pine Ln Queensbury NY 12804

MILLER, TERRY BURNS, Music Teacher & Choir Director; *b:* Huntington, WV; *m:* Larry K.; *c:* Matthew, Jeremy; *ed:* Marshall Univ (BA) Music Ed 1980; *cr:* Lincoln Cty Schls Band Dir 1980-81; Wayne Cty Schls HS, MS, Elem Schl Music Tchr 1981-90; Fairland Schls MS, HS Music Tchr 1990-95; Chesapeake Schls MS, HS Music Tchr 1995-; *ai:* Handbell Choir; HS Chorus Spon; Dir of HS Play; Previous Amer Pride Instr; NEA 1980-; OEA 1990-; *office:* Chesapeake Union Exempted Schl 10183 Co Rd 1 Chesapeake OH 45619

MILLER, THEODORE RAY, Soc Stud Tchr & Dept Head; *b:* Beverly, NJ; *m:* Susan C.; *c:* Theodore Jr, Michelle Faulkner, Ross; *ed:* Keene St Coll (BED) Soc Stud Ed 1968, (MED) His Ed 1971, (MAT) Geog Ed 1993; *cr:* Thayer HS Soc Stud Tchr 1969-74; Nathaniel Hawthorne Coll Adjunct Lecturer His 1984-85; Franklin Pierce Coll Adjunct Lecturer Ed, Govt 1986-93; Keene St Coll Adjunct Lecturer Ed His, Geog 1981-82, 1985-; Keene HS Soc Stud Tchr 1974-; *ai:* Wellness Comm, Fac Rep; NEA 1969-; ASCD 1991-; Natl Geographic Sco 1991-; Natl Cncl Geographic Ed 1991-; Natl Geographic Soc Tchrs Consultant Ogrn 1990; Russian Amer Improvement Geog Ed Seminar 1993; Journal of Geog Art 1994; Gamma Theta Upsilon Geog 1992; Cert Geog Ed 1993; Geog Prof Cert 1993; *office:* Keene Sr HS 43 Arch St Keene NH 03431

MILLER, THOMAS EDWARD, Campus Minister; *b:* Annapolis, MD; *ed:* Loyola Coll (BA) Philosophy 1983; Addl 12 Credit Hrs Theology; *cr:* Ronald Mc Donald House Mgr 1983; Assoc Cath Charities Cnslr 1983-84; St Elizabeth Ann Seton Parish Dir of Youth Ministry 1984-89; Archbishop Spalding HS Campus Minister, Rel Stud Fac 1989-; *ai:* Retreat Dir; Schlsp, Stu Svcs Comms; Sr Class Moderator; NCEA 1989-; Greater Baltimore Bd of Realtors 1992-; Cert of Achvmt Youth Ministry; For God, Youth Awd from Archdiocese of Baltimore; *office:* Archbishop Spalding H S 8080 New Cut Rd Severn MD 21144

MILLER, TIMOTHY I., Retired MS & HS Teacher; *b:* Canton, OH; *m:* Jill Syler; *c:* Scott, Matthew, Sheri Miller Davies; *ed:* OH Northern Univ (BS) PE 1964; Univ of Akron (MA) Ed 1970; *cr:* Walker Jr HS Math, Sci Tchr 1964-69; Canton S HS Head Bsbl Coach 1964-93; Faircrest Jr HS PE Instr 1970-93; Canton S HS Summer Schl Instr 1978-91; Faircrest Jr HS Bsktbl Coach 1970-91; *ai:* Bsbl, Ftbl, Bsktbl Ath Dir; PE Dept Head; Cty PE Comm; Pres of St Bsbl Coaches Assn; Northeastern Buckeye Conf, Bsbl Coach of Yr; Stark Cty, Bsbl Coach of Yr 1993, 1995; OH HS; Bsbl Coaches Hall of Fame Inducted 1991; Greater Canton, Bsbl Hall of Fame Inducted 1986; All OH Coach 1984; OH Northern Univ, Letterman Bsbl 4 Yrs, Ftbl 2 Yrs, Bsbl Team Capt, PE Major of Yr 1964; Cath Comm League, 22 Yrs; Canton Twp, Zoning Bd 6 Yrs; Yth Action, Ldr 3 Yrs; OH Bsbl Coaches Assn 25 Yrs, Pres Hall of Fame; Canton Local Ed Assn, OEA, NEA 24 Yrs; Twp Zoning Comm 7 Yrs; Articles Pub; *home:* 4055 Dueber Ave SW Canton OH 44706

MILLER, TITUS ALFRED,III, 5th Grade Teacher; *b:* York, PA; *m:* Gertrude Finman; *c:* Tanya Leigh, Tammy Renee; *ed:* Lock Haven St Coll (BS) Elem Ed 1964; Kutztown St Coll (MED) Elem Ed 1966; 37 Credits Leadership Dev; Archaeology, Cmptr Sci, Ec, Oceanography; *cr:* Hamburg Area Schl Dist 4th Grd Tchr 1964-69, 5th Grd Tchr 1969-; Rdng Area Comm Coll Cmptr Prgramming 1987-89; East PA Valley YMCA Adult Ed Cmptr Programming 1984-86; *ai:* Tutoring Prgm; Prof Dev Advy Comm; Stu Cooperative Tchr; Tchr Advy Panel; Metropolitan Edison Corp; Earth Day Comm 1995-; Hamburg Area Ed Assn 1964-, Fac Rep; HAEA Treas, Pres 1992-94, Chief Negotiator; VP 1994-; Lenhartsville Fish & Game Assn 1968-, Hunter Safety Instr PA Game Commission, 18 Yr Awd; PA Jaycees; *office:* Hamburg Area School Dist Windsor St Hamburg PA 19526

MILLER, TODD ALLEN, Social Studies Teacher; *b:* Dayton, OH; *ed:* Ball St Univ (BS) Scndry Ed, His 1992; 9 Credit Hrs Comprehensive Soc Stud Univ of Dayton; Anthropology & Humanities; Grad of Honor Coll; *cr:* Arcanum Butler Local Schls Asst Var Track Coach 1992-93, Head Var Cross Cntry Coach 1993-95, Head Var Track Coach 1993-; Ansonia Local Schls 6th Grd, HS Soc Stud Tchr, Asst Ath Dir 1995-; *ai:* Asst Ath Dir; Var Track & Cross Cntry Coaches Arcanum-Butler Local Schl Dist; Phi Alpha Theta His 1991-; Honors Thesis Pub Ball St Univ; DeptHonors in His Ball St Univ; *office:* Ansonia Local Schl Dist 200 W Canal St Ansonia OH 45303

MILLER, VICTORIAN LEE, English Instructor; *b:* Wooster, OH; *c:* Steven Kiley, Terry Baughman; *ed:* OH St Univ (BA) Eng 1972, (MA) Eng 1978; Masters Plus 60 Qtr Hrs; *cr:* Upper Arlington HS Eng Tchr 1972-; *ai:* Coaching Positions; NEA, OEA 1972-; *home:* 991 Manor Ln Unit M Columbus OH 43221

MILLER, VIRGINIA YASKULKA, First Grade Teacher; *b:* Stafford Springs, CT; *m:* James George; *ed:* Cntrl CT St Univ (BS) Ed 1963; Univ of CT (MA) Ed 1967; *cr:* Northeast Elem Schl 1st Grd Tchr 1963-; *ai:* NEA, CT Ed Assn, Vernon Ed Assn 1963-; *office:* Northeast Elem Schl 69 East St Vernon Rockville CT 06066

MILLER, WENDY DIBBLE, Chemistry Teacher; *b:* Westfield, NY; *m:* R. Max Jr.; *c:* Kelly Jean, John Peter; *ed:* Wittenburg Univ (BA) Chem 1972; Attnd Univ of MN, Rochester Inst of Tech, Univ of Jacksonville, Univ of Cntrl FL, Univ of FL; *cr:* St Petersburg Sr High Chem Tchr 1972-76; Pt Charlotte Jr High 7th-8th Grd Sci Tchr 1988-91; Our Lady of Peace Schl 7th-8th Grd Sci Tchr 1991-93; Mercy Hurst Prep Chem Tchr 1993-; *ai:* PA Jr Achvmt of Sci Spon; Travel Club Adv for Easter Trip 1997; Sunday Schl Tchr; Amer Chem Soc; NSTA 1995-; Jr Womens Club 1977-, Pres; YMCA Bd 1986-; Fawcett Memrl Hosp Advy Bd; Charlotte Cty Yth Bd; Our Lady of Peace Schl Bd 1994-, VP; Pinellas Cty Outstdng Edctr 1976; *home:* 3402 Delmar Dr Erie PA 16506

MILLER, WILLIAM C., Anatomy & Physiology Teacher; *b:* Harrisburg, PA; *ed:* Lebanon Vly Coll (BSE) Pre-Med Bio 1973; Shippensburg Univ (MS) Bio 1975; 17 Courses in Voc Stud; Post Grad Stud in Educl Scndry Admin; *cr:* Northern Lebanon Schl Dist Sub Tchr 1975; Susquehanna Twp Schl Dist Sub Tchr 1975; Harrisburg Schl Dist Tchr 1975; *ai:* Audio Visual Club Adv; Audio Visual Coord; Bldg & Tech Comms; HEA 1975-; NEA 1975-; Harrisburg Area Comm Coll 1993-, Respiratory Therapy Bd Mentor; Harrisburg Mini Grant Campus Floral Dev; Tchr of the Month (Twice); APOB Pat on the Back Awd (3 Times); *office:* Harrisburg HS 2451 Market St Harrisburg PA 17103

MILLER, WILLIAM H.,III, Span Tchr & Frgn Lang Dept Chm; *b:* Phillipsburg, NJ; *m:* Christine R. Milner-Miller; *c:* Kristen, Megan, Sarah; *ed:* East Stroudsburg Univ (BSEd) Span, Scndry Ed 1984; Middlebury Coll (MA) Span Lang, Lit 1991; Grad Ed Stud at IN Wesleyan Univ 1995, Ogontz Coll 1993; Univ De Valencia Bac Ed, Span Stud 1983; *cr:* Malvern Prep Schl Span, Fr Tchr 1984-85; Downingtown HS Span Tchr 1985-86; Stroudsburg Area Schl Span, Fr Instr 1986-; *ai:* Frgn Lang Dept Chm, Strategic Plan for Lang Comm Chr; Span Club Co-Adv; Stu Asstance Team Core Mem; Head Cross Cntry, Track Coach; AATSP 1984-; MLA, PMLA 1993-; NEA, PSEA, SAEA 1985-; Stroudsburg Wesleyan Church 1994-95, Bd of Chrstn Ed; Career Missionary to Costa Rica for Tchng, Translating 1996; *office:* Stroudsburg Area Schl Dist 1100 W Main St Stroudsburg PA 18360

MILLER, WILLIAM THOMAS, Assistant Dean of Students; *b:* Rahway, NJ; *m:* Barbara Huestis; *c:* Kerry Schneeberger, Courtney, Ryan; *ed:* Norwich Univ (BS) PE, Bio 1975, (MS) Admin 1976; *cr:* John F Kennedy HS PE, Hlth Tchr 1976-77; Gettysburg Coll Assoc Prof Hlth Sci 1977-85; Richards Ins Acc Exec 1985-90; Brattleboro Union HS Asst Dean 1990-; *ai:* Head Ftbl Coach; Natl Ftbl 1977-; NEA, Bd of Dir Natl Ftbl & Coll Hall of Fame Vt Chptr; Outstanding St Coach of VT 1993-; Shrine Ftbl Team Coach 1994; *home:* 5 Myrtle St Brattleboro VT 05301

MILLER, WINIFRED E., MS Math Teacher; *b:* Providence, RI; *m:* William; *c:* Kim, Rebecca; *ed:* Mercy Coll (BSEd) Ed 1960; RI Coll (MED) Guid & Cnslng 1972; 40 Credit Hrs in Schl Psych Pgm; *cr:* Pvt Schls Tchr 1960-67; Cranston Pub Schls elem Guid Pgm 5th & 6th Grd Tchr 1968-72; Western Hills MS Math Tchr 1995-; *ai:* Odyssey of the Mind Coach; AFT 1968-; Warwick Symphony Orch 1975-95, Bd Mem; Local Grants; *office:* Western Hills MS 400 Phenix Ave Cranston RI 02920

MILLER-COLLINS, DEBORAH ALBRA, English Teacher; *b:* Rochester, NY; *m:* Paul; *ed:* Brockport SUNY (BS) Eng 1985; Geneseo SUNY (MS) Rdng Specialist 1989; *cr:* Honeoye HS 8th Grd Eng Tchr 1985-87, 11th & 12th Grd Eng Tchr 1989-; *ai:* Yth to Yth Adv.

MILLETT, CAROLE DUNBAR, 7th Grade Math Teacher; *b:* Portland, ME; *m:* Everett R.; *c:* Thaddeus, Lucinda, Rebecca; *ed:* Gorham St Tchrs Coll (BS) Jr High Math 1965; Univ of ME at Orono (MS) MS Ed 1994; *cr:* Windham Jr HS Math Tchr 1965-69; Jordan Small Schl Math Tchr 1971-73; Windham MS Math Tchr 1983-; *ai:* Team Ldr; NEA, MT 1983-; NCTM, ATOMIM 1990-; *office:* Windham MS 408 C Windham ME 04062

MILLETT, NADINE M. ORSKI, Business Ed Tchr & Chairpe Brooklyn, NY; *m:* Stephen E.; *c:* Scott S., Jeffrey M.; *ed:* Suff Comm Coll (ABS) Bus Admin 1966; Husson Coll (BS) Bus Ed, 1969, (MBS) Bus Sci 1985; IBM Atlanta Network Admin Trng; Hrs Masters Level Univ of GA; 6 Credit Hrs Cmptr Sci Univ of Orono HS Bus Ed Tchr 1969-73; Bangor Adult Ed Schl Bus Tchr Husson Coll Prof Stud Instr 1980-; John Bapt Meml HS Bus Dep Cmptr Admin 1983-; *ai:* Key Club Adv; Dept Chair, Bd of Dir Fin Comp Admin; Tech Comm Chprsn; Curr Comm Sec; Bus Ed Assn 1969-; Eastern Bus Ed Assn 1990-; ME Assn of Pub Schl Adult Tchr of Yr 1979; St Patricks Episcopal Church 1989-, Layreader; Schl Admin & Tchr 1985-, Supt; Adult Edctr Voc Tchr of Yr 1979; Coll Bus Tchr Advy Bd; *office:* John Bapst Memorial HS 100 Br Bangor ME 04401

MILLETT, ROBERT EUGENE, Mathematics Teacher; *b:* Ale Bay, NY; *m:* Cathy Lynn Conti; *c:* Andrea, Matthew; *ed:* Jefferson Coll (AS) Math Sci 1971; St Univ NY at Oswego (BA) Math E (MSED) Math 1981, (CAS) Schl Admin 1988; 36 Credits at St La Univ 1969-70; Adj Prof Cert Cmptr Engrng 1986 at Syracuse U Liverpool HS Math Tchr 1973-, Ice Hockey Coach 1973-82, Extend Day Instr 1981-; 1000 Islands River Boat Pilot 1978-86; *ai:* Liverpool Fac 1973-; Onordaya Cty Math Tchr Assn 1973-89; Mids Hockey Assn 1983-, Coach; Cntrl HS Hockey League 1977-7 Baldwinsville Hockey Booster Club 1995-, Pres; NY Perm Tchng C Perm Schl Dist Admin Cert; US Coast Guard 100 Ton Master o Lakes License; *office:* Liverpool HS 800 4th St Liverpool NY 130

MILLETTE, ROBERT E., Grenadais Ambassador; *b:* Grenada Indies; *m:* Denise; *c:* Wayne, Donna, Abena, Dalia; *ed:* Brooklyn Co Sociology 1974; New Schl (MA) Sociology 1977, (PHD) Sociolog *cr:* Talladega Coll Tchr 1979; Grenada's Ambassador to United 1995-; *ai:* Lincoln Univ Sociology, Anthropology Dept Chair Caribbean Stud Assn, Former Pres; Grenada Mutual Assn, Pres 1 Ldrshp Awd 1990; Lincoln Univ Distngd Fac Awd Excl Tchng 199 of Yr 1991; Co-Ed of Exploring The African-Amer Experience.

MILLIGAN, COLLEEN LOUGHRAN, Sixth Grade Teach Frankfurt, West Germany; *m:* William F.; *cr:* Corpus Christi Schl Grd Tchr 1985-88; Holy Saviour-St John Fisher Schl 6th-8th Gr 1988-; *ai:* Mrktg Comm Chprsn; NCEA 1985-; *office:* Holy Sav John Fisher 122 E Ridge Rd Linwood PA 19061*

MILLIKEN, MARIAN D., Health & Physical Ed Teacher; *b:* Ridle PA; *m:* C. Craig; *c:* Lisa R., Christine D. Mc Call, Troy E.; *ed:* Tre Coll (BS) Hlth, PE 1979, (MEJ) Hlth, PE 1985; *cr:* Newton Jr HS H Tchr 1980-; *ai:* Stu Assistance Prgm; SADD; Jogging Club Adv, NEA, CREA 1980-; Northampton Twp Park, Recreation Bd 19 Hammond Svc Awd Trenton St Coll 1979; *office:* Newtown Jr H Richboro-Newton Rd Newtown PA 18940

MILLIKEN, PATRICIA KOPPENHAUER, Biology Teacher; *m:* *ed:* Bloomsburg St Coll (BS) Bio 1970, (MED) Bio 1972; Duquesn (MS) Spec Ed 1982; Attnd PA St Univ, Univ of Pittsburgh, Univ Cornell Univ; *cr:* Cornell Univ Rsrch Specialists 1972-76; Bowling Schl Tchr 1977-79; Mt Lebanon Schl Dist Tchr 1979-80; North Hil Dist Tchr 1980-; *ai:* Strategic Planning & Recommendation Improvement, Project Voyager Curr Dev Comms; NABT; NSTA; W PA Bio Tchrs; PSTA; NEA; PSEA; Delta Kappa Gamma; St Afters Pittsburgh Spectroscopy Soc Grant 1992; Woodrow Wilson B Flwshp 1991; Spec Ed Equipment Grants 1985, 1987; Tchr Excl Awd *office:* North Hills Sr HS 53 Rochester Rd Pittsburgh PA 15229

MILLIKEN, TERESA MALEY, Music Teacher & Choir Director; *b* Liverpool, OH; *ed:* Youngstown St Univ (BMUS) Ed, Voice 197 Lincoln Jr HS Music Tchr 1974-80; North Jr HS Music Tchr 1980 NEA, OEA, Youngstown Ed Assn 1984-; Music Edctrs Natl Con Music Ed Assn 1988-; YSU Alum Assn 1983-; Jennings Scholar Awd *home:* 2536 Center Rd Poland OH 44514

MILLIS, JOANNE M., Art Teacher; *b:* Flushing, NY; *m:* Albert; *c:* Bryanna; *ed:* Beaver Coll (BFA) Fine Arts 1964; Coll of St Rose (Art Ed 1991; *cr:* Freelance Artist; St Catherine of Siena Schl Ar 1989-; East Greenbush Schl Art Tchr 1993-; *ai:* NYSATA 1990-; N 1991-; DCC 1979-; Juror.

MILLMANN, LOUISE M., Photography Teacher; *b:* Huntington, N Schl of Visual Arts (BFA) Art 1986; SUNY at Story Brook (MLS) Lb 1989; *cr:* Northport UFSD #4 Tchr 1989-; *ai:* Mail Art Wall Coord; T Dir; Performance Art Design; Photography Exhibition; NYSUIT, NY 1989-; *office:* Northport HS Laurel Hill Rd Northport NY 11768

MILLS, CAROL LYNN, 7th & 8th Grade Math Teacher; *b:* Suffern *ed:* Hartwick Coll (BA) Elem Ed 1978; Long Island Univ (MS) Cm Ed 1986; CCNY (MA) Scndry Ed Math 1995; *cr:* Upper Nyack Sc Grd Tchr 1980-81; West Point Schl 7-8 Grd Math Tchr 1983-; *ai:* 8t Memory Book Adv; NCTM 1989-; *office:* West Point Schl Bldg 705 Rd West Point NY 10996

MILLS, DENISE GIANADDA, Associate Professor of Spanis Buffalo, NY; *m:* Richard V.; *c:* Anna, Nicholas, Laura; *ed:* LeMoyn (BA) Modern Lang 1974; SUNY at Buffalo (MA) Span 1976, (PHD) 1988; *cr:* SUC Instr 1978-83; Medville Coll Instr 1984-87; Daemen Assoc Prof 1988-; *ai:* Stud Abroad Prgms Adv; Phi Sigma Iota WNYFLEC 1989-; NEH Grant 1991, 1995; Articles Pub; *office:* Da Coll 4380 Main St Amherst NY 14226

MILLS, EARL ALLEN, Science Teacher; *b:* Randolph, VT; *m:* N Davis; *ed:* Plymouth St Coll (BA) PE, Sci 1970; Assumption C Credits; Attnd Univ of ME; *ai:* Var Cross Cntry, Track & Field Coach Sci Curr Comm; NEA 1970-; NHSTA 1995-; Cross Cntry Coach 1985, 1987; Tchr of Yr 1994-95; *office:* Newfound Regional HS R Newfound Rd Bristol NH 03222

MILLS, FRED W., Social Studies Teacher; *b:* Cleveland, OH; *m:* B L. Petre; *ed:* Muskingum Coll (BA) Soc 1970; Cleveland St Univ (M 1980; Archaeological Field Schl Cleveland Museum of Natural His; Univ Urban Geography Inst 30 Addl Post Grad Hrs; *cr:* Wiley MS Sp Tchr 1970-72; Cleveland Heights HS Tchr 1972-; *ai:* Mock Trial Coach; Juggling Club Adv; AFT Local 795 1972-; NCSS 1980-; U Chicago Outstdng Tchr Awd 1989; *office:* Cleveland Heights HS 1 Cedar Rd Cleveland Heights OH 44118*

MILLS, JUDITH ZILLA, English Teacher; *b:* Springdale, PA Kenneth W.; *c:* Jeffrey, Steven; *ed:* IN Univ of Pa (BSEd) Ed, Eng OH Univ (MED) Scndry Ed, Rdng 1971; *cr:* Freeport HS Sr Eng 1964-66; Evans City Jr HS 7th Grd Rdng Tchr 1966-67; Athens HS Tchr 1967-69; Grove City Jr HS 7th-8th Rdng, Eng Tchr 1978-85; C City HS 9, 11 Eng Tchr 1985-; *ai:* PSEA, NEA 1980-; NCTE; Delta K Gamma 1981-; G. C. Comm Lib Bd 1982-86, Pres 1984-86; Ge Electric Fellow, Career Ed at Univ of SC 1983; Dept Chair 1985-90; *o* Grove City HS 511 Highland Ave Grove City PA 16127

MILLS, LORI ANN, Government & US History Tchr; *b:* Paintsville, *ed:* OH Univ (BS) Soc Stud 1988; *cr:* World Harvest Chrstn Acad H Gov Tchr 1990-; *ai:* Career Day, Stu Cncl & Debate Team Adv; Courtr 'ar Games Simulations & Entrepreneur Bus Pgms; Girls Var Asst Prom Comm; Sr Act Comm; Columbus Cncl on World Affairs OH Ed Assoc; *office:* World Harvest Christian Acad P O Box 32932 us OH 43232*

, SUSAN SHATZER, Business Education Teacher; *b:* ersburg, PA; *m:* Thomas Lloyd; *ed:* Penn St Univ (BS) Mrktg 1989; isburg Univ (BS) Bus Ed 1991; Wilmington Coll (MED) Admin *cr:* Corning Revere Mrktg Correspondence 1989; Brooklane atric Hosp Therapeutic Recreation Tchr 1989-91; Caesar Rodney HS Tchr 1991-; *ai:* New Tchr, Stdnts At Risk Mentor; Instrl Cncl; 1995-, Rep; *office:* Caesar Rodney HS 239 Old North Rd Camden ng DE 19934*

, THOMAS EDWARD, Science Teacher; *b:* Washington Cty, MD; Lynn Workman; *c:* Tanner, Conner; *ed:* Shepherd Coll (BA) Scndry 8; 30 Addl Hrs; *cr:* Frederick Cty Bd of Ed Tchr 1989-; *ai:* 9th Grd Coach 1990-; Integrated Sci Curr Comm 1991-; Schl Improvement 991-93; NEA, Frederick Cty Tchrs Assn 1989-; Brook Hill United hurch 1991-; Energy Grant Potomac Edison 1992.

, WILLIAM ANDREW, 7th-8th Grade Math Teacher; *b:* and, OH; *ed:* Univ of Dayton (BS) Elem Ed 1978; *cr:* St Francis of Schl 7-8th Grd Math Tchr 1981-87; St Margaret Mary Schl 6-8th th Tchr 1987-94; St Mary's Chardon Schl 7-8th Grd Sci Tchr 1995; ame Elem Schl 7-8th Grd Tchr 1995-; *ai:* Stu Cncl, Yrbk Adv; Plain Crystal Apple Awd 1992; *office:* Notre Dame Elem Schl 13000 Rd Chardon OH 44024

, ZIPPORIAH PORTIS, Sixth Grade Teacher; *b:* Brooklyn, NY; ren; *c:* Zakiya, Jelani, Jabari; *ed:* Hunter Coll (BA) African Stud & 4; Adelphi Univ (MS) Rdng Ed 1988; *cr:* PS 273 Tchr 1984-; *ai:* Chorus Co-Dir; Track Team Parent Coord; Schl Wide Pgms Comm United Fed of Tchrs 1984-; Bd for the Ed of People of African ry 1992-; *office:* PS 273 Wortman 923 Jerome St Brooklyn NY

SPAW, MARY LOUISE, Fifth Grade Teacher; *b:* Waterloo, OH; *c:* w, Mark; *ed:* Grad Hrs at Ashland Univ; *cr:* Hebron Elem 4th Grd 961-90; Lakewood MS 5th Grd Tchr 1990-; *ai:* PFO Fac Rep; LTA, st Vice; COTA, OEA; NEA; *office:* Lakewood MS 9380 Lancer Rd OH 43025

UZZO, KATHLEEN A. O'LEARY, Assistant Director; *b:* ster, MA; *m:* Salvatore J.; *ed:* Worcester St Coll (BS) His, Soc Sci Assumption Coll (MA) His 1973; Candidate, Doctor of Arts, His, gie-Mellon Univ; *cr:* Diocese of Worcester Schl Elem Soc Stud Tchr 9; City of Worcester Schl Scndry Soc Stud Tchr 1969-89; Sylvan ng Ctr Dir of Ed 1989-91; Quincy Coll at Plymouth Asst Dir Lbrl Site Coord, Asst Dir 1991-; *ai:* MTA, NEA, NCSS 1969-; Amer cal Assn 1970-; Kappa Delta Pi; Andrew Carnegie Schlsp Doctoral Master Thesis in Pub Lib; *home:* 1 Ridgewood Dr Auburn MA 01501

IOE, MARIJANE J., 8th Grd Social Studies Teacher; *b:* Buffalo, *:* Michael; *c:* Mary Rogers, Kathy Taylor, Anne Trachtenberg, , Michael, Jack; *ed:* LeMoyne Coll (MS) Sociology, His 1958; Attnd se Univ; *cr:* Canastota Cntrl Schl 4th Grd Tchr 1958-60, 5th-6th Grd Canastota Jr Sr HS 8th Grd Tchr; *ai:* Jr HS Stu Govt Adv; Pub Lib 38-92, Pres 1992; *home:* 115 Stroud St Canastota NY 13032

E, HENRY U., Sci Dept Chairperson & Teacher; *b:* Washington, : Lisa Oneto; *c:* Jason Cullins; *ed:* Frostburg St Coll (BS) Bio Ed *cr:* Kensington Jr HS Math, Earth Sci, Life Sci Tchr 1967-69; omery Hills Jr HS Earth Sci 8 Tchr 1970-71; Robert Frost MS Life Earth Sci 8 Tchr 1971-91; Cabin John MS IRT, Sci Dept Chair 1992-; ch, Liaison, Stu, Staff Recognition Comms; NEA 1967-; MSTA, 1991-; METEC 1996; 4 Sci Units Pub; 1 Unit Written for Educl Film ; Stipends Given for Writing; *office:* Cabin John MS 10701 borough Rd Rockville MD 20854

E, SANDRA CARPENTER, Second Grade Teacher; *b:* Mc ort, PA; *m:* Jack; *ed:* Slippery Rock Univ (BS) Elem Ed 1967; Attnd t, Millersville; *cr:* Butler Schl Dist Third Grd Tchr 1967-68; Norwin Dist Elem Tchr 1968-; *ai:* NEA 1967-; *office:* Scull Elem Schl 780 Hill Rd North Huntingdon PA 15642

E, VICTORIA WILSON, Social Studies Teacher; *b:* Johnson City, : Robert M.; *c:* Joshua, Jenny; *ed:* Cayuga Cty Comm Coll (AS) l Arts 1984; St Univ of NY at Oswego (BS) Scndry Ed 1986, (MA) Dev 1992; *cr:* East Syracuse Minoa HS Soc Stud Tchr 1987; insville HS Soc Stud Tchr 1987-88; Liverpool HS Soc Stud Tchr *ai:* Operation Cooperation-Lip Cap Facilitator; Conflict Mediator; NYSUT, NYSCSS, CNYSCSS 1987-; Marcellus Free Lib Bd, Treas; e of Marcellus Planning Bd, Sec; Literacy Vols; Soph Class Past Adv.

IER, DONNA A., Medical Assistant Instructor; *b:* Germantown, PA; lliam D. Jr.; *c:* Amanda; *ed:* Temple Univ Voc Ed Cert 1991; Bucks ech Schl Licensed Practical Nurse 1979; Certified Medical Asst 1988, Holy Family Coll Enrolled in BSN Prgm; *cr:* Woodbourne Medical Licensed Practical Nurse 1979-86; Olsten Temporary Svcs Licensed cal Nurse 1988-; Bucks Cty Tech Schl Medical Asst Instr 1987-; *ai:* Voc Industrial Clubs Adv; Curr Comm Chair; PA St Ed Assn 1987-, Level Mem of Voc & Practical Arts Ed Division; Rotary Dist #7450 chng Excl Awd 1993,95; Curr & Instrn Assn Awd 1995-; *office:* Bucks y Tech Schl Wistar Rd Fairless Hills PA 19030*

DN, RONALD ANTHONY, Instr of Political Science; *b:* Buffalo, *d:* St Univ of NY at Brockport (BS) Pol Sci & His 1987; Univ of io (MA) His 1989; New Schl for Soc Research (MA) Pol Sci 1995, A) Intnl Affairs 1995; *cr:* St Univ of NY at Brockport Summer Instr ; John Jay Coll Adjunct Govt Instr 1989-92; Nassau Comm Coll His 1992-94; Boricua Coll Facilitator & Instr 1993-; *ai:* Stu Cncl Adv ; Acad of Pol Sci 1989-; Amnesty Intnl 1992-; NYS Bd of Regents ate-at-Large; New Schl Fellowship 1993-95; Ralph J Bunche v on United Nations 1989-92; *office:* Boricua Coll 186 N 6th St lyn NY 11211*

DS, FRED L., Latin & French Teacher; *b:* Passaic, NJ; *ed:* Seton Hall (BA) Classical Langs 1959; NY Univ (MA) Fr 1974; Fr Stud nbia Univ; Speed Rdng US Army; Piano, Organ Private Stud; *cr:* St s HS Eng Tchr 1961; Clifton HS Latin, Eng Tchr 1961-62; New rd HS Fr Tchr 1967-69; Saddle Brook HS Fr, Latin, Eng Tchr 76; Lakeland Regnl HS Fr, Latin, Eng Tchr, Japanese Facilitator ; *ai:* Latin Club Adv, Spon; NJ Classical Assn 1970-; NEA, NJ Ed 1961-; St Matthew's Luth Church 1980-85, Music Dir; First Church 1990-, Organist; US Army 1962-64, Soldier, Instr; Pub Articles; ared on Latin; Bass with Berkshire Choral Festival; All-Arts actions Chorister; Piano Soloist.

OSEVIC, MICHELLE, 9th-12th Grd Mathematics Tchr; *b:* Parma, *n:* David; *ed:* Univ of Akron (BA) Math Ed 1989; Cleveland St Univ Adult Learning & Dev 1993; 8 Post-Grad Credit Hrs; *cr:* Garfield s HS Math Tchr & Adult Ed Instr 1989-; Old Trail Schl Summer Math Ldr 1992-; Ashland Univ Wkshp Facilatator 1994-; *ai:* Var Girls Coach; NEA, OEA, NCTM, OCTM 1989; GHTA 1989-, Bldg Rep; eld Hghts City Schls Outstanding Educator 1995; Awded GTEs th Initiatives for Tchrs Grant; *office:* Garfield Heights HS 12000 e Leaf Dr Cleveland OH 44125

MILOSEVICH, MICHAEL ROBERT, Lang Arts & World His Tchr; *b:* Steubenville, OH; *m:* Mary Wolford; *c:* Richard, Mark, Faith, Edward; *ed:* West Liberty St Coll (BA) Elem Ed 1973; Franciscan Univ of Steubenville (MS) Ed Admin 1995; Stud in Principalship; *cr:* Bantam Ridge Elem 5th Grd His & Sci Tchr 1990-91; Hills Elem Schl 5th & 6th Grd His & Sci Tchr 1991-93, 6th Grd Lang Arts & World His Tchr 1995-; Mingo MS 5th Grd Math, Sci & US His Tchr 1993-95; *ai:* Just Say No Adv; Field Trip Coord; ICEA 1990-; NEA 1990-; Steubenville Twp Trustee 1988-, Pres of Bd; Loyal Order of Moose 1994-; Received Jefferson Cty Bd of Ed Mini-Grants 1992 & 1995; *home:* 252 Hallock Ave Mingo Junction OH 43938

MILOVANOVICH, ZORAN M., Law & Criminal Justice Prof; *b:* Belgrade, Yugoslavia; *m:* Nevenka Gruzinov; *ed:* Univ of Belgrade (LLB) Law 1976; George Washington Univ (MFS) Forensic Sci 1981; Univ of Belgrade (LLM) Criminal Law, Justice 1982, (PHD) Criminal Law, Justice 1987; *cr:* Univ of Belgrade Law Schl Asst Prof 1982-88, Assoc Prof 1988-91; Loyola Univ Law Schl Fulbright Visiting Prof 1991-92; Lincoln Univ Assoc Prof 1992-; *ai:* Adv Stu Chapter NABCJ, Sociology Club; Bd Mem Ctr Pub Policty, Diplomacy's Fac Adv, Honorary Degrees, Writing Comms; Ad-Hoc Grad Cncl; ACJS 1993-; NEACJS 1995-; AAFS 1992-; AAUP 1994-; Natl Schlsp Holder 1978; Fulbright Flwshp 1980-81, 1991-92; Forensic Sci Dictionary; *office:* Lincoln Univ Dept Sociology& Crim Justice Lincoln University PA 19352*

MIL'SHTEIN, SAMSON, Professor of EE Department; *b:* Vinitza, Ukraine; *m:* Inna; *c:* Mark, Valery; *ed:* St Univ of Odessa, USSR (MSSC) Semiconductor Physics 1963; Univ of Jerusalem, Israel (PHD) Solid State Physics 1976; *cr:* Inst of Solid St Physics Acad of Sci, USSR Rsrch Fellow 1966-72; Univ of Jerusalem Sr Lecturer 1974-76; Univ of Ben-Gurion Sr Lecturer 1976-82; AT&T Bell Labs Visiting Scientist 1982-84; Cabat Corp Sr Scientist 1984-87; EE Dept U MASS at Lowell Full Prof 1987; *ai:* Coord of Gifted HS Stdnts Pgm; Mater Rsrch Soc 1984-; NEA 1987-; IEEE 1987-; Natl Undergr Rsrch Cncl 1995-; 1st Prize for Rsrch Achvmts from ISSP, Acad of Sci, USSR; Pub & Presented at Confs Numerous Papers & Patents; *office:* Univ Of MA At Lowell 1 University Ave Lowell MA 01854

MILSON, LINDA OPDYKE, 4th Grade Teacher; *b:* Phillipsburg, NJ; *m:* James W.; *ed:* Monmouth Univ (BS) El Ed 1973; 3 Credit Hrs Grad Stud Johnson St Coll; 10 Hr Course Tech Univ of CT Schl of Ed; *cr:* Franklin Twp El Schl 2nd Grd Tchr 1973-95, 4th Grd Tchr 1995-; *ai:* Sunshine Comm;, PTA Exec Comm Tchr Liaison; Doris Kirick Schlsp Fund Trustee; Brian Teasers Club Adv; Cmptr Curr Comm Chprsn; PTA, NEA, Franklin Twp Tchrs Assn, Monmouth Univ Alumni Assn, NJEA 1973-; TAWL 1992-; VTAWL 1994-; St Joseph's Cath Church; Natl Wildlife Fed, Nature Conservancy, Natl Parks & Conservation Assn 1995-; Tchr of Yr 1989; *home:* 28 Kinnaman Ave Washington NJ 07882

MILSPAW, THOMAS HENRY, Physical Science Teacher; *b:* Oil City, PA; *m:* Grace Ann Cress; *c:* Michael T., John L.; *ed:* Elon Coll (BA) Bio 1968; Univ of DE (MS) Voc Stud 1988; 63 Credits Post Grad, Inservice; *cr:* Reidsville City Schls Bio Tchr 1968; Sussex Cntrl MS Phys Sci Tchr 1969-89; Indian River HS Phys Sci Tchr 1990-; *ai:* Sr Class Adv; Sci Olympics Coach; NEA, DSEA 1969-; IREA 1969-, Treas; Little League 1990-, Dir.

MILSPAW, YVONNE JEAN, Eng & Humanities Assoc Prof; *b:* Sacramento, CA; *m:* Douglas R. Evans; *c:* Wesley K. Evans, Brandt D. Evans; *ed:* Mary Washington Coll of Univ of VA (BA) Eng 1967; IN Univ (MA) Folklore 1969, (PHD) Folklore 1975; *cr:* WV Univ Eng Instr 1971-74; PA St Univ Capitol Campus Amer Stud Asst Prof 1974-81, 1984-88; Harrisburg Area Comm Coll Eng, Hum Assoc Prof 1989-; *ai:* Phi Theta Kappa Adv; Prof Growth, Dev Comm; Hum Prgm Coord; Fac mentor; Amer Folklor Soc 1968-, Exec Bd, Nominating Comm; Mid Atlantic Folklife Assn 1976-, Past Pres; PA Folklore Soc 1974-, Past Pres; Middletown Area Historical Soc 1975-88, Ed; First PA Feminist Credit Union 1975-78, Sec; WITF-TV, FM Acution 1980-, Gallery 33 Advy Bd; Articles Pub; *office:* Harrisburg Area Comm College 1 HACC Dr Harrisburg PA 17110*

MILTNER, DANIEL SCOTT, Mathematics Teacher; *b:* Plainfield, NJ; *m:* Kerri McClimen; *ed:* Univ of IA (BS) Math 1991; Starting Grad Degree; *cr:* Good Cncl HS Math Tchr 1991-; *ai:* Bskbl & Sftbl Coach; Fac Staff Cncl Head; *office:* Good Counsel HS 11601 Georgia Ave Silver Spring MD 20902

MILZ, MICHAEL ANDREW, History Teacher; *b:* Wilkes-Barre, PA; *m:* Patricia Monaghan; *c:* Andrew, Martin, Christian; *ed:* King's Coll (BA) His 1972; *cr:* Bishop Hoban HS Tchr 1975-; *ai:* NACST 1978-, Exec VP, Sec, Trea 1981-95; Scranton Diocese Assn Cath Tchrs 1978-, Pres 1978-; *office:* Bishop Hoban H S 159 S Pennsylvania Ave Wilkes Barre PA 18701

MILZA, PETER JOSEPH, Social Studies Teacher; *b:* Staten Island, NY; *ed:* St Univ of NY at Albany (BA) Amer His 1994; *cr:* Moore Cath HS Soc Stud Tchr 1994-; *ai:* Newspaper Moderator; Asst Coach Girls Golf Team; *office:* Moore Catholic HS 100 Merrill Ave Staten Island NY 10314

MINARDI, THOMAS R., English Teacher & Dir of Drama; *b:* New York City, NY; *m:* Christine M. Spring; *c:* Jessica, Sara, Christopher, Jacob, Tessa; *ed:* St Univ of NY at Cortland (BA) Eng & Drama 1970; 30 Post Grad Hrs in Theatre Arts at St Univ of NY at Oswego; *cr:* Liverpool HS Eng Tchr 1970-; *ai:* Drama Dir; NYSUT 1970-; *office:* Liverpool HS 4338 Wetzel Rd Liverpool NY 13027

MINCH, ELLEN SOMERVILLE, Art Teacher; *b:* Bedford, OH; *m:* Thomas Joseph; *c:* Morgan Ann; *ed:* Kent St Univ (BED) Art Ed 1979; Art His Medieval Art 1984, Life Drawing; Tchng Children to Read 1989-90, Avt Spec Needs Stus; Theory, Practices in Tchng Rdng 1990; *cr:* Aurora Children's Day Ctr Curr Dir, Tchr 1979-80; Roxbury Elem Schl 1-4 Grd Art Tchr 1980-; *ai:* Annual Art Exhibit; Art Enrichment; Solon Ed Assn 1980-; OH Avt Ed Assn 1981-; Artist in Residence Grants 2 Yrs OH Fine Art Seminar; *office:* Roxbury Elem Schl 6795 Solon Blvd Solon OH 44139*

MINCIELI, MICHAEL VINCENT, Guidance Counselor; *b:* Bronx, NY; *ed:* Fordham Coll (BA) Sociology 1964; Fordham Schl of Soc Sci (MSW) Group Work 1966; Fordham Grad Schl of Arts & Scis (PHD) Sociology 1972; *cr:* Nativity Mission Ctr Cnslr, Group Worker 1961-71; Nativity Mission Schl Prin 1971-78; Regis HS Guid Cnslr 1978-; *ai:* Head Var Bsktbl Coach; Natl Assn of Soc Workers 1965-; NY Cnslng Assn 1992-; Assn for Supervision & Curr 1994-; *office:* Regis HS 55 E 84th St New York NY 10028

MINCIO, RONALD A., Sixth Grade Teacher; *b:* Ossining, NY; *m:* Karen Sherer; *c:* Eileen, Kevin, Matthew, Rebecca; *ed:* SUNY New Paltz (BS) Elem Ed 1966, (MS) Elem Admin 1969; 60 Hrs In-service, Grad Credits; *cr:* Ossining Pub Schls 4th-5th Grd Tchr 1966-69; Bay Shore Pub Schls 6th Grd Tchr 1969-80, Enrichment Tchr 1980-85, 6th Grd Tchr 1985-; *ai:* Math Comm; 7th Grd Stu Cncl Adv; Schl Improvement Team; Acad Excl Comm; Bayshore Classroom Tchrs Assn 1969-; NYSUT; NCTM; ACE; ASCD; Good Shepherd Parish 1971-, Rel Ed Tchr; Precana Eucharistic Minister; *home:* 2 Tory Ct Holbrook NY 11741*

MINCOLLA, MICHELE MARANO, French Teacher; *b:* Syracuse, NY; *m:* Vincent A. Jr.; *c:* Michael, Alex; *ed:* LeMoyne Coll (BA) Ed 1971; SUNY Coll at Oswego Permanent Ed 30 Hrs 1976; *cr:* Franciscan Acad Fr Tchr 1973-87; Henninger HS Fr Tchr 1988-90; Baldwinsville Schl Dist Fr Tchr 1990-; *ai:* Lang Dept Chprsn 1973-87; Fr Club Moderator 1994-; NHS Moderator 1973-77; Stu Cncl Adv 1976-80; Prins Advy Cncl Rep 1991-94; Prof Dev Comm Rep 1994-; Bldg Planning Team Subcommittee 1996; NYSAFLT, FLACNY 1974-; NEA 1990-; AATF; Northstars Soccer Club Boosters 1995-; Rel Ed Tchr 1993-; *office:* Durgee Jr HS E Oneida St Complex Baldwinsville NY 13027*

MINDER, JUDITH MOWRY, Eight Grade Teacher; *b:* Greensburg, PA; *m:* Walter James; *c:* Michael J., Lisa Ann; *ed:* West Liberty St Coll (BA) Soc Stud, Art 1963, (BA) Scndry Ed 1973; WV Univ (MA) Rdng 1992; Attnd Franciscan Univ of Steubenville; Univ of Dayton; *cr:* St Mary Cntrl Eight Grd Tchr 1973-; Belmont Tech Coll Adj Instr 1991-93; *ai:* Schl Newspaper The Tiger Times Publisher; Amerigo Vespucci Geog Awareness Prgm Innovator; Right to Read Yr Annual Celebration Co-Chair; OH Cath Ed Assn 1973-; Winner OH His Day St Awds 1979, 1984; *office:* St Mary Cntrl Schl 24 N 4th St Martins Ferry OH 43935

MINDERLEIN, JAMES LLOYD, Naval Science Instructor; *b:* Baltimore, MD; *m:* Diann Marie Ratchford; *c:* Jeff, Amy; *ed:* US Naval Acad (BS) Naval Engrng 1965; *cr:* US Navy USN Capt & Naval Aviator 1965-89; Northern HS Naval Jr Reserve Officers Trng Corps Naval Sci Instr 1989-; *ai:* Boys & Girls Cross Country Coach; NJROTC Drill Team & Color Guard Coach; US Naval Acad Alumni Assn 1965-; Southern MD Athletic Conf Coach of Yr 1993-95; NJROTC Drill Team Natl Champions 1994-95; *office:* Northern HS 2950 Chaneyville Rd Owings MD 20736

MINEHAN, PAUL RICHARD, Contract Law Teacher; *b:* Philadelphia, PA; *m:* Nancy Ladden; *c:* Kevin Michael, Janine Marie, Molly Marie, Kaitlyn; *ed:* LaSalle Univ (BS) Bus 1964; Post Grad Scndry Ed; *cr:* Cardinal Dougherty HS Tchr 1964-; *ai:* Asst Cross Cntry & Track Coach Girls Team Ocean City HS; *home:* 4 Gilbert Ln Ocean City NJ 08226

MINELLA, ANN BARRETTE, Sixth Grade Reading Teacher; *b:* Pittston, PA; *m:* James P.; *c:* James M.; *ed:* Wilkes Coll (BA) Elem Ed 1972; Univ of Scranton (MS) Elem Ed 1976; *cr:* Pittston Area Schl Dist Elem Tchr 1972-; *ai:* Pittston Area Fed of Tchrs 1972-; St Mary's Advy Bd 1989-91; *home:* 1147 Pittston Ave Old Forge PA 18518

MINELLI, REGINA PURSELL, Third Grade Teacher; *b:* Trenton, NJ; *m:* James K. Sr.; *c:* James Jr., Christopher; *ed:* Trenton St Coll (BS) Elem Ed 1971; ECE Cert 1984; *cr:* St Anthony Schl Third Grd Tchr 1978-; *ai:* Mid Sts Evaluation Comm 1993-94; NCEA 1978-; *office:* St Anthony Schl 530 S Olden Ave Trenton NJ 08629

MINEO, JEANNE PARLATO, Upper Grade Elem Schl Tchr; *b:* Brooklyn, NY; *w:* Charles (dec); *c:* Diane Barba, Gina Blanco, Andrea; *ed:* Fordham Univ (BS) Elem Ed 1959; Adelphi Univ (MS) Soc Stud 1992; 30 Credits Above MS in Ed; *cr:* PS 58 Tchr 1959-62, Tchr 1988-; Merrill Lynch Inc Customer Svc Mgr AVP 1978-85; Eabank Customer Svc Mgr AVP 1985-87; *ai:* Consultation Comm; Spec Ed Liaison; Grd Ldr; UFT & AFT 1988-; Girl Scout Brownie Ldr 2 Yrs; Adult Ed Tchr Nassau Cty 2 Yrs; Disabled Veterans On-Going, Bronze Ldr Commanders Club.

MINER, CAROL C., Biology Teacher; *b:* Amsterdam, NY; *m:* William J.; *ed:* St Univ of NY at Albany (BS) Bio 1973, (MS) Ed & Bio 1978; Cmptr Scis, Biotechnology & Ed; *cr:* Scotia-Glenville Cntrl Schls 7th & 8th Grd Sci Tchr 1973-75, Non-Regents Bio, Earth Sci & Bus Math Tchr 1976-79, 10th Grd Bio & Hlth Tchr 1980-85, 10th Grd & Advanced Placement Bio Tchr 1986-; *ai:* Botany Club Adv; Numerous Schl Comms; AFT 1973-; Assn of Curr & Supervision 1995-; Amsterdam Golf Assn 1990-; Amsterdam Couples League 1985-; Tandy Tchr; GE Star Awd Winner 3 Times; Grant From Golub Corp & Sterling Winthrop for Biotechnology; *office:* Scotia Glenville HS 1 Tartan Way Scotia NY 12302

MINER, JEFFREY T., English Teacher; *b:* Providence, RI; *ed:* RI Coll (BA) Eng 1973, (MA) Eng 1977; 36 Addl Hrs; *cr:* Pilgrim HS Eng Tchr 1973-; *ai:* Head Coach Girls Cross Cntry Team; Asst Coach Girls Outdoor Track Team; AFT, RIFT, Warwick Tchrs Union, RI Cncl Tchrs of Eng, NCTE 1973-; City of Warwick Juvenile Hearing Bd 1993-, Chm; Smithsonian Inst Natl Seminar, RI Consortium on Writing Fellow; Steering Comm RI Stwide Writing Assessment Mem; Fac Consultant to Educl Testing Svc Natl Tchr, Advanced Placement Exam; *office:* Pilgrim HS 111 Pilgrim Pkwy Warwick RI 02888

MINER, LORRAINE E., Spanish Teacher; *b:* Queens, NY; *m:* Keith H.; *c:* Victoria; *ed:* Siena Coll (BA) Span & Ed 1984; SUNY at Albany (MA) Span Lit & Ed 1985; Post Grad Courses; *cr:* Coxsackie Athens HS Span Tchr 1989-90; Siena Coll Adj Span Tchr 1989-91; SUNY at Albany Adj Span Tchr 1989-; Cairo-Durham HS Span Tchr 1990-; *ai:* NYSAFLT 1989-; ASCD 1995-.

MINER, MARGARET HOLBROOK, Special Education Teacher; *b:* Westfield, NY; *m:* Charles Bradley; *c:* Curt, Jason; *ed:* Univ of Rochester (BA) Eng 1965; Kent St Univ (MED) Gifted 1981; 30 Addl Credits; *cr:* Pittsford HS Eng Tchr 1965-67; Baldwin Elem Schl Tutor of LD 1978-79; Hudson HS Tudor of LD, Tchr of LD 1981-; *ai:* Acad Decathlon Head Coach 7 Yrs; *office:* Hudson HS 2500 Hudson Aurora Rd Hudson OH 44236

MINETOLA, ALBERT J.,JR., Head Teacher; *b:* Kutztown, PA; *m:* Janice R. Bender; *c:* Craig, Eric; *ed:* Futz Town St Coll (BS) El Ed 1971; Univ of Scranton (MS) El Ed Admin, Level I 1983; Attnd Penn St, Mansfield Univ; *cr:* Bethlehem Steel Corp Laborer 1967-71; ACME Mkts Clerk 1969-71; Self Employed Paintor 1970-71; Camptown Elem Schl 6th Grd Head Tchr 1971-; *ai:* Game Mgr, Time Clock Ofcl HS Aths; Ftbl Ofcl Jr HS; PSEA, NEA, WAES 1971-, Treas; Amer Red Cross 1979-, Bd of Dir; Wyal Vol Fire Co 1974-; Wyal Ambulance Dr 1980-; PA Math League Dir Test Admin & Tutoring; *home:* PO Box 104 Wyalusing PA 18853*

MINETOLA, JANICE R., First Grade Teacher; *b:* Muir, PA; *m:* Albert J. Jr.; *c:* Craig, Eric; *ed:* Mansfield Univ (BS) Elem Ed 1981, (MA) Elem Ed 1987; Attnd Binghamton Univ; Mansfield Univ Rdng Cert 1992; *cr:* Migrant Ed Prgm Tutor 1981-83; Wyalusing Area SD 6th Grd Tchr 1983, ELem Librn 1983-084, 1st Grd Tchr 1984-95; *ai:* Supt Cncl Comm; NEA, PSEA 1983-; Delta Kappa Gamma 1993-, Recording Sec; *home:* PO Box 104 Wyalusing PA 18853*

MINGRONE, JOSEPH A., English Teacher & Drama Dir; *b:* Brooklyn, NY; *ed:* St Francis Coll (BA) Eng 1976; *cr:* St Sergius HS Eng Tchr 1976-78; Bishop Ford HS Eng Tchr 1978-; *ai:* HS Dir; St Francis Coll Dir of Drama; NCTE 1978-; Educl Theatre Assn 1993-; Lay Fac Assn 1995-; *office:* Bishop Ford C C H S 500 19th St Brooklyn NY 11215

MINIERI, JAMES JOHN, Social Studies Chairman; *b:* Philadelphia, PA; *m:* Carmela B. Francesco; *c:* Traci Ann, Lisa Ann; *ed:* Penn St Univ (BS) Scndry Ed 1972; Glassboro St (MA) Soc Stud Ed 1977; Attnd Univ of PA 9 Grad Hrs, St Josephs Univ 3 Grad Hrs & Gettysburg Coll 3 Grad Hrs; *cr:* St John Newmann HS His Tchr 1972-81; Bishop McDevitt HS Soc Stud Chm 1981-; *ai:* NHS Adv; Dance Comm & Sr Prom Moderator; Recruitment & Retention Comm; Diocesan Schlrs; NACST 1972-, Union Rep 6Yrs; PA Cncl of Soc Studs & Philadelphia Cncl of Soc Stud 1972-; Univ of PA NEH Schlr; St Joseph Univ Taft Inst of Politics; Gettysburg Coll nEH Vietnam Experience; *office:* Bishop McDevitt HS Royal Ave & Mulford Rd Wyncote PA 19095*

MININBERG, MARY ELLEN MURHY, English Tchr & Stu Cncl Adv; *b:* New Haven, CT; *m:* Ian; *c:* Mark; *ed:* Albertus Magnus Coll (BA) Eng & His 1949; Fordham Univ (MA) Eng 1951; Southern CT St Coll Amer His & Rdng Tchng; Fairfield Univ Ed Courses; *cr:* St Mary HS Eng Tchr 1950; Sheridan Jr HS Eng Tchr 1951-58; Albertus Magnus Coll Eng Tchr 1963-69; Southern CT St Coll Eng Tchr 1970-77; Edgewood Schl Tchr & Dir Creative Arts Pgm 1974-77; Wilbur Cross High Eng Tchr 1977-; *ai:* Stu Cncl Adv; Dir Bloodmobiles; Schl Spirit Week; Thanksgiving Food Drive;

Citywide Ldrshp Conf Comm; New Haven Democratic Party, Sec, 26th Ward Chprsn; St Aedan Schl Bd; Cath Family Svc Bd 1989-; New Haven Tchr of the Yr 1980.

MINIUM, LINDA LAIRD, Communication Teacher; *b:* Lewisburg, PA; *ed:* Lock Haven St Coll (BS) Elem, Early Chldhd 1969; Bucknell Univ (MSEd) Ed 1979; Penn St Univ Post Grad Credits in Parks & Recreation; *cr:* Mifflinburg Area Schl Dist Second Grd Tchr 1969-71, Fifth Grd Tchr 1972-80, Eighth Grd Tchr 1981-; *ai:* Dist Outdoor Ed Prgm 1972-; NEA, PSEA, MAEA 1969-; Merrill Lynn Land & Waterways Conservancy 1991-, Bd of Dir; *office:* Mifflinburg Area MS 151 E Market St Mifflinburg PA 17844

MINK, SANDRA PHILLIPS, Business Education Teacher; *b:* Pittsburgh, PA; *c:* David, Daniel, Jennifer Porter, Margaret Kowalewski; *ed:* Westminster (BBA) Acctng 1960; Youngstown St (MBA) Acctng, Fin 1979; *cr:* Penn OH Univ Tchr 1960-63; South Range Tchr 1963-; *ai:* NHS; Stu Cncl; Acad Challenge; Stu Bus Ldrs; NEA, OEA 1963-; NEOEA 1963-, Recording Sec, Exec Comm; SREA 1963-, Pres; *office:* South Range HS 11836 South Ave North Lima OH 44452

MINKLEIN, SHARON ELIZABETH, Teacher of Gifted & Talented; *b:* Buffalo, NY; *ed:* D'Youville BS Liberal Arts; Univ of Buffalo (MS) Elem Ed; Attnd San Francisco St, Somona St Univ of CA, Univ of HI, Univ of Edingburgh, Scotland, Univ of London; *cr:* Maple Elem Schl 2nd, 3rd Grd IDEAS Tchr 1966-89; Williamsville Cntrl Tchr, Trainer Peer Coaching 1985-92; Maple Elem Gifted Talented Tchr 1990-; *ai:* Dist Staff Dev; Strategic Plan; Fac Liaison; AFT; Phi Delta Rappa 1985-; Alpha Delta Kappa 1970-, Pres, Recognition for 25 Yrs; ASCD; Amer Assn Univ Women Ed Chair; Buffalo Lille Assn Elem Coord; PTA Awd 25 Yrs of Svc; Article Pub on Best Practices; Nom for Williamsville Cntrl PTA Prof Awd.

MINKOFF, SANDRA G., First Grade Teacher; *b:* NY City, NY; *m:* Bernard; *c:* IRA; *ed:* Bklyn Coll (BA) Ed 1951; Hofstra Univ (MS) Ed 1971; *ai:* VP Bellmore Fac Org; Curr Advy, Staff Dev Comm; AFT, NYSUT 1968-.

MINNICOZZI, DONNA JILL, English Teacher; *b:* Bronx, NY; *m:* Dr. Michael; *c:* Jason, Samantha; *ed:* Montclair St Coll (BA) Eng 1991; Addl 6 Post Grad Credits Rdng Specialist & Rdng Tchr Cert; *cr:* East Brunswick HS Eng Tchr 1991-92; Dwight Morrow HS Eng Tchr 1992-; *ai:* NEA, NCTE 1991-; NYRRC; *office:* Dwight Morrow HS 274 Knickerbocker Rd Englewood NJ 07631*

MINNIEAR, JOSEPH C., High School English Teacher; *b:* Anderson, IN; *c:* Sean, Paul, Charles, James; *ed:* Univ of IN (BA) 1964, (MS) Eng, Sec Ed 1967; *cr:* Rancocas Vly Regnl HS Eng Tchr 26 Yrs; *ai:* Lit Publication Adv; NSEA, NEA 1970-; *office:* Rancocas Valley Regional HS Jacksonville Rd & Ridgeway St Mount Holly NJ 08060

MINO, JACK JOSEPH, Professor of Psychology; *b:* Astoria, NY; *m:* Dorothy Meyer; *c:* Jesse, Jane; *ed:* SUNY Stonybrook (BA) Psych 1978; Univ of WA (MSW) Soc Work 1983; *cr:* Berkshire Comm Coll Lecturer & Soc Work 1984; Holyoke Comm Coll Psych Prof 1986-; *ai:* Learning Comms in Sci & Hum Co-Dir; NEA & MTA 1987-; Grant: NEH, NSF & FIPSE 1993-; Marrieb Tchng Excel Awd 1994; Conf Presenter Tchng & Learning; Articles Pub; *office:* Holyoke Comm Coll 303 Homestead Ave Holyoke MA 01040

MINOR, ANNETTE POLLARD, Cosmetology Instructor; *b:* Opelika, AL; *c:* Marceline Y., Ursa R.; *ed:* Kent St Univ (Voc) Ed 1990; Youngstown St Univ (BS) Ed 1991; Ashland Univ Grad Stud; *cr:* Joseph long Schl of Cosmetology Jr Instr 2 Yrs; Annettes Designed Hair Care Salon Owner & Operator 15 Yrs; Trumbull Cty JVS Cosmetology Instr 4 Yrs; *ai:* Organizer & Planner Black His Pgms Triedstowe Bapt Church; Yth Ldr for Childrens Church Triedstowe Bapt Church; Coach Yth in Speech Preparation & Presentation; NEA 1991-; Trumbull Cty NAACP 1995-; Awds: Persuasive Speaking Forensic Team YSU; Beauty in Motion Production at Packard Music Hall; *office:* Trumbull County Joint Voc Schl 528 Educational Hwy NW Warren OH 44483

MINOR, BRIAN RICHARD, 5th Grade Teacher; *b:* Elmira, NY; *m:* Debora Faith House; *c:* Blaine, Brianne, Brendan; *ed:* Mansfield Univ (BS) Elem Ed 1973; Elmira Coll (Masters) Elem Ed 1978; *cr:* Penn Yan Cntrl Schls 4th-6th Grd Tchr 1973-; *ai:* Asst Var Ftbl Coach Defensive Coord; Co-Chm Just Say No Comm; NEA 1973-; Penn Yan Tchrs Assn 1973-; Elks Lodge 1722 1976-, Elk of Yr 1993; *office:* Penn Yan Cntrl Schl Dist 3 School Dr Penn Yan NY 14527

MINOR, LORNA H., High School History Teacher; *b:* New York, NY; *m:* Miller G.; *ed:* Coll of Mt St Vincent (BA) Soc Stud, His 1965; Bowling Green St Univ (MA) Amer His 1967; 60 Credits Beyond Masters; *cr:* Mamaroneck HS His Tchr 1968-; *ai:* NHS Adv; Jr Stman Adv; Mamaroneck Tchrs Assn 1968-, Pres 1988-1995; NCSS, NYSCSS, WCSS 1970-; AFT, NYSUT 1968-; NEH Fellowship Inst Women's His 1978-79; *office:* Mamaroneck HS 1000 W Boston Post Rd Mamaroneck NY 10543

MINOR, MARY ANGELA, 3rd-4th Grd Teacher; *b:* Hazelton, PA; *ed:* Marywood Coll (AB) Elem Ed, Music 1978; Instructional I, II Certs; Diocesan Cert Catechist; *cr:* St. Nicholas 3rd-5th Grd Tchr 1979-81; McAdoo Catholic Schl K-6th Grd Tchr 1981-; *ai:* CCD Instr; Church Organist, Guitarist, Vocalist; St Jude's Hosp Bike A Thon Co-Chprsn; ADLTA, NCEA 1979-; Hazelton Hist Soc 1982-84; *office:* McAdoo Catholic Schl 35 N Cleveland St Mc Adoo PA 18237

MINOR, MARY L. (MYER), Math, Art & Music Teacher; *b:* Lancaster, PA; *m:* Rodney; *c:* Adrienne, Allison; *ed:* Elizabethtown Coll (BS) Elem Ed 1978; *cr:* New Covenant Chrstn Schl Math, Art, Music Tchr 1991-; *ai:* Richland Church of Brethren Rejoice Club Dir; Drama Club Coach; *office:* New Covenant Chrstn Schl 1275 Birch Rd Lebanon PA 17042

MINOR, TOM W., Chemistry & Physics Teacher; *b:* Dayton, OH; *m:* Mary Ellen Brady; *c:* Faith Powell, Matthew, Elizabeth, James Paul; *ed:* Asbury Coll Wilmore KY (BA) Chrstn Ed 1970; Wright St Univ Dayton OH (MEd) Scndry Sci 1975; Partners Terrific Sci Miami Univ 1989-90; HS Chem Tchr Prgm Paper Sci Dept; *cr:* Dayton Chrstn Schls Bio, Chem, Music, Human Anatomy, Physics Tchr 1970-, Sci Dept Chm 1978-; *ai:* Sci Fair Coord; Montgomery Cty Sci & Engineering Fair Chm 1989-93; TEAMS, 5 Yrs Jr HS Soccer Coach; West Dist Sci Day 1980-, Tchr of Yr 1984; AAPT 1988-; Amer Chem Society 1987-; Montgomery Cty Sci Day 1978-, Chm 3 Yrs; Assn of Chrstn Schls, Sci Fair Chm 8 Yrs; Fac of WISE Prgm at Wright St Univ 1986, 1987, 1988, 1991; Tchr of Yr at Univ of Dayton; Tchr of Yr Acken Awd West Dist Sci Day; Batelle Awd; *office:* Dayton Chrstn HS 325 Homewood Ave Dayton OH 45405*

MINTCHELL, BEVERLY MOSELEY, Third Grade Teacher; *b:* Owensboro, KY; *m:* Gary Alan; *c:* Heather, Derek; *ed:* Cedarville Coll (BA) Elem Ed 1968; Attnd Univ of Dayton, Wright St Univ; *cr:* Ft Jennings Local 6th Grd Tchr 1968-69; New Carlisle 6th Grd Tchr 1969-70; Botkins Local 6th Grd Tchr 1971-73; Fairlawn Local 3rd Grd Tchr 1980-; *ai:* Strategic Plan Comm; NEA, OEA, FEA 1980-, Past Pres; SCIRA 1985-, Publicity Dir; Womens Circle 1985-, Past Sec; Hospital Auxiliary 1996; *office:* Fairlawn Elem Schl 18800 Johnston Rd Sidney OH 45365

MINTEL, SUSAN TERNISKY, Math Teacher; *b:* Canandaigua, NY; *m:* John L.; *c:* Sarah, Benjamin, Michael; *ed:* Le Moyne Coll (BA) Math 1987; Nazareth Coll (MS) Scndry Ed 1992; *cr:* Manchester Shortsville Cntrl Schl 7-12 Math Tchr 1987-; *ai:* AFT, NEA 1987; *office:* Manchester Shortsville C Schl Rt 21 Shortsville NY 14548

MINTON, MICHAEL VERNON, Sixth Grade Teacher; *b:* Middlesboro, KY; *m:* Paula Suzette Curtis; *c:* Mary Kaye Apke, Laura Lee, Angela Hope; *ed:* Campbellsville Coll (BS) Elem Ed 1967; Univ of Cincinnati (MS) Elem Ed 1977; Working Toward Masters In Law Ed; *cr:* Lebanon City Schls Tchr 1967-72; North College Hill City Schls Tchr 1972-; *ai:* NEA, OH Ed Assn 1969-; North College Hill Ed Assn 1972-, Pres, VP, Treas, Outstanding Treas Awd; Gideons Intnl 1994-, VP; Co-Authored OH Bar Assn Law Curr for Elem Schls; *office:* North College Hill City Schls 1498 W Galbraith Rd Cincinnati OH 45231*

MIORI-MEROLA, DOREEN M., English Teacher & Yearbook Adv; *b:* Syracuse, NY; *m:* Albert Joseph Merola Sr.; *c:* Nila; *ed:* Oswego St (BS) Scndry Ed, Eng 1975; Attnd Syracuse Univ, St Univ of NY; *cr:* Solvay HS Eng Tchr 1976-; *ai:* Yrbk; NHS; Dist Ldrshp Team; Schls of Character Project; Ftbl Camera Person; Tchrs Org Publicity Dir; AFT, NYSUT 1976-; Jr Girl Scouts 1992-, Ldr; US Power Squadron 1992-; Tyrol Club of Solvay 1970-; Solvay Centennial Comm; Co-Author Book-One Hundred Yrs of Tradition; Cited by Sen John D. Francisco Good News, Kids Prgm; *office:* Solvay HS 600 Gertrude Ave Solvay NY 13209*

MIRABELLA, THOMAS PATRICK, Theology Teacher; *b:* Philadelphia, PA; *ed:* Allentown Coll of St Francis de Sales (BA) Theology, Philosophy 1991; Working Toward Admin Degree, Cert; *cr:* Bethlehem Cath HS Theology Tchr 1992-; *ai:* Key Club Adv; JV Bsbl Asst Coach; Sports Videographer; Schl Maintenance Supvr; Allentown Tchrs Assn, NCEA 1992-; Kiwanis Club 1992-, Outstdng Svc Awd; Key Club Dir 1992-, Adv; Allentown Coll Pres Medal, Individual of Yr, Phi Delta Kappa Awd 1991; *office:* Bethlehem Catholic HS 2133 Madison Ave Bethlehem PA 18017

MIRACLE, KATHY TURPIN, Mathematics Teacher; *b:* Pineville, KY; *m:* Gary Dale; *c:* David; *ed:* Cumberland Coll (BS) Math 1972; Morehead St Univ (MA) Ed 1979; 30 Hrs Past (MA) Ed; Addl Hrs OH St Univ 3 Math, Univ of Cincinnati 3 Math, Ashland Univ 2 Ed; *cr:* Bourbon Cty HS Math Tchr 1972-74; Boyd Cty HS Math Tchr 1974-92; Springboro HS Math Tchr 1992-; *ai:* Stu Govt Adv; Pride Comm Chprsn; Grdng Comm; NEA 1972-; OMTA 1991-; 1995 Tchr of Excl; *office:* Springboro HS 1605 S Main St Springboro OH 45066

MIRACLE, MARY ANN HAVLENA, Retired Fifth Grade Teacher; *b:* Cleveland, OH; *c:* Jeffrey P., Gregory S.; *ed:* Miami Univ (BS) Elem Ed 1956; Xavier Univ (MED) Elem Cnslr 1976; Mid, Jr HS Math; Comm Intervention; Prespectives on Family Violence IV; Disruptive Child; Substance Abuse; Tchng Through Learning Channels; Prof Refinements in Dev Effectiveness; Project TEACH; Curr, Strategies for the Gifted; *cr:* Goshen Local Schls 5th Grd Tchr 1958-62, 1968-87, K-6 Grd Elem Cnslr 1987-89, K-6 Grd Substance Abuse Coord 1988-89, 5 Grd Tchr 1989-94, 5-6 Grd Career EdCoord 1990-93; *ai:* Served 5th Grd Rep to Clermont Cty Lang Arts, Sci Curr Comms; Math Minimum Competency Comm; NEA; OH Ed Assn; Goshen Ed Assn; OH Schl Cnslrs 1987-89; Pregnancy Help Ctr 1995-, Vol, Information Systems Person; Madeira Church of Christ Nursery Vol 1986, Vacation Bible Schl Registrar 1993, Prepare Communion, Mt. Healthy Serve Lunch 1994; OH Arts Cncls Arts in Ed Prgm Artist in Residency Grant Comm 1996-; Nom Tchr of Yr.

MIRACLE, RONALD BRYCE,SR., Carpentry Instructor; *b:* Zanesville, OH; *m:* Carol Ann Jack; *c:* Ronald Sr., Mellony Schoeppner, Rhonda Sapienea; *ed:* OH St Voc Carpentry 1980; *cr:* Omar Bakery Supvr 1956-65; M&E Inc Mgr 1965-68; Miracle Gen Contractor Owner 1968-80; Muskingum-Perry Career Ctr Carpentry Instr 1980-; *ai:* VICA Club Adv; Comms; NEA, OEA, Carpentry Advy Comm 1980-; Wildwood Church of Christ 1962-, Sunday Schl Tchr; Muskingum Homebuilders 1965-, Bd Mem 15 Yrs; St Homebuilders Assn; Natl Homebuilders Assn; BSA 8 Yrs, Order of Arrow; Army Reserves Honorable Discharge 1955; Outstdng Stu Job Placement; Zanesville Outstdng Performance Housing Rehabilitation Prgm, Sr Citizen & Disabled Winterazation Prgm; *office:* Muskingum-Perry Career Ctr 400 Richards Rd Zanesville OH 43701

MIRAGLIOTTA, SANDRA ANNE KAUBEK, Seventh Grade Teacher; *b:* New York City, NY; *m:* Vincent; *ed:* Fordham Univ (BA) His & Pre Law 1985; Jersey City St Coll Rdng 1986-87; *cr:* St Paul of the Cross 4th Grd Tchr 1985-86, 7th Grd Tchr 1986-; *ai:* Chprsn & Mem of Middle Sts Evaluation Team; NJEA 1985-; NCEA 1985-; *office:* St Paul Of The Cross Schl 211 Sherman Ave Jersey City NJ 07307

MIRAKIAN, JAMES EDWARD, High School Music Teacher; *b:* New Haven, CT; *m:* Catherine; *c:* Lauren, David; *ed:* Univ of CT (BS) Music Ed 1974; Univ of IL (MM) Choral Conducting 1979; 30 Hrs in DMA Prgm; *cr:* Meml Boulevard Schl Music Tchr 1974-77; Univ of IL Tchng Asst 1977-79; RHAM HS Music Tchr 1979-; *ai:* Drama Asst Dir; Tech Consultant & Asst; Schedule Planning Comm; Ind Stud Spon; Fine Arts Task Force; NEA, CEA, REA 1979-; MENC, ACDA 1974-, CMEA 1974-, Eastern Region Chorus Chm; Phi Delta Kappa 1985-; Amer Fed of Musicians 1992-; RHAM Music Boosters 1979-, Fac Chm; AHM Summer Theater 1990-, Music Dir, Outstanding Svc Awd; Music Ed Tchrs Assn 1989-; Town of Hebron Citizen of Yr Awd 1992; *office:* Rham Sr HS 67 Rham Rd Hebron CT 06248

MIRAND, JOHN PAUL, 8th Grade Social Studies Tchr; *b:* Kenmore, NY; *m:* Dawn Ferrara; *c:* Caralyn; *ed:* St Univ Coll at Buffalo (BS) Elem Ed 1985; Canisius Coll (EDM) Scndry Ed 1991; 48 Post Grad Credit Hrs; *cr:* Williamsville Schls Tchr Aide 1981-83; Clarence Jr HS Tchr Aide 1985-88; Clarence MS 8th Grd Soc Stud Tchr 1988-; *ai:* Musical & Variety Show, 8th Grd Promotion Dirs; Stu Cncl, Yrbk Advs; MS Advy Comm; NYSUT, AFT 1988-; Neighborhood Planning Advy Bd 1995-, Comm Mem; Golden Apple Awd Excl in Tchng 1994; *office:* Clarence MS 10150 Greiner Rd Clarence NY 14031

MIRANDA, CAROLINA HENRIQUES, Spanish Teacher; *b:* Waterbury, CT; *m:* Benjamin P.; *c:* Paul B., Carrie A.; *ed:* Univ of Hartford (BS) Span & Scndry Ed 1972; Southern CT St Univ (MS) Biling Ed 1978; 6th Yr Admin 1992; *cr:* Amity Reg #5 HS Span Tchr 1972-; *ai:* Natl Span Hnr Soc Adv; Dist Staff Dev Comm Bldg Rep; Bldg Based Staff Dev Comm Chprsn; CEA & NEA 1972-; AATSP 1984-; COLT 1984-; Spcl Olympics 1995-; Celebration of Excl Honorable Mention; *home:* 45 Heritage Dr Prospect CT 06712*

MIRESSI, RUTH SCHERER, Kindergarten Teacher; *b:* Kingston, NY; *c:* Adam, Jill, Anna Susan; *ed:* Marist Coll (BA) Ed 1972; SUNY at New Paltz (MS) Elem Ed 1975; *cr:* St Augustine Schl 6th Grd Tchr 1973-75; Kingston Cath Schl Kndgtn Thr 1975-; *ai:* Directed Numerous Theatrical Productions for K-8 Grds; *office:* Kingston Catholic Schl 159 Broadway Kingston NY 12401

MISENER, CHRISTINE CAMANDONA, Assoc Professor of Nursing; *b:* New Bedford, MA; *m:* Alan F.; *c:* Eric Alan, Craig Emile, Darren Frank; *ed:* U of MA (BSN) Nrsng 1965; SUNY at Stony Brook (MALS) Ed 1970; 3 Credits Cnslng U of MA; 6 Credits Ed Westfield St; *cr:* Holyoke Hosp Schl of Nrsng Instr 1965-67; Suffolk Comm Coll Assoc Prof Nrsng 1967-; *ai:* Nrsng Club Adv; Nrsng Curr, Coll Hnrs Comms; Assoc Womens Hlth Obstetrics & Neonatal Nrsng 1983-; SWR HS Connection 1985-, Advy Bd; St Ansens Episcopal Church 1993-; Vestor Companies That Care for Kids 1996, Bd Dirs; Reviewing Nrsng Textbooks; Outstdng Adv 1994; *office:* Suffolk Comm Coll 533 College Rd Selden NY 11784*

MISENHIMER, DEBORAH MCMANAMA, HS English Teacher; *b:* Holland, MI; *m:* Michael; *c:* Sarah, Myleah, Mikayla; *ed:* St Rose (MA) Eng 1983; Siena Coll (BA) Eng 1983; St Univ at Albany Eng; *cr:* Middleburgh Cntrl Schl Eng Tchr 1981-; Coll of St Rose Instr of Eng 1990-91; *ai:* Sr Adv; Drama & Poetry Coach; NYSUT 1981-; Gir Ldr; Timothy Murphy Players Dir; Hilltown Players Dir & Actress; Choir Dir; Poetry Books: Pilgrim Soul & Between the Lines; *office:* Middleburgh Cntrl Schl Main St Middleburgh NY 12122*

MISENKO, NANCY BECK, English Teacher; *b:* Syracuse, NY; *m* J.; *c:* Eric, Darren; *ed:* Potsdam Coll (BS) K-9 Ed Eng 1969; S Oswego (MS) Ed; Addl 24 Grad Hrs Beyond Masters; *cr:* Cntrl S 9-10th Grd Eng Tchr 1969-73; Phoenix Cntrl Sub Tchr 1983-87; A 10-11th Grd Eng Tchr 1987-; *ai:* Compact Dist Team; Comm Sc NCTE, APWTA 1987-; *office:* Altmar-Parish-Williamstown HS Cc 22 Parish NY 13131*

MISENTI, NICHOLAS CHARLES, Asst Prof of Acctng & Bus Middletown, CT; *m:* Julianne Connors Long; *c:* Kali, Zachary, Forrest; *ed:* Cntrl CT St Univ (BS) Acctng-Summa Cum Laude 198 of CT Schl of Law Juris Doctor Law 1983; *cr:* Capital Comm Te Asst Prof 1984-; *ai:* Acad Policies Comm Mem & Chprsn 1 Promotions Comm Chprsn 1995-96; Acad Adv; CT Dept Hig Consultant; ST of CT Attorney at Law; St of CT Certfd Pub Acc Internal Revenue Svc Vol Awd 1993 & 1994; *office:* Capital Com Coll 61 Woodland Street Hartford CT 06105

MISER, KATHARINE KOVACIK, First Grade Teacher; *b:* Steub OH; *m:* Richard L.; *c:* Brandon, Kaci; *ed:* Kent St Univ (BS) Elem E Univ of Dayton (MS) Rdng Ed 1988; *cr:* Westgate Elem 2nd G 1973-78; Jewett Elem Chptr Rdng Tchr 1978-80; Hopedale Elem Tchr 1985-89, 1st Grd Tchr 1989-; *ai:* Co-Jr Class Adv Jewett-S 1994-; Jr High Chrldng Adv 1989-94; NEA 1973-; OH Ed Assn Harrison Hills Tchrs Assn 1973-, Sec; Jewett Jr Womens Club 1 Pres & Sec-Treas; GFWC 1983-85, OH Jr Arts Chm; Jewett-Sc Boosters 1988-; Jewett-Scio Band Boosters 1988-; *home:* PO B Jewett OH 43986

MISHKIN, HAL RICHARD, Social Studies Tchr & Coord; *b:* Br NY; *m:* Carol Apelskog; *c:* Ross; *ed:* Stony Brook Univ (BA) Sc 1975, (MALS) Eng 1986; NY Univ Dist Ed Adm 1988; *cr:* St Josep Instr 1994-; South Manor Schl Dist Soc Stud Coord 1990-, Soc St 1978-; *ai:* Girls Vlybl; Yrbk Adv; Educl Dev Comm; Shared De Making Bldg Level Team; Rep for Eastern Hamptons Trng Ctr; Long Cncl for the SS 1995-; South Manor T A, AFT, NEA, NYST 1978-; Joe Basel Sports Cnsl 1993-; *office:* South Manor Schl Dist Dayt Manorville NY 11949

MISHLER, JOHN MILTON, Professor of Biology; *b:* Cairo, Sigrid Ruth Elisabeth Fischer; *c:* Joshua Evan; *ed:* Orange Coast Co Bio 1966; Univ of CA at San Diego (ABSCM) Melecular Bio, Engr 1971; Univ of Oxford England (PHD) Immunohaematology 1978 Royal Coll of Pathologists England FEC Path 1992; *cr:* Natl Inst Branch Chief 1980-82; Univ of MO Prof of Medicine 1983-89; Univ Eastern Shore Prof Nat Sci 1989-94; DE Vly Coll Dean 1994-95, B 1994-; *ai:* Master Plan Adv Comm; Budgeting, Policy Cncl; M Biomedical Rsrch Support Prgm Comm; Grad Fac Cncl; Sigma Xi Soc of Rsrch Admin 1987-, 1989 Excl Awd; Ctr Bus Innovation 19 of Dir; Bucks Assn Retarded Citizens 1994-, Bd of Dir; Sr Rsrch F Outstdng Admin Svc Awd 1987; 109 Scientific Articles Pub; Bo 1982; Mc Gew Overseas Flwshp Oxford Univ 1978; *office:* De Valley Coll 700 E Butler Ave Doylestown PA 18901*

MISHLEY, JOSEPH J., 8th Grade Science Teacher; *b:* Natick, M Marcia Piecewicz; *ed:* Univ of New England (BA) Environment 1976; Framingham St Coll (MED) Spec Ed 1989; 15 Hrs Advanc Stud Sci, Spec Ed; *cr:* Natick HS 9th Grd Sci Tchr 1985-86; Sherborn HS 9th-10th Grd Sci Tchr 1986-87; Hudson HS 8th Grd Sc 1987-; *ai:* 8th Grd Class Adv; Assessment Activity Chprsn; Transition Comms; MTA, NEA, HEA 1987-; Stow Historical Comm 1988-, Vice-Chm; *office:* Hudson HS 69 Brigham St Hudson MA 0

MISIOLEK, WOJCIECH ZBIGNIEW, Materials Engrng Assoc P Zabrze, Poland; *m:* Teresa Maria Korta; *c:* Michal W., Tomasz A.; *ed* of Mining & Metallurgy at Krakow Poland (ME) Metallurgy 1980, Metallurgy 1985; *cr:* Inst for Non-Ferrous Metals Rsrch Engr 19 Univ of Mining & Metallurgy Asst Prof 1984-88; Lehigh Univ V Rsrch Scientist 1987-88; Rensselaer Polytechnic Inst Rsrch Asso 1988-; *ai:* Confs, Seminars, Wkshps Comms Mem; ASM Intl 1988-, Awd; The Materials Soc 1988-; Amer Powder Metallurgy Inst Theodore M. Hebsburgh Awd 1995; ASM Alfred H. Geisler Mem Kosciuszko Fnd Flwshp 1987; AA, AEC Best Tech Paper Awds; Ove Tech Papers; One Patent; *office:* Rensselaer Polytechnic Inst 110 Troy NY 12180

MISIOREK, THOMAS, Fourth Grade Teacher; *b:* Norwich, C Louise Vocatura; *ed:* Southern CT St Univ (BS) Scndry Ed 1971; Cn St Univ (MS) Elem Ed; *cr:* Norwich Schl System 4th-6th Grd Tchr *ai:* IM Sports, Coaching; Bldg Mngmnt, Instrl Team; NEA, CEA *office:* Veterans Meml Schl 80 Crouch Ave Norwich CT 06360

MISMAS, LARRY J., Mathematics Lecturer; *b:* Greenburg, PA; Vincents Coll (BA) Math 1976; Duquesne Univ (MA) Math 1978; U Pittsburgh Grad Stud; *cr:* Duquesne Univ Tchng Asst 1976-78; U Pittsburgh Tchng Asst 1978-83; St vincents Coll Instr 1983-; *office:* Vincents Coll & Sem Latrobe PA 15650

MISRA, PRABHAKAR, Associate Professor; *b:* Lucknow, Ind Suneeta; *c:* Isha, Uday; *ed:* Univ of Calcutta (MS) Physics Carnegie-Mellon Univ (MS) Physics 1981; OH St Univ (PHD) P 1986; *cr:* OH St Univ Postdoctoral Rsrch Assoc 1986-88; Howard Asst Prof 1988-92, Assoc Prof 1992-; *ai:* Natl Sci Fnd Rsrch P Review; Natl Insts Hlth, Agency Intnl Dev; Prgm Comm Mem; Rsrch Sessions Chair Intnl Confs Lasers 1993-94; Amer Phys Soc 1984; Assn for Advancement of Sci, Amer Assn of Univ Profs 1994-; V Scholar Chem Dept Northwestern Univ 1990; Rsrch Grants Receive Environmental Protection Agency 1993-, NASA Lewis Rsrch Ctr Wright-Patterson Air Force Base 1990-94; *office:* Howard Univ D Physics & Astronomy 2355 6th St NW Washington DC 20059

MISSILDINE, KATHRYN LONG, English Professor; *b:* Dayton, O Daniel W.; *c:* Nathaniel, Whitney, Nina; *ed:* Univ of CT (BA) Eng Trinigy Coll at Hartford 24 Grad Credits; Univ of IA 9 Grad Credit Broadway HS Eng & Speech Tchr 1972-75; Lorain Co Comm Col Instr 1981-84; York Coll of PA Adj Eng Instr 1985-, Coord of Advising 1993-; *ai:* Advising Enhancement Comm Co-Chair; Stu Disabilities Comm Chair; Summer Lang Inst; Amer Assn Univ W 1979-, VP 1981-82 & Pres 1982-83; Lit Cncl 1986-; NOW 1985-; York Coll Of PA Country Club Road York PA 17405

MISSLER, CHARLES W., High School English Teacher; *b:* Broc MA; *ed:* Bridgewater St Coll (BA) Eng 1967; Cambridge Coll (MS) 1995; Anna Maria Coll 6 Credit Hrs; Fitchburg St Coll 9 Credit Hr Franklin Jr HS Eng Tchr, Coord 1967-91; Franklin HS Eng Tchr 1991 Head Ftbl Coach; MA Tchrs Assn, NEA 1967-; Franklin Ed Assn 1 Pres; MA Cncl Tchr of Eng 1992-; *office:* Franklin HS Oak St Franklin 02038

MISTRETTA, ANTOINETTE CARREA, Math & Algebra Teache Plainfield, NJ; *c:* Amanda; *ed:* Kean Coll of NJ (BA) Elem Ed 1977 Edison HS 9-12 Grd Compensatory Ed Math Tchr 1977-78; UFRES Grd Tchr 1978-82, 7-8 Grd Math Tchr 1982-; *ai:* Yrbk, 8th Grd Advs ıt Ldr; NEA 1977-; NJEA, UFREA 1978-; NCTM 1985-; Monmouth ıl Tchr of Yr 1989-90; Distinguished Svc Awd 1991; *office:* Upper d Regnl Elem Schl 27 High St Allentown NJ 08501*

HELL, ANNE MARIE, High School Mathematics Tchr; *b:* Troy, · Thomas A.; *c:* Carrie, Jennifer, Ryan; *ed:* Siena Coll (BA) ting & Math 1987; St Univ of NY at Albany (MS) Curr Dev 1990; ussell Sage Coll TI-81 Graphing Calculator Inst 1993; Statewide ele-Inst 1990; *cr:* Heatly HS Bus Ed Instr 1986-87; Troy City Schl ıth Instr 1987-88; Brittonkill Cntrl Schl Dist Math Instr 1988-; *ai:* :s & Fitness Assn of Amer Aerobics Instr; Brittonkill Fnd Grant for ıg Calculators Purchase 1996; MathCounts Coach 1988-92.

HELL, BARBARA CHAMPAGNE, English Teacher; *b:* Troy, NY; ı M., Amy M. Richter; *ed:* Coll of St Rose (BA) Eng 1961, (MA) ch 1973, (MA) Eng 1979; St Univ of NY at Albany 18 Grad Credits Supervision; North Adams St Coll 12 Grad Credits Admin, ssion; *cr:* Soc Security Admin Claims Rep 1961-62; St Peters Acad d Tchr 1970-71; Keveny Meml Acad HS Eng Tchr 1971-74; ɔrd-Halfmoon HS Eng Tchr 1974-; *ai:* BOCES, Waterford Distance ıg Comms; Tchrs Assn Rulse Rules, Curr Comm; ASCD, NCTE, NY Cncl, IRA, AFT, WTA; Delta Epsilon Sigma Alpha Chi Chapter; ɑwd Greater Capital Dist Tchr Ctr 1985; Natl Endowment for Hum 1985; Turnkey Trainer Lang Arts NY St Ed Dept; Local, Regnl, St s Presenter; *office:* Waterford-Halfmoon Elem Schl 125 Middletown erford NY 12188

HELL, BRUCE C., Science Coordinator; *b:* Gardner, MA; *m:* en Ann Cormier; *c:* Lisa M. Merrit, Jennifer Feyrer; *ed:* Fitchburg (BS) Bio 1969, (MA) Bio 1975; Post Grad Work in Psych, Cmptr Archeology; *cr:* Mahar Regnl Schl Sci Tchr, Sci Coord 1969-; *ai:* r, Sr Class Adv; Girls Jr Var Vlybl; Jr Var Bsbl; Jr High Ftbl; MTA ɜd; Manar Tchrs Assn 1969-, Past Pres; MA Tchrs Assn, NEA 1969-; s of Columbus 1982-; MA St Conservation Awd 1995; *office:* Ralph ar Regional HS S Main St Orange MA 01364

HELL, CHRISTINE DIXON, Vocal & Gen Music Teacher; *b:* gton, DC; *m:* David; *c:* Stephanie, Keith; *ed:* Univ of MD (BS) Ed 1975; Montgomery Cty MD (MEQ) Ed 1981; *cr:* Francis Scott HS 7-9 Grd Vocal, Gen Music Tchr 1975-84; Montgomery Blair HS rd Vocal, Gen Music Tchr 1984-89; Paint Branch HS 9-12 Grd Vocal, usic Tchr 1989-; *ai:* Stu Govt Assn; Music Dept Chprsn; NEA, 1975-; Organist for Washington Bullets 1973-83, Washington s 1973-, Georgetown Hoyas 1973-; *office:* Paint Branch Sr HS Old Columbia Pike Burtonsville MD 20866

HELL, CORINNE F., English Teacher; *b:* Boston, MA; *m:* William Courtney, Michael; *ed:* Bridgewater St Coll (BA) Eng 1969; Univ of A) Amer Stud 1993; *cr:* Broad Meadows Jr HS Eng Tchr 1971-84; Pub Schls Eng Tchr 1971-; North Quincy HS Eng Tchr 1984-; *ai:* Ed Assn, MA Tchr Assn, NEA 1971-; NCTE 1990-; MCTE 1993-; Boston Regnl Ed Cncl 1985-90; *office:* North Quincy HS 316 :k St North Quincy MA 02171

HELL, DANE EDWARD, English Teacher; *b:* Sharon, PA; *m:* :e Rhodes; *c:* Brian, Lorraine; *ed:* Geneva Coll (BA) Eng 1969; *cr:* HS Lang Arts Tchr 1969-; *ai:* Acad Competition Team Spon; OEA 1969-; Jamestown Presbyn Church 1977-; Mercer Cty Sportsmens 91-; *office:* Badger HS Box 99 Main St Kinsman OH 44428

HELL, DAVID E., Math Teacher; *b:* Biddeford, ME; *m:* Dawna J. re; *c:* Jill, Tracy, Jessica Amy; *ed:* Springfield Coll (BS) PE, Math *cr:* Kennebunk HS Math Tchr 1982-; *ai:* Consulting Tchr K-12th Curr, Innovation, Alternative Ed, Schl Improvement, Tchr Support Springfield Coll Interview Team; Ftbl Game Announcer; NEA, 1982-; Math Application Rocketry Made Easy; *home:* 9 Fieldcrest ınebunk ME 04043

HELL, DONNA TABORN, English & Social Studies Tchr; *b:* Perth , NJ; *ed:* Monmouth Coll BS Soc Stud, Ed 1970; Georgian Court MA) Admin, Supervision 1995; *cr:* Asbury Park HS Engl, Soc Stud 970-; *ai:* Dir of Pub Relations; ADEA, NEA 26 Yrs; NCTE, NJ ıl for the Soc Stud; Delta Zeta 1967-; Whos Who in Amer Ed 1972.

HELL, EDWARD J., History Teacher; *b:* Camden, NJ; *m:* Patricia ; *c:* Daniel, Kelly, Leigh; *ed:* Albright Coll (BA) His 1980; Beaver MA) Hum 1992; *cr:* Lenare HS His Tchr 1980-; *ai:* Ftbl Head Coach; Var Club Adv; Weight Room Supvr; NEA 1980-; Amer Ftbl Coaches 986-; *office:* Lenape HS 235 Hartford Rd Medford NJ 08055

HELL, ELAINE MARIE (ESTELLE), Fifth Grade Teacher; *b:* , OH; *m:* Alfred Sr.; *c:* Alfred Jr., Michael A., Marlita L.; *ed:* Univ edo (BA) Elem Ed 1982; Improving Stu Achvmt & Behavior; Positive line with Jane Nelsen; Empowering Young People with H. Stephen ; Cooperative Learning Levels I & II; *ai:* David Carter Symphonic 1986-; Natl Assn Advancement of Color People 1983-; First Church d, Sanctuary Choir 1975-; *home:* 2858 Scottwood Ave Toledo OH

HELL, GEORGE FREDERICK,JR., Technology Education er; *b:* Newark, NJ; *m:* Cheryl Joan; *c:* Taylor, Cameron, Morgan; *ed:* Coll of NJ (BA) Industrial Arts 1976, (MA) Admin, Supervision *cr:* Rahway Bd of Ed Industrial Arts Tchr 1976-86; Jackson Meml ch Ed Tchr 1986-; *ai:* Ski Club Adv; Asst Girls Soccer Coach; NEA, 1976-; JEA 1986-; *office:* Jackson Memorial HS Don Connor Blvd ɔn NJ 08527

HELL, GLENDORA WHITE, First Grade Teacher; *b:* Gaston Cty, : George William; *c:* Gordon, Glenda Evans; *ed:* J.C. Smith Univ Elem Ed 1965; Johns Hopkins Univ, Loyola Coll, Morgan St Univ alency, Advance Cert; *cr:* Baltimore City Dept of Ed Tchr 1964-; *ai:* grad Stu Tchrs Co-operative Tchr; Tessaract Prgm Math Peer Coach Demonstration Tchr; Mentor Tchr; AFT; BTU; NCTM; Girl Scouts; Jill of Amer; Delta Sigma Theta; *home:* 6732 Kincheloe Ave nore MD 21207*

HELL, GRANT JOSEPH, Director; *b:* Montpelier, VT; *m:* Michele ıey; *c:* Colton, Austin; *ed:* Univ of VT (BS) Ag 1975; 35+ Credits in ɔnmental Stud, Human Hlth & Wellness; *cr:* S Burlington HS Hlth 1975-77; Mt Mansfield UHS Sci & Math Edctr 1977-86; Stowe HS dctr & Dept Chm 1986-87; Winooski HS Sci & Hlth Edctr 1988-95; ıture Schl at NAWA Dir 1995-; *ai:* Adventure Sports Coord; Dir of Adventure Sports Guide Trng Pgm; WWOGA 1995-; AGVT 1995-; A 1996-, Bd of Dirs; Amer Red Cross 1972-, Instr; Mountainside ess Conf Planning Team 1991-; VT Dept Travel & Tourism 19968 ɔor Task Force; Implementation & Directorship of VT First Fully rated Scndry Curr; Licensed Ships Capt; *home:* RR 1 Box 28 ɪown VT 05660*

HELL, HELENA THERESA (SEKULAR), Sixth Grade Teacher; rain, OH; *m:* George E.; *c:* Brian L., Philip M.; *ed:* OH St Univ (BA) cis 1964, (BS) Soc Sci, Scndry Ed 1964; Wright St Univ (MS) Cnslng Attnd Youngstown St Univ, Univ of Dayton; *cr:* City Columbus ation Ldr I 1964-66; Miami East Jr HS Sci, Soc Stud Tchr 1968-; ston Elem Schl 5th Grd Tchr 1968-69; St Patrick Elem Schl 7th Grd 1979-89; Cookson elem Schl 6th Grd Tchr 1989-; *ai:* Substance e, Sci Fair Coord; Assessment, Soc Stud, Prof Dev Comms; OEA, 1989-; South Whole Lang 1991-; Kappa Delta Pi 1976-; St Patrick Church 1966-; Amer Assn Univ Women 1994, 1995; Lang Arts Presenter Statewide Convention; *home:* 644 S Market St Troy OH 45373

MITCHELL, JACQUELYN A., Chem, Math & Phys Sci Tchr; *b:* Palmerton, PA; *ed:* Immaculata Coll (BA) Bio & Chem 1984; Attnd LaSalle Univ Tchng Cert; Allentown Coll MED Prgm Degree Pending; *cr:* Panther Valley MS 7th Grd Earth & Space Sci Tchr 1988-89; Cardinal Brennan HS Chem, Sci & Math Tchr 1989-; *ai:* Stu Cncl Moderator; Sr Class & Grad Adv; Amer Chem Soc 1984-; Amer Inst of Chemists 1984-, Outstanding Coll Sr Awd 1984; Carbon Cty Democratic Exec Comm 1989-, Sec 3 Yrs; Marian HS Alumni Assn 1989-, Treas 3 Yrs; *office:* Cardinal Brennan H S RD 2 Ashland PA 17921

MITCHELL, JANICE BELL, Language Arts Teacher; *b:* Cleveland, OH; *m:* James Walker; *c:* Jeff Roderick, Jennifer Suzanne; *ed:* OH St Univ (BS) Elem Ed 1967; Cleveland St Univ (MA) Curr, Instruction 1982; *cr:* Cleveland Pub Schls Lang Arts Tchr 1967-75; Warrensville Hghts City Schls Lang Arts Tchr 1977-; *ai:* NEOEA, NEA & OEA 1967-; WEA Tchrs Assn 1978-; Metropolitan Cleveland Alliance of Black Schl Educators 1989-; Delta Sigma Theta 1965-; *office:* Randallwood M S 21865 Clarkwood Pkwy Warrensville Hts OH 44128*

MITCHELL, JIMMIE F., Teacher; *b:* Athen, GA; *m:* Jean; *c:* Randall; *ed:* Bachelor of Sci (BA) Bus Mgmt 1982; Spfld Tech Comm Coll (BA) Assoc Degree; Tchr Cert Bus Mgmt; *ai:* Bsktbl & Ftbl Coach; Mediation Tchr; Drug Abuse Trng; *home:* 186 Arcadia Blvd Springfield MA 01118

MITCHELL, JOHN C., Sixth Grade Teacher; *b:* Passaic, NJ; *m:* Eileen Zelinsky; *c:* Christopher, Ian, Tara; *ed:* Paterson St Coll (BA) Elem Ed 1967; William Paterson Coll (MA) Admin & Supervision 1974; Rutgers Univ (EDD) Elem Ed 1981; *cr:* Mt Hebron Schl 5th Grd Tchr 1967-68, 1971-72; US Army 1st Lieut 1968-71; East Dover 6th Grd Tchr 1972-; Cedar Grove Schl 6th Grd Tchr 1972-; *ai:* NEA, NJEA, TREA 1968-; SPEBSQSA 1960-, Dir of Chorus Champion 1968, 1989, 1991; Doctoral Dissertation Improving Spelling in Elem Grds 4-6; *office:* Cedar Grove Elem Schl 173 Cedar Grove Rd Toms River NJ 08753

MITCHELL, JOHN PATRICK, English Teacher; *b:* Brooklyn, NY; *ed:* St Thomas Aquinas (BA) Eng 1976; Fairleigh Dickinson Univ (MA) Eng 1980; St Univ at New Paltz 6 Credits; IONA Coll 3 Credits; *cr:* Pomona HS Eng Tchr 1979; Emerson HS Eng Tchr 1984-85; Nanuet HS Eng Tchr 1979-84; Dominican Coll Adj 1985-; *ai:* Modified Ftbl, Girls JV Bsktbl Coach; AFT 1979-, Bldg Rep; *office:* Nanuet HS 103 Church St Nanuet NY 10954*

MITCHELL, JOSEPH, Retired Fourth Grade Teacher; *b:* Auburn, NY; *m:* Joanne Leonard; *c:* Joseph, William, John, Laura; *ed:* SUNY at Oswego (BS) Elem Ed 1961, (MS) Elem Ed 1978; Addl Credit Hrs; IDEA Trng Group Process Facilitation; *cr:* Genesee St Sch Tchr 1961-63; Mark Loveless Sch Tchr 1963-79; Morgan Rd Sch Tchr 1979-94; *ai:* Liverpool Schl Dist Educl Cncl 1991-94; United Liverpool Fac Assn 1963-, VP, Treas; NYS United Tchrs 1963-; AFT 1972-.

MITCHELL, JUDITH UNZICKER, Third Grade Teacher; *b:* Chicago, IL; *m:* James; *ed:* Knox Coll (BA) Ed 1968; Wm Paterson Coll of NJ (MS) Ubun Ed, Comm Affairs 1981; 12 Credits Supervision, Prin Cert Kean Coll 1995-; Addl PHD Ed Credits La Salle Univ; *cr:* Hickory Hills Elem Schl Kdg Tchr 1969-70; New Brunswick Elem Schl K-3 Grd Tchr 1970-; *ai:* Dance Club, Baton, Drum Corps Spon, Dir; Young Inventors Clubs, Olympics of Mind, Cognetics 1984-90; NBEA 1970-, Rep; NJEA 1970-; IEA 1969-70; NJAHPERD 1986-, Convention Dance Wkshp; Phi Mu 1964-; New Brunswick Tchr of Yr 1989; Tchr of Yr 1984-85, 1996; Middlesex Co Elem Sci Tchr of Yr 1988; NJ Governors Awd 1989, 1995; *office:* Woodrow Wilson Schl 133 Tunison Rd New Brunswick NJ 08901

MITCHELL, KAREN FOLSOM-TILTON, Chemistry Teacher; *b:* Lewiston, ME; *m:* Walter Mitchell; *c:* Bethany Lake, Barbara Tilton; *ed:* Univ of ME at Orano (BSEd) Chem 1968; Univ of Southern ME (MSEd) Sci 1981; *cr:* Jay HS Chem, Sci Tchr 1968-; *ai:* Follow-Up Comm NEASC Accreditation Process Chair; St Sci Olympiad Event Capt; NEA, MEA, JTA 1968-; NEST 1991-, Exec Comm, ME Tchr of Yr 1994; Univ of ME Pulp & Paper Fnd Tchr of Yr 1994; Edcore IP Fnd Grant Recipient 6 Yrs; *office:* Jay HS 4 School St Jay ME 04239

MITCHELL, KEVIN JOHN, Professor of Mathematics; *b:* Providence, RI; *m:* Ellen Jean Duncan; *c:* Dorothy A., Dianne M.; *ed:* Bowdoin Coll (AB) Math & Philosophy 1975; Brown Univ (PHD) Math 1980; *cr:* Hobort & William Smith Coll Math Prof 1980-; *ai:* Queensland, Australia Term Dir Coll; AMS 1974-; MAA 1981-; COMAP 1983-; ASANA 1995-; Geneva Concerts 1994-, Bd of Trustees; NSF ILI Grants 1989, 1991; Author of Fnd of Analysis Test.

MITCHELL, LILLIAN LEE, Academic Affairs Dean; *b:* Baltimore, MD; *w:* Donald J. (dec); *c:* Suzanne Wilburn, Patrick; *ed:* Towson St Univ (BS) Ed 1959; Johns Hopkins Univ (MED) Ed 1962; Cath Univ (PHD) Cnslng 1972; 18 Credit Hrs Rdng Specialist Cert Loyola Coll; *cr:* Balto Pub Schls Tchr 1959-61; US Dept of Army Tchr 1961-62; Balto Pub Schls Tchr 1962-71; Garrett Co Pub Schls Cnslr 1971-72; Garrett Comm Coll Psych Prof 1972-85, Acad Affairs Dean 1985-; *ai:* MD Psychological Assn 1980-; Amer Assn of Comm Clg 1988-; Phi Theta Kappa 1961-; Delta Kappa Gamma 1972-, 2nd VP; *home:* 539 Mitchellee Ln Oakland MD 21550

MITCHELL, MARY J., Mathematics Teacher; *b:* Kenton, OH; *m:* Earl; *ed:* OH Northern Univ (BA) Math 1969; Addl Course Work at Bowling Green St Univ, Saint Marys Coll & Ashland Univ; *cr:* Fremont Ross HS Math Tchr 1969-71; Bellevue Sr HS Math Tchr 1971-; *ai:* Schl Tech Comm; Bellevue Ed Assn 1971-, Treas, Exec Bd; OEA, NEA 1969-; OCTM, NCTM 1978-; Bellevue Heritage Museum 1989-, Trustee, Sec; *office:* Bellevue Sr HS 200 Oakland Ave Bellevue OH 44811

MITCHELL, MEGAN J., History, AP Government Teacher; *b:* Alexandria, VA; *ed:* LA St Univ (BA) His 1991, (MA) Scndry Soc Stud Ed 1992; British His Univ of Cambridge England 1994; *cr:* Phoenixville Area HS US His, AP Govt Tchr 1994-; *ai:* NHS Adv; GATE Internship, AP Coord; NEA, PSEA 1994-; *office:* Phoenixville Area HS Gay & City Line Ave Phoenixville PA 19460*

MITCHELL, MELODYE A., Science Teacher; *b:* Frederick, MD; *c:* Katie Garner, Michael Garner, Benjamin Garner; *ed:* Univ of MD (BS) Botany 1973; Grad Schl Botany; *cr:* Bowie HS Chem Tchr 1973-76; Eleanor Roosevelt HS Bio, Chem Tchr 1976-87; DuVal HS Bio, Chem, Art Tchr 1988-; *ai:* Bio Club Spon; Fac Advy Comm; Sci Fair Coord; NABT, NEA, MSTA 1975-; AAAS 1987-; Laurel Boys, Girls Club 1990-, Coach; Appleman-Norton Awd for Excl in Botany 1973; NSTA, NASA Natl SSIP Tchng Awd 1985; Outstdng Scndry Tchr Awd, PEPCO, PGCO Pub Schls 1995; *office:* Du Val Sr HS 9880 Good Luck Rd Lanham MD 20706*

MITCHELL, RICHARD ANTHONY, English Professor; *b:* Johnson City, NY; *c:* Richard, Marissa, Michael; *ed:* Broome Comm Coll (AA) Liberal Arts 1968; SUNY at Oswego (BA) Eng, Amer Lit 1970, (MA) Eng, British Lit 1977; Univ of NV at Reno (PHD) Eng Renaissance 1982; *cr:* St Univ of NY at Delhi Asst Prof 1978-85; North Cty Comm Coll Asst Prof 1985-86; St Univ of NY at Alfred Prof 1986-; *ai:* MLA 1978-; Marlowe Soc 1988-; ADE 1990-; Speaking of Seed & Night Chiron Review Press; *office:* S U N Y Coll Of Tech At Alfred SDC 327 Alfred NY 14802*

MITCHELL, ROBERT WILLIAM, Teacher; *ed:* Boston Coll (BA) Latin-Cum Laude 1971, (MA) Latin-Distinction 1975, (MA) Greek-Distinction 1982; MA Dept of Ed Tchrs Cert 1974; PHD Prgm: Johns Hopkins 1984-85, Brown Univ 1985-87; *cr:* Beaver Cntry Day Latin Tchr 1971-73; Weymouth South HS Latin Tchr 1975-80; Boston Coll Latin Tchr 1980-81; Waltham HS Latin Tchr 1982-83; St Sebastian Cntry Day Schl Latin Tchr 1983-84; Johns Hopkins Latin Tchr 1984-85; Franklin & Marshall Coll Ctr Academically Talented Youth Tchr 1984; Summer Semester Latin Tchr 1984, Greek Tchr 1984; Brown Univ Discussion Group Ldr Fall Semester 1986; Regis Coll Latin Tchr 1987; Newton North HS 1990-; Newton Amer His, Soc Stud FA Day JHS Tchr 1991-92; Boston Coll Latin Tchr 1991-92, Greek Tchr 1992; *ai:* Boston Marathon Running 1972-; Ultra Distance London to Brighton England 1975; Triathlons; Alpha Sigma Nu Jesuit Honor Soc 1979; Laborer's Intnl Union North Amer 1968-, Construction Laborer; Cane, Classical Assn New England Shakespeare Oxford Soc, Mem.

MITCHELL, SANDRA MUNDORFF, 2nd Grade Teacher; *b:* Bolivar, PA; *m:* James E.; *c:* Kristin S. Stiffey, Charles D.; *ed:* Indiana Univ of PA (BS) Elem Ed 1966; Master Equivalency 1992; *cr:* Ligonier Valley Schl Dist 1st Grd Tchr 1967-72, 2nd Grd Tchr 1980-; *ai:* Pilot Prgm for Cross-Grd Tchng of 2nd & 3rd Grd 1993-94; Discipline Comm 1990-; Sci Comm 1993-;Sci Comm 1993-4; Stategic Plnng Comm for ligonier Valley Schl Dist 1994-5; Reprt Crd Comm 1994-5; PSEA, NEA & Ligonier Valley Ed Assn 1980-; Seward United Meth Church 1967-, Chair of Ed; Seward Area Comm Ctr 1987-, Sec, Dir, Chair of Recreation; Pa Cleanways 1992; Seward Recreation Bd Chm 1995; Ligonier valley Endowment comm 1996-; *office:* Laurel Valley Elem Schl RD 1 New Florence PA 15944*

MITCHELL, SCOTT NATHAN, Middle Level Tchr & Asst Prin; *b:* Augusta, ME; *m:* Jude Liston; *ed:* Univ of ME at Farmington (BA) Elem Ed 1983; 21 Credits Towards Admin Masters; *cr:* Athens Elem Schl Mid Level Tchr 1983-; *ai:* HS Girls JV Bsktbl, Co-Ed MS Soccer Coach; Skowhegan Elks Club 1996-; *office:* Athens Elem Schl PO Box 167 Athens ME 04912*

MITCHELL, VIOLET LORETTA, Elem Schl Guidance Counselor; *b:* Plainfield, NJ; *ed:* St Pauls Coll at Lawrenceville (BS) Elem Ed 1973; Kean Coll at Union (MS) Cnslr Ed 1992; *cr:* Plainfield Bd of Ed Elem Grd 4-6 Tchr 18 Yrs; Plainfield Bd of Ed Elem Schl Guid Cnslr 4 Yrs; *ai:* Jr Gentlemen's Club; Creative Arts Club Adv; Stdnt Cncl; Bsktbl; Ldrshp Inovation & Change Cncl Comm Dist, Schl; Comm Planning Process Design Team Liaison; Schl Partnership Comm; Self-Esteem Jams; Black His; Quiz Bowl; Guid Newsletter; Easter Seal Campaign; Bonding Ties; Symposium for Parents; Men Involved; NEA, NJEA 1973-; Plainfield Ed Assn 1973-, Rep Cncl, VP, Pres, Recording Sec; NJ Cnslrs Assn, Natl Cnslrs Assn, NJ Schl Cnslrs Assn 1992-; Plainfield Family Yth Club 1992-, Support Group; Ath Comm Corp 1966-, Bd Mem; Schl Based Yth Svcs 1994-; Plainfield Family Net Advy Bd 1994-, Co-Chprsn 1994- 95, Sec 1995-; Governors Recognition Tchr of Yr 1987; *office:* Evergreen Elem Schl 1033 Evergreen Ave Plainfield NJ 07060

MITRA, INDRANI, English Professor; *b:* Calcutta, India; *m:* Ravi Subramaniam; *ed:* Calcutta Univ (BA) Eng Lit 1979, (MA) Eng Lit 1982; Kent St Univ (PHD) Eng Lit 1992; *cr:* Mount Saint Mary'S Coll Asst Prof 1991-; OR St Univ Ctr for Hum Fellow 1995-; *ai:* Modern Lang Assn 1990-; Numerous Publications & Conf Presentations; *office:* Mount Saint Marys Coll Emmitsburg MD 21727

MITSAKOS, DONNA DEFUSCO, Fifth Grade Teacher; *b:* Webster, MA; *m:* Nicholas P.; *c:* Nicholas W.; *ed:* Cardinal Cushing Coll (BA) Ed K-8 1971; *cr:* Webster Pub Schl System 5-6 Grd Elem Schl Tchr 25 Yrs; *ai:* 5th-6th Grd Schl Bank Co-Adv; Coord Partnership for Raising Funds with Schl & Peace Corps for Kutna Hora Lib in Czech Republic; Multi-Age Writing, Rsrch Project Comm Founder; NEA, MTA, WEA 1971-; *office:* Anthony J. Sitkowski Schl Negus St Webster MA 01570

MITSTIFER, ARWOOD E., Retired Teacher; *b:* Williamsport, PA; *m:* Walburg R. Scholz; *c:* Romy Young; *ed:* Lycoming Coll (BS) Sociology 1963; Penn St (MED) Admin 1976; *cr:* Liberty Elem Schl Tchr 27 Yrs; *ai:* NEA, PSEA 1963-.

MITTELSTAEDT, JAMES ROBERT, Associate Professor; *b:* North Tonawanda, NY; *m:* Susan Gaspari; *c:* James, Jennifer, Jill; *ed:* Empire St Coll (AS) Criminal Justice, (BS) Criminal Justice 1986; SUNY Coll at Buffalo (MS) Criminal Justice 1988; *cr:* NY ST Police Investigator 24 Yrs; Niagara Cty Comm Coll Assoc Prof 1989-; SUNY Empire St Coll Mentor 1990-; Niagara Cty Law Enforcement Acad Instr 1990-; *ai:* Mid Sts Steering, Acad Grievance Comms; Judicial Bd of Conduct; Stu Criminal Justice Assn Adv; NEA 1989-; Amer Corr Assn 1990-; North Tonawanda Yth Bd 1990-94; NYS Retired Troopers Assn 1989-; Niagara Cty BOCES Advy Bd 1990-; Dev Criminal Investigations Course Grant 1994; Rrrch Attrition CRJ Curr Grant 1994; Outstdng Contribution Stu Acts Prgm Awd 1995; Stu Senate Extra Mile Awd 1991; Stu Sentate Contribution & Achievement Awd 1990; *office:* Niagara County Comm Coll 3111 Saunders Settlement Rd Sanborn NY 14132*

MITTELSTEADT, VIVIAN LEE, Spanish Teacher; *b:* Buffalo, NY; *ed:* Alfred St Coll (AAS) Ag Sci 1967; St Univ of NY at Buffalo (BA) Bio 1975, (MSEd) Eng as Second Lang & Foreign Lang 1993; 20 Credit Hrs at St Univ of NY at Buffalo in Span; 6 Credit Hrs at Daemen Coll Tchr Cert; 12 Credit Hrs at Univ Iberoamericana at Mexico City; *cr:* Lewiston-Porter HS Sub Tchr 1988-89; Buffalo Pub Schl 71 Span Tchr 1989-90; Lewiston-Porter HS Span & Bio Tchr 1990-91, Span Tchr 1991-; *ai:* Schl Site Base Mgmt Team; Western NY Foreign Lang Fair Judge, Presenter & Participant; WNYFLEC 1989-, 1st VP, Conf Presenter 1992; NYSAFELT 1991-, Conf Presenter; ACTFLT, NNELL 1995-; Dodge NEH Foreign Lang Fellow 1996; *office:* PS 71 156 Newburgh Ave Buffalo NY 14211*

MITTLER, DAVID E., Language Teacher; *b:* Oberlin, OH; *m:* Mona; *c:* Rebecca; *ed:* Otterbin Col (BA) Eng 1972; 5 Addl Hrs Towards Masters at Baldwin Wallace Coll; *cr:* Holy Trinity Schl 7th-8th Grd Eng Tchr 1973-74; St Christopher Schl 7th-8th Grd Rdng, Eng Tchr & Admin Asst 1975-88; Lorain Cty Comm Coll Eng & Writing Tchr Part Time 1988-93; St Richard Schl 7th-8th Grd Lang Tchr 1989-; *ai:* Adv for Schl Newspaper, Yearbook; NCEA 1973-; *office:* St Richard Schl 26855 Lorain Rd North Olmsted OH 44070

MITTLER, DIANNE BENTLEY-BURK, Gifted Resource Teacher; *b:* Lakewood, OH; *m:* Glenn Douglass; *c:* Stephen, Laurie; *ed:* Kent St Univ (BA) Spec Ed, Gifted 1980; Post Grad Stud in Spec & Elem Ed, Curr Dev; *cr:* Lorain City Schls Kndgtn Tchr 1984-85, Third Grd Gifted Tchr 1985-95, Gifted Resource Tchr 1995-; *ai:* NEA, LEA 1984-; ASAD 1993-; *office:* Meister Road Elem 3301 Meister Rd Lorain OH 44052*

MITTLER, DONNA S., Speech & Theatre Teacher; *b:* Worzburg, Germany; *ed:* Bowling Green St Univ (BS) Ed, Gen Speech 1977; Univ of Akron (MA) Theatre 1988; Post Grad Stud 17 Hrs; *cr:* Brunswick HS Tchr 1977-; *ai:* VOD, Rotary Speech Contents, Theatre Dept Coord; Dir 2 Main Stage Shows; Thespian, Theatre Club Spon; Perennial Peace Garden Supvr; NEA, OEA, BEA, OTA, ITS 1977-; *office:* Brunswick HS 3851 Center Rd Brunswick OH 44212

MITTMAN, NINA SIMON, 5th Grade Teacher; *b:* New York, NY; *m:* Stephen Mittman; *c:* Howard, Seth; *ed:* CW Post Coll at Greenvale (BS) 1969; Stony Brook Univ (MS) Lbrl Stud 1994; 30 Grad Credits; *cr:* Los Angeles City Schls Tchr 1969-70; Glen Cove Pub Schls Tchr 1970-77; Mark Cntry Day Schls Tchr 1980-83; William Floyd Schl Dist 1983-; *ai:* Stu Cncl & Newspaper Co Adv.

MJAANES, HOLLY (WALKER), 8th Grade English Teacher; *b:* New York City, NY; *m:* Alfred J.; *ed:* Barrington Coll (BA) Ed, Bible 1966;

Queens Coll (MA) Cnslng, Guid 1971; *cr:* Lawrence Summer Schl Spec Ed, Cmptrs, Math, Rdng, Lang Arts, 10th-11th Gr Eng Tchr 1967-95; #2 Schl 4th-6th Grd Tchr 1966-87; Lawrence HS Adult Ed Abnormal Psych Tchr 1967-79; Lawrence MS 6th Grd Tchr 1987-95, Adult Basic Educa Tchr 1979-, 8th Grd Eng Tchr 1995-; *ai:* Prin Advy, Report Card Comm; Grouping Task Force; Vlybl Captain; Natl Spelling Bee Coord; NYSUT 1967-; Lawrence Tchrs Assn, PTA 1966-; Soc Guid Cnslrs Queens Coll 1971-; Hnr Citation Dedicated Svc 1990; Literacy Tchr of Yr Nassau Cty 1990; No Absences 25 Yrs Letter Supt of Schls; *office:* Lawrence Pub Schls 195 Broadway Lawrence NY 11559

MLYNIEC, RICHARD ALEXANDER, Business Teacher; *b:* Rochester, NY; *m:* Susan Johnson; *c:* Jennifer, Jessica; *ed:* Rochester Inst of Tech (BS) Bus Admin 1974; Buffalo St Coll (MS) Voc Tech 1981; Educl Admin Cert SUNY at Brockport; *cr:* Ellenville Cntrl Schl Bus Tchr 1977-78; Avon Cntrl Schl Bus Tchr 1978-83; Bloomfield Cntrl Schl Bus Tchr 1983-84; Mt Morris Cntrl Schl Bus Tchr 1984-; *ai:* Dist, Bldg Decision Making, Introduction to Occupations Curr Teams; MM Tchrs Assn 1984-, VP; NYS BTA, MC BTA 1978-; NYS VEA 1984-; Knights of Columbus 1992-, Grand Knight; Mc Quaid Assembly 1994-, Faithful Navigator; Batavia Clippers Inc 1993-, Direction; WY Cty Fair Assn 1994-; Articles Pub; Turn Key Trainer; Curr Presenter; NY Ed Dept Comm; *office:* Mt Morris Central Schl Bonadonna Ave Mount Morris NY 14510*

MOALLEM, FILOMENA VISCARDI, English Department Chairperson; *b:* St Peter, Italy; *ed:* Jersey City St Coll (BA) Eng, Scndry Ed 1978; MA in TESOL Tchrs Coll, Columbia Univ 1995; *cr:* Jewish Educl Ctr Eng Tchr 1988-89; Holy Family Acad Eng Tchr 1989-91, Eng Dept Chprsn 1991-; Adjunct Instr Bloomfield Coll; *ai:* NCTE 1988-; TESOL 1991-; *office:* Holy Family Acad 239 Ave A Bayonne NJ 07002

MOBLEY, NANCY HRIMNAK, Language Arts Teacher; *b:* Mt Pleasant, PA; *m:* Kenneth E.; *c:* Sharon, Robert; *ed:* Bowling Green St Univ (BS) Ed 1971; Post Grad Credits from St Joseph Univ, Rosemont Coll & West Chester Univ; *cr:* Interboro Schl Dist Math Tchr 1971-73, Lang Arts Tchr 1988-; *ai:* Spelling Bee Coord; Tinicum Instrl Support Team; NEA 1988-; *office:* Tinicum Schl 1st & Seneca St Essington PA 19029

MOCCIA, MADELINE MARY, Seventh Grade Teacher; *b:* New York, NY; *ed:* Iona Coll (BBA) Acctng 1988; 15 Credits Ed Grad Stud; *cr:* St Clare's Schl Seventh Grd Tchr 1989-; *home:* 1906 Hone Ave Bronx NY 10461

MOCEK, BRENDA M., German Teacher; *b:* Toledo, OH; *w:* Albin M. Mocek (dec); *c:* Dana, Michael, Libbe; *ed:* BGSU (BSEd) Ger 1972; 46 Grad Hrs Scndry Ed Univ of Toledo; *cr:* Libbey HS Eng Tchr 1972-73; Rogers HS Eng, Ger Tchr 1973-79; Devilbiss HS Ger Tchr 1985-90; Start HS Ger Tchr 1991-; *ai:* Ger Club; Delta Epsilon Phi Club Adv; AFT 1973-; ACTFL 1995-; OFLA, AATG 1985-; St Johns Luth Church 1950-, Church Cncl VP, Bldg Comm, Yth Advy Comm, Prsnl Comm; Celebration of Excl Commended Tchr; Commended by Red Cross & United Way for Work with Stdnts; *office:* Roy C. Start HS 2100 Tremainsville Rd Toledo OH 43613

MOCHEL, AUDREY K., English Teacher; *b:* Buffalo, NY; *m:* Ken; *c:* Jim, David; *ed:* SUNY at Geneseo (BA) Eng 1984; Middlebury Coll (MA) Eng 1989; *cr:* Warsaw HS Tchng, Tchng Asst 1976-84; Canisteo HS Eng Tchr 1984-; *ai:* Musicals Dir.

MOCIK, WAYNE KENNETH, Science Instructor; *b:* Jersey City, NJ; *m:* Cleone Witkofsky; *c:* Wayne Kenneth, Chad Evan, Natalie Cleone; *ed:* Parsons Schl (BA) ELem Ed 1970; Loras Univ Elem Schl Supervision; 9 Credit Hrs Fairleigh Dickinson Univ Sci Specialist; *cr:* Guttenberg Elem Schl 5th, 6th Grd 1970-79; Mt Olive Dist Schl 6th, 7th Grd Sci Tchr 1979-; *ai:* Model Bldg Adv; Garden Club Adv; Karate Club Adv; Stu Cncl Adv; Peer Tutoring Adv; Supt Cncl; Ed Specification Comm; Scheduling Comm; Caldendar Comm; Enviromental Camp Adv; NEA 1970-; NJEA 1979-; NJSTA 1990-; BSA Comm Chair 1970-, Scout Master; Cub Scout 1979-, Chm; Colonial Musketerr 1980-, VP, Pres, No East Champions; Fife, Drum Corps 1987-, Dir NJ, NY St Champions; Grand Prize Winner Recycling Awd 1992; Natl Gardening Grant 1993; Who's Who AAT 1993, 1996; *office:* C. M. Stephens Mt Olive MS 99 Sunset Dr Budd Lake NJ 07828

MOCKUS, CAROL, Chemistry Teacher; *b:* Philadelphia, PA; *ed:* Holy Family Coll (BA) Chem 1980; Villanova Univ (MA) Chem 1985; *cr:* Nazareth Acad HS Chem Tchr 1980-; *ai:* NCEA 1980-; NSTA 1980-; CSC 1980-, Moderator for Adv Bd 1988-, Moderator of the Yr; Natl Cath Yth Conf 1994-, Chprsn for Spcl Svc; CSC Moderator of Yr Awd; Nazareth Acad Alumnae Assn Hnr Awd in Ldrshp & Svc; *office:* Nazareth Acad HS 4001 Grant Ave Philadelphia PA 19114

MOCKUS, JOHN, Guidance Counselor; *b:* Philadelphia, PA; *m:* Audrey Golomb; *c:* Kate; *ed:* Penn St (BA) Lib Arts, His 1968; Glassboro St Coll (MA) Stu Prsnl Svc 1973; Admin Cert Glassboro St Coll; Substance Awareness Coord St Cert Jersey City St Coll; *cr:* Greenwood Schl Dist Eng, His Tchr 1968-69; Clearview Regnl HS Eng, His Tchr, Cnslr 1969-91; MT Holly Twp Schls Cnslr, Sub Aware Coord 1991-92; Rancos Vly Regnl HS Cnslr 1992-; *ai:* Peer Mediation; NEA, NJEA 1969-; *office:* Rancocas Valley Reg HS 572 Jacksonville Rd Mount Holly NJ 08060

MODIC, EUGENE LEIGH, Biology Teacher & Dept Liaison; *b:* Sewickley, PA; *m:* Louise Marion Morelli; *c:* Paul E., Gregory T., Alyssa M.; *ed:* Indiana Univ of PA (BSEd) Bio, Ed 1970; Slippery Rock Univ of PA (MED) Bio 1977; *cr:* North Allegheny Schls Tchr, Liaison 1970-; *ai:* Supvr Evening Aquatics Prgm; Instr, Trainer Lifeguards, Swim Instrs; AFT 1970-; Western PA Bio Tchrs Assn 1996; Mason Blue Lodge 1990-; York Rite Masonry, Shriners 1991-; Safari Club Intnl Amer Wilderness Ldrshp Schlsp Awd; *office:* North Allegheny Intermdte H S 350 Cumberland Rd Pittsburgh PA 15237

MOECKEL, ILONA CISLAK, Fifth Grade Teacher; *b:* Clinton, MA; *c:* David J., Melissa A., Christopher H.; *ed:* Worcester St Coll (BS) Ed 1961; 30 Hrs Ed; *cr:* Lancaster Meml Schl Grd 4 Tchr 1961-71; Lancaster MS Grd 5 Tchr 1971-; *ai:* Natures Classroom Coord; Lancaster Tchrs Assn 1961-, Pres; Nashoba Regnl Ed 1995-, Pres; MA Tchrs Assn, NEA 1961-; *office:* Lancaster MS Hollywood Dr Lancaster MA 01523*

MOEGLING, LAWRENCE ANTHONY, Spanish Teacher; *b:* Canton, OH; *m:* Mary Lou; *c:* Lori, LeeAnn; *ed:* Bowling Green St Univ (BS) Span & Eng 1975, (BA) Span & Eng 1975; Marietta Coll (MA) Liberal Stud 1981; OH Univ (MAEd) Scndry Ed 1989; *cr:* Ft Frye HS Span Tchr 1975-; Washington St Comm Coll Span Adjunct Instr 1993-; *ai:* Span Honor Soc; OEA & NEA 1975-; FFTA 1975-, Pres, VP, Treas; OFLA; Knights of Columbus 1985-, Grand Knight, State Dir; NEH Awds & Grant; NCTE Article; *office:* Fort Frye Jr/Sr HS 5th St Beverly OH 45715*

MOEHN, JULIETTE MARIE, High School Science Teacher; *b:* Princeton, NJ; *ed:* Univ of CT (BS) Cytogenetics 1991; Med Lab Sci Cytogenetics 1991; 16 Grad Credits at Montclair St Univ; *cr:* Metpath Inc Cytogeneticist Internship 1991; Novo Nordisk Pharm Inc Product Safety Consultant 1991-92; Kearney HS Sci Tchr 1992-; *ai:* Bio Sci League Adv; Rennaisance Comm; NJEA 1992-; NJSTA 1994-; Vol at Great Swamp Outdoor Ed Ctr; *office:* Kearny HS 336 Devon St Kearny NJ 07032*

MOELLER FOSTER, DORIS PRICE, HS Math Tutor; *b:* Peconic, NY; *c:* Linda Moeller, Rik F. Moeller (dec); *ed:* STC at New Paltz (BE) Ed 1943; Attnd Corenll Univ 1955, SUNY at SCCC 1967, LIU Southampton 1968, C W Post 1968; *cr:* Hampton Bays Schl 3rd Grd Tchr 1943-44; Southold Schl 4th Grd, Jr High Math, Summer Schl Math & Adult Ed Math Tchr 1955-77; *ai:* Math Tutor 1977-; NYSUT 1955-; SCMT 1955-; AMTNYS 1966-; NCTM 1966-; *home:* 3600 Little Neck Rd Cutchogue NY 11935

MOENICH, KENNETH MICHAEL, Second Grade Teacher; *b:* Parma, OH; *m:* Kathryn Ann Liberatore; *c:* Faith Alexandra; *ed:* Cleveland St Univ (BA) Elem Ed 1988, (MS) Cmptr Uses in Ed 1992; *cr:* Arlington Elem Schl Fifth Grd Tchr 1988-93; Pleasant Vly Elem Schl Second Grd Tchr 1993-; *ai:* Safety Patrol Adv; NEA, OEA 1988-; *office:* Pleasant Valley Elem Schl 9906 W Pleasant Valley Rd Cleveland OH 44130

MOENK, JEANNE A., Assistant Professor of Math; *b:* Cleveland, OH; *ed:* Notre Dame of OH (BA) Math 1968; Notre Dame Institute (MA) Rel Ed 1980; John Carroll Univ (MA) Math 1987; *cr:* Regina HS Tchr 1968-75; Notre Dame Acad Tchr, Dept Head 1975-78; Regina HS Tchr, Dept Head 1978-94; Notre Dame Coll of OH Asst Prof 1994-; *ai:* Curr Comm; Grd 11 Moderator; Career Exploration Dir; NCTM 1975-; MAA 1985-; OCTM 1972-; GCCTM 1968-, Cath Schl Bd Member 1978-80; Gesu Church Choir 1994-; Speaker OCTM Conventions, GCCTM Meetings; *office:* Notre Dame Coll of OH 4545 College Rd South Euclid OH 44121*

MOFFATT, BARBARA BRASKEY, Second Grade Teacher; *b:* Cumberland, MD; *m:* Charles Dennis Sr.; *c:* Charles Jr., Carey, Joseph; *ed:* Frostburg St (BA) Early Chldhd 1970, (MA) Early Chldhd 1976; *cr:* Fountain Elem 1st Grd Tchr 1970-71; Mt Savage Schl 3rd Grd Tchr 1972; Cntrl Elem 3rd & 1st Grd Tchr 1972-75; George's Creek Elem 1st, 2nd & 3rd Grd Tchr 1975-; *ai:* NEA; MSTA; AFT; George's Creek Library Fund Co-Chprsn 5 Yrs; *office:* Georges Creek Elem Schl Rt 36 Lonaconing MD 21539

MOFFETT, DORIS HENDRICKS, School Nurse; *b:* Felton, DE; *m:* Michael Edward; *c:* Michael, Brenda, John, Pamela Sotton, David, Stacey Bishop; *ed:* Milford Meml Hosp Schl of Nursing (RN) 1956; Attnd Univ of DE; *cr:* Milford Meml Hosp Staff Nurse 1956-64; Gen Foods Indstrl Nurse 1964-1966; Lake Forest Schl Dist Schl Nurse 1967-; Milford Hosp Part-time OB Staff Nurse 1968-; *ai:* Past Majorette Adv 8 Yrs, Chrldng Coach 15 Yrs; DE St Ed Assn 1980-; DE Schl Nurse Assn 1980-, Treas; Milford Mem Hosp Alumni, Sec; Lake Forest Well Ctr, Advy Bd 1993-; *office:* Lake Forest HS 5407 Killen's Pond Rd Felton DE 19943

MOFFETT, SHARON MC CLOSKEY, Seventh Grade Lang Arts Tchr; *b:* Drexel Hill, PA; *m:* J. Wilson; *c:* Courtney, Bethany; *ed:* Elizabethtown Coll (BS) Elem Ed, His 1976; Temple Univ (MS) Elem Ed 1990; *cr:* Garrettford Elem Schl Third Grd Tchr 1977; Drexel Hill Elem Schl First, Second, Third Grd Tchr 1977-81; Bywood Elem Schl Fourth & Fifth Grd Tchr 1981-95; Drexel Hill MS Seventh Grd Tchr 1996; *ai:* PSEA 1977-, Sec; NEA 1977-; Schl Bd Rep 1992-; PTO Grant Publishing Ctr; Article Pub; *office:* Bywood Elem Schl 3001 State Rd Drexel Hill PA 19026*

MOFFITT, JOHN, Math Dept Chairman; *b:* Lewiston, ME; *m:* Anne Tardif; *c:* Jennifer; *ed:* UMPG (BS) Math 1968; USM (MS) Ed 1972; Attnd Advanced Placement Calculus Symposium 1985 & Windham Tchrs Acad 1989, 95; USM 15 Hrs Towards Doctrine Degree; USM Project Aspire Calculus I & II Summer of 1992 & 1993; *cr:* Casco Bay Coll Math Tchr 1974-79; Windham HS Math Tchr 1968-, Math Chm 1974-; *ai:* K-12th Grd Cmptr Comm; WEA 1968-, Welfare Comm 1980-83; MTA & NEA 1968-; Maine Horse Assn 1984-, 1st Pl Open Jumper 1984-89; New England Horse Assn 1984-, 2nd Pl Open Jumper 1985; ME Tchr of Yr 1985; Attnd Excl in Ed Symposium at Capitva FL 1985; *office:* Windham H S 406 Gray Rd Windham ME 04062

MOGENSEN, CAROL ONEIL, 6th Grade Teacher; *b:* Holyoke, MA; *m:* Harry; *c:* Ellen, Joanne Deitsch; *ed:* Emerson (BA) Eng 1955; *cr:* Burlington Comm Action Comm Literacy Tchr 1962-65; Willingboro Elem Schl 3rd Grd Tchr 1966-67; St Charles Borromeo 6th Grd Tchr 1972-; *ai:* NCEA 1972-; Outstdng Cath Edctr 1996 St Charles Schl; *office:* St Charles Borromeo Schl 2500 Branch Pike Riverton NJ 08077

MOGLIA, ALLEN WILLIAM, 7th-8th Grade Social Stud Tchr; *b:* New Brunswick, NJ; *m:* Patricia Fantini; *c:* Ryan, Justin; *ed:* Rutgers Univ (BA) Ec 1977; 12 Addl Credit Hrs Industrial Ed; *cr:* Self-Employed 1970-80; Spotswood HS Tchr 1983-84; Joyce Kilmer Schl Tchr 1985-; *ai:* 8th Grd Class, Youth in Govt Prgm, Stu Cncl Adv; Asst Coach; NJ Ed Assn 1983-; Natl Cncl for Soc Stud, NJ Cncl for Soc Stud 1989-; Milltown Rangers Ath Club 1978-, Pop Warner Chprsn; Milltown Teen Cncl 1992-, Adv; Govs Tchr Recognition Awd; *office:* Joyce Kilmer Elem Schl W Church St Milltown NJ 08850

MOGRO, PATRICIA, Assoc Prof of Spanish & Psych; *b:* La Paz, Bolivia; *m:* Antonio; *c:* Patricia Bosak, Cynthia Andrews, Cristina; *ed:* Schenectady Cty Comm Coll (AA) Hum, Soc Sci 1983; Univ of St of NY (BS) Lbrl Arts 1986; St Univ of NY at Albany (MA) Span 1989; 30 Credits Psych; *cr:* St Pius Schl Span Tchr 1984-87; St John the Evangelist Schl Span Tchr 1984-89; Schenectady Cty Comm Coll Asst Prof 1989-92, Instr 1992-95, Assoc Prof 1995-; *ai:* Span Club Adv; Curr Comm; Lang Lab Supvr; Capital Org of Lang Tchrs 1993-, VP, Pres; NY St of Frgn Lang Tchrs, NEA, NYEA 1990-; Our Lady of Fatima Church 1975-; Hispanic Heritage Inst 1988-; South Amer Club 1990-; Fnd Awd for Excl in Tchng 1994; St Univ of NY Chancellor's Awd Excl in Tchng 1995; *office:* Schenectady County Comm Coll 78 Washington Ave Schenectady NY 12305

MOHAN, JUDE FRANCI, English Teacher; *b:* Quincy, MA; *m:* Jane McInerney; *c:* Cassandra, Jude, Chandra, Michaela, Damien; *ed:* Saint Marys Coll at Winona (BA) Classics & Eng 1969; Univ of IL (MA) Classical Langs 1972; Lehigh Univ (MA) Ed 1974; *cr:* North Hunterdon Regnl HS Dist Eng & Latin Tchr 1974-; *ai:* Acad Team, PSAT & SAT Preparatory, & Frosh Class Adv; Frosh Discovery Summer Prgm Coord; NJEA 1974-, Local VP; NJ Schl Bds Assn 1990-, Bd of Ed Pres; Governors Tchr of Yr Awd; *office:* Voorhees HS 256 County Road 513 Glen Gardner NJ 08826*

MOHAPP, LES STEVEN, High School English Teacher; *b:* Newtown, PA; *m:* Janice E. Criswell; *c:* Pat O'Neill, Tara O'Neill; *ed:* Point Park Coll (BA) Jrnlsm & Comm, Sec Ed Comm Cert, Grad Magna Cum Laude 1984; 24 Addl Credits Eng Lit Bucknell Univ; *cr:* Middleburg HS Eng Tchr 1985-; *ai:* Var Girls Bsktbl Coach 1989-92; Asst Girls Bsktbl Coach 1986-89; Jr High Girls Bsktbl Coach 1985-92; Jr High Boys Bsktbl Coach 1985-86; Equestrian Club 1993-94, Key Club 1985-86 Advs; PSEA, NEA 1990-; Sigma Tau Gamma 1982-, VP 1983; Alpha Chi PA ETA 1983-; Mifflin Cty Dog Trng Club 1992-; Mifflin Cty Equestrian Clb 1995-; *office:* Middleburg HS 546 E Main St Middleburg PA 17842

MOHLENHOFF, BRUCE R., 8th Grade Teacher; *b:* Staten Island, NY; *ed:* Wagner Coll (MSED) Scndry Ed 1974, (BA) His 1971; Addl 15 Credits; *cr:* St Adalbert Schl Tchr 1971-; *ai:* Summer Co-op Schl; Soc Stud Fair; Yrbk Adv; Grad Coord; Federation of Cath Tchrs 1971-, Union Del; NCSS; NCTM; Staten Island Historical Soc; St Johns Luth Church 1949-, Finance COmm Chm 1986-, Schl Bd, Church Cncl, Usher, Lector, Communion Asst; *office:* St Adalbert Schl 355 Morningstar Rd Staten Island NY 10303

MOHLER, LEONARD H., Bible & Science Teacher; *b:* Lodi, OH; *m:* Judith M. Knowlton; *c:* Leon M., Rollin L., Neil H.; *ed:* Cedarville Coll (BA) Pre-Seminary Bible 1975; Grand Rapids Bapt Seminary (MRE) Chrstn Ed 1993; *cr:* Elyria Chrstn Acad Bible, Sci Tchr 1977-87; Maranatha Chrstn Schl Bible, Sci Tchr 1987-; *ai:* Sci Dept, Sci Fair Prgm Chprsn; *office:* Maranatha Chrstn Schl 4663 Trabue Rd Columbus OH 43228

MOHNEY, THOMAS LEE, High School Supervisor Teacher; *b:* Kittanning, PA; *m:* Christine Kirsch; *c:* Christopher, Thomas Jr., Hope, Charity, Patience, Joshua; *ed:* IN Univ of PA (BS) Scndry Ed, S 1969; FL Inst of Tech (MS) Logistics Mngmt 1978; US Army Com Gen Staff Coll; *cr:* US Army LtCol 1969-91; Temple Univ A 1987-90; Bethel Chrstn Acad Supvr Tchr 1992-; *ai:* Bsbl, Sftbl Ass Bethel Assembly 1991-, Deacon; *office:* Bethel Christian Ac California Ave Pittsburgh PA 15212

MOHR, DOROTHY ANN, English & Journalism Teacher; *b:* LaR France; *ed:* Bemidji St Univ (BS) Eng Ed 1979; Antioch Grad Sch Ed 1991; 16 Credit Hrs Toward Doctorate at Walden Univ; *cr:* O HS Eng Tchr 1979-80; Pelham HS Eng & Jrnlsm Tchr 1987-; *ai:* Newsletter Adv; Weighing Comm; NEA, PEA 1987-, Negotiator; P Kappa, ASCD 1990-; NEATE 1987-; *office:* Pelham HS 85 M Pelham NH 03076

MOHR, NORMA BATESON, Sixth Grade Teacher; *b:* Tontogany, Royce E.; *c:* Sondra Roberts, Ronda Corpus; *ed:* Bowling Green (BS) Elem Ed 1960; *cr:* Westwood Schl Dist Jr High Lang Arts Tc Grand Rapids Local 4th Grd Tchr 1960-68; Grand Rapids Elem 4t Grd Tchr 1968-; *ai:* APEX & Sci Curr Comm; NWOEA 1960-, S OH Ed Assn & NEA 1960-; Otsego Edctrs 1968-, Bldg Rep, Sec Calvary United Meth Church 1978-, Chm of Bd; Order of Eastern S Point; Rebekah Lodge, Noble Grand; Historical Soc; Otsego Tc 1986-87; *home:* PO Box 115 Grand Rapids OH 43522

MOHR, TIMOTHY A., Asst Prof of Electrical Engrg; *b:* Pittsbur *ed:* MT St Univ (BS) Electrical Engrg 1980, (MS) Electrical Engr (PHD) Electrical Engrg 1991; *cr:* Bendix Guid Systems Div Ass 1981-85; MT St Univ Adj Math & Engrng Prof 1991-93; Grove C Electrical Engrng Asst Prof 1993 -; *ai:* IEEE Club Adv; IEEE 19 Branch Adv.

MOHR, WILSON DAWSEY, Math Chairman; *b:* Staten Island, Dolores Rose; *c:* Brittany, Taylor; *ed:* Oswego St (BA) Bio 1979; SI (MS) Scndry Ed & Sci Concentration 1986; 6th Yr Scndr Supervision 1990; *cr:* Dreyfus IS 49 Math Tchr & Chm 1981-; R & Sci Supvr 1982-; *ai:* Math Team Coach; UFT & AFT 1981-, Awded; St Johns Church 1980-94, Vestry Mem; All Saints Church Asst Treas; Several Grants; NY St Tchr of the Yr Nom; Natl Ma Nom; *office:* IS 49 Bertha Dreyfus 101 Warren St Staten Island NY

MOKE, MARTIN C., Health, PE & Math Teacher; *b:* Philadelph *m:* Marie T. Basso; *c:* Nicole M.; *ed:* West Chester Univ (BS) H 1974, (MED) Hlth, PE 1977; Supvrs Cert Rowan Coll NJ 1996; Ma 1989; *cr:* St James Cath HS Tchr 1974-89; Bishop Eustace Prep Sc 1989-; *ai:* Head Ftbl Coach; Numerous Articles Pub 1979, 1995; Ph League Ftbl Coach of Yr, Phila Daily News City Ftbl Coach of Y *office:* Bishop Eustace Prep Schl Rt 70 Pennsauken NJ 08109

MOLCHAN, JANE BANKER, Sixth Grade Teacher; *b:* Lawrenc *m:* Stanley James; *c:* Tasha; *ed:* Salem St Coll (BS) Elem Ed 197 MS Admin 1996; *cr:* Searles Schl 5 Grd Tchr 1971-75; Tenney MS Tchr 1975-90; Comprehensive Grammar Schl Grd 6 Tchr 1990-; *ai:* Club Adv; Schl Cncl; Recycling Chairwoman; NEA 1971-; Comprehensive Grammar Schl 100 Howe St Methuen MA 01844

MOLDOVAN, MICHAEL JOHN, English Instructor; *b:* Lorain, Frances Zackeroff; *c:* Maria, Nicole, Elaine; *ed:* Bowling Green S (BS) Eng 1977; Westminster Coll (MS) Admin 1995; *cr:* JFK HS En 1977-90; Chamberlin HS Eng Tchr 1990-; *ai:* Asst Ftbl Coach; NEA Twinsburg Ed Assn 1990-; *home:* 2101 Timber Way Dr Cortland OH

MOLESKY, GEORGE ANDREW, 7th-8th Grade Math Teacher; Eagle, PA; *m:* Kathleen Bednarczyk; *c:* Mark, Maria, Elaine, Rebec Univ of PA at California (BS) Scndry Math 1973; 24 Hrs Permaner *cr:* Kitt Energy Corp Purchasing Agent 1973-88; Bellmar MS Ma 1993-; *ai:* MS Adv & Advisec; PSEA 1993-; NEA 1993-; BVAEA Charlerio Sportsmen 1970-, Recording Sec; Smithton Conservation *office:* Bellmar MS 500 Perry Ave Belle Vernon PA 15012

MOLEY, EDWARD C., Science Department Chairperson; *b:* Rahw *ed:* Seton Hall Univ (BSEd) Bio, Minor Fr 1962; Alexander Art C Salem Cert Oil Painting Instr 1988; *cr:* St Mary's HS Sci Tchr 196 Dir 1967-69, Sci Curr Consultant, Asst Prin 1986-89; *ai:* Oil P Club; NCEA, NBTA 1965-; NSTA 1970-; Elizabeth Republican 1978-; NJ St Assembly Candidate 1979; Mayor of Elizabeth Ca 1980; *office:* St Mary-Assumption H S 237 S Broad St Elizabeth NJ

MOLEY-PALACIOS, MARY, English Teacher; *b:* Newfane, N Donald Rey; *c:* Peter Rey, Marie Theresa; *ed:* Niagara Cty Comm Lbrl Arts 1977; SUNY at Geneseo (BA) Speech Comms 1979; Em Coll (BA) Eng 1986; Niagara Univ (MS) Cnslng 1992; *cr:* Wilson Schl Eng Tchr 1984-; *ai:* SADD, Ski Club Adv; Acad Stans, Prof Sta Comms; Proposal Chprsn; Newspaper Adv 1984-89; Hiring Comm MS Transition Team 1995-; NYSTA 1984-; Wilson Tchrs Assn E 1992; PTA 1983-, Steering Comm; Niagara Cty Victim Impact Panelist; Local Bone Marrow Dr 1990-, Organizer; Our Lady of the Parish Cncl Sec; *office:* Wilson Cntrl Schl 374-80 Lake St Wils 14172*

MOLIN, MAURICE JOHN, Social Studies Teacher; *b:* Pottsville, P East Stroudsburg Univ (BS) Soc Stud, Scndry Ed 1976, (ME) His 19 Pocono Cntrl Cath HS Soc Stud Tchr; East Stroudsburg HS Soc Stud *ai:* Asst Soccer Coach 1977-81; Asst Track Coach; Model United N Adv; Wallyball IM Prgm; Acad Achvmt Prgm; Phi Delta Kappa Omicrun Delta Kappa 1995-; NEA 1990-; Phi Alpha Beta 1975-; 1990-; Alpha Chi Rho 1974-, Pres, Bldg Assn Chm; Outstdng B Outstdng Alumni; East Stroudsburg Univ, Bd Mem of Alumni Assn Chair; Tchr of Yr 1990-91; Ziegler Awd 1989; Outstdng Young Amer 1982; Who's Who in Amer Ed 1989; *office:* E Stroudsburg HS Courtland St East Stroudsburg PA 18301*

MOLINA, KAREN KINZER, Spanish & French Teacher; *b:* Butle *c:* Sara; *ed:* Bowling Green St Univ (BA) Fr Lang & Lit 1970; NY (MA) Span & Hispanic Lit 1979; 30 Credit Hrs; *cr:* Madrid Spa Tutoring in Eng & Fr 1971-81; Whitingham Schl Lang Dept Chair 1981-; *ai:* MS Drama Coach; Ldrshp Project Coord; Drug Free Sc Comms Advy Cncl; 9th Grd Class Adv; Homestay in Spain S Chaperone; Fac Cncl; VT Frgn Lang Assoc 1981-; Windham SW Assoc 1981-, Pres, VP, Negotiator; Deerfield Vly Farmers Day 1987-, Chprsn Photo Division; Deerfield Vly Hlth Ctr 1994-, T Whitingham Schl Dirs Cert of Appreciation 1987; Univ of VT Outstd Tchr Awd 1988; *office:* Whitingham Schl PO Box 199 Jacksonvil 05342

MOLINARI, LINDA VIOLONE, 4th Grade Teacher; *b:* Jersey Cit *m:* Joseph; *c:* Michael; *ed:* St Thomas Aquinas Coll (BA) Elem Ed Jersey City St Coll (MS) Urban Ed 1995; ESL Cert; *cr:* Husdon Sc Grd Tchr 1984-; *ai:* NEA 1984-; *office:* Hudson Elem Schl 167 1 Union City NJ 07087

MOLINARO, JOHN JOSEPH, Social Studies Teacher; *b:* Carbor PA; *m:* Dianne M. Rupp; *c:* Frank, Janine; *ed:* Univ of Scranton Scndry Ed & Soc Stud 1975; *cr:* Carbondale Area Jr Sr HS Jr HS Leve Stud Tchr 1977-; *ai:* Soph Class Adv; PSEA, NEA 1977-; CAEA Pres & VP; PTA 1977-; CA Booster Club 1980-; *office:* Carbondale Jr Sr HS Rt 6 Brooklyn St Carbondale PA 18407

MOLL, ANGELA MARIE, Latin, Classical Greek Teacher; *b:* Have MA; *ed:* Wellesley Coll (BA) Latin, Philosophy 1991; Rivier Coll (

5; cr: Haverhill HS Latin, Greek, Span Tchr 1992-; ai: Latin Club urr Frameworks, Task Force Review Comms; Schl Site cncl; al Assn of New England, Amer Classical League, MA Frgn Lang 992-; St Joseph Church 1969-.

, **CHARLES STANLEY,** Vocal Music Teacher; *b:* Arlington, VA; ne Miller; *c:* Sara Elizabeth, Charles Frederick, Russell Eaton; *ed:* hester Univ (BS) Music Ed 1971, (MA) Music Performance 1979; g on PHD; *cr:* South Mountain Jr High Vocal & General Music Tchr 5; Downingtown Sr HS Vocal Music; *ai:* Music Theater; Mens, s, Show & Chamber Choir; Barbershop; Sweet Adelines; Chi Alpha; & ITG 1971-; ACDA 1979-; ASCAP 1974-; Composer Childrens Music Dir for Bi-Centennial of Chester Cty; Coach Horn Awd 1st orse Show, Devon Horse Show, Newport & Gladstone; Composer & an of Coach Horn Music; *office:* Downingtown Sr HS 445 Manor wningtown PA 19335

, **SUZANNE HUBER,** Mathematics Teacher; *b:* Northampton, PA; ney W.; *c:* Alison L., Lori C.; *ed:* Kutztown Univ (BSEd) Math MED) Math 1970; La Salle Univ 3 Credit Hrs; 7 In-Service Hrs; *cr:* s HS Math Tchr 1967-73; Boyertown Area Sr HS Math Tchr ; Emmaus HS Math Tchr 1981-; *ai:* Math Club Adv; Math Curr, Ed Comms; EPEA, NCTM 1981-; EPCTM 1985-; PSEA; NEA; Arts Soc of Upper Perkiomen Valley 1983-, Bd; Bd of Auditors Hanover Township Chm 1979-; Upper Perkiomen Vly Library Bd *office:* Emmaus HS 851 North St Emmaus PA 18049

ENKOTT, VIRGINIA RAMEY, Professor of English; *b:* lphia, PA; *c:* Paul F.; *ed:* Bob Jones Univ (BA) Eng Lit 1953; Univ (MA) Eng Lit 1955; NY Univ (PHD) Eng Lit 1964; *cr:* n Coll Eng Dept Chair 1955-63; Nyack Coll Eng Dept Chair 7; Wm Paterson Coll Eng Prof 1967-, Dept Chair 1972-76; *ai:* Eng Comm & Promotions Comm; Bd of Advs Upper Room AIDS y; Pacem in Terris Bd; AFT 1971-; Modern Lang Assn 1960-, Regnl Milton Soc of Am 1964-, Exec Comm; Natl Cncl of Churches, ve Lang Lectionary Comm; Amer Bible Soc, Stylistic Consultant, tl Version of Bible; Andiron Awd; Penfield Fellowship, Founders vd; Integrity Awd; Honorary D. Min Samaritan Coll; Author of Many s & Eleven Books; *office:* William Paterson Coll of NJ 300 Pompton yne NJ 07470

ER, JUDY O'ROURKE, Third Grade Teacher; *b:* Brooklyn, NJ; *m:* ; *c:* Rick, Mark, Wendy; *ed:* Brooklyn Coll (BA) Sociology 1959; n St (MA) Dev Rdng 1982; 74 Addl Credits; *cr:* Spruce Run Schl l Grd, Basic Skills Tchr 1979-90; Patrick Mc Gaheran Schl 3rd Grd 990-.

ICA, FERNANDO, Italian Tchr; *b:* Ripi, Italy; *m:* Palmina Lunghi; cello; *ed:* Queens Coll (BA) Lang 1972, (MA) Italian 1975; Univ of Or Eng; NY Univ PHD Pgm in Italian; *cr:* Scusla Mastai Rome Elem chr 1962-70; Queens Coll Tchr of Italian & PT Lecturer 1972-73; 2 Brooklyn Tchr of Italian 1973-86; Forest Hills HS Tchr of Italian *ai:* AATI 1972-; ITA 1972-; UFT 1974-; *office:* Forest Hills HS 10th St Flushing NY 11375

OCK, CLARENCE B., Art Teacher; *b:* Easton, MD; *m:* Sharon a Hawkins; *c:* Clarence Brandon, Michael Aaron; *ed:* Bowie St Univ cndry Ed in Art 1972; Towson St Univ (MED) Art Ed 1985; *cr:* ood Sr HS Art Tchr 1973-; Catonsville Comm Coll Adj Fac Art Instr me) 1991-; *ai:* Art Club Co-Spon; Forensics Judge; Ad Hoc Curr, lity Comm; Harford Cty Ed Assn, MD St Tchrs Assn, NEA 1973-; Circle of MD 1993-; Edgewood Comm Planning Cncl 1995-, Art *office:* Edgewood Sr HS 2415 Willoughby Beach Rd Edgewood MD

O-HOLMES, LINDA STEO, Jr HS Mathematics Teacher; *b:* yn, NY; *m:* Michael; *c:* Jamie Lynn Mollo, Marion, Michael, Jr.; *ed:* Univ (BA) Math, Ed 1976; Coll of Staten Island (MS) Scndry Math 12 Free Credits Dwight D. Eisenhower Brooklyn Coll; *cr:* Notre HS Scndry Math Tchr 1976-84; Mc Kinley Jr HS Math Tchr 1984-; Ridge Comm Cncl; Essay Contest Chprsn; Staten Island Gen Math 976-84; Fort Hamilton Alumni Assn 1982-, VP; Bay Ridge Citizen Team; *office:* Mc Kinley IS 259 7301 Fort Hamilton Pky Brooklyn 228

OSKY, CAROLYN (KARNS), Health Teacher; *b:* Hornell, NY; *c:* , James; *ed:* SUC at Brockport (BS) Hlth & PE 1969; Niagara Univ Ed; Addl 60 Hrs Above Masters Degree Ed; *cr:* Lewiston Porter PE 969-71; Hlth & PE Long & Short Term Sub Tchr 1973-80; Wilson 7th & HS Girls Hlth Tchr 1981-; *ai:* DARE Educator; Wellness Champion & Stu of Month Comms; WTA 1981-; AFT, NYSUT Immaculate Conception Church, Caregivers group 1995-; New ons Awd for Drug Ed Given by Lions Intnl 1992; Niagara Cty olism Cncl Prevention & Ed Awd; Jr HS Tchr of Yr 1984-88; 2 Yrs mm Awareness Presentations for WCS Dist AIDS Task Force; A; *office:* Wilson Central Schl 412 Lake St Wilson NY 14172

OY, BARRY M., 7th-12th Grd English Teacher; *b:* Queens, NY; *m:* a O'Brien; *c:* Barry, Erin, Michael, Kaithlin; *ed:* Dowling Coll (MS) Ed 1986; Addl 60 Credits Stonybrook Univ, Dowling Coll, Long Univ; *cr:* Rocky Point Jr-Sr HS Eng Tchr 1976-; *ai:* Frosh Class Var Golf Coach; VP Coaches Assn; Tchrs Assn 1986-; Grad Hnr Soc ng Coll; *office:* Rocky Point Jr Sr HS 82 Rocky Point Yaphank Rd Point NY 11778*

OY, LINDA DANKESE, English Teacher; *b:* Brighton, MA; *m:* . Jr.; *c:* John J., Justin M.; *ed:* Boston Coll (BA) Eng, Ed 1971; urg St coll (MED) Media Literacy 1995; Grad Work at Tufts Univ, n Coll, Merrimack Ed Ctr, Harvard Grad Schl of Ed-Inst Media Ed; llerica Meml HS Eng Tchr 1971-; *ai:* Comm Svc Adv; Billerica er-Equity Comm; Educl Tour Ldr; AFT 1971-; Edctrs for Soc nsibility 1990-; Amer Craft Cncl 1990-; Commonwealth of MA t Alliance; *office:* Billerica Memorial HS 35 River St Billerica MA

NAR, WILLIAM, Honors Chemistry Teacher; *b:* Hoboken, NJ; *m:* Anne; *c:* Jennifer, Allyson; *ed:* Jersey City St Coll (BA) Scndry Sci 65; Montclair St Coll (MA) Chem, Physics 1971; Univ of CA at ley Post-Grad Schl Chem; San Diego St Univ Post-Grad Schl s; Polytechnic Inst of Brooklyn Post-Grad Schl Systems Engr; NJ f Tech Post-Grad Schl Physics, Environmental Engr; *cr:* Ramway HS , Algebra II, Geometry Tchrs 1965-66; River Dell Regnl HS Chem, gy, Astronomy Tchrs 1966-; *ai:* Quiz Bowl Coach; JETS Team Adv; eam Coach; Acad Decathlon Coach; RDEA, NJEA, NEA 1965-, VP iations 5 Yrs; Amer Chemical Soc 1968-; NJ Sci Tchrs 1975-; Bergen oaches Assn 1968-; Natl Sci Tchr 1980-; NJ Earth Sci Tchr 1978; Museum of Nat His 1970-, Educator Consultant; Amer Red Cross , First Aid, CPR, Water Safety, Instr; NJ Governor Tchr of Yr Awd Spec Recognition NASA-JPL HS Sci Tchr; Summer Sabbatical rch & Video of Geology of NJ; Sabbaticical Internet & Sci Team; ; River Dell Regnl Sr HS Pyle St Oradell NJ 07649

ONEY, MARY F., High School Math Teacher; *b:* Bayonne, NJ; *ed:* er's Coll (BA) Math 1974; Jersey City St Coll (MA) Stu Personnel 1978; SPC Urban Ed Summer Inst; *cr:* Washington Schl 7-8th Grd Tchr 1974-79; Bayonne HS 10-12th Grd Math Tchr 1979-; *ai:* Curr ion, Schl of Excl Comms; Pi Mu Epsilon; Hudson Cty Tchr Recognition Program; NEA, NJEA, BTA 1974-; AMTNJ, NCTM 1985-; *office:* Bayonne HS Avenue A & 29th St Bayonne NJ 07002*

MOLOUGHNEY, VINCENT F., Math Teacher & Dept Chair; *b:* Jersey City, NJ; *m:* Patricia Glanville; *c:* Caitlin M., Vincent P.; *ed:* Seton Hall Univ (BS) Math 1969; *cr:* Pequannock Twp HS Math Tchr 1970-; *ai:* NEA, NJEA 1970-; Pequannock Twsp Ed A 1970-, VP 1990-; NCTM; AMT NJ; Natl HS Coaching Awd 1988 Golf Coack Silver Awd; *office:* Pequannock Township H S 85 Sunset Rd Pompton Plains NJ 07444

MOLUSH, EDWARD NICHOLAS,JR., English Teacher; *b:* Philadelphia, PA; *c:* Jeffrey; *ed:* Temple Univ (BSC) Scndry Eng Ed 1972, (MA) Eng Lit 1988; Addl 18 Grad Hrs, M Sec Ed; West Chester St Univ, 6 Grad Hrs M Eng Ed; *cr:* J. P. Mc Caskey HS Eng Tchr, Head Bsbl Coach 1976-77; La Salle Coll HS Eng Tchr, Head Bsbl Coach 1979-85; *ai:* Yrbk Co-Moderator Writing; Head Bsbl Coach Haverford Coll 1987-; NCTE 1980-; MLA 1989-; Lower Merian Twp Sports Assn 1994-; Bard Coll Writing Wkshp 1989; Univ of NH Writing Wkshp 1990; Westtown Tchrs Conf 1993; NEH Grant 1992; *office:* Lasalle College HS 8605 Cheltenham Ave Wyndmoor PA 19038*

MOLYET, ANNE MARY M., Counselor; *b:* Upper Sandusky, OH; *ed:* Walsh Univ (BA) Psych 1978; Univ of Dayton (MA) Schl Cnslng 1991; Bowling Green Univ Certified in Ed 1982; *cr:* Ladyfield 7th Grd Tchr 1984-1988; St Marys 8th Grd Tchr 1988-1992; Cntrl Cath HS Tchr & Schl Cnslr 1992-1993, Admin Asst to Prin & Schl Cnslr 1993-; *office:* Central Cath HS 2250 Cherry St Toledo OH 43608

MOLYNEAUX, JAMES LEVAN, 6th Grade Teacher; *b:* Oswego, NY; *m:* Carol L. Taylor; *c:* Joel, Andrew, Laurel; *ed:* Buffalo St Univ Coll (MS) Elem Ed 1972; 52 Addl Grad Credit Hrs; NYS Rdng Cert; *cr:* Portville Cntrl 6th Grd Tchr 1965-; *ai:* Former Cross Cntry & Bsktbl Coach; Referee; Yrbk Adv; 6th Grd Ecology Camp Co-Dir; AFT 1992-; BSA 1965-, Scoutmaster, Silver Beaver; First Bapt Church 1978-, Trustee; VFW 1991-; 6th Grd Ecology Trip Founder 1969; *office:* Portville Central Schl Elm St Portville NY 14770

MOMBERGER, SHERRY M. SHERWOOD, Reading & English Teacher; *b:* Normantown, WV; *m:* Carl Henry II; *c:* Sarah, Carl III; *ed:* Glenville St Coll (BA) Elem Ed 1964; George Washingtown (MA) Rdng; *cr:* Kent Island Elem Tchr 1965-66; Glenwood MS Tchr 1967-68; Calvert MS Tchr 1979-92; Plum Point MS Tchr 1992-; *ai:* Speech Contest Participants; Delta Kappa Gamma, VP; NEA; CEA; MSTA; *office:* Plum Point MS 1475 Plum Point Rd Huntingtown MD 20639*

MONACO, ARTHUR JOHN, Tchr of Learning Disabilities; *b:* Newark, NJ; *m:* Florence Jusinski; *c:* Arthur Jr., Michael, Jason, Robert; *ed:* Seton Hall Univ (BS) Elem Ed 1972; Montclair St Coll (MA) Learning Disabilities 1977; 32 Post Grad Credits Admin Cert; *cr:* Franklin Schl Elem Tchr 1973-78; Kearny Spec Svcs LDT-C Tchr 1978-; *ai:* HS Head Wrestling Coach; NJ Wrestling Coaches Assn 1978-, Treas 1980-; NEA, NJEA 1973-; Rick Cerone Little League Assn 1988-; Dist Coach of Yr 1979, 1982, 1985, 1993; Region Coach of Yr 1993; *office:* Kearney Dept of Spec Svcs 336 Devon St Kearny NJ 07032

MONACO, RALPHAEL CHRISTOPHER, 5th Grade Teacher; *b:* Tiffin, OH; *c:* Shelby Lauren; *ed:* Mount Union Coll (BA) Elem Ed 1977; US Sports Acad (MSS) Sports Admin 1990; Amer Inst of Massotherapy (MT) Massotherapy Candidate; Attnd Bowling Green St Univ, Drake Univ, Ashland Coll; *cr:* Tiffin St Mary's Elem Schl 7-8 Grd Tchr 1977-79; Bucyrus City Schls Headstart Tchr 1979-81; New Washington Buckeye Cntrl Local Schls 6th Grd Tchr 1981-83; Fostoria City Schls Sub Tchr 1983-85; Clyde-Green Springs Schls 5th Grd Tchr 1985-; *ai:* 5-6 Grd Boys, Girls Bsktbl Coach; Levy, Schl Advy Comm; Camp Adv OH Northern Univ, Bobcat BsktblCamp; NEA 1977-; OH Ed Assn 1979-; Amer Inst of Massotherapy 1993-, Bd Mem; Who's Who in Amer Colls & Univs 1977; *home:* 182 Jackson St Tiffin OH 44883

MONACO, SUSAN OBERKIRCH, First Grade Teacher; *b:* Brooklyn, NY; *m:* Joseph; *c:* Jason, Rebecca, Rachel; *ed:* SUNY at New Paltz (BA) Ed 1972, (MS) Spec Ed; Addl 12 Credits; Trained in Responsive Classroom Soc Curr; *cr:* Kingston City Schls 1, 3, 5 Grd Tchr 1972-85; Whitehall Cntrl Schls 1, 3, 3-4 Combined, 5 Grd Tchr 1985-; *ai:* Adj Prof in Ed Green Mtn Coll; Consultant, Wkshp Presener St Tchrs Confs; NY St Eng Cncl 1989-, Past Regnl Dir, Exec Bd; AFT 1974-; Whitehall Tchrs Assn 1985-; IRA; Poultney Schl Bd 1990-Clerk; Poultney Woman's Club 1988-; Grants Rec'd Capital Region Tchr Ctr Dev Interdisciplinary Tchng Units; Article Pub 1993; *home:* RR 2 Box 510 Poultney VT 05764*

MONACO-HANNON, KELLI ANN, English Teacher; *b:* Buffalo, NY; *m:* Mark D. Hannon; *c:* Dominic J. Hannon; *ed:* St Univ of NY Coll at Buffalo (BS) Scndry Eng 1991, (MS) Eng Ed 1992; *cr:* Mount St Mary Acad Eng Tchr 1991-, Dept Chair 1995-; *ai:* Yrbk Adv 1992-; Newspaper Moderator 1991-92; *office:* Mt St Mary Acad 3756 Delaware Ave Kenmore NY 14217

MONAGHAN, JOHN MICHAEL, Western World Soc Stud Teacher; *b:* Chester, PA; *m:* Lori Ann; *c:* Mollyfay; *ed:* Kutztown Univ (BS) Criminal Justice, Pol Sci 1986; Cheyney Univ Tchng Cert Soc Stud 1993; Beginning Masters Prgm in Ldrshp Penn St; *cr:* W. C. East HS Soc Stud Tchr 1993-; *ai:* Boys Soccer Team Asst Coach; Class of 1998 Adv; NEA, PSEA 1993-; US Army Reserves 1982-, Capt Transportation Corp; *office:* West Chester East HS 450 Ellis Ln West Chester PA 19380

MONAGHAN, KEVIN MATTHEW, Science Teacher; *b:* Pittsburgh, PA; *m:* Christina Beth Bowman; *ed:* CA Univ of PA (BS) Bio 1990; Tchng Cert 1991; *cr:* Peters Twp HS Sci Perm Sub, Soccer Coach 1990-92; South Fayette Jr, Sr HS Sci Tchr, Soccer, Bsbl Coach 1993-; *ai:* Var Soccer, Bsbl Coach; Tech Comm; NEA 1992-; Caring Prgm for Kids; Beta Testing for Wheeling Jesuit Coll; South Fayette Twp Summer Recreation Prgm Organizer; *office:* South Fayette Jr Sr HS 2254 Old Oakdale Rd Mc Donald PA 15057*

MONAGHAN, MAUREEN, 6th-8th Grade Teacher; *b:* Rockville Centre, NY; *m:* Thomas; *c:* Timothy, Steven; *ed:* Hofstra Univ (BS) Elem Ed 1966, (MA) Elem Ed 1969; *cr:* Deer Park Schl 6th Grd Elem Ed Tchr 1967-68; St Catherine of Sienna 6th-8th Grd Tchr 1982-; *ai:* NCEA 1982-; *office:* St Catherine of Sienna Schl 990 Holzheimer St Franklin Square NY 11010

MONAHAN, ANNE LOFTUS, Reading & Writing Teacher; *b:* Pittston, PA; *m:* Joseph T.; *ed:* Marywood Coll (BA) Elem Ed 1964; Attnd Montclair Univ, Kean Coll, Gesell Inst of Child Dev; *cr:* Parisippany-Troy Hills Bd of Ed Primary Grds Tchr 1965-70, Title I Grant Dir 1970-72, Asst to Supt of Schls 1972-74, Tchr 6th Grd Self-Contained 1974-86, MS Tchr 1986-; *ai:* PTHEA, NJEA, NEA 1965-; Marywood Coll Alumni Assn, Pres NJ Chapter; Distngd Fac Awd; *office:* Brooklawn MS 250 Beachwood Rd Parsippany NJ 07054

MONAHAN, CHRIS, Math Teacher; *b:* New York City, NY; *m:* Diane Hartman-Treanor; *c:* Kathryn, Brendon, Andrew, Kristen; *ed:* Manhattan Coll (BS) Math 1976; Colgate Univ (MAT) Math 1977; *cr:* Tompkins Cortland Comm Coll Adj 1981-95; Ithaca Coll Adj 1980-95; Newfield Cntrl Schl 1977-81; Ithaca HS Math Tchr 1981-82; Newfield Cntrl Schl 1984-92; Ithaca Hs Math Tchr 1992-95; Scotia-Glenville HS Math Tchr 1995-; *ai:* Class Adv; NEA 1992-; AMTNYS 1989-; Presenter Hudson-Mohawk Vly Area Math Conf 1996; *home:* 22 Hearthstone Dr Gansevoort NY 12831*

MONAHAN, EMILY J., Sixth Grade Teacher; *b:* Haverstraw, NY; *m:* Michael Jurkovic; *ed:* St Univ of NY at New Platz (BA) N-9th Grd Eng 1989, (MS) K-6th Grd Rdng 1993; *cr:* The Primary Schl 2nd & 3rd Grd Tchr 1989-91; Gardnertown Fundamental 6th Grd Tchr 1991-; *ai:* Safety Patrol & Peer Mediation Dir & Adv; Kappa Delta Pi, Sigma Tau Delta 1989-; AFT, NYSUT 1990-; Green Peace 1991-; Amnesty Intnl 1991-; Unpublished Spelling Manual for Curr Integration, Integrated Units for Intermediate Grds, Cookbook Geared Towards Family Involvement in Meal Preparation; *office:* Gardnertown Fndmntl Mgnt Schl 6 Plattekill Tpke Newburgh NY 12550

MONAHAN, MARTIN J., AP History Teacher; *b:* Troy, NY; *m:* Patricia Clancy; *c:* Stephen, Conor; *ed:* Siena Coll (BA) His, Ed-Cum Laude 1969; NY Univ (MA) His 1971, (PHD) His, Mid Eastern 1991; Persian Lang Stud Firdousi Univ at Mashad Iran 1978; *cr:* Averill Park HS Soc Stud Tchr 1970-, Soc Stud Chm 1978-81; Siena Coll Adjunct Prof His 1980-; ACC Adjunct Prof His 1992-95; HVCC Adjunct Prof His 1996-; *ai:* Citizen Bee Coord 1989-94; APHS Renaissance Prgn; AFT 1973-; NYSUT 1970-, Bldg Rep; Siena Coll Alumni 1970-, Class Rep 1970-78; Iranian Stud Assn 1992-; Phi Delta Kappa 1995; NYSCSS; CDCSSS 1970-, Treas; Pahlavi Fnd Fellowship Stud Iran 1978; Research Grant British Lib India Office 1981, 1983; Golub Fnd Stu Scholar Recognition Awd 1991, 1992, 1994; *office:* Averill Park HS 146 Gettle Rd Averill Park NY 12018*

MONAHAN, RITA DOLORES,OV, Secondary Theology Teacher; *b:* Jersey City, NJ; *ed:* Assumption Coll for Sisters (AA) 1971; Immaculata Coll (BA) His 1973; Attnd Loyola Coll of Baltimore; *cr:* Msgr O'Dwyer Retreat House Asst Dir & Retreat Dir 1989-90; St John Neumann Regnl Schl Prin 1991-92; Allentown Cntrl Cath HS Scndry Theology Tchr 1992-; *ai:* Pastoral Life Spec Events Adv; NCEA 1973-; Crime Victims Cncl 1996, Sexual Assault Cnslr; Habitat for Humanity 1987-; Spec Olympics 1987-; Amer Heart Assn 1995-; Loyola Coll of Baltimore Ldrshp Schlsp 1987; Article Pub Catholic Teen Magazine 1987; Master Tchr Awd Diocese of Paterson 1979; *office:* Allentown Central Cath HS 4th & Chew Sts Allentown PA 18102*

MONAHAN, TAMMY SUE, Math Teacher; *b:* Salem, NJ; *ed:* Rowan Coll (BA) Math 1988; *cr:* Pennsgrove HS Math Tchr 1988-89; Vineland HS Math Tchr 1989-; *ai:* NEA 1988-; Aerobics, Fitness Assn of Amer 1987-, Cert Instr; Co-Writer Innovative Project Grant; *office:* Vineland HS 3010 E Chestnut Ave Vineland NJ 08360*

MONAHAN-DINOIA, KELLY ANN, Latin Teacher; *b:* Southington, CT; *m:* Paul L. DiNoia; *c:* Riley M.; *ed:* St Josph Coll (BA) Scndry Ed 1988; Trinity Coll (BA) Classical Langs 1988; Cntrl CT St Univ (MS) Scndry Ed 1993; St Joseph Coll Span Cert 1988-92; Attnd St Joseph Coll, Univ of Hartford, Tunxis Comm Coll Cert Span; *cr:* Enfield HS Frgn Lang Tchr 1988-90; E Hartford HS Latin Tchr 1990-; *ai:* Latin Club; Svc Club; Adv Class of 1997; Co-Chprsn Cultural Diversity Team; Founding Mem Stu Assistance Team; PTO; Classical Assn of CT 1988-, Exec Bd, Publicity Chair, Mbrshp Chair; Classical Assn of N England, Amer Classical League, CT Cncl of Lang Tchrs 1988-; St Joseph Church Ladies Guild 1990-, Sec; E Hartford Tchr of Yr 1996; Finalist CT Tchr of Yr 1996; Walt Disney Salutes the Amer Tchr 1996; Outstdng Grad Stu of 1993 from Cntrl CT St Univ; CT Excl in HS Tchng Awd 1992, 1995; J. C. Penney Golden RuleAwd 1994; *office:* East Hartford HS 869 Forbes St East Hartford CT 06118*

MONASTRA, RICHARD J., US History, Psych & Soc Tchr; *b:* Philadelphia, PA; *c:* Rachel Versace; *ed:* La Salle Univ (BA) Amer His 1968; Temple Univ (MA) Amer His 1973; Drexel Univ (MS) Ec 1975; *cr:* Interboro HS AP US His, Psych, Sociology Tchr 1973-89; Delaware Co Coll US His, Ec Instr 1977-; Buena Regnl HS AP US His, Psych, Sociology Tchr 1989-; *ai:* Interboro HS Stu Cncl & Class Adv 14 Yrs; NCSS 1970-; NEA, NJEA, PSEA, BREA 1968-, Fac Rep, PR Chm, IHS 10 Yr Svc Awd; Ec Fellowship Drexel Univ; Tchr of Yr Awd Interboro HS; Gould Awd Nom DE Co Coll; *office:* Buena Regional HS Weymouth Rd Buena NJ 08310

MONAT, STEVEN M., Mathematics Teacher; *b:* Goshen, NY; *m:* Kathryn Winant; *c:* Temina; *ed:* Rider Coll (BA) Math 1973; 61 Credit Hrs Ed, Cmptr Sci, Psych; *cr:* NY St Division for Youth Ed Coord 1975-80; High Point Rgnl HS Math Tchr 1984-; *ai:* NCTM 1984-; Natl Ski Patrol 1968-; *office:* High Point Rgnl HS 299 Pigeon Hill Rd Sussex NJ 07461*

MONBERG, ALDEN GATES, Associate Professor of Math; *b:* San Antonio, TX; *m:* Thomas D.; *c:* Robert, James, Erin, Brooke, Christian; *ed:* Univ of ME (BA) Math 1984, (PHD) Applied Math, Coastal Processes 1994; *cr:* Bangor HS Math Tchr 1985-87; Univ of ME Math Instr 1990-91; ME Maritime Acad Math Prof 1991-; *ai:* Stu Advising; NEASC Steering Comm; All-Coll Cncl; Orono Schl Comm 1993-, Chair; NSF Grad Flwshp Applied Math; *office:* Maine Maritime Acad Castine ME 04420*

MONBORNE, EDWARD H., Associate Prof of Accounting; *b:* Ebensburg, PA; *m:* Barbara Degretta; *c:* Edward W., Mary Christine Lamanna; *ed:* St Francis Coll (BS) Acctng 1961; Duquesne Univ (MS) Acctng 1975; St of PA Certfd Pub Accountant 1965; Ed Credits; *cr:* St Francis Coll Asst Prof of Acctng 1966-75, Assoc Prof of Acctng 1975-; *ai:* Fac Salary, Benefits Comm; Stu Vol Svc for Internal Revenue Svc Fac Liaison; Sigma Beta Delta, Fac Adv; Beta Gamma Sigma; Alpha Kappa Psi; Phi Chi Theta; *office:* St Francis Coll Box 600 Loretto PA 15940

MONCRIEF, CATHY PETERKA, Spanish Teacher; *b:* Camden, NJ; *c:* Kelly, Shannon; *ed:* Montclair & Rutgers (BA) Span 1971; Glassboro (MA) Span Curr & Instruction 1980; Prin & Supvr Cert +15 Credits; *cr:* Washington Twp Span Tchr 1971-; Camden Cty Coll Adj Span Prof 1991-; *ai:* Span Club Adv; NEA, NJEA & WTEA 1971-; Bd of Ed 1991-, VP; Sftbl Team Coach; *office:* Washington Township HS 529 Hurffville Crosskeys Rd Sewell NJ 08080*

MONCRIEF, DOLORES TYLER, First Grade Teacher; *b:* Meshoppen, PA; *m:* Stephen B.; *c:* Dorothy, Deborah; *ed:* Wilkes Coll (BA) Elem Ed, Span 1972; 18 Post-Grad Courses; *cr:* Wyalusing Area Schl 2nd Grd, Basic Skills Tchr 1972-74; Deefield Twp Schl 7th Grd, Basic Skills Tchr 1983-85; Stow Creek Twp Schl 1st Grd Tchr 1985-; *ai:* Sci Fair Coord; Affirmative Action Ofcr; Stowcreek Tchrs Assoc 1985-; NJEA 1983-; NEA; WCTU 1978-90, Pres; Shiloh 7th Day Bapt Church 1978-, Deaconess, Yth Group Ldr; Stowcreek Twp Pub Asst Bd 1978-; Governors Recognition Awd St of NJ 1990; Tchr of Yr 1990; *home:* 385 Jericho Rd Bridgeton NJ 08302*

MONDA, KAREN ANN, MS Sci & HS Chem Teacher; *b:* Paterson, NJ; *ed:* Seton Hall Univ (BS) Chem 1982; Montclair St Coll Tchng Cert Sci 1987; Currently Attending Immaculate Conception Seminary in So Orange NJ Part-Time Working Toward a MS Degree; *cr:* MEM Co Inc Chemist 1983-84; Hawthorne Bd of Ed Sci Tchr 1984-; *ai:* Multicultural Comm; NJEA 1983-; HTA 1983-; NJAAPT 1990-; St Anthonys R C Church 1988-94, Liturgy Comm Mem, Adult Facilitator & Founder of Quest Young Adult Group; Diocese of Paterson 1994-, Young Adult Task Force Mem; *office:* Hawthorne HS Parmelee Ave Hawthorne NJ 07506

MONDESIRE, LINDA MARIE, 2nd Grade Teacher; *b:* Bronx, NY; *c:* Ijah Mondesire-Crump; *ed:* Lehman Coll (BA) Comm 1989; The City Coll (MA) Elem Ed 1995; Lyons Educl Ctr Radio Broadcast Division Cert NY Schl of Announcing & Speech 1976; NY Trng Inst Tech Cnslng & Writing 1974; *cr:* WRAP-AMRollins Broadcasting Radio Announcer 1979-80; WSRC-AM Carolina Radio of Durham Announcer, Pub Affairs Host, Newscaster 1980-81; WQDR-FM Durham Life Broa dcasting Staff Announcer 1981-82; WWDC Capitol Broadcasting Air Personality Washington DC 1982-85; Bd of Ed CS 146 Common Branches Tchr 1989-; *ai:* Moet Chess Club Adv; Dev & Implemented Lobby Displays; World Jaycees Outstdng Svcs Comm Supporter Awd 1980; WTVD TV Channel 11

Broadcast & Career Goal Biography 1981; Guest Host WDVM PM Magazine; Cert of Appreciation Outstdng Presentation Awd; *home:* 4120 Hutchinson River Pkwy E Apt 4G Bronx NY 10475

MONDSCHEIN, JOHN F., Business Teacher; *b:* Allentown, PA; *m:* Linda S. Castor; *c:* Ashley, Lindsay, Matthew; *ed:* Bloomsburg Univ (BS) Bus Ed 1978; 30 Grad Credits Bus, Ed; *cr:* Parkland HS Bus Tchr 1978-; *ai:* Jr Class Adv; Track Coach 1978-; NEA, PSEA, PEA 1978-; Good Shepherd LC Church Cncl 1984-, VP 1994-; *office:* Parkland HS 2675 PA Rt 309 Orefield PA 18069*

MONETTE, MITCHELL, Sixth Grade Teacher; *b:* Winooski, VT; *m:* Nancy Mc Fadden; *c:* Chris, Tom, Lisa, Tim, Matt, Patrick; *ed:* SUNY at Plattsburgh (BS) Ed 1967, (MS) Ed 1972; 72 Grad Hrs; *cr:* Veeder Elem Schl 6th Grd Tchr 1967-70; Peru Intermediate Schl 6th Grd Tchr 1970-; *ai:* Peru Assn Tchrs, NEA of NY, NEA 1967-; *office:* Peru Intermediate Schl School St Peru NY 12972

MONETTE, NANCY ANN, Spanish Teacher; *b:* N Syracuse, NY; *m:* Bruce; *c:* Ashley, Bruce; *ed:* SUNY at Plattsburgh (BS) Intnl Bus & Span 1986, (MA) Ed 1992; *cr:* St Regis Falls Cntrl Schl Span Tchr 1986-87; Southwest Airlines Employment Coord 1987-88; St Lawrence Cntrl Schl Span Tchr 1988-91; Franklin Acad Span Tchr 1991-; *ai:* Fr Club Adv; Span Club; NYSAFLT 1989-; AATSP 1992-; Ladies of Elks 1303 1989-; Coll Club 1995-; NYS Multicultural & Comparative Ed Schlsp; *office:* Franklin Acad State St Malone NY 12953

MONEY, MATTHEW MICHAEL, Bio, Chem & Physics Teacher; *b:* Dayton, OH; *m:* Nicole Ann Dixon; *c:* Matthew William; *ed:* Univ of Dayton (BA) PE 1985; 7 Hrs; Univ of Dayton Grad Schl 9 Cr; Wright St UnivGrad Schl 8 Cr; *cr:* Precious Blood Schl Tchr, Sci Chair 1986-91; Our Lady of the Rosary Schl Tchr, Sci, PE Chair 1991-; *ai:* Eaton HS Boys Head Soccer Coach; Jump Rope for Your Heart, Sci, His Fair Coord; Soccer Player 24 Yrs; Bowler; Drummer; Powerlifter; Amer Coll of Sports Med, Natl Strength, Conditioning Assn1990-; OAAPHRD 1994-; Sci Equipment Grant 1992; Cert Strength, Conditioning Specialist NSCA 1993; Cert Hlth Fitness Instr 1992; *home:* 1001 Colwick Dr Dayton OH 45420*

MONFETT, CHRISTINE ANN, Science Teacher; *b:* Hollis, NY; *m:* Roger R.; *c:* Michael, Matthew, Meghan; *ed:* SUC at Oneonta (BS) Bio, Chem 1974; Stony Brook Univ (MS) Ed 1978; 30 Addl Hrs; *cr:* Sagamore Jr HS Sci Tchr 1975-79; Sachem HS South Earth Sci, Bio Tchr 1980-; *ai:* Hnr Soc, Rich Di Martino Schlsp Fund Selection Comms; NYSUT 1975-; *office:* Sachem HS South 51 School St Ronkonkoma NY 11779

MONFETTE, LINDA POPE, Third Grade Teacher; *b:* Jamacia, NY; *m:* Raymond; *c:* Marion; *ed:* SUNY at New Paltz (BS) Ed, Early Chldhd 1963; 15 Grad Credits Ed; SUNY at Albny 12 Grad Credits Lib Sci; *cr:* Greenville Cntrl Schls Third Grd Tchr 1963-66; Kingston Schls Consolidated Kndgtn-First Grd Tchr, Third Grd Tchr, Librn 1966-; *ai:* KFT 1967-; Klyne Historical Soc 1985-; Port Ewen Reformed Church 1966-, VP, Fin Chair; St Remy Reformed Church 1991-, Choir Dir, Fund Raising Chair; *office:* Chambers Elem Schl 945 Albany Avenue Ext Kingston NY 12401

MONFILS, LORA F., High School Math Teacher; *b:* New Brunswick, NJ; *c:* Kristin; *ed:* Boston Univ (BA) Fine Arts 1972; Rutgers Univ (MED) Math Ed 1985; 53 Additional Credits; *cr:* Westfield HS Math Tchr 1993-94; Franklin HS Math Tchr 1994-; *ai:* Frosh Class & Prevention Using Stu Help Adv; Franklin Township Instrl Cncl; NJEA 1983-; NEA 1983-; NCTM 1985-; *office:* Franklin HS 415 Francis St Somerset NJ 08801*

MONICA, FREDRIC, Guidance Counselor & Coach; *b:* Newark, NJ; *m:* Patricia; *c:* J. Thomas; *ed:* Rutgers Univ (BS) PE 1961; Montclair St Coll (MA) Stu Prsnl Services 1967; Over 40 Credits in Addition to Masters Work; *cr:* Oakland Acad PE Dir, Tchr 1961-62; DePaul HS Tchr, Coach 1962-64; Lakeland Regnl HS Tchr, Guidance Cnslr, Coach 1964-; *ai:* Head Var Girls Bsktbl Coach; Defensive Coord, Var Ftbl Tchr; Stu Asst Team; Schl Liason Passale Cty Coaches Assn; NEA; NJEA; NJPCA; NJTFOA; PCEA, PC Coaches Assn; Jaycees; Wanaque Jaycees Educator of Yr 1987; Passale Cty Coaches Service Awd 1986, Bsktbl Coach of the Yr; NISI AA Schlar, Ath Coach 1991; NAC Bsktbl Coach of the Yr; NJICA All-Star Bsktbl Coach; *office:* Lakeland Regnl HS 205 Conklintown Rd Wanaque NJ 07465

MONICO, SUEANN LEANDRI, 6th Grade Social Studies Tchr; *b:* Kingston, PA; *m:* John J.; *c:* Kristen, Brian; *ed:* Coll Misericordia (BS) Elem Ed 1969; Masters Equivalency 1991; *cr:* Collings Lake Elem 3rd Grd Tchr 1969-70; WY Vly West Sch Dist 4th Grd Tchr 1970-74, 5-6th Grd Eng Tchr 1975-78, 6th Grd Eng Tchr 1978-, 6t Grd Soc Stud Tchr 1996; *ai:* Stu Assistance Team; Mentor Tchr; NEA 1970-; PSEA 1970-; *office:* WY Vly West MS 201 Chester St Kingston PA 18704

MONIZ, KAREN MARIE, Mathematics Teacher; *b:* Warwick, RI; *ed:* Saive Regina Univ (BAS) Math & Ed 1989; Providence Coll (MED) Cnslng 1994; *cr:* W Warwick HS Math Tchr 1990-; *ai:* MS Girls Bsktbl Coach 1990-; HS Var Girls Bsktbl Coach 1995-; AFT 1990-; RIMTA 1990-; NCTMA 1990-; WWTA 1990-; WBCA 1995-; RIHSGBCA 1995-; NFICA 1990-; *office:* W Warwick HS 4 Webster Knight Dr West Warwick RI 02893

MONK, MELCHER I., Principal; *b:* Philadelphia, PA; *m:* Dawn Price; *ed:* Oakwood Coll (BA) Chem 1982; Tchrs Coll (MA) Educl Admin 1993; Attnd Andrews Univ; *cr:* Shiloh Acad Sci Tchr 1982-85; Excelsior Elem Schl Prin 1990-91; Northeastern Acad Prin, Chem Tchr 1986-90, 1991-; *ai:* Spon Yrbk, Short-Term Missions; Acad Standards Comm Chprsn; NASSP 1991-; ASCD 1990-; Giraffe Univ Yth Org 1993-; Harlem YMCA 1989-; Minority Stdnts Awd; Jewish Child Care Agency Svc Awd; *office:* Northeastern Acad 532 W 215th St New York NY 10034*

MONROE, BETTY MINOR, Lit, Eng & Soc Studies Teacher; *b:* Bridgeport, CT; *m:* Martin; *c:* Ebony Nicole; *ed:* Univ of Bridgeport (BS) Elem Ed 1980; Widender Univ (MS) Ed 1996; Curr, Instruction Supvr Cert; *cr:* Penns Grove MS Tchr 1980-; *ai:* Mentor Prgm; Peer Mediation Supvr; Stu Support Team; Subject Area Coord 1991-93; Kids for Saving Earth Adv 1991-92; NJEA, NEA 1980-; ASCD, Southern NJ Rdng Cncl 1993-; Kappa Delta Pi 1996; Favorite Tchr of Yr 1995-; *office:* Penns Grove MS 351 Maple Ave Penns Grove NJ 08069*

MONROE, DAVID DUBOSE, Life Science Teacher; *b:* Jersey City, NJ; *m:* Heidi Elisabeth Kurbjeweit; *c:* Adam, Scott; *ed:* Jersey City St Coll (BA) Ed 1968; Columbia Univ (MA) Ed 1973; Bacteriophage Cloning, Dev Behavior Genetics William Patterson; *cr:* West Essex Jr HS Sci, Life Sci, Bio Tchr 1968-; West Essex HS Sci, Life Sci, Bio Tchr 1968-; *ai:* NJSTA; NSTA; NJSBA 1987-; NJEA, NEA 1968-; Hope Twp Bd of Ed 1987-, Former VP, Pres; Woodrow Wilson Flwshp Princeton Univ; *office:* West Essex Regnl Jr HS W Greenbrook Rd North Caldwell NJ 07006

MONROE, JANE HAMILTON, Retired Fourth Grade Teacher; *b:* Albemarle, NC; *m:* Harold; *c:* Gloria Lavy, John, Barbara Shackelford; *ed:* Drake Univ (BA) Ed 1968, (MS) Ed 1970; *cr:* Saydel Consolidated Schl Dist Third Grd Tchr 1968-69; Des Moines Pub Schls Third Grd Tchr 1969-72; Loveland City Schl Dist Fourth Grd Tchr 1973-90; *ai:* NEA 1968-; PEO 1992-, Chaplain; Jennings Scholar Lectures 1980-81; *home:* 202 Rollins Dr Loveland OH 45140

MONROE, SUZANNE ABDO, Fifth Grade Teacher; *b:* Olean, NY; *m:* Mark Douglas; *c:* Cheryl, Matthew; *ed:* St Bonaventure Univ (BS) Elem Ed 1970, (MS) Advanced Tchr Ed 1975; *cr:* Olean Cath Schl 3rd Grd Tchr 1 Yr; Otto-Eldred Schls 3rd-4th Grd Tchr 1970-74; Olean Schls Permanent Sub 1975-79; St Marys Elem Kndgtn & 6th Grd Tchr 1979-85; Washington West Elem 5th Grd Tchr 1985-; *ai:* Lang Arts Comm; Discipline Comm Chprsn; Flower Fund Chprsn; Past Math Comm; NEA 1985-; Conflict Resolution Presentations; *office:* Washington West Elem Schl 1626 Washington St Olean NY 14760

MONROE, VICTOR ALLEN, English Teacher; *b:* Marion, OH; *m:* Michelle Bovesen; *ed:* Humboldt St (BA) Eng 1987; San Diego St (MA) Eng 1989; *cr:* Sacred Heart Schl Eng Tchr 1989-90; St Margaret's Mc Tenan Schl Eng, Drama, Coach 1990-92; Dar Al Fikir Schl ESL Tchr 1992-93; Gilmour Acad Eng, Cmptr Tchr, Coach; *ai:* Stu Cncl Adv; Soccer Coach; Schl Culture, Tech Comms; NCTE 1989-; Comm on Post-Scndry Information, Dissemination 1993-; AFCD 1994-; Inst for Human Stud 1995-; Various Short Stories, Poems Pub, Paper on Ethnocentric Rdng Interpretation; *office:* Gilmour Acad 34001 Cedar Rd Gates Mills OH 44040*

MONS, JOAN DIXON, Chemistry Teacher; *b:* Buffalo, NY; *m:* Roy J.; *ed:* Southern IL Univ (BS) Zoology 1974; Nazareth Coll (MS) Ed 1982; *cr:* Gananda Cntrl Schl Sci Tchr 1980-82; Fairport HS Chem Tchr 1983-; *ai:* NYSUT 1982-; Fairport Edctrs Assn 1982-, Treas, Bldg Rep; Church Pianist; *office:* Fairport HS 1358 Ayrault Rd Fairport NY 14450

MONTANEZ, JOHN M., Dir of Grants & Adj Instructor; *b:* Caguas, PR; *m:* Carolyn Thomas; *c:* Robert, Gregory; *ed:* St Johns Univ (BA) Psych 1976; Tchrs Coll of Columbia Univ (MA) Psych 1979; *cr:* Hudson Cty CC Cnslr 3 Yrs; Hostos CC CUNY Spcl Asst to Pres 3 Yrs; BMCC CUNY Dir of Continuing Ed 5 Yrs; BMCC CUNY Dir of Grants & Dev 3 Yrs; *ai:* NY St Assn Cont Ed 1987-; NCRD 1989-; *office:* Borough Of Manhattan Comm Coll 199 Chambers St New York NY 10007

MONTANEZ, MARIE-JOSEE BEROTTE, ESL Coord & Lang Dept Chprsn; *b:* Port-au-Prince, Haiti; *m:* Benigno; *c:* Jason, Victoria; *ed:* Hunter Coll (BA) Romance Langs 1976; Columbia Univ (MA) TESOL 1982; Bank St Coll of Ed (MED) Educl Ldrshp 1988; *cr:* NY City Bd of Ed Elem Tchr 1977-86; Nyack Pub Schls ESL Tchr, Chprsn 1986-; *ai:* Haitian Culture Club Adv; Multicultural Comm; Trainer for Ldrshp Trng Groups; TESOL 1985-; NYSAFLT 1994-; IFG Prod 1990-, Comm Vol, Person of Yr; Ramapo Town Cncl 1994-, United Amers; Received Title VII Flwshp MA Degree Grad Stud; *office:* Nyack HS 360 Christian Herald Rd Nyack NY 10960

MONTANTE, JOSEPH R., Mathematics Teacher; *b:* Buffalo, NY; *ed:* SUNY at Buffalo (MED) Math Ed 1992; *cr:* Seneca Voc HS Math Tchr 1987-90; Sweet Home Cntrl Schls GED Instr 1987-90; Frederick Law Olmsted Schl Math Tchr 1990-; SUNY at Buffalo Lecturer & Gifted Math Pgm Tchr 1995-; *ai:* Math League Coach; NYSUT 1987-; NCTM 1993-; BSA 1983-, Scoutmaster & Comm Mem, Distngd Scoutmaster, Vigil Hnr & Scouters Key; Amer Mensq Ltd 1988-, Treas; Intl Soc for Philosophical Enquiry 1989-; Fulbright Grant 1996; *office:* PS 56 Frederick Law Olmsted 716 W Delavan Ave Buffalo NY 14222

MONTE, ANTHONY JOHN, Science Teacher; *b:* Brooklyn, NY; *ed:* Dowling Coll (BA) Natural Sci, Math 1987; Stonybrook Univ (MA,LS) Sci 1995; *cr:* Sachem HS Sci Tchr 1987-89; Acad of St Joseph Sci Tchr 1990-; *ai:* Sci Olympiad, Vlybl Coach; Presidential Awd for Excl in Sci, Math Tchng Nom 1995; *office:* Acad of Saint Joseph Brentwood Rd Brentwood NY 11717

MONTECALVO, ALBERT M., Music Director; *b:* Bridgeport, CT; *m:* Karen Bowe; *c:* Alisyn, Nancy Dill Zangre, Robin Dill Herde, Deborah Dill, Ken Dill, Melissa Dill; *ed:* Western CT St Univ (BA) Music Ed 1964, (MS) Music Ed 1970; Southern CT St Univ 6th Yr Admin, Supervision 1989; Attnd Berklee Schl of Music, Goddard Coll, Drake Univ, George Washington Univ, KS St Univ Ed, Music, Lang; *cr:* Stamford Pub Schls Instrumental Music Tchr 1964-68; Carmel Cntrl Schl Dist Instrumental Music Tchr 1968-89, Music Dir 1989-; *ai:* Dance, Jazz Band, Holiday Winds Dirs; Co-Chm Inclusion Comm; Carmel TA, AFT, NYSUT 1968-, Bldg Rep, 25 Yr Silver Cup; CEA 1964-68; Amer Fed Musicians 1960-; Putnam Cnty Music Edctrs Assoc Pres; CHS Site Based Comm Co-Chr; Curr Cncl Chr; Spcl Area Comm; Sonny Carroll Jazz Orchstra; Pub Music NYSSMA Manual; Performer Bridgeport, New Haven, Ridgefield Symphonies, Summer Music on Hudson, Free Lance; Conn Inst of Mrtl Arts Taekwon Do Blck Blt 1995; *office:* Carmel Cntrl Schl Dist 30 Fair St Carmel NY 10512*

MONTEFUSCO, YOLANDA BIANCANIELLO, English & Journalism Teacher; *b:* Astoria, NY; *m:* John Anthony; *c:* Audra Ann; *ed:* Hofsta Univ (BA) Eng 1971; St Univ of NY at Stony Brook (MLS) Liberal Stud; 70 Post Grad Credits; *cr:* Lindenhurst HS Eng & Jrnlsm Tchr 1971-; *ai:* Charles Street Times Newspaper Adv; Tchr Assn of Lindenhurst, AFT, NEA, NYSUT 1971-; Jrnlsm Ed Assn 1992-; The Columbia Scholastic Press Advs Assn 1994-; *office:* Lindenhurst Sr HS 300 Charles St Lindenhurst NY 11757

MONTELEONE, JOHN, 5th Grd Teacher & Bldg Chprsn; *b:* Brooklyn, NY; *ed:* Pace Univ (BA) His 1967; Univ of Dayton (MA) His 1970; C. W. Post (PHD) Admin 1982; Traffic Driving Safety, Spec Ed Cert; *cr:* Most Holy Trinty HS Tchr 1968-72; Bishop Ford HS Dir of Act, Tchr 1972-75; Seaford HS Tchr 1975-78; Candlewood Jr HS Tchr 1978-83; Abbey Lane Schl Chprsn, Tchr 1983-; *ai:* Drug Ed Bldg Coord; Levittown After Schl Prgm Dir; NEA; AFT 1983-, Bldg Rep; AFS Admin 1985-; Amer Legon 1971-; Vly Stream Vol Fire 1974-; Grad Assistanship Univ of Dayton; *home:* 1725 Greene Ave Ridgewood NY 11385*

MONTELEONE, VINCENT JOSEPH, Instrumental Music Teacher; *b:* Butler, PA; *m:* Celeste Michelotti; *ed:* Duquesne Univ (BS) Music Ed 1969, (MM) Music Performance 1971; Post Grad Stud Univ of Denver; Private Stud; Bob McCoy; NBC Orch; NYC; *cr:* Diocese of Pittsburgh Instrumental Music Tchr 1969-71; Duquesne Univ Adjunct Prof of Trumpet 1971-91; Pittsburgh Pub Schls Instrumental Music Tchr 1971-86; Freelance Musician, Soloist, Commrcl Rcrdng Artist, Bndldr; Sterrett Classical Acad Music Dept Head 1986-; *ai:* Stage Crew; Instructional Cabinet; Parent, Schl, Comm Cncl; AFT 1971-; Intnl Trumpet Guild 1986-; Amer Fed of Musicians 1967-; Pittsburgh Vintage Grand Prix Car Cncl 1994-95; Sports Car Club of Amer; Selected Mem Yamaha Music Personalities 1971-73; Twice Nom Pittsburgh Thanks to Tchrs Awd 1992, 1993; Sch Dist Txtbk & Curr Comms; *office:* Sterrett Classical Acad 7100 Reynolds St Pittsburgh PA 15208*

MONTELLA, ENNIS JOSEPH, Mathematics Professor; *b:* Lawrence, MA; *m:* Virginia Shaw; *c:* Sharon, Diane; *ed:* Boston Coll (AB) Math 1950, (MA) Math 1956; *cr:* Army Map Svc Supervisory Mathematician 1951-56; Merrimack Coll Math Prof 1955-93; Avco Mathematician 1962; Merrimack Coll Adj Lecturer 1993-; *ai:* Math Club Adv 1957-90; MAA 1955-; Outstdng Tchng Awd 1969-70; Pub 1955, 1961; Assoc Prof 1970; *office:* Merrimack Coll 315 Turnpike St North Andover MA 01845

MONTEMBEAU, JEANNE A., Sixth Grade Teacher; *b:* Biddeford, ME; *ed:* Univ of ME at Gorham (BS) Eng, Soc Stud 1972; *cr:* Guilford MS 4 6 Grd Tchr 1972-73; St Andre Schl 6 Grd Tchr 1973-86; Biddeford MS 6 Grd Tchr 1987-; *ai:* Natl Jr Hnr Soc, Peer Mediation Adv; Stu Assistance Team Mem; Delta Kappa 1990-95, VP; Tchr of Yr 1986; *office:* Biddeford MS 335 Hill St Biddeford ME 04005*

MONTENARE, KATHRYN PRIN, Secondary English Teacher; *b:* Brooklyn, NY; *m:* Gene; *c:* Eugene, Meredith, Michael; *ed:* Molloy Coll (BA) Eng 1969; SUNY at Stoneybrook (MS) Lbrl Stud 1974; Addl 60 Hrs; *cr:* Patchogue-Medford Schl Eng Tchr 1972-; *ai:* GATE Prgm; De Tchr; Rsrch Curr Dev Pgrm; Drama Coach Adv; AFT 1972-, Bl NEA, NCTE 1972-; Natl Assn Univ Women 1986-; Stonybroc Alumni Assn 1972-; *office:* Patchogue-Medford HS Buffalo Ave N NY 11763

MONTESANO, MARILYN CARDINALE, English Teacher; *b.* NY; *m:* William S.; *c:* Amanda, Marc; *ed:* SUNY at Fredonia (B. Scndry Ed 1976, (MS) Ed, Learning Disabilities 1977; Cert Elem E *cr:* SUNY at Fredonia Tchng Asst Psychological Fnd 1977; Oneid Eng, Writing Tchr 1977-85; New Hartford Sr HS Eng, Rdng, Writi 1985-; *ai:* Adv Chrldng, Zonta Club; AFT, NEA 1977-; NCTE 198 1977-; Grad Tchng Asst Flwshp 1977; Kappa Delta Pi 1976; Whe Among Stdnts in Colls 1976; Delta Kappa Gama 1983; Outstdr Recognition 1995; *office:* New Hartford Sr HS 33 Oxford Rd New H NY 13413*

MONTESANO, ROCCO ANTHONY,JR., Social Studies Teac Utica, NY; *m:* Jan Belton; *c:* Lauren, Marie; *ed:* St Lawrence Un His 1974; St Univ at Albany (MS) Educl Comm 1975; Tchr Cert 1 Tamarac MS 8th Grd Soc Stud Tchr 1976-77; Averill Park-Algonq 8th Grd Soc Stud Tchr 1977-87; Burnt Hills-Ballston Lake MS 8th Stud Tchr 1987-; *ai:* Bldg Pres; Co-Chm Mid Schl Cncl; Comm B Sftbl Prgm Coach; Rel Ed Tchr; Recreation Dir Summer Recreatic 1977-91; Averill Park HS Head Ftbl Coach 1977-85; NY St Unitec AFT 1976-, Bdlg Pres 1991-; Tchng & Comm Svc Awd 1993; *office* Hills Ballston Lake MS Lakehill Rd Burnt Hills NY 12027

MONTESI, FRED JOSEPH, 4th Grade Teacher; *b:* Springfield, Patricia A. LaPorte; *c:* Michelle Picher, Marlo, Michael; *ed:* Am Coll (MS) Ed 1967; Amer Intnl Coll (BS) Elem Ed, (BS) Prsnl Western New England Coll Mechanical Engrng 1 Yr; *cr:* Anna E Ba 5th Grd 1967-67; Granger Elem Schl 4th Grd Tchr 1967-; *ai:* MTA NEA 1965-; AEA 1965-, Ins Comm Neg Team, Nom Tchr of Agowan UICO, Mental Hlth Comm Chprsn; Sacred Heart Church Usher, Cath Charities; Coach Sacred Heart, Sftbl & Ice Hockey Camp Rainbow, Asst Dir & Cnslr; Nom Tchr of the Yr; Asst Prin; S & Schl Cncl; *office:* Clifford M Granger Schl 31 S Westfield St Hills MA 01030*

MONTFORD, CLAUDIAN HAMMOND, 5th Grade Teacher; *b:* C GA; *m:* Redolphus; *c:* Randolph, Rudolph; *ed:* Newark St Coll (BA Ed, Early Chldhd 1969; Fairleigh Dickinson Univ (BA) Elem Sci 1 Peter's Coll, Urban Schls Pgrms 3 Credits; Christ Church Coll Zealand Whole Lang 3 Credits; Rutger's Univ Children's Writin Cert; *cr:* Bank Street Coll Consultant Tchr 1972-73; Plainfield Bd E Tchr 1969-72, Tchr 1973-; *ai:* NJSSI Participant, Rep; Family Sc After-Schl Sci, Math Club Tchrs; Cmptr Tech, School-Wide S Coord; Seed Rep; PEA, UCEA, NJEA, NEA 1969-; ASCD 1995-; 1996-; AT&T Tech Awd 1995-; New Zealand Stud Tour Schlsp Westry G. Horne Excl Ed Awd 1988; Governor's Tchr Reco Recipient 1986; NJ St Mini Grant 1983; Outstanding Tchr Awd *office:* Evergreen Elem Schl 1033 Evergreen Ave Plainfield NJ 070

MONTGOMERY, BRIDGET WADE, High School Choral Direc Waynesburg, PA; *m:* Greg; *c:* Benjamin; *ed:* Fairmont St Coll (BA) Ed 1978; WV Univ (MA) Scndry Ed 1986; Attnd Vandercook Music, West Minster Choir Coll; *cr:* Cntrl Greene Schl Dist Tchr *ai:* PMEA; Grange 1988-; *office:* Waynesburg Cntrl HS RD 2 Waynesburg PA 15370

MONTGOMERY, CHRISTINA LYNN, Vocal Music Teacher; City, PA; *c:* Pamela Fellner, Michelle Kunkle; *ed:* Clarion Univ Music Ed 1987; Edinboro Univ (MA) Scndry Guid 1994; *cr:* Youn MS, Sr HS Vocal Music Instr 8 yrs; *ai:* Silver Eagle Adv; Production Dir; PMEA, MENC 1987-, Cty Rep; NEA, WCEA Philomel Tchr of Yr 1992; Article Pub; *office:* Youngsville MS, Sr College St Youngsville PA 16371

MONTGOMERY, JO ANNE, 6th Grade Teacher; *b:* Johnstown, Susan De Anne Smith; *ed:* Bowling Green St Univ (BA) Ed, El Ed Wright St Univ (MA) Master Tchr 1979; 50 Hrs BGSU, Lourdes Co St, Univ of Toledo; *cr:* Lakota Schl Dist 1st Tchr 1968-71; Vandalia Schl Dist K-3rd Grd Tchr 1971-79; Findlay City Schls DPPF, Tutor Term Sub Tchr 1979-82; Liberty Benton Schl Dist 6th Grd, Long Te Tchr 1982-84; Lake Local Schl Dist 1st, 3rd, 6th Grd Tchr 1984-; *ai:* Cty Young Writers Conf Comm Mem; NW Regnl Prof Dev Ctr Bd LEA Exec Bd Mem; Stu Cncl Adv Top Natl Stu Cncl Awd 1995; NEA 1971-, Del, Rep Assembly; LEA 1984-, Pres, Treas, NW Svc Awd; 1973-, St Pres; Wood Cty Republicans 1984-, Precinct Comm; Wo Republican Woman 1984-, Past VP; Co-Author; Lake Dist Tchr of Yr Co-Grant Writer Three Grant; OH Hall of Fame Schl Fac Mem; St Gold Medal Natl Awd 1995; *office:* Lake Elem Schl 28140 Lemoy Millbury OH 43447*

MONTGOMERY, LARRY C., Guidance Counselor; *b:* Mc Keespo *c:* Leah; *ed:* Langston Univ (BA) Soc Stud Ed 1970; Univ of Pitts (MED) Cnslr Ed 1974; Attnd CA Univ of PA; *cr:* W Mifflin HS So Tchr 1972-76; Homeville Jr HS Guidance Cnslr 1976-83; *ai:* AFT Omega Psi Phi 1969-; *office:* West Mifflin MS 371 Camp Hollow R Mifflin PA 15122

MONTGOMERY, MARJORIE A., 8th Grade Social Studies T Framingham, MA; *m:* Michael J. Shea; *ed:* Wheaton Coll (AB) E 1963; Wesleyan (MALS) Intellectual His 1970; *cr:* Newton Pub Schl 1965-; *ai:* Time Ed Prgm, Sports Illustrated for Kids, Time for Writing, Advy Bd; NCSS 1980-, Writer Natl Stans; NASCD 1995-; MTA, NEA 1963-; CRADLE 1985-, Trustee; MALRE 1980-, Pres, T Yr; Bill of Rights Ed Project 1990-, Advy Comm; MA Tchr of Yr Disney Tchr 1989; Writings Pub; *office:* Frank Ashley Day MS 21 Pl Newtonville MA 02160

MONTGOMERY, MELODY WARKE, 8th Grd Amer His Teach Allentown, PA; *m:* William; *c:* Marc Mertz, Matthew Mertz; *ed:* V Coll (BA) His 1968; Western CT Univ (MS) Adolescent Psych 19 Ldrshp Prgm Southern CT Univ; *cr:* Haworth Pub Schl Tchr, Dept 1968-74; Great Vly Schls Tchr, Dept Head 1974-83; Radnor Schls Dept Head 1983-84; Danbury Schls Tchr, Dept Head 1984-; *ai:* Yrbk Tech Comm; NEA 1968; CEA 1984; KSUCC Trustee 1984; *office:* F Park MS 21 Memorial Dr Danbury CT 06810

MONTGOMERY, MICHELLE LOLLI, Science Teacher; *b:* Chi IL; *m:* Robert; *c:* Stephen, Francis, James; *ed:* Bucks Cty Comm Coll Bio 1969; Framingham St (BA) Bio 1971; 32 Addl Credit Hr Presentation BVM Schl AV Coord & 1st-8th Grd Sub Tchr 1976-85; W Hallahan HS Sci Tchr 1985-; Philadelphia Coll of Textiles & S Prof 1992-95; *ai:* SAP; Sunshine Club Dir; Bowling Coach 2 Yrs; Schl Discipline Bd Arbitrator; Career Dev at Risk Yths Stu Adv; 1986-; NACST 1986-; NAAEE 1994-; *office:* John W Hallahan HS 19th St Philadelphia PA 19103*

MONTGOMERY, PATRICK LAWRENCE, Science & PE Teach Cincinnati, OH; *m:* Suzanne Rebecca; *c:* Elizabeth, Matthew Morehead St Univ (BS) PE & Bio 1977; Xavier Univ (MED) Ed A 1981; *cr:* Middletown Madison Jr HS 8th Grd Bio Tchr 1977-78; Syca Jr HS 8th Grd Bio & Chem Tchr 1978-; Sycamore HS 9th Grd PE 1978-; *ai:* 8th Grd Ftbl; 7th & 8th Grd Girls Track; 7th & 8th Grd Ski

›EA & SEA 1978-; *office:* Sycamore Jr HS 5757 Cooper Rd ati OH 45242*

GOMERY, RAE BRINKLEY, Third Grade Teacher; *b:* Newark, Craig; *ed:* Trenton St Coll (BA) Elem Ed 1963; Kean Coll (MA) urr, Inst 1989; *cr:* Benjamin Franklin Schl Third Grd Tchr 1963-; ning Com; Cultural Arts Chprsn; Assembly Show Coord; PTA, ETEA, MCEA 1963-; NEA 1963-, Sec; Plainfield Beautification 94-; Tchr of Yr 1987; *home:* 323 Hillcrest Ave Plainfield NJ 07062*

GOMERY, STEPHEN R., 11th & 12th Grd Soc Stud Tchr; *b:* , FL; *m:* Christine A.; *c:* Bryan C., Kelsey M.; *ed:* Mohawk Valley) Lbrl Arts 1976; SUNY at Oswego (BA) Scndry Ed & Soc Stud UNY at Cortland (MS) Scndry Ed & Soc Stud 1982; CAS Pgm at Cortland; *cr:* Camden HS 9th-12th Grd Soc Stud Tchr 1978-; Rome Summer Schl Tchr 1994-95; *ai:* JV Ftbl 1978-83; Var Boys 1978-85; Head Var Ftbl 1983-86; JV Girls Bsktbl 1990 & 1991; 1995-; *office:* Camden Cntrl Schl Oswego St Camden NY 13316

GOMERY, SUZANNE T., 4th Grade Teacher; *b:* Bellaire, OH; *m:* ..; *c:* Stacey Carlo, Denise; *ed:* OH Univ (BS) Elem Ed 1968, (MS) d 1978; *cr:* Bellaire City Schls 5th Grd Tchr 1964-66, 1st Grd Tchr), Head Start Tchr 1969; Shadyside Schls 2nd Grd Tchr 1969-70; land of OH Schls 1st, 3rd & 4th Grd Tchr 1972-; *ai:* NEA, OEA & 1964-; SOEA 1972-; Delta Kappa Gamma 1984-, Mem & Rsrch ffice: Switzerland of OH Schls 125 2nd St Powhatan Point OH

I, JOSEPH FRANK, History Teacher; *b:* Jersey City, NJ; *ed:* St Coll (BS) His 1964; Kean Coll (MA) Soc Stud 1967; Seton Hall EdS) Admin, Supv 1979; *cr:* Hasbrouck Hts HS His Tchr 1964-88, ad Dept Chprsn 1974-88; Toms River HS East His Tchr 1988-; *ai:* e People Lecture Series Dir; NJEA 1964-; Phi Delta Kappa 1978-; Group 1995-; DAR NJ Outstdng His Tchr Awd 1985; Valley Forge ns Fnd Awd Outstdng Contributions to Ed 1986; Amer Ex-POW iation Awd 1991; NJ Legislative Resolution for Tchng Armenian de 1993; SAR Outstdng Citizenship Awd 1995-; *home:* 26 Morton allette NJ 08735

I, PATRICK A., Accounting Teacher; *b:* Syracuse, NY; *m:* en P. Barry; *ed:* Niagara Univ (BS) Commerce 1968, (MS) Ed 1971; ous Philosophy & Coaching Courses; *cr:* Bishop Neuman HS Bus Coach 1968-69; Niagara Falls HS Bus Tchr 1969-70; Bishop Duffy tbl Coach 1969-72; LaSalle HS Bus Tchr 1972-; *ai:* Boys Var Bsktbl 1975-; AFT, NEA, NYSTA 1968-; Niagara PAL 1981-; Niagara Girls Club 1985-; NYS Section VI Coach of Yr 1988, 1991 & 1995; LaSalle Sr HS 1500 Military Rd Niagara Falls NY 14304*

'I-BOVI, LOUISA NORA, English Teacher; *b:* Waterbury, CT; *m:* ; *c:* Max; *ed:* St Josephs Coll (BS) Eng, Ed 1974; SCSU Rdng 1984; tertown HS Eng Tchr 1974-; *ai:* Honor Soc, Homecoming, Jr Prom Morale Comm; Staff Fund Coord; WEA, CCET 1974-; *office:* own HS 324 French St Watertown CT 06795

'ICELLO, CHARLES E., 4th-12th Grd Musical Director; *b:* PA; *ed:* West Liberty St Coll (BA) Music Ed 1978; Univ of Dayton Educl Admin 1985; *cr:* Grove UP Church Choir Dir 1977-; ville HS Dir Musical Stud 1978-; Dance Band Musician, Mgr 1975; Grd Class Spon; Marching, Concert, Pep, Stage, County Band; Chorus; Concert Choir; Percussion Ensemble; Folk Music Ensemble; 1978-; MENC-; Loyal Order of Moose, Masons 1980-; *office:* ville H S PO Box 262 Beallsville OH 43716

'PLAISIR, RENE EDWARD, 8th Grade Science Teacher; *b:* ester, NH; *m:* Barbara G. Fraser; *c:* Bethany, Brandon; *ed:* St ns Coll (BA) Natural Sci, Bio, Chem 1969; 30 Credits 1969; *cr:* own Jr HS 7-8 Grd Sci Tchr 1969-73; Goffstown Area Schl 8th Grd hr 1973-91; Mountainview MS 8th Grd Sci Tchr 1991-; *ai:* NH Assn Bd Mem; Jr HS Sftbl Umpire; NEA 1969-; NEA NH, GEA Pres 1973-76, VP 1971-72; Goffstown Ed Assn 1969-, Chm nce, Negotiation Comms, VP 1992-; NSTA; Mt William Pond Assn Pres 1986-; *office:* Mountain View MS 41 Lauren Ln Goffstown NH

'ROSS, CAROL STORY, Mathematics Teacher; *b:* Kingston, PA; eodore S.; *c:* Bryan E., William A., Erin E.; *ed:* Bloomsburg Univ Math & Fr 1963; *cr:* Marhsall HS Math Tchr 1963-64; Longview HS Math Tchr 1965-66; Tunkhannock HS Math Tchr 1983-; *ai:* NEA, 1983-; Jr Choir 1990-, Dir; *office:* Tunkhannock HS 120 W Tioga St annock PA 18657

'ROSS, H. CHRIS, Guidance Counselor; *b:* Wilkes-Barre, PA; *m:* Diane Denison; *c:* Shane; *ed:* Mansfield Coll (BS) Elem Ed 1971; wood Coll (MA) Cnslng 1988; Stu Assinstance Trng; *cr:* Elk Lake Dist 4th Grd Tchr 1972-78, 5th, 6th Grd Modified Section Tchr 88, AV Coord, Daily Replacement Instr 1985-86, 5th, 6th Grd ied Tchr 1987-92, Jr HS Cnslr 1992-; *ai:* Stu Support Team; United rs Peer Ldrshp; Natl Jr Hnr Soc; Susquehanna Cty Children & Yth Bd; PSEA, NEA 1971-; ELEA 1971-, Rep; Chi Sigma Iota 1988-; nic Blue Lodge 1984-, Worshipful Master; Keystone Consistory Shriner 1986-; *office:* Elk Lake Schl Dist PO Box 100 Dimock PA

'TROY, BECKY DUPREY, 7th-8th Grade Math Teacher; *b:* sburg, NY; *c:* Leon III, Kara; *ed:* SUNY at Potsdam (BA) Math, Ed Working on Masters; *cr:* Heuvelton Cntrl Schl MS Math Tchr 1993-; ath Counts Team Coach; NCTM, AMTNYS 1992-.

TS, EILEEN MC MANUS, English Teacher; *b:* Framingham, MA; ry; *c:* Paul, Timothy; *ed:* Univ St of NY (BS) Eng 1987; 18 Credit Women's Stud & Native Amer Stud; *cr:* Bethel Elem Schl Rdng Tchr 92; Whitcomb HS Eng Tchr 1992-; *ai:* Sr Project Coord; Sr Class Schl Improvement, Fac Advy, Scheduling, Curr Review Comms; VEA, BEA, NCTE 1992-; Intnl Rdng Assn 1995-; Natl Endowments um Flwshp; Outstdng Tchr Awd Univ of Chicago 1995; Yrbl ation 1995; *office:* Whitcomb HS Pleasant St Bethel VT 05032*

'CHLER, OLIVE PARSONS, 5th-7th Grade English Teacher; *b:* ill, NY; *m:* Frederick A.; *c:* Nicholas J., Amelia Moochler necky, Frederick C.; *ed:* Wells Coll (BA) Eng 1967; Elmira Coll (MS) 976; SUNY at Cortland 30 Credit Hrs NY Cert 1974; *cr:* Union gs Cntrl Schl MS Eng Tchr 1967-80; Wells Coll Assoc Dir of ssions 1980-85; Insts for Achvmt of Human Potential Home Tchr & pist 1985-88; The Key Schl MS Eng Tchr 1988-; *ai:* Admissions & Head Search Comms; Bach Meistersingers 1989-93, Pres 1992; St Episcopal Church Choir 1989-; Wells Coll Master Tchr 1980-85; : The Key Schl 534 Hillsmere Dr Annapolis MD 21403

'DY, DOUGLAS W., English Teacher; *b:* Camden, ME; *m:* Shelley ; *ed:* Univ of ME at Orono (BS) Ed 1970; Univ of Southern ME) Rdng 1976; *cr:* Rockland Jr HS Rdng Tchr 1970-71; Erskine Acad Stud Tchr 1971-74; Gray-New Gloucester Jr HS Tchr of Spec Ed 80; Westbrook HS Tchr of Spec Ed & Eng Tchr 1980-; *ai:* Girls r Track Head Coach; Girls Outdoor Track Asst Coach; NEA, MEA ; *office:* Westbrook HS 125 Stroudwater St Westbrook ME 04092

'DY, JUDITH CECCARELLI, Kindergarten Teacher; *b:* Charleroi, ; Raymond Jr.; *c:* Mary Lou Moody Hasson, Marci Lin, Raymond P.; A St Coll (BS) Ed 1969; 24 Credit Hrs Toward Masters; *cr:* Belle on Area Schl Dist Kndgtn Tchr 1969-72; St Sebastian Schl Kndgtn Tchr 1979-; *ai:* NCTA 1980-; Annitta Gabaldi Soc 1985-; *home:* 547 Green St Belle Vernon PA 15012

MOODY, TIMOTHY ROBERT, Sixth Grade Teacher; *b:* North Conway, NH; *m:* Kathy Sue Carver; *c:* Erik, Kristopher, Keegan; *ed:* Univ of ME at Machias (BS) Elem Ed 1981; *cr:* South Aroostook Comm Schl 5th Grd Tchr 1981-82; MSAD #57 Lyman Elem 6th Grd Tchr 1982-; *ai:* 1st-6th Grd Bsktbl Coach & Coord; 6th Grd Math Club Adv; NEA, MEA 1981-; *office:* Lyman Elem Schl RFD 1 Box 2790 Kennbunk Pond Rd Kennebunk ME 04043*

MOOG, HELENE LOUISE, Fourth Grade Teacher; *b:* Bryan, OH; *m:* Lyle D.; *c:* Lyle Anthony, Jennifer; *ed:* Bowling Green St Univ (BS) Ed 1970; OH Northern Univ 1 Yr Credit; *cr:* Millcreek West Unity Schls Second Grd Tchr 1968-71; Bryan City Schls Fourth Grd Tchr 1971-; *ai:* Curr Comms; Delta Kappa Gamma 1993-; NEA, OEA, BEA 1971-; Bryan Tree Commission 1989-, Sec; Amer Legion Auxiliary 1946-; Wesley Unified Meth; *home:* 618 Cardinal Dr Bryan OH 43506

MOOK, DELO EMERSON, Prof of Physics & Astronomy; *b:* Cleveland, OH; *m:* Kathryn Jo Hiltner; *c:* Richard, Robert; *ed:* Univ of MI (PhD) Astronomy 1970; *cr:* Dartmouth Coll Asst Prof 1970-76, Assoc Prof 1976-79, Prof 1980-; *ai:* Articles in Astrophysical Journal, Astronomy & Astrophysics; Book with Thomas Vargish Inside Relativity; *office:* Dartmouth Coll 6127 Wilder Laboratory Hanover NH 03755

MOON, BONNIE YOUNG, First Grade Teacher; *b:* Cincinnati, OH; *c:* Caroline Donnelly, John, Chris, Michael, Cathy; *ed:* Wilmington Coll (BA) Elem Ed 1974; Miami Univ OH (MED) Elem Ed 1989; *cr:* Clinton Massie Schl Rdng Tchr 1983-85, Kndgtn Tchr 1985-86, First Grd Tchr 1986-; *ai:* NEA 1984-; CMEA 1984-, VP; Earthwatch 1995-; OEA John F. Kennedy Schlsp 1986; Exceptional Achvmt Awd 1993; *office:* Clinton Massie Elem Schl 2556 Lebanon Rd Clarksville OH 45113

MOON, RICHARD E., Science Teacher; *b:* Scranton, PA; *m:* Kay; *ed:* Temple Univ (EDD) Sci Ed 1988; *cr:* Schl Dist of Philadelphia Tchr 1975-; *ai:* Philadelphia Fed Tchrs 1975-; Phi Delta Kappa, Natl Assn of Sci, Tech & Soc 1988-; *office:* HS Creative & Performing Arts 11th & Catherine Sts Philadelphia PA 19147

MOON, STEPHEN R., English Teacher & Coach; *b:* Providence, RI; *m:* Kathy Schuman; *c:* Joanna, Jesse, Kristin; *ed:* Bapt Coll (BA) Ed 1978; Univ of RI Post Grad Stud; *cr:* Evangel Chrstn Schl HS Tchr, Coach 1978-82; North Stonington Chrstn Acad HS Eng Tchr, Coach 1982-94; Cornerstone Chrstn Schl HS Eng Tchr, Coach 1994-95; West Bay Chrstn Acad 8th Grd Eng Tchr, Coach 1995-; *ai:* Vars Soccer, Bsktbl Coach 1980-95; Drama Adv 1991-94; Natl Assoc Soccer Coaches of Amer 1987-; ACSI 1984-.

MOONE, PATTY ARLENE, English Teacher; *b:* Columbus, OH; *m:* Samuel; *c:* Brian, Kelly; *ed:* OH Dominican Coll (BA) Eng 1967; Mt St Joseph Coll (MA) Ed 1986; 40 Addl Hrs; *cr:* St James Grd Schl Lang Arts Tchr 1967-68; Mt St Joseph 10th Grd Eng Tchr 1968-69; Pickerington HS Eng Tchr 1969-; *ai:* Vol Conduct Stdnts Grief Support Grp; OEA, NEA PEA 1969-, Bldg Rep; Eastwood Village Civic Org 1980-; Jennings Scholar; Carnegie Grant Awd; *office:* Pickerington HS 300 Opportunity Way Pickerington OH 43147

MOONEY, CHRISTOPHER P., Philosophy Professor; *b:* Mineola, NY; *ed:* Columbia Univ (BA) Philosophy 1969; Fordham Univ (MA) Philosophy 1971, (PHD) Philosophy 1981; *cr:* Nassau Comm Coll Philosophy Tchr 1971-; *ai:* NEH Flwshp 1988; Schalkenbach Fnd Grant 1981; 25 Articles Pub; *office:* Nassau Comm Coll 1 Education Dr Garden City NY 11530

MOONEY, D. MICHAEL, English Teacher; *b:* Cincinnatti, OH; *m:* Judy Woodring; *c:* Christopher Stephen; *ed:* Hanover Univ (BA) Eng 1965; Univ of Cincinnati (MED) Scndry Admin 1973; *cr:* Glen Este HS Tchr 1965-67; Princeton Jr HS Tchr 1967-; *ai:* Eng Dept Head; NEA, OEA & PACE 1967-; NCTE 1992-; OH Writing Project Fellow; *office:* Princeton Jr HS 11157 Chester Rd Cincinnati OH 45246

MOONEY, DONALD FRANCIS, Religion Teacher; *b:* Jackson Heights, NY; *ed:* Fordham Univ (BS) Philosophy, Theology 1983, (MS) Rel Ed, Youth Ministry 1989; Scripture, Church His Courses St Joseph's Seminary; *cr:* John F. Kennedy HS Rel Tchr 1983-86; St Joseph's Grammer Schl Rel Tchr 1983-90; Cardinal Spellman HS Rel Tchr 1986-; *ai:* Mock Trial Club Moderator; Helpers of God's Precious Infants; C Y O Bsktbl Coach; Lay Fac Union 1987-; Grad Magna Cum Laude Fordham Univ; Distinguished Svc Awd NY Bd of Ed for Work with Mock Trial Club; *office:* Cardinal Spellman HS 1 Cardinal Spellman Pl Bronx NY 10466

MOONEY, ELLEN PATRICIA (DEVANEY), Social Studies Teacher; *b:* Brooklyn, NY; *m:* Michael Francis; *c:* Michael Andrew; *ed:* St Joseph's Coll at Brooklyn (BA) Eng 1963; 35 Addl Grad Credits in Eng Brooklyn Coll 1964-68; *cr:* Montauk Jr HS Eng Tchr 1963-67; Boody Jr HS Rdng Tchr 1967-69; Seneca Jr HS Soc Stud Tchr 1970-71; Holy Angels Regnl Schl Soc Stud Tchr 1980-; *ai:* Soc Stud Chprsn; Tech, Guid Coord; NCEA 1980-; Long Island Cncl for Soc Stud 1981-; BSA 1983-, Comm Sec; *office:* Holy Angels Regnl Schl Division St Patchogue NY 11772

MOONEY, JENNIE LYNN, 6th Grade Teacher; *b:* Batavia, NY; *m:* Patrick J.; *c:* Peter Fowler, Cory Fowler, Jeffrey Fowler; *ed:* SUNY at Cortland (BA) Elem Ed & Soc Sci 1970; SUNY at Brockport 30 Grad Hrs; *cr:* Batavia City Schls Sub, 1st & 4th Grd Tchr 1970-76; Robert Morris Elem Resource Room Tchr 1976-77; McGraw Elem Schl 6th Grd Tchr 1979-; *ai:* Shared Decision Making Bldg Team; Author Visit & PARP Comms; NEA 1979-, Sec; MFA 1979-, Pres; Seven Vly Rdng Cncl 1986-; Delta Kappa Gamma 1992-; Cortland Memrl Hosp Auxiliary 1994-; *office:* Mc Graw Elem Schl W Academy St Mc Graw NY 13101*

MOONEY, JOSEPH PATRICK, 6th Grade Teacher; *b:* Boston, MA; *m:* Jane Burke; *c:* Katherine, Christine; *ed:* Dakota Wesloyan Univ (BA) Elem Ed 1968; Boston St Coll (MED) Ed 1981; Boston St Coll Masters Degree & Addl 30 Hrs; *cr:* Brockton Schl System 5th Grd Tchr 1968-70; Norwood Schl System 5th & 6th Grd Tchr 1970-; *ai:* HS Var Ftbl Coach; NEA, MTA, Norwood Tchrs Assn 1968-; Westwood Bsktbl & Sftbl Assn, Coach; *office:* Norwood Jr HS Washington St Norwood MA 02062

MOONEY, M. PATRICIA DUFFY, HS Business Instructor; *b:* Johnsonburg, PA; *m:* F. Joseph; *c:* P. J., Joseph; *ed:* Mercyhurst Coll (BA) Bus 1953; Attnd Clarion Univ, PA St Univ; *cr:* DuBois Area HS Bus Instr 13 Yrs; DuBois Bus Coll Bus Instr 3 Yrs; Brockway Area HS Bus Instr 15 Yrs; *office:* Brockway Area Jr Sr HS 100 Alexander St Brockway PA 15824

MOONEY, MARK PATRICK, Anatomy & Physiology Asst Prof; *b:* Chicago, IL; *m:* Patti J. Dinwiddie; *c:* Meghan; *ed:* Western IL Univ (BS) Psych 1978, (MS) Biopsychology 1980; Univ of Pittsburgh (PhD) Physical Anthropology 1986; *cr:* Univ of IA Research Asst II 1979-83; Univ of Pittsburgh Research Asst Prof 1986-91, Asst Prof 1991-; *ai:* Lambda Chi Alpha Fac Adv; AAPA, ACPCFA 1984-; IADR 1995-; Over 100 Articles & Abstracts on Cranifacial Growth & Dev Pub; *office:* Univ Of Pittsburgh Pittsburgh PA 15261

MOONEY, STEPHEN VINCENT, School Social Worker; *b:* Boston, MA; *m:* Sharon Irene Sunega; *c:* Matthew; *ed:* Univ of CN (BA) Eng 1975, (MSW) Casework 1982; *cr:* St Receiving Home Childcare Worker 1975-77; Dept of Children, Families Case, Soc Worker 1977-83; Newington Childrens Hosp Psychiatric Soc Worker 1983-89; Somers Pub Schls Soc Worker 1989-; *ai:* Stdnts Supporting Stdnts Peer Cnslng Prgm Adv; Elem Schl Cross Grd Team Ldr; Natl Assn Soc Work 1983-, Mem; *office:* Somers Pub Schls Ninth District Rd Somers CT 06071

MOONEY, SUSAN P., High School Science Teacher; *b:* Hanover, NH; *m:* Robert E.; *ed:* Univ of NH (BA) Zoology 1971, (MS) Bio 1983; 60 Credit Hrs from Univ of MA, Univ of CT, Salem St, Leslie Coll & Notre Dame Coll; AP Bio Inst; DNA Inst; *cr:* Haverhill HS Sci Tchr, Bio & AP Bio Tchr 1973-; The Coll Bd Office of Acad Affairs Consultant 1994-; *ai:* Ecology Club Adv 1973-85; Acad Decathlan Adv 1984-; Steering Comm; MEAP Mentor 1993; NEA, MTA & HEA 1973-; NABT 1980-; AAAS 1993-; NSTA 1994-; Opera League of NH 1994-; Sierra Club 10 Yrs; NH Forest Soc 10 Yrs; Rsrch in Microbiology at UNH for Minority Stdnts; Horace Mann Grant 1980; Ecology Slide Show Series of Local Habitats; *office:* Haverhill HS 137 Monument St Haverhill MA 01832

MOONEY, VINCENT JAMES, English Teacher; *b:* New York City, NY; *m:* Celia Mascioli; *c:* Christopher, Erin; *ed:* Marist Coll (BA) Eng 1969; SUNY at New Paltz (MA) Eng 1975; 30 Addl Grad Credits; *cr:* Arlington Jr HS Eng Tchr 1969-75; Arlington Sr HS Eng Tchr 1975-; *ai:* NYSUT, Arlington Tchrs Assn 1969-; LaGrange Little League 1988-, Coach; LaGrange Bsktbl League 1988-; LaGrange Soccer League 1985-.*

MOONITZ, DANIEL ALEXANDER, Band Director; *b:* Cincinnati, OH; *m:* Abby Woods; *c:* Edward, Timothy, Melody; *ed:* Boston Univ (BM) Music Ed 1971; Univ of Cincinnati (MM) Music Performance 1974; *cr:* Ross MS Elem, Jr HS Band Tchr 1979-82; Ross HS Band, Music, His & Theory Tchr 1982-; *ai:* MENC, OMEA 1979-; ITG 1994-; Nationally Registered, Certfd Music Edctr; OH Dept of Ed Tchr Scholar Prgm; *office:* Ross HS 3425 Hamilton Cleves Rd Hamilton OH 45013

MOONO, STEADY HATUKALI, Upper School Administrator; *b:* Mazabuka Zambia, Africa; *m:* Kelly Gaugler; *c:* Micah; *ed:* Messiah Coll (BA) Ed 1985; Biblical Theological Seminary (MA) Theology 1987; Beaver Coll (MA) Eng 1993; Temple Univ PHD Stu; *cr:* Pinebrook Jr Coll Eng Tchr 1985-87; PA Chrstn Acad Eng Instr 1987-89, Upper Schl Admin 1989; *ai:* Soccer Coach; Self Stud Chprsn; ACSI 1989; Natl MS Assn 1993-; ASCD 1994; *office:* Penn Christian Acad 50 W Germantown Pike Norristown PA 19401

MOORE, ALVIS JAMES, Commnctn Theatre Arts Teacher; *b:* Winston-Salem, NC; *m:* Pearl Smith; *c:* Scott, Dustin; *ed:* Rio Grande Univ (BA) Commnctn Comp 1974; Attnd OH St Univ, Otterbien Coll; *cr:* The Columbus Urban League Tchr & Cnslr 1 Yr; Columbus Pub Schls Tchr, Adv & Coach 21 Yrs; Franklin Broadcasting Co Radio Personality 8 Yrs; Wilmington Coll Multicultural Wkshp Facilitator 2 Yrs; *ai:* Advy Bldg Cncl; Theatre Arts Dir; Future Edctrs of Tomorrow; Peer Mediators Group; Wilmington Coll Multicultural Seminarist; Columbus Ed Assoc 1975-, Bldg Rep; OH Ed Assoc 1975-; NEA 1975-; Whos Who in Amer Colls & Univ 1973; Radio Personality of Yr 1991; Edctr of Yr 1992; *office:* Whetstone HS 4405 Scenic Dr Columbus OH 43214*

MOORE, ANITA CROWE, English Teacher; *b:* New Egypt, NJ; *m:* William J.; *c:* Kelly; *ed:* Edinboro Univ of PA (BS) Scndry Eng Ed 1986; 6 Grad Hrs; 12 Grad Hrs at Duquesne Univ; *cr:* Lakeview HS Eng Tchr 1986-87; Vincentian HS Eng Tchr 1988-89; North East HS Eng Tchr 1989-; *ai:* Ftbl Ticket Booth; PSEA, NEA & NWCTE 1990-; *office:* North East Schl Dist 1901 Freeport Rd North East PA 16428

MOORE, ANN G., Science Department Chairperson; *b:* Lewiston, ME; *m:* Joseph F.; *c:* Jennifer A., Sean J.; *ed:* Bates Coll (BA) Bio, Psych 1978; *cr:* St Dominic Reg HS Biological, Scis, Psych Tchr 1977-, Sci Dept Chprsn 1992-; *ai:* Sr Class Moderator; NHS Adv; NSTA; APA 1993-; TOPSS 1993-, St of ME Coord; NASAA; General Electric Awd; *office:* St Dominic Regnl HS 179 Blake St Lewiston ME 04240

MOORE, ANN OPPEDISANO, Social Studies Teacher; *b:* Rochester, NY; *m:* Richard F.; *c:* Catherine, Jennifer, Mary; *ed:* Niagara Univ (BA) His 1974, (MA) Ed 1993; *cr:* Sacred Heart Schl 6th, 7th, 8th Grd Soc Stud Tchr 1975-79, 1986-90; Niagara Wheatfield Sr HS 9th, 10th Grd Soc Stud Tchr 1990-; *ai:* 1997 Class Adv; Care Team; AFT 1990-; *office:* Niagara Wheatfield Sr HS 2292 Saunders Settlement Rd Sanborn NY 14132

MOORE, ARLENE GREINER, Social Studies Teacher; *b:* Newburgh, NY; *m:* Michael Thomas; *c:* Michael, Colleen; *ed:* NY Univ (BA) His 1970; CA St U (MA) Hum 1992; 27 Credits Comparative Lit Hofstra Univ Grad Schl; Theoretical Fnds of Rdng 6 Grad Credits; *cr:* Harmony Hghts Schl Soc Stud Tchr 1990-; *ai:* Fac Adv Stu Pol Journal; *office:* Harmony Heights Schl 60 Walnut Ave East Norwich NY 11732

MOORE, ARMAND L., 4th Grade Teacher; *b:* Philadelphia, PA; *m:* Linda Durham; *c:* Kelli Jane, Bradley Durham; *ed:* Cheyney St Univ (B) Elem Ed 1969; Glassboro St Coll (MA) Elem Ed 1991; Johns Hopkins Univ Cert Ed 1975; Cheyney St Univ Cert Human Growth, Dev, Ed 1973-74; Glassboro St Coll Cert Elem Sci Tchng, Learning Inst 1988; *ai:* WTEA 1977-; NJEA 1971-; NEA 1969-; Phi Delta Kappa 1992-; Governors Tchr Recognition Awd 1989; Mc Siip Fellow 1989; Trained Mentor Cert 1991; *office:* Winslow Twp BOE Schl #5 Oak Leaf Rd Cedar Brook NJ 08018*

MOORE, BARBARA HARMONY, Retired Elementary Teacher; *b:* Sidney, OH; *m:* Thomas Herndon; *c:* James Elliott II, Nancy Moore Zwiep, Elizabeth; *ed:* Towson St Tchr Coll (BA) Elem Ed 1957; *home:* 6277 Lilbur Ln Cincinnati OH 45230

MOORE, BERNICE GHEE, US History Teacher; *b:* Monroeville, AL; *c:* Alberta Marye, Jayson Alexander; *ed:* AL St Univ (BS) His, Eng Tchr 1967; Univ of Cincinnati 72 Hrs His, Ec 1976; Miami Univ 15 Hrs Great Rels 1983; Xavier Univ 12 Hrs US Presidents 1990; Browns Univ 12 Hrs Schl Reform; 18 Hrs Conflict Mngmt; *cr:* Summer Yth Employment Asst Dir 1980, Dir 1981; Brown Univ Coalition of Essential Schl Trainer 1990-94; Peace in Ed UC Peer mediation, Conflict Mngmt 1992-; *ai:* Peer Mediation Trainer Spon, Mediator; Wkshp Facilitator, Fall Forum Del; Site, Instrl Ldrshp Team Mem; Inclusion Wkshp Trainer; CFT, AFT 1976-; Parent Orient Comm 1993-; Critical Friend 1995-; New Life Bapt Church 1977-; *office:* Woodward HS 7001 Reading Rd Cincinnati OH 45237*

MOORE, CLARE PEOPLES, Social Studies Tchr & Dpt Head; *b:* Wilmington, DE; *c:* David, Brian, Nancy; *ed:* Immaculata Coll (BA) Soc Stud, Ed 1972; Post Grad Stud Univ of DE; *cr:* Immacualta Heart of Mary 5th & 6th Grd Tchr 1972-74; St Mary Magdalen Schl 5th & 6th Grd Tchr 1980-; *ai:* Soc Stud Dept Head; NCEA 1980-; *office:* St Mary Magdalen Schl 9 Sharpley Rd Wilmington DE 19803*

MOORE, DAVID ALLEN, Social Studies Teacher; *b:* Gallipolis, OH; *m:* Judith Kathleen; *c:* Heather, Matthew; *ed:* Rio Grande Coll (BA) Soc Stud Comp 1979; Univ of Dayton (MS) Scndry Admin 1984; *cr:* Gallia Cty Local Schls Tchr, Coach 1979-; *ai:* Beta Club, Sr Class Adv; JV Vlybl, Girls Var Bsktbl Coach; OEA 1979-; GCLEA 1979-, Tchr of Yr; *office:* River Valley HS 1482 Little Kyger Rd Cheshire OH 45620

MOORE, DAVID EDWARD, History Teacher; *b:* Medford, MA; *m:* Lynne Rachlis; *c:* Daniel; *ed:* Boston Coll (BS Ed) His 1966, (MAT) Urban Ed & His 1968; 30 Credit Hrs in Post Grad Work Harvard & Boston Univ; *cr:* Boston Pub Sch MS Tchr 1966-68; Arlington Pub Schl East Jr High Tchr 1968-70; Newton Pub Sch Weeks Jr High Tchr 1970-76; Newton Pub Schl Day Jr High 1976-83; Newton North HS Tchr 1983-; *ai:* NEA, MTA 1968-; Newton Tchrs Assoc 1970, Sec 1996; Outstdng Tchrs Awd 1993 1993; *office:* Newton North HS 360 Lowell Ave Newton MA 02160*

MOORE, DAVID R., History Teacher; *b:* Pottsville, PA; *m:* Nancy; *c:* Matt, Ashley; *ed:* Mansfield St (BS) His 1973; *cr:* Zuni HS His Tchr

1976-78; Redbank Vly His Tchr 1979-; *ai:* Ftbl Coach 1979-; Girls Bsktbl Coach 1995-; NEA 1979-; *home:* RR 1 Box 657 Rimersburg PA 16248

MOORE, DENISE ELLEN, Health Teacher; *b:* Boston, MA; *m:* Mark Mc Glone; *ed:* Univ of Lowell (BS) Hlth Ed 1983; Northeastern Univ (MS) Ed 1994; *cr:* Milford Area Sr HS Hlth & Sci Tchr 1985-87; Lowell HS Hlth & PE Tchr 1987-91; Plymouth Regnl HS Hlth, Sci & PE Tchr 1991-; *ai:* Girl's Frosh Bsktbl Coach; Winter Carnival, Soph Class Adv; Hlth Fair Coord; Hlth Curr Comm; NEA, AAHPERD 1985-; Plymouth Fire Fighters Aux 1993-; Amer Cancer Soc 1983-, Bd of Dirs; Amer Red Cross 1983-, CPR Instr; Teen Smoking Cessation Grant; Hlth Curr Guide; *office:* Plymouth Regional HS 1 Old Ward Bridge Rd Plymouth NH 03264*

MOORE, DONNA NEGRINI, 5th Grade Teacher; *b:* Pittsfield, MA; *m:* Lorence E.; *c:* James, Thomas; *ed:* North Adam St Coll (BS) Elem Ed 1977; Lesley Coll (MED) Curr Dev 1992; *cr:* Lenox Pub Schls 2nd Grd Tchr 1980-81, 3rd Grd Tchr 1983-88, 4th Grd Tchr 1990-94, 5th Grd Tchr 1988-89, 1991-93, 1995; *ai:* NEA, LEA 1983-; *office:* Camaron Elem Schl 109 Housatonic St Lenox MA 01240

MOORE, EDMUND TIMOTHY, Asst Prof of Pan African Stud; *b:* Cleveland, OH; *m:* Debra DeLacy Washington; *c:* Candace, Elliot; *ed:* Kent St Univ (BFA) Graphic Design 1973, (MA) Graphic Design 1977, (MFA) Graphic Design 1983; *cr:* Kent St Univ African Amer Inst Grad Asst 1974-77, Pan African Stud Instr 1977-83, Pan African Stud Asst Prof 1983-, Pan Africa Stud Acting Chair 1994; *ai:* Hnrs Coll Policy Cncl; Lovelight Inc Bd Chm; KSU Policies Ed Cncl; Diversity Sub-Comm; Stu Harassment & Discrimination Review Comm 1994-95; Stdnts Achieving & Reaching for Success Advy Bd 1994-95; Natl Org Black Designers 1994-; Minority Empowerment Prj Portage Cty 1993-; Omega Psi Phi Awd Appreciation KSU 1989; Arts & Scis Stu Advy Awd Distngd Tchng 1992; Cleveland Magazine Edctr of Month 1994; Mortar Bd 2 Tchng Recognitions 1994; Honorary Mem Alpha Lambda Delta 1995; KSU Distngd Tchng Awd 1993; *office:* Kent St Univ 117 Oscar Ritchie Hall Kent OH 44242*

MOORE, ELAINE, Social Studies Teacher; *b:* Washington, DC; *c:* Eva Yolanda; *ed:* Federal City Coll (BA) African-Amer Stud 1972; George Washington Univ (MA) Uban Stud 1977, (EDD) Ed Admin 1987; Trng Mid Coll HS Shelby St Coll 1989; Univ of MD Nrsng 1966-68; *cr:* Washington Hosp Ctr Nurses' Aide, Unit Clerk 1967-72; Natl Portrait Gallery Tour Guide, Rsrch Aide 1971; Dist of Columbia Pub Schls Soc Stud Tchr 1972-87, Adult Ed Eng Tchr 1973-74, DC His Pilot Tchr 1978, Instr DCPS Tchrs 1981, Geog Curr Writer 1981, Schl Assessment Writer 1987, Systematic Tchr Preparation Prgm Monitor 1987-89; Univ Dist of Columbia Human Ecology Recruitment Coord 1988; Dist of Columbia Pub Schls 1989; Mac Farland Jr HS Soc Stud Tchr 1989-93; Dist of Columbia Pub Schls Curr Writer 1991, 1993; Coolidge Sr HS Soc Stud Tchr 1993-; *ai:* Testing Comm Chprsn; Mid St HS Accreditation Comm; Stu Cncl Spon; AFT 1972-; Phi Delta Kappa 1979-; Natl Cncl Negro Women 1988-; David Clark DC City Cncl 1993, Campaign Election Comm Chm; Alexis Roberson DC Ward Four 1992, Four Election Comm; Charlene Drew Jarvis DC Mayoral Election Comm 1990; ASCD 1981-; Metropolitan Bapt Church Sr Choir 1978-; Ward 5 Mayoral Election 1978; DC Statehood Comm 1978-79; Dist of Columbia Pub Schls Vol Svc Awd 1987, 1988, Outstdng Stu Svc Ldrshp Awd 1986, Soc Stud Cert 1985, Outstdng Tchrs Awd 1984-86; Cmptr Trng Cert 1983; Bunker Hill Elem Schl Cert of Appreciation 1987; Mac Farland Jr HS Cert of Participation 1987; Who's Who in the East 1985; Honorable Marion Barry Jr. Mayor Letter of Commendation 1983; Rsrch Club of Washingon DC Outstdng Svc Awd 1973; Outstdng Young Woman of Amer 1980; Congressman Walter Fauntroy Letter of Commendation 1979; Rabaut Jr HS Masters Degree Awd 1977, Cert of Merit 1976, Doctoral Degree Awd 1988; *office:* Coolidge Sr HS 5th Tuckerman St NW Washington DC 20011*

MOORE, EMELIA AMENDOLA, Fifth Grade Teacher; *b:* Kingston, NY; *m:* Shannings G.; *c:* Shane; *ed:* SUC at New Paltz (BA) His 1968, (MS) Ed 1978; Addl Post-Grad 15 Hrs; *cr:* Kingston City Schls Elem Tchr 1968-; *ai:* GATE Rep; Kingston Tchrs Fed 1968-, Sec; NY St Unified Tchrs, AFT 1968-; Delta Kappa Gamma 1991-; NY PTA 1984-, Honorary Life Mem; *home:* 112 Benson Ct Hurley NY 12443

MOORE, EVA ANNETTE, Second Grade Teacher; *b:* New Bern, NC; *c:* Derrick B.; *ed:* Fayetteville St Univ (BS) Elem Ed 1966; 60 Grad Hrs in Ed; 8 Credit Hrs Math & Sci; 2 Credit Hrs Conflict Resolution; *cr:* Bridgeton Elem Schl 1st Grd Tchr 1966-67; Eugene Meyer Elem Schl 1st Grd Tchr 1967-68; J F Cook Elem Schl 1st & 2nd Grd Tchr 1968-72; P R Harris 1st & 2nd Grd Tchr 1972-; *ai:* Hnrs & Awds Comm; March of Dimes Comm; AFT 1968-; Washington Tchrs Union 1968-.

MOORE, JACQUELYN ZAMARRA, Biology Teacher; *b:* Newark, NJ; *m:* William N. Jr.; *c:* Stephanie, Andrew; *ed:* Lycoming Coll (BA) Bio, His 1982; Georgian Court Coll (MA) Ed 1988, (MA) Bio Prgm; *cr:* Point Pleasant Borough HS Bio Tchr 1983-; *ai:* Pupil Asst Comm Chprsn; NEA, NJEA 1983-; Point Pleasant Ed Assn 1983-, Recording Sec; Governors Tchr of Yr 1994; *office:* Point Pleasant Borough HS Laura Herbert Dr Point Pleasant NJ 08742

MOORE, JAMES, Assistant Principal; *b:* Kenmore, NY; *m:* Donna Marie Palmer; *c:* Allyson; *ed:* Salisbury St Univ (BA) Lbrl Arts 1982, (MED) Ed 1995; Certfd DARE Instr at OH Hwy Patrol Acad 1992; *cr:* West Nottingham Acad Soc Stud Tchr, Coach 1982-84; Blue Ridge HS Soc Stud Tchr, Coach 1984-86; St Marys HS Soc Stud Tchr, Coach 1986-88; Sts Peter & Paul HS Ath Dir, PE Instr 1990-95; North Caroline HS Asst Prin 1995-; *ai:* Schl Improvement Team; Stu Assistance Prgm; NASSP 1995-; MD Assn of Scndry Schl Prins 1995-; MD St Ath Dirs Assn 1992-, Exec Comm, Dist Rep, Ath Dir of Yr Dist 7; Town of Ridgely 1993-, Commissioner 3 Yr Term; Parks, Recreation Comm 1992-, Chm; Chesapeake Coll Human Kinetics & Wellness Advy BD 1992-94, Bd Mem; Caroline Co Dept of Soc Svcs 1993-95, Licensed Foster Parent; Coach of Yr Wrestling VA Prep League 1986.*

MOORE, JAMES CARL, Psychology & Economics Teacher; *b:* Philadelphia, PA; *m:* C. Sue Edwards; *c:* James C. III, Erin Leigh; *ed:* Maryville Coll (BA) His 1969; Xavier Univ (MED) Curr Design 1974; Attnd NSF Psych Inst, Beaver Coll 1972; *cr:* Miami ELem Schl 5th Grd Tchr 1969-70; Milford HS HS Tchr, Staff Dev Tchr; Dept Chair 1970-; Madeira Sellman Schl Asst Prin, Dept Chair Soc Stud 1978-79; *ai:* Tennis Coach; Dept Chprsn Soc Stud; Milford Ed Assn 1969-; OEA; NEA; Kiwanis 1986-90 Treas; Milford United Meth 1972-94 Chprsn Admin Bd; Christ United Presbyn 1969-72, Elder, Sunday Schl Tchr; Knox Presbyn Church 1994-; *home:* 788 Bay Harbor Dr Maineville OH 45039*

MOORE, JAMES EDWARD, 7th Grade Language Arts Tchr; *b:* Washington, DC; *m:* Mary H.; *c:* Meghan, Beth, Lauren, Caitlin; *ed:* Loyola Coll (BA) Elem Ed 1973, (MED) Curr & Instruction 1983; *cr:* St Anthony of Padua Grd 3-8 Tchr 1973-80, Vice Prin 1980-84, Prin 1984-86; Westminster East MS Grd 7 Lang Arts Tchr 1986-; *ai:* NEA, MSTA, CCEA 1987-; Knights of Columbus 1991-, Warden, Family of Yr; *office:* Westminster East MS 170 Longwell Ave Westminster MD 21157*

MOORE, JANICE ALEXANDER, Mentor, Tchr & Spiritual Adv; *b:* Portsmouth, VA; *w:* James Arthur (dec); *c:* Willie Lewis Brown, Denene Dezell Brown, Isaac Emanuel Brown, Morris Anthony Brown; *ed:* Jericho Christian Tra Cnt Coll Ministry Chronology 1991-92, Ministry Christopiogiles 1992-94, Ministry the Book of Revelation 1994; Currently taking Telep Comm in Offices; *cr:* C. w. Medical Term; Trng DC Govern Office Skills; DC Fin Man Sys Age T & A I, Ii Classes; CPR Instr 1982-87; Cmptr Trng 1988-; *ai:* Incarcerated Correspondence Classes at Jericho Instr; Jericho Chrstn Trng Coll for Youth Overseer; Jerich Bapt Church Upperoom Prayer Cnslr; New Mem Prayer Partner; Civil Service 1967-, Cert; Office Skills & Machines 1966-, Cert; Office Machines & Eng Math, Data Entry 1968-, DC Skill, Cert; Transcription of Dr; Orders; *home:* 3772 Hayes St NE Apt 5 Washington DC 20019

MOORE, JAY, Business Education Teacher; *b:* Bangor, ME; *m:* Nancy Allison; *c:* Emily; *ed:* Husson Coll (BS) Bus Tchr Ed 1987; 6 Credit Hrs Ec; 3 Credit Hrs Exceptionality in the Classroom; 3 Credit Hrs High Performing Tchrs; *cr:* Wells HS Bus Tchr 1987-; *ai:* Var Boys Bsktbl Coach; ME Career Advantage Prgm Coord; Oguquit CSD Strategic Planning Comm; ME Tchrs Assn, NEA 1989-; Received a Grant to Fund a Schl to Work Prgm called Maine Career Advantage Prgm; *office:* Wells HS Sanford Rd Wells ME 04090

MOORE, JEANNE ACKLEY, Resource Room Teacher; *b:* Sayre, PA; *m:* Robert Anthony; *c:* Laurel Anne, Robert Ackley; *ed:* Mansfield Univ (BS) Spcl Ed 1976, (MS) Spcl Ed 1982; *cr:* Elmire Schl Dist Cnslr of Spcl Needs 1977; Waverly Mid & Sr HS Resource Room Tchr 1977-94; Lincoln St Elem Schl Resource Room Tchr 1994-; *ai:* NEA 1977-; NYNEA 1977-; WTA 1977-; Seven Lakes Girl Scout Cncl Inc 1994-, Brownie Ldr 1994-95, Jr Ldr 1995-; *office:* Lincoln St Elem Schl 45 Lincoln St Waverly NY 14892

MOORE, JENNIFER CAMBERG, English Teacher; *b:* Altoona, PA; *m:* Dennis Joseph Jr.; *ed:* PA St Univ (BA, BS) Eng, Scndry Ed 1991; Working Toward Masters in Lib Sci at Kutztown Univ; *cr:* Hollidaysburg Area Jr HS Eng Tchr 1992; Fleetwood Area HS Eng Tchr 1992-; *ai:* Newspaper, Band Front Adv; NCTE 1990-; NEA, PSEA, FEA 1992-; *office:* Fleetwood Area HS 409 N Richmond St Fleetwood PA 19522

MOORE, JENNIFER CECILE (LEDBETTER), English Teacher; *b:* Little Rock, AR; *m:* Sylvester; *c:* DeNieko, Stefan; *ed:* Univ of AR at Litle Rock (BA) Comm 1973, (BSE) Ed 1975; SUNY at Brockport (MA) Eng 1990; *cr:* AR Power & Light Co Salesperson 1976-77; Rochester City Schls #35 Performing Arts Tchr 1978-80; Rochester City Schls #39 Performing Arts Tchr 1980-82; Wilson Magnet HS Eng Tchr 1984-; *ai:* Homebase Tchr; Multi-Cultural, Black His, Recruitment, Instrl Comms; Former K-Club Adv; NYSUT 1984-; K-Club Adv; Solicitor for Heart Fund Assn; *office:* Wilson Magnet HS 501 Genesee St Rochester NY 14611

MOORE, JERRY E., Associate Professor; *b:* Gloversville, NY; *m:* Janice M.; *c:* Michelle, Brian; *ed:* Potsdam St (BS) Physics 1974; Union Coll (MA) Cmptrs 1986; Working on Masters in Electrical Engrng; *cr:* Hudson Valley Comm Coll Tech Specialist 1979-81; Schenectady Cty Coll Assoc Prof 1982-; *ai:* Tech Club Adv; Engrng Tech Assn; *office:* Schenectady County Comm Coll 78 Washington Ave Schenectady NY 12305

MOORE, JERRY LEE, 5th & 6th Grade Teacher; *b:* Indiana, PA; *m:* Beth Noel Wright; *ed:* Geneva Coll (BS) Elem Ed 1986; *cr:* Clearfield Chrstn Elem Tchr 1986-; *ai:* Ftbl & Track Coach; Int Hockey Coord; Stu Cncl Adv; *home:* RR 1 Box 619 Mahaffey PA 15757

MOORE, JIMMY-LEE, 4th-7th Grd Resource Room Tchr; *b:* Baltimore, MD; *m:* Joyce Morris; *c:* N'Koy, Zena; *ed:* Fisk Univ (BA) Elem Ed 1976; Southern CT St Univ 30 Hrs; Univ of Cntrl FL 3 Hrs; *cr:* New Haven Pub Schls 2-3, 5-7 Grd Tchr, Talented, Gifted Prgm Edctr 1976-, Summer Remedial Prgm Tchr, Acting Prin 1987; CT Pre-Engrng Summer Eng, Guid Head Tchr 1989-, Parent, Guid Coor 1991-; *ai:* Chm: Cooperative Educl Planing Comm, Black Parent Tchrs Org; Parent Tchrs Stu Org VP; Exploring Race Relations Comm; AFT 1976-, Exec Bd; CT Assn for Gifted 1990-; Tchr Ctr Inc 1980-, Bd Mem; Literacy Vols 1987-, Bd Mem; NAACP 1993-; Ed Excl Awd; 2 Initiative for Excl Grants; Yale 1988 Kenya, Zanzibar, Tanzania Outreach Curr Project; Guidebook, Resource Handbook Pub; *office:* New Haven Bd of Ed 54 Meadow St New Haven CT 06519

MOORE, JOSEPH, Chemistry Teacher; *b:* Shenandoah, PA; *ed:* Penn St Univ (BS) Sec Ed 1974; Bloomsburg St Univ (MED) Chem Ed 1981; *cr:* North Pocono HS Chem Tchr 1975-; *ai:* NEA, PSEA 1975-; ACS 1981-; *office:* North Pocono HS 701 Church St Moscow PA 18444

MOORE, JOSEPH SEAN, Physics Teacher; *b:* Bainbridge, NY; *m:* Laura Lee Facey; *c:* Chelsea, Carly; *ed:* Springfield Coll (BS) Hlth & Fitness 1981; Univ of MD (MA) Ed 1993; *cr:* Glen Burnie Sr High Physics Tchr 1991-; *ai:* Stu Govt Assn Co-Adv; NEA 1991-; TAAC 1991-; Anne Arundel Cty Sci Tchr of Yr 1994-95; *office:* Glen Burnie HS 7550 Balto Annapolis Blvd SE Glen Burnie MD 21060*

MOORE, KENNETH RODNEY, Sixth Grade Teacher; *b:* Hamilton, OH; *ed:* Miami Univ (BSEd) Elem Ed 1985; *cr:* Libertytown Elem Schl 4th Grd Tchr 1985-86; Walter Shade Elem 6th Grd Tchr 1986-91; Harold Schnoll Elem 6th Grd Tchr 1991-; *office:* Harold Schnell Elem Schl 5995 Student St Dayton OH 45449

MOORE, KEVIN MORRIS, Professor of Music & Bus Law; *b:* Ogdensburg, NY; *ed:* St Univ Coll at Potsdam (BM) Piano Performance 1971; The Manhattan Schl of Music (MM) Piano Performance 1972; NY Univ (PHD) Music Theory & Performance 1979; Syracuse Univ Coll of Law (JD) Commercial Law 1986; *cr:* St Univ at Potsdam Admissions Cnslr 1972-73, Instr of Music 1973-74; Onondaga Comm Coll Prof of Music & Bus Law 1975-; Attorney at Law 1986-; *ai:* Sabbatical Leaves Comm; NY Bar Assn 1986-; Civic Morning Musicals Inc 1975-, Bd Mem; Syracuse Camerata Inc 1988-, Bd Mem; Carnegie Recital Hall Debut 1976; Articles Pub 1986; Choral Work Pub 1996; Prof Concert Pianist; *office:* Onondaga Comm Coll Rt 175 Syracuse NY 13215

MOORE, LAURA ROGERSON, English Teacher; *b:* Boston, MA; *m:* Robinson Chase; *c:* Grace Sargent, Katherine Rogerson, Elibet Andres; *ed:* Harvard-Radcliffe (BA) Eng 1982; Attnd 1985 Summer Dance Prgm-Modern, Ballet & Jazz; *cr:* Applewild Schl Tchng Intern 1982-83; Lawrence Acad Dance, Latin, Eng & Dorm Tchr & Lang Arts II Creative Writing Prof Adv 1983-; *ai:* Early Intervention Team; Schl Lit Magazine Fac Adv; Lawrence Acad Departmental Chair for Excl in Tchng 1991-92; Poem Pub in Mothering Magazine 1994, Rubens Quarterly 1994; Story Pub in Granite Review 1995; *office:* Lawrence Acad PO Box 992 Groton MA 01450

MOORE, LINDA DAWSON, Science & Lang Arts Teacher; *b:* Phialdelphia, PA; *m:* Michael F.; *ed:* West Chester Univ (BS) Elem Ed 1969; PA Dept of Ed M Equiv Elem Ed 1981; Post Grad Stud 60 Credit Hrs; *cr:* Westbrook Park Elem Sch 5th Grd Tchr 1969-89; Drexel Hill MS 6th Grd Tchr 1989-; *ai:* Dist Strategic Planning Comm; Upper Darby Ed Assn 1969-, Bldg Rep; PA St Ed Assn, NEA 1969-; *office:* Drexel Hill MS 3001 State Rd Drexel Hill PA 19026

MOORE, LINDA KAY (GRIMES), 9th & 10th Grade English Tchr; *b:* Steubenville, OH; *m:* David Lee; *c:* Jessica, Mallory, Matthew; *ed:* West Liberty St Coll (BA) Eng 1977; Univ of Dayton Credit Hrs; *ai:* NEA 1978-; WIBC 1978-; *home:* 813 Logan St Toronto OH 43964

MOORE, LONNY RUSSELL, PE Teacher & Chm; *b:* Norristown, PA; *m:* Joyce Martine Shaner; *c:* Amanda Martine O'Leary; *ed:* West Chester Univ (BS) Hlth PE 1963; Univ of Bridgeport (MS) Hlth PE 1973; West Chester Univ 24 Credit Hrs; PA St Univ 54 Credit Hrs; *cr:* Spring-ford Schl Dist Hlth PE Edctr 1963-65; Phoenixville Schl Dist Hlth PE Edctr 1965-; *ai:* Hlth, PE Dept Chm; Asst Ftbl Coach 1966-; Asst Track Coach 1966-; Boys Var Jr Class Adv; Head Wresting Coach 1966-83; NEA, PSEA 1963-; Masonici Temple 190 1964-; Tall Cedar DIAA Dist I Wresting CHm; *home:* 776 Mennonite Rd Royersford PA 19468*

MOORE, LOWELL CORNELIUS, Physical & Business Ed Tea Sharpsburg, MD; *m:* Jo Anne M.; *c:* Billie-Jo, Mary-Beth; *ed:* S Coll (BS) Bus Admin 1960; Univ of NC (MED) PE 1961; Attnd Tov St Mary's Coll, Univ of MD; *cr:* Mars Hill HS Tchr, Coach 1 Yr; Park HS Tchr, Coach 9 Yrs; Great Mills HS Tchr, Coach 24 Yrs; *ai:* Dept Chprsn; Local Tchrs Assn, MSTA, NEA 1962-; SMAC Coach Times; MD Svc Awd Wrestling 1989; MD St Wrestling Hall of Fam *office:* Great Mills HS Great Mills Rd Great Mills MD 20634

MOORE, LYNN EDWARD, 9th-12th Grd Spanish Teac Parkersburg, WV; *m:* Kelley Stricklin; *c:* Neil D., Luke E., Brady West Liberty St Coll (BA) Span & Soc Stud 1970; Univ of Dayt Guid Cnslng 1986; 6 Hrs Span Jaime Balmes Univ at Guadalajara I Hrs Guid Univ of Dayton; 6 Hrs Span Centro de Idiomas at Mer Linsley Inst Span Tchr 1970-78; Bridgeport HS Span Tchr 1980-; Club, Span NHS Spon; U-16 in Wheeling Amateur Soccer Assn NEA, OEA 1980-; Bridgeport Ed Assn 1980-, VP, Pres; Dallas Church 1967-, Trustee, Elder; Upper OH Vly Presbyn 1967-, Missi *office:* Bridgeport HS 501 Bennett St Bridgeport OH 43912

MOORE, LYNN WILSON, Social Studies Teacher; *b:* Lewes, Judy Davis; *c:* Lisa Ann, Christy Lynn; *ed:* Univ of DE (AA) E Salisbury St Univ (BA) His 1973, (MA) His 1983; *cr:* Self En Farming Bus 1973-80; Self Employed Real Estate Bus 1980-; Ja Groves Adult HS Part-time Tchr 1982-95; Epworth Chrstn Schl P US His, Govt Tchr 1993-; Wilmington Coll Part-time Instr 1994-; Boys Bsktbl Head Coach; AACE Adult Ed 1982-, Tchr of Yr 19 Assn of Realtors 1988-; Georgetown Little League Coach, All Sta 1994; Sussex Cty Prothonotary 1985-88; Elected Ofcl; Flwsh League Pres 1978-; Tchr of Yr 1993; Conservationist of Yr 1995 RR 3 Box A10 Georgetown DE 19947

MOORE, MARI LOU ANTIN, High School English Teac Ironwood, MI; *c:* Joy Ann; *ed:* Gogebic Comm Coll (AA) Eng, 1968; Northern MI Univ (BA) Eng, Sec Ed 1970; Univ of Dayto Tchng, Sec Ed 1979; 36 Addl Sem Hrs Ed, Cnslng; *cr:* Fairmont Eng Tchr 1973-83; Kettering Fairmont HS Eng Tchr 198 Co-Facilitator Support Groups; Kettering Educ Assn 1973-, Rep, 1988-90, HS at Large; NEA 1973-; OH Educ Assn 1973-, RA Del; Mc Gregor Schl of Antioch Univ 1994-, Tchr Cert Prgm Advy Ashland Oil Golden Apple Achiever Awd 1990; Kettering Schls ST 1989; *office:* Kettering Fairmont HS 3301 Shroyer Rd Kettering OH

MOORE, MARSHA J., Home Economics Teacher; *b:* Philadelph *m:* James E.; *c:* Shawn, Michael, Ryan; *ed:* Glassboro St (BA) H Ed 1987; Enrrolled in MA program Reading Edu Rowan Coll of Pinelands Regnl HS Home Ec Tchr 1987-; *ai:* FHA; Schlsp Comm NJEA 1987-; Phi Theta Kappa 1980-; Kappa Omicron Phi 1986 Mae Awd 1987; Helped Prepare, Win Voc Ed Grant for Food Sci; Several Curr in Curricular Area; *office:* Pinelands Regnl HS Nug Rd Tuckerton NJ 08087

MOORE, MARTA L., Assistant Professor; *b:* Lock Haven, PA; *e* Haven Univ (BS(Kndgtn, Elem Ed 1971; PA St Univ (MS) Human Family Stud 1982, (PHD) Human Dev & Family Stud 1991; Per Tchng Cert 1974; Advanced Trng Play Therapy; *cr:* Keystone Cn Dist Elem Ed Tchr 1971-78; PA St UNiv Instr, Rsrch Asst, As 1978-91, Affiliate Prof 1991-; Lock Haven Univ Asst Prof 198 Practice Play Therapist 1994-; *ai:* Clearfield Campus Mid Sts Advy Assn of PA St Coll & Univ Fac 1989-; Phi Kappa Phi, Kappa Omic 1983-; Centre Cty Advy Cncl to PA Human Relations Commission Tchr of the Yr 1991-92; Articles Pub; *home:* PO Box 302 State Coll 16804*

MOORE, MARTHA ADELE, English Teacher; *b:* Charlottesville, Erika; *ed:* Wartburg Coll at Waverly (BA) Eng 1971; Univ of W (MA) Eng 1973; 10 Post Grad Hrs; 9 Addl Credits; *cr:* Prince Comm Coll Instr, Career Eng, Part-time 1977-84; Winston Churc Jrnlsm Tchr 1984-85; Holy Cross Acad Eng Tchr 1985-86; Holy Sp Eng Tchr, Dept Chair 1986-89; St Francis Xavier Schl Eng, His, R 1989-91; US Senate Page Schl Eng Tchr 1991-95; Yeshiva of Grea Eng Tchr 1995-; *ai:* Girl Scouts 1957-86, 1990-; Ldr, Trainer; Luth of the Cross 1965-, Dir of Pub Relations, Drama Dir; *home:* 1240 Mill Rd Silver Spring MD 20906

MOORE, MARVA ANN (RUCKER), School Counselor; *b:* Crysta *m:* Gerald; *c:* Jacqueline A., Juliette A.; *ed:* Bluefield St (BS) Bio & 1958; Wright St Univ (MS) Schl; Post Grad Credits Univ of D Wright St Univ; *cr:* Dunbar HS Sci Tchr 1967-70; Longfellow MS Math Tchr 1973-81; E J Brown MS Schl Cnslr 1982-89; Patterson Acad 1990-91; Colonel White Schl Cnslr 1991-; *ai:* NHS & Clas OEA & NEA 1973-; Delta Sigma Theta 1995- Pres; Wright St Univ Adv Bd; *office:* Colonel White HS 501 Niagara Ave Dayton OH 45

MOORE, MORNA RUTH W., Retired 3rd Grade Teacher; *b:* Corsi *m:* Robert I.; *c:* Morna Katherine, Melody Troup, Robert, James K Hamel; *ed:* Maryville Coll (BS) ELem Ed 1952; Ohio St Univ EL *cr:* Easton Schl Dist 3rd Grd Tchr 1952-56; Columbus Schl Dist 4 Tchr 1956-63; New Waterford Dist Schl 6th Grd Tchr 19 Williamsport Schl Dist Emotional Disturbed K-6 Grd Tchr 1969- Sub Work; NEA 1952-; Church 1939-, SS Tchr, Yth Dir, Women Choir.

MOORE, NANCY J., Associate Professor of English; *b:* St Louis *m:* John Lucarelli; *c:* Laura J. Crary-Ortega, James M. Crary; *ed:* H Coll (AA) Lbrl Arts 1954; WA Univ (AB) Eng 1958; Carnegie-Mello (MA) Eng 1969; Italian, Fr, Math Courses at Instituto Dante Al Florence Italy; *cr:* Penn St Univ Adj Eng Fac 1968; CCAC Eng Tchr Univ of Pittsburgh Adj Eng Fac 1976-82; *ai:* Societa Dantre Al 1986-; Jane Austen Soc 1993-; Dickens Flwshp 1994-; Friends 1990-; Historical Soc of Western PA 1983-; Alliance for Menta 1993-; Western PA Conservancy 1980-; Tchng Excl Awd 1996; A Pub; 1 Yr Tchng Exch at Modesto Jr Coll CA; *office:* Comm Coll Al Algny Cmps 808 Ridge Ave Pittsburgh PA 15212

MOORE, NANCY STEWART, English Teacher; *b:* Rimersburg, David R.; *c:* Matthew David, Ashley Dyan; *ed:* Clarion Univ of P Eng 1972; Penn St Univ 3 Credit Hrs; 21 Addl Credit Hrs; *cr:* W Valley HS Eng & Rdng Tchr 1972-76; Zuni HS Rem Rdng & ESL 1976-78; Redbank Valley HS Sub Tchr 1983-85, Eng Tchr 1985-; *ai:* Lab Monitor; SAT Preparation Class Instr; Peer Tutor Pgm Adv; PSEA & RVEA 1985-, Fac Rep; NCTE 1990-; Western PA Tchr 1992-; *office:* Redbank Valley HS 920 Broad St New Bethlehem PA

MOORE, NELSON JAY, Professor of Biology; *b:* Greenvile, O Janet Felix; *c:* Neil Arthur, Heather Lynne; *ed:* Manchester Coll (BA Chem 1963; OH St Univ (MS) Zoology 1968; Univ of AZ (PHD) Z 1972; *cr:* OH Northern Univ Prof of Bio 1972-; *ai:* Sigma Theta E Adv; Mem at Large Univ Cncl; Fac Welfare Comm Chair; Ornithological Union 1970-; Assn of Field Ornithologist 1984-; O Banding Assn 1980-; Silver Creek Enviromental Ed Ctr 1985-; Tri-M Audubon Soc 1980-, Past Pres; Scioto River Watch 1990-, Sec; Arts Distngd Fac Awd 1984, 1986, 1990, 1994; Alpha Xi Delta Distngd Fa 1993; Phi Eta Sigma Fac Awd 1977; Biological Scis Dept Chair 198 *office:* OH Northern Univ Lincoln Ave Ada OH 45810

E, PATRICIA G., PE, Health & Drivers Ed Tchr; *b:* Elizabeth, NJ; wark St Coll (BA) K-12 PE, Hlth 1971; Kean Coll (MA) K-12 Supervision 1980; Jersey City St Coll (SAC) Drug Abuse Cnslr 'ert Driver Ed 1988; Post-Grad St Peter's Coll, Discipline; *cr:* St s HS PE Tchr 1966-68; St VincentsAcad PE Tchr 1968-69; S ld HS PE, Hlth Tchr 1971-72; Harrison HS PE, Hlth Tchr 1972-; Soc Adv; Girls' Var Vlybl Coach; Intl Women's Day Comm; HEA, NEA 1971-, Bldg Rep; AAHPERD 1971-; Hudson Cty Vlybl s Assn 1992-, Sec; NFOCA, NASAA 1994-; Tall Timbers Condo 74-88, VP, Recognition Awd; Red Cross 1981-88, 5 Yr Pin; Eastern 54-, 25 Yr Pin; Tunkhannock Twp Residents Comm 1991-, Chprsn; hprsn 1981-89; Mid Sts Assn Recognition 1981-82; Natl Safety tation 1982; *office:* Harrison HS 1 N 5th St Harrison NJ 07029*

E, RICHARD EDWARD,JR., Humanities Teacher; *b:* lphia, PA; *m:* Loraine Fischer; *c:* Richard III, Ian G.; *ed:* Mansfield Sec; Penn St (MED) Ed & Psych 1991; 30 Addl Credit Hrs; *cr:* Rock Schl Dist Tchr 1987-; *ai:* Yrbk Adv; Ftbl & Bsbl Coach; Ed Dept Chair; Crowding Comm Chm; Prin Search, Act 178 & c Plan Comms; CREA 1987-, Bldg Rep; PSEA & NEA 1987-; /ho in the East 1981-82; Natl Stu Register 1969-70; *office:* Holland 00 E Holland Rd Holland PA 18966

E, RICHARD EMIL, Instrumental Music Teacher; *b:* Akron, OH; nt St Univ (BA) Music Ed 1979, (MED) Music Ed 1981; 19 Grad Hrs Kent St Univ, Baldwin-Wallace Coll, Walsh Univ; *cr:* North City Schls 5-6, 9-12 Grd Instrumental Music Tchr 1982-; *ai:* ng Band, Flag Line, Concert Band, Jazz Ensemble Dir; Pvt Tchr nstruments; Prof Musician Drums; NEA, MENC 1982-; Amer Fed ans 1976-; OH Music Edctrs Assn Adjudicator Jazz 1996; *office:* HS South 605 S Fair Oaks Ave North Canton OH 44720

E, ROBERT JAMES,JR., Social Studies Teacher; *b:* Sayre, PA; nise Ann Pelton; *c:* Seija, Lindsey, Kylee; *ed:* Mansfield Univ Soc Stud 1987; 29 Grad Hrs; *cr:* Northeast Bradford HS Scndry d Tchr 1987-; *ai:* Head Girls Var Bsktbl Coach; Positive Peers Adv; PSEA 1987-; Northeast Stu Loan Fund 1989-; *office:* Northeast d Jr Sr HS RR 1 Box 211b Rome PA 18837*

E, RONALD LEE, Lang Arts Tchr & Bldg Coord; *b:* Zanesville, Marjorie L.; *c:* Brian, Jennifer Stanchin; *ed:* OH Univ (BA) Ed MA) Ed Leadership 1990; Prin Admin 1991; Addl 30 Grad Hrs Coll t Joseph & OH Univ; *cr:* Morgan Local Schls Tchr 1986-, Building 1988-; *ai:* Safety Patrol; Strategic Planning; Course of Stud Head; scipline Comm; MLEA 1968-, BR 24 Yrs; OEA 1968- SEOC 24 Yrs; 968-, Rep 28 Yrs; Six Cty 1991-94; Valdictorians Awd 1990; Poetry ffice: McConnelsville Elem Schl 21 E Jefferson St Mc Connelsville 756*

E, SANDRA (STEWART), 7th & 8th Grd Lang Arts Tchr; *b:* OH; *m:* Gary M.; *c:* Erik, Lizabeth; *ed:* Univ of Akron (BA) Comm MS) Tech Ed 1993; *cr:* Norton HS Eng Tchr 1980-91; Norton MS Grd Tchr 1991-; *ai:* Preparing Stdnts to Complete ICP Folders; OEA, PTA 1981-; Stark Cty Historical Soc; Queen of Heaven ; Girl Scouts of Amer Brownie Ldr; Recipient of Several Grants to nent Career Ed at MS Level; *office:* Norton MS 3390 Cleveland on Rd Norton OH 44203

RE, SHEILA GOODMAN-COUNCIL, Business Teacher; *b:* ore, MD; *m:* Michael J.; *c:* Nicole A., Michele D. Moore-Barnes; organ St Univ (MS) Bus Ed 1977, (BS) Bus Ed 1979; George gton Univ Bus Ed Partnership-Transition 33 Credit Hrs & Doctoral ; *cr:* IBM Customer Support Rep 1977; Western Voc Tech Medical arial Coord 1978-80; Comm Coll of Baltimore Instr Coord 1980-82; HS Bus Tchr 1982-; *ai:* Natl Honor Soc Spon Adv; Steering Comm Mid States; Stu of the Month Selection Comm; Sunday Schl Tchr; VA 1977-; MBEA 1987-; NBEA 1980-; NASSP 1993-; Charles Cty Coll 1990-, Advy Bd Accounting; Links Inc 1991-, Publicity Chair; P 1992, Youth Chair; Natl Pol Congress of Black Women 1989, ing Sec; *office:* Calvert HS 600 Dares Beach Rd Prince Frederick 678*

RE, STEPHANIE LOIS (DAVIS), Social Studies Teacher; *b:* l, DE; *m:* Michael E.; *c:* Carter Q.; *ed:* Salisbury St Univ (BA) His, ad, Sec Ed 1992; Wilmington Coll 12 Credit Hrs; Shepherd Coll 30 Hrs; *cr:* Colonel Richardson HS Soc Stud Tchr 1992-94; Seaford HS d Tchr 1994-; *ai:* Key Club Adv; Colonel Richardson HS Class Adv; Adv; European Tour Spon; Hnr Soc Comm; Schl Wide Cnslng Team NEA 1992-; DE St Tchrs Assn 1995-; MD STA, Caroline Cty TA 4; *office:* Seaford HS N Market St Seaford DE 19973

RE, SUSAN, Reading Teacher; *b:* Lawrence, MA; *ed:* Fitchburg St BS) Elem Ed 1969; Salem St Coll (MED) Rdng 1973; *cr:* Lawrence chls Grd 1 Tchr 1969-88, K-2 Grd Rdng Specialist 1988-89, Title I Specialist 1989-; *ai:* Lang Arts; Rdng Curr Cncl; LTU, MFT, AFT IRA 1990-; Bread & Roses Local Soup Kitchen 1985-, Vol; Cncl of nes 1994-, Del; *office:* South Lawrence East Schl 65 Crawford St nce MA 01843

RE, THERESA DEPASQUA, English Teacher; *b:* Derby, CT; *m:* d A.; *ed:* Southern CT St Univ (BS) Eng 1984; Sacred Heart Univ Ed 1991; *cr:* Illing Jr HS 7th Grd Stu Tchr 1983; Manchester HS 2th Grad Eng Permanent Sub 1984; St Bridget Schl 6th-8th Grd Tchr 1984-85; Shelton HS 9th Grd Eng Tchr 19d85-; *ai:* Adv Frosh, sses; NEA 1985-; CCTE 1984-; St Anthony's Parish 1978-82, CCD office: Shelton HS 120 Meadow St Shelton CT 06484

RE, THOMAS EDWARD, Sixth Grade Teacher; *b:* Wilkes-Barre, Mary Theresa Mc Donagh; *c:* Michael, Mary Ellen; *ed:* King's Coll Ec 1964; Attnd St Univ of NY; *cr:* St Patricks Schl 5th Grd Tchr 65; Chenango Forks Schls 4th Grd Tchr 1965-68; S & S Meml SChl d Tchr 1968-82; Calvin Elem SChl 6th Grd Tchr 1982-84; Mackin Schl 6th Grd Tchr 1984-; *ai:* NEA, PSEA 1968-; WBAEA 1968-, Rep; Ancient Order of Hibenians 1985-; Donegal Soc 1980-; *home:* illow St Wilkes Barre PA 18702

RE, TRINA DENNISTON, Drill Team Co-Director; *b:* Cincinnati, : F. Scott; *c:* Sarah E.; *ed:* Attnd Northern KY Univ 1978-79; *cr:* Hosp Kenwood Ward, Med Recs Clerk 1979-93; Lockland HS Drill Co-Dir 1991-; GRE Insurance Underwriting Processor 1993-94; Hlth Assocs Med Recs Clerk 1994-95; *ai:* Alumni Assn 1992-; Pub; *office:* Lockland HS 249 W Forrer St Cincinnati OH 45215

RE, TRUDY E., Coordinator of English; *b:* Philadelphia, PA; *m:* W.; *c:* Kimberly Lynn; *ed:* Grove City Coll (BA) Eng 1965; Temple (MED) Eng Ed 1968; *cr:* William Tennant HS Eng Tchr 1964-73; gfield HS Eng Tchr 1973-, Coord of Eng & AP Tchr 1983-; *ai:* Class, udio Adv; Lit Magazine Spon; STEA 1969-; PSEA, NEA 1965-; ng Tchr; Article Pub; Consultant Coll Planning; *office:* Springfield 01 Paper Mill Rd Glenside PA 19038

RE, WILLIAM L., Mathematics Teacher; *b:* Lewistown, MD; *m:* Louise Harding; *c:* Shannon, Sean, Bridget; *ed:* Frostburg St Univ Eng 1964; San Jose St Univ (MA) Math 1969; Attnd Univ of Santa Loyola Univ, Mt St Marys Coll; *cr:* Elm St Jr HS Eng, Soc Stud Tchr 66; Andrew P. Hill HS Math Tchr 1966-71; Frederick HS Math Tchr 83; Elm St Alt Schl Math Tchr 1985; Frederick HS Math Tchr 1987-; ed Co Tchrs 1971-, Pres 1983-85; SERTOMA 1985-, Pres; St John's Schl Bd 1985-87; NSF Prgms; *office:* Frederick HS 650 Carroll Pky Frederick MD 21701

MOORE, WILLIAM N.,JR., High School Soc Stud Tchr; *b:* Neptune, NJ; *m:* Jacquely A. Zamarra; *c:* Stephanie, Andrew; *ed:* Widener Univ (BA) Pol Sci 1981; 12 Credit Hrs Jersey City St Coll; *cr:* Point Pleasant Borough HS Soc Stud Tchr 1982-; *ai:* Boys Var Soccer, Girls JV Soccer, Frosh Girls Bsktbl Coach; Key Club Adv; NEA, NJEA 1982-; PPEA 1990-, Bldg Rep; Kiwanis 1988-, Key Club Adv, Outstdng Adv; *office:* Point Pleasant Borough HS Laura Herbert Dr Point Pleasant NJ 08742

MOORE, YVONNE PEARSON, 6th Grade Teacher; *b:* Akron, OH; *m:* Les R.; *c:* Dale L., Brian M.; *ed:* Kent St Univ (BS) Scndry Bus Ed 1978, (BS) Kndgtn & Elem Ed 1986; 48 Post Grad Hrs; *cr:* Mantaline Corp Inside Sales Rep 1978-84; Aurora City Schls Sub Tchr 1983-84; Ravenna City Schls Sub Tchr 1983-84; Crestwood Local Schls Bus Ed & Sub Tchr 1983-85, 6th Grd Tchr 1986-; *ai:* Fieldhouse Bldg Fund Treas; Ftbl Treas; 6th Grd Spelling Bee Coord; Steering Comm, Displine Org 1994-95; Levy Comm 1990-; Lang Arts Txtbk Selection Comm 1995; JV & Var Bsktbl Statician 1994-; Ftbl & Bsktbl Parent Rep 1993-; NEA, OH Ed Assn & Crestwood Ed Assn 1987-; Portage Faith Meth Church 1983-; Crestwood Ath Boosters 1991-; Crestwood Womens Club 1991-, Sec; Crestwood Curr Cncl 1987-92, Sec; Maplewood Mini-Grant Winner 1988; 1994 Recipient OH Jaycees Outstanding Young Educator; *office:* Crestwood MS 10880 John Edward Dr Mantua OH 44255

MOORE, ZENOLA HUBBARD, Third Grade Teacher; *b:* Philadelphia, PA; *m:* James; *c:* Marlon, Michael; *ed:* Fayetteville St Univ (BS) Elem Ed 1972; Post Grad Stud Saint Joseph's; *cr:* William B. Mann Elem Schl Second Grd Tchr 1974-; *ai:* Rdng, Soc Stud Comms; Fayetteville St Univ Alumni Phila Chptr 1987-, VP; Alpha Kappa Alpha 1996; *office:* Thomas M Peirce Elem Schl 23rd & Cambria Sts Philadelphia PA 19132

MOORE-GREEN, DONNA MARIE, Fifth Grade Teacher; *b:* Philadelphia, PA; *m:* Raymond; *ed:* Oakwood Coll at Huntsville (BS) Music Ed 1985; Elem Ed SDA Cert; Coppin St at Baltimore Grad Stud; *cr:* Baltimore Jr Acad K-12 Grd Music Tchr 1985-88, 5th Grd Tchr 1988-; *ai:* Schl Musical Prgm Coord; Organize Schl Fairs Talent Prgm, Musical Entertainment, Homecoming Choirs; Co-Author K-8 Music Prgm Pub 1993; Tchrs Inservice Music Prgm Spokesperson 1994; *office:* Baltimore Jr Acad 3006 W Cold Spring Ln Baltimore MD 21215*

MOORE-LEAMON, SILVER, Studies Director & Math Tchr; *b:* Reading, PA; *c:* Ann Leamon, Rebecca Leamon, John Leamon, Tom Leamon; *ed:* Bates Coll (BS) Chem 1955; Unif of S ME (MSEd) Counseling 1988; *cr:* Mary C Wheeler Schl Math Tchr 1956-60; Hebron Acad Math Tchr, Dir of Stu Services 1987-95, Math Tchr, Dir of Stud 1995-; *ai:* Stu Cncl Adv; Day Stu Coord Comms; NCTM; ASCD; United Church of Christ 1964-, Deacon, Moderator; Schl Bd 1974-77, Chair, 1982-85; *office:* Hebron Acad PO Box 309 Hebron ME 04238

MOORE-PALUMBO, SUSAN T., Biology Teacher; *b:* Syracuse, NY; *m:* Frank Palumbo; *c:* Colin Emerson, Peter Francis; *ed:* SUNY Coll of Environmental Sci & Forestry (BS) Forest Bio 1984; Syracuse Univ (MS) Scndry Sci Ed 1986; St Univ of NY at Albany 33 Credits hrs Ed Admin; *cr:* Levy Jr HS Sci Tchr 1985-86; Albany HS Bio Tchr 1986-; *ai:* Club Adv Theta Alpha Sigma Lit Club; Mediator Dispute & Resolution Team; NABT 1990-; NY St United Tchrs, Albany Pub Schl Tchrs Assoc, AFT 1986-; Literacy Vol of Amer 1990-, Pres Bd of Dir; Friends of Saratoga Springs Pub Lib Inc 1989-, Sec Bd of Dir; *home:* 6 Anyhow Ln Gansevoort NY 12831*

MOORE-WLEKLINSKI, PATRICIA M., English Teacher; *b:* Syracuse, NY; *m:* John; *c:* Alyssa; *ed:* SUNY at Cortland (BS) Elem Ed 1978, (MS) Elem Ed 1990; *cr:* Onondaga Madison BOCES Sign Lang Interpretutor; West Genesee Cntrl Schls 6th Grd Tchr 1980-82; St Ann's 4th, 5th Grd Tchr 1982-85; Chrstn Brothers Acad Jr HS Eng Tchr 1985-; *ai:* Jr High Stu Senate Adv; Fac Cncl; Var Cheerleading Coach 17 Yrs; NCTE 1995-; NCEA 1985-; Section III Cheerleading Comm 1990-, Sec; Empire Games 1985-, Bsktbl Vol Coord; *office:* Christian Brothers Acad 6245 Randall Rd Syracuse NY 13214

MOORMAN, JANET BOUTEILLER, HS Social Studies Teacher; *b:* New Haven, CT; *m:* Thomas W.; *c:* Jennifer E., James I.; *ed:* Pine Manor Coll (AA) 1960; Boston Univ (BA) His 1963; Assumption Coll (MA) Ed & His 1977; Trinity Coll 33 Credit Hrs His; Attnd Framingham St Coll; *cr:* Woodrow Wilson MS Fr Tchr 1966-67, Soc Stud Tchr 1967-70; Newington HS Soc Stud Tchr 1970-71; Assabet Valley Reg Voc HS Soc Stud Tchr 1973-; *ai:* Coach Citizen Bee; AFT 1966-, Local Pres, St VP; NCSS & MCSS; Trinity Coll Fellow; Acad Tchr of Yr Assabet Valley Reg Voc HS 1992; *office:* Assabet Valley Reg Voc HS Fitchburg St Marlborough MA 01752*

MOORMAN, MARY METCALF, Math, Science & Soc Stud Tchr; *b:* Cairo, GA; *m:* Swede L.; *c:* Swede II, Miko, Kim; *ed:* Cntrl St Univ (BS) Elem Ed 1971; Univ of Dayton (MS) Admin 1988; Wright St Math Specialist Project Prime 1992; Univ of Dayton 6 Credit Hrs Post Grad 1991; *cr:* Longfellow Mid IGE Magnet Schl 6-8 Grd Tchr 1974-81; Univ of Dayton Summer Urban Prgm Co-Dir, Math Tchr 1987-88; Stu Tchr Supvr 1987-90; Univ of Dayton Urban Prgm Dir 1989-; St of OH Governor's Gifted Inst Dir 1990-93; Lincoln IGE Magnet Schl 4-6 Grd Tchr 1993-; *ai:* Unit Ldr; Univ of Dayton Sci Course Stud Revision Comm; Dist Math Competency Prgm St of OH; Textbook Adoption, Scndry Math Curr Comms; UD Sci Course Stud Revision of City of Dayton Pub Schls Sci Curr; Dayton Pub Schls Annual Space Symposium, Math Course of Stud; Math Curr Dev Comm Chprsn; Dist Math Coord; Schl Banking Prgm, Career Days, Drug Prevention Days Chprsn; NEA, OEA, DEA 1971-; OH Tchr Cncl for Math & Sci 1990-; Daymont West 1987-, Chprsn 1989-90, 1993-94, Bd of Dirs; Univ of Dayton Minority Task Force 1986-87; City of Dayton Staff Dev 1988-89, Presenter; Trotwood Madison City Schl Dist Strategic Planning Process 1991-; Citizens of Trotwood Madison Tax Levy 1986-; Trotwood Redistricting Comm 1985-86; United Way Bldg Coord 1987-93; Trotwood Boy's Bsbl Club Trustee 1985-86; Girl Scout Ldr 1986-87; Career Day Bldg Coord 1992-93; Drug Prevention Coord 1991-93; Dayton Pub Schls Outstdng Math Tchr 1987-89, 1992-93; Tchr of Month Staff Awd 1991; WKEF TV 22 Tchr of Week Awd 1991; Dayton Pub Schls Math Coord Cert for Math Prgm 1988-90, Math Olympics Judge 1991-93, Site Base Mngmt Pilot Prgm Participant 1990-91; Dare Prgm Cert of Recognition 1991-93; Proclamations Office of Mayor City of Dayton 1989-92, St Rep Rhine Mc Lin 1992-93; Cert of Recognition Bd of Ed Mem for Math Specialitst; Outstdng Math Tchr 1992-93; *office:* Lincoln Ige Magnet Schl 401 Nassau St Dayton OH 45410*

MOORS-DRESSING, MARY ELLEN, English Teacher; *b:* Cincinnati, OH; *m:* Steve; *c:* Michael, Melaina; *ed:* Miami Univ (BSEd) Comm Ed 1979; Grad Work at Miami Univ, Xavier Univ; *cr:* New Richmond HS Eng, Rdng Tchr 1979-80; Lockland HS Dept Chair, Eng, Speech, Jrnlsm Tchr 1980-83; Mc Auley HS Eng Tchr 1988-89; Roger Bacon HS Eng Tchr 1983-88, 1990-; *ai:* Newspaper; Yrbk; Hands Across the Campus; NHS; NCTE 1980-; Kindervelt 1987-, Sec 6 Yrs; Active in Church 1982-; Flwshp to OH Writing Project 1988; Designed Women Authors Class 1993; Ldr of Schls Ethnic Group 1994; Designed Fac In-svc on Diversity 1995-; Nom Ashland Oil's Tchr of Yr 1996; *office:* Roger Bacon HS 4320 Vine St Cincinnati OH 45217

MOQUIN, LYNN GERRISH, Sixth Grade Teacher; *b:* North Kingstown, RI; *m:* Randall K.; *c:* Jennifer, David; *ed:* Lesley Coll (BS) Elem Ed, Spec Ed 1979; *cr:* Kolburne Preparatory Schl Spec Educator 1979-80; Raymond MS Spec Educator 1986-89; Iber Holmes Gove MS 6th Grd Educator 1989-; *ai:* NEA 1986-; Chester Congregational Bapt Church 1987-, Bible Schl Dir, Chrstn Ed Chair, Sunday Schl Supt; *office:* Iber Holmes Gove MS School St Raymond NH 03077*

MORA, ROBERT T., AP Biology Instructor; *b:* Teaneck, NJ; *m:* Diane Gagen; *c:* Kimberly, Kerri; *ed:* Montclair St Coll (BA) Bio 1965; Rutgers Univ (MS) Zoology & Physiology 1971, (PHD) Zoology & Physiology 1974; *cr:* West Orange HS Bio Tchr 1965-; Rutgers Univ Cell Bio & Lab Instr 1971-76; Kean Coll of NJ Bio Instr 1975-83; *ai:* Bio II Team Adv; NEA 1965-; NJEA & WO EA 1965-; Amer Soc of Zoologists 1971-; Washington Twp Vol Ambulance Corps 1985-, Pres 2 Yrs; Hoffmann LaRoche Inst for Molecular Bio Flwshp 1993; Howard Hughes Fndtn Grant 1995; *office:* West Orange HS 51 Conforti Ave West Orange NJ 07052

MORABITO, ANTHONY RICHARD, Coach; *b:* Rochester, NY; *m:* Karen Montcrieff; *c:* Christopher, Joseph; *ed:* First Aid, Advanced CPR, Mngmt Diploma; *cr:* GRS Supvr 1974-; Gananda JV Girls Sftbl Coach 1993-, JV Girls Bsktbl Coach 1994-; *ai:* Summer Clinics & Teams, Scouting; Walworth Vol Fire Dept 1983-, Pres, Rescue, Lt Truck Captain; *home:* 3252 Day Spring Rdg Walworth NY 14568

MORABITO, DONALD VINCENT, Social Studies Teacher; *b:* New Castle, PA; *m:* Paige Nicole Bradley; *c:* Bradley Cicco; *ed:* Penn St Univ (BS) Scndry Ed & Soc Stud 1991; Attnd West Chester Univ Pursuing Masters in Geog & Planning; *cr:* Great Vly HS Soc Stud Tchr 1993-; *ai:* Stu Cncl Co-Adv; Color Guard Instr; AV Coord; Sexual Harassment Prevention Trainer & Liaison; Peer Mediator Trainer; Mountain Biking Club Adv; GVEA, PSEA & NEA 1993-, Pol Action Local Chair; NCSS 1993-; Natl Assn of Stu Act Advs 1995-; *office:* Great Valley HS Rt 401 & Phoenixville Pike Malvern PA 19355

MORACHE, DENISE MARIE, Span Tchr, Frgn Lang Dpt Chpsn; *b:* Meriden, CT; *ed:* Cntrl CT St Univ (BS) Span, Italian 1978; The Monterey Inst of Intnl Stud (MA) Hispanic Stud 1987; Malaca Inst of Intnl Stud Summer Stud Prgm 1990; *cr:* St Mary's HS Span, Italian Tchr, Frgn Lang Dept Chair 1979-91; Cheshire Acad Eng as Second Lang Tchr 1990-93; Sacred Heart HS Span, Italian Tchr 1991-92; St Paul Cath HS Span Tchr, Frgn Lang Dept Chair 1993-; *ai:* Jr Class, Span Hnr Soc Adv; NHS Fac Cncl; Fac Dev Comm Chprsn; NEASC Self-Stud Steering Comm; Fulbright Alumni Assn 1983-; CT Org of Lang Tchrs 1978-; Amer Assn of Tchrs of Span, Portuguese 1986-; Cultural Heritage Alliance Assn 1982-; Fulbright Scholar Italy 1983; CT Coll Natl Endowment for Hum Grant 1984; Archdiocese of Hartford St Elizabeth Seton Grants 1986, 1990; Alpha Mu Gamma; Kappa Delta Pi; *office:* Saint Paul Catholic HS 1001 Stafford Ave Bristol CT 06010

MORAES, ROBERT LLEWELLYN, Team Leader & Soc Stud Tchr; *b:* Marlboro, MA; *m:* Eleanore D. Mahalick; *c:* Robert Anthony; *ed:* Wm Paterson Coll (BA) Gen Elem Ed 1969, (MA) Soc Stud 1989; 15 Credits Soc Stud Jersey City St Coll; 15 Credits His Rutgers Univ; *cr:* Vly View Schl Grd 5 Tchr-in-Charge 1970-89; Robert R. Lazar MS Team Ldr, Grd Six Soc Stud Tchr 1989-; *ai:* Lions Club Eye Mobile; Lions Quest Skills for Adolescence; GATE Prgm; NEA, NJEA 1969-; Montville Ed Assn 1969-, Acting Pres, VP; Assn of Soc Stud 1985-; Lion's Club 1980-86, VP, Treas, Appreciation Awd 1985; NJ Tchng Acad 1988; NJ Gov Tchr Recognition Awd 1994; Initiated & Implementated Participation Carmen San Diego TV Prgm 1992-94; Docant Wm Paterson Coll 1991; *office:* Robert R Lazar MS 123 Changebridge Rd Montville NJ 07045

MORAHAN, JOHN KELLY, HS Soc Stud & Drivers Ed Tchr; *b:* Scranton, PA; *m:* Kristen Mary Walsh; *c:* Sean, Caitlin; *ed:* Univ of Scranton (MS) Scndry Schl Admin 1995; PA Prins Cert 1995; *cr:* Pocono Cntrl Cath HS Soc Stud Chprsn, Ath Dir, Coach 1981-88; Notre Dame HS Girls Bsktbl Coach, Soc Stud Tchr 1988-89; Elk Lake HS Coach, Soc Stud, Driver Ed Tchr 1989-; *ai:* PA Assn of Safety Edctrs 1994-; NEA, PSEE 1989-; Elk Lake Ed Assn 1989-, HS Rep-Exec Comm; Who's Who Among Amer Coll & Univ 1995; *office:* Elk Lake HS PO Box 100 Dimock PA 18816

MORAL, AURORA EMELINA, Spanish Teacher; *b:* Havana, Cuba; *m:* Armando F.; *c:* Armando E., Carmen Moral DiPasquale; *ed:* Temple Univ (MA) Fgn Lang Ed 1972; Escuela Normal de La Habana Educacion & Pedagogia; 65 Credit Hrs After Completion of MAED Univ of PA, Villanova Univ, West Chester Univ, Marywood Coll Penn St Univ & Many Others; *cr:* Instituto Edison Elem & Scndry Tchr 1960; Greater Chester Movement Biling & ESL Tchr 1968-70; Radnor MS 7th & 8th Grd Span Tchr 1970-71; Springfield HS Span Tchr 1971-; *ai:* Span Club Adv 17 Yrs; NEA, PSEA & SEA 1970-; Amer Assn of Tchrs of Span & Portugese 1970-; Amer Cncl of Tchng of Fgn Lang 1970-; Natl Fed of Modern Lang Tchrs 1971; Delta Kappa Gamma Intnl 1981-, VP, Sec & World Flwshp Chm; BSA Mothers Auxiliary; Delaware Vly Translators; Top 10 Percent of Class; Jose Marti Awd; Articles Pub.

MORALES, IRIS DELIA, Spanish Teacher; *b:* Rio Piedras, PR; *m:* John; *c:* Jason, Lisa, Denise; *ed:* Westchester Comm Coll (AS) Hum 1987; Pace Univ (BS) Span, Scndry Ed 1989; Iona Coll (MS) Scndry Ed, Span 1993; Writers as Witnesses of Their Times at Tchrs Consortium of SUNY Purchase Manhattanville Coll 8 Inservice Credits; Superviory Tchr Trng 3 Grad Credits; *cr:* White Plains HS Span Tchr 1989-90; Yorktown HS Span Tchr 1990-92; Brewster HS Span Tchr 1993; Walter Panas HS Span, AP Tchr 1993-; *ai:* Hispanic Outreach Prgm for Enrichment Club Adv; WISE Prgm Mentoria; Span Trip Organizied, Ldr; ASCD 1996-; WAFLE 1989-; Frgn Lang Hnr Soc 1988-, VP; NY St Challenger Awd 1991; Who's Who Among Amer Coll Stdnts 1989; *office:* Walter Panas HS 300 Croton Ave Cortlandt Manor NY 10566*

MORALES, MANUEL JOSEPH, Spanish Teacher; *b:* Barcelona, Spain; *m:* Pam Myers; *c:* Andrew, Anna; *ed:* Lancaster Bible Coll (BS) Bible Ed 1996; Millersville Univ 19 Credit Hrs of Grad Stud; *cr:* Auburn Chrstn Acad Sr High Supvr 1988-89; Chrstn Schl of York Sr High Span Tchr 1990-; Lancaster Bible Coll Continuing Ed Course & Introduction to Span 1996; *ai:* Karate Club; Frgn Lang Comm; ACSI 1990-; Span Lib Bd of York 1994-, Advy Bd; *office:* Christian Schl Of York 907 Greenbriar Rd York PA 17313

MORALES, RICHARD, Associate Professor; *b:* Durand, MI; *m:* Sharon Kay Perrine; *c:* Darrell Jon, Christine Marie; *ed:* MI St Univ (BA) Psychiatric Soc Work 1965; St Univ of NY at Brockport (MA) Pub Admin 1974; Syracuse Univ (MSW) Organization & Planning 1977; The Maxwell Schl of Citizenship & Public Admin at Syracuse Univ (PHD) Soc Sci Rsrch 1985; St Johns Univ; *cr:* Keuka Coll Adj Fac 1 Yr; St John Fisher Coll Consultant & Trainer 7 Yrs; Cornell Univ Adj Fac 7 Yrs; SUNY Clinical Asst Prof 11 Yrs; Rochester Inst of Tech Assoc Prof 20 Yrs; *ai:* SHPE & RIT & Latina Sorority Adv; United Way of Greater Rochester 1969-, Citizenships Awds; Mental Hlth Assn 1986-; Articles & Rsrch Reports Pub; *office:* Rochester Inst Of Tech 1 Lomb Memorial Dr Rochester NY 14623

MORAN, ANN KAELIN, 5th Grade Teacher; *b:* Rockville Center, NY; *m:* Matthew; *c:* Joseph Russo; *ed:* Oneonta St Univ (BS) Elem Ed, HS Soc Stud 1964; Post Grad Hrs Hofstra Univ, C W Post Univ; *cr:* Brookside Jr HS 7-8 Grd Soc Stud Tchr 1964-68; Commack Jr HS 7-8 Grd Soc Stud Tchr 1968-69; Jos A Edgar Schl 5th-6th Grd Spec Ed Tchr 1969-; *ai:* Grd Leve Coord; Grievance Comm; NYSUT 1964-, Local Pres 7 Yrs, Svc Awd; Fire Dept Ladies Aux 1991-, Pres; *home:* 30F Floyd Bennett Dr Sound Beach NY 11789*

MORAN, ANNA (LADUE), Social Studies Teacher; *b:* Springfield, MA; *m:* David George; *c:* Grant Thomas, David-Paul; *ed:* Bemidji St Coll (BSEd) Soc Stud 1967; *cr:* Holy Family Schl 5th Grd Tchr 1968; Gilbert Jr Sr HS 8-10th Grd Soc Stud Tchr 1968-69; Dept of Army USDESEA PREP 9-12 Grd Soc Stud Tchr 1972-74; Holy Name of Jesus Schl 6-8 Grd Soc Stud, Sci Tchr 1974-85; Holy Cross Schl 6-8 Grd Soc Stud Tchr 1986-; *ai:* Soc Stud Curr Coord; MA Bar Assn Mock Trail Team Coach; Natl Geog Bee Jr Achvmt 6th-8th Grd; Global Challenge 7th-8th Grds; Natl Current Events League 6th Grd; NCRA 1986-; Springfield Girls Club Family Ctr Inc 1990-, Camp Dir; Ludlow CYO Bsktbl Assn 1993-, Sec; Sallie Mae Tchr Awd 1991 Newsweek.

MORAN, CYNTHIA ANN WEHLE, Mathematics Teacher; *b:* Rochester, NY; *m:* James R.; *c:* Paige Caitlin, Kayleigh Shea; *ed:* SUC at Brockport (BS) Math & Music 1975, (MS) Ed 1979; Attnd Univ of Denver 1970; Berklee Coll of Music Music 1973; *cr:* Wheatland-Chili HS 7th-8th Grd Math Tchr 1976-78; Churchville-Chili HS 9th-12th Grd Math Tchr 1978-; *ai:* Video Club Adv for St Puis X; CML Adv; NEA 1978-, Bldg Rep; AFT 1967-78; St Pius X Schl Advy Bd Mem 1991-93; *office:* Churchville-Chili HS 5786 Buffalo Rd Churchville NY 14428*

MORAN, DANIEL, English Teacher; *b:* Perth Amboy, NJ; *m:* Deirdre; *ed:* Rutgers Coll (BA) Eng 1990, (MA) Eng 1993; *cr:* East Brunswick HS Eng Tchr 1991-; *ai:* Drama Club Adv; Natl Endowment for Hum Fellowship 1994; *office:* East Brunswick HS 380 Cranbury Rd East Brunswick NJ 08816

MORAN, DIANA WHALEN, Biology Teacher; *b:* Hartford, CT; *c:* James, Sean, Tighe, Ian, Tara; *ed:* Marymount Coll (BA) Chem 1961; Fairfield Univ (MA) Scndry Ed 1964; Attnd Sacred Heart Univ, Wesleyan Univ, Quinnipiac Coll; *cr:* Naugatuck HS Chem Tchr 1963-68, Bio Tchr 1978-; *ai:* NEASC Comm; CEA, NEA, NTL 1963-; Sweet Briar Coll Parents Assn; Villanove Univ Parents Assn; Marymount Coll Alumnae Assn; Natl Trust; Smithsonian Museum; Museum of Natural His.

MORAN, JAMES MARTIN, Religious Studies Teacher; *b:* New York City, NY; *ed:* St Thomas Aquinas Coll (BA) Comm Arts 1985; Grad Stud Immaculate Conception Seminary Theology; Seton Hall Univ Educl Cnslng; Montclair St Univ Ed; *cr:* Queen of Peace HS Rel Stud Tchr 1990-; *ai:* Frosh Class, NHS Adv; Prin Advy Comm; NCEA 1990-, Del to NCEA Conventions New Orleans 1993, Anaheim 1994; Serve Amer Hitachi Corp Svc Grant, Pilot Svc Prgm Queen of Peace HS, St Lucy Filippini Acad Sponsored by NJ Dept of Ed 1993-94; Rediscovering the Encounter The Worlds of 1492 Grant NJ Comm for Hum Endorsed by NJ Ed Assn Prof Dev Inst 1992; *office:* Queen Of Peace HS 191 Rutherford Pl North Arlington NJ 07031*

MORAN, JAMES PATRICK, Oceanography Instructor; *b:* Yonkers, NY; *m:* Judity Gostic; *c:* Alison; *ed:* Iona Coll (BS) Bio 1960; NY Univ (MA) Sci Ed 1964; 85 Credits Sci, Ed; *cr:* Rice HS Sci Tchr, Coach 1960-61; Isaac E. Young Jr HS Sci Tchr, Coach 1962-66; Elwood Jr HS Sci Tchr 1966-85; John Glenn HS Sci Tchr 1985-95; Suffolk Cty Comm Coll Oceanography Instr 1995-; *ai:* NY St United Tchr 1966-; Knights of Columbus 1993-, Trustee; NSF Grant; Tchr Rsrch Assoc Grant Brook Haven Natl Lab; Article Pub; *home:* 21 Kenny St Hauppauge NY 11788

MORAN, JOYCE LEONARDO, High School Italian Teacher; *b:* New York, NY; *m:* Stephen; *ed:* Queens Coll (BA) Italian, Fr 1968; SUNY at Stony Brook (MS) Eng 1992; *cr:* North Babylon HS Italian, Fr Tchr 1968-; *ai:* AFT; NEA; *office:* North Babylon HS Deer Park Ave North Babylon NY 11703

MORAN, KARIN BARRICK, Business Teacher; *b:* Coshocton, OH; *m:* Brian; *c:* Brianna, Justine; *ed:* Malone Coll (BA) Math, Basic Bus, Bookkeeping, Scndry Ed, Steno, Typing, Keyboarding 9-12 1989; *cr:* Cochocton Cty JVS Adult Keyboarding Tchr 1990-92; CORC Job Trng HS Stdnts Math Tutor 1990-92; River View HS Proficiency Tutor, Remedial Instr Summer 1994, Math Cmptr, Bus Tchr 1989-; *ai:* Asst Dir Color Guard 1991-93; Club Adv Exec Bears 1990-94; Adv Dist Newspaper 1992-94; Class Adv, Chm Soph Class; Bus Dept Chprsn 1993-; Peer Mediator Comm; NHS Cncl 1992-94; OEA, NEA 1989-95, Local Treas 2 Yrs; North Cntrl Math Org, Orgnl Mem 2 Yrs; Sigma Zeta 1988-; Kappa Phi Delta; 4-H Advy Comm Mem 2 Yrs; Pastor Parish Comm Mem 2 Yrs; Evaluator for Cty 4-H Awds; Comm Mem for Parent Visitation 2 Yrs; *office:* River View HS 26496 Sr 60 N Warsaw OH 43844*

MORAN, KATHLEEN A., Social Studies Dept Chprsn; *b:* New York, NY; *ed:* Long Island Univ (BA) Pol Sci 1977; C. W. Post Campus (MS) Elem Ed 1982; *cr:* St John the Evangelist Sixth Grd Tchr 1978-89; Holy Trinity HS Soc Stud Tchr 1989-; *ai:* Stu Cncl Adv; Mid St Evaluation Steering Comm; Univ of CT Tech, Learning In Svc Ldr; NCSS 1980-; NCEA; *office:* Holy Trinity HS 98 Cherry Ln Hicksville NY 11801*

MORAN, KENNETH PAUL, Mathematics Teacher; *b:* Bridgeport, CT; *m:* Diane Sidorwich; *c:* James Joseph, Daniel Patrick; *ed:* Sacred Heart Univ (BA) Math 1970; Fairfield Univ (MA) Admin, Supervision 1980; 6th Yr Admin, Supervision 1988; *cr:* Stamford Cath HS Math Tchr 1970-78; Bassick HS Math Tchr, Ath Dir, Sftbl Coach 1978-87; Cntrl HS Math Tchr, Ath Dir, Sftbl Coach 1987-; *ai:* Girls Head Sftbl Coach; BEA, CEA, NEA 1978-; *office:* Central Magnet HS 1 Lincoln Blvd Bridgeport CT 06606

MORAN, MICHAEL LEE, Assistant Prof of Phys Therapy; *b:* Batavia, NY; *m:* Jeanne Grunau; *c:* Katie, Michael; *ed:* SUNY Stony Brook (BS) Phys Therapy 1978; Univ of Scranton (MS) Admin 1983; Nova Univ (SCD) Cmptr Tech 1991; *cr:* Moran Phys Therapy Owner 1984-88; Manor Hlth Care Phys Therapist 1988-92; Coll Misericordia Asst Prof 1992-; *ai:* Parent Advy Comm, Phys Therapy Club Adv; Amer Phys Therapy Assn 1980-, Ed of Issues on Aging, Jrnl; Books Pub Cmptr Principles for Phys & Occupational Therapists, Clinical Cases in Phys Therapy; Numerous Articles Pub; *office:* Coll Misericordia 301 Lake St Dallas PA 18612

MORAN, MICHAEL PAUL, Music Teacher & Band Director; *b:* Bethlehem, PA; *m:* Robin Harrison; *ed:* West Chester Univ (BS) Music Ed 1991; 3 Grad Credits; 3 Grad Credits Villa Nova Univ; *cr:* Lincoln MS Music Tchr 1991-92; Elizabeth HS Music Tchr, Asst Band Dir 1992-94; Spring-Ford HS Music Tchr, Band Dir 1994-; *ai:* Marching, Jazz Bands, Musical Pit Orch, Choral Dir; NEA, PMEA, MENC 1994-; Host PMEA Region VI Band Festival 1995; *home:* A8-168 Westridge Gardens Phoenixville PA 19460

MORAN, SEAN PATRICK, History Teacher; *b:* Baltimore, MD; *ed:* Loyola Coll (BA) His 1987; Univ of Md, Balto CO (MA) His 1995; *cr:* Calvert Hall Coll HS Lang Specialist 1987-88; Mount de Sales Acad AP His Tchr 1988-; *ai:* Var Cross Cntry, Indoor Track, Outdoor Track Coach; Dev Comm; Mid Sts Accreditation Comm; Acad Adv; Citizen Bee Coord; Eucharistic Minister; NHS Adv; Irish Dance Club Moderator; NCSS 1991-92; Natl Park Service VIP, 5th US Cavalry 1986-; Mid Sts Accreditation Visiting Team; *office:* Mount De Sales Academy 700 Academy Rd Catonsville MD 21228

MORAN, SHARON ANN, AP Government Teacher; *b:* Hartford, CT; *ed:* Albertus Magnus (BA) Amer Stud 1966; Trinity Coll (MA) Pol Sci 1977; UCLA Constitutional Stud; UCSB Early Amer Values in Religion; CSULB Enlightenment Philosophers; Yale Federalism; BU Federalist Papers 1995; *cr:* South Windsor HS Soc Stud Tchr 1966-; *ai:* Natl Bicentennial Competition Adv; CT Mock Trial Competition, Sr Class Adv; Fac Advy Cncl; Natl Review Bd for Govt & Civics; NCSS 1989-; CCSS 1970-; NEA, CEA, SWEA 1966-; CT Cncl for Law & Civic Ed 1990-, Law Tchr of Yr; Natl Endowment for Hum Fellowships 1989-92; CCE Constitutional Stud Consultant 1990-; Close-up USA/Japan Cultural Exchange 1993; CT Celebration of Excellence Recipient 1994; AFT Democracy/Intl Instr Dev Nations How To Teach Democracy 1995-; *office:* South Windsor HS 161 Nevers Rd South Windsor CT 06074*

MORAN-HARR, NANCY OCHS, Fifth Grade Teacher; *b:* Wilkinsburg, PA; *m:* John C. Harr; *ed:* Slippery Rock Univ (BS) Elem 1968; Post Grad Stud IN Univ of PA, PA St; *cr:* Centennial Elem Schl Second, Fifth Grd Tchr 1968-81; Cornell MS Fifth Grd Tchr 1981-; *ai:* NEA, PSEA 1968-; MAEA 1968-, Bldg Rep; WOTM 171 Chptr 1993-; Amer Cancer Soc 1989-, Daffodil Ball Comm Co-Chm, Sepc Projects Chm; PTA 1968-; *office:* Cornell MS 1600 Cornell St Mc Keesport PA 15132

MORANO, JOHN DAVID, Professor of Journalism; *b:* E Rockaway, NY; *ed:* Clark Univ (BA) Eng & Film 1982; Penn St Univ (MA) Print Jrnlsm 1987; Adelphi Univ Tech Cert 1988; *cr:* Modern Screen Magazine Managing Ed 1983-84; Rockbeat Magazine Ed-In-Chief 1988-89; Monmouth Univ Assoc Prof 1988-; *ai:* Stu Newspaper, Stu Govt & Div I Mens Bsktbl Team Adv; Soc of Prof Journalists 1989-; NJ Press Assn 1989-; Book: A Wing and a Prayer; Monmouth Univ Stu Choice Awd 1992-95, Nom 1991; Monmouth Univ Celebration of Tchng Awd 1994; Monmouth Univ Distngd Fac Mem Awd Nom 1994-96; *office:* Monmouth Univ Dept of Commnctn West Long Branch NJ 07764

MORANT, MERVALIN ANDERENE, Asst Prof of Plant Pathology; *b:* Jamaica; *ed:* Tuskegee Inst (BS) Plant & Soil Sci 1981, (MS) Plant & Soil Sci 1983; Purdue Univ (PHD) Botany & Plant Pathology 1988; Post Doctoral Rsrch Assoc Molecular Plant Pathology Univ of IL at Champaign-Urbana; *cr:* Univ of MD Eastern Shore Visiting Rsrch Assoc 1991-93, Asst Prof 1993-; *ai:* Ag Sci Club Adv; Minorities in Ag Co-Adv; Natural Resources & Related Sci Club; Grad & Undergraduate Stdnts Adv; Univ Comms; Sigma Xi, Alpha Kappa Mu 1982-; Amer Phytopath Soc 1983-; Prin Investigator on Over 8 Competitively Funded Grants; Co-Prin Investigator on Competitive Grants; Pub Rsrch Articles; Reviewer of Manuscripts for Scientific Competitive Events; Invited to Judge Stdnts Entries in Cty Fairs 3 Yrs; *office:* Univ Of MD Eastern Shore Dept of Agriculture Princess Anne MD 21853

MORASKI, HELENA HUNT, Resource Center Teacher; *b:* Yonkers, NY; *m:* Raymond Mitchell; *c:* Sean Mc Cann, Moira Mc Cann, Brayn Mc Cann; *ed:* Marymount Coll (BA) Eng 1961; City Univ of NY (MS) Elem Ed 1969; Fairleigh Dickinson Univ (MA) Learning Disabilities 1979; Fordham Univ Prof Diploma Supervision & Admin 1988; *cr:* Upper Saddle River Schls 3rd Grd Tchr 1977-79, 4th Grd Tchr 1979-81, 5th Grd Tchr 1981-82, Percep Imp 1982-83, 2nd Grd Tchr 1983-94, Resource Ctr 1994-; *ai:* Spec Ed Advy Comm; NEA, NJEA, BCEA 1977-; Upper Saddle River Lib Bd; Active Church of Presentation 1973-; Tchr of Yr 1992; Grade Chprsn 1991-94; Wkshp Presenter Math Curr 1992-93; *office:* Robert D Reynolds Primary Sch 395 W Saddle River Rd Upper Saddle River NJ 07458

MORDAN, CAROL RITTER, Third Grade Teacher; *b:* Danville, PA; *m:* Lloyd S.; *c:* Jan Carol, Lloyd H.; *ed:* Williamsport Area Comm Coll (AA) Psych 1973; Bloomsburg Univ (BS) Elem 1975, (MS) Elem 1979; *cr:* George A. Ferrell Elem Schl 2nd-3rd Grd Tchr 1975-; *ai:* Kids for Saving Earth Club Adv; Outdoor Classroom, Power of Positive Stdnts Prgm Coord; ELEA, PSEA, NEA 1975-; PTAC Exec Bd 1976-, Prgm Chprsn, Tchr Rep; Beta Sigma Phi 1977-, Extension Ofcr; Prof Ed Cncl 1990-; Hill's Environmental Ed Grants; Danville St Mental Inst, Schl of Hope Vol; Employee of Month; Dev 2 Week Dist, Comm Local His Unit; *office:* George A. Ferrell Elem Schl 34 Court St Picture Rocks PA 17762*

MOREAU, PETER L., Mathematics Teacher; *b:* Providence, RI; *ed:* Dartmouth Coll (AB) His, Fr 1974; Assumption Coll (MAT) His 1978; Courses at Providence Coll, RI Coll, Comm Coll of RI; *cr:* Lincoln Jr Sr HS Tchr of Math, Soc Stud, Fr Tchr 1974-; *ai:* LTA Schlsp Comm; AFT 1974-, VP Local; DIG of RI, Treas; Lincoln Land Trust, VP; Apeiron Fnd, Treas; Szumita Meml Pl Comm, Bd; Amer Fr Genealogical Soc; Numerous Local Environmental Clean-ups; Local Historic Tours; Pub Articles; *office:* Lincoln Jr Sr HS 135 Old River Rd Lincoln RI 02865*

MOREHOUSE, DANIEL E., Fourth Grade Teacher; *b:* Philadelphia, PA; *c:* Courtney; *ed:* Temple (BSEd) Elem Ed 1978; (ME) Elem Ed 1986; 40 Addl Credits; *cr:* Pearl Buck Elem Schl 4th Grd Tchr 1978; Walter Miller Elem Schl 3rd & 4th Grd Tchr 1978-80; Tawanka Elem Schl 5th Grd Tchr 1980-83; Pearl Buck Elem Schl 6th Grd Tchr 1983-84; Albert Schweitzer Elem Schl 2nd Grd Tchr 1984-87; Herbert Hoover Elem Schl 2nd & 4th Grd Tchr 1987-; *ai:* Mentor Tchng New Employees; 3rd & 5th Grd Writing Assessments Comm Mem; Eng Tutor Second Lang; AFT 1985-; Neighborhood Home Owners Assn 1986-; Doylestown Shade Tree Commission 1990-; Svc Pin 15 Yrs Employment; Subject of Newspaper Articles; *office:* Herbert Hoover Elem Schl 501 Trenton Dr Langhorne PA 19047

MOREHOUSE, SHEILA M., Professor of Chemistry; *b:* Auburn, NY; *m:* Francis S.; *ed:* Salve Regina Univ (BS) Chem; Cornell Univ (MS) Inorganic Chem; Columbia Univ (PHD) Inorganic Chem 1971; Rsrch Asst MIT; Attnd Imperial Coll of Sci, Tech; *cr:* Manhattanville Coll Prof Dept Chr 1971-; Yale Univ Visiting Assoc Prof 1980-81; Columbia Univ Visiting Scientist 1985-87; Yale Univ Rsrch Assoc 1981-85; Natl Rsrch Cncl Fellow Imperia Coll; *ai:* Steering Comm; Pre-Med Comm Chair; Status Comm; Adv Pre-Med Soc; Amer Chem Soc; Sigma Xi; NY Acad of Scis Advy Bd Mem Chair, Organometallic Section; Fac Flwshp Columbia Univ; NIH Pre-Doctoral Flwshp Columbia Univ; Rsrch Corp Grant; NIH Rsrch Grant; Numerous Publications; *office:* Manhattanville Coll 2900 Purchase St Purchase NY 10577

MOREHOUSE, TERRY, English Composition Teacher; *b:* Newark, OH; *c:* Seth, Eric; *ed:* Univ of Cincinnati (MA) Eng 1975; *cr:* Walnut Hills HS Eng Tchr 1969-79; Seven Hills Schl Eng Tchr 1980-84; Univ of Cincinnati Composition Tchr 1988-; *ai:* Books: Basic Projects & Plantings for the Garden, Gardening Basics; *office:* Univ of Cincinnati 346 1 Edwards Ctr Cincinnati OH 45221

MOREIRA, DONNA MARIE, High School Art Teacher; *b:* Plainview, NY; *m:* John Jr.; *c:* Justin, John; *ed:* SUNY at New Paltz (BS) Art Ed 1983; Dowling Coll (MS) Elem Ed 1990; 3 Credit Hrs Advertising Art; 50 Credit Hrs Airbrush Basics; *cr:* Christ the King K-8th Grd Art Tchr 1986-87; Schl of the Holy Child K-6th Grd Art Tchr 1987-88; William Floyd Schl Dist 7th Grd Art Tchr 1988-89; Malverne Schl Dist 5th-12th Grd Art Tchr 1989-; *ai:* Mural Club; Schl Musical Bus Mgr; Cooperating Tchr for Coll Stu; NAEA 1985-; *office:* Malverne HS 80 Ocean Ave Malverne NY 11565*

MORELAND, DAVID S., Social Studies Teacher; *b:* New Brunswick, NJ; *m:* Sandra Lee Stedman; *c:* Andrew, Benjamin; *ed:* St Univ of IA (BA) His 1964; Boston St Coll (MED) Ed, US His 1968; Grad Work Harvard, Bridgewater St Coll; *cr:* Silver Lake Regnl Jr HS Soc Stud Tchr 1968-; *ai:* Chess Tournament Adv; NEA, MA Tchrs Assn 1968-; Silver Lake Ed Assn 1968-, VP, Exec Comm; Plymouth Town Meeting 1995-; Article Pub; *office:* Silver Lake Reg Jr HS 80 Learning Ln Pembroke MA 02359*

MORELAND, MURIEL REYNOLDS, Retired Classroom Teacher; *b:* Pittsburgh, PA; *m:* William H.; *ed:* Waynesburg Coll (BA) Eng 1950; Univ of Pittsburgh (MED) Ed 1956; *cr:* Keystone Oaks Schl Dist Classroom Tchr 1953-92; *ai:* Delta Kappa Gamma, Pi Lambda Theta, Pres; Pittsburgh Blind Assn, Vision Testing, Vol; Classroom Creative Writing Lessons, Vol; Storyteller, Vol; Extra Mile Awd 1986; Achvmt Awd Congressm[illegible] Walgren; Excl Amer Family Inst.

MORELAND, SUSAN K. (RAMSEY), Choral Music Director; *b:* [illegible] OH; *m:* Wayne Steven; *ed:* Baldwin-Wallace Coll (BME) Vocal [illegible] Univ of Akron (MM) Vocal Ed 1983; *cr:* Pleasant Vly Jr HS Voca[illegible] Tchr 1971-85; Greenbriar Jr HS Vocal Music Tchr 1985-87; Parm[illegible] Choral Dir 1987-; Shiloh Jr HS Vocal Music Tchr 1994-; *ai:* Parma[illegible] Show Choir Dir, Drama Club Dirs Asst; PEA, OEA, NEA 1971-[illegible] 1987-; Phi Mu 1969-; Cleveland Shetland Sheepdog Club 1979-, [illegible] Medina Cty Woman of Distinction Awd 1992; *office:* Parma Sr H[illegible] Ridge Rd Parma OH 44129

MORELLE, BERYL GAIL (MACK), Second Grade Tea[illegible] Woonsocket, RI; *m:* Paul J.; *c:* Meredith; *ed:* Univ of RI (BA) [illegible] Psych 1969; RI Coll (MED) Cnslng 1974; Credit Hrs Spec Ed; [illegible] St Schl 3rd Grd Tchr 1969-84; Globe Park Schl 2nd Grd Tchr 1[illegible] Cooperating Tchr; CAP-CAST Comm; Bldg Steward; AFT #95[illegible] Rep Assembly, Fin Sec; Alpha Delta Kappa 1990-, Treas; RIF[illegible] Quest Comm; Amer Heart Assn 1986-, Bd Dir; AFT Newspap[illegible] *office:* Globe Park Elem Schl 192 Avenue A Woonsocket RI 0289[illegible]

MORELLI, JEAN ANN, English Teacher; *b:* Boston, MA; *ed:* B[illegible] Coll (BA) Eng 1968, (MED) Guid, Cnslng 1974; Addl 30 Credit Hr[illegible] Schl Admin; *cr:* Grover Cleveland MS Eng Tchr 1968-74; Hyde [illegible] Eng Tchr 1974-89; Hyde Park HS Eng Dept Head 1989-92; Bost[illegible] Schl Dept Head, Eng Tchr 1992-; *ai:* NASSP Evaluating, Curr Co[illegible] Support Svcs; Valedictory Coach; AFT 1968-; Golden Apple Aw[illegible] *office:* Boston Latin Schl 78 Avenue Louis Pasteur Boston MA 02[illegible]

MORELLI, PAULA SAVANOVICH, High School English Tea[illegible] Rochester, PA; *m:* Ronald L.; *c:* Pamela, Nathan; *ed:* Indiana Uni[illegible] (BS) Eng Ed 1977; PLS 9 Credits, 12 Credit Hrs Duquesne Univ, [illegible] Univ, Slippery Rock Univ for Masters Equivalency; *cr:* Rocky Gr[illegible] Dist Eng Tchr 1977-78; Center Area Schls Scndry Eng Tchr 19[illegible] Penn St Univ Consortium of Eng Tchrs; PSEA, NEA, CAEA 1978-[illegible] Ctr Area Schls 160 Baker Rd Ext Monaca PA 15061

MORELLI, PHIL ANTHONY, Director; *b:* Pittsburgh, PA; *m:* [illegible] Vossler; *c:* Phil A., Mark J.; *ed:* Univ of Pittsburgh (BS) Hlth & P[illegible] Carlow Coll (MED) Educl Leadership 1994; Admin I Primary-Scn[illegible] 1993; Diocese of Pittsburgh Prospective Prins Prgm 1992-94, A[illegible] Cert 1992; *cr:* St Bartholomew Schl Math & Sci Tchr 1[illegible] CCAC-Boyce Campus Math Tchr 1986-87; Carlow Coll Campus Sc[illegible] & Religion Tchr 1990-91, Tchr & Upper Schl Coord 1991-93, Di[illegible] *ai:* Boys Jr HS Bsktbl Coach; Schls Advy Cncl Mem; Search Comm[illegible] ASCD 1991-; MEEN 1993-; NCEA 1990-; Carnegie Sci Ctr 1994[illegible] Hills Bsbl Assn 1995-; *office:* Carlow College Campus Schl 3333 [illegible] Pittsburgh PA 15213*

MORELLI, RICHARD, Span Tchr & Frgn Lang Dept Chm; *b:* Ro[illegible] PA; *m:* Janet Caprelli; *c:* Jessica, Amanda; *ed:* St Francis Coll (B[illegible] 1969; Duquesne Univ (MSEd) Scndry Ed 1972; Pitt Univ Post Gr[illegible] Eng; *cr:* Aliquippa HS Span Tchr 1969-81; Corabel HS Span Tchr [illegible] *ai:* Span Club Adv; Asst Bsbl Coach; Discipline, Pres Comm; NEA[illegible] 1969-; AEA, CEA 1969-, Pres, Bldg Rep; Tchr of Month 3 Time[illegible] Mentor; *office:* Cornell Educl Ctr 1099 Maple St Coraopolis PA 1[illegible]

MORENCY, BERTRAM ANTHONY,III, Sixth Grade Teac[illegible] Meriden, CT; *m:* Kathleen Kingsley; *ed:* Cntrl CT St Univ (BS) [illegible] 1974, (MS) Guidance & Counseling 1979; 6th Yr Rdng & Lang Ar[illegible] *cr:* Central Schl 5th-6th Grd Tchr 1974-78; Tootin Hills 6th G[illegible] 1978-; *ai:* 5th-6th Grd Intramurals Schl Dir; Elem Schl Cncl Chprsn ESC Cncl Mem 1993-; Rdng, Sci & Cmptr Tech Curr Revision [illegible] SEA, NEA 1974-; Mentor & Cooperating Tchr in CTs BEST Prgm[illegible] Tootin Hills Elem Schl 25 Nimrod Rd West Simsbury CT 06092

MORENO, PATRICK ANTHONY, World Languages Dept C[illegible] Malden, MA; *m:* Shirley Ann Tuccio; *c:* Paul A., Kristen S.; *ed:* [illegible] Univ (AA) Gen Ed 1957, (BA) Romance Lang 1959, (MED) Roman[illegible] 1964; Middlesex Comm Coll 24 Hrs Tech Writing 1981-84; Harva[illegible] 68 Grad Hrs Frgn Lit 1986-; Univ of MD 9 Under Grad Hrs Fr[illegible] 1965-66; *cr:* Winchester Schls Frgn, Ger Second Tchr 1964-67; Fo[illegible] Employed 1967-81; Family Bus Mgr, Food 1982-84; Plymout[illegible] Italian Second Tchr 1985-91; Carver Schls Fr Tchr, Chprsn 19[illegible] Hobbies Stone Cutting, Bldg & Rowing Crew; NEA, MTA, AATF 1985-; Saute Alighier Soc 1991-; Writing Thesis; *home:* 12 Pat[illegible] Burlington MA 01803*

MOREY, JOHN CHARLES, 6th Grade Teacher; *b:* Canton, [illegible] Susan E. Reidenbach; *c:* John, Joshua, Jessica, Jennifer; *ed:* Malo[illegible] (BA) Elem Ed & His 1971; Akron Univ (MA) Guid & Cnslng 19[illegible] Perry Local Schl Dist Tchr 1972-; *ai:* Ftbl Coach; Strategic P[illegible] Comm; Staff Dev & Tech; NEA 1972-; OEA 1972-; Perry Classroo[illegible] Assn 1972-, Treas, OEA Treas Awd; The Educl Enhancment Part[illegible] 1994-, Comm Mem, Commnctn Consorgium; *home:* 611 Overdale A[illegible] Canton OH 44708

MOREY, MARK V., Physical Education Teacher; *b:* New York, [illegible] Manhattan Coll (BS) PE 1983; City Coll of NY (MS) Ed Supervisio[illegible] 1996; Coll of Mt St Vincent 3 Grad Hrs; Manhattan Coll 12 Grad [illegible] PS 1 Tchr 1983-87; Sacred Heart HS Tchr 1987-94; John F. Kenn[illegible] Tchr 1994-95; Janaica HS Tchr 1995; William Howard Taft HS Tchr *office:* Taft HS 240 E 172nd St Bronx NY 10457

MORFENSKI, MARY PATRICIA MARISKANISH, B[illegible] Education Teacher; *b:* Ann Arbor, MI; *m:* David Marcus; *c:* Kelly Stephen; *ed:* IN Univ of PA (BS) Bus Ed 1972; Masters Equivale[illegible] Grad Hrs IUP; Attnd IU at Edinboro; *cr:* St Marys Area HS Bus E[illegible] 1972-76; Meadville Area Sr HS Bus Ed Tchr 1976-; *ai:* Bus Adv[illegible] CCEA Tchrs Assn 1976-; Greater Assn of Meadville Churches Magazine Pub Word Perfect Tip; *office:* Meadville Area Sr HS N Ext Meadville PA 16335

MORGAN, ANNE MARIE M., School-to-Career Coordina[illegible] Yonkers, NY; *c:* Sharon E. Basso, Keith M. Basso; *ed:* SU[illegible] Plattsburgh (BS) Elem Ed & Bus Ed 1988, (MS) Rdng Specializatio[illegible] *cr:* Saranac HS Bus Tchr & Schl-to-Career Coord 1988-; *ai:* Sr Cla[illegible] 4 Yrs; NHS Adv; Shared-Decision Making Comm; AFT 1988-; Bus Assoc NYS 1988-; Champlain Vly Rdng Cncl 1988-; Goals Adirondack Schl-to-Work Consortium 1995-, Grant to Impleme[illegible] Internships; SUNY at Plattsburgh Valedictorian Winter Commen[illegible] 1988; Katherine Gibbs Bus Schl Full Schlsp.*

MORGAN, BRANCH,III, French & Spanish Teacher; *b:* Baltimor[illegible] *ed:* Washington Univ (BA) Fr 1974; Universite De Strasbourg Fr D[illegible] 1974; Universidad De Madrid Span Cert 1995; *cr:* Baltimore Theatre Dancer, Instr 1975-87; Gilman Schl 1976-79; Atlanta Theatre Dancer, Instr 1979-82; Balto City Pub Schls Fr, Span 1983-87; Baltimore Dance Theatre Dancer, Instr 1988-; Balto C[illegible] Schls Fr, Span Edctrs 1990-92; Balto City Pub Schls Fr, Span 19[illegible] Dunbar Dance Ensemble Founder, Artistic; Class of 1996 Adv; Coach; AFT 1990-; Baltimore Tchrs Union 1983-; MD Foreign Lan[illegible] 1988-, Escola Tchr Incentive Grant; NAACP; ABIRA 1981-; A[illegible] 1990-; Intnl Assoc of Blk Dancers 1993-; MD Showcase Wrks[illegible] Choreographers; City Cnsls Presidential Citation; City Cncl Resolution 20 Yr Apprecition; Katherine Dunham Tech Seminars; Paul L. Dunbar HS 1400 Orleans St Baltimore MD 21231

AN, BYRON E., Hlth & Phys Conditioning Tchr; *b:* Youngstown, Janice; *c:* Jason, Kevin; *ed:* Univ of Findlay (BS) Hlth & PE 1968; leveland St Univ, Akron Univ Hlth & PE; *cr:* Mayfield HS 1972-89; IS 1990-; *ai:* Head Ftbl Coach; Weight Trng & Conditioning Instr; duc Assn 1990; OH Ftbl Coaches, NEA 1976; Greater Cleveland oach of Yr 1981, 1984, 1985; Chagrin Vly Conf Coach of Yr 3; Greater Cleveland Coaches Dan Mormile Awd 1984; astern OH Coach of Yr 1984, 1991; *office:* Solon HS 33600 Inwood n OH 44139

AN, CHARLES B., English, Greek & Latin Teacher; *b:* lphia, PA; *m:* Lynne D'Arcy; *c:* Sarah, Catherine, Anne; *ed:* Univ keley (MA) Eng 1980; Amherst Coll (BA) Classics 1969; *cr:* St chl Tchr 1969-; *ai:* Var Cross Cntry, Var Crew Coach; Outing Club iscipline Comm Chm; Stu Housing Comm Co-Chm; Fac Leadership Ath Assn Mem; Classical Assn of New England 1969-; American aides Assn 1991-; *office:* Saint Pauls Schl 325 Pleasant St Concord 301

AN, CHERYL ANN, PE & Health Ed Teacher; *b:* Rockville, MD; iv of South FL (BA) PE 1973; Montgomery Coll (AA) Cmptr nmer 1983; MD Hlth Ed Cert 1996; *cr:* Churchill HS Vlybl Coach Walter Johnson HS Vlybl Coach 8 Yrs; USA Vlybl Natl Ofcl 16 Yrs; d MS PE Tchr 10 Yrs; *ai:* Wellness Dir; Girls Jr Var, Boys Var Vlybl Intramural Dir; MSTA, NEA, MSPPA 1985-; ABO, USA, NAGUS Vol Childrens Inn 1987-, Sports Dir; USA Vlybl 1975-, Fellowship Olympic Vlybl 1990-, Dir; Big Train Awd 1990, 1992; USA Vlybl ed Gold Div Jr Olympics 1995; Tchr Svc Awd 1995; *home:* 2004 iffe Dr Rockville MD 20851

AN, DAVID LEE, French & German Teacher; *b:* New York, NY; rgan St Univ (BA) Fr 1970, (MS) Ed, Admin, Supervision 1977; redit Hrs Towson St Univ, Millersville St Univ, Dartmouth Coll, MD at Coll Park, La Sorbonne Univ Paris France; *cr:* Pimlico MS 1970-73; Greenspring MS Fr, Ger Tchr 1973-77, 1978-79; Lycee at Cloud Schl Eng Lang Asst 1977-78; Western Sr HS Fr, Ger Tchr *ai:* Intnl Club Co-Adv; Schl Wide Tech Comm; AFT, NEA 1970-; gn Lang Assn 1971-; Amer, Ger Union 1988-; AATG, AATF 1994-; ht Schlsp 1977-78; *office:* Western Sr HS 4600 Falls Rd Baltimore 209

AN, DEBRA HILBERT, Math Teacher; *b:* Hanover, PA; *m:* Jeffrey Millersville Univ (BSE) Math 1993; 9 Credit Hrs Towards Masters Math Ed; *cr:* Columbia Borough HS Math Tchr 1994-; *ai:* Stu Cncl lass 2000 Adv; Track Coach; PSEA, NCTM 1993-; NEA, Columbia sn 1994-; South Western Alumni Assn 1993-, Treas 1993-95; *home:* lemory Lane Ext York PA 17402

AN, GAIL A., Vocational Business Ed Tchr; *b:* Toledo, OH; *ed:* Univ (BS) Ed 1981; OH Univ (MBA) Bus 1990; *cr:* Mid-East OH chr 1981-; *ai:* Bus Prof of Amer Adv; OVA, AVA 1985-; OBTA, NEA 1981-; *office:* Muskingum Perry Career Ctr 400 Richards Rd ille OH 43701

AN, JAMES M., English Teacher; *b:* California, PA; *m:* Jennifer Bethany, Curtis, Brett; *ed:* California Univ of PA (BSEd) Eng 1968, Eng 1974; 15 Addl Hrs; *cr:* Baldwin HS Eng Tchr 28 Yrs; *ai:* Eng hm 4 Yrs; Coached JV Bsbl 5 Yrs; Announcer for Ftbl Games 12 sktbl Games 6 Yrs; BNEA, PSEA, NEA 1968-; *home:* 4571 Echo r Pittsburgh PA 15236

AN, JAMES ROBERT, HS Social Studies Teacher; *b:* Columbus, Debbie; *c:* Justin, Jeremy; *ed:* OH St Univ (BS) Soc Stud Ed 1982; d Credits Racial Equality, Testing & Assessment; *cr:* New Albany -8th Grd Soc Stud Tchr 1984-88; Fremont Jr HS 7-9th Grd Soc Stud 989-91; New Albany HS 9-12 Grd Soc Stud Tchr 1991-; *ai:* Head 3sktbl Coach; Soph Class Adv; Chrstn Discipleship Mentor; NEA, 983-; St Coaches Assn 1984-; Dist 10 Coaches Assn 1984-; *office:* New HS 6425 New Albany-Condit Rd New Albany OH 43054

AN, JAMES T., English Teacher; *b:* Summit Hill, PA; *m:* Catherine cha; *ed:* West Chester Univ (BS) Soc Stud & Eng 1961; Bloomsburg MS) Eng 1974; Lehigh Univ 3 Credit Hrs; Wilkes Univ 12 Credit utztown Univ 3 Credit Hrs; Gratz Coll 12 Credit Hrs; Lehigh Cty Coll 6 Credit Hrs; *cr:* Montgomery Area Schl Dist Eng Tchr 0; Jim Thorpe Area Schl Dist Eng Tchr 1970-; *ai:* PSEA 1964-, Coordinated Bargaining Cncl; NEA 1964-; Jim Thorpe Ed Assn Pres, VP, Chief Negotiator; Allentown Art Museum 1980-; bury Shaker Vlg 1985-; Lehigh Cty Historical Soc 1988-; Natl Rifle 993-, Firearms Instr.

AN, JOHN DONALD, Photography Teacher; *b:* Providence, RI; eryl Smith; *c:* Shayna, Adam; *ed:* RI Coll (BS) Art Ed 1972; AZ St MA) Art Ed 1977; +9 Post Grad Credits in Ed; *cr:* Isaac Schl Dist Grd Art Tchr 1972-79; Bridgewater-Raynham HS 9th-12th Grd Art 980-91; Lincoln Schl 10th-12th Grd Photography, MS Studio Art 992-; *ai:* Admissions & Spiritual Life Comms; Eng Tutor; *office:* n Schl 301 Butler Ave Providence RI 02906

GAN, JOSEPHINE ANNE (DILL), English Teacher & Dept Chair; timore, MD; *m:* Vernon J.; *c:* Michelle, John; *ed:* Towson St Univ Mass Commnctn 1971; The Coll of Notre Dame Working on (MA) Stud Candidate; *cr:* St Clares Schl Lang Arts & Soc Stud Tchr 34; Our Lady of Fatima Schl Lang Arts & Soc Stud Tchr 1984-85; ishop Curley HS Amer & British Lit Tchr & Eng Dept Chair 1985-; k Group Dir; Campus Ministry; Visions Lit Magazine; 10 Yrs Dir of ackfriars Theatre; NEEA 1985-; NCTE 1985-; Theatre Threse 1983-, as; Archbishops Awd for Tchng Excl 1995; Delta Mu Delta Inductee *office:* Archbishop Curley HS 3701 Sinclair Ln Baltimore MD

GAN, KATHLEEN ANN (BERENATO), Home Economics er; *b:* Hammonton, NJ; *m:* Leonard Warner; *c:* Kimberly Ann; *ed:* of Akron (BA) Home Ec 1966; Glassboro St Coll Voc Co-Op Cert *cr:* Overbrook Sr HS Home Ec Tchr 1966-; *ai:* Voc Dept Chprsn; en Cty Coll Instrl Comm; NEA, NJEA, LCCRD #1 Tchr Assn 1966-; 988-; Amer Home Ec Assn 1966-; Wenonah Fire Co Aux 1981-, Pres, eas, Firt Pres, Charter Mem; Wenonah Schl Bd 1984-, Instr Chprsn; vernors Tchrs Awd 1988; *office:* Overbrook Regional Sr HS 1200 rville Rd Pine Hill NJ 08021*

GAN, LARRY L., Bus Ed & Cmptr Sci Instructor; *b:* Point Pleasant, *m:* Sherrie Adkins; *c:* Brian Michael, Bradley Scott; *ed:* Marshall BA) Bus Ed 1969; Post Grad Stud OH Univ; *cr:* Wanama HS Bus Ed 969-72; St Joseph Cntrl HS Bus Ed Instr 1972-76; South Point HS d Instr 1976-78; Chesapeake HS Bus Ed Instr 1979-; *ai:* Asst Ftbl ; Beta Club Co-Spon; Jr Spon; NEA, OEA, SEDEA 1992-; CLTA , Bldg Rep; Chesapeake Little League 1986-93, VP, Treas; JTPA anding Instr; *home:* 146 Township Road 1301 Chesapeake OH 45619*

GAN, LAURA ANSEL, Retired 4th Grade Teacher; *b:* Leckrone, PA; ne Overstreet; *ed:* CA St Coll (BS) Elem 1965; (MEd) Elem 1969; hn F. Kennedy Elem Schl 4th Grd Tchr 1965-93; *ai:* PSEA, NEA ; *home:* 281 Dixon Blvd Uniontown PA 15401

GAN, LAURA BAUM, High School English Teacher; *b:* Canton, *m:* Jefferey S.; *ed:* Dayton Univ (MS) Ed, Schl Cnslr 1995; *cr:* ee Yth Camp Long-term Sub 1990-91; OH Hi-Point JVS Eng, Comm 1991-94; Covington HS Eng Tchr 1994-; *ai:* Vlybl Coach; Sr Class Adv; Staff Dev Comm; Drama Club Asst; NEA, OEA 1994-; NCTE 1992-; March of Dimes Mother 1995-; HS Catechism Class Instr Church; *home:* 313 Lafayette Ave Urbana OH 43078*

MORGAN, LINDA MOORE, Health & Physical Ed Tchr; *b:* Salem, NJ; *m:* Philip M.; *c:* Abby, Ali; *ed:* West Chester St (BS) Hlth & PE 1973; Post Grad Stud in Hlth Related Fields Especially Drug & Alcohol Prevention; *cr:* Gen Wayne Mid Tchr 1973-; *ai:* Creator of Take a Stand & Positive ID; Drug Free & Stu Mentoring Clubs; Stu Assistance Team; Raising Drug Free Kids Facilitator Parent Ed; Great Vly HS Bsktbl Coach; PTO Task Force at Great Vly; NEA 1980-; Womens Ath Booster Club 1992-, Treas; Paoli Meth Church 1993-; *office:* General Wayne MS 20 Devon Rd Malvern PA 19355

MORGAN, LYDIA MARGARET, Kindergarten Teacher; *b:* Catlettsburg, KY; *m:* Stephen D.; *c:* Stephen; *ed:* Morehead St (BA) Elem Ed 1963; Addl 22 Semester Hrs Educl Stud; *cr:* Ararat Elem Schl 1-6 Grd Tchr 1956-57; Ironville Elem Schl Tchr 1957-68; Andis Elem Schl Tchr 1974-92; Monitor Elem Schl Tchr 1992-; *ai:* NEA 1956-; KEA 1956-68; OEA 1974-; DBEA 1974-, Bldg Rep; Alpha Delta Kappa 1992-, Chaplain, Treas; Jennings Scholar 1991-92; *home:* PO Box 55 Rock Camp OH 45675

MORGAN, LYNNE PAUL, Spanish Teacher; *b:* Pittsburgh, PA; *m:* Graham Stephenson; *c:* Stephanie Morgan Havener, Kendall Morgan Manning, Laura Morgan Downie; *ed:* Framingham St (BA) Fr 1980; Cert Span, Eng, Fr; Working on Spanish Master RI Coll; *cr:* Penn Hills HS Span Tchr 1963-64; Robert Frost MS Span Tchr 1964; Memorial Elem Span Tchr 1977-79; Hopedale Jr-Sr HS Span Tchr 1979-; *ai:* Class of 1995 Adv; HTA 1977-, Sec 5 Yrs; NEA; MAFLA; OPA 1972-, Sec, Soc Dir; *office:* Hopedale Jr-Sr HS 25 Adin St Hopedale MA 01747

MORGAN, MARGARET REILLY, AP US History Teacher; *b:* Pittsburgh, PA; *m:* William F.; *c:* Margaret, Mary, Reilly, Honor; *ed:* Marymount Coll (BA) His & Politics 1965; Case Western Reserve (MA) 20th Century British His 1969; Attnd London Schl of Ec 1963-64, Univ of London 1965, The Sorbonne 1965 & Duke Univ 1992; *cr:* Beachwood HS Soc Stud Tchr 1966-69; Warren Area HS Advanced Placement US His Tchr & Adv of Gifted 1988-; Jamestown Comm Coll His Lecturer 1992-; *ai:* Speech & Debate Judge; Phi Alpha Theta 1968-; Warren Concert Soc, Bd Mem, Warren shakespeare Clb; The Coll Bd Amer His Advanced Placement Test Reader & Advanced Placement US His Instr; *office:* Warren Area HS 345 E 5th St Warren PA 16365*

MORGAN, MARILYN ANNE (HOUGHTON), English Teacher; *b:* Theresa, NY; *m:* James; *c:* William, Robert; *ed:* NY St Univ at Albany (BA) Eng 1963; Univ of NH (MST) Writing, Composition 1992; *cr:* North Colonie Jr HS Eng Tchr 1964-67; Upward Bound of Utica Coll Eng Tchr 1976-78; Chadwicks HS Eng Tchr 1979-81; New Hartford Central Schl Eng Tchr 1981-; *ai:* Jr High Shared Decision Making Team; AFT, NYSUT, NCTE, NYSEC 1964-; Article Pub; *office:* Perry Jr HS 9499 Weston Rd New Hartford NY 13413

MORGAN, MORRIS HERBERT,III, Assoc Prof of Chemical Engrng; *b:* Atlanta, GA; *m:* Carolyn Bradshaw; *c:* Eric, Kristin; *ed:* Vanderbilt Univ (BS) Chem Engrng 1969; Univ of Dayton (MS) Chem Engrng 1973; Rensselaer Polytechnic Inst (PHD) Chem Engrng 1978; *cr:* Gen Motors Dev Engr 1969-72; Monsanto Co System Safety Engr 1972-73; Gen Electric Co Staff Chem Engr 1973-82; Rensselaer Polytechnics Inst Chem Engrng Prof 1982-; *ai:* AICHE 1969-; Fine Particle Soc 1990; Sigma Xi 1993-; Amer Statistical Assn 1992-; Sigma Pi Phi 1984-; Author, Co-Author Over 50 Research Artcles; Holder of Four US, 1 European Patents; *office:* Rensselaer Polytechnic Inst 131 Ricketts Bldg Troy NY 12181

MORGAN, RHONDA, 9th & 12th Grade Science Tchr; *b:* St Vincent, West Indies; *ed:* Wiley Coll (BA) Bio 1979; Brooklyn Coll (MS) Sci Ed 1989; Attnd Hunter Coll; Post Grad Supervision & Admin Brooklyn Coll; *cr:* Catherine Mc Auley HS Sci Tchr 1981-84; FDR HS Sci Tchr 1984-86; Brooklyn Tech HS Sci Tchr 1988-; Coll of New Rochelle Adj Prof Bio 1993-; *ai:* Self Defense Club Adv; AFT, UFT 1984-; NBTA; A Cncl of United Negro Coll Fund 1990-; Outstdng Young Women of Amer 1988; Natl Deans List 1979; Phi Beta Kappa 1978; *office:* Brooklyn Technical HS 29 Fort Greene Pl Brooklyn NY 11217*

MORGAN, ROBERT D., HS Band Director; *b:* Hackensack, NJ; *m:* Michele Marie Chabay; *c:* Daniel, Matthew; *ed:* Univ of IA (BMEd) Music 1971; Paterson St Coll Music; *cr:* Clifton HS Music Tchr, Band Dir 24 Yrs; *ai:* Marching Band; Wind Ensemble; Jazz, Brass Band; Clarinet Choir; Flute Consortium; Sax Quintet; Symphony Band; Percussion Ens; Pit Orch; NEA; NJEA, CTA, CHSFO, MENC 1972-; NJMEA 1972-, All St Band Procedures Comm 1987-89, Region I Symphonic Band Conductor 1987; NJ Band Fed, Exec Bd 1977; BSA 1990-, Scout Master; First Luth of Clifton, Church Cncl 1996; Man of Yr Clifton Veterans Alliance 1991; Man of Yr clifton Optimists 1996; Citizen of Merit Clifton Mental Hlth; Clifton Tchr of Yr 1989; *office:* Clifton H S 333 Colfax Ave Clifton NJ 07013*

MORGAN, SHARON LYNN, Second Grade Teacher; *b:* Cumberland, MD; *m:* Harry Alvin; *c:* Matthew, Adam; *ed:* Frostburg St Coll (BS) Elem Ed 1980, (MED) Elem Admin, Supervision 1985; Mngmt Acad WV; Frameworks Facilitator Trng; TESA; *cr:* Hampshire Co Bd of Ed 1, 3, 6 Grd Tchr 1980-89, K-6 Grd Prin 1989-92; Allegany Co Bd of Ed Grd 2 Tchr 1992-; *ai:* PTA South PA; Tchr Asst Team Chprsn; Early Indentification Intervention Prgm Chprsn; Cty Soc Stud Curr Comm; NEA, MSTA, ACTA 1992-; Western MD Rdng Cncl, SOMIRAC 1995-; Wesley Chapel Meth Church 1990-, Dir of Ed, Yth Dir, Admin Bd; Frankfort MS 1992-, Sec; Local Schl Improvement Cncl Frankfort MS 1994-; Mentor Tchr WV; *office:* South Penn Elem Schl 500 E 2nd St Cumberland MD 21502*

MORGAN, SUSAN LORRAINE, Admin Director of Enrichment; *b:* Lock Haven, PA; *ed:* Edinboro St Coll (BS) Elem Ed 1972, (MED) Elem 1976; 9 Grad Credits in Gifted Ed Univ of Ct; *cr:* St Michael Schl 4-5 Grd Tchr 1972-74; St George Cath Schl 3 Grd Tchr 1974-76, 4 Grd Tchr 1976-87, Asst Prin, Gifted Coord Tchr 1987-93, Admin Dir of Enrichment, Gifted Tchr 1993-; *ai:* Coord for Accelerated Reader, 24 Challenge Math, PA Thinking Cap Quiz Bowl, Rainbows; Comm Mem Intnl Schl to Schl Experience; NCEA 1972-; Erie Diocesan Enrichment Core Team 1990-; *office:* St George Schl 1612 Bryant St Erie PA 16509

MORGAN-BELL, PEARL THOMAZENA, English Professor; *b:* Manchester, Jamaica; *m:* Easton Alexander; *c:* Harold, Easton, Ronald, Omar; *ed:* Univ of the West Indies (BA) Eng 1973; Adelphi Univ (MS) Spcl Ed 1980; Tchrs Coll Columbia U (EDM) Psychological Cnslng 1988, (EDM) Educl Admin 1994, (EDD) Educl Admin 1966; 100 Post Grad Hrs Rsrch; *cr:* Northeastern Conf of SDA Edctr, Cnslr & Tchr 1980-93; Med Adj Prof 1993-; CUNY at BMCC Adj Prof 1993-; Coll of New Rochelle Instr 1996-; *ai:* Womens Ministries Dept Coord & Adv; Cnslng Teens & Yth; Fam Life Comm Mem; NTE 1982-; ASCD 1988-; AACD 1989-; NABSE 1990-; Corona SDA Comm 1978-, Church Elder, Womans Ministries Dr, SS Tchr & Supt, AY Ldr; Civic Assoc of East Elmhurst 1988-; Northeastern Acad Outstdng Ldrshp Merit 1982; Natl Defense Inst Whos Who Among Amer Women Edctrs 1988; Whos Who Among Edctrs Awd of Distinction 1989; Intnl Biographies Inst 1990; Tchrs Coll Dissertation Grant & Flwshp 1992-94; Books: Fundamental English for Coll Stu & Natural Wholesome Foods; *office:* Borough Of Manhattan Comm Coll 199 Chambers St New York NY 10007*

MORGAN-FISHER, NAOMI R., Science Teacher; *b:* Monticello, NY; *m:* Michael Fisher; *ed:* Syracuse Univ (BS) Psych 1980; City Coll of NY (MS) Sci Ed 1990; *cr:* Sullivan Cty Probation Dept Probation Ofcr 1982-84; Acad of Environmental Sci Tchr 1984-85; Bridge Schl Grds 6-8th Soc Stud Tchr 1985-90; Woodlands MS 8th Grd Sci Tchr 1990-; *ai:* Jr HS Key Club Adv; Coach Modified Soccer; Shared Decision Making Team Mem 1991-95; Sci Fair Coord; AFT 1984-; STANYS 1986-; NY St Challenger, Natl Sci Schlsps; *office:* Woodlands MS 475 W Hartsdale Ave Hartsdale NY 10530*

MORGANROTH, PATRICIA A., Nursing Instructor; *b:* Bayonne, NJ; *m:* Joseph H.; *ed:* Villanova Univ (BSN) Nursing 1969; Univ of Cincinnati (MSN) Nursing 1985; Cert Diabetes Educator; Train the Trainer Cert; CPR Instr Amer Red Cross & Amer Heart Assn; *cr:* Bethesda Hospital Inc Diabetes Ctr Dir & Clinical Specialist 1985-90; Bethesda Hospital Inc Clinical Staff Dev Instr 1990-95; Cincinnati St Tech & Comm Coll Instr 1991-; Bethesda Hosp Inc Lithotrepsy Ctr Staff Nurse 1994-95; Cincinnati St Tech & Comm Coll NATP Prgm Coord 1995-; *ai:* Curr Comm; Fac Org; Safety Comm; Cincinnati St Stu Nurse Assn; Fac Adv; Green & White Club VP; Acad Ceremonies Comm; Summer Schl Task Force; Diabetes Educators of Cincinnati 1985-, Pres & Bd of Dir; Amer Assn of Diabetes Educator, Amer Diabetes Assn 1985-; Amer Red Cross 1992-; Natl League for Nursing 1994-; Natl Stu Nurse Assn 1994-, Adv; Amer Red Cross 1992-, Pat on Back Awd; Bethesda Hospital Speakers Bureau 1985-92; Little Flower schl 1988-, Guest Speaker; PTA, Class Mom; Church Festival Vol; Amer Diabetes Assn Natl Review Panel For Prgms Seeking Recognition for Excellence in Ed 1989-; Contributor to Diabetes Ed is the Key Bethesda Hospital Inc; Sigma Theta Tau Natl Honor Soc of Nursing Grad Stu Research Awd; *office:* Cincinnati St Tech & Comm Coll 3520 Central Pky Cincinnati OH 45223

MORGANS, ELLEN CLEAVES, 7th Grade Teacher; *b:* Van Buren, ME; *m:* John; *c:* Kimberly, Eric, Amanda; *ed:* Univ of ME at Presque Isle (BS) Elem Ed 1974; Univ of ME at Orono (MS) Elem Ed 1980; Post Grad Stud Wesley Theological Seminary; *cr:* Connor Schl Classroom Tchr 1974-80; New Sweden Schl Classroom Tchr 1980-; *ai:* Cooperating Tchr for Stu Tchr; Cert of Tchrs Comm Chair; Dist Tchr Ldr; MEA, NEA 1974-; Northern Educl Partnership Grant; *office:* New Sweden Schl RR 161 New Sweden ME 04762

MORHACK, ANDY, English & Speech Teacher; *b:* Natrona Heights, PA; *ed:* IN univ of PA (BS) Eng & Commnctn 1971; *cr:* Vly HS Eng & Speech Tchr 1971-; *ai:* NKAEA; PSEA; NEA; Natrona Heights Little League 1972-, Bd Mem; St Vincent Coll Tchr Recognition Awd; *office:* Valley HS 703 Stevenson Blvd New Kensington PA 15068

MORIARTY, JEFFREY M., English & Drama Teacher; *b:* Waterbury, CT; *m:* Pamela; *c:* Leah, Connor; *ed:* Eastern CT St Coll (BA) Eng 1982; Southern CT St Univ (MS) Instrl Media & Tech 1991; Lib Information Stud Pgm Courses Include Storytelling; *cr:* West Haven Comm House Alternative Ed & Life Skills Instr 1986-89; Shelton HS Eng, Acting, Playwriting & Theatre Tchr 1983-; *ai:* Theatre Wkshp & SEED Club Advs; Dir of Plays; NEA 1983-; CEA 1983-; SEA 1983-; Diversity in Ed Comm 1995-; Branford Democratic Town Comm 1996-; A World of Difference Southern CT Conf; *office:* Shelton HS 120 Meadow St Shelton CT 06484*

MORIARTY, KEVIN JOHN, Social Studies Teacher; *b:* Springfield, MA; *m:* Karen Kern; *c:* Karolyn, Kevin; *ed:* Amer Intnl Coll (BA) Ec 1965, (MA) Ed 1969, (CAGS) Ed Admin 1980; *cr:* Holyoke HS Tchr 1966-; *ai:* Model United Nations; NEA 1966-; MTA 1966-; Wilbraham Selectman 1988-, Chm, Vice Chm of Bd; *office:* Holyoke HS 500 Beech St Holyoke MA 01040

MORIARTY, MILDRED DE LUGO, Middle School Math Teacher; *b:* New York City, NY; *m:* Charles David; *c:* Erin Helene, Kerry Therese; *ed:* St Joseph Coll (BA) Math 1973; Coll of New Rochele (MSEd) GATE Ed 1991; Confratute Univ of CT 1990; *cr:* St Raphael Schl MS Math Tchr 1977-83; Our Lady of Perpetual Help Schl MS Math Tchr 1984-; *ai:* Fed of Cath Tchrs 1984-; An Inspirational Tchr Awd Fordham Prep Schl 1995; *home:* 255 N Ridge St Rye Brook NY 10573*

MORIARTY, THOMAS F., Professor of History; *b:* Holyoske, MA; *m:* Bonnie R. Mc Lean; *c:* Thomas, Catherine; *ed:* Holy Cross Coll (BA) His 1956; Univ of Notre Dame (MA) Amer His 1958, (PHD) European His 1964; *cr:* Fordham Univ Instr, Asst Prof 1961-68; Talladega College Visiting Asst Prof 1968-69; Elms Coll Assoc Prof, Prof 1969-; *ai:* AAUP 1990-; Amer Cath Historical Soc 1970-; Amer Conperence for Irish Stud 1980-; Chicopee Historical Soc, Ancient Order of Hibermiahs 1980-; Articles, Reviews; *office:* Elms Coll 291 Springfield St Chicopee MA 01013

MORICH, VINCENT A., Social Studies Teacher; *b:* California, PA; *m:* Shannon Mc Bryar; *ed:* CA St Univ (BS) Soc Stud 1970; 40 Addl Credit Hrs Spec, Drivers Ed Cert; *cr:* South Pemiscot HS Tchr, Ftbl Coach 1 Yr; Laurel Highlands HS Soc Stud Tchr, Coach 25 Yrs; *ai:* PCSS 1990-; PSEA, NEA 1970-; YMCA 1985-; *office:* Laurel Highlands Sr HS 300 Bailey Ave Uniontown PA 15401

MORICO, LAWRENCE FRANCIS, Guidance Counselor; *b:* New Haven, CT; *m:* Leatrice Mary; *c:* Paul, David, Kenneth; *ed:* Univ of CT (BA) His 1958; Univ of Bridgeport (MS) Scndry Ed 1961; Southern CT St Univ (MS) Psych, Guid 1970; 6th Yr Schl Admin 1974; Attnd Univ of CT Schl of Law; *cr:* Notre Dame HS Soc Stud Tchr 1959-61; Ridgefield HS Soc Stud Tchr 1961-64; North Branford HS Soc Stud Tchr 1964-66; Wilbur Cross HS Guid Cnslr 1966-; *ai:* AFT, New Haven Fed of Tchrs 1970-; Phi Alpha Theta; Pi Sigma Alpha; Phi Delta Kappa; *home:* 76 Hall St New Haven CT 06512*

MORIN, HOLLY JEAN, Director & Teacher; *b:* Marlboro, MA; *ed:* Univ of RI (BS) Early Chldhd 1984; *cr:* NM Regnl HS Majorette Coach 1984-; Hollys Bunch Studio Schl Dir, Tchr 1984-; *ai:* NBA MA St Twirling Championships Dir; Natl Baton Twirling Assn 1984-, Tchr, Judge; North Middlesex Band Boosters Assn 1984-; North Middlesex Majorettes Champions 1995; MA St HS Team Champions 1995; *home:* 10 Pleasant Ct Marlborough MA 01752

MORIN, LORENE ANN (LAPLANTE), English Teacher; *b:* Ware, MA; *m:* Richard P.; *c:* Melissa A., Robert R.; *ed:* Westfield St Coll (BA) Eng 1966, (MA) Ed, Guidance 1975; Univ of MA 15 Credit Hrs; Mt Holyoke Coll 4 Credit Hrs; *cr:* West Rocks Jr HS Eng Tchr 1966-67; Kosciuzko Jr HS Eng Tchr 1967-69; Holyoke HS Eng Tchr 1972-; *ai:* Chm Stu Svcs Evaluation Comm 1985; Class Adv 1972-83, 1991-; Schl Cncl; Hall of Fame Comm; Archives Founder; Amhurst Coll Asst Prgm Coord; Schl Cncl 1993- Pres; Schl Tech Comm; NEA, MTA 1972-; NCTE 1987-; NCTE 1987-; Horace Mann Grant 2 Yrs; Active Participant Mentor Prgm Holyoke Prof Dev Schl; Hall of Fame Apprec Awd 1995; *office:* Holyoke HS 500 Beech St Holyoke MA 01040*

MORISIE, ROSALIE VALENTI, Mathematics Teacher; *b:* Long Island, NY; *m:* Robert; *c:* Alyssa, Gregg; *ed:* Hofstra Univ (BS) Math 1968; SUNY at Stony Brook (MA) Math Ed 1972; 60 Post Grad Credit Hrs; *cr:* Alva T Stanforth Jr HS Math Tchr 1968-69; North Babylon HS Math Tchr 1969-; *ai:* Math Team Coach; Comp Club Adv; Stu-Tutor Pgm & SAT Prep Coord; Renaissance Comm Mem; North Babylon Tchr Org 1969-, Election Rep; AFT 1969-; NYSUT 1969-; St Thomas More RC Church 1979-, Comm Chprsn; Hauppauge Yth Org 1984-, Asst Treas; Hauppauge Womens Sftbl Team 1990-, Outfielder; Presidential Acad Fitness, News 12 Long Island & NYS Tchr of Yr Awd Nom; *office:* North Babylon HS 1 Phelps Ln North Babylon NY 11703*

MORITZ, KIMBERLY MORMUR, Spanish & Business Teacher; *b:* Pittsburgh, PA; *m:* Derek; *c:* Bryna Ashley, Tallon Thomas; *ed:* Gannon Univ (BA) Comm 1985; SUNY at Fredonia (MS) Ed 1994; *cr:* CVS PHarmacy Store Mgr 1985-88; Tri Cty Meml Hosp Admin Asst 1988-89; St Joseph Schl 8th Grd Tchr 1989-90; Pine Vly Cntrl Span, Bus Tchr 1990-; *ai:* Yrbk, Class Adv; NYSAFLT 1991-; *office:* Pine Vly Cntrl Schl 7827 Rt 83 South Dayton NY 14138*

MORITZ, MICHAEL NICKOLAS, History Teacher; *b:* Kearny, NJ; *m:* Debbie Lorraine; *c:* Amanda Louraine; *ed:* William Paterson Coll of NJ (MA) Soc Sci 1977; WPC of Wayne (MA) Urban Ed 1984; New Paltz Univ (CAS) Admin 1992; US Army Food Service Coorespendence Schl 94B20 & 94B30; PLDC 92 & BNCOC 94 Grad; PLDC 1992; BNCOC 1994; ANCOC 1995; 1st Wrnt Ofcr Co; *cr:* Bartender Weputs Newtorion Inn 1979-84; Eldred Cntrl Schl Tchr Soc Stud 1984-; *ai:* Asst X-Cntry Coach 1991 Class D Girls St Champions NYS; AFL, CIO, NYSUT 7 Yrs; PHI Alpha Theta 1975-, Pres, His Honor Soc; Phi Lamba Theta 1982-, Tchr Honor Soc; USAR Mess Hall Tobyhanna PA Army Military Depot, Sergeant; Amer Lgn Post 1363; USAR Food Svc Wrnt Ofcr 922A; 828th Qutr Co; New Paltz Univ Leadership & Excl Tchng Awd 1987, Sullivan Cty SADD Awd 1986; Started Coll Prgms Area HS; Started Distributive Ed Prgm 2 HS 1991; *office:* Eldred Central Schl Rt 55 Eldred NY 12732

MORMAN, MARIE S., Reading Specialist; *b:* East Stroudsburg, PA; *m:* William B.; *c:* Lester A.; *ed:* East Stroudsburg Univ (BS) Elem 1959, (MED) Elem 1962; Rdng Specialist 1974; *cr:* Nazareth Area Schl Dist 6th Grd Tchr 1959-72, Rdng Specialist 1973-; *ai:* PTA Book Report Project; Books for Babies; Rdng Dept Chair; Breakfast with Dad; NEA, PSEA, NAEA 1959-; CARE, IRA, KSRA 1986-; Nazareth Woman's Club 1965-, Sec, 1st & 2nd Pl Crafts; PTA 1959-, Sec, Life Mbrshp; *home:* 111 Hillendale Ave Nazareth PA 18064*

MORMILE, GAYLE L., French Teacher; *b:* Cleveland, OH; *ed:* Notre Dame Coll (BA) Fr, Eng 1970; John Carroll Univ (MA) Ed 1975; 12 Hrs Translators Prgm Notre Dame Coll; 2 Hrs Lib Sci Kent St Univ; Amer Travel Agents Schl; *cr:* Willowick Jr HS Eng, Rdng, Fr Tchr 1970-84; Kennedy Jr HS Fr Tchr 1983-84; Eastlake North HS Fr Tchr 1984-; *ai:* Fr Club Adv; NHS Advy, Sunshine, Acad Decathalon Comms; 9th Grd Stu Mentoring Prgm; OEA, NEA, WETA, NEOEA 1970-; *office:* Eastlake North HS 34041 Stevens Blvd Eastlake OH 44095

MORO, STEPHEN M., High School English Teacher; *b:* Yonkers, NY; *m:* Jean; *c:* Jonathan, Peter, Alexander; *ed:* Lehman Coll (BA) Eng 1972; Manhattan Coll (MA) Rdng 1976; *cr:* Mark Twain MS Yonkers 8th Grd Lang Arts Tchr 1972-78; Camden-Rockport HS 9th-12th Grd Eng Tchr 1978-, Eng Dept Head 1984-94; Univ of ME System Rdng & Writing Lector 1986-; *ai:* Commencement Act Dir 1986-; William Blake Soc Coord 1994-; NEA 1978-; AFT 1986-; NCTE; Rockport Zoning 1980-88, Bd of Appeals Chm; Freelance Copy Ed; NCTE Article Pub; *office:* Camden - Rockport HS 34 Knowlton St Camden ME 04843

MORONY, ROSEMARIE E., Eng Chprsn & AP Hnrs Instr; *b:* Brooklyn, NY; *m:* Ronald J.; *c:* Angela Ann Purdie, John G.; *ed:* St Josephs Coll (BA) Eng, Scndry Ed 1963; Bowie St Univ (MED) Supervision, Admin 1979; 12 Credits Bowie St Univ; 6 Credits Bemidji St Univ; 6 Credits Coll of Notre Dame; 6 Credits Loyola Univ; *cr:* Eastern Dist HS Eng Fac 1962-64; St Marys HS Eng Fac 1979-; *ai:* Sr Yr, Encounter Club, Choral Group, Poets Corner Moderator; Kappa Delta 1979-, Charter Mem Bowie St Univ; Poetry Pub; Williams Coll Outstdng Tchr Competitor; *office:* St Mary's HS Duke of Gloucester Annapolis MD 21401*

MOROSKI, ENCIE MOSSFORD, English Teacher; *b:* Ashtabula, OH; *m:* Joseph; *ed:* Kent St Univ (BA) Eng 1971; Ednboro Univ of PA (ME) Rdng 1991; *cr:* Harbor HS Eng Tchr 1971-; *ai:* NHS Adv; Newspaper Adv; NEA 1971-; Delta Kappa Gamma 1987-, Yrbk Ed 1990-; Conneaut Comm Ctr 1982-, Pres Bd 1984-85; Ashtabula YMCA 1987-, Sec Bd 1988; Outstanding Educator by Edinboro Univ 1985; Outstanding Grad Stu in Rdng by Edinboro Univ 1991; *office:* Harbor H S 221 Lake Ave Ashtabula OH 44004

MOROSKY, FREDERICK HARRY, Science Teacher; *b:* Erie, PA; *m:* Ruby Lee Hill; *ed:* Edinboro Univ (BA) Bio, Earth Sci 1970; Gannon Univ (MED) Environmental Sci; 30 Post Grad Credits; Towsend St 6 Credit Hrs; *cr:* Duncalx Jr HS Gen Sci Tchr 1973-75; East HS Bio Tchr 1976-79; Wilson Jr HS Gen Sci Tchr 1980-82; Acad HS Earth Sci, Bio Tchr 1983-89; Cntrl HS Earth Space, Bio, Chem Applied Tchr 1990-; *ai:* EEA, NEA, PSEA 1975-; *office:* Cntrl HS 3325 Cherry St Erie PA 16508

MOROTTI, JOSEPH, 7th Grade Social Studies Tchr; *b:* Little Falls, NY; *ed:* SUNY at Oswego (BS) Elem Ed & Rdng 1987; SUNY at Oneonta (MS) His 1992; Attnd SUNY at Albany & Cortland for Educl Admin; *cr:* Little Falls Schl Dist 7th Grd Soc Stud Tchr 1987-, Admin Intern 1994-95; *ai:* Modified Bsbl & Bsktbl Coach 1987- & Var Cross Cntry Coach 1994-95; AFT 1987-; *home:* RR 2 Box 237 Mohawk NY 13407*

MORRILL, ANN CASSIDY, First Grade Teacher; *b:* Providence, RI; *m:* Kenneth W.; *c:* Ann, Daniel, Jeanne, Kenneth, Kathleen Bailey, Rebecca Holter, Thomas Riley; *ed:* RI Coll (BED) Elem Ed 1956, (MED) Ed, Rdng 1971; Cooperating Tchr 15 Addl Hrs; *cr:* Providence Pub Schls 3rd Grd Tchr 1956-58, 1st Grd Tchr 1965-67; Orchard Place Nursery Schl 4 Yr Olds Tchr 1971-74; Seekonk Pub Schls 1st Grd Tchr 1974-; *ai:* SE MA Rdng Assn 1992-; NEA, SEA 1974-; RI Foster Parent 1958-68; Holy Name Church 1934-, Confirmation Tchr; St Xavier Acad Alumnae Assoc 1962-, Sec, VP, Pres; St Xavier Acad Bd of Dir 1983-; Laurel Park Improvement Assn 1963-, Sec, Prop Chprsn, Del KRC; Kickemuit River Cncl 1973-, Sec 17 Yrs, 2nd VP, Vol; Kickemuit River Project, Dir; *office:* George Martin Elem Schl 445 Cole St Seekonk MA 02771

MORRILL, JAMES MARTIN, Bio & Environmental Sci Tchr; *b:* Paterson, NJ; *m:* Harriet Hatcher; *c:* James, Molly; *ed:* Hamilton Coll (BA) Bio 1964; Rutgers Univ (MS) Physiology & Bio Chem 1968; Wesleyan Univ CAS 1978; Bard Univ Candidate for MS Environmental Sci; *cr:* Liceo Calatrava Venezuela Peace Corps Vol 1964-66; Rutgers Prep Schl Bio & Chem Tchr 1968-72; The Hotchkiss Schl Bio & Environmental Sci Tchr 1972-, Dept Chair 1978-88; *ai:* Sci Magazine & SEA Adv; Soccer Club Head; Save the Woods Environmental Comm; CVISSTA 1972-, Pres; NABT 1978-, St Chprsn; NSTA 1978-; OBTA 1992-; Coll Bd Exam Reader & Table Ldr 1981-95, AP Bio, AP Recognition Awd 1992; Coll Bd Consultant Leading Wkshps; Lake Wanonscopomies Assn 1985-, Pres; Pres Awd Winner St Awd 1989; Hotchkiss Summer Grants Environmental Stud 1991-95; Hotchkiss Acad Chair 1993-; Coll Bd NE Region Recognition Awd; Articles Pub; *office:* Hotchkiss Schl PO Box 800 Lakeville CT 06039*

MORRIS, ANDREW XAVIER, 7th Grd Soc Studies Teacher; *b:* Washington, DC; *m:* Linda Hinckley; *c:* James, Sara; *ed:* St Josephs Coll (BS) Elem Ed 1979; Univ of Southern ME (MS) New England Stud 1995-; *cr:* Rath Schl Dist 6th Grd Tchr 1981-86; SAD #75 7th Grd Tchr 1986-; *ai:* Grd 7 Team Ldr, Boys Bsktbl Coach; NEA, MTA 1981-; *office:* Mt Ararat MS 32 Spring St Brunswick ME 04011

MORRIS, ARLENE KOLESARICH, Fifth Grade Teacher; *b:* Perth Amboy, NJ; *m:* Donald; *ed:* Trenton St Coll (BA) Elem Ed 1966; *cr:* Port Reading Elem Schl Sixth Grd Tchr 1966-76, Fifth Grd Tchr 1976-; *ai:* Stu Cncl Adv 1967-77, 1989-; Field Day Coord 1989-; Math Olympics Co-Adv 1995-; NEA, NJEA 1966-; NCTM, AMTNJ 1990-; Governor's Grant Awd Tchr of Yr 1990-91; Woodbridge Twp Ed Fnd Grant Co-Recipient for Mobile Math Lab Project 1994.

MORRIS, CLAIRE PALCHANIS, Art Teacher; *b:* Kingston, PA; *c:* John, Gail, Mark; *ed:* Wilkles Univ (BFA) Art Ed 1972; Univ of Guanaiuato Mexico (MFA) Fine Art 1976; 28 Post Grad Credits in Fine Art & Ed at Kutztown Univ; *cr:* Inst Allende Mexico Asst Instr 1973; Wilkes Univ PA Guest Instr 1980; SoftShell Freelance Art Owner 1985-; Bishop O'Reilly HS Art Tchr 1989-90; Dallas Westmoreland Elem Art Tchr 1990-93; Dallas HS Art Tchr 1993-; *ai:* Art Club Adv; Grad Requirements Comm; NEA, PSEA 1990-; PACE 1991-; NAEA 1990-; Nesbitt Hospital Auxilliary 1974-; Copywrites to Art Work Designed & Produced; Limited Edition of Painting Designed for & Printed by Keystone Pretzel Co; *office:* Dallas Sr HS PO Box 2000 Dallas PA 18612

MORRIS, DEBORAH CABINESS, Assistant Professor of Nursing; *b:* Brooklyn, NY; *m:* Reginald B.; *c:* Cameron, Kimberly, Kanin, Cory; *ed:* Bronx Comm Coll (AAS) Nursing 1971; City Coll (BSN) Nursing 1973; NY Univ (MA) Nursing 1978; 3 Credits on Doctoral Level; *cr:* Bronx Comm Coll Adjunct Instr 1979-86; Lehman Coll Sub Lecturer 1981-83; Bronx Comm Coll Full-Time Lecturer 1986-91, Asst Prof Nursing 1991-, Adjunct Asst Prof 1993-; *ai:* Chprsn St Bd Review Comm for Stdnts; Mem of Fast-Track Prgm Comm for LPN to RN; Course Coord Fundamentals of Nursing; Contractual Nurse for Home Care Agency in Maternal Child Hlth; Ed-in-Chief for City Coll Alumni Nursing Newsletter; Teach Wkshps for Pub Svc Employees; NY St Occupational Ed Assn 1994-; NY City Chapter of Critical Care Nurses 1976-; Amer Assn of Critical Care Nurses 1976-; Amer Nurses Assn 1971-, Tri-Level Membership; Sigma Theta Tau Grad Nursing Honor Soc Upsilon Chapter; People Based Svcs Awd; Author of Calculate With Confidence; Grad Nursing Ed Grant 1977; *office:* Bronx Comm Coll W 181 St & University Ave Bronx NY 10453

MORRIS, DELLA LYN, 7th Grade Life Science Teacher; *b:* Cincinnati, OH; *ed:* Valley City St Coll (BSEd) Bio 1986; *cr:* Fargo Pub Schls Sub Tchr 1987; Kindred Pub Schls Span & Life Sci Tchr 1987-89; Leonard Pub Schls Span Tchr 1988-89; West Clermont Schls Sub Tchr 1989-90; Milford Exempted Village Schls Life Sci & Span Tchr 1990-; *ai:* Site Supvr; Yrbk Photographer; Curr Dev Comm; NJHS Adv; Stud Cncl Adv, Dept Chm; *office:* Milford Jr HS 5735 Pleasant Hill Rd Milford OH 45150

MORRIS, ELENE S., Third Grade Teacher; *b:* Syracuse, NY; *c:* Gary, Alan, Daniel; *ed:* Syracuse Univ (BSA) Elem Ed 1957; Nazareth Coll Elem Ed Grad Schl; *cr:* Chestnut Hill Elem 4th Grd Tchr 1 Yr; Council Rock Schl 1st Grd Tchr 1 Yr; Brighton Schls 2nd-5th Grd Rdgn & Math Tchr 13 Yrs; Fr Rd Schl 3rd Grd Tchr 1987-; *ai:* Parent-Tchr-Stu Assn, Stu Crisis Team & Stu Asst Team Rep; 3rd Grd Team Ldr 3 Yrs; NEA; Brighton Tchrs Union; Wood Creek Homeowners Assn 11 Yrs; Temple Brith Kodesh Sisterhood; Hadassah; *home:* 141 Wood Creek Dr Pittsford NY 14534

MORRIS, ELIZABETH CAROL, English & Reading Teacher; *b:* Waterbury, CT; *ed:* Univ of Bridgeport (MS) Ed 1992; *cr:* Bassick HS Eng Tchr 1994-; *ai:* NEA, CEA 1994-; *office:* Bassick HS Clinton Ave Bridgeport CT 06601

MORRIS, GEORGE JOSEPH, ESL Teacher; *b:* New York City, NY; *ed:* Iona Coll (BA) Span, Ed 1970, (MSEd) Span, Ed 1974; 75 Addl Hrs Bilingual Ed, Cmptr Applications, Latin, Arabic; *cr:* Yonkers Pub Schls ESL, Foreign Lang Tchr 1970-; Coll of New Rochelle Educ Adjunct Instr 1988-; *ai:* Ed 2000 Steering Comm; NY St Tchrs of Eng to Speakers of Other Langs 1976-, First VP; Amer Classical League 1987-; New Rochelle Schl of Rel 1966-, Bd of Dirs, Vice Chm; New Rochelle Pub Lib Fnd 1994-; Hispanic Prof Assn 1991-; Natl Endowment for Hum Stud of Arabic Grant 1994-; *office:* Charles E Gorton HS 100 Shonnard Pl Yonkers NY 10703

MORRIS, KAREN LEA, Spanish Teacher; *b:* Buffalo, NY; *m:* James P.; *c:* Jacob; *ed:* Buffalo St Coll (BS) Ed,Span 1989, (MS) Ed 1993; 6 Credit Hrs Span, His, Culture,Grammar 1988; *cr:* Royalton-Hartland Cntrl Schl Span Tchr 1989-94; *ai:* Span Club Adv; Prof Cncl 1991; Soc Skills Comm 1992; AFT NY Tchr 1989-; NYSAFLT, WYNYFLEC 1989-; Immersion Day; *office:* Royalton-Hartland Cntrl Schl 54 State St Middleport NY 14105

MORRIS, KARL A., English Teacher; *b:* Warren, OH; *m:* Jeannine Beagle; *c:* Christopher, Gregory, Timothy; *ed:* Kent St Univ (BS) Eng Ed 1961, (MED) Eng 1966; Summer Inst Rdng; *cr:* West Jr HS Eng Dept Chair, Newspaper, Yrbk Adv 1961-84; Warren Western Reserve HS Eng Tchr, Yrbk, Newspaper Adv 1984-90; W. G. Hardint HS Eng Tchr 1990-; *ai:* Past Yrbk 1964-90, Newspaper 1962-90 Adv; NEA, OEA 1961-, Life mem; Warren e. Assn 1961-, Newsletter Ed, Exec Com; NCTE 1961-; Second Chrstn Church 1961-79, Deacon, Elder, Congregation Chm, Choir; St Pauls Luth Church 1980-, Church Cncl, Choir, Sunday Schl Tchr; Exec Tchr 1972-82; Jennings Scholar 1972-73; Warren City Schls Tchr of Yr 1988-89; Whos Who in Amer Ed 1989-90; *home:* 197 Adelaide Ave SE Warren OH 44483

MORRIS, KATHLEEN ANTHONY, English Department Chairperson; *b:* Winchendon, MA; *m:* John L.; *ed:* Coll of Our Lady of Elms (BA) Eng 1967; Assumption Coll (MA) Eng 1970; 36 Credit Hrs; *cr:* Narragansett Regnl HS Tchr 1967-79, Eng Dept Chprsn 1979-; *ai:* NHS Adv; NEA, MTA, NCTE, MCTE 1967-, NDEA 1967-, Pres, Treas; *office:* Narragansett Regnl HS 464 Baldwinville Rd Baldwinville MA 01436

MORRIS, KATHLEEN FOY, Language Arts & Rdng Teacher; *b:* Flushing, NY; *m:* Donald Woodfiel; *c:* Gayle Eliz; *ed:* Frostburg St Coll (BS) Elem Ed 1977; Bowie St Coll (APC) Guidance, Counseling 1986; Sterling Inst Career Mngmt Series II; *cr:* Comsewogue Elem Schl Kndgtn Tchr 1977-78; Matthew Henson MS Lang Arts, Rdng Tchr 1978-; *ai:* 7-8 Team Ldr 1990-92; Ryken Eng Competition Adv; Book Store Mgr 1982; Test Coord; Sit MSPAP 1988; MD Univ Coll Awareness Prgm at Rish Stdnts; Spelling Bee Adv; Dept Chair 1992-; Site- Based Mgmt Tm 1993-; NCTE 1990-; ASCD 1993-; MD Assessment Grp 1994-; Sacred Heart R. C. Church 1989-; Dr. James Craik Elem Schl PTO 1995-; MD Writing Test Scoring Comm 1993-98; 2 Grants by SAC 1991, 1993; Charles Co Bd of Ed Regntn for Exemplary Tchng 1995; Nom for Outstanding Staff Develper 1996; *office:* Matthew Henson MS 3535 Livingston Rd Indian Head MD 20640

MORRIS, LARRY BERNARD, Economics Tchr & Athletic Dir; *b:* Palmerton, PA; *m:* Sheryl J.; *c:* Jennifer, James; *ed:* Lafayette Coll (BA) His, Govt 1967; East Stroudsburg St (MA) His, Govt 1970; 31 Addl Credits at Kutztown Univ, Penn St Univ, Lehigh Univ; *cr:* Parkland Jr HS Tchr, Coach 1967-70; Upper Perkiomen HS Tchr, Coach, Ath Dir 1970-; *ai:* Ftbl, Bsktbl, Tennis Coach; Investment Club Adv; NEA, PSEA 1967-; UPEA 1970-; Jaycees Young Edctr of Yr 1976; Coaches Awd 1980, 1986; *office:* Upper Perkiomen HS 2 Walt Rd Pennsburg PA 18073*

MORRIS, LARRY D., Animal & Diary Science Prof; *b:* Chillicothe, MO; *m:* Lucinda A. Moore; *ed:* Northwest MO St Univ (BS) Dairy Sci 1971, (MS) AS Ed 1975; Addl Credit Hrs: Univ of DE Animal Sci, IA St Univ Ag Ed; *cr:* IA Pub Schls Voc Ag Instr 1972-76; Northwest MO Univ Dairy Sci, Ag Ed Instr 1975; DE Valley Coll Asst Animal, Dairy Sci Prof 1976-77; *ai:* Intercollegiate Dairy Cattle Judging Team Coach; Prof Dev Comm Chair; Dairy Soc Adv; ADSA 1977-; PDK 1972-; NMC 1988-; NACTA 1982-; Outstanding Dairy Sci Tchr 1982; *office:* Delaware Valley Coll 700 E Butler Ave Doylestown PA 18901*

MORRIS, LIDA M., 5th Grade Teacher; *b:* Wilmington, DE; *m:* Hugh J. III; *c:* Kenneth, Karyn, Daniel; *ed:* Nyack Coll (BA) Ed 1962; Attnd Univ of DE Elem Ed 1965-66; *cr:* DE Power & Light Co Office Clerk 1957-58; Wilmington Chrstn Schl 5th Grd Tchr 1962-67; Pub Schl System Grd K-9 Sub Tchr 1962-83; New Castle Bapt Acad 3rd, 5th Grd Tchr 1983-; *ai:* Violin Tchr; Active Church, Orch; *office:* New Castle Baptist Ac[illegible] Basin Rd New Castle DE 19720

MORRIS, MARGARET A., Mathematics Teacher; *b:* Gowanda, Dale J.; *c:* Stephanie, Caitlin; *ed:* Fredonia St Coll (BS) Ed 197[illegible] Ed; 15 Credit Hrs Undergrad Univ of Copehagen; 10 Credit Hrs Po[illegible] *cr:* St Aloysius Schl Jr High Math & Lang Arts Tchr 1974-80; Cat[illegible] Cntrl Jr High Math Tchr 1980-84; Holland Cntrl HS Math Tchr 19[illegible] Soph Class Adv; 4-H Ldr; CCD Tchr; *office:* Holland Cntrl S[illegible] Canada St Holland NY 14080

MORRIS, MARGUERITE MARY, Social Studies Teacher; *b:* N[illegible] NY; *ed:* Fairleigh Dickinson Univ (BA) Soc Stud, Scndry E[illegible] Montclair St Univ (MS) Stu Personnel Svcs, Psych, Soc Stud; *cr:* C[illegible] Jr HS Tchr 1970-; Cresskill Sr HS Tchr 1970-; *ai:* 8th Grd Team[illegible] NEA, BCEA, CEA 1970-; *office:* Cresskill Jr Sr HS 1 Lincoln Dr C[illegible] NJ 07626*

MORRIS, MARTHA, Social Studies Teacher; *b:* Grand Rapids, Western IL Univ (BS) Corrections Ed 1977; Fairfield Univ Counseling Schl & Comm 1991; *cr:* Dept of Children & Fami[illegible] Juvenile Cnslr 1975-; K D Waldo Jr HS Tchr 1977-85; Norwalk H[illegible] 1985-; *ai:* Sftbl Coach; Corrections Ed Assn 1977-; NEA 197[illegible] 1985-; ACA 1990-; *office:* Norwalk HS 23 Calvin Murphy Dr Norw[illegible] 06851

MORRIS, MARTHA I., English Teacher; *b:* Brooklyn, Christopher; *c:* Jason, Daniel; *ed:* Wagner Coll (BA) Eng 1967; Univ (MAT) Eng 1977; Various Courses for Recertification Including Writing, Cmptrs, Womens Stud; *cr:* Fair Lawn HS E[illegible] 1967-69; Spaulding HS Eng Tchr 1969-; *ai:* Drama Coach; Pub R[illegible] Coord; Writer of Press Releases for Local Paper; NEA, VEA[illegible] Shepherd of Hills Luth Church 1978-, Sec of Church Cncl, Sun[illegible] Tchr; Cub Scouts, Den Mother; Tchr of Yr Spaulding HS 1987; Spaulding H S Ayers St Barre VT 05641

MORRIS, NEIL WARD, Social Studies Instructor; *b:* Brookville, Sally Alsbaugh; *c:* Heather M., Michael G.; *ed:* Edinboro Univ ([illegible] Stud 1972; Gannon Univ (MA) Soc Sci 1978; *cr:* Maplewood HS S[illegible] Instr 1974-; *ai:* Head Wrestling Coach 1990-95; NEA 1974-; PA H[illegible] Bicentennial Bill of Rights Scholar; *office:* Maplewood H S RD Mills PA 16327

MORRIS, ROBERT A., Bus Ed Instructor & Ath Dir; *b:* New Cas[illegible] *m:* Diann H.; *ed:* Westmar Coll (BS) Bus Ed 1968; Drake Univ Gra[illegible] Slippery Rock Univ Drivers Ed Cert; *cr:* Norwalk HS Bus Ed Tchr 1968-72; Laurens HS Bus Ed Tchr, Coach 1973-77; Private Bus Co 1977-84; West Middlesex HS Bus Ed Instr, Coach 1984-; *ai:* Hea[illegible] Track, Boys & Girls Cross Cntry Coach; FBLA Adv; West Middle[illegible] Assn, PSEA, NEA 1984-; Ducks Unlimited 1982-; PA Track Coach 1989-; PA Ath Dir Assn 1994-; *office:* West Middlesex HS 3591 Sh[illegible] West Middlesex PA 16159*

MORRIS, ROY ANTHONY,JR., Naval Sci Instr; *b:* Glendale, Daphne L. H.; *ed:* CA St Univ at Los Angeles (BS) Bus Admin 196[illegible] of CO (MA) Pub Admin 1975; CA Western Schl of Law 10 Addl [illegible] *cr:* US Navy Aviation Fighters 1965-84; USS Ranger Navigator 1[illegible] Chief of Naval Ed Training Inspector Gen 1986-89; MIami Univ Naval Sci 1989-91; McKinley HS Naval Sci Instr 1991-93; *ai:* V[illegible] Coach; Military Order of the World Wars 1994-; Retired Ofcr Assn[illegible] *office:* Friendly HS 10000 Allentown Rd Fort Washington MD 207[illegible]

MORRIS, SERENA J., Biology & Chemistry Teacher; *b:* New CT; *m:* Roy Chuck; *c:* Jennifer Pottle, Nicholas Pottle, Samuel; *e[illegible]* of ME (BS) Enviromental Sci 1978, (MS) Sci, Spec Ed 1996; Scn[illegible] Ed Tchng Cert 1984; *cr:* Soil, Water ConservationDist Tech 1[illegible] Shead HS Sci Tchr 1984-85; Hampden Acad Sci Tchr 1985-; *ai:* J[illegible] Adv; MS Cross Cntry Coach; NSTA, NABT, NEA, MEA 1985-; Justice Ctr 1990-, Mem; Appointed by Governor of ME to Serv[illegible] Panel for Children with Disabilities; *office:* Hampden Acad Mai[illegible] Hampden ME 04444

MORRIS, SIDNEY BROCK, Technology Coordinator; *b:* Bryn PA; *m:* Margaret Denham Knight; *c:* Lily, Elliot; *ed:* Univ of M[illegible] Elem Ed 1975; Harvard Univ (MED)) Ed 1992; *cr:* Sant Bani S[illegible] 1986-92; Oak Bluffs & W Tisbury Project Broker 1992-94; Oak Blu[illegible] Tech Coord 1994-; *ai:* MV Educl Collaborative; MV Tech Advy Chappaquiddick Comm Ctr 1986-, Founding Bd Mem; Marthas V[illegible] Pub Charter Schl 1994-, Founding Bd Mem; *home:* HC 61 B[illegible] Edgartown MA 02539

MORRIS, SONYA KRAININ, Fifth Grade Teacher; *b:* Brooklyn, Eugene; *c:* Beth Susan, Stephen James; *ed:* Lesley Coll (BS) Ed Credit Hrs Penn St; *cr:* Newton Pub Schls 6th Grd Tchr 1957; A[illegible] Pub Schls 4th Grd Tchr 1957-58; Columbiar Pub Schls 1st-6th Gr Supvr 1958; Dentsville Pub Schls 6th Grd Tchr 1959; Hopewell Are[illegible] 5th Grd Tchr; *ai:* NEA, Hopewell Ed Assn 1967-; *office:* Hopewel[illegible] 2121 Brodhead Rd Aliquippa PA 15001

MORRIS, TINA SOCHIA, Instrumental Music Teach[illegible] Baldwinsville, NY; *ed:* West Chester St Coll (BS) Music Ed 1982; MA (MMus) Conducting 1984; Conducting Master Class; *cr:* Joan[illegible] HS Instrumental Music 1984-86; Union-Endicott HS Instrumental 1987-89; Dundee Jr, Sr HS Instrumental Music 1989-; *ai:* Hon[illegible] Comm; Marching Band; Savona, Vestal Winterguard; Mentor Spectrum Drum, Bugle Corps; Horseheads Marching Band; AFT NYSUT, MENC NYSSMA 1984-; MYCGC 1987-, VP; NY Schl Assn Adjudicator, Fed of Contest Judges.

MORRIS, WALTER, Social Studies Teacher; *b:* Pendelton, C[illegible] Maryanne; *ed:* Nassau Comm Coll (AA) Gen Lbrl Arts 1972; St U[illegible] NY at Stony Brook (BA) Pol Sci, His 1974; Hofstra Univ (MA) Scn[illegible] His 1975; PD Rdng K-12 1986; PD Schl Dist Admin Dowling Col[illegible] *cr:* Wyandanch Meml HS 7-12 Grd Soc Stud Tchr 1985-; *ai:* Var Ft[illegible] Coach; Act Supvr; NEA 1985-; NCSS, NY, Suffolk Cty Cncl So[illegible] Tchrs, Natl, NY, Suffolk Cty Rdng Tchrs 1985-; *office:* Wyandanc[illegible] Dist Straight Path Wyandanch NY 11798

MORRIS, ZELENA MC FADDEN, English Teacher; *b:* Baltimore *m:* Steve Leonard; *c:* Charlie, Adam, Leslie, Rachel; *ed:* Coppin S[illegible] (BS) Eng 1974; Morgan St Coll 6 Hrs; Coppin St Coll 6 Hrs; Howar[illegible] 25 Hrs; *cr:* Patapsco MS Eng Tchr; Hammond HS Eng, GATE Tchr *ai:* Awds Comm 1992-; NEA, Howard Cty Ed Assn, MD St Tchr 1974-; Chamber of Commerce Awd for Ed 1989; Howard Com[illegible] Evening of Excl 1989; Sr Class Tchr Awd 1990-91, 1993-; Hammond HS 8800 Guilford Rd Columbia MD 21046*

MORRISON, BRIAN VINCENT, Mathematics Teacher; *b:* Bron[illegible] *m:* Deirdre Clare; *c:* Patrick, Diane, Matthew, Christopher; *ed:* ST Univ (BS) Mrktng & Minor Math 1977; CW Post (MS) Math Ed 19[illegible] ST Dominic HS Math Tchr 1978-81; Holy Cross HS Math Tchr 19[illegible] Smithtown East HS Math Tchr 1982-83; Island Trees HS Math Tchr *ai:* Asst Var Ftbl Coach; AFT 1992; Wrote Entire Math Curr for Seq[illegible] Regents Pgm in our Dist; *home:* 71 Amy Dr Sayville NY 11782*

MORRISON, DONNA HASKINSON, In-School Suspension Teac[illegible] Zanesville, OH; *m:* Michael Ray; *c:* Phillip Michael, Katlin Don[illegible] Univ of Akron (BA) Hlth Ed 1985, (BS) PE 1985; Post Undergr[illegible] Work Behavior Mngmt, Childrens Lit, Child Growth & De[illegible] Scandinavian Hlth Spas Nutrition Cnslr, Trainer 1985-86; Self-Em[illegible]

Tchr 1988-93; Morgan Local Schl System Sub Tchr 1993-94, 5-12th Schl Suspension Tchr 1994-; *ai:* Var Vlybl Coach; JV Sftbl Coach; s Adv; OHSAA 1994-, Dist Pres Elect; DAR 1995-; Pisgah United Church 1961-, HS Tchr; Soccer Assn 1994-, Bd of Dir; *office:* HS 800 Raider Dr Mc Connelsville OH 43756

ISON, DONNA LEE, Math Teacher; *b:* Sanford, ME; *ed:* Husson BS) Legal Secretarial Sci 1977; Univ of South ME (BS) Math 1984; agmt Course; *cr:* Deering HS Math Tchr 1984-; *ai:* NEA 1985-; Deering HS 370 Stevens Ave Portland ME 04103*

RISON, EDDIE RAY, Spanish Teacher; *b:* Greenville, SC; *ed:* SC l (BA) Span 1986; Trinity Coll 21 Semester Hrs; *ai:* Male ement Network Mentoring Pgm Spon 1993-95; AFT 1993; *office:* Madison MS 7300 Woodyard Rd Upper Marlboro MD 20772

RISON, JENNIFER E., English Teacher; *b:* Carlisle, PA; *m:* Aaron aron Andrew, Alexander Barrett; *ed:* Shippensburg Univ (BA) Eng, Arts 1977; Tchr Cert Eng & Comm Arts 1990; *cr:* Letterkenny Army Prgm Analyst 1979-80; PA Dept of Gen Svcs Mngmt Analyst 4; West Perry Sr HS Eng Tchr 1993-; *ai:* Peer Mediation Club Adv; upport Team; NEA 1994-; Landisburg Fire Co & Ambulance Assn Yth Sports Assns.

RISON, JENNIFER LYN DYDO, English Teacher; *b:* Sacramento, Heath E.; *ed:* Coll of William & Mary (BA) Eng, Math, Ed 1991; g Toward MA, ADv Spec Stu Univ of MD at Coll Park; *cr:* Ferguson Tchr 1991; Stephen Decatur MS Eng Tchr, Dept Chair 1991-94; ce HS Eng Tchr, Team Ldr 1994-; Sylvan Learning Ctr Eng, Math 1995-; *ai:* Site-Based Mngmt Team; Pom-Pon Squad Coach; SAT s; NCTE 1993-; MSTA, NEA 1991-; Proofread Coll Calculus ok; NEH Tchng Shakespeare Inst; Multicultural Shakespeare Video Project Grants; Tchr of Yr 1994; *office:* Westlake HS 3300 town Rd Waldorf MD 20603*

RISON, JUDITH PEITSCHER, Language Arts & Soc Stud Tchr; *b:* ster, NY; *m:* Lane; *c:* Peter, Jackie, Jennifer, Justine; *ed:* Univ of VT cndry Ed-His 1967, (MA) His 1975; 30 Credit Hrs St Michael's Coll, oaf Schl of Eng; *cr:* Sullivans Schl MS Tchr 1967-70; Mt Abraham s, Eng Tchr 1986; Hinesburg Elem Schl MS Tchr 1987-; *ai:* Schl Spelling Bees Adv; Soc Stud, Lang Arts Curr Comm; NEA 1984-; Wallace-Readers Digest Fellow at Bread Loaf Schl of Eng, burg Coll; *office:* Hinesburg Elem Schl RR 1 Box 1800 Hinesburg 461

RISON, KAREN JOHNSTON, 9th & 10th Grade Business Tchr; *b:* y, PA; *m:* C. Thomas; *c:* Christie, Julie; *ed:* New Castle Bus Coll xec Secretarial 1961; Ferris St coll (BS) Bus Ed, Eng 1973; Slippery niv, Wilkes Univ, Butler Cty Comm Coll, Midwestern Intermediate V, IN Univ Completed Several 3 Credit Courses in Cmptr Tech, Courses While Attending These Insts; *cr:* Butler Area Schl Dist Sub 980-86; Butler Co Comm Coll Adult, Continuing Ed Tchr 1983-93, me Bus Instr 1986-93; Butler Area Schl Dist Bus, Cmptr ations Tchr 1993-; *ai:* FBLA Club Adv; Crisis Mngmt Team; Prom, Comms; NEA, PSEA, BEA 1993-; YMCA, Bd Mem 3 Yr Term, p, Maintenance, Advertising; Butler Jr Women's Club 8 Yrs, Holly Chprsn; Welcome Wagon of Butler 8 Yrs, Sec, Served on Comms; nited Presbyn Church, Elder 3 Yr Term, Nature Comm Chprsn; Penn wim Club 1985-, Pres, Treas; Cert of Achvmt GFWC-PFWC Butler d of Women's Clubs; *home:* 110 Cresthaven Dr Butler PA 16001*

RISON, NANCY L., Second Grade Teacher; *b:* Old Town, ME; *m:* H.; *c:* Amy Morrison Fletcher, Eric R.; *ed:* Univ of ME (MS) Ed *cr:* Union 90 Milford Elem Tchr 1973-74, 1981-; *ai:* ME Tchrs Assn, 982-; Jaycees 1970-80; *office:* Doctor Lewis S Libby Schl 8 County lford ME 04461

RISON, RICHARD L., Mathematics Teacher; *b:* Westfield, NY; *m:* A. Szymczak; *c:* Bethany, Stephanie, Jennifer, Kristin; *ed:* SUNY at ia (BS) Math, Ed 1983, (MS) Math, Ed 1990; *cr:* Conway Jr HS Tchr 1983-84; New Symrna Sr HS Math Tchr 1984-85; Westfield Math Tchr 1985-; *ai:* Coach Girls Bsktbl Jr HS, Var Levels; NEANY Westfield TA 1985-, Negotiator; *office:* Westfield Acad E Main eld NY 14787

RISON, RUTH M., History & English Teacher; *b:* Alexandria, MN; lliam L. II; *ed:* Moorhead St Univ (BS); Post Grad Work; *cr:* Svc dv; Curr Dev Chprsn; Preparing For Adult Living Adv; 8th Grd Adv; opkinton Congregational Church, Womens Ministries Dir; Author, er; *office:* LaHer Rain Chrstn Acad 280 Pleasant St Ashland MA

RISON, WILLIAM FRANCIS, Business Education Teacher; *b:* ss Hills, PA; *ed:* Indiana Univ of PA (BSEd) Bus Ed 1984, (MED) Penn St Part-Time Stud; *cr:* Windber Area HS Bus Ed Tchr 1984-; s Club Adv; Drill & Show Designer; Marching Band & Indoorguard NEA, PSEA 1984-; Natl Judges Assn 1990-; Windber Area Band ers, Steel City Drum & Bugle Corps 1984-; Westshoremen Drum & Corps 1988-; Pitt-Johnstown Cmptrs in Ed Wkshps; IUP G G Hill Outstanding Jr in Bus Ed 1983; Whos Who in Amer Colls & Univs WJAC Television Cmptrs in Classroom Participant; *home:* 1527 2nd ltoona PA 16602

RISSEY, CHARLES RICHARD, 5th Grade Teacher; *b:* New , CT; *m:* Janice Holly; *c:* Charles R. Jr., Amy, Melissa, Jennifer, er; *ed:* Providence Coll (AB) Ec 1964; Southern CT St Coll (MS) Ed 1968; 6th Yr Prof Diploma Admin, Sup 1973; 24 Credit Hrs Post Prof ma Math; *cr:* Fair Haven Jr HS Grd 8 Sci, Grd 9 His Tchr 1964-65; e Day Schl Grd 4 Tchr 1967-68; Clintonville Elem Schl Grd 5 Tchr, rd Unit Ldr 1968-; *ai:* Cmptr Facilitator 1990-; Phi Delta Kappa , Newsletter Ed, VP Projects, Photography Intnl Awd; NHEA, CEA, 1968-; CT Best Prgm 1986-, St Assessor New Tchrs, Cooperoting Rodrigo Cncl #441 1975-, Grand Knight, Paul May Awd, Outstdng ibutions; 2nd Governors Foot Guard 1995-; Amer Legion 1975-; Highland Pipe Band 1991-, Stu Piper; *office:* Clintonville Elem Schl lintonville Rd North Haven CT 06473

RISSEY, HELEN LARKIN, Substitute Teacher; *b:* New York City, : Robert F.; *c:* Kevin F., Deirdre L.; *ed:* Marymount-Manhattan Coll Psych 1965; *cr:* St Rose of Lima Schl 5th Grd Tchr 1978-85; Sts Methodius Schl 8th Grd Tchr 1986-95; South Orange MS Sub Tchr ; *home:* 6 Robin Pl Fairfield NJ 07004

RISSEY, SONJA RUTH, English Teacher; *b:* New York City, NY; n Patrick; *c:* Lisa K. Mann, Stephen R.; *ed:* SUNY at Cortland (BA) 60, (MS) Ed, Eng 1964; Experiment in Intnl Living 8 Credit Hrs Elmira Coll 6 Hrs Grad Work; Cornell Univ 6 Hrs Grad Work; use Univ Adj 6 Hrs Grad Work; *cr:* Owego Jr HS Eng Tchr 1960-67; o Free Acad Eng Tchr 1979-; *ai:* Class Adv 12 Yrs; Dept Eng Chprsn Stu Tchrs 3 Yrs; Syracuse Adj SUPA 7 Yrs; NYS United Tchrs 1986-; o-Apalachin Tchrs Assn 1980-; Christ the King Luth Church 1968-; Tchr Awd of Excl 1994.*

RO, THOMAS G., Dev, Legal Studies Professor; *b:* Jersey City, NJ; ordham Univ (BA) Philosophy 1975; St John's Univ Schl of Law (JD) 1978; *cr:* Self-Employed Attorney 1979-86; Donnelly Inds Chief ating Ofcr 1986-92; Sussex Cty Comm Coll Legal Stud, Dev Stud Prof ; *ai:* Asst Girls Bsktbl Coach 1993-94; Head Girls Bsktbl Coach 95; Passaic-Sussex Soccer Ofcls 1991-; USSF Ofcl Grd 7 1993-; NJSBUA 1991-; Assn Builders, Contractors 1988-, Dir; Northwest NJ Dog Trng Club 1984-, Pres; Jersey Skylands Labrador Ret Club 1990-, Pres; Mid-Jersey LRC 1985-, Sec; Wallkill Vly Soccer Club 1988-, Coach; Wallkill Vly Ranger Sports 1990-, Coach; *office:* Sussex County Comm Coll College Hill Newton NJ 07860

MORRONE, MICHAEL JOSEPH, Associate Prof of Cmptr Sci; *b:* Philadelphia, PA; *m:* Joyce Ballone; *c:* Amanda, Alyssa; *ed:* St Josephs Univ (BS) Math 1972; *cr:* Unisys Corp Systems Analyst 1966-84; Montgomery Cty Comm Coll Assoc Prof 1981-; Lockheed Martin Staff Engr 1984-; *ai:* Engrng Process Improvements Phases I, II; *office:* Montgomery County Comm Coll 340 Dekalb Pike Blue Bell PA 19422

MORROS, JAMES A., Health & Physical Ed Teacher; *b:* Bristol, CT; *m:* Emiko Itosu; *c:* Sean, Kelley, Kazu; *ed:* Springfield Coll (BS) PE 1970; Fairfield Univ (MS) Admin 1977; Southern CT St Univ 6th Yr Hlth 1986; *cr:* Joel Barlow HS Hlth, PE Tchr 1970-; *ai:* Drivers Ed; IM Act; Before Schl Bsktbl Prgm; NEA, CEA, JBHS 1971-; JOPHER 1989-; Article Pub 1974-75; *office:* Joel Barlow HS 100 Black Rock Tpke Redding CT 06896

MORROW, FARRA MCCARTNEY, Communication Arts Teacher; *b:* Phoenixville, PA; *m:* Thomas Oliver; *c:* Millersville St Coll (BA) Eng 1970; Temple Univ (MED) Ed 1974; *ed:* Multiple Courses; Edward Hand Jr HS CA Tchr 1970-; *cr:* 9th Grd Team Capt; SAP Team; Hnr Soc, Peel Ldr Adv; *ai:* Grace Brethren Church of Lititz 1979-; Tchr of Yr; *office:* Edward Hand Jr HS S Ann & Juniata St Lancaster PA 17602

MORROW, KATHRYN BOARD, Third Grade Teacher; *b:* Parkersburg, WV; *m:* Daniel E.; *ed:* Muskingum Coll (BA) Eng, El Ed 1980; Attnd Walsh, Ashland, Drake Univs; *cr:* West Muskingum Schls 1st-2nd Grds Tchr 1980-84; Warren Local Schls 3rd Grd Tchr 1984-85, 4th Grd Tchr 1985-86, 3rd Grd Tchr 1986-; *ai:* Church Pianist; Piano Ychr; Choir Dir; Right to Read Comm; NEA, OEA 1980-; YWCA Vol of Yr; Tchr of Month; *home:* RR 1 Box 69 Fleming OH 45729

MORROW, KIMBERLY JO, MS Mathematics Teacher; *b:* Waynesboro, PA; *ed:* Shippensburg St Coll (BS) Math Ed 1978; Wilkes Univ (MSEd) Ed 1990; *cr:* Greencastle-Antrim High Math Tchr 1978-95, Math Dept Chair 1988-92; Greencastle-Antrim Mid Math Tchr 1995-; *ai:* Ping Pong Club Adv; NEA, PSEA, GAEA 1978-; NCTM 1985-; Evangelical Luth Church 1956-; Outstanding Young Women of Amer 1985, 1987; *home:* 8659 Picadilly Cir Waynesboro PA 17268

MORROW, RAYMOND ALLEN, Director of Jazz Ensembles; *b:* Portland, ME; *cr:* City of Pub Schls Dir of Jazz Ensembles 1984-87; Waynflete Schl Dir of Jazz Ensembles, Individual Saxophone Lessons 1987-; *ai:* S Portland Jehovahs Witness 1979-, Elder; *office:* Waynflete Schl 360 Spring St Portland ME 04102

MORROW, ROBERT B., Graphic Arts & Arch Instr; *b:* Pittsburgh, PA; *m:* Jane Shirer; *c:* Sarah, Robert, Rebecca, Benjamin; *ed:* CA St Coll (BSEd) Indstrl Arts 1974; *cr:* Wellington HS Indstrl Arts Instr 1974-75; Valley HS Indstrl Arts Instr 1975-; *ai:* PSEA, NEA, NKAEA 1975-; Innovative Tchng Grant 1993-94; Thanks to Tchrs Finalist 1993-95; Cert of Spec Congressional Recognition 1994-95; Academia Meritorious Outstndg Achvmt Awd 1994-95; *office:* Valley HS 701 Stevenson Blvd New Kensington PA 15068

MORROW, VALERIE AUSTIN, Assistant Principal; *b:* McKeesport, PA; *c:* Eric, Tanya; *ed:* Penn St (BS) Sci & Bio 1970; Hood Coll (MS) Sci & Bio Admin 1983; 18 Hrs Admin & Supervision; *cr:* Northern MS 8th Grd Sci Tchr 1980-94, Resource Tchr 1994-95, Asst Prin 1995-; *ai:* Cty Projects Evaluation Task Force, SIT Task Force, OM Coach; Team Ldr; WCTA, MSTA, NEA 1980-95; NASSP 1995-; Washington Cty Tchr of Yr Awd 1992; Presentor Natl MS Conf, MD St Sci Conf; *office:* Northern MS Northern Ave Hagerstown MD 21742

MORSCHAUSER, RICHARD A., Math Teacher & Coach; *b:* Yonkers, NY; *m:* Helen Niemiec; *c:* Karen, Michael; *ed:* Concordia Jr Coll (AA) Sci Tchr 1968; Manhattan Coll (BS) Math Tchr 1970; Univ of Bridgeport (MSEd) Curr Dev 1975; 33 Addl Hrs Manhattan Coll, LIU, LaSalle Univ, SUNY at Purchase; *cr:* Hathorne Jr HS Math Tchr 1970-73; Yonkers HS Math Tchr, Asst Coach Ftbl, Track 1973-85; Gorton HS Math Tchr, Track Coach 1985-; *ai:* Girls Spring Track Coach; Boys, Girls Winter Track Coach; Sr Prom Adv 1982, 1985, 1992, 1994; NEA, YFT 1970-; AMTNYS, NCTM 1975-; ACDS 1995-; Knights of Columbus 1990-; Ushers SOC I(**_: Site Based Mngmt 1991-93; Team Mahopac JHS 1992-, Treas; Mahopac Var Gymnastics Booster Comm; Mellon Fnd Grant 1988; Mid St Evaluation Comms 1985-; *office:* Charles E Gorton HS 100 Shonnard Pl Yonkers NY 10703*

MORSE, BRENDA HENDRICKS, English Teacher; *b:* Detroit, MI; *m:* George Le Grand; *c:* Sarah Maurine, Todd LeGrand; *ed:* St Univ of NY Coll at Buffalo (BS) Scndry Ed, Eng-Summa Cum Laude 1971, (MA) Eng 1972; *cr:* St Univ of NY Coll at Buffalo Grad Tchng Asst 1971-72; Hamburg Cntrl HS 10-12 Grd Eng Tchr 1972-75; West Seneca West HS 10-12 Grd Eng Tchr 1981; West Seneca West Jr HS 9 Grd Eng Tchr 1981-82; Springville Griffith Inst HS 11-12 Grd Eng Tchr 1982-; *ai:* Mentor for New Tchrs; NHS Tchr, Fac Advy Comms; Tchr, Coord HS GATE Prgm & SAT Preparation Course; Coll Day Prgm, Tickets Ushers Refreshments for Schl Musicals Coords; Sr Class, NHS Advs; Its Acad Coach; Dir of Schl Play; AFT, NYSUT 1971-; Griffith Inst Fac Assn 1982-; Phi Delta Kappa 1985-; NCTE 1972-; Grad Flwshp 1971-72; Tchr of Eng for Hnrs 11 & 12 AP; Speaker at Coll Conf First Yr Tchrs Can & Do Make A Difference 1972; NY St Tchr of Excl 1985; Exceptional Tchr Who Had Greatest Impact on Their Ed SUNY Coll at Fredonia 1991, 1992, 1994; *office:* Springville-Griffith Inst HS 290 N Buffalo St Springville NY 14141*

MORSE, DONNA MARIE, Teacher; *b:* Rumford, ME; *m:* Stanley B.; *c:* Darcy, Darin; *ed:* Univ of ME at Farmington (BA) Elem Ed 1974; *cr:* Meroby Elem Schl 5th Grd Tchr 1974-; *ai:* NEA 1974-; MEA 1974-; *office:* Meroby Elem Schl 28 Cross St Mexico ME 04257

MORSE, JAMIE P., Art Photography & Art His Tchr; *b:* Providence, RI; *m:* Helene S.; *c:* Julia, Betsy; *ed:* Philadelphia Coll of Art (BFA) Painting 1975; Cuyahoga Comm Coll Photography Credits; *cr:* For Art's Sake Mgr 1975-80; Sendetl's Gallery Buyer, Appraiser, Mgr 1980-83; Hathaway Brown Schl Art, Photography, Art His Tchr 1983-; *ai:* Acad Dean 10th Grd Level; 10th Grd Level, Sr Speech, Art Club Adv; Sftbl Coach; New Org Visual Artists 1988-; Catalyst Fund Grant 1990; Anne Cutter Coburn Chair Tchng Excl 1991; *office:* Hathaway Brown Schl 19600 N Park Blvd Shaker Heights OH 44122

MORSE, PATRICIA STANLEY, 7th-8th Grade Science Teacher; *b:* Bristol, England; *m:* Alan E.; *c:* Tracey; *ed:* Towson St Univ (BS) Geog, Psych 1967; Grad Courses Towson SU; In Svc Environmental Ed; *cr:* Roland Park Jr HS Geog, His Tchr 1967-73; Holy Rosary Schl Sci Tchr 1984-89; Shrine of Little Flower Schl Sci Tchr 1989-; *ai:* Safety Patrol; Sci Dept Chprsn; Chesapeake Bay Environmental Grant; *home:* 2832 Forest Glen Dr Baldwin MD 21013

MORSE, RAYMOND FRANK, Fifth & Sixth Grade Elem Tchr; *b:* Attleboro, MA; *ed:* Bapt Bible Coll (AA) Gen 1981, (BA) Bible 1983, (MS) Elem Ed 1992; *cr:* Perth Bible Chrstn Acad Tchr 1983-; *ai:* Chess Club; Cmptr Class; Church, Children's Ministries Dir; *office:* Perth Bible Chrstn Acad 1863 Co Hwy 107 Amsterdam NY 12010

MORSETTE, GALE MARIE, 11th Grade English Teacher; *b:* Brooklyn, NY; *ed:* SUNY at Stonybrook (BA) Eng 1980, (MA) Eng 1989; 60 Addl Hrs Post Grad, In Svc Courses; *cr:* Copiague Chrstn Acd Eng Tchr 1984-86; Gen Douglas Mac Arthur HS Eng Tchr 1988-; *ai:* Peer Ldrshp Comm; AFT 1988-; Co-Wrote New Tchrs Handbook; *office:* General Douglas Mac Arthur HS Old Jerusalem Rd Levittown NY 11756*

MORSTATTER, LIELA M., Math Teacher; *b:* Petersburg, OH; *m:* Miles F.; *c:* Fred; *ed:* Youngstown St (BA) Math 1968; Kent St (MED) Ed & Math 1975; *cr:* Greenford HS Math Tchr 1968-69; Clifton HS Math Tchr 1969-70; Copley HS Math Tchr 1970-; *ai:* OEA & NEA 1970-; NCTM 1968-; CTA 1970-, bldg Rep; *office:* Copley HS 3807 Ridgewood Rd Copley OH 44321*

MORT, LORI LEE (TRIMBLE), 7th-12th Grd Lrng Support Tchr; *b:* New Castle, PA; *m:* Douglas C.; *ed:* Slippery Rock Univ (BA) Spec Ed, Elem 1981; 24 Post Grad Hrs; *cr:* Shenango Area Schl Dist Learning Support Tchr 1981-; *ai:* Spec Depts Chprsn; Sr Class, Stu Cncl Adv; NEA, PSEA, SAEA 1981-; *home:* 512 Shenango Park Dr New Castle PA 16101*

MORTENSEN, EARL MILLER, Chem Dept Chair & Assoc Prof; *b:* Salt Lake City, UT; *m:* Sharlene Wilcox; *c:* Eric A., Brian D., Russell J., Mark A.; *ed:* Univ of UT (BA) Chem 1955, (PHD) Chem 1959; NSF Post Doctoral Fellow 1959-60, Lawrence Radiation Lab 1960-62 Univ CA at Berkeley; *cr:* Univ of MA Chem Asst Prof 1962-69; Cleveland St Univ Chem Assoc Prof 1969-; *ai:* BSA Unit Commissioner, Asst Cubmaster; Amer Chemical Soc 1962-; Amer Phys Soc 1957-; Sigma Xi 1960-; *office:* Cleveland State Univ Dept of Chemistry 1983 E 24th St Cleveland OH 44115

MORTIMER, CAROLYN G., High School Art Instructor; *b:* Elmer, NJ; *m:* David Sr; *c:* David Jr., Kate, Jessica, Rebekah; *ed:* Univ of DE (BA) Art Ed 1975; *cr:* Brandywine HS Art Tchr 1975-76; Elmer Elem 1979-81; AP Schalick HS 1987-; 20 Yrs of Pri Studio Instruction & Gallery Exhibitions; *ai:* Art Club; Natl Art Hnr Soc; Soc of NJ Artists 1985-; NAEA 1987-; FOTA; Whos Who in Amer Art 1980; Purchase Awds from City or Atlantic City; Purchase Awd in 1985 Miss Amer Baordwalk Art Festival & Exhibit; Limited Edition Prints Released 1991; *office:* Arthur P Schalick HS Pittsgrove Twp Elmer NJ 08318

MORTIMER, ELIZABETH ANN, French Teacher; *b:* Baltimore, MD; *ed:* Susquehanna Univ (BA) Fr 1990; *cr:* Univ of Agri Eng Tchr 1992-93; Tome Schl Fr, Eng, Latin Tchr 1993-94; Kenwood HS Fr, Span, IB Fr Tchr 1994-; *ai:* NHS Adv; Multicultural Liaison Comm Tchr, SponUkrainian Exch 1996; 11th Grd Recognition Comm; NEA 1994-; *office:* Kenwood HS 501 Stemmers Run Rd Baltimore MD 21221

MORTIMER, GEORGIANNE R., Second Grade Teacher; *b:* Chester, PA; *m:* Martin M.; *c:* Kelli Anne, Marty; *ed:* West Chester Univ (BA) Elem Ed 1964, (MS) Elem Ed 1970; *cr:* Ogden Elem Schl First Grd Tchr 1964-70; Boothwyn Elem Schl First Grd Tchr 1970-73; Chichester Schl Dist Summer Headstart Dir 1972-82; Marcus Hook Elem Schl First Grd Tchr 1979-83, Second Grd Tchr 1983-; *ai:* PSEA, NEA 1964-; *home:* 5 Kimbrough Ct Wilmington DE 19810

MORTIMER, MARILYN WELCH, Math & English Teacher; *b:* Salisbury, MD; *m:* Bill; *ed:* Univ of DE (BS) Eng Ed 1975; Rowan (MA) Eng Ed 1992; Post Grad Stud Six Hrs; Univ of DE 33 Hrs; *cr:* VISTA Vol 1975-76; Woodstown Schls Tchr 1976-; *ai:* Eng Club; Fac Alliance; Curr Cncl; Employee Month, Yr, Alternative Scheduling Comms; NJEA, NCTE, 1977-, WPREA 1977-, Pres; Delta Kappa Gamma 1988-, 1st VP; Tchr Yr Dist; Violence Prevention Wkshp, Authentic Assessment Trainer; *office:* Woodstown HS 140 East Ave Woodstown NJ 08098

MORTON, CARMELLA SYE, Jr High Science Teacher; *b:* Camden, NJ; *m:* Derrek; *c:* Derrek II, Jasmine; *ed:* Rutgers Univ (BS) Home Ec & Early Chldhd Ed 1982; Univ of Toledo (MS) Ed Curr 1992; PHD Ed Admin Candidate; *cr:* BCCAP Headstart Pgm Coord 1982-87; LaPetite Acad Pgm Dir 1988-90; DeVeaux Jr High Sci Tchr 1992-; *ai:* African Amer Club Adv; NEA 1992-; AFT 1992-; ASCD 1995-; Gold Leaf Fin 1992-, Bd Sec; Jack & Jill of Amer Inc 1995-; Carmella Sye Morton Awd; *home:* P.O. Box 352862 Toledo OH 43635*

MORTON, DONNA JEAN, 4th Grade Teacher; *b:* Portland, ME; *m:* David; *c:* Benjamin, Jennifer; *ed:* Univ of Southern ME (MS) Ed 1977, (MS) Ed 1984; 15 Addl Hrs 1988; EDIS 943-51 1994; Tele Comm 1994; Tchr Academ 1993; Multi Media 1992; *cr:* Manchester Schl 4th Grd Tchr 1977-; *ai:* Bldg Cmptr Coord; Dist Tech Comm; WEA, MEA, NEA 1977-; ATNE 1994-; BSA 1988-, Ldr; Girl Scout 1994-, Ldr; Casco Park Comm 1994-; Casco Halloween Comm 1985-; ME Top Ten Tchr of Yr 1986; Aspirations Grant 1993; Windham PTA Grant 1995; Windham Focus Presentor 1990; *office:* Manchester Schl 709 Roosevelt Trl Windham ME 04062

MORTON, JOE, Professor of Philosophy; *b:* Budapest, Hungary; *c:* Rebecca, Jason, Paul; *ed:* Amherst Coll (BA) Philosophy 1959; John Hopkins Univ (PHD) Philosophy 1968; *cr:* Goucher Coll Appointed Instr 1964-95; *ai:* Peace Stud, Frosh Care Prgm Dir; ACLU, Amnesty Intnl, AFSC, SPLC, WILPF; *office:* Goucher Coll Dulaney Valley Rd Baltimore MD 21204

MORTON, LINDA LOVETT, 4th Grade Teacher; *b:* Springfield, VT; *m:* Seeley W.; *c:* Kevin, Beth; *ed:* Castleton St Coll (BS) Elem 1970; Attnd Univ of VT, Norwich Univ; *cr:* Chester Andover Elem Schl 3rd Grd Tchr 1970-88, 4th Grd Tchr 1988-; *ai:* Chester Ed Negotiations Team; VT NEA 1970-, Bldg Rep; St Josephs Parish Cncl 1994-; VT Outstanding Tchr 1986; Delta Kappa Gamma 1988; *home:* RR 5 Box 60 Chester VT 05143*

MORTON, ROBERT S., Chemistry & Physics Teacher; *b:* Wilmerding, PA; *m:* Barbara Donlin; *c:* Shawn, Sarah; *ed:* MA St Coll at North Adams (BS) Sci 1964; Wesleyan Univ (MA) Physics 1972; Credits from Various Colls & Univs; *cr:* Ledyard Jr-Sr HS Jr HS Sci Tchr 1964-67; Arlington Meml HS Jr-Sr Sci Tchr 1967-68; Cambridge Cntrl Schl Physics & Chem Tchr 1968-; Adirondack Comm Coll Chem Adjunct Prof 1993-; *ai:* Presch Tutor; AFT, NYSUT 1968-; CFA 1968-, Pres, VP, Chief Negotiator; 1985 Stu Awd for Tchr Who has Done Most For Stdnts; *home:* RR 1 Box 92 Buskirk NY 12028*

MORTON, SUSAN ELIAS, Mathematics Teacher; *b:* Danbury, CT; *m:* Patrick C.; *c:* Erin E.; *ed:* WCSU (BS) Elem Ed, Math 1982, (MS) Math 1988; Cmptr Sci Ed 21 credits Fairfield Univ; *cr:* Immaculate HS Math Tchr 1982-; Bethel HS Continuing Ed, GED Math 1994-; *ai:* Math League, Stock Market Game Adv; ATOMIC, NCTM 1993-; NSF Fellowship at Fairfield Univ 1991-94; Tandy Tech Scholar 1993; *office:* Immaculate HS 73 Southern Blvd Danbury CT 06810*

MORTON, THOMAS RICHARD, 5th Grade Teacher; *b:* Corry, PA; *m:* Paula Sankey; *c:* Karen Matsick, David Hauser, Ryan; *ed:* Slippery Rock Univ (BS) Elem Ed, Scndry Eng 1970; 33 Grad Credits; *cr:* Dassa McKinney Elem Schl Tchr 1970-; *ai:* Moniteau HS Var Bsktbl Coach 1991-; MEA, PSEA 1970-; Bsktbl Coach of Yr 1992-93; *office:* Dassa Mckinney Elem Schl 391 Hooker Rd West Sunbury PA 16061

MORTON, WILLIAM HAROLD, History Teacher; *b:* Portland, ME; *m:* Dianne; *c:* Deborah Rideout, Becky Andrews, William James; *ed:* Gorham St Coll (BS) Soc Sci 1968; 15 Addl Hrs at Univ of ME 1984; *cr:* Telstar HS His Tchr 1968-; *ai:* NHS Selection Comm; HS Jr Var Bsktbl Coach; Scheduling & Curr Comm; NEA, ME Educators Assn, Telstar Educators Assn 1968-; *office:* Telstar HS 284 Walkers Mills Rd Bethel ME 04217

MORTON, WILLIAM HEYWOOD, 7th-8th Grd Soc Studies Tchr; *b:* New York City, NY; *m:* Paula K.; *c:* Bradley, Abby; *ed:* Heidelberg Coll

(BA) Elem Ed 1970; Univ of Dayton (MS) Ed 1982; *cr:* Sedalia Elem Schl 5-6th Grd Tchr 1970-78; Dunloe Elem Schl 5th Grd Tchr 1978-94; Groveport Madison MS North 7-8th Grd Soc Stud 1994-; *ai:* Asst Ath Dir; OEA, NEA 1970-; Groveport Madison Local Ed Assn 1970-, Pres.

MORVAN, HANNAH RIKERT, Teacher; *b:* Providence, RI; *m:* Raymond Sr.; *c:* Raymond Jr., William; *ed:* Middlebury Coll (BA) His 1970; Vaddo at Folkhogskola (3rd Yr Degree) Swedish Crafts 1971; ATTND UVM, Johnson St Coll, Coll of St JOSEPHS, CO SCHL OF Mines, Lyndon St Coll; *cr:* Roxbury Village Schl 1st-3rd Grd Tchr 1973-80; Northfield Elem Schl 1st Grd Tchr 1980-; *ai:* Tech Comm; K-1 Decision Unit Head; After Schl X-C Ski Pgm; VEA & NEA 1976-; VSTA 1980-, Bd of Dirs; NSTA 1985-; VT Philharmonic Orch 1974-; United Church of Northfield 1978-; Jaycees Outstdng Young Edctrs Awd Runner Up; Tchr of the Yr Northfield Rotary Club; *office:* Northfield Elem Schl 1 Garvey Hl Northfield VT 05663*

MOSCA, JENI A., Athletic Director & PE Tchr; *b:* Berlin, NH; *ed:* Univ of NH (BS) PE 1983; Antioch Grad Schl (MED) Admin & Supervision 1996; *cr:* Sacred Heart Schl PE Tchr, Coach & Ath Dir 1983-87; Sanborn MS PE Tchr, Coach & Ath Dir 1987-; *ai:* Girls MS Soccer, Bsktbl, Sftbl & Track; Girls Frosh Bsktbl; Girls Var Sftbl; NEA & NH Assn of PE Rec & Dance 1987-; *office:* Sanborn MS 31-A W Main St Newton NH 03858

MOSCHETTI, ANGELA ANN, First Grade Teacher; *b:* Jersey City, NJ; *ed:* St Thomas Aquinas Coll (BS) Ed 1963; Manhattan Coll (MA) Latin 1970, (MS) Educl Admin 1978; 9 Credits Eng Lit 1971-72; Fordham Univ 6 Credits Educl Television 1963; *cr:* St Anthony Schl 4th-5th Grd Tchr 1960-62; St Theresa Schl 1st Grd Tchr 1962-63; St Vito Schl 3rd-4th Grd Tchr 1963-64; Sacred Heart Schl 7th-8th Grd Tchr 1964-66; St Rita Schl 8th Grd Tchr 1966-67; Immaculate Heart of Mary 7th-8th Grd Tchr 1967-68; Saints Peter & Paul HS 9th-10th Grd Tchr 1968-69; St Edmund Schl 7th-8th Grd Tchr 1969-71; Most Precious Blood Schl 7th-8th Grd Tchr 1971-72; St Theresa Schl Prin 1972-74; Cardinal Mc Closkey Child Care Agency Dir of Ed 1974-80; Robert Fulton Schl 2nd Grd Tchr 1980; Mt Vernon HS 9th-12th Grd Tchr 1980; Pennington-Grimes Schl 1st Grd Tchr 1980-; *ai:* 1st-6th Grd Tutorial Sessions; Kappa Delta Pi 1977-; Alpha Delta Kappa 1992-; NYSUT 1980-; PTA 1980-, Jenkins Awd; Police Capts, Lts, Sgts Assn 1996-; AARP 190-; Tchr Conf Presentations 1963-64; Tchng Stdnts with Spec Needs Wkshp 1978; *office:* Pennington Grimes Elem Schl 20 Fairway St Mount Vernon NY 10552*

MOSCOWITZ, DENNIS, High School Math Teacher; *b:* New York, NY; *m:* Louella Demira; *c:* Jason, Kelly; *ed:* City Coll of NY (BS) Math 1966; St Johns Univ (MA) Math 1971; 45 Credit Hrs Post-Masters Degree in Assorted Courses; *cr:* US Peace Corps Vol 1966-68; Benjamin Franklin HS Math Tchr 1968-72; John F Kennedy HS Math Tchr & Pgm Chm 1972-80; John Bowne HS Math Tchr & Pgm Office 1980-; *ai:* Winter Carnival Auctioneer; Prom Chaperone & Adv; Pgm Office Comm; AFT 1968-; NYSUT 1968-; UFT 1968-; Knight of Pythias 1970-; Bsktbl Buddies of Bayside 1975-, Sec & Pres; Returned Peace Corps Vols of Amer 1972-; Reliance Awd 1993; Borough of Queens HS Tchr of the Yr; *office:* John Bowne HS 63-25 Main St Flushing NY 11367*

MOSCOWITZ, MARLENE DOBRIN, Spanish Teacher; *b:* Newark, NJ; *m:* Alan S.; *c:* Barry Edan, David Stuart; *ed:* Rutgers Univ (BA) Fr, Span 1964; Seton Hall Univ (MA) Judaeo, Chrstn Stud 1988; *cr:* New Milford HS Fr, Span Tchr 1964-66; Abraham Lincoln Jr HS Fr, Span Tchr 1966-68; West Orange Schl Sys Sub Tchr 1972-77; Governor Livingston RHS Span Tchr 1987-; *ai:* Jr Class, Pep Club, Span Club Adv; Fall, Winter Chrldng Coach; Track Timer; Key Comm; Span Tutorial Prgm Instr; AFT, ACTFL, FLENJ, AATSP, PTA 1987-; AATSP NJ 1987-, Bd Mem; Phi Delta Kappa 1993-; Natl Cncl of Jewis Women 1980-; US Holocaust Meml Museum; Tempel B'Nai Abraham 1966-, Ritual Comm Mem; King Juan Carlos Flwshp 1993; Scott Foresman In-Svc Prgm; NDEA Span Inst; Org, Implemented Span Exch Prgm 1995; *home:* 70 Warren Rd West Orange NJ 07052*

MOSELEY, SANDRA L., 10th Grade English Teacher; *b:* Willoughby, OH; *c:* Erika K. Carter, Timothy S.; *ed:* Kent St Univ (BS) Scndry Ed, Eng 1970; Post Grad Stud OH Univ, Coll of Mount St Joseph, Miami Univ, Kent St Univ; *cr:* Geneva Jr HS 7-8 Grd Eng Tchr 1967-69, 1970-71; Ashtabula HS 10th Grd Eng Tchr 1971-, Eng Dept Chair 1991-92; *ai:* Jr Class, SophClass, Stu Cncl Advs; Saturday Schl Detention Supvr, Monitor; After Schl Stud Time Supvr; Career Ed Cnsltnt; AAEA, NEOEA, OEA, NEA 1971-; NCTE 1976-; Northeast OH Sports Car Club 1968-, Pres 1981, 1982, 1984-, Mem of Yr 1986; Geneva Grape Jamboree Bd 1984-, Comm Chairs; *office:* Ashtabula HS 401 W 44th St Ashtabula OH 44004*

MOSELEY, THOMAS ROBERT, Professor; *b:* Lanchout, China; *m:* Josephine Mary Modafferie; *c:* Thomas, Patricia, Pamela Kay Patton; *ed:* Wheaton Coll (BA) His 1942; NY Univ (MA) His 1947, (PHD) His, Sociology 1963; OK Univ Cert Linguistics 1947; Yale in China Chinese Lang, Culture 1947; *cr:* Amer Schl in Vietnam Tchr 1948-52; Nyack Coll Prof 1952-62; SUNY Rockland Comm Coll Prof 1962-; *office:* St Univ of NY Rockland Comm Coll College Rd Suffern NY 10901

MOSER, BARBARA ANNE, French Teacher; *b:* Columbus, OH; *m:* Michael L.; *ed:* Wittenberg Univ (BA) Fr 1974; Kent St Univ MED) Scndry Ed 1980; Universite de Haute at Bretagne 1972-73; Centre d'Etudes Linguistiques d'Avignon 1992; *cr:* Glen Oak HS Fr Tchr 1975-; *ai:* Fr Club & Chrldng Adv; N Central Accrediation Steering Comm; Stu Groups to France; ARC Foreign Exch Stdnts Cnslr; *office:* Glen Oak HS 2300 Schneider St NE Canton OH 44721

MOSER, CHARLES W., Mathematics Teacher; *b:* Norristown, PA; *m:* Alberta Cameron; *c:* Kimberly Kathleen, Charles Cameron, Lisa Jeannine; *ed:* Lock Haven St Coll (BS) Math, Physics 1965; 45 Grad Credit Hrs Math, Ed; *cr:* Upper Merion Area HS Math Tchr 1965-; *ai:* Asst Ftbl Coach; PSES, Upper Merion Area Ed Assn 1965-; NEA 1970-; *office:* Upper Merion Area HS 440 Crossfield Rd King Of Prussia PA 19406

MOSER, DAVID DEAN, Communications Instructor; *b:* Butler, PA; *m:* Nancyann Begnoche; *ed:* Western OK St Coll (AA) Jrnlsm 1984; Slippery Rock Univ (BS) Scndry Ed, Comm 1987, (MA) Eng 1989; *cr:* Butler Cty Comm Coll Instr 6 Yrs; *ai:* Adv Stu Newspaper; Coll Media Advs 1992-; Soc Prof Journalists 1992; Soc of Environmental Journalists 1992-; *office:* Butler County Comm Coll College Drive Oak Hills Butler PA 16001*

MOSER, MICHAEL L., Mathematics Teacher; *b:* Massillon, OH; *m:* Barbara Britton; *ed:* OH St Univ (BS) Scndry Ed 1971; Kent St Univ (MED) Math Ed 1979; *cr:* Glen Oak HS Math Tchr 1972-; *ai:* NEA, OEA, OH Cncl Teach of Math 1972-; *office:* Glen Oak HS 1044 44th St NW Canton OH 44709

MOSER, PATRICIA JUDGE, Biology Teacher; *b:* Silver Spring, MD; *m:* Timothy Moser; *c:* James; *ed:* Univ of Scranton (BS) Sec Ed Conc Bio 1989; Univ of MD 8 Grad Hrs,30 Grad Hrs MEQ; *cr:* Springbrook HS Sci Tchr 1989-; *ai:* Cheerleading Coach; 9th Grd Transition Team Comm; NEA, MCEA, MSTA 1989-; MD Higher Ed Commission Grant 1992; *office:* Springbrook HS 201 Valley Brook Dr Silver Spring MD 20904*

MOSER, STEVE WILLIAM, Mathematics Teacher; *b:* Lewisburg, PA; *m:* Janet Louise Klein; *c:* Laura, Todd; *ed:* Bloomsburg Univ (BS) Math 1972; 42 Addl Hrs Masters Equivalency; *cr:* Danville Jr HS Math Tchr 1972-88; Danville Sr HS Math Tchr 1988-; *ai:* DEA, NEA, PSEA 1972-; NCMT 1972-; *home:* 144 Liberty Valley Rd Danville PA 17821

MOSER, THOMAS MARK, Biology Teacher; *b:* Bradford, PA; *m:* Alice E. Root; *c:* Mark; *ed:* Univ of Pittsburgh (BS) Ed, Bio, Chem 1974; Addl Hrs St Bonaventure Univ, SUNY at Geneseo, SUNY at Buffalo, Coll of St Rose, Cornell Univ; *cr:* Olean City Schl Dist Tchr 1975-; *ai:* Sci Dept Chm; NY St Bio Mentor; Self-Esteem Comm; NEA, NYEA, Olean Tchrs Assn 1975-; Cornell Univ Inst for Bio Tchrs 1 of 20 Chosen; Tchr of Month; *home:* 1653 Haskell Rd Olean NY 14760

MOSES, BARBARA STUMPT, Sixth Grade English Teacher; *b:* Jamaica, NJ; *c:* Sanford III, Allison; *ed:* Wheelock Coll (BS) Early Chldhd Ed 1958; 3 Hrs At SUNY at Stonybrook; 30 Hrs at Southampton Coll; *cr:* Darien Pub Schls 3rd Grd Tchr 1958-59; Riverhead Cntrl Schls 5th Grd Tchr 1969-86, 6th Grd Personal Dev 1986-95, 6th Grd Eng Tchr 1995-; *ai:* Summer Migrant Ed K-6 1973-80; Summer Spec Ed Cmptrs 1981-94; EXCEL Cmptrs; Jrnlsm Club Adv; Ethnic Sharing Comm; Mentor, Adv; AFT, Riverhead Fac Assn 1969-; Riverhead Townscape 1985-; Riverhead Cntry Fair 1980-; Wheelock Coll Distgnd Alumni 1988; *office:* Riverhead MS 600 Harrison Ave Riverhead NY 11901

MOSES, CAROL TOPICZ, Sixth Grade Teacher; *b:* Cincinnati, OH; *c:* Joseph; *ed:* Mt St Joseph (BA) Sociology 1962; Addl Ed Credits Univ of Cincinnati; *cr:* Cath Charities Soc Worker 1962-65; Spec Svcs US Army Recreation Dir 1965-66; Austin Schl Tchr 1967; Assumption Schl Tchr 1968-; *ai:* Fac Rep PTO; Soc Stud Chprsn; NCEA; Inspiration Awd 1993, 1996; *home:* 5385 Boomer Rd Cincinnati OH 45247

MOSES, KAREN DONAHUE, Title I Rdng & Lang Arts Tchr; *b:* Indianapolis, ID; *m:* Ronald; *c:* Amy, Molly, Rebecca, Cedric, Mark, Kaithys; *ed:* Wright St Univ 14 Credit Hrs MA Tchr Ldr; *cr:* East Schl Title Rdng, Lang Arts Tchr 1993-; *ai:* Literacy Team Head; Intervention Asst Team; Lang Arts Task Force Hlth Impaired Tutor Mem; NEA 1990-, Pres, SEA; ASCD 1996-; 4-H 1986-, Adv; *office:* Hollingsworth East Elem Schl 506 Aukerman St Eaton OH 45320

MOSES, KAREN PERROTTO, Jr High Math Teacher; *b:* Erie, PA; *m:* Scott Allen; *ed:* Edinboro Univ of PA (BAMA) Math 1993; 18 Grad Ed Courses; *ai:* Head of Stu of Month; NEA, PSEA 1991-; *office:* Galeton Area Jr Sr HS Bridge St Galeton PA 16922*

MOSES, LORETTE, Kindergarten Teacher; *b:* Brooklyn, NY; *c:* Nanewa Dai Gause; *ed:* Pace Univ (BA) Early Chldhd & Elem Ed 1980; Adelphi Univ Working Towards Masters Early Chldhd & Elem Ed 1996; *cr:* VA Day Care Ctr Asst Gr Tchr 1970-73; Howard O Walker Day Care Ctr Gr Tchr & Parent-Tchr Wkshp Facilitator 1973-83; Williamsburg Head Start Bd of Dirs 1982-83; Pub Schl Kndgtn Tchr 1983-; *ai:* UBC Learning Ctr Coord of Yth; African Amer Cultural Enrichment Pgm; UFT African Amer Heritage Comm; ABENY 1996; UBC Yth Ministry 1990-, Cnslr; UBC Hospitality Guild 1993-, Hostess.

MOSES, NOEL, Engineering & Mathematics Tchr; *b:* Georgetown, Guyana; *c:* Nyerere, Kwame, Akini, Sharlene; *ed:* City & Guilds of London (OTD) Electrical Engrng 1978; Univ of Guyana (BSCEE) Digital Systems 1983; Long Island Univ (MSC) Ed 1992; Advanced Cert Schl Admin, Supervision Brooklyn Coll 1993; *cr:* NY Power Authority Engr 1985-86; AT&T Paradyne Engr 1986-87; Aero Tech Engrng Consultant 1987-89; Bd Ed Tchr 1990-; *ai:* Schl Base Mngmt; Tech Sci, Tech Soc Adv; NCTM 1994-; Poem Pub 1995; *home:* 718 Jerome St Brooklyn NY 11207*

MOSHIER, MELINDA MUTO, Physical Education Teacher; *b:* Blossburg, PA; *m:* David B.; *c:* Lindsey Renee; *ed:* Lock Haven Univ (BS) Hlth, PE, Recreation 1984; Wilkes Univ (MS) Ed 1990; *cr:* Mansfield Jr-Sr HS PE Tchr 1985-; *ai:* Head Vlybl Coach IM; Class of 1997 Adv; Quality Schls Comm; PSEA, NEA, STEA 1985-; PA Vlybl Coaches Assn 1987-; Corey Creek Ladies Golf Assn 1993-, Bd Mem; Outstdng Young Women of Amer 1991; Jaycees Yth Ldr Awd; NTL West Vlybl Champions 1986, 1989; Dist IV Vlybl Champions 1989.

MOSIER, DOUGLAS WAYNE, Head Wrestling Coach; *b:* Ashland, OH; *m:* Alphy Ann Collins; *c:* Bryan, Bradley; *ed:* USAF Fire Sci, Ph Ed, Ldrshp; St of OH Sports Med; *cr:* Mansfield St Peter's Schl Head Wrestling Coach 1986-92; Mansfield Sr HS Head Wrestling Coach 1993-; *ai:* Founder of CLAWS Biddy Wrestling Prgm, Children Learning About Wrestling K-6th Grd; OCSEA Union 11-7010 1987-, Exec Bd 1990-95, Pres 1995-, Appreciation Awd; USAF Spec Achvmt; Coach's Awd 1987; *office:* Mansfield Sr HS 145 W Park Blvd Mansfield OH 44906

MOSKOWITZ, ANDREA HARROW, Sixth Grade Teacher; *b:* Brooklyn, NY; *c:* Erick Graham; *ed:* Queen Coll (BA) Ed 1970, (MS) Sci Ed 1972; Scndry Math License 1983; 80 Addl Credits Various Colls; *cr:* Tioga Hills Elem Schl 3rd Grd Tchr 1970-71; Sycamore Avenue Elem Schl 4-6 Grd Tchr 1972-85; Cherokee St Schl 6th Grd Tchr 1985-; *ai:* Math Team Adv; NCTM; NCAMS; AFT, NYSUT 1970-, CT Tchrs Assn 1972-, Parliamentarian; *office:* Cherokee Street Schl 130 Cherokee St Ronkonkoma NY 11779

MOSLEY, ROGEE YVETTE, Earth Science & Biology Tchr; *b:* Washington, DC; *m:* Tony Duwayne; *c:* Emerald, Jade, Toni II; *ed:* VA St Univ (BS) Bio 1984; Norfolk St Univ Cert of Ed 1987; 34 Hrs Ed, Environmental Stud, Meteorology, Astronomy, Geology, Bio; *cr:* Kettering MS 8th Grd Phys Sci Tchr 1987-88; Amer Embassy Zaire Pouch Supvr, Sub Tchr 1988-91; Suitland HS 9th Grd Earth Sci & Bio Tchr 1991-; *ai:* Earth Sci Division Chprsn; Bio Club; Mentor; Tutoring; Cooperative Learning Ctr; NEA, PGCEA 1987-; NSTA 1991-; Bethal AME Church 1995-; Highbrige Comm Assn 1996; Beta Beta Beta Biological, Beta Kappa Chi Scientific Hon Socs; Who's Who Among Colls; *office:* Suitland HS 5200 Silver Hill Rd Forestville MD 20747

MOSPAW, KATHAN JUDITH, Eighth Grade Soc Stud Tchr; *b:* Woonsocket, RI; *c:* Jennifer A., Elizabeth K.; *ed:* Syracuse Univ (AB) Pol Sci 1967; RI Coll (MEd) Elem Ed 1977; Southern New England Schl of Law (JD) Law 1993; 45 Hrs Grad Credit in Ed Post Masters; *cr:* William L. Callahan Schl Classroom Tchr 3rd-6th Grds 1969-89; Burrillville MS 8th Grd Soc Stud Tchr 1989-; *ai:* Mock Trial Coach; Segue Drama Club Adv; We the People Coach; NEA 1969-; NEA RI 1969-, Exec Comm 1990-; Burrillville Tchrs Assn 1969-, Pres 1990-; ABA 1995-; Burrillville Chamber of Commerce 1983-, VP 1986-95; Northern RI Cncl of the Arts 1981-, Chm 1984-90; RI Legal Educl Partnership 1990- Dir 1993, Pres 1995; Jasper Ballet Bd of Dir 1995, VP 1995; RI Law Related Ed Tchr of Yr 1992; Admitted To MA Bar 1994; *office:* Burrillville MS 2220 Broncos Hwy Harrisville RI 02830

MOSS, ARMENTHA DARLEEN, French Teacher; *b:* Parkersburg, WV; *m:* Walter S.; *c:* Mari Alistine, Shannon; *ed:* Hampton Univ (BA) Fr Ed 1968; Malone Coll (MS) Curr & Instruction 1992; Attnd Inst Filologia de Saltillo Mexico, Akron Univ, Wayne St Univ; *cr:* Detroit Pub Schls Tchr 1968-72; Trinity Chrstn Schl Tchr 1983-85; Canton City Schls Tchr 1985-; *ai:* Fr Club; Timken Bible Club; A3 Power Club; NAACP Yth Adv; ACT-SO Comm; Natl Alliance of Black Schl Edctrs 1992-, Ed Awd 1993; Kappa Delta Pi Honorary 1992-; OH Alliance of Black Schl Ed 1994-, Co-Chprsn & Conf; OH Frgn Lang Assn; NAACP 1992-, Yth Adv; Urban League Guild 1994-; Rockefeller Flwshp 1988; Yth Ldrshp Awd for Scndry Ed; Tchr of the Yr Finalist Awd; Impact II Grant Awds; *home:* 1601 Harvard Ave NW Canton OH 44703

MOSS, ELAINE GINGER, 5th Grade Teacher; *b:* New York City, NY; *m:* Richard W.; *c:* Jennifer, Sara, Eileen; *ed:* Queens Coll at NYC (BA) Ed 1967; Attnd Wright St Univ, Univ of Dayton; *cr:* Raleigh City Schls 3rd Grd Tchr 1967-68; Fairborn City Schls 3rd Grd Tchr 1969-72; Beavercreek City Schls 5th Grd Tchr 1988-; *ai:* Schl Spelling Bee Coord 1995 OEA, WOEA 1988-; *office:* Beavercreek City Schls 2940 Dayton X Dayton OH 45434

MOSSER, SYLVIA ECKENRODE, Language Arts Teacher; *b:* Cty, PA; *m:* Bruce Thompson; *c:* Mark, Marsha; *ed:* Shippensbu (BS) Scndry Ed 1971; Penn St Univ (MED) Ed 1993; *cr:* North Ca Scndry Lang Arts Tchr 1971-75; Spring Grove HS Scndry Lang A 1985-; *ai:* Adv Stu Cncl, Project Harmony; NEA, PSEA, NCTE 19 Bd 1984-; Spring Grove PTA 1983-; York Human Relations Com 1993; *office:* Spring Grove HS Hanover & Jackson St Spring G 17362*

MOSSER, VON WILLIAM, Physics Teacher; *b:* Cumberland, Linda Jean Brown; *ed:* WV Univ (BS) Scndry Ed, Physics & Gen 1988; 36 Grad Hrs at Frostburg St Univ; *cr:* Catoctin HS Physics Sci Tchr 1988-89; Northern MS 8th Grd Sci Tchr 1989-94; N Garrett HS Physics Tchr 1994-; *ai:* Band Asst Dir; Sr Class Adv; Ja Adv; NEA 1988-; MD Virtual HS 1995-; Past Prom Comm; Marietta Grad Fellows Prgm 1995; NEWMAST at Goddard Spac Ctr 1993; MD Governors Acad 1991; *office:* Northern Garrett HS Pkwy Accident MD 21520

MOSSER, WILLEDA WILSON, Fourth Grade Teacher; *b:* Cum MD; *m:* Von A.; *c:* Von William; *ed:* Frostburg St Univ (BS) Elem E (MED) Ed 1967; *cr:* West Side Schl Third Grd Tchr 1960-64; Wes Elem Third & Fourth Grd Tchr 1964-72; Fountain Elem Fourth G 1972-73; Westernport Elem Fourth Grd Tchr 1973-; *ai:* After Schl Prgm; NEA, MSTA & Allegany Cty Tchrs Assn 1960-; PT Membership; Fountain EB in Christ Choir 1971- Dir; *office:* Wers Elem Schl Church St Westernport MD 21562

MOSSMAN, CLAUDIA, HS Business Education Teacher; *b:* Huds *ed:* Cntrl CT St Univ (BS) Bus Ed, Dis Ed 1969; SUNY at Albany(M Ed, Dis Ed 1975; SUNY at Cobleskill Bus Admin 1965; Souther Univ Admin 1989; *cr:* Northwestern HS Tchr 26 Yrs; *ai:* Adv Clas House Cncl; Act Coord; NTA, CEA, NEA, CBEA 1969-; NIA, Pres, Northwestern Regional HS 100 Battistoni Dr Winsted CT 06098

MOSSMAN, RICHARD PHILLIP, Social Studies Tchr & Ath Hudson, NY; *m:* Linda Hedin; *c:* Brett, Jennifer; *ed:* SUNY at Alba His 1970, (MA) Ed 1973; Post Grad Stud; *cr:* Chatham Cntrl Sch Coord 1970; Germantown Cntrl Schl Soc Stud Tchr 1970-; *ai:* Ath D Stud Master Tchr; AFT 1970-; *office:* Germantown Central Schl 12 St Germantown NY 12526*

MOSTELLER, GWEN THERESA, Life Science & Biology Tea Elizabeth, NJ; *ed:* Clarion Univ (BS) Scndry Ed Bio, Gen Sci Shippensburg Univ (MED) Educl Admin 1995; 4 Credit Hrs Sci, Tec *cr:* Williams Vly Schl Dist Life Sci, Bio Tchr 1990-; *ai:* Environmental Club Adv; Stu Assistance; Distance Learning Proje Peer Helper; Peer Mediator Adv; Head Swim Coach; NEA, PSEA, 1990-; NASAA, NASSP 1992-; Luth Home Meals on Adopt-A-Hwy 1993-; *office:* Williams Valley Jr Sr HS Rt 209 Tow PA 17980*

MOSTERT, DARLENE, Teacher; *b:* Grimsby ON, Canada; *m:* Rachel; *ed:* Calvin Coll (BA) Ed & Lang Arts 1986; 3 Credit Co Brock Univ; 1 Credit Course at Redeemer Coll; *cr:* Calvin Meml 2nd-4th Grd Sub Tchr 1986-93; *ai:* OCSTA 1986-, Mem.

MOSTOLLER, CYNTHIA SCHOLZ, Soc Stud & Amer His T Medina, OH; *m:* Karl Evangelisti; *ed:* Univ of Akron (BA) His 1983 Trinity Coll, Lewis & Clark Univ, Univ of Northern CO, Howar Western KS Univ & Portland St; *cr:* Deal Jr HS Soc Stud Tchr 19 Stu Cncl Co-Adv; Restructuring & Schl Chapter Advy Comms; Dep WA Tchrs Union 1986-; DC Geographic Alliance 1993-, Steering DC Historical Soc, His Bd; Presidential Tchr Awd 1995; Parents Cornerstone Awd 1995; Agnes Myer Candidate 1994; *office:* Alice HS Ft Dr & Nebraska Ave NW Washington DC 20016*

MOSTOW, ROBERT ALAN, Theatre, Television & Eng T Washington, DC; *m:* Quincy; *c:* Samantha, Megan; *ed:* Univ of College Park (BA) Scndry Ed 1975, (MA) Scndry Ed 1985; Attnd A fo Stanislavski Theatre Art, Univ of UT; *cr:* Leland Jr HS Theat Tchr 1976-79; Paint Branch HS Theatre, Television, Eng Tchr 19 Mid Sts Production Comm Chprsn 1994; Theatre Dir 1979-84, 19 Forensics Coach 1989-; Jr Var Bsbl Coach 1984-87; Weight Roo 1992-; MSTA, MCEA, NEA 1976-; Rockville Little Theatre 1992- Hat Awd; Attnd Seminar by Dir of Moscow Art Theatre Columbia *home:* 3208 Llewellyn Field Rd Olney MD 20832

MOTELL, PHIL, High School English Teacher; *b:* Scranton, Suzanne T.; *c:* Nicole Dimatos, Phillip A., Jason J., Michael; *ed:* Scranton (BA) Eng 1965, (MS) Rdng 1968; Binghamton Univ Sa Leave 1984; *cr:* Owego Appalachian Schls Eng Tchr 1966-; *ai:* A Instr Syracuse Univ; AFT 1970-; O-A Tchrs Assn 1966-; Binghamto Rdng Cncl 1973-, Treas; Dollars for Scholars, Treas; NY Cncl for Local Coord; Supts Educl Advy Cncl Chm; Natl Fellowship for In in Hum Cncl for Basic Ed 1987; Natl Seminar for Schl Tchrs 1988, NY St Eng Cncl Tchr of Excl; *office:* Owego Free Acad George St NY 13827

MOTKO, JO RENEE, Second Grade Teacher; *b:* Butler, PA; *m:* Da Lauren, Mindi; *ed:* Indiana Univ of PA (BS) Elem Ed 1973; Slipper Univ (MS) Elem Ed 1976; *cr:* Jefferson Elem Schl Second Grd Tchr *ai:* PSEA 1973-; *office:* Jefferson Elem Schl 650 Saxonburg Rd Bu 16001

MOTT, DIANNE ILLSLEY, Instrumental Music Teache Gloversville, NY; *m:* John; *c:* Andy; *ed:* Roberts Wesleyan Col Music Ed 1984; Coll of Saint Rose (MA) Music Ed 198 Oppenheim-Ephratah Cntrl Schl Instrumental Music Tchr & Music 1984-; *ai:* Marching Band; Jazz Ensemble; Concert Band; OE Quartet; "J" Jazz; Cadet Band; FCMEA 1984-; Herkimer All-Cty Conductor 1993; Disney World Band Guest Conductor 1992; Sp Amer Marching Band European Tour 1990; *home:* 263 Lakesi Mayfield NY 12117*

MOTT, NANCY FRASER, Sixth Grade Teacher; *b:* Takoma Park *m:* Robert O.; *c:* Robert K., Jennifer L., Susan E.; *ed:* Cornell Univ Home Ec 1964; Eastern Nazarene Coll (MED) Ed 1991; Post Grad W Bridgewater St Coll, OK St Univ, Embry-Riddle Aeronautical Un Brockton Chrstn Schl 6th Grd Tchr 1988-; *ai:* Yrbk Adv; Soccer Video Teams Adv; Quilting Club Adv; Schl Tech Advy Comm; S Coord; Natl His Day Adv; ACSI 1988-; NSTA 1993-; MMED 199 1971-, Ldr, MA Salute to Excl Winner; Addison-Wesley Tchr F NASA Newest Hnr Tchr; *office:* Brockton Chrstn Schl 1367 M Brockton MA 02401

MOTTER, MELISSA MARY, Fifth Grade Teacher; *b:* Johnstown, P Univ of Pittsburgh (BS) Elem Ed 1987; Western MD Coll (MS) Curr 1994; *cr:* New Market Elem 5th Grd Tchr 1987-; *ai:* Math Ldr; M Planning Comm; NEA, Frederick Co Tchrs Assn 1987-; *office:* Market Elem Schl PO Box 284 New Market MD 21774*

MOTTICE, WILLIAM, 7th Grade Teacher; *b:* Akron, OH; *m:* Jo Donald, William, Gregory, Melissa; *ed:* Kent St Univ (BS) Soc Stud Masters Equivalency in Credit Hrs Akron Univ; *cr:* Stow City Schls Coach 1964-; *ai:* Girls Jr Var, Asst Var Bsktbl Coach; NEA, OEA hrs Assn 1964-, Negotiator 5 Yrs; Successful Businessman; *office:* ı MS 380 N River Rd Munroe Falls OH 44262

LESSEAUX, KAREN LYNN, Secondary English Teacher; *b:* City, NY; *ed:* SUNY at Cortland (BA) Scndry Eng Ed 1988, (MS_ Eng Ed 1991; *cr:* Greene Cntrl Schl Scndry Eng Tchr 1988-; *ai:* CTE 1988-; *office:* Greene Cntrl Schl 40 S Canal St Greene NY

OULIS, MARY PITSILOS, Third Grade Teacher; *b:* Lefkara, Isld us; *m:* Thomas; *c:* Bill; *ed:* Moravian Coll (BS) Elem Ed 1966; ehigh Univ, Penn St Univ, Stroudsburg Univ; I. U. 20 Ed; *cr:* w Schl 6th Grd Tchr 1969-82; William Penn Elem Schl 3rd Grd 83-; *ai:* Stu Cncl Adv 1984-94; BEA, PSEA, NEA 1969-; Dream rue Bd 1982-92, Dream Maker Awd; Camelot House for Children 5-93; Bethlehem Bulletin Feature Writer; Globe Times Pet Tchr; 301 Lord Byron Dr Bethlehem PA 18017

TON, CLAUDIA JEAN, Kindergarten Teacher; *b:* Potsdam, NY; niv Coll At Brockport (BS) Elem Ed 1969; 30 Plus Hrs Permanent Univ Coll at Potsdam; *cr:* Madrid-Waddington Elem Schl First Grd 69-85, Kndgtn Tchr 1985-; *ai:* JV Girls Bsktbl Coach 1981-82; ; Madrid-Waddington Tchr Assn 1969-, Treas; 4-H Mem, Ldr; Girl Scouts 1969-, Jr GS Ldr, Brownie GS Ldr, Daisy GS Ldr; earning Ctr Grant.

TON, DONNA CARVOTTA, High School Math Teacher; *b:* MA; *m:* Howard A.; *c:* Jeffrey, Anthony; *ed:* Univ of MA (BA) ED, 69; 33 Post Grad Credits Salem St & Fitchburg St Coll; *cr:* Digital ent Co GED Instr 1975-80; Austin Prep HS Math Tchr 1980-85; H HS Math Tchr 1985-1986; St John's Preparatory HS Math Tchr i: NHS Adv; Admisions Comm; NASAA 1990-; *office:* Saint Johns hl 72 Spring St Danvers MA 01923

TON, TAMMY LYNN FRITH, Science & Mathematics Teacher; hegan, ME; *m:* Nathan; *c:* Kassandre, Krysta; *ed:* Univ of ME at (BS) Elem Ed 1986; Project Adventure Ropes Trng, Portfolio nent, Main Streaming, Research in Classroom, Outdoor dness, MS Inst; *cr:* Athens Elem Schl 7th & 8th Grd Sci & Math 86-; *ai:* Boys Bsktbl Coach; Steering Comm Beacon Grant; Sci Fair NEA 1986-; *office:* Athens Elem Schl Main St PO Box 167 Athens 12

EN, ROSEMARY THOMPSON, Third Grade Teacher; *b:* Fresno, Jamal; *ed:* CT Coll (BA) Studio Art, Certfd Elem Ed 1973; n Univ (MALS) Arts, Lit 1983; 3 Credits Towards CAS; *cr:* A. W. m Schl 4th Grd Tchr 1973-74, 3rd Grd Tchr 1974-; *ai:* NEA, CEA, 73-, Negotiating Team, VP, Bldg Rep; *office:* A W Cox Elem Schl ee Mile Crse Guilford CT 06437

DSCHEIN, RICHARD JOSEPH, Mathematics Teacher; *b:* wn, PA; *m:* Christina Lynn Thomas; *c:* Stefanie, Steven; *ed:* va Univ (BS) Math 1976; *cr:* Daniel Boone Schl Dist Math Tchr ; Emmaus HS Math Tchr 1979-; *ai:* Curr Revision Comm Geom; 977-; NEA 1977-; PCTM 1977-; NCTM 1977-; *office:* Emmaus HS th St Emmaus PA 18049

TAIN, CARLETON JOHN, US History & Government Tchr; *b:* ster, MA; *m:* Virginia Craig; *c:* Aaron Craig, Allix Craig; *ed:* rg St (BS) His 1973, (MED) US His 1978; *cr:* North Middlesex S US His, Gov't Tchr 1973-; *ai:* MA Stu Gov't Act; NM Tchrs Assn, rs Assn, NEA 1975-; Town of Ashby Bd Selectmen 1978-85, Chm; tice of Peace 1985-; *home:* 240 South Rd Ashby MA 01431

TCASTLE, DEIRDRE DEGARMO, First Grade Teacher; *b:* re, NY; *m:* John; *c:* Sean, Trevor; *ed:* Southampton Coll (BA) Eng . W. Post (MS) Elem Ed 1971; 60 Addl Credits at Coll of St Rose, chelle; *cr:* Eastport Schl 2nd Grd Tchr 1969; Rocks Village Schl Tchr 1970; Babylon Elem Schl 1st Grd Tchr 1971-; *ai:* Storytelling Teach Adults; AFT, NEA 1969-; St Peters Theater Group 1969-; Stu 986-; *office:* Babylon Elem Schl 171 Ralph Ave Babylon NY

TFORD, MARTHA THURLOW, English Teacher; *b:* South ME; *c:* Andrew, Joseph; *ed:* Univ of ME (BS) Ed, Eng 1971; *cr:* chl 7th Grd Lang Arts Tchr 1973-74; Jordan Small Schl 4th Grd hr 1974-76; Windham HS Eng Tchr 1976-; *ai:* Windham Educators E Educators Assn 1976-; MCELA 1988-; *office:* Windham HS 406 d Windham ME 04062

TFORD, ROXANNE D., English Professor; *b:* Kansas City, KS; iam F. Endres; *ed:* Malone Coll (BA) Eng 1984; OH St Univ (MA) 89, (PHD) Eng 1991; *cr:* OH St Univ Tchng Asst 1984-89, Admin 89-90; Otterbein Coll Adj Fac 1990-91; Rensselaer Poly Inst Asst 91-; *ai:* Adv Women Stdnts Assn; Chair Women, Gender Stud Prgm; ive Learning Task Force; Modern Lang Assn 1990-; NCTE 1987-; c Soc of Amer 1992-; Shenendehowa K-12 Lang Arts Comm 1992-, ep; Regents Coll 1995-, Univ Consultant; Grants: Distngd Tchng 1992-94, Rsrch 1989-90, 1993; Numerous Articles, Book Chptrs

TS, DOROTHY L., Math Teacher; *b:* Philipsburg, PA; *m:* Joel E. Brent; *ed:* Clarion Univ (BS) Math 1972, (MA) Math 1974; *cr:* Du rea HS Math Tchr 1972-; *ai:* NEA, PSEA 1972.

ER, JOYCE ELAINE, 3rd Grade Teacher; *b:* Springfield, OH; *m:* l D.; *ed:* OH St Univ (BS) Elem Ed 1970; Wright St Univ (ME) Tchr 88; *cr:* Northeaster Bd of Ed Tchr of Neurologically Handicapped 7th & 8th Grd Tchr 1971-72, 6th Grd Tchr 1973-76, 2nd Grd Tchr 9, 5th Grd Tchr 1979-80, 3rd Grd Tchr 1980-; *ai:* NEA & OEA NELEA 1972-, Sec & Bldg Rep; OSU Alumni Assoc 1971-; Wright nni Assoc 1988-; *home:* 2944 Malibu St Springfield OH 45503

'ON, PATRICIA P., English Teacher; *b:* Biltmore, NC; *m:* Stephen l; *c:* David, Joanna; *ed:* Maryville Coll (BA) Eng 1961; Syracuse MS) Rdng Ed 1979; Syracuse Univ Advanced Lit Theory; *cr:* North se Cntrl Schls Rdng Tchr 1961-70, Eng Tchr 1979-81; Liverpool chls Eng Tchr 1981-; *ai:* NYSUT 1979-; Delta Kappa Gamma 1985, JS Distinguished Tchr 1986; Tchr of Excl Eng 1989; NEH Fellow r Seminar 1987, Inst 1990; *office:* Liverpool HS 4338 Wetzel Rd ool NY 13090*

'ON, STEPHEN EDWARD, HS English Teacher; *b:* Philadelphia, Patricia Anne Penland; *c:* David, Joanna; *ed:* Maryville Coll (BS) Eng 1959; 42 Credit Hrs Permanent Scndry Eng Cert Syracuse r: Roxboro Rd Jr HS Eng Tchr 1960-63; Gillette Rd Jr HS Eng Tchr 7; Cicero HS Eng Tchr 1968-84; Cicero-N Syracuse HS Eng Tchr *ai:* Drama, Co-Dir Schls Musical, Fall Play 28 Yrs; Subscription ance Syrause Stage Spon; Acad Decathalon Preparation Coach; AFT NSEA 1960-, Bldg Rep; Cicero Amateur Summer Theater 1969-86, ounder; NYS Eng Cncl Tchr of Excl Drama 1986; *office:* -North Syracuse HS Rt 31 Cicero NY 13039

BRAY, JOHN SCOTT, PE Teacher; *b:* Hagerstown, MD; *m:* e Fry; *ed:* Frostburg St (BA) PE 1985; Western MD (MS) Ed 1995; shington Cty B of Ed Tchr, Coach 1986-; *ai:* Var Boys Bsktbl Coach; 986-; *home:* 13308 Birchwood Ln Hagerstown MD 21740

CHAN, LINDA MARIE, Russian Teacher; *b:* Huntingdon, PA; *ed:* son Coll (BA) Russian Lang, Lit, Russian, Soviet Areas Stud 1992; sville Univ Cert in Russian 1996; 9 Credits Univ of Pittsburgh; 15 Credits Millersville Univ; 3 Credits Saint Francis Coll; *cr:* Grier Schl Eng as Second Lang Tchr 1995; Tussey Mountain HS Russian Tchr 1992-; *ai:* Russian Class, NHS Adv; Stu Assistance Prgm; Omicron Delta Kappa 1992-; Dobro Slovo 1991-; *home:* RR 1 Box 242 Hesston PA 16647

MOWEN, ROBERT EARL,JR., Automotive Technology Instr; *b:* Dayton, OH; *m:* Julia D.; *c:* Robin Layne, Angela, Robert A., Dennis; *ed:* Univ of Cincinnati (BA) Voc Ed 1982; General Motors Trng Ctr 15 Yrs; North Western Auto Coll 10 Yrs; Sinclaire Coll 2 Yrs; *cr:* Barry Chev Old & Buick Line Mechanic 1968-76; Mowens Pennzoil Self-Employed Full Svc Station 1976-78; OH Vly Voc Schl Automotive Tech Tchr 1978-; *ai:* VICA Club Adv 1987-; Adams Cty Jr Fair Adv 1989-90; VICA Club of Amer Club; NEA 1978-; AUTO 1985-, Southwest Rep; Adams Cty Spcl Olympics 1988-, Coord; ASE Master Certfd Mechanic since 1976; Top 10 Voc Tchr by St of OH; *home:* Star Rt 41 #8652 Aberdeen OH 45101

MOWERY, CHARLES G., High School Business Teacher; *b:* Bloomsburg, PA; *m:* Sara Lynn Miller; *c:* Rebecca, J. Aaron; *ed:* Bloomsburg Univ of PA (BS) Bus Ed 1968, (MEd) Bus Ed 1980; Multnomah Bible Coll at Portland Cert 1974; Shippensburg Univ of PA 6 Credits; *cr:* Highlands Chrstn Acad Bus Tchr 1974-77; Mount Union Area HS Bus Tchr 1978-; *ai:* Sr Class, FBLA & Power Source Adv; Adv & Techs Comm Mem; NEA & PSEA 1978-; MUAEA 1978-, Treas; C&MA Church 1979-, Treas; US Naval Reserves 1978-; *office:* Mount Union Area HS 706 N Shaver St Mount Union PA 17066

MOWREY, JAMES, Graphic Design Program Coord; *b:* Wooster, OH; *ed:* OH St Univ (BSID) Visual Comm Dsgn; Temple Univ (MFA) Visual Design; ME Coll of Art Summer Prgm Graphic Design; *cr:* Battelle Meml Inst Display Technician 1986-88; Fitch Richardson Smith Production Designer 1989; Visual Snytax Inc Designer 1990; Tyler Schl of Art 1991-93; Marywood Coll Full-Time Fac, Graphic Design Prgm Dir 1993-; *ai:* Comms Acad Computing Advy, Womens; Graphic Identity Sub Comm; Type Dir Club 1993-; AIGA 1986-; Amer Ctr for Design; Philharmonic League of Scranton Design; Scranton Mac Users Group Liason; Designer for Scranton Singers Guild; Pub in Print Magazine; Clients PGSA, Fox 38, Contemporary Gallery, Marywood Coll; *home:* RR 3 Box 3468 Union Dale PA 18470

MOYER, BRUCE EUGENE, Professor of Bible & Theology; *b:* Lexington, KY; *m:* Ruth Alice Atherton; *ed:* Vennard Coll (BA) Bible & Theology 1975; Wesley Biblical Coll (MDIV) Pastoral Stud 1980; Trinity Intnl Univ (THM) Systematic Theology 1986; Marquette Univ (PHD) Historical Theology 1992; *cr:* St Paul Theological Seminary La Paz Bolivia Dir 1982-85; Vennard Coll Prof Bible & Theology 1988-90, 1992-95; Circleville Bible Coll Prof Bible &Theology 1996; *ai:* Commission On the Discipline The Evangelical Church; Wesleyan Theological Soc 1980; City of University Park 1993-95, Councilman; Delta Epsilon Chi; Alumnus of Yr 1995 Wesley BiblicalSeminary; Pub 2 Vol Systematic Theology, Monthly Devotionals in Daily Thoughts on Holiness; *office:* Circleville Bible Coll PO Box 458 Circleville OH 43113

MOYER, CHARLES N., Teacher of the Gifted; *b:* Reinholds, PA; *ed:* Millersville Univ (BA) Elem Ed 1981; Post-Grad Work Gifted Ed; *cr:* Muhlenberg Schl Dist 5th Grd Tchr 1982-83; Berks Cty Intermediate Unit #14 Tchr of Gifted 1983-91; Conrad Weiser Area Schl Dist Tchr of Gifted 1991-; *ai:* NEA; Gifted Ed Assn of Rdng Awd 1989; *office:* Conrad Weiser Area Schl Dist 347 E Penn Ave Robesonia PA 19551

MOYER, CYNTHIA L., Art Supervisor & Teacher; *ed:* Millersville St Coll (BS) Art Ed 1971; Kutztown St Coll (MA) Art Ed 1975; Supervision Cert in Art Ed 1993; Pratt Inst Fashion Design 1966-68; *cr:* Hempfield Schl Dist JH Art Tchr 18 Yrs, 9th-12th Grd Art Supvr & Tchr 7 Yrs; *ai:* NEA & PSEA 1971-; NAEA & PAEA 1989-; Amer Cncl of the Arts 1989-; Amer Craft Cncl 1989-; Scholastic Art Awds, Regnl Advy Comm; Governors Schl of the Arts, Selection Comm; CreARTivity Gifted Pgm of Art, Artist in Residence; *office:* Hempfield HS 200 Stanley Ave Landisville PA 17538

MOYER, DAVID ROY, Math Teacher; *b:* Millerstown, PA; *ed:* Shippensburg Univ (BSEd) Math 1986; *cr:* Bishop Mc Devitt HS Math Tchr 1986-; *ai:* Jr Class Stu Cncl Moderator; Stu Assistance Team; NCEA 1986-; PASAP 1990-; *office:* Bishop Mc Devitt HS 2200 Market St Harrisburg PA 17103

MOYER, JOHN THAYER, Language Arts Teacher; *b:* Meadville, PA; *ed:* Edinboro St Coll (BS) Sec Ed Eng 1977, (AS) Cmptr Tech 1983; Edinboro Univ of PA (MED) Sec Schl Admin 1990; The Univ of Akron PHD Curr Stu 1991-; *cr:* Mc Dowell Intermediate HS Eng Tchr 1978-88; James S. Wilson MS Lang Arts Tchr 1989-; *ai:* NEA, PSEA, MEA 1989-; Outstdng Young Eductr Awd Presque Isle Jaycess 1979-80; Pub Article; *office:* James S Wilson MS 901 W 54th St Erie PA 16509

MOYER, JOY CHARMAINE, Physical Education & Hlth Tchr; *b:* Lancaster, PA; *ed:* Washington Bible Coll (BA) Bible, PE 1990; 3 Addl Credits Columbia Univ; *cr:* Chapel Chrstn Acad PE, Hlth Tchr, Var Coach 1990-; *ai:* Class of 1996 Adv 4 Yrs; Girls Vlybl, Bsktbl, Sftbl Var Coach; Sports Camps; *office:* Chapel Christian Acad 378 W Ridge Pike Linfield PA 19468

MOYER, KAREN LYNN, Health Related Tech Tchr; *b:* Ashiya, Japan; *m:* Barry Keith; *c:* Stephanie, David; *ed:* Moravian Coll (BS) Medical Tech 1978; Lehigh Univ (MED) Scndry Ed 1990; *cr:* Saint Lukes Hospital Hematology Instr & Medical Tech 1978-86; Christopher Dock HS Chem & Physics Tchr 1986-88; Saint Marys Area HS Hlth Related Tech, Bio & Chem Tchr 1988-; *ai:* HOSA Club Adv; Cross Cntry, Track & Swimming Boosters; PSEA, NEA 1990-; Article Pub; *office:* St Marys Area HS 977 S Saint Marys Rd Saint Marys PA 15857*

MOYER, LUTHER SAMUEL, Mathematics Teacher; *b:* Guntur, South India; *m:* Veronica Kathleen Rugg; *c:* Kathleen Billings, David Covert, Christina Shulman, Ed, Eric, Kelly Adams; *ed:* Muhlenburg Coll (BA) Psych, Math 1961; Montclair Coll (MA) Psych of Tchng 1977; 24 Addl Hrs St Peter's Coll; *cr:* Asbury Pk HS Math Tchr 1961-; *ai:* Church Choir; Soccer Referee; NEA, NJEA, MCEA, APEA 1961-; AMTNJ 1964-; Jaycees 1968-, Treas, Spark Plug; *office:* Asbury Park HS 1001 Sunset Ave Asbury Park NJ 07712

MOYER, MARY LAUBACH, Business Education Teacher; *b:* Danville, PA; *m:* Robert Mc Clellan; *ed:* Lock Haven St Coll (BS) Hlth, PE 1973; Bloomsburg Univ (BS) Bus Ed, Acctng 1984; 45 Addl Credits UT St Univ; *cr:* Cntrl Columbia HS PE Tchr 1974; Sullivan Cty HS PE Tchr 1974-84; Williamsport Area Comm Coll PE Tchr 1985-86; Millville Area HS Bus Ed 1986; Sullivan Cty HS Bus Ed 1986-; *ai:* FBLA; Frosh Class Adv; NEA, PSEA 1974-; AAHPERD 1969-; NBEA 1986-; AAUW 1996; Delta Kappa Gamma 1992-; Sull Co Schlsp Assn 1990-, Bd of Dir; *office:* Sullivan Cty HS PO Box 98 South & Beech Sts Laporte PA 18626*

MOYER, MARY JANE CLARK, 7th Grd Social Studies Teacher; *b:* Norristown, PA; *m:* Robert F.; *c:* R. Scott, Christopher M., Megan E. Seiber, Sean M.; *ed:* East Stroudsburg Univ (BA) Elem Ed; Rosemont Coll 2 Yrs Undergraduate; Shippensburg Univ Post Grad Stud; *cr:* Blain Jr HS Eng, PE Tchr 1966-68; West Perry Jr HS PE, Hlth Tchr 1970-71; Green Park Elem Schl 6th Grd Lang Arts Tchr 1975-91; West Perry MS 7th Grd Soc Stud Tchr 1991-; *ai:* HS Field Hockey Coach 21 Yrs; Dist Staff Dev, Strategic Planning Comms; WPEA; PSEA; NEA; South Cntrl PA Lead Tchr Advy Bd; Perry Hlth Ctr Bd of Dirs 1970-, Sec; Norristown HS Hall of Fame; Lead Tchr Grants; Field Hockey Coach of Yr; *office:* West Perry MS RR 2 300 W High St New Bloomfield PA 17068

MOYER, PATRICIA MARINO, 2nd Grade Teacher; *b:* Clearfield, PA; *m:* Larry K.; *ed:* Edinboro Univ (BS) Elem Ed 1975; *cr:* Girard Elem Schl 2nd Grd Tchr; Clearfield Area Schl Dist; *ai:* NEA 1976-.

MOYER, PETER CLAYTON, Soc Studies Tchr & Swim Coach; *b:* Waynesboro, PA; *m:* Sue Ann; *c:* Christopher, Jeffrey; *ed:* Bucknell Univ (BS) Ed, Sociology 1976; Attnd Penn St Univ, IN Univ of PA; *cr:* Waynesboro Area Schl Dist Tchr 1976-77; SC Schl Dist Tchr, Swim Coach 1977-; *ai:* Various Schl Clubs; NEA 1976-; NCSS 1986-; Am Swim Coaches Assn, Natl Interscholastic Swim Coaches 1980-; PA St HS Swim Coaches, 1st VP 1989-91, Pres 1991-93; YMCA 1985-; Local Recreation Assn, Bd Mem; Several Articles on Swimming Pub; *office:* Park Forest MS 2180 School Dr State College PA 16803*

MOYER, R. BRUCE, Secondary Mathematics Teacher; *b:* Sellersville, PA; *m:* Jodelle Detweiler; *c:* Cheramie Noelle, Caleb Luke; *ed:* Bluffton Coll (BS) Math 1965; Attnd Bowling Green St Univ, Penn St Univ at State College, Lehigh Univ at Bethlehem; *cr:* Bluffton HS Scndry Math Tchr, Asst Ftbl 1965-66, Scndry Math Tchr, Head Ftbl, Track Coach 1967-69; Pennridge HS Scndry Math Tchr, Asst Ftbl Coach 1970-86, Scndry Math Tchr, Head Ftbl Coach 1987-89, Scndry Math Tchr 1990-; *ai:* OSEA 1965-69; NEA 1965-; PEA 1970-; Buck's Cty Bd of Realtors 1982-; Blooming Glen Mennonite Church 1959-, Adult Chrstn Ed, Yth Chrstn Ed, Usher Coord; Ftbl Coach of Yr Toledo Blade Awd 1969; Ftbl Coach of Yr Lima News Awd 1969; *office:* Pennridge HS 1228 N 5th St Perkasie PA 18944

MOYLAN, EILEEN RICCI, 6th & 7th Grade Science Tchr; *b:* Bristol, CT; *m:* Thomas Michael; *c:* Amy E., Megan L.; *ed:* CCSU (BS) Elem Ed 1973, (MS) Elem Ed 1980; Sci Wesleyan Univ 1992; *cr:* J.J. Jennings Pub Schl 4th & 5th Grd Tchr 1974-76; Ivy Dr Pub Schl 4th Grd Tchr 1976-77; Ms Porter's Private Schl 1987-90; Greene Hills Pub Schl 6th Grd Tchr 1990-91; Memorial Blvd Pub Schl 6th & 7th Grd Sci Tchr 1991-; *ai:* AFT 1974-; NSTA 1984-; *office:* Meml Boulevard Schl 70 Memorial Blvd Bristol CT 06010

MOYNIHAN, BETSY, Business Teacher; *b:* Amsterdam, NY; *ed:* Nazareth Coll of Rochester (BS) Bus 1973, (MS) Bus Ed 1988; Addl Grad Courses at Coll of St Rose at Albany NY; SUNY at Oswego; Syracuse Univ; SUNY at Albany; *cr:* West Genesee HS Bus Tchr 1973-, Bus Dept Chprsn 1984-92, Bus, Hlth, Home Ec, Tech Bus Coord 1993-; *ai:* Tchrs Assn 1974-; *office:* West Genesee HS 5201 W Genesee St Camillus NY 13031

MOYNIHAN, JEROME DANIEL, Adj Instr of Economics & Bus; *b:* Natick, MA; *m:* Lorraine Asselin; *c:* Kathryn, Elizabeth; *ed:* Univ of RI (BA) Pol Sci 1974; Bryant Coll (MBA) Mngmt 1982; *cr:* Johnson & Wales Univ Adj Instr, Ec, Bus 1983-92; Fisher Coll Adj Instr Ec 1984-; *ai:* Natl Inst Govt Procurement 1995-; Natl Ass Purchasing Mgrs 1986-; RI Municipal Purchasing Agents Assn 1982-; Certfd Purchasing Mgr 1986; Certfd Pub Purchasing Ofcr 1995; *office:* Fisher Coll 70 Holcott Dr Attleboro MA 02703

MOYNIHAN, JUDITH TOMOLO, 7th Grd Math & Science Teacher; *b:* Clinton, MA; *m:* John T.; *c:* Timothy C., Mary Pat, Michael J.; *ed:* St Coll at Fitchburg (BS) Ed 1958; Post-Grad Stud at St Coll of Ma at Fitchburg, Worcester & Lowell; *cr:* West Boylston Jr Sr HS 7-8th Grd Math & Sci Tchr 1958-60; Regnl Cath Elem 4-6th Grd Soc Stud, Rel & PE Tchr 1973-75; Clinton MS 5th Grd Math & Sci Tchr 1975-88, 7th Grd Math & Sci Tchr 1988-; *ai:* Clinton Tchrs Assn 1975-, Exec Bd 1975-86; MA Tchrs Assn, NEA 1975-; Delta Kappa Gamma 1984-; Friends of Clinton Lib Treas; George Weeks Fund Trustee; Confraternity of Chrstn Doctrine Educator 23 Yrs; 4H Cooking Instr; Clinton Little League Sec; Cub Scout Mother & Ldr; Historical Soc Curator; St Johns Chrch Lector; RCIA Yth Instr; Confraternity of Chrstn Doctrine Tchr of Yr 1992; Nanco Assoc of the Presentation of the Blessed Virgin Mary Order of Nuns; *office:* Clinton MS 100 W Bolyston St Clinton MA 01510*

MRAVINTZ, ANNE MARIE DIVELBISS, Kindergarten Teacher; *b:* Natrona Heights, PA; *m:* Jeffrey Alan; *ed:* Edinboro Univ (BS) Elem Ed, Early Chldhd 1991; 12 Addl Hrs; *cr:* Vly Comm Svcs K-4th Grd Tchr 1991-93; Highlands Schl Dist Kndgtn Tchr 1993-; *ai:* NEA, HEA 1993-; *office:* Highlands Schl Dist 1415 Freeport Rd Natrona Heights PA 15065

MRAZEK, MARK EDWARD,JR., Physics & Environmntl Sci Tchr; *b:* Chicago, IL; *m:* Suzanne Nelson; *ed:* Univ of Dayton (BSME) Mechanical Engrng 1991; Tchng Prgm Kent St Univ; *cr:* Rsrch Engr 1991-93; Regina HS Physics & Env Sci Tchr 1994-; *ai:* Physics Club, Environmental Club Moderators; JV Sftbl Coach; Schl Newspaper Co-Moderator; Drama Asst; NCEA, NDEA 1994-95; *office:* Regina HS 1857 S Green Rd South Euclid OH 44121

MRISS, PAUL E., Guidance Services Coordinator; *b:* Lehighton, PA; *m:* Ruth Ann Nothstein; *c:* Michael E., Patrick J., Allison L.; *ed:* Univ of Scranton (BS) Eng Ed 1973; Lehigh Univ (MED) Cnslng 1976; Univ of Scranton Admin Cert; *cr:* Bethlehem Cath HS Eng Tchr 1973-76; St Joseph's Schl 7th Grd Tchr 1976-78; Marian HS Guid Cnslr 1978-81; Hamburg Area HS Coord of Guid Svcs 1981-; *ai:* Heat Team; Prin Advy Cncl; Career Ed Consortium; NEA, PSEA 1981-; PA Schl Cnslrs Assn 1979-; Lehighton Fire Dept 1972-, Treas; Franklin Twsp L. L. 1988-, Coach; Lehighton Band 1968-; Lehighton Band Booster 1993-, Treas; *office:* Hamburg Area HS Windsor St Hamburg PA 19526

MROWKA, WILLIAM FRANCIS, Chemistry Teacher; *b:* New Haven, CT; *m:* Colleen Marof; *c:* Kate Victoria; *ed:* Quinnipiac Coll (BS) Psychobio 1987; Sacred Heart Univ (MAT) Ed 1990; Southern CT St Univ 6th Yr MS ISIS Sci 1996; *cr:* Dodd MS Sci Tchr 1992-94; Cheshire HS Chem Tchr 1994-; *ai:* Bsbl Coach 1988-; CT Ed Assn 1992; CT HS Coaches Assn 1990-; *office:* Cheshire HS 525 S Main St Cheshire CT 06410

MRVA, KIMBERLY ANN, HS Mathematics Teacher; *b:* Rochester, NY; *ed:* St Univ of NY at Geneseo (BA) Math & Scndry Ed 7th-12th Grd 1993; Working Toward Masters in General Scndry Ed at Nazareth Coll; *cr:* Greece Arcadia HS Math Tchr 1993-; *ai:* Assembly & Alternative Ed Comms; Peer Mediation Prgm; Bldg Mgmt Team; Mathematical Assn of Amer 1993-; NCTM 1992-; NEA 1993-; Assn of Math Tchrs of NY St; *home:* 45 Beatty Rd Rochester NY 14612*

MUCCOLINI, GENE PAUL, 9th-12th Grd Soc Stud Instr; *b:* Allentown, PA; *m:* Nancy Frable; *c:* Michael; *ed:* Kutztown Univ (BS) Scndry Ed 1964; Glassboro St (MA) Soc Sci 1970; Addl 15 Hrs Jr Coll Tchng; *cr:* Palmyra HS Instr 1964-; *ai:* Sftbl Coach 6 Yrs; Photography Adv 20 Yrs; Dir Cultural Affairs, Spec Pol Conf, Seminars Pol Sci Interest Stdnts; NEA, NJEA 1964-; Palmyra Ed Assn 1964-, VP 2 Yrs; Recognition Rutgers Uni One of Top 58 HS Tchrs in St 1990; Recognition Palmyra Schl Bd First Cert Excl Given to Tchrs 1991.

MUCHA, MARLENE M.,SSJ, Eng Tchr & Dept Chair; *b:* Whitinsville, MA; *ed:* Coll of Our Lady of the Elms (BA) Eng; Rhode Island Coll (MA) Eng; *cr:* Marianhill HS Eng Dept Chair, Tchr1965-69; Holyoke Cath HS Eng Dept Chair, Tchr 1969-; Honors Eng 4, Eng 4, Lit Explrtns, AP Eng Tchr; *ai:* Sr Class Adv; Accreditation Steering Com; Literary Club, Acad Bd; Craft Club; Alumni Bd; NCTE, MCTE, NCEA; Golden Apple Ed Awd; Galleon Awd in Journalism Yrbk; *office:* Holyoke Catholic H S 91 Chestnut St Holyoke MA 01040

MUDGE, JANE BENNIGHOFF, 2nd Grade Teacher; *b:* New Tripoli, PA; *m:* Terry; *c:* Kimber Lee, Bradley; *ed:* Mansfield St Coll (BS) Ed Elem

1967; Elmira Coll (MS) Ed 1975; *ai:* HS Bsktbl Team Scorekeeper; STEA, PSEA, NEA 1967-; Mansfield Univ Alumni Assoc 1967-, VP, Pres, Elsie Burke Svc Awd.

MUDGE, RANDY ALBERT, Athletic Dir & PE Teacher; *b:* Stamford, NY; *m:* Anne Truesdell-Mudge; *c:* Gregory Thomas, Zachary Lauren; *ed:* SUNY at Cobleskill (AA) Liberal Arts 1980; SUNY at Cortland (BSE) PE 1983; SUNY at Albany (MS) Ed Admin 1990; *cr:* Schenevus Cntrl PE, Hlth Tchr 1986-87; Hunter-Tannersville Cntrl Ath Dir, PE Tchr 1987-, Interim Prin 1995; *ai:* Var Sports Club Adv; Girls Var Soccer, Boys Var 4th-6th Grd Bsktbl, Bsbl Coach; DE Cty Leage Alignment, DE League Merger, Section IV Ethics & Task Force, Acad Eligibility, Fac Hiring Comm; DE Cty League Sect IV Rep; Sports Booster Club Liason; AFT, NYSUT 1986-; Hunter-Tannersville Tchrs Assn 1987-, VP, Negotiator; Headwaters Soccer Club 1990-, Bd Mem; *office:* Hunter-Tannersville Cntrl Schl Main St Tannersville NY 12485

MUDRA, JAMES GREGORY, 8th Grd American History Tchr; *b:* Cleveland, OH; *m:* Cynthia Sue Elmer; *c:* Mitchel, Brady; *ed:* OH Univ (BSEd) His Govt 1973; Attnd Ashland Univ; *cr:* Ontario MS 7th Grd Geography & 8th Grd Amer Hist Tchr 1973-79; Appleseed MS 8th Grd Amer His Tchr 1979-89; Malabar MS 8th Grd Amer His Tchr 1989-; *ai:* NEA 1977-, Past Local Pres Ed Assn Ontario; OH MS Assn 1979-; Tchr Educator of Yr 1983-84; *office:* Malabar MS 205 W Cook Rd Mansfield OH 44907

MUDRICK, SUSAN ELLEN, Assistant Dean; *b:* Chester, PA; *ed:* Temple Univ (BA) Psych 1973, (MA) Psych 1974; LaSalle Univ (MBA) Mrktg 1984; *cr:* Bridge Therapeutic Ctr Therapist 1975-81; LaSalle Univ Mngmt Adj Prof, Asst Dean 1984-; *ai:* NACADA 1995-; *office:* La Salle Univ School of Business 1900 W Olney Ave Philadelphia PA 19141

MUEHLBAUER, ERIC MARK, Biology Teacher; *b:* Brooklyn, NY; *m:* Esther Indelman; *c:* Stefan, Evan, Sarah, Mikael; *ed:* Hobart Coll (BA) Bio 1976; NY Univ (MS) Bio 1981; Bank Street Bilingual Ed, Spec Ed; *cr:* Walden Schl Bio Tchr 1982-84; Forest Hills HS Bio, Gen Sci Tchr 1984-; *ai:* Comm Work on Dev New Bio Curr for NY St Bio Regents; AFT, UFT 1984-; ACLU 1993-; Nature Conservancy 1985-; Brooklyn Botanic Garden 1978-; *home:* 6516 Cromwell Cres Rego Park NY 11374*

MUELLER, CAROL A., Instr of Hosp & Culinary Ed; *b:* Bronx, NY; *ed:* State Coll (BSEd) PE 1961; NH Coll (MS) Bus Ed 1993; 28 Credit Hrs Adult Ed at Boston Univ; *cr:* Boston Univ Cnslng 1963-65; Australia PE 1967-73; Loon Mountain Corp chef, Mgr 1978-81; Bus Owner 1981-89; NH Coll Culinary Co-op Dir 1989-; NH Tech Coll Consultant 1994-; *ai:* Curr Comm; SOS Taste of Nation Culinary Stdnts; Fr Hospitality Schl Liason; Coop for Culinarians Dir; CHRIE, ACF 1990-; BPWNH Inc 1978-, Local Pres, St Legislative Chair; HOBY 1992-, Bd Mem, St Level; Women of Yr Lincoln-Woodstock NH Area BPW; CHRIE Food & Beverage Exec; *office:* NH Coll 2500 N River Rd Manchester NH 03104

MUELLER, DONALD JOHN, Social Studies & Religion Tchr; *b:* Buffalo, NY; *ed:* Franciscan Coll (BA) Philosophy 1972; Saint Anthony on the Hudson (MTH) Theology 1977; Post Grad Stud at Canisius; *cr:* Blessed Sacrament Tchr 1972-80; Saint Joachim Prin 1980-83; Saint Gregory the Great Tchr 1983-; *ai:* Stu Cncl Adv; Soc Stud Chprsn; 8th Grd Adv; DETA 1993-, Rep; Soc Stud Of WNY 1991-, Rep; Natl Cath Educators 1986-; Response to Love Ctr 1993-, Adv, Svc Awd; World Univ Games Lesson Plan; Holocaust Museum WA Lesson Plan; *office:* St Gregory The Great Schl 250 Saint Gregory Ct Williamsville NY 14221

MUELLER, INGRID WALTRAUD, Lecturer in Nursing; *b:* Bremen, Germany; *ed:* Hunter Coll (BS) Nursing 1983; Hunter coll (mS) Psychiatric Nursing 1986; Attnd Pace Univ in Family Nurse Practioner Prgm Grad in July 96; *cr:* Cabrini Hospice RN 1986-90; NY Hospital Coswell Psychiatric RN 1990-91; St Lukes Hospital Home Care Nurse 1990-91; Bronx Comm Coll Lecturer 1991-; *ai:* Continuing Ed & Admition & Promotion Comm; Lailou to The Voice Coll Newspaper; Sigma Theta Tau 1982-, Membership, 1982; Leadership Awd Hunter Coll; For Presidency of Grad Stu Org 1986-; Lake Peekskill Civic Org 1990-, Bod; Lecture Sexuality & Intimacy in the Elderly at Sunnyside Sr Citizens Ctr; Queens & BCC Wkshp Kids & Hlth at Lake Peekskill; *office:* Bronx Comm Coll W 181 St & University Ave Bronx NY 10453

MUELLER, JACQUELINE GASIOR, English Teacher; *b:* Cleveland, OH; *m:* Leo J. Jr.; *c:* John, Christopher, Julie; *ed:* OH Univ (BS) Commnctn 1973; 24 Grad Hrs in Ed; Permanent PA Cert; *cr:* Strongsville Sr High 10th-12th Grd Eng & Jrnlsm Tchr 1973-76; St Athanasius Schl 7th-8th Grd Eng & Rel Tchr 1976-79; St Teresa Schl 7th-8th Grd Eng Tchr 1979-80, 7th-8th Grd Eng & Rel Tchr 1990-; *ai:* Forensics Moderator; NCEA 1990-; WPTE 1992-; NCTE 1994-; SPFL 1987-, Commnctn Coord; *office:* St Teresa of Avilla Schl 800 Avila Ct Pittsburgh PA 15237

MUELLER, JANYCE MORTE, Health Occupations Teacher; *b:* Yuma, AZ; *m:* Eric J.; *ed:* Univ of Portland (BSN) Nursing 1978; Oklahoma City Univ (MBA) Bus 1986; Grad Stud PA St Univ 16 Hrs Towards Masters in Voc Ed; Grad Command & General Staff Coll, US Army 1992; *cr:* US Army Clinical Head Nurse 1980-83; Great Plains Area Vo Tech LPN Instr 1984-86; York Hospital Staff Nurse 1989-93; York Cty Area Vo-Tech Hlth Occupations, Allied Hlth Sci Tchr 1992-; *ai:* Hlth Occupations Stdnts of Amer Adv; Amer Voc Assn 1993-; Amer Nurse Assn 1980-, VP PNA; Amer Red Cross 1982-, Instr; HOSA Adv 1991-; Army Commendation Medal; *office:* York Cty Area Voc-Tech Schl 2179 S Queen St York PA 17402

MUELLER, RAY W., Third Grade Teacher; *b:* Kaiserslautern, Germany; *m:* Barbara Jean Marshman; *c:* Robert David; *ed:* Temple Univ (BSEd) Elem Ed-Summa Cum Laude 1975; Lehigh Univ (MS) Admin, Supervision 1982; *cr:* Ringing Rocks Elem Schls 3rd Grd Tchr 1975-79, 5th Grd Tchr 1976-77, 2nd Grd Tchr 1979-87, 4th Grd Tchr 1987-90, 3rd Grd Tchr 1990-; *ai:* In-Svc, Long Range Planning Comms; Child Stud Team; NEA 1975-78, VP; AFT 1978-90, Bldg Rep; NEA 1990-; UCC Church 1978-, Planning; In-Svc Prgms Math Wkshps Tchr; *office:* Ringing Rocks Elem Schl 1301 Kauffman Rd Pottstown PA 19464*

MUELLER, ROBERT K., Assoc Prof & Acting Chm; *b:* Ellwood City, PA; *c:* Matthew, Brian, Emily; *ed:* Grove City Coll (BA) Math 1980; Syracuse Univ (MS) Math 1982, (MS) Electrical Engineering 1985, (PHD) Electrical Engineering 1989; *cr:* General Electric Prgm Engr 1982-85, Advanced-Course Supvr 1985-88, Systems Engr 1988-89; Grove City Coll Engineering Prof 1989-; EE Dept Chair 1994-; *ai:* Beta Sigma & Sr Design Project Adv; Pre-Prof Comm; IEEE 1987-; Borough Parks & Recreation Cncl 1994-; Summer Fac Research Prgm 1990-91, 1993; CISS 93 Article Pub; *office:* Grove City College 100 Campus Dr Box 2658 Grove City PA 16127

MUELLO, MARY JANE J., Health & Physical Ed Coord; *b:* Arlington, MA; *ed:* Bridgewater St Coll (BS) Hlth & PE 1978, (MS) PE 1990; *cr:* Haverhill HS PE Tchr & Coach 1979-81; Dana Hall Private Schl PE Tchr & Coach 1981-88; Wareham Pub Schls Coord Hlth & PE Tchr 1988-; *ai:* Peer Ldrshp & Mediation Adv; Hlth Advy Comm; NEA 1988-; MTA 1988-; WEA 1988-; MAHPERD 1992-; Tchng Prof Hnr Awd Plymouth Cty Ed Assn; *office:* Wareham Public School System Viking Dr Wareham MA 02571*

MUENCH, PHYLLIS AGRESTA, 4th Grade Teacher; *b:* Jersey City, NJ; *m:* Michael J.; *c:* Hope May, Philip May; *ed:* Lenoir Rhyne Coll (BA) Elem Ed 1964; *cr:* Quantico Dependents Schl System 2nd Grd Tchr 1964-66; Durham City Schls 3rd Grd Tchr 1966-70; South Mountain Elem Schl Compensatory Ed Tchr 1978-81; Immaculate Heart of Mary Schl 4th Grd Tchr 1982-; *ai:* NCEA 1982-; *office:* Immaculate Heart Of Mary Schl 276 Parker Ave Maplewood NJ 07040

MUENCHEN, G. JOE, Individual Instr & Pgm Coord; *b:* Cincinnati, OH; *m:* Moura Connolly; *ed:* Northern KY Univ (BA) Comm 1984; Univ of Cincinnati (MED) Spec Ed 1988; *cr:* Connelly Home Schl Pgrm Dir 1983-86; LaSalle HS Tchr 1987-; *ai:* Asst Bsktbl, Cross Cntry Coach; Frosh Moderator; Orton-Dyslexia Soc 1992-; Assn for Retarded Citizens 1984-; Oasis of Peace, Helping Hands 1995-, Bd Mem; Best Friend to Kids Cincinnati Magazine 1991; *office:* La Salle HS 3091 W North Bend Rd Cincinnati OH 45239

MUENZEN, MARIE, Second Grade Teacher; *b:* New York City, NY; *ed:* Fordham Univ (BS) Ed; Attnd St Joseph's Seminary Theology; *cr:* St Joseph Schl Second Grd Tchr 1956-59; Immaculate Conception Second Grd Tchr 1959-69; St Stanislaus Rel Ed Dir 1970-77; Immaculate Conception Schl Second Grd Tchr 1977-; *ai:* Immaculate Conception Church, Children's Catechumenate; *office:* Immaculate Conception Schl Winterhill Rd Tuckahoe NY 10707

MUESER, JOHN ALAN, Sixth Grade Teacher; *b:* New York, NY; *m:* Eileen Conde; *c:* James, Catherine; *ed:* Columbia Univ (BA) Eng 1971, (MA) Ed 1975, (MED) Admin 1986; *cr:* Mediator Day Schl Grd 1 Tchr 1970-71; St Hilda's & St Hugh's Schl Grd 5-6 Tchr 1971-80; Riverdale Cntry Schl Grd 6 Tchr 1980-; *ai:* After Schl Prgm, Summer Day Camp Dir; NCTM 1991-; Co-Author Practicing Rdng, Vocabulary; *office:* Riverdale Country Schl 5250 Fieldstone Rd Bronx NY 10471

MUFFLEY, JAMES DANIEL, Chemistry Teacher; *b:* Allentown, PA; *ed:* LaSalle Univ at Philadelphia (BA) Chem, Ed 1966; Villanova Univ at Philadelphia (MA) Chem 1973; Notre Dame Univ (MA) Theology 1983; Attnd LaSalle Univ, Duquesne, Wheeling Jesuit, Phila Coll of Textiles & Sci, St Mary's Coll of CA Courses in Ed, Chem, Theology; *cr:* Cntrl Cath HS Tchr, Dept Chair 1966-76; West Phila Cath HS Tchr, Dept Chair 1976-85; Bishop Walsh HS Tchr, Dept Chair 1985-88; West Phila Cath HS Tchr, Dept Chair 1988-93; Cntrl Cath HS Tchr, Dept Chair 1993-; *ai:* Musical Dir Asst; Band, Stu Cncl Moderator; NSTA 1970-; ACS Western PA; Brothers of Chrstn Schls 1961-; Sci Curr Comm Chair; Church Ministry Prgm; *office:* Central Catholic HS 4720 5th Ave Pittsburgh PA 15213

MUGGLESTON, PATRICIA GREENE, Language Arts Specialist; *b:* Fall River, MA; *m:* Robert Graham; *c:* Robert Jr., Laura; *ed:* SCSU (BS) Ed 1975; UCONN (Ma) Rdng 1994; 30 Addl Post Grad Credits CT Coll, Wesleyan, St Joseph, Fairfield Univ; Writing Project Columbia TC; *cr:* Clinton Glenwood Schl 1st Grd Tchr 1975-76; Madison-Ryerson 5th Grd Tchr 1976-77; Acad Elem Sch 3rd, 5th Grd Tchr 1977-88, Lang Arts Specialist 1988-; *ai:* Stu Cncl, Newspaper Adv; SE CT Rdg Assoc, Recording Sec 1995-; IRA; NCTE; TAWL; Phi Lambda Theta 1994; PEO; Essek Comm Fund, Past Pres; CT Celebration of Excl by SNET 1986; *office:* Acad Elem Schl 4 School St Madison CT 06443*

MUGLER, DALE H., Professor; *b:* Denver, CO; *m:* Karla E. Trechel; *c:* Paul, Emily; *ed:* Univ of CO (BA) Math 1970; Northwestern Univ (MA) Math 1971, (PhD) Math 1974; *cr:* Syracuse Univ Asst Prof 1974-75; Santa Clara Univ Asst Assoc Prof 1975-88; Univ of Akron Prof 1989-; *ai:* Church Youth Choir Dir; Math Asst Stu Chapter Adv; OH St Math Asst,Stu Comm Act Chair; Math Asst of Amer 1975, Tchng Awd 1993; Soc Industrial. Applied Math; IEEE; AJEE; Alexander von Humboldt Fellowship 1983-84; NAJA Summer Fac Fellowships 1988-89, 1991, 1992; *office:* Univ Of Akron Dept of Math Akron OH 44325

MUGNO, ALBERT MARK, Industrial Technology Coord; *b:* Paterson, NJ; *ed:* Montclair St Coll (BS) Tech Ed 1992; Montclair St Univ (MA) Industrial Ed & Tech 1995; 30 Post MA Credits; Cooperative Industrial Ed Cert; Supvrs Cert; *cr:* Kennedy Ind Arts Tchr 1992; Jersey City PS #14 5th-8th Grd Ind Arts Tchr 1992-93; Northern Highlands Regnl HS Industrial Tech Tchr 1993-; *ai:* Frosh & Soph Class Adv; Frosh Boys Soccer, JV Boys Asst Bsktbl & Var Asst Spring Track Coach; SAC & BRITE Comms; Bsktbl Interview Comm; Educl Tech & Commencement Goals Comms; Cafeteria & Foods Comm; Passaic Sussex Soccer Ofcls Assn 1989-; Phi Sigm Pi 1990-; NEA 1992-; NJEA 1992-; Episilon Pi Tau 1992-; Mike Mugno Schlsp Fund 1988-, Co-Chprsn; Knights of Columbus 1991-; Bergan Cty Soccer Coaches Assn 1996-; Article Pub 1988; Tech Stu of Yr MSC 1992; Outstdng Sr MSC 1992; *office:* Northern Highlands Reg HS Hillside Ave Allendale NJ 07401*

MUHA, ARLA H., English Teacher; *b:* Pittsburgh, PA; *ed:* Duquesne Univ, (BED) Scndry Ed, Eng 1962, (MA) Eng 1969; Comparative Ed Univ of London England; *cr:* Pittsburgh Pub Schls Eng Tchr 1962-; *ai:* Instructional Cabinet; Arts Propel Team; Delta Kappa Gamma 1978-, Pres 4 Yrs; NCTE 1965-; PNCTE 1980-; AFT; Bd of Trustees of Comm Lib of Castle Shannon 1984-, VP; Tchr of Yr St of PA Finalist 1991; Thanks to Tchrs Finalist; Speaker of NCTE Natl Convention; Pub Poetry; *office:* South Vo Tech HS 930 E Carson St Pittsburgh PA 15203

MUHILLY, MARYANN, English Teacher; *b:* Boston, MA; *ed:* Emmanuel Coll (BA) Eng 1975; Univ Coll of Dublin (MA) Anglo Irish Lit 1976; 45 Credit Hrs Beyond Masters; *cr:* Northern Essex Comm Coll Composition I-II Tchr 1977-; St Johns Prep Schl Eng Tchr 1980-; Northeastern Univ SAT, GMAT & LSAT Testing 1985-94; *ai:* NEA 1980-; NCTE 1980-; MTA 1990-; 2 NEH Flwshps; Northeastern Univ Tchng Excl Fac Awd; *office:* Saint Johns Prep Schl 72 Spring St Danvers MA 01923*

MUHLENBRUCK, RICHARD O., Science & History Teacher; *b:* Ney York, NY; *m:* Eileen Brennan; *c:* James, Lucy, Jill; *ed:* City Univ of NY (BA) Sci Ed 1975; Georgian Ct Coll (MA) Sci Ed 1991; Monmouth Coll Sci Ed Course; NJ Audobon Schl for Environmental Ed; *cr:* Brielle Elem Schl Night Custodian & Sub Tchr 1978-84; Spring Lake Hghts Schl 7th & 8th Grd Sci & His Tchr 1984-; *ai:* IM Dir; Boys & Girls Bsktbl Coach 1984-94; Schlsp Comm; Nat Geographic Soc 1976-; NEA 1984-; YMCA 1964-; NJ Governors Tchng Recognition Pgm SLH Tchr of the Yr 1987; *office:* Spring Lake Heights Elem Sch Rt 71 Spring Lake NJ 07762*

MUHLICH, ILONA MANOR, English Teacher; *b:* Lawrence, MA; *m:* Leonard R.; *c:* Jeremy, Sara; *ed:* Univ of NH (BA) Eng Ed 1963; SUNY at Albany (MA) Eng Ed 1975; Tufts Univ 6 Hrs; Union Coll 6 Hrs; Coll of St Rose 6 Hrs; *cr:* Glens Falls HS Eng Tchr 1963-65; Columbia HS Eng Tchr 1965-; *ai:* NYS United Tchrs 1963-; E Greenbush Tchrs Assn 1965-; AFT; NDCA Grant; *office:* Columbia HS Luther Rd East Greenbush NY 12061

MUIRHEAD, BRIAN WILLIAM, Earth Science & Health Teacher; *b:* Hartford, CT; *ed:* SUNY at Fredonia (BS) Earth Sci 1992; 12 Credit Hrs Beyond Degree; *cr:* Southwestern HS Sci Tchr 1993-; *ai:* Sci Club; NEA 1993-; *office:* Southwestern HS 600 Hunt Rd Lakewood NY 14750*

MUKUNGURUTSE, MANOMANO MARAINI MOYO, Prof of Philosophy & Sociology; *b:* Harare, Zimbabwe; *ed:* Univ of Pittsburgh (BA) His & Politics 1971-, (BA) Sociology & Philosophy 1971, (MA) Sociology & Anthropology 1974; Duquesne Univ (PHD) Candidate in Philosophy; Univ of London Law Stud Via Correspondence; *cr:* Allegheny Coll Asst Prof 1976-81; Chatham Coll Lecturer 1982-85; Allegheny Comm Coll Prof 1985-; Duquesne Univ Adj Prof 1994-; *ai:* Soccer Coach; Yth Inst Adv; Boys Club Adv; Amer Sociological Assn 1980-; African Stud Assn 1980-; Amer Philosophical Soc 1990-; Speakers Bureau Assn In 1980-; MADD 1990-; Lib Bd 1991-; African Amer Inst Schlsp Awd 1968-71; Univ of Pittsburgh Grad Flwsp 1971-75; Duquesne Univ Grad Flwsp
Numerous Articles Pub; *home:* 5506 5th Ave # B115 Pittsburgh PA

MULCAHY, NORANNE, Biology & Chemistry Teacher; *b:* Gle
NY; *ed:* Coll of New Rochelle (BA) Bio 1966; Long Island Univ (
1970; Attnd Rensselaer Polytechnic Inst, Union Coll; *cr:* Fort Edv
Bio & Chem Tchr 1969-; *ai:* Class Adv; Bio Club Adv; NYSU
STANYS 1972-; Amer Chemical Soc 1991-; Glens Falls Count
1978-, Governor; NSF Grant for DNA & Engrng from Union Coll;
Hughes Grant for DNA Stud at RPI; *office:* Ft Edward Jr Sr
Broadway Fort Edward NY 12828*

MULDOON, KATHERINE KERSWELL, High School Art Tea
North Tonawanda, NY; *m:* John R.; *ed:* St Univ Coll at Buffa
Interior Design 1984; St Univ of NY at Buffalo (MAH) Art His,
1993; St Univ Coll at Buffalo Tchr Cert Art 1986; Stud Abroad Ma
England 1982; *cr:* Tonawanda Sr HS Drama Dir 1986-90; Niagara F
Art Tchr 1987-95; Niagara Falls HS Art Tchr 1995-; *ai:* Drama Di
Class of 1999 Adv; LaSalle MS Drama Dir 1988-94; Friends of
Univ Theatre 1995-, Bd of Trustees; Presenter of Wkshp on
Interdisciplinary Subject NYS MS Conventions; 1993 Coord & Or
Stu Art Exhibit at Buffalo St Coll; *office:* Niagara Falls HS 1201 F
Niagara Falls NY 14301

MULHERIN, ROSEANNE CAVALLARO, French Teach
Philadelphia, PA; *m:* Mark J.; *c:* Tom; *ed:* Temple Univ (BA) F
Boston Conservatory of Music 1 Yr 1976-77 Towards BS Music
Classical Piano Stud Phila, PA 1962-74, Rouen, France 1974-76,
MA 1978-80; *cr:* CES Fontenelle Giraudoux Rouen, France Eng T
Prgm 1974-76; St Gregory HS Fr, Eng Tchr 1978-82; Milton HS
Tchr 1983-87; J. R. Masterman Lab & Demonstration Schl Fr Tch
ai: Sr Class Adv; HS Fr Club Spon 1991-; Piano Accompanist to M
Choirs 1993-; World Affairs Cncl of Phila Comm for Schls of Excl
1991-95; PFT, AATF 1991-; Summa Cum Laude Temple U 1974;
Kappa 1974; Presidential Schlr Temple U 1974; Recipient of Temp
Dept Tchng Exch Schlsp 1974; Dean's List Boston Conservatory o
1976-77; *office:* J R Masterman HS 17th & Spring Garden Sts Phila
PA 19130*

MULHERN, DOROTHY, Language Arts Teacher; *b:* Brooklyn,
St John's Univ (BS) Ed 1971, (MS) Ed 1974; *cr:* St Brigid Sc
1959-63; St Mary's Schl Tchr 1963-67; St Gerard Schl Tchr 1967-
Trinity Schl Tchr 1973-87; Mercy Ctr Ministries House Dir 1987-
Angels Regnl Schl Tchr 1990-; *ai:* NCEA 1973-; Mercy Elem Ed
1991-; *office:* Holy Angels Regnl Schl Division St Patchogue NY

MULHERN, PATRICIA ANN,OSU, Junior High English Teach
Cleveland, OH; *ed:* Marygrove Coll (BA) Eng 1969; Ursuline Co
Admin 1987; Stud in Cooperative Ed; *cr:* Underwood-Olivetti C
1956-67; Holy Cross Schl 3rd Grd Tchr 1969-75, 8th Grd Soc St
1986-88; Ursuline Nuns Rel Sister 1975-; Immaculate Concepti
2nd, 6th-7th Grd Tchr 1976-80, 7th-8th Grd Eng Tchr 1988-; Ch
King Schl 8th Grd Sci Tchr 1980-83; St Charles Schl Prin & 8th G
Arts Tchr 1983-86; *ai:* Safety Patrol; Comms for Revision
Handbook & Stud of Textbooks; NCEA 1969-; OH Cath Ed Assn
office: Immaculate Conception Schl 37940 Euclid Ave Willoug
44094

MULHOLLAND, BETTY JANE RUPE, Second Grade Teac
Bridgeport, CT; *m:* John; *ed:* Southern CT St Coll (BS) Intern
Upper Ed 1970, (MS) Rdng 1976; Fairfield Univ CAS 6th Yr GAT
cr: Grasmere Schl 2nd-3rd Grd Tchr 1970-1981; Riverfield Schl
Tchr 1981-; *ai:* PTA Tchr Rep; Annual Earth Week Comm Chm;
of Beautification, Staff Handbook, Tech Comm; Geology Gra
Wkshps; NEA, CEA, Fairfield Ed Assn 1970-; Phi Delta Kappa
Hands Across Fairfield Co-Chm 1986; Lit Unit, Sci Unit Grants; S
Grant Geology; NASA Tchr in Space Applicant; *office:* Riverfie
Schl 1525 Mill Plain Rd Fairfield CT 06430

MULHOLLAND, KATHLEEN ANN, Fine Arts Teacher; *b:* Wash
DC; *ed:* The OH St Univ (BA) Art Ed 1987; Trinity Coll (MAT) E
9 Credit Hrs in Painting & Printmaking; *cr:* Lanman Progress
Customer Rep & Comp Lithography 1987-90; Harry C Johnson & S
Antique Restorer 1988-82; Allyson Louis Gallery Sales & Rsrch 1
Magruder HS Long Term Sub Art & HS Art Tchr 1992-; *ai:* V
Hockey 1990-; Var Womens Bsktbl 1995-; AFT 1996-; US Field
Assoc 1991-, Futures Field Hockey Coach; *office:* Colonel
Magruder H S 5939 Muncaster Mill Rd Rockville MD 20855

MULHOLLAND, KIMBERLY ANN, Chemistry Teacher; *b:* Bro
m: Patrick; *c:* Amanda, Ryan; *ed:* SUNY Coll at Purchase (BS)
Chem 1988; City Coll of NY Masters in Progress in Environmental
Clarkstown HS North Chem Tchr 1993-; *ai:* Sci Club Adv; Sci O
Team Coach; NYSUT & AFT 1993-; *office:* Clarkstown HS North
Rd New City NY 10956

MULHOLLAND, MARY JANE, English Dept Director; *b:* Portla
ed: Univ of MA (BA) Eng 1964; Cambridge Coll (MED) Ed 1990
Salem St Coll, Emerson Coll; *cr:* Lynn Classical HS Eng Tchr 196
Dept Dir 1993-; *ai:* Huntington Theatre Tchrs Advy Cncl Mem; Ly
Dev Comm; AFT 1986-94; NCTE 1986-; Delta Kappa Gamma
Chptr 1993-; Numerous Poetry, Fiction & Non-Fiction Publications
Classical HS 33 N Common St Lynn MA 01902

MULHOLLAND, SUSAN STEELE, Teacher of the Gifted; *b:* Wh
WV; *m:* David B.; *c:* Christopher Steele, Casey Steele; *ed:* WV Un
Elem Ed, Drama 1965; 66 Post Grad Credit Hrs; 30 in Sch
Matriculated at Univ of PA, Temple, Penn St, Trenton St, Widener C
Rador Twp Schl Dist 5th Grd Tchr 1965-70; Central Bucks Schl
Grd Tchr 1973-74, Nursery Schl in HS 1974-79, Gifted Ed 1980-;
Saudi Arabia Intnl Schl 3rd Grd Gifted Spec Tchr 1983-85; Holi
High 7th Grd 1995-; *ai:* Supts Advy Bd; Dimontions, Portfolio,
Schl, PEN Comms; 6th Grd PEN Play Dir; NEA, Rep to Nat Conve
Yrs; Cntrl Bucks Ed Assoc, Sec 1992-94; PA Assn for Gifted Ed 1
Educators Museum Bd 1993-; Delta Kappa Gamma 1990-, Prgm
Producer, Dir of Art Beat 1988-92, Producer, Dir, Interviewer,
Writer, Ace Awd for Cable Excl 1990; Cntrl Bucks Educl Grants f
Prgms; Block Grant for Schl Curr Requests; *office:* Gayman Ele
Point Pleasant Pike Danboro PA 18916*

MULHOLLAND, WILLIAM DANIEL, Professor of Busin
Northampton, MA; *m:* Catherine N.; *c:* Michael; *ed:* Berkshire Com
(AS) Bus 1973; North Adams St Coll (BS) Bus Admin 1976; Weste
England Coll (MBA) Bus Admin 1982; Textron Exec Dev Prgm H
Schl of Bus; *cr:* SHeaffer Eaton Textron Plant Controller 1
Materials Mgr 1983-84, Plant Mgr 1984-85; Berkshire Stationary I
1986-88; N Adams St Coll ADjunct Fac 1989; Berkshire Comm C
of Bus 1989-; *ai:* Fac Adv Amer Production, Inventory Control S
Chapter; APICS 1990-, Adv, Achvmnt Awd; MA Assoc of Acctn
office: Berkshire Community College West St Pittsfield MA 01201

MULILIS, JOHN-PAUL, Psychology Professor; *b:* Boston, M
Shirley Ann Fleetwood; *c:* Timari Fleetwood, Erika; *ed:* CA St
Long Beach (BS) Engrng 1969, (MSCE) Engrng 1970; Univ of
Berkeley (MSE) Engrng 1974, (PHD) Engrng 1975; CA St
Fullerton (MA) Psych 1985; Univ Southern CA (PHD) Psych 19
Northland Pioneer Coll Psych Prof 1992-94; Univ of Phoenix Psy
1993-94; Northern AZ Univ Psych Prof 1993-94; PA St Univ Psy

ai: Exec Ofcrs Comm Chair; Lbrl Arts Coll Rep; Acad Affairs Exec Comm Fac Cong, Grad Schl Fac 1995-; Fac Congress 1994-; y Soc 1990-; Amer Psy Assn 1986-; Soc Advance Soc Psy 1984-; sn Alcoholism Cnslrs 1979-; 18 Journal Articles Pub; 14 Rsrch, Grants; 11 Conf Papers Presented; 2 Invited Colloquia Presented iums; *office:* PA St Univ Brodhead Rd Monaca PA 15061*

LIS, AMANDA GELAZIS, Math Department Chairperson; *b:* i, Lithuania; *m:* Algirdas P.; *c:* Elena Greene, Jonas, Saulius, *d:* Ursuline Coll for Women (BS) Chem 1960; Cleveland St Univ Curr & Instruction, Math & Sci 1980; New Math Standards; e-Melon Univ, Cmptr Sci Pascal; Baldwin Wallace, Assertive ne; *cr:* Maple Heights HS Chem, Math Tchr 1960-61; Euclid City ubstitute Tchr 1962-74; Borromeo HS Physics Tchr 1975; St ne Acad Tchr, Math Dept Chair 1976-; *ai:* Ski Club; ASCD 1980-; 1979-; Amer Prof Partnership for Lithuanian Ed 1991-; Lithuanian ssn 1956-, Ldr 1956-; Lithuanian Saturday Schl 1969-82; Martha Jennings Fnd Grant 1986; US Army Summer Prgm Associateship A Lewis Research Ct 1988; Translator Lithuanian Version Golden Childrens Dictionary Mano Zodynas 1975; First Grd Workbook ian Ed Cncl in USA 1974; Cath Diocese of Cleveland Outstanding d 1991; A.P.P.L.E. Seminars in Lithuania Coord & Lecturer 1993-; St Augustine Acad 14808 Lake Ave Lakewood OH 44107*

MARIANNE J., Senior High Math Teacher; *b:* Punxsutawney, PA; ence R.; *c:* Lawrence J., John M.; *ed:* Univ of Pittsburgh (BS) Math MED) Math 1975; Post Grad Stud PA St Univ, Robert Morris Coll, of PA; *cr:* North Allegheny Intermediate Math Tchr 1972-88; llegheny Sr High Math Tchr 1989-; *ai:* AFT 1972-; PCTM 1975-; North Allegheny H S 10375 Perry Hwy Wexford PA 15090

ANE, ANN MARY MC MILLAN, Business Education Teacher; *b:* City, NJ; *m:* Robert John; *c:* Meredith, Mariclare; *ed:* St Peters Coll rban Stud, Bus 1975; 30 Cr Hrs Grad Psych Montclair St Univ; 24 Ed Kean Coll; Attending Jersey City St Coll MA Spec Ed; *cr:* Queen HS Bus Ed Tchr 1990-92; Nutley HS Bus Ed Tchr 1993-; *ai:* Class Adv; NJEA 1993-; St Stephans CYO Bd 1995-96, Sec.

ANE, ROBERTA M., English Department Supervisor; *b:* West d, CT; *ed:* St Joseph Coll (BA) Eng 1965; Boston Coll (MA) Eng Sixth Yr Cert in Ed Admin; *cr:* Simsbury Pub Schls Eng Tchr , 1968-69; CT Assn of Ind Insurance Agents Exec Asst 1970-71; ry Pub Schls Eng Tchr 1971-85; The Travelers Insurance Co g Specialist & Supvr 1985-89; Simsbury Pub Schls Eng Dept Supvr ai: Grad Speakers Adv; Simsbury Ed Assn 1965-, Pres; CT Ed Assn 1965; NCTE 1989-; CCTE 1992-; St Joseph Coll Alumnae Assn Pres Hartford Branch; Tchng Assistantship During Grad Stud at Coll; *office:* Simsbury HS 34 Farms Village Rd Simsbury CT 06070

ANEY, EDWARD L., 7th-8th Grd Social Stud Tchr; *b:* Flushing, St Univ of NY at Stonybrook (BA) Scndry Ed 1987; Western CT (MA) Amer His 1990; 30 Post Grad Hrs Ed, Amer Lit; Permanent ert Scndry Eng; *cr:* Somers MS Soc Stud Tchr 1991-; *ai:* Stu Cncl d 6, 7 & 8; 8th Grd Class Adv; Coord Annual 8th Grd Trip to gton DC; Soc Stud Curr Comm; AFT 1988-; NY St United Tchrs Prof Musician, Guitarist & Vocalist; *home:* RD 4 Plumbrook Rd n NY 10536

ANEY, KATHERINE DIPPOLD, Fourth Grade Teacher; *b:* St PA; *m:* Michael L.; *c:* Patrick, David, Matthew; *ed:* Indiana Univ BED) Math 1971; 24 Grad Credits Penn St, Gannon; *cr:* St Marys S 6-8th Grd Math Tchr 1973-74; Ridgeway Area HS 8-10th Grd chr 1973-74; Queen of the World 5 Grd Tchr 1974-75; St Boniface 8 Grd Tchr 1986-; *ai:* St Marys Area Boys Bsktbl Booster Club NCEA 1986-; St Marys Recreation Bd 1984-92-, Chm; *office:* St e Parish Schl 359 Main St Kersey PA 15846*

EN, ELISABETH MANCUSI, Chemistry Teacher; *b:* New York, Alfred J.; *c:* Marc, Meredith; *ed:* St John's Univ (MA) Sociology 47 Credit Hrs Chem, Bio; 9 Grad Credits Spec Ed; *cr:* Avard g Ctr Spec Ed Tchr 1970-73; Our Lady of Victory Schl 8th Grd Sci 984-91; Sacred Heart Acad Chem, Bio Tchr 1991-; *ai:* Dean of Frosh Class; NSTA, STANYS 1991-; Hospice Vol 1992-; Sons of 993-; Hebrew Theological Seminary Grant for Star Lab Trng; *office:* Heart Acad 47 Cathedral Ave Hempstead NY 11550

EN, GERALDINE, 6th Grade Teacher; *b:* Pittsburgh, PA; *ed:* (AA) Eng 1971; Slippery Rock Univ (BS) Eng 1973; 24 Post Grad St Albert the Great Upper Elem Tchr 1978-92; St Bernard 6th Grd 992-; *ai:* Spelling Bee; JV Bsktbl Coach; Soc Stud Dept Chm; Mid nm; NEA 1978-; FPDT 1992-; *office:* Saint Bernards Schl 401 gton Rd Pittsburgh PA 15216*

EN, JAMES LAURENCE, Secondary English Teacher; *b:* ock NB, Canada; *m:* Darice Dawn; *c:* Jessica, Victoria; *ed:* on Coll (BA) Eng 1986; SUNY at Geneseo (MS) Scndry Ed 1991; a Cntrl Schl Sec Eng Tchr 1986-87; Fillmore Cntrl Schl Sec Eng 987-; *ai:* Yrbk Adv; Var Boys Soccer, JV Bsktbl, Var Tennis Coach; Coord; Class Adv; NEA 1987-; Houghton Wesleyan Church 1981-, Schl Tchr; *office:* Fillmore Cntrl Schl 144 W Main St Fillmore NY

EN, ROBERT, Grammar & Composition Teacher; *b:* Paterson, NJ; zabeth Kelly; *c:* Scott, Kelly; *ed:* Seton Hall Univ (BS) His, Eng 1967, (MA) Spec Ed 1973; 45 Addl Credit Hrs; *cr:* US Army 2 Lt Military Police 1967-69; Woodrow Wilson MS 7th Grd His, Eng i: Schl Store; Team Ldr for Team Tchng; NJEA, NEA, PCEA 1969-; Tchrs Assn 1969-, Pres Elect, Pres; Amer Legion 1993-; Reserve rs Assn 1969-; DCM 1987-; Essex Troop 1994-; Army Reserve 28 Yrs Retired Ltc 1995 Awds, Medals, Ribbons; *office:* Woodrow MS 1400 Van Houten Ave Clifton NJ 07013

EN, ROBERT JAMES, 8th Grade Social Studies Tchr; *b:* own, PA; *m:* Ann; *c:* Katie, Emily, Tim, Dan; *ed:* East Sturounsburg Social Studies 1994; East Stroudsburg Master in Soc Stud 1994; *cr:* haels Tchr 1976-79; Nortre Dame HS Tchr 1980-89; Black River MS 989-; *ai:* Former Asst Coach; NEA, NJEA; YMCA Coach; Tchr of 5; *office:* Black River MS RR 513 Chester NJ 07930*

EN, SHARON GRIFFIN, Spanish Teacher; *b:* Morristown, NJ; *m:* F.; *c:* Melissa Ann; *ed:* Montclair St Coll (BA) Span 1974; sbury Coll (MA) Span 1980; Attnd NY Univ, Univ of Salamanca; *cr:* Vly Reg HS Span Tchr 1974-; *ai:* NHS, Span NHS Advs; Schlsp ion Comm; NJEA, NEA 1974-; FLENJ 1976-; AATSP 1978-; Lenape Girl Scouts 1993-, Ldr; West Morris YMCA 1991-, Girls Rep; Green Twp Zoning Bd of Adjustment 1991-, Trng Facilitator; Shepherd Church 1980-, CCD Tchr; Rockefeller Fellowship 1986.

EN, WALTER H., Language Arts Teacher; *b:* Ashtabula, OH; *m:* a Ann Seward Peterman; *c:* Rdith Linz, Stacy Peterman; *ed:* Capital BS) Eng 1969; Kent St Univ (AA) Criminal Justice Stud 1975; *cr:* bula Area City Schls Eng, Lang Arts Tchr 26 Yrs; *ai:* Natl Jr Hnr Soc Bd; AATA 1968-; OEA; NEOTA; NEA; *office:* Columbus Jr HS 1326 bus Ave Ashtabula OH 44004

LENIX, DAVID RAY, Social Studies Teacher; *b:* Akron, OH; *m:* Ann; *c:* Michael, Tisha, Matthew; *ed:* Kent St (BA) Soc Stud Comp *cr:* Rootstown HS Tchr 1979-; *ai:* Frosh Class Adv; Boys JV Bsktbl; Girls Head Sftbl Coach; NEA, OEA, RTA 1979-; Rootstown Boosters 1979-; *office:* Rootstown HS 4190 St Rt 44 Rootstown OH 44272

MULLER, CHARLOTTE ANNE, English Teacher; *b:* Jersey City, NJ; *m:* Louis Robert; *c:* Erica, Jessica; *ed:* Jersey City St Coll (BA) Eng 1968; Grad Work St Peter's Coll at Jersey City NJ; *cr:* Thorne Jr HS Grd 7-9 Eng Tchr 1968-72; St Catherine's Grd 4 Tchr 1982-88; Thorne MS Grd 8 Eng Tchr 1988-90; Keyport HS 9-12 Grd Eng Tchr 1990-; *ai:* Life Line; Core Team; PAC; Discipline, Prin Advy Comms; Mentoring; Sr Class Adv; Frosh & Soph Class Adv; Peer Mentoring Comm; NEA, NJEA 1968-; MCRA 1994-; NJRA 1990-; *office:* Keyport HS 351 Broad St Keyport NJ 07735

MULLER, ELIZABETH COREILL, High School English Teacher; *b:* Decorah, IA; *m:* Kurt E.; *ed:* Luther Coll (BA) Eng 1970; Rutgers Univ (MA) Eng 1978; Attnd Rutgers Univ Eng; NEH Summer Insts; Dodge Poetry Seminars; *cr:* Ft Dodge HS Eng Tchr 1970-71; Westfield HS Eng Tchr 1971-; *ai:* Prof Dev Co-Chair; Restructuring Comm; NEA, NJEA, WEA, NCTE 1971-, WEA Sec, Exec Cncl; Natl SEED Project 1981-; AAUW; NWSA; Governor's Awd Excl in Tchng; NEH Flwshp Grant; Local Tchr Awds; *office:* Westfield HS 550 Dorian Rd Westfield NJ 07090

MULLER, MARY D'AQUILA, High School Math Teacher; *b:* Astoria, NY; *m:* Henry III; *ed:* Queens Coll (BA) Math 1979, (MS) Math, Scndry Ed 1982; 30 Post Grad Credits; *cr:* Norman Thomas HS Math Tchr 1980-88; Murry Bergtraum HS Math Tchr 1989-; *ai:* Math Team Coach, Adv; AFT, NYSUT, UFT 1980-; Cooperative Planning, Tchng Grant 1992; *office:* Murry Bergtraum HS 411 Pearl St New York NY 10038

MULLER, WILLIAM GEORGE, Professor of Visual Arts; *b:* New York City, NY; *m:* Linda M.; *c:* Stephanie, Nathan, Anne; *ed:* St Johns Univ NY (BA) Rhetoric 1965; NEW York Univ (MS) Spe Path & Aud 1967; Rensselaer Polytechnic Inst Comm Psych 64 Hrs Toward PHD; *cr:* St John's Univ Lecturer 1966-68; Hudson Vly CC Prof 1968-; *ai:* Acad Senate; Stu Life, Educl Policies, Fac Hnrs Comms; Jaycees 1976-, Pres; Parish Cncl 1976-, Pres; Excl in Tchng Pres Awd; SUNY Chancellor's Awd Excl in Tchng; *office:* Hudson Valley Comm Coll 80 Vandenburgh Ave Troy NY 12180*

MULLIGAN, ANNE, English Teacher & Dept Chprsn; *b:* Brooklyn, NY; *ed:* St Joseph's Coll (BA) Summa Cum Laude Eng, Sec Ed Minor 1975; NY Univ (MA) Eng 1978; Doctoral Candidate in Eng; Several Courses in Admin Fordham Univ; *cr:* St Joseph's Coll Instr 1981; Bishop Kearney HS Eng Tchr 1975-, Tchr of Advanced Placement 1984-; *ai:* NCTE 1975-; NCEA; Alumni Exec Bd St Joseph's Coll, VP; Who's Who in American Univ & Coll; Sigma Iota Chi; Delta Epsilon Sigma; Kappa Gamma Pi; *office:* Bishop Kearney HS 2202 60th St Brooklyn NY 11204

MULLIGAN, DAVID F., Health & Physical Ed Teacher; *b:* Erie, PA; *m:* Carol McLean; *c:* Shanna, Kyle, Kalie; *ed:* Slippery Rock Univ (BA) Hlth & PE 1980; PA Instructional II Cert; *cr:* Erie Schl Dist Sub Tchr 1980-85; Erie Acad HS Hlth & PE Tchr 1986-87; Erie Wayne MS Hlth & PE Tchr 1988-92; Erie Strong Vincent HS Hlth & PE 1993-; *ai:* Hlth & PE Chprsn; Iroquois HS Diving Coach; NEA 1985-; Erie Ed Assn 1985-; Wayne MS Tchr of Yr 1989; *office:* Erie Strong Vincent HS 1330 W 8th St Erie PA 16502

MULLIGAN, EUGENE DENNIS, Science Teacher & Dept Head; *b:* Philadelphia, PA; *m:* Rosalie Ann; *c:* Donna Marazzo, Eugene III, Dennis William; *ed:* Villanova Univ (BS) Sci 1964; Temple Univ (BS) Sci Ed 1968; *cr:* Tilden MS Sci Tchr 1964-70; Bartram HS Bio, Chem Tchr 1970-71; Stetson MS Sci Tchr 1971-; *ai:* Energy Bow Team Spon 1992-; WCAEA, PSEA, NEA 1971-; NSTA 1992-; Local Parish Ed Comm 1976-78, Chm; Mullico Construction Pres 1977-; *office:* G A Stetson MS 1060 Wilmington Pike West Chester PA 19382*

MULLIGAN, JAMES FRANCIS,SSJ, Fac, Eng & Writing Lab Coord; *b:* Meadville, PA; *ed:* Villa Maria Coll (BA) Eng 1947; Marquette Univ (MA) Eng 1957; Attnd Cath Univ, Pitt Univ, Univ of VT; *cr:* Villa Maria Acad Fac 1947-48; Diocesan Elem Schl Fac 1948-51; St Leo HS Fac 1951-57; Villa Maria Coll Assoc Prof, Chprsn 1957-81; St Mark Seminary, Cathedral Prep Fac 1981-; Gannon Univ Adj Prof 1981-; *ai:* Acad Challenge, Whiz Kids, Acad Sports League, Acad Decathlon Coach; Advy Bd Fac Rep; NCTE 1980-; NWPCTE 1980-, Sec; NCEA 1981-; Books for Kids 1989-, Vol; Span Apostolate 1990-, Vol; VMC Alumna of Yr Svc 1975, Alumna of Yr Career 1976; NSF Grant Cmptrs in the Hymanities; NWPCTE Awd Outstdng Tchr of Yr 1995; *office:* Cathedral Prep Schl 225 W 9th St Erie PA 16501

MULLIGAN, JANET H., 1st Grade Teacher; *b:* Lowell, MA; *ed:* Univ of Lowell (BA) Elem Ed & Eng 1982; Notre Dame Coll of Manchester (MS) Interdisciplinary Stud 1991; Completed Work on Curr Revision; *cr:* Rosary Acad 1st Grd Tchr 1983-85; Salem Schl Dist 1st Grd Tchr 1985-; *ai:* SEA 1985-; *office:* Walter Haigh Elem Schl 24 School St Salem NH 03079

MULLIGAN, JOSEPH PAUL, Music Director; *b:* Beverly, MA; *m:* Jen Mazzetta; *ed:* Univ of Lowell (BA) Music Ed 1992; Univ of MA at Lowell (MA) Music Performance 1994; *cr:* Reading Mem HS Brass Coord 1990-; Univ of MA Grad Asst Brass Stud 1992-94; East Coast Jazz Brass Coord 1993-; Winthrop Pub Schls Music Dir 1994-; *ai:* Concert Band; Jazz Band; Colorguard; MMEA 1995-; MENC 1989-; IAJE 1994-; East Coast Jazz 1993-, Brass Coord; *office:* Winthrop Pub Schls 400 Main St Winthrop MA 02152

MULLIGAN, MAXINE ROGERS, Ninth Grade English Teacher; *b:* Vineland, NJ; *m:* Rodney W.; *c:* Kelly; *ed:* Glassboro St (BA) Scndry Eng 1980, (MA) Scndry Eng 1987; *cr:* Vineland Schl System Educl Sec 1954-80; Holly Heights Schl Eng Tchr 1980-81; Vineland HS North 9th Grd Eng & World Cultures Tchr 1981-; *ai:* After Schl Assistance Prgm 1994-; Role Playing Club 1994-; Sports Hall of Fame Selection Comm 1994-; NEA, Cumberland Cty Ed Assn, NJ Ed Assn 1980-; Vineland Ed Assn 1980-, Bldg Rep; Vineland HS all-Sports Booster Club 1987-, Treas 1990-93, VP 1994-, Outstanding Contributions to HS Ath Awd; Governors Recognition Prgm Tchr of Yr 1986; Whos Who in Amer Ed 1989; Intnl Bio Ctr Cambridge England Degree of Merit 1994; *office:* Vineland HS North 3010 E Chestnut Ave Vineland NJ 08360

MULLIGAN, PATRICIA J., Eng Tchr & Newspaper Adv; *b:* Brooklyn, NY; *m:* Donald G.; *c:* Timothy, Sean; *ed:* CSI CUNY (MSEd) Scndry Eng 1986; SUNY 27 Credits Grad Eng; *cr:* SUNY Resident Hall Dir 1971-73; Msgr Farrell HS Eng Tchr 1974-78, 1981-84; St Peters Boys HS Eng Tchr & Newspaper Adv 1992-; *ai:* The Eagle Fac Adv; Var & JV Bowling Coach; Im Bowling League Coord; NCTE 1973-; WIBC 1978-; SI Southshore YMCA 1984-; *office:* Saint Peters Boys HS 200 Clinton Ave Staten Island NY 10301*

MULLIKIN, TERRI EVETETT, Seventh & Eighth Grade Teacher; *b:* Bristol, PA; *m:* Jeffrey; *c:* Kristie, Crystal; *ed:* Bloomsburg Univ (BS) Elem Ed 1977; WA Coll (MA) His 1985; Loyola Coll Admin, Supervision Cert 1995; *cr:* Chestertown MS 7th-8th Tchr 1978-82; Rock Hall MS 6th Grd Tchr 1982-83; Millington Elem Schl 4th Grd Tchr 1984-85; Rock Hall MS 7th-8th Grd Tchr 1985-; *ai:* Stu Govt Adv; Svc Learning Coord; Schl Improvement Team; NEA 1978-, Local Secy; ASCD 1994-; Girls Scouts 1962-, Trainer, Seagull Awd, Outstdng Ldr, Adult Apprec Pin; Kent Co Red Cross 1978-, Instr, Bd Mem; Rock Hall Parks, Rec 1984-; Employee of Month 1994-95; MICCA Grant Recipient; *office:* Rock Hall MS 21203 Sharp St PO Box 719 Rock Hall MD 21661*

MULLIN, JEROME L., Associate Prof of Chemistry; *ed:* LeMoyne Coll at Syracuse (BS) Chem 1977; Univ of NH (PHD) Analytical Chem 1983; *cr:* Univ of NH Post-Doctoral Rsrch Assoc 1983-84; Univ of WI Chem Asst Prof 1984-90; Univ of New England Chem Asst Prof 1990-93, Chem Assoc Prof 1993-; *ai:* Womens & Mens Cross Cntry Head Coach; Amer Chemical Soc 1977-, ME Section Sec; Sigma Xi 1984-; Kennebunkport Conservation Trust 1993-, Bd of Dirs; 3 NSF Grants; EOSAT Corp Grant; US Fish & Wildlife Svc Grant; Numerous Articles Pub; *office:* Univ Of New England 11 Hills Beach Rd Biddeford ME 04005*

MULLIN, SUSANNE KAHN, Guidance Counselor; *b:* Bryn Mawr, PA; *m:* William J.; *c:* Geoffrey, Ryan; *ed:* Susquehanna Univ (BA) Fr Ed 1969; Shippensburg Univ (MS) Guid, Cnslng 1982; *cr:* Pan Amer World Airways Flight Attendant 1970-76; Cumberland Vly Schl Dist Guid Cnslr 1986-; *ai:* Peer Helpers; Comm Bus Partnership; NEA, PSEA, CVEA 1986-; Keystone Cnslrs Assoc 1987-, Sec; St Paul's UCC 1976-, Chair of Chrstn Ed; *office:* Eagle View MS 6746 Carlisle Pike Mechanicsburg PA 17055

MULLINS, KELLI OLIVER, Language Arts & Reading Tchr; *b:* Oak Hill, OH; *m:* Teddy; *c:* Logan; *ed:* Rio Grande Coll (BA) Elem Ed 1984; Univ of Dayton (MS) Ed, Counseling 1993; *cr:* Hamden Elem 5th-8th Grd Rdng Tchr 1984-85; Wilton Elem 5th-8th Grd Lang Arts, Rdng Tchr 1985-88; Vinton Cty Jr High 7th Grd Lang Arts, Rdng Tchr 1988-; *ai:* NEA, OEA, VLTA 1984-; Emmanuel Bapt Church; Southern OH Coal Co Grant Rdng Project; *office:* Vinton County Jr HS Rt 1 Box 667 Mc Arthur OH 45651

MULLINS, MURRAY NEIL, Social Studies Teacher; *b:* Birmingham, AL; *m:* Katherine Hunter; *c:* Melissa Mullins Rhoads, Meredith, Elizabeth; *ed:* West Chester Univ (BS) Scndry Ed 1966; Univ of AK (MED) Educl Admin 1969; Addl Grad Courses Penn St Univ, St Josephs Univ, The Chester Cty Intermediate Unit; *cr:* Green Rdige Elem Schl Tchr 1966-67; Barnette Schl Tchr 1967-69; North Pole Schl Asst Prin 1969-71; Marshall St Schl Tchr 1971-72; Hillside Schl Tchr 1972-87; Vly Forge MS Tchr 1987-; *ai:* Team Ldr, Facilitator; Vlybl, Bsbl Coach; Chm & Co-Chair Positions on Curr Cncls; Strategic Planning; Liaison with Chester Cty Historical Soc; NEA 1966-; PSEA, TEEA 1972-; Involve in Church & Area Pol Comm; *office:* Valley Forge MS 105 W Walker Rd Wayne PA 19087*

MULLINS, SHIRLEY STROHM, Music Educator; *b:* Clinton, IA; *m:* William H.; *c:* Amy Mullins Ceney, F. Arthur, Wendy, W. Michael; *ed:* Univ of IA (BA) Music Ed 1957, (MA) Music Performance 1958; Grad Hrs at Univ of MI & IN Univ; *cr:* Cntrl St Univ Adj Fac in Music Ed 1963-93; Yellow Springs Pub Schls Orch & Strings Tchr 1970-; Antioch Coll, Wittenberg, Cedarville Coll & Univ of Dayton Music Ed Classes & Applied Cello Tchr 1975-; *ai:* Summer Strings Pgm; Music Yr Round for Srs & Presch Children; Mentor Tchr; MENC 1970-, Prof & Natl Certfd; OMEA 1970-, Southwest Region Chair 1976; ASTA 1975-, OH Branch Tchr of the Yr 1993; NSOA 1975-; Yellow Springs Yth Orch Assn 1965-, Co-Founder & Adv; OH Arts Cncl; Books: Teaching Music, The Human Experience 1985 & Faces of America 1988; Numerous Articles Pub; Consultant to Instrumentalist Magazine; OH Dept of Ed Tchr Scholar 1996; Guest Conductor Music Festivals; Lecturer Music Conventions; *home:* 537 Ridgecrest Dr Yellow Springs OH 45387*

MULNICK, LINDA, First Grade Teacher; *b:* New York, NY; *m:* Jerrold; *ed:* Brooklyn Coll (BA) Sociology 1964; Univ of MI (MA) Ed 1965; Post Grad Stud at NY Univ; *cr:* PS 2 Remedial Rdng Tchr 1965-67, 2nd Grd Tchr 1967-84, 3rd Grd Tchr 1984-87; Staff Dev Whole Lang 1987-91; 1st Grd Tchr 1991-; *ai:* AFT & NYSUT 1965-; IRA 1987-; NCTE 1987-; Dist 2 Mini Grants; *office:* Meyer London Pub Schl 2 122 Henry St New York NY 10002*

MULRANE, DONNA ABBATO, 5th Grade & Basic Skills Tchr; *b:* Jersey City, NJ; *m:* Patrick E.; *c:* Patrick Jr., Joseph, Chris, Greg; *ed:* Georgian Ct Coll (BA) Elem Ed, Early Chldhd 1985; *cr:* Cedar Grove Schl 5th Grd Tchr 7 Yrs, Basic Skills Math Tchr 3 Yrs; *ai:* Basic Skills EXCEL Prgm; NEA 1985-; Tchr of Yr 1991-92; *office:* Cedar Grove Elem Schl Cedar Grove Rd Toms River NJ 08753*

MULRANE, JEANIE COURTNEY, Fifth Grade Teacher; *b:* Findlay, OH; *ed:* IN Univ (BS) Elem Ed 1970; Attnd Milligan Coll 1966-68; Post Grad Coursework Miami Univ of OH, Bowling Green St Univ, OH St Univ, Univ of Toledo; *cr:* Butler Co Schls 7-8 Grd Sci, Math Tchr 1970-71, 4 Grd Tchr 1971-73; Findlay City Schls 4-5 Grd Tchr 1973-; *ai:* Drama Club Coach; Prof Rights & Responsibilities, Soc Stud Curr Comms; NEA, OEA, FEA 1982-; NCSS, OCSS 1989-; Arcadia United Meth Church 1992-; Findlay Soc Stud Tchr of Yr 1989; Rotary Golden Apple Awd Finalist 1994; OH His Acad 1992; *office:* Chamberlin Hll Intrmdiate Schl 600 W Yates Ave Findlay OH 45840

MULREADY, SEAN MICHAEL, English Teacher; *b:* Quincy, MA; *m:* Verna VonIderstein; *c:* Jessica, Susan; *ed:* Northeastern (BA) Eng 1972; Univ of MA at Boston (MA) Eng 1989; Suffolk Univ Ed Cert Ed 1972; *cr:* Weymouth High Eng Tchr 1972-73; Quincy High 1973-; *ai:* Stu Page in Regnl Paper Adv-Spon; Tennis Coach; MTA & NEA 1973-; NCTE 1987-; *office:* Quincy HS 52 Coddington St Quincy MA 02169

MULVANEY, DONNA MORAN, English Teacher; *b:* Jersey City, NJ; *m:* Eugene M.; *c:* Tim, Patrick; *ed:* St Peter's Coll (BS) Elem Ed 1973; Yeshiva Univ (MA) Curr, Instruction 1976; *cr:* St Peter's Coll Adj Fac 1977-92; Msgr Donovan HS Eng Tchr 1989-; *ai:* Mid Sts Accreditation Steering Comm Chprsn; Discipline Comm Rep; Substance Abuse Cnslr; NCEA 1989-; St Joseph Church 1979-, Eucharistic Minister; St Joseph Schl PTA 1985-, VP, Sec; *office:* Monsignor Donovan HS 711 Hooper Ave Toms River NJ 08753*

MULVANEY, LOUISE M., Associate Professor of English; *b:* Hudson, NY; *m:* peter; *c:* Molly, Lara, Barbara Singleton, Susan; *ed:* LeMoyne Coll (BS) Eng, Philosophy 1963; Siena Coll (MS) Ed 1970; 30 Hrs St Rose in Albany; *cr:* Waitress 1959-86; Palmyra-Macedon-Canandaigua Schls Sub Tchrs 1974-77; Geneva Cntrl Schsl Eng Tchr 1977-79; Finger Lakes Comm Coll Eng Prof 1979-; *ai:* Phi Theta Kappa 1984-, NY Region Exec Bd, Chptr Adv; NEA 1978-; NYS Excl in Tchng 1995; Phi Theta Kappa Distngd Adv 1993, Hnrs Inst Seminar Ldr 1992; *office:* Finger Lakes Comm Coll 4355 Lakeshore Dr Canandaigua NY 14424

MULVEY, MICHAEL PATRICK, English Teacher; *b:* Nashua, NH; *ed:* Univ of NH (BA) Eng 1990; Notre Dame Coll (MED) Scndry Ed 1994; *cr:* Manchester HS West Eng Tchr 1992-; NH Coll Adj Prof 1993-; *ai:* Forensics Team; Drama, environmental Clubs; Accreditation Comm; US First Team; NFA 1993-, Sr Rep; *office:* Manchester HS West 9 Notre Dame Ave Manchester NH 03102*

MULVEY, WILLIAM,JR., Technology Ed Tchr & Dept Chm; *b:* Geneva, NY; *ed:* SUNY Coll at Oswego (BS) Tech Ed 1976, (MS) Tech Ed 1983; *cr:* Geneva HS Tchr, Tech Ed Tchr 1977-, Chprsn Dept of Tech Ed 1985-; SUNY Coll Adj, Asst Prof 1987-93; *ai:* Dist Coord of Instrl Tech; NEA, Geneva Tchrs Assn 1977-; NYS Tech Edctrs Assn 1975; Christa Mc Auliffe Edctr by NEA's Natl Fnd for Improvement of Ed 1991; Frequent Presenter in Area of Comm Tech; *office:* Geneva HS 101 Carter Rd Geneva NY 14456*

MUMIE, ELIZABETH JANE (BLACKBURNE), Math Teacher; *b:* Glendora, NJ; *m:* Walter R.; *c:* Jeffrey Warren, Jill Elizabeth; *ed:* Rutgers South Jersey (BA) Math 1966; *cr:* Haddon Hghts HS Math Tchr 1966-67; Sterling HS Math Tchr 1967-; *ai:* Class Adv 1968-71, 1977-78; Tutorial Prgm 1991-93; NJEA, NEA 1967-; OES 1968-; *office:* Sterling HS Warwick Rd & Preston Ave Somerdale NJ 08083

MUMMA, JUDITH E., Special Education Teacher; *b:* Detroit, MI; *m:* Jack W.; *c:* CHeryl D. Cira, Steven P.; *ed:* Hiram Coll (BA) Elem Ed 1962; LD & BD Cert 12 Hrs; *cr:* Berea City Schls Kndgtn Tchr 1962-64; Wynford Schls SLD Tutor 1983-85; Carey Ex Village Schls SLD Tchr 1985-; *ai:* Advy, Curr Cncls Carey E V Schls; NEA, OEA, CEA 1985-; *office:* Carey Elementary School 357 E South St Carey OH 43316

MUMMENTHEY, CARL J., English Teacher; *b:* Brentwood, NY; *ed:* St Univ of NY Coll at Oneota (BS) Scndry Eng Ed 1993; Univ of NH Eng Dept; *cr:* Coxsackie-Athens MS Sr HS Eng Tchr 1993-94; *ai:* Boys Jr Var Soccer Coach; Yrbk Adv; Bldg Ldrshp Team; Catskill Area Tchrs of Eng, Natl Cncl Tchrs of Eng 1992-; BSA 1982-, Cncl Camping Comm Mem; Eagle Scout 1988; Amer Red Cross 1992-, Hlth, Safety Instr; OutstdngAchvmt Eng Ed at SUNY 1993; *office:* Unatego Jr Sr HS RR 1 Box 451a Otego NY 13825*

MUNCUSO, ANNE MARIE DIMILLO, 2nd Grade Teacher; *b:* Lockport, NY; *m:* Ronald A.; *c:* Marci Ann, Todd Ronald; *ed:* St U at Brockport (BS) Elem Ed 1968; St U at Buffalo (MS) Elem Ed 1974; 33 Grad Hrs; *cr:* John Pound Elem 1st Grd Tchr 1968-69; Parker Elem Schl 3rd Grd Tchr 1970-73; Boston Vly Elem Schl 2nd Grd Tchr 1984-; *ai:* ETTA Sec; BVS Unit Team Core Mem; Staff Dev Team; AFT 1970-; NYSUT 1970-; PDK 1996-; Phi Delta Kappa; Clinical Field Supvr; Assoc Fac in Ed Stud; *office:* Boston Valley Elem Schl 7476 Back Creek Rd Hamburg NY 14075*

MUNDAY, JOHN HENRY,JR., Science Dept Chm & Teacher; *b:* Hagerstown, MD; *ed:* Hagerstown Jr Coll (AA) Chem 1973; Shepherd Coll (BS) Chem 1975; Attnd Shippensburg Univ; *cr:* Saint Maria Goretti HS Sci Dept Chm, Sci Tchr 1976-; *ai:* NHS Adv; WA Cty Genealogical Soc 1975-, Treas; Hagerstown WA Cty Chamber of Commerce Excl in Ed Awd 1985; *home:* 848 Jefferson Blvd Hagerstown MD 21740

MUNDELL, CHARLES LEO, Program Director & Instructor; *b:* Washington, DC; *ed:* Univ of MD (BS) Urban Stud 1975; WA Theological Univ (MTS) Theology 1988; *cr:* Prince George Comm Coll Career, Life Planning Instr 1989-90; Delaware Tech Comm Coll Career, Life Planning Instr 1992-; *ai:* Stu Support Svcs Club Adv; DSTO 1992-, Pres, Outstdng Svc Awd 1995; MEAEOPP 1993-, Bd Mem, Outstdng Svc Awd 1995; MACCA 1988-, Treas, Bd Mem; CPC Annual; *office:* DE Tech & Comm Coll At Dover 1832 N Dupont Hwy Dover DE 19901

MUNDIE, TAMMY LOUISE, Math, Computer Science Teacher; *b:* Prince George's Co, MD; *ed:* Univ of MD Balto Co (BS) Math, Cmptr Sci 1987; Towson St Univ Cert Scndry Ed Cmptr Sci 1991, MA Equiv Ed, Cmptr Sci 1995; *cr:* Milford Mill Acad Math Tchr 1991-94; Hereford HS Math, Cmptr Sci Tchr 1994-; *ai:* Var Field Hockey Coach; Tech Team Tchr Rep; Tech Comm; NEA, TABCO, NCTM 1991-; *office:* Hereford HS 17301 York Rd Parkton MD 21120

MUNDY, CONNIE JARRELL, First Grade Teacher; *b:* Chelyan, WV; *m:* Jeffrey T.; *c:* Amanda; *ed:* Concord Coll at Athens WV (BS) K-8 Ed 1973 at Athens WV; *cr:* Smoot Elem Kndgtn Tchr 1973-79; McArthur Elem First Grd Tchr 1979-; *ai:* NEA 1973-; OEA 1979-; VLTA 1979-; Delta Kappa Gamma Soc Intnl 1987-; United Meth Women 1979-; McArthur Bus & Prof Women 1995-; Girl Scout 1984-, Ldr; Vinton Co Band Boosters 1994-, VP; Advy Bd of Rainbow for Girls 1990-, Chprsn; Jennings Scholar 1985-86; *home:* 414 McArthur Ave Mc Arthur OH 45651

MUNDY, MICHAEL FRANCIS, American History Teacher; *b:* Coatesville, PA; *m:* Vicki Lynn; *c:* Denise Copeland, Jason, Megan; *ed:* York Jr Coll (AS) Liberal Arts 1968; Millersville St Coll (BS) Soc Sci, His 1970; West Chester St Coll (MED) 1976; *cr:* Octorara Intermediate Schl US-World Geography, Amer His 6-8 Grd Tchr 1970-, Gifted, Talented Grds 5-8 Tchr 1984-86; *ai:* Coaching Bsktbl, Intramural Sports Prgms, Odyssey of Mind Gifted, Talented; Pres Octorara Area Ed Assn, VP; Tchrs Negotiations Team; PA St Ed Assn, NEA 1970-; QUEST 1986-; Lions Club 1974-75; Odyssey of Mind First Place Dist, Regnl, St Competitions, Sixth Natl, World Competition 1984-85; Chester Cty Outstanding Tchr of Amer His 1991; *home:* RR 3 Box 337A Coatesville PA 19320

MUNDY, RICHARD, High School Biology Teacher; *b:* New York City, NY; *m:* Anne; *c:* Maryanne; *ed:* Marist Coll (BA) Bio 1967; MI St (MS) Bio 1972; Attnd Univ Louisville KY, Pace Coll NYC, Jersey City St NY; *cr:* Brentwood HS Tchr 1969-; North Cntry Outfitters Pres 1982-; NY St Licensed Guide 1988-; *ai:* AFT 1980-; BTA 1969-; Smithtown Twp Arts Cncl 1993-; Brookhaven Arts Cncl 1995-; Wet Paints 1990-; Alaskan Watercolor Soc 1989-; North Cntry Outfitters 1982-, Pres; *office:* Brentwood HS Third Ave Brentwood NY 11717

MUNGALSINGH, MICHAEL, Engineering & Math Teacher; *b:* Trinidad, West Indies; *m:* Grace M.; *c:* Paul D.; *ed:* City Univ NYCTC (AAS) Mechanical Engrng Tech; City Univ (BS) Electrical, Mechanical Engrng 1985; PolyTechnic Univ (MS) Mechanical, Indstrl Engrng 1987, (PHD) Mechanical Engrng 1989; 30 Addl Credit Hrs in Ed; *cr:* Texaco T'dad Inc Engrng 1966-79; Amstar Corp Engrng 1979-88; NY City Tech Coll Prof Electrical, Mechanical, Electro-Mechanical Engrng 1986-; Brooklyn Tech HS Engrng, Math, Sci Tchr 1988-; *ai:* Chess Club, Team Adv; Indian Culture Club, Stageworks Adv; UFT 1988-; Instrument Soc of Amer, Amer Soc of Metals 1982-; ASME, NICET, ASCET 1983-; Ebasco Awd Excl 2 Merit in Mech Engrng; Sid Avener Awd Most Outstdng in Mechanical Engrng Dept; Golden Key Natl Hnr Soc Scholastic Achvmnt; *office:* Brooklyn Tech HS Fort Green Dekalb Ave Brooklyn NY 11217*

MUNGAN, MARY JANE, Developmental Reading Teacher; *b:* Flushing, NY; *ed:* Fordham Univ (BS) Eng Ed 1959; Coll of St Rose (MA) Eng 1966; St Joseph Seminary (MA) Rel Stud 1990; 60 Credits Ed, Supervision Beyond Masters; NY St Cert K-6, Eng 7-12, Rdng, Admin, Supervision, Dist Supt; *cr:* St Eugene Schl Grd 3, 6 Tchr 1952-56; Holy Name Schl Grd 6 Tchr 1956-60; Sc Clare Acad Grd 9-11 Eng Tchr 1960-62, Prin 1962-70; St Gabriel HS Rel, Eng Tchr, Head of Eng Dept 1970-71; Somers MS Dev Rdg Tchr 1972-; *ai:* Admin Duty; Run, Plan Prgms, Schedules for Stdnts, Fac During 2 Trip Weeks; St Mary Parish 1972-95, Chaired Parish Cncl, Chaired Lit Comm; *office:* Somers MS Rt 202 Somers NY 10589

MUNGER, SARAH VIRGINIA (QUARLES), Retired Teacher of GATE; *b:* Coraopolis, PA; *w:* Cornelius Stanley Sr. (dec); *c:* Belinda Joyce Bunting, Cornelius Stanley Jr.; *ed:* Univ of Pittsburgh (BS) Elem Ed 1951; Penn St 12 Credits Elem Ed 1957-59; *cr:* Pittsburg Schl Dist 2 Grd Tchr 1957-67; Cornell Schl Dist 5 & 6 Grd Tchr 1967-72, Remedial Rdng Tchr 1972-76, GATE Tchr 1976-88, Sub Tchr 1988-; *ai:* NEA; PSEA; St Paul AME Zion Church, Sunday Schl Tchr, Supt of Vacation Bible Schl, Spon of Yth Choir & Rdng for Fun Prgm; Cornell Area Comm Advy Cncl; Cornell Dist, First African-Amer Tchr; Founder Cornell Bsktbl Mothers; *home:* 525 Mount Vernon Ave Coraopolis PA 15108

MUNGIGUERRA, CARL, Chemistry Teacher; *b:* New Haven, CT; *m:* Joan; *c:* Karen Morcaldi, Janet Zachey; *ed:* Yale Univ (BS) Chem 1958; Fairfield Univ (MA) Ed 1966; Wesleyan Univ (CAS) Sci 1973; 15 Credit Hrs Southern CT St Univ; *cr:* King Schl Sci Tchr 1958-64; Hamden HS Chem Tchr 1964-; *ai:* Hamden Adult HS Coord; NEA 1964-; CT Ed Assn 1964-; Hamden Ed Assn 1964-, Pres 1986-92; NSF Grants 1964-73; New Haven Area Outstdng Chem Tchr & Hamden Tchr of Yr 1986; *office:* Hamden HS 2040 Dixwell Ave Hamden CT 06514

MUNGO-MORTON, RUTH YVONNE, English Teacher; *b:* Greenville, SC; *m:* George Cleveland Morton; *c:* Marlon; *ed:* Livingstone Coll (BA) Eng 1965; St Univ of NY at Buffalo (MA) Eng 1977; St Univ of NY (MS) Displinary Measures 1984; Benedict Coll Elem Ed Cert 1967; Post Grad Hrs St Univ of NY; *cr:* Lancaster Cty Schl System Eng Tchr 1965-72; Cath Charities Soc Worker 1972-73; Niagara Falls Schl System Eng Tchr 1973-79; Buffalo Schl System Eng Tchr 1979-; *ai:* Buffalo Traditional Schls Stu cncl Adv; Production Guild Black His Act Chprsn; Stu Govt Inter High Staff Mem; NEA 1965-; NYEA, Bfo Tchrs Fed 1979-; Natl Assn for Stu Act 1992-; NCTE 1990-; Delta Sigma Theta; Stu Cncl Adv; Natl Cncl of Negro Woman; Buffalo Innovators, Pres, Founder; Buffalo Ambassador; *office:* Buffalo Traditional Schl 450 Masten Ave Buffalo NY 14209

MUNIZ, RAYMOND C., English Teacher; *b:* Palmerton, PA; *m:* Theresa; *c:* Christian, Jessica; *ed:* E Stroudsburg Univ (BS) Eng 1968; Temple Univ (MS) Ed 1974; *cr:* John Adams Jr HS Eng Tchr 1968-70; J P Steven HS Eng Tchr 1970-72; Louis E Dieruff HS Eng Tchr 1972-; *ai:* Key Club; Golf Coach; Curr Adv; Fac Senate; OBE Comm; Drama Tchr; Drama Coach; Allentown EA, Penn EA, NEA 1972-; *home:* 2606 Valley Rd Orefield PA 18069*

MUNK, JANET T. KLIMCHAK, Third Grade Teacher; *b:* Brooklyn, NY; *m:* William J.; *c:* Christopher, Amy; *ed:* Long Island Univ Brooklyn Ctr (BS) Elem Ed 1969; Seton Hall Univ (MA) Ed 1993; Merck Ldr Tchr Inst Instrl Team 1995; Reasington-Merck Summer Sci Inst 1994; Quest-Princeton Univ Summer Sci Inst 1993; Merck-Retgers Summer Ldrshp Inst 1992; Ele Hwy Navig Rariton Vly Comm Coll 1995; Cmptr, Internet Courses; *cr:* St Brendans Elem Schl 4th Grd Tchr 1967-68; Three Bridges Elem Schl Third Grd Tchr 1977-; *ai:* St Systemic Initiative 3rd Grd Telecommunic Project; Merck Ldr Tchr Assessment Investigation Team; Merck Inst for Sci Ed Advy Comm; Quest Stud Groups; Fac Advy Comm; 3rd Grd Rep; Math, Sci Curr Comm; Sci Fair Comm; NEA, NJEA 1977-; Rdng for Ed Assn 1977-, Mbrshp Chprsn; NCTM; NJSTA; NSTA; St Elizabeth Ann Seton Parish 1985-, Rel Ed Tchr, Eucharistic Minister, Sacristan, Bell Choir; DE Vly Unit Herb Soc of Amer; Clinton Museum Ed Comm; Earth Sci Instrl Team Merck Ldr Tchr Inst 1995-; Lifetouch Enrichment Grant, Increase the Peace Awd for Quiltmaking Idea 1996; Mid Sts Evaluation Tema 1991, 1994; *office:* Three Bridges Schl PO Box 443 Main St Three Bridges NJ 08887

MUNLEY, ELIZABETH ANN, Latin, Spanish & French Tchr; *b:* Scranton, PA; *m:* Paul J.; *c:* Paul Jr., John, Brian, Kevin; *ed:* Marywood Coll (BA) Latin & Fr 1965; Elmira Coll (MS) Scndry Ed 1980; *cr:* Windsor Cntrl Latin & Fr Tchr 1965-68; Broome Comm Coll Span Instr 1981-83; Johnson City Cntrl Latin, Span & Fr Tchr 1984-; *ai:* NEA, Johnson City Tchrs Assn 1984-; *office:* Johnson City HS 666 Reynolds Rd Johnson City NY 13790

MUNLEY, FRANK M., Retired Teacher; *b:* Jamaica, NY; *m:* Annette E. Kita; *c:* Cynthia Thiel, Patricia; *ed:* Mansfield St Coll (BS) Soc Stud 1961; Marywood Coll (MS) Guid Cnslr 1974; *cr:* Blairstown HS Soc Stud Tchr 1961-63; Cntrl Schl Soc Stud, Govt Tchr 1963-91; *ai:* 7-8th Grd Bsbl, Bsktbl Coach; 7-8th Grd Debating Club Adv; NJEA, NEA 1991-; Knights of Columbus 1991-; Warren Cty Democratic Comm 1982-; Governor's Tchr Recognition Awd 1991; Independence Twp Comm Cert of Resolution for 28 Yrs of Dedicated Svc to Twp Stdnts; *home:* 10 Barkers Mill Rd Hackettstown NJ 07840

MUNLEY, KATHLEEN PURCELL, Assoc Professor of History; *b:* Carbondale, PA; *ed:* Marywood Coll (AB) His 1960; Univ of PA (MA) His 1962; Lehigh Univ (PHD) His 1980; *cr:* Keystone Jr Coll His Prof 1964-67; Marywood Coll Asst & Assoc His Prof 1967-; *ai:* His & Soc Sci Majors Adv; Mem Various Coll Comms; Phi Alpha Theta & Intnl His Honor Soc Advisor; Oral His Assn 1990-; Soc Sci & His Assn 1990; PA His Assn 1990-91; Bd of Mental Hlth Assn of Lackawanna Cty 1986-92; Friendship House 1987-93; Girl Scout Cncl 1986-92; Eleanor Roosevelt Grant; Marywood Cultural Diversity Awards; Numerous Articles Submitted for Publication & Conferences Attended; Paper Delivered; FDR Lib (PHD) Research; *office:* Marywood Coll PO Box 704 LAC 82 Soc Sciences Dept Scranton PA 18509

MUNN, DAVID ALAN, Associate Professor of Soils; *b:* Elyria, OH; *m:* Marilyn McBride; *c:* Laurie, Jeffrey; *ed:* OH St Univ (BS) Ag 1970, (MS) Soils 1972, (PHD) Soils 1974; 24 Hrs of Engrng, Geology, & Ec Completed at Univ of Akron 1981-93; *cr:* NC St Univ Soil Sci Dept Research Assoc & Visiting Asst Prof 1974-76; OH St Univ Asst Prof 1976-82; Agricultural Tech Inst Assoc Prof 1982-; *ai:* Co-Adv to Ag Tech Inst Phi Theta Kappa Chapter; Amer Soc Agronomy 1970-; Soil Sci Soc Am 1970-; Church of Cross United Meth 1979-, Sunday Schl & Adult Bible Tchr; 1970 Ag Bachelor Degree-Summa Cum Laude; 1974 Chapter Mem Sigma XI OH St Univ; Assoc Ed 1985-88 & Ed 1989-93 of Journal of Natural Resources and Life Sci Ed; *office:* OH St Univ Agri Tech Inst 1328 Dover Rd Wooster OH 44691

MUNNING, MARY ANNE, Second Grade Teacher; *b:* White Plains, NY; *m:* Philip P. Jr.; *c:* Philip P. III, Catherine; *ed:* Glassboro St Coll at Rowan (BA) Elem Ed 1982; Univ of PA Post Grad; *cr:* Westville Pub Schl 4th Grd Tchr 1986-88, 2nd Grd Tchr 1988-; *ai:* Staff Dev, Schl Based Planning Comms; WEA, NJEA 1986-; Governor's Tchr Recognition Awd Tchr of Yr 1995-; *office:* Parkview Elem Schl Birch & High Sts Westville NJ 08093

MUNNS, JOYCE ANN, English Teacher; *b:* Pittsburgh, PA; *c:* Justin; *ed:* Carlow Coll (BA) Eng, Ed 1967; Univ of Pittsburgh (MS) Eng 1971; *cr:* Knoxville Jr HS Eng Tchr 1967-70; Allegheny HS Eng Tchr 1970-83; Langley HS Eng Tchr 1983-84; Taylor Allderdice HS Eng Tchr 1984-; *ai:* AFT, PFT 1967-; Awds Tchr of Yr, Pittsburgh Northern Sphere 1977, Duquesne Univ 1992, Tufts Univ 1990, Carleton Coll 1987, Univ of Chicago 1989, 1991, Outstnd Tchr Recognition, All-Star Edctr Pittsburgh Area 1991.*

MUNOZ, CHARLOTTE FAELLA, English Teacher; *b:* Providence, RI; *m:* Michael J. Sr.; *c:* Michael Jr., Cheryl Munoz Tryticlo, Jeff, Christopher; *ed:* Salve Regina Univ (BA) Eng 1962; Univ of RI (Masters) Eng 1970; Masters Courses Eng, AP Eng & Muliticultural Lit SUNY at Oswego; *cr:* East Greenwich HS Eng Tchr 1962-66; North Syracuse HS Eng Tchr 1970; Cicero HS Eng Tchr 1978-79; Liverpool HS Eng Tchr 1981-; *ai:* Genesis Adv; ULFA 1981-; *office:* Liverpool HS 4338 Wetzel Rd Liverpool NY 13090

MUNROE, NORMA GOYETCHE, Fifth Grade Teacher; *b:* Gloucester, MA; *m:* Alan M.; *c:* Alan Jr., David, Lisa; *ed:* Bridgewater St Coll (BS) Elem 1956; Cambridge Coll (MED) Ed 1991; 90 Hrs Past (MEd); *cr:* Beeman Schl 4th Grd Tchr 1956-59; Fuller MS 7th Grd Soc Stud Tchr 1976-81; O'Malley MS 7th-8th Grd Soc Stud Tchr 1981-87; Fuller Elem Schl 5th Grd Tchr 1987-; *ai:* Delta Kappa Gamma Intnl Honor Soc 1981-; Alpha Upsilon St, Omega Chapter 1981-, Exec Bd, Sec; Gloucester Tchrs Assn 1956-, Exec Bd; NEA, MTA 1956-; College Womens Club 1992-, Exec Bd; BTC Alumni Assn 1956-; Horace Mann Tchr 1987; Speaker, Supts Conf 1990; Pub Article 1991; Ma Distinguished Tchr Awd MA Assn of Tchr Educators 1992; *office:* Milton Fuller Elem Sch 99 School House Rd Gloucester MA 01930

MUNSEE, SANDRA NUPP, Math Teacher; *b:* Erie, PA; *m:* Lloyd L.; *c:* Andrea, David; *ed:* Penn St Univ (BS) Sec Ed Math 1971, (MED) Sec Ed Math 1974; *cr:* Philipsburg Osceala SD Math Tchr 1971-82; Southwestern Cntrl SD Math Tchr 1983-; *ai:* Natl Jr Honor Soc Adv; Pi Lambda Theta 1970-; NCTM 1971-; NEA 1971-; AMTNS 1983-; Presbyn Church 1961-, Session Ruling Elder; Lakewood Womens Club 1991-, Corresponding Sec; *office:* Southwestern Cntrl Schl Dist 600 Hunt Rd WE Jamestown NY 14701

MUNSEY, SANDRA MORGAN, 6th Grade Teacher; *b:* Canton, James W. (dec); *ed:* Univ of Akron (BS) Elem Ed 1971; 35 Credit H of Akron, 5 Credit Hrs Bowling Green St Univ; *cr:* Lodi ELem S 4th, 5th Grd Tchr 1971-76; Hopewell Loudon Elem Schl 4th G 1976-78; Van Buren Elem Ed 5th, 6th Grd Tchr 1978-; *ai:* Neg Comm Contract; NEA, OEA 1971-; First Presbyn Church Deacon Elder 1992-95; *office:* Van Buren Elem Schl Main St Van Buren O

MUNSKY, TERRY L., Special Education Teacher; *b:* Brooklyn, Ronald; *c:* Stefanie, David; *ed:* Brooklyn Coll (BA) Elem Ed 197 Math 1976; Kean Coll Tchr of the Hanidcapped Cert 1992; *cr:* NY of Ed PS 91 Elem Schl Tchr 1974-81; Elizabeth HS Spcl Ed Tch *ai:* NJEA 1991-; Cncl for Exceptional Childern 1992-; *office:* E HS 600 Pearl St Elizabeth NJ 07202*

MUNSON, ALICE FAYE OWENS, First Grade Teacher; *b:* Cir OH; *m:* Karl Eric; *ed:* Univ of CT (BS) Elem Ed 1972; Miami Ur of Mt St Joseph Grad Stud; *cr:* Madison Local Schl Dist Kndg 1973-95, First Grd Tchr 1995-; *ai:* Safety, Right to Read Comms; Unit Ldr; NEA, OEA, Madison Tchrs Assn 1973-; Zeta Tau Alp 1968-70; Outstdng Elem Tchr of Amer 1975; *office:* Madison Lo Dist 6600 Trenton Franklin Rd Middletown OH 45042

MUNSON, SALLY SCOFIELD, Retired 6th Grd Lang Arts Tchr; MI; *m:* Philip Reynold; *c:* Scott, Melinda Munson, Timothy; *ed:* H Coll (BA) Econ, Eng1950; 60 Hrs Elem Ed LIU 1970-76; *cr:* IBM Svc 1950-57; South Cntry Schls Tchr 1968-92; *ai:* womar Patchogue 1991-; Bellport Garden Club 1992-; PEO 1955-, Pres 167 S Country Rd Bellport NY 11713

MUNT, MARGARET STAPLES, 1st & 2nd Grade Teacher; *b:* C NH; *m:* John Michael Lyman; *c:* Vanessa, Evangeline; *ed:* Univ of Ed 1976; 21 Addl Credits; *cr:* The Children's Schl Asst Tchr, Tchr 1 The Schoolhouse Tchr 1976-78; The Children's Schl Tchr 1 Williston Cntrl Schl Tchr 1983-; *ai:* Schl Report Card Comm; NE Bd; *office:* Williston Central Schl 705 Williston Rd Williston VT

MUNTEAN, JANE PEEL, First Grade Teacher; *b:* Sharon, Richard; *ed:* Edinboro (BA) Elem 1967; Westminster (MA) Elem 1 Farrell Elem Schl Tchr 25 Yrs; *ai:* Mentor; Co-operating Tchr; PSE 1971-; *office:* Farrell Area Elem Schl 1600 Roemer Blvd Farrell PA

MUOIO, DOMINIC, Italian Teacher; *b:* Paterson, NJ; *ed:* Fordha (BA) Comm 1971; Rutgers Univ (MA) Frgn Lang Ed Italia Montclair St Coll Tchr Cert; Kean Coll Admin, Supervisio Universita per Stranieri Perugia Italy; Universita di Firenze Floren Universita del Sacro Cuore Rome Italy; *cr:* Watchung Hills Reg H of Italian 1973-; *ai:* Italian Club, Amnesty Intl Adv; Fulbright 1982-87; Tchr of Yr 1988; *office:* Watchung Hills Reg HS 108 Sti Warren NJ 07059

MURACCO, LINDA LOUISE, Science Teacher; *b:* Scranton, Gary R.; *ed:* Marywood Coll (BS) Bio, Scndry Ed 1990; Complete II Cert; *cr:* Dunmore HS Sci Tchr 1991-; *ai:* NHS Adv; Strategic P Comm; AFT 1991-; PSTA 1992-; *office:* Dunmore H S Quincy Warren St Dunmore PA 18512

MURADIAN, ANDREA LYNNE, English Teacher; *b:* Whitinsvil *ed:* Worcester St Coll (BA) Eng 1969; Assumption Coll (MA) En CAGS Eng 1983; *cr:* Northbridge HS Eng Tchr 1969-; Fisher Adjunct Instr 1976-85; *ai:* Class of 1996, Mentor Adv; Northbridg Assn 1969-, VP 1993-95; MA Tchrs Assn, NEA 1969-; Congregational Church; Whitinsville Soc Lib, Corporator; Northbridge HS 171 Linwood Ave Whitinsville MA 01588

MURAK, RICHARD JAMES, Soc Stud Tchr & Chprsn; *b:* Buffa *m:* Deborah J. Ray; *c:* Melanie, Elizabeth, Rebecca, Rachel, David John Vianney (BA) Philosphy, Theology 1969, (MDIV) Theology 1 Univ of NY Dept of Philosphy 80 Grad Hrs; *cr:* Madonna HS R 1973; Archbishop Carroll HS Rel Tchr 1976-77; Bishop Mc Ma Rel, Soc Stud, Latin Tchr 1977-87; Bishop Turner Carroll HS Sc Chprsn, Tchr 1987-; *ai:* Textbook Coord; SLTA, NCEA 1977-; Turner-Carroll HS 185 Lang Ave Buffalo NY 14215

MURANO, DONNA HEMPHILL, 9th-11th Grd English Teac Cleveland, OH; *m:* Frank Salvatore; *c:* Kathryn Elizabeth; *ed:* S Oswego (BS) Scndry Ed & Eng 1973; Nazareth Coll (MS) Scndry E *cr:* Greece Olympia HS Eng Tchr 1973-; *ai:* Staff Stu Recognit Facilitator; NEA 1976-; NYSEC 1995-; Penfield HS Forum 1993-; Greece Olympia H S 1139 Maiden Ln Rochester NY 14615

MURAWSKI, CORINNE MARKO, Mathematics Teacher; *b:* M Rocks, PA; *m:* John P.; *ed:* PA St Univ (BS) Scndry Ed 1986; Du Univ (MS) Educl Stud 1994; 9 Credit Hrs Curr, Instruction, Super *cr:* Beaver Cty Intermediate Unit Summer Enrichment Instr 1 Beaver Area Schl Dist Math & Sci Tchr 1989-; Geneva Coll Part-Tim 1994-; *ai:* Co-Spon Bobcats Against Self-Harm 1990-92, Jr & S 1992- 94; Spon Jr Class 1992-; Math Dept Head 1994-; NCTM 1989-; ASCD 1992-; Holy Trinity Parish; Local Dist Grant He Internet Access in Schl Dist; *office:* Beaver Area Middle-HS Gyps Rd Beaver PA 15009

MURDOCK, BEVERLY A., English Teacher; *b:* Albany, NY; *m:* S *c:* Suzanne Rodio, Stanley Jr.; *ed:* Utica Coll (BA) Eng 1980; C SUNY (MS) Rdng 1987; *cr:* Little Falls HS 10th Grd Eng Tchr 19 Adv Schl Newspaper, Class 1997; NCTE 1985-; AFT 1990-; NEA *office:* Little Falls HS 1 High School Rd Little Falls NY 13365

MURDOCK, KATHRYN A., Social Studies Teacher; *b:* London, En *m:* Stephen; *c:* Peter, Robert; *ed:* Hunter Coll (BA) His 1960; 30 Hrs; Inservice Masters; *cr:* Hackensack HS Soc Stud Tchr 1960; Da HS Soc Stud Tchr 1975-; *ai:* Mock Trial Coach; MSTA; *office:* Da HS 25921 Ridge Rd Damascus MD 20872

MURDOCK, WANDA BROOKS, Home Ec & Consumer Sci T Cincinnati, OH; *m:* H. Michael; *c:* Karman, Erica, Michael; *ed:* O (BS) Home Ec Ed 1972; Univ of Cincinnati (BS) Sci Ed 1973; Attnd Univ Post Grad Stud; *cr:* Shroder Jr High Tchr 1972; Peoples Jr Hig 1973-76; Walnut Hills HS Tchr 1976-; *ai:* Chrldng Adv; Track & Coach; Lead Tchr; Dept Head; Kappa Delta Pi 1971-; AFT 1972- Sigma Theta 1969-, Pres, Schlsp; Govt Consumer Sci Corp to Abroad; Consultant for & on Teen Pregnancy; *office:* Walnut Hil 3250 Victory Pky Cincinnati OH 45207*

MURINKA, NANCY YURA, 4th Grade Teacher; *b:* Auburn, NY; *m* Anthony; *c:* Jennifer, Julie; *ed:* Auburn Comm Coll (AAS) Lbrl Arts, Applied Sci 1971; SUNY at OSWEGO (BS) Elem Ed 1973; SU Cortland (MS) Elem Ed 1976; *cr:* A A Gates Elem Schl 4th Grd El Tchr, Dept Chm 1973-; *ai:* Dept Chm 10 Yrs; Odyssey of the Mind 1975; Costumes Elem Play Chm 1992-94; Schl Budget Comm 199 Byron Tchrs Assn 1973-; NYSUT; AFT; Rel Ed Tchr 1987-; Seward Historic House 1980-, Vol; 5 Mini Grants from Local Tchr Ctr C Onondaga; Presenter NY Historical Assn Yorkers Conf 1990; *office* Gates Elem Schl Maple Ave Port Byron NY 13140

MURNION, WILLIAM EDWARD, Philosophy Professor; *b:* New NY; *m:* Deborah Cary; *c:* William C., Gregory T.; *ed:* St Josephs S Coll (BA) Philosophy 1954; Gregorian Univ (STL) Theology 1958, Philosophy 1970; *cr:* Duquesne Univ Asst Prof 1967-68; Boston Co Fellow 1968-69; Newton Coll Asst Prof 1969-72; Ramapo Coll Prof

ampus Planning Comm; APA 1970-; AAR 1970-, Regnl Pres Elect; 1970-; NEH Summer Seminar for Schl Tchrs Dir 1992, 1995; The ng Of Act In Understanding Rome 1973; Numerous Articles Pub; p to Inst for Ecumenical & Cultural Stud 1974-75; *office:* Ramapo of NJ 505 Ramapo Valley Rd Mahwah NJ 07430

NO, ELEANOR COSTELLO, Social Studies Teacher; *b:* Brooklyn, *:* Michael Joseph; *c:* Kathleen, Michael, Jennifer; *ed:* Brentwood BSEd) His 1970; Richmond Coll CUNY His; William Paterson Coll s Second Lang; *cr:* Our Lady of Refuge Schl 5th Grd Tchr 1970-71; f Wayne Sub Tchr 1984-88; Passaic Cty Tech Inst Soc Stud Tchr, ESL 1988-; *ai:* NJEA 1988-; NJTESOL 1993-; PCTEA 1988-, iations Team; Annunciation Church 1978-, Pastoral Cncl, Financial ı, Chair; BSA 1985-, Merit Badge Cnslr; *office:* Passaic County Tech : HS 45 Reinhardt Rd Wayne NJ 07470

PH, MARGARET SHELTON, Fifth Grade Teacher; *b:* Greenville, *:* Ronald; *c:* Ronald Jr., Ryan; *ed:* Univ of Cincinnati (BS) Elem Ed (MS) Elem Ed 1972; *cr:* Sharonville Schl First Grd Tchr 1971-73; meade Elem Schl Second Grd Tchr 1973-75; Heritage Hill Elem Schl ı, Sixth, Fifth Grd Tchr 1995-; *ai:* Hlth Rep Princeton City Schls; Kappa Alpha 1989-; Delta Kappa Gamma 1989-, Pres 1996-98; OEA 1971-; Tchr of Yr Brookmeade Elem Schl 1974; *office:* ge Hill Elem Schl 11961 Chesterdale Rd Cincinnati OH 45246

PHY, ALICE HUGHES, English Dept Chair & Teacher; *b:* ton, PA; *m:* John D.; *c:* Maureen; *ed:* East Stroudsburg Univ (BS) Eng 66; 35 Grad Credits Penn St at Westchester; *cr:* Hazleton Area HS 'chr 1966-68; Owen J. Roberts MS Eng Tchr 1968-74; Twin Vly HS ıg Tchr, Dept Chair 1984-; *ai:* MCTE 1984-; *office:* Twin Valley HS Elverson PA 19520

PHY, ANN MARIE CALLAHAN, Language Arts Teacher; *b:* Jersey NJ; *m:* Robert P.; *c:* Robert P. Jr., Christine Wright, Heather Holmes, ɪn Krass, Thomas C. Krass; *ed:* St Thomas Aquinas (BS) Ed 1970; ım Paterson Coll 15 Hrs Whole Lang Across Curr, Integrating Lit, K-8; *cr:* Mt Carmel Schl 6th Grd Tchr 1970-73; Bergen Cty Schls Sub 1977-85; St John the Evangelist 8th Grd Tchr 1985-87; St Therese th-8th Grd Lang Arts Tchr 1987-; *ai:* 8th Grd Yrbk Coord 1987-; Dir ays 1992-94; Stu Cncl Moderator 1993-; Schl Photographer 1988-; oncerns Moderator 1993-; 8th Grd Fund Raiser Coord 1987-; NCEA ; Peer Nomination Archdiocese of Newark 1996 Tchr of Yr; *office:* erese Schl 220 Jefferson Ave Cresskill NJ 07626*

PHY, BARBARA FIELEK, Third Grade Teacher; *b:* Perth Amboy, *:* Glassboro St Coll (BA) Primary Ed 1967; 30 Grad Credits; *cr:* ester Twp Schls 1st Grd Tchr 1967-69; Pennsville Schl System 1st chr 1969-70; Perth Amboy Schl System 3rd Grd Tchr 1971-; *ai:* PTO n; Lit Club; Curr Comm; AFT 1970-; NJ Rdng Assn 1990-; Raritan Hosp Auxiliary 1985-; Roosevelt Hosp Auxiliary 1990-; NJ Governors gnition Awd 1994; *office:* Thomas Mundy Peterson Elem Sch 274 St Perth Amboy NJ 08861

PHY, BRIDGET GORMAN, 8th Grade Teacher; *b:* Brooklyn, NY; seph; *ed:* St Joseph's Coll at Brklyn (BA) Child Stud 1974; 3 Grad ts Cuny Pol Sci; 3 Grad Credits Fordham Art; 15 Grad Credits Bklyn Ed; *cr:* St Athanasius Second Grd Tchr 1974-75; St Edmund Kndgtn 1975-76; St Rose of Lima Fifth Grd Tchr 1978-82, Sixth-Eighth Grd 1982-; *ai:* HS Choices Cnslr; NCEA 1974-; Taft Inst Grad Course Awded Free Tuition; Mentor Tchr 1994-95; *office:* St Rose Of Lima 154 Beach 84th St Rockaway Beach NY 11693

PHY, BYRON GIRARD, Mathematics Tchr; *b:* Wilmington, DE; *m:* tte E. Kuzmack; *ed:* Univ of DE (BS) Electrical Engrng 1987; 30 t Hrs Tchng Cert; 15 Hrs Towards MSEd; *cr:* Middletown HS Math 1991-; *ai:* Class Adv; Dramatic Dir; Chm Middlestates Accreditation ı; NCTM, ASCD 1995-; Pub Article; *office:* Middletown HS 504 S St Middletown DE 19709

PHY, CAROLYN CORRELL, German Teacher; *b:* Carbondale, IL; aul Joseph; *c:* Michael; *ed:* Univ of CO (BA) Ger 1967; Masters alancy Linguistics West Chester Univ 1988; *cr:* Lakewood HS Ger 1967-68; Amos Alonzo Staff HS Ger Tchr 1968-69; North Penn HS 'chr 1980-; *ai:* Exch Stu, Ger Club Adv; PSEA 1980-; Montgomery 985-, Pres; Tchrs of Frgn Lang 1989-93; Amer Assn of Univ Women , Pres, Mem Chair, Outstdng Woman 1979; *home:* 1687 Jacks Cir lale PA 19446*

PHY, CAROLYN MANCINI, Mathematics Teacher; *b:* Providence, : Grayson P.; *c:* Christopher, Pamela N. Colin R.; *ed:* RI Coll (BA) 1962; 30 Hrs Masters Equivalency; *cr:* Parkview Jr HS Math Tchr 63; George West Jr HS Fr Tchr 1964-66; Lincoln HS Math Tchr 73; Cumberland HS Math Tchr 1973-; *ai:* NCTM Stans; Providence Critic Tchr; NEA 1973-; Greenpeace 1988-; Amnesty Intnl 1985-; at 1991-; Pres Awardee Excel in Tching Math 1993; *home:* 3249 ond Hill Rd Cumberland RI 02864*

PHY, CAROLYN ROYE, Art Teacher; *b:* Huntington, NY; *m:* ard C.; *c:* Elizabeth L., Catherine R.; *ed:* Syracuse Univ (BFA&Ed) d 1969, (MS) Photography & Cinematography 1974; 18 Hrs Advaced Painting; *cr:* Fayetteville-Manlius K-6th Grd Art Tchr 1969-72; ham Pub K-6th Grd Art Tchr 1972-76; Jamesville-Dewitt Art ultant 1980-81; Onondaga Cntrl HS & MS Art Tchr 1981-; *ai:* Class t Club Adv; Tchrs in Positive Attitude Towards Learning Pgm cipant & Trainer; ML 21 Pgm Participant; 4th-6th Grd Guid Coord; UT 1969-; NEA 1969-; OCSFA 1969-; Syracuse Univ Orange Pack & Davis Club 1975-; Onondaga Cntrl Schl Staff Advy Bd 1983-89, Art Head; Pebble Hill Presbyn Church 1988-90, Deacon; Contributor & bitor Juried Shows at Everson Museum; LeMoyne Coll Wilson Art ry 1 Person Show; Syracuse Univ Lone Art Ctr Group Show; *office:* daga Cntrl Schl Dist 201 Hudson Ave Nedrow NY 13120

RPHY, CATHERINE E., Dance Teacher & Choreographer; *b:* ing, NY; *m:* William F.; *c:* Ryan; *ed:* Queens Coll CUNY (BA) tre, Dance 1982; NY Univ Gallatin Schl (MA) Dance 1992; *cr:* St cis Prep HS Dance Tchr, Choreographer 1983-84; Holy Trinity esan HS Dance Tchr, Choreographer 1985-; *ai:* Musical Productions, al Dance Concerts, Seasonal Concerts Choreographer; Amer Dance l; AAPEHRD; NDA; *office:* Holy Trinity Diocesan HS 98 Cherry Ln sville NY 11801

RPHY, CHRISTINE S., English Dept Chairperson; *b:* Phillipsburg, *:* John J.; *c:* Michael; *ed:* Trenton St Coll (BA) Eng 1970, (MED) Eng ; *cr:* Bridgewater Raritan HS Eng Tchr 1970-72; La Reine HS Eng 1972-78; Immaculata Preparatory Eng Tchr 1983-86; Visitation aratory Tchr 1986-, Eng Dept Chair 1993-; *ai:* Honor Bd Moderator; , NCTE 1972-; *office:* Georgetown Visitatn Prep Schl 1524 35th St Washington DC 20007

RPHY, CHRISTOPHER ANTHONY, Social Studies Teacher; *b:* poc, CA; *ed:* St Banaventure Univ (BA) Jrnlsm 1987; Univ of ester (MS) Ed 1994; Albertus Magnus Coll 6 Credits Hrs Lbrl Stud; Murphy Publishing Owner, Ed 1988-91; Albertus Magnus Coll Grad 1992-93; Univ of Rochester Grad Asst 1993-94; Wilby HS Soc Stud 1994-; *ai:* Stu Cncl Club Adv; Ec Club Adv; New England Curr ew; NEA, WTBY Tchr Assn, CT Ed Assn 1994-; City of New Haven Grad Awd 1993; Articles Pub Univ of Rochester Journal 1994; *home:* Schraffls Dr #106 Waterbury CT 06705

MURPHY, CHRISTOPHER JOHN, Latin & World History Teacher; *b:* Westminster, MD; *ed:* Univ of MD at Baltimore (BA) Ancient Stud-Cum Laude 1984; Attending Univ of MD Schl of Medicine; *cr:* West Baltimore MS Latin Tchr 1987-89; Randallstown HS Latin, World His Tchr 1989-94; Hereford HS Latin Tchr 1984-; *ai:* Odyssey of Mind Coach WBM, RHS.

MURPHY, DANIEL BARKER, Emeritus Prof of Chemistry; *b:* Richmond Hill, NY; *m:* Lorraine Carey; *c:* Daniel, Kathleen Civetta, Brien, Kevin; *ed:* Fordham Coll (BS) Chem 1947; Fordham Univ (MS) Chem 1949; PA St Univ (PHD) Fuel Sci 1958; *cr:* Univ of Scranton Instr 1949-51; Picatinny Arsenal Rsrch Chemist 1951-54; Hunter Coll Assoc Prof 1957-68; Lehman Coll Prof 1968-91, Emeritus Prof 1991-; *ai:* Amer Chemical Soc 1948-; Amer Carbon Soc 1974-; Royal Soc of Chem 1963-; Sigma Xi 1969-, Past Chptr Pres; Fnds of Coll Chem J. Wiley; Gen Chem Coll Quiz Series; Numerous Rsrch Papers Pub.

MURPHY, DANIEL PATRICK, High School Teacher; *b:* Lowell, MA; *m:* Joan Marie Bovitz; *c:* Grainne, Daniel, Patrick; *ed:* St Anselms Coll (BA) Eng 1971; Univ of MA (MEd) Ed Admin 1979; Northeastern Univ (MEd) Pysch & Family Therapy 1980 & 1982; 160 Grad Credits at Summa Cum Laude; *cr:* Lowell Schl System Tchr 1971-; *ai:* Creative Writing Club; Univ of MA Boston Ctr for Learning & Tchng Awd; AFT 1971-, Mem; NEA 1971-, Mem; NE Poets Club 1986-, Mem; Amer Assn of Marriage & Family Therapists 1985-, MA Family Therapists 1985-, Mem; Book of Poetry, The Fractured Emerald; Numerous Awds; Short Story Writer; Tufts Univ Outstdng Tchr Awd.*

MURPHY, DARIA FEDOROVICH, Library & Media Specialist; *b:* Chester, PA; *m:* William R.; *ed:* California Univ of PA (BS) Elem Ed 1974; Duquesne Univ (MS) Lib Sci 1983; *cr:* Ringgold Schl Dist Classroom Tchr, GATE Instr, Elem Librn 1975-85; Lower Dauphin Schl Dist Coord of Libs 1985-88; York Cty Area Voc Tech HS Lib, Media Specialist 1988-; *ai:* Stdnts Win at Tech Team Founder, Adv; VICA, HOSA, DECA Stu Ldrshp Orgs; Commencement Stu Speakers Coach; PA Schl Librn Assn 1981-; Phi Delta Kappa 1992-; PA Assn Curr, Dev 1993-; NEA; PSEA; YCVTEA; Pittsburgh Steelers Fan Club of York; York Cty Indstrl, Ag Museum, Educ Advy Bd 1990-; York Little Theatre; *office:* York Co Area Voc Tech Sch 2179 S Queen St York PA 17402

MURPHY, DAVID JOHN, Government & Psychology Tchr; *b:* Herkimer, NY; *m:* Kathy L.; *c:* Karen, Kimberly, Katherine, Kristina; *ed:* SUNY at Brookport (BS) His & Ed 1973; Ed & Admin 40 Grad Hrs; *cr:* New Hartford Cntrl 6th Grd 1973-86, 10th-12th Grd His 1987-; *ai:* Jr High Track Coach 12 Yrs; Sophmore Class Adv 3 Yrs; Sr Class Adv 2 Yrs; Girls Sftbl Coach 4 Yrs; AFT 1973-; NSUT 1973-; *office:* New Hartford Sr HS 33 Oxford Rd New Hartford NY 13413

MURPHY, DAVID THOMAS, English Tchr & Rdng Specialist; *b:* Philadelphia, PA; *ed:* Temple Univ (BS) Eng Ed 1977; Temple Univ (MED) Psych of Rdng 1983; *cr:* Temple Univ Part Time Lecturer 1975; Schl Dist of Philadelphia Eng Tchr 1977-80; Philadelphia Literacy Inst Eng Tchr 1980-81; Lenape HS Eng Tchr, Rdng Specialist 1982-; *ai:* Adv Knowledge Bowl, Renaissance Club; Coach Karate Club; Adv Future Tchrs Of Amer; NEA, NCTE 1982-; Phi Delta Kappa 1985-; NEH Summer Seminar Nietzsche 1988, NEH Ind Stud 1989, Lenape Dist Excl in Ed Grant 1988, 1994; TV Prgms Producer & Creator; NEH Summer Semnr goethe 1995; Geraldine R Dodge Fndtn Flw 1995; *office:* Lenape Regnl HS Church & Hartford Rds Medford NJ 08055*

MURPHY, DONNA HURST, Guidance Counselor; *b:* Baltimore, MD; *m:* Kevin Michael; *c:* Shaun, Jeffrey, Daniel, Anthony; *ed:* Loyola Coll at Baltimore (BA) Psych 1982, (MED) Guidance & Counseling 1990; *cr:* Arthur Slade Regnl Cath Schl Tchr 1983-85; Arthur Slade Regnl Ed-Care Admin 1985-89; The Seton Keough HS Guidance Cnslr 1989-; *ai:* SADD Moderator; Soph Class Coord; AACD, Amer Schl Cnslr 1990-; Arthur Slade Schl Bd 1990-, Sec, VP; *office:* Seton Keough HS 1201 S Caton Ave Baltimore MD 21227*

MURPHY, EDWARD JEROME,JR., Senior Army Instructor; *b:* Baltimore, MD; *m:* Patricia Ann Repine; *c:* Edward J. III, Timothy Patrick; *ed:* Loyola Coll (BS) Pol Sci 1958; Catholic Univ 3 Credit Hrs 1978; *cr:* Military Svc Military Ofcr 1958-78; Treadwell HS Sr Army Instr 1982-88; Calvin Coolidge HS Sr Army Instr 1988-; *ai:* Jr ROTC Drill Team; Partnership Comm; Prsnl Admin, Washington HS Summer Camp; Reserve Ofcrs Assn 1982-; *office:* Calvin Coolidge Sr HS 5th & Tuckerman Sts NW Washington DC 20011

MURPHY, E.J. JOSEPH, 7th Grade Reading Teacher; *b:* Pittston, PA; *m:* Deborah Jean Orlando; *c:* Mark; *ed:* East Stroudsburg Univ (BS) Elem Ed, PE 1972; Masters Ed East Stroudsburg St & PA St Univ; *cr:* Pittston City Elem 6th Grd Math, Rdng, Soc Stud Tchr 1972-82; Pittston Area MS 6th-7th Grd Math, Rdng, Soc Stud, Sci Tchr 1982-; *ai:* HS Bsbl Coach 1972-87; AFT 1972-; Knights of Columbus 1976-; *office:* Pittston Area MS New St Pittston PA 18640

MURPHY, GAYLE RICHARDSON, 11th Grade English Teacher; *b:* Woburn, MA; *m:* Robert B.; *c:* Shannon, Brian; *ed:* Merrimack Coll (BA) Eng 1973; Cambridge Coll (MED) Ed 1994; *cr:* Kennedy Jr HS Eng Tchr 1974-82; Woburn HS Eng Tchr 1987-; *ai:* Prof Dev Comm Fac Cncl; NCTE 1992-; MA Tchr Assn, NEA 1974-; *office:* Woburn Sr HS 88 Montvale Ave Woburn MA 01801

MURPHY, GLENN ELLSWORTH, Mathematics Teacher; *b:* Uniontown, PA; *m:* Beverly Ann Murphy; *c:* Kimberly, Colleen; *ed:* Clarion Univ (BS) Math 1969; Addl 60 Hrs Post Degree; *cr:* Wyalusing Jr & Sr HS Math Tchr 1969-; *ai:* Aviation Ground Instr; Wyalusing Area Ed Assn 1969-, Pres, VP; Penn & Ed Assn 1969-, St Comm Spec Svcs; NEA 1969-; Camptown Comm Church 1970-, Trustee; Camptown Mens Club 1970-8 Pres, Treas; Choir 1970-; Wyalusing Lodge #618 1992 F&AM Mem; Ancient Accepted Scottish Rite 1992; Irem Temple AAONMS 1992; *home:* PO Box 112 Camptown PA 18815*

MURPHY, GWENDOLYN BOLTON, 7th Grade English Teacher; *b:* York, PA; *m:* Rodger Dale II; *ed:* Millersville Univ (BA) Scndry Ed Eng 1984; Shippensburg Univ (MED) Eng 1990; 45 Addl Educl Credits; *cr:* Red Lion Area Jr HS 7th Grd Eng Tchr 1985-; *ai:* Stu Cncl, Yrbk Advs; Fun Day Comm Chprsn; Schl Act Comm; NEA 1985-; Tchr of Month; Dist Mentor Tchr; *office:* Red Lion Area Jr HS 200 Country Club Rd Red Lion PA 17356

MURPHY, IRENE E., Biology Teacher; *b:* Southington, CT; *m:* Larry; *c:* Kim, Erica, Ben; *ed:* Univ of ME at Fort Kent (BS) Bio 1975; *cr:* Comm HS Bio Tchr 1975-; *ai:* Prof Dev Comm; Support System Chprsn; Trainer Cooperative Learning; Sci Olympiad & Envirothon Team Coach; NHS Adv; Dimensions of Learning Trainer; Curr Tm Ldr K-12 of Sci, Hlth, Phys Ed; MTA, NEA, NATA 1975-, Sec 1988; ATONIM Mem, MSTA; Recreation Bd 1987-; *office:* Community H S 55 Pleasant St Fort Kent ME 04743

MURPHY, JAMES EDWARD, English & Social Studies Tchr; *b:* Titusville, PA; *ed:* Edinboro Univ (BS) Scndry Ed 1960, (MS) Ed 1966; Attnd Gannon Univ; *cr:* Randolph East Mead HS Tchr 1960-75; Maplewood MS Tchr 1975-90; Maplewood HS Tchr 1990-95; *ai:* SADD Adv; Act Ldr; Hiking Club; Stu Asst Team Tutor; Soph Retreat Facilitator; PSEA 1960-, Pres 1965-66, Life Mem; NEA 1960-, Life Mem; Northwestern Cncl Tchrs of Eng; Knights of Columbus 1990-; CCD Tchr 1960-; Parish Cncl; Sierra Club; *office:* Maplewood HS RR 1 Guys Mills PA 16327

MURPHY, JAMES MICHAEL, 8th-9th Grade English Teacher; *b:* Pittsburgh, PA; *m:* Rita K. Stern; *ed:* Univ of Pittsburgh (BA) Eng 1976; Univ of Pittsburgh (MA) Speech, Theater Arts 1986; Penn St Admin Cert 1995; *cr:* Moon Twp Jr High Eng Tchr 1982-83; Downingtown Area Sr High Eng Tchr 1983-84; Hollidaysburg Area Jr High Eng Tchr 1984-; *ai:* Hollidaysburg Area Ed Assoc 1983-, Pres; *office:* Hollidaysburg Area Schl Dist 1000 Hewitt St Hollidaysburg PA 16648

MURPHY, JAMES WILLIAM, Sixth Grade Teacher; *b:* Providence, RI; *m:* Kathleen; *c:* Christopher, Ryan; *ed:* Providence Coll (BA) Ed 1973, (MA) Admin 1977; 30 Addl Hrs His, Rdng, Spec Ed, Cmptr RI Coll; *cr:* Burrillville HS Soc Stud Tchr 1973-83; Burrillville Jr HS Geog Tchr 1983-89; Burrillville MS House Supvr 1989-92, 6th Grd Geog Tchr 1992-; *ai:* Coach Hockey Jr HS 7 Yrs, Var 4 Yrs, Summer Camp 12 Yrs; Rhode Ornithology Club 7 Yrs; Elem PTO GEM Awd 1995; HS Hockey RI Coach of Yr 1983; *office:* Burrillville MS 2220 Broncos Hwy Harrisville RI 02830*

MURPHY, JANE ZAMPITELLA, Classroom Teacher; *b:* Revere, MA; *m:* William Z.; *ed:* Boston St Coll (BS) Elem Ed 1968, (MED) Cnslng 1973; 60 Addl Credit Hrs; *cr:* Linden Elem Schol 1968-; Weight Watchers Group Inc Lecturer 1974-; *ai:* Federal Aviation Assn Schl Partnership Steering Comm 1995-; Report Card Comm 1994-; Assessment Advy Comm 1995-; Malden Tchrs Assn 1968-, Sick Bank Comm; NEA 1968-; Sacred Heart Parish Comm 1983-, Chprsn Chrstn Worship Commission 1990-92; *office:* Linden Elem Schl 29 Wescott St Malden MA 02148*

MURPHY, JANET COMPTON, Sixth Grade Teacher; *b:* Latrobe, PA; *m:* Paul M.; *c:* Brian, Stephen; *ed:* IN Univ of PA (BS) Elem Ed 1972, (MED) Elem Ed 1981; Addl 6 Credit Hrs; *cr:* Blairsville Schl Sub Tchr 1974-77, 5th Grd Tchr 1977-78, 6th Grd Tchr 1978-79, 5th Grd Tchr 1979-81, 4th Grd Tchr 1981-86, 5th Grd Tchr 1986-95, 6th Grd Tchr 1995-; *ai:* Blairsville Saltsbury Ed Assn, PA Ed Assn, NEA 1977-; Trinity Presbyn Church 1974-79, Tchr; Chrstn Ed 1975-80; Sunday Schl 1985-87, Sec; KARE Project Cert; *home:* RR 1 Box 573 Saltsburg PA 15681

MURPHY, JEAN TROJANOSKI, 5th Grd Lang Arts & Rdng Tchr; *b:* New Haven, CT; *m:* Thomas C.; *c:* Timothy, Cynthia; *ed:* Southern CT St Univ (MS) Rdng 1981; *cr:* Turkey Hill Schl 5th Grd Tchr 1964-65; St Catherine of Siena Schl 8th Grd Tchr 1982-86; Daniel Farm Schl 5th Grd Tchr 1986-; *ai:* Stu Cncl Adv; Stu Assistance Team Mem; TEA, Rep; CEA, NEA; League of St Josephs Manor 1990-; St of CT Mentor Tchr 1991-; CT Pot Woman of Substance 1993; *office:* Daniels Farm Schl 710 Daniels Farm Rd Trumbull CT 06611

MURPHY, JEREMIAH NATHANIEL, Vocal Music Teacher; *b:* Washington, DC; *ed:* Oberlin Coll (BM) Piano, (MMT) Music Ed 1979; *cr:* Spaulding Jr HS Vocal Music Tchr 1981-82; Andrew Jackson MS Vocal Music Tchr 1984-88; DuVal HS Vocal Music Tchr 1988-89; Largo HS Vocal Music Tchr 1990-; *ai:* EMA Music Inc 1993-, Pres; Leading Commandment Church 1956-, Bd Mem; Gospel Music Wkshp of Amer 1991-; Gospel Music Assn 1993-; Recording Released 1993; *office:* Largo HS 505 Largo Rd Upper Marlboro MD 20774*

MURPHY, JEROME, Eng, French Teacher & Ath Dir; *b:* Tokyo, Japan; *ed:* LeHigh Univ (BA) Eng 1990; Sacred Heart Working for MAT to Grad 1997; *cr:* Nantes France Semi-Pro Ftbl Quarterback 1990-91; ABC Sports Asst Pub Relations 1991-92; Black Goose Grille Mgr 1992-94; St Thomas More Eng, Fr Tchr & Ath Dir 1994-; *ai:* Ftbl Coach; Numerous Articles Pub; *office:* St Thomas More Schl 45 Cottage Rd Oakdale CT 06370*

MURPHY, JOAN MURPHY, 3rd Grade Teacher; *b:* Attleboro Falls, MA; *w:* Lawernce William (dec); *c:* Kellie Murphy-Tolo; *ed:* Bridgewater (BA) Elem 1955; Credit Hrs Art Courses, Whole Lang, Portfolio Assessment, Math Manipulatives, Cooperative Learning, Peer Power, Stress Mngmt; *cr:* John Woodcock Schl Grd 2 Tchr 1955-57; Verplanck Schl Grd 2 Tchr 1957-59; Roosevelt Ave Schl Grd 3 Tchr 1967; Joseph Martin Schl Grd 3 Schl 1967-; *ai:* Schl Cncl Sec 1994-; AFT 1967-; NEA 1955-60; My Most Memorable Tchr Awd; *home:* 17 Stagecoach Rd North Attleboro MA 02760

MURPHY, JOHN J.,JR., Religious Educator; *b:* Bronx, NY; *ed:* St Marys Coll (BA) His Psych, Theology 1972; Manhattan COll (MA) Rel Stud 1978; Fordham Univ Inst of Rel Ed; *cr:* New Rochelle HS of Rel Asst Dir 1965-87; Dodge City Rel Ed Prgm Asst Dir 1970-71; Mount St Michael Acad Rel Ed Tchr, Club Moderator 1974-; *ai:* NCEA 1974-; Spec Olympics 1982-; Amer Red Cross Ldrshp Awd; New Rochelle HS of Rel Alumni Awd, Svc Awds; Stu Cncl Svc Awd; *office:* Mount Saint Michael Acad 4300 Murdock Ave Bronx NY 10466

MURPHY, JULIA MARY, Social Studies & Science Tchr; *ed:* Molloy Coll (BS) Soc Stud, Ed; C. W. Post Coll (MA) Soc Stud, Ed; *cr:* St John the Bapt HS 9th-10th Grd Soc Stud, Sci Tchr 1973-; *ai:* Big Brother, Big Sister; Frosh Stu Cncl; L I Soc Stud Cncl; *office:* St John the Bapt Diocesan HS 1170 Montauk Hwy West Islip NY 11795

MURPHY, KATHARINE PHILLIPS, Principal; *b:* Suffern, NY; *m:* Robert; *c:* Jamie, Sean, Kyle, Erin; *ed:* Long Island Univ (MS) Ed; Wilson Coll (BA) Bio 1975; Attnd Fordham Univ; *cr:* Cimmaculate Conception Tchr, Prin; St Paul the Apostle 7th Grd Tchr; Robin Hill Schl Nursery Tchr 1976-; *ai:* Ladies Auxiliary 1995-; Wayne Hose Fire Dept; *office:* Immaculate Conception Schl 24 E Main St Stony Point NY 10980

MURPHY, KATHERINE ANN, Religion Teacher; *b:* Washington, DC; *ed:* James Madison Univ (A) His 1989; Cath Univ of Amer (MA) Rel Ed 1992; 9 Hrs at Washington Theological Union; *cr:* The Good Shepherd Eng Schl Japan Eng Tchr 1989-90; Archbishop Carroll HS Religion Tchr 1993-; Summer Youth Employment Summer Mgr 1995-; *ai:* Bsktbl & Soccer Coach; Hiking Club Moderator; Soph Class Svc Coord; Scheduling Comm; NCEA 1993-, Mem; Maryknoll 1996, Mem; Grant-Tchng for Spiritual Growth Inst at Harvard 1994; *office:* Archbishop Carroll HS 4300 Harewood Rd NE Washington DC 20017

MURPHY, KATHLEEN ANN, Mathematics Dept Chairman; *b:* Pittsfield, MA; *ed:* North Adam St Coll (BA) Math 1969; SUNY at Albany (MA) Math 1970; *cr:* Pittsfield HS Math Tchr 1970-88, Math Dept Chm 1988-; *ai:* NEA, NCTM, MAA 1970-; *office:* Pittsfield HS 300 East St Pittsfield MA 01201

MURPHY, KATHLEEN SUE, Science Teacher; *b:* Cleveland, OH; *c:* James Globokar, Leo, Kristine; *ed:* Cleveland St Univ (BS) PE 1978; Ashland Coll (MSEd) Sports Sci 1995; *cr:* Parma Holy Name HS Ath Trainer, Sci, Hlth, PE Tchr; North Royalton HS Head Ath Trainer, PE Tchr 1983-86; Lorain Clearview HS Sci Tchr 1986-87; Twinsburg Chamberlin HS Sci Tchr 1993-95; *ai:* NEA 1983-; NATA 1974-; OH HS Ath Assn 1976-; Twinsburg Educ Assn 1993-; North Shore Coll Umpires 1994-; Suburban Umpires 1990-; NE OH Vlybl Ofcls Assn 1983-; Pub Masters Practicum HS Ath Trng Curr Ashland Coll; *office:* Twinsburg Chamberlin HS 10270 Ravenna Rd Twinsburg OH 44087*

MURPHY, KEVIN JAMES, Fourth Grade Teacher; *b:* Nashua, NH; *m:* Sandra Ferguson; *c:* Galen, Joshua; *ed:* Univ of NH (BS) Bus Admin 1973; Antioch Grad Schl (MED) Elem Ed 1977; *cr:* Milford Elem 1-3, 5 Grd Tchr 1977-90; Halvorsen Elem Rhein Air Base Tech, Grd 1 Tchr 1990-92; Milford Elem Schl Grd 4 Tchr 1992-; *ai:* Elem Schl Tech Facilitator; After Schl Ski Prgm Coord; Space Needs Comm; NCTM 1993-; NHATMNE 1994-; NEA 1977-; Excl in Elem Math Presidential Awardee St, Natl 1995; *home:* 287 Federal Hill Rd Milford NH 03055

MURPHY, KEVIN OWEN, Social Studies Teacher; *ed:* Dowling Coll (BA) His 1990; *cr:* Crawford & Co Claim Adjuster 1992-93; ITT Hartford

Litigation Specialist 1993-94; *ai:* Track Coach; *office:* West Islip Sr HS 1 Lions Path West Islip NY 11795

MURPHY, KIMBERLY JANET, Music Director; *b:* So Weymouth, MA; *m:* Peter F.; *c:* Nicholas; *ed:* Duquesne Univ at Pittsburg (BSME) Music Ed, Music Therapy 1983; Attnd Boston Univ Schl of Fine Arts 1978-79; Univ of Southern ME Post Grad Stud; *cr:* The Matheny Schl Music Therapist RMT-BC 1983-96; United Cerebral Palsy Music Therapist RMT-BC 1987-88; Oak Hill HS Music Tchr 1988-; School Union #44 Music Tchr 1988-; *ai:* ACDA 1989-; MENC, MMEA 1988-, Sec Dist III; NEA, Oak Hill Tchrs Alliance 1988-; Camp Happy Times, Music Act Dir, Cnslr; Gaslight Theater 1990-, Bd, Actress, Costume Designer; Comm Little Theatre 1991-; Prince of Luth Church, Misic Comm; Boothbay Playhouse Actress; Pub Children Musical Tape; Soloist for First Church of Christ Scientist; Lead Roles im Comm Musicals; *office:* Oak Hill HS PO Box 400 Sabattus ME 04280*

MURPHY, LAURIE JOHNSON, History & German Teacher; *b:* Sussex, NJ; *m:* James K.; *ed:* Boston Coll (MA) European His 1990; *cr:* Hackettstown HS His, Govt, Sociology Tchr 1990-91; Phillipsburg HS His, Ger Tchr 1991-; *ai:* Asst Track & Field Coach; Debate Club Adv; Ger Club Adv; NEA 1990-; NCSS 1991-; Phillipsburg HS Boosterettes 1986-; *office:* Phillipsburg HS 675 Corliss Ave Phillipsburg NJ 08865

MURPHY, MARTIN VINCENT, Teacher; *b:* Peabody, MA; *m:* Margaret L. Butler; *c:* Jennifer; *ed:* Phoenix Comm Coll (AS) Cmptr Sci 1977; Northshore Comm Coll (AA) Bus Admin 1980; Salem St Coll (BS) Acctng Bus 1982; 45 Credit Hrs Salem St; *cr:* NS Regnl Tech HS Tchr 1982-; *ai:* Newspaper Adv; NEA, MTA 1982-; NSEA 1982-, Pres; NRA 1962-; Conservation Commission 1995-; Cntry Pond Fish, Game 1995-, Treas; *office:* North Shore Regnl Tech HS 30 Logbridge Rd Middleton MA 01949

MURPHY, MARYANN, Sixth Grd Mathematics Teacher; *b:* New Brunswick, NJ; *c:* Jason; *ed:* Trenton St Coll (BA) Elem Ed 1965; Newark St Coll (MA) Supervision, Admin 1980; *cr:* Lincoln Schl 6th Grd Tchr 1965-66; AlexanderSchl 6th Grd Tchr 1966-67; Parkway Schl 6th Grd Tchr 1967-70; James Madison Inter Schl 6th Grd Tchr 1972-85; Woodro w Wilson MS Math, 6th Grd Tchr 1985-; *ai:* NEA, NJEA 1965-; ETEA 1972-.

MURPHY, MICHAEL FRANCIS, Mathematics Teacher; *b:* Elizabeth, NJ; *m:* Glenda Sharp; *c:* Michael S., Timothy L.; *ed:* Seton Hall Univ (BS) Scndry Ed 1965; 4 NSF Math Grants; Keane Coll Math Supervision; Trenton St Coll Ed; *cr:* Holy Trinity HS His Tchr 1962-63; Union Cath HS Math Tchr 1963-65; St Jospeh HS Math, His, PE Tchr 1965-67; Colonia HS Math Tchr 1967-71; North Marion HS Math Tchr 1971-72; Franklin Elem Schl Math Tchr 1972-73; Metuchen HS Math Tchr 1973-75; Highland Park HS Math Tchr 1975-85; Flemington-Raritan MS Math Tchr 1985-; *ai:* Co-Ed Winter & Girls Spring Track; NEA, NJEA 1967-; Flemington-Raritan Ed Assn 1986-; NJ Coaches Assn 1994-; NJ Track Ofcls Assn 1972-; Hillsborough NJ Bd of Ed 1968-71; Hillsborough Recreation Comm 1969-71; Hillsborough Jaycees 1969-70, Pres; Amer Legion 1994-; US Marine Corps League 1995-, Commandant; Woodbridge Twp Ath Hall of Fame; NJ St Coaches Hall of Fame; My Teams Won St Titles in Groups I, II, III & IV; St Championships Cross Cntry, Winter Track, Spring Track; *office:* Reading Fleming MS 50 Court St Flemington NJ 08822*

MURPHY, MICHAEL JOSEPH, 6th-8th Grade Multi-Age Tchr; *b:* Portland, ME; *m:* Beth Hamilton; *c:* Meaghan, Erin, Sean; *ed:* Univ of Southern ME (BS) Elem Ed 1986; *cr:* Thornton Acad HS Aide 1986-87; Scarborough MS 6th-8th Grd Tchr 1987-; *ai:* Var Golf 1988-; Var Bsktbl 1989-; Tennis 1988-; ME Bsktbl Coaches Assn 1987-; *office:* Scarborough MS Gorham Rd Scarborough ME 04038

MURPHY, MICHELE, Math Teacher; *b:* Chester, PA; *ed:* Alvernia Coll (BA) Math, Scndry Ed 1973; Kutztown Univ (MED) Math, Scndry Ed 1976; *cr:* St Pius X HS Math Tchr 1973-; *ai:* Mathletes, IM Bowling Moderator; Math Dept Chprsn; ATMOPAV; NCTM; Dstngd Cath Edctr 1994.

MURPHY, NATALIE ANN, English Teacher & Dept Chair; *b:* Lynn, MA; *ed:* Salem St Coll (BA) Eng 1971; Plymouth St Coll (MED) Ed 1979; Bates Coll Course to Teach AP Eng; *cr:* Winthrop Jr HS Eng Tchr 1971-74; Newfound Regnl HS Eng Tchr 1974-, Dept Chair 1986-; *ai:* Steering Comm NEASS & C Evaluation; Curr Comm; Class Adv; NCTE 1974-; Phi Delta Kappa 1991-; NEA-NH 1971-; New England Assn Tchrs of Eng 1980-; ASCD 1988-; NATA 1976-; Dev Dist ESL Policy 1989; NH Tchr of Yr Nom; St Cert Bd; Prin Search, Curr, GATE, MS Reorganization Comm; *office:* Newfound Regional HS Rt 104 Newfound Rd Bristol NH 03222

MURPHY, NEIL P., English Teacher; *b:* Lowell, MA; *m:* Anne Madigan; *c:* Maryanne, Elizabeth; *ed:* Boston Coll (BS) Eng 1961; Salem St Coll (MED) Eng Ed 1964; Boston Coll (MA) Eng Lit 1967; Univ of Notre Dame (ABO) Eng Renaissance; 30 Addl Hrs; *cr:* Dracut HS Eng Tchr 1961-67; Univ of Notre Dame Tchng Asst 1967-70; Univ of MA at Lowell Instr 1971-73; Acton Boxborough Reg HS Eng Dept Chm 1973-94, Eng Tchr 1994-; *ai:* NEA, MTA 1961-; AEA 1973-; Cert Awareness Hammond, MIT, Tufts, Univ of Chicago.*

MURPHY, PAMELA NORTHCUTT, High School English Teacher; *m:* Michael; *c:* Mackenzie Jordan; *ed:* Univ of Cincinnati (BA) Eng 1975; Xavier Elem (MS) Admin 1992; Post Grad Work Eng Univ of NC; *cr:* Lakota HS Eng Tchr 1975-80; Providence Day Schl Eng Tchr 1980-82; Madeira HS Asst Prof 1991-94 & Eng Tchr 1982-; *ai:* NHS & Jr Class Adv; Design Team Comm; NCTE 1980-; OCTCLA 1985-; United Meth Women 1996; Great People Make Great Schls Madeira Awd; Articles Pub; *office:* Madeira Jr Sr HS 7465 Loannes Dr Cincinnati OH 45243*

MURPHY, PATRICIA, Mathematics Department Chm; *b:* Chester, PA; *ed:* Alvernia Coll (BA) Math 1973; Kutztown Univ (MED) Math 1976; 15 Hrs in Bus at Alvernia Coll; *cr:* Holy Name HS Tchr 1973-; *ai:* Intramural Bowling Moderator; NHS Fac Cncl; NCTM, PCTM & NCEA; *office:* Holy Name H S 955 E Wyomissing Blvd Reading PA 19611

MURPHY, PATRICK M., Business Teacher; *b:* Camden, NJ; *m:* Theresa Budesa; *c:* Casey, Ryan, Theresa Mary; *ed:* Glassboro St (BS) Admin Stud 1982; *cr:* Gloucester Cath HS Bus Tchr 1983-; *ai:* Dev Dir; Bus Dept Chprsn; A-V Moderator; Mrktg Team; NCEA, NJBA 1983-; Dist Tchr of Yr 1995-96; *office:* Gloucester Catholic HS 333 Ridgeway St Gloucester City NJ 08030

MURPHY, PATRICK MICHAEL, Guidance Counselor; *b:* Chicago, IL; *m:* Irene Therese; *c:* Keith, Christine, Ryan, Timothy; *ed:* Marist Coll (BA) His 1962; St John's Univ (MA) His 1969, (MS) Cnslng 1972; Attnd Bowie St Univ, Catholic Univ, Rutgers NDEA Grant, Trinity Coll at Washington; *cr:* Christ the King HS Tchr 1962-75; Douglass HS Tchr 1975-76; High Point HS Cnslr 1977-82; Eleanor Roosevelt HS Cnslr 1983-; *ai:* Schl Comms; Cross Cntry, Indoor, Outdoor Track Coach 10 Yrs; Wrestling Coach; NEA; Knights of Columbus 1977-, Chair of Church Comm, Right to Life Chair, Lecturer; Oakland Mills Soccer Booster Chm; NDEA Grant; *office:* Eleanor Roosevelt HS 7601 Hanover Pky Greenbelt MD 20770

MURPHY, RAYMOND JOSEPH, Retired Teacher; *b:* Rome, NY; *c:* Christopher, Michael, Megan; *ed:* Syracuse Univ (BA) Bus Ad, Acct, Elem Ed 1963; Attnd SUNY at Oswego, Elmira Coll, Utica Coll; *cr:* Parmalee Elem Schl Tchr 1964-81; Gansevoort Elem Tchr 1981-93; *ai:* NYSUT 1964-; Rome Tchrs Assn 1964-, Tchr Rep; K of C 1956-.

MURPHY, ROBERT JAMES, Mathematics Teacher; *b:* Toledo, OH; *m:* Ann Elizabeth Oberkiser; *c:* Shawn; *ed:* Univ of Toledo (BED) Math 1970, (MS) Rsrch, Statistics 1976; Guid, Cnslng Cert; *cr:* Kroger Co Clerk 1963-69; Libbey-Owens Ford Tech 1964-65; Anthony Wayne HS Math Tchr 1970-; *ai:* Coached Ftbl, Bsbl; NEA 1970-; OEA 1970-, Rep Assembly Del; AWEA 1970-, Pres, Chief Negotiator; OCTM; GTCM; Perrysburg Jaycees, Pres, Jaycee of Yr 1980; OH Ed Grant for Math Lab; Presidential Awd for Excl Nom 1993; *office:* Anthony Wayne HS 5967 Finzel Rd Whitehouse OH 43571

MURPHY, SUE JEMISON, Sixth Grade Teacher; *b:* Parkersburg, WV; *m:* Michael J.; *c:* Jason; *ed:* OH St (BS) Elem Edu 1972, (MA) Stu Personnel in Higher Ed 1974; Post Grad Work Environmental Ed; *cr:* Ashton MS 6th Grd Tchr 1974-; *ai:* Outdoor Ed Coord; Peer Ldrshp Adv; NEA, OEA, REA 1974-; OH Conservation Outdoor Ed Assn 1974-, Bd Mem; Reynoldsburg Recreation Commission 1981-, Chair, Vice Chair; Jaycee Tchr of Yr 1983; Tchr of Yr 1995; Drug-Free Consortium Achvmt Awd 1992-93; *office:* Hannah J. Ashton MS 1482 Jackson St Reynoldsburg OH 43068

MURPHY, THOMAS WILLIAM,JR., Amer Govt, Ec & US His Tchr; *b:* New Haven, CT; *m:* Shirley Goetsch; *c:* Shauna, Nathaniel; *ed:* Univ of NE (BA) His 1966; 15 Credit Hrs Univ of NE; *cr:* Milliar Jr HS Soc Stud, Eng Tchr 1967-68; Bourne HS Soc Stud Tchr 1968-72; Kennebunk HS Soc Stud Tchr 1972-80; State Rep Ldr Minority 1980-88; Kennebunk HS Soc Stud Tchr 1988-; *ai:* Interact Club; Pol Affairs Club; Chm ME Republican Party Pres Appointment 1982-89; Advy Cncl to Sec of Defense Dept of Defense Overseas Dependent Schls; *home:* 1 Gilpatrick Shipyard Ln Kennebunk ME 04043

MURPHY, TYLER L., Science Teacher; *b:* Langhorne, PA; *m:* Elizabeth Bloomer; *ed:* Messiah Coll (BS) Bio, Ed 1992; *cr:* Mercer Chrstn Acad Sci Tchr 1992-; *ai:* Bsktbl Coach; Stu Cncl Adv; Vlybl IMs; Sci, Math Coord; *office:* Mercer Christian Acad 2015 Pennington Rd Ewing NJ 08618*

MURPHY, WENDY LORRAINE, Social Studies Teacher; *b:* Rockville, MD; *m:* Patrick S.; *ed:* York Coll of Pa (BA) Soc Stud 1992; 9 Credit Hrs Beaver Coll, Penn St Univ; *cr:* West York Sr HS Soc Stud Tchr 1993-; *ai:* Sr Class, Project Harmony Adv; Liasion Comm; PSEA Bldg Rep; NEA, PSEa 1993-, Bldg Rep; VFW 1995-, Ladies Aux; NSF Tchng Psych as Natural Sci Beaver Coll 1994; *office:* West York Area HS 1800 Bannister St York PA 17404

MURPHY-CRANSTON, DONNA LEE, Special Education Teacher; *b:* New London, CT; *m:* James Spencer; *c:* Kenzie Wenk, J. Walker; *ed:* Eastern CT St (BS) Elem Ed 1980; Univ of CT (MS) Spcl Ed 1988; *cr:* Sacred Heart 6th Grd Tchr 1984-85; LEARN Spcl Ed Tchr, SEM Classroom Tchr 5 Yrs & Tchr of Developmentally Disabled 2 Yrs 1988-; *ai:* Prof Dev 4 Yrs, Curr Dev 3 Yrs & Strategic Planning 1 Yr Comms; Developmentally Delayed Team Ldr 1 Yr; CEA & NEA 1989-; PLEA Project LEARN 1989-, Chprsn; Ed Assn, Nom & Tchr Appreciation Day Comm; Girl Scouts of Amer 1981-, Asst Ldr; American Cancer Soc 1981-Annual Ball Chprson; E Lyem Yth Chrldng 1995-, Support Team; *office:* Project Learn-Old Lyme MS 44 Hatchetts Hill Old Lyme CT 06371

MURR, PAUL WILLIAM, Frgn Lang Dept Chair & Tchr; *b:* Lancaster, PA; *m:* Deborah Kay Riedel; *c:* Paul A., Amy M.; *ed:* Millersville Univ (BS) Span 1969, (MA) Span 1976; ESL Credits Temple Univ; *cr:* Ephrata HS Tchr & Dept Chair 27 Yrs; *ai:* Stu Cncl Adv; NEA 1969-; PSEA 1969-; EAEA 1969-; PSMLA 1992-; Guy K Bard Educl Fund 1985-, Trustee; Ephrata Jaycees Tchr of the Yr 1974; *office:* Ephrata Sr HS 803 Oak Blvd Ephrata PA 17522*

MURRAY, CATHERINE HOFFMAN, Fourth Grade Teacher; *b:* Lewisburg, PA; *m:* John S. Jr.; *c:* Vaughn, Jeffrey; *ed:* Bloomsburg St Coll (BS) Elem Ed 1960; *cr:* Grant Schl Third Grd Tchr 1960-65; Millward Schl Second Grd Tchr 1972-73; Montandon Elem Schl Fourth Grd Tchr 1973-77; Milton Elem Schl Fourth Grd Tchr 1977-80; Montandon Elem Schl Fourth Grd Tchr 1980-; *ai:* Milton Area Ed Assn; Schl Bd Rep; PSA Rep; PSEA, NEA 1972-; MAEA 1972-, Schl Bd Rep; Montandon Bapt Church 1950-, Sunday Schl Sec; *home:* PO Box 242 Montandon PA 17850

MURRAY, COLLEEN M., Middle School Teacher; *b:* Milford, CT; *m:* Shawn R.; *c:* Stash Kamykowski, Austin Kamykowski, Beau Kamykowski, Shawn; *ed:* Southern Ct St Univ (BS) Ed 1979; Masters Prgm in Progress; *cr:* St Gabriel's Schl 1-2 Grd Tchr 1979-82; St Mary's Schl Kndgtn Tchr 1988-89, Grd 5 Tchr 1989-94; Harborside MS Grd 6 Math, LA Tchr 1994-; *ai:* NEA 1994-; Christ the Redeemer Ladies Guild 1979-, Sec; Milford Co-op Nursery Schl 1984-87, Sec; *office:* Harborside MS High St Milford CT 06460*

MURRAY, DANIEL KEVIN, English Teacher; *b:* Latrobe, PA; *m:* Kathleen Marie Ellwood; *c:* Jennifer, Elizabeth; *ed:* OH Univ (BS) Comm 1985; CA Univ of PA (MA) Comm 1996; 50 Post Bac Credits Seton Hill Coll Tchng Cert; *cr:* NBC's Late Night with David Letterman Intern 1984-85; Nancy SEltzer & Assoc Jr Publicist1985-86; Asbestos Claims Fac Comm Liaison 1986-89; Gateway Schl Dist Tc hr 1991-; *ai:* Forensic Team Coach; NEA, GEA, PSDA, NFISDA 1991-; Holy Family Church, Cnslr Marriage Prep; Yo Instrl Bsktbl League Coach; Univ of Pittsburgh Pos Gazette All Star Edctr 1994; Am Family Inst Gift of Time Honoree 1992; *office:* Gateway Sr HS 2629 Mosside Blvd Monroeville PA 15146*

MURRAY, DAVID F., Fifth Grade Teacher; *b:* Poughkeepsie, NY; *ed:* St Univ of NY at New Paltz (BS) His 1981, (MS) Elem Ed 1984; Credit Free Classes-Civil War & Span I; Masters Plus 4; 15 Clock Hrs; *cr:* Chancellor Livingston Elem 5th Grd Tchrs Aide 1981; Saint Georges Schl 3rd & 4th Grd Tchr 1981-87; Nassau Spackenkill Elem 5th Grd Tchr 1987-; *ai:* Scheduling Comm; Cmptr Club Adv; Tchrs Vlybl Team Mem; Schl Plays Stage Crew Mgr; PTA Mem & Rep; Kappa Delta Pi, New Paltz Alumni Assn 1981-; Spackenkill Tchrs Assn 1987-; Hyde Park Recreation Commission 1992-, Commissioner; First Bapt Church 1959-; Glory Ringers-Handbells 1975-; Choir 1985-; FDR Alumni Band 1979-, Dir; Outstanding Sci Tchr Awd 1990; Hyde Park Tchrs Assn Schlsp; Extensive Travel of US, Canada, Mexico, Europe, Israel & Scandinavia to Supplement Curr; *office:* Nassau Spackenkill Elem Sch 8 Nassau Rd Poughkeepsie NY 12601

MURRAY, EDWARD JOSEPH, English Teacher; *b:* New York City, NY; *m:* Marjorie A. Cox; *c:* Susan B., Kathleen F.; *ed:* Seton Hall Univ (BA) Classical Lang 1957, (MA) Personnel & Guidance 1964; Natl Defense Ed Act 1964; Attnd Fordham Univ, Columbia Tchrs Coll, Montclair St Coll; *cr:* Pope Pius XII HS Eng & Latin Tchr 1955-60; North Bercen HS Guidance Cnslr 1960-64; Northern Highlands HS Guidance Cnslr 1964-66; Coll of Ins Dir of Admission 1966-70; Waldwich HS Eng Tchr 1970-; Fairleigh Dickinson Univ Psych Tchr 1970-; *ai:* Yrbk 1970, 1982, 1993; NEA, NJEA, WEA, AAVP 1970-; Knights of Columbus 1950-, Deputy Grand Knight; NOEA counseling Rutgers Univ 1964; Outstanding Faculty Awd 1980; Natl Fnd for Hum Sarah Lawrence Coll World Lit 1984, Rutgers Univ Leonardo De Vinci Inst 1988; NJ Writers Conf 1981; Outstanding Story Awd Authors, Writers Network Alumni House Montclair St Coll, Creative Writing; Pub Magazines; NJ Governor's Tchg Awd 1991; *office:* Waldwick HS Wycoff Ave Waldwick NJ 07463*

MURRAY, EDWARD RICHARD, English & Drama Teacher; *ed:* C. W. Post Center of Long Island Univ (BA) Theatre, Eng Ed 1983; SUNY at Stonybrook (MALS) Lib Stud Ed 1988; *cr:* William Paca Jr HS Eng Tchr 1983-88; Mineola HS Eng, Drama Tchr 1990-; *ai:* Thespian Troupe Adv; Dir of Fall Play; Dir, Choreographer Spring Musical Production; *office:* Mineola HS 10 Armstrong Rd Garden City NY 11040*

MURRAY, ELEANOR L., Foreign Language Teacher; *b:* Boston *ed:* Emmanuel Coll (BA) Ger 1971; Boston Coll (MA) Ger 1972; St Coll (MED) Cnslng 1980; Attnd Tufts Univ, Schiller Coll, Goeth *cr:* Boston Coll Rsrch Asst Germanic Stud Dept 1971-72; Weymou Voc Tech HS Frgn Lang Tchr 1972-; *ai:* WTA, NEA, AATG Classical Assn 1981-; Municipal Commission 1993-; Family, (Monitoring Comm 1992-; Natl Endowment for Hum, Flwshp at Cl Inst; Fulbright Goethe Inst Scholar; Anderson Fnd Grant; Mem England Assn of Schls, Coll Accredidatition Team; *home:* 377 Linc Duxbury MA 02332

MURRAY, ERWIN L., Technology Education Teacher; *b:* Harrisbu *m:* Debra A. Jackson; *c:* Amber, Autumn; *ed:* CA Univ (BE) Ed 1968; Penn St, Univ of WY, Goddard Coll; *cr:* Murray's Svc Mechanic, 1962-; Cameron Cty HS Tchr 1968-; *ai:* Tech Advy Comm; PSEA 1968-; Cameron Cty Ed Assn 1968-, Past Treas, Pres; Tech Ed Assn 1968-; Keystone Airport Club 1968-94, Treas; Emporium Fire 1968-78, Captain; Cameron Cty Historical Soc 1976-; Emergency Tech 1968-78; Presenter Various Prgms Tech St & Natl Confs; Cameron Cty HS 601 Woodland Ave Emporium PA 15834

MURRAY, FERNLEY A., Eng & Contemporary Issues Tchr; *b:* FL; *m:* Gwendolyn Douglas; *c:* Connie Williams; *ed:* IN Univ Speech, Theatre, Eng 1961; Nova Univ (MS) Rdng, Admin 1984; Univ of Miami; City Univ of NY, Columbia Univ, Fordham Un Miami Northwestern Sr HS Eng Tchr, Drama Coord 1963-69; JHS 1 Tchr, Rdng Coord 1969-83; Music 13 Eng Tchr, Rdng Coord 19 Creative Learning Comm Schl Asst Dir Eng, Rdng 1990-; *ai:* Guid HS Articulator for 9th Grd; Sr Activity Dir; VFT 1969-, Schl Rep 1973-; Assn of Black Edctrs of NY 1973-, Past Pres; NAACP 1985-; Alpha Psi 1959-, Past Polemarch, Svc Awd; Manna House Jazz W 1989-, Pres of Bd; DuBois Fnd of NY 1990-; Structured Tchng in A Rdng & Writing Co-Ed 1977; Outstdng Vol Awd Presented by Na Women of Amer; Spec Recognition Ed Awd by Kiwanis Intnl Afro of Greater Miami; *office:* Creative Learning Comm Schl 1573 Madis New York NY 10029*

MURRAY, JACQUELINE NICHOLSON, 5th Grade Teache Baltimore, MD; *m:* Ellwood Louis; *ed:* Morgan St Univ (BS) Ele 1969, (MS) Elem Ed 1972, (MS) Elem-Mid Admin, Supervision 197 Thomas Johnson Elem Schl Tchr Grd 1-6 1969-; *ai:* Schl Support, Comm; Schl Improvement Team; 5th Gr Fundraiser Coord; BTU Bld Gr Group Tchr; Combined Charity Schl Coord; AFT, NEA, BTU Combined Charity Coord 100% Schl Awd 3 Yrs; *office:* Thomas Jo Elem Schl 100 E Heath St Baltimore MD 21230

MURRAY, JAMES PHILLIP, Computer Programming Ins Riverdale, MD; *c:* Christopher, David; *ed:* Univ of MD (BS) Ed 1972 Math 1996; *cr:* Anne Arundle Pub Schls Tchr 1971-72; Calvert Ct Schls Data Proc, Bus Ed, Adult Ed, Comp Pgm & Math Tchr 197 FBLA & VICA Spon; NEA, MSTA & CEA 1972-; Babe Ruth League, Coach & Mgr; *office:* Calvert Career Ctr 330 Dorsey Rd Frederick MD 20678

MURRAY, JOHN JOSEPH, Social Studies Teacher; *b:* Nyack, N Oswego St Coll (BA) Ec 1976; Iona Coll (MS) Ed 1996; *cr:* Nyack H Stud Tchr 1988-91; Tappan Zee HS Soc Stud Tchr 1991-; *ai:* Ftbl (9th Grd Team Ldr; Bldg Liaison Comm; Asian Amer Soc 1991-; 1988-; NYSUT 1990-; Educl Assoc of S Orangetown 1991-, Rockland Cty Coaches Org 1988-; Empire Hook & Ladder 1971-, Tr Police Ath League 1988-; Spec Olympics 1993-; *home:* 27 Terra Nyack NY 10960

MURRAY, JOYCE SMYTHE, Fifth Grade Math & Sci Tc Canandaigua, NY; *m:* John Ralph III; *ed:* Elmira Coll (BA) His, Scnc 1967; Oakland Univ (MA) Elem Ed; OH St Univ, NJ Jersey City St, MI St Univ 30 Addl Credits; *cr:* Vicksburg Elem 3rd & 5th Grd 1967-69; Plain City Elem 5th Grd Tchr 1969-72; Woodhaven Elem 1- Tchr 1972-76; Summit Pub Schl 4th-5th Grd Tchr 1976-; *ai:* Alt Route Tchr Mentor; Leadership in New Tchr Trainer; Curr Dev C Summit Ed Assn 1976-, Treas, VP; NJ Ed Assn 1976-; NEA 1967- Math 1988-; Women's Auxilary New Vernon; Vol Dept 1977-; NV Pr Church 1976-, Deacon; Mt Kemble Assn 1976-, Bd Mem; Summit E Awd for Sci Kits; NJ Math Conf Spring, Fall Confs Presentor; NJ Dis Awd; Soc Stud in Class DAR Awd; *office:* Franklin Elem Sch Blackburn Rd Summit NJ 07901*

MURRAY, JUDITH L. (ENMAN), Lang Arts Teacher, Dept Chpr Fitchburg, MA; *c:* Richard J.; *ed:* Worcester St Coll (BSEd) Eng 19 Grad Credit Hrs Fitchburg St Coll; *cr:* Gardner Jr HS Tchr 1966-, Chprsn 1992-; *ai:* Schl Newspaper Adv; Curr Comm; NCTE 1993-; GEA, NEA 1966-; *office:* Gardner Jr HS 62 Waterford St Gardne 01440

MURRAY, KAREN J., Mathematics Teacher; *b:* Torrington, C David; *c:* David; *ed:* Cntrl CT St Univ (BS) Math 1984, (MS) Math Fairfield Univ (CAS) Cmptrs in the Classroom 1996; Woodrow W Insts for Algebra, Modeling & Change; *cr:* Avon HS Math Tchr Litchfield HS Math Tchr 1986-87; Gilbert Schl Math Tchr 1987-; *ai:* League, JETS & UCONN All-Star HS Acad Bowl Coach; NCTM, AT 1984-; COMAP 1990-; NEA, CEA 1987-; NSF Fellowship 1991, 1993; PIMMS Fellowship 1995, 1996; *office:* Gilbert Schl 200 Wi Ave Winsted CT 06098*

MURRAY, KATHLEEN GALVIN, Child Care Teacher; *b:* Melrose, *m:* Richard; *c:* Christopher, Matthew, Susan; *ed:* Univ of NH Occupational Ed 1995, (BS) Home Ec 1979; *cr:* Salem Recreation Presch Tchr, Dir 1979-80; Salem HS Child Care Tchr 1988-; *ai:* H NVTHS Adv; Child Care Advy Comm; NEA 1988-; AVA 1989-; A Pub; *office:* Salem HS 44 Geremonty Dr Salem NH 03079

MURRAY, KAY CAMERON, 8th Grade Math & Algebra Tch Philadelphia, OH; *ed:* Miami Univ (BS) Math Ed 1970; Cleveland S Curr, Inst 1977; *cr:* Parkside MS 8th Grd Math, Algebra Tchr 1970 Penny Project; Intervention Asst Team; Environmental Club; Teen Support Group; WTA 1970-, Treas 1980-81; OEA, NEA 1970-; Lifetime Mbrshp Awd 1988; *office:* Parkside MS 24525 Hilliard Westlake OH 44145

MURRAY, KEVIN JOHN, English Teacher; *b:* Morristown, N. Debra; *c:* Ryan, Kyle; *ed:* St Bernard Coll (BA) Eng 1969; Addl Jersey City St; *cr:* Morristown HS Eng Tchr 1976-77; Whippany Par Eng Tchr 1977-80; Morris Knolls HS Eng Tchr 1980-81; Parsippany HS Eng Tchr 1981-; *ai:* Head Coach Bsbl Team; Drug, Alcohol Identification Team; Stu Discipline Comm; NEA, NJEA 1971-; IABB #168 1980-, Exec Cabinet Chm; NJSIAA Coaches Assn 1990-, Jersey Rep; Morris Cty Bsbl Coach of Yr 1995; Tchr of Month PHHS Oxford Scholar 1989; *home:* 31 Wiltop Rd Netcong NJ 07857

MURRAY, MABEL LAKE, Human Growth & Dev Stud Coor Baltimore, MD; *m:* Elmer; *c:* Mark A. Butler, Sarita, Linda W. Butle Coppin St Tchrs Coll (BS) Elem Ed 1956; Loyola Coll at Baltimore (Rdng 1969; VA Tech (CASE) Instruction 1981, (EDD) Curr 1982 Baltimore City Pub Schls Classroom, Rdng Resource Tchr 1956-69; P George's Cty Rdng Clinician 1969-71; Baltimore City Schls Pr KAPS-Clinician 1971-72; Univ of MD LRC Rdng Coord 1972-76; C Cty Pub Schls Supvr of Rdng, Learning Disabilities 197 Sojourner-Douglas Coll Human Growth, Dev Stud Coord; *ai:* Ed

iltant NAACP 1990-; IRA 1968-, Pres, Carroll Cty Rdng Edctr of Yr; ll Cty Edctrs 1980-; Baltimore City Tchrs Assn 1958-; Delta Sigma 1992-, Chptr Pres, Pub Svc Awd; Nalt Alliance of Black Schl Edctrs ; Instruction Exec Bd Chair; Delta Sigma Theta, Kappa Alpha Psi, en Power Awds; Speaker at Freedom Fund Dinners for NAACP; *home:* ridge Ct Randallstown MD 21133

RAY, MARGARET ROSE, Teacher of Gifted & Talented; *b:* worth, OH; *m:* David Guy; *c:* Megan K., Allison A.; *ed:* Capital Univ Elem Ed 1969; Attnd Bowling Green St Univ, Univ of Toledo, Ashland *cr:* Tiffin City Schls 4th & 5th Grd Tchr 1969-86, Tchr of Gifted & ted 1986-, 2nd Grd Thinking as a Skill Tchr 1993-; *ai:* Tiffin Ed Assn , Sec; NEA 1969-; OH Ed Assn 1969-; OH Assn for Gifted Children ; First Luth Church 1970-, Pres, Sec; Jr Womens League; Tchr OH na (Japan) Exch; *home:* 126 Rosa St Tiffin OH 44883

RAY, MARY A., Social Studies Teacher; *b:* Niagara Falls, NY; *c:* rd Byrd; *ed:* Niagara Univ (BA) His 1988, (MS) Ed 1989; 30 Addl Grad Hrs; *cr:* Lockport HS Soc Stud Tchr 1989-; *ai:* AFR-AM Stud Adv; Global Stud Coord; Lockport Mentor Prgm Comm; AFT, CSS 1989-; *office:* Lockport HS 250 Lincoln Ave Lockport NY *

RAY, PATRICIA CALVIN, Vocal Music Teacher; *b:* Teaneck, NJ; bert Theadore; *c:* Maureen Elizabeth; *ed:* Rutgers Univ (BA) Music 86; NY Univ (MA) Educl Theatre 1994; *cr:* Lincoln Schl 4th-6th Grd Music Tchr 1986-87; Ho-Ho-Kus Pub Schl K-8th Grd Vocal Music 1986-94; Northern Highlands Regnl HS Coord of the Fine & rming Arts Dept 1994-; *ai:* Conductor of Concert Choir, Vocal nble, & Madrigal Singers; Dir of Musical Theatre Production; Liaison ergen Cty Teen Arts Festival; MENC 1985-; NJEA 1986-; *office:* ern Highlands Reg HS Hillside Ave Allendale NJ 07401

RAY, SUSAN DAWN, Sixth Grade Elementary Teacher; *b:* Muncy y, PA; *m:* James C.; *c:* Meagan; *ed:* Lycoming Coll (BA) Sociology, Ed 1974; Bloomsburg Univ 28 Credit Hrs Remedial Rdng; *cr:* gomery Elem Schl 2nd Grd Tchr 1975; East Lycoming Schl Dist 3rd chr 1975-84; Title 1 Summer Schl Tchr 1975-82; East Lycoming Schl 6th Grd Tchr 1984-; *ai:* Bldg, Elem Discipline Comms; Elem Yrbk 5 Yrs; Elem Sci Fair Coord 8 Yrs; Mentor Tchr 6 Yrs; Cheerleading 1976-77; Prof Ed Comm; Christ United Meth Church 1965-; Who's 1992, 1994; *office:* Joseph C. Ashkar Elem S Broad St Hughesville 1737

RAY, TED WILLIAM, Marketing Education Coord; *b:* Wabash, IN; icky Pohlamus; *c:* Heath, Heather; *ed:* Vincennes Univ (AS) Bus n 1970; Bowling Green St Univ (BS) Mrktg Ed 1972; Univ of Dayton Ed Admin 1978; Voc Supervision Wright St Univ; *cr:* Miami tries Sales 1972-73; Huber Heights City Schls Tchr 1973-; *ai:* DECA ; Schl Store Supvr; Staff Dev Comm; Renaissance Comm; OEA, A, NEA 1973-; OVA, AVA; OMEA, MEA 1986-; Troy BPOE 833 ; Troy Bsbl Parents 1987-; Troy All Sports Booster 1986-; Troy l Parents 1987-91, Treas; Troy Soccer Parents 1990-; *office:* Wayne 400 Chambersburg Rd Huber Heights OH 45424

RAY, THOMAS M., Retired Music Teacher; *b:* Sharpsville, PA; *m:* a Jean Carr; *c:* Thomas, Nicholas, Mark; *ed:* Younstown Univ (BM) : 1961; Edinboro St Univ (MA) Ed 1976; *cr:* Sharpsville HS Music 1961; Geneva Area Schls Music Tchr 1961-63; Conneaut Lake HS : Tchr 1963-93; *ai:* NEA 1961-; PA St E Assn 1963-; Am Fed of Mus ; *home:* 6877 Lake Rd Atlantic PA 16111*

RAY, TIMOTHY WAYNE, Physics, Chem & Anatomy Tchr; *b:* usky, OH; *m:* Holly Marie Pry; *ed:* Bowling Green St Univ (BA) y Ed 1993; *cr:* Edon Northwest Schls Physics, Chem, Anatomy Bio, Sci Tchr, Var Bsbl & Bsktbl Coach, Cross Cntry Coach, Envirothon, Coord 1993-; *ai:* JV Bsbl Coach; NEA 1993-; *office:* Edon Northwest 309 W Indiana St Edon OH 43518

RAY, TRACY GLENN, Choral Director; *b:* Newark, NJ; *ed:* clair St Coll (BA) Music Ed 1985; *cr:* Immaculate Conception HS al Dir 1985-86; East Brunswick HS Choral Dir 1986-87; Union HS & Farms Schl Choral Dir & General Music Tchr 1987-90; South field HS Choral Dir 1990-; *ai:* Traveling Choir; Schl Musical Music nd Dir; Madrigals, Boys & Girls Choir; Amer Choral Dirs Assn & c Educators Natl Conf 1990-; Phi Mu Alpha Sinfonia 1981-; NJ All-St a Festival Conductor of Chorus 1993; *office:* South Plainfield HS 200 St S Plainfield NJ 07080

RRELL, DAISY MAE (GOOLSBY), Business Education Teacher; *b:* y, NC; *w:* James R. (dec); *c:* Robert Fitzgerald; *ed:* D. C. Tchrs Coll Bus Ed 1969; Federal City Coll (MBE) Bus Ed 1975; 24 Credit Hrs Grad Stud in Bus Ed, Cmptr Courses, Real Estate; 6 Credit Hrs of , Cert Income Tax Preparer; *cr:* Amer Aviation Publication Clerk, st 1963-65; Gen Svcs Admin IBM Keypunch Operator, Verifier -67; Peace Corps Clerk, Typist 1967; Veteran's Admin Clerk, Typist, 967-68; D. C. Pub Schls Bus Tchr 1969-; *ai:* Co-Spon FBLA; DCBEA ; NBEA, EBEA 1985-; Simmons Acres HOA 1992-, Chm Budget, Fin n; Ebony Schlsp Soc 1983-, Advy Bd; FBLA Adv Awds for Outstdng Vol Svc Awds; *office:* Theodore Roosevelt Sr HS 4301 13th St NW ington DC 20011

RRIN, KATHLEEN ANNE, AP US History & Govt Teacher; *b:* nton, PA; *ed:* Marywood Coll (AB) Soc Stud 1967; Univ of Scranton Amer Stud 1969; 12 Credits Laral Univ at Quebec; 40 Credits NY ; *cr:* Scranton Cntrl HS Tchr 1967-91; Scranton HS Tchr 1991-; *ai:* l Rsrch & Discrimination Resource Link; Dist Mentorship Prgm Tchr or; AFT 1970-; Amer Historical Assn 1972-; Natl Genealogical Assn -; Scranton Singer's Guild 1978-, Sec; Women's Philharmonic League -; Lackawanna Cty Hist Soc 1967-; Everheart Museum Soc; *office:* nton HS 721 Adams Ave Scranton PA 18510

RTAGH, LINDA CHRISTINE, 7th Grade Science Teacher; *b:* ingham, MA; *c:* Joey Messina, Vincent Messina, Erin; *ed:* Anna Maria (AB) Bio 1964; Worcester St Coll (MED) Scndry Ed 1972; ingham St Coll (MED) Rdng, Lang Arts 1979; Tech Writing, Cmptr ramming, Math, Cooperative Lrng; *cr:* Worcester Fnd for rimental Bio Research Asst 1964-65; Worcester Mem Hospital Lab nician 1965-66; Hudson Pub Schls Tchr 1970-; *ai:* Natl His Day Adv; Dev, Tech, Recycling Comms; NEA, MTA 1972-; ASCD 1992-; Natl nce for the Mentally Ill 1991-; Horace Mann Grant 1987; *home:* 20 and St Hudson MA 01749*

RTAUGH, CYNTHIA ANN, Language Arts Teacher; *b:* DuBois, PA; onald E.; *c:* Erin Delle, Brian James; *ed:* Clarion Univ of PA (BS) Ed 1980; 36 Post Grad Credit Hrs in Elem Ed; Rel Instruction Cert; E Valley Schl Dist 3rd-4th Grd Tchr 1980-84; Highlights for Children ner Balser Ed Publishers Asst Editor 1984-87; St Vincents Schl Lang Tchr 1987-; *ai:* Stu Cncl Adv; Free-Lance Writer, Ed & Copy Ed; h Rel Instr; Girl Scouts 1989-, Asst to Troops & Asst Ldr; Grade Level or: Zaner-Blaser Spelling Connections; *office:* St Vincent's Schl 329 St Honesdale PA 18431

RTHA, CAROLE TREMLETT, Asst Professor of Nursing; *b:* Boston, *m:* Thomas J.; *c:* Thomas, Katherine, Megan; *ed:* Boston Coll (BSN) g 1965; NY Univ (MA) Nrsng 1970; 15 Addl Credits Rutgers Univ of Ed; *cr:* Camden Cty Hlth Svc Clinical Nurse Specialist, Psych -82; Widener Univ Asst Prof Nrsng 1982-89; Childrens Hosp of Phila Staff Nurse Pediatrics 1987-94; Gloucester Cty Coll Asst Prof Nrsng 1989-; *ai:* Haddon Heights Local Assistance Bd Sec 1981-; Local Standing Comm; Acad Adv; AFT 1989-; NJSNA 1974-, Local-Area Bd Mem; ANA 1974-; Sigma Theta Tau; Haddon Heights Lab 1981-, Sec; Haddon Glen Swim Team Comm; Contributor RN Magazine 1992-, CEU Prgm; Tchr of Yr 1995; Stu Govt Org; *office:* Gloucester County Coll 1400 Tanyard Rd Sewell NJ 08035

MURTHA, EDWARD KEVIN, Professor of English; *b:* New York City, NY; *ed:* Montclair St Univ (MA) Hlth Ed 1982; Jersey St Coll (MA) Eng & Eng as Second Lang 1989; *cr:* New York Infirmary Hospital Dir of Respiratory Therapy 1973-76; Bergen Comm Coll Prof 1976-; *ai:* Eng Lang Resource Ctr Project Co-Dir; NEA, NJEA 1976-; TESOL 1989-; Federal Grants Cmptr Assisted Lang Learning 1994, Multimedia Dev in Eng as Second Lang 1995, Multimedia Dev in Voc Ed 1996; *office:* Bergen Comm Coll 400 Paramus Rd Paramus NJ 07652

MUSA, BEVERLY (STEVENS), Math Teacher; *b:* Johnson City, NY; *m:* Anthony; *c:* Scott, M. Lynne, Karen; *ed:* Marymount Coll (BA) Math 1964; Syracuse Univ (MS) Math 1968; Attnd SUNY, Binghampton U, Harpur Coll; *cr:* Binghampton North HS Math Tchr 1964-65; ME Endwell Sr Hs Math Tchr 1965-; *ai:* Z Club Co-Adv; Key Club Adv; SAT Prep Class Tchr; Math Action Team M-E Dist; NEA 1964-, Corr Sec; *office:* Maine Endwell Sr HS 720 Farm to Market Rd Endwell NY 13760

MUSACCHIO, OLGA, French Teacher; *b:* Liege, Belgium; *m:* Paul; *c:* Nina, Katya; *ed:* CUNY at Brooklyn Coll (BA) Fr & Russian; Universite de Nancy (CELG); Attnd Fairfield Univ; *cr:* St Josephs Tchr 1968-71; Branford HS Tchr 1971-76; The Salisbury Schl Tchr 1976-77; The Morgan Schl Tchr 1978-; *ai:* Fr Club; NHS; Fr Exchange Pgm Dir; Dist Curr Comm; St Curr Com Guide for Fgn Lang Comm; NEA 1968-; CT Cncl for Fgn Lang Tchrs, Bd of Dir; AATF; ACTFL Oral Proficiency Tester; Rockefeller Flwshp; Univ of Chicago Outstndg Tchr Awd; *home:* Tuttles Pt Guilford CT 06437

MUSCATO, LORETTA CATALDO, Fourth Grade Teacher; *b:* Buffalo, NY; *m:* Charles J.; *ed:* Buffalo St Coll (BS) Elem Ed 1968; Canisius Coll (MS) Elem Ed 1974; 2 Credit Hrs; *cr:* Starpoint Cntrl Schl Fourth Grd Tchr 1968-; *ai:* Report Card Revision, K-12 Math Curr, Cafeteria Incentive Prgm Comm; AFT, NY St United Tchrs 1968-; Starpoint Tchrs Assn 1968-, Wing Rep.

MUSCH, LINDA LAPIENE, Culinary Arts Instructor; *b:* Middletown, CT; *m:* Ronald R.; *c:* Randy, Phillip, Veronica; *ed:* Johnson Wales (AS) Culinary arts 1981, (BS) Food Svc Mngmt 1982, (BS) Culinary Ed 1988; *cr:* Chariho Career & Tech Ctr Chef, Instr 190-; *ai:* Class VICA Adv; NEA 1990-; Amer Culinary Fed 1990-, Treas; *office:* Chariho Career & Tech Ctr 459 Switch Rd Wood River Jt RI 02894

MUSCORFITI, JEANNE T., Spanish Teacher; *b:* New York City, NY; *m:* Robert; *c:* Wendy, Michelle; *ed:* Stoney Brook Univ (MA) Span 1972; Ladycliff Coll (BA) Span; *cr:* South Huntington Schls Span Tchr 1970-86; Roslyn HS Span Tchr 1986-87; Wantagh HS Span Tchr 1987-; Adelphi Univ Span Tchr 1987-; *ai:* Span Club Adv; AFT & NYSUT 1970-; Wantagh Union of Tchrs 1987-; *office:* Wantagh HS Beltagh Ave Wantagh NY 11793

MUSCOTT, HOWARD STEVEN, Assoc Prof of Ed & Spec Ed; *b:* New York City, NY; *m:* Amy Jo Shuster; *ed:* St Univ Coll at Buffalo (BS) Ed & Mental Retardation 1977; George Washington Univ (MA) Ed, Human Dev & Early Chldhd Soc Ed 1980; Columbia Univ Tchrs Coll (MED) Instructional Practices In Spec Ed 1986, (EDD) Spec Ed & Emotional Disturbance 1991; *cr:* Baltimore Cty Pub Schls Tchr of Spec Ed 1977-79; Parry Ctr for Children Tchr of Resource Room & Transition Specialist 1980-81, Educl Chprsn & Prin 1981-84; Columbia Univ Tchrs Coll Coord of Stu Tchng & Instr 1984-87; French Hill Learning Ctr Prin 1987-89; Wolden Schl Prin 1989-92; Rivier Coll Assoc Prof of Ed & Dir of Spec Ed Prgms 1992-; *ai:* Sr Class Adv; Comm on Acad Stans & Educl Policy Chprsn; Stu Dev & Tech Comms Fac Rep; Cncl for Exceptional Children 1977-, Natl Newsletter Ed 1994-, Northeast Regnl Sec 1996, Fnd Comm Chprsn 1994-; Cncl for Children with Behavioral Disorders, Cncl of Admins in Spec Ed, ANYSEED; NH ASCD 1994-, Consulting Ed Ed & Treatment Children 1995-, Field Ed Beyond Behavior 1995- & Perceptions 1988-; SNH CHADD 1995-, Advy Bd Mem; NH Inst on Disability & Emotional Disability 1992-, Advy Comm; Grant Co-Awded Promoting Inclusion Tchr Ed 1995 & Tchr Practices 1994; Rivier Coll VPs Awd for Outstanding Leadership 1996; Grant Co-Awded Americorp NH Conacct 1995; Outstanding Fac Mem for Stu Dev 1993; Doctoral Research Grant NY St CEC 1990; 15 Articles & 1 Book Pub; *office:* Rivier Coll 420 Main St Nashua NH 03060*

MUSHRUSH, DAVID E., Algebra & Geometry Teacher; *b:* Erie, PA; *m:* Paula Lukac; *c:* Christopher, Jason; *ed:* Edinboro Univ (BA) Ed, Math 1971; Indiana U of PA (MS) Math Ed 1975; *cr:* Woolslair Elem Schl 5th Grd Math, Sci Tchr 1971-79; Sterrett Classical Acad Algebra, Geometry, ITL Tchr 1979-; *ai:* Fund Raising; Math Competitions; Cross Cntry Coach; AFT 1971-; Champions Assoc Cert of Appreciation; Tchr of Yr 1984-85; *office:* Sterrett Classical Acad 7100 Reynolds St Pittsburgh PA 15208*

MUSITANO, CHARLES A., Biology Teacher; *b:* New Castle, PA; *m:* Karen M.; *ed:* Penn St Univ (BS) Ed & Bio 1974; Bloomsburg Univ Post Grad Stud; *cr:* Benton Area HS Bio Tchr 1974-; *ai:* Environmental Club Adv; Sci Dept Chm; *office:* Benton Area HS RD 2 Park St Benton PA 17814

MUSKAUSKI, JUDY MORRASH, Fifth Grade Teacher; *b:* Wilkes-Barre, PA; *m:* Charles; *c:* Lauren; *ed:* Bloomsburg St Coll (BS) Elem Ed 1975; Johns Hopkins (MS) Elem Ed 1980; Cert Spec Ed; 30 Addl Hrs; *cr:* Gray Manor Elem Schl 5th Grd Tchr 1976-78; Bears Creek Elem Schl 5th Grd Tchr 1978-80; Mars Estates Elem Schl 5th Grd Tchr 1980-82, 3rd Grd Tchr 1982-86; Shady Spring Elem Schl 3rd Grd Tchr 1987-89, 4th Grd Tchr 1989-95, 5th Grd Tchr 1995-; *ai:* Substance Abuse Facilitator; Stu Ambassadors Chprsn; Organizer Wee Deliver Postal Act; NEA, MSTA 1976-; TABCO 1976-, Homework Hotline Chair; *office:* Shady Spring Elem Schl 8868 Goldenwood Rd Baltimore MD 21237*

MUSKO, KAREN WASLO, Learning Support Teacher; *b:* Ambridge, PA; *m:* George Dennis; *c:* Brooke, Faith, Breanna; *ed:* Slippery Rock Univ (BS) Elem, Spec Ed 1975; Grad Stud Carlow Coll at Pittsburgh, Univ of AL Southeast; *cr:* Intermediate Unit #4 Spec Ed, Perm Sub Tchr 1988-89; Allegheny Vly Schl Spec Ed Tchr 1990; Butler Jr HS Spec Ed Tchr 1990-; *ai:* Co-Spon Stu Spirit Star, Get Organized & Learn Prgms; Spon Casual Dress Day Fac Prgm; Alameda Swim Team Parent Assn 1994-, Pres; *office:* Butler Jr HS 225 E North St Butler PA 16001

MUSOLINO, JAMES ALLEN, Science Instructor & Director; *b:* Bradford, PA; *m:* Rosemary Bryan; *c:* Bryan, Megan; *ed:* Indiana Univ of PA (BS) Physics & Math 1968, (MED) Physics & Math 1970; Post Grad Stud at Univ of IA; Univ of Pittsburg; *cr:* Plumboro Schl Dist Math Instr 1968-69; New Kensington-Arnold Schl Dist Sci & Cmptr Instr & Educl Tech Coord 1969-; *ai:* Physics Club Spon; Head Var Soccer Coach; Chapter II Advisory Comm; AAPT 1970-; NKAEA, PSEA & NEA 1968-; NSTA 1984-, Excl in Sci Ed Awd 1984; PA Sci Supvrs Assn 1984-, Bd of Dirs, Dist Service Awd 1988; Spectroscopy Soc of Pittsburgh 1984-, Keivin Burns Citation 1983; BSA 1958-, Asst Scout Master, Dist Awd of Merit, St George Awd; St Margaret-Mary Youth Group, Adv 1987; Bd of Dirs 1971-,1996, Chrmn 1996; Leechburg Area Park & Pool Inc; New Kensington Fire Dept Band; Armstrong Band; Kiski Valley Band; Tri-City Jaycees Outstanding Young Educator 1984; NSTA Monograph Pub Tchrs Honors Wkshp in Laser Physics 1984; NSTA Tchrs Honors Cmptr Wkshp 1985; NASA Tchr in Space Citation 1985; NASA NEWMAST Honors Awd 1987; US Physics Olympiad Awd 1987; Westinghouse Sci Talent Search Cert of Honor 1987; NSTA NASA Space Sci Stu Involvement Prgm Citation 1985 & 1987; Innovative Tchng Grant; Chamber of Commerce New Ken 1992, 1994; Arnold Chamber of Commerce Hall of Fame for Exel in Acad 1995; PA House of Rep & PA Senate Citations for Acad; US House of Rep Cert of Special Rec; KDKA Thanks to Tchrs 1995; *office:* Valley H S 703 Stevenson Blvd New Kensington PA 15068*

MUSOLINO, JOSEPH, Business Teacher; *b:* Syracuse, NY; *m:* Maria; *c:* Dominick, Casandra, Andrea; *ed:* LeMoyne Coll (BS) Bus Ed 1992; 15 Credit Hrs in Voc Technological Ed Masters Prgm at St Univ of NY at Oswego; *cr:* East Syracuse Minoa Schls Bus Tchr 1994-; *ai:* DECA Co-Adv; Class of 1997 Adv; Stu of Month Comm; CII; Workforce Prep; Natl Tchrs Assn, NY St Bus Tchrs Assn 1994-; *office:* East Syracuse-Minoa HS Fremont Rd East Syracuse NY 13057

MUSSELMAN, SUSAN EDENS, English & Speech Teacher; *b:* Frankfurt, Germany; *m:* Larry; *c:* Cheri Welsh, Lucy Pratt, Gavin, Jason, Lauren; *ed:* Denison Univ (BA) Speech 1968; Post Grad Univ of Akron, Malone Coll, Duquesne Univ, Indiana Univ of PA, Seton Hill Coll; *cr:* Lake Local Schl Dist Speech, Eng Tchr 1968-71; Nations Bank Properties Ofcr 1977-79; Kiski Area Schl Dist Speech, Eng Tchr 1981-; *ai:* Sr, Jr Class Co-Spon; Drama Club Play Dir; NEA, KAEA, PSEA 1981-; Jr League of Pittsburgh 1981-, Bd Mem; *office:* Kiski Area HS 200 Poplar St Vandergrift PA 15690

MUSSELMAN, SUZANNE, Mathematics Dept Chairperson; *b:* Lambertville, NJ; *ed:* Ursinus Coll (BS) Math 1964; Univ of CA Math 1969; Trenton St Coll (MA) Math 1970; *cr:* Antheil Jr HS Demonstration Tchr for Trenton St Coll 1970-74; Antheil MS Head of Math Dept 1974-79; Ewing High Schl Math Tchr 1979-, Dept Chprsn for Math 1992-; *ai:* Part of Presentation Team Inservicing Staff on Instructional Theory into Practice; NCTM 1965-; Assn of Math Tchrs of NJ 1990-; Mercer Cty Tchrs Federal Credit Union 1966-, Chm of Bd; Lawrence Twp Arbitration Panel 1990, 1991, 1992; Natl Sci Fnd Grant to Stu Math at Univ of CA at San Diego 1969; *office:* Ewing HS 900 Parkway Ave Trenton NJ 08618*

MUSSER, KAREN WEAVER, Biology Teacher; *b:* Lewisburg, PA; *m:* Robert Curtis; *c:* Bradley, Mark, Taylor; *ed:* Bloomsburg Univ (BS) Ed & Bio 1988; 15 Addl Credit Hrs; *cr:* Mifflinburg HS Bio Tchr 1991-; *ai:* Stu Assistance Prgm Mem; Stu Govt Adv; PSEA, NEA 1991-; Beta Beta Beta Biological Honor Soc; Phi Kappa Phi; Mifflinburg Home & Schl Assn 1990-; *office:* Mifflinburg Area HS 1st & Market Sts Mifflinburg PA 17844

MUSSER, ROBERT M.,II, Instrumental Music Teacher; *b:* Harrisburg, PA; *ed:* West Chester Univ (BS) K-12 Music Ed 1973; *cr:* Whitehall HS Instrumental Music 1973-74; Penns Grove MS Instrumental Music 1975-77; Penns HS Instrumental Music 1977-90; Eastern HS Instrumental Music 1990-; *ai:* Marching, Jazz Band; Indoor Guard; NJEA, MENC 1975-; Natl Judges Assn 1972-, South Jersey Coord; *office:* Eastern HS Laurel Oak Rd Box 2500 Voorhees NJ 08043*

MUSSINA, MARK ANDREW, Sports Talk Show Host; *b:* Williamsport, PA; *ed:* Susquehanna Univ (BA) Math 1994; *cr:* Owings Mills HS Scndry Math Tchr, Long Term Sub 1995; *home:* 1302 Spruce St Montoursville PA 17754

MUSTER, NAOMI L., Retired 3rd-5th Grade Teacher; *b:* Kimbolton, OH; *ed:* Kent St Univ (BSEd) Elem Ed 1960; *cr:* Atwater Local Schl 3rd Grd Tchr 1960-63; Madison Ave Schl 5th-6th Grd Tchr 1963-67, 4th Grd Tchr 1967-95; *ai:* Talent Show Dir; ESP Ldr; PTEA, NEOEA, OEA, NEA 1967-; Meth Women; Sweet Adelines 1974-; Meth Church 1974-, Chair.

MUTH, ROBIN B., Language Arts Teacher; *b:* Bridgeport, CT; *m:* Marcel; *ed:* Univ of Bridgeport (BS) Ed; Fairfield Univ (MS) Ed; St Joesphs 6th Yr Ed; *cr:* Chapter I 5th Grd Elem Tchr 1970-77; Tchr of Gifted 1977-89; Lang Arts, Eng Team Ldr 1985-; *ai:* Natl Jr Honor Soc, Yrbk Adv; SEA; NEA; Stratford Comm Team; Celebration of Excl Awds 1993, 1995; *office:* Wooster MS 150 Lincoln St Stratford CT 06497*

MUTHERSBAUGH, DAVID HOWARD, Mathematics Teacher; *b:* Cleveland, OH; *m:* Donna Sagert; *c:* Scott, Mark; *ed:* Miami Univ (BS) Math 1971; Cleveland St Univ (MA) Ed 1977; IN Univ Alternative Ed; Edctrs in Industry, Entrepreneurship, Algebra for Tchrs; Baldwin Wallace Coll Assertive Discipline; *cr:* Cleveland Heights HS Tchr 1971-72; Parma-Pleasant Vly Jr HS Tchr 1972; Cleveland Heights HS Tchr 1972-; *ai:* HS Sunshine Fund Chm; Acad Awds Ceremony Co-Coord; Presenter of Mitchel Gubkin Meml Schlsp; AFT 1971-, Bldg Steward; NCTM, OCTM, GCCTM 1991-; Residents & Edctrs for Action, Treas; *office:* Cleveland Heights HS 13263 Cedar Rd Cleveland Heights OH 44118

MUTRIE, MARTHA CHRISTIAN, English Teacher; *b:* Attleboro, MA; *m:* George J. Jr.; *c:* Jake, Timothy, Katherine; *ed:* Bridgewater St Coll (BA) Eng 1969; Wroxton Coll at Oxfordshire (MA) British Lit 1975; Harvard Grad Schl of Ed (CAGS) Tchng & Learning 1988; *cr:* Silve Lake Regnl HS Eng of Tchr 1970-; Massasoit Comm Coll Adj Eng Instr 1981-86; Folger Shakespeare Lib Master Tchr 1986, 1988, 1990; *ai:* NEA, NCTE 1970-; Terrific Tchr Awd; Interview 1995; *office:* Silver Lake Reg HS-Kingston 132 Pembroke St Kingston MA 02364*

MUZER, FREDERICK CARL, Fifth Grade Teacher; *b:* Middletown, CT; *m:* Mary; *c:* Kari Anne; *ed:* Eastern CT St Univ (BA) Eng 1985, (MS) Sci Ed; *cr:* Ryerson Elem Schl 3rd Grd Tchr 1985-89; Acad Elem Schl 5th Grd Tchr; *ai:* Cmptr Coord; Math, Cmptr Clubs; NSTA; MEA, 1985-, Schl Rep 1993-; CEA, NEA 1985-; CECA 1989-; Pimms Fellow 1989; Celebration Excl 1992; Outstdng Tchr Awd; *office:* Acad Elem Schl 4 School St Madison CT 06443*

MUZIO, KIMBERLY ANN, High School Guidance Counselor; *b:* Long Island, NY; *m:* Frank; *ed:* Syracuse Univ (BS) Advertising 1986; Hofstra Univ (MS) Educl Cnslng 1989; Admin Stud 6 Credit Hrs; *cr:* Commack HS Guid Cnslr 1989-92; Lynbrook HS Guid Cnslr 1992-; *ai:* SADD Club Adv; *office:* Lynbrook H S 9 Union Ave Lynbrook NY 11563

MUZYK, BARBARA R., Sci, Chem Tchr & Dept Chprsn; *b:* Trenton, NJ; *m:* Daniel; *c:* Ryan, Jon; *ed:* Trenton St Coll (BA) Sci Ed 1970, (MED) Sci Ed 1982; Attnd Rider, Newton Coll of Sacred Heart & Taft Schl of Ed; *cr:* Reynolds Jr High Tchr 1970-74; Steinert HS Tchr 1974-81; Nottingham HS Tchr & Chair 1982-; *ai:* NHS; NJEA & NEA 1970-; HTEA 1970-, Rep; NJSTA 1980-; Jaycees 1971-77, All Offices, Outstanding Local Pres in St; Elks & Ladies Auxiliary 1989-, Sec; St Johns Preschool ed 1979-, Tchr; Tchr & Staff Mem of Rutgers Inst for New Tchrs past 7 Yrs; Staff Mem NETS Wkshp Presenter 4 Yrs; *office:* Nottingham HS 1055 Klockner Rd Trenton NJ 08619*

MUZZY, MARTHA DILWORTH, Learning Support Teacher; *b:* Bryn Mawr, PA; *m:* Terrence R.; *c:* Taylor, Christopher; *ed:* Millersville Univ (BS) Elem & Spcl Ed 1974; West Chester Univ (MED) Spcl Ed 1987; Comp Courses; *cr:* Devereux Fndtn Cnslr 1973-76; Chester Cty Intermediate Unit Spcl Ed Tchr 1974-92; Downingtown Schl Dist Learning Support Tchr & Dept Chair 1992-; *ai:* NEA 1974-; Honey Brook Lib 1988-, Bd Mem, Friends Comm; Honey Brook BSA 1993-, Advancement Chprsn; Honey Brook Cub Scouts 1995-, Sec; Co-Operative Learning Pgm Educl Grant; Chester Cty Intermediate Unit Outstdng Staff Awd; *office:* Downingtown Sr HS 445 Manor Ave Downingtown PA 19335

MYER, DEBRA LEE, High School Math Teacher; *b:* Kingston, NY; *ed:* St Univ of New Paltz (BS) Math 1979, (MS) Math 1981; *cr:* Kingston HS Math Tchr 1979-; *office:* Kingston HS 403 Broadway Kingston NY 12401

MYERS, BRENDA WILKINSON, Ed Pgms Supvr & Prof Dev Tchr; *b:* Cortland, NY; *m:* Larry J.; *ed:* SUNY at Oneonta (BS) Ed 1984, (MS) Rdng 1988; SUNY at Cortland (CAS) Educl Admin 1993; *cr:* Bainbridge-Guilford SD 3rd, 6th Grd, Rdng Tchr, Lang Arts Coord 1984-93; Broome-Tioga BOCES Supvr, Educl Prgms, Prof Dev Tchr 1993-; *ai:* Adjunct Instr, Grad Ed SUNY at Oneonta; IRA 1988-, Outstanding Rdng Prgm; Phi Delta Kappa, ASCD, Natl Staff Dev Cncl 1993-; Hoyt Fnd, Goals 2000 Grants; Mailbox Magazine Contributor; *office:* Broome-Tioga BOCES Glenwood Rd Binghamton NY 13905*

MYERS, CHARLES STELZIG, Band & Choir Director; *b:* Kittanning, PA; *m:* Elizabeth Howell; *c:* Steven, Jeff, Brian; *ed:* Miami Univ (BSME) Music Ed 1973; 3 Hrs Univ of WI at Whitewater; 1 Hr Bowling Green St Univ; 3 Hrs Duquesne Univ; *cr:* New Lebanon Local Schls Band Dir 1973-76; Kalida Local Schls Band, Choir dir 1976-; *ai:* Marching, Pep Bands; Show Choir Musical; MENC 1973-; OMEA 1973-, Marching Band Judge; Phi Mu Alpha 1970-, Chapter Sec; Kappa Kappa Psi 1971-, Chapter Sec; 1st Presbyn Church 1979-, Session Clerk, Pastor Nominating Comm Chm; Kalida Marching Band Superior Ratings St Band Competition 8 Yrs, Appeared in Philadelphia Thanksgiving Parade 1989; *office:* Kalida HS Box 269 Kalida OH 45853

MYERS, CHRISTY KATHLEEN, First Grade Teacher; *b:* Bristol, PA; *ed:* Rider Univ (BA) Elem Ed 1989; *cr:* Our Lady of Sorrows Schl Fourth Grd Tchr 1990-91; Immaculate Conception Schl Sixth Grd Tchr 1991-94, First Grd Tchr 1994-; *ai:* Math Chprsn; Spelling Bee Coord; *office:* Immaculate Conception Schl 520 Chestnut Ave Trenton NJ 08611*

MYERS, CLARE DRAPER, Kindergarten Teacher; *b:* Wilkes-Barre, PA; *m:* Ellis R.; *c:* Andrew E., David J.; *ed:* Wilkes Univ (BS) Elem Ed 1965; Univ of NC (MED) Elem Ed 1967; *cr:* Crestwood Schl Dist Elem Tchr 1978-; *ai:* Crestwood Ed Assn 1978-, VP, Treas; *office:* Crestwood Schl Dist 117 Spruce St Mountain Top PA 18707

MYERS, CONNIE ROSE (BARLEY), Former Teacher; *b:* Dallastown, PA; *m:* Charles Ronald; *c:* Marnette, Jenna; *ed:* Millersville St U (BS) Elem Ed 1966, (MED) Elem Ed 1970; *cr:* Red Lion Area Schl Dist Kdgtn Tchr 1966-70, 1st Grd Tchr 1976-89, Pre-First Grd Tchr 1989-95; *ai:* PSEA 1976-; NEA 1966-; Yorkshire U M Church Choir 1989-, Treas; Comfort Caring Canines 1993-.*

MYERS, DAVID R., Science Dept Chair & Teacher; *b:* Easton, MD; *m:* Sherry Swank; *c:* Trysta Sears; *ed:* Johns Hopkins Univ (BA) Physics 1965; Univ of MD (MED) Sci Ed 1975; Trng Physics Tchng Resource Agent Northern AZ Univ 1985; Nuclear Concepts Inst Penn St Univ 1986; *cr:* Crossland HS Physics, Chem Tchr 1965-76; Prince George's Comm Coll Tchr for Phys Sci Inst for Tchrs 1991-95; Loyola Coll Tchr for Phys Sci for Elem Tchrs 1992-95; Eleanor Roosevelt HS AP Tchr Physics C, Rsrch Practicum, Sci Dept Chair 1993-; *ai:* NHS Adv; Schl Instructional Cncl; Physics Olympics Team Spon; NEA, MSTA, PGCEA 1965-; AAPT 1973-; NSTA 1975-; MD Assn Sci Tchrs 1990-; First United Meth Church 1955-, Lay Ldr, Sunday Schl Tchr, Choir Mem, UMM; Presidential Awd for Excl in Sci, Math Tchng St Finalist 1991; Ed Fellow of Optical Soc of Amer 1988; PEPCO, Prince George's Co Outstdng Sci Tchr Awd 1987; Ldr Numerous Wrkshps; *office:* Eleanor Roosevelt HS 7601 Hanover Pky Greenbelt MD 20770*

MYERS, DORA P., Secondary English Teacher; *b:* Brooklyn, NY; *m:* Andrew M. Jr.; *ed:* St Univ of NY at Oneonta (BA) Early Scndry Eng 1970; Russell Sage Coll Addl 30 Hrs Permanant Cert 1970-75; *cr:* Shenendehowa Cntrl-Gowana Jr HS Eng Tchr 1970-; *ai:* Drama CLub Dir 1970-; Asst 7th, 8th Grd Girls Track Coach 1985-; AFT, NYSUT, Shenendehowa Tchrs Assn 1970-; PTSA 1970-, Tchr Liason, Honorary Life Mbrshp; Named Twice Golub Select Seminars; NY St Cncl of Tchrs of Eng Recognized Achvmnts Working Stdnts in Theatre; *office:* Gowana Jr HS 970 Route 146 Clifton Park NY 12065

MYERS, ELLINOR ELIZABETH, English Teacher; *b:* Baltimore City, MD; *ed:* Towson St Univ (BA) Eng 1971; Towson St Univ (MS) Writing 1991; Univ of MD, Univ of Baltimore, Towson St Univ Grad Courses Eng, Theater Arts; *cr:* Dumbarton Jr HS Eng Tchr 1971-81; Parkville HS Eng, Theater Arts Tchr 1981-85; Dumbarton MS Eng Tchr 1985-; *ai:* Kiev Club Spon; Fac Cncl; NEA, MSTA, TABCO 1971-; Book: Algebra of Hooves; Art in Progress, Dancing Shadow Review Various Poetry; *office:* Dumbarton MS 300 Dumbarton Rd Baltimore MD 21212

MYERS, EMILY JANE (BRICKNER), English Teacher; *b:* Tiffin, OH; *m:* Gary P.; *c:* Hilary, Kevin; *ed:* Marian Coll at Indianapolis (BA) Eng 1974; Heidelberg Coll 2 Credit Hrs; *cr:* Ottawa-Glandorf HS Ger, Eng 1974-81; Columbian HS Ger Tchr 1987-88; Calvert HS Eng, Ger Tchr 1988-; *ai:* Eng Dept Chprsn; Tutor 9th Grd Proficiency Testing; NHS Fac Cncl; NCEA 1993-; Calvert HS Music Booster 1995-, Exec Bd; *home:* 188 Coe St Tiffin OH 44883

MYERS, JOHN THOMAS, Fifth Grade Teacher; *b:* Johnstown, PA; *m:* Cynthia Greggo; *c:* Abby, Sam; *ed:* Clarion St Coll (BA) Elem Ed 1979; Youngstown St Univ (MS) Elem Admin 1989; *cr:* Jeff Davis MS 5th Grd Tchr 1979-80; Randallwood MS 5th Grd Tchr 1980-93; *ai:* Wrestling Coach; Drama Club Spon; NEA 1980-; *home:* 3755 Mercedes Pl Unit 10 Canfield OH 44406

MYERS, KEITH JOSEPH, American History Teacher; *b:* Philadelphia, PA; *m:* Eileen Denneny; *c:* Christopher, Heather; *ed:* LaSalle Coll (BA) Soc Stud Ed 1973; Temple Univ (MS) Soc Stud Ed 1976; Univ of PA His; *cr:* Archbishop Wood HS for Boys Soc Stud Tchr, Dept Chm 1973-88; Medill Bair HS Soc Stud Tchr 1988-; *ai:* NEA, PEA 1988-; NEH Inst Local His Flwshp 1984, Text Toleration Flwshp 1985; BCU Perf Assessment Project 1995; *office:* Medill Bair HS 608 S Olds Blvd Fairless Hills PA 19030

MYERS, KENNETH JAMES, Mathematics & Science Teacher; *b:* Cassandra, PA; *m:* Mary Alice Donohoe; *c:* Benjamin, Molly, Andrew, Hannah Jo; *ed:* St Francis Coll (BS) Elem Ed, His, Govt 1971; 39 Post Grad Hrs; *cr:* Penn Cambria Elem Schl Tchr; Penn Cambria MS Tchr, Adult Ed Tchr; *ai:* NEA, PSEA 1917-; *home:* 215 A Frame Rd Ebensburg PA 15931

MYERS, LARRY ROBERT, Psychology Teacher; *b:* Washington, PA; *ed:* PA St Univ (BS) Rehabilitation Ed 1976; Attnd California Univ of PA Scndry Tchng Cert & 36 Grad Credits Toward MS in Schl Psych; *cr:* Allegheny Valley Schl Behavior Mgmt Coord 1976-80; Trinity HS Soc Stud Tchr 1989-; *ai:* Girls Vlybl Head Coach; Jr Class Adv; NEA, PSEA 1995-; APA 1996; AVCA 1985-; PVCA 1983-, Dist Rep; *office:* Trinity HS 231 Park Ave Washington PA 15301

MYERS, LENON PAGE, High School Mathematics Tchr; *b:* Perth Amroy, NJ; *m:* Susan Lynn Ritchie; *ed:* Wheaton Coll (BA) Math, Scndry Ed 1995; *cr:* Timothy Chrstn Schl Math Tchr 1994-; *ai:* Gospel Choir Dir; Var Soccer Asst Coach; Var Bsbl Head Coach; Men's Small Group Ldr Adv; NSCAA Soccer 1995-; *home:* 66C Old New Brunswick Rd Piscataway NJ 08854

MYERS, LINDA SAYLER, 6th Grd Lang Arts & Math Tchr; *b:* Gettysburg, PA; *m:* Donald Vincent; *c:* Vincent, Anthony; *ed:* Frederick Comm Coll (AA) General Stud 1982; Western MD Coll (BA) Eng & Elem Ed 1984, (MS) Gudiance & Cnslng 1991; 34 Addl Credit Hrs; *cr:* Bd of Ed of Fred Cty Adult Ed Recruiter & Aide 1976-82, Acad Aide 1984-86; Frederick Cty Pub Schls Tchr 1986-; *ai:* Lang Arts Dept Chprsn; Stu & Family Cnslr; NCTE 1987-; NCTM 1990-; FCTA, NEA & MSTA 1986-; Toms Creek United Meth Church 1960-, Sunday Schl Tchr, Lay Speaker, Chprsn of Ed; Suburban Kiwanis Club Achvmt Awd 1992; Chamber of Commerce of Frederick Cty Tchr Excl Awd 1990; *office:* Thurmont MS 408 E Main St Thurmont MD 21788*

MYERS, MARY DAHER, Math & Reading Teacher; *b:* Norristown, PA; *m:* William M.; *c:* Todd, Chad; *ed:* West Chester Univ (BS) Elem 1972; Penn St Univ (MA) Elem 1982; *cr:* Gay St Elem Schl 5th Grd Tchr 1972-79; Barkley Elem Schl 5th Grd Tchr 1980-91; Phoenixville Area MS 6th Grd Math, Rdng Tchr 1991-; *ai:* Annual Spring Show Musical Costume Coord 1990; Comm Space 1989, Planning 1990; PSEA, PAEA, NEA 1972-; Babe Ruth League 1987-90, Treas, 1988-89, 1992-, Chprsn St Tournament.*

MYERS, MARY KATHRYN TOOLE, Second Grade Teacher; *b:* Pittston, PA; *m:* Sylvester T.; *c:* Michael; *ed:* Coll Misericordia (BS) Elem Ed 1968; 36 Grad Credits; *cr:* Pittston Area Schls Geography Tchr 1968-69, 4th-6th Grd Rdng Tchr 1969-72, 2nd Grd Tchr 1972-; *ai:* Mid Sts Evaluation Comm; PAC Reader Pgm; AFT 1968-; Luzerne Cty Rdng Assn 1989-; *office:* Pittston Area Schl Dist New St Pittston PA 18640

MYERS, MICHAEL RAYMOND, Biology & Accelerated Bio Tchr; *b:* Lancaster, OH; *m:* Sonia Marie Crozier; *c:* Moriah; *ed:* Capital Univ (BA) Bio & Scndry Ed 1989; Univ of Dayton (MS) Supervision 1995; School Finance 3 QT Hrs; Pub Relations 3 QT Hrs; Field Stud 3 QT Hrs; *cr:* Jonathan Alder HS & Jr HS 8th Grd Sci & General Sci Tchr 1989-91; Fairfield Union HS Bio II & Accelerated Bio Tchr 1991-; *ai:* Fairfield Union Ed Assoc 1991-; OH Ed Assn 1991-; NEA 1991-; Grace Luth Church Cncl 1991-, Elder; Moneta Weihl Awd for Outstdng Achvmt in Ed 1989; Governors Awd for Excl in Youth Sci Opportunities 1995; *office:* Fairfield Union HS 6401 Cincinnati Zanesville Rd Lancaster OH 43130*

MYERS, ROBERT WILLIAM, English & Theater Teacher; *b:* Meadville, PA; *m:* Lise Therrien; *c:* Annie L., Dominic A., Israel A., Billee E.; *ed:* Edinboro Univ of PA (AA) Speech Commnctn 1987, (BSEd) Eng 1992; Ambassador Univ (BA) Theology 1990; *cr:* Ft LeBoeuf HS Eng & Theatre Tchr 1993-; *ai:* PSEA 1993-; NEA 1993-; NCTE 1993-; *office:* Fort Le Boeuf HS 931 N High St Waterford PA 16441

MYERS, ROSE ANN BURNHAM, Fifth Grade Teacher; *b:* Theresa, NY; *m:* Wayne C.; *c:* Alicia Weber, Michelle Fisher, Gail Mc Donald, Anne Green; *ed:* SUNY at Oswego (BS) Elem Ed 1972; Perm 1977; 46 Post Grad Hrs; *cr:* Pulaski Day Care Ctr Prgm Dir 1972-73; Parish Elem Schl K, 4-5th Grd Tchr 1974-; *ai:* Bldg Site Shared-Decision Making Comm; NY St United Tchrs 1974-, Bldg Rep, VP; Oswego Rdng Cncl 1984-; Elks Auxiliary 1984-; Church, Choir, Comms; *office:* Parish Elem Schl PO Box 579 PO Box 579 Union St Parish NY 13131

MYERS, SANDRA ELLEN, Eighth Grade English Teacher; *b:* Clearfield, PA; *m:* Mark; *c:* Robert; *ed:* Slippery Rock Univ (BS) Elem Ed, Lib Sci 1985; Attnd PA St Univ; *cr:* Centre Elem Schl Kndgtn Tchr 1990-91; Clearfield MS Eighth Grd Eng Tchr 1991-92, Eighth Grd His Tchr 1992-93, Eighth Grd Eng Tchr 1993-; *ai:* Memory Book Adv; PSEA; NEA.

MYERS, SHARON BACK, Sixth Grade Teacher; *b:* Middletown, OH; *m:* Stephen Ray; *c:* Jessica, Stephen Scott, Tara; *ed:* Morehead St Univ (BA) Elem Ed 1979; Wright St Univ (MA) Tchr Ldr 1996; *cr:* Taft Elem Schl Kndgtn 1982-85; Mc Kinley Elem Schl 5th Grd Tchr 1985-89; Amanda Elem Schl 6th Grd Tchr 1989-; *ai:* Mc Kinley Thunder Bird Adv 1986-89; Right to Read Adv 1987; Amanda Soc Com Chprsn 1989-93; Comm Relations 1994-; MTA, OEA, NEA 1982-; *office:* Amanda Elem Schl 1212 Girard St Middletown OH 45042

MYERS, STEPHEN GROVE, Science Teacher; *b:* Carlisle, PA; *m:* Bonnie L.; *ed:* Shippensburg St Coll (BA) Bio, Ed 1969, (MED) Bio 1972; *cr:* Charles Boehm HS Scndry Bio Tchr 1969-90; Medill Bair HS Scndry Bio Tchr 1991-; *ai:* HS Talent Show Dir, Spon; Schl Choral Concerts, Plays, Musicals Percussion Accompaniment; NEA, PEA 1969-; Pi Nu Epsilon 1968-, Pres; Kappa Delta Pi 1967-; Westshoremen Inc 1975-, Percussion Instr; Cornwells United Methodist Church, Missions Comm Chr, Adult Ed Ministry; *office:* Medill Bair HS Olds Blvd Fairless Hills PA 19030

MYERS, TONYA EVANS, Fourth Grade Teacher; *b:* Springfield, OH; *m:* William Dean; *c:* Hannah Janess; *ed:* Cedarville Coll (BA) Elem Ed 1988; Attnd Univ of Dayton, Wright St Univ; *cr:* Clark Cty Pub Schls Sub Tchr 1988; Miamisburg City Schls Fourth Grd Tchr 1988-; *office:* Mound Elem Schl 1108 Range Ave Miamisburg OH 45342

MYFELT, CAROL J., Fourth Grade Teacher; *b:* Elmira, NY; *ed:* Mansfield Univ (BS) Elem Ed 1971; Grad Prgm for PA Cert Elmira Univ; *cr:* W. R. Croman Elem Schl 5th Grd Tchr 1971-86, Lang Arts Specialist 1986-91, 3rd Grd Tchr 1991-92, 4th Grd Tchr 1992-; *ai:* NEA, PSEA, TAEA 1971-; Daggett United Meth Church 1962-; *home:* RR 2 Box 115D Ulster PA 18850

MYKUT, TERESA A. (LOS), Mathematics Teacher; *b:* Huntingdon, PA; *m:* Peter S.; *c:* Peter, Nathan; *ed:* Shippensburg St Coll (BS) Scndry Math 1985; 24 Credits for Level II Cert; *cr:* Middletown HS Sec Math Tchr 1985; MUA Jr Sr HS Sec Math Tchr 1985-; *ai:* NEA, PSEA, MUEA; *office:* Mt Union Area Jr Sr HS N Shaver St Mount Union PA 17066

MYLES, TRACEY A., High School Math Teacher; *b:* Mineola, NY; *m:* Joseph; *c:* Hayley; *ed:* St Johns Univ (BA) Math 1992; 7 Credit Hrs Completed in Spec Ed at Queens Coll; *cr:* Lawrence Woodmere Acad HS Math Tchr 1993-; *ai:* Sr Class Adv; Math Club Supvr; *office:* Lawrence Woodmere Acad 336 Woodmere Blvd Woodmere NY 11598

MYLOTT, GARY DAVID, Mathematics Teacher; *b:* Glenns Falls, NY; *m:* Karen Barber; *c:* Amanda, Christine; *ed:* Siena Coll Loudonvill NY (BA) Math 1974; SUNY at Buffalo 31 Credit Hrs; *cr:* Crown Point CSD Math Tchr 1975-78; Cairo-Durham HS Math Tchr 1978-; *ai:* NYSUT 1975-; AFT 1975-; *office:* Cairo-Durham Jr Sr HS Rt 145 Cairo NY 12413

MYOTT, RICHARD STEWART, Science Teacher; *b:* Glens Falls, NY; *m:* Vickie; *c:* Richard, William; *ed:* SUNY at Plattsburg (BS) Scndry Ed Physics 1985, (MS) Ed 1990; *cr:* Argyle Cntrl Schl Physics & Chem Tchr 1986-; *ai:* Class, Sci Club & Yrbk Adv; Argyle Tchr Assn 1985-, VP; NYSUT 1985-; *office:* Argyle Central Schl Sheridan St Argyle NY 12809*

MYRABO, LEIK NORWALD, Assoc Prof of Engrng & Physics; *b:* Sioux Falls, SD; *m:* Christie Lee Eckes; *c:* Tregenna, Danielle; *ed:* IA St Univ (BS) Aerospace Engrng 1968; Univ of CA at San Diego (PHD) Engrng Physics 1976; *cr:* Physical Sciences Inc Prin Scientist 1976-77; W. J. Schafer Assoc Scientist, Consultant 1977-80; BDM Corp Scientist, Consultant 1980-83; Rensselaer Polytechnic Inst Assoc Prof 1983-; *ai:* AIAA 1976-; EAA 1975-; SSI 1993-; Whipstock Hill Preservation Soc 1994-, Pres; Bennington Region Preservation Trust 1994-, Dir; Mt Anthony Preservation Soc 1994-, Dir; Tri-St Taconic Audubon Soc 1995-, Dir; Book: The Future of Flight Co-Author 1983; *office:* Rensselaer Polytechnic Inst Undergraduate Admissions Ofc 15th St Troy NY 12180

MYRICK, TERRY DARNELL, Performing Arts Teacher; *b:* Tampa, FL; *c:* David Baker; *ed:* FL A&M Univ (BS) Mrktg 1981; City Coll of NY (MS) Elem Ed 1992; *cr:* Benjamin Franklin Jr HS Music, Math Tchr 1981-83; King HS Bus Ed Tchr 1983-84; Intermediate Schl 136 Math Tchr 1986-87; Bridge Schl Performing Arts Tchr 1987-; *ai:* Head Performing Arts Dept; Chorus Dir; Drama Coach; 7th-8th Grd Dean; UFT 1987-; CCNY Alumni Assn 1992-; Operation Pride Awd 1988; *office:* Bridge Schl 141 E 111th St New York NY 10029

MYSLIWIEC, MICHAEL JOSEPH, Mathematics & Theology Te *b:* Troy, NY; *ed:* Siena Coll (BA) Rel Stud 1984; CQ Provisional Cert 1992; Hudson Vly Comm Coll 16 Hrs; Univ at Albany 27 Hrs; *cr:* HS Theology Tchr 1984-85; St Henry's Church Rel Ed Coord 19 Bell's Driving Schl Instr 1987-93; St Henry's Church Catechist Form coord 1990-92; Troy HS Summer Schl Math Tchr 1993-95; Cath Cn Math, Theology Tchr, Dept Chair 1985-; *ai:* Folk Group, Arbor Moderator; St Henry's Church 1980-, Choir; *home:* 1861 9th Watervliet NY 12189

N

NABINGER, PATRICIA WEMPLE, Vocal Music Teache Gloversville, NY; *m:* Richard; *c:* Christine N., Carolyn N., Laur Leanne N.; *ed:* Crane Schl of Music (BS) Music Ed Voice 1971; 30 Hrs; *cr:* Lisbon Cntrl Schl K-12th Grd Gen Music & Vocal Tchr 197 Pvt Piano Tchr 1971-; United Ministry of Delhi Organist 1989-; W Cntrl Schl 6th-8th Grd & HS Choirs Conductor 1991-; *ai:* ME NYSSMA 1991-; ACDA 1995-; *office:* Walton Cntrl Schl 47-49 Sto Ave Walton NY 13856

NACE, KEVIN D., Social Studies Teacher; *b:* Danville, PA; *m:* McClelland; *ed:* E Stroudsburg Univ (BS) Scndry Ed 1991; 12 Cred Toward Masters; *cr:* E Stroudsburg Schl Dist 8th Grd Tchr 199 10th-11th Grd Tchr 1993-; *ai:* Asst Ftbl Coach; NEA 1992-; PSEA 1 *office:* E Stroudsburg Area Schl Dist 279 N Courtland St East Stroud PA 18301

NACE, SHARON KAY, Fourth Grade Teacher; *b:* Harrisburg, PA Harrisburg Area Comm Coll (AA) Pre-Elem Ed 1984; Penn Harrisburg (BELED) Elem Ed 1986, (MED) Tchng & Curr 1995; Di Stud Diploma Bible Truth Inst 1977; Math Conf for Ldrs CEU Awded Rdng Specialist Cert 1991; *cr:* Upper Dauphin Area Schl Dist 3rd Grd 1986-87; Halifax Area Schl Dist 5th Grd Tchr 1987-91, Chptr I Rdng 1991-92, 4th Grd Tchr 1992-; *ai:* NEA 1986-; Penn St Alumni Assoc Millersburg Area Art Assoc 1995-; Ned Smith Ctr for Nature & Art Gift of Time Awd 1995; *office:* Halifax Area Elem Schl 3940 F Mountain Rd Halifax PA 17032

NACHBY, HELEN GOMBERG, Art Teacher; *b:* Brooklyn, N Alysha Dawn, Loren Nachby Walker; *ed:* St Univ Coll At Buffalo (BS Ed 1967; Bridgeport Univ (MS) Art Ed 1970; Hopkins Loyola, Towsor Scndry Prin, Supervision 1992; Univs Addl 60 Credit Hrs 1994 Baltimore Cty Pub Schls Art Tchr, Chair, Team Ldr 10 Yrs; Roton M Tchr 3 Yrs; Van Sickle Jr HS Art Tchr 1 Yr; Beverly HIlls Jr HS Art 1 Yr; Univ of SC Art Instr 1 Yr; *ai:* Baltimore Cty Yth Art Month C Co-Chair; Inbound Frgn Stu Exch Prgm Coord; Outbound Frgn Exch F Coord; Yrbk Adv; NEA, MD Ed Assn, TABCO, PTSA 1986-; Had 1975-; Micro Soc 1994-95, Natl Confs Presenter; Nom for MD St Tc Yr, Baltimore Cty Tchr of Yr 1995; Nom for Fulbright Tchr Exch BSA Outstdng Svc 1993; Intnl Ed Forum Top Coord 1994; *home:* Peace Chimes Ct Columbia MD 21045*

NACRELLI, CATHY SINGLETON, Language Arts Teache Abingdon, VA; *m:* Robert A. Jr.; *c:* Robert, Annette; *ed:* Emory & H Coll (BA) Elem Ed 1978; Widener Univ (MED) Rdng Ed 1991 Broadmeadow Schl Sci Tchr, Dept Chair 1979-81; Caravel Acad LA MS Coord 1987-93; Perryville MS Lang Arts Tchr 1993-; *ai:* MD De Ed Content Stands, Schl Improvement, Recognition, Literacy Co SHOUT Spon; Odyssey of the Mind Coach; ASCD 1992-; NMSA, C 1993-; Book Discussion Club 1995-; Holy Angels Parish 1985-; *o* Perryville MS 850 Aiken Ave Perryville MD 21903

NADARESKI, MARISA PERTELESI, Former Science Tuto Peekskill, NY; *m:* Christopher A.; *c:* Teresa C., Benjamin J.; *ed:* Coll Rose at Albany (BS) Elem Ed, Bio 1983; SUNY at Albany (MS) ACT Ed 1986; *cr:* Coll of St Rose Botany Lab Asst 1982-83; SUNYA Tchrs 1985-86; Orville A. Todd MS Life, Phys, Regents Earth Sci Tchr 198 Coll of St Rose Sci Tutor; *ai:* Coord Odyssey of the Mind; Environm Club Adv; STANYS, Kappa Gamma Pi 1983-; Who's Who in Amer & Colls 1979; Grants; Thinking Skills Wkshp Presenter for NYS Eng 1987.*

NADEL, COLLEEN DIANE, 8th Grd Social Studies Tch Philadelphia, PA; *c:* Ian, Michael; *ed:* Metropolitan St Coll (BA) H Svcs 1986; Metropolitan St Coll Tchng Cert Soc Scis 1989; 12 Credi Wilmington Coll Grad Prgm Scndry Schl Admin; *cr:* Cntrl MS 8th Gr Stud Tchr 1989-; *ai:* CMS Comm Svc Club Adv; Odyssey of the Coach; Chm of CMS Awd Comm; CEA Exec Bd; CEA Ldrshp Team; Advy Comm; Chm of Inst Prof Dev Comm; Capital Schl Dist Negoti Team; NEA, DE St Edctrs, Capital Ed Assn 1989-; Cntrl MS Tchr 1993; Nom for DE Cncl of Soc Stud Tchr of Yr; *office:* Dover Centra 1 Delaware Ave Dover DE 19901

NADIG, JOHN CLYMER, Mathematics & Cmptr Sci Tchr; *b:* Allent PA; *m:* Jane Louise Miller; *c:* Bonnie Joy, Jonathan Miller; *ed:* Kutz St Coll (BS) Math 1970; Trenton St Coll (MA) Math 1983; *cr:* Trent Coll Instr 1984-88; Pennsbury HS Tchr 1970-; *ai:* Chess Club Spon; 1970-; *office:* Pennsbury HS 705 Hood Blvd Fairless Hills PA 19030

NADJAR, ESTHER VICKIE, History & Judaic Studies Tch Brooklyn, NY; *ed:* Brooklyn Coll (BA) His 1991; Attnd Mich Jerusalem Coll Women, Nishmat, NYU Skirball Dept of Judaic Stud Saphardic Bikur Holim 1989-91; Bnei Shaare Zion Prgm Coord 199 Magen David HS Stu Act Dir 1992-; *ai:* Comm Outreach Prgms; Wee Seminar Retreats; Spec Assemblies, Lectures; Yrbk Adv; Ismel Pa Coord; NASSP 1992-; Sephardic Bikur Holim, Bnei Shaare Zion 1 Phi Beta Kappa; *office:* Magen David Yeshivah HS 7801 Bay Pky Broo NY 11214

NADLER, GAIL (WIRTH), First Grade Teacher; *b:* New York City, *c:* Laurie; *ed:* Brooklyn Coll (BA) Elem Ed 1963; 30 Addl Credits W Univ; *cr:* NY Bd of Ed K-1st Grd Tchr 1963-67; ID Falls Dist #91 1st Grd Tchr 1974-77; Assoc for Help of Retarded Ch Tchr 1979-84; N of Ed 1st Grd Tchr 1985-; *ai:* UFT, AFT 1963-; NEA 1974; *office:* PS Ocean Schl 825 Hicksville Rd Far Rockaway NY 11691

NADLER, SHEILA ORLINSKY, English Teacher; *b:* Brooklyn, N Joseph H.; *ed:* Simmons Coll (BS) Soc Scis 1957; Montclair St Univ Human Resources 1981; *cr:* Wareham Schl System Eng Tchr 1957 Belleville Schl Eng Tchr 1958-61; San Towel Svc Sec, Treas 196 Verona HS Spec Svcs Tchr 1971-72, Eng Tchr 1972-89, Eng Dept Coord 1977-81; Univ of St Martin Adj Prof 1989-90; Verona HS Eng 'chr 1990-; *ai:* 1 of 200 Tchrs in US Attnd Conf on Holocaust Stud DC 1994; Clinical Adj Fac Montclair St 1994; Ed Advy Comm -94; Tchr of GATE 1990-91; Advy Cncl Consultant Holocaust, cide & Prejudice Reduction 1987; Honored by Museum Amer Folk . Seton Hall Univ Curr Dev; NCTE; NEA, NJ Cncl Tchrs of Eng; NJ Assn; Verona Ed Assn; Simmons Coll Club of NJ Sec 1958, Co-Pres 91; Educl Prgm Dev & Presentation Designed Led Wkshps NJ Cncl hrs of Eng, PA Cncl Tchrs of Eng, NJ Advy Cncl on Holocaust; Dev Materials; Mngmt & Admin, Prepared, Submitted Line Budget, ed, Held & Assisted Departmental & Interdepartmental Meetings, vised, Wrote Curr, Evaluator of Eng & Lib Svcs; *office:* Verona HS airview Ave Verona NJ 07044*

LER, THOMAS EDWARD, Mathematics Department Chair; *b:* St sburg, FL; *m:* Barbara G.; *c:* Laura, Michelle, Martin; *ed:* Eastern KY (BS) Elem Ed 1968; Xavier Univ (MED) Guidance 1971; *cr:* Lakota Schl Dist Tchr 1968-; *ai:* LEA 1968; OEA 1968-; NEA 1968-; : Hopewell Jr Schl 8200 Cox Rd West Chester OH 45069

ORI, BARBARA GENTILE, Third Grade Teacher; *b:* NYC, NY; *m:* h; *ed:* Queens Coll-CUNY (BA) Elem Ed 1967, (MA) Elem Ed 1972; atute U Ct Renzulli Trng 2 Weeks; Univ of NH Masters in Rdng Prgm edits; *cr:* PS 171 Schl 2-5 Grds Tchr 18 Yrs; PS 122 Acad, Magnet for Gifted Pupils 4 Grd Tchr 8 Yrs; Oyster River Schl Dist Chptr 1 d 1 Yr; Mast Way Elem Schl 3 Grd Tchr 1 Yr; *ai:* Co-Chair Parent ership Comm; French Club; NEA 1996; AFT 1967-; NH Assn for d Ed, Mini-Grant for Shakespeare Project; Oyster River Schls Svc 1994; Piloted Magnet Schl Project Gifted Ed.

ASH, BARBARA MARGARET, 8th-12th Grade French Teacher; *b:* n City, NJ; *ed:* Montclair St (BA) Fr, Eng 1967; NYU New York, Paris Fr Lang, Civilization 1979; 3 Credits Italian; *cr:* Palisades Park Jr Sr r, Eng Tchr 1967-; *ai:* Lit Magazine Adv 1978-93; NHS Comm 1980-; Sts Evaluation Foreign Lang Chrp 1982, 1993; NJEA, NEA 1967-; 1967-, Treas 1978-; Governor's Awd Excl in Tchng 1989; Princeton's nguished Tchr Nom 1988, 1990; *office:* Palisades Pk Jr Sr HS E Ruby terans' PL Palisades Park NJ 07650*

FIN, CHARLOTTE OURSLER, Latin & French Teacher; *b:* our, IN; *m:* Jerry R.; *c:* Matthew; *ed:* IN Univ (BA) Latin 1970; Coll lliam & Mary (MA) Ed Specializing in Classics 1977; *cr:* Kempsville atin & Fr Tchr 1970-75; Denbigh HS Latin Tchr 1975-77; Rdng HS & Fr Tchr 1984-; *ai:* Jr Classical League Spon; NEA 1984-; Amer sical League 1989-; PA Classical League 1994-; Classical Assn of atic Flutes 1995-; *office:* Reading Sr HS 801 n 13th St Reading PA 4

AI, THERESE MIDORI, Math Teacher; *b:* Kilauea, HI; *ed:* St Univ Y at Oswego (BSEd) Sci 1963; Univ of HI (MSEd) Chem 1966; lrow Wilson Inst Tchrs of Sec Sch Math 1987-88; Pre-Calc, Calculus ; *cr:* St Francis HS Sci, Math Tchr, Sci Dept Chr 1963-68; Assumption HS Sci, Math Tchr 1968-70; Sacred Heart HS Sci, Math Tchr -71; D. R. U. HS Sci, Math Tchr 1971-72; Riverdale Cntry HS Sci, Tchr 1972-; *ai:* Stds Color Coalition Co-Adv 1993-; Fac Grants m 1988-92; Gr 7-8 Awds Com Chair 1985-89; Stu-Fac Cncl 1988; le of Color Ind Schls 1993-; Nepperhan Com Cntr 1994-, Vol Math ; Habitat for Hum, Southern Poverty Law Ctr 1992-; Natl Parks ervation Assn 1993-; Hudson River Clearwater 1985-; NSF Grants: Jr Math Tchr Syracuse Univ NY 1963, Acad Yr Inst Univ of HI 1965-66; ap Ldr Asian-Am Comm NYC 1993.*

AO, CAROL PRICHETT, Art Teacher; *b:* Millville, NJ; *m:* C. Scott; ott T., Michael; *ed:* Glassboro St Coll (BA) Art Ed 1974; Fairleigh inson Univ (MA) Human Dev 1984; *cr:* Millville Sr HS Art Tchr -; Cumberland Co Coll Adj Fac Watercolor & Design 1991-94; *ai:* Sr Drama & Musical Productions Art Dir; Millville Ed Assn 1975-, Tchr Awd 1989; NJEA 1975-; NEA 1975-; Japanese Amer Citizens League -, Sec, Bd Mem, Silver Svc Pin; Cumberland Co United Way Tennis nament Comm 1994-; Millville Jaycees Outstdng Young Edctr 1989; *e:* Millville Sr HS 200 Wade Blvd Millville NJ 08332

ASE, GORO, Professor of Mathematics; *b:* Tokyo, Japan; *m:* Takako la; *c:* Terumi, George; *ed:* Univ of Tokyo (BS) Bio 1960; Univ of HI Zoology 1963; Univ of DE (PHD) Mathematical Statistics 1972; *cr:* oln Univ Prof 1971-; *ai:* Lindback Distngd Tchng Awd 1979; 13 Prof rs Publications; *office:* Lincoln Univ Dept of Math Lincoln University 9352

EL, BARBARA ANN, Health & Physical Ed Teacher; *b:* Lima, OH; Bowling Green St Univ (BS) PE 1973; Wright St Univ Bio; Univ of on Ath Trng; *cr:* Wapakoneta St Joseph Schl PE, Bio Tchr 1973-74; ht St Univ Womens Sftbl Coach 1974-75; Tecumseh HS Bio, PE, Hlth 1975-; *ai:* Var Sftbl Coach; Fall Weight Room Supvr; Steering Comm; PE Dept Chprsn; Vlybl Ofcl; OEA, NEA, TEA 1985-; OH St Sftbl ches Assn 1980-, Dist Treas, 200 Victories Awd; Dist Vlybl Coach of 987, 1991; Clark Co Sftbl Coach of Yr 1991; *office:* Tecumseh HS W National Rd New Carlisle OH 45344

EL, CHRISTOPHER ANDREW, English Teacher; *b:* Charleston, *m:* Lisa S. Nagel-Thoft; *ed:* Westminster Coll (BA) Theatre 1988; of Pittsburgh (MFA) Tchng 1993; *cr:* Bethel Park HS Eng, Theatre 1993-; *ai:* Drama Club, Thespian Spon; Fall Play, Spring Musical Dir; AFT, NTA 1993-; BPFT 1995-, At-Large Rep; Written Curr atre Arts I, II.*

EL, KATHLEEN PETERS, Kindergarten & Music Teacher; *b:* North awanda, NY; *m:* Kenneth Howard; *c:* Tristan D'Angelo, Devin; *ed:* alo St Coll (BS) Elem Ed 1965, (MS) Supervision Magna Cum Laude ; Grove City Coll, Concordia Coll; *cr:* Tonawanda Pub Schls Elem 1965-77; North Tonawanda Pub Schls Elem Tchr 1977-79; St Paul Schl Kndgtn Tchr 1979-; *ai:* Direct Schl Musical; Early Chldhd Cncl /NY; NAEYS; Niagara Cty Music Educators Assn; Coord Chrstn Ed United Meth Church 1978-, Tchr & Youth Adv; Choir; Buffalo St nni Assn Sec 1969-71; Schlsp Comm Chm Buffalo St Alumni Assn -73; *office:* Saint Paul Lutheran Schl 453 Old Falls Blvd North awanda NY 14120

ELBERG, MARC MORRIS, Learning Center Teacher; *b:* Brooklyn, *m:* Barbara E. Kramer; *c:* Scott, Michael; *ed:* Hofstra Univ (BA) His), (MS) Spec Ed 1970, (CAS) Educl Admin 1982; Addl Courses RC, SCOPE, C. W. Post Coll, Hofstra Univ; *cr:* Copiague Jr HS Tchr 7th-8th Grd SS, EMR 1970-80; Copiague HS 10th-12th Grds elopmental Learning Ctr Tchr 1980-85; Great Neck Rd Elem Schl DLC V Tchr 1985-; *ai:* Dist-Wide TAG; Shared Decision Making Comm; TA, NYSUT 1970-; AFT, NEA 1980-; NYSSE 1985-; Knights of ias 1985-, Exec Bd, Outstdng Job Awd; Kiwanis Club 1980-, Sec, s; Dir of Adult Ed Copiague Pub Schls; Cnslng Ctr for Learning Educl Disabilities-Prof Bus Newsletters, Newspaper Articles, Seminars; inal Justice Prgm HS, Jr HS, Suffolk Co Police; *home:* 406 Brookside opiague NY 11726

GELE, DOROTHY C., Third Grade Teacher; *b:* Elizabeth, NJ; *m:* neth; *c:* Peggy Nagele Honore, Nancy; *ed:* Newark St Coll (BA) Elem 966; *cr:* Rahway Bd of Ed 1st Grd Tchr 1966-69, Home Instr 1981-83; en Bd of Ed Home Instr & Supplemental Tchr 1982-83; St Hedwigs 1st Grd Tchr 1983-84; Timothy Chrstn Schl 3rd Grd Tchr 1984-; *ai:* Fair Coord; *office:* Timothy Christian Schl 2008 Ethel Rd Piscataway 08854

NAGLE, BRIAN M., Accounting Professor; *b:* Glen Cove, NY; *c:* Kristin; *ed:* Siena Coll (BBA) Acctng 1983; St Univ NY at Albany (MS) Acctng 1986; St Louis Univ (PHD) Acctng 1994; *cr:* Marist Coll Asst Prof 1986-89; St Louis Univ Instr 1983-93; Duquesne Univ Asst Prof 1993-; *ai:* Amer Acctng Assn 1991-; Amer Acad of Acctng & Fin 1995-; AACSB Doctoral Flwshp; Deloitte & Touche Doctoral Consortium Fellow; Certfd Pub Accountant; *office:* Duquesne Univ A. J. Palumbo School of Bus Pittsburgh PA 15282*

NAGLE, LINDA (FORTUNA), Spanish Teacher; *b:* New York, NY; *m:* Joseph Michael; *c:* Lauren, Matthew; *ed:* Iona Coll (BA) Span 1974, (MS) Ed Span 1978; 45 Addl Credits Schl Admin; *cr:* Port Chester MS Span Tchr 1976-; *ai:* New Tchr Mentor; Advy Ldr; Co-Founder School-wide Positive Behavior Prgm; Scheduling Comm; World Difference Comm; Liaison Spec Subject Tchrs; AFT, NYSUT 1976-; St Joseph Schl Mothers' Club 1989; Prin Advy Comm 1994-, Parent Rep; *office:* Port Chester MS 113 Bowman Ave Port Chester NY 10573*

NAGLER, MICHAEL P., Assistant Principal; *b:* Brooklyn, NY; *ed:* St Univ of NY at Binghamton (BA) His 1987; Brooklyn Coll (MA) His 1990, (AC) Admin & Supervision 1992; Doctorate Candidate at Columbia TC; *cr:* David A Boody Jr HS Soc Stud Tchr 1987-95; David A Boody Intermediate Schl Asst Prin 1995-; *ai:* Spec Olympics Certified Coach; AFT 1987-; Columbia Assn of Bd of Ed 1993-; *office:* IS 228 David A Boody 228 W 5th St Ave S Brooklyn NY 11223

NAGROSKY, JOYCE, English Teacher; *b:* Long Branch, NJ; *ed:* Cedarcrest Coll (BA) Eng 1961; *cr:* Keyport HS Tchr 1961-; *ai:* Keymax; KTA, NJEA, NEA 1961-; NOW 1992-; Humane Soc, SPCA 1991-; Governors Recognition Tchr of Yr; CTN Golden Apple Tchr.

NAGY, CHRISTOPHER JOSEPH, Assistant Principal; *b:* Harrisburg, PA; *ed:* St John Lateran Univ (PHB) Philosophy 1984, (THB) Theology 1987; Angelicum Univ (MA) Elumenism 1988; Lehigh Univ (MED) Educl Ldrshp 1993; Prin Cert 1996; Doctoral Candidate in Educl Ldrshp; *cr:* St Ignatius Loyola Parish Assoc Pastor 1988-89; Notre Dame HS Prof 1989-92; Allentown Coll Adj Prof 1990-; Notre Dame HS Vice Prin 1992-; *ai:* Key Club Adv; Tech Comm; Disciplinarian; NCEA, ASCD 1992-; NADEO 1990-; Kiwanis Club 1989-; Rotary Club 1992-; *office:* Notre Dame HS 3417 Church Rd Easton PA 18045

NAGY, JOAN B., Vocational Education Teacher; *b:* Hartford, CT; *ed:* Univ of Hartford (AS) Secretarial 1968; Cntrl CT St Univ (BS) Secretarial Sci, Soc Bus 1972, (MS) Admin, Supervision 1981; *cr:* Allen Mfg Clerk Typist, Teletype Opr 1956-57; Travelers Ins Co Keypunch Opr, Cmptrs 1957-63; Retirement Assocs Admin Asst 1963-69; Newington HS Tchr 1972-; *ai:* Curr Comm; Newington Tchrs Assn, NEA 1972-; Alpha Delta Kappa 1976-, Corresponding Sec, Historian; Photography Clubs 1957-; Univ of CT Alumni Assn Tchng Excl Awd; *home:* 104 Episcopal Rd Berlin CT 06037

NAGY, NANCY MAMMARELLA, Asst Prof of Graduate Ed; *b:* Port Griffith, PA; *m:* Attila; *c:* Amy Wallace; *ed:* Wilkes Univ (BA) Elem Ed 1978, (MS) Elem Ed 1982; Temple Univ (PHD) Ed 1993; Rdng Specialist Cert 1981; *cr:* Wyoming Seminary Lower Schl 1st & 4th Grd Tchr 1978-87; Kean Coll of NJ Acad Specialist & Adjunct Prof 1991-93; Marywood Coll Asst Prof & Dir of Grad Rdng Prgms 1993-; *ai:* Middlesex Rdng Cncl 1987-, Pres, Bd of Dirs, Pres Club IRA; Org Tchr Ed in Rdng 1995-; Coll Rdng Assn 1996; Pho Delta Kappa 1993-; Luzerne Cty Rdng Cncl 1983-, Bd of Dirs; NJ Rdng Assn 1987-, Bd of Dirs; *office:* Marywood Coll 2300 Adams Ave Scranton PA 18509*

NAGY, PATRICIA A., Fourth Grade Teacher; *b:* Cleveland, OH; *ed:* Cleveland St Univ (BS) Elem Ed 1983, (MA) Curr, Instruction & Spcl Rdng 1990; *cr:* Cleveland Cath Diocese 3rd-4th Grd Tchr 1983-86; Parma City Schls 3rd-5th Grd Tchr 1986-; *ai:* Safety Patrol Adv; Pleasant Vly Pride; NEA 1986-; *office:* Pleasant Valley Elem Schl 9906 W Pleasant Valley Rd Cleveland OH 44130

NAGY, ROBERT STEPHEN, History Teacher; *b:* Trenton, NJ; *m:* Ruth Edith Mouton; *ed:* Seton Hall Univ (BS) His 1971, (MA) Scndry Ed 1973; US Army Reserve Army Advanced Course, Army Command & General Staff Course; *cr:* Fisher Jr HS His Tchr 1971-; *ai:* Boys Intramural Athletic Prgm Dir; Tchrs Liaison Comm; NJEA, ETEA & MCEA 1971-; Us Army Reserve 1973-, Co Commander, Army Commendation Medal 1986; Clover Rod & Gun Club 1983-, VP 2 Yrs; J B Sportsmen Club 1985-; Fisher Jr HS Tchr of Month; BOLD Tchr of Yr Awd 1995; *office:* Fisher Jr H S 1325 Lower Ferry Rd Trenton NJ 08618

NAIRUS, JUDITH (KORTSEHL), Latin & English Teacher; *b:* Milwaukee, WI; *m:* John P.; *c:* John, James, Theresa, Mark; *ed:* Mt Mary Coll (BA) Latin, Eng 1963; 15 Semester Credit Hrs Ed 1987-95; *cr:* Cleveland Bd of Ed Latin, Eng Tchr 1963-66; Highland Local Schls Latin, Eng Tchr 1991-; *ai:* NEA 1991-; NCTE 1996; St Antela's Guild 1978-, Sec; St Angelas Couples Club 1977-, Pres, Treas; Partial Coll Schlsp; *office:* Highland Local Schls 3880 Ridge Rd Medina OH 44256*

NAJLIS, MYRA LEE, Lang Arts & Reading Teacher; *b:* Brooklyn, NY; *m:* Pierre R.; *c:* Paul, Robert; *ed:* Bergen Comm Coll (AAS) Early Chldhd Ed 1980; William Paterson Coll (BA) Elem Ed 1983; Rdng Tchr Cert 1984; Musical Stud, Piano; *cr:* Self Employed Piano Tchr 1961-71; YMCA of Ridgewood Early Chldhd Prgm Dir 1978-79; Young World Day Schl Prgm Coord, Head Tchr 1979-84; Irvington HS Rdng Tchr 1984-85; Ramapo Ridge MS Lang Arts, Rdng, Soc Stud Tchr 1985-; *ai:* Scheduling Comm; MEA 1984-; ASCD 1995-; Pi Lambda Theta; Phi Theta Kappa; *office:* Ramapo Ridge MS 150 Ridge Rd Mahwah NJ 07430

NAKOFF, MICHAEL H., Prof of Business Computer Sci; *b:* Cincinnati, OH; *m:* Juanalda Voncile Steele; *c:* Keith Michael, Mark Mihail; *ed:* Univ of Cincinnati (BS) Admin Mgmt 1974; Xavier Univ (MED) Prsnl Ed, Trng & Dev 1994; LaSalle Univ Cmptr Sci 15 Hrs; *cr:* CST&CC Instr, Prof 1977-; *ai:* Governance Comm Mem; Sabbattical Comm Adv; Stu Career Adv for Data Processing Industry; Assn for Computing Machinery 1984-; Natl System Prgmr Assn 1989-; Boston Cmptr Soc 1990-; AAUP 1990-; Civil Air Patrol 1985-, Squadron Commander; Certified Computing Prof 1985 ICCP; *office:* Cincinnati St Tech & Comm Coll 3520 Central Pky Cincinnati OH 45223

NALITZ, JANICE A., Religion Teacher; *b:* Pittsburgh, PA; *ed:* Univ of Pittsburgh (BA) Sec Ed, Classics & Rhetoric 1976; Duquesne Univ (MA) Theology 1986; Post Grad Stud Span; Univ of Pittsburgh Lang Comm Masters Equiv; *cr:* Pittsburgh Pub Schls Eng, Latin, Span Tchr 1976-79; Diocese of Pittsburgh Schl Rel, Eng, Latin, Span Tchr 1979-; St Joseph HS Rel Tchr 1991-; *ai:* Stu Cncl; Ldrshp Cncl; Jr Class Prom; Ministry Team; Our Lady of Most Blessed Sacrament Parish, RCIA Dir; *office:* St Joseph HS 800 Montana Ave Natrona Heights PA 15065

NALLY, JAMES THOMAS, Health & Physical Ed Teacher; *b:* Cleveland, OH; *m:* Vickie Denise Gainer; *c:* Lisa, Brian; *ed:* Bowling Green (BS) PE 1977; Cleveland St (ME) Ed, Human Performance 1986; *cr:* Mayfield MS Hlth Tchr 1977-84; Mayfield HS Hlth, PE Tchr 1984-; *ai:* Asst Var Ftbl, Frosh Bsktbl, Asst Var Bsbl Coach; OH Ed Assn, NEA 1977-; *home:* 5690 Hawthorne Dr Highland Heights OH 44143

NAMESTNIK, ALBERT JOHN, Fifth Grade Teacher; *b:* Cleveland, OH; *m:* Gail Meilander; *c:* Sarah, Marcy, Seth; *ed:* Ashland Coll (MA); Attnd Lakeland Comm Coll, Baldwin Wallace 1977; *cr:* North Royalton Schl 5th Grd Tchr, Coach 1977-; *ai:* Stu Cncl, IM Adv; Started Mohican Outdoor Ed; NEA, OEA, NREA 1977-; Jennings, Cuyahoga Voc Grants; PTA Lifetime Mbrshp Awd; Plain Dealer's 150th Yr Anniversary Crystal Apple Awd Candidate.*

NAMETH, JOSEPH LOUIS, Aerospace Instr AF JROTC; *b:* Reed City, MU; *m:* Rilla Foster; *c:* Joseph H., Andrea R.; *ed:* Univ of Mi (BA) Psych 1963; Pepperdine Univ (MA) Ed 1972; Troy St Univ (EDS) Admin 1976; *cr:* US Air Force Col 1964-93; *ai:* Fairfax Optimist Club 1992-, Fellowship Chm.

NAMETH, VICKI J., Sixth Grade Teacher; *b:* Miles City, MT; *m:* Thomas; *c:* Yvette; *ed:* Carroll Coll (BA) Elem Ed 1969; St Univ of NY at Albany (MS) Rdng 1974; Addl 30 Post Grad Hrs Various NY & CT Univs; *cr:* Bishop Gilmore Elem 5th Grd Tchr 1968-69; Staatsburg Elem 5th Grd Tchr 1969-79; North Park Elem 6th Grd Tchr 1979-; *ai:* Bldg Level & Dist Compact for Learning Teams; AFT, NYSUT 1972-; Hyde Park Tchrs 1969-, Bldg Rep; Good Shepherd Choir 1982-; *office:* North Park Elem Schl PO Box 722 Hyde Park NY 12538

NAMI, THOMAS ANTHONY, Music Teacher; *b:* Syracuse, NY; *ed:* Onondaga Comm Coll (AAS) Music 1985; St Univ of NY at Potsdam (BM) Music Ed 1988; Coll of Saint Rose (MS) Music Ed 1995; *cr:* Cath Diocese of Syracuse PreK-6th Grd Vocal Music Tchr 1988-89; Mohawk Cntrl Schl 1st-6th Grd Vocal Music Tchr 1989-92; Mount Markham CSD K-3rd & 9th-12th Grd Vocal Music Tchr 1992-95; Fulton City Schl Dist 9th-12th Grd Vocal Music Tchr 1995-; *ai:* Sr High Musical; Select Choir; MENC 1985-, Mem; NYSUT 1989-, Mem; *home:* 8426 Theodolite Dr Apt 809 Baldwinsville NY 13027*

NAN, KELLY SAMUEL, 10th Grade US History Teacher; *b:* Norwalk, OH; *m:* Pamela Lynn Luther; *c:* Samantha, Nicholas, Ethan, Evan; *ed:* Masters of Ed Degree in Scndry Schl Cnslng; 52 Hrs of Post Grad Stud at Slippery Rock Univ; *cr:* Heart of the Earth Survival Schl tchr 1984-85; Shippensburg HS Tchr & Coach 1985-86; Grove City HS Tchr & Coach 1986-; *ai:* Retired Head Coach Var Ftbl; NEA, PSEA, GCEA; Bd Deacons E Main Presbyterian Church 1992-94, Deacon; WFMJ-TV "Class Act Awd", Article Pub in PA Coaching Journal 1987; *office:* Grove City Area Sr HS 511 Highland Ave Grove City PA 16127

NAPIER, ANDREW R., Technology Ed Tchr & Dept Chm; *b:* Buffalo, NY; *m:* Lynn Reiber; *c:* Andy Jr., Jodi; *ed:* Buffalo St Coll (BS) Indstrl Arts 1967, (MS) Indstrl Arts 1970; Univ of Buffalo Cmptrs 15 Hrs 1985; *cr:* Cheektowaga Cntrl Schl Tchr, Dept Chair, Coach 1967-; *ai:* Ftbl, Bsbl Coach; Schl Improvement Team Chm; NYSTEA 1980-; WNYTEA 1970-; Jr Jaycees 1967-; Yth for Christ 1984-; Epsilon Pi Tau; *office:* Cheektowaga Cntrl HS 3600 Union Rd Cheektowaga NY 14225

NAPIER, KEVIN JOHN, Social Studies Teacher; *b:* Atlantic City, NJ; *m:* Felicia Pipitone; *c:* Kelly M.; *ed:* Glassboro St Coll (BA) Elem Ed, His 1988; *cr:* Sacred Heart Elem Schl 5, 6th Grd Tchr 1988-90; Sacred Heart HS Soc Stud Tchr, Dept Chprsn 1990-; *ai:* Stage, Set Construction, Production Mgr Schl Plays; Boys, Girls Track, Field Coach; NCEA 1991-; *office:* Sacred Heart HS 22 N East Ave Vineland NJ 08360

NAPLES, A. RICHARD, Math & Science Teacher; *b:* New Haven, CT; *m:* Karen P.; *c:* Jeffrey, Lisa; *ed:* Southern CT St Univ (BA) Ed 1967, (MS) Media Tech 1971; 6th Yr Admin 1974; *ai:* Lib Power Grant Initiative; Schl Planning, Mngmt Team; Carnegie Fnd Schl Grant; AFT 1967-; Wilsonian Mens Club 1985-; Knights of Columbus 1975-; *office:* Betsy Ross Arts Magnet Schl 185 Barnes Ave New Haven CT 06513

NAPOLITAN, RICHARD A., Choral Director; *b:* Johnstown, PA; *w:* Jeanne C. Cassidy (dec); *c:* Richard Charles, Alice Jean; *ed:* IN Univ of PA (BS) Music 1956; Duquesne Univ Masters Music 1962; 70 Post Grad Credits; *cr:* Garfield Jr HS Theory, Harmony Choral Dir 1956-73; Gr Johnstown Voc Tech Theory, Harmony Choral Dir 1973-87; PA Governors Schl of Arts Theory, Harmony Choral Dir 1988-92; Bishop Mc Cort HS Theory, Harmony Choral Dir 1990-; *ai:* Golf Coach; PMEA; PASR; IUP Alumni Assn; AFM Local #41; Played Prof 52 Yrs; Former Mem River City Brass Band, Johnstown Jazz Wkshp, Johnstown Symphony Orch; Rockefeller Grant Oberlin Conservatory Tchrs Perf Inst; *office:* Bishop Mc Cort HS 25 Osborne St Johnstown PA 15905*

NAPOLITANO, DANIEL C., Dept Regligious Stud Faculty; *b:* Biloxi, MS; *m:* Karen B.; *c:* Elena; *ed:* St Pius X Coll (BA) Philosophy 1982; Cath Univ (MA) Philosophy of Ed 1989; *cr:* Holy Cross Acad Fac 1984-88; Immaculata Coll HS Fac, Dept Chm 1989-90; Georgetown Prep Fac 1990-; *ai:* Oasis Music Club; Pub The Performing Songwriter; SAW Awds; *office:* Georgetown Prep Schl 10900 Rockville Pike Rockville MD 20852

NAPOLITANO, RALPH ANTHONY, High School Principal; *b:* Manhattan, NY; *m:* Joann Frangella; *c:* Marc, Scott, Christa; *ed:* St John's Univ (BA) His 1972, (MS) His 1977, (PHD) Ed 1985; PD Admin & Supervision SAS, SDA; *cr:* St Theresa Schl Tchr 1973-77; Frank Whalen MS Tchr 1977-79; Coll of Mt St Vincent Dir of Ed Dept 1979-87; St Catharine Acad Prin 1987-; Pleasantville HS; *ai:* ASCD, NASSP, NCEA 1987-; Research, Project Grants 15 Yrs; Articles Written; Recognized Outstanding Prin; Excl Tchng Awd; *office:* Pleasantville HS Romer Ave Pleasantville NY 10570

NAPPER, SHIRLEY M., Second Grade Teacher; *b:* Atlantic City, NJ; *ed:* Howard Univ (BA) Elem Ed 1967; City Coll (MS) Remedial Rdng 1972; *cr:* PS 186 First Grd Tchr 1967-78; PS 153 Spec Needs Assessment Prgm Tchr 1978-79, Second Grd Tchr 1979-; *ai:* Multicultural Comm; Stu Dance Club; UFT, AFT 1967-.

NAPPI, MARIE TERESA VALENT, 7th & 8th Grd Math Tchr; *b:* Brooklyn, NY; *m:* John G.; *c:* John C., Joseph V.; *ed:* Hunter Coll (BA) Math & Ed 1974; Adelphi Univ (MA) Ed 1992; *cr:* St Raphaels Jr HS Math Tchr 1986-92; St Eliz Ann Seton Jr HS Math Tchr 1992-; Nassak Comm Coll Math Adj Prof 1992-; *ai:* Math & AV Coord; Yrbk Adv; Natl Jr Hnr Soc Comm; NCEA 1986-; NCTM 1992-; Nassan Cty Math Tchrs Assn 1992-, Math Tchr of Yr 1992; N Bell & N Merrick PTA; *office:* St Elizabeth A Seton Rgnl HS 600 Newbridge Rd East Meadow NY 11554

NAPPO, ANTHONY JOSEPH, Social Studies Instructor; *b:* Suffern, NY; *m:* Janice G.; *c:* A. J., Nicholas; *ed:* John Carroll Univ (MA) Soviet Amer Relations 1976, (BA) US His & Elem Ed; Univ of CO Inst for Comparative Ideologies 1977; *cr:* John Carroll Univ Grad Asst 1974-76; Gilmour Acad Instr 1976-78; Middletown HS Instr 1978-; *ai:* AFT, NYSUT 1978-; Middletown Tchrs Assn 1978-; *office:* Middletown HS Gardner Ave Ext Middletown NY 10940*

NAPPO, JANICE TARALLO, HS English Teacher & Director; *b:* Richmond Hill, NY; *m:* Anthony Joseph II; *c:* Anthony J. III, Nicholas J.; *ed:* Keuka Coll NY (BA) Eng & Scndry Ed 1971; SUNY at New Paltz 36 Credit Hrs Towars Masters & Tchng Cert; Cornell Univ Schl of Labor Relations 18 Credit Hrs; *cr:* Middltown MS 7th-8th Grd Eng Tchr 1971-93; Middletown HS 9th-10th Grd Eng Tchr 1993-; Middletown Tchr Staff Dev Ctr Dir 1995-; *ai:* Policy Bd & Exec Comm of Ctr; Magnet Schl Comm; Schl-To-work Partnership; AFT & NYSUT 1971-, Del; Middletown Tchrs Assn 1971-, Pres 1981-87; NYS Cncl of Eng Tchrs; NYS Rdng Assn; ABC Rdng Cncl 1991-; Lower Hudson Tchr Ctr Network 1995-, Sec; Womens Univ Club 1995-; PTO; *office:* Middletown HS Gardner Ave Ext Middletown NY 10940

NAPPO, VINCENT, Physical Ed & Health Teacher; *b:* Englewood, NJ; *m:* Barbara Ann Villiard; *c:* Christine Mc Carthy, James Vincent; *ed:* Murray St Univ (BS) Hlth, PE, Sociology 1966; *cr:* Croydon Hall Acad Sociology, PE, Hlth Tchr, Coached Ftbl, Bsktbl, & Bsbl 1967-69; Avon Elem Schl Hlth, PE Tchr, Coached Soccer, Bsktbl, Track, Sftbl 1969-; *ai:* Coached St

Rose Var Girls Bsktbl 5 Yrs; Div Champs Twice; St Semi-finalists Twice; Coached JV Girls Bsktbl St Rose HS 5 Yrs; Avon Ed Assn 1969-, Pres; NJEA, NEA 1969-; Vol Fireman 7 Yrs Lieutenant; First Aid Squad 7 Yrs; *office:* Avon Elem Schl 505 Lincoln Ave Avon By The Sea NJ 07717*

NARAIN, VANDANA DOLLY, Science Teacher; *b:* Meerut, India; *ed:* N Wadia Coll at Pune (BS) Chem, Botany, Zoology 1986; Rajasthan Univ at Jaipur (MS) Radiation Bio 1988; Long Island Univ (MSE) Bio, Scndry Ed 1991; St John's Univ Prof Diploma Schl Admin, Supervision 1994, Pursuing EDD Schl Admin, Supervision; *cr:* St Angela's Elem Schl Tchr 1988-89; James Reynolds Jr HS Tchr 1990-91; Richmond Hill HS Tchr, Chem Lab Coord 1991-; *ai:* Fashion, Talent Show Coord; Sr Class, Sci Rsrch Club, Key Club Adv; Bio Regents Tutor; Sunshine Comm; Staff Dev; Natl Inst of Hlth Grant; Articles Pub; Miss Wadia Coll 1984-86; Coll Pres; HEOP Cnslr; Univ Ladies Rep; *office:* Richmond Hill HS 89-30 114th St Richmond Hill NY 11418*

NARDINE, ANGELA WAGNER, Lang Arts & Soc Studies Tchr; *b:* New York City, NY; *m:* Ronal Everett; *c:* Julia; *ed:* CCSC (BS) Elem Ed 1974; CCSU (MS) Elem Ed 1978, (MS) Schl Cnslng 1994; *cr:* Northwest Elem Schl 5th Grd Tchr 1974-75; Martin Kellogg MS 6th Grd Soc Stud Tchr 1975-80; E Green Elem Schl 3rd Grd Tchr 1982; John Wallace MS 7th Grd Lang Arts, Soc Stud Tchr 1982-; *ai:* Schl Bookstore 1984-94; Stu Assistance Team 1993-95; Staff Dev Comm 1985-; Activity Period Comm 1995-; NTA Bldg Rep, Exec Bd 1994-; Newington Tchr Assn, CT Ed Assn, NEA 1974-; Alpha Delta Kappa 1993-95; *office:* John Wallace MS 71 Halleran Dr Newington CT 06111

NARDINO, ANTHONY GARY, Latin & Bus Education Teacher; *b:* Passaic, NJ; *m:* Esther Marie DeBlasio; *c:* Joseph D., Anthony R.; *ed:* Seton Univ (BA) Classical Lang 1969; Notre Dame Univ (MSA) Admin 1984; Istituto Dante Alighieri Rome Italian Cert; Seton Hall Schl of Theology 30 Credit Hrs Theology; *cr:* Archdiocese of Newark Parochial Vicar 1973-80; Msgr Domoran HS Latin Tchr, Frgn Lang Dept Chm 1985-92; Wall HS Latin, Bus Ed Tchr 1992-; *ai:* Tennis Coach; Latin Club Comoderator; NJ Classical Assn 1985-; NJEA 1992-, Comm Rep; St Joseph Church 1985-; *office:* Wall HS 18th Ave & New Bedford Rd Wall NJ 07719*

NARDONE, CLAUDINE PISTONE, First Grd Tchr & Curr Mentor; *b:* Bronx, NY; *m:* Jerry; *c:* Claudine, Jennifer, Lauren, Jerry; *ed:* St John's Univ (AA) Elem Ed 1970, (BS) Elem Ed 1972; Coll of New Rochelle (MS) Remedial Rdng 1974; Columbia Univ Pelham Inservice Courses, Writing Process & Rdng Process; *cr:* Prospect Hill Schl Stu Tchr 1971-, Prospect Hill Schl First Grd Tchr 1972-81; Colonial Schl First Grd Tchr 1981-; *ai:* Dev Guidelines Groundbreaking Comm; Helped to Establish Prof Dev & Became Prof Dev Comm Mem; Tchr Chm of Curr Cncl; Curr Mentor; Assoc Rep for Tchrs Assn; UFT, NYSUT 1972-, Tchr; Pelham Tchrs Assn 1972- VP & Bldg Rep; Lincoln Ctr 1968-, Stu Awd; Rdng Comm 1974-; Fitness Fun Instr, Schl Enrichment; Tchrs Advy Cncl 1988-; Pub Ctr Grant; Coordinated Major Schl Events; Established Schl Bd Pub Ctr; *office:* Colonial Elem Schl 315 Highbrook Ave Pelham NY 10803*

NARDONE, SAMUEL ALEX, Spanish Teacher; *b:* Ellwood City, PA; *m:* Cynthia Hornacek; *c:* Dominic, Leslie; *ed:* Slippery Rock Univ (BS) Ed, Elem, Scndry Span 1988; Addl Credit Hrs; *cr:* Freedom HS Span Tchr 1989-95; Blackhawk HS Span Tchr 1995-; *ai:* Ftbl Head Coach Freedom HS; PA St Ftbl Coaches Assn 1993-; NEA, PA St Ed Assn 1989-; *home:* 132 Burns Ave Beaver Falls PA 15010

NARGES, BARBARA ZANKL, German Teacher; *b:* Toledo, OH; *m:* Michael E.; *c:* Eric M., Christina M.; *ed:* Univ of Toledo (BED) Ger, Span 1968; *cr:* Portsmouth HS Span Tchr 1968-69; Newport HS Span Tchr 1969-70; Cntrl Cath HS Span Tchr 1970-73, Ger Tchr 1991-; *ai:* Ger Club Moderator; AATG, NCEA 1991-; *office:* Cntrl Cath HS 2550 Cherry St Toledo OH 43608

NARINE, KESHAW, Science Teacher; *b:* Rosignol, Guyana; *m:* Amy E.; *c:* Shobha, Ravina; *ed:* Mc Gill Univ (BS) Geology 1971; London Univ (MS) Mineral Exploration 1978; 18 Ed Credits in His of Amer Ed, Psych of Ed, Advance Tchng Practice, Span, Tech for Tchrs; *cr:* Geologist 1971-74; Mine Supt 1974-77; Planning Engr 1978-86; Sci Tchr 1986-; *ai:* Sci Club Moderator; Black Active Stdnts Assn Moderator; Soc of Mining Engrs 1980-; *office:* Bishop Kearny HS 2202 60th St Brooklyn NY 11204

NASCA, LINDA ANN, Social Studies Teacher; *b:* Buffalo, NY; *ed:* Villa Maria Coll of Buffalo (AA) Elem Ed 1970; SUCB (BS) Elem Ed Extension 1972, (MS) Elem Ed 1976; 9 Hrs in Gifted Ed, Psych & Multicultural Ed; *cr:* Galax Elem 5th Grd Tchr 1974-76; Diocesan Educl Campus 6th-8th Grd Soc Stud Tchr 1978-88; Catholic Cntrl Schl 6th-8th Grd Soc Stud Tchr 1988-; *ai:* Teach Needlepoint; NCSS 1988-; Soc Stud Cncl of Wstrn NY Cath Schls Sec, Treas; *home:* 50 North Dr Amherst NY 14226

NASH, DELORES ANNE, Retired Social Studies Teacher; *b:* Morgantown, WV; *w:* Hubert (dec); *c:* Verna Swaby; *ed:* Mercy Coll (BS) Soc Stud 1972; Montclair St Univ (MA) Sociology 1990; 30 Grad Hrs Ed; *cr:* Nyack Pub Schls Soc Stud Tchr 1972-95; *ai:* African Amer Club Adv; AFT 1977-; NEA 1976-, Local Pres; Alpha Kappa Alpha 1994-, Financial Sec; Black Pol Caucus 1977-, Chprsn, Outstdng Svc 1985; NAACP LIfe Mem; RO Comm Svc Org 1978-, Vice Chprsn; Martin Luther King Pub Svc Awd 1986; Rockland Bapt Church Mother of Yr 1992-93; Rockland Cty Distngd Svc Awd 1985; *home:* 4 Keim Dr Pomona NY 10970*

NASH, FERN, Music Teacher; *b:* Brooklyn, NY; *c:* Meredith Leigh; *ed:* St Johns Univ (MS) Elem Ed, Gifted 1991; *cr:* PS 220 Q Cluster LIb, Sci, Music Tchr 1987-88; PS 139 Q Cluster Lib, Sci, Music Tchr 1987-88, 6th Grd Tchr 1988-91, Music Tchr 1991-; *ai:* Dir Glee Club; Tchr Hunter HS Prep Course The Amer Musical Theater; MENC 1992-; Glee Club Performed at Madison Sq Garden for NY Knicks; John Bunzel Awd 1988 by ATSS, UFT, Soc Stud Supvrs Assn of NY City; *home:* 1558 212th St Bayside NY 11360

NASH, MILDRED J., BEAM Teacher; *b:* Sharon, PA; *m:* James A.; *c:* Noreen, Rebecca; *ed:* Grove City Coll (BA) Eng 1960; Harvard Univ (EdM) Poetry 1977; *cr:* Burlington Schls BHS Eng Tchr 1979-83; Marshall Simonds MS Tchr of Gifted, Talented 1984-; *ai:* Odyssey of Mind Teams Coach 1987-; NEA 1979-; Poetry Soc of Amer 1977-, Emily Dickinson Awd; New England Poetry Club 1977-, Sec, Power Dalton Awd; Burlington Town Meeting 1972-, Rep; Numerous Poems in Magazines, Anthologies Pub; Book: Beyond Their Dreams; World Order of Narrative Poets Numerous Prizes Winner; Terrific Tchrs Making a Difference Awd 1992; *office:* Marshall Simonds MS Winn St Burlington MA 01803

NASS, JOHN PHILLIP,JR., Asst Prof of Anthropology; *b:* Saginaw, MI; *m:* Jean L. Montgomery; *c:* Erin E.; *ed:* MI St Univ (BA) Anthropology 1974; Western MI Univ (MA) Anthropology 1980; OH St Univ (PHD) Anthropology 1987; *cr:* Archaeological Svcs Consultants Inc Sr Archaeologist 1987-90; California Univ of PA Asst Prof of Anthropology 1990-; *ai:* Women Stud, Univ Rsrch, Schlsp Comms; Soc for Historical Archaeology 1975-; Soc for Amer Archaeology 1976-; Sigma Xi 1985-; Lambda Alpha, Adv; Trinity United Presbyn Church, Local Missions Comm Chprsn; Numerous Book, Monographs Chptrs, Journal Articles Pub; *office:* California Univ Of PA 250 University Ave California PA 15419

NASSAR, ELIZABETH FOX, Resource & Consultant Teacher; *b:* Binghamton, NY; *m:* Robert Ward; *c:* Matthew Robert, Kristin Elizabeth, Jamie Fox; *ed:* Syracuse Univ (BS) Spec Ed 1978; SUNY at Binghamton (MS) Spec Ed, Rdng 1982; *cr:* Chenango Forks MS Resource Room Tchr 1978-79, 1983-87; Chenango Forks HS Resource Room Tchr 1979-82; Norwich HS Resource Room Tchr 1987-; *ai:* Pi Lambda Theta 1978-; BOD Gathering Place 1990-, Past Pres; Girl Scouts 1992-, Troop Ldr; *office:* Norwich HS Midland Dr Norwich NY 13815

NASSAU, CAROL DEAN, French Teacher; *b:* Omaha, NE; *ed:* Univ NE at Kearney (BA) Translation & Interpretation 1976; Binghamton Univ (MA) Comparative Lit 1983; (EdD) 40 Hrs, (MAT) 32 Hrs; *cr:* Unatego Cntrl Schl Fr & Span Tchr 1987-88; Oneonta City Schl Fr Tchr 1988-; *ai:* Ski, Drama Clubs Adv; NEA 1988-; NYSAFLT 1987-; AERA 1994-; Binghamton Univ Couper Fellowship 1994-95; Article Pub Amer Schl Bd Journal 1995, Learning 1996; NYSAFLT St Conf Presenter 1995; *office:* Oneonta MS East St Oneonta NY 13820*

NASSER, BERNARD SAMUEL, Eng & Creative Writing Tchr; *b:* Wilkes-Barre, PA; *m:* Ellen Shepherd; *c:* Bernard S. Jr., Daniel J.; *ed:* King's Coll (BA) Eng, Ed 1972; Southern CT St Univ (MS) Ed 1981; 6th Yr Admin, Supervision 1983; *cr:* R. E. Fitch Sr HS Eng, Pub Speaking Tchr 1972-; Mitchell Coll Assoc Prof 1988-92; *ai:* Head Boy's Soccer Coach; GATE Prgm Coord; Acad Decathlon Team Coach; Schl Improvement Team Facilitator; Attendance, Assessment Comms Chm; CHSCA; CIAC; Groton Ed Assn, Negotiations Team, St Del; NEA; CEA; CT Interscholastic Wrestling Ofcls 1974-, Pres 1991-93; NFICA; NFIOA; Groton Lodge of Elks 1985-, Schlsp, Italian Night Comms Chm; St of CT Best Mentor Prgm; *office:* Robert E Fitch Sr HS 101 Groton Long Point Rd Groton CT 06340*

NASTASI-COTEY, RITA, Spanish Teacher; *b:* Camden, NJ; *m:* Gus Jr.; *ed:* Rutgers Univ (BA) Span-High Hnrs 1973; Exch Stu La Coruna Spain 1969 6 Credits; Univ of Madrid Spain 1972 8 Credits; Glassboro St Coll 1975 2 Post Grad Credits; *cr:* Friedman Schl Remedial Rdng Tutor 1969-72; Overbrook Jr HS Span Tchr 1973-82; Overbrook Regnl Sr HS Span Tchr 1982-; *ai:* Stu Tchrs Cooperating Tchr; Bedside Tutor; Span Club Adv; NJEA 1973-; Cherry Brook Farms Civic Assn 1983-; Span IV Hnrs Tchr; Magazine Article 1981; Discipline Strategies Course 1986; Effective Trng Wkshp 1987; Natl Crisis Prevention Course 1 Equivalency Credit 1988; Inservice Wkshp for the Blind 1991; Power of Comm Skills for Women Ethnic Day Awd 1985; Tchng Methodologies Wkshps; Music Booster Awd 1990; NJEA Discipline Conf South 1991; Textbook Selection Comm 1983; *office:* Overbrook Regnl Sr HS 1200 Turnersville Rd Pine Hill NJ 08021

NASTO, DOLORES POLYNIAK, Mathematics Teacher; *b:* Passaic, NJ; *m:* Charles; *c:* Danielle; *ed:* Jersey City St Coll (BA) Math 1971; Master Equivalent 30 Credits; *cr:* Roxbury HS Math Tchr 1971-; *ai:* NHS Adv; NJEA, NEA, MCCEA 1971-; *office:* Roxbury HS 1 Bryant Dr Succasunna NJ 07876

NATALE, BARBARA JONES, 5th-8th Grade Media Specialist; *b:* Rio Piedros, PR; *m:* Frank L.; *c:* Carl, Beth; *ed:* OH Northern U (BA) Eng 1963-; Kent St U (MA) Lib Sci 1992; *cr:* Lime Sr High Eng Tchr; Leetonia HS Eng Tchr; Crestview MS Media Specialist; *ai:* NEA; OEA; Crestview Ed Assn, Pres; ALA; *office:* Crestview MS 3062 Fairfield School Rd Columbiana OH 44408

NATALE, LORRAINE MARCIA, Guidance Counselor; *b:* Providence, RI; *m:* Gregory; *c:* Gregory; *ed:* RI Coll (AB) Scndry Educ, Fr 1970; Providence Coll (MED) Cnslng K-12 1973; HS Prin Cert Admin 1985; MS Prin Cert 1994; Supt Cert 1996; *cr:* Johnston HS Fr Tchr 1970-76; Ferri MS Cnslr 1977-81; Johnston HS Cnslr 1981-91, Guidance Dir 1991-94; Ferri MS Guidance Tchr 1994-; *ai:* Train Guidance Interns Providence Coll; AFT 1970-, Sec, Treas, Chprsn, JF7 Schlsp Comm; Rotary Club, Amy Fordad Elderly Ctr 1994-; Slected Serve Evaluation RI Coll Guidance, Cnslng DED7 1988, 1990; Steering Comm Accreddation 1991.*

NATALI, MAUREEN GILLIGAN (BIOLK), English Teacher & Drama Dir; *b:* New York City, NY; *m:* Gary L.; *c:* Kristofer, Elizabeth; *ed:* SUNY at Brockport (BS) Eng, Theatre 1974, (MA) Speech Ed 1979; Syracuse Univ (PHD) Mass Comm 1996; *cr:* The Sawyer Schl Prgm Coord 1977-82; Bryant, Stratton Bus Inst JTPA Coord 1982-87; East Syracuse Minoa Eng Tchr 1987-; Syracuse Univ Adjunct Prof 1992-; *ai:* Drama Club Dir; CII Comm; Master's Schlsp; Who's Who 1992, 1994; ESM Excel in Tchng Awd 1989 & 1994; *office:* East Syracuse-Minoa Schls Fremont Rd East Syracuse NY 13057

NATALIE, JOAN MARILYN, Art Teacher; *b:* Jamaica, NY; *ed:* Hofstra Univ (BS) Art Ed 1962; Univ of HI (MA) Eastern Art His 1967; 60 Addl Hrs Fashion Inst of Tech, C. W. Post, Adelphi Univ, Nassau Comm Coll, Art Inst at San Miquel D'Allende; *cr:* Floral Park Meml HS Art Tchr 1962-; H. Frank Carey HS Art Tchr 1962-; *ai:* Co-Adv Art Palettes; Adv Animation Club; Art Dept Rep; Sunshine, Schlsp Comms; NYSATA 1962-, Comm Chm, HS Stdnts Art Shows; NEA 1972-; AAUW 1980-; Hofstra Alumni Assn Inc 1962-, Chm, Pres, VP, George M. Estabrook Awd; East West Ctr Alumni Assn 1967-, NY Rep; East West Ctr Schlsp Univ of HI 1965-67; Summer Fulbright Italy 1969; Summer Stud Grants India 1970, Egypt 1972, Poland 1974; 3 Indonesian Culture Filmstrips Pub 1975; Lincoln Ctr Prgm for Tchrs 1980-.

NATALIZIA, ELENA MARIA, Criminal Justice Instructor; *b:* Providence, RI; *ed:* Salve Regina Univ (BA) His, Pol Sci 1971; Northeastern Univ (MS) Criminal Justice 1979; *cr:* R. I. Justice Alliance Dir 1986-91; Amer Friends Svc Comm Criminal Justice Coord 1991-93; Mt Wachusett Comm Coll Criminal Justice Instr 1993-; *ai:* Criminal Justice Dept Chprsn; Long Range Planning Comm Co-Chprsn; Criminal Justice Club Co-Adv; Assn of Criminal Justice Scis, Citizens for Juvenile Justice, Amer Correctional Assn 1994-; NEA 1993-; ACLU RI Bd of Dirs 1988-; *office:* Mount Wachusett Comm Coll 444 Green St Gardner MA 01440

NATHAN, ROBERT, Mrktg Tchr & DECA Advisor; *b:* Miami Beach, FL; *m:* Ramona Savocchia; *ed:* IN Univ of PA (BS) Distributive Ed 1973; Univ of Pittsburgh (MA) Voc Ed 1976; *cr:* Riverside HS Bus Tchr 1973-; *ai:* Golf Coach; Bsktbl Announcer; Frosh Class & SADD Spon; PSEA, NEA 1973-; DECA 1973-, Pres, Bd of Trustees; Jaycees Young Educator of Yr; Dept of Ed Outstanding Leadership Awd; Jerry Lewis Citation of Merit; Sears & Roebuck PA DECA Tchr of Yr; Dist II DECA Tchr Yr 5 Consecutive Yrs; Riv Riverside HS Tchr of Yr 1995; *office:* Riverside HS Country Club Dr RR 2 Box 4010 Ellwood City PA 16117*

NATILI, ARMAND LOUIS,JR., Asst Professor of Psych; *b:* Butler, PA; *m:* Rosanne Amendolea; *c:* D'Ante; *ed:* Bethany Coll (BA) Psyc 1980; Slippery Rock Univ (BA) Elem Ed 1981; Univ of Pittsburgh (MA) Coun Ed 1986; Duquesne Univ (MA) Lbrl Stud 1994; Inst Trng & Cert Ctr for Journal Therapy; *cr:* St Josephs Schl Elem Ed Tchr 1982-85; Luth Yth, Family Child Care Specialist 1985-86; Seneca Vly Schl Dist Elem Ed Tchr 1987-89; Butler Co Comm Coll Asst Prof of Psyc 1989-; *ai:* Shorin-Ryu Karate Club; PSEA, BCEA 1993-; Outstdng Fac Mem 1993, 1995; Rev. Joseph P. Slater Fac Enhancement Awd 1995-96; *office:* Butler County Comm Coll Box 1203 Butler PA 16003

NATOLI, ANNE LAURAINE WALKA, Computer Creative Writing Tchr; *b:* Jersey City, NJ; *m:* Joseph Edward; *ed:* Montclair St Univ (BA) Eng 1982; NY Univ (MA) Cinema Stud 1984; Montclair St Univ (MA) Eng 1990; Southern IL Univ ABD Eng, Theatre, His, Screenwriting; Children's Lit Inst Children's Writing; *cr:* Belleville HS Math Tchr 1984-87; Montclair St Univ Adj Eng Dept 1987-; Southern IL Univ Grad Tchng Asst 1990-92; Immaculate Conception HS Drama, Math, Writing Tchr 1994-; *ai:* Drama Coord; Newspaper Adv; Cmptr Club Moderator; PCA 1994-; NCTE 1980-; Amer Film Inst 1981-; MLA 1989-; Soc for Cinema Stud 1992-; Soc for Animation Stud 1991-; Rosary Soc 1994-; CAST 1993-, Actor; ISIA 1980-, Ice Skater; USFSA 1981-, Ice Skater; 5th Sparrowgrass Poetry Contest 1994; Outstdng Grad Asst Tchng Awd 1992; Who's Who in Amer Ed 1989-; *office:* Immaculate Conception Cottage Pl Montclair NJ 07042*

NATOLI, JOSEPH R., School Guidance Counselor; *b:* Akron, O Susan L.; *c:* Sara Webb; *ed:* Univ of Akron (BS) Eng, His, Sec Ed (MS) Guid & Cnslng 1972; 80 Addl Hrs in Educ AdminGrad Leve Crs Undergraduate; *cr:* Hyre MS Eng Tchr 1969-72, Guid Cnslr 197 Akron Ed Assn 1969-; *office:* Hyre MS 2443 Wedgewood Dr Akro 44312

NATOLI, TAMARA CHRISTINE, Spanish Teacher; *b:* Syosset, N Erik Clifford Mattsen; *ed:* SUNY at New Paltz (BA) Span, Scndry Ed (MS) Span, Scndry Ed 1995; Attnd Univ of Sevilla Spain 198 Kingston Jr HS Span Tchr 1990-91; Pine Bush HS Span Tchr 199 Yrbk Adv; Bldg Ldrshp Team; Multi-Cultural, Pub Relations Co NYSAFLT, NYSUT, ALOUD 1990-; Paul Douglas Tchrs Schlsp; Pine Bush HS Rt 302 Pine Bush NY 12566

NATOLI, THOMAS AURELIUS,JR., Chemistry Teacher; *b:* New NY; *m:* Carol I. Kent; *c:* Thomas III, Tamara; *ed:* Queens Coll (BS 1965, (MS) Sci Ed 1968; 26 Credits Towards Administrative Ce Shimer Jr HS Sci 1965-72; M. Clifford Miller Jr HS Phys Sci 19 Kingston HS Chem 1988-; *ai:* Hockey Club Adv; Honor Soc Sel Comm; NY St United Tchr 1965-; Sci Tchr Assn of NY 1984-; Mid H Renewoble Energy Assn 1980, Pres; Tchr Adv Panel Cen Hudson Elec Corp 1984-; 1984 Outstanding Phys Sci Tchr Awd; SE Section St Sci Tchrs Assn; *office:* Kingston HS 403 Broadway Kingsto 12401*

NATONICK, MARLYS-JEAN SCHILLER, Third Grd Teacher & Prin; *b:* Bridgeport, CT; *m:* George Walter; *c:* Mathew, Jonathar Valparaiso Univ (BS) Elem Ed 1967; Lewis & Clark Coll (MAT) Lang Art 1971; San Jose City Coll 3 Credits Span; Univ of MD at Col 3 Grad Credits Rdng; *cr:* W. Powellhurst Elem Schl Second Grd 1968-77; Immanuel Luth Schl Fourth Grd Tchr 1979-80; Calavary Schl Third Grd Tchr 1981-, Asst Prin 1994-; *ai:* Schl Newslette Parent-Tchr Cncl Fac Staff Liaison; Ways N Means Comm; Sign Consultant; Vol Sign Lang Interpreter; Campaign Comm Sc Candidate 1992-; Wkshp Presenter at Tchr Conf, Sign Lang in Class Creating a Welcoming Classroom Environment; *office:* Calvary Lut Schl 9545 Georgia Ave Silver Spring MD 20910

NAUGHTON, INGRID EMELDA, English Teacher; *b:* Christians C, VI; *ed:* City Univ of NY (AAS) Bus Admin 1985, (BA) Eng Lit 24 Credit Hrs Cath Univ of Amer; 3 Credit Hrs Univ of FL; *cr:* CAP Citicorp Exec Sec 1989-90; Presbyn Church Admin Asst 199 Macfarland Jr HS Eng Tchr 1992-93; Abraham Lincoln Multicultura Eng Tchr 1993-; *ai:* Local Schl Restructuring Team Mem 1992-, Sec Pom Dancers, Majorettes, Flag Girls Spon, Adv; Hosp Comm Mem; 1993-; Amer Soc Exec & Prof Women 1987-; Southeastern Conso Minorities in Engrng 1994-, Asst Coord; Zeta Phi Beta 1987-, Pre Acad Scholar; Natl Cncl Negro Women 1989-; Southeastern Conso Min in Eng Stipend Undergraduate of Yr Schlsp 1989; *home:* 2100 B Dr Apt 414 Forestville MD 20747*

NAUGHTON, JOHN PATRICK, Lang Arts, Soc Stud, Rdng Tc Wilmington, DE; *ed:* Univ of DE (BA Dramatic Arts & Speech Ed Scndry Eng Cert 1975; Addl 30 Hrs Beyond BA in Eng, Theater 1982; H B Studio Acting, Trng 1982-87, 1991; *cr:* Comm Jrnlsm Ad 1976-78; Henry C. Conrad HS 10-12 Grd Theater, Speech, Eng 1974-78; Wilmington HS 10-12 Grd Eng, Jrnlsm Tchr 1978-79; Holy Schl 6 Grd Tchr 1982-83; St Josephs Schl of Yorkville 7-8 Grd Lang Tchr 1986-88; Our Lady of Good Cnsl 7-8 Grd Lang Arts, Rdng, Soc Tchr 1989-; *ai:* Past Cross Cntry, Drama, Newspaper Coach; CFT, Rep.*

NAUGHTON, WILLIAM B., English Teacher; *b:* Boston, MA; *m:* N *c:* Nathaniel, Joshua, Matthew; *ed:* Univ of MA at Boston (BA) Eng Boston Univ (MED) Rdng 1975; *cr:* Boston Pub Schls Rdng Tchr, Head 1970-82; Arlington Cath HS Eng Tchr 1982-; *ai:* IRA 1970-; N 1971-; Boston Minuteman Cncl BSA 1979-, Cncl Commissi Associated Landscape Contractors of MA; MA Nursery & Land Assn; *office:* Arlington Catholic HS 16 Medford St Arlington MA 02

NAUGLE, GLORIA ANDOLINA, 4th Grd & Instrl Support Tc Pittsburgh, PA; *m:* Larry; *c:* Greg, Courtney; *ed:* California Univ (BS) Elem Ed 1970, (MS) Elem Ed 1973; 6 Addl Hrs; 3 Hrs Un Pittsburgh at Johnstown; *cr:* Montour Schl Dist Elem Ed 1970-73; Star Schl Dist Elem Ed 1973-; *ai:* PSEA, NEA 1970-; AYSO Amer Soccer Org 1990-, Bd Sec; *home:* 615 Mississippi St Boswell PA 15

NAUGLE, JUDITH (PULLIAM), Mathematics Teacher; *b:* Washin DC; *m:* Edwin V.; *c:* Patrick; *ed:* Frostburg St Univ (BS) Math Western MD Coll (MS) Curr, Instruction 1991; *cr:* Cntrl HS Math, Sci 1965-67; DuVal HS Math Tchr 1967-70; Prince George's Cty Home, Tchr 1976-86; Forestville HS Math Tchr 1986-; *ai:* Math Tutoring; Preparation; Fac Advy Cncl; Curr, Testing Comms; PGCEA, NEA, M 1965-; NCTM 1971-; Fish, Wildlife Svc Vol Bird Bander 1976-86; *o* Forestville HS 7001 Beltz Dr Forestville MD 20747

NAUMAN, DEBORAH FREDRICK, Eighth Grade Reading Teache East Stroudsburg, PA; *m:* Steven; *c:* Nicole Graffin, Jill; *ed:* Stroudsburg Univ (BS) Elem Ed 1982, (ME) Rdng 1989; Attnd Kutz Univ Fr; *cr:* East Stroudsburg Area Schl Dist 8th Grd Rdng Tchr 1985 Bulletin Bds Supvr; NEA 1985-; *office:* East Stroudsburg Area Schl Courtland St East Stroudsburg PA 18301*

NAUMANN, PAUL SCHILLER,SJ, English Instructor; *b:* Syracuse, *ed:* Boston Coll (BA) Eng 1956, (MA) Philosophy 1957, (BA) Theo 1964; Attnd Intl, Shakespeare, Eng Lit Summer Schls in Cambridge *cr:* St Peter's Prep Eng Tchr 1957-60; Canisius HS Eng Tchr 1965-9 Moyne Coll Eng Instr 1994-; *ai:* Bene Merenti 20 Yr Svc Awd; Ar Pub; *office:* Le Moyne Coll Le Moyne Heights Syracuse NY 13214

NAVAL, MADELINE FERRARA, Second Grade Teacher; *b:* Long Is NY; *m:* Arthur E.; *ed:* St Univ at Oneonta (BA) Elem 1964; 30 Addl *cr:* Barnum Woods Elem 2nd, 3rd, 6th Grd Tchr 32 Yrs; *ai:* Ment Inexperienced Tchrs; AFT, NEA 30 Yrs; East Meadow Union Pres; Bldg Treas; *office:* Barnum Woods Elem Kalda-May Ln East Meadow 11554*

NAVARRO-GOVELOVICH, TERESA M., Supervisor of Stu Teachers; *b:* Harrisburg, PA; *m:* Nicholas S.; *c:* Alexander N., Andre *ed:* Elizabethtown Coll (BA) Span 1971; Millersville Univ (MA) 1977; Shippensburg Univ (MED) Educl Admin 1995; *cr:* Susquehanna Span, Fr Tchr 1971-76; Harrisburg Area Comm Coll Span Instr 197 Milton Hershey Schl Span, Fr Tchr 1989-94, Supvr Stu Tchrs 1994 Future Edctrs of Amer Adv; ASCD 1995-; NEA, PSEA, MHSEA 1994- Delta Kappa 1994-, Fnds Rep; Church Bd 1991-, Vestry Women.

NAVE, JOANNE PENNESI, High School English Teacher, Hagerstown, MD; *c:* Kristoffer J. Lescalleet; *ed:* Shepherd Coll (BA) Arts 1974; Shippensburg St Univ (MEA) 1987; *cr:* South Hagerstown Eng Tchr 1976-80; Boonstown HS Eng Tchr, Jrnlsm Dept Chair 1980- Aldus Pagemaker; Microsoft Works; SAT Wkshp; AP Eng Instr; D Alcohol Seminar; Newspaper, Prom Promise Campaign Adv; Improvement Team; Antietam Lioness 1995-, Second VP; Ray Kroc

:l 1995; Washington Cty Excl Ed Awd 1995; Tchr of Yr Awd Nom 95; Curr Guides, Pilot Prgms Pub; *office:* Boonsboro HS 10 Campus oonsboro MD 21713*

IRA, DEBRA L., Substance Abuse Prevention; *b:* New York City, : Rafael III; *ed:* Herbert H. Lehman (BA) Psych 1994; *cr:* Evander HS Educl Assoc 1978-89; Project Esteem CSD #11 Drug Prevention Substance Abuse Prevention, Intervention Specialist 1989-; *ai:* :t Esteem Peer Ldrshp, After Schl Prgms.

ROCKI, DANIEL A., Guidance Counselor; *b:* Erie, PA; *m:* Janet r; *c:* Daniel, Anne Lawson, John, Steven; *ed:* Gannon Univ (BA) 1963, (MED) Guid 1970; 6 Credit Hrs Earth Sci; 9 Credit Hrs gy; 3 Credit Hrs Cmptr Prgm; *cr:* Roosevelt MS Sci Tchr 1963-78; HS Sci Tchr 1978-87; Tech Meml HS Guid Cnslr 1987-91; Cntrl HS Cnslr 1991-; *ai:* Adult Evening Schl Cnslr; NEA, PSEA, EEA 1969-, Pres; *office:* Central HS 3325 Cherry St Erie PA 16508

)AN, WILLIAM JOSEPH, Music Teacher & Choral Dir; *b:* Trenton, *n:* Catena Messina; *c:* William Michael, Mary Katherine; *ed:* ette Coll (BA) Russian, Ger 1978; Temple Univ (MA) Opera rmance 1983; Chestnut Hill Coll Music Ed Cert; Attnd Westminster Coll, West Chester Univ; *cr:* Cntrl Bucks West HS Vocal Music Tchr 91; Hatboro-Horsham HS Vocal Music Tchr 1991-; Lafayette Coll l Activities Dir 1992-; *ai:* Vocal Ensembles & Activities Dir; MENC, A 1982-, Dist 11 Pres 1990-92, Citation of Excl 1990; ACDA, NATS ; Champions of Learning Tchr of Yr 1993-94; *office:* ro-Horsham HS 899 Horsham Rd Horsham PA 19044*

:R, SOFYA, Asst Professor; *b:* Russia; *m:* Yakov; *c:* Irene; *ed:* echnic Inst of Moscow (BA) & (MS) Mechanical Engrng 1972; nbia Univ Tchrs Coll (EDD) Coll Tchng of Math 1993; Attnd Adelphi Comp Programming 1982; *cr:* Moscow Coll of Engrng Prof 1972-80; attan Comm Coll Asst Prof 1982-; *ai:* Hnrs, Math Dept Calculus & Dept Major Comms; NYSMATYC 1989-; Article Pub; *office:* agh Of Manhattan Comm Coll 199 Chambers St New York NY 10007*

)WITH, NANCY M., Health & PE Teacher; *b:* Philadelphia, PA; *ed:* Stroudsburg Univ (BS) Hlth, PE 1983; *cr:* John Moffet Elem Schl Hlth chr 1987-93; Overbrook HS Hlth, PE Tchr 1993-; *ai:* Jr Var Girls l, Sftbl Coach; Outward Bound Fac Adv; AFT, PFT 1984-; *office:* orook HS 59th & Lancaster Philadelphia PA 19131

ZARO, EDWARD MICHAEL, World Languages & ESL Tchr; *b:* , NJ; *ed:* Univ of PA (BA) Span 1973, (MS) Ed 1973; Columbia Univ Coll Candidate for EDD; *cr:* Randolph HS Tchr 1973-77; Dover HS Chprsn 1977-; *ai:* Intnl Club; Goals 2000 Comm; NJEA 1973-; ASCD ; El Primer Paso Ltd 1994-, Bd of Trustees; PR Rockefeller Fndtn 1988; Portugal Fullbright Tchr Exch 1990; *office:* Dover HS 100 St Dover NJ 07801

ZARO, JOANN M., English & Journalism Teacher; *b:* Rahway, NJ; chael; *ed:* Rutgers Univ (BA) Eng, Ed 1983; Kean Coll (MA) Educl n 1993; *cr:* Rahway HS Eng Tchr 1983-; *ai:* Jrnlsm Adv; NEA, REA ; *office:* Rahway HS 1012 Madison Ave Rahway NJ 07065

ZARRO, JO ANN M., English Teacher; *b:* Rahway, NJ; *c:* Michael; utgers Univ (BA) Eng, Ed 1983; Kean Coll (MA) Educl Admin 1993; ddl Hrs; *cr:* Rahway HS Eng Tchr 1983-; *ai:* Yrbk Co-Adv; NJEA, 1983-; *office:* Rahway HS 1012 Madison Ave Rahway NJ 07065*

ATOU, GILBERT, Computer Science Professor; *b:* Nkongsamba, eroon; *m:* Victorine Feuyong; *c:* Edgar, Francine, Tatiana; *ed:* nde Univ at Cameroon (BS) Math 1980, (MS) Math 1981; Coll of n Island (MS) Cmptr Sci 1987; CUNY Grad Schl (PHD) Cmptr Sci ; 3 Credits in Exceptional Child Tchng; 3 Credits in Mainstreaming r: Ivory Coast Ministry of Ed HS Math Tchr 1981-84; Coll of Staten l Lecturer Cmptr Sci 1986-87, Grad Asst Cmptr Sci 1987-92; William son Coll Asst Prof Cmptr Sci 1992; *ai:* Cmptr Sci Dept Curr & ing Comm Chair; AFT 1986-; ACM 1989-; Flwshp Grad Schl of Y 1988-89, 1990-92; Grant from Ctr of Rsrch 1995; Pub, Present s.*

MA-OGAR, PETER ODOK, Professor; *b:* Bendege Afi-Ikom, West a; *m:* Margaret; *c:* Elton, Kenneth, Wilson, Perpetua; *ed:* Cntrl St at Edmond Asst Prof 1981-82; Tillards Corp VP Mktg 1982-83; A&T iv Asst Prof 1983-89; Lime Stone Coll Assoc Prof 1989-90; Kean Coll Prof 1990-; *cr:* Cntrl St Univ Edmond OK Asst Prof 1981-82; Tillards VP Mktg 1982-83; A&T St Univ NC Asst Prof 1983-90; Kean Coll of of 1990-; *ai:* Amer Mktg Assn 1978-, Adv, Acad; Amer Mngmt 1990-; Grant; AMA Awd; *office:* Kean Coll Of NJ 1000 Morris Ave Union 7083

L, BENNIE FRANK, Reading & Social Studies Tchr; *b:* Manchester, *m:* Dianna L.; *c:* Tiffany, Bennie, Brittany, Joseph; *ed:* Fort Valley St (BS) His 1979; Attnd Cleveland St Univ Rdng 1990; Cleveland Hum nst; Summer Writing Inst for Tchrs; Ed Leadership Awareness ork; Cleveland Tchrs Union Leadership Project; *cr:* Glenville HS Grd Rdng Tchr 1984-85; James Ford Rhodes HS 11-12 Rdng Tchr -88; Willson Intermediate Schl 8th Grd Rdng Tchr 1989-90; Harry E. s Intermediate Schl 7th-8th Grd Rdng Tchr 1990-; *ai:* Head Girls ol Coach; Detention Room Supvr; Alpha Phi Alpha 1977-, Pres; Phi Kappa 1992-; Cleveland Tchr Union 1984-, Bldg Chair; Emerald lace Tchrs Network 1992-, Pres; BSA 1990-, Cub Master, Merit Awd; Erie Girl Scouts 1984-, Asst Ldr, Father of Yr; Lillie Hinds Rdng Org ; Plain Dealer Crystal Apple Awd 1992, 1995; CAV's Tchr of Month Ashland Oil Tchr of Yr Nom; Carnegie, Venture Capital, Small, na Holden Jennings Grants; *home:* 1347 E 92nd St Cleveland OH 6*

L, DEBORAH T., Math Teacher; *b:* Somerville, NJ; *c:* Sean M.; *ed:* nova Univ (BS) Ed, Math 1978; West Chester Univ (MED) Scndry Ed , Grad Courses in Counseling & Tchng Techniques; *cr:* William Penn Dist Math Tchr 1978-86; Downingtown Schl Dist Math Tchr 1986-; S SAP Team 4 Yrs; PSEA 1978-; NCTM 1988-; PASAP 1991-; *office:* ningtown Sr HS 445 Manor Ave Downingtown PA 19335

L, EUGENE E., Middle School Band Director; *b:* Brooklyn, NY; *m:* ane Clancy; *c:* Eugene, Ellis, Ereka; *ed:* Union Coll (BA) Music, Piano ; Post Coll (MD) Music 1984; *ai:* MS Concert, Jazz Bands; Yth at *office:* Westbury MS 455 Rockland Westbury NY 11590*

L, GINA M., Social Studies Teacher; *b:* Philadelphia, PA; *c:* David; UNY at Potsdam (BA) His 1991; 28 Credits Hrs SUNY at Albany; *cr:* lsor HS Tchr 1993-; *ai:* Crusader Yrbk, 1997 Class & SIPP Adv; Bldg np Team & 9th Grd Mod Comms; AFT 1993-; NY Cncl for Soc Stud ; *office:* Windsor HS 215 Main St Windsor NY 13865

L, JANNIE M., Teacher of Gifted & Talented; *b:* Paulsboro, NJ; *c:* ifer Robinson, Tracy Byarm; *ed:* Cheyney Univ (BS) Elem Ed 1967; oudenslager Schl 2nd Grd Tchr 1967-89, Tchr of Gifted, Talented -; *ai:* Enrichment Comm; Multicultural Comm Chair; Advy Comm r Supt; NJEA 1967-; Gloucester Cty Educ Assn, Minorities vement Comm Chair; Sigma Gamma Rho, Basilus; 2nd Bapt, nist, Choirs Directress; Cheyney Alumni Outstdng, Dedicated Svc eciation Cert 1983; Outstdng Edctr of Amer for Ed Advancement anitarian, Svc Awd NAACP; 1st Governors Tchr of Yr Awd; Tchr posium.*

NEAL, JERRY D., Sixth Grade Teacher; *b:* Punxsutowney, PA; *m:* Betsy Ann Preisel; *c:* Kristi, Kelly, Kyle; *ed:* Clarion Univ (BS) Elem Ed 1975, (MS) Elem Ed 1978; *cr:* Bell Township ELem Schl Intermediate Rdng Tchr 1975-76; Parkview Elem Schl Intermediate Rdng Tchr 1976-95; Big Run Elem Schl Intermediate Math, Sci Tchr, Head Tchr 1995-; *ai:* Head Tchr; Jr HS Boys Bsktbl Coach; HS Asst Bsbl Coach; NEA, PSEA 1975-; Punxsy Little League Coach, Bd, Umpire 1977-; *office:* Big Run ELem Schl Main St Big Run PA 15767

NEAL, KATHY SUZANN, Home Economics Teacher; *b:* Akron, OH; *ed:* Univ of Akron (BA) Home Ec 1969; Post Grad Stud Nutrition, Child Dev Ed, Family Life, Tailoring; *cr:* Roberts MS Home Ec Tchr 26 Yrs; *ai:* Operation of Stu Bus; Proud Warrior Award Comm; CFEA, NEA, OEA 1970-; PTA 1970-, Tchr Liason Outstdngt Edctr; Cuy Falls Dist Tchr of Yr; Red Lobster Tchr of Yr; PTA Tchr Yr; *office:* Roberts MS 3333 Charles St Cuyahoga Falls OH 44221*

NEAL, KIMBERLY SHARER, Instructor of Education & Dir; *b:* Tarentum, PA; *c:* Brandon Wade; *ed:* IN Univ of PA (BS) Elem Ed 1974, (MED) Rdng Specialization 1992; Penn St Univ Elem Ed; *cr:* Norfolk City Schls Kndgtn Tchr 1974-77, First Grd Tchr f1977-79; US Naval Amphibious Base Chapel Dir of Rel Ed 1979-81; PA St Univ Instr of Ed & Dir Tech Prep Tutorial Prgm 1991-; *ai:* Phi Theta Kappa Co-Adv; Tech Prep Spec Populations Comm Dir; Campus Plan for Plan Sub-Comm Chprsn; PROV DUS Adv; Svc Learning Comm; Recruitment FTCAP; Tech Prep Curr Comm; Integrative Skills Sub-Comm; Tech Prep Task Force; Kappa Delta Pi, Phi Delta Kappa 1992-; IRA, Keystone St Rdng Assn, Westmoreland Rdng Cncl, Natl PTA 1991-; ASCD 1994-; PA Assn of Dev Edctrs, Intnl Soc Exploring Tchng Alternatives 1995-; Nom Outstdng Tchr of Yr 1994-95; PA Assn Dev Edctrs Proceeding 1996; PA Assn Two Yr Coll Journal Two Articles; Journal of PA Acad of Sci 1995; *office:* The Pennsylvania St Univ 3550 7th Street Rd New Kensington PA 15068*

NEAL, ROBERTA L., English Teacher; *b:* Youngstown, OH; *ed:* OH Dominican Coll (BA) Eng 1982; OH St Univ (MA) Eng Ed 1985; *cr:* Hamilton HS Eng Tchr 1985-; *ai:* Writing Contest; Lit Mag Coord; Eligibility Comm; Steering Comm; HCTA; OEA; NEA; Outstanding Catalyst Awd 1991-92; Fellowship OH St Univ; Outstanding Catalyst Aw 1994-; *office:* Hamilton HS 1165 Eaton Ave Hamilton OH 45013

NEAL, SANDRA H., 5th & 6th Grade Teacher; *b:* Christiansburg, VA; *m:* Stephen; *c:* Melanie Mae; *ed:* WV Inst of Tech (BA) Soc Stud Ed, His & Govt 1985; Western MD Coll Curr & Instruction 1991; *cr:* Ansted MS 6th-7th Grd Lang Arts Tchr 1985-86; Berwyn Bapt Schl 5th-6th Grd Lang Arts, Soc Stud Tchr 1986-; *ai:* Delta Kappa Gamma 1994-, Recording Sec; Phi Alpha Theta 1985-; *home:* 7230 Carriage Hill Dr Laurel MD 20707

NEAL, TAMMORAH MAE, Aide & Coach; *b:* Albion, NY; *m:* David Albert; *c:* Spencer, Amber; *ed:* 12 Addl Credit Hrs GCC; *cr:* Albion Cntrl Schl Tchrs Aide 3 Yrs, Pool Aide 1 Yr; *ai:* 7-8th Grd Vlybl, JV Vlybl Coach; First Bapt Church, Yth Group Ldr; *office:* Albion Cntrl Schl 302 East Ave Albion NY 14411

NEALE, JO-ANN, Third Grade Teacher; *b:* Leechburg, PA; *c:* Brian Scott; *ed:* Univ of Pittsburgh (MED) Curr & Supervision 1969; Curr & Supervision 1988; *cr:* Penn Hills Schl Dist 3rd Grd Tchr 1963-; *ai:* PSEA, NEA, PHEA 1963-; *home:* 613 Newport Dr Pittsburgh PA 15235

NEALE, MARGARET DUKES, United States Government Tchr; *b:* Thomasville, GA; *m:* Alvin Morris; *c:* Alvin Morris Jr., Kevin Alonzo; *ed:* Savanna St Coll (BA) Soc Sci 1969; Cath Univ of Amer (MA) Scndry Ed 1970; Trinity Coll 18 Hrs; Howard Univ 6 Hrs; Univ of DC 33 Hrs; Univ of VA at Charlottesville 3 Hrs; Amer Univ 3 Hrs Admin & Supervision; *cr:* Paul Jr HS Soc Stud Tchr 1969-70; Woodrow Wilson Sr HS Soc Stud, Yrbk Tchr 1970-77; Ballou Sr HS US His, Yrbk Tchr 1977-89; Mulicultural Values Ed Office Tchr Trainer, Comm Svc Coord 2989-93; Eastern Sr HS US Govt Tchr 1993-; *ai:* Yrbk; Sr Class Spon; Coll Bureau; Mid Sts Philosophy Comm; PTSA Paat Pres; Assembly Prgm Comm; AFT Local #6 1970-; ASCD 1982-; NCSS; Prince Georges Cty Charities, Chaplain; CPR, Blood Specialist 1990-, Pres; Alpha Kappa 1966-, Reporter, 25 Yr Silver Star; ASED 1982-, Convention Presenter 1992; Pub Schls Perfect Attendence Awd 3 Yrs; Ballou Sr HS Tchr of Yr; Prince Georges Cty Outstdng Vol Awd; *office:* Eastern Sr HS 17th & E Capitol Sts NE Washington DC 20003*

NEALEIGH, THOMAS T., French & Hum Tchr; *b:* Shelbyville, IN; *m:* Katheleen E.; *c:* Thomas M., M. Deirdre; *ed:* Miami Univ (BA) Fr 1965; Wright St Univ 41 Quarter Hrs Toward Master of Hum; Univ of Northern IA 12 Quarter Hrs 1982-1991 Degree; Fr Lang, Culture, Civilization 1987; *cr:* Woodstock HS Fr Tchr 1965-67; Barrington HS Fr Tchr 1967-72; Tri-Village HS Fr, Cmptr Sci & Hum Tchr 1980-; Self-employeed Weaving, Spinning, Lace Making 1973-81; *ai:* Drama & Fr Club; Muse Machine-Arts Org; Dir of Schl Plays & Musicals; TVHS Acad Team Avd; Natl Honor Soc Adv; NEA, OEA, TVEA 1980-; OFLA 1984-; Darke Cty Civic Theatre 1984-, VP-Sec 1990-91; Tri-Village Tchr of Yr Dist-wide 1986 & 1994; Dayton Area Harp Ensemble 1983-90-Asst Conductor 1987-90; Arts-in-the-Schls Darke Co OH 1988-92; Arts-in-the-Schls Darke Co OH 1991-92 One-man Shows; Selected to Perform Intnl Ediburgh Festival Scotland 1990; Ashland Oil Golden Apple Awd 1993; Fulbright Tchr Exchange Grant 1993 & 1994; OH Conf of Gifted Coord & Tchrs Keynote Speaker 1990; Darke Co Tchr of Yr 1994; *office:* Tri Village H S S Main St New Madison OH 45346*

NEALY-CLARKE, MARTHA PATTON, 8th Grade Language Arts Tchr; *b:* Bardstown, KY; *m:* Maceo; *c:* Darren Nealy; *ed:* KY St Univ (BA) Elem Ed 1966; Wright St Univ (MA) Curr, Supervision 1978; Addl Credit Hrs Univ of Dayton; *cr:* Residence Park Elem Schl 8th Grd Lang Arts Tchr 1966-73; Fairview Elem Schl 8th Grd Lang Arts Tchr 1973-80; Brown MS 8th Grd Lang Arts Tchr 1980-86; Fairview MS 8th Grd Lang Arts Tchr 1986-; *ai:* Fac Cncl Chprsn; Writing, Speech Contests Adv; Partners Ed Rep; Cluster Ldr; NEA, OEA, NCTE 1966-; Parish Cncl 1994-; Spiritual Life Commission 1993-, Chprsn; NAACP 1992-; *office:* Fairview MS 2408 Philadelphia Dr Dayton OH 45406

NEANEN, RONALD D., Guidance Counselor; *b:* Dayton, OH; *m:* Cindy Lucas; *c:* Jessica, Sadie, Maggie; *ed:* Defiance Coll (BA) Elem Ed 1979; Univ of Toledo (MS) Ed Cnslng 1986; *cr:* Defiance MS Grd 5 Tchr 1979-87; Eaton MS 6-7 Grd Tchr 1987-82; Eaton HS Guid Cnslr 1992-; *ai:* Head Ftbl Coach; Sr Class Adv; Eaton Classroom Tchrs Assn 1987-; OH Assn of Coll Admin Cnslrs, OH St Schl Cnslrs Assn 1992-; Miami Valley Ftbl Coaches Assn 1988-; *office:* Eaton HS 307 N Cherry St Eaton OH 45320

NEARON, LAURIE A., Mathematics Teacher; *b:* Bronx, NY; *ed:* Columbia Coll (BA) Math 1984; Queens Coll (MS) Scndry Ed Math 1990; The Prins Inst Bank St Coll of Ed (EDM) Educl Ldrshp 1995; Columbia Univ Schl of Engrng; Mercy Hosp Cancer Care Unit Vol Trng Pgm; Day Star 2 Yr Scripture Stud Pgm; *cr:* TRT Telecommunications Corp Asst to Admin Supvr 1982-84; Ronkin Educl Group & Quest Learning Ctr SAT Math Instr 1991-93; York Coll Adj Prof 1992; Springfield Gardens HS Math Tchr & Programming Asst 1984-; City Coll 1996; *ai:* Math-Sci Initiative Comm Supt; Cath Tchrs Assn; AFT & UFT 1984-; Queen of Peace Nursing Home, Vol; BCIA Team at St Clares RC Church 1992-; NSF Grant; Natl Conf of Chrstns & Jews Human Relations Awd; Monsignor Thomas F Noonan Ed Awd; 2 Plaques from Amer Cancer Soc & Millard Fillmores for Raising Money; Springfield Gardens HS Hall of Fame.*

NEASE, DAVID GEORGE, Fine Arts Department Chair; *b:* Buffalo, NY; *ed:* SUNY at Albany (BA) Philosophy 1966; Canisius Coll (MS) Ed 1977; *cr:* St Bernard Schl Jr HS Tchr 1966-70; St Francis HS Tchr, Music Dir 1970-; Our Lady of Victory Basilica Music Dir 1980-; *ai:* Male, Mixed Chorus; Performing, Visual Arts Soc; Acad Cncl; Liturgical Music; Annual Musical Producer; Choirmaster; MENC, NYSSMA 1972-; ACDA 1978-; NPM 1980-, Chapter Dir; Church Musicians Guild 1960-, Pres; Dioc Liturgical Comm, Music Sec; Outstdng Scndry Educator 1973; Tchr of Yr 1995; NPM Regnl Convention Chair 1988; Articles Pub; *office:* St Francis HS 4129 Lakeshore Rd Athol Springs NY 14010

NEDOH, SANDRA WHEELER, Art Teacher; *b:* Wadsworth, OH; *m:* David A.; *c:* Brett Farkas, Russell Edward Farkas; *ed:* Univ of Akron (BS) Scndry Ed, Art K-12-Magna Cume Laude 1979, (MS) Educl Admin 1989; 41 Post Grad Hrs; *cr:* Avon Corp Dist Mgr 1973-74; Edgewater Quality Care Admin Trainee 1974-79; Rittman Sr HS Tchr 1979; Wadsworth City Schls Tchr 1979-; *ai:* Pastor Parish, Music & Worship Comms; Young Authors Choir Instr 7 Yrs; Medina Co Bd of Ed Enrichment Acad Art Instr 8 Yrs; North Cntrl Auxiliary Chair; OAEA, NEOTA, WEA 1979-, Bldg Rep; Kappa Delta Pi 1978-; Kappa Kappa Iota 1985-, VP; Pi Lambda Theta 1977-; Medina Co Art League 1978-, Pres; Tri Co Soc of Fine Arts 1975-; FPA 1968-, Pres; Cuyahoga Vly Art Club 1994-; Article Pub; Tape Placed in Univ of Akron's Lib; Prof Artist One-Man-Art-Shows; *office:* Wadsworth Sr HS 625 Broad St Wadsworth OH 44281

NEE, EDWARD J., Mathematics Teacher; *b:* Brooklyn, NY; *m:* Colleen M. Crean; *c:* James, Kevin, Kathleen; *ed:* SUNY Coll at Cortland (BS) Early Scndry Math 1971; SUNY Coll at Potsdam (MS) Ed 1975; Attnd St Lawrence Univ Admin & SUNY Coll at Plattsburgh Counseling; *cr:* Hermon DeKalb Cntrl Schl Tchr 1972-; *ai:* Soccer Coach; Hermon DeKalb Tchr Assn 1972-, Pres 1976, Treas 1989; NYSUT 1972-, Del 1976; AFT 1972-; St Mary's Bd of Ed, Pres & VP; St Mary's Home & Schl Assn, Pres; Canton Pee Wee Assn, Hockey Commissioner & Coach, Bsbl Coach; *office:* Hermon De Kalb Central Schl E De Kalb Rd De Kalb Junction NY 13630

NEE, JOANN WHEELER, Vocal Music Teacher; *b:* Uniontown, PA; *ed:* Penn St Univ (BS) Music Ed 1972; Hood Coll (MS) Scndry Ed 1983; Western MO Coll Currently Working Toward Masters in Counseling; *cr:* West Frederick Jr HS Vocal Music Tchr 1972-79; New Market MS Vocal Music Tchr 1979-88; Frederick HS Vocal Music Tchr 1988-; *ai:* Concert & Show Choirs Fundraisers Spon; FCTA 1972-, Sec, Bd of Dirs 2 Yrs; NEA 1972-; Amer Guild of Organists 1995-; Frederick Cty Hotline 1996; *office:* Frederick HS 650 Carroll Pky Frederick MD 21701*

NEEDHAM, DONNA L., English Teacher; *b:* Yonkers, NY; *ed:* Univ of MA (BA) Eng 1966; Northeastern Univ (MED) Ed 1972; 78 Credit Hrs; *cr:* Danvers HS Eng Tchr 1966-; *ai:* Danvers Tchrs Assn 1966-, VP; MTA, NEA, NCTE 1966-; *office:* Danvers HS 60 Cabot Rd Danvers MA 01923

NEEDHAM, RICHARD JOHN, Social Studies Teacher; *b:* Irvington, NJ; *c:* Erica; *ed:* St Frances Coll (BA) His & Ed 1977; *cr:* Good Cnsl HS Soc Stud Tchr 1978-87; Essey Cath Girls HS Soc Stud Tchr 1987-88; Acad of St Aloysius Soc Stud Tchr 1988-; *ai:* Girls Vllybl & Sftbl Coach; NCEA.

NEEDLE, DONNA VOGT, Fam & Consumer Sci Tchr; *b:* Pittsburgh, PA; *m:* Richard Hale; *c:* Timothy Hale, James Hale; *ed:* Indiana Univ of PA (BS) Voc Home Ec 1969; Received Masters Equivalency in Ed Penn St Univ 1976; *cr:* Homeville Jr HS Home Ec Tchr 1969-83; West Mifflin MS Home Ec Tchr 1983-87; West Mifflin Area HS Fam & Consmr Sci Tchr 1987-; *ai:* Wall of Fame Artist; Grad Comm; Prom Promenade Spon; Strategic Planning Comm; Future Educator Prgm Facilitator; Titan Tribune, Titan Tidbits & Future Homemakers Spon; PTSA Schlsp Comm Chair; Comm Comm; PTSA Membership Chair; "Jeaniaticics" 1996; AFT 1972-; Amer Home Ec Assn, Home Ec Assn Allegheny Cty & PA Home Ec Assn 1990-; Amer Sewing Guild 1989-, Educator; PA PTSA 1991-, Honorary Life Mem, PTA Tchr of Yr 1991 Mon-Yough Cncl; W Mifflin Area HS PTSA Historian; Mon Valley Partners Comm Service 1990-, Author Grant Recipient 1993; The Great Kennywook Caper; 1991 Thanks to Tchrs Nom; 1994, 1995 Thanks to Tchrs Fin, 1993 Disney Amer Tchr Nom; Mon Valley Ed Consortium 5 Time Grant Winner Tchr Level & Schl Level Grant Winner; Pub Journal of Home Ec 1994; Butterick Home Catalog 1993; Leadership for Stu Act; PA Journal of Tchr Leadership Dist Dir for Tribute to Mr. Fred Rogers 25th TV Anniversary; *office:* West Mifflin Area HS 91 Commonwealth Ave West Mifflin PA 15122

NEEDS, DAVID WAYNE, 6th Grade Teacher & Coach; *b:* Marietta, OH; *m:* Kimberly Joanne Vaughan; *c:* Andrea Nicole, Jennifer Leigh, Justin Hahns Winer, Kaitlan Maryanna; *ed:* OH Univ (BS) Elem Ed 1977; 18 Addl Hrs in Ed Marietta Coll; *cr:* Belpre City Schls Elem Tchr, Coach 1977-; *ai:* Boys & Girls Cross Cntry Coach 12 Yrs; Girls Var Asst & JV Coach 15 Yrs; Sci Course of Stud Comm; BEA, NEA, OH HS Bsktbl Coaches Assn 1977-; Amer Fed of Musicians; Masonic Lodge #609 F&AM 1986-; Belpre Congregational Church 1982-, Bd of Deacons; Girls B-Ball Team Perfect Seasons, Conf Champs 1994-95; Boys Cross Cntry TVC, SEO Div III Dist Champs 1994, 10 TVC Conf Championships; *home:* 908 Blennerhassett Ave Belpre OH 45714

NEELEY, G. STEVEN, Asst Professor of Philosolphy; *b:* Cincinnati, OH; *m:* Ann Marie; *ed:* Univ of Cincinnati Coll of Law (JD) Law 1985; Univ of Cincinnati (MA) Philosophy 1987, (PHD) Philosophy 1989; *cr:* Xavier Univ Visiting Asst Prof 1989-92; Coll of Mount Saint Joseph Adjunct Prof of Philosophy 1992-93; Saint Francis Coll Philosophy Asst Prof 1992-; Law Offices of G S Neeley Esquire Private Practice 1995-; *ai:* Saint Francis Coll Ethics Inst, Judicial Appeals Bd, Honors Prgm, Interim Dir, Curr & Tchng Comm, Acad Standing Comm, Deans Cncl, Law Schl Endowment Comm, Working Group on Governing Bd, Org, Admin & Governance; Commonwealth Of PA Bar 1994-, Attorney-At-Law; OH St Bar 1985-, Attorney-At-Law; Amer Philosophical Assn 1983-, Excl in Tchng Awd 1994; Intnl Assn Phil of Law & Soc 1990-; North Amer Schopenhauer Soc 1984-; Pub Book & Numerous Articles; Saint Francis Honor Soc Distinguished Fac Awd 1994; Bishop Fenwich Tchr of Yr Awd 1991; Greater Cincinnati Corsortium of Coll & Univ Celebration of Tchng Awd 1991; Charles Phelps Taft Meml Fellowship 1987-88, 1988-89; Univ Research Cncl Fellowship 1987; *office:* Saint Francis Coll 122 Raymond Hall Loretto PA 15940

NEELY, CAROLYN BURKEY, K-12 Art Teacher; *b:* Cumberland, MD; *m:* George E.; *c:* David, Jennifer; *ed:* Frostburg St Univ (BS) Art 1965; Grad Credit; Art Inst of Pittsburgh & Savannah Coll of Art & Design Summer Tchr Sessions; *cr:* North Potomac MS 7-8th Grd Art Tchr 1965-69; Allegany HS Art Tchr 1969-70; SS Peter & Paul 1-8th Grd Art Tchr 1980-81; St John Neumann Schl K-5 ARt Tchr 1981-; Bishop Walsh MS & HS 6-12th Grd Art Tchr 1991-; *ai:* Outreach Prgm; Cath Schls Wk Comm; Fine ARts Dept Chair; Acad Cncl; NAHS Co-Moderator; MS Newspaper & Annual Co-Mod; NCEA, NAEA, ESTA of Archdiocese of Baltimore; Ursuline Assoc; Allegany Arts Cncl; *office:* Bishop Walsh MS HS 700 Bishop Walsh Rd Cumberland MD 21502

NEELY, EDNA LORAINE, English & Journalism Teacher; *b:* Roaring Spring, PA; *ed:* PA St Univ (BS) Scndry Ed 1969, (MA) Eng 1975; Post Grad Credits at Amer Univ, Georgetown Univ, IN Univ, Millersville Univ; *cr:* Altoona Area HS Tchr 1969-; *ai:* HS Newspaper, Lit Mag, Yth Ed Assn, Quill, Scroll Club Adv; NEA, NCTE 1970-; PSEA, AAEA 1970-, Bldg Rep; Delta Kappa Gamma; PA Soc Children of Amer Revolution 1982-, Sr St Pres, Editor St Newsletter; Numerous Articles Pub; CARE Awd; *office:* Altoona Area HS 1415 6th Ave 6th Ave & 14th St Altoona PA 16602

NEELY, FRED EUGENE, Biology Teacher; *m:* Nancy Bryant; *c:* Amanda, Burke, Clark; *ed:* Warren Wilson Coll (BA) Bio 1974; Susquehanna Univ Tchrs Cert Ed 1989; *cr:* Self Employed Carpenter 1974-75; Warren Wilson Coll Dir Cattle Feed Research 1975-76; Sire Power Inc AI Tech 1976-78; Self Employed Dairy Farmer 1978-86; West Perry Schl Dist Bio & Earth Sci Tchr 1986-; *ai:* Enviromental Club Adv; NEA, PSEA, WPEA 1986-; PA Farm Bureau 1978-; Agway, Local Dir; Peery Co Soil Conservation Dist, Local Dir; Sire Power, Local Dir; Centre Presbyn Church Mem; 4-H Adv; *home:* RR 2 Box 73 Loysville PA 17047*

NEELY, MARY BETH, Social Studies Teacher; *b:* Martins Ferry, OH; *m:* Arthur Stalbow; *c:* Amy Smith, Jeff Smith; *ed:* Coll of Wooster (BA) His 1969; Northwestern Univ (MAT) His, Ed 1970; *cr:* ME South HS Intern Tchr 1 Yr; Glen Rock Jr-Sr HS Soc Stud Tchr 1 Yr; Monroe-Woodbury HS Soc Stud Tchr 24 Yrs; *ai:* NHS, Class of 1997 Adv; AFT, NYSUT, MWTA 1972-; *home:* 14 Winston Dr Goshen NY 10924

NEELY, SANDRA HELMER, 5th Grade Teacher; *b:* Philadelphia, PA; *c:* Michele; *ed:* Utica Coll of Syracuse Univ (BA) Soc Stud 1970; 30 Credit Hrs SUNY Upper Division at Cortland 1974; *cr:* Dolgeville Elem 3rd-5th Grd Tchr 26 Yrs; *ai:* Effective Schls Comm; Conflict Resolution Comm Chm; NY St United Tchrs 1970-; AFT 1970-; Dolgeville Tchrs Assoc 1970-; *home:* 11 W Faville Ave Dolgeville NY 13329

NEFF, ROSE ANN, Associate Professor; *b:* Lewisburg, PA; *ed:* Lock Haven Univ (BS) Hlth, PE 1973; Penn St Univ (MS) PE 1980, (PHD) Hlth Ed 1990; *cr:* Ephrata HS Tchr Hlth, PE 1973-74; Susquehanna Univ Instr PE Dept 1974-78; Lock Haven Univ Assoc Prof, Rec Dept 1979-; *ai:* Aerobics Club 1988-; LDSSA Club Adv 1994-; Tenure Comm 1992-; AAHPERD, PSAHPERD 1986-; PASTS 1991-; Relief Soc 1992, Pres; Family Planning Bd 1994-; Tchng Coll 1990; Classroom Comm 1989; *office:* Lock Haven Univ 23 Honors Bldg Lock Haven PA 17745

NEGER, ELIZABETH WILLIS, French Teacher; *b:* London, England; *m:* Nial; *ed:* Smith Coll (BA) Govt 1969; Yale Univ (MAT) Fr 1970; Baccalaureat de Philosophie From Lycee Francais de Londres 1965; 60 Credit Hrs Fr, Span, Admin NY Univ, Fairfield Univ; *cr:* Roger Ludlowe HS Fr, Span Tchr 1970-87; Fairfield HS Fr Tchr 1987-; *ai:* Fr Exch Prgm Coord 1974-; Fr Hospitality Club Adv; Natl Fr Contest, St Fr Video Contest Coord; HS Prgm Comm; NEA, CEA, FEA 1970-; AATF 1970-, Exec Bd; CT Org Lang Tchrs 1970-; AATF Natl Task Force Promotion of Fr in US 1995-; Fairfield Cty Chorale 1972-; Smith Club 1994-, Candidates Comm; Delta Kappa Gamma 1980-95, Schlsp Chm; *office:* Fairfield HS 755 Melville Ave Fairfield CT 06432

NEGER, NIAL E., Mathematics Dept Chairman; *b:* New York, NY; *m:* Elizabeth W.; *ed:* Univ of Bridgeport (BA) Math 1964, (MS) Math 1968; Southern CT St Univ 6th Yr Supervision, Admin; 15 Credits Grad Math Fairfield Univ; *cr:* Trumbull HS Tchr 1965-84, Dept Chm 1984-; *ai:* TEA, CEA, NEA 1965-; ATOMIC 1975-, Exec Bd 1988-93; NCTM, MAA 1975-; *office:* Trumbull HS 72 Strobel Rd Trumbull CT 06611

NEGLEY, HESTON RACHAL (MUSKO), Mathematics Teacher; *b:* Butler, PA; *m:* John L.; *ed:* Grove City Coll (BA) Math, SEED 1991; *cr:* Knoch HS Math Tchr 1992-; *ai:* Chrldng Adv 1992-94; Fac Bsktbl, Vlybl; Donkey Bsktbl; PSEA, NEA 1992-; Butler Cty Jr Miss Pageant 1995-, Bd Mem.

NEGRO, FRANK JOSEPH,JR., Science Teacher; *b:* Dunkirk, NY; *m:* Sandra E. Vought; *c:* Michael Clark, Jennifer Dian; *ed:* Mt St Marys Coll (BS) Bio 1970; Western MD Coll (MED) Admin 1977; Univ of MD College Park 8 Hrs Grad Stud; *cr:* Montgomery Hills Jr HS 7th Grd Sci Tchr 1970-72; Robert Frost Intermediate Schl 7th, 8th Grd Sci Tchr 1972-78; Northwood HS 9-12 Grd Sci Tchr 1978-83; Wheaton HS 9-12 Grd Sci Tchr 1983-; *ai:* Cross Cntry, Indoor & Outdoor Track, Field Head Coach; Class Spon 1981, 1986, 1989; MCEA, MSTA, NEA 1970-; Flower Hill Civic Neighborhood Org 1983-, VP, Pres; Montgomery Cty Swim League, Pres, Chair Competition Comm; *office:* Wheaton HS 12601 Dalewood Dr Silver Spring MD 20906

NEHER, DONNA S., Art Teacher; *b:* Warren, OH; *m:* Randall R. Bare; *c:* Maxwell A. N. Bare, Zoe S. N. Bare; *ed:* Kent St Univ (BSEd) Art 1972; OH Univ, John Carroll Univ Grad Work; *cr:* LaBrae Local Schls 1-7 Grd Art Tchr 1972-74; Athens City Schls K-5 Grd Art Tchr 1976-77; Elyria City Schls K-6 Grd Art Tchr 1977-; *ai:* Art Club Adv; Fine Arts Fair Coord; Fine Arts Comm; Transition Team; OAEA 1977-, Circa Soc; NEA, OEA 1972-; EEA 1977-, Bldg Rep; Emmanuel Luth Church 1982-, Church Counsel; Tchr Endowment Fund Grant; *office:* Windsor Elem Schl 264 Windsor Dr Elyria OH 44035*

NEIDER, MARY ANN (BARTHOLF), Sixth Grade Teacher; *b:* Batavia, NY; *m:* James B.; *ed:* Roberts Wesleyan Coll (BA) Elem Ed 1971; SUC at Brockport (MS) Elem Ed 1976; Elements of Inst; *cr:* Alexander Cntrl Schl First Grd Tchr 1971-72, Sixth Grd Tchr 1972-82, Fifth Grd Tchr 1982-84, Sixth Grd Tchr 1984-; *ai:* AFT, NYSUT 1971-; Stafford Garden Club 1994-; Museum Quilt Guild 1996; *office:* Alexander Central Schl 3314 Buffalo St Alexander NY 14005

NEIGEL, GLADYS MAE (FELTMAN), Business Education Teacher; *b:* Bridgeton, NJ; *m:* Fred; *c:* Michele Dauns, Christina Ann; *ed:* Ball St Univ (BS) Bus Ed 1969; Andrews Univ 16 Addl Hrs; *cr:* Indiana Acad Bus Ed Tchr 1964-65; Garden St Acad Bus Ed Tchr 1969-76; Atlantic Union Coll Bus Ed Tchr 1980-84; Mt Vernon Acad Bus Ed Tchr 1989-; *ai:* FBLA Adv & Founder 1990; Svc Recognition Awd Adv 1993; Cert of Recognition Great Ideas for Tomorrow Prgm FBLA Natl Leadership Conf 1993; *office:* Mount Vernon Acad 15 Fairgrounds Rd Mount Vernon OH 43050

NEIGHBORS, SHIRLEY MOSS, Bio, Anatomy & Physiology Tchr; *b:* Buckingham, VA; *m:* William E. Jr.; *c:* Tabitha, Tamara; *ed:* Shaw Univ (BS) Bio 1966; Univ of Bridgeport (MS) Scndry Ed 1976; *cr:* Central HS Bio Tchr 1966-69; Bassick HS Bio Tchr 1970-71; Career HS Bio Tchr 1972-; *ai:* NHS, Scientific Investigation For Research & Dev Sci Club Adv; Prins Advisory Comm Co-Adv; Extended Day Acad Supvr; AFT, NSTA & Natl Assn of Stu Activity Advs; Zeta Phi Beta 1964-; United Congregational Church of Bridgeport 1975-; Amer Cancer Soc & Daffadil Soc 1985-, Schl Chm; Soc Dev Comm 1988-; Woman's Guild; Chrisian Concerns Bd Mem; Sigma Xi Outstanding HS Tchr 1991; Presidential Awd for Excl in Sci Tchng for Scndry Tchrs Cert of Participation; TAPS Outstanding Distinguished Service Awd 1989; Yrbk Dedication 1989; Yale Univ, Schl of Medicine In-Service Tchr 1993, Research Apprentice Prgm; Yale Medical Schl Anatomy and Bio II Lab Co-Founder; Ed Ldrshp Team; *office:* Career H S 21 Wooster Pl New Haven CT 06511

NEIGHOFF, CAROLYN SUE, Physical Ed & Hlth Dept Head; *b:* Baltimore, MD; *c:* Krista Meyer, Seth Meyer; *ed:* Univ of ME (BS) PE 1989; Masters in PE 1996; *cr:* Hodgkins Jr High Tchr Asst 1989-90; Gardiner MS Hlth & PE Tchr 1990-91; Cony HS Hlth Tchr 1991-93, PE Tchr 1993-; *ai:* Var Boys Tennis St Champs 1993; Var Field Hockey St Champs 1995; Key Club Adv; AAHPERD 1995-; MEA; NEA; Bread of Life Ministries 1984- Chm of Bd; Water of Life Luth Church 1995-; *office:* Cony HS 104 Cony St Augusta ME 04330*

NEIKAM, WILLIAM CHARLES, Professor of Chemistry; *b:* Upland, PA; *m:* Ann L. Crowe; *c:* Diane Carter, Christopher, Derrick; *ed:* St Joseph's Coll at Phila (BS) Chem 1957; U of FL (PHD) Phys Chem 1961; Post Doctoral Flwshp Columbia U 1962; *cr:* Sun Oil Co Rsrch Chemist 1963-73; West Chester St Coll Asst Prof Chem 1973; Plymouth St Coll Prof of Chem 1973-; *ai:* Chair Boyd Hall Maintance Comm; Amer Chemical Soc 1961-; 14 Referred Publications 1961-90; 5 Patents 1963-73; Chm Natural Sci Dept 1988-91; Dir Planetarium 1990-91; Chm Energy Conservation Comm 1976; *office:* Univ Of NH Plymouth St Coll Plymouth NH 03264

NEILL, MARGARET DAUGHERTY, Third Grade Teacher; *b:* Dayton, OH; *m:* David G.; *c:* Andrew, Timothy; *ed:* Worcester St Coll (BS) Elem Ed 1967; Cambridge Coll (MED) Ed 1991; *cr:* Forbes Schl 1st-2nd Grd Tchr 1967-77; Hovey Schl 2nd Grd Tchr 1978-80; West Parish Schl 2nd-3rd Grd Tchr 1980-; *ai:* West Parish Schl Culture Team; NEA 1967-; MTA 1967-; GTA 1967-; *office:* West Parish Elem Schl 10 Concord St Gloucester MA 01930

NEILL, STEPHANIE LYNN, English Teacher; *b:* Southampton, NY; *m:* Michael J.; *c:* Caitlin M.; *ed:* SUNY at Fredonia (BA) Eng 1987; SUNY at Stonybrook (MS) Eng 1991; Addl Post Grad Stud; *cr:* Miller Place Schl Eng Tchr 1987-; *ai:* Yrbk, Newspaper Adv; Curr Work; Integrating Curr Supts Day Presenter; *office:* North Country Road Schl 191 N Country Rd Miller Place NY 11764*

NEISWENDER, PATRICIA HUGHES, English Teacher; *b:* Plattsburgh, NY; *m:* J. Kurt; *c:* Mark, Laura; *ed:* Coll of St Rose (BA) Eng, Scndry Ed 1975; St Univ of NY at Albany (MA) Advanced Classroom Tchng-Eng 1979; Staff Dev-Inservice Capital Distr Writing Project, Jr Great Books Ldr Course, ETM-M Hunter's Model, Cooperative Learning, Classroom Mgmt, Learning Styles, Portfolio Assessment, Macintosh for Tchrs; *cr:* South Lelonie Cntrl Schl 7 Grd Eng Tchr 1975-76; Shenendhowa Cntrl Schl 7-9 Grd Eng Tchr 1976-; *ai:* Union Newsletter Ed Shenendhowa Tchrs Assn; Advy Bd Cooperating Tchr, Stu Tchrs SUNY; Yrbk, Magazine Adv; Ski Club, Stu Cncl Acts, Class Trip Chaperone; Stud Recognition, Pub Relations, Reconfiguration, K-12 Lang Arts, Dev of Stans, Lit Text Selection Comms; NY St United Tchrs 1976-; Kappa Gamma Psi, Delta Epsilon Sigam 1975-; St Rose Alumni Assn 1976-, Phon-A-Thon Vol; Shenendehowa Excl Ed Awd; Who's Who in Amer Ed 1989-90, Young Amer Profs 1988-89; Eng Majors Awd Coll of St Rose 1975; *office:* Shenendehowa Cntrl Schl 970 Route 146 Clifton Park NY 12065

NEISWENTER, PHOEBE ANN A., Jewelry & Metals Teacher; *b:* Harrisburg, PA; *c:* John Fisher III, Kristin Fisher, Lindsey, Jeffrey Markle; *ed:* Kutztown St Univ (BS) Art Ed 1961; Numerous Credit Hrs in Silversmithing, Weaving, Ldrshp Skills, Comm, Pub Speaking, Cooperative Learning, Assessment; *cr:* Harrisburg Pub Schls Outdoor Ed, Art 1965-68, Elem Art 1968-73; Concord Pub Schls Dist Art Coord 1973-92; Concord HS Jewelry & Metals Tchr 1992-; *ai:* Originated & Toured with Dance Troup; Ldrshp Team Ldr; NEA 1965-; NHEA 1973-; NH Art Edctrs Assn 1980-; NAEA 1980-; League of NH Craftsmen 1980-, Bd of Trustees, Mrktg Prgm 5 Yrs, Pres 2 Yrs, Governing Bd, Concord Shop; NH Art Edctr 1986; Outstdng NH Edctr 1989; Presentor at Regnl Art Ed Confs, Crafts Bus, 18th Century Crafts 1978-87; *office:* Concord HS 170 Warren St Concord NH 03301

NEKUZA, KATHLEEN M. BREINDEL, 6th Grade Teacher; *b:* St Marys, PA; *m:* Lawrence Alan; *c:* Timothy Alan; *ed:* Villa Maria Coll (BS) Ed, Minor His 1969; Post Grad Stud Penn St, Clarion, Gannon; *cr:* Sptruce St Pub Schl 2nd Grd Tchr 1969-71; St Marys Parochial Schl 3rd-7th Grd Tchr 1972-; *ai:* Tooth Tchr; Tchrs in Trng Mentor; Laurel Rdng Cncl 1990-; *home:* 208 Martin Rd Saint Marys PA 15857*

NELLI, GAIL BECKER, English, Theatre & Speech Tchr; *b:* Rochester, NY; *m:* Robert J.; *c:* Rachel, Ryan; *ed:* SUNY at Oswego (BA) Scndry Ed, Speech, Theatre 1972; SUNY at Buffalo (MA) Hum, Scene Design, Amer Lit 1990; 30 Grad Hrs SUNY at Oswego, SUNY at Geneseo; *cr:* Romulus Cntrl HS Eng Tchr 1972-74; SUNY at Oswego Speech Instr 1974-75; R. L. Thomas HS Eng, Theatre Tchr 1975-76; York Cntrl HS Eng Tchr 1978-79; Alexander Cntrl HS Eng, Theatre, Speech Tchr 1979-; *ai:* Drama Club Adv; Theatre Dir; Scene Designer; Write Theatre Curr NYS Ed Depts Curr Framework Arts; Curr Chprsn NYS Theatre Ed Assn; NYSUT, AFT 1972-; New York St Theatre Ed Assn 1982-, Pres 1992-94; Alexander United Tchrs 1979-, St Del; Amer Alliance Theatre, Ed 1992-; St Thomas Aquinas Roman Cath Church 1980-, Lector; Geneseo Comm Players 1978; Numerous Articles Pub; *office:* Alexander Central Schl 3314 Buffalo St Alexander NY 14005*

NELSON, BARBARA CACKOWSKI, Kindergarten Teacher; *b:* Staten Island, NY; *m:* William M.; *c:* Drew, Brooke; *ed:* Wagner Coll (BS) Elem Ed 1967, (MS) Elem Ed 1971; Addl 30 Credit Hrs; *cr:* Pub Schl 14 2nd & 3rd Grd Tchr 1967-71; Pub Schl 39 Kndgtn & 3rd-5th Grd Tchr 1973-; *ai:* Women in His Coord; UFT 1967-; SI Band Parents Club 1986-93, Treas 4 Yrs; *office:* Public Schl 39 Sand Ln & McFarland Staten Island NY 10305

NELSON, BETH MIKESELL, Language Arts Teacher; *b:* Columbus, OH; *m:* Steven K.; *ed:* The OH St Univ (BS) Elem Ed 1978; Ashland Univ (MA) Curr, Instruction 1996; OH Univ, Coll of Mt St Joseph Post Grad Stud; *cr:* Warsaw Elem Schl First Grd Tchr 1978-81; River View Jr HS 8th Grd Lang Arts Tchr 1981-; *ai:* Yrbk, Show Choir, Drama Club Adv; Acad Achvmt Comm; Fac Cncl Dept Chair 1996; RVEA, OEA, NEA 1978-, Bldg Rep, Past Pres; Delta Kappa Gamma; 4-H Coshocton Co 1984-, Key Ldr; Coshocton Cty Chamber of Commerce Comm Improvement Awd 1994; YWCA-BPW Women of Achvmt Awd in Ed 1996; Coshocton Cty Ldrshp 1995.

NELSON, BETTY FALCO, 6th-8th Grd Science Teacher; *b:* Bridgeport, CT; *m:* David Arthur; *c:* Jennifer, Melissa; *ed:* Sacred Heart Univ (BA) Bio-Magna Cum Laude 1972; *cr:* Natl Marine Fisheries Svc Phys Scientist 1972-76; Sub Tchr 1983-84; Saint Mary Schl Sci Tchr 1983-; *ai:* NSTA 1990-; *office:* St Mary Schl 72 Gulf St Milford CT 06460

NELSON, BEVERLY JEAN, English Teacher; *b:* Wauseon, OH; *m:* Richard A.; *c:* Megan Dion, J. W.; *ed:* Houston Bapt Univ (BS) Eng & His 1973; Univ of Toledo (MS) Eng Ed 1992; Attnd Taylor Univ for Eng Stud; Received Bowling Green St Univ Rdng Cert; *cr:* Wauseon HS Eng & Speech Tchr 1984; Napoleon HS Eng Tchr 1984-; *ai:* Advanced Placement Lit & Composition; Napoleon HS Asst Var Sftbl Coach 1993-; Asst Summer League Sftbl Coach 1993-; Napoleon Faculty Assn 1984-, Sec 5 Yrs; OH Ed Assn, NEA & NCTE 1984-; Stratford Shakespearean Festvl Mem; Evangelical Mennonite Church 1963-, Choir Dir & Pianist; Natl Endowment for Hum Schlsp Recipient 1988 & 1989; Presidential Scholars Distinguished Tchr Awd 1989; Whos Who Among Human Services Profs; OH Ed Assn Service Awd 1994; *office:* Napoleon HS 701 Briarheath Dr Napoleon OH 43545

NELSON, BRONWYN JONES, Chemistry Teacher; *b:* Cincinnati, OH; *m:* David W.; *c:* Sallie, Jill, David; *ed:* Univ of MI (BS) Chem & Zoology 1969; Univ of Cincinnati (MED) Curr & Sci Instr 1980; Attnd Xavier Univ; Hope Coll, Miami Univ; Bath Univ; *cr:* Shriners Burns Inst Rsrch Assoc 1969-71; Cincinnati Pub Schls Sci & Math Tchr 1975-76; Miami Univ Visting Scholar 1994-95; Fairfield HS Chem Tchr 1976-; *ai:* Terrific Sci Club; Awds & Rewards Comm; Amer Chem Soc HS Chem Com Test Writing Comm; NEA 1977-; NSTA 1980-; ACS 1983-, Environmental Chair, 2 Educl Grants; Iota Sigma Pi 1985-, Mbrshp Comm; Immanuel Presbyn Church 1957-, Elder, Deacon; GTE Growth Initiatives for Tchrs Fellow 1995-96; Rural Electric Natl Grant 1995; Pres Excl Awd Nominee; Article Pub; *office:* Fairfield HS 1111 Nilles Rd Fairfield OH 45014

NELSON, CAROL A., Spanish Teacher; *b:* Buffalo, NY; *m:* William; *c:* Mark; *ed:* DYouville Coll (BA) Span 1969; Attnd Marquette Univ; *cr:* West Seneca Cntrl Schls Span Tchr 1970-75; Hamburg Cntrl Schls Span Tchr 1984-; *ai:* AFT; NY St United Tchrs; *office:* Hamburg Junior High School 360 Division St Hamburg NY 14075

NELSON, CRAIG ROBERT, Fifth Grade Teacher; *b:* New Orlean *m:* Virginia Ondecko; *c:* Craig Nelson Jr., Laura, Eric; *ed:* U Bridgeport (BA) Sociology 1969, (MA) Sociology 1970, (MS) El 1972; 15 Addl Hrs Admin; *cr:* St Andrews Schl 5-6 Grd Tchr 197 Side MS 7-8 Grd Tchr 1970-74; Stony Brook Schl 5-6 Grd Tchr 19 Stratford Acad 5-6 Grd Tchr 1981-; *ai:* Stu Asst Team Chm; 6 Grd A Class Trip; Schl Improvement Comm; Town of Stratford Continu Prgm Facilitator; GED Tchr; Statford Ed Assoc 1974-; CT Ed Assoc 1970-; Ansantawae Lodge #89 1981-; Pyramid Temple Shriners *office:* Stratford Acad 719 Birdseye St Stratford CT 06497

NELSON, DANIEL A., Technology Instructor; *b:* Ballston Spa, N Rose T.; *c:* Joanne; *ed:* Mohawk Valley CC (AAS) Mechanical Tech St Univ of NY at Oswego (BS) Industrial Arts & Tech 1969; St Univ at Albany (MS) Educl Comms 1972; Adirondack CC (AS) Geology Attnd St Univ of NY at Buffalo, rensselaer Polytechnic Inst & OK St *cr:* Shenendehowa HS Tech Instr 1969-; Adirondack CC Adjunct & Instr 1989-; *ai:* Research Project Adv; Greater Capital Region Engrng Fair Planning Comm; Northeast Chapter-Amer Nuclear Soc Exec Comm; NYSUT 1969-; Northeast Sustainable Energy Assn Intnl Tech Ed Assn; Civil Air Patrol 1988-, Aerospace Ed Mem; Am of Chemical Engrs Natl Environmental HS Sci Tchr of Yr 1994; NY of Prof Engrs Outstanding Contributions to Ed St Awd NASA-NEWMAST Grant NASA Goddard Space Flight Ctr 1993; Sci Congress Planning Comm 1991-92; *office:* Shenendehowa H Route 146 Clifton Park NY 12065

NELSON, ELIZABETH, Math Teacher; *b:* Cleveland, OH; *ed:* OH (BS) Math, Scndry Ed 1993; 18 Hrs Grad Prgm John Carroll Un Martin L. King HS Math Tchr 1994-; *ai:* Jr Class Adv 1995-; Earth EPA Prgm; *office:* Martin L King HS 1651 E 71st St Cleveland OH

NELSON, ELLEN VALENTINE, Language Arts Teacher; *b:* Logan *m:* Christopher; *ed:* WV Univ (BS) Scndry Eng, Jrnlsm 1989; *cr:* Pa Sr HS Eng Tchr Grd 10 1 Yr; St Elizabeth Elem Schl Lang Arts Tc 7-8 4 Yrs; *ai:* Forensics Moderator; St Louise de Marillac Guild Nom Golden Apple Awd; *home:* 863 Boulder Dr Bethel Park PA 15

NELSON, GEORGE WINSTON, Social Studies Teacher; *b:* Duluth *m:* Catherine Cressor; *ed:* West Chester Univ (BSEd) Soc Stud Ed (MA) His 1993; *cr:* Lionville Jr HS 7th Grd Soc Stud Tchr 1989-; *a* Adv; Pub Schl Newspaper; PA St Ed Assn 1989-; *office:* Lionville 50 Devon Dr Downingtown PA 19335

NELSON, HYLTON RICHARD, Honors Chemistry Teacher; *b:* Panama; *ed:* Panama Univ (BS) Pharmacy, Chem 1969; Adelphi Univ Scndry Ed 1990; Instituto Justo Arosemena Lic Elem Ed 1959; Spec Credit Hrs; Rsrch Stud in Chem; Mngmt Courses in Biling Ed; Tch Prin Cert; *cr:* US Defense Schls Elem Schl Tchr 1955-71, Sci 1963-71; Octavio Mendez Inst Chem, Physics Intruct 1964-68; C Images Inc Acctng Mgr 1972-80; Park West HS Bio, Chem Tchr 198 Biling, ESL Dir; Parents Advy Comm Facilitator; Tchr Mentorship, Sr Awds, Srs Ranking Comms; Sci & Tech Contest Adv; AFT 1960-; 1965-; NYSUT 1980-; ASCD 1994-; Biling Parents Assn 1980-, Parents Appreciation Awd; Govt Outstdng Tchr Awd; US Defense Outstdng Tchr Awd 1969; US Canal Zone Distngd Svc Awd 1971; Ra City Parent-Tchr Assn Comm Svc Awd 1971; Rainbow City Alumni Edctr of Yr 1985; NYC Manhattan Supt Tchr of Yr 1992; Tchr of Yr NY City Bd of Educ Bright Lights Awd for Distngd Tchng in Math Finalist.*

NELSON, JEFFREY ALAN, Eighth Grade Math Teacher; *b:* Bronx *m:* Barbara Cohen; *ed:* Queen Coll (BA) His 1969; St Johns Un Credits in Cnslng; La Guardia Comm Coll 16 Credits in His of NY; *c* 141 Queens Math Tchr 1969-82; JHS145 Queens Math Tchr 1981-83 Newton Schl Math Tchr 1983-; *ai:* UFT Chptr Ldr 1991-; Math Coach; *office:* Isaac Newton Jr HS E 116th St & Fdr Dr New Yor 10029

NELSON, JOAN M., Third Grade Teacher; *b:* Keene, NH; *m:* John Christie J. Tarpey, Timothy J.; *ed:* Keene St Coll (BED) K-8th El 1952; *cr:* St Joseph Schl 2nd Grd Classroom Tchr 1952-54; Parker Sc & 2nd Grd Classroom Tchr 1954-63; Pawtucketville Memrl Schl 2r & 5th & 6th Grd Tchr 1970-; *ai:* 636 Steering Comm Mem; Lib Task Adv; MTA 1970-; NEA 1970-; Small Grants for Tchrs Awded U Lowell Coll of Ed 1987; *office:* Pawtucketville Memorial Schl 4 Meadow Rd Lowell MA 01854*

NELSON, JOANNE M., Fourth Grade Teacher; *b:* Mannington, N William C.; *c:* Sarah, Katie; *ed:* Glassboro St Coll (BA) Kndgtn, Pr Ed 1974; Addl 12 Hrs Cert Early Chldhd Ed; *cr:* Salem City 4-Y Kndgtn Tchr 1975-77; John Fenwick Schl Basics Skills Tchr 197 Salem MS Classroom Tchr 1978-95; John Fenwick Schl Fourth Grd 1995-; *ai:* Schl Morale-Climate, Spirit Comm; NJEA 1978-, Assn STA 1978-, VP; *office:* John Fenwick Schl 183 Smith St Salem NJ 0

NELSON, JUDITH, First Grade Teacher; *b:* Brooklyn, NY; *ed:* St J Coll (BA) Ed, His 1970; Queens Coll (MS) Elem Ed 1975; *cr:* PS 169 1971-; *ai:* UFT 1970-; *office:* PS 169 Sunset Park 4305 7th Ave Bro NY 11232

NELSON, JUDITH BINNER, French Teacher; *b:* Quakertown, F Kenneth S.; *ed:* Temple Univ (BMUS) Music-Magna Cum Laude Univ of PA (MA) Fr 1986; Grad Stud Princeton Seminary; Diplomas Univ of Brussels W-Hons, Univ of Stockholm, Univ of Strast L'Institut Catholique W-distinguished Hnrs; *cr:* Saint Isidore's Schl Rdng, Soc Stud Tchr 1974-75; Gullmarsplans Vuxen Gymnasium Eng 1980-83; Univ of PA Fr Tchng Fellow 1984-86; Perkiomen Vly HS Fr 1986-87; Lower Merion Sch Dist Fr Tchr 1987-; *ai:* Fr Club Adv; Coach; AATF 1994-; NEA 1986-; LMEA 1987-; Beckford Walking 1991-; Acad Schlsp Temple Univ; Notation with Hnrs from Free Ur Brussels with Notation Distngd Hnrs Univ of Stasbourg, L'In Catholique; Tchng Fellow Univ of PA; Excl Tchng Penn Course G *office:* Lower Merion HS 245 E Montgomery Ave Ardmore PA 1900

NELSON, JUDITH CARVELLI, Guidance Counselor; *b:* Camder *m:* Karl; *c:* Patrick, Brett, Angelina; *ed:* Glassboro St Coll (BA) Soc Ed 1982; Rowan Coll of NJ (MA) Stu Personel Svcs 1994; *cr:* Washi Twp HS US His Tchr 1984-93, Guidance Cnslr 1993-; *ai:* NHS Co- NEA, NJEA, WTEA 1984-; Tchr of Yr 1992; *office:* Washington Tow HS 529 Hurffville Cross Keys Rd Sewell NJ 08080

NELSON, MALCOLM A., Distinguished Professor of Eng Carbondale, IL; *m:* Elizabeth Hoffman; *c:* Michael, David, Laurie, Bernie; *ed:* Williams Coll (BA) Eng 1955; Northwestern Univ (MA Lit 1957, (PHD) Eng Lit 1961; *cr:* Northwestern Univ Tchng Asst 195 Miami Univ Instr, Asst Prof 1959-65; Grinnell Coll Asst Prof 196 SUNY Assoc Prof, Prof, Distinguished Prof Eng 1968-; *ai:* Lit Soc AFT 1969-; NYSUT 1969-, Dir 1980-82; United Univ Professions 1 Nina Mitchell Svc Awd; Phi Beta Kappa 1954-; Modern Lang Assn 1 Little League, Former Coach; Everywoman's Opportunity Ctr, Forme Tyng Fnd Fellowship; Books: The Robin Hood Tradition in the Renaissance, A Collection of Catches, Canons & Glees, Epitaph & I Field Guide to the Old Burying Grounds of Cape Cod, Martha's Vine Nantucket; *home:* 120 W Main St Brocton NY 14716

NELSON, MARGARET, English Director; *b:* New York, NY; *ed:* Am (BA) Eng 1966; St Univ at Oneonta (MA) Eng Ed 1968; Hofstra (

n 1981; Univ of PA Grant Eng Lit 1969; Portland St Univ Irish Poetry Univ of CA Irish Short Story 1990; *cr:* Westbury HS 9-12th Grd Eng 1967-69; Kings Park HS 9-12th Grd Eng Tchr 1969-95, Tchr & n 1973-90, Eng Dir 1996-; *ai:* NCTE, NYSUT, NYS Eng Cncl Tchr cl Awd; *office:* Kings Park HS Rt 25A Kings Park NY 11754

SON, MARY CAMPBELL, Social Studies Teacher; *b:* Worcester, m: Donald R.; *c:* Tammy Carr, Cheri Pillarella, Kenneth; *ed:* Anna Coll (BA) His 1967; Assumption Coll (MA) His 1972; 45 Hrs Post Stud Anna Maria Coll, Worcester St Coll; *cr:* David Prouty HS Soc Tchr 1967-; *ai:* Soc Stud Frameworks, Block Scheduling Comms; Fr ass, NHS, Sr Hnr Soc Adv; Spencer-East Brookfield Tchrs Assn, MA Ass, NEA 1967-; Delta Kappa Gamma 1975-, Sec, VP Alpha Alpha; : David Prouty HS 302 Main St Spencer MA 01562

SON, MARYLOU PICKELL, Retired K-2nd Grade Teacher; *b:* rville, NJ; *m:* Edward A. J.; *c:* Kenneth Edward, Linda Diane Ward, erine Elizabeth; *ed:* Beaver Coll (BS) K-Elem Ed 1959; *cr:* West End 2nd Grd Tchr 1959-60; Chester Elem Schl 2nd Grd Tchr 1960-61; Mt Elem Schl 2nd Grd Tchr 1963-64; Willingboro Bd of Ed Kndtn, 1st, Grd Tchr 1970-92; *ai:* First United Meth Church, Bldg, Church, Soc ns; United Meth Women; *home:* 750 McElwee Rd Moorestown NJ

SON, NANCY WEISS, Jr HS Science Teacher; *b:* Cleveland, OH; *m:* rt; *c:* Rob, Justin; *ed:* Saint John Coll (BSE) Elem Ed 1971, (MSE) seling 1974; 30 Hrs Beyond Masters in Sci & Counseling Classes; *cr:* eland Pub Schls 3rd Grd Tchr 1971-78; Newbury Schls Spec earning Disabilities, Jr HS Sci, His, Lang Arts, Math, Algebra & Rdng 1979-; *ai:* NEA 1982-; AFT 1971-78; *office:* Newbury Schl 14775 rn Rd Newbury OH 44065

SON, PATRICIA MORA, Spanish Teacher; *b:* Attleboro, MA; *c:* l, Dennis, Jennifer; *ed:* Muhlenberg Coll (AB) Span, Soc Sci 1973; CT St Univ (MS) Span 1978; *cr:* Simsbury HS Span Tchr 1973-; *ai:* Trivia Team Coach; NEASC Follow UP, Frgn Lang Curr Review ns; COLT 1975-; NEA, CEA, SEA 1974-; *office:* Simsbury HS 34 s Village Rd Simsbury CT 06070

SON, PAULA PERKINS, Business Education Teacher; *b:* Pittsburgh, : Donald G.; *ed:* Geneva Coll (AA) Secretarial 1968; Grove City Coll Bus Ed 1970; Univ of Pittsburgh (MED) Bus Ed 1974; Robert Morris 15 Credit Hrs; *cr:* Comm Coll of Beaver Co Instr 1986-92; Western er HS Bus Ed Tchr 1970-; *ai:* Bus Club Spon; NEA, PSEA, WBEA , Treas; Tri-State Bus Tchrs 1970-; Delta Pi Epsilon Honorary Bus *ffice:* Western Beaver HS 216 Engle Rd Industry PA 15052

SON, ROBERT SCOTT, English Teacher; *b:* Brooklyn, NY; *m:* Linda eck; *c:* John, Peter, Caroline; *ed:* St Francis Coll (BA) Eng, Sec Ed SUNY at Stony Brook (MA) Lbrl Stud 1980; *cr:* Mt Sinai HS Eng 1980-; *ai:* Stu Ath Adv; NYSUT, AFT 1980-; *office:* Mount Sinai HS ude Goodman Dr Mount Sinai NY 11766

SON, ROBERTA BUDD, Art Teacher; *b:* Harrisburg, PA; *m:* Eric V.; A St Univ (BS) Art Ed 1964; Addl 27 Hrs in Art at Owswego St Univ 3 Hrs in Art at Elmira Coll 1975; *cr:* Chenango Valley Cntrl Schl Art Mexico Cntrl Schls Art Tchr; Romulus Cntrl Schl Art Tchr 1974-; *ai:* Leadership Comm; NYSATA 1970-; NYSUT 1975-; Delta Kappa na; Amer Craftsman 1995-; Meml Art Gallery 1994-; *office:* Romulus Schl 5705 Main St Romulus NY 14541

SON, RONALD HARRY, Bible & Science Teacher; *b:* Bellevue, OH; ynn Rochelle Gunter; *c:* Caleb, Nathan; *ed:* OH Univ (BS) Geology (MS) 1967; *cr:* Foote Mineral Co Field Geologist 1967-74; Heritage n Schl Bible & Sci Tchr 1977-; *ai:* Cleveland Bapt Church 1977-, on; Curr Materials in Print; *home:* 4473 W 137th St Cleveland OH 5*

SON, SADIE YVONNE, Teacher; *b:* Townsend, GA; *m:* Howard; *c:* , Barry, Reginald, Nadine, Nichole, Kyle, Keir; *ed:* NYC Comm Coll) Lbrl Arts 1974; Medgar Evers (BS) Elem Ed 1976; Tchrs Coll at mbia (MA) Spec Ed Mentally Retarded 1980; 21 Credit Hrs; *cr:* Bd of ducl Asst, Rdng, Math Tchr 1970-80, Rdng Tchr 1980-81, Spec Ed 1981-; *ai:* Stu Govt Adv; Schl Base Mngmt Team; Assembly Coord; ; Rachel Jean Mitchell Awd; *office:* IS 55 Oceanhill-Brownsville 2021 en St Brooklyn NY 11233

SON, THOMAS JOHN, Band Teacher; *b:* Fort Monmouth, NJ; *m:* Ann Roupp; *ed:* West Chester Univ (BS) Music Ed 1992; 10 Post Grad Manfield Univ; *cr:* St Josephs Schl K-8 Classroom, Vocal Music Tchr -93; Allentown HS Instrumental Teacher 1992-93; Williamson Jr Sr Band Tchr 1993-; R. B. Walters Elem Schl Band Tchr 1993-; *ai:* Jazz, hing Bands; Soph Class Adv; NEA, PMEA 1993-; PAS 1992-; *home:* Box 84A Liberty PA 16930

SON, TIMOTHY TAFT, English Teacher; *b:* Hamilton, OH; *m:* la Louise Smith; *c:* Erin, Megan; *ed:* Eastern KY Univ (BA) Eng ; Attnd Miami Univ at Oxford OH, Univ of Cincinnati; *cr:* Garfield Jr Eng Tchr 1984-; *ai:* NEA, OEA, HCTA 1984-; NRA 1987-; Izaak on League 1988-; *office:* Garfield Jr HS 250 N Fair Ave Hamilton OH 1

SON, WILLIAM T., Eng, Drama & Television Tchr; *b:* Buffalo, NY; ois E. Duffield; *c:* Jessica, Jonathan; *ed:* Univ of Hartford (BA) ter Arts, Television 1985; SUNY at Albany (MA) Tchng 1989; Eugene ill Theater Ctr Natl Theater Inst Grad; *cr:* Drury Lane Theater Actor -84; Theaterworks, USA Actor 1986-87; Schalmont Schl Dist Eng 1990-91; Greater Amsterdam Schl Dist Eng, Drama, TV Tchr 1991-; Drama Club; Superteams Trng Group; NYSUT, AFT 1991-; Actors ty Assn 1983-; United Presbyn Church 1992-, Session, Clerk of ion, Sunday Schl Moderator; *office:* Amsterdam HS Saratoga Ave terdam NY 12010

ICHICK, MARK ALLAN, Physics Teacher; *b:* McKeesport, PA; *m:* my Lee Schaup; *ed:* CA Univ of PA (BS) Physics 1992; *cr:* Steel Vly Physics Tchr 1992-93; McKeesport Area HS Physics Tchr 1993-; *ai:* Track Coach; PSEA 1992-; MAEA 1993-; *office:* Mc Keesport Area 960 Eden Park Blvd Mc Keesport PA 15132

IECEK, ANTHONY JOSEPH, English, Speech & Debate Tchr; *b:* Fernando Vly, CA; *m:* Caroline Hickinbottom; *c:* Max, Lucy; *ed:* OH niv (BA) Eng 1983; John Carroll Univ (MED) Eng, Speech Ed 1990; Cleveland Cntrl Cath HS Eng, Rdng Tchr 1985-86; Cleveland Hghts HS Speech Tchr 1987-; Cleveland St Univ Access to Careers in neering Prgm Tchr 1994-; *ai:* Speech, Debate Team Coach; Steering m; AFT 1988-, HS Chief Steward 1993-; OH HS Speech League, eland Dist Chm 1993-; Natl Forensic League, Diamond Awd, OH h Coast Dist Comm; St Paul's Cooperative Nursery Schl, VP; ointed Dist Mentor; St of OH Tchr of YR 1992; *office:* Cleveland ghts H S 13263 Cedar Rd Cleveland Heights OH 44118*

IERGUT, DOLLY E., Bilingual Science Teacher; *b:* Santurce, PR; *m:* P.; *c:* Nicole Veronica, Ivan Byice, Aidan Sam; *ed:* Rutger-Cook Coll) Enviromental & Ed 1990; Middlesex Cty Coll Chem Tech 1982; Grad of Ed; Biling Ed; *cr:* FMC Rsrch Ctr Residues & Metabolism Tech 2-84, Analytical Chem Tech 1984-87; Perth Amboy HS Biling Sci, Bio arth Sci Tchr 1994-95; McGinnis MS Biling Sci Tchr 1995-; *ai:* Grad of Ed Biling Endorsement Pgm; NEA 1990-; AFT 1994-; TESOL -; Mobile Corp Sci Grant 1982; *office:* William C McGuinnis MS 271 St Perth Amboy NJ 08861

NEMET, RIMA ROSSIN, First Grade Teacher; *b:* Brooklyn, NY; *w:* Jordan H. (dec); *c:* Karen Nemet Betsy, Richard B.; *ed:* Brooklyn Coll (BA) Elem Ed 1959; William Paterson Coll 9 Spec Ed Credits; *cr:* Plainview-Old Bethpage Schl Dist Second Grd Tchr 1959-62, Third Grd Tchr 1963-64; PS 153 Manhattan Second Grd Tchr 1986-91, First Grd Tchr 1991-; *ai:* AFT 1986-; UFT 1986-, Excl in Tchng 1994; Temple Beth Tikvah, Choir; *office:* PS 153 Adam Clayton Powell Jr 1750 Amsterdam Ave New York NY 10031

NEMI, DAVID MICHAEL, Asst Professor of Business; *b:* Lockport, NY; *m:* Anna Skakuj; *c:* Christy, Jillian, Robert, Allison; *ed:* Niagara Cty Comm Coll (AAS) Bus Admin 1978; St Univ Coll at Buffalo (BS) Mrktg & Distributive Ed 1980, (MS) Mrktg & Distributive Ed 1984; *cr:* Erie Cty Comm Coll Instr 1981-85; Niagara Cty Comm Coll Asst Prof 1986-; Small Bus Dev Ctr Mrktg Consultant 1991-; *ai:* Mens Bsbl Coach 1984-; Curr, Distngd Stu Schlsp & Kalifas Awd Comms; Pres Awd for Excl in Advisment; NEA 1986-; Assn of Mrktng Edctrs 1987-; Credit Union Exec Soc 1990-; Unit I Federal Credit Union 1988-, Treas & Bd of Dir; St Anthonys Parish 1990-, Parish Cncl; Tony Nemi Sportsmans League 1992-, Bd of Dir; AN & JO Bsbl League 1992-, Coach; Pres Awd for Excl Advisment at Niagara CCC 1992; Distngd Alumni Awd 1995; Book: Promotion A Small Business Guide; Guest Speaker Niagara Falls Chamber of Commerce Bus Seminars 1991-; *office:* Niagara County Comm Coll 3111 Saunders Settlement Rd Sanborn NY 14132*

NEMOTKO, ANITRA DOUGHERTY, Chrpsn & Instr of Sci Dept; *b:* Dunmore, PA; *ed:* Marywood Coll (BS) Bio & Chem 1959; Villanova Univ (MS) Bio 1967; Univ of Pgy (PHD) Sci Ed 1990; Attnd Wilkes Univ, Univ of VT Med Schl, Temple Univ; *cr:* Univ of Pgy PHD Tchng Flwshp 1983-88; Marywood Sci Dept & Fac Mem 1988-93, Chprsn & Fac Mem 1993-; *ai:* Bio Club, Acad, Pre-Med & Sci Ed Adv; Tchr Ed & Field Experience Advy Bd; Acad Computing & Allied Hlth Comms; NSTA 1989-; AAAS 1989-; NARST 1989-; ABTA 1989-; PA Jr Acad of Sci 1980-, Advy Bd; NSF Equipment Grant; *home:* 1338 Madison Ave Scranton PA 18509

NENOW, WILLIAM EDWARD, 7th-8th Grade Science Teacher; *b:* Phillipsburg, NJ; *m:* JoAnn Adrienne Bergeron; *c:* Jennifer, Adrienne; *ed:* Rider Coll (BA) His 1969; Attnd Lehigh Univ 15 Grad Credit Hrs, Allentown Coll, Lafayette Coll 9 Credit Hrs, Trenton St Coll 12 Credit Hrs; *cr:* Bloomsburg Elem 6th-8th Grd His, Sci & Eng Tchr 1969-72; Greenwich Twp Elem 6th-8th Grd Sci Tchr 1973-; *ai:* Sci Dept Head; Bsktbl Coach; IM Sports; NJEA 1969-; NCTE 1973-; Masonic Lodge 1977-; US Coast Guard; NJ Governors Tchr Recognition Pgm; *office:* Greenwich Twp Elem Schl 269 S Main St Stewartsville NJ 08886

NEONAKIS, IRENE KIVLEN, French Teacher; *b:* Summit, NJ; *m:* John; *c:* Dimitra, Nicholas, Alexia, Peter; *ed:* Coll of St Elizabeth (BA) Fr 1961; Attnd Univ of Paris 1961-62 Fr Lang & Culture, Univ of Athens 1967 Greek Lang; *cr:* Summit HS Fr Tchr 1962-67; Summit MS Fr Tchr 1982-; *ai:* Fr Club; Chaperone of Annual Stu Trip to France; AATF 1982-; *office:* Summit MS 272 Morris Ave Summit NJ 07901

NEPTUNE, DIANE MIGNELLA, Fifth Grade Teacher; *b:* Youngstown, OH; *m:* Larry Edward; *c:* Allison; *ed:* Youngstown St Univ (BA) Elem Ed 1974; Univ of Dayton 8, Univ of Seattle Pacific 5, Coll of Mt St Joseph 6 Post Grad Quarter Hrs; *cr:* Diana Shop Asst Credit Mgr 1974-75; Carlisles Dept Store Dept Mgr 1975; Edison Local Schls Tchr 1975-; *ai:* John Gregg Sci Fair Chm; Sci Dept Chprsn; CBE Math Test Formation Comm; Past Cheerleading Adv 1975-78; ELEA, OEA, NEA 1975-; Richmond Lioness Club 1985-88; St Level Math Resource Tchr 1990-92; *home:* B7343 Stuart Mnr # R2 Steubenville OH 43952*

NEPTUNE, LARRY EDWARD, Science Teacher; *b:* Fairmont, WV; *m:* Diane M.; *c:* Allison; *ed:* W Liberty (BA) Bio 1974; Univ of Steubenville Math Cert 1976; *cr:* Jefferson Union HS Math & Sci Tchr 1974-88; Edison South HS Sci Tchr 1988-93; Edison HS Math & Sci Tchr 1993-; *ai:* Ftbl, Bsktbl & Track Coach 1974-86; Frosh Class Adv 1988-89; NEA & OEA 1974-; Edison Local Ed Assn 1974-, Bldg Rep 1976-86; Richmond Lions Club 1972-; Jefferson Cty Schls Courses of Stud, Textbook Selection & CBE Test Formation Comms; *office:* Edison HS RD 1 Box 308 Richmond OH 43944

NERI, ANTHONY JOSEPH, Biology Teacher; *b:* Jersey City, NJ; *m:* Sandra S. Gerak; *c:* Christopher, Theresa; *ed:* Jersey City St (BS) Sci Ed 1966, (MS) Sci in Sp Ed 1980; 30 Credit Hrs Human Physiology, Marine Bio; *cr:* NNMC Bethesda Tchr OR Tech 1968-69; Woodbridge Adult Schl Bio Tchr 1971-75; Raritan HS Bio Tchr 1968-; *ai:* Drill Team & 4-H Club Adv; Class Adv 1972, 1991; Sci League Adv 1989-92; Stu Cncl Adv; NJEA, NEA 1968-; Hazlet Tea Assn 1968-, Bldg Rep; Bio Tchr Assn, NJSTA 1975-; St Mary's Church Parish Cncl 1979-, VP; Woodbridge Jaycees 1970-71; Ciba Gigy Phar Fellowship; Tchr of Yr; NJ Dept of Head Cmptr Network; *office:* Raritan HS 419 Middle Rd Hazlet NJ 07730*

NERI, ROSANNE, ESOL Teacher; *b:* Bridgeport, CT; *c:* Jeremy K. Saladyga, Ian A. Saladyga; *ed:* Sacred Heart Univ (BA) Eng, Scndry Ed 1968, (MAT) Lit 1988; Southern Ct St Univ 6th Yr Rdng, Lang Arts, Consultant, K-12 ESOL Specialist 1994; *cr:* Warren Harding HS Scndry Eng Tchr 1968-71, Intnl Inst of Conn Inc Dir of ESOl Svcs, ESOL Tchr to Adults 1978-84; Warren Harding HS ESOL Tchr LAG Monitor Scndry 1984-; *ai:* LAU Monitor; LAU Tester ESOL B/L Dept; NEA, CEA, BEA, CA BBE 1984-; Natl Assn of Univ Women Grant; Graduated 1st in Class Sacred Heart Masters Prgm 1988; *office:* Warren Harding HS 1734 Central Ave Bridgeport CT 06610

NERL, THOMAS G., Assistant Prin & Alegbra Tchr; *b:* Cincinnati, OH; *m:* Julianne M.; *c:* Kevin Thomas, Eric Gerard; *ed:* Xavier Univ (BS) Math 1986; *cr:* Purcell Marian HS Math Tchr 1986-, Summer Schl Prin 1994-, Asst Prin 1995-; *ai:* Head Bsbl, Asst Ftbl Coach; NCTM 1986-; Southwest OH Bsbl Coaches Assn 1986-, Treas; *office:* Purcell Marian HS 2935 Hackberry St Cincinnati OH 45206

NERO, JOSEPH MICHAEL, Business Teacher; *b:* Hudson, NY; *m:* Tina Mary Fish; *c:* Erik, Jamie, Gregory; *ed:* Columbia-Green Comm Coll (AS) Bus 1971; SUNY at Albany (BS) Bus Ed 1973; 33 Credit Hrs; *cr:* Red Hook Cntrl High Bus Tchr 1973-; *ai:* AFT 1973-; NYSUT 1973-; Red Hook Fac Assn 1973-; Red Hook Little League 1987-, Pres; Red Hook Sports Club 1993-; *home:* 101 W Market St Red Hook NY 12571

NERO, MICHELE, 5th Grade Teacher; *b:* Brooklyn, NY; *c:* Kyree Nero-Hattley, Kaliq Nero-Scott; *ed:* Fordham Univ (BA) Ed, Soc Stud 1971; Columbia Univ (MA) Curr, Tchng 1972; Kingsborough Comm Coll Addl 30 Hrs; *cr:* PS 181 Schl 4 Gr Tchr 1972-76; IS 61 Oceanhill Schl Eng Tchr 1976-77; PS 279 Schl 4 Gr Tchr 1977-79; PS 235 4, 5 Gr Tchr 1980-90; PS 221 5 Gr Tchr 1990-; *ai:* Multicultural Coord: Stu Tchr Prog Medgar Evers Coll, Bklyn Coll; UFT 1972-; *office:* PS 221 Empire 791 Empire Blvd Brooklyn NY 11213*

NERSESIAN, ROY L., Associate Prof of Management; *b:* Bayshore, NY; *m:* Marie D. Kotasey; *c:* Diane, Julie, Catherine, Eric; *ed:* Rensselaer Polytechnic Inst (BS) Physics 1961; Harvard Bus Schl (MBA) 1971; *cr:* US Navey Engr Ofcr Polauis Sub 1961-69; Zapata Naess Shipping Proj ect Analyst 1971-73; Manufacturers Hanover Bank Shipping Loan Ofcr 1973-76; Poten & Partners Maritime Consultant 1976-85; Monmouth Univ Assoc Prof 1985-; *ai:* Fac Adv Phi Sigma Kappa; Books: Ships & Shipping, Cmptr Simulation in Bus Decision Making, Corp Planning & Cmptr Simulation; Cmptr Simulation in Fin Risk Mngmt, Global Mngmt Acctng, Cmptr Simulation in Logistics; *office:* Monmouth Univ Schl of Bus West Long Branch NJ 07764

NERTI, DAVID MICHAEL, Senior Soc Studies Head Tchr; *b:* Ellwood City, PA; *m:* Cheryl A. Lewis; *c:* Nicole, Angela; *ed:* Slippery Rock Univ (BS) Soc Stud 1977; Masters Equivalency Duquesne Univ 1992; *cr:* Union Area Schl Dist Soc Stud Tchr 1982-94, Head Tchr 1994-; *ai:* Sr HS Class Adv; Disciplinarian Mid HS; Former Head Ftbl Coach; NEA, PSEA 1982-; Union Area Ed Assn 1982-, VP; Chewton Vol Fire Dept 1982-, Chief, Pres; Wayne Twp Planning Comm 1994-; PA Governing Bd Prof Dev; PA Regency Bd Governors for Prof Dev; *office:* Union Area Schl Dist 2106 Camden Ave New Castle PA 16101

NERVEGNA, MARY H., Mathematics Teacher; *b:* Carbondale, PA; *m:* Gene; *c:* Louis, Margaret; *ed:* Marywood Coll (BA) Chem 1962, (MS) Sci-Math Ed 1970; *cr:* Overlea Sr HS Chem Tchr 1962-63; Lakeland Schl Dist Sci & Math Tchr 1963-76; Carbondale Area Sub Tchr 1985-86; Scranton Hebrew Day Schl Math Tchr 1986-90; Holy Rosary Elem Schl Math Tchr 1990-; *ai:* 6th Grd Homeroom Tchr & Adv; NCEA 1990-; PSEA (Now Retired) 1963-1986; Girl Scouts of Amer 1989-, Troop Adv; *office:* Holy Rosary Elem Schl 316 William St Scranton PA 18508*

NESHOFF, DARLENE, Business Education Teacher; *b:* Braddock, PA; *ed:* Indiana Univ of PA (BS) Bus, Distributive Ed 1983; Working Towards MS in Cmptr Sci; *cr:* Mc Keesport Area HS Bus, Distributive Ed Tchr 1 Yr; West Mifflin Area HS Bus Ed Tchr 11 Yrs; *ai:* Asst Vlybl, Seventh Grd Girl's Bsktbl Coach; Key Club Spon; Sr Awds Chprsn; AFT 1985-; Mon Vly Partners 1994-, Spon; *office:* West Mifflin Area HS 91 Commonwealth Ave West Mifflin PA 15122

NESLEY, MAUREEN LEE, French Teacher; *b:* Canonsburg, PA; *m:* Todd J.; *c:* Cortland; *ed:* Penn St Univ (BS) Scndry Ed Frgn Lang 1987; *cr:* St Coll Area Schl Dist Fr Tchr 1987-88; Steel Vly Schl Dist Fr Tchr 1988-89; Pocono Mountain Schl Dist Fr Tchr 1989-90; Stroudsburg Area Schl Dist Fr Tchr 1991-; *ai:* Fr Club & NHS Adv; NEA 1989-; PSEA 1989-; SAEA 1991-; *home:* 22 Balson Rd Stroudsburg PA 18360*

NESNAY, ELISA SAKOSITS, Fifth Grade Teacher; *b:* Englewood, NJ; *m:* Jeffrey; *ed:* Seton Hall Univ (BS) Elem Ed 1976; Attnd Jersey City St Coll; *cr:* Bergenfield Pub Schls First Grd Tchr Compensatory Ed Title I Instr 1977-82; Byram Twp Pub Schls Fifth Grd Tchr 1982-; *ai:* NJEA 1982-; NEA 1982-; Byram Tchrs Assn 1982-; NW Jersey Rdng Cncl 1991-; Byram PTA 1982-, 3rd VP 1994-95; 1988 Governors Tchr Recognition Awd; 1990 Byram Tchr of the Yr; *office:* Byram Intermediate Schl 12 Mansfield Dr Stanhope NJ 07874

NESSELROAD, MICHAEL A., Chemistry Teacher; *b:* Pomeroy, OH; *m:* Tania Bichsel; *c:* Coree Rae, Andrew T.; *ed:* Rio Grande Coll (BA) Bio, Chem 1979; Attnd Ohio St Univ, Ashland Univ Admin; *cr:* Greenfield Mc Clain HS Chem Tchr 1979-84; Delaware Hayes HS Chem Tchr 1984-; *ai:* Head Golf Coach; OEA, NEA 1979-, Bldg Rep; Grad Speaker 1993; *office:* Delaware Hayes HS 289 Euclid Ave Delaware OH 43015*

NESSEN, RICHARD STEPHEN, Principal & Teacher; *b:* Brookline, MS; *m:* Kathryn Raymond; *c:* Pamela, Peter, Annie, Abigail; *ed:* Yale Univ (BA) Eng 1967; Stanford Univ (MA) Ed 1968; Univ of MA ABD; UVM Spec Ed Credit; *cr:* Mead Schl Tchr, Staff Dir 1972-75; Middlebury Coll Lecturer 1975-80; Bridge Schl Co-Founder, Tchr 1981-; *ai:* NATM 1988-; *office:* Bridge Schl PO Box 27 Middlebury VT 05753

NESTER, CAROL BAIRD, 4th Grade Teacher; *b:* Bethel Park, PA; *m:* Arthur F.; *c:* Genna; *ed:* Univ of Pgh (BS) Elem Ed 1973, (MED) Elem Ed 1976; *cr:* Lib Elem Schl 5th Grd Tchr 1974-76, 4th Grd Tchr 1976-; *ai:* PSEA 1974-; *office:* Library Elem Schl 6450 Pleasant St Library PA 15129

NESTLER, PATRICIA CUNDIFF, Associate Professor of English; *b:* Bryn Mawr, PA; *m:* David Donald; *ed:* Gettysburg Coll (BA) Eng 1972; Univ of NC at Chapel Hill (MA) Eng 1973; 15 Credit Hrs at Villanova Univ & Northeastern Univ; *cr:* TV Guide Magazine Readers Svc Dept 1973-74; Villanova Univ Part-Time Eng Instr 1977; Montgomery Cty Comm Coll Assoc Prof of Eng 1974-; *ai:* Writers Club Adv 1982-; Annual Writers Club Conf Coord 1988-; Headed Spring Writers Forums 1991 & 1992; Amer Assn of Univ Profs 1980-82; AFT 1984-; NCTE; Modern Lang Assn; MCCC Speakers Bureau 1990-; MCCC Norristown Pub Lib, Liaison, Applying for Poets in Person Grant 1995; Wkshp Ldr at Philadelphia Writers Conf 1990; Stu Affairs Outstdng Svc Awd 1991; Outstdng Contributions Made to Montgomery Cty Comm Coll Pres Awd 1993; *office:* Montgomery County Comm Coll 340 Dekalb Pike Blue Bell PA 19422*

NESTOR, MARY MAXWELL, Art Teacher; *b:* Brooklyn, NY; *m:* Edward Gerard; *c:* Mary, Edward, Brian; *ed:* St Johns Univ (BS) Art, Ed 1965; Brooklyn Coll (MS) Art, Ed 1980; Attnd Brooklyn Gardens Cert Floral Design, Art Courses, Water Colors, Botanicals, Landscaping; NY Pub Schl License K-8 Grd; *cr:* St Michaels Grammer Schl 1, 8 Grd Tchr 1961-66; PS 140 2 Grd Tchr 1966-68; Sub Work Pub Pvt Schl K, 8 Grd Tchr; St Agnes Seminary K-8 Art Tchr 1980-82; Bishop Kearney HS Art Tchr 1982-; *ai:* Fashion Design Club; Fac Cncl; Group Ldr Mid Sts Presch; Tchrs Union 1982-; Brklyn Museum, Met Museum, Women's Museum 1990-; Block Assn 1 Yrs, Pres Monies for Block Improvement; Rosary Soc 10 Yrs.

NESTRA, JOHN E., Teacher; *b:* Detroit, MI; *ed:* Bowling Green St Univ (BS) Elem Ed 1967, (MED) Guid, Cnslng 1971; *cr:* Margaretta Local Schls Tchr 1964-; *ai:* Swim Coach 1970-76; NEA; OEA; SECO; Fullbright Grant; *office:* Bogart Elem Schl 5906 Bogart Rd W Castalia OH 44824

NETCHER, JAMES HARLAND, Junior High Math Teacher; *b:* Elmore, OH; *m:* LInda Sue White; *c:* Cheryl D.; *ed:* OH St Univ (BS) Ag Ec 1967; Addl 14 Credit Hrs; Bowling Green St Univ 47 Credit Hrs 1968-73; Univ of UT 4 Credit Hrs 1973; Walsh Coll 3 Credit Hrs 1994; *cr:* Bellevue City Schls Sixth Grd Tchr 1968-82, Fifth & Sixth Grd Tchr 1983, Sixth Grd Tchr 1984-92, Jr HS Math Tchr 1993-; *ai:* Chm Math Textbook, Schl Levy, Middle Schl Comms; Jr Var Bsktbl Coach; Bellevue, OH Ed Assns, NEA 1968-; OH HS Bsktbl Coaches Assn 1978-; US Tennis Assn 1984-; OH HS Bsktbl Coaches Hall of Fame; Bellevue Gazette Tchr Awd; Selected to Attnd Martha Holden Jennings Conf; Nom Master Tchr Awd Martha Holden Jennigs Fnd.

NETH, JOHN WATSON,III, Biology Teacher; *b:* Indianapolis, IN; *m:* Linda Gene Gray; *c:* Christena Ruth, John Watson IV; *ed:* Milligan Coll (BS) Bio, Chem 1968; OH St Univ (MS) Zoology 1971; Attnd Ashland Univ, Barry Univ, FL Inst of Tech, Southern Univ of NY, Univ of ID at Moscow, Univ of WY at Laramie; *cr:* Groveport-Madison HS Bio, Physics, Zoology, Int, Environmental Sci Tchr 1971-; Milligan Coll Summer NSF Instr 1982-85; Ashland Univ Adj Tchr 1995; *ai:* Sci Curr Comm; Wild, Aquatic, Wet Projects Facilitator; NSTA; MSTA; ABIS; SECO, On Site Registration St Conf; Natl Geographic 1957-; Wheaton Club 1985-; OH Cued Speech Assn 1980-, Co-Pres; Natl Cued Speech Assn; Project Discovery Cntrl Dist 1990-, Steering Comm; Milligan Coll Outstdng Biological Sci Stu 1968; OH Acad of Sci Acker Outstdng Sci Tchng Awd; Denison Univ Outstdng Tchng Awd; Sci Dept Chm 19 Yrs; *home:* 634 Elm St Groveport OH 43125*

NETTI, PATRICIA ANN, English & Journalism Teacher; *b:* Bronx, NY; *ed:* Iona Coll (BA) Speech, Theatre 1984, (MS) Ed 1987; *cr:* St Mary Star of the Sea 4th Grd Tchr 1984-85; Herbert H. Lehman HS Eng, Jrnlsm Tchr 1985-; *ai:* Schl Newspaper Adv; Chrldng Coach; UFT, AFT 1985; Quill & Scroll Intnl 1995-; Rookie Tchr of Yr 1989; Tchr of Yr 1989; *office:* Herbert H Lehman HS 3000 E Tremont Ave Bronx NY 10461*

NETTLETON, RUTH ALEXANDER, Retired First Grade Teacher; *b:* West Haven, CT; *w:* Willis (dec); *c:* Wesley, Martha Pacilio, Nancy Jackson; *ed:* Tchrs Coll of CT (BS) Elem Ed 1949; Southern CT St Coll (MB) Rdng 1973; *cr:* Wethersfield CT Bd Ed First Grd Tchr 1949-50; Guilford CT Bd Ed Third Grd Tchr 1950-52; Cox Schl First Grd Tchr 1964-89; *ai:* Lead Rdng Tchr 3 Yrs; NEA 1964-88; *home:* 464 Tanner Marsh Rd Guilford CT 06437

NETTNIN, PATRICIA KECKLEY, Professor of Computer Science; *b:* Sidney, OH; *m:* Thomas; *c:* Kristopher, Jonathan; *ed:* Bowling Green Univ (BS) Math & Minor Cmptr Sci 1974; St Univ of NY at Brockport (MA) Math & Emphasis Cmptr Sci 1980; Attnd Nazareth Coll & RIT Credit Hrs in Cmptr Sci; *cr:* Eastman Kodak Systems Analyst 1974-78; Gates-Chili HS Math & Cmptr Sci Tchr 1979-85; Finger Lakes Comm Coll Prof of Cmptr Sci 1985-; *ai:* Cmptr Sci Adv; Bargaining Cncl Officer; ACM 1988-, Reader, Schlsp Conf Presider 1995; NYSMATVC 1985-; Author of Introduction to the IBM Personal Cmptr & Interactive Guide; *office:* Finger Lakes Comm Coll 4355 Lakeshore Dr Canandaigua NY 14424

NETTROUR, ELIZABETH LYNN, English Graduate Tchng Fellow; *b:* Annapolis, MD; *ed:* Allegheny Coll (BA) Pol Sci 1990; Duquesne Univ (MA) Eng 1993; Working on Doctorate in Eng; *cr:* Duquesne Univ Eng Tchng Fellow 1993-; *ai:* Duquesne Awded Fellowship so i Could Complete Doctoral Stud; Presented Scholastic Papers at Confs Held at Notre Dame, RI Coll & Univ of Louisville; *office:* Duquesne Univ Eng Dept Pittsburgh PA 15282*

NEU, BRENDA GREENWELL, Mathematics Tchr & Asst Prin; *b:* Louisville, KY; *m:* Mark A. II; *c:* Mark A. III, Matthew A., Ashley L., Amanda E.; *ed:* Eastern KY Univ (BA) His & Soc Stud 1973; 24 Hrs for Elem Ed Cert; 5 Hrs Towards Masters in Admin; Courses Towards Religion Tchng Cert; *cr:* Middletown Schl Dist Tutor 1973-74; John XXIII Elem Tchr 1974-80, Tchr & Admin 1980-; *ai:* Math Counts Adv; Active Pride Awd Coord; NCEA 1981-; Archdiocesan Math Curr Dev Comm Mem; Diocesan Comm for the Harvest Mem; Schl Policy Comm Mem; Prin Search Comms Mem; Miami Univ OH Math Wkshp Planning Comm; 8 Hrs Math Wkshps; *office:* Pope John XXIII Elem 3806 Manchester Rd Middletown OH 45042

NEU, PETER SCOTT, Band Director; *b:* Bethlehem, PA; *ed:* Philadelphia Univ of Arts (BME) Music Ed, (BA) Music Performance 1985; Grad Stud Temple Univ, Westchester univ, Villonova Univ, Vandercook Coll of Music; *cr:* North Penn HS Jazz, Asst Marching Dir 1985-; North Penn Jr HS Band Dir 1985-94; Upper Moreland HS Asst Marching Band Dir 1989-; Pennbrook MS Band Dir 1994-; *ai:* Concert, Marching Band; Jazz, Brass Ensemble; Intnl Jazz Edctrs Assn, MENC, PA Music Edctrs Assn 1985-; Natl Band Assn 1988-; NEA 1985-; Amer Fed of Musicians, Intnl Trumpet Guild 1983-; Conducted Band Performances Intnl Jazz Edctrs Conventions 1993, 1996, PA Music Edctrs Assn Conf 1989, 1992, 1996, MENC 1993, Music Fest USA Jazz Ensemble Silver Medal 1989; *home:* 115 Kent Dr North Wales PA 19454

NEUBAUER, JOHN JOSEPH, EFL & FL Teacher; *b:* Baltimore, MD; *ed:* Towson St Univ (BA) Fr Lit 1984; Universite de Paris la Sorbonne Work Abroad Pgm 1984; 15 Credit Hrs in Educl Supervision at Loyola Coll; *cr:* The Baltimore City Coll FL Tchr 1987-95, Summer Scholars Pgm Dir 1994-95; Univ of MD ICONS Tchr & Asst Dir 1991-95; Amer Acad of Eng EFL Tchr 1995-; *ai:* MFLA 1988-, VP 1988-91, Pres 1991-92; AATF 1990-; MD Lang & Linguistic Soc 1993-; Baltimore Cncl of Frgn Affairs 1994-; Maryland Historical Soc 1994-; Walters Art Gallery 1995-; Bridge Pgm Supplement of 2nd Yr Latin 1992; Pub Numerous Journal Articles; Film Project Icons: The Ed of the Gifted & Talented; *office:* The Amer Acad of Eng Ul Jozefezaka 27A 41-902 Bytom Poland XX*

NEUBIG, MIKE A., Language Arts Teacher; *b:* Westerville, OH; *m:* Caroline Rieser; *c:* Emily, Megan; *ed:* Otterbein Coll (BA) Hlth Ed 1990; Working on Masters in Schl Cnslng at the OH St Univ; *cr:* Walnut Springs MS Lang Arts Tchr 1990-; *ai:* Head MS Ftbl & Asst Var Track Coach; OEA 1990-; NEA 1990-; *office:* Walnut Springs MS 888 E Walnut St Westerville OH 43081

NEUDING, MARY GAIL, English & Communications Tchr; *b:* Marion, OH; *m:* Karl D.; *c:* Aaron, Benjamin; *ed:* BGSU (BS) Ed 1975; OH St Univ (MS) Ed 1989; *cr:* Fremont Ross HS Comm, Eng Tchr 1975-85; Gahanna Lincoln HS Comm, Eng Tchr 1985-89; Kent City Schl HS Eng Tchr 1989-91; Hoban HS Eng Tchr 1991-92; Copley HS Eng, Comm Tchr 1992-; *ai:* Judge Speech Tournaments; Delta Kappa Gamma, Sec, Grad Schlsp 2 Yrs; 1st United Meth Church; *office:* Copley HS 3807 Ridgewood Rd Copley OH 44321*

NEUFANG, RICHARD, Mathematics Teacher; *b:* Geneva, NY; *m:* Carol Phelps; *c:* Donna Landwehr, Jill King, Mark; *ed:* Alfred St Tech (AAS) Electronic Comm 1962; Univ of Rochester (BA) Math 1965; Bowdoin Coll (MA) Math 1972; 15 Addl Grad Hrs; *cr:* Marcus Whitman Jr Sr HS Dept Chprsn 1970-91, Math Tchr 1965-; *ai:* AFT & Marcus Whitman Tchrs Assn 1965-; F&AM 1967-; Marcus Whitman Tchr of Yr Awd 1985; Natl Sci Fndtn Awd 169-72; *office:* Marcus Whitman Jr Sr H S Baldwin Rd Rushville NY 14544

NEUFELD, VALERIE THALROSE, English Teacher; *b:* New York, NY; *w:* George (dec); *c:* Joshua, Zachary; *ed:* (BA) 1971; (MS) 1976; 30 Post Grad Credits; *cr:* Sub Tchr 1971; PS 52 Fifth Grd Tchr 1976-77; PS 178 Fifth Grd Tchr 1977-78; PS 305 Third Grd Tchr 1978-84; MS 67 Q Eng Tchr 1984-; *ai:* UFT 1977-.

NEUHARD, TODD ANTHONY, Asst to Prin & HS Math Tchr; *b:* Danville, PA; *m:* Megan E.; *ed:* Bloomsburg Univ (MS) Scndry Ed 1992; Attnd Shippensburg Univ working on MS in Scndry Admin; *cr:* Northern Lebanon HS Scndry Math Tchr 4 Yrs, Asst to Prin 1 Yr; *ai:* Var Ftbl Asst Coach 4 Yrs; Jr High Wrestling Head Coach 4 Yrs; NEA 1992; *office:* Northern Lebanon HS 1 School Dr Fredericksburg PA 17026

NEUMAN, JERALD, Mathematics Teacher; *b:* Allentown, PA; *m:* Rita Marie Imp; *c:* Erin Raecke, Elissa; *ed:* Kutztown Univ (BA) Scndry Ed, Math 1967; 21 Credit Hrs Temple Univ; 6 Credit Hrs Penn St Univ; *cr:* Salisbury HS Scndry Ed Math Tchr 1967-95; *ai:* PA Math League Adv; NEA, PSEA 1967-; NCTM; *office:* Salisbury Sr HS 500 E Montgomery St Allentown PA 18103

NEUMANN, CAROLYN A., Mathematics Teacher; *b:* Somerville, NJ; *m:* Charles; *c:* Jennifer; *ed:* Trenton St Coll (BA) Math 1964; 15 Credit Hrs Beyond Masters in Cmptrs; *cr:* Bridgewater Raritan HS Math Tchr 1964-; Rutgers Univ Part- Time Math Lecturer 1994-; *ai:* Bridgewater Raritan Ed Assn, Somerset Cty Ed Assn, NJEA, NEA 1964-; Branchburg Republican 1990-94; Dist Comm, Elected Office; Courier News Best Tchr 1994; *home:* 172 Tanglewood Dr Somerville NJ 08876

NEUROTH, JOAN FERRIGNO, Sixth Grade Teacher; *b:* Lakewood, NJ; *m:* Michael; *c:* Ellen Marie, Robert Michael; *ed:* Bloomsburg St Coll (BS) Elem Ed 1973; *cr:* Tuckerton Elem Schl 5th Grd Tchr 1973-76, 1st Grd Tchr 1977-80, 1984-88, 6th Grd Tchr 1988-; *ai:* Schl Store; Schl Safety Patrol; Announcement Bd; Club Adv; NEA, NJEA, TEA 1973-, Pres, VP, Sec, Treas; NJ Curr Framework Math Comm; Pinelands HS PTA 1989-, Sec; Governor's Tchr Recognition Awd 1992; *office:* Tuckerton Elem Schl PO Box 217 Marine St Tuckerton NJ 08087

NEUSTEIN, SONDRA MIRIAM (LIPP), French & Spanish Teacher; *b:* Pittsburgh, PA; *m:* Ronald Joel; *c:* Hallie, Micah; *ed:* Univ of Pittsburgh (BA) Ed Emphasis in Fr & Span 1975; CA St Univ at Northridge 13 Credit Hrs, 3 Credit Hrs Chicano Culture; Indiana Univ of PA 3 Credit Hrs Art of Translation & Interpretation & 3 Credit Hrs Hispanic Cult Thru Lit; Wright St Univ 4 Credit Hrs Span Composition & 3 Credit Hrs Ed Courses; *cr:* Conejo Valley Unified Schl Dist Fr & span Tchr 1984-84; Norwin HS Fr Tchr 1985-86; Sacred Heart HS Fr Tchr 1986-87; Hoffman Estates HS Fr & Span Tchr 1989-91; Alter HS Fr & Span Tchr 1991-; *office:* Archbishop Alter HS 940 E David Rd Kettering OH 45429*

NEVERDON-MORTON, CYNTHIA, Professor of History; *b:* Baltimore, MD; *m:* Lonnie George; *ed:* Morgan St Coll (BA) His 1965, (MS) His 1967; Howard Univ (PHD) His 1974; *cr:* Baltimore City Pub Schls His & Geog Tchr 1965-68; Inst Afro Amer Stud Curr Dev & Instr 1968; Univ of MN Admissions Assoc 1968-69, Coord Spcl Pgms 1969-71; Coppin St Coll Asst Dean of Stus 1971-72, His Prof 1972-; Dept of Defense HBCU Fac Fellow 1986-95; *ai:* His Club & Book Club Adv; Fac Senate; ASALH 1971-, Exec Cncl, Svc Awd 1996; Southern Historical Assn 1980-; Amer Historical Assn, Wesley-Logan Book Comm; NEA & MSTA 1990-; Delta Sigma Theta 1962-, Pres; Black Women Historiaans 1979-, Parliamentarian; Great Blacks in Wax, Bd Mem; Travel & Study Grants 1974 & 1979; NEH Flwshp for Coll Tchrs 1981; Fulbright Flwshp 1981; ASALH Scholar in Residence 1995; Numerous Articles, Monographs, Tchng Modules & Fact Sheets Pub; Book Pub; *office:* Coppin State Coll 2500 W North Ave Baltimore MD 21216

NEVES, DAVID, Band Dir & Music Supervisor; *b:* Central Falls, RI; *m:* Janice Povlin; *c:* Kristin, Jennifer, Amanda; *ed:* Berklee Coll (BM) Music Ed 1976; RI Coll (MAT) Music 1981; 15 Credits Admin; Supervisory Cert 1985; *cr:* Scituate HS Choral Dir 1976-79, Band Dir 1979-, Supvr of Music 1979-; *ai:* Jazz Ensemble; NEASC Chair 1991; RI Music Ed Assn 1976-, Pres, Meritorious Svc Awd 1993; NEA RI 1976-; Natl Band Assn, Intl Assn Jazz Ed 1979-; ASCD; Amer Band 1979-, Prin Saxophone; RI Milken Educator Awd 1991; Scituate Tchr of Yr 1989; RI Music Educators Review Ed 1991-93; Exec Bd RI Music Ed Assn 1984-; *home:* 260 Phenix Ave Cranston RI 02920*

NEVIN, RICHARD L., Elem Gen Music & Chorus Tchr; *b:* Washington, PA; *m:* Janet Stamm; *ed:* West Liberty St Coll (BA) Music Ed, Piano 1975; 25 Credit Hrs Elem Ed Cert CA Univ of PA 1982; *cr:* Bethlehem-Center Schl Dist 7-12 Grd Gen Music, Choirs Tchr 1976; Washington Schl Dist 5-7 Grd Gen Music Tchr 1977; Trinity Area Schl Dist 6-8 Grd Musical Arts, Band, Percussion Tchr 1979; Bentworth Schl Dist Elem Gen Music, Elem, HS Chorus Tchr 1980-; *ai:* Sr HS Chorus; MENC, BEA, PSEA, NEA 1980-; *office:* Bentworth Schl Dist PO Box 610 29 S Main St Ellsworth PA 15331

NEVINS, REGINALD ALAN, Mathematics & Science Teacher; *b:* Anderson, IN; *m:* Darlene A. Davinsizor; *c:* Angel, Ty, Alicia; *ed:* Slippery Rock Univ (BS) Elem Ed 1976; Post Grad Stud Penn St Univ, Millersville Univ; *cr:* Spring Cove Schl Dist Remedial Rdng Tchr 1976-78, 5th Grd Tchr 1978-81, 6th Grd Lang, Art Tchr 1981-86, 6th Grd Math, Soc Stud Tchr 1986-91, 7th-8th Grd Math, Sci Tchr 1991-; *ai:* Sr HS Boys Bsktbl Coach with 2 Dist Titles; Sr HS Bsbl Asst Var Coach; *office:* Spring Cove MS 1150 E Main St Roaring Spring PA 16673

NEW, WENDY ROSE, Fourth Grade Teacher; *b:* New York, NY; *m:* Dennis J. Riedmiller; *c:* Lauren Gibberman, Beth Riedmiller; *ed:* Stoney Brook Univ (BA) Elem Ed 1971; Cntrl CT St Coll (MS) Elem Ed 1974; Supervisory Cert from Univ of Cincinnati; *cr:* E Hartford Conn Schls 3rd-5th Grd Tchr 1972-75; Yavneh Day Schl 3rd Grd Tchr 1975-77; Forest Park Schls Tutor to Learning Disabled 1977-80-; Fairfield City Schls 3rd-5th Grd Tchr 1980-; *ai:* Writing Sci Course of Stud for Dist; ASCD 1995-; NEA, OEA 1980-; Womens Amer ORT 1990-, Pres; Supts Innovaton Grant 3 Yrs; Ashland Oil Nom; *office:* Fairfield S Elem Schl 5460 Bibury Dr Fairfield OH 45014

NEWBERRY, DEANA CAPUTY, Spanish Teacher; *b:* Buffalo, NY; *m:* Robert; *c:* Anthony Robert; *ed:* Buffalo St Univ (BS) Span, Scndry Ed 1991; Univ at Buffalo (MS) Frgn Lang Ed 1995; 24 Credit Hrs Biling Spec Ed Buffalo St Coll; 9 Credit Hrs Span Lit, Culture NY St Univ; Studied Span Univ of Salamanca 1990, 1992; *cr:* St Francis Elem Span Tchr 1990-91; West Seneca East Sr HS Span Tchr 1991; West Seneca East MS Span Tchr 1991-; *ai:* Natl Jr Hnr Soc Adv; JV Sftbl Coach; Union Rep; Shared Decision Making Team; WNYFLEC 1991-; *office:* West Seneca East MS 1445 Center Rd West Seneca NY 14224

NEWBOLD, ARDITH HANSON, 1st Grd Tchr of Gifted Stdnts; *b:* Visalia, CA; *m:* Dwight B.; *c:* Soon Hee, Jamie, Sandra; *ed:* Pacific Union Coll (BS) PE 1969; MD St Advance Prof Cert Early Chldhd 1987; Univ of MD Kinesiology; Western MD Coll Deaf Ed; Hood Coll & Frederick Comm CollEarly Chldhd; *cr:* MD Schl for the Deaf PE, Art Tchr 1972-77; Home Stud Intnl K-5 Tchr 1979-84; Brunswick Elem Schl First Grd Tchr1987-89; Monocacy Elem Schl First Grd Tchr 1989- 94; N Frederick Elem Schl First Grd Magnet Tchr 1994-; *ai:* Hands on Sci Instr; Software Review Comm; Sci Fair Judge; Math Manipulative Cadre; Tech & Educ Cadre; Writing, Sci Summatives; Stu Tchr, Mentor; MD St Tchrs Assn 1987-; NCTM, Convention Presenter; MD Dept of Natural Resources, Quail Lic 1994-; NSTA 1985-, Convention Presenter; MSTA Conf 1987-, Conf Presenter; SDA Schl Bd Mem 1982-84; Frederic Comm Coll 1983-86, Interpreter, Tutor for Deaf; Chamber of Commerce Tchr Excl Awd 1995; NASA Lunar Sample Wkshp; eisenhower Sci Ed Grant; Washington Post Grant 1992-93, 1994-95, 1995-; Natl Sci Ed Stans 1996 Stdnts Photos Quail & Duck Photos Pub; *office:* North Frederick Elem Schl 1001 Motter Ave Frederick MD 21701

NEWBOLD, TERRIE LEE (WARD), Fifth Grade Teacher; *b:* Elizabeth, NJ; *m:* Henry A.; *c:* Corbin Phillip; *ed:* Bank St Coll (BS) Elem Ed 1969; Kean Coll at Union (MA) Stu Prsnl Svcs 1977; Seton Hall Univ Post Grad in Supervision; *cr:* Columbus Schl Kndgtn, 3rd-4th Grd Tchr 1970-73; Mtn View Schl 1st, 3rd, 5th & 6th Grd Tchr 1973-; *ai:* Mountain View Concerns Comm 1993-; Supts Cncl 1993-; Dist Evaluation Revision Comm 1994-; Mt Olive Admin Internship Pgm 1995-; Natl Tchr Cert Assessor 1996; EAMO, NJEA & NEA 1970-; ASCD 1993-; Long Vly Womans Club 1988-, Vice-Chm, Craft Awds 1989-90; Mt Olive Mtn View Schl Tchr of Yr 1992; Geraldine R Dodge Celebration of Tchng 1993-94; Metropolitan Opera Guild, Dodge Fndtn & GE Fndtn Grant 1994; *office:* Mountain View Schl 118 Cloverhill Dr Flanders NJ 07836*

NEWBY, JUDY ANN, 7th Grade Language Teacher; *b:* Rochester, MN; *m:* Robert; *c:* Stephen, Debra Williams, Kelly Malin; *ed:* Wilmington Coll (BA) Elem Ed 1980; Post Grade Work Wright St Gifted Ed, Miami Univ Sci; SBH LD Cert Wilmington Coll; *cr:* Washington Elem Schl 5th Grd Tchr 1980-84, Severe Behavior Handicapped Class 1985; Hillsboro HS SBH 1986-87; Washington Elem Schl 5th Grd Tchr 1988-93; Hillsboro MS 7th-8th Grd Lang, Rdng Tchr 1994-; *ai:* MS Power of Pen Team Coach; Elem OM Coord 1991-93; Martha Holden Jennings Scholar; Scioto Paint Vly Mental Hlth Awd of Merit; Parent Advy Execptional Achvmt Awd; Cncl & the Hopewell SERRC.

NEWCOMB, GLENDA DALE, Fourth Grade Teacher; *b:* Keyser, WV; *m:* Louis; *c:* Matthew, Autumn; *ed:* Frostburg St Univ (BS) Elem Ed 1970; 30+ Grad Credit Hrs; WV Univ; *cr:* Bloomington Elem 2nd & 3rd Grd Tchr 1970-77; Pre Schl Dev Ctr Owner & Operator 1984-89; Southern HS 9th-12th Grd Career Employability 1990-95; Red House Elem 4th Grd Tchr 1995-; *ai:* NEA 1970-; Jr Womens Civic Club 1982-89, VP, Sec & Pres; Brownie Scout Ldr 1985-86; *home:* 179 Mitchell Dr Oakland MD 21550

NEWCOME, CONNIE LARSON, Fifth Grade Teacher; *b:* Kane, P. Arthur H.; *c:* Dirk Wooser, Megan; *ed:* Gettysburg Coll (BA) Eng, 1961; Temple Univ (MED) Educl Media, Elem 1971; 8 Hrs Cmptrs, 3 Elem Ed, 9 Hrs Mngmt Courses, 6 Hrs Bus Ed Stock Market Cour Hrs Tax Courses at Univ of Pittsburgh, NY Univ, St Bonaventure Uni Robert A. Becker Med Adv Media Specialist 1962-65; Warminster Schls Tchr of Gifted 1971; Smethport Area Schls Media Specialist 1966-; *ai:* NEA 1966-; PA St Ed Assn 1966-, Pres, Treas; Delta K Gamma; Church; Senatorial Schlsp, Tchr of Yr 1973.

NEWELL, GERALD LYNN, Social Studies & US His Tchr; *b:* Ca OH; *m:* Janet Carol Morris; *c:* David, Robert; *ed:* Malone Coll (BS) Ed 1969; 23 Hrs Ashland Univ, Kent St Univ, Akron Univ; *cr:* Carr Ex Village Jr HS Math, US His Tchr 1968-77; Minerva Local Schls 6t Tchr 1977-87, 7th & 8th Grd Soc Stud Tchr 1987-; *ai:* Minerva HS Chptr Parent, Soc Stud Comm; MLEA, NEA 1977-; OEA 1 Nutritution Grant 1994-95; *office:* Frances Hazen Jr HS 401 N Mar Minerva OH 44657

NEWELL, GRAHAM STILES, Latin Instructor; *b:* St Johnsbury, V Univ of Chicago (AB) Pol Sci 1938, (AM) Latin Lang & Lit 1949; Grad Stud His of Culture at Univ of Chicago 1949-51; *cr:* St John Acad Latin & His Tchr 1938-47; Lyndon St Coll His Prof 195 Johnsbury Acad Latin I-IV Tchr 1982-; *ai:* St johnsbury Acad Sc Bowl Coach; VT Historical Soc 1952-, Pres 1965-69; VT Ge Assembly 1953-79, Senate Ed Comm Chm 20 Yrs; Intergovernm Relations Advisory Commission 1962-64; Cncl of St Govts Bd of 1953-79.

NEWELL, JUDITH (SWEET), 7th Grade Mathematics Teache Cambridge, MA; *m:* Arthur; *c:* Paul, Robert, Daniel; *ed:* Framingha St (BS) K-8th Grd Ed 1965; 16 Credit Hrs North Adams St C Fitchburg St Coll; Cooperative Lrng Cert 1990-91; 45 Credit Hrs M Burns Math 1994; *cr:* Hilltop Schl 2nd Grd Tchr 1 Yr; Yakota AFB K & 4 Yr Old Tchr 1 Yr; Mohawk Trail Regnl Schl Dist Title I & Chptr I & Essential Skills Dir 11 Yrs, 7th Grd Tchr 8 Yrs; *ai:* MS Cty All Steering Comm Mem 1994-; Prior 7th Grd Class Adv 1992-93; NEA 1 MTA 1988-; Mohawk Tchrs Assn 1988-; Prior Local Educl Cncl 199 Chptr I & NELMS Annual Confs 1978-; Fed Recognition Chptr I S Pgm 1985; Trained Provider of Quest Lions Club Skills for Adoles 1991; NELMS Presenter How to Provide a Math Rsrch Fair Provi 1995; *home:* 136 Clesson Brook Rd Charlemont MA 01339*

NEWELL, SHEILA SCHNEIDLER, Retired Elementary Teache New York, NY; *m:* Bruce; *c:* Fayth, Scott; *ed:* Monmouth Univ (B 1960; *cr:* Long Branch Bd of Ed Schl 2nd Grd Tchr 1960-63; Neptun of Ed Schl 2-5th Grd Tchr 1963-92; *ai:* Neptune Twp Educ Assn, VP, 2 Terms; Hosp Worker for Veterans; O'Brien Major VFW 1 Conductress, Trustee; *home:* 84 Bennett Ave Neptune NJ 07753

NEWHOUS, NATALIE F., Teacher of Handicapped; *b:* Painesville, *ed:* Mount Union Coll (BS) Elem Ed 1964; Univ of MI (MA) Spec Ed Kent St 9 Hrs Post Grad; *cr:* Touslee Elem Schl Tchr 1964-66; Ma Ave Elem Schl Tchr of Orthopedically Handicapped 1967-73; Ho Elem Schl Tchr of Orthopedically Handicapped 1973-77; Royalview Schl Tchr of Orthopedically Handicapped 1977-; *ai:* NEA, OEA 1 Delta Kappa Gamma 1991-; Univ of MI Govt Fellowship; CEC Ch #261 Spec Tchr of Yr 1976; Tchr of Yr 1983-84; *office:* Royalview Schl 31500 Royalview Dr Willowick OH 44095

NEWKIRK, JACK ANGLE,II, Business Education Teacher Hagerstown, MD; *m:* Amy Michele Rupert; *ed:* Shippensburg Univ (B Bus Ed 1991; Johns Hopkins Univ (MS) Bus, Fin 1996; *cr:* Frankli Area Vo-Tech Schl Bus Data, Processing Tchr 1991-92; Adult Ed C Tchr 1992-; Kenwood HS Bus Ed Tchr 1992-; *ai:* Soph Class, FBLA Soc Comm; SIT Team; Mentor Tchr; MD Bus Ed Assn 1992-, MVA Parlimentarian; MD Voc Assn 1992-, MBEA Rep; MD Conf Svcs 1 Registration Chair; NEA 1991-; AF&AM #58 Columbia Lodge 1 Outstdng Rookie Tchr 1992; Curr Dev 1994, 1995; *office:* Kenwoo 501 Stemmers Run Rd Baltimore MD 21221

NEWKIRK-SQUIRE, SHEILA D., Secondary Special Ed Teache Gainsville, FL; *m:* Oscar; *c:* Eliza, Lee; *ed:* Denison Univ (BFA) Ar 1973; LeHigh Univ (MED) Spec Ed 1983; *cr:* Centennial Schl Pvt Tchr Asst 1980-81; Union Terr Schl Elem Spec Ed Tchr 1989-91; Allen HS Scndry Spec Ed Tchr 1991-95; *ai:* Achvmt Club Adv; Sc Instrl Support Tchr; Conflict Resolution Prgm Dev, Orginal Coord; Exec Comm 1993-95; PSEA-NEA; NEA; All Amer Culture Ctr Bd 1 Pres; Black Interest Coalition Exec Bd 1986-; Child Abuse Preve Effort 1975-78, Chair Pub Relations Comm; LeHigh Vly Summer B Advy Bd 1994-; Natl Coalition Bldg Inst 1994-; Edctr of Merit 199 Jr Achvmt Tchr of Yr; Outstdng Young Woman of Yr 1981.*

NEWLAN, CATHY SUE TIEMAN, Seventh Grade English Teache Portsmouth, OH; *c:* Jeremy, Bryan, Jason, Ashley; *ed:* OH Univ (BA 1984; Morehead Univ (MS) Curr Design 1991; *cr:* Friendship Elem Grd Tchr 1986-88; Dry Run Elem 1st Grd Tchr 1989-90; Nauvoo Jr H Grd Eng Tchr 1990-; *ai:* Career Ed Prgm; OH Educl Assn 1986-; L Tchrs Union, Sec 1991-92, Bldg Rep 1995-; NEA 1986-; Church gr Youth Adv; Jr HS Chrldr Adv 1991-93; *office:* Nauvoo Jr HS 3543 Ca Ln West Portsmouth OH 45663*

NEWLAND, JANET FOSTER, Spanish Teacher; *b:* Dayton, OH; Miami Univ (BS) Scndry Ed, Eng, Span 1970, (MA) Span 1977, Versailles HS Span Tchr 1970-73; Connersville Jr HS Span, Eng 1974-78; St Bernard-Elmwood Pl HS Eng, Span Tchr 1978-85; Gre HS Span Tchr 1985-; *ai:* Adv Span Hnr Soc; AFT 1985-, Bldg Rep 2 Amer Assn of Tchr of Span & Portuguese 1988-; Assistantship in Span, Portuguese 1976-77.

NEWLAND, LINDA MARIE (WEISS), Math Teacher; *b:* Cheverly, *m:* Robert L.; *ed:* OH St Univ (BS) Math Ed 1975; 38 Addl Hrs Hastings MS Math Tchr 1975-; *ai:* Team Tchng Ldr; Class Trip Co-Co Upper Arlington Ed Assn, OH Ed Assn, NEA 1975-; Upper Arlingto Fund Summa Cum Laude Awd 1987; Tchr of Yr 1990-91; Sallie Mae Tribute Awd 1991; Tchr of Month 1995; *office:* Hastings MS 1850 Hast Ln Columbus OH 43220

NEWMAN, BETTY MC LAUGHLIN, Retired Third Grade Teache Chambersburg, PA; *m:* Lawrence; *c:* Larry, Sherry Disney; Shippensburg Univ (BS) Eng, Soc Stud 1952; 36 Credit Hrs Penn Shippensburg Univ to Complete Permanent Cert Elem, Scndry Work 1 *cr:* Tuscarora Schl Dist Third Grd Tchr 1952-58, 1962-93; *ai:* NEA 19 PSEA, Life Mem; Franklin Co Chptr PA Assn Schl Retirees; Civitan 19

NEWMAN, F. DAVID, English & Drama Teacher; *ed:* Oberlin (Speech 1962; Yale (MRA) Playwriting 1966; *cr:* North Shore Cntry Schl Drama Tchr 1966-70; Expedition for Cultural Stud Staff 1970 Oberlin Coll Drama Asst Prof 1971-79; CO Acad Artist in Res 1980 Saint Pauls Schl Tchr 1983-; *ai:* Visiting VIPs Conroy Comm; AC CATCH 1990-; *office:* Saint Pauls Schl 325 Pleasant St Concord 03301*

NEWMAN, GARY GORDON, Social Studies Teacher; *b:* Denver, *ed:* St Univ of NY at Geneseo (BA) His 1968; St Univ of NY at One (MS) Soc Stud 1973; Attnd Elmira Coll Adult Ed, Syracuse Univ Ec & Coll of Saint Rose Ed; *cr:* Rome Schl Dist Soc Stud Tchr 1968-; St U of NY at Oneonta Pol Sci Grad Asst 1972; Utica Urban Ctrs Youth P

)76-77; Rome Tchr Resource & Cmptr Trng Ctr Dir 1986-90; Elmira instr 1991; *ai:* AFT, NYSUT 1968-; Rome Tchrs Assn 1968-, Exec Election Chair, Staff Dev Chair; ASCD 1989-; NYS Staff Dev Cncl ; Men of Achvmt 1989; Bicentennial of US Constitution Grant 1989; IA Grant 1989; Title II EESA Grant 1986, 1987 & 1988; Whos Who er Ed 1988; Fulbright Grant Peru 1986; Sabbatical 1985, 1978; Govt anada Fellowship 1982; Project Move-Voice Sex Equity Grant 82; Natl Sci Fnd Grant 1981; Fulbright Italy 1980; Pol Sci antship 1972; NYS Speech Inst Grant 1970; *office:* Rome Free Acad urin St Rome NY 13440

MAN, INA M., PE & Health Dept Chairperson; *b:* Ambler, PA; *ed:* St Univ (BS) PE, Hlth Ed 1960; Antioch Coll (MED) Scndry Urban '75; 30 Credit Hrs Scndry Ed St Joseph's Univ; 15 Credit Hrs Admin le Univ; *cr:* Coach 35 Yrs; Tchr 35 Yrs; Simon Gratz HS Co-Chrprsn Learning Comm Springboard 3 Yrs, Chprsn PE, Hlth Ed Dept 5 Yrs; rls Bsktbl Coach; AFT; WBCA; PHPERD; *office:* Simon Gratz HS & Hunting Park Ave Philadelphia PA 19140*

MAN, JACQUALYN JAMES, Social Studies Teacher; *b:* dsburg, PA; *c:* Sharon Levergood Vermeulen, Andrea Levergood rty, James Charles Levergood; *ed:* Bucknell Univ (BA) Psych, logy; East Stroudsburg Univ (BS) Scndry Ed, Soc Stud 1968; Lehigh (MED) Guidance & Counseling 1974; Amer Stud Fellowship Eastern ITEC Lehigh Unvi, INSYS; Penn St; *cr:* Stroudsburg HS Psych, US chr 1968-; *ai:* Chrldr Coach 1968-1974; Presdntl Clsrm Coord; SATA, 1968-; Amer Psych Assn, Affiliate HS Tchr 1970-; Monroe Cty ral Authority 1972-, Chm; Phoenix Players Theater 1970-, Sec; o Medical Center Auxillary 1980-; Big Pocono Ski Club 1992-, ; *office:* Stroudsburg HS 1100 W Main St Stroudsburg PA 18360

MAN, JOAN SMITHWICK, Kindergarten Teacher; *b:* Brooklyn, : Bert; *c:* Kathe Newman Schell, Richard (dec); *ed:* Danbury St (BS))66; Long Island Univ (MS) Ed 1992; 90 Grad Credits; *cr:* Carmel Schl Tchr 30 Yrs; *ai:* Instr Mag Adv 5 Yrs; Budget Comm; Cmptr rer; AFT, NEA 1966-, Mem; Hudson Valley Rdng Assn 1994-, Mem; Trustees 1980-85, Sec; Math Grant; *office:* Kent Primary & Elem Rt 52 Carmel NY 10512*

MAN, MARIE A., 5th Grade Teacher; *b:* Stoneham, MA; *m:* Dennis; sten, Danielle, Melissa; *ed:* Mass Bay Comm Coll (AS) Liberal Arts Boston St Coll (BA) Span, Scndry Ed 1973; Cambridge Coll (MED) Ed 1993; 9 Grad Credits Salem St Coll; 3 Grad Credits Lesley Coll; Natl Acad of Learning Styles; *cr:* Immaculate Conception Schl 5th Tchr 1984-95; 6th Gr Tchr 1995-; *ai:* Stu Cncl Adv; Extended Day Prgm, 5th-6th Grd Ski Trip Coords; NCEA 1984-; *office:* Immacualte eption Schl 306 Highland Ave Malden MA 02148

MAN, PAULINE, First Grade Teacher; *b:* Dunkirk, NY; *m:* Daniel Lynne Zasucha, David; *ed:* SUNY Coll at Fredonia (BA) Elem Ed , (MS) Rdng 1969; *cr:* Dunkirk Elem Schl Five First Grd Tchr -78; Dunkirk Elem Schl Six First Grd Tchr 1979-; *ai:* DTA, NYSUT, 1967-; *office:* Dunkirk Elem Schl 6 55 E Benton St Dunkirk NY 14048

MAN, PETER HENRY, English Dept Head & Teacher; *b:* New York, n: Andrea Kadar; *c:* Daniel, Mara Katelin; *ed:* Lafayette Coll (AB) 1973; Lehigh Univ (MA) Eng 1980; NEH Shakespeare Inst; *cr:* reth Schl Dist Eng Tchr 1973-, Eng Dept Chair 1987-; *ai:* Curr Cncl; egic Planning; Bldg Mngmt Team; Long Range Comm Committee ; Mid Sts Communication Comm Head; NEA, PSEA, NAEA 1973-; ams Twp Soccer 1989-, Head Coach, Garcia Awd; Temple Covenant ace 1986-, Prin 1990-92; *office:* Nazareth Area Schl Dist Center & ry Ln Nazareth PA 18064

MAN, WILLIAM EDWARD, Adjunct Professor of History; *b:* eck, NJ; *m:* RoseMary Fratinardo; *c:* Steven, Lawrence, Suzanne; *ed:* clair St Univ (BA) His 1954, (MA) His 1956; Rutgers Univ Prof Deg rvision, Curr 1960; Minors in Bio, Eng, Elem Ed; Stud in Opera, nber Music, Asian His; *cr:* Northern Vly Reg HS Tchr, Supvr 1956-92; Record Music Critic, Feature Writer on Music, Films 1962-70; Natl rer on Native Amers, JFK Death, Music, His 1961-; Ramapo Coll Adj of His 1990-; Montclair St Univ Adj Prof, Supvr, Stu Tchrs 1993-; *ai:* y Lecturer for GATE Prgm in HS Dist; His, Music Club Adv; Wrote Supervisory Model for Northern Vly Regnl HS Dist; Wrote Project 95 l Dists for the Dist; NCSS, NJ Cncl for Soc Stud 1961-; Mid Sts Cncl oc Stud 1961-, Gold Medal for Rsrch, Writing; ASCD 1961- Dist; ont Planning Bd 1971-75; Dumont Pub Lib 1972-, Pres; Numerous les Pub; DAR His Tchr of Yr Awd 1984; Mid Sts Cncl for SS Rsrch, g Gold Medal 1990; Book, Cassette Veri as a Revolutio nary; Articles is, Music, JFK Assassination, Native Amers, Tchng, Book Reviews Journals; Author Prgm Notes Various Musical Grps in NYC; *office:* apo Coll Of NJ 505 Ramapo Valley Rd Mahwah NJ 07430*

MAN, WILLIAM JOSEPH,JR., High School Science Teacher; *b:* ille, NJ; *m:* Ann Winiecki; *c:* Juliana; *ed:* VA Tch (BS) Chem 1986; of CT (MS) Chem 1988; Trenton St Coll (MA) Tchng 1991; Supvrs , *cr:* Univ of CT Tchng Asst 1986-88; Perth Amboy HS Sci Tchr -93; Montgomery HS Sci Tchr 1993-; *ai:* Class of 1988 Adv; Sci mpiad Coach; NEA 1988-; Cranbury Historical Soc 1993-; ol-Myers Squibb Internship 1989, 1990; Union Carbide Internship , 1993; Princeton Plasma Physics Lab Internship 1994; Hoechst nes Internship 1995; Masterton Tchng Awd 1987, 1988; *office:* tgomery HS 375 Burnt Hill Rd Skillman NJ 08558*

MAN-LEVY, SANDRA S., Fashion Instructor; *b:* Island Fall, ME; ay E. Levy; *ed:* Univ of ME at Orono (BS) Mrktg 1973; Cambridge (MED) Integrated Stud 1996; Salem St Coll Environmental Stud; *cr:* ra Newman Design Owner 1982-; Endicott Coll Instr Fashion Dept Cad Apparel Design, Flat Pattern Dev 1986-88; Lasell Coll Instr ion Dept 1993-; *ai:* Marathons; Amer Sewing Guild 1986-, Regnl Ldr; r Home Sewing & Craft Assn 1987-; Pub Article; Inventor & Marketer ewing Related Products; *office:* Lasell Coll 145 Cabot St #2 Beverly 01915

VMARK, LESLIE PAUL, Math Teacher; *b:* Port Amboy, NJ; *m:* garet T. Dugan; *c:* Lorraine Mann; *ed:* Nova Univ (MS) Cmptr ning 1992; *cr:* Auenel Jr HS Math Tchr, Wrestling Coach 14 Yrs; nia Jr HS Math Tche, Wrestling Coach 1 Yr; J.F. Kennedy Meml HS Tchr 15 Yrs; *ai:* NTEA, WTEA, NEA 1966-, Bldg Rep; Jaycees 5074 Treas, Dist Svc; *office:* John F Kennedy Memorial HS Washington Iselin NJ 08830*

VPHER, NANCY A., 6th Grade Teacher; *b:* Lancaster, PA; *ed:* etown Univ (BS) Elem Ed 1968; Millersville Univ (MED) 1976; 60 l Ed Credits; *cr:* Twin Vly Elem Schl 5th Grd Tchr 1968-89; gantown Elem Schl 6th Grd Tchr 1989-91; Twin Vly MS 6th Grd Lang Tchr 1991-; *ai:* 1st Team Ldr; NEA 1968-, Pres, Sec, Bldg Rep, shp Chprsn, VP; *office:* Twin Vly MS RR 3 Elverson PA 19520

VSOME, GARY LEE, Asst Principal & Athletic Dir; *b:* Portsmouth, *m:* Victoria Lee Evans; *c:* Jillian, Christian, Marie; *ed:* Olivet arene Univ (BS) Ed 1974; Chicago St Univ (MS) Scndry Ed 1982; Hrs cl Admin Xavier Univ, Univ of Dayton; *cr:* Blanchester HS Eng, PE 1974-77; Green HS PE Tchr 1977-80; Olivet Nazarene Univ Asst Prof)-82; Wheelersburg HS Eng Tchr 1982-83; Paint Vly HS Elem, Asst HS 1983-; *ai:* Head Ftbl Coach Green HS, Paint Vly HS 16 Yrs; Head Bsbl en HS, Paint Vly, Olivet Nazarene 5 Yrs; OH Elem Prins 1988-; OH HS Coaches 1974-, VP; ASCD 1989-92; FCA 1974-, Huddle Ldr, Supvr; 2 Articles Pub; Speaker at Orgs, Churches; *office:* Paint Vly HS 7454 US Rt 50 Bainbridge OH 45612

NEWTON, CAROL SMITH, Special Education Teacher; *b:* Valley Stream, NY; *m:* William E.; *c:* David, Peter, William; *ed:* Univ of Bridgeport (BS) Elem Ed 1962; Adelph Univ (MS) Spcl Ed 1985; *cr:* Comsewogue Elem Tchr 1961-62; Fairmont Elem Tchr 1962-63; Oneida City Schl Kndgtn Tchr 1971-73; Port Jefferson Schl Tchr 1983-85; Longwood Cntrl Schls Spcl Ed Tchr 1985-; *ai:* Peer Tutoring; Liberty Partnership; AFT 1962-; NEA 1962-; MITA 1985-; United Meth Church 1951, 1962, 1995-; *home:* 114 Hoyt Ln Port Jefferson NY 11777

NEWTON, DAVID ALAN, Band Dir & Woodwind Instructor; *b:* Ravenna, OH; *m:* Barbara Blair; *ed:* Baldwin-Wallace Coll (BM) Music Clarinet 1968; Manhattan Schl of Music (MM) Music Clarinet 1972; New Paltz SUNY Ed Courses; Hart Schl of Music Courses; *cr:* Newburg Schl Dist Elem Instrumental Music Tchr 1972-80; Washingtonville Cntrl Schl Dist HS Instrumental Music Tchr, Band Dir & Woodwinds 1980-; *ai:* Pep Band Dir; Mid St Philosophy Comm; AFT, NEA 1972-; Musicians Union Local 291 1971-, VP; Music Performance Trust Fund 1980-, Chm; Vestry St Johns Episcopal Church 1971-, Warden; Co-Founder NE Arts Ensemble; St & Cty Grants; Baldwin-Wallace Coll Disrngd Alumni Awd; Pub Instrumentalist Magazine 1975; *office:* Washingtonville HS 54 W Main St Washingtonville NY 10992

NEWTON, EVANS KENDRICK,III, Spanish Teacher; *b:* Princeton, IN; *m:* Celmira Montilla de Newton; *c:* Lina Yvette, Windie Adriana; *ed:* Brown Univ (BA) Pol Sci 1964; IN Univ (MAT) Span 1971; *cr:* Peace Corps Trng Ctr Puerto Rico Lang Prgm Coord, Span Tchr 1967-69; Canastota HS Span Tchr 1971-73; Christian Bros Acad Span Tchr 1973-77, Dept Chr 1978-81; Westtown Schl Span Tchr 1981-, Dept Chair 1989-93; *ai:* Mexican Exchange Prgm Coord; Intnl Stu Org, Jr Class Adv; Adv, Trainer of Math Tutors; Teach Eng Migrant Workers; Fac-Stu Comm Multi-Cultural Awareness; Fac Mentor for New Tchr; Stu Cncl Adv; Awarded Ford Fnd Flwshp Stud Intnl Dev 1967; Commonwealth Fellow Span 1988; *home:* PO Box 1799 Westtown PA 19395*

NEWTON, JAMES L., Teacher; *b:* Olean, NY; *m:* Carolyn S.; *c:* Christopher, Anthony, Laurie; *ed:* Mansfield Univ (BS) Math 1964; Rutgers The St Univ (MS) Math 1971; Attnd RIT, Alfred Univ, Elmira Coll, Highlands Univ NM, Corning Comm Coll; *cr:* Corning Comm Coll Instr1971-89; Boces Tchr Ctr Instr 1982-94; CPP East HS Tchr 1967-; *ai:* Sr Class Adv; Christmas Happening Coord; CTA 1967-; Southern Tier Apple Users 1982-, Pres, VP; NYS Cmptr, Tech 1982-; AFT; Jaycee, Local Man of Yr; United Way Bd of Dir; Corning Chamber of Comm; Yrbk Dediction; Excl in Cmptr Tchng; Who's Who in Amer Young Mens Awd; Neophyte to Neophyte Conf Coord; *office:* Corning Painted Post East HS 201 Cantigny St Corning NY 14830

NEWTON, JANICE EHLERS, Retired Elementary Teacher; *b:* Flint, MI; *m:* David C.; *c:* Carol Newton Cooper, Gail; *ed:* Central CT St Univ (MS) Elem Ed, Sci, (BS) Elem Ed, Amer His; *cr:* Farmington CT Elem Schls 1-2 Grd Tchr 1972-75, Kndgtn Tchr 1975-91, 3rd Grd Tchr 1991-95; *ai:* NOah Webster House Historical Interpreter, Schl Lib Vol; NEA, CEA, Farmington Ed Assn 1972-, Assoc Rep, Sec, Pres 1 Yr; Retired Tchrs of CT 1995-.

NEWTON, JUANITA WILLIAMS, Business Teacher; *b:* Albany, GA; *c:* Martin, David, Valarie; *ed:* Clark Coll (BA) Sec Sci 1960; Cleveland St Univ (BA) Admin 1972; Addl 30 Hrs Rdng Cert; *cr:* Attorney C. B. King Legal Sec 1960-61; Glenville HS Bus Tchr 1966-67; East Technical HS Bus Tchr 1968-; *ai:* Stu Act Chprsn; PA Comm; Big Buddy, Little Buddy; Cleveland Area Bus Tchr Assn; CABES; Phi Delta Kappa 1990-, Sec; *office:* East Technical HS 2439 E 55th St Cleveland OH 44104

NEWTON, ROSLIN DICKINSON, Assistant Professor of Nursing; *b:* Buffalo, NY; *m:* William R.; *c:* Rochelle Lyn; *ed:* Capital Univ (BSN) Nrsng 1974; St Univ of NY at Buffalo (MSN) Nrsng, Adult Hlth 1984; Nova Southeastern Univ (DED) Higher Ed; Univ of NV at Reno Rural Nurse Practitioner Cert 1977; *cr:* Lockport Meml Hosp Staff, Charge Nurse 1975-76; Washoe Med Ctr Staff, Charge Nurse ICU 1977-79; WCA Hosp Clinical Nurse Specialist 1981-91; Jamestown Comm Coll Part-Time Clinical Instr 1980-82, Asst Prof Nursing 1991-; *ai:* Chautauqua Co Fair Bd 1992-, Bd Mem; Cornell Cooperative Extension 1982-, 4-H Vol, Sec, Pres Comm, Bd of Cooperative Extension, Kazon Mosher Meml Awd Outstdng Ldrshp; Nurse Reviewer 20 Topics Med, Surgical Text Pub Little Brown & Co; *office:* Jamestown Comm Coll 525 Falconer St Jamestown NY 14701

NEWTON, TRINA SMITH, 8th Grade Science Teacher; *b:* Beckley, WV; *m:* J. Scott; *ed:* Jamestown Comm Coll (AS) Math, Sci 1987; SUNY at Fredonia (BS) Ed 1989, (MS) Ed 1994; *cr:* Washington MS Sci Tchr 1989-; *ai:* Ski Club Adv; Sci, Environmental Club Founded, Adv; NEA-NY 1989-, Region IV Del; Delta Kappa Gamma 1993-; Chautauqua Cty Sci Tchr Assoc 1989-; Jamestown Schl Forest 1992-, VP, Bd of Dir; YWCA 1993-, Bd of Dir; Roger Tory Peterson Ins 1990-; Presenter NYS Mid Level Conf Cornell Univ; NTE Revision Process, NASA-ARC Math Sci Camp; *office:* Washington MS 159 Buffalo St Jamestown NY 14701

NEY, CASSI E., English Teacher; *b:* Towanda, PA; *m:* Wim Ney; *c:* Sebastiaan, Quinn; *ed:* Eastern Coll (BA) Writing, Lit 1983; Tchng Cert Scndry Ed Mansfield Univ 1985; Post Grad Stud Writing, Lit Millersville Univ, Penn St Univ; *cr:* Dover HS Eng Tchr 1986-; *ai:* Mentor New Tchr, Cooperating Tchr; NEA, DAEA 1986-; PSEA 1985-; Capital Area Writing Project 1992-; Pub Article The Messerge.

NEYE, LUCILLE LORENA, Social Studies Teacher; *b:* Jersey City, NJ; *ed:* Jersey City St Coll (BA) Ed 1973; Wm. Paterson Coll (MA) Urban Stud 1981; Stu, Prsnl Guidance Cert 1981; *cr:* St Michael Grammar Schl Tchr 3 Yrs; Union City Schl Dist Grds 3-5, 7-8 Tchr 23 Yrs; *ai:* Peer Adv; Stu Cncl; Grad Tchr; Yrbks; Union City Ed Assn 1973-, Sec 1990; NJEA 1995-, Mentor Tchr, Curr Comm; NJ Tech for Children Awd 1985; *home:* 7416 3rd Ave North Bergen NJ 07047

NEYLAND, DIANA LYNNE (FORTE), English Teacher; *b:* Brooklyn, NY; *m:* Thomas Patrick; *c:* Morgan, Cory; *ed:* Queens Coll of CUNY (BA) Eng 1969; Columbia Tchrs Coll (MA) Tchng Scndry Eng 1972; 9 Credits Eng Atlanta Univ 1969; 2 Credits Childrens Lit Southampton Coll of SUNY 1974; *cr:* Maria Regina Diocesan HS Eng Tchr 1972-74; St John's Univ Lecturer-Introductory Writing Prgms 1975-77; Allstate Insurance Co Claims Adjuster 1978; Lawrence Road Jr HS Eng Tchr 1979-; *ai:* Uniondale Tchrs Assn 1979-; Cub Scouts Pack 18 Merokee Dist 1985-91, Scout Ldr, Comm; *office:* Lawrence Road Jr HS 50 Lawrence Rd Hempstead NY 11550

NG, MARY GEE, ESL Kindergarten Teacher; *b:* New York City, NY; *m:* Raymond C.; *c:* Nicholas; *ed:* Queens Coll of the City Univ of NY (BA) Elem Ed 1981, (MSEd) Children's Lit 1986; *cr:* Chinatown Planning Cncl Daycare Ctr Tchr 1981-83; PS 2 Meyer London Schl Tchr 1983-; *ai:* United Fed of Tchrs, AFT, NY St Tchrs Assn 1983-; *office:* PS 2 Meyer London 122 Henry St New York NY 10002

NGATCHOU, JEAN-CLAUDE N., Assistant Prof of Computer Sci; *b:* Bangangte, Cameroon; *m:* Catherine Henry; *c:* Anita, N-Neka, Zanne, Ziena; *ed:* Yaounde Univ (MA) Math 1981; City Coll of CUNY (MS) Cmptr Sci 1987; City Univ of New York (PHD) Cmptr Sci 1995; *cr:* New York City Dept Mental Hlth Programmer 1985-; City Coll Adj Lecturer 1985-90; Coll Staten Island Adj Lecturer 1987-92; Jersey City St Coll Asst Prof 1992-; *ai:* Parkchester N Condominium Bd Mgr; AFT 1992-; City Univ NY 1990-92; NY St Flwshp 1991; *office:* Jersey City State Coll 2039 Kennedy Blvd Jersey City NJ 07305

NGUYEN, CHARLES C., Professor of Electrical Engrng; *b:* Danang, Vietnam; *m:* Kim-Bang Pham; *c:* Carissa Thuy-Duong, Olivia Quynh-Duong; *ed:* George Washington Univ (MS) Control System 1980, (DSC) Control System 1982; Konstanz Univ Germany Dipl-ing Electrical Engrng 1978; *cr:* Siemens Corp Engr 1977-78; Cath Univ of Amer Asst Prof 1982-86, Assoc Prof 1986-91, Prof 1991-, Dir of Control & Robotics Lab 1986-; *ai:* Founder & Ed-In-Chief of Intnl Journal of Intelligent Automation & Soft Computing; Assoc Ed Ind Journal of Cmptrs & Electrical Engrng; Editorial Bd of Journal of Intelligent & Fuzzy System, Journal of Engrng Design & Automation; IEEE 1982-, Sr Mem; Sigma Xi 1983-; Tau Beta Pi 1983-, Mem & Fac Adv; SME 1986-, Sr Mem; Robotics & Intnl 1986-, Sr Mem; Amer Biographical Inst 1986-, Rsrch Bd of Advs; Intnl Biographical Centre 1985-, Advy Cncl; Acad VP Rsrch Excl Awd; Best Univ Grad in 1978; NASA, ASEE Flwshp Awds 1985-86, 1994-95; Natl Acad of Sci Sr Rsrch Assoc Awd 1990; Prin Investigator of 16 Rsrch Projects; Pub Articles, Books, Technical Reports; *office:* The Catholic Univ Of America Dept of Electrical Eng 620 Michigan Ave NE Washington DC 20064*

NGUYEN, HO N., Professor of Economics; *b:* Ninh-Binh, Vietnam; *ed:* Univ of CA (BA) Ec 1969; Univ of Calgary (MA) Ec 1971; Dalhousie Univ (PHD) Ec 1976; *cr:* Lakehead Univ Ec Prof 1975-79; St Mary's Coll of MD Ec Prof 1979-; *ai:* Division Head; Dept Chair; East Asian Stud Club, Amnesty Intnl Campus Group Advs; AEA 1976-; NAEF 1983-; Amnesty Intnl 1973-; Fulbright Hays; *office:* St Marys College of Maryland Eng Dept Saint Marys City MD 20686

NGUYEN, LORI RIMAR, 4th Grade Teacher; *b:* Warren, OH; *m:* Viet H.; *c:* Benjamin Joel; *ed:* OH St Univ (BS) Elem Ed 1980; *cr:* Darbydale Elem 2nd-3rd Grd Tchr 1981-85; Phanat Nikhom Refugee Camp Vietnamese Schl Supvr 1987-88; Prairie Norton Elem Schl 3rd-5th Grd Tchr 1988-; *ai:* Vietnamese Children Sunday Schl Tchr; *office:* Prairie Norton Elem Schl 117 Norton Rd Columbus OH 43228

NGUYEN, THIEU TRUNG, Social Studies Tenured Teacher; *b:* Kien An, Vietnam; *m:* Lien Tran; *c:* Khanh, Dan; *ed:* Dalat Univ Vietnam (BA) His 1966; Dickenson Law Schl (JD) Bus Law 1982; *cr:* Kleckner & Parren Law Firm Law Clerk 1981-82; Brighton HS Tenured Soc Stud Tchr 1982-; *ai:* Stdnts Act Organizer & Adv; BH Vietnamese Stdnts Alumni Assn Adv; *office:* Brighton HS 25 Warren St Brighton MA 02135*

NICALEK, KENNETH A., Health & Physical Ed Instr; *b:* Youngstown, OH; *m:* Janet L. Zuretti; *c:* Judith W. Weiland, Amy L.; *ed:* Springfield Coll (BS) Hlth, PE 1971; Anna Maria Coll (MA) Guid Psych 1978; *cr:* Assabet Vly Regnl Voc HS Hlth, PE Instr 1973-, Dept Lead Tchr 1986-, Dir of Ath 1981-86; *ai:* Girls Soccer, Boys JV Bsbl Coach; AFT, MAPHERD 1974-; MAVA 1990-; *home:* 340 Brigham St Northborough MA 01532

NICASTRO-BALDWIN, GENA SUE, Math & Computer Teacher; *b:* Lakewood, OH; *m:* Mark Baldwin; *ed:* Baldwin Wallace Coll (BS) Math 1991, (MSEd) Admin 1995; *cr:* Firelands Schls Math Tchr, Math Lab Developer, Cmptr Instr 1992-; *ai:* Girls Head Vlybl Coach; Var Swim Coach; Co-Ed IM Vlybl Coach; Newspaper, Stu Cncl Adv; Peer Mediator, Drug Free Schls Coord; NCTM, OCTM, NEA 1991-; FEA 1992-, VP; Compeer 1991- Treas, Vol; Alpha Xi Delta 1987-, Pres, Sister of Yr; *office:* Firelands Local Schl Dist 152 W Main St South Amherst OH 44001

NICHOL, JAMES J., 6th Grade Teacher; *b:* Staten Island, NY; *m:* Martha Goodwin; *c:* Scott, Amy, Jeffrey; *ed:* SUNY at Oswego (BS) Elem Ed 1968; SUNY at New Paltz 33 Addl Grad Hrs; *cr:* Myers Corners Elem 6th Grd CSD Tchr 1968-74; Violet Ave Elem 5th Grd Tchr 1974-79 & 6th Grd Tchr 1979-94; Haviland MS 6th Grd Tchr 1994-; *ai:* MS Comm 1987-89; Dist Standards Comm 1994-; AFT 1968-, Bldg Rep 1989-91 & 1993-; Town of Hyde Park Recreation Comm 1979-83, Commissioner; NYS HS Sftbl Ofcls 1982-, Sec Dutchess Chapter; Morgan Sports Car Club 1972-, Pres 1983-84, VP 1984-85; Hyde Park Little League 1984-, coach 1989-93; *office:* Haviland MS Box 721 Haviland Rd Hyde Pard NY 12538

NICHOL, SANDRA MARY, Math Teacher; *b:* Bennington, VT; *m:* Larry; *c:* Erin Riley, Mark Riley; *ed:* Univ of VT at Burlington (BS) Math, PE, Hlth 1973; 45 Credit Hrs Ed, Pursuing Cert in Middle Level Ed; *cr:* Arlington Schl K-12th Grd PE, 7-8th Grd Hlth, Math Alg I Tchr 1972-73; Poultney HS PE, Hlth, 7-8th Grd Math Tchr 1985-; *ai:* 8th Grd Class Adv; 7-8th Grd Girl's Soccer Coach; 9-12th Grd Var Golf Coach; NCTM 1994-; Outstdng Tchr at Univ of VT 1994; *office:* Poultney HS E Main St Poultney VT 05764*

NICHOLAS, JEFFREY JOHN, Fifth Grade Teacher; *b:* Akron, OH; *m:* Hope-Anne Cady; *c:* Isaac G.; *ed:* Walsh Univ (BA) Elem Ed 1977; Kent St Univ 8 Addl Hrs; Ashland Coll 4 Addl Hrs; Akron Univ 3 Addl Hrs; *cr:* Highland MS Eng & Lit Tchr 1977-84; Hinckley Elem Fifth Grd Tchr 1984-; *ai:* Dir of HS Plays; Coached MS Bsktbl & Wrestling; Instr Illustrating & Cartooning Classes Saturday Enrichment Prgm; OEA, NEA 1977-, Rep; Authored & Illustrated the Recently Pub Book Mr Gathers Alphabetical Adventures a Tchng Manual for a Co-Dev Alphabet Learning Prgm; Recieved Cty Tchr of Excl Awd 1993; *home:* 505 Ringer St Wadsworth OH 44281*

NICHOLAS, LEONARD H., Technology Teacher; *b:* Brooklyn, NY; *m:* Joyce; *c:* Len, Joyce; *ed:* SUNY at Oswego (BA) Indstrl Arts 1970; 37 Post Grad Hrs; *cr:* Oswego Cath HS Driver Ed Tchr 1970-71; Indian River HS Indstrl Arts, Tech Tchr 1971-; *ai:* AFT, NEA, NYSTA 1971-; Knights of Columbus 1995-, Recorder, 2nd Degree; Amer Motorcycle Assn 1992-, Field Rep, Bronze.

NICHOLAS, LESLIE JAMES, English Teacher; *b:* Kingston, PA; *m:* Jo Ann Macario; *c:* Jordan; *ed:* Wilkes Coll (BA) Eng, Ger, Ed 1981; Univ of PA at Philadelphia (MA) Educl Ldrshp 1985; *cr:* Wyoming Vly West HS Eng Tchr 1981-; *ai:* Adv Radio Club 1981-, Yrbk, Hnr Soc 1989-; Girls' Winter, Spring Track Coach 1981-; Kingston Municipality, Councilman 1983-93, VP 1988-89, Pres 1990-91; PA Schl Press Assn St Bd 1993-; Natl Textbook Co Reviewer 1993; Hoyt Lib Bd of Dirs 1990-91, 1993, Road Run Race Dir 1988-93, Auction Comm 1988-; Who's Who in Amer Ed 1988; WVW Mid Sts Evaluation Steering Comm 1991; Times Ldr Track Coach of Yr 1993-94; Project LEARN Lang Arts Comm, Presenter 1994; Times Ldr Newspaper in Ed Advy Bd 1994-95; *office:* Wyoming Valley West HS Wadham St Plymouth PA 18651

NICHOLAS, TODD, 6th Grade Social Studies Tchr; *b:* Palmerton, PA; *m:* Roxann; *c:* Joshua, Michael; *ed:* Wilkes Univ (BA) Elem Ed 1982, (MS) Educl Dev, Strategies 1991; *cr:* Pleasant Valley Schl Dist 6th Grd Soc Stud, Sub 3rd, 5-6th Grd Tchr 1982-; *ai:* PVEA, NEA 1984-.

NICHOLS, BETSY L., Asst Prof of Education; *b:* Bronxville, NY; *c:* Courtney Ryan, Kimberly Ryan; *ed:* Denison Univ (BFA) Music 1974; SUNY at Cortland (MS) Early Chldhd 1984; Ithaca Coll (MM) Music Ed 1986; Syracuse Univ (PHD) Ed 1993; *cr:* Cornell Univ Tchng Support Specialist 1981-95; Tompkins Cortland Comm Coll Instr 1985-94; Ithaca Coll Adj Asst Prof 1990-94; Muskingum Coll Asst Prof 1994-; *ai:* Tutoring, Coach, Coll Prgms for At Risk Kidz Adv; Grad Prgm Comm; CEC 1994-, Adv, Nom Adv of Yr; NAEYC 1994-; Article Pub; *office:* Muskingum Coll Dept of Ed New Concord OH 43762

NICHOLS, DAVID MILLER, Physical Education Teacher; *b:* Brooklyn, NY; *m:* Linda Minutillo; *c:* Lori Garone, Jason, David; *ed:* Northwestern

St Coll (BS) PE & Sociology 1969; Adelphi Univ 18 Hrs Grad Courses; Dowledge Coll 12 Hrs Grad Courses; *cr:* Tremont Ave Schl PE Tchr 1970-71; Saxton St Schl PE Tchr 1972-73 & 1977-; Eagle Elem Schl PE Tchr 1974-76; *ai:* Ftbl, Weightlifting & Spring Track Coach; AFT 1970-; *office:* Saxton MS 123 Saxton St Patchogue NY 11772

NICHOLS, DENISE VALLET, Frgn Lang Dept Chair & Fr Tchr; *b:* New York City, NY; *m:* Robert J.; *c:* Caitlan, James; *ed:* St Univ Ctr at Albany (BA) Fr, Ed 1974; St Univ Coll at New Paltz (MS) Scndry Fr Ed 1978; *cr:* Cornwall Cntrl HS Fr Tchr 1974-, Frgn Lang Dept Chprsn 1986-; *ai:* NYSUT, NVSAFLT 1974-; ACTFL 1993-; Rockefeller Flwshp Frgn Lang Tchr 1987; Northeast Conf Presenter 1988; Fr Inst Writers as Witnesses of Their Times 1994-95, Natl Endowment for Hum; *office:* Cornwall Central HS 122 Main St Cornwall NY 12518

NICHOLS, DONNA EILEEN, Music Teacher; *b:* Hartford, CT; *ed:* Castleton St Coll (BA) Music Ed 1992; Hartt Schl of Music 15 Addl Credits; *cr:* Whitehall Schls Trng Music Tchr 1992; Proctor HS Music Tchr 1993-; *ai:* Flag Squad; Jazz, Marching Band; Chamber Ensembles; MENC 1989-; NEA 1993-; Church Choir 1987-; Lakes Region Yth Orch 1991-, Mgr, Bd Mem; *home:* RR 2 Box 2271 Florence VT 05744

NICHOLS, EDWARD LEE, 6th Grade Teacher; *b:* Marion, OH; *m:* Vicki Ann Rickolt; *c:* John, Chris; *ed:* Univ of Akron (BA) Electronic Tech 1975; Berea Coll (BA) Elem Ed 1980; Kent St Univ (MED) Elem Math 1984; 12 Grad Credit Hrs; *cr:* Dryden Combined Schl 6th Grd Tchr 1980-83; Crestwood MS 6th Grd Tchr 1984-; *ai:* Ftbl, Bsktbl Coach; Ski Club Spon; Tech Comm; NEA, OEA 1984-; *office:* Crestwood MS 10880 John Edward Dr Mantua OH 44255

NICHOLS, GAIL BRENNEMAN, Retired Teacher; *b:* Portersville, PA; *m:* William J.; *c:* Timothy, Melinda Wendell, Sally Hiers, Bill; *ed:* Taylor Univ (BS) Elem Ed 1954; Westminster Coll (MS) Rdng 1975; *cr:* Star Schl 3rd Grd Tchr 1954-56; Martin Schl 2-3rd Grd Tchr 1956-57; Hanna Schl 4th Grd Tchr 1957-59; Amish Schl 1-8th Grd Tchr 1972-93; East Lawrence Elem Schl 1st Grd Tchr; *ai:* PASR 1994-; Rescue Mission Auxillary 1994-; New Castle Chrstn Women 1994-, Prayer Adv; *home:* 227 N Mercer St New Wilmington PA 16142

NICHOLS, JAMES FLINT, Health & Physical Ed Teacher; *b:* Roxboro, NC; *m:* JoEllen Forker; *c:* Christine; *ed:* Western Carolina Univ (BS) Hlth, PE 1973; 6 Credits Ed Trenton St Coll; *cr:* Ethel Mc Knight Elem Schl Hlth, PE Tchr 1973-78; Hightstown HS Hlth, PE Tchr 1978-; *ai:* Asst Ath Dir; Girls Sftbl Coach; Affirmative Action Cncl; Discipline comm; NJ Ed Assn, NEA 1973-; East Windsor Ed Assn 1973-, Past Chprsn, Negotiation Comm; Amer Red Cross 1988-, Instr; MADD 1988-; VFW; Vietnam Veteran, Staff Sgt.

NICHOLS, KAROLYN KREIDER, High School English Teacher; *b:* Erie, PA; *ed:* IN Univ of PA (BS) Scndry Eng 1966; Univ of Pittsburgh (MED) Rdng, Lang Arts 1972; Edinboro Univ of PA Rdng Supvr 1975; 60 Addl Hrs Alleghany Coll, Edinboro Univ, Gannon Univ, Columbia Univ, Northeastern Univ Classes in Lit, Methods in Tchng, Frgn Lang Italian, Case Stud Rsrch; *cr:* Girard Sch Dist 8th Grd Rdng Tchr 1974, Elem Rdng Supvr 1977-82, HS Eng Tchr 1983-; *ai:* AFT 1972-, Local Pres, Sec, Outstdng Ldrshp; PDK 1976-; NCTE 1980-; Roadhouse Theatre 2 Yr Term, Bd of Dirs; Eric Cty IRA, Pres Several Yrs; Keystone St Rdng Assn, Served Local Rep; Presented Original Work at Local Univs Conf on Lang; Presented at ST Level Rdng, Eng Conventions; *office:* Girard HS 1135 Lake St Girard PA 16417*

NICHOLS, KENT L., Biology Teacher; *b:* Charleroi, PA; *m:* Cindy Shelapinsky; *c:* Brody, Aubrey; *ed:* California Univ at PA (BS) Bio 1976; Post Grad Credits Prins Prgm; *cr:* Charleroi Area HS Stu Tchng 1976; S Fayette Jr Sr HS Bio Tchr 1976-; *ai:* Former Ftbl Coach; California Univ at PA Belle Vernon HS; Ringgold HS Position QB & Received Coach; NEA 1976-; *home:* 10 Carroll Way Monongahela PA 15063*

NICHOLS, LESLI FARNHAM, English Teacher; *b:* Winsted, CT; *m:* Scott; *c:* Justin, Tyler; *ed:* Maranatha Bapt Bible Coll (BS) Scndry Ed & Eng 1991; *cr:* Emmanuel Chrstn Acad Eng Tchr 1991-; *ai:* Vlybl & Cheerleading Coach; Speech & Drama Dir; *office:* Emmanuel Christian Acad 569 Maple Hill Ave Newington CT 06111

NICHOLS, LOIS A., Teacher of the Gifted Ed; *b:* Springfield, OH; *c:* Scott, Nan Nichols-Miller; *ed:* OH Univ (BS) Elem Ed 1970; Gifted Certfd 1986; *cr:* Springfield OH Pub 2nd & 3rd Grd Tchr 1954-55; US Army at Ft Riley HS Eng 1956; Nordonia Schls 6th Grd Tchr 1960-67; Portsmouth OH 2nd Grd Tchr 1970-77; Oak Hills Local Schls 4th Grd Gifted 1977-; Mt St Joseph Coll at Cinn Ed Classes; *ai:* Soc Comm; Delta Kappa Gamma; Cin Recreation Health Club; Jaycee Wives 1968-, Pres; Tchr of Yr Portsmouth OH; Coaching Knowledge Master Team & Thinking Cap Quiz Bowl Team 1996; *home:* 1071 Celestial St # 80J Cincinnati OH 45202

NICHOLS, MARIE JOANNE, Band & Orchestra Teacher; *b:* Salem, OR; *m:* Timothy Michael; *c:* Jonathan David; *ed:* Bob Jones Univ (BS) Music Ed 1986, (ME) Music Tchng 1990; *cr:* Licking Co Christian Acad Elem, Scndry, General Music, Choral, Instrumental Tchr 1986-92; Elem, Scndry General Music, Choral, String Instrument Tchr 1992-93, Jr Sr Hs Strings Tchr 1993-; JH, HS, Choir 1994-95; Elem, JH, HS Band 1994-; *ai:* Private Music Instruction; Vocal, Instrumental Solo & Ensemble Coaching; MENC 1989-95, Natl Guild of Piano Tchrs 1990-95; LWelsh Hills Symphony, Trumpet; *home:* 17 S 6th St Newark OH 43055

NICHOLS, MARY A. (NEWMAN), High School Guidance Counselor; *b:* Lansing, MI; *c:* Victoria; *ed:* Bowling St Univ (BAE) Eng, Psych 1985, (MED) Guid & Cnslng 1993; Post Grad Work in Word Processing; Adolescent & Adult Addiction; *cr:* Napoleon HS Eng Tchr 1985-95, Guid Cnslr 1995-; *ai:* Pale Noon Lit Magazine Adv 1985-95; Hi-Y Comm Svc Club Adv 1985-; NEA, OEA, NFA 1985-; OSCA 1995-; Early Chldhd Ed Advy Bd; Teen Task Force 1995-; Rdng Intern at BGSU Summer of 1992; *office:* Napoleon HS 701 Briarheath Dr Napoleon OH 43545

NICHOLS, MARY RUTH CYR, French Teacher & Librarian; *b:* Van Buren, ME; *m:* Richard Kenneth; *c:* Jennifer, Heidi, Jonathan; *ed:* Univ of ME at Presque Isle (BS) Ed 1966; Univ of ME at Orono (MS) Ed 1980; 6 Hrs Univ of Caen Normandy France; 21 Hrs Lib Sci; *cr:* Skyway MS Fr, Span Tchr 1966-67; Univ of ME at Presque Isle Fr Tchr 1979-83; Presque Isle HS Fr Tchr 1968-84; Easton HS Fr Tchr, Librn 1984-; *ai:* Fr Club Adv 1970-; Easton Tchrs Assn 1984-85, VP; ME Tchrs Assn, NEA 1966-; Phi Kappa Phi, Reflect Regnl Frgn Lang Coming Together 1980-; Frgn Lang Assn of ME 1980-; ME Edcl Media Assn 1987-; Involved With Exch Prgms; Wrote 2 Articles Le FAROG Forum; Pub Museum Booklet; Tour Organizer, GUide for European Trips; Co-Authored Innovative Grant 1986-87; *office:* Easton HS PO Box 66 Main St Easton ME 04740*

NICHOLS, NANCY SHEA, French Teacher; *b:* Pittsfield, MA; *m:* William W.; *c:* Judith, Anne; *ed:* Park Coll (BA) Fr, Span 1960; Univ of MO, Denison Univ 25 Credit Hrs; *cr:* Parkville HS Fr, Span Tchr 1960-61; Univ of MO Fr Instr 1963-65; Denison Univ Fr Instr 1974-75; Granville MS Fr Tchr 1975-; *ai:* NEA, OEA, GEA, AATF 1975-; OFLA 1989-; *home:* 17 Samson Pl Granville OH 43023

NICHOLS, REBECCA SCHROEDER, Guidance Counselor; *b:* Portsmouth, OH; *m:* William R.; *c:* Amy; *ed:* OH Univ (BSEd) Ed 1977; Xavier Univ (MED) Guid, Cnslng 1983; Post Grad Classes Oh Univ, Xavier Univ; *cr:* Nauvoo Elem Schl Tchr 1977-89; Wheelersburg Elem Schl Guid Cnslr 1989-; Wheelersburg HS Guid Cnslr 1989-; *ai:* Scioto Co Crisis Intervention Core, Wheelersburg Crisis Intervention Teams; Conflict Resolution Comm; NEA, OEA 1977-; Am Schl Cnslr Assn, OH Schl Cnslr Assn 1989-; Scioto Co Schl Cnslrs Assn 1989-, Sec, Treas.

NICHOLS, SCOTT THOMAS, History Bible Teacher & Coach; *b:* Marshaltown, IA; *m:* Lesli Farnham; *c:* Justin, Tyler; *ed:* Maranatha Bapt Bible Coll (BS) Yth Ministries 1991; *cr:* Hartford Courant Dist Mgr 1991-; Emmanuel Chrstn Acad Tchr & Coach 1991-; *ai:* Bsktbl & Soccer Coach; *office:* Emmanuel Christian Acad 569 Maple Hill Ave Newington CT 06111

NICHOLS, SUSANNE ALBERT, Art & Computer Teacher; *b:* Baltimore, MD; *m:* John C.; *c:* John C. Jr., Marion Woodward Hasslinger; *ed:* Notre Dame (BA) Art 1955; Cath Univ (MFA) Art 1967; MD Inst of Art 30 Credits 1967-76; MD Inst Coll of Art Cmptr 1990; *cr:* Notre Dame Preparatory Art Dept Tchr 1960-; *ai:* NEA 1970-; *office:* Notre Dame Prep Schl 815 Hampton Ln Towson MD 21286*

NICHOLS, TED R., Chemistry Teacher; *b:* Lancaster, PA; *m:* Carol A.; *c:* Mark; *ed:* Millersville St Coll (BS) Comprehensive Sci 1966; Temple Univ (MS) Phys Sci 1972; Attnd Penn St, West Chester Univ, Franklin & Marshall; *cr:* Northern Lebanon HS Earth & General Sci Tchr 1966-68; Conestoga Valley Jr High Phys Sci Tchr 1968-87; Conestoga Valley HS Acad & AP Chem 1987-; *ai:* Bsbl Coach 1970-79; Scuba Club 1992-; Internet Comm 1995-; NEA, PSEA 1966-; Redeemer Luth Church 1970-, Soc Ministry; Howard Hughes Fnd & Natl Inst of Hlth Grant for Yr Research in Inorganic Chem 1990-91; *office:* Conestoga Valley HS 2100 Horseshoe Rd Lancaster PA 17601*

NICHOLS, THOMAS E., Library Media Specialist; *b:* Westfield, NY; *m:* Linda A. Scott; *c:* Jeffrey, Keith; *ed:* Empire St Coll (BS) Pub Relations 1986; St UNiv of NY at Buffalo (MLS) Lib Media 1987; Finger Lakes Comm Coll (AA) Radio, TV, Theatre 1979; Simmons Inst of Funeral Svc; *cr:* Corning Pub Lib Reference Librarian 1985-87; Penn Yan Pub Lib Youth Librarian, Reference 1987-89; Rsrch Lib Cncl Hosp Lib Prgm 1989-92; Romulus Cntrl Schl K-12 Librarian 1992-93; Dundee Jr, Sr HS Lib Media Specialist 1992-; *ai:* DCS Club Adv; DCS Principal's Cabinet; NYSET 1992-; Schl Librns of Southerntier; Kaiser Frazer Owner's Club 1990-; Naval Enlisted Reserve Assn 1995-; Milo Masonic Lodge #108 1986-, Sec; US Naval Reserve 1978-, Chief Petty Ofcr; Traveling Parnassas Awd; Corning Pub Lib; Outstanding Young Men of Amer Nom 1986; Navy Commendation Medal Outstanding Svc Operation Desert Storm; *office:* Dundee Jr Sr HS 55 Water St Dundee NY 14837

NICHOLSON, DAVID ALLEN, Choral Dir & Music Theory Tchr; *b:* Johnstown, PA; *ed:* IN Univ of PA (BS) Music Ed K-12 1970; Attnd PA St Univ, Villanova, Duquesne Univ Grad Course Work; *cr:* US Army Band Clarinetist 1970-72; So York Co Schl Dist Choral Instr 1972-; Union Luth Church Music Dir 1980-; *ai:* Fine Arts Chm; HS Steering, MS Steering Comms; HS Auditorium Mgr; Schl Musicals Vocal Coach; Private Voice Tchr; NEA, PSEA, SYCEA, MENC, PMEA 1972-; PA Music Edctrs Citation of Excl Awd Dist 7 1991; *office:* Susquehannock HS PO Box 128 Glen Rock PA 17327

NICHOLSON, JAMES JOSEPH, Cmptr Aided Drafting Instr; *b:* Columbus, OH; *m:* Melissa J. Rose; *c:* Kaitlyn; *ed:* Franklin Univ (BSMET) Mech Engrng 1989; OH St Univ Cert Trade, Indstrl Tech 1994; *cr:* Cardinal Industries Inc CAD Oper 1986-88; J. S. Mac Lean Co Detail Engr 1988-89; Mc Donald-Cassell-Basset Design Engr 1989-91; Mid-East OH Voc Schl Dist Cmptr Aided Drafting Instr 1991-; *ai:* VICA Chptr Adv; Muskingum Tech Coll Adj Fac; NWA 1991-, OVA 1093-, MEEA 1991-, Sec; K of C 1994-; Elks Lodge #509 1992-; Muskingum Cty Bd of Ed Cert of Recognition; *office:* Mid-East OH Voc Schl Dist 400 Richards Rd Zanesville OH 43701

NICHOLSON, THOMAS CHARLES, Health & PE Teacher; *b:* White Plains, NY; *m:* Luanne; *c:* Emily; *ed:* St Univ of NY at Cortland (BS) PE 1985, (MS) Hlth 1990; Addl 18 Credit Hrs Educl Admin; *cr:* Rhinecliff Union Free Schl Hlth & PE Tchr 1985-89; Berlin Cntrl Schl Dist Hlth & PE Tchr 1989-; *ai:* Boys Bsbl Coach; AFT 1985-; Capital Dist Bsbl Umpires Assn 1990-; Article Pub Educl Change Fall 1986; *office:* Berlin Central Jr Sr HS PO Box 259 Berlin NY 12022

NICHOLSON, WILLIAM G., English Teacher; *b:* Greenfield, MA; *m:* Cornelia Downes; *c:* Alexandra, Christopher D., Hugh R.; *ed:* Brown Univ (AB) Eng 1958; OH St Univ (MA) His 1963; *cr:* The Columbus Acad Eng Tchr 1958-63; The Cate Schl Eng Tchr 1963-65; Charlotte Country Day Schl Eng Dept Head & Dean of Fac 1965-68; Birmingham Univ Schl Headmaster 1968-69; The Taft Schl Eng Tchr, Dir of Coll Placement & Holder of Independence Fnd Chair 1969-; *ai:* Soc for Amer Bsbl Research 1972-; Watertown Commission on Aging 1988-90; Watertown Redevelopment Agency 1989-92, Chm; Watertown Bd of Ed 1991-95; Columbus Acad Seminars Ed 1963; Pete Gray One-Armed Major Leaguer 1976; The Taft-Thacher Letters Ed 1986; Those Who Served 1990; More Than 50 Articles; *office:* The Taft Schl 110 Woodbury Rd Watertown CT 06795*

NICKERSON, BRADFORD DREW,JR., Spanish Teacher; *b:* Framngham, MA; *m:* Christine L. Holloran; *c:* Sean, Kevin; *ed:* Framingham St Coll (BA) Span 1986, (BS) Comp Sci 1986; SUNY at Geneseo 18 Grad Hrs; *cr:* Framingham Pub Schls Span Tchr 1986-91; Albion Cntrl Schl Span Tchr 1991-; NY Army Natl Guard Logistical Ofcr 1991-; *ai:* Span Club Adv; NEA; AFT; MAFLA 1991-, Tchr of the Yr; *office:* Albion HS 302 East Ave Albion NY 14411*

NICKERSON, EDWARD A., Math & Computer Sci Teacher; *b:* Utica, NY; *m:* Paulette Zitko; *c:* Diane N., Paul N.; *ed:* Utica Coll of Syracuse Univ (BS) Physics 1966; Coll of Tech (BS) Cmptr Sci 1985; *cr:* Strough Jr HS Math Tchr 1966-79; Rome Free Acad Math Tchr, Coord, Cmptr Sci Tchr 1978-; *ai:* Hnr Soc; Math; AFT, NYSUT 1966-; Rome Tchrs Assn 1966-, Treas, Exec Comm; Runaway, Homeless Yth 1986-; *office:* Rome Free Acad 500 Turin St Rome NY 13440*

NICKERSON, JILL ANN, French Teacher & Yrbk Advisor; *b:* Camp Hill, PA; *m:* Michael J.; *ed:* Millersville Univ (BS) Scndry Ed & Fr 1988; West Chester Univ (MS) Scndry Ed 1994; Attnd Universite de Haute Bretagne at Rennes; *cr:* Souderton Area Schl Dist Sub Tchr 1989; Methacton Schl Dist Fr Tchr & Yrbk Adv 1989-; *ai:* Stu Groups Travel Ldr; NEA & MCATFL 1989-; PA St Modern Lang Assn 1992-; *office:* Methacton Sr High 1001 Kriebel Mill Rd Norristown PA 19408

NICKERSON, LUCY ELIZABETH, Math Teacher; *b:* Lawrence, MA; *m:* Stephen; *c:* Geoffrey; *ed:* Merrimack Coll (BA) Lib Arts Math 1966; Grad Course Boston Coll; Salem St Coll; Univ of MA; *cr:* St Mary HS Math Tchr 1966-69; Tyngsboro Jr Sr High Math Tchr 1969-; *ai:* NCTM 1966-; NEA 1969-; MTA 1969-; Liturgy Comm 1988-; Yrbk Dedication to Myself & My Husband; *office:* Tyngsborough Jr Sr HS 36 Norris Rd Tyngsboro MA 01879

NICKERSON, MARY DAVIS, Vice President of Academics; *b:* Bangor, ME; *m:* Richard Andrew; *c:* Jason Andrew, Timothy Donald; *ed:* Univ of Southern ME (BA) Sociology 1976, (MS) Adult Ed 1995; *cr:* Andover Coll Fac Mem 1987-89, Lbrl Stud Dept Chair 1989-93, Dean of Stdnts 1993-95, VP Acad 1995-; *ai:* Stu Senate Adv; Ethics, Promising Scholer, Fac Inservice Comms; Bus Ed Assn of ME, Amer Cncl on Ed 1990-; Scarborough HS Lib 1996-, Advy Bd; Guest Ed Two Textbooks; *office:* Andover Coll 901 Washington Ave Portland ME 04103*

NICKERSON, PENNY J., Social Science Teacher; *b:* Carlisle, PA; *ed:* St Mary's St Coll of MD (BA) Soc Sci, Sec Ed 1976; Dowling Coll (MSEd) Scndry Ed, Rdng 1987; 81 Addl Credits; *cr:* Univ of Esfahan Eng Tchr 1976-78; Palm Beach Gardens HS Soc Stud Tchr 1981-82; Ctr Mo HS Soc Stud Tchr 1983-84; Longwood Sr HS Soc Sci Tchr 1984-; *ai:* MITA 1983-; Mestract Tchng Grant 1995; Prins Awd; *office:* Longwc HS 100 Longwood Rd Middle Island NY 11953

NICKERSON, RICHARD GEORGE, Choral Music Directo Newcastle NB, Canada; *m:* Sabrina Taliento; *c:* Arianna, Sarah; *ed:* of ME (BME) Music Ed 1986; Currently Pursuing MM in C Conducting; *cr:* 5th St MS Music Tchr 1986-87; Windham HS Chor 1987-; *ai:* Chamber Singers Conductor; Class Adv; Amer Choral Dirs 1984-, Pres Elect; ME Music Edctrs Assn 1984-, Choral VP; Music E Natl Conf 1984-; NEA & ME Ed Assn; ME Tchr of Yr Finalist Invitation to Perform for Music Edctrs Natl Conf 1995; Elected to Pi K Lambda Natl Music Hnr Soc 1995; *office:* Windham HS 406 Gr Windham ME 04062

NICKERSON, WILLIAM WHITMAN, 8th Grade Science Teach Brockton, MA; *ed:* Bridgewater St Coll (BA) Earth Sci 1971; *cr:* Me HS 8th Grd Sci Tchr 1981-; *ai:* Organizer, Dir of Several Seven- Cross Cntry Summer Trips Involving Area Teenagers 1983-89, 199 Honored by Local Supt for Putting 8th Grd Sci Course on Video *office:* Memorial Jr HS 219 N Main St Middleboro MA 02346

NICKERSON-PLOCK, PAULA, 5th Grade Teacher; *b:* Boston, M Ronald W.; *ed:* North Adams St Coll (BS) Elem Ed 1973; Univ of VT Curr & Instruction 1987; Bridgewater St Coll, Cape Cod Comm Coll, of MA 36 Additional Hrs; *cr:* Stamford Schl Tchr 1973-94, Asst 1975-94, Curr Coord 1990-94; Williamstown Elem Schl Tchr 1994 Past Rdng is Fundamental Prgm Dir 1981-94, Licensing Standard 1992-94, CORE 1989-94, Lang Arts & Sci Dist Curr Comm, Lectu Presented Workships at Univ of VT, Central CT Coll, North Adams St Clarksburg Schl System, RAP Prgm of St of VT; Lang Arts, Hlth Comm; NEA 1975-84, 1994-; Lib Trustees 1987-, Chprsn 1991-; *o* Williamstown Elem Schl 96 School St Williamstown MA 01267*

NICKLES, JOHN HENRY, Chemistry Professor; *b:* Pittsfield, M Elizabeth Ann Pflegl; *c:* John Arthur; *ed:* Union Coll (BS) Coll 1960; of NH (MA) His 1968; SUNY at Albany 9 Credit Hrs His of Sci 197 *cr:* NY St Hlth Dept Sanitary Chemist 1960-62; Monroe Cty Hlth Lab 1962-63; Hudson Vly Comm Coll Instr & Prof 1965-; *ai:* HVCC Senate Vice-Chprsn; AAAS 1966-; SUNY Chancellors Awd for Ex Tchng 1993; *office:* Hudson Valley Comm Coll 80 Vandenburgh Ave NY 12180

NICKLOS, RICHARD WOODY, Principal; *b:* Pittsburgh, PA; *m:* Pa Ann; *c:* Richard R. J., Eric Scott; *ed:* Point Park Coll (AA) Ed 1965; of Pittsburgh (BS) Ed 1966, (ME) Ed 1970; Prin Cert; *cr:* Lemington Schl Tchr 1966-70; Manchester Elem Schl Asst Prin 1970-71, 197 East Hills ISA Prin 1981-; *ai:* NEED Schlsp Comm; Pittsburgh A Assn 1980-; *office:* East Hills Intl Studies Acad 2150 E Hills Dr Pitts PA 15221

NICODEMUS, JAMES RAY,JR., Carpentry Teacher; *b:* Pittsburgh *m:* Bonita Peffer; *c:* James, Michael, Gregg, Karen; *ed:* CA Univ Industrial Arts 1973; Univ of Pittsburgh (MS) Voc Ed 1975; Ca Making; Carpentry; Cmptrs; *cr:* Butler HS Cabinetmaking Tchr 197 Butler Co AVTS Carpentry Tchr 1979-; *ai:* Butler Co Voc Ed Assn 1 NEA, PSEA 1973-; Butler Co Woodworkers 1989-; Arts, Craft Spec Army; *office:* Butler Co Area Voc Tech School 161 New Castle Rd E PA 16001

NICOLAI, MAUREEN MC PARTLAND, Social Studies Teache Hempstead, NY; *m:* Robert; *c:* Erin; *ed:* Lehigh Univ (BS) Bus, Ec Adelphi Univ (MA) Scndry Ed 1990; *cr:* St Dominic HS Soc Stud 1990-; *ai:* Var Vlybl, JV Sftbl, Bowling Coach; Stu Cncl, Jr Class, Trial Team Adv; Long Island Cncl for Soc Stud 1990-; *office:* Dominic HS 110 Anstice St Oyster Bay NY 11771

NICOLAISEN, ELENA PETRELLA, First Grade Teacher; *b:* Lawr MA; *m:* Michael J.; *c:* Andrea; *ed:* Univ of MA at Lowell (BS) Ele 1970; Early Lit Inservice Course; Early Lit Advanced Tchr Trn Strategies; Observation Survey Trng Prgm; *cr:* No Andover Schl Sy First Grd Tchr 1970-; *ai:* No Andover 350th Anniversary Comm; Comm; No Andover Tchrs Assn 1970-, Former Bldg Rep; MA Tchrs NEA 1970-; *office:* Franklin Schl 2 Cypress Ter North Andover MA 0

NICOLAYSEN, LUCILE MARTINEZ, Spanish Teacher; *b:* New City, NY; *m:* John E.; *c:* Pamela, Cristina; *ed:* Hunter Coll (BA) Span, Soc 1966; Montclair St Univ (MA) Span Lit 1979; Wm Paterson (MA) Admin, Supvr 1994; *cr:* NYC Bd of Ed Span Tchr 196 Bergenfield Bd of Ed ESL Tchr 1978-84; Literacy Vol, Bergenfield Coord ESL, Literacy 1981-85; Northern Vly Regnl Dist Span Tchr 1 *ai:* Span Club Adv; Project 95, 2000, Average Stu, Schlsp Comms; A FLENJ, NEA, NJEA 1986-; Pi Lamda Theta, Beta Chi 1992; Girls S of Amer 1979-84, Ldr, Parade Chprsn; AP Fac Consultant 1 Governors Tchr Recog 1990; *office:* Northern Valley Regnl HS Central Old Tappan NJ 07675

NICOSIA, SALVATORE CHARLES, Dir of Counseling Svcs; *b:* York, NY; *m:* Mary Alesi; *c:* Joseph, Joan Nicosia Karpf; *ed:* City Coll Yorm (BS) Ed 1956; Hofstra Univ (MSEd) Admin 1962; OR St Univ (F Counseling, Psych 1967; C. W. Post Univ Counseling; *cr:* Suffolk Cty Consumer Aff Deputy Commissioner 1980-82; Patchogue-Medford S Attendance Dir 1982-85, Cnslr 1985-86; BOCES Suffolk Cty Consu 1986-89; Smithtown Chrstn Schl Dir Counseling Svcs 1989-; *ai:* Adv Govt; NHS Comm; NYSUT 1962-, Pres Local 1630, VP, Del; Suffolk Salvation Army, Advy Bd 1977-, Chm; Big Brother Prgm 1971-75; Sa Lib Bd Trustee 1973-88, Pres; NDEA Schlsp Federal Grant 1 Candidate US Congress Republican Party Designee 1976; Cand Suffolk Cty Legislature Republican Party Designee 1977; *of* Smithtown Chrstn Schl Higbie Dr Smithtown NY 11787

NICOTERA, CATHY MONESCALCHI, English Teacher; *b:* Utica, *m:* Anthony Nicotera; *c:* Marisa, John; *ed:* State Univ of NY at Al (BA) Eng 1979; State Univ of NY at Cortland (MS) Rdng 1982; *cr:* U City Dist Desktop Publishing Coord Rdng Enhancement Prgm 197 Frankfort Schuyler Central Schl Eng Tchr 1981-87; Sauquoit V Central Schl Eng Tchr 1987-; *ai:* Yrbk Adv; Shared Decision Making Planning Team; Jr Class Adv; Amer Youth Soccer Org 1993-; Utica Rotary Club Tchr of Yr Awd 1992; *office:* Sauquoit Valley Central 9449 Jennifer Ln Sauquoit NY 13456

NIEBAUER, BERNARD ANDREW, Mathematics & Computer Tea *b:* Fairview, PA; *m:* Rosemary Marz; *c:* Amanda, Elizabeth; *ed:* Edin St Univ (MED) Ed 1980; Gannon Coll Under Grad Stud; *cr:* Cochra HS Tchr 1976-; *ai:* NHS Adv; Meadville HS Girls Jr Var Bsktbl Co Seton Schl Jr Var Bsktbl Coach; NEA, PSEA & CCEA 1976-; Saint Ag Church 1976-, Eucharistic Minister & Lector 1982-; Seton Schl Fin Comm 1982-, Treas; *office:* Cochranton Jr/Sr HS 2nd St Cochranton 16314

NIEBAUER, MARTIN ANTHONY, Mathematics & Computer Chn Erie, PA; *m:* Marilyn Dahlkemper; *c:* Martin Jr., Michelle, Michael; Gannon Univ (BS) Math 1972; Edinboro Univ (MMEd) Math Ed 1 Manhattan Coll 3 Credits; Intermediate Unit 3 Credits; *cr:* Acad HS Cn Math Tchr 1972-91; Behrend Coll Adj Fac Math 1981-, Penn St Adj Math 1981-; Gannon Coll Math Lecturer; Villamaria Coll Math Lectu Mercyhurst Coll Math Lecturer; Cntrl HS Math, Cmptr, AP Calculus

-; *ai:* Math, Cmptr Chprsn; NHS, Chess Club, PEP Spirit Club Adv; r Trainer; NEA, PSEA, EEA 1972-, Bldg Rep; MAA 1994-; Natl Assn udnt Act Advs 1993-; Erie Jaycees, Outstdng Tchr; Waterford Lions 1993-; St Joseph, Food Pantry Worker, Pre-Cana Lead Couple, Lenten Supper Worker, Eucharitic Minister; Wrestling Booster; Outstdng ; 5 Gallon Donor Erie Comm Blood Bank; Jefferson Playground Svc Cntrl Track, Vlybl, Wrestling Teams Svc Awd; *office:* Central HS Cherry St Erie PA 16508*

BERDING, JAMES EDWARD, Social Studies Dept Chair; *b:* eland, OH; *m:* Alberta M. Scharf; *c:* Christopher, James, Catherine is; *ed:* John Carroll Univ (BA) His 1952, (MA) His 1953; Attnd eland St Univ; *cr:* St Edward HS Tchr, Dept Chm 1955-; *ai:* World rs Cncl; Diocesan Soc Stud Tchrs Assn 1965-80, Pres, Two Svc Awds; Cncl for Soc Stud; Henning Awd 1989; *office:* Saint Edward HS 13500 oit Ave Lakewood OH 44107

BERGALL, JOANNE, 2nd Grade Teacher; *b:* Brooklyn, NY; *m:* am; *ed:* Suffolk Comm Coll (AA) Lbrl Arts 1972; Stonybrook Univ Elem Ed 1974, (MA) Elem Ed 1980; 75 Credit Hrs; *cr:* Aquebogue 1st-3rd Grd Tchr 1974-; *ai:* Bldg Rep; Site Based Mgmt Team; Comm ter Troup, Pres 1990; Soc Comm; Schlsp Fund; Riverhead Fac Assn -, Bldg Rep, Soc Comm & Many Other Comms; Comm Theater 1984-, lem; 2 Stu Tchrs from Southampton Coll; 2 Stu Observers from St ohs Coll; *office:* Aqueboque Elem Schl Main St Aquebogue NY 1*

O, JOHN A., Librarian; *b:* Danville, PA; *m:* Barbara Kolet; *c:* John, ew, Matt, Mark; *ed:* Millerville (BA) Lib 1962; Villanova (MS) Lib ; Post Grad Work at OK & Penn St; *cr:* Danville Jr High Librn -76; Danville HS Librn 1976-; *ai:* NEA, PSEA & DEA 1962-; PHLA -; Several Publication Latest in Book Report 1992.

DERER, JOAN ANNECHINI, Sixth Grade Teacher; *b:* Trenton, NJ; lark Robert; *ed:* Buck Cty Comm Coll (AA) Elem Ed 1970; West ster Univ (BS) Elem Ed 1972; 24 Credit Hrs Holy Family Coll, Penn xtension; *cr:* Queen of Universe 5-8 Grds Tchr 1972-85; Hun Schl of ceton Sixth Grd Tchr 1985-; *ai:* Yrbk, Newspaper, Chrldrs Adv; Sftbl ch; Sixth Grd Lead Tchr; Discipline Comm for Upper Schl; NJ MS 1986-94; Gold Awd MS Yrbk; *office:* Hun Schl Of Princeton 176 erstoune Rd Princeton NJ 08540

HAUS, SUSAN JANE, Math Teacher; *b:* Cincinnati, OH; *m:* Daniel *c:* Amy, Molly, Robby, Maggy; *ed:* Coll of Mt St Joseph (AB) Math ; Ed Miami Univ 1990; Ed Xavier Univ 1989; *cr:* Badin HS Math Tchr -; *ai:* NHS; NCEA 1979-; OCEA 1979-; Butler Cty Medical Auxillary -; *office:* Stephen T. Badin HS 571 New London Rd Hamilton OH 3

HOFF, KARISSA LYNN, Health & PE Coordinator; *b:* St Louis, MO; Univ of MA at Amherst (BS) Prof Preparation in PE 1988; 56 Credit Latin Ed, Classics Major Brown Univ; 18 Credit Hrs Masters Degree Ed Southern CT St Univ; *cr:* Greenwich Pub Schls PE Long-TermSub 1988-90; Joel Barlow HS PE, Hlth Tchr 1990-92; Bethel MS PE Tchr 2-93; Litchfield HS K-12 Grd Hlth & PE Coord, Pers onal Wellness 1993-; *ai:* Var Field Hockey, Girls Bsktbl Coach; Stu Cncl, Peer Edctr ; Ldrshp Cncl; Blue Ribbon Writing Team; Litchfield Prevention Cncl; 1990-; CAHPERD 1990-, VP Elect Hlth, Scndry Hlth Edctr of Yr 3-94; ASCD 1993-; US Olympic Comm, Del & Ed Comm; US Del to l Olympic & Canadian Olympic Acads; US Field Hockey Assn 1990-; rnational Fed d'Eucation Physique 1995-; Conntent Exam Review im 1994-; CT Hlth Ed Standards Comm; Intnl Olympic Yth Camp nta 1996, Group Ldr; 21st Century Outstdng Edctr of NE 1993-94; IPERD Hlth Edctr of Yr 1993-94; Outstdng Edctr Litchfield Prevention l; St Class S Field Hockey Coach of Yr 1995; First Natl Olympic Acad Yth Ldrshp US Olympic Comm Co-Organizer 1996; *office:* Litchfield 14 Plumb Hill Rd Litchfield CT 06759*

KAMP, JENNIFER RITTER, 7th-12th Grade Science Teacher; *b:* St ys, OH; *m:* Randall William; *c:* Sarah, Emily; *ed:* Wright St Univ (BS) Ed 1990; Univ of Dayton (MS) Ed 1994; *cr:* Botkins Schls 7-12 Sci r 1990-; *ai:* NEA, OEA 1990-; Copeland Grant; *office:* Botkins Local ls 208 N Sycamore Box 550 Botkins OH 45306

LANDER, BARBARA BENJAMIN, 4th Grade Teacher; *b:* Olean, *m:* William Jr.; *c:* Zachary, Kyle; *ed:* SUNY at Cortland (BA) Elem Ed 5; Nazareth Coll (MS) General Ed 1989; *cr:* Rochester City Schl Dist 6th Grd Tchr 10 Yrs; *ai:* Chprsn Peer Mediator Trainer & Coord; Schl mate Comm; RTA, NYSTA 1986-; *home:* 1568 Snowberry Cres worth NY 14568

ELSEN, KAREN ENGLEHARDT, English Teacher; *b:* Massillon, OH; Charles Allen; *c:* Edward C., Melora L.; *ed:* Capital Univ (BA) Eng Ed 6; Grad Hrs in Ed, Cmptrs & British Lit; *cr:* Roosevelt Jr HS Eng Tchr 6-70; Longfellow Jr HS Learning Disabilities Tutor 1973-74; Tuslaw Eng Tchr 1975-; *ai:* NHS; N Cntrl Evaluation Team 1984, 1990 & 1992; Pg Admin; Tech Comm; NEA & OEA 1975-; Tuslaw Classroom Tchrs n 1975-, Sec 1989-90; NCTE & OCTELA 1990-; Amer Heart Assn 0-, Vol; March of Dimes, Vol; Jennings Scholar 1990-91; Yrbk dicatee & Outstanding Tchr 1982; Tchr & Ldr Network 1990-91; land Oil Golden Apple Awd 1993; Martha Holden Jennings Master ir 1994; Stark Cty Enrty Yr Mgmt Team; *office:* Tuslaw HS 1723 nchester Ave NW Massillon OH 44647

ELSEN, THOMAS JOSEPH, Mathematics Teacher; *b:* St Albans, NY; Susan Elisabeth Robak; *c:* Jonathan; *ed:* Queens Coll (BA) Math 1967; fstra Univ (MA) Scndry Math Ed 1972; St Univ of NY at Albany 30 edit Hrs; *cr:* Elmont Meml HS Math Tchr 1967-; *ai:* Sr Class Adv 1974, 9; NEA 1967-; *office:* Elmont Memorial HS 555 Ridge Rd Elmont NY 003

ELSEN-PERCY, ANNI, French Teacher; *b:* Amsterdam, NY; *m:* nold; *ed:* SUC at Fredonia (BA) Fr 1983; OH St Univ (MA) Fr 1986; rney Towards Literacy Conf; Westchester Comm Chorus Concert Tour Greece; *cr:* OH St Univ Fr Tchng Assoc 1984-86; Schenectady City ils Jr High Fr Tchr 1986-89; Clifton-Fine Cntrl Schl HS Fr Tchr 1989-; Fr Club Adv; NYSUT-AFT 1986-, Local Treas; Amer Assoc Tchr of Fr 36-; Amer Cncl on Tchng Frgn Lang 1986-; East Pittcairn Wesleyan urch 1994-, Communicant; *office:* Clifton-Fine Central Schl Box 75 ain St Star Lake NY 13690

EMCZURA, M. A., German Teacher; *b:* Palmer, MA; *ed:* Univ of idelberg (BA) Ger Lang, Lit, Culture, His & Geography 1965, (MA) Ger ng, Lit, Culture, His & Geography 1966; Univ of CO (BA) Ger Lang & 1967; Vanderbilt Univ (MA) Ger Lang & Lit 1973, (PHD) Ger Lang & 1974; Post Grad Stud 1991; *cr:* TN Technological Univ Ger Asst Prof 67-72; Old Dominion Univ Ger Adjunct Prof 1972-75; Norfolk City hls Ger Tchr 1972-83; North Syracuse Schls Ger Tchr 1983-; Adelphi iv Ger Adjunct Prof; *ai:* AAUP 1967-72, Sec; AATG 1967-; ACTFL, L 1989-; NYSAFLT 1983-; Fulbright Fellowships 1990-91, 1994-95; ckefeller Fellowship 1990; Bus Week Awd for Innovative Tchng 1989; 'SAFLT Grants 1989 & 1991; CNY Tchng Ctr Grant 1989; Ger Club Adv TN Technological Univ & Norfolk City Schls; *office:* Cicero-North racuse HS Rt 31 Cicero NY 13039

EMEYER, CONNIE PHILLIPS, Chemistry Teacher; *b:* Dayton, OH; George E.; *c:* Craig, Lynne, Kirk; *ed:* Miami Univ (BS) Math & Sci 58; OH St Univ (MA) Math Ed 1963; Post Grad Stud Wright St Univ, Bowling Green St Univ, Univ of Dayton; *cr:* Lima Sr HS Math Tchr 1958-66; Lima Branch of OH St Univ Math Instr 1960-66; Wapakoneta Jr HS Math & Sci Tchr 1975-79; Wapakoneta HS Chem Tchr 1979-; *ai:* WEA, OEA, NEA 1975-; Alpha Delta Kappa 1984-; SECO; Jr Svc League; The Irving Club GFWC 1968-, Pres; 3 Natl Sci Fnd Grants to Obtain MA Degree; *office:* Wapakoneta HS 1 W Redskin Trail Wapakoneta OH 45895

NIEMI, PETER ANDREW, Rdng & Lang Arts Specialist; *b:* Plymouth, MA; *ed:* Northeastern Univ (BS) Speech, Hearing & Pathology Lang 1972, (MED) Curr & Instruction 1973; Addl Credit Hrs Rdng Diagnostics, Research Lit, Whole Lang Theory & Applications, Portfolio Assessment Methodology & Co-Operative Learning & Peer Obsrvtn; *cr:* Whitman Pub Schls 2nd Grd Tchr 1973-87, Rdng Tchr Specialist & Chapter I Rdng Bldg Coord 1987-; Rdng, Lang Arts Coord 1993; Tchng Asst Princ 1989-91; Title I Coord; *ai:* Whitman Tchrs Assn Prof Rights & Responsibilities Comm; Schl Cncl; Curr Frameworks; IRA, NEA & MA Tchrs Assn 1973-; MA Rdng Assn 1990-; Phi Kappa Phi Honor Soc 1971-, Schlsp & Acad Performance Awd 1972; Kappa Delta Pi Honor Soc 1970-; Natl Cncl of Tchrs of Eng 1992-; So Shore Rdng Cncl 1992-; Assoc for Supv & Curr Dev 1994-; Plymouth Cnty Ed Assoc Cit Award 1992; MA Assn for Sup & Curr; Chapter I Grant to Coord Lit into the Rdng Prgm; *office:* Frank Holt Elem Schl 1 Essex St Whitman MA 02382*

NIENBURG, GORDON WILLIAM, 9th Grade Science Teacher; *b:* Jersey City, NJ; *m:* Mary Ann Makoski; *c:* Tina, Toni, Marc; *ed:* Monmouth Coll (BS) Math 1967; Kean Coll (MA) Math 1977, (MA) Admin, Supervision 1979; *cr:* John Adams Jr HS 7th Grd Math, 7th-9th Grd Sci Tchr 1968-80; J. P. Stevens HS 9th-11th Grd Sci Tchr 1980-; *ai:* Girls Soccer, Boys, Girls Winter Track, Girls Spring Var Coach; NJEA, NEA, ETEA 1968-; NJ Soccer Coaches Assn 1992-; NJ Sci Tchrs Assn 1985-; K of C 1968-; Westfield Soccer Assn 1981-, Pres; St Helen's Parish Cncl 1984-, Pres; Westfield HS Boosters 1988-; *office:* John P Stevens HS 855 Grove Ave Edison NJ 08820*

NIES, BARBARA, 4th Grade Teacher; *b:* Jersey City, NJ; *c:* Randy; *ed:* William Paterson U (BA) Ed-Suma Cum Laude 1974; Fairleigh Dickinson U (MS) Human Dev 1985; *cr:* Englewood Bd of Ed 3rd-4th Grd Tchr 21 Yrs; *ai:* Englewood Tchrs Assn 1974-, Bldg Rep; NEA 1990-, Natl Convention Del; A+ for Kids; *office:* Cleveland Schl 325 Tenafly Rd Englewood NJ 07631*

NIESE, BECKIE A. (HONIGFORT), Elem Art Teacher; *b:* Ottawa, OH; *m:* Michael V.; *c:* Michelle, Kristi, Taryn, Jaclyn; *ed:* Bowling Green St Univ (BFA) Fine Arts & Art Ed 1981; Attnd OH St Univ, Univ of Findlay, Ashland Univ; *cr:* Leipsic Elem Schl Art Tchr 1982-; *ai:* Enrichment for Talented & Gifted Art Stdnts Instr; NEA 1982-; OAA 1982-; LEA 1982-; Mothers Club 1983-, VP, Sec; *office:* Leipsic Local Schl 232 Oak St Leipsic OH 45856

NIESE, KARLA ANN, Music Dir & Dept Chm; *b:* Sandusky, OH; *m:* Mark Charles; *c:* Jessica Faye, Aaron Joseph, Kevin James; *ed:* Heidelberg Coll (BM) Music Ed, Trumpet Performance, Brass Pedagogy, Studio Mngmt 1986; Youngstown St Univ (MM) Music Ed Trumpet Performance 1988; Music Bowling Green St Univ; *cr:* Byzantine Cath Schl Elem, Jr HS Music Dir 1986-88; Lorain Cath HS Instrumental-Vocal Music Dir, Dept Chm 1988-93; St Joseph Acad Instrumental-Vocal Music Dir, Dept Chm 1993-; *ai:* Pep Band; OMEA, MBNA 1986-; WBNA 1993-; TAU 1984-; Natl Coll Achvmt Awd; *home:* 1373 Cleveland Rd W Apt 305 Huron OH 44839

NIESTEMSKI, JOYCE A., HS Teacher; *b:* Derby, CT; *ed:* Southern IL Univ (BS) PE, Hlth 1966; Southern CT St Univ (MS) PE, Hlth 1972; Attnd Southern CT St Univ Ed 1982; Post Grad Stud Supervision, Admin, Vagiellonia Univ Exchange, Ed; *cr:* Pomperaug HS Tchr, Jr Class Adv, Stu Cncl, Dean 1966-; *ai:* Jr Class, Stu Cncl Adv; NASAA Rep Divison Stu Achvt; NEA, CEA, Pomp Ed Assn 1966-; DKG 1979-, Sec; St Thomas Ladies Guild 1979-, VP; Fullbright Scholar 1976; Kosciuszko Fnd Scholar 1979-80; CT Assn of Stu Cncl Adv of Yr 1994; *office:* Pomperaug Regional HS 234 Judd Rd Southbury CT 06488

NIEWIAROSKI, TRUDI OSMERS, Social Studies Teacher; *b:* Jersey City, NJ; *m:* Donald; *c:* Donald Jr., Margaret Annie Mouna, Donna, Nancy Comez; *ed:* Ucsala Coll (AB) His, Ger 1957; Mont Cty Pub Schl (MED) Ed 1992; *ai:* Spon Acad, Intl Club; PTSA Tchr Rep; Coord Mid States Accreditation 1996; NCSS, MD Cncl Soc Stud, Asia Soc 1984-; Amer Assn Univ Women, NCSS Spec Interest Group Korea, Natl Soc Stud Supvr Assn, MD St Tchrs of Yr Assn 1995-; Smithsonian Institution, NCSS Special Interest Group China 1987-; NCSS Special Interest Group Japan 1990-; ASCD 1992-; MD Bus Roundtable Ed, Kappa Delta Pi, Natl St Tchrs Yr Assn 1993-; Local Citizens Assn 1970-, Pres, Treas 1977-81; Local Swim Club 1970-, Pres 1981-82; MCRS Instrl Mat Comm, Chair 1971-75; Bd Cotopaxi Acad Ecuador, Dir 1965-66; Girls Scouts, Ldr 1975-76; MD Tchr of Yr, Natl Tchr of Yr Finalist 1993; Univ MD Mexican Art, Culture Flwshp 1995; Del Eisenhower People to People Edctrs Vietnam 1993; Milken Fnd Natl Educator Awd 1994; Japan Keizai Koho Ctr Flwshp 1992; Advy Cnsl Milken Fnd 1994-; Upsala Coll Distngd Alumni Awd 1993; Fulbright Flwshp India 1985, China 1990; Numerous Publications, Curr Guides; Undergrad Schlsp 1953-57; Valedictorian Undergraduate; Phi Beta Kappa Awd; *office:* Richard Montgomery HS 250 Richard Montgomery Dr Rockville MD 20852*

NIGGLI, CAROL APPLEBY, Sixth Grade Teacher; *b:* Cortland, NY; *m:* Wayne V.; *c:* Brent, Karen, Denis; *ed:* SUNY at Cortland (BS) Elem Ed 1979, (MS) Elem Ed 1985; Misc Grad & Inservice Hrs; *cr:* Cincinnatus Cntrl Schl Elem Tchr 1981-83; Marathon Cntrl Schl Kndgtn, 5th & 6th Grd Tchr 1983-; *ai:* Effective Schl Dist Team; Discipline Comm; Schl Cabinet; Prof Dev Team; Girls Ldrshp Wkshp Adv; NEA & NY 1980-, Recording Sec, Pres; Marathon Village Bd 1995-, Trustee; Marathon Alumni Assoc, Pres; NYS Rdng Conf Presenter; NYS Eng Cncl Presenter; *office:* Appleby Elem Schl Albro Rd Marathon NY 13803*

NIGHTENGALE, RUSSELL E., Counselor; *b:* Wheeling, WV; *m:* Marjorie K. Gehringer; *c:* Russell Scott, Melissa Nightengale Geric; *ed:* West Liberty St (BA) Bio 1960; Edinboro St (MED) Guid & Cnslng 1973; Cleveland St Univ (MED) Admin 1984; *cr:* Triadelphia HS Bio Instr & Coach 1961-70; Eastlake North Cnslr, Coach & Chprsn 1970-84; Willoughby Tech Ctr Admin 1984-92; Ledgemont HS Cnslr 1992-; *ai:* OEA & NEA 1970-; Willoughby-Eastlake Tchrs 1970-, Tchr of Yr Awd; St Pauls Presbyn Church 1993-, Trustee; Mens Bsktbl Coach of Yr 1969; Cross Cntry Coach of Yr 1970; Womens Bsktbl Coach of Yr 1977-79; *office:* Ledgemont HS 16700 Thompson Rd Thompson OH 44086

NIGHTINGALE, BONNIE MAGAR, Social Studies Teacher; *b:* Rochester, NY; *m:* William Walter; *c:* Richard; *ed:* SUC at Brockport (BA) His 1971; Nazareth Coll (MS) Ed 1983; 3 Grad Hrs His; *cr:* John Marshall HS Soc Stud Tchr 6 Yrs; Wilson Magnet Schl Soc Stud Tchr 1 Yr; Frederick Douglas MS Soc Stud Tchr 2 Yrs; St Charles Boromeo Schl Soc Stud, Rdng Tchr 5 Yrs; *ai:* Schl Based Planning Team Comm, Tchr Contituency; Rochesters Tchrs Assn, AFT 1988-; *office:* John Marshall HS 180 Ridgeway Ave Rochester NY 14615

NIGRI, JOHN,III, Social Studies Teacher; *b:* Winsted, CT; *ed:* Northwestern CT Comm Coll (AS) Gen Stud 1992; Westfield St Coll (BA) His, Ed 1994; *cr:* Agawam HS Soc Stud Tchr 1995-; *ai:* Orange & Brown Acad Achvmt, Mayor's Appreciation Awds 1995; Nom NHS 1996.*

NIGRO, JOSEPH PHILIP, Biology Teacher; *b:* Milford, MA; *m:* Elaine Gogliormella; *c:* Tracy, Rebecca, Joseph, Ashley; *ed:* Boston Coll (BS) Bio, Ed 1965; Framingham St Coll (MED) Ed 1971; Univ of MA at Boston 4 Hrs Biochem; Framington St Coll 15 Hrs Inst; Boston Coll 4 Hrs Mass Biotech; *cr:* Holliston HS Sci Tchr 1965-, Sci Dept Chprsn 1968-82; *ai:* HS Cncl; Fac Cncl; Globe, Greenhouse Prject; Stu Biotech Rsrch, Stud Group; MCET 3 Hrs Rsrch Inst Wkshp; AFT, Phi Delta Kappa 1965-; Milford MS Cncl 1995-; Knights of Columbus 1985-; Holliston Ed Fnd Grant for Greenhouse Sci Project 1994-95; *home:* 370 Ramble Rd Milford MA 01757

NIHOFF, JOSEPH JOHN, Instr of Hospitality Mngmt; *b:* North Ft Myers, FL; *ed:* Duquesne Univ (BS) Soc Stud 1976; Univ of Pittsburgh (BS) Ec 1977; Duquesne Univ (MS) Psych 1978; *cr:* Chez Robert GM 1980-82; Bellevue-Stratford Hotel F&B Mgr 1982-85; Superior Wine & Spirits Wine Mgr 1985-87; Kasscrs Distillers Wine Dir 1987-91; Culinary Inst of Amer Instr, Hospitality Mngmt 1991-; *ai:* Chaine des Rotisseues 1989-, Bailli, Medal of Excl Bronze Star; Catering de Medicci 1990-, Schlsp of Commitment; Chevalliers des Tasteuin 1995-, Candidate of Hnr; *office:* Culinary Inst Of America 433 Albany Post Rd Hyde Park NY 12538*

NIILER, KRISTINE CARLSON, Math Teacher; *b:* St Albans, NY; *m:* Craig J.; *c:* Kurt; *ed:* Univ of CT (BS) Chem 1985; Plymouth St Coll (MED) Math 1986; *cr:* Kingswood Regnl Schl Math Tchr 1986-; *ai:* Math Team Adv; Field Hockey, Head Ski Team Coach; MS Team Ldr; Dist Math Curr Comm; Quiz Bowl Adv; NCTM, NH Sci Tchrs Assn 1986-; Church Folk Music Group; *office:* Kingswood Regnl MS 404 S Main St Wolfeboro NH 03894

NIJHUIS, MARGARET JOHNS, Mathematics Teacher; *b:* Richmond, VA; *m:* Rolf H.; *c:* Michelle; *ed:* Coll of William & Mary (BA) Math 1963; NY Univ at New Paltz (MA) Math, Ed 1974; Addl Hrs Cmptr Sci; *cr:* Huguenot Acad Tchr 1963-64; Carey HS Tchr 1964-65; Blacksburg HS Tchr 1965-67; Arlington Jr HS Tchr 1967-68; Our Lady of Lourdes HS Tchr, Dept Chair 1968-; *ai:* Ski Club, Jr Class, Sr Class Moderator; NYS Math Tchrs 1983-; Am Assn Univ Women 1967-, Pres, Schlsp; Mid Hudson Alumni Panhellenic 1975-, Pres; Tchr of Yr Blacksburg Jaycees; *office:* Our Lady-Lourdes HS 29 N Hamilton St Poughkeepsie NY 12601

NIKLAUS, WILLIAM MICHAEL, Psychology Teacher; *b:* Manhasset, NY; *m:* Mary Ellen; *c:* William Christopher; *ed:* St Johns Univ (BA) Psych, Sociology 1984, (MS) Ed 1986; *cr:* Archbishop Molloy HS Psychology Tchr, Soc Stud Dept Chm 1984-; *ai:* Var Golf Coach, Golf Chm CHSAA; Newspaper Moderator; Soc Stud Dept Chm; USGA 1986-; APA 1990-; *office:* Archbishop Molloy HS 8353 Manton St Briarwood NY 11435

NILSEN, ADRIENNE PRETEROTI, Latin & English Teacher; *b:* Newark, NJ; *m:* J. Kent; *ed:* Montclair St Coll (BA) Latin, Eng-Cum Laude 1974; NJ St Tchng Cert 1974; *cr:* St Thomas Aquinas HS Latin, Eng Tchr 1974-76; St Peters HS Latin, Eng Tchr 1976-80; Merril Lynch Realty Assoc Realtor 1980-85; George A. Fuller Co Western Reg Exec Asst 1980-85; L. A. Rams Chrldng, Entertainment, PR 1980-85; Rogue Sportswear Invoicing, Acctng 1980-85; R. E. Scott Mortgage Co Underwriter 1985-89; Anthony Mortgage Co Office Mgr 1985-89; St John Vianney Regnl HS Latin I-V, Eng I, II, World His, Sociology Tchr 1989-; *ai:* Key Club, Lit, Art Journal, Creative Writing Club, Latin Club Adv; NCEA; Amer Classical League; Natl Jr Classical League; Frgn Lang Edctrs of NJ; Shore Latin Cncl; Kiwanis; Kappa Delta Pi; Project Discovery Spec Appointment to Southern UT Univ; *office:* St John Vianney Reg HS 94 Line Rd Holmdel NJ 07733*

NILSEN, FRANCIS, Drafting Teacher; *b:* Brooklyn, NY; *m:* Sheryl Ann Schott; *c:* Nicholas, Kenneth, Matthew, Thomas; *ed:* SUNY at Delhi (AS) Building Construction 1979; Attnd City Coll of NY, SUNY at Stony Brook; *cr:* Thomas Construction Carpenter 1982-85; Francis Nilsen Carpentry Owner, Carpenter 1985-; Boces 2 Asst Tchr 1990-93; Eastern Suffolk Boces Drafting Tchr 1993-; *ai:* VICA Adv; Boy Scout Den Ldr; NAAUG 1993-; ALIVE 1995-; CHADD 1994-; *office:* Eastern Suffolk Boces Schl 350 Martha Ave Bellport NY 11713

NILSON, LINDA MAXSON, Reading Support Teacher; *b:* Gloversville, NY; *m:* Arthur H.; *ed:* Skidmore Coll (BS) Elem Ed 1973; Attnd Univ of MN, St Univ at Oneonta, Elmira Coll; *cr:* St Clements 3rd Grd Tchr 1967-71; McNab Elem Schl Transitional 1st Grd Tchr 1973-79; Lansing Elem Schl Kndgtn, 1st & Transitional 1st Grd Tchr 1982-90; Bristol Consolidated Schl Rdng Support Tchr 1991-; *ai:* Selected to Participate in Production of Tchr Recruitment Video Video for NY St; *home:* 162 Round Pond Rd Medomak ME 04551

NILSSON, CHRISTOPHER NILS, Science Teacher; *b:* New York, NY; *m:* Patricia Anita Holtzner; *c:* Nancy Noel; *ed:* Univ of VT (MS) Comp Sci 1975; Attnd Rutgers Univ, McGill Univ, John Hopkin Univ, Union Coll; *cr:* Baltimore Pub Schls 5th Grd Tchr 1961-63; IBM Corp Comp Scientist 1965-90; Winoski HS Math Comp Tchr 1990-91; Enosburg Falls HS Sci Tchr 1991-; *ai:* Physics Team Adv; Tech Comm Mem; NHS Selection Comm; NEA 1990-; AAPT 1991-; SEA 1991-; Democratic Party 1965-, Town Chm; Natl Ski Patrol 1986-; US Coast Guard Honorable Discharge; IBM Division Awd 1985; EFHS Outstdng Achvmt Awd 1992; NSF, IBM, Eisenhower & Chptr II Grants; *office:* Enosburg Falls Jr-Sr HS School St Enosburg Falls VT 05450

NIMBLETT, JAMES F., Mathematics Teacher; *b:* Winthrop, MA; *m:* Sally Mills; *c:* Thomas, James (dec), Ruthie, Robert; *ed:* Salem St (BSEd) Math, Sci Tchng 1965; Boston St (MSEd) Scdnry Ed 1982; 30 Addl Credits; *cr:* Winthrop Jr HS Math Tchr, Coach 1965-84; Winthrop HS Math Tchr, Coach 1984-; *ai:* Asst Girls Bsktbl, Sftbl Coach; NEA, MA Tchr Assn 1965-; Winthrop Tchrs Assn 1965-, VP 1973, Excl in Ed 1996; NCTM 1994-; BPOE Elks 1966-.

NIMMER, TIM, Social Studies Teacher; *b:* San Francisco, CA; *m:* Mary; *ed:* SUNY at Stony Brook (BA) Pol Sci, His 1986; Columbia Univ (MA) Soc Stud Ed 1990; 18 Post Grad Credit Hrs; *cr:* Colonie Cntrl HS Soc Stud Tchr 1991-; *ai:* Girls, Boys Var Tennis Team; Chess Club; NYSASA Ldrshp Conf; NCSS 1996; NYSUT 1990-; *office:* Colonie Central HS 1 Raider Blvd Albany NY 12205

NIMS, CAROL L., Second Grade Teacher; *b:* Jamestown, NY; *m:* David A.; *c:* David Wayne, Charis Lynn; *ed:* Cedarville Coll (BS) Elem Ed 1967; Addl Hrs Univ of Dayton, Wright St Univ; *cr:* Beavercreek Bd of Ed First Grd Tchr 1967-73, Second Grd Tchr 1974-; *ai:* NEA; *office:* Beavercreek Bd of Ed 2940 Dayton Xenia Rd Beavercreek OH 45434

NIRO, DONNA HEINRICH, Fifth Grade Teacher; *b:* E Cleveland, OH; *m:* William; *c:* Kimberly, Ryan; *ed:* OH St Univ (BS) 1-8 Ed 1967; 30 Grad Hrs; *cr:* Cobb Cty Schls 1st Grd Tchr 1967-68; Wickliffe City Schls 5th Grd Tchr 1968-71; Strongsville City Schls Chptr I Tutor 1986-88, 5th Grd Tchr 1988-; *ai:* Strongsville Tchrs Assn, NEA, OEA 1988-; Cleveland Plain Dealer Crystal Apple Awd; *office:* Strongsville City Schls 16400 Park Lane Dr Strongsville OH 44136

NISH, GERALDINE VALONIS, Language Arts Teacher; *b:* Dickson City, PA; *m:* Peter M.; *c:* William P., Jennifer M., Peter C.; *ed:* Marywood Coll (BA) Eng & Scndry Ed 1963, (MS) Eng 1970; *cr:* Chenango Forks HS Eng & Fr Tchr 1963-66; Dickson City HS Eng Tchr 1966-67; Dunmore Cntrl Cath HS Eng & Soc Stud Tchr 1968-73; East Stroudsburg HS Eng Tchr 1985-87; Pocono Jr HS Lang Arts Tchr 1987-; *ai:* PSEA 1987-; NEA 1987-; Womens Guild of Church 1990-; *office:* Pocono Mountain Jr HS Box 200 School Rd Swiftwater PA 18370

NISIVOCCIA, PATRICIA (ROSACE), 7th-8th Grade English Teacher; *b:* Jersey City, NJ; *c:* Jennifer; *ed:* Fairleigh Dickinson Univ (BA) Elem Ed

1970; Jersey City St Coll (MA) Rdng 1975; 15 Credit Hrs Learning Disabilities Tchr, Consultant; *cr:* Bayonne Bd of Ed Tchr 22 Yrs; *ai:* Peer Mediation Adv; Pupil Assistance Comm; NJEA, NEA, Bayonne Tchrs Assn 1970-; NJ Governor's Tchr Recognition Prgm 1990.

NISSLY, JOSEPH A., Frgn Lang Coord & Span Tchr; *b:* Denver, PA; *ed:* Penn St Univ (BA) Span 1961; Middlebury Coll (MA) Span 1967; Post Grad Stud Escuela Normal at Saltillo Mexico, Universidad De Los Andes at Bogota Columbia; *cr:* Tamanend Jr HS Span Tchr, Dept Coord 1961-70; Cntrl Bucks West Schl Span Tchr 1970-71; Cntrl Bucks East Schl Span Tchr, Dept Coord 1971-; *ai:* CBEA, PSEA, NEA, AATSP 1961-; ATFL-BC 1990-; Phi Sigma Iota 1961-; NDEA Frgn Lang Tchrs Inst 1962; Fulbright Schlsp Columbia 1964; Citation of Merit Northwood Inst MI 1991; *office:* Central Bucks-East HS PO Box 405 Buckingham PA 18912

NISTA, JOSEPH VINCENT, Mathematics Teacher; *b:* Bronxville, NY; *m:* Antoinette R.; *c:* Danielle; *ed:* Iona Coll (BS) Math 1987; Fordham Univ (MA) Ec 1988; Manhattanville Coll Ed Credit Hrs; *cr:* Fordham Univ Adj Ec Prof 1989; Iona Coll Adj Ec Prof 1989-91; Scarsdale Pub Schls Math Tchr 1989-92; Nanuet Pub Schls Math Tchr 1993-; *ai:* JV Soccer & Boys Soccer Coach; NCTM 1990-; AFT 1993-; NYSMT 1993-; NYSUT 1993-; *office:* Nanuet HS 103 Church St Nanuet NY 10954

NITKIN, RISA M., 11th-12th Grade English Tchr; *b:* New Haven, CT; *ed:* Univ of CT (BS) Eng & Fr 1971; Southern CT St Univ (MS) Emot; BEST & Mentor Pgms; TESA; *ai:* Schl Newspaper & Bus Adv; NEA; Top Ten Tchr of Yr; Intl Baccalarreate Pgm Recognition; *office:* Hamden H S 2040 Dixwell Ave Hamden CT 06514*

NIUTTA, MARIA SOLURI, Mathematics Teacher; *b:* Port Chester, NY; *m:* Benito; *c:* Carla, Daniela, Gildo; *ed:* Brown Univ (BA) Math 1964; Hofstra Univ (MA) Math 1978; 39 Addl Credit Hrs; *cr:* Harrison HS Math Tchr 1964066; Amer Can Co Mngmt Sci Analyst 1967-69; Bradford Investor Data Svcs Mgr Client Liasion 1969-73, Mgr Spec Projects 1976-79; Northern Vly Regnl HS Math Tchr 1989-; *ai:* Math Team Adv; Fac Advy Comm; PTSA; NEA, NJEA 1989-; NCTM 1995-; *office:* Northern Valley Regnl HS 100 Central Ave Old Tappan NJ 07675

NIX, RONALD JAMES, 6th Grade Teacher; *b:* Chicago, IL; *m:* Sue Jacoby-Nix; *c:* JOanna O'Brien Jeff Krakowka, Carrie Krakowka, Andrew Krakowka; *ed:* 30 Post-Grad Hrs SUC at Oswego; *cr:* Fitzhugh Park Schl Elem Tchr 27 Yrs; *ai:* OCTA Schlsp, Shared Decision Making Comms; NYSUT 1969-; Elks Club 1967-; *office:* Fitzhugh Park Elem Schl E 10th & Bridge Sts Oswego NY 13126

NIXON, BARBARA WARD, Chemistry Teacher; *b:* Auburn, NY; *m:* Terrence H.; *ed:* Wilkes Univ (BA) Chem 1971; Johns Hopkins Univ (MS) Adult Ed 1979; Univ of MD 12 Credit Hrs Earth Sci; *cr:* Severna Park Jr HS Sci Tchr 1971-75; Severn River Jr HS Sci Tchr 1975-77; Chesapeake Sr HS Chem Tchr 1977-85; Severna Park HS Chem Tchr 1985-; *ai:* Tutoring; NEA & MSTA 1971-; MD Assn of Sci Tchrs 1977-; NSTA 1980-; Natl Mole Fnd 1991-; PTSO; Amer Fed of Aviculture 1988-; Eastern Star 1971-; Chem Tchrs Club of NY 1995; Dryefus Wkshps; Presenter at ACS Meeting in Washington DC, ChemEd 91 & Local Wkshp; Local TV Station Class Act Awd; A.A. Co. Tchr of Month 1996; *office:* Severna Park H S 60 Robinson Rd Severna Park MD 21146*

NIXON, GEORGE E., Math Teacher; *b:* Morristown, NJ; *m:* Linda D. Eckardt; *ed:* Rutgers Univ (BA) Russian Area 1962; NY Univ (MA) Russian Lang 1970; NY Univ (MSMS) Math 1978; *cr:* Morris Tolls HS Math Tchr 1966-; *ai:* NEA; NTOM; NCTM; MAA; Woodward Wilson Scholar; *home:* 38 Wash Valley Rd Morristown NJ 07960

NIXON, JANE E., 8th Grade Teacher; *b:* Bronx, NY; *w:* John R. (dec); *c:* Robert, Elizabeth Hearne, Pamela Kropilak; *ed:* William Patterson (BA) Elem Ed 1970; 60 Credits in Ed William Patterson, Bridgeport Univ, Jersey City St 1975-92; *cr:* Ascension Schl Tchr 1966-68; St Joseph's Schl Tchr 1968-70; Paramus Schl System Tchr 1970-; *ai:* Dungeons & Dragons Moderator; Odyssey of Mind Coach 1 Yr, Judge 4 Yrs; Renaissance Club Co-Moderator; Rdng, Report Card, Soc Stud Comm; EAP, BCEA, NJEA, NEA 1970-; CYO 1960-72, Adv, Treas; Parish Steering Comm 3 Yrs, Mem; Parish Cncl 2 Yrs, Mem; Vol Englwood Hosp 3 Yrs, Vol; *home:* 49 Forest Pl Rochelle Park NJ 07662

NIXON, LOIS TORRENCE, Special Education Professor; *b:* Washington, DC; *m:* Walter Wadsworth; *c:* Stacie Nicole Nixon Lyons, Walter Wadsworth II; *ed:* Coppin St Coll (BS) Spec Ed MR 1969, (MA) Spec Ed ED 1971; Union Grad (PHD) Psych 1977; *cr:* Baltimore City Pub Schls Spec Educator 2 Yrs; Coppin St Coll Prof 24 Yrs; *ai:* Office of Field Svcs Coord; Cncl for Exceptional Children Co-Adv; Dept Prsnl, Division Hospitality, Tchr Ed Cncl, Admin Cncl, Scndry Ed Planning Comm & Mentoring Comm Mem; CEC 1971-; Fed of Tchrs 1985-; Natl Black Child Dev Inst 1992-; Foster Care Review Bd 1985-; Baltimore City Schl Mentor 1990; Baltimore City Circuit 1993-; HOPE 1988-, Aids Ministry; Pub 1 Article; Written & Submitted for Publication 2 Articles; Written 2 Proposals; Participated as Mem 2 Grants; *office:* Coppin St Coll 2500 W North Ave Baltimore MD 21216*

NIZNIK, JUDITH POWELL, Mathematics Teacher; *b:* Wilkes-Barre, PA; *m:* John; *c:* Jennifer, John E.; *ed:* Wilkes Univ (AB) Math 1962, (MS) Math Ed 1971; Addl 6 Hrs Amer Univ, 6 Hrs Lehigh Univ, 30 Hrs William Paterson Coll; *cr:* Hawthorne HS Math Tchr 1962-64; Mount Vernon Seminary Math Tchr 1964-68; Coughlin HS Math Tchr 1968-70; Hawthorne HS Math Tchr 1980-; *ai:* NHS Adv; NEA, NJEA, PCEA, HTA, NCTM, AMTNJ 1980-; Tandy Tech Awd; *office:* Hawthorne HS Parmelee Ave Hawthorne NJ 07506

NOAKES, MARY CLAIRE WATSON, Third Grade Teacher; *b:* Utica, NY; *m:* Alan V.; *c:* Jean Ann S. DeCelle, John Brian Shattuck, John Alan, Jeffrey Carl Shattuck; *ed:* SUNY at Plattsburgh (BS) Elem Ed 1964; Attnd SUNY at Albany, Montclair Coll, St Coll of PA; *cr:* Keeseville Elem Schl & Peru Ctrl Schl 2nd Grd 1963-65; Hadley-Luzerne Ctrl 1965-, 3rd Grd 17 Yrs, 6th Grd 10 Yrs, 4th Grd 2 Yrs, Kndgtn Music & Art 1 Yr, Remedial HS Soc Stud 1 Yr; *ai:* Yrbk Adv; Chrldng Coach; Chess & Checker Club; Drama & Elem Musicals; Hadley-Luzerne Tchrs Assn 1965-, Pres; NY St United Tchrs 1965-, Altern Del; Tri-Cty Tchrs Assn 1966-, Sec, Treas; Delta Kappa Gamma Soc Intnl 1970's, Pres Alph Epsilon Chptr; HL Tchrs Assn 1964-, VP, Pres, Del; Hadley-Luzerne Lidness 1980-, Sec, VP, Pres, R Uplingler Awd for Svc; Chamber of Commerce 1982-, Del; 2 WSY Wish Grants to Help Children; Sci Tchr of Yr Warrea Cty.*

NOBILE, WILLIAM MICHAEL, Linguistics & Spanish Teacher; *b:* Latrobe, PA; *ed:* Masters Equivalency; PA St Univ Educl Computing Cert; Span, Eng, Commnctn Post Bachelors Certs; *cr:* Hamburg Area HS Scndry Tchr 1980-; *ai:* Church 1983-, Worship Ldr; Hamburg Arts Guild 1995-; *office:* Hamburg Area HS Windsor St Hamburg PA 19526*

NOBLE, ANNETTE, Mathematics Professor; *b:* Monroe, LA; *ed:* Grambling St Univ (BS) Math Ed 1969; Clarkson Coll of Tech (MS) Math 1971; Northeast Univ; Univ of MD at Coll Park; *cr:* Langston Univ Instr 1971-74; Univ of MD Eastern Shore Lecturer of Probability & Statistics 1975-; *ai:* Crisfield Open Tennis Tournament Winner; Avid Bowler; Math Tutor for HS Stdnts; Delta Sigma Theta 1968-, Princess Anne Alumnae Chptr, Charter Mem; MD Cncl of Deltas 1979-, Sec; St Francis de Sales Cath Church; NSF CISE Co-Prin Investigator; Institutional Infrastructure Grant 1990-92; NBLIC-RIE Project Assoc; *office:* Univ Of MD Eastern Shore Dept of Mathematics Princess Anne MD 21853*

NOBLE, DANA L., English Teacher; *b:* Galion, OH; *m:* Ginger A.; *c:* Nathan, Evan, Nora; *ed:* Akron Univ (BA) Eng 1973; Cleveland St Univ (MS) Rdng 1985; *cr:* Fairless Local Schls Eng Tchr 1975-78; Tallmadge HS Eng Tchr 1978-81; Shaker Hts Schls Eng Tchr 1981-; *ai:* Japanese Frgn Exch Prgm Coord; NCTE 1978-; Supplement, Appendix to Traditions by Regie Routman; *office:* Shaker Heights HS 15911 Aldersyde Dr Shaker Heights OH 44120

NOBLE, ELI SIDNEY,JR., Vice Principal; *b:* Brunswick, GA; *m:* Thelma; *c:* Kimberley Audra; *ed:* St Augustines (BA) PE 1966; Univ of AZ (MED) Hlth Ed 1971, (EDD) Ed Curr 1981; *cr:* Pima Comm Coll Tchr, Coach, Dept Head 1971-89; Essex Cty Voc Schl Vice Prin 1990-; *ai:* Wrestling, Judo; Pac, Core Team; MEA 1971-; PSA 1990-; AASCD 1994-; Naacp 1961-; Omega Psi Phi 1964-; Urban League 1975-; *office:* Essex County Voc Tech Schl 209 Franklin St Bloomfield NJ 07003*

NOBLE, JO ANN, Secondary Science Teacher; *b:* DuBois, PA; *ed:* Univ of Pittsburgh (BS) Bio 1989; Tchr Cert Ed 1990; Chem Cert 1995; *cr:* Mars Area HS Bio Tchr 1991; Rochester Area HS Scndry Sci Tchr 1991-; *ai:* Frosh & Soph Class Spon; NSTA 1994-; PA Sci Tchrs Assn 1991-; W PA Bio Tchrs Assn 1995-; Shenendoah Ski Club 1993-; Sierra Club 1995-; *office:* Rochester Jr-Sr H S 540 Reno St Rochester PA 15074

NOBLE, LINDA ANN, Physics Teacher; *b:* Cincinnati, OH; *ed:* Edgecliff Coll (BS) Bio, Chem 1979; Xavier Univ (MA) Physics 2nd Ed 1988; *cr:* Bishop Brossart HS Tchr 1979-81; Lakota HS Tchr 1981-; *ai:* Sci Dept Chair; AAPT 1987-; PTRA-PLUS; Fermilab Natl Modern Physics Prgm; Project Chosen 1996 C3P CD-ROM; *office:* Lakota HS 5050 Tylersville Rd West Chester OH 45069*

NOBLE, NADINE MORSE, Fr Tchr & Frgn Lang Dept Chair; *b:* Binghampton, NY; *m:* John W.; *c:* Elizabeth, Thomas, William; *ed:* Chestnut Hill Coll (AB) Fr 1970; Univ of NC at Chapel Hill (MA) Fr 1972; 45 Credit Hrs Univ of DE Eng & Linguistics; Univ of Laval Quebec Canada; Bryn Mawr at Avignon France; *cr:* Dover AFB HS Fr, Span & Eng Tchr 1971-79; Caesar Rodney HS Fr & Span Tchr 1980-; *ai:* Fr Club; NHS Adv; Curr Cncl; NEA & AATF 1971-; DECTFL 1980-; Dover Symphony 1971-; Grants to Stud in Avignon, Attnd AP Wkshp at LaSalle Univ & Rassias Inst at Tollison St Univ; *office:* Caesar Rodney HS 239 Old North Rd Camden Wyoming DE 19934*

NOBLE, RICHARD A., 8th Grade Health Teacher; *b:* Columbus, OH; *m:* Kathy A. Spiers; *c:* Matt, Mark; *ed:* Capital Univ (BA) Hlth Ed 1978; Mount St Joseph (MS) Ed 1988; Walsh Univ (MS) Ed 1995; Attnd OH St 1985, Ashland Univ; *cr:* Pickerington Local Schls K-8 Grd PE Stu Tchng 1978; Groveport Local Schls 8th Grd Hlth Tchr 1978-; *ai:* 8th Grd Head Ftbl Coach 18 Yrs; 7-8th Grd Wrestling Coach 15 Yrs; 8th Grd Bsbl Coach 18 Yrs; IM dir 18 Yrs; Ath Dir 10 Yrs; BLT Team; Advy, Site Base, Tech, Curr Comms; Washington DC Coord; NEA, OEA, GMLEA, COBA 1978-; Optimist Club 1978-82; Wagram United Meth Church 1980-, Communion Steward; Pickerington Ath Boosters Club 1990-; *office:* Groveport-Madison MS North 5474 Sedalia Dr Columbus OH 43232*

NOBLE, RONALD ERNEST, 10th-12th Grd Social Stud Tchr; *b:* Providence, RI; *m:* Linda Butera; *c:* Ronald Jr., Jonathan; *ed:* RI Coll (BA) His 1971; Bryant (MBA) Acctng 1988; *cr:* Cumberland HS Tchr 1972-; *ai:* Tchr Advy Comm; Schl Cabinet Mem; Bd of Dirs Cumberland Employees Credit Union; NEA 1972-; CTA 1972-; *office:* Cumberland HS 2600 Mendon Rd Cumberland RI 02864*

NOBREGA, OTILIA M., French & Spanish Teacher; *b:* Sao Miguel Azores, Portugal; *m:* John; *c:* Derek; *ed:* URI (BA) Fr, Scndry Ed 1981; RI Coll (MAT) Span 1994; Working on MA Fr Lit; *cr:* Cumberland HS Guid Cnslr Liason 1985-86; Lincoln Jr Sr HS Long Term Sub Eng Tchr 1986-87; Scituate HS Fr, Span Tchr 1987-; *ai:* Philosophy, Tech Comm; NHS Advy Bd; NEA, RIFLA 1987-; *office:* Scituate HS 94 Trimtown Rd North Scituate RI 02857

NOCE, GENE, Head of High School; *b:* Jersey City, NJ; *ed:* St Peters Coll (BA) Classical Lang 1975; OH St Univ (MA) Classical Lang 1978; *cr:* OH St Univ Tchng Assoc 1976-78; The Hudson Schl Tchr 1981-, Assoc Dir 1986-, Head of HS 1993-; *ai:* Amer Classical League 1986-; NCTE 1990-; *office:* Hudson Schl 506 Park Ave Hoboken NJ 07030

NODECKER, JOHN RAYMOND, Behavioral Management Teacher; *b:* Syracuse, NY; *m:* Joanne; *c:* Kelly, Christopher, Sarah; *ed:* Univ of Houston (MS) Educl Psych 1988; *cr:* Houston Ind Schl Dist Crisis Intervention Tchr 1983-87; Upper Merion Area Schl Dist Tchr Emotional Support 1988-; *ai:* Boys Cross Cntry, Winter Track, Spring Track Head Coach; NEA 1988-; Philadelphia Area Coaches Assn 1987-; Outstanding Tchr Harper Alternative Schl 1987; Finalist Tchr of Yr Dist 1987; *office:* Upper Merion Area HS 435 Crossfield Rd King Of Prussia PA 19406

NODIFF, RUTH ABRIN, Vocal Music Teacher; *b:* New York, NY; *m:* Jack; *c:* Debra, Eric, David; *ed:* Queens Coll-CUNY (BA) Music 1954, (MA) Performance 1976; Ed Stud Staten Island Coll 1983-87; *cr:* Fivetowns Music & Art Fnd Piano Tchr 1960-65; United Choral Soc Accompanist 1970-72; Cathedral Schl, St John the Devine Music Tchr 1976-79; Shore Road Schl Music Tchr 1980-83; Daniel Carter Beard Jr HS Vocal Music Tchr 1983-; *ai:* Adv Arista Honor Soc; AFT 1980-; UFT 1983-; MEANYC 1990-; Friday-Woodmere Music Club 1960-; Concert Pianist, Accompanist Performances; *home:* 6 Emmet Ave East Rockaway NY 11518*

NODRUFF, SANDRA JAYNE, Retired Music Teacher; *b:* Benton Harbor, MI; *ed:* Baldwin-Wallace Coll (BME) Music Ed 1963; *cr:* Bedford City Schls K-9th Grd Vocal Music Tchr 1963-66; Vinton Co Schls K-8th Grd Vocal, Gen Music Tchr 1967; Wellston HS Choral, Play, Show Choir Dir 1968-87, Music His Tchr, Band Dir 1988-94; *ai:* Past Chrldr, Stu Cncl, Tri-Hi-Y Adv; NEA, OEA, OMEA, MENC 1963-; Delta Kappa Gamma 1980-, Pres 2 Yrs; Martha Holden Jennings Scholar; *home:* 109 E 6th St Wellston OH 45692

NOE, WILLIAM LEEDS, Special Education Teacher; *b:* Abington, PA; *m:* Debra Langley; *c:* Stephen, Damon; *ed:* The Citadel (BA) Eng 1965; *cr:* Lower Cape May HS Tchr 1980-; *office:* Lower Cape May Reg HS 687 Route 9 Erma NJ 08204

NOECKER, MARTHA ELLEN, Retired Third Grade Teacher; *b:* Camden, NJ; *ed:* Rowan Coll (BA) Elem Ed 1961; *cr:* Camden Bd of Ed 5th Grd Tchr 1961-66; Cinnaminson Bd of Ed 4th Grd Rdng, Demonstration Tchr, 3rd Grd Tchr 1966-95; *ai:* Bldg Advy & Focus 2000 Comms; Home & Schl Fac Rep; New Tchr Mentor 1993-95; Concert Script Writer, Poetry, & Creative Wrtng Tchr; Life Learning Inst Mem 1995-; Intnatl Soc of Poets 1994-; Cinnaminson Ed Assn, NJEA, NEA 1966-; Burlington Cty Retired Tchrs Assn 1995-; Governor's Awd 1987; Grant to Write Booklet about Comm of Cinnaminson 1993-95; Poetry Pub.*

NOEL, EDWARD JOHN, Mathematics Teacher; *b:* North Adams, MA; *m:* Judy Benedetti; *c:* Kimberly Christiansen, Kirby; *ed:* North Adams St Coll (BA) Math 1967, (MS) Ed 1984; *cr:* Brayton Jr HS Math Tchr 1967-75; North Adams MS Math Tchr 1976-81; Drury HS Math Tchr 1982-; *ai:* Yrbk Adv; North Adams Tchr Assn, Music Tchrs Assn, NEA 1967-; *home:* 43 Hathaway St North Adams MA 01247

NOFFSINGER-SPURRIER, LOIS BAUMGARDNER, Kindergarten Teacher; *b:* Frederick, MD; *m:* W. M. Ray; *c:* David P., James W., Daniel J., John R., Margaret V.; *ed:* Hood Coll (BA) Early Chldhd Ed 1964; Attnd Frederick Comm Coll; Numerous In Svc Courses; *cr:* Days Inn of Frederick Night Mgr; Visitation Acad Kndgtn Tchr 1965-80; Good Shepherd Nursery-Kndgtn Schl Kndgtn Tchr 1980-; Frederick Co Bd Parent-Child Summer Prgm Tchr 1981-84; *ai:* Music Coord; Frederi Early Chldhd Ed Assn 1985-; Sunday Schl Tchr 1957-; Frederick Co Bureau 1966-, Ed Chprsn; Frederick Womens Civic Club; Amer L Aux; Frederick Cty Tourism 1986-; Several Childrens Books Pub; 411 Delaware Rd Frederick MD 21701*

NOGA, ANDREW F., Latin Teacher; *b:* Parma, OH; *ed:* Coll of the Cross (AB) Classical Langs 1990; *cr:* Dwight Schl Latin & World His 1993-94; Saint Peters Prep Latin Tchr 1994-; *ai:* Cross Cntry & Lac Coach; Ski Club Moderator; Amer Classical League 1993-; Classical of Atlantic Sts 1993-; Fulbright Assn 1995-; Amer Acad in Rome Ful Classics Fellow; Geraldine R Dodge Ind Rsrch Grant; Columbia Tchrs Coll Klingenstein Ctr Fellow; *office:* St Peters Preparatory H Grand St Jersey City NJ 07302*

NOGA, PAULA, Second Grade Teacher; *b:* Waukegan, IL; *m:* Micha Shannon, Brittany; *ed:* Univ of WI (BS) Elem Ed 1971; Math Their II; Act Integrating Math & Sci I, II; Apple Works for Edctrs; Understa Tchng I; 4 Mat; *cr:* St Mary's Schl 2-3 Grd Tchr; Hilltop Schl 1 Grd Page Hilltop Schl 2 Grd Tchr; *ai:* AIMS Dist Liaison; Fitchburg S Stdnts Cooperating Tchr; Rdng, Writing, Report Card, Sci Comms; MTA, ATA 1971-; M2E 1990-; St Therea's Church 1971-; Beta Sigm 1990-, Publicity Chair; Eisenhower Grant; *office:* Page Hilltop Elem 117 Washington St Ayer MA 01432*

NOGAY, BRIAN MICHAEL, Science, Biology & Chem Tchr; *b:* Spring, MD; *m:* Donna Reid; *c:* Jonathan, Justin, Mary Jordan; *ed* Univ (BS) Plant, Soil Sci 1980; Tchng Grad Courses 18 Hrs; *cr:* Fai Cath Grd Schl Sub, Full Boys Gym Instr 1981; Bishop Mc Nama Chem, Bio, Dev Geometry, Anatomy, Physiology, Honors Bio, Chem 1981-90; Good Counsel HS Chem, Anatomy, Physiology, Environmental Sci Tchr 1990-; *ai:* Frosh Ftbl, Wrestling, Girls Coach; Jr, Sr Retreat Moderator; *office:* Good Counsel HS 11601 Ge Ave Wheaton MD 20905*

NOLAN, DAVID, Mathematics Professor; *b:* Port Jefferson, NY Arlene; *c:* Jessica, Eric, Kimberly; *ed:* Saint Francis Coll at Brooklyn Math 1966; Saint Johns Univ (MA) Math 1968; *cr:* Saint Johns Univ Asst 1966-68; Suffolk Cty Comm Coll Math Fac 1968-; *ai:* Various & Intra Acad Comms; Ways & Means Dept, Division Tri-Car Pre-Calculus Dept, Acad Standards, Calculus Reform & Gra Calculator Comms; AFT, NYSUT 1968-; NEA, NYSMATYC; N Chancellors Awd Nom 1970-71, 1980; Made a Difference Awd SUNY Spec Prgm Awd 1992; *office:* Suffolk Comm Coll Ammerman 533 College Rd Selden NY 11784

NOLAN, EDWARD CHARLES, Mathematics Teacher; *b:* Silver Sp MD; *m:* Michele Lamphier; *c:* Calvin; *ed:* Univ of MD (BS) Scndry Ed 1990; Western MD Coll 18 Credit Hrs Educl Admin; *cr:* Gaithers MS Math Tchr 1990-94; Eastern MS Math Dept Chair 1994-95; Forest MS Math Dept Chair 1995-; *ai:* Odyssey of the Mind Coach; NCTM 1 Montgomery Cty Math Tchrs Assn 1991-, Pres; MD CTM 1991-; Forest Oak MS 8100 Midcty Hwy Gaithersburg MD 20877

NOLAN, EDWARD L., 9th Grd Govt & Earth Sci Tchr; *b:* Keyser, *m:* Catherine Marley; *c:* Sean, Marlay; *ed:* Frostburg St Univ Georgraphy 1971, (MED) Ed 1976; *cr:* Fort Hills HS 9th Grd Sci, Soc Tchr 1971-; Allegany Comm Coll Part Time Fac, Geography Tchr 1 *ai:* NEA, ML St Tchrs Assn, Allegany Cty Tchrs Assn 1971-; Allegany Historical Soc, Allegany Cty Soc Stud Cncl 1990-; Frostburg Ambulance 1980-91, EMT; Frostman Fireman 1984-91, Vol; *office:* Hill HS 500 Greenway Ave Cumberland MD 21502

NOLAN, GARY L., Physics, Chem & Algebra Instr; *b:* Richmond, IN Wright St Univ (BS) Sci, Math-Summa Cum Laude 1975; OH Nor Univ (JD) Law 1980; *cr:* Ayersville Local Schls Sci, Math Instr 1 Crestview Local Schls Sci Instr 1982-84; Lincolnview Local Schls Math Instr 1984-; *ai:* NHS, Soc Comms; Schl Tutor; ABA; OSBA; MC Sec; NEA; OEA; AEA; LEA; Phi Alpha Delta; Phi Eta Tau; Kappa D Pi; Mendon Church of God, Sunday Schl Tchr, Church Cncl VP; Mc Cty Crippled Children & Adults, Dir; Celina Area Jaycees, Dir; Sir Alive, VP; Celina Lions Club; Spon 3 Stdnts to Intnl Sci & Enginee Fair; *home:* 445 Johnson Ave Celina OH 45822

NOLAN, JOHN ROBERT, Mathematics Teacher; *b:* Arlington, MA Elaine W. Johnson; *c:* Brian, Kevin, Mark; *ed:* Boston St Coll (BS) Math 1969, (MED) Scndry Admin 1973; Post Grad Ed, Cmptr Northeastern Univ; *cr:* Burlington HS Math Tchr 1969-; *ai:* Burlingto Assn 1969-, Bldg Rep, Negotiation Rep; MA Tchrs Assn, NEA 19 Menotomy Minute Men 1980-, Past Captain; Knights of Columbus 19 *office:* Burlington HS 123 Cambridge St Burlington MA 01803*

NOLAN, JOSEPH A., Latin Teacher & Dept Chprsn; *b:* Philadelphia, *m:* Ann Marie Yerbury; *ed:* St Bonaventure Univ (BA) Philosophy, En His 1955; CUNY, Montclair & Earher La-Salle Univ 45 Hrs Beyond *cr:* Holy Name Province of Franciscan Fathers Stu for Priesthood 1950 John J Nolan & Assoc Electronics Manufacturers Rep 1958-59; Charities Group Soc Worker 1959-61; Cliffside Park HS Eng Tchr & Coach 1961-62; Wardlaw Schl Eng & Latin Tchr & Ftbl, Bsktbl & Coach 1962-76; Bishop George Ahr HS Eng & Latin Tchr, Dept Cha Golf Coach 1976-; *ai:* Lang Dept Chprsn; Verbal SAT Preparation; NJ 1980-; Formerly Lions Club & Kiwanis; *home:* 16 Burrows Bernardsville NJ 07924

NOLAN, KATHLEEN M., Professor of Teacher Education; *b:* Erie, *c:* Tyler Nolan Morgan, Adam Nolan Morgan; *ed:* D'Youville Coll Spec, Elem Ed 1972; George Washington Univ (MA) Ed, Therapeutic 1977; St Louis Univ (PHD) Spec Ed 1982; *cr:* Montgomery Cty Pub S Spec Ed Tchr 1972-78; Fontbonne Coll Spec Ed Asst Prof 1978-83; Misericorida Tchr Ed Prof 1986-; Ed Dept Chair 1987-94; *ai:* Chu Related Act with Yth Groups; Cub Scouts Asst; Consultant to Local S Dists; PA Certifying Ofcr in Tchr Ed; Cncl for Exceptional Children 19 Tchng Excl & Campus Ldrshp Awd 1990; Dir of Summer Camp for S Needs Children 1987-93; *office:* Coll Misericordia 301 Lake St Dallas 18612

NOLAN, MARIANN GARDINIER, Study Skills Teacher; *b:* Little F NY; *m:* Daniel M.; *c:* Chas, Cory, Caitlin; *ed:* SUNY at Geneseo (BS) 1974; SUNY at Cortland (MS) Ed & Rdng; Working on CAS 18 Completed; *cr:* Ilion Cntrl Schl Classroom Tchr & Elem 1974-76; U Schl Classroom Tchr & Elem 1976-79; Mohawk Cntrl Schl Classroom T & Scndry Stud Skills 1979-; *ai:* K-12th Compensatory Ed Coord; NYS *office:* Mohawk Cntrl HS 28 Grove St Mohawk NY 13407*

NOLAN, PATRICIA, English Teacher; *b:* Brooklyn, NY; *ed:* St Jo Univ (BA) Eng 1955; The Coll of St Rose (MA) Eng 1971; NY Uni Credit Hrs Tchng Jrnlsm, 9 Credits Tchng Rdng; *cr:* Good Shepherd E Schl 1-7 Grd Tchr 1946-56; Dominican Commercial HS Eng Tchr, D Chair 1956-59; All Saints HS Eng Tchr, Dept Chair 1959-69; Domini Commercial Eng Tchr, Dept Chair 1969-; *ai:* Immigrant Ed Dir; NC 1956-; Brooklyn-Queens Eng Cncl 1968-, Treas; Tchrs of AP Eng Gr Colgate Univ.

NOLAN, THOMAS J., Secondary English Teacher; *b:* Rockville Cen NY; *m:* Suzanne Guertin; *c:* Brian, Ian, Leiana; *ed:* Worcester St C (MED) Marticulating Ed, (BA) Eng 1987; *cr:* South HS Eng Tchr 1987- Trinity Cath Acad Eng Tchr 1988-90; North Brookfield HS Eng T

-91; South HS Eng Tchr 1991-; *ai:* A World of Difference Facilitator; :r Beginnings Staff Coord; MTA 1987-; NCTE 1996; *office:* South Comm Schl 170 Apricot St Worcester MA 01603

AN, WILLIAM H.,III, Social Stud Dept Chair & Tchr; *b:* Bay Shore, *n:* Brenda Lynn Pettit; *c:* Kelsie Michelle, Brett William,; *ed:* St Univ Y at Fredonia (BA) His & Scndry Ed 1980, (MS) Scndry Ed & Soc 1987; *cr:* Dunkirk HS Substitute Tchr 1980-82; Fillmore Cntrl Schl : 11th Grd Soc Stud Tchr 1982-93, 7th & 12th Grd Soc Studies Tchr -; Dept Chm 1985-; *ai:* Sr Class Adv 1985 & 1991; Boys Jr Var Soccer h 1982-86; Girls Var Tennis Coach 1987-; Boys Jr Var Bsbl Coach -91; Girls Var Sftbl Coach 1992; Girls Jr Var Bsktbl 1980-82; Jr HS Bsktbl Coach 1984-; NHS Comm 1991; Open House Comm 1992; gany Cty Govt Intersnhip & Amer Legion Oratorical Contest Liason -; NEA 1980-, Local Pres 1994-; *office:* Fillmore Central Schl 104 St Fillmore NY 14735

AND, PATTI MUNSEY, Biology & Physiology Teacher; *b:* sville, VA; *w:* John R. (dec); *c:* Holly Nicole, Melody Noel; *ed:* Univ N (BS) Natural Sci 1963; 25 Extra Grad Hrs at Miami Univ, Univ of on, Wright St Univ, Ohio Univ; *cr:* Hampton Bennett Jr HS Sci & Tchr 1963-65; Franklin Jr HS Bio & General Sci Tchr 1966-70, Bio th Tchr 1978-82; Franklin HS Bio & Physiology Tchr 1983-; *ai:* Sci Chprsn; North Cntrl Steering, Sci Course of Stud & Sr Assembly ms; OEA, NEA & FEA 1963-; Faith United Meth Church 1978-, ees; *home:* 8076 Eastlawn Dr Franklin OH 45005

D, JAMES JAY, 7th Grade Science Teacher; *b:* Amherst, OH; *m:* Lisa Lang; *c:* Kaylee Virginia; *ed:* Kent St Univ (BS) Elem Ed 1988, (MS) Curr 1994; *cr:* Brecksville-Broadview Hghts 6th Grd Tchr 1988-89; son Local Schls 7th Grd Sci Tchr 1989-; *ai:* HS Var Ftbl 7 Yrs; JV Bsbl s; NEA, OEA 1988-; OH MS Assn 1990-; *office:* Hudson MS 77 N tt St Hudson OH 44236*

DE, FRANK E., Social Studies Teacher; *b:* New York, NY; *m:* Carol henson; *c:* Clarissa E., Jonathan T.; *ed:* Middlebury Coll (BA) pean His 1959; Columbia Univ (MA) US His 1968; *cr:* Roosevelt Int Soc Stud Tchr 1960-; *ai:* Westfield Ed Assoc 1960-, Speaker of Del embly; NJ Ed Assoc, NEA, NCSS 1960-; Natl Trust for Historic ervation 1973-; Preservation NJ 1985-; *office:* Roosevelt Intermediate 301 Clark St Westfield NJ 07090

E, RUTH A., Fifth Grade Teacher; *b:* Scranton, PA; *cr:* Campbell 5th Grd Tchr 32 Yrs; *ai:* SREA 1962-, Head Bldg Rep; MCEA, NJEA, 1962-; Domestic Violence Cnslr 1992-; *office:* Campbell Schl 22 d St South River NJ 08882

EN, HOWARD EARL, Social Studies Teacher; *b:* Gadsden, AL; *c:* n, Lonnie, Scott, Sarah; *ed:* Youngstown St Univ (BS) Ed & Psych ; Univ of Pittsburgh (MA) Ed 1977; Attnd Clayton Coll, Penn St Univ; St Alphonsus Schl Tchr 1970; Allegheny Vly Schl Dist Tchr & Coach ; Freeport Area Schl Dist Tchr & Coach 1977-; *ai:* Stu Cncl Adv; Bsbl ch; Stu Instrl Support Team; Freeport Area Care Team SAP; NEA -; PSEA 1977-; FEA 1977-; Natrona Hghts Little Lg 1970-, Bd of ; Tarentum His & Landmarks Fndtn 1973-, Charter Mem; Freeport Little Lg 1989-; WPIAL Dist X Bsktbl Champions 1987-88; Natl Zeta Tau Fndtn Awd; ZBT Einstein Awd for Scholastic Achvmt; Dist 26 e League Championships (4 Times); *office:* Freeport Jr HS 325 4th St port PA 16229*

LF, GAIL H., Business Dept Chair; *b:* Troy, NY; *ed:* Bloomsburg Univ) Bus 1977; LeHigh Univ (MBA) Bus 1982; Cert Bus at Gwynedd cy 1992; *cr:* Salisbury MS Comp & Bus Tchr 1990-91; Liberty HS eer Ed Tchr & Bus Chair 1992-; *ai:* Bus Dept Chair; MS Bsktbl Coach; ous Comms; Little League Coach; Dewey Fire & Ambulance Crew n; Hellertown Lower Saucon Little League Coach; *office:* Liberty HS 5 Linden St Bethlehem PA 18018

LL, AMY MARIE, 9th-12th Grade Orchestra Tchr; *b:* Madison, WI; Milton Coll (BA) Music Ed 1978; Long Island Univ CW Post (MS) sic Ed 1990; *cr:* Sun Prairie Pub Schls 5th-12th Grd Orch Tchr 1979-85; ksville Pub Schls 9th-12th Grd Orch Tchr 1987-; *ai:* Modern Music sters Adv; String & Chamber Ensembles Dir; ASTA 1979-; NMEA 7-; NYSSMA 1987-; MENC 1987-; HCT 1987-; Hicksville PTA 1987-; 1987-; NSOA 1991-; Hicksville Tchr Excl Awd 1990; Hicksville PTA nders Day Awd 1995; All-St Peformance Hicksville String Ensemble 5; *office:* Hicksville HS Division Ave Hicksville NY 11801

LL, MARK VINCENT, Social Studies Teacher; *b:* Loch Haven, PA; Karen Hersh; *c:* Austin; *ed:* IN St Univ of PA (BS) Ed 1978; Millersville S) Amer His 1990; *cr:* York Cty Vo-Tech Soc Stud Tchr 1981-83; llastown Area Soc Stud Tchr 1983-; *ai:* Cross Cntry, Winter Track & ck & Field Head Coach; NEA 1995-; *office:* Dallastown Area MS 700 v School Ln Dallastown PA 17313

LL, MARY KEEFE, Retired First Grade Teacher; *b:* Boston, MA; *m:* bert L.; *c:* Rob, Chuck; *ed:* Bridgewater St Coll (BSEd) Elem Ed 1958, ED) Elem Ed 1963; Penn St Univ Grad Courses; *cr:* Stoughton Schl Dist st Grd Tchr 1958-62; US Army Dependents Schls First Grd Tchr 52-64; Penns Vly Schl Dist First Grd Tchr 1971-93; *ai:* Textbook ection Comms; Supt Search; Act 211 Drug, Alcohol Prevention; Hlth r Dev; NEA, PSEA 1971-, Bldg Rep, Del; Penns Vly Ed Assoc 1971-, ; Phi Delta Kappa 1988-; Delta Kappa Gamma, 1st VP, Pres; Church ighborhood Svc 1990-; Cty Extension Vol Tchr; Presenter Wkshps on tical Thinking; *home:* 134 W Marylyn Ave State College PA 16801

LL, RICHARD GREGORY, English Department Head; *b:* Pittsburgh, ; *w:* Constance Margaret (dec); *c:* Sharon M. Andrews, Susan R. ndley; *ed:* CA Univ (BS) Comp Eng 1966; California Univ of PA (MA) g, Lit 1972; *cr:* Fort Cherry HS Dept Head 16 Yrs, Eng Dept 30 Yrs; *ai:* wspaper; NEA, PSEA, FCTA 1966-; Meth Churches Lay Speaker 22 s; *office:* Fort Cherry Jr Sr HS 110 Fort Cherry Rd Mc Donald PA 15057*

LLEZ, KERWIN R., Reading Teacher; *b:* Chattanooga, TN; *m:* ances Wilson-Nollez; *c:* Dana; *ed:* Richmond Coll (BA) Eng 1979; nhattan Coll (MA) Rdng 1982; Tchrs Coll (EDD) Higher Ed 1995; *cr:* tivity Schl Rdng Tchr & Supvr, Asst Prin 1982-88; Borough of nhattan Comm Coll Rdng Tchr 1988-; PS 133 Manhattan Rdng Tchr 95-; *ai:* Bowling Club, Chess Club Coach; Story Telling Club Adv; *ice:* Borough Of Manhattan Comm Coll 199 Chambers St New York NY 007

OONAN, JOSEPH P., Theology Tchr & Dev Dir; *b:* Lima, OH; *m:* eryl; *c:* Emily, Meredith, Billy, Joey; *ed:* Univ of Toledo (BS) Ed Tech, edia 1980, (MS) Admin, Supervision 1988; 30 Addl Hrs Univ of Dayton, niv of Toledo; *cr:* St John's Jesuit HS Tchr, Librn, Asst Ftbl Coach 80-87; Univ of Toledo Rsrch Asst 1987-88; Calvert HS Prin 1988-94; St seph Cntrl Cath HS Dev Dir, Theology Tchr 1994-; *ai:* Asst Ftbl Coach; mm Svc Coord; ASCD; NASSP; OCLMA; NCEA; Knights of olumbus; *office:* St Joseph Ctl Cath HS 702 Croghan St Fremont OH 420

OONAN, KAREN A., Nursing & Allied Health Chprsn; *b:* Cleveland, I; *ed:* Coll of Mt St Joseph on the OH (BSN) Nrsng 1967; Boston Univ S) Psychiatric Nrsng 1969; Post-Grad Cources Boston Coll, Boston niv; *cr:* NHTC NSG, Allied Hlth Chprsn 1986-; Central CT St Univ NSG, llied Hlth Chprsn 1986-; Boston Coll NSG, Allied Hlth Chprsn 1986-; *ai:* dagogy, Curr Comm; Dept Chprsn; Amer Nurses Assn; NH Nsg Assn; gma Theta Tau; NH Cncl Nurse Edctrs; SHARE 1995-; Ldrshp Seacoast 1996; Pedagogy Journal Bd of Ed NHTC, Inst System 1995; Bd of Ed Coping with Illness 1981; Bd of Ed Journal Nsg Ed 1979; *office:* NH Technical College-Stratham 277 Portsmouth Ave Stratham NH 03885

NOONE, LANA MAE, Music Teacher; *b:* New York, NY; *m:* Byron Michael; *c:* Heather (dec), Jennifer, Jason; *ed:* SUNY at Albany (BA) Music 1988; Mannes Coll of Music (BS) Music; Addl Credits SUNY at Potsdam, Regents St Coll; *cr:* Eglevsky Ballet, Long Island, Nassau Symphony Orchestras, Amer Concert Band, Orchestra Flute Musician 1972-; St Christophers & St Patricks Music Tchr 1987-; Nassau Comm Coll Adjunct Music Prof of Flute 1975-; Garden City Summer Music Prgm Tchr 1992-; *ai:* MENC, NYSSMA 1993-; NMEA 1992-; Long Island Flute Club 1985-, Bd, Previous Co-Founder; Garden City Comm Church 1978-, Previous Chm, Bd of Chrstn Soc Responsibility; Island Chamber Symphony; Pub Article; Honoree Whos Who Amer Ed, in the East; Intnl Bio Dictionary of Musicians; Emerging Ldrs of Amer.*

NOONE, MARY ELLEN, Learning Center Teacher; *b:* New York, NY; *ed:* St Francis Coll (BA) His 1959; Stony Brook Univ (MSLS) Ed 1973; *cr:* St Joseph Schl 2nd Grd Tchr 1950-51; Holy Name 1st Grd Tchr 1951-55; St Patricks 4th Grd Tchr 1966-67; SS Cyril & Methodius 1st Grd Tchr 1967-72; Most Precious Blood 1st Grd Tchr 1975-93, Learning Ctr Tchr 1994-; *ai:* After Schl Prgm; Parish Minister.

NORCROSS, DARRY R., US History & Government Tchr; *b:* Plattsburgh, NY; *m:* Beverly J.; *c:* Kevin, Brian; *ed:* Plattsburgh St (BA) Soc Stud 1965; Post Grad Stud; *cr:* Saranac HS 11th Grd Soc Stud Tchr 1966-; *ai:* Ath & Coaching; NYSUT 1966-; Youth Commission 1961-, Bsbl Coach; *home:* 11 Park Row Cadyville NY 12918

NORCROSS, JOHN C., Psychology Professor; *b:* Camden, NJ; *m:* Nancy A. Caldwell; *c:* Jonathan, Rebecca; *ed:* Rutgers Univ (BA) Psych 1980; Univ of RI (MA) Clinical Psych 1981, (PHD) Clinical Psych 1984; Internship Brown Univ Schl of Medicine Clinical Psych 1985; *cr:* Univ of RI Rsrch Fellow 1982-86; Univ of Scranton Psych Prof 1985-; Psych Ctr of Northeast PA Clinical Psych 1986-; *ai:* Psi Chi Moderator; Elder Rosetl Instr; Amer Psychological Assn, Krasner Meml Awd, Fellow; Amer Assn of Univ Profs; PA Psych Assn, Fellow; Co-Author, Ed of 10 Books; Pub 100 Scholarly Articles; Served on 10 Editorial Bds; CASE PA Prof of Yr; *office:* Univ Of Scranton Dept of Psychology Scranton PA 18510

NORD, PETER DALBY, English Teacher; *b:* Cohasset, MA; *c:* Kevin, Valerie Mc Intyre, Nicole; *ed:* Bridgewater St Coll (BS) Eng 1963; Lesle Coll (MA) Fiction Writing 1992; Attnd Wesleyan Univ, Umass Amherst, Bard Coll, Boston Univ; *cr:* Dighton Rehoboth Regnl HS Eng Tchr 1963-65; Hingham HS Eng Tchr 1965-66; Scituate HS Eng Tchr 1966-; *ai:* Yrbk Adv; Fac Senate; Curr Dev Comm; NEA, MA Tch Assn 1963-; Scit Tch Assn 1966-, Bldg Rep, Negotiation Team Crisis Comm; NCTE 1975-; AMVETS 1992-; DAV 1990-; US Holocaust Museum Comm 1994-; USMC Veteran 1953-56; Commencement Speaker 1992; Tchr of Month; Bridgebuilder Awd; *home:* PO Box 9 15 Riverview Pl Scituate MA 02060

NORDBYE, MARK STEVEN, 6th Grade Teacher; *b:* Abington, PA; *ed:* Grad Bloomsburg Univ 1982 With Degree in Elem Ed; *cr:* Council Rock Schl Dist Tchr 1983-; *ai:* Jeopardy Club for 5th-6th Grd; After Schl Sports Prgm for 5th-6th Grd; *office:* Rolling Hills Elem Schl 340 Middle Holland Rd Southampton PA 18966

NORDE', GERALD SIDNEY,SR., Sociology Professor; *b:* Bridgeport, CT; *m:* Jane Littleton; *c:* Derek G., Gerald S. Jr., Eugenia S., Carla A.; *ed:* Southern IL Univ (BA) Span 1971, (MSEd) Ed Admin 1975; Univ of DE (PHD) Sociology 1985; *cr:* WA DC Pub Schls Dir, Teen Father Prgm 1986-90; Lincoln Univ Prof 1992-92; Cntrl St Univ Prof 1992-; *ai:* Coord Natl Achvmt Week; Million Man March Local Organizing Comm Chprsn; Sociology Club Adv; Amer Assn Univ Profs 1991-; Amer Sociological Assn 1986-; Amer Bridge Assn; Omega Psi Phi 1993-; Univ of DE 1st Black Am PHD Grad Sociology 1979-85, Grad Flwshp 1981-83; Southern IL Univ at Edwardsville Martin Luther King Jr Schlsp 1970-71; *office:* Central St Univ Dept of Sociology Wilberforce OH 45384

NORDLE, DOLORES RICHARD, Jr High Teacher; *b:* Manchester, NH; *m:* Brian F.; *ed:* Keene St Coll (BS) Sec Ed Soc Stud 1978; Guid, Cnslng at Univ of NM 1981-83; *ai:* NEA 1985-; *home:* 36 Purgatory Pond Rd Dunbarton NH 03045

NORDONE, JAMES PAUL,JR., Adjunct Instr of Psych Dept; *b:* Mt Vernon, NY; *m:* Stephanie Heth; *c:* Mackenzie Heth; *ed:* Westchester Comm Coll (AA) LA, SS 1981; Western CT St Univ (BA) Dev Psych 1984, (MS) Guidance, Counseling 1988; Southern CT St Univ 21 Credits Toward 6 Yr Prof Diploma in Admin, Supervision, Educl Found; *cr:* Naugatuck Valley Comm Tech Coll Cnslr II, Adjunct Fac Mem, Stud Skills Courses, Psych Tchr 1987-; *ai:* Stu Handbook Ed; New Stu Orientation Dir, Comm Chprsn; Handbook, Stu Affairs, Acad Stands Sec Comm Chprsn; Pres Cncl for Total Quality Svc Newsletter, Cultural Diversity, Emergency Intervention Comm Mem; Womens Sftbl Coach; Amer Assn for Counseling, Dev 1987-92; Pi Lambda Theta; AFT 1987-, Mem; Cystic Fibrosis Fnd, Wethersfield Chapter Comm Mem; *office:* Naugatuck Vly Comm Tech Coll 750 Chase Pky Waterbury CT 06708

NORDQUIST, STACY STURMER, French Teacher; *b:* Harrisburg, PA; *m:* John Bruce; *c:* Jon-Erik, Alexander Reid; *ed:* Middlebury Coll (BA) Fr 1980; Saint Michaels Coll (MA) Ed 1996; Prof Cert Conf Interpreting Fr, Eng, Fr GA St Univ 1983; Jr Yr Abroad Univ de Paris X, Nanterre, Inst dEtudes Politiques 1978-79; *cr:* INTERAC Japan ESL, Fr Tchr 1983-86; Burlington HS Fr Tchr 1991-92; Peoples Acad Fr Tchr 1992-; *ai:* Fr Trip Primary Fundraiser, Chaperon; VT For Lang Assn 1991-, Bd of Dir, 1992-, Sec 1993-; *office:* Peoples Acad RR 3 Box 40 Copley Ave Morrisville VT 05661

NORELLI, ELAINE, Mathematics Teacher; *b:* Bronx, NY; *m:* Edward Drach; *ed:* Fordham Univ (MS) Math 1978; Manhattan Coll (MS) Schl Admin 1988; 20 Hrs Tchr Dev Ctr; *cr:* Gorton HS Math, Cmptr Tchr 1974-82; Lincoln HS Math, Cmptr Tchr 1974-82; White Plains HS Math, Cmptr Tchr 1982-; *ai:* AFT 1974-; White Plains Tchr Assn 1990-, Liason Chm, Bldg Rep; *office:* White Plains HS 550 North St White Plains NY 10605

NORMAN, DAVID ALAN, Vocal Music Tchr & Interim Dir; *b:* Rockville Centre, NY; *m:* Starr Kathryn Allison; *c:* Kathryn E., Julie A., Thomas A.; *ed:* SUNY Coll at Potsdam (BM) Music Ed 1978; SUNY at Albany (MS) Ed 1983; Attnd Boston Univ, SUNY Coll at Oswego; *cr:* Carthage Cntrl Schls Vocal Music Tchr 1978-81; Schenectady City Schls Vocal & Instrumental Music Tchr 1981-87; West Genesee Cntrl Schls Vocal Music Tchr 1987-; *ai:* Music Theatre Production Producer; MENC 1978-; NYSSMA 1978-; AFT & NYSUT 1978-.

NORMAN, RICHARD E., Spanish Teacher; *b:* Canton, OH; *m:* Sandra J. Kerber; *c:* Laura, Rick, Lisa; *ed:* OH Univ (BSC) Bus 1961, (BSEd) Span 1962; OH St Univ (MA) Frgn Lang Ed 1965; Attnd MI St Univ, Baldwin-Wallace Coll, Purdue Univ, Univ of Akron, Univ of Oaxaca Mexico; *cr:* Dayton City Schls Span, Bus Tchr 1962-64; Rocky River Schls Span Tchr 1965-; *ai:* Adult Ed Supvr; Frgn Lang Dept Coord; Rocky River Tchrs, OH Educ Assn, OH Frgn Lang Assn 1965-; Chemical Abuse Reduced thru Ed 1983-86; Presentation Natl Endowment for Hum Seminar Purdue Univ; Martha Holden Jennings Awd for Distngd Tchng; *office:* Rocky River HS 20951 Detroit Rd Cleveland OH 44116

NORMAN, SHARON LYNN (CREECH), Library Media Specialist; *b:* Dayton, OH; *m:* Ronald M.; *c:* James C.; *ed:* Miami Univ (BS) Ed 1974; Wright St Univ Lib, Gifted, Cmptrs, Tech Trng at SOITA on Cmptrs, Instrl TV Wkshps; *cr:* OH Appalachian Cooperative for Ed Svcs Prof Librn 1974-77; Fayetteville-Perry Schls First Grd Tchr 1977-79; Jefferson Twp Schls 3-4 Grd Remedial Rdng Tchr 1979-80; C R Coblentz Schls K-8 Grds Media Specialist 1980-; *ai:* Coblentz Classroom Tchrs Assn 1985-; NEA, OEA 1985-; Delta Kappa Gamma Delta Omega Chprt 1983-; *office:* C. R. Coblentz Schls 115 N Spring St New Paris OH 45347

NORMILE, NICHOLAS JOHN, Guidance Counselor; *b:* Troy, NY; *m:* Elizabeth B. Kauffman; *c:* Nicholas (dec); *ed:* Siena Coll (BA) His 1957, (MS) Ed 1961; His Grad Stud Siena, Coll of St Rose 30 Hrs; Guid Grad Stud Siena, SUNY at Albany 30 Hrs; *cr:* Heatly Jr Sr HS Latin Tchr 1960-66, Social Stud Tchr 1960-, Guid Cnslr 1975-; *ai:* Former Class, Yrbk, Key Club Adv; Stu Cncl; Capital Dist Cnslng Assn, NY Cnslng Assn 1970-; Green Island Tchrs Assn 1960-, Pres; *office:* Heatly Jr Sr HS 171 Hudson Ave Green Island NY 12183

NORRIS, JOANNE LEDONE, Sixth Grade Teacher; *b:* Perth Amboy, NJ; *m:* E. Thomas; *c:* Jaclyn Anne, Katherine Jean; *ed:* Glassboro St Coll (BA) Elem Ed 1987; *cr:* Holy Spirit Schl 2nd, 5th Grd Tchr 1968-71; St Michael Schl 4th Grd Tchr 1971-76; St Mary of Lakes 6th Grd Tchr 1989-; *ai:* Mission Club Adv; NCEA 1989-; *office:* St Mary Of The Lakes Schl RR 70 Medford NJ 08055

NORRIS, MARY ZIPF, Teacher of Gifted & Talented; *b:* Newark, NJ; *m:* William R. II; *c:* William III, Kerry; *ed:* Upsala Coll (BA) His 1967; Kean Coll (MLAS) Lbrl Stud 1982; Attnd St Peters Coll Grad Stud; *cr:* Clark Pub Schls Eng Tchr & Tchr of Gifted 1967-; *ai:* Odyessy of Mind Coach; UC G&T Assn Rep; PAC Comm; NEA 1967-; NJEA 1967-; VCEA 1967-; CEA 1967-; AHSA; Prof Grafter Assn; NJPHA; Tchr of Yr 1991; Commendation 1992-93; *office:* Kumpf MS 59 Mildred Terr Clark NJ 07066

NORRIS, PARRY L., Fifth Grade Teacher; *b:* Columbus, OH; *m:* Judith Sarber; *ed:* OH Univ (BSEd) Elem Ed 1978; Univ of Dayton (MSEd) Rdng Ed 1987; Addl Trng Educl Admin; *cr:* Bloom Schl Tchr 1978-; Carroll Schl Tchr 1978-; *ai:* Coord Outdoor Ed Prgm; Rdng, Lang Arts Curr, Tech Comms; NEA, OEA 1978-; Bloom-Carroll Ed Assn 1978-, Past Pres; Martha Holden Jennings Scholar; *office:* Carroll MS 69 S Beaver ST Carroll OH 43112*

NORRIS, RHONDA JOYCE, Jr High English Teacher; *b:* Wilmington, DE; *m:* Mark Steven; *ed:* Liberty Univ (BS) Eng Ed 1986; *cr:* New Castle Bapt Acad Sr HS Eng Tchr 1986-92; Red Lion Chrstn Acad Jr HS Eng Tchr 1992-; *ai:* Missions Comm; Music Performance Related; 7th Grd Spon; Poetry Pub; *office:* Red Lion Christian Acad 1400 Red Lion Rd Bear DE 19701

NORRIS, STEVEN JOSEPH, 5th Grade Teacher; *b:* Huntingdon, PA; *m:* Wendy Munch; *c:* Ian Thomas, Justin Wade, Brea Lynn; *ed:* Juniata Coll (BA) Elem Ed 1975; Edinboro Univ MA Equiv Elem Admin Emphasis 1992; Staff Dev Trng as Tchr, Presenter; *cr:* Yth Corp Juveniles Ath Dir, Environmental Ed, Acad Instr 1975; Warren Co Schl Dist Sheffield Elem 6th Grd Tchr 1975-83, Irvindale Elem 5th-6th Grd Tchr 1983-88, Beaty W MS 5th Grd Sci, Hlth Tchr 1988-; *ai:* Geog Club; Asst Ftbl, Girls Vlybl, Cross Cntry, Track, Girls Bsktbl, Asst Boys Bsktbl Head Coach; Sprints, Hurdles, Throwing, Track Coach; Weight Lifting Trainer; NEA, WCEA 1975-; Educl Staff Dev 1990-93, Presenter; Elks Lodge BPOE 223 1992-; Spec Olympics, Past Helper; Newspaper Distance Running Advice Column; Book Dedication; *office:* Beaty Warren MS 3rd St Warren PA 16365*

NORRIS, WILLIAM RUSSELL, Elementary Principal; *b:* New York, NY; *m:* Mary Eileen Zipf; *c:* Robin Van Over, Kristin, William, Kerry; *ed:* Montclair St Coll (BA) Soc Stud 1963; Seton Hall Univ (MA) Admin 1974; Attnd Rutgers Univ Taft Inst, Antioch Coll Ctr for Understanding Media, Keane Coll of NJ Schl Finance; *cr:* Linden HS Tchr 1963-64; Clark Pub Schls LA, SS Tchr 1964-90. Admin Asst 1990-91, Prin 1992-; *ai:* NJEA, CEA, NEA 1963-, Pres, Outstanding Educator; NAESP, NJPSA 1992-; NJSBA 1988-, Pres; Jaycees 1965-; Branchburg Bd of Ed 1988-, Pres; NJ Schl Bds Assn 1988-, Continuing Ed; Robert A. Taft Fellow; Ctr for Understanding Media; *home:* 1011 Hillcrest Dr Neshanic Sta NJ 08853*

NORSTRAND, THOMAS FLETCHER, Social Studies Teacher; *b:* Brooklyn, NY; *ed:* Wisner Coll (BA) His 1968; LIU Masters Ed 1978; *cr:* William McKinley I.S. 259 Tchr 1968-; *ai:* G.O., Arista, Yrbk Fac Adv; AFT, UFT 1968-; Appalachian Mountain Club 1973-; *office:* William McKinley Intrmdt Schl 7301 Fort Hamilton Pky Brooklyn NY 11228

NORTH, DEBORAH, Second Grade Teacher; *b:* Gallipolis, OH; *ed:* Rio Grande Coll (BS) Elem Ed 1972; *cr:* Roosevelt Elem Tchr 1973-77; OH Valley Chrstn Tchr 1977-; *ai:* Amer Assn of Chrstn Schls; *office:* Ohio Valley Christian Schl P O Box 755 Gallipolis OH 45631

NORTH, JAMES B., Professor of Church History; *b:* Hammond, IN; *m:* Martha Sue Dean; *c:* Cynthia, Jennifer; *ed:* Lincoln Chrstn Coll (BA) Ministry 1982; Lincoln Chrstn Seminary (MA) Church His 1983; Univ of Chicago (MA) Church His 1967; Univ of IL (PHD) Amer His 1973; *cr:* San Jose Bible Coll Prof of His 1972-77; Cincinnati Bible Coll & Seminary Prof of Church His 1977-; *ai:* Amer Soc of Chrstn His 1965-; Conf on Faith & His, Disc of Christ His Soc 1973-; Book: From Pentecost to the Present 1983, Union In Truth 1994; *office:* Cincinnati Bible Coll & Sem 2700 Glenway Ave Cincinnati OH 45204

NORTH, KEVIN W., Third Grade Teacher; *b:* Glens Falls, NY; *ed:* SUNY at Genesee (BS) Elem Ed 1986; Coll of St Rose (MS) Spec Ed 1989; Castleston St Coll 12 Credit Hrs Post Grad Work; Adirondack Comm Coll Addl Credits in Math, Soc Sci for Soc Stud Cert 7-12 & Math Cert 7-9; *cr:* Hartford Cntrl Schl Remedial, Math, Process Writing Tchr 1986-88, 6th, 7th, 9th Grd Math, Lang Arts, Soc Stud Tchr 1988-92, First Grd Tchr 1992-94, Second Grd Tchr 1994-95, Third Grd Tchr 1995-; *ai:* FFA Adv; Budget, Crisis, Orientation for New Tchrs, Scheduling, Tchr Interview Comms; NYSUT HFA 1986-, Negotiations Ofcr; ASCD; IRA; NCTE; NCTM; NCSS; *office:* Hartford Central Schl Rts 40 & 149 Hartford NY 12838*

NORTH, MARY ELLEN VILLARREAL, Fourth Grade Teacher; *b:* Hollister, CA; *m:* Stephen D.; *c:* Maria, Patrick; *ed:* Gavilan Jr Coll (AA) Bus 1968; Earlham Coll (BA) Elem Ed 1973; Wright St Univ (MS) Ed 1990; *cr:* West Elkton Elem Schl DH Intermediate Level Tchr 1968-69; West Alexandria Elem Schl DH Primary, LD Primary 2nd Grd Tchr 1969-75; Bruce Elem Schl DH Intermed Level 3rd-5th Tchr 1986-; *ai:* Outdoor Sci Lab Establishing Schl Site Outdoor Sci Lab Areas; Earth Day Coord; NEA, OEA, Eaton Classroom Tchrs Assn 1986-; Preble Co Hist Soc 1984-, Bd Mem, Ed Comm; Alpha Kappa 1974-; *office:* Bruce Elem Schl 201 E Saint Clair St Eaton OH 45320

NORTH, ROBERT D., Physical Ed Teacher & Coach; *b:* Dunkirk, NY; *m:* Melissa Mansfield; *c:* Tyler Robert, Trey Richard; *ed:* Slippery Rock Univ of PA (BS) Hlth, PE 1985; Fredonia St Univ of NY (MS) Elem Ed 1991; *cr:* Westfield Acad HS PE Tchr 1985-; Cntrl Schl HS PE Tchr 1985-; *ai:* Girls Var Vlybl, Sftbl, Boys Var Bsktbl Coach; NEA 1985-; Loyal Order of Moose 1995-; Boys Bsktbl Coach of Yr 1991; Girls Sftbl Coach of Yr 1993; *office:* Westfield Acad E Main St Westfield NY 14787

NORTHCRAFT, SHERRY L., 4th Grade Teacher; *b:* Warfordsburg, PA; *ed:* Shippensburg Univ (BS) Elem Ed 1984; *cr:* Waynesboro Area Schl Dist 6th Grd Tchr 1984-93, 4th Grd Tchr 1993-; *ai:* WAEA & NEA 1984-;

Marion Mennonite Church Mem; 4th Grd Lead Tchr 1993-94; *office:* Waynesboro Area Schl Dist 210 Clayton Ave Waynesboro PA 17268

NORTHRUP, JANET M., English Teacher; *b:* Englewood, NJ; *m:* David M.; *c:* Victor, Mark; *ed:* SUNY at Fredonia (BA) Eng 1967; Grad Hrs SUNY at Albany, Univ of Rochester; *cr:* Fairport Cntrl Schls Eng Dept, Lead Tchr 1967-; *ai:* Lit Magazine Club Adv 1985-; Curr Planning Comm 1989-95; NYSEC; NCTE; Fairport Educators Assn 1967-; Lang Arts Ldrs Assn; Writers, Books 1991-; Rochester Arts, Lectures 1994-; People to People Stu Trip Chaparone 1992; Pub in Eng Journal 1989; Univ of NH PTSA, NYS Cncl on Arts Fellowships; *office:* Fairport HS 1358 Ayrault Rd Fairport NY 14450*

NORTHWOOD, WILLIAM CAMPBELL, Retired Fifth Grade Teacher; *b:* Wilkinsburg, PA; *m:* Barbara Hempstead; *c:* William H., Rebecca S. Warner; *ed:* Bapt Bible Coll (BRE) Chrstn Ed 1961; St Univ of NY at Cortland (MS) Ed 1965; ETTA Tchrs Diploma; Attnd Broome Comm Coll; *cr:* Floyd Bell Elem Schl Fourth Grd Tchr 1961-81; Susquehanna Vly Cntrl Schl Rdng Specialist 1975; C. R. Weeks Elem Schl Fifth Grd Tchr 1981-95; *ai:* Windsor Tchrs Assn 1961-95; NYSUT 1961-66; Town of Conklin Zoning Bd of Appeals 1970-, Chm; Comm Advy Bd WSKG-TV 1981-; Multi Dist Supts Conf Chm; *home:* 6 Tiffany Ave Conklin NY 13748

NORTON, DONNA MARIE, Vice Principal; *b:* Syracuse, NY; *m:* Michael; *c:* Joseph, Jacob; *ed:* LeMoyne Coll (BA) Bio 1985; SUNY Geneseo (MA) Bio 1987; Attnd Syracuse Univ, Rutgers Univ, Manhattan Coll; *cr:* Christian Bros Acad Bio Tchr 1988-, Sci Dept Chair 1992-, Vice Prin 1996-; *ai:* Jr Prom Adv; Eligibility Comm; NHS Adv; Tandy Schlsp; *office:* Christian Bros Acad 6245 Randall Rd Syracuse NY 13214

NORTON, EMILY FINE, Science Teacher; *b:* Norwood, MA; *m:* John W.; *c:* Kevin Powers, Laurel Powers; *ed:* Bates Coll (BS) Bio 1976; Courses Bridgewater St Coll, Stonehill Coll, Framingham St Coll; *cr:* North Attleboro HS Sci Tchr 1977-81; Sharon HS Sci Tchr 1988-; *ai:* Sharon Tchrs Assn; MA Tchrs Assn; NEA; CESAME Grant 1994-95; *office:* Sharon HS 180 Pond St Sharon MA 02067

NORTON, LISA ANN HOLL, First Grade Teacher; *b:* Erie, PA; *m:* Henry Z.; *ed:* Villa Maria Coll (BA) Elem Ed, Early Chldhd Ed 1982; ACES, ITEC, NIE; *cr:* St James Schl Tchr Various Grds 1980-; *ai:* Supvr Before Schl Care; NCEA 1980-; Kappa Gamma Pi 1982-; Flagship Niagara League 1991-; Natl Trust 1988-; Friends of the Lib 1994-; Smithsonian 1986-; 15 Yr Svc to Diocese of Erie as Tchr Co-Writer, Collaborator for Diocesan Prgm; *home:* 2621 Bird Dr Erie PA 16510

NORTON, RICHARD WALKER, Multi-Age Teacher; *b:* Dunkirk, NY; *m:* Sandra Lamphear; *c:* Erin, Emily; *ed:* Fredonia St Univ (BS) Elem Ed 1987, (MS) Curr & Instruction 1994; *cr:* Forestville Cntrl Schl 4th Grd Tchr 1988-92; Silver Creek Cntrl Schl 4th-5th Grd Multi-Age Tchr 1993-; *ai:* Jr Var Boys & Girls Bsktbl Coach; Swimming Asst Coach; Var Soccer, Jr Var Soccer, Var Golf & Medified Ftbl Intramural Dir; Adult Ed; SCCS Tchrs Assn 1993-, Union Rep; FCS Tchrs Assn, NYSUT 1987-; Parks & Recreation Commission 1995-; *office:* Silver Creek Cntrl Schl Dickinson St Silver Creek NY 14136*

NORTON, THOMAS EMMETT, Retired 5th Grade Teacher; *b:* Rochester, NY; *m:* Add Midora; *c:* Kelly, Kristin, Kevin; *ed:* SUNY at Brockport (BA) Ed 1961; C. W. Post (MS) Guid, Cnslng 1969; *cr:* Dinklemeyer Elem Schl 5th Grd Tchr 1961-89; *ai:* North Bellmore Tchrs Assn 1961-; AIT AFL-CIO.

NORTON, WILLIAM, Social Studies Teacher; *b:* Pottsville, PA; *m:* Bonnie Moran; *c:* Sharon Rossi, Kim; *ed:* Millersville Univ (BA) Soc Stud 1967; Bloomsburg Univ (MA) Soc Stud 1977; Scanton Univ (MED) Admin 1986; 200 Hrs Crisis Intervention; *cr:* Schuylkill Haven Schl Tchr 1967-68; Nativity BVM Tchr 1968-; *ai:* Chess Club Moderator; Stu Assistance Team Coord; Crisis Intervention Specialist; NCEA; NCSS; Mayor's Commission Drug, Alcohol Abuse 1988-93; Cty YMCA 1990-, Vice-Chm Bd Dirs; Cited Crisis Action by Mayor 1982; DARE Prgm Awd 1991; B'Nai, B'Rith Awd Tchng Excl 1968; *office:* Nativity BVM HS 1 Lawton's Hill Pottsville PA 17901

NORTON-SMITH, THOMAS MICHAEL, Assoc Professor of Philosophy; *b:* Springfield, IL; *m:* Linda Lee; *c:* Michael Chandler, Kathryn Greigh; *ed:* MO Southern St (BS) Math 1979; Pittsburg St Univ (MS) Math 1981; Univ of IL at Urbana (PHD) Philosophy 1988; *cr:* Kent St Univ Asst & Assoc Prof 1988-; *ai:* Univ Priorities & Budget Advy, Fac Ethics, & Regnl Campuses Fac Advy Comms; Fac Senate; Fac Cncl Chair; Exec Comm & Promotion, Tenure & Reappointment Comm Chair; Amer Philosophical Assn 1985-; Hum & Tech Assn 1991-; OH Philosophical Assn 1992-; Cntrl St Philosophical Assn 1993-; Great Lakes Historical Soc 1989-; Stark Cty Historical Soc 1991-; Numerous Articles Pub; 9 Presentations at Natl & Regnl Confs; 1991 Kent St Univ Stark Campus Distngd Tchng Awd; *office:* Kent St Univ Stark Cmps 6000 Frank Ave NW North Canton OH 44720

NORWOOD-DOBBINS, CORNELIA LEVON, Business Teacher; *b:* New York, NY; *m:* Michael J. Dobbins; *c:* Charnetta, Christopher; *ed:* Univ of DC (BS) Bus Ed 1973, (MBA) Fin, Ec 1977; *cr:* Potomac HS Bus Tchr 1973-; *ai:* FBLA Adv; Perkins Chprsn; Schl Planning Mngmt Team; Instrl Cncl; Bus Dept Chprsn; Schl Store; IBM Cmptr Lab Lans Mgr; AFT 1980-; NBEA, EBEA 1989-; MBEA 1973-, Treas 1993-95; PTA 1973-; NAACP 1995-; ACT-SO 1994-; FBLA Outstdng Svc; *office:* Potomac HS 5211 Boydell Ave Oxon Hill MD 20745*

NOSSEK, WILLIAM L., Seventh Grade Teacher; *b:* Cleveland, OH; *ed:* KS St Univ (BA) Ed 1970; *cr:* St Stanislans Schl 7th Grd Tchr 1972-80; St Joseph Schl 7th Grd Tchr 1980-.

NOSTI, ANNA MARIE TERES, Fifth Grade Teacher; *b:* Newark, NJ; *ed:* Coll of St Elizabeth (BS) Elem Ed 1966; In-Svc Whole Lang, Calligraphy; Pupil Asst Cnslr Trng; Assertive Discipline; *cr:* Archdiocese of Newark Schls Primary Grds Tchr 1959-67; Matawan-Aberdeen Regnl Schl Dist 2,3,5, LEC Sci, Cmptr Tchr 1968-; *ai:* Chess, Decorating, Frgn Lang, Quilting Clubs; Fac Adv Bd; PAC Team; Math, Rdng Tutor; MRTA, NJEA, NEA 1968-; Rdng Tchrs Assn of NJ 1992-; St Clement Choir 1992-; *office:* Cliffwood Elem Schl 422 Cliffwood Ave Cliffwood NJ 07721*

NOSTRO, BEVERLY, Biology Teacher; *b:* Port Chester, NY; *ed:* SUNY at Geneseo (BED) Ed 1966; Attnd OH St Univ & SUNY at New Palz; *cr:* Van Wyck Jr HS 7th Grd Sci Tchr 1966-85; John Jay HS Bio Tchr 1985-; *ai:* AFT 1970-, Bldg Rep; *office:* John Jay HS Rt 52 Box 38 Hopewell Junctio NY 12534

NOSTRO, NEIL R., 8th Grd Social Studies Teacher; *b:* Port Chester, NY; *m:* Fernande; *ed:* Bridgeport Univ (BS) Scndry Ed 1972; *cr:* Port Chester Schls Spec Assignment Tchr 1972-73, Soc Stud Tchr 1974-; *ai:* Schl Tutor Prgm 1983-; Peer Mediation Adv 1995-; 8th Grd Team Ldr 1995-; NYSUT 1974-; Tchr of Yr Nom 1995; Humanitarian Awd 1992; *home:* 20 Whittemore Pl Rye Brook NY 10573

NOTAR, JOAN, Third Grade Teacher; *b:* Hackensack, NJ; *m:* Robert; *c:* Kelly, Michael; *ed:* Fairleigh Dickinson (BA) Elem Ed 1971; Grad Credits Cmptr, Whole Lang; *cr:* Garfield Schl #8 Remedial Rdng Spec 1972-73; Garfield Schl #4 1-2, 4 Grd Tchr 1974-79, 3 Grd Tchr 1980-; *ai:* AFT 1980-; NJEA 1979-; Governor's Tchr Recognition 1989-90; *office:* Washington Irving Elem Sch 4 12 Madonna Pl Garfield NJ 07026

NOTAR, MICHAEL ROBERT, Sixth Grade Teacher; *b:* Sharon, PA; *m:* Tabitha Lyn; *ed:* Youngstown St Univ (BA) Elem Ed 1993; Univ of Dayton Masters Degree in Educl Admin; *cr:* Ottoville Elem 5th Grd Tchr 1993-95, 6th Grd Tchr 1995-; *ai:* Jr High Boys Bsktbl 1993-95; JV Bsbl 1993-; Var Girls Vllybl 1995-; NEA 1993-; Putnam Cty Drug & Alcohol Coord 1993-, Contact Person; Putnam Cty Curr Dir of Sci 1995-, Coord; Received Stu Tchr of Yr Awd in 1993; *office:* Ottoville Elem Schl PO Box 248 Ottoville OH 45876*

NOTARI, RICHARD PAUL,SR., Mathematics Teacher; *b:* Scranton, PA; *m:* Diane Barbara Lesneski; *c:* Rick, Robert, Timothy; *ed:* Wilkes Univ (BA) Math 1969; 36 Credit Hrs Post Grad Stud at Leigh Univ, Temple Univ, Trenton St, Rider, Rutgers Univ in Scndry Ed & Cmptr Tech; *cr:* N Brunswick HS Tchr 1969-74; Old Forge HS Tchr 1974-; *ai:* Math Dept Chm; Dir Ath; Head Golf Coach; OFEA, PSEA 1974-; NEA 1969-; Won St Cmptr Grant To Start Elem Cmptr Lab; *office:* Old Forge H S Marion St Old Forge PA 18518

NOTARI, ROBERT JOHN, Music Teacher; *b:* Old Farge, PA; *m:* Carol Ann Marie Boyle; *c:* Denise Ellyn Endieveri, Kenneth John; *ed:* West Chester Univ (BS) Music Ed 1964; IN Univ (MM) Clarinet Preformance 1967; Univ of IL (EdD) Mus Ed; *cr:* Glen Falls City Schls Instrumental Music Tchr 1964-66; Queensbury Schls Music Tchr 1967-; Adirondack Comm Coll Clarinet, Saxaphone Instr 1982-; *ai:* Key Club Adv; Jazz Band Dir; Site-Based & MS Quality Review Comm; AFT 1982-; NYSSMA 1964-, Adjudicator; MENC 1964; Saratoga Warren Cty Music Educators Assn 1982-, Pres; Glen Falls Comm Theater 1964-, Musical Dir; Church of the Annunciation 1964- Parish Cncl VP; Habitat for Humanity 2 Yrs; QBY Kiwanis 5 Yrs; MENC Journal Article; Assistantship Univ IL Edit Crime Journal; Guest Coord NYSSMA Area All St Bands, VT Area All- State Band, All Cty Elem Jr & Sr High Bands; *home:* 2 St Andrews Dr Queensbury NY 12804*

NOTARNICOLA, JOYCE BARCLAY, French Teacher; *b:* Buffalo, NY; *m:* Mark; *c:* Christopher; *ed:* St Univ Coll at Oswego (BA) Fr 1982; SUNY at Albany (MA) Fr 1992; 17 Grad Credit Hrs; *cr:* Dundee Cntrl Schl Fr & Span Tchr 1986-87; Catskill Cntrl Schl Fr Tchr 1987-; *ai:* Yrbk & Fr Club Adv; NY St Frgn Lang Tchrs Assoc 1987-; Rockefeller Schlsp Grant to Stud in France for Summer; *office:* Catskill HS 347 W Main St Catskill NY 12414

NOTO, CAROLINE DEGENNARO, Kindergarten Teacher; *b:* Brooklyn, NY; *m:* Pete; *c:* Josette, Pietra; *ed:* St Joseph's Coll (BA) Child Dev 1967; Hunter Coll (MS) Ed 1972; 18 In-Svc Credits NYC Bd of Ed; *cr:* PS 345 Kndgtn, Third, Second Grd Tchr 25 Yrs; PS 72 Third Grd Tchr 1 Yr; *ai:* Fac Adv; UFT, AFT 1967-; Cath Tchrs Assn 1989-; Afghan Club 1990-; Parents Club Kellenberg Meml HS 1993-; St Boniface Parish 1974-; St Rita's Alumni Assn; United Fed of Tchrs Mini-Grants 1995-96; *office:* PS 345 Robert Bolden 111 Berriman St Brooklyn NY 11208*

NOTO, MICHAEL JAMES, Social Studies Teacher; *b:* Rochester, NY; *m:* Martha Tisher; *c:* Christopher, Alison; *ed:* Univ of Rochester (BA) His & Pol Sci 1980, (MS) Human Dev 1983; *cr:* Brighton HS Soc Stud Tchr 1983-; *ai:* Chprsn for Brighton HS Comm Planning Team Comm; Mem & Speaker for Ad Hoc Comm on Soc Stud Stan; *office:* Brighton HS 1150 Winton Rd S Rochester NY 14618*

NOTTO, ROBERT VINCENT, Music Teacher & Band Director; *b:* Brooklyn, NY; *c:* Brynn E.; *ed:* Hofstra Univ (BS) Music Ed 1978; Queens Coll Aaron Copland Schl of Music (MS) Music 1983; 30 Addl Credit Hrs George Mason Univ, LIU at C. W. Post, Brooklyn Coll; *cr:* Baldwin Harbor Elem Schl Tchr, Instrumental Music, Orch 1978-81; Milburn Elem Schl Tchr, Instrumental Music, Orch 1978-81; Baldwin HS Tchr, Instrumental Music, Orch, Marching Band 1978-83; Plaza Elem Schl Tchr, Instrumental Music, Orch 1981-83; Baldwin Jr HS Tchr, Instrumental Music, Band Dir, Marching Band, Jazz Ensemble 1983-; *ai:* Jazz Ensemble, Marching Band 1983-; MENC, Nassau Music Edctrs Assn, NYSUT 1978-; Long Island String Festival Assn 1978-82; PTA 1978-; Helen Slonim Meml Awd Tchr of Yr 1993; In Recognition Excl Awd 1994; *home:* 8 Meadow Rd Massapequa Park NY 11762*

NOVAK, BARBARA LONG, Science Teacher; *b:* Medford, MA; *m:* Scott C.; *c:* Brain, Marc; *ed:* Univ of CT (BS) Hlth, PE 1975; Cntrl CT Univ (MS) Guid, Cnslng 1981; 6th Level Sci, Bio 1984, 30 Credit Hrs; *cr:* Enfield HS PE Tchr 1975-76; Kosciuszko Jr HS 7-9 Grds PE Tchr 1976-82; John F. Kennedy MS 7-8 Grds Sci Tchr 1982-; *ai:* Running Club Adv; NEA, CT Ed Assn, Enfield Tchrs Assn 1975-; *office:* John F Kennedy MS 155 Raffia Rd Enfield CT 06082*

NOVAK, JEAN FINNEGAN, Eighth Grade Teacher; *b:* Pittsburgh, PA; *m:* John J.; *c:* Amy, John; *ed:* DuQuesne Univ (BS) Elem Ed 1972, (MS) Rdng & Lang Arts 1986; *cr:* Pittsburgh Pub Schl First Grd Tchr 1973; St Piux X Schl 3rd Grd Tchr 1973-78; St Sebastian Schl 5th Grd Tchr 1979-80; St Alphonsus Schl 8th Grd Tchr 1985-; *ai:* Sacrament Preparation Confirmation; Stu Cncl Moderator; NCEA, Diocesan Fed of Tchrs 1980-; Golden Apple Awd Diocese of Pittsburgh 1993; *office:* St Alphonsus Schl 201 Church Rd Wexford PA 15090

NOVAK, JOSEPH D., Mathematics Teacher; *b:* Allentown, PA; *m:* Dianne Sibree; *c:* Nicholas; *ed:* Kutztown Univ (BS) Math, Ed 1989; *cr:* J. S. Bunnell Jr HS Math Tchr 1989-90; Franklin HS Math Tchr 1991-; *ai:* HS Sftbl Coach; NJEA, NEA, NCTM, AMTNJ 1992-; NJ New Math Tchr Inst Rutgers Univ Staff Mem; *office:* Franklin HS 415 Francis St Somerset NJ 08873*

NOVAK, NANCY MLAKAR, Consumer, Family Life Sci Tchr; *b:* Sharon, PA; *m:* Gerald P.; *ed:* Villa Maria Coll of Gannon Univ (BS) Home Ec Ed 1972; Penn St Univ 15 Post Grad Hrs; *cr:* Kennedy Chrstn HS Home Ec Tchr 1972-83; JTPA West Cntrl Summer Supvr 1984; Trumbull Co Vo-Tech Displaced Homemaker Coord 1984-85; Wilmington HS Home Ec Tchr 1985-86; Neshannock Jr Sr HS Home Ec Tchr 1986-; *ai:* Stu Invironmental Action Cncl Adv; Comm Svc Coord; NEA 1989-; *office:* Neshannock Jr Sr HS 301 Mitchell Rd New Castle PA 16105

NOVAK, PATRICIA E., Teacher of Enrichment Programs; *b:* Hudson, NY; *m:* Walter M. Jr.; *c:* Alessandra; *ed:* St Univ of NY at Oswego (BS) Elem Ed 1965; Coll of Saint Rose (MS) Rdng 1975; *cr:* Mohanasen Cntrl Schls K-2nd Grd Elem Tchr 1965-81, Remedial Rdng Tchr 1977-78, Gifted, Talented & Enrichment Tchr 1982-; *ai:* Phi Delta Kappa 1990-; AFT; NYS Rdng Assn; Rotterdam Lioness Club 1985-; Goals 2000 1991-; *office:* Pinewood Elem Schl 901 Kings Rd Rotterdam NY 12303

NOVAK, PATRICIA GAIL, Eng, Soc Studies & Rdng Tchr; *b:* Stambaugh, MI; *ed:* Northern MI Univ (BA) Eng 1971; CA St Univ at Dominguez Hills (MA) Hum 1985; *cr:* West Iron Cty Pub Schls Scndry Tchr 1971-74; Dept of Defense Schls Scndry Tchr 1974-; *ai:* Tchng Module Study Bldg Based Facilitator; Curr Dev, Target Comms, Outcomes Accredidation Chair; AFT, OFT 1974-, Sec; PDK 1983-90, VP, Pres; SETAF Comm Outstdng Performance Recognition 1987, 1991; Vicenza SETAF Comm Recognition for Outstdng Performance 1987, 1991; *office:* Vicenza American HS Unit 31401 Box 11 APO AE 09630

NOVAK, ROBERT JAMES, Fourth Grade Teacher; *b:* Babylon, NY; *m:* Elizabeth Helen Millican; *c:* Jason N.; *ed:* Fredonia St Univ (BS) Elem Ed, Pol Sci 1975; Ashland Univ (MSEd) Elem Admin 1985; 12 Addl Post Grad Hrs Cooperative Ed, Sci, Using Discovery World; *cr:* Whipple Heights Elem Schl First Grd Tchr 1976, Second Grd Tchr 1977-80; T. C. Knapp Elem Schl Fourth Grd Tchr 1980-; *ai:* Negotiating Team 6 Yrs; Perry Classroom Tchr Rep 18 Yrs; PTO Tchr Rep 15 Yrs, Comm Rep 8 Yrs; NEA, OEA 1976-; Perry Local Tchrs Assn 17 Yrs, Tchr Rep, Negotiating Team 6 Yrs; Apples for Tchr Awd 1994; Canton Chamber of Commerce Tchr Nom 1990; PAKT Svc Awd 1990; First Stu, Tchr Recognition B Edctr Awd 1989; Perry Pride Pin 1985-86; *office:* T C Knapp Eler 5151 Oakcliff St SW Canton OH 44706

NOVAK, RONALD JOHN, Government Teacher; *b:* Cleveland, O Ann; *c:* Chris, Kathy Novak Boff, Joseph, Jennifer; *ed:* John Carroll (BA) His 1962, (MA) His 1965; Cleveland St Guid Cert 1987; Sovi Stud 18 Addl Hrs; TAFT Govt Stud 18 Addl Hrs; *cr:* Berea Schl S Tchr 1963-68; Padua Franciscan AS Dept Head Tchr 1968-; *ai:* Clo Cleveland City Club; Sports Referee; OHSAA 1975-; Citizens L 1960-; Pol Candidate for US House of Rep; Councilman for Clevelan

NOVAK, SCOTT C., HS Social Science Teacher; *b:* Hartford, C Barbara Long; *c:* Brian, Marc; *ed:* Cntrl Conn St Coll (BS) Soc Sci (MS) Counseling 7 Human Relations 1982; 30 Addl Credit Hrs Gener *cr:* Vernon Ctr MS Gifted & Talented Tchr 1976-77, Soc Stud & Lan, Tchr 1977-88; Rockville HS Soc Sci, Psych, World His 1988-; *ai:* S Adv; NEA, CT Ed Assn. Vernon Tchrs Assn 1976-; East Windsor S Assn 1993-; *office:* Rockville HS Loveland Hill Rd Vernon Rock 06066

NOVAK, STEVE, Government Teacher; *b:* Newark, NJ; *m:* Barba Steven; *ed:* Seton Hall Univ (BS) Ed 1969; Kean Coll (MA) Admin *cr:* South Plainfield HS Tchr & Vice Prin 1969-; *ai:* Var Soccer & Coach; Stu Cncl Adv; NEA; North Plainfield, Mayor 1974-88, 1971-74; Recreation, Dir 1989-; North Plainfield HS Hall of Fame C Mem Grad 1965; Home Town of North Plainfield Man of Yr 3 Times of Yr 1991; NJIAA Coaching Awd; Bsbl Coach of Yr 6 Times; S South Plainfield HS Pom Pon Girls.

NOVAK, WALTER JOSEPH, Technology Education Teacher; *b:* Ch PA; *ed:* Delaware Cty Comm Coll (AA) Lbrl Arts 1971; Mansfield S (BA) Psych 1973; Cheyney Univ Tchng Cert Tech Ed Indstrl Arts Immaculate Coll Tchng Cert Comp Soc Stud 1975; Enrolled Wilmi Coll Instruction; *cr:* Penn Delco Schl Dist Soc Stud Tchr 1974-77; C Upland Schl Dist Soc Stud Tchr 1977-81; Chichester Schl Dist Soc Tchr 1981-88, Indstrl Arts Tchr 1988-91; Brandywine Schl Dist Te Tchr 1991-; *ai:* Tech Stu Assn, Jr Solar Spring, Engrng Club Adv; DE Educl Assn, BEA 1991-; NEA 1974-; BSA 1992-, Merit Badge Adv; Springer MS 2220 Shipley Rd Wilmington DE 19803*

NOVELLI, ROBERT JOHN, Adjunct Prof of Liberal Art Philadelphia, PA; *ed:* Bloomsburg St Coll (BS) Gifted Ed Bloomsburg Univ (MA) Speech Comm 1985; *cr:* Montgomery Cty C Coll Adjunct Prof 1987-; Chestnut Hill Coll Adjunct Prof 1989-; DE V Coll Adjunct Prof 1991-; Thomas Jefferson Univ Adjunct Prof 1991- Pi Kappa Delta 1980-; Philadelphia Cactus & Succulent Soc 1 Numerous Pub Speaking Awds; 1st Place Natl Champion for Ori Poetry 1991; *home:* PO Box 1174 Skippack PA 19474

NOVEY, JUDY, Art Teacher; *b:* NYC, NY; *c:* Dora Novey Buttfiel Philadelphia Coll of Art (BFA) Studio Art 1975; Rutgers Univ (Studio Art, Painting 1982; *cr:* Cncl Rock Pub Schls Art Fac 197 1982-84; North Yarmouth Acad Chair, Arts Dept 1984-85; Maine C Art Admin Asst 1985-87; Waynflete Schl Art Fac 1987-; *ai:* Stu Adv Display; Portfolio Dev; Union of ME Visual Artists; NAEA; Innov Classroom Grant ME Dept of Ed & Cultural Resources 1989; Pres Assn of Ind Schl of New England 1995; *office:* Waynflete Schl 360 S St Portland ME 04102

NOVOTNEY, FRANK A.,JR., Science Dept Chair & Teache Brownsville, PA; *m:* Anastasia Tatar; *c:* Nathan, Sean; *ed:* St Vincent (BS) Chem 1967; Post Grad Stud Seton Hill Coll, Penn St, IN Univ, Carnegie Mellon, Univ of CA at Berkeley; *cr:* Greensburg Cntrl Cat Sci Tchr 1969-71; Brownsville Area HS Sci Tchr 1971-; *ai:* Competition Team; Instrl Design Team; Sr Class Spon; Tutoring Coord, Publicity Box Office for Schl Musical; NEA, PSEA 1971-; N 1990-; Greater Uniontown Chorale 1985-, Pres, Bd of Dir; YMCA, V Yr; Church Bd 1971-, Sec; TRAC Fellow; NSF Fellow; Rsrch In Howard Hughes Grant; Tchr Enhancement Coord; *office:* Brownsville HS Brashear Ave Brownsville PA 15417*

NOVOTNEY, VIRGINIA DISNEY, Sixth Grade Teacher; *b:* Elmh IL; *m:* David; *ed:* IL St Univ (BSEd) Jr HS Ed 1973; Georgetown (MAEd) Elem Ed 1988; Post Grad Stud at OH St Univ & Univ of Da *cr:* College Heights Chrstn Schl 6th Grd Tchr 1979-83; Dallas Chrstn Instr 1985; Lexington Chrstn Schl 6th Grd Tchr 1986-88; Tree of Chrstn Schl 6th Grd Tchr 1988-; *ai:* ACSI 1979-; NCTM 1974-79 Space Fnd NASA Fellowship to Class Called Getting Comfortable T with Space; *home:* 1850 Dandridge Dr Columbus OH 43229

NOVOTNY, DEBRA A., American History Teacher; *b:* Uniontown, *ed:* California Univ of PA (BS) Ed, His 1972, (MA) His 1978; 15 Hrs Grad; *cr:* Brownsville Cath Schl Soc Stud Tchr 5 Yrs; Gettysburg J World His Tchr 2 Yrs; Gettysburg HS Amer His Tchr 16 Yrs; *ai:* N Gettysburg Area Ed Assn 1980-; Adams Cty Historical Soc 1978-; War Table 1975-, Exec Bd; Assn of Licensed Battlefield Guides 1 Treas; *office:* Gettysburg Sr HS Lefever St Gettysburg PA 17325

NOVOTNY, JOSEPH M., Technology Teacher; *b:* Garfield Hts, OH Liza M. Pugliesi; *c:* Milena; *ed:* CA Univ of PA (BS) Tech Ed 1991; Lo Coll of MD Admin & Supervision; *cr:* Hayfield Scndry Tech Tchr 1991 Burleigh Manor HS Tech Tchr 1992-; *ai:* Centennial HS Ftbl & Coach; NEA, MSTA & HCEA 1992-; TEAM 1993-; ITEA 1994-; *of* Burleigh Manor MS 4200 Centennial Ln Ellicott City MD 21042

NOWACK, GEORGE P., Language Arts Teacher; *b:* Pittsburgh, PA Carolyn R.; *ed:* Duquesne Univ (BSEd) Eng 1970; Trenton St Coll (Eng 1974; Duquesne Univ (MED) Rdng Specialist 1976; VA Union Botany 1964; Univ of Pittsburgh Psych 1977; CA St Coll Writing; South River HS Dir of Dramatics, Eng Tchr 1970-74; Pgh Pub Schls L Arts Tchr 1974-; *ai:* Allegheny Star Ed 1983-91; Players Dir 1990 Yrbk Spon 1983-89; Treas 1994-; Stu Cncl Adv 1990-91; AFT, PFT 19 Kappa Phi Kappa 1968-, Pres, Outstdng Grad; Natl Carousel Assn 19 South River Jaycees 1971-, Pres; Garden St Arts Festival Outstdng 1972-74; Allegheny Comm Dev Conf Grant 1981-83; PSPRA Excl 1987; Champions Assn Outstdng Tchr 1992-94; Who's Who in Amer 1992-93; Who's Who in the East 1992-95; Author Grounds Fee; *off* Allegheny MS 810 Arch St Pittsburgh PA 15212*

NOWAH, GERALDINE, Religion Teacher & Coord; *b:* Buffalo, NY; Medaille Coll (BS) Ed 1965; St Univ Coll (MS) Ed 1969; Christ the K Seminary (MA) Theology 1976; *cr:* Newman Ctr St Univ Chap 1975-79; St Joachim Schl 6-8 Grd Rel Ed Tchr 1979-81, Prin 1981 Nativity of Our Lord Schl 1-6 Grd Rel Ed Tchr, K-8 Grd Rel Ed C 1982-; *ai:* Schl Photographer; NCEA 1982-; NCCC 1984-; Buffalo A Sacred Heart 1995-, Schl Bd; Experienced Tchr Flwshp Prgm 1968; Edctr of Yr 1985; *office:* Nativity Of Our Lord Schl 4414 S Buffal Orchard Park NY 14127

NOWAK, ADELA G., Mathematics Teacher; *b:* Utica, NY; *ed:* SUNY Albany (BA) Math 1964; 36 Grad Hrs Var Insts; *cr:* Utica City Schl HS Math Tchr 32 Yrs; *ai:* AFT, Oneida Cty Math Tchrs, NY St Math T Assn 1964-; Kopernik Meml Assn 1984-, VP; Polick Comm Club 19 Treas; Na-Ki-Yan Klub 1990-, Pres, VP; NSF Summer Grants Tw *office:* T. R. Proctor Sr HS Hilton Ave Utica NY 13501

AK, DENISE O'GORMAN, Biology Teacher; *b:* Yonkers, NY; *m:* *ed:* Manhattan Coll (BS) Bio Ed 1991; NY Univ (MS) Sci Ed 1995; ddl Credit Hrs Fordham Univ, Lehman Coll, Westchester Comm Coll; : Witt Clinton HS Bio Tchr, Sr Adv 1991-; *ai:* Boys & Girls Var Vlybl ı; Sr Trip Coord; Upside Down Club Adv; ASCD 1992-; NYSBT, UFT 1991-; Amer Red Cross 1985-; NYU Dewight D Eisenhower ient; Paul Douglas Schlsp; NYS Challenger Schlsp; *office:* De Witt on HS 100 W Mosolu Pkwy Bronx NY 10468*

AK, RUTH ANN PIFER, 6th & 8th Grade Art Teacher; *b:* Niagara NY; *c:* Laura Clair; *ed:* Buffalo St Coll (BA) Art Ed 1966, (MS) Art 973; *cr:* Orchard Park Schls Art Tchr 29 Yrs; *ai:* Yrbk Adv 1967-72; action Ldr Art Dept 1991-; Comp & Learning Styles Comms 1991-; ibute Stu Work to Artsplash K-12; AFT 1967-; NEA 1967-; Town Hall rtwork Exhibit 1991-, Comm Mem; Awded Laser Disc Natl Gallery t; *office:* Orchard Park Cntrl Schl Lincoln Ave Orchard Park NY 7

AK, TOPHIE KATHERINE, 6th Grade Teacher; *b:* Montague City, *ed:* Greenfield Comm Coll (AS) 1965; Amer Intnl Coll (BS) Elem Ed ; Springfield Coll (MED-GPS) Guid 1971; 36 Credit Hrs Ed; mplated Courses for 6th Level Recognized Enfield Bd of Ed; *cr:* ard Schl 3rd Grd Tchr 2 Yrs; Henry Barnard Schl 4-5 Grd Tchr 5 Yrs; an Hale Schl 5-6 Grd Tchr 22 Yrs; *ai:* Town Wide Staff Dev Comm 28 Schl Family Nite Act Chair; PTO Sec; Yrbk Adv; After Schl PE Prgm nvention Convention Prgm Chm; NEA, CEA, ETA 1969-, VP, El Ed 4 Enfield Town Republican Comm 1979-; Dist Capt, Candidate Review n Chair; Enfield 4th of July Bd of Dir 1992-, Dir; Enfield Womens blican Club, Comm Chair 1982; Justice of the Peace 1984; *office:* an Hale Elem Schl 5 Taylor Rd Enfield CT 06082

AKOWSKI, JOSEPH MARK, Asst Professor of Economics; *b:* ona Heights, PA; *m:* Laura Dane Johnston; *ed:* Duke Univ (BA) Ec ; UNC Chapel Hall (PHD) Ec 1993; *cr:* UNC Greensboro Lecturer, 1990-93; Muskingum Coll Asst Prof 1993-; *ai:* Lambda Sigma Fac AEA, SEA, ACES 1990-; *office:* Muskingum Coll 131 Cambridge New Concord OH 43762

ICKI, CHRISTINE CURRY, Middle School Librarian; *b:* burgh, PA; *c:* Scott, Robert; *ed:* Edinboro Coll (BS) Lib Sci 1972; cuse Univ (MLS) Lib Sci 1977; Mansfield Univ, Penn St Univ Grad se Work; *cr:* Oriskany Cntrl Schl Librn 1972-74; Dryden Cntrl Schl ı 1974-77; Cntrl NY Hosp Assn Hlth Care Coord 1978-80; Mc Call Librn, Tchr of Gifted 1982-; *ai:* Stu Assinstance Prgm; Schl Store, lerated Rdng Prgm Adv; Lib Dept Dist Chprsn; Battle of Books h; Montoursville Area Ed Assn 1983-, Sec; PA Assn of Stu Assistance ; PA Schl Lib Assn; BSA 1993-, Sec; Our Lady of Lourdes Church r, Yth Group Adv; *office:* C E Mccall MS 600 Willow St Montoursville 7754

ICKI, JILL GERCKEN, Child Care Teacher; *b:* Pittsburgh, PA; *m:* ard R.; *c:* Stacy L., Jennifer L.; *ed:* IN Univ of PA (BS) Home Ec ; CA Univ of PA 9 Credit Hrs; PA St Univ 26 Credit Hrs; *cr:* Churchill S Home Ec Tchr 1967-74; Comm Coll Allegheny Coll Parenting Tchr -89; Forbes Road East AVTS Child Care Svc Tchr 1989-; *ai:* Natl Voc Soc, Portfolio Dev Comms; Child Care Svcs Voc Ind Clubs Amer Spon, ; PSEA, NEA, NHEA 1989-; Freavts Ed Assn 1989-, Sec; St adette Guild 1978-; PTG 1979-; Consumer Ed Grants 1972, 1973; *e:* Forbes Road East AVTS 607 Beatty Rd Monroeville PA 15146

VORYTA, VICTORIA SWISHER, Math Teacher; *b:* North awanda, NY; *m:* Michael V.; *ed:* SUNY at Buffalo (BA) Scndry Math 969, (MS) Scndry Math Ed 1974SUNUY; *cr:* Cheektowaga Cntrl HS h, Pre Calculus, Calculus Tchr 1969-; *ai:* Soph Class Adv; Tchr ognition, Report Card Comms; NEA 1969-; *office:* Cheektowaga ral H S 3600 Union Rd Cheektowaga NY 14225

ES, DEBRA SUTTON, Asst Prof of Trvl & Tourism; *b:* Little Falls, *m:* Stephen; *ed:* Bryant-Stratton PBI (AOS) Exec Sec 1981; SUNY of Tech (BPS) Bus, Pub Mngmt 1983; Binghamton Univ (MS) Mngmt 1991; 15 Credit Hrs Travel & Tourism Courses; *cr:* Herkimer Cty m Coll Travel & Tourism Asst Prof 1988-; *ai:* Travel Club Adv; Acad, Events, Wall St Journal Awd, Coll Day Comms; Gerontology Speakers eau; Travel & Tourism Advy Bd; NYSUT, CHRIE, ASTA 1991-; kimer Cty Historical Soc 1992-; Amer Cancer Soc 1991-, Bd Mem, Pub Chair; Authored & Received Fnd Fac Dev Grant; Awded Cert for Svc cl Inst of the Amer Hotel & Motel Assn; Amer Express Svc Excl Awd; stdng Young Woman of Am er; *office:* Herkimer County Comm Coll ervoir Road Herkimer NY 13350

ES, SUSAN POTTER, Former English Teacher; *b:* Lynn, MA; *m:* glas G.; *c:* Laura, Matthew, Karolyn; *ed:* Univ of NH (BA) Eng, (MED) 1996; *cr:* Concord Chrstn Schl HS, MS Eng Tchr 1989-93; *ai:* Yrbk ; Jrnlsm Tchr; Pub Schl Newspaper; Speech Coach; *home:* 2 Betty Ln NH 03304

GENT, EDWARD ROY, Fifth Grade Teacher; *b:* West Stewartstown, *m:* Lenora Jane Rich; *c:* Ben, Sarah; *ed:* Lyndon St Coll (BS) Elem Ed 4; 15 Addl Credits; *ai:* Chair Local Civic Oration; Fairbanks Museum cl Curr Adby Bd; Aft Schl Sftbl Coach; NEA, VEA 1974-, Bldg Rep, otiator 10 Yrs; Nom Outstdng Tchr of Yr 1982; *home:* 49 Pleasant St ıt Johnsbury VT 05819

GENT, JULIA T., 7th Grade Life Science Teacher; *b:* Trinidad, West es; *m:* Bernard; *c:* Christian, Patrick; *ed:* Queens Coll (BA) Bio 1985,) Sci Ed 1993; 28 Grad Level Credits; *cr:* Hamilton Mills Traffic nt Imported Products 1995-; IS 125 Tchr 1996; *office:* Woodside IS 125 2 47th Ave Flushing NY 11377*

GENT, VINCENT WILLIAM, English Teacher & Dept Chm; *b:* oklyn, NY; *m:* Jean Karole; *c:* Caitlin Jean, Brendan Patrick, Moira herine; *ed:* Marist Coll (BA) Eng, Ed 1978; SUNY at New Paltz (MS) cl Media 1982; 31 Addl Grad Hrs; *cr:* F. D. Roosevelt HS Eng Tchr 8-79; Rhinebeck HS Eng Tchr 1979-; *ai:* Eng Dept Chm; Drama Club forming Arts Dir; AFT, NYSUT 1978-; Rhinebeck Tchrs Assn 1978-, Sec, Pub Relations Coord; Myer Schl PTO 1989-; NYS Eng Cncl Edctr Excl; Dutchess Cty Area Fund Grant 1990, 1995; Hudson Vly Portfolio ject; *office:* Rhinebeck HS Box 351 N Park Rd Rhinebeck NY 12572

KALA, DANIEL GUY, Lang Arts & Composition Tchr; *b:* Knox, IN; IN Univ (BS) Eng 1974; Univ of CA at Berkeley Bay Area Writing ject; Univ of IA Jrnlsm; Univ of Conn TAG with Dr Joe Renzuui; *cr:* er Schl Eng, Drama Tchr 1975-77; Gary Emerson HS Speech Tchr 7-79; Zweibruecken HS Eng, Drama, Jrnlsm Tchr 1979-93; Ramstein Eng Tchr 1993-; *ai:* Sr Clas, Drama Spon; Phi Delta Kappa 1991-, wsletter Ed, Outstdng Newsletter 1994-95, Edctr of Yr 1993; FEA, NEA 3-; NCTE 1995-; Outstdng Tchr Kaiserslautern Dist, Do DDS 1995; Play The Write Stuff; Presenter Confs Edctr Days on Tchng of Writing; *ne:* PSC Box 2 Box 8892 APO AE 09012*

LL, PATRICIA CAMPAGNA, Business Education Teacher; *b:* iladelphia, PA; *m:* Gregory K.; *c:* P. John, Jodi; *ed:* Rowan Coll (BA) s Admin, Ed 1979; Rider Univ (MA) Bus Ed, Supervision; *cr:* Audubon Bus Ed Tchr 1979-80; Plantation HS Bus Ed Tchr 1980-82; Haddon ights HS Bus Ed 1986-92; Camdem Cty Vo Tech Allied Hlth Tchr 2-95; Haddon Heights HS Cooperation Ed Coord 1995-; *ai:* Schl to rk Coord; HOSA Adv 1993-95; Advy Comm; NEA, NJEA 1986-; EA, NJBEA 1987-; FBLA, HOSA 1992-95; Sturbridge Woods Swim Club 1993-, Swim Team Coord; *office:* Haddon Heights High School 301 Second Ave Haddon Heights NJ 08035

NU'MAN, VIVIAN SEIDAH, Middle Grades Teacher; *b:* Jacksonville, FL; *c:* Robert Nunn, Fernando Nunn; *ed:* Jersey City St Coll (BA) Elem Ed 1976, (MA) Scndry Ed, Urban Stud 1979; Post Grad Stud 28 Credit Hrs; *cr:* Whitney M. Young Elem Schl Tchr 1976-77; St Mary's Grammar Schl Tchr 1977-78; Watchung Elem Schl Tchr 1978-79; Pub Schl Number 29 Tchr 1979-82; Pub Schl Number 14 Tchr 1982-; *ai:* NEA 1976-; Hudson Rdng Cncl 1994-; Tchr Recognition of Excl Merrill Lynch Mc Millan, Mc Govern; Hudson Cty Tchr of Excl 1994; Outstdng Tchr of Yr 1995; *home:* 29 Virginia Ave Jersey City NJ 07304

NUNES, LUCILLE SOUSA, Second Grade Teacher; *b:* Ludlow, MA; *m:* Manuel C.; *c:* Paul V. Nunes, Odette Nunes-Turcotte, Jane Nunes-Campolo; *ed:* Univ of MA (BA) Elem, ESL, Bilingual Ed 1977; *cr:* Ludlow Pub Schl Elem Bilingual, ESL Tchr 1973-95, 2nd Grd Tchr 1995-; *ai:* Bldg Based Support Team 4th Yr; Tech Comm; Parents Advy Cncl Organizer; Admin of MA Eng Lang-Oral Assessment Asst Resource Specialist; NEA, MEA, LEA, MABE 1973-; TESOL 1992-; ASCD 1989-; Portguese-Amer Citizens Club, Portguese Women's Auxilary 1950-; Western MA Portuguese Radio Hour Co-Host 1950-83; *home:* 329 East St Ludlow MA 01056*

NUNZIENTE, PETER, Pastor; *b:* Brooklyn, NY; *m:* Teresa Nunziante; *c:* Nathaniel, Valerie, Joshua; *cr:* Upper Room Chrstn Schl Cnslr 1981-; Upper Room Ministries Pastor 1982-; *ai:* Higher Ground Drug & Rehabilitation Pgm Overseer; *home:* 47A Hilltop Ln Wheatley Heights NY 11798

NURSE, ORAL, Math Teacher; *b:* NYC, NY; *m:* Michele; *c:* Julian, Oral; *ed:* Queen Coll (BA) Acctng 1984, (MS) Math 1988; *cr:* William A. Maxwell VHS Stu Acts, Attendance, House, Lunchroom Coord 1989-; *ai:* Boy's Handball Coach; Parent Involement Comm; Classical Guitar Tchr; AFT 1986-; NCTM 1989-; *office:* Wm H Maxwell Voc HS 145 Pennsylvania Ave Brooklyn NY 11207*

NURZYCK, VICTORIA J., Second Grade Teacher; *b:* Steubenville, OH; *m:* William J.; *c:* Jean Ann, B.J.; *ed:* Univ of Steub (BS) El Ed 1971; *cr:* St Anthony Schl Third Grd Tchr 1971-76; Stueb City Schls LD Tutor 1982-83; Aquinas Cntrl Schl Second Grd Tchr 1984-; *ai:* First Penance, First Communion Sacramental Coord; NCESA 1971-; Amer Cancer Soc 1979-85, VP, Pres; *office:* Aquinas Central Schl RD 3 Lovers Ln Steubenville OH 43952*

NUSSBAUMER, JILL D., English Teacher; *b:* Uniontown, PA; *ed:* Univ of Pittsburgh (BA) Eng 1992; Prof Instrl Cert 1993; *cr:* James M Bennett HS Eng Tchr 1993-; *ai:* Sr Class & Upward Bound Adv; NEA 1993-; WCEA 1993-; MSTA 1993-; *office:* James M Bennett HS 300 E College Ave Salisbury MD 21804

NUSSEY, MICHAELINA (QUARELLA), First Grade Teacher; *b:* Fitchburg, MA; *m:* Scott Philip; *c:* Joshua, Justin; *ed:* Fitchburg St Coll (BS) Elem Ed 1974, (MS) Elem Ed 1985; *cr:* Westminster Elem Schl First Grd Tchr 1974-93; Meetinghouse Schl First Grd Tchr 1993-; *ai:* Schl Cncl; Math Focus Group; NEA, UTA 1974-; Westminster Tchrs Assn 1974-, Pres; Ashburhan-Westminster Tchrs Assn 1982-, Prof Rights & Responsibilities Comm; Westminster Woman's Club 1980-, Bd of Dirs, Intnl, Ed Comm Chprsn; *office:* Meetinghouse Schl 8 South St Westminster MA 01473*

NUTT, RICKI LEE, Professor of Religion; *b:* Kansas City, MO; *m:* Mary Gene Boteler; *c:* Mary Rebekah, Hannah; *ed:* Univ of MO at Kansas City (BA) His 1975; Louisville Presbyn Theological Seminary (MDIV) 1980; Vanderbilt Univ (PHD) Church His 1986; *cr:* Muskingum Coll Religion Prof 1988-; *ai:* Prof Dev, Ecumenical Schlsp Comms; Ctr for Church Life; Amer Church His, Presbyn Historical Socs 1984-; Amer Acad of Religion 1985-; Guernsey Meml Hospital 1992-, Ethics Advy Bd; Pub Books; *office:* Muskingcom Coll Brown Chapel New Concord OH 43762

NUTTALL, LINDA LAWRENCE, Secondary English Teacher; *b:* Rochester, NY; *m:* Clifford J. III; *c:* Clifford, Trevor; *ed:* Bucknell Univ (BA) Eng 1969; Post Grad Hrs; *cr:* Lewisburg Area HS Scndry Eng Tchr 1969-73, 1975-; *ai:* SAT Private Tutoring; Grading Comm; Tech-Prep Comm; NEA, PSEA, LAEA 1969-; Milton Area Comm Pool 1993-, Bd of Dirs; Bucknell Univ Home Club 1995-, Bd of Dirs; *office:* Lewisburg HS 815 Market St Lewisburg PA 17837

NUTTING, THOMAS K., Spanish Teacher; *b:* Charleroi, PA; *ed:* CA St Coll (BS) Scndry Span 1970; Univ of Pgh (MA) Span 1991; *cr:* Uniontown Area Schl Dist Span Tchr 1970-; *ai:* Span Club, Stu Cncl & Lettermens Club Spon; Asst Swim Coach; NEA 1970-; UAEA 1970-; PSMLA 1980-; Knights of Columbus 1972-, Treas, Grand Knight, Knight of Yr Awd 1993; St Vincent Coll Great Tchr Recognition Pgm; Westminster Coll Outstdng HS Tchr; *office:* Uniontown Area HS 146 E Fayette St Uniontown PA 15401*

NUTTYCOMBE, THOMAS HOPKINS, 5th Grade Teacher; *b:* Honesdale, PA; *c:* Elizabet, Wallace; *ed:* Univ of Scranton (BS) His Ed 1970; East Strandsburg St 24 Credit Hrs; Marywood Coll 7 Credit Hrs; *cr:* Narrowsburg Cntrl Schl 5th Grd Tchr 1971-; *ai:* NYSUT 1971-, Past Pres; Honesdale Borough Cncl 1972-80, Pres 1976-80.

NUVALLIE, ANTHONY JOSEPH, Business Management Professor; *b:* North Adams, MA; *c:* Anthony Jr., Gianina; *ed:* Cambridge Coll (MED) Admin, Mgt 1982; Cert Comm Intensive; Life Underwriter Trng Cncl Diploma Ins Mrktg; Lee Inst Cert Real Estate; *cr:* NOBARC Voc Svcs Dir 1984-85; N Berkshire CRIL Project Dir 1985-86; Southern VT Coll Fac 1986-92, Dir Bas Mgt Dept 1992-; *ai:* SVC Bus Club Adv; Fac Dev Comm; NBEA 1988-; Amer Mrktg Assn, Amer Mgt Assn, Soc for Advancement of Mgt 1992-; N Adams Comm on Disabilities 1987-; Outstanding Fac Mem Southern VT Coll 1988-89; *home:* 306 Walker St North Adams MA 01247

NUZZI, ELIZABETH ROSE, Third Grade Teacher; *b:* Shenandoah, PA; *m:* Anthony; *ed:* Caldwell Coll (BA) Elem Ed 1965; Fairfield Univ (MA) Ed 1970; Rowan (MA) Media Specialist 1977; Scndry Eng, Supvr Certs; *cr:* St Luke's Schl 5-6 Grd Tchr 1958-70; St Anne's Schl 5-8 Grd Tchr 1958-70; Immaculate Heart Acad 9-12 Grd Tchr 1958-70; St Genevieves Schl 9-12 Grd Tchr 1958-70; St Mary's Schl 7-8 Grd Tchr 1958-70; Deepwater Schl 4-5 Grd Tchr 1970-82; Penn Beach Schl 3 Grd Tchr 1982-; *ai:* Delta Kappa Gamma Corresponding Sec; NEA, NJEA, SCEA, PEA 1970-, Former Assn Rep; Amer Assn Univ Women 1993-; Assn Supervision, Curr; Natl, NJ PTA; Cub Pack #215 1992-, Honorary Mem; NDEA Eng Summer 1966; 25 Yr Tchr; *office:* Penn Beach Schl 96 Kansas Rd & Salem Dr Pennsville NJ 08070

NUZZI, MARIE GRACE, Spanish & ESL Teacher; *b:* Jamaica, NY; *ed:* Molloy Coll (BA) Span Ed 7-12 1975; Hofstra Univ (MA) Biling Ed 1977; 60 Addl Credits; *cr:* Dominican Commercial HS Dean of Discipline 1981-85, Frgn Lang Dept Chprsn 1984-86; Garden City HS Span Tchr 1988-, ESL Tchr 1995-; *ai:* Natl Span Hnr Soc, Natl Span Exam Adv; NYSUT, AATSP, NYSAFLT 1986-; US Marine Corps Reserve 1982-, Staff Sgt, Hnr Grad; Women Marines Assn 1982-, WMA Recruit Awd, Desert Storm Medal; Hofstra Univ Biling Ed Full Flwshp; *office:* Garden City HS 170 Rockaway Ave Garden City NY 11530

NUZZO, CHARLES, Seventh Grade Teacher; *b:* New Haven, CT; *ed:* St Thomas Aquinas Coll (BA) Eng 1974; St John's Univ (MA) Theology 1988; *cr:* Holy Ghost Schl Tchr 1974-75; Holy Cross Schl Tchr 1980-81; Holy Redeemer Schl Tchr 1981-82; St Gabriel Schl Tchr 1982-; *office:* St Gabriel Schl 9702 Astoria Blvd East Elmhurst NY 11369

NWAEZE, EMEKA T., Accounting Professor; *b:* Obollo-Afor Nsukka, Nigeria; *ed:* Southern Univ at Baton Rouge (BS) Acctng 1986, (MPA) Acctng 1987; Univ of CT (PHD) Acctng 1992; *cr:* Rutgers Univ Acctng Asst Prof 1992-; *ai:* Coord Acctng, Fin Research Wkshp; Fac Adv; Natl Assn of Black Accountants Camden Chptr; Amer Acctng Assn 19880; European Acctng Assn 1993-; AAUP 1992-; Beta Gamma Sigma; Doctoral Consortium Fellow; *home:* 81 Chateau Ridge Pine Hill NJ 08021

NWOKEAFOR, COSMAS UCHE, Communication Professor; *b:* Portharcourt, Nigeria; *m:* Catherine Adaku Anyandu; *c:* Uchenna, Nneka, Chinwendu, Chinedu; *ed:* Alvan Ikoku Coll of Ed (NCE) Tchr Ed 1983; Howard Univ (BA) Broadcast Jrnlsm 1986, (MA) Mass Comm 1990, (PHD) Mass Comm 1992; *cr:* Howard Univ Lecturer 1990-92; Bowie St Univ Asst Prof 1992-; GA Mason Univ Adj Prof 1993-; *ai:* Family Adv PRSSA; Commencement, Fac Elections, Stu Outcomes Assessment Comms; AEJMC 1988-; African Cncl for Comm Ed, ECA, ICA, PRSA 1993-; Knight of Columbus 1986-; Book Reviewer; Co-Authored Two Chptrs; Pub Journal Articles; Poynter Inst Flwshp Awd 1995; Minority Jrnlsm Flwshp Awd 1994; All-Amer Scholar Flwshp Awd 1991; *office:* Bowie St Univ 14000 Jericho Park Rd Bowie MD 20715

NYANG, SULAYMAN SHEIH, African Studies Dept Professor; *b:* Banjul, West Africa; *m:* Wiriya Noiwong; *c:* SulaymanJr., Edna Elizabeth; *ed:* Hampton Univ (BA) Pol Sci 1969; Univ of VA (MA) Pub Adm 1971; Univ of VA (PHD) Govt 1974; *cr:* Howard Univ Asst Prof 1972-75, Acting Dir 1973-75; Gambia Govt Deputy Ambassador 1975-78; Howard Univ Assoc Prof 1978-86, Howard Univ Dir, Full Prof 1986-93, Prof Dept of African Studs; *ai:* Africa & Intnl Comm Chm; NAACP Montgomery Cty MD Adv; African Stdnts Assn Adv; African Studs Assn 1972-, Bd Mem; Assn of Muslim Social Scientists 1980-, VP, Pres; Amer Cncl for the Stud of Islamic Socs 1986-, VP; Amer Muslim Cncl 1992-, Adv; Washington Interfail Conf 1993-, Bd Mem; Thomas Jefferson Fellow, Univ of VA; Phillip Dupont Fellow, Univ of VA; Islam, Christianity, & African Identity 1984; Reflection on the Human Condition 1981; *office:* Howard Univ Grad Schl PO Box 472 Washington DC 20059*

NYE, CYNTHIA ROGERS, Choral & General Music Teacher; *b:* Philadelphia, PA; *m:* George R. A.; *c:* Cheryl Wagner, Brian Krause, Jennifer Wenrich; *ed:* Penn St Univ (BA) Music Ed 1963, (MED) Music Ed 1969; 18 Grad Credits Music, Ed; *cr:* Ledyard Schls Elem Music, Vocal Tchr 1963-65; Coolville Schls Grd 1-12 Vocal Music Tchr 1965-66; Derry Twp Schls Grd 1-12 Vocal Music Tchr 1970-; *ai:* Vocal Coach; HS Musical Dir Show Choir; Cty Dist Regnl, All-St Festival Participants Coach; NEA, PSEA, HEA 1970-, Welfare Chair; MENC, PMEA 1970-; PEO 1969-, Pres; *office:* Hershey HS PO Box 898 Homestead Rd Hershey PA 17033

NYE, DIANNE A., Parks & Recreation Director; *b:* Methuen, MA; *m:* David A.; *c:* Jonathan, Amanda, Michael; *ed:* Merrimack Coll (BS) Sociology, Ed 1980; *cr:* Child & Family Svc Cnslr 1981-83; Plaistow Parks & Recreation Dir 1990-; *ai:* Timberlane Jr Ftbl Chrldrs 4 Teams, Minor League Sftbl Coaches, Plaistow Cmptr Comm Co-Chair; VP Timberlane Jr Ftbl; Timberlane Bud Comm 1987-93, Chair; Timberlane Schl Bd 1993-95, Chair 1995; Seacoast Coach of Yr Chrldng 1994.

NYE, JOHN BOLAND, Mathematics Teacher; *b:* Harrisburg, PA; *m:* Judith A.; *c:* Catherine, Stephanie, Jennifer; *ed:* Lock Haven Univ (BS) Math 1957; Univ of DE (MED) Math, Ed 1967; Lehigh Univ (ES) Ed Admin 1974; CA Coast Univ (DED) Ed Admin 1978; Grad Stud Penn St Univ 1957; Grad Stud Purdue Univ 1980; Grad Stud Harvard Univ 1983, 1988; *cr:* Kennett HS Math Tchr 1957-68; Pleasant Valley HS Prin 1968-73; Pleasant Valley Schl Dist Supt of Schls 1973-88; MSAD #51 Supt of Schls 1988-90; Notre Dame HS His, Math Tchr 1990-; *ai:* Phi Delta Kappa 1980-, Pres; NCEA 1990-; Pr Ret Supt Assn 1993-; Monroe Co Ret Tchrs 1994-; Diocese of Scranton 1995-, Bd of Edctrs; Easter SEals Adv Bd 1994-; IHM Natl Adv Bd 1994-; Outstdng Young Edctr 1964; Outstdng Citizen 1966; Excl of Purpose Awd 1968; *home:* PO Box 466 Mountainhome PA 18342

NYE, JUDITH L., Psychology Professor; *b:* Madison, WI; *m:* Richard G. Su; *ed:* VA Commonwealth Univ (BS) Psych & Sociology 1982, (MS) Soc Psych 1985, (PHD) Soc Psych 1988; *cr:* Monmouth Coll Asst Prof 1987-94; Monmouth Univ Assoc Prof 1994-; *ai:* Undergraduate Rsrch Conf Coord; Fac Adv; Gamma Sigma Sigma Reviewer; Jr Sci Symposium; Amer Psychological Assn 1983-; Amer Psychological Soc 1990-; Amer Assn of Univ Women 1993-; Book Ed: Whats Social About Social Cognition? Research on Socially Shared Cognition in Small Groups 1996; Numerous Articles Pub; *office:* Monmouth Univ West Long Branch NJ 07764

NYGREN, ROY R., Physical Ed & Health Teacher; *b:* Upper Saddle River, NJ; *m:* Judy R.; *c:* Lindsay, Julia, Garrett; *ed:* William Paterson Coll (BA) PE 1982; *cr:* Hasbrouck Heights Schl K-6th Grd PE, Hlth Tchr 1982-85; Midland Park HS 7th-12th Grd PE, Hlth Tchr 1986-88; Elizabeth Morrow Schl PreK-6th Grd PE, Hlth Tchr 1988-90; Haledon Pub Schl K-8th Grd PE, Hlth Tchr 1990-; *ai:* 6th-8th Grd IM Bsktbl; 6th-8th Grd Schl Bsktbl Team; 8th Grd Chaperone; Var Boys Soccer Coach; NJEA 1982-; Glen Rock Jaycees 1993-; Glen Rock Soccer Club 1994-; NJ Soccer Coach of Yr 1993; Cty Coach of Yr 1993; Hall of Fame Induction 1995; *office:* Haledon Public Schl 91 Henry St Haledon NJ 07508

NYROD-DUNN, SUSAN KELLY, Geometry & Pre-Chemistry Tchr; *b:* Columbus, OH; *m:* James Dunn; *c:* Trey, Melissa; *ed:* OH St Univ (BS) Chem, Math 1968; Cleveland St Univ (MS) Guidance, Cnslng 1988; Addl 30 Semester Hrs Ashland, Baldwin Wallace, John Carroll; *ai:* Strongsville Amer Assn of Univ Women VP; Tennis-USTA; OEA; NEA; OSC; *office:* Center Jr HS 13200 Pearl Rd Strongsville OH 44136

NYSTEDT, CLIFFORD P., Art Teacher; *b:* New York, NY; *m:* Kathleen Kubicke; *c:* Christine Mirante, Scott, Stephanie; *ed:* Suffolk Comm Coll (AA) Art 1972; SUNY at Stony Brook (BA) Fine Arts 1974, (MFA) Fine Arts 1979; LIU at Southampton Tchr Cert 1975; *cr:* Centereach HS Art Tchr 1975-; USDAN Ctr for Creation & Performing Arts Summers 1984-88; *ai:* Natl Art Honor Soc Adv; Art Club; Tech Comm; AFT, NYSUT, NEA, NAEA 1975-; Southampton Artists Assn 1986-, VP, Pres; Annual One Man Shows 1988-; Various Group Shows; NY Armory Show 1991; Lithograph Pub 1990; Many Local Bios, Artwork Pub; *office:* Centereach HS 14 43rd St Centereach NY 11720*

O

OAKES, GENE, Guidance Counselor; *b:* Old Town, ME; *m:* Kathryn Ryan; *c:* Lisa, Ryan; *ed:* Univ of ME at Orono (BS) Ed, Soc Stud 1970, (MEd) Guid, Cnslng 1973; 27 Post Grad Credits; *cr:* Cntrl Jr Sr HS Math

Tchr 1971-73; Winslow Jr HS Guid Cnslr 1974-77; Camden-Rockport HS Guid Cnslr 1977-92; Nokomis Regnl HS Guid Cnslr 1992-; *ai:* HOPE, Friends, Pep Band Adv; NEA 1971-, Chief Negotiator; MEACD 1974-; Tchr, Staff Mem of Yr 1995; *office:* Nokomis Regional HS RR 2 Box 4800 Newport ME 04953

OAKLEY, CAREY FRANCIS, Language Arts Teacher; *b:* Louisville, KY; *m:* Carolyn Jane Osborn; *c:* Colleen Conners, Chawn, Clark, James; *ed:* Otterbein Coll (BA) Ed 1964; Bowling Green Univ (MA) Ed 1972; Attnd Univ of Toledo; *cr:* Oak Harbor HS Lang Arts Tchr 1964-; *ai:* NEA, OEA 1964-; Oak Harbor United Meth Church 1964-, Lay Person, Chprsn Admin Cncl.

OAKLEY, DONALD L., Professor of Science; *b:* Port Washington, NY; *m:* Jane Shellenberger; *c:* Judith, Daniel; *ed:* Gettysburg Coll (AB) Chem 1961; Cornell Univ (MST) Sci Ed 1968, (PHD) Sci Ed 1971; 3 Chautauqua Insts; *cr:* North Penn HS Chem & Physics Tchr 1965-68; Cornell Univ Asst Dir & Acad Yr Instr 1969-71; Lock Haven Univ Prof of Sci 1971-; *ai:* Sci Ed Coord; Pa-Step Instr; Schl Sci Ed Consultant; Wkshp Coord & Instr; NSTA 1970-; Amer Chemical Soc 1971-, Section Chair, Post-Scndry Dir; PA Sci Tchrs Assn 1971-; Phi Delta Kappa; Phi Kappa Phi; Assn for Ed of Tchrs of Sci; Amer Cancer Soc 1978-, Bd Mem; United Luth Church 1939-; Sound Tchng; *office:* Lock Haven Univ 205 Ulmer Hall Lock Haven PA 17745

OAKLEY, HARRIETT HUTCHINSON, Professor of Nursing; *b:* Pittsburgh, PA; *m:* James; *c:* Anthony, Andrea, Andrew, Aneida; *ed:* Comm Coll Allegheny Co (AS) Nrsng 1971; Duquesne Univ (BSN) Nrsng 1975; Univ of Pittsburgh (MED) 1980, (MSN) Pulmonary Nrsng 1985; *cr:* Columbia Hosp Staff Nurse 1971-72; Comm Coll Allegheny Co Asst Instr 1972-74, Prof 1978-; *ai:* Allegheny Campus Nrsng Prgm Advy Comm; MRRTP, Acad Affairs Comms; AFT 1980-; CCAAC 1990-, Parlimentarian, Sec, Campus Rep; Natl Cncl in Black Amer Affairs 1994-; Written Several Retention Grants, Stud Guides Nrsng Stdnts; *office:* Comm Coll Algny Co Algny Cmps 808 Ridge Ave Pittsburgh PA 15212

OAKLEY, MOLLY S., Fifth Grade Teacher; *b:* Baltimore, MD; *m:* Robert P.; *ed:* Jackson Coll (BA) Sociology 1968; Brillantmont Cert de L'Universite de Nancy France 1964; 45 Post Grad Credits in Elem Ed, Arch, His; *cr:* Schenectady Pub Schls Second Grd Tchr 1970-71; Cambridge Cntrl Schl 2nd-5th Grd Tchr 1971-; *ai:* Shared Decision Comm Elem Rep; NYSUT, AFT-CIO 1970-; Hubbard Hall 1975-, Bd of Trustees; Pub Article 1979; Lila Wallace Arts Intnl Grant 1994; Rsrch 1994; *home:* PO Box 191 Shushan NY 12873*

OATMAN, JON P., Drafting Teacher; *b:* Lancaster, PA; *ed:* (BS) Ind Arts, Ed 1973; (MED) Ind Arts, Ed 1976; Supervisory Cert Tech Ed 1991; 45 Grad Hrs Beyond Masters; *cr:* US Air Force Aircraft Electronic Instrument Tech 1962-66; Trojan Boat Co Time Stud Technician 1966-70; Millersville Univ Stu 1970-73; Self Employed Bookbinder & Restorer 1977-88; Penn Manor Schl Dist Tchr 1973-; *ai:* Advanced Drafting Club Adv; NEA, PSEA, Tech Ed Assn of PA, Epsilon Pi Tau 1973-; Outstdng Young Edctr 1979; Articles Pub; *office:* Penn Manor Schl Dist PO Box 1001 Millersville PA 17551

OBAR RAND, ANNA MARIE, Fifth Grade Teacher; *b:* Ft Fairfield, ME; *m:* Steven Garth; *c:* Dennis Scott, Jamie Michelle; *ed:* Univ of ME at Presque Isle (BS) Ed 1970; Univ of Southern ME (ME) Ed 1979; Univ of Southern ME Math 1979; 30+ Hrs; *cr:* Herbert Gray Schl 5th Grd Tchr 1970-72; Manchester-Arlington Schl 5th Grd Tchr 1982-89, 6th Grd Tchr 1989-90, 5th Grd Tchr 1990-; *ai:* Prof Dev Comm Bldg Chm; Resident Supervisory Support for Tchrs 1985-; NEA, Windham Educl Assn 1982-; PTO, Pres, Treas; PTA 1982-; Mini-Grants G-T 1994, CGC-PDT 1989; *office:* Manchester-Arlington Schl 709 Roosevelt Trl Windham ME 04062*

OBARSKY, ANTHONY RAYMOND, Science Teacher; *b:* Johnstown, PA; *m:* Susan M.; *c:* Luke David; *ed:* Duquesne Univ (BS) Bio 1982; Penn St Univ (BS) Biological Scis & Scndry Ed 1987; 3 Credit Hrs Juniata Coll; 3 Credit Hrs Sci, Tech & Soc; *cr:* Bishop McCort HS Sci Tchr 1988-89; Bishop Guilfoyle HS Sci Tchr 1989-92; Forest Hills HS Sci Tchr 1992-; *ai:* Girls Vllybl Team Head Coach; Forest Hill Ed Assn 1992-, Bldg Rep; PA St Ed Assn 1992-; NEA 1992-; Republican Party 1995-, Comm Person; Roxbury Church of Brethren, Sunday Schl Tchr & Childrens Church Ldr; *office:* Forest Hills Sr HS 489 Locust St PO Box 325 Sidman PA 15955

OBASOGIE, FAITHE TRENT, Lead Teacher; *b:* Parksley, VA; *m:* A Osa; *c:* Tinyan, Osagie; *ed:* Bennett Coll (BS) PE & Bio 1964; Univ of Cincinnati (MA) Spcl Ed 1981; 30 Post Grad Credit Hrs; *cr:* Accomack Cty Schls Tchr 1964-75; Cincinnati Pub Schls Tchr 1975-; *ai:* Local Schl Advy Comm; Girls Club Adv; Sunday Schl Tchr; Mentor; AFT 1975-; Order of Eastern Star 1960-; Univ of Cincinnati Flwshp 1980; *office:* Withrow HS 2488 Madison Rd Cincinnati OH 45231*

OBBEY, KIMBERLY PAWLIZAK, K-8th Grade Guidance Counselor; *b:* Columbus, OH; *m:* Elliot G.; *c:* Jordan, Alexander; *ed:* Bowling Green St Univ (BS) Elem Ed 1983, (ME) Schl Guidance 1986; *cr:* Univ Schls 7th Grd Eng Tchr 1983-90, 8th Grd Lit Tchr 1984-90, 9th Grd Eng Tchr 1987-90, K-8th Grd Schl Cnslr 1990-; *ai:* IEF Coord; NEA 1983-; OSCA & ACA 1993-; *office:* Amherst Schools 571 Lincoln Amherst OH 44001*

OBDYKE, PHOEBE STAMBAUGH, Director & Curator of Museum; *b:* Green Park, PA; *m:* William E.; *c:* Kimberly Shunk, Kurtis Shunk, Terril Douglas; *ed:* Dickinson Coll (BA) Psych 1955; OH Wesleyan Univ (MA) Psych 1956; Penn St Univ 6 Post Grad Hrs; Cheyney St UNiv 24 Hrs for Tchng Cert; *cr:* Sidney Smedley Schl Elem Ungraded Schl Tchr 1969-76; Springfield Schl Dist Elem Gifted Prgm Developer, Tchr 1976-85; E. T. Richardson MS Math Tchr 1985-93; Springfield Histocial Soc Heritage Museum Dir, Curator 1994-; *ai:* Served on Staff Dev, Stragetic Planning Comms, Advy Cncl; NEA 1969-; Springfield Historical Soc 1992-; Amer Assn Univ Woman 1970-; Tchr of Yr E. T. Richardson MS 1992; Dev Booklet Used to Promote Springfield Schl Dist.

O'BEIRNE, MARGUERITE J., Former Principal; *b:* County Sligo, Ireland; *ed:* Neuman Coll (BA) Eng 1968; Millersville Univ (MA) Eng 1977; Fordham Univ (PHD) Admin, Supervision 1984; Attnd St Bonaventure, Trenton St Coll, Boston Coll; *cr:* Corpus Christi Schl Elem Tchr 1962-68; St Anthony Schl Jr HS Tchr 1968-72; Holy Trinity Schl Prin 1972-77; Sisters of St Francis Schl Ed Coord 1977-83; Mc Corristin HS Prin 1983-95; *ai:* Sabbatical Prgm; NCEA 1962-; Phi Delta Kappa 1983-; ASCD 1972-; St Francis Hosp Bd; Jr Achvmt; Cath Charities Bd; Univ of FL NSF; Boston Coll Connolly Fnd Grant; Ed Svc St Recognition Citations; Articles Pub.*

OBEL-OMIA, MICHAEL CHARLES, English Tchr & Dean of Stdnts; *b:* Albany, NY; *m:* Carolyn Haviland Campbell; *ed:* Middlebury Coll (A) Amer Lit 1988; Bread Loaf Schl of Eng (MA) Eng Lit 1992; *cr:* Perkiomen Schl Eng Tchr, Coach, Dormitory Parent 1988-90 The Roxbury Latin Schl Eng Tchr 1990-, Dean of Stdnts, Admissions Ofcr, Wrestling, Bsbl Coach 1990-; *ai:* Coach JV Wrestling, Var Bsbl; Acad Adv; Admissions Ofcr; NCTE 1995-; Martin Luther King Address Saddle River Schl 1993; Trey Whitfield Meml Address Brewster Acad 1994; Commencement Address Bethlehem Bapt Acad 1994; Recruiting New Tchrs Featured in Brochure 1994, 1996, Appeared in Commercial 1996; *office:* Roxbury Latin Schl 101 Saint Theresa Ave West Roxbury MA 02132*

OBENAUF, GREGG L., Assistant Principal; *b:* Salem, OH; *m:* Diane Scobell; *c:* Tyler; *ed:* OH St Univ (BS) Comprehensive Soc Stud 1970; Cleveland St Univ (MA) Scndry Admin 1975; Addl 18 Semester Hrs; *cr:* North Olmsted Jr HS Soc Stud Tchr 1970-74; Columbia HS Asst Prin 1974-79; Fairport HS Asst Prin 1979-; *ai:* Act Coord; Pub Addr & Cable TV Sports Announcer; Supvr Club Advs; NY St Adv, Stu Assn 1982-, Sec 1993-, NY St Admin of Yr; Schl Admins Assn of NY St 1979-; Masonic Lodge, Seneca Lodge #797 1985-; *office:* Fairport HS 1358 Ayrault Rd Fairport NY 14450

OBENOUR, ROBERT B., Social Studies Teacher; *b:* Fostoria, OH; *ed:* Univ of Toledo (BE) Scndry Soc Stud 1988; Pursuing Stud in Athletic Admin at Bowling Green St Univ; *cr:* Van Buren Local Schls Scndry Soc Stud Tchr 1989-; *ai:* Boys & Girls Var Track & Field Coach 1995-; Frosh Boys Bsktbl Coach 1995-; OEA, NEA 1995-; Saint Marks Church 1976-, Sunday Schl Tchr; *office:* Van Buren Local Schls 217 S Main St Van Buren OH 45889*

OBERDORF, NANCY DEMKO, Seventh Grade Reading Teacher; *b:* Toledo, OH; *m:* Larry W. Sr.; *c:* Larry Jr, Laurie, Robert, William; *ed:* Univ of Toledo (BE) Elem Ed 1969; Bowling Green St Univ (ME) Rdng 1981; Addl 10 Credit Hrs; *cr:* Lagrange Elem Kndgtn Tchr 1969-71; Burroughs Elem 2nd Grd Tchr 1971; Rossford Jr HS Rdng Tchr 1986-; *ai:* HS Wrestlerette Adv; Jr HS Lang Arts Dept Chm; NEA, OEA, RACT 1986-; IRA 1988-; Delta Kappa Gamma 1992-; Bowling Green St Univ Grad Assistantship in Ed; OH Dept of Ed Fine Arts Grant; Hunt Wesson Grant to Purchase Books for Holocaust Unit; *office:* Rossford Jr HS 651 Superior St Rossford OH 43460*

OBERDORFER, CARMEL JANOTA, Spanish Teacher; *b:* Akron, OH; *m:* Carl William; *c:* Julian Janota; *ed:* Univ of Akron (MA) Multicultural Ed; 18 Post Grad Credit Hrs in Comp Courses; *cr:* Findlay Elem Span Tchr 1983-84; Robinson Elem Span Tchr 1983-85; East HS Span Tchr 1984-85; Cntrl-Hower HS Span Tchr 1984-; *ai:* NHS Adv; NEOLA 1989-, Steering Comm Chair; OFLA 1994-; Martha Holden Jennings Grant; Gund Fndtn Grant; *office:* Central Hower HS 123 S Forge St Akron OH 44308*

OBERHOLTZER, WILLIAM IRVING, Senior Army Instructor; *b:* Harrisburg, PA; *m:* Patricia A.; *c:* Matthew; *ed:* FL St Univ (BS) Ed Admin 1975; Webster Univ (MA) Mngmt 1982, (MA) Human Relations 1982; CA St Univ 26 Hrs Toward MA Natl Security; Command & Gen Staff Coll Grad 1985; Defense Systems Mngmt Coll Grad 1994; *cr:* Armored Systems Modernization Rsrch, Dev Coord 1989-91; Nato Land Forces Southeast Chief Command & Control, Maneuver, Exercises 1991-93; Army Rsrch Lab Chief Armor Tech Weapons Test Dir 1993-94; Mount Pleasant HS Sr Army Instr 1994-; *ai:* Drill, Rifle Teams; Color Guard; AUSA 1972-; TROA 1990-; ADPA 1989-; Airborne; Ranger; Pathfinder; Air Assault; Underwater Operations; EIB.

OBERHOLZER, CECILIA GARVIN, Chem Tchr & Sci Dept Chairman; *b:* Philadelphia, PA; *m:* John C.; *c:* John Jr., Mark, Matthew, Christopher; *ed:* Holy Family Coll (BA) Chem 1962; St Josephs Univ (MS) Ed 1991; Grad Cmptr Courses Philadelphia Coll of Textiles & Scis; *cr:* Carl F. Norberg Res Ctr Research Chemist 1962-65; Bishop Kenrick HS Math & Sci Tchr 1980-82; North Cath HS Cmptr Sci Tchr 1982; Little Flower HS Phys Sci & Chem Tchr 1982-, Sci Dept Chm 1991; *ai:* Chm Blood Mobile Drive; Cmptr Club; Wardrobe; NSTA 1985-; Kappa Gamme Pi 1962-; Aid for Friends 1986-; Outstanding Young Women of America 1963; Little Flower HS Distinguished Educator 1985; Published Experiment Project Labs Rohm & Haas 1990; Outstanding HS Sci Tchr Professional Engr of PA 1991; Article Journal of Applied Polymer Sci 1963.

OBERLANDER, LOIS BERLIN, Guidance Dept Chairperson; *b:* New York City, NY; *m:* Morris; *c:* Marcus; *ed:* Trenton St Coll (BA) Soc Stud Ed 1968; Monmouth Coll (MSEd) Stu Prsnl Svcs 1972; Cmptr Literacy, Suicide Prevention Credits; Supervisory Cert 1993; *cr:* Ocean Township HS Soc Stud Tchr 1968-69; Wall Intermediate Schl 7th Grd Soc Stud Tchr 1969-72; Wall HS Guid Cnslr 1972-, Guid Dept Chprsn 1992-; *ai:* Kwanis Hnr Soc Advy; NHS Comm Workline Dir; Weighting Comm Co-Chm; Quality Asst Cycle Guid Co-Chm; Momoc Dev Cncl Coord; WTEA, NJEA, NEA 1969-; Monnouth City Guid Dirs 1993-; VP, Pres, Founder Caring Awd; Mohmouth City Schl Cnslrs 1972-, Sec, Pres, Exec Bd; Amer U Eagle Club 1995-; Working at Schl Grant; Monmouth Cty Founded Caring Awd; *office:* Wall HS 18th Ave Wall NJ 07719*

OBERMAN, DIANA BOUND, English Teacher; *b:* San Antonio, TX; *m:* Robert Thomas; *c:* Jared; *ed:* AR Univ (BA) Eng 1970; Attnd La Salle Coll; Spec Ed, Human Relations, Cmptrs Grad Work; *cr:* Kings Park MS Eng Tchr 1 Yr; Barnstable MS Eng Tchr 20 Yrs; *ai:* Stu Cncl; Mentor Prgm; Yrbk; Drama Club; NEA, BTA, MTA, Natl Rdng Cncl 1972-; *office:* Barnstable MS 730 Osterville W. Barstable Rd Marstons Mills MA 02648

OBERT, KATHRYN F., English Teacher; *b:* Towanda, PA; *c:* James Stepanski Jr., Dr. Catherine Stepanski; *ed:* Bloomsburg St Coll (BS) Scndry Eng 1967; Mansfield Univ Elem Cert 1981; Penn St Univ Masters Equivalency 1992; *cr:* Northeast Bradford HS Eng Tchr 1967-70; Tioga Cntrl MS Eng Tchr 1983-86; Northeast Bradford HS Eng Tchr 1986-; *ai:* Publicity & Classic Movie Clubs; NEA, PSEA, NEBEA 1986-; DAR 1985-; OES 1970-; *home:* RR 3 Box 3097 Rome PA 18837

OBEY, ERICA FRANCES, Speech World Hums Adj Lecturer; *b:* Springfield, OH; *m:* George Baird III; *ed:* Yale Univ (BA) Ec 1981; Creative Writing CCNY; Comp Lit CUNY; *cr:* CCNY 1991-; *home:* 675 Academy St Apt 4D New York NY 10034*

OBI, CHINWE ILOABACHIE, French Teacher; *b:* Udi, Nigeria; *c:* Chukwunwike, Ogidi; *ed:* Fed Advanced Tchrs Coll (NCE) Fr, Eng, Ed 1966; Douglas Coll-Rutgers Univ (BA) Fr 1971; Rutgers Univ (MA) Fr 1980; Univ of Dakar Cert Oral Proficiency; Pursuing Cert Supervision at Rider Univ; *cr:* Ogidi Girls Sec Schl Fr Tchr 1965; Aggrey Meml Scndry Schl Fr Tchr 1967-68; Franklin HS Fr Tchr 1971-; *ai:* Fr Natl Exam Contestants Adv; Ed Advy Comm Princeton Univ 1992-, Founding, Bd Mem; Foreign Lang Edctrs of NJ 1988-, Bd Mem, Publisher-Liason, Reg 3 Rep, Stu Schlsps; Amer Assn of Fr Tchrs; Home Friends 1993-; Grants Mini Princeton Univ Dept of Cncl of Regnl Stud, Rotary Intnl for Summer Stud France; *office:* Franklin HS 415 Francis St Franklin Twp Somerset NJ 08873*

O'BIER, MARY LOUISE LONG, First Grade Teacher; *b:* Shamokin, PA; *m:* Donald M. Jr.; *ed:* Univ of DE (BA) Elem Ed 1972; Salisbury St Univ (MS) Elem 1977; 60 Plus Credits Above Master's Wilmington Coll, Inservice Credits; *cr:* Benjamin Banneker Elem Schl First Grd Tche 21 Yrs; Morris Early Chldhd Ctr First Grd Tchr 3 Yrs; *ai:* MEA, DSEA, NEA 1992-; Alpha Delta Kappa 1995-; Avenue Presch Bd, Avenue Meth Church 1995-; Alternatives to Violence Prgm; Conflict Resolutions Ldrshp Conf; Basic Schl, Integrated Curr Author; Schl Rep Site Based Mngmt; *office:* Morris Early Chldhd Ctr 103 3rd St Lincoln DE 19960

OBNEY, NORA CAVANAUGH, Social Studies Dept Chairman; *b:* Canton, OH; *m:* James Marshall; *c:* James A. MD., Mary Elizabeth Obney Freihofer; *ed:* Mount Union Coll (BA) Ec, Accounting, Scndry Ed 1956, (BA) Elem Ed 1960; Attnd Oh St, Bowling Green St, Ashland, Kent St Univs, Univ of PA, Univ of Akron; *cr:* Alliance Pub Schls 5 Grd Tchr 1956-66; Lake MS 7-9 Soc Stud Tchr, Dept Chm 1971-; Youngstown Univ Tchr Asst, Consultant 1992-95; Akron Univ Tchr Asst Cnsltnt 1994-95; *ai:* Dept Chm; Stark Cty Soc Stud Curr Comm; NEA, OEA, Lake Local Ed Assn 1971-93; OH Cncl of Soc Stud 1971-93, Dist Rep; Delta Kappa Gamma 1974-, Treas; BSA, Merit Badge Cnslr; Alpha Chi Omega 1953-; Tchr of Yr 1993; OH Cncl of Soc Stud; Recipient of Freedom Fnd Fellowship; Natl Geographic Alliance Wkshp, Trng as Tchr Consultant; Critiqued Textbook for Publishing Co; OH Dept of Ed Tchr Mentor; Lake MS 12001 Market Ave N Hartville OH 44632

O'BOYLE, MARIA RODEGHIERO, Biology Teacher; *b:* Wilkes-PA; *m:* Joseph; *ed:* Univ of Scranton (BS) Bio 1984; Grad Credits Univ, Penn St Univ, Performance Learning Systems; *cr:* Tunkhannoc HS Bio Tchr 1986-; *ai:* Post Spon Bio Club; PSEA, NEA, TAEA *office:* Tunkhannock HS 120 W Tioga St Tunkhannock PA 18657

O'BOYLE, M. PAULA MC NAMARA, Social Studies Teacher; *b* York City, NY; *m:* M. Joseph; *c:* Timothy, Christopher, Kerry Maureen; *ed:* Empire St Coll (BS) Home Ec, Soc Stud 1979; Tow Univ (MED) Scndry Ed 1995; 51 Credits Univ of MD, Loyola; Ac Prof Degree in Spec Ed, Soc Stud, Home Ec; *cr:* NYC Parochial Elem Tchr 1958-61; Adult Ed Tchr 1972-79; Seton HS Home Ec, So Tchr, Chprsn 1979-88; Seton Keough HS Soc Stud, Spec Ed, Ho Tchr, Chprsn 1988-; *ai:* Foods, Sewing Clubs; Fin Comm; Acad Cncl Chprsn; Cncl for Learning Disabilities 1994-; NCEA, Amer Home E 1979-; Natl Soc Stud Assn 1983-; St Vincent de Paul Assn, Adult Women's League 1968-72; *office:* Seton Keough HS 1201 S Cato Baltimore MD 21227

O'BRIAN, CINDY J., Fourth Grade Teacher; *b:* Salem, OH; Douglas; *c:* Michael, Matthew; *ed:* Youngstown St Univ (BA) Elem E & Sci 1980, (MS) Gifted & Talented 1987; Current Post-Grad fc Masters in Cnslng; Attnd Kent St, Drake Univ; *cr:* Salem Schls 3rd-4th Grd & Gifted 4th & 6th Grd Tchr; *ai:* Odyssey of Mind 1985-94, Local Dir 1987-93, Regnl Coord 1990-93; NEOCA 1980-1985-; Phi Delta Kappa 1993-; Mentor Tchr 1994-; Salem Cntry 1992-, Team & Childrens Act; Salem Visitors & Tourism Bd 1994-Adv; *office:* South East Elem Schl 2200 Merle Rd Salem OH 44460

O'BRIEN, ANGELA ALTILIO, Mathematics Teacher; *b:* Jersey Cit *m:* Christopher; *ed:* Rutgers Univ (BS) Math 1989; Attnd Montclair S Grad Schl; *cr:* Hasbrouck Hghts HS Math Tchr 1990-; *ai:* Soph Class Ring & Chrldr Adv; NEA, NJEA, HHEA, BCEA 1989-, AMT NCTM 1987-; Nancy Higginson Dorr Awd; *office:* Hasbrouck Heigh 365 Blvd Hasbrouck Hts NJ 07604

O'BRIEN, BRENDA HALSTEAD, Health Education Program Coo East Orange, NJ; *m:* John T.; *ed:* Univ of MD (BS) Bio Sci, Ed; R Univ (MS) Physiology; Univ of MA at Lowell 9 Credits; Fitchburg Credits; North Shore Comm Coll 6 Credits; *cr:* Merck Sharp Dohma Rsrch; Abbott Pharmaceutical Researcher; Amersha Searle Radioche Specialist; Wilmington Pub Schls Hlth Edctr; Andover Pub Schl Hl Prgm Coord; *ai:* Comm Hlth Adv Team Chm; St Dept of Ed Framework Comm; Curr Assessment Writing Team; Point to Point C APHA; APHERD; MTA; MAPHEEB; ASCD; COHES; Expl Assistance Prgm; Andover CARES Comm; Unsung Hero Awd 1994; Lyon Awd for Achieving Gender Equity Amer Assn of Univ Women *office:* Andover Pub Schl 36 Bartlet St Andover MA 01810

O'BRIEN, BRIAN ANDREW,SR., English & Computer Sci Teach Worcester, MA; *m:* Colleen F. Wallace; *c:* Brian Jr., Timothy J., Mi P.; *ed:* Assumption Coll (BA) Amer His 1971; Worcester St Coll (Scndry Ed 1980; Addl 15 Credit Hrs Eng; Transitional Stu Course Worcester East MS Eng Tchr 1971-80, Acting Asst Prin 1979-80; Sou Eng Tchr 1980-85; Burncoat Sr HS Eng, Cmptr Sci Tchr 1985-; *ai:* Var Bsktbl Coach Wachusett Regnl HS; Tchr Advy Cncl Chm; NHS NEA, MA Tchrs Assn, Educl Assn of Worester 1971-; MA Bsktbl Co Assn 1982-; Chaffins Recreation Assn 1977-, Coaching Mem; Lesson Written, Pub in Conjunction with Prof Play Being Performed; Curr W Tech Prep, Schl to Work; *office:* Burncoat Sr HS 179 Burncoat St Worc MA 01606*

O'BRIEN, CAREN SCHMIDT, French Teacher; *b:* Somerville, M Michael A.; *ed:* Cntrl CT St Coll (BS) Fr 1970; Assumption Coll (M 1979; LaSorbonne Univ de Paris 2 Cources Adv Grammar & Phon Summer 1969; *cr:* Wolcott HS Fr Tchr 1970-71; Marlboro HS Fr 1971-, Dept Chprsn 1986-91; *ai:* Schl Cncl Fac Rep; Adv for Spring to Quebec City 1996; NEA 1971-; MAFLA & AATF, Schl Mem; Cntr For Lang Alliance 1995-; Hopkinton Cultural Cncl 1994-; Translate Book on Ninnuck; *home:* 140 Spring St Hopkinton MA 01748*

O'BRIEN, CAROLINE SAMANTHA, 6th Grade Teacher; *b:* Charle WV; *ed:* Bowling Green St Univ (BS) Ed 1993; Working Towards Ma in Ed OH St Univ; *cr:* Shawnee MS 6th Grd Tchr 1994-; *ai:* Shawne Var Girls Soccer Coach 1994-; 7th Grd Girls Bsktbl Coach 1994-; Sha Ed Assn 1994-; NEA 1991-; *office:* Shawnee MS 3235 Zurmehly Rd OH 45806

O'BRIEN, CATHY A., Foreign Language Dept Chprsn; *b:* Queens, *ed:* SUNY at Albany (BA) Span 1975; Instituto Intnl Madrid Span Keene St Coll 6 Credits Span; Taft Schl 3 Credits Span II Tchng Charlotte Valley Cntrl Schl Span Tchr 1976-77; Monadnock Regn Span Tchr, Dept Chair 1977-; *ai:* Foreign Lang Dept Chprsn; NEA; *of* Monadnock Regional HS 580 Old Homestead Hwy Swanzey NH 034

O'BRIEN, DAVID EDWARD, 8th Grade Social Studies Tchr Syracuse, NY; *m:* Valerie Szancilo; *c:* Colleen, Jennifer Hike; Lemoyne Coll (BS) Pol Sci 1964; 30 Hrs SUNY at Cortland 1965; Summer Prgm Potsdam St 1967; 8 Hrs Geog 1970; 9 Credit Hrs Pots St 1972-73; *cr:* Leonardsville Cntrl Schl Grds 8-12 Soc Stud Tchr 1965 Carthage Cntrl Grd 8 Soc Stud Tchr 1968-; Carthage MS Grd 8 Soc Tchr 1968-; *ai:* JV Bsktbl Coach 1965-68; Jr HS 1978-94; Ftbl Coach Warner 1970-72; HS Fr 1973-75; Fr1980-85; Intercultural Aware Mastery Learning, Schl Quality Review, Schl Discipline Comms; NY 1965-; CTA 1968-; Carthage Elks 1970-; Carthage Knights of Colu 1975-; Carlowden Cntry Club Bd of Dirs 1980-, VP 1988; NY St Sur Conf Inductive Learning 1967; Natl Sci Fnd Grant Geog WI St at Claire 1970; *home:* 34 N Main St Carthage NY 13619*

O'BRIEN, DONALD GENE,JR., English Teacher; *b:* Ft Wayne, IN Suzanne S.; *c:* Hadley E., Jonathan D.; *ed:* IN Univ (BA) Eng 1967, (Eng 1970; Doctoral Stud Miami Univ of OH; *cr:* Weisser Park Jr HS Tchr 1967-70; Univ of Evansville Eng Instr 1970-73; Miami Univ Asst 1973-74; Lakota HS Eng Tchr 1974-; *ai:* Acad Quiz Team Co NEA 1974-, Bldg Rep; *office:* Lakota HS 5050 Tylersville Rd West Ch OH 45069

O'BRIEN, DONNA HENDERSON, Spcl Ed & Sr Homeroom Tchr Boston, MA; *m:* James F. Jr.; *c:* Caitlin, Jay; *ed:* Boston St Coll (MA) Ed 1975; 45 Addl Credits; *cr:* Boston Pub Schls Tchr 1971-; *ai:* Sr C Adv; Prom Coord, Sec; Schl Site Cncl; Clinic, Downtown Evening Pilot Schl Advy Bd; Boston Tchrs Union Bldg Rep; Mgr Schl Suns Fund; AFT 1971-; MFT 1971-, Del; BTU 1971-, Bldg Rep, Bldg Rep 1982; Greater Boston Labor Cncl 1981-, Del; West Dennis Yacht 1989-, Mbrshp Chair; Mt Alvernia Acad Parent Advy Bd 1991-92, Mary's Parish 1992-, Marriage Preparation Comm; Impact II Grant; Ctr Grant; Schl to Career Basic Skills Curr Writing Team; *office:* Bos HS 152 Arlington St Boston MA 02116*

O'BRIEN, EDWARD JOSEPH, Professor & Chair of Grad Dept Parsons, KS; *m:* Jean Patrice Losco; *c:* Caroline Lovise, Lindsey Jean; Univ of KS at Lawrence (BA) Psych 1972; Univ of MA at Amherst (Clinical Psych 1975, (PHD) Clincial Psych 1980; Residency Clin Psych Univ of TX Hlth Sci Ctr at San Antonio; *cr:* Univ of MA at Amh Prof Staff Assoc 1978-81; Bucknell Univ Asst Prof 1981-83; Maryw 'rof 1983-; *ai:* Sftbl, Soccer, Kingston Girls Asst Coach; Recreational ıes; Amer Psychological Assn 1978-; Book; Principal Investigator Sci Fnd ILI Grant Rsrch Trng in Psych 1995-; *office:* Marywood Coll Adams Ave Chs Adams Ave Scranton PA 18509

IEN, EMILY S., Sixth Grade Teacher; *b:* Huntington, NY; *m:* ıd F.; *c:* Joseph, Jessica, Julie; *ed:* SUNY at Cortland (BS) Elem Ed, Scndry Math 1985; C. W. Post Coll (MS) Elem Sci 1989; Ldrshp MS Cert Hofstra Univ; Sci Mentor Cert; Trng Cold Spring Harbor Lab in ;ics for MS Stdnts; *cr:* Plainview-Old Bethpage MS 6th Grd Tchr ; *ai:* SADD Adv; Title IV Comm; Tchr Mediator; NEA 1985-; PTA ıme Mbrshp Awd; *office:* Plainview Old Bethpage Mdl Sch 121 al Park Rd Plainview NY 11803*

RIEN, GLORIA NORAT, ESOL Teacher; *b:* Aibonito, PR; *m:* Mark ıas; *c:* Julia Maria, Christina Joann; *ed:* Univ of MD (MED) Eng ·y Ed 1980; 30 Post-Grad Hrs ESOL Cert Pgm; 6 Post-Grad Hrs ıg Pgm; *cr:* Upward Bound Cnslr & Tchr 1974-76; Gordon Intnl Schl Tchr 1976-78; Prince Georges Cty Schls: Northwestern HS Tchr ·79, Hill HS Tchr 1980-88, High Point HS Tchr 1988-; *ai:* TESOL; ESOL; PGCEA; *home:* 4210 Ulster Rd Beltsville MD 20705*

RIEN, GREGORY MICHAEL, Art Teacher; *b:* Taunton, MA; *m:* a Paulson; *c:* Brendan M., Erin E.; *ed:* Bridgewater St Coll (BS) Elem 973, (MAT) Creative Arts 1996; St of DE Practical Nrsng License; *cr:* Martin Schl MS Art Specialist 1972-; *ai:* Fac Senate; TEA 1972-, Ex n; MT A 1972-; NEA 1972-; Taunton Arts & Berkley Arts Lottery n; Taunton Civic Chorus; City of Taunton Desert Storm Recognition ion 1991; Grants: Southeast MS Alliance 1995-96; *office:* J H Martin 131 Caswell St East Taunton MA 02718

RIEN, JAMES DANIEL, Technology Education Teacher; *b:* ville Centre, NY; *m:* Francine; *c:* James Jr., Kevin; *ed:* SUNY at ego (BS) Indstrl Arts 1973, (MS) Indstrl Arts 1974; Attnd NY Inst of , Western CT St Coll, SUNY at Stony Brook; *cr:* Syracuse City Schl, wood JR HS Indstrl Arts Tchr 1973; Cold Spring Harbor Jr Sr HS rl Arts Tchr 1973-75; Gifted, Talented Prgm Robotics Tchr 1985-; ers HS Tech Ed Tchr 1975-; *ai:* Fac Adv HS Tech Stu Assn, Olympics ind; Fac Co-Adv Schl Newspaper; Co-Coord Cmptr, Tech Ed; AFT -; NYS Tech Ed Assn 1975-, Regnl Pres, Regnl Tech Tchr of Yr; ers Fac Assn 1975-, Bldg Rep; BSA 2 Yrs Weblo Ldr; North Salem ervation Advy Bd 2 Yrs; WCC Comm Bd 1976-, VP; AYSO 2 Yrs, er Coach; HS PTA Tchr of Yr; Presenter Numerous NYSTEA Confs, Dept Regnl Confs, Desktop Publishing, Cmptr Aided Drawing; *e:* Somers HS PO Box 640 Lincolndale NY 10540*

RIEN, JAMES EDWARD, Chem Tchr & Sci Dept Chm; *b:* Malden, *m:* Patricia Anne Wasilewski; *c:* Joseph E., James M., Jason T., Jeffrey *d:* Boston Coll (BA) Bio & Chem 1965; Wesleyan Univ (MAT) (CAS) & Ed 1968; Southern CT St Univ Sci & Admin Courses; *cr:* The gan Schl Tchr 1967-, Chm 1989-; *ai:* NHS Adv; SADD Co-Adv; NEA, 1970-; CT Sci Tchrs Assn 1972-; CT St Sci Supvrs 1989-; Guilford hdown Club 1992-, VP; *office:* The Morgan Schl 27 Killingworth Tpke ton CT 06413

RIEN, JAMES O.,JR., History & Government Teacher; *b:* Bronx, NY; St John's Univ (BA) Pol Sci, His 1989; New Schl for Soc Research 3 lits; Rutger's Univ Grad Schl 12 Credits; *cr:* Carteret Schl Dist Sub 1987-90; Our Lady of Good Counsel HS Tchr, Dept Chm 1989-; *ai:* esty Intl HS Group, Yrbk Adv; Jr Statesman of Amer Adv 1992-93; ling Coach 1995-; NCEA 1989-; Carteret Democratic Org 1988-, -Chm, Treas; Carteret Lib Bd 1990-93, Treas 1990-91, Pres 1992-93; Sen Frank Lautenberg, Intern 1988; Gov Mario Cuomo, Intern 1989; eret Councilman 1994-; Acad Excl Cert 1988; Gold Pin Acad Excl); Lambda Kappa Phi SJU 1989; Kappa Gamma Phi 1989; *home:* 779 sevelt Ave Fl 1 Carteret NJ 07008*

RIEN, JEANNE FALIERO, Second Grade Teacher; *b:* Buffalo, NY; eborah Mascia, Thomas J. II; *ed:* St Univ Coll at Buffalo (BS) Elem 1961; Univ of Buffalo (MS) Elem Ed 1970; Post Grad Cert Creative 1993; 60 Post Grad Hrs Including Cooperative Learning, Creative blem Solving & Cmptrs; Internship Nancie Atwell Writing Process; *cr:* ence Cntrl Schls Summer Schl Remedial Rdng Tchr 16 Yrs; Sheridan Elem 1st Grd Tchr 1961-76; Ledgeview Elem 2nd Grd Tchr 1976-; *ai:* otr Specialist; Tchrs Ed & Prof Stans Comm; Clarence Tchrs Assn Exec Clarence Cntrl Schls Federal Credit Union Loan Officer; AFT, NY St ted Tchrs, Clarence Tchrs Assn 1961-; ASCD, Elem Ed & Rdng Alumni apter 1989-; Clarence Comm Ed 1994-; Clarence Rotary Club, dowing Prgm, Citizenship Awd; Clarence Jaycees, Pumpkin Run Vol; ence Cntrl Schls Compact 2000 Strategic Planning Shared Decision king & Tech Comm Mem; NYS Smoke-Free Class 2000 Videotape ntest 1st Place Awd; Inclusion Presentation at NYS Assn of npensatory Educators Region XI 1994; Wynroth Math Presentation at S Cncl for Children Conf 1988; *office:* Ledgeview Elem Schl 5150 Old odrich Rd Clarence NY 14031*

BRIEN, JEANNE PETRA, Physical Education Teacher; *b:* Boston, ; *m:* Robert; *c:* Rachael, Samuel; *ed:* Boston Univ Sargent Coll (BS) 1967; Univ of NH (MS) PE, Spts Soc 1979; Grad Stud Ed Univ of VT; Belmont Day Camp Waterfront Dir 1965-70; Needham HS Var nnastic Coach 1968-69; Harwood Union HS 7-12 PE Instr 1969-78; iv of NH Grad Asst PE 1978-79, Recreational Sports Coord 1979-82; ford Area Sr HS 9-12 PE Instr 1982-; *ai:* Natl HS Fed Field Hockey es Comm Natl Coaches Rep 1989-1992, 1994-; NH Interscholastic Ath n Exec Cncl 1992-; Chm NHIAA Field Hockey Comm; Gymnastics nm; Outcome Based Ed Steering Comm 1993-; Sr HS Staff Dev Comm 84-; NH Coaches Assn Pres 1992, Sec, Treas 1994-; NH Alliance for h PE Recreation & Dance 1980-, Pres 1993, VP 1991-92, Mbrshp prsn 1986; Eastern Dist Assn AAHPERD, Chrprsn, Hon Awds Comm 92, Cncl Conventions Comm 1987-91, Presidential Comm 1983-84, ndry Schl Task Force 1982-84, Fin Comm 1980-83, Nom Comm 79-82, Chprsn Cncl for Svcs 1977-79, VT Rep 1974-79;NH Rep HPERD-NAGWS 1989-93; NH Field Hockey Coaches Assn, Sec-Treas; Coaches Assn 1980-, Pres; NEA, NHEA 1969-, Dist Rep; Natl HS Fed aches-Umpires Ass; Girl Scouts 1989-, Ldr; NHFHUA 1982-, Sectional; GWS Pathfinder Awd 1993; *home:* 39 Hawkstead Holw Nashua NH 063*

BRIEN, JILL WATERSON, English Teacher; *b:* Lawrence, MA; *m:* nnis F.; *c:* Kate, Jack; *ed:* Trenton St Coll (BA) Eng, Lang Arts 1987, S) Ed 1995; *cr:* Neshaminy HS Eng Tchr 1990-; *ai:* Drama Asst Dir; T 1990-; *office:* Neshaminy HS 2001 Old Lincoln Hwy Langhorne PA)47

BRIEN, JOHN JOSEPH, Retired Social Stud Dept Head; *b:* Worcester, A; *m:* Ann M. Thomas; *c:* John J. Jr., Maeve E. Mickle, Elizabeth A., ul M., James V.; *ed:* Coll of the Holy Cross (BS) Pol Sci 1955; Boston ll (MA) His, Govt 1957; 60 Credits Post Grad Stud Boston Coll, amingham St Coll; In-Svc Credits; *cr:* Dracut HS Soc Stud Tchr 58-60; Framingham HS Soc Stud Tchr 1960-63; Framingham North HS c Stud Tchr 1963-91, Dept Head 1980-91; Framingham HS Dept Head 91-95; *ai:* Class Adv; Bsbl Coach; Intnl Relations Club Founder, Adv; c Advy Comm Chair; Philosophy & Objectives Comm Chair; Comm Svc gm Dir; NEA, MTA, Soc Stud St & Natl Orgs 1960-; FTA 1960-, VP, lary Comm Chair; NEASSC 1971-, Visiting Evaluation Comm; ASCD 81-; Rel Orgs, Bds, Act, Chair; Pearl Street House, Bd of Dirs; Christa's Tchr 1996; Curr Design, Implementation Articles Pub; Prof Curr & Curr Integration Wkshps; *home:* 140 Oaks Rd Framingham MA 01701

O'BRIEN, JOYCE BRADY, Math & Religion Teacher; *b:* New York, NY; *w:* Francis T. (dec); *ed:* St Johns (BA) Soc Stud 1972, (MS) Elem Ed 1974; Theology, Lions Quest & Comp Math 3 Credit Hrs Each; Environmental Ed & Art 1 Credit Hr Each; Ldrshp Pgm 9 Credit Hrs; *cr:* Annunciation 1953-55; St Catherine of Siena Tchr 1955-57; OLPH Tchr 1957-59; St Francis of Assisi Tchr 1959-67; Crum & Forster Ins Clerk 1967-69; St Nicholas of Tolentine Tchr 1969-; *ai:* After Schl Pgm; Stu Cncl.

O'BRIEN, KATHLEEN DEACON, 8th Grade Language Arts Tchr; *b:* Jamaica, NY; *m:* Fred James; *c:* Patrick, Christine, Thomas; *ed:* Monmouth Univ (BS) Elem Ed 1971; Grad Credits Georgian Court Coll; *cr:* Ardena Schl Lang Arts Tchr 1971-94; Howell MS Lang Arts Tcgr 1994-; *ai:* Lang Arts Curr Comm; New Tchr Mentor; Cath Yth Group Adv; NEA, NJEA, HTEA 1971-; NCTE 1989-; Allentown HS Band Parents 1986-, Pres, VP, Sec; St John's Confirmation 1988-90, Instr; Assumption Church Confirmation 1993-, Instr; *office:* Howell MS 501 Squankum-Yellowbrook Rd Howell NJ 07731

O'BRIEN, LEE ANN ATWOOD, Instrumental Music & Span Tchr; *b:* Duluth, MN; *m:* Mac Gregor; *ed:* Univ of MO (BS) Music Ed 1978, (MED) Music 1984; Addl 30 Hrs Course Work St Cert Tchng Span; *cr:* Univ of MO String Project Tchr 1977-78; Allegany Cty Bd of Ed Resource Tchr 1979-; *ai:* Allegany Cty Yth, Elem Orch Co-Dir; MENC 1977-; Amer String Tchrs Assn 1978-; NEA, Allegany Cty Tchrs Assn 1979-; Music & Arts Club 1979-, St Treas 1993-95; Allegany Cty Music Advocacy Cncl 1995-, Bd of Dir; Allegany Arts Cncl 1980-; Frostburg Comm Theatre 1979-, Pres; MD Symphony Orch 1982-84; Western MD Symphony Orch 1994-; *office:* Braddock MS 909 Holland St Cumberland MD 21502*

O'BRIEN, LINDA JEAN VELARDOCCHIA, Kindergarten Teacher; *b:* Medford, MA; *ed:* Mass Bay Comm Coll (AA) Lbrl Arts 1971; Salem St Coll (BS) Elem Ed & Art 1973; 30 Credit Hrs; *cr:* Robin Hood Schl 1st Grd Tchr 1974-82; South Schl 1st Grd Tchr 1982-87, 4th Grd Tchr 1987-91, Kndgtn Tchr 1991-; *ai:* Hospitality Comm; NEA 1974-; MTA 1974-; STA 1974-, Bldg Rep; Stoneham HS Yrbk Favorite Tchr 1993; Dev Own Phonics Pgm; Working on Alphabet & Poetry Book Geared for K-2nd Grds; Dev a Line of Childrens Clothing & Accessories Patterned Teddy Tot; *office:* South Elem Schl 11 Summer St Stoneham MA 02180*

O'BRIEN, MARGARET K., Chemistry Teacher; *b:* Philadelphia, PA; *m:* James L.; *c:* James Scott, Claudia; *ed:* Gettysburg Coll (BA) Chem 1959; Worcester Polytechnic (MS) Natural Sci 1988; Attnd Bridgewater St Coll, Temple Univ; *cr:* Rohm & Haas Co Rsrch Assoc 1959-60; Mellon Inst Rsrch Assoc 1960-62; Duxbury Jr-Sr HS Chem Tchr 1975-; *ai:* Acad Decathlon Adv; DJSHS Schl Cncl; NEACT 1976-; NEA, MTA, DTA 1977-, Past Pres, VP; Phi Beta Kappa, ACS 1959-; ST John Evangelist Church Layreader; *office:* Duxbury Jr Sr HS 130 St George St Duxbury MA 02332*

O'BRIEN, MARGARET MARY, Chemistry Teacher; *b:* New York, NY; *ed:* Hunter Coll (BA) Chem 1962; Univ of Notre Dame (MS) Chem 1971; St Joseph Cathiecial Inst (MA) Scripture 1982; *cr:* Jr HS 115M Sci Tchr 1961-62; Preston HS Sci Tchr 1965-68; John F. Kennedy HS Chem Tchr 1968-69; New Rochelle HS Chem Tchr 1969-; *ai:* Golf; NSTA 1969-p NEA 1970-; STANY 1971-; Univ of Notre Dame NSF; *office:* New Rochelle HS 265 Clove Rd New Rochelle NY 10801

O'BRIEN, MARY NIEWIERSKI, Second Grade Teacher; *b:* Canton, OH; *m:* David Edward; *c:* Megan, Erin; *ed:* Kent St Univ (BS) Ed 1971; Enrolled Ashland Univ Master's Prgm; *cr:* E. G. Bowers Elem Schl Second Grd Tchr 1971-; *ai:* Math, Sci, Report Card Comms; Assessment Team; Tchr Rep Parent Org; NEA, OEA, MEA 1971-; *office:* Bowers Elem Schl 1041 32nd St NW Massillon OH 44647

O'BRIEN, MAURA KENNEDY, HS Social Studies Teacher; *b:* Acton, MA; *ed:* Coll of the Holy Cross (BA) Pol Sci 1989; Univ of MA (MED) Scndry Soc Stud 1992; *cr:* North Middlesex Regnl HS Soc Stud Tchr 1992-; *ai:* Var Field Hockey, Var Boys Tennis Coach; NHS Adv; NEA, MTA 1992-; *home:* Fire Rd 12 Spec Pond Lancaster MA 01523

O'BRIEN, MICHAEL J., Principal; *b:* Ithaca, NY; *ed:* Buffalo St Coll (BS) Elem Ed 1974, (MS) Early Scndry Ed 1978; Canisius Coll (MS) Educl Admin 1985; *cr:* St Marys Buffalo 6th-8th Grd Tchr 1974-83; St Marys Lancaster Prin 1983-89; Buffalo St Coll Asst Prof & 6th Grd Tchr 1989-93; Campus West Prin 1993-; *ai:* Exec & Mission Vision Goals Comms; Buffalo Cncl of Schl Admin; Buffalo Bd Of Ed; Martin Luther King Jr Memrl Inst at SUCB; Curr Comm for the Infusion of African Amer His in Sch Curr; NEA 1980-; BCSA 1990-; CEC 1991-; Ldrshp Buffalo 1994-; NFTA Adv to Commissioner; Speaker at Natl Conf at Atlanta GA 1989, Natl Conf at Univ of Notre Dame 1990; *office:* Campus West Buffalo Pub Schl 1300 Elmwood Ave Buffalo NY 14222*

O'BRIEN, MICHAEL PATRICK, Dean of Students & His Tchr; *b:* MA; *m:* Lois N.; *c:* Patrick; *ed:* Norwich Univ (BS) Ed, Soc Stud 1979; Bridgewater St Coll Grad Stu Admin; *cr:* The Winchendon Schl Tchr, Coach 1979-81; Perkiomen Schl Tchr, Coach 1981-83; VA Episcopal Schl Tchr, Coach 1983-84; Bishop Stang HS Dean of Stdnts 1986-; *ai:* Asst Var Ftbl Coach; Outing Club Dir; MA Scndry Schl Admin Assn, NASSP 1993-; NCSS, MA Cncl Soc Stud, NCEA 1984-; Track Coach of Yr Awd 1987, 1988; Grant Outward Bound Educl Course 1982; *office:* Bishop Stang HS 500 Slocum Rd North Dartmouth MA 02747

O'BRIEN, PATRICIA WOOD, English Teacher; *b:* Hartford, CT; *m:* William P.; *c:* Kevin, Meghan; *ed:* Emmanuel Coll (BA) Eng, Philosophy 1974; Univ of Hartford (MED) Ed 1983; *cr:* South Cath HS Eng Tchr 1975-90; Rocky Hill HS Eng Tchr 1990-; *ai:* NEA, CEA 1990-; Langford Schl PTO 1992-; Tchr of Yr 1995-; *office:* Rocky Hill HS 50 Chapin Ave Rocky Hill CT 06067

O'BRIEN, PAUL JAMES, English Teacher; *b:* Troy, NY; *m:* Deborah Damm; *ed:* Iona Coll (BA) Eng 1965; Cath Univ (MA) Ed 1967; SUNY at Albany (MA) Eng 1975, (DA) Eng 1995; *cr:* Notre Dame HS Eng Tchr 1967-75; Notre Dame-Bishop Gibbons Schl Eng Tchr 1975-; *ai:* Schl Newspaper, Spelling Bee Team Moderator; Eng Dept Chair; Pub Relations Liaison; NCTE 1975-; NCEA 1989-; NYSEC 1986-; Capital Dist Eng Supvrs Assn 1975-, Co-Chair; Schenectady Human Rights Commission Recognition; NYS Ed Dept Document on Tchng Film; Essays Pub; Edmund Rice Distngd Edctr Awd; *office:* Notre DAme-Bishop Gibbons Schl 2600 Albany St Schenectady NY 12304*

O'BRIEN, PAUL JAMES,JR., Religion Teacher; *b:* Washington, DC; *ed:* Borromeo Coll of OH (BA) Philosophy & Eng 1987; *cr:* Mt Olivet Cemetery Sales Cnslr 1987-90; Magoos Irish Pub Bartender & Waiter 1990-92; St Vincent Pallotti HS Rel Tchr 1992-; *ai:* Var Sftbl Asst Coach; Game Day Club Moderator; Retreat Team Co-Fac Adv; JV Ftbl Stud Hall Moderator; Salary & Benefits Comm; *office:* St Vincent Pallotti HS 113 Saint Marys Pl Laurel MD 20707

O'BRIEN, RICHARD LARENCE, English Teacher; *b:* Brockton, MA; *ed:* Univ MA Amherst (BA) Eng 1967, (MAT) Ed & Eng 1969; (CAS) Tchng & Curr 1978; Huntington Theatre; Boston Coll; *cr:* Brockton High Tchr 1969-; *ai:* NEA 1969-; MCSS 1969-; MCT Eng 1974-; Huntington Theatre Tchrs 1994-, Advy Cncl; Tufts Univ Tchr who Made a Difference; Univ of Chicago Outstdng Tchr; *office:* Brockton HS 470 Forest Ave Brockton MA 02401*

O'BRIEN, ROBERT BURKE, OWE Coordinator; *b:* Youngstown, OH; *m:* Eileen J.; *c:* Erin E., Meghan M.; *ed:* Youngstown St Univ (BS) Bus Admin 1973, (MS) Curr & Instruction 1993; Kent St Univ (BS) Industrial Tech 1978; OH St Univ OWA Cert 1993; Kent St Univ OWE Cert 1994; *cr:* General Motors Corp Engr 1973-74; East HS Industrial Tech Tchr 1974-90, OWE Coord 1993-; Hayes Upper Learning Ctr OWA Coord 1990-93; *ai:* Adult Basic Ed Tchr; Homeless Yth Adv; Laubach Literacy Tutor; OH Industrial Tech Assoc 1974-89; NEA, OEA & YEA 1981-; Tri-Cty Coords Assoc 1991-, Pres; OH Voc Assoc 1992-; OWECA 1993-; IA Convention Best in Show 1979; OH Insurance Schlsp Awd 1982; *office:* East HS 1544 E High Ave Youngstown OH 44505

O'BRIEN, SUSAN D., Advanced Placement Eng Tchr; *b:* Harrisburg, PA; *m:* Michael L.; *c:* Maureen, Michael; *ed:* Shippensburg Univ (BA) Eng 1966; 30 Grad Credits; *cr:* Morrisville HS Tchr 1967-70; Susquehanna Twp HS Tchr 1986-; *ai:* Newspaper, Magazine & Television Show Adv; Character & Value-Discipline Comms Chm; *office:* Susquehann Township HS 3500 Elmerton Ave Harrisburg PA 17109

O'BRIEN, THOMAS FRANCIS, Assistant Principal; *b:* Woburn, MA; *m:* Elizabeth Parent; *c:* Tom Jr., Lynne, Tracey, Laura; *ed:* Fitchburg St Coll (BSE) Spec Ed 1966; Salem St Coll (MED) Schl Admin 1976; 30 Addl Credit Hrs; *cr:* Billerica Meml HS Spec Ed Tchr 1968-86, Asst Prin 1986-; *ai:* Dir Driver Ed 1970-; NEA 1968-; *office:* Billerica Memorial HS 35 River St Billerica MA 01821

OBRIEN, THOMAS JOHN, District Art Director; *b:* Rochester, NY; *m:* Nancy Jean Lux; *c:* Thomas Jr., Meghan; *ed:* Rochester Inst of Tech (BFA) Advertising 1962, (MFA) Fine Art Painting 1971; Post Grad Courses at St Univ of NY at Brockport & Ithaca Coll; *cr:* Tioga Cntrl Schl Art Tchr 1962-64; Pittsford Cntrl Schl Art Tchr & Art Dir 1964-; *ai:* 10th Grd Adv; Art Club; NEA, NYSTA 1962-; NAEA 1971-; Pittsford Historical Preservation Bd 1984-88; Pittsford Zoning & Planning Bds 1988-92; Pittsford Trustees 1992-; Amer Beautiful Fnd Awd 1985; Outstanding Tchr Awd Rochester Inst of Tech 1989; Outstanding Tchr Awd Univ of Rochester 1984; Outstanding Tchr Awd Cornell Univ 1993; Outstanding Alumni Rochester Inst of Tech 1991; *office:* Pittsford Central Schls 42 W Jefferson Rd Pittsford NY 14534*

O'BRIEN, TIM, Social Studies Teacher; *b:* Utica, NY; *m:* Mary Elizabeth Sowers; *c:* Robert, Kevin; *ed:* Niagara Univ (BA) 1980; Loyola Coll (MED) Ed Mgmt 1988; *cr:* Archbishop Curley HS His Tchr 1980-83; Cardinal Gibbons HS Soc Stud Tchr 1983-86; Hammond HS Soc Stud Tchr 1986-87; Oakland Mills HS Soc Stud Tchr 1987-93; *ai:* Stu Govt Assn & NHS Advs; Var Bsbl Coach; Schl Improvement Comm; NEA 1987-; MD St Bsbl Coaches Assn 1989-, Bd of Dirs & Sec; Twice Pub in Scholastic Coach Magazine; Howard Cty Outstdng Tchr Awd 1993; *office:* Oakland Mills HS 9410 Kilimanjaro Rd Columbia MD 21045*

O'BRIEN, WILLIAM HENRY, Physics & Mathematics Teacher; *b:* Cambridge, MA; *m:* Loretta Ann; *c:* Katharine Ann, Rebecca Ann; *ed:* Boston Univ (BS) Aeronautical Tech 1965; Univ of MA at Boston (MED) Sci Ed 1966; Boston Univ (EDD) Sci Ed 1980; Attnd Harvard Univ, Bridgewater St Coll; *cr:* Randolph HS Physics Tchr, Sci Dept Chm 1967-; Massasoit Comm Coll Physics, Astronomy Tchr 1981-; Univ of MA at Boston Acad, Voc Ed Tchr 1993-; *ai:* Schlsp Comm Chm 15 Yrs; Teen Forum Cnslr 3 Yrs; NEA, MS Tchrs Assn 1967-; AAPT 1971-; Astronomy Soc of Pacific 1981-; Knights of Columbus 1980-, Grand Knight, Gold Star Awd; St John's Church 1985-, Eucharistic Minister; Girl Scouts of Amer 1983-85, Asst Ldr; Boston Fireman's Band 1963-74; Patriot Ledger Golden Apple Awd 1995; Amer Astronomical Soc Astronomer for Day 1989; Westinghouse Sci Tchr Talent Search Hnr Cert 1994; Tchr, Adv, Semi-finalist NYNEX Tech Awd 1994; *office:* Randolph Jr Sr HS 70 Memorial Pky Randolph MA 02368*

OBRIST, LEDEA M. (QUATTRONE), Chemistry & Physics Teacher; *b:* Pittsburgh, PA; *m:* John H. III; *ed:* Penn St Univ (BS) Scndry Ed, Chem 1990; Sacred Heart Univ (MA) Chem; *cr:* Sullivan Jr-Sr Schl Chem, Physics Tchr 1 Yr; Western MS Gen Sci Tchr 3 Yrs; New Brighton HS Chem, Physics Tchr 2 Yrs; *ai:* Lioness Club Spon; Asst Coach Girls Vlybl; Nom Outstdng Stu Tchr 1990; *home:* 121 Clearbrook Dr Cranberry Twp PA 16066*

OBSTARCZYK, MICHAEL FRANCIS, Science Teacher; *b:* Lackawanna, NY; *m:* Deborah; *c:* Zoe Elizabeth; *ed:* SUNY Coll at Buffalo (BS) Bio, Scndry Ed 1987; Pursuing MS; *cr:* St Bernard Schl Sci Tchr 1988-95; Kensington HS Sci Tchr 1995-96; Lincoln Acad Sci Tchr 1996-; *ai:* NEA 1995-; 865th Gen Hosp 1990-; US Army Reserve.

OBUCH, DOLORES GRADY, Principal; *b:* Yonkers, NY; *m:* Joseph; *c:* Kim Obuch Shepcaro, Kerry Obuch Limongelli; *ed:* SUNY at Purchase (BA) Eng, His 1984; T C Columbia Univ (MA) Eng 1986; Coll at New Paltz (SAS) Supervision 1989-SDA; MA Candidate Lehman Coll CUNY Lit; *cr:* John F. Kennedy HS Coll Bound Tchr 1984-86; Port Chester HS Eng Chprsn 1986-; Coord Language Arts 7th-12th; *ai:* Texaco Acad Team Coach; NTE, AFT, Westchester Cncl Eng Educators 1986-; Dist Curr Comm 5 Yrs; SUNY at Purchase Partnership 5 Yrs.

O'BYRNE, BRUCE RAYMOND, Phys Ed & Co-Ath Director; *b:* Manhatten, NY; *m:* Joy Elizabeth Roe; *c:* Bryce Christian; *ed:* Houghton Coll (BS) PE 1988; US Sports Acad (MSS) Sports Mngmt, Sports Coaching 1993; *cr:* Houghton Coll Vol Asst Womens Bsktbl Coach 1989-91; Springhill Coll Vol Asst Womens Bsktbl Coach 1991-92; Keuka Coll Vol Asst to Ath Dir 1993; South Shore Chrstn Schl Phys Edctr, Co-Ath Dir 1994-; *ai:* Var Girls Bsktbl Coach; Class of 1997 Adv; WBCA 1996.

OBZUT, JANET CAESAR, Communications Teacher; *b:* Elizabeth, NJ; *m:* Kenneth W.; *c:* Keith; *ed:* Douglass Coll (BA) Speech 1971; William Paterson Coll (MA) Urban Ed 1976; 30 Addl Hrs; *cr:* New Brunswick Pub Schls Communications Tchr 1971-; *ai:* Peer Leadership Coord 1986-; NEA, NJEA, MCEA 1971-, Del to Natl Convention 1975-79; New Brunswick Ed Assn 1971-, VP 1975-80; NBC Natl Tchrs Awd 1988; Tchr Scholar to NJ Governors Schl 1988; NJ Governors Awd 1987; New Brunswick Tchr of Yr 1987; *home:* 13 Saratoga Ct East Brunswick NJ 08816

O'CALLAHAN, JOHN DOWD, 5th Grade Math & Science Tchr; *b:* Cambridge, MA; *m:* Karen Kelley; *c:* Erin, Ryan; *ed:* Northeastern Univ (BS) Elem Ed 1971; Museums for Tchng Sci (MITS) 1987; Process Sci Skills Boston Coll 1975-76; IBM System Operators Course 1993; AIMS Math Course; Challenger Ctr Tchr Trng 1995; *cr:* Holliston MS 5th-7th Grd Lang Art Tchr, 5th-6th Grd Math, Sci Tchr 1975-86; Miller Elem Schl 1st-4th Grd Sci Tchr 1986-88; Holliston MS 5th-6th Grd Soc Stud, Rdng Tchr 1988-89, Grd 4 Coord 1990-92, 5th Grd Math, Sci Cmptr Systems Operator 1993-, Sci Coord 1995; *ai:* Head, JV Coach Vlybl Holliston HS 1975-88, Girls Outdoor Track 1978-86; Head Coach Boys Swimming Framingham North HS 1977-86; HS Bsktbl Official 1985-; RI Indoor Soccer Champs, Coach 1994, Outdoor Champs 1995; Holliston Fed of Tchrs, MA Fed of Tchr, AFT 1971-; US Army Reserve 1971-79, Captain; Middlesex Bd of Officials 1985-; Treas; Smithfield Youth Soccer Assn 1991-, Coach Competitive Div; Directed & Dev Sci Prgm for Environmental Day Camps 1975-85; 1993 Awd Grant from Holliston Ed Fnd; Sam Placentino Fund Grant 1995; TEC Collaborative Consultant 1993-; *office:* Holliston MS 100 Linden St Holliston MA 01746*

OCCASO, MARIA M., Language Teacher; *b:* Licata, Italy; *m:* Filippo; *c:* Claudia, Cristina; *ed:* Hunter Coll (BA) Italian 1973; Univ of Bologna (MA) Italian Lit 1974; *cr:* John Jay HS Lang Tchr 1974-84; W C Bryant HS Lang Tchr 1984-; *ai:* Italian Club Adv; UFT 1974-; ITA 1974-; NYC Mentor 1992-; FLES Pgm Contributed to W C Bryants Winning of HS of

Yr Sponsored By Newspaper Newsday 1985; FLES Coord; Articles Pub; *office:* William C Bryant HS 4810 31st Ave Long Island City NY 11103*

OCCHINO, ROSEMARY ANDREANA, First Grade Teacher; *b:* Gloversville, NY; *m:* Joseph C.; *c:* Martin J., Alan A., Jason C.; *ed:* Castleton St Coll VT (BS) Elem Ed 1969; Attnd Univ of VT at Burlington, SUNY at Oswego at NY, College of St Rose; *cr:* Gloversville Enlarged Schls 5-6 Grd Tchr 1968-70; Fulton City Schls Grd 3 Tchr 1970-71; Northeast Supervisory Dist Spec Ed, Level I, II Tchr 1971-73; Fulton City Schls Sub Tchr 1973-83, Grd 1 Tchr 1983-; *ai:* Staff Dev, BIAC, Positive Schl Climate Comms; Fulton Tchrs Assn, NYS United Tchrs Assn 1983-; AFT, AFL, CIO 1983-; Fulton Cncl of Chrstn Churches 1989-, Pres; Who's Who Among Stdnts; *office:* Granby Elem Schl RR 1 Box 20a Fulton NY 13069*

OCCHUIZZO, JOHN, Science Teacher & Dept Chm; *b:* Greensburg, PA; *ed:* St Vincent Coll (BS) Physics, Math 1965; Univ of Pittsburgh (BED) Scndry Ed 1969, (DED) Sci Ed 1993; Post Grad Johns Hopkins Univ, Penn St; *cr:* Norwin HS Physics Tchr 20 Yrs, Dept Chm 25 Yrs; Univ of Pittsburgh Programming Instr 4 Yrs, Cmptr Tech Tchr 2 Yrs; *ai:* Sci Dept Chm Grds K-12th; NSTA, PSTA 1968-; PSTT 1968-; ASCD 1991-; St Pauls Church 1955-; PITT CHS Prgm 1980-, 15 Yr Pin; Physics Lab Investigations Textbook; Of Bytes & Bits Workbook; Dissertation Tech in Sci Ed; *office:* Norwin Sr HS 281 McMahon North Hunting PA 15642*

OCHS, ROBERT L., Science Teacher; *b:* Columbus, OH; *ed:* OH St (BS) Sci Ed 1965; Univ of CT (MA) Curr 1971; Univ of RI (MA) Lib & Media 1993; *cr:* Reynoldsburg HS Tchr 1966; Norwich Free Acad Sci Tchr 1971-; *ai:* Sci, Astronomy & Ham Radio Clubs; Planetarium; Observatory; NSTA, NEA 1971-; AAPT 1990-; Elks 1976-; *office:* Norwich Free Acad 305 Broadway Norwich CT 06360*

OCHS, SCOTT ARMIN, Sociology Instructor; *ed:* SUNY at Cortland (BA) Sociology 1980; John Jay Coll of Criminal Justice at NY (MA) Criminal Justice 1983; NYS Cert Security Guard Instr 1994; *cr:* NYS Div of Probation Prgm Consultant 1987-90; Cortland Cty Comm Action Homeless & Runaway Svc Dir 1990-93; LeMoyne Coll Adj Instr Sociology 1990-; Tompkins Cortland Comm Coll Sociology Instr 1993-; *ai:* Club Adv Black Stu Union; Human Svcs Prgm Review Chair; Fac Stu Assn Bd of Dir; Coll Tchng Ctr Bd of Dir; Alcohol & Drug Abuse Cnslng Prgm Dev & Advy Comm Lead Fac; NEA, Acad of Criminal Justice Sci 1993-; Village of Homer Recreation Commission 1992-; Cortland Cty Yth Bd 1989-92, Pres; Pub Summary Report 1995; Wrote Grants Runaway & Homeless Yth & Adult Homeless Prgms 1990-93; Presented NY St Socological Assn Annual Mtg Prisons of Ed 1996; Nom SUNY Chancellor's Excl Tchng Awd 1993; *office:* Tompkins Cortland Comm Coll 170 North St PO Box 170 Dryden NY 13053*

O'CONNELL, CATHERINE,OP, Religion & Reading Teacher; *b:* Manhattan, NY; *ed:* Dominican Coll (AAA) Ed 1954; Fordham Univ (BS) Ed 1964; Manhattan Coll (MA) Cnslng Psychology 1974; *cr:* St Pius Prov RT 7 Gr Math, 7-8 Gr Eng Tchr 1964-68; Sts Philip & James Schl 7 Gr, 5-8 Gr Eng Tchr 1968-70; St Raymond Schl 8 Gr, 5-8 Eng Tchr 1971-73, Prin 1973-89; St Augustine Schl 8 Gr, 6-8 Gr Rel, 4-6, 8 Rdng Groups 1989-; *ai:* Supervise 7th-8th Graders Who Voluntarily Visit Residents in Cherry Hill Nursing After Schl; NCEA 1960-; NY St Educ DEpt 1974-, Permanent Cert Nursery Kg 1-6; Dominican Sisters of Bluavelt NY 1950-; *office:* St Augustine Schl 635 Mount Pleasant Ave Providence RI 02908

O'CONNELL, CHARLES F., Social Studies Teacher; *b:* New York, NY; *ed:* Cath Univ (BA) His 1971; Syracuse Univ (MS) Ed 1978; NY Univ (MA) His 1980; 72 Addl Credit Hrs His Syracuse Univ; *cr:* Chrstn Brothers Acad Tchr 1971-76, Asst Prin 1976-78; Manhattan Coll Instr 1983-86; La Salle Acad Tchr 1988-; *ai:* Global Stud Newsletter Adv; Phi Beta Kappa; Syracuse Univ Grad Flwshps; NY St Tchr Cert; *office:* La Salle Acad 44 E 2nd St New York NY 10003

O'CONNELL, CHRISTINE A., 8th Grade Teacher; *b:* Buffalo, NY; *m:* Joseph; *c:* Sara, Joseph; *ed:* Medaille Coll (BS) Elem Ed 1979; *cr:* St John Evangelist Schl 5 Grd Tchr 1979; St Ambrose Schl Tchr 1979-83; Our Mother of Good Cnsl Tchr 1984-; *ai:* Asst Prin; Learning Fair Coord; NCEA 1979-; Rel Educator of Yr 1988; *office:* Our Mother Good Counsel Schl 15 Oakwood Ave Blasdell NY 14219

O'CONNELL, CHRISTINE BISS, Eighth Grade English Teacher; *b:* Baldwinsville, NY; *c:* Tim, Mary Kathleen; *ed:* SUNY at Cortland (BA) Eng 1968; Grad Credits Eng SUNY at Binghamton 1969; *cr:* Chenango Forks Jr, Sr HS Eng Tchr 1968-70; Shenendehowa Cntrl Schls Eng Tchr 1971-; *ai:* Past Chrldr, Great Books Club, Newspaper Club; Hnrs Level Classes Tchr; Tchr of Focus; NEA 1968-; Shen PTSA 1990-; Burnt Hills PTSA 1984-; *office:* Shenendehowa Cntrl Schl 790 Rt 146 Clifton Park NY 12065

O'CONNELL, CONSTANCE SPANARELLI, French & Italian Teacher; *b:* Brooklyn, NY; *m:* Edward J.; *c:* Gabrielle, Mark; *ed:* Saint Joseph Coll (BA) Fr 1967; SUNY New Paltz (MS) Fr Ed 1976; 24 Credit Hrs Italian Cert; *cr:* Maxson Jr HS Fr Tchr 1967-68; Westbrook Jr HS Fr Tchr 1968-70; Hillburn Slatsburg Schls Fr Tchr 1970-71; Blue Mountain MS Fr, Italian Tchr 1984-; *ai:* Tchrs Assn Exec Bd; PTO Tchr Rep; Cmptr Implementation, Increasing Enrollment Comms; NYSAFLT, NYSUT, AFT 1984-; Delta Kappa Gamma Soc Intnl 1992-; Ossining Pub Lib, Vol Tchr, Literacy, ESL; Grant Readers Digest Mini Grant for Tchrs 1991-92, Hudson Vly Tchrs Ctr 1989-90; *office:* Blue Mountain MS PO Box 14 Montrose NY 10548

O'CONNELL, DANIEL C., Staff of Spiritual Dev; *b:* Boston, MA; *ed:* St John's Seminary (BA) Philosophy 1979, (MDiv) Divinity 1983; Attnd Preaching Inst, Cath Univ of Americs at Washington DC, Boston Theological Inst; *cr:* St Patrick Parish Assoc Pastor 1983-88; Sacred Heart Parish Assoc Parish 1988-93; St Bernard Parish Assoc Pastor 1993-; Office of Spiritual Parish Liason 1993-; Boston Cath Television Talk Show Host 1993-; *ai:* Yth Programming Boston Cath Television; HS Rel Tchr; Wkshp Presenter Rel Ed Conventions; HS Chaplain 1983-88; *office:* St Bernard Parish 1529 Washington St W Newton MA 02165

OCONNELL, DANIEL TIMOTHY, Foreign Languages Department; *b:* Philadelphia, PA; *ed:* Magara Univ (BA) Span 1989; St Josephs Univ (MS) Educl Admin 1995; *cr:* Immaculate Conception Fac 1981-88; St Michael the Archangel Fac 1988-89, 1989-; *ai:* Phi Sigm Iota 1989-; AATSP 1990-; ACTFL 1990-; ASCD 1994-; *office:* Nazareth Acad HS 4001 Grant Ave Philadelphia PA 19114*

O'CONNELL, ELLEN, English Teacher; *b:* Bronx, NY; *m:* Joseph; *c:* Joseph; *ed:* Mercy Coll (BS) Eng Lit 1989; Iona Coll (MA) Eng Lit 1993; *cr:* St Barnabas HS English Tchr 1989-95; Acad of Our Lady of Good Council HS Engl Tchr 1995-; *ai:* Co-Moderator Stu Cncl; Moderator Archdiocesan Instructional TV; Instr SAT Prep Course; SADD Moderator; NY St Engl Council Educator of Exel.

O'CONNELL, EUGENIE, Music Teacher; *b:* Boothbay Harbor, ME; *m:* John; *c:* James, Maeve; *ed:* Attnd Metropolitan Opera Guild; *cr:* Boothbay Region Elem Schl Music Tchr 1993-; *ai:* Dir of Original Opera Prgm; Dir of Bands; *office:* Boothbay Region Elem Schl 156 Townsend Ave Boothbay Harbor ME 04538

O'CONNELL, J. BRIAN, Principal; *b:* North Adams, MA; *m:* Linda M. Neveu; *c:* Shaun P., Christopher B.; *ed:* North Adams St Coll (BS) Ed 1969, (MED) Ed 1974; Addl 30 Credit Hrs; *cr:* USN Radarman 3rd Class 1959-63; Conte MS Asst Prin 1993-95, Prin 1995-; *ai:* Co-Chprsn Schl Improvement Cncl; PTG; North Adams Tchrs, MA Tchrs Assn, NEA 1969-; BSA 1982-, Asst Scout Master, Dist Awd; *office:* Silvio Conte MS 191 E Main St North Adams MA 01247

O'CONNELL, JAMES PATRICK, Business Education Teacher; *b:* Pittsburgh, PA; *ed:* Univ of PA Wharton Schl of Bus (BS) Acctng 1969; Univ of Pittsburgh Ed Cert; Attnd Robert Morris Coll; *cr:* Canevin Cath HS Bus Ed Tchr 1970-; *ai:* FBLA, Rotary Interact Club Adv; Diocese of Pittsburgh Subject Area Coord; Fac Schlsp Fund Chm; NBEA; PA Bus Ed Assn; Eastern Bus Ed Assn; Tri-St Bus Ed Assn; FBLA Outstdng Adv 1994, 1996; St Vincent Coll Great Tchr Recognition Prgm Awd; Duquesne Univ Excl Tchng Awd; *office:* Canevin Catholic HS 2700 Morange Rd Pittsburgh PA 15205

OCONNELL, MARY ELLEN, Physical Education Teacher; *b:* Massena, NY; *ed:* Ithaca Coll (BS) PE 1992; SUNY at Brockport 18 Credit Hrs; *cr:* Wellsville HS PE Tchr 1992-; *ai:* JV Soccer, Var Bsktbl & Asst Golf Coach 4 Yrs; NEA 1992-; WBCA 1992-; *office:* Wellsville Cntrl Schl 126 W State St Wellsville NY 14895*

O'CONNELL, RICHARD M., Teacher; *b:* Philadelphia, PA; *m:* Barbara Spilker; *c:* Michael, Jennifer, Craig; *ed:* Bucks Co Comm Coll (AA) Jrnlsm 1967; Millersville St (BS) Ed 1969; Attnd Trenton St & Penn St Univ; *cr:* Charles Boehm HS 10th Grd Eng Tchr 1969-80; Pennwood MS 8th Grd Eng Tchr 1981-95; William Penn MS 8th Grd Eng Tchr 1995-; *ai:* Millard Fillmore Miniature Golf Team & Marching Kazoo Band Spon; NEA, PSEA, PEA 1969-; *office:* William Penn MS 1524 Derbyshire Rd Yardley PA 19060

O'CONNELL, SHIRLEY TUTTLE, 4th Grade Teacher; *b:* Ware, MA; *c:* Karin lieberman, Susan Drummey, Daniel, Nan Maley; *ed:* Univ of MA (BS) Home Ecs, Ed 1955; *cr:* Richer Elem Schl 5th Grd Tchr 1969-75, 4th Grd Tchr 1975-92; Bigelow Elem Schl 4th Grd Tchr 1992-; *ai:* Marlboro Tchrs Assn, MA Tchrs Assn 1969-; MA Assn of Sci Tchrs; *office:* Bigelow Elem Schl Orchard St Marlborough MA 01752

O'CONNOR, ANNE L., 7th Grade Teacher; *b:* Holyoke, MA; *m:* Thomas B. Jr.; *c:* Bridget, Brian, Kimberly; *ed:* Coll of Our Lady of the Elms (BA) Sociology 1972; *cr:* Kelly Schl 4th & 6th Grd Tchr 1974-78; Blessed Sacrament Schl 7th Grd Tchr 1990-; *ai:* 7th Grd Class Adv; NCEA 1990-; HCHS Soccer Club 1990-94, Pres, Vol Svc Awd; *office:* Blessed Sacrament Schl 21 Westfield Rd Holyoke MA 01040

O CONNOR, BERNARD, Sci Supvr & Physics Tchr; *b:* New York, NY; *m:* Angela T. Siciliano; *c:* Heather, Karen; *ed:* Hamilton Coll (BA) Physics 1962; Adelphi Univ (MS) Math 1966; St John's Univ (PD) Admin & Supervision 1982; Yeshiva Univ Grad Physics 18 Hrs; *cr:* Floral Park Mem HS Sci Supvr 14 Yrs, Sci & Math Tchr 34 Yrs; *ai:* NY St Physics Mentor; SAANYS 1982-; AAPT; Co-Author Review Book; Ed Brief Review; *office:* Floral Park Memorial HS 210 Locust St Floral Park NY 11001*

O'CONNOR, CAROLYN WOODS, Rdng Specialist & US His Tchr; *b:* Boston, MA; *m:* David; *c:* Sarah, Jeremy, Adrian; *ed:* Boston Univ (BA) Pol Sci-Cum Laude 1966; Seton Hall Univ (MA) Rdng-Summa Cum Laude 1982; Supvrs Cert 1989; Credit Hrs Marquette Univ, Villanova Univ; Johnson & Johnson Cooperative Learning Trng Session Advanced 1989; *cr:* Edison MS Rdng Specialist 1985-; Cooperative Learning Trainer 1990-93; Seton Hall Univ Adj 1992-93; Edison MS US His Tchr 1993-; *ai:* Stu Cncl Adv; Dist Style Manual Dev Comm; IRA 1982-; NJ Rdng Assn 1983-; Seton Essex Rdng Assn, Pres, Sec, VP; Prospect Presbyn Sunday Schl Tchr 1985-, Westminister Bell Choir; IRA Contribution Awd 1996; Mini Grant Interdisciplinary Project 1985; Author Bio Lab Plus; Co-Author The Biology Teacher; Tchr of Yr Awd 1994; *home:* 27 Salter Pl Maplewood NJ 07040

O'CONNOR, CAROLYNN FLOHR, Science Teacher; *b:* Endicott, NY; *m:* Terrence James; *c:* T. J., Jacqueline; *ed:* SUNY (BS) Geology 1988; Tchr Ed SUC Cortland; *cr:* Pemberton HS Sci Tchr 1992-93; H G Hoffman HS Sci Tchr 1993-; *ai:* Class of 1998 Adv; NEA, NJEA 1992-' SAEA 1993-; *office:* H G Hoffman HS 249 John St South Amboy NJ 08879

O'CONNOR, DAVID, Health & Physical Ed Teacher; *b:* Buffalo, NY; *m:* Jacqueline Ann Price; *c:* Kelly Ann; *ed:* Ithaca Coll (BS) PE 1987; MS Ed Candidate Canisius Coll; *cr:* Orchard Park HS Sub Tchr 1989-90; *ai:* Cross Cntry, Outdoor, Indoor Track Coach; Educl Frameworks Comm; North Tonawanda Mentor Prgm; NY St Champion 1990, All Amer Distance Runner, NY Cross Cntry Girls Section Champs Coach; *home:* 988 Mill Rd East Aurora NY 14052*

O'CONNOR, DAVID L., History Teacher; *b:* Baldwin, NY; *m:* Alicia Sheehan; *c:* Mackenzie, Brenna, Olivia; *ed:* St Univ of NY at Stony Brook (MA) His 1985; AZ St Univ (BA) His-Summa Cum Laude 1987; (PHD) Candidate; *cr:* John Jay HS at Brooklyn His Tchr 1988-91; Schreiber HS His Tchr 1991-; *ai:* Chess Club Adv; Soccer, Bsktbl, & LaCrosse Coach Weber Jr HS; AFT 1988-; NYSUT 1988-; Amer Historical Assoc 1992-; Eastern Surfing Assoc 1992-; Golden Key NHS; Dobro Slovo Natl Slavic Honor Soc; *office:* Paul D Schreiber HS 101 Campus Dr Port Washington NY 11050*

OCONNOR, EDWIN JOSEPH, Business Teacher; *b:* Holyoke, MA; *m:* Claire M. Meckel; *c:* Rosemarie Sicard, Kirsten Murdock, Edwin, Tara, Timothy, Sean; *ed:* St Michaels Coll (BA) Bus Admin 1959; Westfield St Coll 18 Credits; IBM Schl of Data Processing; *cr:* Holyoke HS Bus Tchr & Acctng 1963-, Tchr & Data Proc Dir 1965-69; Quincy Coll Acctng Instr 1992-; Holyoke Comm Coll Acctng Instr 1995-; *ai:* Stu Tchrs Mentor; HHS Bus Accreditation; Rising Star Pgm; Holyoke Tchrs Assn 1965-; NEA 1965-; Elks 1964-68; *office:* Holyoke HS 500 Beech St Holyoke MA 01040

O'CONNOR, ELIZABETH HESTEN, French & Literature Teacher; *b:* New York, NY; *m:* Thomas Patrick; *c:* Thomas, Michael, Veronica, Peter, Elizabeth, Paul; *ed:* Lady Cliff Coll (BA) Eng Lit 1963; New Paltz Univ (MS) Ed 1988; Post Grad Creative Writing 1989-90; Fordham Univ Eng Lit 1963-64; *cr:* Astor Home Tchr, Permanent Sub Tchr 1963-64; Regina Coelie 3rd & 4th Grd Tchr 1964-66; St Christopher 3rd Grd Tchr 1966-67; Our Lady of Mt Carmel 4th-8th Grd Tchr 1985-; Manist Coll Writing Instr 1989-91; *ai:* NCTE 1988-; Lambda Iota Tau 1963-; Grants, Area Fund Writing Prgm 1989; Rsrch Project 1992; *office:* Our Lady-Mt Carmel Schl 15 Mount Carmel Pl Poughkeepsie NY 12601

O'CONNOR, GREGORY JOHN, High School Math Teacher; *b:* Schenectady, NY; *m:* Hilary S.; *ed:* Hudson Valley CC (AA) Liberal Arts 1984; St Univ Coll at Oneonta (BA) Statistics, Math 1987; Union Coll (MAT) Tchng, Math Cert 1993; *cr:* Chrstn Brothers Acad Math Tchr 1993-94; Stillwater HS Math Tchr 1994-; *ai:* Asst Ftbl Coach; 10th Grd Adv; NYs Certified Ofcl Soccer Referee 1992-; *office:* Stillwater Central HS 334 Hudson Ave Stillwater NY 12170*

O'CONNOR, ILETT KEREEN, Social Studies Tchr & Grd Adv; *b:* Jamaica, West Indies; *ed:* Brooklyn Coll (BA) Sociology 1977; Adelphi Univ (MA) Ed 1988; Attnd Long Island Univ, Fairfield Univ, Bridgeport Univ, Fordham Univ & Coll of St Rose; Addl 60 Credits Post Grad Working Towards Career in Guidance; *cr:* John Adams HS Soc Stud Tchr 1992-, Grd Adv 1995-; *ai:* Tutored Homeless Girls at Wayside Home; AFT 1992-; Old Stndts Assn Awd; *office:* John Adams HS 101-01 Rockaway Blvd Ozone Park NY 11417

O'CONNOR, IRENE, 5th Grade Teacher; *b:* Cincinnati, OH; *ed:* Univ of Cincinnati (BS) Elem Ed 1965, (ME) Ed & Cnslng 1968; 15 Credit Hrs 1975-95; Cnslr Cert 1976; Grad Courses Completed Math, Sci & Outdoor Ed; Comp Trng Completed; *cr:* Ann Weigel Elem 4th-6th Grd Tchr 1965-72; Summer Schl Math & Rdng Tchr 1966-70; Colerain MS Bsktbl Coach 1979-82; Colerain Elem 5th-6th Grd Tchr 1972-; *a* Mem; Comp Comm Mem; Dir Musicals; NEA & OEA 1965-; HCEA SWOEA 1965-; NAE & NWTA 1965-; OH Womens Caucus 1972-; N 1985-; Univ Cincinnati Alumni Band 1968-; Cincinnati Horsemen 1969-, Sec; OH Horsemens Cncl 1975-, Trustee; Colerain Lift-a-Thon, Spon 1993; Colerain Elem PTA; Spcl Ed Classroom Tch 1989; Math Adoption Comm; Stu Tchr Cooperating Tchr; *office:* C Elem Schl 4850 Poole Rd Cincinnati OH 45251

O'CONNOR, JACQUELYN, Special Education Teacher; *b:* Bro NY; *ed:* Long Island Univ (BS) Hlth Ed 1985, (MS) Spec Ed 1993; *c* Tchr 1985-87; West Islip HS Hlth Ed Tchr 1987-90; St John the Bap Spec Ed Tchr 1993-; *ai:* NYSUT, AAHPERD 1992-; West Islip Cancer Coalition 1993-; *office:* St John the Bapt HS 1170 Montauk West Islip NY 11795

O'CONNOR, JOHN M., Professor of Philosophy; *b:* Evanston, Emily, Amanda; *ed:* Cornell Univ (BA) Philosophy 1959; Harvard (MA) Philosophy 1962, (PHD) Philosophy 1965; *cr:* Vassar Coll Inst Prof 1964-68; Case Western Reserve Univ Asst Prof, Assoc Prof 19 Amer Philosophical Assoc Exec Sec 1977-83; Natl Hum Ctr As Prgms 1983-87; William Paterson Coll Hum Dean 1987-92, Philo Prof 1987-; *ai:* Promotion Comm; Amer Philosophical Assn 1964-, Sec 1977-83; Ed 1968; Co-Ed 1969, 1974; Author Prof Journals Ar *office:* William Paterson Coll 300 Pompton Rd Wayne NJ 07470

O'CONNOR, LINDA NAUGLE, Mathematics Tchr & Dept He Gettysburg, PA; *m:* Ronald; *c:* Sean Michael, Emily Catherine; *ed:* Chester St Coll (BS) Math 1969; Western MD Coll (MED) Math Lehigh Univ 8 Hrs; Penn St Univ 3 Credits; Western MD Coll Super Cert; *cr:* Littlestown HS Math, Sci Tchr, Dept Head 1969-; *ai:* Sci, Curr Comms; Math Club, Parent Advy Comm; NCTM 1978-; PCTM NSTA, PSTA 1989-; Delta Kappa Gamma 1987-; Jr Women's Club Pres, Woman of Yr 1991; Articles Pub; Eisenhower Funds to Rewrite Curr; Provide Wkshp to Inservice Tchrs; *office:* Littlestown HS Myrtle St Littlestown PA 17340*

O'CONNOR, MARLEEN TREDY, Guidance Counselor; *b:* Jersey NJ; *m:* Wayne Thomas; *c:* Erin, Courtney; *ed:* St Johns Univ (BA) Ed (MA) Counseling 1981; HIV Trng; Grad Courses Counseling, Sci, M Hum; Star Lab Trng; *cr:* St Pauls Schl Tchr 1976-77; P. S. #34 1977-78; P. S. #27 Tchr of G & T & Guidance Cnslr 1978-; *ai:* Girl Ldr; Children Accepting Responsibilities Everyday Club Adv; Hudso Guidance Cnlsrs & NJ Counseling Assn 1994-; NJ Sci Assn 1980-; Assn & Jersey City Ed Assn 1977-; Girl Scouts of Amer 1987-, Civ Patrol 1984-; Air Force Assn 1984-; Young Astronauts 1984-, Exec B Force Assn; Parent Tchr Assn; NJ Ed Assn Awd; Outstndng Ldr Awd; of Yr Awd; Outstndng Educator Awd; Hgts Pride Awd; Air Force Assn Awd; *office:* Public Schl #27 201 North St Jersey City NJ 07307*

O'CONNOR, MATTHEW J., Junior Religion Teacher; *b:* Holyoke, *ed:* Saint Marys Seminary (MDiv) Theology 1981; Loyola of Ch (MA) Arts 1981; Univ of Montreal Diplome en Philosophie Worchester Post Grad Stud Theology at Assumption Colls Eccum Inst; Post Grad Ed at Our Lady of the Elms Chicopee; *cr:* Cathedra Tchr 1962-72; Saint Josephs HS Tchr 1972-76; Cathedral HS Tchr 1 *ai:* Camp Holy Cross Dir; *office:* Cathedral HS 260 Surrey Rd Spring MA 01118

O'CONNOR, ROBERT CHARLES, Biology Teacher; *b:* Buffalo, N Cheryl A. Turvey; *c:* Robert T.; *ed:* Buffalo St Coll (BS) Bio S Ed-Summa Cum Laude 1993; Working Toward Masters; *cr:* Kenmore Sr HS Tchr 1994-; *ai:* Respect Design & Ownership Design Teams; Comms; NSTA 1992-; Church, Bd of Dirs 1993-; *office:* Kenmore E HS 350 Fries Rd Tonawanda NY 14150

O'CONNOR, TIMOTHY ROCH, Math Teacher; *b:* Columbus, OH OH St Univ (BS) Math Ed 1976, (MA) Educl Admin 1990; *cr:* B Watterson HS Math, Physics Tchr 1976-86; Dublic Coffman HS Math 1987-; *office:* Dublin Coffman HS 6780 Coffman Rd Dublin OH 430

O'CONNOR, YVETTE SILVER, Social Studies Teacher; *b:* S Island, NY; *m:* Brian P.; *c:* Beth Ann, Andrew Paul; *cr:* NYC Bd of Yrs; Marlboro Twp Tchr 19 Yrs; *ai:* Natl Geographic Geography Affirmative Action Dist Comm Rep; PTA Tchr Rep; NJEA 1974-, I Yrs; Monmouth Cty Rdng Tchrs Assn.

O'DANIEL, SUSAN PHILPUTT, Instrumental Music Teache Bennington, VT; *m:* Michael; *c:* Meghan, Sharon, Nancy, Cathy, James Boston Univ (BA) Music Ed 1978; Post Grad Courses Instrum Conducting, Repair, Instrumental Music New England Conservatory, of ME at Orono, Hartt Schl of Music, Cntrl CT St, Plymouth St Coll, of VT; *cr:* Vergennes Union HS Instrumental Music Tchr 1978-; *ai:* Ensemble Dir; Marching Band; Musical Production; Music Dir, Produc Coord; Dist, St, New England Festival Competitions; MENC 19 Instrumental Music Coord; VT, Local NEA, New England Music Fest 1978-; Green Mountain Music Dist, Pres, VP; Vergennes Congregati Church 1988-, Choir Dir; Vergennes City Band 1980-, Conduc Champlain Brass Quintet 1991-, Fr Horn; Univ of VT Outstdng Tchr 1985; *office:* Vergennes Union HS 50 Monkton Rd Vergennes VT 054

ODDIE, DONNA-JEANNE MARY, 8th Grd Sci Tchr & Team Leade Norwalk, CT; *ed:* U CT (BA) Lbrl Arts 1970; So Ct St U (MA) Ed 1 Quinnipiac Schl of Law (JD) Gen Law 1987; U of Salamanca Span Cu 1971; *cr:* Hamden Elem Schl Tchr 4-6 Grd Tchr 1980-90; Hamden MS Tchr 1990-93, Eng Tchr 1993-94, Team Ldr, Sci Tchr 1994-; *ai:* Team Stu Cncl Adv; NEA; NSTA 1990-; Hamden Gd Assn 1971-, Griev Chair; Conn Sci Tchrs Assn 1990-; NY St Sci Tchrs Assn 19 Celebration of Excl St of Ct Awd 1990, 1992; Ed Grant 1992; Natl Awd 1993; Pub in Contemporay Poets of America & Britain 1994; *of* Hamden MS 555 Newhall St Hamden CT 06517*

ODDOU, WILLIAM E., Professor of Kinesiology; *b:* Fort Wayne, IN; Ball St Univ (BS) PE, Hlth 1972; Univ of AZ (MS) Exercise Physio 1975; OR St Univ (PHD) Exercise Physiology 1985; *cr:* St Cloud St U Instr 1980-81; ND St Univ Asst Prof 1981-85; OR St Univ Lect 1985-86; Temple Univ Assoc Prof 1986-; *ai:* Coord Exercise Sci Pr Amer Coll Sports Medicine; *office:* Temple Univ Dept of Kinesiol Pearson Hall Philadelphia PA 19122

ODELL, KATHLEEN LOUISE, Project Counselor; *b:* Dayton, OH; Anne Arundel C C (AA) Bus Admin 1988; Univ of Baltimore (BS) Admin 1990, (MS) Applied Psych 1992; *cr:* Univ of Baltimore Stu Asst 1989-91, Career Dev Grad Asst 1991-92; Baltimore City C.C. Tran Cnslr SSS 1992-94, Project Cnslr SSS 1994-; *ai:* MECEO, MEAE 1993-; *office:* Baltimore City Comm Coll 2901 Liberty Heights Baltimore MD 21215

O'DELL, KIMBERLY FUDGE, English Teacher; *b:* Newark, OH; Kemp; *ed:* OH St Univ (BA) Eng, Hum 1986, (BS) Scndry Eng Ed 19 *cr:* Newark HS Sub Tchr 1990-91, Eng Tchr 1991-; *ai:* Lang Arts Comm; Faculty Adv for S.T.A.R.T.; Co-Facilitator of Dist Multicultrl T Force; NEA 1990-; OH Cncl Tchr of Eng Lang Arts, Cntrl OH Tchrs A 1991-;NCTE; NCSS; *office:* Newark HS 314 Granville St Newark 43055

ODGERS, JOHN ABBOTT, Science Teacher; *b:* Glen Cove, NY; Maude Crawford; *c:* Heidi Mayfield; *ed:* Coll of Santa Fe (BS) Chem 19

Baccalauret Tchr Cert Keene St Coll; *cr:* St Patricks Schl Sci Tchr 94; Keene St Coll Physics Tchr 1994-95; Keene HS Sci Tchr 1994-; oss Cntry Ski Team Coach, Odyssey of Mind Team Coach, Coord; A, NEA 1995-; Experimental Aircraft Assn 1978-, Chptr Sec, Tech , *home:* 130 4 Winds Farm Rd Peterborough NH 03458

EN, RICHARD L., 5th Grade Teacher; *b:* Buffalo, NY; *m:* Joyce S.; arc, Jennifer; *ed:* Buffalo St Tchrs (BS) Ed 1971, (MS) Ed 1973; 20 Credit Hrs at Buffalo St; *cr:* Depew Pub Schl Tchr 1971-; *ai:* Girls wim Coach 4 Yrs; Swim Ofcl WNY 20 Yrs; *office:* Depew Pub Schl nsit Rd Depew NY 14043

ARDI, JOSEPH M., English Teacher; *b:* Pietranico, Italy; *c:* Elisa; airfield Univ (BA) Eng 1970, (MA) Ed 1974; Fairfield Univ 6th Yr n Supervision 1979; *cr:* Assumption Schl Eng Tchr 1971-76; rest Jr HS Eng Tchr 1976-86; Trumbull HS Eng Tchr 1986-; *ai:* Tech n Trumbull Schl Dist; Sftbl Coach; Shakespeare Soc Adv; NEA -; CEA 1976-; TEA 1976-, Bldg Rep; *office:* Trumbull HS 72 Strobel rumbull CT 06611

M, PATRICIA A., 7th Grade Teacher; *b:* Atmore, AL; *c:* Idrissa; *ed:* of MA (BA) Human Svcs 1990; Eastern Nazarene Coll (MA) Modern Needs & Ed 1994; *cr:* Boston Pub Schls Tchr 1989-; *ai:* Compass Schl Pgm; Davin After Schl Club; Tchr & Math Tutor; Stdnts Mentor; Edctr of MA 1989-, Fundraising Comm; *office:* Patrick Gavin MS Dorchester St South Boston MA 02127

NISH, JOHN MICHAEL, Sixth Grade Teacher; *b:* Warren, PA; *m:* anne A. Jessy; *c:* Kristina, Zachary, Adam; *ed:* Edinboro St Univ (BA) Ed 1969; Clarion St Univ (MS) Sci Ed 1987; *cr:* McMillen Lumber Machine Operator 1964-65; Kane Area Schl Dist Tchr 1969-70 & ; US Army 101st Avionics Vietnam 1970-72; *ai:* Sci Olympiad h; Sci Curr Steering Comm; NEA 1969-; PSEA 1969-; KATA 1969-, ms; Built Sci Olympiad Team 4th Place; *home:* 410 Greeves St Kane 6735

ONNELL, EUGENE J., Adjunct Assistant Professor; *b:* Brooklyn, *ed:* John Jay Coll (BS) Criminal Justice 1982; Touro Coll Schl of Law Law 1988; *cr:* John Jay Coll Adj Asst Prof 1991-; *ai:* NYC Bd of Ed; k Trail Comp 1990; Articles Pub; *office:* John Jay Coll 899 10 Ave New NY 10019

ONNELL, JAMES C., English Dept Chair & Teacher; *b:* Portland, *m:* Diana T.; *c:* James M., Joshua J.; *ed:* Univ of South ME (BS) Ed ndry 1971, (BA) Eng 1971; *cr:* Brunswick HS Eng Tchr 1971-84, Eng Chair 1984-; *ai:* Lit Magazine Adv; NEA; ME Cncl Tchrs of Eng, E 1971-; *office:* Brunswick HS Maquoit Rd Brunswick ME 04011*

ONNELL, JAMES HOWLETT,III, History Professor; *b:* Memphis, *m:* Mabry Miller; *c:* John, Anne, Susan; *ed:* Lambuth Coll (BA) His ; Duke Univ (MA) His 1961, (PHD) His 1963; *cr:* Radford Coll Prof is 1963-69; Mariette Coll Prof of His 1969-; *ai:* Coll Lecture Series rd; Phi Alpha Theta Adv; Sou His Assn 1963-; OH Acad of His 1969-, Cncl; Organ of Amer Historians; Omicron Delta Kappa; Amer Cncl ned Societies Fellow; Southern Indians in Amer Revolution 1972; heastern Frontiers: Critical Bibliography 1982; *home:* 118 Meadow Ln ietta OH 45750

ONNELL, JOSEPH N., 7th Grade Mathematics Teacher; *b:* kinsburg, PA; *m:* Ann Marie Szwarc; *ed:* Univ of Pittsburgh (BS) dry Ed 1973, (MA) Math 1975; *cr:* North Hills Schl Dist Math Tchr 5-; *ai:* PSEA, NEA 1975-; *office:* North Hills Jr HS 53 Rochester Rd sburgh PA 15229

ONNELL, JOSEPH REGAN, Social Studies Teacher; *b:* ensburg, NY; *ed:* SUNY at Potsdam (BA) His 1991; *cr:* Lyme Cntrl Soc Stud Tchr 1992-; *ai:* Class of 1998 Adv; LaCrosse, Bsbl, Soccer ch; Soc Stud Curr Comm; *office:* Lyme Central Schl PO Box 219 demy St Chaumont NY 13622*

ONNELL, KAREN LUCIANO, Assoc Prof Developmental Stud; *b:* eva, NY; *m:* John Patrick; *c:* Sean, Christopher; *ed:* St Bonaventure (BA) His 1974; Purdue Univ (MS) Ed 1979; *cr:* Holy Ghost Schl Jr Sci, Soc Stud Tchr 1975-78, 1980-81; Prairie St Coll Instr, Learning Coord 1982-86; Finger Lakes Comm Coll Instr, Asst Prof, Assoc Prof 6-; *ai:* Curr Comm Sec; Subbatical Comm Chair; Tchng Ctr Planning United Way Rep; Fac, Stu Mentor Prgm; CATS Mentor; Chronicle orial Bd; IRA 1980-; NYCLSA 1986-, Regnl Rep; LCC of IRA 1986-, s, VP, Cncl Svc; AAWCC 1994-; St Francis, St Stephens Schl Bd 1988-, s, VP; GVA Historical Soc 1988-, Ed Comm Mem; Childrens Museum nning Bd 1995-, Schl Comm Mem; St Francis, St Stephens HSA 1986-, as; LIVE, Family Literary Grant; Numerous Articles Pub; Adhoc iewer; JAAL, Book Reviewer; Who's Who Amer Women; Who's Who Amer; *office:* Finger Lakes Comm Coll Lake Shore Dr Canandaigua NY 24*

DONNELL, LEO EDWARD, 5th Grade Teacher; *b:* Hazleton, PA; *m:* e Zurn; *c:* Erica, Brad, Brian; *ed:* Bloomsburg St (BS) Elem Ed 1976; rl II Permanent Cert 24 Credit Hrs; *cr:* St John Neumann Regnl Schl Grd Schl Tchr 1977-; *ai:* Little League Bsbl Coach; Bsktbl Coord; St es Math-A-Thon & Talent Show Coord; Asst Adv of Stu Cncl & Yrbk; EA 1977-78; ADLTA 1982-; Diocesan Lay Tchrs of Allentown Diocese; ights of Columbus 1968-; Jim Thorpe Civic League 1970-, mmissioner, 25 Yrs Svc; 15 Yrs Svc Recognition by Diocese; *home:* 429 nter St Jim Thorpe PA 18229*

DONNELL, MABRY MILLER, Prof of Speech Communication; *b:* ntsville, AL; *m:* James Howlett III; *c:* John, Anne, Susan; *ed:* Stephens ll (AA) 1965; LA St Univ (BA) Government 1967; Univ of AL (MA) eech 1969; Bowling Green St Univ (PHD) Speech Comm 1977; *cr:* rietta Coll Prof of Speech Comm 1969-; *ai:* Forensics Coach; Pi Kappa lta, Omicron Delta Kappa Adv; Lib Comm; Coll Planning Advy Cncl; rk Stud, Speech Lab Supvr; Basic Speech Prgm Dir; Fac Marshal; ster Seals, Advy Bd 1995; OH Forensics Assn; OH Speech Comm Assn; Alpha Theta; Delta Gamma, Order of Omega; Marietta Rdng Club; rness Fellow 1992-95; Mc Coy Prof 1994-; Coll Tchr of Yr 1994; Pub ticle Interpersonal Comm; *office:* Marietta Coll 215 Fifth St Marietta 45750*

DONNELL, MARJORIE MAZIARZ, Professor of Office Admin Dept; Chicopee, MA; *w:* Fred (dec); *c:* Jerome E. Kane, Carolyn Kane Collins; Amer Intnl Coll (BS) Bus Admin 1969, (MAT) Ed & Tchng 1973; Univ MA CAGS Ed-Adult Learning 1985; *cr:* Secretarial Positions 1949-69; ngmeadow HS Bus Dept Chm 1969-73; Springfield Tech Comm Coll of 1973-; *ai:* Fac Adv; STCC Chptr; Collegiate Secs Intnl; MA Tchrs sn 1969-, Del; MA Literacy 1986-88, Vol Tutor; Alcohol & Drug Svcs Greater Springfield 1994-, Dir; *office:* Springfield Tech Comm Coll One mory Square Springfield MA 01105

DONNELL, MARY E. CORCORAN, English Teacher; *b:* Bronx, NY; Thomas E.; *c:* Deborah Roulston, Jackie Dumbroff, Ken; *ed:* St Johns iiv (BS) Ed 1961, (MA) Eng 1962; Attnd Stony Brook Univ, Adelphi iiv, Univ of HI at Honolulu, Cambridge Univ, Middlebury Coll; *cr:* lley Stream North Schl Eng Tchr 1962; Northport HS Eng Tchr 1977-; Tutoring & Vol Work with Parish Outreach at St Anthony of Podus; CTE 1980-, Presenter 1989, 1992 at Louisville; United Tchrs of orthport & AFT 1975-; Atlanta, GA Presenter 1990; Parent Tchr Stu Assn, onoree 1977-; NYSTU; Middlebury Coll Writers Conf Grant 1988; ambridge Summer Inst Grant 1989; North port HS Boys & Girls St Competition Organizer 1990-; Young Writers of New England Conf Organizer; NCTE Writing Contest Spon; Hum Inst Grant to Study at Cambridge Univ, England (Trinity Coll) 1994; Hum Inst Grant to Study at Trinity Coll in Dublin, Ireland for Summer 1996; *office:* Northport H S 210 Elwood Rd Northport NY 11768

O'DONNELL, PATRICIA, 8th Grade Teacher; *b:* New Brunswick, NJ; *ed:* Immaculata Coll (BA) Eng, Ed 1983; Trenton St Coll Educ Admin 30 Hrs; *cr:* Immaculate Conception 6th Grd Tchr 1986-87; St William Schl 6th Grd Tchr 1987-90; Holy Family Schl 8th Grd Tchr 1990-; *ai:* Stu Cncl, Yrbk Moderator; Choir Dir; NCEA 1986-; NCTM 1990-; *office:* Holy Family Schl 555 S 25th St Harrisburg PA 17104

O'DONNELL, PATRICIA LEE, 5th Grd Tchr & Building Asst; *b:* Boston, MA; *ed:* Boston St Coll (BSEd) Elem Ed 1975, (MED) Elem Ed 1980; Working on Masters Spec Ed, Moderate Spec Needs K-22, Certfd Elem Prin Boston St Coll; *cr:* City of Woburn Grd 4 Tchr 1975-77, Grd 1 Tchr 1977-78, Grd 6 Tchr 1978-79, Grd 5 Tchr 1979-80, Grd 6 Tchr, Chptr One Specialist 1981, Region Resource Room Tchr 1982, Resource Room Specialist 1982-87, Grd 5 Reg Ed Tchr 1987-; *ai:* PTO; Improve Schl Comm, Math Stans Comms; Comm to Interview for Spec Ed Asst Dir; Woburn Tchrs Assn, MA Tchrs Assn, NEA 1975-; *office:* Malcolm S. White Elem Schl 36 Bow St Woburn MA 01801

O'DONNELL, TIMOTHY MICHAEL, HS Math Teacher & Coach; *b:* Louisville, KY; *m:* Joyce Repko; *c:* Colleen, Danny; *ed:* (MS) Math, Cmptr Sci 1972; 18 Credit Toward Masters Temple Univ; *cr:* Paul VI HS Math Tchr 1972-81; Bally's Golden Nuggett Casino Games Supvr 1981-89; Atlantic City Schl Math Tchr 1989-; *ai:* Head Track, Little League, Yth Soccer, Bsktbl Coach; Atlantic Cty Party & Charter Boat Assn 1988-, Pres; Margate Yacht Club 1990-, Bd of Dirs; Longport Planning Bd 1990-, Chm; Longport Recreation Dept 1992-, Dir; *office:* Atlantic City HS 1400 Albany Ave Atlantic City NJ 08401

O'DONNELL, VINCENT PATRICK, 12th Grade Biology Teacher; *b:* Fountain Springs, PA; *m:* Florence Breitmayer; *c:* Jennifer, Brendan; *ed:* St Josephs Univ (BS) Bio 1968; West Chester Univ (MA) Bio 1980; 30 Credits Beyond Masters; *cr:* Archbishop Ryan HS Bio Tchr 1968-70; Cardinal O'Hara HS Sci Dept Chair 1970-93; Delaware Cty Comm Coll Co-Adjutant Prof 1992-; Unionville HS Bio Tchr 1993-; *ai:* Link Adv; Bio Curr Comm; Sci Fair Adv & Judge; PA Jr Acad of Sci Judge; NSTA 1970-; NEA, PEA 1993-; Amer Fed Herpetoculturists, Paleontological Research Inst 1988-; Mid Amer Paleontological Soc 1985-; Delaware Cty Paleontological Soc 1980-, Pres 1988-90; GE Star Tchr Awd 1988, 1990; Tchr of Yr 1989 Cardinal O'Hara HS; *office:* Unionville HS 750 Unionville Rd Kennett Square PA 19348

O'DONOGHUE, MARY JOANN, Religious Educator; *b:* Brooklyn, NY; *ed:* St Johns Univ (BS) Mrktg 1979, (MS) Scndry Ed 1991; Fordham Univ (MA) Rel Ed 1993; *cr:* St Johns Prep HS Rel Edctr 1987-; *ai:* Adolesent Cnslr; *office:* Saint Johns Preparatory HS 21-21 Crescent St Astoria NY 11105

O'DONOHUE, SUSAN M., Third Grade Teacher; *b:* New York City, NY; *ed:* Marymount Coll of VA (AA) Lbrl Arts 1968; St Univ of NY at New Paltz (BS) N-6 Psych & Elem Ed 1970; C. W. Post Coll (MS) Elem Ed Specialization Rdng 1975; *cr:* Our Lady of Lourdes Schl Second Grd Tchr 1970-80, Third Grd Tchr, Rdng Coord 1980-; *ai:* Latch Key Coord Supvr 1987-92; Tutoring K-6 Rdng, Math, Related Subjects; Participated, Helped Organize Safety Watch, Patrol Apartment Bldg; NEA 1970-; *office:* Our Lady Of Lourdes Schl 76 Park Blvd Malverne NY 11565*

O'DONOVAN, RICHARD A., AP Amer His Tch & Soc Stud Chm; *b:* Newburgh, NY; *m:* Judith Buchanan; *c:* Mark, Timothy, Michael; *ed:* Millersville St Univ (BS) Sec Ed Comprehensive Soc Stud 1967; Temple Univ (MA) Pol Sci, Amer Govt, Internal Pol 1974; Cheyney Univ Supvr Cert 1982; Franklin Life Ins Co Series 6 License Sell Annuities, Securities 1983; *cr:* Lansdowne-Aldan HS Driver Ed Supvr 1967-69; Methacton HS Soc Stud Tchr 1969-; Franklin Life Ins Co Agent 1971-; St Francis Coll Instr 1994-; *ai:* NEA, PA Ed Assn 1967-; NCSS 1975-; CYO Bsktbl Coach 1984-89; Amer Legion Bsbl Coach 1994-; Pres St Pius X Ath Assn 1984-92; HS Yrbk Dedication 1985; PA Cncl Soc Stud Presenter 1976, 1995; *office:* Methacton HS 1001 Kriebel Mill Rd Norristown PA 19408

ODUM, CHRISTOPHER YORK, English Educator; *b:* Sicily ; *m:* Kathleen M. Costello; *ed:* Corning Comm Coll (AS) Lbrl Arts 1986; Elmira Coll (BA) Eng 1989, (MS) Eng 1996; *cr:* Quinsigamond Comm Coll Writing Instr; Valley View Farm Schl Eng Tchr; Horseheads HS Eng Tchr 1996; *ai:* Co-Adv Drama Club; Asst Dir Productions; Dir Schl Musicals; NCTE; *office:* Horseheads HS 1 Raider Ln Horseheads NY 14845

ODUM, LORI LYN, Eighth Grade Teacher; *b:* Philadelphia, PA; *m:* John W.; *ed:* Cabrini Coll (BA) Arts Admin 1983; St Joseph's Univ (MS) Elem Ed 1994; *cr:* Transfiguration Schl Fifth, Sixth Grd Tchr 1986-92; Roberts Vaux MS Seventh, Eighth Grd Tchr 1992; *ai:* Acads Plus Comm; Project Exposure Adv; NCTM 1995-; *office:* Roberts Vaux MS 24th & Master Sts Philadelphia PA 19121*

OERTEL, VIRGINIA ANN PERLEY, Secondary Social Studies Tchr; *b:* Flushing, NY; *m:* Paul L. Jr.; *c:* Paul L. III, Geoffrey Kenneth; *ed:* Good Counsel Coll (BA) His 1964; Univ of TX (MA) His 1967; *cr:* Austin Pub Schls Scndry Soc Stud Tchr 1964-67; Prince Georges Pub Schl Scndry Soc Stud Tchr 1967-69; Newark Pub Schl Scndry Soc Stud Tchr 1967; Pittsford Cntrl Schls Scndry Soc Stud Tchr 1976-; *ai:* Academically Talented Dist & Bldg Comms; Team Ldr; House & CI Comms; RACSS 1985-; NYSUT, AFT 1980-; *office:* Pittsford MS 75 Barker Rd Pittsford NY 14534

OEXMANN, NORVAL L., Retired Math Teacher; *b:* Decker, IN; *m:* Rita J. Mouzin; *c:* Ram Rotterman, Kim Harris, Debbie Brill; *ed:* IN St Coll (BS) Sec Ed, Math 1952; Purdue U (BSEE) Elect Eng 1962; Wright St U (MS) Sec Schl Admin 1976; Systems Analysis; U of MD Equivalent to Masters in Ec; *cr:* USAF Retired as Colonel 1952-75; Centreville HS Math Tchr 1976-96; *ai:* Var Sftbl Coach; NEA, TROA 1976-; Air Force Assn 1955-; Outstanding: Young Men of Amer, Personalities of South; Meritorius Svc Medal, Legion of Merit; *home:* 2825 Swigert Rd Kettering OH 45440

OFFER, SHARON JONES, History Teacher; *b:* Salisbury, MO; *m:* Roland W.; *c:* Carley; *ed:* Morgan St Univ (BA) His 1970; 30 Hrs Grad Credit Hrs Black His Masters Equivalent; Rdng, Spec Ed In-Svc Courses; *cr:* Eastern Sr HS Tchr 1970-80; Baltimore Polytechnic Inst Tchr 1980-; *ai:* Black Awareness Club Adv; Schl Improvement Team; AFT 1970-; *office:* Baltimore Polytechnic Inst 1400 S Coldspring Ln Baltimore MD 21209*

OFFUTT, SHELLY WYLIE, Teacher of Gifted; *b:* Port Arthur, TX; *m:* Steven Brett; *c:* Tyler; *ed:* TX A&M Univ (BS) Elem Ed & Math 1984; Grad Stud; *cr:* Cy-Fair Schl Dist Tchr 1984-89; West Shore Schl Dist Tchr 1989-; *ai:* Math Counts; Acad Bowl; NEA, PSEA & WSEA 1994-; WHTM TV Channel 27 Recognized as Tchr of Week 1992; *home:* 45 Gary Player Dr Etters PA 17319

OFMAN, RONALD JOSEPH, Second Grade Teacher; *b:* Johnstown, PA; *m:* Eileen M. Yeckley; *c:* Timothy, tyler; *ed:* IN Univ of PA (BA) Elem Ed 1981; 33 Addl Hrs IN Univ; *cr:* United Schl Dist Third Grd Tchr 1985, Second Grd Tchr 1986-; *ai:* Sci Steering Comm; Fac Fin Comm Treas; !SEA, NEA, IRA 1981-; Clyde Vol Fire Co 1989-, Treas; Clyde Playground Comm 1995-, Treas; Blue Ribbon Grant 1996; *office:* United Elem Schl PO Box 168 Armagh PA 15920

OGDEN, MELANIE ANNE, Student Assistance Counselor; *b:* Elizabeth, NJ; *ed:* Trenton St Coll (BS) Hlth & PE 1978; Kean Coll of NJ (MA) Stu Prsnl Svcs 1982; Rutgers Univ (EDD) Spec Ed 1990; *cr:* PE & Hlth Tchr 1978-81; Spec Ed Tchr 1982-93; Old Bridge HS East Campus Stu Assistance Cnslr 1994-; *ai:* Var Girls Tennis Coach; NJEA, NEA 1978-; ASAP 1993-; *office:* Old Bridge HS East Campus Rt 516 Old Bridge NJ 08857

OGDEN, PHILIP MYRON, Natural Science & Math Chprsn; *b:* Nampa, ID; *m:* Edna Irene Mudge; *c:* Carl, Karen Pereira; *ed:* Seattle Pacific Univ (BS) Physics & Math 1959; Univ of CA at Berkeley (PHD) Physics1964; *cr:* Seattle Pacific Univ Asst Prof of Physics, Assoc Prof of Physics 1964-69; Roberts Wesleyan Coll Assoc Prof of Physics 1969-74, Assoc Prof of Physics, Prof of Physics, Chair Div Nat Sci & Math 1974-; *ai:* Hnrs Cncl Chair; Amer Phys Soc, AAPT 1964-; Amer Scientific Affil 1966-, Fellow; Rochester Comm for Scientific Information 1974-; Pearce Meml Free Meth Church 1969-, Chair, Ofcl Bd; Who's Who in Amer Coll & Univ; Summa Cum Laude Seattle Pacific Univ 1959; Articles Pub; *office:* Roberts Wesleyan Coll 2301 Westside Dr Rochester NY 14624

OGG, CAROL RUTH, Special Education Teacher; *b:* Wilkinsburg, PA; *c:* Terri Schrecengost Belcher, Greg Schrecengost; *ed:* Clarion Univ (BS) Elem, Spec Ed 1963, (MED) Spec Ed 1973; *cr:* Westfield NJ Tchr 1963-64, Sub Tchr 1965; Plainfield NJ Sub Tchr 1965; NJ & PA Sub Tchr 1966; Elk Co Pub Schls Sub Tchr 1967-70; St Marys Area Schl Dist Tchr 1971-; *ai:* Mentor; NEA, PSEA 1970-; Kappa Delta Pi 1972-; Seneca Highlands Ed Assn 1971-92, VP, Sec; Elk Co Cntry Club 1973-76, Women's Golf Chair-Woman, Club Championship 1976; Elk Co Crippled Children 1968-, Bd Mem; Mothers Stud Club 1968-78, Pres; St Marys Area Schls Scndry Tchr of Yr 1995-; Helen Kellers Tchr Anne Sullivan Awd; *office:* St Marys Area MS 979 S Saint Marys Rd Saint Marys PA 15857*

OGG, KAREN HAND, Art Teacher; *b:* Salem, MA; *m:* Jamerling; *c:* Dewey, Emma; *ed:* Univ of Southern ME (BFA) Fine Art 1983; Painting; Attn Art Ed Inst; Exceptionality in Art Ed; *cr:* Hinckley Home Schl Farm Family Live-in Tchr, Art Edctr 1983-85; Acad Hill Schl Art Edctr 1984-85; Mt Ararat Schl Art Edctr 1985-86; Edward Little HS Art Edctr 1986-; *ai:* Block Schedule Dev Comm; Stu Crisis Assistance Team Dev; NEA 1984-; Auburn Ed Assn 1986-; Childrens Discovery Ctr 1996, Parent Bd; ME Ed Assessment Tests Dev of Hum 1990, 1993, 1995; Area Artists Show 1994-95; VSM Ceramics Studio Guest Speaker 1994; *office:* Edward Little Sr HS 1 Auburn Hts Auburn ME 04210*

OGILBEE, BARBARA LOUISE (SETZER), 8th Grade Teacher; *b:* Bellaire, OH; *c:* Kyle, Courtney, Brock; *ed:* OH Univ (BSEd) Soc Stud Scndry Ed 1975; *cr:* St Marys Cntrl 7th Grd Tchr 1976-81, 8th Grd Tchr 1991-; *ai:* 8th Grd Power of the Pen Writing Team Coach; Stu Cncl & Schl Newspaper Adv; Art Fair Chm; Diocese of Steubenville for Soc Stud Curr Dev Comm; 8th Grd Grad; OCEA 1991-, Presenter of Paddle-Wheel Talk at St Convention 1993; CWC 1980-, Craft Fair Chm; St Marys Cntrl Endowment Bd 1993-, Originial Mem Appointed to Begin Bd; *office:* St Mary's Cntrl Schl 226 W Main St Saint Clairsville OH 43950

OGILVIE, CAROL RUTH, English & Journalism Teacher; *b:* Nashville, TN; *m:* Edwin B. Stevenson; *c:* Sean Stevenson; Michelle Stevenson; *ed:* Virginia Polytechnic Inst (BA) Eng 1973; Shippensburg Univ (MED) Eng 1976; New Ed Strategies & Newspaper in Ed Applications Courses; *cr:* VPI & SU Eng Grad Tchng Asst 1973; Cumberland Vly HS Eng, Jrnlsm Tchr 1974-81; Carlisle HS Eng Tchr 1985-86; Cumberland Perry Vo-Tech Instrl Support Asst Tchr 1991-94; Hershey HS Eng, Jrnlsm Tchr 1994-; *ai:* Newspaper Adv; Newspaper in Ed Comm Spon Patriot News; NEA; PA Schl Press Assn; Jrnlsm Ed Assn; Newspaper in Ed; Past Phi Kappa Phi Mem; Girl Scouts, BSA Ldr; Various Comms; *office:* Hershey HS Homestead Rd Hershey PA 17033

OGNIBENE, JOHN ROBERT, Sixth Grade Teacher; *b:* Jamestown, NY; *m:* Kimberly Ann Swan; *c:* Jonathan, Alex; *ed:* Clarion Univ of PA (BS) Elem Ed 1981; Fredonia St Coll (MA) Curr & Instruction 1987; Jamestown Comm Coll (AA) 1978; 6 Addl Credit Hrs; *cr:* Cassadaga Valley Cntrl Schl 5th & 6th Grd Tchr 1981-83; Aldine MS 7th Grd Math Tchr 1983-84; Cassadaga Valley Cntrl Schl 6th Grd Tchr 1984-; *ai:* Var Soccer, Var Wrestling, Asst Golf Coaches; AFT 1981-; Village Zoning Bd 1993-; Chautauqua Cty Ath Assn 1981-, Exec Bd; Southern Tier Wrestling Coaches 1981-, Pres; *office:* Cassadaga Valley Central Schl Rt 60 Sinclairville NY 14782

OGNIBENE, RICHARD THOMAS, Chemisty & Physics Teacher; *b:* Rochester, NY; *ed:* Siena Coll (BS) Chem 1985; Univ of Rochester (MS) Chem 1987; *cr:* Perry HS Jr HS Sci Tchr 1986-90; Caledonia-Mumford HS Chem Tchr 1990-92; Monroe Comm Coll Adj Prof of Chem 1990-; Fairport HS Chem, Physics Tchr 1992-; *ai:* Class of 98 Fac Adv; Brotherhood, Sisterhood Comm; VP Fairport Ed Assn; STANYS, NY St United Tchrs 1986-; Caledonia-Mumford Tchr of Yr, Commencement Speaker 1992; Comencement Speaker 1995; *office:* Fairport HS 1358 Ayrault Rd Fairport NY 14450

OGORZALEK, MARGARITA PARRILLA, Language Arts Teacher; *b:* Comerio, PR; *m:* Wayne L.; *c:* Wayne P., Wesley K.; *ed:* Trinity Coll of VT (BA) His 1963; Cntrl CT St Univ (MS) Ed 1969; *cr:* John Barry Schl 2nd Grd Tchr 2 Yrs; Jefferson Jr HS ESL Tchr 3 Yrs; Platt HS Home Schl Coord 22 Yrs; Lincoln MS 8th Grd ILA Tchr 6 Yrs; *ai:* Stu Cncl Co-Spon; Schl Improvement Comm; Meriden Fed of Tchrs 1970-, Co-Chaired Project Excel Schlsp Prgm; Meriden CT Federal Schl Employees Credit Union 1963-, Sec, Bd of Dirs; Honored by CT Puerto Rican Parade St Comm for Dedication, Contributions to Meriden Hispanic Yth; Who's Who in Amer Ed 1994-95; *office:* Lincoln MS 164 Centennial Ave Meriden CT 06450*

O'GRADY, CLOE GISSINGER, 8th Grade Math & Science Tchr; *b:* Philadelphia, PA; *m:* Kevin; *c:* William, Shannon, Brian; *ed:* Holy Family Coll (BA) Elem Ed 1982; Addl Credit Hrs Sci Ed; Scndry Cert Math; *cr:* St Marth Schl 8th Grd Tchr 1987-; *ai:* CYO Dance Moderator; NEA 1987-; *office:* St Martha Schl 11321 Academy Rd Philadelphia PA 19154*

O'GRADY, MARK DANIEL, Assoc Prof of Art & Chprsn; *b:* Salem, MA; *m:* Marijo Russell; *ed:* Cooper Univ (BFA) Studio Art 1976; LA Tech Univ (MFA) Studio Art 1984; *cr:* MA Coll of Art Instr of Art 1978-80; Art Inst of Atlanta Instr of Art 1984-85; Rivier Coll Assoc Prof of Art 1985-; *ai:* Fine Art Soc; Adopt-a-Schl Prgm; Comm Mural Project; Coll Art Assn; Fnds in Art Theory & Ed; Boston Visual Artists Union; NY Artists Equity; Exhibits at STEP Gallery New York NY, Savacon Gallery New York NY, Winfisky Gallery Salem St Coll & Kingston Gallery Boston MA; *office:* Rivier Coll 420 S Main St Nashua NH 03060

O'GRADY, TERENCE J., Geography & Soc Stud Teacher; *b:* New York, NY; *m:* Jennifer Skemp; *c:* Terence O., John P., Robert E., Catherine E.; *ed:* Univ of Bridgeport (BS) His-Scndry Ed 1965, (MS) Soc Stud Scndry Ed 1969; 6th Yr CAS Admin, Supervision 1974; 9 Addl Hrs in Reality Ed, Tchr Effectiveness Trng, Effectiveness Trng & Curr; *cr:* Assumption Schl Math, Sci & Lit Tchr 1965-66; Wilton Jr HS Geography & US His Tchr 1967-70; Middlebrook Sch Geography, Cultures & His Tchr 1971-; *ai:* Beginning Ed Support & Trng Comm; CT Geographic Alliance Tchr Consultant; Capricorn Exchange 1993-94; 1st US-Australia Tchr Exch; Natl Geographic Soc Geography Bee Coord; NEA, CT Ed Assn 1967-; CT Soc Stud Cncl 1980-; ASCD; Hiram Lodge #18 AF&AM 1978-, Tiler, Master Mason; Governor's Youth Action Awd 1981; Fac & Schl Received Pres Awd Excl in Ed 1982-83; 8th Grd Classes Won CT Originals Exemplary Writing Awd 1989; Pres Environmental Youth Awd 1990; 7th &

8th Grader Won CT Originals Exemplary Writing St Awd 1990; ASCD Displayed Co-Authored Curr 1991; Presenter at Unified Arts Conf in Sturbridge MA 1995; Presenter on Integrated Curr at New England League of Midd Schls Natl Conf in Providence RI 1996; *office:* Middlebrook Schl 131 School Rd Wilton CT 06897*

OGREN, S. ROBERT, Retired Mathematics Teacher; *b:* Mc Keesport, PA; *m:* Jane Freeland; *c:* David, Chad; *ed:* Edinboro Univ (BS) Math Ed 1965; IN Univ of PA (MED) Math 1970; *cr:* Bethel Park HS Math Tchr 1965-95; *home:* 132 Audrey Dr Pittsburgh PA 15236

O'HANLON, CYNTHIA MARIE, Kindergarten Teacher; *b:* Philadelphia, PA; *m:* William P. Sr.; *c:* Kevin, Billy Jr., Cindi; *ed:* Cabrini Coll (BA) Eng & Commnctn 1979, (BS) Elem Ed 1979; *cr:* Cabrini Coll Resident Dir 1980-81; Holy Savior-St John Fisher Schl 2nd Grd Tchr 1981-93, Kndgtn Tchr 1993-; *ai:* Yrbk; Primary Level Coord; Emergency Response Team; Rel Comm; NCEA 1980-; Ulster Project 1991-, Act Dir; *office:* Holy Saviour-St J. Fisher Schl 122 E Ridge Rd Linwood PA 19061

O'HANLON, JOAN MARIE CASABONA, Eng & Language Arts Instructor; *b:* Brooklyn, NY; *m:* W. Reese Jr.; *c:* Reese Nolan; *ed:* St Joseph's Coll (BA) Eng 1969; Adelphi Univ (MA) Eng 1973; St John's Univ (PD) Admin, Supervision 1979; In Dissertation Phase of Doctor of Arts Degree in Eng St John's Univ; *cr:* Half Hollow Hills HS East 12 Grd Eng, Advanced Placement, Coll Eng, Lang Arts Instr 1970-; *ai:* NHS Adv; Supvr Bldng Asst & Eng, Lang Arts Dept; Phi Delta Kappa 1979-; NY St United Tchrs 1970-; NCTE 1970-; Finalist as Regnl Summer Schl Prin 6-12 Grd at Western Suffolk BOCES; Shared Decision Making Team 1994-; *office:* Half Hollow Hills HS E 50 Vanderbilt Pky Dix Hills NY 11746

O'HARA, BRYAN, Secondary Mathematics Teacher; *b:* Youngstown, OH; *m:* Kathryn Jones; *ed:* Youngstown St Univ (BS) Comp Tech 1986, (MS) Ed 1995; 2nd Math Tchng Cert 1988; *cr:* Girard HS 2nd Math Tchr 1988-93; Liberty HS 2nd Math Tchr 1994-; *ai:* Asst Bsktbl Coach Girard HS 1981-93; Head Bsktbl Coach 1994-; Martha Jennings Scholar; Kent St Univ Tchng Awd; *office:* Liberty HS 317 Churchill Hubbard Rd Youngstown OH 44505*

O'HARA, CAROL JEANNE, First Grade Teacher; *b:* Newark, NJ; *ed:* Kean Coll of NJ (BA) Elem Ed 1969; Grad Studies Bank Street Coll of Ed, Caldwell Coll, Antioch Coll; Credit Hrs Soc for Dev Ed; *cr:* Spring Garden Schl Tchr 1969-; *ai:* Hnr Roll, Citizenship Prgms Coord; Curr Dev Comm; NEA 1969-; Acad Booster Club 1990-; *office:* Spring Garden Elem Schl 59 S Spring Garden Ave Nutley NJ 07110*

O'HARA, DAVID ALVIN, Computer Teacher; *b:* Spangler, PA; *m:* Sedona Ann Sunseri; *c:* Taylor James; *ed:* Indiana Univ of PA (BS) Scndry Math 1985; California Univ of PA (MS) Math, Comp Sci 1991; *cr:* Rockwood Schl Dist Math Tchr 1985-86; Carmichaels Schl Dist Cmptr Tchr 1986-; Mount Aloysius Coll Intro to Comp Tchr 1992; Univ of Pitt Assoc Prof Comp Sci 1994-; *ai:* Sr Class Adv; Sr High Cmptr Coord; NEA, PSEA 1986-; Presbyn Church 1993-, Yth Adv; Goals 2000 Grant Applicant; Army Achvmt Awd; Distngd Hnr Grad, Military Schooling; 4MAT Trainer; *home:* 1010 Peach St California PA 15419*

O'HARA, ELIZABETH ANN, Fr Tchr & Frgn Lang Dept Ldr; *b:* Yonkers, NY; *m:* Frederick H.; *c:* Amy, Claire; *ed:* Univ of Rochester (BA) Fr Lang, Lit 1972; Syracuse Univ (MA) Fr Literat 1975; Span, Cmptr; *cr:* LeRoy Cntrl Schl Fr Tchr 1972-74; Syr Univ Tchng Asst 1974-75; Baker HS Fr Tchr 1975-88; Westhill HS Fr Tchr 1988-; *ai:* Fr Exchange 30 Stdnts Hosted Fr Counterparts 1995, Will Visit France; Fr Club; AATF 1972-, Treas; NYSTAFCT 1972-; NEA; Grants Tchrs Ctr 12 Times, Schl Curr 3 Times; Seminars for Profess Org Cooking, Fr Lang, Exchanges; *office:* Westhill Sr HS 4501 Onondaga Blvd Syracuse NY 13219

O'HARA, JAMES D., Social Studies Teacher; *b:* Brighton, MA; *m:* Denise Lavely; *c:* Emily, Zachary; *ed:* Framingham St Coll (BA) US His 1977; Lesley Coll (MED) Spec Needs 1981; 3 Hrs Tchng World Geog Bridgewater St Coll; 3 Hrs Tchng His, Soc Stud Univ of MA at Dartmouth; *cr:* Mc Lean Hosp Spec Needs 1979-81; Kino MS Spec Needs Tchr 1981-82; Westport MS Spec Needs Tchr 1984-88, Soc Stud Tchr 1988-; *ai:* Geog Club Adv; Yth Bsktbl Coach; AFT 1984-; South Eastern MS Geographical Network 1992-; Dartmouth Yth Act Assn 1995-; YMCA Bsktbl 1988-; Dartmouth Girls Little League 1993-; Mustard Seed, Horace Mann Grant; John Riley Geog Tchr of Yr Awd; *home:* 64 Prospect St South Dartmouth MA 02748

O'HARA, KEITH ARMSTRONG, English & Spanish Teacher; *b:* Oak Park, IL; *ed:* Middlebury Coll (AB) Eng Lit 1982; Trinity Coll (MA) Eng 1994; *cr:* Lyman Meml HS Eng, Span Coach 1989-90; Marianapolis Preparatory Schl Dept Chair Span, Eng Coach 1990-; *ai:* Girls Var Soccer Head Coach; Boys Var Tennis Head Coach; Asst Ath Dir; NCTE 1990-; BSA, Vol, Contributor, Former Scout, Eagle; *office:* Marianapolis Preparatory Schl The Common Rt 200 Thompson CT 06277*

O HARA, RICHARD, English Teacher; *m:* Margaret W.; *ed:* St Francis Coll (BA) Eng 1967; John Carroll Univ (MA) Eng 1970; Montclair St (MA) Rdng 1977; Columbia Univ Writing, Philosophy; *cr:* Morris Cath HS Eng Tchr 1971-73; Metuchen HS Rdng Tchr 1973-74; Montgomery HS Eng Tchr 1974-; *ai:* Lit Magazine; Intnl Rdng Assn 1975-; NJ Cncl of Tchrs of Eng 1980-; *office:* Montgomery HS Burnt Hill Rd Skillman NJ 08558

O'HARE, MICHAEL JAMES, Social Studies Teacher; *b:* NY; *m:* Deborah; *c:* Maureen, Brendan; *ed:* St Vincent Coll (BA) His 1969; St Johns Univ (MA) Asian His 1974; Stony Brook Univ 15+ Cr; *cr:* R C Murphy Jr HS Tchr 1969-; *ai:* Stock Market Game; Dist Curr Dev Comm; Soc Stud Task Groups; Stu Tchr Mentor; AFT 1969-; NYSUT 1969-; 3 Village Tchrs Assn 1969-; DAR Awd Outstdng Tchr of His 1995; *home:* 58 Farm Rd W Wading River NY 11792*

O'HARRA, SUSAN LOOBY, Mathematics & Business Teacher; *b:* Columbus, OH; *m:* Hal; *ed:* Otterbein Coll (BS) Acctng, Bus Admin 1985, (MA) Ed 1994; Scndry Math Bus Cert; *cr:* West Jefferson MS Math Tchr 1989-91; West Jefferson HS Math, Bus Tchr 1991-; *ai:* Soph Class Adv; Jr Achvmt Coord; Jennings Scholar Lecture Prgm; NEA, WJEA 1989-; *office:* West Jefferson HS 561 W Jefferson Kiousville Rd West Jefferson OH 43162*

O'HEARN, JAMES B., English Teacher; *b:* Arlington, MA; *m:* Lynne A. Hedin; *c:* Timothy, Kylen; *ed:* Univ of MA (AB) Eng 1964; Amer Intnl Coll (MED) Ed 1971; IN Univ Linguistics; *cr:* East Longmeadow Pub Schl Tchr 1965-; *ai:* Tech Comm; NEA, MTA, ELEA; Elks Lodge #61 1978-; East Longmeadow Cable Access Television 1991-; Springfield Coll Sports Announcer; *office:* Birchland Park MS 50 Hanward Hl East Longmeadow MA 01028

OHEARN, MAUREEN ANN, 1st Grade Teacher; *b:* Everett, MA; *ed:* Regis Coll (BA) His & Eng 1966; *cr:* St Bridgets Schl 1st Grd Tchr 1966-68; CW Holmes Schl 1st Grd Tchr 1968-; *ai:* MEA 1968-; Malden Tchrs Assn 1968-; *office:* CW Holmes Schl 257 Mountain Ave Malden MA 02148

OHLSON, HELEN, English Teacher; *b:* Philadelphia, PA; *ed:* West Chester Univ (BS) Scndry Ed 1967; Widener Univ (MED) Lang Arts 1988; Eastern WA Univ, Univ of DE, Penn St Univ Addl 30 Credit Hrs; *cr:* Great Falls Mt Schl Dist Eng Tchr 1967-69; St Div Soc Svcs Soc Worker 1970-74; Interboro Schl Dist Eng Tchr 1975-; *ai:* Writing Wkshp Presenter, Critique Group Organizer, Mentor; NEA 1967-70, Bldg Rep Comm Mem 1975; DE Lit Connection 1995-, Dir of Ed; Friends of Caleb Pusey 1984-, Bd Mem; Lit Newsletter Articles Pub; *office:* Prospect Park Schl 9th & Pennsylvania Avenues Prospect Park PA 19076

OHLSON, MATTHEW PAUL, Physics Teacher; *b:* Kingston, NY; *m:* Mary S. Garcia; *ed:* OH St Univ (BS) Sci 1980; Akron Univ (MS) Ed 1990; Attnd Ashland Univ; *cr:* West Holmes Schl Sci Tchr 1980-84; Southeast Local Sci Tchr 1984-85; Green Local Sci Tchr 1985-93; *ai:* Stu Cncl; Wrestling, Ftbl & Track Coach; Various Comms; NEA, OEA & NSTA 1985-; AAPT 1989-; Tchr of Yr 1991; *office:* Green HS PO Box 218 Greensburg OH 44232

OHMAN, SHERRI LYNN, 7th-8th Grade Teacher; *b:* Detroit, MI; *m:* Steven David; *ed:* Pensacola Chrstn Coll (BS) Elem Ed 1989; *cr:* Trinity Chrstn Schl 4-6 Grd, 11-12 Grd Speech, 9-10 Grd Bio Tchr 1989-, 7-8 Grd Tchr 1993-; *ai:* Var Cheerleading Coach; Yrbk Adv; Jr Class Spon; Elem & HS Dramatic Productions; Stu Tchr Awd 1989; New England Assn of Chrstn Schls Speaker; *office:* Trinity Christian Schl 80 Clinton St Concord NH 03301

OHMELA, JANET M., Social Studies Teacher; *b:* Manhattan, NY; *m:* Stephen; *c:* Stephen, Janeen; *ed:* Queens Coll (BA) His 1966; Addl 30 Post Grad Credits Ed; *cr:* John Bowne HS Soc Stud Tchr 1966-79; Sachem HS Soc Stud Tchr 1980-; *ai:* NYSUT, NCSS 1966-; SCTA 1980-; *office:* Sachem HS South 51 School St Ronkonkoma NY 11779

OHREN, JUDY BEARMAN, Kindergarten Teacher; *b:* Brooklyn, NY; *m:* Sheldon I.; *c:* Holly, Jennifer, Richard; *ed:* Brooklyn Coll (BA) Ed-Early Child 1958, (MS) Ed-Early Child 1963; Lincoln Ctr Julliard Schl 4 Credit Hrs; *cr:* PS 114 Kndgtn Tchr 1958-66; PS 219 Kndgtn Tchr 1970-71; PS 68 Kndgtn, Second Grd Tchr 1981-; *ai:* Early Childhood Assn; *home:* 12 Hastings Rd Monsey NY 10952

OHRT, JOSEPH GLEN, Director of Choral Activities; *b:* Manteno, IL; *m:* Susan Elizabeth Crawford; *c:* Elija River; *ed:* Westminster Choir Coll (BM) Music Ed 1987, (MM) Music Ed 1995; Tchng Cert Choral Music Experience Inst; Kodaly Musical Trng Inst; *cr:* Linden Elem Schl Vocal Music Tchr 1987-91; Cntrl Bucks HS W Choral Dir 1991-; Youngsingers of PA Choral Dir 1991-; *ai:* Dir Men's Ensemble, Women's Ensemble, Chamber Choir, Madrigal Choir, Voix D'esprit; Harlequin Productions; ACDA 1987-, R & S Chair PA; MENC 1987-; *office:* Central Bucks-West HS 375 W Court St Doylestown PA 18901*

OILER, JAMES WILLIAM, Science Teacher; *b:* Columbus, OH; *m:* Margaret Elizabeth; *c:* Seth, Emily Hall, Deidra Hall; *ed:* Warren Wilson Coll (AA) Bio 1966; Berea Coll (BA) Bio 1968; Eastern KY Univ (MAEd) Bio 1975; *cr:* North Gallia HS Sci Tchr 1968-92; River Valley HS Sci Tchr 1992-; *ai:* Sci Club Adv; NEA & OEA 1968-; NSTA 1980-; OH Acad of Sci Tchrs Awd; Acker Outstanding Tchr 1983-84; *home:* 80 Wayne Ln Thurman OH 45685

OJA, LINDA PALUMBO, Sixth Grade Teacher; *b:* Brooklyn, NY; *m:* David E.; *c:* Matthew David, Kristen Elizabeth, Katherine Ann; *ed:* Syracuse Univ (BS) Elem Ed 1975; 42 Credit Hrs; *cr:* West Genesee Schl Dist Math, Resource Room Tchr 1975-76; East Syracuse Dist-Wide Math Specialist 1976-80; Fremont Elem Enrichment Math Tchr 1980-86; Kinne St 6th Grd Tchr 1986-; *ai:* Syracuse Chargers Youth Dev Prgm Vol Coach; Syracuse Festival of Races Asst Race Dir; Susan G Komen Breast Cancer Fndtn Race for Cure; AFT, NYSUT, ESMUT 1976-; YMCA Comm Fitness Awd; Syracuse Chargers Track Club 1977-, Soc Chprsn, Vol of Yr 1981, 1993; Volntr Chrprsn; ES M Tchr of Exclnc 1994, Chrpsn 1994-; *office:* Kinne Street Elem Schl 230 Kinne St East Syracuse NY 13057*

O'KEEFE, BRIAN DAVID, Biology & AP Biology Instr; *b:* Baldwin, NY; *m:* Patricia A. Kosters; *c:* SUNY Cortland (BS) Bio 1969; *ed:* Cortland, SUNY (BS) Bio 1969; SUNY Oswego, ESF, Albany 43 grad hrs; *cr:* Albany HS Sci Tchr 1969-70; Chittenango HS Bio Tchr 1970-; *ai:* CTA, AFT 1970-; NABT 1985-; NY St Regents Bio Inst Instr 1979-; Examagen Corp Counsltant; Primary Bio Inc Pres, CEO; NSF Grant 1974-75 SUNY Oswego, Ithaca Coll 1990-; *office:* Chittenango HS Genesee St Chittenango NY 13037*

O'KEEFE, DANIEL PATRICK, Asst Prin, Eng & French Tchr; *b:* New York, NY; *c:* Erin; *ed:* Cathedral Coll (BA) Eng Lit 1987; St Josephs Seminary (MA) Rel Stud 1993; Post-Grad Stud in Ed at NY Inst of Tech; *cr:* Cardinal Hayes HS Tchr 1987-88; John S Burke Cath HS Tchr 1988-91; Newburg City Schl Tchr 1991-92; Cathedral Prep Seminary Tchr & Asst Prin 1992-; *ai:* Stu Cncl; Bookstore; Cross Cntry; Indoor & Outdoor Track; *office:* Cathedral Prep Seminary 5625 92nd St Elmhurst NY 11373

O'KEEFE, ELIZABETH, High School Librarian; *b:* New York, NY; *ed:* St Thomas Aquinas (BSEd) Ed 1958; St Johns Univ (MLS) Lib Sci 1965; Attnd Manhattan Coll, Iona Coll, Fordham Univ; *ai:* Recruitment, Alumni Comm; Transportation Coord; Adjunct Librn; Fed of Cath Tchrs 1974-; Cath Lib Assn; NY St Grant for Comm Arts at SUNY Potsdam; *office:* Monsignor Scanlan HS 915 Hutchinson River Pkwy Bronx NY 10465

O'KEEFE, LAWRENCE, Middle School Teacher; *b:* Westerly, RI; *ed:* St Michael's Coll (BA) Ed 1965; Univ of VT (MED) Soc Sci, Ed 1985; 30 Addl Credit Hrs; *cr:* Edmunds MS Tchr 1966-, Vista Del Mar Schl Dist 1994-; *ai:* Paradise Project; Educl Consultant; NEA 1966-, Rep Cncl; BSTA; NCSS; Natl MS Assn; BSA 1949-, Scoutmaster, Eagle, Silver Beaver; Historical Soc 1967-; Distngd Tchr Awd; Natl Tchrs Forum; Natl MS Assn, 100 Exemplary MS Prgms; Excl in Tchng Presidential Awd; *office:* Edmunds MS 275 Main St Burlington VT 05401*

O'KEEFE, MARY KATE MCGOLDRICK, English Teacher; *b:* Greenwich, CT; *m:* Timothy Charles; *c:* Timothy Charles Jr.; *ed:* Providence Coll (BA) Eng 1986; RI Coll (MAT) Eng 1990; *cr:* Bay Bank Credit Analyst 1986-88; Portsmouth HS Eng Tchr 1990-; *office:* Portsmouth HS 1 Education Ln Portsmouth RI 02871

O'KEEFFE, KATHLEEN F., Social Studies, AP US His Tchr; *b:* Brooklyn, NY; *ed:* St Josephs Coll (BA) His; Fordham Univ His; NY Univ His Ed; *cr:* Cardinal Newman Coll Admissions Cnslr 1977-78, Admissions Dir 1978-79; Newtown HS Tchr, Tchr Cnslr 1982-; *ai:* Schl Safety, Schl Planning Comms; Dept Soc Act Co Chair; ATSS 1984-, Exec Comm; UFT 1984-, Delegate at Large; Hosp Light House, Vol; Stu Handbook Editor; Dev Occupational Ed Grant; Dev 9th Grd Curr Queensboro Comm; Multicutural Ldrshp Prgm Manual; *office:* Newtown HS 48-01 90th St Elmhurst NY 11215

O'KEEFFE-BOOGS, COLETTE D., Physical Education Teacher; *b:* New York, NY; *m:* Phillip Baker Boogs; *ed:* Univ of Ulster in Northern Ireland (BA) Sports Sci 1980; Post Grad Cert in Ed 1986; *cr:* Dana Hall PE, Acad & Class Adv, Coach, Soc Comm 1988-; *ai:* Soc Comm Coord for MS; Coach Field Hockey, Bsktbl, LaCrosse; *office:* Dana Hall Schl 45 Dana Rd Wellesley Hills MA 02181

OKIN, JASON, History Teacher & Debate Coach; *b:* New York, NY; *m:* Jerilyn M. Kossack; *c:* Jobi, Jordana; *ed:* Montclair St Univ (BA) Soc Stud 1964; NY Univ (MA) His 1967; Post Grad Stud Cornell Univ; *cr:* West Kinney Jr HS Span Tchr 1964-67; Ramapo HS His Tchr 1967-; *ai:* Debate Coach; NEA & NJEA 1967-; NCSS 1989-; Ringwood NJ Democratic Comm 1980-86, Municipal Chm; Lakeland Regnl HS Bd of Ed 1987-, VP, Pres; NDEA Grant at Cornell Univ 1969; *office:* Ramapo HS George St Franklin Lakes NJ 07417*

OKONKWO, EMEKA C. J., Prof of English & Linguistics; *b:* Awka Anambra St, Nigeria; *m:* Luz Delagado; *c:* Ucheamaka, Chimaobi; *ed:* Alvan Ikoku Coll of Ed Nigeria (NCE) Eng, Fr 1965; St Univ of NY at Buffalo (MA) Linguistics 1972; SUNY at Buffalo (PHD) Linguistics *cr:* Univ of Jos Nigeria Lecturer 1977-79; Coll of Ed Assoc Prof, H Dept 1979-92; Medgar Evers Coll Adj Assoc Prof 1993-; BMCC Adj Assoc Prof 1993-; *ai:* 20 Journal Articles, Publications; Borough Of Manhattan Comm Coll Dept of English 199 Chambers S York NY 10007

OKONKWO, VALERIE MAUREEN (BROWN), Social Studies Te *b:* St Ann's Bay, Jamaica WI; *m:* Sylvester U.; *ed:* Univ of West Indie Lib Stud-Hon 1983; Herbert H. Lehman Coll (BA) Psych 1986; Br Coll Working Towards MA Experimental Psych; *cr:* Brown's Town Coll His, Ec, Prins of Bus Lecturer 1983-84; Theodore Roosevelt H Stud Tchr 1985-86; IS 232 Winthrop Intermediate Schl Soc Stud 1986-; *ai:* Prof Dev Lab, Cancer Day Planning Comms; African-Am Month Competition; *office:* IS 232 Winthrop 905 Winthrop St Br NY 11203*

O'KONSKI, BARBARA A., French Teacher; *b:* Wilkes Barre, P Thomas E.; *c:* Christine, Michael; *ed:* Coll Misericordia (BA) Fr Bloomsburg Univ (MED) Fr 1973; 18 Addl Hrs; *cr:* Hanover Area Tchr 1968-; Hanover Sr HS Fr Tchr 1968-; *ai:* Hanover Area Chpt Adv; HAEA, PSEA, NEA 1968-; Amer Assn Tchrs of Fr 1974-; Hanover Area Jr Sr HS 1600 Sans Souci Pky Wilkes Barre PA 1870

OKOREN, CAROL A., Retired PE Teacher & Coach; *b:* Brooklyn *ed:* St Univ Coll at Cortland (BS) PE 1963; Attnd St John's Univ, St Coll at Albany, Guidance, CO St, AZ St, St Univ at New Paltz, P Onteora Cntrl Schl PE, Coaching 1963-; *ai:* STEP Prgm; Coach Var Field 1971-; Var Field Hockey Coach 1973-93; Var Bsktbl Coach 19 Coached Var Vlybl, Winter Track, JV Bsktbl; AFT, AAH NYSAHPERD, US Field Hockey Assn 1963-; Onteora PTSA 1978-; Coach of Yr 1982; Empire St Games Field Hockey Coach 13 Yr Medals; Natl Women Sport Day Honoree Awd 1995; GWS Project Ac Awd.

OKULSKI, GLORYIA LENZI, Literature Teacher; *b:* Italy; *m:* Jo Liberty; *ed:* Wells Coll (BA) Frgn Langs; Columbia Univ (MA) Eng *cr:* Rockville Comm Coll Eng Tchr; NY Pub Schls 9-12th Grd Eng NJ Pub Schls 9-12th Grd Tchr; Utica Comm Coll Communication Tch Lean Schl Lit Tchr 1984-; *ai:* NCTE; Small Victories Chptr Devo Me; *office:* Mc Lean Schl Of Maryland 8224 Lochinver Ln Potoma 20854

OKWU, AUSTINE S. O., Professor & Director; *b:* Egbu Owerri, Ni *m:* Beatrice N.; *c:* Nkem, Edo, Ndi, Chichi, Emeka; *ed:* Univ of Du (BA) Ec 1958; Southern CT St Univ (MA) His 1971; Columbia Univ (His 1978; Inst for Stud of Ec 1964; *cr:* Civil Admin Dist Ofcr195 Diplomatic Svc Frgn Svc 1961-71; Bloomfield Coll Assoc Intern 197 Naugatuck Vly Comm Coll Dir Soc Sci 1985-; *ai:* 4CS, ECCSSA 1 Distngd Svc, Acad Excl Awd; *home:* 14 Pine Rock Rd New Have 06511*

OLBRYS, DONNA MARIA, Spanish Teacher; *b:* Newark, NJ Edward; *c:* Tara; *ed:* Bloomfield Coll (BA) Span- Summa Cum L 1979; *cr:* Paul VI Regnl HS Span Tchr 1981-87; Pinelands Regnl HS Tchr 1989-; *ai:* Span Club Adv; Span Honor Soc Coord; Class of 19 1999 Co-Adv; NEA, NJ Foreign Lang Educator Assn & Amer Assn of of Span & Portuguese 1981-; Bloomfield Coll Svc Key & Schlsp Key *office:* Pinelands Regional HS 565 Nugentown Rd Tuckerton NJ 080

OLDFIELD, BRUCE K., Assoc Professor of Phys Sci; *b:* Baltimore, *m:* Teresa Fallon-Oldfield; *c:* Jennifer, Bethany; *ed:* Broome Comm (AAS) 1971; SUC at Cortland (BS) Geology 1973; Binghammon (MA) Geology 1989; *cr:* Broome Comm Coll Assoc Prof 1988-; *ai:* Theta Kappa Hnr Soc Adv; Young Peoples Geology Club Co-Adv; Hnrs Inst Seminar Ldr; Palesntological Soc, Wray Trust Rsrch G Palesntological Rsrch Inst; Intnl Assoc for Stud of Fossil Cidarian; Y Peoples Geology Club, Adv; Each One Teach One Eastern Mineological Scis 1989; NYS Chancellors Awd for Excl in Tchng 1 NIS Excl Awd 1995; Phi Theta Kappa Most Distngd Adv & Paragin 1995; *office:* Broome Comm Coll PO Box 1017 Binghamton NY 139

OLDHAM, SALLY NIMOCKS, 4th Grade Teacher; *b:* Columbus, OH Jerry L.; *c:* Keith, Peter, Collin; *ed:* OH Dominican Coll (BS) Elem 1973; Attnd OH St Univ, OH Univ at Zanesville, Xavier; *cr:* Licking Head Start Tchr 1973-74; Maybury 2nd Grd Tchr 1973-75; Eastha 1st-5th Grd & Currently 4th Grd Tchr 1975-; *ai:* Safety Patrol Adv; Re Panel Mem Co-Chair; Strategic Plan Schl Reform Comm; Project SH Tchr Ldr; COTA 1973-; OEA & NEA 1973-; Cols Ed Assn 1973-, E Governor at Large, CEA Mem of Yr 1988 & Outstdng Rac Rep (3 Tim Buckeye Lake Civic Assn 1980-; WBNS-TV Tchr of the Week 1993; *off* Easthaven Elem Schl 2360 Garnet Pl Columbus OH 43232

OLDROYD, CAROLYN A., Math & Spanish Teacher; *b:* Elmira, NY; Mansfield Univ (BS) Math Ed 1972; Elmira Coll (MS) Math Ed 1979; Horseheads Chrstn Schl Math, Span Tchr 1974-76; Twin Tiers Bapt Math & Span Tchr 1976-; *ai:* Sr Class Adv; *office:* Twin Tiers Baptist PO Drawer K Breesport NY 14816

O'LEARY, ANNE SWARTHOUT, HS Social Studies Teacher; *b:* Tol OH; *m:* Timothy Patrick; *c:* Todd, Andrew, Thomas; *ed:* Univ of Tol (BE) His, Geog 1993; *cr:* Springfield HS Soc Stud Tchr 1994-; *ai:* PEA Team Coord; NEA 1994-; NCSS, OCSS 1993-; Kappa Delta Pi; *off* Springfield HS 1470 S Mc Cord Rd Holland OH 43528

O'LEARY, MICHAEL PAUL, Guidance Counselor; *b:* Boston, MA; Patricia Ann Hegarty; *c:* Kristen O'Sullivan, Michael S.; *ed:* Boston (BS) Eng & Ed 1964; Univ of MA at Boston (MED) Guid & Cnslng 1 63 Credit Hrs beyond MS from: Boston Univ, Northeastern Univ, Uni MA & Boston Fitchburg St Coll; *cr:* Cambridge Rindge & Latin HS Tchr 1964-67; Chelmsford Jr HS Guid Cnslr 1970-70; Dracut HS G Cnslr 1970-90; Englesby Jr HS Rdng Tchr 1990-92; Dracut HS Guid C 1992-; *ai:* Peer Medition Coord; Occupational Cnslr for Division Employ & Trng in MA; Summer Schl Eng Tchr; Tutor for Home-Bo Stdnts; NEA 1964-; MA Schl Cnslrs Assn 1967-; Dracut Tchrs Assn 19 Northeast Cnslrs Assn 1975-; *office:* Dracut HS 1540 Lakeview Ave Dra MA 01826*

O'LEARY, PATRICIA, English Teacher; *b:* New York, NY; *m:* Paul; Deirdre, Julie; *ed:* Hunter Coll (BA) Eng, (MA) Eng, Comparative Lit; Credit Hrs Post Grad Stud Hofstra Univ, Brooklyn Coll; *cr:* Willi Cooper Jr HS Eng Tchr 3 Yrs; Forest Hills Adult Ctr Asst Prgm Dir, Tchr 12 Yrs; Elmont Meml HS Eng Tchr 8 Yrs; *ai:* Yrbk, Lit Magaz Advs; NEA 1988-; NCTE 1991-; Tchr of Month Awd 3 Times; Outst Tchr Awd Univ of Chicago; *office:* Elmont Memorial HS 555 Ridge Elmont NY 11003

O'LEARY, PATRICIA ANN, Science Teacher; *b:* Bridgeport, CT; Jennifer Feola, Michael Feola, Elizabeth Feola; *ed:* Souther CT St U (BS) Bio 1968, (MS) Bio 1985, (MS) Environmental Ed 1986; Outw Bound Educators Course; NOAA Grant Marine Inst Key Largo; NSF Gr Project Porifera Thames SS New London CT; CT Mentor Tchr Tr Cooperative Tchr Trng; *cr:* Westbrooke HS Sci Tchr 1968-70; C Saybrook HS Sci Tchr 1980-; Dist Sci Coord K-12; *ai:* Jr Class Adv; P Dev, Stu of Month, Scheduling, Stu Acts Fund Raising Comms; Ra Music Boosters; PTO; NEA, CEA, OSEA 1980-, Exec Comm OSE NSTA, CSTA 1986-; Judy Lubber's Fellowship; NSF Grant; Tchr of

Outward Bound Schlsp; *office:* Old Saybrook Sr HS 1111 Boston .d Old Saybrook CT 06475*

ARY, TERESITA DWYER, English Teacher; *b:* Rouses Point, NY; :hael K.; *c:* Anne, Teri; *ed:* Hunter Coll (MA) Eng 1970; Coll of New lle (BA) Eng 1963; Columbia Univ Tchng the Gifted; Coll of New lle Remedial Rdng; *cr:* Guadalupe Schl Elem Tchr 1963-65; NYC chls JHS Tchr & Adult Ed 1966-73; Immaculate Conception MS 84; St Michael Acad Eng Tchr 1984-; *ai:* Yrbk 1984-93; Poetry ıp 1993; Eng Dept Chair 1987-1992; *office:* Saint Michael Acad 425 d St New York NY 10001

:HNOWICZ, REBECCA ANN (QUINN), First Grade Teacher; *b:* Castle, PA; *m:* Richard Joseph; *c:* Joseph, Michael, Mary Beth; *ed:* oro St (BS) Elem Ed & Early Chldhd 1972; Akron Univ (MS) Elem 95; Addl 30 Credit Hrs From Kent St, Ashland & Walsh; *cr:* Towslee Kndgtn Tchr 1974-77, 2nd Grd Tchr 1977-81; Huntington Elem 1st chr 1981-; *ai:* Brunswick Ed Assn, OEA, NEA 1974-; Saint Ambrose PTO, Pres, Presch Religion Tchr; Tchr of Week Awd-Thanks to Tchr Channel 8 WJW Cleveland Television Station; *office:* Huntington Schl 1931 Huntington Cir Brunswick OH 44122

KSAK, SHARON DANIELS, Health & Physical Educator; *b:* sville, OH; *m:* Michael Carl; *c:* Kellen Michael, Kyle Patrick; *ed:* ıng Green St Univ (BS) HPER 1978, (MED) Hlth Ed 1980; 17 Post Hrs at Univ San Diego, Clarion Univ of PA, Fresno Pacific Coll, ery Rock Univ of PA; *cr:* Swanton HS Tchr, Coach 1978-79; Bowling ı St Univ Grad Asst, Asst VB Coach 1979-80; John Carroll Univ ng Lecturer 1980-81; Clarion Univ of PA Assoc Prof, VB Coach 85; Temple Univ Women's Vlybl Coach, BB Coach 1985-90; Mentor PER Tchr 1991-; *ai:* Steering, Hlth Review of Curr, PE Curr Review n; Girls Bsktbl Coach 1992-95; AAHPERD 1977-; NEA 1991-; giate VB Coaches Assn 1981-; Venture Capital Grant for Team Tchng; : Articles; *office:* Mentor HS 6477 Center St Mentor OH 44060

NDZENSKI, MICHAEL FELIX, Composition & Lit Professor; *b:* n, MA; *ed:* Mc Gill Univ (BA) Eng 1972, (MA) Eng 1978; Univ of FL) Eng Ed 1991; *cr:* SUNY Ed Instr 1978-80; Plymouth-Carver Regnl ng Tchr 1980-82; Univ of FL Writing Ctr Coord 1987-88; Utica Coll yracuse Univ Eng Asst Prof 1988-90; Cape Cod Comm Coll osition, Lit Prof 1990-; *ai:* Writing Coord; Curr & Prgms Comm ; Poetry Club Adv; NEA; NCTE; Intnl Arthurian Soc, North Amer ch; Ed Arthurian Fiction and Criticism, Poetry Journal; *office:* Cape Comm Coll 2240 Iyanough Rd West Barnstable MA 02668*

NIK, PETER MATTHEW, Physical Education Teacher; *b:* Queens, *m:* Jennifer Ann Regan; *ed:* SUNY at Cortland (BSE) PE 1992; phi Univ Grad Stu Hlth Stud 21 Credit Hrs; *cr:* Meadowbrook Elem PE Tchr 1994-; *ai:* JV Boys Bsktbl Coach; JV Boys & Girls Tennis h; AAHPERD 1992-; NYSAHPERD 1992-; East Meadow Tchrs Assn -; *office:* Meadowbrook Elem Schl 241 Old Westbury Rd East Meadow 1554

.NYCH, THOMAS STEVEN, Language Arts & Soc Stud Tchr; *b:* ıgstown, OH; *m:* Elisa Jill Patterson; *c:* James, Jeffrey, Lyndsay; *ed:* ıgstown St (BS) Elem Ed 1981, (MS) Curr 1984; 15 Quarter Post Grad *cr:* Southside MS Tchr 1981-; *ai:* Intramural Dir; Soc Stud Comm ; CEA, OEA, NEA 1981-; Boardman Lions 1993-; Mahoning Cty Cncl Retarded Citizens 1989-, Pres; *home:* 43 S Shore Dr Youngstown OH 2*

SKA, CARLA MARIE,SSJ, Coord of Spcl Pgms & Adj Asst; *b:* ucket, RI; *ed:* Coll of New Rochelle (BA) Eng & Philosophy 1975; of RI (MA) Eng 1981, (PHD) Eng 1992; *cr:* Elms Coll Adj Asst Prof -, Acad Cnslr for CE 1989-93; Spcl Pgm Coord 1990-; Acting Dean of ts 1993-94; *ai:* Coll Strategic Planning Process Oversite, Coll ntion & Intnl Womens Day Comms; Delta Epsilon Sigma 1992-; JW 1993-; NAWCHE 1993-; Kappa Gamma Pi 1975-; Latino Schlsp m 1993-, Bd Mem; Diocesan Comm on Violence 1994-; Natl Task e for US Fed of Srs of St Joseph; Hum Grant for Course Design; ertation Selected for Entry in Northeast Outstdng Dissertations; *office:* s Coll 291 Springfield St Chicopee MA 01013*

EXIK, WILLIAM A., Professor of Biology; *b:* Mc Keesport, PA; *m:* ına Howard; *ed:* Memphis St Univ (BS) Zoology 1966, (MS) Vertebrate logy 1968; *cr:* KS St Coll of Pittsburg Bio Instr 1968-69; Univ of nsville Bio Instr 1969-70; York Coll Bio Instr 1970-72; Montgomery Bio Prof 1972-; *ai:* Bio Dept Computing Coord; AAUP 1976-, Chptr 1988-89; Anatomy & Physiology Lab Manual, Prgm Coord; *office:* ntgomery Coll At Rockville 51 Mannakee St Rockville MD 20850

EY, NANCY HURWICH, Prof of Psychology; *b:* New York, NY; *m:* lan R. Pola; *c:* Loren B.; *ed:* Barnard Coll (BA) Psych 1967; Columbia v (PHD) Experimental Psych 1973; FL St Univ Post Doctoral Fellow chobiology; Tchrs Coll at Columbia Post Doctoral Fellow ıropsychology; *cr:* Augustana Coll Asst Prof Psych 1974-76; Ctr for dache Care Dir Neurodiagnostic Lab 1983-87; Trinity Coll Asst Prof ch 1976-83; Medgar Evers Coll Psych Prof 1988-; *ai:* Psych Club Spon; Coll Cncl Rep; Fac Senate Vice Chair; Annual Greater NY Conf Soc Rsrch Prgm Comm; NY Neuropsychology 1987-, Bd of Dirs; tern Psychological Assn, Soc for Neuroscience 1980-; NY Acad of Sci 9-; 25 Publications; 20 Grants for Rsrch, Tchng Equipment or Softwre 9-; Columbia Univ Fac Flwshp; NIMH Post Doctoral Flwshp; Psi Chi; ce: Medgar Evers Coll 1650 Bedford Ave Brooklyn NY 11225

INGER, LESTER LEE,JR., Retired Social Studies Teacher; *b:* shington, DC; *ed:* Univ of MD (BA) Sociology, Pol Sci 1957, (BA) Pol 1966; Duke Univ 1 Yr Law, Various Addl Courses; *cr:* Bethesda-Chevy ass HS Soc Stud Tchr 1961-95; *ai:* Timekeeper, Ftbl, Bsktbl; Model UN; A, MSTA, MCEA 1961-; St Luke Luth Church 1951-; Various nmendations Colls, Univs.

IO, DAVID MICHAEL,JR., English Teacher; *b:* Richmond, VA; *m:* esa M. Creeden; *c:* Cassidy, David III; *ed:* St Michaels Coll (BS) Bus min 1986; Cntrl CT St Univ (BS) Scndry Ed Eng 1992; Trinity Coll 3 edits; *cr:* Northeast United Mrktg Agent 1987-92; Cathedral HS Eng ır 1993-; *ai:* Debate Coach; NE Assn Tchrs of Eng 1992-, Mbrshp Chair; TE 1992-; Bd of Fin 1990-92; Western MA Writing Project Writing ant; Article Pub.*

ISKY, JOHN JOSEPH, Theology & Psychology Teacher; *b:* Sayre, ; *ed:* Boston Coll (BA) Eng & Comm 1978; Elmira Coll NYS Cert ndry Ed 1981; *cr:* Notre Dame HS Theology & Psych Tchr 1981-; *ai:* Jr ass Moderator; Dept Chair; *office:* Notre Dame HS 1400 Maple Ave nira NY 14904

.IVEA, CHARLES LAURENCE, History Teacher; *b:* New York City, ; *m:* Mary; *c:* Peter, Gordon; *ed:* New Paltz SUNY (BS) Mis, Pol Sci 65, (MS) His, Ed 1970; 15 Grad Credits Amer His Cntrl CT St; *cr:* Jr HS roject Tchr, Tech writer 1967-69; Praxis Corp Tech Writer 1969-70; enham Correctional Facility Tchr 1970-71; Shepaug Vly HS His Tchr 71-; *ai:* Ad Hoc Comms; NEA 1980-; Cub Scout Master 3 Yrs; Flwshp aders Urantia Book 26 Yrs; Numerous His Articles Pub; Stu Guide esis Writing His; *office:* Sheapaug Vly HS 159 South St Washington Gr T 06793

.LIVEIRA, ANNE MARIE, Science Teacher; *b:* New Bedford, MA; *m:* wrence; *ed:* Bridgewater St Coll (BS) Bio 1983, (MA) Bio 1987; Tufts niv 70 Hrs in Human Genetics & Bioethics; *cr:* Normandin Jr High Sci Tchr 8th Grd 1987-88; New Bedford HS Sci Tchr 1988-; *ai:* NEA, MTA, NBEA 1987-; *office:* New Bedford HS 230 Hathaway Blvd New Bedford MA 02740

OLIVEIRA, LOUISE A., Social Studies Dept Chprsn; *b:* Providence, RI; *m:* Neil A. Barker; *ed:* RI Coll (BA) Scndry Ed, Soc Stud 1976, (MED) Cnslr Ed 1979; Providence Coll (MA) His 1989; Brown Univ Scndry Ed Tchrs Insts; Television Production, Cmptr Programming Post-Grad Work; *cr:* St Mary's Acad Soc Stud Tchr 1979-87, Asst Dir Guid 1987-90; Exeter-West Greenwich HS Soc Stud Dept Chprsn 1990-; *ai:* Model Legislature, United Nations; NEA 1990-; RI Soc Stud Assn 1980-; Wheelchair Sports, Recreation Assn 1990-, Adaptive Kayak Prgm; New England Prgm Tour Recipient 1989; Vietnam War Curr Co-Author; New England Regnl Soc Stud Conf 3 Time Presenter; *office:* Exeter-West Greenwich Jr Sr HS 930 Nooseneck Hill Rd West Greenwich RI 02817

OLIVER, DARLENE HOOKER, High School Mathematics Tchr; *b:* Manchester, KY; *m:* Jean Blair; *c:* Jason, Candace; *ed:* Eastern KY Univ (BS) Math & PE 1965; Univ of OR (MS) Tchng HS Math 1970; 20 Credit Hrs Montgomery Cty Dept of Continuing Ed; *cr:* Clay Co Bd of Ed HS Math Tchr 1965-66; Knightstown Pub Schl HS Math Tchr 1966-68; Eugene Pub Schls Jr HS Math Tchr 1968-70; Montgomery Cty Bd of Ed HS Math Tchr 1980-; *ai:* Educl Visioning Action Team; NEA 1980-; MSTA 1980-; MCTA 1980-; Bradley Hills Presbyn Church 1983-; Montgomery Cty 15 Yr Tchng Pin; *office:* Bethesda-Chevy Chase HS 4301 E West Hwy Bethesda MD 20814

OLIVER, DOMINICK MICHAEL, Acctng, Bus & Cmptrs Instr; *b:* Niagara Falls, NY; *m:* Vicki Anne; *ed:* Niagara Co Comm Coll (AAS) Acctng 1982; Niagara Univ (BS) Bus Admin 1984, (MS) Ed 1986; *cr:* The Edwin Mellen Press Co Accountant 1988-89; Kelly Bus Inst Bus Instr, Dean 1988-91; Cheryl Fell's Schl of Bus Instr 1991-92; Bryant Stratton Bus Inst Instr 1992-; *ai:* Acctng Curr Advy Bd; NYS Bus Tchrs Assn 1986-; Friends of Niagara Falls Pub Lib 1979-; Buffalo, Erie Cty Naval, Servicemen's Park 1991-, Life Mem; Fac Mem of Quarter; *office:* Bryant Stratton Bus Inst Buflo 1028 Main St Buffalo NY 14202*

OLIVER, EDWARD ALAN, Secondary Science Teacher; *b:* New Hartford, NY; *m:* Julianne Orobona; *ed:* SUNY at Geneseo (BS) Bio 1992; SUNY at Potsdam Working on MS Scndry Sci Ed; *cr:* Lyme Cntrl Schl Scndry Sci Tchr 1992-; *ai:* Jr Class, NHS Adv; Effective Schls Comm; Model Schls Rep; Odyssey of Mind Coach; NYSUT 1992-; *office:* Lyme Central Schl 11868 Academy St Chaumont NY 13622

OLIVER, EDWARD DONALD, 7th-12th Grade Teacher; *b:* Pittsburgh, PA; *m:* Beverly Sue Dobransky; *c:* Christy, Holly, Rachel; *ed:* Slippery Rock Univ (BS) Soc Stud, Dr Ed 1973; Attnd Univ of Pittsburgh, Moody Bible Inst, Allegheny Intermediate Unit; *cr:* Essex Intnl Production Scheduler 1974-75; Handee Marb Inc Mgr 1975-88; Portersville Chrstn Schl Tchr 1988-; *ai:* HS Chorus; Past Jr Class Adv; PMEA 1988-; ASCD 1992-; 27th Ward Girls Sftbl 1987-, Asst Coach; North Side Saints Ftbl 1990-, Parents Assn; Harmony Zelenople UM Choir 1988-, Dir; *home:* 1432 Reuben St Pittsburgh PA 15212

OLIVER, GRACE RETHARTHA, Library Media Specialist; *b:* Bridgeport, CT; *m:* William J. III; *ed:* Southern CT St Univ (BS) Eng, Scndry Ed 1986, (BS) Lib Sci 1993; 15 Addl Credits Intermediate Admin Cert; *cr:* Stratford HS Eng Tchr 1986-93; Second Hill Lane Elem Schl Lib Media Specialist 1993-94; Ctr Elem Schl Lib Media Specialist 1993-95; Wooster MS Lib Media Specialist 1994-; *ai:* SEA, NEA 1986-; CEMA 1993-; *office:* Wooster MS 150 Lincoln St Stratford CT 06497

OLIVER, JUDY LYNNE, High School English Teacher; *b:* Hazleton, PA; *m:* Steven Neil; *c:* Stephanie, Caitlin; *ed:* IN Univ of PA (BS) Scndry Eng 1974; Millersville Univ Remedial Rdng Cert 1979; Attnd Wilkes Coll, PA St 52 Grad Credits 1986; *cr:* Allentown Schl Dist Eng Tchr 1974-76; Eastern Lebanon Cty Schl Dist Eng Tchr 1976-; *ai:* Steering, Curr for Intensive Scheduling & Grad Requirements Comms; Eng Mentor; NEA 1974-; PSEA 1974-; AEA 1974-76; ELCEA 1976-; *office:* Eastern Lebanon Cty HS 180 Elco Dr Myerstown PA 17067*

OLIVER, LINDA NEWHOUSE, Eng, Bus Law, Para-Legal Instr; *b:* Pautuxent, MD; *m:* James Robert; *c:* Matthew, Patrick; *ed:* Univ of MN at Minneapolis (BA) Eng 1968; Frostburg St Univ 15 Credit Hrs Post Grad MBA Prgm; Univ of MN Paralegal Cert; *cr:* R. J. Cooney & Associates Para-Legal 1985-88; St Farm Insurance Agent 1989-90; Cambria-Rowe Bus Coll Instr 1991-; *ai:* In-Svc Coord; NALS, PALS, PBSA 1991-; *office:* Cambria-Rowe Business College 221 Central Ave Johnstown PA 15902

OLIVER, LLOYDANNE ELLEN, Gifted Program Teacher; *b:* Providence, RI; *ed:* RI Coll (BA) Elem Ed, Psych 1986; Edctr of Gifted Cert 1989, Enrolled Masters Ed Admin; Attnd RI Schl of Design; *cr:* Alice M. Waddington Schl Gifted Prgm Tchr 1987-; *ai:* Odyssey of Mind Coach, Safety Patrol Copord; Schl Site Grant Comm; NEA 1987-; E Prov Educ Assn 1987-, Bldg Del; RI St Cncl on Arts; Oddsy of Mind, St Grant Recipient; Lifetime Mem PTA; *office:* Alice M Waddington Schl 101 Legion Way Riverside RI 02915

OLIVER, MARION KERCHER, 8th Grd Lang Arts Teacher; *b:* Mt Holly, NJ; *m:* David G.; *c:* David R., Matthew M.; *ed:* Juniata Coll (BA) Elem Ed 1964; Kean Coll (MS) Curr, Instruction 1984; Early Chldhd Cert 1975; *cr:* Von E Mauger MS 6th, 8th Grd Tchr 1964-68, 1978-; *ai:* Teach Academically Talented Eighth Grds; MEA, MCEA, MEA 1964-; NCTE; Bound Brook Presbyn Church 1978-, Elder; Juniata Coll Alumni 1964-, Class Agent; NJ Governors Tchr Recognition Awd; Educl Testing Svc Tchr Assessment Consultant; *office:* Von E Mauger MS Fisher Ave Middlesex NJ 08846

OLIVER, SANDRA FOWLKES, Seventh Grade Teacher; *b:* Jersey, NJ; *m:* Reginald Joseph; *c:* Wesley; *ed:* Trenton St Coll (BS) Elem Ed 1977; 8 Post Grad Credits; *cr:* Pub Schl Twenty-Two Elem K-8 Tchr 1978-; *ai:* Jersey City Ed Assn, NJ Ed Assn, NEA 1978-; Alpha Kappa Alpha 1975-; Hudson Cty Tchr of Yr 1992-93; Tchr Recognition Awd; *home:* 73 Christopher St Montclair NJ 07042*

OLIVER, TROY C., MS Mathematics Teacher; *b:* Dayton, TN; *ed:* Wheaton Coll (BS) Math 1988; Moody Bible Inst 1983-84; *cr:* Glenbard South HS Spec Ed Aide Tchr 1988; Cristobal HS Math Scndry Tchr 1989-95; Curundu MS 6 Grd Math Tchr 1995-; *ai:* HS Boys Tennis, Vlybl Coach; Crossroads Bible Church 1983-, Deacon; *office:* Curundu MS Dodds Panama Region APO AA 34002

OLIVERA, IGDALIA, Guidance Counselor; *b:* Lajas, PR; *m:* Jaime A.; *c:* Yessennia; *ed:* HCC (AS) Child Care 1976; Univ of Bridgeport (BA) Elem Ed 1980, (MS) Cnslng 1985; 6th Yr Degree 1987; *cr:* Bridgeport Bd of Ed Tchr 1981-85, Biling Tchr 1985-92, MS Elem Schl Cnslr 1992-94, Guid Cnslr 1994-; *ai:* BEA 1981-; NEA 1983-; NEACAC 1994-; *office:* Bassick HS 1181 Fairfield Ave Bridgeport CT 06605

OLIVERA, MARIA MERCEDES, Spanish Teacher; *b:* Adjuntas, PR; *c:* Diego J. Gerrish; *ed:* Univ of PR (BA) Scndry Ed His, Soc 1967; Tchrs Coll Columbia Univ (MA) Curr, Tchng Biling Ed 1988; 30 Grad Credits Ed, Guidance Brooklyn Coll, Univ of MN, Long Island Univ 1973-77; *cr:* Dept of Ed His, Soc Stud Tchr 1967-71; NY City Bd of Ed Schl, Comm Relations Biling Tchr 1971-79, First Grd Span Biling Tchr 1979-85; HS Span Tchr 1985-; *ai:* ASPIRA Youth Leadership Club Adv; Multi Cultural Curr Comm; AFT 1972-; NYSAFLT 1985-; AATSP 1988-; Tchrs Coll, NY City Bd of Ed Fellowship to Stud Biling Ed 1982-84; CUNY Grad Ctr, NEH Inst Latin Amer Lit Culture 1989; Colgate Univ, NYCH Humanities Inst 500 Yrs Re-Discovering Amers 1991; *office:* Brooklyn Tech HS 29 Ft Green Pl Brooklyn NY 11217*

OLIVER-GREEN, NANCY, English Teacher; *b:* Bethesda, MD; *m:* John Gruen; *ed:* Univ of NH at Durham (BA) Theatre Arts 1977, (MAT) Theatre Arts, Ed 1978; *cr:* Univ of NH Tchr, Radio Drama 1978; Phillips Andover Acad Tchr, Radio Production 1977-78; Exeter HS Eng Tchr, Drama Adv 1978-81; Marshwood HS Eng Tchr, Drama Adv 1981-; *ai:* Talent Show, Drama Club, IMPACT, INTERN Adv; Multiple Schl Comms; New England Theatre Assn, Bd of Dirs; Salmon Falls Friends of Music 1980-; Tchr of Yr; Singer; Songwriter; *office:* Marshwood HS 204 Dow Hwy Eliot ME 03903

OLIVERI, JOSEPH, Social Studies Teacher; *b:* Everett, MA; *m:* Marilyn Linda Horgan; *ed:* Boston St Coll (BS) His 1968; Bridgewater St Coll (MS) Ed 1973; Attnd Duquesne Univ, StoneHill Coll, Fitchburgh St Coll, World of Difference Inst; *cr:* Coll Acad Summer Prgm for Gifted Tchr 1990-91; College GATE Summer Prgm for Gifted Tchr, Admin 1992; LaLiberte Jr HS 7th-8th Grd Soc Stud Tchr 1969-; *ai:* Chm Elizabeth Keneally Schlsp Comm; Co-Chm Stu of Month Comm; Co-Dir Mock Trial Club, 50's, 60's Show; Schl Site Cncl; Raynham Ed Assn 1969-, VP, Treas; MA Tchrs Assn, NEA 1969-; Easton Historical Soc 1993-; Soc Preservation New England Antiguities 1993, Natl Trust Historic Preservation 1993-; Founding Pres Mu Iota Chptr of Phi Alpha Theta 1967-68; 2 Horace Mann Grants Dev Spec Prgms; *office:* LaLiberte Jr HS 777 Pleasant St Raynham MA 02767

OLIVERI, JUDITH M., Secretarial Instructor; *b:* Rochester, NY; *m:* William; *c:* Carin Adams, Pamela, Stacey, Jodi; *ed:* Bryant & Stratton (AOS) Admin Systems 1981; Nazareth Coll (BS) Eng 1987; 6 Credit Hrs Grad Cert Adult Ed Trng the Trainers Prgm Elmira Coll; 6 Credit Hrs; *cr:* Ind Instr Writing Curr, Tutoring, Presentry Seminar 1989-; Amer Inst of Banking Coll Eng Instr 1992-; Monroe Bd of Cooperative Ed Adult Ed Instr 1992-; Bryant & Stratton Secretarial Instr 1993-; *ai:* First Prize Doris Weber Jones Excl in Integration of Lang Awd Nazareth Coll; Rochester Area Coll Outstdng Stu Awd Nom Nazareth Coll; *home:* 28 Chimney Hill Rd Rochester NY 14612

OLIVERI, NATALIE ANNE, Communication Department Prof; *b:* Jersey City, NJ; *m:* Gerald Anthony Madek; *c:* Christina Madek, Jonathan Madek; *ed:* Univ of VA (MA) Eng 1970; Boston Univ (MED) Cnslng Psych 1976; *cr:* Chamberlayne Jr Coll Eng Instr 1970-73; Bunker HIll Comm Coll Eng Prof 1973-; *ai:* Stu Adv; Curr Comm; MTA, MECC 1975-; NCTE 1992-; Wrote Article; Presentation NERC Conf 1994, CCCC Conf; *office:* Bunker Hill Comm Coll New Rutherford Ave Boston MA 02129

OLIVERO, RON, 7th & 8th Grd Soc Studies Tchr; *b:* Wechawken, NJ; *m:* Anastasia Metaxas; *c:* James, Michael; *ed:* Jersey City St Coll (BA) Elem Ed 1970; *cr:* PS #2 Tchr 24 Yrs; *ai:* CORE,PAC Chm; Schl Improvement Team; NEA, NJEA 1972-; WNYEA 1972-, Bldg Rep; Little League Coach; NJ PTA 1984-; *office:* Pub Schl Number Two 52nd St & Broadway W New York NJ 07093

OLIVIA, SUSAN (REHRIG), Sixth Grade Teacher; *b:* Palmerton, PA; *m:* Christopher D.; *c:* Kristin Olivia; *ed:* Lehigh Cty Comm Coll (AA) Elem 1970; Kutztown Univ (BS) Elem 1972; Lehigh Univ (MED) Rdng Specialist 1976; 60 Credits Marywood Coll, Allentown Coll, Wilkes Coll; IU 21 Hrs; *cr:* Palmerton Elem Schls 6th Grd Tchr 1972-; *ai:* NEA, PSEA 1972-; PAEA 1972-, Sec 1978-79; Concourse Club 1976-; Bus & Prof Women 1979-; *office:* S. S. Palmer Elem 3rd & Lafayette Ave Palmerton PA 18071

OLIVIERI, MARTIN JOHN, Science & ESL Teacher; *b:* Bronx, NY; *ed:* Universita di San Tommaso in Urbe (SPL) Philosophy 1987; Univ of Toronto Honours (BA) Philosophy & Mediaeval Stud 1985; 36 Addl Credits Toward Masters in Sci Ed at City Coll, CUNY to be Granted in 1996; *cr:* Dollar Dry Dock Savings Sales Rep 1989-90; Castle Hill 127 MS Tchr 1990-; *ai:* Schl Collaborative Comm; AFT 1990-; UFT 1990-; Grant from ITI Prgm for ESL Cert; *office:* MS 127 Castle Hill 1560 Purdy St Bronx NY 10462

OLKIEWICZ, DIANE PLATANIA, English Teacher; *b:* Bayonne, NJ; *m:* Peter; *ed:* Jersey City St Coll (BA) Eng 1971; MA Equivalence 1996; *cr:* Woodrow Wilson Schl 7-8th Grd Eng Tchr 1972-; *ai:* Acad Challenge, Drama Coach; Yrbk; Newspaper; Career Ed Adv; PTO Rep; NJEA, NEA 1972-; NJ Rdng Cncl 1973-; NJ Environmental Coalition 1985-; NJ Governor's Awd Excl in Tchng; Cty Tchr Recognition 1995.

OLLO, MICHAEL ANTHONY, Social Studies Teacher; *b:* Newark, NJ; *m:* Maura Lucy Fitzmorris; *c:* Peter Michael, Amelia Lucy, Elizabeth Mary; *ed:* Caldwell Coll (BA) Soc Stud & Pol Sci 1992; 36 Hrs Toward Masters; Attnd Univ of VT Schl of Intnl Trng 16 Hrs, Univ of Miami Univ of Air Force 2 Yrs; *cr:* Project Link Ed Ctr Tchr 1984-89; Dome Project Inc Tchr 1989-93; Lakeland Regnl HS Tchr 1993-; *ai:* Boys Bsktbl Coach; Sr Class Adv; NJEA, LRHSTA 1993-; LRHSPTSO 1995-; IAABO 1992-; Lake Winona Civic Assn 1993-, Trustee; Caldwell Coll Dr Cullen-Bender Grad Schlsp Awd; San Vito AS Italy Most Outstanding Influence on Youth; *office:* Lakeland Regional HS 205 Conklintown Rd Wanaque NJ 07465*

OLMSTEAD, DORIS EDNA, Administrative Assistant; *b:* Bennington, VT; *m:* Craig N.; *c:* Jennifer M., Megan R., Nathan L.; *cr:* Chrstn Heritage Schl 7-12 Grd Tchr, Eng Dept 1989-95, Yrbk Adv 1988; *ai:* Fine Arts Competition, Speech Categories Adv; Yrbk Publication 1988-93 Adv; Voice of Amer VFW Contest Adv; Chrstn Schl Fine Arts Competition Judge; VT Assn of Chrstn Schls 1989-; NE Assn of Chrstn Schls 1989, 5 Yrs Svc; Auditors Town Halifax 1988-, Chm; Bd of Deaconesses 1993-94, Chm.

OLNOWICH, LARRAINE BARNES, Drama & English Teacher; *b:* Liverpool, England; *m:* Howard T.; *c:* Frank Raponi, Gayle Larson, Gary; *ed:* Harpur Coll (BA) Eng, Gen Lit 1966; SUNY at Binghamton (MA) Theatre 1989; *cr:* Binghamton Schl Dist Eng, Drama Tchr 1966-; *ai:* Drama Club Adv; NEA 1966-; NYSTEA 1995-; NYSEC 1995-, Prgm Excl Awd; Southern Tier Inst for Arts in Ed 1994-, Bd Mem; *home:* 2922 Twilight Dr Endicott NY 13760

OLORE, GINA MARIE, Business Teacher; *b:* Presque Isle, ME; *ed:* Northern ME Tech Coll (AS) Exec Secretarial 1986; Husson Coll (BA) Bus Tchr Ed 1988; *cr:* Ellsworth HS Bus Tchr 1988-89; Bonny Eagle HS Bus Tchr 1989-; *ai:* FBLA Adv; Bus Ed Assn of ME 1988-; *office:* Bonny Eagle HS 700 Saco Rd Standish ME 04084

OLORE, TIMOTHY MARK, 8th Grd Social Studies Teacher; *b:* Presque Isle, ME; *m:* Carole Marie Theriault; *ed:* UMPI (BA) Behavior Sci 1983; Scndry Tchg Cert in Soc Stud 1986; Prof Tchng Accreditation in Soc Stud 1991; Mainstreaming Endorsement 1991; Eng, Lang Arts Endorsement 1992; *cr:* Skyway MS 8th Grd Soc Stud Tchr 1986-; *ai:* Founder & Directed Annual Var Bsbl Spring Trng Trip to FL 1987-; Presque Isle Babe Ruth Coach 1986-; 6th, 8th Grd Bsktbl Coach 1992-; Boys Var Bsbl Coach 1985-; Boys Jr Bsktbl Coach 1985-91; Founder & Dir of Wildcat Bsbl Schl 1989-; Presque Isle Recreation Summer Bsbl Prgm Dir 1991-; MSAD #1 Staff Dev Comm; ME Bsbl Coaches Assn 1993-, Sec; MTA, NEA 1986-; Amer Bsbl Coaches 1986-, Plaques for 100 & 150 Wins; Bsbl Coaches of Amer 1986-, Natl Yth Sports Coaching Assn 1990-; ME St Coaches Assn 1986-, Certfd Coach ASEP 1995-; Golden Spike Awd Amateur Coach 1987; Big East Coach of Yr 1990-91; Aroostook Cty All-Star Coach 1992, 1995; *office:* Skyway MS 569 Skyway St Presque Isle ME 04769

OLOW, FRANCES ADAMS, 8th Grade Mathematics Teacher; *b:* Okinawa, Japan; *m:* John L.; *ed:* Chaminade Univ (BA) Elem Ed 1972;

Univ of HI (MA) Elem Ed 1977; *cr:* Acad of the Pacific Math, Eng, Soc Stud Tchr 1973-77; St Charles Borromeo 7th-8th Grd Math Tchr 1977-78; Mac Arthur MS 6th-8th Grd Math Tchr, Math Dept Chair 1978-95; Crofton MS 7th Grd Math Tchr 1981-82; Windsor Knolls MS 8th Grd Math Tchr 1995-; *ai:* Math Counts, Challenge 24 Math Coach; St Mathalon Comm Co-Chprsn; Capital Area Math Meet Host; NEA 1978-; NCTM; MD Cncl Tchrs of Math; Anne Arundel Cty Edctr of Month; *home:* 16180 A E Mullinix Rd Woodbine MD 21797*

OLSAVSKY, JOHN, Asst Professor of Accounting; *b:* Uniontown, PA; *ed:* Indiana Univ of PA (BS) Bus Mngmt, Accounting 1975; Robert Morris Coll (MS) Taxation 1982; SUNY Coll at Fredonia Post Grad Stud in Ed; *cr:* SUNY Coll at Fredonia Asst Prof 1982-; *ai:* Accounting Soc Adv; Alumni, Personnel, Curr & Cmptr Resources Comms; Inst of Mngmt Accountants 1979-; Amer Accounting Assn 1982-; *office:* St Univ of NY at Fredonia W311 Thompson Hall Fredonia NY 14063*

OLSEN, BRUCE, Theology Tchr, Campus Minister; *b:* East Meadow, NY; *ed:* Cathedral Coll of Immaculate Conception (BA) Eng 1978; Seton Hall Univ (MA) Ed 1992; Working Towards MA Theology; *cr:* Our Lady of the Vly Schl 7th, 8th Grd Tchr 1983-84; Assumption Schl 7th, 8th Grd Tchr 1984-88; Bayley-Ellard Cath HS Theology Tchr, Campus Minister 1988-91; Paramus Cath HS Theology Tchr, Campus Minister 1991-; *ai:* Dev, Supervise Peer Ministry Prgm; Moderate Liturgy Club; Train & Moderate Eucharistic Ministers; Organize & Conduct Retreats; Dev & Coord Svc Prgm; Asst Spring Track Coach; Prin Advy Cncl; Kappa Delta Pi 1988-; Knights of Columbus 1982-; St Therese Church, RCIA Catechist, Liturgy Comm, Eucharistic Minister, Lector, Cantor; Outstdng Young Man by Outstdng Young Amers 1988; *office:* Paramus Cath HS 425 Paramus Rd Paramus NJ 07652

OLSEN, GARY ALAN, Mathematics Teacher; *b:* Orange, NJ; *ed:* Wheaton Coll (BS) Math 1989; 28 Credit Hrs Montclair St Univ; *cr:* Midlantic Natl Bank Customer Svc Rep 1989-92; Hawthorne Chrstn Acad Tchr 1992-; *ai:* NCTM 1993-; *office:* Hawthorne Christian Acad 2000 Rt 208 Hawthorne NJ 07506

OLSEN, JEANNE BROPHY, Span Tchr & Frgn Lang Dpt Head; *b:* Cleveland, OH; *m:* Richard; *c:* Matthew, Margaret; *ed:* Notre Dame Coll (BA) Span, Ger, Eng 1958; Kent St Univ (MED) Rdng, Writing 1991; Post Grad Stud Case-Western Reserve Univ, Georgetown Univ, Akron Univ; Grad Work Fresno Pacific Coll; *cr:* St James Schl Fourth Grd Tchr 1958-60; North Royalton HS Eng, Span Tchr 1960-66; Normandy HS Span, Ger, Eng, ESL Tchr 1969-; *ai:* Var Sftbl Coach; Asst Ath Dir; Foreign Lang Trip Coord; North Cntrl Comm Writing Chprsn; PEA, NEOEA, OEA, NEA 1969-; AATSP 1987-; OSBA 1970-78; North Royalton Bd of Ed 1970-78, Pres 2 Yrs, VP 2 Yrs; Concessionaire 1979-; Levy Vol; Interpreter; Grants St of OH 1970, Eastern OH ABLE Consortium, Grant-Kurdziel Fnd 1993; PEA Schlsp 1989; Foreign Lang Workbooks, Learning Packets, Article Pub; Co-Author of On Speaking Terms, 1994; Writing Team for Venture Capital Grant; *office:* Normandy HS 2500 W Pleasant Valley Rd Parma OH 44134*

OLSEN, KAREN NIMAL, Choral Director & Teacher; *b:* Indianapolis, IN; *m:* Kenneth Eric; *c:* Brian, Jonathan, Lauren; *ed:* Glassboro St Coll (BA) Music Ed 1969; 30 Grad Credits Glassboro St Coll, Westminster Choir Coll of Rider Univ; *cr:* Barrington Jr HS Tchr, Choral Dir 1969-72; Ocean Twp Jr HS Tchr 1972-73; Ocean Twp HS Tchr, Choral Dir 1992-; *ai:* HS Chorus, Wanamassa Schl Chorus Dir; NKEA, NEA 1992-; All-Shore Chorus Inc 1992-, Pres 1995; *office:* Ocean Township HS 550 W Park Ave Oakhurst NJ 07755*

OLSEN, KRISTINE E., Mathematics Tchr & Dept Chprsn; *b:* Windber, PA; *ed:* IN Univ of PA (BS) Math 1961, (MED) Cnslng 1965; *cr:* Greater Johnstown Schls Math Tchr 1961-; *ai:* Sr Class Adv; Co-op Tchr Stu Tchrs; Y-Teens; Mentor Prgm; NEA, PSEA, GSEA 1961-; Delta Kappa Gamma 1973-, Treas; AAUW 1965-; *office:* Greater Johnstown Sr HS 222 Central Ave Johnstown PA 15902

OLSEN, LINDA ELIZABETH, Fifth Grade Teacher; *b:* Brooklyn, NY; *m:* Stephen Roberts; *c:* Craig Walters; *ed:* SUNY at New Paltz (BS) Early Chldhd Ed 1973, (MS) Elem Ed 1975; *cr:* Arlington CSD 2nd Grd Tchr 1973-76, 3rd Grd Tchr 1976-82, 5th Grd Tchr 1982-; Asst to Prin 1991-; *ai:* Dist Curr Comm; Sci Bldg Mentor; Dist Sci Cncl; Bldg Site Based Mngmt Team; ArlingtonTA 1973-, Sr Rep; Mid Hudson Rdng Cncl 1991-; Save the Rainforest 1991-; Nature Conservancy 1990-; Syefest; Natl Sci Fnd Grant; Lead Tchr; *office:* Noxon Road Schl Old Noxon Rd Poughkeepsie NY 12603

OLSON, BEVERLY LYNN, High School Math Teacher; *b:* Youngstown, OH; *ed:* Wittenberg Univ (BA) Elem & Scndry Ed, Geography 1977; Youngstown St Univ (MS) Master Tchr Scndry, Curr; Attnd Kent St Univ; *cr:* Southeast Local Schls MS Math Tchr 1977-80; Boardman Local Schls MS Math, Eng Tchr 1980-81, HS Math Tchr 1981-; *ai:* NHS Advy Comm; NEA, OEA 1977-; BEA 1980-; Jr League 1978-, Publications Comm; BTSC 1988-, Pres; *office:* Boardman HS 7777 Glenwood Ave Boardman OH 44512

OLSON, CHARLES RICHARD, Associate Professor of Art; *b:* Pittsburgh, PA; *m:* Marie Odile Thomas; *c:* Jeremy, Alexandra; *ed:* IN Univ of PA (BSA) Art Ed 1974, (MA) Painting 1976; Post Grad Credits in Painting Tyler Schl of Art Temple Univ PA; *cr:* Saint Francis Coll Assoc Prof of Art 1976-; *ai:* Fine Arts, Fac Affairs Chm; Deans Cncl; Fac Senate; Adv Multiculture Awareness Group; Univ Museum Bd; Associated Artists of Pittsburgh 1978-; Univ Museum Former Pres, Sec; James Stewart Museum Chair, Installation Comm; Sold Numeros Exhibitions; Work in Numerous Pub, Private Collections; *office:* Saint Francis Coll 100 College Ave Loretto PA 15940

OLSON, CHRISTINE A., Kindergarten Teacher; *b:* Binghamton, NY; *m:* Mark H.; *c:* Joshua Mark, Abby Christine; *ed:* SUNY at Oneonta (BS) Elem Ed 1972; 16 Grad Hrs SUNY at Binghamton; 15 Grad Hrs Elmira Coll; *cr:* Vestal Hills Schl First Grd Tchr 1972-79; Glenwood Schl Kndgtn Tchr 1979-81; Nathan T. Hall Schl Pre-First Grd Tchr 1982-84; Glenwood Schl Kndgtn Tchr 1985-88, Second Grd Tchr 1988-89; Clayton Ave Schl Kndgtn Tchr 1989-; *ai:* Vestal Tchrs Assn, NEA, NEA NY 1972-; *office:* Clayton Ave Elem Schl 201 Clayton Ave Vestal NY 13850

OLSON, CLIFFORD ARTHUR,JR., Language Arts Teacher; *b:* Fort Knox, KY; *m:* Doris E. Koch; *c:* Alexander; *ed:* Shippensburg Univ (BSEd) Soc Stud 1975; (MSEd) Rdng Specialist 1981; 15 Hrs Rdng Johns Hopkins Univ; 15 Hrs Elem Cert Wilson Coll at Chambersburg; *cr:* Md Corr Inst ABE, GED Tchr 1977-85; G.D. MS Rdng Tchr 1985-93, Lang Arts, Eng & Rdng Tchr 1993-; *ai:* Golf Club Adv; Tae Kwon Do Instr; Camp Cnslr United Church of Christ; PSEA, NEA, GAEA 1985-; Articles Pub; *office:* Greencastle-Antrim MS 500 Leitersburg St Greencastle PA 17225*

OLSON, DANIEL ANTHONY, Soc Studies Dept Chm & Tchr; *b:* Spencer, IA; *m:* Patricia Ann Dugan; *c:* Mary Pat, Laura Ann, Erik Daniel; *ed:* SUC at Plattsburgh (BS) 2nd Ed Soc Sci 1973; Carleton Univ of Ottawa (MA) Inst of Canadian Stud 1977; Elmira Coll (MS) Soc Sci Ed 1987; Attnd Univ of Rochester, Nazareth Coll, SUC at Geneseo, SUC at Potsdam & SUC at Brockport; *cr:* CAFOP de Korhogo Coted Ivoire Africa Peace Corps Vol 1973-75; Carleton at Ottawa Tchng Asst 1975-77; Geneva Jr HS Soc Stud Tchr 1977-79; Victor Sr HS Soc Stud Tchr & Dept Chair 1979-; *ai:* Acad Decathlon Team & Master Mind Team Coach; Victor Film Soc Adv; Victor Cntrl Schls Instrl Cncl 1981-90; Wayne Finger Lakes Soc Stud Cncl 1979-, Dir, Tchr of Yr 1995; NY Cncl for Soc Stud 1979-; NY St Assn for Africa Stud 1980-, Planetary Soc 1985-; Wayne Cty Republican Comm 1981-, Chm; NY Rep St Comm 1982-89, Del 1992 Natl Convention; Bob Oaks for Assembly 1992-, Chm; Univ of Rochester Awd for Excl in Scndry Tchng 1985 & 1992; *office:* Victor Sr HS 953 High St Victor NY 14564

OLSON, DONNA MARIE, Arts Educator; *b:* Suffern, NY; *m:* Richard William; *c:* Kristopher Loretz; *ed:* Alfred Univ Coll of Ceramic Art, Design (BFA) Sculpture 1971; 5 Yrs Rel Stud; *cr:* Town of Southbridge Spec Ed Liason 8 Yrs; St Anne's Shrine Rel Ed Dir 3 Yrs; St Mary's Schl 3-5 Grd Art Tchr 3 Yrs; Trinity Cath Acad K-8 Grd Art, Music, Theatre Tchr 6 Yrs; *ai:* Brownie Troop 338 Ldr; Youth Choir, Drama Club Dirs; NCEA 1986-; St Vincent de Paul 1996-; AIDS Support Group 1995-; Peer Recognition Article 1995; *office:* Trinity Catholic Acad 11 Pine St Southbridge MA 01550*

OLSON, JOYCE FOGEL, MS Mathematics Teacher; *b:* Sunbury, PA; *m:* Ronald E.; *c:* Angie M., Ronald E. Jr., Matthew G.; *ed:* Bucknell Univ (BA) Math 1962; 18 Addl Grad Credits; *cr:* Mifflinburg Jr & Sr HS Math Tchr 1962-66; Shikellamy Schl Dist Math Tchr 1975-; *ai:* Stu Assistance Team; Instructional Support Team; Stu Cncl Adv; Bucknell Alumni Club of the Susquehanna Valley 1987-, Sec & Treas; *office:* CW Rice MS 4th & Hanover Streets Northumberland PA 17857

OLSON, KAREN A., Hnrs Science Research Teacher; *b:* Richmond, VA; *m:* Daniel C.; *c:* Sarah, Kirsten; *ed:* OH Univ (BS) Zoology 1966; OH St Univ (MS) Cell Bio 1969; 18 Hrs Gifted Ed St Thomas Aquinis; Tchng Rsrch Sci Westchester BOCES; *cr:* Ithaca HS Bio Tchr 1970-73; Suffern HS Bio, Sci Rsrch Tchr 1973-; *ai:* Sci Olympiad Head, Events Coach; Sci Enrichment Prgm; AFT 1969-, STANYS 1982-; NEA; AAABS 1985-; STANYS Outstdng Sci Tchr Southeastern Zone; *home:* 1141 Union Ave Newburgh NY 12550

OLSON, LINDA (WALLIN), Mathematics Teacher; *b:* Olean, NY; *m:* Kurt E.; *c:* Jaime; *ed:* Edinboro Univ of PA (BS) Math 1973; Addl Hrs for Masters Equivalency; *cr:* Fairview HS Math Tchr 1973-; *ai:* Math Dept Chprsn; Amer HS Math Exam Spon; PA St Ed Assn PSEA, NEA 1973-; NCTM 1986-; *office:* Fairview HS 7460 Mccray Rd Fairview PA 16415

OLSON, SANDRA IRENE (RYAN), English Teacher; *b:* Philadelphia, PA; *m:* Vernon B.; *c:* Vernon L., Douglas P., Christina L.; *ed:* Bloomsburg Univ (BS) Ed, Eng 1966; Attnd Clarion Univ, PA St, Lock Haven Univ; *cr:* Kane Area Schl Dist Eng Tchr 1966-67; Warren Area HS Eng Tchr 1967-74; Sheffield Area Jr Sr HS Gifted Itinerant, Eng Drama Tchr 1975-; *ai:* Drama Dir 1986-, Adv; NEA, PSEA 1966-; WCEA 1968-; NWPCTE 1989-; Clay Street PTA 1977-, Pres 1980; WA Cty Fellowship 1990; *office:* Sheffield Area Jr Sr HS St Rt Box 600 Sheffield PA 16347

OLSON-HOLMES, DEBORAH, Fourth Grade Teacher; *b:* Sac City, IA; *c:* Kate, Charles; *ed:* Univ of SD (BS) Elem Ed 1969; Univ of VT Grad Level Course Work; Johnson St Coll Working Towards MS in Curr & Instruction; *cr:* Sioux City Schl Third Grd Tchr 1969-74; Germany DOD Overseas 2nd Grd Tchr 1974-76; Great Falls Schl 4th-5th Grd Tchr 1976-78; Milton Elem Schl 4th Grd Tchr 1985-; *ai:* Dev, Facilitate Summer Sci Inst; Prof Dev Comm 1990-94; Lang Arts Curr Comm; Soc Stud Comm 1995-; ASCD 1990-, IRA 1988-; VT Elem Sci Project 1991-; Friends of Milton Lib 1986-; PTA 1985-; Parent Advy Cncl 1993-; Booster Club 1993-; Amer Legion & Schlsp Comm Tchr of Yr Awd 1993; Presidential Awd for Excl in Sci & Math Tchr Nom 1992-; *home:* 228 Poor Farm Rd Milton VT 05468*

OLSZEWSKI, SUZANNE SUMMERVILLE, English Teacher; *b:* Rimersburg, PA; *m:* William; *c:* Danielle, Logan; *ed:* Clarion Univ (BS) Eng, Scndry Ed 1978, (MA) Eng 1986; *cr:* Union Schl Dist Eng Tchr 1979-87; Mars Area Schl Dist Eng Tchr, Dept Chair 1987-; *ai:* NCTE, PCTE, WPCTE 1987-; Butler Musical Theatre Guild 1983-; Butler Little Theatre, Butler Cty Humane Soc 1987-; Amer Family Inst Gift of Time Tribute; Chamber of Commerce Awd for Extra-Curr Work; *office:* Mars Area Sr HS Rt 228 Mars PA 16046

OLTZ, MARGARET D., Fifth Grade Teacher; *b:* Waterloo, NY; *c:* Necole Vitale, Stephanie Vitale; *ed:* St Univ of NY at Geneseo (BS) Ed N-6 1971; 30 Hrs Post Grad Work St Univ of NY at Brockport; *cr:* Perry Elem Schl 4th Grd Tchr 1971-82, 3rd Grd Tchr 1983-89, 5th Grd Tchr 1989-; *ai:* Perry Tchrs Assn 1971-, Sec 2 Yrs; NYSUT, AFT 1971-; NEA; Girl Scouts of USA 1957-, Life Mem; Former 4th Grd Sci & 6th Grd Stu Govt Adv; *office:* Perry Cntrl Schl Dist 59 Leicester St Perry NY 14530

OLVANY, TARA ANN, Social Studies Teacher; *b:* Smithtown, NY; *ed:* Mt Saint Mary's Coll (BA) His, Ed 1985; Lehigh Univ (MED) Admin & Supvr 1988; *cr:* Prince William Pub Schls Tchr 1988-93; South Plainfield Schls Soc Stud Tchr 1993-; *ai:* Var Co-Ed Chrldng; Frosh Girls Bsktbl; Frosh Field Hockey; Appeals Comm; Spec Ed Comm; NEA, NJEA 1993-; NY Cares Day 1993-; Pilot Inclusion Prgm.

O'MALLEY, CATHERINE B., Health & Religion Teacher; *b:* Cleveland, OH; *ed:* Notre Dame Coll (PB) Hlth, PE 1961; Miami Univ (MA) Hlth Ed 1985; Attnd Dayton Univ, John Carroll Univ; *cr:* Notre Dame Acad Tchr 1961-72; Regina HS Tchr, Ath Dir 1973-84; Notre Dame Acad Tchr 1984-88, Tchr 1988-; *ai:* Alumni Coord; NCEA 1970-; NDEA 1990-; AAHPERD 1962-; Amer Red Cross 1970-, 25 Yr; *office:* Notre Dame Cathedrl Latin Schl 13000 Auburn Rd Chardon OH 44024

OMALLEY, E. EILEEN, High School Math Teacher; *b:* Audubon, NJ; *ed:* Glassboro St Coll at Rowan (BA) Math Ed 1969; Purdue Univ (MAT) Math Ed 1973; Jersey City St, Trenton St Coll Addl Credits; *cr:* Cinnaminson HS Math & Comp Tchr 1969-; Burlington Cty Comm Coll Adj Math Tchr 1979-82; *ai:* Class of 1988, Chrldng & Math League Adv; Project Grad Comm; Comp Wkshp; NEA, NJEA & BCEA 1969-; Cinnaminson Ed Assn 1969-, Pres, VP Mbrshp & Negotiations Chprsn; HS Home & Schl Assn Liaison 1986-; Cinnaminson HS Tchr of Yr 1988; NSF Grant; *office:* Cinnaminson HS Riverton Rd Riverton NJ 08077*

O'MALLEY, MARTIN, History Teacher; *b:* Phila, PA; *ed:* Worcester St Coll (BS) Soc Stud 1967; Northeastern Univ (MA) European His 1971; Ball St Univ 28 Credits; Univ of MD 3 Credits; *cr:* Francis Scott Key Jr HS Tchr 1970-71; Frederick Sasscer Jr HS Tchr 1971-73, 1975-80; Zwibrucken Amer HS Tchr 1973-75; Crossland HS Tchr 1980-; *ai:* Game Mgr Sporting Events; AFT 1976-; Book Review Article Schl Lib Journal; Influential Tchr Awd St Mary's Coll; Outstanding Educator Prince George's Cty Schl 1989; *office:* Crossland HS 6901 Temple Hills Rd Temple Hills MD 20748*

O'MALLEY, PATRICK EDWARD, Math Teacher & Computer Coord; *b:* Winchendon, MA; *m:* Mary J. Decato; *c:* Shawn, Kevin; *ed:* Fitchburg St Coll (BS) Mathematics Ed 1963; Framinghham St Coll (MED) MAth 1969; Fitchburg St Coll 24 Credit Hrs; *cr:* Murdock Jr Sr Hs Math Tchr 1963-64; Nagog Elem Schl Math Specialist 1964-65; Fitchburg St Coll Visiting Lecturer 1976-; N Middlesex Reg HS Math, Cmptr Sci 1965-; *ai:* Asst Bsktbl Coach 1965-66; Math Team Coach 1976-80; Math Dept Chm1970-87; Supt Advy Comm 1993-; Prin Search Comm 1980-; MTA, NEA 1963-, Pres Local; NCTM 1964-; Cable Commission 1990-, Sec; N Amer Family Camping Assn 1976-, Natl Pres; Cable Pub Svc Awd for Ldrshp; *office:* North Middlesex Regional HS 19 Main St Townsend MA 01469

O'MARA, DAULETTE PESTONJI, Retired 4th Grade Teacher; *b:* Calcutta, India; *m:* Denis G.; *ed:* Plymouth St Coll (BED) Elem Ed 1956; 50 Addl Hrs Post Grad Stud; *cr:* Woodland Hghts Elem Schl 4th Grd Tchr; *ai:* NEA 1957-93.

O'MARA, EVA POZMANN, Art Teacher; *b:* Hodmezovas[...] Hungary; *m:* Michael; *ed:* Baldwin Wallace Coll (BA) Art 1972; Cl[...] Inst of Art 15 Hrs Graphic Design; Kent St Univ 15 Hrs Ed; 20 Hrs [...] Cert Prgm; *cr:* Brecksville Broadview Hghts High Art Tchr 1[...] Brecksville Broadview Hghts Schl Elem Art Tchr 1985-90; Birm[...] Comm Schls Adult Ed Supvr, Adult ESL Tchr 1990-94; Brec[...] Broadview Hghts High Art Tchr 1994-; *ai:* Soph Class, Art Clu[...] Brecksville Ed Assn Exec Bd Rep, Negotiations Team Mem; St[...] Planning Comm; Brecksville Ed Assn 1980-, Exec Bd Rep; OEA[...] OAEA; NCEA; Art Mart Parents Schlsp Fundraiser Comm Mem; [...] Outcomes for Adult Ed Comm Mem St of MI; Soc of Weatherhea[...] Fellows Participant Weatherhead Schl of Mgmt, Case Western R[...] Univ; *office:* Brecksville-Broadview HS 6376 Mill Rd Broadview [...] OH 44147*

O'MEARA, H. SELMA HOKANSON, Spanish Teacher; *b:* Mo[...] NJ; *m:* Robert A.; *c:* Derrick A., Timothy A., Jocelyn O'Meara Ca[...] *ed:* Tchrs Coll Columbia Univ Psych, Ed; Coll of St Rose at Alba[...] Elmira Coll Ed; 75 Addl Hrs; *cr:* Holland Patent Cntrl HS 9th-12[...] Span Tchr 1978-; *ai:* Adv of SADD; Formerly Liaison, P[...] Reinforcement, Marking Period Assessment Comm; NY St Assn o[...] Langs 1078-; Frgn Lang Assn of Cntrl NY 1978-, Stu Awds; First P[...] Church 1972-, Bd of Deacons; AFS Rome Area 1982-, Comm to [...] Candidates; Tchrs Assn 1978-; Juan Carlos Quincentennial Prgm; [...] of Schlsp 1989; Panel Ldr for Frgn Lang Assn of Cntrl NY; James E[...] Awd; *home:* 1904 Roser Ter Rome NY 13440

O'MEARA, JACKLYN ARMOUR, Acctng & Computer Tech T[...] Long Beach, CA; *m:* T. Michael; *c:* Patrick, Christopher, Zachar[...] Westminster Coll (BA) Bus Ed 1970; Attnd OH St Univ 21 Hrs V[...] Ed, Youngstown St Univ 45 Hrs Scndry Ed; *cr:* Columbus Pub Sc[...] Level Voc Ed Tchr 1970-74, 1976-78; Ashtabula Cty Joint Voc Schl [...] Level Computerized Office Skills Tchr 1987-94, HS Level Accou[...] Computer Tech Instr 1994-; *ai:* Bus Profs of Amer Chapter Adv; [...] 1987-; Bus Profs of Amer 1994-, Adv; *office:* Ashtabula Co Joint Vo[...] 1565 State Route 167 Jefferson OH 44047*

OMWAKE, JANE ELLEN, First Grade Teacher; *b:* Bucyrus, O[...] Miami Univ (BS) Elem Ed 1975; *cr:* Buckeye Cntrl Remedial [...] 1977-85, 1st Grd Tchr 1986-; *ai:* NEA, OEA & BCEA 1977-, Pres, [...] IRA, ORA & CCIRA 1977-, Pres, Sec; TLC Preschool Bd 1987-, [...] *home:* 3233 Albaugh Rd Bloomville OH 44818

ONCAY, BARBARA SHARP, German & French Teacher; *b:* Darb[...] *m:* Daniel W. Pritchett; *c:* Ruthy Papp, Deborah Papp, Michael Pap[...] St Joseph's Univ (BS) Scndry Ed, Fr 1969; Villanova Univ (MA) Rel[...] Stud 1976; Cath Univ Amer PHD Stu for Religious Stud; Grad Co[...] Ger, Fr, Latin, Greek, Hebrew, Syriac, Span; *cr:* Hdy Cross Jr High 7[...] Grd Eng 1982-83; Dover AFB HS Dir, Adult Religious Ed 1983-84; [...] HS Foreign Lang Tchr 1984-; *ai:* Ger Club Adv; Dover HS Fac Com[...] Schl Reorganization; AATG, AATF, DCTFL 1985-; ASCD 1992-; D[...] NEA 1984-, Pol Action Chair; Capital Improvement Assoc 1991-, Fo[...] Dir; Democratic Comm Woman 1990-; Tchng Fellow Univ of DE [...] *office:* Dover HS 625 Walker Rd Dover DE 19901*

ONDER, KRISTINA MANUEL, English Teacher; *b:* Austin, T[...] Stephen; *ed:* Bowling Green St Univ (BS) Eng 1985; 30 Addl Cred[...] in Eng from Queens Coll; *cr:* Arcadia Local Schls Eng Tchr 1986-8[...] Fleming Schl Eng Tchr 1988-90; Xenia HS Eng Tchr 1990-; *ai:* S[...] Team & Lit Magazine Adv; Staff Dev Liason; Stu Assistance Team; [...] 1985-; OEA 1990-; YMCA 1977-; Short Story Pub in Writing Text[...] Articles Pub in Cath Digest, Cath Telegraph & Natl Cath Register; [...] Xenia HS 303 Kinsey Rd Xenia OH 45385

ONDERDONK, RICHARDSON DIXON, Biology Teacher; *b:* S[...] Springs, MD; *m:* Christine Louise Miller; *c:* Skyler; *ed:* Bard Coll [...] Bio 1980; Antioch New England Grad Schl (MST) Environmental [...] 1982; SUNY at New Paltz Credits; *cr:* Poughkeepsie Day Schl K-1[...] Sci Tchr 1982-84; Kingston HS Bio Tchr 1984-; *ai:* Environm[...] Awareness Club, Envirthon Adv; Watershed Yth Summit 1996 Adv; [...] 1986-; *office:* Kingston HS 403 Broadway Kingston NY 12401

ONEAIL, PATRICIA BACKER, Fifth Grade Teacher; *b:* Grassmere, [...] *m:* John Joseph; *c:* John, Joseph, Jeffery, Jason, Jeremy, Ian; *ed:* Un[...] NH (BA) Psych 1968; Masters of Ed Lesley Coll Boston; *cr:* Seab[...] Elem 4th & 5th Grd Tchr 1968-; *ai:* NHEA, SEA, NEA 1968-; *o*[...] Seabrook Elem Schl 256 Walton Rd Seabrook NH 03874

O'NEAL, CHRISTIAN MICHAEL, History Teacher; *b:* Newark, N[...] Howard Univ (BS) Sociology, His 1968, (MA) Scndry Ed 1969 [...] Neptune Twp HS Tchr 1969-70; Eastside HS Tchr 1970-84; Science [...] Tchr 1984-; *ai:* Speech Team Coach; Comm Svc Adv; NCSS, AFT, AS[...] Princeton Univ Awd Distinguished Practice; NJ Governors Awd [...] Tchng; Rutgers Univ Tchr Appreciation Awd; *office:* Science HS 40 R[...] St Newark NJ 07102*

O'NEAL, FRANCES ALVEY, English Teacher; *b:* Evansville, IN [...] William Joseph; *ed:* St Mary of the Woods Coll (BS) Ed 1962; The [...] of Toledo (MS) Liberal Stud 1987; Ball St Univ Seminars on World [...] Miami Univ of OH Lang Arts Wkshps; Sienna Hghts Coll Wkshp[...] Advanced Placement Eng; Toledo Museum of Art Classes; *cr:* Ca[...] Pub Schl Lang Arts Tchr 1962-64; McMillan Schl Lang Arts Tchr 1964[...] Russell Blvd Schl Lang Arts Tchr 1965-69; Oregon Schls Lang Arts [...] 1969-78; St Francis De Sales HS Eng Tchr 1978-; *ai:* Pres of Arts & [...] Alumni Affiliate; Host for Foreign Stu Exch; Vol Tutoring; NEA 1[...] NCEA 1978-; NCTE 1980-; SMW Alumae Assn 1962-; UT Alumni A[...] NEH Fellowship; Evaluator N Cntrl Evaluation Comm; *home:* [...] Potomac Dr Toledo OH 43607

O'NEIL, D. MICHAEL, Assistant Prinicpal; *b:* Massena, NY; [...] Elizabeth Arguette; *ed:* Plattsburg (BA) Sci & Soc Stud 1972; Castl[...] (MS) Admin 1989; *cr:* Queensbury Schl Dist 5th & 6th Grd Tchr 1973[...] Admin 1989-; *ai:* 7th & 8th Grd Bsbl, Jr Var Bsktbl, Bsbl, Var Bsktbl, [...] Golf, 7th & 8th Grd Ftbl & 5th & 6th Grd Intramural Ftbl Coach; SAA[...] 1989-; *office:* Queensbury Elem Schl 431 Aviation Rd Queensbury [...] 12804

O'NEIL, FRANCES L., Professor of Psychology; *b:* Weymouth, MA [...] Robert, Stephen, Kevin; *ed:* Stonehill (AB) Psych, Eng 1959; Univ of [...] (MED) Psych, Ed 1967; Univ of CT (PHD) Psych, Ed 1980; Post Doct[...] Stud Yale Univ at New Haven, Amer Hypnosis Trng Acad at WA [...] Mental Rsrch Inst at Palo Alto; *cr:* Cntrl CT St Univ Adj Prof 1971-[...] Univ of CT Adj Prof 1976-83; Tunxis Comm-Tech Coll Prof of P[...] 1983-; *ai:* Psi Beta, Acad Adv; APA 1983-; AAUP 1985-; World Ed Flw[...] 1970-, VP; Soc for Educl Reconstruction 1968-, Sec, Treas; High[...] Scholastic Average Awd Stonhill Coll; Doctoral Dissertation Flwshp [...] Univ of CT; Mellon Fnd Grant Yale Univ; Article Pub; *office:* Tu[...] Comm-Tech Coll Routes 6 And 177 Farmington CT 06032

ONEIL, GAYLE LYNN, Kindergarten Teacher; *b:* Newark, NJ; [...] Newark St (BA) Elem 1968; Kean Coll (MA) Early Chldhd 1977; [...] Middletown Twp Sch Grd 1 Tchr 1968-87, Pre 1 Tchr 1987-91, Knd[...] Tchr 1991-; *ai:* NEA, NJEA, MTEA 1968-; Withecomb Fnd Grants; *off*[...] River Plaza Elem Sch 59 Tindal Rd Middletown NJ 07748

O'NEIL, KELLEY SUE, Social Studies & French Instr; *b:* Erie, PA; [...] Slippery Rock Univ (BS) Ed & Soc Stud 1993; Attnd Clarion Univ, Cu[...] of Quebec at Trois Rivieres & Gannon Univ; *cr:* Ridgway HS Soc Stu[...]

· 1993-; *ai:* Var Soccer Coach; Jr Class Adv 1994-95; Sr Class Adv 6; Sec of Ridgway Area Tchrs Assn; Curr Writer; Homebound Instr; em; PSEA, NEA 1993-; Tchr of Yr at Ridgway HS 1994-95.*

L, MARY A. OKEEFE, English Language Teacher; *b:* Buffalo, NY; mas A. Sr.; *c:* Thomas, Mary Wallace, Daniel; *ed:* Framingham St 3SEd) Ed 1959; St of MA K-3rd Grd & 1st-6th Grd ESL Cert 1996; mingham Schl Dept 3rd Grd Tchr 1959-61; Natick Pub Schls Sub 974-82, Elem ESL Tchr 1982-; *ai:* Multicultural Comm Co-Chair; 984-, Bldg Rep; MA Tchrs Assoc 1984-; Jiffy-Lube Excl Tchr Awd *office:* Memorial Elem Schl 107 Eliot St Natick MA 01760

L, PATRICK MICHAEL, Humanities & Soc Sci Asst Prof; *b:* ch, NY; *ed:* St Univ of NY at Binghamton (BA) Eng Lit 1969, (MA) (MA) Philosophy 1979, (MA) His 1981, (PHD) His 1993; *cr:* e Comm Coll Asst Prof, Humanaites & Soc Scis 1985-; *ai:* Stu Govt dv; Amer His Assn, Amer Philosophical Assn, Amer Acad of Pol Sci lem; Pub Articles; *home:* 75 Colfax Ave Binghamton NY 13905*

L, TERRY MC GUIMESS, Biology Teacher; *b:* Pontiac, MI; *m:* el; *c:* Mikala, Kelsey; *ed:* Univ of NH (BA) Microbiology Lab Tech (MED) Scndry Ed 1987, (MED) Cnslng 1995; *cr:* Lahey Clinic Med icrobiology Lab Technician 1985; Nashua Sr HS Bio Tchr 1986-; *ai:* ss Adv; St Championship Odyssey of Mind Coach; Fac Advy Comm; Instrl Soccer Coach; AFT, NEA 1986-; NARAL 1988-; *office:* a Sr HS 36 Riverside Dr Nashua NH 03062*

L, THOM, Coordinator of Gifted; *b:* Indianapolis, IN; *m:* Diana L. ; *c:* Corrie F., Brennan M.; *ed:* In Univ at Purdue (BS) Mrktg, e & Ec 1983; Tchr Cert from Shippensburg Univ 1992; 9 credit Hrs ted Ed Toward Masters from Millersville Univ; *cr:* Dean Witter lds Stockbroker Fin Ctr Mg 1984-90; W H Newbolds Stockbroker 91; Woodside Detention Ctr Juvenile Detention Specialist 1991-92; pring Schl Dist Coord of Gifted 1992-; *ai:* Fall Play Dir 1992-; onmental Club Adv 1992-; Shakespeare Festival Judge; NEA 1992-; nted the First Fac Written Production of a Christmas Carol; Instituted ide Recycling Prgm; *office:* Big Spring HS 45 Mount Rock Rd ille PA 17241*

IL, VIDA JEAN, History & German Teacher; *b:* McKeesport, PA; obert Patrick O'Neil; *ed:* Westminster Coll (BA) Ger 1968; Univ of urgh (MA) Germanic, Lang, Lit 1972; 34 Credit Hrs in His, Sci-Tech Local His & Ethnic Stud; Real Estate License; Oxford Univ, Eng Art ry 1995; *cr:* Univ of Pittsburgh Ger Instr 1969; McKeesport Schl Dist His Tchr 1969-; PA St Univ Adjunct Ger Prof 1988-93; *ai:* Auberle for Boys Tutor; Field Trips Org; Stdnts to Europe 1980-; AATG ; NEA 1972-; Outstanding Tchr Coll Frosh; Woodrow Wilson Natl wship Fnd Grant 1993; *office:* McKeesport HS 1960 Eden Park Blvd eesport PA 15132

ILL, BARBARA LEROY, Science Teacher; *b:* Bridgeport, CT; *m:* l Franc; *ed:* Western CT St Univ (BS) Hlth Ed & Sci 1985; Cntrl CT iv (MS) Sci Ed 1993; 15 Post Grad Credit Hrs Above Masters; *cr:* y HS Sci Tchr 1988-; *ai:* Vllybl & Sftbl Coach; Sci Review Curr n; Positive Discipline Comm; Soph Class Adv; CSTA 1988-; NEA -; CEA 1988-; WTA 1988-; All Saints Church 1993-, Vestry.

EILL, BERNARD L., Social Studies Teacher; *b:* Denver, CO; *m:* ude Nargan; *c:* Katie, James, Sean; *ed:* Univ of N CO (AB) His 1961; Jose St Univ (MA) US His 1970; Doctoral Cadidate 1993; *cr:* klin-Mc Kinley Schl Tchr 1961-69; Woodbridge HS Tchr 1971-74; bart HS Tchr, Admin 1975-93; Heidelberg HS Tchr 1993-; *ai:* Frosh s Spon; Stu Sponsorship; Lionhearts Svc Org; NEA 1961-; PDK 1981-.

EILL, BRIAN F., Assistant Professor; *b:* Pittsburgh, PA; *ed:* Univ of burgh (BA) Admin of Justice 1981; Marywood (MSW) Soc Work 1988; Stu City Univ of NY at John Jay; 33 Addl Credits Criminal Justice; dolphi Village Cnslr 1981-83; Comm Commitment Inc Cnslr 1983-91; ntown Coll Asst Prof 1991-; *ai:* Schl-Wide Guest Speakers, ormers; Dev New Course Race & Ethnic Relations; IM Sports; Stu Life m; Criminal Justice Club Adv; Stu Adv; Internship Supvr; AD-HOC m on Drugs & Alcohol; Hispanic Initiative; Natl Acad of Criminal ce 1995-; WMUH 1984-, Disc Jockey, Vol; PA Prison Soc 1992-, Vol; of Recognition Lehigh Co Prison 1994; Cert of Appreciation ntown Diversity Fair 1992; *home:* 1238 Seidersville Rd Bethlehem PA 5

EILL, CHRISTINE P., Eighth Grade Math Teacher; *b:* Queens, NY; *c:* ; *ed:* Kean Coll of NJ (BA) Ed 1973, (MA) Math Ed 1984; 32 Credits d Past MS; *cr:* Bedminster Bd of Ed 5th Grd Tchr 1973-76; Glen Ridge of Ed Basic Skills Math Tchr 1977; Ringwood Bd of Ed 7th-8th Grd h Tchr 1977-80; West Orange Bd of Ed 8th Grd Math Tchr 1980-; *ai:* Grd Fundraiser, Williamsburg 8th Grd Trip & Math Contests Coord; k & Memrl Day Ceremony Adv; NEA 1973-; NJEA 1973-; NJ ernors Tchr of Yr Awd 1990; *office:* Edison MS 75 William St West nge NJ 07052

EILL, CYNTHIA BENANTI, Biology Teacher; *b:* Hackensack, NJ; ohn F.; *c:* Eve, Elizabeth; *ed:* Indiana Univ of PA (BS) Ed 1973; 24 dit Hrs Bio Ed; *cr:* North Allegheny Schls 9-10 Grd Bio Tchr 1973-74, Life Sci Tchr 1974-85, 9-10 Grd Bio Tchr 1986-; *ai:* Spon Project Earth ronmental Club; Sci Ed Team; Hlth & Safety Comm; Girls Scouts -, Troop Ldr; Woodhaven Oaks Civic Assn 1987-, Newsletter Ed; Nom r Excl Awd, Amway Environmental Awd; Gift of Time Awd 1990; W PA Sci & Engineering Fair Awds; Pres Aw for Ecell in Sci Tchng Nom 6; *office:* North Allegheny Interm HS 350 Cumberland Rd Pittsburgh 15237

EILL, DANIEL JOSEPH, Social Studies Teacher; *b:* New York City, *m:* Pat Sutphen; *c:* Cindy Sutphen, Susan Sutphen; *ed:* Saint aventure Univ (BS) Ec 1973; Saint Johns Univ (MBA) Marketing nt 1978, (MA) His 1992; Rockville Centre Diocese Pastoral Formation Completed 2 Yr Prgm for Spiritual-Theological Formation 1993-95; Textile Industry Sales & Mrktg 1973-88; D P Murphy Co Parish nsultant 1989-91; Saint Anthonys HS Soc Stud Tchr 1988-89, 1991-; *ai:* sh Bsktbl Moderator; *office:* St Anthony's HS 275 Wolf Hill Rd Melville 11747

NEILL, DAVID, Social Studies Teacher; *b:* Somerville, NJ; *ed:* Raritan Comm Coll (AA) Lbrl Arts 1989; Trenton St Coll (BA) His 1992, AT) Ed 1993; *cr:* Linden HS World, US His Tchr 1993-94; Mc Donough US His, Govt Tchr 1994-; *ai:* Ftbl, Sftbl Coaches; Class of 1998 Spon; bate, Forensics, Mock Trial Clubs Advs; NEA 1993-; *office:* Maurice donough HS 7165 Marshall Corner Rd Pomfret MD 20675

NEILL, JANE SCHARLE, Chemistry Teacher; *b:* Allentown, PA; *m:* ristopher R.; *c:* Christopher, Sean, Kyle, Colleen; *ed:* Villanova Univ CE) Chemical Engrng 1979; Allentown Coll of St Francis de Sales ndry Ed Cert Chem 1994; 34 Post-Grad Credit Hrs; *cr:* SunTech Rsrch gr 1979-80; Notre Dame HS Chem Tchr 1994-95; Allentown Cntrl Cath Chem Tchr 1995-; *ai:* NCEA 1994-; Allentown Diocese Lay Tchrs sn 1994-; Scout Vol 1987-; Cathedral Church Parish Cncl 1992-; Cedar est Coll Eisenhower Grant 1995; *office:* Allentown Cntrl Cath HS 301 N St Allentown PA 18102

NEILL, JOHN WILLIAM, Hotel & Restaurant Mgmt Prof; *b:* Troy, ; *m:* Alicia Kay Fitzgerald; *c:* Michael J.; *ed:* Cornell Univ (BS) Hotel lmin 1984; NY Univ (MS) Real Estate 1994; Walt Disney Productions ngmt Trng Prgm; Hyatt Corp Mngmt Trng Prgm; *cr:* Hyatt Corp Mgr 1984-87; Marriott Intnl Hotel Dev Mgr 1987-90; Holiday Inn Worldwide Market Planning Dir 1990-91; Coopers & Lybrand Sr Consultant 1991-94, Johnson & Wales Univ Prof 1994-; *ai:* Cncl on Hotel, Restaurant, Institutional Ed; MENSA; Appraisal Inst 1991-, MAI Designation; Amer Hotel & Motel Assn; RI Bd of Real Estate Appraisers; Articles, QuotationsPub; *office:* Johnson And Wales Univ 8 Abbott Park Pl Providence RI 02903

O'NEILL, JULIE K., 3rd-4th Grade Tchr & Asst Prin; *b:* Merrill, WI; *m:* David Charles; *c:* Alyxandra Michelle; *ed:* Working on MS Learning, Behavioral Disorders Buffalo St Coll; St Univ at Buffalo 9 Credits, 36 Quality Points Towards MS Exceptional Ed; *cr:* St Mark Luth Schl 3-4 Grd Tchr 1984-, Admin 1988, Asst Prin 1988-, 2-3 Grd Tchr 1989-90; *ai:* Vacation Bible Schl Coord; Sunday Schl, Piano, Flute Tchr; Dir Christmas Prgm; Wkshp Ldr; Coord Parenting Classes; Co-Dir Schl Musical; LCMS Stu Aid, Recruitment Bd 1992-95; St Mark Bd of Ed 1986-95, Tchr Adv; St Mark Bd of Stewardship 1994-95, LCMS Educl Subcomm 1994-; Mem of Ntnl Schl Accredidation Tm 1995-96, St Matthew Schl; Marquis Who's Who Am Educ; 1993- Elem Educator of Yr; LCMS Nom 1990 Thanks to Tchrs Excl Awd; Wrt Lang Curriculum; *office:* Saint Mark Lutheran Schl 1135 Oliver St North Tonawanda NY 14120*

O'NEILL, KATHLEEN QUINLAN, Guidance Counselor; *b:* Mineola, NY; *m:* Sean E.; *ed:* Long Island Univ (BS) Eng Ed 1988, (MS) Guid Cnslng 1985; 6 Post Grad Credits Psych, Cnslng; *cr:* Ballmore Merrick Schl Dist Sub Tchr 1982; Sacred Heart Acad Eng Tchr 1982-91, Guid Cnslr 1991-; *ai:* Adult Enrichment Prgm; Spiritual Life Comm; Spec Events Coord; ASCD 1990-; NCA, CCA 1991-; NCTE 1983-91; *office:* Sacred Heart Acad 47 Cathedral Ave Hempstead NY 11550

O'NEILL, KEVIN, English Teacher; *b:* Cambridge, MA; *m:* Sheri Henderson; *c:* Erin, Jared; *ed:* Ramapo Coll of NJ (BA) Eng, Comparative Lit 1980; William Paterson Coll of NJ (MA) Eng, Writing 1992; *cr:* Park Ridge HS Eng Tchr 1981-; *ai:* Tennis Coach; Supt's Advy, PAC Comms; NEA, NJEA, PREA 1981-; *office:* Park Ridge HS 2 Park Ave Park Ridge NJ 07656

O'NEILL, LINDA SYLVESTER, First Grade Teacher; *b:* New Castle, PA; *m:* Robert F.; *ed:* Franciscan Univ (BA) His, Soc Stud 1969; Westminster Coll (MED) Elem Ed 1971; Cert Elem, MS Prin 1982; Credit Hrs Essential Elements of Instruction; *cr:* Union Meml Elem Schl Third Grd Tchr 1971-73, Fourth Grd Tchr 1973-74, First Grd Tchr 1974-; *ai:* Acad Banquet; Amer Ed Week, Parent Vol, Research Comms; Staff Dev; Curr; Fac Adv; Long Range Planning; Stud for Rdng; Evaluating Team; Lawrence Cty Rdng Cncl; Mentor Prgm; Discipline; NEA 1971-, Sec; PSEA 1971-, Negotiations Soc Prof Dev Comm; MADD, Boosters 1990-; Amer Red Cross 1975; Cancer Soc, Heart Fund 1986-; Youngstown St Univ Prof Prgm Awd; Gift of Time Tribute 1994-95; *home:* 5670 Lockwood Blvd Boardman OH 44512*

O'NEILL, ROBERT MARTIN, High School English Teacher; *b:* Lancaster, NY; *w:* Louraine (dec); *c:* Andrea Roberts, Martin, Margaret; *ed:* Canisius Coll (BA) Latin, Greek 1961; Fordham Univ (MA) Latin, Creek 1962; 64 Addl Hrs in Eng, Educl Admin; *cr:* Depew HS Latin & Eng Tchr 1962-; *ai:* Ftbl PA Announcer; Depew Tchrs Org, NY St United Tchrs, AFT 1962-; Loyal Order of Moose 1954-; Natl Endowment for Hum 1984, Ind Stud 1985, Summer Seminar 1989, Summer 1993.

O'NEILL, STEPHEN PAUL, Prof of Reading & Study Skills; *b:* New York City, NY; *ed:* Cath Univ of Amer at WA DC (BA) Eng Lit 1959; Fordham Univ (MSE) Educ Psych, Measurement in Guid 1964; NY Univ (MA) Educl Psych, Rdng 1967; Manhattan Coll (MA) Rel 1970; Nova Univ Higher Ed 1990; St John's Univ Prof Diploma Cnslr Ed 1975; Attnd Walden Univ, Univ of San Diego, Bronx Comm Coll CUNY, Manhattan Coll; *cr:* Ascension Schl 4th, 6th, 8th Grds Tchr 1958-63; St John's Schl 8th Grd Tchr 1963-65; Sacred Heart Schl 8th Grd Tchr, Asst Prin, Prin 1965-70; LaSalle Acad HS Rdng Tchr, Cnslr 1969-70; Baruch Coll CUNY Adj Eng Lit; Coll of New rochelle Adj Rdng, Study Skills, Ed; Manhattan Coll Adj Rdng, Stud Skills, Ed; Bronx Comm Coll CUNY Rdng, Stud Skills, Ed, Former Deputy Chprsn 1971-; *ai:* Fac Coord for Basic Dev Rdng Course; Dept Liason Evening Fac; Departmental Prsnl & Budget Comm; Irish Cultural Soc; NY Metropolitan Assoc for Div Ed 1984-, Conf Chair, Exec Cncl, Former Pres, Svc Awd; IRA 1980-; People to People Intnl 1991-; Archdiocese of NY Dist 12 S Bronx Awded Svc Plaque; Pub Articles; *office:* City Univ Of NY Bronx Comm Col 181st St & University Ave Bronx NY 10469

O'NEILL, THOMAS EUGENE, Art, Crafts & Photography Tchr; *b:* Teaneck, NJ; *m:* Rosalie Rizzo; *c:* Scott, Todd; *ed:* Syracuse Univ (BFA) Advertising Design 1961; NY Univ (MFA) Art Ed 1968; 45 Addl Hrs; *cr:* Leonia HS Art Tchr 1968; Fairlawn HS Art Tchr 1968-; *ai:* North Jersey Stu Craftsman Fair Sec 20 Yrs; Set Design, Painter Schl Musical 5 Yrs; NJEA, NEA, AEW 1968-; Fair Lawn Edctrs Ed 1968-; Midland Pk Magic 1992-; Tchr of Yr 1994; Citizen of Yr 1976; *office:* Fair Lawn HS Berdan Ave Fair Lawn NJ 07410*

O'NEILL-BURNS, SHEILA, 8th Grd Lang Arts & Rdng Tchr; *b:* New Haven, CT; *m:* Christopher; *c:* Dayna Roper, Eric Burns, Kelly Burns; *ed:* Southern CT St Univ (BS) Intermediate, Upper Ed 1965; SCSC (MS) Spec Ed 1973; Fairfield Univ 6th Yr Project Teach 1980; *cr:* Temple St Elem Schl 3rd-4th Grd Tchr 1965-76; Green Acres Elem Schl 2nd Grd Tchr 1977-78; Montowese Elem Schl 2nd-4th Grd Tchr 1978-91; North Haven MS 8th Grd Lang Arts Tchr 1991-; *ai:* Elem Schl Drama Club Coach 13 Yrs; Tchrs Choral Club; Cath Charities; Friends in Residence Adv, Advisee; Promoting Young Authors; Comm to Restructure Jr HS To MS; Early Intervention Project Elem 10 Yrs, MS 2 Yrs; Stdnts Visit Retirement Homes; 2nd-8th Grd Field Trip Experiences; Elem Schl Fairs 26 Yrs;Star Trek, Danci ng for Boys I, Boys & Girls II, Predators and Their Worlds Clubs; Elem IM Sports; Recycling, Extended Day Comms; Elem Soc Stud, Sci Comms; NHEA, NEA, CEA 1965-; Negotiation Team 1965-, Exec Bd 10 Yrs; Grievance Comm 1965-, Exec Bd 10 Yrs; Bldg Rep 20 Yrs; Greenpeace 1965-; Spec Olympics Vol 1965-78; PTA Exec Bd 1965-, Elem Tchr Rep 26 Yrs; Leukemia Soc, NMDP Bone Marrow Fund Raiser; SCSC, Fairfield Univs Alumni; North Haven, New Haven Project Concern; Alumni Univ Women; Alternative Ways to Evaluate Stu Progress; CT Rdng Assn Summer Librn 4 Yrs; Planning For Stdnts with Alternative Educl Needs; Jaycee Outstdng Yng Edctr of Yr Awd 1978; Elem Master Tchr, Mentor 15 Yrs; *office:* North Haven MS 55 Bailey Rd North Haven CT 06473

ONEY, BRYAN L., 6th & 7th Grade Science Tchr; *b:* Willard, OH; *m:* Wendy Leber; *ed:* Ashland Univ (BS) Comprehensive Sci 1988; Working On Masters in Cmptr Ed 17 Semester Hrs; *cr:* South Cntrl Schls 6th & 7th Grd Sci Tchr 1988-; *ai:* Stu Cncl Adv; NEA 1988-; North Fairfield Vol Fireman 1985-, Firefighter; *home:* 110 N Main St North Fairfield OH 44855

ONOFRIO, MARSHALL PAUL, Associate Professor of Music; *b:* New Haven, CT; *m:* Susan Levering Barclay; *c:* James, Anne; *ed:* Univ of CT (BS) Music Ed 1977, (BM) Trumpet 1978; Univ of IL (MM) Trumpet 1979; Univ of NE at Lincoln (MM) Composition 1982; OH St Univ (DMA) Composition 1987; Rutgers Univ Summer Inst on Jazz Ed 1988; *cr:* Midland Coll Asst Prof of Music 1979-83; Muskingum Coll Asst Prof of Music & Chair 1983-86; OH St Univ Grad Assoc Music 1985-87; SUNY at Plattsburgh Assoc Prof of Music & Coord 1987-; *ai:* Coord of Heisler Music Schlsp Prgm; Adv to Music Minor & Musi Concentration Prgms; UUP 1987-; Amer Federation of Musicians 1971; Intnl Assn of Jazz Educators 1979-; Intnl Trumpet Guild 1977-; Music Educators Natl Conf 1979-; NY St Schl Music Assoc 1987-; Bd of the Champlain Valley Oratorio Soc 1989-93, Comm Consult; Plattsburgh Arts Coalition 1995-, Exec Comm; Article on Jazz Improvisation Published in May 1989 Intnl Trumpet Guild Journal; Music, Book & Record Reviews Published; Thrice Awded Discretionary Merit Increases in Highest Categories at SUNY at Plattsburgh; *office:* SUNY at Plattsburgh 231 Myers Fine Arts Bldg Plattsburgh NY 12901*

ONORATO, ROBERT ANTHONY, US History & Law Teacher; *b:* Montclair, NJ; *m:* Kathleen O'Mara; *c:* Lauren, Matthew; *ed:* Rutgers Coll (BA) Pol Sci 1979; Cumberland Schl of Law (JD) 1982; Rugers at Newark (MAT) Amer His 1992; Montclair St Univ; *cr:* Essex Cty Superior Court Law 1982-83; Law Offices of Paul Ainge Attorney-At-Law 1983-86; Ridgewood Pub Schls Soc Stud Tchr 1986-; *ai:* Yrbk, Mock Trial Club & Model UN Club Adv; ASCD 1974-; NJEA 1986-; NEA 1986-; Helped Establish Exch Pgm Between Ridgewood HS & Paterson Eastside HS; Wrote Curr for Introduction to Law Course & Curr for Amer Govt & Pol AP; *office:* Ridgewood HS 627 E Ridgewood Ave Ridgewood NJ 07450

OPALKA, JULIANNE T. KUPCHIK, 9th-12th Grd Chem & Bio Tchr; *b:* Scranton, PA; *m:* John D.; *ed:* IN Univ of PA (BS) Sci Ed, Bio, Chem 1988; Masters Candidate Thesis Effects Constructivist Tchng Methods Acad Achvmt HS Bio, Chem Stdnts; *cr:* Pillsbury Corp Mgr 1979-81; Marriott Corp Mgr 1981-83; Apollo Ridge HS Sci Tchr 1988-; *ai:* Tech, Learning Festival K-5 Comm; NEA 1988-; Outstdng Conservation Ed Armstrong Cty 1990; *office:* Apollo Ridge HS Star Rt Box 46A Spring Church PA 15686

OPDYKE, KRISTEN MARIE, Biology Teacher; *b:* Dover, NJ; *ed:* Bucknell Univ (BS) Scndry Ed 1993; *cr:* Freehold Boro HS Bio, Earth Sci Tchr 1993-94; Toms River HS E Bio, Tchr 1994-; *ai:* Girls Cross Cntry, Spring Track Coach; Reaching Out Chstn Bible Club; NEA, NJSTA 1993-; USA Track & Field 1994-; Article Pub; *office:* Toms River HS East Raider Way Toms River NJ 08753*

OPINANTE, PHILIP N., School Social Worker; *b:* Brooklyn, NY; *m:* Joan Nedza; *c:* Victoria; *ed:* Univ of Dayton (BA) Psych 1974; Fordham Univ (MSW) Soc Work 1977; Post Grad Cert in Ed Admin Brooklyn Coll 1987; *cr:* St Vincents Hall Inc Soc Worker & case Mgr 1974-80; NY City Bd of Ed Schl Soc Worker 1980-; *ai:* Adv to the Stu Govt; Boys & Girls Vlybl Team Coach; NASW 1978-; *office:* Sheepshead Bay HS 3000 Avenue X Brooklyn NY 11235*

OPLINGER, DIANE LEACH, Social Studies Teacher; *b:* Akron, OH; *m:* Douglas J.; *c:* Danielle, Justin, Jaclyn; *ed:* Univ of Akron (BSEd) Elem Ed 1976; Ashland Univ (MED) Curr, Instruction 1995; GATE, Supervision Cert; Attnd Summit Cty Tech Acad; *cr:* Springfield Twp Schls 3rd-6th Grd Tchr 1977-; *ai:* Tech Comm; SLACT,NEOEA, OEA 1977-; OAGC 1995-; Akron Yth Symphony Parents 1993-, VP; *home:* 4556 Arlington Rd Uniontown OH 44685

OPYR, LINDA ELENA, English Dept Chairperson; *b:* Astoria, NY; *ed:* Springfield Coll (BS) Sociology, Psychology 1974, (ME) Guidance, Psych Svc 1975; St Johns Univ (EDD) Eng, Amer Lit 1988; CW Post Educl Admin Prof Diploma 1993; NYS Coaching Cert; *cr:* Sewanhaka HS Eng Tchr, Var Soccer, Stbl Coach 1976-91; Sewanhakan Cntrl HS Dist Gifted, Talanted Coord 1986-91; Floral Park Meml HS Eng Dept Chprsn 1991-; *ai:* Yrbk Adv; Dist Tchr Prof, 5 Yr Plan Comms; NCTE 1976-; ASCD 1986-; LI Poetry Collective 1992-; Amer Acad of Poets; Rosebud Ed Bd; Group for South Fork 1990-; Nature Conservancy; Pub Poetry Numerous Times; *office:* Floral Park Meml HS 210 Locust St Floral Park NY 11003

ORAM, CHERYL SILLETTI, English Teacher; *b:* Morristown, NJ; *m:* George; *c:* Jordan Petrill, Blake Petrill; *ed:* Fairleigh Dickinson Univ (BA) Eng Ed 1976; Rutgers Univ (MED) Eng Ed 1982; *cr:* Kean Coll Asst Dir of Admissions 1976-77; Somerville HS Eng Tchr 1977-; *ai:* NHS Adv; Athletic Hall of Fame Soc 1991-, Sec; Tchr of Yr 1990; *office:* Somerville HS 222 Davenport St Somerville NJ 08876

ORANGE, LINDA C., Math Teacher; *b:* Painesville, OH; *c:* Julie; *ed:* Kent St Univ (BS) Spcl Ed Gifted 1971; Baldwin Wallace Coll Grad Courses; *cr:* Willoughby-Eastlake 4th-6th Grd Tchr 1971-77; Pre-Schl Tchr 1983-89; Lake Ridge Acad Mid & Upper Schl Math 1990-; *ai:* MS & Comm Svc Adv; Math Lab Coord; Summer Schl Algebra & Stud Skills; Tchr-Mentor; NCTM 1990-; *office:* Lake Ridge Acad 37501 Center Ridge Rd North Ridgeville OH 44039

ORAVEC, RONALD DAVID, Pastor & Catechism Instructor; *b:* Cleveland, OH; *m:* Lana Mae Herbert; *c:* Daniel E., David A., John C.; *ed:* Concordia Seminary at St Louis (MDiv) Theology 1971; Dr of Ministry Prgm 15 Credit Hrs; *cr:* St Stephen Luth Church Pastor 1971-76; St John L. C. at Rome Pastor 1976-81; St John L. C. at N. Tonawanda Pastor 1981-; *ai:* St John Schl Chess Team Coach, Adv; Boys Bsktbl Team Asst Coach; St Johnsburg Vol Fire Co 1981-, Chaplain; *office:* St John Ev Luth Church & Schl 6950 Ward Rd North Tonawanda NY 14120

ORAVECZ, JULIA LOOKABILL, High School English Teacher; *b:* Pulaski, VA; *ed:* Longwood Coll (BA) Eng 1966; Johns Hopkins Univ (MA) Lbrl Arts 1978; Admin Course; *cr:* Brookville HS Tchr 3 Yrs; Northeast HS Tchr, Eng Dept Chm 7 Yrs; Chesapeake HS Tchr, Eng Dept Chm 13 Yrs; Glen Burnie HS Tchr 7 Yrs; *ai:* Human Relations, Curr, Writing Comms; Jr, Sr Class Adv; Drama Coach 3 Yrs; MCTELA, NEA 1969-; NCTE 1966-; TAAAC 1969-, NEA Rep 6 Yrs, Bd of Dirs 2 Yrs; Stu Tchr Adv 5 Yrs; *office:* Glen Burnie Sr HS 7550 Baltimore Annapolis Blvd Glen Burnie MD 21060

ORBAKER, DANIEL LEE, Physics & Chemistry Teacher; *b:* Rochester, NY; *m:* Darlene K.; *c:* Colton, Caleb; *ed:* SUNY at Brockport (BS) Bio 1984, (MS) Ed 1989; *cr:* Lyons HS Tchr 1984-85; Holley HS Tchr & Coach 1985-; *ai:* Var Boys Soccer, Var Girls Bsktbl & Sftbl Coach; Ski Club & Holley Soccer Club Adv; AFT, NYSUT 1984-; NSCAA 1985-; *office:* Holley HS Lynch Rd Holley NY 14470

ORBANN, CAROL A., Reading & Basic Skills Teacher; *b:* East Orange, NJ; *m:* Herbert F.; *c:* Alyson E. Bellotti, Karen G. LaFragola, Melissa A. Remo; *ed:* William Paterson Coll (BS) Elem Ed 1958; Kean Coll 30 Post Grad Credits; Cert Pgm Rdng; *cr:* East Orange Pub Schls Elem Grds Tchr 1958-64; F H Morrell HS Rdng & Basic Skills Tchr 1980-; *ai:* IEA 1980-; NJEA 1980-; NEA 1980-; Local Assistance Bd Union NJ 1988-, Chprsn; Union Twp Bd of Ed 1988-91, Elected Mem, Ed Chprsn; Comm Dev Union NJ 1995-.

ORCHARD, ROBYN BAILEY, Former Eng Tchr & Drmtcs Dir; *b:* Baltimore, MD; *m:* Christopher R.; *c:* Anthony, Jeremy; *ed:* Sweet Briar Coll (BA) Eng 198; Lynchburg Coll (MEd), Scndry Eng Ed; *cr:* Amherst Cty HS Tchr 1986-90, 1992-95; *ai:* Spon & Founder of Dramatic Soc 1986-90, 1993-95; Odyssey of the Mind Coach 1993; NEA 1986-95; Amherst Cty HS Tchr of the Yr 1990.*

OREFICE, VLADIMIRO, Italian Teacher; *b:* Enna Sicily, Italy; *m:* Norma Myers; *c:* Brian, Sharon, Gina; *ed:* CCSU (BS) Fr, Italian 1971; AIC (MED) Ed 1975; *cr:* Enrico Fermi HS Italian Tchr 1971-80; Bloomfield HS Culinary Arts Tchr 1990-91; Agawam HS Italian Tchr 1991-; *ai:* Future Tchrs Club Adv; Discipline Comm; NEA 1990-; MITA, MAFLA 1992-; Orange & Brown Awd; *office:* Agawam HS 760 Cooper St Agawam MA 01001

O'REGAN, MAUREEN MC AULEY, Retired Sixth Grade Teacher; *b:* New York City, NY; *m:* Charles; *c:* Jeanne Marie; *ed:* Hunter Coll (BA) His 1960, (MA) Elem Ed 1970; *cr:* PS 109 Schl Second Grd Tchr 1960-61; Mc

Kinley Schl First Grd Tchr 1961-62; PS 109 Schl First-Second Grd Tchr, Supvr 1962-69; PS 79 Schl Six Grd Tchr 1969-95, Gifted Class Tchr 1989-91; *ai:* Fac Adv Schl Lit, Art Magazine Rhapsody 1989-91; UFT 1960-; AFT 1970-; NY St Cncl Rdng Tchrs 1980-; Cath Trs Assn 1960-, Schl Rep 1985-.

OREILLY, H. GORDON, Professor; *b:* Boston, MA; *m:* Priscilla P.; *c:* Pamela Lamie, Steven, Scott; *ed:* Northeastern Univ (AS) Civil Engrng 1962, (BS) Indstrl Tech 1972; *cr:* Steco Engrng Structural Designer 1962-67; Blue Hills Tech Inst Tchr 1967-85; Massasoit Comm Coll Prof 1985-; *ai:* Track Coach; Fac Adv Stu Senate, Civil Engrng Club; NEA, MA Tchrs Assn 1967-; Am Soc of Engrng Ed 1990-; Boston Soc of Civil Engrs 1970-; *office:* Massasoit Comm Coll 900 Randolph St Canton MA 02021

OREM, WALTYNE BROOKS, Fifth Grade Teacher; *b:* Baltimore, MD; *m:* Quinten Edward; *c:* Winnee O. Chavis, Quandra E., Q. Jason; *ed:* Coppin St Coll (BA) Elem Ed 1961; Johns Hopkins Univ (MS) Ed 1974; *cr:* Patapsco Elem #163 1st Grd Tchr 1961-64; Rosedale Elem #148 1st-2nd Grd Tchr 1965-70; Westside Elem #24 4th-5th Grd Tchr 1970-; *ai:* Globetrotters Jr Geog Club; Schl Improvement Team Chprsn; After Schl Tutor; AFT, Balto Tchrs Union 1974-; Girls Scouts 1990-, Jrs Ldr; Trinity Bapt Church 1990-, Church Schl Supt; *office:* Westside Elem Schl 24 2235 N Fulton Ave Baltimore MD 21217*

OREN, JAMES L., Retired Elementary Teacher; *b:* Randolph County, IN; *m:* Juanita Myrtle Reid; *c:* Timothy; *ed:* Taylor Univ (BA) Sociology 1960; 35 Semester Hrs Miami Univ; *cr:* Miamisburg City Schls Elem Tchr 32 Yrs; *ai:* META 1970-.

ORENDORF, DEBRA D., French, English & Jrnlsm Tchr; *b:* Meyersdale, PA; *ed:* Clarion Univ of PA (BS) Ed 1979, (BA) Fr 1980; Cert to Teach Fr & Eng; *cr:* Meyersdale Area HS Fr, Eng Tchr 1982-83; Berlin Brothersvalley HS Fr, Eng Tchr 1983-; *ai:* Schl Newspaper, Fr Club, Quill & Scroll Adv; Schlsp Comm; NEA 1983-; PSMLA; AATF; *office:* Berlin Brothersvalley HS 1025 E Main St Berlin PA 15530

ORENDORFF, LAURENCE F., Guidance Director; *b:* Gettysburg, PA; *m:* Jean Elizabeth Topper; *c:* Jennifer A. Triaca, Tara, Gail; *ed:* Towson St Univ (MED) Sci, Ed 1973; Masters Equivalent Guid & Admin; *cr:* Baltimore Cty Pub Schls Tchr 1965-78, Dept Chair 1973-78, Cnslr 1978-, Dir of Guid 1990-; *ai:* Recruitment Incoming Ninth Grd; Stu Svc Team Tchr; Admission Review Dismissal, Schl Performance Teams; Phi Delta Kappa 1980-; Chi Sigma Iota 1989-, Life Mbrshp; Natl Bd for Certfd Cnslrs 1984-, NCC; Amer Cnslng Assn 1987-; Knights of Columbus 1963-; *office:* Eastern Tech HS 1100 Mace Ave Baltimore MD 21221

ORFANELLA, LOU, 7th-8th Grade English Teacher; *b:* Bronx, NY; *m:* Marie Inghilterra; *c:* Justin; *ed:* Columbia Univ (BA) Eng & Psych 1982; Fordham Univ (MA) Commnctn 1983; *cr:* Dover UFSD Tchr 1987-88; Dutchess Comm Coll Adj 1987-; Webutuck Cntrl Schls Tchr 1988-93; Western CT St Univ Adj 1988-; Valhalla Schl Dist Tchr 1993-; *ai:* Debate Coach; Newspaper & Lit Magazine Adv; NCTE; NYSUT; Numerous Articles Pub; *office:* Valhalla MS 300 Columbus Ave Valhalla NY 10595

ORFE, MICHAEL, Eng, US His, Hum & Soc Tchr; *b:* Riverside, NJ; *m:* Gay Ann Anderten; *c:* Michael J. Taryn Pomponio, K.C.; *ed:* Montclair St (BA) Eng, Soc Stud 1968; Seton Hall Univ (MA) Amer Stud 1973; Addl 45 Credits Including Cert Supvr, Prin; *cr:* Scotch Plains-Fanwood HS Eng Tchr 1968-74; Mendham HS His, Eng Tchr 1974-, Coord Stu Act 1978-86; *ai:* Golf Coach 1979-; Stu Acts Coord 1978-86; Hum Festival Adv; NEA; NJEA; WMREA; EC; USGA; Lebanon Twp AA 1978-89; Pub Poet, Two Short Pieces of Fiction; Visiting Mem Mid Sts Comm Scndry Ed 4 Times; *home:* 6 Heather Hl Port Murray NJ 07865

ORFEI, FRANK J., Secondary History Teacher; *b:* White Plains, NY; *m:* Gail M.; *c:* Adam, Gabrielle; *ed:* SUNY at Albany (BA) Amer His 1977; Manhattanville Coll (MA) Scndry Soc Stud 1982; Attnd Cleve Coll, Cambridge Univ, London Univ; *cr:* Pelham Meml HS Soc Stud Tchr 1978-; *ai:* Amer Field Svc Club, Yrbk Fac Adv; Soc Stud Curr Revision Comm; Supts Advy Comm Fac Rep; AFT, NY St United Tchrs 1978-; Woodrow Wilson His Scholar Flwshp; NYS Cncl on Hum Latin Amer Flwshp; *office:* Pelham Memorial HS Colonial Ave Pelham NY 10803*

ORFF, THOMAS MARTIN, Music Director; *b:* Pottsville, PA; *m:* Mary Louise Smith; *ed:* Gettysburg Coll (BS) Music Ed 1987; Attnd Villanova Univ, Univ of the Arts, Millersville Univ, Clarion Univ, Vandercook; *cr:* Cardinal Brennan HS Music Dir 1987-89; Schuylkill Haven Area HS Music Dir 1989-; *ai:* Band & Choir Dir; Yrbk Adv; Tech Comm; MENC 1983-; PA Music Edctrs Assn 1983-; Schuylkill Cty Band Assn 1987-, Sec; NEA & PSEA 1989-; Pottsville 3rd Brigade Band 1980-, Dir 1993-95; Schuylkill Symphony Orch 1988-, Prin Tuba; *office:* Schuylkill Haven Area HS 120 Haven St Schuylkill Haven PA 17972

ORGANSKY, FLORENCE DAYTON, 5th Grade Teacher; *b:* Philadelphia, PA; *m:* Peter P.; *c:* Theresa Conway, Edward Conway; *ed:* St Josephs Univ (BA) Elem Ed 1980; *office:* Saint Anselm Schl 12670 Dunks Ferry Rd Philadelphia PA 19154*

ORIA, MARIA CRISTINA (GONZALEZ), Third Grade Bilingual Teacher; *b:* Cardenas Matanza, Cuba; *m:* Modesto; *c:* Mario M., Julia C.,Oria; *ed:* St Peters Coll (BA) Ed 1978; Jersey City St Coll Bilingual Cert 1980; Fairleigh Dickinson Univ Post Grad 30 Credit Hrs; *cr:* Vineland Bd of Ed Bilingual & Multicultural Elem Tchr 1978-; *ai:* Bilingual Curr Comm; NEA 1978-; NJEA 1978-; Vineland Ed Assn 1978-, Rep; Vineland PAL 1994-, Svc Awd; Carmen Gonzalez Baton Twirlers 1995-, Svc Awd; Span Cath Ctr Church; Bilingual Multicultural Conf Presentor 1995; *office:* Marie Durand Elem Schl 317 W Forest Grove Rd Vineland NJ 08360

O'RIELLY, BARBARA STEINKUHLER, English Teacher; *b:* Lockport, NY; *m:* Kevin; *c:* William Edward, K. Michael; *ed:* Rosary Hill Coll (BA) Eng 1970; Niagara Univ Ed 1972; *cr:* Lockport HS Eng Tchr 1972-; *ai:* NEA, AFT, Lockport Ed Assn 1971-; *office:* Lockport HS 250 Lincoln Ave Lockport NY 14094

O'RILEY, JOHN GEORGE, Secondary English Teacher; *b:* Montague, MA; *m:* Lynn Blake; *ed:* Assumption Coll (BA) Eng 1969; *cr:* Turners Falls Jr HS Eng Tchr 1969-85; Turners Falls HS Eng Tchr 1985-; *ai:* Class of 1999 Adv; Schl & Comm Cncl; Montague Tchrs Assn, MA Tchrs Assn, NEA 1969-; BPOE Yth Act Comm 1975-; Montague Excl in Tchng Awd 1991-92.

ORINTAS, BERNADINE CLAIRE, Second Grade Teacher; *b:* Waterbury, CT; *ed:* Cntrl CT St Coll (BS) Elem Ed 1966; Southern CT St (MS) Remedial Rdng 1971; St Joseph Coll 30 Credit Hrs Educl Ldrshp; *cr:* Region 16 2nd Grd Tchr 1966-; *ai:* PTO Exec Bd; Chair Character Counts, Vol Tea Comm; Prins Advy Bd; Children's Corp of CT Chm, CEO; NEA, CEA 1966-; Region 16 Ed Assn 1969-; Comm Vision for Waterbury 1994-, Image, Downtown Comm; Local Church, Writer, Dir of Play; Choir, Parish Cncl, Chprsn; Pub Article; Nom Tchr of Yr; *office:* Algonquin Elem Schl 30 Coer Rd Prospect CT 06712

ORISS, JAMES J., Guidance Counselor; *b:* Pittsburgh, PA; *m:* Lois Ann Leist; *c:* Lisa Anne Sands, Amy Beth; *ed:* Juniata Coll (BS) His, Pol Sci, Span 1962; Indiana Univ of PA (MED) Cnslr Ed 1972; *cr:* Alexander M. Scott HS Tchr, Cnslr 1962-68; General Braddock HS Cnslr 1968-72; Woodland Hills HS Cnslr 1972-; *ai:* NEA, PA St Ed Assn 1962-; Woodland Hills Educl Assn 1977-; Dropout Prevention Network 1992-; Educator of Yr 1995; *office:* Woodland Hills Sr HS 2550 Greensburg Pike Pittsburgh PA 15221*

ORKFITZ, JANET ELAINE, K-6th Grade Vocal Music Tchr; *b:* Philadelphia, PA; *m:* William Charles III; *ed:* Temple Univ Coll of Music (BMEd) Music Ed 1965; *cr:* Toms River Schls Vocal Music Tchr 1965-1970; Island Heights Schl Vocal Music Tchr 1971-72; Seaside Heights Schl Vocal Music Tchr 1971-72; Toms River Schls Vocal Music Tchr 1972-; *ai:* Omni Musci Opera Class; Chorus; TREA 1972-.*

ORLANDO, ANTHONY PAUL, Phys Ed & Health Teacher; *b:* Passaic, NJ; *m:* Katherine Kohler; *c:* Kara, Lisa, Jenna; *ed:* Montclair St Coll (BS) Phys Ed, Hlth 1980, (MA) Tchng of Phys Ed 1987; Addl 30 Credit Hrs Sixth Yr Level Montclair St Coll, Jersey City St Coll; *cr:* Clifton Bd of Ed Phys Ed, Hlth Tchr 1980-, Phys Ed, Hlth Dept Head 1991-; *ai:* Asst Ftbl, Asst Girls Bsktbl, Asst Lacrosse Coach; Schl Based Mngmt Comm; NEA, NJEA, Passaic Cty Ed Assn 1980-; Governors Tchr Recognition Awd 1992-93; *office:* Christopher Colombus MS 350 Piaget Ave Clifton NJ 07011

ORLANDO, LISA MARIE SOMMELLA, Vocal Director; *b:* Gloversville, NY; *m:* Thomas J.; *c:* Nicholas A., Dominic J.; *ed:* Crane Schl of Music at Potsdam (BM) Music Ed 1987; Coll of Saint Rose (MM) Music Ed 1995; NYS Cert Piano Pedagogy 1995; Crane Schl of Music Cert Piano Pedagogy 1987; *cr:* Monticello Cntrl Schl Vocal Dir, MS Gen Music Tchr 1987-88; Pvt Piano Stuido Owner 1988-92; Ft Plain Cntrl Schl Vocal Dir, Gen Music Tchr 1992-93; Oppenheim-Ephratah Cntrl Schl Vocal Dir, Gen Music Tchr 1994-; *ai:* Select Choir Adv; MENC, NYSSMA 1995-; NYS Tchrs Assn 1987-; PTA Tchr of Yr 1994; *office:* Oppenheim-Ephratah Cntrl Schl 6486 State Highway 29 Saint Johnsville NY 13452*

ORLANDO, MARYANN JOAN, English Teacher; *b:* Revere, MA; *ed:* Salem St Coll (BA) Eng, Drama 1975; Univ of MA at Boston (MA) Applied Linguistics 1989; *cr:* Arlington HS Eng Tchr 1977-89; Gibbs Jrs HS Eng Tchr 1989-91; Arlington HS Step Prgm Eng Tchr 1991-; *ai:* Strategic Planning Comm; TESOL 1989-; NEA 1977-; Pub Textbook Series: Night & Day 1, 2 & 3 1994.

ORLANDO, SAMUEL JOSEPH, Retired Teacher; *b:* Geneseo, NY; *m:* Dianna Bentley; *c:* Samuel, Joel, Deborah; *ed:* SUNY at Geneseo (BS) Soc Stud 1958; 50 Hrs in Soc Stud, His Field; *cr:* Bloomfield Cntrl Schl Jr-Sr High Soc Sts Tchr 1958-87; *ai:* NEA 1958-; Bloomfield Tech Assn 1968-, Pres; Fire Dept 1963-, VP, Pres, Firemen of Yr; Town Bd 1964-74, Bd Mem; Town Justice 1964-94, Judge; *home:* 23 Maple Ave Bloomfield NY 14469

ORLEANS, MICHAEL SALVATORE, Jr High Teacher; *b:* Cleveland, OH; *m:* Ruth Minick; *ed:* Youngstown St Univ (BS) Bus, Acctng, Mngmt 1969, (BS) Elem Ed 1974; Univ of IA, Coll of Mount St Joseph Post Grad Stud; *cr:* Southington Local Schls Jr HS Tchr 1969-; *ai:* Math Dept Chprsn; Head Bsbl, Golf, Jr HS Ftbl Coach; Ftbl, Bsktbl Asst; Future Tchrs of Amer; OEA, NEA 1969-; St Jude's Childrens Hosp Cert; *home:* 551 Willow Dr SE Warren OH 44484*

ORLEMANN, KAREN SERGI, Private Tutoring; *b:* Baltimore, MD; *m:* Richard Kerr; *c:* Carlos; *ed:* Millersville Univ (BS) Spec Ed 1979; Credit Hrs Kutztown Univ; *cr:* Lehigh Chrstn Acad K Grd Tchr 1979-88; Bethlehem Chrstn Schl 2-4 Grd Tchr 1989-91; Full Time Pvt Tutor 1991-95; *ai:* Lehigh Univ Schlsp; *home:* 1434 Bushkill St Easton PA 18042*

ORLOFF, DIANE A., Second Grade Teacher; *b:* Amsterdam, NY; *m:* John C.; *c:* John C Jr.; *ed:* SUNY Brockport (BA) Elem Ed 1970; *cr:* Broadalbin-Perth Cntrl Schl 2nd Grd Tchr 1974-; *ai:* NY Tchrs Assn; Amer Fed of Tchrs; *office:* Broadalbin-Perth Cntrl Schl 100 Bridge St Ext Broadalbin NY 12025

ORLOSKI, SHARON GLORIA, Biology Teacher; *b:* Taylor, PA; *ed:* Central CT St Coll (BS) Bio 1965; Univ of CT (MS) Zoology 1970; Wesleyan Univ 6th Yr Degree Sci 1972; 9 Cr Hrs Span, 6 Cr Hrs Fr; Quinnipiac Coll Cmptrs Bio 1990; Choate St Paul's Cold Spring Harbor Reccumbinant DNA Course 1987; CT BEST Tchr Mentor Prgm 1994; *cr:* Cntrl HS Bio Tchr 1965-; City of Bridgeport Homebound Gen Sci, Bio Tchr 1966-67; Central Adult Evening HS Gen Sci Tchr 1966-68; Stud Master Tchr 1974; *ai:* NEA, CEA, BEA, 1970-; Univ of CT Alumni Assn 1989-, Life Mem; Cntrl CT Alumni, Life Mem; Madison Gardens Condo Assn Bd of Dirs 1988-, Sec, Pres; NSF Grant to Attnd Wesleyan Univ; NABT Regnl Embryology Bowdoin Coll 1967; Envir Prot Agency Awd to Attnd Washington DC Conf 1990; *office:* Central HS 1 Lincoln Blvd Bridgeport CT 06606*

ORLOSKY, JANET ANN, Resource & Math Teacher; *b:* Williamsport, PA; *m:* Francis J.; *c:* John, Sherri; *ed:* Indiana Univ of PA (BS) Elem Ed 1967; Johns Hopkins Univ (MS) Ed 1982; Confratute for Gifted, Talented Tchng Univ of CT; *cr:* Portage Area Elem Schl 3rd Grd Tchr 1967-68; Margaret Edmonston Elem Schl 3rd Grd Tchr 1968-69; Dasher Green Elem Schl 5th Grd 1981-84, Resource Tchr 1984-; *ai:* Math Comm Chprsn; Schl Improvement Team; NEA 1967-; HCEA 1981-; NCTM; Cmptr Comm Chprsn; Gifted & Talented Pilot Prgm 1984-85; *office:* Dasher Green Elem Schl 6700 Cradlerock Way Columbia MD 21045

ORLOV, PAUL A., Assistant Professor of English; *b:* Chicago, IL; *m:* Deborah O'Brien; *ed:* MI St Univ (BA) Eng-Honors 1969; Univ of Toronto (MA) Eng 1970, (PHD) Eng 1978; Addl Post Doctoral Stud at Cambridge Univ 1988; *cr:* Univ of Montreal Writing & Lit Lecturer 1978-79; Clemson Univ Visiting Asst Prof of Eng 1979-81; Univ of Louisville Visiting Asst Prof of Eng 1981-82; Penn St Univ-Delaware Cty Campus Asst Prof of Eng 1982-; *ai:* Fac Senate VP; CEO Admin Staff Group Mem; Coll of Liberal Arts Stu Adv; Amer Culture Assn 1984-; Northeast Modern Lang Assn 1991-; Amer Lit Assn 1990-; Intnl Dreiser Soc 1991-, Sec, Treas; NEH Summer Fellowship 1981; Penn St Grants for Scholarly Activity RDG & FSSF; Articles Pub in Modern Fiction Stud, Amer Lit Realism, Walt Whitman Quarterly Review, Journal of Narrative Technique & Parts of Several Books; *office:* PA St Univ Delaware Cty Cmps 25 Yearsley Mill Rd Media PA 19063

ORLOWSKI, DONALD LOU, Science Teacher; *b:* New Kensington, PA; *m:* Dayna M. Ligoon; *c:* Rebecca, Matthew, Jessica; *ed:* IN Univ of PA (BS) Bio, Gen Sci 1974; 30 Post Grad Credit Hrs; *cr:* MT St Peters Schl Tchr 1970-80; Kiski Area Schl Dist Grd 9 Bio, Grd 8 Phys Sci Life Sci, Grd 7 Earth Sci Tchr 1980-81; Freeport Area Schl Dist Grd 7 Life Sci, Grd 8 Earth Sci, Phys Sci Tchr 1981-; *ai:* Sportsments Club; Tech Task Force; PSEA, NEA 1979-; PSTA 1994-; Tri Cty Trout Club 1981-, Pres, Treas, Bd of Dir; *office:* Freeport Jr HS 325 4th St Freeport PA 16229*

ORLOWSKI, NANCY LAUBENTHAL, Second Grade Teacher; *b:* Toledo, OH; *m:* David; *c:* Tiffany; *ed:* BGSU (BS) Elem Ed 1967; 30 Hrs Elem Ed at Toledo Univ; *cr:* Lark Elem Schl Kndgtn Tchr 1967-72, 3rd Grd Tchr 1972-73, 2nd Grd Tchr 1973-; *ai:* Tech Comm; NEA 1967-; Athletic Boosters 1992-; *office:* Lark Elem Schl 331 Andrus Rd Northwood OH 43619

ORME, JESSICA LYNN (BURKARD), Eng Tchr & Girls Soccer Coach; *b:* New Brunswick, NJ; *m:* Paul Anthony; *ed:* Taylor Univ (BS) Elem Ed, Jr High Eng 1992; *cr:* Sugarcreek Riding Ctr Riding Instr 1992-; Dayton Chrstn Schls HS Eng, Hlth, PE, Var Girls Soccer Coach 1992-; *ai:* Riding Ctr Mgr; Lesson Instr; Var Soccer Coach; CYO MS Soccer Dir; ACSI 1992-; Ron Pinsenshaum All Area Soccer Coach Of Yr Awd; *home:* 2325 Cross Village Dr Miamisburg OH 45342*

ORMISTON, TODD GRAHAM, Math Teacher; *b:* Oneonta, NY; *ed:* St Lawrence Univ (BA) Ec 1991; Natl Ski Coachs Schl 1993; *cr:* Colby Sawyer Coll Asst Soccer Coach 1991; Williams Coll Asst Ski 1991-92; Vermont Acad Tchr, Coach, Dorm Parent 1992-; *ai:* Ath Head Alpine Ski Coach; Acad Adv; US Ski Assn 1991-; St Lawren Admissions Assoc 1992-; *office:* Vermont Acad PO Box 500 Saxtor VT 05154

ORMOND, TERRI CRUMRINE, French Teacher; *b:* Hanover, Robert Louis; *c:* Michael Ryan; *ed:* Bloomsburg St Coll (BS) Scr Fr 1971; Attnd Penn St York & Western MD Coll 30 Addl Credits Eng; *cr:* Spring Grove Area Fr Tchr 1971-; *ai:* NEA, PSEA & 1971-; AATF & PSMLA 1975-; *office:* Spring Grove Area Sr HS H & Jackson St Spring Grove PA 17362

ORMSBY, DEBRA, Principal; *b:* Buffalo, NY; *m:* Wayne; *ed:* Hilb (AA) Liberal Arts 1972; SUNY at Fredonia (BA) Scndry Ed Eng (MA) Eng 1976; CAS Ed Admin, SDA, SAS Cert 1987; *cr:* Pine Cntrl Schl Tchr 1974-90, Eng Dept Chair 1978-86, Asst Prin 1986-9 1990-; *ai:* SAANYS 1990-; Amer Assn of Univ Women 1986-, VI Eng Cncl Tchr of Excl Awd 1987; NYS Collegiate Achvmt Awd 198 Young Careerist 1978; *office:* Pine Valley Mid Sr HS 7827 Rt 83 Dayton NY 14138

ORNER, CAROL LYNNE (PAYNE), English Teacher & Dept Ch East Orange, NJ; *c:* Charles Brian, Bradley Payne, Leslie Joan; *ed:* City Coll (AB) Eng & Soc Stud 1958; Shippensburg Univ (ME 1967; Attnd Western MD Coll; *cr:* Carlisle Schls 6th Grd Eng Tch Tyrone Schls 7th Grd Eng Tchr 1 Yr; Churchill Schls 7th-9th Grd Span Tchr 1 Yr; Messiah Coll Adjunct Comms; 10th-12th Grd Eng T Yrs; *ai:* Sr Class Adv; Eng Mentor; Eng Dept Chair; Honor Soc Ad Coach of Yr 2 Yrs; Debate Judge; Tennis Coach 17 Yrs; NEA 1952-; Presbyn Church, Elder, Deacon.*

ORNER, DONALD JAMES, HS Art Teacher; *b:* Harrisburg, PA; *m* McNear; *c:* Melissa Orner-Lorenz; *ed:* Kutztown Univ (BS) Art Ed 24 Credits at Millersville Univ; *cr:* Oxford Area HS Art Tchr 196 Fac Cncl; NEA 1965-; PSEA 1965-, Rep Chief Negotiator; OAEA Oxford Chamber of Commerce 1992-; Oxford Meth Church 1977-, Finance, Ad Bd, Worship Comm; Mid States Steering Comm 19 Chair; Sent More Than 80 Stdnts to Art Colls; *home:* 2700 Union Rd Oxford PA 19363

ORNOVITZ, IRENE M., Biology Teacher; *b:* Minneapolis, M Henry; *c:* Avital, Jenny; *ed:* WA St Univ (BS) Home Ec Ed 1976; Fa Dickenson Univ (MA) Elem Sci; Central WA Univ 5th Yr Cert Ed *cr:* Leavenworth HS Home Ec Tchr 1976-79; Irvington HS Food Sv 1982-85; Union HS Bio Tchr 1990-; *ai:* Girl Scout Ldr; Teach Afte Hand on Sci Course; NJEA 1981-; NJSTA 1993-.

ORNSTEIN, AVI, Science Teacher & Educl Dir; *b:* New York, N Bernice Nowak-Ornstein; *c:* Satya, Joshua, Alia; *ed:* MIT (BS) Bio Cntrl CT St Univ (MS) Sci Ed 1991; Attnd Harvard Univ, Boston S St Joseph Coll, Curry Coll, Univ of Hartford, Quinnipiac Coll, Univ at Amherst; City Coll of NY & Hunter Coll; *cr:* Blackstone-Millville 7th, 8th Grd Math, Sci Tchr 1974; Waterbury Cath HS Chem Tchr 19 Holy Cross HS Chem, Phys Sci, Math Tchr 1975-80; Berlin HS De p 1986-90, Chem, Physics Sci Tchr 1980-94; Little Scientists Tchr 1995-; *ai:* Comm Svc Club, Chem Team Adv; Creativity Competition First Coord; Knowledge Master Open; Schl Improvement Cncl; Honc Selection Comm; New England Sci Tchrs 1989-, Editor, Exec Bd, CT of Yr; NSTA 1976-; CT Sci Tchr Assn 1975-; New England Assoc of Tchrs 1990-; New Britain Youth Museum, Bd of Dir 1991-; Alph Omega 1968-, Adv, Distinguished Svc Awd; Excl Awd; Dow- Summer Wkshp; NSTA Grand Illuminator Competition Winner; Artic NEACT, Chemical Ed, CT for Sci Ed Journals; Chem 13 News, Spe of Safety & Chem Guild Newsletter; *office:* Little Scientists Schl 497 St Ansonia CT 06401

O'ROURKE, AARON D., Sixth Grade Science Teacher; *b:* Hornell *m:* Shelly Perry; *ed:* SUNY at Cortland (BS) Elem Ed 1989; Alfred (MS) Schl Cnslng 1994; *cr:* Naples Elem Schl 6th Grd Tchr 1989-; *a* Bsbl, Girls Bsktbl; NTA 1989-; *office:* Naples Elem Schl 2 Acader Naples NY 14512

O'ROURKE, GAIL ANN, Computer Science Dept Chprsn; *b:* Yor NY; *ed:* Hunter Coll (BA) Math, Ed 1968; Manhattan Coll (MS) Guid 1972, Iona Coll (MS) Cmptr Sci 1988; Fordham Univ 18 Credit Hrs; M Coll 9 Credit Hrs; Yonkers Bd of Ed 12 Credit Hrs; *cr:* Emerson Jr HS Tchr 1968-72; Gorton HS Math Chprsn 1974-84, Math & Cmptr Sci 1972-, Cmptr Chprsn 1981-; *ai:* Ed 2000 Dist Steering & Cycle I Redesign Steering Comms; Schl Improvement & Cmptr Sci Compe Teams; Ftbl & Bsktbl Announcers Statisticians; Gender Equity Task F All Sports Awd Dinner Coord; AFT, Yonkers Fed of Tchrs 1968 Anthony RC Church 1952-; Kiwanis of Yonkers Tchr of Yr 1988-89; H Jenkins Meml Tchrs Awd 1975, 1978; NYSPTSA Permanent Life Membership Awd 1986; Tchrs Tchr Awd 1990; 4 Yrbk Dedications; Women's Action Alliance Equity Expert Grant; *home:* 105 Clunie Yonkers NY 10703

O ROURKE, MARY CURTIN, Spanish Teacher; *b:* Columbus, OH Daniel T.; *c:* Danny, Meghan, Caitlin; *ed:* OH St Univ (BS) Ed & For Lang 1977, (MA) Ed Foreign Lang 1982; *cr:* Franklin Alternative Span Tchr 1978-89; McCord MS Span Tchr 1989-; *ai:* Foreign Lang Multicultural Comm; Ventures for Excl; OH Foreign Lang Assn, 1978-; WEA 1989-; CCD Tchr Religon Tchr 1990-; WCBE Span R Series Creator; OSU Honoring Excl in the Teaching Profession 1992-93; *office:* Worthington Kilbourne HS 1500 Hard Rd Worthington 43235

O'ROURKE, MARY JANE J., English Teacher & Dept Chair Cumberland, MD; *m:* Thomas M.; *c:* Colleen; *ed:* Immaculata Coll Eng 1975; Bowling Green St Univ (MA) Eng 1979; Grad Credit Hrs i at Frostburg St Univ; *cr:* Ft Hill HS Eng Tchr 1975-; *ai:* Newsletter Dept Chair; Delta Adv; Publicity Chair; Functional Testing Tutor for F & Eng; MSTA & NEA 1975-; Christopher Columbus Festival Comm 19 Sec & Worker; S Cumberland Lib Bd 1995-, Sec; Ft Hill Outstdng Awd 1993; Stu Stud Skills; *office:* Fort Hill HS 500 Greenway Cumberland MD 21502

O'ROURKE, WILLIAM JOSEPH,JR., Helping Tchr & Suite Admin Troy, NY; *m:* Dorothy Costello; *c:* Laura, Sarah, Erin; *ed:* St John Fis Coll (BA) Span 1969; SUNY at Brockport (MS) Educl Admin 1974; Webster HS Span Tchr 1969-90; Webster Schl Dist Curr Supvr 1990- Webster Jr HS Helping Tchr, Suite Admin 1991-; Thomas MS Help Tchr, Suite Admin 1991-; Webster HS Interim Asst Prin 1994; *ai:* Web HS Stu Cncl, Span Club, Span Hon Soc Adv 1969-90; Grad Lipe-Up Su 1970-89; Boys Var Bsktbl Coach 1978-; NYSUT, NYSAFLT, WTA 19 ASCD 1994-; Webster Yth Bureau Advy Bd 1989-91; St Rita's Chu Parish Ctr Fund Drive 1995-, Co-Chprsn; Webster Citizen of Yr 1984; St Senate Cert of Merit 1984; Section 5 Bsktbl Coach of Yr 1988- All-Greater Rochester Coach of Yr 1988; Article Pub 1984; *office:* Thor MS 800 Five Mile Line Rd Webster NY 14580

ORR, BARBARA DILLWORTH, Span Tchr & Foreign Lang Chair Painesville, OH; *m:* James S.; *c:* Carol L. Kelly, Jason A. Spilis; Bowling Green SU (BS) Bio, Span 1965 Lake Erie Coll (MSEd) Gifted 1992; Kent SU 1986-88; Garfield Sr Coll 1980; *cr:* Toledo Pub Schls S JHS Tchr 1965-66; Xenia Pub Schls Bio Tchr 1972-73; Madison Lo Schls Span HS Tchr 1981-82; Ledgemont Local Schls Span HS Tchr 198

Ledgemont Schls GED Tchr 1984-88; *ai:* Span Club, Frosh, Golf, , Soph, Sr Class, Chrldr Adv; NEA 1981-; Martha Holden Jennings irant; *office:* Ledgemont HS 16700 Thompson Rd Thompson OH

DARLENE COLE, Music Teacher; *b:* Nashville, TN; *c:* Jennifer, a; *ed:* Jordan Coll of Music (BSME) Music Ed 1963; Attnd Butler r: North Allegheny Schl Dist Music Tchr, Choir Dir 1971-; *ai:* Fifth orus, Schl Plays, Concerts Dir; Fifth Grd Small Ensemble Dir; gh Concert Chorale; PAFT, PMEA 1971-; ACDC 1994-; *office:* Mc Elem Schl 200 Hillvue Ln Pittsburgh PA 15237

JOSEPH H., Industrial Technology Instr; *b:* Dayton, OH; *m:* Karen OH Univ (BA) Sec Ed, Indstrl Tech 1986; Attending California Univ MS Sec, Sch Admin; *cr:* Milton Union MS Indstrl Tech Jr HS, HS 87-90; Eagles Landing HS Indstrl Tech Instr 1991-93; Chartiers Vly strl Tech Instr 1993-; *ai:* Stu Support Team; Head Wrestling Coach; 993-; ITEA 1987-; TUT 1994-; Pub Textbook; Tchr of Yr Eagles g HS 1993; *office:* Chartiers Valley HS 50 Thoms Run Rd ville PA 15017*

MARIAN ANDREA, Counselor; *b:* McKeesport, PA; *ed:* Univ of Slippery Rock (BS) Eng & Rdng 1970; Univ of Pittsburgh (MEd) 1973, (PHD) Admin 1985; Carnegie Mellon Univ (MPM) Bus, Ed & Human Resources 1996; Attnd Harvard Univ, Penn St & CA cr: McKeepsport Schl Dist Eng Tchr & Cnslr 1970-76; Upper St Schl Dist Cnslr 1976-; *ai:* Phi Delta Kappa 1986-; Dissertation; Upper Saint Clair HS 1825 Mclaughlin Run Rd Pittsburgh PA 15241

SARA-JANE GERHARD, Substitute Teacher; *b:* Lancaster, PA; *m:* n P.; *c:* Peter D., Matthew B.; *ed:* Ursinus Coll (BS) Hlth, PE & ical Scis 1963; PA Tchng Cert Kutztown Univ; *cr:* Warren Cty Coll Adjunct Bio Tchr 6 Months; Lehigh Chrstn Acad PE, Sci & Tchr 6 Yrs; N FL Chrstn Schl Resource Room Tchr & Coach 3 Yrs; g Schl Dist PE & Hlth Tchr 3 Yrs; All Saints Regnl Schl Sci Tchr 6 ib Tchr; *ai:* Stu Cncl Adv; Bsktbl, Sftbl, Vllybl Coach.

SUE MOORE, Second Grade Teacher; *b:* Shelby, OH; *m:* Gilbert Douglas, Gregory; *ed:* Bowling Green Ashland Univ (BS) Elem Ed Addl 24 Credit Hrs; *cr:* Bedford Elem Third Grd Tchr 1965-68; ille Elem Second Grd Tchr 1970-; *ai:* NEA, OEA 1965-82; AFT Bldg Rep; CFVTA 1970-; *home:* 2360 Ranchwood Dr Mansfield OH

CO, AMY WILLSON, English & Theatre Arts Tchr; *b:* Camden, NJ; eph S.; *c:* Alison, Nicole; *ed:* Glassboro St Coll AT Glassboro (BA) n, Eng Theatre 1981; Salem St Coll (MA) Schl Admin 1996; *cr:* ern Regnl MS 7-8 Grd Eng Tchr 1981-82; Edward Devotion Schl 7-8 ng Tchr 1983-84; Cranford HS 10-12 Grd Eng, Theatre Tchr 1985-87; tically Kids Schl K-8 Grd Tchr 1989-92; Sandwich HS 9-12 Grd Writing Lab, Radio, TV Tchr 1992-; *ai:* Musical, Play Dir; Knight e co Adv; Schl Cncl; Cape Cod Consortium of Tchrs; Curr Dev NEA; ETA; Southern Regnl MS Tchr of Yr 1982; *office:* Sandwich 5 Quaker Meeting House Rd E Sandwich MA 02537

S, DALE ALVIN, Instrumental Music Dir; *b:* Sunbury, PA; *m:* Jo rd; *ed:* Susquehanna Univ (BM) Music Ed 1975; Univ of Cincinnati Trumpet 1978; *cr:* Susquehanna Univ Trumpet Instr, Jazz Ens Dir Horry Cty SD MS Band Dir 1985-87; Lewisburg Area SD HS mental Music Dir 1988-; *ai:* HS Marching Band; Jazz-Rock able; HS Pit Orchestra; InstrlLdr; Unification Team; Ath Comm; Booster Adv; MENC, IAJE, NEA 1985-; PMEA 1988-, Dist 8 Jazz Performed with Glenn Miller Orchestra, Buddy Rich Band; Various s; Guest Soloist; *office:* Lewisburg Area HS 815 Market St burg PA 17837

AG, JAMES O., Social Studies Teacher; *b:* Aliquippa, PA; *m:* Norma ni; *c:* James Jr.; *ed:* Edinboro Univ of PA (BS) Scndry Ed 1961; Univ sburgh (MS) Scndry Ed 1967; *cr:* Rochester Jr-Sr HS Soc Stud Tchr *ai:* Afro-Amer Club Spon; NEA, PSEA, RAEA 1961-; BPOE 1980-; Rochester Area HS 540 Reno St Rochester PA 15074

ENE, MARK STEVEN, Mathematics Teacher; *b:* New Haven, CT; Williams Coll (BA) Astrophysics 1978; Yale Univ (MS) Geophysics Cntrl CT St Univ Tchr Cert Prgm; *cr:* CIGNA Corp Group Insurance writer 1978-81; St Joseph HS Earth Sci Tchr 1984; Simsbury HS Tchr 1984-; *ai:* Fac Advy & Statement of Schl Philosophy Comm; Dances & Fundraisers Vol; Amer Assn Advancement of Sci 1981-; CEA, SEA 1984-; Phi Beta Kappa & Sigma Xi 1978-; Articles Pub lativistic Astrophysics; Sloan Fnd Research CT Tchrs Incentive & A Grant; NCTM Conf; *office:* Simsbury HS 34 Farms Village Rd bury CT 06070

I, MARTHA D., Adjunct Professor of English; *b:* Newark, NJ; *c:* s P., Michael D., David G.; *ed:* Bucknell Univ (BS) Sec Ed, Eng 1963; ers Univ Masters Equivalency Eng, Amer Lit 1965; *cr:* Thomas Edison S Eng Tchr 1963-67; Cinnaminson HS Eng Tchr 1968-69; Valley m North HS Eng Tchr 1969-70; Moravian Acad Sub Eng, Fr Tchr -89; Northampton Comm Coll Adj Prof Eng 1989-; *ai:* Lehigh Vly of Acad Women 1991-; NCTE 1986-90; Amer Assn of Univ Women -, Legislative, Educ Fnd Chair; Article, Book Chptr Pub; *office:* hampton Comm Coll 3835 Green Pond Rd Bethlehem PA 18017

LEY, LORI BOCEK, High School Counselor; *b:* Niagara Falls, NY; erry; *c:* Sean; *ed:* Alfred Univ (BA) His, Scndry Ed 1967, (MS) Guid, ng 1971; Post Masters Cert Guid Montclair St Univ; *cr:* Hornell HS Stud Tchr 1967-70; Middletown Jr HS 7&8 Grd Soc Stud Tchr -74; Middletown HS 9-12 Grd Cnslr 1974-; *ai:* Turnaround Tchr; hool Club Adv; Schl Improvement Team; NYSUT 1970-; MTA 1971-; A 1975-; Amer Cancer Soc 1985-, Yearly Campaigner; March of es 1990-, Mothers March Campaign Yearly; *office:* Middletown HS ner Avenue Ext Middletown NY 10940

O, JOYCE GROSSO, 5th Grade Teacher; *b:* Waterbury, CT; *m:* o F.; *c:* Jennifer Anne; *ed:* Cntrl CT St Univ (BS) Elem Ed 1973, (MS) y Chldhd Ed 1977; Trinity Coll of VT 6th Yr, 15 Addl Hrs Gen Ed 1995; Bucks Hill Elem Schl Tchr Grd 5 1973; Washington Elem Schl Tchr 3 1973-76; Slocum Elem Schl Basic Skills Tchr 1976-77; Kingsbury Schl Tchr Grd 4 1977-83; Bunker Hill Elem Schl Tchr Grd 5 1983-84; hington Elem Schl Tchr Grd 5 1984-; *ai:* Math Cadre Improving & sing Elem Curr; NEA, CEA, Waterbury Tchrs Assn 1973-; *home:* 234 wood Rd Waterbury CT 06706

SON, SHEILA ROSENTHAL, First Grade Teacher; *b:* New York City, *c:* Andrea Charney, Richard A., Stephanie Korostoff; *ed:* Hofstra Univ Span, Elem Ed 1966; *cr:* East Meadow Schls 6th Grd Tchr 1967, 2nd Tchr 1968-70, 1st Grd Tchr 1971-; *ai:* Character Values Ed Comm; SUT 1967-; NY St United Tchrs; AFT; PTA 1996, Founders Day Nom; oree PTA Founder's Day Nom 1996; *home:* 2379 Warren Ave North more NY 11710

TIZ, LINDA, High School Spanish Teacher; *b:* Staten Island, NY; *m:* ph Salamon; *c:* Chad, Amber; *ed:* Hartwick Coll (BA) Span, Eng 1969; t St Univ (MA) Span 1972; Attnd Univ of Madrid 1967-68; *cr:* burne Earville Cntrl Schl Span, Eng Tchr 1969-70; LaBrae HS Span Tchr 1972-; *ai:* Span Club Adv; NEA, OEA, LTA 1972-; *office:* Labrae 4651 W Market St Leavittsburg OH 44430

WICK, LANE NESTLERODE, Fourth Grade Teacher; *b:* Altoona, *m:* Rick; *c:* Alicia Wilson, Zac Wilson (dec), Aaron; *ed:* Lock Haven St Coll (BS) Elem, Spec Ed 1968; IN Univ of PA (MA) Elem Ed 1990; Addl 80 Credit Hrs; *cr:* Penns Vly Schl Dist 4 Grd, Primary Spec Ed Tchr 1968-73; Bellefonte Area Schl Dist 1st, Spec Ed Tchr, 4th Grd Tchr 1974-; *ai:* Church Tchr In-Svc Ldr, Visiting Tchr; NEA 1964-; Kappa Delta Pi; Penn St Rhetoric Project 1982; *office:* Pleasant Gap Elem Schl 230 S Main St Pleasant Gap PA 16823

ORZA, ANTHONY JOSEPH, Spanish Teacher; *b:* New York City, NY; *m:* Paula Carollo; *c:* Nina; *ed:* Fordham Univ (BA) Span 1969; Attnd SUNY at Buffalo, Univ Intnl Menendez Pelayo; 6 Hrs Univ of Salamanca; 6 Hrs NYU Inst of Hispanic Culture; *cr:* SUNY at Buffalo Tchng Asst 1969-70; Ulster Cty Comm Coll Span Instr 1970-71; Onteora HS Span Tchr 1971-72; Rhinebeck HS Span Tchr 1972-; *ai:* Spain Summer Prgm Dir; 5 Week Madrid HS Prgm; NY Fed Tchrs 1972-; Madison WI Fellowship; Awded Diploma Superior en Lengua, Espanola; *home:* 144 Main St Lake Katrine NY 12449

ORZEL, MARGARET DUCKETT, Second Grade Teacher; *b:* Binghamton, NY; *m:* John; *c:* Emily, Andrew; *ed:* St John's Univ (BA) Ed 1970; Cortland (BS) Ed 1972; *cr:* Whitney Point Schl Tchr; Central Schl Kndgtn, 3rd, 4th, 2nd Grd Tchr 1972-; *ai:* Dist Soc Stud, Assessment Comms; Family Fun Carnival; WPCS Tchrs Assn, AFT, NYSUT 1972-; Shakespeare Club 1982-, Sunshine Comm, VP; *office:* C. E. Adams Schl Keibel Rd Whitney Point NY 13862

ORZO, ANTHONY J., Assistant Principal; *b:* New York, NY; *m:* Diane; *c:* Anthony; *ed:* Queens Coll (BA) Music, Ed 1981; Coll of New Rochelle (MS) Spec Ed 1985, (PD) Schl Admin, Supervision 1995; *cr:* PS 156 Tchr 1981-90; PS 157 Spec Ed Supvr 1990-91; IS 131 Asst Prin 1991-; *home:* 15 Maple Ave Bronx NY 10465

OSBORN, DAVID FRANCIS, Guidance Counselor; *b:* Lowell, MA; *m:* Nancy; *c:* Cara, Keith; *ed:* Univ of MA at Amherst (BA) Psych 1974; Springfield Coll (MED) GPS 1975; *cr:* Springfield Comm Coll Psych Instr 2 Yrs; Milford Area HS Guid Cnslr 9 Yrs; Butler Jr HS Guid Cnslr 4 Yrs; Mountain View MS Guid Cnslr 6 Yrs; *ai:* Tennis Instr; NH NEA, NH ACA 1990-; *office:* Mountain View MS 41 Lauren Ln Goffstown NH 03045

OSBORN, MARLENE HAZLETT, Science Teacher; *b:* Tarentum, PA; *m:* Robert Allan; *c:* Jennifer, Matthew; *ed:* Kent St Univ (BA) Bio, Sociology 1967; Univ of Akron (BA) Sec Ed, Comp Sci 1987; Kent St Univ (MA) Bio 1996; Attnd Sea Base Inst; *cr:* Summit Cty Welfare Soc Worker 1967-69; West Jr HS Bio Tchr 1969-71; Roberts MS Life Sci Tchr 1989-; *ai:* Hnrs Sci Club; Sci Curr Comm; Recycling Prgm; NSTA 1990-; CFEA, NEA, OEA 1989-; ASCD 1996; PTA 1989-, Outstndg Edctr; KSU 1995-, ATTEP Mentor; Kent St Grad Schl Schlsp; Cuyahoga Falls Schls Fnd Grant; BGSU Pi Beta Phi Parent of Yr 1994; Tchr of Month 1995; Inventure Place Exemplary MS Sci Tchr 1991; Keep OH Beautiful Merit Awd.

OSBORN, RANDY R., Science Teacher; *b:* Hartford, CT; *m:* Diane Lynn Mc Kamish; *c:* Kelli, Jacob, Kristi, Joseph, Kimberly; *ed:* Taylor Univ (BS) Hlth Ed 1979; Amer Coll (CLU) Life Insurance 1988; Fin Consulting 1989; Attnd Ball St Univ, Capitol Univ, Clarion St Coll, Hamline Univ, Kearney St Coll, OH St Univ; *cr:* Huntington Coll Head Wrestling Coach 1976-79; Taylor Univ PE Instr, Wrestling Coach 1979-80; Brown Cty HS Hlth Tchr, Wrestling Coach 1980-81; Franklin Univ Interim Bus Instr; Liberty Chrstn Acad Sci, Bible Tchr 1990-; *ai:* Wrestling Coach; BSA 1992-, Charter Silver Mem; CRS 1990-; Columbus R&P City Wrestling Championship Team Coach 1995-; Tchr of Yr 1991-92; HBCC Wrestling Coach of Yr 1980; *office:* Liberty Christian Acad 4938 Beatrice Dr Columbus OH 43227*

OSBORNE, EDWARD HENRY, Accounting Professor; *b:* Connersville, IN; *m:* Karen Collins; *c:* Amy, David; *ed:* IN Univ at Bloomington (BS) Accounting 1964, (MBA) Accounting 1965; *cr:* Arthur Andersen & Co Sr Auditor 1965-71; Marietta Coll Prof 1971-; *ai:* Fac Cncl 3 Terms; Omicron Delta Kappa, Fac Sec, Leadership Honorary; Inst of Mngmt Accounting 1972-, Pres Regnl Cncl, Local Chapter; Amer Red Cross 1975-, Chm Bd of Dirs; Univ of Pittsburgh's Ctr for Russian, E European Stud Accounting Grant; Southwestern Univ of Finance & Ec Chengdu China Visiting Prof; *home:* 906 Glendale Rd Marietta OH 45750

OSBORNE, HILDA BARNES, English Teacher; *b:* Carrsville, VA; *m:* Johnnie T.; *c:* J. T., Shannon; *ed:* Hampton Univ (BS) Eng Ed 1973; *cr:* Franklin HS Eng Tchr 1973-74; La Plata HS Eng Tchr 1976-; *ai:* Yrbk Spon; NEA, MSTA, EACC 1976-; Delta Kappa Gamma 1980-; Allen Chapel AME Church 1976-, Stewardess Bd Pres; Natl Capital Area Writing Project Fellow; *office:* La Plata High School 6035 Radio Station Rd La Plata MD 20646

OSBORNE, JAMES P., Physical Ed Tchr & Coach; *b:* Geneva, OH; *m:* Jennifer Ours; *c:* Tige, Tia; *ed:* Wittenberg Univ (BSEd) PE & Hlth 1967; OH Univ (MED) Scndry Admin 1971; *cr:* Northwestern HS Hlth & PE Tchr 1967-69; Gallia Acad HS Hlth-PE Tchr & Coach 1969-; *ai:* Drivers Ed; Head Coach Bsktbl, Bsbl & Tennis; Var Track Asst; Bsktbl Coaches Assoc, Pres & Treas; Var G Alumni Treas; NEA, OEA & GEA 1967-; OHSBCA 1969-, Longevity Awd; Dist #13 BCA 1970-, Pres, Coach of the Yr 3 (Times); OHSTA 1985-, Coach of The Yr 7 (Times); *office:* Gallia Acad HS 340 4th Ave Gallipolis OH 45631

OSBORNE, JEFFREY DUANE, Mathematics Teacher; *b:* Bloomsburg, PA; *m:* Joanne Grajewski; *ed:* Lebanon Valley Coll (BS) Math 1990; 25 Grad Credits; *cr:* Bloomsburg HS Math Tchr 1990-94; Cntrl Columbia HS 1994-; *ai:* Ftbl Coach; Weight Trng, Head Ftbl Coach (CCHS) 1995-; NEA, PSEA & BAEA 1990-94, CCEA 1994-; *office:* Cntrl Columbia HS 4777 Old Berwick Rd Bloomsburg PA 17815

OSBORNE, KAREN S., HS Math Teacher; *b:* Philadelphiia, PA; *ed:* Glassboro St Coll (BA) Jr HS & MS Math 1988; Rowan St Coll Master Math Ed; *cr:* St Charles Borromeo Elem Schl 7th & 8th Grd Math Tchr 1988-90; Washington Twp HS Math Tchr 1991-; *ai:* Stu Cncl Co-Adv; NEA 1991-; NJAMT 1991-; *office:* Washington Twp HS 509 Hurftville Cross Keys Sewell NJ 08080*

OSBORNE, KEN, Assistant Principal; *b:* Prestonsburg, KY; *m:* Sidney Chaffin; *c:* Kim Parsons, Ashly; *ed:* Morehead St Univ (BA) Industrial Arts & PE 1962, (MED) Admin 1964; Attnd Miami Univ, Xavier Univ, St Marys Coll, Univ of Dayton, Santa Clara Univ, Azusa Pacific Coll; 40 Semester Hrs; *cr:* Williamsburg HS Tchr, Ath Dir, Asst Prin, Prin Coach 33 Yrs; Carter City HS Tchr & Bsktbl Coach 1 Yr; *ai:* Ath Dir, Ftbl Coach; CCTEA 1962-; WEA 1962-; NEA 1962-; OHSFLA 1962-; SWOFLA 1988-; St Ftbl Coach of Yr 1980; League Ftbl Coach of Yr (Nine Times); *home:* 416 S Broadway St Williamsburg OH 45176

OSBORNE, MARY JEAN, Assistant Professor of Nursing; *b:* Scranton, PA; *m:* Thomas; *c:* Jennifer, Kathleen; *ed:* Mercy Hosp Schl of Nrsng (RN) Nrsng 1977; Marywood Coll (BSN) Nrsng-Summa Cum Laude 1984; Widener Univ (MSN) Burn Emergency Trauma Nrsng 1986; CCRN 1984; Advanced Trauma Life Support Instr 1968-; TQM 1993-; *cr:* Milton S Hershey Med Cntr Staff Nurse; Mercy Hosp Staff Nurse; Leigh Vly Hosp Clinical Nurse Specialist 1986-; Northampton Comm Coll Asst Prof of Nrsng 1993-; *ai:* NCC Lib Advy Comm; LVH PCC Comm; Amer Assn of Critical Care Nurses 1984-; Sigma Theta Tau 1984-; AFT 1993-; Natl League of Nrsng 1993-; Amer Trauma Soc 1986-; Farm Safety for Just Kids 1994-; Cathedral Parish Retreat Team 1995-; Speaker at Natl Tchng Inst 1989 & 1996; Natl Scholastic Hnr Soc; Numerous Articles Pub; *office:* Northampton County Area Coll 3835 Green Pond Rd Bethlehem PA 18017

OSBURN, SUSAN BOTTORFF, Spanish Teacher; *b:* Tecumseh, MI; *m:* Jeffrey B.; *c:* Adam, Ben, Matthew; *ed:* MI St Univ (BA) Spanish 1969; Univ of NH (MA) Span Lit 1990; *cr:* Pinckney HS Span Tchr 1969-73; Derryfield Schl Span Tchr 1987-88; Concord HS Span Tchr 1990-; *ai:* Span Club Adv; 9 to 12 Trans Team; Schl Sen; RHS Ldrshp Team; NEA, CEA 1990-; NH Foreign Lang Tchrs 1992-.

OSENBACH, ROBERT JOHN, 7th-8th Grd Math Teacher; *b:* Lykens, PA; *m:* Karen Yvonne Headdings; *c:* Andrew, Matthew; *ed:* Shippensburg Univ (BS) Elem Ed 1982; Post Grad 12 Credit Hrs Wilkes coll; *cr:* Halifax MS Rdng, Math & Soc Stud Tchr 1982-; *ai:* Var Girls Bsktbl Coach; MS Stu Cncl & Var Club Adv; NEA 1982-; PSEA 1982-; Halifax Ed Assn 1982-, Pres 1989-90; Word of Life Chapel 1990-; *office:* Halifax School District 3940 Peters Mountain Rd Halifax PA 17032

OSEPCHUK, DEBORAH CHURCHILL, Middle School Art Teacher; *b:* Newark, NJ; *m:* John W.; *c:* Caitlin; *ed:* Kean Coll (BA) Fine Arts Ed 1972; Grad Stud Univ of Oslo Norway; *cr:* Parsippany-Troy Hills BOE Art Tchr 1972-77; R-Stuff Miniatures Partner 1976-85; Gordon Danielli Design Fabricator 1980-81; Eko Gallery Owner & Partner 1989-90; Howell Twp BOE Art Tchr 1981-; *ai:* Art Club; Art Show Coord; NEA 1972-; NJEA 1972-, Bldg Rep; Homeowners Assn 1985-; Ocean Grove Historical Soc 1990-; Neptune Bd of Architechtual Review 1993-; R-Stuff Miniatures Featured in Reproducing Period Furniture 1981; *office:* Howell Twp MS 501 Squankum Rd Howell NJ 07731*

OSGOOD, ANN FLEWELLING, Business Instructor; *b:* Presque Isle, ME; *m:* Thomas F.; *c:* Matthew, Michael, Michelle; *ed:* NMTC (AS) Secretarial 1974; Univ of ME at Machias (BS) Bus Ed 1976; Husson Coll (MS) Bus 1993; *cr:* St Joseph Hosp Admin, Assist, Exec Sec to CEO 1978-79; Aroostook Med Ctr Sec to Dir of Fiscal Affairs, Med Staff 1979-80; Northern ME Tech Coll Bus Instr 1980-; *ai:* Grad Comm; Stdnts Acad Adv; ME Ed Assn, Fac Assn, NBEA 1980-; Easton Wesleyan Church, Jr Church Dir; Co-Authored Publication; *office:* Northern ME Tech Coll 33 Edgemont Dr Presque Isle ME 04769

O'SHAUGHNESSY, JANE JACKSON, College Counselor; *b:* Dayton, OH; *m:* Thomas F.; *ed:* The OH St Univ (BS) Ed 1970, (MA) Guidance, Counseling 1975; 15 Addl Credit Hrs Beyond Masters; *cr:* Hilliard HS Span Tchr 1970-76; Hilliard MS Schl Cnslr 1976-88; Hilliard Frosh Bldg Schl Cnslr 1988-89; Hilliard HS Schl Cnslr 1989-92, Coll Cnslr 1992-; *ai:* Future Problem Solver Team Coach; OACAC 1991-; HEA, OEA, NEA 1970-; NHS Tchr Honoree; *office:* Hilliard HS 5100 Davidson Rd Hilliard OH 43026

O'SHEA, TERRY V., Honors English & Psych Teacher; *b:* Pittsburgh, PA; *m:* Hollis C.; *c:* Melissa, Amy, Terry Jr.; *ed:* Lock Haven Univ (BS) Eng 1963; Duquesne Univ (MA) Ed Admin 1979; 30 Addl Grad Credits; *cr:* Montour Jr HS Eng Tchr 1963-68; Montour Sr HS Soc Stud Tchr 1968-77, Eng Tchr 1977-, Psych Tchr 1991-; *ai:* Mid Sts Evaluation Co-Chair; NEA 1963-; TRSC Soccer 1980-, Pres; CIT Bsbl 1982-, VP; Crafton Swim Team 1980-, Head Coach; *home:* 71 Kingston Ave Pittsburgh PA 15205

O'SHELL, MARTHA LOUISE, First Grade Teacher; *b:* Lewistown, PA; *m:* Donald R. Sr.; *c:* Donald Jr., David; *ed:* Diploma Bible At Appalachian Bible Inst 1968; Music at Messiah Coll 1960-62; *cr:* Greater Beckley Chrstn Schl K-5 Grd Tchr 1 Yr; Mt Zion Bapt Schl Eng Tchr 1 Yr; West Side Chrstn Schl First, Second Grds Tchr 1 Yr; Red Lion Chrstn Schl First Grd Tchr 15 Yrs; *ai:* Tchr of Yr from Keystone Chrstn Ed Assn; *office:* Red Lion Christian Schl 105 Springvale Rd Red Lion PA 17356

OSHIMA, HEIDRUN BECKER, Language Instructor; *b:* Dusseldorf, Germany; *m:* Don; *c:* Michele, Marc; *ed:* Univ of MN (BS) Span, Fr, Ger 1963; Rutgers Univ (ME) Admin, Supervision 1984; Univ of MN Ger Prgm 1980; Univ of Guanajuato Mexico 1961; Grad Courses Pedagogy at Montclair St Univ 1994-; *cr:* US Army Ed Ctr Germany Ger, Eng Tchr 1963-65; Ramsey Jr High FL Tchr 1965-68; Souk Comm Schl ESL Tchr 1968-73; Parsippany Comm Adult Schl ESL Supvr 1973-76; Parsippany HS Span, Fr, Ger Instr 1976-, FL Dept Head & Lead Tchr 1984-; *ai:* NHS, Asian Amer Club Adv; Cntrl Curr Planning, Mascot Comms; Stu Tchr Mentor; Phi Delta Kappa 1985-, Newsletter Ed; AATSP 1987-, St Exec Bd Mem; FLENJ 1980-; PTHEA, NJEA, NEA 1976-; ASCD 1985-94; LWV of Morristown 1976-86; LWV of Richfield 1965-73; Ger Lang Schl of Morristown 1974-83, Pres 3 Yrs, Exec Bd 8 Yrs; King Juan Carlos I Fellowship; *office:* Parsippany HS 309 Baldwin Rd Parsippany NJ 07054*

OSHIN, RICHARD KENT, Instrumental Music Teacher; *b:* Newark, NJ; *m:* Coletta Digman; *c:* Rebecca; *ed:* Motclair St Coll (BA) Music Ed 1973; *cr:* Hudson St Schl Gen Music Tchr 1973-75; Yetter Schl Gen, Instrumental Music Tchr 1975-94; Meml MS Instrumental Music Tchr 1994-; *ai:* Band Dir; NEA, NJEA 1975-; Who's Who Among Coll & Univ Stdnts 1973; *office:* Meml MS Grant Ave Eatontown NJ 07724*

OSINSKI, RONALD C., HS Physical Education Teacher; *b:* Schenectady, NY; *m:* Jill M. Howenstein; *c:* Corey, Kevin; *ed:* Orange Cty Comm Coll (AA) PE 1971; SUNY at Brockport (BS) PE 1973; St Rose (MS) Ed Psych 1986; *cr:* Schalmont Cntrl Schls PE Tchr 1986-; *ai:* Var Bsktbl Coach 20 Yrs; NYSUT 1992-; Elks 1980-; 210 Career Var Bsktbl Wins; *office:* Schalmont Cntrl Schls 1 Sabre Dr Schenectady NY 12306

OSLER, KATHY A., Spanish Teacher; *b:* Rockville Centre, NY; *m:* Dr. Thomas J.; *c:* Eric, William; *ed:* Rowan Coll (BA) Span 1986; *cr:* Millville HS Span Tchr 1986-87; Bridgeton HS Span Tchr 1987-88; Glassboro HS Span Tchr 1988-; *ai:* SADD Club Adv; SERC Japanese Facilitator; Tech Comm; NEA 1986-.*

OSSONT, DAVID ROBIN, Science Teacher; *b:* Amsterdam, NY; *m:* Pamela Stone; *c:* Kyle David; *ed:* SUNY Empire St (BS) Environmental Sci 1977; SUNY Cortland (MS) Ed 1991; *cr:* NY St Dept Env Conservation Fish, Wildlife Technician 1977-85; Oneida Cty Cooperative Extension Environmental Specialist 1985-86; Oneida City Schls 7th-8th Grd Sci Tchr 1986-91, 7th Grd Sci Tchr, Dean of Stdnts 1991-95, 7th Grd Sci Tchr 1995-; *ai:* Sci Tchrs Assn of NYS, NYSUT 1986-; Natl Sci Tchrs Assn Cert; Articles in Sci Scope, Stanys Bulletin; *office:* Otto L Shortell MS 716 Markell Dr Wampsville NY 13163

OSTE, MARLA JOHNSON, Womens Physical Education Tchr; *b:* Westfield, NY; *m:* Randall Scott; *c:* Scott Randall, Marc Daniel; *ed:* Jamestown Com Coll (BA) PE 1976; Brockport St (BS) PE 1979, (MS) 1983; *cr:* Maple Grove Jr, Sr HS Womens PE Tchr 1979-; *ai:* Pep Club; Stu Cncl Adv, Jr Class; NEA 1979-; Boy Scouts 1994-, Den Mother; Bemus Point Yth Soccer 1995-, Coach; Who's Who of Amer Stdnts 1974; *home:* PO Box 15 Bemus Point NY 14712

OSTERBERG, KRISTEN CALOUN, Middle School Science Teacher; *b:* Davenport, IA; *ed:* Univ of DE (BA) Bio Ed 1993; Grad Courses Spec Ed West Chester Univ, PA St Univ; *cr:* NBMS 7th-8th Grd Sci Tchr 1993-; *ai:* Spirit Club Co-Adv; NEA, PSEA, CATA 1993-; *office:* North Brandywine MS 200 Reeceville Rd Coatesville PA 19320

OSTERFIELD, BARBARA CONNICK, Biology Teacher; *b:* Lynn, MA; *m:* John; *c:* Tanya, Nicole; *ed:* Salem St Coll (BA) Bio 1969, (MED) Ed 1974; *cr:* Avon Jr High Sci Tchr 1969-70; Lowell Jr High Sci Tchr 1970-74; Burke Elem Spcl Ed Tchr 1988-89; Peabody HS Bio Tchr 1989-; *ai:* Sr Class Adv; Mass Curr Frameworks Sci Comm; AFT 1988-; Bio Edctrs Assoc 1988-; CPMSIE 1990-; Comm Covenant Church 1980-; *office:* Peabody Veterans Memorial HS 485 Lowell St Peabody MA 01960

OSTERMANN, EDWIN PAUL, Environmental Science Teacher; *b:* Aguano, Guam; *m:* Kathleen Joanne; *c:* Laura, Kyndall; *ed:* Miami Oxford

(BS) Ed 1977, (MED) Ed 1982; Attnd Wright St, Univ of Dayton, Sinclair Comm; *cr:* Lakota HS Sci Tchr 1978-84; Franklin HS Sci Tchr 1985-; *ai:* Wrestling Coach; Sci Olympiad; Envirothon; Warren Cty Litter Prevention, Soil & Water Conservation Tchr of Yr 1991; Adams Cty Stewardship Awd 1995; MML League Wrestling Coach of Yr 1988-90; *office:* Franklin Sr HS 750 E 4th St Franklin OH 45005*

OSTORGA, ALCIONE, Educational Facilitator; *b:* Sao Paulo, Brazil; *m:* Jose Guadalupe; *c:* Oliver; *ed:* Staten Island Coll (AA) Lbrl Arts 1974; Queens Coll (BA) Elem Ed 1979; Aldephi Univ (MS) Spcl Ed 1982; Fordham U 18 Credits Towards PHD; *cr:* St Christophers Homes Developmental Specialist 1982-83; The Child Schl Spcl Ed Tchr 1983-84; Queens Luth Schl Elem Schl Tchr 1984-89; Boricua Coll Educl Facilitator 1990-95; *ai:* Kappa Delta Pi 1979-, Ed Hnr 1979; ASCD 1995-; *office:* Boricua Coll 9 Graham Ave Brooklyn NY 10032*

OSTRANDER, TERRANCE FRANCIS, Physical Ed Teacher & Coach; *b:* Buffalo, NY; *m:* Margaret; *c:* Christopher, Kathryn; *ed:* Canisuis Coll (BS) PE 1981, (MS) 1988; *cr:* Diocese of Buffalo PE Tchr 1981-85; Frontier Coll PE Tchr 1985-; *ai:* Vars Ftbl, Indoor Track, Boys Outdoor Track Coach; AAPHER 1988-; Orchard Park Little League Bsbl 1990-; W Senecca Hockey 1994-; Coach of Yr Awd 1991 Channel 7 Buffalo NY; *office:* Frontier Central HS S-4432 Bay View Rd Hamburg NY 14075

OSTRIN, STEVE H., History & Social Science Tchr; *b:* Brooklyn, NY; *m:* L. Judith Fermin; *c:* Chiara Evelyn; *ed:* Brooklyn Coll (BA) Sociology, Psych 1975, (MA) Soc Stud, Scndry Ed 1995; Gemological Inst of Amer Gemologist 1978; Conflict Resolution, Mediation; *cr:* Lincoln HS Tchr 1987-89; Mc Kee Voc HS Tchr 1989; Maxwell Voc HS Tchr 1989-90; Boys & Girls HS Tchr 1990-93; Brooklyn Tech Hs Tchr 1993-; *ai:* Magazine Adv, Coord; After Schl Global Regents Tutor; Peer Mediation, Negotiation Cnslr; Mentor, Buddy Tchr; AFT 1987-; Vietnam Vets of Amer 1982-, Drug Prevention, Cnslng; *office:* Brooklyn Technical HS 29 Fort Greene Pl Brooklyn NY 11217*

OSTROSKY, BARBARA (MIRANTI), Fourth Grade Teacher; *b:* Bridgeport, CT; *m:* Raymond E.; *c:* Jason, Ryan, Kerri; *ed:* Sacred Heart Univ (BA) Eng, Elem Ed 1969; Fairfield Univ (MA) Elem Ed 1972; *cr:* Booth Hill Schl Grd 6 Tchr 1969-72, Grd 2 Tchr 1972-75, Grd 6 Tchr 1975-86, Grd 4 Tchr 1986-; *ai:* Soc Stud, Eng, Math, Curr Comms; Spelling Bee, Schl Store Adv; PTA VP; NEA, CEA, SEA 1969-; *office:* Booth Hill Schl 544 Booth Hill Rd Shelton CT 06484

OSTROV, LYN K., Art Director; *b:* Akron, OH; *m:* Terry F. Lewis; *ed:* MD Inst Coll of Art (BFA) Painting 1976; Mt Royal Schl of Painting (MFA) Painting 1979; Univ of PA 1972-74; Kent St Univ 1972-73; York Archaeological Trust 1974; *cr:* Bowie St Coll Art Instr 1979-81; Comm Coll of Baltimore Art Instr 1981-85; Baltimore Schl for Arts Art Instr 1985-89; Friends Schl of Baltimore Art Dir 1989-; *ai:* AIMS Acad Adv Cncl Ind MD Schls Assn; Prsnl Comm Fac-Admin Bd Friends Schl; Dismissal, Discipline, Schedule, People for Sexual Tolerance Comm; NAEA MD Chptr; Artists Equity; Amnesty Intl; Eagle Voice Ctr 1982-; Bd Mem; Included in Book Titled Pub Art; Ivan Karp Awd Artscape Baltimore Arts Festival 1980; *office:* Friends Schl Of Baltimore 5114 N Charles St Baltimore MD 21210*

OSTROWSKI, DEBRA W., Mathematics Teacher; *b:* Glens Falls, NY; *m:* Paul; *c:* Alexandra, Mark; *ed:* St Univ of NY at Cortland (BS) Early Chlhd Ed 1984; State Univ of NY at Brockport (MS) Scndry Math Ed 1989; *cr:* Albion HS Math Tchr 1984-; *office:* Albion HS 302 East Ave Albion NY 14411

OSTROWSKI, LOIS BAKER, Mathematics Teacher; *b:* Pittston, PA; *m:* Michael Mark; *c:* Samantha, Christopher; *ed:* Coll Misericordia (BS) Math 1973; Wilkes Univ (MS) Math, Ed 1975; In-Svc Credit Hrs Luzerne Intermedidate Unit; PHD Pgrm Math Ed PA St Univ; *cr:* PA St Univ Adj Fac Math 1985-92; Pittston Area Schl Dist Scndry Math Tchr 1973-; *ai:* Math Coach; Advanced Math Club Adv; SAT Prep Instr; Goals 2000 Integrated Curr Project; NCTM, PCTM, PADE, MAA, ASCD 1985-; AFT, PAFT 1974-; WY Valle Yth Soccer 1984-, Vol; Rsrch Grant PA Cncl of Tchrs of Math; Article Pub.

O'SULLIVAN, BRIDGET TERESA, Religion Teacher; *b:* New York, NY; *ed:* Fordham Univ (BC) Ed 1955; Manhattan Coll (MA) Rel Stud 1973; Misericordia Home Ec Cert 1967; *cr:* St Rose Schl Elem Ed Tchr 1949-55; St Teresa Schl Elem Ed Tchr 1955-62; Aquinas HS Rel, Home Ec Tchr 1962-67; Msgr Scanlan HS Rel Tchr, Chair 1967-; *ai:* NCEA 1967-; *office:* Monsignor Scanlan H S 915 Hutchinson River Pky Bronx NY 10465

O'SULLIVAN, CYNTHIA ELLEN, First Grade Teacher; *b:* Springfield, MA; *ed:* Coll of Our Lady of the Elms (BA) Sociology 1968; Post Grad Stud Ed Amer Intnl Coll, Westfield St Coll, Cambridge Coll, Anna Maria Coll; *cr:* Green Meadows Schl Spec Ed Tchr 1968-69, Second Grd Tchr 1969-93; Hampden Schl System GATE Coord 1984-90; Green Meadows Schl First Grd Tchr 1993-; *ai:* NEA, MTA 1968-; Hampden Ed Assn 1968-, Pres 1978-83; IRA 1990-; NCTM, NCTE 1993-; Planned, Organized & Opened First Lib at Schl; Horace Mann Tchr 1987; Nom MA Tchr of Yr 1991; *office:* Green Meadows School 38 North Rd Hampden MA 01036*

O'SULLIVAN, MICHAEL, English Teacher; *b:* Norwalk, CT; *m:* Mary Ellen Moylan; *ed:* Boston Univ (BA) Eng 1983; Worcester St Coll (MED) Scndry Ed 1993; *cr:* Burncoat MS Eng Tchr 1989-91; South High Comm Schl Eng, Jrnlsm Tchr 1991-; *ai:* Schl Newspaper Adv; Lang Arts Curr Comm 1994-; NEA, Educl Assn of Worcester 1993-; 1 Yr Flwshp Hiatt Ctr Urban Ed Clark Univ at Worcester 1994-95; *office:* South High Comm Schl 170 Apricot St Worcester MA 01603

O'SULLIVAN, PETER VINCENT, Mathematics Teacher; *b:* Lawrence, MA; *m:* Deborah Alfieri; *c:* Rebecca A., Tatum K., Kendra A.; *ed:* Boston Coll (BA) His 1971; Univ of Lowell (MS) Math 1979; *cr:* St Joseph Schl Tchr 1971-75; Cntrl Cath Schl Tchr 1975-; *ai:* Cross Cntry, Indoor & Outdoor Track Coach; Math Chm; *office:* Central Catholic HS 300 Hampshire St Lawrence MA 01841

OSWALD, MARY GOODMAN, Learning Specialist; *b:* Tampa, FL; *m:* John S. II; *c:* Steven, Mark; *ed:* SUNY at Oswego (BS) Math Ed 1963; Rivier Coll (MED) Learning Disabilities Ed 1991; 30 Grad Hrs SUNY at Oswego, Univ of MS, Syracuse Univ; *cr:* US Pub Schls Math Tchr 1963-72; NHTC Learning Specialist, Math Tchr 1991-; *ai:* LDA 1987-; CHADD 1990-; NCTM; *office:* NH Tech Coll At Nashua 505 Amherst St Nashua NH 03060

OSWALD, RONALD R., Equipment Repair Instructor; *b:* Erie, PA; *m:* Charlene L.; *c:* Ryan M.; *ed:* IN Univ of PA Voc 2 Voc Ed 1992; *cr:* Butler Cty Arts Schl Instr 1980-; *ai:* Mentor Tchr; Induction Team Mem; Schl Resource Person-IN Univ of PA; PA St Inspection Cert Instr; BCAVTSEA 1980-, V-P; Cochranton Jaycees 1981-, HH Chm, JC of Yr 1986, 1988, 1990; Pub Schl Shop Magazine; *office:* Butler Cty Area Voc-Tech Schl 161 New Castle Rd Butler PA 16001

OTERMAT, VIRGINIA BOK, Retired Second Grade Teacher; *b:* Mark Center, OH; *m:* Larry L.; *c:* Megan, Kyle, Gretchen; *ed:* Defiance Coll (BSEd) Elem Ed 1963; OSU 3 Hrs; Eastern MI 6 Hrs; Ashland Univ 9 Hrs; *cr:* Edison Schl 2nd Grd Tchr 1963-65; Garden City Schls 5th Grd Tchr 1965-66; Edison Schl 1, 2, 3rd Grd Tchr 1965-94; *home:* 214 Parkside Dr Ashland OH 44805

OTERO, VICTOR R., Bilingual & Science Teacher; *b:* Santurce, PR; *m:* Brenda I.; *c:* Victor E.; *ed:* Univ of PR (BA) Ed & Sci 1981; Rutgers Univ Sci Courses; *cr:* Jose N. Landron HS Math Tchr 1981-83; Woodrow Wilson HS Sci Tchr 1985-87; Rutgers Univ Asst Coord for Pharmacy Ed Pgm 1988-92; Perth Amboy HS Sci Tchr 1993-; *ai:* Perth Amboy HS After Schl Learning Pgm; HSPT Prep Course PAHS Math Tchr; Biling Pgm Comm for the Mid St Evaluation; Adult Schl Sci Tchr; NEA 1981-; PR Tchrs Assn 1981-; NJEA 1985-; United St Dept of Energy & Tchr Rsrch Assoc Pgm 1995; *home:* 51 Smith St Perth Amboy NJ 08861*

OTIS, CAROL D. FALLENI, Family & Consumer Sci Teacher; *b:* Jersey City, NJ; *m:* Donald; *c:* Wendy Otis-Lavrenov, Kevin, Jennifer; *ed:* Douglas Coll (BS) Home Ec 1961; Rutgers Univ (MED) Family Life Ed 1967; Addl 22 Credits Fairleigh Dickinson Univ Cmptr, 9 Credits Jersey City St Coll Sociology, 8 Credits Rutgers Univ Consumer Ed Family; *cr:* Hackensack HS Family Life, Home Ec, Voc Ed Tchr 1961-63, 1971; Emerson HS Home Ec, Family Tchr 1963-64; Teaneck HS Family & Consumer Sci Tchr 1978-80, 1990-95; Benjamin Franklin MS Home Ec, Wellness Tchr 1980-; *ai:* FHA; NEA, NJEA, BCEA, TTEA 1961-64, 1977-, NEA Del, Secret to TTEA; NJAFCS NJ Assoc Family & Consumer Sci 1961-, Treas Elect; AAFCS 1961-; BPAFCS 1961-; Voc Home Ec on Ed Assn of NJ 1st VP Mbrshp; FHA Alumni 1957, 1961-62, 1977-, Pres Elect, Adv, Natl FHA Ldrshp Hall of Fame 1995; Comm Schlsp 1974-, Pres; Comm Chest 1974-, Treas; Evening Mbrshp Women's Club 1974-, Sec, Treas, Chm, St Hnr Roll; Teaneck Swim Club Trustee 1981-, Fin Sec; St Anastasia 1964-, Parish Cncl Instr of Rel Classes; FHA Adv to Adv Natl Prgm; Honored by PTA for Svc 1989; Consumerism Soc Svc Grad Flwshp Rutgers 1970-; Kappa Delta Pi; Cert Family & Consumer Sci Edctr.*

OTIS, DOUGLAS B., Music Director; *b:* NY City, NY; *ed:* Mercy Coll (BA) (BS) Bio, Math, His 1971; Westchester Conservatory of Music (BA) (BS) Music Perf, Music Comp 1985; NY Univ (MS) Composition, Piano 1991; Fordham Univ (MS) Ed 1995; West Con Music Prof Arts Diploma; 30 Credits Hrs Columbia Univ 1972; *cr:* Mt St Ursula Acad Bio, Earth Sci, Music Tchr 1992; Fordham Prep Schl Bio, Music Tchr 1996; *ai:* Dir of Music, Orch, Band & Musical; NSTA 1971-; Prof Artists of Westchester 1985-; *office:* Fordham Prep Schl 441 E Fordham Rd Bronx NY 10458*

OTIS, JANET E., Third Grade Teacher; *b:* Madison, ME; *m:* Gordon A.; *c:* Michael, Stephen, Roberta Bailey; *ed:* Univ of ME at Orono (BS) Ed 1973; *cr:* Schl Admin Dist #49 Classroom Tchr 1973-; *ai:* Team Ventures Steering Comm Mem; NEA, ME Educl Assn 1973-; Schl Admin Dist #49 Tchrs Assn 1973-, Bldg Rep; *office:* Benton Elem Schl 62 Old Benton Neck Rd Benton ME 04901

OTLEY, GLORIA BEERS, 9th-12th Grd Math Teacher; *b:* Danbury, CT; *m:* Victor C. Jr.; *c:* Victor III, Clark, Brian; *ed:* Bryant Coll (BS) Acctng & Fin 1959; Montclair Univ (MA) Tchng 1985; *cr:* Wayne Hills HS Tchr 1986-; *ai:* NEA 1986-; WEA 1986-; NCTM 1986-; *office:* Wayne Hills HS 272 Berdan Ave Wayne NJ 07470*

O'TOOLE, BERNARD JOHN, English Teacher; *b:* New York City, NY; *m:* Anne; *c:* Bernard; *ed:* City Coll of NY (BA) Eng 1965; City Univ of NY (MA) Eng 1970; *cr:* All Hallows Inst Eng Tchr 1967-77; Spellman HS Eng Tchr 1977-86; Horace Mann Schl Eng Tchr 1986-; *ai:* Book Club; Soc for Stud of Medieval Lang, Lit 1993-; *office:* Horace Mann Schl 231 W 246th St Bronx NY 10471

O'TOOLE, CHRISTOPHER JOHN, AP Mathematics Teacher; *b:* Brooklyn, NY; *m:* Grace Smith; *c:* Christopher, Edward, Donald, John, Hugh, Andrew, Marianne; *ed:* Western CT St Univ (MS) Sec Math Ed 1977; *cr:* Bishop Loughlin Meml HS Latin, Math Tchr 1956-64; Lakeland Sr HS Math Tchr 1964-; Pace Univ Assoc Prof Math 1978-; *ai:* AFT 1970-; Phi Delta Kappa 1977-; MAA 1989-; NSF: Yale 1965, Wayne St Univ 1970-72, Hope Coll Inst of AP Math 1973, Columbia 1977; *home:* 260 Austin Rd Mahopac NY 10541

O'TOOLE, JOANNE RINDENELLO, Spanish Teacher; *b:* Utica, NY; *m:* Thomas P.; *c:* Catherine, Patrick, Devin; *ed:* SUNY at Binghamton (BA) Span 1978; SUNY at Oswego (MS) Ed 1991; Universidad De Salamanca 1992; *cr:* Baldwinsville Cntrl Schls Span Tchr 1988-; *ai:* NYSAFLT & FLACNY 1988- VP 1996; NEA 1991-; St Johns Church 1984-; Anthony J. Papalia Foreign Lang Research Awd 1992; Multinational & Comparative Ed Schlsp Winner 1992; Article Pub "Foreign Lang Anxiety" in NYSAFLT Bulletin 1993; Pub Article 1995; *office:* C W Baker HS 29 E Oneida St Baldwinsville NY 13027*

O'TOOLE, SUSAN RENNER, Chemistry Teacher; *b:* Rochester, PA; *c:* Catherine; *ed:* Duquesne Univ (BS) Biochemistry 1977, (MS) Biochemistry 1980, (MS) Scndry Ed 1988; Post Grad Credits Drexel Univ, Gannon Univ, Univ of CA at Berkeley, West Chester Univ; *cr:* Duquesne Univ Tchng Asst 1977-80; B. Reed Henderson HS Chem Tchr 1986-; *ai:* Amer Chemical Soc 1975-; NSTA, PA Sci Tchrs Assn 1987-; West Chester Area Ed Assn, NEA 1986-; Girls Scouts of Amer 1993-; Attnd Inst Chemical Ed Instrumentation, ACS Chem in the Comm; Demos, Writing, Thinking Act Presenter at PSTA Conventions; *office:* Henderson HS Lincoln & Montgomery Aves West Chester PA 19380

OTRUPCHAK, ROBERT P., High School Psychology Teacher; *b:* Morristown, NJ; *m:* Karen; *c:* Kristin Siciliano, Inga Holmes, Karen Jeanne; *ed:* Rutgers Univ (BA) His 1965; Kean Coll (MA) Stu Prsnl Svcs 1978; Rutgers Univ (MA) Psych 1985; Cert for Psych 30 Credits; Prins & Supvrs Cert 18 Credits; Guidance Cert 36 Credits; *cr:* Red Bank Regnl HS Instr of Psych 1965-, Instr of US His 1965-, Boys Bsktbl Coach 1965-73; *ai:* Girls Bsktbl Coach 1992-; NEA, NJEA 1965-; APA 1973-; Ocean Twp Little League 1981-, Commissioner; Amer Sftbl Assn 1986-, Commissioner; Sabbatical Leave Grants 1985 & 1990; Summer Stud Grants 1970, 1971, 1974, 1976, 1977 & 1978; Pub Article Bsktbl Coach 1971; *office:* Red Bank Reg HS 101 Ridge Rd Little Silver NJ 07739

OTT, BARBARA BARKMAN, Family & Consumer Science Tchr; *b:* Somerset, PA; *m:* Harold Richard; *c:* Karen Ball, Brian; *ed:* IN Univ of PA (BS) Home Ec 1964, (MS) Equivalency Home Ec 1991; 3 Grad Credits Clarion St Univ; 6 Grad Credit Duquesne Univ; 12 Grad Credits PA St Univ; *cr:* Mercer Cty Voc Tech Food Svc Instr 1983-84; Lakeview Jr, Sr HS Home Ec Tchr 1984-87; Centre Cty Voc Tech Interior Design Instr 1988-; Penns Vly Jr, Sr HS FCS Tchr 1988-; *ai:* Final Evaluations, Grad Requirements Comms; PVEA, NEA 1988-; Fac Womens Club 1987-, VP Prgms; Hosp Aux Antique Show 1992-, Hospitality Chm; Hosp Aux Antique Show 1993-, Dlrs Co-Chm; *office:* Penns Valley Jr Sr HS RR 2 Box 116 Spring Mills PA 16875*

OTT, MARY LOU, Sophmore English Teacher; *b:* Malvern, OH; *m:* William A.; *c:* Char; *ed:* Univ of Akron (BA) Ed 1971, (MA) Family Stud 1982; Cert of Adulthood & Aging; *cr:* First Chrstn Church Chrstn Ed Dir 1983-86; Wane Gen & Tech Coll Part Time Instr 1983-86; Wadsworth City Schls 8th Grd Eng Tchr 1986-92; Wadsworth City Schls Soph Eng Tchr 1992-; *ai:* Adv Stu Operated Bookstore; OCTELA, NCTE 1986-; 1st Chrstn Church 1974-, Elder; Grant to Operate a Stu Bookstore; People to People Ambassador with NCTE to Russia 1995; *office:* Wadsworth City Schls 625 Broad St Wadsworth OH 44281

OTTAVIANI, VIRGINIA OTTOBRE, Business Ed Tchr & Dept Chprsn; *b:* Ellwood City, PA; *m:* John; *c:* Darin; *ed:* Geneva Coll (BS) Bus Admn 1971; Univ of Pittsburgh Graduate Studies 1972-73; *cr:* Lincoln HS Bus Ed Tchr 1971-; *ai:* NEA, PSEA, EAEA, Tri-St Bus Ed Assn 1971-; EAEA Past Sec Bldg Rep, Soc Comm Co-Chprsn; Purification BVM Church, Parish, Cncl Lector; *home:* 910 Skyline Dr Ellwood City PA 16117

OTTE, RANDON C., Accounting Professor; *b:* Punxsutawney, PA; *m:* Kathy J. Evans; *ed:* Clarion St Coll (BS) Bus Admin 1973, (MBA) Acctng 1974; Addl Grad Work Univ of Pittsburgh; *cr:* Root Spitznas & CPAs Auditor 1974-76; Clarion Univ of PA Asst Prof 1976-; *ai:* Ce Accountant St of PA; Amer Inst of CPAs, PA Inst of CPAs 1977 Acctng Assn 1979-; *office:* Clarion Univ Of PA 304 Still Hall Cla 16214

OTTEN, DANIEL J., Dev Handicapped Coach; *b:* Dayton, Bowling Green St Univ (BA) Spec Ed, Elem Ed 1977; *cr:* Fairview Spec Ed Tchr 1977-80; Celina Sr High Spec Ed Tchr 1980-; *a* Soccer Coach; Asst Jr Class Adv; Head Cross-Cntry Coach; Ass Coach; NEA, OEA & CEA 1977-; *office:* Celina HS 715 E Wayne S OH 45822

OTTERSON, SHARON R., Reading Specialist; *b:* Hanover, NH Michael; *c:* Katy M., Kristopher M.; *ed:* Keene St Coll (BS) Elem E Antioch New England Grad Schl (MA) Early Chldhd 1985; Notr Coll (MA) Reading Specialist 1991; Reading Recovery Trng 1993 Hillsboro-Deering Elem Schl 1st-3rd Grd Tchr 1970-87, Rdng Sp Coord 1987-91, Rdng Recovery Tchr, Rdng Specialist, Asst Prin 19 Tchr Mentor; IRA 10 Yrs; AFT 15 Yrs; Design Team 4 Yrs; Outstd Awd; Tchng Svc Awd; *office:* Hillsboro-Deering Elem Schl 4 Hi Hillsboro NH 03244*

OTTEY, HYPHA ANN, Chemistry & Biology Teacher; *b:* K Jamaica, West Indies; *ed:* Polytechnic Univ (BS) Chem 1984; A Columbia Univ Sci Ed; *cr:* Brooklyn Tech HS Chem & Bio Tchr 19 UFT 1987-.*

OTTO, FRED BISHOP, Associate Professor of Physics; *b:* Bang *m:* Alma Merrill; *c:* Janet L., Nancy L. Jessen, Robert M., Katl Ward; *ed:* Univ of ME (BS) Engrng Physics 1956; Univ of C Physics 1960, (PHD) Physics 1965; *cr:* Colby Coll Asst Physi 1964-68; Univ of ME Asst Electrical Engrng prof 1968-74; Maritime ACad ASsoc Physics Prof 1982-; *ai:* APS 1963-; AAPT IES 1972-; BSA 1947-, Silver Beaver Awd; *office:* Maine Maritim Castine ME 04420

OTTO, JUDITH COLEMAN, HS Physical Ed Tchr & Coa Lockport, NY; *m:* Marvin William; *c:* Aaron, Alexander; *ed:* Slippe Univ (BS) Hlth, PE & Rec 1974; SUNY at Buffalo (MS) Hlth Ed 19 Barker Cntrl Schl MS & HS PE 1975-; *ai:* Head Field Hockey Team 21 Yrs; AFT 1975-; NEA 1975-; Started BCS Girls Pgm Niagara-Orleans League 20 Yrs Coaches Awd 1994; *office:* Barker Schl 1628 Quaker Rd Barker NY 14012

OTTO, NORA KATHRYN, Retired Elementary School Tchr; *b:* PA; *m:* John H.; *c:* Peter S.; *ed:* West Chester Univ (BS) Elem Ec Bloomsburg Univ (MS) Elem, Rdng 1974; *cr:* Upper Dauphin Sch Classroom Tchr 1957-63; Tri Vly Schl Elem Classroom Tchr 1963- TVEA 1963-; PSEA, NEA 1957-; PASR-R, PSEA-R 1993-; Churc Craftfaire Caregiver, Vol; New Stringer for Local Radio Station Lance Writer for Local Newspaper; Tutored Elem, Coll Prep, Cu Tutoring; *home:* 815 Chestnut St Hegins PA 17938

OTTOCHIAN, FRANK JOHN, Visual Art Teacher; *b:* Brooklyn, Celia Mary; *ed:* William Patterson Coll (MFA) Visual Arts 19 Credits Beyond Masters Ed 1994; *cr:* Warwick NY Construction Co 1970-90; Teaneck NJ Visual Art Tchr 1973-; Sulyer Loaf NY Art Owner 1980; *ai:* Ftbl Coach 1973-75; Photography Club Adv 1991- Class Adv 1992; Beautification Adv 1994-; Spring Play Set De Little League & Soccer Coach; Art Act Dir; NJEA 1973-; Conodm of Mgrs 1980-82, Bd Mem; Art Exhibit at Forbes Magazine 1992; Teaneck HS 100 Elizabeth Ave Teaneck NJ 07666

OUELLETTE, LYNETTE (LANDRY), French Teacher; *b:* New Be MA; *m:* Normand E. Ouellette; *c:* Robert; *ed:* Annhurst Coll (BA) Fr Bowdoin Coll Cert 1962; Univ of Rennes Cert Fr 1964; Boston Co Stud Fr 1967; *cr:* Hastings MS Fr, Latin Tchr 1961-68; Fairhaven Bio Tchr 1970-71; Notre Dame Schl Eng Tchr 1982-84; Westport Eng, Span Tchr 1984-; *ai:* Fr Club; Schl Cncl; Westport Tchrs, M Tchrs, AFT 1984-; MA FLA 1992-; Franco-Amer Civic League 1965 Ladies Guild 1990-, VP, Pres, Sec, Diocesan Treas, Lady of Yr; 1962-64; *office:* Westport HS 19 Main Rd Westport MA 02790

OUELLETTE, ROGER J., Fifth Grade Teacher; *b:* Tiverton, RI; *ed* Univ of Amer (BA) Amer His 1964; RI Coll (MED) Elem Ed 1969; Brown Univ, Salve Univ & Univ of RI; *cr:* La Salle Military Acad 9 Soc Stud Tchr 1964; Saint Augustine HS 9th Grd Soc Stud Tchr 19 J F Wilbur Schl Elem Tchr 1965-; *ai:* Math Club; Sci Fair; 8t Moderator; Testing Coord; Francophone Assn; RI Ed Assn 1965-; 1966-; LCTA 1965-, Pres 4 Yrs, VP 4 Yrs, Sec 4 Yrs, Treas 2 Yrs; Conservancy 1995-; Thames Sci Ctr 1993-; Whos Who in Am 1989-90; Eisenhower Grant for Bio from Salve Univ 1994; Waters Prgm; *office:* Wilbur-McMahon Schl Commons PO Box 178 Compton RI 02837

OUELLETTE, THOMAS PETER, History Teacher & Dept Chpr Springfield, MA; *m:* Marion Roberts; *c:* Michele Bigda, Tami K Michael; *ed:* Amer Intnl Coll (BA) His 1967, (MA) Ed 1971; 6th Admin 1980; *cr:* Endfield Pub Schls Tchr 1967-; *ai:* Model UN, Clo Adv; ETA 1967-, PAC Chprsn; CEA; NEA; *office:* Enrico Fermi HS Maple St Enfield CT 06082

OUELLETTE, VIVIANNE L., Math Teacher; *b:* Fall River, M Henry C.; *c:* Paul, Steven; *ed:* Clark Univ (BA) Math, Eng 1972; Wor St (MS) Cmptr Ed 1980; 45 Addl Credits; *cr:* Holden Jr HS Math, Eng 1976-80; Jefferson MS Math Tchr 1980-90; Mountview MS Math 1990-; *ai:* Interdisciplinary Team Ldr; Math Task Force Co-Chprsn; Comm; NCTM 1976-; Helped Pub Problem Solving, Geometry Source Books; *office:* Mountview MS 270 Shrewsbury St Holden 01520

OUTMAN, KENNETH RONALD, Mathematics Teacher; *b:* Olean *m:* Susan E. Ryan; *ed:* SUNY at Albany (BS) Math 1965, (MS) Math 1969; Union Coll (MS) Math 1976; *cr:* South Colonie Ctrl HS Math 1965-; *ai:* NYSUT; AFT; NEA; *office:* South Colonie Ctrl Schl 1 Ra Blvd Albany NY 12205

OUTT, DAINA ASHLEY, Mathematics Teacher; *b:* Philadelphia, P Pamela Ellen Moore; *c:* Ashleigh; *ed:* Univ of Cincinnati (BS) Ed, 1984; Masters Work Northern KY Univ Admin; *cr:* Glen Este HS Tchr 1985-; *ai:* Jr Class Adv 1986, 1996; Sr Class Adv 1987; Asst Var Soccer Coach 1986-88; Pep Club Adv 1992-; Intervention Team NCTM 1990-; Eagles 1985-; Tchr of Yr 1993; Nom Tchr of Yr 1992, 1995; *office:* Glen Este HS 4342 Glen Este Withamsville Rd Cincinnat 45245*

OUYANG, BENJAMIN T., Resource Counselor; *b:* Rochester, NY; *m* Shieu Lee; *ed:* Univ of Rochester (BA) Pol Sci 1988; Univ of MD (M Schl Counseling 1990; 15 Credit Hrs Towards PHD; *cr:* Fairfax Cty Schls Schl Cnslr 1990-92; Montgomery Cty Pub Schls Schl Cnslr 1 *ai:* MSAP Peer Mediation; NEA, MSTA; Asian Amer Ed Assn; Al GAC 1995-, Mem; *office:* Redland MS 6505 Muncaster Mill Rd Rock MD 20855

OVER, PHILIP R., Mathematics Teacher & Ath Dir; *b:* Roaring Sp PA; *m:* Renee M.; *c:* Susan R. Dawson, Phillip R. Jr., David A.; *ed:* Ju Coll (BS) Math 1959; Univ of PA (MS) Guid, Cnslng 1962; Attnd P Univ; *cr:* Red Lion Area Sr HS Math Tchr 1959-60; Beverly Hills J Math Tchr, Ath Dir, Coach 1960-80; Upper Darby HS Math Tchr, Ath ai: NEA, PSEA, UDEA 1959-; office: Upper Darby HS 601 N wne Ave Upper Darby PA 19082

RENEE MACFADYEN, Second Grade Teacher; b: Philadelphia, Philip Ralph; c: Susan Dawson, Philip Jr., David; ed: Juniata Coll em Ed 1959; Univ of PA (MS) Rdng 1962; cr: Red Lion Area Schl st Grd Tchr 1959-60; Upper Darby Twp Schl Dist First Grd Tchr 4; Haverford Twp Schl Dist Chptr I, Rdng Tchr 1978-80, Second r 1980-; ai: NEA; PSEA.

DORFF, MARJORIE KELLER, Elementary Music Specialist; b: lsville, PA; m: Gary Paul; c: Jeffrey Alan, Wwndy rff-Dodson; ed: IN Univ of PA (BS) Music Ed 1965; Addl Stud g Green St Univ, Memphis St Univ, Sam Houston St Univ, PA St r: Lock Haven Schls Elem Music Supv 1965-68; Livinston Schls Music, PE Tchr 1969-73; Maysville Local Schls Elem Music ist 1973-; ai: Soc for Gen Music St Comm; Music Wkshp Coord; Steering Comm; NEA, OEA 1973-; MENC, OMEA 1973, Dist St Comm 25 Yr; Amer Orff-Schulwerk Assn 1974-, Delta Omicron Thurday Music Club 1978-, Treas; Delta Kappa Gamma 1987-, Co-chair; Hospice of Bethesda 1994-; Martha Holden Jennings 993-94; Newton Tchr of Yr 1995; office: Maysville Local Schls inkerton Rd Zanesville OH 43701

HISER, JAMES LEWIS, 8th Grd Physical Science Tchr; b: ır Falls, NY; m: Sandra Tuthill; c: Ryann; ed: Corning Comm Coll ci, Lib Arts 1977; Cortland St (BS) Scndry Ed, Biochemistry 1980, Sci Ed & Bio 1982; Oneonta St, Univ of Binghamton, Penn St 28 Hrs Beyond MSE; cr: Ithaca HS Permanent Sci Sub Tchr 1980-81; ad St Grad Tchng Asst 1981-82; Groton Cntrl Schl Sci Tchr, Dept 982-; Cortland St Adjunct Lecturer, Ed Dept 1994-; ai: Cross Cntry 1982-; Jr High Honor Soc Adv; Dist Tech Comm; NY St Gas & c Ed Advy Panel; NY St Sci Mentor; Natnl Tchr Training Inst Master STANYS 1986-; NSTA 1993-; NEA 1982-; Pres Awd for Excl in c Sci Tchng Nom 1986, 1991-96; Sigma XI Scientific Research Soc Corp Pub Broadcasting, Natl Tchng Trng Inst, Texaco Inc 1995-96 f Yr; office: Groton Cntrl Schl 400 Peru Rd Groton NY 13073

HOLT, ROBERT ALLAN, Advanced Chemistry Teacher; b: ıs, OH; m: Donna L. Fischer; c: Richard, Rebecca Sendi; ed: berg Coll (BS) Physics & Math 1960; Miami Univ of OH (MAT) 1972; cr: Univ of Pittsburgh Grad Stu Asst 1960-61; Thompson HS 961-70; Bellevue HS Tchr 1970-83; Tiffin Columbian HS Tchr ai: Environmental Club Adv; STAND Adv; OH Ed Assn 1961-; NEA Tiffin Ed Assn 1984-; North Cntrl Sci Soc 1980-, Past Pres, ng Tchr Awd; Habitat for Hum 1986-, Treas; Church Cncl 1994-; 1st Bd of Dirs 1996-; VFW Chptr Tchr of the Yr; Habitat for Hum Pub wd; office: Tiffin Columbian HS 300 S Monroe St Tiffin OH 44883*

HOLTS, JUDY L., Third Grade Teacher; b: Hamilton, OH; m: Eric Laurie Solazzo, Jay; ed: Miami Univ (BS) Elem Ed 1982; cr: St Julie t Schl Third Grd Tchr 1983-; ai: Commission Ed, Safety Cncl Reps; 7 Hollowtree Ct Hamilton OH 45013

HOLTZER, DAVID CRAIG, Instrumental Music Teacher; b: town, PA; m: Amy Walz; ed: IN Univ of PA (BS) Music Ed 1993; cr: Penn Jr HS Indoor Color Guard Instr 1994; Lackey HS Instrumental Tchr 1994-; ai: Marching Band, Jazz Ensemble Dir; Spring Musical Dir; AFT, NEA 1993-; MSTA 1994-; office: Lackey HS 3000 moxen Rd Indian Head MD 20640

MAN, HOWARD ANTHONY, Phys Ed & Health Teacher; b: vater, OH; m: Patricia Hoying; c: Kelli, Doug, Marcus; ed: Univ of n (BS) PE 1980, (MS) Admin 1986; Working Towards Prins Cert; cr: Lehman HS His Tchr 1980-81; Wapakoneta City Schls PE Tchr 93; New Bremen Local Schls PE, Hlth Tchr 1993-; ai: Head Ftbl ; Weight Room Coord; NEA 1981-; New Bremen Tchrs Assn 1993-; d Assn 1981-; Yth Bsktbl Coach 1996; Yth Bsbl Coach 1995-; office: Bremen Schl 202-210 S Walnut St New Bremen OH 45869

MILLER, LAURIE (WEINFURTNER), Art Teacher & Dept b: Ashland, KY; m: James M.; c: Simon, Celeste; ed: Eastern KY (BA) Art Ed 1975; 24 Credit Hrs in Ed at Penn St Univ; cr: Spring Area Schl Dist Art Tchr 1982-86; York Cath HS Art Tchr 1987-; ai: Club Moderator; Set Design Co-Ordinator for Plays & Musicals; 1987-; office: York Catholic HS 601 E Springettsbury Ave York PA

MYER, ANNE DIBERT, Kindergarten Teacher; b: Toledo, OH; m: t; c: Kerri, Laura; ed: Bowling Green Univ, Toledo Univ, Ashland Credit Hrs; cr: Fremont-Atkinson Schl 1st Grd Tchr 1970-72, Kndgtn 86, K-Pre-first 1986-95, Kndgtn 1995-; ai: FEA, NEA, OEA 1970-; ay Schl Tchr 1978-; Church Cncl 1994-; Yth Church Ldr 1985-94; ion Bible Schl Tchr 1978-80; Learning & Liberty Grant; Excl in n Awd 1985, 1989; office: Atkinson Elem Schl 1100 Delaware Ave ont OH 43420

RTON, DOROTHY JEAN, Biology Teacher; b: Darlington Cty, SC; lelvin Lionel; c: Lionel Sean, Kareef; ed: Benedict Coll (BS) Bio , Bowie St Univ (MS) Scndry Admin, Supervision 1980; Scndry Schl Phase 1-2 Ldrshp Trng; Family Life & Sex Ed; Strategies & Prgms ifted Stdnts; Effective Schls & Tchr Behavior Modification; cr: e George's Cty PS Bio Tchr 1970-71; Gaithersburg Jr HS Sci Tchr -89; Takoma MS Sci Tchr 1989-93; Walter Johnson HS Bio Tchr -; ai: Stu Govt, Ecology Club Adv; GATE, Stu At Risk Coord; Pom Spon; NEA 1964-; MSTA, MCEA 1972-; Delta Sigma Theta 1980-, Ladies of Colesville 1970-, Treas; Progressive Club 1978-, Pres.*

RTON, PAULETTE CULLUM, Sixth Grade Science Teacher; b: n, SC; m: Louis Overton; c: Rachael L.; ed: MO Bapt Coll (AA) Elem 973; Cntrl MO St Coll (BSE) Elem Ed 1976; 12 Quarter Hrs Sci eland St Univ; cr: Go Vallee Elem Schl Third Grd Sub Tchr 1977-78; ard Elem Schl Sixth Grd Tchr 1978-93; Whitney M. Young Schl Sixth Sci Tchr 1993-; ai: Sci Lead Tchr, Proficiency Curr Alignment Writer, ciency Presenter; Union Conf Comm; Vlybl, Asst Track Coach; NSTA ; AFT 1980-; Vol Tutor Comm Ctr; Two Grants Cleveland Ed Fund; resenter NSTA Anaheim; Nom OH Tchr Participant Wake Forest Univ cy Inst; Sci Ed Cnslr OH.*

RTON, THERETHA DARIYAH, HS Vocal Director; b: Cleveland, m: William Samuels; c: Celeste Y. Melton; Nneka; ed: Cleveland St (BMUS) Music Ed 1994; Augsburg Music Acad, Cleveland Inst of c Privated Stud Voice; cr: Yth Dev Ctr Yth Ldr for Ages 12-18 Yrs -80; ai: Arican-Amer Heritage Comm Co-Chair; Gospel Choir Adv; Phi Epsilon Gamma Phi Chptr 1989-, Pres 1989-92, Most Active Chptr ; office: James Ford Rhodes HS 5100 Biddulph Rd Cleveland OH 4

RTON, WINNIFRED HELEN, Physical Education Teacher; b: sville, KY; m: Blair P. III; c: Blair IV, Scot; ed: Shepherd Coll (BS) 965; Bowie St Univ (MS) PE 1979; cr: DuVal HS 10th-12th Grd PE 1965-68; Francis T Evans Elem K-6th PE Tchr 1977-79; Key Schl 7th Grd Sci Tchr 1982-85; Kenmoor Elem K-6th PE Tchr 1985-92; tpelier Elem K-6th Grd PE 1992-; ai: NEA 1965-; MSTA 1965-; EA 1965-; office: Montpelier Elem Schl 9200 Muirkirk Rd Laurel MD 8

EN, PATRICIA LYNNE, English Teacher; b: Massillon, OH; c: gan Oakleaf; ed: Kent St Univ (BA) Eng, His 1968; Ashland Univ (BS) Elem, Scndry Ed 1992, (MED) Ed 1994; Portfolio Assessment, Lang Arts Duquesne Univ 3 Hrs; OH Univ Cmptrs in Classroom 3 Hrs; Lorain Cty Comm Coll Ed 8 Hrs; cr: Fairless Local Schls 4th Grd Classroom Tchr; Kent Cty Libs Asst Librn; St Thomas Aquinas Elem Schl 1st-8th Grd Media Specialist 1984-87; Lorain Comm Hosp Med Librn 1987-94; Elida Local Schls Eng, Scndry, Creative Writing Tchr 1994-; ai: Coalition Essential Schls Team; Mentorship Prgm Boosters; Venture Capital, Schl Improvement, Regnl Prof Dev Comms; Elida Ed Assn 1994-; ALA, MLA 1987-; OEA, NEA 1990-; Harbortown Historic Dist 1988-, Festival Chprsn; Med Lib Assn 1988-, Reference Comm, Acad Hlth Information Specialists; Alpha Gamma Delta 1966-, Svc; Univ Schlsps, Acad, Panhellenic; Bldg Comm Partnership Grant; office: Elida HS 101 E North St Elida OH 45807*

OWEN, WENDY EMERSON, English Dept Chair; b: New York, NY; ed: Univ of PA (BA) Eng 1975; Oxford Univ (MA) Eng 1980; Yale Univ (PHD) Eng 1986; cr: Claremont Coll Asst Prof of Eng 1985-87; Univ of MD Asst Prof 1987-94; Park Schl Eng Dept Head 1994-; ai: Fac Adv Lit Magazine, Book Club; Admissions, New Tchr Comms; Yale Univ, Yale Prize Tchng Flwshp; Claremont Tchng Prize 1986-87; office: The Park Schl 2425 Old Court Rd Brooklandville MD 21022*

OWENS, DARLENE J., Owner & Teacher; b: Latrobe, PA; c: Ryan; ed: Bus Career Inst; cr: Darlene's Dance Studios Owner & Tchr 1965-; Derry Area Sr HS Choreographer 1967-70, 1988; Ligonier Vly Players Choreographer 1971-72; Westmoreland Comm Coll Tchr 1980-81, 1994; ai: PDTA; Excl Awd I Love Dance Pageant 1992; Stdnts Natl Awd Winners Summer Dance Festival; Stdnt Won Highest Score Awds Rising Star Talent Comp, I Love Dane Pageant; Performance Plus Dance Comp; home: 3000 Williamsburg Dr Latrobe PA 15650

OWENS, ELOISE SUZANNE, Professor of Arts & Humanities; b: Cleveland, OH; ed: Miami Univ (BA) Eng 1976; Coll of William & Mary (MA) Eng 1977; The OH St Univ (PHD) Eng & Art His 1982; Post-Doctoral Fellow; Schl of Criticism & Theory Northwestern Univ 1983; cr: Winthrop Univ Eng 1979-80; Univ of FL Eng 1981-83; OH St Univ Eng 1983-85; Ursuline Coll Eng 1985-88; Lorain Cty Comm Coll Arts & Hum 1991-; ai: Chair: Gen Ed Comm, Ctr for Tchng Excl & Women in Ldrshp Cncl; Modern Lang Assn 1985-; Amer Stud Assn 1986-; Coll Eng Assn OH 1991-; NTCE 1992-; Phi Beta Kappa 1976-; Greater Cleveland Assn of Phi Beta Kappa 1986-, Trustee; Women Historians of Greater Cleveland 1986-; Numerous Articles Pub; office: Lorain County Comm Coll 1005 N Abbe Rd Elyria OH 44035

OWENS, MICHAEL ROBERT, English & Latin Teacher; b: Cincinnati, OH; m: Joan Hittner; c: Mark, Katie, David; ed: Loyola Univ at Chicago (BA) Classics 1968; Xavier Univ (MA) Eng 1969; OH Writing Project at Miami Univ OH; cr: Gordon Tech HS Eng Tchr 1969-72; Loyola HS Eng Tchr 1972-76; LaSalle HS Eng & Latin Tchr 1976-; ai: Eng Dept Chair; Asst Kairos Retreat Dir; Natl Cncl of Tchrs of Eng 1980-; Awds: Ashland Oil Golden Apple Achiever, LaSalle HS Hall of Fame & Bro James Daniel; office: La Salle HS 3091 W North Bend Rd Cincinnati OH 45239

OWENS, RICHARD FRANCIS,JR., Mathematics Teacher & Supvr; b: New York City, NY; m: Mary Beth Joyce; c: Ryan Richard; ed: St Johns Univ (MA) Math 1969; Adelphi Univ (MS) Math 1975; C W Post Supvr Cert 1988; cr: Carle Place HS Math Tchr & Supvr 1970-; Queensborough Comm Coll Math Adj Prof 1978-; ai: MS Bsktbl Coach; NCTM 1973-; Assn of Math Tchrs of NY St 1975-; Nassau Cty Assn of Math Tchrs 1980-; NSF Grand for Grad Stud at Adelphi Univ; office: Carle Place Jr, Sr HS Cherry Ln Carle Place NY 11514

OWENS, SCOTT T., Agricultural Education Instr; b: Gonzales, LA; m: Bonnie L. Colantoni; ed: Penn St Univ (BS) Ag Ed 1987, (MED) Ag Ed 1993; cr: Keystone Cntrl SD Ag Instr 1987-; ai: FFA Adv; SAP Team Mem; NEA 1987-; PVATA Region VP; PA Trappers Assn 1990-; PA Farm Bureau 1995-, Head Ed Comm; Outstdng Young Tchr Awd 1988; Outstdng Voc Tchr Awd 1989; office: Keystone Cntrl SD RR 2 Box 10 Loganton PA 17747*

OWENS, SUSANNE KELLEY, Social Studies Teacher; b: Brooklyn, NY; c: Linda, Robert H.; ed: Immaculata Coll (BA) His 1961; Attnd Hofstra Univ, St Johns Univ, Univ of VT, Freedoms Fnd; cr: Sewanhaka Schls Soc Stud, Eng Tchr 1961-64; Garden City HS Soc Stud, Eng Tchr 1964-65; Whitehall Cntrl Schl Soc Stud, Eng Tchr 1965-67; Granville Cntrl Schl Soc Stud, Eng Tchr 1968-; ai: Granville Tchrs Assn 1968-, Bldg Rep; AFT; office: Granville Jr Sr HS Quaker St Granville NY 12832

OWENS, VICKI DAFFARA, Art Teacher; b: Alexandria, VA; m: Paul Owens; c: Jason, Joy; cr: Strafford HS Art Tchr 1 Yr; D. C. Pub Schl Lower Schl Art Tchr 1 Yr; Carvel Acad PT Art Tchr 8 Yrs; ai: Odyssey of Mind Coach; Cornerston United Meth, Jr HS Yth Ldr; office: Caravel Acad 2801 Del Laws Rd Bear DE 19701

OWENS, WILLIAM JUDE, Social Studies Teacher; b: Brooklyn, NY; m: Patricia Ann; c: Timothy, Terence, Ryan; ed: Adelphi Suffolk Coll (BS) Ed 1966; Adelphi Univ (MA) Ed 1972; St Univ at Stony Brook 15 Hrs; cr: Hicksville Jr HS Soc Stud & Eng Tchr 1967-87; Hicksville HS Eng & Soc Stud Tchr 1987-; ai: Defensive Driving at Hicksville Continuing Ed Prog; HCT 1969-; Natl Safety Cncl 1990-; home: 154 4th St Saint James NY 11780

OXENDINE, ELNORA COLEY, Music Teacher & Coord of GATE; b: Wilson, NC; m: James Emerson; c: Johnny Steele, Lori JaMez; ed: NC Cntrl Univ (BA) Music 1950; 28 Hrs GATE Trinity Coll; 9 Hrs Bus Mngmt; cr: Rocky Mount City Schls Music Supvr 1952-63; Spingarn HS Music Tchr 1969-71; Anthony Bowen Schl Music Tchr 1971-79; Ferebee Hope Elem Schl Music Tchr, Spec Tchr Chm, GATE Coord 1979-; ai: W. T. Union Ldrshp Dev, Reorganization Comms; AFT 1969-, Exec Bd; GATE Comm 1979-, Judge Odyssey of Mind Competitions; Bd of Dirs 1991-; NADAA 1962-; Women's Intnl Rel Flwshp 1975-, US Performing Arts Coord; Anthony Bowen Schl Tchr of Yr 1974; home: 5958 Westchester Park Dr College Park MD 20740*

OXLEY, MARGARET STEWART, Second Grade Teacher; b: Petaluma, CA; m: Joseph Hubbard; c: Linda, Carol Greiner, Joan Willis, Joseph, James, Laura; ed: OH St Univ (BS) Ed Elem-Summa Cum Laude 1973, (MA) Lang Arts, Lit, Rdng 1984; Rdng, Writing, Lit Stud Tour Great Britain Summer 1985; cr: St Paul Schl 2nd Grd Tchr 1973-; ai: Presenter in Field; Inservice, Wkshps for Tchrs; Presentations Local & Natl Confs; The Literacy Connection 1984-, Pres; NCTE, OCTELA 1984-; NCTE Childrens Lit Assembly 1984-, Ways & Means Chair; NCTE Notoble Childrens Bks Comm 1993-, Chair 1995-; IRA 1984-, Celebrating Literacy Awd Exemplary Svc 1991; OCTECA Outstdng Eng Lang Arts Elem TChr 1990-; Phi Kappa Phi 1984-; Pi Lambda Theta 1995-; Intnl Hnr & Prof Assn in Ed; Awds OH St U Mary Karrer 1994, Diocese of Cols Distngd Tchng 1988, St Paul Schl Tchr of Yr 1980; Co-Author Reading & Writing Where it All Begins 1991; Contributing Author Teaching with Children's Book, Paths to Literature Based Instruction 1995; Article Pub; office: St Paul Schl 61 Moss Rd Westerville OH 43082

OXNAM, PHILIP LINTON, Theatre Director; b: Pomona, CA; m: JoAnne Buck; ed: Norwich Univ (BA) His & Govt 1963; Amer Acad of Dramatic Art (aA) Theatre Arts 1972; Addl 270 Credit Hrs in Theatre,Arts, & Film; cr: Acting is Easy Owner & Coach 1982-; Acting Lab Owner & Dir 1985-89; Lamoille Union HS Dir of Theatre Arts 1990-91 & 1993-; ai: Dir of Theatre, HS Play & Tech Dir, MS Play & Musical Dir; Asst Coach; NEA 1994-; home: PO Box 426 Warren VT 05674*

OYER, W. BRIAN, Secondary Earth Science Tchr; b: Buffalo, NY; m: Marjorie Fischer; c: Beth Schwartz, Mark, Anne; ed: Univ of Rochester (BA) Geology 1966, (MS) Paleontology 1970; cr: Greece Olympia HS Phys Sci & Chem Tchr 1968-69; Greece Athena HS Earth Sci Tchr 1969-; ai: Greece Tchrs Assn, NEA 1968-; Rochester Acad of Sci Astronomy Section 1990-, Project Scope Coord; office: Greece Athena HS 800 Long Pond Rd Rochester NY 14612

OYLER, DIANE WILLIAMS, 6th Grade Teacher; b: Roaring Spring, PA; m: Eugene M.; c: Gregory, Brian, Brenda, Ted; ed: Dickinson Coll (BA) His 1951; Elem Ed Cert PA St 1970; 56 Credit Hrs In Service Eastern Coll, PSU; cr: Scotland Elem 3rd 1951-52; Park Forest Elem 5th, 6th Grd 1971-95; Park Forest MS 1995-; ai: SCAEA, NEA 1971-; Dist Art Mini Grant 1986; Eastern Coll Amer Stud Fellowship 1983; St Coll Magazine Named One of Top Ten Best Tchrs in St Coll Area Schls 1987-88; Mid Level Stud Comm SCA Schl Bd 1990-91; Gifted Review Task Force 1985-86; PSEA, PDE Outcome Based Education Cadre 1992-; Presenter PSEA Hershey Conference 1992-93; PSEA Regnl Conference 1991-92; SCASD Strtgc Plan Steering Comm 1994-95; office: Park Forest MS 2180 School Dr State College PA 16803

OYSTER, BETTY JEAN (NIGHTINGALE), 6th Grade Teacher; b: Salem, OH; m: James C.; c: Michael, Brian, Greg, Erin; ed: OH St Univ (BS) Elem Ed 1984; Currently Working Toward Masters Hum CA St Univ; cr: Silver St Elem Schl 5 Grd Tchr 1985-93; Baker MS 6 Grd Tchr 1993-; ai: NEA, Marion Ed Assn 1985-; OH PTA, Natl PTA 1993-; PTA Tchr of Yr 1993; office: Baker MS 400 Pennsylvania Ave Marion OH 43302

OZIEMBLO, JOANNE MARIE, Vice Principal & 8th Grd Tchr; b: Jersey City, NJ; ed: St Peter's Coll (BA) Elem Ed 1974, (MA) Admin, Super 1982; Cert Soc Stud, Eng; Caldwell Coll 3 Credits; cr: Our Lady of Mt Carmel Schl Tchr 1974-87; Sacred Heart Schl Prin 1987-89; Hudson Cty CYO Summer Site Supvr Food Prgm 1989-91; CYO Day Camp Summer Camp Dir 1992-93; Mt Carmel Schl Tchr, Vice Prin 1989-; ai: Vlybl Coach; Bowling, Chess, Mission Clubs Moderator; Schl Newspaper Adv; Archdicese of Newark Yth Advy Bd; NCTM, AMTNJ 1994-; NCEA 1974-; Girl Scouts 1970-, Ldr, St Anne Awd; St Peter's Coll GEA 1982-, Treas; Mt Carmel Church 1976-, Lector, Eucharistic Min, Parish Merit Awd; office: Our Lady Of Mount Carmel Schl 95 Broadway Jersey City NJ 07306*

OZOG, RICHARD PETER, Spanish Teacher; b: Welland, Ontario Canada; m: Anne Louise Shipley; c: Peter Richard Joseph; ed: Univ of Western Ontario (BA) Span Lang, Lit 1982, (MA) Span 1983, (BED) Span 1984; Post Grad Stud Curr Brock Univ at St Catharine's 1984-85; cr: Waterloo Jr HS Span Tchr 1985-87; Keuka Coll Span Lecturer 1988-93; Saint Joseph's Schl Span Tchr 1988-; ai: Natl Jr Hnr Soc Adv; Cath Tchrs Assn 1988-; St Mary's Church 1985-; Ontario Grad Schlsp 1984-85; Deans Hnr List 1982; Grad Tchng Flwshp Univ of Western Ontario 1982-83; home: 44 W Elisha St Waterloo NY 13165

OZOLINS, LOUISE DEANGELIS, Language Arts Teacher; b: Brooklyn, NY; m: Karl; c: Aleksander; ed: Montclair St Univ (BA) Speech, Drama 1970, (MA) Stu Prsnl Svcs 1979; Post Grad Stud; cr: Thomas Edison Elem Speech Therapy Tchr 1970-71; Nishvane Schl Drama Tchr 1971-72; Mt Hebron Schl Drama, Lang Arts Tchr 1972-79; Glenfield Schl Drama, L A Tchr 1979-84, 1989-; Bradford Schl Lang Arts Tchr 1984-89; ai: Directed Musicals; NEA 1970-; office: Glenfield MS 25 Maple Ave Montclair NJ 07042

OZUG, CHARLES DAVID, English Dept Chprsn & Tchr; b: Fall River, MA; m: Mary Ann Pietraszek; c: Matthew, David; ed: Assumption Coll (BA) Eng 1973; Bridgewater St Coll (MAT) Eng 1977; Univ of NH (MA) Eng Writing 1983; Bridgewater St Coll (CAGS) Schl Admin 1994; Enrolled EDD Prgm, Lang Arts, Lit Univ of MA at Lowell; cr: Milton Acad Summer Writing Prgm Tchr 1978-88; Hingham HS Eng Tchr 1973-95; Falmouth HS Dept Chair, Tchr 1995-; ai: NCTE 1975-; MCTE 1980-; Witter Bynner Fnd Poetry Grant 1994-95; Horace Mann Grants; Recipient of Sabbatical Tchng of Writing; Poet of Yr Awd NEATE; office: Falmouth HS Gifford St Falmouth MA 02540

OZUK, CHRISTINE M., English Teacher; b: Findlay, OH; ed: Bluffton Coll (BA) Eng & Communication 1989; Bowling Green St Univ (MS) Eng 1995; cr: Allen East HS Eng Tchr 1989-; ai: Cheerleading Coach; Jr Class Adv; Mentor; office: Allen East HS 105 N Washington St Lafayette OH 45854*

P

PABST, KAREN MARIE, 6th Grade Teacher; b: Ridgewood, NJ; m: Neal; ed: William Paterson St Coll (BA) Early Chldhd 1985; Masters Equivalency Paterson 28 In-Svc Credits; Post Grad Course Dev Psych I 3 Credits; cr: Schl #26 Unassigned Tchr 1985-86; Schl #5 4th Grd Tchr 1986-87, 5th Grd Tchr 1987-91, 6th Grd Tchr 1991-; ai: Tchr Rep Drug, Alcohol Core Team 1993-; 4th Grd Tchr for After Schl Skills Improvement Prgm 1996; Liasion, Chaperone CYTEC Industries; Inspire a Dream Prgm 1995-; NJ Ed Assn, NEA, Paterson Ed Assn 1985-; 1994-95 Governor's Tchr Recognition Awd; 1992 Completed 4MAT-Fundamental Trng Session; home: 633 Indian Rd Wayne NJ 07470*

PACE, CAROLYN WEST, Asst Professor of Humanities; b: Philadelphia, PA; m: Kevin; c: Frances, Daniel; ed: Syracuse Univ (BS) Music 1974, (MA) Art His 1985, (MPhil) Hum, Art His 1993, (ABD) Hum, Art His 1993; cr: Ithaca Coll Adj Prof 1988; Cazenovia Coll Lecturer 1990; Syracuse Univ Instr 1987-90; Mohawk Vly Comm Coll Asst Prof 1990-; ai: Coll Arts Assoc 1991-; Cntrl NY Music Tchr 1986-; Natl Endowment for the Arts, Amer Assoc of Comm, Jr Colls Advancing the Hum Awd 1993; Florence Flwsp; office: Mohawk Valley Comm Coll 1101 Sherman Dr Utica NY 13501

PACE, ELLEN S., Physical Education Teacher; b: Brooklyn, NY; ed: Brooklyn Coll (BS) PE 1977; FL St Univ (MS) Sport Psych 1979; Post Grad Ctr for Mental Hlth NY Clinical Cnslng 1986; Brooklyn Coll Inst for Schls of the Future 1995; cr: Miami-Dade Comm Coll Instr 1979-80; Kaliski Day Cntry Schl Tchr 1980-81; Ditmas Intermediate Schl Tchr, Stu Act Coord 1981-; Luth Med Ctr Cnslr, Tchr 1993-; ai: UFT, AFT 1981-; Amer Cnslng Assn 1986-; Private Psychotherapy Practice 1986-; Natl Distngd Svc Registry Cnslng & Dev 1990; office: Ditmas Intermediate Schl 62 700 Cortelyou Rd Brooklyn NY 11218*

PACE, JOHN P., Professor of Mathematics; b: Newark, NY; m: Herta Georgia; c: Angela, Sarah; ed: NJ Inst of Tech (BS) Industrial Engrng 1965; Montclair St Univ (MA) Math Ed 1969; NJ Inst of Tech (MS) Math

1979; Rutgers (EDD) Math Ed 1989; ID St Univ 18 Credits Dr of Arts in Math; Natl Sager Fnd Chattaqua Short Course in Calculus in Context; *cr:* Essex Cty Coll Instr 1973-79, Asst Prof 1980-85, Assoc Prof 1986-90, Math Prof 1991-; *ai:* Fac Adv, Stu Govt Assn; Fac Newsletter Columnist; NEA 1970-, Local VP; Articles on Math, Math Ed, Educl Psych; Ed Dept Newsletter; Amer Math Assn Founding Ed; Newsletter Reviewer for Math Cmptr Ed at 2 Colls.

PACE, KAREN E., Third Grade Teacher; *b:* Torrington, CT; *ed:* Boston Coll (BA) Elem Ed 1987; Cntrl CT (MS) Rdng 1992; *cr:* Forbes Elem Classroom Tchr 1987-; *ai:* Lang Arts Textbook Adoption & Curr Comms; Torrington Ed Assn 1987-, Sec; NEA, CEA 1987-; Alpha Sigma Nu 1987-; Boston Coll Alumni Assn 1989-, Interviewer; Salvation Army Vol; *office:* Forbes Schl 500 Migeon Ave Torrington CT 06790*

PACE, KAREN GREENE, Fifth Grade Teacher; *b:* Neward, NJ; *m:* Benjamin Albert III; *c:* Daniel, Timothy; *ed:* Montclair Univ (MA) Stu Prsnl Svcs 1991; Masters Plus 30 Admin & Supervision; *cr:* 5-8th Grd Tchr 1983-; *ai:* Stu Govt; Newspaper; Harrison Ed Assn 1993-, Bldg Rep; *office:* Lincoln Schl 15 S Frank Rogers Blvd Harrison NJ 07029*

PACHECO, DEBRA INSLEY, Dance Teacher; *b:* Baltimore, MD; *m:* Carmine Arthur; *c:* Thomas Arthur; *ed:* Goucher Coll (BA) 1980; Dance Masters of Amer Kent St Univ Dance Tchr Cert; *cr:* Anita's Dance Studio Owner, Choreographer, Tchr 20 Yrs; Notre Dame Prep Dance Tchr 2 Yrs; *ai:* Performing & Competition Groups Vol; Natl Assn of Dance & Affiliated Artists 1988-, VP 3 Yrs; *office:* Anita's Dance Studio 8908 Harford Rd Baltimore MD 21234

PACHLA, JAMES DAVID, Mathematics Teacher; *b:* North Tonawanda, NY; *m:* Holly Dilamarter; *ed:* St Univ of NY at Buffalo (MS) Educl Computing 1994; Admin Course; *cr:* Niagara Wheatfield Sr HS Math Tchr 1989-; *ai:* Var Vlybl Coach; AFT 1990-; *home:* 433 Adelaide Pl North Tonawanda NY 14120*

PACHMAN, ARLEEN ROSEN, Fifth Grade Teacher; *b:* Bronx, NY; *c:* Dayna Sloane; *ed:* Natl Coll of Ed (BED) Ed, Math 1966; *cr:* Yonkers Bd of Ed First Grd Tchr 1967-69; Miskayuna Bd of Ed Pre-First Grd Tchr 1969-70; Neshaminy Bd of Ed First, Fourth Grd Tchr1970-72; Bazellel Hebrew Day Schl First Grd Tchr 1972-73; Freehold Reg HS 9-12th Grd Basic Skills Read, Math Tchr 1980-81; Lincroft Elem First, Fifth Grd Tchr 1981-84; Woodland Wlem Fifth Grd Tchr 1984-; *ai:* Monroe Township Ed Assn 1984-; NJ Ed Assn 1980-; B'nai Brith 1970-; Hadassah 1978-; ORT 1970-, VP; Sisterhood B'nai Assn 1977-, VP; *home:* 215 Rutledge Dr Red Bank NJ 07701

PACI, JAMIE AMATO, Spanish Teacher; *b:* Waynesburg, PA; *m:* Anthony Joseph Jr.; *c:* Nicole; *ed:* CA Univ of PA (BS) Span 1970; Masters Equivalent from WV Univ, Western MD & MD St Dept of Ed; *cr:* West Union HS Span & Eng Tchr 1 Yr; Smithsburg HS Span Tchr 23 Yrs; *ai:* Los Conquistadores Span Club, Class of 1994, Prom Promise Adv; AATSP & MFLA 1971-; ACTFL; VFW Ladies Auxiliary 1994-; St Ann Choir 1987-; *office:* Smithsburgh HS 66 N Main St Smithsburg MD 21783*

PACKARD, HARVEY B., History Teacher; *b:* Springfield, MA; *m:* Janet Fessler; *c:* Heidie, Brent; *ed:* Chaminade Coll of Honolulu (BGS) Pol Sci 1974; Naval War Coll at Newport; *cr:* US Coast Guard Surface Operations Ofcr 1959-79; Calvary Chrstn Schl His Tchr 1979-; *ai:* Yrbk & Newsletter Adv; Granite St Challenge Coach; Ret Ofcrs Assn 1994-; Amer Legion 1994-; *office:* Calvary Christian Schl 145 Hampstead Rd Derry NH 03038

PACKARD, TERESA (KORALIN), English Teacher; *b:* Cleveland, OH; *m:* Robert W.; *c:* Nicole, Nathan; *ed:* OH Univ (BSEd) Eng 1966; Attnd Ashland Univ 1992; *cr:* New Philadelphia HS Eng Tchr 1966-69; Fairfield Union HS Eng Tchr 1969-; *ai:* NEA, OEA 1966-; *office:* Fairfield Union Schl 6401 Cincinnati Zanesville Rd Lancaster OH 43130

PACKER, PAULA GRUBB, Associate Professor; *b:* Lock Haven, PA; *m:* Michael E. Packer; *c:* Amanda, Rachael; *ed:* PA St Univ (MED) Curr & Instruction 1974, (DED) Curr & Instruction 1990; *cr:* Asst Prof 1986-93; Early Chldhd Ed Prof Semester Team Ldr 1992-; Assoc Prof 1993-; Early Chldhd Ed Prog Coord 1995-; *ai:* NAEYC; ASCD; ACEI 1990-; Phi Delta Kappa; Keystone Cntrl Schl Dist 1993-, Curr Comm Chair, Inclusion Comm, Vice-Chair of Prsnl, Tech Comm Mem, Vice-Pres of Bd, Chair of Fin Comm, Pres of Bd 1996; Task Force for the Homeless, Bd of Dirs 1991-94, Sec & Treas 1991-92, Vice Pres 1992-93, Pres 1993-94; Young Children & Journal Writing Project with Keystone Cntrl Schl Dist 1992-94; United Way, Bd Mem, Rep for Infant Dev Pgm 1991-93; Phi Delta Kappa Rsrch Awd 1990; Clinton Cty United Way The Process of Filial Therapy Extra Mile Awd for Svc 1993; Grants: PA Higher Ed Initiative 1994-95; PA Higher Initiative 1995-96; *office:* Lock Haven Univ N Fairview St Lock Haven PA 17745

PACKIS, JOHN THOMAS, Physics & Physical Sci Teacher; *b:* Cleveland, OH; *m:* Sandy Elios; *ed:* Cleveland St Univ (BS) Physics 1987; Baldwin Wallace Coll (MA) Supervision 1993; *cr:* Beaumont Schl Physics Tchr 1987-88, Sub 1988-90; Westlake HS Math, Physics Tchr 1990-; *ai:* Acad Challenge Team Adv; Ski Club Chaperone; AAPT 1987-88; NEA 1988-89; Tchr of Yr Nom 2 Yrs; 1st Pl Conf Acad Challenge Team 4 Yrs; *office:* Westlake HS 27830 Hilliard Blvd Westlake OH 44145

PACOS, ROGER L., High School Technology Teacher; *b:* Dunkirk, NY; *ed:* St Univ of NY Coll at Buffalo (BSEd) Tech Ed 1986; Bowling Green St Univ (MED) Career & Tech Ed 1988; NY St Permanent Driver Ed Cert; *cr:* General Dynamics Material Planning Analyst 1988-89; Fredonia Cntrl Schls Tech Tchr 1989-; *ai:* Stu Cncl, Schl Store Adv; Dept Chm; Curr Cncl; Cmptr Comm; Epsilon Pi Tau 1985-; NY St Tech Ed Assn, ITEA 1986-; NYSUT 1989-; Knights of Columbus 1985-; Article Pub; *office:* Fredonia Sr HS 425 E Main St Fredonia NY 14063

PACSI, FRAN, Computer Education Teacher; *b:* Farrell, PA; *m:* Robert A.; *c:* Rob, Stephanie; *ed:* Mercyhurst Coll (BA) Elem Ed 1969; 15 Addl Credit Hrs John Carroll Univ Admin; *cr:* Irving Pub Schls First Grd Tchr 1969-70; St Joseph Grd Schl Seventh, Eighth Grd Tchr 1972-77; Eber Baker MS Sixth Grd Tchr 1977-81; St Monica Schl Sixth Grd Tchr 1981-89, Cmptr Sci Tchr, 8th Grd Algebra, Math Tchr 1989-; *ai:* HS, Fac, Media & Tech, Schl Test Coords; Soc Comm, Magazine Drive Chms; Schl Newspaper Adv; Schl Discipline Prgm, Before & After Care Prgm Dirs; NEA 1969-; NCEA 1972-; ASCD 1980-; St Monica PTU 1981-; St Monica Parent Advy Bd 1993-; Jr Womans Guild 1979-; WJW Channel 8 TV We Salute Tchrs Awd; Marion City Schls Tchr Excl Awd.*

PACZKOSKI, RICHARD, Fifth Grade Teacher; *b:* Brooklyn, NY; *m:* Anita Snyder; *c:* Cheryl Lee; *ed:* Lehman Coll (BA) Pol Sci 1971; Univ of Western CT (MA) Elem Ed 1974; Attnd Sci Inst 1994; *cr:* Mahopac Pub Schl 4th-6th Grd Tchr 1971-; *ai:* Sci, Mahopac Dist Report Card Comms; AFT, NYSUT 1971-; Fulmar Rd PTO; Natl Schl of Excl Awd Writing Team.

PADALINO, LEO P., Retired HS Social Studies Tchr; *b:* Brooklyn, NY; *m:* Carla J.; *c:* Mary Elizabeth, Lisa Rose, Deborah Anne; *ed:* Fordham Univ (BS) Ed 1962, (MS) Admin 1968; *cr:* Long Beach HS Soc Stud Tchr 1962-95; *ai:* NYS United Tchrs 1962-.

PADDOCK, SHERRI M., Mathematics Teacher; *b:* Anchorage, AK; *ed:* Springfield Coll (BS) Scndry Ed, Math 1991, (MED) Ed 1992; *cr:* HS of Commerce Math Tchr 1990-91; Morris Hills HS Math Tchr 1992-; *ai:* Girls Cross Cntry, Indoor, Outdoor Track & Field Head Coach; Morris Cty Track Coaches Assoc VP; NJEA 1994-; NCTM, AMTNJ 1992-; Daily Record Girls Track & Field Coach of Yr 1995; *office:* Morris Hills HS 520 W Main St Rockaway NJ 07866

PADOBRICK, GARY W., 7th Grade Math Teacher; *b:* Sharon, PA; *c:* Nicole Lynn; *ed:* Edinboro Univ (BA) Ed 1970; Slippery Rock Univ (MS) Spec Ed 1977; Attnd Intermediate Unit IV, IN Wesleyan Univ; *cr:* Farrell Area Schl Elem, Spec Ed, Pre-Algebra Tchr 1970-; *ai:* Ftbl, Track Coach; Chess Club Adv; Friday Dress Down Fund Comm; NEA, PSEA 1970-; Sr Class Tchr Made the Most Impact on Their Lives 1992; *home:* 2775 Michael Ln Hermitage PA 16148

PADOVANO, ANTHONY T., Professor of Lit & Rel Studies; *b:* Harrison, NJ; *m:* Theresa Lackamp; *c:* Mark Anthony, Andrew, Paul, Rosemarie; *ed:* Seton Hall Univ (BA) Classical Langs 1956; Gregorian Univ (STB) Theology 1958, (STL) Theology 1960, (STD) Theology 1962; St Thomas Intnl Univ (MA) Philosophy 1962; NY Univ (MA) Lit 1971; Fordham Univ (PHD) Lit 1980; *cr:* USA Colls & Univs Visiting Prof; *ai:* Lit Chprsn; Danforth Fellow; Numerous Books & Articles Pub; Natl Cath Book, Golden Angel Holywood & Fred & Florence Thomas Awds; *home:* 9 Millstone Dr Morris Plains NJ 07950*

PADUANO, LESLIE MARIE, Health & Physical Ed Teacher; *b:* Newport, RI; *ed:* IN Univ of PA (BS) Hlth, PE 1987; Shippensburg Univ Spec Ed; *cr:* Silver Springs Elem Schl K-5 Elem PE Tchr 1988-; *ai:* Coaching Var Girls Bsktbl, Soccer; Elem Bsktbl Coord; Township Soccer Coach; PSEA, NEA 1988-; Inclusion Awd 1994-95; *home:* 329 Lamp Post Ln Camp Hill PA 17011

PADWA, LINDA BAUM, Science Teacher; *b:* London, England; *m:* Stephen L.; *c:* Daniel, Robin, Howard; *ed:* Queens Coll (BA) Chem 1967; Harvard Univ (MAT) Sci Ed 1968; *cr:* Suffolk Cty Comm Coll Adjunct Staff 1973-87; Port Jefferson Pub Schls Sci Tchr 1987-; *ai:* MS, HS Acad Team Coach; Regnl Quiz Bowl Founder, Dir; STANYS; ACS; AAUW; NSTA; Gender Equity in Math, Sci Seminar, Chem Ed Wkshps for Tchrs; NY St Mentor for Chem Estrn Suffolk BOCES; Recpt of CMA Regl Catalyst Awd 1994; *office:* Port Jefferson MS, HS Old Post Rd Port Jefferson NY 11777

PAGANO, ANNETTE MAYO, Instructor; *b:* Brooklyn, NY; *m:* Robert G.; *c:* Gavin Mc Gerald, Avery Mc Gerald, Tucker Mc Gerald, Thomas; *ed:* Nassau Comm Coll (AAS) ECE 1972; Rivier Coll (BS) Psych 1985, (MA) Cnslng 1987; Fielding Inst PHD Candidate Human Dev; *cr:* Growing Tree Child Dev Ctr Dir, Owner 1976-83; Wang Labs Inc Ed Specialist 1984-88; Mount St Mary Guid Dir 1989-90; Rivier Coll Instr, Acad Adv, Adult Stu Recruiter 1991-; *home:* 24 Swart Ter Nashua NH 03060

PAGANO, JOAN ROMANO, Fourth Grade Teacher; *b:* Newark, NJ; *m:* Frank; *c:* Richard, Thomas; *ed:* Kean Coll (BA) Elem Ed 1967; 36 Grad Credits MS Equivalency; *cr:* CT Farms Schl Third Grd Tchr 1967-77, Fourth Grd Tchr 1977-; *ai:* NEA, NJEA, UTEA 1967-; Alpha Delta Kappa 1978-, Treas; *office:* Connecticut Farms Elem Schl 711 Stuyvesant Ave Union NJ 07083

PAGE, B. LOUISE DAVIS, 4th Grade Teacher; *b:* Pittsburgh, PA; *c:* Daniel S.; *ed:* CA St Coll (BSEd) Elem Ed 1965; 24 Post Grad Credits Penn St Univ; *cr:* Young Sch Dist 7th-8th Grd Rdng Tchr 2 Yrs; Laurel Highlands Schl Dist 4th Grd Tchr 27 Yrs; *ai:* Co-operating Classroom Tchr for Penn St Univ Stu; NEA, PSEA, LHEA Local 1969-; Grace Brethren Church 1991-, Bible & Sunday Schl Tchr, Jr Church, Girls Club; *home:* RR 1 Box 170A Vanderbilt PA 15486

PAGE, ELMA MAY, Sixth Grade Science Teacher; *b:* Wilmington, DE; *m:* Richard; *c:* Richard Brian, Robert Michael; *ed:* Univ of DE (BS) Elem Ed 1966; Post-Grad Stud; *cr:* Baltz Schl 3rd Grd Tchr 1966-71; St Helena's Schl 4th-6th Grd Tchr 1981-85; St John's Schl 6th Grd Tchr 1985-88; Stanton MS 6th Grd Tchr 1988-; *ai:* Team Ldr; Sci Club Spon; Sci Olympiad Coach; DTS 1981-; NEA 1988-; EPA Region III Conservation Tchr of Yr; Red Clay Schl Dist Tchr of Yr; DE Nature Ctr Tchr of Yr; *office:* Stanton MS 1800 Limestone Rd Wilmington DE 19804

PAGE, HARRIET, Science Teacher; *b:* Newburyport, MA; *m:* Harold J.; *c:* James, Janine, Joseph; *ed:* Emmanuel Coll (BA) Chem 1969; Northeastern Univ Schl of Pharmacy & Allied Hlth Scis (MS) Medicinal Chem 1976; *cr:* Notre Dame Acad Chem, Physics Tchr 1969-72; Marblehead HS Chem Tchr 1976-77, 1989-90, 1995-; Our Lady of Nazareth Acad Chem, Physics Tchr 1990-91, Math & Sci Dept Chprsn 1992-94; Lynnfield HS Chem Tchr 1994-95; *ai:* NHS, Environmental Club Moderator; Earth Shuttle Adv; NSTA, Natl Assn of Stu Act Advs, MA Assn of Sci Tchrs, NCEA 1990-; Natl Sci Supvrs Assn, Natl Assn of Scndry Schl Prins, North Shore Sci Supvrs Assn, MA Assn of Sci Supvrs 1993-; North Shore Physics Tchr Assn 1992-; Marblehead PAC 1992-; *office:* Marblehead High School Duncan Sleigh Square Marblehead MA 01945

PAGE, LYMAN ALEXANDER, Associate Professor; *b:* San Francisco, CA; *m:* Elizabeth Olson; *c:* Brent, James, William; *ed:* Bowdoin Coll (BA) Physics 1978; MIT (PHD) Physics 1989; *cr:* MIT Post-Doc 1989-90; Princeton Univ Instr 1990-91, Asst Prof 1991-95, Assoc Prof 1995-; *ai:* Adv Undergraduates; Undergraduate Tchng Awds; Cottrell Flwshp; David & Lucile Packard Flwshp; Natl Young Investigator; *office:* Princeton Univ Dept of Physics PO Box 430 Princeton NJ 08544

PAGE, VIRGINIA VANDERWARKER, Earth Science Teacher; *b:* Taunton, MA; *m:* Gene Field; *ed:* Bridgewater St Coll (BS) Geography, Earth Sci 1962, (MS) Scndry Ed 1964; Fordham Univ (MS) Spec Ed 1985; Attnd MS St Univ, Coll of St Rose, Ithaca Coll, Pratt Coll of Sci & Engineering, St Univ of NY at New Paltz; *cr:* Cohannet Schl Geography, Sci Tchr 1963-66; Roy C. Ketcham HS Earth Sci Tchr 1967-68; John Jay Sr HS Earth Sci Tchr 1969-; *ai:* AFT; NY St United Tchrs; Natl Ea Sci Tchrs; Sci Tchrs Assn of NYS; Eastern & Amer Fed Mineralogical Socs; Editorial Collaborator; Bk Co-Auth; *home:* 2 Haskins Pl Beacon NY 12508

PAGLIA, RHONDA THOMPSON, 4th Grade Teacher; *b:* Greenville, PA; *m:* Anthony G.; *c:* Anthony, Cara, Jessica; *ed:* Univ of VA, Slippery Rock Univ, Clarion Univ, Carlow Coll Credits Masters Equivalency St of PA Elem Ed; *cr:* Greenville Schl Dist Elem Tchr 1971-73; Fairfax Cty Schl Dist Elem Tchr 1973-75; Heritage Schl Dist Elem Tchr 1985-; *ai:* Bus Owner; St Johns Recorder Consort; Notre Dame Folkgroup; Former Girls Sftbl Coach, Shenango Vly Chorale, Mentor Tchr; PSEA, NEA, HEA 1985-; St Johns Recorder Consort 1985-; Notre Dame Hope Line 1994-, Comm Co-Head; Hermitage Girls Sftbl League, Team Coach; Notre Dame Choir 1991-; Thanks to Tchrs Finalist 1991; *office:* Hermitage Elem Schl 233 N Hermitage Rd Hermitage PA 16148

PAGLIONE, LORI, French Teacher; *b:* Leamington, CN; *ed:* Rowan Coll of NJ (BA) Fr Lang Lit 1990; K-12 Tchr Cert, Grad Prgm Scndry Schl Admin; *cr:* Collingswood HS Fr Tchr 1991-; *ai:* Fr Club Adv; Prepare Stdnts Natl Fr Exams; Induct Stdnts Natl Fr Hnr Soc; Fr Exch Prgm Coord; Bldg Improvement Team, Liaison Comms; AATF, FLENJ 1991-; Phi Delta Kappa 1994-; Tchr of Yr 1993-94; Fr Lang, Lit Excl 1990; *home:* 164 Tavistock Cherry Hill NJ 08034

PAGLIUCA, RICHARD, Guidance Counselor; *b:* Flushing, NY; *ed:* Central Ct St Univ (BS) Elem Ed 1970, (MS) Guid 1972; *cr:* St Paul Jr HS Elem Schl Tchr 1970-75; St Thomas Aquinas HS Guid Cnslr 1975-76; St Bernard HS Guid Cnslr 1976-; *ai:* Co-owner of Slamma Jamma Bsktbl Camps for Girls, Boys; *home:* 9 MacKenzie Rd Waterford CT 06385

PAGNANELLI, EDWARD VICTOR, High School Math Teacher; *b:* Steubenville, OH; *ed:* Franciscan Univ of Steubenville (BA) His, Math Ed 1974; Univ of Notre Dame Engrng, Bus Admin; Post Grad Stud Univ of Dayton Cnslng; Post Grad Stud OH St Univ Cmptr Ed; C Calculator OH St Univ Seminar & Ed; *cr:* Holy Rosary Elem Schl Grd Math, His Tchr, Bsbl Coach 1976-79; Bishop Ready HS M Tchr, Bsbl, Cross Cntry 1979-85; Columbus Schl for Girls Ma Bsktbl Coach 1985-86; Bishop Ready HS Math Tchr, Dept Chpr Coach 1986-; *ai:* Var Bsbk Coach; Jr House Adv; Sr Homeroom A Advy Bd; Acad Cncl Comm; Natl Hnr Soc Selection Comm; Fac C Blue Ribbon Schl Application; Math-A-Thon Chprsn; NCTM, OH 1980-; OH HS Ath Assn, OH HS Bsbl Coaches Assn 1979-; Hub 1986-, Dist All-Star Game Ofcl 1995; OH Historieon Soc 1994-, Cntrl OH Radio Rdng Svc 1988-, Vol Svc; Natl Fed of Inter Sc Ofcls Assn 1986-; Bishop Ready Awd of Achvmt for Tchng Excl; Vlybl Assn Officiated Sect Dist 1992-95, Regnl 1995; Bsbl Coa Runner-up 1982, St Semi Finalist 1984, League Champion 1990 Corp Outstdng Math Tchr Finalist 1993; *office:* Bishop Ready Salisbury Rd Columbus OH 43204*

PAGNANO, KAREN B., Health, PE Teacher & Coach; *b:* Boston, M Springfield Coll (BS) PE 1988; Univ of ME Adapted PE Pgrm 19 Medomak Vly HS Hlth & PE Tchr, Var Soccer, Gymnastics, Track 1988-; *ai:* PAWS Adv; Gymnastic KVAC League Champions 1994; KVAC Champions 1995; Ran Boston Marathon 1995; *home:* 5 Augusta Rd Waldoboro ME 04572*

PAGNI, ELIZABETH M., 6th & 8th Grd Math Teacher; *b:* Gro PA; *m:* Reni A.; *c:* Charlotte, Cheri Griffith, Anne Reiplinger, Mitchell, Matthew; *ed:* Slippery Rock Univ (BS) Elem Ed & Spcl E (ME) Rdng Specialist 1976; *cr:* Slipperty Rock MS 6th Grd Ma 1971-94, 6th & 8th Grd Math Tchr 1994-; *ai:* Former Gifted Coo Yrs; PSEA 1971-, Bldg Rep; *office:* Slippery Rock MS Keister Rd S Rock PA 16057

PAGONIS, LOUIS, Teacher; *b:* Kriopigi Karditsis, Greece; *m:* V *c:* Dean, Zoe; *ed:* Montclair St Univ (BA) Pol Sci, Soc Stud 197 York Univ (MA) Pol Sci 1975, (PHD) Pol Sci 1980; Montclair St U Stud Cert; *cr:* Cresskill HS Tchr 1977-; Montclair St Univ Adj Prof Union Coll Adj Prof 1977-83; New York Univ Adj Prof 19 Bloomfield Coll Adj Prof 1986-87; *ai:* Stu Govt Adv; NJEA, NEA VP; AAVP; Constitutions of the Countries of the World Greece, W Rights and Political Participation in Europe, The Problem of War a Issue, War & War Prevention Author; *office:* Cresskill HS 1 Linc Cresskill NJ 07626

PAICE, BETTE S., Fifth Grade Teacher; *b:* Baldwinsville, NY; *m:* C F.; *c:* Kim, Richard, Courtney, Brett; *ed:* St Univ of NY at Osweg Ed N-6 1985, (MS) Ed N-6 1992; *cr:* North Rose Elem 5th Grd Tchr 4th Grd Tchr 1 Yr; *ai:* His Bowl Coach; Dist Curr Cncl Rep for Invention Convention Chm; Seven Stu Tchrs Master Tchr; NEA Local Tchrs Assn 1985-; *office:* North Rose Elem Schl Salter rd Nort NY 14516*

PAIGE, PAMELA ARCHAMBAULT, Spcl Education & English T Woonsocket, RI; *m:* Gregg; *c:* Rebecca, Gregg, Jonathan; *ed:* Newpo (BA) Spec Ed 1980; Attnd Salva Regina Univ Elem Ed, Soc Providence Coll 21 Credits, RI Coll 9 Credit Hrs; *cr:* Woonsocket M Ed Tchr 1980-81; Winsed Schl HS Spec Ed Tchr 1981-82; Globe Park Schl Presch Tchr 1982-84; Woonsocket MS Spec Ed Tchr 1990-; *a* Field Hockey, MS Sftbl Coach; Woonsocket N Stars Yth Hockey 19 of Dir, Tournament Dir; *home:* 75 Halsey Rd Woonsocket RI 02895

PAINTER, ALICE MANEY, First Grade Teacher; *b:* Asheville, N George R.; *c:* Karen Painter Scarpignato, Keith; *ed:* Meredith Coll Elem Ed 1961; Attnd Loyola Coll; *cr:* Louise Luxford Elem Schl 4 Tchr 1961-62; Clarence Poe Elem Schl 4th Grd Tchr 1962-63; Brook Elem Schl 4th Grd Tchr 1963-65; Atholton Elem Schl 1st Grd 1977-79; Clemens Crossing Elem Schl 1st Grd Tchr 1979-85; Bushy Elem Schl 1st Grd Tchr 1985-; *ai:* NEA; MSTA; HCEA; *office:* Park Elem Schl 2670 Rt 97 Glenwood MD 21738

PAINTER, CAROLYN WILSON, Lang Arts & Gifted Teach Canton, OH; *m:* William E.; *c:* Kimberly, Wm; *ed:* Kent St (BSEd) Speech, Ed 1971; Ashland Univ Grad Hrs; *cr:* Stow City Schls Scndr Tchr 1980-88, Eng, Gifted Tchr 1989-; *ai:* Cheerleading Coach; Fac Comm; OH Future Problem Solving Coach; NEA, OEA 1980-; Cuy First Meth Church 1976-; Children's Med Ctr of Akron 1980-; Kimpton MS 380 N River Rd Munroe Falls OH 44262

PAIR, GLENN CLEVELAND, Social Studies Teacher; *b:* Emporia *m:* Beverly Stewart; *c:* Shayla, Glenn II; *ed:* Saint Paul's Coll (BS) P Ed 1972; Bowie St Univ (MS) Sec Ed, Admin, Superv 1979; *cr:* Clark Elem Schl Tchr 1972-73; Northeast HS Tchr 1973-; *ai:* Frosh Class Close Up Club Founder, Adv; Frosh Interdisciplinary Team C Multicultural Liason Tchr; NEA 1973-; TAAAC 1973-, Rep; Faith Church, Trustee; Faith Ame Church Man of Yr; Faith Chrstn Boys Ministry Dir, Founder.*

PAJAK, LOUISE BEARS, Orchestra Director; *b:* Summit, NJ; *m:* Alan; *c:* Johanna; *ed:* Hartt Schl (BM) Music 1978; Univ of NH Music 1990; *cr:* Atkinson Acad Music Tchr 1978-82; Timberlane Sch Strings Tchr 1982-86; Timberland MS, HS Orch Dir 1987-; *ai:* HS A Spring Musical Music Dir; AFT 1993-; MENC 1978-, Cert Mus Ed; Music Honor Soc 1996-; *office:* Timberlane Regional H S 36 Green Rd Plaistow NH 03865

PAKALUK, MICHAEL, Associate Prof of Philosophy; *b:* Mineola *m:* Ruth VanKooy; *c:* Michael, Maximilian, John Henry, Maria, Th Sarah, Sophia; *ed:* Harvard (AB) Philosophy 1980, (PHD) Philos 1988; Edinburg (M Litt) Philosophy 1982; *cr:* Clark Univ Asst 1988-94, Assoc Prof 1994-; Brown Univ Visiting Prof 1995; *ai:* BA 1988-, Dir; APPI 1990-, Founding Mem; Worcester Public Lib 1995 of Dir; Marshall Schlrshp; *office:* Clark Univ 950 Main St Worceste 01610

PALADINO, RICHARD, Physical Education Teacher; *b:* Port Che NY; *m:* Joyce Traverse; *c:* Lisa P. Verboys, Ricky; *ed:* Plymouth St (BED) PE 1967; Grad Work, Permanent Cert NY Univ, Univ of Bridge *cr:* Rye Neck HS Head Ftbl Coach 1974-79; Fordham Schl Asst Ftbl C 1980-83; Scarsdale HS Head Ftbl Coach 1984-93; Fox Lane HS Coach 1967-; *ai:* Ski, Golf Coach; Section One Ftbl Coaches 1967-; Ftbl Fnd 1970-; Metropolitan Golf Assn 1976-; Gannett Newspaper, Daily News, Cable 3 TV Ftbl Coach of Yr 1987; *office:* Fox Lane H 172 Bedford NY 10506*

PALAGYI, LORNA (HAAPANEN), Fourth Grade Teacher; *b:* Conne OH; *m:* James A.; *c:* Lisa Mathews, Wendy, Paul; *ed:* Kent St Univ Elem Ed 1963; 46 Post Grad Hrs Elem Ed; *cr:* Red Bird Elem 5th Grd 1963-66, Math Tutor & Sub Tchr 1969-84; Madison Meml MS Math 1986-87; North Madison Elem 4th Grd Tchr 1987-; *ai:* ASCD 19 Madison Ed Assn; NME Parent-Tchr Org; Meals on Wheels Sub; Mad Ed Fnd Grant-Playground Map; Madison Educators Awd 1988 & Banking Prgm; OH Hall of Fame Schl Awd; *home:* 6142 Little Green Madison OH 44057

PALAKOVICH, FRANK EMIL, Fifth Grade Teacher; *b:* Rochester, *m:* Betty J.Thompson; *c:* Frank, Lori; *ed:* Geneva Coll (BA) His, Soc 1964; PA St (ME) Elem, Psych 1968; Slippery Rock (MS) Elem Ed 1 *cr:* Rochester Area Schls 6th Grd Tchr 1964-72, 4-8th Grd Sci 1973-82, 5th Grd Tchr 1983-; *ai:* Run Scoreboard For BSktbl Pr ic Planning Comm; RAEA, PSEA, NEA 1964-; Croatian Lodge 85 lia's Church 1965-; Perfect Attnd Awds; Amer Family Inst Gift of rgm; *home:* 702 Elm St Rochester PA 15074

ZZO, JOSEPHINE MELE, Fourth Grade Teacher; *b:* Youngstown, Joseph Anthony; *c:* Kimberly Howe; *ed:* Youngstown St Univ (BS) 3; Diocese of Youngstown (MA) Rel Ed 1982; Youngstown St Univ rad Stud Ed; *cr:* Immaculate Conception Schl Third Grd Tchr 4, Sixth Grd Tchr 1974-88, Fourth, Fifth Grd Tchr 1988-92, Fourth chr 1992-; *ai:* Chprsn Fund Raising Events Center City Schls stown OH; ICS Rep to Mahoning Cty Math Wkshps; Chprsn ICS Concerts; Mentor Youngstown St Univ Stu Tchrs; IRA 1973-; Eastern OH Cncl of Tchrs of Math, OCEA 1974-; Magna Cum Youngstown St Univ 1973-; Youngstown Cursillio 1970-; St ay's Parish 1927-, Latin Culture Fnd 1960-; Youngstown Urban Cath ng 1995-; Deans List Youngstown St Univ 1969-73; Vienna Boys 1995; Hiram Coll Cert of Recognition Prof Svc to Ed of Tchrs; *home:* olonial Dr Youngstown OH 44505*

HO, KAREN D., Art Teacher; *b:* Pittsburgh, PA; *ed:* PA St Univ rt Ed for Soc & Culutural Agencies 1982; Kuztown Univ (MED) Art 0; *cr:* NU Art Graphics Screen Printer; Kelsch Assocs Soc Worker; issing Area HS Art Tchr 1987-; Amer Intnl Schl of Luxembourg g Art Tchr 1992-93; *ai:* Art Club Adv Stu Art Collection, Outreach Natl Cncl for Ed in Ceramic Arts; NEA 1986-; Natl & PA St Art Ed 987-, Presenter 1994-95; Berks Art Cncl 1993-; Penn St Berks Fine ncl 1994-, Ed Coord; Wyomissing Inst of Art 1988-, Presenter 1990; Grout-Kauffman Exhibit Awd Penn St Berks; Regnl, Local Presentor Curr & Nicaraguan Ceramics; 1992 Cncl for Basic Ed & Natl ment for Arts Grant; *office:* Wyomissing Area Jr Sr HS 630 Evans yomissing PA 19610*

ZAK, STUART JOHN, Social Studies Teacher; *b:* Amsterdam, NY; anna; *ed:* St Univ of NY at Albany (BA) Pol Sci 1987, (MA) Ed 1988; atego Jr Sr HS Soc Stud Tchr 1989; Amsterdam HS Soc Stud Tchr *ai:* Asst Var Wrestling Coach; Class 1993 Adv; Yth Cart HS Coord; Task Force; Bldg Rep; AFT & NYSUT 1989-; NY St Cncl for Soc 1992-; Section II Asst Wrestling Coach of the Yr 1995; *office:* rdam HS Saratoga Ave Amsterdam NY 12010*

EY, THOMAS JOSEPH, Sixth Grade Teacher; *b:* Ashley, PA; *m:* rine Regan; *c:* Thomas Jr., Cassie, Grant, Regan; *ed:* Wilkes Coll Scndry Ed 1965; Elem Ed Cert NJ & PA; *cr:* Kingwood Twp Elem ixth Grd Tchr 1965-70; Wilkes-Barre Area Schl Dist Sixth Grd Tchr *ai:* Dodson Safety Patrol Supvr; Wilkes-Barre Area Ed Assn, PA Ed PSEA 1970-; NEA 1965; Hanover Twp Reycling Comm 1 Yr; Albright Church 1990-, Youth Supvr 2 Yrs, Admin Bd 2 Yrs, Bd of Trustees 2 Meth Urban Ministry Rep 2 Yrs; Environmental Awd for Outstanding rvation Tchr from Luzerne Cty Conservation Dist; Steering Comm s-Barre Areas MS Evaluation 1982-83; Mid Sts Evaluation Team 84; *home:* 22 High St Wilkes Barre PA 18702

NKAS, ALEXIS M., 6th Grade Teacher; *b:* Passaic, NJ; *ed:* Wm on Coll (BA) Elem Ed 1968; Long Island Univ (MS) Ed 1991; *cr:* rn Elem Schl Tchr 1968-92; Thomas Jefferson MS Tchr 1993-95; *ai:* 1968-; NJEA & BCEA 1968-; FLEA 1968-; City of Hackensack & Co-Op Unit Owners Advy Bd 1990-, Chprsn; *office:* Thomas son MS 35-01 Morlot Ave Fair Lawn NJ 07410

KA, JANET WIGHT, Assoc Professor of Biology; *b:* Pittsburgh, PA; rl J.; *c:* John J., William C., Timothy A.; *ed:* PA St Univ (BA) Bio Duquesne Univ (MS) Physiology 1968; Univ of Pittsburgh Post Grad *cr:* Chatham Coll Instr 1980-85; Comm Coll of Allegheny Cty Assoc 987-; *ai:* Acad Adv; Phi Theta Kappa Spon; Acad Affairs Comm; Phi Kappa Distngd Adv Mid Sts 1995; *office:* Comm Coll Algny Co Cmps 808 Ridge Ave Pittsburgh PA 15212

KOVIC, CAROL LEE, English Teacher; *b:* Breckenridge, MN; *m:* hy John; *c:* Antonia, Matthew; *ed:* Moorhead St Univ (BS) Eng 1971; burgh St Univ (MS) Ed 1976; 24 Addl Hrs Cmptr Literacy, Writing; eru Cntrl Schl Eng Tchr, Dept Chair 1973-; Plattsburgh St Univ Adj eech, Comm 1981; Isothermal Comm Coll Adj in Eng & Speech 87; *ai:* Bldg, Liaison, Schl Musical Make-up Comms; Lobby Day PAT's Team Literacy Bowl; Presentation Hode Podge Books Whole Wkshp; NEA, NEA, NY 1973-; Peru Assn of Tchrs 1973-, Bldg VP, Grant GATE; 2 SARA Grant Wkshps; *office:* Peru Central Schl 17 ol St Peru NY 12972

LADINO, ANTHONY, Third Grade Teacher; *b:* Brooklyn, NY; *ed:* St Univ (BS) Elem Ed 1968; C W Post (MS) Elem Ed 1971; Attnd phi Univ 45 Hrs Beyong MS; *cr:* Floral Pakr Bellerose 3rd Grd Tchr -73, 4th Grd Tchr 1973-75, 6th Grd Tchr 1975-76, 3rd Grd Tchr 1976-; YSUT 1971-; AFT 1971-, Union Pres; *office:* Floral Pk-Bellerose Schl Ave Floral Park NY 11001

LADINO, JOAN PHELPS, Professor & Dance Pgm Coord; *b:* New ord, CT; *ed:* Springfield Coll (BS) Dance, PE 1964; 14 Credit Hrs os Pillow; MA Equivalency Plus 30 Addl Credit Hrs Dance Stud; *cr:* Coll Coord of Dance, Dir Tchr Choreographer1964-; USA dencies Dir, Tchr Choreographer Modern Dance 1964-; Television s on Role of Dance in Ed 1966-80; *ai:* Ed Comm Bd of Trustees; e Co Dir; Strategic Plng; Reacreditation Steering Comm; Dance dicator New England & Caribbean; MA Assn of Hlth, PE Rec & Dance -75, Dance Chair; New England Fnd for Arts 1975-80, Panelist; MA nce for Arts Ed 1973-82, Treas; Danny Sloan Dance Co 1981-88, Bd ir, Chair; Researching Dances of the Caribbean; Who's Who in Amer en; World Who's Who of Women in Ed; Notable Amer Awd; Honorary Alumna; 12 Original Dance Productions; 10 New Choreographies -; *office:* Dean Coll 99 Main St Franklin MA 02038*

LADINO, MARY SWEET, Mathematics Teacher; *b:* Elizabeth, NJ; obert T. (dec); *c:* Timothy, Susan, Joseph; *ed:* Univ of Notre Dame Math 1975; Allentown Coll of St Francis de Sales (MED) Comps in 995; 30 Post-Grad Credits Penn St, East Stroudsburg & West Chester ; *cr:* AT&T Engrng Assoc 1975-78; Bell of PA Engrng Assoc 1978-79; ertown Area Schl Dist Long-Term Sub Tchr 1989-90; St Pius X HS & Sci Tchr 1990-91; Spring-Ford HS Math Tchr 1991-; *ai:* Radio Moderator; Acad Team Coach; New Tchrs Mentor; Bldg Level Tech d; NCTM 1975-; ATMOPAV 1990-; *office:* Spring-Ford HS 413 S is Rd Royersford PA 19468

LADINO, ROSEANNE M., Social Worker & Counselor; *b:* abeth, NJ; *m:* Anthony V.; *c:* Mary K., Robin L., Aime E., Ann V.; *ed:* rini Coll (BS) Ed 1962; Rutgers Univ (MSW) Soc Work 1989; Attnd rgian Court Coll Post Grad, Ocean Cty Coll Humanistic Stud, okdale Comm Coll; *cr:* 6th-8th Grd Tchr 1962-69; Real Estate Vol & Tchr 1970-85; Private Schl sex Ed Tchr 1985-89; CST Soc Worker & r 1989-; *ai:* Private Cnslng Bus 5 Yrs; Clinical License Soc Worker SW; NASW 1989-; NJEA, NEA 1962-; NJSW 1989-; Brisbane Child atment Ctr, Bd of Trustees; TAP, Bd of Trustees; Awd for Appreciation Boyton Bros Bus; Appreciation Plaques from Various Org & PTAs; ships for Tchr in Other Dists; *office:* Brick Twp HS 346 Chambersbridge Brick NJ 08723

LANT, MARILEE LEHMAN, English Teacher; *b:* Dayton, OH; *c:* Lynn; *ed:* Ohio Univ at Athens (BS) Comprehensive Eng & Ed 1969; phen F Austin St Univ at Nacogdoches (MA) Amer Lit & Writing 1973; d Miami Univ at Oxford, Wright St Univ at Dayton, OH St Univ at Columbus; *cr:* Vinton G Consolidated HS Eng Tchr 1967-; Franklin-Monroe HS Eng Tchr 1968-69; Arcanum HS Eng Tchr & Dept Chprsn 1973-86; Writer Poet Free Lance 1978-; Tippecanoe HS Eng Tchr 1986-; *ai:* Birdbark Lit Magazine Adv; Prins Advy Comm; Verse Writers Guild of OH 1978-; NFSPS 1978-; OH Writing Fellow Miami Univ OH Writing Project 1984-; Natl Endowment for Hum Flwshp 1984; Outstdng Scndry Lang Arts Tchr for OH 1993 OCTELA; Ashland Oil Co Tchr of Yr 1994; Sega Schl Sci-Mat Flwshp Cncl for Basic Ed 1994; OH Arts Cncl Flwshp Tchr & Writer 1995; Poems Pub; *office:* Tippecanoe HS 555 N Hyatt St Tipp City OH 45371*

PALLANTE, MARTHA IRENE, Assistant Professor of History; *b:* Youngstown, OH; *m:* Glen A. Schaefer; *c:* Sara Schaefer, Laura Schaefer, Paula Schaefer; *ed:* Youngstown St Univ (BA) His & Anthropology 1977; Coll of William & Mary (MA) His & Historical Archaeology 1982; Univ of PA (PHD) Amer His 1988; *cr:* Penn St Visiting Asst Prof 1992-93; Hiram Coll Asst Prof 1984-91; Youngstown St Univ Asst Prof 1991-; *ai:* Fac Adv to Stu Govt; Acad Rsrch & Animal Care & Use Comms Am Studiest Bd; His Day; Niles Fire Brick Project; Adv to Womens His Collective; Phi Alpha Theta; Amer Hist Assoc; Org of Amer Historians; Amer Stud Assoc; Womens Hlth Information Network 1993-, Trustee; Natl Breast Cancer Coalition 1993-, Coord for OH; Numerous Articles Pub; *office:* Youngstown St Univ 539 De Bartolo Hall Youngstown OH 44555*

PALLANTE, MARY R., Supervisor of Student Teachers; *b:* Newark, NJ; *m:* Michael A.; *c:* Michael C., Paul, James; *ed:* Caldwell Coll (BA) His 1956; Seton Hall Univ (MA) His 1963; Univ of HI Supervision, Admin 12 Hrs; Jersey City St Coll Career Ed 12 Hrs; *cr:* Weequhic HS Soc Tchr 1956-75; Newark Bd of Ed Soc Stud Supvr 1971-72; Montville HS Soc Stud Tchr 1975-95; Coll of St Elizabeth Supvr of Stu Tchng 1995-; *ai:* Former Mem Bicentennial Club, Jerseymen Historical Club, Presidential Debate, Amnesty Intnl, Debate, Stu Cncl, NHS; NJEA 1975-, Local Treas; Delta Epsilon Sigma, Kappa Gamma Delta 1956-; Young Dems, St Committeewoman; PTA, Treas, Sec; Outstdng Tchr 1965-; NJ Governor's Tchr Recognition Prgm: Selection 1974, Nom Several Times; 8 Practice Tchrs; Bell Atlantic Scholar Presidential Classroom 1990; Morris Cty Alcohol, Drug Abuse Schlsp Rutgers Univ 1990; *office:* Coll of St Elizabeth 2 Convent Rd Morristown NJ 07045*

PALLO, JANET LEE, 5th Grade Teacher; *b:* Ashtabula, OH; *m:* John David; *c:* Matthew Jason; *ed:* Kent St (BA) Ed 1968; Garfield Sr Coll (MS) Ed 1977; 36 Addl Hrs Varous Inst John Carroll, Case, Edinburough; *cr:* North Kingsville Schl 5 Grd Tchr 1968-82, 3-4 Grd Tchr 1982-88, 5th Grd Tchr 1988-; *ai:* FPS Coach; Schl Newspaper Ldr; OEA, NEA 1968-, Head of Pub Relations 2 Yrs; Beta Sigma Phi Inter 1970-; Jaycees; CCD Tchr 34 Yrs; Astitabula Historical Assn Brd Mem; Astitabula Woman's Club Bd Mem; Owner One of a Kind Museum of Jefferson Victorian Perambulator; Victorian Baby Carriages Book Co-Authored; Buckeye Local Schls Tchr of Yr 1994-95; 1st Runner-up Ash Co Tchr of Yr 1985; *home:* 482 Owl Pt Rock Creek OH 44084*

PALLO, LAUREL SEXTON, Language Arts & Lit Teacher; *b:* Toledo, OH; *m:* James M.; *c:* Erica R., Evan J.; *ed:* Georgetown Coll (BA) Eng 1969; Post Grad Stud Required 1-8 Cert Xavier Univ; *cr:* OH Bureau of Employment Svcs WIN Cnslr 1970-79; Queen of Peace Elem Schl 7-8th Grd Tchr 1990-; *ai:* Schl Newspaper; NCEA 1990-; OH Writing Project 1990; *office:* Queen Of Peace Elem Schl 2550 Millville Ave Hamilton OH 45013

PALLOTTA, LUCILLE IZZO, Asst Professor of Fr & Italian; *b:* Troy, NY; *m:* Augustus G.; *c:* Sanford, Ellis; *ed:* St Univ Coll at Oneonta (BA) Elem Ed-Summa Cum Laude 1967; Syracuse Univ (MA) Fr 1970, (MA) Italian 1987; Harper Coll 45 Credit Hrs; McGill Univ 6 Grad Hrs; *cr:* Syracuse Univ Fr Tchng Asst 1967-70, Italian Adj Instr 1979-89; LeMoyne Coll Italian Adj Instr 1970-90; Onondaga Comm Coll Fr & Italian Asst Prof 1989-; *ai:* Intnl Ed Comm Mem; Stud Abroad Subcommittee Convener; Intnl Club Adv; Curr Proctor; NYSAFLT 1980-, 12th Annual Culture Fair Chprsn; FLACNY 1980-, Exec Bd Del at Large; AATF 1991-; Order Sons of Italy in Amer 1991-92; Rotary Intnl Tchr Exch Schlsp 1991; Awds: OCC Trustees 1992, Fac Appreciation 1994; Numerous Articles Pub; Intnl Assoc of Italian Amer Scholars Directory; *office:* Onondaga Comm Coll Dept of Mod Langs Syracuse NY 13215

PALLOZZA, FRANCES BERNADETTE, Music Teacher; *b:* Philadephia, PA; *ed:* Chestnut Hill Coll (BSME) Music 1970; West Chester Univ (MM) Music 1975; *cr:* Elem Schls Music Tchr 1958-65; St Hubert HS Music Tchr 1965-68, 1991-; West Cath HS Music Tchr 1968-75; Chestnut Hill Coll Asst Prof of Music 1975-90; *ai:* Orch, String Ensemble Dir; MENC, NCEA 1991-; *office:* St Hubert Cath HS for Girls 7320 Torresdale Ave Philadelphia PA 19136

PALM, DEBORAH SNELLING, Assistant Elementary Principal; *b:* San Antonio, TX; *ed:* OH St Univ (BS) Early & Mid Chldhd Ed 1976; Xavier Univ (Masters) Elem Admin & Supv 1985; 21 Post Grad Hrs; *cr:* Lakewood Local Schls Classroom Tchr 1976-91, Asst Prin 1991-; *ai:* PTO; Just Say No Clubs; Stu Cncl; Martha Holden Jennings Grant; Conservation Tchr of Yr; Dow Chemical Excl in Tchng Awd.

PALM, JEANNE S., English Teacher; *b:* Rockville Centre, NY; *ed:* Cortland Coll (BA) Eng 1969; Hofstra Univ (MA) Lit 1974; Story Brook Univ (PHD) Renaissance LF 1990; *cr:* Kings Park HS Eng Tchr 1970-; *office:* Kings Park HS 200 Route 25A Kings Park NY 11754

PALM, KITTIE A., High School Fine Arts Teacher; *b:* Ludington, MI; *m:* Irv Oslin; *c:* Ramona Palm Oslin; *ed:* OH St Univ (BAEd) Art Ed 1974, (MA) Art Ed 1986; OH Meth Theological Schl Post Grad Stud; *cr:* Var House Sportswear Commercial Artist 1975-76; South-Western City Schls Elem Art Tchr 1976-80; Bishop Hartley HS Art Tchr 1984-; *ai:* Yrbk Moderator; Ski Club Head Moderator; Columbus Diocesan Ed Assn 1984-; First UU Church 1988-, Bd of Trustees; Builders of the Adytum 1982-, Co-Regnl Cnslr; Phi Kappa Phi; Adult Ed Wkshps 1976-81; OSU Inst for GATE in Arts Tchr 1995; *office:* Bishop Hartley HS 1285 Zettler Rd Columbus OH 43227*

PALMACCIO, MARY L., Intermediate Teacher; *b:* Brooklyn, NY; *m:* George; *c:* Charles; *ed:* Boricua Coll (BS) Elem Ed 1991; Columbia Univ Tchrs Coll (MA) Biling Ed 1994; *cr:* IS 162 Tchr 1991-; *ai:* Debate Coach; Adult Ed Vol; Dr. Evelina Antonetti Acad Excl Awd 1991; Who's Who Amongest Stdnts in Amer univs & Colls 1990-91.

PALMATIER, BARBARA J., 7th Grade English Teacher; *b:* Gloversville, NY; *w:* Richard W. (dec); *c:* Brian Charles; *ed:* KY Wesleyan Coll at Owensboro (BA) Eng Ed 1966; St Univ of NY at Albany (MA) Eng Ed 1972; *cr:* Lansingburgh HS 10th-12th Grd Eng Tchr 1966-69; Cazenovia HS 12th Grd Eng Tchr 1969-70; Lansingburgh HS 11th Grd Eng Tchr 1970-76; Knickerbacker MS 7th-9th Grd Eng Tchr 1976-77, 1980-; *ai:* Spelling Bee, Prom Organizer, Co-Adv; Jr Sr Class Past Adv; 8th Grd Dance Comm; Lansingburgh Tchrs Assn, Bldg Rep; AFT; NEA; NCTE; BSA, Positive Reward Comm; Tchr of Yr Awd 1985; Who's Who Nom 1988; *office:* Knickerbacker MS 320 7th Ave Troy NY 12182

PALMER, BARBARA ANN, Special Education Teacher; *b:* Goshen, NY; *m:* Jeffrey; *c:* Megan; *ed:* Orange Cty Comm Coll (AA) Lbrl Arts 1980; SUNY at Oneonta (BS) Elem Ed 1982; SUNY at Albany (MS) Spec Ed 1983; *cr:* Vly Cntrl HS Spec Ed Tchr 1983-95, Spec Ed Dept Chprsn 1995-; *ai:* Vly Cntrl TA, NYSUT 1983-; *office:* Valley Central HS 1175 Rt 17k Montgomery NY 12549

PALMER, BARBARA FODERARO, 4th-5th Grade Teacher; *b:* Cleveland, OH; *m:* Gary L.; *c:* John M., Jeffrey G.; *ed:* OH Univ (BSEd) Elem Ed 1967; Univ of Akron (MED) Elem Ed; Grad Hrs Ashland Univ; *cr:* Parma City Schls 3rd Grd Tchr 1968; Medina City Schls 5th Grd Tchr 1978-92, 4/5 Mulit-age Team 1992-; *ai:* MCTA; NEA, OEA; Phi Delta Kappa 1994-; Articles Pub; Medina City Outstdng Tchr 1994; Plain Dealer Crystal Apple Awd; *office:* Ella Canavan Elem Schl 825 Lawrence St Medina OH 44256*

PALMER, BARBARA SUE (HENSON), Art Teacher; *b:* Portsmouth, OH; *c:* Michael; *ed:* Kent St Univ (BFA) Art 1967; OH Cert 157 Hrs; Attnd Chautauqua Summer Schls; *cr:* Adkin Sr HS Art Tchr 1967; Claymont HS Art Tchr 1968-69; Chautauqua Summer Schls Art Tchr 1969-70; Jewett-Scio HS Art Tchr 1969-70; *ai:* NEA, OH Art Ed, Harrison Hills 1971-; Art Schlsp Stu Chautauqua Inst; OH Governors Youth Art Exhibition Regnal Excl Stu Work; Art Awds; *office:* Jewett Scio Jr Sr HS 322 W Main St Scio OH 43988

PALMER, BARRY KEITH, Tech Coord & Math Teacher; *b:* Johnstown, PA; *m:* Sheila Ditzler; *ed:* Lebanon Valley Coll (BS) Math 1978; Wilkes Univ (MS) Ed Computing 1996; 36 Addl Grad Credit Hrs; *cr:* Tri-Valley Schl Dist Tchr, Tech Coord 1978-; *ai:* Ftbl, Bsktbl Coach; Weightroom Supvr; Stu Trainer, Cmptr Club Adv; PSEA, NEA 1978-; NSF Grant for AP Cmptr Programming 1985; *office:* Tri-Valley HS 155 E Main St Hegins PA 17938

PALMER, BONNIE HANCHER, English Teacher; *b:* Johnstown, PA; *m:* Robert Keith; *c:* Greta Lynn, Douglas Robert; *ed:* Elizabethtown Coll (BA) Eng 1964; Univ of MD Masters Equivalency; *cr:* Sligo Jr HS Eng Tchr 1964-69; Montgomery Blair HS Eng Tchr 1979-; *ai:* Mentor; Soc Comm Chm; Montgomery Cty New 9th Grd Curr Writing Comm; Woodmoor Civic Assn; Shakespeare Inst of Univ of MD; Wrote Curr for Adult Ed that Was Pub; *office:* Montgomery Blair HS 313 Wayne Ave Silver Spring MD 20910*

PALMER, FRAUKE, Physics Teacher; *b:* Gottingen, Germany; *m:* William F.; *c:* Jocelyn Alford, Stephanie Christopher; *ed:* Goucher Coll (AB) Physics 1965; OH St Univ (MA) Sci, Math Ed 1984; *cr:* Bishop Hartley Tchr 1978-80; Worthington Kilbourne Tchr 1980-, Dept Chair 1989-93; *ai:* Physics Club; Project Engrng; Discipline, NHS Comm; AAPT 1980-; US Dept of Ed 1st Grant Project Dir; *office:* Worthington Kilbourne HS 1499 Hard Rd Columbus OH 43235

PALMER, GALE L., Biology Teacher; *b:* Quincy, MA; *ed:* Sterling Coll (BA) Divisimac Sci 1966; Northeastern Univ at Boston (MS) Bio 1983; Trained Mediator; Noise & Noise Control Ed Cert; *cr:* Hingham Pub Schls Sci Tchr 1966-68; Quincy Coll Bio Lab Instr 1971-73; Quincy Pub Schls Bio, Sci Tchr 1968-; *ai:* Stu Handbook Comm Chprsn; Tchr Adv; Judging HS Sci Fair Chprsn; Stu-Fac Production Cast Mem; St Reform Schl Cncl Mem; NEA 1966-; QEA 1968-, High Dir, Exec Bd; MTA; Schl Comm Campaign 1991-92; Cystic Fibrosis Prudential Stairclimb Support Team 1990-; Northeastern Univ Sigma Phi Sigma Beta Nu Chapter; *office:* North Quincy HS 316 Hancock St Quincy MA 02171

PALMER, HARVEY JOHN, Professor of Chemical Engrng; *b:* Richmond Hill, NY; *m:* Donna M. Partigan; *c:* Harvey, Thomas, Angeline; *ed:* Univ of Rochester (BS) Chemical Engrng 1967; Univ of WA (PHD) Chemical Engrng 1971; *cr:* Univ of Rochester Asst Prof 1971-77, Assoc Prof 1977-84, Assoc Dean for Grad Stud 1983-89, Prof 1984-, Chemical Engrng Dept Chair 1990-; *ai:* Transmation Inc Bd of Dirs; Amer Inst of Chemical Engrs 1971-; Sigma Xi 1975-; Tau Beta Pi; ACS 1995-; Honeoye-Falls Lima Schl, Bd Mem 1983-92, Pres 1990-91; 30 Plus Tech Articles Pub; 6 US Patents Issued; Co-Author of 40 Plus Tech Presentations at Tech Confs; Undergraduate Tchng Awd in Schl of Engrng 1979 & 1982; *office:* Univ Of Rochester Dept of Chemical Engrng Rochester NY 14627

PALMER, HENRY ROBINSON, Seventh Grade Math Teacher; *b:* Westerly, RI; *ed:* Boston Univ (BA) Elem Ed 1977; Univ of RI (MA) Rdng 1985; *cr:* West Vine Schl 6th Grd Classroom Tchr 1977-83; Pawcatuck MS 6th-8th Grd Classroom Tchr 1983-; *ai:* MS Boys Bsktbl Coach; Dist Math Comm; NEA, CEA 1977-; NCTM 1991-; Pawcatuck Fire Dept 1981-, Captain; Pawcatuck Lions 1987-, Treas; Pawcatuck Little League Distngd Svc Awd; *office:* Pawcatuck MS 40 Field St Pawcatuck CT 06379

PALMER, KATHLEEN ANN, 3rd Grade Teacher; *b:* Westfield, MA; *m:* Terry L.; *c:* Matthew, Jessica; *ed:* Westfield St Coll (BA) Elem Ed 1969; *cr:* City of Westfield Spcl Staff 1967-68; Needs Summer Pgm Dir 1969-78; City of Westfield 3rd Grd Tchr 1969-; Headstart Pgm Tchr 1978-80; Westfield Summer Childrens Theater Dir 1995; *ai:* Kids Act Theater Group; NEA 1969-; MTA 1969-; WEA 1969-; Westfield Theater Group 1994-; Westfield Womens Club 1994-; Horace Mann Grant; Theater Grant from Office of Grants & Rsrch in Westfield; Childrens Theater Trng & Performing 1991-; *office:* Southampton Rd Elem Schl 330 Southampton Rd Westfield MA 01085

PALMER, MARK A., Adj Asst Prof of Materials; *b:* Greenwich, CT; *ed:* Rensselaer Polytechnic Inst (BS) Materials Engrng 1987, (PHD) Materials Sci & Eng 1995; NSF Fac Enhancement Prgm; *cr:* Gen Electric Co-op Technician 1985; Rensselaer Polytechnic Inst Rsrch Asst, Tchng Asst 1987-95; Rsrch Asst, Tchng Asst 1987-95, Rsrch Asst, Instr 1992-95, Post Doc, Adj Asst Prof 1996; *ai:* Fac Mentor; Scoutmaster, Bridge Heop Instr; ASCE 1995-, Apprentice Fac Grant; ASM Intnl, TMS, Amer Ceramic Soc 1985-; Elks 1992-, Third VP; Co-Author of Materials Chem Textbook; Kodak Flwshp; 10 Publications; *office:* Rensselaer Polytechnic Inst 110 8th St Troy NY 12180

PALMER, MARLYS ANN, Prof of Health & Physical Ed; *b:* Berkeley Springs, WV; *ed:* Penn St (BS) Hlth & PE 1968, (MED) PE 1972, (DED) Hlth Ed 1994; Shippensburg Univ Course Work in Spcl Ed; *cr:* Elizabethtown Schl Dist Elem PE Tchr 1968; Chambersburg HS Scndry Hlth & PE Tchr 1968-70; Grier Schl Scndry PE & Bio Tchr 1970-72; Wilson Coll Hlth & PE Tchr & Coach 1973-76; Hagerstown Jr Coll Hlth & PE Tchr & Coach 1979-; *ai:* Head Coach Womens Vllybl & Bsktbl; Reg Vllybl Chprsn; Womens Bsktbl Reg Sec; Kodak All Amer Selection Comm; Curr & Staff Dev Comms; Hlth & PE Coord; AAHPERD 1986-; AVCA 1989-, Reg Coach of Yr Awd; ABCA 1992-; Chambersburg Road Runners 1980-; Dist 14 Vllybl Coach of the Yr 6 Times; Eastern Reg AVCA Coach of the Yr 1995; Tri-State Area Women on the Move; *office:* Hagerstown Jr Coll 11400 Robinwood Dr Hagerstown MD 21742*

PALMER, MARTHA MALONEY, Mathematics Teacher; *b:* Dansville, NY; *m:* Edward; *c:* Jennifer; *ed:* Geneseo (BS) Ed 1963, (MS) Ed & Math 1964; *cr:* Livonia Cntrl Math Tchr 1964-; *ai:* Help Coach Jr HS Math Team; CTA; *office:* Livonia Jr Sr HS PO Box E Livonia NY 14487

PALMER, MELVIN L., Spanish Teacher; *b:* Raleigh, NC; *ed:* Univ of NC (AB) Span 1971; NC Cntrl Univ (JD) Law 1974; Howard Univ, Johns Hopkins Univ Credits Towards Masters; *cr:* Eastern Sr HS Span Tchr 1985-89; Bell Mult-Cultural Sr HS Span Tchr 1989-91; Calvin Coolidge Sr HS Span Tchr 1991-94; H. D. Woodson Sr. HS Span Tchr 1994-; *ai:* NHS Co-Adv; Hospitality, SCAC Comms; Washington Tchrs Union, Amer Assn of Tchrs of Foreign Lang; St Lukes Episcopal Church, Schl Tchr; Alpha Phi Alpha; *office:* H D Woodson SR HS 55th & Eads St N E Washington DC 20019*

PALMER, NANCY H., Retired Fourth Grade Teacher; *b:* Rochester, NY; *c:* Susan Riggs, Margaret Sombathy, Sharon Youngman; *ed:* OH Wesleyan Univ (BA) Elem Ed 1957; Credit Insvc Hrs Williamson Cntrl Schl; *cr:*

Williamson Cntrl Schl 4th Grd Tchr 1957-58; Loudonville Elem Schl 4th Grd Tchr 1958-60; Sodus Cntrl Schl Sub Tchr 1961-67; Williamsonville Cntrl Schl 4th Grd Tchr 1969-95; *ai:* Delta Kappa Gamma 1977-; NYSUT, AFT 1969-; Williamson Fac Assn 1969-, VP, Pres, Tchr of Yr 1987, Newsletter Ed, Bldg Rep; Tchr of Yr 1987.

PALMER, RAYMOND TYRONE, Teacher; *b:* Brooklyn, NY; *m:* Kim Yvette; *c:* Tiffany; *ed:* Pace Univ (BA) Finance 1988; Brooklyn Coll (MA) Scndry Ed; *cr:* Office of Pub Transportation Accountant 1985-91; Edward R Murrow HS Tchr 1990-91; S Shore HS Tchr 1991-; *ai:* African Stud Club; *office:* South Shore HS 6565 Flatlands Ave Brooklyn NY 11236

PALMER, REBECCA LYNNE, Fourth Grade Teacher; *b:* Akron, OH; *ed:* Kent St Univ (BA) Ed 1966, (MS) Ed 1972; *cr:* Brookridge ELem Schl 5th Grd Tchr 10 Yrs, 4th Grd Tchr 20 Yrs; *ai:* 3rd-6th Grd Math Coord; Grant Team; Curr Cncl; Cultural Arts Club Adv; Brooklyn Ed Assn 1966-, Negotiations Team; OH Cncl Tchrs of Math 1966-; NEA, OEA 1966-; Compass South Homeowners Assn 1985-, Pres, Treas; Brooklyn Employees Credit Union 1966-, Credit Chm Debit-Asset Awd; Jennings Schlr Twice; Delta Kappa Gamma; Grant Team Capital Grant for Brookridge Elem Schl; *office:* Brookridge Elem Schl 4500 Ridge Rd Brooklyn OH 44144

PALMER, SALLY ANN (MATTHEWS), Fourth Grade Teacher; *b:* Warren, OH; *m:* James W.; *c:* James M.; *ed:* YSU (BS) Elem Ed 1970; *cr:* Cortland Elem Schl 1st, 4th Grd Tchr 1970-; *ai:* OEA 1970-; *office:* Cortland Elem Schl 264 Park Ave Cortland OH 44410

PALMER, SANDRA CIRA, 7th Grade Science Teacher; *b:* Rochester, NY; *m:* Bruce K.; *ed:* Cambridge Coll (MS) Ed 1993; 48 Addl Credit Hrs Ed; *cr:* Rochester City Schl Dist 7th-12th Grd PE Tchr 1969-82; Forfar Field Station Schl Marine Bio Tchr 1982-83; South Shore Natl Sci Ctr Ed Dir 1985-87; Hanover MS Sci Tchr 1987-; *ai:* Scheduling Comm; NEA 1987-; PALMS 1994-; Project Swims Flwshp 1993-94.

PALMER, T. KATHERINE, Lang Arts & Reading Teacher; *b:* Warren, OH; *m:* Robert G.; *c:* Scott, Kimberly; *ed:* Edinboro Univ (BS) Elem 1962; Attnd East Stroudsburg Univ, Kent St Univ; *cr:* Madison Local Schls Sixth Grd Tchr 1962-67; Jamestown Schls Sixth Grd Tchr 1967-69; Buckeye Local Sub Tchr 1973-84, Fifth Grd Tchr 1984-85; Conneaut Area City Schls Sixth Grd Tchr 1985-; *ai:* Stu Cncl Adv; NEA, OEA, CEA 1962-69, 1984-; Ashtabula Woman's Club 1989-, Mbrshp, Prgm Chair; *office:* Rowe MS 360 Rowe St Conneaut OH 44030

PALMER, VINCENT LOUIS,JR., Professor of Education; *b:* Erie, PA; *m:* Christine Kay Supplee; *c:* Lauren N., Leanne C.; *ed:* Clarion Univ of PA (BS) Ed 1978; TN Temple Univ (MS) Educl Admin 1982; Univ of Pittsburgh (PHD) Instruction, Learning Sci Ed 1992; PA Tchng Cert in Chem, bio, Math, Gen Sci; PA Admin Cert in Scndry Rd; Grad Stud in Chem, Cmptr, Lab Interfacing; *cr:* Shady Side Acad Chem Tchr, Gen, Environmental Lab Master, Coach 1978-80; North Hills Chrstn Schl Sci, Math, Bible Scndry Tchr, Coach 1983-86; Quaker Vly Schl Dist Chem, Bio, Math Scndry Tchr, Coach 1986-93; Bapt Bible Coll Prof of Ed, Coach 1993-; *ai:* Cross Cntry Coach; Serve on Stu Affairs Bd; Heavily Involved in Curr Dev; AAAS 1984-; NARST 1989-; NCTM 1992-; Bapt HS Bd 1994- Chm; Heritage Bapt Church 1993-, Sunday Schl Class Tchr; Wkshp Speaker in 1993-95 for Tchrs, Admins in Keystone Chrstn Ed Assn; *office:* Bapt Bible Coll & Sem Po Box 800, 538 Venard Rd Clarks Summit PA 18411

PALMERI, KANDY BEANE, 2nd Grade Teacher; *b:* Titusville, PA; *m:* Salvatore; *c:* Kelly Lynn; *ed:* St Univ Coll of NY at Buffalo (BA) Elem Ed 1972, (MS) Elem Ed Rdng 1977; *cr:* Akron Cntrl Schls K-2nd Grd Tchr 1972-; *ai:* AFT 1972-; NY St United Tchrs 1972-, Local Ch VP 1995-; Ldrshp Awd, Comm of Rep; CARE for Lancaster 195-, Charter Mem, Svc Org; Outstdng Grad Tchr at St Univ Coll 1973; *home:* 5815 Genesee St Lancaster NY 14086

PALMERO, JUDITH ANN, French & Spanish Teacher; *b:* Lancashire, England; *ed:* Hunter Coll (BA) Fr 1966, (MS) Guid, Cnslng 1970; NY Univ, Hunter Coll SUNY at Albany 60 Credits Beyond Masters in Ed, His, Lang, Admin, Supervision, Eng 1970-92; *cr:* JHS 139 Fr Tchr 1966-80; IS 145 Fr Tchr 1980-87; Corinth HS Fr, Span Tchr 1987-; *ai:* Adv 4 Yrs; Frgn Lang Club, Hnr Soc Co-Adv; Advy Comm; Frgn Lang Coord; UFT, AATF 1966-; AFT 1970-; CTA 1980-; Grant Written; *office:* Corinth Cntrl Schl 105 Oak St Corinth NY 12822

PALMERO, LEO JOHN, Tenth Grade Biology Teacher; *b:* Wilmington, DE; *m:* Joan F.; *c:* Joanna; *ed:* CO St Univ (BS) Bio 1966; Iona Coll (MS) Bio 1971; 60 Credits Beyond Masters; *cr:* North Rockland HS 10th Grd Bio & Advanced Placement Bio Tchr 1966-; *ai:* Biotechnology Ctr Dir; NY St Ed Dept Regnl Bio Mentor; U of WI Madison, Northern AZ Univ, CO St Univ, Ontario Sci Ctr Tchr Facilitator; Ed Comm of the Biotechnology Industry Org 1990-93; NABT, STANYS; NSTA Local Ldr; Outstanding HS Tchr of Yr Awd 1993; Sigma Xi-Manhattan Coll; Rockland Westchester Sci Supvrs Assn Outstanding Sci Recognition Awd 1993; Amer Inst of Chemical Engrng Tappan Zee Section Outstanding HS Tchr Awd 1993; *office:* North Rockland HS Hammond Rd Thiells NY 10984

PALMIERI, SUSAN LAURA, Speech Teacher; *b:* Brooklyn, NY; *c:* Dylan; *ed:* St John's Univ (BA) Speech, Theatre 1972; Brooklyn Coll (MA) Speech 1985; CUNY Staten Island Campus (MA) Cinema Stud; CUNY 20 Credit Hrs Cinema Stud 1988; Yale Univ 5 Credit Hrs Directing 1993; *cr:* St Mary Mother of Jesus Schl Eng Tchr, Chprsn 1972-80; Chaminade Coll Prep Eng Tchr 1980-81; Chaminade HS for Boys Eng Tchr 1981-82; Charon Williams Coll ESL Tchr 1982-83; Wagner Coll ESL Tchr 1983-85 1983-85; Brooklyn Tech HS Speech Tchr, Coord T & LA Dept 1985-; *ai:* Dir Schl Plays; Spon Intnl Thespian Honor Soc; Adv Tech Players Drama Club; Certified Producer Cable Television; Awd Winning Video Staten Island Film Festival; 1988 Entitler Circle of Confusion; Best Video; Best Screen Play; Best Dir; Best Actress; *office:* Brooklyn Tech HS 29 Fort Greene Pl Brooklyn NY 11217

PALMIOTTO, SUSAN LEVY, Stained Glass Teacher & Dean; *b:* Lodz, Poland; *m:* Frank J.; *c:* Danielle, Nicole; *ed:* Long Island Univ (BS) Bus Admin 1965, (MS) Cnslng 1972; Pratt Inst, Westchester Comm Coll Stained Glass, Jewelry Courses; *cr:* Morris HS Tchr, Dean 1967-80; Bronx Regnl HS Tchr, Grd Adv 1980-86; Dodge Voc HS Tchr, Dean 1986; Hostos Lincoln Acad Tchr, Dean 1986-; *ai:* SADD, Peer Counsel, Stained Glass Course, Parent Involvement Prgm Adv; Bus Ed Assn 1967-, Ed, Newspaper; UFT 1967-; NASSP 1986-; Tchr of Yr 1992; *home:* 42 Barnes Rd Ossining NY 10562*

PALMISON, DENISE, First Grade Teacher; *b:* Cleveland, OH; *c:* Monique, Brent; *ed:* Lakeland Comm Coll (AS) Early Chldhd Dev 1975; Kent St Univ (BA) Early Chldhd Ed 1980; KSU Story Telling 2 Credits; *cr:* St Joseph Schl First Grd Tchr 15 Yrs; *ai:* Soc Comm; Latchkey Coord; *office:* St Joseph School-Randolph # 1 2617 Waterloo Rd Mogadore OH 44260*

PALOMBO, CHRISTEN M., Art Teacher; *b:* Pittsburgh, PA; *m:* Frank Dominic; *c:* Nicole; *ed:* VA Commonwealth Univ (BFA) Art Ed 1979; Univ of Pittsburgh (MS) Spec Ed 1987; Attn La Roche Coll Commercial Art 2 Yrs; *cr:* Byrd Primary Schl Elem Art Tchr 1981-82; Comm Coll of Allegheny Cty Art Tchr Emotionally Dist 1983-89; Pace Schl Ceramics Tchr 1989-91; Bethe Park Schl Dist HS Art Tchr 1989-; *ai:* Art Club Spon; Scenery Painting Spon; NAEA 1986-; USC League for the Arts 1988-, Exhibit Dir, VP, Class Dir; Jaycees 1987-, VP, Several St Level Speech Awds, Best Comm Project; Flwshp Grant; Biannual Tchr, Artist Exhibit 2 Yrs; PFAE Arts Grant; *office:* Bethel Park Sr HS 309 Church Rd Bethel Park PA 15102

PALUMBO, JERI, World Cultures Instructor; *b:* New Castle, PA; *ed:* Slippery Rock St Coll (BS) Scndry Ed 1971; 6 Credit Hrs Intnl Stud Westminster Coll 1980; 26 Credit Hrs His, Soc Stud 1971-; *cr:* LCAVTS World Cultures Instr 1974-; *ai:* Stu Assistance Prgm 1995-; Prof Voc Indstrl Clubs of Amer Mem 1996; PSEA, NEA, Sec 1977-84, Exec Comm 1994-, Prof Dev Comm Ldrshp 1995, Admin, Tchr Liaison Comm Chprsn 1996; St Vincent De Paul, CCD Instr 1974-85; Amer Family Insts Gift of Time Tribute 1994; *office:* Lawrence Cty Area Voc Tech Sch 750 Phelps Way New Castle PA 16101

PALUMBO, JILL A., English Teacher; *b:* Newark, NJ; *c:* Cara DiGiovine, Elijah de la Campa; *ed:* Kean Coll of NJ (BA) Eng, Speech, Theatre 1975; Substance Abuse Cert 1993; 12 Credit Hrs NY Univ Drama 1983; *cr:* Harding Schl 7 & 8 Grd Rdng Tchr 1978-80; Elizabeth HS 9-12 Grd Eng, Theatre Tchr 1980-; *ai:* Schl Literary Magazine Moderator; NJEA 1978-; NCTE 1994-; CASA 1993-; *office:* Elizabeth HS 500 Pearl St Elizabeth NJ 07202

PALUMBO, MICHAEL A., Science Chairperson; *b:* Union City, NJ; *c:* Michael, Steven; *ed:* Jersey City St Coll (BA) Sci Ed 1966, (MS) Sci Ed 1969; Montclair Univ (MS) Sci Ed 1973; 45 Addl Hrs; *cr:* Cliffside Park HS Sci Chem Tchr 1966-, Sci Chprsn Supvr 1972-; *ai:* Running Cross Cntry Coach; Bergen Cty Championships 1973, 1978; NJEA 1966-73; NJSSA, NJPSA 1973-; Phi Delta Kappa; Honored for Sci Rsrch; Paper Pub; *office:* Cliffside Park HS Palisade And Riverview Aves Cliffside Park NJ 07010

PALUMBO, RAFFAELE, Technology Teacher; *b:* San Benedetto, Italy; *m:* Laura Danner; *c:* Tav-Fiavo, Chad-Joseph; *ed:* Monroe Comm Coll (AAS) Mechanical Tech 1967; St Univ Coll at Buffalo (BS) Tech 1970, (MS) Tech 1974; *cr:* West Seneca East Sr HS Tech Tchr 26 Yrs; *ai:* Var Boys Soccer Coach 20 Yrs; Yrbk Adv 12 Yrs; Various Stu Recognition Comms; AFT West Senea Tchr Assn 1970-; West Seneca Soccer Club 1975-, Pres 1975-80, Founder; *office:* West Seneca East Sr HS 4760 Seneca St West Seneca NY 14224

PALYA, JOSEPH JOHN, Social Studies Teacher; *b:* Yonkers, NY; *ed:* Manhattan Coll (BA) His 1968; Lehman Coll (MA) His 1972; Addl Credit Hrs Manhattan Coll, Pace Univ, Manhattanville Coll, Iona Coll; *cr:* Charles E. Gorton HS Soc Stud Tchr 1968-, Dept Chair 1979-80; *ai:* Schl Newsletter Ed; Pub Relations Liaison; Shrd Dcsn Mkng Comm; Yonkers Tchrs Fed 1968-, Bldg Rep, TIC; NCSS, NY St Soc Stud Cncl 1968-; Westchester Soc Stud Cncl 1968-, Sec, VP, Svc Awd 1993; PTSA 1968-, VP, Outstanding Svc Awd 1981; NYS Regents Test Bd Comm 1990-; Outstanding Scndry Educators of Amer 1974; PTSA Jenkins Awd 1977; Robert A. Taft Govt Inst Taft Fellow 1978; Who's Who in East 1984; HS Wall of Fame 1994; *office:* Charles E. Gorton HS 100 Shonnard Pl Yonkers NY 10703

PANAGGIO, JANET LEONE, 2nd & 3rd Grade Teacher; *b:* Revere, MA; *m:* Orry; *c:* Billy; *ed:* Boston Univ (BS) Elem Ed 1970, (MED) Rdng Cert 1979; Lesley Coll (MED) Creative Arts & Learning 1990; Continued Course Work in Inclusion, Cooperative Learning & Tech; *cr:* Williams Elem Schl Classroom Tchr 1970-94; Boston Coll Clinical Fac & Supvr 1989-92; Angier Elem Schl Classroom Tchr 1994-; *ai:* Cooperating Tchr for Interns; Diversified Assessment Practices Pilot Tchr; Tech Related Confs Presenter; Newton Tchrs Assn, MA Tchrs Assn, NEA 1970-; Newton Schls Fnd, Bd Mem; *office:* Angier Elem Schl 1697 Beacon St Waban MA 02168

PANARIELLO, ROSEMARY PASCONE, Mathematics Teacher; *b:* Brooklyn, NY; *m:* Robert; *c:* Giana Rose; *ed:* Hofstra Univ (BA) Math 1989; SUNY at Stony Brook (MA) Ed 1992; *cr:* Copiague Summer Schl Math RCT Tchr 1989; West Islip HS Math Tchr 1989-91; Hauppauge HS Math Tchr 1992-; *ai:* Math Team Adv; JV Sftbl Coach; NYSUT 1989-; *office:* Hauppauge HS Lincoln Blvd Hauppauge NY 11788

PANATIER, CAROLYN CRONIN, Former Teacher; *b:* New York, NY; *m:* Christopher M.; *c:* Annie C.; *ed:* Villanova Univ (BA) Eng 1987; St John's Univ (MS) Elem Ed 1992; *cr:* St Martin of Tours Schl Fourth Grd Tchr 1987-88, Third Grd Tchr 1988-90, Second Grd Tchr 1990-92; Child's Play Intnl Preschl 2-4 Yr Olds Instr 1992-93; La Salle Regnl Schl K, 2, 4 Grd Long Term Sub Tchr 1993-95.

PANAYIOTOU, ANNA STEPHANOU, Teacher; *b:* Asgata Limassol, Cyprus; *m:* Andreas; *c:* Savva, Suzanne; *ed:* Hilda Jaba Tchng Method 15 Credits; Bank St Coll 24 Credits; Meet the Mac Comp 3 Credits; *cr:* St Peters Coll Rdng Cntr Tchr 1970-81; Bayonne Bd of Ed Tchr 1972-; *ai:* New England Maritime Tour 5th & 8th Grds 1988-; NEA 1972-; Asgata Org 1980-; St Annas Philoptochus 1983-; Bayonne Historical Soc 1993-; Bayonne 2000: Cleaner & Greener 1993-, Founder, Coord, Green Comm Awd; NJ Dept of Forestry Svcs SBA Grant to Plant Trees; NJ Dept of Forestry Svcs Grant to Publish Brochure; *office:* Vroom Learning Ctr 18 W 26th St Bayonne NJ 07002*

PANCHUCK, PAULA DEANGELIS, Dir of Early Chldhd & Elem Ed; *b:* Natick, MA; *m:* Michael; *c:* Melissa; *ed:* Univ of MA at Amherst (BS) Scndry Ed 1970; Framingham St Coll (MED) Elem Ed 1975; Lesley Coll (PHD) Adult Dev & Aging 1994; Early Chldhd Ed Cert Courses 1978-80; *cr:* Natick HS Tchr & Dir 1971-76; Lasell Coll Prgm Dir & Assoc Prof 1985-; *ai:* Fac Chair 1995-; Project HEARTS HIV-AIDS Ed Dir; CampColors for HIV-AIDS Children, Co-Dir; Aging Stud Research Grants; Joy of Aging Prin Researcher, Pub Survey Research; Author Caring for Children with HIV-AIDS; Distinguished Svc Rainbow Awd for HIV-AIDS Ed 1996; *office:* Lasell Coll 1844 Commonwealth Ave Newton MA 02166

PANCIERA, CARLA MARIE, English Teacher; *b:* Westerly, RI; *m:* Dennis Donoghue; *ed:* Univ of NH (BA) Eng 1985; Boston Univ (MA) Creative Writing 1987; Univ of MA at Boston (MED) Scndry Eng 1990; 60 Plus Credit Hrs; *cr:* Burlington HS Eng Tchr 1989-; *ai:* Lit Art Magazine, Newspaper Adv; MTA, NEA 1989-; Pub Poetry; *office:* Burlington HS 123 Cambridge St Burlington MA 01803

PANCIONE, LORETTA HARRILL, Honors & Academic Bio Teacher; *b:* Hamlet, NC; *m:* Michael C. Jr.; *c:* Michael; *ed:* Wake Forest Univ (BS) Bio 1966; Temple Univ (MED) 1974; MS Equivalency Sci Penn St; 60 Hrs Hlth Scis, Hlth Ed, Hlth Admin; *cr:* Cheltenham HS Sci Tchr, Bio, Chem, Phys Sci, Botany 1966-; *ai:* Sponsorship Ind Sci Rsrch Projects; NEA 1966-; Montgomery Co Sci Tchrs 1967-, Sci Fair Judge, Worker; NSTA, Prgm Presenter; Gardners of Crooked Billet 1969-, Pres, Prgm, Lib Chm; Jarrettown United Meth Church, Chm Trustees 1970; Upper Dublin Parents Org; Marcellus Waddell Excl Tchng Finalist 1995; Sci Fair Judge Awd 1993-95; 25 Yr Tchr Recognition Awd; NSF Grant 1968; Intnl Sci Fair Spon; *office:* Cheltenham HS Rices Mill & Carlton Aves Wyncote PA 19095

PANCOE, CRAIG ALBIN, 6th Grade Teacher; *b:* Coaldale, PA; *m:* Deborra Sines; *c:* Adrienne, ALycia, Stefan; *ed:* Bloomsburg St Coll (BS) Elem Ed 1970; Lehigh Univ (MED) Elem Ed 1972; Addl 30 Credits Antioch Coll, Chectnut Hill Coll, Marywood Coll, PA St Univ, Univ of PA; *cr:* Hatboro-Horsham Schl Dist 6th Grd Tchr 1970-; *ai:* Create, Discipline Comm; SAP Team; NCTM 1989-; PSTA 1985-; *office:* Keith Valley MS 227 Meetinghouse Rd Horsham PA 19044

PANCOST, LOIS ELAINE, Mathematics Teacher; *b:* Tiffin, Bowling Green St Univ (BS) Geog, Math 1971, (MS) Scndry E Tchrs Summer Math; *cr:* South Jr HS 7-9 Grd Math Tchr 1971-8 Adult Ed Math Tchr 1974-77; Dover HS Math Tchr 1986-; NH T at Berlin Math Adj Prof 1988-90; Franklin Pierce Coll Math Adj Fa *ai:* Math Team Coach; NCTM, NEA 1971-; NHATMNE, DTU 198 Sci Fnd Grant 1985; *office:* Dover HS 25 Alumni Dr Dover NH 0

PANDALIANO, DONNA JEAN, Science Teacher; *b:* Islip, NY; *ed:* Hofstra Univ (BA) Bio 1992; Dowling Coll (MS) Scndry Ed 1 Vly Stream Cntrl Schl Sci Tchr 1994-; *office:* Valley Stream Ce 135 Fletcher Ave Valley Stream NY 11580

PANDER, BETTY J., Marketing Tchr & Coordinator; *b:* Sewick *m:* Larry; *c:* Cliff Price, Jeremy Price; *ed:* IN Univ of PA (BED) Ed 1976; *cr:* York Cty AVTS Mrktng Tchr, Coord 1976-78; Aliqu Mrktng Tchr, Coord 1978-79; Moon HS Mrktng Tchr, Coord 19 Deca Club Adv; MEA, PSEA, NEA 1983-; *office:* Moon Sr HS 904 Grade Rd Moon Twp PA 15108

PANEBIANCO, COLLEEN T., US History & Govt Teacher; *b:* NY; *m:* Anthony F.; *c:* Sara, Anthony; *ed:* Marquette Univ at Mil (BA) His 1970; SUNY at Cortland Ed 1981; 30 Grad Hrs Coll of S *cr:* Oswego Cty Dept of Soc Svcs Child Protective Worker 1971- Mills HS Scndry Tchr 1985-; *ai:* Previous Sr Class Adv 10 Yrs; Mc Adv 3 Yrs; Stu Cncl Adv 1 Yr; Prof Ed Comm 5 Yrs; Bldg Ldrshp Yrs; Tchr Ctr Bd 5 Yrs; NYSUT 1983-, Sec & Delegate; Cncl for S 1985-; Cntrl NY Soc Stud 1985-; New Hartford Hardwood Club B 1993-, Treas; Tchr of Yr 1986; *office:* New York Mills Jr Sr HS 1 M Blvd New York Mills NY 13417

PANEK, DOROTHY RYAN, Literature & Composition Tchr; *cr:* HS Lit, Composition 9 Tchr 1974-; *office:* Auburn HS Lake Ave NY 13021

PANEK, JUDY, 6th Grade Teacher; *b:* Elyria, OH; *ed:* Saint Jo (BS) Ed; Post Grad Stud; *cr:* Saint Boniface Schl 4th & 5th Gr Assumption Schl 6th-8th Grd Tchr; Asst Prin; *ai:* NCEA; Assumption Schl 9183 Broadview Rd Broadview Hts OH 44147

PANETSKI, STANLEY FRANK, Art Dept Tchr & Chair; *b:* Buffa *c:* Stanley K., Taner Colbert; *ed:* NY St Univ Coll at Buffalo (BS) 1969; SUCB (MS) Art Ed 1971; Eastern IL Univ (MA) Art C Sculptur 1985; Attnd Savanna Coll of Art & Design; *cr:* Lewiston Schl Jr HS Art Tchr 1969-84, Sr HS Art Tchr 1985-, Grds K-12 A Chair 1988-; *ai:* Ski Club Adv; Build Shared Decision Comm SCM Quality Cir; NYSATA 1970-, Convention Photographer & Stud Ar Comm; NYSUT 1969-, Comm of 100 & Del; AFT 1969-, Del; LPUT Bld Vice Pres, Negotiation; B; Skidmore Summer Flwshp; Eastern I Grad Asst Flwshp; NYS Ed Dept Judicator St Media Art Summer S

PANETTA, JUDITH M., Special Education Teacher; *b:* Camden, Bryant Coll (BS) Bus Ed 1976; Rowan Coll Spec Ed Cert 1992, 18 C *cr:* Wildwood HS Bus Tchr 1976-79; Bally's Park Place Chief C Front Desk 1979-85; Paulsboro HS Bus Tchr 1986-89; Egg Harbor T Bus, Spec Ed Tchr 1989-; *ai:* Class of 1997 Adv; Winter Var C Coach; Asst Drama Dir; Ticket Seller Ftbl Games; NJEA, NEA BEST Mem 1988-, Coll Rep; *office:* Egg Harbor Twp HS 24 High Dr Egg Harbor Townshi NJ 08234*

PANFILO, FRANCESCA, French Teacher; *b:* Staten Island, NY; *e* Univ (BA) Fr, Anthropology, Pre-Med Prgm 1993; *cr:* Moore Cath Italian Tchr 1993-; *ai:* Lang Club Coord, Adv; Prom, European Exc Coord; AATF 1993-; Honored in the Fr Review for Producing Wir Natl Fr Contest 1994; *office:* Moore Catholic HS 100 Merrill Ave Island NY 10314

PANIAN, MARY FRANCES F., Principal; *b:* Pittsburgh, PA; *ed:* Dame of MD (BA) Biological Sci 1973; Univ of Pittsburgh (MA 1974; *cr:* St Philomena Schl Tchr 1975-85; St Mary Schl Tchr & As 1985-95; St Irenaeus Schl Prin; *ai:* Moderator of Echo; Dir of Olympiad; NCTM 1989-; PCTM 1992-; *office:* St Irenaeus Schoo Fourth St Oakmont PA 15139

PANICH, DIANE, Fine & Performing Arts Dir; *b:* Philadelphia, F Jonathan Loftus; *ed:* Seton Hill Coll (BA) Printmaking 1969; PA St (MA) Printmaking 1970; Masters Degree +60 Credits; Fine Arts Dir *cr:* Blackwood MS Art Tchr 1970-71; Pollard MS Art Tchr 19 Needham Elem Schls Art Tchr 1984-90; Needham HS Art Tchr 19 Fine & Performing Arts Acting Dir 1995-; *ai:* Assessment, Tir Learning & Schl Reform Comms; Map on Schl Playground, Murals i Lib & Cafeteria Supvr; NEA 1970-; MA Tchrs Assoc & Local Assoc NAEA 1989-; MA Art Ed Assoc 1989-; Presentations on Assessment Art Ed Assoc; NEF Money for Equipment; Horace Mann Grant; Exch Needham England; MA Coll of Art Exhibit; Supts Awd (2 Times); Needham HS 609 Webster St Needham MA 02194

PANICO, SAMUEL JOHN, 8th-12th Grade Art Instructor; *b:* Ell City, PA; *m:* Patricia Mack; *c:* Samuel Mark, Noah John; *ed:* Edi Univ (BS) Art Ed 1961; Indiana Univ of PA (MED) Art Ed 1964 Ellwood City Area Schls Elem Art Tchr 1961-64, Scndry Art Tchr 1 *ai:* Art Club Spon; EFTA, PFTA & AFT 1988-; *office:* Lincoln HS Crescent Ave Ellwood City PA 16117

PANIGROSSO, DIANA BAUMLIN, Dept Chprsn & English Teach Perth Amboy, NJ; *m:* S. Louis; *c:* Geraldine Bayles, Diana Wilim Marie; *ed:* Coll of Notre Dame (BA) Eng 1968; *cr:* John Adams Jr HS Tchr 1968-70; Monmouth Cty Ed Svc Comm Tchr 1980-81; Saint Regnl HS Eng Tchr 1981-; Better & Better Korean Acad Eng Part-Time 1994-; *ai:* Eng Dept Chprsn; Yrbk & Newspaper Mode Comptr; Jrnlsm; NATE 1980-; Sodality 1975-, Moderator; CWV L Auxiliary 1968-; *office:* St Mary's Regnl HS 310 Augusta St South Ar NJ 08879

PANITZ, THEODORE, Engineering & Mathematics Prof; *b:* New NY; *m:* Patricia Snyder; *c:* Michael William, Andrew Adolf; *ed:* Co Univ (BS) Chemical Engrng 1968; IL Inst of Tech (MS) Chemical En 1970; Boston Univ (EDD) Ed 1982; *cr:* IL Inst of Tech Instr 1968-72 DuPont Co Engr 1972-74; Parkersburg Comm Coll Asst Prof 197 Cape Cod Comm Coll Prof 1976-; *ai:* Developmental Ed C NEMATYC Mem; NEA 1974-; MTA 1976-; Barnstable Town 1990-94, Pres; Centerville Civic Assn 1985-90, Pres; Lilly New Eng Conf Presenter 1995; NEMATYC Confs Presenter 1990-94; Consulta New Bedford Jr HS on Cooperative Learning; *office:* Cape Cod Comm 2240 Iyanough Rd West Barnstable MA 02668*

PANKA, JEANNE BROSTEK, Bio & Environmental Sci Tchr Syracuse, NY; *m:* Lawrence James; *c:* Kimberly Szyikowski, L Szyikowski; *ed:* SUNY at Oswego (BS) Bio & Scndry Ed 1 Post-Graduate SUNY at Oswego Permanent Cert NY St; *cr:* Gillette MS Sci Tchr 1970-76; Roxboro Road MS Sci Tchr 1977-82; N Syracuse Jr High Sci Tchr 1982-86; Cicero-North Syracuse High Bi Environmental Sci Tchr 1986-; *ai:* Adv Environmental Consc Organized Stdnts; Coach Sci Olympiad, Envirothon Team; Bldg Plan Team Sec 6 Yrs; Alternative Assessment Dist Plan Team; Time Mng Comm; NSTA 1986-; NBTA 1992-; STANYS 1982-; Excl in Tchng Syracuse Univ 1992; Learning Styles Trainer for Dist 1993-; *off* Cicero-North Syracuse HS Northstar Dr Cicero NY 13039*

W, MARY, Span Tchr & Frgn Lang Chprsn; *b:* Rosenheim, y; *ed:* OH St Univ (BS) Span, Russian 1968; Kent St Univ (MA) 74; Attnd Univ of Madrid, Univ of Northern IA, CSU, Univ of ica, Oberlin Univ, Akron U, Univ of the Amer Mexico, John Carroll otre Dame Coll; *cr:* Vly Forge HS Span Tchr 1969-, Frgn Lang ead 1979-; *ai:* Span Club Adv; Trip Chaperone; PEA, NEOEA)EA; NEA; OFLA; Church; OFLA Presenter; *office:* Valley Forge) Independence Blvd Parma OH 44130

, CHERYL SLOMA, Spanish Teacher; *b:* Johnson City, NY; *m:* William; *c:* Margarita, Christopher; *ed:* Broome Comm Coll (AA) Arts 1976; SUNY at Fredonia (BA) Span Scndry Ed 1978; Bingham (SEd) Rdng Ed 1983; *cr:* Chenango Forks Schsl Span Tchr 1978-; Comm Coll Span Adj Fac 1991; SUNY Albany Span Adj Fac 1993-; n Club Adv; CF Tchrs Assn, NYSUT, AFT 1978-; AATSP 1986-; Chenango Forks HS 1 Gordon Dr Binghamton NY 13901

BAKER, FRANK ALLEN, Assistant Principal; *b:* Baton Rouge, Cynthia; *c:* Niechelle, Chris; *ed:* Clarion Univ (BS) Elem Ed 1980; rg St Coll (MED) Guid & Cnslng 1986; Shippensburg Univ (MED) alship Scndry 1993; *cr:* Rockwood Schl Dist 3rd-4th Grd Elem Ed 80-86; Conewago Vly Schl Dist Guid Cnslr 1986-93; Spring Cove st Asst HS Prin 1993-; *ai:* Asst Jr High Wrestling Coach.

S, HELEN A., Assoc Prof of Travel & Tourism; *b:* Oakland, NJ; nolas; *c:* Dianne Pannes-Mc Cann, Peter, Sue; *ed:* Herkimer Cty Coll (AS) Travel & Tourism; SUNY at Utica, Rome (BA) Bus Ed SUNY at Oswego (MS) Ed 1987; Walt Disney World Mngmt s; System One Airline Cmptr Trng; *cr:* Buck, Seifert & Jost Sec 7; Wall St Journal Advertising Asst 1967-68; Dolgeville HS Tchr 3; Herkimer Cty Comm Coll Assoc Prof 1983-; *ai:* Travel Club Adv; omm; Trip, Tour Organizer, Escort; Leatherstocking Cntry 1985-; storical Soc 1988-; Amer Soc of Travel Agents 1989-; Mohawk Vly Arts 1995-; Ilion Fnd Bd 1994-, Sec; Herkimer Cnty Chamber of rce Tourism Bd 1988-; Chancellors Awd Excl in Tchng; HCCC Fnd Articles Pub; *office:* Herkimer County Comm Coll Reservoir Road er NY 13350

ESI, MARIANN, 5th Grade Teacher; *b:* Boston, MA; *ed:* Suffolk S) Elem Ed 1965, (MED) Prsnl mgmt 1984, (CAGS) Ldrshp 1985; tertown Pub Schls Tchr 1965-, Asst Prin 1984-87; *ai:* Watertown Assoc Exec Bd; NEA 1965-; MA Tchrs Assoc 1965-; Watertown assoc 1965-, Pres; Town Meeting Mem 1974-81; Conservation 1978-84; Town Cncl 1985-92, VP; *office:* Hosmer Schl 1 Concord ertown MA 02172

ONE, JOSEPH JOHN,JR., English Teacher; *b:* New Brunswick, Susanna Saluga; *ed:* Rider Coll (BA) Scndry Ed Eng 1975; Trenton (MA) Eng 1993; Trenton St Coll Supervision Cert 1995; Inst for ced Placement; 3 Credits Wilkes Univ 1995; *cr:* Pemberton hip Schl Dist Eng Tchr 1977-, 7th Grd Soc Stud Tchr 1977-85; h Grd Eng Tchr 1986-, AP Lit & Comp 1994-, Alternative Pgm Supv *ai:* Winter Indoor Head Track Coach; Environmental Club Adv; ative Pgm Supv; NEA & NJEA 1977-; ASCD 1995-; *home:* 77 er Rd Wrightstown NJ 08562

Y, ROBERT J., Social Studies Teacher; *b:* Newark, NJ; *m:* Kathyn; ohanie; *ed:* Muhlenberg Coll (BA) Pol Sci 1989; Kutztown Univ Ed Cert 1992; *cr:* Whitehall MS Soc Stud Tchr 1994-; *ai:* Ftbl NCSS, NEA 1992-; *home:* 4954 Shawnee Ct Schnecksville PA

E, PETER CHARLES, Third Grade Teacher; *b:* Brooklyn, NY; *m:* E. Daly; *c:* Peter, Donald, Virginia Williams, Kenneth; *ed:* Hofstra BS) Bus Admin 1953, (MSEd) Elem Ed 1954; *cr:* Sears, Roebuck & vision Mgr 1945-54; Franklin Sq Pub Schls Tchr 1954-; *ai:* NEA, 54-; NYSUT-AFT; Franklin Sq Tchrs Assn 1954-, VP; East Meadow Club 1972-, Pres, Sec, Treas; Long Island Jr Soccer League 1972-, Hall of Fame; Nassau Cty Soccer Ofcls Assn 1958-, Pres, VP, ary Life Mem; PTA Awds 1973, 1982, 1993; Town of Hempstead Pub itation; *office:* Washington Street Schl Washington St Franklin NY 11010

ALEO, RICHARD P., Band Director; *b:* Monongahela, PA; *m:* a Karabin; *c:* Katherine, Regina, Richard; *ed:* IN Univ of PA (BS) Ed 1969; The Univ of TX at Austin (MM) Music Ed 1973; Attnd of Cincinnati, Univ of Hartford, Penn St Univ; *cr:* Ringgold Schl Dist mental Music Tchr 1969-; *ai:* Jazz Band; Usherettes; Tri-M Music oc; MENC & PMEA 1969-; NEA & PSEA 1969-; Soc for Rsrch in Ed 1969-; Intnl Assoc Jazz Ed 1970-; Percussive Arts Soc 1970-; and Assoc 1970-; Amer Schl Band Dir Assoc 1988-; MENC Cert Edctr; *office:* Finley MS Rt 88 Finleyville PA 15332*

ELLA, JANET MARIE, Biology Teacher; *b:* Lehighton, PA; *ed:* own Coll (BS) Bio 1984; E Stroudsburg Univ (MS) Bio 1992; *cr:* auqua HS Bio Tchr 1984-; Lehigh Cty Comm Coll Adjunct Bio Tchr *ai:* NHS Adv; Sec Steering Comm Mid Sts Evaluation; Dist Rep Prep Prgm; NSTA 1993-; NEA, Catasauqua Area Ed Assn 1984-; Mem 1995-; Eisenhower Sci Grant Prgm 1992-; Woodrow Wilson Fellowship Awd Princeton Univ; *office:* Catasauqua HS 850 Pine St auqua PA 18032

UOSCO, JOHN JOSEPH, Business & Special Ed Tchr; *b:* gfield, MA; *m:* Michelle Ann Belmer; *c:* John Joseph, Nicholas ny, Lucia Michelle, Joseph Wayne; *ed:* Univ of Tampa (BA) Bus nt 1984; Westfield St Scndry Ed Cert Bus Mngmt; *cr:* Our Lady of d Heart Math, His Tchr 1984-86; Children's Stud Home Tchr 87; Cathedral HS Math, Ec Tchr 1987-94; Longmeadow HS Bus, Spec Ed Tchr 1994-; *ai:* Var Boys Soccer Coach; Var Boys Track n Cathedral HS; MTA 1987-; Longmeadow Ed Assn 1994-; Natl er Coaches Assn 1989-; Western MA Soccer Coaches Assn, Pres; : Longmeadow HS 95 Grassy Gutter Rd Longmeadow MA 01106

JCCI, KELLY DEEP, 10th-12th Grade English Tchr; *b:* Pittsburgh, *m:* Mario; *ed:* Univ of Memphis (BA) Eng 1991; Univ of Pittsburgh Ed 1993; *cr:* NJC Architects Sec 1990-91; Univ of Pittsburgh Tchng 1991-92; North Allegheny Schl Dist Intern 1992-93; Quaker Vly Sr ng Tchr 1993-; *ai:* Girls Tennis Coach Moon HS; Boys Tennis Coach; PSEA 1993-; Phi Kappa PHi; Nom Sallie Mae Tchr Awd; *home:* 345 Lynn Dr Moon Twp PA 15108*

Y, EDWARD A., Teacher; *b:* Northampton, PA; *m:* Barbara; *c:* ann Madden; *ed:* Kutztown St Tchrs Coll (BS) Soc Stud 1958; (MA) Stud; *cr:* Northampton Sr HS Amer Govt, World His, Ec & 10th Grd His Tchr 1958-; *ai:* Numerous presentations on Local His Topics to orical Socs & Civic Org; Working on a Museum of Local His; ingon Atlas Cement Co Mem Museum; NEA, 36 Yrs; AFT; PSEA, er Local VP; His Articles Pub in Newspaper; His Museum Displays ement Industry in the LeHigh Valley & Research on the Immigrants Made Them; *office:* Northampton Sr HS 1619 Laubach Ave nampton PA 18067

LA, EVELYN JOAN, Fourth Grade Teacher; *b:* Brooklyn, NY; *ed:* St 's Univ (BS) Ed 1957, (MS) Guid, Psych 1959; *cr:* Newbridge Road 1st, 3rd, 4th Grd Tchr 1957-76; Barnum Woods Schl 4th Grd Tchr -; *ai:* PTA Tchr Del; Grd Level, Consumer Ed Club Chprsn; Comm to New Progress Report 1994-95; Comm to Revise Growing Healthy n Grd 4 Natl Inst of Hlth 1985-93; AFT; NYSUT; Barnum Woods TA 1976-; East Meadow TA 1957-, Newbridge Tchr Rep; March of Dimes 1994-, Chain Reaction Fac Adv; Nassau Cty Dept of Drug & Alcohol Abuse, Growing Healthy Prgm Trainer 15 Yrs; East Meadow Dev 4th Grd Soc Stud Curr, Elem Guid Curr; *office:* Barnum Woods Elem Schl 500 May Ln East Meadow NY 11554

PAOLELLA, PATRICIA MULLIS, 7th & 8th Grade English Tchr; *b:* Albemarle, NC; *m:* Richard; *c:* Amy; *ed:* Pfeiffer Coll (BA) His 1967; *cr:* Albemarle Sr HS Soc Stud Tchr 1967-68; South Stanly HS Soc Stud Tchr 1968-70; Sub Tchr 1985-88; St Joseph Schl 5th-8th Grd Eng Tchr 1989-; *ai:* Natl Cath Edctrs 1989-; *office:* St Joseph Schl 115 Telford St East Orange NJ 07018

PAOLILLO, LORIANNE, Eighth Grade Algebra Teacher; *b:* Riverside, NJ; *ed:* Univ of DE (BS) Elem Ed, Discipline in MS Math 1989; 15 Grad Credits; *cr:* Gunning Bedford MS 8th Grd Pre-Algebra, Algebra Tchr 1989-; *ai:* Chrldng Coach 1990-; Stu Cncl Adv 1989-; Team Ldr 1992-; NEA, DSEA 1989-; *office:* Gunning Bedford MS Cox Neck Rd Delaware City DE 19706

PAOLINO, FRANK J., 4th Grade Teacher; *b:* New Haven, CT; *m:* Roseann Cusano; *c:* Frank, Michael, DeAnna; *ed:* Southern CT St Univ (BS) Elem Ed 1977, (MS) Safety Ed 1981; *cr:* Washington Magnet Schl 5-6 Grd Tchr; Seth G Haley Elem Schl 4-6 Grd Tchr 1985-; *ai:* St of CT Assessor of Tchr, Mentor Beginning Tchr, Support Tchr Tchrs in Trng; AFT, Local PTA 1977-; WHFT 1977-, Steward; West Haven Italian Amer Civic Assn 1977-, Pres 1986; Shore Haven Jr Bsbl League 1988-, Coach; West Haven Playground Comm 1992-, Childrens Comm Co-Chprsn; Nom Tchr of Yr 1989; Pilot Tchr Saxon-Larson Math 4 1993-95; *office:* Seth G Haley Elem Schl 148 South St West Haven CT 06516*

PAOLONE, REYNALD JOSEPH, Jr HS Soc Stud & Rdng Tchr; *b:* Youngstown, OH; *m:* Brenda Sue Griffiths; *ed:* Youngstown St Univ (BSEd) Geography & 7th-12th Grds His 1978, (BSEd) 7th-12th Grds Comprehensive Soc Stud 1990, (BSEd) 1st-8th Grds Elem 1991; *cr:* Our Lady of Mount Carmel Tchr 1979-; *ai:* Athletic Dir; Safety Patrol Spon; Jr HS Ftbl Prgm Coord; NCEA 1979-; City of Girard 1994-, Councilman at Large; Chamber of Commerce 1994-; *office:* Our Lady Mt Carmel Schl 309 N Rhodes Ave Niles OH 44446

PAOLOZZI, ANTHONY S., English Dept Chairman & Tchr; *b:* New York, NY; *ed:* Fordham Univ (BA) Eng & Philosophy 1984; Loyola Univ of Chicago (MA) Philosophy 1986; *cr:* Xavier HS Eng Tchr 1988-; *ai:* Asst Ath Dir; NCTE 1992-; ASCD 1995-; *office:* Xavier HS 30 W 16th St New York NY 10011

PAOLOZZI, LINDA ANN, Fourth Grade Teacher; *b:* Providence, RI; *ed:* Mount Saint Joseph Coll (BA) Elem Ed 1970; Attnd RI Coll, Univ of RI; *cr:* RI Coll Girls Bsktbl Head Coach 1976-80; G J West Elem Tchr 1970-; Mount Pleasant HS Girls Bsktbl Head Coach 1980-; *ai:* Hope HS Sftbl Coach; Officiating at Girls Bsktbl,Fast Pitch & Slow Pitch Sftbl; AFT 1970-; Global Ed 1994-; Schl Improvement 1990-; *home:* 5 Paradise Ln Johnston RI 02919

PAONE, THOMAS JOSEPH, Hlth Educator Coord & Teacher; *b:* Troy, NY; *m:* Andrea Lynn Pelletier; *c:* Kathryn Lynn; *ed:* Hudson Vly Comm Coll (AS) PE 1984; Russell Sage Coll (BS) Hlth Ed 1986; The Sage Colls (MS) Hlth Ed 1991; Coll of St Rose Educl Admin; *cr:* Albany HS Hlth Educator 1986-; *ai:* SADD Co Adv; NYSFPHE 1986-, Regnl Pres; APSTA, Albany HS PTSA 1986-, Tchr of Yr 1994; Albany City Schl Dists Hlth Ed Advy Cncl 1995-, Co-Chair; Albany Co Substance Abuse Prevention Prgm Awd of Merit 1995; Albany Co Stop DWI Comm Svc Awd 1994; *office:* Albany HS 700 Washington Ave Albany NY 12203*

PAPA, CHRISTOPHER M., Jr HS Language Arts Teacher; *b:* Albany, NY; *m:* Marika T.; *c:* Victoria Heather; *ed:* Siona Coll (BA) Eng Ed 1977; St Univ of NY at Albany (MA) Eng, Advanced Classroom Tchng 1985; Attnd Harvard Univ Grad Schl of Ed, Inst of Rdng, Writing, Civic Ed; *cr:* Sacred Heart of Mary 6, 7, 8th Grd Eng Tchr 1979-80; Keveny Meml Acad 9-12th Grd Eng Tchr 1981-83; Gardner Dickinson 7, 8, 9th Grd Lang Arts Tchr 1983-; *ai:* Girls Soccer Coach; NYSTU, AFT 1983-; NYSEC 1995-, Tchr of Excl; DARE Advy Comm 1988-; NY St Tchr of Excl 1995-; Flwshp Awded 1991; *office:* Gardner-Dickinson Schl East Ave Wynantskill NY 12198

PAPA, EILEEN MARIE, Mathematics Teacher; *b:* Albany, NY; *ed:* Potsdam Coll (BA) Math, Scndry Ed 1989; SUNY at Albany (MA) Math Ed 1993; *cr:* Tamarac HS Math Tchr 1990-; *ai:* NHS Adv; AFT, BTA, NCTM 1990-.*

PAPADOPOULOS, EFTEHIA KOCONIS, Retired Scndry Math Teacher; *b:* Cleveland, OH; *m:* Socrates Demetrios; *c:* Demetrios, Evangeline Mirkov; *ed:* Case Western Reserve Univ (BA) Math 1960; Cleveland St Univ (MA) Curr & Instruction 1988; John Carroll Univ 3 Hrs; OH Dominican Coll 6 Hrs; Kent St Univ 24 Hrs; Univ of Akron 9 Hrs; *cr:* Cleveland City Schls Hrs Geometry, Hrs Alg, Math Tchr 1960-72; Brecksville City Schls Title I Math Tutor 1974-75; North Royalton City Schls Hrs Alg, Hrs Math Tchr 1975-94; Allegheny Coll Math, Area Instruction Ctr Math & Cmptrs Method Instr 1982-87; *ai:* Problem Solvers Club Adv; Textbook Selection, Competency Testing, Dist Math, Prins Comm, North Cntrl Evaluation Comms; NCTM 1975-; OCTM 1975-, Buck Martin Outs Teach 1984; GCCTM 1975-, Dist Dir, NE Dist Outs Teach; NEA, OEA, NREA 1975-95; Hellenic Preservation 1993-, Ed Comm; St Paul Philoptochos, Pi Lambda Theta 1984-; PTA 1960-, St Hon Life Mem; Eisenhower Grant Recipient 1992; Jennings Scholar 1984, 1990; 3rd Pl Sec Division Natl Ec Software Ed Compt 1983; Wkshps, Sessions OCTM, GCCTM, ACEI, CCEE, NCTM, NOTCC; Author, Programmer DANDEE Software TRS80; *home:* 6103 Millwood Dr Broadview Heights OH 44147*

PAPAGNI, NICK, Middle School Science Teacher; *b:* Brooklyn, NY; *m:* Marigrace; *c:* Emma; *ed:* SUNY at Buffalo (BS) Earth Sci, Sec Ed 1989; Working on Masters Earth Sci Sec Ed; *cr:* Clarence Jr High Sci Tchr 1991-93; Alden Cntrl Schls Sci Tchr 1993-; *ai:* Sci Fair Coord; Rocket Club Adv; AFT, NYSUT 1993-; STANYS 1994-; *office:* Alden MS Crittenden Rd Alden NY 14004

PAPAHAGIS, SANDRA L., Third Grade Teacher; *b:* Boston, MA; *m:* Francis D'Alessandro; *c:* Deborah Zinck, Sarah Eastham; *ed:* Boston St Coll (BS) Elem Ed 1963; Hundreds of Post Grad Hrs in Various Educl Stud; *cr:* Nathaniel Hawthorne Schl 2nd & 3rd Grd Tchr 1963-73; Dr Wm H Ohrenberger Schl 3rd Grd Tchr 1973-; *ai:* Mentor Tchr for Tchng Interns from Local Colls & Univs; Chprsn & Lead Tchr Multi-Cultural Schl Prgm; Cheerleading Coach; Boston Tchrs Union 1963-, Bldg Rep, 30 Yrs Svc Awd; MA Fed of Tchrs, AFT 1963-; Impact II Tchr Networking Prgm Grant & Awd Twice; Boston Voyages in Learning Grant from Boston Globe Fnd; Horace Mann Curr Project Grant; Boston Pub Schls Consultant for Soc Stud Textbook; *office:* Dr Wm H Ohrenberger Schl 175 W Boundary Rd West Roxbury MA 02132*

PAPALIA, FRANK R., Spanish & English Teacher; *b:* East Meadow, NY; *m:* Madeline M. Angelucci; *c:* Michele; *ed:* Albright Coll (BA) Span 1961; Syracuse Univ (MA) Span 1967, (MS) Rdng 1976, (CA) Rdng 1985; Studies in Spain, NDEA Govt Schlsp; *cr:* Otisville Union Free Schl Span Tchr 1961-64; North Syracuse HS Span, Eng Tchr 1964-; Syracuse Univ Summer Inst 1976-; *ai:* Tech, Attendance Comms; Optimist Club 1980-85; Zoning Bd Appeals 1982-92, Chm; Fed Govts Schl Excl Comm 1985-86; Presidential Schl Comm 1988-; NDEA Schlsps; *office:* Cicero-North Syracuse HS Rt 31 Cicero NY 13039

PAPANDREA, MARIANNE PETRUS, English Chair; *b:* Hartford, CT; *m:* John F.; *c:* Anne Marie, Mary Rose, John Jr.; *ed:* St Joseph Coll (BA) Eng 1957; Trinity Coll (MA) Eng 1959; SCSU 6th Yr Admin 1993; *cr:* Maloney HS Eng Tchr 1985-; *ai:* Class Spon; NCTE 1985-; CT Cncl of Eng Tchrs 1985-; Public Lib 1995-, Bd of Dirs; *office:* Maloney HS 121 Gravel St Meriden CT 06450

PAPARELLA, FRANCIS CHARLES, Middle School Math Teacher; *b:* Utica, NY; *ed:* SUC at Oswego (BS) Ed Math 1968; 30 Credit Hrs 1969; *cr:* Fulton Jr HS Math Tchr 1969-; *ai:* AFT, NYSUT, Fulton Tchrs Assn 1969-; *office:* Fulton Consolidated Schls 129 Curtis St Fulton NY 13069

PAPAS, FRAN S., Cooperative Bus Ed Coordinator; *b:* Warren, OH; *m:* Ted J. Jr.; *c:* Ted III, Michelle West; *ed:* Youngstown St Univ (BS) Comprehensive Bus Ed 1968; Kent St Univ (MS) Bus Ed 1971; Voc Ed Cert Youngstown St 1991; *cr:* Howland HS Bus Tchr 1968-71; Niles McKinley HS Bus Tchr, CBE Coord 1973-; Kent St Univ Part Time Instr 1994-; *ai:* Cooperative Bus Ed Club Adv; NEA, OEA 1968-; NCTA 1973-; NBEA 1992-; Zonta 1996; *office:* Niles Mc Kinley HS 616 Dragon Dr Niles OH 44446

PAPAS-KAVALIS, HELEN, Pediatrics Nursing Instructor; *b:* New York City, NY; *m:* George; *c:* Maria, Christina, Anthony; *ed:* NY Univ (BS) Nursing 1979, (MA) Nursing 1985; *cr:* Hillcrest Hospital Newborn Nursery Head Nurse 1983; Schneider Childrens Hospital LIJ Neonatal Nurse 1983-85; Westchester Cty Medical Ctr Pediatric Clinical Nurse Spec 1985-93; Bronx Comm Coll Pediatric Nursing Fac 1993-; *ai:* Review Network Nursing Educator Conultant to Prepare Grad Nurses for NCLEX Exam 1994-; Pre-nursing Stndts & Actual Nursing Stdnts Acad Adv; Successful Blood Drives Chprsn on Campus; Nursing Curr Comm & Admissions & Promotions Comms Active Mem; Assn of Pediatric Oncology Nurses 1993-; Amer Heart Assn 1985-; Amer Nurses Credentialing Ctr 1987-, Certified as Pediatric Nurse; Numerous Continuing Ed Seminars-Women & Hiv-AIDS-A Life Span Approach, Test Construction Wkshp, Legal Implications to Nursing Fac, Self Stud by AJN; Primary Data Collector for Multi-Institutional Research Stud Focusing on Pediatric Intensive Care Factors Related to Patient Outcomes in Collaboration with The Childrens Medical Ctr in Washington DC 1990; Mem of CORE Planning Comm for 2 Day Nursing Symposium; Pub in Amer Nurse; Dev Numerous Educl Offerings; *office:* City Univ Of NY Bronx Comm Col W 181 St & University Ave Bronx NY 10453*

PAPENFUSS, LYNNE MARIE, English & History Teacher; *b:* Toledo, OH; *ed:* Univ of Toledo (BED) Eng, (MA) Amer His 1982; Some Work Toward Doctorate; Attnd OH Univ; *cr:* Heath City Schls Tchr 1983-93; Fairlawn Local Schls Tchr 1984-; *ai:* Academia, Soc Stud Competition, Chess & Sr Class Adv; NEA 1990-; New Choices Abuse Shelter 1994-, Renovation Dir; Habitat for Humanity 1987-; Grad Fellowship; *office:* Fairlawn Elem Schl 18800 Johnston Rd Sidney OH 45365

PAPETTI, JANET GAIS, Guidance Counselor; *b:* Elizabeth, NJ; *m:* Joseph; *ed:* Kean Coll (MA) Stu Personnel Svcs 1984; Montclair St Coll (BA) Home Ec Ed 1975; *cr:* Elizabeth Bd of Ed Home Ec Tchr 1976-86, Guidance Cnslr 1986-; *ai:* Project Grad Comm; Core Team Substance Abuse Prgm; Elizabeth Ed Assn 1976-; NJ Ed Assn 1976-; NEA 1976-; *office:* Elizabeth HS 600 Pearl St Elizabeth NJ 07202

PAPETTI, LINDA LOPEZ, Fourth Grade Teacher; *b:* Brooklyn, NY; *m:* Joseph M.; *c:* Jennifer, Michael; *ed:* Finch Coll (BS) Ed 1974; *cr:* Morris Schl Dist Basic Skills Tchr 1 Yr; West Dover 4th Grd Tchr 10 Yrs; *ai:* Invention Convention Adv; Handbook Comm; NEA 1986-; Governors Recognition Awd, Christie Whitman; *office:* West Dover Elem Schl Blue Jay Dr Toms River NJ 08755

PAPIN, DEBORAH SHIPPEE, 11th-12th Grd English Tchr; *b:* Watertown, NY; *c:* Daniel, Molly; *ed:* St Lawrence Univ (BA) Eng & Writing 1984; St Univ Coll at Potsdam (MA) Lit 1994; Assorted Ed Classes; *cr:* Jefferson Cty Schls Sub Tchr 1984-91; Jefferson Comm Coll Adj Eng Instr 1984-95; Indian River Cntrl HS Eng Tchr 1992-; *ai:* Yrbk Adv 1992-; NYSUT 1992-; BSA 1995-, Pack Ldr; *office:* Indian River Central H S Rt 11 Philadelphia NY 13673

PAPINEAU, MARGARET SABETTI, Spanish Teacher; *b:* Providence, RI; *m:* David Michael; *c:* Philip; *ed:* Salve Regina Coll (BAS) Scndry Ed, Span 1988; RI Coll (MED) Scndry Ed, Span 1995; *cr:* St Mary's Acad Span Tchr 1988-90; Mt St Charles Acad Span Tchr 1990-92; Ponaganset HS Span Tchr 1994-; *ai:* NEA 1994-; RIFLA 1988-; *office:* Ponaganset HS Anan Wade Rd No Scitvate RI 02814

PAPOULA, MANNY, Middle School Mathematics Tchr; *b:* Fall River, MA; *ed:* Boston Coll (BS) Math 1966; Bridgewater St Coll (MED) Scndry Admin 1968; 30 Grad Credits Beyond Masters Degree; *cr:* Somerset Jr High Math Tchr 1966-67; Rodman Job Corps Ctr Math Tchr 1967-68; Tiverton HS Math Tchr 1968-70; Memorial MS Math Tchr 1970-; *ai:* Math Team Coach; Bsktbl Club Adv; NEA 1968-; Vol Math Tutor with HS Dropouts 1980-90; tchr of the Yr at Memorial MS 1987; Begen Cty Citizen of the Yr 1993; NJ Citizen Of Yr 1995; *home:* 36 Avenue D Lodi NJ 07644

PAPP, CYNTHIA M., Chem, Bio & Earth Sci Tchr; *b:* Oak Park, IL; *m:* John; *ed:* The Coll of Wooster (BA) Chem 1986; OH St Univ Grad Level Work; *cr:* Worthington City Schls Sci Tchr 1988-; *ai:* Head Coach Girls Vlybl Prgm; NSTA & NEA 1993-; Tchr of Yr 1991-92; *office:* Worthington Kilbourne HS 1499 Hard Rd Columbus OH 43235

PAPPALARDO, PETER E., Teacher; *b:* E Stroudsburg ; *m:* Lynn; *c:* Chris, Alex, Peter, Aaron; *ed:* Juniata Coll (BS) Bio & Chem 1976; Duke Univ (MEM) Resource Policy 1977; Sci & Eng Cert ESU Eng Lit 1996; *cr:* Pocono Mountain HS Tchr 1982-85; East Stroudsburg Univ Prof Tutor 1986-; Pleasant Vly HS Tchr 1985-; *ai:* Coord SAP Pgm; Class Adv 1986-90; Track Coach 1986-87; Dept Head 1988-90; PA Sci Tchr Assn 1986-; PA Assn of Stu Asst Prof 1988-, Coord; Developmental Ed 1984-, Treas; United Way 1994-; 4 Completed Fiction Manuscripts; Numerous Articles; *office:* Pleasant Valley HS Rt 209 Brodheadsville PA 18322

PAPPANO, CAROL ANN, Mathematics Teacher; *b:* Waterbury, CT; *m:* Frederick Leonard; *c:* Stacy Marie, Anthony Joseph; *ed:* Sacred Heart Univ (BA) Math 1969; Fairfield Univ (MA) Comp Sci 1987; 36 Credit Hrs Psych Western CT 1969-70; 3 Credit Hrs Ed Tech Weslyn Univ 1995-96; 18 Credit Hrs Admin Cert 1989, 18 Credit Hrs Math Cert 1990-93; *cr:* Notre Dame Math Tchr 1969-70; Waterbury Cath HS Math Tchr 1970-73; Holy Cross HS Math Tchr 1978-85; Sacred Heart Univ Adj Asst Prof 1977-; Naugatuck HS Math Tchr 1985-; Naugatuck Valley Comm Tech Coll Adj Instr 1989-; *ai:* Greater New Haven Math League Coach & Treas 6 Yrs; Curr Comm; NEA 1985-, Schl Rep; Atomic; CEA 1985-; NCTMM; Historical Soc 2 Yrs; NSF 3 Yrs Fairfield Univ Pgm; PIMMS Fellow 2 Yrs Weslyn Univ; Est Pgm-Mentor & Cooperative Tchr; *office:* Naugatuck HS 543 Rubber Ave Naugatuck CT 06770

PAPPAS, CAROL SCHMOUTH, 9th-10th Grd World His Teacher; *b:* Boston, MA; *m:* William; *c:* Nicholas, Peter; *ed:* Univ of NH (BA) His 1962, Univ of Southern ME (MS) Adult Ed 1991; Post Grad 18 Credit Hrs Univ of NH His; Attnd Dartmouth Coll; *cr:* Kennebunk HS Eng, His Tchr 1962-70; South Portland HS Eng Tchr 1982-; Portland HS His Tchr 1983-; *ai:* Tchr Mentor for Tchrs Needing Re-Cert; Achvmt, Placement Action Team, NHS Comm; NEA, MEA, PEA 1983-; Tchr Acad Grants; Classical Assn of New England Grant; *office:* Portland HS 285 Cumberland Ave Portland ME 04101

PAPPAS, CAROLE E., Social Studies Tchr & Dept Chm; *b:* High Splint, KY; *m:* John E.; *c:* Michael J. Oglesbee, Eric J. Oglesbee; *ed:* Wright St Univ (BS) Elem Ed 1969, (MS) Elem Ed 1973; Addl 30 Credit Hrs Beyond Masters; *cr:* Ankeney Jr High 7-8th Grd Tchr 1969-95; *ai:* Soc Stud Dept Chair; NEA, OEA, BEA 1969-95; Miami Valley Folk Dancers 1974-, Chprsn, Sec, V-Chair, Honorary Couple of Yr 1993; Yugoslav Club of Greater Dayton 1974-, Del to Dayton World A Fair, Bd Mem; Dev Intervention Packet for Citizenship Proficiency; Helped Write Curr Guides at Local Level & Course of Stud at Cty Level; *office:* Ankeney Jr HS 4085 Shakertown Rd Beavercreek OH 45430

PAPPAS, JAMES PETER, Mathematics Teacher; *b:* Brooklyn, NY; *m:* Nancy V.; *c:* Alicia; *ed:* Dowling Coll (BA) Math 1980; SUNY at Stony Brook (MS) Math 1983; 60 Addl Hrs; *cr:* Kings Park HS Math Tchr 1980-; *office:* Kings Park HS 200 Route 25a Kings Park NY 11754*

PAPPAS, MARIE, Theology Teacher; *b:* Manhattan, NY; *ed:* Coll of St Rose (BA) Rel Stud 1978; Angelicum St Thomas Univ (MA) Rel Ed 1985; Fordham Univ (APD) Rel Ed 1996; Cert Spiritual Direction Archdiocesan Schl Spirituality; *cr:* Immaculate Conception Schl Tchr 1975-80; St Ann's Schl Tchr 1980-85; Maria Regina HS Tchr, Theology Dept Chprsn 1985-; *ai:* Young Cath Ldrshp Club; News, Views; Pub Speaking; Folk Group; NCEA 1985-; News, Views Moderator of Yr; NCEA Nom Tchr; Curr Scndry Rel Ed to be Pub; *office:* Maria Regina HS 500 W Hartsdale Ave Hartsdale NY 10530*

PAPPAS, NICHOLAS, Spanish Teacher; *b:* New York, NY; *ed:* LIU (BA) Psych & Span 1968, (MS) Guid & Cnslng 1971; LaGuardia Comm Coll Film & Hum Cert 1995; Attnd Queens Coll CUNY Admin & Supervision, The New Schl Psych; *cr:* Jr HS 133 Span Tchr 1968-74; IS 193 Span Tchr & Guid Cnslr 1974-82; Jr HS 104 M Span Tchr & Guid 1982-; *ai:* After Schl Intramurals; Tutorial; UFT 1968-; Gateway Plaza Tenants Assn 1985-, VP; *home:* 355 S End Ave Apt 4E New York NY 10280

PAPPAS, OLGA, Teacher; *b:* Webster, MA; *ed:* Clark Univ (BA) Sociology 1974; Assumption Coll (MS) Rehab Cnslng 1977; Nichols Coll (MBA) Bus Admin 1982; North Easterix Univ Post Grad 15 Credit Hrs; *cr:* Park N Shop Supermarket Front End Mgr 1943-74; Shepherd Hill Regnl Dist Ed Tchr 1975-76; Bay Path Voc Dist Ed Tchr 1976-79; Bartlett HS Mrktg Tchr 1979-; *ai:* DECA Club Adv; MTA 1974-; Redevelopment Authority 1983-, Chm; Philoptochos Soc 1943-, Sec.

PAPPAS, SUSAN CHIRUMBOLO, 5th Grade Teacher; *b:* Canton, OH; *m:* Thomas L.; *c:* Nathan, Kara; *ed:* Kent St Univ (BS) Elem Ed 1974; Ashland Univ Credit Hrs; *cr:* Martin Elem 6th Grd Tchr 1975-84; Fairmount Elem 5th Grd Tchr 1984-; *ai:* NEA, OEA, CPEA 1975-; Grant for Listening Skills 1990; *office:* Fairmount Elem Schl 2701 Coventry Blvd NE Canton OH 44705

PAPPAS, THOMAS FRANCIS, Assistant Principal; *b:* Worchester, MA; *m:* Christine J. Carlson; *c:* Nicholas, Zachary, Alexander; *ed:* Framingham St Coll (BS) Elem Ed 1977; Worcester St Coll (MED) Educl Adm 1981; 30 Addl Hrs; *cr:* Lake St Schl Tchr 1977-85; Elm Pk Comm Schl Asst Prin 1993-; Chandler Elem Comm Schl Comm Sch Adm 1994-; *ai:* Pub Schl Staff Dev, Multicultural Steering, Exec Comms; Pub & Work Voc Schl; MA Comm on Comm Educ; Governance Cncl; MA Tchrs Assn, NEA 1977-; Educl Assn of Worcester 1986-; Advocates for Yth, Healthy Neighborhoods 1994-; Cntrl MA Conf Ftbl Off 1980-; Christ the King Cath Church 1982-; Grant Designed to Fit; Co-Nect Proposal; *office:* Tatnuck Magnet Schl 1083 Pleasant St Worcester MA 01602

PAPPO, STANLEY, Mathematics Teacher; *b:* Long Beach, NY; *m:* Robin Trust; *c:* Jennifer; *ed:* C W Post (BS) Math 1971, (MS) Math 1974; *cr:* Sheepshead Bay HS Math Tchr 1971-72; East Meadow Jr HS Math Tchr 1972-73; Farmingdale HS Math Tchr 1973-78; Half Hollow Hills HS Math Tchr 1978-; *ai:* Math Research Dir; AFT 1972-; Recognized by Westinghouse Talent Search; Saint Johns Symposium; NY St Talent Search; NY St Energy Competition for Finalists; Nom by Tufts Univ for Recognition as an Outstanding Tchr; *office:* Half Hollow Hills HS East 50 Vanderbilt Pky Dix Hills NY 11746*

PAPROCKI, WALLACE COATES, Latin Teacher; *b:* Hartford, CT; *m:* Theodore F.; *c:* Anna Isozaki, Lee; *ed:* CT Coll (BA) Latin 1963; Trinity Coll (MA) Ed, Latin & Eng 1966; *cr:* Daniel Hand HS Latin Tchr 1964-67; Adirondack Comm Coll Eng Instr 1981-82; Salem HS Eng Tchr 1982-83; Cambridge Cntrl Schl Latin Tchr 1983-; *ai:* Classical Assn of Empire St, Classical Assn of New England 1980-; AFT 1982-; Girl Scouts 1970-80, Ldr; NHS Adv 1984-90; *office:* Cambridge Central Schl S Park St Cambridge NY 12816

PAPSON, REBECCA JO, Science Teacher; *b:* Washington, PA; *m:* Frank J. Jr.; *c:* Greg, Michael; *ed:* CA Univ of PA (BS) Elem Ed 1972; *cr:* John F. Kennedy MS Sci Tchr 1978-; *ai:* PA Jr Acad of Sci Spon.

PAQUETTE, EVELINE GAIL, Visual Arts Teacher; *b:* Providence, RI; *ed:* RI Coll (BS) Art Ed 1975; Lesley Coll (MS) Integrated Arts 1978; Providence Coll, MA Coll of Art, RI Coll, Univ of RI, 42 Grad Credits, Sci Courses for Cert Scndry Bio, Gen Sci; *cr:* Woonsocket Jr HS Art Edctr 1975-90; Woonsocket Sr HS Art Edctr 1990-, Mentor 1995-; RI Schl of Design Critic Tchr 1992-; *ai:* AFT 1975-; NEA 1991-; Conanicut Art 1990-; RI Art Tchrs Assn 1975-94, Pres, VP, Sec, Photography RI Art Edctr; Arts & Act, Schl Arts Magazines; RI Art Edctr of Yr 1984 NAEA; *office:* Woonsocket Sr HS 777 Cass Ave Woonsocket RI 02895*

PAQUETTE, LINDA PARSONS, 7th-12th Grd Lang Arts Teacher; *b:* Bangor, ME; *c:* Jennefer P. Eaton, Sean; *ed:* Univ of VT (BS) Scndry Ed 1975; +30 Post Grad Stud Castleton St Coll; *cr:* Poultney Elem Tchng Asst 1984-87; Poultney HS 7th-8th Grd Lang Arts Tchr 1989-91, 8th Grd Soc Stud & Lang Arts Tchr 1993-; ME Trauma Ctr Residential Instr 1991-93; *ai:* Sr Class Adv 1995; NHS Adv 1995-; 8th Grd Class Adv 1996-; Schl Newspaper Adv 1996-; Goals 2000 Literacy Comm 1996-; Act 230-504 Team 1996-; VAMLE 1995-; NCTE 1995-; ASCD 1995-; Poultney Facilities Comm 1996-, Tchr Rep; *office:* Poultney HS E Main St Poultney VT 05764*

PAQUETTE, PAUL ROGER, 8th Grade Social Studies Tchr; *b:* Lowell, MA; *m:* Deborah Lee Monroe; *c:* Brian, Michael, David, Jason Julie; *ed:* Notre Dame Coll (BA) Soc Stud, Ed 1990; *cr:* Iber Holmes Grove MS 8th Grd Soc Stud Tchr 1990-; *ai:* Adv Debate, Mock Trial Team; Yrbk; Var Bsbl Coach; 8th Grd Fundraising Coord; NEA 1990-; *office:* Iber Holmes Gove MS School St Raymond NH 03077

PAQUIN, JOSEPH V., Geology & Science Teacher; *b:* Fall River, MA; *m:* Sarah E. Porter; *c:* Paddy, Yin; *ed:* Univ of RI (BS) Zoology 1976; 8 Credits Particle Physics, Astrophysics Harvard Univ; 6 Credith Biotech, Anthropology Providence Coll; *cr:* Diman Voc Schl Physics Tchr 1984-89; Cumberland HS Physics, Astonomy, Geology Tchr 1989-93; Toll Gate HS Physics, Bio, Geology, Environmental Sci 1993-; *ai:* Founded Musicians Club; Class 1989 Yrbk Dedicattee; *office:* Toll Gate HS 575 Centerville Rd Warwick RI 02886

PARADIS, KAREN DUTTON, Teacher of the Gifted; *b:* New Britain, CT; *m:* Robert M.; *ed:* Cntrl CT St Univ (BS) Elem Ed 1969, (MS) Art Ed 1979; 36 Hrs 6th Yr Step Gifted Ed, Curr; *cr:* Flanders Elem Schl Fourth Grd Tchr 1969-75, Sixth Grd Tchr 1976-77; Cntrl Elem Schl 4-6 Grd Systemwide Tchr of Gifted 1977-; *ai:* Gifted Curr Comm; Womens Stud MS; CEA, NEA 1969-; CAG 1989-, Bd of Dirs; Our Lady of Grace Church 1990-, Parish Cncl; *office:* Central Elem School 100 Victoria Dr Southington CT 06489*

PARADIS, PIXIE BERGEZ, Second Grade Teacher; *b:* Benton Harbor, MI; *m:* Arthur Joseph; *c:* Todd Joseph, Desiree Danielle; *ed:* Loyola at Baltimore (MS) Rdng 1989; *cr:* John Nevins Andrew 2nd Grd Tchr 18 Yrs; Adjunt Prof At Columbia Union Coll 1995-; *ai:* Mid States Evaluation Mem; Wheaton Seventh Day Adventist Church Kndgtn Ldr; Wheaton Pathfinders Asst Ldr; Potomac Conf General Conf of Seventh Day Adventist Church Commissioned Licensed Tchr; *office:* John Nevins Andrews Schl 117 Elm Ave Takoma Park MD 20912*

PARADISE, NANCY A., Pre-K Teacher; *b:* Bayshore, NY; *m:* Jeffrey W.; *c:* Heather, Jeffrey; *ed:* Georgian Court Coll (BA) Elem Ed 1975; Southampton Coll (MS) Elem Ed 1981; Addl 75 Credits Grad & Inservice Courses; *cr:* South Haven Schl Tchr Asst 1978-79, Kndgtn Tchr 1979-81, Kndgtn T., Creative Writing Tchr 1986-87, Pre-K At Risk Tchr 1987-91; Brookhaven Elem Schl Pre-K At Risk Tchr 1991-; *ai:* Union Bldg Rep; Bldg Team; AFT 1987-, Union Rep; Natl Assn for Early Chldhd Ed 1991-; Outstdng Elem Ed Major Georgian Court Coll 1976; Articles Pub; Cert of Commendation Bd of Ed 1991-92; Produce Early Chldhd Video 1991; Governor's Early Chldhd Career Recognition Awd 1992; *office:* Brookhaven Elem Schl 101 Fireplace Neck Rd Brookhaven NY 11719

PARADOWSKI, NATALIE LAMB, Fourth & Fifth Grd Tchr; *b:* Batavia, NY; *m:* David P.; *ed:* Roberts Wesleyan Coll (BA) Sociology & Social Work 1974; NY St Univ 30 Hrs Post Grad Work; *cr:* Gladstone South Elem Schl at Gladstone Queensland Australia 3rd & 4th Grd Tchr 1975-76; Albion MS 5th Grd Tchr 1979; Colden Elem Schl 4th & 5th Grd Tchr 1980-; *ai:* Colden PTA VP; AFT 1980-; NYSUJ 1980-; Adirondack Mountain Club 1990-, Sec; Sweet Adelines Lake Effect Harmony 1993-, Sec; Springville-Griffith Inst Tchr of the Yr 1990; *office:* Colden Elem Schl PO Box 197 Colden NY 14033*

PARADY, ROGER JAMES,JR., High School Soc Studies Tchr; *b:* Gloucester, MA; *m:* Phyllis Laiachino; *c:* Joseph P., Paula C.; *ed:* North Shore Comm Col (AS) 1969; Salem St Coll (BS) Ed, Soc Stud 1971; *cr:* Milton Fuller Schl Jr HS Soc Stud Tchr 1972; Ralph B, O'Maley MS Soc Stud Tchr 1973-85; Gloucester HS Soc Stud Tchr 1985-; *ai:* NHS Selection, Scheduling Review Comms; GHS Site-Based Mgmt Team; Middle to HS Transition Comm; GHS Handbook Comm; NEA, MTA, GTA 1972-; Elks Club Post 892 1977-; Amer Legion Post 2 1980-; *office:* Gloucester HS Leslie O. Johnson Rd Gloucester MA 01930

PARANDELIS, ROSEMARY SANTIAGO, HS Religion Studies Teacher; *b:* Harlem, NY; *m:* Robert; *c:* Raina, Rhea; *ed:* Seton Hill Coll (BA) Art 1962; Notre Dame Univ (MA) Art 1967; St Joseph's Seminary (MA) Ministry 1990; *cr:* Sacred Heart HS Tchr, Rel Stud Dept Chair 1989-95; Acad of Resurrection Rel Stud Tchr; Yonkers Tchr Ctr Calligraphy Tchr 1990-95; Coll of New Rochelle Adjunct Prof, Calligraphy Tchr; *ai:* Clown Ministry; Emotions Anonymous 1989-95, Chprsn; Natl Cncl of Chrstn & Jews Woman of Valor Awd; *office:* Sacred Heart HS 34 Convent Ave Yonkers NY 10703*

PARASKEVOPOULOS, ANTHONY ANDREW, High School Music Teacher; *b:* Limassol, Cyprus; *m:* Margaret; *ed:* OH Wesleyan Univ (BM) Music Ed 1971; Manhattan Schl of Music (MM) Music Ed 1975; Teachers Coll Columbia Univ (EDD) Music Ed 1989; Juilliard Schl of Music Choral Conducting 1979; Natl Conservatory of Greece Piano Cert 1966; Multicultural Music Byzantine Music 1994; *cr:* Greek Archdiocesan Schl System Choral, General Music Tchr 1975-82; JHS Choral, General Music Tchr 1982-84; Bayside HS Piano Prgm Dir 1984-; *ai:* Annual Piano Recital Coach, Dir; Philosophy Club Adv; UFT 1982-; Tchrs Coll Stu Senate 1987-, Music Dept Rep; Kappa Delta Pi 1984-, Natl Honors in Ed; Makarios Awd 1979; Lectures Interdiciplinery Curr Physics of Music, Latin, Music, Byzantine Music, Reviewer Multicultural Curr Bd of Ed 1993; *home:* 375 Riverside Dr Apt 6G New York NY 10025*

PARATORE, ANTHONY JOHN, Advanced English Teacher; *b:* Syracuse, NY; *m:* Mary Lou Skahen; *c:* Anna, Greg, Beth; *ed:* LeMoyne Coll (BA) Eng 1968; Syracuse Univ (MA) Eng & Ed 1970; 30 Credits Inservice Courses; *cr:* Levy Jr High & 7th-9th Grd Eng & Latin Tchr 1968-77; Nottingham High 9th-12th Grd Eng & 10th-11th Grd Advanced Eng 1977-; *ai:* Dept Chprsn; Site Based Action Ldr; Final Exam & Portfolio Comm; NYSUT 1968-; Syracuse Tchrs Assn 1968-, Alternate Rep; AFT 1968-; Nottingham Outstdng Tchr Awd 1989; Tchr of Excl Awd NY St Eng Cncl 1990; *office:* Nottingham HS 3100 E Genesee St Syracuse NY 13224

PARCELLA, MARY MCPOYLE, Spanish Tchr & FL Chprsn; *b:* Norristown, PA; *m:* Richard D.; *c:* Elizabeth, Richard Luis, Gregory; *ed:* Georgetown Univ (BSFS) Intnl Relations 1961; Fairfield Univ (BA) Span 1968; SCSU Cert as Chprsn; Ed Courses at Villanova Univ; *cr:* Bishop Shanahan HS Span & Eng Tchr 1961-64; Hamden HS Span Tchr 1964-74; Amity Regnl Jr HS Span Tchr 1985-86; Quinnipiac Coll Span Adjunct Prof 1986-88; Amity Regnl HS Span Tchr 1986-89; Jonathan Law HS Span Tchr 1991-, FL Chprsn 1995-; *ai:* NHS Fac Adv; MEA, NEA 1991-; AATSP 1964-74, 1991-; CCD Tchr 1984-; taft Schl Advanced Placement Span Lit Wrkshps; NDEA Inst at Vanderbilt Univ; *office:* Jonathan Law HS 20 Lansdale Ave Milford CT 06460

PARCELS, MARTHA S., First Grade Teacher; *b:* Hillsboro, OH; *m:* Karl E.; *c:* Bryan, Barry, Brent, Karla Giddens; *ed:* Urbana Univ (BS) Elem Ed 1969; Wright St Univ (MA) Rdng Specialist 1980; Post-Grad Stud; *cr:* Urbana City Schls Tchr 1969-; *ai:* NEA, OEA 1969-; UACT 1969-, Sec 1985; Urbana Area Chamber Commerce 1986-89, Bd Dir; Awd Merit 1989; Certs Mert 1991, 1992, 1994; *office:* Urbana City Schls 626 N Russell St Urbana OH 43078

PARDINE, JOSEPH,JR., Mathematics Teacher; *b:* East Orange, NJ; *m:* Sandra MacGowan; *c:* Eric, Timothy, Jonathan, Andrew, Jeffrey; *ed:* Montclair St Coll (BA) Math 1971; 18 Addl Hrs; *cr:* Elmwood Park HS Math Tchr 1971-72; John F. Kennedy HS Math Tchr 1972-; *ai:* Ath Treas; Math Tutor; NEA 1972-; PEA 1978-; Madison Avenue Bapt Church 1969-, Deacon 9 Yrs; NJ Governor Tchr Recognition Awd 1988-89; *office:* John F. Kennedy HS 61 Preakness Ave Paterson NJ 07522

PARE, BRIAN JOSEPH, Dean of Students; *b:* Providence, RI; *m:* Sharon Lynn Decker; *c:* Carole Dutchka, Christen Dutchka, Jason Dutchka, Jonathan Dutchka; *ed:* Framingham St Coll (BA) Pol Sci 1978; Attnd Assumption Coll; *cr:* Medfield St Hosp Occupational Therapy Asst 1982-84; Marlboro Hosp Mental Hlth Cnslr 1984-86; Hillside Schl Tchr, Coach & Dean of Stdnts 1986-; *ai:* Admissions Person 1990-95; Placement Dir 1990-; Var Bsktbl Coach; Calesa Fndtn Terrific Tchr Awd 1993; *office:* Hillside Schl Robin Hill Rd Marlborough MA 01752*

PARE, DANIEL B., Social Studies Teacher; *b:* Nashua, NH; *m:* Holly B. Upton; *c:* Nathaniel; *ed:* Univ of NH at Manchester (NA) His 1992; Working on MAT; *cr:* Wilton-Lyndeborough Co-op Soc Stud Tchr 1993-; *ai:* Stu Senate, Granite St Challenge Adv; NEA 1995-; NHCSS 1994-; Church Sr Yth Group Adv; Governor's Success Grant; James Madison Fellow; *office:* Wilton-Lyndeboro Jr Sr HS 59 School Rd Wilton NH 03086

PARE, MARILYN WARREN, 8th Grade Teacher; *b:* Boston, MA; *m:* William P.; *c:* Krysia Hudson, Amelia Pare-Park, Mark, Amanda; *ed:* Boston Coll (BS) Ed 1963; Univ of NH (MS) Psych 1964; Loyola Coll Rdng 18 Hrs; Univ of DE Adult Ed; Towson St ECE; *cr:* Chesapeake Job Corps GED Instr 1980-82; Good Shepherd Schl 3rd, 8th Grd Tchr 1982-87; Univ of DE Coll Intensive Literacy Instr 1987-; Mt Aviat Acad 7th, 8th Grd Tchr 1987-; *ai:* LACC; Delmarva Rural Ministries 1991-92; St Agnes Guild 1970-; Thanks to Tchrs Finalist 1990; *office:* Mount Aviat Childs Rd Childs MD 21916*

PARENT, DANIEL PAUL, Social Studies Teacher; *b:* Cleveland Sherri Loreen Demarco; *c:* Brandon, Christopher, Nichalous; *ed:* Green St Univ (BA) Comprehensive Soc Stud 1985; Ashland U Miramar HS Soc Stud Tchr 1985-88; J P Taravella HS Soc S 1988-90; Westlake HS Soc Stud Tchr 1990-91; Marion L Steele Stud Tchr 1991-; *ai:* Var Ftbl & Wrestling Coach; Weight Coach; Tchrs Assn 1990-; NEA 1985-; *office:* Marion L Steele HS 450 Wa St Amherst OH 44001

PARENT, JAMES THOMAS, Math & Computer Science Prof Buren, ME; *m:* Cynthia Lois Conrad; *c:* Faith Hendrickson, Jil Heather, Elizabeth, Eric; *ed:* Ricker Coll (AA) Math, Chem 19 Math 1958; Univ of ME (MA) Math 1959; Self Stud Fractals Algebra Systems, Cmptr Programming Langs; *cr:* Dutchess Cor Math Tchr, Asst Prof 1959-65, Cmptr Ctr Dir 1965-73; Dutchess C Commissioner Cmptr Info Systems 1973-76; Empire St Coll Cmpt 1977-82; Schenectady Cty Comm Coll Math Prof 1982-; *ai:* Schlsp NEA, NYSMATYC 1982-; Excl in Tchng Awd 1988; St Univ Chancellor's Awd for Excl in Tchng 1989; Univ of Austin, Kell Intnl Medallion Awd for Excl in Tchng 1990; Stu Govt Assn C Achvmt, Dedication Cert of Merit 1994-95; *office:* Schenectady Comm Coll 78 Washington Ave Schenectady NY 12305

PARENT, MARILYN JEAN (D'AMORE), Spanish Teac Providence, RI; *m:* Roger R.; *c:* Michael, Matthew; *ed:* RI Co Scndry Ed, Fr, Span 1972; Attnd Univ of RI, Providence Coll; *cr.* R. Cole Jr HS 7-8th Grd Span Tchr 1972-; *ai:* Coach for Stdnts in N Exam 1988-; NEA, RATSP, RI Frgn Lang Assn 1972-; *office:* A Cole Jr HS 100 Cedar Ave East Greenwich RI 02818

PARENT, MICHAEL J., High School Special Needs Tchr; *b:* MA; *m:* Margaret Gibson; *c:* David, Mikaela; *ed:* Northern Esse Coll (AA) Liberal Arts 1980; Fitchburg St Coll (BA) Spec Ed 1 Credits in Educl Leadership; *cr:* Westford Acad Spec Needs Tch *ai:* Var Sftbl Coach, Asst Ftbl Coach 1982-; Class Adv 1983-86 1986-89; MA Tchrs Assoc, Ftbl Coaches Assoc, Sftbl Coache 1982-; Dracut Recreation Commission 1982-, Vice Chm; *office:* V Acad Patten Rd Westford MA 01886*

PARENT, ROBERT C., 7th Grd Math & Science Teacher; *b:* H MA; *m:* Noreen M. Briere; *c:* Christopher, Benjamin; *ed:* Westfield (BA) Ed 1972; PALMS 196 Hrs, Poercoaching 30 Hrs, Effective Practices 60 Hrs, Conflict Resolution 18 Hrs, Thinking Skills Discipline With Dignity 6 Hrs; *cr:* Park Street Schl 6th Grd Self Co 1972-76; White Brook MS 7-8th Grd Transitional Classroo 1976-81, 6th Grd Math & Sci Tchr 1981-93, 7th Grd Math & S 1993-; *ai:* Coach Var Swim Team 1976-96, Agegroup Swim 1976-8 Schl Cncl 1990-, Adv Comm 1988-90, Discipline Comm 1987-88, Valley Alliance- Acad of Excl 1995-, Dist Cncl Mem Communications Comm 1994-; Easthampton Ed Assn 1972-, Pres 1 MA Tchrs Assn, NEA 1972-; Town Meeting Mem 1983-89 Precin *office:* White Brook MS 200 Park St Easthampton MA 01027

PARENTI, ROBERT BERNHARD, Senior Parole Officer; *b:* Akro *m:* Bonita Joyce Grimes; *c:* Ashley, Amber; *ed:* Univ of Akro Sociology 1973; Attnd US Army Intelligence Schl, OH St Corr Acad, OH Peace Ofcr Trng Acad, OH Drug Stud Inst; *cr:* US Infantry, Interrogator 1966-68; OH Adult Parole Authority Sr Paro 1973-; *ai:* SEIU 1986-; Stark Co Alcohol & Drug Abuse Svcs Bd 1 VP; Firearms, Drug Identification Instrs; Acting Dist Supvr.

PARETS, PAUL L., Director of Bands; *b:* Bangor, ME; VanDerGraaff, Meredith Anne; *ed:* Cntrl MI Univ (BA) Music Ed Univ of MI, Univ of MD Grad Hrs; *cr:* Croswell-Lexington HS Bands 1966-76; Alexis I. duPont HS Dir of Bands 1976-; *ai:* M Band; MENC 1976a-;DE Music Edctrs 1976-, Past Pres; Lions Intnl Delaware City, Cncl Mem 1994-; DE Tchr of Yr 1987; MENC R. M. Outstdng Achvmt Awd Indianapolis Natl Convention; Named Nation's 10 Top Edctrs Instr Magazine 1988; *office:* Alexis I DuP 50 Hillside Rd Wilmington DE 19807

PARHAM, BETSEY L., Fourth Grade Teacher; *b:* Camden, NJ; *m.* Richard; *ed:* Rowan Coll (BA) Elem Ed 1972; *ai:* Safety Patro Consortium Comm; AFT 1976-.*

PARIS, ANITA, Sixth Grade Team Leader; *b:* Brooklyn, NY; *ed:* at Cortland (BS) Eng 1957; Hofstra (MS) Ed 1962; Post Grad 60 *cr:* West Babylon Schls 2nd Grd Tchr 1957, 6th Grd Tchr 1958-; Grd Stu Cncl Adv; Lit Magazine Club; Shared Decision Making, Awds, Thematics Comms; Union Rep; *office:* West Babylon Jr HS 2 Farmingdale Rd West Babylon NY 11704

PARIS, FRANCIS JOSEPH, Assistant Principal; *b:* Philadelphia, Jane Barnes; *c:* Scott F., Laura J.; *ed:* Temple Univ (BS) Elem Ed (MED) Elem Ed Curr 1974; Post Grad Stud in Educl Admin; *cr:* No Schl Elem Tchr 1971-86, MS Tchr 1986-89, Asst Prin 1989-93, Ele 1993-95, Asst Prin 1995-; *ai:* NEA 1971-; PSEA 1971-; Interbo 1971-; BSA Troop 55 1992-, Treas; *office:* Norwood Schl 558 Sene Norwood PA 19074

PARISE, DENNIS WILLIAM, 8th Grade Science Teach Youngstown, OH; *m:* Laura Jean Gostey; *ed:* Youngstown St Univ (B 1989, (MS) Curr 1996; *cr:* Youngstown City Schls Sci Tchr 198 Youngstown St Geological Soc; Ftbl, Bsktbl, Track Head Coach, 1989-, Bldg Rep; *office:* Youngstown Adams Jr HS 2537 Coo Youngstown OH 44502

PARISH, MARIAN MAYER, Science Teacher; *b:* Philadelphia, Mel; *ed:* Rutgers univ (BS) Bio, Chem 1977; Glassboro St Coll Ed Attnd Villanova; *cr:* Rutgers Univ Microbiology Lab Asst 19 Philadelphia Police Craim Lab Forensic Cherm 1974-77; Thomas Jef Univ Biologist 1977; Cherry Hill Pub Schls Bio, Chem Tchr 198 Curr Dev; Peer Mediation; NSTA, NEA, NJEA 1979-; Pub Articles; Cherry Hill Pub Schls Cropwell Rd Cherry Hill NJ 08003

PARISH, MARY REED, Second Grade Teacher; *b:* Caledonia, O Joseph William; *c:* Noelle; *ed:* OH St Univ (BS) Elem Ed 1975; Coll St Joseph (MA) Ed 1987; *cr:* River Vly Local Schls Tchr 1976-; M City Schls Adult Basic Literacy & Ed Tchr 1988-95; *ai:* Waldo Elem Comm; Chrstn Edctrs Assn Intnl 1994-; Phi Delta Kappa 1987-; Bibl Flwshp 1994-, Discussion Ldr; *office:* River Vly Schls 300 N Mar Waldo OH 43356

PARISI, GILDA HALUSKA, German Teacher; *b:* Mason City, I Philip Lee; *c:* Paul, Mark, Allison; *ed:* New York St Univ at Buffalo Russian 1973; New York St Univ at Brockport (MA) Lbrl Stud 1994 Stud at Univ of VA 1973-75; Grad Course at Univ of Rochester 198 Univ of VA Tchng Asst 1973-75; Brighton MS Spanish Tchr 198 Greece Athena HS German Tchr 1988-; *ai:* NYSAFLT 1987-; Greece Assn 1988-; AATG 1989-; Phi Beta Kappa; *office:* Greece Athena H Long Pond Rd Rochester NY 14612

PARISI, LORI ANN, Math Teacher; *b:* Lakewood, OH; *ed:* Univ of (BA) Scndry Ed 1989; Baldwin Wallace Coll Grad Stud; *cr:* Rockfeller Schl Span Tchr 1989-92; Collinwood HS Math Tchr 1992 Proficiency Math Tchr; In Charge of Proficiency Cmptr Lab; Chrldng Coach; John Carroll Univ Master Teach; Leading Tchng Svc st Cath Young Adults 1993-, Pres 2 Yrs, Treas 1 Yr; Cleveland Ctr Bulletin Bd Winner; *home:* 3868 W 160th St Cleveland OH 44111*

I, PATRICIA ANDREWS, Fourth Grade Teacher; *b:* Providence, Joseph M.; *c:* Matthew, Laura; *ed:* RI Coll (BS) Elem Ed 1975; ly Pursuing Masters Elem Ed; *cr:* St Elizabeth Schl 5-8 Grd Rdng 975-77, 4 Grd Tchr 1985-87; Colt-Andrews Elem Schl 4 Grd Tchr *ai:* Intnl, Rdng Week Comms; NEA 1987-; IRA; *office:* ndrews Elem Schl 574 Hope St Bristol RI 02809

I, PHYLLIS DIMARIA, Second Grade Teacher; *b:* New York, NY; minic; *c:* Gerlando, Teresa Parisi-Alvarez; *ed:* Hunter Coll (BS) Ec 1955; *cr:* Benjamin Franklin Schl #13 Second Grd Tchr 1956-62; Schl #12 Second Grd Tchr 1962-; *ai:* Drama Adv; Sci Comm; PTA J; NEA, NJEA 1956-; UCEA, EEA 1956-, Bldg Rep; Elizabeth Gen l Ctr Ladies Auxiliary1989-; Governor's Tchr Recognition Awd Project Teach Grants 1987-90; *office:* Elmora Schl #12 638 Magie zabeth NJ 07208

I, ROBERT V., Instrumental Music Director; *b:* Philadelphia, PA; n Quintavalle; *c:* Michelle; *ed:* Temple Univ (BA) Music Ed 1971; Coll (MS) Music Composition 1977; 8 Post Grad Credit Hrs Temple Post Grad Credit Hrs Villanova Univ; *cr:* John Paul Jones Jr HS iental Music Dir 1972-87; Mc Kinley Elem Schl Instrumental Music 72-87; Frankford HS Instrumental Music Dir 1987-; *ai:* Marching azz Band, Orch, Pep Band; AFT, PFT, MENC, PMEA 1972-; *office:* ord HS Oxford Ave & Wakeling St Philadelphia PA 19124

DAVID GLENN, Spanish Teacher; *b:* Homestead, PA; *m:* Maria Huambachano; *c:* Quilla I.; *ed:* San Francisco St Univ (BA) Span MA) Span 1989; 30 Credit Hrs of Ed Courses for Cert Univ of PA 5 Post Grad Credit Hrs Ed Courses at Gannon Univ; *cr:* Linesville n Tchr 1992-93; Fairview HS Span Tchr 1993-; *ai:* Stu Assistance n Adv; Frgn Lang Strategic Plan Comm; NEA 1992-; PSEA 1992-; 992-; Outstdng Stu Tchr 1992 IN Univ of PA; *office:* Fairview HS Accray Rd Fairview PA 16415

EDWARD DUANE, Bio Chem Teacher; *b:* Silver Creek, NY; *m:* I.; *c:* Michael, Catherine, Rebecca, Nathan, Daniel; *ed:* SUNY at ia (BS) Bio & Ed 1971; NY Inst of Tech (MS) Educl Tech 1996; Hrs; *cr:* Roscoe Central Sci Tchr 1971-84; Fallsburg Central Bio Tchr 1984-; *ai:* Sci Olypiad Co-Coach; Sports Ofcl; AFT 1971-; urg Tchrs Assn 1984-; Roscoe Cty Schl Bd of Ed 1989-, Pres; ns 1990-; *office:* Fallsburg Central Schl Brickman Rd Fallsburg NY

, SECHOUL, Accounting Professor; *b:* Seoul, South Korea; *m:* oung Won; *c:* Danny; *ed:* IN St Univ (MBA) 1984; Univ of MD Acctng 1992; *cr:* Hyundaz Corp Mgr 1972-82, Gen Mgr of Midwest 984-87; Morgan St Univ Asst Prof 1992-; *ai:* AAA 1987-; AFA, 1993-; KASEA 1994-; Ciber Grant 1994; Morgan Rsrch Grant Article Pub; *office:* Morgan St Univ Cold Spring La-Hillen Rd ore MD 21239

ER, ALYSSON B., English Teacher; *b:* New London, CT; *ed:* Univ thern ME (BS) Eng 1990; Univ of NH (MS) Eng 1995; MED Work k Univ at Boston; *cr:* Pembroke Acad Eng Tchr 1990-; *ai:* Spring Coach 1990-92; Outing Club Chaperone, Co-Adv; Class of 1997 Accompanist Stu Talent Show; Stu Fac Attendance Comm; NHATE, 1990-; NOW 1985-; Pub Poetry, Short Fiction; Fulbright Flwshp xchange Prgm; *office:* Pembroke Acad 209 Academy Rd Pembroke 275*

ER, CAROLYNN STOCKWELL, School Counselor; *b:* port, CT; *m:* Alan Douglas; *c:* Lucas, Corey, Erica; *ed:* Emerson Coll Theatre Arts 1986; Univ of NH (MED) Counseling 1990; *cr:* ster Schl Cnslr 1990-93; Whitcomb HS Cnslr 1993-; *ai:* Wellness ; Drama Coach; VT Counseling Assn 1993-; White River Valley s 1991-; *office:* Whitcomb HS Pleasant St Bethel VT 05032

ER, CHANDLER B., History Teacher; *b:* Manchester, NH; *m:* ; *c:* Katherine; *ed:* Univ of MI (BA) His 1959; Wesleyan Univ (MA) 968; Harvard Univ (CAS) Admin 1977; *cr:* UA Peace Corps Tchr 56; Brookline HS Tchr 1967-69; Hill Schl Tchr 1970-73; Andover HS 986-; *ai:* NEA 1986-, Bldg Rep.

ER, CHRIS, Second Grade Teacher; *b:* Martins Ferry, OH; *c:* Arik c); *ed:* OH Univ (BSEd) Elem Ed 1966; Attnd Barry Univ, Dayton OH Univ at Belmont & OH Univ at Zanesville; *cr:* St Clairsville and Schl Dist Spec Ed Tchr 1966-69; Flushing Elem Schl 1st Grd 969-72; Morristown Elem Schl 2nd & 3rd Grd Tchr 1972-; *ai:* OH sn & NEA 1966-; Assn of Classroom Tchrs 1969-; Morristown Parent Org 1969-; Martha Holden Jennings Scholar 1994-95; *office:* stown Elem Schl Union Local Schl Dist PO Box 1 Morristown OH

ER, DAN M., ROTC Instructor; *b:* New York, NY; *m:* Isabel E.; *c:* , Geoffrey, Rebecca; *ed:* Belmont Abbey Coll (BA) His 1967; Pacific Univ (MA) Human Relations 1977; Boston Univ Germany 18 Credit *r:* US Army Army Officer 1967-87; Dept of Defense Dependent Schls Instr 1987-; *ai:* Outdoor Ed; AP Coord; Schl Advy Cncl VP; German e Club 1983-; Otters Svc Team 1991-, VP; Parish Cncl Chapel 1994-, *office:* Augsburg American HS Unit 25001 APO AE 09178*

ER, DELORISE W., Elementary Teacher; *b:* Suffolk, VA; *ed:* lyn Coll (BA) Sociology, Psych 1975; Long Island Univ (MS); City of NY 21 Credits Supervision Admin; Coll of New Rochelle 6 Credits gy; Medgar Evers Coll 3 Credits Bus Admin; *cr:* Agency for Child Pre-Schl Tchr 1975-81; Bd of Ed Tchr of Common Branches, Elem 981-; *ai:* Discipline, Compact for Learning Comms; After-Schl Rdng Tchng Rdng Vol; Parent Involvement Prgm 1993; UFT 1981.*

ER, DEWAYNE GORDON, 6th Grade Teacher; *b:* Washington, : Destiny; *ed:* Howard Univ (BA) Elem Ed 1985, (MA) Rel 1993; house Schl of Rel 1 Yr; Trinity Studying for MA Ed; *cr:* Atlanta Pub Tchr 1985-87; DC Pub Schl Tchr 1987-; Evangel Missionary Bapt h Pastor 1991-; *ai:* Black His Bee Spon; Run for Arts Coord; Bsktbl ; 6th Grd Chm; Concern Black Men Inc; Church Minister; DC Tchrs 1987-, Tchr of Yr 1993; Bapt Minister Conf 1991-, Speaker 1991; gel Missionary Bapt 1991-, Pastor, Pastor of Wk 1991; Phi Delta a 1993; Math, Sci & Tech Inst Flwshp; Outstdng Dresser 4 Yrs; *office:* Burroughs Elem Schl 18th & Monroe St NE Washington DC 20018*

KER, GALE J. KEMP, First Grade Teacher; *b:* Port Jefferson, NY; ames D.; *ed:* SUNY at New Paltz (BS) Early Chldhd Ed 1964; LIU Early Chldhd Ed 1988; 50 Credt Hrs; *cr:* Kerhonkson Elem Schl n Tchr 1964-65; Hope Elem Schl 1st Grd Tchr 1965-66; Charlestown Schl Kndgtn, 1st Grd Tchr 1966-68; Laurel Schl 1st-2nd Grd Tchr -72; Hampton Bays Elem Schl Kndgtn, Transitional 1st Grd, 1st Grd, 3rd Tchr 1972-; *ai:* Prof Church Organist, Choir Dir; HBTA 1972-, ; E Suffolk Rdng Cncl 1968-85, Treas; Amer Guild of Organists -, Exec Bd; Mother's Club 1972-90, Exec Bd; HB PTA 1990-; *office:* pton Bays Elem Schl 72 Ponquogue Ave Hampton Bays NY 11946*

KER, JAN, Professor of Economics; *b:* Bangor, ME; *ed:* CT Coll Ec 1954; Univ of CT (MA) Ec 1956; Brown Univ 64 Credits Hrs nd MA ABD 1956-60; MA Inst of Tech Visiting Scholar 1967-68; *cr:* esley Coll Ec Instr 1960-64; Wheaton Coll Asst Prof Ec 1964-67; et Briar Coll Assoc Prof of Ec & Dept Chair 1968-70; Slippery Rock oll Asst Prof of Ec & Bus 1970-72; NM St Univ Asst Prof of Ec 1972-74; Suffolk Comm Coll Asst to Prof of Ec 1975-; *ai:* AEA 1959-; *office:* Suffolk Comm Coll Western Cmps Crooked Hill Road Brentwood NY 11717

PARKER, JANET ELAINE, Vocal Music Director; *b:* Huntington, NY; *m:* Loren Jay; *ed:* Ithaca Coll (BM) Mus Ed 1970, (MM) Applied Voice 1976; Tri Cities Opera Apprenticeship; *cr:* Huntington USFD 3 Vocal Music Tchr 1970-71; ME Endwell Schls Vocal Music Tchr 1976-78; Oswego Apalachin Schls Vocal Music Tchr 1989-; *ai:* NY St Schl Music Assn; Zone 3 Pub Relations Dir; Womens Afterschool Ensemble; Tioga Cty Music Edctrs Assn; Public Relations Dir; Govt Relations Rep; AGMA 1976-89; AFT 1989-; NYSSMA 1989-; ACDA 1989-; TCMEA 1989-; *office:* Owego Free Academy George St Owego NY 13827

PARKER, JILL MARIE, HS Social Studies Teacher; *b:* Quincy, MA; *ed:* Univ of MA at Lowell (BA) His 1969; Tufts Univ (MA) His 1979; *cr:* E.N. Rogers Schl 7th-8th Grd Soc Stud Tchr 1969-79; Lowell Adult Ed Schl GED Tchr 1980-84; Lowell HS Soc Stud Tchr 1985-; *ai:* Drama Club, Indian Club Adv; Univ of MA at Lowell Tsonpas Industrial His Ctr 1990-Tchr Advy Bdmem; NEA 1969-83; Lowell Tchrs Org 1969-83, Pres, Grievance Chprsn; AFT 1984-; Natl Park Svc Grant; *office:* Lowell HS 50 Fr Morrissette Blvd Lowell MA 01852*

PARKER, JUDITH K., Family & Consumer Sci Teacher; *b:* Honolulu, HI; *m:* Kenneth A.; *c:* Cheryl, Christopher; *ed:* Univ of MA (BS) Home Ec 1963, (MS) Home Ec Ed 1983; Spec Needs Cert; Hlth Ed Cert; *cr:* Smiths Voc Schl Spec Needs Tchr 1982-85; Peck MS Home Ec Tchr 1985-91; Agawam HS Home Ec Tchr 1991-92; Holyoke HS Child Dev Tchr 1992-; *ai:* MA Home Ec Assn 1983-; Western MA Home Ed Assn 1983-, VP 1995-; *office:* Holyoke HS 500 Beech St Holyoke MA 01040

PARKER, KATHLEEN KELLY, Eng & Reading Tchr of Gifted; *b:* Akron, OH; *m:* James C.; *c:* Phoebe Bleichrodt, Melissa Heinl, Kristin; *ed:* Kent St Univ (BA) Eng 1968, (MS) Educl Admin 1978; Currently Taking Courses for Gifted Cert; *cr:* Stow Schls 8th Gr Eng Tchr 1968-, Acclerated Rdng Tchr 1995-; *ai:* MS Reorganization Comm; Stow Tchrs Assn 1968-, Exec Bd; *office:* Kimpton MS 380 N River Rd Munroe Falls OH 44262*

PARKER, MARY JUNELLEN, Social Studies Teacher; *b:* Toledo, OH; *ed:* Univ of Toledo (BAEd) Comprehensive Soc Stud & Speech 1970, (MS) Admin & Supervision 1988; *cr:* Toledo Pub Schls Tchr 1970-; *ai:* Girls Bsktbl Coach; Chrldr, Natl Honor Soc & Soph Class Adv; Curr & Book Selection Comm; TFT Bldg Rep & Bldg Comm; AFT 1970-, Bldg Rep; TFT 1970-, Bldg Comm; Toledo Zoo Guild 1991-, Chm of Fund Raising Comm; *office:* Rogers HS 5539 Nebraska Ave Toledo OH 43615

PARKER, RANDY PAUL, Science & Computer Teacher; *b:* Meadville, PA; *m:* Carol S.; *c:* Erin, Megan, Sean; *ed:* Gannon Univ (BS) Gen Sci 1982; Edinboro Univ Instrl I Cert 1991; *cr:* Cathedral Prep Sci Tchr 1982-85, Sci, Cmptr Tchr 1991-; *ai:* Var Ftbl Asst Coach; Discipline Bd; Alternative Scheduling Comm; Co-Spon of Grant for Purchase of New Sci Equipment; *office:* Cathedral Prep Schl 225 W 9th St Erie PA 16501

PARKER, RICHARD K., Technology Teacher; *b:* Hinton, WV; *m:* Sharon K. Milliron; *c:* Kerry, Nikki, Brent; *ed:* Kent St Univ (BS) Indstrl Arts 1970; Grad Credit Ashland Univ, Baldwin Walace Univ; *cr:* Marlington Schls Ind Arts Tchr 1969-71; Lake Local Schls Ind Arts Tchr 1971-75; Louisville Schls Ind Arts Tchr 1975-80; Babin Bldg Ctr Retail Mrktg Mgr 1980-90; Lorain City Schls Tech Ed Tchr 1990-; *ai:* Var Asst Bsbl Coach; Leo Club Adv; Learning Environment, Site Based Comm Chm; NEA, OEA, LEA, OTEA, ITEA 1990-; Lion Club 1980-, Dist Governor, Melvin Jones Awd; Elyria Acessment Bd 1980-; Lorain Endowment Grant 1996; *office:* Lorain Admiral King HS 2600 Ashland Ave Lorain OH 44052*

PARKER, RICHARD MYRON, Chemistry Teacher; *b:* Biddeford, ME; *m:* Janine A. Bertrand; *c:* Douglas S., Kristan D. Gross; *ed:* Univ of ME (BS) Chem 1964; Univ of Southern ME (MS) Ed 1971; Addl 24 Credits; 6 Credits Univ of New England; *cr:* St Francis Coll Chem Instr 1970-71; Thornton Acad Chem Tchr 1964-; *ai:* ME Ed Assn 1964-, Rep Assembly; Thornton Acad Tchrs Assn 1964-, Pres, Negotiator; NEA 1964-; FOE 1974-, VP, Chaplain; BPOE 1995-.

PARKER, ROBERT PLEWES,II, Mathematics Teacher; *b:* Danville, VA; *m:* Christy Hampton Guy; *c:* Elizabeth Christian Parker, Robert Plewes III; *ed:* Randolph-Macon Coll (BS) Math 1970; Westchester Univ (MA) Math 1982; *cr:* Mercersburg Acad Math Tchr 1970-71; Harvey Schl Math Tchr 1971-77; Hill Schl Math Tchr 1977-; *ai:* Soccer, Squash Coach; NCTM 1977-; AP Reader in Math; *office:* Hill Schl 717 E High St Pottstown PA 19464

PARKER, SUSAN ROBINSON, Tchr of Gifted & Talented Prgm; *b:* Lowville, NY; *c:* John Frederick; *ed:* SUNY at Potsdam (BS) Ed 1961; Univ of CT at Storrs Confratute, GT Ed Post Grad Stud; *cr:* Guilderland Elem 3rd Grd Tchr 1961-63; Jamesville-Dewitt Elem 2nd Grd Tchr 1964-65; Jhllo Boces Chapter 1 Rdng, GT Tchr 1979-85; Lowville CS GT Coord, Tchr 1985-; *ai:* Effective Schls Comm; Drama, Musical Dir; AFT; Delta Kappa Gamma 1985-, Music Chm; AGATE; Lib Bd, Co-Chair; Art Cncl, Dir; NYSCA Decentralization Comm; Chair, Bd Mem; Planned Parenthood, Bd Pres; NYS Ed Commissioner's Gifted & Talented Ed Comm; *office:* Lowville Acad & Cntrl Schl 7668 State St Lowville NY 13367*

PARKER, TAXI JOHN, Physical Education Teacher; *b:* Springfield, OH; *m:* Christina; *c:* Ana Jean, Joan; *ed:* Wilmington Coll (BS) PE, Ath Adm 1967; Xavier Univ (MED) Ath Admin 1973; Attnd Wright St Univ, OH Univ, Central St Univ; *cr:* Greenfield Cith HS PE, FB, BK, Swim Tr 1967-68; Springfield City Jr HS PE, FB, BK, TR 1968-71; Mont Co Bd PE, BK, Ath Dir Cur 1971-73; Irwin Co HS PE, FB, BK 1973-77; Natl Trail PE Ath Dir BK 1977-80; Northridge PE Tchr 1980-; *ai:* NEA 1967-, Schl Rep; AHPER 1967-; Optomists VP; Lions Club Sgt Arms; Coach of Yr 1974-75, 1977-78; *office:* Northridge-Morrison School 2235 Arthur Ave Dayton OH 45414

PARKER, THOMAS M., Social Science Teacher; *b:* Jersey City, NJ; *m:* Mary Lou; *c:* Sharon; *ed:* Seton Hall Univ (BS) His & Eng 1966, (MA) His 1973; William Patterson Post Grad Stud; Addl Post-Grad Stud; Prin & Supvrs Cert; *cr:* North Jr HS Soc Sci Tchr 1969-81; Bloomfield Sr HS Soc Sci Tchr 1981-; *ai:* Key Club & Voice of Democracy Adv; DARE Coord; BEA, NJEA & NEA 1969-; *office:* Bloomfield Sr HS 160 Broad St Bloomfield NJ 07003

PARKER, TOM R., Science Teacher; *b:* Mc Comb, OH; *m:* Andrea Ione Bennett; *c:* Sheryl; *ed:* Findlay Coll (BS) Elem Ed 1976; Post Grad Stud Environmental Sci; *cr:* Pandora-Gilboa Schls Jr High Sci Tchr 1076-; *ai:* Ftbl Coach 1976-89; Jr High Bsktbl Coach 1977-78; NEA, OEA 1976-; PGEA 1976-, Pres 1986; Flag City Classics 1986-, Pres 1992; Benchmark; Ottawa First Presbyn, Elder; TKE; Jerry Acker Awd; Battelle Prof Dev Grant; Who's Who Among Amer Edctrs; *home:* 103 Sugar St Ottawa OH 45875

PARKER, WENDY ANN (MC NAMEE), 5th-6th Grd Language Arts Tchr; *b:* Baltimore, MD; *m:* Edward M. Jr.; *c:* Patrick M., Jacqueline A.; *ed:* Towson St Univ (BS) Elem Ed 1970; Stan Prof Cert 1 1970-73, Cert 2 1987-94, Advanced Prof Cert 1994-; *cr:* Balto Cty Bd of Ed 5th Grd Lang Arts Tchr 1970-73; Balto Cty Bd of Adult Ed Adult Basic Ed, GED Tchr 1979-82; St Clement Mary Hofbauer Schl 5th-6th Lang Arts Tchr 1984-; *ai:* Eng Curr Coord; NEA, MSTA, TABCO 1970-73; ESTA 1996-; Writing Project Tchr Consultant 1992-; *office:* St Clement Mary Hofbauer Schl 1216 Chesaco Ave Baltimore MD 21237

PARKER-CAPOLINGUA, JOAN MARIE, First Grade Teacher; *b:* Philadelphia, PA; *ed:* Temple Univ (BS) Early Chldhd Ed 1984; Chestnut Hill Coll 6 Credit Hrs; *cr:* Saint Monica Schl Third Grd Tchr 1986-88, Fourth Grd Tchr 1984-85, 1988-93, First Grd Tchr 1993-; *ai:* Math Curr Coord Grds K-4; NCEA 1990-; *office:* Saint Monica Schl 1720 Ritner St Philadelphia PA 19145

PARKHURST, LEODA GIROUX, English Department Chairperson; *b:* Providence, RI; *m:* Edward; *ed:* Univ of RI (BA) Eng, Ed 1969, (MA) Remedial Rdng Specialist 1974; Post Grad Work Rdng, Cmptrs in Rdng Curr, Writing Consortium RIC; *cr:* Smithfield HS Eng Instr 1969-, Remedial Rdng, Title I Tchr 1975-90, Eng Dept Chprsn 1991-, URI Adjunct Fac 1995-, Writing 101, Basic Coll Composition Tchr; *ai:* Writing Lab Coord, Writing Club Adv 1991-; Former 10-12th Grd Class Adv 5 Yrs, Act Dir, Stu Cncl Adv 5 Yrs, Revise Stu Handbook Comm; NEA, RIEA, SEA 1969-; GSDC of Amer 1985-, Mem; GSDC of RI 1985-, Pres, Bd Mem; GSDC of NH 1990-, Bd Mem; Writing Curr; *office:* Smithfield HS 272 Pleasant View Ave Smithfield RI 02917*

PARKS, CAROL (DAVENPORT), Mathematics Department Chprsn; *b:* Rahway, NJ; *m:* John H.; *c:* Amy C., Matthew J.; *ed:* Kean Coll (BA) Math 1963; *cr:* Scotch Plains-Fanwood Schl System Jr HS Math Tchr 1963-69, Math Dept Chprsn 1966-69; Vineland Schl System MS Math Tchr 1975-, Math Dept Chprsn 1979-; *ai:* Peer Tutoring, NJ Math League, St Jude Math-A-Thon Coord; Data Team for Schl System; Math Curr Comm; NEA, NJEA, VEA, NCTM, AMTNJ 1975-; Womans Club of Vineland 1973-; DAR 1986-; Outstanding Tchr in Governors Recognition Prgm 1986; Author of Math Reference Book; *office:* Landis MS 61 W Landis Ave Vineland NJ 08360

PARKS, ELSIE B., Fourth Grade Teacher; *b:* Jersey Shore, PA; *m:* William R.; *c:* Sharon Hackenberg, Penny, Wendy, Terri Baier; *ed:* Lock Haven Univ (BS) Elem Ed 1972; PA St Univ (MED) Developmental & Remedial Rdng 1978; Addl Post Grad Stud at Penn St, Mansfield Univ & Wilkes Coll; England Stud Tour; *cr:* Oval Elem 2nd Grd Tchr 1972-75; Jersey Shore Elem 4th Grd Tchr 1975-76; Salladasburg Elem 4th Grd Tchr 1976-; *ai:* NEA 1972-; Jersey Shore Area Ed Assn 1972-; Literacy Vol 1990-; Arthritis Fund 1990-, Chprsn; *office:* Salladasburg Elem Schl RR 3 Box 98 Jersey Shore PA 17740*

PARKS, KEITH, Spanish Teacher; *b:* Bedford, OH; *m:* Carol Ann Foster; *c:* Tracy Ann, Lisa Lynne; *ed:* Baldwin-Wallace (BA) Span 1962; Kent St Univ (MED) Span 1969; Baldwin-Wallace (MED) Ed 1977; Addl 15 Hrs Post Masters Grad Stud; *cr:* Strongsville HS Span Tchr 1962-66; Center Jr HS Span Tchr 1966-; *ai:* Span Club; OH Mod Lang Assn 1964-; NEA, OEA & NEOEA 1962-; Church Choir 1972-, Soloist; Church Comms 1978-89; Strongsville Tchr 1983-84; OH St Tchr Yr Semi Finalist 1983-84; Jennings Scholar 1984-85; Baldwin Wallace Alumnus of Yr 1984-85; *office:* Strongsville Ctr Jr HS 13200 Pearl Rd Strongsville OH 44136

PARKS, LANETTA WOLFE, Librarian & Lang Art Tchr; *b:* Baltimore, MD; *m:* Floyd L. Jr.; *c:* J. Manly, Zachary D. Jared R.; *ed:* Univ of MD (BA) Eng 1963, (MS) Lib Sci 1967; Attnd WA Coll, Villanova Univ; *cr:* Enoch Pratt Free Lib Young Adult Specialist 1963-69; Kent School Inc Librn, Tchr 1981-; Queen Anne's Co Pub Lib Reference Librn Part-time 1986-90; *ai:* Stu Govt Adv; Drama Coach; AIMS 1981-; Friends of Kent Co Pub Lib 1972-, Organizing Chair, Pres, MO St Vol of Yr MLA; Downtown Chestertown Assn 1994-, Exec Comm 2-VP; Presbyn Church of Chestertown 1985-, Organ Comm, Elder 1993-95; Coll Comm Chorus 15 Yrs; Numerous Articles Pub; Co-Author Annotated Bibliography, Roll Call: Kent County in the Civil War; *office:* Kent Schl Inc 6788 Wilkins Ln Chestertown MD 21620

PARKS, LORI K., English Teacher; *b:* Hagerstown, MD; *ed:* Towson St Univ (BS) Bus Admin, Eng 1983; The Johns Hopkins Univ (MLA) Lbrl Arts 1992; Hood Coll 16 Credits Ed, 3 Grad Credits; Shepherd Coll 15 Credits Ed; *cr:* Boonsboro HS Eng Tchr 1987-93; Williamsport HS Eng Tchr 1993-; *ai:* Adv Acad Team; *office:* Williamsport HS 5 S Clifton Dr Williamsport MD 21795

PARKS, MARILYN JAYNE (RILEY), Kindergarten Teacher; *b:* Akron, OH; *m:* Dr William H. Jr.; *c:* Susan; *ed:* The Univ of Akron (BS) Ed 1970; Attnd Ashland Univ, Kent St Univ 33 Credit Hrs; Univ of Akron 25 CEU Credits; Master Equivalency Earned 1977; *cr:* Harris Elem Schl Kndgtn Tchr 1971-; *ai:* Harris Schl Disciplinary Review, Bldg Priority & Bldg Use; Thematic Unit Writing, At-Large Whole Lang Comms; Kndgtn & Sci Adv Bd; Akron Pub Schls "Teaching Tools Comm"; OAYEC Pre-K to 3 Special Interest Grp Steering Comm; OH Elem Kndgtn Nursery Ed Bd; Akron Pub Schls Sci, Soc Stu; Akron Ed Assn 1970-; Pi Lambda Theta 1987-, Outstanding Tchr Awd 1987; Phi Delta Kappa 1992, Outstanding Tchr Awd 1987; Natl Assn For Ed of Young Children 9 Yrs; Elem Kndgtn Nursery Educators of OH 9 Yrs; Intnl Rdng Assn; TAWL Tchrs Applying Whole Lang; GATELA 3 Yrs; OH Conservation & Outdoor Ed Assn 2 Yrs; Delta Kappa Gamma 5 Yrs; GAME; Assn for Supvr & Curr Dept Early Childhood Ed; The Amer Heart Assn, Comm Service Awd 1988; The Univ of Akron Coll of Ed, advisory Bd 2 Yrs; Akron Dental Auxiliary 10 Yrs; Trainer of Heart Treas Chest for the Amer Heart Assn; OH Heart Assn Distngd Achvmt Awd; Impact II Disseminator Grant 1992-,1993; GAR Fnd Grant for the Establishment of Classroom Project 1990; Akron Pub Schls Outstanding Performance Awd 1986; Wkshp & Lecture Presentor to St & Local Ed Groups; Akron Tchr of Yr 1986-87; Akron Hlth Dept Spec Recognition, PTA Silver Acorn Awd, Akron Pub Schl Outstanding Performance Awd, Amer Heart Assn Commendation for Outstanding Comm Service & Phi DeltaKappa-Pi Lambda Theta Outstanding Tchr Recognition 1987; Akron Bd Cert of Commendation for Prof Excl, Univ of Akron Cert of Commendation, AAAEYC Child Care ProfAwd, Alpha Delta Pi Comm Involvement Awd, Our Lady of the Elms; Univ of Akron Alumni Prgrm of Yr 1993; Outstanding Pi Lambda Theta 1993; First Intnl FranchiseofHealthy Happy Heart Restaurant 1993; Akron Pub Schls Ambassador Awd 1991-93; *office:* Harris Elem Schl 959 Dayton St Akron OH 44310

PARKS, MARYANNE, Fifth Grade Teacher; *b:* Bayonne, NJ; *c:* Michael; *ed:* CA St Univ at Long Beach (BA) Sociology 1977; Kean Coll of NJ Tchng Cert Elem Schl Tchr Cert Prgm 1987; *cr:* Henry E Harris Elem Schl 5th Grd Tchr 1988-; *ai:* Peer Leadership Prgm 1989-; NEA 1988-; CSULB Alumni Assn 1977-; Kappa Delta Pi Intnl Honor Soc Since 1987; *office:* Henry E Harris Schl Avenue C & 5th St Bayonne NJ 07002

PARKS, SUSAN MARIE (SHERMAN), Algebra & Pre-Algebra Teacher; *b:* Norwalk, OH; *m:* Charles A.; *c:* George, Charlie; *ed:* Otterbein COll (BS) Math, PE 1968; Mt Union Coll Ed 1970; Learning Disabilities 16 Addl Hrs; *cr:* Alliance Pub Schls 7-8th Grd Math Tchr 1970-75; Seneca East Schls LD Tutor 1981-84; Bellevue City Schls Math Tchr 1984-; *ai:* Mathcounts Adv; Jr HS Prgm Coord for Aths; NEA, OBE 1970-; BEA, OCTM 1984-; Eastern Star 1976-, Worthy Matron; *office:* Bellevue Jr HS North St Bellevue OH 44811*

PARKS, TERRY V., Communications & English Tchr; *b:* Eldorado, OH; *m:* Barbara J. Schwartz; *c:* Shawn; *ed:* Cumberland Coll (BS) His, Eng 1973; Wright St Univ 29 Hrs Towards MA His, Comm; *cr:* C. R. Coblentz Local Schl Tchr, Ath Dir, Coach 1973-91; MVCTC Tchr 1991-92; *ai:* Negotiations Comm 1991-; AFT, OFT 1991-, Pres 1995-; NEA; Edctrs Investment Group 1995-, Pres 1995-; 1994 Natl Convention Tech Writing Speaker;1995 St Convention Tchl Writing Speaker; *office:* Miami Vly Career Tchnlgy Ctr 6800 Hoke Rd Clayton OH 45315

PARKS, TRUDI JAMES, Clinical Coord & Radiography; *b:* Springfield, OH; *c:* Suzanne; *ed:* Western MI Univ (BS) Hlth Ed; Ferris St Univ; Baldwin Wallace Coll; Akron Gen Hosp Schl of Rad Tech; Univ of MI Post Grad; *cr:* Cleveland Clinic Instr & Radiographer 9 Yrs; *ai:* VP Fac LGCC 2 Terms; Several Comm Mbrshps; Amer Soc of Rad Tech 1964-; OH Soc of Rad Tech 1964-, Past Pres & Past Chief Bd; Cleveland Soc of Rad Tech 1968-, Past Pres; Amer Assn Ed in Rad Sci; Christ UM Church; Northern OH Yth Org Treas; Radiography Article 1990; CDROM Encyclopedia Contributor 1996; Major Med Dictionary Consulting Bd; *office:* Lorain County Comm Coll 1005 N Abbe Rd Elyria OH 44035

PARKS-LEE, BARBARA EVANS, 9th & 11th Grade Teacher; *b:* Washington, DC; *m:* Willie Lee Jr.; *c:* Claire D. Parks, Clarence J. Parks, Terrence Lee; *ed:* D. C. Tchrs Coll (BS) Eng 1967; Univ of Dist of Columbia (MA) Admin, Supervision 1987; Post Grad Stud Trinity Coll, Howard Univ, George Washington Univ; *cr:* Terrell Jr HS Eng & Speech Tchr 1967-68; East Technical Sr HS Eng, Speech, Writing Lab Tchr; Woodson Sr HS Eng, Rdng Lab Tchr, Eng, Hums, Speech Tchr; *ai:* Pen Power Adv; PEN Faulkner Writers in Schls Spon; NCTE, DC Cncl Tchrs of Eng 1970-; Folger Lib Bd of City Edctrs 1985-; Text Alive Folger Shakespeare Theater 1983-; Book: Connections A Collection of Poems, Short Stories, & Essays with Lessons; Article Pub; *home:* 3330 M St SE Washington DC 20019*

PARMENTER, FREDRICK A., Culinary Arts Instructor; *b:* Maspeth, NY; *m:* Lucia Alzate; *c:* Fredrick A., Alexandra E., Steven M.; *ed:* Food Svs, Food Mngmt, Food Production, Baking Certs; Gen Ed Hospitality Mngmt; *cr:* Acad of Culinary Arts Tchr; Cumberland Cty Tech Ed Ctr Culinary Arts Instr 1994-; *ai:* Culinary Competitions, Food Salons; Soccer Coach; Prof Chef Assn of South Jersey, Sergeant at Arms; Amer Culinary Fed; VICA, Adv; NJEA; NEA; *office:* Cumberland Cty Tech Ed Cntr 601 Bridgeton Ave Bridgeton NJ 08302

PARMENTER, ROBERT MAURICE, AP Social Studies Teacher; *b:* Amsterdam, NY; *m:* Marion Badgley; *c:* Heather, Jerry; *ed:* SUNY at Potsdam (BA) Soc Stud Scndry Ed; SUNY at Albany (MA) Soc Stud Scndry Ed; *cr:* Guilderland Cntrl HS Soc Stud, European, Global Stud Hnrs & Regents Tchr 1966-; *ai:* War Games Club Adv; Level Change & Summer Curr Planning Comms; AFT; NYSUT; Town of New Scotland Historian; *office:* Guilderland Cntrl HS PO Box 37 Guilderland Center NY 12085

PARMERTER, ROBERT KNAPP, MS Social Studies Teacher; *b:* Goshen, NY; *m:* Dorothy G. Noges; *c:* Mark, Brad M.; *ed:* St Univ at Oneonta (BS) Soc Stud Ed 1964; Post Grad Stud; *cr:* Schenevus Cntrl Schl Soc Stud Tchr 1964-; *ai:* Dist Planning Team; Union Grievance Comm; NYSUT 1964-; NEA 1964-, Life Mem; Schenevus United Tchrs 1964-, Pres, VP, Chief Negotiator; AFT 1969-; Amer Aviation Hist Soc 1970-; Twin Beech Assn 1988-, Historian; Town Planning Bd 1993-, Sec; Grant to Pub Cty Tchr Resources; Numerous Articles Pub; *office:* Schenevus Central Schl 100 Main St Schenevus NY 12155

PARMLEY, STARR RAYMOND, Health Sci & PE Instructor; *b:* Oswego, NY; *c:* Barbara Kay Parmley Maniatakis, Mary Starr, E. K.; *ed:* Murray St Univ (BA) Hlth, PE, Bio, Psych 1965; Post Grad Hlth Ed; *cr:* US Army Chaplins Asst 1959-62; Louisville, Nashville R R Machinist 1963-65; St of KY Juvenile Cnslr 1965-67; Marsteller Jr HS PE Tchr 1967-68; Altmar Parish Williamstown HS Instr, Hlth Coord 1968-; *ai:* Hlth, Wellness Team Adv; Teen Stress Group Co-Adv; NY St Tchrs Assn, NEA, Oswego Co Tchrs Assn 1971-; NYSAHPERD 1993-; Tug Hill Sporting Assn, Dir; *office:* Altmar Parish Williamstown HS PO Box 97 Rt 22 Parish NY 13131

PARNELL, FRANCIS JAMES, 8th Grade Science Teacher; *b:* Caledonia, NY; *m:* Kathrine Brown; *c:* Kathrine, Katrine, Nicholas; *ed:* Brockport St (BS) Sci Ed 1966, (MS) Ed 1974; 24 Hrs Clarkson Inst of Tech; 9 Hrs Boston Coll; *cr:* Gen Crushed Stone Adm 1962-68; Mac Leod Assocs Land Surveyor 1970-90; Churchville Schls Tchr 1966-; *ai:* Bsbl Coach; NEA 1966-; *office:* Churchville-Chili MS 139 Fairbanks Rd Churchville NY 14428

PARRILLO, MATTHEW ANTHONY, Science Teacher; *b:* Bronx, NY; *m:* June; *c:* Matthew, Jenna; *ed:* SUNY at Maritine Coll (BS) Meteorology 1977; Manhattanville Coll (MA) Math & Ed 1982; Iona Coll (SDA) Admin 1986; *cr:* Mt Vernon Alternative Schl Math & Sci Tchr 1977-79; Nichols MS Math & Sci Tchr 1979-85; North Rockland HS Math & Sci Tchr 1985-; *ai:* Alternative Pgm PM Schl Supvr; NYSUT 1979-; NYSTA 1979-; Middletown Little League 1989-; NY St PTA Tchr of Yr Awd 1984; *office:* North Rockland HS Hammond Rd Thiells NY 10984

PARRIS, DAVID CHRISTIAN, Curator of Natural History; *b:* Mc Pherson, KS; *m:* Susan Connolly; *c:* William N., Daniel S., Timothy P.; *ed:* NM Inst Mining, Tech (BS) Geology 1966; SD Schl Mines, Tech (MS) Paleontology 1968; Princeton Univ (MA) Geology 1970; *cr:* NJ St Museum Sci Regstrar 1972-73, Asst Sci Curator 1973-85; SD Schl Mines, Tech Instr, Field Paleontology 1986-; NJ St Museum Curator of Natural His 1985-; *ai:* Adult Vol; BSA; Soc Vertebrate Paleontology 1969-; Paleontological Soc 1974-; Sigma Xi 1968-; Archaeological Soc of NJ 1972-, Appreciation Awd; DE Vly Paleo Soc 1993-, Honorary Life Mem; Soc Amer Archaeol 1969-; SD Archaeological Soc 1989-; NSF Grant 1980; Nat Geog Soc Grants 1986, 1988-89; Numerous Articles, Reviews, Abstracts Pub; *office:* New Jersey State Museum 205 West State St #CN-530 Trenton NJ 08625

PARRISH, DOUGLAS D., Secondary Mathematics Teacher; *b:* Defiance, OH; *m:* Glola Bidlack; *c:* Carrie, Kendra, David; *ed:* OH Northern Univ (BA) Math 1970; Univ of Dayton (MA) Ed 1979; 12 Hrs Post Grad at Bowling Green St Univ; *cr:* Kenton City Schls Math Instr 1971-76; Van Wert City Schls Math Instr 1976-; *ai:* Math Dept Chair 1976-; AFT, OFT 1979-, Treas; NCTM 1984-; Dir of Ath 1978-95; *office:* Van Wert HS 305 W Crawford St Van Wert OH 45891

PARRISH, KAREN I., Social Studies Dept Chair; *b:* Akron, OH; *c:* Brian John, Jeffrey David; *ed:* Kent St Univ (BA) Soc Stud Comp 1963; Ashland Univ (MS) Curr & Instruction 1991; Attnd 3 Hrs at Univ of Akron Abnormal Psych, 3 Hrs at OH St Univ Child Psych, 5 Hrs at Chapman St Coll Drug Intervention, 3 Hrs at Xavier Coll Working with the Difficult Stu; *cr:* Cuyahoga Falls City Schls Tchr 1963-68; Hamilton City Schl Tchr 1968-69; Marion City Schls Soc Stud Dept Chair & Advanced Placement Govt Tchr 1980-; *ai:* Mock Trial; Youth in Govt Prgm; Sr Class Adv; Soc Stud Curr & Grade Card Comms; HEAT-Interviewing Prospective Soc Stud Tchrs; NEA 1963-, Natl Del; OH Ed Assn 1963-, Rep Del; Marion Ed Assn 1986-, Sec; Marion Pop Corn Festival 1987-90, Sec; Marion General Hospital 1977-80, Vol; Red Cross 1976-77, Vol; Jennings Scholar; Taft Inst; Pub Article in Clearing House; Pub Weekly Articles in the Falls News.

PARRISH, KAREN KING, Kindergarten Teacher; *b:* Evanston, IL; *m:* Dennis L.; *c:* Ryan, Adam; *ed:* Bowling Green St Univ (BSED) Elem Ed 1973; Post Grad 18 Credit Hrs; *cr:* St Mary Schl Kndgtn Tchr 23 Yrs; *ai:* HUGS OH Child Conservation League; Asst Brownie League; Cub Scout Ldr; NCEA 1973-; *office:* St Mary's School 702 Washington Ave Defiance OH 43512*

PARROTT, BOYD DENNIS, Librarian; *b:* Brooklyn, NY; *m:* Linda Diane King; *ed:* Long Island Univ (BA) Ed & Eng 1968; Brooklyn Coll (MS) Ed 1972; Admin; Art & Dance; *cr:* PS 21 Schl Aide & 3rd, 5th & 6th Grd Paraprofessional Tchr 1968-83; PS 308 6th Grd & 7th Grd Soc Stud Tchr 1983-93, Gifted Coord Schl Librn 1995-; *ai:* Rsrch, Schl Lit & Rdng Clubs; Book Fair & Writing Essay & Poetry Contest Coord; Storytelling Club Chm & Coach; Amer & African Crafts Club; AFT 1968-; NEA 1968-; Media Edctrs Assn 1985-; ASCD 1989-; Dist Tchr of Yr (Twice Honored); Honored at 20th Anniversary of the Clara Cardwell Schl for Yrs of Dedicated Svc; *office:* PS 308 Clara Cardwell 616 Quincy St Brooklyn NY 11221*

PARROTT, LORI MARIE, Social Studies Teacher; *b:* Hackensack, NJ; *m:* Eric M. Roskelly; *c:* Lauren, Kurt; *ed:* Montclair St Univ (BA) Pol Sci 1979; Attnd East Stroudsburg Univ, St Peter's Coll, Rosemont Coll; *cr:* Vernon Twp HS Soc Stud Tchr 1983-91; Wallkill Valley Regnl HS Soc Stud Tchr 1991-; *ai:* Mock Trial Adv; NJ Ed Assn, NEA 1983-; Wallkill Valley Ed Assn 1991-; Vernon Recreation Coach 1993-; Vernon Bd of Ed Citizen Advy Bd 19950; Tchr of Month; *office:* Wallkill Valley Reg HS 9 Grumm Rd Hamburg NJ 07419

PARROTTE, KEITH ERIC, Jr High Math & Sci Teacher; *b:* Plattsburgh, NY; *ed:* Plattsburgh St Univ (MS) Elem Ed 1984; 15 Addl Hrs Plattsburg St Univ of NY; *cr:* St Alexander's Schl Jr HS Math Sci5th-8th Grd Tchr 1984-; *ai:* 3 Yr Sequential Math Instr; Schl Newspaper Ed in Chief; Introduction to World Processing; CSAANYS 1992-; Creative Writing Awd 1994; *office:* St Alexander's Schl 2155 State Route 22b Morrisonville NY 12962

PARRY, CYNTHIA, 4th Grade Teacher; *b:* Islip, NY; *m:* William; *c:* Danielle; *ed:* SUNY at Oneonta (BS) Elem Ed, Psych 1986; Dowling Coll (MA) Rdng 1988; 30 Addl Credit Hrs; *cr:* Longwood Cntrl SD Tchr Asst 1986-87; Miller Place Schls 4th Grd Tchr 1987-; *ai:* Homework Club Moderator; Lit Club; *office:* Sound Beach Schl 197 N Country Rd Miller Place NY 11764

PARRY, CYNTHIA E., English Teacher; *b:* Freeport, NY; *ed:* SUC at Oneonta (BA) Eng, Sec Ed 1973; Art Stdnts League of NY; Parsons Schl of Design Huntington Extension Suny Stony Brook 45 Grad Credit Hrs; *cr:* South Cntry Schls Eng Tchr 1973-; *ai:* NEA; Long Island Suffolk Writers Project Fellow 1994; Fulbright Exch Prgm 1993; Art Stdnts League of NY Mert Schlsp 1988.

PARRY, DAVID G., Driver Education Instructor; *b:* Philadelphia, PA; *m:* Kathi Birmingham; *c:* Michael, Kevin, Kyle, Nicholas; *ed:* East Stroudsburg Univ (BS) Hlth, PE 1979; 12 Post Grad Credits; *cr:* Northern HS Driver Ed Instr 1980-; *ai:* Head Boys Cross Cntry Coach 9 Yrs; Asst Track Coach 14 Yrs; Head Indoor Track Coach 12 Yrs; Ping Pong Club Adv; PA Track, Field Coaches Assn 1982-; Governor's Hwy Safety Awd 1990; *office:* Northern HS 655 S Baltimore St Dillsburg PA 17019

PARRY, RITCHARD GEORGE, Chemistry Teacher; *b:* Kingston, PA; *m:* Charlotte Dymond; *c:* Brenda Schick, Ritchard, Brian; *ed:* Muhlenberg Coll (BS) Natural Sci 1957; Brown Univ (MS) Chem 1963; Attnd Syracuse Univ, PA St Univ; *cr:* Cncl Rock HS Sci Tchr 1957-67; Lower Moreland HS Chem Tchr 1967-; *ai:* Bsbl & Wrestling Coach; Jr Class Adv; Sci Curr Design Comm; LMTEA, MCSTA 1967-; PSEA, NEA 1957-; 2 Natl Sci Fund Grants; *office:* Lower Moreland HS 555 Red Lion Rd Huntingdon Valley PA 19006

PARRY, VALERIE LOVELL, Third Grade Teacher; *b:* Dumont, NJ; *m:* John R. Jr.; *c:* Vanessa, Taylor; *ed:* VA Polytechnic Inst & St Univ (BA) Eng 1975; Post Grad Stud Univ of PA; *cr:* Pleasant Vly Nursery Schl Early Chldhd Tchr 1975-77; The Moore Schl Tchr, Mom & Me Prgm Coord 1979-80; Westfield Friend Schl Third Grd Tchr 1985-; *ai:* NJ PIRG 1992-; *office:* Westfield Friends Schl Riverton Rd Cinnaminson NJ 08077

PARRY, W. DAVID, Health & Physical Ed Teacher; *b:* Greensburg, PA; *m:* Becky J.; *c:* Heather, Jessica, Sarah; *ed:* Tarkio Coll (BS) PE & Hlth 1965; Attnd Penn St Univ; *cr:* Norwin Schl Dist PE & Hlth Tchr 30 Yrs; *ai:* Track Coach 28 Yrs; Norwin Ed Assn 1968-; PSEA 1968-; NEA 1968-; Jaycees, Pres; United Way; Community Picnic Comm; Track Official; *office:* Norwin MS East 1 Main St Irwin PA 15642

PARSONS, CRAIG LLOYD, Fifth Grade Teacher; *b:* Reading, PA; *m:* Mary Mellers; *c:* John, Victoria; *ed:* Temple Univ (BA) Ed 1972; Villanova Univ (MA) Educl Admin 1983; 24 Addl Hrs; St Joseph's of Philadelphia 6 Addl Hrs; *cr:* Upper Dublin Schl Dist Tchr 1972-; *ai:* IMS 1972-90; Heritage Comm 1983-89; NEA, PSEA, UDEA 1972-; Temple Univ Var Club, Under Grad Letter Winner; Mid Atlantic Conf Ftbl Champions 1967; Villanova Chapter Kappa Delta Pi; Newspaper Article Featured Edctr 1990.

PARSONS, CYNTHIA HAYDEN, Fourth Grade Teacher; *b:* Oakland, MD; *m:* Don R. Jr.; *c:* Mathew; *ed:* Frostburg St Univ (BS) Ed 1991; 24 Addl Hrs; *cr:* South Penn Elem Schl 4th Grd Tchr 2 Yrs; Oldtown Schl 4th Grd Tchr 2 Yrs; *ai:* MD Quiz Bowl Coach; NEA 1992-; Meth Church 1989-, Sunday Schl Tchr.

PARSONS, DONALD RUSSELL, 4th & 5th Grade Teacher; *b:* Philadelphia, PA; *ed:* Belmont Abbey Coll (BA) His 1964; SUNY at Cortland (MS) Elem Ed 1970; Resident Outdoor Ed Camp Dir Trng 20 Hrs 1981; Individualized Lang Arts Courses 12 Hrs 1984; Prgm for More Effective Tchng 27 Hrs 1988; *cr:* Maine-Endwell Schl Dist 4th-6th Grd Tchr 1965-93; *ai:* Asst Var Boys Soccer Coach & Scorekeeper; Asst Var Girls Gymnastics Team Coach; Dist Wide Lang Art Comm; ME-Endwell Tchr Assn, NEA & NYS Tchr Assn 1975-; NY St & Natl PTA 1965-; Natl Geographic Soc 1966-; Phi Kappa Theta 1961-; the Cousteau Soc 1985-; Boat-US 1981-; *home:* 512 Reynolds Rd # E-22 Johnson City NY 13790

PARSONS, IVOR RICHARD, Social Studies Chairman; *b:* Exeter, England; *m:* Donna Elizabeth Dubrul; *c:* Devon, Heather, Aimee; *ed:* SUNY at Pittsburgh (BA) His 1968; MI St Univ (MA) Sec His 1969; Long Island Univ (PD) Pol Sci 1981; Columbia Univ (EDD) Schl Admin 1991; CUNY NY TAFT Fellow 3 Credits; *cr:* US Army GED Dir Vietnam 1970-71; Locustd Vly Mid, HS Soc Stud Tchr 1971-89, Chm Soc Stud 1990-; *ai:* Mock Trial Team; Long Island Cncl of Soc Stud Tchrs, NY St Cncl of Soc Stud Tchrs 1989-; NCSS 1987-; Locust Vly Soccer Club 1978-, Pres; Oyster Bay Yth Cncl Coach 1984-; Taft Inst Fellow 1992; NY St Ed, Bar Grant; Dissertation Retaining Effective Tchrs; AP Consultant US His 1995-; *office:* Locust Vly Mid-HS Horse Hollow Rd Locust Valley NY 11560*

PARSONS, JERRY LEE, Choir & Music Theory Teacher; *b:* Columbus, OH; *m:* Laurie Lee Brown; *c:* Rebecca Lee, Daniel Lee; *ed:* Otterbein Coll (BME) Music Ed 1983; Masters of Arts in Ed 45 Quarter Hrs; *cr:* Rosemore Jr HS Choir, Gen Music Tchr 1983-86; Worthingway MS Choir, Gen Music Tchr 1986-91; Thomas Worthington HS Choir, Music Theory Tchr 1991-; *ai:* Fine Arts Dept Chair; Musical Dir; Curr, Music Cncl; Wrestling Coach 1983-89; OEA, NEA, ACDA 1983-; OH Music Ed Assn 1980-, Solo, Ensemble, Large Group Adjudicator; 7 St Plaques Superior Ratings OMEA Contest; OMEA Prof Conf Performance 1995; *office:* Thomas Worthington HS 300 W Granville Rd Worthington OH 43085

PARSONS, LINDA, Second Grade Teacher; *b:* Philadelphia, PA; *ed:* Westchester St Univ (BS) Elem Ed 1972; Salisbury St Univ (MED) Elem Ed, Rdng 1980; *cr:* Denton Elem Schl Resource Room Tchr K-3 Grd 1972-77, First Grd Tchr 1977-78, Second Grd Tchr 1978-; *ai:* NEA, MSTA 1972-; IRA; Alpha Delta Kappa 1979-, VP, Sec, Treas; *office:* Denton Elem Schl 303 Sharp Rd Denton MD 21629

PARSONS, MADELYN MATTINGLY, Retired 1st Grade Teacher; *b:* Pikeville, KY; *m:* Alvin Gregory; *c:* Jennifer P. Pryor, Benny F., Karen P. Hall; *ed:* Pikeville Coll (BS) Elem Ed 1970; *cr:* Pike Co Schls 1 Room Schl Tchr 1947-50; Jenkins Ind Schl Tchr 1950-55; Dorton Schl 7th Grd Tchr 1955-57; Pike Co Schls 1 & 2 Room Schl Tchr1962-64; Huntington Elem Schl First Grd Tchr 1964-88; *ai:* NEA, OEA, ORTA, Ross Co Ret Tchrs, Life Mem; Liberty Hill Church 1976-; *home:* 12736 State Ro Chillicothe OH 45601

PARSONS, MARGARET LOCONTO, Physical Education Tea Peekskill, NY; *m:* William J.; *ed:* Montclair St Coll (BA) Hlth & F Western CT St Coll (BS) Scndry Ed & PE 1981; Attnd CW Pc Manhattan Coll, St Univ of NY at New Paltz; *cr:* Croton Harmc K-2nd Grd PE Tchr 1975; Ardsley Schl Dist 5th-8th Grd PE Tch *ai:* Var & Modified Girls Soccer Coach; NYSUT 1975-; AFT Section I Soccer Coaches Assn 1981-; PTA 1985-; Ardsley Day Car Dir; Lower Hudson Ath Conf Soccer Coach of the Yr 1987-88; Ardsley Schl Dist 500 Farm Rd Ardsley NY 10502

PARSONS, MARK LANE, Assistant Professor of Music; *b:* Pi NC; *ed:* TN Temple Univ (BA) Sacred Music & Vocal Performanc Eastern MI Univ (MA) Vocal Performance 1986; *cr:* Big Oak Chrs Dir of Fine Arts & Classroom Tchr 1982-88; Saint Andrews Presb Instr of Music & Theatre 1988-90; NC Pub Schls Choral Dir & Cla Tchr 1990-94; Green Mountain Coll Asst Prof of Music 19 Music-Choral Club Adv; Dir & Founder of Cantare Prof Vocal En Dir & Founder of Jubilate Alumni Group-Choir of NC Governc Chorus Alumnae 1988-; Phi Mu Alpha Sinfonia 1984-; Phi Ka 1986-; MENC 1978-; Amer Choral Dirs Assn 1984-; NEH Fellow Summer 1995; *home:* 32 Church St Poultney VT 05764*

PARSONS, PATRICIA BROOKS, Math Teacher; *b:* New Haven Laura A., Michael J.; *ed:* Southern CT St Coll (BS) Math 1968; Un (MA) Math 1969; *cr:* Amith Sr HS Math Tchr 1969-; *ai:* NCTM CEA, ATNME, AEA, ATOMIC 1970-; Recording for Blind 1994-; Amity Sr HS 25 Newton Rd Woodbridge CT 06525

PARSONS, STEPHEN FRAZIER, History & Bible Teac Rochester, NY; *m:* Sandra Jean Dunnett; *c:* Benjamin, Jonathan, Ba Bapt Bible Coll (BRE) Pre-Seminary 1979; Bapt Bible Schl of Th (MDiv) 1982, (ThM) Old Testament 1985; Rutgers Univ (MA) Ar 1995; 18 Hrs Toward Masters in Ed at Philadelphia Coll of Bible; c HS Tchr 1986-; *ai:* Guidance Cnslr; ACSI; *office:* Baptist HS 3rd & Aves Haddon Heights NJ 08035

PARTELOW, SUSAN M., French Teacher; *b:* Torrington, CT; *m:* F *c:* Ryan, Lindsey; *ed:* Cntrl CT St Univ (BS) Fr 1978; MS in Admi F Kennedy Jr HS Fr & Span Tchr 1978-79; Schaghticoke MS Fr Tchr 1979-; *ai:* Intramural Tennis Coach; Intnl Celebratin Co-A Cncl Adv; Foreign Lang Curr Comm; Fac Cncl; COLT 1980-; CEA 1978-; *office:* Schaghticoke MS 23 Hipp Rd New Milford CT 0677

PARTON, ALVES P., HS & MS Science Teacher; *b:* Ohatchee, Jacksonville St Univ (BS) Bio 1951, (MS) Cnslng 1970; 30 Hrs Masters Sci; *cr:* USAF Med Lab Tech 1951-55; Ohatchee H 1955-58; US Govt DODDS HS, MS Tchr 1958-; *ai:* Ath Dir, T Bsktbl Coach; SIP Comm; Advy Cncl; FEA, NEA 1958-, Local Pres Legion 1955-; Meth Church; *office:* Brussels Amer Schl PSC Box 003 APO AE 09724

PARTRIDGE, CHARLES A., Social Studies Teacher; *b:* Geneva, Mary Bishop; *c:* Emily, Jessica; *ed:* St Univ of NY at Brockport (E 1983, (MA) Liberal Stud 1991; *cr:* Lyndonville HS Soc Stud Tchr 19 Hilton HS Soc Stud Tchr 1986-; *ai:* Var Wrestling Coach; Peer Me Team Mem; Bldg Advy Comm; AFT 1985-; Univ of Rochester Tchng Awd 1990; Genessee Region League Wrestling Coach of Y Monroe Cty West Wrestling Coach of Yr 1996.

PARTRIDGE, DARLENE SMIGIEL, 9th Grade US History Teac Pittsburgh, PA; *m:* Richard J.; *ed:* Duquesne Univ (BA) His 1971, His 1976; *cr:* Sto-Rox HS His Tchr 1971-; *office:* Sto-Rox HS 1105 St Mc Kees Rocks PA 15136

PARTRIDGE, DEBORAH, Art Teacher; *b:* Suffern, NY; *c.* Donnellan; *ed:* Ladycliff Coll (BS) Art Ed 1974; Coll of New R (MS) Studio Art 1991; 30 Addl Credits Studio Art 1995; Art Stdnts NY 1989; Attnd St Univ of NY at Purchase 1977, Rockland Ctr for t 1976; *cr:* Rockland Ctr for Arts Art Tchr 1978-88; Archdiocese of Tchr 1985-87; Suffern HS Art Tchr 1987-95; Suffern MS Art Tchr *ai:* Co-Adv Natl Art Honor Soc 1990-95; NY St Art Tchrs Assn 198 Stdnts League 1989-; Coll Art Assn 1990-; Rockland Ctr for Arts Article Pub 1992; 1989 Art Stdnts League Best In Show Mixed Painting, Vriesland Inc Artist Studio Space Awds; CETA Grant 197

PARTRIDGE, RICHARD, 9th Grade Mathematics Teach Pittsburgh, PA; *m:* Darlene F. Smigiel; *ed:* Thiel Coll (BA) Math Univ of Pittsburgh (MED) Math 1976; *cr:* Vincentian HS Mat 1975-79; Shaler Area Schl Math Tchr 1979-; *ai:* Sr Class, NHS Sp Army Reserves 1971-, Master Sergeant; *office:* Shaler Area Sr H Wible Run Rd Pittsburgh PA 15209

PARTRIDGE, VICKI VEE, English Teacher; *b:* Sharon, PA; *m:* Jo *c:* John Jr., Wendy, Christopher, David, Mike; *ed:* Clarion Univ Scndry Ed 1969; *cr:* WMHS Tchr 27 Yrs; *ai:* Yrbk; Newspaper 1969-; PSEA 1969-; WMEA 1969-; Juvenile Diabetes Fndtn; *office* Middlesex HS Sharon-New Castle Rd West Middlesex PA 16159*

PARTS, CATHERINE MARIE, English Teacher; *b:* Dayton, OH; *m* William Geis; *ed:* Ohio St Univ (BA) Jrnlsm 1987; Rhode Island Col Scndry Eng Ed 1992; 9 Credit Hrs Cinema, Film Theory; 25 Cre Eng, Amer Lit; Univ of Cincinnati Rdng Cert Specialist 1996; *cr:* Ma Comm Group Editorial, Mrktg Asst 1990-92; Taylor HS Eng Tchr 19 Mt Healthy HS Eng Tchr 1993-; Univ of Cincinnati Literacy Ctr Rdn 1995-; *ai:* Acad Team Coach; Chaperone for Jr Class; NCTE, OC 1992-; NEATE 1991-92; Literacy Vol of Amer 1990-92; Dev Ed of 2 Books Pub; *home:* 3424 Brookline Ave Apt 6 Cincinnati OH 45220*

PASANEN, JACK M., English Teacher; *b:* Fitchburg, MA; *m* Henderson; *c:* Gretchen Anthony, John, Jennifer Jeffers; *ed:* Univ (BA) Eng 1960; Middlebury Coll (MA) Eng 1969; *cr:* Indian Mt Sc Dept Chm 1960-66; Emma Willard Schl Eng Dept Chm 19 Northshore Cntry Day Schl Eng Dept Chm 1984-86; Ithaca Coll L Eng Instr 1986-90; The Hunger Project UK Educl Prgms Dir 1990-92 Porter's Schl Eng Tchr 1992-; *ai:* Schl Newspaper Adv; Tech, Benefits Comms; Hunger Project 1977-, Key Vol; NDEA Fellowshi Mott Tchng Chair; Pub Books: Confront, Construct, Complete Vol *office:* Miss Porter's Schl 60 Main St Farmington CT 06032

PASCALE, JOHN PAUL, Science Teacher; *b:* Passaic, NJ; *m:* And Verga; *ed:* Seton Hall Univ (BS) Scndry Ed 1986; St Peters Coll Admin & Supvr 1990; Don Bosco Coll Seminary 32 Credits Beyon 60 Post Grad & Inservice Credits; *cr:* Don Bosco Prep HS Sci 1987-90; Mahwah HS Sci Tchr 1990-; *ai:* Sci League Chem & Bio Mem of Attendance Apeal & Mem of Interruptions Comms; NSTA NEA 1990-; NJEA 1990-; NJSTA 1990-; Tchr of the Yr 1994-95; T Bio, Chem, Physics & Phys Sci.

PASCERI, CYNTHIA ESMARK, Instructional Support Teach Phila, PA; *m:* Vincent I. Jr.; *c:* Kim Rogal de Oliveira, Scott V., Eli L.; *ed:* Temple Univ (BS) Ed 1971; Beaver Coll M Equiv Ed 1973-88; Penn St Univ, Marywood Coll; *cr:* Abington Schl Dist Tchr 19 Instructional Support Tchr 4-6 Grds 1994-; *ai:* Homework Club; Lan Comm; AEA, PSEA, NEA 1972-; Delta Kappa Gamma; Natl Hol Museum; Art Museum of Phila; PA Holistic Scoring Table Ldr; P Conf Schlsp; Rdng Tchr Article; Learning Magazine Tchr Idea Articl *office:* Mc Kinley Elem Schl 370 Cedar Rd Elkins Park PA 19027*

YN, KWITOSLAWA SALUK, English Teacher; *b:* Jaroslau, ; *m:* Dan Paschyn; *c:* Alex, Meka; *ed:* Kent St Univ (BS) Eng & 1965; Old Dominion Univ (MA) Eng 1970; 15 Credit Hrs in Post Courses; *cr:* Prince Georges Pub Schls Eng Tchr 1973-; Squire Dempsey Law Firm Office Mgr 1992; *ai:* NEA 1990-; PGCEA Jkrainian Natl Womens League 1980-, VP; Article Pub; *office:* Roosevelt HS 7601 Hanover Pky Greenbelt MD 20770

ZZI, EDWARD, Physics Teacher; *b:* Huntington, NY; *ed:* St Univ at Stony Brook (BS) Physics, Astrophysics, Planetary Sci 1988, hysics Ed 1993; *cr:* Vanderbilt Planetarium Astronomy Lecturer, 83-95; Brookhaven Natl Lab Physics Assoc 1989; Glen Cove HS Tchr 1993-; *ai:* Sci Rsrch Journal Club; Long Island Physics Tchrs 92-, Newsletter Ed; AAPT 1992-; Edward Lambe Sci Tchng Awd arol Escobar Amusement Park Physics Honorable Mention Awd stromony for all Ages Book Pub 1994; Article Pub in The Physics 1991-92; Numerous Honorable Mentions for Hosp Photography s 1990-93; *office:* Glen Cove HS 150 Dosoris Ln Glen Cove NY

ZZO, JOAN AUDREY, Retired Sixth Grade Teacher; *b:* Richmond Y; *m:* Richard James; *c:* Jill Seymour, Jane Michalek, Richard Jr.; NY at Oswego (BS) Ed 1954; SUNY at Geneseo (MS) Ed 1959; *cr:* low Schl Elem Tchr 1954-55; CO Springs CO Sub Tchr 1955-56; ntrl Schl Tioga Ctr Elem Tchr 1956-92; *ai:* Adv Stu Cncl 1983-92; 1956-; NEA 1963-; TCTA 1956-; Tioga Cty Historical Soc 1960-; ty Cncl Arts 1990-; Tioga Cty Human Svcs Comissioner; Booster c Awd 1986; MS Tchr of Yr 1990; Awd Established in Name for 6th y, Girl.

TINER, LEE, AP Biology Teacher; *b:* Yonkers, NY; *m:* Judith; *c:* Michael, Scott; *ed:* St Univ at Brockport (BS) Sci Ed 1954; Penn St io 1957; Hofstra Univ Scndry Schl Prin & Dept Chr Cert; Attnd at Stonybrook, Pace Coll, Columbia Univ; *cr:* Lindenhurst HS AP r 1957-; *ai:* NHS, Stu Cncl Adv; Stu Act Treas; AFT, NEA, NABT, Sci Tchrs Assn; Wrote HS Bio Text.*

WICH, BROOKE VACCARINO, Health & PE Teacher; *b:* th, NJ; *m:* Edward; *c:* Heather, Christopher; *ed:* Trenton St Coll th & PE 1971; Kean Coll (MA) Curr 1989; Jersey City St Drugs & Substance Abuse Cert 1993; Supvrs Cert 1996; *cr:* Highland Park n & PE Tchr 23 Yrs; *ai:* Conflict Resolution; Gymnastic Ofcl; ance Intervention Chprsn; NAHPER 1996; NEA 1971-; D-CARE 1990-, Support Person; *office:* Highland Park HS N 5th ghland Park NJ 08904

, JENNIFER ANN, Dept Chairperson & Eng Tchr; *b:* lphia, PA; *m:* Joseph S.; *c:* Nathan, Luke; *ed:* Millersville Univ of Ed) Eng 1984; Thirty Credits in Post Grad Stud Ed; *cr:* Solanco HS hr 1985-; *ai:* Chprsn of Quality Ed Comm; Staff In-Service Comm er; NCTE 1993-; NEA, PSEA 1986-.

JALE, CHARLOTTE MC DADE, Resource Teacher; *b:* Reading, Don Pasquale; *c:* Jeffrey, Staci Basolis; *ed:* Immaculata Coll (BA) 3; Rowan Spec Ed Cert; *cr:* Twin Vally HS Art Tchr 1 Yr; Minatola Grd Tchr 1 Yr; Vineland Bd of Ed Spec Ed Tchr 21 Yrs; *ai:* NEA NJEA 1975-; *office:* Vineland HS North 3010 E Chestnut Ave nd NJ 08360

JINE, MARILOU CAREY, English Teacher; *b:* Brockton, MA; *m:* ; *ed:* Framingham St Coll (BA) Eng & Ed 1987; Bridgewater St Coll Eng & Ed 1991; *cr:* Silver Lake Reg HS Eng Tchr 1987-88; on HS Eng Tchr 1988-91; North Attleboro HS Eng Tchr 1991-; *ai:* areness Comm & Yrbk Fin Adv; AFT 1991-; North Attleboro Tchrs 991-; *office:* North Attleboro HS Landry Ave North Attleboro MA

JINO, WILLIAM A., 8th Grade Social Studies Tchr; *b:* Warren, Patricia Ann Spatafore; *c:* Joellen; *ed:* Millersville Univ (BS) ehensive Soc Stud 1969; 28 Grad Credit Hrs; *cr:* Swift MS Tchr ; *ai:* NEA, PSEA, SEA 1969-; *office:* Swift MS 1866 Robert Fulton uarryville PA 17566

BET, KIMBERLY RING, Reading Teacher; *b:* Zanesville, OH; *m:* Vincent III; *c:* Nicholas, Kelly Anne, Christopher; *ed:* Bowling St Univ (MED) Elem Ed 1989; Rdng Recovery Tchr Trng; *cr:* Bay st & 2nd Grd Tchr 1984-87; Bataan Elem Schl 1st-3rd Grd Tchr 0; Portage Elem 3rd Grd Tchr 1990-95; Bataan & Jefferson Elem Rdng Tchr 1995-; *ai:* Rdng Recovery Tchr in Trng; AFT 1987-, ponding Sec; IRA 1987-; P E Jr Womens Club 1990-; *office:* Port City Schls Portage Dr Port Clinton OH 43452

NESE, SALVATORE MICHAEL, Professor of Biology; *b:* a Falls, NY; *m:* Lillian Marie Stanwich; *ed:* Niagara Cty Comm Coll Math, Sci 1973; St Univ Coll at Buffalo (BA) Bio 1975; Niagara Univ Bio 1977; St Bonaventure Univ (PHD) Bio, Microbiology 1988; *cr:* a Univ Tchng Asst 1975-77; St Bonaventure Univ Tchng Asst 0; Niagara Cty Comm Coll Prof 1980-; *ai:* Bio Dept, Med Assisting NEA 1980-; ASM, AAAS, NY Acad of Sci 1977-; Niagara Univ, St enture Univ Full Schlsp; Articles; Textbooks; Pres Awd Tchng Excl Alumni Awd 1993; *office:* Niagara County Comm Coll 3111 ers Settlement Rd Sanborn NY 14132

ARELLI, HENRY DAVID, Fifth Grade Teacher; *b:* Clearfield, PA; rion J. Collin; *c:* David, Sue-Lynn, Darlynn; *ed:* Erie Cty Comm Food Svc 1962; St Univ Coll at Buffalo (BA) Ed 1968, (MS) Ed 1971; Dept Mental Hygiene Alcohol Problems; *cr:* Sweethome Elem Schl Ed, 4th-5th Grd Tchr 1966-76; Dexter Terrace Schl 3rd Grd Tchr 39; Heritage Heights Schl 5th Grd Tchr 1989-; *ai:* Cmptr Sci Tech; Report Card Comms; 5th Grd Peer Coord; Sweethome Educl Assn ; Natl Geograpic Soc 1975-; NY St United Tchr 1966-; UAW 73; Trinity United Meth Church, Pastor Relation Comm; Trinity h, Admin Bd Chprsn; Eagle Scout; God & Cntry Awd; Asst Scout r; *office:* Heritage Hghts Elem Schl 2545 Sweet Home Amherst NY

AS, NIKOS, Criminology Professor; *b:* Athens, Greece; *m:* Hilli; *ed:* of Athens (ILB) Law 1981; Univ of Paris II (DEA) Criminology & gy 1982; Univ of Edinburgh (PHD) Law & Sociology 1988; *cr:* Univ nburgh Cncl of Europe Fellow 1984-85; Univ Coll London Rsrch 1989; Temple Univ Asst Prof 1989-95, Assoc Prof 1995-; Univ of at Cardiff Visiting Prof 1995-; *ai:* ASC 1989-; ASA 1989-; Law & ssn 1990-; ACJS 1991-; Northeastern Univ Press 1994-, Series Ed on national Crime; Ctr for Hellenic stud 1995-, Assoc Dir; Univ of urgh Post-Doc Flwshp; European Union Grants for Rsrch; Pub 20 es & Book Chptrs; Edited Books: Organized Crime, the Future of ic Theory; *office:* Temple Univ 529 Gladfelter Hall Philadelphia PA

ENTI, ROBERT JOHN, Music Department Coordinator; *b:* Jersey NJ; *m:* Paula Lanzo; *c:* Nicole; *ed:* Jersey City St Coll (BA) Music 83; Masters of Music Ed Prgm; *cr:* Pub Schls 3, 6 Gen Music Tchr 88; Meml HS Band Dir 1988-94, Coord Music Dept 1994-; *ai:* hing, Concert, Jazz Bands; NEA 1984-; Amer Fed of Musicians ; Sons of the Amer Legion 1995-; *office:* Memorial HS 5501 Park Ave New York NJ 07093

ERO, WENDY NOKES, Spanish Teacher; *b:* Melrose, MA; *m:* r Michael; *c:* Cynthia, Michael, Clifford; *ed:* Univ of NH (BA) Span 1968; Cambridge Univ (MED) Ed 1993; Attnd Univ of Valencia at Valencia; *cr:* Beverly HS Span Tchr 1968-69; Winnacunnet HS Span Tchr 1970-77; Exeter Area HS Span Tchr 1983-; *ai:* Sociedad Honoraria Hispanica Spon, Adv; Span Natl Exam; AATFL, ATSP, NEA, Exeter Ed Assn 1983-; BSA 1981-, Cubmaster, Merit Badge Cnslr; St Theresa Cath Church 1979-, Eucharistic Minister, Parish Cncl; *office:* Exeter Area HS 30 Linden St Exeter NH 03833*

PASSIFIONE, EDWARD, Sixth Grade Teacher; *b:* Seneca Falls, NY; *m:* Ann Ferrara; *c:* Edward Jr., Mary T. Jones, Jennifer, Elizabeth; *ed:* SUNY Geneseo (BS) Ed 1963; Post Grad SUNY Cortland, SUNY Oswego, Syracuse Univ; *cr:* Ovid Cntrl Schl Tchr 1963-69; Seneca Falls Cntrl Schl Tchr 1969-; *ai:* NEA NY 1963-; NYS Cncl of SS; Wayne Finger Lakes Cncl of SS; Women's Rights Natl Park 1992-, Tchr Advy Comm; St Patricks Church 1995-, Rel Ed Comm; *home:* 4135 Sunrise Pass Seneca Falls NY 13148

PASSUCCI, FRANK MARTIN, Principal; *b:* Passaic, NJ; *m:* Diane J. Sinatra; *c:* Dana, Camille; *ed:* Glassboro St Coll (BA) Elem Ed 1977; William Paterson Coll (MA) Admin & Supervision 1985; Jersey City St Coll 30 Credits Occupational Therapy; *cr:* Abraham Lincoln Elem K-8th Grd Rdng Tchr 1977-78; Garfield HS 9th-12th Grd Basic Skills Math Tchr 1978-80; Washington Irving Elem 8th Grd Math Tchr 1980-91, 6th Grd Tchr 1991-93; Abraham Lincoln Elem K-6th Grd Tchr, Prin 1993-; *ai:* NAESP, PSA 1993-; *office:* Abraham Lincoln Schl No 6 111 Palisade Ave Garfield NJ 07026

PASSUITE, FRANCIS J., Retired 7th Grd Soc Stud Tchr; *b:* Lockport, NY; *m:* Kathryn A. Pshirrer; *c:* Mark, David; *ed:* Edinboro Scndry, Soc St 1961; 31 Cr Hrs SUNY at Buffalo, SUNY at Brockport; *cr:* Barker Cntrl Schl 6th Gr Tchr 1961-62; Emmet Belknap 7th Gr Soc St Tchr 1962-95; *ai:* LEA, NYSUT 1962-; NPPA 1969-; Military Svc 82nd Airborne Div 1954-56; *home:* 6448 Hope Ln Lockport NY 14094

PASTER, JOAN HOBBS, High School History Teacher; *b:* Spartanburg, SC; *m:* Darrell L.; *c:* Rachel, Katie; *ed:* Salem Coll (BA) His 1969; Vanderbilt Univ (MA) His 1972; *cr:* Greenwich Acad Dean of Stdnts, His Tchr 1971-80; The Nightingale Bamford Schl His Tchr 1980-85; Oak Knoll Schl His Tchr 1990-96; *ai:* Sr Class Homeroom Tchr; Cum Laude Pres; Long Range Planning Steering Comm; *office:* Oak Knoll Schl 44 Blackburn Rd Summit NJ 07901

PASTERNAK, CAROL DEAKYNE, 8th Grade Language Arts Tchr; *b:* Plainfield, NJ; *m:* William; *c:* Marc, Jennifer Pasternak Zeran, Jeffrey, Amanda; *ed:* Middlesex Cty Coll (AA) Lbrl Arts 1969; Glassboro St Coll (BA) Ed, Sec Eng 1971; Georgian Ct Coll (MA) 1996; Rdng Specialist Cert; Diversity Ed; CHEER Conf; Holocaust Ed; NJ Trainer, Consultant; *cr:* St Bartholomew Schl 8th Grd Eng Tchr 1971-72; St Dominic Schl 6th-8th Grd Eng Tchr 1977-87; Cntrl Regnl MS Lang Arts Tchr 1990-; *ai:* Adv Peer Mediation; Pupil Assistance, Strategic Planning Comm; Curr Cncl; NEA, NJEA, NCTE 1990-; Ardena Bapt Church 1993-, Chrstn Bd of Ed; Tchr of Yr 1992-93; *office:* Cntrl Regnl MS Forest Hills Pkwy Bayville NJ 08721

PASTERNAK, CHARLES JOHN, Social Studies Teacher; *b:* DuBois, PA; *m:* Rebecca Gilbert; *c:* Casey; *ed:* IN Univ of PA (BS) Soc Sci Ed 1993; 9 Grad Credits Gannon Univ; *cr:* DuBois Area HS Soc Stud Tchr 1993-; *ai:* JV Bsbl, 9th Grd Ftbl Coach; Vlybl Club Adv; Prin Advy Comm; NEA, PSEA, DAEA 1993-; United Way 1994, Fund Raising Vol; *office:* Dubois Area Sr HS 400 Orient Ave Du Bois PA 15801

PASTIR, LINDA RUFF, Biology Teacher; *b:* Newark, NJ; *m:* Mark R.; *c:* Susan, Kristen; *ed:* Kean Coll (BA) Bio Ed 1969; Montclair St Coll (MA) Bio 1976; *cr:* Westfield HS Tchr 1969-; *ai:* Prins Liaison & Dist Sci Review Comms; Natl Assn of Bio, NJ Sci Tchrs Assn, NEA, NJEA, WEA 1969-; Bio Tchrs Assn of NJ 1990-; PTA, PTO & Sp F Music Boosters; NJ BISEC Clinical Inst Grant; Dist Nom Presidential Awd for Excl in Sci Tchng; Natl Ed Honor Soc, Kappa Delta Pi; Honor Soc of Phi Kappa Phi; The Shen Distinguished Tchr Awd; *office:* Westfield HS 550 Dorian Rd Westfield NJ 07090*

PASTO, RONALD J., Science Teacher; *b:* Elmira, NY; *m:* Ellen; *c:* Ronald Jr., Toivo; *ed:* SUNY at Cortland (BS) Chem 1964; Penn St (MED) Phys Sci 1967; Attnd Franklin & Marshall Coll, Bucknell Univ, Syracuse Univ, SUNY At Oneonta; *cr:* Owego Free Acad Sci Tchr 1964-; SUNY at Binghamton Adj Phys Dept 1980-85; Owego Free Acad Chem, Physics Tchr, Sci Dept Chprsn 1991-; *ai:* Bike Club Adv; Learn to Ski Prgm; Supt Budget Advy, Prins Ed Advy, Frameworks, Dimensions Learnng Comms; Past Bowling Coach; Owego Apalachian TA 1964-, Pres, VP, BR, ED 11 Del; NYSUT, AFT 1970-; Amer Assn Physics Tchr 1985; *office:* Owego Free Acad George St Owego NY 13827

PASTOR, RENEE S., Jr High Lang Arts Teacher; *b:* Elyria, OH; *ed:* Notre Dame Coll (BA) Eng 1972; John Carroll Univ (MED) Rdng 1980; *cr:* St Leo's Schl Jr HS Tchr 1979-82; Loyola Press Textbook Writer for Christ Our Life Series 1982-84; St Benedict's Schl Tchr, Prin 1984-93; St Francis Schl Jr HS Tchr 1993-; *ai:* Stdnt Cncl Moderator; Peer Mediation Moderator & Trainer; Creative Writing Coach; *office:* St Francis Schl 7206 Myron Ave Cleveland OH 44103

PASTORESSA, MARIANNE PUGLIESE, Biology & Chemistry Teacher; *b:* Flushing, NY; *m:* Joseph C.; *c:* Christina Marie, Joseph Michael; *ed:* SUNY at Stony Brook (BS) Bio & Chem 1980; Hofstra Univ (MA) Comp Sci 1986; *cr:* Half Hollow Hills Schl Dist HS & Jr HS Sci Tchr 1980-; *office:* Half Hollow Hills West Schl 375 Half Hollow Rd Dix Hills NY 11746

PASTORINO, LINDA SCHLEGEL, Fifth Grade Teacher; *b:* Brooklyn, NY; *m:* Timothy; *c:* Amy, Katherine; *ed:* William Paterson Coll (BA) Elem Ed 1969; *cr:* Forest Glen Elem Schl Fifth Grd Tchr 1969-76; Fairview Elem Schl Fifth Grd Tchr 1976-85; Carteret Elem Schl Fifth Grd Tchr 1987-; *ai:* Tech Comm; Chess Adv; NEA 1969-; Girl Scout Ldr 1988-89; *office:* Carteret Elem Schl 158 Grove St Bloomfield NJ 07003

PASTORIZA-CRESPO, NELIDA, Registrar & Adjunct Lecturer; *b:* Arecibo, PR; *c:* Ninoska, Isalia; *ed:* Manhattan Comm C CUNY (AAS) Data Processing 1972; Lehman Coll CUNY (BA) Puerto Rican Stud 1974; Hunter Coll CUNY (MS) Biling Ed 1977; *cr:* Hostos Comm Coll Exec Asst to Pres 1975-80, Asst Dir Stud, Adm Serv 1980-84, Adj Lecturer 1983-95, Registrar 1988-; *ai:* Stu Govt, Latin Amer Stdnts Union Club Adv; ACROO Cncl Registrar's 1988-, Sec; AAUW 1984-; AFT, PSC-CUNY 1980-; *office:* City Univ Of NY Hostos Coll 500 Grand Concourse Bronx NY 10451

PASTULA, GALE P., English Teacher; *b:* Jersey City, NJ; *c:* Daniel; *ed:* Elizabethtown Coll (BA) Eng 1974; *cr:* South Plainfield HS Eng Tchr 1974-; *ai:* Sr Class Adv; Antique Car Show Chprsn; AFT; NEA, SPEA 1974-; *office:* South Plainfield HS 200 Lake St S Plainfield NJ 07080

PASUIT, MARY ANN T., 6th Grade Teacher; *b:* Passaic, NJ; *m:* Paul H.; *c:* Tom, Michael; *ed:* Wm Patterson Coll (BA) Spec Ed, Tchr of Hand 1973; Long Island Univ (MA) Elem Ed 1991; 30 Addl Credits Post Grad Stud; *cr:* Lincoln Schl Tchr of Handicapped 1973-76; Wilson Schl 1, 4 Grd Elem Ed Tchr 1978-80; Lyncrest Schl Compensatory Math Tchr 1985-86; Hilltop Schl NI Spec Ed Class Tchr 1986-87; Warren Point Schl 1, 6 Grd Elem Ed Tchr 1987-93; Thomas Jefferson MS 6 Grd Tchr 1993-; *ai:* Stu Cncl, PTA Fac Adv; Soc Stud, Tchr Assessment, Evaluation Comm; NEA 1973-; Fair Lawn Hockey Assn 1994-, Exec Bd, Vol Svc Awd; Pub Svc Announcement Aired WOR-TV; Stu Incentive Prgm Dev New Jersey Devils; *office:* Thomas Jefferson MS 35-01 Morlot Ave Fair Lawn NJ 07410*

PATCH, ALYSON L., 6th Grade Teacher; *b:* Middlebury, VT; *ed:* Castleton St Coll (MED) Ed 1983; Bates Coll (BA) Psych 198; *cr:* Townshend Elem 5th-6th Grd Tchr 1982-85; Shutesbury Elem 5th-6th Grd Tchr 1985-86; Sanderson Acad 5th-6th Grd Tchr 1986-; *ai:* Tekkids; Ashfield Youth Commission 1992-, Chprsn; Ashfield Historical Soc 1990-, Former Trustee; Fellow Tchr Scholar Prgm Natl Endowment for Hum 1994-95; *office:* Sanderson Acad 44 Buckland Rd Ashfield MA 01330

PATCH, RICHARD C., Physics Teacher; *b:* Boston, MA; *ed:* Northeastern Univ (BSME) Mechanical Engrng; Univ of WI (MST) Physics 1970; Univ of SD (MNS) Earth Sci 1975; Attnd Univ of Dallas 3 Credit Hrs, Univ of Hartford 6 Credit Hrs & Univ of Washington at Seattle 4 Credit Hrs; *cr:* Holliston HS Physics Tchr 1965-67; Salem HS Math & Physics Tchr 1967-84; Marblehead HS Physics Tchr 1984-.*

PATCHEN, LYNN HEDGES, Second Grade Teacher; *b:* Lancaster, OH; *m:* David; *ed:* OH Univ (BA) Elem Ed 1974, (MA) Elem Ed & Rdng Specialist 1980; *cr:* Crooksville Schl Kndgtn & 4th Grd Tchr 1975-77; Fairfield Union Schls 2nd Grd Tchr; *ai:* OEA, NEA 1975-; Forgotten 4-Paws 1995-, Sec; Jennings Scholar 1986-87; *office:* Pleasantville Elem 225 Lincoln Ave Pleasantville OH 43148

PATEL, SURYAKANT C., Science Teacher; *b:* Kampala, Uganda; *m:* Kiran Suryakant; *c:* Jatin, Rajvi; *ed:* Makerere Univ (MS) Chem & Physics 1972; 6 Addl Credit Hrs; *cr:* Walworth Sec Schl London Sci Tchr 1974-84; East Orange HS Sci Tchr 1985-; *ai:* Sci Club Adv; Amer Inst of Chemists 1989-; Prins Awd for Outstndg Edctr in Sci 1990-91; *office:* East Orange HS 34 N Walnut St East Orange NJ 07019*

PATENAUDE, CYNTHIA RUTH, Secondary English Teacher; *b:* Mechanicville, NY; *m:* Henry Schmeer; *ed:* SUNY at Geneseo (BA) Eng 1987; SUNY at Albany (MA) Eng Ed 1989; *cr:* Reimer & Braunstein Law Firm Data Processor 1987-88; Main Tane Contracting Hazardous Commnctn Coord 1988-90; Mount Morris Cntrl Eng Tchr 1990-; *ai:* Class of 1999, NHS & Schl Newspaper Adv; NEA 1990-; NASAA 1993-; PTA Spcl Person Awd 1991; MMCS Tchr of Yr 1992 & 1994; U of Rochester Awd for Excl in Scndry Schl Tchng 1993; *office:* Mt Morris Central Schl Bonadonna Ave Mount Morris NY 14510

PATENAUDE, DAN ROBERT, College Placement Counselor; *b:* Lowell, MA; *m:* Loretto Margaret Fromm; *ed:* Bridgewater St Coll (BA) Pol Sci 1979; Assumption Coll (MA), (CAGS) Rehabilitation Cnslng 1987; Chicago St Univ Ed Cert 1983; Rivier Coll MA Tchr Cert; *cr:* Tyngsboro Jr Sr HS Soc Stud Tchr 1979-81; Marist HS Soc Stud Tchr 1981-85; St Peter-Marian Jr Sr HS Guid Cnslr 1987-; *ai:* Coach Soph Ftbl 1981-85, Frosh Bsbl 1982-85, Var Ftbl 1987-89, JV Bsbl 1988-; Substance Abuse Prevention Coord 1991-95; MASCA, Worc Cty Prsnl & Guid Assn, Natl Rehabilitation Assn 1987-; *office:* St Peter-Marian Jr Sr HS 781 Grove St Worcester MA 01605

PATENAUDE, DIANA L., Multi-Age Teacher; *m:* Michael; *c:* Nathan, Megan; *ed:* Castleton St (BS) Ed 1971; Univ of VT (MED) Curr Dev 1985; *cr:* St Albans City Elem Tchr 1972-; *ai:* Mem of the Franklin Cntrl Local Stans Bd for Relicensing Edctrs; Ad Hoc Comm for Behaviorally Challenging Stdnts; NEA; VEA; Franklin Cntrl Sup Union Tchrs Ed Assn, Exec Comm; PTA; Schl Bd Awd 1986 for Outstdng Svc; Co-Founder Mentor Pgm; *home:* 6 Burnell Ter Saint Albans VT 05478

PATEREK, PAMELA ANN (SIGLOCH), Amer History II Teacher; *b:* Elizabeth, NJ; *m:* Raymond Richard; *c:* Elizabeth Marie; *ed:* Kean Coll (BA) Soc Stud Ed 1972; Addl Astronomy, Chem I & Physics I Stud 1978-80; *cr:* St Mary of the Assumption Elem Schl 7th & 8th Grd Soc St & Eng Tchr 1974-93; St Mary of the Assumption HS Amer Hist II Tchr 1993-, Dept Chprsn 1995-; *ai:* 8th Grd Grad & Craft Fundraiser Moderator; Soc Stud Chprsn 1974-80; Patrol Supvr; Class Plays 1976-80; Yrbk Moderator & Asst 1993-94; Stu Cncl Moderator 1994-; NCEA 1974-; Roselle Vol Ambublance Corps 1973-80, Emergency Medical Technician 1974-77; Schl Evaluation Comm Chprsn 1979; *office:* St Mary-Assumption H S 237 S Broad St Elizabeth NJ 07202

PATERNA, JOAN OSIPOWITZ, Asst Professor of Psychology; *b:* Neptune, NJ; *m:* Andrew; *c:* Christopher, Adam; *ed:* Montclair St Univ (BA) Fr 1970; Cntrl CT St Univ (MS) Cnslng 1974; Tchng Cert 1970; 6 Credit Hrs Rdng 1986-87; *cr:* Quinnipiac Coll Cnslr 1974-75; Univ of CT Asst to Dean of Stdnts 1975-84; Pvt Practice Cnslr 1984-85; CT Wellness Ctr Cnslr 1985-86; Manchester Comm Coll Asst Prof of Psych 1987-; *ai:* Psych Club & Psi Beta Psych Hnr Soc Adv; Fac Senate Exec, Awds Reception & Gen Ed Comms; Amer Psychol Assn 1987-; Amer Psychological Soc 1991-; South Windsor Supts Advy Comm 1993-; South Windsor HS Prins Advy Group 1993-.

PATERNO, MATTHEW JOHN, Instrumental Music Director; *b:* Rahway, NJ; *ed:* Rutgers Univ Mason Gross Schl of Arts (BM) Music Ed 1989; *cr:* Keansburg HS Band Dir; Keansburg Summer Music Schl Co-Dir 1989-90; Mt Tabor Summer Music Schl Low Brass Instr, Jazz I, Wind Ensemble, Marching Band 1991-; Pvt Drill Designer & Clinician 1993-; Pvt Brass Inst 1992-; Asst William Paterson College Summer Band 1993-; Wayne Hills HS Instrumental Music Dir 1990-; *ai:* Marching & Jazz Bands; Pit Orch; Small Ensembles; Music Theory; Asst WPC college band; MENC 1989-; Natl Band Assn 1993-; North Jersey Area Band Conductor Symphonic Band 1995; North Jersey Region I NJ Allstate; NJEA Arts Cncl Coop; Wayne Friends of Music 1990-, Co-Pres 1991-; Hanover Wind Symphony 1990-; Imperial Brass Band 1991-; William Paterson College Concert Band 1992-; Mt Tabor Alumni Jazz Ensemble 1991-; Metropolitan Bass Band co-founder, co-conductor; *office:* Wayne Hills Sr HS 272 Berdan Ave Wayne NJ 07470

PATERSON, WILLIAM M., English Teacher; *b:* Niagara Falls, NY; *m:* Joan L. Genovese; *c:* William E., Jeffrey M.; *ed:* NY St Univ Coll at Buffalo (BS) Scndry Ed 1968; Niagara Univ (MA) His 1974; Addl Post Masters Stud Soc Stud, Eng, Ed; Facilitator Lang Arts; *cr:* NY Power Authority Comm Realtions Tchr, Visitor 1973-; Niagara Power ProjectTchr; City of Tonawanda Pub Schl System Eng, His, Soc Stud Tchr 1968-; *ai:* Prof Dev Schl Cncl, Fac 1995-; Veterans US Navy Operation Deep Freeze Antartic Svc; Tonawanda Ed Assn 1968- Exec Bd, Bldg Rep, Del; Niagara Falls Municipal Housing Authority 1985-91 Bd Chair, Vice Chair, Sec, Commissions Chm; Niagara Falls Municipal Planning Bd 1976-78; IBEW Local 2104 Steward, Recording Sec, Exec Bd Mem, Vice Chm, Trial Bd Mem, Ed of Local Publications 1983-91; Niagara, Orleans Cntrl Labor Cncl Del; Annual Progess Meeting 1983-91, Sec; *office:* Tonawanda Sr HS 150 Hinds St Tonawanda NY 14150*

PATKA, JOYCE CASINO, Business Education Teacher; *b:* Schenectady, NY; *m:* Edward W.; *c:* Sue, Michelle; *ed:* Castleton St (BS) Bus Ed 1969; Albany St (MS) Bus Ed 1973; Distributive Ed Cert; *cr:* Mohonasen HS Bus Tchr 1969-; *ai:* DECA Adv; Stu Store; MTA 1969-; NYSTA 1969-; *office:* Mohonasen HS 2072 Curry Rd Schenectady NY 12303

PATNETT, EARNESTENE ENOCENCIA, Seventh & Eighth Grade Teacher; *b:* San Ignacio, Belize; *m:* Damacio; *c:* Brian, Angelique, Andre; *ed:* Univ of Miami (BSC) Math 1980; *cr:* St Andrews Elem Schl 1st-7th Grd Tchr 1961-71; R. M. Bailey Jr, Sr HS 7th Grd Tchr 1971-72; L. W. Young Jr, Sr HS 7th Grd Tchr 1972-73; C. C. Sweeting Sr HS 10th Grd Tchr 1973-87; O. L. Victory Elem Schl 7th-8th Grd Tchr 1987-; *ai:* William E. Simon Fund for Educl Opportunity Yth Coord; Friends in Support of The Diocese of Belize 1989, VP, 1994, Treas; St Andrews Schl Assn 1989-, Pres; Nutrition Grant for Schl; Awd for Participation in William E. Simon

Fund for Educl Opportunity; Rel Level I Cert; *office:* Our Lady Of Victory Schl 38 N 5th Ave Mount Vernon NY 10550

PATRICK, BONNIE MC KEE, Second Grade Teacher; *b:* New Castle, PA; *m:* William; *c:* Michael Ernst, Patricia Ernst; *ed:* 45 Grad Hrs John Carroll Univ, Cleveland St Univ, Kent St; *cr:* Sebring Schl 5th Grd Tchr 1967-68; Ridgebury Schl 3rd Grd Tchr 1968-69; South Euclid-Lyndhurst 2nd Grd Tchr 1975-; *ai:* At Risk Kids Group Facilitator; Bldg Assistance Team; CORE Team; Curr Advy, Soc Comm; OH Ed Assn, NEA, South Euclid-Lyndhurst Teach Assn 1968-; Meals on Wheels, Vol; Cmptr Grant ECCO; *office:* S Euclid-Lyndhurst Schl System 5044 Mayfield Rd Lyndhst-Mayfld OH 44124

PATRICK, CAROL A., English Teacher; *b:* Orange, NJ; *m:* Stephen B.; *c:* Elizabeth, Margaret, Robert; *ed:* Douglass Coll (BA) Eng Ed 1963; *cr:* Morristown HS Eng Tchr 1963-66; Baumholder Schl W Germany U S Army Librn 1966-68; Atlantic Cty Schls Substitute & Long-Term Substitute Tchr 1976-80; Holy Spirit HS Eng Tchr 1980-; *ai:* Sr Class Moderator; Annual Musical Costumes; Schl Nwspr Adv; CEA 1980-; NCTE 1986-; Scndry Contracted Tchrs Org 1984-; Northfield Pub Lib Assn 1969-72, Pres 1969-72; Northfield Cultural Comm 1972-, Chprsn 1972-; Library on the Move; Historic Houses of Northfield; More Historic Houses of Northfield; *office:* Holy Spirit H S New Rd & California Ave Absecon NJ 08201

PATRICK, DAVID GEORGE, Assistant Professor; *b:* Cambridge, NY; *m:* Nancy Pederson; *c:* Christa, Matthew, Ryan; *ed:* Univ of PA (BS) Phys Therapy 1979; Temple Univ (MS) Phys Therapy 1993; Northwestern Univ Cert Prosthetics & Orthotics 1985; *cr:* John Heinz Inst Dir of Phys Therapy 1982-85; Northeastern Prosthetics-Orthotics Staff Prosthetist-Orthotist 1985-87; Allied Svcs Rehabilitation Hospital Dir of Phys Therapy 1987-93; Coll Misericordia Asst Prof of Phys Therapy Prgm 1993-; *ai:* Amer Phys Therapy Assn 1987-; PA Phys Therapy Assn 1987-, Bd of Dirs; Northeast Dist PPTA 1987-, Dir, Vice-Chair; Temple Bapt Church, Youth Spon; Allied Svcs, Home Hlth Advy Bd; Youth Bsktbl League, Coach; 2 Case Stud Contributions in Clinical Cases in Phys Therapy; Chapter in Saunders Manuel of Phys Therapy; Article Issues on Aging; *office:* Coll Misericordia 301 Lake St Dallas PA 18612

PATRICK, DONNA C., Principal; *b:* Hershey, PA; *m:* Kenneth E.; *ed:* Shippensburg Univ (BS) Elem Ed 1970, (MED) Elem Ed 1972; Temple Univ Prins Cert 1992; Millersville Univ Supvr Elem Ed; *cr:* Northern Lebanon Schl Dist 1st Grd Tchr 1970-74; Derry Twp Schl Dist 1st Grd Tchr 1974-90, Elem Ed Coord 1990-92, Elem Prin 1992-; *ai:* NAESP, PAESP 1992-; ASCD, PASCD 1989-; PAFPC 1993-; *office:* Hershey Intermediate Elem Schl Homestead Rd Box 898 Hershey PA 17033

PATRICK, EVA E., Biology Teacher; *b:* Lynchburg, VA; *m:* Howard L. Tucker Jr.; *c:* Bernadette Tucker, Dawn Tucker; *ed:* VA St Coll (BS) Bio 1962; Wilkes Univ (MS) Ed 1990; 12 Hrs Penn St Tchrs Cert; 12 Hrs Temple Univ; *cr:* Philadelphia Schls Edctr 1963-67, Harrisburg Schl Edctr 1968-; *ai:* Sci Dept Rep; Curr Comm; Sci Fair Coord; NEA 1968-, Bd Mem 8 Yrs, Legislative Chair Hlth Comm; PA St Ed Assn 1968-, Bd Mem 8 Yrs; Phi Delta Kappa; Delta Sigma Theta 1990-, Soc Action Chair; Greater Zion Missionary Bapt Church; *office:* Harrisburg HS 2451 Market St Harrisburg PA 17110*

PATRICK, IRENE JOYCE, High School Art Teacher; *b:* Pittsburgh, PA; *m:* Regis L.; *ed:* Edinboro Univ of PA (BS) Art Ed 1964; Attnd Indiana Univ of PA; *cr:* Bethel Park Schl Dist Art Tchr 1964-66; Norwin Schl Dist Art Tchr 1966-; *ai:* Art Dept Chprsn; Mentor Tchr; Cooperating Tchr for Seton Hill Coll; NEA 1964-, Soc Chprsn, Bldg Rep; *office:* Norwin Sr HS 251 Mc Mahon Dr North Hunting PA 15642

PATRICK, KATHLEEN A., Science Teacher; *b:* Rochester, NY; *ed:* Monroe Comm Coll (AAS) Recreation Supervision, Therapeutic Recreation 1975; St Univ Coll at Brockport (BS) Hlth Ed 1980; Alfred Univ (MS) Ed 1991; *cr:* Saint Agnes HS Sci Tchr 1980-82; Caledonia-Mumford Cntrl Schl Sci Tchr 1982-86; Andover Cntrl Schl Half Time Sci Tchr & Whitesville Cntrl Schl Half Time Sci Tchr 1987-; *ai:* Yorks Corners Mennonite Church 1992-; *office:* Andover Central Schl 31-35 Elm St Andover NY 14806

PATRICK, PATRICIA KINKELA, 6th Grade Social Studies Tchr; *b:* New Castle, PA; *m:* Ronald J.; *ed:* Slippery Rock Univ (BS) Elem Ed 1963; Addl 12 Grad Hrs; 18 Grad Hrs Coll of Notre Dame; *cr:* Laurel Elem Schl 1st Grd Tchr 1963-67, 4th Grd Tchr 1967-88; Harlansburg Schl Head Tchr 1974-79; Laurel Elem Schl 6th Grd Lang Arts Tchr 1988-91, 6th Grd Soc Stud Tchr 1991-; *ai:* Acad Assistance; Detention Supvr; 6th Grd Field Trip Coord; NEA, PSEA 1963-; Laurel Ed Assn 1963-, Sec, Treas, Fac Rep; YM-YWCA 1973-, Vol, Water Safety & Lifeguard Instr, Lifeguard; Amer Red Cross, Vol Cardiac Pulmonary Resuscitation Instr; Mary Mother of Hope Parish 1968-, Sunday Schl Tchr; *office:* Laurel Elem Schl Rd 4 Box 52 New Castle PA 16101*

PATRICK, ROBYN D., Science Teacher; *b:* Dayton, OH; *m:* Joseph; *c:* Nicholas, Zachary; *ed:* Kent St Univ (BA) Elem Ed 1982, (MED) Comm Cnslng 1995; *cr:* Southeast Local Schls 7th & 8th Grd Sci, Rdng Tchr 1994-; *ai:* Local Sci Fair Coord, Rep; NEA, NEOEA, SELDTA 1984-; Kappa Delta Pi 1982-; Chi Sigma Iota 1994-; Dalta Gamma Alumnus 1982-; *office:* Southeast Local Schls 8301 Tallmadge Rd Ravenna OH 44266

PATRICK, THOMAS RICHARD, Mathematics Teacher; *b:* Younstown, OH; *m:* Christine Frazis; *ed:* Younstown St Univ (BS) Math 1969; Univ of Dayton (MS) Math Ed 1973; Cleveland State Univ 3 Hrs Grad Stud; Case Western Reserve Univ 6 Hrs Grad Stud; Cleveland St Univ 6 Hrs Post Grad Stud; John Carroll 8 Hrs Post Grad Stud; OH Weslyan Univ 1 Hr Post Grad Stud; *cr:* Woodbury Jr HS Math Tchr 1969-83; Shaker Hghts HS Math Tchr 1983-; *ai:* Amer HS Math Examination Schl Mgr; Advance Placement Math Instr; Shaker Hghts Tchr Assn 1969-, Treas, Svc Awd 1987; NWTF 1981-94, OH St Bd; NRA 1989-; SHTA Fellowship; PTA Tchr Fellowship Grant; Natl Sci Fnd Grant 1970-73; SHTA Negotiating Team; Coll Bd Educt Testing Svc, Advanced Plcmnt Calc Exam Reader; *office:* Shaker Heights HS 15911 Aldersyde Dr Cleveland OH 44120

PATRONE, EILEEN CIMINERO, American History Teacher; *b:* Warren, OH; *m:* Thomas R.; *c:* Matthew; *ed:* Youngstown St Univ (BSEd) His, Pol Sci 1972; Grad Courses YSU, Kent St Univ, Univ of Dayton, Ashland Coll, Drake Univ; *cr:* Warren G. Harding HS Soc Stud Tchr 1972-79; H. B. Turner Jr HS Geography, Am His Tchr 1979-90; Warren Western Reserve Jr HS Amer His Tchr 1990-; *ai:* Bldg Improvement Comm; Chrldg Adv 1974-76 Warren G Harding; Sr Class Adv WGH 1976; WGH Asst Speech Team Coach 1972-74; NEA, OH Ed Assn, Warren Ed Assn 1972-; Niles Mc Kinley Band Boosters 1993-, Sec 1994-; Our Lady of Mt Carmel Church; H. B. Turner Jr HS & Warren City Schls Tchr of Yr 1988; Nom OH Tchr of Yr 1988; Nom Natl Band Certification 1995; *office:* Warren Western Reserve Jr HS 200 Loveless St SW Warren OH 44485*

PATSOLIC, SANDY A., Eighth Grade Teacher; *b:* Flushing, NY; *m:* Joseph; *c:* Lindsay, Jessica; *ed:* Shippensburg Univ 33 Hrs Rdng Specialist; Shippensburg Univ 33 Hrs Rdng Specialist; *cr:* PA Assn for Blind Pub Rel Dir 1974-76; YWCA Tchr 1986-88; St Patrick Schl Tchr 1988-; *ai:* K-8 Grd Lang Arts, in-schl Educl Prgms Coord; Eighth Grd Grad, Reception, Fund Raising Class Trips Coord; Liaison to HS Curr Planning; Civic League 1980-90; ABC Nursery Schl VP; Crestview Elem PTO Bd 1987-88, Sec; Authored Article; Outstanding Quality, Exceptional Acad Performance from Profs Dr. Wm Anderson, Dr. Ann Fordham; *office:* St Patrick Schl 87 Marsh Dr Carlisle PA 17013

PATTEN, BRENDA LUSSIER, Sixth Grade Teacher; *b:* Acushnet, MA; *m:* Paul W.; *c:* Audrey, Jennifer, Thomas; *ed:* Bridgewater St Coll (BS) Elem Ed 1975, (MS) Rdng 1982; Cmptrs, Gifted & Talented, Cooperative Ed; Fitchberg St Coll Cmptr; *cr:* Norton MS 3rd-4th Grd Tchr 1975-78; Cathedral Schl 5th-6th Grd Tchr 1978-80; Dighton Elem 4th-5th Grd Tchr 1980-82; Dighton MS 6th Grd Tchr 1982-; *ai:* Girls Bskbl Coach 1983-90; Girls Sftbl Coach 1983-90; Arts & Crafts Adv 1983-; Enrichment Task Force Comm 1991-; Soc Stud Task Force 1989-90; 6th Grd Team Ldr 1987-89; Soc Stu Task Force II 1996-; NEA, MA Tchrs Assn, Dighton Educators 1980-; Plymouth Bay Girl Scouts 1987-, Ldr; Geography Achievement Awd 1988; Golden Apple Awd 1992; *home:* 650 Regan Rd Somerset MA 02726

PATTEN, DARLENE DUFAULT, First Grade Teacher; *b:* Hartland, ME; *m:* Donald I.; *c:* Holly, Dawn, Kate; *ed:* Univ of ME at Farmington (BA) Spec Ed 1975; *cr:* Guilford MS Spec Ed Tchr 1975-81; Abbie Fowler Schl First Grd Tchr 1981-; *ai:* NEA 1975-; SAD #4 Tchrs Assn 1975-, Sec 3 Yrs; *office:* Abbie Fowler Elem Schl School St Sangerville ME 04479

PATTEN, SUSAN SHIREY, English Teacher; *b:* Coudersport, PA; *m:* Michael; *c:* Tracy, Sean, Ryan; *ed:* Lock Haven Univ (BS) Comm 1974; PA St Univ MS Eqs Dev, Remedial Rdng 1983; SAP Trained; 40 Grad Credit Hrs; *cr:* Brockway Jr Sr HS Eng Tchr 1974-76; Piper Aircraft Corp Indstrl Relations Rep 1977-80; Penns Vly Jr Sr HS Eng Tchr 1980-; *ai:* Drama Club; Sr Class Adv; PASS Team; NEA, PSEA 1974-; PVEA 1980-, Bldg Rep; *office:* Penns Valley Jr Sr HS RD 2 Box 116 Spring Mills PA 16875*

PATTERSON, CAROL KING, Kindergarten Teacher; *b:* Plainfield, NJ; *m:* Gary Thomas; *c:* Julie, Tina Fyvie, Crystal Keicher, Stacey Almeter, Scott; *ed:* Houghton Coll (BS) Soc Sci 1967; Fredonia St Coll (MSEd) 1972; *cr:* Randolph Cntrl Schl 1st & 2nd Grd Tchr 1967-74, Kndgtn Tchr 1974-; *ai:* PARP & Staff Morale Comms; NYSTA 1967-; NEA 1967-; *home:* 11219 Benson Rd Randolph NY 14772

PATTERSON, CHARLES E., 5th Grade Teacher; *b:* Sayre, PA; *m:* Constance Ruth Bennett; *c:* Alexander William; *ed:* PA St Univ (BS) Elem Ed 1989; Western MD Coll (MS) Counseling 1995; Pursuing MS in Schl Admin; *cr:* Dallastown Area Schls 5th Grd Tchr 1989-; *ai:* Intramural Sports Instr; Safety Patrol Ldr; Sci Comm Mem; Gift of Time Tribute; *office:* York Twp Elem 2500 S Queen St York PA 17402

PATTERSON, CHARLES WILLIAM, High School Teacher; *b:* Wilmington, DE; *m:* Kimberley A. Kaufman; *c:* Charles III, Luke; *ed:* Temple Univ (BS) Soc Stud Ed 1968, (MED) Adult & Continuing Ed 1974; West Chester Univ 6 Credits Ed; *cr:* Marpue-Newton Sr High His Tchr 1969-71; Chrstn Acad Jr High Tchr 1982-87; Kings Chrstn Schl HS Prin 1987-90; Delaware Cty Chrstn Schl His Tchr 1990-; *ai:* Jr Class & Black His Comm Adv; Track & Cross Cntry Coach; Curr Comm & Advy Cncl Mem; Regnl Assn VP; Stu Act Coord; Amer Historical Assn 1991-; Malta Boat Club 1973-, 1st & 2nd Lieut; *office:* Delaware County Christian Schl 462 Malin Rd Newtown Square PA 19073*

PATTERSON, ELIZABETH HOSTETLER, 7th Grd Math & Reading Tchr; *b:* Madison Cty, OH; *m:* Allan Alexander; *c:* Katherine, Laura, Matthew; *ed:* Lorain Cty Comm Coll (AA) Gen Stud 1994; Ashland Univ (BS) Elem Ed 1995; 3 Sem; Baldwin Wallace Coll 27 Qt Hrs; Cleveland St 7 Qt Hrs; Oberline Tchrs Acad 3 Sem; John Carroll Univ 3 Sem; *cr:* Prospect Elem Schl 5th Grd Tchr 1 Yr; Langston MS 8th Grd Math Tchr 2 Yrs, 6th Grd Tchr 1 Yr, 7th Grd Math Tchr 3 Yrs; *ai:* Peer Mediation Adv; Site Mngmt; Tech Comm; Curr Coordinating Cncl; Family Night Coord; BUGS Co-Coord; NEA, OEA, NEOEA 1988-; NCTM 1994-; OCTM 1990-; Kappa Delta Pi 1985-; Voices for Children Vol 1996; Wkshp Presenter; Project Discovery Participant; *office:* Langston MS 150 N Pleasant St Oberlin OH 44074

PATTERSON, JANE K., 10th Grade Biology Teacher; *b:* Ridgewood, NY; *m:* Robert; *c:* Jessica, Jason, Matthew; *ed:* SUNY at New Paltz (BS) Scndry Ed, Bio 1972, (MS) Scndry Ed, Bio 1975; *cr:* Catskill Cntrl Schl Sci Tchr 1972-; *ai:* Child Stud Team; Prins Advy Comm; STANYS, NYSUT, AFT 1972-; Accepted into Cornell Inst for Bio Tchrs 1995; *office:* Catskill Cntrl Schl Dist 347 W Main St Catskill NY 12414

PATTERSON, JOHN E., English Teacher; *b:* Clifton Springs, NY; *m:* Mary Ann Hughes; *ed:* SUNY at Oswego (BA) Eng, Ed 1972; Post Grad Stud; *cr:* Auburn HS Eng, Hum Instr 1973-; *ai:* Fac Advy Comm; Hist Club Co-Adv; Dist Based Team; Auburn Tchrs Assn 1973-, 1st VP 1990-; NYSUT 1973-, Rep Assembly Del; NCTE 1973-; Auburn Zoning Bd of Appeals 1987-; Served Auburn's Dist Planning Team to Create Plan for Participation for A New Compact for Learning; *office:* Auburn HS Lake Ave Auburn NY 13021

PATTERSON, JOHN ROBERT, Chemistry & Mathematics Tchr; *b:* Corry, PA; *m:* Sally Mae Land; *c:* Steven Vinciguerra, Lauri Keller; *ed:* Edinboro Univ (BS) Chem 1966; 18 Hrs Geology; Attnd Toledo Univ 9 Hrs Chem, City Coll of NY 15 Hrs Chem, Buffalo St Univ 3 Hrs Chem, Univ of MO 3 Hrs Chem; *cr:* Sherman Cntrl Schl Sci & Math Tchr 30 Yrs; *ai:* Advanced Placement Chem Coord-Adv; NEA, NYSTA; *office:* Sherman Central Schl Park St Sherman NY 14781*

PATTERSON, KAREN O. (KING), Latin Teacher; *b:* Utica, NY; *m:* Jon M.; *c:* Susan V., Emily A.; *ed:* St Univ of NY at Albany (BA) Latin 1964; Univ of KS (MA) Classical Stud 1976; *cr:* Clarence Cntrl Schl Latin Tchr 1966-68; Univ of KS Latin Tchr 1968-71; Roland Park Cntry Schl Latin Tchr 1981-87; Clarence Cntrl Schl Latin Tchr 1987-; *ai:* Classical Assn of Western NY 1987-, Treas 1990-; Classical Assn of Empire St 1987-; Amer Classical League 1981-; Alpha Delta Kappa 1988-, Treas 1992-; *office:* Clarence MS 10150 Greiner Rd Clarence NY 14031*

PATTERSON, LILLIAN COOPER, Dept of Human Services Prof; *b:* Providence, RI; *m:* John Alexander; *c:* Jason R. Pariseau; *ed:* RI Coll (BED) Elem Ed 1965; Univ of MD (MED) Spec Ed 1967; DeLaSalle Univ Philippines (PHD) Counseling Psych ABD; *cr:* Warwick Schl Dept Tchr of Spec Ed 1967-69; RI St Trng Schl Tchr of Sped Ed 1969-71; Comm Coll of RI Human Svcs Prof 1972-; *ai:* Human Svc Club & Acad Advy Comm Adv; NEA 1967-, Exec Com, Negotiating Team; Cncl of Churches 1975-89, Ministry Bd, Co-Chair, Chair; St Advy Bd-Spec Ed 1980-, Pres, Co-Chair 1983-85; Fellowship Grad Stu at Univ of MD; *office:* Community College Of RI 400 East Ave Warwick RI 02886

PATTERSON, LINDA A., English Teacher; *b:* Philadelphia, PA; *m:* Glenn E. Soloner; *c:* Alexander; *ed:* Beaver Coll (BA) Eng 1976; West Chester Univ (MA) Eng 1970; St Josephs Univ Post Grad Work; *cr:* Palmyra HS Eng Tchr 1970-; *ai:* Yrbk Adv 1970-78; Drama Dir 1983-85; NHS Adv 1986-94; NEA 1970-; NJEA 1970-; NCTE 1972-; PEA, Asst Negotiator 1975-80; Palmyra HS Tchr of the Yr Governors Awd 1993.

PATTERSON, LINDA (DIVIRGILIO), 1st Grade Teacher; *b:* Mt Pleasant, PA; *m:* George; *c:* Megan, Rebekah; *ed:* CA Univ of PA (BA) Early Chldhd 1971, (MS) Elem Ed 1974; *cr:* Marion Elem Schl 2nd Grd Tchr 1971-72, 1st Grd Tchr 1972-; *ai:* NEA & PSEA 1971-; Olive Branch Bapt Church 1971-, Deaconess, Chrstn Bd of Ed & Dir of Childrens Work; Great Idea Grant 1990; Thanks to Tchrs 1996 Honoree Nom; *office:* Marion Elem Schl 500 Perry Ave Belle Vernon PA 15012*

PATTERSON, MARILYN, English Teacher; *b:* Pittsburgh, PA; *m:* Mark S.; *c:* Karrie, Carly; *ed:* Clarion Univ (BS) Eng 1969; 36 Hrs Post-Grad; *cr:* West Allegheny HS Eng Tchr 1969-71; Laurel HS Eng Tchr 1971-72; Warren Co Schl Dist Eng Tchr 1989-; *ai:* NEA; NCTE; *home:* 101 E 3rd Ave Warren PA 16365

PATTERSON, MARILYN AMY, English Teacher; *b:* Camden, James G.; *c:* Daniel Mark Favilla, Sara Lynn; *ed:* (BA) Scndry En *cr:* Eastern Regnl HS Eng Tchr 1968-77; Edgewood Sr HS Eng Tch *ai:* Lower Camden Cty Inter Dist Curr Consortium, Stu Recognitior Mem; Newspaper Adv 1987-94; Alpha Delta Kappa 1993-; NJE 1968-; Tchr of Yr Stu Govt 1988.

PATTERSON, PATRICIA FORDYCE, Professor of English; York, NY; *c:* Todd, Scott, Melissa; *ed:* Adrian Coll (BA) Eng, G Duquesne Univ (MA) Eng 1981; *cr:* English Prof 1983-; *ai:* Comm Allegheny Cty Eng Prof 1983-; Acad Affairs, Diversity, Re Part-time Fac, 089 Textbook Cmm, Eating in Classroom Comm Hearing Bd; *office:* Comm Coll Algny Co Algny Cmps 808 Ri Pittsburgh PA 15212*

PATTERSON, PAULA STANYARD, English & Reading Tea Sewickley, PA; *m:* John J.; *c:* Barry, Mandee; *ed:* Geneva Coll 1966; Kent St (MEd) Curr & Instruction with Rdng Specializatio Addl Hrs Bachelors Geneva Coll 1975-76; Addl Hrs Grad Co Joseph, Ashland Coll, Kent St; Addl Hrs Youngstown St Univ; Liverpool Jr HS Fr & Eng Tchr 1966-68; Bradford MS Eng & L 1968-70; Bohemia Manro HS Fr & Eng Tchr 1970-72; Crestview & Rdng 1974-; *ai:* Soph Class Adv; EECAP Comm; NEA, OE 1974-, Sec 1991-, Building Rep 1990; NCTE 1991-; Phi Delta 1990-; United Presbyn Church 1984-, Stewardship 1992-95, Nom Comm 1991; Amer Legion Auxiliary; Penn OH Model A Club; Holden Jennings Scholar 1987 & 1993; Tchr of Yr Bohemia Ma 1972; *home:* 1851 State Route 165 East Palestine OH 44413

PATTERSON, ROBERT SLOANE, English Teacher; *b:* New Yo NY; *m:* Carol J. Walker; *c:* Douglas, Seth, Jessica, Robert, Rolli Russell Lee, Lucy Cate; *ed:* Cornell Univ (BA) Eng Lit 1969; C (BA) Music 1980; 9 Credits Eng Univ of WI at Madison; *cr:* F Valley Schl Eng Tchr, Chm Music Dept 1970-78; CO Opera Festiv Dir 1980-82; Freelance Writer, Composer 1982-90; Cincinnati Cn Schl Eng Tchr 1990-, Chm of Dept 1991-93; *ai:* Lit Magazine Adv Dept Act, Performances; Fac Advy Comm; *office:* Cincinnati Coun Schl 6905 Given Rd Cincinnati OH 45243*

PATTERSON, SANDRA CLARK, Kindergarten Teacher; *b:* Gre PA; *m:* Gerald; *c:* Rachelle, Justin; *ed:* Edinboro Univ of PA (BS) E 1970, (MED) Elem Ed 1972; Rdng Specialist 1978; Westminster C Prgm Spec Stu; *cr:* Reynolds Schl Dist K-1st Grd Tchr 197 Commadore Perry Schl Dir 6.5 Yrs; *home:* 442 Yeager Rd Clarks M 16114

PATTERSON, THOMAS M., Technology & Technical Teac Dunkirk, NY; *m:* Bonnie L.; *ed:* SUNY at Buffalo (BS) Indstrl 1983; SUNY at Albany (MS) Curr Planning, Dev 1986; *cr:* Mont P HS Technology, Tech Tchr 1983-92; Schenectady HS Technology Tchr 1992-; *ai:* Wilderness Outing, Tech Svcs Clubs Co-Adv; Saf Prgm Cmptr Lab Coord; Auditorium Mgr; CTF 1984-, Act Schenectady City Schl Dist Tchr of Yr 1993; Sparkman Ctr Gran CTF Young Achiever Awd, Rsrch Flwshp 1986; GE Corporate Rsr Summer Internship 1991; *office:* Schenectady HS The Plaza Sche NY 12308

PATTERSON-VAITI, TERESA VANATTA, Social Studies Teac Long Branch, NJ; *w:* Victor F. Vaiti (dec); *c:* Dale Greengrove, Meahan, Julie Y. Patterson; *ed:* Elmira Coll (BA) His 1963; Kean NJ 15 Credits His, Ed 1984-85; Rutgers 3 Grad Credits Geography Monmouth Univ 6 Grad Credits Toward Masters in Ed 1995; *cr:* HS His Tchr 1963-64; Freehold Regnl HS Soc Stud, Intnl Stud Spec Learning Ctr Tchr 1987-; *ai:* Dev Current World Stud Curr Comm Mid Sts Evaluation Team; Octagon Club Adv 1991-; NEA, NJEA Ocean Twp Bd of Ed 1981-89, Pres, VP; *office:* Freehold Township Elton Adelphia Rd Freehold NJ 07728

PATTI, CHERYL ANN WHITE, Fifth Grade Teacher; *b:* Jersey Ci *m:* Richard; *c:* Christopher, Candice; *ed:* Jersey City St Univ (BA Ed 1970; St Peters Coll Post Grad Urban Ed 1991-95; *cr:* Horace Schl Tchr 1984-86; Bayonne HS Tchr 1986-94; Midtown Comm Sch 1994-; Jersey City St Coll Gifted, Talented Tchr 1996; *ai:* Discipline Expo Comm; NEA, NJEA, BTA 1984-; AMTNJ 1986-; Montclair C Guild 1988-; Project Seaquest Mini Grant 1995; *office:* M Community Schl 550 Avenue A Bayonne NJ 07002

PATTON, BARBARA YOEST, Math Teacher; *b:* Sharon, PA; *m:* W.; *c:* Eric, Neil, Valerie, Matthew; *ed:* Indiana Univ of PA (BSEd 1974; Westminster Coll (MSEd) Elem Ed 1977; *cr:* Sharpsville HS Tchr 1976-; *ai:* Yrbk, Newspaper Co-Adv; NHS Adv; NEA, Shar Tchrs Assn 1976-; *office:* Sharpsville HS 301 Quarry Way Sharpsv 16150

PATTON, DAVID RICHARD, Third Grade Teacher; *b:* Millerstow *c:* Vanessa J.; *ed:* Messiah Coll (BA) Elem Ed 1972; Shippensburg (MED) Rdng 1976; *cr:* Greenwood Schl Dist Third Grd Elem Tchr *ai:* NEA, PSEA 1972-; Greenwood ED Assn 1972-, Sec 2 Yrs; Gree PTO 1980-; Perry Cty Historical Soc 1972-, Bd of Dir; *office:* Gree Schl Dist 405 E Sunbury St Millerstown PA 17062

PATTON, R. SCOTT, Technology Education Teacher; *b:* Pittsburg *m:* Maureen Miller; *ed:* CA Univ of PA (BS) Industrial Arts 1969, Edcn 1973; *cr:* Mt Lebanon HS Scndry-Tech Ed 1969-; Comm C Allegheny Co Industrial Edcn Instr 1972-74; *ai:* Wrestling Co WRAL; Instructional Cabinet; NEA, PSEA, TEAP 1969-; *offic* Lebanon Sr H S 155 Cochran Rd Pittsburgh PA 15228

PATTON, SCOTT GARDNER, Technology Education Teacher; *b:* Chester, PA; *m:* Carol L. Hollowell; *c:* Timothy F., Stephen G Millersville Univ (BSEd) Indstrl Arts 1975; Temple Univ (MED) Arts, Tech Ed 1981; West Chester Univ, PA St Univ, Great Vly C Grad Stud 6 Hrs; *cr:* Upper Merion Area Jr HS Ind Arts, Tech E 1975-79; Upper Merion Area HS Ind Arts, Tech Ed Instr 1979-; *ai:* Crew Lighting, Sound Design& Equipment Adv; Stu Ldrshp Con NEA, PSEA Upper Merion Ed Assn 1975-, VP, Negotiator, Bldg Re Tech Ed Assn 1976-; Dev Summer Camp Prgm for Mentally Handic Yth, Adults; Participated in Dev of Stu Ldrshp Trng Wkshp; C Wkshps for Stdnts; Low Income Home Repair Vol Org Regular Partic Work Crew Ldr; *office:* Upper Merion Area Schl Dist 435 Crossfie King Of Prussia PA 19406

PATTON, SHANNON SHEPHARD, World Cultures & Ec Teach Buffalo, NY; *m:* Douglas; *ed:* Westminster Coll (BA) Pol Sci Edinboro Univ (MA) Sec Ed Admin 1995; *cr:* Mc Dowell Interm HSWorld Cultures, Ec Tchr 1992-; *ai:* Adv Campus Store Entrepren Prgm; Track Statistician; Young Republican's Clb Adv; NEA 1992-; Mc Dowell Intermediate HS 3320 Caughey Rd Erie PA 16506*

PATTON, SUSAN MIDKIFF, Third Grade Teacher; *b:* Mc Arthur, O David E. (dec); *ed:* OH Univ (BA) Elem Ed 1973; *cr:* Worthington Second Grd Tchr 1973-79; Scioto Schl Third Grd Tchr 1979-; *ai:* OH Ed Assn 1973-; Jackson City Ed Assn 1979-; Martha Holden Jen Scholor Chillicothe & Jackson City Schls; *home:* 3 Pleasantvie Jackson OH 45640

PATZELT, KAREN E., Seventh Grade Teacher; *b:* Fairfield, CT; *e* Salle Univ (BA) Elem, Spec Ed 1991; Enrolled in Biling, Bicultural Prgm; Univ of PA MS Prgm in Rdng, Writing, Lit; *cr:* Immaculate

:hl Seventh Grd Tchr 1991-; *ai:* Stu Cncl, Schl Newspaper Adv; ion ERIC 1992; King Juan Carlos Flwshp Univ MN 1996; *office:* late Heart Mary Schl 815 E Cathedral Rd Philadelphia PA 19128

, **MARK LEE,** Associate Professor; *b:* Oakland, MD; *m:* Diane :row; *c:* Doug, Johua, Jonathan; *ed:* Columbia Union Coll (AA) ory Therapy 1981, (BS) Respiratory Therapy 1982; Univ of Cntrl H) Pub Hlth 1985; FL St Univ (PHD) Adult, Continuing Ed, Policy 90; *cr:* Frederick Mem Hosp Respiratory Therapist 1979-83; FL itical Care Therapist, Ed Coord 1983-89; FL A&M Univ Clinical st Prof Respiratory Therapy 1986-89; Frederick Comm Coll Prgm oc Dir Respiratory Therapy 1989-; *ai:* Adv RT Stu Org; Structural tion Comm; Choir; RT Advy Bd; AARC 1978-; APHA 1985-; 1987-; Amer Lung Assn of MD 1977-, Bd Mem 1990-93, Excl for ;vc 1979, 1982; St Josephs Parish Cncl 1990-, Sec 1991-94; Article 8; Hlth Manpower Grant 1994-95; *office:* Frederick Comm Coll)ossumtown Pike Frederick MD 21702

CAROL A., Associate Professor of Biology; *b:* Brockton, MA; *m:* D.; *c:* Christin M., Dana J., Stephanie F., Robert R., Paul Tetreault; v of MA (BS) Bio & Chem 1958; RI Coll (MAT) Bio & Ed 1968; Jniv (MAT) Bio 1970; Boston Univ (EDD) Educl Admin 1978; *cr:* hore Comm Coll Asst Prof & Asst Dean 1969-78; NJ Dept of Higer er Planner 1978-80; Fairleigh Dickinson Univ Assoc VP 1980-86; Comm Coll VP Acad Affairs 1986-94, Assoc Prof 1994-; *ai:* Mid 1 Comm; Curr Comm; Phi Delta Kappa 1976-; Pi Lamda Theta Suffolk Fac Assn 1994-; NSTA 1994-; League of Women Voters NSF Brown Univ 1968-69; Whos Who of Amer Women 1993-; Whos Amer Ed 1993-; Whos Who in East 1993-; *office:* Suffolk Comm nmerman Cmp 533 College Rd Selden NY 11784*

CHARLES H., Music Teacher; *b:* Audubon, NJ; *m:* Holly Little; ey, Kerri; *ed:* Glassboro St Coll (BA) Music Ed 1980; 15 Grad Rowan Coll of NY, Westminster Chair Coll; *cr:* Hammonton HS Music 1980-; *ai:* Select Singers; Schl Play Dir, Music Dir; Band NEA, MENC 1980-; NJMEA 1980-, St Bd of Dirs, Choral ures; NJEA 1980-; S Jersey Choral Dir Assn 1980-, Reg Rep, tor All-South Jersey Chorus 1990; 27 Music Compositions Pub ng 2 Major Works for Orch & Choir; *office:* Hammonton HS N St Hammonton NJ 08037*

DIANE JENDRYSIK, Second Grade Teacher; *b:* Springfield, MA; k T.; *ed:* North Adams St Coll (BS) Elem Ed 1976; *cr:* Our Lady of al Help Schl Kndgtn Tchr 1978-79, 2nd Grd Tchr 1979-; *ai:* Yrbk NCEA 1978-; Pioneer Valley Rdng Assn 1994-; MA Rdng Assn Polish Falcons of Amer 1958-; *office:* Our Lady Of Perpetual Help Chestnut St Holyoke MA 01040

JAMES J., Fifth Grade Teacher; *b:* Hartford, CT; *m:* Melanie A. n; *c:* Douglas Hazelton, Elizabeth Hazelton; *ed:* Westfield St Coll Elem Ed 1972; Univ of NH (MED) Admin, Supervision 1986; UNH dit Hrs Writing Process; UNH 12 Credit Hrs Span; *cr:* Merrimack Tchr 1972-82; Londonderry Schls Tchr 1982-84; Raymond Schls in, Tchr 1986-88; Goffstown Schls Tchr 1988-; *ai:* ASCD 1986-; umane Ed Assn 1993-; NEA Essay Awd 1990, 1995; *office:* ain View MS 41 Lauren Ln Goffstown NH 03045

JOHN, School Minister, Theology Tchr; *b:* Phila, PA; *ed:* St s Borrome Seminary (BA) Philosophy 1968, (MDIV) Theology Villanoua Eng; LaSalle Psychology; *cr:* Archbishop Kennedy HS gy Tchr 1974-75; Bishop McDevitt HS Theology Tchr, Schl er 1975-86; St James HS Theology Tchr, Schl Minister 1987-90; shop Kennedy HS Theology Tchr, Schl Minister 1990-93; dy-Kenrick Schl Theology Tchr, Schl Minister 1993-; *ai:* Pro Lite *office:* Kennedy-Kenrick Catholic HS 250 E Johnson Hwy own PA 19401

JOHN DONALD, 5th Grade Teacher; *b:* Cleveland, OH; *m:* a Metzger; *c:* Jodi; *ed:* Cleveland St Univ (BA) Elem Ed 1970-71; 9 ath, Advanced El Ed; 9 Hrs Math, Advanced El Ed Baldwin Wallace *r:* Vly Vista Elem Schl 1-2 Grd Tchr 1970-1; Beach Schl 5-6 Grd 972-81; Kensington Intermediate Schl 4-5 Grd Tchr 1981-; *ai:* Var st 1 Yr, Boys 7-8 Grd Bsktbl 3 Yrs, Girls JV Tennis 3 Yrs, Head ar Tennis 1 Yr, Head Girls Var Fast-Pitch Sftbl 3 Yrs Coaches; Math 4 Yrs; Stu Cncl 4 Yrs, Safety Patrol 15 Yrs Advs; OEA, NEA, Rocky Tchrs Assn 1970-; *office:* Rocky River City Schl Dist 20140 Lake Rd River OH 44116

LESLIE BERRY, Third Grade Teacher; *b:* Boston, MA; *m:* Donald Geoffrey, Jon; *ed:* Barrington Coll (BA) Elem Ed 1967; *cr:* gton Schl 2nd Grd Tchr 1967-68; Karamursel Turkey Ed Office Consultant 1969-70; Goddard Schl First, Second Grd Tchr 1970-74; n Schl First, Second, Third & Fourth Grd Tchr 1975-; *ai:* Coyle & y HS Mothers Club, Music Parents Assn; Allin Congregational Benevolence Comm, Co-Chm; NEA, MTA, BEA 1967-; Natl ces Trust 1982-, Prgm Act, Dir NRT Fair; *office:* Franklin Elem Schl ytell Ave Brockton MA 02402

, **ROBERT J.,** Music Teacher; *b:* Philadelphia, PA; *m:* Ann-Ellen; *c:* Ross; *ed:* Temple Univ (BA) Music Ed 1973; Beaver Coll (MA) Ed Addl Courses in Leadership & MGT; Cert as Elem & Scndry Prin in NJ; Supvr of Curr & Instruction Letter of Eligibility Schl Supt; ed in Doctoral Prgm; *cr:* Parochial Schls Music Tchr 1972-78; r Coll Percussion Tchr 1976-81; Mount Sinai Schl Dist Tchr 84; Lenape HS Tchr 1989-; *ai:* Band; Marching & Jazz Bands; Orch Gifted & Talented Review Comm; At-Risk Stdnts Fac Mentor; line Comm; Curr; MENC, South Jersey Band & Orch Dirs 1989-; Publications Buddy Rich Pub Awd Music & Class Drum Method; aphee Who's Who in the East 25th Ed; Who's Who in the World; 1546 Stoney Ln # B Philadelphia PA 19115*

, **RODNEY GEORGE,** Science Teacher; *b:* Ashland, PA; *m:* Linda ouser; *c:* Rodney, Karen; *ed:* Bloomsburg St Coll (BS) Earth, Space 71; West Chester Univ (MA) Phys Sci 1984; Bucknell Univ Prin's 991; 97 Post Grad Credits; *cr:* Quakertown Schl Dist Sci Tchr 79; North Schuylkill Jr-Sr HS Sci Tchr 1979-; *ai:* NEA, PSEA 1971-; Nuclear Sci Tchr Assn 1983-; Borough Cncl Ashland 1988-92; North Schuylkill Jr Sr HS RR 2 Box 47 Ashland PA 17921

, **RONALD M.,** Academy of Health Director; *b:* New York, NY; *m:* ra Ellen Young; *c:* Mindi Paul Weiner; *ed:* City Coll of NY (BS) Bio (MA) Ed 1971; Manhattan Coll Guid Courses 6 Credits; *cr:* Dewitt n HS Bio & Gen Sci Tchr 1968-75; Bronx Comm Coll Adj Lecturer rary 1971-75; William H Taft HS Dir Acad of Hlth & Bio Tchr 1976-; Y Bio Tchrs Assn 1968-; Phi Beta Kapp Merit Awd; Ward Medal for n His; William H Taft HS Tchr of the Yr Awd 1988; Finalist NY ice for Pub Schls Outstdng Tchr; Cert of Commendation 1988; *office:* m Howard Taft HS 240 E 172nd St Bronx NY 10457

, **TIMOTHY,CFX,** Assistant Principal; *b:* Old Town, ME; *ed:* n Univ (BA) Bio 1971; Northeastern Univ (MS) Microbiology 1979; St Coll (MED) Schl Admin 1996; Harvard Univ, Northeastern Univ Sci; Salem St Coll Bio; *cr:* Xaverian Brothers HS Tchr 1971-73; St eth's Hosp Lab Technologist 1974; St John's Prep Tchr, Dept Chm 93, Asst Prin 1993-; *ai:* Bd of Dirs CPMSIE Salem St Coll; North Sci League Past Pres; Adv Planning Comm; No Shore Sci Supvrs 1980-, Pres; NABT, NSTA, ASM 1974-; Sci & Math Tchng Presidential Awd; Harvard Book Awd for Tchng; Tandy Tech Scholar Awd; *office:* Saint Johns Prep Schl 72 Spring St Danvers MA 01923

PAULEY, JOHN S., Social Studies Teacher; *b:* Reading, PA; *m:* Joanne Raffeo; *c:* Tim, Joe; *ed:* Ursinus Coll (BA) His 1970; Villa Nova Univ (MA) His 1972; Attnd York Jr Coll; Cabrini Coll Tchng Cert; Penn St Univ Supvrs, Prins Cert; *cr:* Marple-Newtown Sr HS Soc Stud Tchr 1973-83; Penncrest HS Soc Stud Tchr 1983-; *ai:* Stu Cncl, Sr Class Spon; Soc Stud Bldg Coord; PA Cncl of Soc Stud, NCSS 1987-; Upper Marion Rowing Assn 1990-.

PAULEY, MARY-ANN MELCHIONDA, Transitional Teacher; *b:* New Haven, CT; *m:* Robert; *c:* Micheljon Wolfe; *ed:* Southern CT St Univ (BS) Early Chldhd Ed 1969, (MS) Early Chldhd Ed 1978; Anna Maria Coll 6th Yr Cert Educl Stud; *cr:* Stevens Schl 3rd Grd Tchr 1969-72; Parker Farms Schl 2nd Grd Tchr 1972-83, 3rd Grd Tchr 1981-83; Highland Schl Transitional Tchr 1983-; *ai:* NEA 1969-; *home:* 12 Blossom Ln Wallingford CT 06492

PAULINE, ANNA MARIE, Spanish Teacher; *b:* Hazelton, PA; *ed:* Bloomsburg Univ (BS) Scndry Ed, Frgn Langs 1977; 24 Hrs Rel Stud Marwood Coll; Ed Scranton Univ; *cr:* Msgr Molino Schl Tchr 1977-81; Bishop Hafey HS Span Tchr 1981-; *ai:* Yrbk, NHS Adv; Intnl Club, Span Travel Club, Span Contest Club, Hispanic Comm Svc Club Moderator; Stu Life Comm; Eucharistic Minister; Amer Assn Tchrs of Span & Portuguese 1981-; NCEA 1977-; Lower Anthracite Project, Hispanic Comm Svc 1990-; Holy Trinity Elem Span Prog 1988-; Red Cross Translator 1993-; Finalist Jaycess Tchr of Yr Awd; Pius Awd Rel Ed; AATSP Awd Natl Span Contest; *office:* Bishop Hafey HS 1700 W 22nd St Hazleton PA 18201

PAULL, SUSANNE KAY, Mathematics Teacher; *b:* Lewiston, PA; *m:* Frank; *c:* Rebecca Ann; *ed:* Lock Haven Univ (BS) Scndry Ed Math 1970; Attnd Westchester Univ, Kutztown Univ; *cr:* Twin Valley HS Math Tchr 1970-; *ai:* Sr Class Adv, Dept Chair; NEA, PSEA, TVEA 1970-; NCTM 1996-; *office:* Twin Valley HS RD 3 Box 52 Elverson PA 19520*

PAULO, WILLIAM DAVID, Information & Technology Tchr; *b:* Fall River, MA; *m:* Patricia Ann Farrell; *c:* William Jr., Richard, Timothy, Andrew, Amy; *ed:* Southeastern MA Univ Bus Mgmt 1969; 24 Credit Hrs; *cr:* Attleboro HS Bus, Information & Tech Tchr 1969-95; *ai:* Bsbl, Bsktbl & Sftbl Coach; MTA 1969-; Attleboro Tchrs Assn 1969-; *office:* Attleboro HS Rathbun Willard Dr Attleboro MA 02703

PAULSEN, PATRICIA O'REILLY, French & Spanish Teacher; *b:* Toronto, ON; *m:* Joseph J.; *c:* Modena E. Magallan, Erik S., Emily C.; *ed:* York Univ Toronto Canada (BA) Fr 1969; SUNY at Albany (MA) Fr Ed 1973; Attnd St Rose Coll, Siena, Hudson Valley Comm Coll; *cr:* Schodack Cntrl Fr Tchr 1970-71; East Greenbush Cntrl Part-Time Fr & Span Tchr 1985-87; Lansingburgh Cntrl Fr & Span Tchr 1987-; *ai:* Positive Rewards Comm; PTA; AFT 1982-; NYSUT 1982-; NYSAFLT 1985-; Trinity Luth Church 1974-, Sun Sch Supt & Cncl Mem; PTA Lifetime Mbrshp Awd; *office:* Lansingburgh HS 320 7th Ave Troy NY 12182

PAULSON, CAROL PHILLIPS, 3rd & 4th Grade Teacher; *b:* Columbus, OH; *m:* H. William; *c:* David (dec), Mary, Joseph; *ed:* Mt Vernon Nazarene Coll (BS) Elem Ed 1979; Ashland Univ 30 Grad Credit Hrs; *cr:* Mt Vernon MS Learning Disabilities Tchr 6th-7th Grd 1 Yr; Greater Baltimore Jr Acad 1st-2nd Grd Tchr 1 Yr; Silgo SDA Elem Schl 3rd-4th Grd Tchr 3 Yrs; Mt Vernon SDA Elem Schl 3rd-4th Grd Tchr 12 Yrs; *ai:* IRA 1991-; The Compassionate Friends 1982-, Chapter Ldr, Regnl Coord; 1988 Natl Chprsn Natl Conf; The United Way 1985-; Dir Compassionate Friends, Founder; Natl Sibings Pen Pal Clb 1994-; 1988 Jefferson Awd for Outstanding Comm Serv; 1990 Zapara Awd Excl in Tchng; 1992 Alma Mc Kibben Sabbatical Awd for Excl in Tchng; Ashland Chemical Golden Apple Awd for Excl in Tchng 1995; Community Life Awd 1995; OH Conf of SDA for Recognition of Outstanding Community Service 1995; Natl Speaker of Edctrs; *office:* Mount Vernon SDA Elem Schl PO Box 891 221 Sychar Rd Mount Vernon OH 43050

PAULSON, CHARLANE SUSAN (MC DANIEL), Seventh Grade Teacher; *b:* Bathesda, MD; *m:* Steven Roy; *c:* Devon Marie; *ed:* Univ of ME at Machias (BSEd) Ed 1977; *cr:* Ella Lewis Schl 6th Grd Tchr 1977-79; D. W. Merritt Elem Schl 7th Grd Tchr 1979-89; Harrington Elem Schl 7th Grd Tchr, 6th-8th Grd Departmental Eng Tchr 1989-; *ai:* Eighth Grd Grad Adv; Church of God 1982-; *home:* RR 1 Box 209 Milbridge ME 04658

PAULSON, STANLEY ALBERT, Math, Science & Tech Teacher; *b:* Kingston, PA; *m:* Jeanette Anne; *c:* Jennifer Anne; *ed:* King's Coll (BA) His 1966; Temple Univ (MS) Ed 1982; 45 Grad Credits Ed Penn St Univ, Rutgers Univ; Glassboro St Coll; *cr:* Sudlersville HS Soc Stud Tchr 1966; Wyalusing HS Soc Stud, Eng Tchr 1966-68; Woodglen Schl Math, Sci, Tech Tchr 1968-; *ai:* Ath Dir, Detention Supvr; LTEA, NJEA, NEA 1968-; Tech for Children Tchr of Yr 1977; Governor's Awd Tchr of Yr 1995; *home:* 733 Franklin St Belvidere NJ 07823

PAULUS, KIM SMITH, English & Journalism Teacher; *b:* Cumberland, MD; *ed:* Potomac St Coll (AA) Arts & Scis 1984; Frostburg St Univ (BA) Ed & Eng 1986, (MS) Admin & Supervision 1993; *cr:* Alleghany Cty Bd of Ed Eng & Jrnlsm Tchr 1988-; Frostburg St Univ Upward Bound Lit Tchr 1990-; *ai:* Ft Hill Tennis Coach; Yrbk, Newspaper, Ski Club & Bicycle Club Adv; Career Ctr Stu Lit & Wellness Coord; Fac Advy Comm; ACTA 1988-; MSTA 1988-; Allegany Cty Hlth Advy Bd 1995-; *office:* Center For Career/Tech Educatn 14211 McMullen Hwy SW Cumberland MD 21502

PAUPE, MARY JOANN (COYLE), RN & Hlth Occupations Instr; *b:* Cumberland, MD; *ed:* Meml Hospital (RN) Nursing 1953; Univ of MD (BA) Voc Ed Nursing & Hlth Occupations 1981; Gerontology-Multiple Stud; Home Care R N Multiple Stud; Pub Hlth Nursing; Lab Tech Multiple Stud; *cr:* Prince Georges Hospital Supvr of Hospital 1954-64; Countries in Asia Vol in Asian Orphanages 1966-75; Price Georges Hospital Gerontology Wards Supvr 1976-81; Prince Georges Cty Hlth Dept Geriatric Evaluation Svc Supvr 1976-78; Crossland HS Hlth Occupations Instr 1978-; *ai:* Prince Georges Comm Coll for Higher Learning of HS Stdnts Adv; Intergration of Hlth & Sci Into Career Tech Classes; HS Job Placement of Hlth Occupations Stdnts Coord; Voc Industrial Clubs of Amer; Amer Voc Assn 1980-, Mem; ANA 1954-, Mem; PTA 1978-, Mem; BPOE 1778 Ladies of the Elks 1964-, VP, Svc to Comm Awd, Youth Drug & Prevention of Violence in Youth Svc Awds; White House Conf on Aging Mem; Article Pub-Hospital Aseptic Technique; USAF Awd for Svc to Military NCIOC Officers; Grant From Prince Georges Comm Coll for Integration of HS Stdnts with Medical Prof; *office:* Crossland HS 6901 Temple Hill Rd Temple Hills MD 20748

PAUTALEO, GIACOMO, History & Math Teacher; *b:* Brooklyn, NY; *m:* Rita M.; *c:* Joseph Mark, Jack Daniel; *ed:* Dowling Coll (BA) Soc Sci 1971; LIU C W Post (MS) His & Ed 1977; 28 Credit Hrs Math Enrichment; *cr:* Holy Family Regnl Schl 7th & 8th Grd soc Stud & Math Tchr 1972-; *ai:* Photo Club; *office:* Holy Family Regnl Schl 2 Indian Head Rd Commack NY 11725

PAVELKO, PENNY LAAKSO, Mathematics Chairperson; *b:* Warren, OH; *c:* Matthew J., Clinton T.; *ed:* Youngstown St Univ (BA) Math 1970; Coll of Mt St Joseph (MSED) Ed 1990; *cr:* Austintown Fitch HS Math Tchr 1970-71; Lordstown HS Math Tchr 1971-75; Youngstown St UnivAdjunct Fac, Math Tchr 1980-87; Leetonia HS Math Tchr, Chair 1987-; Math Consltnt Saxon Pub Inc 1990-; *ai:* Acad Team, Physics Olympics Adv; NCTM, OH CTM, NEA 1987-; BSA 1986-93, Troop Comm 1986-93; Youngstown St Alumni Assoc, Rd Rnnr; Tandy Tech Scholar Natl Semi-FInalist 1990, 1991; Martha Holden Jennigs Scholar 1990-91; Who's Who in Amer Ed 1992, 1993; *office:* Leetonia HS 181 Walnut St Leetonia OH 44431*

PAVIO, A. NICHOLAS, Soc Stud Tchr & Dept Chm; *b:* Geneva, NY; *m:* Jennifer Jill Artman; *c:* Anthony Nicholas III, Julia May; *ed:* Cayuga Cty Comm Coll (AA) Hum & Soc Sci 1978; SUNY at Geneseo (BA) His 1981, (MS) Scndry Ed 1991; *cr:* Honeoye Cntrl Schl 7th-12th Grd Soc Stud Tchr 1988-; *ai:* Var Tennis Coach; Natl Cncl for Soc Stud & NY St Cncl For Soc Stud 1988-; Phi Delta Kappa 1986-; *office:* Honeoye Central Schl PO Box 170 Honeoye NY 14471

PAVLANSKY, DAVID S., English Teacher; *b:* Akron, OH; *m:* Kathleen S.; *c:* David, Sarah; *ed:* Drury Coll (BA) Eng, Ed 1982; 18 Sem Hrs Coaching Sci Miami Univ 1985; 20 Sem Hrs Grad Level Ed Courses Ashland Univ; COMP Cert Ashland, Vanderbilt; *cr:* Charlotte HS Eng Tchr 1982-84; Port Charlotte HS Eng Tchr 1984; Cooper City HS Eng Tchr 1987-89; Boardman HS Eng Tchr 1989-; *ai:* Asst Ftbl Coach; Asst Track Coach IMS; Eng Dept Remedial, Inclusion Section; NEA, Boardman Ed Assn 1989-.

PAVLANSKY, THOMAS H., Social Studies Teacher; *b:* Youngstown, OH; *m:* Kathleen A. Fechtel; *ed:* OH St Univ (BA) Comprehensive Soc Stud 1991; 15 Addl Hrs CO St Univ; *cr:* Lakeview HS Soc Stud Tchr 1992-; *ai:* Var Asst Ftbl, 9th Grd Bsktbl Coach; NCSS 1995-; *office:* Lakeview HS 300 Hillman Dr Cortland OH 44410*

PAVLICK, JOYCE M., Fifth Grade Teacher; *b:* Pittston, PA; *ed:* Coll Misericordia (BS) Early Child & Elem Ed 1974; Attnd Penn St Univ & Wilkes Univ; *cr:* Pittston Area Schl Dist Elem Tchr 1974-; *ai:* AFT 1975-; Luzerne Cty, Rdng Cncl; Keystone St Rdng Assn; *office:* Pittston Area Intermediate Defoe St Pittston PA 18640

PAVLICK, JUDITH E. NORTH, Physical Education & Swim Tchr; *b:* Hazleton, PA; *m:* Stan J.; *c:* Christopher, Gabrielle; *ed:* East Stroudsburg Univ (MED) Hlth & PE 1988; *cr:* West Hazleton HS PE Tchr 1981; Hazleton Area HS PE & Swim Tchr 1981-82; Heights Terrace Elem PE & Swim Tchr 1983-; *ai:* PSEA 1991-; PHERD 1981-; PSCA 1992-; WY Valley Conf Swim Coach of Yr 1993; Hazleton HS Swim Coach 1981-92; Hazleton Area HS Swim Coach 1992-94; *home:* 870 Branch Ct Hazleton PA 18201*

PAVLICK, RONALD JAMES, Art Teacher; *b:* Sharon, PA; *m:* Diane; *c:* Kristin, Jonathan; *ed:* Penn St (BS) Art Ed 1980, (MS) Curr & Instruction 1983; Prin Cert 1994; *cr:* Downingtown Art Tchr 4 Yrs; Devereaux Fndtn Art Tchr 1 Yr; Allentown MS Art Tchr 1 Yr; *ai:* Sr Class Play Art Coord; Soccer Coach; NEA 4 Yrs; Free Lance Artist.

PAVLIDIS, ANITA MARIE, Nursing Professor; *b:* Burlington, VT; *m:* Arthur; *ed:* St Mary's Schl of Nrsng (RN) Nrsng 1972; Salem St Coll (BSN) Nrsng 1982; Boston Univ (MS) Nrsng Admin 1985; *cr:* St Mary's Hosp Staff Nurse 1972-74; Beth Israel Hosp Staff Nurse, Clincial Adv 1975-85; Rhode Island Hosp Head Nurse Neuro Unit 1985-87; St Joseph Hosp Head Nurse ICU-CCU 1987-88; NH Tech Inst Nrsng Prof 1989-; *ai:* NH Nurses Assn 1987-, Chprsn Comission on Ed; Sigma Theta Tau 1982-; NH Cncl Nurse Edctrs 1989-; Nieghbor to Neighbor, Vol; 1 Article Pub; *office:* NH Tech Inst 11 Institute Dr Concord NH 03301

PAVLIK, DIANE DAY, Special Ed Resource Tchr; *b:* Upland, PA; *m:* Melvin D.; *c:* Jonathan W.; *ed:* Glassboro St Coll (BA) Elem Ed 1963; OH St Univ (MA) Exceptional Ed 1975; 69 Credit Hrs Supervision; Certfd Supervision Rdng, Exceptional Ed; *cr:* Aura Bd of Ed 4th Grd Tchr 1963-66; Washington Twp Bd of Ed 4th Grd Tchr 1966-70, Elem Rdng Tchr, Coord 1970-73; Cambridge Bd of Ed Spec Ed Resource Tchr 1973-; *ai:* Cambridge Cooperative Cncl; Cambridge Discipline Task Force; Inservice Comm; OH Ed Assn Legislative Commission; OH Classroom Mngmt System St Planning Comm; Oakland-OH Classroom Mngmt System Team; Eastern OH Ed Assn Exec Comm; Cambridge Ed Assn 1973-, VP, Pres; NEA, OEA 1973-, Del to Rep Assemblies; Cncl for Exceptional Children 1983-; Cncl for Edctrs of Exceptional Children 1989-; OSU Alumni Assn 1985-; OEA Resolutions Commission Cert of Honor; OEA Stu Discipline Task Force Svc Awd; OEA Mega Conf Presenter; Organizer, Trainer Parent Vols; Inservice Presenter Local, Dist, St Levels; *office:* Oakland Elem Schl 1300 Clairmont Ave Cambridge OH 43725

PAVLIK, JAMES WILLIAM, Chemistry Professor; *b:* Chicago, IL; *m:* Maryann Lang; *c:* Claire, David, Anne; *ed:* Carthage Coll (BA) Chem 1959; VA Polytechnic Inst & St Univ (MS) Chem 1961; George Washington Univ (PHD) Organic Chem 1970; *cr:* Prempeh Coll at Kumasi Chem Instr 1961-63; Addis Ababa Univ Asst Chem Prof 1967-70; Univ of WI at River Falls Asst Assoc Chem Prof 1970-74; Worcester Polytechnic Inst Assoc Chem Prof 1974-; *ai:* Amer Chem Soc 1960-; Inter-Amer Photochemical Soc 1990-; WPI Bd of Trustees Awd for Outstdng Tchng 1981; Numerous Rsrch Articles Pub Intnl Journals & Presentations Given at Natl & Intnl Meetings; *office:* Worcester Poly Inst 100 Institute Rd Worcester MA 01609

PAVLIK, MICHALYN C., French Teacher; *b:* Youngstown, OH; *ed:* Youngstown St Univ (BA) Fr, Eng Cum Laude 1972, (MA) Guid Cnslng 1991; *cr:* Trumbull Cty Pub Schls Fr, Eng Tchr 1973-88; Harford Cty Pub Schls Fr Tchr 1988-; *ai:* Fr Club Adv; Fr NHS Adv; NEA 1972-; Harford Cty Ed Assn 1988-; Natl Assn of Tchrs of Fr 1990-; Schlsps Awded; *office:* Edgewood HS 2415 Willoughby Beach Rd Edgewood MD 21040*

PAWLIK, W. TIMOTHY, Band Director & Music Teacher; *b:* Scranton, PA; *m:* Patricia L. King; *c:* Grant A., Trevor R.; *ed:* Marywood Coll (BM) Music Ed 1985; Wilkes Univ (MS) Ed 1995; *cr:* Bishop Hoban HS Band Dir, Music Tchr 1986-89; Old Forge Schl Dist Band Dir, Music Tchr 1989-; *ai:* Marching, Jazz Bands; PSEA 1989-; MENC 1981-; PMEA 1986-; *home:* RR 3 Box 3037 Moscow PA 18444

PAWLOSKI, WILLIAM ANTHONY, Physical Education Instructor; *b:* Natrona Heights, PA; *c:* Becky, Jozef, Laura, Matthew; *ed:* Alliance Coll (BS) Ed 1970; Oswego St (MA) Ed 1977; Syracuse Univ (MS) PE 1982; *cr:* Plainfield MS Instr 1970-71; Oswego HS Instr 1971-77; Myrtle Beach HS Instr 1977-78; CBA HS Instr 1982-84; Camden Cntrl HS Instr 1987-; *ai:* Camden Cntrl Schl Dist Ftbl Coord, Strength & Conditioning Coach; AFT, NEA, NYSUT 1971-; Amer Coaches of Amer Fed 1987-; Amer Legion 1990-; *office:* Camden Central HS Rt 13 Camden NY 13316

PAWLOWSKI, STELLA MARIE, First Grade Teacher; *b:* Hazleton, PA; *m:* Walter N.; *c:* Walter, Joseph; *ed:* E Stroudsburg Univ (BS) Elem Ed 1974; Scranton Univ (MEquiv) Elem Ed 1985; 12 Credits Wilkes Univ; 9 Credits Penn State Univ; *cr:* St Joseph Memorial 3rd Grd Tchr 1974-78; Transfiguration 3rd Grd Tchr 1978-89; *ai:* NEA 1989-; *office:* Valley Elem Schl 100 Rock Glen Rd Sugarloaf PA 18249

PAX, JULIANNA B., Chem & Nutrition Sci Teacher; *b:* Minster, OH; *m:* Charles; *c:* Christina, Nancy, Joseph; *ed:* Univ of Dayton (BS) Chem 1960; Univ of MI (MS) Nutrition Sci 1976; Univ of MD (PHD) Nutrition Sci 1991; *cr:* Univ of MD Asst Instr Summers 1991-94; Montgomery Cnty Schls Tchr 1976-; Walt Whitman HS Tchr 1992-; *ai:* Chemathon Competition Univ of MD; Chem Club; NEA; MSTA; NSTA; ACS; Dev New Curr for Nutrition Sci, Instrumentation Inservice for Tchrs; *office:* Walt Whitman HS 7100 Whittier Blvd Bethesda MD 20817

PAXSON, ALICE BOYD, Elementary Gifted Ed Tchr; *b:* Portland, OR; *m:* John Rodger Jr.; *c:* Catharine E.; *ed:* Univ of ME (BS) Elem Ed 1975; Shippensburg Univ (MED) Elem Ed, Gifted 1979; *cr:* Natl Tchrs Corps

Intern Tchr 1973-75; Lincoln Intermediate Unit No 12 Gifted K-8 Grd Tchr 1977-83; Bermudian Springs Schl Dist K-5 Grd Elem Gifted Ed Tchr 1983-; *ai:* Jr Great Books Lit Prgm Tchr; *office:* Bermudian Springs Elem Schl 7335 Carlisle Pike York Springs PA 17372*

PAXTON, DOUGLAS JOHN, History Teacher; *b:* Brooklyn, NY; *m:* Sheila M. Overhiset; *c:* Brooke, Bradley; *ed:* St Univ at Buffalo (BA) His 1967, (MS) His 1971; *cr:* Pub Schl #77 Tchr 1968-77; Pub Schl #33 Tchr 1977-87; Buffalo Acad Visual & Performing Arts Tchr 1987-; *ai:* Asst Scout Master; Debate Team Coach; NEA 1967-; AARP 1995-; Church, Elder 1978, Mission Dept Chm; *office:* Buffalo Acad Vsl/Perf Arts 333 Clinton St Buffalo NY 14204

PAXTON, JUDITH A., Third Grade Teacher; *b:* San Diego, CA; *m:* Timothy A.; *c:* Matthew, Kevin; *ed:* OH Univ (BS) Ed 1973; Pursuing Masters Degree Ed Ashland Univ; *cr:* St Rose Schl 7th, 3rd Grd Tchr 1970-74; New Lexington City Schls Rdng, K-3rd Grd Tchr 1976-95; *ai:* New Lexington Tchrs Assn 1984-, VP, Sec; Junction City Lioness 1983-; St Patricks 1993-, Rel Ed Coord; Martha Jennings Grant 1983; Ashland Tchr Runner Up 1995.*

PAYACK, CHRISTINE A., Amigos Prgm & 6th Grd Eng Tchr; *b:* Denville, NJ; *ed:* Univ of MA at Amherst (BS) Individual Concentration in Animal Ecology & Conservation 1979; Attnd Harvard Extension Schl Bio of Marine Invertebrates 1992, Ocean Environments 1993, Museum Inst for Tchng Sci Summer 1990, 1994-95, Prospect Archive & Ctr for Ed & Rsrch Summer Inst I, II; *cr:* Tobin Schl Extended Term Sub 4-6th Grd Tchr 1983-84; Tobin Schl Follow Through Prgm 5-6th Grd Tchr 1984-87, 6th Grd Tchr 1987-89; R. F. Kennedy Schl Follow Through Prgm 4-5th Grd Tchr 1989-91, 6th Grd Tchr 1991-92; R. F. Kennedy Schl Amigos Prgm 5-6th Grd Eng Tchr 1992-93, 5th Grd Eng Tchr 1993-94, 6th Grd Eng Tchr 1994-; *ai:* Ed Docent Franklin Park Zoo; Cooperting Tchr; Field Placement; Consulting Tchr for Curr Wkshps & Lib Prgms; MTA, NEA 1984-; Lib Power Kennedy Schl Comm 1993-; Conservation Tchr of Yr 1995; Living is for the Elderly Recognition of Svc Awd 1989; *office:* Robert F. Kennedy Schl 158 Spring St Cambridge MA 02141

PAYNE, ANDREA J., Health Teacher; *b:* Passar, NJ; *m:* William; *c:* Trudi Hart, William; *ed:* Springfield Coll (BS) PE 1964; SUNY Stony Brook (MED) Ed 1970; 60 Post Grad Hrs; *cr:* Sachem Schls PE, Hlth Tchr 1964-; *ai:* Jr & Sr Act Vol Chaperone; Sachem Cent Tchrs Assn, NY St Tchrs Assn 1970-; Womans Club of Patchogue 1984-, Exec Bd; Bellport Meth Church 1966-, Pres Ex Bd; Bellport Clipper Club 1984-, Pres; Hearth Club 1982-; Pub Article; *office:* Sachem HS North 212 Smith St Ronkonkoma NY 11779

PAYNE, DAVID MINTON, Associate Professor of English; *b:* Elizabeth, NJ; *m:* Andrea Janasie; *c:* Allison Derrickson, Ellen Mc Laughlin, David Jr., Catherine, Susan; *ed:* St Peter's Coll (BA) Eng 1958; Seton Hall Univ (MA) Eng 1967; NY Univ 30 Credit Hrs Amer Stud 1970-72; *cr:* Keyport HS Eng Tchr 1961; Westfield Bd of Ed Eng Tchr 1961-67; Fairleigh Dickenson Univ Part-time Eng Tchr 1965-67; Coll Misericordia Assoc Prof of Eng 1967-; *ai:* Div of Hum Chair; Fac Status Comm; Dean of Admissions 1976-90; PA Occupational Therapy Assn Awd 1984; Division of Prof Stud, Alternative Learners Prgm Awds 1990; *office:* Coll Misericordia 301 Lake St Dallas PA 18612

PAYNE, DEBORAH SCHEPSIS, 4th Grade Teacher; *b:* Utica, NY; *m:* Richard C. Sr.; *c:* Richard Jr., Sarah; *cr:* Kemble St Schl 4th Grd Tchr 1972-76; Sauquoit Elem 4th Grd Tchr 1986-; *ai:* Curr Area Coord for Lang Arts K-5th Grd; Mem of Ctr St Tchr Ctr-Policy Bd; NYSUT & AFT 1986-; Sauquoit Vly Tchrs Assoc 1986-; Utica Area TAWL, Sec & Chprsn; *home:* 15 Bonnie Brae Utica NY 13501

PAYNE, JEFFERY M., 8th Grade Language Arts Tchr; *b:* Silver Creek, NY; *m:* Lisa F.; *ed:* St Univ of NY at Fredonia (BA) Eng Ed 1990; Working Toward MA in Eng Ed; *cr:* Pine Valley Cntrl Schl Temporary Eng Tchr 1991; Westfield Cntrl Schl 8th Grd Lang Arts Tchr 1991-; *ai:* 8th Grd Class, Stu Newspaper Adv; Bowling Coach; NCTE 1995-; NEANY 1991-; *home:* 229 Eagle St Fredonia NY 14063*

PAYNE, KATHY LOUISE (LITTER), Reading & Language Arts Tchr; *b:* Delaware, OH; *m:* Tom; *c:* Jordan, Ashton, Lincoln, Makiah; *ed:* Morehead St Univ (BA) His, Speech 1982, (MS) Comm 1983; Working on Prins Cert, Elem Tchng Cert 1986 OH Univ; Law Stu Capital Univ Law Schl 1985; Scndry Tchng Cert 1982; *cr:* Hazard Comm Coll Comm 1983-84; Ross Co Child Care Network Coord 1986-87; Chillicothe City Schls HS, El, Mid Tchr 1984-; *ai:* Chair Acad Fair, Intertainment Comm; Mentor Adv; Advy, Curr Cncl; Prin Internship; Phi Delta Kappa,Coach YMCA Bsktbl, Yth Sftbl; Sunday Schl Teach; NEA, OEA 1984-; Natl Speakers Assn, OH Speacker Forum 1983-; Phi Kappa Phi 1982-; *office:* Smith MS 235 Cherry St Chillicothe OH 45601*

PAYNE, REBECCA PHILLIPS, English Speech & Drama Teacher; *b:* Huntington, WV; *m:* William Scott; *c:* Philip Wilcox, Melissa Wilcox, Susan Wilcox Perry, Wesley, Scott, Corey; *ed:* WV Univ (BS) Speech & Eng 1966; 50 Post-Grad Hrs Marshall Univ; 1 Credit Hr OH St; *cr:* Huntington HS Eng Tchr 1966-68; West Jr HS Eng & Speech Tchr 1968-70; Commack Jr High Eng Tchr 1970-73; Clay Battelle HS Eng & Creative Arts Tchr 1975-77; Chesapeake HS Eng & Speech Tchr 1977-; *ai:* Thespian Troupe; Forensics; Eng Dept Chprsn; The All-Schl Play; NEA 1966-; Bapt Temple Church 1944-, Sunday Schl Tchr & Adults Choir; Comm Players 1962-; Marshall Univ The Studio of Theatre Arts for Children 1988-, Dir; Sweet Adelines Accapella Singing Group 1994-, Bd Mem; Musical Arts Guild 1996; *office:* Chesapeake HS PO Box 10 Chesapeake OH 45619

PAYNE, RICHARD W., High School Teacher; *b:* Worcester, MA; *m:* Phyllis Cary; *c:* Erica, Tyler; *ed:* Clark Univ (BA) Eng 1968; Tufts Univ (MA) Eng 1969; Boston Univ (MED) Ed 1973; Suffolk Univ (JD) Law 1981; *cr:* Dedham HS Eng Tchr 1973-; *ai:* Interact Club Adv; NCTE; NEA, MA Tchrs Assn 1973-; Dedham Ed Assn 1973-, VP; Norfolk Cty Tchrs Assn 1973-; Horace Mann Grant Recipient; *office:* Dedham HS 140 Whiting Ave Dedham MA 02026

PAYNTON, KRISTA I., Animal Science Teacher; *b:* Attleboro, MA; *m:* Richard; *c:* Alex, Taylor; *ed:* Univ of MA (BS) Animal Sci 1980; Univ of NH (MS) Animal Sci 1984; *cr:* Bristol Cty Agricultural HS Animal Sci Tchr 1982-; *office:* Bristol County Agri HS 135 Center St Dighton MA 02715

PEABODY, TIMOTHY JOHN, Physical Education Teacher; *b:* Nyock, NY; *m:* Margaret Bryant; *ed:* St Univ Coll at Cortland (BSE) PE 1985; Lehman Coll Hlth Ed 12 Credit Hrs; *cr:* Alberton Magnus HS Dean of Stdnts, PE, Hlth Tchr 1985-94; Pearl River HS PE Tchr 1994-; *ai:* Albertus Magnus Womens Var Soccer Coach 1988-94, Var Boys Lacrosse Coach 1985-92; Womens Var Soccer Coach 1995-; Womens Var Lacrosse Coach 1996; NEA; Natl Lecrosse Coach Assn, Natl Soccer Coach Assn 1985-; Eastern Olympic Dev Prgm 1995-, Trainer, Coach; Rockland Westchester Coaches Assn, Pres 1994-; *home:* 517 Mountainview Ave Valley Cottage NY 10989*

PEACE, WILLIAM E., Biology Teacher; *b:* Waltham, MA; *m:* Katharine T. Reid; *c:* Johanna, Andrew, Marielle; *ed:* Tufts Univ (BS) Bio 1973, (MA) Ed 1976; Addl Credits Beyond Masters from Salem St Coll, Fitchburg St Coll, Anna Maria Coll; *cr:* New England Deaconess Hospital Lab Asst 1969-73; Dennis-Yarmouth Regnl HS Sci Tchr 1973-; Fisher Coll Adjunct Instr of Anatomy & Physiology 1986-; *ai:* NEA, MA Tchrs Assn 1973-; Author of Its A Comet Xerox-Weekly Reader Books 1985; Author & Publisher The Cape Cod Bike Book 1984-96; Author of Shareware Cmptr Pgrms, GradePlus 1995, Bankonit 1987, Just To Quote 1993, Attendance Moniter 1994, Vocabucomp 1994; *office:* Dennis-Yarmouth Regional HS 210 Station Ave South Yarmouth MA 02664

PEACHEY, RAYMOND SCOTT,SR., English Teacher; *b:* New Brunswick, NJ; *m:* Katharine Bevins-Peachey; *c:* Raymond Jr., Lynn, Michael; *ed:* Rutgers Univ at New Brunswick (BA) Eng, His 1970; Rutgers Grad Schl Ed (EDM) Eng Ed 1973; Supervision Cert 1991; Peer Leadership Advs Cert 3 Credits Princeton Ctr for Leadership Trng 1993; Rdng Across the Curr, Rdng for Scndry & Coll 6 Credits 1993; NJ Writers Project 6 Credits 1993; Schl & Comm 3 Credits 1992; Assessment 3 Credits 1992; *cr:* Hilcrest Elem Schl 5th Grd Perm Sub 1970; Roosevelt Intermediate Schl 5th Grd Perm Sub 1971; South Brunswick HS Eng Tchr 1973; Somerville HS Eng Tchr 1973-; *ai:* Head Boys Soccer, Head Boys Tennis Coach; Peer Leadership, Stu Cncl Adv; Somerville Educ Assn 1973-, Treas; NJEA, NEA, NCET 1973-; NJ Soccer Coaches Assn; Rutgers Prep Ath Hall of Fame 1992; Gob's Rec Aw 1995; Newark Star Ledger Somerset Cty Boys Soccer Coach of the Yr 1995; *office:* Somerville HS 222 Davenport St Somerville NJ 08876*

PEACHY, IRENE PAPPIANOU, Reading Teacher; *b:* Cheverly, MD; *m:* Nicholas; *c:* Jane, Margaret; *ed:* Mount Holyoke Coll (BA) Philosophy 1973; IN Univ (MS) Ed 1974; *cr:* Somerset HS Rdng Tchr 1974-; *ai:* Schl Newspaper Adv; IRA, NEA, MTA 1974-; *office:* Somerset HS Grandview Ave Ext Somerset MA 02726

PEACHY, NICHOLAS, English & History Teacher; *b:* Bangor, ME; *m:* Irene Pappianon; *c:* Jane, Margaret; *ed:* Bowdoin Coll (BA) His 1972; IN Univ (MA) Russian His 1974; Brown Univ (MAT) Soc Stud 1975; Working To PHD Russian His IN Univ; Courses Cmptr Sci, Tchng Gifted Stdnts; *cr:* IN Univ Tchng Asst 1972-74; Somerset HS Eng, His Tchr 1975-; *ai:* Head Wrestling, Sftbl Coach; NEA, MTA 1975-; N England Hist Tchrs Assn; Southeastern Cncl Soc Stud; NCTE; Amer Sftbl Assn 1992-, Coach; *office:* Somerset HS Grandview Ave Ext Somerset MA 02726

PEACO, RAY F., Senior High Business Teacher; *b:* Pittsburgh, PA; *m:* Marcia Schaffer; *c:* Megan, Morgan; *ed:* IUP (BS) Ed 1983; Robert Morris (MS) Bus Ed 1994; *cr:* Mars HS Tchr 1983-84; Seneca Valley HS Tchr 1984-; *ai:* NHS Spon; Track & Field Asst Coach; 9th Grd Girls Bsktbl Coach; NEA 1984-; *office:* Seneca Valley HS 128 Seneca School Rd Harmony PA 16037*

PEACOCK, JAMA LORYNN, Biology & Chemistry Teacher; *b:* Greenfield Ctr, NY; *ed:* Cntrl Coll at Pella (BA) Chem 1988; Union Coll at Schenectady (MS) Bio 1993; Union Coll at New York (MAT) Ed 1994; *cr:* Taconic Hills HS Bio, Chem Tchr 1994-; *ai:* Vlybl 1995-, Track 1995-, Wgt Lifting 1996 Coach; Newspaper Adv 1995-; NEA 1994-; ACS 1996; *office:* Taconic Hills HS PO Box O Philmont NY 12565

PEACOCK, WRAY PASH, English Teacher; *b:* Rocky Mount, NC; *m:* Vincent Gerard; *ed:* Hampton Univ (BA) Ent 1966; Queen Coll (MS) Cnslng 1977; *cr:* Roosevelt Co-Operative Comm Coll Eng Tchr 1970-71; Huntington HS Eng Tchr 1966-; *ai:* ATH 1966-; NCTE 1977-; NYSEC 1990-; Huntington Cncl Task Force 1993-; Western Suffolk Focus 1992-, Corresponding Sec; New Audience Advy Comm-Heckscher Museum 1994-; Suffolk Chptr Delta Sigma Thera 1974-, Corresponding Sec; Awd of Exl Tchng Eng Huntington Pan African Coalition 1987; Edctr of Excl Awd NY St Eng Cncl 1994; *office:* Huntington HS Oakwood & Mc Kay Rds Huntington NY 11743

PEARCE, DONALD N., Physics & Physical Sci Teacher; *b:* Binghamton, NY; *m:* Sue E. Hurley; *ed:* St Univ Coll at Cortland (BS) Sci Ed 1964; St Univ of NY at Buffalo (MS) Physics Ed 1973; Boston Coll NSF Summer Sequential Prgm 1965-68; Kent St Univ Solid St Physics NSF Summer Inst; Erie Comm Coll Cmptr Programming & Operations Prgm 1969-70; St Univ Coll at Geneseo Project Physis Inst 1972; Coll of St Rose at Albany Earth Sci NYS Cert Prgm 1985; *cr:* Haverling Cntrl Schl MS Sci Tchr 1964; Cheektowaga Cntrl Schl Research & Dev Dir 1969-73, Continuing Ed Dir 1975-82, Physics, Phy Sci Tchr 1964-; St Univ Coll Lab Instr Summer Physis Wkshp 1990-; *ai:* MS Promotional Review, Sci Exploration Day Coorination, Darien Lake Park Org Physics Day Comms; NSTA, NYSUT, AFT 1964-; NY St Sci Tchrs Assn 1964-, Treas 1975-, Svc Awd 1986; Phi Delta Kappa 1985-, 10 Yr Awd 1994; Niagara Frontier Sci Supvrs 1978-, Vice Chm, Chm; AAPT 1966-; Cheektowaga Cultural Soc 1968-74, Pres; Cheektowaga Comm Symphony Orch 1966-74, Pres; Cheektowaga Sr Cit Cncl 1966-82; Niagara Frontier Adult Ed Cncl 1972-82, Pres; Amer Chemical Soc Outstanding Tchr 1987; Sigma Psi Research Soc Calspan Corp Outstanding Tchr Awd 1988; NYS Ed Dept Gen Physics Syllabus & Testing Comms 1967-72; STANYS Svc Awd 1986, Fellow 1983; STANYS Service Award 1995; *office:* Cheektowaga Cntrl Schl 3600 Union Rd Cheektowaga NY 14225

PEARCE, MARY NANTELL, History & Literature Teacher; *b:* Cleveland, OH; *m:* Lawrence V.; *c:* Matthie U.; *ed:* Cleveland St Univ (BA) His, Eng, Scndry Ed 1969; Addt Post Grad Courses; Attnd Inst of Urban Stud, Cleveland St Univ; *cr:* St Colman Schl 7th Grd Jr HS Tchr 1969-70; Lourdes Acad 11th-12th Grd Tchr 1970-72; Erieview Cath HS 11th-12th Grd Tchr 1971-73; Urban Rsrch, Planning Consultant 1973-75; Strose of Lima Jr HS 6-8 Grd Tchr 1975-77; St Rose of Lima Jr HS 6-8 Grd Tchr 1988-; *ai:* Natl Jr Hnr Soc; NEOTA 1988-; Natl Assn of St Activity Advs 1990-; *office:* St Rose Of Lima Schl 1441 W 116th St Cleveland OH 44102

PEARCE, MICHELE DEEGAN, Secondary Guidance Counselor; *b:* DuBois, PA; *m:* Bill; *ed:* IN univ of PA (BA) Psych 1990, (MED) Scndry Guid 1992; *cr:* Adelphoi Village Resident Cnslr 1990-91; DuBois-Jefferson Mental Hlth Crisis Cnslr 1992; Marion Ctr Jr Sr HS Jr Hs Guid 1992-; *ai:* Co-Spon Stu Cncl, SADD; Supvr Afterschool Tutoring Prgm; SAP Team Equity Comm; PSEA, IN Cty Cnslrs Assn 1992-; *office:* Marion Ctr HS Box 156 Marion Center PA 15759*

PEARL, GARY S., HS Biology Teacher; *b:* Manhattan, NY; *m:* Denise; *c:* Megan, William; *ed:* Fairleigh Dickinson Univ (BA) Biol, Ed 1981; Montclair St Coll (MA) Bio 1984; *cr:* Cliffside Park HS Bio Tchr 1981-82; Essex Cty Coll Tech Trng Project Bio, Chem Instr 1984-90; Livingston HS Bio Tchr 1991-92; Paramus HS Bio Tchr 1992-; *ai:* Acad Decathlon Team Asst Coach; NEA, NJEA 1992-, NABT 1991-; NMEA; NJMEA 1995-; *office:* Paramus HS E 99 Century Rd Paramus NJ 07652

PEARLMAN, JEFFREY LAWRENCE, Earth Science Teacher; *b:* Brooklyn, NY; *m:* Mimi; *ed:* Oswego St Univ (BS) Bus Admin 1983; City Coll of NY (MA) Sci Ed 1986; *cr:* Robt A VanWyck Jr HS Sci Tchr 1984-; *ai:* Audio-Visual & Drama Club Adv; IM Ath Coach; Sci Fair Coord; United Fed of Tchrs 1984-; Roses Cantina Music Assn 1991-, Bus Mgr; *office:* Robert A VanWyck Jr HS #217 85-05 144th St Jamaica NY 11435

PEARLMAN, PAULA SCHWARTZ, Fourth Grade Teacher; *b:* Fall River, MA; *m:* Earl H.; *c:* Lisa, Marc; *ed:* St Coll at Bridgewater (BS) Elem Ed 1964; Act Integrating Math, Sci Summer Prgm; *cr:* Westfall Schl 6th Grd Tchr 1964-65; Lilja Schl 6th Grd Tchr 1965-66; Ft Irwin Schl 3rd Grd Tchr 1966-67; Fall River Schl 3rd Grd Tchr 1967-68; Stonewall JAckson Schl 3rd Grd Tchr 1968-69; Henry P. Clough Schl 3rd Grd Tchr 1977-78; Meml Schl 3rd-4th Grd Tchr 1978-81; Henry P. Clough Schl 4th Grd Tchr 1981-; *ai:* Fac Senate; Curr Planning, Math Curr Comms; Natures Classroom; Mendon-Upton Regnl Tchrs Assn 1977-; MA Tchrs Assn, NEA 1964-; *office:* Henry P. Clough Schl PO Box 5 10 North Ave Mendon MA 01756

PEARO, MICHAEL CHARLES, Social Studies Dept Chprsn; Albans, VT; *ed:* Univ of VT (BS) Ed 1962; Saint Michaels Coll (M 1969; Post Grad Stud at Univ of HI Asian Stud, Univ of Tel Aviv M Stud, Univ of Kyoto Japanese Stud & Beijing Normal Coll Culture; Champlain Coll; *cr:* Rice Memorial HS Tchr & Dept 1962-; *ai:* Var Bsbl Coach; European Comparative Cultures Prgm D Dir; NACST 1962-; VT Bsbl Coaches Assn 1966-; Outstanding Educator 1969; Governors Awd in Intnl Ed 1974; Univ of VT Outs Scndry Schl Tchr 1990; Trinity Coll Outstanding Scndry Schl Tch Rice mem HS Ath Hall of Fame; *office:* Rice Memorial HS 99 Proc S Burlington VT 05403

PEARSALL, KENNETH GORDON, Science Teacher; *b:* Baysh *m:* Julia Messenger; *c:* Shannon R., Gregory Allen; *ed:* SUNY Brook (BS) Bio, Sec Ed 1975; 6 Grad Credits at U of MT; 3 Grad U of HI; 15 Grad Credits at SUNY at Stony Brook; 9 Grad Credits Tech; 3 Grad Credits at Rensellaer Poly Tech; 3 Grad Credits at Bio Tchrs Inst; *cr:* Sachem HS Sci Ed Tchr 1976-82; Auburn HS Tchr 1982-; *ai:* Environment Club Adv; Ocean Sci Field Course Ins NYSUT 1975-; ATA 1982-; Cty-Wide Environmental Liason to N Dept; WCNY Grant To Produce Watershed Video; Article Pub; Cay Outstdng Conservation Awd; Governors Citation; NACO, Deu Recognition Awd Conservation Ed; *office:* Auburn HS Lake Ave NY 13021*

PEARSON, JUDITH CLARK, English Teacher; *b:* Bonham, David Earl; *ed:* Southwestern Union Coll (AS) Music Ed 1966; Uni (BS) Music Ed 1970; Pan Amer Univ (MEd) Scndry Ed, Eng Specia 1980; Attnd Columbia Union Coll; *cr:* Shenandoah Valley Acad Tchr 1970-71; Valley Grande Acad Music, Eng Tchr 1973-8 Mountain Acad Eng Tchr 1980-82; Grand Ledge Acad Music, E 1982-84; Mount Vernon Acad Music Tchr 4 Yrs, Eng Tchr 1984-; Assn Spon; Pub & Jrnlsm Adv; Bd of Trustees Staff Rep; Acad Stan Sec; NCTE 1988-; NASAA 1990-; NEH Fellowship 1993; Zapara Tchng 1990; McKibbin Sabbatical Awd 1991; Whos Who A 1989-90; *office:* Mount Vernon Acad 15 Fairgrounds Rd Mount Ver 43050

PEARSON, LISA MARA, Mathematics Teacher; *b:* Worcester, Richard L.; *c:* Shannon, Erin; *ed:* Worcester Polytechnic Inst (MM 1986; AP Insts by Coll Bd; *cr:* East Bridgewater Schls HS Ma 1977-81; Walpole Pub Schls HS Math Tchr 1981-; *ai:* Stu Cncl Ad Cncl Mem; HS Will, K-12 Tech Comms; Fac Sentate; MTA, NEA Walpole Tchrs Assn 1981-; *office:* Walpole HS 257 Common St MA 02081*

PEARSON, MARIANNE P., High School Science Teacher; *m:* J *c:* Jane, Carolyn; *ed:* Univ of Toledo (BA) Ed, Comprehensive Sc Addl Classes MED; *cr:* Blessed Sacrament 7-8th Grd Tchr 1 Swanton HS 9-12th Grd Tchr 1991-; *office:* Swanton HS 206 Ch Swanton OH 43558*

PEARSON, PATRICK J., Prof of Accounting; *b:* Niagara Falls, Judith S. Sharo; *c:* Christina Rose, Patrick Jr.; *ed:* SUNY at Alba Bus Ed 1965, (MS) Bus Ed 1965; 21 Credit Hrs Syracuse U Continuing Prof Ed Units Annually; *cr:* Jefferson Comm Coll Acct 1965-87, Bus Division Chair 1987-93; Patrick J. Pearson CP Account Firm 1982-; Jefferson Comm Coll Acctng Prof 1993-; Acctng Club; Bus Division Mrktg Plan Comm; Inst of Mgnt Acco 1992-, VP Comm; AICPA, NYSSCPA 1983-; NATP 1993-; Amer Assn 1985-; Tchrs of Acctng at Two Yr Coll 1987-; Amer Heart Assn Treas 1984, Vol of Yr 1979; NYS Affiliate AHA 1984-, Audit Comn 1993-95, Vol of Yr 1985; Sacred Heart Fnd 1994-, Treas 1995-; Church, Awd Pro Ecclesia Et Pontifice 1995; 1996 TACTYC Annu Session Presenter Intermediate Acctng Roundtable.

PEASE, JOHN ALAN, Associate Prof of Sociology; *b:* Grand Rap *c:* Leah K. Harrington, Jay R.; *ed:* Western MI Univ (BS) Sociolog MI St Univ (MA) Sociology 1963, (PHD) Sociology 1968; *cr:* Univ Assoc Prof 1967-; *ai:* Amer Sociological Assn 1960-; DC Sociologi 1967-, Pres 1974-75, Sec; Numerous Articles Pub; Books: Sociolo Social Life & Attrition of Graduate Students at the Ph D Level Traditional Arts and Sciences; *office:* Univ Of MD Dept Of So College Park MD 20742

PEASE, LINDA MARIE DOLLOFF, Language Arts Teac Damariscotta, ME; *m:* Alan Richard; *c:* Zachary; *ed:* Univ of South ME (BS) Ed 1985; 6 Credits In Educl Admin; *cr:* Prescott Meml Schl Tchr 1985-87; Miller Schl Grd 6 Tchr 1987-95; A. D. Gray MS Grd Arts Tchr 1995-; *ai:* Yrbk, Schl Newspaper Adv; In-Dist Peer Co Dist Curr Meetings Facilitator; In-Svc Writing Wkshps Ldr; ME Assn 1985-; *office:* A. D. Gray MS Waldoboro ME 04572

PEATTIE, PATRICIA KANOUSE, English Teacher; *b:* Morristow *m:* Bruce R.; *c:* Jeffrey, Megan; *ed:* Bloomsburg St Coll (BS) Scn Eng 1974; 17 Credit Hrs; *cr:* Kittatinny Reg HS 7-12 Grd Eng Tchr *ai:* Class of 1997 Adv; Peer Ldrshp Facilitator; NHS Fac Comm 1975-; *office:* Kittatinny Regnl HS 77 Halsey Rd Newton NJ 07860

PECHILIS, WILLIAM C., High School Mathematics Tchr; *b:* Ip MA; *m:* Anne Low; *c:* Jason, Eric; *ed:* Gordon Coll (BA) Math 19 Credit Hrs Masters Equivalency Ed; *cr:* Georgetown Mid HS Mat 1976-; *ai:* Frosh Bsktbl Coach; Jr Var Bsbl Coach; NEA & MA Tchr 1976-; Georgetown Ed Assn 1976-, Negotiating Team Chm; Georgetown Mid HS 1 Winter St Georgetown MA 01833

PECK, ARDEN RAY, High School Science Teacher; *b:* Paulding, C Sharon Lee Bennett; *ed:* Defiance Coll (BS) Bio Sci 1969; St Franc (MS) Scndry Ed, Sci Comp 1975; Post Grad Stud at Toledo Univ, B Green Univ, Akron Univ, Dayton Univ; *cr:* Columbus Groveland S HS Sci Tchr, Coach 1970-71; Paulding Exempted Vlg Schl HS Sc 1971-; *ai:* Bsktbl, Ftbl Jr HS, Frosh Coach 2 Yrs; Sci Olympiad Adv 1969-; OEA; PEA; Project Aware OH Ed Environmental Fund Martha Holden Jennings Grant Biotechnology Ed at HS Bio Level; Paulding Exempted Vlg Schls 405 N Water St Paulding OH 45879

PECK, NANCY CREGAN, Pre Kindgergarten Teacher; *b:* Horne *m:* William; *c:* Andrew Vowles, Katie Vowles; *ed:* Nazareth Col Elem Ed 1974, (MS) Soc Sci 1979; *cr:* Mother of Sorrows Schl 1st-3 Tchr 1974-78; ST Pius 10th Schl Pre-Kndgtn & 6th Grd Tchr 19 1985-88; ST Rita Schl Pre-Kndgtn Tchr 1988-; *ai:* Early Chldhd C *office:* St Rita Schl 1008 Maple Dr Webster NY 14580

PECK, ORION NOBLE, Chemistry & Physics Teacher; *b:* Waterbu *m:* Robert Edwin; *c:* Brendan, Amber, Candice; *ed:* Waterbury S (AA) Chemical Tech 1966; Southern CT St Univ (BS) Physics Courses His of Sci, Demonstrations; *cr:* Anaconda Amer Brass Infor Retrieval Tech 1966-69; Engineered Environments Environmenta 1969-73; TImex Safety Rep 1973-77, Quality Control Lab Tech 19 Bassick HS Chem, Physics Tchr 1993-; *ai:* Jets Team; CT Assn P Tchrs 1992-; CT Sci Tchrs Assn 1994-; Girl Scout Ldr; PTO, Rec Sec, VP, Pres; Multiple Bd Ed, Subcommittees; *home:* 230 Straitsvi Prospect CT 06712

PECK, SHARON BENNETT, Fifth Grade Teacher; *b:* Defiance, O Arden; *c:* Joanna Lee, Jamison Ray; *ed:* Defiance Coll (BS) 1-8 Ele K-12 Rdng 1981; Coll of Mt St Joseph (MS) Ed 1987; *cr:* Sub 1981-82; Wayne Trace Schls Tchr 1982-; *ai:* Guiding Footsteps CCL

›d United Meth Church; *office:* Wayne Trace Schl Grover Hill Bldg nroe St Grover Hill OH 45849*

:R, MARSHA JURNOVOY, Assistant Principal; *b:* Philadelphia, Fred; *c:* Michael, Craig; *ed:* Temple Univ (BA) Eng 1969, (MED) Instr 1972; Beaver Coll (MED) Ed Ldrshp 1992; *cr:* Cherry Hill hl Eng Tchr 1986-89, Asst Eng Chprsn 1989-94; Beck MS Sci 1994-95; Cherry Hill East Schl Asst Prin 1995-; *ai:* Chprsn Star Advy Bd 1990-, Parent Advy Bd for Gifted Ed 1984-90; *office:* Hill HS East Kresson Rd Cherry Hill NJ 08003*

IAM, DIANA J., English Teacher; *b:* Quincy, MA; *m:* Barry E. ı; *c:* Alexandra, Sean, Katherine; *ed:* Springfield Coll (BS) Eng ieorgetown Univ (MS) Sociolinguistics 1988; Univ of MD 6 Credit idgewater St Coll 3 Credit Hrs for MA St Tchrs PE, Hlth Cert; *cr:* : Cty Agricultural HS PE, Hlth Tchr 1976-80; Mc Donough HS Eng ›81-87; Broadneck HS Eng Tchr 1987-88; Brooklyn Park Jr Sr HS Lang Arts Tchr 1988-89; Annapolis HS Eng Tchr 1989-; *ai:* Hnrs ıciplinary Comm; Fac Cncl; NHS Fac Cncl; It's Acad, Newspaper lass Spon; Field Hockey, Girls Cross Cntry Coach; Track & Field ›ach; Lit Magazine, Class, Theater Arts, Chrldng Adv; Ath Trainer; ıl & Sexual Hlth Coord; NEA 1976-; MSTA 1981-; TAAAC 1987-; 1982-; Dow Jones Newspaper Fund Flwshp 1983; FFA Honorary 980; *office:* Annapolis HS 2700 Riva Rd Annapolis MD 21401*

:, DONALD JOSEPH, Social Studies Teacher; *b:* Adams, MA; *m:* M. St Cyr; *c:* Anne; *ed:* North Adams St (BA) His 1966; Siena (MA) ›9; John Hay Fellow Williams Coll Addl 57 Hrs; *cr:* Drury HS Tchr Dept Head Team Ldr 1979-; North Adams St Adjunct Prof 1984-; ıch Acad Decathlon Team; Sr Class Adv; Schl Cncl; North Adams 967-, Past Exec Bd; MTA, NEA 1967-; Zoning Bd 1988-, Clerk; nial Comm 1993-; NASC Alumni Cncl 1980-, Past Chm; NASC Fnd Marion B Yelly Tchr of Yr 1992; Three Horace Mann Grants; John llow Williams Coll; Author Curr Guide Women's His; *office:* Drury hurch St North Adams MA 01247

RI, SUSAN HORVATH, English Teacher; *b:* Pittsburgh, PA; *m:* ‹.; *c:* James Jr., Angela, William, Peter; *ed:* Clarion Univ (BA) Eng Penn St Univ; *cr:* Sto-Rox Schl Dist Eng Tchr 1968-; *ai:* Dept ; SREA 1968-; AWPET 1995-; *office:* Sto-Rox Schl Dist 1105 St Mc Kees Rocks PA 15136*

CH, ROBERT D., Guidance Counselor; *b:* Lackawanna, NY; *m:* ı Patterson; *c:* Lisa, Jason, Kelly, Sean; *ed:* St Univ Coll at Fredonia d 1970, (MS) Ed 1979; NYS Cert Schl Cnslr 1988; *cr:* Cassadaga hl Tchr 1970-88, Cnslr 1988-; *ai:* NHS Selection Comm; SUNY Tech Schl Cnslr Advy Bd; Yth Empowerment Svc, Impact Team; Co Cnslrs Assn 1988-, VP; NYS Cnslrs Assn 1988-; Phi Delta Kappa BPO Elks 1983-; Free & Accepted Masons 1984-; *office:* Cassadaga Central Schl Rt 60 Sinclairville NY 14782

IE, CAROL E., Vocal Music Teacher; *b:* Cleveland, OH; *ed:* Univ ami at Coral Gables (BMEd) Music Ed-Cum Laude 1972; n-Wallace Coll (MAEd) Ed 1992; Supvr, HS Prin Certs; *cr:* Boca HS Vocal Music Tchr 1972-75; Lorain HS Vocal Music Tchr 5; Lorain Admiral King HS Vocal Music Tchr 1995-; *ai:* Chamber ›, Producer Annual Broadway Musical Dirs; NEA, OEA, LEA, 1980-; Church Choir Dir, Soloist 1980-; Full 4 Yr Schlsp Violin to f Miami.

DAVID WILLIAM, Agriscience Dept Chprsn; *b:* Redbank, NY; *m:* :; *c:* Kristyne, David J.; *ed:* DE Vly Coll of Sci & Ag (BS) Animal ndry 1978; Rutgers Univ (ME) Vo-Tech Ed 1984; MT St Univ 'e Mngmt, Sec Ed; *cr:* Voorhees HS Ag Tchr 1979; Newton HS Ag, l Resource Mngmt Tchr 1979-; *ai:* FFA Adv; Ag & Applied Tech 'hair; Var Sftbl Coach; NEA; Trout Unlimited 1980-, Pres; Tchr of ognition 1988; Progressive Tchr of Yr 1995; *office:* Newton HS 44 n Ave Newton NJ 07860

RSEN, ANNE GREER, Senior Riding Instructor; *b:* Rochester, NY; ›ert P.; *c:* Rachel A.; *ed:* Monroe Comm Coll (AA) Bus Admin 1978; ith Manor Schl of Horsemanship, Riding Master IV 1977; Amer Instr Cert Prgm Instr Beginner-Advanced 1993; *cr:* Cicero Schl of ınanship Riding Instr 1978-83; Anne Greer Schl of Riding Owner, 984-88; *ai:* Coach Teams for Empire St Riding Acad Series Horse ; Prof Horseman Assn 1995-; Amer Horse Show Assn 1996-; *office:* Stables 1942 Turk Hill Rd Fairport NY 14450

RSEN, ARNE A., Physics Teacher; *b:* Brooklyn, NY; *m:* Joyce Fein; ooklyn Coll (BS) Chem 1967; Richmond Coll CUNY (MS) Scndry ı 1975; 34 Grad Credits Organic Chem Polytechnic Inst of Brooklyn ›9; *cr:* Tottenville HS Physics Tchr 1969-; *ai:* NHS Adv; Acad ics Coach; UFT 1969-; Physics Club of NY 1989-; Pub Article in l of Research in Sci Tchng 1976; Tchr Trainer 1986-90; Examination Subjct Matter Specialist for Bd of Ed 1988-91; *office:* Tottenville HS ıten Ave Staten Island NY 10312

RSEN, DOLORES WELLER, Fifth Grade Teacher; *b:* Hackensack, Ejanr C.; *c:* Tina, Mary; *ed:* NJ St Coll at Jersey City (BS) Elem 57; Seton Hall (MA) Admin-Sup 1965; Jersey City St Coll Cmptrs 3 ›; *cr:* Lincoln Schl 3rd Grd Tchr 1956-60; US Dependents Schl 3rd chr 1960-62; Driftwood 3rd Grd Tchr 1962-63; Holdrum 6th Grd 963-65; Meml 5th Grd Tchr 1978-80; A.S. Faust 7-8th Grd Eng Tchr ›0, 5th Grd Tchr 1990-; *ai:* NEA, NJEA 1957-; BCEA 1963-; *office:* S Faust Intrmediate Schl Uhland And Grove Sts East Rutherford NJ

RSEN, ERIC RANDALL, Associate Professor of English; *b:* na, NY; *m:* Patricia Telesz-Pedersen; *c:* Travis S., Jeffrey G.; *ed:* ›f SC (BA) Eng 1971, (MA) Eng Modern Amer Lit 1974; VA Comm Writing Project Fellow 1982; George Mason Univ 6 Credit Hrs, 12 Hrs Addl 19 Total; *cr:* Univ of SC at Columbia & Aiken Tchng Asst, ıc 1971-73; Greenville Tech Coll Eng Instr 1973-78; Danville Comm ing Instr 1978-95; Butler Cty Com Col En g Assoc Prof 1985-; *ai:* dv Writer's Club, Lit Magazine FACETS; Mem Fac Enhancement ı; Act 101 Bd Chair; WPCTE 1988-, Honoree; NEA 1992-; PCEA ; McConnell's Mills Pres Assn 1991-, Comm Work; Western PA rvancy 1985-; Amer Rivers Assn 1988-; Three Rivers Paddling Club ; *office:* Butler County Comm Coll PO Box 1203 Butler PA 16003

:RSEN, LARRY DAVID, Chemistry Associate Professor; *b:* ıci, AZ; *m:* Emily Elizabeth Frye; *c:* Jorgen; *ed:* Clarkson Univ (BS) 1969; Yale Univ (MPhil) Organic Chem 1976, (PHD) Organic Chem Post Doctoral Fellow Univ of British Columbia; *cr:* Chemtrend Inc Dir 1983-85; Techesives Co Owner, Pres 1985-; DE Vly Coll Adj ›f Chem 1987-90; Coll Misericordia Assoc Prof of Chem 1990-; *ai:* ›o Orienteering Club Pres; Dead Alchemist Soc Adv; Fac Senate; Chemical Soc 1965-; Cncl on Undergrad Rsrch 1994-; US teering Fed 1979-, Pres; Wagner Forest ParkAssn 1990-; 4 :ations in Journals; 3 US Patents; *office:* Coll Misericordia 301 Lake llas PA 18612

, MARY CATALDO, Language Arts Teacher; *b:* Boston, MA; *m:* ›ny D. Jr.; *ed:* Univ of MA (BS) Scndry Eng, Ed 1971; Summer Inst ›n Coll 1994, St Michael's Coll 1995; Electrology Inst of New ınd 1996; *cr:* Paul Revere Schl Eng Tchr 1971-90; Garfield MS ›n Lang Arts 1990-94, Cluster Ldr 1994-95, Lang Arts, Mentor Tchr *ai:* Hum Prgm Curr Ldr; Yrbk Adv; Mentor Tchr; Revere Pub Schls Frameworks Stud Group; Metro N MS Alliance Group; Natl Team Transformations Project Coordinating Tchr; NEA, MTA, RTA 1971-; Whole Lang Tchrs Assn 1994-; NCTE 1995-; Flint Lib 1979-; Museum of Sci 1972-; ADASTRA 1979-; Inst of Noetic Sci 1985-; Cousteau Soc 1980-; *office:* James Garfield Cmty Magnet Sch 140 Garfield Ave Revere MA 02151*

PEDISICH, DINA, Spanish Teacher; *b:* Port Jefferson, NY; *ed:* Salve Regina Univ (BA) Span Lit 1986; Univ of RI (MA) Span Lit 1989; *cr:* Pensacola HS Span Tchr 1989-93; Pensacola Jr Coll Span Tchr 1991-93; Southbridge HS Span Tchr 1993-; Quinsigamond Comm Coll Span Tchr 1995-; *ai:* Co-Adv Class 1995; Yrbk Adv 1994-; AATSP 1989-; Ma FLA 1993-; *office:* Southbridge HS 25 Cole Ave Southbridge MA 01550

PEDROTTI, MICHELE ELLEN, Social Studies Teacher; *b:* Syracuse, NY; *m:* Dennis; *c:* Ashley, Kayla, Colin; *ed:* SUNY at Oswego (MS) Elem Ed 1989; SUNY at Cortland (MS) K-12 Rdng 1994; *cr:* Syracuse City Schls Resource Tchr 1990; SCSD Project Success Tchr 1990-91, 7th Grd Soc Stud Tchr 1992-; *ai:* Site Based Planning Team; Movie Club Adv; Bldg Comm; Cntrl NY Cncl Soc Stud 1992-; AFT 1986-; *office:* Clary Magnet MS Amidon Dr Syracuse NY 13205*

PEEBLES, MONICA LOUISE, History Teacher; *b:* Wheaton, MD; *ed:* Univ of MD (BS) Ed 1994; *cr:* Richard Montgomery High His Tchr 1994-; Teens Camping Tour of the West Staff Cnclr 1995-; *ai:* Schl Newspaper Spon; Inservice, Sunshine & Open-Lunch Comms; NEA 1994-; *office:* Richard Montgomery HS 250 Richard Montgomery Dr Rockville MD 20852*

PEEBLES, TIMOTHY L., English & Drama Teacher; *b:* Canton, OH; *m:* Sheila Palmer; *c:* Erin; *ed:* Kent St Univ (BFA) Theatre 1969, (BS) Ed 1970; Cleveland St Univ (MED) Schl Admin 1975-; *cr:* Midpark HS Eng, Drama Tchr 1970-; *ai:* Dramatics Dir; BFT, AFT 1970-; Masonic Lodge 1984-; Fullbright Tchr Exch to Great Britain 1986-87; Original Play Produced off-Broadway; *office:* Midpark HS 7000 Paula Dr Cleveland OH 44130

PEEL, CAROL BERBERICH, Amer History & Govt Teacher; *b:* Pittsburgh, PA; *m:* Robert W.; *c:* Nancy Horne, Margaret Golden, James, Susan Marchetti, Roberta Quinn; *ed:* Clarion Univ (BSEd) Scndry Soc Stud 1962; Univ of Pittsburgh (MED) Soc Sci 1968; Westminster Coll 6 Credit Hrs Am His 1966; CA Univ 6 Credit Hrs Am Stud 1969; *cr:* North Allegheny Schls Soc Stud Tchr 34 Yrs; *ai:* Pi Gamma Mu 1962-; PA Cncl Soc Stud 1965-; AFT 1685-.

PEELING, MICHELLE L., English Teacher; *b:* Charleston, SC; *ed:* Shippensburg Univ (BA) Eng 1983; Tchng Cert Eng 1987; Currently Pursuing Grad Work at Penn St; *cr:* Chambersburg Area Sr HS Scndry Eng Tchr 1988-; *ai:* Drama Club Adv; Dir of Musicals & Plays; Forensics Team Coach; NEA, PSEA 1988-; *office:* Chambersburg Area Sr H S 511 S 6th St Chambersburg PA 17201

PEER, LARRY E., Science Teacher; *ed:* Clarion Univ (BS) Scndry Ed, Earth & Space Scis, Comprehensive & Phys Scis & Geography 1971; Duquesne Univ (MS) Admin; *cr:* Norwin Schl Dist Sci Tchr 1971-; *ai:* Var Ftbl Asst Coach, Offensive Coord; NEA, PSEA, Norwin Ed Assn 1971-; Saint Agnes Athletic Assn 1986-, Treas; Saint Vincent Coll Tchr Enhancement Inst Participation Awd 2 Yrs; Former Bsktbl & Track-Field Coach; *office:* Norwin Sr HS 251 Mcmahon Dr North Huntingdon PA 15642

PEER, PENNY MAY, Chemistry Teacher; *b:* Columbus, OH; *m:* Teddy Glen Bostic Jr.; *c:* Kelsey Amelia, Matthew Glen Bostic; *ed:* OH Dominican Coll (BS) Chem 1988, (BA) Ed 1990; Attnd OH St Univ Coll of Ed; Working on Masters in Curr Dev at Otterbein; Seattle St Univ Learning with Mult Intelligences Stud; *cr:* St Charles Prep HS Chem Dept Tchr 1990-; *ai:* Dev of Diocese Sci Prgm Curr Comm; Prom Adv; NSTA 1991-; ICE 1994-; ACS 1987-; *office:* St Charles Prep HS 2010 E Broad St Columbus OH 43209*

PEERY, BARBARA JONES, First Grade Teacher; *b:* Steubenville, OH; *m:* Thomas Brady; *c:* Ross, Tyler; *ed:* Bowling Green St Univ (BS) Elem Ed, LBD 1978; Attnd OH Univ, Marietta Coll; *cr:* Warren Elem Schl Kndgtn Tchr 1978-83, First Grd Tchr 1983-; *ai:* NEA, WLEA 1978-; Mid-OH Vly Mothers of Twins Club 1987-, Treas 2 Yrs; *office:* Warren Elem Schl RR 2 Box 138 Marietta OH 45750

PEETS, BARBARA POWERS, 7th-10th Grade English Teacher; *b:* Troy, NY; *c:* Shawn W. West; *ed:* SUNY at Plattsburgh (MA) Lbrl Stud, Eng 1986; *cr:* Chateaugay Cntrl Schl 7th Grd Eng Tchr 1984-86; F-E-H BOCES 7th-10th Grd Eng Tchr 1986-; *ai:* Site-Based Comm for Shared Decision Making; NYSUT 1984-; F-E-H BOCES Tchrs Assn 1986-, Sec; NCTE 1986-; Outstdng Svc Employee of Yr 1992; *office:* North Franklin Ed Cntr 52 State St Malone NY 12953

PEFFLEY, BRUCE ELVERT, Sci Chm, Chem & Physics Tchr; *b:* Dayton, OH; *m:* Lynn Doreen Smyth; *c:* Laura A., Paul M.; *ed:* Cornell Univ (BA) Chem 1972; Columbia Univ (MA) Computing, Tech Ed 1987; Addl 42 Grad Hrs Sci, Ed; *cr:* Campbell Cntrl Schl Sci Tchr 1972-92; Campbell-Savona Cntrl Schl Sci Dept Chm, Tchr 1992-; *ai:* Boys, Girls Cross Cntry Coach; HEAL Club Adv; STANYS 1972-; NSTA 1980-; Corning Sister Cities 1985-, Pres; Corning 1st United Meth Church 1975-, Bd of Trustees, Sec; *office:* Campbell Savona Central Schl 8455 Cty Rt 125 Campbell NY 14821

PEGELOW, THOMAS RAY, Special Ed Teacher & Coach; *b:* Terrae Haute, IN; *m:* Maureen Cole; *c:* Nate, Nick; *ed:* Old Dominion Univ (BS) Hlth, PE 1977; IN-Purdue Univ (MS) Scndry Ed 1980; DE St Univ Spec Ed Cert; *cr:* Garrett Jr Sr HS Tchr, Coach 1977-85; Woodbridge Jr Sr HS Tchr, Coach 1985-89; Seaford MS Tchr, Coach 1989-91; Seaford Sr HS Tchr, Coach 1991-; *ai:* Var Bsbl Coach; Asst Var Ftbl Coach; NEA 1985-; SEA 1989-, Negotiation Team; BCA; DBCA, Blue Gold All-Star Game Chm; DE St Bsbl Coach of Yr 1993-94; Henlopen Conf Coach of Yr 1994; USA Bsbl, Topps Amateur Bsbl Coach of Yr 1994; *office:* Seaford Sr HS 399 N Market St Seaford DE 19973

PEGG, ANN M., 5th Grade Math & Science Tchr; *b:* Boston, MA; *m:* William J.; *c:* Amanda, Ian; *ed:* Fichburg St Coll (BSED Spec Ed, Elem 1967; Boston Coll (MED) Ed; Simmons Coll; Eastern Nazarene Coll Sea Ed Assn; *cr:* Quincy Pub Schls Spec Needs Tchr 1967-76, 1-5th Grd Tchr 1976-; *ai:* Acting Asst Prin, Tchng 5th Grd; Present Wkshps; NSTA; MA Assn of Sci Tchrs; Soc for Elem Presidential Awardees; Cncl for Elem Sci Intnl; MA Marine Edctrs; Pres Awd for Excl in Sci, Math Tchng 1993; Presenter for MA Corporation for Educl TeleCommunications Tchr in Electronic Residence 1995; *office:* Merrymount Elem Schl 4 Agawam Rd Quincy MA 02169*

PEIFER, LAUREL DENISE, Spanish Teacher; *b:* Danville, PA; *ed:* Asbury Coll (BA) Span Ed 1993; *cr:* Montoursville Area Sr High Span Tchr 1994-; *ai:* Class Adv; PSEA & NEA 1995-; *office:* Montoursville Area Sr HS 100 N Arch St Montoursville PA 17754

PEIFFER, DEREK WILLIAM, Social Studies Teacher; *b:* Allentown, PA; *m:* Ann Jeanette Ruggiero; *c:* Emily Elizabeth; *ed:* Kutztown Univ (BS) Soc Stud 1989; 12 Credit Hrs Lehigh Univ Educl Ldrshp; *cr:* Sacred Heart Schl 7th Grd Tchr 1990-91; Emmaus HS Soc Stud Tchr 1992-; *ai:* Boys Bsktbl Coach; Dept Chprsn; Stu Asst Prgm; NEA, PSEA, EPEA 1992-; St Anne's Church 1991-, Yth Leader; TPA 1991-; *office:* Emaus H S 851 North St Emmaus PA 18049

PEIFFER, H. KIRK, Mathematics Teacher; *b:* Westminister, MD; *ed:* Univ of Richmond (BA) Math & Ger 1990; Univ of MA at Amherst (MED) 1993; *cr:* Southegan HS Math Tchng 1993-; *ai:* Math, Sci Fellow; Natl Re Learning Fac Through Coalition of Essential Schls; *office:* Souhegan HS PO Box 1152 Amherst NH 03031*

PEIFFER, SUSAN MARIE, Middle School Math Teacher; *b:* Reading, PA; *m:* Cory D.; *c:* Nathan, Rebecca; *ed:* Millersville Univ (BS) Math Ed 1986; 25 Grad Credits; *cr:* Lebanon MS 7th Grd Math Tchr 1986-; *ai:* Team Ldr; Curr Coord; NEA 1986-; NCTM 1986-; *office:* Lebanon MS 350 N 8th St Lebanon PA 17046*

PEIL, MANFRED HEINZ, English Teacher; *b:* Bensheim, Germany; *ed:* Rutgers Coll (AB) Eng 1971, (EDM) Eng, Ed 1974, (EDS) Labor Ed 1989; *cr:* East Brunswick HS Eng Tchr 1971-; *ai:* NEA, NJEA, MCEA, EBEA 1971-, Del; MENSA 1967-; East Brunswick Pub Schls Tchr Recognition Awd 1993-94; NJ Governor's Awd 1993; Who's Who in Amer Ed 1989-90; Article Pub; Poem Pub; *office:* East Brunswick HS 380 Cranbury Rd East Brunswick NJ 08816*

PEITZ, TIMOTHY CHARLES, Chemistry Teacher; *b:* Newark, NJ; *m:* Susan Brown; *c:* Adam, Joshua, Katharine, Jonathan; *ed:* Newark Coll of Engrng (BS) Chem Engrng 1974; Kean Coll Phys Sci Tchr Cert 1993; *cr:* EI DuPont Engr 1974-84; Heubach Inc Production Supvr 1984-87; Woodbridge Twp Bd of Ed Sub Tchr 1990-93; Woodbridge HS Chem Tchr 1993-; *ai:* Chem Club; NJEA, NEA 1991-; NJSTA, ACS Tchr Affiliates 1993-; G&T PTO 1986-, Pres; Avenel Colonia FAS 1985-89, Pres; Union Carbide Summer Internship Prgm; NJ Bisel Tchr Internship Prgm; Union Carbide Fnd Grant; *office:* Woodbridge HS Kelly St Woodbridge NJ 07095

PEKALA, DOROTHY A., Third Grade Teacher; *b:* Windber, PA; *ed:* St Francis Coll (BS) Elem Ed 1969; Shippensburg St Univ (MED) Ed 1973; Univ of Pitt at Johnstown (BA) Ec 1987; *cr:* Richland Schl Dist Elem Tchr 1970-; *ai:* RIchland Ed Assn, PSEA, NEA 1970-; *office:* Rachel Hill Elem Schl 338 Theatre Dr Johnstown PA 15904

PEKALA, DOROTHY OLSEN, Mathematics Teacher; *b:* Staten Island, NY; *m:* Andrew J.; *c:* Andrea, Jennifer, Amy, Christina; *ed:* Merrimack Coll (BA) Hum 1964; Univ of MD 30 Credit Hrs Post Grad; Charles Cty CC 21 Credit Hrs; Wagner Coll 10 Credit Hrs; *cr:* Crestview Elem 6th Grd Tchr 1965-68; James Ryder Randall 6th Grd Tchr 1970-72; Friendly HS Math Tchr 1985-91; Surrattsville HS Math Tchr 1991-92; John Hanson MS Math Tchr 1992-; *ai:* CCD Tchr 1978-92 & 1995; EACC 1992-; MSTA 1992-; NEA 1992-; NCTM 1992-; Laurel Acres Comm Assoc 1974-, Treas 1981-; *home:* 6680 Oakwood Cir Indian Head MD 20640

PELLEGRINI, NANCY CICCHINO, Business Teacher; *b:* Campobosso, Italy; *m:* Dennis; *c:* Carl Anthony; *ed:* Middlesex Cty Jr Coll (AA) Secretarial Stu 1968; Montclair St Coll (BA) Bus Ed 1970; Various Courses Montclair St Coll, Jersey City St Coll; *cr:* Parsippany Hills HS Bus Tchr 26 Yrs; *ai:* Class of 1997 Adv; Renaissance, Bridges Comms; NJEA, NEA, MCEA, PTHEA, NBEA 1970-; *home:* 5 Heather Ct Dover NJ 07801

PELLEGRINO, CAROL BARTO, Music Teacher; *b:* Greenwich, CT; *m:* Gerard; *c:* Lauren, David, Kristen; *ed:* SUNY at Potsdam (BS) Mus Ed, Violin 1957; Eastman Schl of Music (MM) Mus Ed 1962; *cr:* Greenwich Pub Schl Music Tchr 1957-62; Coventry Music Tchr 1962-63; RI Philharmonic Orch Violinist 1963-75; Warwick Pub Schl Music Tchr 1975-; *ai:* RI Music Ed Chprsn Jr & Sr HS All-St Orch; AF of M 1963-; AFT 1975-; Mus Ed Natl Conv 1957-; RI Music Ed Assn 1962-, Bd Mem; Am String Teach Assn 1955-; RI String Teach Assn 1962-, Treas; Warwick PTA Cncl Outstanding Tchr Awd 1983 & 1993; RI Arts Ed in Ed Model Prgm 1989-90; RI Mus Ed Review Strings Ed; Orch 1st Place; Gold Medal Winner Outstanding Instrumental Group; 1st Orch Muited to Perform in Lord Mayor of Westminster, New Year's Day Celebration, Royal Albert Hall.*

PELLEGRINO, DIANE ELAINE (PERRETT), High School Nurse; *b:* Melrose, MA; *m:* Joseph A.; *c:* Jason, Tanya; *ed:* New England Coll (AS) Behavoral Sci 1986; Melrose Wakefield Schl of Nrsgn Diploma Nrsng 1973; *cr:* Bon Secours Hosp Staff, OB Nurse 1973-86; Methuen Pub Schls MS, ELem Nurse 1986-92, HS Nurse 1992-; Holy Family Hosp Per Diem OBS Nurse 1988-; *ai:* Pert Team 1992-; Hlth Advy Cncl 1993-; Dating Violence Grant 1995-; MA Nurses Assn 1986-, Chprsn; Amer Red Cross 1986-, CPR-First Aid Instr; *office:* Methuen HS Merrimack St Methuen MA 01844

PELLEGRINO, HELENMARIE, 9th-12th Grd Art Teacher; *b:* Camden, NJ; *m:* Rick; *ed:* Rowan St Coll (BA) Art Ed 1965; Kean Coll (MA) Fine Arts Ed, Painting 1970; Tchrs Coll Columbia Univ (EDD) Analysis of Art Tchng & Supervision 1983; Doctorial Dissertation Art Ed in the Pub Schols of Newark NJ; Prin, Supvr Cert; Elem, Scndry Cert Art Ed K-12; *cr:* Elizabeth Pub Schls Art Tchr 1965-68; New Brunswick Pub Schls Art Tchr 1968-69; Sussex Ave Elem Schl Art Tchr 1969-79; Madison Ave Elem Schl Art Tchr 1969-79; Eastside HS Art Tchr 1979-; *ai:* Natl Art Hnr Soc Established, Adv; Yrbk Adv; Awded Second Place Recognition by Columbia Scholastic Press Assn; Organized Stu Art Work Display Newark Intnl Airport, Smithsonian Inst, Trenton St Museum, Newark Museum; Natl Art Ed Assn 1965-, Recorder, Evaluator; Cncl of Art Ed; Art Edctrs of NJ St Assn 1970-; Art Edctrs of Newark Dist Assn 1971-; Art Edctrs of NJ 1970-, Yth Artmonth Co-Chprsn, Film Festival for Fall Conf Chprsn; Westfield Art Assn 1994-; Two Curr Dev Mini-Grants Awded by NJ St Dept of Ed 1971-71; Two Governors Awds for Yth Art Month 1986-87; Wkshps; Lectures; Slide Presentations; Art Exhibitions; Certs of Appreciation, Commendations Newark Muncipal Cncl 1991, Channel 13 1989, Annual Stdnts Art Festival; Commendation Cert Arts & Crafts Materials Inst 1985.

PELLEGRINO, JOSEPHINE L. (CEVETTO), Sixth Grade Teacher; *b:* Newark, NJ; *w:* Anthony J. (dec); *c:* Cynthia Anne Mc Mahon, Nancy A., Carolyn M., Anthony; *ed:* Newark St Tchrs Coll (BA) Elem Ed 1956; *cr:* Newark Pub Schls 1st-2nd Grd Tchr 1956-60; Vineland Pub Schls Sub Tchr 1975-80; Saint Francis of Assisi Schl Sub Tchr 1981-83; Saint Mary's Schl 6th Grd, Sub Tchr 1984-86; *ai:* Rel Coord; After Schl Prgm Supvr; Amer Fed of Women's Club 1974-, Newcomers Club VP; *office:* St Leo Schl 123 Myrtle Ave Irvington NJ 07111

PELLEGRINO, MARK BARRETT, Biology & Physics Teacher; *b:* Buffalo, NY; *ed:* SUNY at Buffalo (BS) Biological Scis 1986, (MS) Natural Scis 1987; 24 Credits Tchng Cert SUC at Buffalo; 10 Credits Physics Monroe Comm Coll; 30 Credits Eng CLEP Prgm Educl Testing Svc; *cr:* Roswell Park Meml Inst Rsrch Tech 1985-87; Niagara Cty Comm Coll Adj Fac 1988-90; Holland Cntrl Schl Sub Tchr 1990; Gananda Cntrl Schl Tchr 1990-; *ai:* Sr Class Adv; Drama Club Dir, Adv; Var Chrldng Coach; Acceleration Comm Chm; Tchr Selection, NHS Speaker, Comms; NABT 1990-; STANYS 1991-; ASCD 1993-; Univ of Rochester Excl Tchng Awd, Gananda Employee of Yr 1993; Tandy Tech Scholar 1994-95; Article Pub 1988; Peak Learning Systems Inc Educl Consultant; *office:* Gananda Cntrl Schl 1500 Dayspring Ridge Walworth NY 14568*

PELLEGRINON, MARY ZOELLNER, Sixth Grade Teacher; *b:* Portsmouth, OH; *m:* Jack Edward; *c:* Emily; *ed:* OH Univ (BS) Elem Ed 1972; Xavier Univ (MED) Ed Admin 1977; *cr:* Wheelersburg Elem Chapter I 1969-74, 5th Grd Tchr 1974-90, 6th Grd Tchr 1990-; *ai:* NEA, OEA 1969-; Wheelersburg Ed Assn 1969-, Pres 1980; Delta Kappa Gamma 1981-; *office:* Wheelersburg Elem Schl 1760 Dogwood Ridge Wheelersburg OH 45694

PELLETIER, DEBORAH JEAN, Physical Education Teacher; *b:* Attleboro, MA; *ed:* Westfield St Coll (BS) PE 1985; *cr:* Hampshire Regnl HS PE Tchr 1989; Westfield Pub Schls PE Tchr 1989-; *ai:* Head Coach Vlybl 1992-, Swimming 1989-, Track, Field 1988-; MTA, WEA, NEA 1989-; AAHPERD, MAHPERD 1981-; WMTFOA 1994-, Exec Bd; *office:* Southampton Road Schl 330 Southampton Rd Westfield MA 01085

PELLETIER, MARK CHARLES, Fifth & Sixth Grade Teacher; *b:* Troy, NY; *m:* Mary Anne Conrad; *c:* Adam, David; *ed:* St Univ of NY at Delhi (AAS) Liberal Arts 1977; Eastern MI Univ (BS) Elem Ed, Speech & Lang Imp 1980, (MA) Speech, Lang Impaired 1981; *cr:* Rutland NE Supervisory Union Speech & Lang Pathologist 1981-85; Sudburys Cntry Schl Tchng Prin 1985-89, Tchr 1989-95, Team Admin 1995-; *ai:* NEA, VTEA 1982-; *office:* Sudbury Country Schl Box 1300 Sudbury VT 05733

PELLETIER, RAE HARMON, Choral Director; *b:* Presque Isle, ME; *c:* Ernest Josef III, Daniel Phillip; *ed:* Boston Univ Schl of Fine & Applied Arts (B-Mus) Music Ed 1961; Long Island Univ (MS) Elem Ed 1989; *cr:* South Paris K-12th Grd Music Tchr & Dir 1961-63; Orono K-6th Grd Music Tchr 1963-64; East Ramapo Schl Dist 10th-12th Grd Music Tchr 1968-; *ai:* Madrigal Singers, Vocal Jazz Ensemble, Show Choir & Performing Troupe Dir; NEA 1961-; NYSSMA 1968-; *office:* Ramapo Sr HS 400 Viola Rd Spring Valley NY 10977

PELLETIER, VALERIE MAE, Music Dir & Teacher; *b:* Lowell, MA; *m:* George Ray; *c:* Christopher G., Jarod Allan; *ed:* Berklee Coll of Music Piano, Instrumental Band, Choral; *cr:* St Mary of the Bay Organist, Cantor, Jr-Sr Choir Dir 1970-86; Our Lady of Mt Carmel Organist, Cantor, Jr Choir Dir 1986-90; St Elizabeths Schl Pre K-8 Grd Music Tchr, Liturgical Dance, Theater Dir 1990-; *ai:* Liturgical Comm; Dir, Organize Pre K, K, 8th GrdGrads; Christmas Pageants Dir 256 Children; Tch Liturgical Dance; MADD 1990-; *home:* 17 Tobin Ln Bristol RI 02809*

PELLETIER-MYERS, LISA JEAN, Art Dept Chair & Teacher; *b:* Rochester, NY; *m:* Paul N.; *c:* Katherine, Paul Christopher; *ed:* Nazareth Coll (BS) Art Ed 1986; *cr:* Macedon Elem Schl Art Tchr 1986-88; Bishop Kearney HS Art Dept Chprsn, Tchr 1989-; *office:* Bishop Kearney HS 125 Kings Hwy S Rochester NY 14617

PELLICANO, BARBARA, Spanish Teacher; *b:* Rochester, NY; *ed:* Nazareth Coll of Rochester (BA) Span, Ed 1988, (MS) Ed 1990; *cr:* Webster Jr HS Span Tchr 1988-91, Sr HS Span Tchr 1992-93, Span Tchr, Foreign Lang Dept Ldr 1993-; *ai:* Span Club Adv 1988-; Field Trips Chaperone; NYSAFLT 1988-; WTA; NYSUT; NY Assn Foreign Lang Tchrs James E. Allen Distinguished Foreign Lang Dept Prgm Awd 1994; *office:* Webster HS 800 Five Mile Line Rd Webster NY 14580*

PELOSI, DELORA MARY, Latin Teacher; *b:* Waterbury, CT; *ed:* Cath Univ (PHD) Latin Patristics; Trinity Coll (MA) Latin, Ed 1974; Seton Hill Coll (BA) Classics, Fr 1971; *cr:* Holy Cross HS Latin, Fr, Eng Tchr 1972-76; Wilde Lake HS Latin, Fr Tchr 1976-77; St John's Military Coll HS Latin Tchr 1977-78; Cath Univ Tchng Asst 1977-80; St Anselm's Abbey Schl Latin Tchr 1979-; *ai:* Natl Latin Exam Coord; Moderator Latin Club; Latin Competition Coach; St Chair MD-DC Jr Classical League; Host St Convention; Plan & Org Group for Attendande at Natls 1993; St Anselm's Boy Elected 2nd Natl VP 1994; St Anselm's Stu Natl Pres 1995; Natl Jr Classical League 1990-, Coord of Chpt, St Chair 1990; Amer Classical League 1986-; Washington Classical Soc 1985-; Vergilian Soc 1986-; Fulbright Scholar 1986; Schlsp PHD Stud Cath Univ; Fulbright Insterivew Comm Regnl Chair.*

PELOSI, EVELYN TYMINSKI, Science Dept Chairman & Tchr; *b:* Chicopee, MA; *m:* Stanford S. Jr.; *c:* Sharon Mane, Steven Michael; *ed:* Univ of MA (BS) Chem 1960; Univ of NH (MS) Org Chem 1963, (PHD) Org Chem 1965; SUNY at OneontaEd; Woodrow Wilson Inst for Chem SUNY at Oneonta; *cr:* Norwich City Schls Asst Prof, Chem Tchr 1978-; Norwich HS Chem Tchr 1978-, Dept Head Sci 1995-; *ai:* Chptr of Natl Hnr Soc Adv; Dist Site Based Comm; Instrl Cncl; NEO Bldg Rep; NEA 1978-, Bldg Rep; Amer Chem Soc 1958-, Pres Stu Affiliate, HS Cord; NYS Sci Tchr Assn 1989-; NYS Sci Supvrs Assn 1995-; NYS Chem Mentor for DCMO-BOCE'S; Gen Chem Turnkey Trainer for NYS; *office:* Norwich HS Midland Dr Norwich NY 13815

PELOSO, JOHN RICHARD,III, Chief Instructor; *b:* Hartford, CT; *ed:* Univ of CT (BS) Pathobiology 1987; *cr:* USA TaeKwon-Do Team Gold Medalist 1989, Bronze Medalist 1991, Coach 1992; USA Jr TaeKwon-Do Team Dir 1993, Adv, Coach 1995-; *ai:* Intnl TaeKwon-Do Fed Certfd 4th Degree Black Belt, Class A Umpire; Kore Amer TaeKwon-Do Union Certfd Class A Instr, Referee; Hwangs Black Belt Assn Sr VP, Chief Umpire, Rules & Regulations Comm Head, Tournament Comm Chm; Instr of Yr 1989; *office:* Hwangs Schl of Tae Kwon-Do Ste 311 13 Summit St East Hampton CT 06424

PELTA, MAUREEN, History of Art Assoc Prof; *b:* Phila, PA; *m:* Alan M. Feldman; *c:* Erica, Julia; *ed:* Temple Univ (BA) Fine Art, Art His 1975, (MA) Art His 1979; Bryn Mawr Coll (PHD) Art His 1989; *cr:* Moore Coll of Art & Design 1986-; *ai:* Acad Standards, Stu Judiciary, Admissions & Sesquicentennial Celebrations Comm; Coll Art Assn & DE Valley Medieval Assn 1990-; AAUW 1993-; Jewish Comm Relations Cncl 1992-, Exec Bd; Fac Dev Grant MCAD 1993; NEH Summer Seminar in Rome 1992; Mordechai Anielewicz Awd 1994-95; Articles in MacMillan Dict of Art, Aeon, Journal of Medieval & Renaissance Stud; *office:* Moore Coll Of Art & Design 20th And Race Streets Philadelphia PA 19103*

PELTIER, SARAH M., Vocal Music Director; *b:* Pittsburgh, PA; *m:* David Paul; *c:* Dawn Weaver, Darren Paul, Drew Allen; *ed:* King's Coll (BS) Music Ed 1960; Univ of DE Elem Ed Cert 1962; Attnd Capital Univ, West Chester Univ, Univ of Dayton, OH St Univ, Bowling Green Univ; *cr:* Stanton Schl Dist 5th Grd Tchr 1960-64; So Tioga PA Schl System Elem Music Tchr 1979; Ada Exempted Village Schls Elem Music Tchr 1981-87; Hardin Northern Schls 1-12 Grd Vocal Music Dir 1987-; *ai:* Prins Blue Ribbon Comm; NEA, OEA, HNEA 1987-; MENC, OH Music Edctrs Assn 1981-; OH Choral Dirs Assn 1994-; Ada UMC, Admin Comm, Worship Comm, Adult Choir Dir 1990-; PEO Sisterhood, Music, Prgm Ch; Harvest & Herb Festival, Entertainment Chprsn 1986-; Martha Holden Jennings Scholar for Excl in Tchng 1991-92; Nom by Supt for OH Tchr of Yr 1993; Hardin Cty Mentor Trng Prgm 1992-93.*

PELTON, CAROLINE BROWN, Secondary English Teacher; *b:* Leesburg, VA; *m:* Rodney Arthur; *ed:* Earlham Coll (BA) Eng 1962; Howard Univ (MAT) Eng & Ed 1969; Georgetown Univ (MALS) Lbrl Stud 1987; 18 Credit Hrs in Eng & Lbrl Stud; *cr:* Peace Corps Roosevelt Schl for Girls in Freetown Sierra Leone Eng Tchr 1962-64; Cardozo HS Eng Tchr 1964-69; Western HS Eng Tchr 1970-74; Ellington Schl of the Arts 11th-12th Grd Eng & 12th Grd AP Eng Tchr 1974-; *ai:* Eng Dept Chair; Integrated Curr Project Adv; NCTE 1987-; ASCD 1991-; VASCD 1996; Waterford Fndtn 1987-, Dir 1993-; *office:* Duke Ellington Schl Of Arts 35th & R Sts NW Washington DC 20007*

PELTON, ROBERT DANIEL, Social Studies Teacher; *b:* Bowling Green, OH; *m:* Linda Eachus; *c:* Laura Ann, Jennifer Marie; *ed:* OH Northern Univ (BA) His, Pol Sci, Comprehensive Soc Stud 1977, (JD) Law 1980; *cr:* Hauser & Atkinson Law Assoc 1980; Four Cty Joint Voc Schl Adult Ed Instr 1990-; Hicksville Exempted Village Schls Tchr, Chprsn 1981-; *ai:* Hicksville Ed Assn 1981-; OH Bar Assn 1983-; Amer Bar Assn 1984-; Grace United Meth Church 1981-; *office:* Hicksville HS 105 E Smith St Hicksville OH 43526

PELUSO, JOSEPH FRANK, Social Studies Teacher; *b:* Hartford, CT; *m:* Nancy Tinkham; *c:* Michael; *ed:* Cntrl CT St Univ (BS) His 1978, (MA) His 1989; Post Grad Stud CT Coll 1984; *cr:* Guilford HS Soc Stud Tchr 1978-; *ai:* Close-up Tchr Coord; NEA, CEA 1979-; Deep River Congregational Church, Deacon; Deep River Bd of Ed, Chm, Vice Chair; Natl Endowment for Hum Grant; *office:* Guilford HS New England Rd Guilford CT 06437

PELUSO, PATRICK ANTHONY, 5th Grade Teacher; *b:* Troy, NY; *ed:* St Univ of NY at Plattsburgh (BS) Elem Ed 1973; Coll of St Rose Comm Disorders 1978; *cr:* Shenendehowa Cntrl Elem Tchr 1973-; *ai:* Photography Club & Tchr; Yrbk Adv; Adult Ed; Shared Decision Making Comm; NYSUT 1973-, Bldg Chair; *office:* Shenendehowa Central Schl Rt 146 Clifton Park NY 12065

PELZEL, MICHAEL J., Fourth Grade Teacher; *b:* Cincinnati, OH; *m:* Nancy L. Thatcher; *ed:* Thomas More Coll (BA) Elem Ed 1973; Post Grad Work Xavier Univ; *cr:* St James Schl 3 Grd Tchr 1969-70; St Margaret Mary Schl 2-5 Grd Tchr 1970-; *ai:* Conducting After Schl Ger Lang Classes; NCEA 1970-; Hamilton Cty Genealogical Soc 1990-; Ger, Bohemian Heritage Soc 1991-; Kolphing Soc 1996-; Author 3 Books 1989-; Researcher, Lecturer Ger Genealogy; Articles Pub USA, Germany, Czech Republic; Greater Cincinnati Fnd Ger Stud Grant; *home:* 6205 Twinwillow Ln Cincinnati OH 45247

PELZER-BROWER, ROSE VERNITA, Magnet Coordinator; *b:* Santee, SC; *m:* Jerry Brower; *c:* Brenton, Gerard; *ed:* Claflin Coll (BS) Bio 1979; SC St Coll (MED) Ed 1981; Univ of MD Post Grad Stud Educl Doctorate Degree; *cr:* SC St Coll Shaw Air Base Educl Coord 1981-84; Francis Scott Key MS Sci Tchr 1984-92; Drew-Freeman MS Magnet Coord 1992-; *ai:* Sci, Engrng, Comm & Math Enrichment Clubs Spon; Sophisticated Sisters Co-Spon; Sci Fair Coord; Schl Bd Mgmt Team Mem; Testing Comm Mem; PGCEA, NEA 1984-; *office:* Drew-Freeman MS 2600 Brooks Dr Suitland MD 20746*

PEMBERTON, GLADYS FITZHUGH, Business Teacher; *b:* Fredericksburg, VA; *m:* Ronald Ambrose; *c:* Ron II, Melodi; *ed:* VA St Univ (BS) Bus Ed 1968; Howard Univ (MED) Guid & Cnslng 1972; *cr:* Theodore Roosevelt HS Bus Tchr 1968-; *ai:* Chair FBLA-PBL Natl Bd of Dirs; Fin Sec VSU Local Alumni Assn; FBLA, Sr Class, NHS Adv; AFT, WTU 1970-; NBEA, EBEA 1993-; DC_BEA 1975-, Bd Mem; NAFE 1993-; VSU Alumni Assn 1968-, VP, Treas, Fin Sec, Outstdng Mem; Delta Sigma Theta 1994-; Nations Bank Money Sills Adv Panel 1994; FBLA Mid Level Curr Adv Cncl 1993; DC-FBLA Adv of Yr Awd; Cafritz Fnd Tchr Fellow; FBLA Adv Natl Wall of Fame; *home:* 5910 Colfax Ave Alexandria VA 22311*

PEMBERTON, LAWRENCE,JR., Sixth Grade Math & Rdng Tchr; *b:* Huntington, WV; *c:* Adam, Amie; *ed:* OH Univ (BS) Ed 1980; 16 Grad Hrs Marshall Univ; 16 Grad Hrs OH Univ; *cr:* Chesapeake MS 5th-6th Grd Tchr 1980-; *ai:* 8th Grd Boys Bsktbl, HS Girsl Sftbl Coach; NEA, OEA 1990-; *office:* Chesapeake MS 10255 Cty Rd 1 Chesapeake OH 45619

PEMBROKE, JAMES, HS Guidance Counselor; *b:* Rochester, NY; *m:* Maureen Hayes; *c:* James Jr.; *ed:* Univ of New Haven (BA) Pol Sci 1972; Suffolk Univ (MED) Cnslr Ed 1976; *cr:* WRHS Guid Cnslr 1989-; *office:* Winnisquam Reg HS 367 W Main St Tilton NH 03276

PEMBROOK, LINDA A., Math Teacher; *b:* Elmira, NY; *ed:* SUNY Brockport (BS) Math 1972, (MS) Educl Math 1978; 27 Credit Hrs Cmptr Ed, Guid, Math; *cr:* Pavilion Cntrl Schl Math Tchr 1972-; *ai:* COMPACT Learning Comm; NYSUT 1972-; NCTM 1971-; NYS Math Tchrs Assn; St Joseph's Sodality 1994-; Tchr of Yr 1988; *office:* Pavilion Central Schl 7014 Big Tree Rd Pavilion NY 14525*

PENCAK, JOSEPH MICHAEL,JR., 6th-12th Grd Band Director; *b:* New Kensington, PA; *m:* Heather Renee Walker; *ed:* IN Univ of PA (BS) Music Ed 1993; *cr:* New Kensington Arnold Schl Dist Music Tchr, Band Dir 1993-; *ai:* Marching Band Dir; Music Edctrs Natl Conf, NEA 1993-; Percussive Arts Soc 1988-; WCMEA 1993-, NK Musical Soc 1986-; Parish Cncl 1993-, 1st VP; Parish Yth Group Coord 1995-; *office:* Valley HS 703 Stevenson Blvd New Kensington PA 15068*

PENCEK, DIANE R., First Grade Teacher; *b:* Pittsburgh, PA; *m:* Jack; *c:* Matthew, David; *ed:* East Stroudsburg U (BA) Elem Ed 1964; 48 Post Grad Credits; *cr:* Lackawanna Trl Schl System 1st Grd Tchr 1964-69, 1974-; *ai:* Strategic Planning & Course Dev Sci Comms; NEA 1964-; PSEA 1964-; Lackawanna Trl 1964-; *office:* Lackawanna Trl Elem Ctr College Ave Box 85 Factoryville PA 18419

PENCEK, THOMAS ANDREW, Assistant Professor of Finance; *b:* Dunkirk, NY; *ed:* SUNY Coll at Fredonia (BS) Acctng; MI St Univ (MBA) Fin 1982, (DBA) Fin 1988; *cr:* Rhode Island Coll Asst Prof 1984-88; Eastern IL Univ Asst Prof 1988-90; SUNY Coll at Fredonia Asst Prof 1990-; *ai:* Adv Fredonia St Bus Club; Fredonia Hlth Svc Advy Cncl; Fac Cncl; Fin Mngmt Assoc 1982-; Decision Scis Inst 1984-, Campus Rep; Acad of Fin Svc 1988-; Kociuszko Fnd 1995-; Articles Pub; Taught Eng in Poland Summer Lang Immersion Camp; *home:* 290 Temple St Fredonia NY 14063

PENDER, KAREN FRANZ, Language Arts & Reading Tchr; *b:* New York City, NY; *m:* Michael J.; *ed:* Queens Coll (BA) Eng, Scndry Ed 1980, (MS) Eng, Scndry Ed 1983; Addl 15 Credits; *cr:* Mark Murphy Schl SAT, Co-op Preparation Tchr; St Joseph Schl 7, 8 Grd Lang Arts, Rdng Tchr 1980-; *ai:* Coord 8th Grd, Grad, Spelling Bee, Lang Arts, Assembly; HS Adv; After Schl Ctr Tchr; Peer Group Facilitator; NEA, NCTE, Kappa Delta Pi, NCEA 1980-; John Golden Park Block Assn 1994-, VP; EBHA 1995-; Nature Conservancy 1980-; Winner NY St Eng Cncl 1990; Excl Tchng Awd; *office:* St Joseph Schl 2846 44th St Long Island City NY 11103*

PENDERGAST, JUDITH O'NEIL, Second Grade Teacher; *b:* Lynn, MA; *m:* David L.; *c:* Christine N., David J., Dana T., Dennis M., Daniel J., Cathleen T. Shay, Derek L.; *ed:* Salem St (BS) Elem Ed 1960; Rivier Coll (MA) Cmptrs in Ed 1987; Post Grad 30 Credit Hrs; *cr:* Nashua Pub Schls First Grd Tchr 1960-61; Derry Pub Schls First, 3rd Grds 1964-66; Private Kndgtn Owner, Tchr 1968-73; Bus Sales Person 1973-77; Derry Pub Schls Remedial Rdng Tchr 1 Yr, First Grd Tchr 10 Yrs, Cmptr Coord 3 Yrs, Second Grd Tchr 5 Yrs; *ai:* NG Kids Net Natl Geographic Cmptr Club Teach Two Sessions After Sch; 4th Grd Hello Unit; 5th Grd Solar Energy Unit; NEA, NH 1978-, Pres; Phi Kappa Delta 1988; *office:* South Range Schl 1 Drury Ln Derry NH 03038*

PENDERGRASS, JOHN R., 5th Grade Teacher; *b:* Cambridge, NY; *m:* M. Eileen Hopkins; *c:* John Jr.; *ed:* SUNY at Plattsburgh (BS) Elem Ed 1972; 30 Addl Hrs at SUNY at Oneonta; *cr:* Richmondville Cntrl Schl 5th Grd Tchr 1972-93; Cobleskill- Richmondville Cntrl 5th Grd Tchr 1993-.

PENDZIWIATR, WILLIAM J., Band Director & Music Teacher; *b:* Brooklyn, NY; *m:* Laverne Kindler; *c:* Jennifer; *ed:* St Univ of NY Coll at Fredonia (BM) Music Ed 1971, (MA) Music Ed 1995; PA Dept of Ed Masters Equivalency Music Ed 1991; Post Grad Courses & 2nd Elem Ed Cert Marywood Coll 1980; Working on Masters in Music Ed; *cr:* Prof Road Musician Flute, Sax, Piano Player 1972-74; Crestwood Schl Dist Music & Elem Tchr 1977-93; *ai:* Marching, Concert, Rock Bands; Jazz Ensemble; PSEA, NEA 1977-, Bldg Rep; PMEA, MENC 1983-; Started Music Prgm in Schl Dist; *office:* Crestwood HS 281 S Mountain Blvd Mountain Top PA 18707*

PENESTON, JEFFRY EDWARD, Science Teacher; *b:* Syracuse, NY; *m:* Jan Marie Hugo; *c:* Matthew, Kelly; *ed:* SUNY at Plattsburgh (BA) Environmental Sci, Geog 1981; Univ of VT (MS) Natural Re Planning 1983; Addl 45 Credits SUNY Coll of Environmental Sci, I Toward PHD; *cr:* Liverpool Schl Dist Sci Tchr 1986-; *ai:* Sci Ol Team Coach; Stu Rsrch Projects Adv; Stdnts Competing in In Engrng Fair Adv, Escort; NSTA 1986-; Camp Fire Boys, Girls Museum of Sci, Tech Most Outstdng Vol 1995; Greater Syracuse R Fair; *home:* 566 Cty Rt 54 Pennellville NY 13132*

PENG, GRACE N., Accounting Professor; *b:* Shanghai, China; *m* Hsiao-Ming; *c:* Althea L.; *ed:* Natl Taiwan Univ (BBA) Acctng 196 of DE (MBA) Acctng 1982; Attnd OH Univ; *cr:* Conrail Corp S Intern 1980; Pension Benefit Guaranty Corp Summer Intern Burroughs Corp System Analyst 1982-83; Muskingum Coll Acctng Sci Lecturer 1984-85; Muskingum Area Tech Coll Acctng Coo 1985-; *ai:* Acctng Club Adv; Fin Resourses; Prof Dev, Salary, Comms; OH Soc of CPAs 1985-, Quality Ed Task Force Mem; Gir Cncl 1993-, Bd Mem, Treas; *office:* Muskingum Area Tech Co Newark Rd Zanesville OH 43701

PENN, CARLTON A., Supvr of Media Services; *b:* Lakewood, Patricia Yohn; *c:* Theresa Ann, C. Samuel; *ed:* Glassboro St Coll (I Stud 1972, (MS) Educl Media 1977; Supvr Cert; *cr:* Southern Re Media Specialist 1972-79; Pineland Regnl HS Media Specialist, Dist Supvr of Media Svc; *ai:* NHS Adv 1980-; Restructuring, Comm; Pub Relations Supvr; Golden Age Club; Intergenerationa Stage Crew; WCAT-TV HS Channel; Amer Lib Assoc 1972-; Educ Assn 1982-; Lib Assoc of OCean Cty 1973, Pres 1976-78; Cntrl Regnl Lib Cooperative 1995; Ocean Cty Bd; Stafford Twp Histori 1976-; St Francis Parrish pre Canna Team 1986-; St Francis Rel E Tomas 1995; *office:* Pinelands Reg HS 565 Nugentown Rd B Tuckerton NJ 08087

PENN, DEBORAH, Assistant Professor; *b:* Stockton, CA; *m:* I Alan; *c:* Josh, Jeremy, Jessica; *ed:* Vennard Coll (BA) Bible & Ch 1978; Western Evangelical Seminary (MA) Rel Ed 1980; *cr:* Venna Asst Prof 1988-95; Circleville Coll Asst Prof 1996-; *ai:* Delta Epsil *office:* Circleville Coll PO Box 458 Circleville OH 43113

PENN, LARRY DARNELL, Administrator; *b:* Martinsville, VA; *m* Shayne; *c:* Daryl, Shayne; *ed:* Univ of MD Eastern Shore (BS) Ind 1973; Johns Hopkins Univ ME 1983; Bowie St Univ (ME) Supervision 1994; MS Equivalencey Admin, Supervision John H Univ; *cr:* Arnold Jr HS Instrl Arts Tchr 1973-76; Bayview MS Inds Tchr 1976-80; Bates MS Tech Ed Tchr 1980-94; Annapolis MS Vi 1995; *ai:* Sisters United Prgm Adv; Incentive Comm Chm; Tchrs A Anne Aundel Co 1973-; NEA 1974-; ASCD 1995-; Natl Assn of Prins 1995-; Tech Ed Assn 1989-; Omega Psi Phi 1972-; *office:* An MS 1399 Forest Dr Annapolis MD 21403

PENN, PATRICIA YOHN, Family & Consumer Sci Teac Somerville, NJ; *m:* Carlton Alfred; *c:* Theresa Ann, C. Samuel; *ed:* Madison Univ (BS) Home Ec Ed 1972; *cr:* Southern Regnl HS Tchr *ai:* Family & Consumer Sci Schlsp Comm; Southern Regnl HS S Comm; Sr Adult Schl Tchr; Homebound Instr; SNN Cooks; NEA NJEA 1972-; NJEA & NEA 1972-; St Francis Pre Cannon Comm Rel Ed 1990-; Taxpayer Org of Manahawkin & Surrounding S 1996-; *office:* Southern Regional HS 600 N Main St Manahawkin NJ

PENNA, JOHN PETER, Honors & AP Chemistry Teacher; *b:* Island, NY; *m:* Mary Ann Zaczyk; *c:* Paul, Joseph; *ed:* Cath Univ o (BA) Chem 1964; Rensselaer Polytech Inst (MS) Natural Sci 1971; R Univ EDD Pgm Sci Ed 21 Credit Hrs; OH St Univ Geology 9 Cred Monmouth Coll Supervision & Admin 6 Crdit Hrs; City Univ of NY 21 Credit Hrs; Kean Coll Geology 3 Credit Hrs; Montclair S Cooperative Learning 12 Credit Hrs; *cr:* DeLaSalle HS Chem, Earth Algebra Tchr 1964-69; CBA Sup of Sci & Chem Tchr 1969-72; St Chem Tchr 1972-73; Gov Livingstons Sci Sup, Chem, Earth Sci & A Tchr 1973-; *ai:* Sci Olympiad Coach St Champs 1994 & 1995; Jets Coach 2nd in St; Track & Tennis Coach 20 Yrs; NHS Adv 20 Y League Adv 10 Yrs; Panasonic Design Competition & St Sci Bowl St Sci Day Competition Adv; NJ Sci Convention 1980-, Presenter ACS Tchrs Affiliates 1990-, Chprsn 1994 & 1995, Merrill Awd; Tchrs Alliance Group 1992-; BSA 1954-, Dist Adv Chm, Cath Sc Awd; Fish Needy Family Group 1976-; Summer Pl Swim Club 1980 Piscataway Environmental 3 Yrs; St Sci Olympiad Outstdng Coac 1994 & 1995; Bisec Grant; Princeton Awd Finalist 1995 & 1996 Merrill Awd 1995; Tandy Prize for Tchng Excl 1996; Union Cty Re of the Yr; NSF Grant; *office:* Gov Livingston Reg HS 175 Watchun Berkeley Heights NJ 07922

PENNANZIO, JANET FRAILE, School Psychologist; *b:* Young OH; *m:* Hugh Barton; *ed:* Youngstown St (BA) Eng 1966; Kent S (MED) Cnslng 1968; 2 Yrs Post Masters Schl Psych; Case Western R 2 Hrs; Cleveland St 3 Hrs; *cr:* Youngstown City Schls Eng Tchr 19 Warrenwville Heights Schl Tchr, Cnslr 1967-68; Girard HS Cnslr 19 Austintown Schls Schl Psych Intern 1970-71; State of OH Psych 1971-72; Southeast Local Schls Schl Psychologist 1972-78; Diagno Evaluation Ctr Psychologist 1978-79; Campbell City Schls Psychologist 1979-; *ai:* Eng Dept Chprsn; Spec Ed Advy Comm; Ca Ed Assn; OEA; NEA; KASSP; OSPA; Happy Days BD; Butler A 1992-; Youngstown Historical Soc 1992-; BEAD Grant; Math Improv Grant; Playground Improvement Grant; *office:* Campbell City Sch 6th St Campbell OH 44405

PENNELL, DONALD KENNETH, Music Teacher & Choral D Newark, NJ; *m:* Suzanne Roemmele; *ed:* Kean Coll of NJ (BA) Mu 1974; Seton Hall Univ (MA) Ed 1978; Working on MM at Westm Choir Coll in Music Ed; Manhattan Schl of Music Piano Major; *cr:* Cty Coll Music Tchr 1978-81; Hillside Schl Dist Music Tchr 19 Holy Family Church Choir Dir & Organist 1989-; Rahway HS Cho 1983-; *ai:* Music Dir Schl Play; REA 1983-, Pres; NJEA, NEA NJMEA 1983-; ACDA 1983-; Kappa Delta Pi 1978-; Bloomfield Chorus 1986-92, Conductor; *office:* Rahway HS 1012 Madiso Rahway NJ 07065

PENNELL, KENT JOHN, Instrumental Music Teacher; *b:* Trento *m:* Gloria Holland; *ed:* West Chester Univ (BS) Music Ed 1979; U IL (MA) Music Composition 1982; *cr:* Saddle Brook HS Music Tchr, Dir 1982-85; Morris Knolls HS Asst Marching Band Dir 19 Bergenfield HS Music Tchr, Band Dir 1987-; *ai:* Jazz Ensemble, Ma Band, Stage Lighting Dir; North Jersey Band Festival Exec, HS Musi Comms; NJEA, BEA, MENC, NJMEA, MEBCI, IAJE 1987-; N 1987-, Region I Audition Chm; Hawthorne Caballeros 1975-, DCA Champions 1976, 1984-85, 1995; Guest Conductor NJ Band Festival *office:* Bergenfield HS 80 S Prospect Ave Bergenfield NJ 07621

PENNELL, MELISSA MC FARLAND, Associate Professor of En *b:* Lorain, OH; *m:* Stephen A.; *ed:* Coll of William & Mary (BA) Sociology 1977; Brown Univ (MA) Eng 1981, (PHD) Eng 1984; *cr:* MA at Lowell Lecturer 1983-85, Asst Prof Eng 1985-91, Asst to Pr 1994-, Assoc Prof Eng 1991-; *ai:* Adv Lit Soc 1992-95; Co-Chair S Action Team, Advising Task Force; Lib Futures, Gen Ed, Comm Svc Dept Outreach Comms; Modern Lang Assn 1984-; Northeast Mod Assn 1987-, Session Chair; Amer Stud Assn 1987-; Exemplary Fa 1994; Articles Pub; Regnl Judge Natl His Day; Deliver Papers Prof C Talk, Lead Discussions, Wkshps Local Libs, Museums; *office:* Univ O At Lowell 1 University Ave Lowell MA 01854

ER, BETTY, Chemistry & Physics Teacher; *c:* Ted, Jo Ann Meyer, *l:* Defiance Coll (BS) Ed, Math Sci 1963; Bowling Green St Univ d 1985; *cr:* Oakwood HS Sci, Math Tchr 1962-63; Jewell HS Sci, chr 1963-64; Tinora Jr HS & HS Sci, Math Tchr 1965-66, 1972-74; w HS Sci, Math Tchr 1978-; *ai:* Adv NHS, Stu Cncl; Jets Teams SECO 1982-; Sherwood United Meth 1979-; Martha Holdings Scholar; *office:* Fairview HS 6289 US Highway 127 Sherwood OH

EWELL, MARGARET ANNE, Eng, Psych & Journalism Tchr; *b:* ry, MD; *ed:* Salisbury St Univ (BA) Eng 1968, (MA) Psych 1978; tna Life & Casualty Group Hlth Claims Processor 1968-69; ter Cty Schl Tchr 1970-75; Holly Ctr Cottage Dir 1975-78; mery Cty Schl Tchr 1979-81; Worcester Cty Schl Tchr 1981-; *ai:* aper Adv; Humane Soc of Wicomico Co 1970-, 20 Yrs on Bd Achvmt t John's Meth Church, Lifetime Mem; Master's Thesis Rsrch ed at Amer Psychological Assn 1979; *office:* Snow Hill HS 305 S St Snow Hill MD 21863

EY, LINDA HELEN, Music Teacher & Drama Instr; *b:* nock, NJ; *ed:* Fordham Univ (MS) Ed. Admin 1986; Univ of CT Music 1996; Hartt Schl of Music B in Music Ed 1979; Attnd Univ of d; *cr:* Middletown HS Choral Dir 1979-82; Bronxville MS, HS Choral Dir, General Music Instr 1983-87; Canaan Pub Schl Music 1987-89; Ardsley MS, HS Choral Prgm, Drama Dir 1989-93; Port HS Choral Prgm, Drama Dir, Music Theory, Harmony, AP Theory 93-; *ai:* Fall, Spring Dramatic & Musical Performances; NY Area Music Festival, NY All-St; Select Choral Ensemble, Private Music MENC, WCSMA, NYSSMA, IAJA, AAVW, ACDA; MENC red Music Ed; Whos Who in Amer Ed; *home:* 151 Fenimore Rd Apt Mamaroneck NY 10543

INGTON, GALINDA OSTRINSKI, Russian & Spanish Teacher; *b:* ques, Venezuela SA; *m:* Robert T.; *c:* Andrew, Robert, Katherine; thern CT (BS) Span, Russian 1972; Cntrl CT Univ (MS) Span 1976; cott Jr HS Span, Russian Tchr 1972-79; Hall HS Span, Russian Tchr Conard HS Span, Russian Tchr 1983-; *ai:* Span Club Adv; ACTR COLT; NEA 1972-; Tchng Russian Using Teleconferencing nition; Assisted Congressional Office of Tech Assessment in ation of Video Tape; Presenter at Teleconferencing Presentations; Hall HS 975 N Main St W Hartford CT 06117

INGTON, JOHN ROBERT, Science & Biology Teacher; *b:* East and, OH; *m:* Heather Gambrill; *c:* Nathan, Michael; *ed:* Lakeland Coll (AA) Lbrl Arts 1976; Lake Erie Coll (BS) Ed & Bio-Magnum aude 1978; 7 Grad Credit Hrs Environmental Sci; *cr:* Willowick Jr ci Tchr 1978-84; Willoughby South High Sci & Bio Tchr 1984-; *ai:* lon Team Asst; NEA, OEA, WETA 1978-, Mem; Red Oak Camp Inc Cnslr & Dir; Holden Arboretum 1966-; Lake Erie Coll Awd of tion in Field of Bio 1977; Whos Who Among Amers Coll & Univ 1977; Martha Holden Jennings Summer Sci Participant 1986; *office:* ghby South HS 5000 Shankland Rd Willoughby OH 44094

ISI, ANNETTE BONVENTRE, Chairperson & Spanish Teacher; *b:* ork City, NY; *m:* Albert; *c:* Christopher, Christiane; *ed:* St Johns BA) Span 1966; Columbia Univ (MA) Span 1974; *cr:* Hewlitt HS chr 1966-67; Island Trees HS Span Tchr & Chprsn 1989-; *ai:* Pupil Mid Sts Steering & Stu of Month Comms; LiLT 1989-; NYSAFT FLACS 1995-; *office:* Island Trees HS Straight Ln Levittown NY

ISI, RONALD ANTHONY, Biology Teacher; *b:* New York City, Myrna Garayua; *c:* Jason, Jessica; *ed:* SUNY Stony Brook (BS) Bio MA) Lbrl Stud 1974; 90 Addl Hrs; *cr:* Newfield HS Sci Tchr 1970; T, Middle Cntry Tchrs Assn 1970-; MCTA Grievance Comm 1980-, hprsn; Nature Conservancy 1990-; Pine Barrens Soc 1993-; *office:* eld HS 145 Marshall Dr Selden NY 11784

ISI, TERRI LAREAU, Prof of Business Admin; *b:* Albany, NY; *m:* t; *c:* Matthew, Jarad, Nathan; *ed:* SUNY at Albany (BS) Bus Ed MS) Bus Ed 1975; *cr:* St of NY Municipal Rsrch Asst 1970-72; Cath HS Bus Instr 1972-78; Hudson Vly Comm Coll Prof 1979-; *ai:* Fac VP; HVCC Fac Hnrs Comm; Affirmative Action Advy Panel; HVCC Awd for Excl in Tchng; *office:* Hudson Valley Comm Coll 80 nburgh Ave Troy NY 12180

OCK, HOLLY A., Professor of Psychology; *b:* Syracuse, NY; *m:* E.; *c:* David H., Jessic A.; *ed:* SUNY at Oswego (BS) Elem Ed Russell Sage Coll (MA) Comm Psych 1983; *cr:* Rush Henrietta Cntrl chr 1965-69; Windemere Blvd Schl Tchr 1969-70; Carandaigua City Dist Tchr 1970-74; Hudson Vly Comm Coll Prof 1981-; *ai:* Acad Sec; Coord Coll Forum; Educl Policies, Stans Comm; Assessment Chair; Fac Handbook Comm Chair; NYS Assn Two Yr Colls 1988-, gion IV Act; AAUW 1990-; Amer Psychological Assn 1980-; Trinity Church 1978-, Chair Worship Commission; Amer Heart Assn 1996-, Tournament Comm; Pres Awd Excl Tchng; Chancellors Awd Excl Nom; Gen Ed Assessment Author, Presenter; Writing Across the resenter; Admin Intern Office of Pres; *office:* Hudson Valley Comm 0 Vandenburgh Ave Troy NY 12180

Y, PATRICIA ANN, Sixth Grade Teacher; *b:* Dayton, OH; *m:* R. as; *c:* Scott, Tricia; *ed:* Miami Univ (BS) Ed 1963; Wright St U (ME) Concord Schl Fifth, Sixth Grd Tchr 1961-92; Hook Schl Sixth Grd 1995-; *ai:* NEA, OEA 1961-; TCEA 1964; TWIG 1992-, Chprs, ; *home:* 2590 Seneca Dr Troy OH 45373

, DOUGLAS R., Ecology & Biology Teacher; *b:* Cortland, NY; *m:* Davies; *c:* Amy Lynn, Chad Michael, Matthew Douglas; *ed:* St Univ at Cortland (BS) Scndry Bio Ed 1967, (MS) Environmental Sci 1971; of Northern CO (PHD) Alpine Ecology; Attnd CO St Univ 18 Hrs, ll Univ 18 Hrs, Stony Brook Univ 12 Hrs; *cr:* Cortland HS Sci Tchr 58; South Huntington Schls Bio Tchr 1968-70; New Hartford Sr HS Ecology Instr 1970-; *ai:* Outdoor Ed Coord; Ecology Club, Zooster C Adv; Envirothon Coach; SOS Adv; Track Coach; Sigma Xi 1984-; 1986-, NYS Bio Tchr of Yr 1987; NYS Conservation Cncl, rvation Educator of Yr 1995; NSF Research in Boreal Ecology; ll Inst for Bio Tchrs Hughes Grant; Co-Author of Birds of the ndacks & Wildflowers of the Northeast; EPA Spec Awd of Merit; New Hartford Sr HS 33 Oxford Rd New Hartford NY 13413*

OLA, CATHERINE A., English & Philosophy Teacher; *b:* Mineola, *m:* Peter F. Randazzo; *c:* Sarah; *ed:* SUNY at Stony Brook (BA) sophy & Comparative Rels 1982, (MA) Lbrl Stud 1990; 60 Addl Hrs; *cr:* Patchogue-Medford HS Eng & Philosophy Tchr 1986-; *ai:* T 1986-; NYSUT 1986-; *office:* Patchogue-Medford HS Buffalo Ave ord NY 11763*

VOSE, CINDY MC KEE, Instrumental Instructor; *b:* Clearfield, PA; istina, Kelley; *ed:* Clarion Univ (BS) Music 1980; *cr:* Taught ely 1981-86; West Branch Elem Schl Tchr 1986-; *ai:* NEA, PSEA, A, MENC 1986-; *office:* West Branch Elem Schl Rd 2 Box 194 sdale PA 16858*

ZA, CHARLES,JR., High School English Teacher; *b:* Hammonton, *l:* Saint Josephs Univ (BA) Eng 1990; *cr:* Mainland Regnl Eng Tchr ; *ai:* Boys Tennis Coach; Tchr of Yr 2nd Runner-Up; *office:* Mainland nal Schl 1301 Oak Ave Linwood NJ 08221

PEOPLES, JOYCE LEE (DENNIS), Fifth Grade Teacher; *b:* Cambridge, OH; *m:* Timothy E.; *c:* Brian, Brad; *ed:* Muskingum Coll (BSME) Music Ed 1979, (BSEE) Elem Ed 1979; Univ of Dayton (MED) Cnslng, Child Yth Dev 1993; *cr:* Dexter City Jr HS 7th-8th Grd Sci Tchr 1979; Caldwell MS 5th-6th Grd Tchr 1979-82, 5th Grd Tchr 1982-88; Caldwell Elem Schl 5th Grd Tchr 1988-; *ai:* Soc Stud Textbook Adoption Comm; Curr Comm; Math Competency Testing; NEA, OEA, Caldwell Tchrs Assn 1979-; PTO 1980-81; Church of Christ.*

PEPE, JOHN JOSEPH, Band Director; *b:* Newark, NJ; *m:* Linda Fabian; *c:* Sarah, Jennifer, Joseph, William; *ed:* Kean Coll (BA) Music 1975; Grad Stud Westchester Univ; *cr:* Belleville MS Instrumental Music, Band Dir 1975-77, Band Dir 1977-78; Englewood MS Instrumental, Band Dir 1978-81; Manville HS Band Dir 1985-; *ai:* Marching, Stage, Concert Bands Dir; Percussion Ensemble Dir; Weight Room, Fitness Coach; NEA, NJEA 1975-; Snare Drum Solo Paul Price Publications; *office:* Manville HS 1100 Brooks Blvd Manville NJ 08835*

PEPEKANOS, GEORGE, Teaching Assistant; *b:* Athens, Greece; *ed:* Univ of Patras (BA) Math 1989; Univ of DE (MS) Applied Math 1993; Working Towards PHD; *cr:* Univ of DE Tchng Asst 1991-93, Rsrch Asst 1993-94, Tchng Asst 1994-; *ai:* Siam Journal of Applied Math 1982; Amer Mathematical Soc 1992-; *office:* Univ Of DE Dept of Mathematics Newark DE 19716

PEPIN, LINDA SAYWARD, Spanish Teacher; *b:* Burlington, VT; *m:* Arthur L. Jr.; *c:* Melissa Brady, Christopher Arthur; *ed:* Cntrl CT St Univ (BS) Fr Lit 1966; Univ of CT (MA) Latin Amer, Caribbean Stud 1987; Trinity Coll 30 Hrs Toward MA; Attnd Forester Lang Inst, Lit Intnl Stud Inst, Cntrl CT St Univ; *cr:* Bloomfield HS Fr Tchr 1966-68; Newington HS Fr, Span Tchr 1976-; *ai:* Span Natl Hnr Soc Adv; Sister Schl Prgm Coord 2nd Grd, HS Inner City Stdnts; Frgn Lang Curr Comm; Fac Advy Bd; NHS Selection Comm; AATSP 1986-, Natl Chptr Awd Long Term Act 1995; CT Org of Lang Tchrs 1976-; NEA, CEA 1976-; New England Cncl of Latin Amer Stud 1984-; Casa de Elderly Lang Tutor Vol; Warren Bourgue Awd; Prgm Dev Span IV Grant; Capitol Region Ed Cncl Sister Schl Grant 1995-96; *office:* Newington HS 605 Willard Ave Newington CT 06111*

PEPITONE, BRENDA KOLENTUS, English Teacher; *b:* Richmond, IN; *c:* Staci; *ed:* Univ of Dayton (BA) Eng 1963, (MS) Ed, Eng 1978; OH Writing Project Miami Univ at Oxford 1980; Freedom Fnd 1984; Wright St Univ Grad Eng Classes; *cr:* Milton Union HS Sub Tchr 1974-76; Huber Hghts Schl Eng Tchr 1976-; Advanced Placement ETS Reader 1990-; *ai:* Lit Magazine Adv; NEA, OEA 1980-; Tchr of Yr 1984; *office:* Wayne HS 5400 Chambersburg Rd Dayton OH 45424

PEPOLI, ANTHONY GERARD, 6th-8th Grade Science Teacher; *b:* Pottsville, PA; *m:* Sandra Ann Tutko; *ed:* Kutztown Univ of Pa (BS) Ed, Elem & Sci 1989; 21 Grad Credit Hrs Cnslng; *cr:* Ammunciation Schl MS Sci Tchr 1992-95; St Theresa Schl MS sci 1995-; *ai:* italian Lang, Music Appreciation and Guitar instr; Stu Choir; Yrbk; Guitar Folk Group; NCEA 1993-; *office:* Saint Theresa Schl 1200 Bridge Dr New Cumberland PA 17070

PEPONAKIS-MATZNER, ANDREA RUTH, Spanish Teacher; *b:* Astoria, NY; *c:* Thomas, Nicola; *ed:* Queens Coll (BS) Span, Ed 1979; St Johns Univ (MS) Biling Ed 1981, (PD) Admin 1986; 15 Post Grad Credit Hrs; *cr:* Long Island City HS Span Tchr 1979-81; Flushing HS Span Tchr 1081-86; Grover Cleveland HS Span Tchr 1988-89; WM Floyd HS Span Tchr 1990-; *ai:* Key Club Adv Awd 3 Yrs; Mastic Sports Club Spon, Coach 1993-; AFT 1989-; Biling Flwshp Masters Degree; Admin Flwshp Prof Degree; *office:* William Floyd HS 240 Mastic Beach Rd Mastic Beach NY 11951*

PEPOY, MARYA ALEXANDRA, HS PE Teacher & Ath Trainer; *b:* Johnstown, PA; *ed:* Slippery Rock Univ (BS) PE, Hlth 1979, (MED) PE 1988; *cr:* Forest Hills Jr HS PE Tchr, Coach 1979-83; Sacred Heart Elem PE Tchr, Coach 1984; Chamberlain HS PE Tchr, Coach 1984-86; Conemaugh Township HS PE Tchr, Ath Trainer, Strength Coach 1986-; *ai:* Ath Trainer for Sports; Strength Coach; Stdnts Assistance Prgm; AAHPERD, PAHPERD, PSEA, NEA 1986-; NSCA 1990-; Sftbl Coach of Yr Chamberlain HS 1985; Selected for Inclusion of Marquis Who's Who in Amer 1993; *office:* Conemaugh Township Area HS W Campus Ave Davidsville PA 15928

PEQUIGNOT, JANE KREGER, Reading Specialist; *b:* Liberty, PA; *m:* Edward; *c:* Paula, Kelly; *ed:* Mansfield St Coll (BS) Elem Ed 1972, (MS) Elem Ed 1977; Rdng Specialist Cert 1976; Addl 15 Credit Hrs at Various Insts in the Areas of Cmptrs & Cooperative Learning; *cr:* Cogan House Elem Schl Kndgtn Tchr 1973-74, 1st Grd Tchr 1974-78; Liberty Elem Schl 3rd Grd Tchr 1978-79, Transitional 1st-3rd Grd Tchr 1979-80, 1st Grd Tchr 1980-93, Rdng Specialist 1993-; *ai:* Providing Evening Parent Involvement Process Writing Wkshps for Title I Stdnts & Their Parents; PSEA 1972-73; NEA 1973-; Amer Heart Assn, Vol; Presentor at Mansfield Univs Whole Lang Festival April 1992; Mentor for Southern Tioga Schl Dists Tchr Induction Plan 1993-94; *office:* Liberty Elem Schl RR 1 Box 2c Liberty PA 16930

PERARIA, MELISSA KRAMER, English Teacher; *b:* Philadelphia, PN; *m:* Brian C.; *c:* Hope Anne; *ed:* Glassboro St Coll (BA) Eng 1992; *cr:* Edgewood Jr HS Eng Tchr 1992-93; Cherokee HS Eng Tchr 1993-; *ai:* Color Guard for Marching Band 1993-94; Mildred H Maxon Eng Awd; *office:* Cherokee HS Willowbend Rd Marlton NJ 08053

PERCEY, JAMES W., 9th Grade Earth Science Tchr; *b:* Bloomsburg, PA; *m:* Paulette L. Kester; *c:* Jacob Paul, Brandon; *ed:* West Chester Univ (MA) Phys, Earth Sci 1992; *cr:* St Coll Int HS Earth Sci Tchr 1988; North Penn Jr HS Earth Sci Tchr 1988-90; Pleasant Vly HS Earth Sci Tchr 1990-; *ai:* Soccer, Bsbl Coach; Chess Club Adv; PSEA 1988-; NEA 1988-; *office:* Pleasant Valley Schl Dist Rt 115 Brodheadsville PA 18322

PERCUSSI, LINDA A., Math Teacher; *b:* Jersey City, NJ; *ed:* Paterson St Coll (BA) Eng, Math 1969; E Stroudsburg Univ (MED) Schl Admin 1983; Post Grad at Jersey City St Coll; *cr:* Manchester Reg HS Eng, Speech Tchr 1969-71; Morris Cath HS Math Tchr 1971-77; Mt Olive HS Math Tchr 1977-; Centenary Coll Math Instr 1988-90; Sussex Cty Comm Coll Math Instr 1990-93; *ai:* Liaison Comm; Steering Comm for Mid Sts Evaluation Chprsn; EAMO, NJEA, NEA 1977-; N Warren Reg Bd of Ed 1982-85, Pres; Cntrl Schl Adv Comm 1992-93; Independence Tsp Planning Bd 1993-; 6 Mid Sts Schl Evaluations; *office:* Mt Olive HS Cory Rd Flanders NJ 07836*

PERDUE, SHARON M., Fifth Grade Teacher; *b:* Dunkirk, NY; *m:* Larry D.; *c:* Brian L.; *ed:* SUNY at Fredonia (BA) Scndry Soc Stud 1966, (MS) Elem Ed 1969; Grad Courses at Syracuse Univ; *cr:* Bellamy AFB Schl 5th Grd Tchr 1966-67; Gowanda Elem Schl K-6th Grd Summer Rdng Tchr 1968, 5th Grd Tchr 1967-; *ai:* SUNY at Fredonia Summer Sci Wkshps; Impact Team; BOCES Soc Stud Curr Writing; Support Team; Union Negotiatior; Field Trip Coord; Sunshine & Handbook Comm; Mentor; Exit Outcomes Comm, Chrprsn; Bldg Improvement Team; NYSUT 1966-, Wkshps Negotiator; United Meth Women 1990-, VP 2 Yrs, Chprsn; Ecumenical Chrstn Unity, Chprsn; Schl5 Parents Club 1979-80, Pres; DHS Band & Sports Booster; Little League Team Mother; Pastor-Parish Relations, Chprsn; Channel 7 Tchr Recognition Prgm Nom; Most Popular Tchr 1967; *office:* Gowanda Elem Schl School St Gowanda NY 14070

PEREKUPKA, WALTER, Mathematics Teacher; *b:* Philadelphia, PA; *m:* Joan Edna Ault; *c:* Matthew, Michael; *ed:* West Chester Univ (BS) Math 1978; Penn St Univ (MS) Ed 1991; *cr:* Chichester Sr HS Math Tchr 1978-; *ai:* Head Coach Girls' Var Vlybl, Sftbl; Math Club; NEA, PACE, CEA, NCTM 1978-; Springfield AA 1988-; *office:* Chichester Sr HS 3333 Chichester Ave Boothwyn PA 19061*

PEREZ, CATHERINE HERZOG, Chemistry Teacher; *b:* Covington, KY; *m:* Steven; *c:* Julie, Christie Perez-Johnson; *ed:* Univ of South FL (BS) Chem Ed 1967, (MS) Chem 1974; Univ of Rochester (MS) Ed 1994; Currently Working on Doctor of Ed; *cr:* Hillsborough Cty Chem Tchr 1967-69; Fairport HS Chem Tchr 1974-; *ai:* Sci Club Adv; NYSUT; Kappa Delta Pi 1990-; Pi Mu Epsilon; Univ of Chicago Tchr Awd by Stdnts; Sabbatical for Fairport 1990; Masters Thesis Pub; *office:* Fairport HS 1358 Ayrault Rd Fairport NY 14450

PEREZ, CHRISTINE MORALES, Special Education Teacher; *b:* New York City, NY; *c:* Marc Louis; *ed:* Herbert H. Lehman Coll (BA) Music 1973, (MS) Learning Disabilities 1980; 30 Credit Hrs Admin Spec Ed Coll of New Rochelle 1987; 9 Credit Hrs Schl Psych Grad Prgm USM; *cr:* PS 26 Elem Schl Tchr 1973-75; SPS 31 Resource Room Tchr Spec Ed 1979-84; Bronx Spec Ed Regnl Office SETRC Tchr Trainer, Educl Evaluator 1984-87; Phillips MS Composite Room Tchr 1987-; *ai:* MS Yrbk, Schl Newspaper Fac Advs; Stu Store Fac Mgr; MTA, NEA 1987-; CEC 1980-; ME Spec Ed Support Network 1987-; Written Numerous Grants; *office:* Phillips MS RR 1 Box 272 Phillips ME 04966*

PEREZ, EILEEN, Administrative Assistant; *b:* New York City, NY; *ed:* Hunter Coll of CUNY (BA) Psych & Ed 1981, (MS) Ed & Rdng 1985; City Coll of CUNY (MS) Admin & Supervision 1995; 30 Credits Above MS at Coll of New Rochelle & Brooklyn Coll 1993; *cr:* Hunter Coll Office of Tchr Placement Asst to Dir 1978-81; Pub Schl 50 5th Grd Tchr 1981-82; Pub Schl 146 5th Grd Tchr 1981-82, 2nd & 4th Grd After-Schl Tchr 1982-83, 4th & 6th Grd Classes Tchr 1982-93, 2nd Grd After-Schl Rdng Tchr 1988-89, Hnr Roll Mem & Schl Aide Comm Liaison 1989-, 2nd Grd Tchrs Mentor 1990-91, 1st-3rd Grds Supvr 1993-95, Admin Asst & Curr Coord 1993-; *ai:* Design Curr Ldr 1990-; Grad, 6th Grd Consultant, Liasion & Ldr 1991-; Schoolwide Panel for Selection of Prin Mem 1992-93; Dist-wide & Schoolwide Screening Panel for the Selection of the Asst Prin 1993; Dist Pilot Project Mem for Math, Sci, Tech & Urban Initiative Awd Pgm; Kappa Delta Pi 1980-; AFT 1981-; UFT 1981-; PREA 1993-; ASCD 1993-; Sarah F Kramer Post Grad Schlsp; Article Pub.

PEREZ, M. JUDY, HS Spanish & French Teacher; *b:* Oneinda, NY; *m:* Joseph; *ed:* Assumption Coll (MA) Fr 1968; Attnd Sorbonne France & Dante Aligheri Italy; *cr:* Lana HI Lang Tchr 1965-66; Worcester MA Lang Tchr 1966-68; West Islip NY Lang Tchr 1968-71; North Reading MA Lang Tchr 1975-; *ai:* After Schl Tutoring; NEA 1965-; NREA, MTA, MAFLA & AATSP 1975-; Historical Soc 1992-.

PEREZ, MARK DAVID, Band Director; *b:* Perth Amboy, NJ; *ed:* Temple Univ (BSME) Music Ed 1987; Villanova Univ Addl Stud; *cr:* Churchill JHS Band Dir 1987-; *ai:* Wind Ensemble Dir; Chamber Music Ensemble Adv; NEA, NJEA, NJMEA, CJMEA 1987-; Amer Fed of Musicians 1989-; Garden St Symphonic Band 1989-; Cntrl Jersey Music Edctrs Assn, Intermediate Band Conductor 1991, Mgr 1992.

PEREZ, NORA ELENA, Bilingual Kindergarten Teacher; *b:* Santiago, Cuba; *ed:* CCNY (BA) Art, Ed 1979; Queens Coll (MS) Early Chldhd Ed 1985; *cr:* Biling Pupil Svc Bil-Para Prof 1976-79; PS 149 Q Biling K-1 Tchr 1980-94, Biling-ESL Coord 1994-95; Biling K Tchr 1995-; *ai:* AFT, UFT 1976-; *office:* PS 149 Q 93-11 34th Ave Flushing NY 11372

PEREZ, SAUNDRA TROVA, English Teacher; *b:* Pittsfield, MA; *m:* Santiago Marrero; *c:* Peter J., J. Christian, Marcus A.; *ed:* Univ of MA (BA) Eng 1960; Attnd Univ of OK, Besancow France; *cr:* Norton HS Fr Tchr 1960-63; Norton MS Eng Tchr 1978-; *ai:* NEA, NTA 1978-; NCTE 1979-; *office:* Norton MS 64 W Main St Norton MA 02766

PERFECT, KATHY ANN, Fourth Grade Teacher; *b:* Akron, OH; *m:* William H.; *c:* Alisa, Andrew; *ed:* Univ of Akron (BA) Elem Ed 1982; Kent St Univ (MS) Rdng 1991; Kent St Univ Doctoral Candidate 1996; *cr:* St Vincent Grd Schl 4th Grd Tchr 1968-70, 5th Grd Tchr 1971-73; Windham Schls LD Tutor 1983; Crestwood MS 7th-8th Grd Lang Arts Tchr 1983-84; Mantua Village Elem 4th Grd Tchr 1984-, 3rd Grd Tchr 1995-; *ai:* NEA, CEA, NCATE & OCTELA 1983-; IRA 1993-; ASCD; Art Pub Natl Racquetball 1986; *home:* 116 Spell Rd Kent OH 44240

PERFETTO, JANICE PEDOTO, Sixth Grade Teacher; *b:* Hoboken, NJ; *m:* John; *ed:* William Paterson Coll (BA) Elem Ed 1979; 9 Credit Hrs of Post Grad Work; *cr:* Cresskill HS 7th & 8th Grd Title I Tchr 1980-84; Merritt Meml Schl 5th & 6th Grd Elem Schl Tchr 1984-; *ai:* Math, Prins Cabinet & Schedule Comms; NJEA, NEA 1984-; CEA 1984-, Bldg Rep; Recipient of the Governors Tchr Recognition Awd 1994-95; *office:* Merritt Memorial Elem Schl 1 Dogwood Ln Cresskill NJ 07626*

PERGOLA, PHILLIP R., HS English Teacher & Coach; *b:* New Eagle, PA; *m:* Geraldine Francis Haluch; *c:* Ryan, Kevin; *ed:* Clarion Univ of PA (BS) Eng & Rdng 1968; Univ of Pittsburgh (MS) Safety Ed 1973; *cr:* Mon Valley Cath Eng Tchr 1968-71, Driver Ed Instr 1971-82; Carroll Jr High Eng Tchr 1982-85; Ringgold HS Eng Tchr 1985-; *ai:* Yrbk Spon; Var Bsktbl Coach; REA, PSEA & NEA 1971-; Elks 1988-; AP Big Schl Coach of Yr 1990; WPIAL Section Coach of Yr 7 Times; *office:* Ringgold HS Rd 4 Box 604-A Monongahela PA 15063

PERGOLIZZI, GRACE GENOVESI, Italian & Spanish Teacher; *b:* Brooklyn, NY; *c:* Anthony Christopher, Daniel Milo; *ed:* St John's (BA) Romance Lang 1958; New Paltz (MA) Ed 1959; Summer Inst; MC Gill Univ Fr; C. W. Post Span; *cr:* East Meadow Schl 2nd Grd Tchr 1957-58; Plainview Schl 4th Grd Tchr 1959-60; Smithtown HS Span, Italian Tchr 1969-; *ai:* Italian Hnr Soc Founder, Adv for Smithtown HS W 1977-91 Intnl Nights; Italina Nights; NYSUT, LILT 1969-; Smithtown Arts Cncl 1973-, Pres, Founder, Bd Mem 15 Yrs; *office:* Smithtown HS 660 Meadow Rd Smithtown NY 11787

PERILLI, JOSEPH DOMINIC, Sixth Grade Teacher; *b:* Palmerton, PA; *m:* Ruth Lechleitner; *c:* Joseph; *ed:* Bloomsburg Univ (BS) Elem Ed 1968, (MED) Elem Ed 1971; *cr:* Blue Mt Schl Dist 6th Grd Tchr 1968-69; Tamaqua Schl Dist 6th Grd Tchr 1969-, Head Tchr 1976-; *ai:* Tamaqua Ed Assn 1969-, Bldg Rep; PSEA, NEA 1968-; Recipient Gift ot Time Awd 1992; *office:* West Penn Elem Schl RD 2 New Ringgold PA 17960

PERILLO, SUSAN JOAN, Mathematics Teacher; *b:* Southington, CT; *ed:* Albertus Magnus Coll (BA) Math 1981; Cntrl CT St Univ (MS) Math 1988; 18 Post Grad Hrs; *cr:* St Paul Cath HS Math Tchr 1981-88; Ethel Walker Schl Math Tchr 1988-; *ai:* Acad Review Bd Chair; Selecting Educl Enrichment Events Comm; NCTM, ATOMIC 1986-; ASCD 1988-; *office:* Ethel Walker Schl 230 Bushy Hill Rd Simsbury CT 06070

PERILLO, UMBERTA, Italian Teacher; *b:* Italy; *ed:* SUNY at Albany (BA) Eng 1968; 30 Credit Hrs; Middlebury Coll 26 Credit Hrs; St Rose Coll 6 Credit Hrs; *cr:* Schalmont HS Eng Tchr 1968-69; Hudson HS Eng & Italian Tchr 1972-; *ai:* Shared Decision Bldg & Shared Decision Dist Comms; Strategic Planning Dist; AFT 1972-; Bus & Prof Womens Group 1979-82; SCOUT Bus Merchant Group 1979-82; Current Lang Consultant for the St Ed Dept 1983; Test Writer for the Testing Bureau of St Ed Dept; *office:* Hudson HS Harry Howard Ave Hudson NY 12534

PERINI, MARIE HILL, Vocal Music Teacher; *b:* Buffalo, NY; *m:* Richard; *c:* Robert, Michael; *ed:* Rosary Hill Coll (BS) Music Ed 1972; Fredonia St Coll (MM) Music Ed 1980; Post Grad Stud Univ of Buffalo 1990-; Buffalo Schl of the Bible 1995-; *cr:* Sacred Heart Acad Vocal Music

Dir 1977-77; Holland HS Vocal Music Dir 1990-; *ai:* Musical Director, Select Ensemble; NYSSMA Vocal Adjudicator; NYSSMA, MENC 1969-; Erie Cty Music Educators Assn 1990-; Holland Tchr's Assn 1990-; Covenant Comm Church, Music Dir; Nationally Registered Music Educator MENC 1993-; Who's Who 1976,1994; *office:* Holland HS 103 Canada St Holland NY 14080*

PERKEY, SUSAN WALKER, First Grade Teacher; *b:* Camden, NJ; *m:* Richard M.; *c:* Kevin, John; *ed:* OH Wesleyan Univ (BA) Elem Ed 1972; Shippensburg Univ (MA) Rdng 1974; *cr:* West Creek Hills Schl First Grd Tchr 1972-; *ai:* Prof Dev, Math Comms; Mentor, Cooperating Tchr; Kappa Delta Pi 1970-, Sec; East Pennsboro Ed Assn 1972-; *office:* West Creek Hills Elem Schl 400 Erford Rd Camp Hill PA 17011*

PERKINS, BETH ANNE, Lecturer on Philosophy; *b:* Wilmington, OH; *m:* Barry R. Canter; *c:* Julie Jones, Angela Rachel Smith, Robert Partida; *ed:* Univ of Cincinnati (BA) Philosophy 1985, (MA) Philosophy; 322 Grad Credit Hrs Philosophy; *cr:* Northern KY Univ Philosophy Instr 1983-; Wilmington Coll Philosophy Instr 1986-88; Clark St Philosophy Instr 1991-93; Univ of Cincinnati Philosophy Instr 1992-; *ai:* Curr Comm; PIRT Comm Improve Tchng; Soc Women in Philosophy, Amer Philosophical Assn 1981-; Philosophers Concerned for Peace 1985-; Natl Women's Stud Assn 1982-; Taft Fellowship; Univ Grad Schlsp 1981-86; Article Pub; *office:* Univ of Cincinnati Clermont 725 College Dr Batavia OH 45103

PERKINS, CAROL R., Biology Teacher; *b:* Syracus, NY; *c:* Michael James, Shannon Danielle; *ed:* Syracuse Univ (BA) Bio 1979, (MS) Sci Ed 1982; *cr:* Liverpool HS Bio Tchr; *ai:* Cmptrs in Classroom, Curr, Variance Comms; NY ST Summer Inst for Sci, Math 1988-95; NSTA; Cystic Fibrosis 1991-94; *office:* Liverpool HS 4338 Wetzel Rd Liverpool NY 13089

PERKINS, CHRISTINE MARIE, Social Studies Teacher; *b:* Stratford, NJ; *ed:* Trenton St Coll (BA) His, Sec Ed 1993; Currently Working Toward Master Educl Supervision; *cr:* Waldwick HS 8-12 Grd Soc Stud Tchr 1993-; *ai:* Jr Schl Chrldng Coach 1993-95; Asst Coach Winter Track 1995-; Asst Coach Spring Track 1994-; WEA, NJEA, NEA 1993-; Waldwick Ed Fnd Grant; 2 Commercials Encouraging HS Srs Vote; *office:* Waldwick HS 155 Wyckoff Ave Waldwick NJ 07463

PERKINS, DAVID J., Sixth Grade Teacher; *b:* Cambridge, NY; *m:* Deborah Allen; *c:* Jennifer, Valerie; *ed:* SUNY at Plattsburgh (BS) Ed 1970, (MS) Ed 1978; *cr:* Elem Tchr 25 Yrs; *ai:* Girls BB, Ftbl Coach; MS Bldg Ldrshp Team; MS Cmptr Comm Chair; Kingsburg Recreation Commission 1989-; NY Snowmobile Coordination Group Pres 1994, Intnl Snowmobile Family of Yr 1993; NYS Office of Pks 1994-, Meritorious Svc Awd; *office:* Margaret Murphy Elem Schl 2 Clark St Hudson Falls NY 12839

PERKINS, ELAINE FRANCES, Mathematics Teacher; *b:* Binghamton, NY; *m:* Thomas G. Kump; *c:* Katie Ryan, Alex Ryan; *ed:* Elmira Coll (BS) Math 1988, (MA) 1993; 40 Addl Credit Hrs; *cr:* Waverly HS 1988-94, Elmira Free Acad Math Tchr 1994-; *ai:* Class of 98 Adv; AMTNYS 1989-; Phi Beta Kappa 1988-.

PERKINS, ELIZABETH N., Kindergarten Teacher; *b:* Batavia, NY; *c:* Cindy, Michael, Julie; *ed:* Potsdam St Tchrs (BS) Elem Ed 1958; Grad Work at Brockport & Geneseo St Tchrs Colls; *cr:* Batavia Pub Schls 1st Grd Tchr 1958-60; Trinity Episcopal 3rd Grd Tchr 1960-61; Pavilion Cntrl 4th Grd Tchr 1975-76, Kndgtn Tchr 1976-; *ai:* AFT, NEA 1976-; *office:* Pavilion Cntrl Schl 7071 York Rd Pavilion NY 14525

PERKINS, FRANCES B., English Teacher & Hum Chair; *b:* Bristol, CT; *m:* John A.; *ed:* Cntrl CT St Univ (BS) Eng, His 1963, (MS) Ed 1970; Southern CT St Univ Admin Cert 1987; *cr:* Wamogo Regnl HS His, Eng Tchr 1963-; Eng Soc Stud Dept Chrprsn 1980-; *ai:* Sr Class Adv 1988-; Chess Club; Webster Pub Speaking Contest; 7th Grd Class Adv 1995-96; NEA, NCTE 1963-; CT Cncl T of E; ASCD; Excl Tchng Awd Univ of CT; Tchr of Yr 1984.

PERKINS, JANE HURD, Home Economics Teacher; *b:* Olean, NY; *m:* Glenn P.; *c:* Kayle; *ed:* Mansfield Univ (BS) Home Ec Ed 1985; Saint Bonaventure Univ (MS) Counseling Psych 1995; *cr:* Oswayo Valley HS Home Ec Tchr 1986-; *ai:* Sr Class Adv; PSEA, Oswayo Valley Tchrs Assoc 1986-; Cub Scout, Ldr; Pub Relations Comm 1993-; *home:* RR 1 Box 636 Shinglehouse PA 16748*

PERKINS, JUDITH ROBBINS, Home School Teacher; *b:* Honesdale, PA; *m:* David Paul; *c:* Roderick, Marla, J. Michael; *ed:* Roberts Westeyan Coll (BS) Nursing 1963; *cr:* Strong Meml Hospital Staff Nurse, Asst Head Nurse 1964-66, Staff Dev Instr 1966-68; Perkins Home Schl Home Schl Tchr 1982-; Visiting Nurse Svc Private Duty Nurse 1993-; *ai:* Sunday Schl Tchr; Asst Dir of ProTeen Youth Group; *home:* 273 Black Oak Rd Ithaca NY 14850

PERKINS, MARLENE KAY, Third Grade Teacher; *b:* Frostburg, MD; *m:* Verl Allan; *c:* Cynthia, Lisa, Amy; *ed:* Frostburg St Univ (BS) Early Chldhd Ed 1970, (MS) Elem Ed 1980; Addl 21 Credit Hrs; *cr:* Anne Arundel Co Mayo Elem 3rd Grd Tchr 1970-71; Anne Arundel Co Davidson Elem 2nd Grd Tchr 1971-74; Garrett Co Friendsville Spec Ed Tchr 1978-80; Garrett Co Gr antsville Third Grd Tchr 1980-; *ai:* Schl Improvement Team; Frostburg St Univ Prof Dev Ctr Cncl Mem; NEA 1970-95, Schl Rep 3 Yrs; AFT 1995-; *office:* Grantsville Elem Schl Grant St Grantsville MD 21536

PERKINS, MYRNA ORDWAY, Retired Sixth Grade Teacher; *b:* Kane, PA; *m:* G. Raymond; *c:* Thomas W., Christopher J.; *ed:* Slippery Rock St Coll (BS) Elem Ed 1957; Slippery Rock Univ (MS) Elem Coun 1976; Westminister Coll (MS) Elem Prin Cert 1978; Slippery Rock Univ (MS) Scndry Coun 1981; Liberty Univ (MS) Coun Drug & Alcohol Abuse 1989; *cr:* Riverside Schls 4th-5th Grd Tchr 1957-61; Freedom Area Schls 1-6 Grd Tchr 1966-93; *ai:* FAEA 1966-; PSEA, NEA 1966-93; Kiwanis 1994-, Distngd Mem 1995; *home:* RR 1 Box 306 Fombell PA 16123

PERKINS, RICHARD, 6th-8th Grade Soc Stud Tchr; *b:* Norwich, NY; *m:* Pamela Gail Durkee; *c:* Aaron, Grahame, Emily; *ed:* SUNY at Buffalo (BA) Philosophy 1968, (MA) Philosophy 1976, (PHD) Philosophy 1977; Certfd Tchr, Educator in Philosophy for Children Thinking Skills Prgms Inst for Advancement of Philosophy for Children 1989; *cr:* Bennett Park Montessori Ctr Soc Stud Tchr 1981-; Canisius Coll Prof of Philosophy 1990-, Daemen Coll Asst Prof of Philosophy 1990; Canisius Coll Lecturer in Tchr Ed 1995-; *ai:* NEA, Buffalo Tchrs Fed 1981-; Several Monographs, Essays, Articles Devoted to Philosophy; Comparative Lit; Germanic Stud; Fairytale STud; Nietzsche Stud, Ed; Participant in Several NEH Summer Seminars; Dir NEH SSST on Nietzsche's Zarathustra; Neh Summer Stipend 1988; *office:* Bennett Park Montessori Ctr 342 Clinton St Buffalo NY 14204

PERKINS, RICHARD PAUL, PE Teacher & Athletic Dir; *b:* Carbondale, PA; *m:* Elizabeth Marie Tracy; *c:* Brian Scott, Shelby Marie; *ed:* Ulster Comm Coll (AS) Lbrl Arts 1969; St Univ of NY at Brockport (BS) PE 1974; St Univ of NY at Cortland (MS) PE 1979; Attnd St Univ of NY at Binghamton; *cr:* Ulster Comm Coll Instrl Asst 1970-72; Chenango Forks Cntrl Schl PE Tchr 1975-; *ai:* Ath Dir; Wrestling Coach; NYS Section IV Wrestling Chm; Section IV Hall of Fame Comm; AFT 1975-; NY St Coaches Assoc 1975-; NY Ath Admin Assoc 1980-; Amer Red Cross 1967-; BSA 1989-; Amer Civic Assoc 1990-; *office:* Chenango Forks HS 1 Gordon Dr Binghamton NY 13901

PERKINS, ROSE M., First Grade Teacher; *b:* DuBois, PA; *m:* Edwin; *c:* Steven, Christopher; *ed:* Clarion Univ (BS) Elem Ed 1964; *ai:* Music Boosters Pres; Parent-Tchr Adv Comm; PSEA & NEA 1964-; *home:* 119 W 6th St Emporium PA 15834

PERKINS, SCOTT HOWARD, 7th Grade Social Studies Tchr; *b:* Elyria, OH; *m:* Cathy; *c:* Crystal, Tyler, Logan; *ed:* OH Univ (BSED) Soc Stud 1985; Baldwin Wallace Coll (MED) Supervision 1989; *cr:* Northwood Jr High Soc Stud Tchr 1985-; *ai:* Ftbl Coach; EEA, OEA & NEA 1985-; *office:* Northwood Jr HS 700 Gulf Rd Elyria OH 44035

PERKINS, TERESA, Math Teacher; *b:* Coshocton, OH; *c:* Aubrey; *ed:* Malone Coll (BA) Math 1986; Univ of Akron (MA) Scndry Admin 1995; *cr:* Sovers Jr HS Math Tchr 1989-93; Canton McKinley HS Math Tchr 1993-; *ai:* Asst Bsktbl Coach; NEA 1989-; *office:* Canton McKinley HS 2323 17th St NW Canton OH 44708

PERKINS, TYRONE ALONZO, Bible Tchr & Dean of Students; *b:* Brooklyn, NY; *m:* Janet Wright; *c:* Conal Wright, Lloyce, Lynnai, Christel, Caleb, Leyne; *ed:* Princeton Univ (BA) Psych 1974; Seminary of East 2nd Yr MDIV Stu; *cr:* Mercer St Friends Ctr Cnslr, Coord 1974-81, Prgm Dir 1081-90; Westside Bible Bapt Church Pastor 1988-; Mercer Chrstn Acad Bible Tchr, Dean of Stdnts 1990-; *ai:* Oversee Chrstn Svc Prgm; *home:* 25 Atterbury Ave Trenton NJ 08618

PERKOSKI, RIKKI DIANE, English Teacher; *b:* Baltimore, MD; *m:* David J.; *c:* David Rummel, Holly Holm, Erin; *ed:* Towson Univ (MS) Elem Ed 1978; 60 Addl Credit Hrs from Loyola Johns Hopkins, Towson St; *cr:* DOD Schl 7 & 8 Grd Coord, Eng Dept Chair 1966; Victory Villa Elem 6 Grd Eng Tchr 1979-83; MIddle River MS 6 Grd Eng Tchr 1983-85; Gen John Stricker MS 6 & 7 Grd Eng Tchr 1985-89; Loch Raven Academy 7 & 8 Grd Eng Tchr 1989-; *ai:* Parent Advy Bd Chair; Grad Spon; Drama Club 1994; Saturday Schl Prin; NEA 1979-; MCTELA, NCTE 1985-; TABCO 1979-; Cub Hill Civic 1973-; Outstanding Tchr of Yr for Balto Co 1994.

PERL, GARY L., Movies & Media Teacher; *b:* Cleveland, OH; *m:* Joyce Levin; *ed:* LA Vly Coll (AA) Jrnlsm 1972; Touro Coll (BA) Jewish Stud 1977; Adelphi Univ (MS) Spec Ed 1985; *cr:* Yeshiva of Eastern Pkwy Eng Tchr 1978-80; Reynolds Jr HS Spec Ed Tchr 1981-84; John Dewey HS Spec Ed Tchr 1985-86; Marine Park IS Spec Ed, Movies, Media Tchr 1986-; *ai:* Yrbk Adv; Photo Fund Raiser; UFT 1981-; Beta Phi Gamma 1971-; Eta Beta Rho 1972-; Articles Pub; *office:* Marine Park Intermediate Schl 1925 Stuart St Brooklyn NY 11229*

PERLAKY, MARTIN W., Science Teacher; *b:* Toledo, OH; *m:* Suzanne O'Brien; *c:* Samantha, Colin, Patrick, Jillian; *ed:* Bowling Green St Univ (BS) Comp Sci 1991; *cr:* Cntrl Cath Chem Tchr 1991-95; Springfield Local 1995; *ai:* Statistican Girls Bsktbl; *home:* 3548 Terrace Dr Toledo OH 43611*

PERLEE, NANCY SOLOMON, 1st Grade Teacher; *b:* Roseville, MI; *m:* James Henry; *c:* Regen Rose, Kiersta, Laurel Walker, Lori; *ed:* MI St U (BA) Art Ed, Sci 1965; Univ of VT (MA) Rdng, Lang Arts 1987; 30 Credits Areas that Promote Classroom Act; *cr:* Charlotte Cntrl Schl Math Tchr 3 Yrs, Art Tchr 3 Yrs 1965-71; Bristol Ed Schl 1 Grd Tchr 1981-; *ai:* Assessment Comm Dist Prgm Assn; NEA, VEA, IRA, NCTE 1981-; First Bapt Church 1984-, Missionary Bd Mem, Moderator; *office:* Bristol Elem Schl 57 Mountain St Bristol VT 05443*

PERLEY, JAMES E., Professor of Biology; *b:* Hornell, NY; *m:* Delene Domes; *c:* Thomas, Scott; *ed:* Univ of MI (AB) Bio 1960; Yale Univ (MS) Bio 1961, (PHD) Bio 1965; *cr:* Wayne St Univ Asst Prof of Bio 1965-68; Coll of Wooster Asst Prof Bio 1968-; *ai:* AAOP 1973-, Pres 1994-; 15 Articles Pub; *office:* Coll Of Wooster Mateer Hall Wooster OH 44691*

PERLISH, JOEL S., Retired Elementary Teacher; *b:* Philadelphia, PA; *m:* Kate Mc Dermott; *ed:* Temple Penn St (MA) Elem 1985; *cr:* Coopertown Elem Schl 5th, 2nd, 3rd Grd Tchr 1969-79; Manoa Elem Schl 4th, 3rd Grd Tchr 1980-91; *ai:* Schl Paper; Running Club; NEA, HTEA 1969-; Optimists 1990-, Yth Awds; HHS Alumni Assn 1985-, Sec; Local TV Station Person of Month; Schl Run Club Achvmt; *home:* 401 Colfax Rd Havertown PA 19083

PERLMAN, JOHN N., English & Poetry Teacher; *b:* Alexandria, VA; *m:* Janis Lynn Hadobas; *c:* Nicole; *ed:* OH St Univ (BA) Eng 1969; Iona Coll (MSEd) Eng 1981; *cr:* WY Comm Colls Poet-in-Residence 1971-72; Various Schls Visting Poet in the Poet in the Schls Prgm 1971-72; Mamaroneck HS Tchr of Eng, Poetry 1973-; *ai:* HS Lit Magazine Calliope Adv; AFT; NEA; Books: Kachina 1971, Three Years Rings 1972, Dinner 1974, Notes Toward A Family 1974, Nicole 1976, Self Portrait 1978, Swath 1978, The Vineyard 1978, Homing 1981, Powers 1982, A Wake of 1983, Eyes A Light 1989, Beacons Imaging Within As Promises 1990, Imperatives of Address 1992, Anacoustic 1993, Exuviae 1994, The Natural History of Trees Forthcoming; 5 Pub Anthologies; NY Fnd For the arts Flwshp in Poetry 1991; Acad of Amer Poets Prize 1969; Vanderwater Prize 1969; *home:* 38 Ferris Pl Ossining NY 10562

PERLMUTTER, BARRY, Professor of Geoscience; *b:* New York City, NY; *m:* Rebecca Ann Robertson; *ed:* Brooklyn Coll (BS) Geology 1966; IN Univ (MA) Geology 1968; Univ of IA (PHD) Geology 1971; *cr:* IN Univ Tchng Asst 1966-68; Union Oil Co of CA Summer Geologist 1968; Univ of IA Tchng Asst 1968-71; Shell Oil Co Summer Geologist 1969; Jersey City St Coll Prof of Geology 1972-; *ai:* Chair New Fac Position Departmental Search Comm; Paleontological Soc 1974-; Natl Geographic Soc 1981-; Sigma Xi 1986-; NY St Regents Schlsp; KS Geological Survey PHD Rsrch Support; NJ St Rsrch Grant; *office:* Jersey City State Coll 2039 Kennedy Blvd Jersey City NJ 07305

PERNINI, GLENN V., Science Staff Leader & Teacher; *b:* Somerville, NJ; *m:* Nancy Lenner; *c:* Susan, Emily; *ed:* Jersey City St Coll (BA) Sci Ed 1971, (MA) Bio, Admin 1977; *cr:* Woodbridge MS Tchr, Staff Ldr 1971-96, Right-to-Know Ofcr 1988-; *ai:* Sci Curr, Textbook Selection, Writing Project Advy Comms; NJ Ed Assn 1971-; Woodbridge Twp Educl Assn 1971-, VP; NJ Sci Tchrs Assn 1976-; Woodbridge Twp Ed Fnd Excl in Ed Awd 1995; NJ Governor's Awd for Outstndg Tchng 1992; *office:* Woodbridge MS Barron Ave Woodbridge NJ 07095

PERO, LINDA ANNE, Mathematics Teacher; *b:* Brooklyn, NY; *ed:* St Joseph's Coll (BA) Math, Eng 1974; NY Univ (MA) Math 1978; *cr:* Fontbonne Hall Acad Math Tchr 1974-79; St Angela Hall Schl Math Tchr 1979-80; St Joseph's Coll Methods in Math Tchr, Adj Prof 1980-; The Mary Louis Acad Math Tchr 1980-; *ai:* Yrbk Bus Mgr; 60th Anniversary Journal Comm Chprsn; IM Track, Fitness Coach; Alumnae Assn Exec Bd; NCEA 1974-; NCTM 1993-; St Francis Coll Outstndg Tchr Awd 2 Yrs; *office:* Mary Louis Acad 179-21 Wexford Terr Jamaica NY 11432

PERO, LOUISE, Eighth Grade Teacher; *b:* Brooklyn, NY; *ed:* Richmond Coll (BA) Child Psych, Elem Ed 1975; College of Staten Island (MS) Rdng, Elem Ed 1985; 15 Credit Hrs Post Grad Stud Rel Ed Catechist Prgm; 25 Hrs ADAPP Quest Intnl Yth Dev Prgm; *cr:* St Josephs Schl Second Grd Tchr 1979-82, Third Grd Tchr 1982-92, Eighth Grd Tchr 1992-; *home:* 588 W Fingerboard Rd Staten Island NY 10305

PERON, JOHN C., World Langs Curr Chair; *b:* Roudouallec, France; *m:* Agnes K. Biscotti; *ed:* Hartwick Coll (BA) Ed 1969; North Adams St Coll (MED) Ed 1991; Emergency Med Technician Intermediate; *cr:* S Berk Regnl Schl Dist Dept Chair, Span, Fr Tchr 1969-; *ai:* Ldrshp Team Chprsn; Assessment Comm; Crisis Team Facilitator; Co-Chair MA Dept Ed Framework, Assessment Comms; MTA, NEA 1969-; MAFLA, ACTFL 1994-; Amer Heart Assoc 1975-, CPR Instr, Outstdng Svc; S Berk Vol Ambulance Svc 1982-88, VP, Loyal Svc; Kellogg Fnd Flwshp 1993; Pub Lesson Plan 1994; *office:* S Berkshire Regnl Schl Dist PO B Sheffield MA 01257*

PEROSA, RICHARD JOHN, Retired Eng, Sci & Math Tchr; *b* River, NJ; *m:* Judy Dobbins; *c:* Joseph, Christopher, Lisa Howa Miller Scott; *ed:* Seton Hall Univ (BS) Soc Stud, Bus in Ed, Scndr St Cert in Elem Ed K-8; *cr:* St Ladislaus Schl 3rd Grd Tchr 196 Peter's HS World His Tchr 1963-65; Spotswood Schls 5th Grd, Eng, 8th Grd Sci, 6th Grd Sci, Math Tchr 1965-94; *ai:* St Peter's Asst Ftbl Coach; Spotswood Schlsp, T & E, HS Bldg Comms; Spc Fishing Club Adv; NEA, MCEA 1965-; SEA 1965-, VP, Pres, Tcl 1985; Rangers A. C. 1965-, VP, Sec, Treas, Pres; South River Hi Soc 1993-94; *home:* 4593 Heron Rd Springfield OH 45502

PEROTTI, JOHN ALFRED, English Teacher; *b:* New York City, Beverly Nelson; *c:* David, Erik; *ed:* Cntrl CT St Univ (BS) Eng, H Univ of Hartford (MA) Eng, Rdng 1973; Cntrl CT St Univ 6th Diploma Rdng Consultant 1980; *cr:* Martin Kellogg Jr HS Eng, H 1970-71; John Wallace MS Eng, Rdng, His 1971-81; Newington H Consultant 1981-; *ai:* Jr Class, Ski Club, Future Tchrs of Amer Ad 1970-, Local Pres; Phi Delta Kappa 1984-; NCTE 1981-; LIttle Lea 1985-, Pres, Friend of Bsbl Yth; BSA 1985-, Asst Scou Scoutmasters Key; Sounding Bd for Yth 1990-, Councilman; Comm 1990-, Elder; Who's Who in Amer Univ 1970; NERA Grant 1974 Assistantship 1986; St of CT Mentor Tchr 1995; *office:* Newington Willard Ave Newington CT 06111*

PEROTTI, MATTHEW PAUL, World Cultures Teacher; *b:* Abing *m:* Tricia Mc Lane; *c:* Dana, Jacklyn; *ed:* Shippensburg Univ (B. Arts 1981; Temple Univ (MA) Ed 1988; *cr:* Philadelphia Archdic Amer His Tchr 1986-87; Pemberton Twp HS World Cultures Tchr *ai:* Asst Ftbl & Wrestling Coaches; Peer Ldrshp Facilitator; Pr Intensive Scheduling Comms; NEA, NJEA 1988-; Princeton Univ Tchr Awd Nom 1992, 1994; Govenors Awd 1994; Tchr of Yr 1994.

PEROUTY-BYRNE, CYNTHIA L., Biology I & II Instruc Baltimore, MD; *m:* Douglas L. Byrne; *ed:* Townson St Univ (BS) Bi Johns Hopkins 8 Hrs; Harvard Univ 4 Hrs; Hood Coll 32 Hrs; *cr:* C Cty Schls 7th & 8th Grd Sci Tchr 1984; Caroll Cty Pub Schls Bio I, 1984-; MD St Dept Gifted, Talented Enviroment Tchr 1985; Johns H Ctr for Talented Yth First Paced Bio Tchr 1990; Catonsville Com Adj Lab Instr 1990; *ai:* Key Club Adv 1989-95, Keyette Adv 1 Co-Chpsrn Tour Mod Day Comm 1993-94; Chprsn, Tech in Cla Comm 1995-; NEA, MSTA, Carroll Cty Ed Assn 1985-; MD Assr Tchrs 1985-, Field Trip Coord 1986-89; Kiwanis 1989-, Key Clu Carroll Cty Chamber of Comm Outstdng Tchr Nom 1992; Mc D Corp Recognized Tchr 1994; Sigma Phi Recognized Tchr Awd *office:* South Carroll HS 1300 W Old Liberty Rd Sykesville MD 2

PERPETUA, KATHLEEN G., Emotional Supprt, Spec Ed T Corpus Christi, TX; *m:* Joseph V.; *c:* Joseph M.; *ed:* Clarion Uni Spec Ed 1973; 12 Credits Duquesne Univ; Insvc Credits All Intermediate Unit; *cr:* Allegheny Intermediate Schl #3 Learning Tchr 1974-95, Emotional Support Tchr 1995-; *ai:* Little League Bsb Rep 1990; NEA, PSEA 1974-; AIUEA 1974-, Legislative, Nego Comms; Ken Mawr UP Church 1988-, Deacon 3 Yrs, Sunday Sch PTA 1981-; Montour Hockey Assoc 1993-; *office:* Burkett Elem Station Sq 2nd Flr Pittsburgh PA 15219

PERPETUA, MARY, Piano Teacher; *b:* Lowell, MA; *ed:* D'youvi (BA) Ed, Music; Cnslng Salem St, Lowell St; On Going Ed Salem 7th, 8th Grd Math, Eng, Music Tchr 1950-70; St Leo's Schl Piar 1972-77; *ai:* Nrsng Home Vol; Spec Children Prgm; Salem St Grant *home:* 2556 80th St Flushing NY 11370

PERREAULT, BRUCE M., Social Studies Teacher; *b:* Manchest *m:* Christine; *ed:* Keene St Coll (BE) Scndry Soc Stud 1971; Miscell Credits; *cr:* Memorial HS Psych & US His Tchr 1972-; *ai:* Sr Clas Manchester Police Dept DARE Prgm Liaison; Schl Svc Fnd Executc Accreditation Comm; Tchr-Intern Facilitator; Soc Stud Evaluation Chprsn; NEA, NH Ed Assn, Manchester Ed Assn 1972-; 198 Dedication; *office:* Memorial HS South Porter St Manchester NH

PERRECA, JAMES N., Sixth Grade Teacher; *b:* Brooklyn, NY; *c:* *ed:* Brockport St U of NY (BA) Ed 1967; Stonybrook St U of NY Soc Sci; *cr:* Stagecoach Elem Schl 5th & 6th Grd Tchr 1968-87; MS 6th Grd Tchr 1987-; *ai:* Effective Schl Chprsn 1985-86; Plant Cl 1987-; Peer Ldr Club Adv 1990-; NYSUT & AFT 1967-, Del 1 *home:* 38 Reel St East Patchogue NY 11772

PERRECA, PAUL MERCEDES,IHM, Eighth Grade Teac Philadelphia, PA; *ed:* Immaculata Coll (BA) Soc Sci 1970; St Borromeo Seminary (MA) Rel Stud 1983; *cr:* Transfiguration Schl Grd Tchr 1966-72; St Gabriel Schl 7th-8th Grd Tchr 1972-76; Ep Schl 8th Grd Tchr 1977-82; Newtown Sq Cath Schls Prin 1983-88; I Cath Schls Prin 1983-88; Cherry Hill Cath Schls Prin 1983-88; E Virgin Mary Schl 8th Grd Tchr 1988-95; Annunciation BVM Schl 8 Tchr 1995-; *ai:* CCD Tchr; Choir Dir; NCEA 1966-; *office:* Annun BVM Schl 605 W Browning Rd Bellmawr NJ 08031*

PERRI, LAURA AGUE, Librarian; *b:* Huntington, WV; *m:* Vic Jessica, Robert, Victoria; *ed:* Edinboro St Univ (BS) Lib Sci 1979; Pittsburgh Post Grad Stud; *cr:* Jefferson-Morgan Schl Dist Elem 1979-; *ai:* Elem Lib Helpers; PSEA 1979-, Local Bld Rep JMPA 1979-; Greene Cty Librns 1979-; Amer Diabetes Assn 1993-; Franklin Ftbl Boosters 1993-, Treas 1996; *office:* Jefferson-Morga Schl Greene St Box 206 Jefferson PA 15344

PERRIELLO, KATHY GOLDSMITH, Spanish Teacher; *b:* Frederick, MD; *m:* Joseph; *ed:* Towson St Univ (BA) Span, Sec E Univ of MD (MED) Educl Supervision, Admin 1992; Ctr for Biling Cuernavaca Mexico EF Educl Tours; *cr:* Stoddert MS Foreign Lan 1989-92; Westlake HS Foreign Lang Tchr, Dept Chair 1992-; *ai:* F Lang Dept Chair, Enrichment, Accelrated Team Ldr, Var Chrldng AFAA 1994-, Fitness Assn; AAAI 1993-, Fitness Assn; March of Presenter for In-Svc Cooperative Learning, Lesson Design, Clas Mgmt, Framework for Tchng; HS Curr Framework; *office:* Westla 3300 Middletown Rd Waldorf MD 20603*

PERRIGO, JANIS RUTH (HOUCK), Fourth Grade Teacher; *b:* Fa Park, OH; *m:* Michael Eugene; *c:* Michelle C., Melissa S.; *ed:* Ol (BS) Elem Ed 1968; Cleveland St (MS) Emerging Adolescent 19 Semester Hrs Ashland Univ, Baldwin-Wallace, Cleveland St, John S Carroll, Walsh Univ; *cr:* Ridge-Brook Elem Schl Spec Ed Tchr 19 Dag Hammarskjola Elem Schl 4-5 Grd Tchr 1970-75; Ridge-Brook Grd 6 Tchr 1975-79; Ridge-Brook Elem Schl Grd 4 Tchr 1979-; *ai* West HS Acad Challenge Team Coach; Parma Ed Assn Bldg & Eler NEA, DEA, NEDEA, PEA 1968-, Local Bldg Rep, Elem Rep; Par Assn, Local Mbrshp Chair; Alpha Delta Kappa 1990-, Sec, Corres S Lambda Theta 1981-; St James Friendship Circle 1980-, Treas; Lut Mothers Club 1988-, Pres, Schlsp Chair, Boutique Chair; Good Be the World 1987-, Treas; Who's Who in Amer Ed 1989-90; *office:* Brook Elem Schl 7915 Manhattan Ave Parma OH 44129

PERRIGO, KAREN (LEONARD), Associate Prof of Accounti Gowanda, NY; *m:* Dana S.; *c:* Jill; *ed:* Jamestown Comm Coll Accounting 1979; St Bonarenture Law Schl (BA) Accounting 1981 of Buffalo (JD) Law 1989; *cr:* R.A. Mercer & Co CPA 1981-86;

ler 1986-89; SUNY Alfred Assoc Prof 1989-; *ai:* Affirmative Comm Mem; Stu Conduct Bd; Fac Planning Team; NYS Bar Assn AICPA 1983-; Amer Bar Assn 1995-; Cuba Lake Dist 1983-, Chprsn; t 305 Black Creek NY 14714

N, BARBARA, Second Grade Teacher; *b:* Brooklyn, NY; *m:* *c:* Kenneth, Eric; *ed:* Brooklyn Coll (BA) Ed 1966, (MS) Ed 1976; Grad Credits; *cr:* PS 242 Second Grd Tchr 1966-71; PS 219 Grd Tchr 1975-77, 1982-88; PS 138 Second Grd Tchr 1986-; *ai:* City Tchr of Yr Awd Dist 29.

NE, VERONICA BEADER, Choral & Drama Director; *b:* Farrell, Robert Alan; *c:* Natassia; *ed:* Indiana Univ of PA (BS) Music Ed, 977; Kent St Univ (MED) Spec, Gifted Ed 1980; Univ of AL (PHD) Ed, Music 1989; *cr:* Maplewood East Gifted, Music Tchr 1977-82; lem Gifted, Music Tchr 1977-82; J. A. Davis MS Music, Gifted, Tchr 1982-85; Frink MS Music, Chorus, Drama Tchr 1985-88; enoir HS Music, Chorus, Drama Tchr 1985-88; Rehoboth Elem Jr ic, Chorus, Band Tchr 1988-90; Middletown HS Choral, Drama Dir *ai:* Childrens Theatre; Adult, Children Drama Classes; Comm Dir, Choreographer, Performer; Church Choir Dir; Delta Omicron Alpha Psi Omega, Kappa Delta Pi, MENC 1975-; NEA 1977-; OH Ed Mini Grant; Wrote Dissertation; *office:* Middletown HS 504 S t Middletown DE 19709*

NE, NANCY, High School History Teacher; *b:* New York, NY; *ed:* an Coll (BA) His; Fordham Univ (MA) Amer His; Post Grad Work ry Ed; *cr:* Mother Cabrini HS His Tchr 1982-; *ai:* Cabrini Chptr Intnl Moderator; NHS Adv; NCEA 1982-; OAH 1992-; *office:* Cabrini HS 701 Fort Washington Ave New York NY 10040

TTA, ROBERT D.,JR., Elementary Teacher; *b:* New Castle, PA; anne Tedescko; *c:* Lisa, Gina, Annlyn, Joseph, Jenna, Dana; *ed:* Coll (BS) Elem Ed 1982; Baldwin Wallace Univ Campus; *cr:* iation 4th, 6th-8th Grd Tchr 1982-84; West Branch 4th & 5th Grd 84-87; Wilmington Pre-K, 2nd & 4th Grd Tchr 1987-; *ai:* Schl Curr Comms; Started Annual Math Metric Olympic Day; Ftbl & ach; NEA 1987-; WAEA 1987-; NCTM 1993-; *office:* Wilmington hl Dist 350 Wood St New Wilmington PA 16142*

TTA I, JAMES ANTHONY, Social Studies Teacher; *b:* New York Y; *m:* Cynthia A.; *ed:* Bloomsburg Univ (BA) Pol Sci, His 1989; ll Working Towards MA Educl Admin 3 Credits 1995; William n Coll Soc Stud NJ Tchrs Cert K-12 1991; OK City Univ Schl of Credits 1989-90; *cr:* Wayne Hills HS 9 Grd Soc Stud Tchr 1992; r-Colfax JHS 7 Grd Soc Stud Tchr 1992; George Washington JHS Soc Stud Tchr 1992-; *ai:* Site-Based, Tech, Employment Sub Board Games Club Adv; Bedside Instr Infirmed HS Stdnts; Cntrl on Admin; NEA, NJEA, PCEA WEA 1992-; Benevolent, Protective of Elks 1991-; Church Lbrn Grace Reformed Presbyn Church; nominational Yth Bible Stud; *office:* George Washington Jr HS 60 Dr Wayne NJ 07470*

TTO, CAROL F. (MOSER), 5th Grade Teacher; *b:* Erie, PA; *m:* *c:* Karen L. Moses, Teresa L.; *ed:* Edinboro Univ (BS) Elem Ed MA) 1994; *cr:* Harbor Creek Schl Dist 4-6 Grd Tchr 1966-71; Faith resch Dir, Tchr 1976-81; Iroquois Schl Dist K, 4-6 Grd Tchr ; Millcreek Schl Dist 1, 4-5 Grd Tchr 1985-; *ai:* PSEA; NEA; St Mark's Parish Action League 1987-; Rotary Grant; *office:* Belle Elem Schl 5300 Henderson Rd Erie PA 16509

, CHRISTINE ALLISON, HS French & German Teacher; *b:* NY; *m:* William; *c:* Amanda; *ed:* Clarion St Univ (BS) Ger, Fr Attnd Univ of Salzburg Austria 1969; 24 Credits Cert; *cr:* burg Area HS Fr, Ger Tchr 1970-82; Kane Area Sr HS Fr, Ger Tchr *ai:* PSEA, NEA, KATA 1970-; Great United Meth Church 1970-, Schl, Comms 1990-; Fr-Grmn Clb Fndr 1994-95; *office:* Kane Area st 300 Hemlock Ave Kane PA 16735

, DARLENE TERRY, 4th Grade Teacher; *b:* Dansville, NY; *m:* W.; *c:* Kathryn Lee Perry Palmieri, Amy Lynne; *ed:* SUNY at (BS) Elem Ed 1965; 12 Hrs SUNY at Cortland; 12 Hrs SUNY at o; 18 Hrs Coll of St Rose; Addl 12 Hrs; *cr:* Marcellus Cntrl Schl Tchr 1965-68, 5th Grd Tchr 1969-70, Sub Tchr 1973-80, 6th Grd 980-82, 4th Grd Tchr 1983-; *ai:* Fac Admin Comm; Cntrl NY St ncl; Rdng Club Adv; NY St Tchrs Assn 1983-; Cntrl NY St Rdng *ome:* 1 Beach Rd Marcellus NY 13108*

, JILL P., Business Education Teacher; *b:* West Islip, NY; *ed:* St NY at Farmingdale (AAS) Secretarial Sci 1986; Hofstra Univ (BS) Ed 1988; Dowling Coll (MBA) Mgmt 1991; *cr:* Warren, Gorham & Publishers Copy Ed 1988-89; Lindenhurst HS Bus Ed Tchr ; Depository Trust Co Ed Coord 1991-92; Deer Park HS Bus Ed 992-; *ai:* Kickline, Dance Team, & Jr Var Sftbl Coach; Conflict or; Dist-Wide Curr & Schlsp Comm; Deer Park Tchrs Assn 1992-, ep 1994; Coached Undefeated Long Island Kickline Champions nvited Kickline to Perform in NY City Saint Patricks Day Parade Kickline Was Invited to Perform at Divisional Playoff Game at Stadium 1995; *office:* Deer Park Sr HS 30 Rockaway Ave Deer Park 729*

, JOHN R., Math Teacher; *b:* Dunmore, PA; *m:* Barbara Blaetz; *c:* l, Tracy; *ed:* Bloomsburg St Coll (BS) Math, Ed 1968; Temple Univ Math, Curr 1974; 18 Addl Credits; West Chester Univ 8 Credits; PA v 10 Credits; Bloomsburg Univ Supvisory Cert Math 1984; *cr:* urg Schl Dist Math Tchr 1968-69; DE Valley Coll Math Tchr 1989-; ucks Schl Dist Math Tchr, Coord 1969-; AP Calc Coll Brd Exam Math Dept Coord; Mathletes Coach; Var Swim Coach; Var Bsktbl eeper; Started AP Calculus Prgm 1991-92; NEA 1968-; PSEA, 1968-, Bldg Rep; NCTM 1991-; BAA, DAA 1985-, Coach; Univ of nd Cert of Recognition; *home:* 43 Valley Dr Furlong PA 18925*

, JOHN S., Mathematics Department Chair; *b:* Portland, ME; *ed:* Southern ME (BS) Math Ed 1968, (MS) Math Ed 1977, (MS) Educl 1980; Univ of ME (DED) Educl Ldrshp 1996; *cr:* Bonny Eagle HS chr 11 Yrs; Univ of Southern ME Part-time Math Fac 3 Yrs; Sanford ath Dept Chair 11 Yrs; *ai:* ME Educl Assn, NCTM 1968-; ation Pub; *office:* Sanford HS 2r Main St Sanford ME 04073

, JUANITA LAMBRIGHT-LINDER, Fifth Grade Teacher; *b:* gton, DC; *m:* Vincent Charles; *c:* Donna M. Carney, Delores L. Verna C.; *ed:* DC Tchrs Coll (BA) Elem Ed 1957; Attnd Univ of DC, Coll, Minor Tchrs Coll; *cr:* Drew Elem Schl 4th Grd Tchr 1959-88, l Tchr 1988-; *ai:* SAPE Spon; Programming 4th & 5th Grds Chprsn; 976-; DC Tchrs Union 1971-; SAC 1988-; Union Temple B. C., Sr Pastors Aide Club 1971-; Lib Club 1971-, Sec, Treas; Tchr of Yr 5; *office:* Drew Elem Schl 56th Eads St NE Washington DC 20019

Y, KRAIG STREETER, History Teacher; *b:* New Bedford, MA; *m:* M. Bumpus; *c:* Nathan S., Ryan A.; *ed:* Univ of MA at Dartmouth His, Ed 1973; Soc Stud, His, Geography, Rdng; *cr:* Bristol Comm utor 1969-71; Fairhaven Jr HS Rdng, His Instr 1973-87; Fairhaven s, Rdng Tchr 1987-; *ai:* Chess Club Adv Wood Schl; FEA, MTA, 973-; Asst Coaching Staff 1986-; Soccer, Bsbl 1986-91; Polaroid Share a Book Prgm 1990; *home:* 20 Timothy St Fairhaven MA

Y, MARIA ROMANO, Business Teacher; *b:* Hollywood, FL; *m:* n A.; *c:* Jacqueline; *ed:* Pace Univ (BA); Coll of New Rochelle (MS) Rdng 1981; *cr:* St Raymond Acad Bus Tchr 1978-79; Maria Regina HS Bus Tchr 1979-; Maria Regina HS Bus Dept Chprsn 1988-; *ai:* Yrbk Co-Moderator; Prom Comm; *office:* Maria Regina HS 500 W Hartsdale Ave Hartsdale NY 10530

PERRY, MARJORIE BARTLESON, Sixth Grade Teacher; *b:* Lansdale, PA; *m:* Peter M.; *c:* Zachary R., Catherine R.; *ed:* Juniata Coll (BA) Elem Ed 1973; M Equivalency Elem Ed 1987; Addl 30 Post Grad Hrs; *cr:* Buckingham Elem Sch Pre-l, K, 2, 5 Grd Tchr 1973-85; Gayman Elem Sch K Tchr 1979-80; Buckingam Elem Sch 3, 6 Grd Tchr 1985-; *ai:* Act 178, Dist Sci Comms; PTO Rep; Juniata Alumni Assn 1973-; *office:* Buckingham Elem Schl PO Box 158 Buckingham PA 18912

PERRY, MARY JANE DALY, 6th Grade Teacher; *b:* Bronx, NY; *m:* James A. Jr.; *c:* James III, Mark; *ed:* Adelphi Suffolk Coll (BA) Elem Ed 1968; Adelphi Univ (MA) Elem Ed 1972; Addl 75 Hrs; *cr:* Oakwood Rd Schl 3rd Grd Tchr 1968-69; Cayuge Elem Schl 3-5th Grd Tchr 1967-77, 6th Grd Tchr 1977-; *ai:* 6th Grd Adv; PTA Act; SCTA 1969-, 20 Yr Svc Awd; NYSTA 1968-; *office:* Cayuga Elem Schl 865 Hawkins Ave Lake Grove NY 11755

PERRY, MICHAEL JAMES, Principal; *b:* Portsmouth, OH; *m:* Sheryll Peterson; *c:* Benjamin, Nicholas; *ed:* OH Univ (BS) Elem Ed 1976, (MA) Admin 1980; 45 Credit Hrs Admin; *cr:* Westinghouse Elec Corp Quality Control 1966-74; Detroit Steel Corp Maintenance 1968-75; Gallipolis City Schls Elem Tchr 1976-90, Prin 1991-; *ai:* Negotiations Comm; OH Ed Assn 1976-91; OH Assn of Elem Schl Admins 1991-; Gallipolis Ed Assn, Pres; Sunday Schl Tchr; Grants: OH Dept of Ed Venture Capital, Multiage Seed, Spec Ed Inclusion; Martha Holden Jennings Sci Edctr; *home:* PO Box 246 Rio Grande OH 45674*

PERRY, MONZELL, Math Teacher; *b:* Lebanon, KY; *m:* Dennis Allen; *c:* Denny; *ed:* Univ of KY (BA) Math Ed 1975; Continued Math Ed Courses; *cr:* Jefferson Cty Pub Schls Math Tchr 1975-83, Forest Hills Math Tchr 1984-85; Purcell-Marion Math Tchr 1985-86; Norwood Math Tchr 1986-87; Mt Notre Dame Math Tchr 1990-; *ai:* Math Team Coach; Cheerleadign Spon; Class Jr Adv; Teens for Life Club Spon; OCTM 1991-; RCIA Marriage Minister at Church; *office:* Mount Notre Dame H S 711 E Columbia Ave Cincinnati OH 45215

PERRY, PORTIA PERRY, 5th Grade Teacher; *b:* Elizabeth City, NC; *m:* Vernon M. Jr.; *c:* Vernon III, Vera; *ed:* Elizabeth City St Univ (BS) Elem Ed 1966; St Univ of NY at New Paltz (MS) Elem Ed 1976; Coll of William & Mary Post Grad Stud; *cr:* Hampton Schl System Elem Schl Tchr 1967-68; Newport News Schl System Elem Schl Tchr 1968-71; Newburgh Schl Dist Elem Schl Tchr 1972-; *ai:* Safety Patrol Spon; Supervising Tchr; AFT 1974-; Newburgh Tchrs Assn 1972-; NY St United Tchrs Assn 1974-; NY Prince Hall Masonic Org Twilight Chapter 28 OEA 1981-, Worthy Matron 1989; Elejmal Court #171 Daughters of Isis AEAONMS, Marshall 1994-; Outstanding Elem Tchr of Amer 1974; Whos Who Among Stdnts in Amer Univ & Colls 1966.

PERRY, STUART, Business Education Teacher; *b:* New York City, NY; *m:* Janet Tyndall; *c:* Christopher, Joey, Shannon, Brett; *ed:* Rider Univ (BA) Commerce Mrktg 1977; Cntrl CT Univ (MS) Bus Ed 1985; *cr:* Burroughs Corp Salesman 1977-81; Mahopac HS Bus Ed Tchr 1981-; *ai:* Wrestling & Tennis Coach; Little League Bsbl & Soccer Coach; AFT, MTA 1981-; Theta Chi 1975-; *office:* Mahopac HS Baldwin Place Rd Mahopac NY 10541

PERRY, THOMAS ALAN, Earth Science Teacher; *b:* Nyack, NY; *m:* Maryan; *c:* Tyler Andrew; *ed:* Univ of CT (MS) Ecology & Evolutionary Bio 1989; St Univ of NY at Albany (MS) Sndry Sci Ed 1989; New Paltz 6 Credits in Rdng; Credits in Cooperative Learning; *cr:* Nyack HS Earth Sci Tchr 1989-91, Life Sci Tchr 1992-93, Earth Sci Tchr 1993-; *ai:* Ecology Club Adv; Fdn Mem; NSTA, STANYS 1989-; Pilgrim Bapt Church 1994-, Schlsp Comm Mem; Nyack Staff Dev Ctr Minigrant for Maple Sugaring; Westchester-Rockland Sci Supvrs Assn; Awd for Outstanding Sci Tchr; *office:* Nyack HS 360 Christian Herald Rd Nyack NY 10960

PERRY, WAYNE, Math Teacher; *b:* Youngstown, OH; *m:* Gloria; *c:* Marc; *ed:* Youngstown St Univ (BS) Elem Ed 1973, (MS) Elem Ed 1976; *cr:* W S Guy Schl 7th & 8th Grd Math Tchr 1973-; *ai:* NEA 1973-; *office:* W S Guy MS Liberty Local Schls 4115 Shady Rd Youngstown OH 44505

PERRY, YOLANDA BURKEEN, French Teacher; *b:* Chattanooga, TN; *m:* Chatry; *c:* Marcus, Raymond, Jo Anna; *ed:* Hampton Univ (BS) Fr Ed 1970; Pepperdine Univ (MS) Human Resources Mngmt 1978; Attnd Universite de Poitiers, Millersville Univ; *cr:* Lookout Jr HS Span, Eng Tchr 1970-71; De Renne MS Fr, Eng Tchr 1975-78; City Colls of Chicago Eng Tchr 1982-84; Glen Burnie HS Fr Tchr 1985-; *ai:* Model Org Amer Sts, Jack & Jill of Amer-Teen Group Co-Adv; Higher Ed & Campus Ministry Comm; NEA, Tchrs Assn Anne Arunde Cty 1985-; Phi Delta Kappa 1988-; *office:* Glen Burnie Sr HS 7550 Baltimore Annapolis Blvd Glen Burnie MD 21012

PERSCH, MARTIN ORIN, Fourth Grade Teacher; *b:* Grove City, PA; *m:* Terri Collins-Persch; *c:* Kevin, Kendall; *ed:* Thiel Coll (BS) Elem Ed, Eng 1980; Slippery Rock Univ (MS) Elem Ed 1990; *cr:* Glade Elem Schl 5th Grd Tchr 1981; St Anthony's Schl 6th-8th Grd Sci, Soc Stud Tchr 1981-83, Fifth Grd Tchr 1983-84, Tchr of Gifted 1984-85, Fourth Grd Tchr 1985-; *ai:* Curr Cncl; Strategic Planning Comm; NEA 1983-; PSEA 1983-, Local Pres 1987-88; Little League 1993-, Coach; Presbyn Church 1972-; *office:* Oakview Elem Schl 1387 School Rd Stoneboro PA 16153

PERSENAIRE, SUZETTE WADSWORTH, Reading Specialist; *b:* Cleveland, OH; *m:* Thomas A.; *c:* Jenette, Bethany, Benjamin; *ed:* Calvin Coll (BS) Ed 1981; Salem St (MED) Rdng Ed 1989; *cr:* Trinity Chrstn Schl 4th Grd Tchr 1981-84; North Shore Chrstn Schl 4th-5th Grd Tchr 1984-89; Chelsea Pub Schls Rdng Specialist 1989-93; Danvers Pub Schls Rdng Specialist 1993-; Boston Museum of Sci Tchr 1989-; *ai:* Stu Cncl Adv; After Schl Enrichment; MTA, NEA 1993-; North Shore Rdng 1995-; *office:* Great Oak Elem Schl 76 Pickering St Danvers MA 01923

PERSICHINI, CARL JOSEPH, Math Teacher; *b:* Bradford, PA; *m:* Karen Jean Bell; *c:* Kristin, Kelly; *ed:* St Bonaventure Univ (BS) Scndry Ed Math 1973; 6 Grad Credits St Bonaventure Univ, Mt Mercy Coll; 3 Grad Credits Northern CO Univ, Univ of Pitt; 9 Grad Credits Wilkes Coll; *cr:* Bradford Central Chrstn HS Math Tchr of Yr 1975-79; Allentown Central Cath HS Math Tchr 1979-80; East Hills MS Math Tchr 1980-81; Wilson Area HS Math Tchr 1981-; *ai:* Finished 18 Yrs Ftbl Coach; PSEA, NEA 1981-; NCTM 1990-; K of C 1967-; *office:* Wilson H S 22nd & Washington Blvd Easton PA 18042

PERSLEY, KRISTIN, Vocal Music Teacher; *b:* Endicott, NY; *ed:* Ithaca Coll (BFA) Music 1974; Columbia Univ (MA) Music 1989; 31 Credit Hrs in Orchestral, Choral Conducting; *cr:* Prof Singer, Actress Jingles, Opera, Oratorio, Music Theatre 1975-87; Tchrs Coll at Columbia Univ Studio Voice Instr 1985-86; Orpheon Inc The Little Orch Soc Asst Conductor, Music Admin 1986-88; Vestal Cntrl Schl Dist Vocal Music Instr 1989-; *ai:* Annual 8th Grd Musical Dir; Amer Fed of Television & Radio Artists, Actors Equity Assn 1975-; NEA, NEA NY, BCMEA 1989-; Internship in Institutional Planning & Dev Natl Inst Against Prejudice & Violence 1989; *home:* 137 Hazel Dr Vestal NY 13850

PERULLI, LILLIAN, Math Teacher; *b:* Brooklyn, NY; *m:* Pat Louis; *ed:* Hofstra Univ (BA) Fin & Banking 1988; Adelphi Univ (MA) Scndry Ed & Math 1992, (MS) Math 1995; *cr:* Herricks Union Free Schl Dist 9th-12th Grd Math Tchr 1992-; *ai:* World Hunger & Awareness Club Adv; Herricks 2000 Comm; *office:* Herricks HS 100 Shelter Rock Rd New Hyde Park NY 11041*

PERZ, ERVA KAY, Fifth Grade Teacher; *b:* Canton, OH; *m:* Thomas Edward Sr.; *c:* David Huffman, Doug Huffman, Dann Hobson, Kathy, Tom Jr.; *ed:* Kent St Univ (BA) Elem Ed 1964, (MA) Master Tchr 1980; Post Grad Stud Elem Ed 32 Hrs; *cr:* Canton City Schl Tchr 1956-58, 1964-65, 1968-71; Brunswick City Schl Tchr 1972-; *ai:* Mohican Outdoor Schl; Young Author Coord; Brunswick Ed Assn 1972-, Rep; Delta Kappa Gamma 1986-; Tchr of Yr Candidate; *office:* Hickory Ridge Elem Schl 4628 Hickory Ridge Dr Brunswick OH 44212

PESCA, JOSEPH G., Social Studies Teacher; *b:* Brooklyn, NY; *m:* Neile Katzer; *c:* Michael, Lauren; *ed:* St Johns Univ (BS) Ed 1960, (MS) Guid 1963; Addl 60 Post Grad Credits; *cr:* Hewlett Elem Schl 5th Grd Tchr 1960-64; Ogden Elem Schl 6th Grd Tchr 1964-80; Woodmere MS 6th Grd Math, Soc Stud Tchr 1980-; *ai:* Geog Bee Adv; AFT, NEA 1960-; Hewlett Woodmere FA 1960-, Rep, VP; *office:* Woodmere MS 1170 Peninsula Blvd Hewlett NY 11557

PESCATELLO, NANCY NOLIN, Sixth Grade Teacher; *b:* Brattleboro, VT; *m:* Frank C. Sr.; *c:* Jack, Frank Jr.; *ed:* Keene St Coll (BA) His 1969; 18 Hrs Post Grad Stud in Ed; *cr:* Saint Michaels Elem Schl Tchr 1969-74; Saint Edward Elem Schl Tchr 1975-76; Stratford Pub Schls Remedial Math & Rdng Instr 1983-84; Saint Mary Star of the Sea Schl 6th-8th Grd His Tchr 1984-; *ai:* Stock Market Game Moderator; Local Schl Level Natl His Day Coord; Natl His Day Advy Bd Regnl Dist Level; Stu Cncl Moderator; NCEA 1984-; 1992 Natl His Day Tchr of Merit Awd; *office:* St Mary Star Of The Sea Schl 10 Huntington St New London CT 06320

PESCATORE, GLORIA SPROCH, Sixth Grade Teacher; *b:* Aliquippa, PA; *w:* William J. (dec); *c:* Heather J., Leslie A., Nathan A.; *ed:* Edinboro Univ of PA (BS) Elem Ed 1970, (MA) Elem Ed 1973; *cr:* 4th Ward Elem 4th Grd Tchr 1970-75; Latrobe MS 6th Grd Tchr 1975-85; Latrobe Elem Schl 6th Grd Tchr 1985-; *ai:* GLEA, PSEA, NEA 1970-; Latrobe Jr Womens 1972-77, Pres; Holy Family Church, Cncl 1993-; *home:* 1527 Ligonier St Latrobe PA 15650

PESCE, CAROL ANNE, Math Teacher; *b:* Chelsea, MA; *c:* Adam Medeiros, Matthew Medeiros; *ed:* Bridgewater St Coll (BA) Math 1974; RI Coll (MAT) Math 1978; Grad Work Univ of MA at Dartmouth, Univ of MA at Boston, Bridgewater St Coll; *cr:* Dartmouth HS Math Tchr 1974-83; Bishop Connolly HS Physics, Math Tchr 1983-; *ai:* Fac Welfare Comm; *office:* Bishop Connolly HS 373 Elsbree St Fall River MA 02720*

PESCE, LINDA D., Spanish Teacher; *b:* Hackensack, NJ; *ed:* Georgian Ct coll (BA) Span 1977; Univ of AZ (MA) Span 1983; Attnd Univ of Northern AZ, Univ of San Diego at Guadalajara; *cr:* Cntrl Regnl HS Span Tchr 1977-81; Georgian Ct Coll Adj Span Instr 1979-92; Univ of San Diego Summer Span Tchr 1989-; Cedar Dr MS Span Tchr 1981-; *ai:* Yrbk Adv; MS, Liaison Comms; Coord 8th Grd WA Trip; NJEA, NEA, FLENJ, AATSP, ACTFL 1977-; Alpha Delta Kappa 1987-, Pres Elect NJ Iota Chptr; Grants; Governor's Tchr of Yr in Colts Neck Awd; *office:* Cedar Drive MS 73 Cedar Dr Colts Neck NJ 07722*

PESDA, JOHN LAWRENCE, History Professor; *b:* Shamokin, PA; *m:* Pauline; *c:* John, William; *ed:* Bloomsburg St U (BS) His, Scndry Ed 1962; Kent St U (MA) His 1964, (PHD) His 1971; *cr:* Miami Univ Instr His 1968-71; PA St U at Hazelton Adj Instr 1972; Camden Cty Coll Prof 1972-; *ai:* Phi Theta Kappa Adv; NEA 1976-, Local Pres; Lower Camden Co 1978-; Regnl Bd of Ed 1993-, Pres; AAUW NJ 1995-, Exec Bd; Alice Paul Centennial Fnd 1995-; NJ Inst for Collegiate Tchng Fellow 1989; Women's Pol Caucus NJ Good Guy Awd 1993; Camden Cty Women's Commission Awd 1994; TV Talk Show Host Tri Cty Headlines Jones Intercable; *office:* Camden County Coll PO Box 200 Blackwood NJ 08012

PESEK, JAMES GREGORY, Prof of Mgmt & Dept Chair; *b:* Cleveland, OH; *m:* Karen Westfall; *c:* Seth, Bryn; *ed:* Bowling Green St Univ (BS) Ec 1974, (MA) Ec 1975; Univ of Pittsburgh (PHD) Human Resources Mngmt 1984; *cr:* City of Cleveland Labor Market Analyst 1975-77; Mercyhurst Coll Asst Prof of Bus 1977-80; Clarion Univ Prof of Mngmt 1980-; *ai:* Fac Adv; Soc for Human Resources Mngmt Clarion Univ Stu Chptr; Fac Senate; PA St System of Higher Ed Acad Advy Cncl; Acad of Mngmt 1985-; Soc for Human Resources Mngmt 1988-; Clarion Little League 1994-95, Coach, Mgr; First Recipient Dean's Awd for Fac Excl 1991; Grant Recipient PA Acad for Profession of Tchng 1990; Pub Articles; *office:* Clarion Univ Of PA Coll of Bus Admin Clarion PA 16214

PESEK, JOHN RUDOLPH, Science Teacher; *b:* Woodside, NY; *m:* Carol Lynn Dochterman; *ed:* SUNY at Stony Brook (BS) Earth, Space Sci 1972; Univ of VA (MA) Sci Ed 1974; 60 Credits Hrs Grad Level Courses; *cr:* Mid Cntry Schl Dist Sci Tchr 1974-; *ai:* Sci Tchrs Assn of NYS 1992-; NYS United Tchrs, Mid Cntry Tchrs Assn, AFT 1974-; *office:* Centereach HS 14 43rd St Centereach NY 11720

PESKOWITZ, SANDRA, Kindergarten Teacher; *b:* New York, NY; *m:* Bernard; *ed:* Bernard M. BAruch CCNYU (AAS) Bus 1964; City Coll (BBA) bus 1967; Hunter Coll (MS) Ed 1971; *cr:* PS 87 Queens Tchr 1967-; *ai:* Penny Harvest for Needy Children Dir.

PESOTSKI, RONALD ROBERT PETER, Social Studies Teacher; *b:* Chester, PA; *m:* Susan Neely; *c:* Christopher, Carin, Matthew; *ed:* Villanova Univ (AB) His 1968; Univ of DE (MA) Amer Stud 1973; Post Grad Studs Penn St, IN Univ of PA, Widener Univ; *cr:* Pennsville Meml HS Soc Stud Tchr 1968-70; Sanford Schl Soc Stud Tchr 1970-72; Sun Vly HS Soc Stud Tchr 1973-84; DE Cty Comm Coll His Tchr 1984-86; Sun Vly HS Soc Stud Tchr 1987-; *ai:* NEA 1968-, Spec Achvmt 1983; PA St Ed Assn 1973-, Bd of Dir 1978-84; PA Delco Ed Assn 1973-, Pres 1974-79; NCSS 1988-, PA Cncl; PA St Constable 1981-; Bureau of Schl Audits Dir 1985-87.*

PESSAH, NATHAN VICTOR, Science & Health Teacher; *b:* New York, NY; *m:* Robert Palmer Fels; *c:* Tamera, Michelle; *ed:* Brooklyn Coll (BA) Ec 1957; NY Univ (MA) Rdng 1968; St John's Univ (PD) Curr & Tchng 1974; LIU CW Port Campus (PD) Admin & Supv 1988; Attending St John's for Doctorate in Instrl Ldrshp; *cr:* PS 158K Tchr 1966-69; Bronx Comm Coll Rdng Instr, Study Skills 1969-73; Jr HS 50K Rdng Tchr 1973-75; PS 163Q Rdng Tchr, Common Br 1975-, Env Sci, Hlth K-16 Spec Ed 1975-; *ai:* Engaged in Extensive Programming, Leading of Environmental Field Trips; UFT 1968-, Del; Ed for Gateway 1991-, VP Soc Prgms; Elem Schl Sci Assn 1989-; NYSOEA 1993-; Temple Judea of Manhasset 1982-, Trustee; Hudson River Sloop 1990-; ERIC Rsrch in Rdng 1975; *home:* 75 Barberry Ln Roslyn Heights NY 11577

PESSOLANO, CHRISTINE KOWAL, First Grade Teacher; *b:* New Kensington, PA; *m:* James O.; *c:* Diane, David; *ed:* Coll of Steubenville (BS) Elem Ed 1964; Elem Ed Instructional II; *cr:* Plum Boro Schl Dist Fourth Grd Tchr 1964-65; Roanoak Cty Schl Dist Ungraded Primary 1965-66; St. Benedict Schl First Grd Tchr 1978-; *ai:* NCEA 1978-; Nom Simply the Best Tchr; Univ Scholars Prgm Distinguished Tchr of Honors Stdnts PA St Univ; *home:* 228 Maplewood Dr Johnstown PA 15904

PETCHIK, MARIAN, High School Math Teacher; *b:* Baltimore, MD; *ed:* Immaculata Coll (BA) Math 1970; Johns Hopkins Univ (MED) Ed 1974, (MS) Admin & Supervision 1979; 30 Credit Hrs Beyond Masters; *cr:* Towson HS Math Tchr 26 Yrs; *ai:* Open House Comm Chair; Schl & Bus Partnership Comm Mem; Svc Learning Comm Stu Adv; Asst Scheduling of Stdnts; Towson Support Line Comm; NEA 1971-; MSTA 1971-; TABCO 1971-; NCTM 1971-; WEBCO 1971-, Pres 1995; CAC 1974-, Pres 1982-,

Baltimore CAC of Yr 1981; St Ursula Church 1990-, Eucharistic Minister; Delta Kappa Gamma 1992-, Fin Comm Chair; Baltimore Cty Prof Stud Days Math in Art Presenter; *office:* Towson HS 69 Cedar Ave Baltimore MD 21286*

PETE, STEPHEN J., Amer History & Govt Teacher; *b:* Ithaca, NY; *m:* Paula M.; *c:* Stephen, Amy, Joseph; *ed:* SUNY at Brockport (BS) His 1970; 40 Grad Hrs Ed, His; *cr:* Hoover Drive Jr HS Tchr 1971-85; Olympia HS Tchr 1986-; *ai:* Textbooks, Budget Ad Hoc Comms; NEA, NY Ed Assn 1971-; Greece Tchrs Assn 1971-, Bldg Rep 15 Yrs; Hilton-Parma Recreation 1981-93, Coach.

PETELLE, LINDA F., Spanish Teacher; *b:* Willard, OH; *c:* Sheri, Wendy; *ed:* Denison Univ (BS) Span, Fr 1965; Salem St Coll (MED) Guidance 1977, (MED) Admin 1990; *cr:* Danvers HS Span Tchr 1965-86, 1994-; Danvers Pub Scls Dept Chm, Foreign Lang 1986-94; *ai:* MaFLA 1986-; ECLAT 1986-, Chm; Kiwanis 1986-94; *office:* Danvers HS 60 Cabot Rd Danvers MA 01923

PETER, C. LEE, High School Math Teacher; *b:* Hicksville, OH; *m:* Pamela K. Shull; *c:* Chad Peter; *ed:* Defiance Coll (BS) Math 1972; Bowling Green St Univ (MS) Scndry Admin 1982; *cr:* Hicksville HS Math Tchr 1972-; *ai:* Head Bsbl Coach; NEA 1972-; OCMT 1992-; *office:* Hicksville Exempted Vlg Schls Cr Smith & Main Hicksville OH 43526

PETER, SHARON KULP, Third Grade Teacher; *b:* Landsdale, PA; *c:* Elizabeth, Sarah; *ed:* Elizabethtown Coll (BS) Elem Ed 1969; Trenton St Univ (MED) Elem Guidance 1974; *cr:* Harleysville El Schl 4th Grd Tchr 1969-78; St Sylvester El Schl 7th-8th Grd Tchr 1984-89, 3rd-4th Grd Tchr 1989-; *ai:* NEA 1969-78; NCEA 1984-; Woodsfield Presbyn Church 1984-, Elder; *office:* St Sylvester Cntrl Schl 119 Wayne St Woodsfield OH 43793

PETERING, JENNIFER MARIE, Science Teacher; *b:* Oxford, MS; *ed:* Univ of MS (BA) Bio 1990; Towsan St Univ (MED) Scndry Ed 1994; Addl Stud Toxicology Univ of MD; *cr:* Western HS Sci Tchr 1991-94; Hammond HS Sci Tchr 1994-; *ai:* Environmental Club Spon; Crisis Intervention Team; Field Hockey, Sftbl Coach; Soc Comm; NEA, NABT 1994-; Jr Jaycees 1993- Sierra Club 1993-; Save Our Streams 1995-, Bd Mem; Chesapeake Bay Trust Grant; Dept of Natural Resources Grant; Presentation AERA Conf of Masters Rsrch; *office:* Hammond HS 8800 Guilford Rd Columbia MD 21046*

PETERMAN, MARK S., High School Chemistry Teacher; *b:* Muncy, PA; *m:* Robin Nadene Poland; *ed:* Philadelphia Coll Pharmacy & Sci (BS) Bio 1993; Attnd Villanova Univ; West Chester Univ Masters in Chem Pgm; *cr:* Chichester Sr HS Chem Tchr 1993-; *ai:* Environmental Club Adv 1993-; Frosh Ftbl Coach 1994-95; Frosh Bsktbl Coach 1994-; Ski Club Adv 1995-; Sci Olympiad Coach; Environthon Coach; NEA 1993-; *office:* Chichester Sr HS 3333 Chichester Ave Boothwyn PA 19061

PETER-RAOUL, MAR, Rel Studies Asst Professor; *b:* Binghamton, NY; *c:* Jodi Larnerd, Jamie Larnerd, Jory-Pierre Larnerd, Heather Larnerd, Tamathy Larnerd, Heather Larnerd-Eck; *ed:* St Univ of NY at Binghamton (BA) Philosophy, Psych 1979, (MA) Soc Scis 1982; Univ of Notre Dame (MA) Theology 1987; SUNY at Binghamton (PHD) Amer Ethnic Lit 1991; Maryknoll Schl of Theology Advanced Rel Stud in Justice & Peace Cert 1984; *cr:* Broome Comm Coll Adj Prof 1980-84; Coll of Mount St Vincent Continuing Ed Asst Dir 1985-86; SUNY Adj Prof 1988-91; Marist Coll Rel Stud Asst Prof, Praxis Project Coord 1992-; *ai:* Integrative Major Cncl; Holocaust Meml Comm; Hum Lecture Series; Core Organizing Comm for Intnl Peace Conf; Concerned Philosophers for Peace 1993-; Intnl Philosophers for Peace 1994-; Poughkeepsie Inst 1994-95, Organizing Bd; Initiated Praxis Project 1995-; SUNY at Binghamton Adj Fac Outstdng Svc Awd 1991; Danbury Federal Prison Tchr of Yr Awd 1994; Extraordinary Performance Awd 1995-; Articles, Commentary, Poetry, Reviews Pub 1977-; Book: Yearning to Breathe Free, Liberation Thelogies in the US; *office:* Marist Coll 290 North Rd Poughkeepsie NY 12601

PETERS, ANN JULIE,SND, Sr Theology Teacher; *b:* Brooklyn, NY; *ed:* St John's Univ (BA) Eng, Bus 1949; Villanova Univ (MA) Engl959; Fordham Univ (MS) Rel Ed 1972; 6 Credit Hrs St John's Univ Admin; ELI Assoc Cert Effective Admin in Rel Ed; Pastoral Assoc Cert Dioc of Rockville Centre; Harvard Univ Kohlberg Course; *cr:* Remington Rand Inc Sec, AC Payable 1945-49; SS Joachim & Anne Elem Schl 8th Grd Tchr 1952-54; Moylan HS 11-12th Grd Eng, Rel, Bus Tchr 1954-55; Villa Julie Coll Dean of Stdnts, Eng, Bus, Mid Sts Comm 1955-63; Moylan HS 11-12th Grd Eng, Rel Tchr, Guid 1963-64; St Pius X HS 12th Grd Rel Instr, Acad Dean, Mid Sts Chprsn 1964-68; Notre Dame Acad 9-12th Grd Prin 1968-70; St Cath of Genoa Part-Time Dir of Rel Ed 1970-72; St Brigid's Parish Dir of Rel Ed, Pastoral Assoc, Comm Outreach 1972-77; Sacred Heart Acad Theology Chprsn, Retreat Coord, 9-12th Grd Theology Instr 1977-92; St Anthony's HS 11-12th Grd Theology Instr, Campus Ministry Team 1992-; *ai:* Kolbe Soc HS Core Team Retreat Ldrshp Trng; Mid St Dept Chrpsn; NCEA; NDEA; NEA; ASCD; LCWR; NACC; HERMINDAD Bd Mem; Gift of Life Spon; Intnl House of Healing & Hospitality; St Johns Univ Magna Cum Laude Grad; Pub Thesis Medieval Period; *office:* St Anthony's HS 275 Wolf Hill Rd S Huntington NY 11747

PETERS, ANNE, Teacher; *b:* Truro, MA; *ed:* Bridgewater (BS) Ed 1956; Long Island Univ (MS) Tech 1993; *cr:* Woodbury Jr HS Tchr 1956-57; Bergenfield HS Tchr 1957-63; Spring Vly HS Tchr 1963-64; Ramapo Indian HS Tchr 1964-; *ai:* NEA; BCEA; Governor's Tchr Recognition Prgm Outstdng Tchr 1989-90; Establishment of Anne Peters Schlsp by PTSO 1987; Dow Jones Newspaper Spec Recognition Adv 1986.

PETERS, ANTONIA MARI, Assistant Principal; *b:* Washington, DC; *c:* Toyia; *ed:* DC Tchrs Coll (BS) Bus Ed 1976; Univ of DC (MA) Admin, Supervision 1977; 30 Addl Hrs in Rdng; 24 Addl Hrs in Educl Ldrs; *cr:* US Postal Svc Curr Dev Specialist 10 Yrs; DC Pub Schls Rdng Tchr 6 Yrs, Eng Tchr 5 Yrs, Eng Mentor Tchr 2 Yrs, Asst Prin 5 Yrs; *ai:* Local Schl Restructuring Team, Staff Dev, Testing Comm, Pub Relations Admin; HOPE Prgm, Homework Ctr, Amer Ed Week, Pub Address System Coord; Kappa Delta Pi 1976-, Cum Laude; ASCD 1980-; IRA, NCTE 1989-; Downtown Jaycees 1989-, Reviewer; Phi Delta Kappa 1992-; Blue Ribbon Panel 1992-, Evaluator; Agnes Meyer Outstdng Tchr 1989; Ward I Outstdng Tchr; Cafrtiz Tchr Flwshp Grant; Outstdng Coaches Awd for It's Acad Team; Aetna Grant; Region C Outstdng Tchr; *office:* Eastern Sr HS 17th & E Capitol St NE Washington DC 20003

PETERS, ARMAND JOSEPH, Voc Graphic Comm & Prntng Tech; *b:* Berlin, NH; *m:* Teresa H. Holloman; *c:* Danielle, Michelle, Mandy; *ed:* NH Tech Inst (AAE) Electronic Engnrg 1968; Keene St Coll (BSEd) Indstrl Arts 1978, (MAT) Tchng 1993; Naval Air Trng Command; Naval Air Test Ctr Maintenance & Material Mngmt; Naval Air Station Phatom Aircraft Avionics; Naval Air Tech Ctr Aviation Electronics Sci; *cr:* US Navy Electronics Tech 1968-72; Ingersol-Rand Electrical Designer 1972-78; Millpond Graphics Implant Printer 1978-; Nasava Sr HS Voc Graphics Comm & Printing Tech 1978-; *ai:* Graphics Stu Assn Adv; Curr Audit Comm; Hudson Girls Sftbl Team Mgr & League Rep, Umpire; AFT 1978-; Amer Voc Assn 1978-, NH Tchr of Yr 1993; Voc Advy Comm 1978-, Chm, Tchr of Yr 1981; NH Graphic Arts Assn 1980-, Dir, VP, Pres 8 Yrs, Pres Awd 1992, Comm Mem 10 Yrs, H. J. Tyler Awds Comm; Cmptr Grants; Articles Pub; NH Tech Ed Assn Interface; Nashua HS Tchr of Month 1986, 1992; *office:* Nashua Sr HS 36 Riverside Dr Nashua NH 03062*

PETERS, BARBARA LOOMIS, Mathematics Teacher; *b:* New York City, NY; *m:* Douglas Tilghman; *c:* Derek, Kimberly; *ed:* Beaver Coll (MA) Math 1973; Univ of HI (MED) Remedial Rdng 1980; *cr:* Godwin MS Math Tchr 1973; Warrington MS Math Tchr 1974-75; The Kamehameha Schls Math Tchr 1977-80; Brighton HS Math Tchr 1980-; *ai:* Rdng, Writing & Stud Skills Lab Coord; NEA 1980-; Tchr of Yr Awd; *office:* Brighton HS 1150 Winton Rd S Rochester NY 14618

PETERS, BARRY GEORGE, Band Director; *b:* Allentown, PA; *m:* Joanne Ruspantini; *c:* Katrina, Trisha, Michael, Christopher; *ed:* Mansfield Univ (BS) Music Ed 1970, Ithaca Coll (MM) Music Ed 1972; *cr:* Troy Area Schls Band Dir 1970-71; Hammondsport Cntrl Schl Band Dir 1972-80; Canandaigua Acad Band Dir 1981-85; Liverpool Cntrl Schl Band Dir 1986-88; Union Endicott Cntrl Schl Band Dir 1989-95; *ai:* MENC 1970-; NYSSMA 1972-, Marching Band Chprsn; NYS Band Dirs Assn 1990-, Exec Bd; Bands of Amer Natl Championship Finalist; *office:* Union Endicott HS 1200 E Main St Endicott NY 13760

PETERS, BARRY W., English Teacher; *b:* Hartford, CT; *m:* Susan Jane; *c:* Katherine; *ed:* OH Univ (BA) Eng 1982; Wright St Univ Masters Degree, Eng Fiction Wrtng 1995; *cr:* Manchester Journal Inquirer Sports Writer 1983-85; Tiffin Advertiser Tribune Sports Ed 1985-87; Dayton Daily News Sports Layout Ed 1987-90; Centerville HS Eng Tchr 1990-; *ai:* Fiction Writing Wkshp Dir; *office:* Centerville HS 500 E Franklin St Centerville OH 45459

PETERS, BRUCE E., Mathematics Teacher; *b:* Butler, PA; *m:* Karen L. Eroline; *c:* Kirk C., Amber L.; *ed:* Clarion Univ (BA) Math Ed 1969, (MA) Math 1971; 12 Post-Grad Credit Hrs Cmptr Sci; *cr:* Latimer MS Math Tchr 1969-79; Peabody HS Math Tchr, Dept Head 1979-; *ai:* Instructional Cabinet; Engineering, Cmptr Club; Math Team; AFT, PFT 1969-; Lions Club 1982-, Pres, Treas; Phi Sigma Kappa 1967-, Pres, Treas; All Star Educator Univ of PA 1993; Nom Pittsburgh Math Tchr of Yr 1994; Runner Up Western PA Space Camp Tchr Awd 1995; *office:* Peabody HS 515 N Highland Ave Pittsburgh PA 15206

PETERS, CHRISTAL WIKOFF, Secondary English Teacher; *b:* Cincinnati, OH; *c:* Elizabeth Nell, Katherine Grace; *ed:* Miami Univ (BA) Eng 1983, (BS) Ed 1983, (MA) Speech, Orgnl Comms 1984; OH Writing Project 1988; Admin Dev Acad 1985; *cr:* Milford HS Eng Tchr 1984-; Communicate Inst Course Facilitator 1995-; *ai:* Milford United Meth Church, Loveland Stage Co 1989-; Friends of the Groom 1985-; *office:* Milford HS 1 Eagles Way Milford OH 45150*

PETERS, CLIFFORD SIMPSON, Eighth Grade English Teacher; *b:* Greenwich, CT; *m:* Wilhelmina Ossorio; *c:* Pilar, Victoria; *ed:* Rollins Coll (BA) His 1974; Pace Univ (MSEd) Schl Admin 1985; *cr:* Iona Preparatory Schl Comm Arts, Eng Tchr 1982-85; Hackley Schl Eng Tchr 1985-; *ai:* 8th Grd Adv; MS Track & Field Coach; MS Search Comm; HS Boys, Girls Rowing Club Coach 1992-; US Rowing Assn Bronze Medal Natl Championship 1989; *office:* Hackley Schl 293 Benedict Ave Tarrytown NY 10591*

PETERS, DAVID ALLAN, Study Skills Teacher; *b:* Piqua, OH; *m:* Marcia Ann Sprunger; *c:* LaChelle, Matthew; *ed:* Cedarville Coll (BAEd) Speech, 7-12 Eng 1972; Univ of Akron (MAEd) Scndry Prin 1978; Cooperative Learning 2 Hrs; Essential Elements of Instruction 4 Hrs; Ind Stud 2 Hrs; Beyond Assertive Discipline 3 Hrs; *cr:* Buckeye Local Schls 7th-8th Grd Eng Tchr 1972-75; Medina Career Ctr GED Tchr 1976-77; Revere Local Schls 8th Grd Eng, 6-8 Grd Stud Skills Tchr 1976-; *ai:* Spelling Bee Co-Chm; 7-8th Grds Girl's Bsktbl, Track; Revere Ed Assn; OH Ed Assn, NEA 1993-; Gideons Intnl 1982-; Stu, Tchr, Parent Stud Skills Manuals Copyrighted; Hold Parents & Tchrs Wkshps; Tchr of Yr 1986; *office:* Revere Local Schls 3496 Everett Rd Bath OH 44210*

PETERS, DENISE WRIGHT, English Teacher; *b:* Louisville, KY; *m:* Carl D.; *c:* Dora; *ed:* Univ of Louisville (BA) Eng 1977, (MA) Eng 1982; *cr:* Univ of Louisville Dept Asst, Tchng Asst, Lecturer 1977-82; Our Lady of Mercy Acad Eng, Algebra Tchr 1983-85; Holy Cross HS Eng Tchr 1986-; *ai:* NACT, NCEA 1986-; Coalition for Ed Choice 1993-; Pres's, 2 Arts & Scis, 2 Alpha Kappa Gamma Schlsps; Wrote Tchrs Guide; *office:* Holy Cross HS 5035 S Rt 130 Delran NJ 08075

PETERS, DOLORES J., Retired Teacher; *b:* Youngstown, OH; *m:* Thomas E.; *c:* Karen Faiola, Dan; *ed:* Youngstown St Univ (BS) Elem Ed 1966, (MS) Curr 1981; *cr:* Cleveland Elem Schl Tchr 1966-95; *ai:* Stu, Safety Cncl Adv; YEA, OEA, NEA 1966-; PTA Cncl 1966-, Sec; Grant for Rdng Ed 1968; Worked with JAVTS 1995; *home:* 4042 Cascade Dr Youngstown OH 44511*

PETERS, GREGORY G., Music Teacher; *b:* Erie, PA; *m:* Dawn Ellen Naylor; *c:* Adam, Jacqulyn; *ed:* Mercyhurst Coll (BM) Music Ed 1990; Grad Stud Duquesne Univ 9 Credits; *cr:* Fort LeBouef HS Music Tchr 1991; Conneaut Schl Dist Music Tchr 1992-; *ai:* Show Choir, Barbershop Singers & HS Singing Ladies Adv; PMEA 1987-; PSEA 1991-; NEA 1991-; Linesville First Bapt Church Praise & Worship Music Dir & Svc Coord; *office:* Linesville Conneaut Summit HS RR 3 Box 135E Linesville PA 16424

PETERS, JAMES AMBROSE,JR., Math & Cmptr Programming Tchr; *b:* Cincinnati, OH; *m:* Margaret R.; *c:* Carrie, Jamie, Kyle; *ed:* Univ of Dayton (BA) Ec 1971; OH Univ (MA) Ec 1973; Wright St Univ Scndry Schl Cert, Cmptr Programming & Math; Sinclair Comm Coll Cmptr Programming; *cr:* Archbishop Alter HS Math & Cmptr Programming Tchr 1974-; *ai:* Chess Club Adv; Moderator Cmptr Club; NHS Adv; OCEA 1974-; Kettering Amateur Bsbl Commission 1988-, Mgr 1988-; Natl Youth Sports Coaches Assn 1989-; Univ of Dayton Marianist Schlsp Valedictorian HS Class; OH Univ Research Assistantship; *office:* Archbishop Alter HS 940 E David Rd Kettering OH 45429

PETERS, JAMES FLOYD, Physics Teacher; *b:* Larimer, PA; *m:* Bonnie Odeana Pyle; *c:* Douglas J., Erin R.; *ed:* IN Univ of PA (BA) Ed & Phys Sci 1963, (mED) Sci 1969; 12 Credit Hrs Gifted Ed & 4 Credit Hrs Spcl Topics; *cr:* Norwin Schl Dist Phys Sci Tchr 1963-82, Physics Tchr 1982-; *ai:* NEA 1963-; PSEA 1963-; Norwin EA 1963-, Treas, Del; Norwin Tchrs Fed Credit Union 1965-, Bd Mem; *office:* Norwin Sr HS McMahon Dr North Huntingdon PA 15642

PETERS, JEANETTE NEVERS, Health & Physical Ed Teacher; *b:* Island Falls, ME; *m:* Kenneth L.; *ed:* Avoostook St Tchrs Coll (BS) Hlth, PE, Rec 1966; MAHPER, Dance Cert; *cr:* Caribou Jr HS Hlth, PE 1966-68; Eastern HS PE 1969; Ft Fairfield HS Hlth, PE 1970-; *ai:* Sr Class Adv; Head of Dept Hlth, PE; Field Hockey, Soccer, Bsktbl, Sftbl Coach; Stu Asst, Support Team; MTA, NEA 1966; FFTA, ME Coaches Assn 1970-; Svc Learning 1995-; Svc Learning Mentor 1995; Yrbk Dedication 1975, 1994; Natl Girls, Womens Sports UMPI 1992; Tchr of Yr, Ath Hall of Fame at UMPI 1996; *office:* Ft Fairfield HS Presque Isle St Fort Fairfield ME 04742*

PETERS, JOANN TAURA, US His, Govt & Ec Teacher; *b:* Brooklyn, NY; *m:* Brian E.; *c:* Danielle, Gregory, Christopher, Mary; *ed:* Fordham Univ (BA) Scndry Ed 1970, (MS) Scndry Ed 1973, (PD) Admin & Supervision 1977; *cr:* Louis D Brandeis HS Soc Stud Tchr 1970-76; John F Kennedy HS Soc Stud Tchr 1976-78; Ft Hamilton HS Sub Tchr 1982-84; Midwood HS Soc Stud Tchr 1993-; *ai:* Forum Magazine Fac Adv; UFT 1970-; AFT 1970-; ASCD 1973-; *office:* Midwood HS 2839 Bedford Ave Brooklyn NY 11210*

PETERS, KAREN LEE (MARSHALL), French Teacher; *b:* Niskayuna, NY; *m:* Robert Joseph; *c:* Douglas, Steven; *ed:* SUNY at Oswego (BA) Elem Ed, Fr 1969; SUNY at Albany (MS) Educl Comm 1874; *cr:* Altamont Elem Schl Tchr 1969-75; Draper MS Fr Tchr 1985-; *ai:* Rotterdam-Mohonasen Goals 2000 Steering, Scheduling Comm; Lang Club Adv; Jr NHS Advy Cncl; Acad 2000 Goals Comm; Mohonasen Tchrs Assn, NYSAFLT 1985-; AATF 1989-, Prof du 1992, 1994; Sports Boosters 1993-; Music Parents 1989-, Orientation Chprsn; Fisher United Meth Church 1960-, Nor Comm; Rotterdam Neighborhood Watch 1996; *office:* Draper M Curry Rd Schenectady NY 12303*

PETERS, KAREN NELSON, First Grade Teacher; *b:* Bowie, Stephen Forrest; *c:* Alyson Dooley Brown; *ed:* TX Tech Univ (B Ed 1966; Grad Work North TX St Univ Early Chldhd Ed, Millersv Elem Ed; *cr:* Hurst-Euless-Bedford Schl Dist First Grd Tchr Arlington ISD First Grd, Fourth Grd Tchr 1969-79; West Shore S First Grd Tchr 1979-; *ai:* Instrl Support TeamMem; NEA 1966-; P West Shore Ed Assn 1979-; Tchr of Yr Roark Elem 1975; Tchr of Y Elem 1979; *office:* Hillside Elem Schl 7th & Sharon Sts New Cu PA 17070

PETERS, KATHERINE HAYDEN, Secondary English Teac Potsdam, NY; *m:* Fay E. III; *c:* Jeffrey, Jennifer; *ed:* SUNY at (BA) Eng Ed 1972; SUNY at Potsdam 30 Addl Hrs; *cr:* Hermon Cntrl Schl Scndry Eng Tchr 1972-; *ai:* Yrbk Adv; NYSUT 172- Hermon-De Kalb Central Schl 709 E DeKalb Rd De Kalb Junc 13630

PETERS, KATHLEEN ANN, Latin Teacher; *b:* Mansfield, Stephen M., Brian J., Jonathan A.; *ed:* Univ of Dayton (BS) Sc 1969; Univ of CT (MS) Scndry Ed 1974; Univ of Dayton, Miami U Grad Stud; *cr:* Pleasant Run Jr HS Tchr 1969-76; White Oak Jr 1977-78; Wyoming MS Tchr 1982-83; Fairfield HS Tchr 1983-; Club Adv; NEA 1969-; Amer Classical League 1982-; Phi Delta 1995-; *office:* Fairfield HS 1111 Nilles Rd Fairfield OH 45014

PETERS, LARRY E., Professor of Physics; *b:* Hagerstown, MD Inst of Tech (BS) Math & Physics 1965; Univ of Toledo (MS) Eng Sci 1969; *cr:* NASA Nuclear Scientist 1965-73; Westinghouse Corp Sr Engineer 1973-80; Sci Applications Inc Sr Consultant CCAC Physics Prof 1981-; *ai:* Dept Phys Sci Chm; Allegheny Obs Univ of Pittsburgh Observer; Flying; AAPT, AFT 1983-; NASA Achvmt Awd; Pub Articles Nuclear Reactor Operation & Safety; Comm Coll Allegheny County 595 Beatty Rd Monroeville PA 151

PETERS, MARGARET LOUISE, English Teacher; *b:* Roxborou *ed:* Glassboro St Coll (BA) Scndry Eng 1971; Rowan Coll (M Relations 1995; Elem Endorsement Cert Rutgers Univ K-8 Gr Villanova Univ Stu Motivation Course Summer 1987; *cr:* Edgew Schl Eng Tchr 1971-73; Washington Twp Schl MS & HS Eng Tchr *ai:* Girls Bsktbl, Ftbl, Bsktbl, Chrldng Coach; Vol Assist Peer Faci NEA, NJEA 1971-; WTEA Bldg Rep 1992-; WTEA Comm Newsletter Ed 1986-87; Jaycee Bike-Hike-A-Thon 1973-90 Tchr R in Various Fund Raisers for Stdnts; Involved With Preparing C Centered Act; *office:* Washington Twp HS 509 Hurffville Cross Sewell NJ 08080

PETERS, NORAH DUGAN, Sociology Professor; *b:* Darby, PA; Davis; *c:* Reilly Dempsey; *ed:* Rosemont Coll (BA) Sco Sci 197 Mawr Coll (MA) Sociology 1984, (PHD) Sociology 1988; *cr:* Phila Geriactric Ctr Sr Rsrch Scientist 1988-94; Beaver Coll Asst Prof Chair of Sociology & Anthropology 1994-; *ai:* Comm for the Prote Rsrch Subjects; Class of 1998 Adv; Amer Sociological Assoc Geratological Soc of Amer 1989-; Rosemont Coll Friends of the Lib Pres; Natl Inst of Mental Hlth Rsrch Grant; Articles Pub; *office:* Coll 450 S Easton Rd Glenside PA 19038

PETERS, PATRICIA A., Art & Social Studies Teacher; *b:* Lou MO; *ed:* Loyola Univ at New Orleans (BA) Fine Art 1971, (MED Media 1977; Post Grad Work New Orleans & Europe Art, Photo Video, Ed, Soc Stud, Cmptr Tech; *cr:* OK Parochial Schls 6th-7th G 1964-68; New Orleans Parochial Schls 7th-8th Art Tchr 1969-7 Orleans Pub Schls, HS Art, Photography, Media, Soc Stud Tchr 1 Germany Dept of Defense Dependents Schls 7th-8th Grd Tchr 1 Art, Soc Stud HS Tchr 1984-; *ai:* Govt Tech Project Pilot Tchr; CSC for Spec Ed Dept; Site Team AVID Prgm; Art Exhibits; NHS Comm OEA, FEA 1984-; Art Exhitits OK, LA, MO, Germany; Book Illus

PETERS, ROBERT J., Technology Teacher; *b:* Staten Island, Karen Marshall; *c:* Douglas, Steven; *ed:* SUNY at Oswego (BS) 1970; SUNY at Albany (MS) Ed Comm 1976; *cr:* Bethlehem HS Te 26 Yrs; *ai:* Cmptr Club Adv; Curr, Bethlehem Dist Tech, Tech NEA, NY Tchrs Assn, Bethlehem Tchrs Assn, NYS Tech Assn Mohonasen Schl Bd 1981-92, Elected Mem Bd of Ed; Mohonasen Boosters 1993-; MOhonasen Music Assoc 1989-; Rotterdam Neighb Watch 1996-; Fisher United Meth Church 1970-; Dev Engrng Grant; Constructed Homemade Electric Vehicle 1985; NYS Schl Bd Presentor, Mem 1981-92; *office:* Bethlehem Cntrl HS 700 Delawa Delmar NY 12054

PETERS, SAM, Printmaking Instructor; *b:* Princeton, WV; *m:* C Elder; *ed:* Univ of Charleston (BS) His 1961; WV UNIV (MA) Hi Univ of MD (MFA) Printmaking 1986; *cr:* Maryland Inst Coll Part-time Instr Printmaking 1986-; *ai:* MD Printmakers 1989-, F Former Pres; Southern Graphics Cncl 1987-; Amer Print Alliance Sec-Treas; *home:* 410 E 31st St Baltimore MD 21218

PETERS, SUSAN A., Mathematics Teacher; *b:* Allentown, P Kutztown Univ of PA (BS) Sec Ed, Math 1987; West Chester Univ (MA) Math 1991; *cr:* Twin Vly HS Math Tchr 1987-; *ai:* Strategic Pl Comm; NEA, PSEA 1987-; TVEA 1987-, VP; NCTM, PCTM Rutgers Univ Ldrshp Prgm Discrete Math; *office:* Twin Valley HS Box 51 Elverson PA 19520

PETERS, SUSAN BERRY, Mathematics Teacher; *b:* Worchester, Richard James; *c:* Amy M., Mindy N., Christopher M., Andrew Westfield St Coll (BA) Math 1970; Lowell Technological Inst Math 1974; 3 Grad Credits Eastern Nazarene Coll; 3 Grad Southwest TX St Coll; 3 Grad Credits St Mary's Univ; 3 Grad Cred Angeles Metropolitan Coll; 1 Grad Credit Univ of MO; 3 Grad Cred Lady of the Lake Univ; 3 Grad Credits Smith Coll; 3 Grad Credits Acad; *cr:* Carlisle MS Math Tchr 1970-71; Bromfield Schl Mat 1971-76; Del Rio Jr HS Math Tchr 1976-82; Wagner MS Mat 1982-86; Valparaiso Jr HS Math Tchr 1986-89; Okaloosa Walton Coll Math Instr 1989-91; Amherst Regnl Jr HS Math Tchr 1991-92 Springfield Jr HS Math Tchr 1992-93; Longmeadow HS Math Tchr *ai:* Stu Cncl Adv 1991-92; Harvard Tchrs Assn Treas; Del to MTA 19 Fac Rep TX 1977-81; Schl Wide Action Plan 1983-84; Edctrs Day 1984-85; Talent Pool Comm 1984-86; Admissions Comm 1990-91 Ctr Comm 1990-91; Sftbl, Bsktbl, Var, Jr Var Chrldr Coach 1970-76 Leagues Adv, Coach 1977-93; NCTM, NEA 1970-; MTA 1970-76, LEA 1993-; Harvard Org for Parents, Edctrs, Stdnts 1971-74, Ed Journal; Teen Ctr 1973-76, Bd Adv; Explorer Scout 1975-76; Schl Comm 1984-86; Base ADvy Comm 1984-86; Guid Comm 1987-8 Chrpsn 1971-74; Diversay Club 1991-92, Comm; Builders Club 19 Adv; Presentor of Technology Enhanced Teaching Across the Curri 1990 NISOD Intnl Conf; Dev & Implemented Checklist Reporting S 1974, Individualized Instr 1977-78, Enrichment Prgm 1978-79, Syl for Trigonometry Analytical Geometry Calculus for Cntrl TX Coll, Course Math Counts for Addie R. Lewis JHS Textbook Comm 19

asic Math Syllabus for Criminal Justice Dept 1989-90; *office:* eadow HS 95 Grassy Gutter Rd Longmeadow MA 01106*

RSAVAGE, JOHN RICHARD, Comprehensive English Teacher; *b:* gh, PA; *m:* Clara Marie Paoletti; *c:* Joel; *ed:* St Vincent Coll (BA) 72; Duquesne Univ 40 Credit Hrs Eng Stud; *cr:* South Fayette HS Eng Tchr 1972-; *ai:* PSEA, NEA 1972-; BSA 1992-, Den Ldr; ratic Comm 1995-; Cub Scout Klondike Derby 1992-, Chm; rs Dist Greater Pgh Cncl Pack 262 1994-95, Unit Appreciation Awd; South Fayette HS RR 2 Box 207 A Mc Donald PA 15057

RSEN, DAVID A., PE Teacher & Coach; *b:* Amsterdam, NY; *m:* ne M.; *c:* Thomas, Jon, Jennifer, Jeff; *ed:* Univ of WI at Madison 1971; Attnd Albany St & Saint Rose; *cr:* Fonda-Fultonville Dir & r 25 Yrs; *ai:* Indoor & Outdoor Track Coach; FFCS Tchrs, NEA Moose 1986-; Section 2 & Tri-Valley League Track Chm; Empire St St Track Chm; *office:* Fonda-Fultonville Cntrl Schl Cemetery St NY 12068

SEN, JULIANNE ELIZABETH, Social Studies Teacher; *b:* lphia, PA; *ed:* West Chester Univ (BSEd) Soc Stud 1992; Beaver Glenside Working on Masters Educl Ldrshp; *cr:* Abington Jr HS d Tchr 1992-; *ai:* Schl Musical Custume Dir; Multicultural Comm; eam; Instrl Support Team; NEA, PSEA, Abington Ed Assn 1992-; PA Coll & Tchr Edctrs Outstdng Scndry Stu Tchr Awd 1992; *office:* n Jr HS 2056 Susquehanna Rd Abington PA 19001*

SEN, LAUREL SPINA, Tchr of the Gifted & Talented; *b:* Newark, William; *ed:* Montclair St Univ (BA) PE, Hlth 1973, (BS) Math, Sci 1986; *cr:* Our Lady of Good Counsel Tchr 1973-83; Woodbridge r 1986-; *ai:* Acad Competition Club; Future Problem Solving Club; NEA 1986-; Girl Scouts of Amer 1958-, VP, Thanks Badge; *office:* ridge HS 25 Kelly St Woodbridge NJ 07095

RSEN, MAUREEN JANE MCDONNELL, Math Teacher; *b:* Long NY; *m:* Edward A.; *c:* Christopher, Elizabeth, Brian; *ed:* St Johns BA) Math 1970; *cr:* Mater Christi HS Math Tchr 1970-76; aire Acad Math Tchr 1994-; *ai:* Jr Class Moderator; Mission Club ator; Jr & Sr Prom Moderator; *office:* Lacordaire Acad Scndry 155 e Ave Upper Montclair NJ 07043

RSEN, SUSAN HAMILTON, ESL Teacher; *b:* Newark, NJ; *m:* David; *ed:* Montclair St Coll (BA) Speech, Theatre Arts 1973; oll (MA) Rdng Specialization 1979; 30 Addl Hrs; *cr:* Edison Twp chls Tchr 1974-; *ai:* Equity, Safety Comms; Head Fac; World ers Club; NEA, NJEA, MCEA 1974-; ETEA 1974-, Bldg Rep; NJ BE Inc 1986-; JP Stevens Band, Debate Parents 1994-, Bd at Large, SA 1992-, Fundraising Comm Chair; *office:* Woodrow Wilson MS odrow Wilson Dr Edison NJ 08820

RSON, ANN MARIE, Spcl Education Resource Tchr; *b:* Rockville NY; *ed:* Nassau Comm Coll (AA) Lbrl Arts 1973; Hofstra Univ lem Ed, Psych 1975, (MS) Spec Ed 1977; *cr:* Northern Parkway Schl ills Tchr 1979-81; Walnut Dr Schl Spec Ed Resource Tchr 1981-; ithmetic Coach; Site Base Mngmt Team, Sec; SEPTA Bd; Conflict tion Mediator; Bldg Team, Sec; Nom, ReflectionsComms; Vol, one Events, Evening Meet ings; NEA, NYST, UTA 1978-; SEPTA VP; PTA 1978-; SEPTA Mbrshp, Jenkins Awds; *office:* Walnut St 270 Leslie Ln Uniondale NY 11553*

RSON, ANN MARIE GUIDELLI, 5th-8th Grd Social Stud Tchr; *b:* ork, NY; *c:* Kenneth, Kristen; *ed:* Caldwell Coll (BA) His 1968; *cr:* Anthony Schl Tchr 1968-73, 5th-8th Grd Soc Stud Tchr 1979-; *ai:* Rights Club Moderator; Mid Sts Commission Soc Stud Chprsn; ; NCSS; ASCD; Friend of Lib 1993-; Prepared 10 Gridiron aphy Articles for The Record Newspaper; Presented Geography for Record Newspaper at Giants Stadium; St Anthony Schl ee for Edctr of Yr 1994-95; *office:* Saint Anthony Schl 270 Diamond Ave Hawthorne NJ 07506

RSON, BETTY MORGAN, Art Dept Chairperson & Teacher; *b:* gton, OH; *m:* Roger Lee; *ed:* Sinclaire Comm Coll (AS) Fine Art Univ of Dayton (BS) Art Ed 1988; *cr:* Carroll HS Art Tchr, Dept 8 Yrs; *ai:* Art Club Moderator; OH Soc of Nature Artist 1995-; rg Brush & Palette 1980-; Won a Number of Local Art Awds; *office:* HS 4524 Linden Ave Dayton OH 45432

RSON, BRUCE ROBERT, Earth Science Teacher; *b:* Lakewood, *d:* Baldwin Wallace Coll (BS) (BA) Geology & Ed 1972; Edinboro MED) Earth & Space Sci 1973; Dutchess Comm Coll Cmptr mming; Northwest Comm Coll of WY Geology; *cr:* Edinboro Univ Asst-Geology Dept 1972-73; Mahopac MS Earth Sci Tchr & arium Operator 1973-87; Mahopac HS Earth Sci Tchr 1987-; *ai:* Sci Curr Review & Revise Comm-Southern Tier; AFT & NYSUT STANYS 1993-; *office:* Mahopac HS MH5 Baldwin Place Rd ac NY 10541

RSON, CAMILLE DIANE, Reading & History Teacher; *b:* apolis, MN; *m:* George I. Griffith; *ed:* Valparaiso Univ (BA) Soc 970; U of New Orleans (MA) Rdng 1976; Cleveland St Univ Scndry Spec Ed Cert; *cr:* Rocky River Schls Elem Tchr 1970-73, 1973-76, Tchr 1976-78, Coord Learning Resources 1979-84, HS Asst Prin 9, Pupil Svcs Dir 1989-93, Rdng, His Tchr 1993-; *ai:* NEA 1970-; 1980-; IRA 1976-; League of Women Voters 1989-, Nominating ; Rocky River Comm Challenge 1984-, Charter Mem; Pub Book vs Presented at Spec Ed Confs, Tchr In-Service; *office:* Rocky River 31 Lakeview Rocky River OH 44116*

RSON, CAROL LYNN, High School English Teacher; *b:* field, MA; *m:* Mainert Jordan Jr.; *c:* Laurie, Matthew, Lindsey; *ed:* ll (BA) Eng 1967; Southern CT St Univ (MA) Eng 1978; Univ of g Stud Ger, Japanese 1969-70; *cr:* Rochambeau MS 6th-8th Grd chr 1967-68; Guilford Jr HS 7th-8th Grd Eng Tchr 1968-69; Baldwin h-8th Grd Eng Tchr 1970-73 Calvin Leete Elem Schl K-5th Grd ve Dramatics Tchr 1974-75; The Morgan Schl 9th-12th Grd Eng Tchr *ai:* Cooperating Tchr, Mentor; Stu Tchr Spring 1996; NEA 1978-; , New England Wildflower Soc 1993-; Clan Donnachaidh 1992-; Page Centerfold Tchr in Reed & Bergemans 2nd Edition of in the oom An Introduction to Ed; *office:* The Morgan School Rt 81 Clinton 413

RSON, CAROLYN, Biology Teacher; *ed:* Bates Coll (BA) Art & Simmons Coll (MAT) Ed & Bio 1993; *cr:* Nashoba Regnl HS Bio, gy & Botany Tchr 1993-.

RSON, CYNTHIA C. CARLSON, Art Teacher; *b:* W Lafayette, IN; orge E.; *c:* Holly Renee; *ed:* Rockford Coll (BA) Theatre Arts, Art Univ of MN (MA) Theatre Arts 1972; Columbia Pacific Univ (PHD) e Arts 1993; Attnd SUNY at Fredonia; *cr:* MN Centennial Showboat ctress & Choreographer 1970-71; Chautauqua Cty Schl Bds Theatre Summer Enrichment Prgm Dir 1983-; JAmestown Pub Schls Art 972-; *ai:* Class of 1995 Adv; Art Co-Adv; Schl Improvement Comm; Raiders Marching Band Fall Festival Comm; Chautauqua Cty Art Assn 1972-, Artist; Fluvanna Comm Church 1984-, Choir; Defenders dlife; Audubon Sco; Humane Soc; Who's Who Among Stu in Amer Univ; Book Pub; *home:* 3741 Baker Street Ext Lakewood NY 14750

RSON, DANA ANDREW, French Teacher; *b:* Boston, MA; *m:* n Fern Fryer; *c:* Drew, Ethan, James; *ed:* Coll of the Holy Cross (BA) ng, Lit 1982; IN Univ (MA) Fr Linguistics 1986; Attnd L'Universite Paul Valery 1980-81, Puskin Inst 1983; Post Grad Stud Educl Admin; *cr:* Clearview Reg HS Fr Tchr 1988-89; Lawrence HS Fr Tchr 1989-90; Mount St Joseph Acad Fr Tchr 1990-; *ai:* Stu Senate, Fr Club Adv; Vermont For Lang Assoc 1991-; AATF 1995-; Geraldine R. Dodge Tchng Fellow Awd 1989; Excellent Tchr Awd 1995.*

PETERSON, DEB, Vocal Music Director; *b:* Cornwall, NY; *m:* Ken; *c:* Keva Mosher, Kiera Mosher; *ed:* SUNY at Fredonia (BM) Music Ed 1972; Manthattanville Coll MAT) Music Ed 1978; 50 Grad Hrs; *cr:* Robert E Bell Schl Music Tchr 1972-73; Haldane Cntrl Schl Music Tchr 1973-; *ai:* Jr & Sr Musical & Jr & Sr Choral Dir; Dist Compact Comm; MENC & DLMEA 1967-; AFT & NYSUT 1972-; HFA 1973-, VP; PTA 1973-; PEC 1995-, Steering Comm; Honored by Westchester Cty for Vol Work in Local Womens Jail; *office:* Haldane Cntrl Schl Craigside Dr Cold Spring NY 10516*

PETERSON, DONNELL RICARDO, English & Journalism Teacher; *b:* Washington, DC; *ed:* Bowie St Univ (BS) Eng & Scndry Ed 1993; *cr:* Cntrl HS Eng Tchr 1993-; *ai:* Yrbk Adv; Drama Dir; Intnl Baccalaureate Instr; Kappa Delta Pi 1991-; Sigma Tau Delta 1992-; NEA 1994-; Omega Psi Phi 1992-, Interm Pan Pres; Free & Accepted Mason PHA 1993-, Sr Steward; BSA 1993-, Prof Scout; Intnl Baccalaureate Svc Awd; Article Pub; Herff Jones Yrbk Advs Awd; *office:* Central HS 200 Cabin Branch Rd Capitol Heights MD 20743*

PETERSON, ELLEN F., 4th Grade Teacher; *b:* New Brunswick, NJ; *m:* Andrew; *c:* Jenny, Jay, Jill; *ed:* Kean Coll (BA) Elem Ed 1966; *cr:* Toms River Schls Tchr 1966-72, 1986-; *ai:* Porject Pride Supplemental Instr Rdng, Writing; NJEA, NEA 1966-; *office:* North Dover Elem Schl 1759 New Hampshire Ave Toms River NJ 08755

PETERSON, JOAN ASZUK, Fifth Grade Teacher; *b:* Wilkes-Barre, PA; *w:* Milton William (dec); *c:* Barbara Duggan, Pamela Borek; *ed:* Coll Misericordia (BS) Elem Ed 1953; Grad Courses in Spec Ed Seton Hall Univ, Newark St, Temple Univ; *cr:* Plainfield Pub Schls 3rd-4th Grd Tchr 1953-60; South Plainfield Pub Schl 4th-5th Grd Tchr 1961-78; Plainfield Pub Schls 4th-5th Grd Tchr 1979-86; Our Lady of Fatima 5th Grd Tchr 1988-; *ai:* Mid Sts Accreditation Comm; Pro-Schl Choice, HCA Rep; Testing Coord; NCEA, HSA 1988-; Tchr of Yr 1995; Mentor 1996; *home:* 50 Leland Ave Plainfield NJ 07062

PETERSON, JOHN E., Social Studies Teacher; *b:* Providence, RI; *m:* Laura Dibble; *c:* Brandon, Rowan, Colter; *ed:* Brown Univ (BA) Amer Civilization 1979; RI Coll (MA) His; Addl 57 Grad Hrs; *cr:* Old Sturbridge Village Museum Interpreter 1980-85; Rutland HS Soc Stud Tchr 1985-; Coll of Saint Joseph Arts & Scis Dept Adjunct Fac 1995-; *ai:* Curr Assessment Prgm; Soc Stud Comm Mem; Early Involvement Prgm Supervising Tchr; NEA, VEA, REA 1986-; VT His & Soc Stud Alliance 1988-; Brandon Meth Church 1989-, Trustee; Recipient of Olmstead Awd for Tchng from Williams Coll; *office:* Rutland HS Woodstock Ave Rutland VT 05701*

PETERSON, KATHLEEN DETORIE, Art Teacher; *b:* Baltimore, MD; *m:* Robert Frank Jr.; *c:* Lara; *ed:* Towson St Univ (BS) Ed 1978, (MED) Art Ed 1986; 24 Credit Hrs Insvc & Grad Courses; *cr:* Chadwick & Hillcrest Elem Art Tchr 1978-81; Reisterstown Elem Art Tchr 1981-87; Hereford Mid Art Tchr 1987-; *ai:* NEA, MEA, TABCO 1978-; Chamber of Commerce Excl in Ed Awd 1987; *office:* Hereford MS 712 Corbett Rd Monkton MD 21111

PETERSON, LAUREL S., Adjunct Writing Instructor; *ed:* Wheaton Coll (BA) Psych 1983; Manhattanville Coll (MA) Writing 1995; *cr:* Westchester Bus Inst Adjunct Writing Instr & Dept Chair 1992-; Norwalk Comm Tech Coll Adjunct Writing Instr 1996; *ai:* Inkwell Magazine Editorial Bd; NCTE 1995-; Assn Writing Prgms 1994-; *office:* Norwalk Comm Tech Coll 188 Richards Ave Norwalk CT 06854

PETERSON, MARY-RODNEY BROOKS, Ret Fam Lvng & Hum Sex Tchr; *b:* Baltimore, MD; *w:* George Gibbs (dec); *c:* Caroline Bergren, Laura Gibbs Rostow, Geo Gibbs, Mary Brooks Mullahy; *ed:* Coll of Notre Dame (BA) His 1967; Loyola Coll at Balto (MED) Philosophy, Ed 1970; 24 Addl Grad Credits Ed from Trenton St, Towson Univ, Stockton St Plus Med Society of NJ Aids Symposium 1990-92; *cr:* St Annes Parochial Schl Tchr 1965-66; St Pius X Parochial Schl Tchr 1967-68; Mercy HS Tchr 1968-71; Holy Spirit HS Tchr 1972-, Religion Dept Chprsn 1992-94; *ai:* Sr Class Moderator, Baccalaureate, Graduation, Prom, Sr Activities; Discipline Comm NHS Bd; Steering Comm Mid States Evaluation; NCEA 1972-; SCTO 1984-; Diocesan Lay Tchrs Union; Holy Redeemer Hospice 1986-; 16-34 Comm Assn 1981-; Dev Family Living Course, Aids Ed Plan for Schl; Diocesan Comm Sex Ed for Grammar Schls, Continually Update of Courses.

PETERSON, MEG JOANNA, English Assistant Professor; *b:* Peterborough, NH; *c:* Sam Gonzalez, Marc Gonzalez, Max Gonzalez; *ed:* Franklin Pierce Coll (BA) Interdisciplinary 1979; Univ of NH (PHD) Rdng, Writing Instruction 1991; *cr:* Philbrook Ctr Therapeutic Tchr 1979-81; Devon Lane Schl Tchr 1981-85; Univ Cath Madre y Maestra Prof 1987-91; Plymouth St Coll Asst Prof 1991-; *ai:* NCTE 1980-; NEATE 1991-; IRA 1995-; Articles, Stories Pub; *office:* Plymouth State Coll English Dept Rounds Hall Plymouth NH 03264*

PETERSON, ORVAN B., Professor of Humanities & Eng; *b:* Neola, IA; *m:* Joan T. Chew; *c:* Eric, Kirsten Bazos, Lara; *ed:* Dana Coll (BA) Soc Svc 1955; Univ of MO (MA) Eng 1960; PA St Univ (EdD) Higher Ed 1981; *cr:* Auburn Comm Coll Instr of Eng 1961-63; Monroe Comm Coll Asst Prof of Eng 1963-65; SUNY at Albany Instr of Eng 1966-68; Green Mountain Coll Asst Prof Eng 1968-70; Butler Cty Comm Prof of Hum 1970-; *ai:* Adv FACETS; *home:* 216 Center Ave Butler PA 16001

PETERSON, PATRICIA HERNANDEZ, English Teacher; *b:* Kingston, Jamaica; *m:* Eddie L.; *c:* David, Darrell; *ed:* Syracuse Univ (BA) Lbrl Arts, (MS) Ed 1973; 30 Credit Hrs; *cr:* Syracuse Univ Admin Asst 10 Yrs; Syracuse City Schls Eng Tchr 23 Yrs; *ai:* Intnl Cultural Club Adv; Multicultural Comm; Strategic Action Plan; NYSUT 1973-; Syracuse Tchrs Assn 1973-, Rep; Natl Cncl of Negro Women 1967-, Sec; Delta Sigma Theta 1986-, Soc Action Chprsn; *office:* Nottingham HS 3100 E Genesee St Syracuse NY 13224*

PETERSON, REGINA LISCIO, Sixth Grade Teacher; *b:* Philadelphia, PA; *m:* Dale J.; *ed:* West Chester Univ (BS) Elem Ed 1971; Villanova Univ (MA) Admin 1990; Elem Prin Cert 1992; *cr:* Phoenixville Area Schl Dist 6th Grd Tchr 1971-; *ai:* Stu Assistance Prgm; Curr Comms; NEA, PSEA 1971-; Kappa Delta Pi 1989-; *office:* Phoenixville Area MS 1330 S Main St Phoenixville PA 19460*

PETERSON, RICHARD J., Sixth Grade Teacher; *b:* Philadelphia, PA; *m:* Patricia A. Patton; *c:* Tricia, Erik, Lisa; *ed:* Albright Coll (BA) His 1969; Lehigh Univ (MED) Ed 1971; *cr:* George Wolf Elem Sixth Grd Tchr 1969-; *ai:* NEA 1969-; Northeast Little League, 1984-, Sftbl Commissioner; Hurricane Bsktbl Club; *office:* George Wolf Elem Schl Spruce & Allen Sts Bath PA 18014

PETERSON, SUSAN KENNEDY, Child Development Instructor; *b:* Washington, DC; *m:* Kenneth S.; *c:* Erin, Adam; *ed:* Endicott Coll (AS) Child Dev 1973; Univ of ME at Orono (BS) Child Dev 1975; Salem St (MED) Cnslng 1981; *cr:* Hesser Coll Fac 1989-94; Schl for Lifelong Learning Fac 1991-93; Notre Dame Coll Fac, Advising 1994-; *ai:* Chrldng Fac Adv, Pop Worker; NEAMC 1989-; HSDI Historical Soc 1975-, St Governor; DAR 1971-, Numerous Offices, Outstdng Jr Mem; *office:* Notre Dame Coll 2321 Elm St Manchester NH 03104

PETERSON, TAMARA JEAN, Asst Prof of Fndtn Studies; *b:* Pittsburgh, PA; *ed:* Columbus Coll of Art & Design (BFA) Fine Arts, Painting 1983; OH Univ (MFA) Painting 1986; *cr:* Columbus Coll of Art & Design Asst Prof Fnd Stud 1986-; *ai:* Curr, Schlsp Comms; Fac Adv to Admissions 1988-92; Natl, Regnl Fine Art Exhibitions; Greater Columbus Arts Cncl Awds 1989, 1995; *office:* Columbus Coll Of Art & Design 107 N Ninth St Columbus OH 43215

PETERSON, VICKI PIERCE, 3rd Grade Teacher; *b:* Wilmington, DE; *m:* Robert B.; *c:* Charles A. Martin IV, Kristine M. Connors; *ed:* Univ of DE (BS) Ed 1972; Addl 30 Credits Master Degree Prgm at Univ of DE; Addl 15 Credit Hrs; *cr:* Upper Penns Neck Regnl Schl Dist 5th Grd Tchr 1972-73; Lewes MS 6th Grd Tchr 1976-81; Shields Elem Schl 3rd Grd Tchr 1981-; *ai:* After Schl Tutoring; NEA, DSEA 1972-; CHEA 1977-; Delmarva Power Grant 1996; PTA Local Grants 1995; *office:* Richard A Shields Elem Schl Sussex Dr Lewes DE 19958

PETERSON, VIOLET, Arts & Crafts Teacher; *b:* New York City, NY; *c:* Richard, Stephen, John; *cr:* Most Precious Blood Schl Arts & Crafts Tchr 1972-; *ai:* Dir of Origami Club; Contest, Art Fair Coord; NCEA 1986-; *office:* Most Precious Blood Schl 32-52 37th St Long Island City NY 11103

PETERSON-STREIT, JO ANN RUTH, Guidance Counselor; *b:* Grand Rapids, MI; *m:* Allen J. Streit; *c:* Jeffrey H. Peterson, Jonathan M. Peterson, Jennifer Jo Vanslyke; *ed:* St Bonaventure Univ (BS) Elem Ed 1976, (MS) Ed, Schl Cnslng 1979; Canisius Coll (MS) Admin 1988; Advanced Cert of Specialization Schl Cnslng; *cr:* NYS Div of Youth Rdng Tchr 1975-77; Little Vly Cntrl Schl Soc Stud Tchr 1977-80; Orchard Park Hill HS Guid Cnslr 1980-, Guid Instr, Ldr 1992-; *ai:* Chrprsn Comm Spec Ed; Former Chrprsn of Wellness Com; Dist Comm of Substance Abuse; Youth Court of Orchard Park Coord; Guid Dept Instrl Ldr; St Univ of NY Advy Comm; Natl Bd of Cert Cnslrs 1986-; NYSUT 1977-; NYS Cnslng Assn, Amer Cnslng Assn 1980-; Orchard Park Yth Bd 1984-, Sec; Orchard Park Yth Court Exec Comm 1995-, Sec; Delta Kappa Gamma 1992-; *office:* Orchard Park HS 4040 Baker Rd Orchard Park NY 14127

PETKOVSEK, SHERRY J., 4th Grade Teacher; *b:* Cleveland, OH; *ed:* Kent St Univ (BS) Elem Ed 1969, (MED) Rdng Specialization 1974; 84 Semester Hrs Beyond Masters Degree; *cr:* John Muir Elem Schl 3rd Grd Tchr 1969-76, 3rd-4th Grd Tchr 1976-77, 4th Grd Tchr 1977-; *ai:* Effective Schl Process Ldrshp Team; Peer Ldrshp Day Comm; Instrl Design Chm; Classroom Tchr Edctr for Cleveland St Univ; PEA 1969-, Tchr Grant 1989; NEOEA, OEA, NEA 1969-; PTA 1969-, Life Mem, Tchr Grants 1974, 1993; IRA, OH Intnl Rdng Assn 1986-; Cuyahoga-Summit IRA 1975-, Pres 1988-89, Lois Bing Hnr Grant 1990; Alpha Delta Kappa Sigma 1982-, Pres 1988-90, ADK Regnl Grant 1989; Toastmasters Intnl 1991-, Treas 1991-95; Sierra Club 1984-; Jennings Scholar 1987; Parma Tchr of Yr Candidate 1989; Parma City Schls Strategic Planning Team 1991-92; OH Effective Schls, Venture Capital Grant Writing Team 1991-; Presenter OH IRA Conf 1991, Natl IRA Conv 1992; *office:* John Muir Elem Schl 5531 W 24th St Parma OH 44134*

PETORAK, JANICE M., Sixth Grade Teacher; *b:* Carbondale, PA; *m:* Joseph Thomas; *c:* James, Joseph; *ed:* Coll Misericordia (AB) Scndry Ed 1959; Marywood Coll (MS) Elem Ed 1968; Addl 30 Hrs; Attnd Marywood, Villanova, Wilkos, Drexel; *cr:* Johnson City NY Schls Elem Tchr 1959-65; Valley View Schls Elem Tchr 1965-; *ai:* Environmental Smarts, Soc Stud Curr Comm; NEA 1959; PSEA 1965-; Democratic Women 1994-; Kappa Gamma Pi 1959-; *home:* 465 Lincoln Ave Jermyn PA 18433*

PETR, JOHN A., Aviation Mechanics Teacher; *b:* New York City, NY; *m:* Ivette Alejandro-Petr; *c:* John Alexander; *ed:* 172 Credits Thomas Edison St Coll; *cr:* US Navy Aviation Machinist's Mate First class 1977-86; Aviation HS AViation Mechanics Tchr 1986-; *ai:* After Schl Aircraft Restoration Project Dir; AFT, NYSUT, UFT 1986-; FAA Aviation Maint Tech Trng Bronze Awd 1993-94, Silver Awd 1994-95, Ruby Awd 1995-; Certfd FAA Airframe & Powerplant Mechanic; *office:* Aviation HS 36th St & Queens Blvd Long Island City NY 11101

PETRACCHI, HELEN E., Asst Prof of Social Work; *b:* Burlington, WI; *m:* Glenn S. Pawlak; *ed:* Carroll Coll (BS) Soc Work 1978; Univ of WI at Madison (MSSW) Soc Work 1983, (PHD) Soc Welfare 1992; Acad of Certfd Soc Workers 1988; *cr:* Oconomowoc Dev Trng Ctr Soc Worker 1978-1980; Univ of WI at Madison TA, RA, PA 1984-90; Univ of WI at Milwaukee Instr 1990-91; Univ of Pittsburgh Asst Prof 1991-; *ai:* Distance Ed Steering Comm; Natl Assn of Soc Workers 1978-, Treas 1995-; Acad of Cert Soc Workers; Cncl on Soc Work Ed 1984-; Natl Cncl on Family Relations 1991-; Family Hlth Cncl 1991-, Adolescent Resource Network Advy Bd; Numerous Journals Pub; Inst on Race Ethnicity Grant 1990-91; NASW Eileen Blackey Flwshp 1988-89; Trent Rockwell Schlsp 1987-88; Doherty Fnd Flwshp 1986-87; Kiwanis Intnl Schlsp 1986-87; *office:* Univ Of Pittsburgh 2027 C L Pittsburgh PA 15260*

PETRACCIONE, NICOLA, Social Studies Teacher; *b:* Alife, Italy; *m:* Lisa F.; *c:* Joseph, Nicholas; *ed:* St Univ of NY at Morrisville (AS) Design & Drafting 1989; St Univ of NY at Albany (BA) Soc Scis 1992; Union Coll (MAT) Ed 1993; 15 Credit Hrs Post Grad Working Toward 2nd Masters of Admin Degree; *cr:* Niskayuna HS Soc Stud Tchr 1993-; *ai:* Soccer & LaCrosse Coach; NTA, NYS Soc Stud Cncl 1993-; Crossroads Curr-Natl Assessment Curr for 11th Grd; *home:* 2011 Garden Dr Niskayuna NY 12309

PETRARCA, JOSEPH CHARLES, Chemistry Teacher; *b:* Philadelphia, PA; *m:* Joan B. Carnevale; *c:* Laura, Joseph; *ed:* La Salle Univ (BA) Chem 1966; Temple Univ 7 Credit Hrs; Beaver Coll 8 Credit Hrs; *cr:* St John Neumann HS Chem Tchr 1966-; *ai:* Tech Coord; Diocesan Tech Curr, Diocesan Scholar Selection Comms; NCEA 1966; Assn of Cath Tchrs 1970; St John Neumann Distngd Cath Educator 1991-92; Natl Sci Fnd Grant; Chem Instrl Lectures for the Philadelphia Fire Dept Hazardous Materials Unit; Served on Two Visiting Comms for the Mid Sts Assn of Scndry Schls; *office:* Saint John Neumann HS 2600 Moore St Philadelphia PA 19145

PETRAS, RUTH YEATON, Mathematics Teacher; *b:* Farmington, ME; *m:* Robert; *c:* Merinda, Nathan; *ed:* Univ of ME (BA) Math 1969; Classroom Evaluation; Fortran; Critical Skills; CRISS; Assertive Discipline; Cmptr Algebra Systems; Brainstreaming; Cooperative Learning; Socio-Tech Systems; Synectics; Chaos & Fractals; Tchng Exceptional Stdnts; *cr:* Caravel Jr HS Tchr 1970-71; Plum Borough HS Tchr 1980-81; Scarborough HS Tchr 1982-; *ai:* Class Adv; Tech, Cert Comms; Dean of Stdnts; Ldrshp Team; NEA, MEA, SEA 1982-, Sec; NCTM 1986-; ASCD 1992-; Jr League 1983-; STS Design Team 1991-; Presenter Prism Conf; NEASC Comm; Pacesetter Math Scorer; *home:* 16 Blacksmith Rd Wells ME 04090*

PETRE, ROCHELLE MURPHY, Sixth Grade Teacher; *b:* Queens, NY; *m:* Michael; *c:* Michael, Joseph, Teddi Ann; *ed:* St Univ Coll at Buffalo (BA) Elem Ed 1987; SUNY at Stonybrook (MS) Lbrl Arts & Sci Concentration 1992; *cr:* James Wilson Young MS 6th Grd Tchr 1987-90, 1991-92, 1995-; Sylvan Ave Elem Schl 2nd Grd Tchr 1994-95; *ai:* Adv & Comp Comm; AFT 1987-; NYSUT 1987-; *office:* James Wilson Young MS 602 Sylvan Ave Bayport NY 11705

PETRI, CHRISTINE ANN, Choral Music Director; *b:* Trenton, NJ; *m:* Joseph C.; *ed:* Westminister Choir Coll (BME) Voice 1971; Trenton St Coll

(MM) Voice 1984; 15 Credit Hrs Post Grad Stud; *cr:* Hunterdon Cntrl HS Choral Dir 1971-84; Hightstown HS Choral Dir 1984-; *ai:* Musical Adv & Accompanist Chamber Singers, Tenor & Bass Choir, Advanced Choir, Schola Cantorum, HS Choir, Concert Choir; NEA, NJEA, MENC 1971-; Four European Concert Tours HS Choral Groups; *office:* Hightstown HS 25 Leshin Ln Hightstown NJ 08520

PETRIANNI, PAUL DANA, Social Studies Teacher; *b:* Erie, PA; *m:* Constance Diehl; *ed:* Gannon Univ (BS) Bus 1972; Masters Equiv Ed 1989, Post Grad Stud; *cr:* Erie Schl Dist Soc Stud Tchr 1972-91; Cntrl HS Soc Stud Tchr 1991-; *ai:* Frosh Class Adv; Alternative Ed Pgm Instr; PSEA & NEA 1992-; *office:* Central HS 3325 Cherry St Erie PA 16508*

PETRIDES, BETTE COWDEN, English & Journalism Teacher; *b:* New York City, NY; *m:* George Henry; *c:* George; *ed:* Univ of MI (AB) Eng 1965; MI St Univ (MA) Ed 1969; 15 Credit Hrs at Univ of MD 1984-85; 9 Credit Hrs at Montgomery Coll 1995-; *cr:* Assumpta Scndry Schl Nigeria Eng, His & Sci Tchr 1965-66; Kgari Sechele Scndry Schl Botswana Eng, His & Sci Tchr 1966-68; Seneca Valley HS Eng & Jrnlsm Tchr 1985-90; Winston Churchill HS Eng & Jrnlsm Tchr 1990-; *ai:* Schl Newspaper, Press Releases for Schl; MCEA 1985-; Co-Started & was Assoc Ed for A Museum Journal; Have Pub Articles in Several Magazines & Written Materials for The Smithsonian Inst; Edited 2 Books.

PETRIE, CATHERINE S. KRAMER, English Teacher; *b:* Queens, NY; *c:* Amanda S. Sanchez, Renee C. Kerin; *ed:* Laguardia C Coll (AA) Lbrl Arts-High Hnrs 1983; Hunter Coll (BA) Eng-Summa Cum Laude 1986; Queens Coll (MSEd) Tchng Eng Sec Schls 1990; *cr:* St Brigid's Schl Eng Tchr 1986-87; Franklin K Lane HS Eng Tchr 1987-88; Woodcliff Acad Eng Tchr 1988; PS 17 Schl Eng Tchr 1988-89; Bushwick HS Eng Tchr 1989-94; Canarsie HS Eng Tchr 1994-; *ai:* Lincoln Ctr Inst Tchrs Arts in Classroom; AFT 1987-; Marcia G. Rabinowitz, Charlotte Newcombe, Mayor's Schlsps; Who's Who Among Stdnts Amer Univ & Coll 1984-85; Outstdng Young Women Amer 1983-84; Natl Deans List 1983-84; Deans List 1981-86; *office:* Canarsie HS 1600 Rockaway Pky Brooklyn NY 11236*

PETRIE, GLORIA ANN, 8th Grd Soc Stud Teacher; *b:* Kindersley SK, Canada; *m:* Robert; *c:* Heather Crofoot, Elizabeth Grinnell, Lori Doyle, Lisa Manners, Athena Jones; *ed:* Queens Univ at Ontario (BA) Geog, His, Eng 1965; Grad Stud Colgate Univ Permanent NYS Cert; *cr:* Sauquoit Vly MS 9th-10th Grd Eng Tchr 1966-67, 7th Grd Soc Stud Tchr 1967-1990, 8th Grd Soc Stud Tchr 1990-; *ai:* Cmptr Software Tchr to Stu & Prof; Dist & Site Shared Decision Making Teams; Chprsn Soc Stud Dept 6th-8th Grd; AFT, NEA, 1966-, Local Union Rep; Church Choir; Model Schl Prgms Tchr; *office:* Sauquoit Valley MS Sulphur Springs Rd Sauquoit NY 13456*

PETRIE, LEE A., 8th Grade History Teacher; *b:* Sumter, SC; *ed:* Univ of Southern ME (BA) Elem Ed 1988; *cr:* Marshwood Jr HS His Tchr 1988-; *ai:* Boys A Team Bsktbl Coach; Acad Tchng Teams Ldr; Stu Cnsl Adv; *office:* Marshwood Jr HS 49 Academy St South Berwick ME 03908

PETRIE, LINDA JEAN EPPS, Fourth Grade Teacher; *b:* Rumford, ME; *m:* William Leo; *c:* Lee Alan, Jill Marie; *ed:* U of ME at Farmington (BS) Elem Ed, Eng 1963; *cr:* Kimball Schl 2 Grd Tchr 1963-64; Shaw Heights Elem Schl 1 Grd Tchr 1964-65; Chisholm Schl 2 Grd Tchr 1965066; Kimball Schl 5 Grd Tchr 1976-68; Abbott Schl 2 Grd Tchr 1969-73; Kimball Schl Grd 4 Tchr 1970-74; Kimball Jr Sr HS Majorettes Coach, Adv 1971-89; Meroby Elem Schl Tchr 1975-; *ai:* Staff Dev, Soc Stud Curr Comm; Staff Trng Advy Team; NEA, ME Ed Assn, Mt Vly Edctrs Assn 1971-; Dept Educl, Cultural Svcs Nom ME Tchr of Yr 1989; *home:* 60 Middle Ave Mexico ME 04257

PETRIE-FORGEY, SANDRA C., Science Dept Head & Math Tchr; *b:* Decatur, GA; *m:* Dwayne D.; *c:* Christian D., Savannah J.; *ed:* Univ of Rio Grande (BS) Math 1984; Univ of Dayton (MS) Ed Admin 1988; Credit Hrs at Miami OH Univ; *cr:* Beavercreek Schls Math Tchr 1984-85; Rio Grande Comm Coll Math Tchr 1985-91; Buckeye Hills Career Ctr Math Tchr 1985-89; Kyger Creek HS Sci & Math Tchr 1989-92; River Vly HS Sci & Math Tchr 1992-; *ai:* Sci Team Mem; Key Club Adv; NEA & OEA 1984-; NCTM & OCTM 1984-; 1994 GTE GIFT Flwshp; Key Club Outstdng Fav Adv 1994; Tchr of the Yr 1995; *office:* River Valley HS 1428 Little Kyger Rd Cheshire OH 45620

PETRILLO, MIRANDA L., Social Studies Teacher; *b:* Bryn Mawr, PA; *ed:* Univ of MD (BA) Anthropology 1993; Univ of PA (MS) Scndry Ed 1994; *cr:* Spring Ford HS 10th Grd Soc Stud 1994-; *ai:* PSEA & NEA 1994-; Phi Beta Kappa Hnrs Soc; *home:* 342 Hilltop Dr Apt D King Of Prussia PA 19406

PETRILLO, THOMAS FRANCIS, Director of Campus Ministry; *b:* Brooklyn, NY; *ed:* NY Univ (BA) Italian Lit 1979; St Joseph's Seminary (MDiv) Theology 1982; Fordham Univ (MA) Rel Ed 1991; Doctoral Stu Tchrs Coll, Columbia Univ Working Towards EDD Educl Admin; *cr:* St Vito's R C Church Assoc Pastor 1982-86; Cardinal Spellman HS Rel Tchr 1986-91, Campus Ministry Dir 1991-; *ai:* Var Bsktbl, Gospel Choir Moderator.*

PETRINEC, KATHRYN ANN, Global Studies & Psych Tchr; *b:* Buffalo, NY; *m:* Joseph; *c:* Kelly, Chauncey, Kathryn Marie; *ed:* SUNY at Buffalo (BA) His 1989; Hilbert Coll (AA) Liberal Arts 1987; *cr:* Cardinal O'Hara HS Soc Stud Tchr 1990-, Dept Chprsn & Psych Tchr 1995-; *ai:* Soc Stud Dept Chprsn; Stu Cncl Adv; BPW 1994-; Tchr of Yr 1993-94; NHS 1994; *home:* 3805 Dartmouth St Hamburg NY 14075

PETRIZZI, SUZANNE C. RAKOCZY, Teacher of the Handicapped; *b:* Hungary, Europe; *m:* Michael J.; *c:* Suzanne M., Christina E.; *ed:* Jersey City St Coll (BA) K-8, Spec Ed 1967; Boston Coll (MED) Ed 1968; Addl 24 Credit Hrs; *cr:* NY Assn for the Blind Orientation & Mobility Specialist 1968-70; Mt Carmel Guild for the Blind Orientation & Mobility Specialist 1976-86; Lafayette Mills Schl Tchr of the Handicapped 1981-; *ai:* Pupil Assistance Comm; Stu Advocate; SAC; Hmwrk Clb; NEA, NJEA 1981-; AFB 1968-; CEC 1967-; Grad Schl Fellowship; Amer Workers for the Blind Awd; Article Pub; Visually Handicapped Orientation & Mobility Cert; *home:* 183 Longwood Dr Manalapan NJ 07726*

PETRO, ROBERT ANTHONY, Chemistry Teacher; *b:* Plattsburgh, NY; *m:* Robin Beth Corwin; *ed:* Univ of ME (BS) Ed 1965; *cr:* US Peace Corps Tchr 1966-68; Narragansett HS Tchr 1971-; *ai:* NEA, RI Tchr Assn 1971-; New England Assn Chem Tchr 1977-; *office:* Narragansett HS 245 S Pier Rd Narragansett RI 02882

PETRO, THOMAS MICHAEL, Secondary Social Studies Tchr; *b:* Allentown, PA; *m:* Louise A. Karoly; *c:* Emily, Eloise; *ed:* Lehigh Univ (BA) His 1973; Penn St Univ Perm Cert Ed 1974; Colonial Northampton Intermediate Unit 20, Carlow Coll Credits Towards MEd Equivalency 1994; *cr:* Northampton Area Schls Scndry S S Tchr 1975-; *ai:* Var Golf Coach 1988-; Summer Schl Instr 10 Yrs; Homebound Tutor 5 Yrs; PSEA 1975-; Coplay Ath Club 1994-; *home:* 1015 Chestnut St Coplay PA 18037

PETROFF, THEODORA MC GEOGHAN, Art Teacher; *b:* Springfield, MA; *m:* Gary Eugene; *c:* Charles, Manser Hapcook; *ed:* Univ of MA (BFA) Art Ed 1983; 30 Credits Field Stud Painting, Rockport Art Assn, MA Coll of Art at Nantucket Island; Schl of Design NISDA Cross-Cultural Stud; *cr:* Gill-Montague Art Tchr 1983-84; Regnl Schls HS, MS Tchr 1986-; *ai:* HS, MS Art Club; Art Curr Dev Comm; NEA 1983-; Springfield Art League 1992-; CIVA 1995-, Visions Gallery 1995; RAA 1995-; Avis Neigher Gallery 1992-; Northampton Ctr for Arts 1995-; MA Cultural Cncl Grant.

PETRONSKY, REBECCA DIXON, English & AP Teacher; *b:* Pittsburgh, PA; *m:* George J.; *c:* Gordon, Grant, Greg; *ed:* Clarion Univ (BS) Comprehensive Eng 1971; Attnd PA St Univ & Carnegie Mellon Univ; *cr:* Carlynton HS Tchr 1971-; *ai:* AFT; NCTE; First Bapt Church of Carnegie, Moderator & Sunday Schl Tchr; Pitts & Post Gazette Amer Edctrs Awd 1992 & 1995; *office:* Carlynton Jr Sr HS 435 Kings Hwy Carnegie PA 15106

PETROVICH, MICHAEL, Seventh Grade Science Teacher; *b:* McKeesport, PA; *m:* Janice Lenhart; *ed:* CA St Univ of PA (BS) Ed 1969; Morgan St Univ (MS) Ed Admin & Supervision 1979; *cr:* Clarksville MS Sci Tchr 1969-71; Hammond MS Sci Tchr 1971-72; Dunloggin MS Sci Tchr 1972-; *ai:* Team Ldr; Human Relations Comm; NEA, MSTA, HCEA 1969-; Outstanding Tchr Awd 1990.

PETROW, EVELYN MAE, First Grade Teacher; *b:* Paterson, NJ; *m:* Peter J.; *c:* Peter, William; *ed:* Seton Hall Univ (BS) Elem Ed 1972; 30 Credit Hrs; Paterson Equivalentency Courses; *cr:* Schl No 5 Tchr 22 Yrs; *ai:* Second Grd Tchr Mentor; Stu Act Fund Treas 18 Yrs; NJEA, Paterson Ed Assn, NEA 1973-; Grant Making Children Books; *office:* Schl #5 430 Totowa Ave Paterson NJ 07502*

PETRUCCI, BARBARA J., Fourth Grade Teacher; *b:* Greenport, NY; *m:* Bruce; *c:* Jason, Matthew; *ed:* St Univ of NY at Brockport (BS) PE, Hlth Sci 1973; Long Island Univ (MS) Elem Ed; 45 Addl Hrs; *cr:* Southold HS Part-time Hlth, PE Tchr, Study Hall Monitor 1974-76; Mattituck-Cutchogue HS PE Tchr 1978-80; Greenport Elem Schl 4th Grd Tchr 1980-; *ai:* Elem Musicals; Jr HS Field Hockey, Var, JV Sftbl, Bsktbl, Vlybl, Tennis Coach; Save the Bays Prgm; Greenport Tchrs Assn 1980-; NY St United Tchrs 1978-; Peconic Estuary Prgm, Honored Tchr 1995; Citizen's Advy Comm; Greenport PTA; *office:* Greenport Union Free Schl Dist 720 Front St Greenport NY 11944

PETRUCCI, EARL R., Guidance Counselor; *b:* Washington, PA; *m:* Georgiana Riddle; *c:* Michele Petrucci Hating; Lori; *ed:* Clarion Univ (BA) Soc Stud 1964; Duquesne Univ (MS) Guidance 1971; *cr:* Chartiers Valley Schl Tchr 28 Yrs; *ai:* Stu Cncl Adv; Act Dir; AFT 1981-; PASC 1990-, Bd Mem, Adv of Yr 1993; NASC 1990-; *office:* Chartiers Valley HS 50 Thoms Run Rd Bridgeville PA 15017

PETRUNAK, MICHAEL DOMINIC, Mathematics Instr & Dept Chm; *b:* Portage, PA; *m:* Patricia Ann (Ponczek); *c:* Dianne, Eric, Kristen; *ed:* Clarion St Coll (BS) Math 1963; The PA St Univ (MED) Scndry Math Ed 1969; James Madison Univ 1971 6 Post Grad Credits; *cr:* Huntingdon Area Schls Math Instr 1963-65, Math Dept Chair Jr High 1964-65; Jenner-Boswell Schls Math Instr 1966; Forest Hills Schl Dist Math Instr 1967-, Math Dept Chair 88-; Mt Aloysius Coll 1992-93; *ai:* NHS Advy Cncl 10 Yrs; Ret Ftbl Coach 5 Yrs at Forest Hills HS & Bishop Carroll HS 15 yrs; NCTM 1990-; Forest Hills Ed Assn 1967-; PSEA 1963-; NEA 1968-; Natl Sci Fnd Grant Madison Coll 1971; PA Dept of Ed Evaluating Team; *office:* Forest Hills Sr HS 489 Locust St PO Box 325 Sidman PA 15955

PETRUNGER, JEFFREY LOUIS, 7th & 8th Grd Amer His Tchr; *b:* Ashtabula, OH; *m:* Shirley Dalin; *c:* Lee, Kent; *ed:* Kent St Univ (BS) His, Govt 1970; Grad Stud 18 Sem Hrs; *cr:* Our Lady of Mt Carmel Schl Amer His Tchr 7-8 1972-89; Ashtabula Cath Jr HS Amer His Tchr 7-8 1989-92; Ashtabula Cath MS Amer His Tchr; *ai:* Organizer & Adv for 7th Grd Annual Class Trip; *office:* Ashtabula Cath Elem MS 1464 West 6th St Ashtabula OH 44004

PETRUSH, BARBARA JEAN, Math Teacher; *b:* Buffalo, NY; *m:* James G. I; *c:* Andrea, James II; *ed:* Edinboro St Univ (BS) Earth, Space Sci 1981; *ai:* Sr Class Adv; *office:* Warren Co Christian Schl RD 6 Youngsville PA 16371

PETRUSKI, ROBERT M., Peer Education Coordinator; *b:* Perth Amboy, NJ; *m:* Mary T.; *c:* Michael Joseph; *ed:* Shepherd Coll (BA) Hlth, PE 1973; Trenton St Coll Drugs & Alcohol 150 Hrs; *cr:* Toms River Int Schl West 7-8th Grd PE Instr 1974-78; Toms River HS East Hlth, PE Instr 1979-86; Toms River Schls Peer Ed Coord 1986-; *ai:* Girls Cross Cntry Coach Toms River HS East; Toms River Ed Assn 1973-; Shore Coaches Assn 1979-; Manasquan Elks 1975-; Elks Distinguished Citizen Awd 1993; Scholastic Coach Silver Awd; *home:* 1188 Windham Ct Toms River NJ 08755

PETRUSKO, PAM (NUTTER), Mathematics Teacher; *b:* Youngstown, OH; *m:* Michael; *c:* Michael Jr., Joni; *ed:* Youngstown St Univ (BS) Scndry Math 1989; Spec Ed; Grad Schl Master Tchr, Curr, Ins; *cr:* Kent St Univ Cont Stud Instr 1990-95; Hubbard HS Tchr Severe Behavior Handicap 1992-93, Math Tchr 1994-; *ai:* Soph Class Adv; Natl Cncl of Math, OCTM, EOCTM 1990-; NEA, OEA 1992-; Kappa Delta Pi 1989-; *office:* Hubbard HS 350 Hall Ave Hubbard OH 44425

PETRUZZELLI, JOHN PAUL, History Teacher; *b:* Philadelphia, PA; *ed:* St Josephs Univ (BA) His 1990; *cr:* Our Lady of Calvary 7th & 8th Grd His Tchr 1990-92; Bishop Ireton HS His Tchr 1992-93; St Elizabeth HS His Tchr 1993-; *ai:* JV Head Bsktbl Coach; Stu Govt Moderator; Cath Schls Week Comm Chprsn; NCEA 1990-; Our Lady of Calvary Ath Assn 1984-, Bsbl Dir; Hugh OBrian Yth Fndtn Seminar 1985-, Seminar Chprsn; *office:* St Elizabeth High School 1500 Cedar St Wilmington DE 19805*

PETRY, DAWN CAROL, Social Studies Teacher; *b:* Pompton Plains, NJ; *ed:* Centenary Coll (AA) Lbrl Arts 1976; Trenton St Coll (BA) His 1986, (MAT) Tchng 1988; *cr:* Howell HS Soc Stud Tchr 1988-; *ai:* NJ Cncl of SS, NJEA 1988-; *office:* Howell HS Squankum-Yellowbrook Rd RD 2 Farmingdale NJ 07727

PETRY, JEAN WALMSLEY (HEALY), English Teacher; *b:* Lebanon, PA; *c:* J. Scollay, Emily R.; *ed:* Elizabethtown Coll (BA) Eng 1965; Millersville St Univ (mEd) Tchng & Eng 1971; 72 Credit Hr Post Masters Degree; *cr:* John Harris HS Eng Tchr 1967-69; Cedar Crest HS Eng Tchr 1969-; *ai:* SAT Stud Preparation; NEA & PSEA 1967-; CLEA 1969-; NCTE 1974-; AAUW 1993-; *office:* Cedar Crest HS 115 E Evergreen Rd Lebanon PA 17042

PETRY, MARY K., High School English Teacher; *b:* Livonia, MI; *ed:* Miami Univ at Oxford (BS) Eng Ed 1991; Grad Hrs Wright St Univ, Walsh Univ; *cr:* Miamisburg HS Eng Tchr 1991-; *ai:* Stu Govt Adv; Var Track Coach; NCTE 1991-; MC Tchrs Assn, OEA, NEA 1992-; *office:* Miamisburg HS 1860 Belvo Rd Miamisburg OH 45342

PETRYK, PATRICIA NIETRZEBA, Science Tchr & Dept Chprsn; *b:* Toledo, OH; *m:* Edward A. Jr.; *c:* Michelle, Edward III; *ed:* Mary Manse Coll (BS) Math Sci 1970; Univ of Toledo (MED) Sci Ed; Notre Dame Coll; *cr:* St Thomas Aquinas Schl 7th & 8th Grd Math & Sci Tchr 1970-72; Waite HS Tchr 1979-; *ai:* Dept Chprsn; AFT 1979-; AAPT 1989-; *office:* Waite High Schl 301 Morrison Dr Toledo OH 43605

PETSCAVAGE, WILLIAM FREDERICH, Biology & Chemistry Teacher; *b:* Wilkes-Barre, PA; *m:* Rita Marie Toole; *c:* William Jr., Mark; *ed:* Kings Coll (BS) Bio 1967; Trenton St Coll (MA) Sci Ed 1971; *cr:* Sampson G Smith Intermediate Schl 7th Grd Life Sci Tchr 1967-79; Franklin HS Tchr 1979-; *ai:* Dist Calendar Comm Mem; NEA 1967-; NJEA 1967-; SCEA 1967-; FTEA 1967-; Diocese of Metachen Festival Choir 1985-; NJ Governors Tchng Awd 1990; *home:* 65 Van Liew Ave Milltown NJ 08850

PETTA, KATHARINE G., Former Science Teacher; *b:* Jamestown, OH; *ed:* St Coll at Cortland (BS) Early Scndry Sci Ed-Summa Cum Laude 1987; Syracuse Univ (MS) Sci Tchng, Bio 1993; MS Geology in Progress; 7-9 Extension Gen Sci Cert; 7-12 Bio, Gen Sci Cert; *cr:* Jamesville-DeWitt MS 7 Grd Sci Tch r1988-90, 8 Grd Sci Tchr 1990-95; Syracuse Univ Earth Sci Tchng Asst; *ai:* Sci Olympiad Coach, Judge; NSTA 1987-; Sci Tch of NY St 1987-, Mid Level Subject Area Rep 1987-95, St Bd 1987-95; Empire St Tchrs Challenger Schlsp 1987; SUC at C Alumni Assn Awd 1987; Comm Newspapers Tchr of Week 1991; B Inst Syracuse Univ 1991; Numerous Insts Cornell Univ; Nu Wkshps.*

PETTIES, S. ESTELLE JOHNSON, First Grade Teacher; *b:* Pit PA; *m:* Albert W.; *ed:* Geneva Coll (BSEd) Elem Ed 1971; Harty Bi 4 Yrs Completion 1990; *cr:* Neel Elem Schl Elem Tchr 1971-; *ai* 1971-; PTA; Mt Olive Bapt 1971-, Asst Sunday Schl Supt 1992, S Class Instr 1986, Choir Mem 1971, Hospitality Comm VP 1991 Historical Soc Achievers Awd; Esmay Manning Meml Childrens Biblical Instr; *home:* 1225 Midland Ave Midland PA 15059

PETTIGANO, DAWN-MARIE, Music Director; *b:* Paterson, Hartt Schl of Music (BM) Music Ed 1994; *cr:* Manchester HS S 1993-94; Rumson-Fair Haven HS Music Dir 1994-; *ai:* Marchin Color Guard, Asst Musical Dir; FCA; MENC 1991-; NJMEA, NJE All-Shore Band Assn 1994-96; Music Copyright Original Comp 1990; *office:* Rumson-FairHaven HS 74 Ridge Rd Rumson NJ 077

PETTIGREW, CHRISTOPHER ROSS, Spanish & English Tea Scranton, PA; *c:* Justin, Colby; *ed:* Univ of Scranton (BSEd) Sp 1969; PA St Univ Stu Prsnl MED Equivalency 1970; 34 Addl Valley View Sr HS Span, Eng Tchr, Wrestling Coach 1970-; *ai:* N Coach of Yr 1988; NEA, PA SEA 1970-; Mason's Kingsbury Lodge Articles; *office:* Valley View HS Columbus Dr Archbald PA 18403

PETTIJOHN, TERRY FRANK, Professor of Psychology; *b:* Wy MI; *m:* Bernadette M. Ciemierek; *c:* Terry II, Karen, Thomas; *ed* Univ (BS) Psych 1970; Bowling Green St Univ (MA) Psych 1972, Psych 1974; *cr:* OH St Univ Asst Prof Psych 1974-80, Assoc Pro 1980-86, Prof Psych 1986-; *ai:* Psych Club Adv; Psych Underg Prgm, Honors, Cmptr Comms; Amer Psychological Assn 1974- Psychological Soc 1988-; Psychological Soc 1977-; First Presbyn 1975-, Elder; Articles Pub 1992, 1994; *office:* Ohio State Univ 1 Vernon Ave Marion OH 43302

PETTIS, SCOTT TRACY, Social Studies Teacher; *b:* East Lansi *m:* Gwen Annette Geesaman; *c:* Zachary Tracy, Rachel Leigh, Samuel; *ed:* Slippery Rock Univ (BA) His 1978; Tchr Cert at Penn S 36 Grad Hrs Towards Masters Equivalency; *cr:* Harrisburg HS Coach 1982-84; Cedar Cliff HS Tchr & Coach 1984-86; Trinity HS Coach 1986-87; Middletown Area HS Tchr & Coach 1987-; *ai:* Hea Ftbl & Head Bsbl Coach; U N Club Adv; Stu Assistance Team Me Club Adv; NEA 1986-; YMCA 1978-; Selected by Stu of Month With Most Impact on Their Career; Nom Tchr of Yr Middletown Ar Dist; *office:* Middletown Area H S 1155 N Union St Middleto 17057*

PETTIT, CINDY HOLLIS, Second Grade Teacher; *b:* Oswego, Charles; *c:* Mehgan, Courtney; *ed:* SUNY at Oswego (BS) El Ed, C 1979, (MS) Unified Masters 1984; 6 Hrs Math; 3 Hrs Multi-Cultu 1993; *cr:* Cntrl Square Elem Kndgtn Tchr 1979-85; Ctrl Square Second Grd Tchr 1985-93; Millard Hawk Primary Second Grd Tchr *ai:* Stradegic Planning Comm; PTA Tchr Rep 1981-85; Sun Sch 1994; NYSUT 1979-, Bldg Rep 1986-90; NYSRA 1980-; Oswe Rdng Cncl 1980-, Treas 1988-92; Delta Kappa Gamma 1995-; Sit Tchr Rep; PTA 1979-, Tchr Rep 1981-85; United Meth Church Financial Sec 1994-; Schl Based Support Turn-Key Trainer; Trai Early Literacy In Svc; SUNY at Oswego Chancellors Awd, Kappa D Ed Honor Soc; Alpha Iota Chptr DKG; *home:* PO Box 411 Central NY 13036*

PETTITE, CHET A., Business Education Teacher; *b:* Rochester, Janice M. Wagner; *ed:* Curry Coll (BS) Bus Admin 1965; SU Brockport (MAEd) Ed 1977, (CAS) Schl Admin 1982; 30 Addl Gr *cr:* Greece Cntrl Schl Dist Bus Ed Tchr 1966-; *ai:* Greece Supplementary Budget Comm; Greece Tchrs Assn, NEA-NY, NEA *office:* Greece Athena HS 800 Long Pond Rd Rochester NY 14612

PETTITT, RUTH ALLYN (JENISTA), 8th Grade Language Arts T Summit, NJ; *m:* Richard N. Jr.; *c:* Christian; *ed:* Cedarville Coll (BA Ed 1968; Wright St Univ (MED) Elem Ed 1970; 30 Hrs Rdng Cert Univ; *cr:* Parkwood Schl Grd 6, Grd 4-6 Multi-age Tchr 1968-72, Schl 1-2, 5 Grd 1972-75; Stewart Schl 8th Grd Lang Arts Tchr 19 Talawanda MS 8th Grd Lang Arts Tchr 1989-; *ai:* Prins Advy Cabine Chair; NEA, OEA 1968-; TEA 1977-, Pres Grievance Chair; Holden Jennings Scholar; Molyneaux Fnd Grant; AAUW Tchr *office:* Talawanda MS 4030 Oxford Reily Rd Oxford OH 45056

PETTY, DENA, Art Teacher; *b:* Scranton, PA; *ed:* Mansfield Uni Art Ed 1992; *cr:* Abington Hghts Art Tchr 1994-; *ai:* Art Club, St Adv; NAEA 1995-; *home:* 2010 Newton Ransom Blvd Clarks Sum 18411

PETTY, JEFFREY D., Visual Arts Department Chair; *b:* Philad PA; *m:* Judith; *c:* Jonathan; *ed:* Univ of the Arts (BFA) Graphic 1964; Villanova Univ (MA) Educl Admin 1969; Prins Cert K-12 Design; Tchr Cert Art K-12; *cr:* Philadelphia Schl Dist Tchr Re 1967-78, Placement Ofcr 1968-69; Philadelphia Museum of Ar Lecturer 1969-71; Northeast HS Acting Asst Prin 1992-93, Visu Dept Chair 1979-; *ai:* Stu Assistance Prgm Chair; Stu Govt Spon; S Coord; Annual Schl Show Dir; PA Stu Assist Prof 1989-, Bd Mem Phi Delta Kappa 1989-; NAEA 1975-; NEHS Alumni Assn 1987- Liaison; NEHS Home & Schl Assn 1987-, Fac Liaison; NEH Comparative Theatre Stud; *office:* Northeast HS Cottman & Algor Philadelphia PA 19111*

PETTYJOHN, PRISCILLA HOPKINS, Sixth Grade Teach Norwich, CT; *m:* Warren R.; *c:* Jeffrey S., Craig A.; *ed:* West Che Coll (BS) Elem Ed 1968; St of PA (MA) Elem Ed 1972; *cr:* Warwic Dist 4th Grd Tchr 1968-69; Dallastown Area Schl Dist 6th Grd 19 Red Lion Schl Dist 6th Grd 1970-; *ai:* Head Tchr; Strategic Pl Comm; PSTA 1990-; Assoc of Commonwealth Elem Sci Tchng All *office:* Chanceford Elem Schl Rd 1 Brogue PA 17309

PETUCH, CAROL ANN, English Teacher; *b:* Derby, CT; *c:* Ryan, D Matthew; *ed:* Univ of New Haven (BA) Eng 1971; Wesleyan Univ Lbrl Arts 1985; Southern CT St Univ Tchr Cert Ed 1975; *cr:* Hillhou Tchr 1974-75; Lee HS Eng Tchr 1975-88; Career HS Eng Tchr 198 Schls Lit Magazine & Sr Class Adv; Summer Schl Enrichment Pgm AFT 1976-; 2 Curr Units Pub By the Yale Univ Tchrs Inst; Amer L Stud Group Grant to Travel Throughout Europe with Stdnts D Summer 1972.

PETZ, SUSAN L., Teacher of the Deaf; *b:* Cleveland, OH; *m:* Jay Stephanie, Jacqueline, Brittany, Jason, Mary; *ed:* Kent St Univ (BA Ed 1981; Ashland Univ (MA) Rdng Specialist 1993; *cr:* Lakewo Interpreter for the Deaf 1983-84; Lorain City Schls Tchr of the Deaf Ashland Univ Sign Lang Instr 1993; *ai:* Deaf Club Adv; NEA, LEA 1984-; Jr Church Dir 1996-; Endowment Grant Deaf Theater; *office:* Admiral King HS 2600 Ashland Ave Lorain OH 44052

PEVERLY, SUSAN BEASLEY, MS Reading & HS Jrnlsm Teach Dayton, OH; *m:* Dean T.; *c:* Ryan, Amy; *ed:* Miami Univ (BS) Ed 19 Univ (MS) Ed 1992; *cr:* Hicksville HS MS Rdng, HS Jrnlsm Tchr ewspaper Staff Adv; NEA, OEA 1981-; Hicksville Ed Assn 1981-, Rep; *office:* Hicksville HS Smith & Main St Hicksville OH 43526

Y, CATHY DEVOLL, English Teacher; *b:* Cambridge, OH; *ed:* OH BS) Jrnlsm & Ed; Univ of MD (MS) Educl Theatre; Working Toward 1 & Supervision Cert at Johns Hopkins Univ; *cr:* Herbert Hoover Jr chr & Theatre Spon 1978-89; Churchill HS Dir of Theatre 1985-89; ns Mill HS Tchr & Dir of Theatre 1989-; *ai:* NEA 1978-; ETA 1989-; Watkins Mill HS 10301 Apple Ridge Rd Gaithersburg MD 20879

DO, PATRICIA ANN MC KENTY, Second Grade Teacher; *b:* lelphia, PA; *m:* Edward; *c:* Stacey Kemenash; *ed:* Comm Coll (BA) 34; Working Toward BA at Holy Family Coll; *cr:* Red Oak Restaurant ess Summer 4 Yrs; Various Cath Schls Sub Tchr 2 Yrs; Nursery Schl Yr; Saint George Tchr 11 Yrs; *ai:* Childrens Tutor; Aids for Friends y Companion; Saint Hubert Alumni of Yr Awd 1994; Poem Pub rens Lit Honorable Mention Awd.

ROS, MIKHAIL, Physics Teacher; *b:* Riga, Latvia; *m:* Sophia; *c:* *ed:* Riga Tech Coll (BA) Elec Eng 1949; Riga Tchrs Coll (MS) cs, Math 1955; Moscow Acad of Educl Sci (EDD) Physics Tchng odology 1971; *cr:* Riga HS #43 Physics Tchr 1955-61; Riga Tech HS cs, Electronics Tchr, Asst Prin 1961-67; Latvian Rsrch Inst of Ed Sr rcher, Scientific Sec 1967-79; Rockland Comm Coll Asst Prof cs 1981-85; Bronx HS of Sci Physics Tchr 1985-; *ai:* Amer arately Needs Young Physics Tchrs Project; Pub More Than 50 tific Articles, Physics Textbooks & Exercise Books Grds 8-12 in ous Soviet Union & Latvia; 12 Certs for Excl in Tchng from Bd of Ed via; Bronx Schl Dist Awd Organizing & Leading Physics Tchrs ps; *office:* Bronx H S Of Science 75 W 205th St Bronx NY 10458*

EK, JACQUELINE MACFARLAND, English & Social Studies *b:* Utica, NY; *m:* Martin A.; *c:* Martin E., Jared M., Colin R.; *ed:* use Univ (BA) Eng Ed 1975; Elmire Coll (MS) Ed 1991; *ai:* Schl paper Adv; Block Scheduling, Discipline & Dist Tech Comms; sboro Tchrs Assn 1990-; CNYCSS 1995-; *office:* Whitesboro HS Rt 291 Marcy NY 13403

ULLO, BARBARA DIANE (ONDECKO), Library & Media alist; *b:* Bridgeport, CT; *m:* John; *ed:* Southern CT St Univ (BS) Elem 70; Univ of Bridgeport (MS) Elem Ed 1974; Fairfield Univ (CAS) a 1990; *cr:* Jane Ryan Schl 2, 3, 5 Grd Tchr 1970-87, Media Specialist ; *ai:* Lit Week Coord; Schl Newspaper Adv; Staff Dev Comm; CEMA; ; Delta Kappa Gamma 1976-, Pres; Phi Delta Kappa; *office:* Jane Elem Schl 210 Park Ln Trumbull CT 06611

ULLO, JANE DICKSON, 2nd Grade Teacher; *b:* Bangor, ME; *m:* as; *c:* Jessica; *ed:* U of ME at Gorham (BS) Elem Ed 1967; RI Coll) Eng, His 1973; *cr:* West Jefferson Elem Schl 7-8 Grd Tchr 1967-68; een Elem Schl Grd 4 Tchr 1968-69; West Barrington Elem Schl Grd r 1969-79; Primrose Hill Elem Schl Alternative Learning Prgm Grd chr 1979-; *ai:* Portfolio Comm; NEA 1969-; *office:* Primrose Hill Schl ddle Hwy Barrington RI 02806

UTI, VINCENT G.,JR., English Teacher; *b:* Jersey City, NJ; *c:* nt; *ed:* St Peters Coll at Jersey City (BS) Eng 1965; Attnd Seton Hall of Law at Newark; *cr:* Marist HS Eng Tchr 1967-71; St Peters Coll Prof Bus Law 1972-77; Moore Cath HS Eng Tchr 1987-; *ai:* Talent Moderator; *office:* Moore Catholic HS 100 Merrill Ave Staten Island 0314

E, MALGORZATA ZIELINSKA, Professor of Physics; *b:* Bielsko, d; *m:* Jerzy; *c:* Renata, Juseau, Hubert; *ed:* Univ of Warsaw (MSC) cs 1961; Inst of Nuclear Rsrch (PHD) Nuclear Physics 1969; *cr:* Inst iclear Rsrch Warsaw Poland Asst Prof & Assoc Prof 1968-78; elaer Polytechnic Inst Visiting Rsrch 1978-82; Smith coll Prof 1982-; mer Phys Soc 1978-, Chair of New England Section, Fellow; AAPT ; Sigma Xi 1983-; Flwshp for Rsrch in USA Fr, Ger, Italy & alia; Over 80 Articles Pub; Smith Coll Sr Tchng Awd 1985; Distngd Awd 1995; *office:* Smith Coll Elm St Northampton MA 01063

FENROTH, SARA BEEKEY, Professor of English; *b:* Reading, PA; eter Albert; *c:* Elizabeth, Peter C., Catherine; *ed:* Bryn Mawr Coll Eng 1963; IN Univ (MA) Eng 1964; Mid Career Fellow Princeton U 85; Summer Inst for Intercultural Comm 1991, 1992; Fordham Univ Schl of Ed 1994; *cr:* Northwestern MI Coll Instr 1964-66; Middlesex Coll Instr 1966-68; Cty Coll of Morris Prof 1968-; *ai:* Stud Abroad NJCCIIE 1989-, Chair; NJCIGE 1991-, Rep; NJ Poetry Soc 1970-, Ex ane Austen Soc; CCHA; MLA; NAFSA; Morris Area Girl Scout Cncl , Bd of Dirs; German Lang Schl 1978-, Bd of Trustees; Mid St Assn ator; Journal of New Jersey Poets Assoc Ed; Faces & Voices Ed in ; Video Ethics Among Us Sharing Intercultural Views; Project Dir rous Grants; *office:* County Coll Of Morris 214 Center Grove Rd olph NJ 07869*

FENBERGER, SANDY MOELLER, Instrumental & Gen Music *b:* Celina, OH; *m:* Michael E.; *c:* Douglas, Rachelle Ramsey; *ed:* MI iv (BSME) Inst Music 1967; *cr:* Bettsville Local Schls Instrumental Tchr; St Marys City Schls 5th-12th Grd Instrumental Music, 3rd-7th Gen Music Tchr; Troy City Schls 7th-8th Grd Gen Music, 5th-6th, 2th Grd Instrumental Music Tchr 1994-; *ai:* Troy HS Marching Band Dir; MENC; OH Ed Assn; Troy Ed Assn; NEA; *home:* 1954 Laurel Dr Troy OH 45373

FER, JUDITH STERN, Mathematics Teacher; *b:* Washington, DC; illiam Robin; *c:* Alexander, Sarah; *ed:* Univ of CO (BA) Math 1983, Math 1986; *cr:* Ft Lupton MS Math, CS Tchr 1983-85; Ranum HS , CS Tchr 1986-88; Wuerzburg HS Math, CS Tchr 19988-91; east HS Math Tchr 1993-; *ai:* NHS; NEA 1983-; MSTM 1993-.

FER, NANCY LOUISE, Vocal Music Teacher; *b:* Allentown, PA; *m:* am Charles Jr.; *ed:* Moravian Coll (BA) Music Ed 1970; West Chester ill (MA) Music 1973; *cr:* Cheston Elem Vocal Music Tchr 1970-89; h Elem Vocal Music Tchr 1989-91; Easton HS Choral Dir, mpanist, Theory I, Voice & Piano Lab Tchr 1989-; *ai:* Treble & nber Choir Dir; PA St Ed Assn, NEA, MENC 1970-; *office:* Easton HS 2601 William Penn Hwy Easton PA 18045

FER, WILLIAM H., Social Studies Teacher; *b:* New Haven, CT; *m:* orie L.; *c:* Christopher W., Heidi A., Megan V. Power; *ed:* Trinity Coll His 1959; Central CT St Coll (MS) Ed, His 1964; Univ of CT 6 Yr rvision & Admin 1968; *cr:* Hamden High Dept Chair Tchr 1960-, Dept 1970-83; *ai:* Girls Soccer Coach; Ski Club Adv; Tchrs Mentor; S, Hampden EA, CT EA, NEA 1960-; Girls Sftbl Coach; *office:* den HS 2040 Dixwell Ave Hamden CT 06514

FERLE, KATHIE MARIE, Fourth Grade Teacher; *b:* Monroe, MI; Concordia Coll at Ann Arbor (AA) Ed 1970; Concordia Coll at Seward Ed 1972, (MED) Ed, Rdng 1980; 18 Addl Credit Hrs at Cleveland St for OH Permanent Cert; Luth Tchr Diploma; *cr:* Trinity Luth Schl 3rd Grd Tchr 1972-80; Our Shepherd Luth Schl 1st-4th Grd Tchr -; *ai:* Yrbk Adv; Luth Ed Assn; IRA; Past Corresponding Sec for OH Luth Tchrs Conf; *home:* 111 E Jackson St Painesville OH 44077

FER, MYRA PLOVNICK, Kindergarten Teacher; *b:* Queens, NY; ichael Lawrence; *ed:* Hofstra Univ (BA) Ed, Criminology 1969, (MA) Chldhd Ed 1979; Post Grad Stud C.W. Post Long Island Univ Schl ng Courses; *cr:* John DInkelmeyer Schl Second, Third Grd Tchr -71; Saw Mill Road Schl First Grd Tchr 1971-76; John Dinkelmeyer First, Second Grd Tchr 1976-79; Saw Mill Road Schl Kndgtn, 1st Grd Tchr 1979-89; Park Avenue Schl Kndgtn Tchr 1989-; *ai:* Mentor to Beginning Tchr 1989-90 Saw Mill Rd Schl; Shared Decision Making Team 1994-95; No Bellmore Tchrs Assn 1969-, Sec 1986-88 25 Yr Svc Awd 1994, Treas 1988-90; Wantagh Kiwanis Club 1992-94, Sec, Distngd Sec Awd 2 Yrs 1992-93; Pub Article in No Bellmore Tchrs Ctr Newspaper 1988; *office:* Park Avenue Schl 1599 Park Ave N Merrick NY 11566*

PFEIFFER, JACQUELINE CAROL, Third Grade Teacher; *b:* Pittsburgh, PA; *ed:* Clarion Univ of PA (BS) Elem Ed 1973; Univ of Pittsburgh (MED) Elem Ed 1976; Credit Hrs at Univ of AL, Univ of WI, Wilkes Univ, Slippery Rock Univ; *cr:* South Butler Cty Schl Dist Third Grd Tchr 1974-; *ai:* South Butler Cty Ed Assn 1974-, Chief Negotiator; PSEA, NEA 1974-, Retirement, Welfare Comm; Winfield Sewing 4-H 1980-, Ldr; Saxonburg Pub Lib 1995-, Prgm Comm; 3 Weeks Stud Russia at Krasnoyarsk St Univ; Capitol Area Space Ed Washington DC; *home:* 748 Winfield Rd Cabot PA 16023*

PFEIFFER, KATHLEEN WITEK, Family & Consumer Sci Teacher; *b:* Auburn, NY; *m:* Kenneth R.; *c:* Kristen Engler, Kory; *ed:* SUNY at Plattsburgh (BS) Home Ec Ed 1974, (MS) Home Ec Ed 1979; Numerous Inservice Courses Cmptr Use & Applications, Schl to Work Efforts, Spec Needs Stdnts, Home Ec Ed, Cultural Sensitivity & Gender Equity; *cr:* Amsterdam HS Family & Consumer Sci Tchr 1974-; *ai:* Compact Bldg Team 1995-; Wellness Day 1994-; Mediation Prgm 1992-; Lakeside Hlth Promotion Inst 1991-; Supts Day Plan Comm 1993-95; Case Mngmt Team 1992-93; ATA, NYSUT 1974-; NYSFSCE 1994-; Women's Hlth Ctr 1985-95, Advy Cncl; St Stephan's Church 1990-; St Casimars Church 1974-90.

PFEIFFER, KENNETH ROBERT, Tech Drafting Teacher; *b:* Schenectady, NY; *m:* Kathleen A. Witek; *c:* Kory Robert; *ed:* Hudson Vly Comm Coll (AS) Tech, Drafting 1980; Oswego St (BS) Tech Ed K-12 1984; Albany St (MS) Rdng Ed N-6 1988; Hudson Vly Comm Coll Cert 1980; *cr:* Amsterdam HS Drafting Tchr, Mechanical & Architectural1984-; *ai:* Wrestling Coach; AFT, NYSUT 1984-; ATA 1987-, Senator; AVA; *office:* Amsterdam HS 11 Liberty St Amsterdam NY 12010

PFEISTER, RAY L., High School Guidance Counselor; *b:* Barberton, OH; *m:* Bobbie; *c:* Derrick, Ryan; *ed:* Kent St Univ (BA) PE, Hlth 1974; Youngstown St Univ Drivers Ed Cert 1977; Kent St Univ Masters Schl Cnslng; *cr:* Crestwood Schls K-5 PE Tchr 1974-78, 6-8 Grd PE Tchr 1978-79; Painesville Twp Schls 10-12 PE, Hlth Schl 1979-88; Kirtland Schls 10-12 PE, Hlth Tchr 1988-95, 10-12 Guid Cnslr 1995-; *ai:* HS Girls Bsktbl Head Coach; Asst HS Ftbl Coach; Stu Cnslr Adv; OEA, NEA 1974-; *office:* Kirtland HS 9150 Chillicothe Rd Kirtland OH 44094

PFENNIG, JACQUELINE FRISCO, Eighth Grade Science Teacher; *b:* Long Branch, NJ; *m:* Dwight R.; *c:* Brian; *ed:* Tusculum Coll (BA) Elem Ed 1969; Kean Coll (MA) Rdng Specialist 1995; Doctoral Candidate Nova Southeastern Univ; *cr:* Middletown Twp Bd Ed Tchr 1969-; Belford Elem Schl 2nd Grd Tchr 1969-72; New Monmouth Elem Schl 2nd, 3rd, 5th-6th Grd Tchr 1972-86; Thorne MS 6, 8th Grd Tchr 1986-; *ai:* Heterogeneous Grouping, MS Philosophy, Incentive Comm; MS Soc Stud Curr; Ski Trip Adv; MTEA, MCEA, NJEA, NEA 1969-, Bldg, Cty Rep; NJ Assn Mid Level Ed 1991-, Exec Comm; Natl MS Assn 1991-, Presenter; NJ Governor's Tchr of Yr 1986, Tchr Grant 1989; Natl Intl Presenter 5 Yrs; Nom Tchr's Hall of Fame 1994; NJ Women Radio Show 1990; *office:* Thorne MS 70 Murphy Rd Port Monmouth NJ 07758*

PFEUFFER, MARY ANN KRISTOFF, Mathematics & Physics Teacher; *b:* Pittsburgh, PA; *m:* Richard H.; *c:* Cassandra, Richard Joseph; *ed:* Univ of Pittsburgh (MED) Math 1992; *cr:* Univ of Pgh Med Ctr Med Lab Tech 1987-94; Belle Vernon Area HS Math & Physics Tchr 1992-; *ai:* Drillteam Spon; PSEA; *office:* Belle Vernon Area HS RR 2 Crest Ave Belle Vernon PA 15012

PFIRRMAN, NANCY ANN, French Teacher; *b:* Hamilton, OH; *ed:* Miami Univ at Oxford (AB) Fr 1968, (MA) Fr 1970; 30 Hrs Post Grad Stud Ger Cert Xavier Univ; *cr:* Stephen T. Badin HS Fr Tchr 1970-, Ger Tchr 1972-78, Foreign Lang Dept Chair 1972-94, Ger Tchr 1980-85; *ai:* Fr Club Moderator; Schl Musical Voice Dir; OFLA 1992-95; NCEA 1970-; AATF 1994-; Alliance Francaise 1980-93; The Polio Connection 1985-, Admin Liaison; St Ann Parish, Lifetime Mem; Creative Tchng Ideas Pub OFLA Newsletter; Tour Dir 3 Stu Tours Europe; Founder Schl Recycling Prgm; Co-Dir Musicals & Variety Shows; *office:* Stephen T Badin HS 571 New London Rd Hamilton OH 45013

PFISTERER, JAMES RICHARD, Mathematics Teacher; *b:* Wilkinsburg, PA; *m:* Diane Smith; *c:* Emily, Stephen, Michael; *ed:* Edinboro Univ of PA (BS) Math 1968, (MED) Math 1972; *cr:* Academy HS Math Tchr 1968-92; Central HS Math Tchr 1992-; *ai:* NEA, PA St Ed Assn, Erie Ed Assn 1968-; *office:* Central HS 3325 Cherry St Erie PA 16508*

PFLEEGOR, GWENDA LYNN, Graduate Adjunct Professor; *b:* Fort Wayne, IN; *m:* James O.; *c:* Matthew J., Lisa A., Adam G.; *ed:* SUNY at Geneseo (BS) Elem Ed 1974; Elmira Coll (MS) Rdng 1977; 6 Addl Hrs SUNY at Cortland Admin; Elmira Coll Rdng; *cr:* Broadway Elem Schl Rdng Spec 1977-86, First Grd Tchr 1986-92; Elmira Coll Adj-Grad & Undergrad 1990-; Broadway Elem Third Grd Tchr 1992-; *ai:* Continuity of Curr Action Team Chprsn; Chemung Vly Rdng Assn; Elmira Tchrs Assn, NYSUT, AFT 1977-; Sing-Sing HSO 1980-; Grad Tchr of Yr 1995.

PFLEGER, MARY JO, English Teacher; *b:* Portsmouth, OH; *ed:* OH Univ (BA) Ed, Eng 1971, (MA) Scndry Ed 1979; 15 Addl Credit Hrs above Masters; *cr:* Washington Nile Eng Tchr 1974-87; Clay Portsmouth Eng Tchr 1988-; *ai:* NEA, OEA 1974-; *home:* 43 Pfleger Rd Minford OH 45653

PFLUG, BARBARA SIRAVO, 8th Grd Physical Science Tchr; *b:* Newark, NJ; *m:* Gerald C.; *c:* Jason, Jeremy, Jared; *ed:* Rider Coll (BA) Elem Ed 1971; Kean Coll (MA) Rdng Specialist 1981; Addtl 50 Credits Philosophy, Cmptrs, Motivation, Tech Children, Drug, Alcohol Awareness, TESA, MS Philosophy, Subject Area Courses; *cr:* New Monmouth Schl 4th-6th Grd Tchr 1971-87; Thorne MS 6, 8 Grd Eng, Rdng, Sci, Soc Stud Tchr 1987-; *ai:* Schl Wide Incentive Prgm Stdnts; Organizer Cntrl Region Conf NJ Assn Mid Level Ed; Natl MS Assn 1988-; NJ Assn for MS Ed 1990-, Cntrl Region Dir; NEA, NJEA, MCEA, MTEA 1971-; Hazlet Zoning Bd 1982-85, Zoning Ofcr; NJ Governors's Tchr Recognition Prgm 1986, Tchr Grant 1989; Presenter MS Philosophy, Tchr MotivationNatl, St, Local Level 1989-; Natl MS Delegation to Russia 1 995; *home:* 523 S Laurel Ave Hazlet NJ 07734*

PFLUG-FELDER, KAREN N., Science Dept Chair & Teacher; *b:* Philadelphia, PA; *ed:* Dickinson Coll (BS) Bio 1971; Beaver Coll (MAEd) Environmental Ed 1984; Attnd West Chester Univ, Penn St Univ, Temple Univ; *cr:* Perkiomen Vly HS Sci Tchr 1971-72; Methacton HS Sci Tchr, Dept Chr 1972-; *ai:* Class of 1996, Mountain Bike Club Spon; Girls Var Lacrosse Coach; Co-Curr Act Advy Bd; Methacton Ed Assn 1972-; PSEA, NEA 1971-; Phi Delta Kappa 1984-; NSTA; Natl Bio Tchrs Assn; Montgomery Cty Sci Tchrs Assn; Past Sec PA Schl Girls Lacrosse Assn; Dickinson Coll Sports Hall of Fame 1983; *office:* Methacton Sr High 1001 Kriebel Mill Rd Norristown PA 19408

PFRIENDER, MARILYN MARGARET,OP, Math Tchr & Chorus Accompanist; *b:* Glendale, NY; *ed:* St John's Univ (BS) Math 1960; Cath Univ of Amer (MTS) Math 1966; NY Schl of Liturgical Music Diploma1986; *cr:* St Agnes Acad HS Math Chm 1958-66; Maria Regina HS Tchr 1966-68; St AGnes Cathedral HS Math Chm 1968-73; Hicksville Jr HS Tchr 1974-75; St Anthony's HS Math Tchr, Chorus Accompanist 1975-; *ai:* Jr Ring Day Moderator; Rehearsed Spring Musicals Pianist; All Choral Act Accompanist; Amer Guild of Organists 1989-, Nassau Chptr Treas; Sisters of St Dominic 1948-; NSF Grants to Cath Univ, Colgate Univ, Drew Univ, Manhattan Coll; Numerous Wkshps, Summer Prgms Westminster Choir; 3 Concert Tours in Italy; *office:* St Anthony's HS 275 Wolf Hill Rd Huntington Sta NY 11747

PFROGNER, MICHELE MARIE, 8th Grade English Teacher; *b:* Warren, OH; *m:* Thomas D.; *c:* Tracie; *ed:* Wittenberg Univ (BME) Music Ed 1979; Completed Cert Eng 1994; *cr:* St Marys Schls K-8 Grd Music Tchr 1979-80; Springfield City 7-9 Grd Music Tchr 1980-81; Huber Heights 1-9 Grd Music Tchr 1981-94, 8th Grd Eng Tchr 1994-; *ai:* Power of the Pen Coach; NEA 1979-; Phi Delta Kappa 1986-; NCTE 1994-; OCTELA 1995-; Tchr of Yr Weisenborn 1985-86, 1986-87; Article Pub; *office:* Weisenborn MS 6061 Old Troy Pike Huber Heights OH 45424*

PFUND, MARY ANN,SSJ, Religion Teacher; *b:* Teaneck, NJ; *ed:* Millersville Univ (BS) Comprehensive Soc Stud 1972; LaSalle Univ (MA) Rel Ed 1986; 12 Grad Credits Chrstn Spirituality Prgm Creighton Univ at Omaha; *cr:* Fort Lee HS Tchr 1972-73; St Margaret's Schl Tchr 1973-74; St Joseph Schl Tchr 1974-76, 1978-79; St Bartholomews Tchr 1979-86; Our Mother of Sorrows Schl Tchr 1986-88; Holy Family Acad Tchr 1988-; *ai:* Ath Dir; Rel Dept Chprsn; Jr, Sr Class Moderator; NCEA 1988-; *home:* 239 Avenue A Bayonne NJ 07002*

PHAIR, SHANNON SCULLY, Sixth Grade Teacher; *b:* St Catharines ON, Canada; *m:* Stephen James; *c:* Chris, Jamie, Keira Ferriter, Ryan Ferriter, Kate, Pat, Meghan Ferriter, Patrick Ferriter, Ian; *ed:* Univ of ME (BA) Elem Ed 1988; Newspaper in Ed; Inst for Human Rights; Jr Great Books; *cr:* Hitchcock Rehabilitation Ctr Tchrs Aide 1974-76; Mount Merici Elem Schl Sixth Grd Tchr 1988-; *ai:* Stu Thought Enrichment Prgm Coord, Instr; Jr HS CCD Tchr; Notre Dame Parish 1986-.

PHARO, JAMES WILLIAM, Social Stud Tchr & Dept Chm; *b:* Cincinnati, OH; *m:* Kathleen Marie Moore; *c:* Joan, Jennifer, Jimmy; *ed:* Athanaeum of OH (BA) Philosophy 1968; Xavier Univ (MA) Ed 1972; *cr:* Seton HS Tchr & Chm 26 Yrs; *ai:* Sr Homeroom; Blood Drive Coord; OH Cncl of Soc Stud; *office:* Seton HS 3901 Glenway Ave Cincinnati OH 45205

PHEBUS, DEBRA C., Computer Science Instructor; *b:* Richwood, WV; *m:* Stephen; *c:* Ryan, Mark; *ed:* Glenville St Coll (AS) Gen Stud 1987, (BS) Bus, Acctng 1990; Mid TN St Univ (MS) Acctng, Information Systems 1992; *cr:* Mid TN St Univ Grad Tchng Asst 1990-92; Allegany Comm Coll Part-time Instr 1992-; *ai:* PTO Ofcr; Little League, Hot Stove Bsbl, Cub Scouts Parent Vol; IRS VITA Prgm Trainer, Vol; Amer Acctng Assn, TN Soc of CPA's, Inst of Mngmt Accountants 1990-; Order of Eastern Star 1978-; CPA; Tax Articles Pub; *office:* Allegany Comm Coll Willow Brook Road Cumberland MD 21502

PHELAN, MADLYN BARRINGER, English & French Teacher; *b:* Charlotte, NC; *m:* Walter; *c:* Anya, Mara; *ed:* WA Univ (BA) Fr 1975; Univ of CT (MA) Fr 1977; Kean Coll Eng Cert 1978; Saint Peters Coll Eng Grad Credits 1981; Jersey City St Coll Eng Grad Credits 1979; *cr:* West NY Meml HS Fr & Eng Tchr 1978-92; Hudson Cty Comm Coll Adjunct Prof 1981-83; Ellenville HS Eng & Fr Tchr 1993-; *ai:* Newspaper Adv; AFT 1993-; *office:* Ellenville Central Schl 28 Maple Ave Ellenville NY 12428

PHELAN, MICHAEL ROBERT, Computer Teacher; *b:* Somerville, MA; *m:* Sharon Sullivan; *ed:* Wentworth Inst (AS) 1967; Boston St Coll (BS) Math 1972; Attnd Northeastern Univ; *cr:* Burlington HS Instr 1973-; Burlington Adult Ed Instr 1980-; Woborn Racquet Club Tennis Pro 1982-90; *ai:* Boys Var Tennis Coach 1979-; Burlington Cnty Club 1970-, Pres; Boston Globe Coach of Yr 1990; Middlesex League Spring Coach of Yr 1989; *home:* 3 Sunnyfield Ave Burlington MA 01803

PHELAN-SWAN, LORRAINE H. (SOLTYS), English Teacher; *b:* Needham, MA; *m:* Ernest A. Swan; *c:* Joseph R. Phelan, Tania L. Phelan; *ed:* Northeastern Univ (BS) Eng Ed 1966; Lesley Coll (MED) Curr & Instruction Lang Arts 1994; 45 Credits Beyond Masters; *cr:* C W Ruckel Jr HS Eng Tchr 1966-68; Medway HS Eng Tchr 1969-; *ai:* Class of 1983 & 1992 Adv; Yrbk Adv; Co-Chprsn Scholastic Awds; Schlsp Comm; Honor Soc Selection Comm; Chaperone for Canada Trips; Franklin Emblem Club 1971-, Pres; Blackstone Boosters 1989-, Pres; Medway Fed of Tchrs 1969-, VP; NCTE 1966-; NEATE 1980-; AFT 1972-; Yrbk Dedication; *office:* Medway HS 45 Holliston St Medway MA 02053

PHELPS, JANN CAMPBELL, Family & Consumer Science Tchr; *b:* Braddock, PA; *m:* Steven; *c:* Amy Earhart, Stacey; *ed:* Ashland Coll (BSEd) Voc, Home Ec 1967; Addl Grad Hrs Univ of Toledo, Bowling Green St Univ; *cr:* Elgin Schl Dist Voc, Family, Consumer Sci Tchr 1966-70; Fremont City Schls Family, Consumer Sci Tchr 1970-74; Port Clinton City Schls Pub Presch Tchr 1990-92, 7th-8th Grd Family, Consumer Sci Tchr 1992-; *ai:* Natl, OH Family & Consumer Sci, Port Clinton Fed of Tchrs, AFT 1992-; Ottawa Co Extension, Home Economists 1976-; Church Orgs 1974-; Citizens Awareness of Substance Abuse 1987-, Vice Chm; *office:* Port Clinton Jr HS 110 E 4th St Port Clinton OH 43452

PHELPS, JULIANNE JACOBSEN, Media Specialist; *b:* Portland, ME; *m:* Wolcott H.; *c:* Melissa, Rebecca; *ed:* Cntrl CT St Univ (BS) Eng 1984, (MS) Educl Tech, Media 1995; *cr:* Baldwin MS 8 Grd Eng Tchr 1988-94; Brown MS 6-8 Grd Media Specialist 1994-; *ai:* St Curr Framework, Scheduling, Lib Curr Comms; Dist Curr, Tech Advy Cncls; Ldrshp Team; CFA 1988-; Conn Assn of Mid Level Ed 1995-; AASL 1993-; *office:* Brown MS 980 Durham Rd Madison CT 06443*

PHELPS, SUSAN WILLIAMS, Social Studies Teacher; *b:* Johnson City, NY; *m:* Mark A.; *c:* Nathaniel, Joshua, Aaron; *ed:* SUNY at Binghamton (BS) Soc Sci 1980, (MAT) Sec Soc Stud 1991; *cr:* Binghamton HS Soc Stud Tchr 1991-; *ai:* Excl Acad Comm; Phi Delta Kappa 1994-; NEA, Binghamton Tchrs Assn 1992-; AAUW 1991-; Chenango Forks PTA 1987-; St Mark's Epscopal Church 1985-; SUNY Fnd Awd; *office:* Binghamton HS 31 Main St Binghamton NY 13905*

PHELPS, VIRGINIA TAGGART, English Teacher; *b:* Lubbock, TX; *m:* Roland Alan; *c:* Gregory Alan, Melissa Lauren; *ed:* Univ of MD (BA) Eng Ed 1963; Univ of KS Post Grad Stud Eng Ed; Towson St Univ Post Grad Stud Eng Ed Masters Equivalency Earned 1968; *cr:* Dundalk Sr HS Eng Ed Tchr 1963-65; Old Court Jr, Sr HS Eng Ed Tchr 1966-67; Woodlawn Sr HS Eng Ed Tchr 1967-71; Randallstown Sr HS Eng Ed Tchr 1971-73; Liberty HS Eng Ed Tchr 1983-; *ai:* Stu Assistance Team 1985-91; SHOP Adv 1991-; Co-Chprsn Drug & Alcohol Symposium 1992-; Fac Advy Comm 1994-; NHS Bd 1992-95; Awds Comm 1990-; NEA, MSTA, Carroll Cty Ed Assn 1983-; Messiah Luth Church 1963-, Chrstn Ed Comm; Carroll Dale Comm Assn 1975-, Corres Sec; Outstdng Club Awd for Carroll Cty 1994 & 1995; Co-Author Curr Guides3 for Scndry Eng Tchrs; Carroll Cty Tchr, Mentor Mc Donald's Schlsp Recipient 1995; *office:* Liberty HS 5855 Bartholow Rd Sykesville MD 21784

PHETHEAN, NANCY MORRIS, First Grade Teacher; *b:* Ithaca, NY; *m:* David Glenn; *c:* Carol, David; *ed:* Wilkes Univ (BS) Elem Ed 1957; Western CT Univ (MS) Elem Ed 1974; 30 Post-Grad Credits Various Insts in All Areas Relating to Elem Ed; 15 In-Svc Credits Coll of New Rochelle & New Paltz Coll; *cr:* Thomas Jefferson Schl 2nd Grd Tchr 1957-59; Primrose Schl 1st Grd Tchr 1969-; *ai:* Mem of Schl Based Team in Accordance with NY St Compact for Learning; AFT-Union 1969-; Somers Fac Assn 1969-, Sec 1 Yr, Bldg Rep 3 Yrs, Grievance Rep 15 Yrs; Delta

Kappa Gamma 1980-, Treas 10 Yrs, Current Sec 2 Yrs; *office:* Primrose Elem Schl Rt 139 Lincolndale NY 10540

PHIEL, JEAN ELIZABETH, English Teacher; *b:* Columbia, PA; *m:* Larry E.; *c:* Christopher, Lindy, Andrew; *ed:* Millersville St Coll (BS) Eng & Ed 1970; Millersville Univ (MS) Ed 1989; *cr:* Donegal Schl Dist Eng & Math Tchr 1970-77; Eastern York Schl Dist Eng Tchr 1979-82; Columbia Borough Schl Eng Tchr 1982-; Harrisburg Area Comm Coll Adj Prof of Speech & Eng 1990-; *ai:* NEA 1970-; PSEA 1970-; CEA 1982-; Outstdng Edctr in Amer 1973-74; Outstdng Young Edctr Columbia Area Jaycees 1984; Dedication 1984; Coll Stu Journal; *office:* Columbia HS 901 Ironville Pike Columbia PA 17512

PHILCOX, FREDERIC RICHARD, English Department Chairman; *b:* Worcester, MA; *m:* Sharyn; *c:* Dawn, David; *ed:* Worcester St Coll (BSEd) Eng 1964; Harvard Univ (MAT) Eng 1965; *cr:* Algonquin Regnl HS Eng Tchr 1965-86, Eng Dept Chm 1986-; *ai:* Lang Art Comm Co-Chair; Supts Strategic Planning Comm; MA Tchrs Assn, NEA 1970-; Algmouin Regl Tchrs Assn 1965-, Pres, VP, Sec, Negotuting, Comm Chair; Assabet Valley Master Singers 1970-, Pres, VP; Church Newsletter 1993-, Ed; Northboro Cncl on Aging 1980-86, Chm; NCTE Panel Convener 1981; *home:* 31 Westbrook Rd Northborough MA 01532*

PHILIPPONE, REBECCA G., French Teacher; *b:* Norwich, NY; *m:* Mark R.; *c:* Marie-France, Alexandra; *ed:* SUNY at Oswego (BA) Fr 1987; SUNY at Albany (MS) Ed 1991; *cr:* Coll Offenbach at Paris Eng Tchr 1987-88; Oxford Acad Fr Tchr 1991-92; Greene Cntrl Schl Fr Tchr 1992-; *ai:* Fr Club Adv; NEA 1991-; NYSAFLT 1992-; *office:* Greene Cntrl Schl 40 S Canal St Greene NY 13778

PHILIPPY, GARY, Math Teacher; *b:* Manchester, NH; *m:* Claire Gregoire; *c:* Jason, Audra; *ed:* Univ of NH (BS) Math 1970; Lowell Univ (MST) Math 1976; *cr:* Conant HS Math Tchr 1970-71; Memorial HS Math Tchr 1971-; *ai:* Golf, Bsktbl Coach; MEA 1971-; NHEA, NEA 1970-; NH Golf Assn 1981-, Pres; Mc Donough Golf Fnd 1990-, VP.

PHILIPS, CONNIE MC QUIGG, Instructor & Cmptr Pgm Tech; *b:* Mount Vernon, OH; *m:* James Edward; *c:* Jaimie C., Cori D., Casey N., Matthew J.; *ed:* Bowling Green St Univ (BS) Cmptr Sci, Math 1978; *cr:* Owens-Corning Fiberglas Cmptr Programmer 1977-78; North Cntrl Tech Coll Instr, Cmptr Programming 1979-85; Cntrl OH Tech Coll Instr, Cmptr Programming 1987-; *ai:* Cmptr Programming Tech Curr, Bus Division Curr, COTC Curr, Tenure Comms; AFT, UF, COTC 1990-; Tchng Excl Awd 1995; *office:* Central OH Tech Coll University Drive Newark OH 43055

PHILIPS, DAVID WENDELL, History Teacher; *b:* Baltimore, MD; *m:* Alice Patricia Smith; *c:* Scott, Carolyn; *ed:* Towson St Coll (BS) Eng 1965; Morgan St Coll (MA) European Hist 1972; Addl 40 Credits Hum; *cr:* Woodbourne Jr High Eng Tchr 1965-68; Southern HS Eng Tchr 1968-70; Franklin HS Eng Tchr 1975-78; Dumbarton MS Soc Stud Tchr 1978-92; Dulaney HS His Tchr 1992-; *ai:* Photography Club Adv; Bsktbl, Sftbl Coach; Ancient, Honorable Mechanical Co of Baltimore 1994-, Mem; Fulbright Scholar to Cntrl Amer 1991; *home:* 228 Hopkins Rd Baltimore MD 21212

PHILIPS, GARY ROSS, High School Mathematics Tchr; *b:* Bronx, NY; *m:* Sandra Shipos; *c:* Scott, Jonathan; *ed:* Syracuse Univ (BA) Math 1968; St Univ of NY at Oswego (MS) Ed 1974; 12 Grad Credits; *cr:* Liverpool HS Math Tchr 1968-; *ai:* Boys Frosh Soccer, Var Bowling & Girls Frosh Sftbl Coach; Bridge Club Adv & Instr; United Liverpool Fac Assn 1968-; NYSUT 1968-; AFT 1968-; Syr Parks & Rec Sftbl Bd 1975-, VP; Vol Yth Optimist 1991-, Coach; *home:* 4291 Luna Crse Liverpool NY 13090*

PHILIPSON, WAYNE IAN, Biology Teacher; *b:* Utica, NY; *m:* Linda Marie Leffler; *c:* Brent, Rachael; *ed:* Mohawk Valley Comm Coll (AS) Bio, Chem 1970; Brockport St Univ (BS) Bio 1972; Binghamton Univ Permanent Cert Prgm; *cr:* Vestal Mid Jr HS Earth, Life, Phy Sci Tchr 1972-; Binghamton Univ Upward Bound Prgm Instr 1976-; Vestal HS Regents Bio Tchr 1994-; *ai:* Sci Club, Ski Club Adv; Vestal Tchrs Assn 1972-, Pres 1981-82; NEA 1972-; Susquehanna River Otters Lacrosse Club 1995-, Treas; Beaujon Hills Assn 1977-, Treas 1978; WNBF Radio Tchr of Day 1994; *office:* Vestal Sr HS 205 Woodlawn Dr Vestal NY 13850

PHILLIPS, AARON DWAYNE, Assistant Principal; *b:* Grove City, PA; *m:* Audrey Stine; *ed:* IN Univ of PA (BS) Elem Ed 1985; Hood Coll at Fred (MA) Admin, Supervision 1992; *cr:* Frederick Cty Schl 5th Grd Elem Tchr 1985-88, 6th Grd Tchr 1988-92, Asst Prin 1993-; *ai:* Big Brothers & Sisters; NEA 1985-; ASCD 1988-; Suburban Kiwanis Tchr Awd 1992; Who's Who Among Young Amer Prof 1987-88; Who's Who Intnl 1981; *office:* West Frederick MS 515 W Patrick St Frederick MD 21701*

PHILLIPS, ALTON FREEMAN,III, 5th Grade Teacher; *b:* Quincy, MA; *m:* Carla Green; *c:* Alton IV, Geoffrey; *ed:* Eastern Nazarene Coll (BS) His 1969; Bridgewater St (MED) Admin; Lesley Coll; *cr:* Duxbury Schls Tchr 1970-; *ai:* Curr Asst; After Schl Sports, Talent Show, Chapter I Dir; Admin Intern; NEA 1970-, Pres Local Union, Chief Negotiator; *office:* Duxbury Elem Schl 130 St George St Duxbury MA 02332

PHILLIPS, ANNIE NOYES, Science & English Teacher; *b:* Walden, NY; *m:* Thomas A.; *c:* Kathleen, Kevin D., Joseph A., MaryPat Phillips Bowe, Daniel A.; *ed:* Coll of New Rochelle (BA) Chem 1951; SUNY 32 Credits Hlth; Pace Univ 4 Credits Astronomy; Westchester Comm Coll 2 Comp Courses; *cr:* St John the Evangelist Sci Tchr 1968-71; Mother Butler HS Chem & Phys Sci Tchr 1971-74; Marymount Acad Chem & Phys Sci Tchr 1974-76; Sacred Heart HS Chem & Phys Sci Tchr & Dept Head 1976-79; Holy Child HS Chem & Phys Sci Tchr 1979-87; Maria Regina HS Chem & Phys Sci Tchr 1987-88; St Lawrence O'Toole Sci & Eng Tchr 1988-; *ai:* 8th Grd Grad Exercises; 8th Grd Yrbk; NSTA; NYS Sci Tchrs Assn; BSA Dir; Campfire Girls Dir; Schl Groups; PTA Dir; Natl Wildlife Assn; AARP; Elderhostel; *office:* St Lawrence O'Toole Schl Eastview Ave 11 Eastview Ave Brewster NY 10509

PHILLIPS, BEVERLY ANN, Second Grade Teacher; *b:* Dayton, OH; *m:* Myron L.; *c:* Holly Lynn; *ed:* Cntrl St Univ (BS) Elem Ed 1960; 30 Grad Hrs; *cr:* Yellow Springs Pvt Schl Early Chldhd Tchr 1961-64; Engelwood Elem Schl Spec Ed Rdng Tchr 1973; Springfield city Schl Chptr I Rdng Tchr 9174, Elem Second, Third Grd Tchr 1975-; *ai:* Rdng Tchr After Schl Vol; NEA; Rdng, Math, GATE, Sci, Soc Stud Comms.

PHILLIPS, CATHY LORRAINE, Physical Education Teacher; *b:* Plattsburgh, NY; *ed:* Lyndon St Coll (BS) PE 1977; Plattsburgh St Univ (MS) Liberal Arts 1980; Admin, Counseling, Tech; *cr:* Peru Schl Dist PE Tchr 1979-, Grls Var Soccer Coach; *ai:* Family Schl Org; Class of 1986, 1990, 1992, 1996 Advs; Staff Dev Comm; Pro Ed Comm Group; Youth Prgm; Alumni Cncl Lyndon St Coll; Lions Quest Trainer Skills for Adolescence, Growing, Mega Skill Trainer; Grant Writer, Coord; Drug Free Schls; Chem Awareness Coord; Ath Caring Together, Integrating Organinzing, Networking Standing Comm; NYSAHPERD Sec; NYSPHSAA Chem Awrnss Stndng Comm; ACTION Trnr; Mem Peru Ath Contrct Comm, Bldng Lvl Team, Dist Stff Dvlpmnt Comm; Key Tm Coord; Peru Assn of Tchrs 1979-, Pres, VP, Rep Del, Soc Dir, Rep; NEA NY 1979-, Del, Wmn ldrshp Trnr; NYS Assn of Hlth, PE, Dance 1982-, Sec, Treas; Amer Ed Comm Mem; Comm of Pro-Ed in Peru Mem; Mission Stud Peru Comm Church 1993-; Logos Prgm 1992-, Recreation Dir; Finance Comm 1990-92; Peru Youth Commission 1988-90; Phi Delta Kappa Mem; Peru Chrch Sr High Youth Adv, Personnel Comm; Past Recrtn Coor LOGOS Pgm, Past Seton, Past Fin Comm Mem; Past Sun Schl Tchr; Past Peru Twn Yth & Smmr Bureau Mem; NY St Coaches Assn Honor Awd 1993-94; Section 7 Ath Dirs Ray Holmes Phys Educator of Yr Awd 1992-93, CVAC Coach's Sportsmnshp Awd 1992; Tchr of Yr 1992-93; Yrbk Dedication 1986, 1991; St Educ Dept 1990; Acknwldgmnt in Recource Guide, Unin St NY; Yng Wmn of Amer 1988, 1994; Soccer Coach of Yr 1984; Bsktbl Coach of Yr 1982; Dev, Implemented Various Schl Prgms; Dev Peru Schl Dist Referral Pgm, Drug Pgm, Ath Code of Conduct, Ath Drug, Alcohol Policy, Discipline Policy, Stdnt Ldrshp Cls Grds 8-12, Open Gym Pgm Grds 7-12.*

PHILLIPS, CHERYL ANN, Second Grade Teacher; *b:* Cooperstown, NY; *m:* Craig; *c:* Lindsay; *ed:* St Univ Coll (BS) Elem Ed 1976; 33 Credit Hrs; *cr:* Dolgeville Elem Second Grd Tchr 1976-; *ai:* Hlth Advy Comm; NYSUT; Parent Tchr Group 1987-; *home:* 811 Steuben Rd Herkimer NY 13350

PHILLIPS, CHERYL KLEIS, HS Orchestra & Asst Band Dir; *b:* Cleveland, OH; *m:* Craig T.; *c:* Scott, Brian; *ed:* Bowling Green St Univ (BM) Music Ed 1977; Addl Hrs at Cleveland St Univ, Kent St Univ, Baldwin Wallace Coll, Univ of Akron, Coll of Mt St Joseph; *cr:* Parma City Schls Elem Instrumental Music Dir 1978-, Elem Gen Music Dir 1978-87, HS Orch, Asst Band Dir 1987-; *ai:* OMEA, MENC, Parma Ed Assn, NEA 1978-; Amer Guild of Eng Handbell Ringers 1982-; Amer String Tchrs Assn 1988-; Divinity Luth Church 1981-, Handbell Choir Dir; *office:* Parma Sr H S 6285 W 54th St Parma OH 44129

PHILLIPS, CHRISTIE CIANO, Speech & English Teacher; *b:* Anchorage, AK; *ed:* Wright St Univ (BS) Communication 1978; *cr:* Wayne HS Eng Tchr 6 Yrs; Vinton Cty HS Eng & Speech Tchr 11 Yrs; *ai:* Educl Excl Comm; NEA, OEA 1978-; Wellston Patriots 1995-, Bd Pres; Occupational Ed Grant; *office:* Vinton County HS 307 W High St Mc Arthur OH 45651

PHILLIPS, EILEEN M. (CARLSON), Assistant Professor of Math; *b:* Utica, NY; *m:* Brian; *ed:* Utica Coll of Syracuse Univ (BA) Math 1989; SUNY at Potsdam Scndry Math Tchr 1990; *cr:* Whitesboro Cntrl Schl Sub Tchr 1990-92; SUNY at Morrisville Math Specialist 1992-93; Jefferson Comm Coll Asst Prof of Math 1993-; *ai:* Soc Comm; Awds & Recognition Comm; NCTM 1989-; NYCLSA 1993-; NYSMATYC 1994-; Performance Awd 1994-95; *office:* Jefferson Comm Coll Coffeen St Watertown NY 13601

PHILLIPS, ELIZABETH MARTINO, Latin & History Teacher; *b:* Cleveland, OH; *m:* Ron; *c:* Amy, Beth, Robbie; *ed:* Univ of Dayton (BS) Ed, Latin, His 1972; Addl Post Grad Stud Bowling Green St Univ; *cr:* Bryan HS Latin, His Tchr 1974-77, 1985-; *ai:* Latin Club Adv; Strategic Planning Comm at Bryan; Bryan Educl Assn, OH Educl Assn, NEA 1974-; Amer Classical League 1972-; OH Child Conservation League 1986-, Pres, Treas, Acad Booster Club 1990-, Tchr Rep; Bryan Ath, Music Boosters 1985-; *office:* Bryan HS 150 S Portland St Bryan OH 43506

PHILLIPS, FRED CLEVELAND,III, Senior Accounting Instructor; *b:* Easton, PA; *ed:* Husson Coll ME (BS) Acctng, Ed 1971; Churchman Bus Coll Diploma Advanced Acctng 1969; NCPE LA Tax Cert 1990; PA St Univ 3 Credit Hrs Educl Mngmt; *cr:* Laneco Dept Store Mgr 1972-73; Churchman Bus Schl Jr Acctng Instr 1973-84, Sr Acctng Instr 1984-; *ai:* PA Army Natl Guard 1971-; Maintenance Section, Rebuild Shop Mngmt; NCPE 1989-; Free, Accept Mason 1994-, Chprsn; Scottish Rite Mason 1994-; Masonic Hall Assn 1996-; Scottish Rite Ctr 1996-, Vol; *office:* Churchman Business Schl 355 Spring Garden St Easton PA 18042*

PHILLIPS, JAMES WALTER, Electromechanical Tech Instr; *b:* Wilkes-Barre, PA; *m:* AnnMarie Franks; *c:* Benjamin James, Adam David; *ed:* PA St Univ (BS) Voc Indstrl Ed 1988; *cr:* Allied Signal Aerospace Division Technician 1984-90; York Tech Inst Instr 1990-93; Northeastern PA Tech Prep Field Rep 1993; Luzerne Cty Comm Coll Adj Fac 1993-; Lackawanna Cty AVTS Instr 1993-; *ai:* VICA; AFT, CIO 3876 1993-; Masonic Lodge 248 F&AM 1985-; Outstdng Tchr of Yr 1995; *office:* Lackawanna Cty Area Voc Tech 3201 Rockwell Ave Scranton PA 18508*

PHILLIPS, JANE S., Retired Mathematics Director; *b:* East Rochester, NY; *w:* Roland T. Jr (dec); *c:* Roland T. III, Sara Phillips Hinteregger, Patricia L.; *ed:* St Lawrence Univ (BS) Math, (MEd) Guidance, Personnel 1943; *cr:* Boonville HS Instr Math 1943-45; Amityville HS Instr Math 1945-46; Canton HS Inst Math 1946-48; Boston Univ Guidance Cnslr, Asst Prof 1948-52; Abington HS Dir of Math 1971-95; *ai:* Adv Natl Honor Soc; Tech Comm; 3 Adjudication Comm for New England Colls, Univs, HS Cert; NEA, NCTM, ATMIN,1971-; New England Plymouth Cty Tchrs Assn 1971- Honors Awd Schlsp my Name; Rockland Credit Union, Former Dir; Trustee South Shore Hospital 1970-, Fomer Pres Corp 1980-82, Bd Ch; Abington Citizens Schlshp 1959-, Former Pres, Now Honorary Dir; Abington Visiting Nurse Assn 1957-, Former Pres; Abington Camp Fire Girls 1961-, Prgm Dir; Salvation Army Unit 1963-, 20 Yrs; PM Division Rockland Woman's Club 1957-, Former Pres, Choral Dir; Jane S. Phillip's Schlsp Every Yr; Rotary Club Paul Harris Fellow 1990; Abington Bd Selectman Outstanding Tchr, Educator 1991; Patriot Ledger Golden Apple Awds 1990-93; ACSF Schlsp my Name each Yr; Chester Millett Outstanding Tchr of Yr 1993.*

PHILLIPS, KIMBERLY LYNN, Librarian & Media Specialist; *b:* Gallipolis, OH; *m:* Gary A.; *c:* Adam; *ed:* Rio Grande Coll (BS) Math 1981; Marshall Univ (MA) Lib Sci 1994; *cr:* Kyger Creek HS Math, Chem, Cmptr Tchr 1981-83; Southern HS Math, Bio, General Sci Tchr, Librn 1983-; *ai:* NHS Adv; Quiz Team Coach; OELMA 1992-; NEA, OEA 1981-, Bldg Rep; Lib Future Planning Comm 1995-; *office:* Southern HS PO Box 98 Racine OH 45771

PHILLIPS, LOIS INGALLS, French Teacher; *b:* Sweetsburg Quebec, Canada; *m:* Trevor; *c:* David, Janis Bajor, Nancy; *ed:* Bowling Green St Univ (BA) Fr Ed 1975, (MED) Coll Stu Prsnl 1981; Addl 15 Hrs; *cr:* Bowling Green St Univ Office Work 1975-84; Gibsonburg HS 9-12th Grd Fr Tchr 1984-; *ai:* Fr Club Adv; OH Ed Assn, OH Frgn Lang Assn 1984-; League of Women Voters 1963-, Voter Svc, VP, Sec; Martha Holdings Jennings Awd.

PHILLIPS, MARGARET A., Social Studies & Reading Tchr; *b:* Quincy, MA; *ed:* Bridgewater St Coll (BS) Ed 1961; 36 Addl Hrs; *cr:* Shaw Schl 7th Grd Eng, Soc Stud Tchr 1961-63; Bicknell Jr HS 7, 8 Grds Eng, Soc Stud Tchr 1963-80; East Jr HS 7, 8 Grds Soc Stud Tchr 1980-90; East, Adams Intermediate 7 Grd Soc Stud, Rdng Tchr 1990-; *ai:* Schl Newspaper; Drama Club; Stu Cncl; Yrbk 1992-94; Curr, Leveling, Evaluation Comms; Weymouth Tchrs Assn 1961-, Bldg Rep, Negotiating Team; MTA; NEA; Town Meeting Mem 1960-70; Braintree; Democratic Town Comm 1960-70 Sec, Treas; *office:* Adams Intermediate Schl 89 Middle St Weymouth MA 02189

PHILLIPS, MARK O'HARA, Eighth Grade Teacher; *b:* Calcutta, India; *m:* Louise Charbonneau; *ed:* St Andrews Univ (MA) Philosophy-Hnrs 1986; Addl Hrs Univ of Southern ME Instrl Ldrshp; *cr:* Plummer-Motz Schl GATE Tchr K-5 Grds 1988-90; Pownal Elem Schl Grd 8 Tchr 1990-; *ai:* JV Soccer Coach; Lang Arts Curr, Soc Stud Curr Comms; Casco Bay Educl Alliance Summer Inst Facilitator; Probationary Tchr; Pownal Tchrs Assn 1990-, Negotiator; *office:* Pownal Elem Schl 587 Elmwood Rd Pownal ME 04069*

PHILLIPS, MARYANNE FORD, 7th Grade English Teacher; *b:* Philadelphia, PA; *m:* Donald K.; *c:* Allison, Ford; *ed:* West Chester Univ (BS) Scndry Ed Eng & Soc Stud 1961; Univ of PA (MS) Lang & Rdng 1983; 80 Post Grad Hrs; *cr:* Nether Providence HS Tchr 1961-64; Ocean City HS Tchr 1964-66; Lenape Regnl HS Tchr 1966-67; C Intermediate Schl Tchr 1967-71; Downingtown Jr HS Tchr 1981-9 Curr Revision Interdisciplinary, Interdisciplinary Team Bldng C NCTE & DAEA 1981-; PSEA & NEA 1961-; *office:* Downingtown 335 Manor Ave Downingtown PA 19335*

PHILLIPS, NANCY, Fifth & Sixth Grade Teacher; *b:* Rockville C *m:* Stephen Doherty; *ed:* Univ of VT (BA) Art His 1970, (MED) M 1992; Tchr Elem Ed Cert Univ of MA 1972; 21 Hrs Beyond Maste Ed; *cr:* Northfield Elem Schl 1st & 2nd Grd Tchr 1972-74; Warren Schl 5th & 6th Grd Tchr 1974-; *ai:* Math, Sci, Soc Stud & Lang Ar Comms; Placement Comm; Mid Grds Comm; VT-NEA 1978- Newsletter, Grievance Chair, Bldg Rep; NCTM 1984-; VAMLE NELMS 1982-; Greater Mt Rug Hooking Craft Guild 1984-, Treas; 1992-; Mad River Path Assn 1994-; Nom by Schl for Dist Tchr Integrated Stud in Mid Grds Books: Chapter in Inventions, Th Quoted in Teaching with Architecture; *office:* Warren Elem Schl RR 227 Warren VT 05674*

PHILLIPS, PAUL ALLEN, Mathematics Teacher; *b:* Louisville, K Serena Gabriel; *c:* J. T. Ranz, Jason Ranz; *ed:* Miami Univ Oxfor Scndry Math 1993; Miami Univ Oxford Grad Schl; *cr:* Fasterver Industrial Inside Sales 1986-88; Hamilton Fixture Stockroom 1988-89; Miami Univ Hamilton Tutor Math 1990-92; New Mia Scndry Math 1993-; *ai:* Asst Var Bsktbl, Bsbl & SW OH Summer Bsbl Coach; OCTM 1992-; NCTM 1992-; *office:* New Miami Jr Sr H Seven Mile Ave Hamilton OH 45011

PHILLIPS, PAUL T., Criminal Justice Assoc Prof; *b:* Utica, N Annick Lajeunesse; *c:* Paul, Christian; *ed:* Mohawk Valley Com (AAS) Police Sci 1972; St Univ of NY at Utica (BPS) Criminal 1982; St Univ of NY at Brockport (MA) Liberal Stud 1989; *cr:* Lakes Comm Coll Instr of Criminal Justice 1985-89, Asst Prof of Cr Justice 1989-94, Assoc Prof of Criminal Justice 1994-; *ai:* Acad P Comm 1994-; Criminal Justice Educators Assn 1986-; NEA 19 Tchng Fac Bargaining Cncl of FLCC 1994-; *office:* Finger Lakes Coll 4355 Lake Shore Dr Canandaigua NY 14424

PHILLIPS, PETER DOUGLAS, American His & Government T Fishkill, NY; *m:* Cristina Hansen; *ed:* Dutchess Comm Coll (AA) L Arts, His 1969; SUNY at Plattsburg (BS) Scndry Ed, Soc Stud 19 Grad Hrs His & Ed Long Island Univ, SUNY at New Paltz; *cr:* F Ketcham SR HS Amer His Tchr 1974-; *ai:* Yrbk, Stu Cncl, Jr Clas Bowling Coach; AFT 1974-; Dutchess Cty Legislator 1988-, M Whip 1990-93; Fishkill Rural Cemetary 1989-, VP 1989-; Prot Engine Co #1 1966-, Pres 5 Yrs, Fireman of the Yr 1982-, Life Mem Popular Male Tchr 1991-; Consultant Franklin D. Roosevelt Presid Lib; *home:* 4 Maple Ave Fishkill NY 12524

PHILLIPS, RICHARD A., Business Education Teacher; *b:* Elizabe *ed:* Trenton St Coll (MA) His 1975 & (BA) Soc Stud & Bus Ed; St Coll; Montclair St Univ; Rutgers Univ; *cr:* Orange Ave JR HS Tc Stud & Bus Ed 1968-79; Cranford HS Tchr Bus Ed 1979-; *ai:* Clas Yrbk Bus Staff Adv; Fac Advy Comm; NJBEA 1976; NEA 1968-; 1976-; Union Cty Voc; Schl Advy Comm 1994-; *office:* Cranford H W End Pl Cranford NJ 07016*

PHILLIPS, ROBERT JAMES, Mathematics Teacher; *b:* Olean, N Deborah Wdzieczny; *c:* Carlie, Robert Jr.; *ed:* St. Bonaventure Uni Math 1970, (MS) Ed 1973; Applied Math & Trainer Wkshps at Cen Occupational Research & Dev (CORD) at Waco; *cr:* Olean City Scndry Math Tchr 1973-; *ai:* HS Discipline-Attendance Comm Design Team; So Tier Tech Prep Consortium; Olean Dist Stan R Team; Olean Tchr Assoc 1973-, Treas 1977-78; NEA & NEA-NY AMTNYS; Olean BOCES Vo-Tech; Advy Cncl 1994-; Reserve O Assn 1969-, Chapter Sec-Treas; American Legion 1973-, Adjutant *office:* Olean HS 410 W Sullivan St Olean NY 14760

PHILLIPS, ROBERT R., Professor of Biology; *b:* Norfolk, V Phyllis; *ed:* Old Dominion Univ (BS) Bio 1963; Univ of MD (MS) Z 1968, (PHD) Zoology 1971; Univ of HI, OK St Univ Post Grad; *cr:* S of Oneonta Asst Prof Bio Dept 1973-; *ai:* Animal Behavior Soc Amer Soc of Manmalogy 1992-; Audubon Soc 1990-; Papers Pub i Jrnls on Animal Behavior.

PHILLIPS, SARA HUHRA, Teacher of Gifted Education; *b:* Pitts PA; *m:* Byron C.; *ed:* California Univ of PA (BS) Elem Ed 1972; U Pittsburgh (MED) Elem Ed 1976; 30 Addl Hrs; *cr:* Gastonville Ele 5th Grd Tchr 1972-79; Elrama Elem Schl 6th Grd Tchr 19 Monongahela Elem Ctr 4th Grd Tchr 1982-84; Finley MS 6-8 Grd 6th Grd Math Tchr 1984-; *ai:* NEA, Ringgold Ed Assn 1972-; PA M 1992-; PA Assn for Gifted Ed 1993-; *office:* Finley MS Rt 88 Finle PA 15332

PHILLIPS, SUSAN BUCKLEW, Geometry & Alg II Teach Portsmouth, VA; *m:* Craig; *c:* Courtney; *ed:* Walsh Univ (BS) Math Ashland Univ (BS) Curr, Instruction 1995; *cr:* Highland HS Math, Alg II Tchr 1985-; *ai:* USA Vlybl Player, Adult Leagues; NEA, C 1985-; *office:* Highland HS 3880 Ridge Rd Medina OH 44256

PHILLIPS, TERI LEE, Eng Teacher & Dept Chair; *b:* Newark, O Robert Thomas Marrs; *ed:* Miami Univ (BS) Eng 1975, (MA) Comm 36 Post Grad Semester Hrs Toward PHD Eng Lit; *cr:* Mt Healthy H Tchr 1977-, Eng Dept Chair, Scndry Curr Coord 1995-; *ai:* Tomorrows Educl Ldrs; Tech Prep Steering Comm Chair; Grant Venture Capital School-to-Work; NEA, OEA, NCTE 1977-; OH W Project Flwshp 1989; OH Writing Project Advanced Inst Flwshp Numerous Articles Pub; *office:* Mount Healthy HS 2046 Adam Cincinnati OH 45231

PHILLIPS, WILLIAM KENNETH, Fourth Grade Teacher; *b:* Kensington, PA; *w:* Patricia L. Andres; *c:* Bethanne R., Matthew K Clarion Univ (BS) Elem Ed 1970, (MED) Elem Ed 1972; ITEC 3 Cr *cr:* Vally Grove Schl Dist Fifth Grd Tchr 1970-; *ai:* Schlsp, Negot Comms; 5th-6th Grd Cross Cntry Coach; NEA, PSEA 1970-; VGEA Past-Pres; Rocky Grove Vol Fire Dept 1976-; *office:* Rocky Elementary 317 Wiley Ave Franklin PA 16323

PHILLIPS, WINTHROP T., High School English Teache Westminster, MD; *ed:* Washington & Lee Univ (BA) Jrnlsm 198 Portland HS Alternative Ed 1988-93; Massabesic HS Eng Tchr 199 Frosh Ftbl Asst Coach; Wrestling Head Coach; *office:* Massabesic HS Rd PO Box 500 Waterboro ME 04087*

PHILLIS, ROY ANDREW, Mathematics Teacher; *b:* Pittsburgh, P Dorothy Taylor; *c:* Amy Lynn; *ed:* Slippery Rock Univ (BS) Math & 1967; Univ of Pittsburgh (MED) Comprehensive Safety 1970; Ad Credit Hrs in Ed at Various Univs; *cr:* North Hills HS Math Instr 1 Burgettstown Area HS Math Instr 1967-68; Comm Coll of Alleghen Driver Ed Instr Part-Time 1991-; *ai:* Jr HS Ftbl Coach; NEA; PA Assoc; North Hills Ed Assoc; GTE Grant $12000 1995-96; *home* Broad Meadow Dr Pittsburgh PA 15237*

PHILLPS, DILCIA R., Professional Development Coord; *b:* Colon of Panama; *c:* Melbourne Alexander Hewitt Jr.; *ed:* Kingsborough C Coll (AA) L Arts 1977; Brooklyn Coll (MA) Elem Ed 1979, (MS) Cnslng 1982; City Coll of NY Admin, Supv Cert 1993; New Bruns Seminary at St John's Univ; *cr:* NYC Bd of Ed Elem Schl Tchr 198 Dist Chptr I Monitor 1985-86, Multicultural Coord 1986-90, Prof d 1990-; Medgar Evers Coll Adult Ed, ESL Tchr 1993-95; *ai:* gelist; Edith White Ming Missionary Chprsn; Allen Ame Mentor , Assn of Curr Dev 1990-; Rosedale Civic Assn 1985-; *office:* CSD chl 2240 Dean St Brooklyn NY 11233*

INEY-FOREMAN, ANN M., Chemistry Teacher; *b:* Sayre, PA; *m:* as Kevin Foreman; *c:* Brian Foreman, Matthew Foreman, Robert ıan; *ed:* Clarion Univ (BS) Chem Ed 1977; SUNY at Binghamton Tech 1987; Credit Hrs Univ of DE 13, Mansfield Univ 2, Elmira Coll 'niv of NC at Chapel Hill 4; Attnd Salisbury St Coll, SUNY at ase; *cr:* Indian River HS Chem Tchr 1977-80; Northern HS Chem 1980-81; SUNY at Binghamton Cmptr Sci Instr 1988-91; Waverly HS Tchr 1991-; *ai:* Chem Bowl Adv; NHS Selection Comm; NEA Indian 1977-82, Bldg Rep; NEA Waverly 1991-; Waverly Tchrs Local Assn; ; Dads Club 1993-, Worker, Run Concession Stand; St John's Church , Mem, Worker; Chem Bowl Winner 1st Pl 1992-95;NSF, NSTA, M Nom Presidential Awd Excl Sci, Math Tchng; *office:* Waverly Jr-Sr Frederick St Waverly NY 14892*

PEN, MONICA LYNN, Secondary Mathematics Teacher; *b:* use, NY; *ed:* St Univ of NY at Geneseo (BA) Math 1992, (MS) Ed *cr:* Mohawk Cntrl Schl Math Tchr 1994-; *ai:* Mathletics Adv; M, AMTNYS 1991-; MTA 1994-; *office:* Mohawk Cntrl Schl Dist 28 St Mohawk NY 13407

PS, CAROL SWALES, Secondary Social Stud Teacher; *b:* ngton, DE; *m:* Joseph; *c:* Ronald, Robert; *ed:* Univ of DE (BSEd) logy 1978; Washington Coll (MA) His 1985; Fr Cert from ersite Catholique de lOuest 1989; *cr:* Glasgow HS Soc Stud Tchr 83; Lake Forest HS Fr & Soc Stud Tchr 1985-91; Christiana HS Soc Tchr 1991-; *ai:* NEA, DEA, CEA 1985-; Habitat for Humanity 1994-; rk Wesleyan Church 1971-; Univ of DE Tchng Fellowship 1988; Lake Tchr of Yr 1987; *office:* Christiana HS Salem Church Rd Newark 9713*

PS, DAVID EUGENE, School Counselor; *b:* Piqua, OH; *ed:* Bethel BA) Ed 1976; U of Dayton (MS) Cnslng 1984; Various Courses; *cr:* lin Monroe HS Sci Instr 1976-86, Schl Cnslr 1986-; *ai:* Flwshp n Ath; Coach; Club Adv; Jennings Scholar Outstdng Young Men of

PS, DIANNE LAPENTA, Spanish Teacher; *b:* Syracuse, NY; *m:* rd R.; *c:* Kristen, Lauren, Karen; *ed:* Syracuse Univ (BA) Foreign 1964, (MA) Lang Ed 1969; 6 Addl Hrs Rdng; Univ de Valencia Spain of Att 1963; 70 Hrs Inservice Credits; *cr:* Norfolk Cath HS Span, an Tchr 1964-66; East Syracuse-Minoa HS Span Tchr 1968-73; daga Comm Coll Span Instr 1973-79; Syracuse Cty Schl Dist Span 1980-; *ai:* Mentor of Tchrs; Mediator for Stu Disputes; STA; anding Tchr Awd 1989, 1991, 1994; *office:* William Nottingham HS E Genesee St Syracuse NY 13224

PS, TERRY LEE, Professor of Zoology; *b:* Warsaw, IN; *m:* Rita e Sumner; *c:* Heather, Shannon; *ed:* Cedarville Coll (BS) Bio 1970; ıt St Univ (MS) Bio 1974; OH St Unif (PHD) Zoology 1987; *cr:* North Tech Coll Instr 1974-78; Cedarville Coll Bio Prof 1978-; *ai:* Amer for Advancement of Sci 1978-; Amer Soc for Limnology & ıography 1980-; North Amer Benthic Soc 1978-; Greeneview Local 3d 1984-87, Pres; *office:* Cedarville Coll PO Box 601 Cedarville OH

HAI B., Professor of Political Science; *ed:* Boston Univ (PHD) Pol 972, (MA) Pol Sci 1964; Boston Coll (BA) His 1960; *cr:* Lowell St Asst Prof 1968-73; Univ of Saigon Visiting Prof 1973-75; Univ of MA 975-; *ai:* Commonwealth of MA Governor Advy Cncl 1982-; Pol Sci s, Vietnamese, Cambodian Stu Clubs Fac Adv; Amer Pol Sci Assn, or Asian Stud, MA Tchr Assn 1975-; Book: Vietnamese Public gement in Transition 1990; Pub Policy: Immigration, Refugee Policy; Univ Of MA At Lowell 1 University Ave Lowell MA 01854

OFORTE, DONNA REAM, Mathematics Teacher; *b:* Phoenixville, ; Heather F. McGuire; *ed:* Trenton St Coll (BA) Math 1974, (MED) 1978; 33 Addl Grad Credits in Cmptr Sci, Math & Scndry Ed; als, Chaos & Dynamics Symposium Princeton Univ 1994-95; *cr:* Cncl HS Math Tchr 1974-; *ai:* NEA 1975-; NCTM 1987-; BCCTM; MAST Awd 1992; Speaker ATMOPAV Conf 1987; *office:* Council HS 62 Swamp Rd Newtown PA 18940

TIERI, ANTHONY THOMAS,III, Philosophy & Religion Teacher; w York, NY; *ed:* Boston Coll (BA) Eng Lit 1976; Fordham Univ (MS) Rel Ed 1983; 45 Addl Credits Dept Philosophy, Soc Scis; Curr, Tchng; Tchrs Coll, Columbia Univ; *cr:* Reader's Digest Asst Ed, Proof er 1976-81; ABC Television Free-Lance Critic Projects, Scripts 81; Acad of Mt St Ursula Rel Tchr, Yrbk Moderator 1982-87; Xavier Rel Tchr, Yrbk Moderator 1987-89; Fordham Prep Schl Eng, sophy, Rel Tchr, Yrbk Dir 1989-; *ai:* Video, Film Club Dir; NEA, 1982-; JSEA 1989-; Ronald Mc Donald House 1994-; Awded Letter ure 1994; Awd Outstdng Svc 1991, 1992; *office:* Fordham Prep Schl dham Rd Bronx NY 10458*

AK, MARY CLARE, French Teacher & NHS Adv; *b:* Johnstown, PA; t Francis Coll at Loretto (BA) Eng 1978, (MA) Prsnl, Industrial ions 1989; Indiana Univ of PA Permanent Cert Courses 1979-84; PA Enterprise Week for Educators 1991; Stu Assistance Prgm Confs St & 1992-; *cr:* Bishop Mc Cort HS Fr, Eng Tchr 1978-; *ai:* NHS Adv; Stu ance Prgm Team Mem; Forensics Team Competitions Occasional ; NCEA 1978-; Bottleworks Cultural Ctr 1990-, Bd of Dirs; Red , Organize Schl Blood Dr; St Francis Coll Tchr of Yr 1986, Apples ducators Awd Nom 1991; NHS Chapter Distinguished Tchr Awd 1993; anding Educator 1992; Mid States Evaluation Co-Coord 1990-92; : Bishop Mc Cort HS 25 Osborne St Johnstown PA 15905*

EK, REBECCA MARY, Building Principal; *b:* S Amboy, NJ; *ed:* an Coll at Lodi (BA) Elem Ed 1975; Eng at Villanova Univ; Cert: Schl, Eng & Rel Tchr; Prof Recovery Cnslr Trng NJ St; *cr:* Passaic Regnl Tchr 1975-80; Immaculate Conception Schl Tchr 1979-80; St en Campus Schl Prin 1980-87, Bldg Prin 1987-; *ai:* Liturgical Coord; Bd, Home & Schl Assn & Tuition Assistance Comm Mem; Pastoral p Comm Rep; NCEA 1980-; Polish World Amer Citizen of the Yr Cert of Recognition Admins Exch Todays Cath Tchrs; *office:* Saint ens Campus Schl 500 State St Perth Amboy NJ 08861

ZA, FRANCIS JOHN, Retired Language Arts Teacher; *b:* eport, CT; *ed:* Univ of Bridgeport (BA) Eng 1967; Univ of MI (MA) Lang Lit 1970; Fairfield Univ (MA) Amer Stud 1980; North Amer spondence Schl Travel Degree 1991; Intnl Correspondence Schl Asst Degree 1993; *cr:* Stratford HS Lang Arts Tchr 1972-96; *ai:* a Club Adv 1978-88; NEA, SEA, NCTE 1972-.

ZA, RAYMOND L., Asst to the Superintendent; *b:* Bristol, PA; *m:* ra Hart; *c:* Kim Dietzel, Kelly, Andrew; *ed:* East Stroudsburg Univ Ed 1965; Towson St (MS) Ed 1970; Widener Univ Supt Cert; *cr:* on St Coll Instr 3 Yrs; Hamburg Area Schls Elem Admin 9 Yrs; Berks ntermediate Unit Supvr of Staff Devel 11 Yrs; Daniel Boone Area Schl Supt Asst 3 Yrs; *ai:* Phi Delta Kappa 1979-; PA St Assn Prin 1982-; D 1991-; Easter Seals Bd 1988-91; Trinity Learning Ctr Comm ntion 1992-, VP; Partnership of Berks Cty; Article- Catalyst for ge; *office:* Daniel Boone Jr Sr HS PO Box 450 Douglassville PA 8*

PIAZZA, SHIRLEY E., Professor & Advisor; *b:* Easton, PA; *ed:* Kutztown St Coll (BS) Ed 1970; Univ of Cincinnati (MED) Curr & Instruction 1984, (EDD) Educl Fnds 1989; *cr:* Hamilton Cty Comm Mental Hlth Bd Researcher 1986-90; Univ of Cincinnati Adj Instr 1987-; The Union Inst Prof, Adv 1990-; *ai:* Acad Review, Women's Stud Comms; Union Cncl; Institutional Planning Commission; Amer Educl Stud Assn 1990-; The Alliance 1995-; The Grail 1974-; Friends of Jung 1993-; Cincinnati Bus & Prof Women 1995-; Garvin Doctoral Dissertation Awd; Natl Ctr for Rsrch Voc Ed In-residence Awd; *office:* Union Inst 440 E Mcmillan St Cincinnati OH 45206*

PICCINI, LEONARD A., Cosmetology Instructor; *b:* Peckville, PA; *m:* Roseanne Delfino; *c:* Lindsey, Lisa; *ed:* Lackawan Jr Coll (AS) Mngmt 1973; Temple Univ Voc II Master Equivalency; Attnd Carbondale Schl of Cosmetology, Kree Inst of Electrology; *cr:* Lackawanna Cty Area Voc Tech Schl Cosmetology, Long Term Sub 1981-82; Monroe Cty Area Voc Tech Schl Cosmetology Supvr 1982-; *ai:* VICA Adv; Natl Cosmetology Assn; Assn of Voc Tchrs Educating in Cosmetology VP St Level; NEA 1992-, Local Sec, VP; Cancer Soc, Look Good Feel Better Prgm; Outstdng Tchr 1991; *office:* Monroe Co Area Voc Tech Sch PO Box 66 Laurel Lake Dr Bartonsville PA 18321

PICCININ, ROBERTO, French Immersion Pgm Tchr; *b:* Shawinigan Falls, PQ Canada; *m:* Camille Godin; *c:* Dina; *ed:* ST Francis Xavier Univ (BA) Fr 1972; Mt Allison Univ (BED) Fr 1976; Univ De Moncton (MED) Schl Admin 1990, (MA) Fr; *cr:* Marshview MS 6th Grd Homeroom Tchr & 7th & 8th Grd Fr Lang Arts Tchr 1976-81; Hillcrest Schl Homeroom & 7th & 8th Grd Math Tchr 1981-; *ai:* Involved in IM, Assemblies, Stu Trips, Fund Raising & Coach; New Brunswick Tchrs Fed 1976-; New Brunswick Fr Immersion Cncl 1976-; Awd for Excl in Ed 1983; New Brunswick Tchr of the Yr Awd 1995; *home:* 15 Vail St Moncton NB E1A 3L2 Canada CN

PICCININI, MARY JANE MC CAW, English Teacher; *b:* Sewickley, PA; *m:* Samuel R.; *ed:* Westminster Coll (BA) Comm 1976; Ed Cert 1977; Addl Credit Hrs Cert; *cr:* Freedom Area Schl Dist MS Eng 1977-79; Hopewell Area Schl Dist HS Eng Tchr 1980-82, HS Eng Sub Tchr 1982-86, MS Eng Tchr 1987-; *ai:* Jr HS Chrldng Coach; FAEA, PSEA, NEA 1977-; Monaca Turners 1981-90, Pres; *office:* Freedom Area MS 1701 8th Ave Freedom PA 15042*

PICCIONI, PATRICIA BRENNAN, Kindergarten Teacher; *b:* Pottsville, PA; *m:* Thomas Paul; *c:* Thomas, Maria; *ed:* Penn St Univ (BS) EL EP 1970; 24 Grad Credits; *cr:* Minersville Schl First Grd Tchr 1970-71, Second Grd Tchr 1986-87, Third Grd Tchr 1987-88, Fourth Grd Tchr 1988-89, Kndgtn Tchr 1989-; *ai:* NEA; PSEA; Pottsville Mother's Ftbl Boosters Assn 1988-91, Pres; IGA Grocery Store Awd for Nutrition 1st Place Local, 2nd Place St; *home:* 337 N George St Pottsville PA 17901

PICCIOTTI, ROBERT ANTHONY, Eighth Grade Science Teacher; *b:* Quakertown, PA; *m:* Linda Sue Williams; *c:* Robert Jr., Mary Sylvester, Eugene, Ann; *ed:* Mercer Cty Comm Coll (AS) Life Sci 1960; WV Univ (BA) Pre-Medicine 1965; Trenton St Coll (MA) Tchng 1974; 16 Credit Hrs Chem Univ of PA; 8 Credit Hrs Biochemistry Medical WV Univ; 8 Credit Hrs Chem Beaver Coll; *cr:* Pennsbury HS 12 Grd Chem Tchr 1966-72; Medill Bair HS 9th Grd Sci Tchr 1972-73; William Penn MS 7th Grd Sci Tchr 1973-75; Pennwood MS 7th, 8th Grd Sci Tchr 1975-90; Charles Boehm MS 8th Grd Sci Tchr 1990-; *ai:* Ftbl Team Coach; NEA, PSEA, PEA 1966-; Flwshp Univ of PA 1967-69; NSF Grant Beaver Coll 1966; *home:* 664 Trenton Rd Fairless Hills PA 19030

PICHARDO, GLADYS, Bilingual Second Grade Tchr; *b:* Dom Repub; *m:* Rafael Alvarez; *c:* Steve Alvarez, Noel Alvarez, Mariestela; *ed:* City Coll (BS) Biling Ed 1982, (MS) Ed 1986; 27 Credit Hrs Above Masters; *cr:* PS 152 Biling Tchr 1982-; *ai:* New Tchr Mentor.*

PICHENY, JANET L., English Teacher; *b:* Rockville Center, NY; *m:* David; *c:* Michelle, Marisa; *ed:* SUNY At Brockport (BS) Scndry Ed, Eng 1969; Hofstra Univ (MA) Eng, Ed 1974; 9 Hrs C. W. Post Univ Spec Needs; 40 Hrs Orton, Gillingham, Univ of MA Dyslexia Trng; *cr:* Walt Whitman HS Tchr 1969-74; Kings Park HS Tchr 1975-84; Sharon Pub Schls Tchr 1986-; *ai:* Class of 1998 Adv; PTSO Liaison Sharon Tchrs Assn; Core Values Stud; NEA, STA 1993-; NYTA 1969-; *office:* Sharon HS 180 Pond St Sharon MA 02067

PICKARD, BERT KENNETH,III, Secondary Teacher; *b:* Rochester, PA; *c:* Brenda Underwood; *ed:* (MS) Admin 1981; Post Grad Stud Tech Ed; *cr:* Beaver Falls HS Tchr 1979; Freedom HS Tchr 1979-; *ai:* Rifle Club; NEA, PSEA, Tech Ed Assn of PA 1979-; FAEA 1979-, Bldg Rep; Twp Commissioner 1980-90; Beaver Cty Conservation Sportsman of Yr; Intercurriculum Tchng Project Robertson Flwshp Awd Nom; *home:* 602 Division Ln Vanport PA 15009

PICKARD, JAMES E., History Teacher; *b:* Worcester, MA; *m:* Janine M. Czyzewski; *c:* Elizabeth, Rebecca; *ed:* Bridgewater St (BSEd) His 1963; Johns Hopkins (MSEd) Ed 1970; 30 Hrs Beyond Masters Degree; *cr:* Edgewood High Eng & Soc Stud Tchr 1963-65; Edgewood Jr Eng & Soc Stud Tchr 1965-75; Joppatowne High Eng Tchr 1975-77; Haure De Grace Middle Eng Tchr 1977-86; Edgewood Middle Eng Tchr 1986-91; Bel Air High Eng & His Tchr 1991-; *ai:* Stu Cncl Adv; Honors Comm; HCEA, MSTA & NEA 1963-; Deer Creek Friends Meeting 1971-, Cleric, Treas, Clerk of Ministry & Counsel Recording Clerk; *office:* Bel Air HS 100 Hieghe St Bel Air MD 21014

PICKARD, ROBERT HOUGHTON, Science Teacher; *b:* Suffer, NY; *m:* Sharon Creighton; *c:* Sarah Geagon, Matthew, Martha; *ed:* Potsdam St (BA) Scndry Ed 1966, (MS) Scndry Ed; *cr:* Brasher Falls Cntrl Schl Tchr 1966-95; *ai:* Sci Dept Head; NYSUT 1966-.

PICKARD, SUSAN BORYC, Fourth Grade Teacher; *b:* Waukegan, IL; *m:* David Gary; *c:* Amy, David; *ed:* Saint Josephs Coll (BA) Elem Ed 1972; Northern IL Univ (MS) Elem Ed 1977; Attnd Natl Coll of Ed; *cr:* Waukegan Pub Schls 1st Grd Tchr 1973-79; Syracuse Pub Schls Intermediate Grd Tchr 1985-; *ai:* AFT 1985-; *office:* Percy Hughes Magnet Schl 345 Jamesville Ave Syracuse NY 13210

PICKENS, GENEVA MOORE, English Teacher; *b:* Jackson, MS; *c:* LeVert Wendell; *ed:* Alcorn St Univ (BS) Eng, Lit 1971; Jackson St Univ (MAT) Eng, Lit 1980; Northern IL Univ (EDD) Amer Lit, Adult Continuing Ed 1992; *cr:* Northern Il Univ Prgrm Coord 1990-91; Forest Hill HS Eng Tchr 1992; Prince Georges Comm Coll Instr 1994; Oxon Hill HS Eng Tchr 1993-; *ai:* Yrbk, Newspaper Adv; NEA; MSTA, PGCEA 1993-; Vol PGC Exec Affairs of Citizens Svcs, Warner Theater; Carter G Woodson Scholars Awd 1989-90; Rothen A. Smith Flwshp 1989-90; Pub Thesis; Articles Pub; *office:* Oxon Hill HS 6701 Leyte Dr Oxon Hill MD 20745*

PICKLO, JANELLE LITTLE, Mrktg & Distributive Ed Tchr; *b:* Olean, NY; *m:* Bernard J. Jr.; *ed:* IN Univ of PA (BS) Mrktg 1988-, (BS) Office Tech 1991; 33 Credit Hrs Instrl II Cert; City Univ Working on Masters Mrktg; *cr:* Bradford Area HS Sub Tchr 1989-91, Mrktg, Distributive Ed Tchr, DECA Adv 1992-; *ai:* DECA Adv 1992-; Grad Requirements Comm 1993-; Mrktg Ed Assn 1994-; DECA 1989-; Tribute Awd 1995-; *office:* Bradford Area Sr HS 81 Interstate Pky Bradford PA 16701

PICKLO, MARY JO BORECKY, 8th Grade English Teacher; *b:* Johnstown, PA; *m:* Michael David; *c:* Jennifer, Jessica, Juliann; *ed:* Univ of Pittsburgh at Johnstown (BA) Eng 1977; St Francis Coll Scndry Ed Cert 1988, Working towards MED; ITEC Cmptr; Heres Looking at you 2000; Stu Asstance Prgm; *cr:* West End Cath Sub Tchr, Tchr 1976-88; St Patrick Schl Sub Tchr 1982-88; Central Cath Tchr 1988-; *ai:* Forensic Team, Safety Patrol, Stu Newspaper, Grad Act, Stu Asst Team, Adv; Poster, Essay Contest; St Francis Coll Annual Spelling Contest; IRA 1988-; Comm Art Cntr 1986-, Vol; *office:* Central Catholic Elem Schl 751 Railroad St Johnstown PA 15901

PICKUS, ELLEN GORDON, English Teacher; *b:* New York, NY; *m:* Philip; *c:* Robert; *ed:* SUNY at Albany (BA) Eng 1971; Queens Coll (MA) Fine Arts 1978; Addl 80 Hrs; *cr:* Long Beach Schls Eng Tchr 1971-; *ai:* Lit Magazine Adv; Talented Writers Prgm Head; NYSUT; AFT; Union Reform Temple 1976-, Co-Pres Sisterhood; Gilbert & Sullivan Light Opera CO of Long Island 1979-, Sec; Pub Poens.

PICKUT, GAIL (HERBERT), Science Teacher; *b:* Port Clinton, OH; *c:* Ryan; *ed:* Univ of Akron (BA) Comprehensive Sci 1975; Bowling Green St Univ (MS); *cr:* Elmwood HS Tchr 1975-83; Oak Harbor HS Tchr 1983-; *ai:* Sci Club; NEA; NSTA; Presented Natl Conf.

PIECHNIK, JOHN STEPHEN, Social Studies Supervisor; *b:* Albany, NY; *m:* Nikki L. Carter; *c:* Lindsay; *ed:* SUNY at Cortland (BA) Soc Stud 1972; SUNY at Albany (MA) Soc Stud 1977; curr & Instruction; *cr:* Voorheesville CS Soc Stud Supvr, Asst to Supvr, Soc Stud Tchr 1973-89; Bethlehem CS Soc Stud Supvr 1989-; *ai:* NEA, NCSS, NY St Cncl for Soc Stud, United Univ Professions, AFT, Capital Dist Cncl for Soc Stud; BOU 1989-, Former Bd Mem; Amnesty Intnl 1987-; *office:* Bethlehem Central Schls 700 Delaware Ave Delmar NY 12054

PIECHOCINSKI, MICHAEL NEISON, Art Teacher; *b:* Daytona Beach, FL; *m:* Alganesh Tedla; *c:* Sarah; *ed:* Northern MI Univ (BS) Art 1974, (MA) Art Ed 1977; Attnd Flint Inst of Art, Trinity Coll; *cr:* NICE Comm Schls Art Tchr 2 Yrs; MI Dept of Corrections Art Tchr 2 Yrs; Chetnut Lodge Art Tchr 8 Yrs; Montgomery Cty Pub Schls Art Tchr 10 Yrs; *ai:* Art Club; MCEA 1980-; MCAEA 1986-; Natl Endowment Hum Grant 1989; Art of Ethiapis 1989, Review Dumbarton Oaks Byzontine Art Conf 1990 Sacred Art Journal; *office:* Quince Orchard HS 15800 Quince Orchard Rd Gaithersburg MD 20878

PIECK, MICHAEL, Fourth Grade Teacher; *b:* Wilkes-Barre, PA; *m:* Nancy Sokola; *c:* Michael, Holly, Keith, Abigail; *ed:* E Stroudsburg Univ (BS) Elem 1968, (MS) Elem 1972; Univ of Scranton Elem Ed Prin Cert 1974; Attnd Millersville Univ, Marywood Coll; *cr:* Cotton Ave Schl 4th & 6th Grd Tchr 28 Yrs, Head Tchr 21 Yrs; *ai:* Safety Patrol Adv; Wilkes-Barre Ar Ed Assn, PA St Ed Assn, NEA 1968-, Cncl of Rep for Cotton Schls; Plains Lions Club 1968-92; Holy Resurrection Cathedral 1970-, Bd of Trustees, VP; Elem Ed Grant Rocketry Prgm Schl Dist K-6; *home:* 99 Amesbury St Wilkes Barre PA 18705

PIEGARO, KATHLEEN BRANNIGAN, Mathematics Teacher; *b:* Newark, NJ; *m:* Nicholas J.; *c:* Jared, Joel; *ed:* Jersey City St Coll (BA) Math 1963; Attnd NJIT; *cr:* Roosevelt Jr High Math Tchr 1963-72, 1976-80; Edison Jr High Math Tchr 1982-87; West Orange HS Math Tchr 1987-; *ai:* Frosh Class Adv; Tchr Mentor; Attendance Comm; NEA 1976-; AMTNJ 1976-; WOEA; ECEA; NSF Grant; AMTNJ Awd for Tchng Math for 25 Yrs; *office:* West Orange HS 51 Conforti Ave West Orange NJ 07052

PIELIN, GILBERT MARTIN, Chemistry & Biology Instructor; *b:* Pittsburgh, PA; *ed:* Duquesne Univ (BA) Theology 1976, (MS) Bio 1985; PA Certs: Gen Sci 1986, Bio 1986, Chem 1991; *cr:* Diocese of Pittsburgh Scndry Schl Tchr 1976-93; North Allegheny Schl Dist Chem, Bio Instr 1993-; *ai:* Environmental Club, Univ of Pittsburgh Mortar Bd Moderator; Western PA Assn Bio Tchrs 1995-; AFT 1993-, Bldg Rep; Knights of Columbus 1986-; *office:* North Allegheny Sr HS 10375 Perry Hwy Wexford PA 15090*

PIENIAZEK, NANCY, Science Teacher; *b:* Buffalo, NY; *ed:* SUNY Coll at Buffalo (BS) Elem Ed Extension in Sci 1974, (MS) Scndry Ed Sci 1976; 57 Grad Hrs Beyond Masters; Certs in Elem Ed, Earth Sci, Bio, Chem & Math; *cr:* Depew MS 7th-8th Grd Sci Tchr 1974-84; Depew HS 9th Grd Sci Tchr 1984-; *ai:* Depew Tchrs Org 1974-; NYSUT 1974-; AFT 1974-; REST 1986-; *office:* Depew HS 5201 S Transit Rd Depew NY 14043

PIENKOS, SARAH E., Voc Work Prgm Teacher & Coord; *b:* Grafton, WV; *m:* John A.; *c:* John Andrew II, Charles Robert; *ed:* Fairmont St Coll (AB) Ed, Eng, Soc Stud 1963; Attnd WV Univ, OH Univ, OH St Univ; Occupational Work Experience, Voc Ed Cert; *cr:* Mannington HS Tchr 1963-64; East Fairmont HS Eng Tchr 1964-68; Pocomoke HS Tchr 1969-70; Ft Frye HS Tchr 1970-71; Washington Cty Career Ctr Tchr, Coord 1973-; *ai:* VICA, Safety Club Spon, Adv; Pvt, Vol Tutor; NCTE; NEA 1963-; OEA, OWECA, AVA, OVA, AAUW, W C Tchrs Assn, VICA 1973-; Natl Tchrs Scholastic Honorary; Washington Cty Mental Hlth Bd, Cncl on Alcoholism; Buttons & Bows OCCL; BSA Cub Scout, Asst Den Ldr; Kappa Delta Phi, Exec Comm; Southeast OH OWE Tchr of Yr 1983-84; Persian Gulf War Support Group Steering Comm; Operation Santa Claus for Gulf War; Amer Legion OH Svc Awd; Operation Desert Storm Support Group; *office:* Washngton County Career Ctr Rt 2 Marietta OH 45750*

PIERALLINI, MARYANN HUSOVITZ, Instructional Support Teacher; *b:* Charleroi, PA; *m:* David L.; *ed:* PA St Univ (BA) Elem Ed 1969; Univ of Pittsburgh (MED) Curr, Supervision 1974; *cr:* Upper St Clair Schl Dist Elem Classroom Tchr 1969-83, Elem Resource Tchr 1983-94, MS Instrl Tchr 1994-; *ai:* AFT, PFT 1984-; USCEA 1969-, Bldg Rep; *office:* Boyce MS 1500 Boyce Rd Pittsburgh PA 15241

PIERCE, BRADFORD IRVING, Mathematics Teacher & Dept Chm; *b:* Fairhaven, MA; *m:* Rosalyn Wing; *c:* Dana, Gary; *ed:* Bridgewater St (BS) Ed 1951, (MED) Ed 1955f; 60 Addl Semester Hrs Brown Univ, Stonehill Coll, U MA at Darthmouth, Bridgewater; *cr:* Fairhaven HS Math Tchr 1951-54; Tabor Acad Math Tchr Summers 1956-92; Dartmouth HS Math Tchr, Dept Chair 1954-; *ai:* Math Team Coach; NEA 1951-; DEA 1954-, Tchr of Yr; SMC Math League 1965-, Chm; NSF Grants; Newspaper Articles Math Teams; *office:* Dartmouth HS 366 Slocum Rd North Dartmouth MA 02747

PIERCE, BRENDA KAY (BIEHL), 1st Grade Teacher; *b:* Marietta, OH; *m:* David A.; *c:* Bradford, Christopher, Eric; *ed:* Bowling Green St Univ (BS) Elem, LD, SBD 1980; 6 Addl Hrs; *cr:* Fort Frye Schl Dist Chptr Grds 1-6 Rdng & Math Tchr 1980-83, 1st Grd Tchr 1983-; *ai:* Intervention Assistance Team; OH Ed Assn, NEA 1980-; Ft Frye Tchr Assn 1980-, Bldg Rep 1 Yr; First Bapt Church 1985-, Sunday Schl Tchr; *home:* 201 Ellsworth Dr Marietta OH 45750

PIERCE, CHRISTY ANN, Teacher Specialist; *b:* Northampton, PA; *ed:* Beaver Coll (BA) Elem Ed 1971; Kutztown St Univ (MED) Elem Ed 1977; Salisbury St Univ Admin & Supvr Cert 1987; MD Writing Project Tchr Consultant WA Coll 1984; *cr:* Federalsburg Schl Sixth Grd Tchr 1971-88; Greensboro Schl Asst Prin 1988-91; Denton Schl Asst Prin 1991-92; Tchr Specialist 1992-; *ai:* Lang Arts Curr Guide; Accreditation Cty Chprsn; NCTE Achievement Awds Judge; Admin Asst to Prin; Mid-Shore Rndg Cncl 1989-, Sec 1989-91, VP 1991-, Pres 1992-94; IRA 1988-; NCTE 1984-94; NCTM 1995-; NCSS 1995-; Federalsburg Bsbl League 1972-85, Sec 1976-80; Creative Writing Instrs for Gifted & Talented; Summer Centers Prgm 1986-90; MD Writing Project Tchr Research Insts 1986-88; *office:* Federalsburg Elem School 302 University Ave Federalsburg MD 21632

PIERCE, DAN, Science Teacher; *b:* Ridgway, PA; *m:* Teresa Mathias; *c:* Brittany; *ed:* Baker Univ (BS) Bio, Hlth, PE 1973; KS Univ, Penn St Univ, Univ of Pittsburgh Ed, Ed Admin Stud Master Equivelancy; *cr:* North Hills Schl Dist Hlth, PE Tchr 1974-88, Sci Tchr 1988-; *ai:* NEA, PSEA 1974-;

North Hills Ed Assn 1974-, Bldg Rep; Hiland Child Care 1989-, Bd of Dirs; Northern Area Tchr of Yr Nom 1993; *office:* North Hills Schl Dist 135 Sixth Ave Pittsburgh PA 15229

PIERCE, DEBORAH A., Biology Teacher; *b:* New London, CT; *m:* N. Scott; *ed:* Univ of CT (BS) Ed 1976, (MA) Bio 1978; Boston Coll Post Grad Stud Admin in Ed; Harvard Univ Post Grad Stud in Bio; *cr:* North Stonington HS Bio, Chem Tchr 1980-84; East HS Bio, Chem Tchr 1984-87; King Philip MS Bio, Honors Algebra Tchr 1987-89; Bromfield Schl Bio Tchr 1989-; *ai:* Class Adv; Peer Leadership Prgm, NHS Co-Adv; NSTA, MAST, NABT 1989-; Nom for Presidential Awd in Excl Sci Tchng; Awarded Grants for Purchase of Equipment for Enhancing our Schls Prgm in DNA Tech; *office:* Bromfield Schl 14 Massachusetts Ave Harvard MA 01451*

PIERCE, DEREK SCOTT, English Teacher; *b:* Port Chester, NY; *m:* Anja Hanson; *ed:* Brown Univ (BA) Pol Sci 1988; Harvard Univ (MED) Ed 1993; *cr:* Bbrentwood Schl Eng, Drama Rchr 1990-92; Gorham HS Eng Tchr 1993-; *ai:* Drama Club Adv; Boys' Var Tennis Coach; Tchr Ldr; Literacy Comm; NEA, MEA, NCTE 1993-; Article Pub; *office:* Gorham HS 41 Morrill Ave Gorham ME 04038

PIERCE, DONALD A., Spanish Teacher; *b:* Haverhill, MA; *ed:* Boston Coll (BA) Span, Italian, Lang, Lit 1984; Cambridge Coll (MED) 1992; Summer Stud Intensa Inst 1993; *cr:* Masconomet Regnl HS Frgn Lang Tchr 1985-; *ai:* Span Exch Prgm Coord; Class Adv; AATSP, MAFLA 1985-; Essex Cty Orch 1987-, Bassoonist, Bd Mem; *office:* Masconomet Regional HS 20 Endicott Rd Topsfield MA 01983

PIERCE, FRANCES K., Home Economics Teacher; *b:* NJ; *c:* Thomas, Christen; *ed:* Montclair St U (BA) Home Ec Ed 1970; Kean Coll Tchng Cert Early Chldhd Ed; *cr:* Cranford HS Home Ec Tchr 1970-75; Keyport HS Home Ec Tchr 1981; Middletown HS South Home Ec Tchr, Dir of Early Chldhd Ed 1981-; *ai:* Peer Mediators, Pres Cncl Advs; Renaissance Comm Co-Chair; Asst Tech Dir for Productions; NEA 1970-; MTEA 1981-; Board of Trustees of Homeowners Assn 1991-, Sec; Withycombe Grant Pre Schl Math & Sci Ed; *office:* Middletown H S South 501 Nut Swamp Rd Middletown NJ 07748

PIERCE, MAURA B., English Teacher; *b:* East Meadows LI, NY; *m:* Timothy; *ed:* SUNY at Brockport (BA) 1979, (MS) Eng Ed 1983; *cr:* Albion Cntrl Schl Dist Eng Tchr 1979-; *ai:* Schl Improvement Team; NCTE 1995-; Albion Cntrl Schl Dist Edctr of Yr; *home:* 604 W Center St Medina NY 14103

PIERCE, PRESTON EUGENE, Social Studies Teacher; *b:* Canandaigua, NY; *m:* Mary C. Kaschak; *c:* Rebecca, Stephen; *ed:* Westminster Coll (BA) His 1968; Univ of VT (MAT) His 1972; St Univ of NY at Brockport (MSEd) Ed Admin 1974, (CAS) Ed Admin 1975; Univ of Rochester (EDD) Curr 1984; St Univ of NY at Geneseo (MLS) Lib Sci 1985; Boise St Univ (MSIPT) Instr Tech 1995; *cr:* Lehighton Area Schls 9th-12th Grd Soc Stud Tchr 1969-70; Byron-Bergen Cntrl Schl 10th & 11th Grd Soc Stud Tchr 1970-71; Victor Cntrl Schl 7th & 8th Grd Soc Stud Tchr 1971-; *ai:* Natl His Day Coord; Dist Tech & Dist Lib Eval Comms; AFT, NEA 1971-; NCSS, OAH, OHA 1975-; BSA, Dist Chm, Commissioner, Silver Beaver Awd, Awd of Merit, Sea Badger; Amer Legion; NEH Fellowships 1977, 1984, 1989; Co-Author of Book His of Office of Sgt Major of Amry USGPO 1995; Appointed Cty Historian 1983-; *home:* 209 Davidson Ave Canandaigua NY 14424

PIERCE, RAYMOND CHARLES,JR., Music Teacher; *b:* Morrisville, VT; *m:* Janet Milligan; *ed:* Johnson St Coll (BA) Music Ed 1973; *cr:* Fair Haven Grd Schl Music Tchr 1973-; *ai:* Athletic Dir; Soccer Coach; Jazz Band; NFICA, NIAAA, NFIMA, NFIOA 1994-; Brandon Festival Singers 1994-; Saratoga Performing Arts 1984-, Patron; Brandon Congo Church 1993-, Deacon, Music Comm; ARSU Tchr of Yr; *office:* Fair Haven Grade Schl 103 N Main St Fair Haven VT 05743

PIERCE, RICAHRD G., History Teacher; *b:* Schenectady, NY; *m:* Patricia A.; *c:* Ryan C.; *ed:* SUNY at Albany (BA) His 1964; SUNY at Buffalo (MA) His 1969; *cr:* Lancaster HS Tchr 1964-; *ai:* AFT & NYSUT; Lancaster Cntrl Tchrs Assn; Knight of Columbus 1977-, Grand Knight; *home:* 337 Colonial Dr Grand Island NY 14072

PIERCE, RICHARD JAMES, Honors English Teacher; *b:* Rochester, PA; *m:* Kathy Porter; *c:* Richard, Beth Anne; *ed:* Geneva Coll (BS) Elem Ed 1971; PA St Univ (MS) Ed Admin 1976; Geneva Coll Scndry Eng Cert 1985; *cr:* Hopewell Area Schl Dist Elem Tchr 1972-80, Tchr of Elem Gifted 1980-82, Elem Remedial Math Tchr 1983-84, Scndry Eng Tchr 1985-; *ai:* Jr HS Newspaper Spon; Forensics Team Spon, Coach; Odyssey of Mind Club, Lit Magazine Spon; Lang Arts Dept Chair 1992-95; Beaver Cty Chptr PA Assn for Gifted Ed 1978-, Pres 1983-84, Awd for Excl in Tchng 1988; Hopewell Meml Jr HS PTSA 1985-, Natl PTA Phoebe Apperson Hearst Awd Nom 1989; PA Odyssey of Mind 1984-, Bd of Dirs 1984-94; Southwest PA Odyssey of Mind 1984-, Dir 1984-94, Bd of Dirs 1995-; Property Owners' Assn 1982-, Bd of Dirs 1982-; Mount Pleasant Church 1992-, Elder 1994-; Letter of Commendation PA Governor Casey; Amer Family Inst Gift of Time Tribute Awd 1989; *office:* Hopewell Area Schl Dist 2121 Brodhead Rd Aliquippa PA 15001

PIERCE, SUSAN FRATES, 5th Grade Teacher; *b:* Acushnet, MA; *m:* Dana Christopher; *c:* Nathan, Caitlin; *ed:* Bridgewater St Coll (BS) Elem Ed 1973; 30 Addl Credit Hrs; *cr:* Dartmouth MS 5th Grd Tchr 1974-76; George H. Potter Schl 5th Grd Tchr 1977-89; Joseph DeMello Schl 5th Grd Tchr 1990-; *ai:* Sci Ldrshp Team; Outcomes Driven Dev Model Comm; DEA, NEA, MTA 1974-; MAST 1994-; Coll Club of New Bedford 1995-; Lloyd Ctr 1993-; *office:* Joseph DeMello Schl 654 Dartmouth St S Dartmouth MA 02748

PIERCE-COLEMAN, LLOREN CARYL, History General Science Tchr; *b:* Boston, MA; *m:* Scott Pierce; *ed:* Earlham Coll (BA) Peace & Global Stud 1993; *cr:* Olney Friends Schl Tchr, Coll Cnslr, Bsktbl Coach & Dorm Staff Admissions Rep; *ai:* Bsktbl Coach; Soph Class & Coll Adv; Admissions & Project Week Comm; Daily & Weekend Crew Mem; OACAC 1994-; *office:* Olney Friends Schl 61830 Sandy Ridge Rd Barnesville OH 43713

PIERETH, MARY, English Teacher; *b:* Englewood, NJ; *m:* Robert; *ed:* St Univ of NY at Oneonta (BA) Lbrl Arts 1971; Jersey City St Coll (MA) Admin 1981; *cr:* High Point Regnl HS Eng Tchr 1973; *ai:* Project Quest; NEA, NJEA 1973-; Sussex Cty Experiential Ed Assn 1991-; *office:* High Point Regnl HS 299 Pidgeon Hill Rd Sussex NJ 07461

PIERGENTILE, DOLORES ATTINELLO, HS Health & Biology Teacher; *b:* Bronx, NY; *m:* Paul David; *c:* Paul Matthew, Jennifer; *ed:* Herbert H. Lehman Coll of New York City Hlth Ed & Promotion 1991, Hlth Ed 1993; *cr:* St Catharine Acad Hlth, Bio Fac 1991-; *ai:* Mentor Tchr; Cert Hlth Ed Specialist 1993-; NCEA 1991; STANYS; *office:* Saint Catharine Acad 2250 Williamsbridge Rd Bronx NY 10469

PIERMARINI, ERNEST JOSEPH, Superintendent Assistant; *b:* Newark, NJ; *m:* Linda Mc Mahon; *c:* Peter, Craig; *ed:* Monmouth Coll (BS) Scndry Ed 1966; Seton Hall Univ (MS) Educl Admin 1971; SUNY at New Paltz (PD) Educl Admin 1979; *cr:* Jeff Youngsville Cntrl Schl Dist Bus Ed 1966-70; Lakeland Cntrl Schl Dist Bus Ed 1970-81, Chprsn Occupational Ed 1982-93, Asst to Supvr 1993-; *ai:* Past Adv, Founder FBLA Chptr; NBEA, NYS Bus Tchrs Assn, Eastern Bus Ed Assn 1966-; ASCD 1982-; Westchester Cty Bus Ed Assn 1971-; Haldane Bd of Ed 1988-93, Trustee; Little League 1980-88, VP; Babe Ruth League 1989-92, VP; NY St Bus Ed Tchr of Yr 1994-95; Distngd Occupational Ed Tchr of YR 1988; Westchester Cty Bus Ed Tchr of Yr 1983; *office:* Lakeland Cntrl Schl Dist 1086 E Main St Shrub Oak NY 10588*

PIERRE, WILLIS JOHN, Mathematics Teacher; *b:* Allentown, NJ; *ed:* Washington & Jefferson Coll (BA) Math 1961; WA St Univ (MAT) Math 1967; Attnd Lake Foresty Coll, Univ of DE, OH St Univ; *cr:* Lake Forest Acad Math Tchr 1961-70; The Hill Schl Math Tchr 1970-; *ai:* Exec Comm of Fac; Acad Cncl; Fac Cncl; Math Dept Chm; Sftbl Coach; Bsktbl Timer; Sports Club Adv; Work Job Dir; Dinning Hall Supvr; NCTM 1964-; NCTP, ATMOPAV 1984-; Friends of Bsbl Hall of Fame 1962-; Pottstown Sports Hall of Fame 1986-; E PA Sports Collectors Club 1971-; 7 Natl Sci Fnd Grants; 1 Math Ed Trust Grant; 1 Natl Endowment Hum Grant; Kohl Intnl Tchng, Disney Outstdng Tchr Awds; *office:* Hill Schl 717 E High St Pottstown PA 19464

PIERRO, LINDA PFAU, Mathematics Teacher; *b:* Reading, PA; *m:* Daniel A.; *c:* Elissa R. Mogel; *ed:* Millersville Univ (BA) Math 1971; Lehigh Univ (MED) Ed, Math 1972; *cr:* Chichester Sr HS Math Tchr 1971-; *ai:* NCTM, PSEA, CEA 1971-; ATMOPAV 1988-; Girl Scouts 1994-, Asst Ldr; *office:* Chichester HS 3333 Chichester Ave Boothwyn PA 19061

PIERVINCENZI, WILLIAM ARTHUR, Professor of Biology; *b:* Brooklyn, NY; *m:* Edna; *c:* Gina Torre, William, Andrea, Adam; *ed:* Adelphi Univ (BA) Bio 1970, (MS) Marine Sci 1973; *cr:* Nassau Comm Prof 1970-; *ai:* Multi Cultural Club; Little League Coach; Environmental Orgs Consultant; Amateur Inventor; AFT; Nassau CC Fed 1970-, VP; Nassau CC Adjunct Fac Assn 1972-, Del; NY Thoroughbred Breeders Assn 1984-; Pub Two Juvenile Stories Tchng Evolution, Ecology; *office:* Nassau Community Coll Biology Dept Garden City NY 11530*

PIESLAK, JUDITH STAPLES, English & Literature Teacher; *b:* Lynnbrook, NY; *m:* Robert; *ed:* Trinity Coll (BA) Eng 1962; *cr:* Brandywine Schl Dist Eng & Lit Tchr 1981-85; Ursuline Acad Eng & Lit Tchr 1985-86; St Edmonds Acad Eng & Lit Tchr 1989-; *ai:* Dept Chprsn; Curr Revision; Schedule Comm; NCEA 1989-.

PIESTER, JOHN B., Math Teacher; *b:* Hudson, NY; *m:* Mary Ann Nixon; *c:* John D., Michael E.; *ed:* SUC at Cortland (BS) Math 1962; SUC at Binghamton (MS) Math 1971; Attnd Clarkson Engrng; *cr:* Greene Cntrl Schl Math Tchr 1962-63; ME Endwell Math Tchr 1963-; *ai:* Past Bsbl, Track, Ftbl, Bsktbl Coach; 7th-8th Grd Bsktbl Coach; NEA, ME Endwell Tchrs 1963-; BOCES Grant for Developing Math 12 Course; *home:* 317 Skye Island Dr Endicott NY 13760*

PIETARINEN, GEORGE, English Teacher & College Adv; *b:* Bronx, NY; *m:* Carol; *c:* Matthew, Marcey; *ed:* Hunter Coll (BA) Eng 1970; Lehman Coll (MA) Eng 1972; Fordham Univ Prof Diploma Educl Admin & Supervision 1985; 24 Addl Credits Towards PHD Eng NY Univ; *cr:* James Monroe HS Eng Tchr 1970-85; Harry S. Troman HS Eng Tchr 1986-; *ai:* AFT, UFT, NYSUT, NCTE 1970-; Western Lit Inst Participant; *office:* Harry S. Truman HS 750 Baychester Ave Bronx NY 10475

PIETROMICA, RUDOLPH V., 5th Grade Teacher; *b:* Lorain, OH; *m:* Rose; *c:* Jason, Laura; *ed:* Kent St Univ (BS) Elem Ed 1970, (MED) Elem Ed 1975; 30 Addl Hrs; *cr:* Charleston Elem Schl 5th Grd Tchr 1971-80; Meister Road Elem Schl 5th Grd Tchr 1980-; *ai:* LEA, OEA, NEOTA 1971-; *home:* 4930 Hollyview Dr Vermilion OH 44089

PIETRUCHA, HOLLY, Latin Teacher; *b:* Plainfield, NJ; *m:* Raymond; *ed:* Ripon Coll (BA) Classics 1969; Classical Summer Schl of Vergilian Soc Myths, Masterpieces; *cr:* Jackson MS Soc Stud Tchr 1969-71; St Ann Schl Eng, His Tchr 1973-78; St Joseph Schl Math, Sci Tchr 1978-82; Howell HS Latin Tchr 1982-; *ai:* Latin Club; Shore Latin League; ACL 1982-; NJCA 1982-, Bulletin Ed 1986-88; MOCCA 1985-, Founder; FLENJ; NJCL; NUJCL; CAAS; CAES; CSAAR; AIA; ACTFL; Phi Beta Kappa Edna White Rome 1987; Scholar Governor's Outstdng Tchng Awd 1988; Frgn Lang Edctrs of NJ Profl Awd 1991; *office:* Howell HS Squankum Yellowbrook Rd Farmingdale NJ 07727*

PIETRZAK, JAMES KEVAN, English Teacher; *b:* Wilkinsburg, PA; *m:* Carolyn Corace; *c:* Holly; *ed:* California Univ of PA (BS) Eng 1971, (MEd) Eng 1978; *cr:* CA Area Mid & Jr HS Eng Tchr 1973-90; CA Area HS Eng Tchr 1981-; Westmoreland Cty Comm Coll Eng Instr 1991-; *ai:* HS Newspaper Adv; HS Golf Coach; NEA, PSEA & CAEA 1973-; Great Ideas Grants Mom Valley Ed Consortium; *office:* California Area HS 293 Malden Dr Coal Center PA 15423*

PIETRZAK, JOSEPH T., 7th Grade Life Science Teacher; *b:* Buffalo, NY; *c:* Kevin; *ed:* St Univ Coll at Buffalo (BS) Scndry Ed, Sci 1971, (MS) Scndry Ed, Sci 1974; Addl 30 Hrs; *cr:* Barker Cntrl Schl 9th Grd ISCS, 8th Grd Earth Sci Tchr 1975-85; Brockport Oliver MS 7th Grd Life Sci Tchr 1985-; *ai:* Curr, Staff Dev Comm; Phi Delta Kappa; Comm to Rsrch Tech Needs for Sci; Writing Sci Standards Comm; Phi Delta Kappa 1995-; Received Recognition for Writing a Lesson Plan; Mentioned in Educl Ldrshp Magazine; *office:* Oliver MS 40 Allen St Brockport NY 14420

PIEZ-PACHECO, CYNTHIA LYNN, 4th Grade Teacher; *b:* West Union, IA; *m:* William M. Pacheco; *c:* Colby, Brittany; *ed:* Univ of RI (BA) Psych 1976; RI Coll Elem, Spec Ed Tchr Cert 1978; *cr:* South Road Elem Schl Intermediate Self-Contained Tchr 1978-82; Matunuck Elem Schl 2nd-4th Grd Tchr 1982-; *ai:* CAST Mem 3 Yrs; NEA, RI 1978-, Exec Comm; NEA, SK 1978-; *office:* Matunuck Elem Schl 310 Matunuck Beach Rd Wakefield RI 02879

PIFER, BONNIE, Business Teacher & Dept Chprsn; *b:* Dubois, PA; *ed:* Indiana Univ of PA (BA) Bus Ed 1969; Grad Credits Cath Univ; *cr:* Southern HS Bus Tchr 1969-, Bus Dept Chair 1990-; *ai:* Started FBLA Chapter, Sponsored 5 Yrs; Chrldr Coach 12 Yrs; TAAAC, NEA, MVA, AVA, MSTA, MBEA 1969-; *office:* Southern HS 4400 Solomons Island Rd Harwood MD 20776

PIFKO, PATRICIA GILLESPIE, Assoc Prof of Mathematics; *b:* Bridgeport, CT; *m:* Joseph G.; *c:* Kate, Anne, Tricia; *ed:* Emmanuel Coll (BA) Math 1974; Univ of Bridgeport (MS) Scndry Ed 1978; *cr:* Trumbull HS Math Tchr 1975-78; Housatonic Comm Tech Coll Part-time Math Lecturer 1977-83, Math Prof 1983-; *ai:* Chprsn Curr Comm; Mathematical Assn of Two Yr Colls in CT; Amer Mathematical Assn of Two Yr Colls; Assn of Women in Math; 1992 Merit Recognition Awd Bd of Trustees Ct Comm-Tech Colls; 1994 Educl Excl & Distngd Svc Awd; *office:* Housatonic Comm-Tech College 510 Barnum Ave Bridgeport CT 06608

PIGMAN, JAMES FREDERIC, English Dept Chair; *b:* Omaha, NE; *m:* Carole Newhouse; *c:* Stephen James, Emily Anne; *ed:* Univ of CO (BA) Eng 1968; NY Univ (MA) Eng 1972; NEH Renaissance Inst NY Univ; *cr:* Garden Prep Schl Eng Dept Chair 1974-; *ai:* Key Club Adv; Chess & Broadway Clubs; Core Tchr; European Travel Head Tchr; Phi Beta Kappa 1968-; NCTE 1974-; Kiwanis; Friends of the Lib; Juvenile Diabetes fndtn; Garden Prep Writing Project; *office:* Garden Schl 33-16 79th St Flushing NY 11372

PIGNATARO, BARBARA TROIANO, Sixth Grade Teacher; *b:* Bronx, NY; *m:* George; *c:* Jessica; *ed:* St Johns Univ (BS) Ed 1970; Coll of New Rochelle (MS) Rdng 1974; *cr:* Immaculate Conception Schl Rdng Coord 1969-77; Brooklyn Diocese 6th-8th Grd Rdng Tchr 1969-84; Dutch Broadway Schl 3rd, 5th & 6th Grd Tchr 1984-, Core Skills Coord 1991; *ai:* Math Olympiad & Yrbk Adv; Math In-Svc Staff Trainer; Prof Confs Speaker; Stu Tchr Prgm Supvr; NYS United Tchrs 1984-; ASCD 1984-; NCTM 1987-; Nassau Cty Assn of Math Sup 1987-; Presidential Awds for Excl in Sci & Math Tchng Nom 1995; *office:* Dutch Broadway-E Schls 1880 Dutch Broadway Elmont NY 11003*

PIGNATELLO, PAUL, HS Physical Education Teacher; *b:* Passai[c] *m:* Patricia Glowa; *c:* Allison; *ed:* Montclair St Coll (BA) PE 1975; *c*[r:] Marine Corps Capt 1975-78; Clifton HS PE Tchr 1979-; *ai:* Head Coach; NJSIAA, NJBCA 1985-; NEA, NJEA, PCCA 1979-; Passai[c] Coach of Yr 1985, 1987, 1990-91, 1994; ABCA Dist Coach of Yr *office:* Clifton HS 333 Colfax Ave Clifton NJ 07013

PIGUT, EDWARD ANTHONY, English Teacher; *b:* Jersey City, N[J] Monmouth Univ (BA) His 1968, (MA) Tchng 1971; *cr:* Neptune Jr H[S] & Soc Stud Tchr 1971-89; Neptune MS Eng & Soc Stud Tchr 19[8] Neptune HS Eng & Soc Stud Tchr 1991-92, Eng Tchr 1993-; *ai:* NJEA, NTEA 1971-; Phi Alpha Theta 1966-; *office:* Neptune H[S] Neptune Blvd Neptune NJ 07753

PIHLBLAD, NANCY HENDERSON, Reading Teacher; *b:* Barbou[rville] KY; *m:* Daniel J.; *c:* Daniel, Elizabeth, Andrew, Matthew, David Westminster Coll (BA) Elem Ed 1975; SUNY at Fredonia (MS) Rdng *cr:* Ellicottville Jr Sr HS Remedial Rdng Tchr 1975-76; Jack & Jill Nu[rsery] Dir & Tchr 1979-86; Jamestown Comm Coll Eng & Rdng Tchr 198 Maple Grove Jr & Sr HS Remedial Rdng Tchr 1986-; *ai:* Var Girls S & Travel League Soccer U19 Coach; Future Tchrs Adv; NEA 1 Randolph United Presbyn Church 1976-, Elder; *office:* Maple Grove HS Dutch Hollow Rd Bemus Point NY 14712

PIKE, DOUGLAS SNOW, Special Education Case Manage[r] Gloucester, MA; *m:* Brenda; *c:* Isaac, Alicia, Brendan; *ed:* North Ada Coll (BA) Early Chldhd Ed 1974; Salem St Coll (MED) Cnslng 197 Credit Hrs Schl Psych at Univ of MA at Boston, Northeastern Univ, I Coll; *cr:* Gloucester Pub Schls Tchr, Schl Psychologist, Spec Ed Case 1976-; *ai:* Bsktbl Coach; NEA, GTA 1976-; Fac Assn Awd Excl in North Shore Comm Coll; *office:* M. L. Fuller Schl 4 Schoolhous[e] Gloucester MA 01930*

PIKE, JILL AVERY, English Teacher; *b:* Kalamazoo, MI; *m:* Stanton; *c:* Jennifer, Jared; *ed:* Shippensburg Univ (BS) Eng Ed 1988; Stud Tchng Strategies Wilkes Univ at Wilkes Barre, Tchng W African-Amer Lit; *cr:* Cumberland Valley HS Eng Tchr Greencastle-Antrim HS Eng Tchr 1991-, Eng Dept Chprsn 1993-; *ai:* of 1999 Adv; Yrbk Adv 1993-94; NCTE 1994-; Lib Bd 1993-, Tr *office:* Greencastle-Antrim HS 300 S Ridge Ave Greencastle PA 172

PILACHOWSKI, K. JOANN DONNELLY, Assistant Profess[or] English; *b:* Baltimore, MD; *m:* Gerard C.; *c:* Peter; *ed:* Western MD (BA) Eng 1973; Johns Hopkins Univ (MLA) Interdisciplinary Stud *cr:* Arundel MS Eng Tchr 1978-86; Carroll Comm Coll Er Developmental Eng Tchr 1986-; *ai:* Arts, Honors & Acad Svcs Divis Asst; NCTE 1994-; *office:* Carroll Community College 1601 Washi[ngton] Rd Westminster MD 21157

PILANEN, CAROLYN L. (DOHERTY), Choral Director; *b:* Bo MA; *m:* John; *c:* Peter John, Joshua Patrick; *ed:* Univ of Lowell Music Ed 1985; *cr:* Memrl MS Classroom & Vocal Music Instr 198 Beverly HS Choral & Drama Dir 1993-.

PILARCEK, BARBARA A., Spanish Teacher; *b:* Newark, NJ Montclair St (BA) Span 1972; Addl Grad Credits; Numerous I Courses; *cr:* Rutherford HS Span & Fr Tchr 1973-76; Pascack Valley Regnl Span & Fr Tchr 1976-79; Tenafly HS Span Tchr 1979; Riverd HS Span Tchr 1980; Northern Valley Regnl Span & Fr Tchr 1980 Volunteens & Volunteachers; Sr Awds & Stu Recognition Comms; NJEA, BCEA, NVEA; Foreign Lang Educators of NJ 1980-; *office:* Vly Reg-Old Tappan HS Central Ave Old Tappan NJ 07675

PILCHER, PAUL GORDON, Tech Instr & Adj Prof of Math; Zimbabwe; *m:* Paula; *c:* Drew, Dylan; *ed:* CO Mines (BS) Petro Engrng 1980; UC at Davis (MAT) Math 1990; *cr:* Chevron Corp Produ[ction] Engr 1980-86; Sacramento Pub Schls Tchr 1989-90; Woodstock HS 1990-91; Stafford Tech Ctr Tchr 1991-; Castleton St Coll Adj Math 1992-; *ai:* Various Schl Comms; NEA 1990-; Prof Engr; *office:* Sta[fford] Tech Ctr Stratton Rd Rutland VT 05701*

PILCHMAN, PETER, Prof of Biological Sciences; *b:* Brooklyn, N[Y] Bridgit, Rebecca; *ed:* Queens Coll of CUNY (BA) Bio 1965; City Ur NY (PHD) Bio 1972; Post Grad Stud in Nutrition 1988-90; *cr:* Queens of CUNY Tchng Assistantship 1965-70; Kingsborough Comm Coll 1971-; *ai:* Sci Coord; Coll Now Prgm; Sci Tech Entry Prgm Devel Departmental Prsnl & Budget & Curr Comms; AFT, NEA, Co-Authored 4 Textbooks Subject Areas in Anatomy & Physio Nursing Pathology & Nursing Reviews; Co-Authored & Co-Prese[nted] Several Articles & Papers Related to Tchng Techniques in Coll Ana & Physiology Classes; *office:* Kingsborough Community Coll Oriental Blvd Brooklyn NY 11235*

PILE, JEAN A., Third Grade Teacher; *b:* Altoona, PA; *m:* Alan L Ryan, Shane; *ed:* Shippenburg Univ (BS) ELem Ed 1970; 28 Grad Cre *cr:* Huntingdon Area Schls 2-3 Grd Elem Tchr 1970-; *ai:* HAEA Bldg Juniata Coll Pub Schl Advy Bd; Comm for Dev Schl Wide Curr G Grds K-5; HAEA, PSEA, NEA 1970-; Bible Schl Tchr; Amer Family Gift of Time Awd 1995; Co-Operating Tchr for Stu Tchrs from Ju Coll; *office:* Huntingdon Area Schl Dist Box 107 RD 1 Huntingdo[n] 16652

PILGRAM, SUZANNE PHELPS, Fine Arts Professor; *b:* Monclair *m:* Hassan Ghavam; *ed:* The Amer Univ (BA) Art 1967, (MFA) Pain[ting] Printmaking 1970; The Art Stdnts League New York City; *cr:* Co Translation Prof 1973-80; Georgian Court Coll Asst Prof 1981-; *ai:* Art Moderator; Evening Div Bd; Women Stud Cncl; Printmaking Cncl 1981-, Nom Bd of Dirs; Women's Studio Wkshp 1989-; Univ of ID, A in Residence 1993; Art Exhibitions; Fullbright-Hayes Group Pro Abroad, Integrating Multicultural Schlsp into Curr, NJ Cncl for Lecture Series Grants; *office:* Georgian Court Coll Lakewood Lakewood NJ 08701*

PILKERTON, WILLIAM JOHN, Social Studies Teacher; *b:* Harris[burg] PA; *m:* Barbara Hill; *c:* Keri, Brian; *ed:* Shippensburg St (BS) His 1 Post Grad Credits in Counseling; *cr:* Swatara Jr HS Soc Stud Tchr 19 *ai:* Boys Bsktbl Coach; Intramural Sports & Sports Video Club Adv; & PSEA 1974-; Lower Swatara Ath Assn 1987-, Coach; *office:* Swata[ra] HS 1101 Highland Harrisburg PA 17113

PILLIS, PATRICIA KOTZEBUE, Assistant Prof of Accounting; Bragg, NC; *m:* Paul M.; *c:* Fred, Kevin, Shane, Shannon; *ed:* St Uni[v of] NY at Plattsburgh (BA) Accounting 1982; Certified Pub Accountant S 1984; *cr:* Del Monte Hyatt House Account Clerk 1976-78; John S Lar CPA Sr Staff Accountant 1978-83; Patricia K Pillis CPA Owner & 1984-90; Paul Smiths Coll Asst Prof 1991-; *ai:* Koinonia Club Adv; Cncl; Search Comm for Acad Dean; Stu Life Comm; Alcohol & Awareness Vol; AICPA, NYSCPA 1984-; Habitat for Humanity 1993- Mem; Lake Placid Bapt Church 1982-, Treas; *office:* Paul Smiths Co Arts & Sci Rts 86 & 30 PO Box 265 Paul Smiths NY 12970

PILLITER, RICHARD JOHN, Secondary Social Studies Tch[r] Rochester, NY; *ed:* Univ of Windsor (BA) Pol Sci 1967, (MA) Pol 1969; Nazareth Coll, SUNY at Brockport; *cr:* Aquinas Inst Tchr, Cnslr, Dept Chair, Coach 1969-; *ai:* Asst Ftbl, Var Bsbl Coach; Roch[ester] Cncl of Soc Stud 1983-; NYS Soc Stud Cncl, Natl Assn of Soc Stud 19

›lta Kappa 1979-; *office:* Aquinas Inst 1127 Dewey Ave Rochester ›613

TTIERI, BETTY LOU FAULK, Fifth Grade Teacher; *b:* own, NY; *c:* Laura Ann, David Carl; *ed:* SU Coll at Fredonia (BS) Ed 1967, (MA) Rdng 1971; NY St Soc Stud, Math Cert; *cr:* Panama Schl 3rd Grd Tchr 1967-68; Falconer Cntrl Schl 4th-5th Grd Tchr '2; Southwestern Cntrl Schl Librn 1977-83, 4th Grd Tchr 1983-84, d Tchr 1984-85; Pre-First Grd Tchr 1985-88, 5th Grd Tchr 1988-; nana Splits Group; Prof Growth Comm; SW Exec Bd Sec 1988-92; NYS Tchrs Assn 1967-; Chautauqua Cty Chptr NYS Rdng Assn Former Sec; *office:* Lakewood Elem Schl 31 Lakeview Ave ood NY 14750

›, ANGELO J., Retired Band Director; *b:* Batavia, NY; *m:* Sheila tt; *c:* Stephanie Pillo Kellogg, Brian, Valerie; *ed:* SUNY at Fredonia Iusic Ed 1966; Post Grad Stud SUNY at Brockport; 16 Credit Hrs of Buffalo; *cr:* Oakfield Cntrl Schl Jr Band Dir 1966-71; Byron Cntrl Schl Jr Sr HS Band Dir, Dept Chm 1971-96; *ai:* AFT, NY St Assn 1971-; MENC, NY St Schl Music Assn 1966-; Genesee, WY Edctrs Assn 1966-, Festivals Chm 1974-76, Publicity Chm 1986-88, 77-78; *home:* 1812 Roberts Rd Basom NY 14013*

SBURY, CAROLYN B., Teacher of Gifted & Talented; *b:* Plymouth, *l:* Springfield Coll (BS) Elem Ed 1970; 81 Addl Hrs; *cr:* Whitesboro 1-6 Grd Tchr 1970-82, Tchr of Gifted & Talented 1982-; *ai:* matical Olympiad Adv; Effective Schls Teams; Curr Cncl; Tech Task Math Review Team; WTA Schlsp Comm; Prism Review Team ; DOL Training Cadre, Facilitator; Child Study Team; AFT, NYSUT, 1970-; CHAAD 1992-, Advy Bd; AGATE 1982-; *office:* HartsHill Schl Clark Mills Rd Whitesboro NY 13492

T, CHRISTOPHER H., Physics & Mgmt Science Prof; *b:* Windsor o, Canada; *m:* Lisa Lynn Schonblom; *c:* Kira, Juergen; *ed:* Boston BA) Physics 1974; Technische Univ Munich (MS) Physics 1978, Physics 1981; *cr:* McGill Univ & Concordia Univ Part-Time Fac 85; OK St Univ Visiting Asst Prof 1985-86; Univ of Tulsa Asst Prof 89; Applied Insurance Research Research Assoc 1990-91; ME me Acad Asst Prof 1991-92, Assoc Prof 1993-94, Full Prof 1995-; *ai:* ev & Evaluation Comm; Fac Negotiator; Grad Admissions; Grad ch & Dev; Marine Engrng & Tech Majors Adv; APS 1985-; ORSA IPP 1982-; 17 Research Publications; Several Grants Awded to Research; Consult in Field of Risk Analysis & Cmptr Modeling of al Catastrophes; *office:* Maine Maritime Acad Dept of Arts & es Castine ME 04420

LINDA M., English & Theater Teacher; *b:* Hartford, CT; *m:* Richard etano; *ed:* Coll of Mt St Vincent (BA) Eng, Scndry Ed 1974; Emerson MA) Theatre Directing 1984; *cr:* St Mary Schl Eng, Span, Music 1974-76; Acad of Resurrection Eng, Span, Music Tchr 1978-80, alle Acad Eng, Span, Music Tchr 1986-89; Acad Schl Eng, Span, Tchr 1989-92; Glastonbury HS Eng, Theatre Tchr 1992-; *ai:* Artistic ama Club; NEA, CEA, GEA 1989-; Asst to Broadway Dir; Directed *office:* Glastonbury HS 330 Hubbard St Glastonbury CT 06033

AULT, ROBERT WALTER, Business Teacher; *b:* Fall River, MA; bara J. Souza; *c:* Rebecca, Bradford, Bethany; *ed:* Bryant Coll (BS) e 1971; Bridgewater St Coll (MED) Admin 1979; *cr:* B M C Durfee hr & Asst Vice Prin 15 Yrs; Somerset HS Bus Tchr 10 Yrs; Fisher djunct Fac of Accounting 12 Yrs; *ai:* Sr Class Adv; Schl Store & Coord; Yrbk Adv; NEA 1971-; MA Bus Tchrs 1990-; Somerset Lions 1989-, VP, Outstanding Lionism Awd; Leo Club 1990-91, Adv; Mann Tchr; *home:* 26 Robin Ln Somerset MA 02726

ALCIDES F., High School Guidance Counselor; *b:* Brava, Cape *m:* Iolanda Leca; *c:* Michael; *ed:* Bridgewater St Coll (BA) Soc 1986, (BS) Bus Admin 1989, (MED) Cnslng 1993; 18 Credit Hrs d BS in Span; *cr:* Brockton HS Guid Cnslr 1986-90; Massachusetts r Prevention of Cruelty to Children Soc Worker 1990-91; RI Coll ssions Ofcr 1991-92; Wareham HS Guid Cnslr 1993-; *ai:* ultural Club Adv; Wareham Adult Ed Guid Cnslr, Coord; Guitarist; Cod Guid Cnslr Assn; Brockton Coalition for the Homeless Citizens 92; New England Coll Admissions Cnslrs 1989-; Wrote Grant & ed Funds for Promotion of Cultural Act Shawmut bank 1995; Wrote nor's Allience Against Drugs 1989; Obtained Funds for After Schl Brockton HS.

, JUNE MARIE, First Grade Teacher; *b:* New Bedford, MA; *ed:* eastern MA Univ (BS) Elem Ed 1972; 21 Credit Hrs; *cr:* Carney Acad d Tchr 1972-; *ai:* Zeiterion Theatre House Mgr 1994-, Vol Usher 94; Young Friends of Zeiterion Chprsn, Co-Author 1991-95, NEA, edford Edctr Assn 1972-; Zeiterion Theatre 1992-95, Bd of Trustees; e Mann Grant Creative Writing Project 1988-89; Davis Flwshp Awd en's Lit 1989-90; Ec & Soc Justice Awd YWCA 1995; Order of World Patriotism Awd 1988.*

H, PAULA MARIE (YONCHAK), Business Teacher; *b:* Sharon, : Edward D.; *c:* Dennis, David, April Lynn; *ed:* Notre Dame Coll Bus Ed 1974; 24 Credit Hrs in Bus Area; *cr:* West Middlesex HS Bus 974-; *ai:* Girls Bsktbl Coach 1974-86, Co-Coach of Yr 1981; FBLA 988-; Jr Class Adv 1994-; NEA 1974-; PSEA 1975-, Past Pres 1983, *office:* West Middlesex HS 3591 Sharon-New Castle Rd West esex PA 16159

KNEY, ELAINE FAUTEUX, Middle School Principal; *b:* ford, ME; *m:* Gary; *c:* David, Michael; *ed:* Univ of VT (BA) His (MED) Rdng & Admin 1981; St Michael Coll, McGill Univ & Univ ebec 60 Credit Hrs Post Med Work; *cr:* Essex-North Superv Union Ed Dir 1979-81; Morristown Elem Prin 1981-85; Stowe Elem Schl 6th Grd Tchr 1985-94, Enrichment Coord 1992-94; Stowe MS Prin ; *ai:* Assessment & Lang Arts Comms; VT Rdng Cncl 1974-, Pres, ASCD 1981, 1994-; Lamoille South Tchr of the Yr 1989; *office:* Stowe 13 Barrows Rd Stowe VT 05672

, HARRIET NANCY, Teacher; *b:* New York, NY; *m:* Mark M.; *ed:* r Coll at Lehman (BA) Romance Langs 1963; Hunter Coll at New NY (MS) Elem Ed 1966; Addl 30 Credits; *cr:* PS 2 2nd, 4-6th Grd 1963-72; San Francisco Schl System Substitute Tchr 1968-69; PS 160 Grd Tchr, Bridge Class 1972-86, Lib, Reg, Spec Ed Tchr 1986-; *ai:* vised Stu Tchrs Storytelling Coach; Org Schl Lit Club; Taught ted, Gifted Creative Writing Club Members; VFT, AFT, NYSUT ; Hunter Coll Alumni 1963-, Natl Geographic Soc 1971-, Victory ts Homeowners Assn 1976; NY Zoological Soc 1984-; Dean's List r Coll; Outstanding Elem Tchrs of Amer 1972; Outstanding Ldrs Scndry Ed 1976; Dist in Educator of Yr 1991; Coached NY Citywide elling Winner 1993, Borough-wide 1994; Contributed Articles to Magazine; *office:* PS 160 The Walt Disney Parade 4140 Hutchinson Pkwy E Bronx NY 10475

HAM, ALISON DUCKETT, 7th-8th Grade Teacher; *b:* Lawrence, *m:* Dennis D.; *c:* Martin D., Andrew C., Derek J.; *ed:* Univ of ME at ngton (BSEd) Math, Sci 1964; Univ of ME at Gorham (MSEd) dial Rdng 1978; *cr:* York Elem Schl Tchr 1964-67; Pownal Elem Schl 1972-; *ai:* Cert Comm; NEA, MEA 1964-; Pownal Tchrs Assn 1972-, Negotiator; *office:* Pownal Elem Schl 587 Elmwood Rd Pownal ME

PINKHAM, BARBARA M., English Teacher; *b:* Whitefield, NH; *ed:* Plymouth St Coll (BE) Eng Ed 1969; Univ of NH (MA) Eng 1971; *cr:* Univ of NH Frosh Eng Instr 1969-71; Littleton HS Eng Tchr 1971-; *ai:* Fac Cncl; NCTE; Ford Fellowship; *office:* Littleton HS School St Littleton NH 03561

PINKHAM, DAY, Art Teacher; *b:* Ossening, NY; *m:* Susan J. Musial; *c:* David, Heather; *ed:* SUNY at New Paltz (BS) Art Ed 1971, (MS) Art 1975; *cr:* Coxsackie-Athens Schls Art Tchr 4 Yrs; Draper Schls Art Tchr 1 Yr; Taconic Hills Schls Art Tchr 1 Yr; Schalmont Schl Dis Art Tchr 8 Yrs; *ai:* Chess Club Adv; Art Pub; *office:* Schalmont HS 1 Sabre Dr Schenectady NY 12306

PINKHAM, I. J., Math Teacher & Bsktbl Coach; *b:* Milbridge, ME; *m:* Margaret Grover; *c:* Matthew, Timothy; *ed:* Univ of ME at Farmington (BS) Math Ed 1969; Univ of So ME (MS) Scndry Admin 1978; 15 Addl Credit Hrs, CEU's-30; *cr:* Buckfield HS Math, His Tchr 1969-76; Boothbay Region HS Ath Dir 1980-92, Math Tchr 1976-; *ai:* Jr Class Adv 1976-; Coach: Bsktbl 1970-, JV Soccer 1974-76, Sftbl 1970-76; Ath Dir 1980-92; NHS Comm 1994-, Curr Design Team 1995-; NEA, ME Tchrs Assn 1969-; Boothbay Region Tchrs Assn 1976-, Pres 3 Yrs, Chief Negotiator 3 Yrs, ME Assoc of Bsktbl Coaches 1980-, Sec 1990-; Rotary 1981-, Bd of Dir; Drug Awareness Team 1989-95, Ed Comm Chm; Youth Sports Coach 1983-, YMCA Vol of Yr 1991; Pub in Ath Journal 1970; *office:* Boothbay Region HS Townsend Ave Boothbay Harbor ME 04538

PINKNEY, MATTIE GRAY, Business Teacher; *b:* Cliftonville, MS; *m:* Fred Ladell; *c:* Sherita Pinkney-Robertson, Fredrick Ladell; *ed:* Rust Coll (BS) Bus Ed 1970; MI St Univ; *cr:* Vaiden HS Bus Tchr 1971-72; Yokota HS Bus Tchr 1976-81; Wagner HS Bus, Graphics 1981-91; Mannheim HS Bus, Cmptrs 1991-; *ai:* Yrbk; Stu Cncl; Future Bus Ldrs of Amer; Drill Team; Soccer Coach; Step Team Coord; Field Hockey Coach; Frosh, Soph Class Spon; diciplinarian Comm; Stu of Week, Month, Tchrs Insvc Comm; NEA 1971-; EBEA 1992-; NASAA 1993-; Walworth's Pub, Superior Performance Awds; Cash Awds Dodds for Outstdng Performance; *office:* Mannheim American HS Unit 29939 APO AE 09086

PINKOS, STARR JEAN, Spanish Teacher; *b:* Springfield, MA; *ed:* Univ of NH (BA) Span, Scndry Ed 1975; 50 Addl Credit Hrs; Travel, Stud Spain, Costa Rica, Dominican Republic, Mexico, Chile, Argentina, Ecuador, Puerto Rico; *cr:* West Springfield HS Span Tchr 1977; Turners Falls HS Span Tchr 1977-78; Pioneer Valley Regnl Schl Span Tchr 1979-; *ai:* Span Honor & Club Adv; Western MA Regnl Dir NHS; Schl Cncl; Soc Responsibility Comm; MAFLA 1979-; MTA, NEA 1977-; AATSP 1980-; ACTFL 1995-; Dial, Self 1993-; Sigma Delta Pi; Horace Mann Grant; *office:* Pioneer Valley Regional Schl F Sumner Turner Dr Northfield MA 01360

PINNEY, CAROL SUSANNE (ALBRECHT), English Teacher; *b:* Youngstown, OH; *m:* Patrick Chambers; *c:* Laura Megan; *ed:* Mount Union Coll (BA) Eng, Fr & Ed 1965; Youngstown St Univ (MA) Eng 1985; Lib Sci Credit Hrs; *cr:* Ashtabula HS 9th Grd Eng Tchr 1965-66; Zion Jr HS 7th & 8th Grd Eng Tchr 1966; Liberty HS 9th & 11th Grd Eng Tchr 1968-69; Hubbard HS 10th & 12th Grd Eng Tchr 1974-; *ai:* NHS & Prep Bowl Adv; Youngstown St Univ Eng Festival; NEA, OEA, HEA 1974-; Delta Kappa Gamma 1980-, Chapter Pres, Schlsp Recipient; Phi Delta Kappa 1988-; AAUW 1973-, Chapter Pres; *office:* Hubbard HS 350 Hall Ave Hubbard OH 44425*

PINTO, LOIS BLASER, Health & Phys Ed Teacher; *b:* Springfield, PA; *m:* John T.; *c:* John M., Gemella A.; *ed:* Penn St, East Stroudsburg Univ Master Equiv 1994; *cr:* Liberty HS Hlth, PE Tchr 1974-; *ai:* Field Hockey Coach 1974-79; Girls Vlybl Coach 1977-79; PIAA 1979-; *office:* Liberty HS 1115 Linden St Bethlehem PA 18017

PINTUFF, LINDA COOK, High School Math Teacher; *b:* Cortland, NY; *m:* Ronald; *c:* Eric M. Vandenburgh; *ed:* SUNY at Albany (BA) Math 1969, (MA) Ed 1973; *cr:* Shenendehowa Cntrl Math Tchr 1970-; *ai:* Class Adv; NYSUT, AMTNYS 1970-; *office:* Shenendehowa Cntrl Schl 970 Rt 146 Clifton Park NY 12065

PIOLA, ROBERT C., Special Education Teacher; *b:* Waterbury, CT; *m:* Lynn Weyh; *c:* Rachel, Christina, Kathryn; *ed:* Holy Cross Coll (BA) Modern Lang 1971; Southern CT St Univ (MS) Spcl Ed 1985; 36 Credit Hrs Past Masters 6th Yr Equivalent; Certfd Admin & Supervision; *cr:* Eagle Hill HS Spcl Ed Tchr 1974-77; Naugatuck Alternative Schl Spcl Ed Tchr 1977-80; Naugatuck HS Tchr of LD 1980-; *ai:* Fac Advy Comm; Prof Dev Comm; CEA 1978-; NEA 1978-; NTL 1978-; CASCO 1995-; *office:* Naugatuck HS 543 Rubber Ave Naugatuck CT 06770

PIORKOWSKI, JAMES PAUL, Associate Professor of Music; *b:* Kenmore, NY; *m:* Susan Elizabeth Marion; *c:* Jacob, Benjamin; *ed:* SUNY Buffalo (BA) Music Performance 1978; SUNY Fredonia (MM) Composition 1987; Univ of Toronto Grad Work in Performance Classical Guitar; *cr:* SUNY Buffalo Instr 1980-83; SUNY Fredonia Assoc Music, Classical Guitar Prof 1983-; *ai:* Fredonia Guitar Soc Adv; Buffalo Guitar Quartet 1982; Buffalo Guitar Quartet Recorded 4 Albums; Performed in Russia, Poland, Venezuela, Columbia, Perto Rico, Germany, Canada, Czech Republic, Hungary, Slovakia, US; *office:* S U N Y Coll At Fredonia Mason Hall Fredonia NY 14063

PIOTROWICZ, PAUL, Varsity Soccer Coach; *b:* Boston, MA; *m:* Marilyn Ann Bowman; *c:* Toria, Melanie, Ryan, Adam; *cr:* Fontbonne Acad Head Soccer Coach 1987-; Admin for Olympic Dev Girls Soccer S Section MYSA 1988-94; *ai:* Drummer For Schl Plays; JV Sftbl Coach; EMGSCA 1988-; Newspaper Articles Pub; *office:* Fontbonne Acad 930 Brook Rd Milton MA 02186*

PIOTRZKOWSKI, RICHARD ALAN, Chemistry Teacher; *b:* East St Louis, IL; *m:* Anne Burke; *ed:* Purdue Univ (BS) Ed 1980; IN Univ (MS) Chem Ed 1990; *cr:* Greenwich HS Tchr, Coach 1980-; *ai:* Bsktbl Girls Coach; Dir Project 2000; ACS, NSTA 1990-; NEA 1984; Distngd Tchr Awd 1989; *office:* Greenwich HS 10 Hillside Rd Greenwich CT 06830

PIPAK, MICHAEL JOHN, HS Social Studies Teacher; *b:* Latrobe, PA; *m:* Gina Rose Fratto; *c:* Michael; *ed:* Bethany Coll (BA) Ec, Fin 1984; St Vincent Coll Tchng Cert Soc Stud 1986; *cr:* Merrill Lynch Customer Acctng Rep 1984-86; Sacred Heart Schl Tchr 1987-94; Northgate Jr-Sr HS Scndry Soc St Tchr 1994-; *ai:* Asst Var Ftbl Coach; PSEA, NEA 1994-; Holy Name Soc 1992-; *office:* North Gate HS Union Ave Pittsburgh PA 15202*

PIPER, DIXIE CANON, Secondary English Teacher; *b:* Mercer, PA; *m:* Gary L.; *c:* Greta, Deanna; *ed:* IN Univ of PA (BS) Eng Ed 1972; Master's Equivalency; *cr:* Lakeview HS Eng Tchr 1972-73; Clarion Linestone HS Eng Tchr 1983-84; Brookway HS Eng Tchr 1987-88; DuBois Cntrl Chrstn Schl Eng Tchr 1988-90; Brookville HS Eng Tchr 1990-; *ai:* Yrbk Adv; NCTE 1992-; Brookville Comm Theatre; *office:* Brookville Area HS Jenks St Brookville PA 15825

PIPER, MARJORIE A., Math & Computer Teacher; *b:* Teaneck, NJ; *ed:* William Paterson Coll (BA) Elem Ed 1962, (MA) Math Ed 1966, (MED) Schl Admin 1976; *cr:* Teaneck Elem Schl #1 5th, 6th Grd Tchr 1962-65; Teaneck Elem Schl #6 5th, 6th Grd Tchr 1962-65; Charles De Wolf Schl Math, Cmptr Tchr 1965-; *ai:* Northern Valley Regnl Curr Ctr In-Svc Instr; Math Curr Comm; Stevens Inst of Tech CIESE Prgm Mentor Tchr; Tech Comm; NEA, NJEA, BCEA 1962-; Old Tappan Tchr Assn 1965-, Treas, VP, Sec; Hospital Auxiliary 1965-; NJ Gov's Tchr Recognition Awd 1989; Teaneck Primary & Intermediate Soc Stud Tchng GuideCo-Author; *office:* Charles De Wolf Schl 275 Old Tappan Rd Old Tappan NJ 07675*

PIPER, STEPHEN, Health Teacher; *b:* Uniontown, PA; *m:* Patricia Lewis; *ed:* Lock Haven Univ (BS) Hlth 1970; SUNY at Brockport (MS) Hlth 1977; *office:* Hornell HS 134 Seneca St Hornell NY 14843

PIPMAN, MILLIE HAAS, English Teacher; *b:* New Kensington, PA; *m:* Bruce; *c:* Max, Joel; *ed:* Indiana Univ of PA (BA) Eng 1969; Univ of Pittsburgh (PHD) Eng Ed 1983; Working Towards MED in Eng Ed; Great Books Discussion Ldr; *cr:* Kiski Area HS Tchr 1971-; *ai:* Stu Cncl; PSEA; NEA; WPCTE; Tri-City Jaycees Outstdng Young Pennsylvanian 1984; Univ of Pittsburgh Schl of Ed All Star Edctr 1995; Gift of Time Tribute Cert 1996; *office:* Kiski Area HS 200 Poplar St Vandergrift PA 15690*

PIRAINO, CATHARINE MILLER, Retired First Grade Teacher; *b:* Lineboro, MD; *m:* John V.; *ed:* St Tchrs Coll at Towson (BS) ELem Ed 1960; Courses Taken Baltimore Cty Bd of Ed MA Equivalency Elem Ed; *cr:* Elmwood El Schl 1-3 Grd Tchr 1960-92; *ai:* Sub Tchr; Vol Elem Tchr; Tchrs Assn Baltimore Co, MSTA 1960-; NEA 1956-; Nom Excl Ed Sponsored Baltimore Cty Chamber of Commerce 1989-92.*

PIRIE, BARBARA SPRINGMAN, Special Ed Tchr & Adj Instr; *b:* Philadelphia, PA; *m:* Elliott Lindsay; *c:* Eric; *ed:* Mansfield Univ (BS) Elem Ed 1964; Georgian Ct Coll (MA) Spcl Ed 1986; Widener Univ (MS) Ed 1993, (EDD) Admin 1996; Tchr of the Handicapped; Early Chldhd Endorsement; Supvry Cert; *cr:* Abington Schl Dist 4th Grd Tchr 1964-68; Long Beach Island Schl Dist Elem & Spcl Ed Tchr 1974-; Georgian Ct Coll Undergrad Spcl Ed Instr 1990-; *ai:* NEA 1964-; NJEA 1974-, Local Pres; Delta Kappa Gamma 1984-; Kappa Delta Pi 1996-; N Shore Recreation Comm 1980-; Alliance for a Living Ocean 1986-; Article Pub; NJ Tchr Recognition Awd for Long Beach Island Schl Dist 1982; *home:* 16 Warwick Ave Harvey Cedars NJ 08008

PIRLO, FRANCES CHOMOS, First Grade Teacher; *b:* Sharon, PA; *m:* Thomas; *c:* Suzanne; *ed:* Youngstown Univ (BS) Elem Ed 1965; 16 Addl Hrs Post-Grad Work; *cr:* Christ Our King 1st Grd Tchr 1962-65; Brookfield Twp Schls 1st Grd Tchr 1965-66; Hubbard Schls Mobile Unit Learning Disabilities Tutor Part-Time 1977-84; St Rose 2nd Grd Tchr 1984-95, 1st Grd Tchr 1995-; *ai:* NCEA 1984-; Liturgy Comm 1995-; Lector 1996; *office:* Saint Rose Schl 61 E Main St Girard OH 44420*

PIROLI, PATRICIA RHOADS, Fifth Grade Teacher; *b:* Lancaster, PA; *m:* Edward O.; *c:* Deborah M., Rebbica A., Victory S.; *ed:* Slippery Rock Univ (BS) Elem Ed 1974; Grad Credits Penn St Univ; *cr:* Hopewell Area Schls Third Grd Tchr 1975-77; Ambridge Area Schl First Grd Tchr 1977-78; New Brighton Area Schl Sixth- Eighth Grd Tchr 1979-88, Fifth Grd Tchr 1989-; *ai:* PSEA, NEA 1979-; *office:* New Brighton Elem Schl 3200 43rd St New Brighton PA 15066

PIROSO, BETH ANGWIN, Sixth Grade Teacher; *b:* Concord, NH; *m:* Douglas J.; *c:* Douglas S., Mark J.; *ed:* Plymouth St Coll (BS) Elem Ed 1986; Post Grad Credits Ed; *cr:* Washington St Elem Schl Grd 5 Tchr 1986-90; Merrimack Vly MS Grd 6 Tchr 1990-; *ai:* Stu Cncl Adv; Eng Comm Comm; Discipline Comm Chprsn; Stu Tchng Coord; Tchr Mentor; PTO 1990-; NEA 1986-, Negotiations Rep 1986-90; Flwshps Area Nrsng Homes; Pub Svc Help Homeless in Area; Tchr of Yr 1994-95; Articles Pub; *office:* Merrimack Vly MS 14 Allen St Penacook NH 03303*

PIRRELLO, LINDA ESTES, 4th Grade Teacher; *b:* Rochester, NY; *m:* Robert P.; *ed:* St Univ Coll at Potsdam (BA) Elem Ed 1967; St Univ Coll at Geneseo (MS) Elem Ed Rdng 1971; *cr:* Fairport Cntrl Schls Elem Tchr 1967-72, 1974-; Los Angeles City Schls Elem Tchr 1972-74; *ai:* Fairport Educators Assn; AFT Fairport Educators Assn 1967-, Bldg Rep, Prof Advancemen Advancement Chm; Rochester Area Rdng Cncl 1985-; 1992 Fairport Schl Dist Winner of Crystal Apple Awd; *home:* 37 Butternut Dr Pittsford NY 14534*

PIRRO, KATHLEEN BIANCHI, Third Grade Teacher; *b:* Milford, MA; *c:* Kailen, Brien, Ginessa; *ed:* Notre Dame Coll (BA) Ed, Sociology 1972; 24 Credit Hrs Various Educ Courses; *cr:* Chapin Schl First Grd Tchr 1973-74; Oliver Schl First Grd Tchr 1974-79; Woodland Schl Third Grd Tchr 1979-; *ai:* MTA, NEA 1973-; One of 4 Tchrs Wrote & Received $5,000 Grant for Low Income Child 1976; *office:* Woodland Schl N Vine St Milford MA 01757

PIRTLE, SHELBY GENE, English & American His Tchr; *b:* Sedalia, MO; *m:* Scarlett C.; *c:* Sean T., Seth Andrew; *ed:* Central MO St Univ (BSE) Soc Stud 1965, (MA) His 1968, (EDS) His 1974; Attnd Washington Univ, Northeast MO St Univ, Univ of CA at Berkeley; *cr:* Appleton City Schls His Tchr 1965-67; Belton Schls His Tchr 1967-69; Wentworth Military Acad Coll His Tchr 1969-71; St Charles City Schls His & Eng Tchr 1971-89; Zama Amer HS His & Eng Tchr 1989-; *ai:* Tennis, Wrestling, Bsbl Coach; Discipline Review, NHS, Renaissance Comms; NEA 1971-89; OEA 1989-; Youth Svc Act 1989-; Superior Work Performance; Distinguished Tchr Awd; *home:* 17th Asg Cm Box 3353 Unit 45006 APO AE 96338*

PISANESCHI, KATHERINE MARCHETTI, Former Third Grade Teacher; *b:* Virginia, MN; *w:* Alfred (dec); *c:* Alan, Ann, Cheryl, Craig; *ed:* St Scholastica (BA) Elem Ed 1962; St Scholastica Music, Eng 1963; *cr:* St Lukes Schl 2nd, 1st Grd Tchr 1984-86; Resurrection 4, 5, 6 Grd Tchr, Head of Rel Dept 1986-91, 3rd Grd Tchr 1991-94; *ai:* Vulnerability Substance Abuse Rainbow Prgm; EPDT 1988-; AUP 1991-; Vol Kane Cty Nursing HOme 1977-; Vol Soc Svc Church 1995-; *home:* 2047 Rockfield Rd Pittsburgh PA 15243*

PISANI, JOSEPH ANTHONY,JR., Social Studies Teacher; *b:* Bay Shore, NY; *m:* Jennifer A. Hamilton; *ed:* Suffolk Comm Coll (AAS) Criminal Sci 1986; Dowling Coll (BBA) Mgt, Ec 1990, (MS) Ed 1992; 20 Addl Credit Hrs; Coaching Cert NY; *cr:* Dowling Coll Head Lacrosse Coach 1990-92; St John the Bapt DHS Tchr, Coach 1992-; *ai:* JC Head Soccer, Var Head Lacrosse Coach; Lacrosse Coord; Long Island Cncl for SS 1995-; Natl Coaches Assn 1990-, Achvmt Awd 1991; Knights of Columbus 1984-, Second Guard, 3rd Degree; Thesis Pub; Co-Creator Mac Wear Lacrosse Club 1995; Design Specialist; *office:* St John the Bapt HS 1170 Montauk Hwy West Islip NY 11795*

PISANI, LOUIS ANTHONY, Band Dir & General Music Tchr; *b:* Brackenridge, PA; *m:* Judith E. Zenoski; *c:* Louis M., Mark S., Kathleen J.; *ed:* Indiana Univ of PA (BS) Music Ed 1961, (MA) Music Ed 1966; Attnd Penn St Univ Driver Trng 1974 & Duquesne Univ 60 Addl Credits; *cr:* Apollo Schl Dist HS Choir & Girls Chorus & Sextet Tchr 1961-63; Plum Schl Dist HS Band & Choir Tchr & Jr HS Instr 1963-64; Tarentum HS Band & Jr HS & Elem Schl Inst Tchr 1964-68; Highlands HS Band Music Fund & App Tchr 1968-76; Penn St Grad Schl Music Ed Tchr 1986; Highlands MS Band & General Music Tchr 1976-; *ai:* NEA, Highlands Ed Assn; Phi Mu Alpha Sinfonia; Dir of the Band that won 27 Trophies & 15 Plaques 1968-76; *home:* 1510 Carlisle St Natrona Heights PA 15065

PISANI, MARIA CURELLA, Secondary Level Biology Tchr; *b:* Brooklyn, NY; *c:* Jacqueline, Paul, Andrea; *ed:* Brooklyn Coll (BS) Bio 1960, (MS) Bio 1965; Addl 30 Credits Post Grad Stud; *cr:* Lawrence Jr HS Sci Tchr 1960-66; Nassau Schls All Levels Sub Sci Tchr 1980-83; Southside HS Bio Tchr 1984-; *ai:* Sci Fair Project Adv; AFT, RVCTA 1983-; Columnist for Environmental Newslette; Rel Ed Instr; Outdoor Ed Guide; Vol Rdng Instr for Stu with Eng as Second Lang; *office:* South Side HS 140 Shepherd St Rockville Centre NY 11570

PISANO, ROSEMARY HOEY, Fourth Grade Teacher; *b:* New York City, NY; *m:* William C. Sr.; *c:* Jessica Tobin, William C. Jr.; *ed:* Coll of Mt St Vincent (BA) Eng 1964; Harvard Univ (EDM) Ed 1980; Addl 30 Credit Hrs

Post Masters Tufts, Harvard & Lesley Coll; *cr:* Extension Lay Vol Schl 7-8th Grd Tchr 1964-65; St Barnabas Elem Schl 6th Grd Tchr 1965-68; Schl #7 4th Grd Tchr 1968-69; Glover Schl 5th Grd Tchr 1970-71; Winn Brook Schl Enrichment Tchr 1983-88, 4th Grd Tchr 1988-; *ai:* Belmont Schl Advy Cncl; Harvard Univ Peace Games Comm Bd; NEA, BTA 1983-; Edctrs for Soc Responsibility 1987-; *home:* 253 Washington St Belmont MA 02178*

PISCIOTTI, ALFRED R., Industrial Technology Teacher; *b:* New York City, NY; *m:* Gertrude Valmoro; *c:* Anthony, Nicholas; *ed:* Montclair St Coll (BA) Indstrl Arts 1963; Jersey City St Coll Voc Cert; Rutgers Pub; Voc Cert Auto Tech 1970; *ai:* NEA; BTA; HCTA; Recreation Commissioner 1988-; Tchr of Yr 1994; Tchr of Month 1994, 1995; *office:* Bayonne HS 27 St & Ave A Bayonne NJ 07002

PISCITELLI, MICHAEL, Accounting & Marketing Teacher; *b:* Bayonne, NJ; *m:* Christine Wilczynski; *ed:* Saint Peters Coll (BS) Accounting 1965; Trenton St Coll (MED) Mrktg 1973; Attnd Fordham Univ Admin 9 Credits, Georgian Court Coll Admin & Supervision 30 Credits, San Francisco St Univ Peace Corps Trng; *cr:* Dickinson HS Accounting Tchr 1965-67; Old Bridge HS Bus Tchr 1967-; *ai:* Schl Store Adv; Tchr Advy Cncl; Old Bridge Ed Assn 1967-, Budget Chprsn; Middlesex Cty Ed Assn, NJ Ed Assn 1967-; NEA; NJ Bus Ed Assn; Georgian Poetry Soc Poetry Awd.

PISEGNA, JEANNA MARIE, Biology Teacher; *b:* New Castle, PA; *ed:* Youngstown Univ (BA) Bio 1970; John Carroll Univ (MST) Sci Teaching 1972; Kent St Univ (MA) Exercise Physiology 1980; Sci Curr, Dev; *cr:* Brookside HS Sci Tchr, Phys, Bio 1969-75; Kent St Univ Lab Schl Sci Tchr 1976-79; Northeastern OH Univ Coll of Medicine Lab Coord Physiology 1980-83; Kent City Schls MS Life Sci 1983-92, HS Bio, AT Bio 1992-; *ai:* Curr Review Comm; NSTA 1983-; Natl Assn for Research Sci Tchr 1991-; Natl Assn of Bio Tchrs 1993-; Courteau Soc 1990-; Natl Sci Fnd Grant 1970-72; Amer Physiological Society Summer Fellowship 1995; *office:* Kent Roosevelt HS 1400 N Mautua St Kent OH 44240

PITAGNO, ROBERT LOUIS, Science Teacher; *b:* Bay Shore, NY; *m:* Martha Susan Kennedy; *c:* Reed, Max; *ed:* SUNY Cortland (BS) Hlth Ed 1978; Stony Brook Univ (MA) Lib Stud 1991; Nassau Comm Coll Bio Cert; *cr:* West Babylon Jr High Sci Tchr 1987-88; Udall Road MS Sci Tchr 1988-89; Beach Street MS Sci Tchr 1989-90; West Islip Sr High Planetarium Dir & Earth Sci Tchr 1990-; *ai:* West Islip JV LaCrosse & Beach Stree 7th-8th Grd Boys Bsktbl Coach; NY St United Tchrs 1988-; West Islip Tchrs Assn 1989-; Suffolk Cnty Sci Tchr 1990-; *office:* West Islip Sr HS 1 Lions Path West Islip NY 11795

PITBLADO, COLIN B., Professor of Psychology; *b:* Hartford, CT; *m:* Kathleen Parsons; *c:* Bonnie L., John C.; *ed:* Univ of Ct (BA) Psych 1961; Boston Univ (AM) Psych 1963, (PHD) Psych 1966; *cr:* Sperry Rand Research Ctr Research Staff Mem 1964-67; Pacific Univ Asst & Assoc Prof 1967-76; Inst of Living Research Psychologist 1976-83; Eastern CT St Univ Temporary Appointment 1983-84; Teikyo Post Univ Assoc Prof & Prof 1984-; *ai:* Acad Stans Comm; Schlsp Comm; NAIA Fac Athletic Rep; APA 1978-; AAUP 1985-; 28 Publications; *office:* Teikyo Post Univ 800 Country Club Rd Waterbury CT 06723

PITCHER, BETH ANN, Chemistry Teacher; *b:* Dansville, NY; *ed:* Hartwick Coll (BA) Chem, Ed 1991; SUNY at Brockport (MS) Sci Ed 1995; CCFL Bio 12 Credit Hrs; *cr:* Marcus Whitman HS Chem Tchr 1991-; *ai:* Environmental Sci Club; NYSUT 1991-; *office:* Marcus Whitman Jr-Sr HS Baldwin Rd Rushville NY 14544

PITIFER, MARK SALVATORE, Elementary School Counselor; *b:* Geneva, NY; *m:* Leigh Ann Principio; *c:* Nina L. M., Noah M. S., Markie C.; *ed:* Hobart Coll (BA) Psych 1982; SUNY at Brockport (MS) Ed 1984, (CAS) Cnslng Psych 1989; Finger Lakers Comm Coll 30 Hrs PE & Coaching; *cr:* Charters Homes Playground Supvr 14 Yrs; Waterloo Schl Dist Elem Cnslr 11 Yrs; Var Boys track Coach 10 Yrs; JV & Asst Var Bsktbl Coach 9 Yrs; *ai:* Rap & Role Adv; JV & Asst Var Bsktbl, Var Boys Track Coach; NEA 1985-, 10 Yrs Svc Awd; Dr Martin Luther King Citizenship Awd Geneva NAACP 1978; *office:* Waterloo Schl Dist 202 W Main St Waterloo NY 13165*

PITLOCK, ROBERT NEAL, Science & History Teacher; *b:* Warren, PA; *ed:* Edinboro (BS) His 1973; Addl Sci 1975; *cr:* Sheffield Area HS Tchr 21 Yrs; *ai:* NEA, PSEA, WCEA 1975-; *home:* 112 Pickering St Sheffield PA 16347

PITONYAK, FRANK, Math Teacher; *b:* Scranton, PA; *ed:* Temple Univ (BS) Electrical Engr 1972, (MED) Ed 1975, (MS) Statistics 1979; Addl Credits Statistics; *cr:* Pennsbury Schl Dist Math Tchr 1972-; Temple Univ Adjunct Fac, Statistics 1976-80; Bucks Cty Comm Coll Adjunct Fac, Math Tchr 1980-; Instr in the Tchrs Tchng with Tech Prgm by Univ of TX Arlington; *ai:* Bucks Cty Tchrs of Math, NEA 1972-, NCTM; Langhorne Ath Assn 1987-92, VP; *office:* Medill Bair HS 608 S Olds Blvd Fairless Hills PA 19030

PITT, C. LEON, Associate Prof of Sociology; *b:* Rocky Mount, NC; *c:* Umaru J.; *ed:* NC Cntrl Univ (BA) Sociology 1969; WA Univ (MSW) Soc Work 1971; Univ of Pittsburgh (PHD) Soc Work, Sociology 1975; *cr:* Norfolk St Univ Asst Prof of Soc Work 1975-76; Adult Svcs Area Agency on Aging Long Term Care Coord 1976-78; Bd of Allegheny Cty Govt Exec Asst to Cty Commissioner 1980-85; Comm Coll of Beaver Co Assoc Prof of Sociology 1985-; *ai:* Fac Dev Comm, Stu Svcs Accreditation Comm Chprsn; Stu Svcs, Stu Rights Acad Adv, Chprsn; PSEA, NEA 1985-; NAACP 1980-; Shuman Detention Ctr 1984-, Bd; Mental Hlth, Mental Retardation 1984-, Bd; Pub Speaker Soc Orgs; *home:* 7935 Thon Dr Verona PA 15147

PITTAVINO, MARYALYCE FRICK, 3rd Grade Teacher; *b:* Greensburg, PA; *ed:* Geneva Coll (BS) Elem Ed 1970; Univ of Pittsburgh 20 Post-Grad Credits; *cr:* Shaw Elem Norwin Schl Dist 1st Grd Tchr 7 Yrs, 5th Grd Tchr 5 Yrs; Hartford Heights Elem Norwin Schl Dist 5th Grd Tchr 1 Yr, 3rd Grd Tchr 13 Yrs; *ai:* Lang Arts Curr Comm; PSEA, NEA 1970-; Norwin Ed Assn 1970-, Bldg Rep; *office:* Norwin Schl Dist 15020 Ardara Rd North Huntingdon PA 15642

PITTMAN, JIMMY LEE,SR., Art Teacher; *b:* Rocky Mount, NC; *c:* Jimmy Jr.; *ed:* Elizabeth City St U (BS) Art Ed 1974; George WA U (MA) Scndry Ed 1984; *ai:* CEA, NEA 1974-; MAEA, Art Tchr of Yr; Outstng Young Man of Amer; Tchr of Yr; Recognized by the MAEA; *office:* Northern HS 2950 Chaneyville Rd Owings MD 20736

PITTS, BETH NELL, Kindergarten Teacher; *b:* Milwaukee, WI; *c:* Brock C.; *ed:* Heidelberg Coll (BS) Ed 1971; Univ of Toledo (MS) Admin 1984; Addl 18 Hrs; *cr:* Bogart Elem Schl 1st Grd Tchr 1971-72, Kndgtn Tchr 1972-; *ai:* Started Schl Safety Village Prgm 1984; Asst in Kndgtn Screening; Unit Coord 8 Yrs; Tchrs Assn 1971-, Unit Coord 8 Yrs; OAEYC Conf; Write Unpublished Prgms; *office:* Bogart Schl 5906 W Bogart Rd Castalia OH 44824

PITTS, DAVID LAWRENCE, Third Grade Teacher; *b:* Chester, PA; *m:* Sharon A.; *c:* Nathan, Kevin, Jennifer; *ed:* Penn St Univ (BA) Elem Ed 1970; St of PA (ME) Elem Ed 1987; *cr:* Oxford Area Schl Dist Chptr 1 Rdng Tchr 1971; Chichester Schl Dist Elem Tchr 1973-; Delaware Cty Prison Adult Basic Ed Tchr 1973-95; *ai:* NEA 1971-; PSEA, Chichester Ed Assn 1973-; BSA 1989-, Asst Scoutmaster; US Trotting Assn 1970-; Bethlehem United Meth 1983-, Trustee; *office:* Boothwyn Elem Schl 1414 Meetinghouse Rd Boothwyn PA 19061

PITTS, DENISE, HS Bus Ed Tchr & Peer Ldr Trnr; *b:* Paterson, NJ; *ed:* Montclair St Coll (MS) Bus Ed 1988; Montclair St Univ (MA) Admin, Suprvsn 1995; 39 Credit Hrs Admin, Supervision; *cr:* Passaic Cty Tech & Voc HS Sec 1983; SHulton Inc Clerk 1984; Waks & Waks Attorneys at Law Legal Sec 1985-86; First Schl Careers Tchr 1988; Passaic HS Tchr 1988-; *ai:* African Amer Club; Alpha Kappa Alpha 1986-, Sec, Teen Adv; NEA, NJEA 1988-; Phi Delta Kappa 1993-; FBLA 1988-, Prof Mem; Phi Delta Kappa; NAACP; Outstanding Young Women Amer 1991; Passaic Cty Tech & Voc Hall of Fame 1990; Lewin Schlsp Awd Montclair St Coll 1987; Educ of Yr, Passaic NAACP; *office:* Passaic HS 170 Paulison Passaic NJ 07055*

PITTS, MARJORIE B., Business Education Teacher; *b:* West Point, MS; *m:* Lynn B.; *c:* Anthony, Tanya, Timothy, Tracy, Tricia; *ed:* Mary Holmes Jr Coll (AS) Secretarial Sci 1969; Knoxville Coll (BA) Bus Ed 1972; Cincinnati Univ Voc Bus Ed 1975; Word Processing II 3 Credits; Ec I, II 3 Credits; *cr:* Cincinnati Pub Schl Math, Bus Tchr 1972-74; North Coll Hill Schl Bus Tchr 1976-; Cincinnati Chrstn Schl Bus Tchr 1989-; *ai:* JV, Var Chlrdrs Coach 4 Yrs; NEA 1994-; OEA, NCHTA 1980-; *home:* 2176 W Kemper Rd Cincinnati OH 45240*

PITTS, MICHELE LILL, High School Guidance Counselor; *b:* Little Falls, NY; *c:* Jason, Jaime; *ed:* Upsala Coll (BA) Psych 1968; Kean Coll (MA) Stu Prsnl Svcs 1988; Elem Ed Cert K-8 1986; Dir Stu Prsnl Svcs Cert 1993; Presently Pursuing Supervisory Cert; *cr:* Florence Gaudineer Schl 6th Grd Tchr 3 Yrs; Deerfield Schl Guid Cnslr K-8 Grd 2 Yrs; Montclair HS 9-12 Grd Guid Cnslr; Millburn HS 9-12 Grd Guid Cnslr; *ai:* Soc & Welfare, Holiday Comm; CORE Team Mem; NJ Schl Cnslrs Assn 1988-; NJ Coll Assn of Cnslrs 1993-; Essex Cty Guid Assn 1992-; Kappa Delta Pi Honor Soc 1996; *office:* Millburn HS 462 Millburn Ave Millburn NJ 07041

PITTS, RHONDA GRAY, Vice Principal; *b:* New York, NY; *m:* Hercules O.; *c:* Brittany, Maya; *ed:* Northeastern Univ (BS) Elem Ed 1976; Bowie St Univ (MED) Admin, Supervision 1986; *cr:* Matthew Henson Elem Schl Grd 6 Tchr 1978-81; Tulip Grove Elem Schl Grd 5 Tchr 1981-84; Phyllis E. Williams Elem Schl Grd 4 Tchr 1984-87; Thomas Pullen K-8 Arts Magnet Schl Vice-Prin, Tchr 1987-; *ai:* After Schl Stud, Mentoring Prgm Coord; Phi Delta Kappa 1987-; ASCD 1990-; ASASP 1991-; Washington Post, Black Male Achvmt Grants; Who's Who in Amer Coll, Univs; *office:* Thomas G Pullen Magnet Schl 700 Brightseat Rd Landover MD 20785

PITTS-DOWNING, DENISE LACELLE, Science Teacher & 6th Grd Dean; *b:* Philadelphia, PA; *c:* Ajeenah, Anitra, Aleaya; *ed:* Antioch Univ (BA) Ed 1987; Permanent Cert Ed 1994; *cr:* William Dick Elem 5th Grd Tchr 1988-90; James Elverson 6th Grd Sci Tchr 1990-; *ai:* Geog Bowl Wm Dick; Pupil Support Team; Schoolwide Ldrshp Team Sci Chair; Drill Team Coach; Stu Asst Pgm Team Ldr; Bldg Comm; Sci Fair Spon; Straight Talk Girls Club Spon; Young Women & Young Men Day Spon & Founder James Elverson; Phila Fed Tchr 1982-; Noborche 1993-; Scholastic MS Advy Bd 1993-, Adv; Comm Participation Panel 1993-, Panelist; Sci Fair Initiative Grant; Math & Sci Pgm 1991; Tchr of the Yr Awd 1992; Tchr Reviewer Silver Burdett Ginn 1995; *office:* James Elverson MS 13th & Susquehanna Philadelphia PA 19107*

PITTSER, MEDA MARISE, Library Media Specialist; *b:* Detroit, MI; *m:* Robert Jesse Pittser II; *c:* Rob, Jason; *ed:* Union Coll (BA) Eng, Fr 1969; Xavier Univ Ed Media Cert; Working Towards Masters Cmptr Tech Wright St Univ; *cr:* Macon Eastern HS Eng, Fr Tchr 1969-70, 1971-74; Lynchburg-Clay HS Eng, Fr Tchr 1070-71; Georgetown HS Lib Media Specialist 1974-77; Walnut Twp HS Lib Media Specialist 1977-79; Miami Trace HS Lib media, Tech Coord 1979-; *ai:* Lib Club Adv; Fac Soc Comm Chm; Prins Adv Comm; NEA; OEA; South Side Church of Christ 1985-, Tchr, Musician; *office:* Miami Trace HS 3722 State Route 41 NW Washington Court H OH 43160

PITZ, HAROLD L., Retired Science & Math Teacher; *b:* North Lawrence, OH; *m:* Shirley A. Bransteter; *ed:* Otterbein Coll (BA) Chem, Ed 1963; Coll of Wooster (MAT) Tchng Math 1971; Scndry Admin Cert Univ of Akron; *cr:* Northwest HS Sci, Math Tchr 1963-69;Dalton HS Sci, Math Tchr 1969-95; Orrville HS Physics Tchr 1996; *ai:* OH Ed Assn, NEA 1963-; NSTA; Phi Delta Kappa 1985-; *home:* 825 Bennington Ave NE Massillon OH 44646

PITZER, JOANNE E., First Grade Teacher; *b:* Sault Ste Marie ON, Canada; *m:* Donald E.; *ed:* Glassboro St Coll (BA) Elem Ed 1963; 12 Credit Hrs E Stroudsburg St Coll; *cr:* Pocono Mt Schl Dist Tchr 1963-68; Mc Ginley Elem Schl Tchr 1968-; *ai:* NEA, BCEA, WEA 1969-; West Jersey Rdng Cncl 1980-, Bd Mem; Marlton Womans Club 1980-; *office:* J A Mc Ginley Elem Schl Middlebury Ln Willingboro NJ 08046

PIURCK, JOHN S., High School History Teacher; *b:* New Haven, CT; *m:* Denise; *c:* Ryan, Aimee; *ed:* Southern CT St Univ (BA) Pol Sci 1969, (MS) Ed & His 1974; Southern CT St Univ 6th Yr Ed 1990; *cr:* St Vincent de Paul Schl Tchr 1969-71; Chalk Hill MS Tchr 1971-83; Masuk HS Tchr 1986-; *ai:* Soccer, Bsbl & Bsktbl Coach; CT Ed Assn 1971-; NEA 1971-; Monroe Ed Assn 1971-, Former President; CT Cncl for Soc Stud 1994-; CIAC, Ofcl; Nutmeg Player 1986-, Theater Group Past Ofcr; 27th CT Vols 1993-, Civil War Re Enactor; *office:* Masuk HS 1014 Monroe Tpke Monroe CT 06468

PIZA, ROBERTA WATKINS, English Teacher; *b:* Lewes Sussex, England; *m:* Guy; *c:* Jessica; *ed:* Glassboro St Coll (BA) Scndry Ed & Comm 1975; Lehigh Univ (MED) Ed & Rdng Specialist 1979; Post Grad Stud Ed 30 Hrs; *cr:* Montgomery Cty Intermediate Unit Rdng Specialist 1976-79; Upper Perkiomen Schl Dist Rdng Specialist 1983-85, Eng Tchr 1985-; *ai:* NHS Adv; Peer Coaching; Learning Styles; NCTE 1978-; PCTE 1991-; NEA 1990-; *office:* Upper Perkiomen HS 2 Walt Rd Pennsburg PA 18073

PIZANO, DAVID MICHAEL, Mathematics & Physics Teacher; *b:* Wilkes-Barre, PA; *m:* Jean Ann Elizabeth Brennan; *c:* Matthew, Kayla, Anthony; *ed:* King's Coll (BS) Math & Scndry Ed 1984; Physics IN Univ of PA; *cr:* Bishop Hoban HS Math Tchr 1984-88; M.M.I. Preparatory Schl Math, Physics, Cmptr Tchr 1988-90; Luzerne Cty Comm Coll Adj Math, Physics Tchr 1986-; WY Area SD Schl Math, Physics Tchr 1990-; *ai:* Sci Olympiad Coaching; NEA, PSEA 1990-; Swoyersville Little League 1994-, Coach; Scholars Ed Awd PA 1983-84; *office:* Wyoming Area Schl Dist 20 Memorial St Exeter PA 18643*

PIZZA, DOMINIC A., Physical Science Teacher; *b:* Trenton, NJ; *m:* Carol Ann Scanlon; *c:* Kathleen Castro, Kristopher Kile; *ed:* Worcester St Coll (BSEd) Sci Ed 1964; Fitchburg St Coll (MED) Ed 1968; CAGS at Assumption Coll Guidance, Psych; Chem, Physics at Coll of the Holy Cross; *cr:* Lura A. White Schl Tchrs Assn Pres 1967-68; Littleton MS Intramural Dir 1972-80, Audio-Visual Coord 1980-84, Sci Dept Head 1982-87; Littleton Jr Sr HS Ath Dir 1990-; *ai:* 7th-12th Grd Athl Dir; LEA, NSTA 1968-; NEA 1964-; New Hope for Homeless 1988-92, Bd of Dir; Title III Grant Environmental Stud; Presidential Awd for Excl in Sci Tchng Nom 1987; Horace Mann Tchr 1988; Natl Sci Fnd Grants in Chem, Physics; Natl Sci Grant Project Seed Northeastern Univ; *office:* Littleton Jr Sr HS 55 Russell St Littleton MA 01460

PIZZARELLA, PAUL FRANK, High School Art Teacher; *b:* Worcester, MA; *m:* Virginia M. Keddy; *c:* Michael, Kimberly, Joy, Anthony; *ed:* Framinghan St Coll (BA) Fine Arts & Scndry Ed 1989; *cr:* Tourtellotte Meml HS Art Tchr 1990-; *ai:* Gifted & Talented Art Pgrm; Frosh Class Adv; Co-Chprsn Advy Cncl; NEA, NAEA 1990-; CAEA 1993-; *home:* PO Box 83 Grosvenor Dale CT 06246*

PIZZI, PETER M., Dental Laboratory Teacher; *b:* Brooklyn, N
Lucia D. Chiara; *ed:* St Rose (BA) Ed; UFT Course Work; *cr:* Pizzi
Studio Owner 6 Yrs; Clara Barton HS Tchr 5 Yrs; *office:* Clara Bar
901 Classon Ave Brooklyn NY 11225*

PIZZUTELLO, MAUREEN GALLAGHER, French & Spanish T
b: Yonkers, NY; *m:* John; *c:* John, Nicholas; *ed:* Allegheny Coll (
1975; St Univ of NY at New Paltz (MS) Fr & Ed 1990; Attnd LEc
Traduction Et DInterpretation, Univ Paul Valery, Univ De Salamar
Shizuoka Elwa Jogakuin Eng Tchr 1977-79; CMFI Inc Biling Sec 19
Chester Jr & Sr HS Fr Tchr 1986-88; Felix Festa Jr High Spa
1989-90; Nanuet HS Fr & Span Tchr 1993-; *ai:* Class of 1999 Adv;
Club Adv; NYSAFLT 1986-; *office:* Nanuet HS 103 Church St Nan
10954

PLACE, HOLLY LYNN, Home Economics Teacher; *b:* Kenmore,
Gary J.; *c:* Jacob, Nathan; *ed:* Villa Maria Coll at Erie (BS) Home
1986; Buffalo St Coll (MS) Home Ec Ed 1990; *cr:* Kenmore West HS
Ec Tchr 1986-87; Herbert Hoover MS Home Ec Tchr 1987-89; Creek
Cntrl Schls Home Ec Tchr 1989-; Cleveland Hill HS Home Ec Tchr
ai: NYSUT, AFT 1986-; Amer Assn of Family & Consumer Svcs
office: Cleveland Hill HS 105 Mapleview Rd Cheektowaga NY 142

PLACE, TIMOTHY, Guidance Counselor; *b:* Johnson City, N
Jennifer Zak; *ed:* Washington & Lee Univ (BA) Psych 1990; St Univ
at Albany (MS) Cnslng Psych 1991, (CAS) Schl Cnslng 1991; *cr:*
Brothers Acad of Albany Ftbl Coach 1990-91; NY St Dept of Lab
Rep 1992; Greene Cntrl Schl Dist Sr HS Guid Cnslr, Head Var Ftbl
1992-; *ai:* Head Var Ftbl Coach; Coord of Off-Season Condit
Weight Trng Prgm; Asst Var Track Coach; Coord of Greene Ath
Broome-Tioga Cnslr Assn 1992-; Amer Ftbl Coaches Assn, NY St F
Coaches Assn 1994-; Tchr of Yr 1993-94; Coaches 1994 Greene V
Team to The Winningest Record in Schl His; *office:* Greene Cntrl H
Canal St Greene NY 13778

PLAGGE, MAUREEN ANNE, Language Arts Teacher; *b:* Philad
PA; *m:* Christopher J.; *c:* Nicholas, Gabriel; *ed:* Temple Univ (
1971; Immaculata Coll (MA) Educl Ldrshp 1990; K-12 Prin C
Credits Beyond MA; *cr:* St Agnes Schl 6th Grd Tchr 1971-72; St
Schl 5th-6th Grd Tchr 1972-76; St Denis Schl 8th Grd Tchr 1976
Augustine Schl 4th- 8th Grd Tchr 1977-78; Drexel Hill MS 8th Gr
1988-; *ai:* Philadelphia Young Playwright Festival Coord & Tchr Tea
UDEA 1988-; PSEA 1988-; NEA 1988-; PA MS Assn 1993-; Impa
Grant; Tchr of Yr Nom 1995; *office:* Drexel Hill MS 3001 State Rd
Hill PA 19026

PLANK, LOUIS WILLIAM, US History Teacher & Dept C
Hornell, NY; *m:* Cheryl Marie Girton; *c:* Benjamin, Emily; *ed:*
Nazarene Coll (BA) His 1971; St of NY Univ at Potsdam (MS) K-
Stud 1976; St of NY Univ at Oswego Driver Ed Cert 1981; 9 Addl
Hrs; *cr:* Black River Elem Schl Long Term Sub Tchr 1971-72; LaFar
Cntrl Schl His Tchr 1972-; Sackets Harbor Cntrl Schl Driver Ed Tch
1989; *ai:* Prof Growth Comm Chm; His Dept Chm; NY St United
Assn 1972-, VP; AFT 1972-; Lions Club 1992-; Church of the Na
1972-, Trustee, Steward, Comm, 2 Distngd Svc Awds; *home:* PO Bo
Fargeville NY 13656*

PLANO, SANDRA KAY, Scndry English & Reading Tchr; *b:* Bu
OH; *m:* Ronald R.; *c:* Tracy; *ed:* Kent St Univ (BS) Scndry Ed, Eng
Youngstown St Univ (MSED) Rdng Supervision 1981; 18 Hrs Beyon
cr: Cloverleaf HS Eng, Hlth, PE Tchr 1971-73; West Branch HS E
Rdng Tchr 1974-; *ai:* Past Yrbk Adv 1974-87; NEA, OEA, WBEA
Kappa Delta Pi 1971-; Quota Club 1986-90, Sec, VP; Comp
Competency Testing Comm 1983-89; Project Arete at Youngstown S
1983-87; Co-Author of Tchr to Tchr Trait Manual for Tchng Writing
of Yr 1987; 1st Place in OH Grow Tchr Contest 1990; Gold Awd fo
Adv Achvmt 1987; 2 Showcase Awds for Outstanding Yrbks 1987;
West Branch HS 14277 S Main St Beloit OH 44609

PLANSKER, DORIS G., Braillist & Student Assistant; *b:* Mineol
m: Edwin J.; *c:* Michael, Kimberly; *ed:* 14 Credit Hrs Bus Ed C
Frederick Comm Coll; Cmptr Braille MD Schl for the Blind; *cr:* Fre
Co Bd of Ed Admin Asst, Clerical 1984-91, Braillist, Clerical Asst
ai: Natl Braille Assn 1993-; Eastern Star 1966-, Ruth, Esther, Marth
Conductress, 25 Yr Pin.

PLANTE, JEANNETTE THERESE,CSC, Professor of History &
b: North Adams, MA; *ed:* Notre Dame Coll (BA) Latin, His Ed
Duquesne Univ (MA) Classics 1968; 2 Week CANE Inst Classics, E
Inst NH His; 3 Credit Course Learning Styles; *cr:* St Mary Newm
Notre Dame Schls 2 Grd Tchr 1945-57; St Augustine Schl 2, 3 Gr
1957-61; St George, St Aloysius HS Tchng Latin, His 1961-68;
Dame Coll Asst Prof His, Latin 1968-; *ai:* Acad Adv Scndry Soc St
St Jr Classical League Adv; Coll Alumni Bd of Dirs; Supvr His
Radio Station; Amer Classical League 1960-, Natl Prgm Chm, Ou
Emerita Mem; Classical Assn of New Eng 1968-, Comm, Barlow-
Awd; Notre Dame C. Alumni Bd 1994-, Exec Bd, The Lifetime A
Diocesan Museum Commission 1992-, Bd of Dirs; Judge for Bill of
1990-, Judge; Wkshps for Tchrs 1986-, Vol; Wkshps for Women
1988-, Vol; Natl JCL Conventions Exec Comm 1974-85; Yrbk Dedi
Class 1980; Outstdng Fac Mem Tchng Excl, Campus Ldrshp 1990
Annual NH Classics Day 1968-; *office:* Notre Dame Coll 2321 E
Manchester NH 03104*

PLAS, ALAYNE MARQUARD, French & German Teacher; *b:* Lake
OH; *m:* John R.; *c:* Seth, Patrick; *ed:* Cleveland St Univ (BA) Langs
Antioch of New England (MA) Ed 1985; 1st Degree Universite de
Fr 1971; *cr:* Avon Lake HS Frgn Lang Tchr 1973-81; Kimball Union
Frgn Lang Tchr 1981-84; Riverside MS Frgn Lang Tchr 1984-; *ai*
Aerobics Instr Dartmouth Coll; Delta Kappa Gamma 1995-, Schlsp
Pub Cookbook 1995; *office:* Riverside MS 13 Fairground Rd Sprir
VT 05156

PLAT, ROBERT R., Earth Science & Astronomy Tchr; *b:* Natron
PA; *m:* Joan Pastorek; *c:* Sarah Y., Micah M., Elisha L., Joshua J.;
Univ of PA (BS) Geo Sci 1970; 58 Credit Hrs Post-Grad Stu
Pine-Richland Schl Dist Tchr, Dept Chair & Planetarium Dir 1970
PREA, PSEA & NEA 1970-, Rep Cncl; PSTA 1972-; MAPS, GL
PAPA 1991-; Penn Vly Ath Club 1980-, Bd of Dirs; Butler Co Soccer
1981-88, Head Coach Traveling League; Knoch Area Soccer Assoc
Coaching; *office:* Pine-Richland HS 4300 Warrendale Rd Gibson
15044

PLATEK, GARY THEODORE, Mathematics Teacher; *b:* Batavia, N
Geraldine Yarbrough; *c:* Jason, Shannon, Lauren Frantz, Ronald F
ed: SUNY at Brockport (BS) Math 1966; Post Grad Stud Nazareth
cr: Denonville Jr High Math Tchr 1966-73; Penfield HS Math Tchr
ai: Homecoming & Curr Dev Comms; AFT 1966-; NYSUT & Penfi
Assn 1970-; CWNYBOWS Soccer 1985-; CWNYBOWS Sfbl 1974-
Rochester Coll Umpires 1980-, Pres; *home:* 97 Penn Ln Rocheste
14625*

PLATOW, BARRY PAUL, 5th Grade Teacher; *b:* Manhattan, N
Univ of UT (BS) Elem Ed 1971; Western CT St Univ (MS) Ed 197
Ridgecrest Elem 5th Grd Tchr 1971-72; Somers Cntrl Schl 2-3, 5-6
MS Soc Stud Tchr 1972-; *ai:* Math, Soc Stud Curr Ldr; Jr Historica
Ldr; MS Newspaper Club; NCTE, NCSS 1991-; Sigma Alpha E
1968-; *office:* Somers Intermediate Schl Rt 202 Somers NY 10589*

T, IAN R., Band Dir & Elctrnc Music Tchr; *b:* Brooklyn, NY; *m:* Trapp; *ed:* SUNY at Stony Brook (BA) Psych 1975; C. W. Post Coll Music Ed 1977; 60 Addl Hrs; *cr:* Unity Drive Elem Schl Band Dir Shoreham-Wading River MS Band Dir 1979-93, Instrumental Lesson 993-, Band Dir, Electronic Music Tchr 1993-; *ai:* Jazz Band Dir; HS ch; Pvt Lesson Tchr; Music Festivals Participant; SCMEA, NYSUT , NYSBDA 1982-; NYSSMA, MENC 1994-; Shoreham Wading River Band 1990-, Prin Alto Saxophonist; Long Island Aquarium Soc ; *office:* Shoreham Wading River HS Rt 25A Shoreham NY 11786

T, JEFFREY H., Asst Vice-Pres of Stu Affairs; *b:* Lockport, NY; *ed:* iv Coll at Buffalo (BS) Design 1982, (MS) Stu Prsnl 1984; *cr:* ville Coll Admissions Cnslr 1984-85, Asst Dir of Admissions 88, Dir for New Stdnts, Stu Act 1988-94, Asst VP for Stu Affairs ; *ai:* Commuter Cncl Adult Stdnts Adv; Small Coll Consortium of rn NY Chair; NJ Orientation Dir Assn 1995-; AIDS Family Svcs , Bd of Dir; Local Election Vol 1994-; *office:* D'Youville Coll 320 Ave Buffalo NY 14201

T, LINDA SUE, Professor in Athletic Training; *b:* Somerset, PA; *ed:* Haven St Coll (BS) HPER, Ath Trng 1983; WV Univ (MS) Ath Trng Working Toward EdD in Curr at Duquesne Univ; *cr:* Shade Cntrl City lth, Ath Trng Tchr 1983-84; Bellefonte HS Hlth, Ath Trng Tchr 86; Somerset HS Hlth, Ath Trng Tchr1986-92; Duquesne Univ Prof Trng 1992-; *ai:* Past Coach; Stu Ath Trainers, HS Ski Club, Chrldng Practice Plan Comm; Clinical Coord; Natl Ath Trainers 1982-; PA Ath ers Assn 1982-, Liaison to Spec Olympics, Govt Affairs; NEA, PSEA ; PA Spec Olympics 1984-, Med Coord; Somerset Ambulance Assn , Bd; Recognized by Dean of Hlth Scis for Outstdng Tchr 1993-95; es Pub; Submitted Awd of Prof Grants for Stu, Prof Rsrch; *office:* esne Univ 120 Health Sciences Bldg 600 Forbes Ave Pittsburgh PA

T, MYRA SCHNEIDER, Language Arts Teacher; *b:* Brooklyn, NY; wis; *c:* Steven, Stacey; *ed:* Univ of CT (BA) Span 1967; 30 Credit Grad Stud; *cr:* Town of Norwalk 7th-12th Grd Span Tchr 1967-68; of Dedham 10th-12th Grd Span Tchr 1968-70; Town of E Hartford 8th Grd Span Tchr 1970-72; Town of Newington Tchr of 7th & 8th Gifted & Lang Arts 1987-; *ai:* Stu Asst Team; Mentor Pgm; NEA ; ADK 1993-; *office:* John Wallace MS 71 Halleran Dr Newington CT

T, REGINA J. HEGENBART, Social Studies Tchr & Chairman; *b:* klyn, NY; *c:* Thomas J.; *ed:* Notre Dame Coll (BA) His 1962; lyn Coll of the City Univ of NY (MS) Ed 1970; Sophia Univ at Tokyo Asian Stud; Advanced Catechetical Cert Diocese of Rockville Ctr; S 30K NY City Pub Schl System Common Branch Subjects Tchr 67; Goppingen Elem & Jr HS Tchr 1967-69; PS 15K NY City Pub System Tchr, Trainer & Acting Asst Prin 1969-73; Sacred Heart Schl Grd Soc Stud & Rdng Tchr 1986-; *ai:* Stu Svc Adv; Soc Stud Dept n; Calendar & Fine Arts Comm; Natl Jr Honor Soc Adv; Nassau Rdng 1992-; Cath League for Rel & Civil Rights 1994-; BSA 1980-, Chprsn rit Badge Cnslr; Nassau Cty Homemakers Cncl 1977-; Sacred Heart Lay Support Comm; Nassau Cty Bar Assn Bicentennial Quilt Project; Dedicated Svc to Youth; Outstanding Tchr Aw 1995; *office:* Sacred Schl 730 Merrick Ave North Merrick NY 11566

T, SHARON ALBAN, English Teacher; *b:* Hazleton, PA; *c:* Jessica, ; *ed:* East Stroudsburg (BA) Eng Ed 1971; *cr:* Northern Burlington Jr-Sr HS Eng Tchr 1971-; *ai:* Newspaper Adv; Drama Coach; pline Comm; NJEA 1971-; BCEA 1971-, Exec Cncl Grievance Comm Liaison Rep; *office:* Northern Burlington Reg HS 160 Mansfield Rd umbus NJ 08022

TER, BONNIE FOX, French Teacher; *b:* Newark, NJ; *m:* Gerald H.; ayna Lynne, Randy Scott; *ed:* Douglass Coll, Rutgers Univ (BA) Fr, Ed 1976; Montclair St (MA) Admin, Supervision 1983; *cr:* Midland HS Fr Tchr 1977-; Fairlawn Jewish Ctr Music Tchr 1985-95; Temple Rishon Hebrew Schl Tchr 1985-91; *ai:* Fr Club Adv; Schl Level ing Comm; MPEA, NJEA, NEA 1977-; FLENJ; AATF; Radburn Schl 1990-; Thomas Jefferson MS PTO 1996; Temple Beth Sholom 1983-, MPEA Hnr Awd 10 & 15 Yrs Svc; Jewish Ed Beth Rishon Tchr of Yr; Midland Park HS 250 Prospect St Midland Park NJ 07432*

TUKIS, BARBARA WYNN, Principal; *b:* Washington, DC; *m:* ; *c:* Jaime, Gabrielle; *ed:* Bloomsburg Univ (BS) Elem Ed 1972; eigh Dickinson (MA) Human Dev 1978; 60 Post Grad Stud Hrs Jersey St Coll; *cr:* Franklin Elem Schl Grd 5-6 Lang Arts Tchr 1972-73, Grd f-Contained Tchr 1973-78, Grd 4 Self-Contained Tchr 1979-81, itional 2nd Grd Tchr 1981-82, Grd 2 Self-Contained Tchr 1982-87, 4 Self-Contained Tchr 1987-88, Grd 7 Math, Rdg, Soc St Tchr 91, Grd 8 Alg, Pre Alg, Math Tchr 1991-92, Prin 1992-; *ai:* FEA, , NEA 1972-92; NJP, SA, SCAA, ASCD 1992-; *office:* Franklin Elem 50 Washington Ave Franklin NJ 07416

UT, JANE M. RIFENBERG, Art Teacher; *b:* Brooklyn, NY; *c:* d J.; *ed:* NYC Comm Coll (AAS) Commercial Art 1968; Brooklyn BA) Fine Arts 1978; New York Univ (MA) Studio Art 1986; St Joseph Ed Courses 9 Credit Hrs 1987; Bd of Ed Inservice Cmptr Course 1988; sborough Comm Coll Cmptr 4 Credit Hrs 1994; LaSalle Univ nced Placement Studio Art 3 Credit Hrs 1994; Ldrshp Prgm Substance e Prevention 1994; *cr:* St Maurs Intnl Schl Art Tchr 1970; Good herd Schl Art Tchr 1979-82; Our Lady Help of Chrstns Schl Art Tchr -82; Bishop Kearney HS Art Tchr 1982-; *ai:* Yrbk Moderator 1983-87; ography Club Moderator 1988-91; NAEA, Cath Fine Arts Soc 1980-; A 1972-; Lay Fac Assn 1982-; St Francis Coll Outstdng Contribution Certs 1991-92, 1994; Art Shows 1985, 1996, 1988; Group Shows , 1979, 1982-84, 1986, 1988-90; *office:* Bishop Kearney HS 2202 60th ooklyn NY 11204*

VCAN, JOHN C., Physics, Math & Cmptrs Teacher; *b:* Erie, PA; *m:* Liebler; *c:* Jon, Joan Cooper, Jill; *ed:* Gannon Coll (BS) Physics ; Gannon Univ (MS) Physics & Math 1970; Cmptrs Prgmng & ications Stud; *cr:* Union City HS Math Tchr 1963-66; Strong Vincent hysics, Math & Cmptrs Tchr 1966-; Gannon Univ Physics & Cmptr ications Tchr 1979-; *ai:* Prom Banquet; Grad Announcements, Cap & n Oders & Ceremony; Sci Dept Chprsn; Dist Tech & Curr Comm; , NEA & PSEA 1970-; AAPT 1980-; Univ of Chicago Math Project ; ASCD; Apostleship of the Sea 1990-; Wasatch Cmptr Lab Supvr; Dev & Achvmts Articles Pub in Local Paper; Erie Rotary Club Lab ch; Oustanding Tchr Awd; *office:* Strong Vincent HS 1330 W 8th St PA 16502*

YER, GEORGE HENRY, Spanish Teacher; *b:* Boston, MA; *m:* Elaine ayer Hahren; *c:* George M., Kevin M.; *ed:* Northeastern Univ (BA) Fgn 1950; 40 Hrs Grad Courses Emmanuel Coll, Bridgewater St Tchrs & Quincy Jr Coll; *cr:* Weymouth HS Span Tchr 1962-; *ai:* Var Bsktbl Ftbl Coach 19 Yrs; Ftbl Scouting; Span Club Adv 10 Yrs; Evaluation m 7 Yrs; MTA 1962-; NEA 1962-; WTA 1962-; Immaculate eption Mens Choir 1977-; Wollaston Glee Club 1992-94; St Vincent ul Soc 19991. 1994 & 1995; Pro Bsbl Player 8 Yrs; Milwaukee Braves 5 Yrs; Detroit Tigers Org 2 Yrs; Mex Central League Pitcher; MA Bsbl hes Hall of Fame; WHS Hall of Fame Charter Mem.*

ASNICK, ALAN L., American History Teacher; *b:* Cleveland, OH; Alice Brsepke; *c:* Erika, Elizabeth; *ed:* OH St Univ (BS) prehensive Soc Stud 1967, (MA) Amer His 1968; 45 Addl Grad Hrs; *cr:* Norwalk HS Soc Stud Tchr, Dept Chm 1968-; *ai:* Jr Class Adv 5 Yrs; Sr Class Adv 7 Yrs; Former Ftbl, Vlybl Coach; Dist Ath Dir 5 Yrs; Charter Mem Prins Advy Comm; NEA 1968-; Norwalk Tchrs Assn 1968-, Pres, VP; United Way 1979-, Vol; Huron Cty Sheriff's Dept 1970-, Vol Spec Deputy; Natl Amateur Sftbl Assn 1976-, Umpire, Huron Cty Umpire-in-Chief; First Presbyn Church 1963-, Ruling Elder 1981-; BSA, Citizenship Adv 1968-; Univ of WY Robert Loe Outstdng Amer His Tchr Flwshp 1970; Bowling Green St Univ Jennings Scholar Flwshp 1976-77; Wrote Weekly Newspaper Column 1982-83; Univ of Toledo Robert Taft Inst of Govt Flwshp 1979; *office:* Norwalk HS 80 E Main St Norwalk OH 44857

PLERHOPLES, JUDITH STEINMANN, Bio, Chem & Life Skills Tchr; *b:* Newton, NJ; *m:* William; *c:* William, Timothy, Christina; *ed:* Douglass Coll at Rutgers U (BS) Bio 1972; Elmira Coll (MS) Bio, Ed 1981; 90 Addl Hrs Ed Admin; *cr:* Corning Painted Post West HS Sci Tchr 1974-76; Corning Comm Coll Math Instr 1985; Corning Painted Post East Sci Tchr 1987-90; Corning Painted Post West HS Sci Tchr 1990-; *ai:* Acad All Stars Coach 1987-; AFT 1976-; Corning Philharmonic 1976-, VP 3 Yrs; Suzuki Violin Assn 1976-; *office:* Corning Painted Post West HS Victory Hwy Painted Post NY 14870*

PLESA, BOZICA, English Teacher; *b:* Zagreb, Croatia; *m:* Richard Meades; *ed:* Mc Gill Univ (BA) Ger 1972; Queen's Univ (BED) Ger, Fr 1973; Concordia Univ (TESL) Eng 1979; Recreation, Outdoor Ed 18 Credits; *cr:* Verdun Cath HS Fr Tchr 1974-75; E. S. St Thomas Schl Eng Tchr 1975-81; E. S. Jean XXIII Schl Eng Tchr 1981-; *ai:* Eng Variety Show.

PLESNIARSKI, JAMES MAYFRED, Assistant Principal; *b:* Oneida, NY; *m:* Elizabeth LaGreca; *c:* Amber, Courtne, Natali; *ed:* St Univ of NY at Oswego (BS) Industrial Arts Ed 1973; St Univ of NY at Cortland (CAS) (MS) Educl Admin 1992; *ai:* Youth Ice Hockey Coach; NEA; ASCD; *office:* Sherburne-Earlville Cntrl Schl 15 Utica St Hamilton NY 13346

PLESNITZER, ROBERT, Chemistry Teacher; *b:* Brooklyn, NY; *m:* Diane Janette Stecyk; *c:* Kristin, Eric; *ed:* Univ of Toledo (BS) Chem 1967; 48 Post Grad Credits St John's Univ; *cr:* Mobil Oil Corp Analytical Chemist 1967-69; South Side HS Chem Instr 1969-; *ai:* Var Golf Coach; STANYS 1973-; Amer Chem Soc 1984-; Malverne Oaks Civic Assn 1983-, Treas; *home:* 1089 Walden Pl West Hempstead NY 11552*

PLESSL, MARIA ANGELISANTI, German Teacher; *b:* Reading, PA; *m:* Ted William; *c:* Tanja, Thomas; *ed:* Millersville Univ (BS) Scndry Ed, Ger 1974; Lehigh Univ (MED) Scndry Ed, Ger 1978; Philipps Univ 36 Credit Hrs Ger Stud Abroad Prgm; Muhlenberg Coll Span Cert; Cedar Crest Coll 24 Credit Hrs Tchr Dev Prgms; *cr:* Palmerton HS Ger Tchr 1974-, Frgn Lang Dept Chprsn 1976-84; Mid Statis Comm Mem 1988-89, Tchr Induction Coord, Prof Dev Comm Mem 1988-; *ai:* Mentor Tchr; Tchr Induction, Prof Dev Comm Mem; NEA 1974-; ACTFL 1988-; Yrbk Dedication Awd; Ger, Austria, Switzerland Summer Tours Spon for Stdnts, Adults.*

PLESSNER, VON RODERICK, Professor; *b:* Toledo, OH; *m:* Kathryn Ann; *c:* Bruce, Elizabeth Casper, Eric; *ed:* Northwest St Comm Coll (AAB) Cmptr Programming 1985; The Defiance Coll (BS) Bus 1988; Univ of Toledo (MBA) Bus 1990; *cr:* Northwest St Comm Coll Prof 1984-; *ai:* Accounting, Mgmt, Para Legal Dept Chair; ACBSP 1990-; Master Tchr Awd.*

PLETCHER, DUANE K., English Department Supervisor; *b:* Brookville, PA; *m:* Carole H.; *c:* Megan A. Himes, Brooke L.; *ed:* Clarion Univ (BS) Comprehensive Eng 1966; St Bonaventure Univ (MS) Ed, Admin 1990; Grad Stud Gannon Univ, Southern OR St Coll; *cr:* Bradford Area Schls Instr, Dept Supvr 29 Yrs; Jamestown Comm Coll Adj Prof 4 Yrs; *ai:* NCTE 1989-; NEA, PSEA 1967-; PASSP 1990-; *office:* Bradford Area Schls 81 Interstate Pky Bradford PA 16701*

PLEWINSKI, RONALD B., 4th Grade Teacher; *b:* Buffalo, NY; *m:* Joanna Zarajczyk; *c:* Christopher, Jeffrey, David, Pamela Gerace, Alison Pangrazzio, Ronnie, Gillian; *ed:* Buffalo St Tchrs (BA) Elem Ed & Jr HS Lang 1960, (MA) Elem Ed 1963; Elem Principalship Supervision Deg 1965; *cr:* Pine Hill Schl 5th Grd Tchr 1960-68; Union East Schl 4th Grd Tchr 1968-; Summer Schl K-6th Grd Tchr 1996; *ai:* Cmptr Work; Book It; Rdng with Partners; Assembly Prgms; Vol Studio Arena, Shea's Buffalo, Kleinhens Music Hall; NEA, Tchrs Assn, NYS Tchrs Assn, PTSA 1960-; Pius X Church; *office:* Union East Elem Schl 3550 Union Rd Cheektowaga NY 14225

PLITT, VICKIE LYNN, Physical Educator; *b:* Westminster, MD; *ed:* Western MD Coll (BS) PE 1990; Hlth Edctr Cert; *cr:* Glen Burnie HS PE Tchr 1992-95; Jessup Elem Schl PE Tchr 1995-; *ai:* Bsktbl Coach; NEA, MSTA 1991-; *office:* Jessup Elem 2900 Jessup Rd Jessup MD 20794

PLONSKI, JOSEPHINE SKLANKA, Math Teacher; *b:* Scranton, PA; *m:* Frank; *c:* Frank, David; *ed:* Bloomsburg Univ (BS) Spec Ed 1968; Post Grad Stud Penn St Univ, Temple Univ; *cr:* Montgomery Cty Intermediate Unit Interpreter 1987-89; St Stanislaus Elem Schl Tchr 1989-; *ai:* Cath Schls Week Chm; NCEA 1989-; Amer Soc Deaf Children 1980-; Eucharistic Minister 1995-; Tchr of Yr 1994.*

PLOSKUNAK, J. ROBERT, Architectural Drafting Instr; *b:* Latrobe, PA; *m:* Mary Louise Schreiber; *c:* Christopher, Michael, Matthew, Amy, Robert; *ed:* Univ of Pittsburgh Voc Ed 1980; *cr:* Turtle Creek HS Mechanical Design Tchr 1980-88; Woodland Hills HS Architectural Drafting, Design Tchr 1988-; *ai:* Tech, Voc Dept Chm; PSEA, NEA 1990-; ITEA 1992-; ACIAA 1982-; Plum Zoning Bd 1994-; Fac Advy Bd 1992-; Mentor Tchr 1995-; *office:* Woodland Hills HS 2550 Greensburg Pike Pittsburgh PA 15221

PLOSS, ROBERT W., 8th Grade Science Teacher; *b:* Geneva, NY; *m:* June C.; *c:* Robin, Timothy, Sarah; *ed:* Cornell Univ (BS) Ag, Animal Sci 1959; 80 Post Grad Hrs Northwestern Univ, SUNY; *cr:* South Seneca Cntrl Schl Mid Schl Sci Tchr 1964-72; Trumansburg Cntrl Schl Elem, MS Sci Tchr 1974-; *ai:* NEANY 1964-; STANYS 1974-; Ford Fnd Grant 1963; NSF Grant 1967, 1970; *office:* Trumansburg MS 100 Whig St Trumansburg NY 14886

PLOTNICK, FRANCES B., 5th Grade Teacher; *b:* Bronx, NY; *m:* Herbert C.; *c:* Ellen Plotnick Ravenelle, Jeffrey Scott; *ed:* Mitchell Coll (AS) Bus 1953; Eastern CT Univ (BS) Ed 1970, (MS) Ed 1972; *cr:* Gales Ferry Elem Schl 4th Grd Tchr 1969-83, 5th Grd Tchr 1983-93; Juliet Long Elem Schl 5th Grd Tchr 1993-; *ai:* Soc Stud, Career Ed, Multi-Culture, Restructuring Comms; Schl Bus Partnership; BEST Prgm; Child Study Team; NEA, CEA 1970-; LEA 1970-, Sec 4 Yrs, Bldg Rep 6 Yrs; PTO, Tchr Rep; March of Dimes 1986-, Team Capt, High Av Team, Indiv; Vol for Isreal 1985-, Army Vol, Appreciation Awd; Tchr of Yr Nom 1989-90; Celebration of Excl Awd; Salvation Army Awd for Humanitarian Efforts in Classroom; *home:* 72 Pollys Ln Uncasville CT 06382*

PLOUFFE, LORRAINE PATRICIA, Medical Division Dept Chair; *b:* Lewiston, ME; *ed:* Saint Josephs Coll (BA) Natural Sci 1968; Cntrl ME Medical Ctr Registered Nurse in ME 1952; Medical Technologist 1960; Nuclear Medical Technologist 1961; *cr:* Cntrl ME Medical Ctr Nurse 1952-53; Mercy Hospital Nurse 1953-55; Madigan Meml Hospital Nurse 1955-57; Coll Stu 1957-60; Mercy Hospital Nuclear Technologist 1961-73; Coll Stu 1967-68; Medical Oncology Lab Supvr 1973-84; Andover Coll Asst Prof of Medical Division 1986-; *ai:* Medical Adv; Lib, Safety & Educl Comms; Red Cross Membership; Amer Soc Clinical Pathology 1961-; Nuclear Medical Tech 1963-; St Nurses Assn 1973-; Amer Red Cross 1987-, Instr, 5 Yr Pin Awd 1994; Portland Comm Chorus & Magic of Christmas Chorus 1978-, Section Ldr; Mercy Hospital 15 Yr Pin; Ed Coord for Nuclear Medicine; *office:* Andover Coll 901 Washington Ave Portland ME 04103

PLOURDE-OUELLET, VALERIE A., History Teacher; *b:* East Hartford, CT; *m:* Robert; *c:* Aaron, Mitchell; *ed:* Univ of ME (BS) Ed Soc Stud & Eng 1979, (MED) Scndry Schl Admin 1982; *cr:* Van Buren Dist Scndry Schl Soc Stud Tchr 1979-81; Comm HS Soc Stud Tchr 1981-; Univ of ME at Fort Kent Adj Instr of Ed 1986-; Northern ME Tech Coll Adj Instr of Soc Sci 1990-; *ai:* SADD Adv; Warrior Words Adv; ME Ed Assn 1979-; NEA 1979-; ME & NCSS 1979-; Northern Anoostook Tchrs Assn 1981-, Bldg Rep; Bus & Prof Womens Club, VP, Past Mem; Amer Assn of Univ Women VP, Past Mem; *office:* Ft Kent Cmty HS 51 Pleasant St Fort Kent ME 04743*

PLUMER, ELIZABETH A., English Teacher & Dept Rep; *b:* Grand Rapids, MI; *ed:* Thiel Coll (BA) His 1962; Penn St (MED) Scndry Ed 1967; Attnd WV Univ, Allegheny Coll, Carnegie Mellon Univ; *cr:* Penn Hills Schl Tchr 1962-63; Trinity Schl Tchr 1963-; *ai:* NHS Adv; Strategic Planning Comm Grad Requirements; Portfolio Dev; Implementation Team; ACT Inservice Planning; NEA, PSEA 1962-; TAEA 1963-; Delta Kappa Gamma 1967-, Pres; Rdng Group 1980-, Chair; Commonwealth Lit, Soc His NEH; Tchr of Yr 1994; *office:* Trinity HS 231 Park Ave Washington PA 15301*

PLUMLEY, ELLEN HOPP, High School Mathematics Tchr; *b:* Paterson, NJ; *m:* John; *c:* Jennifer, John; *ed:* William Paterson Coll (BS) Math & Ed 1979; Montclair St Coll Math & Ed; *cr:* Pinelands Regl HS Math Tchr 1979-88; Southern Regl HS Math Tchr 1988-; *ai:* Math Club; Var Cheerleading Coach; NJEA, NEA 1979-; Stu Cncl Feature Tchr Awd; *office:* Southern Regional HS 600 N Main St Manahawkin NJ 08050*

PLUMMER, EDUOARD E., Mathematics & Soc Studies Tchr; *b:* Ronda, WV; *ed:* W VA St Coll (BA) His 1957; NY St Univ (MA) His 1963; Sorbonne Univ of Paris Cert His, Fr 1959; City Univ of NY City 30 Credits; *cr:* Wadleigh Scndry Schl Tchr 1963-; *ai:* Wadleigh Schlrs Pgm Founder & Dir; NAACP 1959-; Urban League 1960-; Omega Psi Phi 1966-; Xavier High Achvmt Pgm 1965-; Boys Choir of Harlem 1975-; Manhattan Vly 1995-; Honorary Doctorate Glassboro St Coll; 21 Brand Awd; West St Coll Alumnus Awd of the Yr 1985; Pres Citation Awd from L B Johnson; *office:* Wadleigh Scndry Schl 215 W 114th St New York NY 10026*

PLUNKETT, EDWARD J., Jr HS Social Stud Tchr; *b:* Newark, NJ; *ed:* Univ of Notre Dame (BA) Liberal Arts 1961; Attnd NYU & Greek New Schl for Soc Research Adult Ed Courses, US Army Lang Schl Arabic & Seton Hall Univ 27 Credits Toward MA in Eng Lit; *ai:* Stu Cncl, Art Club Moderator; Natl Cath Ed Assn 1984-; Amer Assn of Tchrs of Span & Portuguese 1990-; *office:* Holy Innocents Schl 249 E 17th St Brooklyn NY 11226

PLUNKETT, EILEEN, Earth Science Teacher; *b:* Brooklyn, NY; *ed:* Suffolk Comm Coll (AS) Sci 1978; SUNY at Oswego (BS) Sec Ed, Sci 1980; SUNY at Binghamton (MSEd) Sec Ed, Sci 1986; 13 Credits Coll of St Rose at Albany, Hamilton Coll at Clinton, IN univ of PA, Cornell Univ at Ithaca, No AZ Univ at Flagstaff, So IL Univ at Edwardsville; *cr:* Cntrl Schls HS Sci Tchr 1981-82; Deposit Ctl Schls HS Sci Tchr, Sci Chprsn 1982-; *ai:* Cl of 90, 94, 97 Adv; HS Yrbk; Weather Watch Team; Dino Diggers Field Rsrch Group; Natl Sci Tchrs Assn 1989-, Local Ldr; Natl Earth Sci Tchrs Assn, Sci Tchrs Assn of NY St, Dinamation Intl Soc 1990-; AFT, NYSUT 1982-; Deposit Tchrs Assn 1982; HS Shared Decision Making Team, BOCES Earth Sci Mentor, BOCES Sci Steering Comm 1994-; Tchr Ctr Tech Comm 1996; DTA Newsletter Co-Ed 1990-; DCS Tchr of Yr Nom 1994; Presidential Awd Excl in Sci & Math Tchng Nom 1996; Panelist Binghamton Univ Women in Sci, Math & Engrng Prgm; Sec Sci Rep Binghamton Univ SUNY Career Day; Presenter STANYS 1995; NSTA 1992-94, 1996; In-Svc Taught Through Tchr Ctr; *office:* Deposit Cntrl Schls 171 2nd St Deposit NY 13754*

PLUNKETT, MARIE SARRIS, Bio, Anatomy & Physiology Tchr; *b:* Norwood, MA; *c:* Christa; *ed:* Framingham St Coll (BS) Bio & Chem 1988; Worcester Polytech Inst Working Towards MS Bio-Chem; *cr:* Framingham North HS Chem Tchr 1988-89; Natick HS Bio, Anatomy & Physiology 1994-; *ai:* MTA 1994-; Women Tech & Sci Pgm Lexington Mid Man HS; Tri Beta Bio Hnr Soc Lifetime Mem.

PLUNKETT, PAUL H., US His & American Govt Tchr; *b:* Eldorado, IL; *m:* Marian Jean; *c:* Michael, Julie; *ed:* Southern IL Univ (BA) His 1969; Grace Theological Seminary (MA) Chrstn Schl Admin 1987; *cr:* Springfield Chrstn Schl Tchr, Admin 1983-; Carehouse Schl Assoc Headmaster 1993-94; *ai:* Drama Group; *office:* Springfield Christian Schl 627 State St Springfield MA 01109

PLUSS, JACQUES ANTHONY, Associate Prof of His & Hum; *b:* Zurich, Switzerland; *c:* Rebecca Anne; *ed:* Lafayette Coll (BA) His 1975; Cambridge Univ (LIB) Roman Law 1980; Univ of Chicago (PhD) Medieval His 1983; Post Grad Stud Ancient Near Eastern Stud Oriental Inst 1975-77; *cr:* Univ of Chicago Instr 1981-84; William Patterson Coll Assoc Prof 1984-; *ai:* Episcopal Church Vestryman; Honors Prgm Coord; His Club Adv; Natl Assn of Scholars 1989-; Medieval Acad of Amer 1979-; Pub Articles Prof Journals 1986, 1989; *office:* William Paterson Coll 300 Pompton Rd Wayne NJ 07470

PLUTA, JOHN WILLIAM, US History & Government Tchr; *b:* Afton, NY; *m:* Virginia Magura; *c:* Elizabeth Lee; *ed:* Oswego St (BA) Ed & His 1974; 39 Credit Hrs Rdng, Effective Tchng & His; *cr:* Harpersville Schls 5th & 6th Grd Tchr 1974-81, 7th, 8th & 10th Grd His Tchr 1981-86; Norwich HS 11th Grd US His & Govt Tchr & Head Ftbl Coach 1989-; *ai:* Var Ftbl Coach; Asst Track Coach; NHS Comm; NY St HS Ftbl Coaches Assn 1994-; NEA 1994-; NY St Section IV Ftbl Coach of the Yr 1992; Binghamton Ftbl Coaches Clinic Coach of the Yr 1992; *office:* Norwich HS Midland Dr Norwich NY 13815

PLYBON, JOHN D.,JR., Construction Trades Teacher; *b:* Paris, KY; *m:* Linda; *c:* Hillary, Hannah; *ed:* Morehead St (BS) Indstrl Ed 1982, (MA) HPER 1983; VOED Kent St 1994; *cr:* Orrville HS LD Tutor 1983-84; Lorin Andrews Indstrl Ed Tchr 1984-90; Massillon WA HS Construction Trades Tchr 1990-; *ai:* Frosh Ftbl Coord; Girls Track; VICA Adv; Chemical Awareness Prgm; NEA, OEA, OITEA 1984-; VICA 1990-; Sports Hall of Fame 1990-, VP; Heartland Ed Tech Planning Comm; Founded OHS Sports Hall of Fame; *office:* Massillon Washington HS 1 Paul E Brown Dr SE Massillon OH 44646

PLYLER, ROBERT W., Social Studies & English Tchr; *b:* Butler, PA; *m:* E. Anne Davis; *c:* Christian R., Garth O., Laura A.; *ed:* Alleghany Coll (BA) His 1970, (MA) Eng 1971; Attnd St Univ Coll at Fredonia & Durham Univ England Post Grad Stud; *cr:* Mercyhurst Coll His & Eng Tchr 1985-90; Jamestown Post Journal Art Critic 1981-; Chautauqua Inst Dev Writer 1989-; Jamestown Comm Coll His, Eng & Music Prof 1990-; Maple Grove HS Eng & Soc Stud Tchr 1971-; *ai:* Jr & Sr Honor Soc Adv; Honors Comm Mem; NEA 1971-, Pres of Local 1980; NY St Cncl for Soc Stud 1983-; Jamestown Concert Assn 1982-, Pres 3 Yrs, Plaque for Outstanding Support of Arts; St Lukes Episcopal Church 1980-, Vestry; Bd of Dir, Das Puppenspiel Puppet Theatre 1995-; Rochester Inst of Tech Honor for Outstanding Tchng; Chautauqua town Meeting in Latvia Del; Selected by Columbia Univ for Conf on Macedonia; Armonk Institute, Study & Travel in Germany 1995; *office:* Maple Grove HS Dutch Hollow Rd Bemus Point NY 14712

PLYTER, CHARLES C., 6th Grade Teacher; *b:* Newark, NY; *c:* Laura, Charles; *ed:* Attnd SUNY at Brockport, SUNY at Geneseo; *cr:* Madison Cntrl Schls 5th Grd Tchr 3 Yrs; Canandaigua City Schls 6th Grd Tchr 32 Yrs; *ai:* AFT 1961-, VP, Negetiater; Ontario Cty Yth Bd 1993-; *office:* Canandaigua Elem Schl Granger St Canandaigua NY 14424

POCIUS, FRANK LEON, Mathematics Teacher; *b:* Riverside, NJ; *ed:* Drexel Univ (BS) Physics 1969, (MS) Physics 1971; *cr:* Moorestown HS Math & Physics Tchr 1971-; *ai:* Educl Systems for Tchng, Counting & Equation Solving Strategies Patent 1991; *office:* Moorestown HS Bridgeboro Rd Moorestown NJ 08057*

POCKLEMBO, ANN MARIE ELIZABETH, Orchestra Director; *b:* Plainfield, NJ; *ed:* Rutgers Univ (BM) Violin Performance 1991; Northwestern Univ (MM) Music Ed 1993; Attnd Southern Meth Univ; *cr:* Monroe-Woodbury HS Orch Dir 1993-; *ai:* Strolling Strings Dir; All-Cty HS Orch Chprsn; MENC 1994-; Amer String Tchrs Assn 1993-; Natl Schl Orch Assn 1995; AFT 1993-; Amer Fed of Musicians 1986-; Midwest String Tchr Conf OH St Univ; *home:* 496 Plainfield Rd Edison NJ 08820

POCOCK, ELIZABETH JANE GOODWIN, Retired Elementary Teacher; *b:* Hackensack, NJ; *m:* Richard C.; *c:* Steven R., Richard D., Daniel B.; *ed:* Houghton Coll (BA) Eng 1956; SUNY at Geneseo Perm Cert Eng 1974; 37 Credit Hrs; *cr:* Hammondsport C. Schl HS Eng 1956-58; Houghton Coll Part-time Eng, Frosh, Jr-Sr Lit Tchr 1959-66; Friendship C. Schl Intermediate El Tchr 1969-95; *ai:* RAP Comm; NYS Eng; NYSUT 1959-95, Publicity Mem; NYSUT 1959-, Schlsp Comm; Plaque Working Stdnts Historical Writing Contests; *home:* 7356 Campus Heights Rd Houghton NY 14744

PODCZASY, ANTHONY PETER,JR., Science Teacher; *b:* Kingston, PA; *m:* Mary Lynda Durkin; *c:* Stephanie; *ed:* King's Coll (BS) Bio 1977; Earth Sci Cert Bloomsburg Univ; Grad Credits Univ of Scranton Ed, Wilkes Univ Cmptr Tech, Univ of Cntrl FL Aerospace Ed; *cr:* Hanover Area Schl Dist Tchr 1977-; Luzerne Cty Comm Coll Instr 1990-; *ai:* PA Jr Acad of Sci Region 2 Dir; Sr Class Adv; Staff Dev Comm Coord; Mid Sts Steering Comm Chm; Project LEARN Steering Comm; PSEA, NEA 1977-; NSTA 1990-; LCSTA 1977-, Pres; PAS; Knights of Columbus 1994-, Recorder; Excl Tchng Awd; *office:* Hanover Area Jr Sr HS 1600 Sans Souci Pkwy Wilkes Barre PA 18702*

PODER, FRANK, 8th Grade Social Studies Tchr; *b:* Pittston, PA; *m:* Diane Barnovsky; *c:* Cody John; *ed:* Kings Coll (BA) Soc Stud 1973; 48 Grad Credits; *cr:* Tunkhannock Area Schl Dist 8th Grd Soc Stud Tchr 1973-; *ai:* Soc Stud Coord; Stu Assistance Team Mem; PSEA, NEA 1973-; *office:* Tunkhannock Area MS Philadelphia Ave Tunkhannock PA 18657

PODKRASH-VEGA, CAROL ANN, Social Studies, Lang Arts Tchr; *b:* Brooklyn, NY; *c:* Daisy, Nancy; *ed:* Boricua Coll (BS) Ed 1987; *cr:* Lexington Schl for Deaf Asst 1985-86; Our Lady of Lourdes Tchr 1986-; *ai:* 8th Grd Cnslr; *office:* Our Lady Of Lourdes Schl 2-12 Aberdeen St Brooklyn NY 11207

PODOL, PETER L., Professor of Spanish; *b:* Chicago, IL; *m:* Joanne Cohen; *c:* Michael, B. Rachel Beckwith; *ed:* Univ of PA (BA) Span 1963; Columbia Univ (MA) Span 1964; Univ of PA (PHD) Span 1968; *cr:* Lincoln Univ Span Instr 1966-68; Dickinson Coll Span, Italian Asst Prof 1968-73; Lock Haven Univ Span Prof 1973-; *ai:* Dept Chair; Mem Univ-Wide Promotins Comm; MLA, AATSP 1966-; NEMLA 1976-; Penn St Tennis Club, St Coll Comm Theater 1973-; Metropolitan Opera Guild 1964-; 2 Books Fernando Arrabal; 5 Essays in Books Antonin Artrud, Contemporary Span Theater, Playwrights, Film etc; 44 Journal Articles; Numerous Book Reviews, Papers Presented Prof Confs; *office:* Lock Haven Univ Lock Haven PA 17745

PODOLAK, JOSEPH J., Math & Physics Teacher; *b:* Rochester, PA; *m:* Lana Ancrile; *c:* Amie; *ed:* Clarion Univ (BS) Comprehensive Sci 1970; 42 Post Grad Credit Hrs; *cr:* Western HS Tchr 1970-; *office:* Western Beaver HS 216 Engle Rd Industry PA 15052

PODWIKA, JOHN EDWARD, 4th Grade Teacher; *b:* New Britain, CT; *m:* Carol; *c:* Dyanne; *ed:* East Stroudsburg (MS) Elem Ed 1966; *cr:* Nazareth Area Schl Dist Tchr 1966-; *ai:* Cross Cnty, Track Head Coach; *home:* 311 Allen Dr Northampton PA 18067

POE, DIANE ROBERSON, Family & Consumer Sci Tchr; *b:* Maysville, KY; *m:* Richard; *c:* Sarah, Jonathon; *ed:* Eastern KY Univ (BS) Voc Home Ec 1979; Univ of KY (MS) Voc Home Ec 1982; Addl 15 Hrs Beyond Masters; *cr:* Newport City Schls Home Ec Tchr 1980-82; Blanchester Schls Home Ec Tchr 1983-84; Washington City Schls Home Ec Tchr 1984-; *ai:* FHA Adv; Voc Dept Head; Tchr Mentor; NEA 1984-; AHEA 1988-; Tiger Club 1995-, Ldr; 4-H 1996-, Adv; Church 1987-, Sunday Schl Tchr; *home:* 6533 Greenfield-Sabina Rd Sabina OH 43160

POE, LARRY WAYNE, World Literature Teacher; *b:* Parkersburg, WV; *m:* Rebecca Lynn; *c:* Joshua, Jason, Lindsay; *ed:* Glenville St Coll (BA) Eng 1973; WV Univ Amer His; WV Grad Coll Hum; *cr:* Wood Cty WV Schls Sub Tchr 1974-76; Belpre City Schls Eng & Hum Tchr 1977-; *ai:* Belpre HS Jr Class Adv; Global Summit Team Adv; Saturday Schl Monitor; NEA 1974-; Belpre Ed Assn 1976-, VP 1978; Bloodmobile Vol; *office:* Belpre HS Stone Rd Belpre OH 45714

POETAIN, CHARLES A., Assistant Professor of Math; *b:* Pittsburgh, PA; *m:* Fidelisa M.; *c:* Angeline Yu, Julia; *ed:* Univ of Pittsburgh (BS) Math 1978; Carnegie Mellon Univ (MS) Math 1979; Worked Toward Doctorate in Math at SUNY; *cr:* St Vincents Coll Math Instr 1986-87; Trinity Schl Math Tchr 1987-88; Comm Coll of Allegheny Cty Asst Prof 1989-; *ai:* AFT 1990-; *office:* Comm Coll Algny Co Algny Cmps 808 Ridge Ave Pittsburgh PA 15212

POETH, MARK B., 5th Grade Teacher; *b:* Williamsport, PA; *m:* Carol Lynn Prowant; *c:* Casey, Matthew, Lauren; *ed:* Bloomsburg Coll (BS) Elem Ed 1978; Marywood Coll (MF) Elem Ed 1984; *cr:* Montgomery Area Schl Dist Elem Tchr 1979-; *ai:* Asst Tennis Coach Girls Var Prog & Girls Bsktbl Coach; PSEA 1979-; NEA 1979-; MAEA 1979; Huntersville Bible Bapt Church 1985-, Deacon; *home:* RR 1 Box 2405 Hughesville PA 17737

POFF, HARVEY EDWARD, Criminal Justice Instructor; *b:* Lebanon, OH; *m:* Doris Rae; *c:* Katrina, Kasey, William, Leigh-Ann; *ed:* Sinclair Comm Coll (AAS) Law Enforcement 1977; Univ of Cincinnati (BS) Ed 1984; Univ of Dayton (MS) Ed Admin 1993; 12 Sem Grad Hrs at Univ of Dayton, OH Voc Ed Ldrshp Inst 1996; 6 Sem Hrs Towards Asst Supt Cert at Univ of Dayton; *cr:* Montgomery Cty Joint Voc Schl Instr 1976-77; Butler Cty Joint Voc Schl Instr 1991-; *ai:* Law Enforcement Color Guard Adv; OH Voc Ed Assn, Amer Voc Assn 1994-; Middletown Safety Cncl 1978-, Past Pres, Carel Cosby Awd; City of Middletown 1987-91, City Commissioner; *office:* D Russel Lee Career Ctr 3603 Hamilton Middletown Rd Hamilton OH 45011

POFFENBERGER, HOWARD WILMER, Coord of Auto Tech & Collision; *b:* Hagerstown, MD; *m:* Janet L. Henson; *c:* Scott; *ed:* Univ of MD (MS) T & I 1977; *cr:* S Hagerstown HS Instr 24 Yrs; Career Stud Ctr Instr 4 Yrs, Coord 2 Yrs; *ai:* Schl Improvement Team; Awds Comm; Auto, Manufacturing Team Ldr; WCTA, MSTA, NEA 1968-; *office:* WA Co Career Stud Ctr 50 W Oak Ridge Dr Hagerstown MD 21740

POGEL, ALAN F., Economics & Soc Problems Tchr; *b:* Niagara Falls, NY; *m:* Mary C. Jasper; *ed:* Valparaiso Univ (BS) Bus 1977, (JD) Law 1982; Niagara Univ (MS) Ed 1993; Trng in Conflict Resolution, Peer Mediation, Therapeutic Intervention, Coaching Skills & Philosophy; *cr:* Valparaiso Univ Developmental Rdng Tchr & Tutor 1977-78; Porter Starke Svcs Inpatient Therapist 1979-82; Town of Niagara Recreation Supvr 1982-92; Niagara Wheatfield HS Tchr 1982-; *ai:* Var Ftbl & Girls Track Coach; FCA Local Huddle Adv; Jerry Butler Aths in Action Camp Cnslr; Weightlifting Club Adv; NYSUT, AFT 1993-; West NY Ftbl Coaches Assn 1985-; Delta Theta Phi 1980-; Amer Bar Assn, Former Meme; Friends of Natl Parks of Gettysburg 1992-; Porter Cty Mental Hlth Assn 1981-82, Former Bd Mem; Colonial Heights First Meth Church; Empire St Tchrs Fellowship Recipient; Author Recommendations to IN St Legistlature on Treatment of Chronically Mentally Ill; Invited Summer Participant Pub Television Inst on Use of Media in Ed; *office:* Niagara Wheatfield Sr HS 2292 Saunders Settlement Rd Sanborn NY 14132

POGUE, LINDA KHOURI, Teacher; *b:* Wilkinsburg, PA; *m:* James N.; *c:* Jennifer; *ed:* Edinboro Univ (BS) Scndry Eng 1970; Edinboro 24 Credit Hrs Educl Psych; *cr:* Westinghouse HS Tchr 1970-73; Brashear HS Tchr 1974; *ai:* Drill Team 1978-80; Yrbk Adv 1987-88; PFT, AFT 1970-.

POHL, DORIS NEILL, Junior High Science Teacher; *b:* Paterson, NJ; *w:* Frederick B. (dec); *c:* Lisa Pohl Converse, Holly, Kristy; *cr:* Maple Rd Schl 7th Grd Team Tchr 1969-73; Ringwood Chrstn Schl 7th & 8th Grd Math & Sci Tchr 1980-; *ai:* Sci Fair Coord; Stu Cncl Adv; Math Team Coach; *office:* Ringwood Christian Schl 30 Carletondale Rd Ringwood NJ 07456

POHLMAN, BEN J., Occupational Work Adj Teacher; *b:* Fostoria, OH; *m:* Wanda June Richendollar; *c:* Clifford J., Timothy J., Steven J.; *ed:* Bowling Green Univ (BS) Soc Stud Com 1971; Attnd OH St Voc Tchng Cert, Findlay Univ Voc Math Tchng Cert; *cr:* Elmwood HS OWA Coord 1971-72; Fostoria HS OWA Coord 1972-; *ai:* NEA, OEA 1986-; Fostoria Lions Club 1983-, Pres 1988-89, Sec 1990-, Zone 2 Chair 1996-98; *office:* Fostoria HS 1001 Park Ave Fostoria OH 44830

POIESZ, PAUL JOSEPH, Math Teacher & Track Coach; *b:* Philadelphia, PA; *m:* Carolyn M Poiesz; *c:* Matthew, Megan, Kaitlin; *ed:* LaSalle Univ (BA) Ec 1982; Beaver Coll (MED) Ed 1995; *cr:* Bishop McDevitt HS Math Ec Tchr & Track Coach 1982-; LaSalle Univ Math Prof Evening 1994-; *ai:* Mens Cross Cntry Coach 1980-; Womens Cross Cntry Coach 1992-; Womens Ath Dir 1983-89; NCEA, ACT 1982-; PA Track Coaches Assn 1980-, Hall of Fame Chrm, All-St Selection Comm, 1993, 1995; Boys Track Coach of Yr; Philadelphia Cath League Coaches Assn 1980-, VP; Bishop McDevitt HS Staff Person of Yr 1989; *office:* Bishop Mc Devitt HS 125 Royal Ave Wyncote PA 19095

POINDEXTER, DAVID EMORY, 6th Grade Teacher; *b:* Philadelphia, PA; *ed:* Antioch Univ (BA) Elem Ed 1985, (MED) Spec Ed 1988; Attnd Univ of PA, St Joseph's Univ, Gratz Coll, Philadelphia Coll of Textiles, West Chester St Univ; Univ of the Arts; *cr:* Mike Douglas Show KYW-TV Production Asst 1971-79; Reynolds Elem Schl Tchr 1982-84; Harrington Elem Schl Tchr 1984-92; Elkins Park Elem Schl Tchr 1992-; Univ of Arts Tchr 1994-; *ai:* Bus Mgr; Music Comm; St Thomas Church Ed Comm; RHO Chptr; Alpha Phi Alpha Inc; NEA, AFT 1984-; Alpha Phi Alpha 1989-; Camp Summer Love 1994-, Bd Mem; Mt Carmel Human Svc Dev Corp; Palmer Funeral Home 1982- Bd Mem; Tchr of Yr Awd; St Thomas Church Acolyte Guild 25, 30 Yr Svc Awd, Mens Flwshp Svc Awd; USS Halsey US Navy Svc Awd; St Thomas Actors Guild Svc Awd; Mt Carmel Bapt Church Choir Music Awd; *office:* Elkins Park Elem Schl 8149 New Second St Elkins Park PA 19027*

POINDEXTER, JAMES ALLEN, Chemistry Teacher; *b:* Lakewood, OH; *m:* Shannon Christine Modar; *ed:* CA Univ of PA (BS) Scndry Ed, Chem 1993; Summer Tchr Enhancement Inst St Vincent Coll 1994, 1995; Working Towards MS Chem Duquesne Univ; *cr:* Geibel Cath HS Chem Tchr 1993-; *ai:* Asst Marching Band Dir; Earth SOS, Christmas Dance Spons; GCTA 1993-; Amer Family Inst Gift of Time Awd Winner 1995, 1996.

POINTER, LINDA MARIE, English Teacher; *b:* Minersville, PA; *ed:* Penn St Univ (BS) Scndry Ed & Eng 1972; Issues in Contemporary Ed at Univ of Arts, Univ of Cntrl Fl; *cr:* Pemberton Township HS Eng Tchr 1973-78; Eastern HS Eng Tchr 1979-; *ai:* Honors Comm Chprsn; Writing Comm; Piloting Writing Prgm; Instructional Advy Cncl; Work with Stu Alliance Prgm; Comm Unity Newsletter; Created Stud Skills Course; Trained Pedagogy Stdnts; NEA, NJEA 1972-; EEA 1979-; Nom for NJs Vol of Yr 1987; *office:* Eastern Sr HS 3500 Laurel Oak Rd Voorhees NJ 08043*

POIRIER, LAUREN ROSE, Language Arts Teacher; *b:* Wakefield, RI; *m:* Kevin J.; *c:* Ryan, Kaitlyn; *ed:* Univ of RI (BA) Speech Commication 1984; Tchr Cert Prgm; Cert in Scndry Eng Completed 1987; Working on Post Grad Stud 1988-; *cr:* South Kingstown Jr HS 7th & 8th Grd Lang Arts Tchr 1990-; *ai:* NEA 1990-; Drama Club Asst 1991-92; 8th Grd Exit Outcomes Comm 1993; Rel Instruction Tchr 1988-90; Tchr & Ed in Chief for Publication of Childrens Books Geared to Specific Younger Audience 1993, 1995-; Chosen to Attend the RI Consortium on Writing An Affiliate of the Natl Writing Project 1995; *office:* South Kingstown Jr HS 301 Curtis Corner Rd Wakefield RI 02879

POIROT, ANNE CICHY, Chemistry Professor; *b:* Wiesbaden, Germany; *m:* Todd A.; *ed:* North Adams St Coll (BS) Med Tech 1981; Univ of RI (PHD) Pharmaceutical Chem 1989; Postdoctoral Rsrch Brown Univ 1991-93, URI 1989-91; *cr:* Western New England Coll Chem Asst Prof 1993-; *ai:* Hnrs Prgm Comm; Fac Adv Pharmacy Honor Soc URI; Amer Chemical Soc 1986-; Several Publications Dissertation, Postdoctoral Rsrch; *office:* Western New England Coll Box 2191 Springfield MA 01119*

POISSON, TERRY EISEMAN, 8th Grade His & Lang Arts Tchr; *b:* Cheverly, MD; *c:* Aimee Lynn, Russell Alexcie; *ed:* Univ of MD (BS) Pol Sci 1975; Attnd Western MD Coll, Bowie St Univ Tchr Cert His 1980; *cr:* Magothy MS 6th Grd Spec Ed Tchr 1991-92; Annapolis MS 8th Grd Soc Stud Tchr 1992-; *ai:* Soc Stud Dept Chair; Yrbk, Newspaper Spon; MSPAP Comm; Team Ldr Schl Improvement Team; NEA, AACTA, MSTA 1992-; *office:* Annapolis MS 1399 Forest Dr Annapolis MD 21403

POIST, BRENDA LORRAINE, Biology & Physiology Teacher; *b:* Baltimore, MD; *m:* Charles; *c:* Jason, Cameron; *cr:* Old Mill HS Bio, Physiology Tchr 1993-; *ai:* TAAAC 1993-; *office:* Old Mill HS 600 Patriot Ln Millersville MD 21108

POLAND, KIMBERLY KAY (JONES), Language Arts Teacher; *b:* Marysville, OH; *m:* Ivan R. Jr.; *ed:* Bowling Green St Univ (BS) Eng Ed 1983; Wright St Univ Working on Masters Curr & Supervision 1994-98; *cr:* Mechanicsburg HS Lang Arts 9th-12th 1983-; *ai:* NHS Adv; Creative Writing Club Adv; Sr Class Adv; Var Ftbl Chrldng Adv; Var Vllybl Coach; Mechanicsburg Tchrs Assn 1983-, Sec, VP; OH Career Ctr Bldg Rep 1983-, HS Rep; OCTELLA 1983-; Champaign Co Steering Comm 1988-, Co-Chair, Frosh Career Day; Champaign Co Bus Advy Cncl 1990-; Campus Life Vllybl Coach of Yr Awd; 2 Pub Articles.*

POLAND, MIRIAM S., English Teacher & Dept Chair; *b:* Vineland, NJ; *c:* John S., Jill Svedas; *ed:* Endicott Coll (AA) 1945; Temple Univ (BS) Ed 1981; *cr:* Vineland CS Music Tchr 1954-55; Faith Chrstn Schl Eng Tchr 1968-, Eng Dept Chprsn 1989-; *ai:* Lib Coord; Accomp for All Choruses; DAR 1960-; Bible Press 1973-, Church of Collingswood 1956-, Organist 1973-; ICCC, ACCC1956-; 15 Yr Svc Plaque; *office:* Faith Christian Schl Haddon Ave & Cuthbert Blvd & Cuthbert Blvd Collingswood NJ 08108

POLASKO, HENRY, Librarian & Speech Teacher; *b:* Windber, PA; *m:* Lorraine; *c:* Penny, Danielle Charvoz; *ed:* Clarion Univ (BS) Eng 1961; Univ of Pittsburgh (MLS) Lib 1970; IN Univ of PA Grad Stud 12 Credit Hrs; *cr:* St Marys HS Eng Tchr 1961; Triangle Area HS Eng Tchr 19 Forest Hills Eng, Speech Tchr & Librn 1967-; *ai:* Interscholatic S Rdng & Mock Trial Coach; Humanitrian Club Adv; NEA 1961-; PS FHEA 1961-, Sec; PSLA; Jaycees 1970-76, Outstdng Edctr 1975; W Area Schl Bd 1973-87, Pres 1981; Holocaust Edctr Awd 199 Interscholastic Rdng Competition Creator & Organizer; Articles Pu Schl Lib Conventions & Keystone St Rdng Assoc Presenter; *home:* Park Ln Windber PA 15963*

POLCE, MARIE MCCULLOUGH, Chemistry Teacher; *b:* Darby, Donald F.; *ed:* Rosemont Coll (BA) Chem 1976; St Josephs Univ Chem Ed 1983; 13 Credits Hrs; *cr:* Merion Mercy Acad Chem 1981-84; Rosemont Coll Chem Tchr 1990-93; Delaware Cty CC Instr 1992-; Nazareth Acad HS Chem Tchr 1993-; *ai:* Jr Hom Moderator; Amer Chemical Soc 1980-; NSTA 1993-; St Josephs Tchng Assistantships 1984-86; *office:* Nazareth Acad HS 4001 Gra Philadelphia PA 19114

POLEFKO, CAROL WALCZAK, Dir of Religious Education; *b:* G Heights, OH; *m:* Roger F.; *c:* Theresa, Timothy, Andrew, Katherin Ursuline Coll (BA) Math, Eng 1973; Attnd Cleveland St Univ, B Wallace Coll, Cleveland Ctr for Pastoral Ldrshp; *cr:* Villa Angela 9th-12th Grd Math Tchr 1973-79; Our Lady of Good Counsel Jr HS Tchr 1984-87; St John Bosco Schl Jr HS Math, Cmptr Tchr 1990- John BOsco Parish Rel Ed Dir 1994-; *ai:* NCEA 1973-; OH Dirs of Org, Cleveland Org of Rel Ed Dirs 1994-; Kappa Gamma Pi 1973- Ribbon Natl Schl of Excl Awd, Writer 1992; *office:* St John Bosco Schl 6460 Pearl Rd Parma OH 44130

POLESKI, KIMBERLY LUISI, Math Teacher; *b:* Pittsburgh, P Steven Daniel; *ed:* Indiana Univ of PA (BS) Math Ed 1991; Attendin Schl; *cr:* Kiski Area HS Math Tchr 1992-; *ai:* Yrbk Adv; *office:* Kisk HS 200 Poplar St Vandergrift PA 15690

POLEWARCZYK, DENISE M., Spanish Teacher; *b:* Clinton, M Worcester St Coll (BS) Span 1979; Addl Post Grad Stud; Attnd Assur Coll; *cr:* Bartlett Jr Sr HS Span Tchr 1979-; *ai:* Jr Class Adv; NEA & WEA 1979-; MAFLA; ASCD 1995-; *office:* Bartlett Jr Sr HS 52 Pky Webster MA 01570

POLICANO, JOSEPH, 8th Grade Social Science Tchr; *b:* Brookly *m:* Nancy McNamara-Policano; *c:* Anthony, Carly; *ed:* Jersey City S (BA) Soc Sci 1983; *cr:* Lincoln Schl 8th Grd Tchr 1984-; *ai:* Sftbl C NEA 1984-; Little League Coach 1995-; *office:* Lincoln Schl 121 Be Kearny NJ 07032*

POLICASTRO, ELLEN, 9th-12th Grd German Teacher; *b:* Roc PA; *m:* Michael; *c:* Jacquelyn, John, Gina, Joseph; *ed:* IN Univ of P Ger 1977; Geneva Coll (BS) Eng 1979; Penn St & Point Park Co Grad Stud; *cr:* Ctr HS Ger Tchr 1978-; *ai:* Ger Club Adv; Str Planning Comm; NEA 1978-; CAEA 1978-; AATG 1990-; *office:* C Baker Rd Ext Monaca PA 15061

POLIKOFF, CAL, Sixth Grade Language Arts Tchr; *b:* Brooklyn, N Susan Jane Pettersen; *c:* Corrie Jane, Kelsey Anne; *ed:* SUNY Co (BA) Elem Ed 1972; SUNY New Paltz (MS) Ed 1977; Post Grad 7 Hrs; *cr:* Pawling Elem Schl 3rd-4th, 6th Grd 1972-; Boys Jr Var Coach 1975-79; Boys Var Bsktbl Coach 1980-85; *ai:* Chm Po Writing, Elem Schl Scheduling Comm; NEA 1972-; Dutchess Cty Bsktbl Assn 1980-84, Sec, Treas; *office:* Pawling Elem Schl 7 Hai Pawling NY 12564*

POLIKOFF, MICHAEL, Fifth Grade Teacher; *b:* Brooklyn, N Margaret Waldes; *c:* Jessica, Howard; *ed:* St Univ of Oneonta (BS) Ed 1967; NY Univ (MA) Elem Ed 1970; 15 Post Grad Credit Hrs in Ed; *cr:* Summit Park Schl 3rd Grd Tchr 1963-69; Polk St Schl 4th-6 Tchr; John St Schl 4-6 Grd Tchr; *ai:* Polk St Drama Club Dir 1973- 1969-, Bldg Rep; NY St Tchrs Assn 1969; Franklin Square Tchrs 1967-, Bldg Rep; Franklin Square PTA 1967-, Tchr Liason, Natl Li Mbrshp; Ramapo Tchrs Assn 1967-69, Bldg Rep; Temple Beth El Re Bd of Ed 1993-, Bd of Ed; Dogwood Franklin Square Civic Assn; F of Bellmore Lib, Ofcr; Summit Park Schl 1968-, Grd Chm; John Stree 1991-93, Grd Chm; Bd of Ed 1995-, Tchr Liason Comm; Polk St Sch of Yr 1968; Tchr Rep Curr Writing Comm Drug Ed 1971; Tchr Re Curr Comm 1992-93.

POLIMENI, JOANNA ANGELA, English & Language Arts Tc Washington, DC; *ed:* Franciscan Univ of Steub (BA) Eng 1968; U Dayton (MS) Ed 1979; *cr:* Grant Jr HS Eng, Lang Arts Tchr 19 Harding MS Eng, Lang Arts Tchr 1982-; *ai:* Steubenville Dist Sp Bees Chprsn; Jefferson Cty Spelling Bee Co-Chprsn; Musical Co-Dir; NEA, OEA, SEA 1968-; Delta Kappa Gamma, Delta Pi 198 1988-90, Pres 1990-92, 1994-; OH Cncl of Tchrs of Eng, Lang Arts *home:* 621 Lawson Ave Steubenville OH 43952

POLIN, PATRICIA YOUNG, Spanish Teacher; *b:* Amityville, N Robert D.; *c:* Kirsten Houghton, Alexander; *ed:* St Univ of NY at A (BA) Span Ed 1970, (MS) Eng as a Second Lang 1975; MS Plus 3 *cr:* Kings Park Schl Dist Span Tchr 1971-; *ai:* Peer Mediation Natural Helpers, Span Club Adv; KPCTA; *office:* Kings Park HS 200 25a Kings Park NY 11754

POLIN, SUSAN, 7th & 8th Grade Teacher; *b:* Philadelphia, PA; *c:* Benitez; *ed:* Temple Univ (BA) Liberal Arts; *cr:* Most Precious Bloo Grd Tchr 1979-86; Cath Home for Girls Supvr 1986-88; St Hugh 8 Tchr 1988-94; Cecilian Acad 7th & 8th Grd Tchr 1994-; *ai:* News Moderator; Schl Anthology of Writings Coord; *home:* 5407 Walk Philadelphia PA 19124

POLING, DEWAYNE O., Carpentry Teacher; *b:* Parkersburg, W Judith Ann; *c:* Lori, Jennifer; *ed:* Fairmont St Coll (BA) Industria 1971; Marshall Univ (MS) Voc Ed 1977; Attnd WV Univ, Ohio St Wright St Univ; *cr:* Parkersburg HS Industrial Arts Tchr 2 Yrs; Washi Cty Career Ctr Carpentry Tchr 21 Yrs, Adult Ed Supv 2 Yrs; *ai:* H Safety Coord; Voc Industrial Club Adv; Credit Comm; Handbook Co Early Placement Comm; Safety Comm; NEA 1994-; OVA 1993-; 1993-; Trout Unlimited 1976-, Bd Mem; Wild Turkey Fed 1986-, Bd NRA 1992-; Article Pub in Amer Voc Ed Journal; Golden Apple A Awd; *office:* Washington County Career Ctr Rt 2 Marietta OH 4575

POLING, RUTH ANN, Second Grade Teacher; *b:* Kenton, OH; *e* Northern Univ (BS) Elem Ed 1968; Bowling Green St Univ Credit H Ridgemont Elem Schl 3rd Grd Tchr 1968-71, 2nd Grd Tchr 1971 Negotiations Comm; OEA; NEA; Delta Kappa Gamma 1974-; Frie Lib 1994-, Sec; Jennings Scholar 1994-95; *office:* Ridgemont Elem 310 W Taylor Mount Victory OH 43340

POLISHOOK, SHEILA STERN, Associate Professor of Histo Brooklyn, NY; *m:* Irwin H.; *c:* Lewis; *ed:* Brooklyn Coll (BA) His Brown Univ (MA) His 1958; Univ of Chicago Work Towards PH Queensborough Comm Coll Assoc Prof of His 1964-; *ai:* AFT AAUP 1964-, Natl Cncl Mem 1970-73; Phi Beta Kappa; Brown Fellow 1956-57; Univ of Chicago La Verne Noyes Schlsp 195 Numerous Articles Pub; *office:* Queensborough Comm Coll Ave-Springfield Blvd Bayside NY 11364

POLISKI, LISA M., Social Studies Teacher; *b:* Jersey City, NJ; Mark; *ed:* Dickinson Coll (BA) His 1987; West Chester Univ (MA 1993; *cr:* Lancaster Cntry Day Schl Soc Stud Tchr 1987-90; Friends' Schl Soc Stud Tchr 1990-91; Padua Acad Soc Stud Tchr 1991-; *ai:*

Moderator; Model UN Moderator 1991-94; Recruitment Retention n; DE Cncl for SS, Mid Sts Cncl for SS, NCEA 1991-; DE Related Ed Project 1993-95; Wilmington Jr League 1993-; St Thomas n Formation Comm 1996; 1994 Superstars! in Ed Awd Winner; *office:* Acad 905 N Broom St Wilmington DE 19806*

SKIN, SANDRA ARMEL, Special Education Teacher; *b:* New York, *:* Ted; *c:* Michele, Dara; *ed:* SUNY at Stony Brook (BA) Psych 1972; an Coll (MS) Spcl Ed 1993; NYU Bus & Fin; *cr:* SUNY Rsrch Coord 74; White Oaks Industries Admin VP 1975-85; PS & IS 187 Spcl Ed 1989-92; Clarkstown HS North Spcl Ed Tchr 1992-; *ai:* ASPIRA Fac Twirlers & Color Guard Co-Adv; Pupil Svcs Soc Comm; ADHD Dist dinating Comm; HYSATH 1992-; Cncl for Exceptional Children ; Clarkstown Tchrs Assoc 1993-; Rsrch Pub; *office:* Clarkstown HS Congers Rd New City NY 10956*

TES, DORIS MORRETTE, First Grade Teacher; *b:* Washington, *:* William F., Robert D., Mark R.; *ed:* Univ of MD (BS) PE 1952; ensburg Univ (MS) Elem Ed 1971; *cr:* Bethesda Jr High PE Tchr 53; New Bern Elem 8th Grd Tchr 1953-54; Parkville Jr Sr High PE 1954-56; Central High PE Tchr 1956-60 Newberry Elem Kndgtn Tchr 67; Central York Schl Dist 1st Grd Tchr 1971-; *ai:* NEA; Red Land ens Club 1972-; Delta Kappa Gamma Soc Intnl 1991-; *office:* dtown Elem Schl 570 Church Rd York PA 17404

TES, OLGA STAVROS, High School English Teacher; *b:* Camden, *:* Michael; *c:* Paula, John; *ed:* LaSalle Univ (BA) Eng 1983; Beaver MA) Hum 1995; *cr:* Paul VI HS Eng Tchr 1982-85; Lenape HS Eng 1985-; *ai:* NCTE 1996; Article Pub; *office:* Lenape HS Church & ord Rds Medford NJ 08055*

TIS, CATHERINE NICOLE, Language Arts & Reading Tchr; *b:* y City, NJ; *ed:* Jersey City St Coll (BA) Early Chldhd, Elem Ed 1974; dits Rdng, Elem Ed 1992-93; St Peter's Coll 3 Credits Sci, Elem Ed *cr:* PS 15 4th Grd Tchr 1974-75; PS 5 8th Grd Tchr 1975-76; PS 14 rd Tchr, 5th Grd Tchr 1976-88; James F. Murray Schl #38 6th, 7th Tchr 1988-; *ai:* After-Schl Club Adv; Alt Site Planning Team; JCEA, A, NJEA, NEA 1974-, Schl Rep 1977-79; ASCD 1993-; Daughters of ope Amer Hellenic Educ Assn 1985-, Dist Marshall, Chap Penelope ; St Anna's Philoptochos 1980-, Treas; AHEPA Cancer Rsrch Fnd , Bd of Trustees; Deborah Heart Fnd 1996-; *home:* 10 Benmore Ter nne NJ 07002

TIS, JANE GWYN, History & Ldrshp Seminar Tchr; *b:* Evanston, : Steven J.; *c:* Yiannis Steven, Katherine Alexandra; *ed:* Standford (BA) Pol Theory 1963; Salem St Coll (MS) His 1971; Attnd San cisco St Coll, Harvard Univ; *cr:* Newburyport HS Soc Stu, His, ership Seminar Tchr 1966-72, 1981-; *ai:* YWCA Vanguard Awd, g Excl 1990; Harvard Inst Rdng, Writing, Civic Ed 1993.*

TO, MARILYN, Assistant Principal; *b:* Worcester, MA; *ed:* ester St Coll (BS) Elem Ed 1966, (MED) Elem Ed 1969; 30 Addl ts; *cr:* Larmartine St Schl Primary Grd Tchr 1966-68; Lake View Primary Grd Tchr 1968-, Asst Prin 1990-95; Rice Square Schl Asst 1995-; *ai:* Schl Cncl; Worcester Educl Assn, MTA, NEA 1966-; PA 1993-; U MASS Medical Ctr 1975-, Vol; Worcester Jaycees, ter II Mini-Grants; Hiatt Fellowship Summer Inst Harvard Univ; *:* Rice Square Schl 76 Massasoit Rd Worcester MA 01604*

TZA, DONNA MARIE, High School English Teacher; *b:* Kulpmont, *ed:* Alvernia Coll (BA) Eng 1973; Bloomsburg Univ (MED) Eng; th Grd Comm Skills Supervisory Cert 1988; N-12th Grd Curr & uction Supervisory Cert 1990; Classes taken in Cooperative Learning, ssment & Portfolio Implementation; *cr:* Line Mountain HS Eng Tchr -; Line Mountain Schl Dist Communication Skills Coord 1985-90; Susquehanna Intermediate Unit 16 Trainer for PA Framework 90; Line Mountain Schl Dist Assessment Coord 1995-; *ai:* Wkshp itator in Assessment, Support & Resource Tchr Comm; Facilitator for Skills, Assessment & Strategic Planning; Forensics Head Coach; Fac te Mem; Drama & Musical Dir; Curr Cncl; Travel Club Adv; humberland Cty Voc-Tech Strategical Planning; PSEA 1973-; IRA -; NEA 1973-; ASCD 1988-; Phi Delta Kappa 1989-; Excl Awd humberland Cty Conservation Dist in Coordination of Speech ests; *office:* Line Mountain HS RR 1 Box 1660 Herndon PA 17830*

K, O. ELMER, Assoc Prof & Acting Chrmn; *b:* Gainesville, FL; *m:* ly A.; *c:* Alexandria, Emily; *ed:* Univ of South FL (BA) Criminal ce 1976; Rollins Coll (MS) Criminal Justice 1979; Sam Houston St (PHD) Criminal Justice 1993; *cr:* FL St of Corrections Probation, e Ofcr 1976-84; Navajo Tribe Yth Svcs 1979-8-; Bexar Cty TX Juv 1984-90; Coppin St Coll 1993-; *ai:* Grad Cncl; Chairs GER, Criminal ce Police Trng, Grad Cert, Lib Resources Comm; Co-Spon Criminal ce Club; Amer Correctional Assn 1980-; Acad Criminal Justice Sci -; Amer Soc Criminology 1994-; MD Criminal Justice Assn Prof Dev m; Numerous Articles Pub; *office:* Coppin St Coll 2500 W North Ave more MD 21216

LACK, BARBARA R., 2nd Grade Teacher; *b:* New York, NY; *m:* y; *c:* Andrew, Justin; *ed:* Queens Coll (BA) Elem Ed 1973, (MA) Elem 976; 33 Post Grad Hrs Prof Enrichment; *cr:* PS 111Q Grd 4-6 Sci Tchr -78; PS 131 Q Spec Ed 1978-80, Elem Ed 1985-; *ai:* Addison, Wesley Consultant; Muscular Dystrophy Fund Raiser; Amer Hearth Assn Raiser; UFT, AFT 1979-; PTA 1986-89, Ofcr 1986-88, Pres 1988-89; g Inventors of Amer Grant; *office:* Abigail Adams PS 131 Q 172nd St th Ave Jamaica Est NY 11432

LACK, CHARLES, Mathematics Teacher; *b:* Newark, NJ; *m:* Ester rief; *c:* Michelle, Michael; *ed:* Buena Vista Coll (BA) Math 1967; ers Univ (MED) Math Ed 1979; attnd Univ of Northern IA, Montclair OH St; *cr:* Newark Bd of Ed Math Tchr 1968-70; Parsippany Bd of Math Tchr 1970-; *ai:* Tennis Coach 1970-; NCTM, AMTNJ 1983-; NEA -; Tennis Coach of Yr; *office:* Parsippany Hills HS 20 Rita Dr ippany NJ 07054

LACK, KAREN, 4th Grade Teacher; *b:* Brooklyn, NY; *m:* Kenneth; lana; *ed:* CCNY (BA) His 1966; Brooklyn Coll Math, Ed 1976; *cr:* PS Tchr 1966-70; PS 198 Tchr 1970-; *ai:* AFT, UFT 1966-; *home:* 2124 rt St Brooklyn NY 11229*

LACK, PAMELA ROBERTS, 7th Grade Teacher; *b:* Freeport, IL; *c:* ifer, Mark; *ed:* Kent St Univ (BSEd) Ed 1971; Ashland Coll (MEd) , Instruction 1996; *cr:* St Jude Schl 3rd-5th, 7th-8th Grd Tchr, 1967-75, -; *ai:* New Frontiers; Martha Holden Jennings Educl Grant for 5 Yrs; *e:* St Jude Schl 594 Poplar St Elyria OH 44035*

LACK, RICHARD DAVID, VP of Rsrch & Information Tech; *b:* on, MA; *ed:* Syracuse Univ (BA) Psych, Ec 1983; Univ of OK (MS) h 1985; Temple Univ (PHD) Psych 1991; *cr:* Merrimack Coll Asst Prof -95; Maguire Assoc Inc VP of Rsrch & Information Tech; *ai:* rgoudi Dissertation Awd Temple Univ 1991; Journal of Constructivist h Ed 1996; Pub Articles.

LACK, SHARON SELMAN, Third Grade Teacher; *b:* Bronx, NY; *m:* rles; *c:* David, Robert; *ed:* NY Univ (BS) His 1965; Lehman Coll (MS) 970; *cr:* CES 55 Bronx 1st Grd Tchr 1965-71; CES 70 Bronx 3rd Grd 1980-; *office:* CES 70 Bronx Schl 1691 Weeks Ave Bronx NY 10457

LARD, GORDON CHARLES, Elementary PE Teacher; *b:* Sidney, *ed:* Orange Cty C Coll (AA) PE 1971; Cortland St Coll (BS) PE 1973,) PE 1978; Practice Bible Coll 6 Credit Hrs; *cr:* Vestal Schls Asst LaCrosse Coach 1973-85, PE Tchr 1973-, Head Cross Cntry Coach 1974-; ME Endwell HS Head LaCrosse Coach 1986-89; Vestal HS Head LaCrosse Coach 1991-92; *ai:* Cross Cntry Head Coach; Dollars for Scholars, Fitness Facility, & Im Comm; NEA & FCA 1973-; NI LA 1973-, Natl Rep; Amer R & Fit 1991-; Yth LaCrosse 1980-, Founder, Outstndg Achvmt; NILA Sectional 1980 & 1994, Man of the Yr; Sertoma 1990-94; LaCrosse Ofcl 1993-; First Presbyn Church 1994-, Moderator, Deacons; *office:* Vestal Schls Main St Vestal NY 13850

POLLARD, JAMES ALFRED,SR., Professor of Religion; *b:* Philadelpha, PA; *m:* Virginia Overton; *c:* James Jr., Joseph, John; *ed:* Phila Coll of Bible (BS) Biblical Stud 1969; Eastern Bapt Seminary (MDIV) Old Testament 1972; Kensington Univ (PHD) Rel, Philosophy 1990; *cr:* Zion Bapt Church Pastor 1970-; Luth Theological Seminary Adj Prof 1980-; Lincoln Univ Adj Prof 1988-; Eastern Coll Adj Prof 1991-; *ai:* Soccer Coach 1989; Ardmore Affondable Housing 1990-, Pres; Founders Bank CRA Comm 1995-; Phila Tribune Newspaper Contributing Writer 1974-; *home:* 221 W Spring Ave Ardmore PA 19003*

POLLATZ, BRIAN MARK, Music Teacher; *b:* Springfield, IL; *m:* Beth Klemp; *c:* Benjamin; *ed:* Concordia Coll (BA) Music Ed 1987; Univ of MI 2 Yrs; 12 Credit Hrs Villanova; Long Island Univ 24 Credit Hrs; *cr:* Long Island Luth HS Music Tchr 1987-; St Paul's Luth Church Part Time DCE 1987-; *ai:* Pep, Jazz, Pit Bands; String Ensemble; Stu Govt; Small Music Ensembles; Jr High Musical; Sr Class Adv; Nassau Music Edctrs Assn, NY St Schl Music Assn, Music Edctrs Natl Conf 1987-; Long Island String Fest Assn1987-; Randi Abbe Awd Chrstn Svc; *office:* Long Island Luth Mid, HS 131 Brookville Rd Glen Head NY 11545

POLLOCK, ALLEN TOM, Sixth Grade Teacher; *b:* Wheeling, WV; *ed:* Coll of Wooster (BA) His, Fr 1971; Cleveland St Univ (MA) Supervision 1979; Post Grad Stud; Orff Inst at Salzburg Austria; Brasstown Folk Inst; *cr:* Lakewood Elem Tchr 1971-81, Music Tchr 1981-89, 6th Grd Tchr 1989-; *ai:* Environment, Fr, Drama Club; Orff Instrument Ensemble; OH Ed Assn 1971-; Lkwd Tchr Assn 1971-, Newsletter, Rep; OMEA 1981-; OH GATE Assn 1991-; Camp Bd 1979-89, Prgm Chair; Martha Holden Jennings Grant; Margaret Meade Awd; *office:* Emerson MS 13439 Clifton Blvd Lakewood OH 44107*

POLLOCK, ARTHELLA A. (MOTE), Retired Teacher; *b:* Winchester, IN; *m:* Donald K.; *c:* Michael K. (dec); *ed:* Miami Univ (BS) Elem Ed 1971; Wright St Univ (MED) Curr, Supervision 1991; *cr:* C. R. Coblentz Schl Dist Elem Tchr 1965-67; Eaton City Schls Elem, Jr High Math Tchr 1967-93; *ai:* OH Ret Tchrs 1993-; 1st Presbyn Church 1968-, Treas; Women's Church Cir 1991-, Co-Ldr; Puzzle & Fact Page for Dayton Daily News; *home:* 1963 US Route 35 W Eaton OH 45320

POLLOCK, ARTHUR JEROME, Guidance Counselor; *b:* Pittsburgh, PA; *m:* Gloria Florelli; *c:* Emily, Aaron; *ed:* CA Univ of PA (BSEd) Elem Ed 1969; Duquesne Univ (BED) 1973; *cr:* Pittsburgh Pub Schls Tchr 1969-87, Cnslr 1987-; *ai:* Ed of Pupil Svcs Newsletter; CEIP Comm Mem; AFT, PFT 1969-; Point Breeze Neighborhood Assn 1985-, Pres; *office:* Brashear HS 590 Crane Ave Pittsburgh PA 15216

POLLOCK, BARBARA, Second Grade Teacher; *b:* Cleveland, OH; *ed:* St John Coll of Cleveland (BSE) Elem Ed 1967; *cr:* St Clement Schl K-3rd Grd Tchr 1962-, Pub Schl Rel Tchr 1968-72, Asst Prin 1976-91; St Bridget Summer Schl Tchr 1969; Our Lady of Good Cncl Tchr 1970; *ai:* Primary Grd Coord; St Clement Schl Bd 1978-91, Sec; Cox Cable Educl Grant 1995; Stu Tchrs Supvr; Eucharistic Minister; Nom Diocescan Tchr of Yr 1991; *office:* St Clements Schl 14505 Madison Ave Lakewood OH 44107

POLLOCK, GARY JOHN, Mathematics Teacher; *b:* Rochester, NY; *ed:* SUNY at Oswego (BS) Scndry Ed & Math 1984; SUNY at Brockport (MS) Scndry Ed & Math 1989; *cr:* Kendall Jr Sr HS Math Tchr 1984-; *ai:* Boys Var Soccer Coach; Boys Jr Var Bsktbl Coach; Jr Class Adv; NEA 1984-; NSCAA 1988-; 1989 Univ of Rochester "Tchr of the Yr"; GR League Coach of the Yr 1991 & Soccer Coach of Yr 1992, 1994-95; *office:* Kendall Cntrl Schl Dist Rt 18 Kendall NY 14476*

POLLOCK, KAREN PEASE, Health & Physical Ed Teacher; *b:* Columbus, OH; *ed:* Bowling Green Univ (BAEd) Hlth, PEK-12 1969; Continuing Ed OH St Univ; *cr:* Hastings MS Hlth, PE Tchr 27 Yrs; *ai:* Washington DC Chaperone; Upper Arlingotn Hlth, PE Task Force; Hlth, PE Curr Comm; OEA, NEA 1969-; Prof Women's Assn 1970-; *office:* Hastings MS 1850 Hastings Ln Columbus OH 43220

POLLOCK, KEVIN MICHAEL, HS Instrumental Music Teacher; *b:* Lawton, OK; *m:* Kathleen Ferchak; *c:* David, Kerri Beth, Jonathan, Michelle; *ed:* Duquesne Univ (BS) Music Ed 1981, (MM) Music Ed 1989; *cr:* West Mifflin North HS Asst Band Dir 1981-84; Moon Area Schl Dist Permanent Sub Tchr 1984-86; Carlynton Jr, Sr HS Band Dir 1986-87; Franklin Regnl Sr HS Band, Orch Dir 1987-; *ai:* Marching, Jazz, Pep Band Dirs; MENC, PMEA 1981-; PSEA, NEA 1987-; Excl in Tchng Awd Coll of Wooster 1991; *office:* Franklin Regional Sr HS 3200 School Rd Murrysville PA 15668

POLLOCK, MARGARET ARLENE, Fifth Grade Teacher; *b:* Pittsburgh, PA; *m:* William F.; *c:* William A.; *ed:* Kent St (BA) Elem Ed 1968; Akron Univ Addl Credit Hrs; *cr:* St Mary's 5th Grd Tchr 1965-66; West Carlisle 5th Grd Tchr 1966-67; Cuyahaga Falls 5th Grd Tchr 1967-; *ai:* Tennis Coach; Textbook, Curr Comms; NEA, NEOEA 1967-; CFEA 1967-, Bldg Rep; Kappa Kappa Iota 1993-; United Presbyn Church 1958-; US Tennis Assn; Alpha Chi Omega; Tchr of Month; *home:* 3060 W Edgerton Rd Silver Lake OH 44224*

POLLOCK, PATRICIA WOLSKI, High School Teacher; *b:* San Pierre, IN; *m:* Donald R. II; *c:* Philip David Murfitt II, Mark Patrick Murfitt; *ed:* OH Univ (BFA) Painting, Sculpture 1977; *cr:* Unioto HS Math Tchr 1977-78; Bishop Flaget HS Eng Tchr 1978-84; Piketon HS Art Tchr 1984-85; Bright Schl Dist Eng Tchr 1985-86; Zane Trace HS Eng Tchr 1988-; *ai:* NEA; OEA; ZTEA; *home:* 2 Rose Ln Chillicothe OH 45601

POLLOI, JUSTA FRANZ, Religion Teacher; *b:* Koror, Palau; *ed:* Grays Harbor Coll (AA) Sociology 1971; Univ of WA (BA) Sociology 1973; Mother of Life Cert Rel Ed; *cr:* Mindszenty HS Soc Stud Tchr 1973-80, Religion Tchr 1982-; *ai:* Sr Moderator; Schl Liturgical Comm Chprsn; Vicariate Justice Dev 1993-; Sacred Heart Church Choir 1980-.*

POLOMSKI, RAYMOND A., Physics Teacher; *b:* Bayonne, NJ; *m:* Marilyn; *ed:* Jersey City St Coll (BA) Sci 1969; NJ Inst of Tech (MS) Applied Sci 1973; Attnd Montclair St Univ, San Diego St Univ, Stevens Inst of Tech, Fairleigh Dickinson Univ; Seton Hall Univ Admin, Supervision Cert; *cr:* Dumont HS Sci Tchr 1969-; *ai:* Organized Physics Sharing Session for Tchrs in the Area; NEA, NJEA, BCEA, DEA, AAPT, NSTA, NJSTA 1969-; NJAAPT 1977-, VP 1984-86; NSF Grants; 1 of 10 NJ Tchrs Participated in Tchr in Industry Prgm 1988; *office:* Dumont HS 101 New Milford Ave Dumont NJ 07628*

POLSKI, BERNARD JOSEPH, Fourth Grade Teacher; *b:* Braddock, PA; *m:* Sharon Michelle Jeznach; *c:* Timothy, Christopher; *ed:* Clarion Univ (BS) Elem 1970; Penn St Univ 24 Credit Hrs; Univ of Pittsburgh 3 Credit Hrs; *cr:* Westinghouse MS 6th Grd Tchr 1969-70; Park Terrace MS 7th-8th Grd Art, Rdng Tchr 1970-74; Green Valley Elem Schl 3rd-4th Grd Tchr 1975-78; Westinghouse MS 4th Grd Tchr 1978-; *ai:* NEA, PSEA, EAEA 1970-; *office:* Westinghouse MS Marguerite Ave Wilmerding PA 15148

POLUSE, MARTIN, High School Religion Teacher; *b:* Youngstown, OH; *m:* Mary T. Simon; *c:* George, Annette; *ed:* Athenacum of OH (BA) Philosophy 1974, (MA) Biblical Stud 1976; Youngstown St Univ (MA) Amer His 1980; Kent St Univ (PHD) US His 1991; 45 Addl Grad Hrs in Systematic & Pastoral Theology; 12 Addl Grad Hrs in Ed; *cr:* Saint John HS Religion Tchr 1976-81; Saint Vincent-Saint Mary HS Religion Tchr 1981-91; Villa Angela-Saint Joseph HS Religion Tchr 1991-; Notre Dame Coll Theology Dept Adjunct Fac 1992-; *ai:* Yrbk Moderator; Cath HS & Acad Lay Tchrs Assn; Published few Articles; *home:* 505 W Walnut Ave Painesville OH 44077*

POLUSZEJKO, MAUREEN STRAUSS, Senior HS Guidance Counselor; *b:* Sewickley, PA; *c:* David M., Julie; *ed:* West VA Univ (BA) Soc Stud Ed 1971; Univ of Pittsburgh (MEd) Cnslr Ed 1974; Post Masters Work; TX Tech 3 Credit Hrs; *cr:* Beaver Area Schls Teacher 1972-74; North Allegheny Schls Guid Cnslr 1974-; *ai:* Dist Comm; Conflict Resolution; AFT, NAFT 1974-; ACCA 1976-; Quaker Vly Parent Boys Bsktbl Booster Org 1995-; *office:* North Allegheny Sr HS 10375 Perry Hwy Wexford PA 15090

POLYCHRONIOU, CHRONIS, Chair & Assoc Prof of Pol Sci; *b:* Athens, Greece; *ed:* Temple Univ (BA) Philosophy 1980; St Joseph's Univ (MA) Amer Stud 1983; Univ of DE (PHD) Pol Sci 1989; *cr:* Lincoln Univ Chair & Assoc Prof 1986-; *ai:* Pol Sci Club Adv; Former Head Coach Soccer Team; Author, Ed of Several Books on Intnl Pol Economy & Socialist Theory; Articles Pub; Distngd Awd for Excl in Rsrch; *office:* Lincoln Univ Lincoln University PA 19352

POMATTO, CARMELA LINFANTE, Seventh Grade English Teacher; *b:* Jersey City, NJ; *m:* Lawrence T.; *c:* Lawrence Jr., Michael Morris, Laurie Ann; *ed:* Jersey City St Coll (BA) General Elem 1965; *cr:* Jersey City PS #14 4th Grd Tchr 1965-68; Jersey City PS #40 6th & 8th Grd Tchr 1968-77; Duberson MS 7th-8th Grd Tchr 1977-87; Wm Davies MS 7th Grd Tchr 1987-; *ai:* Schl Store; Stu Mentoring Prgm; Davies Digest Writing Staff; NEA, NJEA 1965-; JCEA 1965-77; HTEA 1977-; Egg Harbor Twp Youth Org 1977-93; San Lupo Soc of Jersey City 1944-; Governor's Recognition Awd Tchr of Yr 1992-93; *office:* William Davies MS Vienna Ave Mays Landing NJ 08330*

POMERANTZ, KATHLEEN SUSAN LAUGHLIN, English Teacher; *b:* Windber, PA; *m:* Henry; *c:* Jennifer Minson, Rachel Stup; *ed:* Montclair St Univ (BA) Eng 1965; 15 Credit Hrs Spec Ed Jersey City St Coll; 3 Credit Hrs Cmptr Ed Kittatinny Acad for Tchrs; *cr:* Roxbury HS Eng Tchr 1965-69; Newton Schls Sub Tchr 1976-80; Kittatinny Regnl HS Eng Tchr 1980-; *ai:* HS Stu Cncl Adv 1985-; Fac Sunshine Discipline, Stu Liaison Alcohol, Drug Comm; KEA 1980-; NASSA 1985-; NEA, NJEA, NCTE 1965-; NJASC 1994-, Adv of Yr Runnerup; Newton Meml Hosp Auxiliary 1972-80; YWCA 1974-80, Sec; HS Band Parent 1985-89, VP; *office:* Kittatinny Regnl HS 77 Halsey Rd Newton NJ 07860

POMEROY, PATRICIA WALDRON, Bio, Chem Tchr & Dept Chmn; *b:* Philadelphia, PA; *m:* Paul J. Pomeroy, Jr.; *c:* Paul III, Melissa; *ed:* Gwynedd-Mercy Coll (BA) Bio 1969; Widener Univ (BA) Lbrl Stud 1992, (MED) Ed 1994; Univ of DE 9 Credit Hrs Cmptrs; *cr:* Archmere Acad Tchr, Dept Chair 1976-; *ai:* Sci Show; Olympiad Teams; Physics Olympiad; NSTA, DABT 1976-; Superstars in Ed Awd; *office:* Archmere Acad 3600 Philadelphia Pike Claymont DE 19703

POMMERENING, NANCY KONDAS, History Teacher; *b:* Mentor, OH; *m:* Edward J.; *ed:* Kent St Univ (BA) Ed 1976; Certfd in Gifted Ed; 60 Semester Hrs in Ec, MBA, Gen Ed at Cleveland St, John Carroll, Kent St Univ; *cr:* Lakewood City Schls Tchr 1976-; *ai:* Dance Comm Club Adv; NEA, OEA, LTA 1976-; Soc Stud Cncl 1989-; *office:* Lakewood City Schls 1470 Warren Rd Lakewood OH 44107

POMPA, DANIEL THOMAS, Guidance Counselor; *b:* Bridgeport, CT; *c:* Jennifer; *ed:* Southern CT St Univ (BS) Intermediate Upper Ed 1976, (MS) Cnslng 1985; 6th Yr Schl Psych 1987; *cr:* Pomperaug Reg #15 6th-8th Grd Tchr 1975-85; Bethel 9th-12th Grd Guid Cnslr 1985-; *ai:* Class Adv 1989 & 1995; Stu Cncl, SADD & CORE Adv; NEA 1976-; CT Ed Assoc 1976-, Pub Rel & Human & Civil Rights Commissions; Pomperaug Ed Assoc 1976-85, VP, Pres, Sec & Bldg Rep; Bethel Ed Assoc 1985-, Pres Elect, Pres, Bldg Rep; Phi Delta Kappa 1986-; Pomperaug Region 15 Yth Commission 1982-85; *office:* Bethel HS Educational Park Bethel CT 06801

POMPONIO, ALAN R., Science Teacher; *b:* Brooklyn, NY; *m:* Marie Deeley; *c:* Bernadette; *ed:* SUC NY at New Paltz (BS) Geology 1968; Adelphi Univ (MS) Earth Sci 1972; Lehigh Univ 3 Crecit Hrs Materials Sci & Engineering; NASA-NSTA Newmast Prgm OK St Univ 3 Credit Hrs; SUNY Stonybrook Tchng Ethics in Sci, Mth & Tech; *cr:* Commack Schl Dist Earth Sci Tchr 1968-; *ai:* Site Based Mngmt Comm; Materials Sci & Engineering Grant Lehigh Univ; Newmast & NSF Grant; Tchr of Yr 1993-; Dev of Earth & Moon Simulater & Cmptr Software Prgms; Earth Sci Tutorial Cmptr Prgm 1995; *office:* Commack HS Scholar Ln & Townline Rd Commack NY 11725*

POMPONIO, ANN M., Fourth Grade Teacher; *b:* Inkerman, PA; *m:* Anthony G.; *c:* Thomas, Susan Ryan, Linda Kamor, Diane Katz; *ed:* Marywood Coll at Scranton (BS) Elem Ed 1962; *cr:* Beer Street Schl 1st Grd Tchr 1962; Saint Agnes Schl 4th Grd Tchr 1980-; *ai:* NCEA 1980-; *office:* St Agnes Schl 55 South Ave Atlantic Highlands NJ 07716

PONCHAK, GERARD, Soc Stud Tchr & Dept Chair; *b:* Brooklyn, NY; *m:* Julie Marie; *ed:* St Univ of NY at New Palt (MS) Scndry Ed Soc Stud 1973; Geography Courses 9 Hrs Post Grad Stud; *cr:* James I ONeil Hs Soc Stud Tchr 1969-, Dept Chair 1984-; *ai:* Adv to Youth in Govt of Orange Cty NY; AFT 1969-; NYSUT 1969-; Town of Highlands Tchr Assn 1969-; Mid Hudson Soc Stud Cncl 1989-; *office:* James I ONeill HS Rt 9W South Highland Falls NY 10928

POND, GLORIA DIBBLE, Professor; *b:* Merced, CA; *m:* J. Lawrence; *c:* Scott Lawrence (dec); *ed:* Bennington Coll (BA) Soc Sci 1960; Wesleyan Univ (MALS) Lit 1968, (CAS) Pol Lit 1974; 9 Hrs Advanced Cultural Stud; *cr:* Newsweek Magazine Editorial Asst 1957; Houston Chronicle Editorial Asst 1958; Newsweek Magazine Editorial Asst 1959, 1960; New Haven Univ Hum Lecturer 1967; Naugatuck Valley Comm-Tech Coll Eng Prof 1968-; *ai:* Fresh Ink Lit Magazine Adv; Western CT Bird Club 1980-, Pub Relations 1980-87; YWCA Women in Leadership 1992; NASA Moon Rock Educator 1986; Pub 2 Books, Parts of 2 Other Books & Many Articles; Dev Prizes for Accomplished Arts & Lit Stdnts; *office:* Naugatuck Valley Comm Coll 750 Chase Pky Waterbury CT 06708*

POND, MARTHA FORSYTH, Bio & Life Sci Electives Tchr; *b:* Haverhill, MA; *m:* Christopher R.; *c:* Austin, Melanie; *ed:* Coll of William & Mary in VA (BS) Bio 1986; Univ of NH (MED) Scndry Sci 1993; *cr:* Timberlane Regnl HS Bio, Life Sci Electives Tchr 1988-; *ai:* Track Coach; Action Comm; Class 1992, SADD Former Adv; Former Fac Senate; Fac Liaison; Class Adv; AFT 1992-; NABT 1988-; *office:* Timberlane Regnl HS 36 Greenough Rd Plaistow NH 03865*

POND, ROBERT JOSEPH, Retired Professor; *b:* Hillsboro, OH; *m:* Constance Rae; *c:* David Lee; *ed:* OH St Univ (BS) Ed 1970, (MA) Tech Ed 1974; *cr:* Newark Air Force Base Tech Instr 1962-72; Cntrl OH Tech Coll Prof 1972-95; *ai:* Instrument Soc of Amer Club Adv; Pub Textbooks: Introduction to Engineering Technology 3rd Edition, Fundamentals of Statistical Quality Control; *home:* 1698 Blue Jay Rd Heath OH 43056

PONDO, JULIANN VIRGINIA, First Grade Teacher; *b:* Reading, PA; *m:* Frank J.; *c:* Erno; *ed:* Kutztown Univ (BS) Elem Ed 1983; Attnd Alvernia, Temple Univ & Millersvill; *cr:* Lullabye Nursery & Kindercare Day Schl Tchr 1983-85; Rdng Schl Tchr 1986-; *ai:* NEA & PSEA 1987-;

Greenpeace 1987-; *office:* Thirteenth & Union Elem Schl 1600 N 13th St Reading PA 19604

PONGRATZ, ELAINE M., Title I Reading Specialist; *b:* Hazleton, PA; *m:* Michael DeMarco; *ed:* Bloomsburg St Coll (BS) Eng, Scndry Ed 1973, (MEd) Rdng 1978; Bloomsburg Univ (MS) Exceptionalities 1980; Attending Penn St Univ; *cr:* Norristown HS 10-12 Grd Rdng Specialist 1974-76; CSIU #16 Rdng Specialist Act 89 1976-78; Danville Area Schl Dist Title I Rdng Specialist, Prgm Coord 1978-; CSIU #16 Summer Migrant Ed Prgm 1981-88; Bloomsburg Univ Part-time Fac 1994-95; *ai:* Adult Ed Long Range Planning, Lifelong Learning Strategic Planning Comms Chair; Eng, Rdng, Prof Dev Task Forces; PSEA, NEA, DEA 1976-; IRA, KSRA 1978-; SVRC 1978-, Sec; AAACE 1985-; Natl Comm Ed Assn 1987-; *office:* Danville MS Northumberland Rd Danville PA 17821

PONKOS-MEROLA, BARBARA JOAN, Health Teacher; *b:* Hudson, NY; *m:* John A. Merola; *ed:* St Univ Coll at Oneonta (BS) Elem Ed 1976; St Univ Coll at New Paltz (MS) Elem Ed 1980; Russell Sage Coll at Troy Hlth Ed 1991; 14 Post-Grad Credit Hrs Univ of UT at Salt Lake City; *cr:* Several NY St Pub Schls Elem Tchr 1976-83; Jordan Schl Dist Elem Tchr 1983-85; Ravena-Coeymans-Selkirk CSD Hlth Tchr 1989-90; City Schl Dist Hlth Tchr 1991-; *ai:* SADD, Chrldr, Drama Club Adv; Amer Red Cross, CPR, FPR Instr; AFT 1976-; NYSUT, NYSHPE 1989-; Comm Svc Awd Albany Cty Traffic Safety Ed Dept; *home:* 262 Lenox Ave Albany NY 12208*

PONOS, OLHA BASARAB, French & German Teacher; *b:* Neumarkt, Germany; *c:* Roman, Tania; *ed:* Montclair St Univ (BA) Fr, Ger 1967; Seton Hall Univ (MA) Fr 1980; Parsons Schl of Designs Cert Interior Design; Goethe House Ger Lang, Culture Courses; Post Grad Courses Univ of CT; Higher Order Thinking Skills Course; *cr:* Irvington HS Fr, Ger Tchr 1967; Caldwell Coll Fr, Ger Instr 1988-91; Hanover Park HS Fr, Ger Tchr 1968-; *ai:* Fr Club, Intnl Club Adv; NEA, NJ Ed Assn 1967-; FLENJ; Trends & Friends 1992-; Ukrainian Women's League 1973-, Pres; Ukrainian Branches #75 & #113, Orgnl Sec; NJ St Opera, Interpreter; Ukrainian Artists Org, Interpreter, Faciliator; *home:* 15 Robertson Ct Morristown NJ 07960*

PONTES, JOHN, Health Teacher; *b:* Passaic, NJ; *m:* Carol Ann; *c:* Deirdre, Joseph; *ed:* William Paterson (BA) Hlth, PE 1973; Jersey City St (MS) Hlth Ed 1990; *cr:* Essex Cath HS Hlth, PE Tchr 1974-81; Clifton HS Hlth Tchr 1981-; *ai:* Head Coach Boys, Girls Cross Cntry, Boys Outdoor Track; Asst Coach Boys, Girls Indoor Track; NEA, NJEA, Passaic Cty Coaches Assn 1981-; NJ, Natl Coaches Assn 1984-; US Track, Field Assn 1970-; NYRRC 1975-; Passaic Cty Cross Cntry Coach of Yr 1985, 1987, 1991; *home:* 18 Paranya Ct Clifton NJ 07013

PONTES, JOHN A., English Teacher; *b:* Fall River, MA; *m:* Kristina Connell; *ed:* Georgetown Univ (BA) Eng, Theology 1992; Boston Coll (MA) Theology 1994; *cr:* Bishop Feehan HS Eng Tchr 1993-95; Mansfield HS Eng Tchr 1995-; *ai:* Yrbk Adv; NEA, NASAA 1995-; Guest Speaker NHS 1995; *office:* Mansfield HS 250 East St Mansfield MA 02048

PONTICELLI, RICHARD JAMES, Professor of Math & Dept Chair; *ed:* Univ of MA (BA) Ed 1973; Tufts Univ (MED) Ed 1976; Univ of MA (MS) Math 1988; *cr:* North Shore Comm Coll Math Dept Chair, Full Prof 1989-; *ai:* MA Math League Sec; MAA, AMATYC 1989-; NEA 1979-; Text: Basic Coll Math, Bus Math for Coll; *office:* North Shore Comm Coll 1 Ferncroft Rd Danvers MA 01923*

PONTIUS, BEVERLY JO, Fourth Grade Teacher; *b:* New Castle, PA; *m:* Robin G.; *c:* Ryan Christopher, Autumn Christan; *ed:* Slippery Rock Univ (BA) Ed 1974; 27 Plus Credit Hrs at Westminster Coll, IN Univ & Penn St; *cr:* Midwestern Intermediate Unit IV Title IX Coord, General Ed Diploma Instr, Eng as Second Lang Instr 1975-85; Neshannock Schl Dist Tchr 1985-; *ai:* Dist Newsletter Co-Ed; Pub Relations, Dist Comm, Schl Dirs Appreciation Comms; NEA, PACE, NTEA, PSEA 1985-; New Castle Jr Womens 1987-, Chair of Many Comms; Kappa Delta Pi 1986-, Sec; Amer Cancer Soc 1985-, Auction Gala Chprsn; YWCA 1995-; Exemplary Awd for Excl From the St of PA for Developing a Sex Equity Prgm of Excl Voc Ed Dept 1986; Pub Poetry & in the Natl Lib in Washington DC; Pub Title IX Made Easy for Use in Evaluations of Dists; Power of Partnerships Thanks to Tchrs Awd; *office:* Neshannock Elem Schl 299 Mitchell Rd New Castle PA 16105*

PONZETTI, JANET HASSLER, Math Teacher; *b:* Jersey City, NJ; *m:* Scott; *ed:* Trenton St Coll (BA) Math 1991; *cr:* Millville Sr HS Math Tchr 1991-; *ai:* Key Club Adv; OM Judge; Buddy Prgm Chaperone; Stud Skills Lab TCHR: HSPT Comm; NEA, NJEA, NCTM, AMTNJ 1991-; Make a Wish Fnd 1995-, Coord Charity Golf Tournament, Silent Auction; Sample Lesson Pub; Interviewed for Intnl Newsletter; *office:* Millville Sr HS 200 E Wade Blvd Millville NJ 08332

PONZILLO, LOUIS R.,JR., Social Studies Teacher; *b:* Waterbury, CT; *m:* Beverly Coppeto; *c:* Michael, Elyssa; *ed:* Univ of CT Schl of Ed (BA) His & Soc Stud 1969; Univ of Bridgeport (MS) Scndry Ed 1974; 15 Hrs Eng Cert Cntrl CT St Univ; 6 Hrs Admin Southern CT St Univ; *cr:* Wilby HS Tchr 1969-; *ai:* Waterbury Tchrs Assn 1969-, Bldg Rep; CT Ed Assn, NEA 1969-; *office:* Wilby HS 460 Bucks Hill Rd Waterbury CT 06704

POOLE, BERNARD JOHN, Assoc Prof Ed & Instrl Tech; *b:* Haunton UK, Warwichshire; *m:* Marilyn Giorgio-Poole; *c:* Zsolt; *ed:* London Univ (BA) Eng, His & Fr 1966, (PECE) Ed 1970; West moreland CCC (AAS) Data Processing 1982; Univ of Pittsburgh (MSIS) Information Sci 1983; 12 Grad Credits; *cr:* St Josephs Coll Div Head 1966-74; Mt Carmel Coll Eng Dept Chair 1974-76; Anbercraft Inc Partner 1976-78; Riyadh Schls TOESL Tchr 1978-80; Univ of Pittsburgh Assoc Prof Comp Sci 1983-95, Assoc Prof Ed 1996-; *ai:* Curr Review Comm; Fac Cncl; Fac Senate; Advy Comm for Acad Compng, Rugby Club Adv; ACM 1983-; ASCD 1993-; AAHE 1994-; UPJ Speakers Bureau 1990-; Phi Eta Sigma 1994-, Tchr of the Yr; Books: Education for an Information Age, Teaching in the Computerized Classroom, Essential Microsoft Works: Tutorials for Teachers, Claris Works Step-By-Step, The Resume Writer: Writing it Right; Numerous Articles; *office:* Univ Of Pittsburgh At Johnstwn Schoolhouse Rd Johnstown PA 15904*

POOLE, ROBERT ALAN, MS Guidance Counselor; *b:* Newton, MA; *m:* Ronni Sue Sprung; *c:* James, Jefferson, Lindsay; *ed:* MO Vly Coll (BA) Psych 1969; Cntrl MO St Univ (MS) Scndry Cnslng 1971; 60 Credits Framingham St, Harvard Univ, Emanual Coll; *cr:* Sweet Springs HS Tchr 1969-71; Westborough MS Cnslr 1971-; *ai:* Stu Cncl Adv; Dir IM Sports Prgm; MS Bsktbl, Var Bsbl Coach; MTA 1984-; MA Bsbl Coach Assn 1988-; Middlesex News Coach of Yr 1991, 1995; Mid-Wach B League Coach of Yr 1990; *home:* 49 Bowman St Westborough MA 01581

POOLEY, PATRICIA BROWNLEE, First Grade Teacher; *b:* Sharon, PA; *m:* Robert James; *c:* Erin, James; *ed:* Indiana Univ of PA (BSEd) Elem Ed 1975; Grad Hrs Ashland Univ, OH St; *cr:* Conesville Elem Schl First Grd Tchr 1975-; *ai:* Odyssey of Mind Coach; NEA, OEA 1975-; *office:* Conesville Elem Schl 199 State St Conesville OH 43811

POORMAN, JUDITH (SKWIRA), Mathematics Teacher; *b:* Holyoke, MA; *m:* Michael G.; *c:* Michael Jr.; *ed:* Western New England Coll (BA) Math 1971; Cntrl CT St Univ (MA) Curr, Rsrch, Supervision 1981; *cr:* John F. Kennedy Jr HS Math Tchr 1971-74; Linton HS Math Tchr 1974-75; Schnevus Cntrl HS Math Tchr 1975-76; Newington HS Math Tchr 1977-; *ai:* Math League Adv 1988-91; Soph Class Advisin 1975-76; CT Ed Assn, Newington Tchrs Assn 1977-; NEA 1971-; Celebration of Excl 1988; *office:* Newington HS 605 Willard Ave Newington CT 06111

POPE, ANNA MARIE GOULD, Fifth Grade Teacher; *b:* Martin, OH; *c:* Gregory; *ed:* Siena Hghts Coll (BA) Elem Ed 1962; Sci, Outdoor Ed Classes; *cr:* St Andrew Schl 5th Grd Tchr 1962-63; Graytown Elem Schl 5th Grd Tchr 1963-65; Whiteford Elem Schl 4th Grd Tchr 1965-69; Jefferson Elem Schl 5th Grd Tchr 1969-; *ai:* AFT 1974-, Bldg Rep; Habitat for Humanity 1994-, Habitat Family Spon; Lake Erie Herb Soc 1994-; Project Wild Facilitator; COSI Intern; Outdoor Ed Wkshps Presenter; Sea Grant.

POPE, CHARLENE WHITACRE, Gifted & Talented Prgm Coord; *b:* Port Clinton, OH; *m:* Daniel E.; *c:* Lydia, Adrian; *ed:* Miami Univ (BS) Ed 1973; Bowling Green St Univ (MED) Guidance & Counseling 1978; 23 Hrs Gifted Ed at Ashland Univ & Univ of Toledo; 7 Hrs Tech at Univ of OR; *cr:* Tiffin City Schls Hlth & PE Tchr, Guidance Cnslr & Coord & Tchr of Gifted 1987-, Tech Dir 1995-; *ai:* Acad Decathlon Coach; Coord of Tech; NEA 1973-; COCG & OAGC 1980-; ISTE 1985-; Christ Church 1985-, Pianist; Kiwanis Club Oustanding Educator Awd; NWOET Cmptr Learning Month Awd; *office:* Tiffin City Schls 217 S Washington St Tiffin OH 44883*

POPE, DAVID CALVIN, Physical Education Teacher; *b:* Midland, TX; *m:* Dana Ruth South; *c:* Scott, Andrea; *ed:* Tarleton St Univ (BS) Indstrl Arts 1971, (MED) Educl Admin 1982; *cr:* Garland HS Indstrl Arts Tcgr 1972-75; Bell HS Indstrl Arts Tchr 1975-76; Heidelberg HS PE Tchr 1978-; *ai:* Var Men, Wmon Tennis Coach; Var Women Soccer Coach; FEA, OEA 1978-, Fac Rep; *office:* Heidelberg Amer HS CMR 419 Box 1509 APO AE 09102

POPE, REBECCA K., English Teacher; *b:* Robinson, IL; *m:* Michael S.; *c:* David, Brian; *ed:* Heidelberg Coll (BS) Scndry Ed Eng 1969; Nazareth Coll (MS) Ed 1983; Attnd Interamerican Univ, Wright St Univ; *cr:* York Suburban, Eng Tchr 1969-70; Fall River MA Sub Tchr 1970-71; Fairport Cntrl Schl Eng Tchr 1979-; *ai:* Raider Ranger Club Adv; AFT, FEA 1979-; Missing Children; Jr Golf Prgm; Parent Advs for Spec Ed Awd; 6th Annual NYS Whole Lang Conf Presenter; *office:* Fairport HS 1358 Ayrault Rd Fairport NY 14450

POPIOLKOWSKI, GARY, MS Science & Dept Chairperson; *b:* Canonsburg, PA; *m:* Loreta Castelli; *c:* Jennifer, Matthew; *ed:* CA Univ of PA (BS) Earth Sci 1974; Environmental Ed 1976; Penn St Renaissance Engrng Ed; WV Curr, Instr; George Washington Univ Information, Comm Sci, Tech; Tchrs Level I Prgm; US Space Acad; Univ of MD; CD-RDM Tech Ed; Juniata Coll Environmental Sci 1; *cr:* Chartiers-Houston Jr Sr HS 7th & 9th Grd Tchr 1974-; *ai:* Jr HS PJAS Var Coach Golf, Bsktbl, Bsbl; NEA, CHEA 1974-; NSTA; PSTA; PAECT; NASTS, AAAS 1991-; Challenger Bsbl 1990-, Treas; Talcott Mt Sci Ctr, AAAS Grants; Field Test, Tchr Collaborator TERc; global Lab Project; Co-Presenter 8th NASTS Natl Conf; *office:* Chartiers Houston Jr Sr HS 2050 W Pike St Houston PA 15342*

POPKIE, STEVEN, Fourth Grade Teacher; *b:* Martins Ferry, OH; *m:* Christine R. Collier; *c:* Elisabeth, Joshua; *ed:* OH Univ (BS) Ed 1974; Univ of Dayton (MS) Ed, Admin 1985; *cr:* Buckeye Local Schl LD Tutor 1979-80; Jefferson Cty Chrstn Schl 3-4 Grd Tchr, Prin 1986-89, 3-4 Grd Tchr 1980-; *ai:* Pinewood Derby Coord; Bldg Comm Adv; *office:* Jefferson Cty Chrstn Schl 2501 Commercial Ave Mingo Junction OH 43938

POPKOFF, LAUREN KORN, History & Economics Teacher; *b:* Brooklyn, NY; *m:* Eric Allen; *ed:* Brooklyn Coll (BA) His-Honors 1988, (MA) His 1992; Fordham Univ Credit Hrs; *cr:* IS 234 Tchr 1988; Brooklyn Coll Acad Tchr, Coord 1989-; Undiscovered Equitities Research Inc VP 1996; *ai:* Yrbk Adv 1995-; Cntry Fair Coord 1989-94; Stu Govt Adv 1991-93; UFT, AFT 1988-; Cntr for Educl Change 1994-, Contributor, Presenter; Who's Who of Amer Women 1988; *office:* Brooklyn College Acad 2900 Bedford Ave Brooklyn NY 11210

POPOLIZIO, RICK JOHN, Instrumental Music Teacher; *b:* Bronx, NY; *c:* Sara; *ed:* Fairleigh Dickenson Univ (BA) Music 1973; Kean Coll 21 Addl Credits; *cr:* Prof Musician Perc, Sax 1964-96; Private Tchr Percussion 1972-; Recording Artist Perc 1972-; Pub Schl Instrumental Music Instr 1983-; *ai:* Marching Band, Summer Music Prgm Dir; NJEA, MENC, NEA 1986-; ASCD 1994-; NJ Gov Schl Tchr of Yr 1990-91; Kappa Delta Pi 1995-; *home:* 185 Phelps Ave Bergenfield NJ 07621

POPOVICH, FAITH M., Spanish Teacher; *b:* Wilkinsburg, PA; *m:* Charles G.; *c:* Michael C., Nichole M.; *ed:* IN Univ of PA (BS) Span Ed 1966; Universidad De Las Americas Mexico DF 1st Semeseter Sr Yr of IUP; 18 Hrs Univ of Pittsburgh; 6 Hrs Penn St Univ; *cr:* Charleroi Area HS Span Tchr 1966; Churchill Area HS Span Tchr 1966-72; Penn-Trafford HS 1983-; *ai:* Span Club Adv; Cooperative Tchr for Intern Univ of Pittsburgh; PSMLA; PTEA; AFLA; PSEA; NEA; Pride Awd 1991; Finalist Thanks to Tchrs Univ of PIttsburgh & KDKA 1990-91; All Star Salute Outstdng Edctr Post Gazezze & Univ of Pittsburgh 1994-95t; *office:* Penn Trafford HS PO Box 530 Harrison City PA 15636*

POPP, WILLIAM FREDERICK, Fifth Grade Teacher; *b:* Indiana, PA; *m:* Margaret Deborah; *c:* Anthony, Julianne, Christopher, Benjamin; *ed:* IN Univ of PA (BS) Elem Ed 1972; IUP & Univ of Pitt at Johnsontown Post Grad Stud; *cr:* Blairsville-Saltsburg Schl Dist Elem Tchr 1972-; *ai:* BSEA 1972-, Pres; PSEA 1972-; NEA 1972-; *office:* Blairsville Elem Schl 106 School Ln Blairsville PA 15717

PORA, PATRICIA ANN, Second Grade Teacher; *b:* Pittsburgh, PA; *m:* Charles; *c:* Daniel, Kevin, Beth; *ed:* Edinboro (MS) Elem Ed 1972; *cr:* Millcreek Schls at Tracy 1st Grd Tchr 1970-74; St Pauls Preschool Tchr 1985; Millcreek Schls at Asbury 1-2nd Grd Tchr 1985-; *ai:* Lead Tchr; Instructional Support Team; Millcreek Ed Assn, PA Ed Assn, NEA; PJA 1980-, Bds, Life Membership; Amer Heart Assn, Millcreek Soccer Booster; *office:* Asbury Elem Schl 3814 Asbury Rd Erie PA 16506*

PORADA, CAROL TERESKI, English Teacher; *b:* Newark, NJ; *m:* John; *c:* John, Michele; *ed:* Jersey City St Coll (BA) Eng 1967; *cr:* Abraham Clark HS Eng Tchr 1967-69; Kearny HS Eng Tchr 1969-70; St Mary's Schl Eng Tchr 1983-; *ai:* Peer Cnslng; Yrbk Adv; Mid Sts Co-Chprsn; NCTE 1993-; *office:* St Mary's Schl 25 Pompton Ave Pompton Lakes NJ 07442

PORATH, SHEILA NADILE, English Teacher; *b:* Meriden, CT; *c:* Brett, Stacy; *ed:* Univ of CT (BS) Ed 1959; *cr:* Platt HS Eng Tchr 1959-63; Halldale HS Eng Tchr 1963-68; Cony HS Eng Tchr; *ai:* NEA 1959-; AEA 1981-; *home:* 10 Deer Run Augusta ME 04330

PORCIELLO, KERRI ELLYN, English Teacher; *b:* Huntington, NY; *c:* SUNY at Stony Brook (BA) Eng 1993; *ed:* MA Lbrl Stud will Grad in May 1996; Elwood Schl Dist Eng Tchr 1994-; *cr:* Staff Dev; Stu Advisorship; *ai:* Elwood Tchr Alliance 1994; PTA 1995; *office:* Elwood-John Glenn HS 478 Elwood Rd East Northport NY 11731*

POREDA, EDWARD JOHN, Cross Country Coach; *b:* Trenton, NJ; *m:* Mary Ann Benetto; *c:* Carol Allison, Diana Rees, Edward; *ed:* Syracuse Univ (BA) Recreation 1951; Rutgers Univ (ME) Ed 1970.

POROS, STEPHEN JOHN,JR., Computer & Art Instructor; *b:* Ashtabula, OH; *m:* Pamela Marie Nelson; *c:* Krista, Tara; *ed:* Edinboro St Univ (MED) Ed, Gifted, Art Cmptr 1983; Kent St Univ Ed, Art 1971; *cr:* United Local Schls Art Instr 1968-72; Conneaut City Schls 6th-8th Grd Art, Cmptr Tchr 1972-; *ai:* Head Coach HS Girls Vlybl, 8th Grd Girls Bsktbl; Cmptr Tech Comm; Cmptr Club Adv; GATE Instr in Summer; NEA, OEA 1968-; Conneaut Ed Assn 1972-; OH Art Assn 1978-; United Meth Church Pres, Music Comm, Pastor, Parish Comm, Admin Bd; Scholar Awd Cty Vlybl Co-Coach of Yr 1994; Articles Pub; *office:* Conneaut City 360 Rowe St Conneaut OH 44030*

PORPER, GEORGE FRANCIS, Fourth Grade Teacher; *b:* Bayonn *m:* Deborah Frank; *ed:* Jersey City St Coll (BA) Elem Ed 1969, (MA) Ed 1973; Prin, Supvr Cert; *cr:* Calvin Coolidge Schl 4th Grd Tchr Admin Intern 1986-88, 1990-92, 1995-; *ai:* Hillside Educl Site-Based Planning, Festival of Achvmt Organizational Comms; Hi Ed Assn, NJEA, NEA 1969-; Governor's Tchr Recognition Awd; Awareness Prgm Commendation Cert from Sen. Bradley; Eisenhow Grant Kean Coll; *home:* 96 Joerg Ave Nutley NJ 07110*

PORSIA, MARYELLEN MENNA, Third Grade Teacher; *b:* Philade PA; *m:* Louis; *ed:* Temple Univ (BS) Early Chldhd Ed 1980; *cr:* Edmond Schl 3rd & 4th Grd Tchr 1980-; Tolentine Comm Ctr Adult Ed Tchr 1990-95; *ai:* NCEA 1980-; Nom & Included in Whos Who A Amers Edctrs; *office:* St Edmond Schl 1901 S 23rd St Philadelphi 19145

PORTER, ABIOSEH MICHAEL, Associate Professor of Hur Freetown, Sierra Leon; *m:* Mulsie Cole; *c:* Elizabeth; *ed:* Univ of S Leone (BA) Fr, Eng 1976, (Dip Ed) Ed 1977; Univ of Alberta Comparative Lit 1980, (PHD) Comparative Lit 1984; *cr:* Univ of A Post Doctoral Fellow 1984-85; UMBC MD Post Doctoral Fellow Grambling St Univ Asst Prof of Eng 1985-86; Drexel Univ Assoc P Hum 1986-; *ai:* Pub TV Focus on Africa Bd of Dirs; African Lit 1978-, Assoc Ed; Intnl Comparative Lit Assn 1978-; Lindback Aw Distinguished Tchng; Soc for Hum Post Doctoral Fellowship; Disser Fellowship; Most Distinguished Sr in Fr; *office:* Drexel Univ, Dept of 33rd & Chestnut St Philadelphia PA 19104*

PORTER, BONNIE RUTH, Science Teacher; *b:* Ridgely, TN; *m:* S Jr.; *c:* Shelly III, Sheldon; *ed:* Univ of TN (BS) Elem Ed 1971; Me St Univ (MS) Spec Ed 1977; 5 Credit Hrs Partners Terrific Sci Indstrl Chem Miami Univ; 3 Credit Hrs Effective Tchrs Trng Wright St U Credit Hrs Life Sci, 3 Credit Hrs Geology Univ of Dayton; *cr:* Kendall Elem Schl 6th Grd Tchr 1971-85; F. J. Brown MS Sci, Soc Tchr 1985-87; Wright St Univ Asst Dir, Wright Stepp 1988-95; Fai MS Sci Tchr 1987-; *ai:* Coord Sci Dept, Wright Stepp; Cmptr, Tech C Instrl Support, Monitoring Team; Dayton Ed Assn, OH Ed Assn, 1985-; OH Earth Sci Tchrs Assn 1995-; Partners Ed 1988-, Coord S Month; Delta Sigma Theta 1971-, Treas; AFCEA Sci Tchgn Tolls Presenter SECO Conf; Comm Recognition Awd Ed 1994; Recogr Outstdng Educator; *office:* Fairview MS 2408 Philadelphia Dr Dayto 45406

PORTER, DOUGLAS DEAN, Choral Director; *b:* Watertown, N Lynda Bearup; *c:* Timothy, Seth, Tadam Roemer, Megan Roemer, A *ed:* Ithaca Coll (BM) Music Ed-Voice 1973; SUNY at Albany (MS 1976; Attnd SUNY at Potsdam, Crane Schl of Music, Manhattan Sc Music, Westminster Choir Coll; *cr:* Ticonderoga Cntrl Schls Gen M Tchr, Choral Dir 1973-75; SUNY at Albany Asst Wrestling Coach 197 East Greenbush Cntrl Schls Choral Dir 1976-; *ai:* Fac Senate; Colu Players Musical Dir; NYS United Tchrs, MENC, NYSSMA 1973-; A 1984-; Missions & Soc Concerns 1988-; Spotlight Players Com Th 1979-, Pres, Bd Mem; Albany Pro Musica 1984-; Assoc of Prof Ensembles; Coord Toughlove Group 5 Yrs; *office:* Columbia HS Luth East Greenbush NY 12061

PORTER, EDWARD A., Russian Teacher; *b:* Boston, MA; *m:* Janic *c:* Lisa, Andrea, David; *ed:* Boston Coll (BA) Fr & Eng 1959; Bost Coll (MED) Ed 1960; Boston Coll (MA) Fr 1968; Harvard Univ Ru 1969; Emmanuel Coll Russian 1968-1970; Moscow St Univ Russian *cr:* Weymouth Pub Schls 7th Grd Tchr 1960-62; US Peace Corps UNESCO 1962-64; Weymouth Pub Schls HS Fr & Russian Tchr 1964 Russian Club; Chair of Schl Self-Evaluation 1985; NEA 1960-; A 1990-, Stud Abroad Prgm; Little League Bsbl 1982-87; Pop Warne 1983-88; AFS Exch Tchr in Stauropol, Russian for 3 Months 1989 Grant for Moscow St Univ 1995; *office:* Weymouth HS 1051 Comme St Weymouth MA 02189

PORTER, GAYLE, Asst Professor of Management; *b:* Omaha, N James Quattlebaum; *ed:* Wichita St Univ (BBA) Bus Admin 1979, (M Bus Admin 1982; OH St Univ (MA) Bus Admin 1991, (PHD) C Behavior 1992; *cr:* Peoples Bank of VA Beach Customer Svc 197 Okmar Oil Co Tech Specialist 1973-79; NCR Corp Fin Specialist 197 Friends Univ Curr Dev-Hrm Dir 1986-88; Rutgers Univ Asst Mgmt 1992-; *ai:* Mgmt Soc Fac Adv; Acad of Mgmt 1988-; Numerous Ar Pub; Rutgers Tchng Evaluation Dev Grant; Schl of Bus Tchng Excl *office:* Rutgers St Univ At Camden Schl of Bus 406 Penn St Camde 08102

PORTER, GERALDINE F., Fourth Grade Teacher; *b:* Orange, NJ Newark St Coll (BA) Gen Elem 1970; Post Grad Comp Courses Griebling Schl 3rd Grd Tchr 1970-73; Ardena Schl 4th Grd Tchr 1973 NJEA 1970-.

PORTER, IDA M., Interventionist Teacher; *b:* Beaumont, TX; *m:* Le *ed:* Paul Quinn Coll (BA) Elem & Kndgtn 1963; Addl 24 Hrs A Bachelors; *cr:* Charles Graebner Pre-schl Tchr 4 Yrs; Overbrook Elem 16 Yrs; Joseph Pennell Schl Pupil Support & Interventionist Tchr 9 *ai:* Discipline & Grad Comms; PFT Union 1970-; Positive Tchng 1986; Outstanding Job Performance Pennel Home & Schls 199 Appreciation for Dedicated Svc 1989; *home:* 8303 Williams Philadelphia PA 19150

PORTER, JAMES EARL, Physical Ed & Science Teacher; *b:* Paris, *c:* Michelle, Nikki, James Jr.; *ed:* Lane Coll (BS) Sci, PE 1968; Akron (MA) Ed 1970; *cr:* Franklin D. Roosevelt MS Dept Head, PE Tchr 1 *ai:* Coached Track, Bsbl, Pee Wee Bsbl, Ftbl; Swimming Instr; Cleve Tchrs Union 1970-; Coaches Assn, AFT 1968-; Omega Psi Phi 1969-, of Pledgees; Tchr of Yr 1995-; *office:* Franklin D. Roosevelt MS 800 Dr Cleveland OH 44108

PORTER, JOHN PAUL, Associate Prof of History; *b:* Athens, OH Cheryl Jean Cadwallader; *c:* Catherine Ann Allen, John David; *ed:* Univ (BS) His, Pol Sci 1964; Xavier Univ (MED) His, Pol Sci 1967; Hrs Xavier Univ; *cr:* Hillsboro City Schls Scndry Tchr, His 1964 Tri-Cty Acad Ctr Fac, His 1970-75; Southern St Comm Coll Fac, 1975-; *ai:* Coll Curr Comm; Fac Senate; Fac Assn; NEA 1976-; 1976-; SSEA 1976-, Pres; Org of Amer Historians 1988-; Hillsboro Ch of Christ 1964-, Bd of Elders; Outstanding Fac Mem; *home:* Careytown Rd Hillsboro OH 45133*

PORTER, KAREN L., Sociology Professor; *b:* Syracuse, NY; *m:* R Olson; *c:* Alexa L., Arek A.; *ed:* SUNY Potsdam (BA) Sociology 1 Syracuse Univ (MA) Sociology 1980, (PHD) Sociology 1985 LeMoyne Coll Asst Prof Sociology 1985-86; Alfred Univ Assoc Sociology, Dir Women's Stud Prgm 1995-; *ai:* Consultant Prgm Eval Even Start Prgms; Sociologists Women in Soc 1987-, Chair, Fem Lectureship Cmte; Amer Sociological Assn, NY St Sociological 1985-; Phi Kappa Phi 1987-; AAUW 1995-; 9 Articles Refereed Jour 2 Chapters Books; 1 Rsrch Report; *office:* Alfred Univ Saxon Dr A NY 14802

ER, LINDA, French & Spanish Teacher; *b:* Youngstown, OH; *ed:* stown St Univ (AB) Fr 1977, (MS) Ed, Admin 1983; Attnd Univ de The Sorbonne; Post-Grad Akron Univ; *cr:* Youngstown St Univ Instr, r 1989-92; Howland HS Fr, Span Tchr 1078-; *ai:* Howland oom Tchrs Assn, OH ED Assn, Natl Ed Assn 1978-; Amer Assn of of Fr 1989-; Amer Assn of Tchrs of Span & Portuguese 1992-; Butler Amer Art 1987-; Akron Art Museum 1989-; Youngstown Radio Rdng *fice:* Howland HS 200 Schaffer Dr Warren OH 44484

ER, LORLE, Professor of History; *b:* Mount Vernon, OH; *ed:* Notre (BA) 1960; Boston Coll (MA) Latin Amer 1962; Univ of NM (PHD) val Europe 1965; *cr:* Coll of Steubenville Instr 1962-63; Muskingum of 1965-; *ai:* Fac Affairs Comm; Phi Alpha Theta Adv; OH Acad of 65-; OH Assn Museum & Historical Soc 1970-, 3 Awds Author of ng Region His; Muskingum Cty Tourist Bd; RENEW 1980-, an; Design Review BD Village of New Concord 1990-; Outstdng 1989; Outstdng Alumnae Notre Dame Coll 1993; Western rwood Vly, Roscoe Generations Regeneration, Immigrant Cocoon MA Awds; Discovering OH Hill Cty; *office:* Muskingum Coll New rd OH 43762

ER, LYNDA BEARUP, Middle & High School Math Tchr; *b:* , NY; *m:* Doug; *c:* Megan Roemer, Tad Roemer; *ed:* Vassar Coll Math 1969; SUNY at Albany (MA) Math & Ed 1972; Russell Sage CAC) Cnslng 1991; Post Grad Credits; *cr:* Adirondack Comm Coll Instr 1973-77; Tamarac HS Math Tchr 1978-84; East Greenbush Math Tchr 1985-; *ai:* MS Math Club Adv; EGTA 1984-, Exec Comm p Chm; NYSUT 1970-; AMTNYS 1970-; Renno Cty Environmental League 1994-, Bd Mem; Peace Action Comm 1995-, Bd Mem; ack Vly Assn 1995-; Presidential Tchr of the Yr Awd Nom; Granted etitive Sabbatical to Stud Gender Equity & Math Issues; Pub TV ne Project; *home:* 1523 Sunset Rd Castleton NY 12033

ER, MICHELLE CATINGTON, Art & Photography Teacher; *b:* eville, NC; *m:* Keith Charles; *c:* Kerrie, Craig; *ed:* Western MD Coll Art Ed 1972; Masters Equivalency 30+ Credit Hrs in Ed; Post Grad n Photography 7 Credit Hrs; *cr:* Rising Sun HS Tchr 1975-; *ai:* Schl vement Team; MD Stu Assistance Pgm; Cecil Cty Arts Cncl 1994-; rt Ed Assn Tchr of the Yr for Cecil Cty; *office:* Rising Sun HS 100 Dr North East MD 21901

ER, PETER, Chemistry & Physics Instructor; *b:* Hazleton, PA; *m:* ; *c:* Mark, Julie; *ed:* Penn St (BS) Chem 1970; Duke Univ (MA) 1973; The Restaurnat Schl of Philadelphia; E Stroudsburg Univ Phys 983; *cr:* Lower Moreland Schl Dist Chem Instr 1970-71; Dieruff HS Instr 1972-84; Salisbourg HS Chem & Physics Instr 1985-; *ai:* 1972-; NEA 1986-; AAPT 1986-; NSF Grant for Masters Degree at *office:* Salisbury Sr HS 500 E Montgomery St Allentown PA 18103*

ER, PHYLLIS SKAHAN, English Teacher; *b:* Cambridge, MA; *m:* ; *c:* Jessica; *ed:* Boston St Coll (BA) Eng 1972; Cambridge Coll (MS) 90; Addl Post Grad Courses Tufts, Boston Coll, Harvard Univ; *cr:* HS Eng Tchr 1974-77; West Jr HS Eng Tchr 1977-80; Watertown g Tchr 1981-; *ai:* PTU Grant, Schl Accreditation, Scheduling, Grant rsal, Mass Frameworks, Ind Stud & Interview Comms; Wkshps; 1986-; Watertown Tchr Assn 1974-, Bldg Rep; MA Tchrs Assn, NEA YMCA 1991-; WGBH 1990-; Watertown Ed Fnd Grant 1985; town PTU Mini-Grant; Watertown Schl Dept Funding; *office:* own HS 51 Columbia St Watertown MA 02172*

ER, SHIRLEY LASTER, Lang Arts Teacher; *b:* Chattanooga, TN; wrence E.; *c:* Aqua Y., Angela M.; *ed:* TN St Univ (BA) Eng 1958; t St Univ (MED) 1975; *ai:* Adv for NSH, Sr Grads Comm, Stu Cncl, Achvmt, Wolverine Scholars, Carson-Byans Schlsp, Soc, Courtesy; ring Prgm Coord; NEA 1969-; Phi Delta Kappa 1975-; NASSP TSU Alumni 1965-, Sec; Optimist 1980-, Pres; Alpha Kappa Alpha Pres, Outstdng Mem; The Links Inc 1990-, Comm Chr; NCNW NAACP 1970-; Top Educator; Tchr Appreciation Awd.

ER, STEVEN CLARK, Director of Fine Arts; *b:* NYC, NY; *m:* Rita Iallinan; *ed:* Mannes Coll (BS) Music 1967; Queens Coll-CUNY Music 1967; CUNY Grad Ctr (PHD) Music 1979; LIU (PD) Educl 1984; Musical Theatre Stud with Lehman Engel at NYC; *cr:* s Coll Music, Ed Fac 1967-72; Jericho Pub Schls Chorus, Theatre 972-74; Northport Pub Schls Chorus, Theatre Dir 1975-80; Oyster ub Schls Chorus, Theatre, Grants Dir 1980-84; Binghamton Cty Fine Arts Dir, Head of Serling Schl 1984-; *ai:* Democratic Party date for NY St Senate Dist 51 1992, 1996; BASA 1984-, -Legislative Comm; Kiwanis Intnl 1986-; Lions Intnl 1995-, Guide Dogs; Pub 15 Books on Govt, Ed, Fine Arts, Theatre, 106 Works Since 1970, Over 300 Articles; NY St Chair for Scndry Schl ; Dir Over 25 Musical-Dramatic Productions; *office:* Rod Serling f Fine Arts 31 Main St Binghamton NY 13905*

ER, WAYNE I., Director of Student Services; *b:* Marion, OH; *m:* Martin; *c:* Laura; *ed:* Bowling Green St Univ (BS) Acctng 1967, (MS) & Cnslng 1971; Post Grad Ashland Univ; *cr:* Ridgedale Local Schls Cnslr 1967-76; Tri Rivers Career Ctr Stu Svcs Dir 1976-; *ai:* Asst Var Bsktbl Coach; AVA Assn 1976-; OH Voc Assn 1976-, Stu Svcs Pres, dctr of Yr 1987; Marion Cty Yth Fnd 1986-, VP; *office:* Tri-Rivers r Ctr 2222 Marion Mount Gilead Rd Marion OH 43302

H, CHRISTOPHER FRANCIS, Choir & General Music Director; Paso, TX; *m:* Vanetta Hunter; *c:* Travis O., Austin C., Vanetta H.; *ed:* (BM) Choral, Gen Music 1982, (MM) Choral Music 1983; Addl Ed Cert; *cr:* Highland HS Choir Dir 1983-84; Risinger Primary Schl Music Dir 3 1984-91; J. M. Hanks HS Choirs Dir 1991-94; Hopkinton HS Choirs, Gen Music Dir 1994-; *ai:* Musical Dir, Dist Music Jr, Sr ll-St Music; MENC 1987-; TETA 1988-; ACDA 1995-; Pub Primary Curr; Asst Dir SW Master Chorale; TX All-St Tenor Solo Judge; U horal Contest Div I Rating; Solo, Musical Performance Positions; Hopkinton Jr/Sr HS Hayden Rowe St Hopkinton MA 01748*

O, MARK A., 12th Grade English Teacher; *b:* Teaneck, NJ; *ed:* Hall Univ (MA) Theology, Philosophy 1988; St Mary's Univ at nore MD (STL) Theology 1991, (SJM) Theology 1991; NJ Certs , Elem, Scndry Eng; Working on Cert Scndry Math; *cr:* Dugan-Farley n Asst Dir, Rsrch Dept 1988-90; St John's Univ Adj Instr 1993-95; nsack HS Eng Tchr 1994-; *ai:* Schl Newspaper Adv; Drop In Prgm dv; Adv Inst Tech in Math William Paterson Coll; NJEA 1993-; *office:* nsack HS First & Beech Sts Hackensack NJ 07601*

OLANO, CHARLES JOSEPH, Physical Ed & Health Teacher; *b:* lyn, NY; *m:* Elvira Pisano; *c:* Valerie Marie; *ed:* SUNY at Cortland PE 1974; USAF (AS) Avionics 1977; Adelphi Univ (MS) Hlth Ed NY St Cert Eng, Bio, Earth Sci, Gen Sci; HB Studios at NYC Acting, riting; *cr:* Island Trees HS PE, Hlth Ed Tchr 1981-82; US Post Office , Delivery, Collection 1983-87; Gray Construction Project Mgr, litor 1988-92; Island Trees HS PE, Hlth Ed Tchr 1992-; *ai:* Dir Drama Supvr IM; Goals, Philosophy Comm; NYSUT 1992-, Election Del, Rep; NYSAHPERD 1995-; USTA 1994-; Dedication of 1995 Sr Yrbk; Island Trees HS 59 Straight Ln Levittown NY 11756*

U, CARIDAD, Pre-Kndgtn Teacher & Director; *b:* Caibarien, Cuba; ath Tchrs Coll of Providence RI (BS) Ed 1971; Archdiocese of NY of Ed in Rel Level I & II; *cr:* Acad of St Dorothy 1st Grd Tchr 65; St Francis Schl 2nd Grd Tchr 1961-62; St Patrick Schl 1st Grd 1965-67; St Elizabeth Schl 1st Grd Tchr 1967-69; Acad of St Dorothy 1st Grd, Kndgtn, Pre-Kndgtn Tchr 1969-; *ai:* Tch Rel, Spec Ed After Schl; Support Group for Children; 5 Mile Yrly Walk Amer Cancer Soc, Heart Assn; NCEA 1980-; Early Ed of Staten Island 1989-; Cath Tchrs Conf Day of S I 1962-, Speaker, Wkshp; Cert of Appreciation for Svc in Catechetical Ministry 1986-87; *home:* 1305 Hylan Blvd Staten Island NY 10305*

PORTUONDO, ALICIA E., Span Prof, Frgn Lang Dpt Coord; *b:* Santiago de Cuba, Cuba; *m:* Joaquin; *c:* Alicia Portuondo Ver Hoven; *ed:* Oriente Univ of Cuba (LIC) Span 1952, (LIC) Law 1960; Rutgers Univ (MA) Span 1967; NY Univ (PHD) Span 1976; *cr:* Monmouth Coll Asst Prof 1961-75, Assoc Prof 1975-84, Frgn Langs Dept Chair 1976-85, Prof, Frgn Lang Dept Coord 1985-; *ai:* Eta Pi Spon; Cross Cultural Comm; Span Club Adv; Span Group of Amer Assn of Univ Women Chm; Semester Abroad Comm; AAUP, AAS&P 1965-; Amer Cancer Soc 1965-, Vol; Short Story 1st Awd 1979; Book: Spanish for Social Workers 1981; Woodrow Wilson Natl Flwshp 1985; Distngd Tchr Awd 1983; *home:* 64 Kings Rd Little Silver NJ 07739

PORTZLINE, JOANNE (MARTIN), Third Grade Teacher; *b:* Jackson, MI; *c:* Jeffrey, Jennifer, Eric, Aaron; *ed:* Taylor Univ (BS) Elem Ed 1965; 15 Addl Credit Hrs 1994; Attnd Ashland Univ, OH St Univ, Wright St Univ, Mount Vernon Nazarene Coll, Drake Univ; *cr:* Fort Wayne Comm Schls 1st Grd Tchr 1967, Kndgtn Tchr 1968; Mount Vernon City Schls Tchr 1976-; *ai:* Odyssey of Mind Judge; NEA, OEA 1976-; IRA 1976-86, Sec; Church Chrstn Ed Instr; Mount Vernon Players 1984-, Dir, Pres; Lighthouse Chrstn Cnslng 1994-, Bd Mem; Knox Cty Yth Theatre 1985-91, Founder, Resident Dir; Knox Cty Child Advocate Awd 1991, Mover & Shaker Awd 1990; In Charge of Local Coll Child Abuse Seminar; Copyright Words to Pinocchio Music for Theatre Group; Mentored 13 Stu Tchrs; *home:* 7690 Broadwyn Dr Reynoldsburg OH 43068*

PORUCZYNSKI, CHRISTINA MARIE, Fine Art Teacher; *b:* Bayonne, NJ; *m:* Peter Samuel; *c:* Peter; *ed:* Jersey City St Coll (BA) Art Ed 1970; Kean Coll (MA) Educl Admin 1985; Dist Prof Enrichment Prgms in Cmptr Tech, Word Processing, Desktop Pub, Photo Tech & Graphics; *cr:* Gregory & Lena Conrow Schl Elem Art Tchr 1970-71; M. F. Donohoe Lincoln Elem Art Tchr; John Bailey Roosevelt Vroom Schl Elem Art Tchr 1973-85; Bayonne HS Fine Arts Tchr 1985-; *ai:* Art Club Adv 8 Yrs; Art Schlsp Art Exhibit 5 Yrs; Excl Comm Honors Prgm Mem; AENJ, NJEA 1971-; NJ Ctr for Visual Arts 1988-, Mem; 6 Dist Educl Improvement to Curr Grants; Dist Adopt-A-Schl Prgm Grant; *home:* 101 W 51st St Bayonne NJ 07002

PORVAZNIK, SUSAN JOSEPH, Seventh Grade Teacher; *b:* Pottsville, PA; *ed:* East Stroudsburg Univ (BS) Hlth, PE 1977; Immaculata Coll (BA) Theology 1991; Rutgers Univ 9 Credit Hrs; *cr:* St Bartholomew Schl Tchr 1989-; *ai:* Coord Math-A-Thon, Rel; Mid Sts Steering Comm Co-Chprsn; NCEA, NCTM 1989-; MSA 1992-; Ed Excl Awd Diocese of Metuchen 1993; *office:* St Bartholomew Schl 470 Ryders Ln East Brunswick NJ 08816

PORZUCEK, DONNA, Math Teacher; *b:* Wilkes-Barre, PA; *m:* Joseph; *c:* Laurel, James, Susan; *ed:* Wilkes Univ (AB) Math 1966, (MS) Ed & Cmptrs 1995; 27 Post Grad in Ed; *cr:* Sub Math Tchr 1966-84; Bishop OReilly HS Math Tchr 1984-91; Plains Jr HS Math Tchr 1991-93; GAR Meml HS Math Tchr 1993-; *ai:* NEA, PSEA, WBAEA 1991-; Church Organist, Christman Children Choir Organizer; *office:* G A R Memorial Jr Sr HS 250 S Grant St Wilkes Barre PA 18702

POSATKO, SHEILA FINAN, English & Latin Teacher; *ed:* Marywood Coll (BA) Eng 1964; Univ of Notre Dame (MA) Eng 1969; 45 Credits Univ of DE; *cr:* St Paul HS Eng Tchr 3 Yrs; Newark HS Eng Tchr 3 Yrs; Glasgow HS Eng, Latin Tchr 25 Yrs; *ai:* Classics Club Spon; Classical Assn of DE VP, Pres; Classical Assn of Atlantic Sts; Nat Ed Hums Grants 1991-92, 1994; *office:* Glasgow HS 1901 S College Ave Newark DE 19702

POSEGAY, LINDA ANN STAIB, German Teacher; *b:* New York City, NY; *m:* John S.; *c:* Erik, Marc, Kurt; *ed:* Kutztown Univ (BS) German 1970; *cr:* Parkland Jr HS Springhouse German Tchr 1971-92; Parkland HS German Tchr 1992-; *ai:* German Club Adv; NEA 1971-; *office:* Parkland HS 2675 PA Rt 309 Orefield PA 18069

POSGAI, ROBERT ALEX, Biology Teacher; *b:* Martins Ferry, OH; *m:* Jeanne; *c:* Rob, Ryan, Justin; *ed:* OH Univ (BS) Bio 1971; OH St (MS) Wildlife Mgt 1978; 15 Semester Hrs Scndry Ed, Admin; *cr:* Southern Local Schl Math, Sci Tchr 1971-73; Buckeye Local Schl Biol Sci Tchr 1973-; *ai:* Sci Club, Envirothon Team Spon; Jefferson Cty Course of Stud Comm; OEA 1971-; NEA 1978-; Nature Conservancy of OH 1990-; NSF Summer Stud Grant; Un of Chicago Outstdng Tchr Awd; *office:* Buckeye Local HS Rd 2 Box 475 Rayland OH 43943

POSILLICO, ROSEMARIE ZAFFUTS, Family & Consumer Sci Teacher; *b:* Mt Pleasant, PA; *m:* Joseph C.; *c:* John; *ed:* SUNY at Plattsburg (BS) Home Ec Ed 1977; SUNY at Albany (MS) Curr Planning & Dev 1982; The Coll of St Rose Working on MS in Educl Admin; Inservice Ed Courses Sponsored by NYS Ed Dept & North Colonie Cntrl Schls; Diversified Cooperative Ed Cert; *cr:* North Colonie Cntrl Schls Family & Consumer Scis Tchr 1978-; NYS Ed Dept Consultant 1986-; Shaker HS Family & Consumer Scis Coord 1991-92; *ai:* Assessment & Staff Dev Comms; NYS Family & Consumer Scis Inservice Ed Team Ldr; Chaperone Schl Act & Sport Events; AFT & NYSUT 1977-; NYS Assn of Family & Consumer Sci Edctrs 1978-, St Bd Mem; Amer Assn of Family & Consumer Scis 1988-; Phi Delta Kappa 1992-, Pgm Comm; Amer Voc Assn 1992-; NYS Occupational Assn 1992-; St Rose Coll Educl Admin Assn 1993-; Town of Colonie Partnership 1995-; Capitol Dist Schl to Work Steering Comm 1995-; NYS Home Ec Tchr of the Yr 1992; Shaker Yrbk Dedication 1993; *office:* Shaker HS 445 Watervliet Shaker Rd Latham NY 12110

POSNER, RICHARD, English Teacher; *b:* New York City, NY; *m:* Iris; *c:* Jarrod, Mark, Alayna; *ed:* Hofstra Univ (BA) Dramatic Lit 1965; Dowling Coll (MS) Ed 1976; Queens Coll (MA) Eng Lit 1987; Attnd SUNY at Stony Brook; *cr:* Wm Floyd HS Tchr 1977-78; Sachem HS North Tchr 1978-; *ai:* Schl Newspaper, Lit Magazine Adv; Pianist, Writer Drama & Musical Productions; NYSUT 1976-; NY St Alternate Tchr in Space Prgm 1985; Tchr Excl NYSEC 1990; Publications Eng Journal; 30 Novels; *office:* Sachem HS North 212 Smith Rd Lake Ronkonkoma NY 11779*

POSSEL, CORINNE DENISE, First Grade Teacher; *b:* East Orange, NJ; *ed:* Curry Coll (BA) Ed 1973; Wheelock Coll (MS) Early Child Ed, Dev 1993; *cr:* East Falmouth Elem Schl Kndgtn Tchr 1973-76, First Grd Tchr 1976-; *ai:* NEA, MTA 1973-; Horace Mann Writing Grant; *office:* East Falmouth Elem Schl 33 Davisville Rd E Falmouth MA 02536

POST, ALAN H., Agriculture Teacher; *b:* Celina, OH; *m:* Rose Fullenkamp; *ed:* OH St Univ (BA) Ag Ed 1993; *cr:* Parkway HS Ag Instr 1993-; *ai:* FFA Adv; NEA, Natl Voc Tchrs Assn, OH Ed Assn 1993-; Mercer Cty Ag Soc 1990-; Coldwater Young Farmers 1993-; Mercer Cty Cattlemen 1994-; Mercer Cty Farm Bureau 1995-; *office:* Parkway HS 401 S Franklin St Rockford OH 45882

POST, BARBARA WILBUR, Sci Dept Chair & Chem Teacher; *b:* Boston, MA; *m:* Stanley; *c:* Harry; *ed:* Boston Univ (BA) Pol Sci 1966; Univ of NH 24 Credit Hrs (MEd) Admin Supvr; *cr:* Pittsfield MS Tchr 1985-86; Thom Howard Acad Tchr 1987-89; St Marys HS Dept Chair Tchr 1989-; *ai:* NHS Adv; Jr Var Sftbl Coach; Curr Stu Comm; Pupil Svcs Comm; NASSP 1993-; MAST 1989-; Democratic Town Comm 1995-, Sec; Belknap Cty Democratic Comm 1995-; *home:* PO Box 160 Center Barnstead NH 03225*

POST, DOUGLAS T., Fifth Grade Teacher; *b:* Seaford, NY; *m:* Theresa Cunningham; *c:* Sean, Brendan, Shannon; *ed:* Bloomsburg Univ (BS) Elem Ed 1979; Jersey City St (MS) Ed, Admin 1990; *cr:* Frankford Twp Tchr 1979-; *ai:* Sci Fair Adv; Bus Driver; Problem Solving, After Schl Act Comms; Advy Cncl; FTEA 1979-, Pres, VP; NJEA 1979-, Rep NEA Convention; NEA 1979-; NW Jersey Rdng Cncl; Big Brothers, Sisters Sussex Cty 1982-, Big Brother of Yr; PTA 1979-, Tchr Rep, Vol of Yr; NJ PTA 1979-, Life Membership; Governor's Tchr Recognition Awd; *office:* Frankford Township Schl Pines Rd Box 430 Branchville NJ 07826

POST, EARLE M., Biology Teacher; *b:* Dover, NJ; *m:* Joan E.; *ed:* Montclair St Coll (BA) Sci Ed 1964, (MA) Sci Ed 1969; Addl Credit Hrs; Supvr, Prins Cert; *cr:* Jefferson Twp HS Bio Tchr 1964-; *ai:* NJ St Sci Day Competition Team, Environmental Club Adv; NABT 1968-; Entomological Soc of Amer 1980-; NJ Acad of Sci 1984-; NY Entomological Soc 1990-; Natl Audubon Soc 1975-; Highlands Audubon Soc 1975-, VP, Mbrshp Chair; Branchville Businessman's Club 1994-; North Amer Butterfly Assn 1993-, Regnl Ed; Xerces Soc 1980-; Trng, Present Wkshps NABT; *office:* Jefferson Township H S 1010 Weldon Rd Oak Ridge NJ 07438

POST, GARY ALLAN, Fifth Grade Teacher; *ed:* SUNY at New Paltz (BS) Elem Ed 1966; *cr:* Fishkill Elem Schl Tchr 1966-; *ai:* Stu Govt Adv; Banana Splits; Stu Mentor; Mediation, Substance Prevention & Schl Crisis Teams; AFT 1966-; WCT Local 1966-; Hudson River Sloop Clearwater 1980-, Chair & Bd Mem; Local Zoning Bd of Appeals 1990-, Chair; Mem Natl Drug Free Schl Team Awd 1989; *office:* Fishkill Elementary School Church St Fishkill NY 12524

POST, KAY D. (HOWELLS), Professor of Computer Science; *b:* Pittsburgh, PA; *m:* M. David; *c:* James N. Contakos; *ed:* IN PA of PA (BS) Bus Ed 1962; Univ of MI (MA) Voc Ed, Schl Admin 1976; *cr:* Bethel Park Sr HS Fac 1962-65; IBM Corp Educl Svc Rep 1964-67; L'Anse Creuse Pub Schls Fac 1967-80; St Petersburg Jr Coll Assoc Prof, Corp Train Dir 1980-89; Comm Coll Allegheny Cty Cmptr Sci Dept Chair, Office Tech Dept Head 1991-; *ai:* Dept Chair OAS-CIS; Acad Adv; Acad Affairs Comm; AFT; Word Perfect Pittsburgh Forum 1992-; PA Bus Edctrs Assn, TM St Bus Edctrs 1991-; *office:* Comm Coll Algny Co North Cmps 8701 Perry Hwy Pittsburgh PA 15237

POST, RHODA BABCOCK, Sixth Grade Teacher; *b:* Newburg, NY; *m:* Gary A.; *c:* Allan, Michael; *ed:* St Univ of NY Coll at New Paltz (BS) Elem Ed 1966; 45 Credit Hrs; *cr:* Newburgh Pub Schl System 4th-5th Grd Tchr 1966-68; Wappingers Cntrl Schl Dist 4th & 6th Grd Tchr 1968-; Van Wyck Jr HS Elem Dept Tchr 1993-; *ai:* Sci Olympiad Adv; Turn Key Trainor; CIMS Sci for 6th Grd Tchrs; Schl Dist Rep; Putnam Northern Westchester BOCES Turn Key Trainor WCSD in Learning Styles; AFT 1968-; Wappingers Congress of Tchrs 1968-; Howland 1988-93, Trustee & Pres; Public Lib 1995-; Southeastern Section of Sci Tchrs Assoc of NY St Sci at K-6th Grd Elem Level Outstdng Tchrs Awd; *office:* Van Wyck Jr HS Hillside Lake Rd Wappingers Falls NY 12590*

POST, RICHARD ALLEN, Mathematics Teacher; *b:* Waterloo, NY; *m:* Marlene Joan Mayo; *c:* Kristin, Melissa, Jessica; *ed:* Maranatha Bapt Bible Coll (BS) Bible, Scndry Ed 1982; Owens Tech Coll 4 Credit Hrs 1986; *cr:* Bethany Bapt Church Scndry Math Tchr 1982-90; Emmanual Bapt Chrstn Acad Scndry Math Tchr 1990-; *ai:* Ath Dir; Emmanual Bapt Church 1990-; Prof Reconition Cert Keystone Chrstn Ed Assn 1993; *office:* Emmanuel Bapt Chrstn Acad 4681 E Trindle Rd Mechanicsburg PA 17055

POST, ROBERT JOHN, Spiritual Director; *b:* New York City, NY; *ed:* Iona Coll (BA) Fr 1961; St Johns Univ (MA) Theology 1970; Pacific Western Univ (PHD) Educl Admin 1993; Manahattan Coll 6th Yr Cert Ed Admin; Gonzaga Univ 12 Credits Theology; St Josephs Coll 10 Credits Theology; Chrstn Brothers Coll 16 Credits Theology; *cr:* St Louis Coll Tchr 1961-64; Bishop Gibbons HS Asst Prin 1964-75; Blessed Sacrament HS Prin 1975-79; Trinity Cath HS Spiritual Dir 1984-; Cntrl Cath HS Prin 1989-92; *ai:* Spiritual Adv Var Boys Sports & Trinity Cath Theatre Arts; NCEA 1964-; Belltown Fire Dept 1985-, Chaplain; Stamford Fire Dept 1995-; *office:* Trinity Catholic HS 926 Newfield Ave Stamford CT 06905

POST, RUTH-ELLEN, Paralegal & Legal Studies Prof; *b:* Audubon, NJ; *m:* Dale H. Corliss; *c:* Rebecca Post Corliss, Kenneth D. Karklin; *ed:* Montclair St Univ (BA) Fr, Eng Ed-Cumme Laude 1967; Rutgers-Camden Schl of Law (JD) Law; Syracuse Univ Soc Psych Grad Credits; *cr:* Wahconah Regnl HS Fr Tchr 1967-68; Gen Law Practice 1976-; Part-time Coll Instr 1976-; Rivier Coll Prof, Dept Chair Dept of Paralegal, Legal Stud, His, Pol Sci 1988-; *ai:* Pre-Law, Paralegal Soc Adv; Fac Grievance Comm Chair; Paralegal Advy Bd, Internship Prgm Dir; Amer Assn of Paralegal Ed 1988-, Bd of Dirs 1991-, Ed Comm Awd; Natl Assn of Legal Assts 1994-, Certifying Bd Mem; Amer Bar Assn 1993-, Law Practice Mngmt Section; Town Planning Bd 1986-88; Sierra Club 1990-; Numerous Articles Pub; Paralegal Text Books Ed; Seminars Presenter; Awded Sabbatical 1996-; *office:* Rivier Coll 420 S Main St Nashua NH 03060

POST, WILLIAM L., 5th Grade Teacher; *b:* Poughkeepsie, NY; *m:* Ellen E. Cassetta; *c:* Jennifer Barnaba, Hilarie Larson; *ed:* SUNY at New Paltz (BS) Elem Ed 1963; Grad Hrs Western CT St Coll, SUNY at New Paltz; *cr:* Nanuet Schl Dist 6 Grd Tchr 1963-66; Wappinger Falls Schl Dist 6 Grd Tchr 1966-68; Haldane Schl Dist 4-6 Grd Tchr 1968-; *ai:* Dist Tech, GATE, Dist Safety Comms; NY United Tchrs, AFT 1963-; Haldane Fac Assn 1968-; NY St Retirement Del 1995-; TEG Fed Credit Union Bd of Dir 1972-, Loan Comm Chprsn; Vol Fireman; US Coast Guard Auxiliary Mem; Amateur Radio Operator; *office:* Haldane Cntrl Schl 10 Craigside Dr Cold Spring NY 10516

POSTERARO, CAROLYN AVOLIO, Fifth Grade Teacher; *b:* Pittsburgh, PA; *m:* Gino; *c:* Lauren Eberhardt, Allison Eberhardt; *ed:* Edinboro Univ (BS) Elem Ed 1971; Penn St (MS) Elem Ed 1975; Post Grad Credit Hrs Cmptr Trng, Hyperstudio Creative Drama, Art, Music; *cr:* Northway Elem Schl Third Grd Tchr 1971-73; Seville Elem Schl Fifth Grd Tchr 1973-; *ai:* Producer, Dir Musicals, Talent Shows; Stu Cncl, Newspaper Adv; Lang Arts, Cmptr, Staff Dev, Soc Stud, Rdng Curr Comm; Stu Assistance Intervention Team; NEA, PA St Ed Assn 1971-; North Hills Ed Assn, Bldg Rep 1985-88; Delta Kappa Gamma 1986-88; *home:* 6011 W Grove Cir Gibsonia PA 15044*

POSTERARO, GINO, Elementary Band Director; *b:* Pittsburgh, PA; *m:* Carolyn Avolio; *c:* Julia Lynn, Sara Maria; *ed:* Duquesne Univ (BS) Music Ed 1975, (MS) Music Ed 1979; Addl 21 Credit Hrs Elem Admin 1981-91; *cr:* Avonworth Schl Dist Band Dir 1975-78; North Hills Schl Dist Band Dir 1978-; *ai:* Dist Elem Band Dir; Dist Asst HS Band Dir; Dist NHEA Legislative Chprsn; PSEA Congressional Contact Team; NEA, PSEA 1975-, CCT, LCT; MENC, PMEA 1975-, Festival Host Awd; Pittsburgh Musical Soc 1973-; Trumpeter's Guild 1985-; North Suburband Symphony Band 1992-, Bd; St John Neuman Church 1980-, Brass Ensemble Dir; Gift of Time Awd Amer Family Fnd; Tchr Excl Awd Nom 1993, 1996; *home:* 6011 W Grove Cir Gibsonia PA 15044*

POSTIGLIONE, RALPH ANTHONY, Biology Teacher; *b:* Floral Park, NY; *m:* Florence A.; *ed:* Hofstra Univ (BS) Bio, Chem 1949, (MS) Scndry Ed 1954; 60 Addl Credits; *cr:* Half Hollow Hills Jr HS Sci Tchr 1954-55; Malverne Jr HS Sci Tchr 1955-58; Great Neck Jr HS Sci Tchr 1958-66; Great Neck South HS Sci Tchr 1966-; *ai:* Greenhouse Adv; Ftbl, Tennis Coach; NEA; NYSTA; Natl Assn of Sci Writers; LIFT Tchr Excl Awd 1991; 150 Articles Pub; *home:* 21 Oaktree Ct Albertson NY 11507

POSTLE, KAREN LEE (BURGER), Second Grade Teacher; *b:* Cleveland, OH; *m:* John G.; *c:* Steven, Brian; *ed:* Bowling Green St Univ (BS) Elem Ed 1973; Univ of Akron (MS) Elem Ed 1995; Sev Beh Hand K-12 Cert; Specific LD K-12 Cert; *cr:* Cleveland Pub Schls Rdng Strategy Tchr Grd 2 Tchr 1974-78; Immaculate Conception Schl Grd 4 Tchr

1978-79; Brunswick Schls Sp LD Tutor, Art Tchr, Grd 2 Tchr 1983-; *ai:* NEA 1983-, Bldg Rep; Excl in Ed Tchr Grant 1985, 1993; Huntington Schl Tchr of Yr 1991; *office:* Huntington Elem Schl 1931 Huntington Cir Brunswick OH 44212*

POSTON, LARRY A., Professor of Religion; *b:* Leesburg, VA; *m:* Linda Kay Derksen; *c:* Helena Marie; *ed:* Grace Coll of the Bible (BA) Chrstn Ed 1977; Trinity Evan Divinity Schl (MA) Missiology 1978; Northwestern Univ (PHD) His, Lit of Rels 1988; *cr:* Scandinavian Bible Inst Instr of Missions, Ch His 1981-84; Nyack Coll Missions, Rel Prof 1989-95; Wheaton Coll Inst for Museum Stud Dir 1995-; Nyack Coll Rel Prof 1996-; *ai:* Evangelical Missiological Soc 1990-; Book: Islamic Da'Wah in the West: Museum Missionary Activity and the Cynamics of Conversion to Islam 1992; Numerous Articles, Chptrs Pub; *office:* Nyack Coll 1 South Blvd Nyack NY 10960

POTASNIK, PATRICIA ANN (BORATKO), Business Teacher; *b:* Johnstown, PA; *m:* Gregory Albert; *c:* Alyssa Marie, Amanda Michelle; *ed:* IUP (BSED) Bus 1972; Masters Equiv Bus PA St 1976; *cr:* Johnstown HS Bus Tchr 1972-; *ai:* NEA, PSEA, GJEA 1972-; *office:* Greater Johnstown Schl Dist 222 Central Ave Johnstown PA 15902

POTCHAK, C. DAVID, Junior High Science Teacher; *b:* Johnstown, PA; *m:* Terri Goula; *c:* Amy, Kelly, David; *ed:* Shippensburg Univ of PA (BS) Bio & General Sci 1974; St Francis of PA (MED) Ed 1981; *cr:* Northern Bedford Cty Schl Dist Phys & Life Sci Tchr 22 yrs; *ai:* Var Track & Ftbl Coach 7 Yrs; Ecolgy Clb Adv 10 yrs; Jr High Ftbl Coach 12 yrs; Sci Dept Chprsn 4 yrs; Class Adv 20 yrs; PSEA & NEA 1974-; Northern Bedford Little League 1990-, Vol Coach; *office:* Northern Bedford County HS Rt 1 Loysburg PA 16659

POTENZINI, MONICA L., 7th Grade Reading Teacher; *b:* East Liverpool, OH; *m:* Michael; *c:* Luke Joseph; *ed:* Kent St Univ (BS) Elem & Sec Eng-Cum Laude 1991; Steubenville Univ 12 Grad Hrs; *cr:* Edison North HS 9th & 11th Grd Eng Tchr 1991-92, 7th Grd Eng & OH His Tchr 1992-93; Stanton Jr High 8th Grd US His Tchr 1993-94, 7th Grd Rdng Tchr 1993-; *ai:* Jr Beta Club Adv; Spelling Bee Comm; NEA 1991-; OEA 1991-; *office:* Stanton Jr HS PO Box 158 Hammondsville OH 43930*

POTH, WESLEY STEVEN, Social Studies & PE Teacher; *b:* Columbus, OH; *m:* Cindy Dolan; *c:* Meghan, Kristin; *ed:* Kenyon Coll (BS) His 1969; Xavier Univ (MED) Guidance 1981; *cr:* Northridge HS His & Govt Tchr 1969-70; Blessed Sacrement Schl 6th-8th Grd Soc Stud Tchr & K-8th Grd PE Tchr 1971-; *ai:* Adv to Stu Cncl; Ftbl Coach at Newark Cath HS; Columbus Diocese Course of Stud Comms for Soc Stud, PE & Guidance at Various Times; OH HS Ftbl Coaches Assn 1971-; Amer Legion Auxiliary Citation for Meritorious Svc 1981; Nom for Newark Area Jaycees Outstanding Young Tchr of Licking Cty 1982; Licking Cty League Bsbl Coach of the Yr 1975 & 1977; Asst Coach for the Licking Cty-Muskingum Valley All-Star Ftbl Game 1984, 1987, 1989, 1991 & 1992; *office:* Blessed Sacrament Schl 15 Penney Ave Newark OH 43055

POTLUNAS, JOHN FRANCIS, Instrumental Music Director; *b:* Pottsville, PA; *m:* Michelle Joan Horan; *c:* Michquelena; *ed:* West Chester Univ (BS) Music Ed 1974; PA Dept Ed (M Equivalent) Ed 1984; Attnd West Chester Univ, Univ of MI, Vandercook Coll, Marywood Coll; *cr:* Nativity BVMHS Music Dir Instrumental & Vocal 1974-78; Catasauqua Area HS Music Dir Instrumental & Vocal 1978-79; Williams Valley Jr-Sr HS Mus Dir Instrumental 1980-; *ai:* Marching Band, Jazz Band, Soph Class Adv; Fine & Practical Arts Dept Chm; PMEA & MENC 1974-, Sec Treas, VP, Pres. Inst Auditions Chair; NEA PSEA 1980-; NBA 1980-; Cressona Comm Band 1976- Dir; Schuylkill Yth Symphony 1992-, Dir Conductor; Patriots Vocal Ensemble 1995-; Allentown Diocesian Band Guest Conductor 1981 & 1986; Centre Cty MS Cty Band 1996; *office:* Williams Valley Jr Sr HS Route 209 Tower City PA 17980

POTOCKI, EDMOND JAMES, Sci Dept Chair & Physics Tchr; *b:* Corry, PA; *m:* Mary Jane Pedensky; *c:* Melissa Bahle, Andrew; *ed:* Gannon Univ (BS) Physics 1970; Grad Rsrch; *cr:* Cath Prep Schl Physics Tchr 1969-90; Corry Area HS Physics Tchr 1970-; *ai:* Sci Dept Chair 1975-; Corry Vllybl Club Founding Mem; Internet Trainer for Tchrs; NEA 1970-; PSEA 1970-; CAEA 1970-, Fac Rep; United Way 1970-, Fac Rep; Spartansburg Recreation 1980-, Pres; Corry Schls Federal Credit Union 1970-, Pres; Our Lady of Victory Church 1970-, Parish Rep; Forties Plus Big Band 1984-, Guitar Player; *office:* Corry Area HS 534 E Pleasant St Corry PA 16407*

POTRIKUS, LEO JOHN, Middle School Math Teacher; *b:* Little Falls, NY; *m:* Suzanne Figueiredo; *c:* Alaina, John; *ed:* Herkimer Cty Comm Coll (AS) Math, Sci 1973; SUNY at Oswego (BS) Sec Ed, Math 1975; 30 Addl Credit Hrs Permanent Cert; *cr:* Camillus MS Math Tchr, Math Dept Coord 1975-; *ai:* Bsktbl, Ftbl, Track & Bsbl Coaches; WG Tchr Assn, NYSUT 1975-; Author of Book Tchr BO or Why Our System of Pub Ed Stinks; *office:* Camillus MS 5525 Ike Dixon Rd Camillus NY 13031*

POTRIKUS, SUSAN FRANCES, High School Math Teacher; *b:* Little Falls, NY; *ed:* SUNY at Oswego (BA) Scndry Ed-Math 1973; 30 Grad Credit Hrs; 3 Grad Credit Hrs Coll of St Rose; *cr:* Liverpool HS Math Tchr 1973-; *ai:* Calculus Advanced Placement Exam Preparation, Schl Awds Contest Comm; United Liverpool Fac Assn, NY St United Tchrs, AFT 1973-; Phi Delta Kappa 1995-; Rochester Inst of Tech Distngd Tchr Recognition Prgm 1995; *home:* 105 1/2 Watson Rd North Syracuse NY 13212

POTSIC, ROBERTA K., Teacher & Counselor; *b:* Chicago, IL; *m:* William P.; *c:* Amie, Jordan; *ed:* Univ of IL (BA) Eng 1966; Atlanta Univ (MSW) Soc Casework 1968; Bryn Mawr Schl of Soc Work, Villanova Univ, Cabrini Coll Group Dynamics, Child Dev; *cr:* Atlanta GA Pub Schls Visiting Tchr, Soc Worker 1968-69; United Charities of Chicago Caseworker II 1969-71; Delaware Co Comm Coll New Choices Cnslr 1987-; *ai:* Singles Symposium Wkshp Presenter; NASW 1986-, ACSW; M. L. Unitarian Church 1982-, Bd of Trustees, VP; Women's Resource Ctr; Easttown Twp Lib Friends, PR Dir; *office:* Delaware Cnty Comm Coll 901 S Media Line Rd Media PA 19063

POTTEIGER, CAROL JORDAN, Jr HS Health & PE Teacher; *b:* Harrisburg, PA; *m:* Stephen A.; *ed:* Lock Haven Univ (BS) Hlth, PE 1971; Post Grad Stud West Chester Univ; *cr:* Cntrl Dauphin East Jr HS Hlth, PE Tchr 1971-; *ai:* Spec Olympics Coach; NEA, PSEA, CDEA 1971-; Cntrl Dauphin Distngd Svc Awd; *office:* Central Dauphin East Jr HS 628 Rutherford Rd Harrisburg PA 17109

POTTER, CAROL GALE, 4th Grade Teacher; *b:* Wilmington, DE; *c:* Justin, Brooke; *ed:* Middlebury Coll (BA) Russian 1969; St Michael's Coll (MED) Ed 1977; Trinity Coll CAS Admin; *cr:* Vergennes Elem Schl 1st-6th Grd Tchr 1969-; *ai:* Trinity Coll Stu Tchr Mentor; Conflict Resolution Comm; NEA, VEA 1969-, Bldg Rep, Grievance Comm; Delta Kappa Gamma 1996, Recommended for Mbrshp; Recipient of Local Grants, Mini-Grants; *office:* Vergennes Union Elem Schl 43 East St Vergennes VT 05491*

POTTER, CHRISTOPHER G., Prof of Psych & Counseling; *b:* New York City, NY; *m:* Adrienne M.; *ed:* Hamilton Coll (AB) Psych 1966; Columbia Univ (MA) Counseling & Psych 1972; City Univ of NY Exp Psych Grad Credits; *cr:* Harrisburg Area Comm Coll Psych Prof & Counseling 1972-; *ai:* Natl Bd of Certified Cnslrs 1986-; *office:* Harrisburg Area Comm Coll 1 HACC Dr Harrisburg PA 17110

POTTER, CORY O., Retired English Teacher; *b:* Buffalo, NY; *m:* Howard S.; *ed:* Denison Univ (BA) Eng 1968; Nazareth Coll (BS) Scndry Ed 1976; *cr:* Vermilion Jr HS Eng Tchr 1968-71; Freedom Jr HS Eng Tchr 1971-72; Palmyra-Macedon HS Eng Tchr 1972-95; *ai:* Chrldr Coach 9 Yrs; Class Adv 4 Yrs; Stu Cncl 9 Yrs; Zoning Bd of Appeals 1990-, Chm; United Way 1994-, Bd of Dir; US Coast Guard Auxiliary 1975-, Operations, Commanders Cup.

POTTER, DALE S., Mathematics Tchr & Cmptr Coord; *b:* Elmina, NY; *m:* Pattie Quinn; *c:* Karolee, Eric; *ed:* Corning Comm Coll (AAS) Math, Sci 1964; SUNY Cortland (BA) Math 1967; Elmim Coll (MS) Math 1970; 15 Addl Hrs Cmptr Sci; *cr:* Spencer-Van Etten Cntrl Schl Tchr 1966-; *ai:* Stu Act Treas; NYSUT; AFT; *office:* Spencer-Van Etten Cntrl Schl Daart Crossroad Spencer Ny NY 14889

POTTER, DOUGLAS JOSEPH, Fine Arts Teacher; *b:* Portland, OR; *m:* Elyse Kateman; *ed:* Univ of OR (BS) Fine Arts 1966; NY Univ (BA) Art Ed 1968; *cr:* Adam C. Powell Jr HS Tchr 1968-82; Benjamin N. Cardozo HS Tchr 1982-; *ai:* Art Contests/ Portfolio; UFT 1968-; Finalist Reliance Awds Excl Ed; Nom NY St Tchr of Yr Awd; Recognized Art Excl Scholastic Art Assn; *home:* 8410 Main St Apt 746 Jamaica NY 11435

POTTER, ELIZABETH A., Mathematics Teacher; *b:* York, PA; *m:* Thomas R.; *ed:* Wilkes Univ (MS) Ed 1990; *cr:* Cntrl Dauphin Schls Math Tchr 1987-; *ai:* Key Club Adv; Tchrs Assn Rep; Math Dept Chprsn Grds 7-12; NEA, NCTM, PCTM, Kappa Delta Pi 1987-; PSEA 1987, Sec, Bldg Rep.

POTTER, GEORGE H., Chemistry Professor; *b:* Bolton Landing, NY; *m:* Dorothy K.; *c:* David, Catherine J. Whalen, Richard, Rebecca J.; *ed:* Clarkson Coll (BS) Chem 1953; RPI (PHD) Organic Chem 1958; *cr:* Union Carbide Rsrch Chemist 1958-70; Schenectady Cty Comm Coll Chem Tchr 1976-81, Dept Chm 1981-88, Chem Prof 1988-; Cardin McClaskey HS Chem & Physics Tchr; *ai:* 4H Veg Judge; ACS 1953-; NY St Two Yr Coll Chem Tchrs Assn 1976-, Pres; NSF ILI & Pittsburg Conf Grants; CMA Regnl Chem Tchng Awd 1995; 8 Patents; 2 Articles Pub; 2 Presentations; *office:* Schenectady County Comm Coll 78 Washington Ave Schenectady NY 12305

POTTER, KRISTIN, Occptnl Therapy Asst Pgm Dir; *b:* Tokyo, Japan; *c:* Katrina Bergmann, Daniel Bergmann; *ed:* Freiburg Tchrs Coll (BED) Elem Ed 1971; Boston Univ (MS) Occupational Therapy 1977; *cr:* Clinical Practice Ped Clinician 1977-82; Dominican Coll Pediatric Module Coord 1982-92; Harcum Coll Prgm Dir, OTA Prgm 1992-; *ai:* Dominican Coll Advy Bd; AIM Prgm Advy Bd; AOTA 1977-; POTA 1991-; Unitarian Church, Children's Worship Comm; *office:* Harcum College 750 MontgomeryAve Bryn Mawr PA 19010

POTTER, MARK J., Teacher; *b:* Baltimore, MD; *ed:* Towson St Univ (BS) His 1984, (MED) Scndry Ed 1991; *cr:* Archbishop Curley HS VP for Institutional Advancement & Tchr 1984-; *ai:* Alumni Dir; Sr Class Adv; Var Tennis Coach; NCEA 1984-; Townson St Univ Alumni Assn 1984-, Pres; NEA; Knights of Columbus, Sons of Italy 1991-; St Anthony of Padera Schl Bd 1994-; Speaker NCEA Natl Convention 1995-; Tchr of Yr 1986; Eagle Scout; *office:* Archbishop Curley HS 3701 Sinclair Ln Baltimore MD 21213*

POTTER, RICHARD MICHAEL, Math Teacher; *b:* Staten Island, NY; *m:* Katherine Margaret Byrne; *c:* Kristine, Michael, Sean, Gregory; *ed:* Iona Coll (BA) Math 1970; Richmond Coll (MS) Scndry Ed, Math 1974; 30 Addl Credit Hrs; *cr:* Moore Cath HS Math Tchr, Bsktbl Coach, Drivers Ed Instr, Hnrs Dir 1970-82; Curtis HS Math Tchr 1982-; *ai:* Ath Dir; IB Schlsp Hnrs Prgm Coord; Newman Club Moderator; UFT, AFT, NYSUT 1982-; Natl Assn of Stud Activ Adv 1994-; NY St Ath Admin Assn 1993-; North Shore Democratic Club 1980-; Bread of Life Dr 1994-; Outstdng Scndry Edctrs of Amer 1974; Assn of Tchr of NY Edctr of Yr Awd 1995; Moore Cath HS Hall of Fame 1994; NSF Grant 1973; *office:* Curtis HS 105 Hamilton Ave Staten Island NY 10301

POTTERS, JEAN SHEREDOS, English Teacher; *b:* Plainfield, NJ; *m:* Edward; *c:* David; *ed:* Montclair St Coll (BA) Speech, Theatre Ed 1976; NY Univ (MA) Educl Theatre 1980; *cr:* Red Bank Cath HS Eng Tchr, Forensic Coach 1977-83; Seton Hall Univ Adj Instr 1991-83; Montclair St Coll Adj Instr 1983-87; Lenape Vly Reg HS Eng Tchr 1983-; *ai:* Class Adv 1983-87; Speech, Theatre Assn of NJ 1979-, VP; NEA, NJEA, SCEA, LUEA 1983-; Dover Little Theatre 1989-, Recording Sec; Governors Tchr Recognition Awd; *office:* Lenape Valley Reg HS PO Box 578 Stanhope NJ 07874

POTTS, DAVID KEITH, Sixth Grade Math Teacher; *b:* Uniontown, PA; *c:* Alan, Barbara; *ed:* Morehead St Coll (BA) Elem Ed 1964; Western MD Coll (MA) Adm, Super 1973; MA + 30 in Admin, Supervision 1975; *cr:* Freedom Elem 4th Grd Tchr 1964-66; Sykesville Mid 6th-8th Grd Math Tchr 1966-80; West Mid 6th Grd Math Tchr 1980-; *ai:* Instructional Tech Comm; *office:* Westminster West MS 60 Monroe St Westminster MD 21157

POTTS, DOUGLAS H., 6th Grade Teacher; *b:* Camp Legume, NC; *m:* Kimberlee C.; *c:* Kristee, Brian, Jaclyn; *ed:* Taylor Univ (BS) Elem Ed 1980; Univ of Akron (MS) Elem Admin 1991; Asland Univ 12 Addl Hrs After Masters Degree; *cr:* Southern Wells Local 5th Grd Tchr 1980-82; Osnaburg Local Schls 5th & 6th Grd Tchr 1983-; *ai:* HS Golf Coach; Var Ftbl Games Announcer; Var Girls Bsktbl Games Ofcl Scorer; ECEA, OEA, NEA 1983-, Pres; 1st Baptist Church 1991-, Youth Pastor; Completed Mentor Trng Prgms; *office:* Osnaburg Local Schls Browning St East Canton OH 44730

POTTS, FREDERICK RICHARD,III, Fifth Grade Teacher; *b:* Hudson, NY; *c:* Kelly, Kristie; *ed:* SUC at Brockport (BS) Elem Ed 1973; SUC at New Paltz (MS) Elem Ed 1977; *cr:* Coxsackie-Athens Cntrl Schl 4th-6th Grd Tchr 1973-; *ai:* Rocket Club Adv; AFT, NYSUT, Coxsackie-Athens Tchrs Assn 1973-; NY St Sci Tchrs Assn 1986-; Catskill Fire Dept 1980-, Chief 1989-94; *office:* Coxsackie-Athens Cntrl Schl 24 Sunset Blvd Coxsackie NY 12051

POTTS, KAY MARIE, German & Spanish Teacher; *b:* Pine Grove, PA; *ed:* Susquehanna Univ (BA) Ger, Math 1963; NDEA Ger Inst Albright Coll 1964; Cert Credits Kutztown St Coll 1965-66; Fr Stud Susquehanna Univ 1988-91; *cr:* Evans City HS Ger, Math Tchr 1963-64; Seneca Vly Jr HS Ger Tchr 1964-65; Mahnoy Joint HS Eng, Math Tchr 1965-66; Line Mountain HS Ger, Span, Math, Eng Tchr 1966-; *ai:* Scorekeeper for Wrestling; NEA, PSEA 1963-; LMEA 1966-; AATG, PSMLA 1970-; Idella Rebekah Lodge #58 1974- Recording Sec 1976-85; Sunbury Comm Hosp Vols 1988-; *office:* Line Mountain HS RR 1 Box 1660 Herndon PA 17830

POTTS, LISA ANN, Med, Legal & Fin II Instr; *b:* Barnesville, OH; *m:* Kevin D.; *c:* Dillon Tyler, Taylor Nicole; *ed:* Muskingum Area Tech Coll (AS) Sec Sci 1985; OH Univ (BA) Comprehensive Bus 1985; Kent St Univ 6 Credit Hrs COE & BOE 1985; *cr:* MATC Sec Sci Instr 1984-89; Muskingum-Perry Career Ctr Med, Legal & Fin II Tchr 1985-; *ai:* Bus Prof of Amer Adv; Awds Comm Sec; Octoberfest Chprsn; Christmas Dinner Comm Mem; Mid-East Ed Assn 1985-, Treas; Bus Ed 1985-; NEA & OEA 1985-; AVA 1989-; Tchr of the Quarter; *office:* Muskingum Perry Career Ctr 400 Richards Rd Zanesville OH 43701

POTTS, PATRICIA COOKE, 7th Grade Language Arts Tchr; *b:* Baltimore, MD; *m:* Barry D.; *c:* Joshua, Brady, Bonnie; *ed:* Towson St Coll (BS) Elem Ed 1973; Western MD Coll (MS) Rdng 1980; *cr:* Robert Moton Elem 4th Grd Tchr 1973-78, 2nd Grd Tchr 1981-88; Hampstead Elem 4th Grd Tchr 1978-80; N Carroll Mid 7th Grd Lang Arts Tchr 1988-; *ai:* NEA 1973-; MSTA 1973-; CCEA 1973-, Bldg Rep 2 Yrs; *office:* North Carroll MS 2401 Hanover Pike Hampstead MD 21074

POTTS, PATRICIA FINNEGAN, Mathematics Teacher; *b:* Denv *m:* Mark J.; *c:* Davin M., Kevin J.; *ed:* Fontbonne Coll (BA) Matl Univ of TX at Dallas (MAT) Scndry Math 1984; NSA Summer Inst c Tchng 1994; *cr:* Ladue HS Math Tchr 1967-71; Univ of TX Resour 1984; Brookhaven Coll Instrl Assoc, Math Tchr 1978-85; Ursulin Math, Cmptr Tchr 1985-93; Mercy HS Math Tchr, Tech Resource *ai:* Prom Moderator; Tech Comm Chair; Discipline & Dev Team Sub-Comm for Mid States Self Evaluation Stud for Recertification; 1967-; MCTM 1994-; NCEA 1978-; Archdiocesan TAsk Force fc 1995-; South Meth Univ HS Tchrs Honoree 1990; TX Acad of Math Univ of North TX HS Tchrs Honoree 1990; *office:* Mercy HS Northern Pky Baltimore MD 21239*

POTUCEK, JOSEPHINE SERRANO, Sixth Grade Teacher; *b:* Br NY; *m:* Stephen J.; *c:* Stephen Jr., Frank A.; *ed:* Hunter Coll (BA) En Arts 1973; Brooklyn Coll (MS) Rdng 1975; Hofstra Univ CAS Admin; *cr:* St Patrick's Schl Eng, Rdng Tchr 1973-80; Comm Presch Supvr 1981-84; Shore Road Schl Rdng Readiness Coord 1985-87; J Dinkelmeyer Schl 5th, 6th Grd Tchr 1988-; *ai:* Stu Cncl Rep; Lit Clu Mediation Coord; NYSUT 1988-, Cmptr Linker; *office:* Jo Dinkelmeyer Schl Waltoter Ave North Bellmore NY 11710*

POTVIN, PAUL, Classroom Teacher; *b:* Lewiston, ME; *m:* G. Giroux; *c:* Toby LaCroix, Naomi Lacrois, Andrea, Robert; *ed:* Univ at Machies (BA) His, Elem Ed 1975; Working on Masters Univ c England; *cr:* Campus Schl 4-6 Grd Tchr 5 Yrs; Sabattus Elem 8 Gr 16 Yrs; *ai:* Girls Bsktbl; MS Bldg, IM Prgm's for Studnts, Pub Rel Schl Improvement, Soc Stud Curr Comms; NEA, MEA 1975-; S Tchrs Assn 1980-, Pres, VP; Holy Cross Schl Bd 1993-, Vice Chair; Sabattus Elem Schl PO Box 280 Sabattus ME 04280

POULIN, MARY J., Science Teacher; *b:* Torrington, CT; *w:* Ma (dec); *ed:* Univ of Bridgeport (BS) Elem Ed 1970, (MS) Elem Ed Addl 18 Post Grad Credits in Educl Leadership at Southern CT S *cr:* Franklin Elem Schl 5th Grd Tchr 1970-83; John Winthrop Schl 5th Grd Tchr 1983-84; P L Dunbar Schl 4th Grd Tchr 1984-87, 7th Grd Sci Tchr 1987-; *ai:* Carnegie Fnd Sponsored Team Ldr; Peer Me Adv; Mentor Tchr; Sci Fair Coord; Bridgeport Ed Assn, CT Ed Assn 1970-; Peer Mediation Handbook & Prgm; Certified Mentor Aquaculture Schl Sci Act Coord; *office:* Paul Lawrence Dunbar Ele 445 Union Ave Bridgeport CT 06607*

POULSON, JOHN F., Agriculture Science Teacher; *b:* Bryan, C Lexie M. Zenz; *c:* Jessie L., Shane F.; *ed:* OH St Univ (BS) Ag Ed, 1981, (MS) Ag Ed 1988; 2 Lee Cantner Courses; Tech Update CEU Crestview HS Ag Tchr 1981-88; Pettisville HS Ag Sci Tchr 1990-; *ai* Jr Class Adv; Reserve Bsbl, Summer Rec Coach; OVATA 1981-, Pr Rep, Alumni Rep;AVA, OVA, NVATA 1981-; OEA 1981-88; Lion 1982-, Pres, VP; Farm Bureau 1982-, Yth Cncl Adv; FFA Alumni 19 Reporter; Church; SCS Ag Booster Awd 1994; Triple Crown FFA 1991-95; *home:* V-685 Rd 21 Archbold OH 43502

POULTON, DAVID JOHN, Retired Instrumental Music Dir; *b.* Canada; *m:* A. Doreen Stewart; *ed:* SUCE (BS) Music Ed 1960; St U NY at Potsdam (MS) Music Ed 1966; *cr:* Massena CS Instrumental 1960-64; Hemvelton CS Instrumental Music Dir 1964-92; *ai:* NY 1964-, 25 Yr Pin; NYSUT 1960-; MENC 1964-; SLCMA Music Pres; Lions Club 1986-; Heuvelton Planning Bd 1988-, Chm; *home:* St Heuvelton NY 13654

POUNCIE, BARBARA ELAINE, Artistic Dir & Dance Instr; *b:* FL; *ed:* Purchase St Univ (BFA) Dance, Ed 1979; Attnd City Coll; W Towards MA in Scndry Ed; *cr:* Alvin Ailey Amer Dance Theatre S Prin Dancer 1980-89; Univ of KS Master Dance Tchr 1986; Ju Detention Ctr Dance Instr 1989; PS 26 Dance Instr, Mentor 1992- 84 Dance Instr, Mentor 1992-94; A. Philip Randolph HS Artisti Mentor 1994-; *ai:* A. Philip Randolph Dance Co Artistic Dir; Screen Guild 1977-, Performance; AGMA 1980-, Performance; UFT Children; Salvation Army 1992-, Cnslr & Rec Dir, Enriching Young Drifters Natl Org 1995-, Comm Week; North Manhattan Charity 1979-, Choreographer, Fundraisers; Movie The Wiz Michael Jacksc Dancer 1977; Performed Duet First Black Natl Black Arts Festival; Ailey Amer Dance Theatre Soloist; *office:* A Philip Randolph HS Convent Ave New York NY 10030*

POUND, RICHARD JAMES, Guidance Counselor; *b:* Watertown, N Angelina P.; *ed:* St Lawrence Univ (BA) Sociology 1989, (MED) (1990; Cert Advanced Stud Cnclng 1995; *cr:* J. W. Leary Jr. HS Guid 1990-95; Honeoye Falls-Lima Sr HS Guid Cnslr 1995-; *ai:* Asst Va Strength, Lacrosse Coach; Sons of the Amer Legion 1990-; Honeoye Falls-Lima Sr HS 83 East St Honeoye Falls NY 14472*

POUPKO-REICHMAN, SARA MALKA, High School Teach Queens, NY; *m:* Aaron Don; *ed:* Queens Coll (BA) Educl Psych Michlalah-Jerusalem Tcrsg Degree Judaie Stud 1990; Yeshiva Azrielli Grad Inst Scndry Ed; Bernard Revel Grad Schl; *cr:* Jewis Information Ctr Adv 1989-90; Shaarei Torah HS Tchr 1990-92; H Acad of Nassau Cty HS Tchr 1992-; *ai:* Stu Adv.

POUPORE, LISA A. (BIGNESS), Spanish Teacher; *b:* Malone, N Patrick; *c:* Jessica, Chelsea; *ed:* SUNY at Potsdam (BA) Span & S Ed 1987; SUNY at Plattsburgh Masters MALS 1991; *cr:* Malone MS Tchr 1987-88; Franklin Acad Span Tchr 1988-; *ai:* Span Club Adv; Jr Adv; MFT 1987-; NEA 1987-; AATSP 1991-; NYSAFLT 1987-; *hom* 1 Box 37 North Bangor NY 12966

POVISIL, MARY-JO, Adjunct Prof of Women's Stud; *b:* New York NY; *m:* Leonard Dickens; *ed:* Columbia Univ (BA) His 1989; Univ c (MA) Jrnlsm 1993; Women's Stud Cert; *cr:* Univ of MD Fellow 19 Univ of MD Women's Stud Instr 1991-; *ai:* Producer, Interviewer Affairs Radio Show; Phi Beta Kappa 1989-; Valedictorian Columbi 1989; Nom Outstdng Tchr Pan Hellenic ASsn 1993; Outstdng Tchr C Key Hnr Assn 1993; Master Tchng Asst Ctr for Tchng Excl 1994; Univ Of Maryland Woods Hall Women Studies Dept College Par 20742*

POWE, KAREN DENISE MARCIA, Physics Teacher; *b:* Washi DC; *ed:* Univ of DC (BS) Phys 1989; Univ of Akron (MS) Phys Trinity Coll Credit Hrs; *cr:* Univ of DC Ed Tech 1987-89; Univ of Tchng Asst 1989-93; Univ of A Pre-Coll Prgm Phys Tchr 1993; Eastern HS Phys Tchr 1993-; *ai:* Asst Sftbl Coach; Spec Ed MS A Eval Comm; OBE Problem Based Learning Lesson Plan, Class Demonstration Coord; APS 1990-; MWIS, AFT 1993- Mbrshp Com Usher Bd 1988-; Patricia Roberts Harris Fellow 1991-93; Hlth, Huma Appreciation Awd; Article Pub; *office:* Eastern HS 17th & E Capit NE Washington DC 20003

POWELKO, ANNETTE MAGDALENE, Third Grade Teach Connellsville, PA; *m:* Ronald Edward; *c:* Natalie; *ed:* CA Univ of PA Elem Ed 1974, (MSEd) Elem Ed & Rdng Specialist 1982; Post Grad Supervision 12 Credit Hrs; *cr:* Southeastern Greene Schl Dist 4t Self-Contained Tchr 1978-84, 5th Grd Self-Contained Tchr 1985, 4 Grd Departmental Rdng Tchr 1985-91, ESEA Title I Rdng Tchr 19 3rd Grd Self-Contained & Whole Lang Tchr 1993-95; *ai:* Excel Inc 4 System Advanced Trainer & Facilitator; Dist & Cty Strategic Pla Comm; NEA 1978-; Keystone St Rdng Assoc 1980-; CA Rdng Assoc 1980-, Sec, VP, Pres; McDonalds Corp MAC Grant; Mon-Vly Conso Great Idea Grant; Soc for Analytical Chemists Grant Recipient; PA

Parent Involvement Grant Recipient; Prins Awd; *office:* Bobtown Schl PO Box 397 Bobtown PA 15315*

ELL, BARBARA NELSON, Computer Information Sci Prof; *b:* apolis, MN; *m:* William R.; *c:* Brandon Sodomick, Jeffrey; *ed:* WV BS) Ed, Math, Eng 1970, (MA) Math Ed 1975; 30 Grad Hrs Cmptr *r:* Valley Jr HS Tchr 1971-76; Corning Comm Coll Prof 1981-; *ai:* ssn, Affirmative Action Comms; Rotating Dept Chair; ACM 1981-; Advy Comm to BOE 1987-, Subcommittees Chair; *office:* Corning Coll 1 Academic Dr Corning NY 14830

ELL, D. HUNTER, Sixth Grade Health & PE Tchr; *b:* Hagerstown, *n:* Rosemary; *c:* Tamara, Karyn; *ed:* West Chester Univ (BS) Hlth, 88; Penn St Hlth; *cr:* Donegal Schl Dist HLth-PE Tchr 1988-; *ai:* IM, gh Soccer, HS Track, Coll Bstkbl Coach; Gymnastic-Dance Shows; Track Spon; MS Club Adv; NEA, Donegal Tchr Assn 1988-; Big ers 1985-, Spon; Jaycees Outstdng Comm Fitness Ldr 1991; Tchr of 93; Gift of Time Tribute 1991; *office:* Donegal Schl Dist 1175 River arietta PA 17547

ELL, DAVID JOSEPH, Life Science Teacher; *b:* Sayre, PA; *m:* n Lewis; *c:* Davalyn; *ed:* Lock Haven St Univ (BS) Ed 1972; Western Coll (MS) Ed Guid 1978; USAF Tech Instrs Trng; *cr:* East MS Life chr 1972-; *ai:* NEA, MSTA 1972-; CCEA; *office:* East MS Longwell Westminster MD 21157

ELL, DIANE ELLIOTT, English Teacher; *b:* Canton, OH; *c:* Abbey, *ed:* Malone Coll (BA) Eng & Sociology 1970; Univ of Dayton g; Ashland Coll Gifted & Talented; *cr:* Columbus Pub Schls 7th Grd Arts Tchr 1970-73; Grandview City Schls 7th Grd Eng, G & T Tchr ; *ai:* Yrbk Adv; Directions, Successful Behaviors & Portfolio ns; Lang Arts Curr; Writing Assessment; COGC & OAGC 1989-; LA 1991-; NCTE 1991-; Blvd Presbyn 1976-, Elder, Chair Property; Assoc 1994-; Co-Founder Lost Child Support Group.

ELL, GEORGE DAVID, Science Teacher; *b:* Cincinnati, OH; *m:* B.; *c:* Brian, Mark, Scott; *ed:* Kent State U (BS) Bio 1970; gstown State U (MS) Cnslng 1989; Attnd Case Western Reserve, U, Univ of Akron; *cr:* LaBrae HS Tchr 1970-; *ai:* Beta Club Adv; Chm; NEA 1970-, Comm Chm; Trumbull Co Tchr of Yr Awd 1992; : LaBrae HS 4651 W Market St Leavittsburg OH 44430

ELL, JAMES S., Physics Teacher; *b:* Moira, NY; *m:* Marie ynski; *c:* Elizabeth, Brian, Thomas, Megan, John; *ed:* SUNY at am (BS) Elem Ed 1960, (MS) Ed 1968; Cornell Univ NSF Acad Yr or Sci Grad Stud 1965-66; Utica Coll Grad Work Math; *cr:* Remsen Schl Sci Tchr 1960-65; Utica Free Acad Physics Tchr 1966-90; T. R. or HS Physics Teacher 1990-; *ai:* Utica Tchr Assn, NY United Tchrs, 1966-; Historic Old St Johns Church 1965-, Lector & Vol Worker; Grant Cornell Univ 1965-66; Hnr Tchr of Westinghouse Sci Schlsp Hamilton Coll Sigma Xi Awd 1980; Rotary Outstdng Edctr 1983; Presidential Awds Excl Sci Tech 1986; Employee of Month Utica Schl 1991; *office:* T. R. Proctor Sr HS Hilton Ave Utica NY 13501

ELL, JANET LEE (MC CLISH), Science & Math Teacher; *b:* on, PA; *c:* Joanne; *ed:* Cedarville Coll (BA) Hlth, PE 1964; *cr:* ews HS HPE Sci, Math Tchr 1964-78; Howland Chrstn HS HPE Sci, Tchr 1978-; *ai:* Girls Var Vlybl, Bsktbl; *home:* 870 N State Line Rd asury OH 44438

ELL, JEFFREY W., Physics Teacher; *b:* Utica, NY; *m:* Sharon ck; *c:* Jeffrey, Kellee; *ed:* Ongonta St (BA) Physics 1969; Addl Grad ; *cr:* Oneonta St Physics Instr 1969-70; Baker HS Physics Tchr 1970-; of Concerns Team; NEA, NY NEA 1970-; Baldwinsville Tchrs Assoc -, Chief Negotiator, Past Pres; Integrating Mentally Handicapped s in Sci Classroom Grant; Syracuse NY Chap of Sigma XI Outstndg ci Tchr Awd 1996; *office:* Baker HS E Oneida St Baldwinsville NY 7

ELL, JOLENE D., Biology Teacher; *b:* Sissonville, WV; *m:* William William R., Jeffry S., Jennifer Jo Diley; *ed:* Glenville St (AA) Bio, 960; WV Univ (MS) PE 1963; OH Univ Post Grad; *cr:* Chelyan Schl gh Sci Tchr 1960-65; St. Albans Jr High Sci Tchr 1960-65; Chillicothe Bio Tchr 1978-; Smith Jr High Bio Tchr 1978-; Mt Logan Jr High Bio 1978-; *ai:* CHS, JA Smith Track Coach 12 Yrs; Vlybl Coach 14 Yrs; air Adv GAA Adv; WVEA; CEA, COTA, OEA, NEA 1978-; Tum ch Bd 1966-; Searchers Class Treas; MRDD Bd 1992-, Vice Chr; Beta a Phi 1965-, Pres, VP, Treas, Girl of Yr; *home:* 318 Brennan Rd icothe OH 45601*

ELL, JOYCE DELORES ANDERSON, 8th Grade Language Arts *b:* Greenville, MS; *c:* Calbert K., Janet D. Powell-Trout; *ed:* Univ of do (BE) Soc Stud 1976, (MA) Guid, Cnslng 1979; 38 Post-Grad Hrs ling Green Univ; *cr:* US Army Med Tech 3 Yrs; Receptionist Med 1 pec Svcs US Army Clerk 3 Yrs; Toledo Pub Schls Tchr 20 Yrs, Intern 1 Yr; *ai:* Spon African Amer Club, Adv; AFT, TFT 1976-; Natl Black nce Edctrs, Parents; Zeta Phi Beta; Negro Bus, Prof Women's Club; en AME Church Lay Person 1995; Exec Dir, Founder Warren Church Key Prgm 1994; Pub Svc Awd Presentation of Parenting Wkshp ; *office:* Deveaux Jr HS 2626 W Sylvania Ave Toledo OH 43613

ELL, KARLEEN DYSON (MOORE), Guidance Counselor; *b:* ington, DC; *c:* Catherine Christina; *ed:* Morgan St Univ (BS) Music 976; Bowie St Univ (MA) Cnslng Psych 1980; Pupil Prsnl Worker, in & Supervision Cert; *cr:* G. Gardner Shugart MS Music Tchr -87; Lord Baltimore Acad MS Guid Cnslr 1987-92; Friendly HS Guid r 1992-; *ai:* Instrl Cncl Team Mem; Natl Cncl of Negro Women 1989-; a Kappa Alpha 1973-; MD St Tchrs Assn, NEA 1987-; *home:* 7608 res Ln Brandywine MD 20613*

ELL, KATHARINE JENKS, HS His Tchr & Dept Chair; *b:* ning, NY; *c:* William D., Rebecca J.; *ed:* Hood Coll (BA) His 1964,) Ec 1978; 60 Addl Credit Hrs Beyond Bachelors; *cr:* Walkersville HS 1964-72, 1979-; Hood Coll Soc Stud Methods Instr Part Time; *ai:* s of 1996 Spon; Acad Tournament Adv; FCTA Rep; FCTA, MSTA, 1964-; NCSS, MSCSS & MCSA 1984-; Kappa Kappa Iota 1982-, VP & sec; Church Comm Cncl 1982-, sec, VP & Comm Chair; cersville Almublance Co 1991-; Ec Fellowship at Univ of NC; NEA owship at Wm & mary Coll; Fred Co Innovative Tchr Awd; PTSA Life Awd; *office:* Walkersville HS 81 Fredrick St Walkersville MD 21793*

ELL, KATHLEEN SCEE, Multi-Age Classroom Teacher; *b:* esda, MD; *m:* Mark Richard; *c:* Brian, Kelly, Meghan; *ed:* Towson St (BS) Early Childhood Ed 1976; Loyola Coll (MS) Classroom Tchng ; County Inservice 30 Credit Hrs; Balt Co Inservice 25 Credit Hrs; *cr:* shire Elem Schl 1st Grd Tchr 1976-82; Lansdowne Elem SChl 1st Grd 1982-94, Multiage Classroom Tchr 1994-; *ai:* Girl Scouting, Sftbl ch; Little League Vol; NEA, MSTA, TABCO 1978-; *office:* Lansdowne n Schl 2301 Alma Rd Baltimore MD 21227

ELL, KELLY SUSAN, Former Substitute Teacher; *b:* Norristown, *ed:* East Stroudsburg Univ (BS) Scndry Ed, Eng 1991; Currently NY Masters Prgm 24 Credits Media, Ecology, Dept Culture, Comm; *cr:* sant Vly Schl Dist Sub Tchr 1993-94, Long Term Sub Tchr 11th Grd 1994-95; NY Univ Grad Stu 1993-; *ai:* Conf Papers Delivered; *home:* E 89th St New York NY 10128

ELL, KIPLING JOHN, HS OWA Coordinator; *b:* Oxford, OH; *m:* ny Sue Deaton; *c:* Patrick John, Darcy Marie, Nicholas Paul; *ed:* chester Coll (BA) Environmental Stud, Bio 1979; Wright St Univ (MS) Ed 1994; *cr:* Dayton Jefferson HS Earth Sci, Ecology Tchr 1979-82; Twin Vly North HS Bio, Gen Sci Tchr 1982-83; Preble Shawnee HS OWA Coord 1983-; *ai:* HS, MS Ath Dir; NEA, OEA, 1979-; PSLEA 1983-; Canden Recreation 1988-, Coach; *office:* Preble Shawnee HS 5495 Somers Gratis Rd Camden OH 45311*

POWELL, MARY JANE SIEGLING, Junior HS Language Arts Tchr; *b:* Queens, NY; *m:* J. Edward; *c:* Hilary G., Stacey F. Kipp, Christine J. Lilholt; *ed:* Concordia Jr Coll (AA) Ed, Elem 1961; Concordia Univ (BA) Ed 1979; North Adams St (MA) Eng 1992; *cr:* Berea Schl Kndgtn, Second Grd Tchr 1963-64; Redeemer Schl Kndgtn Tchr 1965-67; St James Schl Jr HS Lang Arts Tchr 1979-; *ai:* 8th Grd, Yrbk Adv; NCEA 1979-.

POWELL, RICHARD ANTHONY,JR., 5th Grade Teacher; *b:* San Diego, CA; *m:* Janice Abramaitys; *c:* Katherine; *ed:* CA St at Northridge (BA) Psych 1970; St Univ Coll at Brockport (MS) Elem Ed 1972; 26 Addl Hrs Educl Psych; *cr:* Lewiston-Porter Cntrl Schl Intermediate Tchr 1972-; *ai:* Ski Club Adv; Vlybl Asst; NYSUT 1972-, Bldg Rep; AFT 1972-; *office:* North Elem 4061 Creek Rd Youngstown NY 14174

POWELL, RICHARD O'BRYAN, High School English Teacher; *b:* Arcadia, KS; *m:* Diana Leah; *c:* Wendy Dawn, Bryan Leon, Shannon Ray; *ed:* OH Valley Coll (AA) Bio 1969; Harding Univ (BS) Scndry Ed 1971, (MED) Bio 1976; *cr:* York Elem Tchr, Coach 1971-77; Morgan HS Tchr, Coach, Intramural Dir 1977-; *ai:* Var Ftbl Defensive Coord; Intramural Dir; Stu Weekly News Broadcast Script Coord; NEA, OEA, SEOEA 1972-; MLEA 1972-, Chm, Grievous Comm, Cal Chair; Pennsville Church of Christ 1970-, Deacon; Penn Vol Fire Dept 1973-; Stockport EMS 1982-85; West Malta Rural Water Bd 1990-, VP; MLEA Outstanding Tchr 1990; Outstanding Elem Tchr of Yr 1974; *office:* Morgan HS 800 Raider Dr Mc Connelsville OH 43756

POWELL, ROSLYN GUNDY, Second Grade Teacher; *b:* Philadelphia, PA; *m:* Lafayette S. Powell Jr.; *c:* Rodney Crawford Jr., Radea Crawford Sharp; *ed:* Temple Univ (BS) Early Chldhd, Elem 1973; Masters' Equivalency Completion; Cmptr Logic Course; *cr:* Intensive Learning Ctr Kndgtn, 2nd-4th Grd Tchr 1973-75; Rowen Elem Schl First Grd Tchr 1975-85; Frederick Douglass Schl Second Grd Tchr 1985-; *ai:* Grds 2nd-4th Acad Ldr; Homeless Initiative Prgm Lead Tchr; Schl Cnsl; Stu Recognition, Math Comms; AFT 1987-; Lombard Cntrl Presby Church 1980-, Sunday Schl Tchr; Girl Scouts 1979-, Ldr; Grant for Alternativies to Violence Curr; Tchr Mentor Awd; *office:* Frederick Douglass Elem Schl 22nd & Norris Sts Philadelphia PA 19121

POWER, BRIAN PATRICK, English Teacher; *b:* Brooklyn, NY; *m:* Myrna Lee Franklin; *c:* Kathleen, Erin Ruth, Tara Meghan; *ed:* Plattsburgh St (BA) Eng 1970; 51 Grad Hrs Scndry Eng; *cr:* NCCS Eng Tchr 1970-; *ai:* Cross Cntry, Bsktbl, Track Coach; Frosh Adv; Hnr Stdnts Annual Coll Visit, Theatre-V Annual Visit Spon; Kappa Delta Pi 1970-, VP; Tchrs Assn 1970-, Pres; AFT 1970-; Noraid 1986-; Organized Annual COTS Walkathon for Homeless; Orgtanized Street Hockey Leagues; Spon Teams at Street Hockey Championships; *home:* 3861 State Route 11 Mooers Forks NY 12959

POWER, GERARD J., PE Teacher; *b:* Bronx, NY; *m:* Kim; *c:* Brian; *ed:* Coll of New Rochelle (BS) Schl Admin 1990; Lehman Coll (BA) Rdng 1995; Cortland St Undergrad BS Elem Ed 1979-85; *cr:* Mt Carmel 5th Grd Tchr 1984-85; PS 41 4th Grd Tchr 1985-86; PS 32 Gym Tchr 1986-; *ai:* Var Bsktbl & Var Tennis Coach; Cath Yth Org 1985-, Bd of Trustees. Honorary Chm; *office:* PS 32 Belmont 690 E 183rd St Bronx NY 10458*

POWER, MARCINE BAUMGARTNER, 5th-6th Grade Math Teacher; *b:* Sarasoto, FL; *ed:* Bowling Green St Univ (BS) Elem Ed 1980; 2 Semester Hrs Math Ashland Coll; 4 Semester Hrs Cmptr Ursuline Coll; 2 Semester Hrs Lit, Lang Arts Kent St Univ; *cr:* St Mary 4th Grd Tch 1 Yr, 6th Grd Tchr 1 Yr, 5th Grd Tchr 4 Yrs; St Brendan 6th Grd Tchr 1986-87; St Paul 3rd Grd Tchr 7 Yrs, 6th Grd Tchr 2 Yrs; *ai:* Math Counts Asst Coach; Math Tutor; Jr HS Girls Vlybl Asst Coach; St Paul Enrichment Comm; CDEA 1986-; *office:* St Paul Schl 61 Moss Rd Westerville OH 43082

POWERS, ALBERT L., Science Teacher; *b:* Nashua, NH; *m:* June H. Beaudet; *c:* Holly Motasky, Cherie Higgins, Heidi; *ed:* Univ of NH (BA) Bio 1960, (MS) Biochemistry 1962; Attnd Dartmouth Medical Schl 1964-66, Cornell Univ Summers of 1968, 1969; *cr:* The New Hampton Schl Sci Chprsn 1962-64; Brewster Acad Sci Chprsn 1966-70; Timberlane Regnl HS Sci Chprsn 1970-74; Concord Carlisle HS Sci Tchr 1974-; *ai:* Sci Olympiad Team Coach; NEA 1970-; NSTA 1964-, Dir, Reg I; MTA 1974-; Concord-Carlisle Schlsp Fnd 1992-, Trustee; Shell Merit Fellow 1968, 1969; Tandy Awd Excl in Sci Tchng 1995; *office:* Concord Carlisle HS 500 Walden St Concord MA 01742*

POWERS, CLAIRE MAHONEY, Science Teacher; *b:* Springfield, MA; *m:* Michael; *c:* Kelly, Michael, Sarah; *ed:* Our Lady of the Elms Coll (BA) Bio 1974; *cr:* Girls Cath HS Sci Tchr 1974-77; Bristol Comm Coll ESL Tchr 1988-90; St John the Evangelist Sci Tchr 1990-; *ai:* Stu Cncl Moderator; Long Range Planning Comm; NCEA 1990-; NSMT 1995-; *office:* Saint John The Evangelist Schl 13 Hodges St Attleboro MA 02703

POWERS, CLINTON H., Math Teacher; *b:* Hartford, CT; *m:* Patricia Q.; *c:* Timothy, Ellen, Sheila; *ed:* Villanova Univ (BS) Soc Stud 1965; Cert Math, His, Gen Sci Soc Stud Cntrl CT St Tchrs Coll 1967; 90 Addl Sem Hrs; *cr:* Hartford Pub HS Math Tchr 1967-; *ai:* Math Team Coach, Adv; AFT 1967-; NCTM 1987-; St Dominic Mens Club 1980-; *office:* Hartford Public HS 55 Forest St Hartford CT 06105

POWERS, FRANKLIN HARRY, Science Teacher; *b:* Marietta, OH; *m:* Sally W.; *c:* Russell Alan, Phillip Franklin; *ed:* Glenville St Coll (AB) Biological, Phys Sci 1964; West VA Univ (MA) Biological, Sci Ed 1967; 6 Post Grad Hrs OH Univ; *cr:* OUZ Spring Botany Lab Instr 1971-72; Caldwell HS Sci Tchr 1964-; *ai:* SADD Adv; Natl Honor Sco Adv 1993; Tech Prep Comm; Sci Dept Chprsn; OEA 1964-, Legislative Comm; NEA 1964-; CTA Local 1964-, Pres; Caldwell Fire Dept 1971-78, Pres 5 Yr Awd; United Ambaulance EMT 1971-93; $5000 Summer Grant 1994; Nashville TN Biochemistry Publication 1971; Croft Sci Techniques Tchrs Sci Article NSF Grant 1971; OH Univ BSCS Bio, Audiotutorial Tchng; *home:* PO Box 146 Caldwell OH 43724*

POWERS, JAMES BRADFORD, Professor of Sociology; *b:* Worcester, MA; *m:* Cynthia Keith Bagster-Collins; *c:* Stephenie, Jeremy, Nicolas; *ed:* Univ ofClark Univ (BSGS) Sociology 1964; Univ of London (MPHIL) Town Planning 1973; Univ of Edinburgh Dip RP Regnl Planning 1969; Northeastern Univ Grad Stud; New Schl for Soc Rsrch; Clark Univ; *cr:* Dean Jr Coll Instr Sociology 1968-70, Registrar 1973-76; Dean Coll Full Prof, Coord Criminal Justice Pgrm 1976-, Assumption Coll Adj Fac 1985-; *ai:* Pre-Law Adv; Hnrs & Awds Comm; Diocese of Western MA Episcopal Church 1980-, Licensed Eucharistic Minster; Outstdng Tchng Awd 1994; Participant Sloan Prgm Harvard Univ 1985; Cert 17th Annual Asian Organized Crime Conf 1995; Book of Rdngs in Sociology 1978; *office:* Dean Coll 99 Main St Franklin MA 02038

POWERS, MARK RICHARD, Guidance Counselor; *b:* Buffalo, NY; *m:* Rita Elaine; *c:* Jennifer Nelson, Michael, Elizabeth; *ed:* Alfred Univ (BA) Speech, Drama & Eng 1968, (MS) Guid & Cnslng 1973; Univ MA at Lowell (MEd) Educl Admin 1981; MS Plus 90 Credit Hrs; CAGS; Schl Psychs 1977; *cr:* US Navy Prsnl Man 2nd Class 1969-71; Avoca Cntrl Schls Eng Tchr 1971-73; No Andover MS Guid Cnslr 1973-; *ai:* Stu Cncl Adv; Numerous Comms; Bsbl & Bsktbl Coach 1985-89; Northeast Cnslrs Assn 1973-; Amer Prsnl & Guid Assn 1973-; MS Cnslrs Assn 1990-, Coord; Cub Scouts of Amer 1984, Pack Ldr; BSA 1987-, Dist Coord; *office:* North Andover Pub Schl System 495 Main St North Andover MA 01845*

POWERS, MARY VICTOR, Principal; *b:* Pittsburgh, PA; *ed:* Seton Hill Coll (BS) Ed 1966; Duquesne Univ (MEd) Admin, Supervision 1969; Notre Dame Univ Rel Stud; *cr:* Cathedral Schl Tchr 1958-59; Saint Jane De Chantal Tchr 1959-64; Immaculate Conception Tchr 1964-65; St Paul Tchr 1965-66; St Edward Prin 1966-78; Cathedral Prin 1978-84; Holy Innocent Prin 1985-90; Word of God Schl Prin 1990-; *ai:* Established Inner City Yth Homework Ctr; Spon Stu of Month Luncheon for Parents & Stdnts; Inaugurated Fine Arts Prgm, Sci Club; Advy Bd Mem; NCEA, ASCD 1966-; PMSA 1993-95; PTO 1990-; IVH Collaborative Cncl 1995-; NSF Grant to Georgetown; SHACC Grant Homework Ctr; PSEA, Giant Eagle Ed Excl Awd; *office:* Word of God Schl 7436 Mc Clure Ave Pittsburgh PA 15218

POWERS, NANCY SPENCER, Biology Teacher; *b:* Boston, MA; *m:* Joseph W. Jr.; *c:* Katelyn, Joseph, Matthew; *ed:* Bridgewater St Coll (BS) Bio 1974; Post Grad Courses Bio, Soc Bio, Hlth; *cr:* Abington HS Bio Tchr 1974-81; Brockton HS Bio, Earth Sci Tchr 1981-82; Abington HS Bio Tchr 1982-; *ai:* Class Adv 12 Yrs; Field Hockey Coach; Hlth Awareness Comm, Stu of Month Comm Adv; AEA, Plymouth Cty Ed Assn, MTA, NEA 1974-; *office:* Abington HS Lincoln Blvd Ext Abington MA 02351

POWERS, PATRICIA MC DONNELL, 4th Grade Teacher; *b:* Holyoke, MA; *c:* Sean, Maurice, Michael; *ed:* Elms Coll (BA) Eng 1966; *cr:* Selser Schl 3rd Grd Tchr 4 Yrs; Litwin Schl 3rd Grd Tchr 3 Yrs; Bowie Meml 4th Grd Tchr 22 Yrs; *ai:* CEA, NEA 1966-; *office:* Bowie Meml Schl 80 Dare Way Chicopee MA 01022

POWERS, RALPH, Physical Education Teacher; *b:* Stoneham, MA; *m:* Gail Maskell; *c:* Daniel, Nancy, Cynthia; *ed:* Boston Univ (BS) PE 1962; Cambridge Coll (EdM) Ed 1992; Framingham St Coll 12 Credits; Salem St Coll 3 Credits; Fitchburgh St Coll 9 Credits; *cr:* Curtis Jr High PE Tchr & Coach 1962-68; Town of Sudbury Recreation Dir 1963-70; Dover-Sherborn Regnl HS PE Tchr & Coach 1968-; *ai:* Boys Var Soccer & Golf Coach; Eastern MA Soccer Assn 1973-, St Coach of Yr Awd 1986 & 1992: Natl Soccer Coaches Ath Assn 1973-; NEA, MTA 1962-; DSEA 1968-; Boys Soccer St Champions 1992; Boston Globe Coach of Yr 1986 & 1992; Eastern MA St Coach of Yr 1986 & 1992; MA St Coach of Yr 1985; *home:* 25 West St Medfield MA 02052

POWERS, ROGER W., Prof of Automotive Technology; *b:* De Ruyter, NY; *m:* Roberta Ossont; *c:* Julie, Derek; *ed:* SUNY at Morrisville (AAS) Auto Tech 1967; SUNY at Oswego (BS) Vo Tech Ed 1971; SUNY Coll of Tech (MS) Vo Tech Ed 1981; *cr:* SUNY Prof 1973-; *ai:* Soc of Automotive Engrs Adv; In Lieu of Credit Comm; UUP 1973-; Chancellors Awd Excl in Tchng 1990; *office:* S U N Y Coll Of A & T Morrisvl Galbreath Hall Morrisville NY 13408

POWERS, WALTER KENNETH, US History & Civics Teacher; *b:* Cincinnati, OH; *m:* Virginia Hafer; *c:* Todd, Mark, Dan, Jay; *ed:* Xavier Univ (BS) Soc Stud & Comm Arts 1968; Post Stud Univ of Cincinnati; *cr:* St John Elem Tchr & Coach 1966-70; Colerain HS Tchr & Coach 1970-72; Northwest HS Tchr & Coach 1972-; *ai:* Boys Track Coach 1966-70; Ftbl & Track Coach 1970-72; Head Ftbl Coach 1972-79; Head Track Coach 1972-; NEA 1969-; OH St Tchr 1976-; City Cncl 1995-, Cncl Mem; Cincinnati Post-Times Coach of Yr 1974; Southwestern Ftbl Coaches Pres 1976; Coach E W All-Stars 1976 & 79; Pam-Am Games Trials Ref 1979; OH Vly Bsktbl Ofcl Pres 1980; Queen City Conf Coach of the Yr 1980; Ashland Oil Outstdng Tchr Nom 1994; *home:* 206 Sunset Ave Harrison OH 45030

POWERS-LAGAC, VIRGINIA, Director of Weekend Coll; *b:* Boston, MA; *m:* Paul A.; *c:* Christopher D., Kevin J.; *ed:* Amer Intnl Coll (BSN) Nrsng 1979-, (MA) Clinical Psych 1981; Univ of CT (PHD) Prof Higher Ed Admin 1995; Nrsng Diploma Malden Hosp Schl of Nrsng 1967; *cr:* Comm Svcs West Outpatient Svcs Supvr 1983-85; Amer Intnl Coll Nrsng Instr 1985-86, Adj 1986-87; Coll of Our Lady of The Elms Asst Prof of Nrsng 1987-89, Asst Prof, Psych Dept Chair 1989-93, Weekend Coll Dir, Adj Fac 1993-; *ai:* Sigma Theta Tau Intnl 1990-; Amer Assn Univ Prof 1989-; Amer Assn of Univ Women 1992-; Delta Kappa Gamma 1989-, Schlsp Comm Chair; Domus Inc 1985-, Bd of Dirs, Past Pres; First Congregational Church, Music Comm 1990-; Publication: Values Clarification Approaches to Pre-Teen Substance Abuse Prevention, Prevention & Treatment of Alcohol & Drug Abuse; *office:* Coll of Our Lady of Elms 291 Springfield St Chicopee MA 01013

POWHIDA, ELIZABETH COOGAN, Spanish & Latin Teacher; *b:* Teaneck, NJ; *m:* Joseph; *c:* Christopher, Catherine, Matthew, Alexander; *ed:* St Univ of NY at Albany (MA) Eng 1968; Span 27 Credit Hrs; Educl Admin, Policy Stud 31 Credit Hrs; *cr:* Ichabod Crane HS Tchr 1969-, Frgn Langs Chair 1985-; Ichabod Crane Cntrl Summer Schl Prin 1992-95; *ai:* Jr Class Co-Adv; Dist Tech, Shared Decision Making, Acad Awds, Drug Free Schls Comms; NY St Tchrs Assn 1969-; NY St Assn Frgn Lang Tchrs 1989-; Sch Dist Employee of Distinction Awd; Anthony Mouse Goes Swimming Children's Book Pub; *office:* Ichabod Crane HS Rt 9 Valatie NY 12184

POWLTER, NELSON M., Eighth Grade Math Teacher; *b:* Waterbury, CT; *m:* Cheryl Ann Wendler; *c:* Devin, Todd; *ed:* Western CT St Coll (BS) Ed 1970; Southern CT St Coll (MS) Ed 1974; *cr:* Newtown MS Tchr 1970-; *ai:* Present Co-Chair Governance Cncl, Girls Sftbl Coach, VP Tchrs Union; Former Yrbk Adv, Math Coord, Co-Founder of Summer Schl Prgm Chess Club & stu Cncl Adv, Bsktbl & Bsbl Coach for Hometwon Children; NFT, AFT 1970-, VP; Stu Cncl Tchr of Yr; *office:* Newtown MS 11 Queen St Newtown CT 06470

POWLUS, GARY RAY, School Counselor; *b:* Berwick, PA; *m:* Teresa L. Adams; *c:* Michael C.; *ed:* Mansfield Univ (BS) Soc Stud 1974; Univ of Scranton (MA) Schl Cnslng 1988; Cert Penn St Univ 1976; *cr:* Benton Area HS Soc Sci Tchr 1974-89; Berwick Area Schl Cnslr 1989-91; Benton Area HS Schl Cnslr 1991-; *ai:* Key Club Adv; PA Schl Cnslr Assn 1989-; PSEA, NEA 1974-; PA Game Commision Hunter's Safety Instr 1978-, 15 Yr Awd; Berwick Golf Club 1979-; *home:* 1025 E 2nd St Berwick PA 18603

POYNTON, JOHN T., US History Teacher; *b:* Darby, PA; *m:* Catherine Schoettler; *c:* Edmund, Patrick, Helen; *ed:* St Joseph Univ (AB) His 1969, (MA) His 1978; Flwshp PA Writing Project; Post-Grad Stud Univ of PA at Lebanon, Valley Coll, Temple Univ; *cr:* Collingdale HS Soc Stud Tchr 1969-79; Ashland MS Soc Stud Tchr 1979-84; Acad Park HS AP US His Tchr 1984-; *ai:* Asst Coach HS Women's Track; Adv Sr Projects; NEA, PSEA, SDEA 1969-, Newsletter Ed; ASCD, NCSS 1990-; *office:* Academy Park High School 300 Calcon Hook Rd Sharon Hill PA 19079*

POYSER, JULIE JOHNSON, Reading & Language Arts Tchr; *b:* Alliance, OH; *m:* Keith W. Jr.; *c:* Kellen E., Kirbi L.; *ed:* Mt Union Coll (BA) Elem Ed 1977; Post Grad Hrs Kent St, Akron Univ, Seattle Pacific Univ; *cr:* Parkway Elem Schl Grds 2-5 Tchr 1977-92, Intermediate Rdng, Lang Arts Tchr 1993-; *ai:* Schl RIF, Dist Curr, Discipline, Schl Net Plus, Testing Comms; Recognition Assembly; Schl Prgm Chr; Host Family Baika Women's Coll Mt Union Coll; IRA; Tchrs Applying Whole Lang; Alpha Xi Delta 1974-, Soc Adv, Unsung Hero Awd, Adv Awd; First Chrstn Church; Alliance Area Chamber of Commerce Edctr of Yr 1991; Stark Cty Tchr of Week 1992; *office:* Parkway Elem Schl 1490 Parkway Blvd Alliance OH 44601*

POZAR, KATHLEEN LOUISE, Speech Arts Teacher; *b:* Pittsburgh, PA; *ed:* Univ of Pittsburgh (BA) Hum 1989; Geneva Coll Speech & Theatre Ed 1970-72; Point Park Coll Theatre Arts & Acting 1972-74; Carlow Coll Cert Scndry Ed, Soc Stud & Commntcn 1990; *cr:* North Hills Schl Dist Asst Dir of Drama & Musical & Asst Forensics Coach 1991-, Speech Arts Tchr 1994-; Comm Coll of Allegheny Cty Applied Acad Curr Writing Team Mem 1992; *ai:* Jr HS Drama Club Spon; Jr High Musical & Play Dir; HS Fall Play & Spring Musical Asst Dir; Asst Forensics Coach; NEA 1994-; PSEA 1994-; Democratic Party 1994-, Chairwoman; Alpha Psi Omega; Natl Forensics League; Thespian Soc; *office:* North Hills Jr HS 55 Rochester Rd Pittsburgh PA 15229

POZNICK, JEFFREY PETER, Social Studies Teacher; *b:* Yonkers, NY; *m:* Nancy Higgins; *ed:* St Univ of NY at Oneonta (BA) Scndry Ed 1969, (MS) Scndry Ed 1976; Attnd Asia Inst Columbia Univ; *cr:* Mildred E. Strang MS Soc Stud Tchr 1969-79; Yorktown HS Soc Stud Tchr 1979-; *ai:* Stu Senate; Alternative Assessment, Regents Variance, Schl Climate Comms; Yorktown Congress of Tchrs, NYSUT, AFT 1969-; Amer Heart Assn 1989-; Heart Care Pub Svc Spots Nyack Hosp 1989-; Nyack Hosp Heart Patient of Yr 1992; Pilot Prgm SUNY at Oneonta 1969; Outstdng Edctr 1995; *office:* Yorktown HS 2727 Crompond Rd Yorktown Heights NY 10598*

POZUN, EDWARD S., Art Teacher; *b:* Johnson, PA; *m:* Frances; *c:* Zachary, Cara, Danielle; *ed:* IN Univ of PA (BS) Art Ed 1975; Masters Equivalency 1986; *cr:* Greater Johnson SD Art Tchr 1975-83; Richland Schl Dist Art Tchr 1983-; *ai:* Art Club; Asst Girls Track Coach; NEA, PSEA 1975-; St, Local Grant Awds; *office:* Richland Sr HS 320 Highfield Ave Johnstown PA 15904

PRACHAR, THOMAS M., Earth & Space Science Teacher; *b:* Allentown, PA; *m:* Diane; *c:* Tom Jr., Shelly, Jeffrey, Jamie; *ed:* Kutztown Univ (BA) Earth, Space Sci 1972; West Chester Univ (MA) Phys Sci 1976; *cr:* Fleetwood HS Sci Tchr 1972-, Var Track, Field Coach 1974-88, Ath Dir 1980-94, Var Bsbl Coach 1989-; *ai:* Outdoor Club Spon; NEA; NSTA; PESTA; PIAA; Optimist; Hawk Mt Assn; *office:* Fleetwood Area HS 409 N Richmond St Fleetwood PA 19522

PRACHER, MARK STEPHEN, High School Band Director; *b:* Huntington, NY; *m:* Laurie Jo; *c:* Erin, Stephen, Kate; *ed:* SUNY at Potsdame Crane Schl of Music (BS) Music Ed 1978; Coll of St Rose (MS) Music Ed 1985; *cr:* Richmondville Cntrl Schl Music Tchr 1980-87, HS Band Dir, Fine Arts Dept Chr 1987-; *ai:* Dir of Jazz, Flute & Brass Ensembles, Musical & Marching Band; Fine Arts Dept Chm; NYSUT, AFT 1980-, Assn Pres; BSA 1992-, Cubmaster, Asst Cubmaster; *office:* Schoharie Central Schl Main St Schoharie NY 12157*

PRAETSCH, PAMELA M., Librarian & College Counselor; *ed:* Wilson Coll (BA) Sociology 1967; *cr:* Woodward Schl Librn, Coll Cnslr & Athletic Dir 1984-; *ai:* Tennis Club Adv; 9th Grd Stdnts Mentor; NEACAC, Cooperative Lib Assn 1985-; Congregational Church 1970-, Treas; Ed Comm for Woodward Schl 1984-; *office:* Woodward Schl For Girls 1102 Hancock St Quincy MA 02169

PRAIL, ROBERT PHILIP, Social Studies Teacher; *b:* Passaic, NJ; *m:* Patricia Schey; *c:* Jonathan, Meredith; *ed:* Rutgers Univ (BA) His 1965; Seton Hall Univ (MA) Gen & Prof Ed 1966; Montclair St Univ (MA) Environmental Stud 1973; *cr:* Schuyler-Colfax Jr HS 7th & 8th Grd Soc Stud Tchr 1969-; *ai:* Girls Track Head Coach; Girls JV Soccer Coach & Asst Coach; Winter Track Asst Coach; NEA 1968-; NJEA 1968-.

PRAIRIE, CHARLES G., HS Social Studies Teacher; *b:* Massena, NY; *m:* Candace M. Lusey; *c:* Trista, Ryan; *ed:* (BA) His, Pol Sci 1973; (MS) His, Ed 1980; *cr:* Massna Jr HS Soc Stud Tchr 1976-77; Brushton Moira Cntrl Schl Scndry Soc Stud Tchr 1977-; *ai:* Bantam Level Hockey Coach; Bldg Improvement Team; *office:* Brushton Moira Central Schl Gale Rd Brushton NY 12916

PRASCHAK, DIANE GIBELLO, Teacher of Gifted & Talented; *b:* Paterson, NJ; *m:* Michael P.; *c:* Kurt, Ilona; *ed:* Montclair Univ (BA) Eng 1958; Wm. Paterson Coll (MA) Parent Ed 1985; Early Chldhd, Supvrs, Elem Ed Certs; *cr:* Lincoln Schl 8th Grd Eng Tchr 1958-62; YMCA Presch Pre-K Tchr 1973-78; N Blvd Schl 1st, 5th Grd Supplemental Instr 1978-85; Pequannock Vly Schl K-8th Grd GATE Tchr 1985-; *ai:* Stu Newspaper Adv; Debate Coach; NJEA, NEA 1981-; NJ Assn Gifted Children 1991-; NJ Consortium for Gifted Ed 1985-; NJ Cncl Ec Ed 1987-, Tchr Resource Person; Pequannock Twp Tchr of Yr 1981-82, 1994-95; NJ Ec Ed Cncl Outstdng Tchr Awd 1989; *office:* Pequannock Valley Mdl Schl 493 Newark Pompton Tpke Pompton Plains NJ 07444

PRASCHAK, DIANE GRIFFITH, Fourth Grade Teacher; *b:* Scranton, PA; *m:* Theodore; *c:* Trina Farrell, Paula, Theodore; *ed:* East Stroudsburg Univ (BS) Elem Ed 1963; Masters Equivalency Cert 1991; 60 Post Grad Credit Penn St, Wilkes Univ; *cr:* Riverside Schl Dist Elem Tchr 1965-; *ai:* IST Team; NEA, PSEA, REA 1965-; Girl, Boys Scouts St Pauls UCC Bd Mem; *office:* Riverside Elem East Sch School & Kreig St Moosic PA 18507*

PRATER, JOSEPH MICHAEL, 8th Grade Amer History Teacher; *b:* Kenton, OH; *m:* Sandra Wierzba; *c:* Lynn Ann, Casey Marie; *ed:* Xavier Univ (BS) Hlth, PE, Pol Sci 1`972; Bowling Green St Univ (BS) His 1989; Addl 15 Hrs His Bowling Green St Univ, 6 Semester Hrs His Univ of MO; *cr:* City of Kenton Parks, Recreation Dir 1972-75; Kenton MS Tchr 1975-; *ai:* Stu Cncl Adv; NEA, OEA, KEA 1975-; Mentorship Prgm 1994-; Meml Park Golf Club 1988-, Pres, VP; Golf Fdn Bd of Dir 1991-; St Presenter OH MS Conf 1986; Jonathan Carter Awd 1989; *office:* Kenton MS 300 Oriental St Kenton OH 43326*

PRATHER, DEBORAH NICHOLS, English Teacher; *b:* Harrisburg, PA; *m:* Alan C.; *ed:* Grove City Coll (BA) Lit 1989; Credit Hrs Univ of Akron 1989, Ashland 1992, Walsh 1994; *cr:* Stow-Munroe Falls HS Eng Tchr 1989-; *ai:* Newspaper Adv 1989-94; NEA 1989-; *office:* Stow-Munroe Falls HS 3227 E Graham Rd Stow OH 44224

PRATOLA, ELIZABETH ANN, Mathematics Teacher; *b:* Long Branch, NJ; *m:* Preston D.; *c:* Stefanie, Sophie; *ed:* William Paterson Coll (BA) Elem Ed 1967; Seton Hall Univ (MA) Prof Ed 1973; *cr:* St Thomas More 3rd-5th Grd Tchr 1970-74; Bayley Ellard HS Math, Eng Tchr 1986-89; St Christopher Schl Math Tchr 1989-; *ai:* Philosophy Comm; NCEA 1989-; Paterson Alumni 1967-; *office:* St Christopher Schl 1050 Littleton Rd Parsippany NJ 07054*

PRATT, BONNIE KORMOS, English Dept Chair & Teacher; *b:* Mc Keesport, PA; *m:* Robert James Sr.; *c:* Meredith N., R. James Jr., Meghan H., Morghan H.; *ed:* IN Univ of PA (BS) Eng Ed 1971; 60 Credit Hrs Post-Grad Stud Ed Advanced Prof Cert; Permanent Cert; *cr:* Bedford HS Eng Tchr 1971-79; St Thomas Elem Schl 5-6 Grd Tchr 1987-88; St Maria Goretti HS 9-12 Grd Eng Tchr 1989-; *ai:* Drama Club Co-Dir; Eng, Sci, Rel Curr Comm; Stu Svc Project Coord; Frosh Class Adv; NCTE, NCEA 1989-; Church Ministry Comm 1989-; Nom MD Cath Tchr of Yr 1992; Tchr of Yr 1995; NEA Shakespeare Flwshp; *office:* Saint Maira Goretti HS 1535 Oak Hill Ave Hagerstown MD 21742*

PRATT, DANIEL WILLIAM, Math Teacher; *b:* Medford, MA; *m:* Gail Tosca; *c:* Lisa Pratt McCormick, Nancy Pratt Mobbs, Barbara Pratt Moser, Casey, Renee; *ed:* Northeastern Univ (BS) Civil Engrng 1964, (MS) Math 1970; 45 Hrs Beyond Masters; *cr:* Boston Tech High Math Tchr 1964-72; Northeastern Schl of Engrng Tech Part-Time Evenings 1967-; Boston Latin Schl Math Tchr 1972-; *ai:* Math & Computer Team Coach; Comp Club Adv; Course Consultant & Curr Developer; Boston Tchrs Union 1965-, 30 Yr Awd; NCTM 1966-; Northeastern Univ 1967-, 25 Yr Awd; Colonial Hlth Club 1994-; Booklet on Casino BlackJack 1978; Article Pub 1978; Boston Latin Comp Team St Championship 1983; *home:* 22 Parkway Rd Medford MA 02155*

PRATT, ISAIAH BAMI JASON, Social Studies, US His Teacher; *b:* Freetown, Sierra Leone; *ed:* Brooklyn Coll (BA) Pol Sci 1975, (MA) Urban Admin 1977; CUNY Grad Schl, Univ Ctr (MA) Pol Sci 1980; Long Island Univ at Southhampton 15 Credits Ed; Fordham Univ 12 Grad Credits Ed; *cr:* Boro of Manhattan Comm Coll Asst Instr 1985-94; CUNY Research Fnd Soc Stud Instr 1987-92; Intermediate Schl 320 Soc Stud Tchr 1988-89; Intermediate Schl 390 Soc Stud Tchr 1989-91; Maxwell Voc HS Soc Stud Tchr 1991-; *ai:* UFT 1988-, Union Del 1994-; AFT, Assn Tchrs of Soc Stud 1988-; CUNY Boro of Manhattan Comm Coll Distinguished Svc Awd 1989, Spec Svcs Merit Cert 1988; *office:* Maxwell Voc HS 145 Pennsylvania Ave Brooklyn NY 11207*

PRATT, RICHARD P.,SR., HS Assistant Principal; *b:* New Castle, PA; *m:* Elaine Miller; *c:* Richard Jr., Michael, Elizabeth, Jeffrey; *ed:* Gannon Coll (BS) Chem 1964, U of Pittsburgh (MED) Sec Ed 1965; Duquesne Univ Prins Cert; Continuing Ed Credits; Penn St Univ Continuing Ed Credits; *cr:* Keystone Oaks Chem Tchr 1965-74, Asst Prin 1974-90, Chem Tchr 1990-93, Asst Prin 1993-; *ai:* PASSP, NASSP 1993-; PSEA, NEA; YMCA South Hills 1982-; *office:* Keystone Oaks HS 1000 Kelton Ave Pittsburgh PA 15216

PRATT, SONIA L., Art Teacher; *b:* Mannington, WV; *m:* Frederick M.; *c:* Devin F., Hagan M.; *ed:* Fairmont St Coll (BA) Art 1972; Attnd WV Univ, Univ of AZ, Guadalajara Mexico Ext, Frostburg St Univ, Navajo Comm Coll at Tsaille; *cr:* Marion Cty Bd of Ed Art Tchr 1972-73; Garrett Cty Bd of Ed Art Tchr 1973-; *ai:* Art Careers Spon; AFT 1976-, John Dewy Awd 1981; AAUW 1996-; Garrett Cty Arts Cncl 1990-, Bd of Dir; MD St Art Ed Assn Outstanding Contribution to Art Ed 1982, 1984; New Forms Regnl Arts Grantee 1994; PA Coun on Arts, Nat Endowment for Arts; Rockefeller Fnd; Andy Warhol Fnd for Visual Arts Inc; *office:* Southern Garrett Sr HS 35 E Oak St Oakland MD 21550*

PRATTS-LOPEZ, LINDA, Science Teacher; *b:* Philadelphia, PA; *m:* Angel P.; *c:* Kristen, Peter; *ed:* West Chester Univ (BS) Hlth & PE 1983; Cabrini Coll (MS) Elem Ed 1990; *cr:* St Josephat Schl 5th Grd, PE Tchr 1984-89; Ethan Allen Elem 6th-8th Grd Sci Tchr 1989-; *ai:* After Schl Bsktbl, Vllybl, Track & Sftbl; PFT 1989-; *office:* Ethan Allen Elem Schl Robbins Battersby St Philadelphia PA 19149

PRAVE, KAREN FAIRCHILD, Science Teacher; *b:* Syracuse, NY; *m:* John Prave; *c:* Kathleen M., Michelle C., John P.; *ed:* SUNY at Oswego (BS) Scndry Sci 1963; SUNY at Cortland Scndry Ed Perm Cert NYS 1970; *cr:* Romulus Cntrl Schl Sci Tchr 1963-69 & 1976-; *ai:* Class Adv 1967, 1970, 1988 & 1991; Prin Advisory Comm; Faculty Assn Membership Comm Chprsn; N.Y.S. Tchrs Retmnt Del; Wellness Comm; Delta Kappa Gamma 1979-, Pres 1984-86 & 1990-92; Pi State Prm Chair 1994-; Romulus Cntrl Schl Parent Support Group Tchr of Yr 1988; *office:* Romulus Cntrl Schl Main St Romulus NY 14541

PRAY, DONALD WALTER, Social Studies Teacher; *b:* Kenmore, NY; *m:* Patricia McCormick; *c:* Sarah; *ed:* SUNY at Buffalo (BA) His & Scndry Ed 1989, (MA) Soc Stud Ed 1994; Working Towards Admin Cert; *cr:* Alden Cntrl Schls Soc Stud Tchr 1989-92; Grand Island Cntrl Schls Soc Stud Tchr 1992-; *ai:* Class of 1997 Adv; Bsktbl Coach; Amer Psychological Assn 1995-; Town of Tonawanda Recreation Dept 1984-, Dir Novice Hockey; Town of Tonawanda Lighting Hockey Org 1992-, Coach Pee-Wee AA Team; *office:* Grand Island HS 1100 Ransom Rd Grand Island NY 14072

PRECOPIO, FOSTER PETER, High School Math Teacher; *b:* Johnstown, NY; *m:* Jeanine Ann Walter; *c:* Gregory, Linda; *ed:* Colgate Univ (BA) Math 1957; Siena (MA) Ed 1964; 30 Hrs SUNY at Albany; 20 Hrs Union Coll; 6 Hrs North Adams; 3 Hrs FMCC; *cr:* Oppenheim Ephratah Schl Math Tchr 1959-62; Greater Johnstown Schl Dist Math Tchr 1962-; *ai:* Golf Coach; Math Club Adv; Head Math Dept; JTA, NEA, NYSUT 1962-; NYMTA 1966-; LOOM 1986-; Tandy Tech Outstdng Tchr of Yr 1995; *home:* 5 ONeil Ave Johnstown NY 12095

PREHODA, CAROL MARIE, Art Teacher & Department Chair; *b:* Granville, NY; *ed:* SUNY at Oswego (BFA) Art 1977; C. W. Post (MS) Art Ed 1989; NYS Permanent Cert in Art K-12 1987; *cr:* Copaigue Schl Dist Art Tchr 1982-83; Hicksville HS Continuing Ed & Adult Ed 1984-; Briarcliff Coll Hum Instr 1990-91; Sacred Heart Acad Chprsn of Art Dept, Coord of Fine Arts 1985-; *ai:* Tech Theatre Dir; Freelance Artist; NYSATA 1987-; CPSA 1993-; BACCA 1994-; Town of Islip Craft Fair Best Of Show Mixed Media; SOHO Art Competition Cert of Excl; *office:* Sacred Heart Acad 47 Cathedral Ave Hempstead NY 11550

PREISER, JOANNE L., English Teacher; *b:* Framingham, MA; *m:* Richard; *c:* Joshua, Daniel; *ed:* Framingham St Coll (BA) Eng 1975; Univ of MA at Boston (MA) Eng 1991; Multi Cultural Lit Curray Coll; 30 Addl Grad Hrs Global Ed, Tchng the Writing Process Framingham St; *cr:* Dover-Sherborn Regnl HS Eng Tchr 1976-; *ai:* Class Adv; Schl Lit Magazine Adv 5 Yrs; Tolerance & Diversity Group Tchr Mem; NEA, MTA, NCTE 1975-; Univ of MA Alvin S. Ryan Awd for Distngd Grad Stud in Eng 1991; Poetry Pub; *office:* Dover Sherborn Reg HS Junction St Dover MA 02030*

PRELLWITZ, NANCY A., Second Grade Teacher; *b:* Chicago, IL; *ed:* Ashland Univ (BS) Ed 1978; Lib Media; *cr:* Frey Elem 1st Grd Tchr 1980-89, 2nd Grd Tchr 1990-; *ai:* NEA 1979-; OEA 1979-; WJEA 1979-, Bldg Rep; Jr League of Columbus 1992-; Christmas in April 1992-; Cntrl OH Tchrs Assn Publicity Grant; *office:* Frey Elem Schl 177 S Frey Ave West Jefferson OH 43162*

PRENCIPE, ARUNDAHTI, Science Teacher; *b:* Cuttack Orissa, India; *m:* Michael; *c:* Joseph; *ed:* St Univ of NY at Stony Brook (PHD) Phys Chem 1987; *cr:* Princeton Univ Undergraduate Labs Coord 1990; Princeton HS Sub Sci Tchr 1991-92; Freehold Twp HS Sci Tchr 1992-; *ai:* NHS Selection Comm; Physics Curr Comm; NEA, NJAAPT 1992-; J. Ghose & A. Kanungo, J. Therm Anal 20 459-462; A. Kanungo & T. Ishida Methyelen Fluoride Clusters Presented Gordon Conf 1984; A. Kanungo, T. Oi, A. Popowicz & T. Ishida, J. Phys Chem 1991; 4198-4203 1987; *office:* Freehold Township HS Elton Adelphia Rd Freehold NJ 07728

PRENDERGAST, THOMAS WILDER, Science Department Chairperson; *b:* New York City, NY; *ed:* Iona Coll (BS) Bio 1981; Harvard Grad Schl of Ed (MED) Math, Sci Ed 1985; Univ of CA at Irvine (MS) Biological Sci; *cr:* Rice HS Sci Instr 1980-82; Cath Mem HS Chair Sci Dept 1983-89; Iona preparatory Schl Chair Sci Dept 1990-; *ai:* Dir Stu Act; Curr Comm Chair; Tennis Prgm Head Coach; Admin & Acad Cncl Mem; Univ of CA Regents Schlsp 1989-90; *office:* Iona Prep Schl 255 Wilmot Rd New Rochelle NY 10804*

PRESBREY, JANICE MATTSON, English Teacher; *b:* Providence, RI; *c:* Univ of RI (BA) Eng & Lbrl Arts 1965; *ed:* Tchng Cert 1966; Grad Credit Tchng of Writing & TET; Cape Cod Comm Coll GED Tchr 1975-85; Dennis Yarmouth Reg HS Permanent Sub Tchr 1982-84; Barnstable MS Eng Tchr 1986-; *cr:* Comm to Integrate Summer Rdng Pgm for MS Stdnts; *ai:* BTA, MTA & NEA 1986-; *office:* Barnstable MS 895 Falmouth Rd Hyannis MA 02601

PRESCAVAGE, EILEEN, Chemistry Teacher; *b:* Wilkes-Barre, PA; *ed:* Coll Misericordia at Dallas (BS) Chem 1972; Univ of Scranton (MS) Biochemistry 1975; Luzerne Cty Comm Coll at Nanticoke Accounting Tech 1985; 36 Addl Credit Hrs Sci; *cr:* WY Area Scn Chem Tchr 1972-, Sci Dept Chprsn 1990-; Misericordia Coll Lecturer 1985-; PA St Univ Chem Lecturer 1995-; *ai:* Sci Olympiad Curr Cncl; Luzerne Cty Sci Tchrs 1973-, Treas 1985-; PA Sci Tchrs Bd of Dirs 1992-; NSTA 1985-; NSTA Chem Tchr Cert 1992; Excl in Awd, Wilkes Univ 1995; *office:* Wyoming Area Secondary Ctr 20 Me St Exeter PA 18643

PRESCOTT, LARRY DEAN, Art Teacher; *b:* Pocatello, ID; *m:* Na Vander Kooi; *c:* Katherine; *ed:* ID St Univ (BA) Art 1985, (BA) E 1988; Stanford Univ Summer 1994; UT St Univ Spring 1994; Bosto 1992-93; *cr:* Indian Hill Elem Schl 6th Grd Tchr 1988-90; Bechte Schl 6th Grd Tchr 1990-92, Art Tchr 1992-95; *ai:* Cmptr Graphic Spon; NEA 1988-; Received Exceptional Rating in DODDS; Re Special Act Awds for Exceeding Performance Standards; Pub Art V Sun Twenty; Pub Article in Entomological Journal; *home:* 1335 Vista Dr Pocatello ID 83201

PRESCOTT, TIMOTHY RAYMOND, Secondary Physical Ed Te *b:* Island Falls, ME; *m:* Julie; *ed:* Univ of ME (BS) PE 1983; *cr:* P Isle HS PE, Hlth Tchr 1984-; *ai:* Girls Jr Var Soccer, Boys Var Bskt Sftbl Coach; ME Tchrs Assn, ME Coaches Assn, ME Assn of Coaches 1984-; Big East Bsktbl Conf Coach of Yr 1992, 1994; ME A Bsktbl Coaches Coach of Yr 1994; *office:* Presque Isle HS 16 Presque Isle ME 04769

PRESKENIS, ANNE M., English Teacher; *b:* Boston, MA; *m:* Rob *c:* Mark, Matthew, James; *ed:* Boston St Coll (BS) Eng, Ed 1966; 18 Hrs Bridgewater St Coll; 18 Credit Hrs Univ of MA; *cr:* Rockland H Dean of Stdnts 1966-74; Plymouth North HS Eng Tchr 1982-; *ai:* Cu Comm 10 Yrs; Portfolio Assessment, Tech Prep Comm; MAED R Assessment; Critical Thinking, Coop Lrng Comm 10 Yrs; NEA 19 1982-; MTA 1966-74, 1982-, Convention Delegate; EAPC 1982-, F MCTE; CCD St Bridget's; Voted Favorite Female Tchr 5 Yrs in a *office:* Plymouth North HS 41 Obery St Plymouth MA 02360

PRESSLEY, JOHNNY GORDON, Professor of Theology & Eth Atlanta, GA; *m:* Jeanette Karen; *c:* Jenna; *ed:* Roanoke Bible Col Chrstn Ministry 1975; Cincinnati Chrstn Seminary (MDiv) Theology Princeton Theological Seminary (THM) His of Doctrine Westminster Theological Seminary (PHD) Reformation Stud 198 Roanoke Bible Coll Prof Theology & New Testament & Dean of 1983-90; Cincinnati Bible Coll & Seminary Prof Theology & Eth Theology Dept Chm 1990-; *ai:* Teach Extension Courses US & Ove Evangelical Theological Soc 1990-; *office:* Cincinnati Bible Coll & PO Box 4320 Cincinnati OH 45204

PRESSLEY, TOMMY L.,JR., Electronics I Instructor; *b:* Warrior, A Veresser Green; *c:* Diana, Kimberly, Dawn, Tommy; *ed:* SUNY C Buffalo (BA) Voc, Tech Ed 1988; Erie Comm Coll Diploma Elec 196 Electrical Union #41 Ibew Electrician 1970-; ATSI Inc Electrical Tech 1979-87; Buffalo Bd of Ed Elec Tchr 1982-84, 1988-; *ai:* Drill Adv; Nat Soc Black Engr; Track Coach 1989-92; NEA, BTF 1982-; 1970-; Genesis Comm Church 1973-, Pastor; *office:* Hutchinson Cntr HS 256 S Elmwood Ave Buffalo NY 14201

PRESSMAN, SYLVIE, French Professor; *b:* Montbeliard, Franc John C.; *c:* Mark L.; *ed:* Univ of Besancon (BA) 1971, (MA) 1976; of Paris IV Sorbonne DEA 1993; Working Towards Doctorate; Bostor 8 Credit Hrs Fr Lit 1989-90; *cr:* CA, MA, MN HS Fr Tchr 1966; F SL Tchr 1971-74; Denver Univ Fr Prof 1976; Intnl Schl Biling 1978-80; Bradford Coll Asst Prof 1986-87; Merrimack Coll Asst 1987-; *ai:* Mullimedia Ctr, Acad Planning, Interdisciplinary Co Continuing Ed Fac Advy Comm Chair, Fr Club Adv; AFT, FMLA, N 1995-; AAUP 1994-; Societe Frangaise of Etudes Americaines 1995- Round Table of UMA Lowell 1974-; Fr Lib Boston; Denver Intnl Fes Judge; La Societe Historigue Franca Americaine; Grants to attend Wkshps; Many Paper Presentations; Articles Pub; *office:* Merrimack 315 Turnpike St North Andover MA 01845*

PRESTON, DENISE DE LARME, Biology Teacher; *b:* Du Bois, P. Michael L.; *c:* Michael, John, Daniel; *ed:* Clarion Univ of PA (BS 1981, (MED) Sci Ed 1989; Credit Hrs Curr & Instruction Penn St Uni Penn St Lab, Technician 1984-88; Clarion Univ of PA Grad Asst Rsrch Asst 1990; Brockway Area HS Bio Tchr 1991-; *ai:* AIMS TEAMS Coach Engrng Competition; Envirothon Coach Environm Competition; Brockway Effective Schl Team; PA Sci Tchrs Assn 1989-, Convention Prgm Chair; PSEA, NEA 1992-; NSTA 1989-; A 1992-94; BSA 1986-, Cub Den Ldr, Comm; PTA 1986-; *home:* 820 Ja St Reynoldsville PA 15851*

PRESTON, JANET REIFENSTAHL, Guidance Counselor; *b:* Colur OH; *m:* Samuel L.; *c:* Jennifer, Samuel III; *ed:* Bowling Green St (BS) Eng, Speech, Drama 1967, (MED) Guid, Cnslng 1971; 30 Hrs Grad Cnslng, Comm; *cr:* Rossford HS Eng, Drama Tchr 196 Woodmore Local Schls Migrant Schl Dir 1975-82; Woodmore Interme Schl Cnslr 1982-84; Woodmore HS Cnslr, Eng, Speech Tchr 1985 Ldrshp Bd, Key Club, Peer Assisting Stdnts Adv; North Coast L Coach; Northwest OH Cnslr Assn 1993-, Treas, Pub Relations; Cnslng Assn 1990-; OH Cnslng Assn 1993-; NCTE; St John United C Christ 1972-, Chrstn Educ Supt, Sec, Longevity; Excl Tchng G 1990-91; Career Edctr of Yr 1991; *office:* Woodmore HS 633 Fremo Elmore OH 43416*

PRESTON, MARY JANE JOHNSON, 4th Grade Teacher; *b:* Louis KY; *m:* John S.; *c:* Kirk S., Joy Kathleen Catlin; *ed:* Duke Univ (B 1964; Univ of Rochestern (MS) Ed 1967; *cr:* Dake MS 6th Grd 1964-70; Chestnut Ridge Schl 4th Grd Tchr 1986-; *ai:* NEA 1 Cephas-Attica Prison Ministry 1992-; NYS Tchr of Yr Nom 1994, *office:* Chestnut Ridge Elem Schl 3560 Chili Ave Rochester NY 146

PRESTON, PHYLLIS R., Perfrmng Arts Coord & Eng Tchr; *b:* New NY; *c:* Nina Rachel Chazin; *ed:* Hunter Coll (BA) Eng, Theater; City (MS) Eng; Moreno Inst Psychodrama Certfd Instr 1980; *cr:* Impoveri Olympics Co-Dir Citywide Competition 1979-90; City-wide Shakesp Competition Co-Dir 1985-92; *ai:* Coord Performing Arts; VFT, AFT 1 NEA 1975-; Tchr of Yr 1989.*

PRESTON, ROBYN RAE (DOSS), 6th & 7th Grd English Teache Portsmouth, OH; *m:* Robert G.; *c:* Kelly Rae; *ed:* OH Univ (BS) Ed (MED) Elem Ed 1973; 4 Addl Credit Hrs; *cr:* Valley Local Elem 1st Grd Tchr 1967-72; Valley Local Intermediate 5th-8th Grd Remedial Tchr 1972-73, 8th Grd Eng Tchr 1973-75, 6th, 7th Grd Eng Tchr 1975 Jr HS Track Coach 10 Yrs; Asst HS Coach Girls Track; NEA, OEA 1 VTA 1967-, VP 1982, Sec 1983-85; OAT, CCC 1992-; ADK 1 Historian, Altruistic Chm 1986-90, Prgm Chm 1990-92; Girl Scouts 1 Troop Ldr 1983-, 10 Yr Awd 1993; *office:* Valley Local MS 393 India Lucasville OH 45648

PRESTOPNIK, RICHARD JOHN, Prof of Electrical Engineerin Little Falls, NY; *m:* Jan Sponenberg; *c:* Nathan, Emily, Adam; *ed:* Moh Valley Coll (AAS) Electrical Tech 1971; Rochester Inst of Tech (E Electrical Engineering Tech 1974; Syracuse Univ (MSEE) C Engineering 1982; *cr:* Intnl Bus Machines Sr Assoc Engr 1974 Fulton-Montgomery C. C. Prof 1980-95, Dean of Career Ed 1995-; *ai:* Prep Coord; ASEE 1988-, Outstanding Educator Awd 1990; IEEE 1 NYSETA 1987-, Campus Rep; Articles Pub; Fac Grant for Improveme rgrad Ed 1986; Who's Who Registry for Bus Ldrs 1992; NASA Fac ıp 1995; *office:* Fulton Montgomery Comm Coll 2805 St Hwy 67 stown NY 12095

TT, LEONORA A., High School Business Teacher; *b:* New York City, *c:* Michele, Michael; *ed:* CCNY Baruch Schl (BBA) Acctng 1963; Y (MS) Ed 1967; C. W. Post Coll, Coll of St Rose, Dowling Coll, L.I. , SCOPE, BOCES, SETRC, NYSUT 81 Coll, In-Svc Credits; *cr:* etquot HS Bus Tchr 1963-70, 1980-; Sayville Schl Dist Sub, Adult Ed Tchr 1964-77; Bayport Schl Dist Sub, Adult Ed Bus Tchr 1964-77; Neck South Jr HS Bus Tchr 1966-67; Peconic Jr HS Bus Tchr -80; *ai:* NY Bus Tchrs Assn 1988-, LI Conf Registration Comm Co r; Suffolk Cty Bus Tchrs Assn 1963-, Pres, VP, Sec, In-Svc Coord, Bd , Suffolk Cty Bus Tchr of Yr Awd 1993; BSA 1983-88, Mother's Club r, Svc Awd; Young Widow, Widowers Group 1989-, Pres, Founder, Svc Bayport Schls 1970-, Curr, HS Weighted Grds Comms, Parents Advy Article Pub; LIBEC, SCBTA Confs Speaker, Panelist; Piloted Cmptr ng Prgms for Mc Graw Hill & Lang Rd Assoc; Supervising Tchr for 3 Tchrs; *office:* Connetquot HS 7th St Bohemia NY 11776

USS, JAMES FRANCIS,JR., 2nd Grade Teacher; *b:* Johnston, PA; Theresa Ann Wojnaroski; *c:* Jessica, James, Jason; *ed:* Univ of burgh at Johnstown (BA) Elem Ed 1977; Intermediate Unit 08; *cr:* East or Elem Schl Tchrs Aid 1975-76, Elem Tchr 1977-; *ai:* HS Jr Var bl, HS Asst Bsbl, Little league Bsbl, Elem Schl Head BsktblCoach; , CVEA 1977-; Conemaugh Fireman 1970-; *office:* East Taylor Elem 1340 William Penn Ave Johnstown PA 15906*

VAS, JOHN, Latin Teacher & Greek Lecturer; *b:* Baltimore, MD; *m:* is Gibson; *ed:* Univ of MD (BA) His 1967, (MA) Pol Sci 1969; Johns kins Univ (MED) Eductl Psych 1974; Antioch Law Schl (MLA) inal Law 1980; Latin Yale Univ 1985; Pol Sci Univ of MD 1982; inal Justice Univ of MD 1984; *cr:* Charles Cty Pub Schls Latin Tchr -; St Mary's Coll Sr Lecturer Pol Sci & Law 1979-85; Towson Univ Sr urer Greek 1995-; *home:* 4000 Cathedral Ave NW Washington DC 6

VOST, CLARICE JACKSON, Principal; *b:* Ft Valley, GA; *m:* ence Nathaniel; *c:* Laurence II, Carla, Lisa, Angela, Nichole; *ed:* ahoga Comm (AA) Early Chldhd 1986; John Carroll (BA) Elem Ed ; Cooperative Learning, Multiple Intelligence Notre Dame; *cr:* St edict Schl Head Start Tchr 1980-84; Mt Pleasant Cath Schl Tchr Asst -80, Tchr 1984-94, Prin 1994-; *ai:* Cath Schls Futuring Chprsn; PSI ; ASCD, NCEA 1990-; St Domonic Women Guild 1990-; Phi Theta pa 1986-; Campfire Girls 1970-, Coord; MPC Schl Bd.*

VOST, GERARD ARMAND, Culinary Arts Instructor; *b:* St sbury, VT; *m:* Crystal Lynn Chandler; *c:* Aimee, Danielle; *ed:* Johnson Vales Univ (AS) Culinary Arts 1978; Attnd Culinary Inst of Amer, son St Coll, Comm Coll of VT; *cr:* St Johnsbury Acad Culinary Arts 1990-; *ai:* Drama Adv; Nordic Ski Coach; Amer Culinary Fed 1985-; ohnsbury Players 1981-, Pres, VP; *office:* St Johnsbury Acad 7 Main St t Johnsbury VT 05819*

VOZNIK, THERSE, Sixth Grade Teacher; *b:* Media, PA; *ed:* Univ of BS) His 1978, (BA) Elem Ed 1978; SHippensburg Univ (MEd) Elem 981; PA St Univ Post Grad 18 Credit Hrs; *cr:* Cape May Court House pter 1 Rdng, Math Tchr 1978-79; Eisenhower Elem Sixth Grd Tchr)-95; Franklin Twp Elem 5th Grd Tchr 1995-; *ai:* Grd Head for Sixth 1991-95; New Stans Project PA Comm; Chapter 1 Outcomes Research ect; MS Task Force; Lang Arts Curr Dev Comm; Stu-Led Conf Wkshp tr; GAEA, PSEA, NEA 1979-, Bldg Rep; Delta Kappa Gamma 1990-; Mini-Grants 1991, 1993; South Cntrl PA Lead Tchr Mini Grant 2-93; Outstanding Young Woman of Amer 1986; *office:* Franklin Twp n 870 Old Rt 30 Cashtown PA 17310

EW, MARY ROSALIE,OP, Fourth Grade Teacher; *b:* East Orange, NJ; Caldwell Coll (BA) Ed & Soc Stud; *cr:* St Mary Schl 1,4,6 Grd Tchr)-69; St Michael Schl 2,6 Grd Tchr 1969-82; Aquinos Acad 4-5 Grd r 1989-91; St Catharine Schl 4 Grd Tchr 1991-; *ai:* Dir of Aftercare; Stud Dept Comm; Rel Dept Comm; NCEA 1969-; St Cath Church ir 1991-; *office:* St Catharine Schl Second & Salem Ave Spring Lake)7762*

EWITT, B. JOANNE HILL, Elementary Teacher; *b:* Albany, GA; *m:* Edward; *c:* Tony Earl (dec), Ricki Edward Hart; *ed:* Albany St Coll) Elem Ed; Attnd Vallejo Coll, San Francisco St Univ, Univ of William Mary, Trenton St Coll; *cr:* Wilkinson Cty GA Schl Elem Tchr; San ncisco USD Elem Tchr; Vallejo USD Elem Tchr; Hampton VA Schl n Tchr; North Hanover Twp Schls Elem Tchr 1972-; *ai:* NHTEA, NEA 2-; Tchr of Yr 1990-91; *office:* C B Lamb Elem Schl 46 Schoolhouse Jacobstown NJ 08562

IANO, MICHAEL,JR., Associate Professor of Biology; *b:* New York , NY; *m:* Lynn; *c:* Donna, Michael III; *ed:* St Univ of NY at Oneonta) Bio 1968; Adelphi Univ (MS) Bio 1974; *cr:* Nassau Comm Coll unct Prof 1972-74; St Univ of NY at Farmingdale Adjunct Prof 3-74; Westchester Comm Coll Assoc Prof 1974-; *ai:* Ecology & Ski bs Adv; AFT 1974-; AAAS 1988-; NY Acad of Sci 1978-; USYSA, ach; Putnam Cty EMC 1990-; Putnam Cty Lake Mgmt Comm 1990-; *ce:* Westchester Comm Coll 75 Grasslands Rd Valhalla NY 10595

ICE, ALMA, Mathematics Teacher; *b:* Kearney, NJ; *m:* David; *c:* Karen licin, David, Tammy, Lori; *ed:* St Univ of NY at Oneonta (BS) Math 3; Addl 45 Hrs at OH St Univ; *cr:* Watertown HS Math Tchr 1963-65; thage HS Math Tchr 1967-; *ai:* Math League Adv; NYSUT 1965-; Amer ion Auxiliary 1964-; Natl Sci Fnd Awd 1970-71; *home:* 31 Liberty St thage NY 13619

ICE, DALE LEE, Mathematics Teacher; *b:* Toledo, OH; *m:* Peggy Jo ffman; *c:* Matthew, Jennifer; *ed:* Univ of Toledo (BA) Math, His Scndry 1982; Bowling Green St Univ (MAT) Mass Comm 1995; *cr:* St Francis Sales HS Math Tchr 1982-83; St Dept of Yth Svcs Math 1983-84; odward HS Math Tchr 1984-; *ai:* Newspaper Asst Adv; GLIPA 1985-, ; AFT, OFT, TFT 1984-; *office:* Woodward HS 600 E Streicher St Toledo 43608

ICE, DENISE G., English Teacher; *b:* Philadelphia, PA; *m:* Lee; *c:* phen, Michael, Stephanie; *ed:* Atlantic Comm Coll (AA) Liberal Arts 72; Glassboro St Coll (BA) Eng 1974; 9 Hrs Grad Credits; *cr:* Atlantic mm Coll ESL, GED Instr 1981-88; Employment Trng Fnd Dir, Educator 88-89; Absegami HS Eng Instr 1990-; *ai:* SAVVY, Train Stu in Conflict, solution Techniques; Human Relations Comm; Natl Hispanic Month ord; NEA, NJEA, OATA 1990-; SAVVY Club Presenter to Train 7th-8th d Stu in Conflict, Resolution Technique; *office:* Absegami HS 201 S angleboro Rd Absecon NJ 08244

ICE, HOLLY WELCH, Coord of Gifted & Talented; *b:* Chicago, IL; Jeremy E. Kay, Nathan H. Kay; *ed:* St Xavier Coll (BA) Eng Lit 1967; Southern ME (MED) Literacy 1985, (MED) Ed of Gifted 1993; *cr:* allett Schl 4th Grd Tchr 1981-88; Cascade Brook Schl 4th Grd Tchr 88-90, 5th Grd Tchr 1990-95; MSAD #9 GATE Coord 1995-; *ai:* yssey of the Mind Coach; NEA 1980-; Natl Assn of Gifted Church 90-; Intnl Paper Edcore Grants U of ME at Farmington Mini Sabbatical; *ice:* ME Schl Adm Dist #9 RR 1 Box 1775 New Sharon ME 04955

RICE, JAMES RAY, POD & Economics Teacher; *b:* Spangler, PA; *m:* na H. Baruch; *c:* James, Joshua, Joe; *ed:* IN Univ of PA (BA) Scndry Soc ıd Ed 1988; 30 Credits Toward MS St Francis Coll of PA: Attnd Univ of Cincinnati; *cr:* Northern Cambria HS His Tchr 1989-92; Purchase Line HS Ec Tchr 1992-; *ai:* Head Var Ftbl Coach; Weightroom Instr; Var, Iron Clubs Fac Spons; NEA, PSEA 1989-; Northern Cambria Civil Defense 1991-; West Cntrl Coaches Assn 1989-, VP, Pres; Southern alleghenies Coaches 1989-, 2nd VP; PA St Coaches Assn 1990-; *office:* Purchase Line HS Box 374 Commodore PA 15729

PRICE, JEFFREY S., Social Studies Teacher; *b:* Bluffton, OH; *m:* Theresa Lynn Crowe; *c:* Amanda Lynn, Matthew Scott, Adrianne Kay; *ed:* Univ of Finlday (BA) Soc Sci & Comprehensive 1983; OH St Univ (MA) General Stud 1985; Attnd Bowling Green St Univ 36 Hrs Toward Masters in His; *cr:* Upper Scioto Valley Schl Tchr 1985-86; Riverdale Schl Tchr 1986-87; Upper Scioto Valley Schl Tchr 1987-; *ai:* Girls Bsktbl Head Coach; Ftbl Asst Coach; Sr Trip Dir; NEA 1985-; Grace Gospel Church 1980-, Bd of Dirs; *office:* Upper Scioto Valley HS 510 S Courtright St Mc Guffey OH 45859*

PRICE, JOHN NICHOLAS, Mathematics Teacher; *b:* Syracuse, NY; *m:* Patricia Barrett; *c:* Andrew, Edward; *ed:* US Merchant Marine Acad (BS) Nautical Sci 1963; Cambridge Coll (MED) Ed 1990; 12 Addl Credit Hrs; Fitchburg St Coll 3 Credit Hrs; *cr:* Furnace Brook MS Math Tchr 1980-83; Martinson MS Math Tchr 1983-91; Marshfield HS Math Tchr 1992-; *ai:* NEA, MTA, PCEA 1983-; *office:* Marshfield HS Forest St Marshfield MA 02050

PRICE, JONATHAN THOMAS, Social Studies Teacher; *b:* Staten Island, NY; *c:* Alexander; *ed:* Trenton St Coll (BA) His 1980; 18 Credits East Stroudsburg Univ Ed; *cr:* N Warren Reg HS Soc Stud Tchr 1989-92; Audicom Inc Sr Telecommunications Consultant 1992-94; Hackettstown HS Soc Stud Tchr 1994-; *ai:* Debate Team Head Coach, Adv; Wargame Club Adv; NEA 1987-; 3 Articles Pub; *home:* 9 Florence Ln Newton NJ 07860*

PRICE, LELA VONETTA, Fifth Grade Teacher; *b:* Margaret, AL; *ed:* Toledo St Univ (BS) Elem Ed 1972, (MS) Elem Ed 1976; 40 Addl Hrs Univ of Toledo; 16 Hrs of Math in Discovery Prgm; *cr:* Longfellow Elem Schl Tchr 15 Yrs; Deveauy Tchr 9 Yrs; *ai:* Intermediate Spelling Bee, Sr Citizen Prgm Coord; Bldg Rep; Rdng Club Adv; Project Discovery Tchr; TFT 24 Yrs, Bldg Rep; Phi Delta Kappa 8 Yrs, 2nd VP; Phi Delta Kappa 12 Yrs; IRA 10 Yrs; Shiloh Bapt Church 45 Yrs; Alpha Kappa Alpha 25 Yrs, Sec; Discovery Project Grant for Math at Univ of Toledo 1995; *office:* Longfellow Elem Schl 4112 Jackman Rd Toledo OH 43612*

PRICE, LUCY CHICCO, 4th Grade Teacher; *b:* Rockville Centre, NY; *m:* Richard; *ed:* New Paltz St Coll (BS) Ed 1972, (MS) Ed 1976; *cr:* Wappingers Schl Dist 6th Grd Tchr 1972-75, 4th Grd Tchr 1976-; *ai:* AFT 1972-; NEA 1972-; Dutchess Cty Area Fund Grant Awd; *office:* Myers Corners Elem Schl 156 Myers Corners Rd Wappingers Falls NY 12590

PRICE, MARY ANN BOLENIUS, Math, Sci, Spelling & Art Tchr; *b:* Lancaster, PA; *m:* Walter V. Jr.; *c:* Walter V. III, Beth Ann, Tracy Price Splain; *cr:* Eastern York Schl Dist 4th & 5th Grd Tchr 1960-62; Donegal Schl Dist 5th Grd Tchr 1962-65; Sacred Heart Schl 7th & 8th Grd Tchr 1976-; *ai:* Safety Patrol Adv; Math Coord; Chprsn St Judes Math-A-Thon; CEA 1976-; Elder Trinity Reformed UCC 1960-, VP.

PRICE, MERIAL H., Spanish Teacher; *b:* Newton Falls, OH; *c:* Heather; *ed:* Kent St Univ (BS) Span & His 1961, (MED) His 1967; PRIDE 3 Semester Hrs; Drug Awareness 4 Semester Hrs; Writing Courses of Stud 5 Semester Hrs; Improving F L Tchng Skills 4 Semester Hrs; *cr:* Warren City Schls Span & His Tchr 1961-70; Farmington Local Schls Span & His Tchr 1979-88; Bristol Local Schls Span Tchr 1988-; *ai:* Beta Club Adv; NEA, OEA 1979-; BASE 1990-; Delta Kappa Gamma 1987-; Williams Jennings Scholar; *office:* Bristol H S 1845 Greenville Rd PO Box 260 Bristolville OH 44402

PRICE, MYRON CHARLES, Mathematics Teacher; *b:* Bloomsburg, PA; *ed:* Bloomsburg St Coll (BSEd) Math 1974; PA St Univ (MED) Math 1978, (MS) Comp Sci 1988; Bloomsburg Univ (BS) Comp & Information 1983; *cr:* Millersburg Area HS Math Tchr 1974-; *ai:* 10th Grd Class Adv; NEA 1974-; PSEA 1974-; MAEA 1974-, Chief Negotiator; *office:* Millersburg Area High School 799 Center St Millersburg PA 17061

PRICE, PATRICIA KATANA, Language Arts & Preschool Tchr; *b:* Pittsburgh, PA; *c:* Kelly; *ed:* Penn St Univ (BS) IFS & Ed 1971; Univ of Pittsburg Post Grad Stud 20 Credits; Pittsburgh Intermediate Univ Post Grad Stud 4 Credits; *ai:* Schl Olympics Dir; Grad Coord; NCTE 1990-; *office:* St Colman Schl 547 Hunter St Turtle Creek PA 15145

PRICE, RENE T., Physical Education Teacher; *b:* New York, NY; *ed:* A & T (BA) Music 1965; 30 Credit Hrs Post Grad Stud Guid; *cr:* Charles Dorsey Schl Tchr 28 Yrs; *ai:* Boys Bsktbl, Colgate Womens Game Coach; Homework Stud Group Tutor; UFT 1970-; Dist 13 PE, Svc Awds; *office:* Charles Dorsey Schl PS 67 51 Saint Edwards St Brooklyn NY 11205*

PRICE, RICHARD DOUGLAS, Fine Arts & Music Chairperson; *b:* York, PA; *m:* Barbara; *c:* Matthew; *ed:* Berklee Coll of Music (BA) Music Performance 1983; Attnd Gettysburg Coll, York Coll, RI Coll; *cr:* Lionel Hampton Orchestra Lead Trumpet, Soloist, Arranger 1985-87; Count Basic Orchestra Lead Trumpet 1987; Night Life Orchestra Lead Trumpet, Soloist 1980-; *ai:* Band Dir; Chess Moderator; MENC, RI MENC 1987-; IAJE 1989-; RI Lib Jazz Series 1994-; Maynard Ferguson Schlsp Awd; Whos Who in RI Jazz; Lionel Hampton Orchestra; RI Matadors Drum, Bugle Corps; LI Sunrisers Drum, Bugle Corps; Rdng Buccanneers Drum Corp; *office:* Bishop Hendricken HS 2615 Warwick Ave Warwick RI 02889

PRICE, SUSAN (RANDOLPH), Home Economics Teacher; *b:* New Kensington, PA; *m:* William D.; *ed:* Mansfield Univ of PA (BS) Home Ec 1967; Penn St Univ Master Equivalency Ed; Course Work Grad Level Univ of Pittsburgh; Cmptr Credits Robert Morris Coll; *cr:* Burgettstown Area SD Home Ec Tchr, Family-Consumer Sci 1967-; *ai:* 9th Grd PA Project Team; Stu Support System; Mentor Sr Exit Interview Project, New Staff; NEA, PSEA, BAEA 1969-, Treas; WA Cty Home Ec Assn 1970-; Allegheny Cty Home Ec Assn 1985-; PA Voc Ed Assn St Comm; Lib Bd, Sec; Train the Trainer Participant; Coord Staff Dev, In-Servicing Home Ec Tchrs.*

PRICE, WOODY, Prof of Visual Communications; *b:* Detroit, MI; *m:* Barbara Riskam; *c:* Jeffrey; *ed:* Los Angeles Trade Tech (AA) Photography 1971; Univ of MD (BA) Visual Comm 1977; Pacific Western Univ (MA) Photography 1984; Comm Coll Air Force (AAS) Visual Comm 1989; Attn NY Inst of Photography; Trade Proficiency Cert; *cr:* US Marines Writer, Photographer 1964-67; Newell Color Lab Photographer 1969-71; Washington Color Lab Photographer 1971-72; Photo Sci Inc Mgr, Photographer 1972-74; Montgomery Coll Prof 1973-; *ai:* USAR, Air Natl Guards; 4-H Photo Instr; Camera Club Guest Lecturer; AAUP; *office:* Mongtomery Comm Coll 51 Mannakee St Rockville MD 20850

PRICE-REAVIS, CHARLES ANTHONY, Adjunct Instructor; *b:* New York City, NY; *c:* Courtney M. Smith; *ed:* Coll of Charleston (BS) Sociology 1987; Univ of South FL (MA) Applied Anthropology 1991; CUNY Grad Schl (MA) Anthropology 1995; Currently Enrolled in PHD Prgm Anthropology; *cr:* FL S Court Stud Comm Ind Researcher 1991; John Jay Coll Crim Justice Adj Instr 1993-; Natl Park Svc, Grant's Tomb Ethnographic Researcher 1994-95; CUNY Queens Coll Adj Instr, PHD Stu 1994-; *ai:* Stu Councilor to Exec Bd Soc for Urban Anthropology; Black Stdnts Alliance Co-Chair 1995-, Exec Comm PHD Prgm in Anthropology Stu Rep; Amer Anthropological Assn 1991-; Soc for Applied Anthropology 1994-; Assn Black Anthro's 1991-; Outstdng Stu in Sociology, Anthropology at Charleston Coll 1987 1987; Delores Auzenne Fellow at Univ South FL 1990; Hugh Culverhouse Schlsp at Univ South FL 1991; President's Fellow 1992-; *home:* 120 W 44th St # 1509 New York NY 10036*

PRICKETT, KAREN L., Second Grade Teacher; *b:* Lakewood, OH; *ed:* Akron Univ (BS) Elem Ed, Rdng Specialist 1975; Addl Stud Baldwin Wallace, Bowling Green Univ; *cr:* St Joseph Elem 5-6 Grd Tchr 1975-80; Avon Lake City Schls 2nd Grd Tchr 1980-; *ai:* Vlybl Referee St of OH; Elem Liaison; Math Comm Co-Chprsn; Cmptr Club Coord; Elem Bsktbl Adv; NEA, OEA, ALEA 1980-; ALEA 1980-, Sec, VP, Pres; NCTE 1990-; Lorain Cty Educl Fnd Grant Lit; Tchr of Yr; Esnhwr Grant; *office:* Westview Elem Schl 155 Moore Rd Avon Lake OH 44012

PRICKETT, KEVIN VERNON, Occupational Work Adjust Tchr; *b:* Chillicothe, OH; *m:* Janet Lee Cryder; *c:* Katrina Marie, Abigail Elnora, Amanda Leigh; *ed:* OH Univ (BSEd) Elem Ed 1985; Ashland Univ (MSEd) Curr Instruction 1995; OH St Univ Occupational Work AdjustmentCert 1995-; *cr:* Zane Trace Local Schls Jr HS Math, Algebra Instr 1985-94; PRJVS, Zane Trace Jr HS Occupational Work Adjustment Tchr 1994-; *ai:* Jr Hnrs Soc Adv; 7th & 8th grd Ftbl Coach; NEA, OEA 1985-; Pickaway-Ross Tchrs Assn 1994-; Kingston OH Village cncl; Kingston OH Village Cncl 1995-, Cncl Mem; Korky's Raiders 1975-, Pres; *office:* Zane Trace Jr HS 39 N Main St Box 615 Kingston OH 45644

PRICONE, STEVEN JOHN, Science & Chemistry Teacher; *b:* Paterson, NJ; *m:* Michele Farley; *ed:* Seton Hall Univ (BS) Bio, Ed 1971; Attnd Montclair Univ, William Paterson Coll; *cr:* Peace Corps Sci, Math Tchr 1971-72; Don Bosco Tech HS Bio Tchr 1972-80; Riverdale Schl Grd 4-8 Sci, Chem Tchr 1980-; *ai:* Newspaper Adv; Boys Bsktbl, Bsbl; NEA 1980-; REA 1980-, Treas; 4 Plays Pub; Geraldine Dodge Fnd Grant 1992; NJ Bisec Grant; NJ Governor's Tchrs Awd 1986; PTA Phoebe Appeason Awd 1987; *office:* Riverdale Elem Schl 52 Newark Pompton Tpke Riverdale NJ 07457

PRIDE, CELIA ANN (GROVES), Fourth Grade Teacher; *b:* Cincinnati, OH; *m:* Richard E.; *c:* Angela Gail, Richard III; *ed:* IN Wesleyan Univ (BS) Elem 1971; Wright St Univ (MED) Ldrshp 1995; *cr:* Batavia Elem Schl Tchr 1971-81; Hamersville Elem Schl 4th Grd Tchr 1985-; *ai:* Worked on St Proficiency Testing; NEA, OEA 1971-; Bethel Nazarene Church, Comm, Work with Mentally Handicapped Sunday Schl; *office:* Hamersville Elem Schl Main St Hamersville OH 45130

PRIDE, JEANNE M., Family & Consumer Science Tchr; *b:* Minneapolis, MN; *m:* Mark F.; *c:* Caleb, Andrew, Luke; *ed:* Univ of MN (BS) Home Ec Ed 1972; Keene St (MAEd) Curr & Instruction 1990; *cr:* Wells Home Ec Tchr 1972-73; Minnehaha Acad Home Ec Tchr 1973-74; Cereal Inst Ed Dir 1975-79; Jeffrey-Rindge MS Home Ec Tchr 1984-90; Conant HS Family & Consumer Sci Tchr 1990-; *ai:* FHA Adv 6 Yrs; FHA St Exec Comm Frosh Adv 2 Yrs; Amer Assn of Family & Consumer Sci 1988-, St Sec 4 Yrs; Cub Scout 1987-93, Chm; Church, Chrstn Ed Co-Chprsn; Upgrade Curr at HS & Toy Booklending Lib for Teen Parents of Children 0-3 Yrs Old Grants from Carl Perkins Homemaking; *office:* Conant HS 109 Stratton Rd Jaffrey NH 03452

PRIEBE-MARCHIOLI, SHANNON, Science Teacher; *b:* Buffalo, NY; *m:* Cesar Marchioli; *c:* Jillian Bryant; *ed:* SUNY Buffalo (BA) Biological Scis 1990; Canisius Coll (MSEd) Scndry Ed 1994; *cr:* Lancaster Cntrl HS Sci Tchr 1992-; *ai:* NHS Adv; Z Club Adv; Sci Olympiad Coach; AFT 1992-; NYSUT 1992-; Amer Assn Physics Tchrs 1995-; Zonta Intnl 1994-; *office:* Lancaster HS 1 Forton Dr Lancaster NY 14086*

PRIEDE, LAURA LYNN, Math Teacher; *b:* Cincinnati, OH; *m:* Mark Zigurds; *c:* Alex; *ed:* Northern KY Univ (MS) Math 1994; *cr:* Milford HS Math, Cmptr Sci Tchr 1983-.

PRIEST, CATHY ANN (WUYAK), HS Social Studies Teacher; *b:* Steubenville, OH; *m:* Thomas E.; *c:* Jade Marie, Thomas Jacob; *ed:* W Liberty St Coll (BA) Eng & His 1972; Muskingum Coll (BA) Ed 1986; OH Univ (MSS) His; Ashland Univ Cmptr Tech & Word Processing; Harvard Inst for Media Ed; *cr:* Coshocton HS Soc Stud Tchr 1986-; Discovery Comm Ed Dept Consultant & Tchr Trainer; Media Lit Tchr Trainer; *ai:* Stu Cncl Adv; Schl & Bus Comm Relations Coord; Video Lib Coord; NEA, OEA & CCEA 1986-; Phi Kappa Phi; Phi Delta Kappa; Red Cross Bloodmobile Coord 1986-; Big Brothers Big Sister 1986-, Fund Raising Act Coord; Discovery-Dimension Cable Championship Team Adv; Cultural Safari Awd 1992; OH Tchr of the Yr 1996; *home:* 780 Ridgewood Dr Coshocton OH 43812

PRIEST, JANET RENN, Fourth Grade Teacher; *b:* Toledo, OH; *m:* Donald E.; *c:* Jason I., Marie E. Shaw, Steven Gilbert, Jonathan Gilbert; *ed:* Bowling Green St Univ (BS) Elem Ed 1968; BGSU (MS) Elem Ed 1977; *cr:* Leipsic St Marys 2nd-4th Grd Tchr 1962-65; Lima Pub Schls 4th Grd Tchr 1965-67; Miller City New Cleveland 1st-8th Grd Rdng Tchr 1968; Toledo St Clement 3th-4th Grd Tchr 1968-72; Wayne Trace 3th-4th Grd Tchr 1972-; *ai:* NEA, OEA 1972-; WTEA 1972-, Pres Treas; Paulding Cty Foster Parent 1983-; EMT Grover Hill Vol FD 1982-; Paulding Cty Mental Hlth 1986-, Bd Mem; St Joseph Church 1972-; Martha Holden Jennings Scholar 1988-89; Ag in the Classroom Awd Winner Local 1989 St 1990; *office:* Grover Hill Elem Schl 101 N Monroe St Grover Hill OH 45849

PRIEST, JOHN MICHAEL, US History Teacher; *b:* Georgetown, DC; *m:* Rhonda C.; *c:* M. Douglas, Jennifer M., Kimberly A.; *ed:* Loyola (BA) His 1972; Hood Coll (MA) Soc Sci 1985; 30 Addl Hrs Scndry Schl Admin; *cr:* Hancock MS Sr HS Tchr 1981-82; South Hagerstown HS Tchr 1982-; *ai:* Acad Team Coach; Helped Stdnts Edit, Pub Civil War Diary, Memoir; MSTA; Fac Civil War Ed Assn 1990-; Pub 8 Civil War His Books; *office:* South Hagerstown HS 1101 S Potomac St Hagerstown MD 21740*

PRIEST, ROBERT A., OWA Coordinator; *b:* VanWert, OH; *m:* Kara L. Fallis; *c:* Ericka Lynn, Robert Tyler; *ed:* Ashland Univ (BSEd) Scndry Ed 1991; Kent St 10 Addl Hrs Voc Ed 1995-; US Sports Acad 2 Addl Hrs Sports Mngmt 1995; *cr:* Findlay HS His Tchr, Asst Ftbl Coach 1992-93; DeFrance HS His Tchr, Asst Ftbl Coach 1993-95; Edon HS OWA Coord, Head Ftbl Coach 1995-; Edgerton HS OWA Coord 1995-; *ai:* Head Boys Track Coach; OHSFCA, NWOFCA 1991-; OAT, CCC 1995-; Denison Univ Outstdng Tchr Awd 1995; *office:* Edon HS PO Box 188 Edon OH 43518*

PRIEST, RONALD EDWARD, Science Teacher; *b:* Rome, NY; *m:* Deborah A. Schue; *ed:* Hamilton Coll (BA) Bio-Honors 1969; Univ of NY at Albany (MS) Bio 1976; Over 30 Post Grad Hrs in Physics, Chem, Bio; *cr:* NY St Schl for Deaf Sci Tchr 1969-71; Simons Rock Coll Chem Instr 1976; Doane Stuart Schl Upper Schl Sci Tchr 1977-; *ai:* Team Earth Adv; NCOG, NYSAIS, Mid Sts Teams 1976-, Evaluator; Nature Conservancy 1976-; Title IV NDEA Fellowship Grad Schl 1971-74; NSF Honors Course for Outstanding Sci, Math Tchrs at Union Coll 1986-87; Pub Sci Books & Films 1986; *home:* 22 Normanside Dr Albany NY 12208

PRIESTER, THOMAS C., Dir of Physical Education; *b:* Erie, PA; *m:* Susan T.; *c:* Shannon L. Zirpolo, Dayne T.; *ed:* Slippery Rock St Coll (BS) PE 1962; Slippery Rock Univ (MED) PE 1970; Fredonia St Coll 6 Credit Hrs; Cortland St Coll 6 Credit Hrs; Univ of Buffalo 6 Credit Hrs; SUNY at Buffalo St Coll 9 Credit Hrs; UNC at Greensboro EDD Pgm 45 Credit Hrs 1974-75; *cr:* Southwestern HS PE Tchr & Coach 1962-; *ai:* PE & IM Ath Dir; Cross Cntry Coach; Chautauqua Cty Ath Assn 1962-, Past Pres, Pres Awd; SW Tchr 1962-; NY St Coaches 1970-; NEA & NYEA; User Comm of Strider Field 1990-; Article Pub 1968; WNY Zone Svc Awd 1980; *office:* Southwestern HS 600 Hunt Rd W E Jamestown NY 14701*

PRIETO, YOLANDA, Professor of Sociology; *b:* Camaguey, Cuba; *ed:* Rutgers Univ (BA) Sociology 1974, (MA) Sociology 1977, (PHD) Sociology 1984; *cr:* Rutgers Univ Tchng Asst 1975-77; Ramapo Coll Sociology Instr 1978-81, Asst Sociology Prof 1981-87, Assoc Sociology Prof 1987-95, Sociology Prof 1995-; *ai:* Prsnl, Acad, Curr Comms; Latin Stdnts Org Past Adv; AFT 1978-; Amer Sociological Assn 1985-; Latin Amer Stud Assn 1977-, Hispanic Task Force; Corpus Christi Parish Cncl 1994-; Ford Fnd Competitive Awd 1977; NY Univ Visiting Scholar, Hispanic Assn Higher Ed Scholarly Achvmt Awd 1990; CUSHWA Ctr Notre Dame Rsrch Awd 1994; Fred & Florence Thomas Tchng Awd 1995; Numerous Publications; *office:* Ramapo Coll Of NJ 505 Ramapo Valley Rd Mahwah NJ 07430

PRIJATELJ, CHARLES ANTHONY, Band Director; *b:* Pittsburgh, PA; *m:* Vickie Jo Greenawalt; *c:* Michael; *ed:* Duquesne Univ (BS) Music Ed 1982; Youngstown St Univ (MM) Performance 1990; Wind Ensemble Conducting, Rehearsal Techniques Duquesne Univ, Indiana Univ of PA, IL St; *cr:* Peterstownship Schl Dist Marching Band Dir 1982; Mars Area Schl Dist Band Dir 1983-; *ai:* Marching Band; Jazz, Percussion Ensemble; Pit Orch; PMEA, NEA 1983-; Merit Citation; *office:* Mars Area Schl Dist 520 Route 228 Mars PA 16046*

PRILLAMAN, DEREK VINCENT, 10th-12th Grd Soc Studies Tchr; *b:* Martinsville, VA; *m:* Sandra Renee; *c:* Taylor; *ed:* West Chester U (BSEd) Soc Stud 1992; 16 Hrs Grad Work; *cr:* Smyrna HS Tchr 1992-; *ai:* Head Bsbl, Asst Ftbl Coach 4 Yrs; NEA, SEA 1992-; DSBCA 1993-; Tchr of Yr 1994-95; *office:* Smyrna HS 85 Duck Creek Pky Smyrna DE 19977*

PRIMM, DAVID EDWARD, Drafting Teacher; *b:* Pittsburgh, PA; *m:* Karen Spahr; *c:* Melinda, Amy; *ed:* CA Univ of PA (BS) Manufacturing Tech 1989; *cr:* CA Univ of PA Energy Project Coord 1989-91; Daugherty Tool & Die Draftsman & Pgm 1991-92; Mon Valley Career & Tech Ctr Drafting Instr 1992-; *ai:* VICA Adv; Schl Newsletter Ed; Strategic Planning Comm; Voc Industrial Clubs of Amer 1993-, Adv; NEA; Municipal Authority of Smithton 1988-, Sec; Amer Legion 1993-, Adj; *office:* Mon Valley Career/Technlgy Ctr 1 Guttman Blvd Charleroi PA 15022

PRIMM, MARY FEY, Eighth Grade Teacher; *b:* Fremont, OH; *m:* Darrell; *c:* Katherine, Adam; *ed:* Univ of Dayton (BS) Scndry Ed, Eng 1980; Attnd Ashland Univ, KS Newman Coll, Wichita St Univ, Portland St Univ; *cr:* LaSalle HS Eng Tchr 1980-82; Bishop Carroll HS Eng Tchr 1982-86; St Jude Schl Eng, 8th Grd Homeroom Tchr 1990-94; St Joseph Schl Eng, 8th Grd Homeroom Tchr 1994-; *ai:* Stu Cncl, Schl Newspaper Adv; Power of Pen Writing Competition Coach; NCEA 1990-; IRA 1995-; OH Child Conservation League, Chrstn Family Movement 1994-; Girl Scout Ldr 1990-; Continental Cablevision Edctrs Awd 1992; New Frontiers Schlsp; *office:* St Joseph Schl 175 St Joseph Dr Amherst OH 44001

PRIMMER, KAREN KITZMAN, Mathematics Teacher; *b:* San Antonio, TX; *m:* David Charles; *c:* Christine, Christopher; *ed:* TX Tech Univ (BA) His, (MA) His; *cr:* James Avery Craftsman Dir of Comm 1984-89; San Antonio Coll His Prof 1989-91; Bandera ISD Math Tchr 1989-91; DODDS Math Tchr 1991-; *ai:* Natl Jr Honor Soc Spon; AVID Coord; Schl Advy Comm Mem; OEA; NEA; PDK; Spirits of Christmas Presents; Book Pub 1988; Articles Pub 1984-91; Newspaper Column; *home:* Cmr 419 Box 1443 APO AE 09102

PRIMOUS, ROSA ANN, Third Grade Teacher; *b:* Shorter, AL; *ed:* Cleveland St Univ (BS) Elem Ed 1976; Kent St Univ (MS) Master of Ed 1982; Grds 1-8 Math Clinician Cert; Grds K-12 Rdng Cert; *cr:* Paul Revere Elem Schl Sixth Grd Tchr 1976-81, 1982-83; Walton Elem Schl Fifth Grd Tchr 1981-82; Woodland Hills Elem Schl Third Grd Tchr 1983-; *ai:* Paul Revere Bowling League Treas 1980-; Act Chprsn 1987-; Union Rep 1991-; AFT 1976-; Cleveland Tchrs Union Local 279; Comm AME Church; Comm AME Laymen's Org, VP; Martha Holden Jennings Scholar 1993-94; First Steps Toward an African Centered Multicultural Curr Cleveland Tchrs Union; *office:* Woodland Hills Elem Schl 9201 Crane Ave Cleveland OH 44105

PRINCE, CHARLES E., Physics Tchr & Sci Dept Head; *b:* Portsmouth, NH; *m:* Chhom Moeng; *c:* Jhen-da; *ed:* Univ of ME (BS) Engrng Physics 1966; Brown Univ (MS) Physics 1971; IN Univ 1 Yr His, Philosophy of Sci; *cr:* Atlanta Univ Sci Tchr 1968-70; Clark Coll Sci Tchr 1968-70; Loyola Acad Physics Tchr 1981-85; St Thomas Aquinas HS Physics Tchr 1986-; *ai:* Sci Dept Chair; Granite St Challenge; Astronomy Club; AAPT; Amer Journal of Physics Letters; *office:* St Thomas Aquinas HS 197 Dover Point Rd Dover NH 03820

PRINCE, EUGENE V., English Second Language Tchr; *b:* Wayne, PA; *ed:* Univ of PA at Philadelphia (BA) Eng & Jrnlsm 1956; Indiana Univ (MA) Eng & Eng Second Lang 1965; Doctoral Prgm, Linguistics at Indiana Univ 30 Hrs; Grad Stud Linguistics at Univ of PA 30 Hrs; Tchng Cert at Temple Univ; *cr:* Various Univs in US & Abroad IL, IN, Saudi Arabia, Malaysia, Indonesia, Spain, Greece Eng Second Lang Instr, Curr Dev Prgm Coord, ESP Tchr Trng 1965-90; Roosvelt Sr HS Eng Second Lang 1990-; *ai:* Eng Second Lang Dept Chm; Local Schl Restructuring Team Sec; Interdisciplinary Coord; TESOL; Educator Exch Prgm to Russia; *office:* Roosevelt Sr HS 13th & Upshur NW Washington DC 20011

PRINCE, TAWANDA ELAYNE, English Teacher; *b:* Bronx, NY; *m:* Wayne K.; *ed:* City Univ of NY Hunter Coll (BA) Eng 1988; Bowie St Univ Masterof Arts in Tchng Candidate; *cr:* PG Cty Bd of Ed Sub Tchr 1992-94; Surrattsville HS Eng Tchr 1994-; *ai:* Praise Team First Bapt Churchof Glenarden; NEA 1995-; Delta Sigma Theta 1981-.

PRINCIPATO, PEGGY MENDOZA, Kindergarten Teacher; *b:* Philadelphia, PA; *m:* Joseph M.; *c:* Matthew; *ed:* Glassboro St Coll (BA) Early Chldhd Ed, (BA) Elem Ed 1979; Acting Schl; Culinary Arts Schl Art Classes; Amer Sign Lang; *cr:* Deptford Twp Schls Comp Ed Tchr 1979; Gloucester Twp Schls Pre-Schl Tchr 1980-81; Gloucester City Schls Kndgtn Tchr 1982-; *ai:* Most Holy Redeemer PTA VP 1993; HS Reunion Comm Co-Chprsn 1988-; Annual MHR Craft Show Co-Chprsn 1993; NEA, NJEA 1979-; GCEA 1981-, Union Rep; Gloucester City Fire Dept Commendation; *office:* Cold Springs Schl Cold Springs Dr Gloucester City NJ 08030*

PRINCIPINO, ORESHIA HYK, Second Grade Teacher; *b:* Rochester, NY; *m:* Paul; *c:* Todd Lee; *ed:* SUC at Brockport (BS) His 1970; Nazareth (MS) Rdng 1977; *cr:* St Josaphat's Ukrainian Schl K-4 Grd Tchr 26 Yrs; *ai:* Channel 21, United Way Rep; Al Sigel Ctr, Inner City Child Tutor; *office:* St Josaphats Ukrainian Schl 910 Ridge Rd E Rochester NY 14621*

PRINTY, DOUGLAS B., Art Teacher; *b:* Rochester, NY; *m:* Janice Hurne; *c:* Douglas Dart, Darrin James, Dale B.; *ed:* Alfred Univ (BFA) Ceramic Design 1966; Addl Grad Work at Univ of HI, SUNY at Potsdam, Oswego; *cr:* Allegany Boces Industrial Design 1966-67; St of HI Art Tchr 1967-68; St Lawrence C Schl Art Tchr 1968-71; Hornell HS Art Tchr 1971-; *ai:* Ftbl, Bsktbl, Hockey, Track; NYSATA; Red Cross Hornell Chapter, Coord; Hillside Bapt Church Trustee, Tchr; Village of N Hornell Trustee, Chm Zoning Bd; *home:* PO Box 88 Bath NY 14810

PRINTZ, PAYTON ARTHUR, Instructor; *b:* Marysville, OH; *m:* Joni L. Mower; *ed:* OH Northern Univ (BA) HPER, Bio 1987; Bowling Green St Univ (MA) Ed 1990; *cr:* OH Northern Univ Instr, Asst FB Coach 1985-90; Arlington HS Stu Tchr 1987-88; Marysville Exempted Village Schls Sub Tchr 1990-91; Lexington Cath HS Bio Tchr 1992-95; Heidelberg Coll Instr, Asst FB 1995-; *ai:* Asst Ftbl Coach; Asst Strength Coach; AFCA 1987-; *home:* 454 E Perry St Tiffin OH 44883

PRIOLA, JOSEPH J., Technology Education Teacher; *b:* Syracuse, NY; *m:* Theresa Carusone; *c:* Joey, Jenna; *ed:* SUNY at Oswego (BS) Ed 1979, (MS) Ed 1988; SUNY at Brockport CAS Educl Admin 30-36 Credit Hrs; *cr:* Brighton Schls Industrial Arts Tchr 1980-82, Tech Ed Tchr 1988-; Burroughs Corp Mrktg Rep 1982-84; Polychrome Corp Tech Sales Rep 1984-86; West Genesee Schl Tech Ed Tchr 1986-88; *ai:* Invention Club Adv; Exploration Club Adv; Team Ldr; Budget Advy Comm; E Cubed Fair Adv; Site Based Mgmt Team; Brighton Liaison to the Challenge Learning Ctr; Bldg Internet Liaison; BTA 1980-; NYSTEA 1986-; Our Lady of Assumption Church 1993-; Life Member NY St PTA; Intnl Tchr Challenger Learning Ctr; Adv to 3 NY St Invention Contest Winners; Newspaper Article Pub; *office:* Twelve Corners MS 2643 Elmwood Ave Rochester NY 14618

PRISCO, LYNN THATCHER, Fine Art Teacher; *b:* Plainfield, NJ; *m:* Michael M.; *c:* Marc, Tony, Cathy, Nanci Colby; *ed:* Syracuse (BA) Art 1960; Monmouth Coll (BS) Art Ed 1983; 30 Grad Credit Hrs; *cr:* Middleton HS South Art Tchr 1983-; *ai:* Art Club Adv; Asst Tech Dir of Plays; NEA & NJEA 1983-; NJ Art Ed 1983-; Alpha Delta Kappa 1995-; Kappa Delta Pi 1982-; *office:* Middletown HS South 501 Nutswamp Rd Middletown NJ 07748

PRISCO, ROSEMARY WINIFRED, Professor of English; *b:* Providence, RI; *ed:* Salve Regina Coll (AB) Eng 1965; Brown Univ (AM) Eng 1974; Working on PHD in Amer Lit; East Asian Conf Wellesley Coll 1994 & 1995; *cr:* E Prov Sr HS Tchr 1965-66; RI Jr Coll Eng Instr 1966-70, Asst Eng Prof 1970-76; Comm Coll of RI Assoc Prof of Eng 1976-83, Prof of Eng 1983-; *ai:* Lit Magazine Adv; NEA 1965-; RIJCFA 1966-; AAUP; AAUW; Natl Museum of Women in the Arts 1989-; RI St Comm 1990-, 1990-91 Sec, 1994 Pres; Articles Pub; Whos Who in RI; Whos Who of Univ Women; *office:* Community College Of RI Lincoln Campus Louisquisset Pike Lincoln RI 02865

PRISER, DENNIS A., Retired Mathematics Teacher; *b:* Dayton, OH; *m:* Marilyn Doris Mead; *c:* Julianne, James Mead; *ed:* Depauw Univ (BA) Math 1963; Miami Univ of OH (MAT) Geography 1968; Addl Stud Dr Ed & Multi Media Projects; *cr:* Springfield South HS Math Tchr 1963-68; Kettering Fairmont HS Math Tchr 1968-95; *ai:* Girls Soccer Head Coach 11 Yrs; Sftbl Head Coach 7 Yrs; Boys & Girls Bsktbl Timer 26 Yrs; NHS Adv; AFT 1963-90, Treas; NEA 1991-95; OCTM 1988-95; AARP 1990-.*

PRISTERA, SALVATORE JOSEPH, Physics & Chemistry Teacher; *b:* Utica, NY; *m:* Mary Lou Ficarra; *c:* Jessica, Adam, Ross; *ed:* Utica Coll of Syracuse Univ (BS) Chem 1968; 72 Credit Hrs Post Grad Syracuse Univ, SUNY at Cortland, SUNY at Utica-Rome, Boston Coll; *cr:* Utica City Schls Sci Tchr 1968-; Utica Coll Adj Fac Chem Tchr 1977-78; *ai:* NYSUT, UTA 1968-; Frankfort Ctr Fire Dept 1974-, Treas; West Frankfort PTO 1985-, Pres; Frankfort Schuyler Music Boosters 1992-, Pres; *office:* T. R. Proctor Sr HS Hilton Ave Utica NY 13501

PRITCHARD, ADAM ROGER, Physics & Computer Sci Teacher; *b:* Liverpool, England; *ed:* London Univ (BS) Physics 1992; Columbia Univ (MA) Physics 1994; *cr:* Universite De Paris-SUD Research Asst 1991; Columbia Univ Tchng, Research Fellow 1992-94; Dominican Acad Tchr 1994-; *ai:* Shakespeare Competition, Ski Trip, Chess Club; *office:* Dominican Academy 44 E 68th St New York NY 10021

PRITCHARD, ARTHUR H., Prof of Biological Science; *b:* New London, CT; *c:* Kerstin B., Ilka Maria; *ed:* Univ of RI (BS) Geology 1962, (PHD) Biological Sci 1966; Outward Bound Inc Tchrs Course at CO; Natl Outdoor Ldrshp Schl Instrs Course; US Army Basic Engr Offcr Course; *cr:* US Army Engrs Capt Svc in Korea, Germany, Vietnam1966-70; Dutchess Comm Coll Asst Prof 1970-76, Assoc Prof 1976-90, Full Prof 1990-; *ai:* Rhinebeck Rotarian NY; Rhinebeck Connections a Drug Prevention Group; NEA 1970-; AARP 1990-; Hyde Park Bd of Ed 1985-88, Pres; Rhinebeck Bd of Ed 1994-; Hyde Park Rotary 1984-92, Pres, Rotarian of Yr 1991-; RhinebeckRotary 1995-; Have Received 50 Grants Which Includes 2 Fipse USDE Drug Prevention Grants, 10 Dwight David Eisenhower Title ITA In-Service & Cooperative, Demonstration Awds, Awds from NY Natural Heritage Trust, Natl Endowment for Humanities, USDI; *office:* Dutchess Comm Coll 53 Pendell Rd Poughkeepsie NY 12601*

PRITCHARD, GEORGE H., Rel & Comp Stud Dept Chair; *b:* Columbus, OH; *m:* Marianne Bailey; *c:* Michael, Maureen, Benjamin; *ed:* Univ of Dayton (BA) Theology & Philosophy 1968, (MA) Theology 1981; Capital Univ & Chaminade Univ Acctng; John Carroll Univ Rsrch for Textbook 1975; Univ of Dayton & Ctr for Yth Stud 1989; *cr:* St Louis HS Rel Tchr 1972-76; Bishop Ready HS Rel & Comp Stud Tchr 1976-; *ai:* Tech Coord; Sci Fair Judge Local, Dist & St; Mentor Tchr; Acad Cncl Schl Bd Rep Pres; CDEA 1976-; OEA 1976-; OSA 1994-; Hilltop Historical Soc 1985-; Tandy Scholar 1994; *office:* Bishop Ready HS 707 Salisbury Rd Columbus OH 43204

PRIVITERA, ANTHONY J., Earth Science Teacher; *b:* Dunkirk, NY; *m:* Sharon Johnson; *c:* Kathleen Sleigh, Marla Dwyer; *ed:* Fredonia St Coll (BA) Sci & Math 1963; Canisius Coll (MS) Sci Ed 1965; *cr:* Silver Creek HS Tchr for 33 Yrs; *ai:* Jr Class Adv; Sci Dept Chm; AFT; NYSUT; Pres of Friends of Banker Lib; Free Lance Writer for The Tonight Show with Jay Leno; *office:* Silver Creek Central HS Dickinson St Silver Creek NY 14136

PRIVITERA, JOANNE URTZ, Kindergarten Teacher; *b:* Ilion, NY; *m:* Robert; *c:* Julie, Peter, Robert; *ed:* Buffalo St Coll (BS) Elem Ed 1969; SUNY at Geneseo 33 Credit Hrs; *cr:* Keshequa Cntrl Schl Elem Tchr 1969-; *ai:* Shared Decision Site Base, SUNY Colloboration, Math Curr Comms; Keshequa Cntrl Tchrs Assn, NEA 1969-; Delta Kappa Gamma 1991-; Pub Lib Bd 1990, VP; Mt Morris PTA 1990-, Pres, VP; Parenting Skills Facilitator 1994-; Catechist St Patricks Church 1980-; *home:* 18 Murray St Mount Morris NY 14510

PROBST, ROBERT ERNEST, 8th Grade REAL Teacher; *b:* Lock Haven, PA; *m:* Carole Bonner; *c:* Dennis, Scott, Amy Houtz; *ed:* Lockhaven Univ (BS) Soc Stud, Geog 1962; PA St Univ (MED) Soc Stud 1976; Accepted Penn St Doctoral Prgm; *cr:* Bellefonte MS Soc Stud Tchr 1962-; *ai:* Stu Cncl Co-Adv; Prin Advy; NEA, PSEA 1962-, Life Mem; Lockhaven Comm Chorus 1972-; IN Univ India Stud 1970; Pub Filmstrips on India; *home:* 390 Irwin St Lock Haven PA 17745

PROCACCINI, FRANK JOSEPH, Social Studies Director; *b:* New York City, NY; *m:* Michelina Consolazio; *c:* David, Micheal; *ed:* St John's Univ (BA) Ed 1969, (MS) His 1972; Long Island Univ Prof Diploma SDA Educl Admin 1991; Addl 96 Credits; *cr:* Babylon Jr, Sr HS Soc Stud Tchr 1969-, DIr Soc Stud 1991-; *ai:* Tchrs Assn Scholastic Awds Comm; Staff Enrichment, Rsrch Coord Comm; AFT, NYSUT, LICSS 1969-; Babylon Tchrs Assn 1969-, Sec; Hauppauge Bd of Ed 1991-, Trustee, Past Pres 1994-95; Chaired Mid Sts Steering Comm; Outstdng Ldrshp Awd; Hauppauge Pub Schls Ldrshp Svc Awd.

PROCOPIO, JUDITH ANN, Secondary English Teacher; *b:* Abbington, PA; *m:* Anthony G.; *c:* Laurie M. Floyd, John A.; *ed:* Bloomfield Coll (BA) Eng & Ed 1965; *cr:* West Orange HS Eng Tchr 1965-68; Roosevelt Jr High Eng Tchr 1969-71; Freehold Regnl HS Adult Supplemental Instruction Tchr 1980-84; St John Vianney HS Eng Tchr 1984-; *ai:* STAND Club Adv; Mid Sts Steering Comm; NACST 1984-; NACST of SJV 1984-; NCTE 1985-, Dept; AAUW 1980-88; NJ Peer Helpers Assn 1993-.

PROCOPIO, RENE,CSSF Principal; *b:* Mount Carmel, PA; *ed:* La Rocise Coll (BS) His 1970; Univ of Pittsburg (MEd) Rdng Specialist; Baldwin-Wallace Admin 1980; *cr:* St Adalbert Schl Prin 1978- Louise De Marillac Tchr 1983-85; St Germaine Schl Prin 1985-95 Spirit Schl Prin 1995-; *ai:* Full Time Prin K-8 Grd Level; Holy Spir Bd & Divine Redeemer Parish Cncl Mem; NCEA 1965-; MSA 1988- Spirit Bd 1995-, Exec Dir; St Germaine Ed Bd 1985-, Exec D Germaine Parish Cncl 1985-; Divine Redeemer Parish Cncl 1995-; Holy Spirit Schl 250 West Ave Mount Carmel PA 17851*

PROCOPIO, RONALD J., Music Teacher; *b:* Providence, R Veronica; *c:* R. J., Kristen, Ryan; *ed:* Barrington Coll (BA) Mus Cranston-Johnston Cath Schl Reg Music Tchr 1973-76; St Margare Tchr 1976-; *ai:* East Providence Comm Chorus Dir, Pres; NCEA; Lions Club Pres; Parish Cncl VP; Democratic Ward Comm; Providence Hall of Fame; *home:* 38 Brentwood Dr Rumford RI 029

PROCTOR, JACQUELINE BROCK, English Teacher; *b:* Sumter, Tracy, Teri; *ed:* Miami Univ (BS) Scndry Eng 1990; 21 Addl Hrs E Great Oaks Career Dev Ctr Tchr 1990-; *ai:* Perfect Attendanc Comm; Learning Prgm Adv; Industry Exch; Camden Church of God 1993-; Ministries; Church Choir, Pub Newsletter; Articles Pub; Poetry *office:* Scarlet Oaks Career Dev Center 3254 E Kemper Rd Cincinna 45241

PROCTOR, PEGGY KUKLA, Physical Education Teacher; *b:* Rive NY; *m:* Scott; *c:* Ken, Laura, Matt; *ed:* SUNY at Cortland (BS) PE 30+ Post Grad Hrs at Old Dominion Univ, Univ of VA & East Ca Univ; *cr:* Granby HS PE Tchr 1974-77; Annunciation Schl PE 1986-89; Webster Jr High PE Tchr 1989-74; Thomas MS PE Tchr *ai:* Var Tennis, Modified Vllybl & Sftbl Coach; IM Dir; WTA Womens Sport Fndtn 1996-; ST Pauls Church 1989-, Parish C Confirmation Ldr; Coach of the Yr 1989-90, 1990-91, 1992-93 & 19 *office:* Thomas MS 800 Five Mile Line Rd Webster NY 14580

PROCTOR, ROBERT BRUCE, Science & Soc Studies Teach Newark, NJ; *m:* Barbara Ann Gaydick; *ed:* Union Coll (AA) Lbr 1968; Paterson St Coll (BA) His 1971; Kean Coll Soc Stud Cert 197 25 Semester Hrs Sci Related Courses 1979-84; Middlesex Cty Coll Physics; Comprehensive Sci Cert 1984; *cr:* St Leo Schl 7-8 Grd Sc Stud Tchr 1971-79; Union Carbide Rsrch, Dev 1979-88; St Ann's Sch Soc Stud Tchr 1991-; *ai:* NCEA 1991-; *office:* St Ann Schl 34 Ross Lawrenceville NJ 08648

PROHASKE, DONNA DIANE, Social Studies Teacher; *b:* West NY; *ed:* Albright Coll (BA) His, Ed 1991; SUNY at Stonybrook Multicultural Ed 1995; *cr:* West Babylon Sr HS Tchr Asst 1992-93 Stud Tchr 1993-; *ai:* Class, SADD Adv; Cmptr Technologists; Sof Comm; Drug & Alcohol Coalition; WBTA 1992-; Who's Who in Tchrs 1995; *office:* West Babylon Sr HS 500 Great East Neck Rd Babylon NY 11704

PROKOPCHAK, PETER ANDREW, HS Instrumental Music Teach New York City, NY; *m:* Diane Rolleri; *c:* Susan, Michelle; *ed:* Orang Comm Coll (AAS) Music Ed 1977; West Chester Univ (BS) Mus 1979; SUNY New Paltz (MS) Elem Ed 1985; NY St Schl Music Adjudicator Woowinds, All-St Woodwinds, Brass, All-St Jazz, Major *cr:* Eldred Cntrl Schl 4th-12th Grd Instrumental Music Tchr 198 7th-8th Grd Gen Music Tchr 1986-88; Pine Bush HS Dept Chair M Dist 1989-92, 9th-12th Grd Instrumental Music Tchr 1988-; *ai:* Mar Band Dir 1988-; Var Sftbl Coach 1981-86; NHS Adv 1984-88; Ph Alpha 1978-; NY St Tchr Assn 1981-; BPO Elks 1993-, Esquirer 1 Esteemed Lecturing Knight 1996; *office:* Pine Bush HS Rt 302 Pine NY 12566

PROKSA, ANITA M., English Teacher; *b:* Pittsburgh, PA; *m:* Jac Jamie Proksa Mac Kay, Paige; *ed:* Clarion Univ of PA (BA) Eng Penn St Cert Eng 1972; *cr:* Plum Borough Schl Dist Rdng Tchr 1968; Mifflin Area Eng Tchr 1968-70, Sub Tchr 1970-93, Eng Tchr 1993-; *a* Assistance Prgm; Vol Schl Chaperoning; Dress Down Day Organizer; 1980-; Tchr of Month Awd; *office:* West Mifflin Area HS Commonwealth Ave West Mifflin PA 15122

PROL, VICTORIA, Spanish Teacher; *b:* New York, NY; *ed:* CCNY Span 1965; Coll of New Rochelle (MS) TESOL 1985; Univ of M Diploma de Estudios Hispanics 1966; CUNY Grad Stud Span, It 1967-72; Yale Summer Lang Inst Italian 1978; Univ Stranieri a Pe 1980; *cr:* NYC Bd of Ed Span Tchr 1966-67; Horace Greeley HS Span 1967-69; Yonkers Pub Schls Span, Italian, ESL Tchr 1970-; *ai:* Frgn Dept Head; AFT, YFT 1970;- NY S Assn Frgn Lang Tchr; Phi Beta K 1975-; *office:* Gorton HS Shonnand Pl Yonkers NY 10703

PROPERT, MADELINE BURGER, English & Pub Speaking Teach Camden, NJ; *m:* Ferdinand Heston; *ed:* Glassboro St Coll (BA) Speaking, Drama 1972, (BA) Eng 1975; *cr:* Oak Knoll Elem Schl Fifth Tchr 1976; Bridgeton HS Eng Tchr 1976-77; Delsea Reg HS Eng & Speaking Tchr 1977-; *ai:* Stu Crudsade for the Homeless Adv; Wood Sketch Club 1976-, Sec, Publicity & Act Dir; Natl Ed assoc, Counc English tchrs; Comm Svc Awd Franklin Twp 1993; Emergency Mngmt 1991-92; Tchr of The Yr Recognition Awd; *office:* Delsea Regional Blackwoodtown Rd Franklinville NJ 08322*

PROPOSKI, WILLIAM J., Math Teacher & Cmptr Specials Lawrence, MA; *m:* Yvette Chasse; *c:* Jeffrey, Christopher, Christa; Merrimack Coll (BA) MATH 1968; Salem St Coll (MA) Math 197 Addl Hrs; *cr:* Gloucester HS Tchr 1968-; Sandy Bay Systems Ow Cmptr Consultant 1985-; *ai:* NEA 1968-, Loc Pres; Tchr of Yr; *home* Story St Rockport MA 01966*

PROSACK, CLAUDIA MARY, Spanish Teacher; *b:* Shenandoah, PA Penn St Univ (BA) Span Linguistics 1978, (MA) Span 1981; Spain Stud; Costa Rica Proft Ecological Stud; Italy Lang Culture, Ort His; Penn St Univ Tchng Ass 1979-81, Cont Ed Instr 1982-84; Linden Hall Tchr 1984-; Tutor US Learning Ct Tchr 1994-; *ai:* Trip Coord 1986, 1 1993, 1996; Stdnts, Class Adv; Lang, Culture Club; AATSP, NAIS 19 PSMLA 1990-; Penn St Lane Co 1994-, Bd Dirs; 1993 Awded Schlsp S Embassy Stud Spain, 1979-81 Tchng Flwshp Penn St; *office:* Linden Schl For Girls 212 E Main St Lititz PA 17543

PROTANO, RALPH DAVID, History Teacher; *b:* Brooklyn, NY; *ed* Francis Coll (BA) Soc Stud 1985; Fordham Univ (MS) Ed 1989; Work Towards Lang, Literacy, Learning PHD; *cr:* St Vincent Ferrer Schl Tchr 1987-90; Bishop Kearney HS His Tchr 1990-; *ai:* Photogra Environmental Awareness Clubs Moderator; AERA 1996-; US Cong Civic Achvmt Awd; Outstanding Young Men of Amer; *office:* Bis Kearney HS 2202 60th St Brooklyn NY 11204

PROTIN, EILEEN DOLAN, Math Teacher; *ed:* Carlow Coll (BA) M Speech 1961; *cr:* Charleroi Area Schls Sub Tchr 1962-75, Mid Sr HS M Tchr 1976-85, Coord Gifted Grds 8-12 1986-95, Mid Sr HS Math 1995-; *office:* Charleroi Mid Sr HS 100 Fecsen Dr Charleroi PA 1502

PROTOS, AMY REED, Math Teacher; *b:* Rochester, NY; *m:* Paul T. Sarah; *ed:* Univ of Dayton (BS) Math 1987, (MS) Interdisciplinary S 1992; *cr:* Archbishop Alter HS Math Tchr 1987-88; Kettering Jr HS M Tchr 1989-94; Kettering MS Math Tchr 1994-; *ai:* Coach Bsktbl, S Power of the Pen; Stu Assistance Coord, Group Facilitator; NCTM 19 Whos Who in Amer Ed 1995.*

PROUDFOOT, JILL LIN, Teaching Fellow; *b:* Dayton, OH; *ed:* OH Univ (BA) Elem Ed 1979; Currently Full Time Grad Stu at Kent St U for Instrl Tech; *cr:* Fairfax Elem 1st & 5th Grds Tchr 1982-95; Tc y & Grad Asst Instr 1996; *ai:* Cleveland Hghts Tchrs Union Pub ons Dir; AFT 1982-, Elem VP 1988-95, Tchr of the Yr 1993; ·oom Grant from Martha Holden Jennings Fndtn 1992; *home:* 2415 d Cleveland OH 44118*

GH, SHERRI LYNN, Health & Physical Ed Teacher; *b:* Wellsboro, : Philip Andrew; *c:* Dylan; *ed:* Lock Haven Univ (BS) Hlth, PE 1991; eld Univ Working Towards MA Pgrm; Penn St Univ 3 Credit Hrs; *cr:* Penn Jr, Sr HS Hlth, PE Tchr 1991-; *ai:* Head Var Vlybl Coach; , NEA 1991-; *office:* North Penn Jr Sr HS 300 Morris St Blossburg 912

JLX, RITA MARIE, Music Teacher; *b:* Sanford, ME; *ed:* Rivier Coll Piano, Organ, Voice 1956; Ed; *cr:* Presentation of Mary Schls ior 1958-88, Prin 1958-74.

JTY, JOHN MARK, Chemistry Teacher; *b:* Canton, NY; *m:* ·lle A.; *c:* Keith W. Jennie R.; *ed:* Roberts Wesleyan Coll (BS) Chem St Univ of NY at Brockport (MED) Physics Ed 1991; *cr:* eld-Alabama Cntrl Chem & Physics Tchr 1987-91; Churchville Chili Chem & Bio Tchr 1991-; *ai:* Track & Field Coach; Amer Chemical 987-; Pearce Meml Free Meth Church, Ofcl Bd 1995-; Univ of ester Tchr of Yr 1994; Monroe Cty Coach of Yr 1994; Univ of ester Summer Research Fellowship 1995; *office:* Churchville Chili Sr 786 Buffalo Rd Churchville NY 14428

UTY, NANCY ZUMWALT, Sixth Grade Teacher; *b:* Ft Ord, CA; *m:* en C.; *c:* Daniel Harrison; *ed:* Westfield St Coll (BS) Elem Ed 1975; CT St Univ (MA) Spec Ed 1981; 30 Credits Beyond Masters; *cr:* ersfield Pub Schls Tchr of 4th-6th Grd Gifted Prgm 1976-90, 6th Grd 1990-; *ai:* Prof Dev Presenter in Areas of Lang Arts; Tech Comm at Level; NEA, CT Ed Assn 1976-; Ed Assn of Wethersfield 1976-, Bldg Wethersfield Distinguished Educator Awd 1986-87; Wethersfield Awd 1992-93; St of CT Celebration of Excl Awd; *office:* son-Williams Elem Schl 461 Wells Rd Wethersfield CT 06109*

UTY, TIMOTHY J., Technology Education Teacher; *b:* Worcester, *m:* Cynthia Worster; *ed:* Fitchburg St Coll (BSEd) Ed 1974, (MSEd) Tech 1991; *cr:* Henry Ford Museum Mgr of Crafts & Presentation -79; Greenfield Village Mgr of Crafts & Presentation 1974-79; Dudley Dist Edctr 1979-; Charlton Schl Dist Edctr 1979-; *ai:* Schl Cncl; SC Curr, Instr Subcommittee; Yrbk Adv; NEA 1982-; MA Tchrs Assn -, VP, Pres; Tech Ed Assn MA 1988-; Knights of Columbus 1991-; Advy Bd 1988-; Article Pub; Tchr of Yr; Lewandowski-Sczlyk ; *office:* Shepherd Hill Reg HS 68 Dudley Oxford Rd Dudley MA 1*

VENCHER, JEANNE STANSFIELD, English & Womens Studies ; *b:* Methuen, MA; *m:* Richard L.; *c:* Matthew, Ryan; *ed:* Newton Coll Eng 1970; Rivier Coll (MA) Writing & Lit 1990; *cr:* St Francis Acad 1970-71; Salem HS Tchr 1971-72; Pelham Memrl Schl Tchr 1983-87; ua Sr HS Tchr 1987-; *ai:* Equity Club Adv; Panther Prints Schl Paper Adv; AFT 1983-; NCTE 1983-; NEATE 1987-; NHATE 1987-; St ryns Church 1986-, Lector; Critical Reader Adventures in eciation, Grammer Wkshp; Contributing Writer Rdng Drama An ology of Plays; *office:* Nashua Sr HS Riverside Dr Nashua NH 03060*

VENZALE, ANTHONY JOSEPH, 7th-8th Grade Science Teacher; leveland Hts, OH; *m:* Laura; *ed:* Baldwin-Wallace (BSEd) Ed 1984; king on Masters GATE Kent St Univ; *cr:* Cleveland Hts Schl Elem, HS Tchr 1984-87; Univ Hts Schl Elem, MS, HS Tchr 1984-87; William ey Harper Elem Schl 5th-6th, MS Sci Tchr 1987-; Whitney Young MS Tchr 1987-; *ai:* AFT 1987-; MDA Walk-A-Thon; Western Reserve orical Soc 1995-, Advy Bd Admin; Helped Start Conflict Mediation ; Set Up Cmptr Lab; Cleveland Fnd Grant; *office:* Whitney Young MS 0 Harvard Ave Cleveland OH 44128

VENZANO, DIANE LOUISE, Science Teacher; *b:* S Weymouth, *m:* Anthony F. Jr.; *c:* Marie, Catherine, Elizabeth; *ed:* Coll of Holy s (BA) Psych 1981; Cornell Univ Med Coll (SA) Surgery 1984; *cr:* ogy Inc Surgical P. A. 1983-85; Sacred Heart HS Sci Tchr 1986-; *ai:* eroom Tchr; Fac, Tchr Enrichment Comm; NEASC, NCEA 1986-; Pol n Comm 1991-; Plymouth Antiquarian Soc 1993-; *office:* Sacred Heart 399 Bishops Hwy Kingston MA 02364

VOST, JANINE MICHELLE, High School Biology Teacher; *b:* ey City, NJ; *ed:* Jersey City St Coll (BA) Art 1980; Rutgers Univ (MS) ecular Bio 1992; Kean Coll 50 Credits Tchng Cert 1987; *cr:* Livingston Bio Tchr 3 Yrs; Rutgers Univ TA-Bio Recitation 1 Yr; West Morris Bio r 2 Yrs; *ai:* Adv Future Physicians Club; Sci League Coach; NJ Sci rs Assn; NABT.

)WELLER, WILLIAM, Retired Art History Professor; *b:* New York, *m:* Thelma Slavin; *c:* Amira, Aaron; *ed:* NY Univ (BS) Art Ed 1953,) Art Ed 1954; Univ of CA (PHD) Art Ed 1961; *cr:* Western WA St Coll His Asst Prof 1961-64; St Univ Coll Prof 1964-95; Univ of Haifa ting Prof 1972-73; *ai:* United Univ Professors 1964-; Coll Art Assn 6-; Pub Svc Organized Pre Coll Prgms Dunkirk HS; Articles Pub; nerous Art Exhibitions.*

)ZIK, JOSEPHINE, Spanish Teacher; *b:* Reggio di Calabr, Italy; *m:* M.; *ed:* Coll of St Rose (BA) Span 7th-12th Grd 1973, (MA) Elem Ed 0; SUNY at Albany 18 Credit Hrs Admin & Supervision; *cr:* Albany HS n Tchr Adult Ed Classes 1974-79; Remedial Math Aide Hackett MS 0-82; Albany Pub Schls Substitute Tchr 1983-83; RCS HS Span Tchr 3-; *ai:* Natural Helpers; Span Club; Coalition Team; SAP; Upper dson Valley Consortium of Foreign Lang Tchr 1985-; Sigma Delta Pi 0-; NY St Assn of Foreign Lang Tchrs; Span Dncrs; *office:* R-C-S HS 9 W Ravena NY 12143

UBAN, DAVID RAY, Former Elementary Teacher; *b:* Beaver Falls, PA; Youngstown St Univ (BME) Music Ed 1980; *cr:* Southern Local Schls 2 Grd Music Ed, Instrumental, Vocal, Gen Tchr 1980-82; Word of Life ·stn Acad Elem Ed, Music Ed Tchr 1982-88; *home:* 1060 Hyde Oakfield N Bloomfield OH 44450

UDEN, BERNADETTE JOANN, English Teacher; *b:* Teaneck, NJ; *m:* ert James; *c:* Daniel; *ed:* Tombrock Jr Coll (AA) Liberal Arts 1968; erson St Coll (BA) Eng, Lang Arts 1971; *cr:* Wyckoff MS Team Aide 1-72; Wood-Ridge HS 7-12th Grd Eng Tchr 23 Yrs; *ai:* Jr Gifted, ented, Frosh Class Adv; Inspirations Lit Magazine; Pep Club; NEA, EA, NJEA 1973-; *office:* Wood Ridge HS 258 Hackensack St Wood lge NJ 07075*

UDEN, MARY A., English Teacher; *b:* Toledo, OH; *m:* w; *c:* Nicola etic, Michelle Donaldson, Amy Pruden; *ed:* Univ of Toledo (BED) Eng 76, (MAE) Eng 1994; *cr:* E. L. Bowsher HS Eng Tchr 1984-85; Morrison Waite HS Eng Tchr 1985-91; Edward D. Libbey HS Eng Tchr 1991-92; y C. Start HS Eng Tchr 1992-; *ai:* Jefferson-Madison Ldrshp Team Adv; T 1984-; Phi Kappa Phi 1976-; Rotary Intl 1993-, Treas; *office:* Roy C. art HS 2100 Tremainsville Rd Toledo OH 43613

UDENTE, CIRO R., Assistant Principal; *b:* Mineola, NY; *m:* Marie F.; Jessica; *ed:* Univ of TN (BS) Ed Eng 1972; Columbia Univ Tchrs Coll A) Ed Eng 1975; Queens Coll (MA) Ed Admin Supervision 1991; Attnd ng Island Univ Post Campus, Stony Brook Campus & Univ of WY TESA adership Trng; *cr:* St John the Bapt HS Eng Tchr 1976-80; East ckaway HS Eng Tchr 1980-85; Plainedge HS Eng Tchr 1985-93; Hofstra niv Adjunct Prof 1991-; Plainedge HS Asst Prin 1993-; *ai:* Staff Dev anning, Dist Rdng, Admin Mgmt, HS Leadership & Renaissance Comm; 9th Grd Team Admin; Tchr Ctr Policy Bd Sec; Schlstc Awds Coord; Tolerance Team Ldr; Dist Rdng Comm; Phi Delta Kappa 1989-; ASCD 1988-; NCTE 1980-; AFT 1980-, Tchr Rep, Recognition of Exemplary Svc; NY St Eng Cncls Tchr of Excl 1989; TESA Leadership Trng; Tchr Ldrshp & Whole Lang Wkshps; *office:* Plainedge HS Wyngate Dr North Massapequa NY 11758*

PRUGAR, JOHN MICHAEL, 5th Grade Teacher; *b:* Greenport, NY; *m:* Lee Ruble; *c:* Heather, Holly; *ed:* St Univ Coll of NY at Oswego (BS) 7th-12th Grd Soc Stud Ed 1968; 39 Credit Hrs of Post Grad Stud; *cr:* Rome City Schl Dist 4th Grd Tchr 1968-69; Watertown City Schl Dist 5th Grd Tchr 1969-; *ai:* Evaluation Comm Mem; PTO Tchr Rep; Watertown Ed Assn 1969-, Bldg Rep & Elections Comm Chm; NY St United Tchrs 1969-; Pi Gamma Mu Natl Soc Stud Hnr Soc; 1st United Meth Church Bd of Trustees Sec 1991-93, Teller & Usher 1991-; Amer Lung Assn Vol; UNICEF Vol; Received 3 PTA Flwshp Awds for Grad Stud; *office:* Harold T Wiley Inter Schl 1351 Washington St Watertown NY 13601

PRUITT, VIRGINIA ANN, Social Studies Teacher; *b:* Tulsa, OK; *ed:* Univ of OK (BA) Eng 1963; NY Univ (MA) Ed 1968; New Schl for Soc Rsrch (MA) Psych 1973; Brooklyn Law Schl (JD) Law 1983; Numerous Prof Dev Courses; *cr:* Peace Corps Vol Tchr 1964-66; Corcoran HS Tchr 1966-67; New York City Pub Schls Tchr 1967-77; Lehigh Univ Adj Instr 1977-78; New York City Pub Schl Tchr 1978-; New York Tech Coll Adj Instr 1984-86; *ai:* Mock Trial Coach; United Fed of Tchrs, AFT 1978-; Returned Peace Corps Vol of Greater New York 1969-, Bd Mem; Natl Endowment Hum Summer Seminar Grant 1995; *office:* The HS For Ldrshp/Public Svc 90 Trinity St New York NY 10006

PRUNTY, MARY MAHONEY, High School Mathematics Tchr; *b:* Jamaica, NY; *m:* James P.; *c:* James J., Elizabeth; *ed:* Marymount Manhattan (BA) Math 1965; Hunter Coll (MA) Math 1966; 9 Grad Credits Math Fordham Univ; 34 Grad Credits Adelphi Univ; *cr:* Lehman Coll of CUNY Lecturer Math 1966-69; Queensboro C C of CUNY Math Instr 1966-72, Asst Prof Math 1972-77; NY Inst of Tech Adj Instr Math 1978-79; St Marys HS Math Tchr 1979-; *ai:* NHS Moderator; Manhasset Tchr Resource Ctr, NCEA 1990-; St Agnes Mothers Club 1978-; Grad Assistantships Hunter Coll, Perdue Univ, Univ of MD, Fordham Univ; NYS Regents Tchng Flwshp; *office:* St Mary's HS 51 Clapham Ave Manhasset NY 11030

PRUSAK, PATRICIA ANN, Reading Resource Teacher; *b:* Clarksburg, WV; *m:* Carl R.; *c:* Deborah, Mark, Matthew; *ed:* Fairmont St Coll (BA) Elem Ed 1964; Baldwin Wallace Coll (MAEd) Rdng 1988; 40 Credit Hrs Beyond Masters; *cr:* Norwood Schl 4th-5th Grd Tchr 1964-65; Coe & Pine Schls 1st-2nd Grd Tchr 1965-68; Butternut Schl 3rd-4th Grd Tchr 1970-72; Crestwood Schl Kndgtn & Title I Tchr 1984-; *home:* 6097 Park Ridge Dr North Olmsted OH 44070

PRUTTING, CAROL WALAKIEWICZ, Fourth Grade Teacher; *b:* Bridgeport, CT; *c:* Charlie Jr.; *ed:* Cntrl CT St (BS) Elem Ed 1973; Fairfield Univ (MS) Ed 1977; Humtoldt St Univ Extended Ed; *cr:* Osborn Hill Elem Schl Grd 4 Tchr 1973-81; Mc Kinley Elem Schl Grd 4 Tchr 1981-; *ai:* NEA, CEA, FEA 1973-; Soc Stud, Sci Bd of Ed Grants; *office:* Mc Kinley Schl 60 Thompson St Fairfield CT 06430

PRYKE, ELIZABETH, History Teacher; *b:* Queens, NY; *m:* Stephen; *ed:* SUNY at Oneonta (MA) Pol Sci 1985; Queens Coll (MS) Scndry Ed 1995; *cr:* Manhattan Dist Attorney 1985-87; Cable & Wireless Comms 1987-88; Lanier Worldwide 1988-91; John Adams HS His Tchr 1993-; *ai:* Negotiation & Conflict Resolution Specialist; Grant Writing Comm; Regents & Rc T Remediation Tchr; Asst Chprsn Soc Stud Dept; Prom Coord; Schl Based Planning Cncl; Tchr Effectiveness Stu Achvmt 1994-; Returned Peace Corp Vols For Global Awareness Coord 1995-; *office:* John Adams HS 101-01 Rockaway Blvd Ozone Park NY 11417

PRYOR, FRANK ANTHONY, Health & Physical Ed Instr; *b:* PA; *m:* Patrica A. Novotnak Pryor; *ed:* WV Univ (BS) Physical, Hlth & Safety Ed 1977, (MS) PE 1979, (CAS) Ath Admin 1983; *cr:* Brownsville Area Schl PE Tchr 1977; WV Univ Grad Asst PE Tchr 1978-80; Bethlehem Ctr Sr HS Hlth & PE Instr 1988-; *ai:* Bsbl Head Coach; Vllybl Asst Coach; Stu Assistance Program; PSEA 1988-; BCEA 1988-; Phi Delta Kappa 1988-; Marianna Volunteer Fire Co 1973; Wash Greene Bsktbl PIAA 1981-, Rules Interpreter; Wash Greene Cty Bsbl & Sftbl Camp 1982-, Dir; Iron City Ftbl PIAA 1990-, VP; Northeast Conference Bsktbl Ofcl Div I 1993; WV Intercollegiate Ath Ofcl Div II 1993; Amer Bsbl Coaches Assn Pub; *office:* Bethlehem Ctr Sr HS 179 Crawford Rd Fredericktown PA 15333

PRYOR, PAUL R., Soc Stud & Pol Sci Teacher; *b:* New Kensington, PA; *m:* Nancy M.; *c:* Paul Jr., Peter Ryan; *ed:* Clarion Univ of PA (BED) His, Ec 1966; California Univ of PA (MED) Soc Stud 1972; Post-Grad Stud Scndry Admin 1982; *cr:* Upper St Clair HS Soc Stud Tchr 1966-, Curr Ldr 1985-; *ai:* Multicultural Club Spon; World Affairs Club Adv; Asst Swim Coach; NCSS 1985-; PACSS 1995-; NEA, PSEA 1966-85; Star Educator Awd 1995; Outstdng Tchr Awd; *office:* Upper St Clair Twp Schls 1825 Mclaughlin Run Rd Upper St Clair PA 15241

PRZEPIERSKI, MARIE STANKAVICH, Eighth Grd Tchr & Asst Prin; *b:* Erie, PA; *m:* Edward; *ed:* Villa Marie Coll, Gannon Univ (BS) Elem Ed, Natural Sci 1969; Post Grad 30 Credit Hrs; *cr:* Springhill Elem Schl Tchr 1069-70; St Paul Schl Tchr 1970-78; St Stanislaus Schl Tchr, Asst Prin 1982-; *ai:* Yth Group Ldr; Safety Patrol Adv; Geog Bee Coord; PA Inventors Soc Adv; Church Commentator, Eucharist Minister; Recipient in Eisenhower Grants for Math, Sci; *home:* 9451 Lake Pleasant Rd Erie PA 16509

PRZYBOJEWSKI, FRANK WALTER, Principal; *b:* Cleveland, OH; *m:* Donna Marie Kisley; *c:* Ruth Rachel, David; *ed:* Borromeo Coll of OH (BA) His, Philosophy 1971; Cleveland St Univ (MA) His 1974; Cuyahaga Comm Coll (MLT) Med Lab Tech 1975; 34 Quarter Hrs Admin Cert Prgm Cleveland St Univ; *cr:* City of Cleveland Mayor's Office Asst Nationalities Dir 1975-78; Mary Crest HS Jr HS Tchr, Stud Skills Coord 1978-81; Jesus & Mary Schl Grd 8 Tchr 1981-94; All Saints of St John Vianney Prin 1994-95; Jesus & Mary Schl Prin 1995-; *ai:* Amer Soc of Clinical Pathologists 1975-, MLT; NCEA 1981-; Amer Nationalities Movement, Polish Natl Alliance 1975-; Civil Won Reenactors Assn 1977-; His Dept Grad Asst Cleveland St Univ 1973-74; *office:* Jesus And Mary Schl 6804 Lansing Ave Cleveland OH 44105*

PRZYBYCIEN, TODD MICHAEL, Chemical Engineering Asst Prof; *b:* Clarkson, NY; *m:* Valerie Patrick; *c:* Jakob; *ed:* WA Univ (AB) Chem 1984, (BS) Chem Engr 1984; Caltech (MS) Chem Engr 1986, (PHD) Chem Engr 1989; *cr:* Monsanto Agricultural Co Sr Rsrch Engr 1989-90; Rensselaer Polytechnic Inst Isermann Asst Prof 1991-; *ai:* Cnslr Hugh O'Brien Yth Ldrshp Fnd Western MA Region; AICHE 1984-, Prgm Coord Area 15C; ACS 1982-; AAAS 1990-; Town of W Stockbridge Water Advy Comm 1994-; NSF Early Career Awd; Howard P. Isermann Asst Prof Chair; 15 Articles Pub; *office:* Rensselaer Polytechnic Inst 110 8th St Troy NY 12180

PRZYBYLA, JOSEPH A., Mathematics Department Chprsn; *b:* Lowell, MA; *m:* Therese Roy; *ed:* Merrimack Coll (AB) Math 1966; Univ of MA at Lowell (MS) 1968; Post Grad Stud in Cmptr Sci; *cr:* Rivier Coll Instr 1968-73; Dracut HS Math Tchr 1973-, Math Dept Head 1987-; *ai:* Cmptr Supvr; NEA, MTA, NCSM, AAPMT, NH ATMNE; Box 52 Assn 1972-; Fellowship Univ of MA at Lowell; Commonwealth Inservice Inst Grant; Math & Sci Connections Grant; *office:* Dracut Sr HS 1540 Lakeview Ave Dracut MA 01826

PRZYBYLA, THERESE ROY, Spanish Teacher; *b:* Lowell, MA; *m:* Joseph A.; *ed:* Univ of MA at Lowell (BA) Fr & Span 1972; Rivier Coll (MA) Fr 1976, (MAT) Span 1996; 42 Post Grad Credits; *cr:* Dracut HS Fr & Span Tchr 1972-; *ai:* Project Santa Org Adv; 3rd-5th Grd Span After Schl Enrichment Prgm; SADD Adv; NHS Comm; Frgn Lang Dept Chprsn; DTA, MTA & NEA 1972-; MaFLa; EMFLA; AATSP; AATF; Horace Mann Grant; *office:* Dracut H S 1540 Lakeview Ave Dracut MA 01826

PRZYBYSZ, CHRISTIE MINOR, Science Teacher; *b:* Cleveland, OH; *m:* David Matthew; *c:* Scott; *ed:* California Univ of PA (BS) Ed 1990; Working on MA at Clarion Univ of PA; *cr:* Elderton Jr, Sr HS Tchr 1992-; *ai:* Tennis, Sci Olympiad Coach; Ski Club, Frosh Class, Drama Club Adv; Play Dir; Stu Assistance Prgm, Scndry Instrl Support Teams; Steering Comm; PSEA, NSTA, AEA 1992-; Written & Received Grants; *office:* Elderton Jr Sr HS PO Box 124 Elderton PA 15736

PRZYSTUP, DONNA W., 7th & 8th Grd Soc Stud Teacher; *b:* Portland, ME; *m:* Leonard Michael; *c:* Deanna Lynn Cook Runeman; *ed:* Univ of ME at Machias (BS) Eng, Minor in His 1966; Addl Courses In Svc, Local CEU's; *cr:* Mattanawcook Jr HS Eng, Rdng Tchr 1966-81, Soc Stud Tchr 1981-; *ai:* 7-8 Grd It's Up to Me Svc Club; 25 Yrs as Jr HS A Team Cheering Coach; After Schl Chess; MEA, NEA 1966-67; Lincoln Lions, Lioness 1973-, Pres, Sec, Dir; Congregational Church 1953-; Lion of the Yr 1995; Lioness Ldrshp Canada, US Awd 1981; J. Herklotz Natl Awd for Schl Elections 1995; Fleet Yth Ldrs 1990, St Awd & Trip to WA; Fleet Yth Ldrs 1991, St Runner-Up Trophy & Schl Plaque; ABC Svc Club 1994 Yth of Amer Awd; Poetry Pub; GATE Grant; Train Stu Tchrs & UME Underclassmen in Ed; 1995 Nom for Jefferson Awd, Spirit of Amer Awd; *office:* Mattanawcook Jr HS 41 School St Lincoln ME 04457*

PRZYWITOWSKI, MARIE B., Sixth Grade Teacher; *b:* Darby, PA; *m:* James S.; *ed:* PA St Univ (BS) Elem Ed 1974; 24 Post Grad Credit Hrs; Arch of Phila Rel Credits; Cert in PA K-6; *cr:* Our Lady of Fatima Schl 5th Grd Tchr 1974-82; Assumption BVM 6th Grd Tchr 1991-; *ai:* Rdng Coord; NCEA 1991-; *office:* Assumption BVM Schl State Rd West Grove PA 19390

PSATHAS, BARBARA (BENNETT), English Teacher; *b:* Easton, PA; *m:* Nicholas; *c:* James, Alexandra, Michael; *ed:* Moravian Coll (BA) Ger Ed 1975; Eng Cert 1979; Attnd Phillips Marburg Univ at Marburg West Germany 1973-74; Kutztown Univ Masters Prgm; *cr:* East Hills Jr HS Lang Arts Tchr 1978-80; St Thomas More Eng Tchr 1985-86; Sts Cyril & Methodius Eng Tchr 1986-87; Cntrl Cath HS Eng Tchr 1987-; *ai:* Oratorical Adv; Soph Cl Adv; Dept Chprsn; Daughters of Penelope 1980-, Pres 1987-89; Cub Scouts 1988-, Den Ldr 1988-90; Bethelehem Soccer Club 1989-; Daughter's of Penelope Dist Treas 1993-; Dist Marshall 1992-93; *office:* Allentown Central Catholic HS 4th & Chew St Allentown PA 18102*

PTAK, BERNADETTE MARIE, Second Grade Teacher; *b:* Uniontown, PA; *m:* John W.; *ed:* CA Univ of PA (BS) Elem Ed 1968; WV Univ (MA) Elem Cnslng 1975; *cr:* Hutchinson Elem Schl 1st Grd Tchr 1968-75, 6th Grd Tchr 1975-87, 4th Grd Tchr 1987-94, 2nd Grd Tchr 1994-; *ai:* NEA, PSEA 1968-; Uniontown Coll Club 1970-; Hutchinson PTO 1968-; *office:* Hutchinson Elem Schl RD 2 Box 492X Uniontown PA 15401

PTASZYNSKI, MARTHA, Tech Coord & Computer Teacher; *b:* Bound Brook, NJ; *ed:* Seton Hall (BS) Elem Ed; Seton Hall (MA) Ed 1972; Attnd St Peters at Jersey City, Univ of AL at Huntsville Space Acad of Edctrs, OK St Univ; *cr:* Our Lady of Mt Virgin Schl 2nd-8th Grd Math, Sci, Cmptr Tchr, Tech Coord 1964-; *ai:* Cmptr Club; Diocese of Metuchen Tech Task FOrce; NCEA 1965-; NSTA 1988-; Middlesex Elks Cert of Awd 1989; Selected & Participated in Star Gazer Prgm 1991; New Mast Hnrs Tchr 1993; Outstdng Edctr 1995; Math & Sci Curr Comm Diocese of Trenton 1973, Diocese of Metuchen 1990.

PUCCI, ANTHONY J., English Department Chairman; *b:* Lawrence, MA; *m:* Cara; *c:* Gina Marie; *ed:* Merrimack Coll (BA) Eng 1971; Elmira Coll (MS) Ed 1979; Duquesne Univ 30 Grad Credits; *cr:* Notre Dame HS Eng Dept Chair 1974-; *ai:* NCTE 1974-; Steele Meml Lib Friends 1974-; Book Review Pub; *office:* Notre Dame HS 1400 Maple Ave Elmira NY 14904

PUCCIARELLI, DONNA JEAN, Business Education Teacher; *b:* Dunkirk, NY; *m:* Joseph A.; *c:* Angela, Joseph F.; *ed:* Hilbert Coll (AAS) Sec Sci 1983; SUNY at Buffalo St Coll (BS) Bus & Distributive Ed 1992; *cr:* Dunkirk HS Sec 1984-93; Pine Vly HS Bus Ed & Schl to Work Coord 1993-; *ai:* FBLA Adv; Fed Schl-to-Work Transition Grant Coord; Chautauqua Cty Bus Tchrs Assn 1992-, Sec; Chautauqua Cty Schl-to-Work Comm 1995-; Brownie Troop 1993-, Vol Ldr; Holy Trinity RC Church 1995-, Children, Family Liturgy Ministry; FBLA Chptr Chartered, Advised 1993-94; 1st Pl NY St Outstdng First Yr Chptr Event FBLA St Ldrshp Conf; *office:* Pine Vly HS 7827 Route 83 South Dayton NY 14136

PUCELL, JANET M.,IHM, Asst Principal of Stu Services; *b:* Philadelphia, PA; *ed:* Immaculata Coll (BA) Math 1972; Villanova Univ (MATM) Math 1980; *cr:* Phila Cath Schls 8th Grd Tchr 1970-85; St Matthew Schl 8th Grd Tchr 1986-90; Bishop Kenrick HS Math, Cmptr Tchr 1990-93; Kennedy-Kenrick Cath HS Dean of Stdnts 1993-; *ai:* NCEA 1980-; CT Ed Support Bd 1988-90; *office:* Kennedy-Kenrick Cath HS 250 E Johnson Hwy Norristown PA 19401*

PUCHINO, RICHARD ANTHONY, Social Studies Teacher; *b:* Philadelphia, PA; *m:* Donna Marie Gehm; *c:* Nicole Marie, Brooke Michelle; *ed:* Shippensburg Univ (BS) Soc Sci 1969; Attnd Penn St, Temple, Trenton St & West Chester; *cr:* Bristol Twp Schl Dist Tchr 1969-; *ai:* Pennsbury Strategic Planning Comm; NEA & NCSS 1969-; PSEA 1969-, Faculty Rep 1987-91; Tullytown Borough Planning Commission 1990-, VP; Pennsbury Schl Dist Strategic Planning Commission; Outstanding Young Men of America 1977; US Bicentennial Constitution Grant; *home:* 32 Serpentine Ln Levittown PA 19055

PUCKERIN, RICHARD KENT, School Counselor; *b:* Trinidad, West Indies; *c:* Jamila; *ed:* Boston St Coll (BS) Sociology 1974; Univ of MA (MED) Psych 1980, (CAGS) Schl Psych 1996; *ai:* Indoor, Outdoor Track, Cross Cntry Coach; AGPA 1987-; Runner of Yr 1995; *home:* 19 Grove St Arlington MA 02174

PUCKETT, JAMES DAVID, Jr High Health & PE Teacher; *b:* Delaware, OH; *m:* Jane Ann Schlater; *c:* Allison, Bradley; *ed:* Otterbein Coll (BA) Ed, Hlth, PE 1982; *cr:* Worthington City Schls Sub, Coach 1982-84; Urbana City Schls Tchr, Coach 1984-; *ai:* Head Jr HS Track Coach; UACT, OEA, NEA 1984-, Bldg Rep 9 Yrs, FAC, Pub Relations 1 Yr; Church Cncl 1993-, Trustee; *office:* Urbana City Schls 500 Washington Ave Urbana OH 43078

PUDHORODSKY, KATHLEEN MADDIGAN, Social Studies Teacher; *b:* Buffalo, NY; *m:* Theodore G.; *c:* Timothy, Matthew; *ed:* Rosary Hill Coll (BA) His, Sociology 1968; Canisius Coll (MSEd) Ed 1988; *cr:* United Airlines Flight Attendant 1968-73; St Martin's Schl Tchr 1973-74; St Jude HS Tchr 1985-89; Cardinal O'Hara HS Tchr 1989-; *ai:* Mock Trail; Newspaper in Ed Coord; Senate Stu Policy Forum; Middle St Evaluation Team; SLTA 1985-; NSSTC 1987-; NHS 1994-; World Wildlife; SPCA; Nature's Conservatory; Natl Audubon; NYPRIG; Diocesan Lay Persons Awd; NHS Awd; *office:* Cardinal O'Hara HS 39 Ohara Rd Tonawanda NY 14150

PUETTNER, ROSEMARIE ELIZABETH,SSJ, Ger Tchr & Frgn Lang Dept Chr; *b:* Philadelphia, PA; *ed:* Chestnut Hill Coll (BA) Ger, Span 1968; Millersville (MA) Ger 1975; Attnd Goethe Inst 1970, 1978, St

Joseoh's Univ 1964-66, Akademie Klausenhof 1981, Case Western Reserve 1968, Univ of Innsbruck 1969; *cr:* St Helena's Third Grd Tchr 1953-54; Our Lady of Mercy First Grd Tchr 1954-60; St John the Evan First, Third, Fourth, Fifth Grd Tchr 1960-64; Little Flower HS Ger Tchr 1964-70; Abp. Ryan HS Ger Tchr 1970-77; Abp. Wood HS Ger Tchr 1977-; *ai:* Dept Chair 1980-; Moderator Ger Club 1964-; Delta Epsilon Phi 1970-; A-V Coord 1979-; Coord Visiting Ger Exch Stdnts, Chaperone Stdnts to Germany 1977-; For Lang Curric Com 1969-80; NCEA 1954-; AATG 1964-; MLAPV 1972-, Corresponding Sec; Mid States Evaluation Comm Hightstown HS 1982, Abington Hgts HS 1980; Ger Comm Internat'l Eucharistic Congress 1976; NFSG, DVFSG Coord of Stu Conventions; Bazaars, Craft Fairs AWHS, Nativity Parish; Grants Goethe Inst; Article Pub 1976; CARE Awd 1991; Tchr of Yr 1990; Speaker AATG 1969; *office:* Archbishop Wood HS 655 York Rd Warminster PA 18974

PUFFENBERGER, JUDITH BURLEY, Third Grade Teacher; *b:* Cumberland, MD; *m:* Carl; *c:* Robert, Amy Cober, Brett; *ed:* Frostburg St (BS) Elem Ed 1963; 12 Addl Credits; *cr:* Allegany Cty MD 3rd-4th Grd Tchr 1963-64; Garrett Cty Md 1st Grd Tchr 1965-67; Rockwood Area Schl Tchr 1976-; *ai:* NEA, PSEA, REA 1976-; Christ U M Church; *home:* RR 1 Box 125 Somerset PA 15501

PUGH, DALE S., Global Studies Teacher; *b:* Utica, NY; *ed:* Buffalo St Univ Coll (BS) His & Sec Ed 1972; 30 Grad Hrs; *cr:* Holland Patent Control Tchr 1972-73; Whitesboro HS Tchr 1973-; *ai:* Girls Summer Sftbl Traveling Team; Former Newspaper Club & SAGA Adv, Asst Sftbl & Girls Ftbl Coach; NEA 1972-; *office:* Whitesboro HS 6000 Rt 291 Marcy NY 13403

PUGH, GLADYS HELEN (BURNISON), Math Teacher; *b:* Huron, SD; *m:* Benjamin; *c:* Amy Melissa, Mary Amanda; *ed:* Dakota St Coll (BSEd) Bus 1972; Univ of Scranton (MED) Math 1982; 6 Credits SD St UNiv, 6 Credits PA St Univ, 6 Credits Wilkes University, 3 Credits Keystone Coll, 5 Credits NEIU Inservice; *cr:* Lakeland Schl Dist Bus Tchr 1973-75; Lackawanna Jr Coll Day Schl Coord, Admissions Rep 1976-77; Scranton Schl Dist Part-time Basic Clerical Skills Instr 1979-80; Northeast Inst of Ed Part-time Bus Courses Instr 1980-81; Scranton Schl Dist Math Tchr 1982-; *ai:* Behavior Mngmnt Support Team; AFT 1982-; Scranton Women Tchrs 1994-; PA Cncl of Tchrs of Math 1982-; Children's Miracle Network Telethon 1990-; Run, Walk a Mile for Mandy Coord; Bus Prof Women's Assn 1975-78; Mental Hlth Assn 1972-79, Bd Mem; Personality of Week 1994; *office:* West Scranton HS 1201 Luzerne St Scranton PA 18504*

PUGH, LUCIA ANN (DELUTIS), Spanish Teacher; *b:* Coatesville, PA; *m:* Cecil Richard; *c:* Richard, John; *ed:* Villa Maria Coll (BA) Span 1971; Masters Equivalency in Ed; *cr:* Abraham Lincoln Jr HS Span Tchr 1971-; *ai:* 9th Grd Party, Natl Jr Hnr Soc, Booster Club 1993 Adv; PSEA, NEA 1971-; Rainbow Elem PTO 1988-; *office:* Abraham Lincoln Jr HS 1001 Lehigh Ave Lancaster PA 17602

PUGLIA, JOANNE Z., Support Tchr of the Gifted; *b:* Jersey City, NJ; *m:* Charles; *c:* Allison, Puglia; *ed:* Beaver Coll (MED) Spec Ed 1981; Elem Principalship Cert 1996; *cr:* Ancillae-Assumpta Acad Admin 1982-89; Hatboro-Horsham Schl Dist Gifted Support Tchr 1989-; *ai:* Mentor Tchr; Stans Comm; Natl Blue Ribbon Comm; Educl Assn, PA Higher Ed Assn 1989-; Medical Coll PA, Hahnemann Univ 1980-, Women's Bd; Educl Fnd Grant; *office:* Hatboro-Horsham Sch Dist 229 Meetinghouse Rd Horsham PA 19044

PUGLIESE, PATRICIA MAUCIONE, Social Studies Teacher; *b:* Newark, NJ; *m:* Robert J. Sr.; *c:* Robert Jr., Carla M.; *ed:* Douglass Coll (BA) Soc Stud 1962; Montclair St Coll (MA) Admin, Supervision 1991; 33 Post Grad Hrs; *cr:* Belleville Elem Schl 7th-8th Grd Soc Stud Tchr 1962-63; Belleville HS Ital Tchr 1963-66, Soc Stud Tchr 1963-; *ai:* Stu Govt Adv; Holistic Scoring Comm; Mid Sts Stu Act Comm Chprsn; Prin Advy, Soc Stud Proficiencies, Curr Revision Comms; NEA, NJEA, Belleville Ed Assn, Essex Cty Ed Assn 1962-; Natl Assn Activity Advs 1977-; Phi Delta Kappa 1994-; Nutley Acad Booster Club 1982-, Treas 1984-86; Elected Cty Comm Woman 1982-; Nutley Friends of Lib 1988-; Carmen Orechio Civic Org 1985-; Phi Beta Kappa 1962; *office:* Belleville HS 100 Passaic Ave Belleville NJ 07109

PUKOWSKI, JOHN PATRICK, Social Studies Teacher; *b:* Philadelphia, PA; *m:* Susan M. Doggett; *c:* Scott, Jeffrey; *ed:* Beaver Coll (ME) Soc Stud 1976; 60 Addl Credit Hrs; *cr:* Klinger MS Tchr 1973-; *ai:* Bsktbl, Sftbl Coach; NEA 1973-; *home:* 298 Hickory Rd Warminster PA 18974

PULASKI, DAVID WALTER, High School Math Teacher; *b:* Westfield, MA; *m:* Wanda Marie Taylor; *c:* David Alan; *ed:* Lowell Technological Inst (BS) I.M. 1963; Westfield St (MS) Scndry Ed 1967; *cr:* Agawan Schl System 1963-; *ai:* Yrbk Phtgrphr 1963-, Dir 1970-; Westfield St Coll Alliance Mentor Prgm C0-Dir; Quill & Scrll Soc; NEA, MTA, AEA 1963-; *office:* Agawam H S 760 Cooper St Agawam MA 01001*

PULICE, MICHELE DAWN, Second Grade Teacher; *b:* Erie, PA; *c:* Nicoletta Cherry, Joseph Cherry II; *ed:* Villa Maria Coll (BA) Elem Ed 1978; Edinboro St Univ (MA) Early Chldhd Ed 1980; *cr:* Our Lady of Peace Schl First Grd Tchr 1976-84; St Gregory's Schl First Grd Tchr 1984-85; Amer Heritage Schl First Grd Tchr 1985-88; Belle Valy Schl Second Grd Tchr 1992-; *ai:* Schl Dist Goals, Drivin Forces of Primary Retention Quality Teams; Piloted Extended Learning Time for At Risk Stdnts; NEA, PSEA, MEA 1982-88, 1991-; CCD Tchr 16 Yrs; Jr League 1985-86; Significant Progress Awd 1995; Team Quality Awd Driving Forces of Primary Retention; *office:* Belle Valley Elem Schl 5300 Henderson Rd Erie PA 16509*

PULICE-LOOMIS, TRACI, 2nd Grade Teacher; *b:* Erie, PA; *m:* Kirk Loomis; *c:* Dillon Lee, Taylor Leigh; *ed:* Edinboro Univ of PA (MED) Elem Ed 1990; *cr:* J. S. Wilson Schl 6th Grd SS Tchr 1982; Grandview Schl Grd 3 Tchr 1992-93; J. S. Wilson 6th Grd Sci Tchr 1983-84; Grandview Schl Grd 3 Tchr 1984-90;Asbury Schl Grd 2 Tchr 1990-; *ai:* PSEA; MEA; Taught a Wkshp at Mercyhurst Coll for New Tchrs-to-be; *office:* Asbury Elem Schl 3814 Asbury Rd Erie PA 16506*

PULITZER, VIRGINIA KUKOWSKI, Teacher of Gifted & Talented; *b:* Utica, NY; *m:* Arthur B.; *c:* Heather Mele, Courtney, Nicole Bachmann; *ed:* Utica Coll of Syracuse Univ (BA) Eng-Magna Cum Laude 1971; SUNY at Corltnad (MA) Eng-Magna Cum Laude 1975; Addl 6 Credit Hrs; *cr:* New Hartford HS Scndry Eng, Theatre Tchr 1971-91; Whitesboro HS Scndry Eng Tchr 1993-95; Whitesboro Elem Schl Prism Tchr, Tchr of GATE 1995-; *ai:* Chprsn Prism Comm; Amer Fed of Tchrs, NY St United Tchrs 1971-; Whitesboro Tchrs Assn 1993-; Munson Williams Proctor Inst 1994-; Cntrl NY Comm Arts Cncl 1995-; Broadway Theatre League 1980-; New Hartford HS Master Tchr Awd.

PULLEN, ARLENE, English Supervisor; *b:* Cream Ridge, NJ; *ed:* Trenton St Coll (BA) Eng & Ed 1960; Columbia Univ (MA) Eng 1964; Nova Southeastern Univ (EDD) Educl Ldrshp 1993; 25 Credits NY Univ; 18 Credits Montclair St Univ, Kean Coll & Rutgers Univ; 6 Credits Hunter Coll; Houston Comm Coll; Oxford Under NYU Auspices 1982; *cr:* North Plainfield HS Eng & Rdng Tchr 1960-62; Raritan HS Eng Tchr 1962-65; Carteret HS Eng Supvr 1965-85; Houston Ind Schls Eng Tchr 1985-86; Marlboro HS Eng Supvr 1987-; *ai:* AP Comm; NCTE 1960-; Prins & Supvrs Assn 1980-; ASCD; NJCTE; Upper Freehold Bapt Church 1952-, Tchr; NDEA Grant 1968; Lilly Fndtn Grant 1972; Articles Pub; Poems Pub; *office:* Marlboro HS 95 N Main St Marlboro NJ 07746

PULLEN, NANCY FOGG, Social Studies Teacher; *b:* Island Falls, ME; *m:* Michael W.; *ed:* Univ of ME at Orono (BSEd) Soc Stud 1973; *cr:* Mt View HS Soc Stud Tchr 1973-79; Old Town MS Soc Stud Tchr 1979-89; Old Town HS Soc Stud Tchr 1989-; *ai:* Sr Class Adv; Schl Improvement Comm; Schl Climate Comm; Co-Chair Evaluation Comm; Recert Comm; ME St Task Force on Learning Results; NEA, ME Tchrs Assn 1973-; Old Town Tchrs Assn 1979-; Delta Kappa Gamma 1990-; *home:* 21 Sargent Dr Old Town ME 04468*

PULLER, JODI STUCK, Fifth Grade Teacher; *b:* Williamsport, PA; *m:* Roy Eugene; *c:* Ethan D.; *ed:* Lycoming Univ (BA) Anthropology, Elem Ed 1985; Wilkes Univ (MS) Elem Ed 1991; *cr:* South Williamsport Schl Dist Kndgtn Tchr 1988-89, Fourth Grd Tchr 1989-90, Third Grd Tchr 1990-91, Fifth Grd Tchr 1992-; *ai:* Interscholastic Rdng Competition Coach; PSEA 1988-; *office:* Duboistown Elem Schl 126 Summer St Williamsport PA 17701

PULLER, LAUREL J., Kindergarten Teacher; *b:* Garden City, NY; *ed:* Westminster Coll (BA) Elem Ed 1982; 15 Credits Towards Masters Degree in Spec Ed; *cr:* Scrolls Schl 2nd Grd Tchr 1982-83; Nativity of Our Blessed Lady Kndgtn Tchr 4 Yrs, Third Grd Tchr 4 Yrs, Fifth Grd Tchr 5 Yrs 1983-; *ai:* Afterschool Prgm Dir 2 Yrs; *office:* Nativity of Our Blessed Lady 3893 Dyre Ave Bronx NY 10466*

PULLI, MICHAEL CHARLES, Fifth Grade Teacher; *b:* Easton, PA; *c:* Michael Jr.; *ed:* Mansfield Univ (BS) Elem Ed 1970; *cr:* Porter Elem Sixth Gde Tchr 1970-76; Cheston Elem Fifth Grd Tchr 1976-; *ai:* Adv Stu Cncl; NEA, PSEA, EAEA 1970-; *office:* Ada B Cheston Elem Sch 723 Coal St Easton PA 18042

PULLMAN, PHYLLIS L., Math Teacher; *b:* New York, NY; *ed:* Queens Coll (BA) Math; Boston Univ (MA) Math; *cr:* Marie Curie MS Math Tchr; *ai:* 9th Grd Math Team Coach; AFT, Produc Curr, Progressive Caucels, Conl Del; NYSUT, Conv Del; UFT, Ldr, Exec Chr, Math Comm, Ely Tract4nberg Awd; NCTM, Co Vice Chair, NE Regnl Mngmt; ATMNYC, Exec Bd, Pres, VP, Sec; AMTNYS, Dist Rep, Cty Chair, JHS LEvel Rep Exec Bd; Jewish Tchrs Assn, Pres 13 Yrs; Cncl of Jewish Org in Civil Svc, Treas; ADL Ed Comm Edctrs Chptr, Jewish Labor Comm, Exec Bd; Numeros Awds; Spoltlight Person in the News; Network of Networks NYC Rep; *office:* Marie Curie MS 158Q 46-35 Oceania St Bayside NY 11361*

PUMA, FRANK JOSEPH, Biology Teacher; *b:* New York City, NE; *ed:* Long Island Univ (BS) Bio 1970, (MS) Bio 1973; NY Univ (PHD) Bio 1980; MA Cert 9-12th Grd Bio 1994; *cr:* Millipore Corp, Pharmaaia Bio-Rsrch Product Specialist 1984-88; Electrophysiological Separatins, Analysis Inc Sr Product Mgr 1988-91; Self Employed Marketing Consultant 1991-93; Acad of Nortre Dame Bio Tchr 1994-; *ai:* MAST 1994-; NABT 1994-; MABT 1995-; Flwshps Natl Inst Hlth, Juvenile Diabetes Assn, Amer Liver Fnd 1980-84; *office:* Acad of Notre Dame 180 Middlesex Rd Tyngsboro MA 01879

PUMPHREY, EUGENE R., Math & Computer Science Tchr; *b:* Hackensack, NJ; *m:* Karen Novotny; *c:* Amy, Gary, Amanda; *ed:* Paterson St Coll (BA) Math Ed 1969; FDU (MAS) Math 1972; 47 Credits Math, Cmptr Sci, Sci Topics; *cr:* Waldwick HS Tchr 1969-; *ai:* Math Team Supvr; NCTM 1988-; *office:* Waldwick Jr Sr HS 155 Wyckoff Ave Waldwick NJ 07463

PUMPHRY, DAVID, Math, Physics & Chemistry Tchr; *b:* Wilmington, OH; *c:* Sarah; *ed:* Kent St Univ (BS) Math 1988; *cr:* Valley View ISD Math Tchr 1991-92; Conotton Valley HS Math, Physics & Chem Tchr 1994-; *ai:* Jr HS Ftbl Coach; Teen Inst Adv; NEA 1995-.

PUNGELLO, JOHANNA MORAN, Fifth Grade Teacher; *b:* Bronx, NY; *m:* Paul; *ed:* Dominican Coll (BA) Psych, Elem Ed 1977; Iona Coll (MS) Urban Ed 1987; 24 Credits Admin Prof Diploma; *cr:* Blessed Sacrament Schl 5th Grd Tchr 1977-81; St Elizabeth's Schl 5th-6th Grd Sci, Rdng Tchr 1982-88; Our Lady of Good Counsel 6th-8th Grd Sci, Hlth Tchr 1988-93, 5th Grd Tchr 1993-; *ai:* Sci Wizards Club; Sci Fair Coord; After Schl Prgm; NCEA 1982-, Tchr Assoc; ASCD 1993-, Prof Assoc; Natl Arbor Day Fnd 1990-; Father's Club Svc Awd 1995; *home:* 24-6 Horseshoe Cr Ossining NY 10562*

PUNTE, AUDREY BOWEN, Junior High Teacher & Coord; *b:* E Pittsburgh, PA; *m:* Eugene F.; *c:* Marianna, Michael, David, Joanne Punte Turgeon; *ed:* Anne Arundel Comm Coll (AA) Elem Ed; Towson St Univ (BS) Ed, (ME) Ed Rdng; Post Grad Courses U of MD, Loyola; *cr:* Anne Arundel Co Part-time Recreation Natl Bowling Instr, Sftbl 1959-84; St Philip Neri Cath Schl 7-8th Grd Tchr 1966-; Archbishop Spalding HS PE Tchr 1967-69; *ai:* GATE Coord; Lang Arts, Farewell Luncheon Chm; NCEA; Towson St Alumnae; N Linthicum Improvement Assn; Cath Daughters; *office:* St Philip Neri Schl 6401 S Orchard Rd Linthicum Heights MD 21090

PUOPOLO, NICHOLAS RALPH, Educational Consultant; *b:* East Boston, MA; *m:* Judith; *c:* Nick Jude, Luke, Christine; *ed:* Boston St Coll (MED) Cnslng, Spec Ed 1970; Post Grad Stud Harvard Univ, Boston Coll, Boston Univ; *cr:* Georgetown Pub Schls Elem Cnslr 30 Yrs; Educl Specialists Assoc Educl Evaluator, Consultant, Mental Hlth Cnslr, Marriage & Family Therapist 1993-; *ai:* NBCC; ACA; MCA, Trustee; North Suffolk Mental Hlth, Past Pres; North Shore Guid Cnslrs Assn, Past Pres; *home:* 19 Neptune Ave Winthrop MA 02152*

PUPINO, MARC STEVEN, Assistant Band Director; *b:* Youngstown, OH; *m:* Diane Medicus; *ed:* Youngstown St Univ (BA) Music Ed 1994; Masters in Ed Admin 9 Hrs Ashland Univ; *cr:* East Palestine Schls Asst Band Dir 1994-; *office:* East Palestine City Schls 360 W Grant St East Palestine OH 44413

PURCARO, MICHAEL JOSEPH, Chemistry Teacher; *b:* Waterbury, CT; *m:* Nancy Bracken; *c:* MIchael Jr., Jennifer, Mary; *ed:* Univ of CT (BA) Bacteriology, Virology 1965; Cntrl CT St Univ (MS) Bacteriology 1967; Addl 15 Hrs; Attnd US Army Field Medical Svc Schl, Kaynor Regnl Tech Schl; *cr:* 1st US Army Research Facility Chief of Medical Lab 1967-68; Wilby HS Chem Tchr 1969-; *ai:* NEA, CT Ed Assn, Waterbury Tchrs Assn 1969-; Amer CHem Soc 1985-; Refrigeration Svc Engineers Soc 1971-; Article Pub for Appliance Talk.

PURCELL, CHRISTINE E., High School English Teacher; *b:* Gloversville, NY; *ed:* Fulton Montgomery Comm Coll (AA) Liberal Arts 1985; St Univ NY at Albany (BA) Eng 1987; Coll of Saint Rose (MS) Spec Ed 1992; *cr:* Fonda Fultonville Central Schl HS Eng Tchr 1987-; *ai:* New Standards Portfolio Project; BOCES Assessment Liason; Exec Bd FFCS Booster Club Mem; FFCS HS Shared Decision Making Team; *office:* Fonda Fultonville Cntrl Schl Cemetary St Fonda NY 12068*

PURCELL, EDWARD A.,JR., Professor of Law; *b:* Kansas City, MO; *m:* Rachel Vorspan; *c:* Daniel E., Jessica V.; *ed:* Rockhurst Coll (AB) His 1962; Univ of KS (MA) His 1964; Univ of WI (PHD) His 1968; Harvard Univ (JD) Law 1979; *cr:* Univ of CA Asst Prof 1967-69; Univ of MO Assoc Prof 1969-77; Wellesley Coll Visiting Assoc Prof 1974-75; NY Law Schl Prof 1989-; *ai:* Soccer & Bsktbl Coach; Org of Amer Historians 1967-; Assoc of Bar of City of NY 1982-; Amer Soc for Legal His 1988-; Soc Sci Rsrch Cncl Fellow 1971-72; Harvard Charles Warren Fellow 1971-72; Crisis of Democratic Theory 1973; Natl Endowment for Hum Fellow 1977-78; Amer Cncl of Learned Soc Fellow 1988-89; Litigation and Inequality 1992; *office:* NY Law School 57 Worth St New York NY 10013

PURCELL, M. LEA KENNEDY, Kindergarten Teacher; *b:* Abbington, PA; *m:* Rick; *c:* H. Dean, P. Ethan, Christopher, Erin; *ed:* Slippery Rock Univ (BA) Elem Ed 1985; *cr:* 2nd Grd Tchr 1985-90; *ai:* K-3rd 4th-6th Grd Field Day Supvr; NEA, PSEA 1985-; Tchr of All Day K

PURCELL, ROBERTA KIRK, Teacher of the Special Nee Weymouth, MA; *m:* Robert; *c:* Michael, Kristin, Brian; *ed:* Fitchb Coll (BS) Spcl Ed 1972; 30 Grad Credits in Spcl Ed, Rdng Instruc Assessment; *cr:* Pentucket Regnl Jr HS Tchr of Spcl Needs 19 Whittier Regnl Voc Tech HS Tchr of Spcl Needs 1973-76; Cohann Tchr of Spcl Needs 1986-; *ai:* Adv & Advisee Pgm for At-Risk S MTA 1972-76, 1986-; NEA 1972-76, 1986-; *home:* 6 Lister Dr Barr RI 02806

PURCELL, THOMAS EDWARD,JR., Psychology Teacher; *b:* M GA; *ed:* Fordham Univ (BA) His, Modern European 1966, (MAT) M of Arts in Tchng 1968; Univ of Sarasota (EDD) Human Svcs Fairfield Univ 66 Credit Hrs Certfd as Schl Psychologist CT 1987 Advanced Stud 1973; Univ of Sorbonne Paris France 6 Credits Fr His *cr:* Danbury HS Soc Stud Tchr 1967-; *ai:* Amer Psych Assn, CT A Schl Psychologists 1990-; Phi Delta Kappa 1987-; NEA 1967-; C Assn; Danbury Educ Assn; Coll Bd AP Tchr Recognition Awd Andrew W. Mellon AP Tchr Flwshp 1992; Natl Defense Ed Schlsp Doctoral Dissertation; *office:* Danbury HS Clapboard Ridge Rd Da CT 06811*

PURNELL, CYNTHIA ADAMS, First Grade Teacher; *b:* Covingtor *ed:* Eastern KY Univ (BS) Elem Ed 1970; Salisbury St Univ (MS) El 1980; Post Grad Hrs Univ of HI 1975; *cr:* Osgood Elem Schl Grd Tw 1971; Sunset Elem Schl Fifth Grd Tchr 1971-72; Beaver Run Elem First Grd Tchr 1972-74; Pittsville Elem Schl First, Second Grd Tchr *ai:* Grd Level Chprsn; MD St Tchrs Assn 1972-; NEA 1971-; Pittsville Elem Schl Old Ocean City Rd Pittsville MD 21850*

PURNELL, JAMES PRESTON, Mathematics Instructor; *b:* New NY; *ed:* City Coll of NY (BA) His, Math 1972, (MS) Ed 1977; *cr:* J Kennedy HS Math Instr; *ai:* Masters Thesis Pub 1977; *home* Columbus Ave New York NY 10025

PURNELL, JANIS GROFT, Fifth Grade Teacher; *b:* Gettysburg, P Michael A.; *c:* Samuel Preston; *ed:* York Coll (BS) Elem Ed 1982; 36 Credits Awded MEQ St of PA 1996; *cr:* Littlestown Area S D 2nd Grd 1984-85, 4th Grd Tchr 1985-86, Tells Math Tchr, Rog Specialist 198 4th Grd Tchr 1987-92, 5th Grd Tchr 1992-; *ai:* Comms Dist Curr, C Arts, Assessment 1994-; Spirit Comm Adv 1992-95; PSEA, NEA LEA 1984, Rep; PA Lead Tchr 1993-; Acad Boosters 1994-; Presente Mid Level Conf; *home:* 185 Kensington Dr Littlestown PA 17340

PURNELL, JOHN C., Sixth Grd Teacher & Asst Prin; *b:* Boston, M Barbara M. Bolduc; *c:* Debra-Ann Conefrey, John C. Jr., Laurie-Le St Coll at Boston (BA) Ed Elem 1968; Bridgewater St Coll (MA) Ele Admin 1973; 86 Addl Hrs; *cr:* Brockton Adult Ed Prgm Tchr; Jo Kennedy Schl Sixth Grd Tchr 1968-73; James Edgar Schl Fourth Grd, Tchr 1973-77; Edward B. Gilmore Schl Sixth Grd tchr 1977-86; Fr Schl Sixth Grd Tchr & Asst Prin 1986-; *ai:* Brockton Schl Dept Crisis Math Comms; NEA, MA Tchrs Assn, Brockton Ed Assn 1968-; *o* Franklin Elem Schl 59 Sawtell Ave Brockton MA 02402*

PURTELL, KAREN BRION, Social Studies Teacher; *b:* Corning, N Gerald R.; *ed:* SUNY at Oneonta (BA) Scndry Soc Sci 1970; Attnd S at Geneseo & Elmira Coll For Permanent Cert in Grad Ed 1973; *cr:* Henrietta Schls Soc Stud Tchr 1970-73; Corning-Painted Post Area Soc Stud Tchr 1973-76; Owego Apalachin Schls Substitute Tchr 197 Soc Stud Tchr 1987-; *ai:* Schlsp Challenge Team Coach; HS Stu T Coach & Adv; Dist Curr Dev & Prin Ed Advisory Comms; NY St Cn Soc Stud 1988-; Owego Apalachin Tchrs Assn & AFT 1987-; St Th Altar & Rosary 1976-; Golden Apple Awd; NY St Dept of St Ce Recognition for NYS Citizen Bee; *office:* Owego Free Acad Geor Owego NY 13827*

PURTILL, JOSEPH JAMES, Mathematics Teacher; *b:* Westerly, R Julie M. Russ; *ed:* Univ of CT (BS) Math 1981; Addl 30 Credits Tow Masters in Arts in Tchng Math RI Coll; *cr:* St Pius X Schl 7th Grd 1985-86; Babcock MS 7th Grd Math Tchr 1986-; *ai:* Womens Soccer Coach; Instrl Coord Math; Classroom Alternative Support Team; 1986-; NCTM 1989-; Colony Cable in The Classroom Awd; A Tc Remember 1992; Who's Who in Amer Ed 1996; *office:* Babcock Highland Ave Westerly RI 02891

PURUS, DANIEL JOSEPH, Computer Coordinator; *b:* New York, NY Lynn M. Alksey; *c:* Jennifer, Amy, Bryan; *ed:* St Johns Univ (BS) E Math 1980, (MS) Scndry Ed & Math 1989; Brooklyn Coll Advanced in Admin & Supervision 1995; *cr:* St Claire Schl Math Tchr 198 Ridgewood Intermediate Schl Math Tchr 1983-92, Stu Perform Assessment & Comp Coord 1992-; Greater Ridgewood Youth Cncl A Dir 1990-; *ai:* Sr Trip Coord; AFT 1983-; UFT 1983-; ASCD 1 Contributions to Textbook 1992; *office:* IS 93 Ridgewood 6656 Forest Flushing NY 11385

PURVIS, DAVID, High School Biology Teacher; *b:* Syracuse, NY; *e* Univ of NY-Environmental Sci & Forestry (BA) Forest Bio 1982; Rut Univ (MS) Microbiology 1985, (PHD) Microbiology 1988; *cr:* Roche of Molecular Bio Post Doctorate Research 1989-90; Kean Coll Sci & Tchr 1990-91; Great Meadows Regnl Schl Dist 6th-8th Grd Sci 1991-95; West Morris HS Bio Tchr 1995-; *ai:* Sci Club; Stu Cncl Adv Sci Tchrs; Busch Predoctorate Fellowship from Rutgers Univ; Geral Dodge Fellowship; *office:* West Morris Central HS Bartley Rd Cheste 07930

PURVIS, SUSAN C., Hlth, Physical Education Tchr; *b:* Philadelphia, *m:* Edward; *ed:* Hlth & PE 1987; *cr:* Montville HS Hlth & PE 1980-83; Springfield HS Hlth & PE Tchr 1983-; *ai:* Girls Var Field Ho Coach; NEA, PSEA 1983-; AAHPER 1980-; Penn St Var S Club 19 Penn St Alumni Assn 1980-; Coach of Yr NJ Coaches League 1983; *off* Springfield HS 49 W Leamy Ave Springfield PA 19064

PUSCAVAGE, DEBORAH A. SCATENA, Fifth Grade Reading Teac *b:* Pittston, PA; *m:* Thomas J. Jr.; *c:* April; *ed:* East Stroudsburg Univ (Elem Ed 1977; Univ of Scranton (MS) Elem Ed 1989; *cr:* St Mary's S Rdng Tchr 1983-; *ai:* Mid States Comm; Forensics Moderator; NC 1984-; Girl Scouts of Amer 1984-; *office:* Saint Marys Schl 742 Sprin Avoca PA 18641*

PUSCHAK, BETH (HORVATH), Reading Specialist; *b:* Coaldale, PA John P.; *c:* Julie, Kate, Christine; *ed:* PA St Univ (BS) Elem, Spec Ed 19 Kutztown Univ (MED) Rdng 1984; 15 Post Grad Credits; R Supervisory Prgm Millersville Univ; *cr:* Saint Ann Schl 6th Grd T 1977-78; Manheim Twp Schl Dist Rdg Specialist 1984-; *ai:* Site B Mngmt Sub Comm; Scorer for PA Assessment Testing; NEA, PSEA 19 Bldg Rep; IRA 1992-; Lancaster Lebanon Rdng Cncl 1990-; St J Neumann 1984-, Rel Edctr; *office:* Manheim Township MS Box 5 School Rd Lancaster PA 17601

PUSHIA, ALFRIEDA COOPER, 4th Grade Teacher; *b:* Kingstree, *m:* Arthur L.; *c:* Aicha LaShene Thomas, Ashanti Lyntoria Edmond, A LaJuan Pushia; *ed:* SC St Coll at Orangeburg (BS) Sociology 1966; Tchrs (BA) Elem Ed 1971; Cath Univ 15 Hrs; Trinity Coll 15 Hrs; Carver HS Tchr 1966-68; Belle View Elem Schl Tchr 1968-69; Martin King Jr. Elem Schl Tchr 1969-; *ai:* AFT, Washington Tchrs Union 196 DCRC of Intnl Rdng Assn 1985-; Largo Comm Church, Dir Wome Flwshp; SCSU Alumni Assn, Mem DC Chptr; Girl Scout Cncl Nat

1976-, Troop Cookie Mgr, Svc Unit Cookie Mgr; Supplement n for DC Pub Schl Tchrs; Facilitator at Two DC Tchrs Annual ntion; *home:* 13 Laughton St Upper Marlboro MD 20774*

REK, PAULA MARIE (FIRST), English & Journalism Teacher; *b:* stown, OH; *m:* Paul J. Sr.; *c:* Paul J. Jr.; *ed:* Mount Union Coll (BA) peech, Comm-Cum Laude 1974; Youngstown St Univ (MA) Eng 30 Addl Hrs from Numerous Univ; *cr:* Springfield Local HS Eng, Tchr 1974-; *ai:* Newspaper, Yrbk Adv; NEA 1974-; SLCTA 1974-, Rep 1994-95; Delta Kappa Gamma 1985-, Recording Sec 1992-94, P 1994-; Phi Delta Kappa 1988-; OCTELA 1980-; HOme, Schl for Family Schl 1990-; PTO 1974-; Walsworth Publishing Companys Cncl 1994; Class Act Tchr of Week 1994; Outstdng Young Women of 1983; *office:* Springfield Local HS 11335 Youngstown Pittsburgh Rd Middletown OH 44442*

A, ROBERT JOSEPH, Art Tchr & Dept Chairman; *b:* Cleveland, *:* Cynthia Marie; *c:* AAron, Katherine, Brian; *ed:* Kent St Univ Art Ed 1975; Post-Grad in MA, Art Ed KSU; *cr:* Kimpton MS Art 975-87; Stow Monroe Falls HS Art Tchr 1987-; *ai:* Dept Chm for Art K-12; Dir of Jr, Sr Class Play; Drama Clb Adv 1994-; Internation ian Soc Spon 1995-; Comm to Dev New Prgms Acd of Theatre Arts fmnc; Schlst Arts Awds Adv Panel K.S.U; Stow Tchrs, OH Ed Assn, 1975-; Awds Childrens Hospital Festival of Trees 8 Yrs; LR Saztis nding Ed Awd 1991-92; PTA Outstanding Ed Awd Kimpton MS 84; Art Shows; Butler Inst of Amer Art; Massilon Museum, Cleveland im of Art May Show; *office:* Stow-Munroe Falls HS 3227 E Graham ow OH 44224*

IAN, STEPHEN M., Mathematics Teacher; *b:* Ogdensburg, NY; *m:* a A. Hawkins; *c:* Morgan, Rachel; *ed:* SUNY at Potsdam (BA) Math 1988, (MS) Instructional Tech; 24 Credit Hrs in Grad Admin Work at Lawrence Univ; *cr:* Tora Farm Dairy Owner & Operator 1974-86; erneur Cntrl HS Math Tchr 1988-; *ai:* Class Adv; NCTM 1990-; n Lions Club 1992-, Tail Twister, Membership Chair, Pres; *office:* erneur Central HS 113 E Barney St Gouverneur NY 13642

IAM, BROCK, History & English Teacher; *b:* Princeton, NJ; *c:* min; *ed:* Amhurst Coll (BA) Dramatic Arts 1970; Brandeis Univ) Directing, Acting 1984; Harvard Univ (EDM) 1987; *cr:* Fessenden Eng, Drama Tchr 1974-77; Rivers Schl Eng, Drama Tchr 1979-80; nden Schl Eng, Drama Tchr 1980-86; New Milford HS His, Eng Tchr ; *ai:* Acad Team Coach; NEA, CEA 1987-, Negotiations Chair A; Roland Wood Flwshp; Celebration of Excl Awd; Jeopardy stant 1996; *office:* New Milford HS 25 Sunny Valley Rd New Milford 5776

IAM, LAURI DUNN, PE Teacher & Athletic Director; *b:* Houlton, *n:* Kimball T.; *c:* Colby; *ed:* Springfield Coll (BS) Pe 1986, (MS) n 1993; Attnd Univ of New England at Biddeford; *cr:* Golden Brook PE Tchr, Ath Dir 1986-; *ai:* Field Hockey Rep; Field Hockey, Bsktbl 1986-94; NHAHPERD, WEA, NEA 1986-; Deacon at Church 1994-; : Golden Brook Schl 112 Lowell Rd Windham NH 03087

IAM, ROBERT ERVIN, Retired Adjunct Faculty; *b:* Northampton, *m:* F. Caroline Wright; *c:* David, Mary C. Bennett, Robert, Andrew; niv of MA (BS) Chem 1950; Univ of IL (MS) Chem 1951, (PHD) 1953; *cr:* E. J. DuPont Rsrch Chemist 1953-58, Res Supvr 1959-80, upt 1980-82, Res Mgr 1983-85; Washington St Comm Coll Chem Adj 985-95; *ai:* Marietta Coll Inst for Learning in Retirement Dir; Univ A, Marietta Coll Chem Dept Advy Cncls; Amer Chem Soc 1948-, OH ect Ch; Amer Assn Adv Sci 1954-, Fellow; Mid-OH Vly Aviation , Treas; Marietta First Unitarian Soc, VP Bd of Trustees; NSF, Univ Flwshp; 20 Articles Pub; 2 Chptrs in Books Pub; 10 Patents Pub; : 100 Alden Ave Marietta OH 45750

IAM, THOMAS WELLS, Seventh Grade Teacher; *b:* Pontiac, MI; *c:* ard; *ed:* Bucknell Univ (MA) Eng 1989; Penn State Doctoral idate 24 Hrs; *cr:* Miller Elem Elem Tchr 1978-79; New Covenant Elem & HS Tchr 1979-89 & 1993-; Penn Tech Engl Tchr 1991-93; ast Adv for Ski Club, Yrbk Staff & Drama Coach; Hamilton-Gibson tre Group 1992-, Founder, Dir; *home:* RR 4 Box 188 Wellsboro PA 1

NICK, MARY ELIZABETH, Asst Professor of Psychology; *b:* ington, DE; *ed:* Bryn Mawr Coll (BA) Psych 1988; Cornell Univ Dev Psych 1991, (PHD) Dev Psych 1993; *cr:* St Francis Coll Asst 1993-; *ai:* Fac Dev Comm Chair; Sorority Adv; Figure Skating; Book: itive & Social Factors in Early Deception; 2 Articles Pub; 6 Prof Conf entations; *office:* Saint Francis Coll Loretto PA 15940

T, HAROLD LEE, Professor of Mathematics; *b:* Clearfield, PA; *m:* Doreen Shorts; *c:* Heather; *ed:* Clarion St Coll (BS) Scndry Ed, Math ; Bowling Green St Univ (MA) Math 1974, (PHD) Math 1977; *cr:* St Univ Math Asst Prof 1977-78; Univ of Akron Math Asst Prof -83; OH Northern Univ Math Assoc Prof 1983-; *ai:* OH Eta Chptr a Mu Epsilon Adv; Epsilon Chptr Sigma Theta Epsilon Spon; Math of Amer 1973-, Dept Rep; Amer Math Soc 1975-; Area Chptr of CISV -, Treas; KEnton Elks Lodge No 157 1992-; Mary Reichelderfer wed Chair for Math, Cmptr Sci OH Northern Univ 1988-90 Acad Yrs; Bowling Green St Univ Outstdng Alumnus Awd; *office:* OH Northern Dept of Math Ada OH 45810

SUSAN T., Kindergarten Teacher; *b:* Sandusky, OH; *m:* John D.; *c:* ara Schlessman, Louise Hoty; *ed:* Bowling Green St Univ (BS) Ed ; 2 Hrs Grad Stud at Toledo Univ; *cr:* Bogart Elem Kndgrtn Tchr -72; St Mary's Elem 1983-; *office:* St Mary Elem Schl 530 Decatur St dusky OH 44870*

A, DIANNE TERHORST, Art Teacher; *b:* Latrobe, PA; *m:* Joseph; N Univ of PA (BSEd) Art Ed 1991; CA Univ of PA 24 Credits Toward ers; *cr:* Mt Pleasant Sr HS Art Tchr 1991-; *ai:* Natl Art Honor Soc & Spon; Art Dept Head; NEA 1991-; NAEA 1991-; Army Reserves -; *office:* Mt Pleasant Area HS Rd 4 Box 2222 Mount Pleasant PA 56

-TIMKO, JENNIFER, Social Studies Teacher; *b:* Islip, NY; *c:* Julia ko; *ed:* Georgetown Univ (BA) His 1989; Amer Univ (MA) Tchng 2; *cr:* Macy's Sales Mgr 1989-91; Gaithersburg HS Tchr 1992-; *ai:* d Coach, Team Founder Women's Lacrosse; NEA, MCEA 1993-; *office:* hersburg HS 314 S Frederick Ave Gaithersburg MD 20877*

E, DEBORAH YATRON, Spanish Teacher; *b:* Reading, PA; *m:* rge H.; *ed:* Albright Coll (BA) Span, Eng 1981; Temple Univ (MS) Ed ; 6 Addl Credit Hrs; *cr:* Wilson Southern Jr HS Span Tchr 1980-; *ai:* Cncl Adv; Chorus Accompanist; Natl Guild of Piano Tchrs; Phi Delta na 1980-, VP.

E, PAUL WILLIAM, Bible Department Head; *b:* Denton, TX; *m:* ette Louise Smart; *c:* Sarah, Nathan, Gabriel, Benjamin; *ed:* Evangel (BS) Eng 1977; Dallas Theological Seminary MA 1994; *cr:* Dayton stn HS Bible Tchr & Dept Chm 1977-; *ai:* Sr Class Adv; Tchr of Yr Awd n; Pub in Alliance Witness Magazine; Contributor Tchrs Manual for liant Life Bible Curr; Chrstn Citizen Monthly Newspaper Ed; Author "Understanding The Times " Bible Curr.

LES, SHERRY GORDON, Pupil Personnel Worker; *b:* Pittsburgh, PA; Donald M. Jr.; *c:* Amberley, Donny, Lyndsay; *ed:* Roanoke Coll (BA) ch 1967; Western MD (MS) Cnslng 1992; *cr:* MD Tomorrow Tchr 0-94; Mt Airy MS Cnslr 1993-94; South Carroll HS Crisis Cnslr 1994-95; CArroll Cnty Bd of Ed Pupil Personnel Worker 1995-; *office:* Carroll Cty Bd of Ed 55 North Court St Westminster MD 21157

PYMN, MARCIA RABLE, Spanish Teacher; *b:* Garfield Heights, OH; *m:* John T.; *c:* Gregory, Katie; *ed:* Univ of Akron (BA) Ed 1980; Attnd Kent & Cleveland St Drug Intervention & Mediation Trng; *cr:* Benedictine HS Span Tchr & Foreign Lang Dept Chair 1980-; *ai:* Span Club; CORE Team; SADD; NHS; Mediation; Acad Cncl; NHS 1995-; *office:* Benedictine HS 2900 Martin Luther King Jr Dr Cleveland OH 44104

Q

QUACKENBUSH, ANN NELSON, Social Studies Teacher; *b:* Jamestown, NY; *m:* Joseph Patrick; *c:* Timothy; *ed:* Houghton Coll (BA) Ed 1971; Elmira Coll (MS) Ed 1976; SUNY at Geneseo Addl Credit Hrs His; *cr:* Hornell MS 7th Grd Soc Stud Tchr 1971-85; Hornell HS Soc Stud Tchr 1985-; *ai:* Red Raider His Club Adv; NEA, NVEA, HTA 1971-; PTA; St Ignatius Church; *office:* Hornell HS Maple City Park Seneca St Hornell NY 14843

QUACKENBUSH, CATHY SEAMAN, Biology Teacher; *b:* West Carthage, NY; *m:* Roger E.; *c:* Thomas Bradford; *ed:* SUNY at Morrisville (AAS) Lab Tech 1969; SUNY at Albany (BS) Sci Ed 1971, (MS) Sci Ed 1976; Attnd Univ of GA 1978, Cornell Univ 1984, Univ of CA 1986, Univ of Albany 1986-87; *cr:* Bethlehem Cntrl MS Sci Tchr 1971-92; Bethlehem Cntrl HS Bio Tchr 1991-; *ai:* Intnl Travel Comm 1985, 1989, 1991, 1994; Bethlehem Cntrl Tchrs Assn, NEA 1971-; Delta Kappa Gamma Sec 1987-90; Bethlehem Opportunities Unlimited 1983-, Bd of Dirs; Grants St Outdoor Ed Inst 1979, DNA Inst MS Tchrs 1990, Human Genetics & Bioethics 1993, Molecular Bio for Tchrs 1993; Co-Instr Molecular Bio for Tchrs 1994-95; Syracuse U Inst for Bio Tchrs 1993; *office:* Bethlehem Central HS 700 Delaware Ave Delmar NY 12054*

QUACKENBUSH, ROGER EUGENE, High School Biology Teacher; *b:* Cooperstown, NY; *m:* Cathy Seaman; *c:* Michele Nagel, Stacey Tully, Thomas; *ed:* St UNiv of NY at Albany (BS) Bio 1961, (MS) Bio 1966; Columbia Pacific Univ (PHD) Curr Dev 1984; Attnd Univ of OK, Wayne St Univ, Univ of CO, Univ of GA, Western WA Univ, Cornell Univ & Ball St Univ; *cr:* Troy City Schl Dist 7-8th Grd Sci & Math Tchr 1961-64; Schuylerville Cntrl HS Regents Earth Sci & Regents Bio Tchr 1964-66; St Univ of NY at Albany Marine Mammal Lecturer 1986; Bethlehem Cntrl Sr HS Regents Bio & AP Bio Tchr 1966-; Cons for AP Bio Niskayuna HS 1995-; St Univ of NY Albany Lecturer, DNA Molecular Bio for HS Stu 1996; *ai:* Cooperating Tchr for Stu Tchrs; TESA Instr; Intnl Travel Advy Comm; Fac Ldr for Stu Trip to Kenya; Instr for Tchr Wkshps in Use of Microcomputers & DNA-Molecular Bio Techniques; Sabbatical Leave 1977; Past Mem Adv Bd of Upstate NY Jr Sci & Hum Symposium; Select Sem on Eval Tchrs 1985; Wells Conf on Regents Bio Syllabus Rev 1991; Wrkshp Presenter on use of TI-82 Calcualtor & CBL Sys in Sci Class; Writer Regents Bio Questions for NY St Ed Dept; NABT 1966-; NEA 1975-; Phi Delta Kappa 1986-; BALSA 1992-; STANYS 1964-, Sec Dir, St Bd of Dir, Sci Congress Dir; Soc of Marine Mammalogy; HS Yrbk Dedication 1979; Tufts Univ Sci Tchr of Yr 1985; NSF Grants 1965, 1967-68, 1972, 1987, 1990; Chapter II Grant 1987; Future Directions Grant 1990; Greenwall Fnd Grant 1993; Honorable Mention Tandy Tech Scholar 1994; Golub SUNY at Albany Scholar Recognition Awd 1989, 1991; Numerous Educl & Scientific Publications; Who's Who in Amer Ed; Who's Who in East; Ed & Writer Alternate Assessments for NY St Ed Dept; Letters of Commendation Univ of Chic 1978, MIT 1985, US Army 1989, Tufts Univ 1990, 1994; Hon Grad Marshal 1991, 1994; Hon NY St Bio Mentor 1995; Outstndg Tchr Awd Univ of Chic 1995; Tandy Tech Schl Prize for Excl in Sci Tchng 1995; Hon Admis Liason Off US Air Force Acad; Men Of Achvt; Intl Book of Honor; Who's Who in Amer; Who's Who in the World; *office:* Bethlehem Cntrl Sr HS 700 Delaware Ave Delmar NY 12054*

QUADAGNO, RONALD THOMAS, Physical Science Teacher; *b:* Portchester, NY; *m:* June Ann Trimarchi; *c:* Jessica, Ashley; *ed:* Western IL Univ (BA) His & Geology 1971, (MS) Ed Admin 1975; Univ of KS (PHD) Higher Ed & Human Dev 1972-79; Addl 35 Credit Hrs; *cr:* Riverdale Jr High 141 Sci Tchr 1980-83; Suffern MS Phys Sci Tchr 1983-; *ai:* AFT 1980-; NY St Tchrs Assn 1981-; STANYS 1990-.*

QUADE, EVELYN CLARE, 7th & 8th Grade Science Tchr; *b:* Albuquerque, NM; *m:* Jeffrey Jay; *c:* Brandi Duso, Joshua Duso, Jeffrey, Joseph, Christina; *ed:* PA St Univ (BS) Home Ec 1972; Seton Hill Coll (BS) Elem Ed 1986; 14 Grad Credits Sci & Ed Wilkes Univ; *cr:* Palymyra MS Home Ec Tchr 1972-73; Apollo Ridge Jr HS Home Ec Tchr & Sub 1974-78; Mt St Peter Schl 8th grd Tchr & 7th & 8th Grd Sci & Soc Stud Tchr 1985-; *ai:* Stu Cncl & 8th Grd Fund Raising Spon; Yrbk & Natl Geog Bee Chprsn; Alle Kiski; Sci Show Schl Contact Tchr; NCEA 1986-; *office:* Mt St Peter Schl 100 Freeport Rd New Kensington PA 15068*

QUAINTANCE, JULIA ANN, Chemistry & Physics Teacher; *b:* Salem, OH; *m:* Thomas Alan; *c:* Kendra Lee; *ed:* Youngstown St Univ (BS) Comprehensive Sci Ed 1984; *cr:* Washington St Comm Coll Chem Tchr, Night Instr 1989-91; Morgan HS Chem, Physics Tchr 1984-; *ai:* Jr Class, Prom Adv; Tech Prep Comm; NEA, OEA 1984-; Sci Ed Cncl OH 1986-; *office:* Morgan HS 800 Raider Dr Mc Connelsville OH 43756*

QUALTIERI, ELLEN S., Spanish Teacher & Dept Chprsn; *b:* Rochester, NY; *c:* Nicole, Joseph A. III; *ed:* SUNY at Oswego (BA) Sec Ed Span 1972; Nazareth Coll (MSE) Ed 1985; Jr Yr Abroad Madrid Spain 1970-71; Univ of PR Summer Stud 1969; *cr:* Border City Schl 3rd Grd Tchr 1985-86; Waterloo HS Span Tchr 1986-; *ai:* Span Club Adv; Class of 1995 Co-Adv; Discipline Comm; Bldg Team; Scndry Curr Cncl; Waterloo Tchrs Assn 1986-, Bldg Rep; NEA, Wayne Finger Lakes For Lang Educatores, NYSAFLT 1986-, WAFFLE 1986-; Delta Kappa Gamma 1993-; Rotary Intnatl 1995; Multicultural, Comparative Schlsp 1989; James E. Allen Awd Distinguished Foreign Lang Dept 1993; *office:* Waterloo HS Center St Waterloo NY 13165

QUAMMA, CAROLE NESTOR, Fifth Grade Teacher; *b:* Canonsburg, PA; *m:* L. Thomas; *c:* Carri, Mike; *ed:* Cal St Univ at Long Beach (BA) Elem Ed 1962; So CT St Univ (MS) Elem Ed 1984; GATE Univ of CT 1985; *cr:* Indian Hill Elem Schl 3rd Grd Tchr 1962-64; North Branford Schl 5th Grd Tchr 1976-82; Killingworth Elem Schl 5th-6th Grd Tchr 1982-; *ai:* Lang Arts, Tech Comms; NEA, CEA 1976-; *office:* Killingworth Elem Schl Rt 81 Killingworth CT 06419

QUANN, THOMAS K., 9th-12th Grd Soc Stud Teacher; *b:* Chester, PA; *ed:* Shippensburg Univ of PA (BS) Scndry Ed & Soc Stud 1976; Addl Grad Credits from Univ of DE; *cr:* Chichester HS Tchr 1976-78; Howard HS of Tech Soc Stud Tchr & Coach 1979-92; Delcastle HS 9th-12th Grd Soc Stud Tchr 1992-; *ai:* Frosh Boys Bsktbl & Bsbl Coach; NEA, DSEA, NCCVTEA 1979-, Treas & Bldg Rep; Dela Geographic Alliance 1995-; Pedals for Progress 1993-; BSA 1962-, Eagle Scout Awd, God & Cntry Awd, Order of Arrow Awd; *home:* 2300 Wilson Ave Claymont DE 19703*

QUANZ, PAULA TARQUINIO, Counselor; *b:* Rochester, NY; *m:* W. Thomas; *c:* David, Peter, Amy, Steven; *ed:* St John Fisher (BS) Bio 1979; Alfred Univ (MS) Counseling 1980; *cr:* SUNY at Alfred Cnslr 1981-82; Stueben Llegany Boces Cnslr 1982-83; Bradford Cntrl Cnslr 1983-86; Canisteo Cntrl Cnslr 1986-; *ai:* NHS, Sr, Jr Class; NYACAC 1994-; Cty Cnslrs, Pres 1983-; NASAA 1993-; *office:* Canisteo Central Schl 84 Greenwood St Canisteo NY 14823

QUARATIELLO, FRANK, Biology Teacher; *b:* Boston, MA; *m:* Sandra Bishop; *c:* Frank, Alice; *ed:* Boston Coll (BS) Bio 1967; Tufts Dental (DMD) Dentistry 1971; Rivier (MBA) Bus 1988, (MED) Ed 1992; *home:* 19 Monza Rd Nashua NH 03060

QUASHIE, LEROY ANDREW, Assoc Professor of Sociology; *b:* Marabella, Trinidad W.I.; *m:* Angelica C. Edwards; *c:* Brent, LeeAnne; *ed:* Warner Southern Coll (BA) Sociology, Psych 1978; Univ of Akron (MA) Child, Family Stud 1982, (PHD) Sociology 1985; Schl of Pub Hlth Univ of Pittsburgh; *cr:* Chatham Coll Asst Prof 1985-88; Ketchum Inc 1988-90; Comm Coll Assoc Prof 1990-; *ai:* AFT 1990-; Sigma Xi 1982-, Pres; Campus Life 1990-, Bd Mem; Pittsburgh Project 1990-, Bd Pres; East Liberty Hlth Clinic 1991-, Bd Mem; Amer Pub Hlth Assn 1982-; US Pub Hlth Schlsp; Fac Fellow Ach Awd Geriatric Ed.*

QUATRANI, ERNEST JOSEPH, English Teacher; *b:* Havertown, PA; *m:* Theresa M.; *c:* Michael, Matthew, Stephen; *ed:* Temple Univ (BS) Comm 1975; Villanova Univ (MA) Admin 1986; St Joseph's Coll Post Bac Eng 1977; *cr:* Upper Perkiomen HS Tchr 1978-; *ai:* Var Bsbl, Powder Puff Ftbl Coach; Vietnam Meml Comm; PA Ftbl Announcer; Amer Bsbl Coaches Assn 1981-; NEA, PA St EA, Upper Perk EA 1978-; NCTE 1982-; Kappa Delta Pi 1986-; Amer Legion Bsbl Coach 1973-79, 1987-; Jaycees Outstanding Young Educator 1984; Yrbk Dedication 1984; Past Pres Upper Perkiomen Coaches Assn; Local Newspaper Coach of Yr 1979; *office:* Upper Perkiomen H S 2 Walt Rd Pennsburg PA 18073*

QUATRINI, MARILYN SCHECKTON, English Teacher; *b:* Amsterdam, NY; *m:* John F.; *c:* Jay, Gregg, Daniel; *ed:* Marywood Coll (BA) Eng & Fr 1963; Coll of St Rose Grad Stud 36 Credit Hrs Eng & Rdng; Attnd TX Tech; *cr:* Greater Amsterdam Schl Dist Eng Tchr 1978-; *ai:* Multicultural Club Adv; Super Teams; AHS Task Force; Goals 2000 Rep; NYSUT 1979-; Hosp Vol; LACCAF Hispanic Achvmt Awd; *office:* Greater Amsterdam Schl Dist Saratoga Ave Amsterdam NY 12010

QUATTLEBAUM, EDWIN G., History & Social Science Instr; *b:* Rockford, IL; *m:* Ruth Flick; *c:* Gus, Hugh; *ed:* Harvard Coll (AB) His 1964; Univ of CA at Berkeley (MA) Amer His 1789 1968; Univ of CA at Berkeley (PHD) Amer Urban His 1972; Inter-Univ Consortium for Pol Rsrch Univ of MI at Ann Arbor Summer 1975; *cr:* St Paul's Schl His Instr 1964-66; UC Berkeley Tchng, Rsrch Asst 1967-72; Phillips Acad His, Soc Sci Instr 1973-; *ai:* Men's Crew Coach; Coord Exeter-Andover Washington Intern Prgm; Chair Donna Brace Ogilvie II Tchng Fnd; Kenan Grant; Dept Chair 1989-94.

QUATTROCCHI, CIRO ANTHONY, Foreign Language Teacher; *b:* Brooklyn, NY; *m:* Angela Taormina; *c:* Maria Anna, Daniela; *ed:* NY Univ (BA) Italian, Span Ed 1981, (MA) Italian Culture, Lang 1987; *cr:* Bishop Ford Cntrl Cath HS Frgn Lang Tchr 1981-; *ai:* Intnl Soc Moderator; NY St Assn Frgn Lang Tchrs; Amer Cncl Tchrs Frgn Lang; Amer Assn Tchrs Italian Lang; St Fortunata Soc 1977-, Pres; *office:* Bishop Ford C C H S 500 19th St Brooklyn NY 11215

QUATTRONE, ELIZABETH GIATAS, ORBITT & PLANET Prgms Coord; *b:* Bradford, PA; *m:* Philip Gerard; *ed:* Sunny Fredonia (BA) Ed 1973, (MS) Curr, Dev Ed 1980; Soc, Emotional Dev of Gifted, Gifted Underachievers,Prgm Dev, Evaluation for Gifted, Staff Dev, Trng for Gifted Ed, Gifted Ed in Regular Schl Prgm; *cr:* St Elizabeth Ann Seton Schl Elem Tchr; SUNY Fredonia Rsrch Fnd Migrant Tutorial Prgm 1980-83, Art Tchr Upward Bound 1992; Boces-Erie II-CC Coord, Tchr of Gifted 1984-; *ai:* Humane Soc; World Wildlife Fnd; Greenpeace; Save the Manatee Club; NYS Gifted Edctrs Trng Sys Networtk 1988-; Natl Assn Gifted 1989-, Ldrshp Comm; NYS Assn GATE Ed 1984-, Presenter; Western NY Consortium for Gifted Edctrs 1988-, Co-Founder; Rockefeller Arts Ctr 1987-, Usher; Fredonia Historical Opera House Usher; Presenter 10th World Congress on Gifted Ed; *office:* Erie II-Chautauqua-Caharaugus 9520 Fredonia-Stockton Rd Fredonia NY 14063

QUATTRONE, KENNETH LEO, Math Chair; *b:* Olean, NY; *m:* Mary Elizabeth Quinn; *c:* Sarah, Mallory; *ed:* SUNY at Brockport (BS) Math 1975; St Bonaventure Univ Perm Cert 36 Hrs & Jamestown Comm Coll Cmptrs 3 Hrs; Dunn & Bradstreet Fundamentals of DOS & BOCES Trng in Intermediate Lotus 1-2-3; *cr:* Alcas Cutlery Cost Accountant 1975-76; Portville Cntrl Schl Math Tchr 1976-77; Jamestown Comm Coll Part Time Math Instr 1984-; Dresser-Rand Industries Part Time Cmptr Consultant & Trainer 1984-; Allegany Cntrl Schl Math & Cmptr Tchr 1977-; *ai:* NHS Selection & ACS Faculty Soc Comms; 9th-12th Grd Fall Sale Coord; Winter Weekend Adv & Chaperon; Past Frosh & Jr Var Ftbl & Jr HS & Jr Var Bsktbl Coach; Past Frosh Class Adv; ACS Math Dept Coord; NEANY, NCTM & NYSTM 1976-; NEA 1976-, Del 4 Yrs; NEA/ACS, Assn Exec Comm 4 Yrs; ALCS Negotiation Team; Knights of Columbus 1986-, 3rd Degree Awd 1989; St Johns Church; Jamestown Comm Coll Math Curr & Cmptr Lotus 1-2-3 Dev & Taught Trng Prgms; NYS Tchr Summer Bus Trng & Employment Prgm 5 Yrs; *office:* Allegany- Limestone Cntr Schl N 4th St Allegany NY 14706*

QUATTRONE, MARK THOMAS, Skill Trades Teacher; *b:* Philadelphia, PA; *m:* Lana Maria Mazzo; *c:* Jenna; *ed:* Rown Coll; Universal EPA Technician Cert; ARI competency TEST HVAC R; *cr:* Camden Cty Voc Tech Skills Trade Tchr; *ai:* Project USE Adv; Southern NJ Crafts Fair Chprsn, Coord; Stu of Month, NHS Fac Comms; ARI & Universal EPA Technician Test Admin; Bldg Trades Prgms Dept Chprsn; RSES 1989-; NEA, NJEA Cam Voc Assn 1987-; Staff Recognition, NHS Svc Awds 1993; Outstdng Support VICA Cert 1993-94; *office:* Camden Cty Vo Tech 343 Berlin Cross Keys Rd Sicklerville NJ 08081*

QUAY, LINDA S., Medical & Human Svcs Teacher; *b:* Brattleboro, VT; *ed:* Univ of NH (BS) Nrsng; Univ of Vt Ed 1988; *cr:* Brattleboro Meml Hosp Staff Nurse 1972; Thompson Schl for Practical Surses Instr 1972-75, Asst Dir 1975-80; Southeastern VT Career Ctr Med, Human Svcs Tchr 1980-; *ai:* Vt Voc Assn 1981-; *office:* Southeast Vermont Career Ed Ct Fairground Rd Brattleboro Center VT 05301

QUAYLE, JULIE SOMSEN, 8th Grd Language Arts Teacher; *b:* Salt Lake City, UT; *m:* William R.; *c:* Douglas Brian, Matthew; *ed:* Univ of UT (BA) Eng 1964; Univ of WY (MA) Eng 1965; Univ of Toledo Grad Hrs for Rdng Cert; Attnd Bowling Green St Univ, John Carroll Univ; *cr:* UT St Univ Eng Instr 1965-66; Gen Motors Inst Eng Instr 1967-69; Corunna Pub Schls Eng Instr 1969-70; Port Clinton City Schls Lang Arts Instr 1989-; *ai:* NCTE 1986-; AFT 1989-; Phi Delta Kappa 1993-; Pub Lib Bd 1993-; Church Vestry 1993-, Clerk; *home:* 4204 E Stonehenge Rd Port Clinton OH 43452*

QUEALY, PHILIP JAMES, Guidance Counselor; *b:* Bronx, NY; *ed:* Cathedral Coll (BA) Psych 1979; St Joseph Seminary (MA) Theology

1982; *cr:* St Brendans R C Church Parochial Vicar 1982-86; St Joseph-St Thomas Church Parochial Vicar 1986-92; Cath Schl Parents Assn Staten Island Chaplain, Moderator 1988-92; Archbishop Stepinac HS Cnslr, Tchr 1992-; *ai:* Moderator, Theatrical Tech Mgr Major Bowes Auditorium & Stage; NCEA, Westchester Cnslr Assn 1992-; AOH 1993-, Chaplain; *office:* Archbishop Stepinac H S 950 Mamaroneck Ave White Plains NY 10605

QUEEN, CHRISTOPHER SCOTT, Dean of Students; *b:* Brooklyn, NY; *m:* Alys Terrien-Queen; *c:* Laura; *ed:* Oberlin Coll (BA) Rel 1967; Union Theological Seminary (MDIV) practical Theology 1972; Boston Univ (PHD) Rel 1986; Post Grad Harvard Divinity Schl; *cr:* Northfield Mt Herman Schl Tchr 1972-75; Boston Univ Adj Asst Prof 1982-89; Harvard Univ Dean of Stdnts, Lecturer on Rel 1989-; *ai:* Dean of Stdnts for Continuing Ed; Amer Acad of Rel 1978-; Brookline Music Soc 1985-, Pres; Plowshares Childcare 1994-, Bd; Homeless Improvement Project 1995-, Bd; Book: Engaged Buddhism; Buddhist Liberation Movements in Asia 1996; *office:* Harvard Univ 51 Brattle St Cambridge MA 02138*

QUEEN, JOYCE E., Primary Science Coordinator; *b:* Cleveland, OH; *m:* Robert Graham; *ed:* Macalester Coll (BA) Bio 1966; Univ of MI (MS) Nat Resource Mngmt 1968; Great Lakes Stud OH St Univ 1990; Aquatic Ecology OH St Univ 1991; *cr:* Rosetree Media Outdoor Ed Tchr, Naturalist 1967; Grand Rapids Pub Museum Exhibitor, Docent 1967-68; Willoughby Schl Tchr, Naturalist 1969-70; Independence Schl Tchr, Naturalist 1970-78; Hathaway Brown Schl Tchr, Prime Sci Coord 1970-; *ai:* Wkshp Ldr Lake Erie Islands His Mus South Bass Island 1992; Presenter Nat Assn Ind Schls 1993; Designer Sci Nature Trail 1986; Designer Sci Classroom & Greenhouse 1990-92; Designer with Colini Landscape of Prime Sci Courtyard 1993; Symposium Sci Wkshp Ldr 1994; Winter Sci Day Coord 1996; Clev Regnl Coun Sci Tchrs; NSTA Sheldon Excl Sci Classroom Design; Clev Cncl Indep Schls; Nat Assn Indep Schls; Wm. Mather Vessel Museum Advy Comm 1992; Holden Arboretum Advy Comm 1992-; Clev Nat Hist Museum; Clev Zoological Pk; World-Wise Schl Exchange Prgm Contributor; Envir Ed Awd OH Alliance Environment 1986; Pres Excl in Elem Sci OH Awd 1992; Sheldon Exemplary Facs Awd NSTA 1992; Great Lakes Lighthouse Keepers Scholar 1992; Marine Ecology Scholar Marine Resources 1989; *office:* Hathaway Brown Schl 19600 N Park Blvd Shaker Heights OH 44122

QUEGUINER, MARGARET LEONE, French Teacher; *b:* Batavia, NY; *c:* Loic, Mia; *ed:* Niagara Univ (BA) Fr 1982; Univ of Rochester (MA) Fr 1987; Universite Catholique de l'Ouest Alliance Francaise Fr 1981; *cr:* Univ of Rochester Grad Asst-Fr Instr 1985-87; Dannemora HS Fr Tchr 1987-88; SUNY Plattsburgh Fr Conversation Instr 1993-94; Beekmantown Cntrl Schl Fr Tchr 1988-96; *ai:* AP Fr Tchr; Item Writer NYS Proficiency Exam in Fr; NYSUT, NYSAFLT 1987-; Phi Sigma Iota 1982-; Grad Fellowship-Univ of Rochester; Niagara Univ Foreign Lang Awd; *office:* Beekmantown Central Schl PO Box 829 Plattsburgh NY 12901*

QUEIJA, JORGE, Spanish Teacher; *b:* Havana, Cuba; *ed:* Salamanca Univ (MA) Theology 1964; Richmond Coll (MS) Ed, Span 1977; Addl Post Grad Stud Hunter Coll Span, Grad Ctr Span; *cr:* Univ Catohca Theology 1968-70; Bolivar Y Garrbaldi Latin, Sp Lit 1965-72; Coll Bello Monte Lit 1965-72; St John's Prep Schl Span Tchr 1978-; *office:* Saint Johns Preparatory HS 2121 Crescent St Astoria NY 11105

QUESADA, BERNARD, English Teacher; *b:* Waynesburg, PA; *ed:* WV Univ (BS) Scndry Eng Ed 1993; *cr:* Brunswick MS Eng Tchr 1993-; *ai:* Asst Ftbl & Track Coach; NEA, MSTA 1993-; *home:* 1337 Taney Ave Frederick MD 21702*

QUESENBERRY, LEGENE, Assoc Prof of Bus; *b:* Billings, MT; *ed:* WA St Univ (BA) Eng 1980; Western WA Univ (MA) Pol Ec 1981; Gonzaga Univ Schl of Law (JD) Law 1984; *cr:* Corpus Christi Army Depot Chief Labor Cnslr 1980-90; Crown Govt Offices Hong Kong Law Clerk 1984-85; US Army Fort Sill OK Admin Law Attorney 1986-88; 8th US Army Korea Criminal Law Chief 1990-92; Clarion Univ of PA Assoc Prof of Bus, Environmental & Amer Indian Law & Attorney 1992-; *ai:* Sigma Pi Fac Adv; Operation Paintbrush Dir; Coll of Bus Admin Undergraduate Policy & Prgms Comm Chair; Brookville Art Inst Consultant; Assn of US Army 1985-; Amer Bar Assn 1994-; ABA Section of Natural Resources, Energy & Environmental Law 1994-; The Army Achvmt Medal 1989; The Army Commendation Medal 1988, 1990 Oak Leaf Cluster; Natl Defense Svc Medal Desert Storm; Army Svc Medal; Overseas Svc Ribbon.

QUEST, RICHARD EDWIN, High School History Teacher; *b:* Binghamton, NY; *m:* Patricia M.; *c:* Crystal L., Richard E.; *ed:* Binghamton Univ (BA) Anthropology 1986, (MA) Soc Sci 1995; Archaeological Field Schl; *cr:* Pub Archaeology Facility Archaeologist 1985-87; Patten of NY Corp Project Mgr 1987-89; Candor Cntrl Schl Tchr, Coach 1990-; *ai:* Var Soccer Coach; NYSUT, AFT 1990-; Candor Yth Commission 1990-94, Chm; Candor Town Planning Bd 1992-, Chm; Tioga Cty Historian 1994-, Historian; *office:* Candor Cntrl Schl Academy St Candor NY 13743*

QUIER, GEOFFREY DOUGLAS, 5th Grade Teacher; *b:* Ravenna, OH; *ed:* Kent St Univ (BA) Elem Ed 1982, (MED) Ed Admin 1988; Prins Cert 1991; *cr:* Kent City Schls 5th Grd Tchr 1982; Maple Hts Schls 4th-6th Grd Tchr 1983-; *ai:* WA DC Trip Coord; Stu Cncl Supvr; MHTA 1983-, Bldg Rep; Young Author's Conf Coord; *office:* Stafford Schl 19800 Stafford Ave Maple Heights OH 44137

QUIGLEY, ANASTASIA MARIE, First Grade Teacher; *b:* Syracuse, NY; *ed:* Marywood Coll (BA) Elem Ed 1977, (MS) Early Chldhd Ed 1989; Numerous Non-credit Classes; *cr:* St Ann Schl First Grd Tchr 1980-84; Epiphany Schl First Grd Tchr 1984-; *ai:* Confraternity of Chrstn Doctrine Instruction; Irish Step-Dancing Instruction; Kappa Gamma Pi, NCEA 1977-; *office:* Epiphany Schl 627 Stevenson St Sayre PA 18840

QUIGLEY, ANNEMARIE FLIEGEL, Fifth Grade Teacher; *b:* Philadelpha, PA; *m:* W. James; *c:* James, William, Thomas, John; *ed:* Chestnut Hill Coll (AB) Bio 1962; Beaver Coll (MED) Elem Ed 1989; *cr:* Villa Joseph Marie HS Math, Eng Tchr 1980-81; St Andrews Schl Fifth Grd Tchr 1981-87; Assumption BVM Schl Fifth Grd Tchr 1987-; *ai:* Sci, Mission Coord; Sacramental Preparation; NSTA 1985-; *office:* Assumption BVM Sch-Feastervlle 55 E Bristol Rd Feasterville Trevo PA 19053

QUIGLEY, KEVIN JAMES, Social Studies Teacher; *b:* Auburn, NY; *m:* Ailish Meagher; *c:* Conor, Sinead, Ciaran; *ed:* Univ of Notre Dame (BA) His 1981; Natl Univ of Ireland (MA) His 1983; Natl Univ of Ireland Ed Diploma Ed 1984; *cr:* St Patricks Coll Ireland His Tchr 1983-84; Blessed Trinity PE Tchr 1984-85; St Marys Schl PE Tchr 1984-85; Auburn HS Soc Stud Tchr 1985-; *ai:* Dir Auburn Moscow Exchange Prgm; Adv Model United Nations Club; Boys LaCrosse Coach 1984-90; AFT 1985-; CNY Cncl for Soc Stud 1987-; *office:* Auburn H S Lake Ave Extension Auburn NY 13021*

QUIGLEY, LORETTA A., English Department Chair; *b:* Scarsdale, NY; *m:* Walter A'Hearn; *ed:* Skidmore Coll (BA) Eng 1970; SUNY at Albany (MA) Eng Lit 1976; Goddard Coll (MA) Creative Writing 1986; Harvard Univ (CAS) Tchng Curr & Learning Environments 1994; *cr:* South Glens Falls Scndry Eng Tchr 1970-; Adirondack Comm Coll Adjunct Eng Professor 1988-91; Russell Sage Coll Adjunct Eng Prof 1987-88; *ai:* Yrbk Bus Adv; AFT 1970-, Delegate 1990-; NYSUT 1970-, Delegate 1981-; SGF Fac Assn 1970-, Pres 1976-77; AAUW, NCTE, ASCD; Greater Capital Region Tchr Center Policy Bd Mem 1989-, Vice Chr 1994-; Articles Pub in The Glens Falls Review, Amecs, An Educ Janus; Scholars Recognition Prgm Honoree 1989 NY Capital Region; Adolescent & Young Adult Eng Stan Comm of Natl Bd for Prof Tchng Stan 1992-; Cornell Univ STAR Awd 1994; *office:* South Glens Falls Sr H S 42 Merritt Rd South Glens Falls NY 12803

QUIGLEY, MARY HALL, Band & Orchestra Director; *b:* Bristol, VA; *m:* William Thomas; *c:* Sarah Beardorff, Elizabeth Marten, Scott; *ed:* Mary Washington Coll (BA) Music 1961; 9 Hrs Univ of IL; 9 Hrs Shenandoah Conservatory of Music; 3 Hrs Univ of Toledo; 3 Hrs Bowling Green; 3 Hrs Brevard; 9 Hrs Vandercook; *cr:* Stafford Cty Schl Elem, Jr Sr HS Bands 1961-65; Winchester Schl Elem, Jr Sr HS Choirs 1966-69; Fredericks Cty Schls Elem Choirs 1976-77; Toledo Pub Schls HS Bands, Orchs 1977-; *ai:* FTA Adv; Concert, Pep, Marching, Jazz Bands; Concert Orch; Choirs Acc; Mu Phi Epsilon 1960-, Sec, Treas, Natl Convention Rep; OMEA, MENC 1975-, Chprsn Dist, St Competitions; Church Choir; Bowling 6 Yrs, Sec, Couple Trophy; Jaycees 5 Yrs, VP; Brownies 4 Yrs, Song Dir; Church Bridge 20 Yrs, 1st Place 3 Times; Aux Rescue Squad 4 Yrs, VP; Music Boosters 20 Yrs; WA Dist Ftbl Ofcls Half Time Awd 1962; One of Tem Most Valuable Tchrs of Yr 1985; OMEA Twenty-Five Pin 1994; Hall of Fame Band Dir of Yr 1995; *home:* 6021 Glenbeigh Dr Sylvania OH 43560

QUIGLEY, MICHAEL, Fifth Grade Teacher; *b:* Buffalo, NY; *m:* Dorene; *c:* Chris, Corey, Bryan; *ed:* SUNY at Geneseo Ed (BS) 1968, (MS) 1973; *cr:* Penfield Cntrl Schls Tchr 1968-; *ai:* Penfield Ed Assn Dist Hlth & Safety Comm Rep; Bldg Level Placement Comm; AFT 1968-, Comms; *home:* 32 Devonshire Dr Penfield NY 14526

QUILLEN, SUSAN HARRIFF, 9th-12th Grd Span & Fr Tchr; *b:* Dover, OH; *m:* Gerald D.; *c:* Joshua, Zachary; *ed:* Kent St Univ (BA) Fr 1974; Ashland Univ (MED) Curr, Instruction 1990; *cr:* Strasburg Franklin Local Schl Fr, Span Tchr 1974-; *ai:* Scholar Challange Coach 8 Yrs; Newspaper Adv; Prin Advy Comm; AFT 1990-; Delta Kappa Gamma 1993-, Schlsp Comm Chm; Tuscarawas Cty Coll Club 1988-; Martha Holden Jennings Scholar 1979; *office:* Strasburg Franklin HS 140 N Bodmer Ave Strasburg OH 44680

QUINCE, CORA BRIDGES, Vice Principal; *b:* Quincy, FL; *m:* Kelvin Craig; *c:* Christina Behlinda, Kaela Cristal, Rory Delone; *ed:* Fisk Univ (BA) Music 1978; Eastern MI Univ (MA) Music 1981; William Paterson Coll (MED) Ed 1991; Univ of South FL 11 Quarter Hrs; *cr:* Willow Run Schl Vocal Music Accompanist 1981-83; River Rouge HS Vocal Music Instr 1983-84; Eastside HS Vocal Music Instr 1985-95; *ai:* Organized Tri-M Music Hnr Soc; NJMEA, PEA 1985-, Schl Del; MENC 1986-; PAA 1995-; Delta Sigma Theta 1986-, Chprsn Arts & Letters, Delta Woman of Yr; Wrigley Park Neighborhood Assn 1990-, Comm Chm; Rosa Parks Condominium Assn Sec 1990-93, Pres 1993-; NAACP 1993-; Calvary Bapt Church Pres Voices of Calvary; Conducted NJMEA All St Opera Chorus; Duke Ellington Music Awd; Appt Vice Prin 1995; Eastide HS Producted & Wrote with Music Stdnts Opera Entitled TAINOS; *office:* John F Kennedy HS 61-127 Preakness Ave Paterson NJ 07522*

QUINLAN, CHERYLL GUDGEON, Instruction Supervisor; *b:* Plainfield, NJ; *m:* Marc; *ed:* Georgian Court Coll (BA) Span 1979; Univ of AZ (MA) Span, L.A. Stud 1985; Jersey City St Coll Admin Cert; *cr:* Toms River Schls Span Tchr 1980-93, Supvr of Instruction 1993-; *ai:* FLENJ 1978-, Exec Bd; AATSP 1990-; ACTFL 1980-; ASCD; NJPSA; PSA; Tchr of Yr; *office:* Toms River HS East 1 Raider Way Toms River NJ 08753

QUINLAN, RONALD JOSEPH, Social Studies Dept Chprsn; *b:* Newark, NJ; *ed:* St Peters Coll (AB) Soc Stud 1973; *cr:* St Vincent Acad Tchr 1977-; *ai:* Women Helping Others Moderator; Spiritual Life Comm; Sftbl Coach; Dir of AV; Chrstn Appalachian Project 1986-, Summer Vol; *office:* Saint Vincent Acad 228 W Market St Newark NJ 07103

QUINLAN, SHARON GUERRO, Math Teacher; *b:* Palmerton, PA; *m:* William R. Jr.; *c:* Rachel; *ed:* East Stroudsburg Univ (BS) Scndry Ed, Math 1987, (MS) Scndry Ed; *cr:* Pocono Mountain Schl Dist Jr HS Math Tchr 1987-91; Montgomery Comm Coll Part-time Math Prof 1991-; Oxford Schl Dist HS Math Tchr 1992; Wyomissing Schl Dist Jr, Sr HS Math Tchr 1992-; *ai:* Peer Mediator, Memory Book Adv; SAT Instr; NEA, PSEA 1987-; *office:* Wyomissing Area Schl Dist 630 Evans Ave Wyomissing PA 19610*

QUINLIVAN, GARY MARTIN, Chairperson & Prof of Economic; *b:* Buffalo, NY; *m:* Sandra Sue; *c:* Vanessa; *ed:* SUNY at Geneseo (BA) Ec 1975; SUNY at Albany (PHD) Ec 1983; *cr:* Saint Vincent Coll Prof 1981-; Carnegie Mellon Univ Adjunct 1989-; Center for Ec & Policy Ed Exec Dir 1991-; *ai:* Republican Club & Ec Club Moderator; Responsible Officer Shandong Univ Affiliation; USIA Rep; Dir of Alex G McKenna Ec Ed Series; Fac Supvr; ASSA; Pittsburgh Ec Club 1981-; Omicron Delta Epsilon 1995-; Amer Red Cross 1993-, Intnl Comm; Ctr for Ec Policy Ed 1991-, Exec Dir; Allegheny Inst 1995-, Advy Bd; Westmoreland Intermediate Unit 1994-, Bd of Dirs; Fulbright in Peoples Republic of China 1988-89; SVC Prof of Yr 1993; Books Culture in Crisis, Ecs in a Cultural Context, Pub Policy & the Restoration of a Civil Soc, Policy Reform & Moral Grounding; *office:* Saint Vincents Coll & Sem 300 Fraser Purchase Rd Latrobe PA 15650

QUINN, ANITA MARIE, Seventh Grade Teacher; *b:* Springfield, MA; *m:* James; *c:* Kellee; *ed:* Framingham St Coll (BA) Eng 1988; Westfield St Coll (MED) Scndry Ed 1993; *cr:* Holy Trinity Schl 6th Grd Tchr 1989-90, 7th Grd Tchr 1990-95; *office:* Holy Trinity Schl 331 Elm St Westfield MA 01085

QUINN, ANITA SAIA, Principal; *b:* Buffalo, NY; *m:* Joseph P.; *c:* Kerry Clair, Joseph E.; *ed:* DYouville Coll (BS) Elem Ed 1965; St Univ Coll at Buffalo (MS) Elem Ed 1976, (CAS) Admin & Supervision 1990; *cr:* Buffalo Pub Schls Tchr 1965-88, Prgm Coord 1988-90, Asst Prin 1990-94, Prin 1994-; *ai:* Buffalo Tchrs Fed, NEA 1965-; BCSA 1990-; Phi Delta Kappa 1988-, Exec Bd, Fnds; NYS Cncl for SS 1988-; ASCD 1990-; Natl Humane Ed Soc 1980-; MADD 1985-; Mothers March of Dimes 1986-; Girl Scout Cncl 1987-; Grd Tchr Magazine Outstanding Tchr of Disadvantaged; 1973 Vol of Outstanding Elem Tchrs of Amer; *home:* 241 Davis Rd East Aurora NY 14052

QUINN, ANN JOHNSON, Spanish Teacher; *b:* New York, NY; *m:* Gregory; *c:* William Joseph; *ed:* Hunter Coll (BA) Span 1970; Lehman Coll (MA) Span 1994; Univ of Salamanca 21 In-Svc Credit Hrs 1989; SUNY at New Paltz Fr 19 Credits, Italian 7 Credits; *cr:* St John Vianney Elem Schl Soc Stud, Lang Arts Tchr 1970-73; Cardinal Hayes HS Frgn Lang Tchr 1973-77; Carmel HS Frgn Lang Tchr 1986-; *ai:* Art in Ed Comm; Manhattan Production Span Repertory Theater Spon; AFT, NYSUT 1986-; NYS Assn of Frgn Lang Tchrs 1994-; Kent Democratic Comm 1993-; NYS Ed Dept & Govt of Spain Multicultural Educl Schlsp to Stud Univ of Salamanca; NYS Assn of Frgn Lang Tchrs Incentive Grant 1995; *office:* Carmel HS 30 Fair St Carmel NY 10512

QUINN, BARBARA FOOTE, Art & Music Director; *b:* Bangor, ME; *m:* Robert L.; *c:* Richard, Christine; *ed:* Univ of NH (BS) Music Ed 1969; Univ of Southern ME (MS) Ed 1980, (MS) Educl Admin 1993; Level III Orff Cert DePaul Univ 1979; *cr:* Dover Schls Elem Music, Elem, Jr High Tchr, Band, Chorus, HS Marching Asst 1969-71; Sacopee Vly Dist Schl Elem Music, Band Tchr 1974-79; Windham Schl Dept Dir of Art, Music, Elem, MS Music 1979-; *ai:* Stu Aspirations 1996; Local Comm for Learning Results, Improving Amer Schls; Founder, Dir Chorus The Generations; NEA; ME Ed Assn; Windham Ed Assn; ASCD Music Ed; Natl Conf, ME Music Ed Assn; North Windham Union Church; ME Women's Fund Woman of Yr 1995; Pub Partners in Learning 1993; *office:* Windham Schl Dept 228 Windham Ctr Rd Windham ME 04062*

QUINN, CAROL REYNOLDS, Kindergarten Teacher; *b:* Osweg[o] *m:* Joseph Francis; *c:* Michael, Maureen Ward, Kevin; *ed:* S[t] Oswego (BS) Ed 1954; 10 Post Grad Hrs; 6 Post Grad Hrs NC St Grad Hrs SUNY at New Paltz; Level I & II Cert for Catechism Arch[diocese] of NY Dept of Ed; *cr:* Baldwinsville Cntrl Schl 4th Grd, Kndg[tn] 1954-58; Maine-Endwell Cntrl Schl K-1st Grd Tchr 1959-61, 196[3] Martin de Porres Schl 5th-6th Grd, Kndgtn Tchr 1977-; *ai:* Euc[haristic] Minister; NEA; NAEYC 1990-.

QUINN, DONALD ANTHONY, NJROTC Naval Science In[structor] Gloucester, MA; *m:* Cynthia Williams; *c:* Brian, Sahm; *ed:* Marquet[te] (BS) Mechanical Engrng 1965; Naval Post Grad Schl (MS) Mete[orology] 1973; SUNY at New Paltz NY Tchr Cert 1994; Defense Lang Inst 1982; *cr:* US Navy Commander 1954-91; MIddletown HS Naval S[cience] 1991-; *ai:* Military Drill Team; Air Rifle Team; *office:* Middleto[wn] Gardner Ave Ext Middletown NY 10940

QUINN, DUANE L., Music Teacher; *b:* Kittanning, PA; *m:* Deb[ra] Foster-Quinn; *c:* Jonathan, Jess, Elizabeth; *ed:* Clarion Univ (BE[d]) Ed 1987, (BM) Mrktg 1987; Grad Courses MA of Music Ed, MI Forest Area Schls Band, Chorus, Vocal Music Tchr 1990-; *ai:* Dram[a] Sr Chorus, Elem Prgm, Sr Band Dirs; Bsbl Coach; MENC, PMEA, C[...] 1990-; *office:* East Forest HS 120 W Birch St Marienville PA 1623[...]

QUINN, EDWARD WILLIAM, Eighth Grade Teacher; *b:* Philad[elphia] PA; *ed:* Immaculata Coll (BA) Elem Ed, Theology, Eng 1971; Row[an] of NJ (MA) Elem Admin 1988; Cert Prgm Theology St Charles Bo[rromeo] Seminary; Postgraduate Stud Ed, Psych Immaculata Coll; Grad Cr[edits] Tech Univ of Southern UT; *cr:* Schls of the Archdiocese Grd 1967-78; Diocese Grds 3-4 Tchr 1978-80; Archdiocese Grd 7-[8] 1980-; Chestnut Hill Coll Adj Fac Ed Dept 1990-; *ai:* Stu Cncl Moderator; Math, Grad Coord; Christmas Prgm Dir; NCTM 1988- Tchrs of Math of Phila 1993-; NCEA 1967-; Elem Math Curr Comm Chprsn 1985-, Svc Awd; Cur Cncl Joint Ele, Scndry 1985-; Math 1985-, Chprsn 1988-; Who's Who in Amer Ed 1992-; Curr Quil[...] Archdiocese of Philadelphia; Distngd Svc to Cath Ed Awd 25 Yrs; Sci Ed Fnd Grant; Articles Pub; *office:* St Francis Xavier Schl 2[...] Wallace St Philadelphia PA 19130

QUINN, JULIE RENAUX, Eng, Speech, Bible & Bus Tchr; *b:* T[...] OH; *m:* Richard L.; *c:* Carrie L., Tracy N., Jason R.; *ed:* Bowling Gr[een] Univ (BAEd) Speech & Drama 1968; *cr:* Davis Jr Coll of Bu[s] 1968-69; Toledo Chrstn Schls Tchr 1986-; *ai:* Stu Cncl Adv; HS Lar[...] Comm Chm; Sr Class Variety Show & HS Speech Meet Coord; S[...] Coord; *office:* Toledo Christian Schls 2303 Brookford Dr Toledo OH

QUINN, KATHLEEN DOUGHERTY, 8th Grade Teacher; *b:* New [York] NY; *m:* Frank; *c:* Francis, Michael; *ed:* Dominican Coll (BS) Ed Manhattan Coll (MA) Rdng 1975; *cr:* Holy Cross Schl 1st, 6th Gr[d] 1968-75; St Francis of Assisi 5th Grd Tchr 1975-77; Annunciatio[n] 6th, 8th Grd Tchr 1977-80; Holy Name of Mary Schl 8th Grd Tchr [...] *ai:* Lang Arts, Soc Stud Chprsn; BSA 1984-, Rel Emblem Awd; A[ncient] Order of Hibernians 1995-; East Rockaway Ftbl League 1988-, Hospi[...] Comm Svc; Lower Westside Comm Org; Holy Cross Parish Awd for [...] Svc; *office:* Holy Name Of Mary Schl 90 S Grove St Valley Strea[m] 11580

QUINN, LEE EMERSON, English Teacher; *b:* Baltimore, MD; *m*[...] P.; *c:* Kelly Quinn McHugh, J. P.; *ed:* Towson St Coll (BS) Elem Ed (MED) Ed & Rdng Specialist 1981; *cr:* Guilford Pub Schl 2nd-3r[d] Classroom Tchr 1964-65; Montebello Pub Schl 2nd-4th Grd Class[room] Tchr 1966-69; St Ursula Schl 2nd-8th Grd Classroom Tchr & Ass[t] 1974-88; Towson Cath HS Theology & Rdng Specialist 1988-91, Eng 1991-; *ai:* Stu Svc Pgm Coord; Yrbk & Creative Arts Magazine Adv Dept Chprsn; NCEA; Cert of Recognition Archbishops Awd for Tchng 1993; *office:* Towson Catholic HS 114 Ware Ave Baltimore MD 212[...]

QUINN, MARY BETH B., Math Tchr & Dept Chair; *b:* Pittsburgh *ed:* Indiana Univ of PA (BS) Math Ed 1973; Penn St Univ Cer[t] Blackhawk Schl Dist Math Tchr 1973-; *ai:* Mathcounts Coach-Club [...] Prof Enrichment, Math Review Comms; Math Dept Chair; NEA, [...] 1973-; Blackhawk Ed Assn 1973, Bldg Rep, Sec, Pres; Delta K[appa] Gamma 1983-; Amer Assn of Univ Women 1978-, Pres, Outsta[nding] Women of Branch Awd; Cath Charities inc 1986-, Comm Advy C[...] Comm Concerts Assn; In Svc Cncl; *office:* Blackhawk HS 500 Black[hawk] Rd Beaver Falls PA 15010*

QUINN, MICHAEL FRANK, English & Speech Teacher; *b:* San R[...] CA; *m:* Maria Fiorella Messina; *ed:* Univ of Portland (BA) Eng 1965 Addl Credit Hrs Univ of CA at Berkeley, Frostburg St, Chapman Co[ll] Mary's Coll of CA, Univ of DC; Attnd CA St Univ at Sonoma 196[...] Novato HS Eng Tchr 1966-68; San Marin HS Eng, Speech Tchr 196[...] Sangley Point Naval Station HS Eng, Speech Tchr 1970-71; Misaw[a] Dormitory Cnslr 1971-72; Pusan HS Dormitory Cnslr 1972-73; Wiesb[aden] HS Dormitory Cnslr 1973-75; Vicenza HS Dormitory Supvr 197[...] Torrejon HS Dormitory Cnslr 1981-83; Sigonella HS Eng, Speech, F[...] Tchr 1983-91; Aviano HS Eng, Speech Tchr 1991-; *ai:* Forensics C[...] Adv; Schl Advy Comm; Overseas Fed of Tchrs 1973-, Local Rep; Di[...] Tchr Awd 1995; 12 Outstdng, Exceptional Awd Ratings; 3 Gradu[ation] Classes Commencement Speaker.*

QUINN, NANCY SHARON, Language & Writing Teacher; *b:* Quee[ns] Albans, NY; *m:* Andrew H.; *c:* Andrew H., Kelly A., Daniel K.; *ed:* M[...] Cath Coll for Women (BA) Eng, Sec Ed 1969; Attnd Rutgers, Rowa[n] John's Univ; *cr:* Cathedral Prep Seminary Grds 9, 11-12 Eng, Speech 1969-70; Nathan Hale MS Grds 7-8th Tchr 1970-71; Charles W. Lewis 5th & 6th Grd Whole Lang Tchr 1984-, Core Ldr 1987-; *ai:* E[...] Consultant & Wkshp Presenter; WJRC; NJEA; NJRA; WJRC Pres[...] 1995; Educl Consultant & Presenter 1995; NJRA Presenter 1994.*

QUINN, SUSAN, English & Drama Teacher; *b:* Elizabeth, NJ; *ed:* Francis Coll (BA) Eng & Scndry Ed 1977; Temple Univ Post Grad Wo[rk] Theater; *cr:* Msgr Donovan HS Eng & Drama Tchr & Theater Dir 19[...] *ai:* Drama Club Moderator; ITS Spon; Alpha Psi Omega 1975-, Chptr F[...] NCEA 1987-; NCTE 1994-; *office:* Msgr Donovan HS 711 Hooper Toms River NJ 08753

QUINN, TAMMY TOWER, Math Teacher; *b:* Boston, MA; *m:* Dan[...] *c:* Steven, Danny; *ed:* Univ of MA at Amherst (BA) Ed 1979; 30 Credit[s] Math for HS Cert; 15 Credit Hrs Toward Masters of Math at Camp[...] Univ; *cr:* Wellesley Schls Title I Tchr 1980; East Side Elem 3rd Grd T[chr] 1980-81, 6th Grd Tchr 1981-83; Norfolk Cty Ag HS Math Tchr 1989- Jr Class Adv; Tech & Curr Comms; NCTM; MFT; ATMIM; Free[...] Centennial Schl Improvement Cncl 1995-; *office:* Norfolk Co Agricul[tural] HS 400 Main St Walpole MA 02081

QUINN, THOMAS JOSEPH, Computer Science Teacher; *b:* Scran[ton] PA; *ed:* Coll of the Holy Cross (AB) Bio 1984; Wilkes Univ (MS) E[d] Computing 1995; *cr:* Saint Bernards Cntrl Cath HS Bio & Phys Sci T[chr] 1984-85; Scranton Prep Schl Algebra, Chem & Cmptr Sci Tchr 1985- Moderator Cmptr Club; Higher Achvmt Prgm Dir; Prins Curr Comm M[...] Mid Sts Comm for the Educl Prgm Chm; *office:* Scranton Prep Schl [...] Wyoming Ave Scranton PA 18509

QUINN, WILLIAM M., Social Studies Tchr & Coord; *b:* Springfi[eld] MA; *m:* Mavreen Doyle; *c:* Sharon, Mary; *ed:* Westfield St Coll (BA) [...] Ed 1971; Univ of CT (MA) Pol Sci 1973; Westfield St Coll (CAGS) [...] 1982; Post Grad Couses; Prof Dev Courses; *cr:* Tunxis Comm Coll T[...]

Agawam HS Tchr 1974-79; Agawam Jr HS Tchr 1979-; *ai:* Soc Stud Coord; Ski Club Adv; Curr Comm; Schl Cncl; Instructional Trust Fnd; MA Cncl for ME Soc Stud, MA Tchrs Assn, Smithsonian Assoc ; Irish Genealogical Assn, Natl Wildlife Fed 1988-; People to People ; Agawon Counseling Ctr 1980-; Aqawon Fed Credit Union 1976-; on Lib Bd of Trustees 1975-; New England Assn of Coll, Schl ation; Amer Field Svc 1974-; Prof Grants; Peope to People ssador; Outstanding Educator of Yr; Pub in Historical Journal of ern MA; *office:* Agawam Jr HS 1305 Springfield St Feeding Hills MA)*

IN-SCHYMANSKI, KATHLEEN E., Cosmetology Teacher; *b:* ic, NJ; *m:* William Schymanski; *c:* Charles L. Qunn, Michael A. i; *ed:* Jersey City St Coll (BA) Voc Ed 1988; Cert WCEP 1990, Tchr andicapped; *cr:* Concord Schl of Hair Design Cosmetology Tchr 85; Monmouth Cty Voc Schl Cosmetology Tchr 1985-87; Matawan HS Cosmetology Tchr 1987-; *ai:* Fac Advy Bd; Pupil Assistance n; Certified Track, Field Ofcl; NJEA 1987-; VEANJ 1991-; Kappa Pi; Awd Dr Henry Dept of Ed-Trenton; *office:* Matawan Regional HS Atlantic Ave Matawan NJ 07747*

NONES, BIENVENIDA E., Science Teacher; *b:* Cavite, Philippines; ilomeno M.; *c:* Nathan, Rowena Q. Martin, Jonathan, Nathaniel, na R.Q. Hudson; *ed:* Univ of Philippines (BS) Chem 1956; *cr:* mission on Volcanology Analytical Chemist 1956-65; Univ of the ppines Instr 1965-69; Calvary Ches Sc Sci Tchr 1971-72; Heritage Sci Tchr 1973-; *office:* Heritage Acad 12215 Walnut Pt W rstown MD 21740

NONES, DIANA CRANE, Foreign Lang & Spanish Teacher; *b:* klyn, NY; *m:* Jose Antonio; *ed:* SUNY at Stonybrook (BA) Hispanic & Ibero Amer Stud 1976; Dowling Coll (MS) Ed; Life Time License Lang; *cr:* Varig Brazilian Airlines Tour Sales 1976-84; Bellport High Cntry Schl Span & Latin Tchr 1985-; *ai:* AATSP 1990-; Classical Assn St 1991-; Intnl Airlines Travel Agent 1989-; *office:* Bellport HS er Dam Rd Brookhaven NY 11719

NTER, VICTORIA (MAUER), Science Teacher; *b:* Sidney, OH; *m:* rice H. Jr.; *c:* Kayla, Brett; *ed:* Univ of Dayton (BS) Bio & Scndry Ed ; Wright St Univ (MED) MS Sci 1990; *cr:* Russia Local Schls Sci Tchr -89f Piqua City Schls Sci Tchr 1989-92; Vandalia-Butler Schls Bio 1992-94; Anna Local Schls Sci Tchr 1994-; *ai:* Stu Cncl & Prom Adv; Olympiad Coach; Shelby Cty Curr Comm; IMS Pgm Master Tchr; A 1987-; NEA 1987-; Natl Bio Tchrs Assn 1990-; ALTA 1994-; Delta a Gamma 1994-; Ft Loramie Yth Org 1990-, Treas; Gym Comm 1991-; E Grant 1992; Project Discovery RTI Grant; Vandalia-Butler eciation Awd 1994-95; Piqua HS Tchr Appreciation Awd 1995; Bro SM Awd of Excl in Bio 1986; *office:* Anna HS 1 McGrill Way Anna 45302

NTERNO, MARIANNE RAO, Chapter I Reading Specialist; *b:* idence, RI; *m:* Frank V. Jr.; *c:* Vanessa, Lauren; *ed:* Rhode Island COll Elem Ed 1975, (MED) Rdng 1987; *cr:* Marreville Elem Schl manent Sub, Preparations Periods 1975-79; Stawberry Patch Chief , Owner 1979-80; Monsignor Bove Schl Grd 2 Tchr 1980, Art, Rdng ourse Tchr 1980-81, Grd 3 Tchr 1983-84, Grd 4 Tchr 1984-85, Grd 2 1985-86; Marieville Elem Schl Chapter I Rndg Tchr 1986-; *ai:* N Prov Arts K-3 Curr Comm, Lang Arts Textbook Comm; LEAP Adv Cncl; ect READ Coord; New England Rdng Assn 1993-; IRA 1986-93; AFT 5-; New England Rdng Assns Meml Grant; *office:* Marieville Schl 1135 eral Spring Ave Providence RI 02904

NTILIANI, GERALD CARMINE, Business & Computer Teacher; *b:* chester, MA; *m:* Patricia Julianne Costello; *c:* Julianne, Janene, hony; *ed:* Salem St Coll (BS) Bus Ed 1974; Suffolk Univ (MS) Bus Ed 5; 75 Credits Beyond Masters Post Grad Stud Suffolk Univ, Cambridge Inservice Courses; *cr:* Quincy HS Bus Tchr 1974-84; North Quincy Cmptr Admin 1985-90, Bus, Cmptr Tchr 1991-; *ai:* Cmptr Club Adv; s of Fac; Advy, Tech, Time & Learning Comms; Tech Prep Home Room r, Adv; NBEA, EBEA 1973-; MBEA 1973-, Cmptr Wkshp Chprsn, rshp Chprsn; NEBEA 1973-, Pres, 1st VP, 2nd VP, Mbrshp, Past Pres; intree Yth Soccer, Bsktbl 1982-; South Braintree Girls Sftbl 1982-, VP, Bd Mem; Who's Who in Amer Coll & Univ 1974; Suffolk Univ ning Division Stu of Yr 1985; Bronze Key Awd 1974; *office:* North ncy HS 316 Hancock St North Quincy MA 02171*

INTIN, ELLEN BONTEMPO, Spanish Teacher; *b:* New Haven, CT; Robert; *c:* Maria, Christine, Elizabeth; *ed:* S CT St Coll (BS) Span 9; Work Towards MS Span; *cr:* Hillhouse HS Span Tchr 1969-74; New l for Young Children Asst Dir 1985-89; Barry Jr HS Span Tchr 1989-92, red Heart Acad Span Tchr 1993-; *ai:* Pro-life Club; Prgm Adv, Advisee; LT 1994-; Awded Schlsp Summer Stud in Guadalajara Mexico 1969; *ce:* Sacred Heart Acad 265 Benham St Hamden CT 06514

INTO, JOHANNA ELEANOR, Pre-School Teacher; *b:* Hoboken, NJ; Coll of St Elizabeth (BA) Elem Ed 1968; Jersey City St Coll (MA) ng 1975; William Paterson Coll Early Chldhd Ed 1985, 21st Annual nf of Young Child 1995; Nursery Schl Tchr, Rdng Specialist Certs 1975; Mt Carmel Schl 1st Gr Tchr 1968-74; St Augustines Schl 4th Grd Tchr 74-77, 7th Grd Tchr 1977-79, Presch Tchr 1979-; *ai:* Art Coord; Rdng v; NCEA 1979-; Cath Yth Org 1975-85, Moderator, Merit Awd 1980; ion City Pub Lib Cert of Appreciation Natl Lib Week 1985; Cert of Awd chdiocese of Newark Presch Curr 1988; *office:* St Augustine Schl 3920 w York Ave Union City NJ 07087

UINTON, ALFRED P., Marketing Professor; *b:* Perth Amboy, NJ; *m:* role; *c:* William, Suzanne Mc Nulty, Carolyn Desmann, Jeannette, alter Smith, Eric Smith; *ed:* Thomas Edison St Coll (BA) Soc Sci 1982; Inst of Tech (MBA) Mngmt 1984; Pace Univ (DPS) Mrktng, Intnl Bus 93; *cr:* R. H. Macy & CO Intnl Mgr 1958-68; Kayser Roth Inc Intnl Mgr 80-85; J. P. Stevens Inc Product Mgr 1986-89; Trenton St Coll Mrktng of 1989-; *ai:* Fac Adv Amer Mrktng Assoc Stu Chptr; Chm Comm on missions, Advisement, Retention; Amer Mrktng Assoc 1986-; Acad of tnl Bus 1989-; Acad of Mrktng Sci 1990-; *office:* Trenton St Coll llwood Lakes Trenton NJ 08650

UIRK, ELLEN FARRELL, English Teacher; *b:* Jersey City, NJ; *m:* chard Gregory; *c:* Peter, Michael, Matthew; *ed:* Union Coll (AA) Lib rts 1977; Rutgers Univ (BA) Eng 1988, (MA) Eng 1990; ost-Baccalaureate Cert Kean Coll 1993; *cr:* NJ Bell Telephone Bus Office apvr 1967-75; Brookdale Comm Coll Adj Instr 1990-93; Middletown HS orth Adv Jrnlsm Tchr 1993-; *ai:* Lion's Roar Stu Newspaper Adv; enaissance Comm; NCTE 1988-; NJEA 1993-; League of Women Voters 93-.

UIRK, JAMES EDWARD, Public Services Dept Chairman; *b:* Camden, J; *m:* Frances PHillips; *c:* Michael, Jamie; *ed:* Wesley Coll (AA) His 964; Univ of DE (BA) Soc Sci 1966; Salisbury St Univ (MED) Ed 1974; ddl 45 Hrs Beyond Masters; *cr:* Caesar Rodney HS Tchr 1966-77; Dover nvironmental Ed Ctr Dir 1978-81; DE Tech & Comm Coll Dept Chm 982-; *ai:* Human Svcs Org Adv; Fac Senate Rep; Hnrs, Mid Sts ccreditation, Prof Dev Comm; NAEYC 1991-; Ctr Stud of Presidency 980-; Amer Psychological Assn 1992-; DE St Ed Assn 1970-, Bd of Dirs; igher Ed consortium 1990-, Bd Mem; tchr of Yr; Co-Authored 2 Trng Manuals for Child Care Providers, Manual for Prof Dev of Child Care roviders; US Dept of Ed Grant for Mentor Trng; *office:* DE Tech & Comm oll At Dover 1832 N Dupont Hwy Dover DE 19901

QUIRK, JANAFE OSMANSKI, Computer & Business Ed Tchr; *b:* Providence, RI; *m:* John P.; *ed:* Bryant Coll Bus (BS) 1972, (MBA) 1977; *cr:* E. R. Martin Jr High Bus Tchr 1973-80; East Providence HS Cmptr Tchr 1980-; *ai:* FBLA Adv; NEA, East Prov Ed Assn 1973-; *office:* East Providence Sr HS 2000 Pawtucket Ave East Providence RI 02914

QUIRK, JOHN P., Economics Teacher; *b:* Providence, RI; *m:* Janate Ann Marie Osmanski; *c:* John Jr., Sharon; *ed:* Providence Coll (BA) His 1966; RI Coll (MED) Urban Ed 1977; Pacific Western Univ (PHD) Curr 1987; Univ of RI 39 Credit Hrs His, 21 Credit Hrs Ec; *cr:* Edward R Martin Jr HS Tchr 1966-80; E Providence HS Ec Tchr 1980-; *ai:* Acad Decathlon Team Coach; NEA & RI Ed Assn 1966-; EPEA 1966-, Pres 1979-80; N Kingstown Little League 1979-86, Coach 1980-82, Bd of Dirs 1982-86; Republican Town Comm 1986-88; *office:* East Providence H S 2000 Pawtucket Ave Providence RI 02914

QUISNO, GARY A., Geometry Teacher; *b:* Port Clinton, OH; *m:* Rebecca Blackburn; *c:* Adam, Amanda; *ed:* Miami Univ (BA) Math Ed 1976; Univ of Toledo (MS) Supervision, Admin 1984; *cr:* Pontiac Cntrl HS Math Tchr 1976-77; Danbury Local HS Math, Bus Tchr 1977-79; Oak Harbor HS Math Tchr 1979-; *ai:* Head Ftbl, Asst Var Track Coach; Asst Ath Dir; Weightroom Supvr; Var Club Adv; Ath Cncl; Bldg Advy Comm; NEA, OEA 1977-; OHEA 1979-; NCTM; OCTM; NWOFCA; OFCA; St Boniface Cath Church; Dist Ftbl Coach of Yr 1991, 1995; *office:* Oak Harbor HS 11661 W State Route 163 Oak Harbor OH 43449*

QUIST, ROBERT MARK, Guidance Counselor; *b:* Worcester, MA; *ed:* Westfield St Coll (BS) Criminal Justice 1982; Univ of Hartford (MPA) Pub Admin 1984; Bridgewater St Coll (MED) Cnslng 1987; Cert Alcoholism Cnslng Stonehill Coll; *cr:* Y O U Inc Clinical Cnslr 1986-87; Malden Cath HS Guid Cnslr 1987-; *ai:* Coach Frosh Ftbl, Asst Indoor, Outdoor Track; MSCA, GBGA 1987-; *office:* Malden Catholic HS 99 Crystal St Malden MA 02148

QUITT, DEBORAH LOBSENZ, History Teacher; *b:* Paterson, NJ; *m:* Martin H.; *c:* Adam, Alisha; *ed:* Douglass Coll Rutgers (BA) His 1966; Brown Univ (MAT) His Ed 1967; *cr:* Brooklins HS Tchr 1968-; *ai:* NEA 1980-; ACLS Tchr Mem 199I-94; NEH Grant 1993; *office:* Brookline HS 115 Greenough St Brookline MA 02146

R

RAAB, GRETCHEN, English Teacher; *b:* Neptune, NJ; *m:* Ivan Kayser; *c:* Jessica Tuchinsky, Adam-Max Tuchinsky; *ed:* Cedar Crest Coll (BA) Eng 1964; Penn St Univ (MA) Eng 1980; *cr:* Upper Perkiomen Schl Dist Eng Tchr 1964-68; Cncl Rock Schl Dist Eng Tchr 1985-; *ai:* Parent Newsletter Ed; Stu Assistance Team; Instructional Support Team; NEA, PSEA 1964-; NCTE 1964-68; AAUW 1968-; *office:* Holland Jr HS 400 E Holland Rd Holland PA 18966

RAATZS, IRENE KITZHOFER, Eighth Grade Teacher; *b:* Letter Hanover, Germany; *m:* Raymond J.; *c:* Kurt, Kate; *ed:* Trenton St Coll (BA) Psych 1990; 12 Addl Credit Hrs; *cr:* Willingboro Pub Schls Sub Tchr 1987-90; Our Lady of Perpetual Help Schl 8th Grd Tchr 1990-; *ai:* Yrbk; Lit Magazine; Lang Arts Coord; Mid Sts Chprsn; Trenton Diocesan Lang Arts Comm; Discipline with Purpose Co-Chair; NCEA, NCTE 1990-; Psy Chi 1989-; Child Abuse Prevention Network 1989-; Outstdng Cath Edctr 1995; Zonta Intnl Grant 1989, 1990; *office:* Our Lady Perpetual Help Schl Main St & Fellowship Rd Maple Shade NJ 08052*

RABBERMAN, ANNA MARIA LEHNER, Social Studies Teacher; *b:* Gyor, Hungary; *m:* Robert C.; *c:* Jeffrey, Brian, Kerri; *ed:* Trenton St Coll (BA) Soc Stud 1974, (MED) Stu Prsnl Services 1978; *cr:* Council Rock HS Cnslr 1984-85, Soc Stud Tchr 1974-; *ai:* Mid Sts Steering Comm Chprsn; Stu Asst Pgm Core Mem; NEA; *office:* Council Rock HS 62 Swamp Rd Newtown PA 18940*

RABENOLD, LAURA C., Fine Arts & Vocal Music Tchr; *b:* Bellevue, PA; *m:* Nelson T.; *c:* Karin, Patrick; *ed:* IN Univ of PA (BS) Music Ed, Piano, Voice 1970; WV Univ (MM) Music Ed 1973; 5 Credit Hrs Post Grad Stud Westminster Choir Coll; *cr:* Bethel Park Schl Dist Elem Vocal Music Tchr 1970-71; West Greene Schl Dist Scndry Gen Music, Vocal Tchr 1973-76; Pvt Studio Pvt Individual Piano, Voice Tchr 1980-86; Maurys Music Store Pvt Piano, Voice Instr 1986-89; William Allen HS Keyboard, Vocal Tchr 1989-92; Whitehall Copley Schl Dist HS Fine Arts, Vocal Tchr 1992-; *ai:* Chorale, Asbury UM Chancel Choir, Spring Musical, Asbury United Meth Church Dirs; Grad Requirements Comm Strategic Planning; MENC, PMEA 1989-, Host, 1994 Dist Chorus; ACDA 1990-; WCEA 1992-; *office:* Whitehall HS 3800 Mechanicsville Rd Whitehall PA 18052

RABENOLD-NORWOOD, GEORGINE, English Teacher; *b:* Bethlehem, PA; *m:* David Norwood; *c:* Karina; *ed:* Moravian Coll (BA) Eng Ed 1989; 24 Grad Credits Ed; *cr:* Pleasant Vly MS Eng Tchr 1991-; *ai:* New Tchr Mentor; Bear Facts Adv 1990-94; PSEA, PVEA 1991-; Instrl Support Cert; Presented at Natl Conf for IST; Initiated a Peer Tutoring Prgm at HS with Christine Raughley; Presented Various Topics for In-Svc; Initiated Team Tchg, Inclusion at HS; *office:* Pleasant Vly MS Rt 115 & 209 Brodheadsville PA 18322*

RABER, LAURA NOFSINGER, Language Arts Teacher; *b:* Massillon, OH; *ed:* The Univ of Akron (BA) Scndry Ed 1986, (MA) Ed 1991; Northwestern Univ Schl of Speech Summer Fellow 1993; 41 Post Grad Hrs at Ashland Univ, Kent St Univ; *cr:* Kent St Univ Part-time Instr 1991-, Tuscarawas Valley HS Lang Arts Tchr 1986-; *ai:* NHS Adv; Stu Tchr Mentor; NCTE, OCTELA 1988-; IRA; OCIAR; NEA; OEA; TVTA; Pythian Sisters, OH Eastern Star 1989-; Phi Delta Kappa Mc Kinley 1994-; Book: The Pen is in My Hand Now What; Articles Pub; Grant from Phi Delta Kappa; *office:* Tuscarawas Vly HS 2637 Tuscarawas Vly Rd Zoarville OH 44656

RABER, SHEILA EDELSTEIN, English Teacher; *b:* Brooklyn, NY; *m:* Roman; *c:* Jennifer, Howard; *ed:* Brooklyn Coll (BA) Eng & Ed 1968, (MA) Art His & Ed 1973; 12 Credits Towards MBA Adelphi 1985; *cr:* Long Beach MS Eng Tchr 1988-91; Long Beach HS Eng Tchr 1991-95; Long Beach MS Eng Tchr 1995-; *ai:* The Tide Newspaper Adv; AFT, NYSUT 1987-; Advised All Columbian HS Newspapers-Medalist Rating CSPA; 2nd Place Best Newspaper in NY St Empire Stu Scholastic Press Assn & Columbia Scholastic Press Assn; *office:* Long Beach HS 322 Lagoon Dr W Long Beach NY 11561

RABII, GAIL THOMAS, Science & Social Studies Tchr; *b:* San Mateo, CA; *m:* Dr Jamshid; *c:* Chris, Lisa, Jeanne; *ed:* Univ of CA at Berkely (BA) Soc Sci 1969; Univ of San Francisco Grad Cert Elem Ed 1970; NASA Aerospace Ed 1991; Princeton Plasma Physics Enhancement Project Sci & Math 1995; *cr:* San Francisco Pub Schls 5th-6th Grd Tchr 1970-71; East Brunswick Pub Schls 5th-6th Grd Sci & Soc Stud Tchr 1985-86, 4th-5th Grd Sci & Soc Stud Tchr 1986-; *ai:* Melville Innovations Grant Coord; NJ Ed Assn 1985-; East Brunswick Ed Assn 1985-, Elem Cncl Mem; NSTA 1986-; NJ Cncl for Soc Stud 1995-; Project GERI 1983-; PTA 1985-; East Brunswick Pub Schls Employee Awd 1989; NASA Newest Hnrs Tchr Awd 1991; NJ Governors Outstdng Tchr Awd 1992; Melville Innovation Grant Cert of Commendation 1993; *office:* Bowne-Munroe Schl 120 Main St East Brunswick NJ 08816

RABIN, MONROE S. Z., Professor of Physics; *b:* Brooklyn, NY; *m:* Joan G.; *c:* Elaine, Carolyn; *ed:* Columbia Coll (AB) Math 1961; Rutgers Univ (MS) Physics 1964, (PHD) Physics 1967; *cr:* Lawrence Berkeley Natl Lab Physicist 1967-72; Univ of MA Assoc Prof 1972-82, Prof 1982-; *ai:* Amer Physical Soc, Sigma Xi 1967-; *office:* Univ Of MA At Amherst Dept of Physics & Astronomy Amherst MA 01003

RABIN, SHEILA J., Assistant Professor of History; *b:* Brooklyn, NY; *m:* William Bregman; *ed:* SUNY at Stony Brook (BA) His 1970; Univ of MI (AM) His 1971; CUNY Grad Schl (PHD) His 1987; *cr:* St Peter's Coll Asst Prof His 1992-; *ai:* His Club Adv; Brooklyn Coll Chamber Chorus; Piano Performance; AHA, Ren Soc of Am 1976-; Medieval Club of NY 1981-, Sec; NY Acad of Sci 1994-; Numerous Articles, Reviews Pub; Conf Papers; *office:* Saint Peters Coll 2641 Kennedy Boulevard Jersey City NJ 07306

RABINE, BRENDA-LEE TYLER, English Teacher; *b:* Glen Falls, NY; *m:* Terry; *ed:* Hamilton Coll (BA) Eng Lit 1988; Siena Coll Scndry Cert 1992; SUNY at Albany 24 Credits Past Masters in Eng, Writing Sequence; *cr:* Chatham HS Eng Tchr 1992-93; Saratoga Springs HS Eng Tchr 1994-; *ai:* Drama Club Adv, Dir; *home:* 1 Sparrow Ct Saratoga Springs NY 12866

RABINO, LINDA, Law & Social Studies Teacher; *b:* New York City, NY; *m:* Isaac; *c:* Tahl Jeanne; *ed:* City Coll of NY (BA) Pol Sci 1962; City Univ of NY (MS) Soc Stud Ed 1965; SUNY at Stony Brook (PHD) Educl Anthropology 1992; *cr:* Macombs JHS Soc Stud Tchr 1964-67; Walton HS Soc Stud Tchr 1967-70; John F. Kennedy HS Amer His Tchr 1970-72; Herbert H. Lehman HS Legal Stud Coord 1975-; *ai:* Moot Court Team Adv; Trainer NYC Law Cluster Curr Writer, Tchr; Legal Stud Prgm Coord; UFT 1960-; NYC Law Cluster 1992-; Impact II Grant NYC Bd of Ed; Natl Endowment for Humanities Summer; Seminar Great Works on Immigration; *office:* Herbert H. Lehman HS 3000 E Tremont Ave Bronx NY 10461*

RABINOWITZ, SHELDON MARK, Fifth Grade Teacher; *b:* Brooklyn, NY; *m:* Paula Sherry Greenberg; *ed:* Brooklyn Coll (BA) Elem Ed, Sociology-Honors 1973, (MS) Elem Ed 1975; *cr:* PS 120 Schl Remedial Rdng, Math Ed Asst Grd 5 1973-74; PS 45 Schl Tchr Emotionally Disturbed Boys Grd 4th-6th 1974; PS 139 Schl 4th Grd Tchr 1974-75; Mary B. Sharpe Elem Schl 5th Grd Tchr 1975-; *ai:* Schl Sci Fair Coord; Soc Stud COmm; NEA, PA St Ed Assn, Chambersburg Area Ed Assn 1975-; Franklin Cty Rock, Minieral Club, Eastern Fed Mineralogical, Lapidary Soc, Amer Fed Mineralogical Soc 1995-; Nom 1990 PA Tchr of Yr; Schl Participation Awd 8 Yrs; *home:* 6485 Grindstone Hill Rd Chambersburg PA 17201

RABINSKY, LEATRICE BERGIDA, English Teacher; *b:* Cleveland, OH; *m:* Irving; *c:* Linda Bensoussan, Rena Kurs, Marc Rabin, David; *ed:* Case Western Reserve Mather Coll (BA) Eng, Fr 1965; CWRU (MA) Eng 1970, (PHD) Ed 1978; Cert Comm Resources 1966; Holocaust Ed Seminar Mercy Coll 1976; Holocaust Edctrs Seminar Philadelphia 1979; Tchrs Conf Holocaust 1986; Yale Univ Confs Holocaust 1984; *cr:* Wiley Jr HS Eng Tchr 1965-71; CWRU Coord Stu Tchng Prgm 1976-78; Ursuline Coll Summer Lecturer, Lit Holocaust 1979; Cleveland Coll Jewish Stud Lecturer 1985-86; Cleveland Hgts HS Eng Tchr 1971-; *ai:* Organizer, Ldr Journey of Conscience; Act Spon Holocaust Outreach, Commemoration Week; Adv Journal Testimony Pub 1995-; North Cntrl Assn Co-Chprsn; Co-Ed Schl Self-Stud 1985, 1992, 2nd Co-Chms 1995; AFT 1970-; NEA 1965-70; NCTE 1975-, Co-Ed Book Genocide, Intolerance; Jewish Comm Fed 1985-, Exec Comm; Cleveland Jewish News 1989-, VP 1993-95; OH Cncl Holocaust Ed 1988-, Chprsn Materials Curr, Co-Ed OH St Curr; Cleveland Yom HaShoah-Holocaust Comm 1980-, Prgm Chprsn 1989, 1994-, The Holocaust Prejudice Unleashed 1977, 1994; Citizen's Advy Comm 1992-95; Co-Author Journey of Conscience, Young People Respond to the Holocaust 1978, Article Contemporary Educl Psych 1979; Natl Cncl Jewish Women Women Who Dared Awd 1995; Excl Tchng Awd 1996; Kol Israel Survivors Group Holocaust Ed Awds 1980, 1985, 1990; Articles Pub; Amer Magen David Adom Woman Valor Awd 1988.*

RABSCHNUK, JULIANNE E., Science Teacher & Dept Chprsn; *b:* Ware, MA; *m:* Joseph; *c:* Scott, Christine; *ed:* Anna Maria Coll (BA) Bio 1962; Grad & In-Svc Courses at Univ of MA, Worcester St Coll & American Intnl Coll 20+ Credits; *cr:* Anna Maria Coll Sci Instr 1962-65; Ware HS Sci Tchr 1970-, Sci Dept Chrprsn 1984-; *ai:* Schlsp Comm; Founder & Mem of Pro Merito Awds Prgm for Stu Scholars; Self Study Comms for HS Evaluation; NEA, MTA & WTA 1970-; MA Sci Supvrs 1990-; Country Bank for Savings 1978-, Corporator; Mary Lane Hospital 1988-, Corporator; MA Exch Del in England at Microelectronics Seminar 1985 & 1987; Visiting Comm Mem of NEASC Evaluating NE HS 9 Times; Outstanding Young Woman of Amer; NSF Grant for Microbiology Research at Cornell Univ; Key Club Recognition Awd; *office:* Ware HS 237 West St Ware MA 01082*

RACCO, LUCIANO, Italian Teacher; *b:* Reggio Calabria, Italy; *m:* Mariella Bagetta-Racco; *c:* Luciano Jr., Tiffany A.; *ed:* Univ of Messina Italy (PHD) Romance Lang, Lit 1977; Attnd Cntrl CT St Univ, St Univ of NY at Albany; *cr:* Cheshire Acad Fr, Italian, Toefl Tchr 1978-85; Ridgefield HS Italian, Span Tchr 1986-88; Mahopac HS Italian Tchr 1988-; *ai:* Italian Club Adv; JV Girls Soccer Coach; AFT 1988-; *office:* Mahopac HS Baldwin Place Rd Mahopac NY 10541

RACER, PATRICIA DOUGHERTY, Second Grade Teacher; *b:* Woodbury, NJ; *c:* Robert, John, Michael; *ed:* Glassboro St Coll (BA) Elem Ed; Catechist Cert; *cr:* St Marys Regnl Second Grd Tchr 13 Yrs; *ai:* Stu Cncl Moderator; PTA Bd, Tchr Liaison; Lang Arts Coord; Sci Acad Awd; *office:* Saint Marys Regnl Schl 31 Oak St Salem NJ 08070

RACHALIS, CHRISTINE FRANCES, Mathematics Teacher; *b:* Elmhurst, NY; *ed:* Kent St Univ (BS) Ed 1974; Montclair St Univ (MA) Schl Prsnl Svcs 1987; *cr:* Randolph MS Math Tchr 1977-; *ai:* NJEA, NEA 1977-; NJAMLE 1991-; *home:* 3 Ventosa Dr Morristown NJ 07960*

RACHBACH, HOWARD L., Chemistry Teacher; *b:* New York, NY; *m:* Barbara Kaplan; *c:* Sharon; *ed:* City Coll of NY (BS) Chem 1953, (MA) Ed 1961; Attnd NYU, CCNY, Earlham 25 Grad Credit Chem 1956-66; Montclair St Coll Educl Supvr Cert 1978; *cr:* Wm C Bryant HS Lab Asst 1956-59; Bryant HS Chem Tchr 1959-64; Bowne HS Chem Tchr 1959-64; LIU Instr, Ed 1961; CCNY Lecturer, Chem 1963, Adj Lecturer, Chem 1965-87; Queens Coll Adj Lecturer, Chem 1965-87; Bronx HS of Sci Chem Tchr 1983-; *ai:* Amer Chem Soc 1954-; NSTA 1959-; Chem Tchrs Club of NY 1956-; Article J Chem Ed Oct 1960; Commendation Inspirational Tchng ACSNY 1977; Outstanding Tchr Awd Univ of Chicago 1985; Tchng Commendations MIT 1985, 1988; *office:* The Bronx HS Of Science 75 W 205 St New York NY 10468

RACHFORD, KAY BARKER, 5th Grade Teacher; *b:* West Liberty, KY; *m:* Thomas M.; *c:* Tobin, Jennifer; *ed:* Eastern KY St Univ (BS) Elem Ed 1965; Penn St Univ (MED) Elem Ed 1976; 15 Addl Grad Credits in Elem Ed; *cr:* Cumberland Vly Schl Dist 1st-5th Grd Tchr 16 Yrs; Woodford Cty

Schls 1st Grd Tchr 1 Yr; *office:* Cumberland Vly Schl Dist 6746 Carlisle Pike Mechanicsburg PA 17055

RACINE, STEVEN R., Sociology & Economics Teacher; *b:* Manchester, CT; *c:* Danielle; *ed:* Southern CT St U (BS) Sec Ed Soc Sci 1982; Kean Coll of NJ Post Bac Cert Recreation Mgmt; *cr:* Morris Cath HS Ath Dir, Coach & Tchr 1981-; *ai:* Var Girls Soccer & Var Spring Track Coach; NCEA 1982-; Natl Soccer Coaches Assoc 1985-; NJ St Girls Soccer Coaches Assoc 1991-; Joey Bella Fund Inc 1987-, Ex Comm; Coach of 8 Consecutive Girls Soccer St Championships 1988-; St Coach of Yr 1989; 6 Morris Cty Championships 1990-; Natl Record for Girls Soccer; 11 Conf Championships; 3 Indoor Track St, Cty & Conf Championships; Area Coach of Yr; 3 Outdoor Track St & Cty Conf Championships Area Coach of Yr (Twice); 7 Conf Championships; 6 Conf Coach of Yr; *office:* Morris Catholic HS 200 Morris Ave Denville NJ 07834*

RACIOPPI, MAUREEN M., 6th-8th Grade English Teacher; *b:* New York City, NY; *m:* Frank G.; *c:* Michael, Elizabeth; *ed:* Fairleigh Dickinson Univ (AA) Bus 1966, (BA) Eng Ed 1984; Seton Hall Univ (MA) Gen Prof Ed 1994; William Paterson Coll, NY Univ, New Schl for Soc Research Lit Credits; *cr:* New York Times Asst Mgr Book Advertising 1969-74; Conway Diet Inst Lecturer 1980-85; Rev. Brown Schl Tchr 1985-; *ai:* Mid Sts Steering, Grad Planning Comms; Lang Arts Dept Chairwoman; Newsletter Ed, Adv; Kappa Delta Pi; NCTE; ASCD; NCEA; *office:* Rev Geo A Brown Memorial Sch 294 Sparta Ave Sparta NJ 07871*

RACKLEY, GAIL MC VAY, English Teacher; *b:* Pittsburgh, PA; *m:* W. John; *c:* Jane, Anne, Emily; *ed:* Carlow Coll (BS) Speech, Comm, Theatre 1973; *cr:* Beaver Area Schls Jr HS Eng Tchr 1974-82, Sr HS Eng Tchr 1990-; *ai:* Yrbk Publication Adv; NEA 1974-; NCTE 1994-; Beaver Cty Lawyers Auxiliary 1976-, Pres; Beaver Tourist Club 1990-, Pres; Park Presbyn Church 1963-; Beaver Band Parents 1994-; *office:* Beaver Area Sr HS Gypsy Glen Rd Beaver PA 15009

RACOWSKI, PAULA BRANNING, Reading Specialist; *m:* Kenneth; *c:* Ken, Joy; *ed:* Keystone Jr Coll (AA) 1972; Mansfield St (BS) Elem Ed 1974; Marywood Coll (MS) Rdng Ed 1981; *cr:* Vly View Elem Schl 1-2 Grd Classroom Tchr 17 Yrs; Vly View MS 5-6 Grd Rdng Specialist 5 Yrs; *ai:* Curr Steering Comm, Staff Dev Co-Chprsn; Northeast PA Rdng Assn, IRA 1992-; PAFPC 1995-; PSEA 1974-; *office:* Valley View Elem Schl Columbus Dr Archbald PA 18403*

RACZKO, TERRENCE MICHAEL, English Teacher; *b:* Toledo, OH; *m:* Karen Clark; *c:* Elizabeth Lodzinski, Lisa Lynott; *ed:* Bowling Green St Univ (BSEd) Eng 1964, (MA) Eng 1967; Case Western Reserve Univ PHD Prog in Eng 18 Semester Hrs; *cr:* Crissey Jr HS Eng Tchr 1964-66; Lake HS Eng Tchr 1966-68; Northern St Coll Asst Prof of Eng 1968-73; Harding HS Eng Tchr 1973-; *ai:* Musical Tech Dir; Fairport Harbor Tchrs Assn 1973-, Past Pres & Past Chief Negotiator; NEA & OEA 1973-; Flwshp to Western Reserve Univ PHD Pgm 1987-91; *office:* Harding HS 329 Vine St Fairport Harbor OH 44077*

RADABAUGH, WILLIAM E., HS Math & Spanish Teacher; *b:* Mt Sterling, OH; *m:* Suellen Graumlich; *c:* Jonathan; *ed:* Columbus Bus Univ (AA) Accounting 1961; Wilmington Coll (BA) Math Ed 1966; Wright St Univ (MED) Master Tchr 1991; Post Grad Stud at Drake Univ, Seattle Pacific Univ, Walsh Coll & Wittenberg Univ; *cr:* Lancaster City Schls Math Tchr 1967-69; Nationwide Insurance Group Ins Acct Mgr 1970-80; Miami Tchr HS Math & Span Tchr 1980-; *ai:* SADD Adv; Adult Basic Ed Tchr 13 Yrs; Sftbl Coach, Tnns; Phi Delta Kappa 1991-; NEA, OEA, MTEA 1980-; Mt Sterling F&A.M. 1978-, Jr Steward; Scottish Rite 1978-; Kiwanis-Lancaster 1968-, D. Deput, Circle K; Fay Co Pilots Assn 1990-, Sec, Treas; EAA 1992-, Newsletter Ed; *office:* Miami Trace HS 3722 St Rt 41 NW Washington Crt Hse OH 43160

RADACK, D. MICHAEL, Elem Mathematics Tchr; *b:* Jamestown, NY; *m:* Mary Anderson; *c:* Emily; *ed:* Brockport St Coll (BS) Sociology 1971, (MS) Ed 1973; *cr:* Jefferson Ave Schl Second Grd Tchr 1972-81, Kndgtn Tchr 1981-90; Dudley Schl First Grd Tchr 1990-93; St Cuthberts RC Primary Schl Reception Tchr 1994-95; Dudley Schl Elem Math Tchr 1993-; *ai:* Mem Golf, Bowling Vlybl, Racquetball Leagues; Coach Yth Soccer League; Fairport Ed Assn 1972-, Rep; NYS Rdng Tchrs 1990-; Dreikurs Assn 1980-; Shared Decision Making Comm 1991-; Fulbright Assn 1992-; Cub Scouts, Weblos Ldr; Nom Who's Who Among Amer Colls, Univs; Fulbright Exchange Tchr to England 1994-95; *office:* Dudley School 211 Hamilton Rd Fairport NY 12240

RADANO, FRANCES J.,JR., TV & Drama Teacher; *b:* Philadelphia, PA; *c:* Francis III, Peter, Christopher; *ed:* St Josephs Coll (BA) Eng Lit 1967; Temple Univ (MS) Commnctn Media 1971; Univ of the Arts Creative Writing, Comp Graphics & Drama 15 Credit Hrs; Univ of PA Cultural Anthropology 18 Credit Hrs; *cr:* Shaw Jr High Eng Tchr 1968-73; Univ City HS Film & TV & Eng Tchr 1973-89; HS for the Creative & Performing Arts TV Production & Drama Tchr 1989-; *ai:* TV Production; AFT & PFT 1968-; Magnet HS Grant for Intercultural Video Project 1994-95; *office:* HS Creative & Performing Arts 11th & Catherine St Philadelphia PA 19147

RADCLIFFE, JENNY ROBINSON, Sixth Grade Teacher; *b:* Uniontown, PA; *m:* Trip; *c:* Chris, Eric, Craig; *ed:* CA Univ (BS) Elem Ed 1973; Post Grad Stud West VA Univ; *cr:* Marshall Elem 5th-6th Grd Tchr 1973-74; Kennedy Elem 1st-2nd Grd Tchr 1974-76; Marshall Elem 2nd Grd Tchr 1976-78; Hatfield Elem 1st Grd Tchr 1985-95, 6th Grd Tchr 1995-; *ai:* NEA 1973-; Ashbury Church, Sunday Schl Tchr; Asbury Bell Choir, Mem; Asbury Bd of Trustees, Sec; *office:* Hatfield Elem Schl 370 Derrick Ave Uniontown PA 15401

RADCLIFFE, SUE ELLEN KINSEY, Physics & Math Teacher; *b:* Pasadena, CA; *m:* Steven E.; *c:* Jaime, Brad, Greg; *ed:* Wright St Univ (BS) Math Ed 1976-, (MED) Tchr Ldr 1985; 19 Addl Hrs Miami Univ, Univ Cincinnati; *cr:* Fairmont East Physics Tchr 1977; Middletown City Schls Math, Sci 1978-; *ai:* Class of 1993 Adv; Class of 1997 Adv; MTA, OEA, NEA, NCTM, OCTM 1978-, SECO 1993-; Middfest 1989-; Academic Boosters 1990-; Pres Awd Excl Math & Sci Tchng Nom 1991, 1992,1995; Crystal Apple Nom 1993/94 1995/96; Breakfast of Champions 1993,1995; Tchr of Yr 1995; Finalist Oh Tchr of Yr 1995; Ashland Oil Golden Apple Awd 1995; *office:* Middletown H S 601 N Breiel Blvd Middletown OH 45042

RADECK, HERMAN JOHN, Calculus Teacher; *b:* St Paul, MN; *m:* Anabeth Hodson; *c:* Rebecca Anne; *ed:* Univ of MN (BS) Natural Sci Ed 1966, (MA) Natural Sci Ed 1969; Attnd Ball St Univ, Univ of UT, MI St Univ, Tel-Aviv Univ, Portland St Univ, Univ of WI; *cr:* White Bear Lake Sunrise Park Jr HS Sci Tchr 1966-68; Johnson Jr HS Sci Tchr 1969-71; Johnson HS Chem Tchr 1971-73; Yokota HS Sci, Math Tchr 1973-; *ai:* Mu Alpha Theta Spon; NEA; Overseas Educ Assn; NCTM.

RADEL, SAMUEL M., Science Teacher; *b:* Toledo, OH; *m:* Marilyn J. Dill; *c:* Tracey, Jody, Samantha; *ed:* The Defiance Coll (BS) Bio 1968; Xavier Univ (MED) Outdoor Recreation 1976; Post Grad Stud Bowling Green SU Marine Bio; *cr:* Mendor-Union HS Sci Tchr 1968-70; New Albany HS Sci Tchr 1970-76; Blanchester HS Occupational Work Adjustment Coord 1973-76; Gibsonburg HS Sci Tchr 1976-80; Oak Harbor HS Sci Tchr 1980-; *ai:* Head Bsktbl Coach 10 Yrs; Head Tennis Coach 2 Yrs; Cross Country Coach 6 Yrs; NEA 1970-; OH Ed Assn 1968-, St Exec Comm; Oak Harbor 1980-, Pres; N Western OH Ed Assn 1976-, Pres, VP, Dist Leadership Awd; Red Cross Trng Instr; Jennings Fellowship Scholar; Natl Sci Fnd Schlsp, Jennings Grants; *office:* Oak Harbor HS 11661 St Rt 163 Oak Harbor OH 43449

RADEN, EVA ROSENBERG, Judaic Studies Teacher; *b:* Budapest, Hungary; *m:* Alex; *c:* Rachel Berg, Dr. Mark, Dr. Robert Zev; *ed:* Boston Hebrew Coll (BA) Ed 1977; Baltimore Hebrew Univ (MA) Hebrew Ed 1985; 30 Credits Post Grad Stud in Hebrew Lit; Recipient of Natl Tchrs License; *cr:* Beth Jacob Rel Schl Tchr 1966-77; Solomon Schechter Day Schl Tchr 1974-77; Beth Israel Rel Schl Tchr 1977-83; Krieger Schechter Day Schl Tchr 1983-; *ai:* Weekly Torah Presentation Adv; Conducts Wkshps for Hebrew Lang Tchrs; Grant Jerusalem Univ Summer Inst; Histagrut Summer Hebrew Lang Wkshp; Pub by Bd of Jewish Ed-Curr of Grd 4; Creative Tchr of Yr Lipset Awd; *office:* Krieger Schechter Day Schl 8100 Stevenson Rd Baltimore MD 21208

RADER, RACHEL M. (OMAN), Mathematics Teacher; *b:* Findlay, OH; *m:* John; *c:* Matthew, Anthony, James; *ed:* Bowling Green St Univ (BS) Math & Elem Ed 1982; Attnd Univ of Findlay; *cr:* Mohawk Local Schl Math Tchr 1984-85; Arlington HS Math & Cmptr Sci Tchr 1986-; *ai:* Tchr of Yr Arlington Schl 1989; *office:* Arlington Local Schl 332 S Main St PO Box 260 Arlington OH 45814

RADLE, WENDY BURRY, High School English Teacher; *b:* PA; *m:* Todd Jeffrey; *c:* Abraham Frederick, Nathanael Paul, Katrina Joy, Tiffany Grace; *ed:* West Chester Univ (BS) Eng 1988; *cr:* Penn Crest HS Sub Eng Tchr 1988-90; Sun Vly HS Sub Eng Tchr 1988-92; West Chester Chrstn Schl 9th-10th Grd Eng Tchr 1993-94; 1st Grd Homeschooling Tchr; *ai:* Speech Coord KCEA competition; PSEA, NEA, NCTE 1988-; *office:* West Chester Christian Schl 1237 Paoli Pike West Chester PA 19380

RADLOFF, JEFFREY EDWARD, Physics & Mathematics Teacher; *b:* Cincinnati, OH; *ed:* Murray St Univ (BS) Math 1990; Attending Ball St Univ Ed in Physics; *cr:* Milford HS Physics, Math Tchr 1991-; *ai:* United Way Drive Bldg Coord; Fac Cncl; HI-Y Yth in Govt Ldr; NEA 1992-; OH Cncl of Tchrs of Math 1992-; Immaculate Heart of Mary Young Adult Group 1990-; Guardian Angels Follies Theatre Prodctn; *office:* Milford HS One Eagles Way Milford OH 45150

RADLOW, STEVEN, Span Tchr & Debate Team Coach; *b:* Brooklyn, NY; *m:* Mona Helane; *ed:* Brooklyn Coll (BA) Span 1969, (MA) Span 1972; Post Grad Courses; *cr:* Marine Park Jr HS 278 Tchr, Dept Coord 1969-; Dist 22 Curr Writer 1987-90; Brooklyn Coll ESL Instr 1993-; *ai:* Fac Adv Yrbk 1972-89, Arista-Archon 1972-88; Debate Team Coach 1989-95; AFT, UFT, NEA 1969-; Columbia & Amer Scholastic Press Assn Awds Yrbk; 1991, 1993, 1994 NYC Championship JHS Debates; Grant Natl Endowment for Hum; Project SALTA Columbia Univ Span Through Authenit Lit & Art; *office:* Marine Park Jr H S 278 1925 Stuart St Brooklyn NY 11229*

RADOCAY, CONNIE MC CLAREN, Math Instructor & Dept Chair; *b:* Pgh, PA; *m:* Marko; *c:* Brandi; *ed:* Slippery Rock St Coll (BSEd) Math, Physics 1962; Univ of AZ (MS) Math 1969; Also Attnd: Univ of Pittsburgh, Duquesne Univ, OH St Univ, Portland St Univ; *cr:* North Allegheny Schls Math, Sci Instr 1962-67; Plum Sr HS Math Instr 1967-; *ai:* K-12 Math Curr Chprn; U of Pgh HS Calculus Chprsn; Ed, Tech Comms; NEA, PSEA 1967-; Plum Ed Assoc 1967-, Local Pres, Negotiation Chprsn; NCTM, PMT, WPTM 1980-; PA Transit; Tribute in Time Awd; Super Cmptr Grand Advy Comm; Hewlett Packard Grant Prgm; Various NSF Grants; *office:* Plum Sr HS 900 Elicker Rd Pittsburgh PA 15239*

RADOSLOVICH, SUSAN MARY, Math & Computer Teacher; *b:* Jersey City, NJ; *ed:* Seton Hall Univ (BS) Math Ed 1976; Lehigh Univ (MS) Educl Tech 1985; 30 Addl Credits; *cr:* Westwood Regnl Jr Sr HS Math, Cmptr Tchr 1976-; *ai:* Cmptr Club Adv; 7th-8th Grd Boys Tennis Coach; NCTM, NEA, NJEA, BCEA 1976-; WEA 1976-, Mbrshp Chprsn; Governor's Tchr Recognition Awd; *office:* Westwood Regnl Jr Sr HS 701 Ridgewood Rd Westwood NJ 07675

RADZA, JOSEPH EDWARD, Science Teacher; *b:* Warren, OH; *c:* Kent St Univ at Trumbull (AA) Gen Stud 1977; Youngstown St Univ (BSED) Hlth Ed, Gen Sci 1980, (MSED) Gifted Ed Specialist 1992; *ed:* Kent St Univ at Trumbull (AA) Gen Stud 1977; Youngstown St Univ (BSED) Hlth Ed, Gen Sci 1980, (MSED) GIfted Ed Specialist; Post Grad Supervisory Courses Youngstown St Univ; Network Mindful Shsl Summer Session IN Univ; Cmptr Tech Trng Ashland Univ; *cr:* Warren Turner Jr Sr HS 7th-8th Grd Life, Earth Sci Tchr 1980-81; Warren City Schls Home Instr All Grd Levels, 9th Grd Sub Tchr, Summer Schl Tchr, Gen Sci Summer Schl Tchr; Girard Prospect Jr HS 7th, 8th Grad Hlth, Life, Earth Tchr 1986-89; Girard Tod Woods MS, Prospect Jr HS 4th-8th Grd Gifted Ed, Sci Tchr 1989-93; Girard Jr, Sr HS 7th, 8th Grd Integrated Sci, Enrichment Tchr 1993-; *ai:* Sci Olympiad, Speech Team Asst Coach; Ldrshp, AIM Resource, Venture Grant Writing, Tech Resource, Sci Curr Dev Team; Phi Kappa Phi 1992-; IN Univ Phi Delta Kappa, Network Mindful Schls 1995-; Giard Ed Assn 1986-; Sci Olympiad Regnl Competition Outstdng Coach Awds 1989- 1 Place, 1990 3rd Pl; Girard City Schls Outstdng Svc Awd 1987; PTSA Cert of Appreciation 1988-89; Nom Ashland Oil Tchr Achvmnt Awd 1989-90; *office:* Girard Jr Sr HS 31 N Ward Ave Girard OH 44420*

RAEHSLER, ROD D., Economics Professor; *b:* St Paul, MN; *m:* Kara D. Campbell; *ed:* Univ of WI at River Falls (BS) Ec, Math 1981; Univ of NE (MA) Ec 1983; Univ of IA (PHD) Ec 1993; *cr:* Clarion Univ Asst Prof of Ec 1991-; *ai:* Alpha Chi Rho, Harrisburg Internship, Omicron Delta Epsilon Adv; Gen Ed Comm; AEA 1990-; APUBEF 1992-, Exec Cncl; PEA 1992-; Habitat for Humanity 1995-, Exec Cncl; Literacy Cncl 1994-; Numerous Articles Pub; *office:* Clarion Univ Of PA 305 Still Hall Clarion PA 16214

RAFAEL, ADELINE FALK, Nursing Professor; *b:* Winnipeg MB, Canada; *c:* Heather Rafael Wise, Paul; *ed:* Univ of Western Ontario (BSCN) Nursing 1989; D'Youville Coll (MSN) Nursing 1993; Completing Dissertation for PHD in Nursing at Univ of CO; *cr:* Adult Occupational Ctr Hlth Svcs Mgr 1979-82; Huronia Regnl Ctr Dir of Nursing 1982-87; Simcoe Cty Hlth Unit Pub Hlth Nurse 1989-92; D'Youville Coll Asst Prof 1992-; *ai:* Fac Adv; NYSNA 1995-; NLN 1993-; Sigma Theta Tau 1988-; Zeta Nu; AAUP 1992-; Univ of CO Grad Fellowshp 1993; Marjorie Stanton Nursing Theory Research Awd 1993; Comm Hlth Nurse Interest Group Fellowship 1990; Mildred I Walker Awd Comm Hlth Nursing 1988; Pub Article ANS 1995; *office:* D'Youville Coll 320 Porter Ave Buffalo NY 14201

RAFETTO, J. SCOTT, Health Teacher; *b:* Chestnut Hill, PA; *m:* Joanne M. Sasse; *c:* Scott, Thomas; *ed:* West Chester Univ (MEQ) Hlth Ed 1985; 20 Post Grad Credits in Hlth, Ed; *cr:* West Chester Univ Grad Asst 1976; Newark Schl Dist Hlth Tchr 1976-77; West Chester Area Schl Dist Hlth Tchr, Ath Trainer 1979-; *ai:* Ath Trainer; Strength Coach; Hlth Ed Dept Chm; NEA 1992-; AFT 1977-; NATA 1976-; PATS 1985-.*

RAFFA, BRENDA KAY ROSE, English Teacher; *b:* Steubenville, OH; *m:* Timothy R.; *c:* Emily Rose, Ashley Robin; *ed:* Kent St Univ (BA) Eng 1982; Franciscan Univ of Steubenville (MS) Ed 1996; Attnd Youngstown St Univ; *cr:* Columbiana Cty Career Ctr Adult Basic Ed Instr 1983-87; The Salem News Reporter 1987-90; Wellsville Schls Eng Tchr 1990-; *ai:* NEA, OH Ed Assn, Wellsville Local Tchrs Assn 1990-; Highlandtown United Meth Church 1973-; Link Grant Youngstown St Univ; *office:* Daw Jr HS 929 Center St Wellsville OH 43968

RAFFA, SANDRA LEE HERMAND, Business Teacher; *b:* East Liverpool, OH; *m:* John Robert; *c:* Timothy, Hope Raffa Goempel; *ed:* Mount Union Coll (BA) Music 1976, (BMED) Music 1979; Comprehensive Bus Ed Cert from St of OH 1991; *cr:* East Liverpool Chrstn Schl Bus & Elem Instrumental Tchr 1978-; *ai:* NHS Adv; NBEA 1993-; Tri-St E Assn 1995-; *home:* 1155 Mick Rd Wellsville OH 43968

RAFFALO, ROBERT GEORGE,SR., Physical Education Teach Hartford, CT; *m:* Judith Kiro; *c:* Robert G. Jr, Kelly M.; *ed:* Linfiel (BS) PE, Hlth 1965; Southern CT St Univ (MS) PE, Recreation 1978 CT St Univ Admin, Supervision 1985; *cr:* Bulkeley HS PE, Hlth Coach 30 Yrs; *ai:* Var Bsbl, Jr Var Bsktbl Coach; Bsbl Club Adv; IM V Lifting Instr; Discipline Comm; PE Curr; AET, HFT, CT HS Coaches 1966-; Ordoer of Elks #2308 1992- House Comm; Pop Warne 1973-75, Head Coach, St Chamionship 1975; Amer Legion 1982-85, Bsbl Coach; Newington Bsbl Assn 1981-89, Fund Raiser Chm; New Little League 1973-78, Asst Coach; Intnl Bsbl Trip 1991; *home* Church St Newington CT 06111*

RAFFELT, TONI BROWN, First Grade Teacher; *b:* Keene, N Thomas Michael; *c:* Thomas Philip, Sarah Elizabeth; *ed:* Keene S (BS) Elem & Spec Ed 1982; *cr:* Winchester Elem Schl Spec Ed Res Room K-3 1983-84, 1st Grd Tchr 1984-85; Mt Caesar Schl 1st & 2n Tchr 1985-; *ai:* NEA 1985-; *office:* Mt Caesar Schl 585 Old Home Hwy East Swanzey NH 03446

RAFFERTY, GREGORY FRANCIS, Physical Education Teach Kingston, NY; *m:* Kathleen B.; *c:* Brendan, Katie, Colin; *ed:* SUI Cortland (BSE) PE 1981; Mount St Mary Coll (MSE) Spec Ed 198 Rhinebeck Cty Schl PE Tchr 1981-84; Guteova Cntrl Schl Elem PE 1984-88; Red Hook Cntrl Schl Elem PE Tchr 1988-; *ai:* Boys, Girls Cntry, Girls Modified Bsktbl Coach; Red Hook Soccer Club 1995 Mem; Parent Advy Bd Parsons Intnl Adoption 1988-91; *office:* Red Cntrl Schl Dist Mill Rd Red Hook NY 12571

RAFFERTY, JAMES JOSEPH, Sociology & History Teache Camden, NJ; *m:* Joan Ferrari; *c:* Theresa, Jimmy; *ed:* Glassboro St Soc Sci 1971; 28 Post-Grad Credits Rowan Coll, Rutgers Univ, Univ o Hartford Univ; *cr:* Delsea Tchr 1971-; *ai:* Asst Var Ftbl, Girls Trac Yrs Coaching; NEA, NJEA 1971-, Pres DEA; NCSS 1971-; Knigh Columbus 1970-; Councilman Boro of Oaklyn 1992-; Tchr of Yr; G St Distinguish Tchr Trenton St Coll; *home:* 79 Kendall Blvd Oakly 08107*

RAFFERTY, JOSEPH G., American & World History Tchr; *b:* Ca City, NJ; *m:* Barbara Doyle; *c:* Joseph, Michael, Patrick; *ed:* Ruger's Cook Coll (BA) Sociology 1983; Criminal Justice Cert; St of NJ T Cert; *cr:* Canden Cty Sheriff Dept Correction Ofcr 1983-; Gloucester HS His Amer World Tchr 1983-89; Cloucester City HS His Amer W Tchr 1989-; *ai:* Asst Ftbl, Track Coach; NEA; Gloucester City Councilman; Gloucester City Charter Stud, Asst Chm; Muddle Ldr; Fl Chrstn Aths; Grant Writer, Coord; *office:* Gloucester City HS 13 Market St Gloucester City NJ 08030*

RAGAN, WALLACE BENNETT, Chair of Classics; *b:* Denver, CO Denver Bapt Coll (BA) Biblical Lang 1974; Univ of CO at Boulder Classics & His 1979, (MA) Classics 1981; Semitic Langs Trinity Div Schl; Amer Schl of Classical Stud Athens Summer Session; *cr:* St Al Schl Hurlburt Chair of Classics 1983-; Georgetown Univ Schl Continuing Ed Fac 1986-; *ai:* Pres Cum Laude Chptr; Fac Spon Clas Soc; Wash Classical Soc 1985-, Pres 1992-95; Amer Classical Le 1984-; Amer Philological Assn 1983-; NEH Tchr, Scholar Awd 19 Rockefeller Flwshp 1992; Fulbright Flwshp 1987, 1989; Co-Dir Sem in Rome; Consultant Natl Latin Exam; AP Latin Exam Reader; *offic* Albans Schl Mount St Alban Washington DC 20016*

RAGANO, WILLIAM JOHN, History Teacher; *b:* Providence, RI Linda Jean O'Brien; *c:* Keith, Ryan, Christopher; *ed:* RI Jr Coll (ASD) Mngmt 1971; Providence Coll (BA) His, Ed 1991; Enrolled Coll Ma His Prgm; *cr:* Retail Mngmt Store Mgr 1968-88; N Prov HS His 1991-; *ai:* Career Life Skills, Work Stu Tchr; AFT 1991-; VFW 196 PEAST LL 1995-, Pres.

RAGER, AMY JORDAN, Business Teacher; *b:* Camp Hill, PA; *m:* F.; *ed:* York Coll of PA (BS) Sec Ed-Bus 1991; *cr:* Cmptr Lear Network Instr 1991-93; Lancaster Cty AVTS Bus Data Processing 1994; Penn Manor HS Bus Tchr 1994-; *ai:* Frosh Chrldng Coach; Clas 1999 Fac Adv; NEA, PMEA 1995-; NBEA, PBEA, EBEA 1990-; *of* Penn Manor HS PO Box 1001 Millersville PA 17551*

RAGIN, JEAN BUSH, Math & Sci Curr Coordinator; *b:* Philadephia, *m:* Robert L.; *c:* Rasheed Jamal; *ed:* Cheyney Univ (BS) Scndry M 1971; Morgan St Univ (MS) Scndry Math 1976; Addl 30 Credit Hrs; Patterson HS Math Tchr 1971-94; Gilman Schl Upward Bound Prgm M Coord 1972-92; Baltimore Ctr for Tchng, Learning Math Site Co Thinking Math Project 1991; UMCP Tchr Collaborative Math, Sci T 1993; Morgan St Univ MESA Coord 1994; Highland Town MS Math D Schl 1994-; *ai:* MESA Math, Engineering, Sci Achvmt Coord; S Improvement Team, Staff Dev; AFT, MCTM, NCTM 1971-; Benja Banneker Assn 1993-; NAACP 1988-; Phi Delta Kappa 1993-; SEMPI 1992-, Brd Mem; Kurt L. Schmoke MD. St Tchr of Yr 1993-, Advy Bltmr Urban Sytmc Iniatire; Advy Bd; Educl Consultant Houghton Mi Book Co; Baltimore Tchrs Union Outstanding Math Tchr 1990; Think Math Project MI St Univ 1991-93; *office:* Highland Town MS 10 Ellwood Ave Baltimore MD 21224

RAGNONI, PATRICK P., Music Chairman; *b:* Brooklyn, NY; *ed:* Rutg Univ (BA) Music Ed 1982; Jersey City St Coll (MA) Supervision, Prin C 1991; Southwestern Univ Law Schl 1983; Webster Univ Music; *cr:* Kea HS Asst Band Dir, Band Dir 1982-92, Music Chm 1992-; *ai:* Acad E Sr Play; Musical; Flute Ensemble; Competitive Marching Band; ME 1994-; NEA, NJEA 1982-; Bergen Co Cadets Alumni 1978-; Town Pa Writer; *office:* Kearny HS 336 Devon St Kearny NJ 07032*

RAGONE, PAUL, PE & Health Teacher; *b:* Vineland, NJ; *m:* Kathl Fannoly; *c:* Jenifer, P. J.; *ed:* Glassboro St Coll (BA) PE 1976; *cr:* M HS PE, Hlth Tchr 1976-94; Vineland HS N PE, Hlth Tchr 1994-; *ai:* B Var Bsktbl Head Coach; VEA, NJEA 1976-; *office:* Vineland HS N 301 Chestnut Ave Vineland NJ 08360

RAGONESE, JAMES A., English Teacher; *b:* West Milford, NJ; *m:* La Melinda Ward; *c:* Cody James, Kaelyn Alleyne; *ed:* East Stroudsburg U (BS) Scndry Eng Ed 1989, (MS) Educl Ed 1996; *cr:* Pocono Mountain S Dist Eng Tchr 1989-; *ai:* Frosh Ftbl Coach 1989-; Weightlifting In 1989-93; Ath Publication Club 1995-; Discipline Comm 1995-; NE PSEA 1989-; *office:* Pocono Mountain Schl Dist PO Box 200 Swiftwa PA 18370

RAGOSTA, STEPHEN W., Horticulture Teacher; *b:* Cranston, RI; Sallyann; *c:* Scott; *ed:* Univ of RI (BS) Horticulture 1974; PA St U (MED) Ag 1978; *cr:* Lehigh Cty Vo-Tech Schl Horticulture, Floral Desi Greenhouse Mngmt, Landscaping Tchr 1974-; *ai:* FFA Adv; Ftbl Coa Prof Dept Comm; Grading Comm; Tchr Mentor; PA St Educl Assn 197 Lehigh Valley Florist Assn 1974-; PA Horticultural Assn 1995-; Lit League Bsbl 1991-; *office:* Lehigh County Vo Tech Schl 4500 Educati Park Dr Schnecksville PA 18078*

RAGWAR, JOANNE DIDONATO, Guidance Counselor; *b:* Lowell, M *m:* James O.; *c:* Akinyi, Aloo, Akello; *ed:* North Adams St (BA) Psy 1976; Fitchburg St Coll (MED) Cnslng 1978, (CAGS) Career, Occ 1980; North Essex Comm Coll (AA) Registered Nursing 1986; Teuksbury HS Career Cnslr 1978-80; Greater Lowell Regnl Voc-Tech Sc Guid Cnslr 1980-; *ai:* Pregnancy & Parenting, Portuguese, African Am rt Group; NEA, MTA, GLRTO 1980-; *office:* Greater Lowell ch Schl Pawtucket Blvd Tyngsboro MA 01879*

IM, CATHERINE LEGER, World & US History Tchr; *b:* Gardner, : David; *c:* Elizabeth, Michelle; *ed:* Fitchburg St Coll (BS) 1971, Ed 1977; Addl 12 Credit Hrs; Several Prof Dev Hrs Higgins Armory m, Prof Dev Inst, Fitchburg St Coll; *cr:* Gardner HS His Tchr 10 Yrs; chusett Comm Coll Part-time Eng Tchr 7 Yrs; Garnder HS Eng, His 0 Yrs; Thomas Passies Elem Schl Rdng Tchr 1 Yr; *ai:* Stu Tchrs rating Tchr; Acccreditaion Comm; NEA, MA Tchrs Assn, Gardner sn 1971-; Gardner Museum 1995-; *office:* Gardner HS 200 Catherine dner MA 01440

MAN, CHERYL BRINSON, ESL Teacher; *b:* New York, NY; *m:* la Noor; *c:* Karriem Rahaman-Bunce, Abdullah Noor II; *ed:* SUNY v Paltz (BA) Scndry Eng Ed 1969, (MS) Spec Ed 1984; N-6, 7-12 SL, Multi-Cultural Ed, Conflict Resolution Certs; *cr:* Hudson Vly unities Industrialization Ctr Ed Coord 1970-73; West Park Union chl Dist Spec Ed Tchr 1973-90; Ellenville Cntrl Schl Dist ESL Tchr . *ai:* Multicultural Club Sr Adv; Stu Peer Mediation Prgm Fac; n to Hispanic Yth Ldrshp Inst; NYSUT 1973-; Ellenville Tchrs Assn , Ellenville Chptr NAACP 1990-; Ulster Sullivan Mediation Svcs , Bd Mem; 101 Black Women on the Move 1996-, Bd Mem, en's Network Chprsn; NAACP Ed, YWCA Ethnic Pride Awds; NY St Bds, Multiple Panels on Racism Presenter; *office:* Ellenville HS 28 Ave Ellenville NY 12428*

AUSER, TOM EDWIN, Spanish Teacher; *b:* Chambersburg, PA; *m:* ; *c:* Eric, Tim, Laura; *ed:* Franklin & Marshall (BA) Span 1978; Penn A) Span Lit 1987; *cr:* Mercersburg Acad Span, Eng Instr, Soccer, Coach 1978-; *ai:* Lang Dept Head; NSCAA; PSCA; Johnston Chair; Mercersburg Acad 300 E Seminary St Mercersburg PA 17236

NFELD, VINCENT D., Instrumental Music Director; *b:* Chicago, IL; ny Lynn Bien; *c:* Michelle Lee, Kimberly Ann; *ed:* Univ of CT Coll rvatory of Music (BA) Music Ed 1980; Xavier Univ (MED) Cnslng Attnd Univ of CT, Drake Univ Addl Post Grad Hrs; *cr:* Milford HS Dir 1980-82; New Richmond HS Band Dir, Music Tchr 1982-89; nore HS Instrumental Music Dir, Guitar Instr, Music Tchr 1989-; *ai:* Ensembles, Guitar Ensemble Dir; Asst Marching Band Dir; honic Band Dir; MENC, OH Music Edctrs Assn 1980-; Natl Assn room Guitar Tchrs 1993-; Sycamore Ed Assn 1989-; CCM Alumni Bd ovenors 1991-93; MENC Nationally Cert Music Edctrs; Pub in als; Guitar Ensemble Performed St, Natl Confs; *office:* Sycamore HS Cornell Rd Cincinnati OH 45242*

CH, MICHAEL J., Sci Dept Chairperson & Teacher; *b:* Johnstown, *n:* Judith A. Garman; *c:* Monica, Georgiana, Matthew; *ed:* Clarion of PA (BS) Geog 1963; IN Univ of PA (MED) Geog 1969; Attnd ord Inst, St Francis Coll for Bus, Univ Pittsburgh for Cmptr Literacy; ochran Jr HS His, Geog Tchr 1963-80; Johnstown Cntrl HS US His, Sci Tchr 1984; Garfield Jr HS Geog, Sci Tchr 1980-; *ai:* Sci Chprsn; er Johnstown Ed Assn, PSEA, NEA 1963-; *office:* Johnstown MS 280 er Ave Johnstown PA 15906

F, SHERYL JABLONSKI, English Teacher; *b:* Buffalo, NY; *c:* n N.; *ed:* D'Youville Coll (BA) Eng 1978; St Bonaventure Univ (MS) Ed 1989; *cr:* Arkport Cntrl Schl Eng Tchr 1979-80; St Andrew Cntry Schl Soc Stud, Rdng Tchr 1980-81; Friendship Cntrl Schl Eng Tchr -; *ai:* Child Study Team; Impact Team; Grading, Stu Discipline ns; NYSUT, AFT 1983-; BSA 1994-; Lighted Schoolhouse Prgm -; *office:* Friendship Central Schl 46 W Main St Friendship NY 14739

NE, JUDITH BOWEN, 6th-12th Grade English Tchr; *b:* Wilmington, *n:* Ronald W.; *c:* Nancy Raine Reddig, Amy Raine Betcher, Ronald F.; Rowan Coll (BA) Elem Ed 1961; *cr:* Pennsville Pub Schls 4th & 6th Tchr 1961-65; Ranch Hope for Boys Rdng Tchr 1970-75; Bethel Bible Supvr 1975-78; Park Bible Acad 6th-12th Grd Eng, Algebra I & Fr & Guidance Cnslr 1979-; *ai:* Schl Newspaper, Radio Talk Show, na Club, Amer Chrstn Honor Soc & Sr Class Adv; Child Evangelism owship 1980-, Sec; Park Bible Church 1979-, Choir, Treas, Sunday Tchr 1980-, Adult Ladies Tchr; *office:* Park Bible Acad 104 Sparks Pennsville NJ 08070*

NEAR, DOUGLAS MICHAEL, Business Education Dept Chair; *b:* geton, NJ; *m:* Fina Sorbello; *c:* Scot, Brad, Kim Angelo; *ed:* Western Univ (BS) Bus Admin, Mrktg-Magna Cum Laude 1971; Glassboro St Ed, Soc Stud; Jersey City St Career Ed, Bus Ed; Attnd Rutgers Univ; Bridgeton HS Bus Ed, Soc Stud, Mrktg Ed Tchr, Cooperative Ed, Mrktg Coord, Bus Ed Dept Chm; *ai:* Upper Deerfield Twp Mayor; 2 Term mitteeman; Utilities Authority Commissioner; NJ League of icipalities; Voice of the Bulldogs 1072-; NEA, NJEA 1971-; berland Cty Cncl Educl Assn 1971-, Exec Comm; BEA 1971-, VP, : Comm Rep, Svc Awd; NJ Realtors Assn; Human Svcs Advy Cncl 3-, Exec Comm; Cty Democratic Assn Exec Comm; Planning Bd Class ayor; Local Assistance Bd; Dev Corp; Voice of Democracy Coord; Hnr Selection Comm; Ath Bus Mgr; Schl Banker; *office:* Bridgeton HS 111 Vest Ave Bridgeton NJ 08302

NES, PAUL R.,JR., Self Employed Agri-Business; *b:* Batavia, NY; *m:* hele S.; *c:* Summer, Kaitlin, Jillian; *ed:* Brockport St Coll (BS) His, Sci 1974, (MA) Amer His 1989; K-6, K-12 Soc Stud Perm Cert 1990; St Vincent's Schl 6th Grd Tchr 1977-78; Blessed Sacrament Jr HS 8th Grd Tchr 1978-90; P&D Equip Sales Self-Employed Sales, Svc 0-; *ai:* Blessed Sacrament Jr HS Former Stu Cncl Adv, IMS Supvr, Asst ; Phi Alpha Theta 1988-; *home:* 2344 Westside Dr Rochester NY 14624

NEY, ANN MARIE KANE, Music Tchr & Choral Director; *b:* anton, PA; *m:* Thomas P.; *c:* Ryan Patrick; *ed:* Marywood Coll (BM) sic Ed 1983; Attnd West Chester Coll; Lafayette Coll; *cr:* Dunmore Schl Elem Music Tchr & HS Choral Dir 1983-; *ai:* HS Choral, Show Choir Musical Theater Vocal Dir; PA Music Edctrs Assn 1983-; AFT 1983-; 1983-; *office:* Dunmore HS 300 W Warren St Scranton PA 18512

NFORD, EVANGELINA THOMPSON, High School Spanish cher; *b:* Panama City ; *c:* Sean, Dominic; *ed:* Univ of West Indies (BA) n-Hnrs 1985; Brooklyn Coll Working on MS; Attnd Fordham Univ, St n's Univ, Univ of Panama; *cr:* PS 219 6th Grd Tchr 1985; Beach annel HS Span Tchr 1987; Jr HS 231 Span Tchr 1991; Hillcrest HS ing Bio, Earth Sci, Span Tchr 1992-; *ai:* AFT 1985-; ASPIRA 1987-, ord; *office:* Hillcrest HS PO Box 541 Aveane NY 11692

INONE, ROBERT PAUL, 7th & 8th Grade Science Tchr; *b:* Jersey y, NJ; *m:* Frances Senatore-Rainone; *c:* Robert Jr., Meredith, Anthony; Jersey City St Coll (BA) Scndry Sci 1968; Elem Cert 1993; *cr:* Anna Klein Schl Sci Tchr 1968-; *ai:* Audio-Visual Dir; Track Team Coach; ttenberg Ed Assn 1968-, Pres; NJ Ed Assn 1968; NEA 1968-; Cliffside k Bsbl Assn 1992-; Cliffside Park Recreation 1992-; Hudson Cty Coord Annual Cty Sci Fair.

INS, DALE RUSSELL, Math Teacher & Dept Chprsn; *b:* Baltimore,); *ed:* Hood Coll (AB) Math 1959; JHU (MED) Math 1980; *cr:* ltimore Cty Math Tchr 1959-67, 1977-78; Anne Arundel Co Math Tchr 78-; *ai:* Math Club Spon; Math Team Coach; MD Assessment nsortium 1992-; MCTM 1987-; MSTA, TAAAC, NEA 1978-; Schl Math ld Group, Writing Team Geometry with Coordinates 1962; *office:* undel HS 1001 Annapolis Rd Gambrills MD 21054

RAINVILLE, KATHLEEN V., Latin & French Teacher; *b:* New York, NY; *m:* Gerard; *c:* Thomas Harmon, Robert Harmon; *ed:* Marywood Coll (BA) Latin 1962; Coll of Notre Dame (MA) Classical Stud 1996; Attnd Laval Univ, Sorbonne, Oxford Univ, St John's Univ, Hofstra Univ, Univ of MD; *cr:* Bay Shore HS Latin, Fr Tchr 1962-66; Bowie HS Latin, Fr Tchr 1972-; *ai:* Frgn Lang Dept Chair; Latin, Fr Hon Socs Spon; WA Classical Assn; GWATFL; Natl Inst for Hum Latin Inst Grant at Coll of Notre Dame; *office:* Bowie HS 15200 Annapolis Rd Bowie MD 20715

RAISER, CHRISTINE RICHER, English Teacher; *b:* Bellefonte, PA; *m:* Michael N.; *c:* Cynthia R., Mark N.; *ed:* PA St Univ (BS) Eng 1963; Attnd William Paterson Coll; *cr:* Phoenixville HS 10-12 Grd Eng Tchr 1963-65; Passaic Vly HS 10-12 Grd Eng Tchr 1965-68; George Washington Jr HS 7-8 Grd Eng Tchr 1982-; *ai:* Site Cncl; WEA, NJEA, NEA, NCTE 1983-.

RAJAN, INDIRA, Biology Teacher; *b:* India; *m:* Raj; *c:* Danny, Ravi; *ed:* Osmania Univ of India (BS) Bio, Chem, Phy 1962, (BEd) Sci Ed 1964; (MEd) 1995; *cr:* Ministry of Ed Ethiopia Tchr 1966-75; Schl Dist of Philadelphia Tchr 1975-; *ai:* Horticultural Club Spon; AFT 1975-; NABT 1980-; NIH Summer Fellow 1990 at Univ of PA; *office:* Philadelphia HS For Girls Broad & Olney Ave Philadelphia PA 19141

RAJCZEWSKI, STAN CHARLES,JR., HS English Teacher; *b:* Yonkers, NY; *m:* Eileen I. Broat; *c:* Meghan; *ed:* Univ of CT (BS) Mrktg 1970; Fairfield Univ (MA) Eng 1977; *cr:* Mt Vernon HS Eng Tchr 1972-; *home:* 21 Bennetts Bridge Rd Sandy Hook CT 06482

RAJSWASSER, BRUCE FARREL, Teacher & FBLA Advisor; *b:* New York City, NY; *m:* Anne Flaherty-Rajswasser; *ed:* Coll of Staten Island (AAS) Bio 1980; Sullivan CC (AAS) Food Svc Mngmt 1981; Coll of Staten Island (BS) Bus Mngmt, Fin 1989; Baruch Coll (MS) Bus Ed 1995; Attnd Champagne & Sherry Inst, Amer Bartending Schl, Natl Food Svc Inst, Cmptr Literacy Prgms; *cr:* NY Food Hotel Mngmt Schl Instr 1 Yr; Kings Borough CC Adj Instr 4 Yrs; Ft Hamilton HS Tchr 7 Yrs; *ai:* FBLA, Yrbk Adv; Cmptr Tech; Print Shop Coord; AFT 1989-; BET 1990-; Knights of Pythians 1972-, Pres; Long Island Brooklyn Tchr of Yr 1994; Coll of Staten Island Alumni Asso Hall of Fame; Tandy Cmptr Sci Tchr 1993; *office:* Fort Hamilton H S 8301 Shore Rd Brooklyn NY 11209*

RAK, FRANCES BONARRIGO, Social Studies Teacher; *b:* Perth Amboy, NJ; *m:* J. Lawrence; *c:* John L. Jr.; *ed:* Kean Coll (BA) Soc Stud 1964; 6 Credits Rutgers St Univ; 6 Credits Univ of MD at Baltimore; 24 Credits Mercer Cty Comm Coll; *cr:* Perth Amboy HS Tchr 1964-65; North Hartford HS Tchr, Title I Grant 1966; Elkton HS Tchr 1966-67; John Adams Jr HS Tchr 1967-73; J. P. Stevens HS Tchr 1976-84; Edison HS Tchr 1984-; *ai:* 1998 Class Adv; NEA, MCTA, ETEA, Tchr of SS 1967-; Beta Sigma Phi 1969-, Pres, VP, Sec, Extension Ofcr, Woman of Yr 1982; Outstdng Yng Woman of Amer; *office:* Edison HS Boulevard Of The Eagles Edison NJ 08817*

RAK, ROBERT STANLEY, World Cultures, Sociology Tchr; *b:* Pittsburgh, PA; *m:* Jane Kidd; *c:* Jennifer; *ed:* Geneva Coll (BA) Soc Stud 1970; Penn St 24 Credit Hrs Soc Stud 1976; *cr:* Head Boys Var Bsktbl Coach 15 Yrs; Asst Boys Var Bsktbl Coach, Western Civ, Adv, Gen World Cultures 11 Yrs; *ai:* Future Tchrs of Amer Spon; HS Disciplinary Comm; NEA, PSEA, RBCEA 1970-; Bsktbl Boys Coaches Assn 1970-, Coach of Yr 1980-81, 1983-84, 1978-79; Most Outstdng Tchr Awd 1980-81, 1983-84; *office:* Riverside HS Rd 2 Courtney Club Dr Ellwood City PA 16117*

RAKATANSKY, LYNN, Mathematics Teacher; *b:* Providence, RI; *ed:* Brown Univ (BA) Math, Eng 1976; Middlebury Coll Bread Loaf Schl of Eng (MA) Eng 1980; *cr:* East Providence HS Math Tchr 1976-81; Cntrl Jr HS Math Tchr 1977-78; Riverside Jr HS Math Tchr 1981-; *ai:* NEA, NEARI, EPEA, NCTM, ATMNE, RIMTA, MCTM 1976-; EPJHS Tchr of Mnth 1992; Presenter, Del First US, Russia Math Edctrs Conf Moscow 1993; RI St Level Presidential Awd Excl Math Tchng 1994; Presenter Math Conf Ontario 1995; Del Initative For Ed, Sci, Tech South Africa 1995.*

RAKER, JILL O'HARA, Teacher of Gifted & Talented; *b:* Wilkes-Barre, PA; *c:* Tim; *ed:* West Chester (BS) Elem Ed 1972; Post Grad Stud Rowan Coll, St Peter's Coll; *cr:* West Bradford Elem Schl Sixth Grd Tchr 1972-73; Philip Baker Schl Fourth Grd Tchr 1973-79; Crest Meml Schl 4-8 Grd GATE Tchr 1983-92, Grd 4-6 GATE Tchr, 7-8 Grd Lit Tchr 1992-; *ai:* Creative Writing Magazine, Stock Market Game Team Adv; Schl Play Dir; Knowledge Bowl Team Coach; NEA, NJEA 1973-; NJEGT 1991-; AAUW 1984-; BSA 1986-; Soccer Booster Club 1994-; *office:* Crest Memorial Schl 9100 Pacific Ave Wildwood NJ 08260

RAKOS, GINA MARIA, 9th Grade Biology Teacher; *b:* Fountain Hill, PA; *m:* Michael S.; *ed:* Kutztown Univ (BS) Scndry Ed 1990; 24 Master Credit Hrs at LeHigh Univ; *cr:* Nazareth HS Bio Tchr 1990-; *ai:* Comm Svc Coord; Peer Mediation; NEA 1990-: NSTA 1990-; PS EA 1990-,VP of Local; Nazareth Area Citizens Advy Bd 1992-94, By-Laws Comm; Learn & Serve Amer Grant; Guest Lecturer; Article Pub; *office:* Nazareth HS E Center St Nazareth PA 18064

RAKOW, SUSAN BOSNICK, Language Arts Teacher; *b:* Flushing, NY; *m:* Larry; *c:* Joshua, Rebecca; *ed:* St Univ of NY at Buffalo (BA) Eng 1970; Cleveland St Univ (MEd) Curr, Instruction, Rdng 1979; Kent St Univ (PHD) Curr, Instruction, Gifted, MS Ed 1994; *cr:* Roxboro Jr HS 7th-9th Grd Eng Tchr 1971-74; Cleveland St Univ Visiting Instr 1979-81; Schl on Magnolia Eng Tchr 1982-83; Beachwood MS Tchr of Gifted, Lang Arts 1983-; Kent St Univ Part-time Adj Prof 1994-; *ai:* Mentor Tchr; Knowledge Master Open, Power of Pen Coach; Women on Wednesdays Adv; Prof Dev Comm; AFT; NCTE; NAGC; ASCD; PDK; NMSA; Reaching Heights, Grant Reviewer; Numerous Articles Pub; Geraldine R. Dodge Fnd Grant; NCTE Your Rdng Reviewer; Dev Kent St Univ Startsmart Beginning Tchrs Course; *office:* Beachwood MS 2860 Richmond Rd Beachwood OH 44122*

RAKOWSKI, JOAN LEVANDOWSKI, 6th & 8th Grade Teacher; *b:* Pittston, PA; *m:* Michael J.; *c:* Michael, Maria; *ed:* Wilkes Univ (BA) Elem Ed, Span 1972, (BA) Fr 1974; Univ of Salamanca Span Grad Courses 1976; Master Equivalency Elem Ed, Span 1995; Staff Dev; Cmptr Courses; Co-operative Learning; *cr:* Sullivan Cty HS Span, Fr Tchr 1972-82; Holy Child 8th Grd Tchr 1988-93; Penn St Summer Prgm Span Tchr 1990-94; Dallas Schl Dist 6th-8th Grd 1993-; *ai:* Detention Monitor; Stu Cncl, Chrldr, Dramatics Club, Lang Club Moderator; PSEA, NEA 1993-; Kids Around Town; *home:* RR 2 Box 260 Hunlock Creek PA 18621*

RAKOWSKY, ADEMAR, Physics Teacher; *b:* Philadelphia, PA; *ed:* La Salle Coll (BA) Geology 1984, (BA) Physics 1984; McGill Univ (MSC) Meteorology 1987; *cr:* La Salle Univ Lecturer of Geology 1986-89; Cardinal Dougherty HS Math Tchr 1989-90; Holy Ghost Preparatory Schl Physics Tchr 1990-; *ai:* Intramural Weight Trng; Pro-Life Club; Astronomy Club; Comm Svc Corps; Stu Assistance Prgm; NSTA 1995-; Assorted Astronomy, Advanced Placement & Physics Tchrs Wkshps; *office:* Holy Ghost Prep Schl 2429 Bristol Pike Bensalem PA 19020

RALEY, JAMES M., Technology Teacher; *b:* Cumberland, MD; *m:* Susan C. Rush; *c:* Sharee, Ainsley; *ed:* CA Univ of PA (BS) Tech Ed 1980; Frostburg St Univ (MA) Admin, Supervision 1984; *cr:* Southern MS Tchr 1980-94; Oldtown, Flintstone Schl Tchr Tchr 1994-; *ai:* MD St Tchrs Assn 1980-, Bd of Dirs; Allegany Cty Tchrs Assn 1994-, VP; NEA 1980-, Del to R. A.; Eastern Garrett Fire Dept 1977-, Chief; Eatern Garrett Park & Rec 1993-, Pres; MD St Firemen's Assn 1990-, Legislative Comm; Garrett Cty Vol Fire & Rescue Assn 1977-, Pres 1996; *home:* 39 Tower Rd Frostburg MD 21532

RALLS, NANCY KAVCAR, Voc Family & Consumer Sci Tchr; *b:* Lakewood, OH; *m:* Craig A.; *c:* Carolyn, Edward, Matthew; *ed:* Kent St Univ (BS) Voc Home Ecs 1976; Attnd Cleveland St, Ashland Univ, Akron Univ, OH St Univ; *cr:* Brooklyn City Schls Voc Home Ec Tchr 1989; Cleveland City Schls Work, Family Coord 1990; Lakewood City Schls Voc Family, Consumer Scis Tchr 1990-; Akron Univ Wkshp Instr 1994-95; *ai:* FHA Club; Group Ldr of Family, Consumer Sci Dept 1993-; LTA, NEOEA, NEA 1990-; PTA 1983-; Sports Booster 1994-; Tchr of Yr 1993; Amer Red Cross Water Safety Instr 1971-; Tchr Ldrshp Inst 3 Yr Commitment for Family, Consumer Sci Statewide; *office:* Lakewood HS 14100 Franklin Blvd Lakewood OH 44107*

RAM, RUSSELL JAMES, Art Teacher; *b:* Buffalo, NY; *ed:* St Univ of NY at Buffalo Painting-Cum Laude 1970; St Univ Coll at Buffalo (MS) Art Ed-Cum Laude 1974; *cr:* Sweet Home Cntrl Schl Art Tchr 1971-; *ai:* NY St Art Tchrs Assn 1990-; Buffalo Soc of Artists 1971-, Pres 1978 & 1985, Bronze Medal 1974 & 1991, Gold Medal 1991; N Coast Collage Soc 1989-; Niagara Frontier Watercolor Soc 1980-; *office:* Sweet Home HS 1901 Sweet Home Rd Amherst NY 14228

RAM, SHUNILA NAOMI, Kindergarten Teacher; *b:* Varanasi Up, India; *m:* Denis; *c:* Namrata Andreissens, Sujata, Kavita; *ed:* Isabella Thoburn Coll (BA) Arts, Geography 1958; Slippery Rock Coll (BSc) Ed 1979; Slippery Rock St Univ (MSc) Elem Ed 1986; 10 Credit Hrs Cmptr Lit; *cr:* Girls HS India Scndry Schl Geography Tchr 1958-61; Jefferson Elem Schl Kndgtn Tchr 1979-; *ai:* Youth Club, Drama Dir; Adult Ed Church Comm Mem; Hand Bells & Chimes Choir Ages 6-12 Dir; NEA 1979-; YWCA 1986-, Bd Mem; League of Women Voters 1990-, Bd Mem; Asian Womens Inst 1981-, Pres; Amer Heart Assn 1990-, Mem; *office:* Jefferson Elem Schl 650 Saxonburg Rd Butler PA 16001*

RAMARGE, MAHLON L., HS Math Teacher & Dept Chair; *b:* Emporium, PA; *m:* Ann Murray; *c:* Kathleen Ramarge Morien, Michael, Kristine Ramarge Ring, Karen Ramarge Orcut, Matthew, Kimberly; *ed:* St Bonaventure U (BS) Math 1962; U of Notre Dame (MS) Math 1968; John Carrol U Physics; U of Buffalo Math; Prgm Systems Inst Cmptrs; St Bonaventure U; *cr:* Olean HS Adult Ed Math Tchr 1964-68, Summer Schl Math Tchr 1974-83; Jamestown Comm Coll Math Instr 1981-90; Hinsdale Cntrl Schl Math Tchr 1962-; *ai:* Bsktbl, Sftbl Coaches; NEA 1962-, St Del RA 1985-95; NEA NY 1962-, Bd of Dir Region; Hinsdale United Tchrs 1962-, Chief Negotiator, St Del, Grievance Comm; Catt Co Classroom Tchrs Org Pres; AMTNYS 1962-; NSF Grant.*

RAMEY, ANN L. (POSEY), 8th Grd American History Tchr; *b:* Chillicothe, OH; *m:* Richard; *ed:* Morehead St Univ (BA) Eng, His 1971; Coll of Mt St Joseph (MS) Rdng 1988; Ashland Univ 13 Hrs; *cr:* Westfall MS Tchr 1971-; *ai:* 7th-8th Grd Ldr Grd Trips to Washington DC, Williamsburg VA; NEA 1978-; OEA 1971-; Westfall Ed 1971-, Pres, Treas, Negotiator; Amer Stu Travel 1992- Advy Bd Mem; Delta Kappa Gamma 1984-, VP; *office:* Westfall MS 19545 Pherson Pike Williamsport OH 43164*

RAMEY, KYLE BRUCE, Science Teacher; *b:* Lancaster, OH; *m:* Phyllis G. Shultz; *c:* Rachel; *ed:* Otterbein Coll (BA) Life Sci 1989; Univ of Dayton (MS) Educl Admin 1993; 40 Addl Post MA Work in Admin; Supvrs Cert; Prin Cert; Stu Assistance Trng; *cr:* Graham HS Sci Tchr 1989-92; Kettering Fairmont HS Sci Tchr 1992-; *ai:* Bsbl, Boys, Girls Golf Head Coach; Chm North Cntrl Comm; Fac Advy, Textbook, Rules, Fairmont 100 Rules Comms, Frosh Class Adv; MVBCA 1989-, VP; NEA, ABCA 1989-; Future Administrators, KEA 1992-; Miami Vly All-Star Head Coach; Oak Leaf Cluster Awd; *office:* Kettering Fairmont HS 3301 Shroyer Rd Kettering OH 45429

RAMIN, TAGHI, Economics Professor; *b:* Tehran, Iran; *m:* Farzaneh H.; *c:* Farzad, Mahrad; *ed:* Natl Univ (BS) Ec 1967; Long Island Univ (MA) Ec 1977; NY Univ (PHD) Ec 1986; *cr:* William Paterson Coll Asst Prof 1984-95, Assoc Prof 1995-; *ai:* Omicron Delta Epsilon Adv; Intnl Hnr Soc in Ec; Atlantic Ec Soc 1994-; Articles Pub; *office:* William Paterson Coll 300 Pompton Rd Wayne NJ 07470*

RAMIREZ, GLORIA J. (FINKENBINDER), Third Grade Instructor; *b:* Carlisle, PA; *c:* Todd Finkenbinder; *ed:* Elizabethtown Coll (BA) Elem Ed 1968; Shippensburg Univ (MS) Elem Ed; Wilkes Coll 3 Credits Cooperative Learning; *cr:* Shaull Elem Schl 3rd Grd Instr 1968-72; Monroe Elem Schl 3rd Grd Tchr 1972-; *ai:* Textbook, AV Comms; Travel Sabbatical Vol Time Bethany Theo Seminary Exch for Room, Bd; NEA, PSEA 1968-; CVEA 1968-, Bld Rep 2 Yrs; BSA 3 Yrs, Den Ldr; Church of Brethren Lifetime, Deacon, Church Bd, Chrstn Ed Comm, Toyfair Chprsn; Letort Quilters 3 Yrs, Sec Auxiliary Group, Camp Cnslr; Handbell Choir 1 Yr; Telephone Crisis Intervention; Messiah Village 2 Yrs, Vol; *office:* Monroe Elem Schl 1240 Boiling Springs Rd Boiling Springs PA 17007*

RAMIREZ, JASON ANTHONY, Fine Arts Dept Chairperson; *b:* New York, NY; *m:* Assunta Ferrara; *c:* Christian; *ed:* Herbert H. Lehman Coll (BA) Speech, Theatre 1992; CUNY Grad Ctr 40 Credit Hrs, Theatre PHD Prgm; *cr:* Cardinal Hayes HS Eng Dept Instr 1 Yr; Preston HS Fine Arts Dept Chm, Eng Dept Instr 2 Yrs; *ai:* Dramatic Soc, Frosh Speech Night Moderator; Musical Dir; IPP Prgm Steering Comm; Assn for Theatre Higher Ed, Doctoral Theatre Stdnts Assn 1993-; Bronx Cncl on Arts 1992-; MAGNET Pres Flwshp 1993-; Latin Amer Writers Conf Awd 1995; Outstdng Mem Cardinal Hayes Comm 1993; *office:* Preston HS 2780 Schurz Ave Bronx NY 10465*

RAMSAY, JOAN LEVASSEUR, Secondary French Teacher; *b:* Edmundston NB, Canada; *m:* Robert W.; *c:* Ryan Lennox, Lauren Rachel; *ed:* Univ of ME (BS) Bio-Tech 1981; Addl 36 Credit Hrs Ed, Frgn Lang; *cr:* Narraguagus HS Fr Tchr, Dept Head 1985-; *ai:* Fr Club Adv; MEA, NEA 1985-; *office:* Narraguagus HS RR 1 Box 489 Harrington ME 04643

RAMSAY, PAULINE ENGLISH, 8th Grade Language Arts Tchr; *b:* Boston Lnclnshire, England; *m:* Walter Gaines; *c:* Christopher; *ed:* Frostburg St Univ (BA) K-8 Ed 1990, (MED) Admin, Supervision 1995; Univ of London Tchrs Cert 1969; Cmptr, Internet Classes; *cr:* King Athelstan Schl 4th Grd Tchr 1969-70; Tabri Intl Schl Prin, Tchr 1970-72; Holton-Arms Schl 3rd, 4th Grd Tchr 1972-83; Bloomington Sch 7th-8th Grd Tchr 1991-92; Southern Mid Schl 8th Grd Tchr 1992-; *ai:* Multicultural Comm Mem Garrett Cty Bd of Ed; Eng Dept Chprsn 1995-; Garrett Cty Humane SOc 1990-, Sec; Foster Parent Assn 1994-; Duke of Edenburghs Awd Scheme Recipient; *office:* Southern MS 605 Harvey Winters Dr Oakland MD 21550

RAMSBURG, JANE SNEDDON, Fourth Grade Teacher; *b:* Salt Lake City, UT; *m:* E. Lee, Jr.; *c:* Beau, Katie, Josh, Langdon; *ed:* Univ of Maryland (BA) Elem Ed 1971; 24 Credit Hrs; *cr:* Lake Normandy Elem 1st-3rd Grd Tchr 1971-73; Waynesboro Area Schl Dist 1st Grd Tchr 1973-75, 1st, 2nd & 4th Grd Tchr 1976-; *ai:* Lead Tchr-2nd & 4th Grd; Discipline Comm; WAEA 1973-; PSEA 1973-; NEA 1973-; 4-H 1991-, Project Ldr; *office:* Waynesboro Area Schl Dist 220 Clayton Ave Waynesboro PA 17268*

RAMSDELL, GREGORY A., Vocal Music Teacher; *b:* Galion, OH; *m:* Cynthia Sue Snyder; *ed:* Bowling Green St Univ (BA) Music Ed 1991; Addl Stud Towards Masters Degree in Music Ed; *cr:* Greenville HS Vocal Music Tchr 1993-; *ai:* Bible Club Supvr; Fine Arts Cognate Ldr; Co-Dir of Spring Musials; NEA 1993-; Erie Philharmonic Chorus, Greenville Civic Chorus 1995-; *home:* 110 W Windridge Rd Greenville PA 16125

RAMSEY, COETTA POE, Second Grade Teacher; *b:* Chambersburg, PA; *m:* Kermit C.; *c:* Michael T., Todd, Troy, Tracy, Rosco Schock, Natasha Schock, Kimberly Schock, Matthew Ramsey; *ed:* Messiah Coll (BA) Behavioral Sci 1972; Shippensburg Univ (MS) Elem Ed 1982; +48 Credit Hrs Beyond Masters PA St Univ; *cr:* Tuscarora Schl Dist Elem Tchr 1976-; *ai:* TEA & NEA 1975-; Dist III Sunday Schl Assn 1986-, Past Pres, Past VP; Gospel Tide Acad 1986-, Past Pres, Past VP; *office:* St Thomas Elem Schl 70 School House Rd Saint Thomas PA 17252

RAMSEY, DAVID CRAIG, Graphic Arts & Phtgrphy Tchr; *b:* Mansfield, OH; *m:* Krista Boss; *c:* Jessa; *ed:* OH St Univ (BS) Ed 1979; Kent St Univ (MA) Educl Media 1986; Supvr Cert Xavier Univ 1996; *cr:* Southeast Local Schls Graphic Arts 8 Yrs; Oak Hills Local Schls Graphic Arts, Photography & Cmptr Technologist 9 Yrs; *ai:* Dist Printing for 9200 Stu Dist; Tech In-Svcs for Tchrs; Dist Strategic Planning & Dist Tech Comms; NEA, OEA 1986-; OITE 1979-; Printing Industries of Amer Grant 1993; *office:* Oak Hills Local Schls 3200 Ebenezer Rd Cincinnati OH 45248*

RAMSEY, KATHRYN A., 4th Grade Teacher; *b:* Toledo, OH; *m:* Richard E.; *ed:* Toledo Univ (BA) Elem Ed 1973; Wright St Ed (MED) 1978; *cr:* Bellefontaine MS 6th Grd Tchr 1973-74; Northeastern Elem Schl 6th Grd Tchr 1974-86, 4th Grd Tchr 1986-; *ai:* Soc Stud Comm; Grd Card Dev Comm; Delta Kappa Gamma 1995-; OEA; NEA; First Luth Church 1982-; Amer Legion Awd 1993-, Tchr Awd; Mary Florence Souers Grant; Martha Holden Jennings Scholar 1980-81; Rotary Tchr of Yr Nom.

RAMSEY, MARGO SALESE, English Teacher; *b:* Beacon, NY; *m:* Raymond W.; *c:* Catherine, Mary; *ed:* Amer Intnl Coll (BA) Eng 1974; 30 Addl Hrs SUNY at New Paltz Eng 1977; *cr:* Beacon HS Eng Tchr 1974-75; Rombout Jr HS Eng Tchr 1975-83; Beacon HS Eng Tchr 1983-; *ai:* NEA 1974-, Sec 1981; *office:* Beacon HS 72 Fishkill Ave Beacon NY 12508*

RAMSEY, MARY ANN, First Grade Teacher; *b:* Portsmouth, OH; *m:* Robert; *c:* Mark, Susan; *ed:* OH Univ (BA) Elem Ed 1973-74; Mt St Joseph (MA) Ed 1988-89; *cr:* Huntington Schls First Grd Tchr 1966-67: Waverly Schls First Grd Tchr 1974-95; *ai:* Girls Little League Coach 4 Yrs; Chrldng Adv 1 Yr; Shaunee St Univ Stu Tchr Comm; OEA, NEA; Alpha Delta Kappa, Sec; Martha Holden Jennings Awd; *office:* Waverly East Primary Schl 5th St Waverly OH 45690*

RAMSEY, PATRICIA GALE, Education & Psychology Prof; *b:* New York City, NY; *m:* Fred Moseley; *c:* Daniel, Andres; *ed:* Middlebury Coll (BA) Amer Lit 1967; CA St at San Francisco (MA) Cnslng 1973; Univ of MA Early Chldhd Ed 1978; *cr:* IN Univ Asst Prof 1978-79; Wheelock Coll Asst Prof 1979-84; Mt Holyoke Coll Asst Prof 1984-89, Assoc Prof 1989-94, Prof 1994-; *ai:* AERA 1978-, Early Chldhd Steering Comm; NAEYC 1978-; SRCD 1979-; Fac Grants & Flwshps 1985, 1986, 1992 & 1995; NIMH Grant 1989-90; Pub 3 Books, 30 Articles & Book Chptrs; *office:* Mount Holyoke Coll 50 College St South Hadley MA 01075

RAMSEY, SARI, Assistant Professor; *b:* Chungli, Taiwan; *m:* Charlie; *ed:* Fu-Jen Univ (BA) World Lit 1985; Southern IL Univ at Carbondale (MS) Educl Psych 1988, (PHD) Comp Based Ed 1993; *cr:* Unity Coll Asst Prof 1993-; *ai:* Northern Lights & Yrbk Tech Adv; Gen Ed Comm; Assn for Dev of Comp Based Instrl Systems 1990-; New England Regnl Computing Pgm 1994-; Natl Educl Computing Assn 1995-; Phi Delta Kappa, Kappa Delta Pi & Phi Kappa Phi; *office:* Unity Coll HC 78 Box 1 Unity ME 04988

RAMSEY, WILLIAM RUSSELL, Biology & Chemistry Teacher; *b:* Oak Hill, OH; *m:* Pamela Joyce Hale; *c:* Jennifer, Aaron, Alison; *ed:* Rio Grande Coll (BS) Bio 1974; Dayton Univ (MS) Educl Admin 1984; Alcohol Abuse Training; IAT Red Cross Cert; CDL Training Tech; *cr:* Oak Hill HS Tchr 1975-84, Tchr, Asst Prin 1985-95; *ai:* United Way Vol; Outstanding Comm Svc Awd; Gallia Bapt Church 1961, Deacon; Outstanding Chem Tchr of OH Univ 1995; *office:* Oak Hill Union High Schls 205 Western Ave Oak Hill OH 45656*

RAMSIER, DENNIS, Dir of External Outreach; *b:* Mt Pleasant, PA; *ed:* Univ of Pittsburgh (BS) Chemical Engrng 1968; Univ of PA (MBA) Intnl Bus 1970; *cr:* Univ of Liberia Mgmt Instr 1971-73; The Riccardi Co VP & Project Mgr 1973-76; Northeastern Univ Asst Undergrad & Bus Dean 1976-95, External Outreach Dir 1995-; *ai:* MBA Alumni Assn Adv; Boston Area Returned Peace Corps Vols 1978-, Mbrshp Comm; Wharton Club of Boston 1980-, Pres, VP Pgms & VP Mbrshp; Our Lady of Good Counsel Church 1982-, Cantor & Lector; Recording for the Blind 1993-, Recording Dir, 100 Hrs Awd; *office:* Northeastern Univ Coll of Bus 412 DG 360 Huntington Ave Boston MA 02115

RAMUNDO, DONNA DERICO, Third Grade Teacher; *b:* Elmira, NY; *m:* Robert; *c:* Jennifer, Peter, Stephen; *ed:* SUNY at Brockport (BS) Psych, Elem Ed 1977; Montclair St (MS) Schl Soc Work, Schl Prsnl 1982; 75 Addl Credits Ed Rockland Tchr Ctr; *cr:* Immaculate Conception Schl Kndgtn Tchr 1977-79; St Paul's Schl Sci Tchr 1979-84; Nyackc Pub Schls Tchr 1984-; *ai:* Site-Based Team; Tech-Linker; NTA 1984-, Chief Bldg Rep, ELem VP; Rockland Cty Girls Scouts 1984-; Project Rainbow; *home:* 115 Gatto Ln Pearl River NY 10965*

RAMUNNO, KERRY KOWALSKI, Fifth Grade Teacher; *b:* Worcester, MA; *m:* Louis Anthony; *c:* Ross E., Mark A.; *ed:* Geneva Coll (BSEd) Elem Ed 1971; Kent St Univ (MSEd) Curr & Instruction 1987; Attnd Clark Univ, Youngstown St Univ, Mount St Josephs, Univ of AK SE, Ashland Univ, Walsh Coll; *cr:* Crestview Schls Kndgtn, Remedial Rdng Tchr 1971-73; Salem City Schls Instr of Visually Impaired 1977-79, 9-12 Grd Learning Disabilities Tutor 1979-88, Fifth Grd Tchr 1988-; *office:* South East Elem Schl 2200 Merle Rd Salem OH 44460

RANAGAN, JOSEPH ANDREW, Physics Teacher; *b:* Orange, NJ; *m:* Lysbeth Beach; *c:* Elizabeth; *ed:* Montclair St Coll (BA) Sci Ed 1965; Temple Univ (MS) Sci Ed 1968; *cr:* Morris Hills HS Sci Tchr 1965-67; Whippany Park HS Sci Tchr 1968-83; Dexter Regnl HS Sci Tchr 1983-; *ai:* AAPT 1985-; NEA 1965-; MEA 1983-; ARRL 1991-; *office:* Dexter Regional HS 12 Abbott Hill Rd Dexter ME 04930

RANALLI, EDWARD F.,JR., Global Studies Teacher; *b:* Rochester, NY; *m:* Sandra J. Finucan; *ed:* Parsons Coll (BA) His 1968; 36 Grad Hrs at St Univ of NY at Brockport in Liberal Stud 1975; 3 Credit Hrs at Creighton Univ in Dev 1982; *cr:* Good Shepherd Schl 4th, 7th & 8th Grd Tchr 1972-79; Saint Bernard Seminary Recruitment Dir 1979-81; Aquinas Inst Dev & Recruitment Dir & Tchr 1989-; *ai:* Frosh Orientation Chair; Rochester Area Soc Stud; Church of The Annunciaton 1990-, Lector; Landmark Soc 1994-; Aquinas Stu Asst Prgm Past Chair; *office:* Aquinas Inst of Rochester 1127 Dewey Ave Rochester NY 14613

RANALLO, JEAN EMRICK, Language Arts Teacher; *b:* Pittsburgh, PA; *m:* Vernon W.; *c:* Gary; *ed:* IN Univ of PA (BS) Eng 1963; *cr:* Plum Sr High Tchr 1963-67; Holy Redeemer Schl Tchr 1977-; *ai:* Lang Arts Dept Chprsn; Newspaper Adv; NCEA 1977-; *office:* Holy Redeemer Schl 49th Ave & Berwyn Rds College Park MD 20740

RAND, CRAIG MARTIN, Asst Professor of Phys Ed; *b:* Akron, OH; *m:* Marianne P. Jung; *c:* Shawn, Justin, Kyle, Connor; *ed:* Ithaca Coll (BS) PE 1978, (MS) PE 1984; Univ of Rochester 27 Hrs Ed; *cr:* Nazareth Coll Head Ath Trainer 1979-85; Elmira Coll Instr, Head Ath Trainer 1985-87; Monroe Comm Coll Asst Prof PE, Head Ath Trainer 1987-; *ai:* Phys Stud Awareness Club Adv; Fac Senator; Supervise Stu Interns Ath Trng; Fitness, Wellness Ctr; Head Coach Mens Lacrosse; Dev Coll Ropes Course; NATA 1980-; NSCA 1985-; Genesee Vly Sports Medicine 1988-, Pres 2 Yrs; NYSUT 1991-; Brighton Bsbl 1993-, Bd of Dirs; Yth Soccer, Bsbl Coach; CYO Bsktbl Coach; Co-Authored The Wellness Workbook, Presented Twice at League of Innovation; Lacrosse Classic Head Coach North JUCO Lacrosse Team 1994; *office:* Monroe Comm Coll 1000 E Henrietta Rd Rochester NY 14623*

RAND, MARK W., World Geography Teacher; *b:* Ware, MA; *m:* Janice Sillars; *c:* Mark L., Deborah L. Waybright, Jennifer, Karl Sandmann; *ed:* Univ of MA at Amherst (BBA) Mrktg 1956; Salem St Coll (MED) Ed 1969; Addl 15 Hrs Geography; *cr:* Beverly Pub Schls 7th Grd Math, Sci, Eng, Geog Tchr 1963-83, World Geography Tchr 1983-; *ai:* Sftbl Coach 5 Yrs; Chm All-Schl Field Day 5 Yrs; Beverly Tchrs Assn 1963-, Mutual Concerns; MA Tchrs Assn, NEA 1963-.

RAND, NANCY KELLEY, Fourth Grade Teacher; *b:* Methuen, MA; *m:* Jeffrey; *c:* Michael, Matthew; *ed:* Plymouth St Coll (BS) Elem Ed K-6 1976; *cr:* North Salem ELem Schl Resource Room Aide 1976-77, Third Grd Tchr 1977-78; Barron Schl Fifth 1978-83, Sixth Grd Tchr 1983-87; Walter Haigh Schl Sixth Grd 1987-93, Fourth Grd Tchr 1993-; *ai:* NEA-NH 1978-, Rep 1994-, A Tchr to Remember 1995; SEA 1978-, Alpha Delta Kappa 1992; *office:* Walter Haigh Schl 24 School St Salem NH 03079*

RAND, SHIRLEY GALLAGHER, Business Admin Professor; *b:* Cleveland, OH; *c:* Connie Rand Kane, Judy Rand Fuschino, Russell; *ed:* Miami Univ (BS) Pol Sci, His; Univ of MO at Kansas City (JD) Law 1974; Elmira Coll (MS) Adult Ed 1983; *cr:* Elmira Coll Adj Prof 1976-84; Coll of Great Falls Paralegal Prgm Dir, Prof 1984-87; Saint Vincent Coll Bus Adm Assoc Prof 1987-; *ai:* Schlsp, Fin Aid, Prof Dev, Pre-Law Comms; Fac Cncl Sub-Comm; Hourly Grievances Fac; Acad of Legal Stud in Bus 1981-, Ethics Intnl Employment, Feminist Sections; Pal Big Bros, Sisters, Bd of Adjustment; Articles Pub; *office:* St Vincent Coll 300 Purchase Fraser Rd Latrobe PA 15650*

RANDALL, SUSAN JANE COUNTRYMAN, 2nd Grade Teacher; *b:* Syracuse, NY; *m:* Gerald; *c:* Jennifer Verbeek, Gregory Jon; *ed:* St Univ of NY at Cortland (BS) Elem 1965; 30 Credit Hrs Grad Courses; *cr:* North Syracuse Cntrl Schls 2nd Grd Elem Ed Tchr 1965-71, Home Bound Instruction 1976-79, Elem Ed Tchr 1979-; *ai:* NYSUT, NSEA 1965-; *office:* Lakeshore Road Elem Schl 7180 Lakeshore Rd Cicero NY 13039

RANDAZZO, CHARLES MICHAEL, Sixth Grade Science Teacher; *b:* Reading, PA; *m:* Susan Eileen Sitlinger; *ed:* Kutztown Univ (BS) Elem Ed 1975; 36 Post Grad Credits Temple Univ, Penn St Univ; *cr:* Tyson-Schoener Elem Schl 6th Grd Tchr 1976-87; Souther MS 6th-7th Grd Sci Tchr 1988-; *ai:* Schl Musical Dir, Producer; MS Bsktbl Coach; Schl Sci Fair Asst Coord; Systems Operator for Bldgs Cmptrs; NEA 1976-, Bldg Rep; Swing Fever Big Band 1984-94, Musical Dir, VP.

RANDAZZO, FRANCES AMANDA (MARCOTTE), Seventh & Eighth Grade Teacher; *b:* Boston, MA; *m:* Philip J.; *c:* Stephanie, Jill; *ed:* Salem St Coll (BS) Elem Ed 1968; *cr:* St Mary's Elem Tchr Grd 3 1968-71; Lynn Pub Schls Sub Tchr Grd K-6 1980-84; Immaculate Conception Tchr Grd 7-8 1984-; *ai:* Accompany, Aid Planning Class Trips; NCEA 1984-; *office:* Immaculate Conception Schl 127 Winthrop Ave Revere MA 02151

RANDELS, DAVID GEORGE, Instrumental Music Teacher; *b:* Bryan, OH; *m:* Esther Zerman; *c:* Kellie Bieber; *ed:* Bowling Green St Univ (BSEd) Music 1965, (MSME) Music 1971; Cert Lib Sci 7-12 Grd; *cr:* Culver Military Acad Summer Instr, Cnslr 1962-67; Port Clinton City Schls Music Instr 1965-; *ai:* Music Dept Head; MENC, OH Music Ed Assoc 1965-; Natl Schl Orch Assoc 1984-, Distngd Svc 1994; AFT 1973-; Port Clint Model RR Club 1975-, Pres 1975-82; US Capital Hist Soc 1975-; Elks 1969-; Phi Delta Kappa 1992-; Noteworthy Tours Inc 1995-, Tour Escort; Port Clinton Fed of Tchrs Lifetime Achie Awd 1984; Bowling Green St Univ Outstdng Bandsman 1965; Kappa Kappa Psi Pres 1965; Drummer Jazz Bands 196)-, Jamie Wight New Orleans Joymakers 1980-; 6 Recordings; *home:* 3635 County Road 182 Fremont OH 43420

RANDLE, BRIAN SCOTT, HS Social Studies Teacher; *b:* Lancaster, PA; *m:* Maria Henry; *ed:* Millersville Univ (BSE) Scndry Ed 1993; *cr:* Joppatowne HS Soc Stud Tchr 1994-95; C Milton Wright HS Soc Stud Tchr 1995-; *ai:* Asst JV Ftbl & Asst JV Lacrosse Coach; NEA 1993-; MSTA 1994-; HCEA 1994-; Joppatowne HS 10th Grd Tchr of Yr 1994-95; *home:* 1620 Denise Dr Apt F Forest Hill MD 21050

RANDOLPH, BRIAN WALTER, Associate Prof of Civil Engrng; *b:* Dayton, OH; *m:* Clare E. Luddy; *c:* Brigid L. Hannah L.; *ed:* Univ of Cincinnati (BSCE) Civil Engr 1982, (MS) Civil Engr 1983; OH St Univ (PHD) Civil Engr 1989; *cr:* Univ of Toledo Instr 1987-89, Asst Prof 1989-93, Assoc Prof 1993-, Dir of Undergraduate Prgm 1994-; *ai:* Chi Epsilon, Hnrs Adv; Environmental Geotechnology Lab Dir; Ctr for Tchng Excl Advy Bd; Amer Soc Engrng Ed 1987-, NEE Exec Bd, Dow Outstdng Young Fac Awd 1993; Amer Soc Civil Engrs 1890-, Toledo Young Engr of Yr Awd 1992; Sigma Xi 1984-; Chi Epsilon 1992-; Toastmasters Intl 1989-, Educl VP, Medal of Hnr 1993; ASCE Tchr of Yr 1988; Who's Who in Sci & Engrng 1994; Coll of Engrng Outstdng Tchr Awd 1994, Fac Tchng Excl Awd 1995; Cvil Engrng Tchr of Yr 1994; Rsrch Grants, Journal Articles; *office:* Univ Of Toledo 2801 W Bancroft St Toledo OH 43606

RANDOLPH, SUSAN I., History & Psychology Teacher; *b:* Jersey City, NJ; *c:* Todd; *ed:* Lindenwood Coll Psych 1967; Univ of ME Orono His & PE 1969; Masters Educl Admin; *cr:* Glen Rock Jr Sr HS His Tchr 1969-78; York HS His & Psych Tchr 1981-; *ai:* Stu Asst Team; Peer Mediation Adv; NEA 1969-; ME Tchr Assn 1981-; Learning Disabilities Assn 1990-; Natl Ctr for Learning Disabilities 1990-; Kennebunk Beach Improvement 1987-; Kennebunk Coastal Assn; West Kennebunk Animal Shelter; *office:* York HS 286 Long Sands Rd York ME 03909

RANGER-DARBY, ROSE NICOTRA, 7th-12th Grd Rdng Specialist; *b:* Syracuse, NY; *m:* Richard P. Darby; *c:* Tyler John Darby; *ed:* Fredonia St Univ (BA) Elem Ed 1985; St Univ of NY at Oswego (MS) Rdng Ed 1989; *cr:* South Jefferson Cntrl Schl 3rd Grd Tchr 1985-87, 6th Grd Tchr 1987-90, Jr HS & Elem Rdng Specialist 1990-92, 7th-12th Grd Rdng Specialist 1992-; *ai:* Model Schls Cmptr Liason; IBM Process Writing Trainer; St Univ of NY at Potsdam & Oswego Stu Tchr Prgm & Potsdam Internship Prgm Mentor; NY St Engrng Cncl 1993-, Educator of Excl 1994; Black River Rdng Cncl, Thousand Island Lit Cncl 1985-, Bldg Rep; Kappa Delta Pi 1983-; SJTA 1985-, Bldg Rep; Veterans of Foreign Wars Ladies Auxiliary 1992-; NY St Engrng Cncl Presenter at 45th Annual Conf 1995; *office:* South Jefferson Central Schl PO Box 10 Adams NY 13605*

RANKIN, CATHERINE PEARCE, Music Teacher; *b:* Pittsburgh, PA; *m:* John F.; *c:* Mary Catherine, Monica; *ed:* Indiana Univ of PA (BS) Music Ed 1970, (MED) Music Ed 1972; Seton Hill (BS) Soc Stud Ed 1986; Liturgical Coord Cert; *cr:* Hempfield Area Schl Dist Elem Music Tchr 1970-73, Jr HS Choral, Instrumental Tchr 1985-87, Elem Music, Gen Inst Tchr 1988-91, MS Instrumental Tchr 1991-; *ai:* Band 1; Band 2-3; Hnrs Bnd; Orch; Strategic Planning Steering Comm; PSEA 1970-73; MENC 1965-70, 1985-; PMEA 1965-73, 1985-; Greensburg Women's Coll Club, Choral Dir 1989-; *office:* Harrold MS RR 6 Box 75 Greensburg PA 15601

RANKIN, HARRY LEE, Social Studies Teacher; *b:* Renovo, PA; *m:* Alice Lee Matthews; *c:* Lee Harry, Eric Phillip; *ed:* Lock Haven Univ (BS) Geog, Soc Stud 1968; Elmira Coll (MS) Soc Stud 1973; 33 In-Svc Credit Hrs; *cr:* Carthage Cntrl Schl Earth Sci, Soc Stud Tchr 1968-69; Addison Cntrl Schl Earth Sci, Gen Sci Tchr 1969-70, Gen Sci, Drivers Ed Tchr 1970-88; Steuben Allegany BOCES Drivers Ed Tchr 1987-; Addison Cntrl Schl Soc Stud, Drivers Ed Tchr 1988-; *ai:* Drivers Ed Instr Addison Youthbuild Prgm; NEA, NY NEA 1968-; Amer Legion 1982-; Royal Order of Green Beret 1964-; Natl Rifle Assn 1979-; *office:* Addison Cntrl Jr S Colwell St Addison NY 14801

RANKIN, NEIL F., Fifth Grade Teacher; *b:* Jersey City, NJ; *m:* Poulton; *c:* Tracy, Kelly, Shaun; *ed:* Trenton St Coll (BA) Elem E Attnd Georgian Ct Coll; *cr:* Silver Bay Elem 5th Grd Tchr 19 Project Excel Tchr; Bsktbl Coach; TREA, NJEA, NEA 1972- Jaycees 1974-, Chm, Jaycee of Yr; Governor's Tchr Recognition Prg of Yr 1993; *home:* 36 Mount Ln Toms River NJ 08753

RANSEY, LINDA MARIE, High School English Teacher; *b:* Toled *ed:* Univ of Toledo (BA) Scndry Ed 1980; 32 Grad Hrs; *cr:* Jesup W HS Eng Tchr 1980-; *ai:* Speech, Debate Coach; 1998 Class Adv 1980-; OABSE 1990-; NABSE 1995-; *home:* 2124 N 13th St Tole 43620*

RANSEY, THERESA MARIE, Sixth Grade Teacher; *b:* Elmira, N Keuka Coll (BS) Elem Ed-Magna Cum Laude 1977; Elmira Coll (M 1990; *cr:* St Mary's Elem Schl 1st Grd Tchr 1977-84; Elmira Corre Facility Chptr I Rdng Tchr 1981-84; Parley Coburn Elem Schl 6th G 1984-; *ai:* Schl Bldg Planning Team; Action Comms; AFT, NY St Tchrs 1984-; Chemung, Schuler Cty Ec Opportunity Prgm 1988-93 Dirs; Chemung Cty Commission on Human Relations 19 Commissioner; Amer Cancer Soc's Fund Raisers, Vol; *office:* Coburn Elem Schl 216 Mount Zoar St Elmira NY 14904

RAPALJE, CHARLES H., 6th Grade Teacher; *b:* Cold Springs, N St Univ at Canton (AAS) Ag 1965; Univ of GA (BS) Ed 1968; St U New Paltz (MS) Elem Ed 1973; *cr:* Balmville Schl Tchr 1968- Newburgh Tchrs Assn, NY St United Tchrs 1968-; AFT; Newburg Warner 1970-85; NFA Booster Club 1970-; *office:* Balmville Schl 4 North Newburgh NY 12550

RAPIEJKO, LISA, Spanish Teacher; *b:* Philadelphia, PA; *ed:* SU Binghamton (BA) Span 1986; Dowling Coll (MS) Scndry Ed 199 Grad Stud Complutense Univ de Madrid; *cr:* East Islip HS Tchr 198 Spring Track Coach; Rotary-Interact Club Co-Adv; Long Island Lang NYS Assn of Frgn Lang Tchrs 1990-; *office:* East Islip HS Redmen S Terrace NY 11752*

RAPISARDA, GREGORY FRANCIS, French, Span & Italian Te *b:* New York, NY; *ed:* Fordham Univ (BSEd) Fr 1961, (MA) Fr 19 Regis HS Fr, Span, Italian Tchr 1961-; *ai:* AATF, AATSP; *office:* HS 55 E 84th St New York NY 10028

RAPISARDI, FRANK, Science Teacher; *b:* Lawrence, MA; *cr:* M Pub Schls 28 Yrs; *ai:* Peer Mediation; MTA; NTA; Knights of Colu *home:* 20 Edgewood Ter Methuen MA 01844

RAPLEE, WILLIAM JOHN, Sixth Grade Math Teacher; *b:* Elmira *m:* Carol Ann Quatrini; *c:* Karen, Christopher; *ed:* Mansfield St Col Elem Ed 1970; Elmira Coll (MS) Ed 1974; *cr:* Hardy Elem Schl Sixt Tchr 1970-82; Parley Coburn Elem Schl Fourth, Sixth Grd Tchr 19 Broadway Elem Schl Fifth, Sixth Grd Math Tchr 1986-; *ai:* Ski Club NY St Certfd Swimming Ofcl; Dist Math Curr Comm; HS Diving C AFT, NEA, NYSUT; Southside Comm Ctr 1986-, VP; *office:* Broa Elem Schl 1000 Broadway St Elmira NY 14904

RAPOZA, CHRISTINE O'CONNELL, 1st-2nd Grade Teache Boston, MA; *m:* John Andrew; *c:* Caleb, Evan, Daniel; *ed:* Lyndon S (BS) Regular & Spec Ed 1992; Addl 15 Hrs HS Sci; *cr:* Behavior Inst Behavior Therapist, Weekend Supvr 1985-87; Woodstructures D 1987-88; Danville Schl First-Second Grd Tchr 1992-; *ai:* Adult Ed W in Cmptr Applications; NEA 1992-; Local Stans Bd 1994-; Explore-Tech Lab Co-Coord; *office:* Danville Schl PO Box 176 Da VT 05828

RAPPA, WILLIAM NEWTON,JR., Fifth Grade Teacher; *b:* Che MA; *m:* Christine Conway Rappa; *c:* Tracy, Lindsay; *ed:* Salem St (MED) Cnslng, Guid; Univ of MA (BA) Psych, Ed 1969; Advanced Stud Boston St Coll; *cr:* WA Comm Magnet Schl Eng Second 1969-72, 5th, 6th Grd Tchr 1972-, MA Migrant Ed Prgm Site Dir 198 WA Comm Magnet Schl Facilitator 1990-; *ai:* Stu Cncl, Schl Patrol Floor Hockey Dir; AFT 1969-; *office:* Washington Cmty Elem Sc Blossom St Lynn MA 01902

RAPPACH, NORMA JEANNE, Diversified Hlth Teacher; *b:* Hast PA; *m:* Ronald M.; *c:* Timothy J. Mrus, Susan Mrus-Hughes, Josep Mrus, Kelley R., Lynn Rappach Paris; *ed:* Kent St Univ (AA) General with Honors 1983; Youngstown St Univ (BS) Nursing-Magna Cum L Trumbull Memorial Hospital Schl of Nursing Diploma RN 1959; Cuya Comm Coll EMT, Paramedic 1978; Kent St Univ Voc Ed Tchr 1996 Dept of Ed EMT Instr Course 1973; Amer Red Cross Instr Cert Course First Aid, CPR 1986; OH Bd of Nursing Nurses Aide TCEP Instr Course 1993; Amer Hearth Assn Heart Saver Instr 1990-; *cr:* Trum Meml Hospital Pediatric Nurse 1960-62; Frank Vargo MD Part- Office Nurse 1960-72; L. .a Swinehart MD Office Obstetrical N 1961-73; Meadows Manor Nursing Home Part-Time Staff Nurse 196 Gillette Nursing Home Part-Time Charge Nurse 1972-74; OH Dept o T&I EMT Instr 1973-78; Packard Electric, Division General M Part-Time Industrial Nurse 1974-76; Lordstown Local Schls K-12th Nurse, Vo-Ed Tchr 1978-93; Gordon D. James Career Ctr Diversified Occupations Vo-Ed Tchr 1993-; *ai:* Voc Clubs of Amer Adv; Red C Blood Driv Spon, Coord; Safety Comm; AIDS Coord 1986-93; Trum Cty Bd of Ed Communicable Disease Task Force 1988; Advy Bd Diversified Hlth 1993-; OH Voc Assn 1993-94; OH, Natl Schl Nurse 1980-93; AFT; Blessed Sacrament Church 1992-94, Parish Nurse; A Heart Assn 1973-86, CPR Instr, Vol; Amer Red Cross 1987-, 1st Aid, Instr; Amer Red Cross 1993-, HIV, AIDS Instr; Trumbull Cty Quota 1986-88; Teen Inst Adv 1981-; Trumbull Cty EMS 1974-75, Past Co Trumbull Cty EMS Comm 1974-75, Past Pres; Howland Fire D Honorary Mem; Trumbull Cty Disaster Drills 1976-77, Vol Co Trumbull Cty Kiwanis Club Nursing 1956, Youngstown St Univ Schol 1986 Schlsp; Trumbull Meml Schl of Nursing 1956-59 Class Pres, NE Treas, Miss Stu Nurse, NE OH Miss Stu Nurse; Trumbull Cty Fair Awd Prof Woman of Yr 1977; Pub Poem Kent St Univ Voc Ed Newsletter 1 Omicron Tau Theta Honorary Chapter Voc Citizenship Awd Kent St U 1994-95; Whos Who in Amer Nursing 1996; *office:* Gordon D. Ja Career Ctr 1824 Salt Springs Rd SW Warren OH 44481

RAPPAPORT, JONATHAN CHARLES, Arts Curriculum Liaison Bronxville, NY; *m:* Rana Gladstone; *c:* Netta, Maya; *ed:* Univ of Der (BME) Music Ed 1969; New England Conservatory (MM) Music Ed 1 Grad Dip Kodaly Musical Trng Inst 1975; Kodaly Cert Liszt Aca Budapest 1975; Post-Graduate Cert Kodaly Ctr Amer 1981; Supvr Cert MA St Coll at Fitchburg; *cr:* Haldane Cntrl Schls K-12 Grd M Tchr 1969-73; W Hartford Schls K-6 Grd Music Tchr 1975-76; Millb Schls K-5 Grd Music Tchr 1976-81; Medfield Schls 4-6 Gr d Music T 1981-82; Kodaly Ctr of America Acad Coord 1982-85; Worcester S Music Tchr 1985-, Arts Curr Liaison 1994-; *ai:* Arts Curr Chp City-Wide Arts Coord; Org of Amer Kodaly Ed 1976-, Exec Sec; East Kodaly Assn, Past Pres; Boston Area Kodaly Ed 1981-, Past Pres; Ir Kodaly Assn; MENC; MMEA; NEA; MA Tchr Assn; Amer Choral Assn; Masonic Lodge 1969-, Sr Deacon, Outstdng Mason; Marlboro Cultural Cncl 1987-89; Compositions Pub; Horace Mann Tchr A Alliance for Ed Minigrants; Lucretia Crocker Flwshp Semi-Finalist; MA Arts Assessment Frameworks Comm; *office:* Worcester Pub Schls Irving St Worcester MA 01609*

OPORT, CHERRY KARL, Assoc Prof of Nrsng; *b:* Baltimore, ; William Arthur; *c:* Jacqueline; *ed:* George Mason Univ (BS) Nrsng (MSN) Gerontological Nrsng 1981; Univ of MD (MA) Instrl Dev King George Hosp RN Diploma; *cr:* Barcroft Inst Dir Nrsng Ed 80; US Soldiers & Airmens Home Dir of Nrsng Ed 1980-81; Pacific n Hosp Night Nurse Ed 1981-85; Chabot Coll Frgn Nurse Grant on 1985-86; Howard Comm Coll Assoc Prof of Nrsng 1986-; *ai:* ry Active Duty 1971-74, 1981- Lt Col Army Nurse Reser; Vac Adv; Recotgition Comm; Sigma Theta Tau 1981-, Prgm Comm Chm 1984; Reserve Ofcrs Assn 1993-; Soc Applied Tech 1995-; AFACCT PTA 1990-, Comm Mem; ANA Cert Gerontological Clinical list; Who's Who Amer Nrsng 1980-89; Articles Pub; *office:* Howard Coll Little Patuxent Parkway Columbia MD 21044*

OPORT, NANCY DICKE, Professor; *b:* Boston, MA; *m:* John; *c:* Ann, Dana Lee; *ed:* Univ of Rochester (AB) Bio 1967; Univ of PA Bio 1969; Univ of MA (MS) Microbiology 1974; *cr:* Springfield Tech Coll Prof 1976-; *ai:* Dept Chprsn; AAAS; ASM; Town Meeting, r Mem; Riverwatch Network 1990-, Vol; Publication: Biochimica et hisical Acta 240 1971; Natl Inst for Staff, Orgnl Dev Excl Awd for ing Tchng, Learning 1994; *office:* Springfield Tech Comm Coll 1 ry Square Springfield MA 01105

DON, ROSEMARY JENKINS, Instructor in Voice; *b:* Grand Island, : C. Wade; *c:* Michael, Geri Ann Socciarelli, Timothy; *ed:* Univ IA a City (BM) Music, Vocal Performance 1971; *cr:* Youngstown St Voice Instr 1971-; *ai:* Sigma Alpha Iota Adv; NATS 1973-; Oratorio no Soloist 15 Works, Recital 41 Yrs; Church Soloist 44 Yrs; Tchr of TS Winners, 1 Metropolitan Opera Dist Auditions Winner; Visting ; Univ of IA Summer Opera Lead Role 1972; *office:* Youngstown St 410 Wick Ave Youngstown OH 44555

CATI, DIANA POLCE, Italian & Spanish Teacher; *b:* Pescara zi, Italy; *m:* Nicholas M.; *c:* Renee, Salvatore; *ed:* Southern CT St (BS) Scndry Ed 1971, (MS) Biling Ed 1989; *cr:* Derby HS Italian 1971-76; St Mary's Grammar Schl 6th Grd Tchr 1982-86; Hillcrest Jr pan, Italian Tchr 1986-87; Hamden MS Italian, span Tchr 1987-93; en HS Italian, Span Tchr 1993-; *ai:* Stdnts Preventing AIDS Club COLT, CITA 1987-; Italian-Amer Historical Soc 1996; *office:* en HS 2040 Dixwell Ave Hamden CT 06514

LE, MICHAEL L., Assistant Spanish Professor; *b:* Massillon, OH; t Union Coll (BA) Span 1966; Kent St Univ (MA) Span, Lang & Lit Post Grad Stud Fr Lang & Lit; *cr:* Canton City Schls Span Tchr 95; Kent St Univ Asst Span Prof 1996; *ai:* Timlen HS Head Sftbl 1984-95; Span Club Adv; Stu Booster Club Adv; Retired from Pub IDEA Univ of Dayton 1967; Ed Professions Dev Act 1969; *home:* W Maple St North Canton OH 44720

KOW, MARION MARIE, First Grade Teacher; *b:* Lawrence, MA; *m:* as Richard; *c:* Thomas Jr., Kevin, Jennifer, Jonathan; *ed:* Lowell St (BS) Elem Ed 1971; 15 Credit Hrs Past BS 1977; 36 Credit Hrs Past 987; *cr:* Memrl Schl 1st Grd Tchr 1971-; *ai:* Enrichment, Budget, etency Skills & Textbook Selection Comms; NEA 1971-; NHEA ; SREA 1971-; Holy Trinity Parents Guild 1981-; Cntrl Cath Parents 1990-; Grant for Purchase of Readiness Materials; *office:* Memorial Schl 31 W Main St Newton NH 03858*

MUSON, NANCY L., Fifth Grade Teacher; *b:* Salt Lake City, UT; *m:* R.; *c:* J. Jason, Zachary B.; *ed:* Univ of UT (BA) Recreational Therapy ; Working for Tchng Cert Fitchburg St Coll; MS Tchr & Tech Trng; Vashington DC Gen Hosp Recreational Therapist 1970-71; Amer Red s Sec & Case Worker 1971; Herbert Lipton Mental Hlth Ctr Soc Work -85; JR Briggs Elem 5th Grd Tchr 1985-; *ai:* Chaperone 5th Grd Sci 0 1985-; Schl Cncl 1992-95; Regnl Prof Dev Comm; MTA 1985-; NEA -; Natl Cncl of Tchrs of Rdng 1990-92; Fitchburg Hospice Org -82, Hospice Vol; Meals on Wheels Vol 1983-84; Church Group -90, Yth Ldr; Salvation Army 1994-, Comm Rep; Oakmont HS Tchr Made a Difference Awd 1995; *office:* John R Briggs Elem Sch 96 ams Rd Ashburnham MA 01430

MUSSEN, OLGA RODRIGUEZ, Religion Department Chair; *b:* lon, England; *m:* Jefdfery P.; *c:* Christian G.; *ed:* Barry Univ (BA) Rel 1977; St Louis Univ (MA) Rel Stud 1980; United Theological inary of Twin Cities (DMIn) Spirituality, Ed 1992; Corp Ministry Prgm 1978; *cr:* Washington Univ Campus Minister 1978-79; John F. nedy HS REl Tchr 1979-80; Convent of The Visitation Schl Dept Chair, Tchr 1981-90; Georgetown Visitation Prep Schl Dept Chair, Campus ster, Rel Tchr 1990-; *ai:* Campus Ministry; Liturgies, Stu & Adult eats; Spritual Mentoring; Dept Chair Curr Comm; Peer Ministry; A; Inst of Noetic Sci; CCMA; AAUW; *office:* Georgetown Visitation Sch 1524 35th St NW Washington DC 20007

SNER, ELENA, French & Russian Teacher; *b:* Moscow, Russia; *m:* ard; *c:* Michael, Ilya; *ed:* Moscow Pedagogical Inst of Frgn Langs D) Fr, Eng & Ed 1967; Moscow Univ 1975; *cr:* Moscow Technological Fr Instr 1967-81; Fort Devens Russian Instr 1984-86; Masconoment al HS Fr & Russian Tchr 1986-; *ai:* Russian Club Adv; AATF 1987-; FLA 1987-; ACTR 1990-; *office:* Masconamet Regional HS 20 Endicott Topsfield MA 01983

SPANTE, PATRICK, Youth Family Minister; *b:* Brooklyn, NY; *m:* bara Sankey; *c:* Paul, Melissa, LoriAnn; *ed:* NY Univ Psych; enborough CC Bus Admin; Diocese of Brooklyn Pastoral Inst Cert in echesis & Yth Ministry; *cr:* St Peter & St Paul Sub Tchr 1973-75; St hael CCD Jr High & HS Tchr 1975-76; St Thomas Aquinas CCD Asst rd & Tchr 1986-92; St Joseph Yth-Family Minister 1992-; *ai:* lerater: Boy Scouts, Cub Scouts, Girls Scouts, OYO Bsktbl, Bsbl, vbl, Brigade Marching Band, Teen & Pre-Teens Clubs, Single Adults, ent-Share, Yth Family Liturgies, Yth-Family Act & Parish Show; ebrate Yth 1992-, Exec Dir; BSA 1992-, Comm Chair; Diocesan Yth nm 1993-; Numerous Articles Pub; Participant in Innovations in Yth istry Conf 1996; *office:* St Joseph R C Church 43-19 30th Ave Astoria 11103

ST, JUDY WITMAN, Health & Physical Ed Teacher; *b:* Lebanon, PA; Wolfgang; *cr:* Fredon Twp Elem Schl K-8th Grd Hlth, PE Tchr 1973-75, th Grd Hlth, PE Tchr 1975-; *ai:* Project Seek, Peer Ldrshp Act; IM ord; NEA, NJEA, SCEA 1973-; AAHPERD, NJAHPERD 1985-; FEA 3-, Co-Pres 1991; *home:* 901 Homestead Dr Newton NJ 07860

TCHFORD, AILEEN CRAWFORD, French Teacher; *b:* Cleveland, ; *m:* Robert L. Jr.; *c:* Christopher, Devon; *ed:* Univ of CO (BA) Fr 1967; v of Dayton (MS) Cnslng 1988; Univ of Toledo Scndry Tchng 1968; Gill Univ Advanced Fr; Univ of Nothern IA Fr; Universila Catholique gers Frances; *cr:* St Louis Inst of Music Piano Tchr; *ai:* Schlsp Banquet mm; Elem Foreign Lang Prgm Adv; OFLA 1980-; SLEA; Boy Scouts; ar of Month Channel 4 TV 1995; *office:* Watkins Memorial HS 8868 tkins Rd SW Pataskala OH 43062

TCHFORD, LINDA M. (STEWART), French & Religion Teacher; *b:* oona, PA; *m:* Gerald; *c:* Scott, Caroline; *ed:* St Francis Coll (BA) Span, 1963; Credit Hrs IN Univ of PA, Altoona Campus of Penn St Univ, stburg St Univ; *cr:* Greater Gallitzin Joint HS Span, Fr Tchr 1963-66; oona Area Schl Dist Sub Tchr 1966-68; Keyser HS Long Term Sub Tchr 75-78; Bishop Walsh Mid HS Fr Tchr, Frgn Lang Dept Chair 1978-; *ai:* -Act Coord; Co-Frosh Class Moderator; Societe Honoraire de Francais oderator; NCEA, AATF, MFLA 1978-; Lasallian Edctr of Yr 1995-; Ray Kroc Edctr Achvmt Awd 1988; *office:* Bishop Walsh Mid HS 700 Bishop Walsh Rd Cumberland MD 21502

RATCLIFFE, HELEN (MAZZA), 5th Grade Teacher; *b:* Lebanon, PA; *m:* Albert J.; *c:* Albert Jr., Vincent; *ed:* RI Coll (BS) Elem Ed 1970, (MS) Elem Ed 1975; Cert Co-operating Tchr for Stu Tchrs, Drivers Ed; *cr:* Calef Schl 3rd Grd Tchr 1970-71; S. D. Barnes Schl 2nd Grd Tchr 1972-76, 5th Grd Tchr 1976-90; Thornton Schl 5th Grd Tchr 1990-; *ai:* Reader, Grader St Writing Assessment Essays; Dev Comms Curr in Sci, Soc Stud, Lang Arts Discipline Code; Teach Summer Rdng High Risk First Graders; AFT 1970-; Natl Tchr of Sci, Natl Tchr of Math 1992-; Nom Presidental Awd Excl in Tchng Math; *home:* 11 Essex St Cranston RI 02910

RATESIC, DOROTHY, English Teacher; *b:* Mc Keesport, PA; *m:* John F.; *c:* Mara Dawn, Marko John; *ed:* Duquesne Univ (BSEd) Eng 1968, (MED) Scndry Ed 1971; Scndry Guid Cnslr 18 Hrs, Elem Ed 24 Hrs 1988; *cr:* South Allegheny Schl Dist HS Eng Tchr 20 Yrs, Elem Sixth Grd Tchr 3 Yrs, Jr HS Eng Tchr 5 Yrs, Gifted Ed Tchr 4 Yrs; *ai:* Tech Planning Comm for Strategic Planning, Curr Review Comm, Redistricting Plan 1993-94; Schl Renewal 1994-95; Dev Act Prgm for Tchrs; NEA, PA St Ed Assn 1968-; South Allegheny Ed Assn 1968-, Sec; Natl Scndry Schl Curr Assn 1991-92; Natl Eng Tchrs Assn; PA Assn Gifted Ed; *home:* 2416 James St Mc Keesport PA 15132

RATH, ERIN KIERNAN, Guidance Counselor; *b:* Providence, RI; *m:* Nicholas; *c:* Adam Gabrault; *ed:* Boston Coll (BA) Ed 1976; Univ of RI (MA) Guid & Cnslng 1988; *cr:* Meadowborok Ferns Schl 3rd & 5th Grd Tchr 1976-79; Eldredge Schl 4th & 6th Grd Tchr 1979-83; Frenchtown Schl 3rd Grd Tchr 1987-88; Cole Jr HS Guid Cnslr 1898-93; East Greenwich HS Guid Cnslr 1993-; *ai:* Stu Cncl Adv; Prom Promise Chprsn; Mem of CAST; NEA 1976-; NACAC 1992-; RI Assn of Cnslrs 1993-; Hugh O'brien Yth Ldrsp Cnslr; *office:* East Greenwich HS 300 Avenger Dr East Greenwich RI 02818*

RATHBUN, ALLAN L., Ag Tchr & Dept Chairman; *b:* Hope Valley, RI; *m:* Marianne Rathbun; *c:* Ryan, Kristen, Lisa; *ed:* Univ of RI (BS) Ag Ed 1973; Attnd Penn St, DE St Univ; *cr:* Caeser Rodney HS Tchr 1973-; *ai:* FFA Adv; Class Adv 5 Yrs; Soccer Coach 17 Yrs; NEA, DSEA, NVATA, DVATA 1973-; HS Tchr of Yr 1982; State Soccer Coach of Yr 1980; *office:* Caesar Rodney Sr HS 239 Old North Rd Camden-Wyoming DE 19934*

RATHBUN, ANGELEE HITCHCOCK, Physical Education Teacher; *b:* Auburn, NY; *m:* Michael D.; *ed:* Ithaca Coll (MS) PE 1991; Attending Cortland St Univ PE; *cr:* Union Springs HS Long Term Sub, Coach 1991-94; Port Byron HS PE Tchr, Coach 1994-; *ai:* Var Field Hockey, Girls Bsktbl, Girls Modified Sftbl Coach; Adv Girls Ath Assn, Class 1995; Team 9 Comm for At Risk Stdnts; STAPEP, AAPHERD 1995-; *office:* Port Byron HS Maple Ave Port Byron NY 13140*

RATHGE, MARK LYNN, Earth Science Teacher; *b:* Napoleon, OH; *m:* Debra Kay Hogrefe; *c:* Austin, Preston, Logan; *ed:* Bowling Green St Univ (BS) Comprehensive Sci Ed 1985; Kent St Univ (MS) Sci Ed 1990; Various Courses at Clarion Univ, Ashland Univ, Cleveland St; *cr:* Lakewood City Schls Sci Tchr 1985-; *ai:* Earth Group Adv; Earth Sci Group Ldr; Saturday Schl Admin; NEA, OEA, Lakewood Tchrs Assn 1985-; Edctrs of Yr Finalists 1994; *office:* Lakewood HS 14100 Franklin Blvd Lakewood OH 44107

RATHKE, ANNE CELLUCCI, Adjunct Fac Med Practice Mgmt; *b:* Philadelphia, PA; *m:* Christopher; *ed:* PA St Univ (BS) Hlth Planning, Admin 1988; St Joseph's Univ (MS) Hlth Ed 1991; Post Masters Hlth Admin 1993; *cr:* Ind Blue Cross Team Ldr 1988-90; PA Blue Shield Account Mgr 1990-95; Pierce Coll Adj Fac 1993-; United Concordia Cos Inc Sr Account Mgr 1995-; *ai:* Cert Hlth Consultant Blue Cross Blue Shield Assn.

RATHMAN, DENISE RENEE, Science Teacher; *b:* Reading, PA; *m:* Todd A.; *ed:* PA St Univ (BS) Scndry Ed 1993; 12 Post Grad Credit Hrs; *cr:* Reading HS Bio Tchr 1993-; *ai:* Sr Project, Act 178 Staff Dev Comms; NEA 1993-; West Lawn United Meth Church, Sunday Schl Tchr; *office:* Reading Sr HS 801 N 13th St Reading PA 19604

RATKEVICH, GEORGE D., Art Teacher; *b:* New Haven, CT; *ed:* Boston Univ (BFA) Art Ed 1988, (MFA) Art Ed 1994; *cr:* Franklin HS Art Tchr 1994-; *ai:* Art Club Adv; NEA 1994-; *office:* Franklin HS 218 Oak St Franklin MA 02038

RATNER, DONNA STRUMEYER, Spanish Teacher; *b:* Far Rockaway, NY; *m:* Mitchell; *c:* Daniel, Gregg; *ed:* SUNY at Albany (BA) Span 1982; *cr:* Fontbonne Hall Acad Span Tchr 1982-84; Hightstown HS Span, Fr Tchr 1984-; *ai:* Israeli Culture, Span Club Adv; NJEA, FLENJ 1984-; Beth El Sisterhood 1994-, Fundraising; Beth El Hebrew Schl 1995-, Ed Comm; Grant from Partners in Ed at Princeton Univ; *office:* Hightstown HS 25 Leshin Ln Hightstown NJ 08520*

RATNER, ELAINE TAXIN, Sr Assoc Prof of Psychology; *b:* Phila, PA; *m:* Arnold; *c:* Abby Simkus, Jim, Craig, Jane; *ed:* Temple Univ (BA) Ed 1960; Beaver Coll (MAEd) Hlth Ed, Psyc 1981; *cr:* Lynnewood Elem Schl 2nd Grd Tchr 1960-61; Manor Jr Coll Sr Assoc Prof 1982-; *ai:* Mid Sts Accreditation Steering Comm; Perr Review Comm; Long Range Planning Comm; NAEYC; APA; *office:* Manor Jr Coll Foxchase Manor 700 Foxchase Rd Jenkintown PA 19046

RATTERAY, ROSE, Technology & Media Teacher; *b:* New York, NY; *m:* Arthur Kelley; *c:* Christopher; *ed:* Marymount Manhattan (BA) Ed 1973; Columbia Univ-Tchrs Coll (MA) Ed 1977; Attnd Lehman Coll, City Coll NY, Kean Coll, Union Coll, Fairleigh Dickinson, St Peters Coll, Jersey City St Coll, New Schl for Soc Rsrch; Jersey City Bd of Ed In-Svcs 1966-; *cr:* J F Murray #38 Schl Elem & Tech Tchr 16 Yrs; C F Bradford #16 Schl Tech & Media Tchr 4 Yrs; *ai:* INTNL BLACK WOMENS CONGRESS NAACP ROSELLE URBAN Safe Harbor League; Plainfield YWCA Womens Group Westfield Area NOW, Past Adv VP, Cert of Recognition 1986; Feminist Book Club Roselle, Founder; Minority Womens Book Club Linden; Sierra Club; Planned Parenthood NJ, Former Bd Mem; Amateur Astronomers NJ; Amer CiviL Liberties; Hyacinth Fndtn; Comm Food Bank Hillside, Vol, Vol Awd 1995; Bellcore Tchrs Inst, Aids Rsrch Fndtn for Children, Vol; St Claire Home for HIV & AIDS Children, Vol; Minority Womens Issues Lecturer; Comm Activist; Rutgers Univ Project ToolChest Comp Awd 1985 & 1990; Women Helping Women Vol of Yr 1987; Parents Cncl Tchr of Yr #38 Schl 1988; Certs of Appreciation: Fortune Soc 1988, Urban League 1989, Bellcore Tchrs Inst 1992; Governors Awd Tchr of the Yr 1990; Geraldine Dodge Fndtn EarthWatch Expedition 1992 & 1995.

RATTIEN, DIANE, Math Teacher; *b:* Brooklyn, NY; *m:* Harry; *c:* Michele, Peter; *ed:* Brooklyn Coll (BA) Math Ed 1973; NY Univ (MA) Math Ed 1975; Guid C.W. Post; Cmptrs Queens Coll; NSF Grant Math Brooklyn Coll; *cr:* Montauk Jr HS Math Tchr 1973; T. Jefferson HS Math Tchr 1973-74; Bayside HS Math, Rsrch Tchr, Prgm Chair 1980-; *ai:* Rsrch Adv; Prgm Chrpsn; NCTM 1985-; ATM-NYC 1982-; Bergen Beach Civic Assn 1978-, Recording Sec, Outstdng Svc; Nasa Educl Wkshp Math & Sci Tech; Tchr of Yr Awd 1994; *office:* Bayside HS 32nd Ave & Corp Kennedy St Bayside NY 11361

RATZER, MARY BOYD, Senior High School Librarian; *b:* Troy, NY; *m:* Philip J.; *c:* Joseph, David; *ed:* Coll of Saint Rose (BA) Eng 1967; Univ of Albany (MA) Eng 1968, (MLS) Lib & Information Sci 1981; Addl 14 Credits in Effective Tchng Model, Cooperative Learning, Internet Trng; *cr:* Shenendehowa Sr HS Schdry Eng Tchr 1968-85; Karigon Elem Schl Lib Media Specialist 1985-89; Shenendehowa Sr HS Lib Media Specialist 1989-; *ai:* Respect Club, Stu Press & Lib Club Adv; NCTE 1968-; NYLA, SLMS 1981-, Roundtable, VP, Pres; ALA, ENSLYMA 1985-; CHORD 1994-; Red Cross 1975-79; Audubon Soc 1973-; Nature Conservancy 1985-; Beta Phi Mu Intnl Lib Sci Honor Soc; Whos Who in Amer; Whos Who in Ed; Pub in SAANYS & Schl Lib Journals; PTA Life Membership & Distinguished Svc; *office:* Shenendehowa HS 970 Route 146 Clifton Park NY 12065*

RAU, GRACE ANN HENDERSON, Instructor of English & Speech; *b:* Rivesville, WV; *m:* Robert L.; *c:* Michael Schenck, Elizabeth Benner, Anne Digges, Stacy Allen, William C. Schenck; *ed:* Fairmont St Coll (BA) Eng, Speech & Drama 1959; Bowling Green St Univ (MA) Speech 1964; Univ of HI 9 Hrs Grad Work in Eng 1983; *cr:* Annapolis Jr HS Eng Tchr 1961-71; Annapolis Sr HS Eng & Speech Tchr, Dept Chair 1972-92; Anne Arundez Comm Coll Eng & Speech Instr 1992-; *ai:* Reader Consultant for ETS, Advanced Placement Lit & SAT II; NEA 1962-92; Tchrs Assn of Anne Arundez Cty 1962-92; MD St Tchrs Assn 1962-92; Natl Endowment for the Hum Summer Seminar 1989; Curr Writing for Speech; Amer Lit Classes for Anne Arundez Cty Bd of Ed.*

RAU, MELINDA SUSANNE, Chemistry Instructor; *b:* Butler, PA; *ed:* Univ of Pittsburgh (BS) Chem 1986; PA St Univ (PHD) Chem 1992; *cr:* Butler Cty Comm Coll Chem Instr 1990-; *ai:* Phi Theta Kappa Co-Adv; Mid Sts Co-Chair; Acad Affairs; Cultural Diversity; Amer Chem Soc 1986-; *office:* Butler County Comm Coll PO Box 1203 Butler PA 16001

RAUB, SARA WILLEMET, Language Arts Teacher; *b:* Bethlehem, PA; *m:* Robert W.; *c:* Elizabeth; *ed:* Bloomsburg Univ (BS) Ger 1972; Lehigh Univ Sec Eng Cert 1988, Post Grad Stud Eng; Colonial Northampton Intermediate UNit Permanent Cert, Credit Hrs; *cr:* Bethlehem Area Schl Dist Sub Tchr 1980-89; Saucon Vly Schl Dist Sub Tchr 1980-89; Saucon Vly Schl Dist Summer Schl Eng Tchr 1990-91; St Theresa Schl Lang Arts Tchr 1989-; *ai:* Dist I CYO Spelling Bee Coord; Spelling Bee Adv; ADLTA 1989-; Saucon Vly Fine Arts 1992-, Summer Theatre Co-Chprsn; Sigma Sigma Sigma 1972-, Lehigh Vly Alumni Pres; *office:* St Theresa Schl 300 Leonard St Hellertown PA 18055*

RAUCH, CATHY LYNN, HS Social Studies Teacher; *b:* Dayton, OH; *m:* Thomas George; *c:* Bryan, Michael, Molly; *ed:* Univ of Dayton (BS) Comprehensive Soc Stud 1971; Cnslr Ed Stud; *cr:* Bellbrook HS Soc Stud Tchr 1971-; *ai:* FLAME; North Cntrl Curr Stud; Attendance Review; St Proficiency Preperation; NEA, OEA, SEA 1971-; Greene Cty Excl in Tchng Awd 1987, 1988, 1990, 1992, 1995; *office:* Bellbrook HS 3491 Upper Bellbrook Bellbrook OH 45305

RAUCH, JUDITH ADAMS, Vocal Music Teacher; *b:* Pittsburgh, PA; *m:* William J.; *c:* Suzane Logan, Juliana, Matthew; *ed:* Wittenberg Univ (BA) Music 1968; Youngstown St Univ (MA) Music 1976; Addl Hrs Ashland Univ, Univ of Akron; *cr:* Rochester City Schls Vocal Music Tchr 1968; Canfield Local Schls Vocal Music Tchr 1973-76; Lakewood Local Schls Vocal Music Tchr 1981-; *ai:* HS Choir; Men's Ensemble; Women's Ensemble; NEA 1981-; ACDA 1982-; MENC 1969-; St Paul's Luth Church 1977-, Music Dir; Weathervane Playhouse 1985-, Musical Dir; Alleluia Series Writer Pub by Augsburg 1980; *home:* 272 Granville St Newark OH 43055

RAUENZAHN, JOHN O., Fifth Grade Teacher; *b:* Pottsville, PA; *m:* Carolyn Quinn; *c:* Lisa Panus, Karen; *ed:* Millersville Univ Elem Ed (BS) 1963, (MEd) 1969; *cr:* Cocalico Union 4th-5th Grd Tchr 1962-64; Blue Mountain 5th Grd Tchr 1964-; *ai:* Cmptr Sci Lead Tchr; Blue Mt Ed Assn 1964-, Pres, VP; *home:* 3 Dogwood Rd Schuylkill Haven PA 17972

RAUSCH, ROBERT FRANKLIN,JR., Industrial Technology Tchr; *b:* Cambridge, OH; *m:* Deanna R. Barrere; *c:* Dana Raeann; *ed:* OH Northern Univ (BS) Indstrl Tech 1993; *cr:* Hiland HS Tchr 1993-; *ai:* Track, Cross Cntry Coach; *office:* Hiland HS 4400 SR 39 Berlin OH 44610

RAUTER, PATRICIA FROST, Arts Dept Chm & Teacher; *b:* Middletown, OH; *m:* Manfred P.; *c:* Audrey, Paul; *ed:* Miami Univ at Oxford (BA) Art Ed 1973, (MS) Art Ed 1975; RIVA Rsrch Inst at Bethesda 1995; *cr:* Poasttown Elem Art Tchr 1973-84; Madison High Art Tchr 1984-; *ai:* Unified Arts Dept Head; Soph Class & Art Club Spon; NEA, OEA & SWOEA; Madison Ed Assn; Phi Delta Kappa; Qualitative Rsrch Consultants Assn; DAV Auxiliary; Middletown Comm Fndtns Crystal Apple Awd 1993; *office:* Madison HS 1368 Middletown Eaton Rd Middletown OH 45042

RAUX, DONALD JAMES, Asst Professor of Accounting; *b:* Ilion, NY; *c:* D. J., Renee Aimee; *ed:* Herkimer Cty Comm Coll (AAS) Acctng; Univ at Albany (BS) Acctng 1971, (MS) Acctng 1990; Working Towards PHD; *cr:* KPMG Peat Marwick Audit Supvr 1971-78; Galka & Raux CPA Partner 1978-82; Donald J. Raux CPA Owner 1982-; *ai:* Cmptr Lab Dir; Hnrs Comm; Acctng Information Systems, Govt Acctng Courses Coord; Amer Inst CPA, NYS Soc CPA 1973-; Healthcare, Fin Mgr, Past Pres, Reeves Fullmer Awd; Certfd Pub Accountant 1973, Govt Fin Mgr 1995; Who's Who in the East; Who's Who Emerging Ldrs in Amer; *office:* Siena Coll 515 Loudon Rd Loudonville NY 12211

RAVAIOLI, CHARLOTTE MCILWEE, Associate Dean of Support Svc; *b:* Scranton, PA; *m:* Albert; *c:* Maria, Trinka, Maggie; *ed:* Marywood Coll (BA) Ed 1968; Univ of Scranton (MA) Eng 1982; Attnd SUNY at Binghamton; *cr:* keystone Coll Fac 1983-95, Div Chair 1990-95, Assoc Dean of Support Svcs, Non Traditional Programming 1995-; *ai:* Various Comm Chair Positions; NCTE 1982-; Mulberry Poets & Writers 1988-, Pres 1988-94; *office:* Keystone Jr Coll Box 5 La Plume PA 18440

RAVAL, SUSHILA NAVNIT, Psychology Professor; *b:* Dakor, India; *m:* Navnit R.; *c:* Pauravi, Kautilya, Arushi; *ed:* Gujarat Univ (MS) Chem 1953; Amer Univ (MA) Psych Ed 1958, (EDD) Cnslng 1962; St of MD Prof Cnslr; *cr:* Prakash HS Tchr 1953-55; NY Univ Asst Prof 1963-66; Coppin St Coll Prof 1966-; *ai:* Psych Club Adv; Fac Mem of Fac Senate; Chair of Dept Peer Review, Collegewide Appeals, Salary Equity, India-Subcontinent Schlsp Comms; Amer Psychological Assn 1963-; Gujarati Samaj 1975-, First Pres 1975-76; Multiculturalism in Curr Grant; *office:* Coppin St Coll 2500 W North Ave Baltimore MD 21216

RAVANELLI, MICHAEL JOSEPH, English Teacher; *b:* Parma, OH; *m:* Mary E. Gale; *c:* Zachary, Dominic; *ed:* Kent St Univ (BA) Scndry Ed, Eng, Speech 1985; Post Grad Baldwin Wallace Coll, John Carroll Univ; *cr:* Cleveland Pub Schls Tchr 1988-92; Parma City Schls Eng Tchr 1993-; *ai:* Jr Var Bsbl Coach; NEA, OEA 1993-; *office:* Parma Sr HS 6285 W 54th St Parma OH 44129

RAVELING, GORDON REYNOLDS, English & Speech Teacher; *b:* Suffolk, VA; *m:* Pamela Hodge; *c:* Ami; *ed:* Univ of Richmond (BA) Speech, Eng 1961; Univ of MD (MA) Speech, Comms 1969; *cr:* Princess Anne HS Speech, Eng Tchr 1962-67; Beltsville Jr HS Eng Tchr 1974-; Bladensburg HS Eng Tchr 1984-90; High Point HS Eng, Speech Tchr 1990-; *ai:* Pub Speaking, Contest Adv; NEA, MSTA, PGCEA 1974-; *office:* High Point HS 3601 Powder Mill Rd Beltsville MD 20705

RAVENSCROFT, ELIZABETH WERRES, Retired Soc Studies & Rel Tchr; *b:* Washington, DC; *m:* F. Ian; *c:* Paul F., Christopher I., Timothy A., Anne E., Katheirne M.; *ed:* Saint Mary's Coll at Notre Dame (BS) Elem Ed 1952; Georgetown Univ at Washington (BA) Amer His 1960; Cert Theological Stud Schl of Continuing Ed 1990; 27 Credit Hrs Towards MA Theology Church His; Cert Primary Grds Univ of MD 1980; *cr:* DC Pub Schls 4th Grd Tchr 1952-53; Annunciation Schl 4th-5th Grd Tchr 1957-59; USAF Brize Norton Sac 1st Grd Tchr 1960; Wilson Lane Schl Co-Founder,

Co-Dir 1963-85; Woods Acad 1st Grd Rel Tchr 1980-81, 8th Grd Soc Stud Tchr 1980-82, 7th-8th Grd Soc Stud Tchr 1982-90, 8th Grd Rel Tchr 1986-90; *ai:* Stu Cncl Co-Moderator; Encouraged, Dir Schl Constitution Written; Liturgy Dir, Co-Planner 1985-90; Co-Spon Drama Club; *home:* 10245 Gainsborough Rd Potomac MD 20854

RAVER, DEBRA ELLEN (ESHELMAN), English Teacher; *b:* York, PA; *m:* David Alan; *c:* Kenton, Caitlin; *ed:* Shippensburg Univ (BS) Eng & Scndry Ed 1971; PA Permanent Cert 1974; Masters Equivalency Course Work Ed 1995; Penn St Univ Post-Grad Stud; *cr:* West York Area Schls 7th Grd Eng Tchr 1971-77; Dallastown Area Schls HS Eng Tchr 1986-; *ai:* DAEA 1971-77 & 1986-; PSEA 1971-77 & 1986-; NEA 1971-77 & 1986-.

RAVERT, E. CAROL HOPKINS, Fourth Grade Teacher; *b:* Philadelphia, PA; *m:* John Alfred; *c:* John Arthur; *ed:* Westchester St Univ (BS) Elem Ed 1956; *cr:* Hartranft Elem Schl Kndgtn Tchr 1956-57; Chester Elem Schl Grd 5 Tchr 1957-58, Grd 4 Tchr 1958-; *ai:* Report Card, Orange Co Historical Exchange Comms; NEA, NYSTA 1957-; Chester Tchrs Assn 1957-, Sec; Negotiation Team 1962-; Lib Bd 1986-; ABC Rdng Assn 1976-; Church Session, Deacon Choir 1957-; Salvation Army 1975-, Rep; Rsrch & Writing of Local His Book for Orange Cty; *office:* Chester Elementary School 2 Herbert Dr Chester NY 10918*

RAWLINGS, ROSS SCOTT, Vocal Music Director; *b:* Baltimore, MD; *ed:* Harford Comm Coll (AA) Music 1985; Towson St Univ (BS) Music Ed, Piano 1993; *cr:* Music Theater Group Music Dir 1985-90; Slayton House Performing Arts Camp Music Dir 1990-95; Toby's Theater Music Dir 1990-; *ai:* Schl Musicals Dir; Women's Choir, Quartet; Men's Quartet, Choir; Gospel, Jazz Choirs; NEA, MMEA 1993-; MENC 1991-; *office:* Atholton HS 6520 Freetown Rd Columbia MD 21044

RAWLINS, W. SCOTT, Assistant Prof of Fine Arts; *b:* New Brunswick, NJ; *ed:* Earlham Coll (BA) Bio 1976; George Washington Univ (MAT) Museum Ed 1981; Univ of MI (MEA) Med & Biological Illustration 1989; Attnd Antioch Coll, USDA Grad Schl, Schl of Visual Arts, Mason Gross Schl of Arts at Rutgers Univ; *cr:* Calvert Marine Museum Dir of Ed 1982-86; Pub Museum of Grand Rapids Curator of Natural Sci 1990-94; Kendall Coll of Art & Design Adj Instr 1991-94; Beaver Coll Asst Prof of Fine Arts 1994-; *ai:* Internship Coord; Acad Standing & Undergrad Acad Pgms Comm; Amer Assn of Museums 1980-; Guild of Natural Sci Illustrators 1980-, Pgms Asst; Amer Museum of Natural His & Calvert Manhe Museum Displayed Illustrations; Beaver Coll Fac Dev Grant; *office:* Beaver Coll 450 S Easton Rd Glenside PA 19038

RAWSKI, MARGARET A., Kindergarten Teacher; *b:* Buffalo, NY; *ed:* Immaculata Coll at Hilbert (AA) Lbrl Arts 1967; Medaille Coll (BSEd) Elem Ed 1969; St Univ Coll at Buffalo (MSEd) Elem Ed; SUNY at Buffalo Addl Stud; Southtowns Tchr Ctr Insvc & Grad Hrs; *cr:* Frontier Cntrl Schl System Elem Tchr 1969-; *ai:* NYSUT 1969-; AFT 1969-; Frontier Cntrl Tchrs Assn 1969-; St Bernadettes RC Church 1981-, Music Ministry, Liturgy Comm, Mission & Renew; Sheas Performing Arts Ctr, Vol Usher; *office:* Cloverbank Elem Schl 2761 Cloverbank Rd Hamburg NY 14075

RAWSON, JULIE, English Teacher; *b:* Steubenville, OH; *ed:* W Liberty St Coll (BA) Eng Ed 1985; Grad Stud at Ashland Univ; *cr:* Steubenville Cath Cntrl Schl Eng Tchr 1985-86; Bridge St Jr HS Eng Tchr 1986-87; Toronto HS & Karaffa MS Eng Tchr 1987-89; Ashland MS Lang Arts Tchr 1989-; *ai:* Chrldng & Power of Pen Coach; Writing Team Adv; Tchr Mentor; Inclusion of All Disciplines Comm Mem; OCTELA; NCTE 1985-; NEA, OEA 1987-; *office:* Ashland MS 345 Cottage St Ashland OH 44805

RAWSON, PAMELA MORIN, Mathematics Facilitator; *b:* Framingham, MA; *m:* David; *ed:* Univ of Lowell (BS) Math 1986; Univ of ME Math; Univ of Southern ME Ed; *cr:* Portland HS Math Tchr 1988-90; Cape Elizabeth HS Math Tchr 1990-95; Brunswick/SAD 75 Beacon Math Fac 1995-; *ai:* Math Team Coach; Co-Dir Southern ME Sci & Math Acad 1993-95; *office:* Brunswick SAD 75 Beacon Center C/O Brunswick Schl Dept Brunswick ME 04011*

RAWSON, PATRICIA ANN, Teacher & Coach; *b:* Southampton, NY; *ed:* SUNY at Brockport (BS) PE, His 1971; Attnd St Bonaventure Univ; *cr:* Cuba Rushford Cntrl Tchr, Coach 25 Yrs; *ai:* Var Vlybl, Girls, Boys Var Sftbl Coach; NY PE, Recreation Assn; NY St Coaches Assn; Allegany Cty Coach of Yr 1986; Cuba Chamber of Commerce Woman of Yr 1986; Western NY PE Tchr of Yr 1995; *office:* Cuba-Rushford Central Schl 15 Elm St Cuba NY 14727*

RAWSON AYERS, NANCY HARRIS, English & Journalism Teacher; *b:* Olean, NY; *m:* Dennis M.; *ed:* St Bonaventure Univ (BA) Eng 1970; Grad Credit Hrs Mansfield Univ, East Stroudsburg Univ, St Bonarenture Univ; *cr:* Oswayo Valley Jr Sr HS Eng Tchr 1970-; *ai:* Schl Newspaper Adv; OVTA 1970-, Past Pres; PSEA, NEA 1970-; Delta Kappa Gamma 1978-; Eureka Chapter #52 Order of Eastern Star 1978-; Amer Legion Auxiliary Post #530 1971-; Shinglehouse United Meth Church; 2 Local Schl Yrbk Dedications 1985 & 1987; Oswago Valley Alumni Assn Tchr of the Yr 1995; *office:* Oswayo Valley Jr Sr HS Box 610 Shinglehouse PA 16748*

RAY, DAWN MAUREEN, 9th-12th Grd Spcl Ed Teacher; *b:* Prince Frederick, MD; *m:* Reginald; *c:* Tonique, Devlyn; *ed:* Coppin St Coll (BS) Spec Ed 1979; Attnd Bowie St Univ, George Washington Univ & Western MD Coll; *cr:* Northern HS Tchr 1980-, Records Coord 1987-; *ai:* NEA 1980-; Learning Disabilities Assn Tchr of the Yr Awd 1990, Employee of the Month; *office:* Northern HS 2950 Chaneyville Rd Owings MD 20736

RAY, DONNA FLANAGAN, Second Grade Teacher; *b:* Fort Devens Ayer, MA; *m:* Shelton Bradley; *c:* Ryan F., Erin D.; *ed:* Endicott Jr Coll (AA) Liberal Arts 1965; Emerson Coll (BS) Speech Audiology, Pathology 1968; *cr:* YMCA Nursery Schl Tchr 1968-69; Headstart Tchr 1969-70; North St Schl Readiness, 1st Grd Tchr 1970-72; Bakersville Schl 2nd, 3rd Grd Tchr 1972-; *ai:* 4-H Vol; NCEA 1970-72; NHEA, MEA 1972-; Auburn Village PTA 1979-89; Meml HS Boosters 1989-93; *office:* Bakersville Schl 20 Elm St Manchester NH 03103

RAY, ELIZABETH GLOVER, English & Language Arts Tchr; *b:* Siler City, NC; *c:* Dalida Devore Ray-Price, Darryl Eugene; *ed:* Manhattan CC (AA) Liberal Arts 1973; Hunter Coll (BA) Studio Art, Elem Ed 1975, (MS) Elem Ed 1981; *cr:* Dist 30Q Schls Para-Prof 1968-79, Per-Diem Tchr 1979-80; IS 145Q-IS126Q Drug Cnslr 1980-82; IS 126Q Tchr 1982-; *ai:* Yrbk Adv; Team Tchr Soc Comm; Restructuring Comm Stu Affairs; NEA & AFT; New Victory Theater Educl Panel 1994-; Lincoln Ctr Ed Panel; Tchr of Yr 1994-95 Dist 30Q; *office:* IS 126 Astoria 31-51 21st St Long Island City NY 11106

RAY, ELLEN EVERETT, English Teacher; *b:* Patterson, NJ; *m:* J. Craig; *c:* Robyn R.; *ed:* Marietta Coll (BA) Eng Ed 1967; *cr:* Bergenfield HS Eng Tchr 1968; Marietta HS Eng Tchr 1968-69; Accotink Acad Classroom Tchr 1985-88; Covington MS Eng Tchr 1989-90; Pottsville Area HS Eng Tchr 1992-; *ai:* Jr Class Adv; NEA 1992-; PSEA 1992-; Schuylkill Cty Symphony Guild 1992-, Sec; Rape Crisis Advy Bd 1996; *office:* Pottsville Area HS 16th & Elk Ave Pottsville PA 17901

RAY, JAMES ELLIOTT,JR., High School Mathematics Tchr; *b:* Fort Dix, NJ; *m:* JoAnn Younger; *c:* James Elliott Ray III; *ed:* Trenton St Coll (BA) Math Ed 1979; *cr:* Ewing HS Math Tchr 1979-; South Brunswick HS Math Tchr 1987-; *ai:* Former Asst Ftbl Coach; Asst Girls Spring Track Coach; Former Head Coach Winter Track 1983-86; Former Frosh Wrestling Coach 1987-89; ETEA 1979-, Treas 1 Yr; NJEA, NEA 1979-; St John Bapt Church 1968-91, Deacon 1984-91; Cntrl Bapt Church 1992-, Chrstn Ed Comm; Govenors Tchr Recognition Awd 1990; Ewing HS ABCD Awd 1990; *office:* Ewing HS 900 Parkway Ave Ewing Twp NJ 08618

RAY, JANE ELIZABETH, English Teacher; *b:* New York City, NY; *c:* Liza Petruzzelli; *ed:* Hunter Coll (BA) Speech, Theatre 1969, (MA) Speech, Theatre 1972; 30 Addl Credits Queens Coll Film Stud, Rsrch; *cr:* L. D. Brandeis HS Eng Tchr 1969-77; Richmond Hill HS Eng Tchr 1981-; *ai:* Coll Adv 1989-93; AFT 1972-; Screen Actors Guild 1982-, Offbeat, Author; Amer Fed TV, Radio Artists 1981-, The Doctors, NBC; Dev Film Stud Curr L. D. Brandeis HS, Richmond Hill HS; *office:* Richmond Hill HS 89-30 114th St Richmond Hill NY 11418*

RAY, JENNIFER LEE (ULREY), English Teacher; *b:* Bethesda, MD; *m:* John W.; *ed:* Bowling Green St Univ (MA) Philosophy 1982; Western MD Coll (BA) Philosophy 1980; Montgomery Coll (AA) Lbrl Arts 1978; Univ of Cincinnati; Admin Acad; Paideia Trng Xavier Univ; *cr:* Aiken HS 9th-12th Grd Eng Tchr 1985-86; Hughes HS 9th-12th Grd Eng Tchr 1986-87; Schroder Paideia Jr High 7th Grd Eng Tchr 1987-89; Hughes Ctr 9th-12th Grd Eng Tchr 1989-; *ai:* Cincinnati Fed of Tchrs 1985-; AFT 1985-; Cincinnati Zoo & Botonical Garden, Vol; Sierra Club 1985-; *office:* Hughes Ctr 2515 Clifton Ave Cincinnati OH 45219*

RAY, MICHELE LYNNE, French & Spanish Teacher; *b:* Elberon, NJ; *m:* Alan; *c:* Brian; *ed:* Montclair St Univ (BA) Fr, Span 1971; Monmouth Univ (Mat) Scndry Ed 1975; *cr:* Manasquan HS Fr & Span Tchr 1971-; *ai:* Fr Club Adv; Led Several Groups to France with Amer Cncl for Intnl Stud; NEA, MEA 1971-; *home:* 67 Cotswold Cir Asbury Park NJ 07712*

RAY, SANDRA GLINKA, Mathematics Teacher; *b:* Nashua, NH; *m:* Peter M.; *c:* Laurie Ann; *ed:* Rivier Coll (BA) Math 1969; *cr:* Mitre Corp Cmptr Programmer 1969-70; Chelmsford MA Schl System Math Tchr 1970-81; Pub Service of NH Systems Analyst 1982-86; Hudson NH HS Math Tchr 1986-; *ai:* Calculus League Adv; AFT, NH-ATMNE; Alvirne HS Tchr of Yr 1989-90; *office:* Alvirne H S Derry Rd Hudson NH 03051*

RAY, SUE ANN, Math Dept Chairperson & Tchr; *b:* Alliance, OH; *m:* Larry A.; *c:* Anthony R., Aleta N.; *ed:* OK Chrstn Coll (BSE) Ed & Math 1982; 15 Grad Level Credit Hrs; Working on Masters at Ashland Univ; *cr:* West Branch Jr High Sub Tchr 1982-83; St Thomas Aquinas HS Math Tchr 1983-; *ai:* Frosh Class Moderator 1988-; New Tchr Mentor 1992-; Math Dept Chprsn 1992-; Stu Tchr Cooperating Tchr 1996; Diocese of Youngstown Confederation of Tchrs 1983-; NCTM 1990-; Grant for Masters Work Kent St Univ 1992; *office:* St Thomas Aquinas HS 2121 Reno Dr Louisville OH 44641

RAY, TROY R., High School English Teacher; *b:* Painesville, OH; *ed:* Univ of ME at Fort Kent (BA) Eng 1990; Kent St Univ (MAT) Eng 1993; *cr:* Lakeland Comm Coll Part-Time Fac & Eng Tchr 1993-94; Kenston HS Eng Tchr 1994-; *ai:* Girls Var Soccer Head Coach; NEA 1994-; *office:* Kenston HS 17425 Snyder Rd Chagrin Falls OH 44023

RAYBUCK, ANNIE FARRELL, Seventh Grade Teacher; *b:* Pittsburgh, PA; *m:* David Edward; *c:* David Emerick, James Farrell; *ed:* Edinboro Univ (BSEd) Elem Ed 1973; Duquesne Univ (MSEd) Theology 1994; Penn St Univ 24 Post Grad Stud Elem Ed; *cr:* Laurenceville Cath MS 6th-8th Grd Tchr 1973-74; Ambridge Area Cath Schl 1st-3rd Grd Tchr 1974-77; Divine Mercy Acad 6th-8th Grd Tchr 1977-; *ai:* Barbershoppe Quartet After Schl Prgm; Dramatic Rel Presentations; Natl Cncl of Geography Ed 1994-, Distinguished Tchr Achvmt Awd; NCEA; St Agatha Church 1994-, Parish Cncl, Worship Comm; Diocese of Pgh Golden Apple Awd; Beaver Cty Edctrs Assn Grants; *office:* Divine Mercy Acad 609 10th St Beaver Falls PA 15010

RAYL, BRIAN LEE, Physics & Chemistry Teacher; *b:* Painesville, OH; *ed:* Lakeland Comm (AA) Math & Sci 1970; Kent St (BS) Math, Physics & Chem 1973; 31 Credit Hrs Physics & Stu Behavioral Cnslrs; *cr:* Fairport Bd of Ed Math Tchr 1974-78; Berkshire Bd of Ed Math & Sci Tchr 1978-85; Willoughby-Eastlake Bd of Ed Physics & Chem Tchr 1985-; *ai:* OEA & NEA 1974-, Local Assn All Offices, Prof Stans Comm Vice-Chair; OCTM 1975-; Tri-Cty Cncl 1974-, Pres; CARES 1973-, Pres, Svc Awd; Lake Co Sheriffs Office 1983-, Dispatcher; Martha Holden Jennings; Featured on CNN; Local Media Items; Sci Tchr of Yr 1994; Sci Fun in the Classroom Seminar Conducter; *office:* North HS 34041 Stevens Blvd Willoughby OH 44095*

RAYMER, ANDREA COLEMAN, Fifth Grade Teacher; *b:* Pittsburg, PA; *m:* Dennis; *ed:* Univ of Clarion (BS) Elem Ed 1966; Penn St Univ Post Grad Stud; *cr:* Hubert St Schl 4th Grd Tchr 1966; Muse & Cecil Elem Schls Kndgtn Tchr 1966-67; Cecil & Hills Hendersonville Schls Kndgtn Tchr 1967-68; Hills-Hendersonville Elem Schl 2nd & 4th-6th Grd Tchr 1968-89; Cecil Elem 4th Grd Tchr 1989-90; Borland Manor Elem Schl 5th Grd Tchr 1990-; *ai:* Natl Geographics Geog Bee Spon 1990-95; Instrl Support Team Mem 1990-95; PSEA 1966-; NEA 1966-; CMEA 1966-; Holy Rosary Altar Soc & Chrstn Mothers Conferternity 1983-, Treas; Canon McMillan Schl Dist Tchr of Yr 1986-87; *home:* 24 Papp Rd Canonsburg PA 15317

RAYMOND, CHRISTOPHER CURTIS, His Teacher & Media Specialist; *b:* Waltham, MA; *m:* Lori Kinley; *c:* Abigail, Wil; *ed:* Lyndon St Coll (BS) Outdoor Ed 1981; Tchng Cert Scndry Ed 1984; *cr:* Daisy Bronson Jr HS Chptr 1 Rdng Specialist 1984-86; Leland & Gray Union HS His Tchr 1986-92; Lyndon Inst His Tchr 1992-; *ai:* Media Specialist; South Vt His Alliance 1988-; Ruffed Grouse Soc 1993-; Boating, Snowmobile Safety Instr 1990-; VT Pub Access Bd 1995-, Treas; VT St Police 1988-, Aux Trooper Commanders Citation; *office:* Lyndon Inst College Rd Box 127 Lyndon Center VT 05850

RAYMOND, JAMES F., Mathematics Teacher; *b:* Philadelphia, PA; *m:* Carolyn D. Wagner; *c:* Kimberly, Sonia, Michele; *ed:* Indiana Univ of PA (BS) Math, Ed 1968; Grad Work at Indiana Univ of PA, PA St Univ, Univ of Pittsburgh; *cr:* Purchase Line HS Math Tchr 1968-, Scndry Gifted Coord 1986-; Univ of Pittsburgh Part-time Instr 1986-; *ai:* NHS Adv; Gray Mattu Team, Quiz Bowl Team Coach; PSEA, NEA, PLEA 1968-; *office:* Purchase Line HS RD 1 Box 374 Commodore PA 15729

RAYMOND, JOHN MICHAEL, Junior HS Mathematics Teacher; *b:* Wheeling, WV; *m:* Susan Kay Leach; *c:* Kim, John T.; *ed:* OH Univ (BSEd) Soc Stud 1973, (BSEd) Elem Ed 1977; 12 Credit Hrs E-Math Prgm 1994; *cr:* Adena-Dillonvale Cath 5th-8th Grd Tchr 1973-77; New Athens Elem 5th-8th Grd Tchr 1977-87; Jewett-Scio Jr HS 7th-8th Grd Tchr 1987-; *ai:* 7th-8th Grd Class Adv; Calendar Comm; NEA 1977-; Cadiz Bsbl Assn 1986-, VP; *office:* Jewett Scio Jr Sr HS 322 W Main St Scio OH 43988

RAYMOND, LANA LIPPOLI, Sixth Grade Teacher; *b:* Williamsport, PA; *m:* John B.; *ed:* Williamsport Area Comm Coll (AAS) Cmptr Sci 1983; Millersville Univ (BS) Elem Ed 1974; 25 Post Grad Credit Hrs PA Permanent Cert Level II Elem Ed; *cr:* Lewisburg Area MS Grd 6 Rdng, Lang Arts, Math Tchr 1974-81; C. E. McCall MS Grd 6 Rdng, Lang Arts Tchr 1985-; *ai:* Spelling Bee Grds 5-8 Co-Spon; Asst Chrldng Coach Lewisburg 2 Yrs; NEA, PA St Ed Assn 1974-81, 1985-; Montoursville Area Ed Assn 1985-; *office:* C. E. Mc Call MS 600 Willow St Montoursville PA 17754*

RAYMOND, MICHLENA P., Mathematics Teacher; *b:* Silver Creek, NY; *m:* Curtis M.; *c:* Renee Raymond Brogger, Ross; *ed:* SUNY at Fredonia (BA) Fr 1965, (MS) Ed 1984; 57 Addl Hrs; *cr:* Silver Creek, Forestville, Lake Shore Cntrl Schls K-12th Grd Tchr 1965-78; Seneca Nation of Indians 7-12th Grd Tchr, Tutor 1978-83; Frontier Cntrl Schl Math Tchr 1983-91; Silver Creek Cntrl Schl Math Tchr 1991-; *ai:* Class Adv; NYSUT, AFT 1983-; Girl Scouts of Amer 1971-82, Troop Ldr; Tri-Cty Cntry Club 1970-; Anderson Lee Lib 1992-, Sec; *office:* Silver Creek Cnt Dickinson St Silver Creek NY 14136

RAYMOND, ROBERT BENJAMIN LUCAS, 7th-12th Grade C Teacher; *b:* Philadelphia, PA; *ed:* Temple Univ (BA) German 198 of Pittsburgh (MAT) Frgn Lang Ed 1992; Attnd Karl Eberhards Philosophy & Modern German Lit 1987-90; *cr:* Concordia Lang V Tchr & Cnslr 1990; Camden City Schls ESL Instr & Elem 1991; Pi Public Schl Ger Tchr 1991-92; Southern Regnl HS Ger Tchr & Coord 1992-; *ai:* Ger Natl Honor Soc Adv; AATG 1991-; NJEA Grad Internships for Tchrs Training Pa St Modern Lang Assn 199 Profs Prize Temple Univ 1987; *office:* Southern Regional HS 600 St Manahawkin NJ 08050

RAYNER, JANICE LEE, English Teacher; *b:* Worcester, MA; *m:* Edward Magiera; *ed:* Univ of MA at Amherst (BA) Eng 1968; Clar (MA) Eng 1980; Comparative Ed Russia, USA Univ of Alburueque *cr:* Clark Univ Tchng Asst 1971-72; Doherty HS Eng Tchr 1968-77; HS Eng Tchr 1978-87; Doherty HS Eng Tchr 1988-; *ai:* Women's 2000 Mem; Raise Arabian Horses 1980-; EAW, NEA, MTA Daybreak Battered Womens Shelter 1978-, Bd of Dir, Hot Line V YES Awd; Book Reviewer, Worchester TeleGram; Gazette 19 Cultural Diversity Wkshp Trainer; Recertification Panel Cntrl Adm Attorney Tchr Ed Partnership Member 1994-; *office:* Doherty Me HS 299 Highland St Worcester MA 01602*

RAYNER, PATRICIA ANN, Science Teacher; *b:* Bridgeport, CT; *m* Edward; *ed:* Western CT St Coll (BS) Scndry Earth Sci 1973; Cntrl Coll (MS) General Sci 1977; Southern CT St Univ 6th Yr Admin Univ of WA Post Grad Stud 1980; *cr:* Madison Jr HS Sci Tchr 19 Turn of River MS Sci Tchr 1979-80; Bethel HS Sci Tchr 1980-; *ai:* of 1999 Adv; Sci Curr, New England Assn of Schls, Colls Comms; M Prgm St of CT; Phi Delta Kappan; NSTA; CEA; NEA; Woodcreek V Condo Assn, Sec; Articles Pub; CONNECT, NE Utilities Grant; Bethel HS Education Park Bethel CT 06801*

RAZAVI, FRANK, Electrical & Cmptr Tech Instr; *b:* Tehran, Ira Anita Anissi; *c:* Christopher, Alexander, Michael; *ed:* St Univ of Buffalo (BS) Electrical & Cmptr Engrng 1984, (MA) Applied Math Worcester Polytechnic Inst (MS) Electrical Engrng 1988; *cr:* N Comm Coll Instr 1988-89; Finger Lake Comm Coll Instr 1989 Sabbatical Comm; Enrollment Mgmt; NEA 1988-; IEEE 1984-; B Advy Bd of Ed 1992-; Grant from Texas Instrument & OH St Univ *office:* Finger Lakes Comm Coll 4355 Lake Shore Dr Canandaigu 14424*

RAZOR, SHARON L., English Teacher; *b:* Mt Sterling, KY; *ed:* E KY Univ (BA) Eng 1969; Xavier Univ (MED) Ed, Eng 1973; Attnd Univ, Univ of Cincinnati, Miami Univ; *cr:* Oak Hills Local Schls Eng 1969-; *ai:* Fac Forum; NEA; OH EA; Oak Hills EA; NCTE; 1983 T Yr; Completed Trng TESA, EHSA, Madeline Hunter Mastery Tchng Writing Project, SW OH Lang Arts Acad Mem; *office:* Oak Hills Schls 3200 Ebenezer Rd Cincinnati OH 45248

RAZUKAS, JOHN M., Electromechanical Engrng Prof; *b:* Brooklyn, *ed:* Polytechnic Inst of NY (BS) Mechanical Engr 1969, (MS) Mecha Engr 1970; *cr:* City of NY Dept of Environmental Protection Admin 1972-84; Pratt Inst Visiting Prof 1982-88; Cooper Union Adj Assoc 1988-; NYC Tech Coll Chm 1984-; *ai:* Dept Chm; Coll Cncl; Prs Budget Comm; Curr Comm; Divisional Admin Cncl; Cncl of Acad Af Amer Soc of Mechanical Engrs 1969-, Exec Comm, Appreciation Aw Chair Prof Dev Comm & Chair Satellite Comm; Polytechnic Tchng Fl 1969-70; *office:* City Univ Of NY NY City Tech 300 Jay St Brooklyr 11201

REA, MARY SCHAUFERT, Assistant Professor of Biology; *b:* Lanca PA; *m:* Mark S.; *c:* Anne C., Katherine M.; *ed:* OH St Univ (BS) Bi 1972; Univ of Ottawa (MS) Bio 1984; *cr:* Dublin MS Life Sci 1972-78; HVCC Adjunct Bio Tchr 1989-92; Russell Sage Coll Adjunc Tchr 1992-94; Sage Jr Coll Asst Prof 1994-; *ai:* Curr Comm; NABT 1 HAPS 1994-; Sigma Xi, ESATYCB 1995-; Phi Theta Kappa Tchr o 1995; Returning Womens Prgm Cert of Recognition 1995 Russell Coll; *office:* Sage Jr Coll Of Albany 140 New Scotland Ave Albany 12208*

REA, RUTH WILSON, Music Teacher & Band Director; *b:* Pittsbu PA; *m:* Richard M. Jr.; *c:* Margaret, Richard III; *ed:* Duquesne Univ Music Ed 1984; 39 Credit Hrs in Music Ed Post Grad; *cr:* Linesville Band Dir 1984-92; Conneaut Lake Sadsbury Elem Classroom M Instrumental 1992-; *ai:* PMEA, NEA, CEA 1984-; Church Choir Ashtabula Symphony Orch, Band 1992-; *office:* Conneaut Lake Sads HS 630 Line St Conneaut Lake PA 16316

REA, THOMAS ROBERT, Chemistry Teacher; *b:* Donora, PA; *m:* D Mary Mc Grew; *c:* Timothy, Paul, David; *ed:* CA St Univ (BS) Chem 1 WV Univ (MS) Chem 1967; Addl 74 Credits; *cr:* Plymouth-Whitem HS Chem Tchr 1967-; *ai:* Colonial Ed Assn, PA ED Assn, NEA 1967- Joseph's Univ Outstanding HS Tchr of Yr 1983-84; Whitemars Women's Club Outstanding Scndry Educator 1983-84; Clark Univ Alu Outstanding Scndry Tchr Awd 1984; Franklin & Marshal Alu Outstanding Scndry Tchr Awd 1984; Finalist PA Tchr of Yr Awd 1986 St Univ Distinguished Tchr of Honors Stdnts Awd 1991; *office:* Plymo Whitemarsh HS Germantown Pike Plymouth Meeting PA 19462

READ, ELLEN HEATH, Business Teacher; *b:* Schenectady, NY Laurel, Melissa; *ed:* Hope Coll (BA) Bus Admin 1970; St Univ of NY (Adv Classroom Tchng 1978; MS Coll of Saint Rose (MS) Educl Ad 1988; *cr:* Schenectady Cty Comm Coll Adjunct Prof 1980-88; Niskay Schls Bus Tchr & Ad Intern 1988-89; Shenendehowa Schls Bus 1989-90; South Glens Falls Bus Tchr 1990-; *ai:* Bus Club Fac Adv; Delta Kappa; NBEA; NYS Bus Tchrs Assn; *office:* South Glens Falls C Schls 6 Bluebird Rd South Glens Falls NY 12803*

READ, EVELYN ROEDEL, First Grade Teacher; *b:* Jamaica Queens, *m:* Arthur John; *c:* Barry David, Gail Patricia Read Spillett; *ed:* St U Coll (BS) Early Chldhd 1963; *cr:* Bicycle Path Elem Schl 1st Grd T 1963-70; Hawkins Path Elem Schl 1st Grd Tchr 1970-; *ai:* NYSUT; Cntry Tchrs Assn; St Univ Coll Oneonta Alumni Life Mbrshp; Kappa De Pi 1963-; PTA; Family Motor Coach Assn; Family Campers & RV Stump Jumpers Camping Club Ex VP, Pres; BSA Merit Badge Cn Jenkins Meml Awd; NY St Congress of Parents & Tchrs Awd Life M *home:* 16 Giant Oak Rd Ridge NY 11961

READ, MAUREEN (HAY), English Teacher; *b:* Philadelphia, PA; Edward; *c:* James, Susan Hirsch, Michael, Anne; *ed:* Byran Coll (BA) Lit 1958; 12 Hrs Undergrad Millersburg St Coll; 6 Hrs Post Grad Tem Univ; *cr:* Boyerstown Area HS Eng, Soc Stud Tchr 1960-63; Leba Evangelical Schl For Girls Eng Tchr 1963-66; Twin Vly HS Eng T 1966-67; Twin Vly Bible Acad Eng Tchr 1975-; *ai:* Drama; Twin Vly Bi Chapel 1978-, Tchr, Ldr Womens Groups, Act; Pub Numerous Articl Books: Like a Watered Garden, The Least One, Earthen Vessel; *home:* Box 39 Narvon PA 17555

READ, ROBERT ALLEN, Band Director; *b:* Pottstown, PA; *m:* R Radakovic; *c:* Brian, Stephanie, Rachel; *ed:* IN Univ of PA (BA) Music 1980, (MA) Music 1989; *cr:* Churchill Schl Dist Band Dir 1980- Gateway Schl Dist Band Dir 1982-; *ai:* Marching, Jazz Bands; Br ıle; Stage Crew; Musical; NEA, PSEA 1980-; Phi Mu Alpha 1978-; Gateway Sr HS 2629 Mosside Blvd Monroeville PA 15146

ROBERT VERNON, Fifth Grade Teacher; *b:* Meriden, CT; *m:* Cosenza; *ed:* Cntrl Conn St Univ (BS) Elem Ed 1968; Southern Conn (MS) Traffic, Safety 1973; Cntrl Conn St Univ 6th Yr Crt Rdng *r:* Mary E. Griswold Elem Schl 5 Grd Tchr 1968-; Berlin HS Driver ırd, Instr 1977-; *ai:* Wallingford TWIST Soccer Tournament Dir; Team; Noon Hr Sports Coach, Prgm Facilitator with Gym Tchr; ating Tchr Coll Prepatory Tchng Prgm; NEA 1968-; CEA, BEA VP Berlin Assn; Assn Supervision, Curr Dev 1995-; Presenter r Wkshp Critical Viewing of Television; Co-Presenter Amer Univ itical Viewing on TV; Berlin Tchr of Yr 1991; *office:* Mary E. ld Elem Schl 133 Heather Ln Berlin CT 06037*

SHIRLEY ZAKRZEWSKI, Science Teacher; *b:* South Amboy, Ernie; *c:* Brad; *ed:* Rutgers Univ (BA) Biological Sci 1972; Working MA Rutgers Grad Schl of Ed; *cr:* East Brunswick HS Sci Tchr *ai:* Sr Class Adv; Environment Club Adv; NEA 1972-; NJ Sci Tchr 980-; Sayreville Environmental Comm 1990-; Howard Hughes Med ant; *office:* East Brunswick HS 380 Cranbury Rd East Brunswick NJ

INGER, MARY LOU, English Teacher; *b:* Lykens, PA; *m:* Gregory : Gregory James, Matthew Daniel, Mary Ann; *ed:* Bloomsburg Univ pan, Eng 1975; *cr:* Tri Valley HS Span, Eng tchr 1976-; *ai:* Quiz Team, Yrbk Advs; PSEA, NEA 1976-, Treas; Little League Assn Pres 3 Yrs; Lead Tchr; Mentor Tchr; Newspaper in Ed Liaison ·; *home:* 433 E Market St Williamstown PA 17098

AN, CHRISTINE M., School Counselor; *b:* Rochester, NY; *ed:* l Univ (BS) Human Dev, Family Stud 1987; Univ of Rochester (MS) 39; Permanent Cert NYS Schl Cnslng; *cr:* Rochester City Schl Dist nslr 1990-91; Elmira City Schl Dist Schl Cnslr 1992-; *ai:* Sr Class Natl Bd of Certfd Cnslrs 1993-; SCT Cnslrs Assn 1992-; Inst for ol Theory Reality Therapy Quality Mngmt, Assoc Mem; *office:* Free Acad HS 933 Hoffman St Elmira NY 14905*

SON, DAVID B., Earth Science & Driver Ed Tchr; *b:* Denver, CO; *m:* Meade; *c:* Matthew, Michael, Bill; *ed:* Univ of CO (BA) Geology Boston Coll (MST) Earth Sci 1968; Peace Corps Trng; Attnd Univ at Kansas City; *cr:* US Peace Corps Peace Corps Vol 1965-67; od Pub Schls Earth Sci Tchr 1967-74; Webutuck Cntrl Schl Earth Drivers Ed Tchr 1974-; *ai:* Drama Club Tech Dir; Track & Cross Coach; NEA 1967-; AFT 1994; Wassaic Fire Co 1975-, Sec; Wassaic e Squad 1978-, Chief; Conservation Advy Commission 1986-, Chm; g Valley Assn & Harlem Valley Rail Trail 1989-; Concerned Citizens Harlem Valley Env, Pres 1995-; *office:* Webutuck Cntrl Schl Box N Rd Amenia NY 12501*

SON, JANET MEADE, Social Studies Teacher; *b:* Sharon, CT; *m:* B.; *c:* Matthew D., Michael R., William J.; *ed:* Wellesley Coll (BA) 967; St Univ of NY at New Paltz (MS) Ed & Scndry Soc Stud 1985; rwood Pub Schls HS Soc Stud Tchr 1967-71; Webutuck Central Schl oc Stud Tchr 1981-; *ai:* Stu Cncl, NHS & Mock Court Adv; ctional Cncl Co-chair; Scheduling Comm; NEA-NY 1981-, Local Webutuck Tchrs Assn, NYSUT & AFT 1992-; S Amenia Presbyn h 1958-, Elder, Sunday Schl Supt & Sunday Schl Tchr; Amenia Jr en's Club 1976-, Pres, Sec; Amenia Day Nursery Bd 1978-83, Pres, Oblong Valley Assn 1989-, VP; Area Fund Grant; SUNY Stu Tchr or Tchr; *office:* Webutuck Central Schl Webutuck School Rd Box N ia NY 12501*

KER, JAMES DALE, Social Studies Teacher; *b:* Plymouth, IN; *m:* le M.; *c:* Tyler James, Austin Michael; *ed:* Ball St Univ (BS) Soc Ed 1984; Xavier Univ (MED) Cnslng 1988; 12 Hrs at Drake Univ; 3 Walsh Coll; *cr:* New Richmond HS Soc Stud, Amer His Tchr 1984-; ar Fastpitch Sftbl Coach; Career Ed Coord; Individual Career Plan tator; NEA, OEA, NREA 1984-; SW Ohio Sftbl Coaches Assn 1990-; nern Buckeye Conf Sftbl Coach of Yr 1990, 1994; *office:* New nond HS 1131 Bethel New Richmond Rd New Richmond OH 45157*

LDINE, DOROTHY S., Secondary Mathematics Teacher; *b:* len, NJ; *ed:* LaSalle Univ (BS) Bus Admin 1984; Rowan Coll of NJ Educl Admin 1994; Scndry Math Supvr, Prin Certs; *cr:* Cherokee HS Tchr 1987-; *ai:* Head Girls Tennis Coach; Core Team; Yrbk Asst-Adv; Term Planning Action Comm; NJEA, NJTA, NCTM, NJMA, ASCD -; Eisenhower Grant 1990-91; Ed Excl Grant 1991, 1993; Burlington Tennis Coach of Yr 1988, 1993; *office:* Cherokee HS Willow Bend & inson Rds Marlton NJ 08053*

LE, CHRISOPHER PAUL, Math & Social Studies Teacher; *b:* nce, OH; *m:* Christine Wetterau; *c:* Andrew, Brian; *ed:* Ohio Univ Ed 1978; Univ of Dayton (MS) Ed 1984; *cr:* Pickenington Elem Schl 3rd Tchr 1978-80; Violet Elem Schl 3rd Grd Tchr 1980-81; Fairfield Schl 3rd, 4th, 5th Grd Tchr 1981-92; Pickering MS 6th Grd Math, Stud Tchr 1992-; *ai:* Jr HS Yth Group Ldr Prince of Peach Luth ch; NEA, OEA 1978-; PEA 1978-, Sec; *office:* Pickerington MS 100 st St Pickerington OH 43147

LER, WENDY, Teacher; *b:* Philadelphia, PA; *ed:* Cheyney Univ (BS) Ed, (MED) Ed Admin; *cr:* Evans Schl Tchr; *ai:* Prof Dev Comm; A; NEA; NAESP; DVASCD; SLC Grant.

LS, REGINA KILGALLEN, Chemistry Teacher; *b:* Schenectady, *m:* Nathaniel; *ed:* Geneseo St Univ (BS) Chem 1988; Albany St Univ Chem Ed 1993; *cr:* Broadalbin Perth Chem Tchr 1989-; *ai:* Sci Honor Adv, Class Adv; STANYS, NSTA, AFT 1989-; *office:* Broadalbin-Perth Bridge St Ext Broadalbin NY 12025

M, ANITA J., English & Journalism Teacher; *b:* Ashland, KY; *m:* lley C.; *c:* Chelsea, Molly, Mason; *ed:* Ashland Univ (MS) Rdng ervision 1987; Morehead St Univ (BA) Eng; *cr:* Plymouth HS Tchr)-86; Shelby City Schls Tchr 1986-; *ai:* Scarlet S Yrbk Adv; NEA)-; OH Cncl of Tchr of Eng & Lang Arts 1986-; First United Meth rch 1991-; St Dept Rdng Grant 1982; *office:* Shelby Sr High 109 W ley Ave Shelby OH 44875

AM, LAWRENCE ROBERT, Industrial Technology Teacher; *b:* veland, OH; *m:* Barbara Karwich; *c:* David, Joseph, Brian; *ed:* Bowling en St Un (BA) Industrial Arts 1964; Attnd Cleveland St, Kent St, John roll; *cr:* Bedford Bd of Ed Tchr 1964-67; Holy Name HS Tchr & Coach 7-; *ai:* Boys & Girls Cross Cntry & Boys Track Coach; Ski Club; ALTA 1975-; MEOTCCA 1989-; Holy Name Soc 1976-, Tres, Sec & VP, of Yr Awd 2 Yrs; All League Coach of Yr 10 Yrs; All OH Coach of Yr r; Greater Cleveland Asst Bsbl Coach of Yr 1 Yr; *office:* Holy Name HS 0 Queens Hwy Parma OH 44130

AMS, LYNN RAY, Retired Eng & Lang Arts Tchr; *b:* Rockford, IA; *m:* queline Yvonne Socha; *c:* Timothy M., Lynn R. II, Robin A. Jones, nadette, Robert K.; *ed:* Youngstown St Univ (BSEd) Ed, Eng 1967; *cr:* th Royalton Local Schls 7-8 Grd Eng Tchr 1967-68; Girard City Schls dry Eng Tchr 1968-71; Maplewood Local Schls Scndry Eng Tchr 2-91; *home:* 603 E Prospect St Girard OH 44420

ARDON, MARY TERESA, Social Studies Teacher; *b:* Boston, MA; Providence Coll (BA) Ed 1981; Suffolk Univ (MED) Ed 1983; Working vards MA in Family Cnslng at Eastern Nazarene Coll; *cr:* St Joseph Schl Stud Tchr 1981-83; St Brigid Schl Soc Stud Tchr 1983-85; Monsignor an Meml HS Soc Stud Tchr 1985-; *ai:* Stu Cncl, Sr Class Adv 1987-; NEA, MTA 1981-; Patriot Ledge Golden Apple Awd 1992; *office:* Monsignor Ryan Mem HS 11 Mayhew St Dorchester MA 02125

REASER, JAMES ROBERT, Vocal Music Tchr & Dept Chm; *b:* Muncy, PA; *m:* Janice Sue Reed; *c:* Amy J. Diggan, Michael B.; *ed:* Susquehanna Univ (BS) Music Ed 1968; Attnd SUNY at New Paltz & Westminster Choir Coll; *cr:* MJM Jr HS General Music & Choral Dir 1968-69; J W Baily Jr HS General Music, Vocal & Choral Dir 1969-72; Shikellamy Schl Dist Elem & Sr HS Vocal & Choral Dir 1972-74; Shikellamy HS Choral Dir, Music Theory, Voice & Electronic Music Tchr 1974-; *ai:* Choir; Chorus; Jubilation Singers; MENC, ACDA, NEA & PSEA; PMEA, Scndry Rep; BSA, Cub Scouts Father of Yr; *office:* Shikellamy HS 6th & Walnut Sts Sunbury PA 17801

REASOR-LEWIS, PHYLLIS MARILYN, 8th Grd Work & Fam Life Tchr; *b:* Akron, OH; *c:* Traci M. Lewis, Cecelia M. Rhasiatry, Chico Rhasiatry; *ed:* Univ of Akron (BS) Scndry, Voc Ed 1976, (MS) Tech Ed, Family LIfe 1981, (MS) Scndry Admin 1990; Cmptr Keyboarding Sci; *cr:* Chartford Jr HS Consumer & Family Life Tchr 1976-77; Teenage Parent Ctr Consumer & Family, Child Dev Tchr 1977-84; Jenning MS Work & Family Life Ed Tchr 1984-91; Perkins MS Work & Family Life Ed Tchr 1991-; *ai:* FHA Yth, Panda, Adv; Work & Family Curr Comm; Greater Akron Home Ec Club; Akron Ed Assn 1977-; Delta Sigma Theta 1989-; OH St Univ Comm Svc Awd; *office:* Perkins MS 630 Mull Ave Akron OH 44313*

REATH, HARVEY D., Computer Sci & Math Teacher; *b:* Norristown, PA; *m:* Evelyn Hoffman; *c:* Kevin, Shannon; *ed:* Houghton Coll (BA) Math 1969; West Chester Univ (MS) Cmptr Sci 1987; *cr:* Chichester Jr HS Math Tchr 1969-85, Cmptr Sci, Math Tchr 1985-; *ai:* Cmptr Sci Moderator; HS Track Coach; NEA, PSEA 1969-; CEA 1969-, VP; First Bapt Church of Oxford 1990-, HS Sunday Schl Tchr; Dev HS Curr Cmptr Courses; Dev, Present Tchr Cmptr Wkshps; *home:* 10 Pawtucket Rd West Grove PA 19390

REAVIS, CHARLES BENTON, Vocal, Gen Music & Drama Tchr; *b:* Salisbury, NC; *m:* Muriel Roberts; *c:* Christopher Benton, Heather Marie; *ed:* Pfeiffer Coll (BA) Music Ed 1969; Salisbury St Univ (MED) Choral Music 1978; 30 Hrs Beyond MED Including Post Grad Courses & Cty Wkshps; Resulting in Adv Prof Degree & Cert in Supervision & Admin; *cr:* Daniels Jr HS Tchr 1969-71; Carnage Jr HS Tchr 1971-73; James M Bennett HS Tchr, Dir & Adv 1973-; *ai:* Drama Club & Troop 2899 Intnl Thespian Soc Adv; Sr & Jr Class Plays, Schl Musicals & Variety Shows Dir; MENC & MMEA 1969-, Cty Mbrshp Chm; NEA, MSTA & WCEA 1973-; St Stephens U Meth Church 1973-, Choir Dir; Salisbury Choral Soc 1992-VP, Soloist & Asst Dir; MD St Curr Comm for Theatre; *home:* PO Box 502 Hebron MD 21830*

REBESCHI, LISA CIRILLO, Assistant Professor of Nursing; *b:* New Haven, CT; *m:* Joseph R.; *ed:* Southern CT St Univ (BSN) Nrsng 1984, (MSN) Nrsng Ed Specialist 1991; Working Toward PHD Nrsng Sci Univ of RI; *cr:* Yale New Haven Hosp Clinical Nurse 1984-; Saint Joseph Coll Nrsng Lecturer 1990-91; Southern CT St Univ Asst Prof, Coord Undergrad Nrsng Stud 1993-; *ai:* Admissions, Acad Standing Comms Chprsn; Mu Beta Sigma Theta Tau 1990-, Pres; Amer Assn Univ ProfS 1993-; Amer Nurses Assn 1995-; Book: Pediatric Survival Guide Co-Author Pub 1996; Nursing Articles Pub; Grant Co-Author; Prof Traineeship Univ of RI 1992-93; Who's Who in Amer Nrsng; *home:* 62 Pistapaug Rd Northford CT 06472*

REBISH, HENRIETTA CHRISTINE, 5th Grade Teacher; *b:* Connelsville, PA; *m:* Robert A.; *c:* Eric Jay; *ed:* CA Univ of PA (BS) Ed 1972; Master Equiv Ed; *cr:* Belle Vernon Area Schl Dist 1st Grd Tchr 1973-74, 4th Grd Tchr 1975-80, 6th Grd Tchr 1980-88, 5th Grd Tchr 1988-; *ai:* Sci Fair, I Was Framed Consortium Grant Coords.

REBMAN, EILEEN S., History Teacher; *b:* New York City, NY; *m:* Jack A.; *c:* James A., Thomas M., Jennifer Jacobs; *ed:* Queens Coll (BA) His 1952; Loyola Coll (MD) Grad Stud Ed Psych 1980; Attnd Columbia Univ Schl of Gen Stud His; *cr:* Ewing Adult Schl Adult Prgm Instr 1970-83; Princeton Univ Supervising Tchr, 1973-74, Undergraduate Tchr Prep Prgm 1976-77; Stuart Country Day Schl His Tchr 1971-86; The Bullis Schl His Tchr 1988-; *ai:* It's Acad Team Coach; Intnl Club Moderator; Org Amer Historians 1971-; Mercer Cty Dept of Womens Affairs, Task Force; Jr League 1970-, Ed Chm CDV; Amer Red Cross 1980-, Outstdng Svc Awd 1983; Amer Schl Tchr Fellow Univ Martinmas 1995; Natl Endowment Hum Summer Stud Grant Univ of KS 1994; Flwsph Awd Natl Cncl Economic Educl Trenton St Coll 1978; *office:* Bullis Schl 10601 Falls Rd Potomac MD 20854

REBOVICH, ELSIE RINALDI, Staff Development Specialist; *b:* Newark, NJ; *m:* Alan George; *ed:* Montclair St Univ (BA) Soc Stud 1967; Kean Coll of NJ (MA) Adm, Suprv 1974; Elem Cert 20 Credits; Math Scndry Cert 30 Credits; 36 Addl Credits; *cr:* Belleville Jr HS Typing Tchr 1967-68; P L Julian MS Sixth Grd Tchr 1968-69; Newark Pub Schls Soc Stud Tchr 1969-71, Admin Intern 1972-75, Elem Tchr 1976-85; Edison Twp Pub Schls Math Tchr 1985-94, Curr Resource Tchr 1994-95, Staff Dev Specialist 1995-; *ai:* Strategic Planning, Curr Coordinating Comms; Mentor Tchr; Stu Cncl Adv; NEA, NJEA, ETEA 1967-; Suprv, Curr Dev Assn 1990-; Math Tchrs of NJ Assn, NCTM 1985-; Amer Assn of Univ Women 1978-; Master Tchr Awd; *office:* James Madison Int Schl 838 New Dover Rd 284 Tingley Ln Edison NJ 08820*

REBUCK, RICHARD HUGH, Adv & Physics Teacher; *b:* Chambersburg, PA; *m:* Carol Graham; *c:* David, Richard, Sherri; *ed:* Shippensburg Univ (BSEd) Physics, Math 1963, (MED) Physics 1968; 45 Addl Hrs; *cr:* Univ of Miami Lab Instr 1963-64; John Dickinson HS Physics Tchr 1964-66; Shippensburg Area Sr HS Physics Tchr 1966-; *ai:* Chess Club Spon; Sr Class Adv; NEA, PSEA, Amer Assn of Physic Tchrs 1966-; Shippensburg Area EA 1966-, Outstanding Tchr 1990-91; Grace United Church of Christ 1953-; Natl Sci Fnd Fellowship; Test Engineer in Electro-Optics at Amp Inc 4 Summers; Article Pub on Optical Fibers; *office:* Shippensburg Area Sr HS 317 N Morris St Shippensburg PA 17257

RECCHIA, CARL, Vocal Music Teacher; *b:* Bronx, NY; *m:* Mary L.; *ed:* Attnd Univ of VT; 9 Grad Credits Multiple Intelligences, Electronic Music; *cr:* Twinfield Elem, HS Vocal, Instrumental Tchr 1978-80; Milford Area HS Vocal Music Tchr 1980-85; High Mowing Schl Vocal, Instrument Tchr 1985-88; Champlain Vly UHS Vocal Music Tchr 1988-; *ai:* South Cty Comm Chorus, Madrigal, Singers, Men's Chorus, Musicals Dir; Auditions Coach; ACDA, MENC 1988-; VMEA 1988-, Auditions Chair; Univ of VT Tchr of Yr 1994-95; VT Music Edctrs Wkshps; Articles Pub; *home:* RR 1 Box 400 N Ferrisburg VT 05473*

RECHT, CHRISTINE BASKIN, Algebra Teacher; *b:* Beacon, NY; *m:* Barry Jay; *c:* Jennifer, Alyssa; *ed:* SUNY Coll at Cortland (BS) Early Scndry Sci, Elem Ed 1977; 7 Credits Data Processing Mercer Cty Comm Coll; 12 Credits Math Ed VA St Univ; *cr:* Brunswick Sr HS Math Tchr 1972-82; Hightstown HS Math Tchr 1984-87; Jackson Meml HS Math Tchr 1988-; *ai:* NJEA 1984-; NCTM 1991-; Child Care Advy Bd 1991-, Co-Chm; *office:* Jackson Memorial HS Don Conner Blvd Jackson NJ 08527

RECOON, SUSAN ELIZABETH, Math & Computer Sci Teacher; *ed:* SUNY at Oswego Hnrs Coll (BS) Scndry Math 1987; SUNY at Buffalo (MED) Scndry Math 1992; *cr:* Buffalo Pub Schls Math Tchr 1988-92; Williamsville North HS Math Tchr 1992-; *ai:* Bldg Tech Facilitator; NCTM, ADT 1992-; *office:* Williamsville North HS 1595 Hopkins Rd Williamsville NY 14221

RECORD, LUCI DEBORAH, English Teacher; *b:* Pawtucket, RI; *m:* James Edward; *c:* James, Stephen, Lauren; *ed:* Boston Univ (BS) Eng, Ed 1965; Bridgewater ST (MA) Eng; 18 Post Grad Hrs Fitchburg St; *cr:* Bristol HS Eng Tchr 1965-68; Silver Lake HS Eng, Writing Tchr; *ai:* Prof Dev Comm; Comm on Diversity; Comm on Raising the Stan; NEA, SLTA, PCEA 1981-; Articles Pub; *office:* Silver Lake Reg HS-Kingston 130 Pembroke St Kingston MA 02364*

RECTOR, MADELYNNE T., Adjunct Associate Professor; *b:* Bronx, NY; *c:* Je Suise; *ed:* City Coll of NY at Cuny (BA) Psych 1970; NY Univ (PHD) Clinical Psych 1984; *cr:* Sydenham Hosp Chief of Psych & Developmental Eval 1972-74; NYU Med Ctr Rsrch Asst 1974-76; NYC Head Start Inc Consulting Psych 1976-86; CUNY Hostos & John Jay Colls Adj Assoc Prof 1986-; NYC Bd of Ed CSD #9 Dist Psych & Spcl Ed Tchr 1986-; *ai:* Consulting Psych for Mind Builders Creative Arts Ctr Bronx NY & Archdioces of NY Dare to Care Project; Career Cnslng Presentations CUNY; NY Assn of Black Psych 1972-; APA 1984-; Grace Bapt Church 1989-; Tremin-Baruch Grant; Scholastic Incentive Awd; Federal Work-Stud Schlsp; NIMH Flwshp; M L King Jr Scholastic Achvmt Awd; Conf Presentations: CUNY, NYC & MTV Bd of Ed, Women for Racial Ec Equality, Early Chldhd Ed Cncl & NY Soc for Adolescent Psychiatry; *office:* City Univ Of NY Hostos Coll 475 Grand Concourse Bronx NY 10451*

REDA, DONNA BALOGH, 1st Grade Teacher; *b:* New Eagle, PA; *m:* Domenic; *c:* Melanie Rae, Christopher Frank; *ed:* CA Coll (MED) Ed 1975; Waynesburg Coll (BA) Elem Ed 1993; *cr:* Gastonville Elem Schl 1st Grd Tchr 1973-75; Elrama Elem Schl 1st Grd Tchr 1975-82; Monongahela Elem Schl Kndgtn Tchr 1983-85, 1st Grd Tchr 1985-; *ai:* NEA, PA St Ed Assn, Ringgold Ed Assn 1973-; Mon Vly Ed Consortium Grants; Publishing a Book Using The Reading-Writing Approach I & II, Supplementing Curriculum Through Children's Literature, Shared Reading with 5th and 1st Graders Here and Beyond, From Reading to Acting; *office:* Monongahela Elem Ctr 1200 Chess St Monongahela PA 15063*

REDD, FERDIE, Library Teacher; *b:* Fairfax, SC; *w:* Curtis (dec); *c:* Anthony, Robin, Jeffrey; *ed:* LaGuardia Comm Coll (AA) Ed 1975; York Coll (BS) Ed 1983; Adelphi Univ (MBS) Ed 1988; 30 Addl Credit Hrs; *cr:* PS 155 Queens Educl Asst 1969-82, Classroom Tchr 1982-92, Lib Tchr 1992-; *ai:* So Oz Pk Taxpayers Assn; 130 St Better Block Assn; Rockaway Blvd Dev Corp; PTA; *office:* PS 155 Queens 130-02 115th Ave So Ozone Park NY 11420

REDDEN, ALONA HOPE JESSON, Mathematics Teacher; *b:* Lockport, NY; *m:* Douglas B.; *c:* Thomas W., Kristina H., Tammy M. Seymour; *ed:* State Univ Coll at Buffalo (BS) Math, 1965, (MS) Math 1967; Univ of PIttsburgh Cmptr Sci 1980-83; *cr:* Newfane Cntrl Schl Dist Math Instr 1964-66; St Univ Coll at Oswego Math Instr 1967; Connellsville Schl Dist Sci Tchr 1967-68; Norwin Schl Dist Math Tchr 1968-; *ai:* Ski Club Spon; Asst Girl Scouts; Adv for Math Contests; Math Tutoring; NEA 30 Yrs; PSEA 28 Yrs, NTEA 27 Yrs; Girl Scouts 8 Yrs; Personal Software Assn 1983-, Sec, Treas 13 Yrs; *office:* Norwin Sr H S 251 Mc Mahon Dr North Huntingdon PA 15642*

REDDER, DEBORAH MUMPOWER, English Teacher; *b:* Providence, RI; *m:* Craig A.; *c:* Emily Closson, Jason; *ed:* Miami Univ (BSEd) Eng 1970; Wright St Univ (MSEd) Learning Disabilities, Behavioral Disorders 1976, (MSEd) Guid 1979; *cr:* West Carrollton HS Eng, LD Tchr, Guid Cnslr 1970-80; Hillel Acad Eng Tchr 1980-86; Berry Co Account Mgr 1986-91; Cath Cntrl HS Eng Tchr 1991-; *ai:* Sr Class, Newspaper, Lit Magazine Adv; Curr Re-design Comm; Selected for Wright St Univ Change Course; Clark Co Outstdng Tchr 1994-95.*

REDDING, J. PATRICK, ESOL & Resource Teacher; *b:* Seattle, WA; *c:* Andrea D., Maytinee J.; *ed:* Southern OR St Coll (BS) Gen Stud 1973, (MS) Ed Scndry 1978; Univ of UT PHD Candidate Comparative Ed 1979; *cr:* US Peace Corps Tchr 1974-76; Ctr Applied Linguistics Cultural Orientation Specialists 1980-83; Intl Cath Migration Commission Deputy Prgm Dir 1983-86; Easy Eng Learning Ctr Owner, Dir 1991-93; Montgomery Cty Pub Schls Tchr, Resource Tchr 1986-; *ai:* Jrnlsm Spon; NEA, MSTA, MCEA 1986-; Several Articles, Monographs, 1 Book Cross-Cultural Trng; *home:* 64 Old S River Rd #34 Edgewater MD 21037*

REDDING, LINDA GAIL, Mathematics Teacher; *b:* Quincy, MA; *m:* Robert W.; *c:* R. Scott, Jennifer G.; *ed:* Univ of MA (BS) Math 1966; Attnd Worcester St Coll, Assumption Coll, Anna Maria Coll; *cr:* Westerly HS Math Tchr 1966-67; Quaboag Reg HS Math Tchr 1967-69; Grafton HS Math Tchr 1984-90; Auburn HS Math Tchr 1990-; *ai:* Class Adv 1989, 1994; Ski Club Adv 1986-89; ATMIN, Auburn Tchrs Assn 1990-; *office:* Auburn HS 99 Auburn St Auburn MA 01501

REDDING, THOMAS H.,JR., English Teacher; *b:* Cleveland, OH; *ed:* Ohio Univ (BSEd) Eng 1973; Kent St Univ (MA) Comparative Lit 1978; *cr:* Grand Valley Schls Lang Arts Tchr 1973-74; Kirtland Schls Eng Tchr 1974-75; Manchester Schls Eng Tchr 1975-77; Akron Pub Schls Eng Tchr 1977-; *ai:* Schl, City Track Meet Dir; Ski Club Adv; *office:* Ellet HS 309 Woolf Ave Akron OH 44312

REDDINGER, ROBERT LEWIS, English Teacher; *b:* Brockway, PA; *m:* Kay A.; *c:* Lynne, David; *ed:* Roberts Wesleyan Coll (BA) Eng 1966; Middlebury Coll (MA) Eng 1971; 30 Addl Post Grad Hrs; *cr:* York Cntrl Schls Eng Tchr 1966-74; Roberts Wesleyan Coll Adjunct Tchr 1989-91; SUNY at Brockport Adjunct Tchr 1980-; Brockport HS Eng Tchr 1974-, Sr AP Eng Tchr; *ai:* NYSUT 1966-; AFT; PTA Fellowship Summer Stud 1969; Univ of Rochester Outstanding Tchr; Pub Poems; *office:* Brockport H S 40 Allen St Brockport NY 14420

REDDINGTON, CECILY ADAMS, Retired English & Latin Tchr; *b:* Pittsburgh, PA; *m:* Laurence J.; *ed:* Carlowe Coll (BA) Eng, Latin 1952; Duquesne Univ (MA) Eng 1955; Addl 36 Credit Hrs Latin, Greek, Ed 1956-60; Post Grad Work Hum Univ of Chicago 1968; *cr:* Canevin HS Head of Classical Lang Dept 1958-62; Pvt Acad Head of Eng Dept 1962-66; Duquesne Coll Adj Prof Eng, Amer Lit 1958-68; Emerson HS AP Eng Tchr Curr Dir 1968-78; T. A. Edison HS Sr Eng, Creative Writing Tchr 1980-90; *ai:* Taught Bus Writing to CPA's; Docent at Arnot Art Museum; Art & Art His Trips; Art & Lit Lectures; NEA, NJEA, NYEA 1968-; Delta Kappa Gamma; Arnot Ait Museum; Sterle Mem Lib Friend; Numerous Articles Pub; Univ of Chicago Grant in Writing; *home:* 98 Rosar Hill Rd Pine City NY 14871

REDDY, ELAINE, English Teacher; *b:* Taunton, MA; *m:* Robert M.; *c:* Susan M., Robert M. Jr.; *ed:* Bridgewater St Coll (BSEd) Eng 1965; Cambridge Coll (MSEd) Ed 1995; 3 Credits Grad Courses Emmanual Coll, Bridgewater St Coll; Enrichment Courses Cape Cod Comm Coll; Real Estate Courses Bristol Comm Coll, Bridgewater St Coll; *cr:* Taunton HS Eng Tchr 1965-68, Eng Tchr 1977-82; Norton MS Lang Arts, 6th, 8th Grd Soc Stud 1982-85; Norton HS 9-12 Grd Eng Tchr 1985-; *ai:* 1999 Class Adv; Schl Cncl; Inclusion, Curr Frameworks Comm; NEA, MTA 1975-68, 1978-; Norton Tchrs Assn 1983-; Delta Kappa Gamma; *office:* Norton HS 66 W Main St Norton MA 02766

REDFIELD, BEVERLY S., Fifth Grade Teacher; *b:* Cleveland, OH; *m:* Bernard; *c:* Shannon Davis, Malcolm; *ed:* OH Univ (BSEd) Elem Ed 1971; Cleveland St (MED) Post Scndry Ed 1985; *cr:* Chesterfield Schl 5th-6th Grd Tchr 1971-81; Anthony Wayne Schl 5th-6th Grd Tchr 1981; Brooklawn Schl 4th-5th Grd Tchr 1981-; *ai:* Guidance Liaison Tchr; Career Day Coord; AFT 1971-; Neighborhood Club 1991-, Sec;

Morningstar Church 1988-, VP, Courtesy Comm Sec; *office:* Brooklawn Elem Schl 11801 Worthington Ave Cleveland OH 44111

REDICAN, J. STACEY, English Teacher; *b:* Philadelphia, PA; *m:* Patricia Krammer; *c:* Lindsay Alison; *ed:* King's Coll (BA) Eng 1966; Beaver Coll (MED) Alternative Ed 1977; 45 Addl Credits; *cr:* Thomas Williams Jr HS Lang Arts Tchr 1967-70; Cedarbrook Jr HS Lang Arts Tchr 1970-71; Alternative Schls Project Eng Tchr, Cnslr 1971-74; Cheltenham HS Soc Stud, Eng Tchr 1974-; *ai:* Fac Advy, Four Sevens Comms; NEA, PSEA 1967-; Cheltenham Edctrs Assn 1967-, VP, Contract Specialist, Sec, Bldg Rep; *office:* Cheltenham HS Rices Mill Rd & Carleton Ave Wyncote PA 19095

REDICK, JANET TAYLOR, Retired Teacher; *b:* Wooster, OH; *m:* John Dayton; *c:* Roberta S. Reed, John T., William T.; *ed:* Kent St Univ (BS) Elem Ed 1957; *cr:* Kirtland Elem 5th Grd Tchr 1957-58; Wooster City Schls 5th Grd Tchr 1958-59; Northwestern Schls 3-6th Grd Tchr 1970-93, Private Tutor 1994-; *ai:* Cheerleading Adv at Kirtland; Northwestern Local Tchrs, OEA, NEA 1970-; EMT New Pittsburg Rescue Squad 1973-88; Farm Bureau Women; St Peter's Church Cncl; Fire Dept Auxiliary 1965-; *home:* 5753 Lattasburg Rd Wooster OH 44691

REDINGER, JANICE C., Home Ec & Child Dev Teacher; *b:* Arlington, VA; *m:* Richard M. Durand; *ed:* Albright Coll (BA) Home Ec 1973; Univ of MD at College Park (MED) Home Ec 1980; 45 Post Grad Credit Hrs; *cr:* Magruder HS Home Ec Tchr 1973-75; Wheaton HS Home Ec Tchr 1975-88; Quince Orchard HS Home Ec & Child Dev Dept Chair & Tchr 1988-; *ai:* NEA, MSTA, MCEA 1974-; AHEA; 1984 Amer Home Ec Tchr of Yr Merit Winner in Family Life Ed; 1984 MD St Home Ec Tchr of Yr; *office:* Quince Orchard HS 15800 Quince Orchard Rd Gaithersburg MD 20878

REDLINE, BARBARA WATSON, Eighth Grade Teacher; *b:* New Castle, PA; *m:* Richard; *c:* Gretchen, Kristina; *ed:* W VA Wesleyan Coll (BS) PE 1963; Edinboro Univ of PA (MED) Biological Sci 1986, (MS) Biological Sci 1986; *cr:* Warren Local Schls Hlth, PE Tchr 2 Yrs; Wallace Braden JHS Hlth, PE Tchr 2 Yrs; Painesville Twp Schls Life & Earth Sci Tchr 1 yr; Assumption Schl 8th Grd Tchr 4 Yrs; *ai:* Stu Cncl Adv; Sci Fair Coord; Delta Psi Kappa 1961-, Pres; Beta Beta Beta 1986-; YMCA, WCA 1970-; United Meth Church 1953-, Music Comm; *office:* Assumption Cath Schl 30 Lockwood St Geneva OH 44041

REDLO, MITCHELL HOWARD, Economics Professor; *b:* Buffalo, NY; *m:* Sarah Lynn Ewald; *ed:* St Univ NY at Buffalo (BA) Ec 1981, (MA) Ec 1987; St Univ NY at Albany (MPA) Pub Finance 1983; St Univ NY at Buffalo 42 Hrs towards PhD in Ec; *cr:* Marine Midland Bank Municipal Bond Analyst 1983-85; Chase Lincoln First Bank Corporate Credit Analyst 1985-86; St Univ of NY at Buffalo Tchng Asst 1986-87; Monroe Comm Coll Ec Prof 1988-; Adj Prof at the New Schl for Rsrch 1996; *ai:* Ec Discipline Coord 1989-94; Mid Sts Assn Accreditation, Enrollment Mngmt, Writing Across the Curr; Senate Exec Comms; Chair Fac Senate Planning & Strategic Planning Comms1994-95; Fac Senate Dept Senator 1993-95; NYSUT, AFT 1988-; Amer Ec Assn 1986-; Author An Introduction to Principles of Microeconomics & Introduction to Market System; Book Reviews; Innovative Technologies Awd; Fac Dev Awd; Made Videos on How to Use Writing in the Classroom; *office:* Monroe Community Coll 1000 E Henrietta Rd Rochester NY 14623*

REDMOND, GARRETT G., Seventh & Eighth Grd Eng Tchr; *b:* Philadelphia, PA; *m:* Leah Ann Haffner; *c:* Garrett, William, David, Timothy; *ed:* East Stroudsburg Univ (BS) Eng 1965; *cr:* Pennridge Schls Gifted Seminar, ESL & Eng Tch 1965-; *ai:* NEA & PEA 1961-; Fish 1970-, VP; *office:* Pennridge Schl Dist 1500 N 5th St Perkasie PA 18944

REDMOND, JAMES JOSEPH, Eng Tchr & 6th Grd Team Ldr; *b:* Cambridge, MA; *m:* Carolyn Gray; *c:* Matthew James; *ed:* Boston St Coll (BA) Eng 1969, (MED) Elem, Scndry Admin 1973; 128 Credit Hrs In-Svc, Other Credits; *cr:* Boston Tech HS Eng Tchr 1969-70; Garrison Annex 7 Grd Math, Geog Tchr 1970-71; West Elem Schl 6 Grd Multidisciplinary Tchr 1971-88; West MS 6 Grd Eng Tchr 1988-; *ai:* 350th Anniversary Comm Rep 1994-; Andover Ed Assn 1971-, Pred, Treas, Bldg Rep, Bargaining Team Mem; MA Tchrs Assn, NEA 1971-; Andover Educl Improvement Assn 1971-, Pres 10 Yrs, Grants Chair; Andover Band Parents 1993-, Equipment Mgr; *office:* Andover West MS Shawsheen Rd Andover MA 01810

REDMOND, MARY JO RUGGIERO, English Teacher; *b:* Long Island, NY; *c:* Ryan, Jocelyn; *ed:* Univ at Albany (BA) Eng 1970, (MA) Eng Ed 1975; Post Grad Stud; In-Service Ed Credit; *cr:* Shenendehowa HS Eng Tchr 1971-73; Koda Jr HS Eng Tchr 1973-; *ai:* Schl Bldg & Dist Comms; NYSUT, AFT 1971-; PTA 1971-, Honorary Lifetime Membership Awd; *office:* Koda Jr HS 970 Route 146 Clifton Park NY 12065

REDMOND, NANCY DUNN, Sr HS Mathematics Teacher; *b:* New Haven, CT; *m:* William; *c:* Shawn; *ed:* Cedar Crest Coll (BA) Math Tchng 1974; Southern CT St Univ (MA) Tchng 1982; *cr:* North Haven HS Temp Math Tchr 6 Months; Amity Reg Sr HS Math Tchr 22 Yrs; *ai:* Staff Dev Comm; NEA, CEA & AEA 1975-; *office:* Amity Regional SR HS 25 Newton Rd Woodbridge CT 06525

REDOS, VICKI CARTER, English Teacher; *b:* Lewistown, PA; *m:* James David; *c:* Christopher; *ed:* Lock Haven Univ (BS) Eng 1971; Hood Coll (MA) Admin & Supervision 1991; 30 Hrs Post Grad Work in Eng; *cr:* Montgomery Hills Jr HS Eng Tchr 1971-76; Damascus HS Eng Tchr 1976-86; Montgomery Voc Trades Fnd Asst Coord 1986-91; Damascus HS Eng Tchr 1991-; *ai:* British Cultural Exch Group & Newspaper Spon; Yrbk & Lit Magazine Asst Spon; NEA, MSTA, MCTE 1971-; ASCD 1991-; Germantown Homeowners Assn 1976-, Sec; Jrnlsm Tchr of Yr; Outstanding Educator Awd; 3 Articles Pub in Educl Journals; *office:* Damascus HS 25921 Ridge Rd Damascus MD 20872

REECE, BETH ELAINE, Music Teacher; *b:* Columbus, OH; *ed:* Capital Univ (BSME) Music Ed 1974; OH St Univ (MA) Ed, Classroom 1987; Capital Univ Art Ed Studios; Columbus Cultural Arts Ctr Classes; *cr:* Southwestern City Schls K-5th Grd Unified Arts Tchr 1974-77; Prairie Lincoln Elem Schl K-5th Grd Music Tchr 1977-; Kingston Ave Schl K-5th Grd Music Tchr 1977-; Prairie Norton Elem Schl K-5th Grd Music Tchr 1977-; *ai:* Fourth-Fifth Grd Choir Dir; Music Course of Stud Comm 1 Yr; NEA 1974-; OH Music Edctrs Assn 1974-, Govt Relations Comm 1995-; Columbus Symphony Chorus 1985-, Singing Alto I; Columbus Son of Heaven Exhibition, Vol; Columbus Ameriflora 1992-, Participant, Performing Groups Escort; 2 Southwestern City Schls Schl Bell Awds, Twenty Yr Awd; *office:* Prairie Norton Elem Schl 117 Norton Rd Columbus OH 43228*

REED, ALFRED T., Human Kinetics Professor; *b:* Chicago, IL; *m:* Lynn Blaha; *c:* Michael, Kathleen, Lora; *ed:* Univ of IL (BS) PE 1965; MI St Univ (PHD)PE 1971; *cr:* Univ of IL at Chicago Lecturer 1965-68; Univ of Ottawa Prof 1971-; *ai:* Dir Clinical Trng, Fitness Assessment, Rehabilitation; Canadian Assn of Sports Sci Achvmt Awd; *office:* Univ Of Ottawa Montpetit Hall Ottawa ON K1N 6N5 Canada CN

REED, BARBARA ANN (CHIRDON), Second Grade Teacher; *b:* Cuyahoga Falls, OH; *m:* D. David; *c:* Terri Siders, Cindi Firebaugh, Kevin, Scott, Lisa Opie, Brett; *ed:* Kent St Univ (BA) Elem Ed 1973; 150 Addl Hrs; *cr:* Chester Elem Schl Sixth Grd Tchr 1973-75, Second Grd Tchr 1975-; *ai:* NEA, OEA, Local NWEA 1973-; Red Haw UM Church 1954-, Bd Chm, Adult SS Tchr 1980-; *office:* Chester Elem Schl 7509 W Smithville Western Rd Wooster OH 44691*

REED, CORLISS A., Seventh Grade Teacher; *b:* Bethlehem, PA; *m:* John F.; *c:* Nathan; *ed:* Thiel Coll (BA) Sociology, Elem Ed 1974; PA St Univ 9 Credit Hrs; IU 3 Credit Hrs, Temple Univ 9 Credit Hrs, East Stroudsburg St Univ 3 Credit Hrs; Allentown Coll 2 Credit Hrs; *cr:* Assumption BVM Sixth Grd Tchr 1974-79; St Michael the Archangel 5-8th Grd Math Tchr; 5th Grd Tchr 1979-89; Our Lady of Perpetual Help 7th Grd Tchr 1989-; *ai:* Mathcounts Coach; Middle Atlantic Sts Co-Chair; PA Jr Acad of Sci Spon; Diocesean Catechist; K-8 Math Coord; 24 Game Coach, Adv; Stu Intervention Team 1-4 Tchr Rep; NCEA 1974-; PJAS 1990-; Musikfest Assn 1987-; Eisenhower Schlsp; *office:* Our Lady Of Perpetual Help Sch 3221 Santee Rd Bethlehem PA 18017

REED, DANA J., English Teacher; *b:* Carbondale, PA; *m:* Kathleen Scorzafava; *c:* Corey; *ed:* Penn St (BS) Scndry Eng Ed 1976; 43 Post Grad Credits Toward Masters Equivalency; *cr:* Western Wayne HS Eng Tchr 1976-; *ai:* Lit Magazine Adv; Fac Advy Cncl Chprsn; Honor Soc Cncl; Attendance Comm; Home Bound Tchr-Tutor; PSEA, NEA 1976-; WWEA 1976-, Union Rep; *office:* Western Wayne HS RR 2 Lake Ariel PA 18436

REED, DEBRA L., Fourth Grade Teacher; *b:* Beaver Falls, PA; *ed:* WV Univ (BM) Music Ed 1975; 27 Hrs Cert Elem Ed Slippery Rock Univ, Geneva Coll; *cr:* Beaver Vly Chrstn Acad Music, Elem Tchr 1976-; *ai:* MENC, PMEA 1994-; *office:* Beaver Vly Chrstn Acad 350 Adams St Rochester PA 15074

REED, ELENA, 6th Grade Teacher; *b:* New York City, NY; *c:* Lisa Dawson, John Bauman; *ed:* Hunter Coll (BAj) Ed, Soc Stud 1956; Stony Brook Univ (MA) Ed, Lbrl Arts 1978; Addl 123 Credit Hrs; *cr:* Gatelot Avenue Schl 3, 5th Grd Tchr 1956-61; Unity Drive Schl 5-6th Grd Tchr 1961-78; Bicycle Path Schl 6th Grd Tchr 1978-87; Selden MS 6th Grd Tchr 1987-; *ai:* 6th Grd Adv; Cultural Club; ABC Quilts; Festival of Trees Cerebral Palsy; Ribbons Intnl; Middle Cntry Tchrs Assn 1961-, Sec; NYSUT, Natl PTA 1956-; NY St PTA 1956-, Tchr of Yr; Welcome Inn 1985-; Outreach Comm 1994-; Social Action Comm 1983-85; How to Teach Tchrs to Write Flwshp; *office:* Selden MS 22 Jefferson Ave Centereach NY 11720*

REED, ELLEN KAY, Learning Support Teacher; *b:* Liberty, PA; *m:* Ronald Allen; *c:* Dean Jay, Andre Richard, Nancy Lynn; *ed:* Mansfield St Coll (BS) Elem Ed 1977; Mansfield Univ (BS) Spcl Ed 1986; *cr:* Blast Learning Support Tchr 1986-91; Southern Tioga Schl Dist Learning Support Tchr 1991-; *ai:* Yrbk Adv 4th Yr; NEA 1986-; PSEA 1986-; STEA 1991-; Boro Auditor 1986-; Liberty Luth Church; *office:* Liberty Jr Sr HS PO Box 135 Liberty PA 16930

REED, HERBERT CHARLES, Fourth Grade Teacher; *b:* Syracuse, NY; *m:* Grace Catherine Wilson; *c:* Catherine, Nora Reed Brow, Blayne, Kolby; *ed:* Potsdam St Univ Coll (BA) Elem Ed, Math 1969; 30 Hrs Grad Courses for Permanent Cert; *cr:* Indian River Cntrl Schl 3rd, 5th, 6th Tchrs 1969-; *ai:* IREA Bldg Pres; Negotiations Team; Primary Action Comm; Bldg Compact Team; AFT, NYSUT 1969-; IREA 1969-, Pres 1980-81, Treas 1974-76; Civic League for Dev, Improvement of Philadelphia, NY 1972-, Treas 2 Yrs; *office:* Indian River Cntrl Schl 3 Sand St Philadelphia NY 13673*

REED, JEFF L., Adjunct Instructor; *b:* Zanesville, OH; *m:* Debra A.; *c:* Erin L., Jeffrey W.; *ed:* OH Univ (BS) Jrnslm 1971, (MA) Govt 1972; *cr:* Bus Coll Adj Instr 1993-; Vanguard-Sentinel Ctrs for Adult Career Dev Human Resource Dev Coord 1995-; *ai:* Vanguard Voc Ctr Employability Skills Advy Bd; Pub Relations Soc of Amer 1985-; Norwalk Chamber of Commerce 1993-; Employment Pool Comm, Sandusky Cty chamber of Commerce, Sandusky Cty Prsnl Assn, Seneca Cty Prsnl Assn 1995-; *home:* 19 Garcia Dr Norwalk OH 44857

REED, JIM NEAL, MS Tchr & HS Golf Coach; *b:* Lancaster, OH; *m:* Portia M Wagner; *c:* Rudy S., Jamie L. Barr; *ed:* OH St Univ (BS) His & Govt 1965; Xavier Univ (MEd) Ed & Admin Cert 1970; Masters Plus 30 1990; *cr:* Liberty Union-Thurston Schls Tchr, Coach, Athl Dir & Adm Asst 1965-; *ai:* Bsbl, Bsktbl, Golf & Ftbl Coach; Ath Dir; NEA, OEA, COTA, LUTCTA 1965-; Coaches Assn 1965-; Griley Museum Consultant 1984-; Local Heritage Consultant & Adopt a Road Supvr 1995-; DAR Outstanding Tchr Recognition; OH Div III Bsbl Coach of the Yr 1994; Golf Team to State Tournament 1992; *office:* Liberty Union-Thurston MS 600 W Washington St Baltimore OH 43105

REED, JOHN L., Social Studies Teacher; *b:* Boston, MA; *m:* Karen G.; *ed:* Univ of MA (BA) His, Ed 1973, (MED) Ed 1980; Attnd Bridgewater St Coll, Lesley Coll; *cr:* Operation Exodus Yth Coord 1968-70; Barnstable Pub Schls His Tchr, Minority Stu Adv 1973-; Southeastern MA Univ Outward Bound Instr 1974-76; Cape Cod & Islands Boy Scouts Cncl Food Svc Dir, Yth Worker 1985-90; *ai:* Imani Club Adv; Town of Barnstable Employee Benefits Comm Chm; Equal Opportunity Compliance Ofcr; NEA 1978-, Northeast Regnl Dir, Black Caucus; MA Tchrs Assn 1973-, Bd of Dirs, Minority Affairs Comm Chm; Barnstable Tchrs Assn 1973-, Pres, VP, Comm Chair; Cape Cod Cncl of Churchrs 1990-, Soc Concerns Comm; Natl Assn for Advancement of Colored People 1980-, Pres, Region II Outstdng Yth Adv; Regnl Employment Bd 1994-, Edctr Rep; Local Hero's Project 1990-, Co-Founder, Fin Comm, Dot Cash Awd; MA Tchrs Assn Human, Civil Rights Awd; Article Pub; Town of Barnstable Pub Svc Distngd Citizen Awd, John Reed Day; *office:* Barnstable HS 744 W Main St Hyannis MA 02601*

REED, KYLE ROBERT, Language Arts Teacher; *b:* Millersburg, OH; *m:* Brenda Sue Goerke; *c:* Kent St Univ (BS) Elem Ed 1987; *ed:* OH St Univ; Kent St Univ 9 Credit Hrs; Columbus Pub Schls 3rd Grd Tchr 1987-88; Canton City Schls 6th-7th Grd Tchr 1989-; *cr:* Ftbl Coach; Ath Dir; *ai:* OEA 1987-; NEA 1987-; CPEA 1989-; Simpson United Meth Church 1990-, Admin Cncl; *office:* Hartford MS 1824 3rd St SE Canton OH 44707

REED, LAWRENCE GRANT,JR., History & Government Teacher; *b:* Norristown, PA; *m:* Beth Garrett; *c:* Dianna Gambone, Debra Yurick, Donna Felice; *ed:* Amer Univ (BA) His 1964; Temple Univ (MED) Ed 1969; Masters +30 Credits; *cr:* Overbrook HS Soc Stud Tchr 1965-93; Cntrl HS His & Govt Tchr 1993-; *ai:* Mentor; Class Adv 10 Yrs; Phila Fed of Tchrs 1987-; East-West Ctr Univ of HI Flwshp in Asian Stud; St Univ of NY at Stoney Brook COE Flwshp in Amer Stud; 2 Flwshps to Freedoms Fndtn at Vly Forge PA; *home:* 1998 Virginia Ln Norristown PA 19403*

REED, LORETTA A. MUISE, Mathematics Teacher; *b:* Danvers, MA; *m:* Gary S.; *c:* Jessica L., Cheryl L.; *ed:* Salem St Coll (BS) Math 1990; 15 Credit Hrs MS Pgm in Math; *cr:* Travelers Insurance Co Claims Specialist 1987-90; Danvers HS Summer Schl Math Tchr 1990-93; Arlington Cath HS Math Tchr 1990-; *ai:* Math Team Adv; Parent Newsletter Comm Chprsn; Natl Tchrs Assoc; Tufts Univ Tchr Awd; Travelers Ins Co Ace Awd; *office:* Arlington Cath HS 16 Medford St Arlington MA 02174*

REED, MARCY J., Mathematics & Computer Teacher; *b:* Philadelphia, PA; *ed:* Univ of Hartford (BA) Music 1973; Univ of MA (MA) Ed 1977; Westfield St (BA) Math 1990; *cr:* Westfield MS Music Tchr 1978-88; Westfield HS Math & Comp Tchr 1988-; *ai:* Math League Adv; MA CUE 1988-, Bd & Conf Chair; *office:* Westfield HS 177 Montgomery Rd Westfield MA 01085

REED, PEG RHOADES, Retired Teacher; *b:* Bellefontaine, OH; *m:* John E.; *c:* Don, Doug, Georganna Buttrick, Jim, Joseph; *ed:* OH St Univ (BS) 1-8 Elem Ed 1969, (MA) Childrens Lit & Rdng 1984; Addl 20 Semester Credit Hrs Beyond Masters Math, Sci; *cr:* Ridgemont Elem Schl Grd Tchr, Team Tchr 1966-86; Wickliffe Elem Schl 3-5 Grd Tc Tchr 1986-95; *ai:* NEA, OEA 1966-; Upper Arlington Ed Ass Literacy Connection 1982-, Founding & Bd Mem; Whole Lang U 1995-; Pub Book: Sunrises & Songs; Rdng & Writing Poetry Classroom; Chptr in Childrens Lit in Classroom; Federal Establish Classroom Based On British Integrated Day Schls.

REED, THERESA SKRIP, English Teacher; *b:* Allentown, Richard S.; *c:* Carolyn, Mark; *ed:* Temple Univ (BA) Eng Lit 197 Univ (MA) Curr, Instr, Supervision 1992; Post Grad Stud St Peter Credit Hrs; 9 Addl Credit Hrs; *cr:* Grice MS Eng Tchr Nottingham HS Eng Tchr 1988-; *ai:* Conflict Resolution Comm, Presenter, SRA Bldg Comm, Mentor Prgm 1994-; 10th Grd Fina Comm 1993-94; NJEA, NEA 1988-; Hopewell Vly Cntrl HS P Booster Club 1994-; Outstdng Stu Tchr Awd Rider Univ; Nottingham HS 1055 Klockner Rd Hamilton NJ 08619*

REEDER, LEONA, 4th Grade Teacher; *b:* Pittsburgh, PA; *m:* Mars *ed:* Univ of Miami (AB) Lbrl Arts 1953; Univ of Shippensburg 4 Hrs Elem Cert 1972; *cr:* Cntrl-Fulton McConnellsburg Elem 4th C 1967-; *ai:* CFEA; PSEA; NEA.

REEDER, PATRICIA ANN, First Grade Teacher; *b:* Williamsp *ed:* PA St Univ (BS) Elem Ed 1962; Masters Equivalency Commo of PA 1985; *cr:* Roosevelt Elem Schl 1st Grd Tchr 1962-67; Uni Elem Schl 2nd Grd Tchr 1968, 1976, 1978, 1st Grd Tchr 1969-7 1979-95; *ai:* Allentown Ed Assn, PSEA, NEA 1962-; Allentown Tchrs' Club 1962-; *office:* Union Terrace Elem Schl 1939 W U Allentown PA 18104

REEDS, NANCY J., PE Teacher & Coach; *b:* Buffalo, NY; *m:* G SUNY at Buffalo (BS) PE 1985; Buffalo St Coll (MS) Spec Ed 1 Var Sftbl Coach at Williamsville South HS; AAHPERD NYSAHPERD 1990-; *office:* Williamsville Cntrl Schls 155 H Williamsville NY 14221

REEDY, GERALD CHARLES, Earth Science Teacher; *b:* Young OH; *c:* Christy, Daniel; *ed:* Youngstown St Univ (BA) Earth Sc (MSED) Supervision 1979; 15 Hrs Past Masters; *cr:* Austintown F Tchr & Coach 1973-; *ai:* Girls Track Coach; NEA, OEA, AEA *home:* 1727 Alverne Dr Poland OH 44514

REEDY, JOHN JOSEPH, Emeritus Prof of Biology; *b:* Buffalo, Joann Elizabeth Walsh; *c:* Kerry, Susan, Mary, Timothy; *ed:* Niaga (BSN) Natural Sci 1948; Univ of Notre Dame (MS) Bio 1950, (PH 1952; Bridgewater St Univ (MED) Ed 1960; *cr:* St Marys Co 1951-52; Univ of Detroit Dental Schl Instr 1952-53; Stonehill Co to Full Prof 1953-60; Niagara Univ Full Prof to Emerito Prof 1960-; Prof Advy GMM Chm 15 Yrs; Sigma Xi 1952-; Delta Epsilon Sigma AIBS 1990-; Sigma Alpha Sigma 1974-; NSF, AEC, Univ Rsrc Monsanto Corp Grants; Numerous Articles Pub.

REEDY, SUSAN REPPERT, 2nd Grade Teacher; *b:* Lebanon, Jeffrey A.; *c:* Joshua, Seth; *ed:* Millersville Univ (BA) Elem Ed Masters Equivalency Elem Ed 1992; *cr:* Jackson Elem Schl 1st Gr 1972-76; Ft Zeller Elem Schl 4th, 5th Grd Tchr 1977-78; Schaeffe Elem Schl 5th Grd 1978-79, 2nd Grd Tchr 1980-; *ai:* Instructional S Team Mem; NEA, PSEA, ELCEA 1972-; Lebanon Cty Ed Honc Renaissance, ELCO Acad Booster Club 1993-, Treas; Schaefferstown Elem Schl PO Box 346 Schaefferstown PA 17088

REEKS, DANIEL M., Social Studies Teacher; *b:* Los Angeles, C Barbara J.; *c:* David, Emily, Michael (dec); *ed:* Los Angeles Harb (AA) Gen Stu 1967; The Amer Univ (BA) His 1969; Univ of MD Co (MA) His, Philosophy of Sprt 1986; 1983 Del Intnl Olympic Acad; US Level II Certfd Track Coach; *cr:* Northwood HS Soc Stud Tchr, Head & Cross Cntry Coach 1974-80; Sligo Jr HS Soc Stud Tchr 19 Wheaton HS Soc Stud Tchr, Swim Coach 1981-; Montgomery Coll Track & Cross Cntry Coach 1983-; *ai:* Head Swim Coach; Peer Med Adv; Head Cross Cntry, Track Coaches Montgomery Coll; MCEA 1970-; Chuf Del Intnl Olympic Acad 1983.*

REESE, JAMES E., Early American History Teacher; *b:* Syracuse *m:* Barbara Lutz; *c:* Darcy, Donald, Renee, Heather; *ed:* York Coll His 1972-; Master Equiv 1995; *cr:* Eastern Jr, Sr HS Tchr 19 Dallastown MS Tchr 1979-; *ai:* Jr Achvmt; Coach Intramural Ftb Pong, Bowling, Vlybl, Soccer, Stu Assistance Team, Summer Outbo Life Skills; Hellam Fire Co 1968-, VP 3 Yrs; KCV Ambulance Corp Pres 2 Yrs, VP 4 Yrs; Eastern Schl Bd 1981-; Crisis Pregnancy Life Maternity Home Bd Mem 1991-1993; Gift of Time Tribute Presen American Family Inst at Valley Forge 1990-92; Jaycees Outstanding Tchr of Yr Awd; *office:* Dallastown M S 700 New Schl Ln Dallasto 17313

REESE, JUDITH RODGERS, Eighth Grade Teacher; *b:* Bethleher *m:* Charles M.; *c:* Alison, Jessica; *ed:* Georgian Ct Coll (BA) Eng 1971; Kutztown Univ (MED) Eng 1974; Attnd Lehigh Univ 1976 Carlow Coll 1990; *cr:* Liberty HS Eng Tchr 1971-72; Freedom H Tchr 1972-81, Eng Dept Chprsn 1979-81; Northampton Comm Co Instr 1981-89; Our Lady of Perpetual Help Schl 7th-8th Grd Tchr *ai:* CYO Adv Dist Spelling Bee, Dist Declamation & Acad Bowl Adv Spelling Bee Competition Coach; NCEA, NCTE & NCTSS 1988-; 1992-; Band Parents Assn 1992-; Home Schl Assn 1983-; Diocesa Tchrs Assn 1988-; *office:* Our Lady Of Perpetual Help Sch 3221 Sant Bethlehem PA 18017

REESE, JUNE BUCCIARELLI, Fourth Grade Teacher; *b:* Doyles PA; *m:* Scott M.; *ed:* Lock Haven St Coll (BS) Elem Ed 1977; Trent Coll Masters Equivalency 1990; Post Grad Stud 20 Credits Plus; *cr:* Bucks Schl Dist 1-4th & 6th Grd Tchr 1978-; *ai:* Mentor; Dist Lang Comm 1989-; St & Dist Writing Assessment Table Ldr 1991-; Por Pilot Tchr 1991-; Presenter for Writing; Portfoloios & Cooper Learning 1991-; NEA 1980-; CBEA 1980-, Bldg Rep 1987-89; *o* Gayman Elem Schl 4408 Point Pleasant Pike Danboro PA 18916*

REESE, LYVITA DEONNA, Fourth Grade Teacher; *b:* Philadelphia *ed:* West Chester Univ (BSEd) Elem Ed 1987; H&R Block Income Preparer Cert 1985; Attending Bowie Univ; *cr:* Bell of PA Customer 1981-83; AT&T Information Systems Accounts Svc Rep 1983-85; P Schl System 5th Grd Tchr 3 Yrs, 6th Grd Tchr 3 Yrs, 4th Grd Tchr 2 *ai:* Discipleship Trng Ldr; 4th Grd Chprsn; PGCEA 1989-, Union NEA, MSTA 1989-; Smithsonian Assocs 1996-; Mt Sinai Bapt Ch Tutorial Coord, Youth Dept; Beulah Bapt Church, Sunday Schl Citizens Concerned for a Cleaner Cty 1989-, Recycling Coord, Chrstn Campers Org 1983-, Camp Cnslr, Tchr; Articles & Booklets LRW Publications Publisher; *office:* Longfields Elem Schl 3300 New Ave Forestville MD 20747*

REESE, TANZA ELOIS TRIM, Work & Family Life Teacher; *b:* Orleans, LA; *m:* Robert L.; *c:* Latarsha, Toyia; *ed:* Southern Univ (BS) Home Ec 1971; Attnd Univ of Dayton, Wright St, Miami Univ; *cr:* Hil Jr HS Tchr 1972-73; Dayton City Schl Tchr 1973; Jefferson Jr, Sr 1974-90; Trotwood Madison HS Tchr 1990-; *ai:* FHA, Class Adv; Bro Ldr; OEA, NEA 1972-; AVA 1973-; AAFCS 1995-; TMEA 1990-; D Sigma Theta 1988-, Second VP, Violet Awd 1989; Trotwood Lioness 1 OH Insurance Inst Grant; VFW Americanism Awd; *office:* Trotw Madison HS 221 E Trotwood Blvd Trotwood OH 45426*

E, THEODORE I., English Tchr & Wrestling Coach; *b:* Dedham, *:* Lynn B.; *ed:* Yale Univ (BA) Eng 1958; Harvard Univ (EDM) Eng Brandeis (MA) Eng 1965, (PHD) Eng 1972; Natl Strength Coaches CSCS 1995; *cr:* Noble & Greenough Schl Eng & Latin Tchr & ling Coach 1959-62; Brandeis Univ Tutor & Wrestling Coach 58; Milton Acad Eng & Latin Tchr, Wrestling Coach & Asst Head IA 1968-74; Camden-Rockport HS Eng Tchr & Wrestling Coach 76; Geager Valley HS Eng Tchr & Dept Head & Wrestling Coach 78; Tabor Acad Eng Tchr & dept Head & Wrestling Coach 1978-81; Eagle HS Eng Tchr & Wrestling Coach 1981-95; *ai:* Wrestling ; Phi Delta Kappa 1965-; NEA 1972-94; NEISWCA 1962, 1968-74, 81 Pres (3 Times); MCA 1982-, Exec Comm & Liaison; MAWA VP; Cert of Meritorious Svc World Cup 1979; FILA Master Coach 1st in USA; ME Coach of the Yr 1984, 1988, 1990, 1993-94; Cert of nt Moscow Inst of Sport 1987; ME Wrestling Hall of Fame 1996; RR 3 Box 122 Gorham ME 04038

Z, JANET CAROL, Third Grade Teacher; *b:* Pittsburgh, PA; *ed:* of WI at Whitewater (BE) Primary Ed 1964; 15 Credits Elem Ed Univ sburgh; 9 Credits Elem Ed PA St Univ; *cr:* North Allegheny Schl Dist Grd Tchr 1964-67; Cartwright Schl Dist Fourth Grd Tchr 1967-69; Richland Schl Dist Second-Third, Fifth-Sixth Grd Tchr 1969-; *ai:* Arts, Title I Rdng Comms; NEA, PSEA, PREA 1969-; Delta Kappa a 1988-.

Z, RANDY L., Instrumental Music Teacher; *b:* Jackson, MI; *ed:* ng Green St Univ (BME) Music Ed 1984; Working Towards MA g; *cr:* Painesville Twp Schls Jr High, Elem Instrumental Music 88; Cleveland Pub Schls Jr High Instrumental, HS Music App 90; Southeast Local Schls 7-12 Grd Instrumental Music 1990-; *ai:* ert, Marching, MS Jazz, Pep Bands; OMEA, MENC 1985-; SELEA ; CORE Team Facilitator of Chem Dependancy Groups; *office:* edale HS Instr Music 9048 Dover Rd Apple Creek OH 44606*

VES, JAMES C., Health Education Teacher; *b:* Washington, DC; *m:* R.; *ed:* Univ of MD at College Park (BS) Gen Biological Sci 1970; 60 t Hrs Post Grad Stud; *cr:* Largo HS Tchr 1970-; *ai:* Hlth Ed Dept sn; PGCEA 1971-; MSTA 1971-; NEA 1971-; Amer Heart Assn 1976-, Instr; Amer Red Cross 1972-82, Advanced 1st Aid Instr, Merit Awd College Pk United Meth Church 1971 Handbell Choir Dir; *office:* HS 505 Old Largo Rd Largo MD 20772

VES, MARY RYAN, Visual Arts Teacher; *b:* New York, NY; *m:* John; n Aylor; *ed:* Hood Coll (BA) Art Ed 1970; 30 Hrs at Western MD coll; runswick HS Art Tchr 1970-72; Middletown HS Art Tchr, Dept Chair -85; Western MD Coll Adjunct Prof 1985; Gov Thomas Johnson Art Dept Chair 1985-; *ai:* Yrbk Adv; FCTA 1970-; Hood Coll Alumnae 1970-, Pres 1991-93; Hood Coll Bd of Assoc 1991-94; Delaplaine Ctr 1995-; Baltimore Water Color Soc 1996-; *office:* Governor Thomas son HS 1501 N Market St Frederick MD 21701

VES, RODNEY, Counselor & Intnl Students Adv; *b:* Chester, PA; *m:* ie Benson; *c:* Erica Nicole, Karla Michelle; *ed:* Cheyney Univ (BA) ology 1969; Univ of DE (MED) Coll Counseling, Stu Dev 1993; 15 Adult Ed; *cr:* DE Tech & Comm Coll Cnslr of Disabled Stdnts, Intnl Ath Acad Adv 1976-; *ai:* NAFSA 1984-; NEA 1974-; Gov Comm for loyment of Persons with Disabilities 1991-95, Chprsn Ed Comm; *e:* DE Tech, Comm Coll Stanton Campus 400 Stanton-Christiana Rd ark DE 19713*

FERT, MARY JANE LAWLER, Theology Teacher; *b:* Cleveland, *c:* Shayna; *ed:* Cleveland St Univ (BA) Psych, Rel Stud 1972; Attnd e Dame Coll, John Carroll Univ, Neuro-Linguistic Programing; *cr:* areth Acad Eductr Theology Dept 1974-78; Brunswick Schl System Ed, Gifted 1979-83; Church of Sacred Heart CCO Coord, Tchr -84; Duchesne Acad Edctr 1984-88; Padua Franciscan HS Edctr -; *ai:* Growth in Cath Lifestyle Stu Text, Tchrs Manual Ctr for ning 1996; *office:* Padua Franciscan H S 6740 State Rd Parma OH 4*

KIN, LOIS E., English Teacher; *b:* New York, NY; *m:* Louis Alvarez; Wesleyan Univ (BA) Eng 1982; Columbia Univ (MA) Eng, parative Lit 1987; NY Univ PHD Candidate in Amer Stud; *cr:* Random se Assoc Ed 1982-86; New Rochelle HS Eng Tchr 1987-88; Fukusawa S Japan Eng Tchr 1988-89; Hunter Coll HS Eng Tchr 1989-; *ai:* Curr m; Adv to Simpsons Appreciation Club, Fac Cncl; PSC, CUNY 1989-, d; NCTE 1988-; Amer Stud Assn 1993-; NEH Summer Seminar owship in Stratford-upon-Avon 1992; Mentor to Several NEH Younger olars; Recipient of Numerous PTA Grants; Pub Study Guide to ompany Yeah, You Rite Educl Video; Presentation at 1992 NCTE Natl f; Tchr Guide to Accompany Nine Plays of the Modern Theatre Author; *e:* Hunter College HS 71 E 94th St New York NY 10128

GAN, DONNA DAMIANO, English Teacher; *b:* Jersey City, NJ; *m:* T.; *c:* Sean, Bryan, Stephanie; *ed:* Jersey City St Coll (BA) Eng Ed ; Drew Univ (MLitt) Hum 1990; William Paterson St Coll ESL 12 lit Hrs, Rdng 18 Credit Hrs Cert; *cr:* Cliffside Park HS Eng Tchr -78; Parsippany Adult Schl ESL Tchr 1983-85; Montville Township Eng Tchr 1985-; *ai:* Frosh Class Adv; NEA, NJEA 1969-; MTEA 1985-; Tchr 1995-; Montville Recreation 1989-, Coach; Schl Comm Self luation Chprsn; Key Club Adv Awd 1994; *office:* Montville Township 100 Horseneck Rd Montville NJ 07045

GAN, JAMES P., Mathematics Teacher; *b:* Boston, MA; *ed:* theastern Univ (BA) Math 1993; *cr:* Dartmouth HS Math Tchr 1994-; Marching Band Instr; Boys Tennis Coach; Chess Club Adv; NCTM 5-; *office:* Dartmouth HS 366 Slocum Rd North Dartmouth MA 02747

GAN, JOHN MICHAEL, Senior English Master; *b:* Boston, MA; *ed:* ton St Coll (BS) Eng, His 1960, (MED) Ed, Eng 1965; 5 Credit Hrs vard Boston Inst Harvard Univ 1967; 15 Credit Hrs Inst of Elizabeth d Univ of VT 1968; 12 Credit Hrs Art, His, Ed Courses Boston St Coll seum of Fine Arts 1979; *cr:* BArnes Jr HS Eng Tchr 1960-74; Another arse to Coll Dir 1974-79; Boston Latin Schl Sr Eng Master 1979-; *ai:* ecting Stdnts in Neil Simons "Rumors"; Isabella Stewart Gardner seum Liason; Teach NEA Sponsored Hum Prgm; Fac Adv; Classical ma Clb; Tchng After Schl SAT PREP Pgm; AFT, MFT 1966-; MIssion Theatre 1964-, Various Positions; Museum of Fine Arts 1975-; ntington Theatre Co 1993; Boston Ballet 1993; Isabella Stewart Gardner seum 1995; 1 of 10 New England Tchrs cited by Pres of Harvard for ceptional Contributions to Scndry Ed; Harvard Club of Boston Book d for Inspiring Curiousity & Excl in Stdnts; Tufts Univ Awd for Work an Inspirational Tchr; Recipient White Huse Commission on Ed tinguished Tchr Awd 1994; *office:* Boston Latin Schl 78 Avenue Louis steur Boston MA 02115*

GAN, MARGARET MANAHAN, Admin Asst & English Teacher; *b:* zabeth, NJ; *m:* John Matthew; *c:* Emily; *ed:* Unif of Dayton (BA) Eng 2; Columbia Univ (MAT) Eng 1976; Lesley Coll (CAGS) Curr & Instr; Inst of Hum Scholar 1993; Attnd Univ of London Extraqcurricular d & Boston Univ Schl of Ed; *cr:* Our Lady of Sorrows Schl Tchr 73-76; Barnstable MS Eng Tchr 1976-81; Barnstable HS Eng Tchr 32-, Admin Asst 1994-; *ai:* Lit Magazine Adv; Schl-Wide Advy Comm; A, Barnstable Tchrs Assn 1976-94; ASCD; Barnstable Admin Org 4-; Natl Endowment for Hum Grant; The Cape Cod Times Columnist; elance Writer.*

REGANSE, ROBERT J., Chair of Coll Preparation Dept; *b:* New York City, NY; *m:* Denise Lisowski; *c:* Alexis Marie, Justin Robert; *ed:* Suffolk Cty Comm Coll (AA) His 1967; Northeastern Univ (BS) His 1969; Stony Brook Univ (MA) His 1971; Empire St Coll (BA) Ec 1985; Stud Roman His at Univ of Rome 1972-74; *cr:* Wyandanch Jr Sr HS Soc Stud Tchr 1971-72; SUNY Dept Chprsn 1974-; *ai:* Founding Mem of UUP-EOC Concerns Comm 1988-; United Univ Professions 1974-, Chptr Pres, Grievance Chprsn, VP for Professions; NY St United Tchrs 1975-, Del; Co-Authored 4 Successfully Funded Grants 1987-89; Loan Exec for Long Island United Way 1988; UUP NY Prof Excl Awd 1991; *office:* S U N Y Coll Of Tech At Frmgdl Rt 110 Farmingdale NY 11735

REGENER, DALE KAY, Earth Sci Chemistry Teacher; *b:* Coatesville, PA; *m:* A. Eugene; *c:* Dawn, Scott; *ed:* West Chester Univ (BSEd) Chem Ed 1990; Chester Cnty Hosp Schl of Nrsng 1967; *cr:* Chester Cnty Hosp Registered Nurse 1967-69; Tel-Hai Nrsng Ctr Registered Nurse 1985-90; Twin Vly HS Registerd Nurse 1991-; *ai:* NEA 1991-; NSTA 1991-; Sandy Hill Mennonite Church 1980-; *office:* Twin Valley HS RR 3 Box 51 Elverson PA 19520

REGER, STEPHEN ANTHONY, Social Studies Teacher; *b:* Dayton, OH; *ed:* Univ of Dayton (BA) Scndry Ed 1993; *cr:* Centerville HS Sub Tchr 1993-94; Indian Hill HS Soc Stud Tchr 1994-; *ai:* Mock Trail Team Coach; NEA, OEA, SWOEA 1994-; Ashland Oil Outstdng Tchr Nom; *office:* Indian Hill HS 6845 Drake Rd Cincinnati OH 45243

REHM, CAROL T., Business Education Teacher; *b:* Utica, NY; *ed:* Utica Coll of Syracuse Univ (BS) Bus Admin 1971; Syracuse Univ Grad Schl Perm Cert Ed 1978; *cr:* Office Secretarial 1959-71; Clinton Cntrl Schl Bus Ed Tchr 1971-75; Hamilton Cntrl Schl Bus Ed Tchr 1977-79; Stockbridge Vly Cntrl Schl Bus Ed Tchr 1979-; *ai:* FBLA, Stu Cncl, SADD, Stu Tchrs, Yrbk Adv; *office:* Stockbridge Valley Cntrl Schl Main St Munnsville NY 13409

REHM, MARYANN, Eng Tchr & Acting Instrl Ldr; *b:* Bethlehem, PA; *ed:* Carlow Coll (BA) Eng, Scndry Ed 1969; Masters Equivalency Univ of Pittsburgh 1969-91; *cr:* Gladstone HS Eng Tchr 1969-76; John A. Brashear HS Eng Tchr 1976-; *ai:* Stage Crew Spon 14 Yrs; Pittsburgh Fed Tchrs, AFT, Western PA Cncl Tchrs Eng 20 Yrs; Western PA Writers Project 1991-; Fellow Western PA Writers Project; Curr Practioner Pittsburgh Pub Schls; Arts Propel Team; *office:* John A Brashear HS 590 Crane Ave Pittsburgh PA 15216*

REHM, PHYLLIS ANDREA CHERNOFF, French & Italian Educator; *b:* Brooklyn, NY; *m:* Rolf L.; *ed:* Queens Coll (BA) Fr 1970; Fairleigh Dickinson Univ (MA) Multilingual Tchng 1976; Cert Fr, Italian, Supervision; Post-Grad Stud Fr, Italian, Ed; *cr:* Mother Cabrini Schl Fr Tchr 1970-71; Frelinghuysen MS Fr Tchr 1972-89; Morristown HS Fr, Italian Tchr 1989-; *ai:* Adv Fr, Italian Clubs; NEA, NJEA 1972-; AATF 1985-; VITA 1994-; FLENJ 1978-, Awd Outstdng Svc 1993, Outstdng Frgn Langs Educator 1993; Grants City Univ 1982, Rutgers Univ 1988, John Jay Coll 1989; Tuition Schlsp 1970; Dept Chair 1994-; Mini Grant Morris Educl Fnd 1995; *office:* Morristown HS 50 Early St Morristown NJ 07960*

REHMEYER, TERRY LOUIS, Health Education Teacher; *b:* York, PA; *m:* Patricia Ann Kroh; *c:* Bryan; *ed:* East Stroudsburg Univ (BS) Hlth & PE 1972; Masters Degree Equivalency; *cr:* Northern HS Hlth Ed Tchr 1972-; *ai:* Dept Chprsn; Northern York Ed Assn, Penn St Ed Assn, NEA 1972-; *office:* Northern York Cty HS 655 S Baltimore St Dillsburg PA 17019

REHN, BRIAN L., Music Teacher & Band Director; *b:* Wiliamsport, PA; *m:* Kimberly Ann; *ed:* IN Univ of PA (BS) Music 1993; 12 Credit Hrs Univ of the Arts Philadelphia PA; *cr:* Mountain View Schl Dist Jr Sr HS Instrumental Music Tchr, Band Dir 1993-; *ai:* Marching, Jazz Band; Jazz Combo; Small Select Ensembles; PMEA, MENC 1989-; NEA 1993-; *office:* Mountain View HS RR 1 Box 339 Kingsley PA 18826*

REHRL-RUGGIO, CARMEN ANTOINETTE, German Teacher; *b:* New York City, NY; *m:* Edward James; *c:* Cyrina, Nicolas; *ed:* SUC at Oswego (BA) Ger, Intl Trade 1977; Syracuse Univ (MS) Foreign Lang Ed 1981, (MA) Ger Lang, Lit 1982; LeMoyne Coll ESL Cert; Julius Maximus Universitat Wurzburg 12 Hrs Federal Rep of Ger; *cr:* Syracuse Univ Ger Tchng Asst 1979-81; West Genesee HS Sub Tchr 1982-83; Liverpoool HS Sub Tchr 1982-83; General Electric Co-Temp Data Production, Tech Support 1985-87; Onondaga Comm Coll Ger Inst Sp 1987; Skaneateles HS Ger, Fr Tchr 1987-93; Mexico HS Ger Tchr 1993-; *ai:* Participate in Ger Club Acts; AATG 1989-; NYSAFLT 1980-; FLACNY, NYSUT 1987-; Phi Sigma Iota 1981-, Sec 1981-82; Delta Phi Alpha 1977-; Ger Consulate Generals Awd Outstdng Tchng 1981-; Stu Presented Honors Convocation Plaque 1993 in Appreciation of Achvmt, Enthusiasm, Love in Ed; *home:* 2299 Mott Rd Baldwinsville NY 13027

REIBER, BARBARA MAE, History Teacher; *b:* New Haven, CT; *c:* Carolyn Reiber Tiroletto; *ed:* Albertus Magnus Coll (BA) Ger 1956; Northwestern Univ (MA) His 1970; 8 Credits Ger Yale Univ; 3 Credits His Trinity Univ; 6 Credits His Southern CT St Univ; *cr:* Michael J. Whalen Jr HS Ancient, Med His, Ger Tchr 1956-65; Hamden HS Ger, His Tchr 1965-; *ai:* Stu Cncl Fac Adv; Parent Tchr Stu Org Fac Rep; Alternative Ed Comm; Mentor Tchr 1994-; NEA 1965-; CT Ed Assn, Hamden Ed Assn 1956-; Delta Kappa Gamma 1992-; Outstdng Young Edctrs Awd Hamden Jaycees 1969; Bd of Ed Bonyai Awd 1988; Bd of Ed PATS Awd 1992; Univ of CT Alumni Assn Awd Excl in Ed 1994.

REICH, DONNA ANANIA, English Teacher; *b:* Des Moines, IA; *m:* Charles E.; *c:* John Francis; *ed:* St Marys Col of Notre Dame at IN (BA) Eng, Scndry Ed 1977; *cr:* Woodrow Wilson Jr HS 9th Grd Eng Tchr 1977-78; North Cath HS 10th Grd Eng Tchr 1978-93; Cntrl Cath HS 9-12th Grd Eng Tchr 1993-; *ai:* Video Club Moderator; Video Yrbk, Creative Writing Contest Coord; Fac Liason Viking Victory Auction; Kappa Gamma Pi 1977-; WPCTE 1978-; NACST, NCEA 1978-; St Marys Notre Dame Alumni Club 1977-.

REICH, RITA S. (EVENSON), ESL Teacher; *b:* Newburgh, NY; *m:* Walter I.; *c:* Stuart J., Lawrence M.; *ed:* St Univ of NY at Albany (BA) Span, Eng 1961; St Johns Univ (MS) Span Tchng 1964; Long Island Univ (MS) TESOL 1987; Span Lang, Culture at Univ of Madrid 1965; Psych Courses at Long Island Univ 1990; Inservice Courses at BETAC-BOCES 1990-; *cr:* Grand Ave Jr HS Span Tchr 1961-66; John F. Kennedy Sr HS Span Tchr 1966-67; Scarsdale Jr HS Span, Eng Tchr 1967-69; Pub Schls of Tarrytowns TESOL Tchr 1987-; *ai:* ESL Team Liason; Wellness Adv Advisee Prgm; AFT, TAT, NYS TESOL 1987-; Tarrytowns PTSA 1987-; Ardsley PTA 1971-, VP; MADD 1984-; Co-Authored, Revised Curr; Co-Taught Sheltered Sci Prgm Under Auspices of NYS Grant for Limited Eng Proficiency Stdnts; *office:* Sleepy Hollow MS-HS 210 N Broadway Tarrytown NY 10591*

REICHARD, DAVID CARL, Prof of Engineering & Math; *b:* Philadelphia, PA; *m:* Margaret Hoffmann; *c:* Suzanne Fratino, Chris; *ed:* Univ of DE (BS) Mechanical Engrg 1966; Univ of MI (MS) Engrng Mechanics 1968; Addl 30 Hrs Engrng, Math, Statistics, Math Ed; *cr:* Gen Motors Inst Assoc Prof 1968-78; US Patent Office Patent Examiner 1978-79; Charles Cty Comm Coll Prof 1979-; *ai:* ASEE; Books Pub: Exploring Cadkey 1988, Exploring Cadkey 3 1989, Exploring Cadkey 1 1990; *office:* Charles County Comm Coll PO Box 910 La Plata MD 20646

REICHARD, GARY GILBERT, Mathematics Teacher; *b:* Wilmington, DE; *m:* Laurie Lynne Gladstone; *c:* Ryan, Kyle, Kelsey; *ed:* Montgomery Coll (AA) Gen Stud 1989; Towson St Univ (BS) Math 1991; *cr:* Duval HS Math Tchr 1992-95; Yeshiva Math Tchr 1995-; *ai:* Bsbl Coach; *home:* 2135 Cedar Barn Way Baltimore MD 21244

REICHARD, TERRY DAVID, Fourth Grade Teacher; *b:* Decatur, IN; *m:* Rebecca Ann Lichtenberger; *c:* Lauren Michelle; *ed:* Defiance Coll (BS) Elem Ed 1972; Wright St Univ (MA) Tchr Ldr 1979; *cr:* Parkway Local Schl 5th-6th Grd Math Tchr 1972-78; Lincolnview Local Schl 4th Grd Tchr 1978-; *ai:* 1st Yr Tchr Mentor; Wrestling Meets Timer; NEA, OEA, LLEA 1972-, Chm of Schlsp Fund, Bldg Rep; Trinity United Meth Church 1982-, Pres of United Meth Men Missions Comm, Choir Mem.

REICHARDT, BEATRICE TAYLOR, Retired Elementary Teacher; *b:* Cincinnati, OH; *c:* L. Dan Taylor, Terral T. Graves, Reed E.; *ed:* Wilmington Coll (BA); Miami U of OH (MA) Ed; Spec Cert Elem Rdng, Art; *cr:* Blanchester Pub Schl First Grd Tchr 3 Yrs; Georgetown Ex Village Schls First, Fourth Grd Tchr 35 Yrs; *ai:* Local, Neighboring Schl, Pub Libs; Elderhostel Part Tutor on Coll Level; Headstart; Fed Arts Prgm; Olympics; Odyssey of the Mind; Elem Tchr Mentor Prgm; Green Key Hnr Soc; Martha Holden Jennings Schlshp; Honorary Resolution from 117th Assembly of OH St Senate.

REICHART, KELLY ANNE, United States History Teacher; *b:* Cleveland, OH; *ed:* Loyola Coll (BA) His 1990; 30 Credit Hrs Beyond BA; Coll of Notre Dame Ed Cert 1991; *cr:* Calvert Hall Coll His Tchr 1991; Loch Raven HS Soc Stud Tchr 1991-; *ai:* Steering Comm Mid Sts; Prins Advy Bd; Spon Jr Class Since 1993; NEA 1991-; IDEA, Fitness 1990-; Writer for US His Curr, US His Countywide Exam; Presenter at Baltimore Museum of Art; *office:* Loch Raven HS 1212 Cowpens Ave Baltimore MD 21286

REICHENBACH, ALLAN J., Mathematics Teacher; *b:* Staten Island, NY; *m:* Sue Ann Eboch; *c:* Scott, Karen, Brian; *ed:* East Stroudsburg Univ (BS) Math Ed 1967; Bucknell Univ (MS) Math Tchng 1970; Attnd Trenton St Coll, Temple Univ; *cr:* Pennsbury Schl Dist Math Tchr 28 Yrs; Rider Univ Adj Instr 25 Yrs; *ai:* Fac Comm Mid Sts Evaluation Chm; Grdng Comm; PIAA 1965-; NEA 1968-; PSEA 1968-; AAUP; Bucks Cty PIAA Bsktbl Ofcls 1968-, Sec, Treas & Assigner; Calvary Bapt Church 1969-, Deacon Bd, Mission Bd Treas, Pastoral Search Comm Vice Chm; Lower Bucks PIAA Track & Field 1980-; *office:* Pennsbury HS Hood Blvd Fairless Hills PA 19030

REICHLE, PHILIP, Admissions Dir & Religion Tchr; *b:* Cincinnati, OH; *m:* Candace Dana Lozier; *c:* Robb Philip, Kelly Ann Brittany Sue, Casey Thomas, Chad Patrick; *ed:* Univ of Cincinnati (AA) Arts 1969, (BSEd) Elem Ed 1975; Working Toward Cert & Masters in Theology; *cr:* St James Schl Tchr 1969-86; LaSalle HS Adm Dir, Tchr, Coach 1986-; *ai:* Key Club Moderator, Ftbl, Bsbl Coach; Work With Stu Trainers; OH Cath Schl Accreditating Assn Comm; NCEA 1986-; NASAA 1990-; OHSBCA 1976-; Hamilton Cty Spec Olympics 1995-, Review Bd; Western Hills Jaycees Young Edctr of Yr Awd 1985; Br. James Daniel Meml Awd; *office:* La Salle HS 3091 W North Bend Rd Cincinnati OH 45239*

REICKEL, ERIC JAMES, English Teacher; *b:* Dearborn, MI; *m:* Becky Schroth; *c:* James, Jack; *ed:* Univ of MI (BA) Eng 1983; Johns Hopkins Univ (MLA) Eng 1988; *cr:* Linganore HS Eng Tchr 1984-1995; Urbana HS Eng Dept Chair 1995-; *ai:* Acad Team Coach; Baccalaureate Speaker Chosen by Sr Class 1993; NEA, MSTA, FCTA 1984-; Tchr of Yr Scndry Schsl Frederick Chamber of Commerce 1993; AP Scorer AP Lit Test Princeton NJ 1992; Outstanding Tchr Awd Natl White House Comm 1990, Mc Donalds Corp 1990; *office:* Urbana HS 3471 Campus Dr Ijamsville MD 21754*

REID, CELESTE CHASSE, English & French Teacher; *b:* Rochester, NH; *m:* David Alexander; *c:* Andrew, Daniel; *ed:* Univ of ME at Orono (BA) Eng 1974; Lesley Coll (MED) Creative Arts 1991; *cr:* Pittsfield HS Eng, Soc Stud Tchr 1974-75; Norwood HS Eng Tchr 1975-77; Salem HS Eng Tchr 1977-, Fr Tchr 1993-; *ai:* Key Club Adv; 10 Yr Re-Accreditation Comm; Inclusion Team; Fr Clb 1995-; Class Adv 1978-82; Granite St Challenge Coach 1986-90; NEA, NHEA 1977-; SEA 1977-, Bldg Rep; NCTE 1993-; NHCTE; Dollars for Scholars 1982-, Pres 1988; ADK Nu Chapter 1992-, Pres 1994-; Salem Tchr of Yr 1986-87; Tufts Univ Outstanding Educator 1993; *home:* 26 Kilrea Rd Derry NH 03038*

REID, ROBERT KOHLER, Bands Dir, Instrumental Music; *b:* Kingston, PA; *m:* Cynthia Carlson; *c:* Adam Kohler; *ed:* Susquehanna Univ (BSME) Music Ed 1979; Advanced Stud Conducting, Admin, Instrument Repair Marywood Coll, Edinboro Univ, East Stroudsburg Univ; *cr:* Wattsburg Area Schls Music Tchr 1980-; Lake Erie Regiment Jr Drum & Bugle Corps Asst Dir 1995-; *ai:* Marching Band, Musical Orch Dir; Phi Beta Mu 1994-; PA Music Ed Assn 1980-, Pres 1991-93, Citation of Excl 1994; Schl Dist Awd for Quality 1994, Awd for Excl 1995; Who's Who Among Young Men in Amer 1989; *office:* Wattsburgh Area Schl Dist PO Box 219 Wattsburg PA 16442*

REID, SHEILA, High School English Teacher; *b:* New York City, NY; *ed:* Bronx Comm Coll (AA) Liberal Arts 1990; Mary Mount Manhatton Coll (BA) Theatre, Eng 1992; Amer Acad of Dramtic Arts Cert Drama 1988; Pursuing Master's Degree in Ed Lehman Coll; *cr:* Sarah J. Hale HS Eng Tchr 1 1/2 Yrs; John Jay HS Eng Tchr; *ai:* Tchng Drama Ages 4-13 at Roots Comm Films Brooklyn NY; *home:* 1140 Woodycrest Ave Apt 3 B Bronx NY 10452

REIDENBACH, ROBERT DAVID, Social Studies Teacher; *b:* Scranton, PA; *m:* Laura Anderson; *c:* Moses, Matthew, Seth; *ed:* Keystone Jr Coll (AA) His 1964; Lebanon Vly Coll (BA) His 1966; Univ of Scranton (MA) his 1970; 45 Credit Hrs Beyond Masters; *cr:* Abington Hghts HS Psych & European His Tchr 30 Yrs; *ai:* Ftbl & Swim Competition Announcer; Track Ofcl; Ski Club Spon; NEA 1966-; PSEA; PA Tchr of the Yr Excl Awd 1972; Freedoms Fndtn Vly Forge; *office:* Abington Heights HS W Grove St Clarks Summit PA 18411

REIDMILLER, F. KEITH, Social Studies Instructor; *b:* Greensburg, PA; *m:* Marsha Ann Bogan; *c:* Stephanie, Matthew, Daniel; *ed:* Shippensburg Univ (BS) Sec Ed 1977; Univ of Pittsburgh Ed Level II Cert 1983; *cr:* Elizabeth Forward HS Ftbl Coach 1986; West Jefferson Hills HS Ftbl Coach 1987; Hempfield HS Ftbl Coach 1988-93; *ai:* Presidential Classroom, Lions Club Schlsps Spon; Var Ftbl Coach; Yough HS Ftbl Coach 1979-85; Yough HS Bsbl Coach 1983; Hempfield HS Ftbl Coach 1988-95; Yearbook & Stud Cncl Spon; NEA, PSEA 1978-; YEA 1978-, Bldg, Grievance Rep; *office:* Yough Schl Dist 99 Lowber Rd Herminie PA 15637

REIDY, GEORGE H., Math Teacher & Dept Chair; *b:* Baltimore, MD; *m:* Evelyne Tanshien Yang; *ed:* Wheeling Coll (BA) His 1972; George Washington Univ (MA) Intnl Ed & Human Resource Dev 1984, (EDD) Higher Ed 1996; *cr:* Dist of Columbia Pub Schls Math Tchr 1975-; *ai:* Co-Chm Tech Comm; Ventures in Ed Consultant; AFT 1975-; WTU 1975-; NSF & DOD Grant in Math Modeling 1996; *office:* Schl Without Walls 21st & G Street NW Washington DC 20037*

REIF, STEPHEN BRUCE, Vocal Music Teacher; *b:* Camden, NJ; *m:* Carol Sue Thomas; *c:* Jason Charles, Brent Thomas, Stephanie Joy; *ed:* Messiah Coll (BS) Music Ed 1977; 2 Grad Credits Chrstn Cnclng, Educl Fnd; 12 Grad Credits Bob Jones Univ; 4 Grad Credits Rider Univ; *cr:* Calvert Chrstn Schl K-12 Grd Music Tchr 1978-79; Baptist HS Vocal, 6-12 Grd Vocal, Instrumental Music Tchr 1980-89; Plumstead Chrstn Schl 6-12 Grd Vocal Music Tchr 1990-; *ai:* Class Adv; Fine Arts Comm; Music Edctrs Natl Conven, PA Music Edctrs Assn, Bucks Cty Music Assn 1990-; Chrstn

Instrumental Dirs Assn 1985-, Northeast Region Sec; *home:* PO Box 453 Silverdale PA 18962

REIGEL, RUSSELL H., Science Teacher; *b:* Shenandoah, PA; *m:* Nancy Jean Cleaver; *c:* Paul R.; *ed:* Elizabethtown Coll (BA) His 1970; 45 Addl Credit Hrs; Lehigh Univ, Kutztown Univ Master's Equivalency 1980; Moravian Coll at PS St Recert Gen Sci 1982; *cr:* Trexler MS Sci, Soc Stud Tchr 1970-84, 1985-; Raub MS Sci, Soc Stud Tchr 1984-85; *ai:* Var Soccer CoachPSEA.; PSEA, AEA, NEA 1970-; NSTA 1985-; Allentown Schl Dist Grant 1988; Rider-Pool Fnd Grant Excl, Innovation in Tchng 1989; *office:* Trexler MS 851 N 15th St Allentown PA 18102*

REIGHARD, DONNA SCALZOTT, Fifth Grade Teacher; *b:* Tarentum, PA; *m:* Thomas H.; *c:* Rachele, Thomas; *ed:* Edinboro Univ (BS) Elem Ed, Early Chldhd 1973; Penn St Univ Stud Elem Ed; *cr:* Bellevue Elem Schl 2 Grd Tchr 1973-75; Weinels Elem Schl 2 Grd Tchr 1975-77, 3 Grd Tchr 1877-78, 5 Grd Tchr 1978-; *ai:* PA St Ed Assn 1973-; Kiski Area Ed Assn 1973-, PR; Gift of Time Recepient 1994; *office:* Weinels Elem Schl 200 Poplar St Vandergrift PA 15690

REIGHARD, KIMBERLY JANE, Health & PE Teacher; *b:* Johnstown, PA; *ed:* Slippery Rock Univ (BSEd) Hlth & PE 1988; *cr:* Ferndale Area Schl Dist Hlth & PE Tchr 1989-; *ai:* Var Girls Vlybl Coach; Sr HS Vlybl Club; PSEA, NEA 1989-; NFIOA, PIAA Ofcl Vlybl 1988-; PVCA 1990-; *office:* Ferndale Area Schl Dist 600 Harlan Ave Johnstown PA 15905

REIGNER, THOMAS E., Civics & World Cultures Tchr; *b:* West Chester, PA; *m:* Helena Ann Ritterson; *c:* Eric, Kevin, Megan; *ed:* Tarkio Coll (BS) Soc Stu, Scndry Ed 1973; Weidner Coll 19 Credit Hrs; PA St 12 Credit Hrs; Intermediate Unit 10 Credit Hrs; *cr:* Showalter MS Soc Stud Tchr 1973-83; Pulaski MS Soc Stud Tchr 1983-90; Chester HS Soc Stud Tchr 1990-92; Chester HS Acad Soc Stud Tchr 1993-; *ai:* Ath & Intramural Dir; Soccer, Track, Wrestling & Bsktbl Coach; Track Ofcl; Class Adv; NEA, PSEA 1973-; CUEA 1973-, Tchr of Yr 1973; North Chester Bapt Church 1949-, Treas, Bd Chm, Fncl & Soc Comms CHm, Servanthood Awd, Sports Awd; US Olympic Comm on Ed, Curr Sub-Comm; Publishing a Curr for Schl on the Olympics; *home:* 3769 Clearwater Ln Brookhaven PA 19015

REIHART, STEPHANY BETTERMANN, World Cultures Teacher; *b:* Johnstown, PA; *c:* Michael J., David C.; *ed:* MIllersville Univ (BS) Geography 1959; Addl 15 Credit Hrs; *cr:* York City Schl 2nd Grd Tchr 1959, Jr HS His, Rdng Tchr 1959-62; Baker HS His Tchr 1963-64; York Suburban HS Soc Stud Tchr 1989-; *ai:* Mock Trial Coach; Frosh Class Adv; Cents Tech Comm; NEA, PSEA, YSEA 1989-; PA Cncl of Soc Stud, Mason Dixon Soc Stud Cncl 1989-; Article Pub; Bassler Geographic Awd 1959; *home:* 1025 Southern Rd York PA 17403

REILLY, BRENDAN, Accounting Professor; *b:* Kearny, NJ; *m:* Claire Dietz; *c:* Lisa, Brendan, Joseph; *ed:* Fairleigh Dickinson Univ (BS) Acctg 1953, (MBA) Acctg 1959; Cert Pub Accountant NJ 1960; *cr:* Central CT St Univ Prof 1968-94; Univ of CT Acctng Prof 1978-; Wethersfield HS Coach 1980-; *ai:* Girls Track, Field, Cross Cntry Coach 17 Trs; *home:* 10 Harvey Rd Windsor CT 06095

REILLY, CATHERINE M., Physical Education Teacher; *b:* Brooklyn, NY; *ed:* Brooklyn Coll (BA) Elem Ed 1984, (MS) Rdng, Ed 1987; Prof Diploma Admin, Supervision 1992; Masters Exercise Sci Rehabilitation; *cr:* PS 105 4-5 Grd Tchr 1984-87, Grd 5 Tchr of Gifted 1987-90, K-5 Grd Rdng Tchr 1990-92, K-5 PE Tchr 1992-; *ai:* Fun Run Organizer; AFT 1984-; Bklyn Rdng Cncl 1987-; Am Coll Sports Med 1996-; Bay Ridge St Patricks Day Parade Comm 1994-, Organizer; Dist 20 Mini Grant 1992; *office:* PS 105 Blythebourne 1031 59th St Brooklyn NY 11219*

REILLY, DAVID JOHN, Chem & Physical Science Tchr; *b:* Wilkes Barre, PA; *m:* Doreen Rose Yankosky; *c:* Coleen, Neil; *ed:* Westchester Univ (MA) Phys Sci 1976; *cr:* Northern Tioga Dist 8th Grd Sci Tchr 1972-73; Downingtown Area Chem Tchr 1973-; *ai:* NEA 1972-; PSEA 1972-; DAEA 1973-; VFW 1977-; *office:* Downingtown Sr HS 445 Manor Ave Downingtown PA 19335

REILLY, DAVID W., Coach; *b:* Washington, DC; *c:* Erika K.; *ed:* The Citadel (BS) Pol Sci 1972; FL Inst of Tech (MS) Contract & Alq Mngmt 1980; *ai:* Asst Ftbl Coach; Head JV Sftbl Coach; JROTC Chprsn; AUSA 1980-; TROA 1991-; *office:* Thomas Stone HS 3785 Leonardtown Rd Waldorf MD 20601

REILLY, DONNA MARIE(LEHMAN), 12th Grade English Teacher; *b:* Pine Grove, PA; *m:* Michael Glennon; *c:* Bret Lehman Reilly; *ed:* Kutztown Univ (BS) Eng Ed 1973; *cr:* Pine Grove Area MS Grd 8 Eng Tchr 1973-82; Pine Grove Area HS Grd 12 Eng Tchr 1982-; *ai:* NCTE 1974-; PCTE 1975-; Kappa Delta Pi 1972-; Amer Legion Auxiliary 1960-; Time Warner Cable Excl in Ed Awd 1995; Tchr of Yr 1992; *office:* Pine Grove Area HS School St Pine Grove PA 17963*

REILLY, DONNA DENISE DOUGLAS, Gifted Program Coordinator; *b:* Manhattan, NY; *m:* John Arthur; *c:* John Jason, Jaida Simone; *ed:* St Joseph's Coll (BA) Child Stud, Ed 1973; Long Island Univ (MS) Elem Ed 1978; Brooklyn Coll Advanced Cert Admin-Supervision 1990; *cr:* John Edward Bruce Day Car Ctr Asst Tchr 1972-73; Brooklyn Jr Acad 1st, 4th Grd Tchr 1973-76; The Lenox Schl PS 235 1st-2nd Grd Gifted Pupil Tchr 1980-87, Coord Gifted Prgm, Supvr of Annex 1987-; Asst Supt of Newlife Ministeries Sunday Schl 1996; *ai:* Activity Spon for Colgate Women's Games, Track & Field; Schl-Comm Liason for CSB #18; Mini Grant Stu Proposal Writing Team; Day Care-Primary Schl Mentor-Adv; AFT, UFT 1977-; ABENY, NYSABE 1988-; ASCD 1990-; New Life Ministries 1990-, Sunday Schl Tchr 1992, Youth Wkshp Ldr, Asst Superintendant 1996-; Keynote Speaker CUNY Forum for Tchng Trng & Educl Opportunities, Grad Speaker Faith Nursery & Day Schl 1993; Grad Speaker P. B. Children's Acad 1992; *office:* The Lenox Schl PS 235 Annex 779 E 49th St Brooklyn NY 11203*

REILLY, GAIL SHERIDAN, Second Grade Teacher; *b:* Brooklyn, NY; *m:* Thomas L.; *c:* Sean Paul, Elizabeth Reilly; *ed:* Jersey City St Coll (BA) Elem Ed 1965; 30 Addl Hrs; *cr:* Slocum Ave Schl Second Grd Tchr 1965-69; Community Nursery Schl Tchr 1975-78; Nutley Elem Schls SCE, Title I, Sub Tchr 1978-85; Yantacaw Elem Schl Fourth, Fifth, Second Grd Tchr 1985-; *ai:* Curr Dev Comms; Stu Cncl Adv 1986-88; Literary Club Adv 1990-; Nutley Crew Booster Assn 1987-89; NEA; NJ Ed Assn; Ed Assn of Nutley; PTA 1977-; *office:* Yantacaw Elem Schl 20 Yantacaw Pl Nutley NJ 07110

REILLY, GEORGE WILLIAM, English Teacher; *b:* Providence, RI; *m:* Mary Elizabeth Mauro; *c:* Elizabeth, Christopher; *ed:* RI Coll (MAT) Eng 1969; 30 Addl Hrs Univ of RI, Brown Univ, RI Coll; *cr:* Smithfield HS Eng Tchr 1965-; *ai:* Coach Acad Decathlon Team; Stu Tchrs Cooperating Supvr 29 Yrs; NEA 1965-; NEA RI 1965-, Del Assembly, St Treas; NEA-Smithfield 1965-, Pres, Negotiating Comm Chair, Grievance Chair, Treas, Hlth Benefits Comm; BSA, Local Troop Bd Mem, Treas; St Augustine Church, Lector, Rel Ed Instr; Booklets Pub; RI St Spelling Bee Judge 1986-; Prov Journal Bulletin News Carrier Schlsp Comm; *office:* Smithfield HS 90 Pleasant View Ave Esmond RI 02917*

REILLY, HELEN FRANCIS,SSJ, Finance Office Assistant; *b:* Philadelphia, PA; *ed:* Chestnut Hill Coll (BS) Ed 1969; *cr:* St Stephen Elem Schl 4th-6th Grd Tchr 1962-66; Ascension of Our Lord Schl 7th Grd Tchr 1966-70; Resurrection of Our Lord Schl 7th Grd Tchr 1970-72; St Helena Schl 5th, 7th-8th Grd Tchr 1972-83; Corpus Christi Schl 4th Grd Tchr 1983-88; Nativity of Our Lord Schl 4th Grd Tchr 1988-89; Ascension of Our Lord Schl Audio-Visula Coord 1989-92; Mount Saint Joseph Fin Office Assistant 1992-; *ai:* Math Grant Northwestern Univ 1971; *home:* 3015 Chestnut St Lafayette Hill PA 19444

REILLY, JEAN FRANCIS, Instrl Aide for Emtnl Sprt Cls; *b:* Columbus, OH; *ed:* Cabrini Coll (BS) Elem Ed & ECE 1973-82; 30 Credits Elem-Spec Ed Penn St; *cr:* St Monica Schl Sub Soc St Tchr 1973; Upper Merion SD Sub Elem Tchr 1973-75; Kinder Care Kndgtn Tchr 1978-82; Hansell Child Care Pre-K, Kndgtn Tchr 1982-95; Devon Elem Schl Instrl Aide 1995-; *ai:* NAEYC 1988-; *home:* 401 Warren Rd Wayne PA 19087*

REILLY, JUDITH G., Physical Science Professor; *b:* Middletown, CT; *m:* James A.; *c:* Thomas E.; *ed:* Clark Univ (AB) Physics 1958, (MA) Physics & Optics 1960; *cr:* Quinsigamond Comm Coll Math & Sci Prof 19630-; Assumption Prep Schl Physics Tchr 1963; Clark Univ Physics Adj Fac 1963-; *ai:* Coll-Wide Governance 25 Yrs; Lib & Media Advy Comm; APT; MCCA; NEA; 2 Books Pub; Numerous Articles Pub.*

REILLY, JUDITH HOWARD, English Teacher; *b:* Pittsburgh, PA; *m:* Michael; *c:* John C., Andrew I., Jill A.; *ed:* Chatham Coll (BA) Eng 1966; Masters Equivalency; *cr:* Upper St Clair HS Tchr 1984-; *ai:* AFT 1984-; *office:* Upper St Clair HS 1825 Mclaughlin Run Rd Pittsburgh PA 15241

REILLY, KATHLEEN MURPHY, Third Grade Teacher; *b:* Newark, NJ; *m:* Francis P.; *c:* Robin, Meghan; *cr:* Harrison Bd of Ed Pre-K & kndgtn Tchr 1970-75, Basic Skills Tchr 1981-82; Jersey City Bd of Ed Basic Skills Tchr 1983, 3rd Grd Tchr 1984-; *ai:* NEA 1970-75, 1981-; NJEA 1970-75, 1981-; Alpha Delta Kappa 1974-; *office:* Martin Luther King Jr PS 11 886 Bergen Ave Jersey City NJ 07306

REILLY, LINDA PRITCHARD, 8th Grade Math Teacher; *b:* Pen Argyl, PA; *m:* Joseph T.; *ed:* Ursinus Coll (BS) Math 1972; Beaver Coll (MED) Ed, Math 1988; *cr:* Plymouth Jr HS Math Tchr 1972-82; Colonial MS Math Tchr 1982-; *ai:* Mathcounts Coach; Pupil Enrichment Prgm Adv; Induction Comm; NCTM 1992-; ATMOPAV 1990-; NEA, PSEA 1972-; Excl in Ed Awd for MS Ed; *office:* Colonial MS 716 Belvoir Rd Norristown PA 19401*

REILLY, SUZANNE SWEENEY, Senior Lecturer; *b:* Philadelphia, PA; *m:* Paul J.; *ed:* MS Coll of Art (BFA) Studio, Art His 1980; Univ of MA at Amherst (MA) Art His 1980; *cr:* Salve Regina Lecturer 1985-86; Wheelock Coll Lecturer 1986-89; Laseil Coll Sr Lecturer 1986-96; Farmingham St Lecturer 1988-89; Fisher Coll Lecturer 1993-; Northeastern Univ Lecturer 1995-; Showa Inst Lecturer 1995-; *ai:* Started Wheelock Slide Lib; Weaver-Artist 1975-; Museum of Fine Arts 1988-; Art News 1986-; Gardner Museum 1992-, Textile Conservator Asst 1994-; Gardner Museum 1994-, Adjunct Tour Guide; *office:* Lasell Coll 1844 Comm Ave Newton MA 02166*

REILLY, THOMAS PATRICK, Russian & Gen Language Teacher; *b:* Waterbury, CT; *ed:* Univ of CT (BA) Fr & Span 1950; Middleburg Coll (MA) Span & Fr 1954; All But Exam for MA in Slavic Lang, Also Have a Total of 100 Credits Beyond the Middlebury MA in Courses in Various Langs, Linguistics, Slavic Studs; *cr:* Canterbury Schl Fr & Span Tchr 1951-52; Horace Mann Schl Fr, Span & Russian Tchr 1952-, Chm of Frgn Lang Dept 1958-90, Tchr of Russian & Gen Lang 1990-; *ai:* Intnl Cncl & Russian Club Advs; Mem of Governing Cncl; Former Fr Club Adv; ATIS 1952-, Recording Sec 6 Yrs; ATR & AATSEEL; Kingsbridge Historical Soc 1973-, Pres 13 Yrs; Bronx Cty Historical Soc 1975-; Cymdeithas Madog Welsh Soc 1985-; Canal Soc of NJ 1986-; Riverdale on Hudson Garden Club 1991-; Rotarty Club Flwshp to Univ of Grenoble France 1950-51.*

REILLY, TIMOTHY EDWARD, English Teacher; *b:* Phila, PA; *m:* Anne Marie Sweeney; *c:* Timothy, Patrick, Meghan, Connor; *ed:* Ursinus Coll (BA) Eng 1981; Beaver Coll (MA) Ed, Eng 1988; 30 Inservice Credit Hrs; *cr:* Lower Moreland HS Eng Tchr 1982-; *ai:* Asst Ftbl Coach; NEA, PSEA 1982-.

REIMERS, CATHERINE KUNZ, German Teacher; *b:* Buffalo, NY; *m:* David M.; *c:* Rosie; *ed:* St Univ of NY at Buffalo (BA) Intnl Stud 1985; St Univ Coll at Buffalo (BS) Multidisciplinary Stud 1989; Working on Span Cert; *cr:* Buffalo Museum of Sci Pub Relations Dept Artist & Pub Relations 1987; Saint Anns Elem Schl 5th Grd Tchr 1987-88; Pembroke Jr-Sr HS Ger & Soc Stud Tchr 1988-92; Kenmore West HS Ger Tchr 1992-; *ai:* Ger & Outdoor Adventure Club Advs; AATG 1992-; Soc for Creative Anachronisms Medieval Renactment 1983-, Dance, Tchng, Calligraphy & Singing Awds.*

REIN, GRACE LOGAY, English Teacher; *b:* Trenton, NJ; *m:* Richard Nicholas; *c:* Benjamin Jason Carey, Maura Faith Carey; *ed:* Glassboro St Coll (BA) Eng Ed 1972; *cr:* Northern Burlington Cty Regnl HS Eng Tchr 1972-; *ai:* NJEA 1972-; NCTE 1980-; BFA Division of NAA 1979-; AKA 1990-; Master Tchr Awd 1985; NJFAA Convention Awd 1994; Article Pub BFA Newsletter 1980; *office:* Northern Burlington Reg HS 160 Mansfield Rd E Columbus NJ 08022*

REIN, STEWART, Social Studies Teacher; *b:* Brooklyn, NY; *c:* Gabriel, Jenny; *ed:* SUNY at New Platz (MS) Soc Stud Ed 1976, (CAS) Educl Admin 1988; *cr:* Hudson MS Soc Stud Tchr 1971-74; Lorge Schl Dir of Admin 1974-75; Wappingers Cntrl Schl Dist Soc Stud, Psych Tchr 1975-; *ai:* Track & Gymnastics Coach; Class Adv; Phi Delta Kappa 1990-, Exec Bd; NYSUT 1971-; Natl Endowment for Hum Grant to Stud & Write about Soc His; *home:* 19 Briarcliff Ave Poughkeepsie NY 12603

REINECK, DRENNA L., Elementary Principal; *b:* Martinsburg, WV; *m:* Steven L.; *c:* Kristin, Jennifer L.; *ed:* Univ of Cntrl FL (BA) Ed 1971, (MED) Ed 1976; VPI CAG8 Ed Admin-Supervision 1987; WV Univ 30 Hrs Gifted Ed; MD Prin Assessment Ctr 1991; *cr:* Orange Co Schl Elem Ed Tchr 1971-80; Berkeley Co Schl Gifted Ed Tchr 1980-87; Orange Co Schl Gifted Ed Tchr 1987-89; Berkeley Co Schl Asst Prin 1989-90; Washington Schl Asst Prin 1990-92; Prin 1992-; *ai:* Report Card Comm Dev Prototype 1993-; Restructuring K-5 Chprsn 1995-; PTA 1971-; Phi Delta Kappa 1980-85; MAESA, WCAESA 1989-, Awd Excl Ed 1992, 1994; WA Cty Pub Schls 1990-; *home:* 1002 Brookside Ct Martinsburg WV 25401*

REINECK, RICHARD JOHN, Mathematics Instructor; *b:* Fremont, OH; *m:* Cynthia L. Baumer; *c:* Scott, Brett, Angela; *ed:* Univ of Detroit (BA) Math 1970; *cr:* St Joseph Cntrl Cath Schl Math Instr 1970-; *ai:* Asst Wrestling Coach 26 Yrs; *office:* St Joseph Ctl Cath HS 702 Croghan St Fremont OH 43420

REINECKER, CHERYL COLLINS, Secondary Social Studies Tchr; *b:* Frankfort, Germany; *m:* David A.; *c:* Andrew, Jonathan; *ed:* Western MD Coll (BA) Pol Sci 1979; Grad Hrs; *cr:* Bermudian Springs HS Soc Stud Tchr, Sr Ec, Govt 1988-; *ai:* Stu Cncl Adv; *office:* Bermudian Springs HS 7335 Carlisle Pike York Springs PA 17372

REINER, SHARYN, Sixth Grade Teacher; *b:* New York, NY; *m:* Peter; *c:* Erica, Alexis; *ed:* Hunter Coll (BA) Anthropology 1967; Coll of New Rochelle (MS) Spcl Ed; 60 Grad Credits; *cr:* NYC Elem Tchr 1967-68; Ft Riley Elem Tchr 1968-70; East Ramapo Schls Elem Tchr 1970-71 & 1986-; *ai:* Schl Fundraising; Yrbk; NEA 1986-; Temple 1982-, Bd Mem; Environmental Grant from O&R Utilities; St Thomas Aquinas Coll Project MC Extend; PTA Life Mem; Facilitator of A World of Difference.

REINERS, DIANNE, First Grade Teacher; *b:* Bay Shore, NY; *ed:* Southern CT SC (BA) Early Chldhd 1977; Adelphi Univ (MA) Spec Ed 1983; 60 Inservice Credits; *cr:* North Babylon UFSD Tchr 1978-; *office:* Woods Road Elem Schl 110 Woods Rd Babylon NY 11703

REINERT, PAUL MICHAEL, School Counselor; *b:* Wilkes-Barre, PA; *m:* Kimberly Ruth Burdick; *c:* Virginia, Jacob, Samuel; *ed:* Univ of Scranton (MS) Cnslr Ed 1991; Addl 54 Credit Hrs; *cr:* Lake-Lenm Dist Jr HS Sci Tchr 1981-93, Schl Cnslr 1993-; *ai:* Peer Helpers Adv PSEA, LLEA 1988-, Pres; *office:* Lake-Lehman Schl Dist PO Lehman PA 18627*

REINFORD, MERLE R., Mathematics Teacher; *b:* Harrisonburg, *m:* Ruth Ann Bauman; *c:* Wanda, Darrel, Sherrie; *ed:* Eastern Mennoni (BS) Math 1972; Millersville Univ (MED) Math 1977; Penn St Univ Grad Credits 1988; 21 Addl Post Grad 1979-93; *cr:* Belleville Mer Schl Math Tchr & Bsktbl, Track & Field & Hockey Coach 19 Lancaster Mennonite HS Math Tchr & Chess Coach 1976-; Mille Univ Adjunct Math Instr 1986-89; *ai:* Chess Coach; PA Cncl Tchr o 1981-; NCTM 1975-; *office:* Lancaster Mennonite HS 2176 Lincol E Lancaster PA 17602

REINHARDT, BARRY L., Health & PE Teacher; *b:* Monongahe *m:* Lucille Berarducci; *c:* Ryan, Bethany; *ed:* Slippery Rock Uni Hlth & PE 1974; Youngstown St Univ (MS) Scndry Admin 198 beyond Masters at Univ of LaVerne & US Sports Acad; *cr:* Howland Schls Tchr & Coach 1974-; *ai:* Wrestling Head Coach; Fac Mgr; Assn, NEA 1974-; Elks 1985-; Numerous Coaching Awds; *office:* Ho HS 200 Shaffer Dr NE Warren OH 44484

REINHARDT, MIRIAM JOSEPH J., Assistant Professor of Mu Texas Township, PA; *ed:* Marywood Coll (BM) Music Ed 1951; Col Univ Tchrs Coll (MA) Music Ed 1958; New York Univ Schl of Ed Music Ed 1971; 1 Credit IN Univ at Bloomington 1975; 9 Credits C Univ of Amer at Washington DC 1980-81; *cr:* Maryland Instru Music Tchr 1951-60; Saint Clare Schl 5th Grd & Music Tchr 19 Saint John HS Music, Vocal & Instrumental Tchr 1966-67; Marywoo Music Tchr 1969-; *ai:* Music Dept Asst Chair & Grad Prgm Dir; Bi Music Alumni & Newsletter Ed; Grad Stdnts Adv; MENC; PMEA C Rep to Dist 9, Curr & Instruction Newsletter Ed, Citation of Exc 1995; DES 1951-; KGP 1951-, Rep; KDP; Pi Kappa Lambda Local Soc of Music Therapy; Amer Musicological Soc; Congregation of of IHM 1963-, Mem; Scranton Schl Prgm for Gifted 1987-, M Marywood Coll Schlsp 1947-51; NEH Fellowship to Princeton Summer 1984; IFCA Schlshp to Catholic Univ Summer 1980 & *office:* Marywood Coll 2300 Adams Ave Scranton PA 18509

REINHART, HARVEY J., 6th Grade Teacher; *b:* Middleburgh, N SUNY New Paltz (BS) Ed 1969; SUNY Albany (MS) Ed 1972; Col Rose Post Grad Credit; *cr:* Schoharie Cntrl Schl 6th Grd Tchr 196 Soc Stud Curr Comm; Bldg Improvement Team; NYSUT, AFT, 1969-; Schoharie Tchrs Assn 1969-, Treas, VP; Kappa Delta Pi; Schoharie Central Schl Main St Schoharie NY 12157

REINHART, JOANNE D., 8th Grade Language Arts Tchr; *b:* Orang *m:* Kurt; *c:* Todd, Joseph; *ed:* Susquehanna Univ (BA) Eng 1968; U DE 6 Credits; Harvard Univ Writing, Rdng, Civic Stud Flwshp; Ha Univ 2 Credits; *cr:* Beaver Springs Jr HS 7th Grd Eng Tchr 196 Christiana HS 10-12 Grd Eng Tchr 1969-73; Avon Grove MS Chptr I Super 1980-82; Caesar Rodney Jr HS 8th Grd Lang Arts Tchr 1984 Drama Coach; Gold Team Ldr; Schl Improvement Comm; Mentor fo Tchrs; DSEA, NEA, NCTE 1984-; Tchr of Yr 1990-91; LA Tchr 1991-92; *office:* Caesar Rodney Jr HS 25 E Camden Wyoming Ave Ca Wyoming DE 19934

REINIGER, MEREDITH ELIZABETH (HORNING), English Tea *b:* Rochester, NM; *ed:* Keuka Coll (BA) Eng 1962; SUNY at Broc (MS) Ed 1971; U of Rochester (EDD) Curr 1982; Attnd Univ of Santa Cruz; *cr:* Natl Tech Ins for the Deaf Research 1980-81; Eastmar of Music Research 1985-86; GOHS Tchr; *ai:* Site Based Mngmt; GT Action; NEA, GTA 1966-; Hazelwood Neighborhood 1986-, Landscaping; GAGV 1983-; Spec Olympics Writers, Books 1982-; Art Gallery; GEVA 1980-; Art Pub Journal of Curr Theorizing, S Learning Resources; Awd for Excl in Sec Sch Tchng; Grants Natl Hum Endowment for Arts; Natl Endowment for Hum; *office:* Greece Oly HS 1139 Maiden Ln Rochester NY 14615*

REINKE, JULIE M., Math & Computer Teacher; *b:* Binghamton, N Charles E. Jr.; *c:* Steven C.; *ed:* SUNY at Geneseo (BS) Math & Ed SUNY at Cortland (MS) Rdng Ed 1991; *cr:* Windsor Jr-Sr HS Math 1987-88; Saratoga-Warren Vo-Tech Ctr Math & Sci Tchr 1988-89; We HS Math & Comp Tchr 1989-; *ai:* Math & Comp Dept Ldr; Dist Comm; NYSUT 1987-; St Johns Church 1990-, Lector & Comment Yrbk Dedication 1992; Westhills Parent Org Hawes Awd 1993; *o* Westhill HS 4501 Onondaga Blvd Syracuse NY 13219

REINKE, PETER H., English Teacher; *b:* Sharon, CT; *m:* Pen Rainey; *c:* Peter H. Jr., Julie Reinke Hazzard; *ed:* Princeton Univ (BA 1955; Brown Univ (MA) Eng 1960; *cr:* Fay Schl Eng Tchr, Coach & I Master 1959-61; William Penn Charter Schl Eng Tchr, Coach & He Upper Schl 1961-76; Medical Coll of PA Adjunct Prof of Hum 197 Germantown Friends Schl Eng Tchr & Coll Cnslr 1976-; *ai:* Chprsn Stans Comm, Coll Cnslng; Woodrow Wilson Fellowship 1958-59; Jo Gummere Distinguished Tchr Awd 1976; Medical Coll of PA Outstan Tchr Awd 1986; CoAuthor of Understanding the Essay; Numerous Arti *office:* Germantown Friends Schl 31 W Coulter St Philadelphia PA 1

REINSTEIN, SUSAN M., 6th Grade English Teacher; *b:* Buffalo, NY Lesley Coll (MED) 1995; *office:* Sarah W. Gibbons MS 20 Fishe Westborough MA 01581

REINSTEIN-POLINS, ANNA T., Art Teacher; *b:* Royersford, PA Eugene R.; *c:* Gregory, Eric; *ed:* Moore Coll of Art (BA) Fas Illustration 1957; Temple Univ (T&I) Voc, Comm Art 1968; Kutztown (MA) Art Ed, Art 1996; Perm Cert PA Art Ed 1979; *cr:* Phoenixville Jr Sr HS Art 9-12 Grd Tchr 1957-60; Northern Chester Cty Tech Comm Art Dir, Tchr 1966-68; Owen J. Roberts HS Art 9-12 Grd 1970-76; St Piux X HS Art 9-12 Grd Tchr 1979-80; Westminster Day Art, All Subj Tchr 1982-83; Episcopal Day Schl Art, All Subj 1982-83; Reading Cntrl Cath HS Art Tchr 1988-; *ai:* Stu Assistance F 1991-; ALDA 1988-; Vly Forge Classroom Tchrs Medal; Willia Horstman Grad Schlrsp Awd; Commissioned Corp Artist.

REISER, KATHLEEN ANN, Fifth Grade Teacher; *b:* Sharon, PA, Gary M.; *c:* Michael, Meghan; *ed:* Youngstown St Univ (BS) Ed 1 (MS) Early Chldhd 1988; Addl Credit Hrs; *cr:* Stevenson Elem Schl T Grd Tchr 1974-95; Addison Elem Schl Fifth Grd Tchr 1995-; *ai:* Stu C Adv; Soc Action Comm for Bldg Tchrs; Bldg Advy Comm; Brookfield of Tchrs 1974-, Bldg Rep; AFT Local 1728, 1974-; Sunday Schl T 1983-, Tchr, Ed Coord; Vacation Bible Schl Dir; Helps Dev Competency Test for Math Grd Three; *office:* Addison Elem Schl Judson St Masury OH 44438

REISMAN, SANDRA (NEUGEBOREN), Mathematics Teacher; *b:* N York City, NY; *m:* Steven H.; *c:* Ira, Lloyd; *ed:* Queens Coll (BA) M 1967, (MS) Math & Ed 1970; Pace Univ (MSEd) Supvr & Admin 1976; Springfield Gardens HS Math Tchr 1967-84; Jamaica HS Math T 1984-95; Francis Lewis HS Math Tchr 1995; Queens bridge to Med M Tchr 1995-; *ai:* UFT 1967-; *home:* 82-40 Bell Blvd Hollis Hills 14427*

REISS, JESSIE D. L., English Teacher; *b:* Bronx, NY; *ed:* Queens C CUNY (BA) Psych 1962; Brooklyn Coll CUNY (MA) Eng Ed 1991; Credit Hrs M Sco Svc, 30 Credit Hrs MS ED IN Univ; Early Ed 12 Cr Hrs Pace Univ; MA Credit Hrs Tchrs Coll Columbia Univ, SUNY Oneo n CUNY; *cr:* Zion Municipal HS Eng Tchr 1 Yr; Willoughby Jr HS hr 3 Yrs; Mark Twain Jr HS Gifted, Talented Eng Tchr 1 Yr; Peter Jr HS Eng Tchr 1 Yr; Brooklyn Tech HS Eng Tchr, Stu Tchrs 9 Yrs; *ai:* Stu Tchrs Mentor Long Island Univ; AFT 1966-; BTHS, 987-; NDEA Fellowships 1965, 1967-68; Tchrs Coll Writing Project peare 1987; NEH Fellowships Columbia Univ 1990, Native Amer 91; Newspaper Articles 1966; Lehman Coll Writing Prgm Grants; Brooklyn Tech HS 29 Fort Greene Pl Brooklyn NY 11217*

FELDER, TYSON PAUL, Biology Teacher; *b:* Somerville, MA; illikin Univ (BS) Bio, Scndry Ed 1986; Plymouth St Coll (MED) nmental Sci 1996; *cr:* Edward Little HS Tchr Asst 1986-87; on HS Bio Tchr 1987-; *ai:* Chest, Model Rocketry Club Adv; ME ors Assn, NEA 1989-; Lewiston Ed Assn 1989-, Prof Image Awd Gamma Beta Prime Chapter Kappa Sigma 1983-, Schlsp Chm, aternity Cncl Pres, Brother of the Yr 1985-86, Kappa Sigma Schlsp, ship Foundation Awd; Order of Omega; *office:* Lewiston HS 156 ve Lewiston ME 04240*

ER, DAISY ZIMMERMAN, Fifth Grade Teacher; *b:* Lewisburg, : Edward Paul; *c:* Edward E., Amy Marie, Elizabeth Ann White, n Marie Ellis, Russell Paul, Ann Marie Myers; *ed:* Penn St Univ Elem Ed 1957; Post Grad Credits Univ Northern CO at Greeley, Inst ldren's Lit; Real Estate Sales Person; *cr:* Hershey Elem Schl Fourth hr 1957-58; Topeka Elem Schl Kndgtn Tchr 1958-59; Red Land Schl Fourth-Sixth Grd Tchr 1959-61; Philipsburg-Osceola ceton-Boggs Elem Schl Fifth Grd Tchr 1975-; *ai:* Integrated Lang Comm; Philipsburg-Osceola Ed Assn, NEA, PA St Ed Assn 1975-; Luth Church 1977-, Choir, Cncl; Toughlove 1983-, Local Chptr er; Arts in Ed Challenge Grant 1980-83; *office:* Wallaceton Boggs Schl Wilson St Wallaceton PA 16876

H, MARY KNISELY, English Teacher; *b:* Kokomo, IN; *m:* David ; *c:* John; *ed:* Ball St Univ (BA) Eng 1963; Miami Univ (MAT) Eng Kent St Univ (MLS) Lib Sci 1976; *cr:* Muskegon HS Eng Tchr 54; Lemon-Monroe HS Eng Tchr 1065; New Miami HS Eng, Jrnlsm 1965-66, 1971-72; Champaign HS Eng Tchr 1970-71; Theodore velt HS Dept Chair 1987-95, Eng Tchr 1973-; *ai:* Lang Arts Comm; Dev Advy Cncl; Kent Tchrs Assn 1972-, Bldg Rep; NCTE 1986-, Kappa Gamma 1976-; Fulbright Assn 1987-; Fulbright Summer v to India 1986; Articles, Journal, Poems Pub; Books; *office:* ore Roosevelt HS 1400 N Mantua St Kent OH 44240

NOUER, GARY LEE, Mathematics Tchr & Dept Chprsn; *b:* ng, PA; *m:* Lisa Barnett; *c:* Amy, Timothy; *ed:* Widener Coll (BS) Ed Millersville Univ (MED) Ed 1992; *cr:* Wilson Schl Dist Math Tchr 82; Solanco Schl Dist Math Tchr, Ftbl, Track Coach 1982-83; The CO gs Schl Math Tchr 1983-85; Milton Hershey SChl Math Tchr, Track 1985-, Dept Chair 1992-; *ai:* Asst Track, Ftbl Coach; Math League NCTM, PCTM, NEA, PSEA 1993-; 1993 Speaker at the NCTM Regnl 1990 & 1992 Served on Visiting Comms for Mid Sts Evaluation; er at PCTM Conf 1995 & 1996; 1994 Selected to Attnd Natl Alliance estructuring Ed & New Standards Conf; *office:* Milton Hershey Schl ox 830 Hershey PA 17033*

Z, CAROL TELLIP, Sixth Grade Teacher; *b:* Scranton, PA; *m:* t; *c:* Justin, Jenna; *ed:* Bloomsburg Univ (BS) Elem Ed 1975; Masters alency + 36 Credits Penn St, Wilkes Coll, St Joseph's Univ; *cr:* rtown Comm Schl Dist Sixth Grd Tchr 1975-; *ai:* Ski Club Adv; , NEA 1975-; NCSS 1995-; Amer Assn of Univ Women 1995-; regational Cncl of Trinity Luth Church 1996; *office:* Quakertown n Schl Dist 600 Park Ave Quakertown PA 18951*

Z, DAVID K., Biology Teacher; *b:* Philadelphia, PA; *m:* Ranee le; *c:* Margaret, Rebecca; *ed:* PA St Univ (BS) Scndry Ed 1967; a Coll at Baltimore (MED) Curr, Sec Ed 1992; Admin & Supervision Salisbury St; *cr:* Easton HS Bio Tchr 1968-; *ai:* Various Comms; NEA ; MD St Tchrs Assoc 1968-; Talbot Cty Ed Assoc 1968, Bldg Rep, tiator; Civil War Reenactment Groups 1994-; Tchr of Yr Nom; Sci Chm 1980-95; Mentor New Tchrs; *office:* Easton H S Mecklenburg Easton MD 21601

TZ, ELLIOTT D., Professor of Biology; *b:* Puxsutawney, PA; *m:* n Ann Kaminos-Reitz; *c:* Elliott II, Melissa, Jeanne, Pamala, Peter, s, Paul; *ed:* Clarion Univ (BS) Biological Sciences 1962; OH Univ Botany 1964; Binghamton Univ (ABD) Bio 1973; 12 Credit Hrs Univ ittsburgh 1965-66; *cr:* Slippery Rock Univ Bio Instr 1964-66; RION Univ Bio Instr 1967-68; Binghamton Univ Grad Scl of Nursing 1980-90; Broome Comm Coll Bio, Intnl Stud Prgm Prof 1974-; *ai:* g Tropical Wildlife Stud Courses in Africa, Australia, Amazon, dor, Virgin Islands; R & R Vintage Racing, Ford Indy Racer & Riley y Racer Owner & Driver, N Amer Road Race from Canada to Mexico, ins Glen Intnl Spdwy Show Wnnr 1994-95; Alpha Delta Nu 1982-, sp; Phi Sigma Pi 1964-, Schlsp; Pi Gamma Mu 1964- Schlsp; Amer eum of Natural His 1980-; World Wildlife Fed 1979-; Nature ervancy 1980-; Audabon Soc 1985-; Antique Auto Club of Amer; 's Who Among Stdnts in Amer Univs & Coll 1961-62; Nom for cellor's Awd 1976, 1982, 1990; Chancellor's Awd for Excellance in g 1990; *office:* Broome Community Coll Front St Binghamton NY 3*

TZ, TEDD A., 6th Grade Teacher; *b:* Canton, PA; *c:* Trudi, Cathi sgrove; *ed:* Bloomsburg Univ (BA) Elem Ed 1970; Attnd Penn St Univ; Middleburg Elem Schl 6th Grd Tchr 1970-; *ai:* Boys Soccer & Bsktbl ch; PA Interscholastic Ath Assn 1968-, Referree in Bsbl, Sftbl & er, Officiated Final 4 in PA St Soccer Tourney; Selinsgrove Speedway 970-, Promoter; Clinton Cty Speedway PA 1989-, Promoter; *office:* ddleburg Elem Schl 600 Wagenseller Middleburg PA 17842

, RAMONDA FITZGERALD, High School Spanish Teacher; *b:* , OK; *m:* Paul August; *c:* Ryan P., Marc K.; *ed:* OK St Univ (BS) Span, 1970; Univ of Dayton (MS) Guid 1982; Ashland Univ 9 Credit Hrs; St 1 Credit Hrs; *cr:* Champion MS 7th-8th Grd Eng, Span Tchr)-75; Champion HS Span, Eng Tchr 1975-; *ai:* Ed Assn 1970-, Sec 2 OH Ed Assn, NEA 1970-; *office:* Champion HS 5976 Mahoning Ave Warren OH 44483

LE, LAURA JEAN (ESTRELLA), Alternative Education Teacher; Manchester, CT; *m:* Gary; *c:* Jonathan James; *ed:* RI Coll (BA) Elem Ed 2; 15 Post Grad Credits for MED in ESL; *cr:* New England Chrstn Acad n Tchr 1983-88, Alternative Ed Dir 1989-, Elem Admin 1989-; *office:* England Christian Acad 271 Sharps Lot Rd Swansea MA 02777*

LOVSKY, JOHN M.,JR., Title I Reading Specialist; *b:* Brownsville; *m:* Patricia Ann Glovola; *c:* Lauren; *ed:* CA St Coll (BA) Elem Ed 2; CA Univ of PA (MS) Rdng Specialist 1977, (MS) Elem Prin 1987; Carmichaels Area Schl Dist 2nd Grd Tchr 1972-75, 4th Grd Tchr 3-84, 1988-93, Title I Rdng Specialist 1984-88, 1993-; *ai:* PSEA 2-; NEA 1972-; St John the Evangelist Parish 1984-, Parish Cncl VP 6-90; Buena Vista Golf League 1987-; Dunbar Twp PTO 1990-; nellsville Slovak Club 1992-; Connellsville Girsl Sftbl League 1994-.

M, MARIE, Spanish Teacher; *b:* Whitestone, NY; *m:* Daniel; *c:* thew, Michael; *ed:* CSR (BA) Span & Fr 1977; SUNYA (MA) Scndry 1982; *cr:* Draper HS Fr & Eng Tchr 1978; Cobleskill Ctrl Schl Span & Tchr 1978-87; DCS Span Tchr 1987-; *ai:* Schl Newspaper Adv; Site ed Mgmt Team 7th-12th; Grading Comm; DCS PTSO 1987-, Sec 1-93; *office:* Duanesburg Ctrl Schl 163 School Rd Delanson NY 12053*

REMBISZ, JAMES THEODORE, Eighth Grade English Teacher; *b:* Carbondale, PA; *m:* Joan Marie Stumpf; *c:* Mark, Gail; *ed:* Shippensburg Univ (BS) Eng 1968; Westchester Univ (MED) Educl Media 1972; 48 Credits Beyond Masters at Penn St Univ, Marywood Coll of Scranton, Durham Univ England, Carlow Coll, Wilkes Coll & East Stroudsburg Univ; *cr:* Unionville-Chadds Ford Schl Dist 7th & 10th Grd Eng Tchr 1968-70; Perkiomen Valley Schl Dist 7th-10th Grd Eng, 8th Grd His & 8th Grd Eng Tchr 1970-; *ai:* Audio-Visual Dir; Japan Exch Coord; 8th Grd Clipboard Newsletter Ed; Saint Mary the Virgin 1975-, Spirit Choir Dir; Marlborough Twp 1994-, Republican Chprsn; STOPP 1990-, Area Dir; Valley Forge Freedoms Fnd 1980-, Medal of Honor Researcher & Archivist, Tchr Medal; 43rd Bombardment Group 1988-; Historical Soc 1988-, Medal of Honor; Sony Corp Tape-Pal Prgm Rep; Researcher for Buicks Heroes Video Series Aired on Arts & Entertainment; *home:* 5852 Upper Ridge Rd Pennsburg PA 18073

REMCHUK, NANCY A., English Teacher; *b:* Floral Park, NY; *c:* Ronald; *ed:* Alfred Univ (BA) Eng 1969, (MS) Ed 1974; *cr:* Hammondsport Cntrl Schl Eng Tchr 1969-; *ai:* SR Class 4 Yr Adv; Current Adv; NHS Adv; NEA 1969-; HTA 1969-, Sec 1 Yr; *office:* Hammondsport Central Schl Main St Hammondsport NY 14840

REMICK, THOMAS B., Industrial Arts & Tech Instr; *b:* Clifton, NJ; *m:* Barbara Nelson; *c:* Brian, Adam; *ed:* Montclair St Coll (BA) Industrial Arts 1970; 30 Post Grad Hrs Career Ed, Media Specialties & CAD; *cr:* US Army 4th Class Sharp Shooter Specialist 1970-72; Roxbury HS Tchr 1972-; *ai:* Dolores Congedo Schlrshp & Other Dist Tech Comms; HS & MS Home Ec & Industrial Arts Depts Lead Tchr; Roxbury Ed Assn 1972-, 1st VP 1994-95; Morris Cty Ed Assn 1972-; NJEA & NEA 1972-; Voc Ed Assn 1972-; Long Vly Land Trust 1994-; Honored By Roxbury Bd of Ed for Beginning Sr Citizen Pgm; *office:* Roxbury HS 1 Bryant Dr Succasunna NJ 07876

REMILLARD, VINCENT LEONARD, Professor of French; *b:* Chicopee, MA; *m:* Joyce; *c:* Michael, Steven, Arthur; *ed:* Univ of MA (BA) Fr 1963; Assumption Coll (MAT) Tchng of Fr 1965; PA St Univ (PHD) Fr 1978; *cr:* Wachusett Regnl HS Fr, Soc Stud Tchr 1964-67; St Francis Coll Prof of Fr 1967-; *ai:* Fr in Quebec Prgm, Russian Inst Dir; PA St Modern Lang Assn 1991-, Exec Bd Mem, Edctr of Yr 1992; Mid Atlantic Conf for Canadian Stud 1982-, Pres; Appalachian Lang Edctrs Soc 1987-, Pres; Holy Name Parish of Ebensburg 1967-, Lecturer; Romance Lang Honor Soc; Quebec Summer Seminar Grant; Excl in Ed Endowment; NEH Summer Seminar Flwshp; *office:* Saint Francis Coll Loretto PA 15940*

REMLAND, NEIL MICHAEL, Mathematics Teacher; *b:* New York, NY; *m:* Marsha Weiss; *ed:* Franklin Coll of IN (BA) Ec 1968; NY Univ (MA) Admin 1974; 30 Hrs Beyond Masters; *cr:* Haaren HS Math Tchr 1968-78; Park West HS Tchr, Coll Adv 1978-94; Murry Bergtraum HS Math Tchr 1994-; *ai:* Accreditation Comm; United Fed of Tchrs Coll Schlsp Fund Asst Dir; AFT 1968-, NYSUT 1968-, Delegate; UFT 1968-, Chapter Ldr Ldr, Smallheiser; NYC Tchr Ctr Consortium 1988-, Policy Bd Mem; *office:* Murry Bergtraum HS 411 Pearl St New York NY 10038

REMLEY, WILLIAM MOORHEAD, Social Studies Teacher; *b:* Berwick, PA; *m:* Suzanne Marion Ames; *c:* David C., Patricia Lynn; *ed:* Bloomsburg St Univ (BS) Soc Stud 1962; St Univ of NY at Brockport (MSP) Ed 1972; Univ of Rochester; *cr:* Hoover Dr MS Soc Stud Tchr 1962-93, Soc Stud Dept Chm 1970-91, 1993-94; Apollo MS Soc Stud Tchr 1993-; *ai:* Schlsp & Service Team Spon & Adv; NEA, NY Ed Assn & Greece Tchrs Assn 1962-; Pittsford Carriage Assn 1972-, Pres 1972-; Amer Driving Soc 1972-, VP 1972-86; Carriage Assn of America 1972-, Bd Mem 1985-88; Articles Pub in Carriage Journal, The Whip, Various Newspapers, Antique Magazines & Journals; NY St Medical Veterinary Assn Awd for Contributions Made in Perpetuating the Growth of Carriage Driving in America; *office:* Apollo MS Greece Cntrl Schl Dist 750 Maiden Ln Rochester NY 14615*

REMMERT, JEAN BOGDONSKI, Second Grade Teacher; *b:* New Brunswick, NJ; *m:* Bill; *c:* Merriditb, Joan Elizabeth; *ed:* Frostburg St Univ (MS) Curr Spec 1983; 15 Addl Hrs; *cr:* Frederick Cty Bd of Ed Classroom Tchr 1978-; *ai:* Team Ldr 8 Yrs; NEA 1978-; Sunday Schl Tchr 1985-, Coord; Vacation Bible Schl Admin 1989-, Coord; Pub Svc Serve at Soup Kitchen 4 Yrs; Help Girl Scouts; *office:* Valley Elem Schl 3519 Jefferson Pike Jefferson MD 21755

REMO, GAIL SENSENBACH, Sixth Grade Teacher; *b:* Bethlehem, PA; *m:* William A. Jr.; *c:* Jonathan, Justin; *ed:* Univ of Pittsburgh (BS) Elem Ed 1969; Attnd East Stroudsburg Univ, Millersville Univ, Kutztown Univ, Lehigh Univ; *cr:* Floyd R Shafer Elem 4th Grd Tchr 1970-74; Lower Nazareth Elem 4th Grd Tchr 1974-79, 6th Grd Tchr 1979-84, 1989-91, 1995-, 5th Grd Tchr 1984-89; *ai:* Just Say No Club Adv; Safety Patrol Coord 1990-; Koalaty Kid Core Team 1991-; IST Validator 1992-95; Peer Mediator Trainer 1995-; NEA 1970-; NAEA 1970-, Pres 1973-74; OES 1970-, Past Grand Ofcr & Grand Rep; *office:* Lower Nazareth Elem Schl 4422 Newburg Rd Nazareth PA 18064

REMONKO, GUY ANDREW, Professor of Percussion Music; *b:* Connellsville, PA; *m:* Janice Marilyn Hughes; *c:* Paul, Sara; *ed:* WV Univ (BM) Percussion Performance 1964, (MM) Percussion Performance 1966; *cr:* Salem Coll Asst Prof of Percussion 1968-72; OH Univ Prof of Percussion 1972-; *ai:* Amer Fed of Musicians 1957-; Percussive Arts Soc 1967-; Articles Pub; *office:* OH Univ School of Music Athens OH 45701

REMPE, ROBERT H., English Teacher & Dept Chair; *b:* Scranton, PA; *m:* Marianne Irene Schmeltzer; *ed:* Univ of Scranton (BS) Eng Ed 1961, (MS) Eng Ed 1967; MI St (PhD) 1995; MI St Univ 1988-; *cr:* Bishop McDevitt HS Eng Tchr, Eng Dept Chair 1962-; Colegio Internacional de Carabobo, Valencia, Venezuela Eng Tchr, Eng Dept Chair 1977-79; MI St Univ Stu in PHD Prgm, Part-time Tchr 1991-92; Part Time Tchr HACC 1995; *ai:* HS Newspaper; NCTE 1965-; PCTE 1980-; CAWP, NWP 1988-, Fellow; PA Dept of Ed Consultant 1989; Fellow MSU London Prgm 1988; Pub Shakespeare & Modern Drama 1990; The Tempest & Tchng 1991; Two Articles Pub 1992cn; Two Articles Pub 1995; *home:* 3211 Schoolhouse Ln Harrisburg PA 17109*

REMY, DELORES STANGEL, German Teacher; *b:* Chicago, IL; *m:* Richard C.; *c:* Steven, Sharon; *ed:* Northeastern IL (BA) Ed 1968; Addl 72 Post Grad Hrs, Including 50 in Ger; *cr:* Hilliard HS Ger Tchr 1992-; *ai:* NEA, Hilliard EA, OFLA, NATG 1992-; IL Tchrs Schlsp; *office:* Hilliard HS 5100 Davidson Rd Hilliard OH 43026

REMZA, FREDRICKA J., 3rd-5th Grd Enrichment Prgm; *b:* Binghamton, NY; *m:* John; *c:* Christine Remza Duffy, Eric; *ed:* SUC at Geneseo (BS) Elem Ed 1966; SUC at Cortland (MS) Elem Ed 1975; *cr:* Maine-Endwell Schl 4th Grd Tchr 1966-67; Union Endicott Schl 1st Grd Tchr 1969-70; Owego-Apalachin Schl 4th Grd Tchr 1972-74, K-3rd Grd Tchr 1979-95, Level 3-5 Grd Enrichment Prgm Tchr 1995-; *ai:* O-A Tchrs Assn 1979-; AFT, NYSUT 1967-; Growing Healthy Trainer of Tchrs; Attnd Space Camp for Tchrs; Grd Level Chprsn 1988-94; Tchr Recognition Awd 1988; *office:* Apalachin Elem Schl 405 Pennsylvania Ave Apalachin NY 13732

RENAUD, RICHARD HENRY, English Dept Chprsn & Teacher; *b:* Holyoke, MA; *m:* Regina M. Rybarski; *c:* Joseph Peter, Jeffrey Richard; *ed:* Western New England Coll (BA) Eng 1970; Ed, Eng Related Courses, Psych, Sociology at Local Colls Univ of MA, Westfield St Coll; *cr:* Monson Jr-Sr HS Eng Dept Chm 1981-, Eng Tchr 1970-; *ai:* Tech, Future Search Restructuring, Search for Vice-Prin Twice, Chm Curr, Acad Honesty, Co-Chm Steering, Schl Cncl, Comms; Schl Plays; Speech Contests; Class Adv; Fac-Stud Acts; Mass Tchrs Assn 1970-, Distngd Svc Awd; Natl Tchrs Assn, Monson Tchrs Assn 1970-; Yrbk Dedications; Set-Up Hnrs Eng Curr; *office:* Monson Jr Sr HS 21 Thompson St Monson MA 01057*

RENAUD, YVONNE M., Science & Mathematics Teacher; *b:* St Mary's, PA; *m:* Thomas; *c:* Michelle Vickery; *ed:* Clarion Univ (BS) Elem Ed, Geog 1966; Post Grad Stud: Univ of Pittsburgh, St Bonaventure Univ, Penn St Univ; *cr:* Bradford Area Schl Dist Intermediate Tchr 1966-67; Limestone Union Free Schl Dist Intermediate Math, Sci Tchr 1967-95; Allegany-Limestone Cntrl Schl Intermediate Math, Sci Tchr 1995-; *ai:* Sci Mentor; NEA 1966-67, 1995-; AFT 1967-95; Limestone Tchrs Assn 1967-95, Sec, Treas, Negotiations; Allegany-Limestone Assn 1995-, Bldg Rep; Tchr of Yr 1973; *office:* Allegany-Limestone Cntrl Schl Main St Limestone NY 14753*

RENDISH, SANDRA MARY, English & Reading Teacher; *b:* Long Branch, NJ; *ed:* Monmouth Coll (BS) Elem Ed 1983, (MS) Rdng Specialist 1995; *cr:* Long Branch MS Eng, Rdng Tchr 1986-; Monmouth Coll Stud Skills Tchr 1989-95; *ai:* Mentor, Vol Stay Smart Univ; Tutor Monmouth Chemical Dependency; NJEA 1986-; Drug & Alcohol Task Force 1993-; *office:* Long Branch MS 364 Indiana Ave Long Branch NJ 07740

RENDZIO, EMIL J., Physical Education Teacher; *b:* Passaic, NJ; *m:* Evelyn; *c:* Edward, Scott, Nicole, Todd; *ed:* Seaton Hall (BS) PE 1962; Montclair (EDD); *ai:* Vllybl; Sftbl; NJEA 1962-; WEA 1962-; NEA 1964-; Bergen Cty Coaches Assn 1990-; NJ Inter Ath Assn Sftbl Grant; *office:* Wallington Elem Schl 106 King St Wallington NJ 07057

RENGUUL, THOMAS, Seventh & Eighth Grade Teacher; *b:* Pelau-Belair ; *m:* Frankie; *c:* Ozella, Anna; *ed:* Schl of Dental Hygiene US Trist Territory (AA) Dental Hygienist at Koror Mac Donald Meml Hosp 1961; Pacific Union Coll (BA) Ed 1968; Andrews Univ (MA) Ed 1974; 40 Addl Credits in Ed at Atlantic Union Coll; 30 Addl Credits Ed at NYC Tchrs Consortium; 18 Addl Credits Ed at Univ of Guam; *cr:* Koror Mac Donald Hosp First Dental Hygienist 1961-64; Palau Mission Acad Boys Dean, Tchr, Prin 1968-75; Brooklyn SDA Schl Tchr, Prin 1978-95; *ai:* Sr Class Adv, Spon; PE Spon; NYC Tchrs Assn 1985-.

RENINO, CHRISTOPHER D., English Teacher; *ed:* Cornell Univ (BS) Indstrl, Labor Relations 1978; Columbia Univ (MA) Eng 1984; *cr:* Scarsdale MS Eng Tchr 1984-88; Scarsdale HS Eng Tchr 1988-; *ai:* NCTE 1985-; Contributing Ed; Consultant at Wkshps & Conventions; *office:* Scarsdale HS Brewster Rd Scarsdale NY 10583

RENKE, JOAN MONKS, Chemistry Teacher; *b:* New York, NY; *m:* Roger S.; *c:* Keith, Christine Renke-Tenney; *ed:* Stony Brook Univ (BS) Bio & Chem 1963, (MS) Tech 1979; *cr:* Lansdale Schls Tchr 1964-66; Rocky Pt Schls Tchr 1967-69; Smithtown Schls Chem Tchr 1975-; *ai:* NSTA 1975-; *office:* Smithtown HS 100 Central Rd Smithtown NY 11787

RENN, VICKI LEE, Art Teacher; *b:* Sunbury, PA; *m:* Paul D.; *c:* Christopher, Jeffrey; *ed:* Kutztown Univ (BS) Art Ed 1971; Credits for Cert; *cr:* Milton HS Art Tchr 1971-77; Sunbury MS Art Tchr 1985-93; Shikellamy HS Art Tchr 1993-; *ai:* Adv for Natl Art Hnr Soc, Art Club; PAEA, NAEA 1992-; NEA 1971-76, 1986-; PA Watercolor So 1977-, Silver Medal; Soc or Animal Artists; Susquehanna Art Soc, Best of Show; Nature Conservency 1995-; Susquehanna Art So Exhibit Second Place; PA Watercolor So Exhibit Purchase Awd; Lewisburg Festival of Arts Best of Show; Bald EAgle Art Exhibit Purchase Awd; *office:* Shikellamy HS 6th & Walnut Sts Sunbury PA 17801

RENNER, MICHELLE, Art Teacher; *b:* Buffalo, NY; *m:* Michael; *ed:* Daemen Coll (BS) Art Ed 1978; Buffalo St Coll (MS) Art Ed 1983; *cr:* Delevan Elem Schl Grds K-4 Art Tchr 1978-89; Pioneer MS Grds 5-8 Art Tchr 1989-; *ai:* Yth Group Adv; Art Dept Chprsn; AFT, NEA 1978-; NAEA 1988-.

RENNEY, LINDA SCHUCKER, 1st Grd Tchr, Math Curr Chprsn; *b:* West Chester, PA; *m:* James E.; *c:* Todd C., Amy L. Sipes; *ed:* West Chester Univ (BS) Ed 1966; PA Equivalency (MS) Ed 1993; *cr:* Bellwood-Antis Schl Dist Sub Tchr 1968-76, First Grd Tchr 1976-, Math Curr Coord 1987-; *ai:* Cooperating Tchr Stu Tchrs; Bellwood Antis Ed Assn, PA St Ed Assn, NEA 1976-; NCTM, PA Cncl Tchrs Math 1987-; Blair Garden Club 1968-, Pres, PA Ed Awd, Natl Ed Awd; Svc Awd; Flower Show Sweepstakes Awd; First Luth Church 1968-, Cncl Sec, Sunday Schl Tchr, Children's Choir Dir, Altar Guild, Chair, Schl Bd, Dist Cabinet; Book Standards K-12th Math Prgms; Presenter NCTM Regnl Cons, PCTM Conf; *home:* 206 College Heights Dr Altoona PA 16601

RENNICK, ROBERT DENNIS, Mathematics Teacher; *b:* Pottsville, PA; *m:* Karen Nunemacher; *c:* Elizabeth, Amanda; *ed:* Penn St (BS) Ed & Math 1969; *cr:* US Army Lt Military Intelligence 1969-71; Pottsville Area Schl Dist Tchr 1971-, Ftbl Referee 1975-; *ai:* PSEA 1971-; NEA 1971-; *office:* D H H Lengel MS 1541 Laurel Blvd Pottsville PA 17901

RENNIE, KATHLEEN DONOHUE, Pub Relation & Advrtsng Prof; *b:* Jersey City, NJ; *m:* David; *ed:* Rutgers Univ (BA) Eng, Comm 1987; Seton Hall Univ (MA) Corporate Comm 1993; Accredited Pub Relations Soc of Amer; *cr:* ARchdiocese of Newark PR Asst 1987-89; NJ Transit Spokesperson 1989-93; Kathleen D. Rennie Freelance Writer, Prof 1990-; Seton Hall Univ Prof 1993-; *ai:* NJ PRSA, Bd Mem; PRSA 1991-, Bd Mem; Seton Hall PRSSA, Fac Adv; WSOU Governing Cncl, Mem; PRSSA Fac Adv of Yr 1995; *office:* Seton Hall Univ 400 S Orange Ave South Orange NJ 07079

RENOLL, DAVID H., German Teacher; *b:* York Cty, PA; *m:* Penelope J. Griggs; *c:* Stephanie, Stacie; *ed:* Millersville Univ (BS) Ger & Scndry Ed 1970; Middlebury Coll (MA) Ger Lang & Lit 1975; 36 Credit Hrs Eng at Univ of Scranton; *cr:* Tunkhannock Area HS Ger Tchr 1970-; *ai:* Dramatics & Asst Band Dir; Key Club Adv; PSEA, AATG 1970-; Kiwanis 1990-; *office:* Tunkhannock Area Schl Dist 120 W Tioga St Tunkhannock PA 18657

RENSEL, AILEEN MC ELHATTAN, Senior High English Teacher; *b:* Vandergrift, PA; *m:* William Donald; *c:* Susan Rensel Shaffner, Eric M.; *ed:* Waynesburg Coll (BA) Eng 1958; Attnd PA St Univ, Clarion Univ, PA River's Writing Course; *cr:* DuBois Bus Coll Eng, Psych, Speech Tchr 1967-73; DuBois Jr HS 7th-8th Grd Eng Tchr 1974-93; DuBois Sr HS 9th-10th Grd Eng Tchr 1993-; *ai:* Speech Club; Pub Relations Person Schl Dist 1991; DAEA, NEA, PSEA 1974-; Cultural Arts Assn, Bd Mem, Ed Comm Letter; Cultural Exch Tchr Russia 1993; Writing, Directing Comm Plays; Poetry Articles Pub; *office:* DuBois Area Sr HS Orient Ave Du Bois PA 15801*

RENSHAW, JOHN HUBERT, US History Teacher; *b:* Hazleton, PA; *m:* Dorothy Sharon Montgomery; *c:* John Michael, Rebecca Lynn; *ed:* East Stroudsburg (BS) Ed, Soc Stud 1961; Univ of DE (MA) His 1965; 30 Addl Credit Hrs Ed, Soc Stud; *cr:* Pocomoke HS Soc Stud Dept Tchr 1961-64; Forwood Jr HS Soc Stud Dept Tchr 1965-78; Springer Jr HS Soc Stud Dept Tchr 1978-81; Hanby MS Tchr, Soc Stud Dept Chm, Curr Head 1981-; *ai:* Drama Adv; Coach HS Bsktbl, Jr HS Bsbl, Sftbl; Audio Visual Dir, Club Adv; Stu Ct Adv; Brandywine Ed Assn Rep; NEA 1961-, Rep; Alfred I DuPont Ed Assn 1965-78; New Castle Ct Ed Assn 1978-81; Brandywine Ed Assn 1981-; Pcomoke Jaycees 1960-; Who's Who Amer Ed; *home:* 2506 Bona Rd Wilmington DE 19810

RENSTROM, SUSAN WARD, Music Teacher; *b:* Tuscaloosa, AL; *m:* Scott; *c:* Daniel, Adam, Leigh Anna; *ed:* TN Temple Univ (BA) Speech

Commnctn 1977; *cr:* Pioneer Chrstn Acad Drama & Music Tchr 1977-78; Cedar Hill Chrstn Schl Music Tchr 1980-; *ai:* Organize & Produce all Schl Pgms; Organize & Supervise Nrsng Home Visits for Elem Stdnts; Teach Private Piano Lessons 20 Yrs; Nottingham Bapt Church 180-95, Music coord & Choir Dir; Chagrin Valley Comm Church 1995-, Music Coord & Choir Dir; *office:* Cedar Hill Christian Schl 12601 Cedar Rd Cleveland OH 44106*

RENTSCHLER, THOMAS C., Social Studies Teacher; *b:* Reading, PA; *m:* Aimee C.; *c:* Luke; *ed:* Penn St (BS) Acctng 1986, (BS) Scndry Ed & Soc Stud 1990; West Chester Univ MED in Progress 24 Credits; *cr:* Arthur Anderson & Co Staff Accountant 1986-87; Penske Track Leasing Dept Accountant 1987-88; Cncl on Chem Abuse Pgm Analyst 1992-93; Souderton Area Schl Dist Soc Stud Tchr 1993-; *ai:* Stu Support Team Mem; SAEA, PSEA & NEA 1993-; PCSS 1993-; *office:* Souderton Area HS 41 N School Ln Souderton PA 18964

RENZETTI, THERESA ANN, English Teacher; *b:* Philadelphia, PA; *ed:* West Chester Univ (BS) Eng 1967, (MS) Eng 1973; Attnd Univ of DE; *cr:* Interboro HS Eng Tchr 1967-; *ai:* SAT's Supvr; Class of 1997, Sr Project Adv; Prins Advy, Horatio Alger, Prins Selection, Grad, Schlsp Comms; Mentor; NEA, PSEA, IEA 1967-; *office:* Interboro HS 16th Ave & Amosland Rd Prospect Park PA 19076

RENZI, EMILIO GERALD, History Teacher; *b:* Buffalo, NY; *m:* Madeline Franchino; *c:* Christine Emily, Mark Andrew; *ed:* St Univ of NY at Albany (BA) His 1966, (MA) Soc Stud Ed 1970; 45 Addl Credit Hrs Coll of St Rose, CO St, Long Island Univ, Drake Univ; *cr:* Rome Free Acad His Tchr 1966-95; *ai:* Rome Tchrs Assn 1966-, Treas 1972-74; NY St United Tchrs, AFT 1967-; Tocculono Club 1988-; Rome Girls Sftbl League 1987-, Coach, Bd of Dirs 1991-93; *office:* Rome Free Acad 500 Turin St Rome NY 13440

RENZULLI, MARY ANN, Science Teacher; *b:* Brooklyn, NY; *m:* Vincent R.; *c:* Richard, Barbara, Anne, Peter, Linda; *ed:* Montclair St Coll (BA) Eng & Sci 1959; *cr:* Edison Bd of Ed Tchr 1982-89; J P Stevens HS Eng Tchr 1989-90; Saint Francis Elem 3rd, 7th & 8th Grd His Tchr 1988-90; Saint Mary of the Assumption Sci Tchr 1990-; *ai:* Frosh Class Adv; Multi-Media Comm-Mid Sts; Final Exam Comm; Frosh, Soph & Sr Classes Co-Adv; NSTA 1993-; NCEA 1989-; Literacy Vols 1995-; Whos Who in Ed; *office:* St Mary-Assumption H S 237 S Broad St Elizabeth NJ 07202*

REPASY, PAUL ALLAN, Biology Teacher; *b:* East Lansing, MI; *m:* Katherine Marie Shinhearl; *ed:* John Carroll Univ (BS) Bio, Chem 1991; Kent St Univ (MA) Bio 1994; *cr:* Shaker Heights HS Sci Tchr 1991-; *ai:* 8th Grd Ftbl, Acad Decathalon Coach; Tutoring Ctr; Schl, Comm Relations Comm; NABT 1991-; Alpha Sigma Nu 1990-; *office:* Shaker Heights HS 15911 Aldersyde Dr Shaker Heights OH 44120

REPICKY, GEORGE JOSEPH, Sci, Comp Sci & Rel Teacher; *b:* Yonkers, NY; *m:* Catherine Ann Powers; *c:* George, Timothy, Sarah, Michael, Joseph; *ed:* Cath Univ (BA) Physics 1965; Union Coll (MS) Physics 1971, (MS) Comp Sci 1990; Grad Work in Geology; *cr:* Chrstn Brothers Acad Physics & Math Tchr 1965-69; St Gregorys Schl for Boys Sci, Soc Stud, Comp Sci & Rel Tchr 1969-; *ai:* Geology Field Trips; Comp Coord; Model Sailplanes; Head Discipline Comm; Cossayond Lake Environmental Comm 1977-85; Heldeberg Wkshp 1985- Bd of Trustees; Environmental Stud Grant; Several Pub Articles on Comp Pgmng; *office:* St Gregorys Schl For Boys Old Niskayuna Rd Loudonville NY 12211*

REPKO, PHILIP E., English Teacher; *b:* Kenilworth, PA; *m:* Julia Humphries; *c:* Philip J., Emily M., Ian C.; *ed:* Ursinus Coll (BA) Eng 1983; Villanova Univ (MS) Educl Admin 1989; *cr:* North Plainfield Jr HS 7th Grd Eng Tchr 1983-84; Boyertown Area Sr HS Grds 10-12 Eng Tchr 1984-; *ai:* Asst Ftbl Coach; Head Bsktbl Coach; Communications Curr, Family & Consumer Scis Curr Comms; *office:* Boyertown Area Sr HS 4th & Monroe Boyertown PA 19512

REPKO, SUSAN MARIE, Social Studies Teacher; *b:* Trenton, NJ; *ed:* Villanova Univ (BS) Ed 1992; 6 Addl Credits Ed; *cr:* Mc Corristin Cath HS Soc Stud Tchr, Coach 1992-; *ai:* Girls Bsktbl, Sftbl Coach; Asst Ski Club Moderator; *office:* Mc Corristin Cath HS 175 Leonard Ave Trenton NJ 08619

REPOLE, SHEILA KATHERINE (NEATE), Social Studies Teacher; *b:* Toronto ON, Canada; *m:* Thomas B.; *ed:* IN Univ of PA (BS) Elem Ed 1979; Duquesne Univ (MS) Rdng, Lang Arts 1985; Washington & Jefferson Coll Soc Stud Cert 1994; *cr:* St Catherine of Siena Schl 7th, 8th Grd Sci, Math Tchr 1979-80; St Joseph the Worker 3rd Grd Tchr 1980-84; Avella Area HS Jr High Rdng, Sr High Soc St 1985-; *ai:* Stu Cncl, Ski Club, Schl Newspaper, NHS Advs; Dir Stu Drama; Asst Tennis Coach; NEA, PSEA, AEA 1985-; WA Hist, Landmarks Fnd 1992-, Burg Friends of Lib 1982-; *office:* Avella Area Jr Sr HS 1000 Avella Rd Avella PA 15312

REPOLI, PETER MICHAEL, Math Teacher; *b:* Newark, NJ; *m:* Ida Mae Scott; *c:* Patrick, Donna Marie; *ed:* Bloomfield Coll (BS) Math 1965; Attnd Montclair St Coll, Caldwell Coll, NJIT, Kean Coll; *cr:* Newark Board of Ed Math Tchr 1967-; *ai:* Sftbl Coach; Math Olympics Team Adv; AFT, NTU 1970-; NAME 1989-; Bloomfield Recreation 1957-; Newark Bd 25 Yr Awd; Tchr of Yr Awd 1973, 1975, 1977, 1978, 1982; *home:* 62 Brookdale Gdns Apt B Bloomfield NJ 07003

REPPEL, JOANNE CAROLE, English Teacher; *b:* Utica, NY; *ed:* Utica Coll (BA) Eng 1962; Syracuse Univ (MA) Ed 1965; Various Other Courses; *cr:* Whitesboro MS Eng Tchr 1962-; *ai:* Oratorical Contest Judge & Preparer of Stndts; NY St United Tchrs; Delta Kappa Gamma, Sec, VP; Whitesboro Tchrs Assn; AFT; PTA, Sec, Class Adv; Magazine Article Pub in 1960 NY St Ed; Schlsp to Freedoms Fnd from Amer Legion; Whitestown Optimist Club Awd; The Amer Legion Dept of NY Red, White & Blue Awd 1995; *home:* 13 White St Whitesboro NY 13492

RESCH, AUDREY LAPINA, 5th Grade Math & Religion Tchr; *b:* Brooklyn, NY; *m:* Joseph R. Jr.; *c:* Joseph III, Stephanie, Jillian; *ed:* St John's Univ (BS) Elem Ed 1960, (MS) Elem Ed 1964; 9 Addl Credits Guidance; *cr:* Sacred Heart Schl 5th Grd Tchr 6 Months; Seaford Manor 3rd-4th, 6th Grd Tchr 10 Yrs; Molloy Coll Adjunct Prof 6 Months; St Agnes Elem 5th Grd Tchr 12 Yrs; *ai:* Math, Grd Coord; NCEA 1984-; Nassau Cty Math Tchrs Assn 1992-.*

RESCH, CYNTHIA FORTES, Spanish Teacher; *b:* Providence, RI; *m:* Joseph B. III; *c:* Jason, Steven, Kayla; *ed:* RI Coll (BA) Fr & Span 1974; Attnd Univ of Paris Sorbonne 1975, Univ of Valencia 1979, Providence Coll 1981; *cr:* North Kensington HS Fr & Span Tchr 1977-; *ai:* Intnl Club Adv; NEA 1977-; NEARI 1977-; RIFLA 1980-; *office:* North Kingstown HS 150 Fairway Dr North Kingstown RI 02852*

RESCINITO, NANCY R. SNYDER, 12th Grade English Teacher; *b:* Clearfield, PA; *m:* Ernest J. Jr.; *c:* Megan; *ed:* IN Univ of PA (BSEd) Eng 1993; St Francis Coll Working on MS Ed; *cr:* Purchase Line 12th Grd Eng 1993-; *ai:* Drama Club Spon; Class Play Dir; NCTE 1992-; NEA 1993-; PLEA 1993-.

RESCONICH, SAMUEL, Chemistry Professor; *b:* Portage, PA; *ed:* St Francis Coll (BS) Chem 1954; Purdue Univ (PHD) Chem 1960; NSF Summer Insts Univ of VA, MI St Univ; *cr:* Purdue Univ Tchng Asst 1954-56, Post Doctorate 1959-60; St Francis Coll Prof 1960-; *ai:* Medical Schl Admissions Comm; Chem Dept Prgm Coord; Amer Chemical Soc 1954-; Soc of Sigma Xi 1956-; Rotary Club 1962-, Pres 1969; Schl Dir 1990-; Outstanding Tchr 1969; Article in Journal of Organic Chem; *office:* Saint Francis College Sullivan Hall Loretto PA 15940

RESEK, MICHELE NODAY, Voc Spcl Ed Coordinator; *b:* Youngstown, OH; *m:* Gary; *c:* Sarah, Katrina; *ed:* Youngstown St Univ (BSEd) Elem Ed & Spcl Ed Rdng 1976; 20 Post-Grad Hrs Cleveland St, Ashland Coll & Bowling Green St Univ; *cr:* OH Yth Commission Scndry Spcl Ed Tchr 1976-78; Beaver Local Schls Primary Spcl Ed Tchr 1978-80; Lorain Cty Voc Schl Voc Spcl Ed Coord 1980-; *ai:* NEA; Elem Schl 1991-, Vol; Comm Church 1992-, Vol; *office:* Lorain Cty Joint Voc Schl 15181 St Rt 58 S Oberlin OH 44074

RESINSKI, BONNIE M. LUCAS, English & Drama Teacher; *b:* Amarillo, TX; *m:* Kenneth L.; *c:* Rachel, Rebecca, Murray; *ed:* Cabrini Coll (BA) Ed & Scndry 1966; IN Univ of PA (MS) Ed & Rdng 1994; *cr:* Ancilla Domini Acad Eng Tchr 1966-67; St Francis Coll Costume Designer 1967-; Northern Cambria SD Eng & Drama Tchr 1989-; *ai:* HS & MS Drama Club Dir; HS Interscholastic Rdng Team Coach; NEA 1988-; Alpha Psi Omega 1966-; Delta Kappa Gamma 1989-; Alpha Delta Kappa 1989-; Duquesne Univ Excl in Tchng Awd; *office:* Northern Cambria HS 807 N 11th St Barnesboro PA 15714

RESNICK, ELIZABETH ANNE, History Teacher; *b:* Livingston, NJ; *ed:* Harvard Univ (AB) Govt 1992; Columbia Univ Klingenstein Summer Inst Fellow 1995; *cr:* St Paul's Schl His, Ath Intern 1992-93; NHM Schl His Tchr 1993-; *ai:* Asst Var Soccer Coach; Head JV Girls Bsktbl Coach; Adv Dorm Parent; *office:* Northfield Mt Hermon Schl 28 Mt Hermon Rd Northfield MA 01360

RESNICK, JEANETTE, Music & Piano Teacher; *b:* Rockville Centre, NY; *m:* Don; *c:* David, Helen; *ed:* Oberlin Coll (BM) Piano 1957; Masters Classes Amherst Coll; Private Stud; Mozarteum Piano 1959; *cr:* Waldorf Schl Music Dept Chm 1958-95; *ai:* Waldorf Tchr Training Fac; New England Waldorf Tchr Trnng Antioch Coll; Waldorf Chamber Players Dir 1985-; Bd of Trustees; NYSSMA 1970-; Prof Concert Series Chamber Artists.

RESNICK, JUDITH POLENBERG, Assoc Professor of Reading; *b:* New York, NY; *c:* Yosef, Andrew, Susan; *ed:* Mill Coll of Ed (BS) Early Chldhd Ed 1961; City Coll of NY (MS) Rdng 1965; Tchrs Coll at Columbia Univ (EDD) Lang, Rdng; *cr:* Passaic Cty Comm Coll Rdng Prof 1977-82; Fairleigh Dickinson Univ Rdng Instr 1982-83; NY Univ Rdnt Instr 1984-85; Borough of Manhattan Comm Coll Assoc Prof of Rdng 1985-; *ai:* IRA 1961-; Coll Rdng Assn, Natl Assn of Dev Edctrs 1985-; Textbooks 1983, 1984; Articles Pub 1993-94; *office:* Borough Of Manhattan Comm Coll 199 Chambers St New York NY 10007

RESSLER, DEBORA JEAN BESECKER, 2nd Grade Teacher; *b:* Rome, NY; *c:* Travis, Tricia; *ed:* Wright St Univ (BA) Elem Ed 1974; Miami Univ of OH (MS) Rdng Supervision 1986; 20 Addl Hrs Univ of Dayton Lang Arts; *cr:* Franklin-Moore Elem Schl 2nd Grd Tchr 1974-75; Arcanum Elem Schl Chptr I Rdng, 2nd Grd Tchr 1977-; *ai:* Young Author's Comm; Phi Delta Kappa 1994-; Potsdam Church of the Brethren 1963-, Bd Chrstn Ed; Wkshps; Presentations OCTELA Conf; *office:* Arcanum Elem Schl 310 N Main St Arcanum OH 45304

RESTAINO, PHILLIP A., High School English Teacher; *b:* Queens, NY; *m:* Monica Ann Bye; *c:* Michael, Serafina, Ian; *ed:* Fordham Univ (BA) Eng 1968; SUNY Stony Brook (MA) Eng 1970; NY Univ (PHD) Comm in Ed 1981; *cr:* Mercy Acad Fr Tchr 1968-69; St Johns HS Eng Tchr 1969-70; New Berlin HS Eng Tchr 1970-72; Mamaroneck HS Eng Tchr 1972-; *ai:* Tech Comm; MHS Cncl; AFT, NEA, NCTE 1970-; Journal, Magazine Articles; *office:* Mamaroneck HS 1000 W Boston Post Rd Mamaroneck NY 10543

RESTAINO-MEROLA, LINDA, Basic Skills Teacher; *b:* Brooklyn, NY; *m:* Louis Merola; *ed:* SUNY at New Paltz (BA) Ed 1967, (MS) Ed 1973; C. W. Post (PHD) Rdng 1977; Post Grad Stud Cmptrs in Ed; *cr:* Peace Corps TESL Tchr 1967-69; Selden MS Rdng, Basic Skills Tchr 1969-; *ai:* Natl Jr Hnr Soc; Scholastic Showcase, Renaissance Comms; AFT 1969-; Orton Dyslexia Soc 1975-; Tchr of Yr; PTA Jenkins Meml Awd; PTA Distngd Svc Awd; *office:* Selden MS 22 Jefferson Ave Centereach NY 11720

RESTORFF, KATHLEEN ANN, Physics Professor; *b:* Meriden, CT; *m:* James Brian; *c:* Cheryl; *ed:* Cntrl CT St Univ (BA) Physics 1971; Univ of MD (MS) Physics 1975; *cr:* Univ of MD Tchng Asst 1971-75, Physics Prof 1979-; Montgomery Coll Physics Prof 1977-; *ai:* Advising Comm; Pgm Coord for Gen Physics; AAPT 1970-; AAUP 1980-; Nat & Audubon Naturalist Soc 1991-; Natl Parks & Recreation Assn 1993-; Nature Conservancy 1993-; ABA 1994-; MOS 1994-; Natl Geographic Soc Consultant 1988-89; Articles Pub; *office:* Montgomery Coll 51 Mannakee St Rockville MD 20850

RETT, KELLY LYNN, Developmental Psych Asst Prof; *b:* Akron, OH; *m:* Christopher Hopkins; *c:* Annamariah; *ed:* Marshall Univ (BA) Elem Ed, Early Chldhd 1980; Plymouth St Coll (MED) Elem Ed, Exceptional Child Stud 1990; Post Grd Hrs Cmptrs, Augmentative Comm Strategies; *cr:* Lyndon Pub Schl Asst Speech Tchr 1989-90; Plymouth St Coll Summer Gifted Prgm Tchr 1990; Head Start WV Tchr Coord 1991-92; Early Intervention Case Worker 1992-93; Washington St Comm Coll Asst Prof 1993-; *ai:* Acad Standards Comm; Early Chldhd Adv; Parent to Parent Inc of WV VP; Party for Children Organizer Stu Senate; Hnr Club Debate; Opportunity Scholars Prgm Speaker; COSI Vol; NAEYC, OAEYC, ACEI, AAUW 1993-; United Way 1993-; Opportunity Scholars Outstdng Tchr Awd 1995; Employee of Month 1992; *home:* 1342 Market St Parkersburg WV 26101*

RETTEL, CHERIE J., School Enrichment Pgm Tchr; *b:* New York City, NY; *m:* Derek A. Hulick; *c:* Michael Hulick; *ed:* Syracuse Univ (BS) Ed 1971; Frostburg St Univ (MED) Admin 1982; WV Univ (BA) Drama; Univ of MD (EDD) Curr, Instruction; *cr:* Northern HS Eng, Speech, Drama Tchr 1973-80; Northern MS GAT, Resource Tchr 1980-86; Area Elem Schls GAT, Resource Tchr 1980-91, Schl Enrichment Prgm Tchr 1991-; *ai:* AFT, GCFT 1974-85; NEA, GCTA 1985-.

RETTIG, THOMAS WILLIAM, Athletic Director; *b:* Lima, OH; *m:* Anne Mc Mahan; *c:* Michele Rettig Gephart, Nicole Rettig Rager; *ed:* Bowling Green St Univ (BSEd) Eng 1967; Attnd Xavier Univ at Cincinnati 1969-71; FL St Univ Cert Renewl 1995; *cr:* Lucas HS Eng Tchr, Boys Asst Bsktbl Coach 1967-68; Bethel HS Eng Tchr, Boys Bsktbl Coach 1968-69; Fairview HS Eng Tchr, Boys Bsktbl Coach 1969-71; Springfield HS Eng Tchr, Var Boys Bsktbl Coach 1971-76; Cardinal Stritch HS Eng Tchr, Var Boys Bsktbl Coach 1976-79; Tippecanoe HS Eng Tchr, Boys Asst Bsktbl Coach 1979-82, Eng Tchr, Girls Var Bsktbl Coach 1982-92, Ath Dir, Girls Var Bsktbl Coach 1992-; *ai:* Var Girls Bsktbl Coach; St Dir OH HS Bsktbl Coaches Assn; OHSBCA 1967-, St Dir, 200 Game Winner; OHSAAA 1992-; NIAAA; NFICA 1976-; Dist 9 Bsktbl Coaches Assn 1979-; St Runner-UP Bsktbl Tournament 1986; Final 4 Appearance St Bsktbl Tournament 1987; Associated Press Coach of Yr Div 2, Natl Fed Distngd Svc Awd 1991; *home:* 1013 Arapaho Trl Tipp City OH 45371*

RETZKO, BARBARA YULICK, Choral Director; *b:* Plainfield, NJ; *m:* Rick; *ed:* Trenton St Coll (BA) Music Ed 1978, (MA) Choral Conducting-Summa Cum Laude 1982; Montclair St Univ Guidance Counseling & Soc Work 40 Credits; *cr:* New Providence HS Choral Dir 1979-80; Wm Annin MS Choral Dir 1980-82; Ridge HS Choral Dir 1982-; *ai:* Mens Chorus; Madrigal Singers; Vocal Jazz Ensemble; Voices of Ridge; Peer Leadership; Class Adv; Concert Choir; 9th Grd Chorus; Acappela Choir; NEA, Amer Choral Dirs Assn, Music Educators Natl Conf 1980-; NJ Choral 1992-94, Procedures Comm; NJ All St Chorus Conductor 1991; Article in Tempo Magazine for NJ Music Educators; *home:* 45 Dayt Bernardsville NJ 07924*

REUBLIN, MARY LOU KLEMENCIC, 6th Grade Teac Cleveland, OH; *m:* Robert; *c:* Susan, Nancy, Patsy, Catherine Gillm Bowling Green St Univ (BS) Elem Ed 1961; Ashland Univ (MS) E Curr & Super 1993; Attnd Univ of CO at Boulder, Univ of North Greeley, CO St Univ & Miamo Univ of OH; *cr:* Talawandu Schls 3t Grd Tchr 1968-74; Boulder Valley Schl 3rd & 5th Grd Tchr 1 Bowling Green City Schl 5th & 6th Grd Tchr 1986-; *ai:* Safety Patr Lang Arts Comm; PTO Tchr Rep; NEA & OH Ed Assn 1968-; CO E 1975-86; IRA 1986-, Pres in CO, Pres in OH; NCTE 1986-; Alpha Delta 1975-86; Amer Cancer Soc 1961-; Boulder Valley Outstandi Stud Tchr; Bowling Green Dist Grants; *office:* Coneaut Elem S Haskins Rd Bowling Green OH 43402

REULBACH, ROSANNE CANGEMI, Eng Tchr & Adj Prof of Jrn NY; *m:* Robert; *c:* Heather, Nicholas; *ed:* Adelphi Univ (BA) En (MA) Eng 1972; 45 Addl Hrs; *cr:* New Hyde Pk HS Eng Tchr 1 Sachem HS Eng, Jrnlsm Tchr 1978-; *ai:* Schl Newspaper; Writin Comm for Planning; NCTE 1969-; Women's Club Civic Org of Mass 1983-, Sec; Grants Natl Endowment of Arts; Tchr of Yr 1985; Sachem HS North 212 Smith Rd Ronkonkoma NY 11779

REUSCHER, MELISSA ROSE, English Teacher; *b:* St Marys, Seton Hill Coll (BA) Eng 1986; Gannon Univ Working Towards MA *cr:* Greensburg Cntrl Eng Tchr 1986-88; Elk Cty Chrstn Eng Tchr *ai:* Drama Dept Dir, Producer; NCTE 1986-; Footlighters 1988-, Bd Cncl 1993-, VP; St Vincent Coll Great Tchr Recognition Prgm 19 Poetry; Eds Aed; *office:* Elk County Christian H S 600 Maurus S Marys PA 15857

REUTHER, MAUREEN WILKINSON, Health, PE Tchr & Co West Chester, PA; *m:* Robert C.; *ed:* Univ of DE (BA) Hlth, PE 198 Chester Univ (MS) Hlth, PE 1987; *cr:* Outward Bound Instr, Cou 1987-90; Cornell Univ Tchr, Coach Outdoor Ed 1990-92; Pennc Hlth, PE Tchr, Coach 1992-; *ai:* Head Field Hockey & Lacrosse NEA 1992-; Full Ath Schlsp to Univ of DE 4 Yrs; Natl Champ Lacrosse 1982-83.

REVER, ELLEN HAMMER, English as a Second Lang Tchr; *b:* N NJ; *m:* Sanford Rever; *c:* Lisa, Scott, Ryan; *ed:* Rutgers Univ (BA) Ed 1964; Kean Coll (MA) Psych 1980; Educl Certs, ESL, Elem, Tchr, Prin, Supvr, Stu Prsnl Svcs; *cr:* Knollwood Schl 5th Gr 1964-66; Union Twp Elem Schls ESL Tchr 1980-89; Union HS ES 1989-; *ai:* Intercultural Stu Org, Peer OrientationComm Adv; NEA, NJ Jesol BE, UTEA Negotiations Team, Philantlropic Chair, Rep; Union HS N 3rd St Union NJ 07083

REVIL, JEAN L., Religious Studies Teacher; *b:* Bridgewater, M Stonehill Coll (BA) Rel Stud 1979; Bridgewater St Coll (MAT) Beh Sci 1986; Natl Ctr for Death Ed Cert in Thanatology 1989; *cr:* Stang HS Rel Stud Tchr 1979-, Rel Stud Dept Chprsn 1986-; *ai:* Soccer Coach; Bicycle Club Adv; NCEA 1979-; Hearts & Hands Inc Bd of Dirs; Coastal Communities Ultreya 1993-, Spiritual Dir; Lect Wkshp Presenter for Local, Regnl & Natl Confs- Topics Include D With Grief & Loss, Sexual Morality, Personal Decision Mak Spirituality; *office:* Bishop Stang HS 500 Slocum Rd North Dartmou 02747

REVTA, JOYCE, Fourth Grade Teacher; *b:* Scranton, PA; *m:* M Richard; *c:* Carolyn; *ed:* Marywood Coll (BA) ELem Ed 1972 Equivalency Marywood Coll Univ of Scranton; *cr:* Dunmore Elem 1st, 4th Grd Tchr 24 Yrs; *ai:* 4th Grd Team Ldr; AFT, PAFT Eucharistic Minister 1991-, Church Pastoral Cncl 1994-, Yth Ad 1990-.*

REX, CATHY J., Commnctn & English Teacher; *b:* Coatesville, Susan Wellhofer, Michael Jr.; *ed:* IN Univ of PA (BS) Spcl Ed Villanova Univ (MA) Theatre & Speech 1988; 60 Credit Hrs Beyon in Hum; *cr:* Avon-Grove Tchr 1974-77; Schl Dist Of PA Tchr & 1977-; *ai:* Schl Newspaper Moderator; Drama Club Coach & Spon 1977-; AFT 1977-; Oak NHS; Kappa Delta Pi; Walt Disney Amer Awds; Outstdng Eng Tchr 1993; Mirabella 1000 1993; Distngd Adv T Univ Press Assoc; NEH Summer Seminars for Tchrs; Shakespeare Fl *office:* Roxborough HS 6498 Ridge Ave Philadelphia PA 19128

REX, JULIA A., Third Grade Teacher; *b:* Lima, OH; *m:* Michael Jared, Rachael, Cara; *ed:* OH St Univ (BS) Ed 1973; Univ of Dayton Cnslng 1986; *cr:* Upper Scioto Vly Schl 2nd & 3rd Grd Tchr 197 Head Tchr of USV Elem Schl; NEA; OEA; Auglaize Bible C Franklin B Walter Outstdng Edctr Awd; *office:* Upper Scioto Vly Sch Courtright St Mc Guffey OH 45859

REX, VIRLYNN LEIGH, 7th & 8th Grade Teacher; *b:* Hicksville *ed:* IN Univ (BS) Elem Ed 1970, (MS) Elem Ed 1976; *cr:* Hicksville 6th Grd Tchr 1972-94; Hicksville Mid Schl Eng Tchr 1994-; *ai:* 6 Grd Summer Schl Tchr; NEA, OCTELA; Village Players 1973, Bd 1996, Best Actress 1992; Grace United Meth Church, Bd Mem, Choir Dir; Undertones Vocal Quartet, KIWANIS; Exch Tchr to 1994; Articles Pub; *office:* Hicksville Elem Schl W Arthur St Hick OH 43526

REXFORD, KATHRYN ANN, Assistant Principal; *b:* Rome, NY; *e* St Univ (BSEd) Eng Comm 1978; Univ of Dayton (MSEd) Schl C 1987; Scndry Principalship 1995; *cr:* Bluffton HS Eng, Jrnlsm, D Speech Tchr 1978-80; Groveport Madison Frosh Schl Eng Tchr 198 Groveport Madison HS Asst Prin 1995-; *ai:* Prof Dev Ldrshp Co-chair; Strategic Planning Action Co-Facilitator; Lang Arts Cou Stud, Band Boosters, Stu Cncl, NHS, Soph, Jr Class Admin Li NASSP, OASSP 1995-; PDK 1990-; ASCD 1988-; Amer Assn of Women 1994-; Martha Holden Jennings Scholar; Muskingum Outstdng Tchr; *office:* Groverport Madison HS 4475 S Hamilto Groveport OH 43125*

REXFORD, PRISCILLA ANN (GREEN), Teacher of the Gifted; *b* City, PA; *m:* Gene; *c:* Gregg Peterson, Kenton; *ed:* Clarion Univ Elem, Spec Ed 1967, (MED) Elem Ed 1970; Clarion Univ of PA Sup Spec Ed 1985; *cr:* Cranberry Area Schl Dist 4th Grd Tchr 1967; Fra Area Schl Dist spec Ed Tchr 1967-73; Clarion Univ of PA Part-time 1975-95; Franklin Area Schl Dist Tchr of Gifted 1979-; *ai:* Cmptr Adv; Gifted Consortium Mem; Strategic Planning Comm; CEC 1990 Assn for Gifted Ed 1985-; Phi Delta Kappa 1980-, 2nd VP, Newslette Alternate Del; NW Med Ctr Corp 1985-; Franklin Arts Cncl 1980-; B Civic Theatre Patron 1980-; *home:* RR 4 Box 773 Franklin PA 16323

REY, LINDA ANN, First Grade Teacher; *b:* Newark, NJ; *m:* Manue Jr; *c:* Jaclyn, Ashley; *ed:* Jersey City St Coll (BA) Elem Ed K-8th 1972; Rutgers Univ 30 Credits Elem Ed 1978; New Brunswic Equivalency; *cr:* Ann Street Schl 1st Grd Tchr 1972-; *ai:* Best F Mentor 1994-; Newark Tchrs Union 1972-; Cranford Historical Soc 1 Cranford Clay Courts Club 1995-; The Governors Tchr Recognition 1991; *office:* Ann Street Schl 30 Ann St Newark NJ 07105

REYDA, MARY PARK, Mathematics Teacher; *b:* Jamestown, NY Joseph A. (dec); *c:* Joseph P., Andrew M.; *ed:* SUNY at Fredonia (BS) Ed 1962; *cr:* Southwestern Cntrl Schl Elem Tchr 1962-68; Sherman Schl Elem Tchr 1979-; *ai:* NEA, NEA of NY 1962-; STA 1979-, T *office:* Sherman Central Schl PO Box 950 Sherman NY 14781

ƐL, JOHN J., History Department Chairman; *b:* Westfield, NJ; *m:* radley; *c:* John J. Jr., Amy Bradley; *ed:* Princeton Univ (BA) His Harvard Univ (MED) His, Ed 1958; Stanford Univ COE Flwshp ast-West Inst Univ of HI Asian Flwshp 1968; Frgn Policy Rsrch Inst Japan 1991, Inventing Democracy 1993; CIEE Japan Summer Stud *r:* USMC Ret Captain 1951-53; Hill Schl Tchr, Coach 1953-56; ceville Schl Headmaster 1973-78; Germantown Acad Chm His Dept *ai:* Upper Schl Dept Chm; Sr Advy; OAH; AHA; NCSS; Whitpain 74-; Democratic Party Comm; Reader Coll Bd AP US His Exams 3; Fulbright Grant Korea 1983; NEH Grant Korean His Culture AP Prgm Outstdng Contribution Coll Bd Awd 1993; *office:* ntown Acad PO Box 287 Fort Washington PA 19034*

S, GLORIA DESIREE, Retired Teacher; *b:* Manila, Philippines; Women's Univ (BSEE) Elem Ed 1953; IL St Univ (MSEd) Spec Ed Attnd Coll Du Leman 1969; Perceptual-Motor Trng Miami Univ Great Books Ldr Trng Course 1989; *cr:* PWU Classroom Tchr 5, 1957-65; Whitaker Schl Intermediate Spec Ed Tchr 1966-83; own Jr HS Spec Ed Tchr 1983-86; Whitaker Schl Classroom Tchr 2; *ai:* Vly Interfaith Food & Clothing Ctr 1995-, Vol; Fulbright Grant 1955; Jr Women's Club of IL Awd 1956; Tchr Ldr Citation Author Writing Prog OH Dept of Ed 1990; Exemplary Ec Edctr Awd cl on Eco Ed 1992; Excl in Ed for Handicapped Children Awd rn OH Spec Ed Regnl Resource Ctr 1986; *home:* 935 Hollytree Dr nati OH 45231

S, RAMON, Spanish Teacher; *b:* Ranama City, Rep of Panama; *m:* Ruth; *c:* Ramon, Monica R., Carl, Daniel, Alex; *ed:* Univ of CO (BA) 962; Univ of OK (MA) Human Relations 1975; Post-Grad 38 Credit & PE; *cr:* Curundu Jr HS Tchr 1965-95; Balboa HS Tchr 1995-; *ai:* pan Club Adv; Var Bsktbl Coach; Past Ftbl, Bsbl & Swimming AFT 1964-; Parish Cncl Church, Pres; Exceptional Performing Awd 1 & 1993-94; Sustained Superior Work Performance 1994-95; PSC Box 2 Box 1323 APO AA 34002*

OLDS, BRUCE C., History Teacher & Coach; *b:* New Castle, DE; , Chad; *ed:* Duke Univ (BA) Ed & His 1971; 30 Credit Hrs Univ of asters Ed Admin 1974; *cr:* William Penn HS Tchr & Coach 1971-; ad Ftbl Coach; Weight Lifting Spon; NEA & DSEA 1971-; DIFCA s Assn 1971-, Pres; St Rep 1984-; St Coach of Yr 1981 & 1995; William Penn HS 713 E Basin Rd New Castle DE 19720

OLDS, CAROL BARBARA, Business & Comptr Sci Teacher; *b:* elphia, PA; *ed:* Bloomsburg Univ (BS) Bus Ed & Accounting 1986; Univ (MS) Ed Tech 1991; Penn St Univ Admin Cert 1995; 30 Credit Addition to Masters; *cr:* Pottsgrove HS Bus Tchr 5 Yrs; o-Horsham HS Bus & Comp Sci Tchr 3 Yrs, Bus & Comp Sci Dept 1 Yr; *ai:* FBLA; Youth Leadership Prgm; Stu Assistance Prgm; NEA, 1987-; MDS Fnd 1993-; Educl Grants, Lehigh Univ; *office:* Hatboro am Sr HS 899 Horsham Rd Horsham PA 19044

OLDS, CAROL F., English Teacher & Dept Rep; *b:* Worcester, MA; lip R.; *c:* James P., Kathleen D., Elizabeth S.; *ed:* Univ of Rochester Eng 1966, (MA) Ed 1968; SUNY at Albany Capital Dist Writing Post Grad Eng Stud; *cr:* R. L. Thomas HS Eng Tchr 1966-69; on Spa HS Eng Tchr 1980-89; Burnt Hills-Ballston Lake HS Eng 989-; St Univ of NY at Albany Writing Tchr 1992-; *ai:* Lefont Lit ine Adv; K-12th Grd Lang Arts Comm; AFT, NYSUT, NCTE, NYS Cncl, Capital Dist Writing Project; Pub in 2 NY St Eng Cncl graphs & NCTE Journal; NEH Smnr Partcpnt; *office:* Burnt Ballston Lake HS Lakehill Rd Burnt Hills NY 12027

OLDS, CHRISTINE M., High School English Teacher; *b:* Little NY; *m:* William G.; *c:* Joshua, Jocelyn, Justin; *ed:* Roberts Wesleyan BS) Elem Ed 1981; St Univ of NY at Oneonta (MS) Eng Ed 1991; *cr:* Falls Bapt Acad HS Tchr 1982-87; Benton Hall Elem 3rd Grd Tchr 91; Dolgeville Cntrl Schl HS Eng Tchr 1991-; *ai:* Musical Theatre al Dir; Choir & Jazz Choir Pianist; Solo Accompanist; SAT Review; Falls Bapt Church, Organist; *office:* Dolgeville Cntrl Schl Slawson ension Dolgeville NY 13329

OLDS, CINDY G., Instructional Support Teacher; *b:* Scranton, PA; arywood Coll (BA) Elem Ed Math 1972, (MA) Rdng Ed 1976; Rdng alists Cert; *cr:* Mountain View Elem Schl Second Grd Tchr 1972-92, Support Tchr 1992-; *ai:* Hands Enlisted by Loving Parents Coord; Lang Arts Comm Chm; Portfolio Comm; Report Card, Assessment ; Dist Bldg Facilities Comm; Delta Kappa Gamma 1977-, Pres; PSEA, MVEA 1972-, Sec; Amer Diabetes Assn 1974-; Harford ultural Assn 1971-, Supt Schl Dept; Intnl Golden Gift Spec Stud d to Write Tchng Prgm for Diabetics; Numerous Articles Pub; *office:* tain View Elem Schl RR 1 Box 339A Kingsley PA 18826*

NOLDS, CONSTANCE MARIE, Chem & Advanced Sci Teacher; *b:* ic City, NJ; *m:* Arthur John; *c:* Jennifer, William, Jessica, Catherine; rexel Univ (BS) 1970; *cr:* The Pilgrim Acad Tchr 1985-; *ai:* Yrbk; Spon & Spring Banquet Decorating Comm Spon.

NOLDS, CRAIG A., Assistant Principal; *b:* Princess Anne, MD; *m:* ly Kujawa; *c:* Stacey Ellice; *ed:* Univ of MD (BA) Govt & Politics (BA) Scndry Ed 1973; Johns Hopkins Univ (MS) Admin & vision 1980; *cr:* Glen Burnie HS Geography & His Tchr 1974-75; Old HS Law Related Ed Tchr 1975-85; Meade Sr HS Asst Prin 1985-93; east Sr HS Asst Prin 1993-; *ai:* Phi Delta Kappa 1986-; AEL, NASSP ; Pasadena United Meth Church 1975-; Riverdale Forrest Comm Assn , VP; Dist 32 House of Dels Schlsp Comm 1990-94; Alpha Phi a; Taught Several Grad Wkshps & Courses in Law Related Ed at us Colls 1978-87; Pub Several Resource & Tchng Aides for Law ed Ed; *office:* Northeast Sr HS 1121 Duvall Hwy Pasadena MD 21122

NOLDS, FAYETTE A., Adj Instr in Human Anatomy; *ed:* William Coll (BA) Bio 1973; SUNY at Brockport (MS) Zoology 1975; Grad g Assistantship & Tuition Waiver; Sigma Xi Awd for Outstdng Rsrch ad Bio; *cr:* Montifiore Hosp Dept of Neoplastics Rsrch Asst 1975-76; VA Med Schl Dept of Pediatrics Clinical Endocrinology Supvr & Assoc 1976-79; Williams Coll Dept of Bio Genetics, Cell Bio & duction Bio Visiting Instr 1979-80, 1987-88; North Adams St Coll of Bio Microbiology & Bio Visiting Lecturer 1981-86; Berkshire n Coll Dept of Scis & Engrng Bio Instr 1992-; *office:* Berkshire n Coll Dept of Sciences & Engrng West St Pittsfield MA 01201

NOLDS, JACQUELINE M., Fifth Grade Teacher; *b:* Cincinnati, OH; erald A.; *c:* Christina Back, Matthew; *ed:* Edgecliff Coll (BS) Ed , Xavier Univ (MED) Ed 1987; Martha Holden Giddinas Summer ; Rdng Renaissance; Algebra, Math Miami; *cr:* St Elizabeth Schl th Grd Tchr 1966-68; St Matthew Schl 5th Grd Tchr 1970-72; nnati Pub Schls Part-time Rdng, Math Tchr 1975-82; Norwood Pub 1982-; *ai:* NEA 1982-; NCTM 1993-; Cincinnati Zoo, Mbrshp Drive; ood YWCA, Bd; *office:* Norwood View HS Carthage & Hannaford Norwood OH 45212

NOLDS, JOHN ANTHONY, Fine Arts Teacher; *b:* Dover, NJ; *ed:* Coll (BA) His 1969; Cath Univ of Amer (MFA) Fine Arts 1984; Ed Seton Hall Univ 1970, 1972; *cr:* Iona Grammar Schl 6th Grd Tchr -74; All Hallows Inst 10th-12th Grd Tchr 1974-75; Sacred Heart of s Elem Schl 5th-7th Grd Art Tchr 1975-, Grd K-8 Tchr; *ai:* After Schl ormance Group Coord, Dir 1983-92; NCEA 1969-; Rel Congregation nrstn Brothers 1965-; *office:* Sacred Heart of Jesus Schl 456 W 52nd ew York NY 10019

REYNOLDS, JOHN DENNIS, Pol Sci & US His Teacher; *b:* Boston, MA; *m:* Judith Conners; *c:* Joshua Thomas, John David, Joanna Lee; *ed:* Univ of MA (BA) Pol Sci 1965; Boston Univ (MED) Systems Dev 1975; Attnd Univ of Lowell Cmptr Sci; *cr:* US Army 1st Lieutent 1966-68; Bedford HS Tchr 1968-; *ai:* Var Golf & Jr Var Bsbl Coach; Stu Govt Adv; Facilities Comm Chm; BEA 1968-, Grievance Chair; MTA & NEA 1968-; MCA 1968-, Golf Coach of Yr 1979 & 1985; *office:* Bedford HS 9 Mudge Way Bedford MA 01730*

REYNOLDS, JOHN E., 6th Grd Social Studies Teacher; *b:* Pittsburgh, PA; *m:* Celia Davis Reynolds; *ed:* CA Univ PA (BA) Elem Ed 1962; Duquesne Univ (MA) ELem Ed 1968; *cr:* Bethel Park Schls Tchr 1962-; *ai:* Team Ldr; Historical Building Comm; Class Trip Spon; AFT, Bethel Park Fed Tchrs 1970-, VP 1978-79, Exec Bd 1991-95; Oliver Miller Historical Soc 1977-, Pres 1977-78; Civil War Reinactor 9th, PA Reserves; Carnegie Civil War Roundtable, Frnds of Gettysburg; Gift of Time Rec 1994 & 1995; *office:* Independence M S Bethel Church Rd Bethel Park PA 15102*

REYNOLDS, JON LEE, Professor of Chemistry; *b:* Anthon, IA; *m:* Evelyn Carr; *c:* Robert, Marta Whalen, Leslie Green, Michael; *ed:* Wayne St Tchrs Coll (BS) Ed 1959; St Univ of SD (MA) Chem 1961; OH St Univ (PHD) Organic Chem 1966; Post-Doctorate 1975; Univ of Montreal Post-Doctorate 1973; SUNY Potsdam Fac Rsrch Flwshp Summer 1970, 1971; Clarkson Univ Fac Assoc Summer 1969; *cr:* Continental Oil Co Rsrch, Dev 1966-68; SUNY Potsdam Assoc Prof of Chem 1968-; *ai:* ACS 1968-; Scott, G.P.; Soong, C.C.; Huang, W.S.; and Reynolds, J.L.,Org. Chem 1964,29,83. Reynolds, J.L.; D. Doshi and Shechter, H., J. Am. Chem. Soc.,1987,109,8032-8041 Forou, M.A. and Reynolds, J.L. Main Group Metal Chem., 1994, XVII,No. 6, 399-402; *office:* S U N Y Coll At Potsdam Pierrepont Avenue Potsdam NY 13676

REYNOLDS, JOSEPH PATRICK, Professor of Chemical Engrng; *b:* New York, NY; *m:* Barbara Geary; *c:* Megan, Marybeth; *ed:* Cath Univ of Amer (BA) Chem 1957; Rensselaer Polytechnic Inst (PHD) Chem Engrng 1964; *cr:* Manhattan Coll Asst Prof 1964-70, Assoc Prof 1970-77, Dept Chm 1976-83, Prof 1977-; *ai:* Amer Inst of Chem Engrs Stu Chptr Adv; Coll Senate; Fac Affairs Cncl; Amer Inst of Chem Engrs 1964-; Air & Waste Mngmt Assn 1970-; Sigma Xi 1957-, Past Pres; Pub 20 Books, Numerous Papers, Several Software Packages; Recipient of Many Govt, Industry, EPA Grants; Dept of Justice Expert Witness; Govt, Industry Consultant; *office:* Manhattan Coll Chemical Engineering Dept Manhattan College Pkwy Bronx NY 10471

REYNOLDS, JOSEPH R., English Teacher; *b:* Worcester, MA; *m:* Donna M.; *c:* Emily M.; *ed:* St Anselm Coll (AB) Philosophy, Eng 1966; Univ of MA (MAT) Ed, Eng 1968; Assumption Coll (MA) Eng 1977; Attnd Univ of RI, Harvard Univ, Tufts Univ; *cr:* Wachusett Regnl HS Eng, Latin Tchr 1968-; *ai:* MA Teachers Assoc, NEA; NEA Fellowship 1985 Bowdin Coll; HEH Fellowship 1995 Univ of WA; Fullbright Fellowship Rome 1982; Articles & Book Reviews in Various Newspapers & Journals; *office:* Wachusett Regional HS 1401 Main St Holden MA 01520

REYNOLDS, JUDITH MALONE, Music Teacher; *b:* Albany, NY; *m:* Keith L.; *c:* Shaun, Kimberly; *ed:* Coll of St Rose (BS) Music Ed 1973; 30 Plus Hrs Grad Stu Elem Ed; Permanent Certification in NY St K-12 Music Ed & N-6 Elem Ed; *cr:* Vincentian Inst Music Dir 1973-77; Holy Cross Schl Vocal Music Tchr K-8th Grd 1978-; *ai:* NCEA 1979-.

REYNOLDS, LINDA JANE, English Teacher; *b:* Lakewood, OH; *c:* Scott Hartley; *ed:* Wright St Univ (BS) Eng Ed 1969, (MED) Ed & Tchr Ldr 1979; *cr:* Piqua City Schls Sub Tchr 1969; Centerville City Schls Eng Tchr 1970-; *ai:* CCTA, OEA, NEA 1969-; ALCU 1990-; Reader-AP Eng Lit ETS 1986-92; Consultant for Coll Bd on AP Tchng 1986-93; Table Ldr Rdng 1992.*

REYNOLDS, MARGARET A., Social Studies Teacher; *b:* Nashua, NH; *ed:* Regis Coll (BA) His 1976; Cambridge Coll (MED) 1990; Attnd Boston Coll, Dartmouth Coll, Northeastern Univ, Univ of Lowell, Univ of NH; *cr:* US Customs Inspector 1976-78; Nashua Pub Schls Soc Stud Tchr 1979-; *ai:* Interact Club, Pathways to Future; AFT 1978-, Bldg Rep; Northern NE Cncl 1992-, Pres; NH Cncl For Soc Stud 1994-; United Way 1995-, Fundraising, Appreciation; Ldrshp Greater Nashua 1994-, Comm Chprsn; Paul Harris Flwshp 1995; Tchr of Yr 1985; *office:* Nashua Senior High School 36 Riverside Dr Nashua NH 03062

REYNOLDS, NANCY ROSE, GATE & Accelerated Math Tchr; *b:* Barnesville, OH; *ed:* OH Univ (BSED) Elem Ed 1965; Gifted Talented Cert 1987; *cr:* Barnesville Ex Village Schls 5-8 Grd Gifted, Math, Soc Stud, Sci, Rdng Tchr 1964-; *ai:* Math Counts; Scholastic Challenge; Knowledge Master; Quest; Math Curr Comm; Geography Bee; NEED Coord; NEA, OEA, EOTA, BEA 1964-; OCTM, OCSS 1964-; OCGC 1987-; Math Awd; First Presbyn Church 1957-, Elder, Deacon, Trustee, Session Clerk; Presbyn Women 1965-, Treas; Belmont Cty Gifted Advisory Cncl 1990-; PTO 1964-, Pres, Treas, Sec, Prgm Chprsn; MS Tchr of Yr Barnesville Educ Fnd 2 Yrs; Article Pub Math Tchr Journal OH & NM; Sunday Schl Tchr 30 Yrs, Part-time Supt; Math Equipment for MS Grant; ZTCG Gifted Tchr of Yr; *office:* Barnesville Elem Schl 210 W Church Barnesville OH 43713

REYNOLDS, RICHARD R., Chemistry Teacher; *b:* Passaic, NJ; *m:* Norma D.; *c:* Richard J., Patricia Ann; *ed:* Fordham Univ Chem 1958; Grad at Montclair St Coll, Jersey City Coll & Seton Hall Univ; *cr:* Marist HS Chem Tchr & Ftbl Coach 1958-60; Northern Vly Regnl HS Chem Tchr & Ftbl & Wrestling Coach 1960-65; Anti-Poverty Pgm Sr Team Ldr 1965-66; Waldwick HS Chem Tchr, Ftbl & Wrestling Coach 1966-; *ai:* Coord Mid Coll Chem Pgm at Fairleigh-Dickinson Coll; NEA, NJEA & BCEA 1960-; WEA 1966-; NJSTA 1970-; Govenors Tchr of the Yr Awd 1989.

REYNOLDS, ROBERT ANDERSON,JR., Pre-Engineering Graphics Tchr; *b:* Toledo, OH; *m:* Roberta S. Miller; *c:* Robert III, Lisa M.; *ed:* Bowling Green St U (BS) Indstrl Arts, Tech 1969; Post Grad Class UT; *cr:* Fremont Ross Jr HS Woodshop Tchr 1969-70; Cardinal Stritch HS Pre-Engrng Graphics Tchr 1970-; *ai:* Asst Ath Site Mgr; North Cntrl Steering, North Centrl Rdng, Writing, Tech Comms; OH Tech Ed Assn 1993-; NCEA; UCT 1990-; Hall of Fame; *office:* Cardinal Stritch HS 3225 Pickle Rd Oregon OH 43616

REYNOLDS, SANDRA LAURIE, French Instructor; *b:* Hempstead, NY; *c:* Delbert, David; *ed:* SUNY at Potsdam (BA) Fr 1985; Purdue Univ (MA) Fr, Span 1987; CUNY Grad Schl PHD Fr; Universite du Quebec Fr Cert 1984; Fordham Univ ESL Ed Credits; *cr:* Martin Luther HS Fr, Span Tchr 1988-90; Olivet Coll Fr Asst Prof 1990-91; St Paul's Coll Fr, Span Asst Prof 1992-93; Raritan Vly Comm Coll Fr, Span Instr 1993-; *ai:* Mentor Prgm; Ethics Comm; FLENJ 1994-; AATF, ACTFL 1995-; Pi Delta Phi 1981-; Cntrl Jersey Master Chorale 1994-; CUNY Rsrch Flwshp 1987-88; Sigma Delta Pi Writing Awd 1985; NSF Ethics, Tech Grant 1995-; *office:* Raritan Valley Comm Coll PO Box 3300 Somerville NJ 08876*

REYNOLDS, SHERRY M., High School English Teacher; *b:* Stoneboro, PA; *m:* Arlo S.; *c:* Shane Daniel, Travis Scott; *ed:* Clarion Univ (BS) Eng 1966; 24 Hrs Slippery Rock Univ; 3 Hrs Bloomsburg Univ; 6 Hrs IN Univ: 3 Hrs Clarion Univ; 2 Hrs Bowling Green Univ; *cr:* Skaneateles Schl Dist Eng Tchr 1966-68; Lakeview Schl Dist Eng Tchr 1968-; *ai:* HS Newspaper, NHS Advs 1976-; NEA 1966-; PSEA 1968-; Lakeview Ed Assn 1968-, Sec 1976-78, Treas 1983-; *office:* Lakeview Schl Dist 2482 Mercer St Stoneboro PA 16153

REYNOLDS, TERRY, Instrumental Music Teacher; *b:* Hartford, CT; *m:* Lori Strelel; *ed:* Univ of CT (BS) Music Ed 1985; Univ of Akron (MM) Music Performance 1987; *cr:* Great Oak MS Instrumental Music Tchr 1987-89; Somers MS Instrumental Music Tchr 1989-91; Somers HS Instrumental Music Tchr 1991-; *ai:* Marching Band & Jazz Ensemble Dir; Winter Guard Adv; WCSMA, AFT, Somers Fac Assn 1991-; NY St PTSA Honorary Lifetime Membership 1993; Recognized by Somers Bd of Ed as One of Five HS Staff Awds 1994; *office:* Somers HS PO Box 640 Lincolndale NY 10540

REZNICK, PATRICIA ANN (PHELAN), 7th-8th Grade Teacher; *b:* Far Rockaway, NY; *m:* Joseph; *c:* Joseph, Timothy, Thomas; *ed:* St Joseph's Coll (BA) Child Stud 1973; Rutgers Univ 3.5 Cr; Fordham Univ 3 Cr; 10 Addl Hrs; *cr:* St Mary Star of the Sea Schl 5th-8th Grd Tchr 1973-75; St Gregory the Great Schl Sub Tchr 1980-89; St Hedwig Schl 1st Grd Tchr 1989-91; Our Lady of Lourdes 7th-8th Grd LA, Rdng Tchr 1991-; *ai:* 8th Grd Guid; Skills for Adolescence, QUEST; Rainbows for All God's Children, Facilitator; LA, Art Coord; NCEA 1990-; *office:* Our Lady Lourdes Schl 92-80 220 St Queens Village NY 11428

REZNIK, RALPH E., Math, Reading & Religion Tchr; *b:* Berea, OH; *m:* Marilyn D.; *c:* Dana Marie; *ed:* Baldwan Wallace Coll (BSEd) Elem Ed 1973; Cleveland St Univ (MAEd) Curr & Instruction 1977; *cr:* St Margaret Mary Schl Tchr Grds 6 & 8 1973-78; St Christopher Schl Tchr Grd 8 1978-; *ai:* Stu Govt Moderator; Right to Life Prgms; Asst Prin; HS Admissions Prgm; NCEA 1973-; SWYMCA Indian Princess Group 1991-; Miriam Joseph Farrell Outstanding Tchr Awd 1984; *office:* St Christopher Schl 1610 Lakeview Ave Rocky River OH 44116

RHEA, JOYCE CUSTER, Vocal Music Teacher; *b:* Somerset, PA; *m:* Dick W. Jr.; *c:* Gretchen J. Swaner, Craig R. Swaner; *ed:* WV Univ (BM) Music 1971; *cr:* Shanksville Stonycreek Schl Dist K-12th Grd Vocal Music Tchr 1971-; *ai:* NEA, PSEA, SSEA & PMEA 1971; *home:* RR 1 Box 150 Friedens PA 15541

RHEAULT, MICHAEL, Music Teacher; *b:* Springfield, MA; *ed:* Univ of MA (BMus) Music Composition & Theory 1978; Working on MBA at Western New England Coll; *cr:* Amer Intnl Coll Choral Dir 1991-93; Bay Path Coll Piano Tchr 1991-93; St Peter & Paul Church Music Dir 1993-; Ludlow HS Music Tchr 1994-; *ai:* Sr Show & Top 40 Advs; MENC 1993-; Amer Guild of Organists 1993-; MA Tchrs Assoc 1994-; Springfield Preservation Trust 1986-; *office:* Ludlow Sr HS 500 Chapin St Ludlow MA 01056

RHEEM, BETH ANN, Chemistry Dept Adjunct Prof; *b:* Saint Marys, PA; *m:* Dean R. Bender; *c:* Paul, Tim; *ed:* Cedar Crest Coll (BA) & (BS) Bio & Chem 1982; Rensselaer Polytechnic Inst (MS) Organic Chem 1984; High Pressure Liquid Chromatography 1989; Tech Writing 1988; Lotus 1-2-3 for Lab 1987; Recombinant DNA 1987; *cr:* Merck & Co Inc Staff Chemist-Process & Dev 1984-87, Research Chemist-Process & Dev 1987-89; Ocean Cty Coll Chem Dept Adjunct Fac 1989; Union Cty Coll Chem Dept Adjunct Fac 1990-; *ai:* Sci by Mail Prgm Vol Scientist; Amer Chemical Soc 1982-; Amer Assn for the Adv of Sci 1985-; *office:* Union County Coll 1033 Springfield Ave Cranford NJ 07016

RHEINECKER, THOMAS C., Physics & Chemistry Teacher; *b:* Cincinnati, OH; *m:* Michelle Carroll; *c:* Michelle, Christine, Valerie, Kathleen; *ed:* Univ of Cincinnati (BS) Chem 1969; Complete Course Work for Masters in Ed; *cr:* Procter & Gamble Chemist 1961-81; Gentek Corp Dir of Quality Assurance 1981-84; Forest Pharmaceuticals Dir of Quality Assurance 1984- 90; Bishop Brossard HS Chem Tchr 1991-92; St Ursula Acad Physics & Chem Tchr 1993-; *ai:* Hold 4 Patents in Chem; *office:* St Ursula Acad 1339 E Mcmillan St Cincinnati OH 45206

RHEM-TITTLE, YVONNE S., Vice Principal; *b:* New York, NY; *m:* James Tittle; *c:* Darlene, Deborah, Joseph, Olga, Augustine, Elizabeth, Nathaniel; *ed:* Antioch Coll (BS) Ed 1976; Bank Street Coll (MS) Ed 1983; Manhattan Coll at Riverdale Schl Admin & Supvr 12 Credits; *cr:* Double H. Trng Center Dir 1974-78; St Augustine Schl Tchr 1976-95, Vice Prin 1995-; *ai:* Rhoer Adv Delta NuSigma Chapter, Northeast Region Phoer Coord; FCT 1976-; NSTA 1984-; Sigma Gamma rho Inc, Chapter Pres; Rhoer Coord 3 Yrs Sigma Gamma Rho; IAMA Tchr 1990; *office:* St Augustine Schl 1176 Franklin Ave Bronx NY 10456

RHETT, CURTIS LEE, 6th Grade Lead Teacher; *b:* Harlem, NY; *m:* Thomasa Guity-Rhett; *c:* Ashaunti; *ed:* Knoxville Coll (BA) Psych, Rsrch 1983; City Univ of NY (MS) Ed 1988; 9 Credit Hrs Toward Admin, Supervision Degree CCNY; Eng as Second Lang, Family Planning, Sex Ed Certs; *cr:* PS 27 St Mary's Schl Math Liaison, Testing Coord 1991-92, 5th-6th Grd Lead Tchr 1992-, 6th Grd Tchr 1994-; Touro Coll Math Prof 1994-; *ai:* Admin Comm 1991-; Math Dept; Sports Fnd, United Way Asst Dir; United Fed of Tchrs 1984-, Outstdng New Tchr Awd; Cath Yth Org 1984-; Alpha Phi Alpha 1983-, Treas, Outstdng Achvmt Awd; Article Pub; Comm Svc Awd 1992; *office:* PS 27 St Mary's Schl 519 Saint Anns Ave Bronx NY 10454*

RHINARD, EDWIN W., Social Science Teacher; *b:* Nanticoke, PA; *m:* Dawn R.; *c:* Christopher, Robert, Allison; *ed:* Bloomsburg St Univ (BS) Soc Stud 1971, (BS) Eng 1976; ME in Soc Sci & Comp Tech 95 Credit Hrs; *cr:* Tunkhannock Area Schls Soc Stud & Eng Tchr 1971-; *ai:* Stu Store; Bsktbl, Soccer & Bsbl Coach; Schedule Coord; Packhorse; NEA; Kiwanis 1992-, Bd of Dir, MISOTY; *office:* Tunkhannock Area Schls Franklin Ave Tunkhannock PA 18657

RHINEHART, SHELBY BREON, English Teacher; *b:* Loganton, PA; *m:* Robert E.; *c:* Gary Lapp, Susan Kirkman; *ed:* Lock Haven Univ (BS) Math, Eng, Soc Stud 1958; *cr:* Lock Haven Jr HS Math, Soc Stud Tchr 1958-61; Jersey Shore Area Sr HS Eng Tchr 1970-; *ai:* Boy, Girl of Month; NHS, Yrbk; NEA, PSEA, JSAEA 1970-; NCTE 1980-; *office:* Jersey Shore Area Sr HS 701 Cemetery St Jersey Shore PA 17740

RHINES, JESSE ALGERON, Asst Prof of African Amer Stud; *b:* Washington, DC; *ed:* Antioch Coll (BA) Pol Commnctn 1974; Yale Univ (MA) African Amer Stud 1983; UCLA (MA) Pol Sci 1986; UC at Berkeley (PHD) Ethnic Stud 1993; NY Univ Film Production Cert 1983; *cr:* YMCA World Ambassador to Hong Kong Summer 1975; Hon Ronald V Dellums Legislative Intern & Admin Aide 1975-76; Mayor Frank Logue Legislative Affairs Ofcr 1978-80; U-Skate Rollerskates Founder 1979-81; Operations Crossroads Africa Mali Group Ldr Summer 1980; IBM Corp Systems Engr 1981-83; St of NY Mortgage Agency Comp Systems Analyst 1989-90; Cineaste Magazine Asst Ed & Co-Ed Race in Contemporary Cinema Section 1992-; Eugene Lang Coll Race, Gender & US Film Distribution System Instr 1993; Rutgers Univ at Newark Afro-Amer Stud Asst Prof 1993-; *ai:* Tchng Excl Ctr Wkshp Tchr & Tchr Evaluation 1994 & 1995; Amer Pol Sci Assn, Fellow 1976; Natl Cncl of Black Pol Scientists, Fellow 1976; Soc for Cinema Stud, Screenings Comm Coord; Black Filmmaker Fndtn, Spon; Ind Feature Project; Natl Asssn for the Advancement of Colored People; Amer Stud Assn; Book: Black Film, White Money; Numerous Articles Pub; Papers Delivered & Scholarly Confs Attnd: Amer Stud Assn Conf 1995, Race & Inequity at Howard Univ 1995, Congressional Black Caucus 1995, Natl Conf on Documentary Film 1995, Natl Assn of Ethnic Stud Conf 1995, Natl Cncl of Black Pol Scientists 1995, The Hosp Ctr at Orange 1995; Bard Coll at Annandale 1995; Smithsonian Inst 1995; Cardinal Schlsp & Black United Fund 1994; African Film Festival at Lincoln Ctr 1994; Soc for Cinema Stud 1994; *office:* Rutgers St Univ At Newark 311 Conkin Hall Newark NJ 07102

RHOADES, JOHN D., Assoc Prof of Anthropology; *b:* Los Angeles, CA; *m:* Mariana Louise Coover; *c:* Kimberly E., G. Thomas; *ed:* Univ of CA at Los Angeles (BA) Anthropology 1962; CA St Univ at Los Angeles (MA) Anthropology 1969; Syracuse Univ (PHD) Anthropology 1976; *cr:* St Univ of NY at Brockport Anthropology Lecturer 1974-75; Saint John Fisher Coll Asst & Assoc Prof, Dir of Intnl Stud Prgm 1976-; *ai:* Amer Anthropological Assn 1964-; Rochester Acad of Sci 1980-, VP, Bd of Dirs; Northeast Medical Group, Bd of Dirs 1985-, Sec; Book Linguistic Diversity & Lang Relief in Kenya; Articles in Amer Anthropologist, Journal of Linguistic Anthropology; *office:* Saint John Fisher Coll 3690 East Ave Rochester NY 14618*

RHOADES, ROBERT JOHN, American & Global Studies Tchr; *b:* Beverly, MA; *c:* Kathleen, Matthew; *ed:* Univ of Southern ME (BS) Soc Stud & Scndry Ed 1974; *cr:* Windham HS Tchr 1974-75; Salem HS Tchr 1975-; *ai:* Boys Cross Cntry Coach; Asst Girls Winter Track Coach; Boys Tennis Coach; SEA, NHEA 1975-; NH Coaches Assn 1975-, Bsktbl Coach of Yr 1980; *office:* Salem HS 44 Geremonty Dr Salem NH 03079*

RHOADS, ANN CLAIRE, Middle School Teacher; *b:* Baltimore, MD; *ed:* The Cath Univ (BA) Elem Ed 1977; Univ of Dayton (MS) Elem Ed 1988; *cr:* St Patrick Richmond Schl Primary Tchr 1978-81; Mother Seton Schl Primary Tchr 1981-90; St Piux X Schl MS Eng Tchr 1990-93; St Dominic Schl MS Math Tchr 1993-94; Mother Seton Acad MS Tchr 1994-; *ai:* Schl Newspaper; NCEA 1978-; Seton Daycare Ctr Bd 1982-87, Sec; Articles Pub; Awd Master Tchr for Stu Tchrs; We Care Comm Grant; *office:* Mother Seton Acad 724 S Ann St Baltimore MD 21231

RHOADS, MICHELLE RENEE, High School Math Teacher; *b:* Medina, NY; *m:* David; *c:* Brendan; *ed:* Syracuse Univ (BA) Math 1990; Franklin Pierce Coll Tchr Cert Pgm 1993; *cr:* Dover HS Tchr 1994-; *ai:* Fr Class Adv; Tech-Prep Comm; NEA 1994-; *office:* Dover HS Alumni Dr Dover NH 03820

RHOADS, SUZANNE HENDERSON, Fourth Grade Teacher; *b:* Lawton, OK; *m:* David Louis; *c:* David, Daniel; *ed:* Trenton St Coll (BS) Elem Ed 1985; *cr:* St Mary's Schl Second Grd Tchr 1965-67; Sacred Heart Schl Second Grd Tchr 1967-72; St Raphael Schl Second, Third Grd Tchr 1977-95; Joyce Kilmer Pub Schl Fourth Grd Tchr 1996; *ai:* Tutor After Schl; NCEA 1977-95; NJEA 1996; Hnr Soc of Phi Kappa Phi 1985-; Capital Club 1988-; Amer Museum of Natural His 1995-; Outstdng Tchr by 3 HS Srs in Hnr Soc as Their Third Grd Tchr; *office:* Joyce Kilmer Schl Stuyvesant Ave Trenton NJ 08610

RHOADS, WILLIAM LEE, Physics Teacher; *b:* Phoenixville, PA; *m:* Barbara Joan Mosser; *c:* Richard, Susan, Karen, Thomas; *ed:* Drexel Univ (BS) Mechanical Engrng 1963; Lehigh Univ (MS) Mechanical Engrng 1964; Post Grad Stud at Penn St Univ; Cert Courses at Immaculata Coll; *cr:* US Naval Ordnance Lab Engr 1964-65; SKF Industries Inc Researcher & Mgr 1965-88; Penn St, Immaculata Coll Lecturer 1987-92; Self Employed Consultant 1988-92; Villa Mary Acad Physics Tchr 1992-; *ai:* Youth Bsbl Coach; AAPT 1992-; Kimberton Youth Athletic League 1974-, Pres, Dir, Svc Awds; BYLSBE Fellowship; US Navy Superior Accomplishment Awd; Numerous Engrng Tech Papers; Several US Patents.

RHOADS-WHITE, DOREEN L., Hlth & Physical Education Tchr; *b:* Norristown, PA; *m:* Dennis H. White; *c:* Tyler Michael White; *ed:* Ursinus Coll (BS) Hlth, PE & Recreation 1975; West Chester St Univ (MED) Hlth, Pe 1977; 32 Credits Above Masters; *cr:* West Chester St Univ Grad Tchng Asst 1975-76; Southern Regnl HS Hlth, PE Tchr, Coach 1977-; *ai:* Gymnastics 4 Yrs, Girls Track 7 Yrs, Girls Var Tennis 14 Yrs, Coach; Dance Club Adv 10 Yrs; Dance Intramurals 4 Yrs; Schl Act Chaperone; NEA, SREA 1977-; *office:* Southern Regional HS 600 N Main St Manahawkin NJ 08050

RHODE, KAREN B., Teacher of the Gifted; *b:* Reading, PA; *ed:* Kutztown Univ (BS) Elem 1972; Masters Equivalency; *cr:* Langswamp Elem 5th Grd 18 Yrs; Dist Topton 1-6th Gifted 6 Yrs; *ai:* Yrbk; Task Force; Elem Environmental Ed Prgm; NEA, PSEA 1972-; PDK (Phi Delta Kapa) 1991-; Tchr of Yr Joycees Awd 1983; PA Tchr of Yr Nom 1987; People to People Delegation Ldr 1996; Safari Club Intnl Amer Wildlife Leadership Schl (AWLS) Participant 1992; *office:* Brandywine Heights Area HS 500 Weis St Topton PA 19562

RHODES, CARMELA SABATIELE, Chemistry Teacher; *b:* Astoria, NY; *m:* Thomas H.; *c:* Thomas Jr., Laurie, Janeen; *ed:* St John's Univ (BA) Chem 1970, (MS) Ed 1975; 60 Post Grad Hrs; *cr:* Mater Christi HS Chem, Bio Tchr 1970-72; Mid Cntry Schl Dist Chem, Bio Tchr 1980-83; Smithtown Schl Dist Chem Tchr 1983-84; William Floyd Schl Dist Chem Tchr 1984-; *ai:* Renaissance Comm Mediator; Museum of Natural His 1988-; NYSUT 1980-; *office:* William Floyd HS 240 Mastic Beach Rd Mastic Beach NY 11951*

RHODES, CAROLINE (PASSAGE), US History & Psych Teacher; *b:* Buffalo, NY; *m:* Robert P.; *c:* Anne K. Rhodes-Kline, Ruth E.; *ed:* Syracuse Univ (BA) Amer Civilization 1960; Edinboro Univ of PA (MA) His 1985; Addl 27 Hrs Tchrs Cert Colgate Univ; *cr:* N Syracuse HS Tchr 1960-61, 1966-68; Liverpool HS Tchr 1962-64; US Peace Corps Tchr 1964-66; Maplewood Jr Sr HS Tchr 1985-; *ai:* Model United Nations Adv; Carnegie Mellon Seminar Soc His; PAEA, NEA 1985-; NCSS 1986-; APA 1990-; Delta Kappa Gamma 1990-, Rsrch Comm Chair; Edinboro Borough Cncl 1976-, Deputy Mayor; Northwest PA Natl Org for Women 1976-, Past Pres; *office:* Maplewood Jr/Sr HS Rd 1 Guys Mills PA 16327

RHODES, CHARLES TIMOTHY, Biology Teacher; *b:* Westerly, RI; *m:* Patricia Ann Devoe; *c:* Christopher, Matthew; *ed:* West Liberty St Coll (BA) Bio 1969; West Virginia Univ 34 Credits; Univ of RI 40 Credits; *cr:* The Austin Schl Bio Tchr 1969-70; Scituate HS Bio Tchr 1971-; *ai:* NEARI 1971-, VP, Pres; *home:* PO Box 17 Bradford RI 02808*

RHODES, DUANE ALLEN, English Teacher; *b:* Troy, OH; *m:* Marie Kline; *c:* Eric Allen; *ed:* Shippensburg St Coll (BS) Eng & Scndry Ed 1975; 24 Credits Beyond Degree; *cr:* Kishacoquillas HS Eng Tchr 1976-88; Indian Valley HS Eng Tchr 1988-; *ai:* Jr Class, Schl Newspaper & Sr Show Adv; NHS Mem; Fac Cncl; Arts in Ed Comm Mem; NEA, PA St Ed Assn, Assn of Mifflin Cty Educators 1976-; Red Cross Bloodmobile 1994-, Chair; MC-2000 1995-, Mem; Quarterly Schl Column for Common Ground Magazine; *home:* 510 Dry Valley Rd Lewistown PA 17044

RHODES, GARY R., Chemistry Teacher; *b:* Altoona, PA; *m:* Carole S. Nuse; *c:* Gary Jr., Tiffany R.; *ed:* Indiana Univ of PA (BS) Bio & Chem 1962, (MED) Bio 1965; 55 Credits Beyond Masters at Penn St Univ; *cr:* Captain Jack HS Sci Tchr 1962-64; Keith Jr HS Tchr of Spec Ed Sci 1964-65; Bishop Guilfoyle HS Bio, Sci & Hlth Tchr 1965-67; Hollidaysburg Area Bio, Chem, Nuclear, Sci, General Sci & Physics Tchr 1967-; *ai:* Boys & Girls Swim Teams Coach; HAEA, NEA 1967-; PSEA 1962-; BSA 1962-, Scoutmaster, Scouters Key; Sunday Schl 1952-, Supt, Tchr, Bd of Trustee, PPRC; Master Mason 1965-; Consistory 1968-; Shrine 1969-; Natl Sci Fnd Grants for Nucleur Engrng Stud & Aerospace Stud; Pittsburgh Plate Glass Grant; *office:* Hollidaysburg Area Sr HS 1510 N Montgomery St Hollidaysburg PA 16648

RHODES, GREGORY LAWRENCE, History Teacher; *b:* Passaic, NJ; *ed:* Newark St Coll (BA) His & Ed 1971; Kean Coll (MA) Admin & Supervision; Montclair St Coll Addl Credits; *cr:* Franklin Schl Soc Stud Tchr 1971-81; Nutley HS His Tchr 1981-; *ai:* NHS Adv; NEA, NJEA, Essex Cty Ed Assn, Ed Assn of Nutley 1971-.

RHODES, KAREN S., Vocal Music Teacher; *b:* Baltimore, MD; *m:* Joseph Timothy; *c:* Christopher David Uhl; *ed:* Towson St Univ (BS) Music Ed 1978; Masters Equivalency 30+ Credit Hrs Grad Work Towson St Univ, Univ of MO; *cr:* Southern MS Vocal, General Music Tchr 1978-83; George Fox MS Vocal Music Tchr 1984-90; Chesapeake HS Vocal, Keyboard Tchr 1990-; *ai:* Choral Dir Concert Choir, Chamber Choir, Vocal Ensemble; Women's Chorus; MMEA, MENC, TAAC, NEA 1978-; ACDA 1994; PTA Lifetime Membership; Anne Arundel Co Tchr of Month 1986; George Fox Mid PTA Tchr of Yr 1986; *office:* Chesapeake SR HS 4798 Mountain Rd Pasadena MD 21122

RHODES, KATHLEEN ANN (BROWN), Teacher of Hearing Impaired; *b:* Ravenna, OH; *m:* Walter Jay; *c:* Jennifer, Jason; *ed:* Kent St Univ (BSEd) Spec Educ, Deaf 1966; Elem Cert 1990; Akron Univ Interpreter Trng 1975; *cr:* Cleveland Pub Schls Tchr of Hearing-Impaired 1966-69, Tchr Head Start Presch 1968, Tchr Adult Ed 1967-69; IN St Schl of Deaf K-1 Tchr H-I 1969-71; Kent City Schls Tchr of Hearing-Impaired 1972-; *ai:* Kent Tchr Assn 1975-, Trustee; Delta Kappa Gamma Gamma Epsilon Chptr 1983-; Great Trail Cncl, Den Ldr; Cub Scouts 1987-, Cubmaster, Comm Chair, Cubmaster Awd; *office:* Roosevelt HS 1400 N Mantua St Kent OH 44240

RHODES, MARGARET ANNE BATTIN, Ninth Grade English Teacher; *b:* Youngstown, OH; *m:* Bill L.; *c:* Thomas K. James, David B. James, Amy M. James; *ed:* Hiram Coll (BA) Sociology & Pol Sci 1962; Youngstown Univ PG Eng, Tchng Cert; Univ of Akron PG Grad Stud, Rdng Cert; *cr:* Joseph Badger Pub Schls; Boardman Pub Schls; Akron Pub Schls; Field Local Schls; *ai:* Former 7th & 8th Grd Chrldr Adv; FLTA 1985-; OEA 1985-; NEA 1985-; *office:* Field Jr HS 1379 Saxe Rd Mogadore OH 44260

RHODES, MARJORIE L., Sixth Grade Teacher; *b:* Celina, OH; *m:* Sam; *c:* Mark, Timothy, Stephen, Gregg; *ed:* Bowling Green St Univ (BA) Elem Ed 1972; IN Univ (MS) Elem Rdng 1981; 30 Hrs Post Grad Stud; *cr:* Cntrl Local Schl Dist Fifth-Sixth Grd Tchr 1967-; *ai:* Tchr Mentoring Prgm; Bldg Rep; Lang Arts Curr Comm; NEA, OH Ed Assn 1970-; TACLS Local Ed Assn 1970-, Exec Sec; Sunday Schl Tchr; Bible Schl Dir, Tchr; Golden Apple Ashland Oil Tchr Achvmt Awd; Martha Holden Jennings Scholar; Lesson Plans Pub; *office:* Fairview MS Rt 1 06289 US #127 Sherwood OH 43556

RHODES, MARK ALLEN, PE Department Head & Teacher; *b:* Celina, OH; *m:* Debra Lou Edwards; *c:* Brady, Brock; *ed:* Defiance Coll (BA) PE 1980; FL St Univ Post Grad Stud; *cr:* Home Savings & Loan Assn Loan Dept Mgr 1981-86; Oakwood Elem Schl PE Tchr 1987-92; Paulding HS PE Tchr 1993-; *ai:* Jr HS Ftbl, Girls Var BsktblHead Coach; Paulding HS Fac Cncl 1995-; Paulding Ed Assn 1987-; OH HS Bsktbl Coaches Assn 1988-; Free Chrstn Church of God 1985-; *home:* 7683 US Highway 127 Sherwood OH 43556

RHODES, MARY BELIN, Mathematics Teacher; *b:* Scranton, PA; *c:* Anthony L.B., Victoria R. Gutpreund, William C.; *ed:* Swarthmore Coll (BA) Ec & Math 1958; Wilkes Univ (MS) Math 1977; *cr:* Tunkhannock Area HS Math Tchr 1961-63; Lackawanna Trail HS Math Tchr 1963-64; Scranton Cntrl HS Math Tchr 1964-66; Abington Heights HS Math Tchr 1966-; *ai:* Scholastic Quiz Prgm Adv; Problem of the Week Admin; nCTM, PCTM 1989-; NPCTM 1989-, Contest Chm; Wilkes Univ 1980-, Stud Affairs Chair; Abington Twp Planning Comm 1975-; Employment Opportunity and Trng Ctr 1988-, Treas; Consultant for AP Calculus; *office:* Abington Heights HS Noble Rd Clarks Summit PA 18411*

RHODES, ROBERT HARLAN, Hum Teacher & Team Leader; *b:* Cleveland, OH; *ed:* Sarah Lawrence Coll (BA) Soc Sci 1990; Working Toward Masters in Urban Admin at Fordham Univ; *cr:* Alternative HS Tchr 1990-93; Schl of Future Hum Tchr & Team Ldr 1993-; *ai:* Bsktbl Coach; Fac Hiring Comm; Dist 2 Stans Group; United Fed of Tchrs 1990-, Schl Rep 1995; Coalition of Essential Schls 1993-; 1993 NEH Inst Grant Folklore; 1992 NEH Seminar Grant Art in Great Depression; *office:* Schl Of The Future 127 E 22nd St New York NY 10010

RHODES, STANLEY WILLIAMS, Physics Teacher; *b:* Syracuse, NY; *m:* Hilda Wright; *c:* Robin E. Astor, Ellen T. Evans, Heather Williams; *ed:* Amherst Coll (BA) Psych 1960; Syracuse Univ (MED) Sci Ed 1961; Fairfield Univ Ed Admin 1977; Attnd Rutgers 1963, Temple 1965, CO 1966; *cr:* Lewis S. Mills Regnl #10 Sci Tchr 1961-66; Staples HS Sci Tchr 1966-72, Asst Headmaster 1972-80, Admin Asst 1980-81, Sci Division Coord 1981-; *ai:* Tech, Arena Comms; Smartnet Think Tank; Cooperating Tchr; NEA, CEA, WEA 1961-, Bldg Rep; NSTA, CSTA, AAPT, NSLEA 1961-; ASCD 1985-; Redding Land Trust 1980-; Redding Republican Town Comm 1992-; Staples Governing Bd 1975-, Treas, Whip, Vice Chair, Chair; Cert of Support CT Bus, Industry Educl Fnd; Who's Who in Amer Educators 1988-89; Distinguished Tchr White House Commission on Presidential Scholars 1994; *office:* Staples HS 70 North Ave Westport CT 06880*

RHODES, THOMAS MICHAEL, Professor of Mathematics; *b:* Gallipolis, OH; *m:* Debra Kay Marcum; *ed:* Rio Grande Coll (BS) Math 1967; Univ of Notre Dame (MS) Math 1971; The OH St Univ (PHD) Math Ed 1983; *cr:* Zane Trace HS Math Tchr 1967-70; Rio Grande Coll Math Prof 1971-80; The OH St Univ Math Grad Tchng Asst 1980-83; Univ of Rio Grande Math Prof 1984-; *ai:* NCTM; OCTM; MAA; OMELC; Chi Beta Phi; Awds: Zane Schl Dist Tchr of Yr 1970, Univ of Rio Grande Edwin A Jones Excl in Tchng, Alumni Citation for Tchng 1986 & 1992; NSF Acad Schlshp 1970-71; Whos Who Among Amer Coll Stu 1967; *office:* Univ Of Rio Grande College Ave Rio Grande OH 45674

RHODY, DAVID, Latin Teacher; *ed:* Coll of Wooster (BA) Greek, Latin 1966; Villanova Univ (MA) Greek, Latin 1980; Attnd Rutgers Law Schl for JD 1990, Amer Acad of Rome; *cr:* Orrville Pub Schls Latin Tchr 1966-67; Moorestown Pub Schl Latin Tchr 1967-; *ai:* Latin Club; Previous Track Coach, Hnr & Svc Soc, Class Adv; NEA, NJEA1967-; MEA 1967-, VP 1990-93; NJ Classical Assn 1967-, Pres 1994; CAAS, PCA, PCS 1980-; Phi Beta Kappa 1966-; NJCA Edna White Rome Scholar 1984; Villanova Univ Alumni Awd 1990; *office:* Moorestown HS Bridgeboro Rd Moorestown NJ 08057

RHONE, DARLENE BANKS, Biology & Anatomy Teacher; *b:* Jamaica, NY; *m:* Darryl; *c:* Darryl, Darnell; *ed:* Morgan St Univ (BS) Bio 1980; Wilson Tech Schl LPN 1976; *cr:* Sacred Heart HS Sci Tchr 1989-; *ai:* Talent Show Moderator; NHS Comm; Natl Assn of Microscopy 1982-; *office:* Sacred Heart HS 21 N East Ave Vineland NJ 08360

RHOTEN, LINDA DUTTON, 5th Grade Teacher; *b:* Findlay, OH; *m:* James Allan; *c:* Alisha; *ed:* OH Northern Univ (BS) Elem Ed 1969; Bowling Green (MS) Media Specialist 1978; Doctoral Hrs Elem Guid Mt St Josephs, BGSU; *cr:* Van Buren 3rd Grd Tchr 1969-77, 4th Grd Tchr 1978-87, 5th Grd Tchr 1988-; *ai:* VBEA 1970-, Sec, Treas, Vp; OEA, NEA 1970-; *office:* Van Buren Middle-HS PO Box 229 Van Buren OH 45889

RHYASON, RODNEY CURRIE, High School English Teacher; *b:* Macklin SK, CN; *m:* Elizabeth Stolee; *c:* Jeff A., Jill K.; *ed:* Univ of Calgary (BED) Scndry Eng 1972; Univ of Lethbridge (DED) Scndry Eng 1991; *cr:* LaCrete Schl Jr, Sr HS Eng Tchr 1973-76; Hanna Jr HS Eng Tchr 1976-80; J. C. Chory Hanna Schl HS Eng Tchr 1980-; *ai:* 12 Grd Grad Adv; ATA, ELAC 1972-; *home:* Box 1064 Hanna AB T0J 1P0 Canada CN

RIB, PATRICIA LYNN (SCHENCK), IPS, Physical Science Tchr; *b:* Vineland, NJ; *c:* Matthew, Jonathan; *ed:* Glassboro St Coll (BA) Phys Sci, Chem 1979; *cr:* Cumberland Regnl HS Earth Sci Tchr 1980; Buena Regnl HS Math, Sci Tchr 1980-81; Landis Intermediate IPS, 7-8th C 1986-; *ai:* 8th Grd Field Trip, Recognition Ceremony, Dance, Lab Comms; NEA, NJEA, VEA 1986-; *office:* Landis Schl 61 W La Vineland NJ 08360

RIBAR, MARGARITA, Associate Professor of Spanish; *b:* Bucar Columbia; *m:* Frank; *c:* Edward Frank, Juliana Margarita, Teresa *ed:* Ministerio Educacion Nacional (BA) Scndry Ed 1961; Duques (MA) Span Lit 1968; 36 Post Grad Credit Hrs in Span Amer Lit Pittsburgh; *cr:* Duquesne Univ Span Instr 1987-88; CA Univ of Instr 1985-90, Asst Prof of Span 1990-92, Assoc Prof of Span 1 Senate Mem; Intnl Ed Cncl Rep; Span Club Adv; Frgn Lang & C Evaluation & Election Comms; Western PA Symposium on W 1986-, Advy Bd; Phi Sigma Iota 1990-; Alpha Mu GAmma 19 Mem; Women's Consortium of the PA St System of Higher Ed 199 Hispanic Stu Org 1995-, Adav; Eberly Fnd 1996, Interpreter, Tra Presented a Concert by Cuarteto Latinoamericano in Cooperation Vira I. Heinz Endowment of Pittsburgh; Created 12 Courses in Stud Cultures; *office:* California Univ Of PA 250 University Ave Califo 15419

RIBO, MARILYN RUTH (YOUNG), French Teacher; *b:* Kent, Joel; *c:* Michael, Meredyth Ribo Makris, Erin; *ed:* Kent St Univ 1965; Cmptr Courses; *cr:* Kent Roosevelt HS Fr Tchr 1965; Clayr Fr Tchr 1965-69, 1981-; *ai:* Fr Club Adv; AATF 1981-; *office:* C HS 215 E 6th St Uhrichsville OH 44683

RICARDS, LYNDA DAWSON, Seventh-Eighth Grade Teac Trenton, NJ; *m:* Bruce Barton; *ed:* Union Coll (BA) Elem Ed 19 Scout Ldr 6 Yrs; Jerseymen Club Advd; Curr Cncl; *cr:* Whisperi Elem Schl First Grd Tchr 4 Yrs; New England Towne Day Sch Fourth Grds Tchr 4 Yrs; Bridgeton MS Fifth Grd Tchr 4 Yrs; St Schl Seventh & Eighth Grd Tchr 2 Yrs; Hopewell Crest Schl Sev Eighth Grd Tchr 9 Yrs; *ai:* Girl Scout Ldr 6 Yrs; Jerseyman Club A Cncl; NJEA, NEA 1976-; GSOA 1985-, Ldr, 10 Yr Awd; Governo of Yr 1993; *office:* Hopewell Crest Schl 122 Sewall Rd Bridg 08302*

RICCI, ANNALEA, Science Department Chair; *b:* Manhattan, Kenneth; *c:* Marco, Lea, Maria; *ed:* Good Counsel Coll (BS) Che Adelphi Univ (MS) Chem 1970; 20 Addl Grad Credit Hrs; *cr* Counsel Acad Math & Sci Tchr 1967-68; Msgr Scanlan HS Chem Tchr 1969-77; Preston HS Chem & Physics Tchr 1978-86; Schl of t Child Chem & Physics Tchr 1986-; Astro & Bioethics Tchr 1993-; Moderator; Sr Class Adv; NHS Adv; STANYS, ALCHEME, Physics Tchrs Club & Chem Tchrs Club; St Augustines Church, 1987-, Eucharistic Minister 1987-, Parish Cncl; Preston HS Alum Steering Comm Holy Child Schls; Woodrow Wilson Fellowship i 1988-, Physics 1989-92; *office:* School Of The Holy Child Westches Rye NY 10580

RICCI, BARBARA ROSE, Fourth Grade Teacher; *b:* Philadelph *ed:* West Chester Univ (BS) Elem Ed 1955; Temple Univ (MS) Gen 1958; Addl 30 Credit Hrs at Univ of the Arts at Philadelphia; *cr:* B Hannah Schl 6th Grd Tchr 1955-58; Anthony Wayne Schl 4th G 1959-65; Chester A Arthur Schl 4th & 5th Grd Tchr 1966-; *ai* Writing Comm; Sci Fair Chprsn; Square Dancing Club; Sci Combined Campaign Chprsn; AFT 1967-, Bldg Rep; Columbus 1970-; Rose Lindenbaum Tchr of Yr Awd 1982; *office:* Chester A Elem Schl 20th & Catharine Sts Philadelphia PA 19146

RICCIARDULLI, SARA LEE (HORVATH), Spanish & English T *b:* Youngstown, OH; *w:* Nicholas J. (dec); *c:* Laura, Nico Youngstown St Univ (MS) Ed, Span 1982; *cr:* John F. Kennedy HS Eng Tchr 1971-76, 1979-; *ai:* Foreign Lang Dept Chprsn; OH Foreig Assn 1990-; NCEA; *office:* John F Kennedy H S 2550 Central Park Warren OH 44484*

RICCIO, JESSICA, 1st Grade Teacher; *b:* Brooklyn, NY; *ed:* S Univ (BS) Ed 1985; Coll of Staten Island (MS) Early Chldhd; *cr:* Tchr 1985-; *ai:* PTA Tchr of Yr 1995; *home:* 28 Bay 20th St Brook 11214*

RICCO, BERNADETTE DEIERLEIN, Coord of Gifted & Talen New Rochelle, NY; *c:* Kevin, David; *ed:* Felician Coll (BA) Spec, Elem Ed-Summa Cum Laude 1980; Coll of New Rochelle (MSEd) Ed-Outstanding Grad Awd 1989; NY Inst of Tech, Coll of St Rose Grad Credits in Gifted Ed, Telecommunications, Self Esteem, Coun Admin; *cr:* Norwood Pub Schl Dist Gifted & Talented Programming 1980-; Gifted Child Soc Curr Coord, In-Svc Instr, Fac 1983-88; New Rochelle Grad Schl Adjunct Fac 1989-90; Fairleigh Dickinso Master Tchr, Trainer 1993-94; Tenafly Pub Schl Dist Summer Enric Instr 1993-; *ai:* Acad Pentathlon, Knowledge Master Open Coach; Interdisciplinary Approach Planning, Time Comms; Focus Group; N for Gifted Children 1990-; Bergen Cty Consortium for Tchrs of 1993-, Historian, Research Librn; Bergen Brain Busters Consortium NEA 1980-; Norwood Ed Assn 1980-, Exec Bd; Franklin Schl Parent 1995-; ASCD Natl Conf 1993-94, NJ Assn for Gifted Children S 1993 Presenter; Northern Valley Ed Fnd Mini Grant Awds; Acad Pen Prgm 1994, The Suitcase Project 1993; Whos Who of Amer 1995-96; Outstanding Grad Awd New Rochelle Coll 1989; *office:* No Public Schl 177 Summit St Norwood NJ 07648

RICE, AGNES M., Retired Kindergarten Teacher; *b:* Newark, Arthur (dec); *c:* Linda Miller, Diane Tilley, Arthur K., Robert (dec); Antoninus Grammer Schl 1st Grd Tchr 1969-74; St Michael's Gr SchlKndgtn Tchr 1974-94; *ai:* Kearny Vol Emergentcy Rescue Auxiliary; *home:* 259 Maple St Kearny NJ 07032

RICE, ANGELA SWANSON, English Teacher; *b:* Washington, D DC Tchrs Coll (BA) Span, Eng 1976; Univ of DC (MA) HRD, Ad 1988; Diploma Universidad de Valencia Spain; *cr:* Rabaut Jr HS Spa 1977-78; Marie Reed MS Eng Tchr 1978-80; Jefferson Jr HS Eng 1980-; *ai:* Coord Best Friends Prgm; Asst Girls Sftbl Coach; Eng Chrprsn; WA Tchrs Union 1977-; AFT 1977-; GEFFEDS 1993-; Recognition Contributions Best Friends Prgm; Best Frnds Frndshp *office:* Jefferson Jr HS 8th & H Sts Sw Washington DC 20024

RICE, BOB, History & Social Sciences Tchr; *b:* New York City, N Saint Bonaventure Univ (BA) His 1971; Univ of South FL (MA) S 1982; Northeastern Univ, Goddard Coll, Western IL Univ Grad & Ind *cr:* Nauset Regnl Tchr 1972-; Brown Univ Inst for Scndry Ed Tchng Vietnam Seminar Co-Ldr 1986; *ai:* Schl Philosophy Comm Mem; 1972-; MTA 1972-, Local VP; Intnl Stud Inst Schlsp 1982; Phi Kapp Honor Soc at USF; Fac Senate Pres; Brown Univ Inst for Scndry E Comm Mem; Past Pres of MA Girls Soccer Coaches; *office:* N Regional HS Cable Rodd North Eastham MA 02631

RICE, CHARLES KEVIN, 7th Grade Science Teacher; *b:* Huntir WV; *ed:* Georgetown Coll (BS) PE, Sci 1980; *cr:* Chesapeake Sch Grd Sci Tchr 1985-; *ai:* Head Bsbl Coach; NEA 1985-; *office:* Chesa Vlg Schls 10181 CR 1 Chesapeake OH 45619

RICE, DOUG F., Asst Professor of English; *b:* Pittsburgh, PA; *m:* A. Birch; *c:* Cory, AnnaLivia; *ed:* Slippery Rock St Univ (BA) Eng Duquesne Univ (MA) Eng 1984; ABD Univ of Pittsburgh Eng Duquesne Univ Eng Instr 1982-84; Univ of Pittsburgh Eng Instr 19 La Roche Coll Eng Instr 1984-90; Kent St Univ Eng Asst Prof 1990-

1984-; AAUP 1995-; NCTE 1994-; Univ Tchng Cncl Grant; Novel n; Casebook on Raymond Federman Co-Ed with Larry McCaffery; Stories in Fiction Intnl, Avant Pop, Black Ice, Cups, New Novel v, Spitting Image; Ed NOBDDADDies; *office:* Kent St Univ Salem 2491 State Route 45 S Salem OH 44460

, ELAINE DAVEY, English Teacher & Dept Chair; *b:* Plattsburgh, : Philip E.; *c:* Davey R., Marcia E.; *ed:* SUNY at Plattsburgh (BS) Scndry, Eng 1961; SUNY at Albany (MS) Eng, Ed 1963; Addl Hrs at Plattsburgh; *cr:* Dolgeville Cntrl Schl 7-8 Grd Eng Tchr 1961-62; Colonie Cntrl Schl Grd 7 Tchr 1963-65; Beekmantown Cntrl Schl 3rd Eng Tchr 1965-; *ai:* NYSEC; NYSUT 1961-; BTA 1965-; Delta Gamma 1992-.

, EUGENE DONALD, Chairman of Liberal Arts; *b:* Manchester, : Natalie Ciechon; *c:* Katherine Dwyer, Matthew LaPointe, Karoline nte; *ed:* Saint Anselm Coll (BA) Fr & Philosophy 1952; NY Univ Ger 1959; Attnd Univ of Munich, Fordham Univ, Middlebury Coll; int Anselm Coll Prof of Ger, Film & Hum 1959-81; NH Tech Coll Hum Instr 1983-; *ai:* Acad Deans Advy Cncl; The Thinking Club & al Thinking Wkshps Coord; NCTE 1984-; Natl Cncl for Excl in al Thinking 1992-; Phi Theta Kappa; 2 Paid Govt Trips to Germany; al Critical Thinking Seminars in Boston; Trng for Critical Thinking rs Wkshp at Sonoma St Univ; *office:* NH Tech Coll At Manchester Front St Manchester NH 03102*

, GARY LYNN, Scndry Math Tchr & Dept Head; *b:* Russellville, : Judy Elaine Godfrey; *c:* Lindsey, Michael; *ed:* AR Tech (BS) Math (MED) Math 1983; *cr:* S Conway Cty Schl Dist Math & Comp Sci 1980-86; Family Chrstn Acad Math & Comp Sci Tchr & Dept Chair 92; Donelson Chrstn Acad Comp Sci Tchr & Tech Coord 1992-93; nnati Chrstn Schls Math Tchr & Dept Chair 1993-; *ai:* NCTM; *home:* Haverstraw Dr Cincinnati OH 45241

, GENE, Prof of Old Testament Lang; *b:* Middlesboro, KY; *m:* Betty Smith; *c:* Jane Hilary Rice Acosta, Jonathan Gregory; *ed:* Berea Coll His, Philosophy 1951; Union Theological Seminary (MDIV) Old nent 1954; Columbia Univ (PHD) Old Testament 1969; Attnd Univ idelberg; *cr:* Howard Univ Schl of Divinity Prof of Old Testament & Lit 1958-; *ai:* Citihope Intnl; Who's Who in Biblical Stud & eology 1993; Soc of Biblical Lit 1964-; Soc of Biblical Lit Atlantic Region 1964-, Pres; Christ Episcopal Church; Nations Under Eerdmans 1990; Articles Pup; *office:* Howard Univ Schl of Divinity Sheperd St NE Washington DC 20017

, JAMES A., Fourth Grade Teacher; *b:* Bowling Green, OH; *m:* een Melling; *c:* Lauren Motrunecs, Lisa, Leslie Pfaff, David; *ed:* ing Green St Univ (BS) Elem Ed 1964; Cleveland St Univ (MED) Ed, n 1979; Post Grad Hrs Admin; *cr:* Parma City Schls 6th Grd Tchr 65; Maple Hts City Schls 6th Grd Tchr 1965-69; Bedford City Schls h Grd Tchr 1971-; *ai:* Intervention Assistance Team; PTA Tchr Rep; OEA, BEA 1964-; Bedford Kiwanis Club 1979-; Bedford Historical 1975-, Treas; Bedford First Meth Church 1975-; Amer Bowling ress 1980-, Pres; *home:* 111 Grand Blvd Bedford OH 44146

, JAMES F., Social Studies Teacher; *b:* Brooklyn, NY; *m:* Lorraine Lorraine Rice Meyer, James F., Terrence, Christine Rice Guilholey; Johns UC (BA) His 1959; Hofstra U (MS) Cnslr Ed 1972; Credits klyn Coll & LIU; *cr:* Eastern Dist HS Tchr 1959-60; Marine Park JHS 1960-63; Eastern Dist HS Tchr 1963-67; Levittown Schl Dist #5 Tchr -; *ai:* Bsbl Coach; Levittown Swim Assn 1968-, Coach; *home:* 7 ght Ln Levittown NY 11756

E, JAMES MICHAEL, 7th Grade Math Teacher; *b:* Worcester, MA; ancy G. Patnode; *c:* Emily, Matthew, Joseph; *ed:* Univ of MA at erst (BS) Sport Mngmt 1984; Worcester St Coll (MS) Ed 1994; Post Ed Cert Worcester St Coll 1984-86; *cr:* W.E. Balmer Elem Schl Grd th, Lang Arts Tchr 1986-91; Northbridge MS Grd 6 Math, Lang Arts 1991-94; King Philip North Jr HS Grd 7 Math Tchr 1994-; *ai:* Ftbl h, Defensive Coord Northbridge HS; IM Involvement; NCTM 1992-; e Lang Tchrs Assn; NEA 1986-; Northbridge Schl Cncl 1993-94; Ath ter Club; Alliance for Ed Grant; *home:* 26 Marywood St Uxbridge MA 9

E, JOHN M., Sixth Grade Teacher; *b:* Watertown, NY; *m:* Ella Black; arie, Ann, John III; *ed:* Rider Coll (BS) Ed 1960; Cert in Elem Ed from on St Coll & St Lawrence Univ; Georgetown Ct Coll Physics & ronment; NSF; *cr:* N Hanover Twp Bd of Ed 4th Grd Tchr 1960-66; rtown Bd of Ed 5th Grd Tchr 1966-67; Indian River Bd of Ed HS Math s Tchr 1967-70; Toms River Bd of Ed 6th Grd Tchr 1970-; *ai:* NJ Ed c 1960-; NEA 1960-; NSTA 1960-; Seaside Park Bd of Ed 4 Yrs; ide Park Bd of Adjustment 6 Yrs; Tchr of Yr Recognition Comm; NJ rnors Tchr of the Yr Awd 1989; Natl Sci Tchrs Honororom.

E, JUDITH S., Mathematics Teacher; *b:* Philadelphia, PA; *m:* Alfred; niv of PA (BS) Math 1954; *cr:* Philadelphia Schl Dist Tchr 1954-58; rford Schl Dist Tchr 1971-; *ai:* Assist with Speech & Debate Club; A, NEA, ATMO PAV 1971-; League of Women Voters of Haverford 1969-, Tres, Pres; Haverford Twp Civic Cncl 1969-; Tchr of Year rford HS 1985-86; *office:* Haverford Twp Schl Dist 200 Mill Rd rtown PA 19083*

E, MARILYN ANN, Physical Education Teacher; *b:* Bangor, ME; *ed:* of ME (BS) PE 1971; *cr:* Fifth Street MS PE Tchr 1971-; *ai:* Bsktbl h; Intramurals Supvr; MAHPERD 1985-; *office:* Fifth Street MS 143 St Bangor ME 04401

E, PETER EDMUND, Social Studies Teacher; *b:* Pittsburgh, PA; *m:* Miller; *c:* Wynn, Kathryn; *ed:* Washington & Jefferson (BA) Ec 1981; of Pittsburgh (MA) Ec 1985; Ed Cert 1992; *cr:* PA Governor's Schl 1992; Franklin Regnl Schl Dist Tchr 1992-; *ai:* Mock Trial; Model ed Nations; Site Cncl; Curr Review Comm; NEA 1992-; PA Assn of s & Tchr Edctrs Stu Tchr of Yr; *office:* Franklin Regnl Schl Dist 4660 William Penn Hwy Murrysville PA 15668

E, SANDRA MCKENNEY, Special Education Tchrs Aide; *b:* Star ; NY; *m:* James L.; *c:* Jodi L., James L. Jr.; *ed:* Univ of WI 6 Credit Childrens Lit, Exceptional Individual; *cr:* Community Bank Head er 1970-74; Clifton-Fine Cntrl Schl Cafeteria 1983-88, Tchrs Aide 3-; *office:* Clifton Fine Central Schl PO Box 75 Star Lake NY 13690

E, THEODORE DELANO, Pre K-6th Grade Art Teacher; *b:* hington, DC; *m:* Carolyn Elaine Dunmore; *c:* Yasmin Elaine Ria, hael Brianna, Nicole Alexandria; *ed:* Tyler Schl of Art Temple Univ) Photography, Art Ed 1978; Univ of DC (MS) Adult Ed 1986; *cr:* DC Schls Art Tchr 1979-84; DC Dept of Corrections Art Educl Specialist 4-86; DC Pub Schls Art Tchr 1986-; *ai:* Art Club Spon; NAEA 1993-; 1981-; Takoma Restructuring Team 1995-, Parent Rep; Bd of Chrstn 1995-; *home:* 5745 9th St NW Washington DC 20011*

E, THERESA RICCARDI, Math Teacher; *b:* Syracuse, NY; *m:* H. ert; *c:* Angela, Marc, Jeffrey, Anthony; *ed:* SUCO at Oswego (BS) dry Ed, Math 1971; Permanent Cert Oswego 1977 30 Hrs; *cr:* Liverpool Math Tchr 1971-80; Westhill HS Math Tchr 1985-92; Cicero-North acuse Math Tchr 1992-; *ai:* Acad Decathlon Coach; Comm nnections, Time Mngmt, Tchng Strategies Comms; Bldg Planning Team; 1971-; N Syr Tchrs, AMTNYS, Onon Co Math Tchrs 1992-; *office:* ero-North Syracuse HS Rt 31 Cicero NY 13212

RICE, VERNON DALE, Health & Physical Ed Teacher; *b:* Sellersville, PA; *m:* Jeanette Kay Eicher Rice; *c:* Timothy, Thomas, Shawn, Sheldon, Vanessa; *ed:* Hesston Coll (AA) 1970; Goshen Coll (BS) Hlth & PE 1972; West Chester Univ (MED) Hlth & PE 1976; Post Grad Stud at Millersville Univ & Sports Acad; *cr:* Lancaster Mennonite HS Tchr & Coach 1972-; *ai:* Boys Var Soccer Coach 1972-; Girls Var Soccer Coach 1990-; Hlth & PE Dept Chprsn; NSCAA 1975-; PSCA Coach of Yr; LLSCA 1981-, VP, 2 Yrs & Coach of Yr Several Times; LLGSCA 1990-, Pres 2 Yrs, Coach of Yr Several Times; Forest Hills Mennonite Church 1975-; Working for MCC 2 Yrs; 1 Wk for Habitat for Humanity; *home:* 48 Lancaster Ave Strasburg PA 17579*

RICE, WILLIAM CRAIG, Expository Writing Preceptor; *b:* Washington, DC; *m:* Carolina Agravante Reyes; *ed:* Univ of VA (BA) Eng 1975; Univ of MI (MFA) Creative Writing 1988, (PHD) Eng 1991; *cr:* Webb Schl Eng Instr 1975-76; Univ of PA Eng Lecturer 1982-83; Temple Univ Eng Instr 1984-86; Harvard Univ Expository Writing Preceptor, Arts & Scis Fac 1992-; *ai:* Assoc Writing Prmgs, Natl Assn Scholars 1983-; Assoc Literary Scholars & Critics 1993-; Pub Book: Public Discourse and Academic Inquiry 1996; Articles, Poems, Stories Pub; *office:* Harvard Univ Vanserg Hall 25 Francis Ave Cambridge MA 02138

RICE, WILLIAM STANTLEY,III, Mathematics Professor; *b:* Washington, DC; *m:* Shebbie Robinson; *c:* David, Alexis, Rahima; *ed:* Yale Coll (AB) Math 1969; Harvard Univ (MAT) Math 1971; *cr:* Roxbury Latin Schl Math Tchr 1969-70; Univ of DC Math Prof 1971-; *ai:* NCTM 1971-; NEA 1980-; Amer Statistical Assn 1990-; All Souls Unitarian Church 1980-; *office:* Univ Of The Dist Of Columbia 4200 Connecticut Ave NW Washington DC 20008

RICH, CAROLE WELLS, 6th Grade Homeroom Teacher; *b:* Cincinnati, OH; *m:* Paul E.; *c:* Bruce, Brian, Leslie A. Downs, Ficki L. Charles; *ed:* Edgecliff Coll (BA) Ed 1978; 18 Post Grad Credits Learning Disabilities Cert 1978; *cr:* St Cecilia Schl 7th Grd Tchr 1962-63, 1976-87; St Ursula Villa Schl 8th Grd Tchr 1987-88; St Vincent Ferrer Schl 6th Grd Homeroom, 7th-8th Grd S S Tchr 1988-; *ai:* Adv, Chaperone OH Stu United Nations Assembley 1994-95; 2 Charles Taft Grants; *office:* St Vincent Ferrer Schl 7754 Montgomery Rd Cincinnati OH 45236

RICH, CYNTHIA GABLE, Third Grade Teacher; *b:* Jamestown, NY; *m:* David G.; *ed:* St Univ at Fredonia (BA) Elem Ed, Eng 1967, (MS) Remedial Rdng, Elem 1971; Univ of Buffalo (EDD) Elem Ed, Rdng, Gifted, Talented, Early Child 1989; Attnd St Univ at Brockport, KY Univ, Canisus, Coll at St Rose; *cr:* Ft Carson Elem Second Grd Tchr 1967-68; Frewsburg Cntrl Schl Third Grd Tchr 1968-; Univ of Buffalo Part-time Ed Tchr 1987-88; *ai:* Parent Stu Tchr Org; Schl Advy, Rdng, Book Selection, Self-Esteem, Tchr Selection, Cncl Spec Ed Negotiations Comms; Chldr Adv; Phi Delta Kappa 1974-, Rec Sec, Historian, VP, Educator & Researcher of Yr 1988; Amer Assn Univ WOmen 1974-, Rec Sec, Membership Chair; Bus & Prof Women 1988-, New & Young Careerist; NYSUT, IRA 1968-; Pi Lambda Theta 1980-; Delta Kappa Gamma 1988-; Kiwanis 1989-, Pres, Pediatric Trauma Ctr Chair, Disting: Pres & Club & 4 Times Mem; Kiwanis Wives Club 1974-, Pres, Disting Pres; Little Theater of Jamestown 1968-, Patron Mem; Order Easter Star 1978-, Aso Matron; Consistory Auxiliary 1978-; Green Thumb Garden Club 1988-; United Meth Church Jamestown 1966-, Educl Commission, Alter Guild, Parish Commission, Exec Bd, UMW; Who's Who: Women Exec, Women in Amer, Amer Ed, Women in World, Amer; Edctr of the Yr 1988; Rsrchr of the Yr 1988; *home:* 4129 Alm Rd Bemus Point NY 14712*

RICH, DON R., Finance Professor; *b:* Pontiac, IL; *ed:* Univ of IL (BS) 1988, (MS) 1989; VA Tech (PHD) 1993; *office:* Northeastern Univ 418 Hayden Hall Boston MA 02115

RICH, EVERETT, Assoc Prof of Communication; *b:* New Brunswick, NJ; *m:* Ellen Reynolds; *c:* Adam, David; *ed:* Emerson Coll (BS) Speech 1964, (MS) Speech Ed 1968; *cr:* Monmouth Univ Assoc Prof of Communication 1966-; *ai:* Oral Interpretation Festival Dir; Radio Station Adv; Natl Broadcasting Soc 1990-, St Dir; Most Distngd Tchr 1985; Sears-Roebuck Fnd Tchng Excl 1991; Stdnts Choice Awd Best Tchr 1986, 1989, 1991; Two 1st Pl Radio documentary Awds from NBS; *office:* Monmouth Univ Cedar Ave West Long Branch NJ 07764

RICH, KAREN ST PIERRE, Math Teacher & Dept Chair; *b:* St Albans, VT; *m:* David J.; *c:* Jason, Shawn, Adam, Aaron; *ed:* Univ of VT (BA) Math 1970, (MED) Tchr Ed 1982; 30+ Credit Hrs Post Grad Stud Beyond MS; *cr:* Essex HS Math Tchr 1970-82, Math Tchr & Dept Chr 1982-; *ai:* Sr Class Adv; Hnrs Night Chair; Schl Climate Comm; Adj Prof UVM; Schl Cncl Co-Chair; SAT Prep Course Tchr; EJEA, VEA & NEA 1970-, Rep; VCTM & NCTM 1975-, Reader for Math Tchr; ATMNE 1975-; Yth Ftbl 1982-84, Pres; UVM Partnership 1993-, Bd Mem; Alpha Delta Kappa 1993-, Comm Chair; Tchr of the Yr; Yrbk Dedication; Finalist Presidential Awd 3 Times; IBM Intern VT Math Coalition; Presdential Scholars Tchr Recognition; *office:* Essex Junction HS 2 Educational Dr Essex Junction VT 05452*

RICH, KERRY ANN, Mathematics Teacher; *b:* Buffalo, NY; *ed:* SUNY at Buffalo (BA) Math 1990, (EDM) Educl Psych 1992, (PHD) Educl Psych 1996; *cr:* Frontier Cntrl HS Math Tchr 1993-; *ai:* NYSC & TE 1988-; NCTM 1989-; Dissertation SUNY at Buffalo 1995; *office:* Frontier Sr HS 4432 Bayview Rd Hamburg NY 14075*

RICH, SUSAN J., Child Studies Program Coord; *b:* Watertown, NY; *m:* Andrew Arrison; *ed:* SUNY at Cortland (BA) Elem Ed 1972; U of VT (MED) Early Chldhd 1978; Boston Univ 48 Credit Hrs EDD; *cr:* Boston Univ Tchng Asst 1986-87; Sharon Pub Schls Kndgtn Tchr 1985-86; Dean Coll Asst Prof 1985-, Child Stud Coord 1991-; *ai:* NAEYC 1982-; Article Pub; *office:* Dean Coll 99 Main St Franklin MA 02038

RICHARD, GEORGE CHARLES, Social Studies Teacher; *b:* Fitchburg, MA; *m:* Lee Twarog; *c:* Jessica, Amanda; *ed:* Fitchburg St (BS) Ed 1968, (MS) Ed 1972; *cr:* Ashby HS Soc Stud Tchr 1968-72; North Middlesex Regnl HS Soc Stud Tchr 1972-, Dept Chprsn 1982-89; *ai:* MA Tchrs Assn, NEA 1968-; *office:* North Middlesex Regional HS Main St Townsend MA 01469

RICHARD, JANET, Mathematics Teacher; *b:* Paterson, NJ; *m:* Robert; *ed:* SUC at Brockport (BS) Math 1969; 100 Credit Hrs Math, Ed; *cr:* Vestal HS Tchr 1969-77; Shenendehowa Centra Tchr 1977-; *ai:* Chrldr Adv; AMTNYS, NCTM 1969-; NYSUT 1978-; *office:* Shenendehowa HS 970 Route 146 Clifton Park NY 12065

RICHARD, LEE TWAROG, High School English Teacher; *b:* New Bedford, MA; *m:* George; *c:* Jessica, Amanda; *ed:* Fitchburg St Coll (BS) Ed 1969; 16 Addl Credit Hrs; *cr:* Ashby HS Eng Tchr 1969-71; North Middlesex HS Eng Tchr 1971-72 & 1978-; *ai:* NHS Co-Adv; Fac Senate; MTA; NEA 1978-; NCTE; *home:* 92 Wilder Rd Lunenburg MA 01462

RICHARD, LINDA R., Teacher; *b:* Rochester, PA; *m:* Christopher M.; *c:* Heather, Sean; *ed:* Penn St Univ (BS) Eng, Ed 1968, (MED) Eng, Ed 1969; *cr:* North Hills Schl Dist Tchr 1969-; *ai:* NHEA, PSEA, NEA 1969-; Northmont Presbyn Church 1983-, Yth Comm; Girl Scouts of Amer 1988-, Ldr; Thanks to Tchrs Nom 1991; Twice Nom Tchr Excl Awd; *office:* North Hills Sr HS 53 Rochester Rd Pittsburgh PA 15229

RICHARD, ROGER L., History Department Chairman; *b:* New Bedford, MA; *m:* Noreen D. Duesel; *c:* Timothy P.; *ed:* Southeastern MA Univ (BA) His 1975; Univ of NH (MA) His 1976; Worcester St Coll (EDM) Educl Admin 1985; *cr:* Wayland Acad His Instr 1976-77; Worcester Acad His Instr 1977-85; Andrews Schl His Dept Chair 1985-; *ai:* Stu Cncl Adv; Host Family Prgm Dir; Jr Class Adv; Curr, Comm Srv, Sr Project Comm; NCSS 1985-; NASAA 1994-; TESOL 1990-; Gund Fnd Fellow 1988-89; Ashbrook Scholar 1992; Co-Authored Book 1996; *office:* Andrews Schl 38588 Mentor Ave Willoughby OH 44094*

RICHARDI, DONNA T., English Teacher; *b:* Newark, NJ; *m:* Anthony M. Salese; *ed:* Jersey City St Coll (BA) Eng Ed 1977, (MA) Rdng Specialist 1983; St Peter's Coll at Jersey City 32 Hrs Ed; *cr:* St Cecilia HS Eng Tchr 1977-80; Essex Cty Coll GED Instr, Adj 1986-90; Belleville MS Eng Tchr 1980-83, Rdng Tchr 1983-86; Belleville HS Eng Tchr 1986-; *ai:* Girls' Gymnastics Var Coach; Affirmative Action Ofcr; BEA 1980-, Rep; NJEA 1980-; *office:* Belleville HS 100 Passaic Ave Belleville NJ 07109

RICHARDS, ALLISON BROWNING, Latin Tchr; *b:* Philadelphia, PA; *m:* Michael L.; *c:* Edythe A., Elizabeth R.; *ed:* Dickinson Coll (BA) Latin 1966; Univ of DE (MI) Instr 1996; *cr:* Cert & Re-Cert Courses at Temple Univ, DE St Coll & LaSalle Univ; *cr:* Caesar Rodney HS Latin Tchr 1966-67; Allen Frear Elem Schl Librn 1967-71; Wesley Coll Librn 1973-84; Caesar Rodney HS Latin & Part-time Eng Tchr 1985-; *ai:* Latin Club Adv; DE Jr Classical League Adv; NEA & DSEA 1966-71 & 1985-; DE Classical Assn 1985-; Amer Classical League 1985-; Classical Assn of Atlantic Sts 1985-; Vergilian Soc 1987-; Pompeiiana 1987-; Amer & DE Cncl Tchrs of Frgn Lang 1994-; Ed for Soc Responsibility 1988-; DE St Frgn Lang Commission & Ldrshp Team; Golden Key Natl Hnr Soc; *office:* Caesar Rodney HS 239 Old North Rd Camden Wyoming DE 19934*

RICHARDS, BETTY B., Director of Guidance; *b:* Bar Harbor, ME; *c:* Michael, Matthew; *ed:* Univ of Southern ME (BA) Soc Work 1973, Counseling 1975; Rutgers Univ Schl for Alcohol Stud Advanced Stud; St Univ of NY at Buffalo Post MA Stud; *cr:* Fillmore MS Guidance Cnslr 1976-77; Massabesic HS Guidance Dir 1977-; *ai:* Class & Foreign Stu Adv; Amer Counseling Assn 1976-; Natl Assn of Alcoholism & Drug Abuse Cnslrs 1990-; Scarborough Amer Little League 1980-89, Treas; Governors Comm for Employment of Handicapped 1983-90; Court Appointed Spec Advocate 1993-; Excl in Counseling Awd Bentley Coll 1992; Several Articles Pub; *office:* Massabesic HS PO Box 500 West Rd Waterboro ME 04087*

RICHARDS, CHERYL MELLO, Fifth Grade Teacher; *b:* Philadelphia, PA; *m:* James William; *c:* Zachary Wm., Travis Clinton; *ed:* Prince George's Comm Coll (AA) General Stud 1975; Univ of MD (BS) Elem Ed 1976; George Washington Univ (MA) Ed, Human Dev 1985; *cr:* Gale Bailey Elem 4 Grd Tchr 1977-78; J. P. Ryon Elem 3, 5 Grd Tchr 1978-87; Malcolm Elem 5 Grd Tchr 1987-; *ai:* Grd Chprsn; Just Say No Spon; Schl Improvement Team; Tchr Mentor Prgm; Charles Cty Ed Assn 1977-; Little League Team Mom 1991-; Charles Co Bd of Ed Exemplary Svc Awd 1986; *office:* Malcolm Elem Schl 14760 Poplar Hill Rd Waldorf MD 20601*

RICHARDS, CYNDEE ANN, Marketing Teacher & Coord; *b:* Washington, DC; *ed:* Univ MD at College Park (BS) Mrktg Ed 1992; Attnd Towson St Univ 1995-, Essex Comm Coll 1994, Johns Hopkins Univ 1993, Montgomery Coll 1986-88; *cr:* Overlea HS Mrktg Tchr 1993-95; Chesapeake HS Mrktg Tchr 1995-; *ai:* DECA, SHOW Adv; Chrldng, Bsktbl Coach; Stadium Lights Comm; Booster Club; MD Mrktg Ed Assn 1991-, Pres; NEA 1993-; MVA, AVA 1991-; MD DECA 1994-, Bd of Govenors Treas; TABCO Rookie Recognition Awd 1995; MD St Dept of Ed Chapter Awd of Excl 1995; 4 Articles Pub 1995-; *office:* Chesapeake HS 4798 Mountain Rd Pasadena MD 21122*

RICHARDS, DENISE MICHAEL, Former 1st Grade Teacher; *b:* El Dorado, KS; *m:* Frederick Ray; *c:* Dustin F., Sarah F., Rebekah M., John Paul J.; *ed:* Bowling Green St Univ (BS) Elem Ed 1982; *cr:* St Mary Elem Schl 1st, 2nd Grd Tchr 1982-85; Our Lady of Perpetual Help Elem Schl 1st Grd Tchr 1986; St James the Less Elem Schl 1st Grd Tchr 1986-87; *home:* 3905 Saddlehorn Dr Columbus OH 43221

RICHARDS, DIANNE M., 6th Grade Teacher; *b:* Bellefonte, PA; *ed:* Penn St Univ (BS) Ek Ed 1976; *cr:* Bald Eagle Area Schl Dist 6th Grd Tchr 1976-83, 3rd Grd Tchr 1984-94, 6th Grd Tchr 1994-; *home:* 955 Woodland Dr Bellefonte PA 16823

RICHARDS, DONNA RILEY, College Scheduler; *b:* Paterson, NJ; *m:* Oakley E.; *c:* Anne, Jocelyn; *ed:* Goucher Coll (AB) Elem Ed 1961; Columbia Univ Tchrs Coll (MA) Supervision, Curr Improvement 1965; *cr:* Summit Pub Schls Elem Tchr 1961-70; Sussex Co Comm Coll GED Instr 1989-94, Coll Scheduler 1992-; *ai:* Sparta Summer Arts Wkshp Bd of Dirs; *office:* Sussex County Comm Coll College Hill Newton NJ 07860

RICHARDS, EDWARD LAMBERT,JR., English Professor; *b:* New York City, NY; *m:* Paula Ann Gills; *c:* Ernest, Edward, Lucy, Cuyler, Rachel Lignar; *ed:* Yale Univ (BA) Eng 1953; Columbia Univ (MA) Eng 1960; NY Univ (PHD) Eng 1975; *cr:* Greenwich Cntry Day Schl 3rd Grd Eng Tchr 1956-60; NY Maritime Coll Eng Instr 1960-62; Pace Univ Eng Prof 1962-70; Norwich Univ Eng Prof 1970-; *ai:* Coach; Sailing Team; Chair Fac Fin & Benefits, Acad Standing & Degrees Comms; AAUP 1963-, Local Pres; NCTE, MLA 1970-; Unitarian Church Montpelier 1988-, Treas; Norwich Univ Ind Stu Leaves 1979, 1985, 1995-; Biography, Critical Evaluation & Checklist; *office:* Norwich Univ Northfield VT 05663

RICHARDS, JEANETTE M. MAE, 6th Grade Math Teacher; *b:* Salem, OH; *m:* Carl E.; *c:* Thomas L., Susan L., Allen C.; *ed:* Kent St Univ (BS) Ed 1973; 150 Addl Hrs; *cr:* Marlington Schl Dist Migrant Prgm 1972-73; Hartville Elem Schl 1st, 3rd Grd Tchr 1973-, Lake Elem Schl 4th-6th Grd Tchr; *ai:* 6th Grd Bldg Level Team Rep; 6th Grd Lake Local Math Comm; Accelerated Schls Comm Venture Capital; Asselerated Schls, Coaches Trng Sanford Univ 1994; Greater Canton Cncl Tchrs of Math 1989-, Dist Contact Person; Nom Tchr of Yr Greater Canton Chamber of Commerce 1987; Dev First Yrbk Lake Elem 1985; *office:* Lake Elem Sch 225 W Lincoln St Hartville OH 44632

RICHARDS, JUDITH JOHNSON, Third & Fourth Grade Teacher; *b:* Buffalo, NY; *m:* McDonald A.; *c:* Xiamara; *ed:* Wheelock Coll (BS) Ed 1971; Grad Work in Ed Admin, Schl Law, Supervision; *cr:* Boston Pub Schls K-1st & 3rd Grd Tchr 1971-73; Cambridge Follow Through Prgm K-3rd Grd Tchr 1973-82; Graham & Parks Schl 2nd-4th Grd Tchr 1982-; Wheelock Coll Instr 1987-; *ai:* Tech & Mass Pep Liaison; NCTM 1982-; NEA 1973-; ASCD 1990-; ADL Fellowship in Math & Sci; Article in Arithmetic Tchr 1992; Chapters in 3 Books-Freedoms Plow, Tchng Malcolm X & Tchng Advanced Skills to At-Risk Stdnts; *home:* 32 Virginia St Dorchester MA 02125*

RICHARDS, KELLY ANNE, 8th Grade Social Studies Tchr; *b:* Long Branch, NJ; *ed:* Douglass Coll (BA) Jrnlsm 1991; Rutgers Univ (MED) Soc Stud Ed 1993; *cr:* Churchill Jr HS 8th Grd Soc Stud Tchr 1993-; *ai:* JV Field Hockey, JV Sftbl Coach; NCSS 1996; *office:* Churchill Jr HS 18 Norton Rd East Brunswick NJ 08816

RICHARDS, KENNETH LYNN, Sixth Grade Teacher; *b:* Millersburg, OH; *ed:* Kent St Univ (BS) Elem Ed, Scndry Ed-Math 1974; Addl Hrs Ashland Univ, Kent St Univ, Coll of Mount St Joseph; *cr:* Fredericksburg Elem Schl 6th Grd Tchr 1974-; *ai:* Spelling Bee, Sci Expo Spvsr; Ashland-Wayne Cty Sci Course Stud Comm, Outdoor Ed Dist Tchr; Career Ed Liaison; NEA, OH Tchrs Assn 1974-; SE Local Tchrs Assn 1974-, Sec, Bldg Rep; Holstein Assn 1973-; Martha Holden Jennings Scholar 1981-82; SE Local Tchr of Yr Finalist 1992; *home:* 7801 Massillon Rd SW Navarre OH 44662*

RICHARDS, LINDA TIERNEY, Singer, Sngwrtr, Envir Ed Tchr; *b:* Hempstead, NY; *m:* Keith Buesing; *c:* Cody, Wyatt; *ed:* Nassau Coll (AA) Lbrl Arts 1977; St Univ at Oneonta (BS) Elem Ed 1979; St Univ at New Paltz (MS) Elem Ed; *cr:* Ashokan Field Campus Instr Residence Prgm 1979-80, Dir Summer Prgm 1980-83; Minisink Vly MS 5th-6th Grd Tchr, 8th Grd Math Remediation Tchr 1981-88, Summer Prgm Instr, Coord 1994-95; Coffee Houses, Schls, Mohonk Singer, Songwriter 1989-; *ai:* Clearwater 1981-; Mohonk Preserve 1981-; Pub Schl Environmental Assembly Prgms 1989-; Article Pub 1988; Nom 1987 NYS Tchr of Yr; *home:* 912 N Mountain Rd Gardiner NY 12525*

RICHARDS, LORI SHEPHERD, 8th Grade US History Teacher; *b:* Cincinnati, OH; *m:* Dirk; *c:* Bailey, Heidi; *ed:* Univ of Cincinnati (BS) Elem Ed 1983; Coll of Mt St Joseph (MA) Ed 1990; Drake Univ 3 Credit Hrs; *cr:* John W. Miles Elem Schl 6th Grd Tchr 1983-84; New Richmond Elem Schl 6th Grd Tchr 1985-86; New Richmond MS Tchr 1986-; *ai:* Sunshine Comm; Soc Stud Dept Chprsn; NREA, OEA, NEA 1985-; Univ of Cinti Alumni Assn 1983-, Young Alumni Bd Mem; Kappa Delta Alumni Assn 1983-, Corres Sec, Rush Recommendations; Kappa Delta Pi 1982-; NR HS & MS PTO 1985-; NR Elem PTO 1993-; Levy Comm 1996-; Ashland Tchr Awds Nom 1988; *office:* New Richmond MS 1135 Bethel New Richmond Rd New Richmond OH 45157*

RICHARDS, LUCINDA BEARD, Honors, AP Biology & Sci Tchr; *b:* Springfield, OH; *m:* John T.; *c:* Julie, Wendy (dec); *ed:* Bowling Green St Univ (BS) Bio 1872; Brockport SUNY (MS) Bio 1989; MI St Univ Food Microbiology 17 Hrs; Brockport Rdng, Elem Cert 6 Hrs; *cr:* West Irondequart Home-Hospital Instr, Sub Tchr 1982-89; Our Lady of Mercy Tchr 1990-; *ai:* Amer Sign Lang Club; Operation Physics 1993-, Instr; CURE 1988-; Church 1974-; Phys Sci Wkshps; Article Pub; *office:* Our Lady Of Mercy Jr HS 1437 Blossom Rd Rochester NY 14610

RICHARDS, MARIE BALDOROSSI, 6th Grade Teacher; *b:* Riverside, NJ; *m:* Marvin; *c:* Cheryl, Jane Gasper, Jim, Bobby; *ed:* Trenton St Coll (BS) Elem Ed 1978; 35 Credit Hrs; *cr:* St Paul Schl Tchr 1978-; H&R Block Income Tax Preparer 1985-; *ai:* Academically Talented 7th Graders SAT; John Hopkins Pgm; Stock Market Club; *home:* 824 Woodlane Rd Beverly NJ 08010*

RICHARDS, PAUL J., English Dept Chairperson; *b:* Woonsocket, RI; *m:* Patricia A. Henault; *c:* Michael, Thomas, Adam; *ed:* Providence Coll (BA) Eng 1972, (MS) Scndry Admin 1994; Univ of MD 30 Credits Eng; *cr:* Our Lady of Providence Schl Tchr 1978-85; Bishop Hendricken Schl Tchr 1985-; *ai:* Lit Magazine Adv; NCTE 1991-; Primrose Vol Fire Dept 1995-, Bd of Dirs Vice Chair; *office:* Bishop Hendricken HS 2615 Warwick Ave Warwick RI 02889

RICHARDS, R. KENNETH, Industrial Arts Instructor; *b:* Akron, OH; *m:* Kathryn Ann Keneaster; *ed:* Kent St Univ (BS) Industrial Arts Ed 1973, (MA) Industrial Arts Ed 1981; Cert Elem Ed; 20 Semester Hrs Post Grad Stud; *cr:* Fairless HS Industrial Arts Instr 1970-77; Perry HS Industrial Arts Instr 1977-78; Sandy Vly HS Industrial Arts & Drafting Instr 1979-; *ai:* Ski Club Adv; Industrial Arts Textbook & Multi-Media Selection Comm; NEA 1970-; OH Ed Assn 1970-; Sandy Vly Ed Assn 1979-; Stark Co Home Builders Model House Competition 1971-, Bd Mem, 4 1st Pl Awds; Kent St Univ Design Competition 1990-, Judge; Adult Basic Ed Tchr & Dir; *office:* Sandy Valley Jr Sr HS 5362 SR 183 NE Magnolia OH 44643*

RICHARDS, ROBERT REYBURN, Art Education Teacher; *b:* Springfield, OH; *m:* Sherri Lynn Miller; *c:* Bryan Timothy; *ed:* Central St Univ (BSEd) Art Ed 1992; Seattle Pacific Univ 5 Credit Hrs; Wright St Univ 1 Credit Hr; *cr:* Central Jr HS Art Tchr 1992-; *ai:* Art Club Adv; Stu Cncl Dance Props & Act Construction Adv; NEA, OEA, Xenia Ed Assn 1992-; Personal Art Work Pub Exhibition; Art Day Prins Awd; Cty Wide Art Ed Prgms Curr Writing Team; *office:* Central Jr HS 425 Edison Blvd Xenia OH 45385

RICHARDS, THOMAS FRANKLIN, Political Science Prgm Chair; *b:* Columbus, OH; *m:* Ann Berger; *c:* John, Lawrence; *ed:* San Francisco St Univ (BA) Soc Sci & Ed 1962; NY Univ (MA) Pol Sci 1963; Univ of CA at Los Angeles (MA) Diplomatic His 1968; Rutgers Univ (EDD) Higher Ed 1988; Scndry & Jr Coll Credential St of CA 1962; Comm Coll Cert 1987; *cr:* Los Angeles Jr Coll Dist Adjunct Tchr 1966-68; New York Cty Schls Tchr 1968-69; Brookdale Comm Coll Pol Sci Chair 1969-; *ai:* Pol Sci Club Adv; Amer Pol Sci Assn 1985-, Spec Svcs Comm; NJ Ed Assn 1969-; NJ Pol Sci Assn 1988-, Pres 1993-95; Phi Delta Kappa 1989-, South Jersey Chapter Historian 1992-94; Mid Sts Soc Sci Assn 1993-; Pax Christi 1993-, Prgm Comm; Project Understanding 1994-; Intnl Cooperation Consortium 1991-, Advy Bd; Brookdale Fnd Grant 1996; Brookdale Gold Star Awd 1991; Brookdale Svc Learning Grant 1995; NJ Historical Commission Grant 1986; Fulbright Egypt Exch Grant 1975; Whos Who in Amer Colls & Univs 1962; *office:* Brookdale Comm Coll Newman Springs Road Lincroft NJ 07738*

RICHARDSON, ANNE OSTRO, English Tchr & Dean of Stdnts; *b:* New York City, NY; *m:* W. Randolph; *c:* Margaret, Nicholas; *ed:* Oberlin Coll (AB) Eng 1983; Wesleyan Univ (MALS) Hum 1993; Klingenstein Summer Inst; Tchrs Coll; Columbia Univl Facing His & Ourselves Inst, Lead Tchr; *cr:* Hamden Hall Ctry Day Schl Eng Tchr 1984-, Dir Comm Svc 1985-, Dir Summer Schl 1990-; Dean MS Stdnts 1993-; *ai:* Ed Comm; 8th Grd Class, Club Advs; Newsletter Ed; CWIS 1993-, Chair 1995-; Downtown Evening Soup Kitchen 1995-, Bd Mem; Class of 1972 Awd 1991; Headmaster Chair Awd 1990; Svc Awd Hill Cooperative Yth Svcs 1990; *office:* Hamden Hall Country Day Schl 1108 Whitney Ave Hamden CT 06517*

RICHARDSON, BRENDA HAUSER, German Teacher; *b:* Elizabeth, NJ; *c:* James Rogers Jr.; *ed:* Muhlenberg Coll (AB) Eng, Ger 1963; Jersey City St Coll (MA) Rdng 1979; NJ Cert Supervision, ESL, Rdng Specialist 1981; *cr:* East PA Union Schl Dist 7th-12th Grd Eng, Ger Tchr 1961-63; Soehl Jr HS Eng, Ger Tchr 1963-70; Linden HS Eng, Ger, Rdng ESL, Dropout Intervention Tchr 1970-; *ai:* Ger Club Adv; Delta Epsilon Phi; Bldng Liaison, Supts Liaison; Monitoring Comm, PTA Parents, Grad Comm Fac Mem; Foreign Lang Stdnts Europe Trips Chaperone 16 Yrs; NHS Fac Mem 1985-91; Mid Sts Eductr 4 Visistations; Chair of Fac Handbk 1994-; Chair Site Based Mngmnt Comm 1994; Chair Mid Sts Comm Lits 1995; Mem Blk Schdlng Comm 1996E; NJEA, AATG 1963-; UCEA 1963-, Fac Rep 2 Yrs; LEA 1963-, Fac Rep 6 Yrs; IRA, NJRA 1976-; Delta Phi Alpha, Chapter Sec; Alpha Upsilon Alpha Honorary Rdng Soc, Treas Local NJ Branch 1988-; St Paul's Church 1950-, Sunday Schl Tchr Supt, Church Cncl 6 Yrs, Mutual Ministry Comm 4 Yrs; Mother's Clb Boy Scouts 6 Yrs; City Tchr of Yr 1990-92; Tchr of Yr 2 Yrs;Cty Tchr of Yr 1991-92; *office:* Linden HS 121 W St Georges Ave Linden NJ 07036*

RICHARDSON, CAL, Chem, Physics & Phys Sci Tchr; *b:* Phila, PA; *ed:* Cheyenne Univ (BS) Comprehensive Sci 1968; Post Grad Credits Chem, Math, Cmptr Programming; *cr:* John Bartram HS Tchr 1967-; *ai:* Head Bsbl & Bsktbl Coach; AFT, NSTA 1975-; AAPT 1985-.

RICHARDSON, CHERYL F., First Grade Teacher; *b:* Middletown, OH; *c:* Jeffery; *ed:* BGSU (BS) Elem Ed 1966; Miami Univ (MS) Elem Cnslng, Prin 1975; 31 1/3 Post Grad Hrs; 27 Post Grad Hrs Wright St Univ; OH Dept of 1.5 Continuing Ed Hrs; *cr:* Mound Elem Schl Tchr 1966-67, 1971-; *ai:* Lang Arts Comm; Lang Arts, Math, Holistic Scoring of Composition; NEA 1981-; Easter Seals, Vol; Comm Schls Fund Raiser Act; Little League, Vol; Free Tutoring Vol Svc; Exemplary Tchr of Yr Awd 1991-92; Tchr Who Made A Difference 1992; Nom Excl Tchng Awd 1991-93; *office:* Mound Elem Schl 1108 Range Ave Miamisburg OH 45342

RICHARDSON, CY B.,JR., Civics Teacher; *b:* Carter City, KY; *m:* Joyce Ann Rogers; *c:* C. B., Martha Ollijean; *ed:* Berea Coll (BA) His & Pol Sci 1965; Xavier Univ (MED) Ed 1970; Attnd Univ of Cincinnati 43 Hrs Post-Grad & Xavier Univ; *cr:* New Richmond HS Soc Stud Tchr 1980-; *ai:* Jr Var Sftbl Coach; NEA, OEA 1965-; NREA 1980-; Bethel Lions 1992-, VP 1995-; Monroe Twp Trustee 1991-, Chm; Clermont Cty Clerks & Trustee Assn 1991-, VP 1995-; *office:* New Richmond HS 1131 Bethel New Richmond Rd New Richmond OH 45157*

RICHARDSON, DANIEL N., Curr Facilitator & Span Tchr; *b:* Quincy, MA; *m:* Maureen LaFleur; *c:* Kevin, Kate; *ed:* New England Coll (BA) Span 1971; Rivier Coll (MED) Admin 1981; *cr:* Concord HS Span Tchr 1971-, Frgn Lang Dept Chair 1982-93, Curr Facilitator 1994-; *ai:* NEA 1971-; NH Assn of Frgn Lang Tchrs 1971-; *office:* Concord HS Warren St Concord NH 03301

RICHARDSON, DAVID L., Eighth Grade Lang Arts Teacher; *b:* Cincinnati, OH; *m:* Angela; *c:* Emily, Andrew; *ed:* Univ of Cincinnati (BS) Eng & Bio Ed 1987; 15 Grad Hrs Concentration Rdng Ed; *cr:* Our Lady of Victory Elem Jr HS Tchr 1988-; *ai:* Supvr for Local Speech Contest; Mem of Discipline Comm; TAWL 1990-; *office:* Our Lady of Victory Elem 808 Neeb Rd Cincinnati OH 45233

RICHARDSON, DEBORAH ANN, Social Studies Teacher; *b:* New York, NY; *ed:* St John's Univ (BA) Scndry Ed 1971, (MS) Scndry Ed 1978; 6 Hrs Grad Credit Ec Queens Coll; *cr:* St Joseph's Schl 7th & 8th Grd Sci Tchr 1974-78; Our Lady of Grace 7th & 8th Grd Sci Tchr 1978-86; The Mary Louis Acad 9th & 10th Global Stud & 12th Grd Ec Tchr 1986-; Sr Dean; *ai:* Chprsn of FSCC; Steering Comm for Mid Sts Eval; Planning Comm for Soph Global Curr; NCEA 1974-; NCSS, ASCD, NYSSSA 1986-; Finalist-Outstanding Alumna for the 50th Anniversary of The Mary Louis Acad; *office:* The Mary Louis Acad 176-21 Wexford Terr Jamaica NY 11432

RICHARDSON, EDWARD C., Sci, Math & Soc Stud Instr; *b:* Sheffield, VT; *m:* Audrey A. Zagorski; *c:* Elizabeth Stevens, David C., Rebecca S. Martin, Barbara M. Tucker; *ed:* Lyndon St Coll (BS) Ed 1969, (MS) Curr, Instruction 1990; *cr:* St Johnsbury MS Sci, Math Instr 1969-; *ai:* Stu Cncl; Odyssey of Mind; Solar Car Race; NEA; Tri Cty Tchrs, Pres; Bapt Church Sunday Schl Tchr, Supt, Deacon, Trustee; Credit Union Dir, Pres, Treas 14 Yrs; Pvt Pilot 1994; *home:* Whispering Brook Farm Sheffield VT 05866

RICHARDSON, JEAN A. TARANTINI, Kindergarten Teacher; *b:* Newark, NJ; *m:* Marius B.; *c:* Peter, Eric, Michael; *ed:* Kean Coll (BA) Early Chldhd 1962; Montclair St Univ (MA) Ed Psych 1977; Credit Hrs Equaling PHD; *cr:* Mc Kinley Schl Kndgtn Tchr 1962-; *ai:* Run Family Rdng Prgm; Schl Improvement Comm; Newark Tchrs Union 1980-; Newcomers & Neighbors Club 1985-; St Pius X Church Choir 1984-; Rosary Soc Mem 1991-; 25 Yrs of Svc Awd; Excl in Tchng Awd V. P. Gladys Bond; *office:* Mc Kinley Elem Schl 1 Colonnade Pl Newark NJ 07104*

RICHARDSON, JEAN CZYZYCKI, Gifted Intervention Specialist; *b:* Cleveland, OH; *c:* Sarah, Rebecca, Michael; *ed:* Miami Univ (BS) Elem Ed 1981; John Carroll Univ (MS) Rdng 1991; Kent St Univ Working Toward Gifted Cert; *cr:* St Justin Martyr 5th Grd Tchr 1981-84; St Mary Chardon 5th Grd Tchr 1984-87; Mayfield City Schls 5th, 6th Grd Tchr of Gifted 1987-; *ai:* Sci Olympiad Coach; Math Counts Coach; Acad Enrichment Prgm Curr Comm; NEA, OEA 1987-; SENG, OAGC 1995-; Acad Booster Club 1995-; Mayfield Excl, Educl Excl Awd; OH Parks & Recreation Prgm Dev Awd; *office:* Mayfield MS 1123 Som Center Rd Mayfield Hgts OH 44124

RICHARDSON, JOHN EDWARDO, Graphic Arts & Printing Tchr; *b:* Washington, DC; *c:* Tiarra Carolyn Nichole; *ed:* Univ of DC (AAS) Printing Tech 1987, (BS) Printing Mgmt 1990; Natl Louis Univ (MED) Ed, Curr & Instruction 1995; *cr:* Cardozo Sr High Graphic Arts & Printing Tchr 1992-; Spingarn STAY High Graphic Arts & Printing Tchr 1995-; *ai:* Asst Bsbl Coach 1993-94; Head Bsbl Coach 1994-; True Success Ministries Disciple Trng Tchr & Founder; Thankful Bapt Church Bsktbl Coach & Deacon in Trng; AVA 1993-; ASCD 1994-; Kappa Delta Pi 1995-, Natl Hnrs; The New St John Missionary Bapt Church 1996-, Pastor & Rev; Awds: ICCS Comm Svc 1991, Outstndg Young Men of Amer 1988, NHS Inductee 1994-95 & Best of Class Acad Achievers 1983 awded by GM & Channel 9; Dept of Ed DC Pub Schls Vol Cert 1991; *home:* 2804 Terrace Rd SE Apt 545 Washington DC 20020*

RICHARDSON, JULIE, Fifth Grade Teacher; *b:* Pocatello, ID; *ed:* Weber St Univ (BS) Elem Ed 1989; Curr, Supervision Natl Louis Univ; *cr:* Weber St Univ Stdnt 1985-89; IRS Tax Examiner, Clerk 1987-89; Navajo Mnt Boardng Schl Fifth, Eighth, Chptr I Tchr, Coord 1989-94; Patch Elem Schl Fifth Grd Tchr 1994-; *ai:* Grd Level Team Ldr; Yrbk Adv; NEA, FEA 1994-; *office:* Patch Elem Schl Unit 30401 Box 4003 APO AE 09131*

RICHARDSON, KATHERINE L., Biology & Anatomy Teacher; *b:* Warwick, RI; *m:* George R.; *c:* Andrew; *ed:* Univ RI (BS) Dental Hygiene 1978, (MS) Sci Ed 1992; Continuing Ed Classes in Bio & Ed; *cr:* Coventry HS Tchr 1987-; *ai:* AFT 1987-; NABT, NSTA 1995-; *office:* Coventry HS 40 Reservoir Rd Coventry RI 02816

RICHARDSON, LINDA ADELE, Language Arts Teacher; *b:* Frederick, MD; *m:* David Thomas; *c:* Ava, Lori, David II, Roxanne; *ed:* Morgan St Univ (BA) Eng 1973; Western MD Coll PLS Courses; Attnd Univ of MD; *cr:* Middletown HS Eng & Fr Tchr 1973-76; Parkway Jr HS Chapter 1 Resource Tchr for Eng 1984-85; DeRidder HS Eng & Fr Tchr 1989-90; New Mrkt MS Lang Arts Tchr 1990-95; *ai:* NCTE; Multicultural Liaison; Eng Lang Arts Curr Review Comm; NEA, MSTA, FCTA 1990-; Human Svcs of Fred Co 1994-; *office:* New Market MS PO Box 58 New Market MD 21774*

RICHARDSON, LINDA SZYMANSKI, Business Education Teacher; *b:* Medway, MA; *m:* Nick J.; *c:* Marybeth, Nick C.; *ed:* St Coll at Salem (BS) Bus Ed 1964; 60 Grad Hrs at Boston Univ, Framingham St Coll, Univ of NY at Southhampton; *cr:* Shelter Island HS Bus Ed Tchr 1964-66; Franklin HS Bus Ed Tchr 1966-; *ai:* NEA 1964-; Franklin Tchrs Assn, MA Tchrs Assn 1966-; MA Bus Ed Assn 1980-; *home:* 23 Holliston St Medway MA 02053

RICHARDSON, MAUREEN MILLIGAN, Teacher of Gifted & Talented; *b:* Hackensack, NJ; *m:* Thomas L.; *c:* Maureen Hermey Castor, Joan Hermey Maciel, Kimberley Hermey; *ed:* Upsala Coll (BS) Eng, Elem 1960; Trenton St Extension 6 Credits; *cr:* Glen Rock Schls Grd 5 Tchr 1960-62; Berkeley Twp Schls Grd 4 Tchr 1964-66; Brick Twp Schls Grds 4-8 Tchr 1967-; *ai:* Yrbk Adv 8 Yrs; Lang, Soc Stud, Rdng Curr Dev Comms; Natl Current Events League Competition Coach; NEA, NJ EA 1960-; Ocean Cty EA 1964-; Brick Twp EA 1967-, Bldg Rep; Lion's Club Women's Aux 1970-, Treas; Tchr of Yr 1995; NJ Governor's Tchr Recognition Awd 1995; Who's Who in Amer's Mid Schls 1994; *office:* Veterans Memorial Mdl Schl 105 Hendrickson Ave Brick NJ 08723*

RICHARDSON, RANDOLPH GARY, History Teacher; *b:* Baltimore, MD; *ed:* Gettysburg Coll (BS) Ec-Bus Admin 1961; Johns Hopkins (MEQ) European His 1975; Morgan St Univ (MS) Amer Stud 1980; 6 Addl Hrs Towson St Univ; 9 Addl Hrs Western MD Coll; *cr:* Sykesville HS Dept Chr 1961-67; South Carroll HS Dept Chr 1968-71; Westminster HS Dept Chr, Tchr 1972-89; *ai:* Var Track Head Coach 1962-72; Var Cross Cntry Head Coach 1962-72; Carroll Cty EA 1961-91, Chr Salary & Compensation Comm; NEA 1961-91; Amnesty Intnl 1985-; ACLU 1981-; Ches Bay Fnd 1986-; HERP 1990-; *home:* 3317 Gamber Rd Finksbu 21048

RICHARDSON, RHONDA ANNE, Associate Professor; *b:* Oberli *m:* Brian K. Bialik; *c:* Jenna Bialik, Logan Bialik; *ed:* PA St Uni Human Dev, Family Stud 1981, (PHD) Human Dev, Family Stud 19 Kent St Univ Temporary Asst Prof 1984-87, Asst Prof 1987-93, Ass 1993-; *ai:* Kappa Omicron Nu Adv; NCR 1982-; SRA 1988-; OCFR Henry A Murray Rsrch Ctr Grant Radcliffe Coll; *office:* Kent St Ur Nixson Hall Kent OH 44242

RICHARDSON, SANDRA MARY, Art & Computer Education T Philadelphia, PA; *m:* Mark H.; *c:* Mark Jr., Juliet, Rebecca, Raqu Burlington Cty Coll (AA) Lbrl Arts-Magna Cum Laude 1994; Rowa of NJ (BA) Art Ed; *cr:* Assemblies of God NJ West Cntrl Section 1988-92; Life Ctr Acad Art, Cmptr Ed 1990-; *ai:* 10th Grd Adv; Care Coord; Cmptr Ed Implementation, Collection Campaign; Glouster C League 1995-; Burlington Cty Coll Alumni Assn 1994-; Coll Fnd S Nom for Bd of Trustees Burlington Coll; *home:* 131 Tuckert Shamong NJ 08088

RICHARDSON, SHARRON YOUNG, 2nd Grade Teacher; *b:* Roc NY; *c:* Gregory, Jill; *ed:* Miami Univ (BSED) Elem Ed 1967; Univ of (MSED) Outdr Ed 1996; Rdng Cert; *cr:* Trenton Schls 1st Gr 1967-69; Strongsville Schl Kndgtn Tchr 1969-70; Troy Local Sch Grd Tchr 1970-71; Medina City Schls Sub, 2nd Grd Tchr 1980-; *ai:* Authors & Illustrators; Right to Read; ECHO; Self Discipline Retirement; Fenntastic Classroom; Writing Competency Tests; Cmp Comm; Dist Strategy; Venture Capital Grant Writing; PDK Trng; OEA, NEOTA 1983-; Lizotte Rdng Cncl; MCTA Bldg Rep 19 Granger United Meth 1978-, Chprsn, Chrstn Ed, Admin Bd, C Ministries; Delta Gamma Alumni; Medina City Schls Fnd Grant Chemical Excl in Tchng Awd 1993; Presentor NEORA, Univ of Wkshp in Creative Writing; Instr Talking With Your Kids About A Mindful Schls; *home:* 781 E Smith Rd Medina OH 44256*

RICHARDSON, SOPHIE KOKEN, Biology Tchr & Sci Dept Chp Oneonta, NY; *m:* Bernard F.; *ed:* Hartwick Coll (BS) Bio 1962; 56 Hrs St Univ Coll at Oneonta, St Univ Coll at Cortland, St Univ C Albany, St Univ Coll at Binghamton; *cr:* Hartwick Coll Lab Preparation 1962-63; Homer Cntrl Schl Jr HS Tchr 1964-66; Unateg HS Sci, Bio Tchr 1966-; *ai:* Advy, Dist Prof Staff Dev, Schedule C Bldg Excl Team; NYSUT 1964-; STANYS; Downtown O Improvement Task Force 1994-, Cncl, Survey & Recruitment Chprsn; Oneonta Bus Woman's Club 1970-, Pres; Sr Class Selecte of Yr; Peers Selected Tchr of Yr; *office:* Unatego Jr Sr HS RD 1 Ote 13825*

RICHARDSON, SUSAN M., Social Studies Teacher; *b:* Passaic, N Daniel J.; *c:* Carrie; *ed:* Felician Coll (BA) Elem Ed 1969; *cr:* Roo No 7 Schl Tchr 1969-95; Thomas Jefferson MS Soc Stud Tchr 199 Schl Based Mgmt Comm; Honors Classes; NJ Ed Assn 1969-; 1988-89 Governors Tchr Recognition Prgm Grant Awd; *office:* T Jefferson MS Alpine St Garfield NJ 07026

RICHARDSON, TERESA, Seventh Grade Teacher; *b:* Philadelphi *ed:* Temple Univ (BS) Elem Ed 1976, (MED) Adult Ed 1980; *cr:* Settlement GED Pgm Coord 1976-78; OIC of Amer Trng Spe 1980-81; St Catherine of Siena Schl 7th Grd Tchr 1981-85; Holy Na Jesus Schl 7th Grd Tchr 1985-; *ai:* Rdng Pgm Coord; NCEA 1981-; Name Alumni Assoc 1993-; Parish Fin Comm 1995-; *office:* Holy Na Jesus Schl E Berks & Gaul Sts Philadelphia PA 19125

RICHARDSON, VIRGINIA MAPP, English Teacher; *b:* Portsmout *c:* David B., Andrew F., Michael H.; *ed:* Coll of William & Mary (BA 1954; George Washington Univ (MA) Rdng Diagnosis 1972; 30 Cred Composition, Writing 1983; 6 Credit Hrs African Stud CUNY at Bro 1991; 6 Credit Hrs So African Stud Williams Coll 1994; *cr:* William Jr HS Eng, Latin Tchr 1954-56; northwood HS Eng, Latin Tchr 195 Seneca Vly HS Eng, Latin Tchr 1975-81; Springbrook HS Eng, Latin 1983-; *ai:* Amnesty Intnl Spon 1992-; Ldrshp Cncl 1993-95; NEA, M Ed, Montgomery Cty Ed Assn 1975-; NCTE 1982-; Network of E Around Cntrl Amer; League of Women Voters 1954-72, Unit C Amnesty Intnl 1989-; Cntrl Amer Task Force RRUC 1984-; Fulb Summer Stud Abroad 1989; Natl Endowment for Hum Summer F 1991, 1994; VA Endowment for Hum Summer Fellow 1992.

RICHARDS-SCHMIT, JAN, English Teacher; *b:* Putnam, CT; *m:* R Hans; *ed:* Univ of CT (MA)-Suma Cum Laude Scndry Ed, Eng Wesleyan (MA) Lit, Art 1981; Sacred Heart Univ Working on Intermediate Cert in Admin; Oxford Univ Working on (MA) Women *cr:* Babcock Jr High 8th Grd Eng Tchr 1974-76; Cromwell Jr High 8t Eng, Rdng Tchr 1976-83; Mitchell Coll Burmese Eng Tchr 198 Tourtellotte HS Eng Tchr 1984-90; Killingly HS Eng Tchr 1993-; *ai:* Improvement Cncl Co-Chair; Poetry Club, Morning Tutorial Both G NEA; Phi Beta Kappa, Phi Kappa Phi 1974-; *office:* Killingly H Westfield Ave Danielson CT 06239*

RICHBURG, CURTIS L., Teacher; *b:* Brunswick, GA; *m:* Judy Harr Curtis Jr., Kirsten, Kristina; *ed:* Savannah St Coll (BS) Sci, Hlth, PE Seton Hall Univ (MED) Prof Ed 1981; William Patterson Coll (MED Admin 1983; Attnd Jersey City St Coll; *cr:* Orange MS Sci Tchr 197 Admin 1991-94; Orange HS admin 1990-91, Sci Tchr 1994-; *ai:* Coach Orange MS; Bsbl Coach; Orange Ed Assn 1975-, Pres 4 Outstdng Pres; NJEA 1975-, Legislative Chm; NEA 1975-, Del; Solomon Lodge #62 1972-; Phi Beta Sigma 1969-, Treas; *home:* 52 St East Orange NJ 07017*

RICHELDERFER, JULIE RIGBY, Social Studies Teacher; *b:* France; *m:* William O.; *c:* Christopher; *ed:* Penn State (BSS) Soc 1983; *cr:* Perry Cty Schls Sub Tchr 1989-94; West Perry HS Soc Stud 1994-; *ai:* Spirit Club & UN Forum Team Adv; Stu Asst Team Mem; W & NEA 1994-; *office:* West Perry HS Rd 1 Box 7 Elliottsburg PA 17

RICHERT, GEORGE DANIEL, Professor of Culinary Arts Bouxwiller, France; *m:* Yolande DesJardins; *ed:* Lycee Bouxuviller Fr (BEBC) 1962; Edole Hoteliere Bouxviller (CAP) Bus, Culinary Nutrition; Cmptr; Curr Dev; *cr:* Aescars Casino Exec S Chef 197 Hunters Run Exec Chef 1982-83; Atlantic Comm Coll Culinary Arts Chair Person 1983-; *ai:* Tutoring; Hot Food Coaching; Pub Article *home:* 5817 Oak St Mays Landing NJ 08330*

RICHETTI, DUANE, English Teacher & Dept Chm; *b:* Jamestown, *m:* Elizabeth; *c:* Amy, Ellen; *ed:* Jamestown Comm Coll (AA) Eng 1 St Univ at Fredonia (BA) Eng 1973, (MA) Eng; *cr:* Falconer Cntrl Sch Tchr 1973-, Eng Dept Chm 1984-; *ai:* Past Yrbk & Current A-plus NYSUT 1973-; Falconer Ed Assn 1973-; NEA 1973-; Phi Delta K 1992-; A Childrens Place 1979-, Past Pres; Dance Conservatory 1980-, Pres; Pub Poet in Local & Natl Presses; Regnl Poetry Contest 1st Buffalo NY Region; *office:* Falconer Cntrl Schl PO Box 43 East Falconer NY 14733

RICHEY, WILLIAM K., Chemistry Teacher; *b:* Xenia, OH; *m:* Bar Ann; *c:* Erica Marie, Tyler William, Jenna Renna; *ed:* Wright St Univ Bio 1984, (MS) Aquatic Bio 1985, (MED) Scndry Ed 1986; Attnd Mia Univ at oxford, Univ of Dayton, Duke Univ Marine Lab Aquatic Bio & Grad Chem Courses; *cr:* Wright St Univ Bio Tchng Asst 1985-86; X em Tchr 1986-; *ai:* Stu Cncl; Sci Comm; XEA, OEA & NEA 1986-; 1990-; First Church of Christ 1987-, Deacon; Sci is Fun Camp for Level 3 Yrs; Presentor at What Really Works in the Classroom bus 1992; OH Sci Ed Cncl 1993-94; NSTA Presenter; *office:* Xenia 3 Kinsey Rd Xenia OH 45385

FORD, CATHERINE ANN, English Teacher; *b:* Morganton, NC; orge F. Jr.; *c:* Daniel; *ed:* Hofstra Univ (BA) Eng 1972, (MA) Scndry 76; Grad Courses in Ed, Eng, Rdng; *cr:* Westhampton Beach HS Eng 972-; *ai:* AFT, NEA, WHB Tchrs Assn 1972-; *office:* Westhampton HS Lilac Rd Westhampton Beach NY 11978

MAN, AARON, High School Math Teacher; *b:* Brooklyn, NY; *m:* ; *c:* Ross, Chad; *ed:* City Coll (BEE) Electrical Engrng 1962; a Univ (MED) Math Ed 1968; NY Univ Electrical Engrng; *cr:* aro Jr HS Math Tchr 1965-67; New Utrecht HS Math Tchr 1967-; *ai:* 1962-; UFT 1962-, Chptr Comm 1970-; Arden Heights Jewis Ctr Founder; Chessed Comm.

MAN, CAROL ANN KOERNER, 6th-8th Grade Teacher; *b:* wken, NJ; *m:* Michael P.; *c:* David, Adam, Ethan; *ed:* Fairleigh son Univ (BS) Elem Ed 1958; Rutger Univ (MED) Guid, Stu Prsnl Univ of VT (CAS) Admin 1988; Attnd NY Univ, SUNY at New Paltz, f VT, St Michael's Coll, Johnson St Coll, SUNY at Plattsburgh; *cr:* Bergen Bd of Ed 4-5 Grd Tchr, HS Guid Cnslr 1958-66; keepsie Bd of Ed Elem Schl Guid Cnslr 1966-68; Millbrook Bd of 2 Tchr 1979-80; Greer-Woodycrest Dir Ed, Accultiaration 1980-83; urg Town Schl Dist 6-8 Mid Grd Tchr 1985-; *ai:* Schl Prgm Cncl MS HS Transition Comm; Schl Sci Fair Coord; Instrl Support Team Stu Peer Ldrshp Group Adv; VT Assn Mid Level Edctrs 1987-; New nd League MS 1995-; Amer Cncl for the Blind 1992-; Nom ential Awd Excel in Sci, Math Tchng 1996; US House of esolution Recognition for Resettlement Ed of Haition Refugees; orated with Natl Captioning Inst Captioning Sci Videos Mid Grd .*

MAN, KENNETH A., Instr of Philosophy & English; *b:* Rochester, *d:* Haverford Coll (BA) Philosophy 1988; Rutgers Univ (MA) ophy 1993, (ABD) Philosophy; *cr:* Haverford Coll Spcl Asst to Dean 89; Rutgers Univ Grad Fellow & Tchng Asst 1989-; *ai:* Tchr Trng os; Amer Philosophical Assn 1989-; Amer Soc 18th C Stud 1992-; Soc 1992-; Articles & Conf Papers Pub; Univ Excl Flwshp Rutgers *office:* Rutgers St Univ At New Brnswck Philosophy Dept New wick NJ 08903

MAN, WENDY DRESNER, Nutrition Instructor; *b:* Philadelphia, *:* Jeffrey; *c:* Jesse, Aliza; *ed:* Penn St Univ (BS) Nutrition 1979; r Coll (MA) Hlth Ed 1980; *cr:* Episcopal Hosp Dietitian 1980-82; gomery Cty Comm Coll Asst Prof 1985-; Penn St Univ Nutrition Instr *ai:* Amer Dietetic Assn 1981-; *office:* Montgomery County Comm 40 Dekalb Pike Blue Bell PA 19422

IMOND, ANITA SMITH, Sixth Grade Teacher; *b:* New York, NY; *c:* , Nicole, Nina; *ed:* Morgan St Univ (BS) Elem Ed 1972; Coll of New lle (MS) Spec Ed 1979; 12 Hrs Admin Trinity Coll; *cr:* Victory Day Ctr Tchr 1972-80; St Luke's Pre-Schl & Kndgtn Dir 1980-83; nediate Schl Spec Ed Tchr 1983-85; Pointer Ridge Elem Schl Sixth Tchr 1985-; *ai:* Multi-Cultural Comm Chprsn; NEA, PGCEA 1985-; Sigma Theta 1969-; Natl Coun Negro Women 1994-; Excl in Ed Awd *office:* Pointer Ridge Elem Schl 1110 Parkington Ln Bowie MD *

IMOND, DEBORAH ANN, Social Studies Teacher; *b:* Baltimore, *ed:* Morgan St Univ (BA) His, Ed 1970, (MS) African Amer Stud 30 Addl Credit Hrs of Inservice, Grad Level Stud at Goucher Coll, a Coll; *cr:* Stemmers Run MS 7-8 Grd Soc Stud Tchr 1971-87; Gen Stricker MS 7-8 Grd Soc Stud Tchr 1987-94; Parkville HS 9-12 Grd tud Tchr 1994-; *ai:* Step Squad Spon; Martin L. King, Black His n Comm; Class of 1999 Co-Spon; NEA, MSTA, TABCO 1971-; Phi Theta 1970-; Morgan St Univ Grad Asst 1970-71.

IMOND, LAWRENCE DAVID, 8th Grade Social Studies Tchr; *b:* son, NJ; *m:* Sharon Weiss; *c:* Nancy, Sandy, Jennifer; *ed:* Monmouth (BA) His 1963; Temple Univ (MA) European & Amer His 1965; *cr:* lapan Englishtown MS Tchr 1966-; *ai:* 8th Grd Boys Bsktbl, Boys r & Track, Girls Soccer; NSEA, NEA 1966-; Prgm Coord Manalapan Summer Recreation Prgm; *home:* 103 Garden Rd Shrewsbury NJ *

INER, NANCY K., ECE Director; *b:* Buffalo, NY; *m:* C. William; *c:* Brett; *ed:* SUNY at Fredonia (BA) Ed 1971, (MS) Ed 1974; Cert ification & Reporting of Child Abuse & Maltreatment; Infection ol for Schl Prsnl; *cr:* Kenmore Town of Tonawanda 1st Grd Tchr -75; St John Luth Rdng & 1st Grd Tchr & ECE Dir 1983-; *ai:* Boys l League Statistician 1989-95; PTL 1983-; Niagara Frontier Rdng 1983-86; Long Range Planning Comm 1990-94; Intership Site Supvr; : St John Lutheran Schl 6950 Ward Rd North Tonawanda NY 14120

ITARIK, DENISE, Resource Teacher; *b:* Warwick, RI; *ed:* RI Coll Ed 1975, (MED) Spec Ed 1979; *cr:* Coventry Pub Schls Resource Spec Ed Tchr 1977-; *ai:* Steering Comm; Tchr Facilitator; AFT -; St Joseph's Choir 1982-; *office:* Tiogue Elem Schl E Shore Dr ntry RI 02816

ITER, AMY FRANKLIN, Band Director; *b:* Morristown, NJ; *m:* E.; *c:* Paul, Elizabeth; *ed:* Manhattan Schl of Music (BM) Obe & rmance 1978, (MM) Ed 1979; Addl 12 Credit Hrs in Supervision & n at NY Univ; *cr:* Packer Collegiate Inst Woodwind Instr 1978-79; phi Acad Music Tchr & Dept Head 1979-83; Union Pub Schls umental Music Tchr 1983-86; Blue Mountain MS Band Dir 1986-; *ai:* ate Woodwind Instr 1978-; MENC 1979-; NYSSMA 1986-; pstown Recreation Dept 1989-, Summer Music & arts Prgm Dir; son Schl PTA 1984-, VP; Fishkill United Meth Church 1993-, Mothers ort Group Ldr; Play Oboe-Eng Professionally in the Tri-St Area; gned a New Jazz Improvisation Curr at Blue Mountain MS 1991; *e:* Blue Mountain MS 7 Furnace Woods Rd Peekskill NY 10566*

ITER, IRENE BERNARDO, French Teacher; *b:* Newark, NJ; *m:* ; *c:* Paul, Daniel; *ed:* Montclair Univ (BA) Fr 1976; Seton Hall Univ) Admin & Supervision 1993; Sorbonne Univ Paris France; *cr:* eville HS Fr Tchr 1976-; *ai:* Foreign Lang Club Adv; Organizer of s to Paris; NJ Foreign Lang Tchrs 1980-; NJ Foreign Lang Tchr Nom ; *office:* Belleville HS 100 Passaic Ave Belleville NJ 07109*

ITER, JOHN DAVID, Comp Sci Instr; *b:* Perham, MN; *m:* Gloria ales; *ed:* Northwest St Comm Coll Assoc Degree Comp Sci 1990; Cert ell Instr; *cr:* Tom Co Plastics Netwoork Coord 1989-90; Northwest St m Coll Comp Sci Instr 1990-, Network Admin 1991-94; J D & Assoc Consultant 1993-; *ai:* NPA 1993-; NUI 1995-; NSCC Comp Advy m 1989-, Adv; Lib Bd 1994-, NSCC rep; *office:* Northwest State m Coll 22-600 Sr 34 Archbold OH 43502

HTER, JOHN LOUIS, Biology Teacher; *b:* Scranton, PA; *m:* leen Roche; *c:* John Jr., Melissa; *ed:* Univ of Scranton (BS) Scndry Ed ; Wilkes Univ (MS) Ed 1995; *cr:* Scranton Tech HS Bio Tchr 1985-86; awanna Trl HS Bio Tchr 1986-; *ai:* Wrestling Coach West Scranton; A, NEA, PSEA 1986-; Red Cross Vol 1995-; *home:* 610 W Locust St nton PA 18504

RICKANSRUD, KIRK MARTIN, Social Science Teacher; *b:* Stilwater, OK; *m:* Harriet Jane Curry; *ed:* Grove City Coll (BA) Pol Sci, His, Ed 1989; 29 Credits Scndry Ed Admin Masters Degree Prgm Rowan Coll; *cr:* Eastern Regnl HS His Edctr, Marching Band Asst 1990-, Class Adv 1990-94, Asst Bsktbl Coach 1991-, Head LaCrosse Coach 1993-; *ai:* Visual Coord; NEA 1989-; Ashland Church 1980-, Trustee; Comm Ed Recreation Camp; Dev 2 Courses Multicultural Ed; *office:* Eastern HS Laurel Oak Rd Box 2500 Voorhees NJ 08043*

RICKARD, VIRGINIA SCOBLICK, Secondary English & Drama Tchr; *b:* Peckville, PA; *m:* Louis; *c:* Brendan D.; *ed:* East Stroudsburg Univ (BS) Scndry Ed 1973; Attnd Univ of Scranton, Scndry Ed; Cath Univ, Speech; Marywood Coll, Ed, Theater; *cr:* North Pocono HS Speech, Eng, Theater Tchr 1974-; *ai:* Acting Coach; PSEA 1974-; Theater Assn of PA; Alpha Psi Omega; Opera IV; St Eulalia's Choir; Actors' Equity Assn Performer, 20 Yrs Experience Stock & Regnl Theater; *home:* 106 Jonslea Ln Moscow PA 18444

RICKELS, DONALD LEE, K-5th Grd PE Teacher; *b:* Towson, MD; *m:* Cathy; *c:* D. J., Samantha; *ed:* West Chester Univ (BS) Hlth & PE 1983; *cr:* Boys Latin Schl K-5 Grd PE Tchr 1984-; *ai:* Var Tennis, JV Soccer, MS Bsktbl Coach; *office:* Boys' Latin Sch Of Maryland 822 W Lake Ave Baltimore MD 21210*

RICKENBACKER, PATRICIA MARSHALL, Guidance Counselor; *b:* Brooklyn, NY; *m:* John Kent; *c:* Kenneth Calhoun, Tanya, John Jr.; *ed:* SUNY at Old Westbury (BA) Sociology 1972; C. W. Post Coll (MS) Schl Cnslng Ed 1982; Union Theological Seminary (MDiv) Theology 1986; *cr:* Brunswick Hosp Ctr Alcohol Cnslr 1983-86; Apple Drug Rehab Drug Therapist 1986-87; Wyandanch Meml HS Cnslr 1987-89; Amityville Meml HS Cnslr 1989-; Bapt Church Living Hope Flwshp Pastor 1991-; *ai:* Anti-Violence, Black His, Curr Comms; BOCES Western Suffolk Liaision Cncl; Amityville Tchrs Assn 1991-; NY St United Tchrs Assn, Western Suffolk Cnslrs Assn, NY St Cnslrs Assn 1987-; Cntrl Long Island Branch NAACP 1972-, Exec Bd; Empire Bapt Congress Chrstn Ed, Fac 1988-, Bd Mem 1990-; North Amityville & Vicinity Ministerial Alliance, 2nd VP 1988-; Guid Excl Awd 1987; United North Amityville Yth Org Spiritual Mentor Awd 1991; *office:* Amityville Memorial HS Merrick Rd Amityville NY 11701

RICKER, JENNIE ANNE, Dance Teacher; *b:* Jersey City, NJ; *m:* Daniel Narden; *ed:* Towson St Univ (BFA) Dance Performance & Ed 1993; *cr:* Howard HS Dance Tchr 1993-; *ai:* Var Chrldng Coach; NEA 1993-; *office:* Howard HS 8700 Old Annapolis Rd Ellicott City MD 21043

RICKERT, JOHN, HS Social Studies Teacher; *b:* Woodbury, NJ; *m:* Carol Palmer; *ed:* Saint John Fisher Coll at Rochester (BA) His & Comm 1992; Coll of Saint Rose at Albany (MSEd) Scndry Ed 1994; 22 Addl Grad Credits in Spec Ed & Educl Admin; *cr:* Capital Region Bd of Cooperative Educl Svcs Tchr of Spec Ed 1992-95; Niskayuna HS Soc Stud Tchr 1995-; *ai:* Var Ftbl Asst Coach; 8th Grd Boys Bsktbl Coach; Awds Comm; Kappa Delta Pi 1993-; AFT 1995-; *office:* Niskayuna HS 1626 Balltown Rd Niskayuna NY 12309

RICKERT, RICHARD EDWARD, Librarian; *b:* Greenville, PA; *m:* Bonnie Gwozdziewicz; *c:* Mindy; *ed:* Clarion Univ (BSEd) Lib Sci 1967; Drexel Univ (MSLS) Lib Sci 1972; Post Grad Work at Slippery Rock Univ, Edinboro Univ & Penn St Univ; *cr:* Reynolds Schl Dist Librn 1967-; *ai:* Lib Club Adv; Star Team; Acad Boosters; Band Boosters; Gridiron Club; Former Ftbl & Bsktbl Coach; Stu Cncl; PSEA 1967-; NEA 1967-; REA 1967-, Past Pres; First Presbyn Church 1980-, Deacon; Bd Of Dir-SWIVC for WQED Pittsburgh; Numerous Articles Pub; Outstanding Tchr; Yrbk Dedication; *office:* Reynolds Jr-Sr HS 531 Reynolds Rd Greenville PA 16125

RICKMAN, MARY L., 6th-12th Grd Art Teacher; *b:* Canandaigua, NY; *m:* Richard E.; *c:* Richard, Rodney; *ed:* Keuka Coll (BA) Art Ed 1981; Rochester Inst of Tech (MFA) Painting 1987; Dev of Child 3 Cr Hrs; Abnormal Psych 3 Cr Hrs; *cr:* Penn Yan Schl Dist Art Tchr 1987-; *ai:* Tchrs Advy Comm; Scholastics Rochester; Dept Chair; Substance Abuse Task Force Comm; Excl, Accountability Comm; NAEA 1994-; NEA 1987-; NYSATA 1988-; *home:* 114 W Lake Rd Penn Yan NY 14527*

RICKS, JANICE D., Math Teacher; *b:* Newark, NJ; *m:* Thomas M.; *c:* Cynthia, Laila; *ed:* Caldwell Coll (BA) Math 1964; Villanova Univ (MA) Tchng of Math 1990; Ldrshp Inst in Discrete Math Rutgers Univ 1991; *cr:* LaReine HS Math Tchr 1976-78; Robert E. Lee HS Math Tchr 1978-86; Friends Select Schl Math Tchr 1988-93; Marple Newton HS Math Tchr 1993-; *ai:* NCTM 1961-; ATMOPAV 1986-, Recording Sec; AWM 1992-; NSF Grant; 2 Articles Pub; Present Wkshps for Tchr In-Svc; *office:* Marple Newtown Sr HS 120 Media Line Rd Newtown Square PA 19073*

RICO, MARIA ELENA ANN, Dance Instructor, Dir & Owner; *b:* Summit, NJ; *c:* Alicia Pagan; *cr:* Anne's Schl of Dance Stu, Stu Tchng 25 Yrs; Broadway Dance Ctr Stu 10 Yrs; *ai:* Theater Groups & Schls Asst Dir, Choreographer; Dance Edctrs of Amer 1983-; *office:* Maria Elenas Schl Of Dance 218 Worth St Iselin NJ 08830

RICOTTA, SANTO JOSEPH, Math & Computer Teacher; *b:* Clearfield, PA; *m:* Elaine Burnworth; *c:* Penny Kilmon, Santo James; *ed:* Clarion St Univ (BS) Math 1970; 24 Credit Hrs Cmptr Sci; *cr:* Punxsutawney Area HS Math Tchr 1970-74; Conemaugh Twp HS Math, Cmptr Tchr 1974-; *ai:* Cmptr Adv; Internet Supvr; Tchrs Assn 1970-, Pres; Tech Steering Comm 1992-, Chm; CTEA, 1992-, Outcomes Based Ed Steering Comm.

RIDARELLI, CAROL MARIE, History Teacher; *b:* New Haven, CT; *ed:* Southern Ct St Univ (BS) Scndry Ed, His 1983, (MS) His 1986; Southern Ct St Univ 6th Yr Intermediate Admin. Sprv 1990; *cr:* St Joseph HS His Tchr 1983-84; Newtown HS His Tchr 1984-; *ai:* Frosh Class Adv; Joseph Korzenik Flwshp Holocaust Tchng 1992; Holocaust, Jewish Resistance Prgm Israel, Poland 1991; Fulbright Hays Seminars Abroad Prgm to Israel 1989; German Exchange Prgm 1985; Pub Articles 1983, 1989; *office:* Newtown HS 12 Berkshire Rd Sandy Hook CT 06482

RIDDELL, HARRY W., Teacher; *b:* Williamsport, PA; *m:* Carol Ann; *c:* Lisa, Sherri; *ed:* Lock Haven Univ (BA) Scndry Math, Physics 1965; Bucknel (MA) Admin Prin 1989; Lock Haven Univ Elem 1967; *cr:* Montgomery Area Schl Dist Tchr, Head Tchr 1965-; *ai:* Church Groups; *home:* RR 1 Box 118-B Allenwood PA 17810

RIDDELL, LINDA, Second Grade Teacher; *b:* Philadelphia, PA; *ed:* Millersville St Univ Elem Ed (BS) 1970, (MS) 1975; Rdng Specialist 1975; *cr:* Brecknock Elem Schl 1st-2nd Grd Tchr 1970-; *ai:* Instructional Support Team; NEA, PSEA, ELCEA 1970-; KRA, LLRA 1975-; Chrstn Ed Comm 1985-; *home:* 12 Oriole Dr Ephrata PA 17522

RIDDICK, KATHERINE VIRGINIA, Third Grade Teacher; *b:* Rocky Mount, NC; *ed:* Coll of Charleston (BS) Elem Ed 1983; Bowie St Univ (MED) Admin & Supervision 1992; *cr:* Bailey Elem Schl Sixth Grd Tchr 1983-85; Dept of Defense Schls Fourth Grd Tchr 1985-87; Kettering Elem Magnet Schl Sixth Grd Tchr 1987-94; Kingsford Elem Magnet Schl Third Grd Tchr 1994-; *ai:* Debate Team Supvr; Odessey of Mind Cty, St Judge; Instrl Cncl; Elem Staff Dev Comm; PGCEA, NEA, MSTA 1987-; Comm & Acad Stud Magnet Curr Writer; Math, Soc Stud Curr; *home:* 2408 Forest Edge Ct Cond E Odenton MD 21113*

RIDDLE, CHARLES HENRY, 7th-8th Grd Soc Stud Teacher; *b:* Sussex, NJ; *m:* Sharon; *c:* Brian C., Matthew J.; *ed:* St Francis Coll (BA) His 1970; Univ of Notre Dame (MA) His 1971; Trenton St Coll (MAT) Ed 1975; K-8 Tchng Cert; K-12 Soc Stud Cert; *cr:* Ethel Hoppock MS 7th-8th Grd Soc Stud Tchr 1971-; Warren Cty Comm Coll Adj His Instr 1987-88; *ai:* 7th Grd Trip Coord, Coach, Referee, Umpire; Coach Team That Won North Hunterdon His Bowl Championships 1986-87; NEA, NJEA, BTEA 1971-; NJ Cncl for Soc Stud 1975-; Annandale Reformed Church 1971-, Deacon, Elder; Annandale Fire Co 1975-83, 1995-, Line Ofcr, Sec, Chaplain; NJ MS Soc Stud Tchr of Yr 1984; Booklet Pub 1975; 5 His Articles Pub 1976; *office:* Ethel Hoppock MS 280 Asbury-W Portal Rd Asbury NJ 08802*

RIDDLE, IRA LEE, HS Mathematics Teacher; *b:* Alameda, CA; *m:* Polly Jean; *ed:* SUNY at Plattsburgh (BA) Math, Speech, Drama 1968; SUNY at Geneseo (MSEd) Speech Ed 1969; PA St Univ (MED) Math Ed 1976; Temple Univ (DED) Math Ed 1990; Attnd Glassboro St NJ, Univ of FL, Univ of DE, Rutgers, Villanova; *cr:* Orange Park Jr HS Math Tchr 1969-70; Penns Grove HS Math Tchr 1970-72; Glassboro HS Math Tchr 1972-74; Centennial Sch Dist 7-12 Grd Tchr 1974-; *ai:* Chess Club; Girls Track Asst Coach; Dramatics; Cent Ed Assn 1974-, Pres 1995-; NEA; PSEA; US Chess Fed 1973-, Reg, VP, Career Svc 1993, Outstdng Comm Chm 1992; *office:* William Tennent HS 333 Centennial Rd Warminster PA 18974*

RIDENOUR, KENNETH ROBERT, Spanish Teacher; *b:* Shelby, OH; *m:* Ann E. Jette-Ridenour; *c:* Nicholas M., Heather L.; *ed:* Pontifical Coll Josephinim (BA) Latin Amer Stud 1973; Wright Univ (MED) Tchr Ldr 1993; Edison St Comm Coll 1981-82; Wright St Univ 1976-79, 1983-84; Univ of Dayton 1986; *cr:* Trotwood Madison Jr HS Span Tchr 1985-; *ai:* Jr HS Wrestling Coach; United Way Building Coord; Family Facilitator; Past TMEA Bldg Rep; NEA, OEA, OFLA 1985-; Franklin Lodge #14 F&AM 1980-, Master 1987; W Cntrl OH Umpire Assn 1976-; Troy Emergency Crew 1974-87; Greene County Umpire Assn 1995-; United Way Outstanding Co Chprsn Avd Nom; *office:* Trotwood-Madison Jr H S 3594 N Snyder Rd Trotwood OH 45426

RIDENOUR, RUTH ANN, Music Chprsn, Choral Music Dir; *b:* Hagerstown, MD; *ed:* Frostburg St Coll (BS) Music Ed 1976; Western MD (MLA) Music Ed; *cr:* Williamsport HS Vocal, Choral Music 18 Yrs; North Potomac MS Choral Music 2 Yrs; *ai:* Drama Club Coach; Show Choir, Madrigal Singers Dir; All Cty Chorus, Music Dept Chair; Restructing Comm; Schl Improvement Team; WA Co Tchr Assn, MD St Natl Ed Assn 1976-; Potomac Playmakers Comm Theatre 1979-, Pres, Costume Chair, Dir; Dir of Choirs Benevola United Meth Church 1974-; WA Cty Tchr of Yr 1992-93; MD Talent Arts Awd for Stu of Coach; *home:* 617 Maryland Ave Hagerstown MD 21740

RIDER, BARBARA JANE, Bus Dept Chairman & Teacher; *b:* Springfield, OH; *m:* Barry A.; *c:* Seth Adam, Amanda Beth; *ed:* Bowling Green St Univ (BA) Bus 1970, (MED) Bus 1971; Numerous Courses Cmptr Tech; *cr:* Erie City Schl Dist Bus Dist Instr 1971-78; Mercyhurst Coll Bus Dist Instr 1985-89; North East HS Bus Dept Chm 1991-; Erie Co Tech Inst Adult Ed Instr 1994-; *ai:* FBLA Adv; NEA; PaBus Tchr Assn; NBEA; Pub Chptr NBEA Yrbk; Organized, Operated Consulting Firm; *office:* North East HS 1901 Freeport Rd North East PA 16428*

RIDER, JON ALLEN, Fifth Grade Teacher; *b:* Malone, NY; *m:* Diane; *c:* Amy Rider Mitchell, Emily; *ed:* St Univ at Potsdam (BA) Ed 1964; *cr:* Malone Cntrl Schls Elem Tchr 1964-69; Clearwater Elem Tchr 1969-70; Malone Cntrl Schls Elem Tchr 1970-; *ai:* Bsktbl Coach 29 Yrs; Bsktbl Adv; Golf Coach; AFT 1964-; NYSUT 1964-; Elks; Bsktbl Coach of Yr (3 Times); *office:* Malone Cntrl Schls 179 Webster St Malone NY 12953

RIDGE, LEWIS O.,JR., 4th Grade Teacher; *b:* Daisytown, PA; *m:* Pamela K. Williams; *c:* Brandon; *ed:* CA St Coll (BS) Industrial Arts 1971; CA Univ of PA (MED) Industrial Arts 1982; Certs Rdng Spec 1986, Elem 1984; *cr:* Caroll Cty Schls Industrial Arts Tchr 1971-72; Bethel Park Schl Dist Electronics Tchr 1972-83; Bethel Park Schl Dist 4th Grd Tchr 1984-; *ai:* In-Schl News Prgm Elem Bldg Tech Adv 3 Yrs; Asst Rifle Team Coach 1973-82; AFT, PAFT, BPFT 1971-; *office:* Bethel Park Schl Dist 301 Church Rd Bethel Park PA 15102

RIDGELY, DEBRAH WUTHNOW, First Grade Teacher; *b:* Lawrence, KS; *m:* Peter T.; *c:* Christopher D., Scott T.; *ed:* Univ of DE (AS) Clothing in Bus & Industry 1970, (BSEd) Elem Ed 1972; Salisbury St Univ (MSEd) Rdng 1984; Addl 15 Credit Hrs; *cr:* Milford MS 6th Grd Tchr 1974-77; Lake Forest South Elem Schl 1st Grd Tchr 1984-; *ai:* 1st Grd Rep; Dist Sci Comm; Report Card Comm; Mentoring Prgm; NEA, DSEA 1974-77, 1984-; LFEA 1984-, Past Bldg Rep; Church, Parish Relations Bd 1995-; South Elem Schl Tchr of Yr 1995-96; *office:* Lake Forest South Elem Schl Dorman St Harrington DE 19952

RIDGEWAY, EDWARD LEROY, Physical Education Teacher; *b:* Salem, OH; *m:* Sandy Belle; *c:* Levi; *ed:* West Liberty St Coll (BA) Comprehensive Soc Stud, PE 1979; 18 Hrs Post Grad Work; *cr:* Beaver Local PE Instr 1981-; *ai:* Asst Var Ftbl; Head Var Track; OH Ed Assn, NEA 1981-; Church HS Yth Ldr 1985-93.*

RIDGEWAY, KENNETH E., 7th Grd Language Arts Teacher; *b:* West Chester, PA; *ed:* West Chester Univ (BS) Eng Scndry Ed 1985; Penn St, Ursinus Coll Permanent Cert 1992; *cr:* Downingtown I&A Schl Remediation Instr Grds 7-10 1985-86; The Phelps Schl Instr 9th, 10th Grd Eng 1986-87; Phoenixville Area MS Instr 7th, 8th Grd Eng 1987-; *ai:* Coach 7th, 8th Grd Phouton Bsbl; Mentor Star Trek Club, Moderator Black His Assemblies; PAEA, PSEA 1987-; Mohawks Yth Club 1970-, Pres; Over & Beyond Club 1977-, Pres; Camp Kweebec 1979-, Radio, Video Specialist, Jack Steven Toran Awd; Coventry Players 1992-, Mediator, Lead Actor, Supporting Actor; *office:* Phoenixville Area MS 1330 S Main St Phoenixville PA 19460*

RIDLEY, OLIVIA P., English Teacher; *b:* Penn Yan, NY; *m:* Ben R.; *c:* Ben Jr., Kirsten Calkins; *ed:* East TX St Univ (BA) Eng, Fr 1962, (MA) Eng, Fr 1963; 5 Addl Hrs Elmira Coll; Attnd SUNY at Binghamton; *cr:* East TX St Univ Grad Asst 1962-63; MacLean Jr HS Fr, Eng Tchr 1963-64; Haverling HS Eng Tchr 1965-; *ai:* Schl Newspaper Adv; NHS, In Service Comm Mem, Sr Pass Advy Comm; NCTE, AFT, NYSUT; JEA Summer Wkshp Schlsp; Article: Eng Journal; *office:* Haverling H S 25 Ellas Ave Bath NY 14810

RIDLEY, VINCENT WILLIAM, Physics & Earth Science Tchr; *b:* Boston, MA; *m:* Grethe Muller Eriksen; *c:* Regina Raustine, Vincent, Erik, Christian; *ed:* Rensselaer Polytechnic Inst (BS) Mechanical Engrng 1957; NY Univ (MS) Nuclear Engrng 1957; Montclair St Univ 56 Addl Credit Hrs; *cr:* George G. Sharp Co Eng 1957-63; Exxon Intnl Co Mgr R&D Marine 1963-86; Kearney HS Sci Tchr 1990-; *ai:* Physics Club Adv; AAPT 1991-; NEA 1989-; Kinnelon Soccer Club 1978-, Sec; BSA 1980-, Unit Commissioner; Optomists Int 1989-; Soc of Naual Architects & Marine Engrs; Best Paper Captain Joseph H. Linnard Prize 1970; Pub Articles; *office:* Kearny HS 336 Devon St Kearny NJ 07032

RIDLON, JAMES A., Professor of Art; *b:* Nyack, NY; *m:* Katherine Rushworth; *c:* James Jr., Kevin, Chris, Kheley; *ed:* Syracuse Univ (BFA) Art Ed 1957, (MFA) Sculpture 1968; San Francisco St Coll Sculpture 1958-59; *cr:* Syracuse Univ Prof 1966-; New York St Summer Schl of Arts, Schl of Visual Arts Artistic Dir 1976-; *ai:* US Sports Acad 1994-, Everson Museum 1996 Trustee; Inst for Arts in Ed at Syracuse Philosopher in Residence 1982-; Sports Artist of Yr 1993; NY St Senate Citation 1990; Book Co-Author; Hum Journal Article; *office:* Syracuse Univ Foundation Dept Shaefer Bldg Syracuse NY 13201

RIEF, LINDA (GUSTAFSON), Language Arts Teacher; *b:* Malden, MA; *m:* George Anthony; *c:* Craig A., Bryan C.; *ed:* Univ of NH (BA) Ger 1966, (MAT) Eng 1980; 30 Grad Credit Hrs; *cr:* Oyster River MS Tchr 1980-;

Univ of NH Instr 1986-; *ai:* NCTE; NEA; NEATE; Kennedy Ctr for Performing Arts Tchr Fellow in Writing 1988; Author Seeking Diversity-Lang Arts with Adolescents; Co-Editor Articles; *office:* Oyster River MS 47 Garrison Ave Durham NH 03824

RIEGAL, MARY CHRISTMAN, 2nd Grade Teacher; *b:* Oak Hill, OH; *m:* Mark; *c:* Tyson, Tara; *ed:* OU at Chillicothe (BA) Elem Ed 1976; *cr:* Scioto Elem 3rd-4th Grd Tchr 1 Yr, 5th-6th Grd Tchr 1 Yr, 2nd Grd Tchr 17 Yrs; *ai:* NEA 1976-; 4-H Adv, 20 Yrs; *office:* Scioto Elem Schl 4701 State Route 776 Jackson OH 45640*

RIEGEL, BRUCE DAVID, Site-Based Management Chrprsn; *b:* Baltimore, MD; *m:* Mary Beth Meyers; *c:* Erin E., David B.; *ed:* Towson St Univ (BS) Bio 1980, (MED) Admin, Supervision 1985; Attnd U of MD Schl of Pharmacy, U of MD Coll Park, Loyola Coll of MD, Johns Hopkins Univ; *cr:* Woodlawn MS Grd 7 Sci Tchr 1980-81; Catonsville Comm Coll Anatomy, Physiology Instr 1981-84; Patapsco MS 8 Grd Sci Tchr 1981-85; Howard Co Pub Schls Asst Prin 1982-85; Howard HS Bio Tchr 1985-; *ai:* Chprsn Site-Based Mngmt Team, Blue Ribbon on Schls Comm, Schl Improvement Team; Stage Production Coord; Phi Delta Kappa 1985-, 10 Yr Svc Awd; HCEA, MSTA, NEA, MAST, MABT, NABT, NAST 1981-; Socc Assoc of Columbia 1992-, Bd of Dir; SAC Coventry Soccer 1995-, Mgr; River Hill Villag Bd 1991-, Bd of Dir; USA Shooting 1994-, Class A cmpetition Ofcl; Co-Author Blue Ribbon Schl of Excl Awd, Tech Vision & Grant Applications, Code of Uniform Behavior, Site-Based Mngmt Team; Author Redbook Excl Schls Awd Application; *office:* Howard HS # 108 8700 Old Annapolis Rd Ellicott City MD 21043*

RIEGER, EDWARD W., Social Studies Teacher; *b:* Pennsgrove, NJ; *m:* Arleen Saleeby; *c:* Edward Jr., Brian, Patricia Hannum; *ed:* Trenton St Coll (BA) Tchng Dev 1967; Glassboro St Coll (MS) Supervision & Curr 1972; Monteclair St Univ (MS) Ec 1975; 47 Hrs Univ of IL Sport Psych; *cr:* Pennsville HS Soc Stud Tchr 1967-; *ai:* Bsbl Coach; NJEA, NEA 1967-; Queen of Apostle Church 1967-, Eucharistic Minister; Jr Achvmt 1985-, Tchr; Articles Pub.*

RIEGER, SAMUEL L., Professor of Chemistry; *b:* Brooklyn, NY; *m:* Wanda Kunkes; *c:* Randall H., Melanie I.; *ed:* Lafayette Coll (BA) Chem 1963; St John's Univ (MS) Organic Chem 1966; Univ of CT (PHD) Organic Chem 1970; *cr:* Univ of CT Teaching Fellow 1966-67, Dupont Fellow Organic Lab Supvr 1967-70; Naugatuck Valley Comm Tech Coll Chem Prof 1970-; *ai:* Fac Adv Amer Chem Society Club; Chem Dept Chm; Amer Chem Soc 1966-; Survivors of Homicide 1994-, Pres; Author Lab Manual; *office:* Naugatock Valley Comm Coll 750 Chase Pky Waterbury CT 06708

RIEHLE, BARRY STEVEN, Physics Teacher; *b:* Cincinnati, OH; *m:* Kathleen A. Giegel; *ed:* Xavier Univ (BS) Physics 1974, (MEd) Physics 1989; Athenaeum of OH (MA) Theology 1978, (MA) Biblical Stud 1979; 4 Hrs Counseling Wright St Univ; 3 Hrs Counseling, 2 Hrs Chem, 2 Hrs Physics Miami Univ; 1 Hr Ec Univ of Cincinnati; 4 1/2 Hrs PE Aurora Univ; *cr:* Cath Central HS Fac & Rel, Sci & Guidance 1978-81; Badin HS Fac Rel 1981-82; St Marys Church Assoc Pastor & Campus Minister 1982-84; Turpin HS Dac Sci 1985-; *ai:* Recycling Club Spon; Mem Care Team; AAPT 1985-; Schl Dist Planning Team 1990-; Tchr of Month 1987, 1989, 1992 & 93; Best Course 1980; NSF Prgm Modern Physics 1985; NSF Prgm Tchng Sci with Toys 1987-88; Topics in Modern Physics at Fermilab 1993; *office:* Turpin H S 2650 Bartles Rd Cincinnati OH 45244

RIELLY, EDWARD JAMES, Eng Prof & Dean of Distance Ed; *b:* Darlington, WI; *m:* Jeanne Marie Smith; *c:* Brendan, Brigid; *ed:* Loras Coll (BA) Eng 1966; U of Notre Dame (MA) Eng 1968, (PHD) Eng 1974; *cr:* St Ambrose Coll Eng Instr 1969-70; St Matthew Cathedral Schl Eng Instr 1974-76; Bishop Dwenger HS Eng Instr 1976-78; St Joseph's Coll Eng Prof 1978-, Dean of Distance Ed 1995-; *ai:* Fac Adv to E. Q., Eng Dept, Interns; Supvr of Writing Tutors; Modern Lang Assoc 1978-; Am Soc for 18th Cent Stud 1982-; Popular Culture Assoc 1993-; Bd of Trustee of Catherine Mc Auley HS 1992-, Vice Chair; Parish Cncl St Edmund'd 1991-, Chprsn; Knight of Columbus 1993-; Family Life Chprsn; Volumes of Poetry Authored: Rain Falling Quietly, Family Portrait; The Furrow's Edge, The Breaking of Glass Horses, My Struggling Soil; Articles & Book Reviews; NEH Grant; Hemingway Fnd Grant; Edited Book; *office:* Saint Josephs Coll 278 Whites Bridge Rd Standish ME 04084

RIENZI, WILLIAM ROBERT, History Teacher; *b:* New Haven, CT; *m:* Geraldine Caciopoli; *ed:* Univ of Bridgeport (BA) His 1967; Southern CT St univ (MA) His 1974; Wesleyan Univ 23 Post Grad Hrs 1974-79; *cr:* Sheridan MS His Tchr 1968-81; Cooperative HS His Tchr 1981-89; Cooperative Arts & Hum HS His Tchr, GATE, Ind Stud, Seminar Prgm 1989-; *ai:* AFT 1968-; New Haven Excl in Ed Grant to Establish Middle East Stud; Mellon Grant for AP European His Wkshp; *office:* Cooperative Arts & Hum HS 444 Orange St New Haven CT 06511

RIEPENHOFF, DOROTHY SANGER, Elementary Music Teacher; *b:* S Hampton, NY; *c:* Arthur Charles, Dorothy Marian, Joseph John, David Alan; *ed:* Averett Jr Coll (AA) Music 1964; Rio Grande Coll (BS) Ed 1969; Coll of Mount St Joseph (MED) Elem Ed 1985; *cr:* Coalton Elem Schl 1st Grd Tchr 1969-70, 1975-79, 4th Grd Tchr 1979-86, Jr HS Math, Music Tchr 1986-87, K-3rd Grd Music Tchr, 5th-6th Grd Band Tchr 1987-; Bundy Elem Schl K-3rd Grd Music Tchr, 5th-6th Grd Band Tchr 1987-; *ai:* Comm Yth Choir Dir; Wellston HS Color Guard Adv; 1st-3rd Grd Choir; NEA, WTA 1969-; OEA, MENC 1987-; Sts Peter & Paul Church, Organist, Choir Dir; *home:* 121 Cedar St Wellston OH 45692

RIEPENHOFF, JOYCE BRADFORD, Spanish Teacher; *b:* Middletown, OH; *m:* David Lous; *c:* Zachary, Rebecca; *ed:* Otterbein Coll (BA) Fr 1971; OH Univ Post Grad Stud Fr 1971-72; Comp Tech at Shawnee St Univ & OH St Univ 1993; *cr:* Clay HS Span & Fr 1973-75; Minford HS Span & Fr 1975-78; Notre Dame HS Span & Fr 1984-88; Wheelersburg HS Span 1988-; *ai:* Span Club Spon; Fac Adv Comm; AATSP 1987-; OH Frgn Lang Assoc 1973-; NEA 1973-; South Cntrl OH Frgn Lang Assoc 1990-, Steering Comm; 4-H Vol Ldr 1994-; St Peters Cath Church 1973-, Organist; Summer Inst on Span Lang & Culture of the Embassy of Spain Schlrshp Winner; Notre Dame HS Tchr of the Yr 1988; *office:* Wheelersburg HS 701 Pirate Dr Wheelersburg OH 45694

RIES, RICHARD L., Retired Eng & Speech Teacher; *b:* Youngstown, OH; *m:* Joan Carol Williams; *c:* Chad, Sean; *ed:* Kent St Univ (BS) Ed, Speech 1966; Westminster Coll (MED) Eng Ed 1974; *cr:* Howland HS Speech, Eng, Broadcasting Tchr 1966-91; Howland MS 7th Grd Eng Tchr 1991-94; *ai:* Head Speech, Debate Coach 1966-81; NEA-R, OEA-R, Trumbull Cty Ret Tchrs, Howland Schls Ret Tchrs 1994-.

RIES, RICK STEPHEN, Fifth Grade Teacher; *b:* Cincinnati, OH; *ed:* Thomas More Coll (BA) Elem Ed 1976; *cr:* Assumption Schl 4th-6th Grd Tchr 1976-; *ai:* Stu Cncl, Acad Team Adv; Cath Schls Comm; NCEA 1976-; Distinguished Grad Awd 1994; *office:* Assumption Schl 1500 Mcmakin Ave Cincinnati OH 45231

RIESELMAN, PAUL JOSEPH, Religious Stud & Spanish Tchr; *b:* Cincinnati, OH; *m:* Mary Lynne Surkamp; *c:* Kathryn Lynne, Heather Elizabeth; *ed:* Xavier Univ (BA) Theology & Span 1972, (MED) Educl Admin 1986; *cr:* All Saints Schl Tchr 1976-78; McNicholas HS Tchr 1978-79; St Bernadette Schl Tchr 1981-85; Gressle Cath Elem Sch Prin 1986-89; St Xavier HS Tchr 1989-; *ai:* All Saints Schl Ed Commission Chair; Ed Comm & Disciplinary Bd; NCEA 1976-; Co-Author Current Soph Text "A Journey of Faith"; *office:* Saint Xavier HS 600 W North Bend Rd Cincinnati OH 45224

RIESS, BARBARA ANN, Physics Teacher; *b:* Brooklyn, NY; *ed:* SUNY at Cortland (BS) Physics 1977; Stonybrook Univ (MALS) Phys Sci 1980; Brooklyn Coll (SAS), (SDA) Educl Admin 1990; Addl 56 Credits Sci, Math, Ed; *cr:* Baldwin Jr HS Sci Tchr 1977-79; Baldwin Sr HS Physics Tchr 1979-96; Brookhaven Natl Lab Particle Physics Tchr 1984-; *ai:* Var Field Hockey, Bowl Team, Sci Hnr Soc Coach; Jr Class, Girls Ath Assn Adv; Shared Decision Making Team; Curr Cncl; Eligibility Comm; Nassau Cty Filt FH Coaches Assn 1984-, Chprsn, Coach of Yr 3 Yrs; AFT, NSTA, LIPTA 1977-; ASCD; NYSUT; STANYS; BTA; PTSA; Baldwin Booster Club 1980-; BEA Educl Grants 1994-95; Tchr of Yr 1994; *office:* Baldwin Sr HS 841 High School Dr Baldwin NY 11510*

RIETHMAN, DENNIS JOSEPH, Agricultural Education Teacher; *b:* Coldwater, OH; *m:* Rita L. Ballmann; *c:* Eric J., Maria D., Kurt G.; *ed:* OH St Univ (BS) Agricultural Ed 1979, (MS) Agricultural Ed 1983; *cr:* Coldwater HS Agricultural Ed 1979-; *ai:* FFA Chptr, Young Farmers Chptr Adv; Coldwater Yth Soccer Coach; Coldwater Tchrs Org 1979-, Sec 3 Yrs; Natl Voc Ag Tchrs Assn, NEA 1979-; Knights of Columbus 1973-; Community Picnic Assn 1983-; Mercer Co Agricultural Soc 1983-; Coldwater PTO 1983-; 5 Amer FFA Degree Recipients; 17 St FFA Degree Recipients; 12 FFA Proficiency Awd Finalist; *office:* Coldwater Jr Sr HS 310 N 2nd St Coldwater OH 45828

RIETZE, PATRICIA MURATORI, Spanish & French Teacher; *b:* New Britain, CT; *m:* Anthony Jr.; *ed:* Cntrl CT St Univ (BS) Fr 1970, (MS) Fr 1976; Italian 1984, Span 1992 Certs 24 Credit Hrs Each; *cr:* St Thomas Jr HS Fr, Italian Tchr 1972-85; Bristol Eastern HS Italian, Span, Fr Tchr 1985-1995; Bristol Cntrl HS Span, Fr Tchr 1995; *ai:* NHS Adv; AFT, Bristol Fed Tchrs, CT Org Lang Tchrs 1985-; NASSP; *office:* Bristol Central HS 480 Wolcott St Bristol CT 06010

RIFE, CONNIE VARSACI, Fifth Grade Enrichment Teacher; *b:* Mount Holly, NJ; *m:* Del; *c:* Steven Ereic, Jeffrey Aaron; *ed:* Bemidji St Coll (BS) Elem Ed 1968; *cr:* Coldwater MI Schls Third Grd Tchr 1968-69; Pemberton Twp Schls Elem Tchr 1969-86, Enrichment Tchr 1986-; *ai:* Sci Fair Chprsn; NEA, BCEA, PTEA 1969-; PTA All Saints Schl 1977-, Pres; Schl Advy Cncl; Harker Wylie Schls Tchr of Yr 1990; *home:* 1411 Noreen Dr Burlington NJ 08016

RIFE, JANE SWEENEY, Retired English Teacher; *b:* Bluefield, WV; *m:* Charles E.; *c:* Mildred B.; *ed:* WV St Coll (BS) Ed Eng 1961; OH St Univ (MA) Ed Rdng 1977; 4 Addl Credit Hrs; *cr:* Starling Jr HS Tchr 1962; Roosevelt Jr HS Eng & Rdng Tchr 1963-76; Briggs HS Eng & Rdng Tchr 1977-94; *ai:* 9th Grd Homecoming Float; NEA, OEA, CEA & COTA 1984-, Outstanding Fr 1988; IRA & ORA 1986-; PTA Outstanding Edctr of the Yr Awd 1994.

RIFFEE, MICHAEL BRIAN, Coordinator; *b:* Portsmouth, NH; *m:* Kate; *c:* Megan, Patrick; *ed:* Coll of Wooster (BA) PE 1980; OH St Univ (MA) Adapted PE 1982; 65 Post Grad Hrs; Certfd Initiatives, High Ropes Instr for Adventure Ed Ctr; *cr:* Beatty Park Elem Schl Tchr of Severe Behavior, Handicapped 1983-87; Centennial HS Occupational Work Adjustment Coord 1987-; *ai:* Head Girls Vlybl, Reserve Girls Sftbl Coach; Bus Dept, Departmental Instrl Support Team Chair; Tech Coord; Dir Adventure Based Substance Abuse Prevention Prgm; CEA, OEA, NEA 1983-; OH HS Vlybl Coaches Assn 1984-, Dist Sec; ASCD 1990-; Phi Kappa Phi 1985-; Colonial Hills Civic Assn 1985-, Sec 1986-87; Edctr of Yr, Columbus City League Vlybl Coach of Yr, Franklin Cty Drug Free Schls Consortium Achvmt Awd 1991; Martha Holden Jennings Scholar Tchr 1995; *office:* Centennial HS 1441 Bethel Rd Columbus OH 43220

RIFKIN, ALYNN SUE, Math Teacher; *b:* Brooklyn, NY; *w:* Ivan Martin (dec); *ed:* Brooklyn Coll (BS) Math 1968; Monmouth Coll (MAT) Math 1976; *cr:* Cedar Ridge HS Math Tchr 1968-94; Old Bridge HS Math Tchr 1994-; *ai:* Asst with Math Team; NEA, NJEA, MCEA, OBEA 1968-; AMTNJ; A2PMT 1980-; *office:* Old Bridge HS 3439 Rt 516 Old Bridge NJ 08857

RIFORGIATO, ROSALIE, 4th Grade Teacher; *b:* Buffalo, NY; *ed:* Bflo St Univ Coll (BS) Elem Ed 1969, (MS) Elem Ed 1971; Inservice Classes; *cr:* East Seneca Elem Schl 4th-5th Grd Tchr 1969-; *ai:* Dist Grd 4 Rep; Bldg Comm; Boces Wkshp; NEA, NYSUT 1969-, Pres; WSTA; PTO 1969-, Pres.

RIGBY, SUSAN HICKEY, Remedial Reading Teacher; *b:* Boston, MA; *m:* Morgan W.; *c:* Brian, Daniel, Matthew, Elizabeth, Jonathan; *ed:* Univ of DE (BSEd) Elem Ed 1977; Attnd Univ of DE Grad Schl Coll of Ed 15 Credits; 40 In-Service Credits; *cr:* Easton MS 8th Grd Tchr 1978-79; W. R. Brown Elem 1, 3, 5 Grd Tchr 1979-; Title I Reading; *ai:* Coach Odyssey of Mind; Math League 1987; NEA, DE St Ed Assn, Caesar Rodney Ed Assn 1978-; WY United Meth Church 1982-, Admin Cncl; Tchr of Yr 1987; Pub in Trade Secrets 1983; *office:* W. Reily Brown Elem 360 Webbs Ln Dover DE 19901*

RIGGS, NANCY STRODTBECK, 1st Grade Teacher; *b:* Hamilton, OH; *m:* Timothy D.; *c:* Jill Marie; *ed:* Miami Univ (BA) Elem Ed 1983; 149 Grad & Post Grad Hrs; *cr:* Hamilton City Schls Elem Tchr 1983-; *ai:* Adopt-A-Schl Bldg Rep; Talent Show Spon; NEA, OEA 1986-, Bldg Mbrshp Rep; Hamilton Classroom Tchrs Assn 1986-; Citywide Adopt-A-Schl Cncl 1991-93, Bd of Dir; HCTA United Way 1995-, Co-Chair, Campaign Co-Chprsn; OH Writing Project Flwshp 1991; *office:* Cleveland Elem Schl 900 S Brookwood Ave Hamilton OH 45013

RIGGS, YVONNE HOLMES, Chem Tchr & Sci Dept Chprsn; *b:* Baltimore, MD; *m:* Charles; *c:* Roxanne, Christopher; *ed:* Morgan Univ (BS) Bio 1965, (MS) Sci Ed 1972; Chem Cert; Post Grad Stud Chem Towson Univ; *cr:* Calvert Cty Bd of Ed Sci Tchr 1965-68; Baltimore Cty Bd of Ed Sci Tchr 1968-; Milford Mill Acad Chem Tchr, Sci Dept Chprsn 1995-; *ai:* Math, Engr, Sci Achvmt, Chemathon, Odessey of the Mind Adv; Chem Tchrs Alliance; MAST 1990-; NEA, TABCO 1968-; NSTA 1995-; Site Base Mngmt 1994-; PTSA 1968-; Zeta Phi Beta 1964-; Cert of Recognition Bd of Ed Balto Cty; Awd Chamber of Commerce; Tchr of Week; Sci Tchr Mentor Awd; *home:* 205 Kearney Dr Owings Mills MD 21117*

RIGHTMYER, JACK KEVIN, 6th Grade English Teacher; *b:* Albany, NY; *m:* Judith Anne; *c:* Erin, Paul; *ed:* Manhattan Coll (BA) Eng & Ed 1980; Notre Dame Coll (MED) Eng & Ed 1987; *cr:* Bishop Gibbons HS 9-12th Grd Eng Tchr 1980-84; Pinkerton Acad 9-12th Grd Eng Tchr 1984-87; Bethlehem MS 6th Grd Eng Tchr 1987-; *ai:* Schl Lit Magazine Moderator; NEA 1987-, Bldg Rep; Awd for Ed Jrnlsm 1995; Schenectady Daily Gazette Writer & Book Reviewer; PBS TV Show Host; *office:* Bethlehem Central MS 332 Kenwood Ave Delmar NY 12054*

RIGIK, ELNORA, Prof of Hum & Dir of Hnrs Prgm; *b:* Thermopolis, WY; *ed:* Linfield Coll (BA) Eng 1964; Harvard Univ (MAT) Eng 1965; Univ of DE (PHD) Eng 1981; *cr:* Anatolia Coll Instr of Eng, Psych 1965-69; Brandywine Coll Asst, Assoc & Prof of Eng 1970-90; Widener Univ Prof of Hum, Dir of Hnrs Prgm 1990-; *ai:* MLA 1975-; CEA 1980-; DE Hum Forum 1980-85; Coll Tchrs Grants Natl Endowment for Hum; Folger Shakespeare Lib Grant; *office:* Widener Univ 1 University Pl Chester PA 19013

RIGNEY, WILLIAM F., Biology Teacher; *b:* Hudson, MA; *m:* Diane Troumpalos; *c:* Cristina, Lauren; *ed:* Framingham St Coll (BS) Bio 1974; Worcester St Coll (MED) Scndry Ed 1979; *cr:* Marlborough HS Bio Tchr 1974-; *ai:* Jr Class Adv; Var Bsbl, Asst Ftbl Coach; Schl Evaluation, Guidance Advisory, Schl Recycle Comm; NHS Fac Cncl; Sci Curr Comm, Schl Cncl & Mediation Cncl; NEA, MA Tchrs Assn 1984-; NSTA MA Bsbl Coaches Assn 1978-; Supervision & Curr Dev Assn 1989 HS Bsbl Coaches Assn 1991-; Natl Assn of Stu Activity Adv 1991-; Marlboro Jr Babe Ruth 1988-; HS Tchr of Yr 1987-88; Tchr of 1987; Tchr of Fall 1985; *office:* Marlborough HS 537 Bo Marlborough MA 01752

RIKE, MARTHA RISH, Foreign Lang Dept Chairperson; *b:* Dayto *m:* William Benton; *c:* David Andrew, Jonathan Charles; *ed:* U Dayton (BA) Fr 1967, (MS) Ed 1986; *cr:* Francis Scott Key Jr HS F Tchr 1968-69; Fairmont West HS Soc Ctr Dir 1971-74; Carroll HS F Lang Dep Chprsn, Fr Tchr 1982-; *ai:* Fr Club Moderator; AATF OFLA 1982-; *office:* Carroll HS 4524 Linden Ave Dayton OH 4543

RIKELMAN, PATRICIA, Computer Dept Chairperson; *b:* Buenos Argentina; *m:* Joshua; *ed:* Westchester Comm Coll (AAS) Bus Sec 1975; Pace Univ (BS) Bus Ed 1991; Mercy Coll ABA Approved Pa Cert; 9 Credits Grad Work Spcl Ed; MS Curr & Instruction; *cr:* West Bus Inst Comp Instr 1985-; Alexander Hamilton HS Bus Ed Stu Tch Pace Univ Information Systems Instr 1992-; Westchester Comm Col Instr 1993-; Bedford Hills Correctional Biling Span Tchr 1995 Westchester Co Bus Ed Assn 1983-; NBEA 1985-; NYSBTA 1990-.

RIKER, RAYMOND, 6th Grade Teacher; *b:* Brooklyn, NY; *m:* Nat Niki; *ed:* St Johns Univ (AA) Bio 1973; Keene St Coll (BA) Elem D. 1977; Univ of NE (MED) Ed 1979; Admin; Univ of VT Guidan Father Flanagans Boys Town 6th-9th Grd Math Tchr 1977-79; Sprir VT MS Spec Ed, Math Tchr 1979-86; Claremont NH Jr High 7th-8 Math Tchr 1987-90; Merrimack Valley MS 6th-8th Grd Math, Sc 1991-; *ai:* Sci Comm; Soccer Coach; NCTM 1987-; *office:* Mer Valley MS 14 Center st Penacook NH 03303*

RILEY, ANGELA JOHNSON, Mathematics Department He Jacksonville, FL; *c:* Corey; *ed:* Lincoln Univ (BA) Math 1971; Univ (MED) Scndry Math Ed 1973; Univ of PA Certs Math, Cur Supvr1986, Scndry Prin, Asst Supt 1992; Temple Univ PHD Can Psycho-Educl Processes, Cmptr Sci Cert Prgm 1987; *cr:* Philadelphi Dist Tchr, Math Specialist, Consultant, Spec Prgms Coord 1971-; A Univ Math, Cmptr Sci Adj Prof 1985-88; Temple Univ Cmptr La 1991-94; *ai:* Mentally Gifted Prgm, Acad Competition Teams Co PRIME, PACT Spon; Schl Recycling Prgm Co-Spon; Annual AIDS Team Spon; NCTM, PCTM, ATMOPAV 1975-; PCSM 1985-; Tabe Bapt Church 1981-, Quest; Alpha Kappa Alpha 1968-, Rec Semi-Finalist Tchr of Yr 1995; NCTM, PCTM, ATMOPAV, Intnl Presenter; Pub Articles; *home:* 53 Bayberry Ln Willingboro NJ 080

RILEY, BRUCE ROBERT, HS Mathematics Teacher; *b:* Havre de MD; *m:* Suzanne Strahorr; *ed:* Univ of MD at Coll Park (BS) M 1987; Loyola Coll of MD (MS) Ed 1996; *ai:* Head Var Ftbl Wrestling Coach; MA Stu Assistance Pgm Team; First Step Parents NEA, MSTA, HCEA 1988-; Harford Cty Yth Ldr Awd 1994; *office:* HS 100 Hieghe St Bel Air MD 21014

RILEY, CAROL SAWICKI, English Teacher; *b:* Queens, NY; *m:* Ke P.; *c:* Kenneth, Dennis; *ed:* Holy Family Coll (BA) Eng 1964; Pos Stud Hunter Coll; *cr:* Christ The King HS Eng Tchr 1964-60; Westfie Schls Vol 1975-86; Roselle Cath HS Tchr 1991-; *ai:* Club Adv Sc Artistic Magazine; NCTE 1991-; *office:* Roselle Catholic HS 1 Rari Roselle NJ 07203

RILEY, CHERYL LEONARD, Span & Frgn Lang Dept Ld Tc Milwaukee, WI; *m:* William; *c:* Sean; *ed:* Univ of FL (BA) Eng 1967; Univ of Hartford, Universidad de Cantabria Spain; Montclair St Jersey City St Coll; Univ of Madrid; *cr:* Ocala FL HS Eng & Spar 1967-69; Roxbury NJ HS Eng & Span Tchr 1969-; *ai:* Sociedad Hon Espanola Adv; Chaperone Study Tours to Spain; Roxbury Goes Under Exchange Prgm Australia; Exchange Prgm Russia; Hands Acro Water Tchr; NJEA, NEA, AATSP FLENJ 1987-; Active in Town P Literacy Vols of Amer ESL Tutor; Resource Guide Translated; Tra Documents for Cty Govt; *home:* 3 Winding Way Denville NJ 07834

RILEY, FRANCES MCFADDEN, Language Arts Teacher; *b:* Haz PA; *m:* Eugene J.; *c:* John, Molly, Catherine; *ed:* Coll Misericordia Eng 1969; Bloomsburg Univ (MS) Early Chldhd & Elem Ed 198 Allen Jr HS Eng Tchr 1969-78; McAdoo Cath Schl Lang Arts Tchr *ai:* Lang Arts & Open House Coord; Drama Dir; Grant Writer; 1981-; Reaching Out 1979-, Pres; Task Force LIU 1985-; Alhambra to Bloomsburg Univ; *office:* Mc Adoo Catholic Elem Schl 35 N Clev St Mcadoo PA 18237

RILEY, GLORIA BERARDUCCI, Pgm Dir, Prof Dental Hygier Charleroi, PA; *m:* Dennis W.; *c:* Lisa; *ed:* Univ of Pittsburgh (RDH) D Hygiene 1969; CA Univ (BS) Ed 1970; John Hopkins Univ (MEL 1977; 8 Post-Grad Credits Beyond Masters; *cr:* Baltimore City Comm Prg Dir, Prof 1971-; *ai:* Amer Dental Hygiene Assn Stu Adv Evaluation, Prgm Evaluation, Fac Senate Exec Comms; Amer D Hygiene 1970-, Delegate; MD St Dental Hygiene 1971-, Pres; Greate Dent Hygiene 1971-, Sec, Delegate; Phi Sigma Alpha Honorary D Hygiene; Pub Articles Amer Assn of Dental Schls Journal; *o* Baltimore City Comm Coll 2901 Liberty Heights Ave Baltimore 21215*

RILEY, KAREN A., 2nd Grade Teacher; *b:* Amsterdam, NY; *m:* Pet *c:* James, Kathleen; *ed:* FMCC (AS) Lbrl Arts 1971; Oneonta (BS) Ed 1973; Permanent Cert 1978; *cr:* Meco Schl 1st, 2nd Grd Tchr 197 Mc Nab Schl 1st, 2nd Grd Tchr 1982-91; Boulevard Schl 2nd Grd 1991-; *ai:* AFT 1973-; Canada Lake Protective Assn 1991-, Bd Mem

RILEY, MARY C., 7th-8th Grd Science Teacher; *b:* West Chester, PA Villanova Univ (BS) Eng, Scndry Ed 1970; 9 Credits Grad Schl; *cr:* Simon & Jude 6th Grd Math, Eng Tchr 1973-75; Catesville Area Cath Schl 7th-8th Grd Eng Tchr 1978-80, Sci Tchr 1980-; *ai:* Chess Club; N 1978-; *office:* Coatesville Area Cath Elem Sch 605 E Lincoln Coatesville PA 19320

RILEY, NEAL ANTHONY, Fourth Grade Teacher; *b:* Worcester, M Mary A. Cencak; *c:* Neal J., Lani K.; *ed:* Univ of MA (MS) Mngmt Anna Maria Coll (MED) Elem Ed 1988; 15 Addl Hrs; *cr:* Rustler House Asst Mgr 1976-79, Unit Mgr 1979-86; Digital Equipment Cafeteria Mgr 1986-87; Paton Eelm Schl Fourth Grd Tchr 1988-; *ai.* Stud Curr Dev Comm; MA Tchrs Assn, NEA 1988-; Millbury Lib 1 Tech Adv; Natl Fnd for Improvement of Ed Grant 1992; Soc Stud Di Grant 1995; *office:* Walter J Paton Elem Sch 58 Grafton St Shrewsbury 01545

RILEY, PAULA GAMACHE, Cmptr Information Tech Instr Middleboro, MA; *m:* Stephen A.; *c:* Patrick; *ed:* Bristol Comm Coll Bus Admin 1979; Johnson & Wales Univ (BS) Acctng 1996; Coopercraft Guild Keypunch, Cmptr Operator, Programmer 196 Sheridan Silver Programmer 1976-80; Old Colony Regnl Voc Tec Shop, Related Instr 1980-; *ai:* Introductory After-Schl Prgm I Teamsters Local 59 1980-; St Bernard's Church 1978-; Tandy Tech Nom 1995; *office:* Old Colony Regnl Voc Tech HS 476 North Rochester MA 02770

RILEY, PETER H., Music & Chorus Director; *b:* Morristown, NJ Martha Francis Bockoven; *c:* Daniel Stanton; *ed:* Gettysburg Coll Music Ed 1969; 12 Addl Hrs Peabody Conservatory; 12 Addl Hrs Chester Univ; 9 Addl Hrs Carlow Coll; 3 Addl Hrs IN Weslayan;

d Area Schls Band Dir 1969-85, Music,Choral Dir1969-; *ai:* All ate & Low Bass Choirs; 3rd & 4th Grd Chorus; Dist Tech Comm; ic Ed Assn 1969-, 25 Yr Awd; PA St Ed Assn 1969-; Fairfeild Ed 69-, Pres 1988-89; BSA 1986-, Asst Scout Master; St James Luth 1973-, Sunday Schl Tchr; *office:* Fairfield Area Schls 4840 d Rd Fairfield PA 17320*

, PETER KEVEN, Business Teacher; *b:* Rome, NY; *m:* Diane Jane ski; *c:* Heidi, Kelli, Nicholas; *ed:* Fulton-Montgomery Comm Coll Bus Mgmt 1970; SUNY at Buffalo (BS) Bus Ed 1972; 37 Hrs of ork SUNY at Potsdam; Permanent Cert SUNY at Oswego; *cr:* Case us Tchr 1972-80; Watertown HS Bus Tchr 1981-83; Pulaski HS Bus 84-; *ai:* Var Boys & Girls Cross Cntry & Var Boys Bsktbl Coach; ı Comm; AFT 1972-; NYSUT 1972-; Pulaski Pub Lib Bd 1988-92, n; *office:* Pulaski Acad & Cntrl Schl 4624 Salina St Pulaski NY

, ROBERT C., Global Studies Teacher; *b:* Saranal Lake, NY; *m:* .; *c:* Marcia, Gregory; *ed:* Paul Smith Jr Coll (AA) Lbrl Arts 1969; at Potsdam (BA) His 1971; SUNY at Albany (MA) His, Ed 1973; th Glens Falls Jr HS Global Stud Tchr 1971-; *ai:* NYSUT, AFT S Glens FAlls Tchrs Assn 1971-, Bldg REp; *office:* South Glen Falls Hudson St South Glens Falls NY 12803*

, ROBERT THOMPSON, Amer & Mid East Studies Tchr; *b:* ton, CT; *m:* Marie F.; *c:* Robert, Dawn; *ed:* WCSU (BA) Elem Ed MA) Scndry His 1980; Span as a Second Lang 3 Credits; *cr:* Morris 5th-6th Grd Tchr 1971-77; Rogers Park Jr HS 7th-8th Grd Tchr); Danbury HS 11th-12th Grd Tchr, Coord 1990-; *ai:* PEACE Prgm; Prgm Wrote, Implemented, Coord; NEA 1971-, Rep; Curr Cncl Class Advs of US 1993-; VF Wars 1975-; Elks, Amer Legion 1980-; y Bd of Ed & Dr Singi Supt Cert of Awd; Wrote, Implemented Asian East Stud Prgm.*

, ROSSANNA V., Spanish Teacher; *b:* Barranquilla, Columbia; *m:* D.; *c:* Carmen Hale; *ed:* Western KY Univ (BS), (BA) Art, Sci, Ed, , Pre-Law 1992; Attnd Vol St Comm Coll 1988-89, Shawnee St Coll at Portsmouth 1984-86, OH Northern Univ 1980-83; Eng as a Lang OH Univ at Athens 1978, 1980, 1983-84, Tulane Univ 1978; Lang & Intercultural Stud Univ de la Costa 1976-79; *cr:* R. V. R. xec Asst 1974-77; Ricardo Viloria Rodriguez Ltd Supervision ees, Inventory Control 1974-77; OH Northern Univ Span Tutor ang 1981-82; Klugge, Donahue & Dugan, Attorneys at Law ter, Translator 1981-82; Court of Appels Court Translator 1982; Pvt utoring 1985; Shawnee St Comm Coll Taught Conversational Span oc Security Admin Data Entry & Location, Govt Formats & Code Bookkeeping, Interviewing, G4 Title II, IV 1985; K-Mart Customer ep 1985-87; Artley's Asst Mgr 1987-88; Howard Elem Schl ised Third-Fourth Grd After Schl Act Prgm 1988-89; Sumner Cty ub Tchr 1992; Vena Stewart Elem Asst Dir After Schl Prgm 1992; sonville HS Span Tchr 1992-93; ACRE Corp Mrktg Consultant 3; PortsmouthWest HS FrgnLang Chprsn 1993-; *ai:* Lang Fair; Span Spanish Talent Show; Mexico, US of Amer Intnl Yth Prgm Coord; a Sister City; South Cntrl OH Frgn Lang Alliance; Oh Frgn Lang OH Vly Frgn Lang Assn; NEA; Phi Sigma Alpha; Sigma Delta, Pres, 0-91, 1995; Royal Acad of Lang; Otway Festival, Coord; Preserving Cty Covered Bridge; Active Church Mem; Western KY Pres List Ashland Oil Golden Apple Achiever Awd 1995; Zprach Diploma Ger Phi Sigma Delta, Epsilon Mu Deans Nomination Span Royal Acad *office:* Portsmouth West HS 1420 13th St Portsmouth OH 45663*

, VERONICA ANNE, English Teacher; *b:* Greenville, PA; *m:* H.; *c:* Susan; *ed:* PA St Coll at Ebinboro (BSE) Eng Ed 1965; SUNY hamton (MSEd) Eng Ed 1987; *cr:* Beaty Jr HS Eng Tchr 1965-67; HS Eng Tchr 1967-70; Whitney Point Cntrl Schl Eng Tchr Eng Tchr 5, Eng Tchr 1987-; *ai:* AFT 1987-; NYSUT 1987-; Whitney Point Assn 1987-; *office:* Whitney Point HS Keibel Rd Whitney Point NY

, VIRGINIA KEYLER, 6th Grade Teacher; *b:* Montclair, NJ; *m:* n Clark; *c:* Erin, Stephen; *ed:* Tusculum Coll (BA) Elem Ed 1973; e Tract Schl 2nd Grd Tchr 1973-80, 4th Grd Tchr 1980-82, 6th Grd 982-; *ai:* Safety Patrol Adv; NEA 1973-; NJEA 1973-, Fac Rep.*

-REID, TREVAR D., English Teacher; *b:* Brooklyn, NY; *ed:* Coll of City Univ of NY (BA) Eng & Commnctn 1989; Rutgers EDM) Scndry Eng Ed 1993; *cr:* Inst for Electrical & Elect Eng Conf 990-93; Plainfield HS Stu Tchr 1993; Highland Park HS Eng Tchr *ai:* Class Adv; Black His Month Comm; NEA, NJEA & NCTE

DORIS STILES, Business Education Teacher; *b:* York, PA; *m:* l K.; *c:* Eric, Andria, Mark; *ed:* York Coll of PA (BS) Acctng, Bus 87; Shippensburg Univ (MED) Bus Ed 1993; 12 Addl Hrs; *cr:* rd-Dale HS Bus Ed Tchr 1987-; *ai:* Schl Newspaper, Stu Secretaries Grad Requirements, Project, Discipline, Schl Life Comms; NBEA, Delta Phi Epsilon 1987-; St Paul Luth Church 1951-, Sec 25 Yrs; RR 3 Box 89A Glen Rock PA 17327*

NG, LOIS ELLIOTT, Second Grade Teacher; *b:* Pittsburgh, PA; *m:* H.; *c:* Kerma Reiss; *ed:* Waynesburg (BED) Ed 1962; Wilkes Coll Ed 1990; *cr:* Philadelphia Pub Schls Grd Schl Art, Rdng Tchr 1962-; s Hopkinson Schl 2nd Grd Tchr 1970-; *ai:* Spon Club for Mentally ; Lititz Moravian Church Sunday Schl Tchr; Daughters of Amer ation Schlrshp Good Citizen Chm; Pilot Prgms for Scholastic in Sci; f PA Linguistic Rdng Prgm 1965, Grd Chair 1994-95.

IER, MARY BONTEMPO, Spanish Teacher; *b:* New Haven, CT; *m:* m D.; *c:* Chloe; *ed:* Drew Univ (BA) Pol Sci, Span Lang 1988; Univ (MA) Span Lit 1994; Cert Southern CT St Univ; *cr:* Mt Pleasant Tchr 1990-; *ai:* Future Edctrs of Amer Spon; La Sociedad Honoraria nia Spon; AATSP 1992-; MAASCUS Grant Future Edctrs of Amer; t FLAIR Comm; *office:* Mount Pleasant HS 5201 Washington Blvd ngton DE 19809*

LDI, KAREN HOLDA, 8th Grd Math & Earth Sci Tchr; *b:* Corona, *l:* Queens Coll (BA) Elem Ed 1975, (MA) Ed 1978; *cr:* Holy Ghost nian Schl 4th Grd Tchr 1976-79; St Joan of Arc Schl 8th Grd Tchr, Coord 1979-; *ai:* Arts, Crafts Act Tchr; Yrbk Adv; NCEA 1979-; St Joan Of Arc Schl 3527 82nd St Jackson Heights NY 11372

LDI, MICHAEL F., 7th Grade Social Studies Tchr; *b:* Stamford, *l:* Southern CT St Univ (BA) Spec Ed 1986; Univ of Bridgeport (MS) Ed 1987; 15 Credit Hrs Towards 6th Yr Educl Mngmt; *cr:* Northeast Schl 5th Grd Tchr 1987-91; Francisco Ramos MS 7th, 8th, 9th Grds chr 1991-92; Turn of River MS Spec Ed Tchr 1992-94; Dolan MS 7th oc Stud Tchr 1994-; *ai:* Cross Cntry Coach; Diversity, Soc Stud Curr s; *office:* Dolan MS 51 Toms Rd Stamford CT 06906*

UDO, THEONE M., Science Teacher; *b:* Hicksville, NY; *m:* Robert Alexa; *ed:* Hofstra Univ (BA) Sci Ed 1988; Stonybrook Univ (MA) d 1993; *cr:* St Andrews Sci Tchr 1982-89; H. Frank Carey Schl Sci 989-; *ai:* Chrldr Adv; Awd Comm; NFT, NEA 1989-; *office:* H Frank HS 230 Poppy St Franklin Square NY 11010*

, ELLIN SALIT, Eng Prof & Commnctn Arts Prof; *b:* Brooklyn, NY; mes F. Fauvell; *c:* David, Patricia, Kate Fauvell, James M. Fauvell; Cornell Univ (BA) Eng 1957; Lehman Coll (mS) Cnslng 1977; lyn Coll 21 Credits Grad Speech & Hearing; NYU 12 Credits Grad Speech & Hearing; New Schl 6 Credits Grad Commnctn Arts; NY Inst Tech 9 Credits; *cr:* York Coll Eng Instr 1984-86; Bronx Comm Coll Eng Instr 1988-91; NY Inst of Tech Eng Instr 1991-; Iona Coll Eng Instr 1994-; *ai:* Schl Newspaper Adv; Intnl Fluency Assn 1993-; Stuttery Resource Fndtn 1987-, Pres; Books; The Stutterer in the Classroom & Directory of Fluency Programs; *home:* 123 Oxford Rd New Rochelle NY 10804

RINDY, PATRICIA PICINO, Business Teacher; *b:* Sharon, PA; *m:* Eugene Edward; *c:* Gina M. Hurton, Jill S. Marooni, John J.; *ed:* Youngstown St Univ (ABA) Bus 1953, (BSEd) Ed 1965, (MSEd) Ed 1976; Post Grad Work; *cr:* US Steel Corp Data Processor 1953-60; Hubbard HS Bus Tchr 1974-; *ai:* FBLA, Stu Cncl, Teen Inst Adv; HEA 1974-, Prepared Publication; OEA, NEA 1974-; ABWA 1979-; Ldrshp, Tech Comms 1995-; Outstdng Tchr Trumbull Cty; Various Stdnts Govt Grants; *home:* 7601 Connelly Rd Masury OH 44438

RINE, JEROME T., Retired 5th Grade Teacher; *b:* Tappahanock, VA; *m:* Bonnie Rider; *c:* Jerome Jr., Joanne Rine Weiss, Kelly James, Jamie R.; *ed:* East Stroudsburg Univ (BS) Elem Ed 1962; 15 Credit Hrs; *cr:* Smithfield Elem Schl 5th Grd Tchr 1962-92; *ai:* East Stroudsburg Ed Assn, PA St Ed Assn, NEA 1962-.

RINE, RUTH KILPATRICK, Varsity Field Hockey Coach; *b:* Philadelphia, PA; *m:* Charles Arlen; *c:* Charles Arlen Jr., Curtis Ethan, Ruth Kristin Rine Barnes, Debra Elizabeth Rine Garcia; *ed:* Gettysburg Coll (BA) Math 1961; *cr:* Northern Burlington Cty Regnl Jr-Sr HS Math Tchr 1961-62; Greencastle-Antrim HS Field Hockey Coach 1985-; Antrim Twp Auditor 1996; PIAA Track & Field Ofcl 1996; *ai:* Vol Inter Lib Loan Prgm, Sci Fair; Long Range Planning Comm; USFHA; PIAA; YMCA Gymnastics Parents Assn 1975-, Treas; GAHS Band Boosters Treas; Sportsmanship Awd 1994-95; Coach of Yr 1995; *office:* Greencastle-Antrim HS 300 S Ridge Ave Greencastle PA 17225

RINEHART, DONALD R., Religion Professor; *b:* Morrow Cty, OH; *m:* Janet Klingensmith; *c:* Melissa Acuna, Melinda Ward, Jonathan Todd; *ed:* Ashland Coll (BSEd) Scndry Ed 1959; Univ of AZ (MED) Ed & Guidance 1962; Ashland Theological Sem (MDiv) Theology 1970; Consort Higher Ed Rel (DMin) Chrstn Ed 1974; *cr:* Tuscon Pub Schl Tchr & Coach 1959-61; Smithville Brethren Church Pastor 1965-69; Ashland Univ Dean of Schl of Arts & Hum 1980-88; Ashland Univ Prof of Religion 1959-; *ai:* United Way of Ashland Cty Campaign Comm; Provost Search Comm Chair; Religion Club Fac Adv; Stu Ctr Capital Campaign Inst Division Chair; AAR 1978-; NAPCE 1989-; Mentor Awd 1986 & 1996, Alumni Distinguished Svc 1982 & 1994, Sr Honorary Soc Awd 1987 from Ashland Univ; General Conf of the Brethren Church Moderator 1983; Article Ashland Theological Bulletin 1976; *office:* Ashland Univ 401 College Ave Ashland OH 44805

RINEHART, JANET L., Teacher; *b:* Goshen, IN; *m:* Don; *c:* Melissa Acuna, Melinda Ward, Todd; *ed:* Ashland Coll (BSEd) Elem Ed 1959, (MED) Curr 1979; 43 Addl Grad Ed Credit Hrs; 16 Grad Credit Hrs Mid Eastern Stud; *cr:* Tucson Pub Schls 6th Grd Tchr 1959-61; Ashland City Schls 6th Grd Tchr 1961-63; Green Local Schls Kndgtn Tchr 1967-68; Ashland City Schls 3-6 Grd Tchr 1972-; *ai:* Ashland City, Ashland Elem Curr Comms; Ashland Univ Acad Affairs Comm; Ashland Univ, Ashland City Schls Consortium; NEA, OEA, ACTA 1984-; Ashland Univ Bd of Trustees 1993-; AUAA 1983-; Jennings Grant Recipiant; Jennings Scholar; Ashland Tchr of Yr; Fulbright Scholar to Israel, Egypt; *office:* Grant St Schl 730 Grant St Ashland OH 44805*

RINEHART, KEN, Director of Guidance; *b:* Galion, OH; *m:* Barbara C. Schmidt; *c:* Tim, Mark; *ed:* Bluffton Coll (BA) Soc Stud Ed 1970; Bowling Green St Univ (MED) Guid, Cnslng 1976; *cr:* Spencerville HS Tchr, Head Bsktbl Coach 1970-78; Ontario HS Cnslr 1978-87; Shelby HS Guid Dir 1987-; *ai:* OH Assn of Coll Admission Cnslrs 1980-; Shelby Ed Assn 1987-; Chrstn Ed Comm 1991-; Trinity Luth Church Comm; Living with AIDS Suport Group 1995-, Group Facilitator; Southern Poverty Law Ctr 1994-.

RINEHART, ROBERT L., Computer Education Teacher; *b:* York, PA; *m:* Maria B.; *c:* Ann M.; *ed:* Millersville Univ (BA) Philosophy 1966; Temple Univ (MA) Philosophy 1975, (MSD) Math 1978; St Joseph Univ Comp Sci 12 Hrs; LaSalle Univ Comp Sci 3 Hrs; *cr:* West Phila HS Math & Comp Sci Tchr 1975-87; Widener Un Adj Comp Ed Tchr 1985-; Carver HSES Comp Sci Tchr 1987-; *ai:* Grants in Comp Ed; *office:* Carver HS for Engrng & Sci 17th & Norris St Philadelphia PA 19121

RINELLA, VINCENT JOHN, Biology Teacher; *b:* Schenectady, NY; *m:* Maria Raymonda; *c:* Cory, Kelsey, Vincent III; *ed:* SUNY at Potsdam (BA) Bio 1974; Elmira Coll (MS) Ed 1976; 24 Credit Hrs Beyond MS; *cr:* Shenendehowa Cntrl Schl Bio Tchr 1975-; *ai:* AFT, NYSUT 1974-; Natl Sci Fnd Grant; GE Star Aw Winner; Reg Outstanding Tchr Aw; *office:* Shenendehowa Sr HS 970 Rt 146 Clifton Park NY 12065

RINELLO, PATRICIA, Teacher; *b:* Port Chester, NY; *m:* Joseph; *c:* Joseph, Heather; *ed:* St Univ at Albany (BA) Eng & Speech 1965; Manhattanville Coll (MA) Hum; *cr:* Hastings HS Speech & Theatre Tchr 1965-69; Port Chester HS Speech & Theatre Chprsn 1969-71; Rye Neck HS Hum & Theatre Tchr & Arts Facilitator 1977-; *ai:* 11th & 12th Grd Class Adv; NEA 1965-; Natl Assn of Stu Activity Adv 1994-; Port Chester Schls 1974-92, Pres 3 Terms, Dist #5 Bd Mem; Westchester-Putnam Schl Bd Assn Awd; Citations for Svc on Schl Bd from NY St Assembly, Cty of Westchester & Villages of Portchester & Rye Brook.

RINEY, DANIEL EDWARD, Amer History & Geography Tchr; *b:* Darby, PA; *m:* Lorana Elizabeth; *ed:* Millersville St (BA) Soc Stud 1968; Antioch Coll (MS) Urban Ed 1975; *cr:* Pulaski Jr Schl Tchr 1968-88; Smedley MS Tchr 1988-92; Main Street Schl Tchr 1992-; *ai:* IM Coord; Chester Upland Ed Assn, PSEA, NEA 1968-; Amer Legion Post 926 1985-, Fin Ofcr; Tchr of Yr Smedley MS 1991; *office:* Main Street Schl 704 Main St Upland PA 19015

RING, CONSTANCE MARIE, Math Teacher; *b:* Dayton, OH; *m:* Matthew; *ed:* Univ of Akron (BA) Sec Ed, Math, Eng 1992; Working Towards MA Univ of Cincinnati; *cr:* Private Math Tutor 1992-; Lebanon City Schls HS Math Tchr 1993-; Univ of Cincinnati Calculus Instr 1996; *ai:* SADD Adv; Soc, Lang Comm Chair; ON TASC; Math Curr Comm; Dist Tchr of Month 1995; *office:* Lebanon HS 160 Miller Rd Lebanon OH 45036

RING, EVELYN B., HS Counselor; *b:* New York, NY; *ed:* Ithaca Coll (BA) Psych 1971; Syracuse Univ (MS) Cnslng Psych 1972; Attnd SUNY at Plattsburgh; *cr:* Queensbury HS Cnslr 1972-79; Clinton HS Cnslr 1979-88; Fayetteville-Manlius HS Cnslr 1988-; *ai:* Crisis Team; Character Ed Steering & NHS Comms; ABC Adv; Guid Advy Cncl Mem; Coll Night Coord; Pupil Prsnl Svcs; NEA, AFT, NYACAC & NYSUT; Comm Connections; Comm Task Force on Violence; A Class Act Awd; *office:* Fayetteville-Manlius HS 8201 E Seneca Tnpk Manlius NY 13104

RINGEL, MARLANE BALDRIDGE, 5th Grade Teacher; *b:* Hamilton, OH; *c:* Michael; *ed:* Miami Univ (BS) Elem Ed 1963; Xavier Univ (MS) Ed 1972; Univ of Cincinnati 18 Quarter Hrs; Miami Univ 15 Addl Hrs; Drake Univ 6 Addl Hrs; *cr:* Amanda Elem Schl 1st Grd Tchr 2 Yrs; Allison Elem Schl 1st Grd Tchr 2 Yrs; Rochester Schls Sub Tchr 1 Yr; Buchanan Elem Schl 1st Grd Tchr 16 Yrs, 3rd Grd Tchr 9 Yrs, 5th Grd Tchr 2 Yrs; *ai:* Mentor Tchr 1990-91; Lang Arts Comm; Math Comm, Lead Tchr; NEA, OEA, HCTA 1990-; Delta Kappa Gamma 1991-; Booster Club 1989-, Advy Bd; Lucky Ladies Stock Club 1995-; IRA 1985-; Jenning Scholar 1983-84; *office:* Buchanan Elem Schl Hancock & Harmon Ave Hamilton OH 45011*

RINGS, MARIANNE HAITE, English Teacher; *ed:* Coll of St Rose (BA) Eng 1965; SUNY at Albany Master Work 1974; *ai:* Prin Advy Comm; Former Class Adv; Yrbk Adv; Chrldng; Pride Club; Waterleit Tchrs Assn 1965-, Pres, VP, Greivance Chair, Bldg Rep; PTA; Jr League of Albany 1982-92; Reg Ford Bank of Northeastern NY 1985-92, Pres of Bd; NY St PTA Schlsp; NY St Eng Cncl Tchr of the Yr 1983; *office:* Watervliet Jr Sr HS Wiswall Ave Watervliet NY 12189

RINGWOOD, DAVID C., History Teacher; *b:* Auburn, NY; *m:* Mary Babiarz; *ed:* LeMoyne Coll (BA) His 1984; SUNY at Cortland (MS) Ed 1990; Schl of Irish Stud Ireland 1983; *cr:* Corcoran HS His Tchr 1984-; *ai:* Discipline Task Force; Schl Improvement Comm; Site Based Facilitator; Mock Trial Adv; Stu Tchr Mentor; Cntrl NY Cncl for Soc Stud 1989-; NYS Cncl for Soc Stud 1995-; NCSS 1993-; Syracuse Tchrs Assn Mini-Grant 1991; NYNEX Grant for Tchr Ed 1990; *office:* Corcoran HS 919 Glenwood Ave Syracuse NY 13207

RINKER, NATALIE ANN (TRPIK), 6th Grade Teacher; *b:* Johnson City, NY; *m:* Duane R.; *c:* Richard Karl, Christine Sears; *ed:* SUNY at Cortland (BSE) Elem Ed 1966; *cr:* George W Johnson Schl 5th Grd Tchr 1976-78; George H Nichols Schl 6th Grd Tchr 1978-82; Charles F Johnson Schl 6th Grd Tchr 1982-; *ai:* Frost Vly Camp Trip Coord; UE PRIDE Comm; NEA 1976-; Endicott Tchrs Assoc 1976-, Bldg Rep; NYSUT; Two Rivers Ethnic Festival Comm 1985-.

RIOLO, LOUIS THOMAS,JR., Secondary Social Studies Tchr; *b:* New York, NY; *ed:* Bucknell Univ (BA) Ec 1988; Fordham Univ (MS) Ed Psych 1992; *ai:* Var Bsktbl & Girls Vllybl Coach.

RIOTTO, MARY DIANE, Second Grade Teacher; *b:* Brooklyn, NY; *m:* Erik D. Johnson; *ed:* Suffolk Cty Comm Coll (AA) Gen Stud 1972; SUNY at Stony Brook (BA) Ed 1974; Dowling Coll (MS) Ed 1978; 75 Addl Hrs; *cr:* William Floyd Elem Schl Grd 3 Tchr 1974-75; Nataniel Woodhull Elem Schl Grd 3 Tchr 1975-80; Moriches Elem Schl Grd 4, 2 Tchr 1980-; *ai:* Stu Tchr Trng 1987-; Bldg Ldrshp Team 1984-93; Brookhaven Natl Lab Elem Sci Fair Judge 1989-; William Floyd United Tchrs 1974-, Bldg Rep 1978-79; NY St United Tchrs, AFT, NEA 1974-; Long Island Symphonic Choral Assn 1977-; NY St Schl Recognition Prgm Exemplary Schl 1986-87; NY St Elem Schl of Excl 1989-90, 1993; Natl Blue Ribbon Schl of Excl 1989-90, 1993-94; *office:* Moriches Elem Schl Louis Ave Moriches NY 11955*

RIOUX, MARGARET ANNE, Math, Science & Reading Tchr; *b:* Fall River, MA; *m:* Armond W.; *ed:* Bridgewater St (BA) Elem Ed 1967; *cr:* Luther Schl Third Grd Tchr 1967-78, Sixth Grd Tchr 1979-85; Joseph Case Jr HS Sixth Grd Tchr 1986-; *ai:* NEA, MTA 1967-; Swansea Edctrs Assoc 1967-, Sec; *home:* 35 Manton St Fall River MA 02724

RIOUX, SUZANNE MARIE, HS Mathematics Teacher; *b:* Weymouth, MA; *ed:* Univ of NH (BS) Jr High, MS Math Ed 1992; HS Cert Through NH Coll at Manchester; *cr:* Alvirne HS Math Tchr 1992-; *ai:* Coach Asst Girl's Cross Cntry, Head Girls Winter, Spring Track; NH-ATMEN 1993-; *office:* Alvirne HS Derry Rd Hudson NH 03051*

RIPCHIK, PAUL JAMES,JR., HS Business Teacher; *b:* Saratoga Springs, NY; *ed:* Siena Coll (BS) Mrktg, Mngmt 1987; Coll of St Rose (MS) Educl Psych 1994; *cr:* Broadalbin-Perth Cntrl Schls HS Bus Tchr 1989-; *ai:* Var Ftbl Coach; Schl Store, DECA Adv; Bsbl Coach Coll of St Rose; NY St Pub HS Ftbl Coaches Org 1996; *office:* Broadalbin-Perth Cntrl Schls 100 Bridge St Ext Broadalbin NY 12025

RIPKE, DAVID CHARLES, Guidance Cnslr & Athletic Dir; *b:* Amarillo, TX; *w:* Marilynn D. Bowditch; *c:* Shannon Krieger, Tamara Mast, Ryan; *ed:* Bluffton Coll (BS) Bio 1967; Univ of Toledo (MED) Guidance & Counseling 1973; *cr:* Pettisville Local Schls Guidance & Ath Dir 1967-; *ai:* Ath Dir; Var Bsbl Coach; Sr Class Adv; Driver Ed Tchr; Pettisville Tchrs Assn 1967-, Pres; Defiance Area HS Bsbl Coaches Assn; 1975-, Treas; *office:* Pettisville HS 232 Summit St Pettisville OH 43553

RIPP, KATHLEEN MARIE, Spanish Teacher; *b:* New York City, NY; *ed:* St Anselm Coll (BA) Span 1993; *cr:* Salem HS Span Tchr 1993-; *ai:* Frosh Class, Span Club Adv; AATSP, ACTFL, NEA 1993-; *office:* Salem HS 44 Geremonty Dr Salem NH 03079

RIPPEL, PATRICIA BLACK, Fifth Grade Teacher; *b:* Derry, PA; *m:* Jerry Mosshart; *c:* Laura Elizabeth Rippel Maxwell, Daniel; *ed:* Westminster Coll (BA) Eng 1955; IN Univ of PA Cert Elem Ed, Grad Credits; *cr:* Blairsville Elem Schl Fourth Grd Tchr 1973-73, Fifth Grd Tchr 1974-; *ai:* NEA, PSEA 1973-; Century Club of Blairsville 1963-, Pres; Duplicate Bridge Club of IN 1980-, Pres; Burrell Twp Lib Bd 1988-90; Judicial Comm to Select Cty Judge 1992; *home:* 60 Dean Dr Blairsville PA 15717

RIPPEY, BETTY THOMPSON, Mathematics Teacher; *b:* Gary, WV; *m:* Will Neeley Jr.; *c:* Will N., George F., Robert D.; *ed:* WV Univ (BS) Math 1951; Dayton Univ (MS) Admin, Supvr 1981; Attnd OH Univ; Wheeling Coll; *cr:* Coalwood Jr HS Math Tchr 1951-52; Gary HS Math Tchr 1954-55; Bellaire HS Math Tchr 1964-66; St Clairsville HS Math Tchr 1967-68; John Yeates Math Tchr 1968-70; Martins Ferry HS Math Tchr 1971-; *ai:* Sr Adv; OEA, NEA 1971-; MFEA 1971-, Treas; OH Cncl Tchrs of Math; Delta Kappa Gamma 1973-; PSi Chapter 1973-, Pres, 1st VP, 2nd VP; *office:* Martins Ferry HS Hanover St Martins Ferry OH 43935

RIPPEY, SANDY SCHULENBERG, Second Grade Teacher; *b:* Buffalo, NY; *m:* Will N. III; *c:* Alison Rochelle, Will N. IV; *ed:* Kent St Univ (BA) Elem Ed 1976; Ashland Univ Continuing Ed Whole Lang, Rdng 1989; *cr:* Kent City Schls 1st Grd Tchr 1977-83, 2nd Grd Tchr 1983-; *ai:* Neighborhood for Amer Heart Assn Chprsn; HS Cheerleading Vol; KEA 1977-; *home:* 534 Bowman Dr Kent OH 44240*

RIPPLE, KEVIN, Science Teacher; *b:* Smithtown, NY; *m:* Dawn M. Francoeur; *ed:* SUNY Coll at New Paltz (BA) Physics Ed 1991; SUNY at Stony Brook (MALS) Sci Ed 1995; *cr:* Port Jefferson UFSD Physics Tchr 1991-92; Ctr Moriches USFD Physics, Sci Tchr 1992-; *ai:* Jr Class Adv; Tech Comm; AFT 1991-; LIPTA, AAPT 1991-, Newsletter Ed; Tchr Rsrch Assoc Brookhaven Natl Lab 1995; *office:* Ctr Moriches UFSD 511 Main St Center Moriches NY 11934

RIPPLE, LEE ALLEN, English Teacher & Dept Chprsn; *b:* Johnstown, PA; *ed:* Saint Francis Coll (BA) Eng 1965; (ME) Eng Ed 1976; 18 Hrs Cmptr Prgmng; Univ of Pittsburgh & Penn St Univ Eng Post Grad Credits; *cr:* Windber Area HS Eng Tchr 1965-, Dept Chprsn 1983-; *ai:* Dramatics Club; WAEA, PSEA & NEA 1965-; PCTE; NCTE; Lib Bd 1966-72, Sec, Pres; Comm Bldg Bd 1980-93, Sec, Cert of Merit; Cty Bd of Assistance 1981-87; Cambria-Somerset Young Woman of Yr Bd 1990-95; OBE Steering Comm; *office:* Windber Area HS 2301 Graham Ave Windber PA 15963

RIPPLE, REA KARU, Math Instructor; *b:* Soltau, W Germany; *m:* William Frederick; *c:* Aleksander; *ed:* Hiram Coll (BA) Ed 1968; Univ of Toledo (ME) Ed 1971; Attnd Hiedelberg Coll, Drake Univ & Ashland Coll; *cr:* Atkinson Schl 1st Grd Tchr 1968-70; Lincolnshire Schl 1st-2nd Grd Tchr 1970-73; Bellevue Jr High EMR Tchr 1973-75; Fremont Jr High His Tchr 1986-87 & Math Tchr 1987-; *ai:* 7th Grd Adv; Youth Tennis Coach; FEA, OEA & NEA 1968-; Delta Kappa Gamma Soc Intnl 1991-; Crystal Apple Awd; *office:* Fremont Jr HS 501 Croghan St Fremont OH 43420

RISCH, THEODORE THOMAS, Second Grade Teacher; *b:* Johnstown, PA; *m:* Judy J. Saylor; *c:* Sarah, Thomas, Timothy; *ed:* Univ of Pittsburg (BS) Elem Ed 1974; *cr:* North Star Schl Dist Sixth Grd Math Tchr 1974-75;

Fourth Grd Tchr 1975-76; Second Grd Tchr 1976-; *ai:* Stu Cncl Adv; Ski Club Adv; Head Tchr; NEA, PSEA 1974-; Somerset Cty ARC 1978-, Treas 4 Yrs,Pres 2 Yrs; Dir Camp PARC 12 Yrs; *office:* North Star West Elem Schl Jennerstown PA 15547*

RISDEN, GERALD ALAN, Band Director; *b:* Long Brandh, NJ; *m:* Marilyn Fuge; *c:* Jeffrey, Susan, Julie; *ed:* Trenton St Coll (BA) Music Ed 1967, (MED) Music 1974; Attnd Philadelphia Coll of Bible Grad Schl; *cr:* Long Branch Jr HS Band Dir & Instrumental Music Tchr 1967-79; Long Branch MS Band Dir & Instrumental Music Tchr 1979-84; Long Branch HS Band Dir & Instrumental Music Tchr 1984-; *ai:* Marching Band; Symphonic Band; Jazz Band; Pit Band; NHS Fac Comm; NEA, NJEA, MCEA & LBEA 1967-; MENC 1967-; NJ Music Edctrs Assn 1967-, Bd of Dir, Exec Bd; Cntrl Jersey Music Ed Assn 1967-, Pres; All-Shore Band Dirs Assn 1967-, Pres 1991-93; Gideons Intnl 1975-, Pres 1977-80; Fifth Ave Chapel 1960-, Elder 1980-; Monmouth Cty Republican Committeeman 1994-; Long Branch HS Tchr of the Yr 1992-93; Conductor NJ Region 2 Wind Ensemble 1992; Awd for Mini-Grant Project in Ed 1993; *home:* 1111 Darlene Ave Ocean NJ 07712*

RISER, JAMILA QAISSAUNEE, 7th Grade Math Teacher; *b:* Kabul, Afghanistan; *m:* Donald; *c:* David, Dannelle; *ed:* DE St Univ (BS) Math Ed 1986; +15 Grad Credits; *cr:* WT Chapman MS Math Tchr 1986-; *ai:* Math Dept Chair; Math Curr Comm; St Steering Comm on Math; Lake Forest Ed Assn 1986-; DE St Ed Assn 1986-; DCTM 1986-; PTO 1993-; Phoebe Hearst Dist Awd; Lake Forest Tchr of the Yr; *office:* W T Chipman MS Dorman St Harrington DE 19952*

RISH, LINDA BOWMAN, High School English Teacher; *b:* Findlay, OH; *m:* James L.; *c:* Ann Stoner Martin, Jenny Stoner; *ed:* Univ of Findlay (BA) Eng 1970; Bowling Green St Univ (MA) Eng 1988; Rdng Tchng Cert BGSU 1980; *cr:* Horewell-Loudon Eng Tchr 1970-78, Eng tchr 1981-97; Triad Local Schls Eng Tchr 1991-; *ai:* OFT 1995-; NEH Awds; *office:* Triad HS 7941 Brush Lake Rd North Lewisburg OH 43060

RISHEL, CRAIG DAVID, Fourth Grade Teacher; *b:* Philadelphia, PA; *m:* Ann Frances Mayerskey; *c:* Leigh Anne Hope; *ed:* West Chester Univ (BSEd) Elem K-8 1965; Temple Univ (MED) Admin Elem 1970; In Svc Trng Staff Dev I; *cr:* Aronimink Elem Schl 6 Grd Tchr 1965-72, 3 Grd Tchr 1972-81, 4 Grd Tchr 1981-84, 3 Grd Tchr 1984-87, 4 Grd Tchr 1989-; *ai:* Yrbk Adv; Cmptr Club Spon, Adv; Drama Coach; Play Dir; NEA, PSEA, UDEA 1965-; Upper Darby Forum 1983-, Dir; Curr Stud 1965-; Bd of Dirs United Meth Ch 1968-78, Chm, Life Achvmt; PA Tchr of Yr Runner-up 1981; Young Authors Tchrs Awd 1986; 25 Yr Svc Awd Upper DArby Schl Dist; Resource Tchr for Doctoral Dissertations; Stu-Tchr Mentor, Co-operating Tchr Univ Level; *home:* 1607 Fairfield Ave Upper Darby PA 19082*

RISHKO, STEPHEN GEORGE, Art Teacher; *b:* Manhattan, NY; *m:* Lori Barbara Bambach; *c:* Eric, Amy; *ed:* Mansfield Univ (BS) Art Ed 1976; Marywood Coll (MS) Studio Art 1983; Univ of Scranton (MS) Admin 1989; Prin Cert 1990; *cr:* Wallenpaupack Area SD Elem Art Tchr 1978-86, Mid Enrichment, Art Tchr 1986-94, Primary Art Tchr 1994-; *ai:* Adult Ed Instr; Middlestates Evaluation Prgm Stud Chprsn; Schl Improvement, Evaluation, Needs Assessment Team NEIU 19; PSEA, WAEA 1978-; Mentorship; *office:* Wallenpaupack Area MS HC 6 Box 6071 Hawley PA 18428*

RISKE, BEVERLY NOGEN, Fifth Grade Teacher; *b:* Cincinnati, OH; *ed:* Univ of Cincinnati (AA) Early Chldhd 1968, (BS) K-8 1970; Mount St Joseph (MA) K-8 1990; Addl 20 Post Grad Credit Hrs Ashland Coll; *cr:* Hoffman Elem Schl Gr 1 Tchr 1970-71; Dallas Acad Spec Ed 1972-73; Northwood Elem Schl Gr 4 Tchr 1976-95, Gr 5 Tchr 1995-; *ai:* Stu Cncl Adv; Mentor Prgm; Prof Growth Comm; Delta Kappa Gamma 1994-; NEA 1982-; *office:* Northwood Elem Schl 1500 School Ave NE North Canton OH 44720*

RISOLI, ALLISON LEE, History Teacher; *b:* Peekskill, NJ; *ed:* Manhattanville Coll (BA) Pol Sci 1982; Fordham Univ (MS) Educl Psych 1986; 15 Addl Credits Purchase Tchrs Acad; *cr:* St Mary's Schl Soc Stud Tchr 1985-87; Sacred Heart Schl Soc Stud Tchr 1987-88; the Hartsdale Schl Soc Stud Tchr, Cnslr 1988-91; Peekskill HS Soc Stuc Tchr 1991-; *ai:* NHS; Class Adv; Interact Club; Fac Cncl; Westchester Cncl for Soc Stud; NY St Cncl for Soc Stud; NCSS; Peekskill Human Relations Commission; Hudson River Regnl Tchr Ctr Policy Bd; Hudson Vly Hosp Ball Comm; Church of the Assumption CYO Adv; *office:* Peekskill H S 1072 Elm St Peekskill NY 10566*

RISSER, BARBARA GAIL, Assoc Prof of English & Rdng; *b:* Syracuse, NY; *m:* Fred; *c:* Emily, Alison; *ed:* Hartwick Coll (BA) Eng Ed 1973; Syracuse Univ (MS) Rdng Ed 1977; *cr:* West Greser Cntrl Schls Eng Tchr 1973-78; Ononlaga Comm Coll Eng, Rdg Dept Tchr 1979-; *ai:* Reappointment, Tenure, Assessment Comms; NY Coll Learning Skills Assn 1981-, Pres; NADE 1988-; Awds Chancellor's Excl Tchng 1995, NISOD Excl 1996, Onondaga Comm Coll Trustee's, Whitney 1990; Supplement Instr-Certfd Trainer; *office:* Onondaga Comm Coll Rt 173 Syracuse NY 13215

RISSER, PASQUALINA CAMPOPIANO, Spanish Teacher; *b:* Puglianello, Italy; *m:* James D.; *c:* Angela Michelle, Stephanie Ann; *ed:* Millersville Univ (BS) Span, Scndry Ed 1970, (MS); *cr:* Conestoga Vly HS Span Tchr 1970-74, Span Tchr 1984-; *ai:* Class, Buddy Club Adv; Schlsp Comm; New Tchr Mentor; CVEA, PSEA, NEA 1984-; ACTFL 1994-; Ballet Theater of Lancaster 1988-, Bd Dir 1996; Flwshp Juan Carlos; *office:* Conestoga Valley Sr HS 2110 Horseshoe Rd Lancaster PA 17601*

RISSINGER, WILLIAM HOFFMAN, Science Coordinator & Teacher; *b:* Hazelton, PA; *m:* Kaye L.; *c:* Lisa, Gregory, Lynne, Lori; *ed:* Kutztown Sc (BS) Sci Ed 1961; Temple Univ (MS) Phys Sci 1965; Rider Coll Supervision, Admin Cert; *cr:* Tremont HS Bio Tchr 1961-65; Cntrl Bucks Schl Sci Tchr, Coord 1965-, Asst Prin 1978-84; DE Vly Coll Genetic Instr 1988-92; Bucks Cty Comm Coll Genetic Instr 1988-92; *ai:* Asst Bsktbl, Ftbl Coach; Head Tennis, Sci Olympiad Team Coach; PSEA; NEA; NAST; Chalfont New Britain Joint Sewer Authority 1968-, Vice Chm, Sec, Treas, Mart Sahl Awd; NSF Grants Franklin & Marshall Coll, Penn St U, Temple Univ; Jaycee Outstdng Young Edctr 1970; Bucks Cty Svc Tchr of Yr 1994-95; Numerous NSF Schlsps; *home:* 94 Blue Jay Rd Chalfont PA 18914*

RISSMEYER, KAREN STARKEY, First Grade Teacher; *b:* Columbus, OH; *m:* Robert C.; *c:* Tara K., Ashleigh L.; *ed:* OH St Univ (BS) Early & Mid Chldhd Ed 1987, (MS) Instr Design, Tech 1994; *cr:* Linden Park IGE Elem 4th-5th Grd Tchr 1988-90; Oakland Park Trad Elem 1st, 4th Grd Tchr 1990-; *ai:* Project Share Tchr Ldr; NEA 1988-; Phi Kappa Phi 1994-; Sweet Adelines Intnl 1995-; Ashland Oil Achvmt Awd 1989; *office:* Oakland Park Traditional Schl 3392 Atwood Ter Columbus OH 43229*

RISTAU, ROBERT JOSEPH, Assistant Professor; *b:* Albany, NY; *m:* Kathleen; *c:* Joseph, William; *ed:* Hudson Valley Comm Coll (AOS) Electrical Construction & Maintenance 1976; SUNY at Oswego (BS) Voc Tech Ed 1992; *cr:* Hudson Valley Comm Coll Asst Prof 1985-; *ai:* EMC Pgm & EMC Club Adv; AVCC Acad Senate Planning Comm Sec; HVCC Acad Senate; ECM Pgm Comm; Intnl Assn of Electrical Inspectors 1985-; *office:* Hudson Valley Comm Coll 80 Vandenburgh Ave Troy NY 12180

RITA, JANE ROBINSON, English Teacher; *b:* Johnstown, PA; *m:* Albert M Jr.; *ed:* WV Wesleyan Coll (BA) Speech, Drama 1965; Fairleigh Dickinson Univ (MA) Eng Lit 1972; Grad Work Wroxton Coll; Ind Stud Chautauqua Inst; *cr:* Harrisburg City Schls Speech Tchr 1965-67; Greater Johnstown Schl Dist Eng Tchr 1967-; *ai:* Delta Kappa Gamma 1977-, Prof Affairs Chprsn; NCTE 1990-; NEA, PSEA 1965-; Greater Johnstown Ed Assn 1967-; *office:* Greater Johnstown Sr HS 222 Central Ave Johnstown PA 15902

RITACCO, JOSEPH S., Middle School Principal; *b:* Pittsburgh, PA; *m:* Christine Stofan; *c:* Joseph, Kari Jo; *ed:* California Univ of PA (BS) Elem Ed 1970, (MED) Elem Ed 1975; Elem Prin Cert; *cr:* Fallowfield Elem Schl Tchr 1970-88; Charleroi MS Prin 1988-; Charleroi Area Schl Dist Federal Projects Dir 1995-; *ai:* Newspaper Spon; PA Assn Federal Prgms Assn 1995-; Charleroi Amer Legion 1974-, Commander; PTA PA Life, Natl Life Mbrshp Awds; *office:* Charleroi MS 100 Fecsen Dr Charleroi PA 15022

RITCH, GREGORY ALLEN, Sixth Grade Teacher; *b:* Connellsville, PA; *m:* Anita Louise Grosso; *c:* Jennifer Lynn; *ed:* CA St Univ (BS) Elem Ed 1973, (MS) Rdng Specialis 1977; 15 Credit Hrs Admin Prgm Prin; 11 Credit Hrs Command & Gen Staff Ofcr Coll Commandants List US Army; *cr:* Connellsville Jr High East Rdng Specialist 1974-83; US Army Exec Ofcr, Co Commander 1983-90; Zachariah Connell Elem Schl Sixth Grd Tchr 1990-; *ai:* Cooperating Tchr for Stu Tchr; Chm Elem Textbook Review Comm; Elem Course Outcome, Elem Sci Comms; Connellsville Area Ed Assn 1974-, VP; PSEA, NEA 1974-; Reserve Ofcr Assn 1978-; Jaycees 1971-, Pres, First Timers Awd; Order of Sons of Italy 1971-, Pres; Amer Legion 1995-; Cville Recreation Bd 1996; Outstdng jr Ofcr US Army Reserve; Grant Soc for Analytical Chemists of Pittsburgh; Nom Presidential Awds for Excl in Sci & Math Tchng; *office:* Zachariah Connell Elem Schl 700 Park St Connellsville PA 15425

RITCH, MARSHA M., Multi-Age Teacher; *b:* Buffalo, NY; *m:* Jerry; *c:* Jared, Amanda; *ed:* Fredonia St (BA) Ed 1973; Univ of Buffalo (MED) Ed 1976; 30 Addl Hrs; *cr:* Lockport Schl Dist Elem Ed Tchr 1973-; *ai:* Shared Decision Making Team; Multi-Age Grant; *office:* Roy B. Kelley Elem Schl 610 E High St Lockport NY 14094

RITCHIE, ELIZABETH ANN, Retired 4th Grade Teacher; *b:* Danville, PA; *m:* Palmer; *c:* Crystal Weidman, Abigail Snyder, Rebecca, Sarah Dunn; *ed:* Bloomsburg St Coll (BS) Elem Ed 1971; Post Grad Stud Bucknell Univ; Addl Courses at Marywood Coll, Susquehanna Univ; *cr:* Second St Elem Schl Grd 4 Tchr 1971-93; *ai:* NEA.

RITCHIE, JOYCE A., Title I Teacher; *b:* Mason, WV; *ed:* OH Univ (BA) Elem Ed 1972, (BSEd) Elem Ed 1979; Emphasis Early Chldhd Ed Ages 3-8; *cr:* Southern Local Chls Tchr 1972-; *ai:* Intervention Team; Career Ed Comm; Acad Banquet Chm; Competeiency Based Ed Test Dev; NEA 1972-, Sec; IRA 1984-; Natl Tchr of Math 1995-; ASDE 1996-; Alpha Delta Kappa 1973-, Sec; Awded Venture Capital Grant Southern Local Schl; Awded Grant Non-Point Source Water Pollution; *home:* PO Box 608 Racine OH 45771*

RITCHIE, LINNEA THORP, English Teacher; *b:* Watseka, IL; *m:* Norman; *c:* Bradford, Brian; *ed:* Eastern IL Univ (BS) Eng Ed 1963; Univ of IL (MED) Educl Psych 1968, Advanced Cert Cnslng & Guid 1970; Natl Endowment for Hum; UNH; Conn Coll; St Anselems; *cr:* Wm Neff HS Eng & Latin Tchr 1963-65; Centennial HS Eng & Latin Tchr 965-69; Salem HS Eng & Jrnlsm Tchr 1978-; *ai:* Schl Newspaper Adv 1985-95; NEA 1978-; NHEA 1978-; SEA 1978-; Dollars for Scholars 1992-95; Big Brothers & Big Sisters 1995-; Alpha Delta Kappa 1996; Eng Honorary; *office:* Salem HS 44 Geremonty Dr Salem NH 03079*

RITCHIE, MERYL (MILANESE), Learning Disabilities Cnsltnt; *b:* Passaic, NJ; *m:* Thomas Ritchie; *c:* Jeffrey (dec), Adam; *ed:* Kean Coll of NJ (BA) Early Chldhd 1978; Montclair St (MA) Learning Disabilities 1985; Jersey City St Post Grad 30 Credit Hrs Admin; *cr:* Clifton Bd of Ed BSI Tchr 1979-82, Kndgtn Tchr 1982-87, Learning Disabilities Consultant 1987-, Child Study Team; *ai:* CTA, NJEA 1979-; *office:* Christopher Columbus MS 350 Piaget Ave Clifton NJ 07011

RITCHOTTE, MICHELLE MARIE, Spanish Teacher; *b:* Lowell, MA; *ed:* Emerson Coll (BA) Theatre Ed 1978; Attnd Merrimac Coll, Univ of MA at Lowell, Universidade de Coimbra, Universidade dos Agores; *cr:* Waltham Pub Schls Elem Drama Aide 1978-79; Lowell Pub Schls Biling Aide, HS Spanish Tchr 1979-92; Fitchburg Pub Schls Span Tchr 1992-93; Lowell Pub Schls Span Tchr 1993-; *ai:* MAFLA 1984-; AFT 1990-; Coll Club of Greater Lowell, Whistler House Museum 1980-; MFA Boston 1990-; Isabella Stewart Gardner Museum 1995-; *office:* Lowell HS 50 Fr Morrissette Blvd Lowell MA 01852

RITENOUR, JAY KENNETH, Fifth Grade Teacher; *b:* Latrobe, PA; *m:* Barbara Jane Hanson; *c:* Kristin, Kyle, Casey, Carrie; *ed:* Slippery Rock St Univ (BS) Elem Ed & PE 1972; Penn St Univ (MED) Elem Ed; *cr:* Seward Elem Schl Head & 6th Grd Tchr 1972-77; Laurel Valley Elem Schl 4th, 5th & 6th Grd Tchr 1977-; *ai:* LVEA, PSEA & NEA 1972-; Hempfield Recreation 1989-, Bsbl Coach 2 Yrs; *office:* Laurel Valley Elem Ligonier Valley Schl Dist RD 1 Box 227A New Florence PA 15944

RITENOUR, LYNNE E. (WHITE), English & Rdng Enrichment Tchr; *b:* Connellsville, PA; *m:* Harry Robert; *ed:* CA Univ of PA (BS) Elem Ed 1971, (MA) Elem Ed 1975, (BS) Scndry Eng 1983; *cr:* Sahlick Elem Tchr 1971-76; Springfield Elem Tchr 1976-79; Bullskin Elem Tchr 1979-82; Jr. HS East Tchr 1982-; *ai:* Yrbk spon; Yearly Awds Day Ceremony Coord; Stu Who Care Club Adv; All Schl Events Photographer; PSCA, NEA 1971-; CGE Assn 1983-, Choir Dir; Great Tchr Recognition Awd; Articles Pub; *office:* Connellsville Jr HS East Locust St Ext Connellsville PA 15425

RITER, BETSY HENDERSON, Teacher of the Gifted; *b:* Bellefonte, PA; *m:* Richard A.; *c:* Joseph H., John T.; *ed:* IN Univ of PA (BS) Bio, Chem-Magna Cum Laude 1973; 20 Credit Hrs MS Bio; 3 Credit Hrs Shippensburg Univ; 6 Credit Hrs Cornell Univ Immunology; 9 Credit Hrs Susquehanna Univ Ed; 30 Credit Hrs Harrisburg Area Comm Coll Math; 6 Credit Hrs Penn St Univ Math; *cr:* IN Hosp Microbiology 1973-78; Cornell Univ Microbiology Rsrch 1978-81; Soldiers & Sailors Meml Hosp Microbiology 1981-82; Milton S. Hershey Med Ctr Microbiology 1982-84; Harrisburg Hosp Microbiology 1984-86; Harrisburg Area Comm Coll Part Time Math Lecturer 1986-89; West Perry Schl Dist GATE Tchr 1986-; *ai:* Families Through Adoption Cntrl PA Adoptive Parents Group; Korean Connection; PA St Univ Master Gardner; Amer Soc Clinical Pathologists 1973-; NEA 1986-; Article Pub 1980; *office:* West Perry Schl Dist RD 1 Elliottsburg PA 17024

RITER, CONNIE, Mathematics Teacher; *b:* Weirton, WV; *m:* Arthur; *c:* James; *ed:* Marygrove Coll (BA) Eng 1962; Univ of Detroit (MATM) Math Ed 1969; Post Grad Stud Syracuse Univ, Brockport, Rochester Inst of Tech, OCC; *cr:* Roxboro MS Math Tchr 1967-68; Cicero North Syracuse HS Math Tchr 1969-; *ai:* Math Chprsn; Schl Cty & St Math League Coach; NCTM 1987-; OCUTA 1967-, Past Pres; NYSUT 1967-; AMTNYS 1967-; Dist Rep; Newmast Alumni 1990; NSF Grants; *office:* Cicero-North Syracuse HS Rt 31 Cicero NY 13039

RITKE, MARK E., Professor of Biology; *b:* Milwaukee, WI; *m:* Mary K. Poirot; *ed:* Eastern IL Univ (BS) Bio 1977; Southwest MO St Univ (MA) Bio 1979; Univ of Memphis (PHD) Bio, Zoology 1987; *cr:* Univ of Memphis Instr 1987-89; Duquesne Univ Asst Prof 1992-93; Carnegie Museum of Natural His Research Assoc 1992-94; Univ of Pittsburgh at Titusville Asst Prof 1994-; *ai:* AAUP 1993-; 21 Presentations at Prof Scientific Meetings; 13 Pub Scientific Papers; *office:* Univ Of Pittsburgh At Titusvle 504 E Main St Titusville PA 16354

RITT, SHARON SHATSKY, Chairperson Information Tech; *b:* NY; *m:* Rickey; *ed:* Herbert H. Lehman Coll (BA) Bus ED 1977; N (MA) Bus ED 1985; *cr:* Berkeley Coll Chprsn Information Tech Rockland Comm Coll Adjunct 1988-; *ai:* Fac Adv Internship Pgr Fac Affairs Comms; NJBEA 1986-; BEANU 1977-; Passaic HS 199 Bd; Tchr of Yr 1983; *office:* Berkeley Coll Of Business 44 Rifle C West Paterson NJ 07424

RITTCHIER, RON EUGENE, Elementary Principal; *b:* Wausec *m:* Carma Jo Fricke; *c:* Josie, Alexa, Stephanie, Katie; *ed:* Bowlin St Univ (BA) Elem, Spec Ed 1979; Toledo Univ (MS) Ed Admin 1 Wauseon Exempted Village Schl 6th Grd Tchr 1979-88; Bryan Cit Admin 1988-; *ai:* OASEA, NAESP 1988-; *office:* Bryan City Sc Avenue A Bryan OH 43506*

RITTENOUR, KIMBERLEY HARPER, Social Studies & Span T *b:* Cincinnati, OH; *m:* John Thornton Jr.; *c:* Brian, William, Johar Eastern KY Univ (AB) Span 1977, (MA) Span 1978; Portugue Histories, Political Sci, Tchng Related Classes; SSU His, Soc S Eastern KY Univ Span Instr 1977-78; Shawnee St Comm Coll Sp 1979-82; Portsmouth City Schls Span Tchr 1982; Pike Cty Schls Sp Stud Tchr 1987-88, 1993-; Dailyville Chrstn Schl Span, Soc Stu Admin 1988-92; *ai:* Tech Comm; Curr Comm; Mock Trial Adv; G Wilson Pub Lib Trustee; NEA; AATSP; ELECTA; OFLA; Piketon UMC; Span, Eng Poetry Pub; WWAAT 1994; *office:* Eastern HS 1 Mill Rd Beaver OH 45613

RITTER, DARLISA PIVOLA, First Grade Teacher; *b:* Derby, Daniel Charles; *c:* Rebecca Colleen; *ed:* Western CT St Univ (BS Ed 1972; Univ of Bridgeport (MS) Elem Ed, Admin 1976; 6th Yr E Admin 1976; Working Towards EDD in Admin, Supervisio Continuing Ed Units; 70 Grad Credits Co-operating Tchr, Me Assessor, BEST Prgm, Intnl Stud, Australia; *cr:* Shelton Pub Ele 1-4, 6 Grd Tchr 1972-; Trumbull Pub Schls Multiage Class Tchr 1 St Dept Ed Celebration of Excl Prgm Chprsn, Pres 1994-; *ai:* US N of Elem Ed Schl Recognition Screener; CT St Dept Ed Accredid Compliance Review Panel Chprsn; CT St Mastery Tests Range Fin St Dept of Ed Talent Pool; US Exemplary Tchr Group; Retired Sr V in Schls Supvr; Grd Level Chprsn; Delta Kappa Gamma, Tchrs A Whole Lang 1992-; NEA, CEA, SEA, PTA 1973-; ASCD, IRA NOLPE 1988-; IMPACT II, League of Women Voters 1990-; Comm Tech Comm 1996; Metropolitan Musem of Art 1988-; CREATE Inter-City Tchr Exch Prgm; Milken Family Fnd Natl Edctr Awd; Tchr of Yr; Weller Grant Selection Mem; Tchrs Network Interac Panelist; *office:* Long Hill Schl 565 Long Hill Ave Shelton CT 06

RITTER, JOHN R., English Teacher; *b:* Allentown, PA; *m:* L Burner; *c:* Seth, Michael, Zacchary; *ed:* East Stroudsburg Uni Scndry Ed & Comm 1977; Kutztown Univ (MA) Eng 1986; Attnd A Coll Psych 1968-70; *cr:* Vernon Twp HS Eng & Comm Tchr 1 Parkland HS Eng Tchr 1980-; *ai:* Amnesty Intnl; NEA, PSEA, PEA Collective Bargaining Chair 1986; Comm Advy Cncl 1992-, Votin Advised Key Club 1980-85; Parkland Jaycees Outstanding Young E 1985; Designed Curr for Stdnts Chosen 1 of 6 in St for Presentatio First Annual Conf for At-Risk Stdnts in Harrisburg PA; *office:* Parkl Rt 309 Orefield PA 18069*

RITTER, LOIS MARVIN, Intermediate Teacher; *b:* Bucyrus, William Edward; *c:* Eric William, Jeffrey David; *cr:* Crestline Ex Village Schls Kndgtn, 4th-8th Grd Music Tchr, Asst Band Dir & Fla 1983-84; St Marys Cath Schl Intermediate Tchr 1985-; *ai:* Notre D Assn 1985-; Natl Cath Ed Assn 1985-; Toledo Choral Soc 1988-; *of* Mary's Schl 217 Page St Toledo OH 43620

RITTER, R. RICHARD, Environmental Science Teacher; *b:* Kn *m:* Melinda Graves; *c:* Stephen, Jason, Daniel; *ed:* WA & Jeffers (BA) Bio 1966; Clarion Univ (MS) Bio, Ecology 1974; 13 G Clarion Univ 1980-81; *cr:* US Army Lieutenant, Med Svc Corps 1 Eisenhower HS Sci Tchr 1969-; Eisenhower HS Sci Dept Chm 19 Ecolab Outdoor Ed Area Dir; Envirothon & Ecomeet Teams Coach 1969-; PA Wildlife Soc 1990-; BSA 1989-94, Committeman; War Conservation Dist 1982-88, Dir; Northern Allegheny Consv Assn Trout Unlimited 1987-; Environmental Edctr of Yr NACA 1 Conservation Tchr of Yr WCCO 1986; *office:* Eisenhower HS Rt 2276 Russell PA 16345

RITTER, ROSS WESLEY, Physical Education Director; *b:* Portla *m:* Judy Anne Smith; *c:* Terri Lynn Scott; *ed:* West Chester Univ (1966; Salisbury St Univ (AP) PE 1976; MS Equivelency PE Salisb Univ of MD 1986; 6 Post Grad Hrs Univ of MD; *cr:* Fruitland Intern Schl Dir of PE 1966-; *ai:* PTA Exec Comm; Schl Advy Cncl; Dis Comm of Fruitland; Field Day Coord; Cty Walk-In Rdng Coord; MC League; Tchr Advy Comm; Tchr in Charge; Jump Rope for Heart Salisbury St Advy Bd Tchr Evaluation; Coord Camp Cha MAPHERD 1994-; Bee Federal Credit Union 1970-, Sec; Schl Co Coord 1970-; Life Mem to MD Congress of Parents & Tchrs Awd Outstdng Elem Tchr of Amer Awd 1972; Key to City of Fruitland Little League Outstdng Achvmt 1992; *office:* Fruitland Intermedia 208 W Main St Fruitland MD 21826

RITTINGER, CHRISTOPHER, PE, Health & Bible Teach Englewood, NJ; *m:* Janine A. Johnson; *c:* Alyssa, Brianna, Hunt Bapt Bible Church (BS) PE, Bible 1986; *cr:* Hackensack Chrstn S Hlth & Bible Tchr 1986-; *ai:* Var Soccer Coach; Dean of Men; Hackensack Chrstn Schools 15 Conklin Pl Hackensack NJ 07601

RITTMAN, ELLEN M., Second Grade Teacher; *b:* New York City, Blair W.; *ed:* Trenton St Coll (BS) K Primary Ed 1958; West Uniov(MS) Elem, Psych Stud 1980; *cr:* Haworth Elem Schl Seco Tchr 1958-61; East Street Schl Second Grd Tchr 1961-63; Hill & Schl First-Second Grd Tchr 1973-; *ai:* Collaborative Learning Disa Model Steering Supt's Advy; Comm Cncl Rdng, Writing Comm Ou Prgm; NEA 1959-; Ct Ed Assn; New Milford Ed Assn 1976-; Ph Kappa 1980-; New Milford Hosp Auxiliary 1967-, Chair Ways & 1968-71; Bd of Ed Outstdng Tchr of Yr in Acad Ldrshp & Projects; 85 Chestnut Land Rd New Milford CT 06776

RITTNER, BARBARA, Asst Prof of Social Work; *b:* Canal Panama; *m:* Peter H.; *ed:* Univ of CT (BA) Eng 1967; Barry Univ (Soc Work 1989, (PHD) Soc Work 1992; *cr:* Barry Univ Adj Prof 19 Univ of NV Soc Work 1992-93; SUNY Schl of Soc Work Asst Prof *ai:* Natl Assn of Soc Workers 1987-, Dade Chptr, Stu of Yr; Cncl Work Ed 1989-; Friendship House Gateway Bd of Dir; Numerous A & Book Pub; *office:* S U N Y at Buffalo School of Social Work 359 Hall Buffalo NY 14260*

RITTS, SAMUEL DONALD, Technology Education Teacher; *b:* PA; *ed:* DE Cty Comm Coll (AA) Drafting, Design 2 Yrs; CA Univ (BSE) Indstrl Arts 4 Yrs; *cr:* Big Springs HS Indstrl Arts Tchr; Gr HS Tech Ed Tchr 1 Yr; Laurel MS Tech Ed Tchr 6 Yrs; Seaford H Ed Tchr 2 Yrs; *ai:* Tech Stu Assn; NEA 1987-; DE Tech Ed Assn Sussex Co Rep; Intnl Ac Tech Ed Assn 1993-; Seaford Ed Assn 1994- Ed Tchr of Yr 1995; *office:* Seaford Sr HS 399 N Market St Seafo 19973

RITZ, ANN GIRARD, Math Teacher & Dept Chprsn; *b:* Waltham *m:* Joseph Paul; *c:* Joanne Keith, Michael, Robert, Jonathan, Margar Canisius Coll (MS) Scndry Ed 1989; Bridgewater St Coll (BS) Scnd

: Sci; Union Coll Gen Electric Sci Flwshp; Attnd Buffalo St Coll; t Bridgewater Jr-Sr HS 7th Grd Math & Sci Tchr; Gloversville HS 10th Grd Sci & Math Tchr; Milford HS 9th Grd Math Tchr; owns Cath Schl 8th Grd Tchr; Immaculata Acad Tchr & Math & s Dept Head; *ai:* NHS Adv; Western NY Physics Tchrs; AMTNYS; ; WNYMTA; SS Peter & Paul Parent Guild Pres & Bd Mem; Buffalo Eisenhower Grant in Physics 1991, 1993 & 1994.

L, DAVID J., Band & Choral Director; *b:* Pittsburgh, PA; *m:* Rosie ; *ed:* Duquesne Univ (BSME) Music Ed 1985; 30 Post Grad Credits l MFA; *cr:* Yough Schl Dist Jr Band & Choral Dir 1988-94; urg Area Schl Dist Sr & Jr Band & Choral Dir 1994-; *ai:* Marching Pep Band; Concert Choir; Drama Dept; MENC & PMEA 1981-; 1984-; NEA 1984-; *office:* Leechburg Area HS 215 1st St Leechburg 56

:RT, TAMMY LYN, Choir Director; *b:* Lakewood, OH; *m:* Frank III; *ed:* Roberts Wesleyan Coll (BS) Music Ed 1990; *cr:* Avon HS hoir Dir 1991-; Avon East Elem Schl 5-7 Grd Gen Music Tchr 1991-; all Ensemble Dir; Private Vocal Instr; Schl Musical Vocal Coach; Avon Tchrs Assn 1991-; Music Edctrs Natl Conf, OMEA 1992-; FBC p Team 1993-; Choir Contest Awds OMEA Superior Ratings 1995-; Avon H S 3075 Stoney Ridge Rd Avon OH 44011*

US, DORIS JEAN, Third Grade Teacher; *b:* Baltimore, MD; *ed:* iv (BS) Spec Ed & Elem Ed 1977; 12 Credit Hrs Toward Masters at nes Univ; *cr:* Licking Cty Chrstn Acad 1st-6th Grd Tchr 1977-79; ille Chrstn Schl 4th Grd Tchr 1979-83; Licking Cty Chrstn Schl f 1st, 5th, 6th, 3rd Grd & Spec Ed 1983-; *ai:* Newark Bapt Temple Choir Sec; *office:* Licking Cty Christian Acad 81 Licking View Dr OH 43056

RD, CAROL MORRIS, Third Grade Teacher; *b:* Lowell, MA; *ed:* St Coll (BSEd) K-12 Elem Ed 1968-; Univ of Lowell (MSEd) , Supervision 1971; 30 Addl Credits; *cr:* E. G. Sherburne Schl Tchr Head Tchr 1980-85, Team Ldr Grd 3 1983-93, Soc Stud Curr, 1983-90; *ai:* IAABO, NHFBWO, OWCA Bsktbl Ofcl; NHWBSBO, A, OWCA, MUBO Sftbl Ofcl; NHFHA Field Hockey 1988-; NEA, 1968-; PEA 1968-, Pres 3 Times; Pelham PTA 1968-, Tchr Rep; St Notary 1991-; MA Approved Bd of Ofcl 1980-, VP, Twice Pres, ; MVBO 1982-, Pres Chprsn, Bsktbl & Sftbl Interpretor; You Make erence Awd 1994; *office:* E G Sherburne Schl 14 Marsh Rd Pelham 076*

, MARY MANGIERO, Computer Teacher; *b:* Staten Island, NY; arles V.; *c:* Christian, Amanda; *ed:* Coll of Staten Island (BA) Psych Wagner Coll (MS) Elem Ed 1977; 15 Credit Hrs Coll of Staten *cr:* St Ann's Schl Tchr 1976-77; St Christopher's Schl Tchr 1; Sacred Heart Schl Tchr 1981-89, Cmptr Facilitator 1989-; *ai:* 1981-; Richmond Adoptive Parent Inc 1988-, Treas 1990-; St a's Mother's Guild 1993-; Adoptive Parents Comm 1988-; Wagner ssistantship 1975; *office:* Sacred Heart Schl 301 N Burgher Ave Island NY 10310

NBURG, GARY ALAN, Instructional Tech Specialist; *b:* Stamford, Jennifer, Ashley; *ed:* SUNY at Oswego (BS) Tech Ed 1990; *cr:* ville-Dewitt MS Tech Ed Tchr 1 Yr; Liverpool Cntrl Schl Tech Ed Yr; Skaneateles Cntrl Schl Tech Ed Tchr 5 Yrs; *ai:* HS Stu Govt Org, ch Club Adv; CNYTEA 1990-; Tech Club of Syracuse 1993-.

RA, ALBERT MICHAEL, Spanish & Business Teacher; *b:* attan, NY; *ed:* Johnson & Wales Univ (AS) Culinary Arts 1989; FL Univ (BS) Bus, Hotel, Rest Mngmt 1991; Working on MST Iona Coll *cr:* Mt St Michael Acad Tchr 1991-; *ai:* Yrbk Adv; Hispanic Heritage Moderator; Champagnat Yth Spirituality; Sr Encounter Movement; Mount Saint Michael Acad 4300 Murdock Ave Bronx NY 10466*

RA, ELIA IRIS, Elementary School Teacher; *b:* Brooklyn, NY; *ed:* Coll (BA) Psych 1983; Queens Coll (MS) Spcl Ed 1986; Working on Schl Psych; *cr:* NYC Bd of Ed Tchr 1984-; *ai:* AFT 1984-; UFT NASP 1995-; 1st Place for Psych Motto at York Coll 1979.

RA, EZEQUIEL R., Prof of Biological Sciences; *b:* Alpine, TX; *m:* ay Koonwong; *c:* Angela Malee; *ed:* Sul Ross St Coll (BS) Bio & 1964; Purdue Univ (MS) Biochemistry 1967; Univ of TX at Austin Botany & Biological Sci 1973; *cr:* US Army Clinical Lab Tech 6th US Army Med Lab Asst Chief Biochemistry 1968; US Army rt Thailand Chief Biochemistry 1969-70; Univ of Notre Dame Asst io 1973-74; Univ of MA at Lowell Asst Prof Bio & Sci 1974-80, Prof Sci 1985-, Mahidol Univ Guest Assoc Prof Trop Med 1981; Univ nan Guest Prof Biologie Animale 1986-87; *ai:* Botanical Soc Amer Amer Soc Plant Physiologists 1972-; Sigma XI Rsrch Soc 1972-, Mass Chptr 1989-93; New England Soc Electron Microscopy 1976-, 83 & Pres 1984; Alpha Chi 1963-; Phi Kappa Phi 1972-; Microscopy mer 1975-; NSF Grant 1981-82; Contributor to Scientific Journals; Univ Of MA At Lowell 1 University Ave Dept of Biological es Lowell MA 01854

RA, SUSAN KOLCZYNSKI, Eng as Second Lang & Rdng Tchr; *b:* ork City, NY; *m:* Carlos Rivera; *c:* Matthew, Paul; *ed:* Middlesex Cty AAS) Tchr Asst 1976; Kean Coll (BA) Elem Ed 1983, (MA) ESL *cr:* Middlesex Cty Coll Tchr Aide 1976-84; Perth Amboy HS ESL, Tchr 1984-; Middlesex Cty Coll ESL Adj Tchr 1985-; *ai:* Tchr tations Stu Achvmt Coord; Biling Sub Comm Mid St Chprsn; NJEA NJITESOL 1985-; *office:* Perth Amboy HS Eagle Ave Perth Amboy 861*

RS, LYNN SALZMANN, Physical Therapy Professor; *b:* Baltimore, *m:* Frederick Jr.; *c:* James, Amanda; *ed:* Univ at Buffalo (BS) Phys py 1985; Buffalo St Univ (MS) Human Resource Mngmt 1995; *cr:* Cty Med Ctr Phys Therapy, Clinical Ed Coord 1985-91; D'Youville Acad Clinical Ed Coord 1991-; *ai:* Amer Phys Therapy Assn 1990-; Phys Therapy Clinical Ed Consortium 1990-, Chprsn 1994-, Sec 94; Buffalo Ambassadors 1994-; Buffalo Ambassador Awd 1995; D'Youville Coll 320 Porter Ave Buffalo NY 14201*

RS, ROBERT D., Assistant Professor; *b:* New York, NY; *m:* Linda; ara, Jonathan; *ed:* Lincoln Univ (BA) Pol Sci & Psych 1955; Brooklyn Schl (JD) Bus Law 1967; *cr:* Boro of Manhattan Comm Coll Adj rer 1988, Asst Prof 1992-; *ai:* Alpha Phi Alpha Grad; Iota Thea Law; Staff Congress CUNY, NY St United Tchrs 1995-; Natl Bar Assn ; Whos Who in Amer Coll & Univ 1955; US Chamber of Commerce ding Young Men in Amer 1965; Whos Who in Law in Amer 1980.

ERE, ROSEMARY, 3rd Grade Teacher; *b:* Jersey City, NJ; *m:* am Paul Jr.; *c:* William, Jennifer; *ed:* Jersey City St Coll (BA) K-8th Ed 1968; Georgian Court Coll Teaching the Gifted 3 Credits; *cr:* oln Schl 3rd Grd Tchr 1968-69; Lanes Mill Schl 2nd Grd Tchr 70; Toms River Schls Supplemental Tchr 1981-85; West Dover Elem rd Tchr 1985-; *ai:* Affirmative Action Liaison; NEA 1985-; NJEA ; CCD Rel Tchr 1993-; *office:* West Dover Elem Schl Blue Jay Dr River NJ 08755

KIN, TOBY, French & Spanish Teacher; *b:* Baltimore, MD; *ed:* Univ Baltimore Cty (BA) Eng, Frgn Lang 1974; Middlebury Coll (MA) Fr , Columbia Univ Tchrs Coll Klingenstein Flwshp Ed 1984-85; 9 ner Courses NEH Grants at Harvard, UVA, Villanova, Y-Plattsburgh, Boston Univ, Univ of Rochester at Fondation des Etats Old Dominion; Several Lang Courses Fr, Span; Stud France at Aix-en Provence 1970-71; Stud in Spain Santander & Madrid 1974; *cr:* Baltimore Cty Schls ESL Tchr 1975-76; Baltimore City Schls Biling Ed Resource Specialist 1975-76; Roland Park Cntry Schl Fr, Span Tchr 1976-; *ai:* Organize & Lead 3 Week Fr Exchange in Paris; Write Fac Skit, Direct It, Create Batik Panels for Sr Day Celebration; Bloodmobile Chair; AATSP, AATF 1976-; Quebec Stud 1984-; Potters Guild 1994-; Girls Just Wanna Drums; Ind Stud Hum Grant Cncl for Basic Ed & NEH to Stud El Ceco; Rockefeller Flwshp Stud Fr, Francophone Theater & Theater Audiences; Wrote Stud Guide for Brooklyn Acad of Music; *office:* Roland Park Country Schl 5204 Roland Ave Baltimore MD 21210*

RIVLIN, TIMOTHY BENNETT, Social Studies Teacher; *b:* New York, NY; *ed:* St Lawrence Univ (BA) Govt 1975; Attnd Syracuse Univ Grad Work; *cr:* Long Ridge Schl K-8th Grd Soc Stud, Fr, Span & PE Tchr 1975-78; Stamford HS 9th-12th Grd Bus Ed Tchr 1979-80; Convent of the Sacred Heart 9th-12th Grd US & European His & Ec Tchr 1981-84; Cardinal Spellman HS 10th & 11th Grd Global II & US His & Govt Tchr 1984-, 12th Grd Govt, Ecnmcs Tchr; Stamford Pub Schls Adult Ed; Horizons Summer Prgm Eng Instr 1979-; *ai:* Jr Var & Var Bowling Coach; Stdnt Govt Moderator 1992-; Lay Faculty Assn 1984-; NCSS 1988-; *office:* Cardinal Spellman HS 1 Cardinal Spellman Pl Bronx NY 10466

RIZER, KELLY DAWN, Reading & English Teacher; *b:* Gallipolis, OH; *ed:* Univ Rio Grande (BS) Comm 1990, (MS) Rdng 1996; *cr:* Southern HS Full-Time Sub 1990-91; Athens HS Rdng & Eng Tchr 1991-; *ai:* Chrldng Adv 1993-95; NEA & OEA 1991-; OCIRA 1991-; Phi Delta Kappa 1994-; Univ Rio Grande Grad Schlrsp Whos Who Among Americas Grad Stdnts; JFK Schlshp Finalist; *office:* Athens HS 1 High School Rd The Plains OH 45780*

RIZZARDI, ANDREW J., High School Math Teacher; *b:* Jeannette, PA; *ed:* Penn St Univ (BS) Acctng 1983; Univ of Pittsburgh Tchng Cert Math 1994; *cr:* J C Penney Co Inc Accntg Mgr 1983-89; Security Bureau Inc Corporate Payroll Mgr 1989-91; Penn Trafford Schl Dist Math Tchr 1994-; *ai:* PIAA Ftbl, Bsbl, Sftbl Ofcl; IM Teams Comprised of Fellow Tchrs; PSEA 1994-; *office:* Penn Trafford HS Rt 130 Box 366 Harrison City PA 15636*

RIZZI, ROBERT B., Spanish Teacher; *b:* Brooklyn, NY; *ed:* Pace Univ (BA) Span 1965; Hofstra Univ (MA) Span 1974; 90 Credit Hrs Span Lit, Italian, Russian, Photography; Cert Attendance Ofcr Tchr; *cr:* Massapequa HS Tchr 1965-; *ai:* Adult Ed Astrology; Renaissance Prgm Photographer; NYSAFLT 1994-; *office:* Massapequa HS 4925 Merrick Rd Massapequa NY 11758*

RIZZIERI, WILLIAM RICHARD, Technology Education Teacher; *b:* Lackawanna, NY; *m:* Nancy Waring; *c:* Meghan, Mary Beth; *ed:* St Univ Coll at Buffalo (BS) Ind Arts Ed 1971; St Univ Coll at Brockport (MS) Ed Adm 1981; *cr:* Auburn HS Tech Ed Tchr 1972-; *ai:* Tech Ed Club Adv; AFT, NYSUT, Auburn Tchr Assn 1971-; Sennett Vol Fire Dept 1975-, Pres, V Pres, Capt, 20 Yrs Life Mbrshp; Town of Sennett 1981-93, Councilman; NY St Gas, Electric Energy Mini-Grant Awd; *office:* Auburn HS Lake Ave Auburn NY 13021

RIZZITANO, JANE ELIZABETH, Spanish Teacher; *b:* Newton, MA; *m:* David H. Thakar; *c:* Elizabeth Thakar, Rebecca Thakar, Joseph Thakar; *ed:* Boston Coll (BA) Span 1979; Cambridge Coll (MED) Span & Eng Linguistics 1987; 45 Credits Beyond Masters in Span & Ed; *cr:* Marshfield HS Span Tchr 1979-80; Canton HS Span Tchr 1980-81; Needham HS Span Tchr 1983-; *ai:* Span Honor Soc Adv; Stu Tchr Comm; NEA 1986-; AATSP 1978-; MAFLA 1983-; MTA; *office:* Needham H S 609 Webster St Needham MA 02194

RIZZO, ANDREA (BONIECKI), Mathematics Teacher; *b:* Brooklyn, NY; *m:* Anthony; *c:* Robert, Cori Marie, Beth Ann, Frank A.; *ed:* Queens Coll (BA) Interdisciplinary 1992; Working Toward Masters in Scndry Math at Saint Johns Univ; *cr:* Saint Stanislaus Bishop & Martyr Schl 8th Grd Tchr 1990-95; Christ the King Regnl HS Math Tchr 1995-; *ai:* MS Accreditation Steering Comm; Diocesan Theatre Guild 1994-; Black Friars Theatre Guild 1992-94; Saint Marys Theatre Guild 1973-91; Holy Cross Choir 1988-, Ldr of Song 1995-; *office:* Christ the King Regnl HS 68-02 Metropolitan Ave Middle Village NY 11379

RIZZO, GARY E., Assoc Dean of Academic Affairs; *b:* Erie, PA; *c:* Brian, Gary Patrick, Thomas A.; *ed:* Gannon Coll (BS) Gen Sci, Bio 1967; Case Western Reserve Univ (MS) Cnslng 1969; Univ of Pitsburg Cnslng 1974; ACE Fellow Acad Admin 1984-85; *cr:* Cuyahoga Comm Coll Cnslr 1969-71; Comm Coll Alleghany Cnslr 1972; Westmoreland Comm Coll Cnslr 1972-82; Montgomery Comm Coll Dir fo Cnslng, Assoc Dean Lifelong Learning, Assoc Acad Dean 1982-; *ai:* Curr, Acad Progress Chprsn, Hnrs, Dev Stud, Ad Hoc Comms; Am Coll Prsnl Assoc 1969-; PA Coll Pers 1972-86, Bd of Dir, Outstdng Contribution Awd; ACE Cncl of Fellows 1985-, Annual Fund & Prof Dev Comms; Cub Scouts of Amer, Cubmaster; Variety of Civic Act, Citizens Comm of Local Schl Dist; Grad Assistantship 1967-69; Doctoral Schlsp; Amer Cncl on Ed Fellow in Acad Admin 1984-85; Visiting Prof Univ of FL, Comm Coll Ldrshp Prgm 1976; Who's Who in East, Human Svcs; *office:* Montgomery County Comm Coll 340 Dekalb Pike PO Box 400 Blue Bell PA 19422

RIZZO, ROBERT WILLIAM, Band Director; *b:* East Liberty, PA; *ed:* PA St Univ (BS) Music Ed 1993; Classes IN Univ of PA; *cr:* East Allegheny Schl Dist Grd 4-12 Band Dir 1993-; *ai:* Lighting Design, Sound System Musical Productions; MENC 1991-; *home:* 282 Hazel Rd Pittsburgh PA 15235*

RIZZO, SANTO D., Prof of Occupational Therapy; *b:* Buffalo, NY; *c:* Christopher; *ed:* St Univ of NY at Buffalo (BS) Ed 1965, (MS) Ed 1974; *cr:* Pembroke Cntrl Schl Instr 1968-70; Erie Comm Coll Prof 1970-; *ai:* Soc of Occupational Therapy Asst Adv; Scheduling Person; Appointments & Evaluations Comms; NEA 1968-; FFECC 1970-, Allied Hlth Rep; AACCF 1970-, Excl in Tchng Awd; Buffalo Craftsman 1970-82; Natl Guard 1968-74; Erie Comm Coll Mini & Video Grants; 1st Place Allentown Art Festival Sculpture; *office:* Erie Comm Coll 6205 Main St Williamsville NY 14221

ROACH, BEVERLY DENNIS, Business & Computer Instructor; *b:* Bellevue, OH; *m:* David P.; *c:* Kelly Diane; *ed:* Bowling Green St Univ (BS) Bus Ed 1975; BGSU-Firelands Br Applied Sci Exec Secretarial 1974; *cr:* EHOVE JVS Exec Secretarial Instr 1978-80; Monroeville HS Bus, Cmptr Instr 1980-; *ai:* Sr Class Adv; Tech Comm 2 Yrs; OEA, NEA 1978-, Pres, Bldg Rep 2 Yrs, Sec 6 Yrs; Acad Boosters, Music Boosters 1994-; *office:* Monroeville HS 101 West St Monroeville OH 44847

ROACH, JOAN BUCSCHER, Retired 4th Grade Teacher; *b:* St Albans LI, NY; *w:* Daniel Joseph (dec); *c:* Daniel J. II, Mary Jo, David, Patrick; *ed:* St John Coll (BSE) Kndgtn-Primary 1952; 9 Credit Hrs; 3 Credit Hrs Notre Dame Coll; 3 Credit Hrs Ursuline Coll; *cr:* Cleveland Pub Schls Kndgtn Tchr 1952-54; St Ann Elem Schl 3-4 Grd Tchr 1966-95; *ai:* Book Talk Coord; Arts Comm; Lit Annual; Help with Fund Raisers; Cath Diocese of Cleveland Best Tchr of Yr Awd 1988-89; *home:* 3090 Yorkshire Rd Cleveland OH 44118

ROACH, KATHLEEN ELIZABETH, Global Studies & French Tchr; *b:* Syracuse, NY; *ed:* SUNY Cortland (BA) Intnl Stud 1988; SUNY Plattsburgh (MALS) Lbrl Stud 1994; Attnd Univ de Neuchafel, Switzerland; *cr:* St John's Acad Fr Tchr 1988-89; Peru Cntrl Schl Global Stud Tchr 1990-95, Fr, Global Stud Tchr 1995-; *ai:* NEA, NEANY 1990-; Peru Assn Tchrs 1990-, Exec Sec; Peru Vol Fire Dept 1992-, Firefighter, EMT, Meritorious Svc; Peru Cntrl Schl Fed Credit Union 1966-, Bd; EMT Commendation CPR Save Reversal of Cardiac Arrest 1994, 1995; Stork Pin Awd Assisted in out of Hosp Live Birth; *office:* Peru Central Schl 17 School St PO Box 68 Peru NY 12972

ROAN, LOU WRIGHT, Guidance Counseling & Chair; *b:* Burlington, NC; *m:* Roger Edward; *c:* Ann Roan Mc Clain; *ed:* Guilford Coll (BA) Sociology 1961; East Carolina Univ (MA) Pub Schl Admin, Supervision, His 1965; Advanced Grad Prgm Psych, Cnslng; *cr:* Lankenau Pvt Schl PE Tchr 1959; Grainger HS His Tchr 1961-63; Sylvan Schl Fine Arts, Hum Tchr 1963-64; Laplata HS His Tchr, Cnslr 1964-69; Smallwood MS Cnslr 1969-; Charles Cty Bd of Ed 1964-; *ai:* Crisis Team Spec Cnslng; Pupil Stud Team Chair; Schl Improvement Team 1985-91; Just Say No Spon 1987-92; Bsktbl, Sftbl Coach 1959, 1963-64; Forensic League Coach 1961-63; Drama, Musical Productions Coach 1963-69; Club Adv 1961-72; Ed Assn of Charles Co, MD St Tchrs Assn 1964-; NEA 1961-, Natl Del; Delta Kappa Gamma, Ofcr, Sec, Schlsp St Comm; Hawthorn Cntry Club 1966-; Good Samaritan Presbyn Church; Quaker Birthright Mem Cane Creek Friends Meeting; Christ Church Schl Bd 1981-83, Chair; Educl Specifications Comm Bd of Ed 1972-80; Outstdng Exemplary Cnslr Bd of Ed; Dept Chair Guid, Cnslng 1969-; 30 Yrs Recognition Bd of Ed 1995; Co-Author MS Cnslng Prgm: Coming Into My Universe Presented Natl APGA, MD ST, Adopted Curr Bd of Ed; *office:* General Smallwood MS RR 210 Indian Head MD 20640

ROANE, LILLIAN E., Math Teacher; *b:* Poughkeepsie, NY; *ed:* Univ of D.C. (BA) Bus Admin, Math 1979; CA St Univ Tchng Cert Ed 1987; 8 Grad Credits Math Georgetown Univ; 3 Grad Credits Math Amer Univ; 6 Grad Credits Math Southeastern Univ; 3 Grad Credits Math, Trinity Coll; *cr:* US House of Reps Caseworker 1969-75, Adm Asst 1982-83; Gen Elec Co Corporate Office Adm Asst 1975-81; Los Angeles USD Math Tchr 1985-88; D.C. Pub Schl System Math Tchr 1989-; *ai:* Schl Spon Yth Chptr Amer Red Cross; Schl Testing, Staff Dev Comms; NEA 1985-88; AFT 1989-; NCTM, DC Cncl Tchrs Math 1993-; Hands Together Neighbor Club 1994-; DCPS Vol Svc Awd 1990-92; Finalist WA Post Agnes Myers Tchr of Yr Awd 1993, 1995; *office:* Eastern HS 1700 E Capitol St NE Washington DC 20003*

ROAR, DANNY JOE, Biology Teacher; *b:* Alliance, OH; *m:* Kathy Lynn Cline; *ed:* Morehead St Univ (BS) Bio 1982, (AME) Sci Ed 1988; Post Grad Hrs OH Univ 1995-; *cr:* Waverly HS Bio Tchr 1982-87, 1989-; *ai:* TEAMS, Sci Club, Envirothon Adv; OEA, NEA, SECO 1982-; *office:* Waverly HS 500 E 2nd St Waverly OH 45690*

ROAT, RANDY SCOTT, Visual Communications Teacher; *b:* Camp Hill, PA; *ed:* Millersville Univ (BSE) Tech Ed 1991; Working on Masters Credits; *cr:* Columbia Jr Sr HS Visual Commnctn Tchr 1991-; *ai:* JV Sftbl Coach; Var Club & Class 1998 Adv; TEAP 1990-; LLTEAP 1991-; PMSA 1995-; *office:* Columbia Jr Sr HS 901 Ironville Pike Columbia PA 17512*

ROBATISIN, CHARLES C., English & Social Studies Tchr; *b:* Bellaire, OH; *m:* Frances Zelechowski; *c:* Charles J., Donnal., Karen M. Zook; *ed:* Univ of Pittsburgh (BS) Bus Admin, Eng 1958; PA St Univ (MBA) (ME) Eng 1970; Geneva Coll; *cr:* Harmony Township Eng, Soc Stud Tchr 1963-67; Quaker Valley Jr HS Eng, Soc Stud Tchr 1967-; *ai:* Admin Comms; NEA, PA St EA 1963-; Quaker Valley EA 1967-; Kiwanis, Lions 1968-; Amer Legion, VFW 1957-.*

ROBB, CAROL E., Retired Math & Cmptr Sci Tchr; *b:* New Castle, PA; *ed:* Slippery Rock Univ (BS) Math Ed 1960; Addl Post Grad Classes in Cmptr Sci; Cmptr Sci Instruction Cert; *cr:* Shenango HS Math & Cmptr Sci Tchr 35 1/2 Yrs; *ai:* Stu-at-Risk Core Team; Mentor Tchr; Stu Tchr Cooperating Tchr; NEA, PSEA & Shenango Area Ed Assn 1960-; Westfield Presbyn Church 1950-, Elder 3 Yrs, Deacon 3 Yrs; Red Cross WSI 1960-, Life Guard I; Morraine Trail BSA 1991-, Dist Chprsn 3 Yrs; Beaver Castle Girl Scouts 1957-92, Pres 2 Yrs, Pres Awd 1988, Thanks Badge 1991.*

ROBBINS, CAROL COULTAS, Sixth Grade Teacher; *b:* Brooklyn, NY; *m:* Gary; *c:* Dana, Lauren; *ed:* Brooklyn Coll (BA) Elem Ed 1970, (MS) Elem Ed, Math & Sci 1973; *cr:* Brooklyn Pub Schl 221 2nd & 3rd Tchr 1970-77; Vacation Day Camp Tchr 1970-76; Lincoln Roosevelt Schl 5th Grd Tchr 1983-84; Roxbury Twp Schls 6th Grd Tchr 1983-; Lincoln Roosevelt Schl 6th Grd Tchr 1984-; *ai:* PTA; Enrichment, Roxbury Twp Schl Facilities & Schl Liaison Comms, Supt Liason, PR & R; NEA & REA 1983-; AFT & UFT 1970-83; BSA, Nominating Comm, Bicentennial Jamboree Chprsn; Kennedy Schl PTA, Pres, Exec Bd, Pres Cncl; Roxbury Day Care, Bd of Dirs 1983-85; Morris Cty Republican Comm 1987-; Dist Trng Prgms Various Courses; *office:* Lincoln/Roosevelt Elem Schl 34 Hillside Ave Succasunna NJ 07876*

ROBBINS, CARSON SUSAN, Social Studies Chair; *b:* Rochester, PA; *ed:* Geneva Coll (BA) His 1972; 35 Credit Hrs Slippery Rock European His; *cr:* South Side HS Tchr, Dept Chair 1973-; *ai:* Assessment Grant Comm; NEA 1972-; NCSS, PCSS 1990-; Istina 1990-, Pres; *office:* South Side HS 4949 St Rt 151 Hookstown PA 15050*

ROBBINS, DENISE STEINER, 9th-12th Grade Art Teacher; *b:* Wadsworth, OH; *m:* Kenneth; *c:* Thegen; *ed:* Kent St Univ (BA) Design & Crafts 1973; Attnd Akron Univ, Ashland Univ, Wright St; *cr:* Wayne Coll Art Tchr 1981-89; Chippewa Local Schl Art Tchr 1973-; *ai:* Comm Intervention Coord; NHS Instr; Teenage Inst Adv; NEA, OEA 1973-; Drug Free Schls Grant 6 Yrs; Tchr of Yr 1986-87, 1990-91; *office:* Chippewa HS 100 Valley View Rd Doylestown OH 44230*

ROBBINS, DONNA REECE, First Grade Teacher; *b:* Muncy, PA; *m:* Dale L.; *c:* Andrea Shultz; *ed:* Lycoming Coll (AB) Psych 1962; Attnd Bloomsburg Univ & Penn St Univ; *cr:* Geo Ferrel Elem Schl 1st-3rd Grd Tchr 1962-71; Ashkar Elem Schl 1st Grd Tchr 1971-82; Carl G Renn Elem Schl 1st Grd Tchr 1982-; *ai:* PSEA 1962-; NEA 1962-; *office:* Carl G Renn Elem Lairdsville PA 17742*

ROBBINS, GEORGE WALTER, Social Science Instructor; *b:* Constantine, MI; *m:* Eileen Reardon; *c:* Nicholas, Anna; *ed:* Univ of MI (BA) Pol Sci 1959, (MA) Pol Sci 1960; Cmptr Classes; *cr:* Prince of Wales Coll Asst Prof 1967-68; Univ of WI at Oshkosh Instr 1968-69; St Univ of NY at Fredonia Instr 1969-70; St Univ of NY at Buffalo Instr 1972-76, 1978-82; Erie Comm Coll Instr 1985-; *ai:* NEA 1989-, Pres, Part-Time Union & Organizer; Peace Ctr 1970-; Former Act-Planning Comm, Stu Life Comm, Stu Link Club & Jr Bsbl; Edwin F Connally Awd in Govt 1966; Univ of MI Grad with Honors 1959; *office:* Erie Comm Coll 121 Ellicott Buffalo NY 14203

ROBBINS, J. WAYNE, Social Studies Professor; *b:* Niles, MI; *m:* Sheri L. Neddell; *c:* Bradley W., J. Blake; *ed:* Hyles-Anderson Coll (BS) Pastoral Theology 1989; *cr:* Twin City Chrstn Schl Yth Pastor, Treas 1989-; *ai:* Sr Class Adv; Bsktbl Coach; Ath Dir; Preacher Boy Club; Teen Cnslr & Ministry; *office:* Twin City Christian Schl 194 Electric Ave Lunenburg MA 01462

ROBBINS, JAMES M., Physics Teacher; *b:* Coudersport, PA; *m:* Kathy Venieris; *c:* Katherine, Laura, Michael; *ed:* St Univ of NY (BS) Physics & Math 1979; 36 Addl Credit Hrs in Ed at Grad Level at Bloomsburg Univ in PA; *cr:* South Williamsport Jr-Sr High Tchr 1984-; *ai:* PSEA 1984-; *office:* South Williamsport Jr / Sr HS 700 Percy St Williamsport PA 17701

ROBBINS, MARK ALLEN, Elem Physical Education Tchr; *b:* Lorain, OH; *m:* Eva Lynette Kincer; *c:* Matthew, Lauren, Heidi; *ed:* Larain Cty Comm Coll (AA) PE 1975; Kent St Univ (BSEd) PE 1977; Ashland Univ (MED) Curr, Instruction 1990; Attnd Cleveland St Univ, Coll of MT at St

Joseph, Walsh Univ, Akron Univ; *cr:* Vanaus Elem Schls PE Instr 1977-82; Larain HS PE Tchr 1982-93; Longfellow Elem Schl K-6 Grd PE Tchr 1993-; *ai:* Southview HS Var Girls Soccer, Asst Girls Bsktbl Coach; NEA, OEA, LEA 1977-; Greater Cleveland Soccer Coaches Assn 1992-; Church of the Open Door, Usher 1985-, Sunday Schl Tchr 1991-; Eric Shore Conf Coach of Yr 1991-92; *home:* 2456 Eastlawn St Lorain OH 44052

ROBBINS, PATRICIA MORAN, English Teacher; *b:* Boston, MA; *m:* Rex; *c:* Margaret, Timothy, Mary Victoria; *ed:* Bryn Mawr Coll (BA) Eng 1957; Columbia Univ (MA) Eng & Comp Lit 1984; *cr:* Birch Walham Schl Eng Tchr 1972-81; Calhoun Schl Eng Tchr 1981-82; Trinity Schl Eng Tchr & 7th-12th Dir of Admissions 1982-; *ai:* Tour Guides Admissions Asst; Hedmasters Admin Staff; Rel & Co-Ed Comm; SEED Ldr; NEH Grant for Summer Stu Harvard 1986; Trustees Travel Grant Trinity 1991; *office:* Trinity Schl 139 W 91st St New York NY 10024

ROBBINS, SUZANNE MARIE, Asst Prof, Dept Educl Techs; *b:* Freeport, NY; *m:* Mark E. Sr.; *c:* Barbara Jean, Mark E. Jr.; *ed:* Bloomsburg St Univ (BS) Elem Ed 1980; Bucknell Univ (MS) Rdng Ed 1982; PA St Univ (PHD) Instrl Systems 1993; *cr:* Governor Mifflin Schl Dist 1st Grd Tchr 1980-81; Faith United Meth Church Nursery Schl Dir 1981-82; Keystone Cntrl Schl Dist Chptr 1 Rdng Specialist 1982-85, Elem Tchr 1985-91, Elem Sci Dist Pgm Ldr 1991-92; PA St Univ Instrl Dev Pgm Asst 1991-92; Lock Haven Univ Asst Prof 1992-; *ai:* Alpha Sigma Tau Zeta Chptr, LHU Womens Rugby & Stu PSEA Adv; Kappa Delta Pi Delta Sigma Chptr Cnslr; Kappa Delta Pi 1979-; PS EA 1982-; NEA 1982-; Phi Delta Kappa 1986-; IRA 1992-; PA Rdng Tchrs Edctrs 1992-; Bald Eagle Rdng Cncl 1992-; ACEI 1994-; Lycoming Co PA; Conservation Dist; Environmental Ed Coord 1994-; Lock Haven Jaycees Outstdng Edctr Awd; Intnl Paper Edcore Fndtn Grant-Writing Awd; PA St Presidential Excl Elem Sci Tchng Awd; PA Electric Assn Pres Awd; Phi Delta Kappa Kozak Memrl Flwshp; ACEI NCATE Folio Reviewer; Whos Who in Amer Ed 1994-95; *office:* Lock Haven Univ 624 Stevenson Lib Lock Haven PA 17745*

ROBELOTTO, RICHARD A., American History Teacher; *b:* Albany, NY; *w:* Carol Bissonette (dec); *ed:* St Univ of NY at Albany (BA) His 1965, (MA) Soc Stud 1966; 30 Grad Hrs His, Educl Admin; *cr:* W.S. Hackett Jr HS Afro Asian Stud Tchr 1966-74; Albany HS Multi-Curr Tchr 1974-; *ai:* Bowling, Golf Coach; Albany Pub Schl TA 1966-, Bldg Rep, Chief Negotiator; NYSUT, AFT 1969-, Del; *home:* 19 McCormick Rd Slingerlands NY 12159

ROBERGE, RICHARD W., Third Grade Teacher; *b:* Biddeford, ME; *m:* Susan G. Skilling; *ed:* Univ of Me (BA) Ed 1973; Post Grad Stud Schl Admin, Environmental Stud, Cmptr Tech; *cr:* Sawyer Schl 3 Grd Tchr 18 Yrs; Brown Elem Schl 3-4 Grd Tchr 5 Yrs; *ai:* Cmptr Tech Comm; Earth Day Coord; NEA, SPTA, MTA 1973-; Conservation Commission 1991-, Dedication of Annual Town Report; Old Orch Bch Tree Bd 1993-, Chm; Old Orch Bch Tree Fund Inc 1993-, Pres; Kind Heart Animal Soc,Pres; Former Chm & Organizer Comm Recycling Prgm; Former Jaycee, Key Man Awd; Organizer ME Coast Marathon.

ROBERSON, CHARLES WILLIAM, Computer Teacher; *b:* Little Falls, NY; *ed:* Western CT St Univ (BS) Scndry Ed Math 1969, (MS) Scndry Ed Math 1976; 20 Hrs Post Grad Cmptr Sci Courses at Northeastern, Harvard & Manhattan; *cr:* Danbury HS Math Tchr 1969-74; West Winfield Math Tchr 1974-79; Joel Barlow HS Math & Cmptr Tchr 1980-86; Milford Cmptr Tchr 1986-; *ai:* Girls Vlybl, Bsktbl & Cmtpr Team Coach; NEA 1975-; *office:* Milford HS 100 West St Milford NH 03055

ROBERSON, VALERIE SPOONER, 6th Grd Lang Arts & Rdng Tchr; *b:* Brooklyn, NY; *c:* Tiya M., Tyren D.; *ed:* Post Grad Stud Western MD Univ Elem Curr; *cr:* Middle Valley Elem Schl Lang Arts, Reading Tchr; *ai:* WA Dist E Yth Dir AME Zion Church; Contee AMEA Church Yth Choir Dir; Black Male Achvmt Coord; Mulitcultural Liaison; NEA 1971-, Del; MSTA 1973-, Del; PGCEA 1973-, Fac Rep.*

ROBERT, CAROLE CARLSON, Mathematics Teacher; *b:* Ridgeay, PA; *m:* John R.; *c:* Justin, David; *ed:* Seton Hill Coll (BA) Math 1964; Attnd Univ of MD, Boston Univ; *cr:* Andover HS Math Tchr 1964-68; Kubasaki HS Math Tchr 1969-72; Wiesbaden HS Math Tchr 1973-; *ai:* Jr Class Spon; Math Dept Chprsn; AFT; OFT; NCTM; *home:* Cmr 467 Box 5074 APO AE 09096

ROBERT, JOHN R., English Teacher; *b:* Erath, LA; *m:* Carole Carlson; *c:* Justin, David; *ed:* U Southwestern LA (BA) Soc St, Eng 1960; Ball St Univ (MA) Ed Psych, Foundations of AM Ed 1978; Post Grad Boston Univ; *cr:* Iberia Parish LA Eng Tchr 1960-65; Baumholder Am HS Eng Tchr 1965-70; Shape AM HS Eng Tchr 1970-72; H. H. Arnold HS Eng Tchr 1972-; *ai:* SCA Adv; AFT; NEA; *home:* Cmr 467 Box 5074 APO AE 09096

ROBERTS, ANITA CLAIRE (MILLER), Enrichment Teacher; *b:* Perth Amboy, NJ; *m:* Russell; *c:* Chad; *ed:* Salisbury St Coll (BS) Elem Ed 1974; 15 Hrs Loyola Coll; *cr:* Overlook Elem Schl 6 Grd Tchr 1974-86; Broadneck Elem Schl 5 Grd Tchr 1986-89; Shipleys Choice Elem Schl 6 Grd Tchr 1989-92; Severna Park MS Enrichment Tchr 1992-95; *ai:* Stu Govt Assn, Schl Newspaper Adv; NEA, TAAC 1974-; PEO 1985-, Sec; *office:* Severna Park MS 450 Jumpers Hole Rd Severna Park MD 21146

ROBERTS, ANNE MARIE LATONA, Chemistry Teacher; *b:* Kingston, PA; *m:* Curtis Wesley; *ed:* Wilkes Univ (BA) Chem 1972, (MS) Chem-Summa Cum Laude 1975; Certfd Interior Design; *cr:* Pittston Area Schl Chem Tchr 1972-; *ai:* AFT, LCSTA 1972-; Amer Chemical Soc Awd for Excl in Chem Tchng; PA St Senatorial Citation for Excl in Chem Tchng; Nominated to Presidential Awds for Excl in Sci, Math Tchng Prgm; Tchr of Yr Nominee; Cert of Recognition Outstdng Svc, Commitment to Tchng; *office:* Pittston Area Schl Dist 5 Stout St Yatesville PA 18640*

ROBERTS, BARBARA J., Resource Room Teacher; *b:* Glens Falls, NY; *m:* Thomas H.; *c:* Susan Dancause, Jennifer, Jason Turcotte, Ryan Turcotte; *ed:* SUNY at Oswego (BS) Elem Ed 1969; Coll at St Rose (MS) Spcl Ed 1977; *cr:* Cazenovia Cntrl Schl 6th Grd Tchr 1969-73; Prospect Schl Spcl Ed Tchr 1973-75; South Glens Falls Cntrl Schl Spcl Ed Tchr 1977-; *ai:* Frosh Class Co-Adv 1978-89; Modified Cheering Coach 1978-90; OM Coach 1983-94; Var Cheering Coach 1990-92; AFT 1969-; NYS Tchrs Assn 1969-; Double H Hole in the Woods Ranch 1993-, Equestrian Dir; *office:* Oliver W Winch Jr HS 99 Hudson St S Glens Falls NY 12801

ROBERTS, EDWIN LEE, Science Teacher; *b:* Wilmington, OH; *m:* Robin Cook; *ed:* OH St Univ (BSEd) Phys Sci Ed 1987; 25 Quarter Hrs Toward MS Sci Ed; *cr:* East Clinton HS Sci Tchr 1988-91; West Jefferson HS Sci Tchr 1991-; *ai:* Head Girls Sftbl & Head Soccer Coach; NEA & OEA 1988-; SECO 1993-; *office:* West Jefferson HS 561 W Jefferson Kiousville Rd West Jefferson OH 43162

ROBERTS, ELIZABETH HAUSNER, Fifth Grade Teacher; *b:* New York, NY; *m:* John Wallace; *c:* Dawn, Deirdre, Amy, Sarah; *ed:* St Univ of NY, Coll of Ed at Cortland (BS) Elem Ed 1960; Univ of Bridgeport (MS) Elem Ed 1984; *cr:* Westport Pub Schls 3rd & 4th Grd Tchr 1960-65; Greenwich Pub Schls 3rd-6th Grd Part-Time Homebound Tutor; Greenwich Cntry Day Schl 3rd-5th Grd Tchr 1982-; *ai:* Comm Work Within Schl; Prof Day & Mission Statemen Comms; NCTM; Jr League of Greenwich 1982-; Saint Catherine Church, Soup Kitchen Vol; Numerous Rdng, Writing & Math Wkshps; *office:* Greenwich Country Day Schl Old Church Rd PO Box 623 Greenwich CT 06836

ROBERTS, ELIZABETH M., 1st Grade Teacher; *b:* Granville, NY; *ed:* SUNY at Cobleskill (AAS) Nursery Ed 1973; SUNY at Oswego (BS) Elem Ed 1975; Addl 30 Grad Hrs Permanent Cert; *cr:* Dolgeville Cntrl Schl Kndgtn Tchr 1976-82, Grd 1 Tchr 1982-; *ai:* Math Comm; Meml Fund Sec; AFT, NYSUT 1976-; DTA 1976-, Sec, RA Del, Exec Comm; *home:* 11 W Spofford Ave Dolgeville NY 13329

ROBERTS, ELIZABETH STEPHENS, Latin Teacher; *b:* Brooklyn, NY; *m:* James; *c:* Sean Michael, Kerri Elizabeth; *ed:* Seat of Wisdon Coll (BA) Latin 1967; Hunter Coll (MA) Eng 1972; LIU-CW Post (PHD) Schl Admin 1976; Theater, Span, Cmptrs & Cooperative Learning Credit Hrs; *cr:* Christ the King Latin & Religion Tchr 1964-73, Tchr & Asst Prin 1973-74; Elwood Jr HS Asst Prin & Eng Tchr 1974-; Touro Coll Eng Prof & Stu Adv 1988-91; Walt Whitman HS Latin Tchr 1990-; *ai:* Latin Honor Soc Adv; AFT & NYSUT 1990-, PDK 1991-; ACL & CAES 1990-; Suffolk Classical Assn & Nassan Classical Assn 1991-; PTA 1986-, Fac VP; NYSCD, NASSP & NAESP Conf Presenter; Who's Who of Amer Women Biographee; *office:* Walt Whitman HS 301 W Hills Rd Huntington Sta NY 11746

ROBERTS, ERIC LEE, Guidance Counselor; *b:* Allentown, PA; *ed:* Univ of Pittsburgh at Johnstown (BA) Scndry Schl Eng 1993; Indiana Univ of PA (MED) Scndry Schl Cnslng 1995; *cr:* Forest Hills Sr HS Eng Tchr 1994; Cambria Cty Area Comm Coll Adj Eng Fac 1994-95; Freedom HS Guid Cnslr 1995-; *ai:* NHS Adv; Big Brother-Big Sister Comm; BEA, PSEA, NEA 1995-; UPJ Alumni Assn 1993-; *home:* 2741 Rickenbacker Ct Orefield PA 18069

ROBERTS, IRENE L., Retired 5th-6th Grade Teacher; *b:* Rochester, NY; *ed:* Nazareth Coll of Rochester (BS) Ed 1959, (BA) Ed 1966, (MS) Ed 1975; 48 Addl Hrs; *cr:* Nazareth Hall Cadet Schl Prin 1966-69; Roch City Schl #34 5th, 6th Grd Tchr 1969-92; *ai:* Mentor Stu, Credited Tchrs; NEA, RTA, AFT 1969-; *home:* 160 Kings Gate S Rochester NY 14617

ROBERTS, J. MICHAEL, Social Studies Teacher; *b:* Bellefontaine, OH; *m:* Debbie Sue Holzbauer; *c:* Emily, Matthew, A. J., Caleb; *ed:* Urbana Coll (BS) Soc Stud Ed 1969; Univ of Northern VA Presidential Scholar; Post Grad Stud Wright St Univ, KS St Univ; *cr:* Indian Lake Eng, His, Govt Tchr 1969-78; Waynesfield World Geography, US His, Govt Tchr 1985-89; West Liberty Salem World Geo, US His, Govt Tchr 1989-; *ai:* Citizen's Bee Team coach; Schl Improvement Steering Comm; Mock Trial Coach; *home:* 4947 County Road 5 N Rushsylvania OH 43347*

ROBERTS, JANE E., First Grade Teacher; *b:* Bethlehem, PA; *m:* Kyle; *c:* Erin; *ed:* Northampton Cty Comm Coll (AAS) Early Chldhd Ed 1985; Bloomsburg Univ (BS) Elem Ed 1987; Kutztown Univ (MS) Rdng Specialist 1991; 7 Post Grad Credit Hrs; *cr:* Salford Hills Elem Schl Third Grd Tchr 1987-88, First Grd Tchr 1988-; *ai:* NEA, PSEA 1987-, SAEA 1987-, Bldg Rep; Dist Spec Mention; *office:* Salford Hills Elem Schl 2720 Barndt Rd Harleysville PA 19438

ROBERTS, JANET H., 3rd Grade Teacher; *b:* Beckley, WV; *m:* H. R.; *c:* Jeffrey, Karen Zelina, Lianne Tedesco; *ed:* Bethany Coll (BA) Elem Ed 1959; Univ of Pittsburgh (MED) Elem Ed 1972; Addl 30 Post-Grd Credit Hrs; *cr:* Bethel Park Schls Tchr 1959-62, 1972-; *ai:* AFT; BPFT; Christ United Meth Church 1962-, Admin Bd Chm 1989-92; Child Care Bd of Dir Prsnl 1992-93; IHN 1995-, Coord; *office:* Bethel Park Schls 515 Clifton Rd Bethel Park PA 15102*

ROBERTS, JEFFREY C., Social Studies Teacher; *b:* Yonkers, NY; *m:* Michelle A.; *c:* David C., Jason W.; *ed:* Pace Coll (BA) Soc Sci 1969; Herbert H. Lehman Coll (MA) Scndry Ed 1972; Concordia Jr Coll Dipl Soc Sci 1967; *cr:* Commerce HS Soc Stud Tchr 1969-74; Goron HS Soc Stud Tchr 1974-; *ai:* Prom Comm Chm; Jr Achvmt Applied Ec Tchr, Spon; AFT, Yonkers Fed of Tchrs 1969-; Westchester Cncl of Soc Stud 1990-; Town of Wappinger Bsbl 1986-, Asst Coach; Jr Achvmt Ed Achvmt Awd 1991; Attnd Jr Achvmt Tchr Flwshp 1994; *office:* Gorton HS Shonnard Pl Yonkers NY 10703

ROBERTS, JOAN SMITH, High School English Teacher; *b:* Lyons, NY; *m:* Kenneth L.; *ed:* Auburn Comm Coll (AA) General Ed 1964; St Univ Coll Buffalo (BS) Scndry Eng Ed 1966, (MS) Scndry Eng Ed 1971; *cr:* Kenmore East Sr HS Eng Tchr 1967-; *ai:* Youth & Adult Yoga Instr; Stu Advocate Design Team; Stdnts at Risk Prgm; Join the Winners Kids Helping Kids; NYSUT, KTA, KETA 1967-; NCTE 1982-; Kenmore East Advisory Bd; Spec Tchr Commendation Fredonia Coll 1990-93; Nom Disneys Americas Greatest Tchr Awd 1991; Pub Poet 1989, 1990; Tchr of Natl Schl of Excl 1993; *office:* Kenmore East Sr HS 350 Fries Rd Tonawanda NY 14150*

ROBERTS, JOHN A., Social Studies Teacher; *b:* Geneseo, NY; *c:* Graig, Adam; *ed:* SUC at Brockport (BS) His, Pol Sci 1974, (MS) His 1979; *cr:* Avon Cntrl Schl 7-12 Grd Soc Stud Tchr 1974-; *ai:* Stu Cncl Adv; Blood Dr; Var Ftbl, Girls Track Coach; Avon Tchrs Assn, NEA 1974-; Nazareth Coll Outstdng Tchr; *home:* 17 Partridgeberry Way West Henrietta NY 14586*

ROBERTS, JUDY BRYANT, English Teacher; *b:* Wilkes-Barre, PA; *m:* Parker; *ed:* Cntrl CT St Univ (MA) Eng 1970; Wesleyan Univ Summer Courses; *cr:* Memrl Schl at Middlefield Fr Tchr 1967-69; Martin Kellogg MS Eng Tchr 1970-76; Newington HS Eng Tchr 1976-; *ai:* Fac Advy Comm Mem; NTA 1970-, Soc Chm; CEA 1970-; NEA 1970-; First Church of Christ 1991-, Choir Mem; *office:* Newington HS 605 Willard Ave Newington CT 06111

ROBERTS, KATHRYN GINTERT, Retired Fourth Grade Teacher; *b:* Warren, OH; *m:* George T.; *c:* Cynthia Roberts Fehr, Thomas; *ed:* Youngstown Coll (BS) Elem Ed 1952; Youngstown St Univ (MS) Ed 1979; *cr:* Austintown Schls 1 GrdTchr 1952-53; Albion Schls 2 Grd Tchr 1956-58; Howland Schls 2-3 Grds Tchr 1958-60; Canfield Schls 2-4 Grds Tchr 1966-91; *ai:* NEA, OEA 1966-; Mahoning Ret T. A., OH Ret Tchrs Assn 1991-; *home:* 182 Talsman Dr Unit B Canfield OH 44406

ROBERTS, LEE MELVIN, Assistant Professor of Chem; *b:* Springfield, MO; *c:* Elizabeth Marie, Karissa Lee; *ed:* Southwestern Adventist Coll (BS) Chem 1984; TX A&M Univ (PHD) Chem 1994; *cr:* Columbia Union Coll Asst Prof 1994-; *ai:* Chem Prgm Dir; Amer Chemical Soc 1994-; *office:* Columbia Union Coll 7600 Flower Ave Takoma Park MD 20912

ROBERTS, MARTEL ZARG, Business Education Teacher; *b:* Little Falls, NY; *m:* John Neff; *ed:* SUNY Inst of Tech (BS) Bus Pub Mgmt & Mktg 1986; Coll of St Rose (MS) Rdng 1995; Siena Cert Bus Ed 1988; *cr:* Fonda-Fultonville Cntrl Bus Ed Tchr 1990-; Ilion Jr Sr High Bus Ed Tchr 1991; *ai:* FBLA Co-Adv; *office:* Fonda-Fultonville Central Schl 112 Old Johnstown Rd Fonda NY 12068

ROBERTS, MARTIN PHILIP, Physics, Chem & Earth Sci Tchr; *b:* Meriden, CT; *m:* Dorothy Cahill; *c:* Kristen, Martin Jr.; *ed:* Southern CT St Univ (BS) Bio 1966; MI St (MS) Bio 1973; Univ of CT 6th Yr Admin 1980; 6th Yr Sci Specialist 1990; Wesleyan Univ 8 Credits Physics, 3 Credits Earth Sci, Geology of CT; Cntrl CT St Univ 3 Credits Statistics; Attnd Univ of Hartford; *cr:* Holy Cross HS Chem Tchr 1966-67; Platt HS Bio, Earth Sci Tchr 1967-80; Glastanbury HS Chem, Earth Sci Tchr 1980-86; Coginchaug HS Physics, Chem, Earth Sci Tchr 1986-; Teckyo Post Univ Part Time Bio Tchr 1987-; *ai:* Boys Cross Cntry, Track; REA, NEA, CEA, CT St Coaches Assn 1967-; CT Physic Tchr Capt; Natl Sci Fnd Grants to MI St, Univ for Sci Specialist.*

ROBERTS, MARY JANE PULEO, History Teacher; *b:* Cleveland, OH; *m:* David Earl; *c:* Lori Lynn, Valerie Ann; *ed:* Case Western Reserve Univ (BA) His 1970; Attnd John Carroll Univ, Mt St Josephs Coll; *cr:* Greenview Jr High Soc Stud Tchr 1970-74; Sub-Mentor Schls Soc Stud Tchr 1979-82; Memrl Jr High-Mentor Soc Stud Tchr 1982-86; Mentor HS Soc Stud Tchr 1986-; *ai:* Sr Project, NHS Selection & MTA Schlsp Comms; NEA, OEA, MTA 1982-; GVS Alumnae Club 1974-, Historian; *office:* Mentor H Center St Mentor OH 44060

ROBERTS, PATRICE HELEN, Mathematics & Science Teacher; York City, NY; *ed:* Saint Thomas Aquinas Coll (BS) Psych 1972 Island Univ (MS) Ed 1992; 45 Credits Toward Doctorate in Instru Leadership at Saint Johns Univ; *cr:* Saint Pius X Schl Tchr 19 Charles DeWolf Schl Tchr 1974-; The Learning Edge Dir of Ed Saint Thomas Aquinas Coll Adjunct Prof of Ed 1996; *ai:* Girls Coach; NEA, NJEA, BCEA 1974-; OTTA 1974-, Pres; ASCD Certified Learning Styles Trainer; Recipient Tchr Incentive Gran Governors Recognition Awd for Outstanding Tchrs; Pub Progr Learning Sequences & Contract Activity Packages by The Learnin Network NY.

ROBERTS, PAUL D., Music Teacher & Choral Dir; *b:* Cincinatti, Frances Coan; *c:* Douglas, Elizabetth; *ed:* OH St Univ (BS) Mu 1966; SUNY at Postsdam (MS) Music Ed 1972; 30 Credits; *cr:* Co Pub Schls Music Tchr 1966-; *ai:* Chamber Choir; SCMEA, Commack Tchrs Assn 1966-; Church Choir 1966-, Sectio Neighborhood Watch 1982-89, Zone Ldr; Boy Scouts 1987-89, Gro Yrbk Dedication Twice; Prof Singer Opera Oratorio; Recordings Soloist; *home:* 15 Nautilus Ave Northport NY 11768

ROBERTS, PAULA M., High School Mathematics Tchr; *b:* Wash DC; *ed:* Charles Cty Comm Coll (AA) General Stud; Univ of MD Park (BS) Math & Scndry Ed, (MA) Math & Scndry Ed; *cr:* McD HS Math Tchr; *ai:* Var Sftbl Head Coach; NCTM; Phi Kappa Phi; Maurice Mcdonough HS 7165 Marshall Corner Rd Pomfret MD 20

ROBERTS, RANDOLPH WILSON, Health & Sciences Ch Scranton, PA; *m:* Ava E. Brown; *c:* Gwendolyn Suzanne, Ryan Wey Franklin & Marshall Coll (AB) Bio 1968, (MA) Geosciences 1974 Univ (MS) Sci Tchng 1977; Western MD Coll (MS) Cnslng 1990; Johns Hopkins Univ, Loyola Coll Sci, Educl Courses, Univ of Ldrshp Courses, Towson St Univ 30 Credits Hlth Ed Courses; *cr:* Ba Cty Pub Schls 7-9 Grd Sci, Math Tchr 1968-89; Woodlawn MS 7-9 G Math Tchr 1968-89; Deer-Park MS 7-9Grd Sci, Math Tchr 19 Franklin MS 7-9 Grd Sci, Math Tchr 1968-89; Loyola HS A Geometry, Physics Tchr 1981-86; Talmudical Acad Bio, Gen Sci, A Geometry Tchr 1983-86; Home & Hosp Ctr Pub Schls Hlth, Sci, Chair 1989-; *ai:* Wellness Coord Home, Hosp Ctr; Curr Consultant 1993, 1995; Cmptr, Tech, Pub Relations Comms; NEA 1968-; MD S Assn 1968-; Phi Delta Kappa 1978-; Eta Sigma Gamma 1993-; Ame for Hlth Ed 1993-; Nature Conservancy, Chesopeake Bay Found Eagle Review Bd; BSA 1954-, Eagle Scout, Webeles, De Advancement Chair; Glendon United Meth Church 1980-, Schlsp Chm, Liturgist, Chrstn Ed Comm; Bare Hills Investment Group 199 Parter, Treas; Natl Sci Fdn Flwshps 1969-74 Amer Univ, 1970-73 Coll; Mem Honorary Hlth Ed Fraternity; Who's Who Among Young Prof 1992-93; Who's Who in The East 1993-94; Who's Who in Ar 1996; Male Tchr of Yr 1982-83; Author Earth Sci Workbook Materials; *office:* Home & Hosp Ctr 6229 Falls Rd Baltimore MD 2

ROBERTS, SADIE JONES, English & French Teacher; *b:* Fre Sierra Le, West Africa; *c:* Ted, Sonia; *ed:* Lincoln Univ (BS) Eng, Fr 1967; Howard Univ (MA) African Stud in Ed 1980; Currently Pos Work; 20 Post Grad Credit Hrs; *cr:* St Edwards HS Tchr 1973-77; A Notre Dame Tchr 1977-80; Automated Bus Systems Tchr 1980-86; D Schls Tchr 1987-; *ai:* Best Friends Club Girls Mentor; Schl New Adv, Ed; DC Tchrs of Eng 1987-; NCTE 1989-; Delta Sigma Theta Undergraduate Schlsp; DC Area Writing Project Grant; Short Stor *office:* Jefferson Jr HS 8th & H Sts SW Washington DC 20024*

ROBERTS, SHARON ANN LEFAUVE, Spanish Teacher; *b:* Buffal *m:* William E.; *c:* Jason, Steven; *ed:* St Univ of NY at Buffalo (BA 1979, (MA) Elem Ed 1990; Canisius Coll; *cr:* Buffalo Acad for Vi Performing Arts Span Tchr 1990-; *ai:* Yrbk & Span Club Adv; NEA NYSAFLT 1992-; *office:* Buffalo Acad Vsl/Perf Arts 333 Clin Buffalo NY 14204

ROBERTS, SUSAN KAY, Asst Prof of PE & Head Coach; *b:* Man OH; *ed:* OH Univ (MED) PE 1975; Univ of AZ (MS) PE 19 Davidson Coll Field Hockey, Bsktbl Head Coach 1976-80; Furmar Field Hockey, Bsktbl Head coach 1980-82; King Coll Vlybl, Bsktb Coach 1983-85; Grove City Coll Asst Prof, Head Coach 1985-; *ai:* Sftbl Head Coach; IMS; Chrldng Adv; Stu Advy Comm; Amer Coaches Assn1983-, Natl Coach of Yr 1985; PAC Coach of Yr 19 1992, 1994-95; *office:* Grove City Coll 100 Campus Dr Grove C 16127*

ROBERTS, TERESA L., Art Teacher; *m:* John J.; *c:* Sujata, Zacha Macalester Coll (BA) Fine Art 1975; Frostburg St Univ (Interdisciplinary Art & Ed 1993; *cr:* Largo HS Scndry Art Tchr 19 Allegany Comm Coll Instr 1988-89; Frostburg St Univ Lecturer 19 Northern HS Scndry Art Tchr 1989-; *ai:* Art Club Spon; Sr Class NAEA, MD Art Ed Assn 1987-; WA Resource Group 1985-; Somers Artist's Assn Juried Exhibit First Place 1989 & 1990; Roy A. Kro Achvmt Awd 1990; *office:* Northern HS RR 2 Box 4 Accident MD 2

ROBERTS, THOMAS GERARD, 9th-10th Grade English Teach Buffalo, NY; *m:* Laura Wilczek; *ed:* Buffalo St Coll (BA) Scndry E 1993; 15 Credit Hrs Univ of Buffalo MA of Eng Ed; *cr:* Depew H Tchr 1993-; *ai:* Class, Newspaper, IM Adv; SAT Instr; Child Stud Acad Stans Comm; Bldg Cncl; NY St United Tchrs, AFT 1993-; I Bd 53 1987-, Bsktbl Ofcl; *office:* Depew HS S 5201 Transit Rd Depe 14043*

ROBERTS, WALTER ERNEST, PE Teacher & Coach; *b:* Lawrence *m:* Patricia Lucas; *ed:* U Mass at Boston (BS) PE, Hlth 1976; Electronics, Instr CPR; *cr:* Honeywell Inc Vender Engr 1980-88; Ol HS PE Instr 1988-90; Pinkerton Acad Tchr 1990-; *ai:* Asst Ftbl, Indoor Track, Head Outdoor Track Coach; Citizenship C NAAHYPERD 1990-; MTCA 1986-; NHCA 1988-; Grace Epis Church From Birth; Coach of Yr Indoor Track 1993; 2 Track & Fi Championships; *home:* 10 Duston Ridge Rd Hampstead NH 03841

ROBERTS-GAITHER, JENNIFER L. JONES, Language Arts Te *b:* Clarksburg, WV; *m:* Roddy Ginley; *c:* Rhoshon, Lawrence, Lakish Coppin St Univ (BS) Ed 1969; Towson St Univ MS Equivalent Ed; *c* 1969-71; Calloway #7 Tchr 1972-73; John Eager Howard 6th Grd 1973-76; Langston Hughes 6th Grd Tchr 1976-78; Liberty #64 6t Tchr 1978-79; Hazelwood #210 6th & 7th Grd Tchr 1982-; *ai:* Chrldr Schl Spirit Comm; Math Tutor; Producer of 4 Major Musicals; AFT BTU 1969-; NAACP 1990-, Minister of Music; Published 2 b Hazelwood Tchr of the Yr 1988, 1993 & 1995; Balto MS Tchr of th 1995; *office:* Hazelwood Elem Sch 210 4517 Hazelwood Ave Balt MD 21206*

ROBERTSON, ANDREW JOHN, 8th Grade Soc Stud Teache Neptune, NJ; *ed:* Quincy Coll (BA) Psych, His 1973; Kean Coll of N Ed Cert 1975; *cr:* Hooper Ave Elem Schl Fifth Grd Tchr 1975-80; River Intermediate West 8th Grd Soc Stud Tchr 1987-90; Toms Intermediate East 8th Grd Soc Stud Tchr 1991-; *ai:* Ed Assn Schlsp C Pine Beach Elem Project Pride; SSTOP Team Conflict Resolution; NJEA 1975-; TREA; *office:* Toms River Intermeidate E Schl Hoope Toms River NJ 08753*

RTSON, CAROL (SHARRON), 4th Grade Teacher; *b:* Plattsburgh, Kelli; *ed:* St Univ of NY at Plattsburgh (BS)-Magna Cum Laude (MS) Ed 1991; Masters +12; *cr:* Plattsburgh City Schl Dist Tchr *ai:* Psi Chi 1983-; Kappa Delta Pi 1984-; NY St Tchrs Assoc 1987-; T 1987-; *office:* Oak Street Elem Schl 108 Oak St Plattsburgh NY

RTSON, GERALD WILLIAM, Senior Prof of Music & Hum; *b:* t, MI; *m:* Deborah Boeshore; *c:* William Stephen, Randal Roy, Risa son Armstrong, Robyn Robertson Sealover, Christopher William; iv of KS (BME) Music Ed 1957; Univ of KS (MME) Music Ed 1967; ced Stud Aesthetic Ed at Univ of IL; *cr:* Herington Pub Schls Music, al Theatre Instr 1957-61; Holliday Jr HS Music Instr 1961-63; nd Park HS Choral Music, Musical Theatre Instr 1963-68; Shawnee n East HS Choral Music, Musical Theatre Instr 1968-69; Harrisburg Comm Coll Music, Hum Sr Prof 1969-; *ai:* Staff Recognition, Helen Schlsp Comms; Music Curr, Adjunct Fac Coord; Salvation Army Advy Bd Chm, Vice Chm, Prgm Dir, Christmas Toy Prgm Coord, Vol of Year; Carlisle Comm Chorus, Music Dir; Natl Endowment for cholar; Young Tchr of Yr 1963; Guest Conductor, Clinician for Band ral Festivals; Created Hum Prgm for Highland Park HS; Created Prgm; *office:* Harrisburg Area Comm Coll 1 HACC Dr Harrisburg 110

RTSON, MARGARET BORGE, Var Bsktbl Chrldng Coach; *b:* ester, MA; *m:* George Frank; *c:* Colleen Sarah, Daniel John; *ed:* 86 Hrs Nrsng Salem St Coll; *cr:* Salem Hosp Delivery RN 1 Yr, ing Room RN 12 Yrs, 6 Yrs; Beverly Hosp Med Surgical RN 8 Yrs, 1989-; *ai:* Var Bsktbl Chrldng Coach; Boys Bsktbl Booster Club; Operating Room Nurses 1990-; Four Conf Trophies; Two Non-Con es; *office:* Beverly HS 100 Sohier Rd Beverly MA 01915

RTSON, SCOTT RAYMOND, High School Science Teacher; *b:* y, NY; *c:* Ariel, Zachary; *ed:* St Univ of NY at Stonybrook (BS) Bio Russell Sage Coll (MS) Ed 1987; 3 Credit Hrs Each at Hamilton Coll of Saint Rose, Smith Coll & St Univ of NY at Purchase; *cr:* al Electric R&D Polymer Chem Research Tech 1981-85; Knowls c Power Lab Chemical & Radiological Controls Instr 1985-88; North n HS Sci Tchr 1987-; *ai:* Outing Club, Gaming Club & Riverwatch hem Lab Team Coord; Envirothon Ldr; NWTA 1987-, Pres; *office:* Warren HS Main St Chestertown NY 12817

RTSON, TIMOTHY W., Academic & Discipline Dean; *b:* and, OH; *m:* Georganne Arion; *c:* Jeffrey, Timothy Jr., Melanie, *ed:* John Carroll Univ (BS) Math 1966, (MS) Math 1969; *cr:* St HS Math Tchr 1967-70, Math Dept Chair 1970-90; Villa Angela HS & Discipline Dean, AP Calculus Tchr 1991-; John Carroll Univ er 1969-; *ai:* Yrbk Photography Dir; Ath Statistics Coord; NCTM OCTM 1975-; GCGTM 1980-; OCEA 1968-; East Side Irish Amer 1980-; *office:* Villa Angela-St Joseph HS 18491 Lake Shore Blvd and OH 44119

RTY, PAULA C., Choral Director & Music Tchr; *b:* Cambridge, *d:* West Chester Univ (BS) Music Ed 1976; Towson St Univ 30 Credit oward MS; *cr:* Bel Air MS Choral Dir & Music Tchr 1976-77; n HS Choral Dir & Music Tchr 1978-82; C Milton Wright HS Choral Music Tchr 1982-; *ai:* Mens Barbershop Chorus Spon; Handbell MMEA 1977-; MEA 1977-; ACDA 1978-; NEA 1995-; Church Accompanist 1977-, Mem, All-Cty Choruses; *office:* C Milton t HS 1301 N Fountain Green Rd Bel Air MD 21015*

Y, JOHN SAMUEL, 7th-8th Grade Math Teacher; *b:* Martinsville, Beth Sadler; *c:* Amy Johnson, Thomas; *ed:* Franklin Coll (BA) His Univ of Dayton (MSE) Admin 1985; *cr:* Brown Cty Elem Tchr 54; Lebanon Elem Tchr 1965-69; Yellow Springs Schls Elem Tchr 82, Jr High Tchr 1982-; *ai:* North-South Skirmish Assn 1962-, ander, Awd of Merit; Natl Rifle Assn 1970-; St Joseph Parish Cncl Pres; St Joseph Choir 1976-, Dir; St Joseph RCIA Team 1991-; 2205 Wrenwood Rd Springfield OH 45505

Y, JUDY SOCHOR, Spanish Teacher; *b:* Putnam, CT; *c:* Jenny, *ed:* Cntrl CT St Univ (BS) Span 1971; Eastern CT St Univ (BS) Ed 30 Addl Hrs; *cr:* Killingly HS Span Tchr 1971-78, 1985-; *ai:* NEA, 1971-; Alpha Mu Gamma 1970-; COLT 1987-; Putnam Bapt Church, y Schl Tchr, Sunday Schl Supt 1993, Chrstn Bd of Ed 1994-; *home:* anyan Rd Putnam CT 06260

Y, MARY FRANCES HUTH, High School History Teacher; *b:* r Falls, PA; *m:* Rodney Clive; *ed:* Seton Hill Coll (BA) His 1963; lair St Coll (MA) His 1973; Attnd Duquesne Univ at Pittsburgh, ry Rock St Coll; *cr:* Southwest Butler Cty Jointure His, Eng Tchr 67; South Orangetown Cntrl Schl Dist His Tchr 1967-69; Northern egnl HS Dist His Tchr 1969-; *ai:* Past Class Adv; Caregivers Fac ; NEA; Bergen Cty Ed Assn; Northern Vly Ed Assn 1969-, Sec, Bldg Action Comm; Schlrshp East-West Ctr Univ of HI; *office:* Northern egnl HS Dist 150 Knickerbocker Rd Demarest NJ 07627

Y, MICHAEL K., Geography & Amer History Tchr; *b:* Wheeling, *d:* OH Univ (BSEd) Soc Stud Comp 1976; MA Scndry Admin Dayton 1983; *cr:* Buckeye Local Schls Dr Ed Tchr 4 Yrs, Soc Stud Tchr 16 *i:* Ftbl, Bsbl, Bsktbl Coach 11 Yrs; Assist Renaissance Prgm; BLCTA ; OEA 1976-, Negotiations; NEA 1976-, Team; NCSS; *home:* 506 and Ave Tiltonsville OH 43963

Y, RONALD R., Dean & Accounting Teacher; *b:* Glen Cove, NY; ebecca W. Barnes; *c:* Steven M., Sara W., Scott D., Susan J.; *ed:* NY of Tech (BS) Bus Admin 1970; Hofstra Univ (MS) Ed 1972; Long Univ (PHD) Schl Dist Admin 1985; *cr:* Oyster Bay HS Bus Ed Tchr ach 1972-81; Elwood-John H Glen HS Dean of Stdnts, Tchr, Coach v 1981-; *ai:* HS Treas Extra Classroom Activity Fund; Site-based & Shared Decision Making Comm; NYSUT 1972-; AFT 1972-; ETA , Treas; Old First Presbyn Church 1979-, Trustee; *office:* od-John Glenn HS 478 Elwood Rd East Northport NY 11731

CHAUX, REBECCA R., Eighth Grade Math Teacher; *b:* Thibodaux, *n:* Jason Anthony; *ed:* Nicholls St Univ (BS) Math Ed 1991; LA St (MA) Math Ed 1994; *cr:* Scotlandville Magnet HS Calculus, Alg I, etry Tchr 1991-95; Autec Schl 8th Grd Math, Cmptr Tchr 1995-; *ai:* Grd Music Tchr; NCTM 1991-.*

LOTTI, JOHN JOSEPH, Social Studies Teacher; *b:* Brooklyn, NY; yce Mary Rich; *c:* Michael, John; *ed:* St Johns Univ (BA) Ed 1967; Island Univ (MA) Amer His 1979; Supervision & Admin St Johns & klyn Coll; Labor Relations Baruch & Cornell MSRL Prgm; *cr:* Eli ney HS Soc Stud Tchr 1967-77; John Dewey HS Soc S tud Tchr 81; Curtis HS Soc Stud Tchr 1981-; *ai:* Curtis Key Club Adv; Schl Mgmt Team; United Fed of Tchrs Union Rep; AFT & UFT 1967-, ter Ldr, Ely Trachtenberg; Assn Tchrs of Soc Stud 1981-, Bd Exec; HS Comm 1981-, Del; BSA 1975-, Scoutmaster, Woodbadge; Civic 1970-, VP; The Most Successful AP European His Courses in Staten ; NYS Ed Dept Review of City HS Reviewing Team; *office:* Curtis 05 Hamilton Ave Staten Island NY 10301*

N, ELAINE DOMBECK, Business Education Coordinator; *b:* , NY; *m:* Stanley David; *c:* Martin, Beth; *ed:* SUNY Farmingdale) Advertising 1962; NY Univ (BS) Bus Ed 1964; Stony Brook SUNY LIb Stud 1983; Tchr Effective Training, Cmptr 60 Addl Hrs; *cr:* Port Schls Tchr 1964-93; MIller Place Schls Bus Ed Coord 1993-; *ai:* Future Bus Ldrs Amer Adv; Renaissance Prgm Treas; BEA, SCBTA 1976-; *office:* Miller Place Schl Dist 191 N Country Rd Miller Place NY 11764*

ROBINETT, ROBENA D., Lead Science Teacher; *b:* Oakland, MD; *ed:* Chesapeake Coll (AA) Lbrl Stud, Sci Core 1973; Salisbury St Univ (BS) Lbrl Stud, Sci Core 1983; Addl 222 Semester Hrs; *cr:* Hosps Emergency Room Technician 1974-85; St & Federal Govt Ag Researcher 1980-86; Bellaire HS Sci Tchr 1992-93; North Caroline HS Sci Tchr 1993-; *ai:* Sci Club, Trek Club, EF Explore Amer Adv; NESTA, NABT, NSTA, NMLSTA, ISC 1988-; NASA Earth & Environmental Sci Tchr Ambassador 1994; UC Berkeley Gloval Systems Sci Intern 1995; *office:* North Caroline HS 10990 River Rd Ridgely MD 21660*

ROBINS, FAYE E., Health Educator; *b:* Brooklyn, NY; *m:* William; *c:* Jeffrey Scott, Rebecca Ann; *ed:* Brooklyn Coll (BS) Hlth & PE 1973, (MS) Hlth Sci 1985; NY Univ (CAS) Ed Admin 1989; 45 Additional Credit Hrs Hlth & Ed; *cr:* Meyer Levin JHS 285 NY City Hlth & PE Tchr 1973-75; Sales & Mrktg Execs Intl Continuing Ed Adm Asst 1975-77; John Jay HS at Brooklyn Hlth & PE Tchr 1977-79; Mid Island YM YW HA Plainview PE Instr 1979-84; Bellport HS at Brookhaven Hlth Edctrs 1985-; *ai:* NYSHAPERD 1973-, Presenters Awd; Plainview Old Bethpage CSD 1984-, PTA Cncl Delegate; Amer Heart Assn 1988-, CPR Instr Life Saving; Temple or Elohin 1990-, Ritual Chair & Bd Trustee; Amer Red Cross 1990-, CPR & First Aid Instr; *office:* Bellport HS Beaver Dam Rd Brookhaven NY 11719*

ROBINS, MARGIE ANN WESTBERG, First Grade Teacher; *b:* Warren, MN; *c:* Debora Robins Piccirilli, Kimberly Robins Piccirilli, Russell H. L.; *ed:* Univ of Bemidji (BS) Elem 1958; Tchng Fellow of Ec Ed Salem St; Eisenhower Project Tufts Univ; *cr:* Bagley Pub Schls 3rd Grd Tchr 1958-59; Huckleberry Hill Schl 3rd Grd Tchr 1959-61; Summer Street Elem Schl 3rd Grd Tchr 1972-94, 1st Grd Tchr 1994-; *ai:* Natl Sci Conventions Rep; MA St Frameworks in Sci; Integrated Curr, Resource Dev; Sci Curr, Writing, Soc Stud Curr Coordination, Basic Skills Improvement Steering, Basic Skills Listening, Staff Dev Comms; Dev Materials, Mngmt System Elem Rdng; Pub Relations Task Force; Search Process for New Admin; NEA, MTA 1972-, Rep; Lynnfield Tchrs Assn 1972-, Exec Bd, Soc Chm; PTO 1985-, Exec Bd; Whole Lang Tchrs Assn 1992-; North Shore Rdng Cncl 1990-; Congregational Church 1988-, Decorating Comm; Kingston House 1995-; YANA Adult Support Group 1995-, Soc Comm; Lucretia Crocker Flwshp Prgm Candidate; Articles Pub; Peabody Sci Resource Ctr Presenter; Schl of Excl Fac Mem 1986; *office:* Summer Street Elem Schl 262 Summer St Lynnfield MA 01940

ROBINS, SANDRA SMOLOWITZ, Fifth Grade Teacher; *b:* Brooklyn, NY; *m:* Jeffrey; *c:* Dara, Lesley; *ed:* Long Island Univ (BS) Elem Ed 1968; Adelphi Univ (MA) Elem Ed 1970; Cert Admin NY Univ 1990; Cert Speech, Theatre; *cr:* Huntington Schl Dist Tchr 1968-73; Brookhaven Cntry Day Presch Dir, Tchr 1980-85; Longwood Schl Dist Tchr 1986-; *ai:* Drama Club Adv; Shared Decision Making Comm; Fac Cncl; NYSUT 1968-; Natl Tay-Sachs 1973-, Treas; Mid East Suffolk Tchr Ctr Grants 1993, 1994; *home:* 12 Segatogue Ln South Setauket NY 11720*

ROBINSON, ALFRED WESLEY, 6th Grade Teacher; *b:* Plattsburgh, NY; *m:* Anitarae Grace Tyner; *c:* Alan, Aaron, Adam; *ed:* SUNY at Plattsburgh (BS) Elem Ed 1966; Attnd SUNY at Oswego; *cr:* Plattsburgh City Schl Dist Tchr 1966-68; Auburn City Schl Dist Tchr 1968-; *ai:* Ski Club Dir; Odyssey of the Mind Coord; NYSUT; *office:* East MS Franklin St Auburn NY 13021

ROBINSON, ANDY, Social Studies Teacher; *b:* Providence, RI; *m:* Jane Mc Clanaghan; *c:* Catherine, Elizabeth; *ed:* Providence Coll (BA) Soc Stud Ed 1971, (MA) Amer His 1974; Attnd Brown Univ, RI Coll, Grad Realtor Inst; *cr:* Burrillville HS Soc Stud Tchr 1971-75; Narragansett HS Soc Stud Tchr 1975-; Bay Realty Ltd Realtor 1985-; *ai:* Mock Trial, Soc Stud Dept Chair; NEA 1971-; RI Natl Soc Stud Assn, RI Natl Bd of Realtors 1985-; Narragansett Lions Club 1981-, Sec; Narragansett Democratic Party 1979-, Sec; Friendly Sons of St Patrick 1982-; RI Air Natl Guard 1968-89, Retired; *office:* Narragansett HS 245 S Pier Rd Narragansett RI 02882

ROBINSON, BARBARA CHAMBERLAIN, Kindergarten Teacher; *b:* Staten Island, NY; *w:* Roland James (dec); *c:* Bethany, Alissa; *ed:* Hunter Coll (BA) Geog & Geology 1968; Univ of ME at Orono (MED) Spcl Ed 1983; *cr:* Rose Gaffney Schl 1st Grd Tchr 1968-70; West Jonesport Schl 1st Grd Tchr 1970-72; Jonesport Cove Schl Kndgtn Tchr 1972-81; Jonesport Elem Schl Kndgtn Tchr 1981-; *ai:* Playground Equipment & Negotiation Comms; Peer Tchng Mentor; NEA 1968-; ME Tchrs Assn 1968-; Moose-A-Bec Tchrs Assn 1970-, Bldg Rep; United Pentecostal Church, Sunday Schl Tchr 1975-, Jr Choir Dir 1984-; Girl Scout Ldr 1984-.*

ROBINSON, BERNARD JEROME, Math Coordinator & Teacher; *b:* Philadelphia, PA; *ed:* Temple Univ (BS) Math Ed 1987; Beaver Coll 4 Grad Hrs Math Ed; *cr:* USAF Reserves Tech Sgt Aero Med Evacuation 1983-91; St Carthage Schl Math Coord 1987-; *ai:* Musical Dir; Black His Act Dir; Chrstn Play Coord; Asst Dir Yrbk Org; NCTM 1996-; Phi Beta Sigma 1987-, Dir of Ed; *home:* 8427 Temple Rd Philadelphia PA 19150*

ROBINSON, BEVERLY ANNE, Remedial Reading Teacher; *b:* Pittsburgh, PA; *c:* Jonathan; *ed:* NY St Coll at Buffalo (BS) Elem Ed 1976; NY St Univ at Buffalo (MS) Remedial Ed 1977; Adv Stud 30 Hrs Post Masters Cert; *cr:* Manatee Cty Schls Rdng Tchr 1980-84; A. G. Edwards & Sons Stockbroker 1984-89; US Peace Corps Vol 1989-91; Norwich City Schls Rdng Tchr 1991-; *ai:* Schl Newspaper Spon; NEA 1991-; Lions Club 1994-, Sec; Pub Svc Awd From Peace Corps; Pub Author; *office:* Norwich MS Midland Dr Norwich NY 13815

ROBINSON, BRUCE H., Associate Professor; *b:* Evansville, IN; *m:* Paula D. Hopkins; *c:* Andre, Adero; *ed:* KS City Art Inst (BFA) Painting 1973; IN Univ (MFA) Painting 1976; *cr:* Johnson Co Comm Coll Instr 1976-77; Columbus Coll Art & Design Assoc Prof 1977-; *ai:* Black Stu Assn Adv; Sr Thesis, Fac Grievance Comm; Juror for OH Governors Yth Art Exhibition; Coll Art Assn 1985-; Best of Show Mus of Sci, Industry Exhibit; Sculpture Art Awd; Fac Stipend; Norfolk Flwshp Yale Univ; *office:* Columbus Coll Of Art & Design 107 N 9th St Columbus OH 43215

ROBINSON, CAROLE ANN, First Grade Teacher; *b:* Elizabeth, NJ; *m:* Neal; *c:* Megan, Jennifer; *ed:* Newark St (BA) Elem Ed 1964; *cr:* Middlesex-Pierce Schl 1st, 3rd Grd Tchr 1964-68; Old Farmers Schl 4th Grd Tchr 1976-82; Kossmann Schl 1st Grd Tchr 1982-; *ai:* 1st Grd Sci Coord; NEA 1964-; *office:* Walter J. Kossmann Schl 90 Flocktown Rd Long Valley NJ 07853*

ROBINSON, CAROLYN MARIE, MS Mathematics Teacher; *b:* Troy, NY; *c:* Teresa M.; *ed:* Saint Bonaventure Univ (BS) Math 1970; Niagara Univ (MS) Guidance 1975; *cr:* Bishop O'Hern HS Geometry, Algebra & Trigonometry Tchr 1970-71; Bishop Timon HS Geometry & Introduction Calculus 1971-85; Buffalo Seminary Geometry, Trigonometry & Introduction Calculus Tchr 1985-87; City Honors Schl 7th Grd Math & Calculus Tchr 1987-88; Seneca Voc HS Course 1 & 2 Tchr 1988-89; Olmstead Schl #56 8th & 9th Grd Math Tchr 1989-90; Campus East Schl #89 7th-9th Grd Math Tchr 1990-; *ai:* Buffalo Tchrs Fed, NEA 1987-; NYS Tchrs of Math 1995-; Orchard Park Comm Ed Adv Bd 1993-, Sec; OPUSA 1991-, Bd Mem; Boys & Girls Club OP 1991-, Tutor Prgm, Comm Svc 1994; Camp Fire 1985-, Ldr; Co-Authored Grant for Ch 1 Math 5000 Dollars Awd 1994; Wrote Review Books for Math 7 & Math 8 1995 & 1993; GM Explore the Possibilities Prgm 1995; Timon HS Chess Team Coach; Seneca HS Drill Team Coach; *home:* 55 Countryside Ln Apt 2 Orchard Park NY 14127*

ROBINSON, CARY SCOTT, Band Director; *b:* Plattsburgh, NY; *m:* Amy Sue Cornwall; *c:* Patrick, Julia; *ed:* SUNY at Potsdam (BS) Music Ed 1970; Manhattan Schl of Music (MA) Bass Trombine Performance 1974; *cr:* Arlington Schls Band Dir 1975-; *ai:* NYSUT 1975-; NYSSMA & MENC 1975-; DCMEA 1985-, Sec; *office:* Titusville MS Green Meadow Pk Poughkeepsie NY 12603

ROBINSON, DAVID EMANUAL, 6th Grade Teacher; *b:* Wilmington, DE; *m:* Vernessa E.; *c:* David E. Jr., Charday; *ed:* Morgan St Univ (BS) Elem Ed 1980; Widener Univ (MED) Ed 1985; Temple Univ Grad Work Ed 1989-; *cr:* Uwchlan Hills Elem Schl 6th Grd Tchr 1980-; *ai:* Safety Patrol Avd; Tchr Mentor Prgm; Soc Stud Task Force; IST Mem; Discipline Comm; Kappa Delta Pi 1978-; NEA, DAEA 1990-; BTA 1986-, Tchr of Yr; NAACP 1977-; Together We Can 1989-, VP; Alpha Phi Alpha 1978-, VP, BA Chptr; Wilmington Improvement Project 1993-; Tart of Solution 1995-, Area Chprsn; Who's Who Amer Univs, Colls 1978, 1979, 1980; Alpha Phi Alpha Natl Schlsp, James Haywood Harrison Meml Schlsp Awds; Raseed Wilson Meml Flwshp 1995; *home:* 214 N Bancroft Pkwy Wilmington DE 19805

ROBINSON, DEBORAH COTNER, Physics Teacher; *b:* Lewisburg, PA; *c:* Arthur Pursel, Jason; *ed:* Bloomsburg St Coll (BS) Math, Physics 1979; Beaver Coll Grad Credits; *cr:* Our Lady of Lourdes Regnl HS Math, Physics Tchr 1979-80; Lewisburg HS Math, Physics Tchr 1980-82; Schuylkill Haven HS Math, Physics Tchr 1984-85; Cocalico HS Math, Physics Tchr 1985-86; Pennridge HS Physics Tchr 1986-; *ai:* Physics Day Trip Spon; NEA, PEA, AAPT 1986-; C. B. Wrestling Fed 1989-94, Treas; *office:* Pennridge HS 1228 N 5th St Perkasie PA 18944*

ROBINSON, DENNIS SEAN, Music Teacher & Band Director; *b:* Fall River, MA; *m:* Marianne Aguiar; *c:* Sarah, Patrick; *ed:* Berklee Coll of Music (BMus) Jazz Compostion & Arranging 1982; Bridgewater St Coll Comm & Theatre; Univ of RI Grad Stud Musical Aesthics & Ed, RI Coll 42 Credit Hrs Completed for MAT Music Ed; *cr:* B M C Durfee HS Music Sub Tchr 1985-87; J M Morton MS Music Sub Tchr 1985-87; Kuss MS General Music Tchr & Chorus Asst Dir 1988-89; B M C Durfee HS Music & Theatre Tchr & Band Dir 1989-; *ai:* Marching & Pep Bands Adv; NEA (FREA & MTA) 1988-; MEN (MMEA) 1989-; Amer Fed of Musicians (Local 216) 1981-; Saint Theresa Church 1987-, Lector, Organist; Fall River Symphony Orch 1982-; Hills Mills Crazy Clown Band 1977-; City Citation for Holiday Performances, The Kidds- R & B Band 1995-; Fall River Herald News Golden Recipient; Apple Awd 1994; *office:* B M C Durfee HS 360 Elsbree St Fall River MA 02720

ROBINSON, DIANE L., Home Economics Teacher; *b:* Coshocton, OH; *ed:* OH St Univ (BS) Home Ec Ed 1978; Univ of Dayton (MS) Ed 1994; *cr:* Chillicothe Smith MS Home Ec Tchr 1980-84; Rosemore Jr HS Home Ec Tchr 1984-; *ai:* Youth to Youth Adv; Girls Vlybl & Bsktbl Coach; HS Track Coach; Musical Asst Dir; NEA, OH Ed Assn, OH St Univ Alumni 1978-; Whitehall Ed Assn 1984-, Bldg Rep, Tchr of Yr 1992; ASCD, Natl MS Assn 1992-; Ath & Acad Boosters, PTA 1984-; Co-Author Venture Capital Grant 1992; 3 Yrs Prgm Dir Rosemores 5 Yr Venture Capital Prgm; *office:* Rosemore Jr HS 4735 Kae Ave Columbus OH 43213*

ROBINSON, DONALD FRANKLIN, Social Studies Teacher; *b:* Ashtabula, OH; *m:* Alice Badia; *c:* Dante, Randy; *ed:* Bowling Green St Univ (BS) Scndry Ed, Comprehensive Soc Stud 1982-; 19 Hrs Bowling Green Grad Schl; 3 Hrs Ashland Univ; *cr:* Fremont Ross HS Soc Stud Tchr 1982-89; Norton HS Soc Stud Tchr 1989-; *ai:* Asst Ftbl Coach; Weight Room Supvr; NEA, OEA 1982-; Norton Classroom Tchrs Assn 1989-; *home:* 3869 Mount Vernon Blvd Norton OH 44203*

ROBINSON, GAIL A., Mathematics Teacher; *b:* Paterson, NJ; *m:* Brian; *c:* Leia, Lauren Nejmeh; *ed:* William Paterson Coll (BS) Math 1969; Montclair St Coll (MS) Cmptr Sci; Grad Courses at Jersey City St Coll, William Paterson, St Peter's Coll; *cr:* Hawthorne HS Math Tchr 1969-; *ai:* Math Tutor Prgm; NEA, NJEA, PCEA, HTA 1969-; NJ-Link 1995-; PTA 1985-92, Chaplain 1990-91; Prospect Park Safety Town 1992-, Head Instr; Hawthorne Ed Action Team 1995-; NSF Grant 1969-70; *office:* Hawthorne HS Parmelee Ave Hawthorne NJ 07506

ROBINSON, JIM A., Industrial Technology Teacher; *b:* Middletown, OH; *m:* Gaylynn M. Leist; *c:* Jessica J., Rebecca M., Erin K.; *ed:* Eastern KY Univ (BA) Industrial Arts Ed 1979; Xavier Univ (MA) Admin 1986; 30 Hrs Beyond Masters; *cr:* Jefferson Twp Schls at Dayton Industrial Arts Tchr 1979-82; New Richmond HS Industrial Arts Tchr 1982-; *ai:* Yrbk & Stud Cncl Adv; Dist Printing; NREA 1982-, Bldg Rep & Negotiation Team; *office:* New Richmond HS 1131 Bethel New Richmond Rd New Richmond OH 45157

ROBINSON, JOAN DIANNE, First Grade Teacher; *b:* Providence, RI; *m:* Roger; *c:* David; *ed:* Univ of RI (BA) Ed 1966; 15 Post Grad Credits; Staff Dev Hrs; *cr:* Summit Ave Schl Second Grd Tchr 1966-67; Lang St Schl First Grd Tchr 1967-90; Interlakes Elem Schl Art Tchr 1970-72, First Grd Tchr 1991-; *ai:* K-2 Grd Primary Environment Stud Chm; Lang St Schl Tchng Prin 1982-86; NEA 1967-; NH Sci Tchrs Assn 1990-; Gilford Hills Tennis Club 1968-; Featured in Project Learning Tree Video; Schl to Schl Partnership Schl Ambassador to Budapest, Hungary; *office:* Interlakes Elem Schl 21 Laker Ln Meredith NH 03253*

ROBINSON, JOAN VERONICA, First Grade Teacher; *b:* Walton, NY; *m:* John A.; *c:* Kristina, Justin, Jarred; *ed:* SUNY at Fredonia (BS) Elem Ed 1974; SUNY at Oneonta (MS) Elem Ed 1977; *cr:* Downsville Cntrl Schl First, Third, Fifth Grds Tchr; *ai:* NEA, DTA 1974-; Sunday Schl Tchr; Yth Group Tchr; Real Estate Assoc Broker; DE Cty Listing Cooperative, Sec; *office:* Downsville Central Schl Maple Ave Downsville NY 13755

ROBINSON, JOHN JAMES, Junior Varsity Ftbl Coach; *b:* Providence, RI; *ed:* The Citadel (BA) Pol Sci 1986; 60 Hrs Dowling Coll Scndry Ed; *cr:* CF Motor Freight Terminal Supvr 1990-; Brentwood HS Ftbl, Sftbl Coach 1987-; *ai:* Citadel Men Assn; Brentwood Ath Booster, Citadel Ftbl Alumni Club; Brentwood Booster Club 1990-, Trustee; Natl Trucking Assn 1994-; *home:* 60 Landview Dr Dix Hills NY 11746

ROBINSON, JOYCE GUINTA (MC PEAKE), Director, Quest Program; *b:* Newark, NJ; *m:* Enders A.; *c:* John Paul Mc Peake, David Samuel Mc Peake; *ed:* Tufts Univ (BA) Eng 1962; Boston Univ (MA) Eng, Ed 1965, (EDD) Rdng, Lang 1979; 6 Credits Amer Lit at Harvard Univ 1980; 6 Credits Creative Writing at Bennington Coll 1985; 4 Credits Multi-sensory Processing at Columbia Univ 1996; *cr:* Boston Univ Asst Dean of Women, Admin Dept 1962-67; Mauter Hall Schl Rdng Specialist 1963-66; Christ Luth Schl Dir 1971-74; Scituate Pub Schls Prin, Rdng Specialist, ESL Tchr 1974-80; St Andrews Schl Chair, Eng, Rdng Tchr 1980-88; Nova Univ Adj Prof 1984-88; St Thomas Univ Adj Prof 1984-88; Broadwater Acad Chair, Eng, LD Prgm 1988-89; Fountain Vly Schl Dir of Learning Resources, Eng Tchr 1989-91; Islamic Saudi Acad Asst Prin 1991-93; Masters Schl Chair, Eng, ESL Tchr 1993-94; Dwight Schl Dir, Quest Prgm 1994-; *ai:* Stdnts Adv; Lib Comm; In-Svc Ed; Cabinet Mem; EERA 1979-, Mbrshp Chm; IRA 1976-; Cum Laude Soc 1987-; Pi Lambda Theta 1979-; CEC 1994-; Orton Soc 1989-; Hemingway Soc 1986-; MLA 1980-; ASCD 1988-; Hamilton Coll Parents Fund 1986-, Fundraiser, Parent Agent; John F. Kennedy Lib 1989-; Museum Mbrshp, Cntrl Park Conservancy 1993-; FCIS Grant 1984; Propeller Club of US, Natl League of Pen Women, Caldwell Theater, Eng Speaking Union Tchr Awds; IRA, NCTE, ASCD, EERA Conf Presentations 1978-; Contributor Tchng Stud Skills 1987;

Author Wordworks 1990; Poem Pub 1986; Numerous Articles Pub; *office:* Dwight Schl 291 Central Park W New York NY 10024*

ROBINSON, JUDITH D., English Teacher; *b:* Acushnet, MA; *ed:* Bridgewater St Coll (BSE) Sec Ed, Eng 1965; RI Coll (MED) Sec Ed, Eng 1975; 45 Addl Credit Hrs Ed, Eng, Lib Sci; *cr:* Dartmouth HS Eng Tchr 23 Yrs, Schl Librn 8 Yrs; New Bedford HS Summer Schl Eng Tchr; Newbury Coll Adult Ed Eng Tchr; *ai:* Schl Improvement, Practice of Tracking Comms; Class Adv; Schl Accreditation Teams; Amer, Intnl Schls Abroad Comm; DEA, MTA, NEA, NCTE, BCTE, NEATE 1961-; Coll Club of New Bedford; Delta Kappa Gamma; *office:* Dartmouth HS 366 Slocum Rd North Dartmouth MA 02747

ROBINSON, KAREN PIAZZA, Biology Teacher; *b:* Winthrop, MA; *m:* Samuel R. III; *c:* Samuel IV; *ed:* Simmons Coll (BS) Bio 1972; Framingham St (MED) Ed, Bio 1980; Attnd Brandeis Univ, Regis Coll, Farmingham St 15 Credits; *cr:* Waltham HS Bio Tchr 1972-; *ai:* NEA, MTA, WEA 1972-; *office:* Waltham HS 617 Lexington St Waltham MA 02154

ROBINSON, LEILA M., Chemistry Teacher; *b:* Somerville, NJ; *m:* Gerald F.; *c:* Gerald T., Margo Clevenger; *ed:* Trenton St Coll (BS) Chem 1988, (MA) Tchng 1992; Credit Hrs LaSalle Univ AP Chem; *cr:* NBC HS Chem Tchr 1992-; *ai:* NEA 1992-; NJSTA 1995-; *office:* Northern Burlington Reg HS 160 Mansfield Rd E Columbus NJ 08022

ROBINSON, LILLIE MAE GUEST, Retired Teacher; *b:* Orangeburg, SC; *c:* Jacqueline Denise, Shernette Yhvonne Denerson, Vinimore Leon Jr.; *ed:* SC St Univ (BS) Elem Ed 1954; 30 Credit Hrs Early Chldhd Hunter Coll 1961; 19 Credit Hrs City Coll 1975; 20 Credit Hrs Bd of Ed 1976; Attnd The St Paul Bible Acad Minister & Evangelist License 1994; *cr:* Dale Elem Schl Tchr 1954-56; Neighborhood Children Ctr Tchr 1956-63; PS 79 Manhattan Tchr 1963-64; Title I Prgm SHARE Exec Dir 1964; PS 57 Manhattan Tchr 1964-69; PS 178 Bronx Tchr 1969-91; *ai:* Multi-Cultural Prgms Spon; Promoting Self Esteem, Self Control Wkshp Spon; Parents of Dist 11 Consultant Sponsoring Wkshp; UFT, AFT, NYSUT 1963-; RTC 1991-; NAACP 1942-, Local Yth Pres; NCNW 1965-, Life Time Mbrshp; Rainbow Coalition 1982-, Mbrshp Drive Chprsn; Northeast Bronx, Co-Chprsn, Voter Registration; PS 111 Bx 1966-71, 1st VP PTA; IS 142 BX, Exec Bd Mem; Mayor David Dinkins Increase the Peace Vol Corps 1992-94; Tapping in the Peace 1994; SC St Coll Alumni New York City Assn Schlsp; Dr J. C. Parler Svc Awd; Helen Shelfield Schlsp Awd; Parent Tchrs Awd for Most Dedicate Tchr PS 57 Manhattan; Soc Stud Awd for Multi Cultural Prgms Bd of Ed; Bi-Centennial Awds Bd of Ed; Tchr of Yr Recognition Awd Bd of Ed; Co-op City Tchr Dedication; Appreciation Awd PS 178 PTA; Recognition for Perform Multicultural Prgms for Sr Citizens; Centerfold in Daily News 1974; Democratic Convention 1 Jesse Jacksons Del 1988; Partners in Ed Tchr of Week, Month, Yr 1989; Coord of Comm to Elect E. T. Marshall to US Congress 1994; *home:* 150-17D Dreiser Loop Bronx NY 10475*

ROBINSON, LOVELL, USAF JROTC Instructor; *b:* Greensboro, AL; *m:* Pauline E. Brown; *c:* Lovetta Smith, Lovell R.; *ed:* Wilimington Coll (BA) Behavior Sci 1980; *cr:* Middletown HS USAF Tchr 1980-; *ai:* NEA 1980-; *office:* Middletown HS 504 S Broad St Middletown DE 19709

ROBINSON, MARIAN CARTER, Third Grade Teacher; *b:* Wilson, NC; *m:* Samuel; *c:* Andrea Yvette Copeland; *ed:* Winston-Salem St Univ (BS) Elem Ed 1964; TN St Univ (MS) Elem Ed 1972; Admin Cert Columbia Univ; NY St Permanent Cert; Admin, Supvr 1976; Post Grad Hrs Elem Ed; *cr:* Elvie St Elem Schl Tchr 1964-68; Richard J. Bailey Schl Tchr 1969-80; Greenburgh Cntrl #7 SD Sci Coord 1980-82; Highview Schl Tchr 1983-; *ai:* Greenburgh Tchr Fed 1982-, Bldg Rep; Natl Alliance of Black Schl Edctrs; Blacks United for Ed 1973-, Pres; PTA; Alpha Kappa Alpha 1992-, Sec; Order Eastern Star 1972-, Worthy Matron; Eureka Grand Chptr OES, Grand Trustee; Elejmal Court #171 Daughters of Isis, Illustrious Commandress; Outstdng Greenburgh Tchr Comm Awd; Prof Dev Grant; Westchester Ed Coalition Grant; Distngd Achvmt Comm Involvement; Pub Articles.*

ROBINSON, MARI-LIN SCHNEIDER, English Teacher; *b:* Urbana, OH; *m:* Arthur L.; *c:* Rachel Lin, Rhonna Lee; *ed:* Urbana Univ (BS) Eng Ed Scndry 1974; Addl 6 Semester Hrs Kent St Univ, 3 Semester Hrs Drake Univ; *cr:* Bristol HS 9-12 Grd Tchr 1974-77; Newton Falls Schls Jr HS Tchr 1977-80, 1986-, Private Tutoring 1980-86; *ai:* Veteran Mentor 1991-; Co-Founder, Dir of Peer Tutoring Prgm 1992-; BLAT, IAT Mem; Trumbull Cty Ldrshp Team; TRESC Schl Improvement Cncl; AFT 1994-; OEA, NEA 1974-94; NFCTA 1992-94, Sec; Selected to Present 1994 Natl Schl Bd Assn Convention Peer-Tutoring Prgm; Selected A+ Tchr 1993; *office:* Newton Falls Jr HS 907 1/2 Milton Blvd Newton Falls OH 44444*

ROBINSON, MARTHA KAY, English Teacher; *b:* Rochester, NY; *m:* Robert Drake; *c:* Seth Ian, Sean Christopher; *ed:* Hartwick Coll (BA) Eng, Ed 1969; 9 Credit Hrs Univ of FL; 30 Credit Hrs SUNY at Geneseo; *cr:* Lyons Cntrl Schl 11th Grd Eng Tchr 1969-70; Palatka Cntrl Schl 11th Grd Eng, 9th Grd Civics, 12th Grd Amer Govt, FL His Tchr 1970-71; Letchworth Cntrl Schl Eng Tchr 1971-; *ai:* Letchworth Cntrl Tchrs Assn, NEA 1971-; Honorary Chapter Farmer Letchworth Chapter FFA, Charles G. May Chapter FFA; Letchworth Cntrl Stu Cncl Tchr of Yr 1992-93; Outstanding Poets of 1993-94 Natl Lib of Poetry; *office:* Letchworth Central Jr Sr HS 5550 School Rd Gainesville NY 14066*

ROBINSON, MARY ELIZABETH, 7th-8th Grade Math Teacher; *b:* Falston, MD; *c:* Jeffrey, Vaughn; *ed:* MD St Coll (BS) Math, Sci 1966; Morgan St Univ (MS) Math 1973; Attnd Baltimore Schl of Bible Church Ministry 1994; Coppin St Coll Ongoing Continuing Ed Courses; *cr:* Riverview HS Tchr 1966-67; Calverton Jr HS Tchr 1967-82; Highlandtown MS Tchr 1982-; Walbrook HS Summer Acad 1983; *ai:* Schl Team Ldr; MESA Adv; Harambee Coord; SIT Team; Tutor for MD Functional Math Wkshps; NEA, Amer Tchrs Assn, Amer Edctrs Assn 1973-; Baltimore Tchrs Union 1967-; Zeta Phi Beta 1963-; Curr, Evaluation Stans Schl Math Grd 6-8; Tchr of Yr Awd 1984, 1986; Outstdng Attendance; Math Counts Prgm Spon; Nom Presidential Awd Excl Tchng Math; *office:* Highlandtown MS 43 101 S Ellwood Ave Baltimore MD 21224*

ROBINSON, MELISSA L., Social Studies Teacher; *b:* Port Jefferson, NY; *ed:* SUNY at Stony Brook (BA) His 1992, (MALS) Tchng Soc Stud 1996; *cr:* Mt Sinai HS Soc Stud Dept Tchr 1993-; *ai:* Drama Dir; NHS Comm; Renaissance.

ROBINSON, MICHAEL EDWARD, English Teacher; *b:* New Brunswick, NJ; *m:* Patricia D.; *c:* Claire; *ed:* Glen Cove Bible Coll (BRE) Ed 1976; The King's Coll (BA) Eng 1981; Gordon-Conwell Seminary (MATS) History, Lit 1986; 9 Credit Hrs Eng; 21 Credit Hrs Ed; *cr:* Loyola HS Eng, His, Rel Tchr 1986-; *ai:* Dir Higher Achvmt Prgm; John Byington Flwshp 1985; *office:* Loyola HS PO Box 6819 Towson MD 21285

ROBINSON, NANCY JEAN, Social Studies Teacher; *b:* Bryn Mawr, PA; *ed:* Susquehanna Univ (BA) His 1979; Credit Hrs Villanova Univ, Jersey City St Coll; *cr:* Montville Twp HS Soc Stud Tchr 1979-; *ai:* NJEA, NEA 1979-; Natl Cncl of His Ed 1995-; *office:* Montville Twp HS 100 Horseneck Rd Montville NJ 07045*

ROBINSON, NANCY WESSELS, English Teacher; *b:* Geneva, IL; *m:* Russell James; *c:* Sarah Arends, James Benjamin; *ed:* OH Wesleyan (BA) Eng 1967; SUNY at New Paltz (MS) Rdng 1980; Penn St Supervisory Cert 1994; *cr:* Kavai HS Eng Tchr 1969-70; Downingtown HS Eng Tchr 1981-; *ai:* Stu Crisis Team; NEA, PSEA, NCTE 1981-; Article Pub; *office:* Downingtown Sr HS 445 Manor Ave Downingtown PA 19335

ROBINSON, PAMELA JEAN, MS Basketball & Track Coach; *b:* Washington c H, OH; *ed:* OSU (BS) Soc Stud 1978; *cr:* Washington City Schls Sub Tchr, Coach 1987-92, 8th Grd Jr HS Bsktbl, Track Aoch 1987-; Calman Inc Assembly Operator 1979-; *ai:* 8th Grd Girls Bsktbl Coach; MS Track Coach; Flwshp of Chrstn Ath Adv; Yth Spon, Bd Mem; Bible Quiz Coach; *home:* 1443 Dennis St Wshngtn Ct Hs OH 43160

ROBINSON, RETIANA BRANCH, Mathematics Teacher; *b:* Baltimore, MD; *m:* Larry James; *ed:* Coppin St Coll (BS) Soc Sci & Math 1973, (MS) Ed 1984; 12 Hrs Post Grad Stud in Scndry Ed at Towson St Univ; *cr:* MD St Police Headquarters Finger Print Asst 1971-73; Baltimore City Pub Schls Math Tchr 1973-; Baltimore City Bureau of Recreation Summer Supvr 1979; MD Conservation Corps Summer Supvr 1980-85; Morgan St Univ Upward Bound Summer Instr 1994-; *ai:* Assembly Prgm Dir; Class Adv; Honor Soc; AFT 1975-; Natl Math Cncl 1974-; Mid Sts Eval 1981 & 1986, Evaluator, Cert; Political Campaign Mgr 1973-; Baltimore City In Schls 1990-, Task Force Mem; Tutorial Prgm 1988-, Tutor; Neighborhood Assn 1993-, Treas; Nom for Tchr of Yr 1987; Local Television Station Champion of Courage Awd 1988; Nom Favorite Tchr 1991; *office:* Northern Sr HS #402 2201 Pinewood Ave Baltimore MD 21214*

ROBINSON, ROBERT D., Agriculture Teacher; *b:* Warsaw, NY; *m:* Martha Kay Wackerow; *c:* Seth, Sean; *ed:* Cornell Univ (BS) Ag Ed 1970; St Univ of NY at Geneseo 48 Hrs; Univ of FL 28 Hrs; *cr:* Livingston Steuben WY BOCES Ag Tchr 1971-83; Perry Cntrl Schl Ag Tchr 1983-90; Medina Cntrl Schl Ag Tchr 1992-; *ai:* Medina FFA; ATANY 1971, Sec; NVATA & AVA 1971-; WY Cty Fair Assn 1971, Asst General Supt; Oakland F&AM 1969-, Master; Outstanding Ag Prgm in NYS 1989; Distinguished Svc Awd NY Assn of FFA; Pub Articles on Ag Ed.

ROBINSON, SANDRA FOGG, English Teacher; *b:* Rochester, NY; *m:* David; *c:* Matthew; *ed:* Univ of Rochester (BA) Eng 1961; Harvard Univ (MAT) Eng Ed 1963; Nazareth Coll Post Grad; *cr:* Plymouth-Carver Regnl HS Eng Tchr; R.L. Thomas HS Eng Tchr; East Lansing HS Eng Tchr; Fairport HS Eng Tchr; *ai:* Intnl Club; Class Adv; Schl Bd 9 Yrs, Pres; *office:* Fairport HS 1358 Ayrault Rd Fairport NY 14450*

ROBINSON, SARA LUCAS, Business Education Teacher; *b:* Union, SC; *c:* Calvin; *ed:* Barber-Scotia Coll (BS) Bus Ed 1970; Kean Coll of NJ (MA) Educl Admin 1996; Guidance & Counseling Addl 12 Credit Hrs; *cr:* Montclair HS Tchr 1985-87; Hillside HS Tchr 1987-; *ai:* FBLA Club Adv; Site Based Planning Comm; NEA, NJEA 1985-; Barber-Scotia Alumni 1970-, Sec; *office:* Hillside HS 1085 Liberty Ave Hillside NJ 07205

ROBINSON, SARAH HEMSTOCK, Spanish Teacher; *b:* Eau Claire, WI; *m:* Perry Hebert; *c:* Ripon Coll (BA) Eng, Span 1989; *ed:* Ripon Coll (BA) Eng, Span 1989; Denison Univ Cert Tchng Eng, Span 1991; *cr:* Lakewood HS Span Tchr 4 Yrs; *ai:* Span, Ski Club Advs; Girls Var Track Coach, Crss Cntry Coach; Lakewood Tchrs Assn 1992-, Bldg Rep; NEA; Cntrl OH Track, Cross Cntry Coaches Assn 1992-; Lakewood Tchrs Assn VP; Alpha Chi Omega 1985-, Pres, Adv; Lakewood Ath Boosters; Chrch Yth Grp Ldr; *office:* Lakewood HS 5222 National Rd SE Hebron OH 43025*

ROBINSON, SHERRY ALFORD, Mathematics Teacher; *b:* Dayton, OH; *m:* Chester K.; *c:* Chester II, Russell, Barrett, Shelli; *ed:* Otterbein Coll (BS) Math, Ed 1966; Wright St Univ (MA) Curr, Supervision, Tchr Ldr 1989; *cr:* Columbus Pub Schls Math Tchr 1968-69; Columbus Tech Instr, Cmptr Dept 1969-70; Dayton Pub Schls Math Tchr 1983-; *ai:* Stu Ldrshp Group, Conflict Resolution Team Co-Adv; Colonel White Staff Focus Group; Dayton Educ Assn, OEA, NEA 1984-; Delta Sigma Theta 1968-, Comm Chair; *office:* Colonel White H S For The Arts 501 Niagara Ave Dayton OH 45405*

ROBINSON, SIGMUND, Electrical Engineering Teacher; *b:* New York, NY; *m:* Peggy; *c:* Randi, Cori; *ed:* (BEE) 1961; (MEE) 1970; (ME) 1972; *cr:* Western Elec Co Comm Engr 1961-67; Grumman Aerospace Corp Digital Engr 1969-73; NY City Bd of Ed Tchr of Engrng 1973-; Queensboro Comm Coll Adj Prof of Engrng 1978-94; *ai:* Schl Play Dir; IEEE 1965-; AFT 1973-.

ROBINSON, STEPHEN E., Eng, His & Psychology Teacher; *b:* Bayside, NY; *m:* Kathleen Mary; *c:* Grace, Thomas, Benjamin; *ed:* SUNY at Geneseo (BA) Sociology 1977; Nazareth Coll of Rochester (MSEd) Comp Tech in Ed 1990; SUNY at Brockport Tchng Cert Scndry His, Eng & Elem Ed 1981; *cr:* Hobart & William Smith Coll Hisorical Indexer 1977-79; Cohocton Cntrl Schl Eng & His HS Tchr 1985-87; Wayland-Cohocton Cntrl Schl Eng, His & Psych HS Tchr 1993-; *ai:* NEA 1985-93, Pres (2 Terms); AFT 1993-; *office:* Wayland-Cohocton Cntrl Schl 2350 State Route 63 Wayland NY 14572

ROBINSON, STUART, English Instr & Ath Asst Dir; *b:* New York City, NY; *ed:* Williams Coll (BA) Eng 1983; Middlebury Coll (MA) Eng 1989; *cr:* Dutchess Comm Coll Eng Instr 1990-94; St Univ of NY at New Paltz Mens Soccer Coach 1992-, Asst Dir of Ath 1994-, Spec Asst to Pres 1995-; *ai:* Pre-Major Acad Adv; Chrldr Adv; Acad Standing, Coll Life & Equal Opportunity Comms; Inmate Ed Coord; St Ed Self-Stud Comm; Dutchess Comm Coll Exploring Transfer Comm; United Univ Prof 1994-; NEA 1990-; Natl Soccer Coaches Assn 1985-; New Paltz Swim Club 1995-, Bd Mem; Article Private Colls & Univs 1988; Essay Active Voices IV 1985; *office:* St Univ of NY at New Paltz 75 S Manheim Blvd New Paltz NY 12561*

ROBINSON, TERRY LYNN, 7th-8th Grade Teacher; *b:* Cambridge, OH; *m:* Shannon Lee Young; *c:* Kylie, Lakyn; *ed:* OH Univ (BA) Elem Ed 1989, (MS) Hlth, Sport Sci 1994; Project Discovery Math 1995; *cr:* Union Local Jr HS Math, Sci Tchr 1989-90; Warren Local Jr HS Math, Sci Tchr 1990-; *ai:* Jr HS Girls Bsktbl; Warren Local Girls Bsktbl Var Asst; Tee-Ball coach Beverly; *home:* 721 Center St Beverly OH 45715*

ROBINSON, THOMAS FRANK, Science Department Head; *b:* Concord, NH; *m:* Hazel Vaughan; *c:* Thomas II, Jay, Kral; *ed:* Keene St Coll (BED) Math & Sci 1959; Univ of NH (MChem) Chem 1967; 30 Credits Holy Cross, Plymouth St, San Diego St; *cr:* Merrimack HS Sci Tchr 1961-; *ai:* Advy Cncl; Joint Mgmt Cncl; NH Sci Tchrs 1980-; Condo Assn 1985-, Treas; Presenter at Natl Local Sci Assn; Presented Wkshps in Chem & Physics; *office:* Merrimack HS 38 Mcelwain St Merrimack NH 03054

ROBINSON, VALERIE A., Instruction Supvr & Guid Dir; *b:* Jamaica Queens, NY; *m:* Bryant O.; *c:* Janelle Robinson Moses, James B.; *ed:* U of VT (BS) Eng & Ed 1964; William Paterson Coll (MA) Rdng & Ed 1983; Supvrs & Prin Certs 1987; Jersey City St Coll Dir of Pupil Prsnl 1990; *cr:* Avery St Schl 1st Grd Tchr 1964-66; Mark Twain Schl 1st Grd Tchr 1966-67; Iona Primary & HS 4th-5th Grd Sci Tchr 1967-68; Ocho Rios Scndry Schl 7th-12th Grd Eng Tchr, Vice Prin & Dist Rdng Coord 1969-75; A B Smith Schl 6th Grd Tchr 1975-76; G White Schl 7th-8th Grd Eng Tchr 1976-90, Instruction Supvr & Guid Dir 1990-; *ai:* 8th Grd Class Adv; ASCD 1989-; NJPSA 1991-; Dr D Goldberg Child Care Ctr 1975-85, Pres & Bd of Trustees; BSA 1977-81, Chprsn; Vesling Holy Trinity 1992-95, Warden; Lib Bd 1992-; Hills Schl & Family Task Force 1992-; *office:* George G White Schl 120 Magnolia Ave Hillsdale NJ 07642

ROBINSON, ZAN DALE, English Professor; *b:* Philadelphia, PA; *m:* Patricia Marion McNaney; *c:* Michael, Zan Jr., Rand, Joan, Marie; *ed:* St Univ Coll at Buffalo (BA) Eng 1975, (MS) Eng 1976; St Univ of NY at Buffalo (PHD) Eng 1990; 30 Hrs Grad Study SUNY Dept Higher Ed; *cr:* Daemen Coll Dir Higher Ed Opportunity Pgm 1976-77; Erie Comm Coll Eng Prof 1978-; St Univ Coll at Buffalo Adj Eng Prof 1982-; *a* Hermanas Unidas & Sigma Lambda Upsilon Adv; Chancellors Awd Co-Chair; Human Resources Comm; Chair Appointments Comm; 1978-; UUP 1982-; NY St Cncl of Affirmative Action Pgms 1976 Eastern Paralyzed Veterans Assn 1978-, Citizen of the Yr 1984; A for Mentally Ill 1982-, Bd Mem; Book: A Semiotic and Psychoar Interpretation of Herman Melvilles Fiction; 9 Books Pub; Nur Articles Pub; Numerous Grants; *office:* Erie Comm Coll North Cmp Main St Williamsville NY 14221*

ROBINSON-DRYJA, DIANE M., First Grade Teacher; *b:* Pittsburg *m:* Mark A. Dryja; *c:* Shawn Robinson, David Robinson, Chris Dryja; *ed:* Univ of PIttsburgh (MAT) Elem Ed 1992; Alle Intermediate Unit 6 Math, 3 Sci Credits; Beaver Intermediate Mentor Credits; Tchr Expectationds Stu Achvmt Prgm 1 Cred Western PA Schl for Blind Voc Specialist 1992-93; Blackhawk Sch 6th Grd Tchr 1993-94; Moon Area Schl Dist Kndgtn, Gifted Tchr 19 1st Grd Tchr 1995-; *ai:* Rdng Comm; PSEA, NEA 1990-; ASCD 199 Stu Tchr Awd 1992; PI Lambda Theta Outstdng Internship Awd *office:* J H Brooks Elem Schl 1301 Coraopolis Heights Rd Coraopo 15108*

ROBITAILLE, JANE KINLOCK, Biology Teacher; *b:* Methuen, M Carol W.; *c:* Michael Stasiak, Bethany Stasiak, Donna Stasiak; *ed:* U NH (BA) Bio 1962; Bridgewater (MAT) Phys Sci 1987; 62 Addtl Hrs From Many Colls; *cr:* Portsmouth NH Schl Dept 8th Grd G 1962-64; Springfield Schl Dept Bio, Phys, Sci Tchr 1970-; Quincy Co Instr, Phys Sci 1996; *ai:* Past Key Club Adv; SCDM Team; Mentor Risk Studnts; MAST; MASS; MME; SEA; MTA; NEA; MJPOA; Cla Duff Soc New England Convener; Western Mass Highland Games Comm Fund Comm; NSF Grant; *home:* 93 Audley Rd Springfiel 01118

ROBITZSKI, NANCY JEAN, 7th-8th Grade Teacher; *b:* Staten I NY; *ed:* Richmond Coll (BA) Eng 1973; *cr:* St Rita 6th Grd Tchr 19 7th-8th Grd Tchr 1975-; *ai:* Yrbk; Choir; Sacrament Prepar Counseling; Cath Youth Org 1975-, Comms; *office:* St Rita Sc Wellbrook Ave Staten Island NY 10314

ROBOTIN, BARBARA ZIELINSKI, Manager; *b:* Trenton, NJ; *m:* John; *ed:* Trenton St Coll (BS) Elem Ed 1972; *cr:* Holy Cross Par Schl 1st Grd Tchr 1973-95; *ai:* Pub Relations; Rdng Coord; Holy Cath War 1980-; Veterans Auxiliary; Holy Cross Advy Cncl 1 Yr, Sec Outstdng Cath Edctr Trenton Diocese 1994; Who's Who in Amer Ed *home:* 330 Montana Ave Trenton NJ 08619

ROBSON, DAVID JAMES, English Teacher; *b:* Philadelphia, P Sonja; *c:* Zeus; *ed:* Temple Univ (BA) Commnctn 1988; St Josephs (MS) Eng Ed 1992; *cr:* DE Cty Comm Coll Eng, Film & Jrnlsm 1991-95; Caravel Acad Eng Tchr 1991-; Neuman Coll Poetry Instr *ai:* Drama Coach 2 Yrs; 10th Grd Adv 1 Yr; Nom for Pushcart Pr Poetry 1996; Numerous Articles Pub; Film Critic for Out & Magazine; Nom for Gould Awd for Tchng Excl; *office:* Caravel Acad Del Laws Rd Bear DE 19701

ROBSON, RICHARD, Guidance Counselor; *b:* Syracuse, NY; *m:* *c:* James, Rick, Sherry, Mike; *ed:* Univ of WY (BA) Pol Sci 1969; U Northern CO (MS) Psych & Cnslng 1973; BYU 3 Credit Hrs; UT Credit Hrs; *cr:* Evanston WY Soc Stud Tchr 1969-73; Cntrl Sq Guid 1973-; *ai:* Bldg Advy Comm; AFT 1973-, Bldg Rep; Article Pub *office:* Central Square MS RR 11 Central Square NY 13036

ROBSON, RUTH DEBO, English Teacher; *b:* Buffalo, NY; *m:* Mark *c:* Kathrine, Timothy, Emily; *ed:* St Univ of NY at Buffalo (BA) Eng SUC at Buffalo (MS) Eng Ed 1986; *cr:* South Park Prepartory Eng 1985-91; South Park HS Eng Tchr 1991-; *ai:* Lit Magazine Adv; 1985-; Northside Writers 1994-, Current Pres; *office:* South Park H Southside Pky Buffalo NY 14220

ROBY, PAMELA CURD, English Teacher; *b:* Ridgewood, NJ; *m:* J *c:* Andrew, Elizabeth; *ed:* SUNY at Geneseo (BA) Fr 1975; Elmira (MSEd) Ed 1980; *cr:* Addison Cntrl Schl Fr Tchr 1976-77; Arkport Schls Eng Tchr 1977-79; Wellsville Cntr Schls Eng Tchr 1979-; *ai:* WEA 1979-; Bd of Canisteo Chrstn Nursery Schl 1986-, Treas; Wellsville Cntrl Schl 126 W State St Wellsville NY 14895

ROCCA, CELIA-ANN MARIA GENUARDI, English, Drama Teac Dir; *b:* Baltimore, MD; *c:* Philip Anthony; *ed:* Mt St Agnes-Loyola (BA) Eng & Drama Sec Ed 1973; Johns Hopkins Univ (MDS) Drama Attnd Amer Univ, Univ of MD, Coppin St, Goucher Coll, Breadloa of Eng, Middlebury Coll 39 Credit Hrs; *cr:* Hampstead Hill Jr Hig Tchr & Drama Dir 1973-82; Baltimore City Coll High Eng Tchr & D Dir 1982-; *ai:* Alameda Players Dir; Restructured Day Comm; Stu Supvr; Performed: Chesapeake Music House, Annapolis Dinner Th Vagabond Players, Cockpit-In-Court Theater, Dundalk Comm Th Fells Point Cabaret, Spotlighters Tagater, Towson St Summer Th Baltimore Lab Theater, Harbour Theater, Theatre Incarnate 1971-; Shakespeare St of the Art U of MD 1986; NEH Coppin Hopkins Seminars 1987-91; NEH Breadloaf Schl of Eng Drama Wkshp 1992 Shakespeare Theatre Wash DC Classical Acting 1995; *office:* Balt City Coll HS 3220 The Alameda Baltimore MD 21218

ROCCHI, LINDA L. KELLER, First Grade Teacher; *b:* New Kensir PA; *m:* John R.; *c:* Kristin; *ed:* Clarion St Univ (BS) Elem 1967; Masters Equiv Elem 1973; *cr:* Plum Boro Schl Dist 2nd Grd Tchr 196 Highlands Schl Dist 1st Grd Tchr 1970-; *ai:* NEA 1967-; Highlan Assn 1970-; Delta Kappa Gamma 1982-; Western PA Assn for Pr Tchrs 1994-; *office:* Heights Elem Schl Freeport Rd Natrona Heigh 15065*

ROCCHINO, ROSANNE, AP English II Teacher; *b:* Philadelphia, PA Glassboro St Coll (BA) Scndry Eng 1964; *cr:* Kingsway Regnl HS Tchr; Glassboro HS Eng Tchr; Cherry Hill HS East Eng Tchr 1972 Founder of Feminine Advancement Stu Clb; SEED Prgm- Educ Involved in Multi-Cultural Stud; NEA & NJEA 1965-; CHEA 1972-, Cert of Acad Achvmt for Johns Hopkins CTY 1988; *office:* Cherry Hi East Kresson Rd Cherry Hill NJ 08003*

ROCCIO, JAMES JOSEPH, Mathematics Department Chair; *b:* Alt PA; *m:* Mary Agnes Aust; *c:* Jacqui (dec), Patrick; *ed:* St Francis Coll Math 1961; Attnd Univ of Southern CA, Holy Cross Coll, Un Pittsburgh, Penn St Univ; *cr:* Bishop Mc Cort HS Math Dept Chm 196 Richland HS Math Dept Chm 1969-; *ai:* Sr Class, Jr Class, Mu Alpha Math Club Adv; Prof Dev Comm; NEA 1969-; PSEA 1969-, Cntrl-We Treas; REA 1969-, Pres; NCTM; PCTM; LHCTM; N Geistown-Richland Kiwanis 1969-83, Pres; Altoona-Johnstown Di Cath Charities 1964-68, Bd of Dirs; LBW Fed Schls Credit Union 1 Bd of Dirs; St Benedict Parish Cncl 1989-, Pres; Family Life Office 1 Bd of Dirs; NSF Grant 1967-68; St Francis Coll Achvmt Awd Outstdng Tchr Awd 1974-75; Who's Who in Amer Ed 1989-90; PA Citation for Svc.

ROCCIO, MARY AGNES AUST, Third Grade Teacher; *b:* Johnstown *m:* James J.; *c:* Jacqui (dec), Patrick; *ed:* Seton Hill Coll (BA) Ele 1963; Attnd IN Univ, Univ of Pittsburgh at Johnstown, PA St Univ; Simon & Jude Schl Tchr 1959-61; Rachel Hill Schl Tchr 1963-; *ai:* Y Astronauts Prgm Spon, Adv; Strategic Planning Comm; NEA, PA S Assn, PTO, IRA 1963-; Richland Ed Assn 1963-, Sec, Negotiation C

Chm; Family Life Office 1964-, Bd of Dirs, Finance Comm, ; Cup Awd 1988; Highland Comm Lib 1991-; CCD Tchr; Delta Gamma 1976-, 2nd VP, Mbrshp Chprsn, World Flwshp Chair, al Records; Bottle Works Ethnic Art Ctr 1995-; Conducted, Wrote, d TV Prgm; Johnstown Jaycee's Outstdng Young Edctr Awd Up; Seton Hall Alumnae Corp Bd of Dirs; Outstdng Ldrs in Scndry, 1976.

), **MARILYN K.**, Home Economics Teacher; *b:* Pittsburgh, PA; *c:* avid; *ed:* IN Univ of PA (BSEd) Home Ec Ed 1979; Grad Credit Woodland Hills East Jr High Curr Coord 1991-93; Woodland Hills ne Ec Tchr 1979-; *ai:* PSEA 1979-; NEA 1979-; IUP Home Ec Assn 1979-; ARC 1986-; Spcl Olympics 1991-; *office:* Woodland HS 2550 Greensburg Pike Pittsburgh PA 15221*

), **RICHARD F.**, English Teacher; *b:* New York, NY; *m:* Patricia Christina, Mary Margaret, Robert; *ed:* C. W. Post Coll (MS) Eng ·: Anacostia HS Fr Tchr 1969-70; Kings Park HS Eng Tchr 1970-; Cty Comm Coll Adj Eng Prof 1980-; *ai:* HS Newspaper Adv; NY of Excl Awd 1993; *office:* Kings Park HS 200 Route 25a Kings Park 54

AT, DENISE, Associate Professor of French; *b:* Cully, Switzerland; rles L. Robertson; *c:* Claudio Rochat-Felix; *ed:* Univ of MA at ıth (BA) Portuguese Stud 1975; Brown Univ (MA) Fr Lit 1977, Fr Lit 1983; *cr:* Smith Coll Instr 1981-83, Asst Prof 1983-89, Assoc 39-; *ai:* MLA 1979-; AATF, NEMLA 1981-; CIEF 1985-; Kenyon ship Brown Univ 1978-79; Numerous Articles Pub; Writes & es Fr Poems into Eng.

E, CHRISTOPHER JOHN, Social Studies Teacher; *b:* Bethpage, Alice Theresa; *c:* Christina Alice; *ed:* Dowling Coll (BA) Soc Sci 989; Taft Schl AP & European His Cert 2 Credits; Queens Coll 20 Irs; *cr:* St Annes Cath Grammar Schl 7th & 8th Grd Soc Stud Tchr ; St Dominic Cath HS Soc Stud Tchr 1992-; *ai:* Var Boys Lacrosse Hockey Coach; LI Cncl for Soc Stud 1991-; NCSS 1995-; Knights mbus 1986-, 3rd Degree Mem; *home:* 77 E 19th St Huntingtn Sta 46*

E, JAMES W., Mathematics Teacher; *b:* Washington, DC; *m:* ne Cordon; *ed:* LaSalle Univ (BS) Math 1957, (MS) Theology 1960; Notre Dame (MS) Math 1964; Grad Credits U of PA, Cornell, U of nple U, Penn St, West Chester, Indiana U of PA, Beaver Coll; *cr:* ath HS Math Tchr 1960-63; LaSalle Coll HS Math Tchr, Dept 1964-68; Merck Scharpe & Dohne Statistical Analyst 1968-70; Tennent HS Math Tchr 1970-76; LaSalle Coll HS Math Tchr, Dept 76-; *ai:* Moderator Mathletes; MAA, NCTM, PCTM, ATMOPAV Shell Merit Flwshp; Article Math Tchr 1993; 4 Addl Expositions hr Tandy Awd; *office:* LaSalle Coll HS 8605 Cheltenham Ave oor PA 19038

E, NANCY MARIE (BRACKEN), Health & Physical Ed Teacher; , PA; *m:* Thomas J.; *c:* Christopher, Alexis; *ed:* Lock Haven Univ th, PE 1984; Gannon Univ (MS) Cnslng Psych 1994; *cr:* Corry Area st Long Term Sub Tchr 1985-87; Clymer Cntrl Schl Hlth, PE Tchr ai: Sr Class Adv; After-Prom Co_chm; Core Team; Var, JV Girls Boys Vlybl Coach; NEA 1988-; AAHPERD 1992-; *office:* Clymer Schl PO Box 580 Clymer NY 14724

E, PATRICIA ABBRUZZESE, 7th Grd Social Studies Teacher; *b:* er, NY; *m:* Andrew John; *c:* Michael, Kevin; *ed:* Monroe Comm S) Liberal Arts 1974; Nazareth Coll of Rochester (BA) His 1976, eneral Ed 1984; *cr:* Blessed Trinity Schl 6-8 Grd Soc Stud Tchr ; Union Springs MS 7th Grd Soc Stud Tchr 1988-; *ai:* Ski Club ; Jr Yorker Club Adv; BSA 1993-, Den Ldr; *office:* Union Springs N Cayuga St Union Springs NY 13160

E, PATRICK GEORGE, Secondary Math Teacher; *b:* Ilion, NY; *m:* ı; *c:* Brianna, Brenden; *ed:* SUNY at Cortland (BS) Scndry Math MS) Scndry Math 1968; 12 Grad Credit Hrs; *cr:* Penn Yan Acad chr 1962-70; Little Falls Sr High Math Tchr 1971-; *office:* Little S 1 High School Rd Little Falls NY 13365

E, PEGGY KEATON, Adjunct Professor of English; *b:* Pittsburgh, John W.; *c:* Morgan, Shannon; *ed:* Slippery Rock St Coll (BS) Ed niv of Pittsburgh (MED) Comm 1976; 12 Credit Hrs Indiana Univ 6 Credit Hrs Point Park Coll; *cr:* Plumborough Schl Dist Tchr); Comm Coll Allegheny Cty Instr, Writing Ctr Coord, Adv to per 1981-; *ai:* Coll Newspaper, Lit Magazine; Writing Ctr Coord; Comm Coll Algny Co Boyce Cmps 595 Beatty Rd Monroeville PA

T, EVANN COX, Earth Science Teacher; *b:* Forest City, PA; *m:* *c:* Nadine, Darren, Rochelle, David, Marissa; *ed:* Marywood Coll o 1965, (BS) Art 1968; Permanent Cert 1968; 6 Addl Hrs Grad Art r: Forest City Regl HS Art & Sci Tchr & Planetarium Dir 1965-72; Wayne HS Sci Tchr 1974-78, Art & Sci Tchr 1988-; *ai:* NEA Delta Kappa Gamma 1976-; Western Wayne Tchrs Assn 1974-; Meml Hospital Auxiliary 1992-, Annual Flea Market Chm; ntship to Saint Louis Univ & Saint Johns Univ at Coll Grad; *office:* Wayne HS RR 2 Lake Ariel PA 18436

, FLORENCE CECILIA, Asst Prof of Psych & Acad Cnsl; *b:* yn, NY; *ed:* Brooklyn Coll (BA) Psych, Sociology 1973; Columbia MS) Soc Work, Casework 1975; Cert in Mngmt Stud Cornell Univ Schl of Indstrl & Labor Relations; *cr:* Greenpoint Hosp Unit Mgr, f Psychiatry 1971-72; City Univ of NY Asst Coord of Cnslng 5, Asst Prof 1991-; *ai:* Block Assn Treas; Battered Women Stdnts of Staff Congress, AAUP 1977-; Dallas Athene 1985-, Curacao, CUNY Office of Stu Affairs & Spec Prgms Cert Awd for Ldrshp Publications Co-Author; Listed in Success Guide 1992; *office:* City f NY City Coll Convent Ave At 138th St New York NY 10031

, PATRICIA LYNCH, Mathematics Teacher; *b:* Bay Shore, NY; *m:* *c:* Michael, Carling, Griffin, Haleigh; *ed:* Dowling Coll (BA) Math SUNY at Stony Brook (MA) Math Ed 1983; 75 Addl Credits; *cr:* t HS Math Tchr 1978-; *ai:* NYSUT, AFT, Bellport Tchrs Assn Fifth Ave PFA Bayshore 1994-; *office:* Bellport HS Beaver Dam Rd aven NY 11719

, RUSSELL L., Principal; *b:* San Francisco, CA; *ed:* Univ of San co (AA) Eng 1956; St Johns at Little Rock (BA) Philos 1958; va Univ (MA) Eng, Ed 1965; Post Grad Credits Temple Univ, Coll; *cr:* Camden Cath HS Admin Asst 1963-69; Gloucester Cath st Prin, Prin 1969-73; St Joseph's HS Prin 1973-76; Paul VI HS Prin *ai:* NCEA 1963-; *office:* Paul VI HS 901 Hopkins Rd Haddonfield 33

ETT, DAVID J., Technology Teacher; *b:* Patchogue, NY; *ed:*) St Coll (BS) Tech Ed 1982; Stony Brook Univ (MA) Liberal Stud r: Ralph G. Reed Jr HS Tech Tchr 1984-; *ai:* 3rd-12th Grd Double Jump Rope Team Coach; STEP Facilitator; Extended Day, Violence tion Prgm Adv; Suffolk Cty Girl Scouts Double Dutch Prgm Coord; Tech Ed Assn, Cntrl Islip PTA 1984-; Natl Jr Honor Soc Honorary Stu Cncl Hall of Fame Winner; Yrbk Dedication; News 12, Hofstra ducator of Yr Awd Nom; The Jenkins Awd Honorary Mem; *home:* ewood St Patchogue NY 11772*

HILL, CONSTANCE EVERETT, Home Economics Teacher; *b:* on Square, NJ; *m:* Harold; *ed:* Drexel Univ (BS) K-12th Grd Home Ec Ed 1972; Rider Univ Credit Hrs; *cr:* Hamilton Township Bd of Ed Home Ec Tchr 1972-; *ai:* Fine Arts Dept Chprsn; Mercer Cty Tchrs Assn 1972-.

ROCKLAND, EDWARD, 8th Grade English Teacher; *b:* Bronx, NY; *m:* Carole Ann Gilbert; *c:* David, Scott; *ed:* City Coll of NY (BSEd) PE 1965; Univ of MA (MS) PE 1970; 60 Addl Credit Hrs; *cr:* U of MA Grad Asst 1965-66; NY Assoc of the Blind Peripatologist 1966-67; Prince Georges Co Tchr 1967-69; Derry Twp Schl Dist Tchr 1969-; *ai:* Yrbk, Newspaper Advs; NEA 1967-; NCTE 1988-; HEA 1969-, Pres; *office:* Hershey MS E Granada Ave Hershey PA 17033*

ROCKLEIN, KATHLEEN FUSCO, Chemistry Teacher; *b:* Jamaica, NY; *m:* E. Timothy; *c:* Daniel T., Diana K., Deirdre L.; *ed:* Cabrini Coll (BS) Chem 1974; SUNY at Stony Brook (MA) Liberal Arts, Sci 1976; 36 Hrs Post Grad in Sci; *cr:* Ward Melville HS Chem Tchr 1974-; *ai:* Schlsp Comm 1995-; Tchr Mentor 1994-; Girls Track, Field Coach 1975-84; TVTA 1974-; EI PTA 1990-; EI Soccer Club 1990-, Coach, Asst Coach; St Peter the Apostle RC Church Family Life Comm 1992-, Rel Ed Instr 1990-; TVCSD 1991, WMHS Outstanding Prof Achvmt Awds; *office:* Ward Melville Sr HS 380 Old Town Rd East Setauket NY 11733

ROCKMORE, MIRIAM MILLER, Second Grade Teacher; *b:* Albany, NY; *m:* Ronald; *c:* Daniel N., Adam J.; *ed:* Brandeis Univ (BA) Hebrew Lit 1955; Tchrs Coll Columbia Univ (MA) Elem Ed 1960; Greenberg Tchrs Inst Jerusalem Hebrew 1956; Kean Coll NJ 1972; Rutgers Univ NJ Math & Comp Ed 1979 & 1984; Institut Catholique Paris French 1987-88; *cr:* Temple Israel Hebrew Tchr 1956-58; Lincoln Mass Pub Schl 5th Grd Tchr 1960; NJ Pub Schl Edison 1st & 2nd Grd Tchr 1971-; *ai:* Kean Coll Supv of Stu Tchrs 1971-; NEA 1969-; NJEA 1969-; ETEA 1969-; Temple Neve Shalom 1963-, Bd of Dirs; Franklin Schl Citizens Comm 1971-, Metuchen Bd of Ed Appointee; NJ Governors Tchr Recognition Pgm 1988; Edison Ed Fndtn Grant 1994-95; *home:* 15 Beacon Hill Dr Metuchen NJ 08840*

ROCKMULLER, CLIFFORD N., Spanish & French Teacher; *b:* Hewlett, NY; *m:* Doris Cavazzini; *ed:* SUNY at New Paltz (BS) Elem Ed 1977, (MA) Span 1982; *cr:* Middletown NY Schl Dist Biling Tchr 1978-86; Rondout Vly NY Schl Dist Span, Fr Tchr 1986-; *ai:* Elem Ftbl Prgm Coord; Model Org Amer Sts; AFT 1978-; NYSFLT 1987-; *home:* 94 Coxing Rd Cottekill NY 12419

ROCKWELL, ANN MULHALL, 5th Grade Teacher; *b:* Meriden, CT; *m:* Lyle Dean II; *c:* Alexandra; *ed:* St Bonaventure Univ (BS) Elem Ed 1986; Elmira Coll (MS) Elem Ed 1991; *cr:* Elm St Schl 6th Grd Tchr 1986-87, 3rd Grd Tchr 1987-91, 1993-94, 1st Grd Tchr 1991-93, 5th Grd Tchr 1994-; *ai:* Spirit Team Adv; NEA, WTA 1986-; *home:* 112 Roosevelt St Sayre PA 18840

ROCKWELL, DIANE MARIE, Biology, Chemistry & Sci Tchr; *b:* Pittsburgh, PA; *ed:* Univ of Pittsburgh (BS) Bio, Chem & Psych 1971; Duquesne Univ (MAT) Ed 1976; Duquesne Univ & Univ of Pittsburgh (PHD) Microbiology; *cr:* St James Schl Sci Tchr 1973-74; Nativity Schl Sci & Math Tchr 1974-78; Sacred Heart Schl 5th Grd Tchr 1978-79; Canevin Cath HS Bio, Chem & Sci Tchr 1979-; *ai:* PJAS, WSHI Stu & Buhl Sci Engineering Fair Spon; Sci Super Bowl Coach; Penn St Coach bowl; NEA 1979-; Alpha Epsilon Delta 1970-; Spectroscopic Soc Grant 1983 & 1991; Analytical Soc of Chem Awd 1988; Kevin Burns Awd 1990; Numerous Other Co Awds at Buhl Sci Engineering Fair; *office:* Canevin Cath HS 2700 Morange Rd Pittsburgh PA 15205*

ROCKWELL, JOHN E., Professor of Education; *b:* Stevens Point, PA; *m:* Margaret Ellen Henry; *c:* Robert, David, Laura, Carolyn; *ed:* Bloomsburg St Coll (BS) Elem Ed 1963; Trenton St Coll (MA) Elem Ed 1966; Temple Univ (EDD) Early Chldhd & Elem Admin 1979; 9 Hrs Penn St Univ; 12 Hrs Trenton St Coll; 3 Hrs; *cr:* IBM Corp Admission Asst 1956-59; Willingboro Twp Schls 4th Grd Tchr 1963-66; Pennsbury Schl Dist 4th Grd Tchr 1966-67; Lock Haven Univ Prof of Ed, Coord, Supvr Philadelphia Area Stu Tchng Pgrm 1967-; *ai:* Elem Ed, Rdng Comms; Campus Crusade Adv 1976-79; SPSEA Adv 1977-79; Summer Urban Seminar Adv; AFT, APSLUF 1970-; Intnl Pigget Soc 1975-79; Curiosity Shoppe Preschl 1982-; Washington Crossing Chrstn Acad 1992-94, Schl Bd Mem; Grad Flwshp Early Chldhd Grad Stu Temple Univ; Urban Ed Grant; Urban Scholars Acad for Profession of Tchng; *office:* Lock Haven Univ Lock Haven PA 17745

ROCKWELL, PHOEBE, Choral Music Teacher; *b:* San Diego, CA; *ed:* Westminster Choir Coll (ME) Choral Music Ed; Attnd Univ Md; *cr:* Robert Frost JHS Choral Dir, Music Chair 1974-80; Rockville HS Choral Dir, Music Chair 1981-90; Watkins Mill HS Choral Dir, Music Chair 1991-; *ai:* Musical Dir; Cty, St Choir Coach; ACDA 1976-; MENC 1974-; NEA 1978-; Choral Arts Soc 1977-78; Mont Co Jr & Sr Yth Choirs Dir; Jr & Sr Perf Arts Sch Vocal Instr; Guest Dir; Choral Arts Soc of Washington Soloist; *office:* Watkins Mill HS 10301 Apple Ridge Rd Gaithersburg MD 20879

RODD, B. DIANE (MATTHEWS), Educational Consultant & Tutor; *b:* Wheeling, WV; *m:* Earl Martin; *c:* Joel, Joshua, Nathanael; *ed:* Coll of Steubenville Franciscan Univ (BA) Eng 1969; Purdue Univ (MS) Eng Ed 1972; St Francis Coll Cnslng Scndry Cert 1973-74; *cr:* Warren Cty MSD Eng, Speech Tchr & Eng Dept Head 1969-73; Southwest Allen Cty MSD Tutor for Home Bound 1973-74; *ai:* Rsrchd Curr from US to Home Edctrs in Australia 1987-89; Curr Cnslng & Design; CHEO 1989-, Conf Speaker 1992-95; Book: Training for Royalty 1991; Numerous Articles Pub; *office:* Abba Inst Of Motivation 2180 Northland Ave Lakewood OH 44107*

RODDY, ROBERT CONLIN,JR., Honors English III Teacher; *b:* Baltimore, MD; *m:* Jacquelyn J.; *c:* Robert III, Rebecca, James, Zachary; *ed:* Slippery Rock Univ (BSEd) Eng Ed 1964; IN Univ of PA (MED) Scndry Ed 1969; *cr:* Richland Jr HS Eng Tchr 1964-68; McDowell HS Eng Tchr 1968-; *ai:* Acad Challenge Team Coach; Schl Literary Magazine Adv; Millcreek Ed Assn, PSEA, NEA 1968-; Distinguished Tchr Recognition Penn St Univ Scholars Prgm; *office:* McDowell HS 3580 W 38th St Erie PA 16506*

RODDY, SCOTT L., Head Football Coach; *b:* Columbus, OH; *m:* Barb; *c:* Erik, Elyse; *ed:* Heidelberg Coll (BA) Hlth & PE 1981; *cr:* Bucyrus HS Head Ftbl Coach & Hlth Tchr 1981-92; Sidney HS Head Ftbl Coach & Hlth Tchr 1993-; *ai:* Weight Room Coord; OHFCA 1981-; N Cntrl Ftbl Coaches Assn 1981-92, Pres; Miami Vly Ftbl Coaches Assn 1993-; Regn II St All-Star Coach 1990; NW Dist & OH Coach of Yr 1990; N Cntrl OH Coach of Yr 1991; Miami Vly All Star Head Coach 1995; *office:* Sidney HS 1215 Campbell Rd Sidney OH 45365

RODE, HELEN TUCCIARONE, English Teacher; *b:* New York, NY; *m:* Jack M.; *c:* David, James; *ed:* Fordham Univ (BS) Eng 1969; Iona Coll (BS) Eng, Ed 1973; *cr:* St Benedicts' Eng Tchr, Chair 1969-79; Orion House Multi Class Tutor 1986-87; White Mts Regnl HS Eng Tchr 1987-; *ai:* Prins Advy, Alternative Scheduling Comms; NEA, NHATE 1987-; *office:* White Mtn Reg HS Rt 3 Whitefield NH 03598*

RODENBAUGH, KAREN ELIZABETH, Advanced Lang Arts & Gate Tchr; *b:* Youngstown, OH; *ed:* Youngstown St Univ (BA) Eng, Scndry Ed 1988; MS GATE Ed Specialist 1997; *cr:* North Jr HS 7-8 Grds Eng Tchr 1988-95, 7-8 Grds Advanced Lang Arts, GATE Tchr 1995-; *ai:* Eng Dept, CORE Team Chprsn; HUGS Club Adv; Odyssey of the Mind Coach; WROTE, OAGC 1995-; NCTE 1996; NEA 1988-; Impact II Ameritech Awd for Innovative Tchng; *office:* North Jr HS 2724 Mariner Ave Youngstown OH 44505

RODENFELS, JEROME FRANCIS, Music Coord, Bands & Orch Dir; *b:* Cincinnati, OH; *m:* Ann Thaman; *c:* Abigail, Taylor; *ed:* Wright St Univ (BM) Music Ed 1981; Youngstown St Univ (MM) Music Ed 1987; Univ of Dayton Post Grad Educl Admin; *cr:* Chamihade Julienne HS Band Asst, Choir Dir 1981; Wooster City Schls Band Dir Grd 5-12 1982-87; Anna Local Schls Band Dir Grd 5-12 1987-89; Mad River Local Schls Music Coord Grd K-12 1989-; *ai:* Marching, Symphonic Bands; Symphonic Orch; OMEA 1981-; NSOA, MREA 1989-; Wright St Univ Distinguished Music Alumni Awd 1993; OMEA Dist Treas, Sec 1994-, Adjudiated Event Chair 1992-, All State Coord; *office:* Mad River Local Schls 1900 Harshman Rd Dayton OH 45424*

RODERICK, DORIS CATANIO, English Teacher & Dept Chair; *b:* East Greenwich, RI; *w:* Anthony M. (dec); *ed:* Univ of RI (BS) His, Eng, (BED) Ed; 12 Addl Credits; Brown Univ 2 Credits; Providence Coll 3 Credits; *cr:* Hope Vly Jr HS Eng Tchr; North Kingstown HS Eng Tchr; East Greenwich HS Eng Tchr, Dept Head 1968-; *ai:* Adv Class of 1996; NEA 1971-, Pub Relations, EG; *home:* 110 Friendly Rd East Greenwich RI 02818

RODGERS, DIANE MARIE, US History & World Geog Tchr; *b:* Zanesville, OH; *m:* John Paul; *c:* Venus Michelle Rodgers Morrison; *ed:* OH Univ (BS) Ed, Soc Stud 1970; Numerous CEUS; 5th Yr of Coll; *cr:* Southern Local Schls Tchr 1970; West Muskingum Schls Tchr 1970-73; Crooksville Schls Tchr 1873-; *ai:* Stu Cncl, Drama Club Adv; OH Cncl of Soc Stud 1986-; Jennings Schlr; *office:* Crooksville Schls 4075 Ceramic Way Crooksville OH 43731*

RODGERS, DONZELLA, ESEA Title, Math Instructor; *b:* Jamestown, NY; *m:* Jimmie Lee; *c:* Jimmie Kizer, Dominique Martin, Chloe Shellee; *ed:* The Univ of Akron (BS) Elem Ed 1977, (MS) Elem Ed 1985; Inst of Children's Lit Writing for Children & Teenagers Diploma 1995; 4 Credits; Kent St Univ 2 Credits; Ashland Comm Coll 4 Credits; *cr:* Fairlawn Elem Schl Third Grd Tchr 1978-82; Rankin Elem Schl Second Grd Tchr 1982-84; Jackson Elem Schl Second Grd Tchr 1985-86; Rankin Elem Schl Third Grd Tchr 1987-92, ESEA Title, Math Tchr 1992-; *ai:* Made Presentations in St, Comm Ctrs; Akron Ed Assn 1978-; Target Assistance Schl Comm 4 Yrs; Fac Cncl Comm 2 Yrs; OH Network Trng & Assistance for Schls & Comms; Self-Help & Re-Ed Inc 1978-, VP; Upper-Room Missionary Bapt Church, Pastor 1990-; NAACP Org 1990-, Bd Mem; Order of Eastern Star Phoenix Lodge 1981-; Carolyn & Co Choir 1993-; Torch Acad In-Progress Exec Dir; Nom Outstdng Sunday Schl Tchr; Natl Bd for Prof Tchng Stans Candidate; OH St Univ Mirror Hnr SocAwd Hnrs; Book: Points Ahead; *home:* 1559 Moreview Dr Copley OH 44321*

RODGERS, JANET E., MS Social Studies Teacher; *b:* Warren, PA; *m:* Lawrence; *c:* Kristal Hungate, Mark; *ed:* Univ of PA at Edinboro (MS) Soc Stud 1961; Syracuse Univ Grad Work; *cr:* Panama Cntrl Schl Soc Stud Tchr 1961-; *ai:* HS Quiz Bowl; Jr Honor Soc; Class Adv; Panama Fac Assn 1961-, Sec & Treas; NEA & Delta Kappa Gamma; Tchr of Month & Grad Speaker; *office:* Panama Central Schl School St Panama NY 14767

RODGERS, JOYCE, Spanish Teacher; *b:* Los Angeles, CA; *m:* Max; *ed:* Northern IL Univ (BA) Span 1966; St Univ of NY at Oswego (MSEd) Curr & Instruction 1991-; 30 Hrs Beyond Master's Degree Taken as Grad Courses & In Svc for Tchrs; *cr:* Dwight Twp HS Span & Fr Tchr 1966-68; Hyde Park Jr HS Span & Fr Tchr 1969-71; Our Lady of Perpetual Help Span Tchr 1971-72; Honolulu, Oahu Pub Schls Sub & Span Tchr 1972-75; Newport News Pub Schls Span & Fr Tchr 1976-85; Camden HS Span & Fr Tchr, Dept Chprsn1985-; *ai:* Frgn Lang Club Spon; Dist Tech Comm; Amer Assn of Tchrs of Span & Portugese 1982-; Camden Tchrs Assn 1985-; NYSAFLT, AFT, NY St Assn of Frgn Lang Tchrs 1985-; UFDC 1986-, Local VP, Pres; *office:* Camden H S Oswego St Camden NY 13316*

RODGERS, LANA LUSCH, Third Grade Teacher; *b:* Lehighton, PA; *m:* Harold E.; *c:* Jacqui Victoria Kirchner, Travis Dustin; *ed:* Kutztown St Coll (BSEd) Elem 1964; Kutztown Univ (MED) Elem 1968; Rdng Specialist 1987; KSC Cert to Teach Visually Handicapped; *cr:* Twin Vly Schl Dist 6th Grd Tchr 1964-67, 1987-88, 3rd Grd Tchr 1988-; Wilson Schl Dist 6th Grd Tchr 1967; *ai:* Sci, Soc Stud Curr Writing; OBE Sci Curr Writing; Several Stu Tchrs from Chester Univ; PSEA, NEA 1964-; TVEA, Local Sec 1965; Amer Assn of Univ Women 1965-67; Girls Scouts 1966-67, Junior, Cadette Troupe; West Lawn Meth Church 1968-, 7th Grd Sunday Schl Tchr 1971-; Berks Cty Literacy Cncl 1977-79; *office:* Twin Vly Schl Dist RD 3 Box 52 Elverson PA 19520*

RODGERS, LUCINDA MAC TAGGART, 6th Grade Teacher; *b:* Corry, PA; *m:* David G.; *c:* Jennifer, Jonathan; *ed:* Edinboro Univ of Pa (BS) elem, Early Child 1973, (MED) Ed 1983; *cr:* Heard Meml Schl 5th Grd Tchr 1977-1992; North East MS 6th Grd Tchr 1992-; *ai:* Kiwanis Builders Club, Vlybl, Schl Store Adv; NEA 1977-, Bldg Rep; PSEA 1977-; North East Support Team 1990-; Jr Women's Club; Sunday Schl Tchr; Chrstn Ed Comm; Rainbow Advy Bd;AAUW; PTA Liason; Stud Yrbk Dedication 1992; Children's Coloring Book Chamber of Commerce; Outsdng Young Edctr; *office:* North East MS 1903 Freeport Rd North East PA 16428*

RODGERS, RAMONA THRAESE, Spanish Teacher; *b:* Altoona, PA; *ed:* St Francis Coll (BA) Span Comm & Mod Lang 1984; IN Univ of PA (MA) Historic Preservation 1993; *cr:* Penn Cambria Tchr 1984-; Mt Aloysius Coll Instr 1985-; *ai:* Ski Club & Jr & Sr Class Adv; Foreign Exch Coord; PSEA & NEA 1984-; PSMLA 1989-; Patton Centennial Comm 1992-, Comm; Gallitzin Tourist Cncl 1990-; *home:* 70 Country Club Rd Cresson PA 16630

RODGERS, THOMAS J., 5th Grade Teacher; *b:* Steelton, PA; *m:* Patricia H.; *c:* Maureen Palese, Katrina, Michael; *ed:* Millersville (BS) Elem 1962; Shippensburg (MED) Elem 1968; Western MD Prin Cert 1972; *cr:* Harrisburg Schl Dist 6th Grd Head Tchr, Ass't Prin 1962-70; Shaull Elem Prin 1970-74; Sporting Hill Elem 5th Grd Tchr 1974-; *ai:* Bsktbl, Track, Flag Ftbl; Steelton Area Jaycees 1968-, Pres, Outstdng Chptr; West Shore Elks 1976-, Exhalted Ruler; Knights of Columubs 1983-, Pres Home Assn; *home:* 9 Highland Dr Camp Hill PA 17011

RODGERS, VINCENT PAUL, Frgn Lang & Speech Arts Chprsn; *b:* Munhall, PA; *ed:* CA St Tchrs Coll (BSEd) Span, Eng 1968; Univ of Pittsburgh (MED) Scndry Ed 1976; *cr:* North Hills Schl Dist Span, Eng Tchr 1969, Span Tchr 1969-, Frgn Lang, Speech Arts Dept Chprsn 1992-; *ai:* Span Club Spon; Forensics Coach, Judge; NHEA, NEA 1969-; Univ of Pittsburgh Nationality Room Comm 1975-, Vice-Chprsn, Lithuanian Room Vice-Chm; *office:* North Hills Schl Dist 53 Rochester Rd Pittsburgh PA 15229*

RODICHOK, JOHN D., Reading Teacher; *b:* Lykens, PA; *m:* Juudith E.; *ed:* West Chester Univ (BS) Elem Ed 1971; Temple Univ (MS) Ed 1974; *cr:* Hegins Hubley Elem 6th Grd Tchr 1971-92; Tri Vly Jr Sr HS 7th-8th Grd Tchr 1992-; *ai:* Asst Ftbl & Jr High Bsktbl Coach; NEA 1971-; PSEA 1971-; *home:* 118 W Maple St Valley View PA 17983

RODKEY, CHARLES, Secondary Gifted Coordinator; *b:* Johnstown, PA; *m:* Mary E. Arthur; *c:* Matthew, Colin, Maura; *ed:* Metropolitan St at Denver (BS) Earth Sci 1986; Addl 26 Hrs Grad Stud Math Univ of Pittsburg; *cr:* Englewood Schls Tchrs Aid-Emotionally Disturbed 1983-86; Comm Coll of Allegheny Cty Instr 1986-88; South Fayette Twp Schls Instr 1989-; *ai:* Cooperative Satellite Learning Project Dir; Supercomputing Project Coor; Med Tech Team Adv; Amer Geophysical Union 1983-; AACE 1989-; PA Assn of Gifted Ed 1995-, Legislative Liason; Cub Scouts 1994-, Den Ldr; Milken Fnd Natl Edctr Awd; CO Scholars Awd; NASA Teamwork Awd; *office:* South Fayette Twp Schls 2254 Old Oakdale Rd Mc Donald PA 15057

RODNEY, NANCY HARTMAN, Therapeutic Foster Mother; *b:* Jersey City, NJ; *m:* Robert Morris Jr.; *c:* David Henry, Elizabeth Jean, Stephen Robert, Susan Kathleen; *ed:* Wellesley Coll (BA) Psych 1961; 15 Addl Hrs CT Tchr Cert K-8 Trinity Coll, Univ of Hartford 1961; Working on St Courses 1 Yr Licensing, Specialized Foster Parenting Univ of CT Schl of Soc Work 1989; *cr:* Westminster Prep Schl Dormitory Supvr, Cnslr, Tutoring 1972-; Hopemeadow Nursery Schl Head Tchr, Dir 1978-87; People's Bank Customer Svc Rep 1987-90; Honolulu Comm Action Prgm Head Start Tchr 1990-91; Meadowbrook of Granby Asst Dir of Day Care 1992-95; The Clark Family Clinic Therapeutic Foster Mother 1994-; Dept of Families & Children Therapeutic Foster Mother 1994-; *ai:* Therapeutic Foster Parents Support Ldr; Interaction Between Sr Citizens & Young Children Wrkshp Presenter; NAEYS, Hartford AEYC 1978-; Phi Beta Kappa 1961-; Hartford Wellesley Club 1961-, Fund Raiser for Schlsps; First Church Granby 1972-, Deacon; First Church Granby 1972-, Moderator, Survival; Simsbury Pub Schls 1972-, Lib Aid, Act Organzier, Room Mother; The Master's Schl at Simsbury 1978-, VP; PTA 1978-, Pres; PTO Simsbury Schl Sponsorship, Activity Facilitator; Five Children's Books Pub; Extensive Course Work Awd.

RODRIGUES, DONNA GHIZE, Dir of Univ Park Campus Schl; *b:* Worcester, MA; *m:* Marco; *ed:* Emmanuel Coll (BA) Span, Eng 1968; Worcester St Coll (MEd) Span 1976; Harvard Univ (MEd) Admin 1995; *cr:* Worcester Pub Schl Span, Fr Instr 1968-, Frgn Lang Dept Chair 1988-; Worcester Pub Schls & Clark Univ Collab Prof Dev Schls Coord 1995-, Dir of UPCS 1996; *ai:* NHS, Jr Class, Natl Span Hnr Soc Adv 1994-; Schl Governance Cncl Rep 1994-; Ldrshp 1996; NEA, MTA, EAW 1968; MFLA, ATSP 1970-; Phi Delta Kappa 1995-; Ldrshp Skills Awd 1995; Amer Cancer Soc 1989-, Vol; Neighborhood Coalition Group 1983-; Hiatt Flwshp to Attend Harvard Univ 1994-95; Resilient Adolescents Publication; Restructuring Grant 1995; *office:* Worcester Pub Schl 170 Apricot St Worcester MA 01603*

RODRIGUES, DOUGLAS MARK, Religious Studies Teacher; *b:* Fall River, MA; *ed:* St John Seminary Coll (AB) Philosphy, Psych 1989; Attnd St Mary's Seminary, Univ INC; *cr:* Family Svc Assn Staff Supvr 1991-92; Bishop Stang HS Tchr 1992-; *ai:* Campus Ministry Dir; Habitat for Humanity Campus Chapter Adv; Habitat for Humanity Fall River Affiliate 1992-94, Bd of Dirs; *office:* Bishop Stang HS 500 Slocum Rd North Dartmouth MA 02747

RODRIGUES, ROBERT M., 9th-12th Grade History Teacher; *b:* Pittsburgh, PA; *m:* Eleanor Ann Srdoch; *c:* Robert, Matthew, Justin, Nicole, Annmarie, Peter; *ed:* Duquesne Univ (BED) Scndry Ed 1969, (MA) Modern European His 1974, (MED) Scndry Admin 1983; 18 Addl Credits at Carnegie-Mellon Univ; *cr:* Bishops Latin Schl Tchr 1969-73; Western PA Schl for the Deaf Tchr 1973-74; Chartiers Valley HS Tchr 1974-; Duquesne Univ Prof 1990-; APEX Co-Dir 1991-; *ai:* NHS Spon; Bsbl Head Coach; Re:Learning Coord; Soc Stud Dept Chm; Cncl for Basic Ed 1985-; West PA Historical Soc 1989-; AFT 1985-; ASCD 1992-; Natl Assn for Core Curr 1994; Natl Cncl for Soc Stud, Teacher of the Year; Natl Cncl for Hist Edctrs; Dormont Lib 1970-; Cncl for Basic Ed Natl Fellowship Awd 1985; Gift of Time 1989-90; VFW Voices of Democracy Awd 1978-; Articles in Journal of Moral Ed 1978, Basic Ed 1989, Soc Ed 1979, The Adjunct Mentor 1992, Univ of Pittsburgh Thanks to Tchrs 1991; Wkshps for Regnl Schl Dist on Integrated Curr, Mult Intelligences Teaming; 1994 PA Outstanding Soc Stud Project Awd; *office:* Chartiers Valley HS 50 Thoms Run Rd Bridgeville PA 15017*

RODRIGUEZ, ADA I., Spanish Teacher; *b:* Vega Baja, PR; *c:* Angel, Joseriberto, Eduardo, Alejandra; *ed:* Univ of PR (BA) Psych 1970; Univ of East Stroudsburg (MED) Scndry & Affective Ed 1996; Instructory Cert Scndry Ed & Span 1989; *cr:* PS 23 Biling Tchr 1972-80; Pleasant Vly HS Span Tchr 1990-; *ai:* Soph Class Adv; Span Club Adv; NEA.

RODRIGUEZ, FERNANDO, Shop Teacher & Grade Advisor; *b:* Brooklyn, NY; *m:* Nereida Gonzalez; *c:* Samuel, Adam, Jaylyn; *ed:* Attnd City Coll of NY Occupational Ed; *cr:* US Navy Plane Capt, Aviation Elec, Inspector 1976-80; Aviation HS Tchr, Grd Adv, Coach 1981-; *ai:* Boys, Girls Var Vlybl Coach; *office:* Aviation HS 36-01 Queens Blvd Long Island City NY 11101

RODRIGUEZ, JACQUELINE (COSBY), Mathematics Teacher; *b:* Richmond, VA; *m:* Francisco A.; *c:* Steven F., Ann Marie; *ed:* PA St Univ (BA) Ene 1965; George WA Univ (MA) Ed Supervision 1975; Math 26 Credits U of MD, Bowie St Coll; Acctng 33 Credits Anne Arundel Comm Coll; *cr:* Alexandria Pub Schls Tchr 1966-67; Albemarle Cty Pub Schls Tchr 1967-68; Anne Arundel Cty Pub Schls Tchr 1968-; *ai:* MD Stu Asst Prgm 3 Yrs; NEA 1966-; MD St Tchr Assoc, Tchrs Assoc of Anne Arundel Co 1967-; NCMT 1994-; St Margarets Civic Assoc 1984-, Sec; *office:* South River HS 201 Central Ave Edgewater MD 21037

RODRIGUEZ, KYRSIS RAQUEL, Professor of Science; *b:* Mayaguez, PR; *ed:* Univ of PR (BS) Bio 1970, (MS) Marine Botany 1974; Univ of MO at Columbia (PHD) Plant Anatomy & Physiology 1982; *cr:* Univ of PR Instr 1974-77; Roxbury Comm Coll Prof of Sci 1983-; *ai:* NEBHE Sci & Engrng Network Mentor; Harvard Univ & Area Hospitals Comm on Microbiological Safety; Biomedical Sci Careers Prgm Inc Bd Mem; NIH Bridges to the Future Reviewer; NEA, MTA, MCCC 1984-; Sigma Xi 1978-; NIH Doctoral Research & AIBS Grants; 2 Ford Fnd & RCC Fnd Awds; MA Pride in Performance Prgm, Latin Amer Stu Assn & Sci Club at RCC Recognition Awds; *office:* Roxbury Comm Coll 1234 Columbus Ave Boston MA 02120

RODRIGUEZ, MAX, Professor of Modern Languages; *b:* Santa Clara, Cuba; *m:* Gisela Ramirez; *c:* Adrian; *ed:* Montclair St Univ (BA) Fr, Lit & Lang 1970; NY Univ (MA) Span Lit 1971, (PHD) Span Lit 1983; *cr:* LaGuardia Comm Coll Asst Prof & Assoc Prof 1972-88, Dept of Hum Chair 1981-83, Asst Dean for Acad Affairs 1984-90, Prof 1988-; *ai:* Modern Langs Coord; CUNY Cncl on Frgn Lang Stud 1978-, Sec 1978-81; AAHE 1985-; Montclair St Univ 1984-89, Exec Bd Mem, Treas 1987-89, Bd of Trustees Rep 1989-90, 75th Anniversary Citation; Title VII Grant 1982; Hispanic Ldrshp Fellow 1983-84; Articles on Transfer 1985 & 1987; *office:* FH LaGuardia Comm Coll 31-10 Thomason ave Long Island City NY 11101

RODRIGUEZ, RAMONA MONTANEZ, Third Grade Teacher; *b:* Manhatten, NY; *m:* Candido; *c:* Cecilio, Anna Maria; *ed:* Brooklyn Coll (BA) Elem Ed 1985, (MS) Elem Ed 1995; Sensa Stud Skill 2 Hrs; Sci 3 Credits; *cr:* PS 213 3rd Grd Bilingual Tchr 1986-87; Our Lady of Refuge 3-4, 6,8, Grd Tchr 1987-; *ai:* 7th Grd Exercise Class; NCEA 1987-; Lecter OLR Church 1993-; *office:* Our Lady Of Refuge Schl 1087 Ocean Ave Brooklyn NY 11230*

RODRIGUEZ, RENEE LYNN, High School Math Teacher; *b:* Cleveland, OH; *ed:* Kent St Univ (BA) Scndry Math 1993; Cleveland St Univ 20 Grad Credit Hrs Comp Ed; *cr:* Garfield Hts HS Math Tchr 1993-; *ai:* Girls JV Bsktbl & Frosh Vllybl Coach; OCTM 1993-; NCTM 1993-; Independence HS Hall of Fame; *office:* Garfield Heights HS 12000 Maple Leaf Dr Cleveland OH 44125

RODRIGUEZ, SAMUEL,JR., Social Studies Teacher; *b:* Newark, NJ; *m:* Eva I. Feliciano; *c:* Yvonne, Nathan; *ed:* Kutztown Univ (BS) Ed 1991; Lehigh Univ Working on MA in Educl Ldrshp; *cr:* Liberty HS Soc Stud Tchr 1992-; *ai:* NEA, Phi Alpha Theta 1991-; Yth Congress Intnl 1995-, Pres; *office:* Liberty HS 1115 Linden St Bethlehem PA 18018

RODWELL, RICHARD CHARLES, Elem Assistant Principal; *b:* Medford, MA; *ed:* Boston Coll (BSBA) Bus Mngmt 1958; Univ of MA at Salem (MED) Educl Admin 1967; 80 Post Grad Credits; Whelock Coll Child Dev; *cr:* US Army Intelligence Corp 1958-62; AT&T Analyst 1962-64; Tyhgborough Ed Dept Elem Tchr 1964-65, Prin 1965-67; Malden Ed Dept Tchr, Asst Prin 1967-; *ai:* Steering, Schl Assessment Comms; Tchr Corp Project Writer; PTO VP; Tchrs Resource Room Planner, Chprsn; Designer Tchr Office Space; Drama Dept; Schl Cncl; Tyngsborough Ed Assn 1964-67, Pres; Malden Ed Assn 1967-; MA Tchrs Assn, NEA 1964-; Daniels Schl Comm Cncl 1979-81, VP; MTA Election Comm 1979-81; Awded Cert Congressional Ldr & Chief Justice Berger Stdnts Participation, Awd; Dev, Wrote System Wide Resource Handbook; *office:* Maplewood Elem Schl 30 Laurel St Malden MA 02148*

ROE, DONALD WINSTON, Physics Teacher; *b:* Catlettsburg, KY; *m:* Betty Jo Bailey; *c:* Sara Nell DiLima, Daniel Winston; *ed:* Marshall Coll (BS) Chem 1955, (MS) Phys Chem 1956; WV Univ (PHD) Phys Chem 1961; *cr:* Sci, Eng Consultant 1968-83; Univ of Tampa Assoc Prof 1968-72; Pineville HS Sci Tchr 1972-81; Gaithersburg HS Physics Tchr 1983-; *ai:* Sci Club Spon 1985-; NEA 1972-; Joint Bd Sci, Engrng WA Acad Sci 1985-, Chm 1990; WA Acad of Sci 1985-; NSF Flwshp; Articles Pub; Electronic Devices Patents; *office:* Gaithersburg HS 314 S Frederick Ave Gaithersburg MD 20877

ROE, GLENN WILLIAM, Science Teacher; *b:* Omaha, NE; *m:* Sheri Schou; *c:* Danielle; *ed:* Univ of NE at Lincoln (BS) Dairy Tech 1968; Ohio St Univ (MS) Dairy Tech 1970; Attnd Howard Univ; Univ of MD 25 Addl Hrs; Univ of Rochester 2 Addl Hrs; Loyola Coll at Baltimore 3 Addl Hrs; *cr:* Southwestern HS Sci Tchr 1971-74; Kenmoor Jr HS Sci Tchr 1974-82; Northwestern HS Sci Tchr 1982-92; Eleanor Roosevelt HS Sci Tchr 1992-; *ai:* Odyssey of Mind Spon; NEA, MSTA 1971-; Pets on Wheels 1991-, Vice Chm; *office:* Eleanor Roosevelt HS 7601 Hanover Pky Greenbelt MD 20770

ROE, HELEN M., Family & Consumer Science Tchr; *b:* Greenfield, OH; *m:* Bill; *c:* Jacob, Joshua; *ed:* OH Univ (BS) Home Ec Ed 1982; Wright St (MS) Ed 1994; *cr:* Clinton Massie MS Home Ec Tchr 1982-83; Greenfield Schls Elem Tchr 1985-87; Greenfield MS 7th, 8th Grd Impact Tchr 1987-; *ai:* FHA; GEVEA, OEA, NEO, OVA 1987-; 4-H 1979-, Adv; Cub Scouts 1994-; *office:* Greenfield MS 200 N 5th St Greenfield OH 45123

ROE, LORI ANN (BUTLER), 6th Grade Math & Science Tchr; *b:* Baltimore, MD; *m:* James D.; *c:* Julie Silberman, Cameron Roe; *ed:* Towson St Univ (BA) Ed 1978-; 15 Addl Hrs U of DE MA Ed; *cr:* Lewes MS Soc Stud 1989-90; Rehoboth Elem Schl Soc Stud 1990-94, Rehoboth Elem Schl Math, Soc Stud 1994-95, Rehoboth Elem Schl Math, Sci 1995-; *ai:* Cmptr Fair Coach; Math League; St Jude's Mathathon Coord; Conflict Resolution Site Coord; Odyessy of Mind Judge; Invention Convention Coord; NEA, CNEA, AFT 1987; Yoga Tchr 1994-; Coastal Arts Comm Planning, Designing, 4-H Involvement; Nom Tchr of Yr 1994-95; *office:* Rehoboth Elem Schl 500 Stockley St Rehoboth Beach DE 19971

ROE, MARTIN JOHN, English Teacher; *b:* Carbondale, PA; *ed:* Mansfield Univ (BS) Eng & Ed 1973; PA St Univ 28 Grad Credits; *cr:* Carbondale Area High Eng Tchr 1974-; *ai:* Stu Cncl Adv 12 Yrs; Ski Club Adv 8 Yrs; NEA 1974-; PSEA 1974-; CATA 1974-; Carbondale Historical Soc, Charter Mem; *home:* 192 Washington St Carbondale PA 18407

ROE, SUZANNE MARY MILLIRON, Fifth Grade Teacher; *b:* Kittanning, PA; *m:* Mitchell D.; *c:* Miles D.; *ed:* Parsons Coll (BS) Elem Ed 1969; Attnd Edinboro Univ, Penn St Univ 1972-75; 24 Hrs Permanent Cert; *cr:* Galesburg Schl 1st Grd Tchr 1969-70; Washington Schl 1st Grd Tchr 1970-72; Crawford Cntrl Schl 1st, 5th Grd Tchr 1972-; *ai:* Meadville Wrestling Booster Club; Pin Club Chm; NEA 1972-; PSEA; CCEA; Boys Town; Defender of Wildlife; Lone Wolk; Humane Soc; Jr Achvmt; *office:* Second Dist Elem Schl 1216 S Main St Meadville PA 16335

ROEBEL, TOM JOHN, Health Teacher; *b:* Cincinnati, OH; *m:* Robin L. Tomer; *c:* Shannon R., Jill M.; *ed:* Miami of OH Univ (BS) Hlth, PE 1978; *cr:* Roger Bacon HS Hlth, PE Tchr 1979-; *ai:* Head Var Boys Bsbl, Asst Var Ftbl Coach; NEA 1979-; *office:* Roger Bacon HS 4320 Vine St Cincinnati OH 45217

ROEBUCK, SHARON JEFFREY, Third Grade Teacher; *b:* New York City, NY; *m:* Gerard; *c:* Jared, Jashaun; *ed:* City Coll of NY Elem Ed (BS) 1977, (MS) 1980; 22 Credits in Rdng; *cr:* P. S. 116 M 4th Grd Tchr 1980-95, 3rd Grd Tchr 1995-; *ai:* NTA 1980-; *office:* P. S. 116 M Schl 210 E 33rd St New York NY 10016

ROEDEL, ROBERT R., Senior Army Instructor; *b:* Hackensack, NJ; *c:* Rob-Roy, Robin L., Kurt; *ed:* Baylor Univ (BA) His 1967; Montclair St Coll (MA) Soc Sci 1984; Boston Univ 16 Credit Hrs His; Natl; *cr:* Jersey City St Coll Asst Prof, Military Sci 1981-85; Boston Univ Asst Prof, Military Sci 1990-93; Thomas Walker HS Sr ARMY Instr 1993-94; Lawrence HS Sr ARMY Instr 1994-; *ai:* Extracurricular Acts Coord; Recruiting Team Spon; NEA 1993-; *office:* Lawrence HS 233 Haverhill St 5 Linlew Dr Lawrence MA 01841*

ROEDER, HAROLD H., Rdng Methods & Microcomp Prof; *b:* Buffalo, NY; *m:* Marcia Schultz; *c:* Lynn, Lisa; *ed:* St Univ Coll at Buffalo (BS) Elem Ed 1958, (MS) Schl Admin 1966; St Univ Coll at Geneso (MSLS) Lib Sci 1965; Univ of Buffalo (EDD) Rdng 1969; Microcomputer Courses; *cr:* Univ of Buffalo Adj Prof 1966-68; St Univ Coll NY Rdng Methods Prof 1968-; *ai:* AAUP 1968-; IRA 1968-; Chautaugua Cty Rdng Assn 1968-; Town of Pomfret 1990-, Planning Bd; 2 NY St Rsrch Fndtn Grants; Numerous Articles Pub; *office:* S U N Y Coll At Fredonia W261 Thompson hall Fredonia NY 14063

ROEDER, NANCY KATHERINE, Professor of Fine Arts; *b:* Wichita Falls, TX; *ed:* Univ of CT (BFA) Drawing; Western MI Univ (MFA) Painting 1977-; *cr:* VA Commonwealth Univ Asst Prof 1979-83; MD Inst, Coll of Art Prof of Fine Arts 1984-; *ai:* Fac Exec Cncl; AAUP 1994-; Ford Fnd Grant; MICA Trustees Grant Excl in Tchng; *office:* MD Inst Coll Of Art 1300 W Mount Royal Ave Baltimore MD 21217*

ROEMER, DENNIS JOHN, Social Studies Teacher; *b:* Buffalo, NY; *c:* Erik, Heather, Andrew; *ed:* Univ of Buffalo (BA) His 1966, (MA) Rdng Ed 1968; *cr:* Woodlawn Jr HS Soc Stud Tchr 1966-67; E Aurora Schls Soc Stud Tchr 1967-; *ai:* NYSUT Inception; Moose Lodge 1990-; Yrbk Tchr of Yr 1974, 1978, 1982; Key Club Tchr of Yr 1994; *home:* David Rd West Falls NY 14170*

ROEMER, ELIZABETH FARRAND, English Teacher; *b:* Syosset, NY; *m:* Scott; *ed:* St Petersburg Jr Coll (AA) Eng 1986; Univ of South FL (BA) Eng Ed 1988; Queens Coll (MA) Eng Lit 1994; *cr:* Island Trees HS Eng Tchr 1989-; *ai:* Var Kickline Coach; Newspaper Adv; *office:* Island Trees HS 59 Straight Ln Levittown NY 11756

ROEMER, HAROLD E.,JR., 5th Grade Teacher; *b:* New York City, NY; *m:* Lois I. Hampton; *c:* Michael, Andrea DeLollo; *ed:* Hofstra Univ (BS) Elem Ed 1964, (MS) Elem Ed 1972; *cr:* Manor Oaks Schl 6th Grd Tchr 1968-69; Countrywood Schl 6th Grd Tchr 1970-76; Maplewood Schl 5th Grd Tchr 1976-; *ai:* Stu Cncl Adv; NYSUT 1968-; South Huntington Tchrs Assn, Bldg Rep; Greenlawn Vol Fire Dept 1979-, Lt., Capt., VP; *office:* Maplewood Intermediate Schl School Ln Huntington Station NY 11746

ROEPCKE, CYNTHIA BOVING, Chemistry Teacher; *b:* Columbus, OH; *m:* Paul S.; *c:* Katie, David, Chris; *ed:* Capital Univ (BA) Chem 1973; Coll of Mt St Joseph (MA) Ed 1987; MT St Univ 6 Sem Hrs; Miami Univ 9 Sem Hrs; Univ of TX at Arlington 2 Sem Hrs; OH St Univ 16 Sem Hrs; *cr:* Licking Heights HS Sci, Chem, Physics Tchr 1973-78; Pickering Chem Tchr, Sci Dept Chair 1979-; *ai:* Sci in Pickerington Camp S Comm 1993-; NSTA 1985-; NCTM 1993-; Epiphany Luth Church Pianist, Jr Choir; GTE Gift Awd 1993-94; Tchr of Yr 1989; Local S Tchr 1989; Amer Chem Soc Cols Section Tchr of Yr 1991; Pickerington HS 300 Opportunity Way Pickerington OH 43147

ROESCH, V. JEAN, Second Grade Teacher; *b:* Amanda, OH; *c:* I Oren; *ed:* Capital Univ (BS) Elem Ed; *cr:* Newton Falls Third G 1955-56; Hamilton Cntrl Third Grd Tchr 1956-60; Marysville Schls Second Grd Tchr 1966-70; Fairbanks Elem Second Grd Tch *ai:* NEA, OEA 1950-; FFA 1976-; *home:* 127 S Maple St Marysv 43040

ROESELER, LISA ANN, 6th-12th Grade Music Teacher; *b:* Medi *m:* Martin C.; *c:* Matthew Philip, Zachary Martin; *ed:* Mansfield PA (BM) Music Ed 1986; St Univ of NY at Buffalo (MM) Music E *cr:* Medina Cntrl Schl Dist Music Tchr 1986-; *ai:* HS Drama Club; Tchrs Assn, Orleans Co Music Educators Assn, NYS Schl Musi Music Educators Natl Conf 1986-; Cath Daughters of the Amer Delta Kappa Gamma 1991-95; Red Cross 1991, Bd of Dirs; *office:* Cntrl Schl Dist 11235 Maple Ridge Rd Medina NY 14103*

ROESER, KATHY L. (HILL), Tchr of Dvlpmntlly Handi Bellevue, OH; *m:* Mark; *c:* Jeffrey; *ed:* Bowling Green St Univ (B Ed, Elem Ed 1987; *cr:* Fremont Jr HS DH Tchr 1987-; *office:* Fre HS 501 Croghan St Fremont OH 43420

ROESKE, ERIC CHARLES, Music Teacher & Band Director; *b:* City, MI; *ed:* Cntrl MI Univ (BME) Music Ed 1985; Univ of AR Music Performance 1987; *cr:* Univ of AR Grad Asst 1985-87 Branch Area Schl Band Dir 1987-89; Bellport HS Music Instr, B 1989-; *ai:* Percussion Ensemble; Clarinet Choir; Percussion Instr; Pit Orch Dir; Marching, Pep Band; PAS; MENC; NYSSMA; CMA; Bellport HS Beaver Dam Rd Brookhaven NY 11719

ROESKE, JOAN N., Business Education Teacher; *b:* Hammonton, William C. Jr.; *c:* Jessica, Heather; *ed:* Trenton St Coll (BS) Bus E *cr:* Oakcrest HS Bus Ed Tchr 1974-83; Egg Harbor Twp HS Bus 1983-; *ai:* NEA, NJBEA, NJEA 1974-; EHTEA 1983-; *office:* Egg Township HS 24 High School Dr Egg Harbor Townshi NJ 08234

ROETH, GARY L., Mathematics Teacher; *b:* Houston, OH; *m:* G F. Mehling; *c:* Andrew, Megan; *ed:* Defiance Coll (BS) Math, Sc Univ of Dayton (MS) Ed 1981; *cr:* Wilder Jr HS Grds 7-9 Math Tch *ai:* Bsktbl Coach 1972; Natl Jr Hnr Soc Adv 1988-92; Math Counts 1985-95; NEA, OEA, PEA 1970-, Sec, Treas, Fac Rep; SPEBSQSA Sec, VP, Pres, Barbershopper of Yr 1982, 1993; Piqua Noon O 1988-; Piqua Tchr of Yr 1987; Western OH Dist Math Tchr of Y *office:* Wilder Jr H S 1120 Nicklin Ave Piqua OH 45356

ROEWE, BARBARA CLANCY, HS English & Journalism T Washington, DC; *m:* George J. Jr.; *c:* G. J. III, Winifred Davis, S *ed:* Wilson Tchrs Coll (BS) Eng 1953; Univ of DE (MED) Scndr 1972; Addl Grad Courses; *cr:* Western Jr High Eng Tchr 1952-5 Grove Jr High Eng Tchr 1954-56; A. T. DuPont High Eng Tchr 19 Adv Tiger Pause Schl Newspaper; Dist Literacy Comm; St Eng La Commission; NCTE & IRA 1972-; DSEA 1972-, Sec; Natl Press DE Press Woman; Delta Kappa Gamma; Unitarian Church 1966- Music Comm; Dixieland Band 1991-; Articles Pub; Tchr of Yr 198 1989-90; Kiwansis Tchr of Yr 1989-90; Preside ntial Scholar Sele Roewe Most Influential Tchr 1989; 1st Pl Natl Press Nwsp Adv; V Media Cont 1994.

ROFFMAN, ROSALY DEMAIOS, Associate Prof of English D New York, NY; *m:* Bernard; *c:* Peter; *ed:* Univ of HI (MA) Lang, Li Eng, Asian Stud; Attnd Univ of CA at Santa Cruz; Univ of Pitt Carnegie Mellon Univ; *cr:* Univ of HI Instr 1961-62; City Coll Lecturer 1962-63; Gakushvin Univ Tokyo Japan, Lecturer 1962; Univ of PA Assoc Prof 1967-; *ai:* Adv Lit Magazine; New Grow Review Founder; Coord Ctr for Stud Myth, Folklore; Co-Ed Aristek Publication; Witter-Bynner Fnd Awd; Natl Endowment Hum; Distr Awd Creative Arts; Writing Flwshp Ed Albee Colony; Studic Centennial Review Awd; Books: Going to Bed Whole, Life on the L Poems, Origins; *office:* Indiana Univ Of PA Indiana PA 15701

ROGALLA, JULIE A., French Teacher; *b:* Pittsburgh, PA; *ed:* Dic Coll (BA) Fr 1991; 18 Credits (MEd) Penn St; *cr:* Lycee Georges de Eng Tchng Asst 1991-92; Huston MS Fr Tchr 1992-; *ai:* French Clu Jaycees 1994-95; *office:* Huston Middle School 1020 Puckety Chu Lower Burrell PA 15068

ROGALSKI, JOHN T., Middle School Teacher; *b:* Philadelphia, Mary Ann Doughten; *c:* John T. Jr., Christopher, Diane; *ed:* Trenton (MS) Ed 1969; Princeton Univ 12 Credit Hrs Urban Yth 1967; *cr:* Two Tchr 1965-68; Memorial Jr HS Tchr 1968-70; Cedarbrook MS Admin 1970-; *ai:* Spec Ed Coord; Co-Athletic Dir; Asst Ftbl Coach Bsktbl Coach; NEA 1965-; PSEA, CEA 1970-; PA St Ath Dir Assn Bucks Cty Cncl BSA 1974-; Knights of Columbus 1988-; Loyal O Moose 1991-; Indepent Scheduling Group 1980-, Pres; *office:* Ceda MS 300 Longfellow Ave Wyncote PA 19095

ROGALSKI, SIGNE, Sixth Grade Teacher; *b:* Hartford, CT; *ed:* W CT St Univ (BS) Ed, Eng 1968; 60 Credits Art, Ed Cntrl CT St Ur Canton Intermediate Schl Sixth Grd Tchr 1969-95; *ai:* Enrichmer Comm; Adv Canton Youth Environment Awareness, Stu Cncl; NEA Ed Bd New Britain Museum Amer Art 1990-; Tchr of Yr Metropolitan Opera Writing Wksp 1990; CT Commission on Arts, Dept of Ed Awd Exemplary Arts Programming; *office:* Canton Interm Schl 39 Dyer Ave Collinsville CT 06022*

ROGAN, ROSLYN BRISK, Reading & Mathematics Teach Brooklyn, NY; *m:* Jack; *c:* Andrea L., Julie H.; *ed:* Finch Coll (B Sociology 1965; Nazareth Coll (MS) Rdng 1980; *cr:* Breece Cntrl 3rd Grd Tchr 2 Yrs; Rochester City Schls Kndgtn Tchr 2 Yrs; Henrietta HS Rdng, Math Tchr 15 Yrs; *ai:* NYSUT, AFT 1980-; Rush Henrietta Sr HS 1799 Lehigh Station Rd Henrietta NY 14467

ROGERS, CAROL ANN, Choral Director & Music Tchr; *b:* Boston *m:* William A.; *c:* Lori J. Sylvia, Richard A., Elise A.; *ed:* NE Conser of Music (BME) Music Ed 1958; 34 Credit Hrs Univ of NH, Keene S Salem St Coll, U MA at Lowell; *cr:* Braintree Pub Schls Music 1958-59; Haverhill Pub Schls 1-6 Elem Music Tchr 1959-80; Haverh 9-12 Choral Dir 1980-; *ai:* HEA 1959-, Comm Mem; NEA, M MMEA 1958-; Church Treas 1988-; Tenney Church, Admin Bd, Fin C NE Jr Dist Girls Chorus Conductor; NE Jr Dist Boys Chorus Mgr, A Sr Dist Chorus Adj; Nom Tchr of Yr 2 Yrs; *office:* Haverhill H Monument St Haverhill MA 01830

ROGERS, CAROLYN HUNTER, Principal; *b:* Florence, SC; *m:* F L.; *c:* Sharon Moses, Craig, Adrieanne, Amada Hunter; *ed:* Morgan S (BS) Elem Ed 1974; Univ of SC (MED) Elem Ed 1987; Attnd OH St *cr:* Holmes Elem Schl Tchr 1974-79; Logan Comm Schl Tchr 19 Gadsden Elem Schl Tchr 1981-85; Lyon St Elem Schl Diagnos 1985-89; Richland Schl Prin Apprentice 1989-90; Lexington Schls 1990; N Linden Elem Schl Prin 1990-; *ai:* Future Scienti mathematicians Dirs; Young Peoples Division of St Paul AME Columbus Curr Coords, Columbus Pub Comm II Steering Comms Assn Elem Schl Prins, Columbus Adm Assn 1991-; Assn Supervis ev 1990-; Alpha Kappa Alpha 1971-; Book Club 1995-, Ed; Admin Acad; Minority Ldrshp Trng Prgm; Tchr of Yr 1983-84; Venture Grant; Total Quailty Mngmt Trainer Efficacy Trng; *office:* North Elem Schl 1718 E Cooke Rd Columbus OH 43224*

RS, DAVID B., Social Studies Dept Chprsn; *b:* Port Jefferson, NY; ce Robins; *ed:* Adelphi Univ (BA) His 1964; 45 Credit Hrs Ed, , *cr:* East Moriches Schl Dist Sci Tchr 1964-67; Ctr Moriches USD id Tchr, Chprsn 1967-; *ai:* Yrbk Adv; IM; Long Island Cncl Soc NYS Soc Stud Cncl, NYS Soc Stud Supvr's Cncl 1976-; Moriches Club 1968-, Pres, Treas; *office:* Center Moriches HS 311 Frowein ater Moriches NY 11934*

RS, DENISE S., Business Teacher; *b:* East Stoudsburg, PA; *m:* r R.; *ed:* Bloomsburg Univ (BS) Bus Ed 1992; *cr:* East Stroudsburg s Tchr 1992-; *ai:* Tech Comm 1995-; FBLA 1992-, Schl Store 1993- Girls Bsktbl Asst Coach 1995-; In Service Instr 1995-; ESEA, NEA, 1992-; NBEA 1991-; *office:* East Stroudsburg HS 279 N Courtland Stroudsburg PA 18301

RS, DONALD FRANCIS,JR., High School Math Teacher; *b:* ore, MD; *m:* Sally Ellen Costello; *c:* Margaret Ellen; *ed:* Duke Univ Mgmt Sci 1980; 36 Grad Credits Towson St Univ, Johns Hopkins : Loyola Coll; *cr:* Gilman Schl Math Tchr 1980-; *ai:* Ftbl, Bsktbl & se Coach 16 Yrs; NCTM 1984-; Dunn Fellowship Gilman Schl 1986; 83 Blondell Ct Timonium MD 21093

RS, ESTHER RAWSON, High School Math Teacher; *b:* Phoenix, Gerald; *c:* Michelle, Sandra; *ed:* SUNY at Oswego (BS) Ed 1962, Math Ed 1965; *cr:* Hannibal HS Math Tchr 1962-; *ai:* SADD Adv; AMTNYS, Hannibal Fac Assn 1962-; Delta Kappa Gamma 1985-, Phi Delta Kappa 1995-; Palermo VFD Auxiliary 1965-, VP; Phi Kappa Tchr of Yr 1991; *office:* Hannibal Jr Sr HS PO Box 66 al NY 13074

RS, GLORIA BENSON, School Counselor; *b:* Philadelphia, PA; nuel A. Jr.; *c:* Lemuel A. III, Lisa A. Maxey, Lawrence A.; *ed:* ey St Tchrs Coll (BS) Elem Ed 1958; St Univ at Brockport (MS) Ed 1973; Cert Advance Stud Cnslng 1982; *cr:* Camden Pub Schls Tchr 1958; Washington Pub Schls Elem Tchr 1959-63; Phila Pub Elem Tchr 1965-68; Roch Pub Schls Elem Tchr 1969-71, Remedial Tchr 1976-79, Cnslr 1979-; *ai:* Double Dutch Club Adv; NY St Schl 1985-, Publisher of Newsletter; Rochester Schl Cnslr 1979-; ster Tchrs Assn 1976-; Alpha Kappa Alpha; *home:* 181 Evandale Rd ster NY 14618*

RS, JAMES EDWIN, Retired Chemistry Teacher; *b:* Hornell, NY; nne Engert; *c:* Lisa Anne Retzke, Lori Anne Buckley; *ed:* NY St Coll rs at Albany (BS) Bio 1959; Cornell Univ (MST) Bio 1963; St Unif at Albany (MS) Educl Admin 1975; 9 Credit Hrs Phys Chem at Coll; 3 Cr Hrs Inorganic Chem at Rensselaer Polytechnic Inst; 2 Cr ug Metabolism at Albany Med Coll; *cr:* Perry Cntrl HS Gen, Phys hr 1959-61, Chem, Physics Tchr 1961-62; Sterling Winthrop Rsrch sst Rsrch Biologist 1963-67, Assoc Rsrch Biologist 1967-68; Averill S Bio, Chem Tchr 1968-84, Chem Tchr 1984-89, Chem Tchr, Sci upvr 1989-94; *ai:* AFT 1968-; NY St United Tchr 1968-, Retiree Averill Park Tchrs Assn 1968-; Adirondack 46ers 1976-; NSF Grants 1; Acad Yr Inst Grant at Cornell 1962-63; Amer Chemical Soc HS Tchng Excl Awd 1986; Scholars Recognition Prgm 1987, 1990; Who in Amer Ed 1992-.

RS, JANICE LYONS, First Grade Rdng Recovery Tchr; *b:* Bristol, Donald E.; *ed:* Central CT St Coll (BS) Elem Ed 1968, (MS) Rdng Univ of CT Rdng Recovery Trng; *cr:* Louis Toffolon Schl First Grd 968-; *ai:* NEA, CEA, EAP 1968-; *home:* PO Box 175 Plymouth CT

RS, JOAN TOMPKINS, Business Education Teacher; *b:* Elgin, Rick Allen; *c:* Kevin, Michael; *ed:* Cumberland Coll (BS) Bus Ed Post Grad Univ of GA, Univ of TN; *cr:* Southeast HS Bus Ed Tchr 79; Mc Donough HS Bus Ed Tchr 1980-; *ai:* Class Spon; Prin Advy, Comms; FBLA Adv; Voc Bus Ed, NEA 1972-; Class Spon, Dedicated stdng Svc Awds; *office:* Maurice J. Mc Donough HS Rt 2 Box 74 Q et MD 20675

RS, K. KELLY, High School Mathematics Tchr; *b:* Canandaigua, *d:* Oral Roberts Univ (BS) Math & Ed 1985; St Univ of NY at eo (MS) Math & Ed 1991; *cr:* New Covenant Schl Math Tchr 92; Honeoye Cntrl Math Tchr 1992; Charles Finney HS Math Tchr 95; *ai:* Vlybl Coach; Math Club; Class Adv; Stu Cncl; Zion ship 1988-, Treas; *office:* Charles Finney HS 2070 5 Mile Line Rd ld NY 14526*

RS, LAURA SWERTFEGER, Social Studies & English Tchr; *b:* k, VA; *m:* James W.; *c:* Noah; *ed:* VA Tech (BA) Eng 1986; Univ of MAT) Scndry Ed 1993; *cr:* Souhegan HS Intern 1992-93; John Stark HS Eng & SS Tchr 1993-; *ai:* Frosh Class Spon; Yth & Govt; ASCD *office:* John Stark Regional HS 618 N Stark Hwy Weare NH 03281

RS, LEE M., Physical Educator; *b:* Fort Momouth, NJ; *m:* Brenda *c:* Tori, Brittany; *ed:* NC Cntrl Univ (BS) K-12 PE 1974; Loyola Coll (MS) Ed 1984; *cr:* Lindale Jr High PE Tchr 1976-80; Arundel HS hr & Coach 1980-; *ai:* Girls Var Vllybl & Bsktbl Coach; Girls sse Asst Coach; NEA 1976-; TAAC 1976-; MSTA 1976-; NFICA Anne Arundel Cty GBB Coach of Yr for Baltimore Sun, MA Capital ette Assoc Press 1995; All Metro GBB Coach of Yr for Baltimore 995; NFICA GBB Coach of Yr 1996; *office:* Arundel Sr HS 1001 olis Rd Gambrills MD 21054

RS, LINDY BRIAN, Earth & Space Science Teacher; *b:* Mt Gilead, *n:* Sheryl Marie Keevert; *c:* Eric, Alison; *ed:* Mt Vernon Nazarene Ed 1972; Moorhead St Univ (BS) Ed Scis 1975; *cr:* West Holmes Tchr & Dept Head 1977-, Tchrs Assn Pres 1992-; *ai:* Ret HS Head ling Coach; Prin Adv Comm; West Holmes Ed Assn 1979-, Pres 3 Yrs, Yrs; Millersburg Elem PTO 1990-; Dist Mentor Tchr; Sci is Fun Prgm Univ; *office:* West Holmes Jr HS 430 E Jackson Millersburg OH *

RS, LOIS COURTER, Retired 5th Grade Teacher; *b:* Mill Hall, Richard Leroy; *c:* Scott, Kristin Cotner; *ed:* Lock Haven St Coll Elem Ed 1962; Addl Classes at Misericordia, Marywood Coll, Clarion Penn St Univ & Lock Haven Univ; *cr:* South Williamsport Schl Dist rd Tchr 1962-65; Lawrence Park Twp Schl Dist Sub Tchr 1969-73; al Intermediate Unit 10 Remedial Rdng Tchr 1973-75; Lock Haven Schl Kndgtn, 3rd & 5th Grd Tchr 1975-93; *ai:* NCEA 1976-; Mount l United Church of Christ 1954-, Church Bd Pres & Sec.

RS, LYNN, First Grade Teacher; *b:* Luzon, Phillipines; *m:* Denis A.; enda, Renee; *ed:* Montclair St Univ (BA) Music Ed, General Elem *cr:* ML King & Monroe Schls Vocal Music Tchr 2 Yrs; Residence e Tutoring, Instr Tchng 7 Yrs; Cornerstone Chrstn 4th-7th Grd, Art, Tchr 1 Yr; Metuchen Chrstn Acad 1st-6th Grd, Music Tchr 10 Yrs; usic for Home Fellowships, Tutoring; Amer Ed Assn 1995-; *office:* chen Christian Acad PO Box 561 Metuchen NJ 08840*

RS, NANCY JENKINS, Business Teacher; *b:* Erie, PA; *m:* Gary E.; dd, Brian, Meghan; *ed:* IN Univ of PA (BS) Bus Ed 1973; Robert s Coll (MS) Bus Ed; Addl 31 Credit Hrs Bus, Cmptrs, Ecs, Ed; Attnd e Enterprise Week; *cr:* Pioneer Cntrl HS Bus Tchr 1973-75; Seneca s Tchr 1986; Harbor Creek HS Bus Tchr 1987-88; Gen McLane HS Bus Tchr 1988-; *ai:* FBLA Adv; Guidance Advy Comm; Learning Systems Team; Gen Mc Lane Educ Assn, PA St Educ 1988-; FBLA 1988-, Adv; Northwestern PA Assn for Educl Computing, Tech 1993-; Tri-Sts Bus Educ Assn 1987-; Delta Pi Epsilon 1991-; Awded Full Grant from Amers for a Competitive Ec System Univ of VA 2 Week Ecs Inst 1995; *office:* General Mc Lane HS 11761 Edinboro Rd Edinboro PA 16412

ROGERS, PATRICIA J., Peer Assistant; *b:* Ironton, OH; *m:* Joseph L.; *c:* Jennifer; *ed:* Coll of St Teresa (BS) Ed 1970; OH St Univ 30 Credits; *cr:* St Francis 1st, 6th & 7th Grd Tchr & Schl Music 1963-68; St Andrew 7th & 8th Grd Tchr & Schl Music 1968-69; Mother Cabrini 5th & 6th Grd Tchr 1969-70; OLPH 1st Grd Tchr & Schl Music 1st-8th Grd Tchr 1970-76; St Anthonys 7th & 8th Grd Tchr 1977-78; Worthington Schls 1st-6th Grd Tchr 1980-93, Dual Peer Asst 1993-; *ai:* Schl Improvement, Facilitation, Dist Mentor Steering & Tchr Ldr Team; Bridge to Future Comm; WEA 1980-; OEA 1980-, Del 1995-96; NEA 1980-, Del 1995-96; *office:* Worthington Bd of Ed 752 High St Worthington OH 43085*

ROGERS, ROBERT ROY, Assoc Prof of Mathematics; *b:* Lackawana, NY; *m:* Cheryll Ann Wilkowski; *c:* Alexander, Amanda; *ed:* SUNY Coll of Buffalo (BS) Math, Cert Scndry Ed 1979; Syracuse Univ (MS) Math 1982; SUNY at Buffalo (PHD) Math 1987; *cr:* Syracuse Univ Tchng Asst 1979-82; SUNY Buffalo Tchng Asst 1982-87; SUNY Coll of Fredonia Asst Prof 1987-94, Assoc Prof 1994-; *ai:* Fredonia St Math Club Adv; Represented Mathematical Profession at Annual Erie Cty Career Fair 1986-92, 1994-; Mathematical Assn of Amer 1987-; Sigma Xi 1994-, Pres; 3 Mathematical Papers Pub; Sr Investigator in NSF Fac Enhancement Grant; *office:* S U N Y Coll At Fredonia SUNY Fredonia Math Dept Fredonia NY 14063*

ROGERS, THOMAS MICHAEL, Biology Teacher; *b:* Troy, OH; *m:* Claudia Pearl Huntsberger; *c:* Thomas Ryan, Lora Lynn, Erin Michele, Kara Elizabeth; *ed:* Earlham Coll (BA) Bio 1969; WA Univ at St Louis (MAT) Bio & Ed 1970; Various Seminars Dealing with Biochemistry; *cr:* Tippecanoe HS Bio Tchr, Sci Chm & Coach 1970-; *ai:* Head Vlybl Coach; Faculty Acad Cncl; Sci Dept Chm; Regnl Steering Comm for Tech Prep; SW Dist 9 Coaches Assn 1985-, Sec-Treas 1993-95, Dist Coach of the Yr 1993; OHSVBCA St Org 1985-, Spec Recog-Achvmt 1993; Several Tipp Fnd Grants for Classroom Act; Martha Holden Jennings Scholar; Tchr of the Yr Awd Twice; *office:* Tippecanoe HS 555 N Hyatt St Tipp City OH 45371

ROGG, ELEANOR MEYER, Professor of Sociology; *b:* New York City, NY; *m:* Gerald; *c:* Schuyler Andrew; *ed:* Hunter Coll (BA) Sociology 1963; Columbia Univ (MA) Sociology 1965; Fordham Univ (PHD) Sociology 1970; *cr:* Wagner Coll Asst Prof 1970-74, Assoc Prof 1974-79, VP Acad Affairs 1988-90, Prof 1979-; *ai:* Adv Fac; Alpha Kappa Delta Fac; Phi Beta Kappa 1963-; Omicron Delta Kappa 1985-, Fac Adv; NYS Sociological Assn 1985-; ESS 1983-; ASA 1984-; Rotary 1989-; SI Chptr Amer Red Cross 1991-, Sec Bd; RSVP Boro Cncl, VP; SI Historical Soc 1989-, Chair Ed Comm Bd Trustees; Book Review Ed 1970-; Books Pub The Assimilation of Cuban Exiles 1974, Adaptation and Adjustment of Cubans 1980; *office:* Wagner Coll 631 Howard Ave Staten Island NY 10301*

ROGOVSKI, ELIZABETH, Assistant Professor; *b:* Washington, DC; *ed:* West Liberty St Coll (BA) Ed 1977; Univ of MD (MSW) Soc Strategy 1981; Pursuing Doctorate at Howard Univ; *cr:* Prince Georges Cty Govt Comm Asst 3 Yrs; Gallaudet Univ Comm Aide 1 Yr; Montgomery Cty Govt Prgm Mgr 9 Yrs; Gallaudet Univ Asst Prof 6 Yrs; *ai:* Soc Work Stu Assn Fac Adv; Healthy Start in Washington DC Research Asst; Continuing Excl in Learning & Tchng; Cncl on Soc Work Ed 1991-; MD Assn of Deaf 1981-; Legislative Chprsn, VP; Several Wkshps; Co-Authored 2 Pub Articles; *office:* Gallaudet Univ 800 Florida Ave NE Dept of Social Work Washington DC 20002

ROHER, ANN MCCLAIN, Senior Composition Instructor; *b:* Huntingdon, PA; *ed:* Kent St Univ (BA) Eng 1971; CA St Univ (MA) Eng 1975; *cr:* Univ of Akron Lecturer III 6 Yrs; Wadsworth HS Eng Tchr 25 Yrs; *ai:* Past Girls Vlybl, Sftbl Coach; Freelance Writer Pub Numerous Articles; *office:* Wadsworth HS 625 Broad St Wadsworth OH 44281

ROHLFING-NAPOLI, MARY KAY, English Teacher & Drama Instr; *b:* Drexel Hill, PA; *m:* Robert Napoli; *ed:* Univ of Scranton (BA) Comm 1988; The Cath Univ of Amer (MFA) Theatre, Acting 1992; Immaculata Coll Cert Courses; *cr:* Cath Univ of Amer Asst to Producer 1991-92; Cultural Arts of Savannah Drama Instr 1992; Villa Maria Acad Eng Tchr 1993-; Archbishop Carroll HS Drama Tchr 1994-95; *ai:* Forensics Team Asst Coach; Pub Relations Dir; Eng Speaking Union Schl Coord; Alpha Sigma Nu 1987-; Theatre Alliance of PA 1995-; US Information Agency Drama Team Mem 1992; Grad Cum Laud; Barrymore Awds Nominator for Theatre Excl in Philadelphia; *office:* Villa Maria Acad 370 Old Lincoln Hwy Malvern PA 19355

ROHLIK, MARGARET REJDAK, AP His, Govt Tchr & Intern Adm; *b:* Cleveland, OH; *m:* James C.; *c:* Jessica, Joshua; *ed:* Marietta Coll (BA) His, Pol Sci 1970; Kent St Univ (MA) Pol Sci 1972; Soviet Stud at John Carroll Univ; Ed Admin Cleveland St Univ; *cr:* Cuyahoga comm Coll Instr 1974-82; Parma City Schls AP His, AP Govt Tchr 1972-; Parma City Schls Asst Prin 1996; *ai:* Stu Cncl, Acad Team Adv; NEA, OEA, PEA 1972-; Martha Holden Jennings Legislative Stud Grant Robert Taft Inst of Govt; *office:* Valley Forge HS 9999 Independence Blvd Parma OH 44130

ROHLOFF, ANDREA FEDELI, 3rd Grade Teacher; *b:* New York City, NY; *m:* Terry J.; *c:* Michael, Jason; *ed:* SUNY at Albany & New Paltz; *cr:* Schalmont Cntrl Schl 1st Grd Tchr 1968-71; Army Schl at Baumholder, Germany 1st Grd Tchr 1971-72; Schalmont Cntrl Schl 1st Grd Tchr 1972-94, 3rd Grd Tchr 1994-; *ai:* Spon Maple Ski Ridge Ski Lessons; NYSUT 1968-, Bldg Rep; Rdng Comm; Schalmont Tchrs Assoc, Bldg Planning Team, Bldg Rep; Mohonasen PTSO 1983-; Our Lady of Assumption 1977-; Vidiotape for Parents Rdng To Your Children.

ROHM, EDDY DUANE, Technology Education Teacher; *b:* Bremerton, WA; *m:* Susan Antoinette Prox; *c:* Megan Jean, Jeffrey David, Ian Joseph; *ed:* Kent St Univ (BSEd) Industrial Arts 1977; Youngstown St Univ (MSEd) Curr & Instruction 1982; Post Grad Degree Elem Cert 1996; *cr:* Mathews Local Schls Tchr 1977-; *ai:* Former Track Coach & Ofcl; Former Ftbl Coach; Local Assn Negotiator for Local Contract; Labor & Mgmt & Tech Dev Comms; NEA, OEA, MEA 1977-, Negotiator Mem Rep.

ROHR, RITA MARIE, Science & Health Teacher; *b:* Columbus, OH; *c:* Michael Brown, Marianne Brown; *ed:* OH Dominican Coll (BS) Elem Ed 1983; Pub Relations; OH St Jrnlsm, Newsletter Writing, Creative Writing, OH Univ Energy Ed Post Grad Stud; *cr:* St Christopher Schl Asst Prin, MS Tchr 1968-71; St Joseph Montessori Schl 1-8 Grd Tchr, Rel Ed Coord 1979-89; St Joseph Montessori Schl Ed Schl Comm Bimonthly Paper 1985-; South-Western City Schls Adult ESL Tchr 1987-; St Joseph Montessori Schl 7th-8th Grd Creative Writing, Lit, Rel, Jrnslm Tchr 1989-; *ai:* NCEA, OCEA 1970-; NSTA 1993-; Pub Fiction; *office:* St Joseph Montessori Schl 933 Hamlet St Columbus OH 43201

ROHRBACH, CAROL HOOD, English Teacher; *b:* Chestnut Hill, PA; *m:* Walter E.; *c:* Jenna, Matthew, Kevin; *ed:* Wilson Coll (BA) Eng 1969; Villanova Univ (MA) Eng 1974; *cr:* Central Bucks HS W Eng Tchr 1965-69; Springfield Twp HS Tchr of Gifted & Eng Tchr 1985-; *ai:* The Chronicle Adv; Stu Assistance Prgm Comm; Prins Advy Cncl; STEA, PSEA, NEA & NCTE 1985-; ASCD 1993-; Writing Assessment Wkshp Presenter; PA Cncl of Eng Tchrs Paper Presentor; PA Writing Assessment Scorer; Tchr Consultant PAWP; *office:* Springfield Twp HS 1801 E Paper Mill Rd Philadelphia PA 19118*

ROHRER, DAVID A., Band Dir & Music Dept Chm; *b:* Frederick, MD; *ed:* Susquehanna Univ (BM) Music Ed 1976; West Chester Univ (MM) Music Ed 1986; Received Supervisory Cert in Music from Millersville Univ 1988; PMEA Ldrshp Conf 1990-95; *cr:* E Pennsboro Area Schl Dist Band Dir & Music Instr 1976-82; US Naval Acad Drum & Bugle Corp Brass Arranger & Instr 1983 & 1984; Carlisle Area Schl Dist Band Dir 1982-; Bluecoats Jr Drum & Bugle Corps 1986-92, Brass Instr; *ai:* HS Jazz Band Dir; MENC & ITG 1976-; NBA 1988-; IAJE 1978-; PMEA 1976-; Carlisle Arts Magnet Schl 1991-; TV 27 PA Proud Awd; Amer Legion Citation for Meritorious Service; PMEA Citation of Excl 1994; Carlisle Area's Finest Fnlst 1995; MENC Nationally Registered Music Edctr 1993; *office:* Carlisle Area Schl Dist 623 W Penn St Carlisle PA 17013

ROHRER, KERRY ANN, Math Teacher; *b:* Lancaster, PA; *ed:* Pensacola Chrstn Coll (BS) Math Ed 1991; *cr:* Heritage Acad Math Tchr 1992-; *ai:* Jr Class Adv; *office:* Heritage Acad 12215 Walnut Point W Hagerstown MD 21740

ROHRS, FRANK LEE, Business Ed & Driver Ed Tchr; *b:* Ft Wayne, IN; *m:* Reesa L. Zachrich; *c:* Rachel, Emily; *ed:* Huntington Coll (BS) PE & Bus Ed 1976; Bowling Green St Univ (MS) PE 1980; *cr:* Lincoln HS Bus Ed 1976-, Drivers Ed 1980-; *ai:* NHS Adv; LLEA, OEA & NEA 1976-; St Marks Evangelical Luth Church 1984-, Sunday Schl Supt 1 Yr, Learning Comm Head 2 Yrs, Church Cncl 4 Yrs; 1 Article PE Journal; Mentor Prgm 6 Yrs.*

ROHRS, HEIDI, German & Social Studies Instr; *b:* Schwetzingen, Germany; *m:* Wilhelm H.; *c:* Angelika, Geerlof; *ed:* Newark St Coll (BA) Fine Arts 1968; Rutgers Univ (MA) Ger Lang, Lit 1982, (PHD) Ger Lang, Lit 1984; Grad Inst of Childrens Lit 1979, Univ Fellowship, Rutgers Univ 1982-83; Frauenfachschule (St Exam) 1955; *cr:* Summit Schl System Fine Arts Tchr 1968-73, ESL Tchr 1974-77; Rutgers Univ Ger Tchng Asst 1977-83; Don Bosco Prep HS Ger Tchr 1984-; Deutsche Sprachschule Inc Prin 1985-; William Patterson Coll German Inst 1983; *ai:* Ger Club Adv; Germany, Austria, Switzerland Ger Tour Guide; Natl German Honor Society; Delta Epsilon Phi Spon; Seasonal Art Exhibits; AATG 1985-; GLSC 1990-, Bd Mem; MPhil Thesis; PHD Dissertation; *office:* Don Bosco Prep Schl 492 N Franklin Tpke Ramsey NJ 07446

ROHRS, TERESA LYNN (BOSTELMAN), Fourth Grade Teacher; *b:* Wuerzburg, Germany; *m:* John Robert; *c:* Zachary, Amanda; *ed:* Bowling Green St Univ (BS) Elem Ed, LS SBH 1981; Math, Sci Credit Hrs; *cr:* Henry Cty Schls Learning Disabilities Tchr 1981-85; Patrick Henry Schls Fourth Grd Tchr 1986-; *ai:* PHEA Tchrs Assn 1985-; St Johns Luth Church 1993-, Sunday Schl Tchr 3 Yrs; Henry Cty 4-H 1994-, Adv.

ROHWER, MARLA FAY, Arts Instructor; *b:* NY; *m:* Raymond; *c:* Sarah; *ed:* SUNY at New Paltz (BS) Art Ed, Art 1974, (MS) Art Ed, Ceramics 1980; Post Grad Stud Robert Piedenberg, Paulus Berensohn, Rudy Autio, Clay Aetists; Studied in Japan, Australia, England, France & Ireland; *cr:* Roy C. Ketchum HS Art Instr, Clay, Jewelry 1974-78; Museum of Hudson Highlands Clay Instr 1976-80; John Jay HS Art Instr, Clay, Jewelry 1978-82; Roy C. Ketchem HS Art Instr, Clay, Sculpture 1982-; *ai:* Stu Mentor; AFT, NEA, NAEA, Amer Crafts Cncl 1974-; Natl Cncl on Ed in Ceramic Arts 1980-; John Burroughs Natural Historical Soc 1987-, Trustee; Ceramics HS NAEA Awd 1980; Mid Hudson Tchr Ctr Dutchess Mini Grant 1995; SUNY at New Paltz Coll Art Gallery Art Shows; Dutchess Comm Coll, Mt Guilian Historical Museum, Museum of Hudson Highlands Art Shows; *office:* Roy C Ketcham H S 99 Myers Corners Rd Wappingers Falls NY 12590*

ROK, JOHN JOSEPH, Mathematics Teacher; *b:* Johnstown, PA; *ed:* Univ of Pittsburgh at Johnstown (BS) Scndry Ed, Math 1991; *cr:* Westmont MS Math Tchr 1992; Conemaugh Valley Jr Sr HS Math Tchr 1992-; *ai:* Jr High Ftbl Asst Coach; Head Jr High Boys Bstkbl Coach; PSEA, NEA, CVEA 1992-; PCTM 1991-; *office:* Conemaugh Valley Jr Sr HS 1342 William Penn Ave Johnstown PA 15906

ROLDAN, FRANCISCO JOSE, Guitar Professor; *b:* Medellin, Colombia; *ed:* Mannes Coll of Music (BA) Guitar Performance 1985, (MA) Guitar Performance 1986; *cr:* Mannes Coll Guitar Instr 1985-; Jersey City Coll Guitar Instr 1992-93; *ai:* Artists Intnl Awd Resulting in Debut at Carnegie Hall; New Schl for Soc Rsrch Cert of Appreciation; *office:* Mannes Coll Of Music 150 W 85th St New York NY 10024

ROLL, JOSEPH, Latin & Philosophy Teacher; *b:* Berwick, PA; *ed:* Cath Univ of Amer (BA) Philosophy 1972; St Univ of NY at Maryknoll (MA) Theology 1978; Fordham Univ (MA) 1989; Undergraduate Stud St Basil Coll at Stamford 1967-69, Bloomsburg Univ 1970; Grad Stud Univ of St Michael's Coll at Toronto 1977, Westminster Choir Schl at Princeton 1986; *cr:* Holy Cross Elem Schl 6th Grd Tchr 1972-74; St Basil Prep Schl Music, Rel, Philosophy, Latin Instr 1978-90; St Basil Coll Seminary Philosophy, Music Tchr 1978-; Greens Farms Acad Latin, Philosphy Instr 1990-; *ai:* St Basil Coll Seminary Liturgical Choir Dir; 9th Grd Class Coord; Natl Assn of Pastorial Musicians 1988-, Bd, Seminary Music Formation; Articles Pub; *office:* Greens Farms Acad 35 Beachside Ave Greens Farms CT 06436

ROLLAND, SHEILA LUCAS, Chemistry Teacher; *b:* Providence, RI; *m:* George M.; *c:* Tracy Ann; *ed:* Salve Regina (BA) Bio & Chem 1972; RI Coll (MAT) Bio 1978; Attnd Brown Univ Inst for Chem; *cr:* Saint Joseph Schl 7th-8th Grd Sci, Math & PE Tchr 1973-74; RI Hospital Genetics Lab Technologist 1974-75; Slater Jr HS 7th-9th Grd Sci Tchr 1975-85; Charles E Shea Sr HS Chem, Bio, Life Sci & Phys Sci Tchr 1985-; *ai:* The King & I Stage Mgr; AFT 1975-; NEACT 1987-; Attnd RI Coll Collaborative Tchng Wkshps; *office:* Charles E Shea Sr HS 485 East Ave Pawtucket RI 02860

ROLLER, GLORIA W., Sixth Grade Language Arts Tchr; *b:* Harrisonburg, VA; *m:* Lawrence W.; *c:* Craig, David, Diane Roller Madey; *ed:* Radford Univ (BS) Elem Ed 1958; 60 Post Grad Hrs Western MD; *cr:* Blacksburg Elem Schl Third Grd Tchr 1958-59; Vly HS Eng Tchr 1959-60; Carroll Manor Elem Schl Second Grd Tchr 1981-87; Walkersville MS Lang Arts Tchr 1987-; *ai:* Chrldr Coach 1959-60; Lang Arts & Soc Stud Dept Chprsns 2 Yrs; NEA, MSTA 1981-; FCTA 1981-, Local Rep; Church Circle 1993-, VP, Pres; *home:* 25 William St Walkersville MD 21793

ROLLER, SUSAN SCHUG, English Teacher; *b:* Camp Lee, VA; *m:* Thomas M.; *ed:* Swarthmore Coll (BA) Eng Lit 1971; Penn St (MA) Eng Lit 1980; 30 Plus Credit Hrs Beyond Masters; Soc Stud Cert, Process Writing Capital Area Writing Project; *cr:* Eng & Soc Stud Tchr 1971-73; Eng & Soc Stud Tchr 1973-76; Penn St Univ Eng Instr 1980-82; Halifax Area HS Eng & Soc Stud Tchr 1983-89; The Harrisburg Acad Eng & Soc Stud Tchr 1989-93, Head of Upper Schl & Eng Tchr 1993-95, Eng Tchr & Coll Guidance Dir 1995-; *ai:* Mock Trial Coach; Sr Internship Comm Mem; Sr Class Adv; NHS Co-Adv; NCTE 1985-; CEEB 1993-; NACAC, PASSCAC 1995-; Save the Bay 1990-; Planned Parenthood 1989-; Nomination for Tchr of Yr Halifax Area Schl Dist 1987-88; *office:* The Harrisburg Acad 10 Erford Rd Wormleysburg PA 17043

ROLLINS, EILEEN CATHERINE (NALLY), English Teacher; *b:* Salem, MA; *m:* Philip Clark; *c:* Timothy James, Christine Marie; *ed:* Salem St (BA) Eng 1967; Fitchburg St (MED) Occupational Ed 1979; Post Grad Stud Adult Ed, Inclusion, Eng Second Lang, Portfolio Writing; *cr:* JFK Jr HS Eng Tchr 1967-; Peabody Meml HS Eng Tchr 1967-; PVMHS Acting Dept Head 1982-83; *ai:* Contemporary Multicultural Lit Stud Group

Facilitator; Networker Eng Dept; AFT, NCTE 1967-; PFT 1967-, Sec 1 Yr; *office:* Peabody Veterans Mem HS 485 Lowell St Peabody MA 01960

ROLLINS, GLOREE M., 6th Grade Teacher; *b:* Waterville, ME; *m:* James Hibbard; *c:* Corey, Anthony; *ed:* Univ of ME at Orono (BA) Eng 1974; *cr:* Upper Kennebee Vly HS Spcl Ed Tchr 1974-87; Quimby Elem 6th Grd Tchr 1988-; *ai:* NEA 1974-.

ROLLINS, PHILIP CLARK, Industrial Technology Teacher; *b:* Beverly, MA; *m:* Eileen Nally; *c:* Timothy, Christine; *ed:* Fitchburg St (BS) Indstrl Arts 1978; Post Grad Stud Tech Prep, Indstrl Tech, Schl to Work; *cr:* Peabody Veterans Meml HS Indstrl Tech, Indstrl Arts 1968-; *ai:* Tech Prep Comm; Schl To Work Adv; AFT 1968-; West Newbury Vol Fire Dept 1994-; Pub Svc First Responder West Newbury Fire Dept; *office:* Peabody Veterans Mem HS 485 Lowell St Peabody MA 01960

ROLLINS-RUFFIN, TAJ-TERESA A., Social Studies Teacher; *b:* Brooklyn, NY; *ed:* Cheyney Univ (BS) Soc Sci Scndry Ed; Tchr Effectivness Trng Cert Jacksonville Univ; Micro Cmptrs in Ed Cert FL Southern; Curr, Ed Procedures Cert Pennsacola Coll; *cr:* Vista Vol At Risk Stu Prgm 1991-92; Wilkes-Barr Schl Dist At Risk Guid Para Prof 1991-92, 8th-10th Grd Soc Sci Tchr 1991-; *ai:* Comm Justice Ed Seminar; Tutorial Soc Sci, Writing; WEBA Tchr Assn 1991-; NCSS 1996; Peace Ctr 1991-, Bd; Temple Bnai Brith 1996, Bd; Temple Schl Tchr 1996; Numerous Articles Pub; *home:* 202 S Franklin St Wilkes Barre PA 18701*

ROLLO, ROBERT ANTHONY, Band Director; *b:* Warren, OH; *m:* Paula Sue Karabin; *c:* Lauren Elizabeth, Jamie Leigh, Emily Madison; *ed:* Youngstown St Univ (BM) Music Ed Jazz Stud 1984; 15 Addl Qtr Hrs; *cr:* Warren City Schl Band Dir, Gen Music Tchr 1985; East Liverpool MS Band Dir, Gen Music Tchr 1985-; *ai:* Jazz Ensamble Dir; HS Marching Band Asst; NEA, OEA, ELEA, MENC, OMEA 1985-; Youngstown Comm Bd 1995-; *home:* 29 Stanton Ave Boardman OH 44512

ROLLSON, ROBERT WARREN, Social Science Dept Prof; *b:* Syracuse, NY; *m:* Celisa L. Campbell; *c:* Joshua, Rhonda, Elijah, Christopher; *ed:* Southern VT Coll (BS) Human Svcs, Soc Psych 1980; Antioch New England Grad Schl (MED) Org & Mngmt Human Svcs 1982; *cr:* Comm Coll of VT Soc Scis Instr 1983-84; Southern VT Coll Fac Soc Scis 1983-; *ai:* Vice-Chair Fac Assn; Chair 504 Comm; Outstansing Fac Mem 1989-90; *office:* Southern Vermont College Monument Ave Ext Bennington VT 05201

ROMA, ANNA MARIE CONTINO, High School Guidance Counselor; *b:* Passaic, NJ; *m:* Joseph M.; *c:* Tony, Joann Koenemund; *ed:* Felician Coll (BA) Elem Ed 1980; Jersey City St (MA) Urban Ed 1983; Eng as a Second Lang Cert 1982; Supervision, Admin Cert 1984; Stu Prsnl Svc Cert 1987; *cr:* Lodi MS 8th Grd Tchr 1980-81; Lodi Elem Schl 6th Grd Tchr 1981-82, K-8 Grd ESL Tchr 1982-89, K-6 Grd Elem Guid 1987-89; Lodi HS 9-12 Grd Guid Cnslr 1989-; *ai:* Pupil Assistance Comm; NEA, Bergen Cty Ed Assn, Bergen Cty Prof Cnslrs Assn 1981-; *office:* Lodi HS 99 Putnam St Lodi NJ 07644

ROMA, JEANNE DUNNE, High School English Teacher; *b:* Niagara Falls, NY; *m:* Ronald G.; *c:* Kelly, Adam; *ed:* St Univ of NY at Fredonia (BA) Eng Ed 1973; St Univ of NY at Buffalo (MED) Scndry Ed 1977; *cr:* Iroquois Cntrl Schl HS Eng Tchr 1973-; *ai:* Iroquois Fac Assn, NYSUT, AFT 1973-; *office:* Iroquois Cntrl HS Girdle Rd Elma NY 14059

ROMAN, GEORGE A.,JR., Social Studies Teacher; *b:* New York City, NY; *m:* Patricia Ann Brock; *c:* Brock, Matthew; *ed:* Appalachian St Univ (BS) HIs, Minor Pol Sci 1969; *cr:* Northern Burlington Cty Regnl HS Soc Stud Tchr, Criminology, US His 27 Yrs; *ai:* NHS Adv 1986-; Past Wrestling Coach 1978-87; Stu Congress, Class Adv; Girls Track, Boys Cross-Country Coach; NEA, NJEA, Burlington Cty Ed Assn 1969-; Northern Burlington Cty Reg Tchrs Assn 1969-, Negotiator, Grievance Comm; Phi Alpha Theta 1969-, Charter Pres; Pi Gamma Mu 1969-, Mem; Northern Burlington NHS Master Tchr of Yr 1991, Honorary Mem 1984; Douglass Coll Tchr Appreciation Awd; *office:* Northern Burlington Reg HS 160 Mansfield Rd E Columbus NJ 08022

ROMAN, JANET MARIE, Art Instructor & Dept Chprsn; *b:* Wilkes-Barre, PA; *ed:* Luzerne Cty Comm Coll (BA) Commercial Art 1981; Penn St Univ (BA) Art 1984; Wilkes Univ PA Tchng Cert K-12th Grd Art Ed 1991; Art Ed Masters Degree Prgm Marywood Coll; *cr:* Our Lady of Lourdes Regnl HS 9th-12th Grd Art Instr 1993-; *ai:* Grotto Yrbk Adv; Acad Cncl; Art Dept Chprsn; Art & Photography Club Adv; Stu Assistance Team; NAEA 1990-; *office:* Our Lady of Lourdes Regnl HS 2001 Clinton Ave Coal Township PA 17866

ROMAN, RUTH M., Mathematics & Physics Teacher; *b:* Kingsley, PA; *m:* Stevan; *c:* John, David, Julie, Amanda; *ed:* Bloomsburg Univ (BS) Scndry Ed, Math, PE 1963; PA St Univ (MA) Math 1967; 12 Hrs Ed Univ of Scranton; 33 Hrs Cmptr Sci SUNY Binghamton Univ; *cr:* Blue Ridge HS Math, Physics Tchr 1963-68; Montrose Area HS Math, Physics Tchr 1985-; *ai:* Sci, Math Curr Team; Prof Dev, Tech Comms; NEA, PSEA 1985-; PCTM 1990-; *office:* Montrose Area HS RR 3 Box 28 Montrose PA 18801

ROMANIC, JENNIFER KENNEDY, Latin Teacher; *b:* Akron, OH; *m:* John Paul; *c:* Katelyn; *ed:* Kent St Univ (BA) Latin, His 1994; *cr:* Ravenna HS Latin Tchr 1994-; *ai:* Latin Club, Jr Classical League Adv; Amer Classical League 1990-; OH EA, NEA 1994-; OH Jr Classical League 1986-, St Chprsn; *home:* 1856 Clearbrook Dr Stow OH 44224

ROMANISKO, JUDITH W., ESL Teacher; *b:* Palmerton, PA; *m:* C. Thomas; *c:* Thomas, Julie; *ed:* Kutztown Univ (BS) Russian, Fr 1964; Grad Work Kutztown Univ, Penn St Univ; *cr:* Stroudsburg HS Fr Tchr 1964-65; Tamaqua HS Fr Tchr 1966-68; Jim Thorpe HS Fr Tchr 1971-92, ESL Tchr 1992-; *ai:* Chrldng Coach; Bicentennial Chorus 1976-, Dir; Olympian Booster Club Woman of Yr; *office:* Jim Thorpe HS 1100 Center St Jim Thorpe PA 18229

ROMANO, ALBERT C., Drama Teacher & Prgm Director; *b:* Philadelphia, PA; *m:* Maria D.; *c:* Julia Rose, Elizabeth Mary; *ed:* Villanova Univ (BA) Eng 1970; Univ of Rochester (MA) Eng 1975; 30 Addl Credits; *cr:* Vail Deane Schl Eng Tchr 1975-78; Trinity Schl Eng, Drama Tchr 1978-88; Pingry Schl Drama Dir 1988-; *ai:* Villanova Univ Schlsp; Univ of Rochester Flwshp; Princeton Univ Prize; Article Pub; *office:* The Pingry Schl Martinsville Rd Martinsville NJ 08836*

ROMANO, BARBARA BUCCI, English Teacher; *b:* Syracuse, NY; *m:* John R.; *c:* Steven, Mark, Kathleen; *ed:* SUNY at Oswego (BA) Scndry Ed, Eng 1966, (MS) Curr Dev 1990; *cr:* Liverpool HS Eng Tchr 1966-68; Northminister Nursery Schl Presch Tchr 1978-81; Syracuse Parochial Schls Jr HS Eng Tchr 1981-92; C. W. Baker HS Eng Tchr 1992-; *ai:* Class Adv; NEA, NCTE 1992-; *office:* Charles W Baker HS 29 E Oneida St Baldwinsville NY 13027

ROMANO, DIANE TUZZIO, Eighth Grade Math Teacher; *b:* Jersey City, NJ; *m:* Alfred; *c:* Christopher, Jonathan; *ed:* Jersey City St Coll (BA) Elem Ed 1971, (MA) Urban Ed ESL 1995; 9 Post Grad Credit Hrs; *cr:* N Bergen Schl System K-2 Grd Tchr 1971-74, 5-6 Grd Tchr 1976-91, 8 Grd Tchr 1991-; *ai:* Stu Cncl Moderator; A-V Coord; AFT 1971-, VP 1974, Exec Bd 1973, Bldg Rep 1971-72; PTA 1971-, Exec Bd; Governor's Recognition Excl Tchng Awd 1990; Northberger Rep for NJ Tchr of Yr 1990; *office:* Horace Mann Elem Schl 9 1215 83rd St North Bergen NJ 07047*

ROMANO, ELIZABETH M., 8th Grade Teacher; *b:* Brooklyn, NY; *ed:* St John's Univ (BS) Mrktg 1982, (MS) Scndry Ed 1991; Ldrshp Prgm Substance Abuse Prevention; *cr:* St Thomas Aquinas Schl 8th Grd, Math, Soc Stud, Lit, Rel Tchr 1986-; *ai:* Yrbk, Math League Adv; NCEA 1986-; Notary Pub 1986-; Elizabeth Ann Seton Awd 1992-93; *office:* St Thomas Aquinas Schl 1501 Hendrickson St Brooklyn NY 11234

ROMANO, JOSEPH A., Physical Education Teacher; *b:* Syracuse, NY; *m:* Connie A.; *c:* Joseph Jr., Nicole; *ed:* Cortland St Univ (BS) PE 1975, (MS) PE 1980; *cr:* Fowler HS 9th-12th Grd PE Tchr 1975-80; Seymour Elem K-6th Grd PE Tchr 1980-85; Grant MS 6th-8th Grd PE Tchr 1985-91; Huntington MS 6th-8th Grd PE Tchr 1991-; *ai:* Ath Coord; Frosh Ftbl Coach Henninger HS; Girls Vllybl & Boys Lacrosse Coach; NYSAHPERD 1991-; *office:* Huntington MS 400 Sunnycrest Rd Syracuse NY 13206

ROMANO, LINDA-MARIE MASCOLO, Social Studies & ESOL Teacher; *b:* Ft Monmouth, NJ; *m:* Joseph R.; *c:* Cari L., J. R., Katherine F.; *ed:* Annhurst Coll at Woodstock (BA) His 1971; Southern CT St Univ (MS) Adult Ed 1991; 30 Credit Hrs His; *cr:* Tantasqua Regnl HS His Tchr 1972-74; Vly Regnl Adult Learning Ctr GED, ESL Tchr 1974-; Watertown HS His, Alternative Ed Tchr 1990-93; Derby HS His, ESL Tchr 1993-; *ai:* Jr Class of 1997 Adv; Derby Ed Assn 1993-, Sec; CEA, NEA 1990-; Conntesol 1992-; CAACE 1975-; *office:* Derby HS 8 Nutmeg Ave Derby CT 06418

ROMANO, MARGARET MEMBRINO, Sixth Grade Teacher; *b:* Leominster, MA; *m:* Peter S.; *c:* Beth Ann, Stephen A., Peter J.; *ed:* Fitchburg St Coll (BSEd) Elem Ed 1965; Addl Courses Taken in MS Ed Gifted & Talented & Math; *cr:* Fitchburg Pub Schls 3rd & 4th Grd Tchr 1965-67; Westminster Elem 2nd, 5th & 6th Grd Tchr 1978-95; Overlook MS 6th Grd Tchr & Team Ldr 1995-; *ai:* Big Help Project Nickelodeon Spon; NEA & MTA; Ashburnham Westminster Tchrs Assoc; Westminster Womans Club 1976-, Mbrshp Chair; Westminster Historical Soc; *office:* Overlook MS 10 Oakmont Dr Ashburnham MA 01430

ROMANO, PATRICIA CAMPBELL, Eighth Grade Science Teacher; *b:* Staten Island, NY; *m:* Andrew J.; *c:* Tricia, Jennifer Genovese; *ed:* Notre Dame Coll (BA) Bio 1968; *cr:* C. W. Goetz MS 7th Grd Math, Sci Tchr 1986-92, 6th Grd Math, Sci, Rdng Tchr 1992-94, 8th Grd Sci Tchr 1994-; *ai:* Stu Acts Adv; Sci Fair Co-Chair; NEA 1986-; PTA 1992-; Governor's Recognition Tchr of Yr 1995; *office:* Carl W Goetz MS 835 Patterson Rd Jackson NJ 08527*

ROMANO, RONALD, World History & Cultures Tchr; *b:* Hackensack, NJ; *m:* Jacqueline Aletta; *c:* Nicole, Victoria; *ed:* Muhlenberg Coll (BA) His 1982; Seton Hall Univ (MA) Educl Admin, Supervision 1988; *cr:* Northern Vly Regnl Schl His Tchr 1982-; *ai:* Stu Cncl Co-Adv; NEA, NJEA 1982-; Northern Vly Ed Assn 1982-, VP, Pres; Dixon Homestead Lib, Trustee; *office:* Northern Valley Regional HS Central Ave Old Tappan NJ 07675*

ROMANO, TERESA, Guidance Counselor; *b:* Pittsburgh, PA; *ed:* Univ of Pgh (BA) Scndry Ed 1978, (MED) Cnslr Ed 1980; Schl Soc Worker Cert; Stu Assistance Prgm Trng; *ai:* Yth Crime Watch Spon; Core Team Coord; *office:* Brashear H S 590 Crane Ave Pittsburgh PA 15216

ROMANO, VIRGINIA BUOYE, Mathematics & Cmptr Sci Tchr; *b:* Orange, NJ; *m:* Frederick P.; *c:* Alfred, Frederick, Thomas; *ed:* Seton Hall Univ (BS) Ed, Math 1964; St Peters Coll (MA) Ed, Cmptr Sci 1989; Post Grad Stud 30 Credit Hrs; *cr:* Our Lady of the Valley HS Math Tchr 1964-65; Garfield HS Math Tchr 1965-66; Queen of Peace HS Math Tchr 1986-92; Kearny HS Math Tchr 1992-; *ai:* Organzed Seminar for QPHS Presented by Stevens Profs Topic Cmptr Software for HS Math Prgms; Participated in Seminar at QP Tchng Peers Cmptr Software; NEA, NJEA KEA 1992-; AMTNJ, NCTM 1965-; Cub Scouts 1974-76, Den Mother Coord; Jr Womens Club of Kearny 1966-70; Vol Tchr Aid QP Elem Schl 1973-81, Rdng, Lib Aid; Geraldine Dodge Fnd Grant for Stud at Stevens Inst for Math Tchrs 1990 Cert Prgm in Cmptr Math; *office:* Kearny HS 336 Devon St Kearny NJ 07032

ROMANSKI, CARL VINCENT, Spanish Teacher; *b:* Wilkes Barre, PA; *m:* Mary Dolores Piatt; *c:* Sally Ann; *ed:* Wilkes Coll (BA) Span 1969; Bloomsburg Univ (MED) Span 1972; Universidad Ibero-Americana at Mexico City, Universidad de Madrid 6 Crd Hrs Each; Universidad de Malaga at Spain Post Grad Studs, Commonwealth Partnership; *cr:* Wyoming Area Jr HS Span Tchr 1969; Danville Area HS Span Tchr 1969-; *ai:* Prins Comm Budget Dev; Software Eval Comm; DEA, PSEA, NEA 1969-; Rio Arriba Chap of AATSP 1978-, Charter Pres; Red Cross Blood Donor 1969-, 10 Gallon Pin; St Joseph Church 1970-, Choir Mem, Cantor, 10 Yr Pin, Eucharistic Minister; 1988 Penna Commonwealth Partnership Co-Dir; Reader Advanced Placement Span Examinations 1994; HS & Coll Evaluations 1976-88; Mentor Tchr for Stu Tchrs 1972-; *office:* Danville HS 600 Walnut St Danville PA 17821

ROMBERGER, MARY J., Mathematics Teacher; *b:* Bethlehem, PA; *m:* Robert A. II; *c:* Jennifer, Kristin; *ed:* IUP (BSEd) Math 1971; Penn St Univ (MED) Tchng & Curr 1992; Addl 45 Hrs Post Masters; *cr:* Cntrl Dauphin Schl Dist Math Tchr 1971-73, 1977-79; HACC Math Tchr 1988-90; Cntrl Dauphin Schl Dist Math Tchr 1989-; *ai:* Honor Soc & Peer Mediation Adv; SA Prgm; Math Help; NCTM 1989-; *office:* Central Dauphin HS 4600 Locust Ln Harrisburg PA 17109*

ROMBERGER, NORMA MC ELHANEY, Soc Studies, Reading, Rel Tchr; *b:* Hagerstown, MD; *m:* Charles J.; *c:* Colin; *ed:* Susquehanna Univ (BA) His, Pol Sci 1971; Lehigh Univ (MA) His 1980; 15 Credits in Theology at Allentown Coll; 6 Credits in Theology at Archdiocese of Philadelphia; *cr:* Christ of King Schl MS Tchr 1970-82; Lehigh Vly Luth Schl Founder, Prin 1983-90; St John the Bapt Schl MS Span, Rel, Rdng, Soc Stud Tchr 1992-; *ai:* Soc Stud Coord; Stu Cncl, Yrbk, 8th Grd Adv; Steering Comm Chprsn for Mid Sts Acceditation; NCEA 1970-; ASCD 1984, 1995; Jr League of Lehigh Vly 1975-, Pres, Sec, Outstdng Vol; BSA 1994-, Merit Badge Cnslr; Lehigh Vly Luth Schl Bd 1983-92, Pres, Treas, Founders Awd; Childrens Theater of Bethlehem 1982-92, Treas; St John the Baptist Church, RCIA Instr; Who's Who in Amer Ed 1986-88; Article Pub; *office:* Saint John The Baptist Schl 4040 Durham Rd Ottsville PA 18942*

ROME, GLENN OWEN, 7th & 8th Grd Reading Teacher; *b:* Jersey City, NJ; *m:* Sharon Mc Andrew; *c:* Matthew, Daniel; *ed:* JCSC (BA) Elem Ed 1972; Seton Hall (MA) Admin 1978; 6 Addl Credits Guid; *cr:* PS #2 Bsktbl, Track, Vlybl Coach 1972-82; PS #2 Tchr 1972-; Meml HS Sftbl, Bsktbl Coach 1982-; *ai:* Head Sftbl, Head Asst Girls Bsktbl, 14-15 Yr Old Babe Ruth Cliffside Park Coach; PTA, NEA, NJEA 1972-; Cliffside Park Little League 1979-, Exec Bd Sec, 1996 Commission of Major Leagues; *office:* Elem Schl 2 5200 Broadway West New York NJ 07093

ROMEO, ANITA MARY (PROCHKO), Fourth Grade Teacher; *b:* Cleveland, OH; *c:* Jonathan; *ed:* Akron Univ (BSEd) El Educ, Music Speciality 1978; El Schl Cnslng 1987; *cr:* Immacykate Heart of Mary 4th Grd Tchr 1978-82; Kent City Schls 4th Grd Tchr 1983-; *ai:* Young Authors Club; Staff Advy Cncl; Conflict Mngmt Team; Staff Dev; Right to Read Week Comm; Kent Ed Assn 1983-; Akron Area IRA 1979-, VP, Pres, Bd Mem; *office:* Kent City Schls 900 Doramor St Kent OH 44240*

ROMEO, BERNADETTE ROSSI, English Teacher; *b:* Elmira, NY; *m:* Dominic J.; *c:* Dominic A., Maria C.; *ed:* DYouville Coll (BA) Eng 1968; Elmira Coll (MEd) Ed 1970; 60 Addl Hrs Beyond (BA); *cr:* Horseheads Jr HS Eng Tchr 1968-70; Jamesville-DeWitt MS Eng Tchr 1970-72; Elmira Free Acad Eng Tchr 1985-; *ai:* Elmira City Schl Dist Elgibility Policy Review Comm; Bldg Planning Team; Dist Compact Cncl; Art Club Adv; NCTE 1986-; NYSUT, NAFTA; League of Women Voters 1992-; St Josephs Auxiliary 1977-; Hammondsport Chamber of Commerce 1993-.*

ROMEO, BONITA A., English Teacher; *b:* Montour Falls, N Mansfield Univ (BSE) Eng Ed 1973, (MA) Eng 1977; Manhatt Advanced Placement Curr 1985; *cr:* Mansfield Univ Composition Asst 1975-77; Newark Valley HS Eng Tchr 1978-; *ai:* NYSUT, N Valley United Tchrs 1978-; Amer Assoc of Univ Women 1993- Legion Auxiliary 1989-; Newark Valley Historical Soc 1990-; Advanced Placement in Distance Learning Ctr; Working on Novel; 279 Main St Apt 1-E Owego NY 13827

ROMEO, FRANCES P., 2nd Grade Teacher; *b:* Massena, NY; Barry Jones; *c:* Daniel Miller; *ed:* Univ of NY at Potsdam (BA Scndry Ed 1969; Univ of VT (MA) Rdng & Lang Arts 1973; 30 Cre Beyond Masters; *cr:* Waddington Elem Schl 4th Grd Tchr 1969-70 Town Elem Schl 4th Grd Tchr 1971-81, 8th Grd Tchr 1982-83, 2 Tchr 1983-; *ai:* Biline Ed Schl Newsletter 1988-92; VT NEA 1971- Yr; VT-NEA Newsletter Excl Awd for Layout & Graphics in 1991; 15 Grandview Farm Rd Barre VT 05641*

ROMEO, RONALD E., High School Band Director; *b:* Rochester, Indiana Univ of PA (BS) Music Ed 1965; Duquesne Univ (MED) M 1969; *cr:* Aliquippa Schls Jr HS Vocal, General Music 1965-68 Instrumental 1968-74, Sr HS Instrumental Band 1974-87; New B Area HS Instrumental Band 1987-; *ai:* PSEA, NEA 1965-; PMEA, 1970-; AF of M Local 82-545 1960-; Sewickley Symphony Mem 19 1976-; *office:* New Brighton Area HS 3200 43rd St New Brighton PA

ROMEO, WILLIAM JOSEPH, English Teacher; *b:* Cleveland, June Hart; *ed:* Kent St Univ (BSED) Eng 1975; Cleveland St Univ Eng 1981; Doctoral Kent St Univ Curr & Instruction, Eng Ed; *cr:* Forge HS Eng Tchr 1975-78; Kent St Univ Ed Instr 1991; Greenbria Eng Tchr 1978-; *ai:* Eng Dept Head; Asst Bsktbl Coach; Eng Lang A of Jr HS Level Course of Stud; NCTE 1973-; Phi Delta Kappa Kappa Delta Pi 1989-; NEA, OEA 1975-; Midwest Medieval Assn Humane Soc 1985-; Smithsonian Inst 1987-; Article in Journal o Experience; OH Cncl of Eng Tchrs Lang Arts Spring 1994 Conf Pre *office:* Greenbiar Jr HS 11810 Huffman Rd Cleveland OH 44130

ROMEU, ALICIA H., High School Spanish Teacher; *b:* Mexic Mexico; *m:* Frank J.; *c:* Diane R. Ekstrand, Laura, Carlos; *ed:* Mo Inst of Tech (MA) Romance Langs-Magna Cum Laude 1963; La Sal (MA) Biling & Bicultural Stud 1988; Villanova Univ (MA) Educl 1992; Foreign Lang Dept Cert; Elem Principalship Cert; Principalship Cert; *cr:* Vista Vol Span Tchr 1969-74; North Penn Second Lang Tutor 1974-82; Green Street Friends Span Tchr 19 Wissahickon HS Span Tchr 1984-; *ai:* World Affairs Club Spon; Intern; MCAFTL 1984-; Phi Beta 1988-; CISU 1980-, Sec; NHS Elem Level Span Tchng Grant; Latin Amer His Book Eng t Translation Grant; Univ of Richmond & Penn St Recognitions; Wissahickon HS 521 Houston Rd Ambler PA 19002

ROMINGER, STACY BRIGGS, Science Teacher; *b:* Dunkirk, Robert; *c:* Nathaniel; *ed:* Univ of Buffalo (BS) Biochemical Pharma 1991, (EDM) Sci Ed 1995; *cr:* Orchard Park HS Sci Tchr 1991-; *ai:* Comm & Stu Govt Adv; HS Wellness Comm; Orchard Park Tchr 1991-; NSTA 1992-; AFT 1991-; Beta Sigma Phi 1994-; *office:* C Park HS 4040 Baker Rd Orchard Park NY 14127

ROMITO, PAMELA JOANNE, Third Grade Teacher; *b:* Kensington, PA; *m:* Robert; *c:* Alexander; *ed:* Indiana Univ of P Elem Ed 1969; 24 Post Grad Credits in Elem Ed; *cr:* Laurel Point S Grd Tchr 1969-70; East Vandergrift Schl 3rd Grd Tchr 1970-74; Point Schl 3rd-4th Grd Tchr 1974-79; Paulton Schl 1st, 3rd Gr 1980-85; Washington Elem Schl Kndgtn-1st Grd Tchr 1985-93; Washington Schl 3rd Grd Tchr 1993-; *ai:* NEA; Tchr of Month Organizer of 3rd Grd Math Challenge; *office:* North WA Elem Schl 66 Apollo PA 15613

ROMMEL, PATRICIA CARI, Spanish & French Teacher; *b:* Island, NY; *c:* Kate E., Michele; *ed:* Coll of St Elizabeth (BA) Fr 19 Span Cert; *cr:* Parsippany Schl Dist 6-12 Grd Span, Fr Tchr 19 Sparta HS 9-12 Grd Span, Fr Tchr 1987-88; Sussex Cty Comm Co Instr 1988-93; Lakeland Regnl HS 9-12 Grd Span, Fr Tchr 1988-; *a* Hnr Soc Adv; Synchronized Swimming Coach, Summer Comm NEH; NJEA 1982-; LRHSEA 1988-; AATSP, FLENJ 1992-; *ho* Division Ln Andover NJ 07821

ROMSPERT, RALPH CARL,SR., Fourth Grade Teach Philadelphia, PA; *m:* Diane Amy; *c:* Bryn, Ralph Jr.; *ed:* PA St Univ Recreation, Parks 1979; Temple Univ (BS) Elem Ed 1982; Stroudsburg Univ (MED) Hlth, PE; Working Toward 60 Addl Hrs; W Toward Strenght Trng, Conditioning Cert; *cr:* Pocono Mt Schl Dist 4 Tchr 1985-; Shawnee Racquet & Fitness Club Fitness Instr 1996-; *ai* 1985-; Masonic Lodge 1985-; *office:* Barrett Elem Ctr Rt 390 Cre 18326

RONALD, THOMAS J., Third Grade Teacher; *b:* Buffalo, N Christi-Carole Esslinger; *c:* Alexandra; *ed:* Erie Comm Coll Nort Liberal Arts & Sci 1976; St Univ Coll at Buffalo (BS) Elem Ed 1981 Elem Ed 1987; Addl 15 Credit Hrs Toward Cert of Advanced S Admin; *cr:* Amherst Windemere Elem 2nd Grd Tchr 1982-83; Cle Hill Elem 3rd, 5th & 6th Grd Tchr 1983-; *ai:* Soc Stud Comm; NYSUT 1983-; Cleveland Hill Tchrs Assn 1983-, Bldg Rep; Cleveland Hill Elem Schl 105 Mapleview Rd Cheektowaga NY 142

RONAN, JOAN LILLIAN, Retired Elementary Teacher; *b:* Newar *m:* Harold; *c:* Debbie Haughwout, Scott, David, Tracey Regrut; *ed:* St (BS) Elem 1952; *cr:* Demerast Schl Tchr 1953-54; Fairview Ele Tchr 1975-95; *ai:* Chrldng Coach; NEA; PSEA.

RONCA, JOAN (PERON), Spanish Teacher; *b:* Pottsville, PA; *m:* J.; *c:* Joseph J. II; *ed:* Bloomsburg St Coll (BS) Scndry Ed, Span 197 Grad Stud Penn St Univ, West Chester Univ, Villanova Univ, Mar Coll; *cr:* Pen Argyl Area HS Span Tchr 1973-; *ai:* NHS Cncl; Station Adv; NEA, Kappa Delta Pi, ACTFL 1973-; Green & WH 1991-; Music Boosters Assoc 1994-; *office:* Pen Argyl Area High S 501 W Laurel Ave Pen Argyl PA 18072*

RONCEK, ROBERT P., Math & Calculus Teacher; *b:* Coaldale, Kathleen Jordan; *c:* Bobby; *ed:* Kutztown Univ (BS) Math Bloomsburg Univ Continuing Ed; *cr:* Shenandoah Vly HS Math 1974-; *ai:* Ftbl Coach; NEA 1974-; PSEA 1974-; *office:* Shenando HS Stadium Rd Shenandoah PA 17976

RONCONI, MARIA LUCIA, Religious Studies Teacher; *b:* Verona, *ed:* Mt St Mary Coll (BA) Rel Stud Sociology 1990; St Joseph Se Inst for Rel Stud (MA) Dogmatic Theology 1994; Attnd Marian Catechism; *cr:* Focolare Movement Youth Coord 1990-93; Preston H 1093-; *ai:* Asst Regnl Dir Focolare Movement; Focolare Movement Dir W Coast; *office:* Preston HS 2780 Schurz Ave Bronx NY 10465*

RONDOSH, ANGELA, 4th Grade Teacher; *b:* Summit ; *m:* Jam Dana; *ed:* Coll of St Elizabeth (BA) His, Eng 1972; *cr:* Holy Famil Tchr 1972-79; St Vincent Martyr Schl Tchr 1979-; *ai:* CTBS Coor Stud Chm, Coord; NCEA 1972-; SEA Alumni Bd 1993-, VP; *hom* Lidgerwood Pl Morristown NJ 07960

RONEY, KELLI ANN (SCHROEDER), Sixth Grade Teacher; *b:* OH; *m:* Mark D.; *c:* Trey; *ed:* Bowling Green St Univ (BS) Elem Ed *cr:* St John Grade Schl Sixth Grd Tchr 1989-; *ai:* St Jude Math-A ıprsn; Math Olympiad Coach; NEA, OSCEA 1989-; NCTM 1995-; : St John Grade Schl 110 N Pierce St Delphos OH 45833

ZONI, ARNOLD DAVID, English Teacher; *b:* Philadelphia, PA; *ed:* le Univ (BA) Eng & Ed 1971; Addl 24 Hrs; *cr:* St John Neuman HS 'chr 1971-82; Little Flower HS Eng Tchr 1982-; *ai:* Newspaper Adv; :ity Dir; Marketing Act Coord; Union Rep; NACT & NTE 1971-; Dow Distinguished Newspaper Adv 1993; Temple Univ Distinguished ɔaper Adv 1989; Distingquished Cath Educator 1994; *office:* Little r Cath HS Girls 1000 W Lycoming st Philadelphia PA 19140*

D, KAREN L., Math & Cmptr Science Teacher; *b:* Passaic, NJ; *ed:* :lair St Univ (BS) Math 1979, (MA) Math 1980; *cr:* Fair Lawn HS Cmptr Sci Tchr 1980-; *ai:* Adv Cmptr League; NJEA, NEA, AMTNJ, 4 1980-; *office:* Fair Lawn HS 14-00 Berdan Ave Fair Lawn NJ 07410

F, JOYCE ANN, Home Economics Teacher; *b:* Sayre, PA; *ed:* Drexel 'BS) Home Ec Ed 1971; Grad Work Mansfield Univ, Penn St, Wilks Coll of Notre Dame; *cr:* Northeast Bradford HS Home Ec Tchr 25 *ai:* Adv Northeast Bradford Comm Svc Club; Chm Mid States ng Comm; NEA; PSEA, NEBEA 1971-, Treas; Delta Kappa Gamma , Treas, Corresponding Sec; Kappa Omicron 1970-; AAFCS, PAFCS ; Amer Cancer Soc 1993-, Bd of Dirs; *office:* Northeast Bradford HS Box 211b Rome PA 18837

F, KIMBERLY HALL, Athletic Dir, Hlth & PE Tchr; *b:* Baltimore MD; *c:* Hunter Peyton; *ed:* High Point Univ (BS) Hlth & PE 1980; Stud at Univ of Richmond, Western MD; *cr:* Meadowbrook HS Hlth Tchr 1980-89; Culvert HS Hlth & PE Tchr 1989-95; Patuxent HS ic Dir & Hlth & PE Tchr 1995-; *ai:* Field Hockey & Sftbl Coach; St Comm Mem; AHPERD 1980-; NSCA 1983-; *office:* Patuxent HS MD 20657*

NEY, DOROTHY, 7th & 8th Grade Teacher; *b:* Philadelphia, PA; *ed:* ephs Univ (BS) Elem Ed 1979; *cr:* Holy Cross 6th-8th Grd tchr 30 *ai:* Yrbk Adv & Coord 7 Yrs; NCEA 1964-; Nominated in 1992 for anding Achvmt in Tchng in US.*

NEY, JOSEPH E., Math Teacher; *b:* Buffalo, NY; *m:* Patricia A. ak; *c:* Sharon Ross, Jeannie Darwin, Susan, James, Kathleen, Mary, Christine, Michael, John, Robert; *ed:* SUNY at Buffalo (BA) Math (MA) Math 1975; Post Grad Stud SUNY at Brockport, SUNY Coll 'falo; *cr:* Orchard Pk HS Math Tchr 1971-; SUNY at Buffalo Lecturer ; *ai:* Chaperone; AFT, NYSUT 1971-; Food Shuttle of WNY 1 Yr; n Tchng Awd; Natl Sci Fnd Grants.

NEY, KATHLEEN,SSJ, Theology Teacher; *b:* Bayonne, NJ; *ed:* rs Univ (BA) Psych 1977; St Michael's Coll (MA) Theology 1993; ɔod Counsel HS Theology Tchr 1984-85; DeLone Cath HS Theology 1985-88; Wildwood Cath HS Theology Tchr, Dept Chair 1988-91; ishop Wood HS Theology Tchr, Dept Chair 1991; *ai:* Sr Prom rator; Mem, Facilitator Stu Assistance Prgm; NCEA 1990-; Master Rel, Catechist Trng Prmg; *office:* Archbishop Wood HS 655 York Rd inster PA 18974

NEY, KATHLEEN A., Math Teacher; *b:* Staten Island, NY; *ed:* rk St (BA) Math 1969; Kean Coll (MA) Educl Supervision 1994; 30 Credits Math Ed Montclair St; *cr:* South Orange Jr HS Math Tchr 80; Columbia HS Math Tchr 1980-; *ai:* Block Scheduling, Stu w Assessment, Ath Eligibility Comms; Assoc Rep; NEA, SOMEA, Cty, NJEA 1969-; *office:* Columbia HS 17 Parker Ave Maplewood 040

P, CLIFFORD EUGENE, Health & Physical Ed Teacher; *b:* Berea, d: Cedarville Coll (BA) PE 1992; *cr:* Orange Chrstn Acad Tchr & ir 1993-; *ai:* Ath Dir; JV Vllybl Coach; *office:* Orange Christian Acad Emery Rd Orange Village OH 44128

SEVELT, BARBARA VEINO, English Teacher; *b:* Troy, NY; *m:* ric; *c:* Frederic, Eric; *ed:* SUNY at Albany (BA) Eng 1985, (MA) Eng 4 Cr Hrs Writing; *cr:* Shaker HS 1985-87; Chatham HS 1987-; *ai:* doscope Adv; Natl Tchrs of Eng 1985-; NEA 1987-, Treas; Numerous es Pub; *office:* Chatham HS 50 Woodbridge Ave Chatham NY 12037

T, KELLIE BOWERS, Fifth Grade Teacher; *b:* Hagerstown, MD; *m:* oseph; *ed:* Liberty Univ (BS) Elem Ed 1991; Attending Frostburg St *cr:* Western Heights MS 8th Grd Math, Cmptr Awareness Tchr 92, 5th Grd Tchr 1992-; *ai:* HS Head Chrldng Coach; Cmptr, Safety ıs; Project Western Heights; Mentor Tchr; Peer Mediation Trainer; 1 1995-; *office:* Western Heights MS 1300 Marshall St Hagerstown 1740

ER, JAMES STEPHEN, Assistant Band Director; *b:* Jackson, MS; slie Carol; *c:* Megan Marie, Christian James; *ed:* Univ of MD at Coll BS) Music Ed 1980; *cr:* Archbishop Carroll HS Band Dir 1981-82; tha Cath HS Band Asst Dir, Chorus Dir 1982-; *ai:* Jazz Lab Band; Dept Chm; MENC, MD Music Educ Assn 1981-; WAMTC 1981-, Treas; MBDA, MCEA 1981-83, Exec Bd; Conducted MD Jr All-St 1991, Tidewater Music Festival 1994; Guest Conducted Univ of MD honic Wind Ensemble 1995; Clinician Cinn Conservatory Music; : DeMatha Cath HS 4313 Madison St Hyattsville MD 20781

SKI, STEVEN JOSEPH, Associate Professor in Biology; *b:* Erie, *n:* Melanie Gustafson-Ropski; *c:* Meaghan K., Nathaniel S.; *ed:* ɔn Univ (BS) Bio, Ed 1978; IN St Univ (PHD) Ecology, Systematics *cr:* Elk Cty Chrstn HS Bio Tchr 1978-79; IN St Univ Grad Asst 84; Gannon Univ Instr, Asst, Assoc Prof 1984-; *ai:* Jr Acad of Sci s Site Organizer; Gen Sci Prgm Dir; Hnrs Ctr Advy Comm; Tri Beta, Regnl Dir; Amer Soc of Mammalogists 1979-, Natl Comm Grad , Undergrad Ed; PA Wildlife Soc 1987-, Bd of Dirs 1992-; Pres Elect 96; Pres 1996; Presque Isle Partnership 1994-, Environmental Comm; bon Soc 1986-, Bd of Dirs, Conservation Comm; Teddy Roosevelt Fac Rsrch, Dev, Audubon Soc Rsrch, Campus Compact Svc Learning onmental Ed Grants; SGA Tchr of Yr 1991, 1993; SGA Tchr of n; PA Jr Acad of Sci Edctr of Yr 1990; Apple Polishing Awd 1994; es Pub; *office:* Gannon Univ University Square Erie PA 16541

UE-BERGONZI, DELIA, Bilingual Kindergarten Teacher; *b:* ıa, Cuba; *m:* Silvio; *c:* Lizette; *ed:* Lehman Coll (BA) Sociology City Coll of NY (MS) Bil Ed 1981; 46 Addl Credits Salary ential; 16 Credits Stud Sabbatical 1994; *cr:* PS 152 M Bil First Grd 1977-78, Bil Kndgtn Tchr 1978-; *ai:* AFT, UFT 1978-; Greenpeace; ıel 13; Kappa Delta Pi; Grant for MA; *office:* PS 152 Dyckman Valley ıgle Ave New York NY 10040

A, MARIE THERESA, Hlth & Physical Education Tchr; *b:* New York NY; *m:* Michael; *c:* Maria; *ed:* Hunter Coll (BA) Hlth, PE, Recreation Brooklyn (MA) Hlth, PE 1972; St John's Univ (MA) Schl Cnslng 30 Addl Credits; *cr:* The Kew Forest Schl 3rd-12th Grd PE Tchr 66; New Hyde Park Meml Schl Hlth, PE Tchr 1966-68; Grover land HS Tchr, Cnslr, Coord 1968-; *ai:* Var Bsktbl, Vlybl, Sftbl, nastics, Track Coach; Cooperative Ed, Ldrshp Prgms Coord; Teen ach Pregnancy Prevention Prgms Group Cnslr; AFT 1968-; ACA ; NYSAPPHER 1972-; NYC Umpire Assn 1972-, VP, Treas; Cath Yth Lecturer, Trainer; Queen Comm Svcs, Group Cnslr; *office:* Grover land HS 2127 Himrod St Ridgewood NY 11385

ANIA, THERESA MARIE, Assoc Professor of Marketing; *b:* rk, NJ; *c:* Michelle Desire Stefanelli; *ed:* Montclair St Univ (BA) His 1975; Fairleigh Dickinson Univ (MBA) Mngmt, Mrktg 1977; Nova Southeastern Univ (DBA) Mngmt, Mrktg 1986; *cr:* Mrktg Mgr, Product Mrktg Mgr, Advertising Dir Consumer, Indstrl Products Natl, Intnl 1966; Trenton St Coll Coord Mktg Dept 1982-86; Allentown Coll St Francis de Sales Asst Prof 1986-90; Kean Coll Assoc Prof 1990-; *ai:* Mu Kappa Tau Adv; Prgm Review, Lib, Schlsp Comms; NAMSB 1995-; Intnl Flwshp 1990; Grant to Rsrch TQM 1992; Ford Fnd Grant Project Lead 1994; Woman of Yr Mrktg 1976; *office:* Kean Coll Of NJ Morris Avenue Union NJ 07083

ROSARIO, OSCAR, Spanish Teacher; *b:* Comerio, PR; *m:* Alicia; *c:* Alyssa Y.; *ed:* Westfield St Coll (BA) Span & Scndry Ed 1977; Emmanuel Bible Seminar Concentration in Theology 1974; *cr:* Holyoke Pub Schls Biling Tchr 1977-86; Mass Migrant Ed Pgm Tchr 1978-86; Assemblies of God Bible Inst Theology Tchr 1980-86; Springfield Pub Schls; *ai:* MTA 1977-; NEA 1977-; STA 1986-; Small Bus Admin 1993-; *office:* HS Of Commerce 415 State St Springfield MA 01105

ROSATI, HELEN DJORDJEVICH, English Teacher; *b:* El Shat, Egypt; *c:* Anthony F.; *ed:* Univ of Buffalo (BA) Eng, Scndry Ed 1970; Buffalo St Coll (MS) Elem Ed N-6 1974; Univ of Buffalo Cert Remedial & Diagnostic Rdng 1980; *cr:* Bethlehem Park Elem Schl Tchr, Librn 1970-72; Wilson Elem Schl Tchr, Librn 1970-72; Bethlehem Park Elem Schl 1st Grd Elem Tchr 1972-77; Lackawanna City Schl Dist K-12 Grd Sub Tchr, Tutor 1978-82; Orchard Park HS Eng Tchr 1983-; *ai:* Soph Class Adv; Wellness, Lib, STAP Comms; Schl Govt; Crisis Response, Intervention Teams; Peer, Stu Mentor; AFT, NYSUT 1970-; OPTA 1983-; St Stephen's Mother's Club 1977-; Church 1970-, Sunday Schl Tchr; Outstdng Young Edctr 1974-75; *office:* Orchard Park HS 4040 Baker Rd Orchard Park NY 14127

ROSATI, JOY (FELKER), 5th Grade Teacher; *b:* Allentown, PA; *m:* Lawrence T.; *c:* Gina Barrinchack, Anthony; *ed:* Kutztown Univ (BS) Elem Ed 1970, (MS) Elem Ed 1976; 9 Grad Credit Hrs East Stroudsburg Univ & Frostburg Univ; 6 Inservice Credit Hrs Intermediate IU Unit; *cr:* Clearview Elem 5th Grd Tchr 1970-77; Miller Hghts Elem 5th Grd Tchr 1977-87; William Penn Elem 5th Grd Tchr 1987-; *ai:* Ec Club for Schl Store; Head Tchr; NEA 1970-; PSEA 1970-; BEA 1970-; Bethlehem Edctrs Assn; *office:* William Penn HS 1002 Main St Bethlehem PA 18018

ROSATO, FLORENCE GENSON, Asst Professor of Accounting; *b:* Cortland, NY; *c:* Richard, Joseph, Debbie, Brian; *ed:* Tompkins Cortland (AAS) Acctng 1982; Empire St Coll (BS) Acctng 1984; SUNY Coll at Binghamton (MS) Ed 1989; Pursuing PHD; *cr:* Smith Corona Quality Control 15 Yrs; Groton Hlth Ctr Jr Accountant 2 Yrs; Tompkins Cortland Comm Coll Learning Specialist 8 Yrs, Instr 3 Yrs, Asst Prof 3 Yrs; *ai:* Acad Stans, Commencement, Twenty-Fifth Anniversary, Acctng & Bus Prgm Comms; NYNEA 1980-; *home:* 255 Cortland-Mc Lean Rd Cortland NY 13045

ROSATO, HELENA RODRIGUES, French & Spanish Teacher; *b:* Melo, Portugal; *m:* Peter; *c:* Stephanie, Anthony; *ed:* Montclair St Coll (BA) Fr 1982; *cr:* St Cecilia HS Fr Tchr 1982-83; Immaculate Conception HS Fr, Span Tchr 1983-88; Hammarskjold MS Fr Tchr 1988-89; St Mary Regnl HS Fr, Span Tchr 1990-; *ai:* Fr Hnr Soc, Frgn Lang Club Adv; Sr Class Moderator 1992-; Fac Advy Bd Mem; AATF 1983-; FLENJ 1990-; *office:* St Mary's Regnl HS 310 Augusta St South Amboy NJ 08879

ROSATO, PHYLLIS P., Math Teacher; *b:* Tacoma, WA; *m:* Thomas; *c:* Cara, Thomas, Enrica; *ed:* City Coll of NY (BA) Math 1977, (MS) Math Ed 1979; *cr:* Mamaroneck HS Math & Sci Tchr 77-79; A Philip Randolph HS Math Tchr 79-81; Catskill HS Math Tchr 81-82; Onteora HS Math Tchr 83-; *ai:* AFT, NYSUT 1977-; NYS Tchrs Math 1977-; *office:* Onteora Jr Sr HS Rt 28 Boiceville NY 12412

ROSCOE, MARY LOU L., Chemistry Teacher; *b:* Daisytown, PA; *m:* Edmund Alex; *c:* Julie, Zachary, Joshua, Tina J. Coyle; *ed:* CA Univ PA (BS) Chem Ed 1968; 28 Grad Credits Chem, Ed; *cr:* Ringgold HS Donora Campus Chem Tchr 1968-80; Ringgold HS Chem Tchr 1980-; *ai:* NEA, PSEA, REA 1968-; Grant Spectroscopy Soc of Pittsburgh; Mon Vly Consortium Great Idea Grant; *office:* Ringgold HS Rd 4 Box 640a Monongahela PA 15063

ROSE, ANITA RUTH (HOOGERHEIDE), Kindergarten Teacher; *b:* Paterson, NJ; *m:* Donald E.; *c:* Jennifer Sue; *ed:* Newark St Coll (BA) Spec Ed & Elem Ed 1970; *cr:* Wayne Pub Schl Tchr of Spec Ed 1970-74; Netherlands Reformed Chrstn Kndgtn Tchr 1979-.

ROSE, ANNE TUCKER, Assistant Professor of Nursing; *b:* Flushing, NY; *c:* John M., Jim W., Elizabeth Rose-Sommers, Stephen J.; *ed:* Union Univ (BS) Nrsng 1954; Russell Sage Coll (MS) Maternal-Child Nrsng 1971; 12 Credit Hrs Cnclng; *cr:* Albany Med Ctr Hosp Head Nurse 1954-57; Albany Med Ctr Schl of Nrsng Instr 1957-59; Hudson Vly Comm Coll Instr PT 1971-79, Instr FT 1979-83, Asst Prof 1983-; *ai:* Course Mgr Nrsng I 1981-86, 1989-1991; Peer Review Comm Chprsn 1990-1994; Hudson Vly CC Fac Assn 1979-; Amer Soc for Psycoprophylaxis in Obstetrics 1970-95; AWHONN 1995-; Guilderland Comm Ctr Bd of Dir 1980-85; Remove Intoxicated Drivers 1983-; Stop DWI Comm Svc Awd 1994-; Guilderland Chamber of Commerce Awd of Merit 1994-; Childbirth Ed, Practice Rsrch, Theory 1985; Articles Pub 1990-94; *home:* 592 Jefferson Ct Guilderland NY 12084*

ROSE, ARCHIE CARL, History & Government Teacher; *b:* Mason, WV; *m:* Debra Lynn Smith; *c:* Tyson, Alison; *ed:* OH Univ (BS) His, Govt 1971, (MA) Principalship 1985; His, Govt OH Northern Univ; Elem Cert 1976; *cr:* Tuppers Plains Elem 6th Grd Tchr 1972-73; Eastern Jr Sr HS 8th Grd Tchr 1973-74, 7th-12th Grd Tchr 1974-; *ai:* Jr & Sr HS Bsktbl, Ftbl Coach; Sr HS Boys-Girls Track Coach; Class Adv; Grd 7-12 Stu Cncl Adv; Soc Stud Chprsn; Sub Bus Driver; Dist Transportation Supvr & Coord; Carmel-Sutton United Meth Churches 1950-, Trustee, Asst Supt, Sunday Schl Tchr; Summer League Sftbl, Coach; Southeastern Ftbl Coach of Yr 1981; *office:* Eastern Jr Sr HS 38900 State Route 7 Reedsville OH 45772*

ROSE, DANIEL J., Junior High School Teacher; *b:* Sandusky, OH; *ed:* Univ of Cincinnati (BSEd) Scndry Ed, Eng 1982; *cr:* Holy Angels Schl Jr HS Tchr 1982-83; Sacred Heart Schl Jr HS Tchr 1984-; *ai:* Stu Cncl Adv; NCTE 1993-; OCTELA 1992-; Parish Liturgy Comm 1991-, Chm; Strs of St Francis 1988-, Co-Mem; *office:* Sacred Heart Schl 500 Smith Rd Fremont OH 43420

ROSE, DWIGHT ARTHUR, English Teacher; *b:* Winnipeg Manitoba, Canada; *m:* Donna J. rose; *c:* Lisa Brucks, Pamela Manassian, Shawna Campbell; *ed:* Univ of Manitoba (BA) Eng, His 1965; Andrews Univ (MA) Schl Admin 1974; Cert Scndry Educ Univ of Manitoba 1966; *cr:* Red River Vly Jr Acad Prin 1966-72; Calgary SDA Schl Prin 1973-74; Churchill HS Tchr, Librn 1974-77; Beirut Overseas Schl Prin 1977-84; Okanagan Adventist Acad Eng Tchr 1984-; *ai:* Careers Coord; NCTE 1993-; Excl Tchng Awd 1992; *home:* 1545 Hollywood Rd S Kelowna BC V1X 4P2 Canada CN *

ROSE, EDWARD JOSEPH, Jr High Teacher; *b:* Sanduksy, OH; *ed:* Bowling Green St Univ (BS) His & Pol Sci Ed 1979; *cr:* Cert Catechist for Diocese of Toledo; *cr:* Sts Peter & Paul 5-8th Grd Tchr 1980-86; St Joseph 6-8th Grd Tchr 1987-; *ai:* Sci Leadership Cncl Rep; Acad Challenge Team Adv; Sci Fair Coord; Retreat Coord; Phi Alpha Theta 1978-; Pi Sigma Alpha 1979-; Sci Ed Cncl of OH 1990-; OH Geographic Alliance 1991-; Sts Peter & Paul Parish 1988-90, Synod Comt Chair; Immaculate Conception Parish 1990-, Rcia Dir; OH Genealogical Soc 1979-; Del to Synod of Diocese of Toledo; Books: Abstract of Monroeville Spectator & Heymans of Kaltenholzhausen; *home:* 138 Greenwood Hts Bellevue OH 44811

ROSE, GEORGE CARL,JR., Business Education Instructor; *b:* Cleveland, OH; *m:* Jane Preston; *c:* Sherry, Jamie; *ed:* Kent St Univ (BS) Soc Stud 1967, (MED) Bus Ed 1970; 14 Addl Credit Hrs Cmptr Instruction; *cr:* Aurora HS Tchr, Bus Dept Chair 1969-; *ai:* Chair Bus Dept, HS Quality Team; Bus Schl Partnership Team; OEA, NEA 1969-; Aurora Ed Assn, Pres 3 Yrs, Treas 15 Yrs; OH BUs Tchr Assn 1969-; First Chrstn Church of Kent 1977-, Elder, Treas 12 Yrs, Chair Stewardship, Fin Comm; Nom Ashland Tchrs Awd; Who's Who Among Scndry Schl Tchrs 1973; *home:* 1768 Elm Dr Kent OH 44240

ROSE, IRENE CARON, French & Latin Teacher; *b:* Oneco, CT; *m:* Perry A.; *c:* Aaron, Dana Rose-Wegiel, Dyana; *ed:* Univ of CT (BA) Fr 1965, (MA) Fr 1967; *cr:* Norwich Free Acad Fr Tchr 1966-71; Plainfield Jr HS FR, Eng Tchr 1975-78; Killingly HS Fr, Latin Tchr 1981-; *ai:* Former Dept Head Frgn Lang; CT Org of Frgn Lang Tchrs, AATF, NAEA, CT Ed Assn 1967-; Justice of The Peace 1971-; *office:* Killingly HS 79 Westfield Ave Danielson CT 06239

ROSE, JEAN BALTZ, Pyramid & Horizons Pgm Dir; *b:* Great Falls, MT; *c:* Mark, David; *ed:* 70 Plus Grad Hrs SUNY at Albany, SUNY at Paltz, Univ of VT & Pepperdine Coll; *cr:* Rosemead Jr HS 1967-68; Scotia-Glenville HS Tchr & Pgm Dir 1975-; Capital Area Schl Dev Assn Asst Dir 1992-95; Acad for Initial Tchr Preparation Clinical Dir 1996; *ai:* Dist Svc Learning Pgm Coord; AFT 1974-; Phi Delta Kappa 1988-; Advy Cncl Cty Office for Aging 1987-94, Sec; Town Sr Citizen Ctr Comm, Resources Comm Chprsn; Christa McAulliffe Flwshp; Honorary PTA Life Mbrshp; Schenectady Cty Human Rights Awd; *office:* Scotia Glenville HS 1 Tartan Way Scotia NY 12302

ROSE, JOAN LEE (TRYTKO), 2nd Grade Teacher; *b:* Wheeling, WV; *m:* Allen Lee; *c:* Johnny, Erin; *ed:* OH Univ (BS) Ed 1970, (MS) Curr, Instruction 1982; *cr:* St John Grd Schl 3rd Grd Tchr 1967-69; Blaine Elem Schl 1st-2nd Grd Tchr 1970-74; Westbrooke Elem Schl 1st Grd Tchr 1974-82; Lansing Primary Schl 2nd Grd Tchr 1982-; *ai:* Bantam Girls Bsktbl Coach 3 Yrs; Parochial Girls Bsktbl Coach 1 Yr; Asst Girls Missy League Sftbl Coach 5 Yrs; Bridgeport Ed Assn 1970-, Various Comms, Rep; OH Ed Assn, NEA 1970-; Cath Womens Club 1973-, Former Sec; PTO 1970-; Home, Schl Assn; St John Cntrl Alumni Assn; Girl Scouts of Amer 1989-, Asst Ldr 7 Yrs; OH Univ Alumni Assn; St Marys Church 1973-, Lector; *home:* 69440 Barton Rd Saint Clairsville OH 43950*

ROSE, JONATHAN E., History Professor; *b:* New York, NY; *m:* Gayle Louise DeLong; *ed:* Princeton Univ (BA) His 1974; Univ of PA (MA) His 1975, (PhD) His 1981; *cr:* Drew Univ Assoc Prof of His 1984; *ai:* Dir Grad Prgm Modern His & Lit; Univ Senate Sec; Univ Lib Comm Mem; Soc for His of Authorshop Rdng & Pub 1991-, Pres & Founder; NE Victorian Stud Assn 1984-, Pres; Authored The Edwardian Temperament 1895-1919; Edited The Revised Orwell; Co-Authored British Lit Publishing Houses 1820-1965; Research Fellowships NEH, Amer His Assn, Eng-Speaking Union & British Inst of US; Articles Pub in Journal of His of Ideas & Journal of British Stud; *office:* Drew Univ History Dept Madison NJ 07940

ROSE, JOYCE LYNNE, English & Writing Lab Teacher; *b:* Lakehurst, NJ; *c:* Gabriel, Toby, Joel; *ed:* Univ of ME at Farmington (BS) Scndry Eng 1987, (BA) Psych 1987; UMO (MS) Literacy 1993; *cr:* Levitt Schl Eng, AP Eng, Writing Lab Tchr 1988-; *office:* Levitt Area HS RR 1 Box 1250 Turner ME 04282

ROSE, KENNETH, Prof of Electrical Engineering; *b:* Bloomington, IN; *m:* Dorcas Baker; *c:* David, Alice; *ed:* Univ of IL (BS) Engrng Physics 1955, (MS) Electrical Engrng 1957, (PHD) Electrical Engrng 1961; *cr:* General Electric Rsrch Lab Physicist 1961-65; Rensselaer Polytechnic Inst Assoc Prof 1965-71, Prof 1971-; *ai:* Solid St Group Coord; IEEE, 1955-, Sr Mem, Cert of Appreciation; AAAS 1964-; MRS 1980-, Symposium Chair; Watervliet Rotary 1985-, Pres; Intnl Assn of Facilitators 1995-; Univ of IL Bronze Tablet 1955; RPI Distngd Fac Awd 1973; Jess E Neal Editorial Achvmt Awd 1980; *office:* Rensselaer Polytechnic Inst 110 8th St Troy NY 12180

ROSE, NANCY SILVIA, French & Spanish Teacher; *b:* Fall River, MA; *m:* Michael; *c:* Mark, Neal; *ed:* Bridgewater St Coll (BA) Fr 1969; *cr:* Fall River Pub Schls Tchr 1969-; *ai:* Fr Club Adv; NEA, MTA 1969-; MAFLA 1985-; *home:* 36 Lancelot Ter Swansea MA 02777

ROSE, PATRICIA COLANGELO, Rdng, Lang Arts & Math Tchr; *b:* PIttsburgh, PA; *ed:* Franciscan Univ (BA) Elem Ed 1969; Duquesne Univ (MS) Rdng 1973; Ed Rsrch, Dev Thinking Math Vol I; *cr:* Brookline Schl Tchr 1969-83; Brookline Elem Tchrs Ctr Dev Demonstration Tchr, Clinica Resident Tchr, Clinic Ldr 1983-89; Brookline Schl Instr Tchr Ldr 1989-; *ai:* Brookline Schl Stu Cncl Spon; AFT, PIttsburgh Fed of Tchrs 1969-, Exec Bd, Elem Group Rep, Bldg Rep; Southwest Reg Lead Tchr Ctr Governing Bd 1989-; Decocratic Comm 1980, Comm Woman; Christa Mc Auliff Flwshp Awds Panel 1987; *office:* Brookline Elem Schl 500 Woodbourne Ave Pittsburgh PA 15226*

ROSE, PATRICIA WALZ, Asst Math Department Chprsn; *b:* Mineola, NY; *m:* William Francis; *c:* Peter Westley, Kristin Rachelle; *ed:* Southampton Coll (BA) Math 1970; Stonybrook Univ (MA LS) Liberal Stud 1974; C. W. Post (PHD) Educl Admin 1987; 75 Addl Credits; *cr:* Riverhead MS Math Tchr 1970-, Asst Dept Chprsn 1985-; *ai:* Suffolk Cty Math Tchrs Assn Coord; Schl Improvement Team; Dist Scndry Curric Comm; NEA, NYSUT, Riverhead Cntrl Fac, NCTM, Suffolk Cty Math Tchrs Assn 1970-; Long Island Learning Disabled Assn 1984-88, Pres 4 Yrs; Westhampton Beach United Meth Church, Admin Bd 10 Yrs, Treas 8 Yrs; Riverhead Cntrl Fac Assn Tchr of Yr 1992; Natl Schl Pub Relations Assn Honor Awd 1989; Who's Who in Amer Edctn 1995; *office:* Riverhead M S 600 Harrison Ave Riverhead NY 11901*

ROSE, PEGGY M., English Teacher; *b:* Rochester, NY; *c:* Jennifer Lapisardi; *ed:* Niagara Univ (BA) Eng 1961, (MA) Eng 1972, (MS) Ed 1984; Attnd St Univ of NY at Fredonia, NY Univ, Long Island Univ; *cr:* Niagara Falls HS Eng Tchr 1961-64, 1968-; *ai:* Lang Arts Dept Chair; Lit Magazine Adv; Shared Decision Making, NFT Bldg Comms; AFT, NYSUT, NCTE, NEA 1961-; *home:* 860 Mohawk St Lewiston NY 14092*

ROSE, RICHARD W., TV Production Teacher; *b:* Sodus, NY; *ed:* Ithaca Coll (BS) Radio & TV Production 1967; SUC at Geneseo (MA) Commnctn 1971; St Univ Coll of NY at New Paltz 18 Creds in Educl Admin; *cr:* Pawling Cntrl Schl Dir of Educl Commnctn 1971-78; Willingboro HS TV Production Instr 1981-90; Bucks Cty Comm Coll Asst Prof Commnctns 1985-90; Hightstown HS TV Prod Tchr Content Specialist 1990; Mercer Cty Comm Coll Asst Prof Commnctns 1991-95; *ai:* HHS Ldrshp Team & Ram Report; EWRSD Tech & Pub Relations Comms; NEA & NJEA 1981-; EW EA 1990-; Amer Legion 1981-; Vietman Veterans of Amer 1994-; VFW 1995-; Bucks Cty Comm Coll Grant; Staff Mem of Month HHS; *office:* Hightstown HS 25 Leshin Ln Hightstown NJ 08520*

ROSE, RICK, Administrator & Football Coach; *b:* Albany, NY; *m:* Margot Johnson; *c:* Lauren; *ed:* Monroe Comm Coll (AAS) Optical Engrng 1977; Southern Meth Univ (BA) Soc Stud, PE, Hlth 1984, (MA) Lbrl Arts 1986; North Adams St Admin; *cr:* Southern Meth Univ Ftbl Coach 1982-86; MacArthur HS Soc Stud, Ftbl, Soccer Coach 1986-90; Lewisville Milliken MS Soc Stud, Ftbl, Track Coach 1990; Troy Cty Schl PE, Ftbl, Hockey, Bsbl Coach 1991; Schenectady HS Admin, Ftbl Head 1992-; *ai:* Head Ftbl, Weight Room Coach; Peer Mediation; Advy Comm; Safe Schls Cmptr; Yth for Understanding 1990-, Coach, US Girls Soccer European Tour 1990-91; Ath, Coaching Schlsp 1982-85; *office:* Schenectady HS 1401 The Plaza Schenectady NY 12308

ROSE, STEVEN A., Mathematics Teacher; *b:* Salem, MA; *m:* Denise; *c:* Michelel Rose Morgan, Scott; *ed:* Bryant & Stratton (AS) Cmptr Programming 1970; Suffolk Univ (BS) Ec 1973; Tchng in Math Lab 1976; Tchng With Logo, Tech in Classroom 1986; *cr:* Milford MS 6th Grd Math Tchr 1974-80; Mid West Schl 7th Grd Math Tchr 1980-95; Stacy MS 7th Grd Math Tchr 1995-; *ai:* Cmptr Club Adv 1986-94; Internet Schl Liaison 1993-; Cmptr Lab Mgr 1986-94; Milford Tchrs Assn, MA Tchrs Assn, NEA 1975-; NCTM; *office:* Stacy MS 66 School St Milford MA 01757*

ROSEBERRY, NINA LOVING, Seventh Grade English Teacher; *b:* Cleveland, OH; *c:* Tiffiany Lilaine; *ed:* Cntrl St Univ (BS) Eng 1968; Cleveland St Univ (MS) Ed & Admin 1986; *cr:* Harry E Davis MS Eng Tchr 1968-74; Lincoln West HS Eng Tchr 1976-79; Wiley MS Eng Tchr 1979-, ESP Coord 1990-94; *ai:* Excl in Stdnts Performance; Cleveland Heights-Univ Heights Schl Dist Coord; Dial-a-Tchr for Cleveland Heights-Univ Heights System Dir; AFT, NEA, OFT 1968-; MS Task Force-Cleveland Heights- Univ Heights 1995-; MS Grouping Comm 1994-95; African-Amer Women Assn Inductee; *office:* Frank L Wiley MS 2181 Miramar Blvd University Heights OH 44118*

ROSE-COLLEY, MARY L., Associate Professor; *b:* Williamsport, PA; *m:* Robert W. Jr.; *c:* Vanessa Leigh; *ed:* Lock Haven Univ (BS) Hlth, PE 1971; PA St Univ (MED) Hlth Ed 1983, (DED) Hlth Ed 1986; *cr:* Bishop Neuman Schl 7th-12th Grd Tchr 1973-82; Penn St Univ Instr 1984-86; East Stroudsburg Univ Asst Prof 1986-90; Lock Haven Univ Assoc Prof 1990-; *ai:* Amer Schl Hlth, Assn Advancement Hlth Ed 1984-; PA Schl Hlth 1984-, Pres, VP, Mbrshp Chair; AAHE Prof of Yr Awd 1993; Distngd Svc Awd; Amer Cancer Soc, Vol; Grants PA Dept of Hlth, USDOE, PA Division ACS; *office:* Lock Haven Univ 114 Himes Hall Lock Haven PA 17745

ROSECRANTS, MARY KATHRYN, English Teacher; *b:* Brockport, NY; *c:* Elizabeth Stull; *ed:* Albion Coll (BA) Eng, Span 1968; SUNY at Brockport (MS) Eng 1972; *cr:* Oneida Cntrl Schl HS Eng, Span Tchr 1968; Brockport Cntrl Schl HS Eng Tchr 1979-; *ai:* Brockport Tchrs Assn Exec Comm; NYSUT, AFT 1982-; Delta Kappa Gamma 1986-; First Presbyn Church 1946-, Pres Bd of Trustees 1979-81, Chprsn Prsnl Comm 1978-79; Steering Comm to Investigate Oversee the Implementtion of a Block Schedule 1992-94; Co-Chair Team to Collect Local Schl, Comm Historical Materials; *office:* Brockport Cntrl Schl 40 Allen St Brockport NY 14420

ROSEGARTEN, MARK HOWARD, Chemistry Teacher; *b:* Poughkeepsie, NY; *ed:* SUNY at New Paltz (MS) Chem, Scndry Ed 1988, (BA) Chem, Scndry Ed 1990; VISION Industry Ed Partnership Prgm; *cr:* Monroe-Woodbury HS Chem Tchr 1988-89; Washingtonville HS Chem Tchr 1989-; *ai:* Sci Club Adv; Hockey Coach; NYSUT 1993-; Amer Online Acad Asstance Ctr 1993-, Chem Tchr; *office:* Washingtonville HS 54 W Main St Washingtonville NY 10992

ROSELLI, ELISE S., Resource Center Teacher; *b:* Newark, NJ; *m:* Frank J.; *c:* Lauren, Stefani; *ed:* Rutgers Coll (BS) Ed 1978; *cr:* Coastal Learning Ctr Tchr for Emotionally Disturbed 1978-85; Toms River Bd of Ed Tchr for Emotionally Disturbed 1985-87, Resource Ctr Tchr 1987-; *office:* Cedar Grove Elem Schl Cedar Grove Rd Toms River NJ 08753

ROSEMAN, MARIA SPEARS, 5th Grade Teacher; *b:* Baltimore, MD; *m:* Jackie; *c:* Pamela, John; *ed:* Coppin St Coll (BA) Elem Ed 1975; Loyola 3 Grad 1994 Tchng High Achievers; STARS Towson 1990; Writing to Learn 1989 Masters Equivalent; *cr:* Baltimore City Pub Schls Tchr 1975-; *ai:* Environmental Tchr Summer Prgm; Church Act; Schl Improvement Team Co-Chprsn; Baltimore City Cncl PTA's Outstdng Tchr 1988; *home:* 3316 Gwynns Falls Pkwy Baltimore MD 21216

ROSEMAN, STEVEN, Marketing Teacher; *b:* Brooklyn, NY; *m:* Maxine Levy Kornblun; *c:* Jennifer, Howard; *ed:* Long Island Univ (BS) Mrktg, Ed 1967, (MBA) Mrktg 1972; Attnd St Johns Univ, Brooklyn Coll; *cr:* John Jay HS Tchr 1966-67; Clara Barten HS Dean, Mrktg Tchr 1967-75; Middlesex Cty Coll Adj Prof 1980-93; Tottenville HS Mrktg Tchr, Co-op Coach, Transportation Testing Coord 1980-; *ai:* DECA Adv; Advertising Club; Driver Ed; NBEA, UFT 1967-; NTS Safety Ed 1970-; Articles Pub; Mrktg Tchr of Yr; Advertising Club Grant; *office:* Tottenville HS 100 Luten Ave Staten Island NY 10312*

ROSEN, CAROL A. (NARDOZZA), Math Teacher; *b:* Lawrence, MA; *m:* Barry S.; *c:* Lindsay M.; *ed:* U Mass at Amherst (BS) Math 1972; Lesley Coll MA Cmptr Ed 1992; Algebra Inst Participant 1992-94; Mentor Tchr Prgm Harvard Univ 1987-89; *cr:* Lawrence HS Math Tchr 1972-; *ai:* Adv NHS; NEA 1972-; *office:* Lawrence HS 233 Haverhill St Lawrence MA 01840*

ROSEN, DIANE L., 7th & 8th Grd Social Stud Tchr; *b:* Brooklyn, NY; *c:* Shari Ascher, Robyn; *ed:* Brooklyn Coll (BS) Psych; 30 Credits Above 30 Grad Credits Psych, Tchng; *cr:* JHS 240 Tchr 16 Yrs; DAvid Marcus Jr HS Tchr, CIT, GATE 9 Yrs; *ai:* Hudde Environmental Action Prgm; Legal Stud Tchr; MSSTNY; NYSST; *office:* JHS 240 2500 Nostrand Ave Brooklyn NY 11210*

ROSEN, EDWARD, Mathematics Teacher; *b:* Hartford, CT; *m:* Karen Macchietto; *c:* Benjamin; *ed:* Univ of CT (BS) Math Ed 1968; Cntrl CT St Coll (MA) Math 1973; RPI-HGC (MS) Cmptr Engrng 1989; *cr:* Weaver HS Math Tchr 1968-94; Univ of Hartford Adjunct Math Instr 1991-; Hartford Pub HS Math Tchr 1994-; *ai:* NCTM 1976-; MAA 1980-; PIMMS Fellow MTI Group; *office:* Hartford Public HS 55 Forest St Hartford CT 06105

ROSEN, EFREM, Professor of Biology; *b:* Brooklyn, NY; *c:* Matthew, Hillary Portnoy, Andrew; *ed:* Brooklyn Coll, Coll Univ of NY (BS) Bio 1957; Long Island Univ (MS) Bio 1961; Rutgers St Univ (PHD) Zoology 1966; Attnd Hofstra Univ Counseling Prgm 18 Semester Hrs; *cr:* Long Island Univ Grad Asst 1959-61; Rutgers Univ Tchng Fellow 1961-66; Hofstra Univ Prof 1966-; *ai:* Self Assessment Comm Chair; Pre-Med Adv; AAUP Exec & Steering Comm; Natural Scis Coord; Adhoc Tenure Comm Chair; AAAS 1967-; AASECT 1974-, Certified Sex Ed Cnslr; ABS 1990-, Certified Sex Therapist; SIECUS, SSSS 1980-; PPNC 1978-; Creative Nurseries 1990-, Bd Mem; Sigma Kappa Alpha, Fac Distinguished Svc Awd; Alpha Epsilon Delta, Honorary Mem; Phi Sigma Soc; Sexuality Counseling Book, 15 Articles in Sexuality 1988; *office:* New Coll 130 Hofstra Univ Hempstead NY 11550

ROSEN, JENNIFER PAYSSE, Bio & Phys Sci Tchr; *b:* Austin, TX; *m:* Freddie Eugene Rosen Jr.; *ed:* IN Univ of PA (BS) Bio in Scndry Ed 1991; Univ of DE Masters of Instruction; *cr:* Laurel Schl Dist HS Sci Tchr 1991-; *ai:* Class of 96 & Sci Olympiad Adv; Discipline, Attendance & Grdng Comms; NEA 1991-; NSTA 1991-; DSEA 1991-; LEA 1991-; DuPont Grant to Attnd Natl NSTA Convention; *office:* Laurel Sr HS 1133 S Central Ave Laurel DE 19956*

ROSEN, SANDRA PLATT, Kindergarten Teacher; *b:* Uniontown, PA; *w:* Samuel (dec); *c:* Mindy Rosen-Stadler; *ed:* Univ of Pittsburgh (BS) Ed 1958, (MED) Ed 1976; *cr:* Lemington 1970-72; Park Place 1972-74; Colfax 1974-77; Crescent Elem Kndgtn Tchr 1977-; *ai:* Pittsburgh Fed of Tchrs 1968-; PA Kndgtn Tchrs 1993-; Allegheny Conf on Comm Dev Awded Nine Grants.*

ROSEN, SUSAN A. C., Assistant Professor of English; *b:* Glen Cove, NY; *m:* Perry; *c:* Sara, Jake; *ed:* St Univ of NY at Albany (BA) His, Ed 1978; Univ of MD (MA) Eng 1983, (PHD) Eng 1994; *cr:* Amer Inst Rsrch Project Dir 1985-90; Univ of MD Eng Instr 1990-94, Adj Asst Prof Eng 1991-; Univ Coll Adj Asst Prof Eng 1991-; Anne Arundel Comm Coll Asst Prof Eng 1994-; *ai:* MLA 1991-; WLA 1989-; ASLE 1993-; Articles Pub; Book Pub Introduction to Writing Course Guide for Eng 101; *office:* Anne Arundel Comm Coll 101 College Pky Arnold MD 21012

ROSENBAUM, MIMI PRAWER, Educational Media Specialist; *b:* Lansberg, Germany; *m:* Steven; *c:* Stacey, Daniel; *ed:* Rutgers Univ at Newark (BA) Soc Stud 1970; Jersey City St Coll (MA) Educl Media Specialist 1985; Post Grad Courses Supvr Cert 1989; Rutgers Univ Tchng Cert 1970; Keane Coll Assoc Media Cert 1973; *cr:* Maple-Lyons Annex Schl Librn 1973-76; Chancellor Ave Annex Schl Librn 1973-76; Ann St Elem Schl Librn 1976-80; Wilson Ave Schl Ed Ctr for Yth Librn 1980-84; East Side HS Head, Staff Librn 1984-; *ai:* Annual Book Fair; Lib Club Supvr; Lincoln-Douglas Debate Coach; Presenting Classes Holocaust; After Schl Tutoring Basic Skills Stdnts; Coord Basic Skills Prgm; Schl Systems Benchmark, Chprsn Media Svcs Mid States Comms; Intnl Night Chprsn; Newark Librns Assn 1973-, Sec; Newark Tchrs Union, AFT 1973-; Essex Cty Librns Assn; Hadassah 1993-; ORT Medwood Chptr 1972-, Bd, Legacy Chprsn, Mbrshp, Installation Comms; *office:* East Side HS 238 Van Buren St Newark NJ 07105*

ROSENBERG, JOHN DAVID, WM Peterfield Trent Eng Prof; *b:* Brooklyn, NY; *m:* Maurine Ann Hellner; *c:* Matthew; *ed:* Columbia Coll (BA) Eng 1950, (MA) Eng 1951; Clare Coll at Cambridge (BA) Eng 1953, (MA) Eng 1958; Columbus Univ (PHD) Eng 1960; *cr:* Columbia Univ Eng Lecturer 1953-54; Coll of City of NY Eng Instr 1954-62; Columbia Univ Eng Asst Prof 1962-65, Eng Assoc Prof 1966-67, Eng Prof 1967-; *ai:* Eng Majors Adv; Composition Comm; Exec Comm Eng Dept; Modern Lang Assn 1962-, Victorian Division Chair; Columbia Coll Alumni Assn 1960-, Bd of Dirs, Hamilton Medal; Phi Beta Kappa 1950-; Guggen Heim Natl Endowment for Hum, Amer Cncl of Learned Socs Flwshps; Articles Pub; *office:* Columbia Univ 116 Street And Broadway New York NY 10027

ROSENBERG, MAXINE H. (EPSTEIN), Elementary Art Teacher; *b:* Rego Park, NY; *m:* Louis H.; *c:* Eric, Leslie, Stacey; *ed:* St Univ Coll at Buffalo (BS) Art Ed 1971; Syracuse Univ 30 Hrs Synaesthetic Ed 1975; *cr:* Chenango Vly Jr HS 7th & 8th Grd Art Tchr 1971-72; Owego-Apalachin Schl Dist K-6th Art Tchr 1972-75; Susquehanna Vly Schls K-6th Grd Tchr 1985-; *ai:* Character Ed & Spring Review Comms; NY St Art Tchrs 1971-; NEA 1971-; Delta Gamma Womens Ed Assn 1994-; Hadassah Womens Org 1975-; Sisterhood at Temple Israel 1975-; Sisterhood at Beth David Synagogue 1981-; Hillel Acad of Broome Cty Bd of Ed 6 Yrs; Binghamton Temple Israel Bd of Trustees 1994-; *home:* 10 Whiting Way Conklin NY 13748

ROSENBERG, MILTON, Professor of English; *b:* Manhattan, NY; *m:* Carole Goldman; *c:* Neil Alan, Brad Prescott; *ed:* Long Island Univ (BA) Eng 1958; New York Univ (MA) Eng 1966; 18 Credits Toward Doctorate at Temple Univ; *cr:* Long Island Univ Adjunct Prof 1961-66; Atlantic Comm Coll Eng Prof 1966-; *ai:* NCTE 1976-; Designer & Developer of Military Simulations-Crisis in Ukraine, Silo 14, Gela Beachhead, Korean Pocket; *office:* Atlantic Comm Coll Rt 2 Mays Landing NJ 08330

ROSENBERG, SCOTT DOUGLAS, Learning Assistance Coord; *b:* Wadsworth, OH; *m:* Patricia L Eckert; *c:* Cara, Jared, Hannah; *ed:* Ashland Coll (BS) Spec Ed & Rdng 1983; Temple Univ MA Prgm Ed Admin; *cr:* Northwestern Local Schl Dist 9th-12th Grd EMR Tchr 1983-84; Schl Dist of Lancaster SMED Tchr 1984-85; Milton Hershey Schl Lang Arts Tchr 1986-90, Learning Assistance Coord 1991-; *ai:* Early Intervention Prgm; *office:* Milton Hershey Schl PO Box 830 Catherine Hall Hershey PA 17033

ROSENBERG, TRACY LEBOWITZ, Performing Arts Teacher; *b:* Brooklyn, NY; *m:* Jeffrey; *c:* Steven; *ed:* Brooklyn Coll (BA) Music Ed 1987, (MA) Music Ed 1996; *cr:* IS 293 Vocal Music Tchr 1987-88; IS 24 Performing Arts Tchr 1988-; *ai:* Spring Musical Production, Traveling Chorus, SI Borough Pres Chorus, PTA Chorus Dir; Sr Orch Conductor; Amer Cancer Soc 1995-; Richmond Theater Collection 1990-, VP; Dist 31 Tchr of Yr 1995, Honorable Mention Tchr of Yr 1994; Nom Patrick Daly Excl in Ed Awd 1994-95; UFT Radio Ads Spokesperson 1996; *office:* IS 24 225 Cleveland Ave Staten Island NY 10308*

ROSENBERG, WILLIAM, Math Teacher; *b:* New York City, NY; *c:* Amy, Matthew; *ed:* C. W. Post (MS) Math Ed 1975; *cr:* Valley Stream Meml Jr HS Math Tchr 1970-80; Valley Stream Cntrl Math Tchr 1980-; *office:* V S Central HS Fletcher Ave Valley Stream NY 11582

ROSENBERGER, LYLE L., Prof of History; *b:* Souderton, PA; *m:* Janet Thuma; *c:* Kathie, Karen, Kyna; *ed:* Millersville Univ (BS) His 1960; Lehigh Univ (MA) Colonial Amer 1966; Ctr for Amer Archaeology Cert; Univ of VA Grad Courses in Archaeology; *cr:* Hempfield HS Tchr 1960-62; Mtshabezi Tchr Trng Inst Instr 1963-64; Leigh Univ Rsrch Fellow 1965-66; Bucks Cty Comm Coll Prof 1966-; *ai:* Tyler Restoration Comm; AFT 1966-; SHA 1981-; Natl Trust 1991-; Natl Endowment for the Hum Yth Pilot Grant 1981; Natl Endowment for the Hum Grant 1988; Bucks Cty Comm Coll Fndtn Grant 1990; Master Tchr Awd; NISOD Intnl Conf on Tchng Excl 1991; *office:* Bucks County Comm Coll Swamp Road Newtown PA 18940

ROSENBERGER, NANCY HARTING, Eng Dept Chprsn & Teacher; *b:* Philadelphia, PA; *m:* Rudy D.; *c:* Philip Boinske, Stefanie Lindquist, Ted Boinske; *ed:* PA St Univ (BS) Eng 1958; West Chester Univ (MA) Eng 1980; 60 Credit Post Grad; Supvrs Cert Eng 1994; *cr:* Hatboro-Horsham Jr HS Eng Tchr 1958-61; Lionville Jr HS Eng Tchr 1970-74; Valley Forge Jr HS Eng Tchr 1974-80; Conestoga HS Eng Tchr & Dept Chair 1980-; *ai:* Philosophers & Thinkers Club Spon; Scholastic Awds, Crisis & Emergency Comms; NEA 1970-; PSEA 1970-; TEEA 1974-; One of Five Finalist PA Tchr of Yr; Natl Endowment for Hum Summer Stud & Ind Study Grants; Pugh Fndtn PA Fellow Grant; *office:* Tredyffrin & Easttown Schl Dis 200 Irish Rd Berwyn PA 19312*

ROSENBERGER, SCOTT EDWARD, Science Teacher; *b:* Allentown, PA; *ed:* Kutztown Univ (BSEd) Bio 1993; Post Grad Stud Kutztown Univ; *cr:* Louis E. Dieruff HS Sci Tchr, ALPFFSS Prgm, Go for Gold Prgm 1993-; *ai:* Key Club Adv; Asst Track, Field Coach; NEA, Allentown Ed Assn 1993-; *office:* Louis E. Dieruff HS Washington & Irving Sts Allentown PA 18103

ROSENBERRY, SUSAN HARTZELL, Fifth Grade Head Teacher; *b:* Chambersburg, PA; *m:* Jeffrey D.; *c:* David G., Timothy J., Shelly R., Chad L.; *ed:* Shippensburg Univ (BSEd) Elem Ed 1985, (MS) Rdng, Rdng Specialist 1992; Admin Courses, UpJohn Co, Kalamazoo Coll Sci; *cr:* Penn St Univ Mont Alto Tutor, Instr for Rdng Dept 1989-94; Chambersburg Area Schl Dist Summer Wkshp, Acad Instr for Sci 1991-94, 5th Grd, Head Tchr 1986-; *ai:* Elem Sci Comm Chambersburg Area Schl Dist; Pilot Pgrms Rdng, Process Writing Chambersburg Schl Dist; PTA; Chambersburg Area Ed Assn, PA St Ed Assn, NEA, NSTA 1989-; Who's Who Women Penn St Univ 1992; Pub Sci Lesson 1992; Tchr of Yr Region 3 Chambersburg Area Schl Dist 1991; *office:* Scotland Elem Schl 3832 Main St Scotland PA 17254

ROSENGARTEN, MARK HOWARD, Chemistry Teacher; *b:* Poughkeepsie, NY; *ed:* SUNY Coll at New Paltz (BA) Chem & Ed 1988, (MS) Chem & Ed 1990; *cr:* Monroe-Woodbury HS Chem Tchr 1989-89; Washingtonville HS Chem Tchr 1989-; *ai:* Hockey Club Adv; Online Tchr Amer Onlies Interactive Ed Svcs; *office:* Washingtonville HS 54 W Main St Washingtonville NY 10992

ROSENSWIE, CARL WILLIAM, Fifth Grade Teacher; *b:* Kane, P Clarion St Univ (BS) Elem Ed 1971; St Bonaventure Univ (MS) Ed A Supervision 1975; Post Master Studies 1992; *cr:* Smethport Area Sc Tchr, Bldg Prin 1971-; *ai:* Safety, Drug Free Schls, Assembly, St Planning, Tech Comms; Dev AIDS Curr; NEA, PSEA, SAEA 1971 C 1978-; *office:* Smethport Area Elem Schl 414 S Mechanic St Sm PA 16749*

ROSENTHAL, LESTER ALAN, Media Generalist; *b:* Brooklyn, N Laurel J. Forcier; *c:* Noel F., Angelica F.; *ed:* Worcester Jr Coll (AA Worcester St Coll (BA) Media, Educl Comm Tech; *cr:* Productio 1976-77; Schl of the Worcester Art Museum, Tchng Asst 19 Goffstown Area HS Media Generalist 1979-; *ai:* Drama Soc Dir NEA-NH 1979-; NHETG 1981-85 Bd of Dir; Educl Theatre Assn Troupe Spon; *office:* Goffstown HS 27 Wallace Rd Goffstown NH 0

ROSENTHAL, MARSHA VYNER, Mathematics Teacher; *b:* New NY; *m:* Richard Lewis; *c:* Scott Nelson; *ed:* OH St Univ (BS) Bus Nazareth Coll (MS) Ed 1980; *cr:* NY St Dept of Labor Claims Ex 1971-75; Mercy HS Math Tchr 1983-84; Mount Saint Joseph HS Mat 1985-87; Saint Marys HS Math Tchr 1987-; *ai:* Frosh Class Ad Dance Comm Chprsn; AMTNYS 1989-; *home:* 186 Schimwo Getzville NY 14068*

ROSENTHAL, NANCY, English Teacher; *b:* Brooklyn, NY; *m:* Pa Brooklyn Coll (BA) His 1965; Boston Univ Grad Schl (MA) Govt Fordham Univ Schl of Ed Rdng Prof Dip 1973; NYU Eng Ed Grad C *cr:* JHS 22 Eng Tchr 1969-80; Louis Armstrong MS Eng Tchr Queens Coll Adj Ed Prof 1985-86; *ai:* Staff Dev Ldr; UFT Exec C Schl Poet, Adv; AFT, UFT 1969-; Natl Acad of Tchng 1982-, VP; 1990-; Jewish Acton Alliance 1992-; Coll, MS Collaborative Prgm; Bitter Honey and Reaching Beyond: Collaborative Learning.*

ROSENZWEIG, JENNIFER LESLIE, English Teacher & Dept Ch New Rochelle, NY; *m:* Jeff; *ed:* Union Coll (BA) Span, Eng 1988; N (MA) Span Lit 1991; Attnd Univ of PA; *cr:* Univ of PA Tchn 1988-89; Lenox Schl Sub Span Tchr 1991; Our Lady of Victory Ac Tchr, Dept Chprsn 1992-; *ai:* Drama, Chrldng Coach; DOROT *home:* 150 East Garden Rd Larchmont NY 10538

ROSEWATER, GAIL ATLESON, French Teacher; *b:* Cleveland, C Robert David; *c:* Amy, Leslie; *ed:* Univ of MI (BA) Fr 1965; Case Univ 15 Hrs; *cr:* Euclid HS Fr, Span Tchr 1965-69; Hawken Uppe Fr, Span Tchr 1970-71; Beaumont Schl Fr, Span Tchr 1985-95; H Upper Schl Fr Tchr 1995-; *ai:* Modern Lang Assn 1965-; Cercle des Francaises 1980-, Sec, VP; Suburban Temple 1971-, Bd Mem; Grant Stud Span; *office:* Hawken Upper Schl 12465 County Line Rd Mills OH 44040*

ROSIC, JEANNETTE LILLY, 1st Grade Teacher; *b:* Fort Knox, K Milija; *c:* Julia, Elizabeth; *ed:* SUC at Buffalo (BS) Elem Ed 1971; at Buffalo (MED) 1975; *cr:* Akron Cntrl Schl 1st & 2nd Grd Tchr *ai:* Lang Art Comm; Bldg Team Chprsn; NYSUT 1972; Akron Fa 1972-; *office:* Akron Central Schl 52 Bloomingdale Ave Akron NY 1

ROSIN, NORMA SILVERMAN, Acad Specialist & Ed Cnsl Boston, MA; *m:* Norman L. M.D.; *c:* Lynn, Jeffrey; *ed:* Boston Uni Ed 1964; Northeastern Univ (MED) Rdng 1967; *cr:* Braintree Pub Remedial Rdng Tchr 1964-68; Northeastern Univ Rdng Clinic 1976-88, Acad Specialist, Instr & Adv 1981-, Ed Consultant 1991-; *a* Tutoring, Comp Assisted Learning & Fac Search Comms; CRA Mem; LAANe 1993-, Bd of Dirs 1995-; NADE 1995-; Temple Action Comm 1993-, Co-Chair 1993-95; *office:* Northeastern Uni Huntington Ave Boston MA 02115

ROSINSKI, CONNIE LOUISE, Mathematics Teacher; *b:* Sandusk *m:* Larry; *c:* Jim Voltz, Ann Marie Valtz Filiere; *ed:* Bowling Green S (BS) Math, Cmptr Sci 1977; Attnd Univ of Toledo, OH St Univ; *cr:* C Local Schls Math Tchr 1977-; *ai:* NHS, Math Club, Math Contes NCTM 1980-; OH Cncl of Tchr of Math 1980-, Tchr of Yr; Greater Cncl of Tchrs of Math 1980-, Rep, Speaker at St & Regnl Confs Martha Holden Jennings Scholar; *office:* Otsego Local Schls PO B Tontogany OH 43565*

ROSKEY, MARY LOUISE VOGEL, 5th Grade Teacher; *b:* Camde *m:* Donald; *c:* Donald Jr., Michael; *ed:* Glassboro St Coll (BA) El 1974, (MA) Commnctn 1984; 30 Grad Credits; *cr:* Jaggard Elem S Grd Tchr 1974-89; Rice Elem Schl 5th Grd Tchr 1989-; *ai:* Sftbl & S Coach; Pride in Ed Comm Chprsn; Evesham Twp Ed Assoc 1974- Rep, Grievance Comm, Ldrshp for Ed Awd 1993-94; NJEA 1974-; 1974-; Waretown Ed Cncl 1995-; Barnegat Soccer League; *home:* 29 Dr Waretown NJ 08758

ROSKO, JOHN A., Computer Technology Instructor; *b:* Mc Kees PA; *ed:* Univ of Pittsburgh (BS) Bus Ed 1986; Robert Morris (MS) 1989; *cr:* Conneaut Lake HS Bus Ed Tchr 1986-90; Cmptr Tech Sch 1990-93; Forbes Rd East Schl Instr 1993-; *ai:* NEA, PSEA 1986-; Pi Epsilon 1987-, Treas; Kenned Twp Fire Dept 1984-, Fund Drive *office:* Forbes Rd E Area Voc Tech Sch 607 Beatty Rd Monroevi 15146

ROSKO, KEITH ALLAN, Art Teacher; *b:* Binghamton, NY; *m:* Lyn Smith; *ed:* Kutztown Univ (BS) Art Ed 1988; Marywood Coll Illustration 1996; *cr:* Chenango Forks HS Art Tchr 1988-; *ai:* Art Adv; Freelance Illustrator, Fine Artist Magazine Pub, Book Cover; Chenango Forks HS 1 Gordon Dr Binghamton NY 13901

ROSKO, KEVIN FRANCIS, PE Teacher & Coach; *b:* Binghamto *m:* Regena Rae Kingsley; *c:* Brett Francis, Megan Elizabeth, Joel Ri *ed:* Cortland St Coll (BS) PE 1980, (MS) PE 1985; Brockport S (CAS) Schl Admin 1990; Driver Ed Cert 1980; *cr:* Moravia Cntrl Sc Dr Ed Tchr, Coach 1980-83; Campbell-Savona CS PE Tchr, Coach Haverling Jr Sr HS Summer Driver Ed Tchr 1988-; *ai:* Girls Soccer, Coach; Wrestling Tournament Dir; Intramural Indoor Soccer, Wre Scoretable, Elem Pee-Wee Soccer Prgm Adv; NYS Coaches Assn Track Honor Awd 1990; Nat Soccer Coaches Assn of Amer 1995-; N NFICA 1980-; NYSAHPERD 1985-; St Joseph's Church 1989-, L Twin Rivers Track Club, Pres; Articles Pub Ath Dir & Coach, Na News; IBC Men of Achvmt Awd 1993; Who's Who Among Amer Edu 1989, 1991-92; *office:* Campbell-Savona Jr Sr HS 8455 County R Campbell NY 14821

ROSKOWSKI, SANDRA LEE, French & Spanish Teache Wilkes-Barre, PA; *ed:* Mansfield Univ (BS) Fr 1971; Bloomsburg Post Grad Fr 24 Credits; Millersville Univ 18 Credits Toward Perm Cert Span; Laval Univ Quebec, Canada 6 Credits Fr; Masters Equiva Fr 1995; *cr:* Crestwood Schl Dist Fr Tchr 1971-, Fr & Span Tchr 199 Trip Adv Fr, Span NYC Annual Trip; NEA, PSEA 1971-; AATF Delta Kappa Gamma 1990-, VP; *office:* Crestwood HS 281 Mountain Mountain Top PA 18707

ROSNER, MERRILY, English Teacher; *b:* Bronx, NY; *c:* Samue Cortland St (BA) Speech & Theater Arts 1972, (MS) Rdng 1980; H Univ (CAS) Ed Admin 1984; *cr:* Ononduga-Madison BOCES GED 1976-80; Start Ctr Rdng Tchr 1980-82; DeWitt Clinton HS Eng Tchr *ai:* Key Club Adv; Tech Preparation Eng Curr Dev; UFT 1986-; *offic* Witt Crinton H S 100 W Mosholu Pkwy Bronx NY 10468

ROSNICK, KATHY CONRAD, Mathematics Teacher; *b:* Mt Ple PA; *m:* William A.; *c:* Leeann; *ed:* WV Univ (BA) Math 1972; Ur urgh (MED) Math Ed; 30 Credits at California Univ of PA 1972; *cr:* rset Area Schls Math Tchr 1973-75; Yough Schl Dist Math Tchr 77; Mt Lebanon Schl Dist Math Tchr 1977-; *ai:* MLEA, PSEA & 1977-; NCTM 1991-; Phi Beta Kappa; *office:* Mt Lebanon Sr H S Mt on Schl Dist 7 Horsman Dr Pittsburgh PA 15228

ICK, ROBERT, Vocational Graphic Arts Tchr; *b:* St Louis, MO; *m:* ope A. Davison; *c:* Vonnie Mull, Avery; *ed:* Kent St Univ (BS) Ed (MED) Voc Ed 1977; *cr:* Barberton HS Graphic Arts Instr 1973-; *ai:* Voc Graphic Arts Club Adv 1973-; NEA, BTA 1973-; *office:* rton HS 489 W Hopocan Ave Barberton OH 44203

, ALLAN F., High School Technology Teacher; *b:* Brooklyn, NY; *m:* ; *c:* Eric, Stacey; *ed:* City Coll of NY (BS) Indstrl Arts Ed 1970, Scndry Ed, Fine Arts 1974; *cr:* Sheepshead Bay HS Indstrl Arts Tchr 73; James Madison HS Indstrl Arts Tchr 1973-75; Tottenville HS Tchr 1976-; *ai:* AVA 1993-; Sweetbrook Civic Assn 1975-, Founding Treas; Coltsbrook Homeowners Assn 1987-, Founding Mem; Tchr of e Gen John A. Lejeune Awd; *office:* Tottenville HS 100 Luten Ave Island NY 10312

, BARBARA, AP Government Instructor; *b:* Brooklyn, NY; *m:* rd; *c:* Garrett, Zachary; *ed:* LIU (BA) His 1968; Brooklyn Coll (MA) ud 1971; *cr:* Brooklyn Tech HS Soc Stud Tchr 1968-; *ai:* UFT 1970-; Brooklyn Tech HS 29 Fort Greene Pl Brooklyn NY 11217

, CARL ANTHONY, Assistant Professor; *b:* New Castle, PA; *m:* e Lynn Baker; *c:* Ashley, Matthew, Eric; *ed:* PA St Univ (BS) Animal 979; Univ of Pittsburgh (BSN) Nrsng 1985; Duquesne Univ (MSN) 1994; Advanced POst Masters Credits 3 Pharmacology, 3 physiology; *cr:* Shadyside Hosp Staff Nurse 1985-89; Shadyside Schl of Nrsng Instr 1989-94; Duquesne Univ Asst Prof 1994-; *ai:* ntnl Nrsng Comm; CPR Instr; Intnl Nrsng Ed Nicaraqua; Amer Assn al Care Nurses 1995-, Wkshp Chair; Sigma Theta Tau 1994-, Pub Fac Dev Frant 1996; 2 Articles Reviewed by Journal of Nurse ; *office:* Duquesne Univ 600 Forbes Ave Pittsburgh PA 15282*

, CAROL FROST, Latin Teacher; *b:* Boston, MA; *m:* Stephen Alan; herine W., Jonathan R.; *ed:* Wheaton Coll (BA) Classics 1964; Bryn Coll (MA) Latin 1966; Dartmouth Classics Summer Inst; Tufts Univ er Classics Prgm; *cr:* Beaver Cty Day Schl Latin Tchr 1966-70; Schl Head Latin Dept Tchr 1979-; *ai:* Yrbk, Comm Svc Adv; Coord al Stud Prgm; Head Adv 9th Grd; Amer Classical League 1964-; Numismatic Soc 1990-; Leap 1992-, Bd Mem; word-Deephaven Camps 1992-, Bd Mem.

, CHARLES DANIEL, 6th Grade Teacher; *b:* Uniontown, PA; *m:* ine T. Hrisoulas; *ed:* CA Univ of PA (BA) Elem Ed 1973; Inst for Therapy 1989; Post Grad Stud Penn St Univ; *cr:* Fox Chapel Area dist 6th Grd Tchr 1973-; *ai:* Girls Var Bsktbl Coach; Born to Run e Commissionaer; Girls Im Dir; Stu Act, SST Comms; Fox Chapel er Club; PSEA Fox Chapel, NEA 1973-; Gift of Time Tribute 1990-, Westinghouse Thanks to Tchrs Nom 1993, 1994; *home:* 412 Clifton lenshaw PA 15116

, CHARLES W.,JR., Science & Chemistry Teacher; *b:* Lake es, LA; *m:* Barbara A. Thomas; *c:* Rhonda C., Andrea E.; *ed:* Howard (BS) Chem 1959; Amer Univ (MSST) Chem, Earth Sci 1975; Grad Howard Univ, NC A&T Univ, Bowie St Univ; *cr:* Cardozo HS Sci Tchr 72; Bladensburg HS Sci Tchr 1972-; *ai:* Sci Dept, Sci Stu Mentors ; Mngmt Team; Instrl Cncl; Awds, Christa Mc Auliffe Awds Selection ns; Grd Level Acad Adv; NEA, MD St Tchrs Assn, Prince George Cty s Assn 1972-; MD Assn of Sci Tchrs 1980-; Alpha Phi Alpha Inc; a Epsilon Lambda Chptr 1956-72, VP, Cor Sec, Rec Sec; Peppermill Civic Assn 1967-; Outstdng Sci Tchng Awd 1991; Washington Post s in Ed Awd 1992; Prince George's Cty Bd of Ed Cert of Recognition *office:* Bladensburg HS 5610 Tilden Rd Bladensburg MD 20710

, ELSE ADELHELM, Sixth Grade English Teacher; *b:* Germany; ward; *c:* Christa Maguire; *ed:* Chesapeake Coll (AA) Hum, Soc Sci, 1972; Salisbury St Univ (BS) Elem Ed 1974, (MED) Ed, Psych 1979; ansgehilfen Brief Germany; *cr:* Lockerman MS 6th Grd Tchr 3 Yrs; sboro Elem Schl 6th Grd Tchr 20 Yrs; Chesapeake Rehabilit Ctr ator 7 Yrs; Roto Gmbht Office Mgr 7 Yrs; *ai:* Chess Club Adv; SIT, Mngmt Comms; MSTA, CCTA, NEA 1972-; Jr Auxiliary Meml Hosp , Information Desk, 1000 Hrs; *home:* 23019 Tuckahoe Springs Dr n MD 21629*

, HILARY KRISTEN, Lecturer in English; *b:* Pullman, WA; *ed:* of CA at Berkeley (BA) Eng 1985; Southern IL UNiv at Carbondale Eng 1989; Attnd ABD, SUNY at Binghamton; *cr:* SUNY at amton Adj Lecturer 1994-; *ai:* Modern Lang Assn 1993-; *office:* at Binghamton Dept of English SUNY Binghamton NY 13902

, JAMES ANTHONY, Math Teacher; *b:* Berwick, PA; *m:* Carol Boone; *c:* Danielle Sadock, Jennifer, Erin Reagan; *ed:* Bloomsburg (BS) Scndry Ed, Math 1969; Kent St Univ Summer Inst 8 Credit hrs; Cmptr Sci, Ed Credits; *cr:* Milton Jr HS Math Tchr 1969; Berwick Schl Dist Math Tchr 1969-; *ai:* BAEA, PSEA, NEA 1969-, Bldg Rep, Sabbatical at Nuclear Trng Ctr 1985-86; *office:* Berwick Area HS Fowler Ave Berwick PA 18603*

, JANET GRIMM, Sixth Grade Teacher; *b:* Celina, OH; *m:* Edward ; *c:* Mark; *ed:* OH St Univ (BS) Elem Ed 1982; Univ of Dayton (MS) Ed 1986, Ed Spec 1996; Course Conversational Japanese; Talents nited Prgm; Ferguson Florissant Writers Project; *cr:* Sidney City 6th Grd Tchr 1982-; *ai:* Sci Fair, Welfare Comm Chm; Curr Cncl Rep; y Ed Assn Rdng & Lang Course Stud Comm; NEA, OEA 1983-; y Ed Assn 1983-, Building Rep 1990 Do'er's Awd 1986; Shelby Cty Rdng Assn 1990-; Women of Moose 1987-; Humane Society 1988; Cancer Society & March of Dimes Vol; Summa Awd OH St Univ Honda of Amer Fnd Eductor to Japan 1988; Sidney City Schl Tchr 1991; Who's Who in Amer Ed 1992-93; *home:* 411 Sunshine Dr y OH 45365

, JOAN HEITZ, Sci & Social Studies Teacher; *b:* Delphos, OH; *m:* ge A.; *c:* John, Amy; *ed:* Coll of St Teresa at Winona (BA) Soc Stud, 955; Attnd Univ of AZ, OH St Univ, Miami Univ, Univ of Cincinnati, ose St; *cr:* Ross HS Sci, Soc Stud Tchr 1955-61; Sycamore HS Soc Tchr 1961-63; Our Lady of Sacred Heart Schl Sci, Soc Stud Tchr 68; St Margaret Mary Sci, Soc Stuc Tchr 1978-; *ai:* Sci Club Adv, ; NCEA 1978-; SECO 1980-; ACS 1995-; Coll Club of Cincinnati -; Fifth, Third Bank Charlotte Schmidlap Grants 1994-95; Amer Chem Grant 1995; Conservation Tchr of Yr 1993; Governor's Sci Awd -95; Sci Tchr of Yr Sigma Xi Miami Univ 1995; Grant to Stud ation San Jose St 1995; Grant Genetic Engrng Miami Univ 1993; es Pub.

, JOHN JOSEPH, Fourth Grade Teacher; *b:* Meshoppen, PA; *m:* cia Jane Davitt; *c:* Lindsey, Jenna; *ed:* Mansfield St Coll (BS) Elem 974; 48 Credit Hrs in Grad Courses; *cr:* Lincolnshire Schl 6th Grd 1974-76; Mill City Elem Schl 4th Grd Tchr 1977-; *ai:* Saint Jude ital Math-A-Thon Project Chm; Local PTA, VP; *home:* RR 1 Box Factoryville PA 18419*

, JULIETTE MARIE (JENEAULT), Mathematics Teacher; *b:* nsburg, NY; *m:* Kevin C.; *ed:* Albany St (BA) Math 1991; Potsdam St redit Hrs; *cr:* Ogdensburg Free Acad Summer Schl Math Tchr -95; Adirondack Cntrl Schl Math Tchr 1992-; *ai:* AFT, NYSUT 1992-, Treas 1995-96; *office:* Adirondack Central School Rt 294 Boonville NY 13309*

ROSS, KAREN SWINEHART, Elementary Kindergarten Tchr; *b:* Ashland, OH; *m:* Ronald R.; *c:* Jacob C.; *ed:* Manchester Coll (BS) Elem Ed 1979; *cr:* Living Vine Chrstn Schl Elem Tchr 1985-86; Chrstn Flwshp Schl Tchr 1986-; *ai:* ACSI 1986-; OSU Acad Challenge Prgm 1991; Presenter Toledo Conf Math Tchrs 1991; *home:* 722 Maple Ave Newark OH 43055

ROSS, LLOYD H., Director of Bands; *b:* Nicholson, PA; *m:* Joan E.; *c:* Sharon Ross Pickersgill, Jeffrey; *ed:* Susquehanna Univ (BS) Music Ed 1970; West Chester Univ (MM) Music Ed 1974; Grad Stud Music Ed 3 Continuing Ed Credits Villanova Univ 1992, 3 Grad Credits Duquesne Univ at Pittsburgh 1992, 5 Grad Credits Univ of DE at Newark 1986, 1991, 2 Inservice Prof Growth Credits Mid Sts Evaluation DPI 1991, 6 Grad Credits West Chester Univ 1977, 1984, 6 Continuing Ed Credits Berklee Schl of Music at Boston 1976, 1979, 3 Grad Credits Ithaca Univ 1976, 10 Continuing Ed Credits Peabody Conservatory at Baltimore 1971, 1976; *cr:* Newark HS Assoc Band Dir, Marching Band Co-Dir 1970-73, Bands Dir 1973-; Susquehanna Univ Part-time Fac 1976; *ai:* BAnd Front, W W Ens Coach; Music Edctrs Natl Conf 1970-, Cty Chair; DE Music Edctrs Assn; Natl Band Assn 1970-; Music Com 1974-, Chair; First St Sym Bd 1978-88, Dir; First St Symphonic Band Conductor 1978-88; New Castle Cty Concert Band Festival Chair 1971; NCC Field Band Festival Chair 1977; Advertising Ed DMEA Notes Chair 1972-78; Tchr of Yr 1990; New Castle Cty Area III Tchr of Yr 1980; Citation Excl Natl Band Assn 1975; Named Outstdng Young Men Amer 1972; *home:* 17 Hillcroft Rd Newark DE 19711

ROSS, MADELINE (LEMBERG), Fifth Grade Teacher; *b:* Brooklyn, NY; *m:* Michael D.; *c:* Lisa, Matthew; *ed:* Brooklyn Coll (BA) Elem Ed 1967, (MS) Elem Schl Math for Tchrs 1970; 60 Addl Credit Hrs; *cr:* P S 279 5th-6th Grd Math Tchr 1967-70; Forest Lake Elem Schl 2nd, 5th-6th Grd Tchr 1983-; *ai:* Parent Tchr Bldg Comm Co-Chair; Wantagh Jewish Ctr Post HS Chprsn; Wantagh United Tchrs 1983-, Exec Bd; Jewish Tchrs Assn 1983-, Schl Rep; Wantagh Jewish Ctr 1972-, Bd of Trustees; ORT 1974-; Hodassah 1987-; Jewish Tchrs Assn Awd; Started Pre-Schl Prgm 1979; *office:* Forest Lake Elem Schl 3100 Beltagh Ave Wantagh NY 11793

ROSS, MARY BETSY, HS English & Journalism Tchr; *b:* Bridgeport, CT; *ed:* St Joseph Coll (BA) Eng 1964; Univ of Bridgeport (MA) Eng 1972; 6th Yr at Fairfield Univ Admin, Supvervision 1979; Trng as a Mentor, Cooperating Tchr; *cr:* Tomlinson Jr HS Eng Tchr 1964-65; Stratford HS Eng, Jrnlsm Tchr 1965-; *ai:* Newspaper Adv; Stering Comm for NEASC Evaluation; Dept Curr Revision Comm; NEA, CT Ed Assn 1964-; Stratford Ed Assn 1965-; NCTE; Black Rock Comm Cncl, Past Recording Sec; Alumni Assn; *office:* Stratford HS 45 N Parade St Stratford CT 06497

ROSS, MARY JO, Fourth Grade Teacher; *b:* Cincinnati, OH; *ed:* Edgecliff Coll of Xavier Univ (BA) Art 1972; Xavier Univ (MA) Elem Ed 1996; Addl Hrs Multiage Classrooms; Child Abuse Prevention Trng; Peer Mediation; Cooperative Learning; Courses from Soc for Dev Trng; CEPUP; Urban Initiatives Summer Inst; *cr:* St Veronica Schl 1-8 Grd Art Tchr 1976-79; St Dominic Schl 4 Grd, Art Tchr 1979-80; Guardians Angels Schl 2, 4, 5 Grds Tchr 1980-89; Cincinnati Pub Schls 3-6 Grd Tchr 1989-; *ai:* PTA Tchr Rep Bd Mem; TBC, Carnival Chpsn; AFT, Cincinnati Cncl of Edctrs, Cincinnati Fed of Tchr 1989-; Eunice Combs Rdng Cncl 1989-, Bd Mem; NSTA Convention, Miami Univ Math, Sci Ed Conf Presenters; Greater Cincinnati Fnd Learning Links Mini-Grant; Charlotte Schmidlapp Fund Grant; *office:* Cincinnati Pub Schls 6829 Stewart Rd Cincinnati OH 45236*

ROSS, PATRICIA MAY (DURKIN), Emergency Med Tech Instr; *b:* Altoona, PA; *m:* William V.; *c:* Cassie Ann, Whitney Marie, William V. Jr., Anthony Thomas, Emily Lynn; *ed:* Southern Alleg EMS Cert Emergency Med Tech 1986; Altoona Voc Tech Licensed Practical Nrs 1993; Commonwealth of PA Continuing Ed Deputy Coroner 1994-95; *cr:* Southern Alleg EMS CPR, EMT Instr 1986-; Duncansville Ambulance Svc EMT Driver 1986-; Mercy Hospital Altoona Skilled Worker in ICCU & Emergency Room 1994-; Blair Cty Coroners Office Deputy Coroner 1994-; *ai:* Firemen Assn 1986-; Coroners Assn 1994-; Vol Fire Co 1986-; *office:* Southern Alleghenies EMS Old Farm Office-1 Carriage House Duncansville PA 16635

ROSS, REBECCA HARRIS, 1st Grade Tchr; *b:* McCook, NE; *m:* Royce A.; *c:* Malcolm, Bruce; *ed:* Houghton Coll (BA) Elem Ed & Soc Sci Tchr 1970; SUNY at Geneseo (MS) Rdng Ed 1973; *cr:* Franklinville Cntrl Schl 1-5th Grd Tchr 1970-; *ai:* Safety & Rdng Comms; NYSUT 1970-; Delta Kappa Gamma 1971-; Presenter St Rdng Convention & NY St Assn of Admins; *office:* Franklinville Central Schl 32 N Main St Franklinville NY 14737

ROSS, ROBERT JON, Social Studies Teacher; *b:* Chicago, IL; *m:* Susan Post; *c:* Jason, Sarah, Peter; *ed:* Beloit Coll (BA) Govt 1966; Univ of WI (MAT) His 1972; Univ of MA 3 Credit Hrs; Westfield St Coll 9 Credit Hrs; *cr:* Mohawk Trail Regnl HS Soc Stud Tchr 1968-; *ai:* Var Golf Coach; MTA, NEA 1970-; ACSS; Woodrow Wilson Fellow 1994; Kennedy Lib Tchr Awd 1990; Horace Mann Grant; Natl Endowment Hum Flwshp 1989; *office:* Mohawk Trail Regional HS Rt 112 Buckland MA 01370

ROSS, ROBERT JON SANFORD, Department Chair of Sociology; *b:* New York, NY; *m:* Marion Karyl Levenson; *c:* Gabriel, Rachel; *ed:* Univ of MI (BA) Pol Sci 1963; Univ of Chicago (MA) Sociology 1966, (PHD) Sociology 1975; Univ of London Post Grad Stud 1963-64; *cr:* New Univ Conf Exec Dir 1968-69; Univ of MI at Ann Arbor Rsrch Assoc 1969-72; Clark Univ Asst to Full Prof 1972-, Dept Chair 1975-78, 1980-81, 1985-86, & 1993-; *ai:* Editorial Bd, Book Review, Socialism, Democracy & Assoc Ed; Amer Sociological Assn; Democratic Town Comm 1982-; Dynamy Ed Fndtn 1993-, Bd of Dirs; Southborough Openland Fndtn 1993-, Bd of Dirs; Wachusset Reservoir Watershed Citizens Advy Bd 1993-; Numerous Articles Pub; Co-Author Global Capitalism 1990; Harvard Univ Hoopes Tchng Awd 1991; *office:* Clark Univ 950 Main St Worcester MA 01610*

ROSS, RONALD OPHERES, Principal; *b:* New York, NY; *m:* Cynthia Chandler; *c:* Erica Chew, Derek, Kelly, Lauren; *ed:* Howard Univ (BA) Pol Sci, Ec 1967; NY Univ (MA) Scndry Ed, Curr 1975, (PHD) Ed Adm; *cr:* James F. Cooper Jr HS Soc Stud Tchr 1969-72; Wingate Prep HS Soc Stud Tchr 1973, Prin 1974-75; HS of Printing Soc Stud Tchr, Dean of Stdnts 1976-80; Park East HS Asst Prin 1982-92; Unity HS Prin 1992-; *ai:* NASSP, ASCD 1991-; Ed Professions Dev Act Fellow 1975-77; *office:* Unity HS 121 Avenue Of The Americas New York NY 10013

ROSS, ROYCE A., 6th Grade Teacher; *b:* Brant Lake, NY; *m:* Rebecca Harris; *c:* Malcolm, Bruce; *ed:* Houghton Coll (BA) Soc Stud 1961; Attnd SUNY at Fredonia, SUNY at Geneseo, Univ of KY; *cr:* Franklinville Cntrl Schl 6th Grd Tchr 1965-; *ai:* Var Sftbl Coach; AFT 1965-; NYSUT 1965-, Pres 3 Terms; *home:* 46 Colonial Village Allegany NY 14706*

ROSS, SANDRA L., Family & Consumer Science Tchr; *b:* Tarentum, PA; *m:* Paul E.; *c:* Kristen, Natalie; *ed:* IN Univ of PA (BS) Home Ec Ed 1974; Univ of Pittsburgh Carlow Coll Grad Work; *cr:* St Joseph Schl Home Ec Instr 1974-77; Highlands HS Family Consumer Sci Instr 1977-; *ai:* Hlth Fair Comm, Svc Learning Comm & Graduation comm Chprsn; Teen Parenting Coord; ASCD 1995-; Holy Martyrs & Chrstn Mother 1985-; Family Ctr Adv Bd 1993-; *office:* Highlands HS Idaho At Pacific Natrona Heights PA 15065

ROSS, SUSAN, Art Teacher; *b:* New York, NY; *c:* Rachel; *ed:* NY Univ (BA) Fine Art 1970, (MA) Fine Art 1975; Parsons Schl of Design; *cr:* Jr HS 51 Art Tchr 1970-75; IS 145 Art Tchr 1979-; *ai:* Spcl Act Coord; Art Dept Chm; Jackson Hghts Beautification Group 1990-, Sec & Dir; *office:* Joseph Pulitzer Jr HS 145 33-34 80th St J Hts Queens New York NY 10021*

ROSS, SUSAN CHASIN, High School Physical Educator; *b:* Brooklyn, NY; *m:* Patrick; *c:* Leigh; *ed:* SUNY at Brockport (BS) Hlth & PE 1966; New York Inst of Tech (MS) Human Relations 1984; 60 Credits Beyond Masters Degree UC Irvine, SUNY at Plattsburgh, CW Post Coll, Hofstra Univ; *cr:* Keeseville Elem Schl PE Tchr 1966-69; Fairfield Elem Schl PE Tchr 1970-81; Massapequa HS PE Tchr 1981-; *ai:* Class of 1997 Adv; Renaissance & Sr Awds Comms; NYSAHPER 1966-; AFT 1970-; NYSUT 1970-; *office:* Massapequa HS 4925 Merrick Rd Massapequa NY 11758

ROSS, THOMAS TOD, English & Reading Teacher; *b:* Columbus, OH; *m:* Anne Marie; *ed:* Bowling Green St Univ (BA) Eng & Tech Writing 1990, (BA) Eng Ed 1992; Rdng Endorsement 1993; Working Toward Masters in Rdng Ed; *cr:* Bowling Green City Schls Eng & Rdng Tchr 1993-; *ai:* Jr HS Ftbl Head Coach; NEA 1996; PTO, HS Rep; *office:* Bowling Green City Schls 530 W Poe Rd Bowling Green OH 43402*

ROSSBACH MC SHANE, NANCY BOURASSA, Third Grade Teacher; *b:* North Adams, MA; *m:* Donald M.; *ed:* North Adams St Coll (BS) Elem Ed 1967, (MS) Elem Ed 1973; 18 Addl Credit Hrs; *cr:* Commercial Street Schl 3rd Grd Tchr 1967-81; Adams Meml Schl 3rd Grd Tchr 1981-94; C. T. Plunkett Schl 3rd Grd Tchr 1994-; *ai:* Schl Cncl; Adams Cheshire Reg Sch Dist Safety Comm; MTA, NEA 1967-; Adams Cheshire Tchrs Assn 1967-, Former Bldg Rep; St Francis Church 1992-, Lector, RCIA Prgm Spon; Williamstown Theater Festival 1990-, Vol Usher; *office:* C T Plunckett Elem Schl 14 Commercial St Adams MA 01220

ROSSELL, JOAN MILLER, 7th Grade Reading Specialist; *b:* Rochester, PA; *m:* David John; *c:* John Charles, James David; *ed:* Slipper Rock Univ (BS) Elem 1970; Millersville Univ (ME) Elem 1989; 15 Addl Hrs; *cr:* Millcreek Schl Dist Elem Tchr 1970-76; Neff Elem Schl Elem Tchr 1987-90; Manheim Twp MS Rdg Specialist Title I 1990-91, Rdg Specialist Title I & Dev 1991-; *ai:* Stu Assistance Prgm; Title I Svcs Planning Comm; Rdng Across the Disciplines Wkshp Presenter; IRA, PA St Ed Assn, Mnaheim Twp Ed Assn, Keystone St Rdng Assn 1989-; Lancaster, Lebanan Rdg Cncl 1989-; Manheim Twp MS PTO 1992-, Tchr Rep; Neffsville Elem PTO 1976-, PA Parent Partner Vol Awd 1986; People to People Literacy Del to China 1993; Article Pub; *office:* Manheim Township Middle Schl 5134 School Rd Lancaster PA 17606

ROSSETTI, PAMELA HAMMOND, Fifth Grade Teacher; *b:* Portsmouth, NH; *m:* David J.; *c:* Erin Lord Mc Allister, Deanna; *ed:* Northern Essex Comm Coll at Haverhill (AS) Mental Hlth 1979; Notre Dame Coll at Manchester (BA) Elem Ed 1982; Lesley Coll at Cambridge (MED) Creative Arts in Ed 1994; Creative Arts & Spec Needs Stu; *cr:* Lincoln Street Schl Sixth Grd Tchr 1982-84; Main Street Schl Fifth Grd Tchr 1984-93; Lincoln Street Schl Fifth Grd Tchr 1993-; *ai:* Dist Ed Improvement Comm; NEA 1982-; Friends of Lib 1989-; *office:* Lincoln Street Schl 25 Lincoln St Exeter NH 03833

ROSSETTI-BAILEY, DONNA L., Art Teacher; *b:* Saugus, MA; *m:* James Joseph Bailey Jr.; *c:* Christina Suzanne Bailey; *ed:* Boston Univ Schl of Fine Arts (BFA) Art Ed 1974; Attnd Bridgewater St Coll, Museum Schl in Boston, South Shore Art Ctr, Duxbury Art Assn, Cambridge Ctr for Adult Ed; *cr:* Rockland Jr HS Art Tchr 1974-78; Rockland HS Art Tchr 1978-; *ai:* Assist with Portfolio Preparation Sr Art Stdnts, Images Art, Lit Publication; NEA, MTA, PCEA 1974-; Advy Bd Scholastic Art Awds 1988-; MA Alliance for Arts Ed 1995-; North River Arts Assn 1988-, Honorable Mention Pastel 1990; South Shore Art Ctr 1990-, 2nd Place Pastel Drawing 1994; Helen Bumpus Art Gallery 1992-93, Bd of Dirs; Outstdng Art Edctr MA Alliance for Arts Ed 1985; Promising Practice Awds 1985; Horace Mann Awd for Innovative Curr 1987; *office:* Rockland HS MacKinlay Way Rockland MA 02370

ROSSETTOS, JOHN NICHOLAS, Professor of Mechanical Engrng; *b:* Nisyros, Greece; *m:* Elizabeth Pureka; *c:* Nicholas, Linda; *ed:* MIT (BS) (MS) Aeronautical Engrng 1956; Harvard Univ (PHD) Applied Math 1964; *cr:* NASA Langley Research Ctr Aerospace Scientist 1964-66; AVCO Corp Sr Staff Scientist 1966-69; Northeastern Univ Mechanical Engr Prof 1969-; MIT Visiting Assoc Prof 1970; Harvard Honorary Research Assoc 1979; *ai:* Senate AEOC Chm; Amer Soc of Mechanical Engrs 1968-, Local Chapter Treas, Named Fellow 1991; Amer Acad of Mechanics 1970-; NASA Langley Res Ctr, NASA Lewis Res Ctr, Contracts Army Materials & Mechanics Research Lab Grants; Book Finite Element Method Pub 1976; *home:* 14 Dana Ave Winchester MA 01890

ROSSI, DOMINIC SAVIO RICHARD, Director of Choral Activities; *b:* Oyster Bay, NY; *ed:* St Vincent Coll (BM) Music Ed 1984; St Vincent Seminary (MDiv) Theology 1991; Carnegie Mellon Univ (MFA) Orch & Choral Conducting 1993; *cr:* St Vincent Coll Chamber Orch Conductor 1987-, Dir Choral Act 1993-; The Abbey Singers Founder, Dir & Counter Tenor 1993-; *ai:* ACDA 1980-, Cty Rep; Chorus Amer 1993-; Conductors Guild 1993-; St Vincents Comerata & Orch Pub Radio Performance; The Abbey Singers won Marvin Hamlisch Awd; Search for a Star Appearing with Pitts Symphony; *office:* Saint Vincents Coll & Sem Latrobe PA 15650

ROSSI, DONNA T., First Grade Teacher; *b:* Bryn Mawr, PA; *ed:* Kutztown Univ (BS) Elem & Early Chldhd 1987; Cabrini Coll (MS) Elem Ed 1997; *cr:* Our Lady of Perpetual Help 4th Grd Tchr 1987-89, 3rd Grd Tchr 1989-91 & 1st Grd Tchr 1995-; Reads Inc Remedial K-8th Grd Math & Rdng Tchr 1992-95; *office:* Our Lady of Perpetual Help 2130 Franklin Ave Morton PA 19070*

ROSSI, JUDITH LABRIOLA, Mathematics Teacher; *b:* Altoona, PA; *m:* Dean M.; *c:* Wayne, Michelle Rossi Wantz; *ed:* PA St Univ (BS) Math 1963; Saint Francis Coll (MED) Scndry Ed 1995; *cr:* Altoona Area Schl Dist Tchr 1963-68; Derry Area Schl Dist Tchr 1968-71; Carlisle Area Schl Dist Tchr 1971-72; Huntingdon Area Schl Dist Tchr 1972-80; Wawasee Schl Corp Tchr 1980-85; Mesa Pub Schls Tchr 1985-88; Hollidaysburg Area Schl Dist Tchr 1988-; *ai:* Assoc Degree Prep Prgm Lead Tchr; Southern Alleghenies Tech Prep Co nsortium; NEA, PSEA 1963-; Hollidaysburg Area Ed Assn 1988-; Outstdng Svc Awd & Outstdng Edctr Awd Wawasee Sr HS; Alumni Awd & Stu Cncl Awd Altoona Campus Penn St Univ; *office:* Hollidaysburg Area Sr HS 1510 N Montgomery St Hollidaysburg PA 16648

ROSSI, KATHLEEN CAREY, Physical Education Teacher; *b:* Teaneck, NJ; *m:* Peter; *c:* Christopher, Jaclyn, Jenna; *ed:* SUNY at Cortland (BS) PE 1979, (MS) PE 1985; *cr:* G Ray Bodley HS PE Tchr 1981-; *ai:* Var Girls Swimming Coach; NHS Adv; AAHPERD 1979-; NYSUT 1980-; NYSAHPERD 1984-; Fulton Ath Booster Club 1983-; Phoenix Sports Boosters 1995-; Onondaga HS League Coaches Awd 1993; Fulton Tchrs Assn Recognition Awd 1995; *office:* G Ray Bodley HS 6 William Gillard Dr Fulton NY 13069

ROSSI, MARGARET A., High School English Teacher; *b:* New York, NY; *ed:* St John's Univ (BA) Eng, Pol Sci 1965; NY Univ (MA) Lit, Drama 1968; St John's Univ (MPH) Lit 1984, (PHD) Lit 1990; Yeats Intnl Summer Schl Sligo Ireland 1995; NDEA Inst Linguistics Columbia U 1967-69; *cr:* Tappan Zee HS Eng Tchr 1967-; St John's Univ Adj Prof Eng 1978-; *ai:* Class of 1999, NHS, Environmental Human Rights Club Advs; Acting Coach Fall & Spring Plays; NCTE, AFT, NYSUT 1967-; AAUP 1978-; NYSTE 1990-; Reader Lighthouse for the Blind NYC; Homeless Shelter Vol; Tchr of Yr 1993; Grad Speaker 1990; Syllabus Maxwell Anderson

Rockland Comm Coll; Yrbk Dedication 1980; *office:* Tappan Zee HS Dutch Hill Rd Orangeburg NY 10962*

ROSSI, MARY LOUISE, 1st Grade School Teacher; *b:* Brooklyn, NY; *c:* Richard, Jon, Nicole; *ed:* Cortland St Tchrs Coll (BS) Elem Ed 1964; Addl 85 Credit Hrs; *cr:* Kreamer Street Elem Schl First Grd Tchr 1964-; *ai:* NEA, AFT 1964-; Bellport Tchrs Assn 1964-, Bldg Rep; Brookhaven Homemakers 1990-; Articles Pub.*

ROSSI, MARY MAY, Sixth Grade Teacher; *b:* Toledo, OH; *m:* Kevin Christopher; *c:* Emily; *ed:* Kent St Univ (BSEd) Spcl Ed 1985; Cleveland St Univ (MS) Curr & Instruction 1989; 45 Hrs Beyond MS; *cr:* Mentor Pub Schls 6th Grd Tchr 1985-; *ai:* Residential Outdoor Ed Tchr; Quality Comm; MTA 1985-; *office:* Mentor Public Schls 8700 Hendricks Rd Mentor OH 44060*

ROSSI, MICHAEL J., Asst Prof of Bio & Environ Sci; *b:* North Hornell, NY; *m:* Ann Marie K.; *c:* Katherine, Elaina; *ed:* Xavier Univ (BS) Bio 1983; Univ of KY (PHD) Bio 1990; *cr:* Univ of FL Post-Doctoral 1989-92; Univ of New Haven Asst Prof 1992-; *ai:* A&S Curr, Fac Welfare Comms; Coord Cellular, Molecular Bio Prgm Grad Level; ASCB 1989-; *office:* Univ Of New Haven 300 Orange Ave West Haven CT 06516

ROSSI, ROSE E., 7th Grade Math Teacher; *b:* Stafford Springs, CT; *c:* Kara; *ed:* Westfield St Coll (BSE) K-9 1972; *cr:* Gerena Comm Schl 3rd, 5th, 6th, 7th Grd Tchr 1984-; *ai:* MTA, SEA, NEA 1985-; Zonta Club of Spfld 1984-, 1st VP; *home:* 127 Valentine St Agawam MA 01001

ROSSI, STEPHEN H., Social Studies Teacher; *b:* Altoona, PA; *m:* Karen Tognoli; *c:* Jessica, Alex; *ed:* Juniata (BS) Soc, Psych 1978; St Francis Coll at Loretto 26 Cred Hrs Tchng Cert; *cr:* Fred S. Engle MS Soc Stud Tchr, Team Ldr 1984-; *ai:* Team Ldr; Soccer Coach; Producer of Variety Show; Intramural 6th Grd Bsktbl; Mentor; NEA, PSEA 1984-, Ofcl; PIAA 1986-, Var Bsbl Ofcl; PIAA 1990-, Var Bsktbl Ofcl; Brandywine Bsbl Chapter 1991-, VP, Playoff Umpire; *office:* Fred S Engle MS 107 Schoolhouse Rd West Grove PA 19390

ROSSI, SYLVIA MITCHELL, Health & Phys Ed Teacher; *b:* Latrobe, PA; *m:* David A.; *c:* Russell; *ed:* Slippery Rock St Col (BA) Hlth, PE, Recreation 1972; *cr:* Kiska Area Schl Dist Hlth, PE Tchr 1976-; *ai:* Red Ribbon Club; Promotes Drug Free Lifestyle; Stu Asst Prgm; *office:* Kiski Area Sr HS 200 Poplar St Vandergrift PA 15690

ROSSI, VIRGINIA F., 6th-8th Grd Sci & Math Tchr; *b:* Brooklyn, NY; *m:* Ronald; *c:* Sheila Albinson, Ronald Jr., Peter; *ed:* Northwestern St (BA) Govt & His 1965; 30 Post Grad Credits from C W Post in Elem Ed; *cr:* Saint John of God Schl 6th Grd Math Tchr 1972-74; Saint Philip & James 6th Grd Tchr 1976-88; Our Lady of Lourdes Schl 6th-8th Grd Math & Sci Tchr 1989-; *ai:* Math Olympiad Coach; Saint Judes MathAThon; Natl Cath Tchr Assn 1970-; Tchr Forum Rep, Zone Rep 3 Yrs; Summer Prgm Westbury Coll Problem Solving; *office:* Our Lady Of Lourdes Schl 44 Toomey Rd West Islip NY 11795

ROSSINI, ARLEEN, 8th Grade Teacher; *b:* Uniontown, PA; *m:* Francis V.; *c:* Melanie, Anthony; *ed:* California Univ of PA (BS) Scndry Ed 1963; *cr:* Redstone HS Jr Sr HS Eng Tchr 1963-70; All Saints Grd Schl 3rd, 8th Grd Tchr 1979-; *ai:* Forensics Spon; Stu Support Team Comm; NCEA 1979-; *office:* All Saints Grade School 100 S Washington St Masontown PA 15461

ROST, MICHELE L., Substitute Teacher; *b:* Williamsport, PA; *ed:* Gettysburg Coll (BA) Hlth, PS 1994; *cr:* Muncy Area HS PE Tchr 1995; Loyalsock HS PE, Hlth, Drivers Ed Tchr 1995; Williamsport HS PE Tchr 1996; *home:* RR 3 Box 372 Cogan Station PA 17728*

ROSTOSKY, DOROTHY ANNA, Middle School English Teacher; *b:* Haverhill, MA; *ed:* Lydon St Coll (BS) Ed 1963; Eng, Ed Grad Work Univ of VT, Lesley Coll, Lowell Univ, Fitchburg St Coll; *cr:* Chelsea Schl Dist Eng Tchr 1963-67; Pentucket Regnl MS Eng Tchr 1967-; *ai:* Dist Team Ldr 1986-; Advisee, Adv Prgm Ldr; Eng Curr Comm; MTA, NEA, PAT 1967-; Republican Comm; Roman Cath Assn 1967-; Co-Author MS Concept; Recipient Arthur Elliot Awd Lyndon St Coll 1963; *office:* Pentucket Regnl MS 22 Main St West Newbury MA 01985*

ROSVALLY, HARRY E.,JR., High School Sci Teacher; *b:* Mt Kisco, NY; *m:* Linda L. Palanzo; *c:* David Herring; *ed:* GA Tech (BEE) Electrical Eng 1987; SUNY at Oneonta (BS) Bus Ec 1987; Western CT St Unv (MS) Ed & Curr 1992; 26 Credit Hrs Toward EDD Tchrs Coll; *cr:* New Fairfield MS 7th Grd Math Tchr & Perm Sub 1991; Broadview Jr HS Math, Sci & EWC Tchr 1991-92; Danbury HS Chem, Phys Sci & Math Tchr 1992-94; Somers HS Physics, Chem & Phys Sci Tchr 1994-; *ai:* Odyssey of Mind Adv; HS Staff Dev Comm; NEA 1991-; AFT 1994-; *office:* Somers HS PO Bos 640 Rt 139 Lincolndale NY 10540*

ROTA, JERRY, High School Math Teacher; *b:* Newark, NJ; *ed:* Kean Coll (BA) Psych 1979; Tchng Cert Math 1995; Pursuing Masters Degree in Scndry Instruction & Curr Math Concentration; *cr:* Exxon Research & Eng Co Research Technician 1979-86; Exxon Chemical Co Sr Research Technician 1986-90; St Marys Tchr 1990-; *ai:* Soph Class Adv; Bowling Coach; NCTM 1991-; *office:* St Mary of the Assumption HS 237 S Broad St Elizabeth NJ 07202

ROTELLA, MARTY JOHN, Seventh Grade Teacher; *b:* Jersey City, NJ; *m:* Pamela Catherine Sidoti; *c:* Michael, Catherine; *ed:* William Paterson Coll (BA) Elem Ed 1978; *cr:* Meml HS Basic Skills Tchr 1978-79; Pub Schl #5 7th Grd Tchr 1979-81, 5th Grd Tchr 1981-86, 7th Grd Tchr 1986-; *ai:* Schl Jr Police Adv; Schl Chorus Piano Player; Schl Fac Chorus Mem; NEA, NJEA 1978-; *office:* P S #5 5401 Hudson Ave West New York NJ 07093

ROTH, BARBARA ANN (ALFONSO), Spanish & French Teacher; *b:* New Bedford, MA; *m:* Patrick D.; *c:* Kristen Ann Roth Schofield, Kara Patrice; *ed:* Stonehill Coll (BA) Fr 1968; RI Coll (MED) Biling Bicultural Ed Portug 1979; 57 Post Grad Credits Certs Span, ESL, Elem Ed, Eng; *cr:* Brockton North Jr HS Fr Tchr 1968-70; Cumberland RI Pub Schls Curr Testing Specialist ESL Tchr 1977-84; Friends Acad Frgn Lang Coord Tchr 1984-94; Coyle-Cass idy HS Fr Span Tchr 1994-; *ai:* NHS, Fr Hnr Soc Co-Moderator; MAFLA 1984-; AATSP 1994-; AATF 1990-; Bay View Corp 1980-, Nominating, Fin Review Comms; Claremont Fnd Grant for World Lang Elem Tutoring Prgm 1996; Canadian Govt Grant for Summer Stud Maritimes 1989; *home:* 64 Beach Ln South Dartmouth MA 02748*

ROTH, CHRISTINE BOBEK, Tech Specialist & Cmptr Tchr; *b:* Allentown, PA; *m:* Thomas C.; *c:* Janet Danenhower; *ed:* Kutztown St Coll (BS) Scndry Ed Eng 1970; Kutztown St Univ (MED) Eng 1973; Lehigh Univ (MS) Educl Tech 1986; 14 Addtl Credits Cmptr Applications, Video Disc, Techniques; *cr:* Hamburg Area HS Eng Tchr 1970-84, Tech Specialist 1984-; *ai:* NEA, PSEA, Hamburg Area Ed Assn 1970-, Rep on Haea Cncl; Phi Delta Kappa 1984-, Newsletter 1995-; Nom By Supt for Berks Cty Trendsetter 1988; Co-Ed of Hawkeye Dist Newsletter 1996; Won Awd of Excl PSPR; *office:* Hamburg Area Jr Sr HS Windsor St Hamburg PA 19526*

ROTH, JOHN MARTIN,JR., High School Guidance Counselor; *b:* Baltimore, MD; *m:* Barbara Ann Flora; *c:* Amy Beth, Eric Raymond; *ed:* Towson St Coll (BA) Geog 1968; Towson St Univ (MED) Scndry Ed 1975; Addl 60 Post Grad Hrs Guid, Cnslng; *cr:* Gen John Stricker Jr HS 7th-8th Grd Soc Stud Tchr 1968-79; Golden Ring Jr HS Cnslr 1979-83; Catonsville Evening Schl 12th Grd Soc Stud Tchr 1981-82, Cnslr, Registrar 1982-93; Woodlawn MS Cnslr 1983-85; Randallstown HS Cnslr 1985-95; Randallstown Evening Schl Cnslr, Registrar 1993-; Herefor dHS Cnslr 1995-; *ai:* Class of 99 Spon; Asst Bsbl Coach; NEA, MSTA 1968-; TABC 1968-, Fac Rep; BCACD 1989-, Treas 1989-92, Pres 1992-95; 40 West Men's Club 1974-, Sec, Treas, VP, Pres; Fulbright Grant for Stud in India 1976; *office:* Hereford HS 17301 York Rd Parkton MD 21120

ROTH, JONATHAN DEAN, Music Teacher; *b:* Rochester, NH; *ed:* Gordon Coll (BME) 5th-12th Grd Band 1988; *cr:* Hillsboro-Deering HS Band Dir 1988-; Smith Congregational Church Music Dir 1993-; *ai:* MENC 1988-; NHBDA 1995-; Withington Tchr of Yr Awd 1990-91; *office:* Hillsboro-Deering HS 12 Hillcat Dr Hillsboro NH 03244

ROTH, RICHARD C., Ninth Grade Math Tchr; *b:* Northampton, PA; *m:* Barbara C. Frisoli; *ed:* East Stroudsburg Univ (BS) Math Ed 1970; Kutztown Univ (MED) Math 1973; Univ of NH (MST) Math 1980; *cr:* Troxell Jr HS Math Tchr 1970-; *ai:* Yrbk Adv; NEA, PSEA, PEA 1970-; NCTM, PCTM, EPCTM 1978-; *office:* Troxell Jr HS 2219 N Cedarcrest Blvd Allentown PA 18104

ROTH, ROBERT CHARLES, Economics & American His Tchr; *b:* Englewood, NJ; *m:* Caroline Ann Trovato; *c:* Christopher, Shaun; *ed:* Fairleigh Dickinson Univ (BA) Ecs 1965; East TX St Univ (MS) His, Govt 1967; Credit Hrs; *cr:* Toms River HS South Senior Tchr 1968-; Ocean Cty Coll Micro Ecs Inst 1982-; *ai:* Textbk Evaluation; Curr Revision; Toms River Ed Ann, NEA1968-; Ocean Cty Coll Adj Assn; *office:* Toms River HS South Hyers St Toms River NJ 08753

ROTH, ROBERT EDWARD, 6th Grade Science Teacher; *b:* Lockport, NY; *m:* Nancy Jo Kolipinski; *c:* Megan, Melissa, Jessica; *ed:* Niagara CCC (AA) Liberal Arts 1970; SUNY at Brockport (BA) PE K-12 1972; 30 Past Masters in Ed; *cr:* Barker Central Schl 6 Grd Soc Stud Tchr 1974-79; 4 Grd Tchr 1979-84; 3 Grd Tchr 1984-85; 6 Grd Sci Tchr 1985-; *ai:* K-6 Sci Dept, 6 Grd Sci Fair Coord; Dist Tech, Dist Grant Writing, Chm of Dist Reforestation Comms; Dist Sci Mentor K-6; Var Golf Coach; Dist Peer Mdtn Comm; MS Hnr Comm; Sci Tchrs Assn of NYS 1985-; NYSUT 1974-; AFT 1974-; Optimists 1988-; YMCA 1974-; Victor A. Fitchlee Youth Conservation Project Grant 1989; Annual St Sci Tchrs Conf 3 Time Presenter; Great Lks Collaborative Grant 1994; Orleans-Niagara Tchr Cntr Mini Grant 1995 & 1996; Eisenhower Prof Dev Grant 1995; *office:* Barker Central Schl 1628 Quaker Rd Barker NY 14012*

ROTH, SUSAN JENNIFER, Office Administration Instr; *b:* Orrville, OH; *m:* Bill; *c:* Jennifer, Alison; *ed:* Univ of Akron (AAS) Secretarial 1973; Bowling Green St Univ (BS) Ed 1996; Bowling Green St Univ 30 Hrs; *cr:* J. M. Smucker Co Sec; Univ of Akron Sec; Fulton Cty Regnl Planning Comm Sec; Terra Comm Coll Instr; *ai:* Svcs & Updating Cmptr Network; NCA Writer for Dept Review Prgm; Prof Dev, Fac Support Comm; Advy Comm Ldr; Lead Tchr for Tech With Adjunct Fac; ASCD, NEA, OEA, Toledo Area Bus Tchrs Voc Ed, OVA, AVA; Tiffin Developmental Ctr Parent Advocate; Advy Comm for Rdng; 1st United Meth Church; Texts Ed; *office:* Terra State Comm Coll 2830 Napoleon Rd Fremont OH 43420

ROTH, TROY ALLAN, High School Math Teacher; *b:* Muskeegan, MI; *m:* Jan Aeschliman; *c:* Chelsea, Morgan; *ed:* Miami Univ (BS) Math Ed 1987; Univ of Toledo (MS) Admin 1994; *cr:* Swanton Local Math Tchr 1988-; *ai:* Ftbl, Wrestling, Sftbl Coach; Math Club Adv; NEA, OEA, SEA 1988-; *office:* Swanton HS 206 Cherry St Swanton OH 43558

ROTHENBERG, RON S., Mathematics Teacher; *b:* Brooklyn, NY; *m:* Diane L. Glasser; *c:* Melanie, Joshua; *ed:* Wagner Coll (BS) Math 1965; City Coll of NY (MA) Math Ed 1969; 30 Post Grad Credits in Math Yeshiva Univ; *cr:* PS 622 Remedial Math Tchr 1965-66; Brentwood South Jr HS Math Tchr 1966-70; Pearl River HS Math Tchr 1970-76; Pearl River MS Math Tchr 1976-82; Pearl River HS Math Tchr 1983-; *ai:* NY St Math League Adv; Pearl River Tchrs Assn 1970-, Treas 1972-80; AFT 1966-; Temple Emanu El 1993-, Comm Mem; Amer Philatelic Soc 1965-; *office:* Pearl River HS 275 E Central Ave Pearl River NY 10965

ROTHENHAUS, ROBERT C., Mathematics Teacher; *b:* Brooklyn, NY; *m:* Wendy Baron; *c:* Amy, Lauren; *ed:* CCNY (BS) Ec 1968, (MA) Ec 1974; Addl Credits At Univ of IL, C W Post, Hunter Coll & NY Univ; *cr:* Jr HS 162 Tchr 1968-69; Long Island City HS Tchr 1969-; *ai:* Curr Writer-ESL Grant; Prgm Chr 1995-; AFT & UFT 1968-; ATMNYC 1970-; *office:* Long Island City HS 14-30 Broadway Long Is City NY 11106

ROTHERMEL, ALAN RICHARD, Chemistry Teacher & Curr Ldr; *b:* Reading, PA; *m:* Debra; *c:* Chris, Carrie; *ed:* Lock Haven St Coll (BA) Chem Ed 1976; Temple Univ (MS) Ed 1985; *cr:* Manheim Cntrl HS Chem Tchr 1978-80; Cedar Crest HS Chem Tchr 1980-; *ai:* Class Adv; PSEA 1978-; Lititz Youth Soccer, Coach; PIAA Soccer Referee; Church Counsil; Distinguished Tchr of Honor Stdnts 1987; Lebanon Valley Chamber of Commerce Ed Excl 1991-92 & 95; ACS Outstanding Chem Tchr 1992; *office:* Cedar Crest HS 115 E Evergreen Rd Lebanon PA 17042

ROTHERMEL, VICTORIA ANNE (SNYDER), HS Math Teacher; *b:* Lykens, PA; *m:* Steven Roger; *c:* Ashley Elizabeth, Kelly Rae; *ed:* Bloomsburg Univ (BS) Elem Ed 1980; Minor in Math; *cr:* Cntrl PA Bus Schl Math & Acctng Instr 1980; Bloomsburg Chrstn Schl Kndgtn Tchr 1986-87, Jr & Sr High Math Tchr 1987-88, 1993-; *office:* Bloomsburg Christian Schl 3300 Ridge Rd Bloomsburg PA 17815

ROTHHAAR, TWILA KAY (MILLER), Fourth Grade Teacher; *b:* Bucyrus, OH; *m:* Michael Wayne; *ed:* Grace Coll (BS) Elem Ed-Cum Laude 1980; Univ of Toledo Addl Credits at Grad Level; *cr:* Toledo Chrstn Schl First Grd Tchr 1980-83, Fourth Grd Tchr 1986-; *office:* Toledo Christian Schl 2303 Brookford Dr Toledo OH 43614

ROTHLISBERGER, PAMELA BERRY, 7th-8th Grd Life Skills Tchr; *b:* Bluffton, OH; *m:* John; *c:* Randy, Tim, Renee Lance; *ed:* Bluffton Coll (BS) Home Ec 1963; OH St Univ Voc Home Ec 1963; Addl 18 Credit Hrs Kent St Univ, Ashland Coll; *cr:* Burton HS 9-12 Voc Home Ec Tchr 1963-67; West Geauga MS Home Ec, Life Skills Tchr 1986-; *ai:* NEA, OEA, OHEA 1963-76, 1986-; Delta Kappa Gamma 1995-; *home:* 13733 Northwood Rd Novelty OH 44072

ROTHMAN, TOVAH G., Resource Teacher; *b:* Flushing, NY; *m:* Robert P.; *c:* Rachel, Aaron, Sarah; *ed:* Syracuse Univ (BS) Ed 1971; Syracuse Univ 36 Grad Hrs, Assistantship Ctr on Human Policy 1971-72; *cr:* BOCES Spec Ed Tchr 1972-75; Fayetteville-Manlius HS Resource Tchr 1984-; *ai:* Class Adv 1991-95; Tchr Rep STPA; Site Based Team Mem; Learning Disability Assn of Cntrl NY, Natl Learning Disability Assn 1984-; Syracuse Univ Summer Orch 1986-; *office:* Fayetteville-Manlius HS E Seneca Turnpike Manlius NY 13104*

ROTHSTEIN, MARK, Retired US History Teacher; *b:* Newark, NJ; *m:* Jo Anne Rosett; *c:* Deborah, Gregg, Evan, Rebecca; *ed:* Univ of Chicago (AB) Liberal Arts 1953; Rutgers Univ (BS) His & Ed 1956, (MED) Pol Sci & Ed 1959; Univ of MO (MS) Ec 1972; Attnd Univ of ME, Ec 1968, Carnegie Mellow Ec 1969, Rutgers Taft Inst Politics 1970; *cr:* Middletown Twp HS US His Honors & Ec Tchr 1959-95; *ai:* Natl Forensic League Double Diamond Coach 1960-75; Mock Trial Team Adv 1988-95; NEA, NJEA, MTEA 1959-; NCSS; NJCSS; Borough Councilman 1973-76; Cty Committeeman 1970-94; Natl Sci Fnd Grad Stud 1971-72.

ROTOLO, JOSEPH PETER, Technology & Drivers Ed Tchr; *b:* New York City, NY; *m:* Mary Jane; *c:* Jason; *ed:* St Univ of NY at Oswego (MS) Industrial Arts 1965, (MA) Ed 1967; *cr:* Marcellus Cntrl Schl Industrial Arts Tchr 1967-80; Oswego HS Tech & Drivers Ed Tchr 1981-; *ai:* Sailing Club Founder & Adv 1981-; Epsilon Pi Tau 1970-; Oswego Maritime Fnd 1981-, Bd of Dirs, Vessel Maintenance Dir; Oswego Sons of Italy 1978-, VP; Oswego Elks 1983-; Oswego Lions Club 1969- 4th of July Parade Float Dir, 1st Place 1972 & 1973; Pioneer of Problem Solving Tchng Approach 1967-79; Article Ground Effect Machines-IAVE, Organizing a Sailing Club-Scots & Water; NY St Fair Comm 1970-78 1st, Place Project 1972-73; Jr North Amer Flying Scot Championships Resatla 1989; Ed Advs Awd for Oswego Sailing Club Winning 1st, 4th & 5th P *office:* Oswego HS 2 Buccaneer Blvd Oswego NY 13126

ROTOLO, LUANN, Spanish Teacher; *b:* Puntsutawnet, PA; *ed:* IN of PA (BS) Span 1975, (BS) Fr 1976; 27 Credit Hrs; *cr:* IN Univ Spar 1982-86; Punxdy HS Eng, Fr Tchr 1983-87; Mapleview Elem Schl Tchr 1988-89; Punxst HS Span Tchr; *ai:* NEA, PSEA 1982-; AP 1986-; *office:* Punxsutawney Area Sr HS N Findley St Punxsutawn 15767

ROTONDO, CINDY KIDD, First Grade Teacher; *b:* Toledo, O Marv; *ed:* Univ of Toledo (BED) Elem Ed 1980, (MED) Curr, Instr 1984, (EDS) Admin, Supervision 1986; *cr:* Our Lady of Perpetua Schl Kndgtn Tchr 1980-81; St John Schl Kndgtn Tchr 1981-83; Geno Local Schls 1st Grd Tchr 1983-; *ai:* Labor Mngmt Comm; Phi Kapp Phi Delta Kappa; Read for Literacy Tutor; Jennings Scholar; Brunner Elem Schl 1224 West St Genoa OH 43430

ROTONDO, STEVEN WILLIAM, School Psychologist; *b:* Provic RI; *m:* Paula A.; *c:* Michael, Billy; *ed:* Providence Coll (BA) Ed, F Lang 1972; RI Coll (MA) Counseling 1975, (CAGS) Schl Psych 198 Bishop Reehan HS Tchr, Cnslr 1972-77; Butler Hospital Mental Worker 1976-78; Barrington Pub Schls Cnslr, Psychologist Counseling & Intervention Services Treatment Cnslr 1985-95; *ai:* Ed; NEA 1977-; RI Schl Psych Assn, Natl Assn of Schl Psychol 1980-; BSA 1980-, Asst Scout Master; *office:* Barrington HS 220 L Ave Barrington RI 02806

ROTS, CHARLA CATANIA, German Teacher; *b:* New Kensingtor *m:* Paul; *c:* Jennifer Demor, Paul (dec); *ed:* IN Univ of PA (BSEd) Span 1967; Duquesne Univ (BSEd) Eng 1980; Overseas Travel wi *cr:* Plum Boro HS Ger, Span & Eng Tchr 1967-68; St Pauls Cath Sc Grd Tchr 1969; E E Smith Sr HS Ger Tchr 1974-77; Montour HS Ger, & Eng Tchr 1978-; *ai:* Ger Club Spon 1974-77; Chrldrs Majorettes 1980-83; Young Republicans Club Spon 1994-; NEA 1967-; PSEA AATG 1979-; MLA 1979-; St Malachy 1978-; Compassionate F 1994-; Italian Sons & Daughters 1995-; Montour HS Class of 199 Dedication; *office:* Montour HS Clever Rd Mc Kees Rocks PA 1513

ROTT, CAROLYN CADE, Health & Physical Ed Teacher; *b:* A City, NJ; *m:* Joseph Charles; *c:* Curt, Heather, Courtney, Brigitte, Shaun, Nicholas; *ed:* Trenton St Coll (BS) Hlth & PE Ed 1969; 9 Hrs Towards Masters; *cr:* Hopewell Vly Cntrl HS & Timberlane Jr H & PE Tchr & Coach 1969-70; Oakcrest HS Hlth & PE Tchr & Coach *ai:* Girls Tennis Coach; Girls Ath Assn Adv; Pres Ath Wall of Fame Bsktbl Coach Port Republic Schl; Delta Psi Kappa 1967-; NEA, N ACTEA 1969-; JPHERD & FCA 1969-; Atlantic Cty Womens Ctr Sexual Assault & Domestic Violence Cnslr, Otustdng Vol Awd 198 Sun Role Model of the Yr 1989; St of NJ Victim of a Violent Outstdng Vol Awd 1990; ABW Outstdng Women of the Yr 1990; Who Help Women Awd 1991; Tchr of the Yr 1992; Princeton Pr Distngd Scndry Schl Tchng Finalist 1994; *office:* Oakcrest HS 1824 Ave Mays Landing NJ 08330

ROTTENBERG, BETTY MAC LELLAN, High School English Te *b:* Youngstown, OH; *c:* Jessica, Heather; *ed:* Westminster Coll (BA 1973; Youngstown St Univ (MA) Eng 1985; *cr:* Howland HS Eng 1973-; *ai:* NEA 1973-, Bldg Rep; *office:* Howland HS 200 Shaffer Warren OH 44484

ROTTINO, ALFRED A., Teacher; *b:* New York City, NY; *m:* Barba Mark, David; *ed:* Iona Coll (BS) Chem, Bio 1961; Notre Dame (MS 1969; Attnd Boston Coll, Univ of CA, Univ of WI, CO Coll, Fordham, Fairleigh, Dickonson Univ, Queens Coll, Coll of New Roc Hope Coll, LIU, SUNY at Stony Brook; *cr:* Blessed Sacrament HS Sc Chm 1961-68; Cath Meml HS Bio, Physics Tchr 1968-69; Half H Hills HS Chem Tchr 1970-; *ai:* Yrbk Adv; Suffolk Sci Tchrs Assn; R Soccer, Lacrosse, Ftbl, Bsktbl; Univ CA at Berkeley, Univ WI, Brook Univ Grants.*

ROULEAU, ANN F., Seventh Grade Teacher; *b:* Rumford, ME; *m:* J.; *c:* Jeffrey A., Terrance A., Wayne S., Smith; *ed:* Univ of Farmington (BS) Elem Ed 1978; *cr:* Rumford Comm Hospital Sec, St Supvr 1968-78; Schl Admin Dist #43 Grd 7 Tchr 1978-; *ai:* Rdng Lang Arts 1983, 1991-93 Currs; Staff Dev 1993-; PRIDE Advy 1989-; Sist Wellness Comm 1993-; Curr Advy Team 1993-; ME Ed 1978-; NEA 1978-; Mntn Valley Tchrs Assn 1978-; RMD Federal Union 1978-, Sec; Mexico Mother's Club 1960- Sec; *office:* Mo Valley MS Highland Terr Mexico ME 04257*

ROUNDS, RONALD JOHN, English Teacher; *b:* Pawtucket, RI; *m:* Alice Clow; *c:* Becky, Sean, Julia Meaghan, Gregory; *ed:* RI Coll (BA 1988; RI Coll 15 Grad Credits; *cr:* Wickford MS Lang Arts Tchr 19 Exeter West Greenwich Sr HS Eng Tchr 1992-; *ai:* Roundstable Talk Classics Movie Club; IM Wall-a-Ball; NEA 1989-; NCTE 1989-; Wa Amer Little League 1992-, Coach & Player Agent; Boys & Girls 1994-, Coach; JC Sparkman Ed & Tech Grant; Exeter West Greenwi Yrbk Dedication 1995; *office:* Exeter West Greenwich Sr HS Nooseneck Hill Rd West Greenwich RI 02817

ROUNDS, THOMAS GERALD, 6th Grade Teacher; *b:* Cleveland *ed:* OH St Univ (BS) Elem Ed 1981; Univ of Akron (MS) Guid C 1988; *cr:* Brunswick City Schls Tchr 1981-; *ai:* Safety Patrol Strategic Plan Comm; Venture Capital Grant Writing, Interve Assistance Team; NEA 1981-, Pub Relations Project Smiles For Mile Miles; OEA, NEOEA, BEA 1981-; Safety Town 1983-, Dir; Bruns Reformed Church, Juvenile Diversion Prgm; OH St Univ Young Ed Yr Awd; Tchr of Yr; *office:* Brunswick's Meml Elem Schl 3845 Ma Dr Brunswick OH 44212*

ROUNSLEY, SUSAN LOUCKS, Mathematics Teacher; *b:* Pitts PA; *m:* R. Mark; *c:* Robert, William; *ed:* Post Scndry Stud U Pittsburgh, Johnstown & Clarion Univ; *cr:* Windber Area Schl Dist Tchr 1970-79; Tri-Cty Intermediate Unit Schl Math Tutor for Cat Prep 1985-86; Mercyhurst Prep Schl Math Tchr 1986-; *ai:* Soph Class NCTM, PCTM 1986-; WAEA 1970-79, Pres; *office:* Mercyhurst Prep 538 E Grandview Blvd Erie PA 16504

ROUNTREE, LEITHA BYERS, Second Grade Teacher; Chambersburg, PA; *m:* Frederick H. II; *c:* Frederick II, Elspeth Jan Shippensburg Univ (BS) Elem Ed 1972, (MED) Elem Ed 1975; 45 Hrs Post Grad Stud; *cr:* Chambersburg Area Schl Dist 4th Grd 1972-73; Lincoln Intermediate Unit #12 Tchr of GATE 197 Chambersburg Area Schl Dist 2nd Grd Tchr 1974-; *ai:* Inclusion Curr Arts Comm; PA St Ed Assn, NEA 1972-; Franklin Cty Lib Bd Recognition Awd 1993; Tchr Tip Pub; *home:* 6834 Lincoln Way W Thomas PA 17252

ROUNTREE, LINDA SIMMONS, Elementary Music Teache Pensacola, FL; *m:* Michael Edward; *c:* Michael Ross, Randi Mathie Univ of West FL (BME) Music Ed 1976; Muse Adventure Tchr Five *cr:* Magruder Elem Schl Music Tchr 1984; Poquoson MS Music 1984-86; Shaw Elem Schl Music Tchr 1988-; *ai:* HS Music, Churc Choir Dir; Bible Stud Flwshp Group Pianist; Muse Machine Pa MENC, OMEA, NEA, BEA 1988-; Comm Theatre 1994-, Musical

Act Tchr Ch 2 TV 1994; *office:* E G Shaw Elem Schl 3560 Kemp Rd
creek OH 45431*

KE, FRANK XAVIER, 7th & 8th Grade Teacher; *b:* Brooklyn, NY; John's Univ (BA) Philosophy 1969; Fordham Univ (MS) Ed, Admin, ision 1988; Hunter Coll 9 Credit Hrs 1970-73; Univ of St of NY Prgm in Drug Ed; Diocese of Brooklyn 2 Credit Hrs Group Skills Drug Abuse Prgm 1985; *cr:* Good Shepherd Roman Cath Schl 5th, d Sci Tchr 1970-75, 5th, 6th Grd Soc Stud Tchr 1975-87, 5th Grd ud, Sci, Math Tchr 1987-88, 7th, 8th Grd Math, Sci, Soc Stud, Rel *ai:* NCEA 1988-; Knights of Columbus 1965-; Natl Geographic Soc Brooklyn Historical Soc 1988-; Edctr of Yr Awd Assn of Tchrs of 91; 25 Yr Awd Diocese of Brooklyn 1995; *home:* 3323 Nostrand Ave yn NY 11229

E, NANCY LYNN (CARNES), Sixth Grade Teacher; *b:* Chicago, Lawrence Howard; *c:* Micholas Leslie; *ed:* TN St Univ (BS) Math Attnd Cleveland St Univ; *cr:* Little Peoples Univ Pre-Schl Tchr 9; Cleveland Hts Schls Sub Tchr 1989-91; St Catherine Schl Tchr *ai:* Stu Cncl, Yrbk Adv; JV Girls Bsktbl, Var Chrldng Coach; Black onth Coord; St Louis Church 1995-, Sec; Cub Pack 171; *office:* St ine Schl 3440 E 93rd St Cleveland OH 44104*

ER, SANDRA MAE, Business Education Instructor; *b:* Fremont, : Donald E.; *ed:* Heidelberg Coll (BA) Comprehensive Bus 1964; ng Green St Univ Voc Ed Tchng Cert 1988; *cr:* Hopewell-Loudon us Ed Instr 30 Yrs; *ai:* Newsletter Adv; Treas Ed Assoc; Head Ticket Ftbl, Bsktbl; NEA, OWEA, NWOEA 1964-; HLEA 1964-, Treas; Kappa Gamma 1968-, Sec; Sunday Schl Tchr; *home:* PO Box 413 ille OH 44815

SE, VALERIE, German Teacher; *b:* Detroit, MI; *ed:* Univ of MI Ger 1974; MI St Univ (MA) Speech Pathology 1980; Attnd Albert g Univ Freiburg Germany 1974-78; *cr:* DODDS Schl Speech Dist 1981-82; Ewa Beach Pub Schls Speech Therapist 1982-84; ine Pub Schls Speech Therapist 1985-86; Needham Pub Schls 7-12 P Ger Tchr 1986-; *ai:* Focus Group Participant; Comprehensive sment System; Ger-Amer Partnership Prgm Coord; AATG 1986-; A 1988-; NEA 1984-; 9 Acad Inst Grants; *office:* Needham Pub 609 Webster St Needham MA 02192*

TH, DELORES CAPEL, Second Grade Teacher; *b:* Baltimore, MD; lliam G.; *c:* Natasha Tina Routh-Smith; *ed:* Coppin St Coll (BA) Chldhd 1974; 15 Hrs Johns Hopkins Univ Guid; *cr:* Sunset Elem Schl n Tchr 1974-89, 1st & 2nd Grd Tchr 1989-; *ai:* Human Rel Comm; nity Affairs, TAAAC Rep; Tchrs Assn A A Cty 1974-, Del; NEA St John United Meth Church 1950-, Sec, Outstdng Svc; Taxpayers vement Assn Patapsco Park Inc 1980-, Sec, Outstdng Svc; Alpha Sigma, Sigma Gamma Rho 1974-, Chp Ldrshp; *office:* Sunset Elem 572 Fort Smallwood Rd Pasadena MD 21122

SIS, JEANNIE, Fourth Grade Teacher; *b:* Brooklyn, NY; *ed:* gh Dickinson Univ (BA) Elem Ed 1972; Montclair St Coll (MA) 1982; William Paterson Coll (MA) Lang Arts 1995; Addl 30 Credits Level Rdng; Cert Teach Greek NY Archdiocese; *cr:* P S #4 Clifton ourth, Fifth Grd Tchr 1972-81; Greek Lang Schl St George Greek dox Church 1972-82; P S #11 Clifton Schl Fourth, Fifth Grd Tchr *ai:* Adv Schl Newspaper Tiger News, Adopt A Grandparent Prgm; n Tchrs Assn 1972-, Del; NJEA, NEA 1972-; Tchr Learning rative 1987-, Pres; Natl Adopt A Tchr, Pi Lambda Theta 1994-, St e Greek Orthodox Church 1968-, Choir; Tchr of Yr 1982; Governor's nition Tchng Excl 1987; Passaic Cty of NJ Tchr of Yr 1994; Several endations 1978, 1981, 1986, 1992, 1994; *office:* Pub Schl #11 147 lis Ave Clifton NJ 07011*

T, DOUGLAS BYRUM, Substitute Teacher; *b:* Evanston, IL; *m:* Margaret Lewis; *c:* Bill, Holly Routt Bushyager, Derek; *ed:* Miami at OH (BS) Aeronautics 1963; Ed Cert Physics 1988; Squadron Ofcrs & Natl Security Mgmt USAF; *cr:* Nichols Schl Earth Sci Tchr & 1987-89; Clarence Jr High Phys Sci Tchr & Coach 1989-94; nce MS Sub Tchr & Wrestling Coach 1994-; *ai:* Wrestling Coach; 1989-; Audubon Bd 1980-, Chm; Sweet Home Schl Bd, 10 Yrs Pres; st Hockey Coach of the Yr; 107th Fighter Group Commander; *home:* lip St Amherst NY 14228

LLI, JOSEPH W., HS Mathematics Supervisor; *b:* Jersey City, NJ; eresa Bianchi; *c:* Joseph, David; *ed:* LaSalle Univ (BA) Math 1968; City St Coll (MA) Math Ed 1979; *cr:* North Bergen Bd of Ed Tchr ministrator 1968-; St Peters Coll Adj Instr 1989-91; Dominican Coll str 1990-; *ai:* Grad Comm; Grant Comm; HSPT Testing Comm; NEA ; NCTM 1989-; IAABU 1972-; Knights of Columbus 1985-; *office:* Bergen HS 7417 Kennedy Blvd North Bergen NJ 07047

ERE, ROBERT JOHN, Chairperson Dept of Languages; *b:* New NY; *ed:* Seton Hall Univ (BA) Fr 1964; NY Univ (MA) Fr 1968; lair St Coll Cert Admin & Supervision; *cr:* St Mary HS Fr Tchr 67; North Bergen HS Fr, Italian Tchr 1967-; Chrprsn Dept of Lngs , *ai:* Project Grad, Staff Dev, NHS Slctn Comm; Fundraiser Show for Project Grad; Mid Sts Evaluator; AFT, NBFT 1967-94; AATI; 1991-; NJEA 1994-; CAS 1994-; AATF; NJFLT; Brooklyn Oratory 94, Lector 1985-94, Faith Dev Comm Chprsn 1993, Comm Cncl *office:* North Bergen HS 7417 Kennedy Blvd North Bergen NJ *

AN, GERALD J., Professor of Art; *b:* Honesdale, PA; *c:* Gabrielle; utztown Univ (BS) Art Ed 1968, (MED) Art Ed 1972; Attnd Univ of rts, Marywood Coll; *cr:* Kutztown Univ TA 1970-72; Northampton coll Prof 1972-; Moravian Coll Adj Prof 1995-; Noravian Coll Adj 995; Allentown Coll Adj Prof 1990-96; *ai:* AFT; Old Allentown rvation Assoc 1990-; Bethlehem Area Vo-Tech 1972, Adv Brd; Lehigh o-Tech Tchr 1972; Numerous Articles; *office:* Northampton Comm 835 Green Pond Rd Bethlehem PA 18017*

AN, GLORIA ALINE, English Teacher; *b:* New York City, NY; *c:* ander Della Rocca; *ed:* Columbia Univ Schl Gen Stud (BA) arative Lit, Ed 1981; Columbia Univ Tchrs Coll (MA) Spec Ed 1985; g Psych 1985; *cr:* ISD 166 Spec Ed Tchr 1982-83; John F. Kennedy ng, Comm Tchr 1982, Eng Tchr 1983-; *ai:* NOIAW 1994-; Wrote at, Interviewed Dr Lydia Soifer for Cable Show 1995.

BOTHAM, BRENDA CALDWELL, First Grade Teacher; *b:* eaut, OH; *m:* Tim B.; *c:* Scott, Michael; *ed:* Kent St Univ (BS) Elem 70; Edinboro Univ (ME) 1974; 30 Credit Hrs 1982; *cr:* Garfield Elem 4th Grd Tchr 1970-71; West Main Elem Schl 2nd Grd Tchr 1971-83, rd Tchr 1983-; *ai:* PTC Schl Rep; Co-Chm Integrated Lang Arts n; CEA 1971-, Bldg Rep; NEA, OEA 1971-; March of Dimes 1992-, 2 Martha Holden Jennings Grants; Tchr of the Month Awd 1992; 1110 Lake Rd Conneaut OH 44030

E, EDWARD J., Mathematics Teacher; *b:* Bridgeport, CT; *m:* Gail iPasquale; *c:* Beth Arcamone, Edward S., Rachel A.; *ed:* Univ of eport (BA) Math 1964, (MS) Scndry Ed 1967; Fairfield Univ (CAS) y Ed Admin 1977; *cr:* Kolbe HS Math Tchr 1964-67; Fairfield Prep Tchr & Var Bsbl Coach 1967-; *ai:* Var Bsbl Coach; Math Team erator; Admissions Comm Mem; NCTM, ATOMIC 1980-; *office:* eld Coll Preparatory Sch N Benson Rd Fairfield CT 06430

E, ELEANOR TURNER, Third Grade Teacher; *b:* Rockville Ctr, : Lawrence H.; *c:* Lawrence C., Chloe E.; *ed:* Saint Francis Coll (BS) Elem Ed 1965; 19 Credit Hrs at Hofstra Univ; 60 Hrs Beyond Bachelors; *cr:* Bellmore Schl Dist 1st Grd Tchr 1965-71; Connetquot C S dist 1st-4th Grd Tchr 1971-; *ai:* Connetquot Tchrs Assn 1971-; NYSUT 1965-; *office:* Cherokee Street Schl 130 Cherokee St Ronkonkoma NY 11779

ROWE, FRANK J., Attendance Coordinator; *b:* Massillon, OH; *m:* Bonnie L. Miller; *c:* Matthew; *ed:* Malone Coll (BA) Eng 1970; Kent St Univ (MED) Admin 1977; Post Grad Stud Kent St Univ, Univ of Akron, Ashland Univ; *cr:* Defiance Jr High Eng Tchr 1970; New Philadelphia HS Eng Tchr 1970-95, Attendance Coord 1995-; *ai:* Prins Leadership Comm; New Philadelphia Ed Assn 1970-, Negotiating Comm Chm; OH Ed Assn, NEA 1970-; Elks 1995-; Dover Band Boosters 1994-, Audit Comm Chm; Winfield United Meth Finance Comm; *office:* New Philadelphia HS 343 Ray Ave NW New Philadelphia OH 44663

ROWE, GLENNA P., Chemistry Teacher; *b:* Greenfield, OH; *m:* William Maurice; *c:* Sara Bethany, William Seth; *ed:* Otterbein Coll (BA) Chem 1981; Wright St Univ (MS) Tchr Ldr 1994; 6 Hrs Post-Masters; *cr:* Washington SR HS Tchr 1981-; *ai:* Sci Dept Chprsn; Block Scheduling Comm; NEA 1982-; SECO 1990-; Greenfield Area Life Squad 1989-, EMTA Vol; Good Shepherd Church Bd & Ldrshp Team 1990-, Asst Chprsn; Natl Karate Assn 1994-; Ashland Chemical Golden Apple Awd; *office:* Washington Sr HS 1200 Willard St Washington Court H OH 43160

ROWE, HOWARD ARTHUR, English Teacher; *b:* Lynn, MA; *m:* Margaret Rose Sylvester; *c:* Michael, Christopher, Kathleen; *ed:* Salem St Coll (BSEd) Eng 1961; Univ of Southern ME (MSEd) Eng 1967; 30 Addl Hrs Eng; *cr:* King Jr HS Eng Tchr 1965-79; Univ of Southern ME Eng Instruction 1970-79; Deering HS Eng Tchr 1979-; *ai:* Acad Decathlon, Future Tchrs of Amer Adv; SIT Chair; NEA, MEA, NCTE 1961-; St Project Grad Task Force 1985-, Sec; BSA 1978-, Comm Chair; Tchr of Yr 1992; Tchng Eng in Japan 1989; Shakespeare in Classroom 1993; *office:* Deering HS 370 Stevens Ave Portland ME 04103*

ROWE, KATHLEEN ELIZABETH, Guidance Counselor; *b:* Norwalk, OH; *c:* Katharine, Allison, Aaron; *ed:* Capital Univ (BA) Ed 1969; OH St Univ (MA) Ed 1972; Post Grad Stud in Ed; Univ of Dayton Licensed Prof Clinical Counseling Prgm; *cr:* Columbus Pub Schls Tchr, Guidance Cnslr 1969-74; Dublin Elem Schls Guidance Cnslr 1984-91; Dublin Coffman HS Guidance Cnslr 1991-95; Dublin Scioto HS Guidance Cnslr 1995-; *ai:* Guidance Dept Chprsn; Intervention Comm; Spec Ed Core Team; OEA, NEA, OSCA 1984-; NACAC, OACAC 1991-; Co Author of A Comprehensive Developmental Guidance Prgm K-5; *office:* Dublin Scioto HS 4000 Hard Rd Dublin OH 43016

ROWE, LEONETTE SUTTER, 6th-8th Grade Teacher; *b:* Akron, OH; *m:* Duane F.; *ed:* Univ of Akron (BS) Bio 1964, (MS) Elem Ed 1980; Attnd Ashland Univ, Univ of CT, OH St Univ; *cr:* Greene MS 7th Grd Tchr 1966-67, 8th Grd Tchr 1967-70, 5th Grd Tchr 1970-77, 6th Grd Tchr 1977-92, 6th, 7th, 8th Grd Tchr 1992-; *ai:* Sci Olympiad Team Coach; Sci Ed Cncl of OH; Dist II Dir 1992-; NSTA; Advy Comm OH Sci Olympiad 1993-95; Jennings Scholar; *office:* Greene MS PO Box 367 Smithville OH 44677

ROWE, PAULA PECK, Science Teacher; *b:* Jackson, MI; *m:* John N.; *c:* John P., Sarah A.; *ed:* Western MI Univ (BS) Bio, Ed 1966; PA St Univ (MED) Bio 1971; 35 Credit Hrs; *cr:* Penns Vly Area HS Sci Tchr 1968-72; Montgomery Cty Pub Schls Sci Tchr 1981-; *ai:* Springbrook HS Stu Med Soc Club Spon, Equestrians Club & Team Spon, Tech & Rsrch Partnership Coord & Tchr; NEA, Montgomery Co Ed Assn 1981-; MD Assn Bio Tchrs 1985-; Natl Soc for Experiential Ed 1994-; Hughes United Meth Church 1974-, Family Coord, Nursery Dir, Circle Chprsn; Natl Soc for Experiential Ed Flwshp & Mini-Grant 1994-; Howard Hughes Medl Inst, Natl Inst of Hlth, Tchr Intern 1993-94; Article Pub in Amer Bio Tchr 1988; *office:* Montgomery Cty Pub Schls 201 Vly Brook Dr Silver Spring MD 20904

ROWE, ROGER PETER, 5th Grade Teacher; *b:* New Rochelle, NY; *m:* Melanie Catherine Ferris; *c:* Scott, Craig; *ed:* Ithaca Coll (BA) His, Soc Stud 1969; New Paltz (MS) Elem Ed 1972; 48 Addl Credit Hrs; *cr:* Roosevelt Schl 4th-5th Grd Tchr 1969-80; Anne M. Dorner MS 6th Grd Tchr 1987-88; Claremont Schl 5th Grd Tchr 1980-; *ai:* Var Ftbl 27 Yrs, Strength Coach; HS Fitness Ctr Dir, Coord; Ftbl Game Day Book Chprsn; AFT, NYSUT 1969-; Elks Club.

ROWELL, KATHERINE R., Assistant Professor; *b:* Lebanon, KY; *m:* Kurt E.; *c:* John, Jack; *ed:* Wright St (BA) Pol Sci 1987, (MA) Applied Beh Sci 1989; OH St (PHD) Sociology 1994; *cr:* Wright St Instr 1993-94; Central St Prof 1996; *ai:* sociological focus deputy ed; Amer Soc Assn 1989-, Honors Prgm Bd; North cntrl Soc assn 1989-, Soc Policy Comm; Greene Cty CPC 1995-, Bd of Trustees; Presidential Fellowship OH St; Tchng Excl Awd OH St 1990-91; *office:* Central St Univ 120 Wesley Hall Wilberforce OH 45384

ROWINSKI, PAMELA ANNE (LETOILE), 8th Grade Teacher; *b:* Haverhill, MA; *m:* Robert F.; *c:* Lisbeth L.; *ed:* Emmanuel Coll (BA) Eng 1972; Salem St Coll (MED) Rdng 1975; 9 Post Grad Hrs; *cr:* Salem HS Eng, Rdng Tchr 1972-78; Northern Essex Comm Coll Rdng Strategies Instr 1980-82; Salem HS Eng, Rdng Tchr 1984-87; Timberlane Regnl MS 8th Grd Tchr 1989-; *ai:* Natl Jr Hnr Soc; Fac Cncl Rep; Former Chprsn Dist Wide Evaluation Comm; AFT 1991-; NCTE 1972-; IRA 1981-; *office:* Timberlane Regnl MS 44 Greenough Rd Plaistow NH 03865*

ROWLAND, STEPHEN C., Mathematics Teacher; *b:* Glen Ridge, NJ; *m:* Deborah D.; *c:* Leah, Abigail; *ed:* Westminster Coll (BS) Math 1970, (MED) Cnslng 1973; *ai:* Regnl Math & Sci Collaborative Steering Comm; IMAST Team Mem; MS Team Ldr; NEA 1970-; PSEA; BWEA; Math Cncl of Western PA; *office:* J E Harrison MS 129 Windvale Dr Pittsburgh PA 15236

ROWLAND, WILLIAM S., English Teacher; *b:* Leominister, MA; *m:* Maria Aiello; *c:* Regina, Lauren; *ed:* Mt St Marys Coll (BA) His & Philosophy-Magna Cum Laude 1967; Hofstra Univ (MS) Fnds of Ed 1978; SUNY at Stony Brook (MA) Eng 1986; 15 Grad Credits Eng 1970-73; Adelphi Univ 15 Grad Credits Eng 1968-70; *cr:* Dawnwood Jr HS Eng Tchr 1968-81; Centereach HS Eng Tchr 1981-; *ai:* AFT & NYS United Tchrs 1968-; NCTE; Natl Endowment for Hum Fellowship 1991; Pub 3 Articles in Journal; Cncl for Hum Ind Stud Basic Ed Fellowship 1992; Natl Endwmnt for Hum Flwshp 1994; *office:* Centereach HS 14 43rd St Centereach NY 11720*

ROWLANDS, KIM R., Fifth Grade Teacher; *b:* N Canton, OH; *m:* Kathryn A. Jackson; *c:* Jason R., Timothy J.; *ed:* Kent St Univ (BA) Ed-Cum Laude 1977; Post Grad Work Desktop Publishing, Use of Media in Ed, Cmptr Stud; *cr:* Westmoor MS 8th Grd Sci Tchr 1980-82; Linmoor MS 8th Grd Algebra, Soc Stud, Math Tchr 1982-83; Georgian Heights Elem Schl 5th Grd Tchr 1983-87; John Burroughs Elem Schl 5th Grd Tchr 1987-; *ai:* Bldg Cmptr Contract Prgm; 5th Grd Outdoor Ed Camp Participant; Cmptr Troubleshooter; CEA, NEA, OEA 1980-; *office:* John Burroughs Elem Schl 2585 Sullivant Ave Columbus OH 43204

ROWLEY, DENNIS, English Teacher; *b:* Trenton, NJ; *m:* Cynthia Baughman; *c:* Robert; *ed:* Rider Univ (BA) Elem Ed 1975, (BA) Eng 1975; Mercer Cty Comm Coll Credit Hrs; *cr:* Grice Jr HS Eng Tchr 1975-76; Hamilton West HS Eng Tchr 1976-; *ai:* Var Cross Cntry, Sftbl Coach 15 Yrs; NEA, HTEA 1976-; *office:* Hamilton West HS 2720 S Clinton Ave Trenton NJ 08610

ROWLEY, LYNNE JOHNSON, Second Grade Teacher; *b:* Geneva, NY; *m:* Norris R.; *c:* Adam, Michael, Joshua; *ed:* Vermont Coll a Division of Norwich Univ (AS) Early Chldhd, Nursery 1974; SUC at Genesco(BA) Spec, Elem Ed 1976, (ME) Spec, Elem Ed 1981; *cr:* Holcomb Campus Schl Tchr Aide 1974-75; Jefferson Primary Schl Spec, Elem Ed Tchr 1977-; Warsaw Elem Schl Spec, Elem Ed Tchr 1977-; *ai:* Stu Cncl, Ski Club, Sunshine Comm Adv; PTA Tchr Rep; Tech Comm; NEA 1977-; PTA Pub Relations Edctrs Asst Prgm; PR, EAP, PTA for Local Org Warsaw Edctrs Assn, Comm Head; *office:* Warsaw Elem Schl 153 W Court St Warsaw NY 14569

ROY, ALICIA M., English Department Chair; *ed:* Providence Coll (BA) Eng, Theatre Art-Suma Cum Laude 1986; E. W. Scripps Schl of Jrnlsm at OH Univ (MS) Jrnlsm 1988; Tchrs Cert Scndry Eng 1989; *cr:* Palmer HS Eng, Hum Tchr 1988-, Eng Dept Chair 1991-; Springfield Tech Comm Coll Instr 1992; *ai:* Yrbk, Lions Club Speech Competition, Stu Literacy Tutors Adv; HS Cncl Tchr Rep; Handbook Comm; Crisis Team; NCTE 1989-; NEA, MA Tchrs Assn 1988-; Literacy Vol of Amer of Quaboag Vly 1993-, Bd of Dirs; Big Sisters 1991-; Kappa Tau Alpha 1987-; Phi Kappa Phi 1988-; MA Tchr of Yr Finalist 1996; Presented at Tech Confs; Huntington Theatre Masterworks Inst Participant; *office:* Palmer HS 4105 Main St Palmer MA 01069*

ROY, CARLETHER POLK, Retired Fifth Grade Teacher; *b:* Lake Charles, LA; *w:* John W. (dec); *ed:* Leland Coll (BS) Eng, Soc Stud 1946; NY Univ (MA) Eng Tchng 1955; Rutgers Univ (EDD) Lang Arts Ed 1991; *cr:* Boston HS Eng, Math Tchr 1946-60; Carver HS Eng, Math Tchr 1960-62; Boston HS Eng, Math Tchr 1962-64; Meml Jr HS Eng, Soc Stud Tchr 1964-65; US Dept of Defense Schls Eng Tchr 1965-68; Conrow Schl Fifth Grd Tchr 1968-94; Anastasia Schl Fifth Grd Tchr 1968-94; *ai:* Sponsored, Initiated Production & Direction of Stu Operettas, Stu Writers Clubs & Fairs, Elem Sci Fair & Career Day Seminar Long Brand Schl Dist; Vol After-Schl Tutoring Site-Based Prgm 2 Yrs; NEA 1960-; MCEA, LBEA, NJEA 1964-, Bldg Rep, Mbrshp Comm Work, Certs & Citations for Outstdng Svcs; NYU Schl of Ed Area Alumni, Coord; John J. Johnson III Schlsp Fnd Bd Mem 1980-, Fund-R Comm; Zeta Phi Beta 1957-, Corresponding Sec; Monmouth Cty Bus & Prof Women's Cncl Inc, Past Pres; Svc Medal; Long Branch Dist Tchr of Yr Awd 1985; Delta Xi Chapter of Kappa Delta Pi 1992; NJ Ed Grant for Hand-On Sci Project 1992; Ft Monmouth Chrstn Ed Prgms Plaque & Certs Awded for Vol Svcs; Dissertation Manuscript Pub 1991; *home:* 355A Long Branch Ave Long Branch NJ 07740*

ROY, GERALD ALLEN, Art Teacher; *b:* HI; *m:* Diane Mc Dermott; *c:* Catherine, Christopher; *ed:* South CT St Univ (BS) Art Ed 1976; Central CT St Univ (MS) Art 1981; *cr:* Bristol Pub Schls K-8 Grd Art Tchr 1976-83, HS Art Tchr 1983-84; Foxborough Pub Schls HS Art Tchr, Art Dept Chprsn 1984-; *ai:* NEA 1984-; NAEA; *office:* Foxborough HS 120 South St Foxboro MA 02035

ROY, REGIS JASON, Fifth Grade Teacher; *b:* Provincetown, MA; *c:* Amanda, Jason; *ed:* Salem St Coll (BS) Elem 1970; Plymouth St Coll (MA) Elem 1975; *cr:* Haverhill Schls 2 Grd Tchr 1970-71, 3 Grd Tchr 1972-73, 4 Grd Tchr 1974-90, 5 Grd Tchr 1991-95; *ai:* Stu Cncl Adv; IST, Math, Eng Curr, Negotiating, Problem Solving, Tchr Evaluation Comms; OM Judge; Spelling Bee Coord; NEA 1975-, Pres; Lib Trustee 1980-; Booster Club 1994-; PTA 1970-; Band Supporter 1993-; *home:* 58 Park St Woodsville NH 03785*

ROY, SAMUEL NORMAND, 8th Grade Religion & Sci Tchr; *b:* Lewiston, ME; *m:* Maureen Emond; *c:* Carleen; *ed:* Saint Michaels (BS) Chem 1962, (MED) Rel Ed 1974; *cr:* Sacred Heart Acad Tchr 1955-58; Sacred Heart Scholasticate Tchr 1958-62; Saint Francis Scndry Africa Tchr 1962-67; Tchr Part-Time & Admin 1967-75; Good Sherpherd Tchr 1975-; *ai:* Girls Bsktbl Coach; NCEA; Diocesan Rel Ed Lecturer for CCD & Cath Schls-Tchr & Adult Ed; *office:* Good Shepherd Jr HS 1210 Mendon Rd Woonsocket RI 02895

ROYAL, PATRICIA LAWSON, Home Economics Teacher; *b:* Hackensack, NJ; *m:* Bobby L. Sr.; *c:* Bobby Jr., Jerrell; *ed:* NC A&T St Univ (BS) Home Ec Ed 1965; Cross Cultural Analysis 3 Credits; Tchr Expectations & Stu Achvmts 3 Credits; *cr:* Pleasantville HS Home Ec Tchr 28 Yrs; Atlantic Cty Job Trng Tchr & Cnslr 6 Months; NC A&T St Univ Resident Cnslr 3 Months; Head Start at Pleasantville Tchr 3 Months; *ai:* Stu Act Coord; TESA Staff Facilitator; NEA 1967-, Elected Convention Del; Pleasantville Ed Assn 1967-, Pres; NJ Ed Assn 1967-, Constitution Review Comm; Atlantic Cty Ed Assn 1992-, Corresponding Sec; NAACP 1990-, Sec; NABSE 1990-, Convention Del; NSide Bus & Prof Women 1990-, Pres; Delta Sigma Theta 1993-, Soc Action Comm Chair; Pleasantville Dist Tchr of Yr; Atlantic Cty Tchr of Yr; St of NJ Governors Tchr Recognition; Zeta Phi Beta Sorority Woman of Yr; Comm Bapt Church Mother of Yr; *office:* Pleasantville HS 350 S Franklin Blvd Pleasantville NJ 08232*

ROYER, JEFFREY ALLAN, Biology & Physiology Teacher; *b:* Baltimore, MD; *m:* Regina Doris; *c:* Lydia, Anne; *ed:* Western MD Coll (BA) Bio 1974; Salisbury St Coll (MA) Ed 1982; Recombinant DNA Tech 1989; *cr:* Wicomico Jr HS Life Sci, GATE, Cmptr Tchr 1978-89; James M. Bennett Sr HS Bio, Physiology Tchr 1989-; *ai:* Model Rocketry Club; NEA, WCEA 1978-; *office:* James M Bennet SR HS E College Ave Salisbury MD 21801

ROYER, RICHARD R., Science & Ag Dept Chair; *b:* Lebanon, PA; *m:* Rosene Schaeffer; *c:* Heather, Rodney; *ed:* Penn St (BS) Voc-Ed, Ag 1968; Addl Curr & Tchr Trng; Millersville Univ Cmptr Programming; *cr:* Conrad Weiser SD Ag Tchr 1968-70, Gen Sci 1970-83, Bio, Cmptr Useage Tchr 1983-91, Bio, Sci Tchr 1991-; *ai:* Sci, Ag Chm; Pub Relations; 10th Grd Curr; Conrad Weiser EA 1968-, Treas, Pres, Past Pres; PSEA, NEA 1968-; So Lebanon Lions 1977-, Pres, Sec, Ldrshp Awd 1985, Outstdng Sec Awd 1986; Mt Lebanon Lodge F&AM 1985-, Master, Sec, Ldrshp Awd 1992.*

ROYER, RONALD PAUL, Activities Director; *b:* Belle Center, OH; *m:* Patricia Mc Intosh; *c:* Melissa, Emily; *ed:* OH Northern Univ (BA) Ed, Bio 1966; Wright St (MA) Curr Supervision 1978; *cr:* Buckeye Local Math, Bio Tchr 1966-70; Benjamin Logan Bio Tchr 1971-93, Act Dir 1993-; *ai:* Head Coach Ftbl, Girls Track; Reserve Girls, Boys Bsktbl Coach; OEA 1966-81; BLEA 1966-81, Pres; Village of Bello Peatea 1986-91, Mayor.

ROYSE, DALE ALVIN, Social Studies Teacher; *b:* Greenfield, OH; *m:* Donna Jean Knowles; *c:* Jennifer Lynne, Chad Austin; *ed:* Univ of Rio Grande (BS) Comprehensive Soc Sci 1979; Univ of Dayton (MS) Ed 1991; *cr:* Green Twp Hs Soc Stud Tchr 1980-; *ai:* Girls Var Bsktbl Coach; OH Ed Assn 1981-; *office:* Green Twp HS Rt 2 Box 18-AA Franklin Furnace OH 45629

ROYSE, LYNN VOLLE, 5th Grade Teacher; *b:* Elmhurst, IL; *m:* Daniel J.; *c:* Matthew, John; *ed:* Penn St Univ & Clarion Univ Masters Equivlancy 1987; *cr:* Marshall Unit Schls 7th & 8th Grd Lit Tchr 1972-74; Danville Dist #118 Tchr 1974-78; St Coll Area Schls 5th & 6th Grd Tchr 1979-; *ai:* NEA 1972-; SCAEA 1979-; Phi Delta Kappa; PSEA 1979-; Jr Womens Club 1978-85, VP; Radio Park PTO 1979-, Treas; St Pauls United Meth Church 1979-; Bsktbl Booster Club 1990-, Treas; Natl Elem Winner TCI Ed Video Awd 1990-91; *office:* Radio Park Elem Schl 800 W Cherry Ln State College PA 16803

ROYSTER, EUGENE CANFIELD, Assoc Professor of Sociology; *b:* New Haven, CT; *m:* Kay McClendon; *c:* Jennyfer, Jeffrey; *ed:* Antioch Coll (BA) Sociology 1953; Yale Univ (MA) Sociology 1957, (PHD) Sociology

1963; Attnd Columbia Univ Schl of Soc Work; *cr:* ABT Assocs Sr Scientist 1975-79; NTS Rsrch Corp Sr Scientist & Dir Ed Eval 1979-82; Univ of Rochester Grad Schl of Ed Prof 1982-89; Cheyney Univ Prof 1989-; *ai:* The Applied Sociology Assn Lester Ward Awd for Lifetime Contribution; *office:* Cheyney Univ Of PA Box 358 Cheyney PA 19319

ROZAN, PAULA MARKOWITZ, Mathematics Teacher; *b:* Newark, NJ; *m:* Dr. Ronald; *c:* Michelle, Gayle; *ed:* Kean Coll (BA) Math Ed; Montclair St Univ (MS) Math Ed 1974; *cr:* Park Jr HS Math Tchr 1970-71; Ben Franklin Jr HS Math Tchr 1971-76; Summit HS Math Tchr 1984-; *ai:* Sr Class Adv; NEA, NJEA, NCTM, AMTNJ 1976-; Summit Ed Assn 1984-; Summit HS Fac Awd; *office:* Summit High School 125 Kent Place Blvd Summit NJ 07901

ROZBICKI, ELLEN A. LATES, 7th-8th Grade English Teacher; *b:* Lackawanna, NY; *m:* Richard S.; *c:* Patricia Leitten, Richard, Joseph; *ed:* St Univ Coll at Fredonia (BA) Eng 1968; St Univ Coll at Buffalo (MS) Eng Ed 1994; 120 Hrs West Seneca Tchrs Ctr 1990-; *cr:* West Seneca West Sr HS 9-12 Grd Eng Tchr 1968-90; West Seneca East Sr HS 9-11 Grd Eng, Writing Tchr 1990-94; West Seneca West MS 7-8 Grd Eng Tchr 1994-; *ai:* Shared Decision Making, Emergency Bldg Team; Bd Games Activity 7th Grd Spon; AFT, West Seneca Tchrs Assn 1968-; NY St Eng Cncl 1989-; 1989 Tchr of Excl NY St Eng Cncl; 1990 Fredonia St Coll Nom by Stdnts for Making Difference in their Lives; *office:* West Seneca West MS 395 Center Rd West Seneca NY 14224

ROZDILSKI, PETER WILLIAM, 7th Grade Math Teacher; *b:* Wilkes Barre, PA; *m:* Suzanne S.; *c:* Claire, Nicholas; *ed:* East Stroudsburg U (BA) Ed 1974; 86 Credit Hrs Beyond BA; *ai:* JV Bsbl Coach; MS Bsbl Club; PSEA 1974-; NEA 1974-; PTA 1974-; Northeastern PA Cncl of Tchrs of Math 1990-; Grace Luth Church 1980-, Church Cncl; Skier Awareness Team Mortage Mt 1990-, Team Ldr; *office:* North Pocano MS 701 Church St Moscow PA 18444

ROZEN, HERSH S., Guidance Counselor; *b:* Johnson City, NY; *m:* Beverly Zalbowitz; *c:* Cory, Steven, Eric; *ed:* Johns Hopkins Univ (BA) Psych 1960; Elmira Coll (MS) Ed 1966; Colgate Univ (MS) Guid 1969; Binghamton Univ Credit Hrs; *cr:* Binghamton North HS Bio Tchr 1961-69, Cnslr 1969-82; Binghamton HS Cnslr 1982-; *ai:* ESOL Cnslr; Commencement Adv; Binghamton Tchrs Assoc 1961-; NYSTA & BTA 1961-; Broome Tioga Cnslrs 1970-; Coll Day Bd 1982-, Treas; Rotary Club 1978-, Rotary Man of the Yr Awd; *office:* Binghamton HS 31 Main St Binghamton NY 13905*

ROZEVINK, LINDA L., Mathematics Teacher; *b:* Defiance, OH; *ed:* Anderson Univ (BA) Math, Acctng 1974; Ball St Univ (MA) Acctng 1977; Attnd Bowling Green St Univ 1981, Kent St Univ 1990-91; *cr:* Fayette Cty Schl Corp Jr HS Math Tchr 1975-79; Lincolnview Local Schls HS Math Tchr 1980-; *ai:* Bd Advy Comm; Scholastic Bowl Team Adv 17 Yrs; Stu Cncl Adv 15 Yrs; Class Adv 9 Yrs; Spirit Club Adv 5 Yrs; Attendance, Textbook Adoption, Weighted Grds Comms; OH Cncl Tchrs of Math 1989-; Big Brother, Big Sister Org, Project You & Me 8 Yrs; Van Wert Area Jaycees Young Edctr of Yr Awd 1989; *office:* Lincolnview HS 15945 Middle Point Rd Van Wert OH 45891*

ROZGONYI, GREGORY ALAN, 9th Grade Health Teacher; *b:* Pittsburgh, PA; *ed:* Slippery Rock Univ (BS) Hlth, PE 1987; CA Univ of PA (MS) Rdng Specialist 1995; *cr:* West Mifflin MS 6-8th Grd Hlth, PE Tchr 1989-92, 9th Grd Hlth Tchr 1992-; *ai:* Cross Cnty, Wrestling, Track & Field Asst Coach; Var Club Spon; AFT 1989-; *office:* West Mifflin Area HS 91 Commonwealth Ave West Mifflin PA 15122

ROZIN, MURIEL ANN LIEBERFARB, Consultant & Resource Rm Tchr; *b:* Brooklyn, NY; *c:* Ian; *ed:* Brooklyn Coll (BA) Speech Therapy, Ed 1967; Tchrs Coll Columbia Univ (MA) Spec Ed 1969; *cr:* PS 327 1968-70; League Schl Spec Ed, Clinical Tchr 1970-79; IS 70 Enrich The Schl for Soc Action Resource Room Tchr 1979-93; IS 70 Physical City Lab Schl Resource Room Tchr 1993-94; IS 70 Upper Lab Museum Schl Resource Room, Consultant Tchr 1995-; *ai:* Schls Tchng Options for Peace Peer Mediation Prgm Coord; Talent Shows; Dances; Proms; Grad; AFT 1969-; NY St Tchrs Mentor; Dia Ctr for the Arts Flwshp; *office:* IS 70 Upper Lab Museum Schl 333 W 17th St New York NY 10011*

ROZITSKI, LORILEE, Secondary Mathematics Teacher; *b:* Wilkes-Barre, PA; *m:* Scott A.; *ed:* Wilkes Univ (BA) Math 1990, (MED) Ed 1993; 18 Addl Hrs; *cr:* Crestwood Area Schl Dist Scndry Math Tchr 1990-; *ai:* Fr Class Adv 1994-; NEA, PSEA 1990-; *office:* Crestwood Schl Dist 281 S Mountain Blvd Mountain Top PA 18707

ROZZELLE, VANESSA K., Instructor; *b:* Rahway, NJ; *c:* Seshat Young; *ed:* Lincoln Univ (BA) Psych 1975; Columbia Univ Tchrs Coll (MA) Cnslng Psych 1976, (MED) Voc, Rehabilitation Cnslng 1977; *cr:* Univ of Calahar Instr 1979-80; Phila Coll of Office Trng Instr 1980-82; Boys Choir of Harlem Instr 1982-87; City Univ of NY BMCC Instr 1989-; *ai:* Coll Discovery Club Adv; Mid Sts Review, Women's His Month Comms; *office:* Borough Of Manhattan Comm Coll 199 Chambers St New York NY 10007

RUANE, NANCY JEANNE, Reading & Writing Teacher; *b:* Jersey City, NJ; *ed:* Saint Peter's Coll (BA) Elem Ed 1974; Montclair Univ (MA) Rdng; 32 Credit Hrs Supvrs, Prins Cert; *cr:* Roosevelt Schl Title I, 3rd, 6-8 Grd Tchr 1974-87; Mary J. Donohoe Schl 6-8 Grd Rdng Tchr 1987-91; Midtown Comm Schl 8th Grd Rdg, Writing Tchr 1991-; *ai:* Peer Meditation, 8th Grd Class, Yrbk Adv; Shared Decision Making Team Ldr; Bayonne Tchrs Assn, NJ Ed Assn 1974-; *office:* Midtown Community Schl 550 Avenue A Bayonne NJ 07002*

RUANE, NOEL A., Business Education Teacher; *b:* Jersey City, NJ; *ed:* Caldwell Coll (BS) Bus Admin 1970; Pace Univ (MS) Bus Ed 1973; Columbia Univ, Fordham Univ Post Grad Stud; *cr:* St Josephs HS Bus Ed Tchr 1970-73; Mother Cabrini HS Bus Ed Tchr 1973-79; Eastchester HS Bus Ed Tchr 1979-; *ai:* Class Adv; Stu Act Treas; NYSUT, WBEA 1979-; BTA 1995-; Impact II Adaptor Grant; Mid Sts Evaluation Comm; *office:* Eastchester HS 2 Stewart Pl Yonkers NY 10707*

RUANE, THOMAS F., History Teacher; *b:* Co Mayo, Ireland; *m:* Monique S.; *c:* Samantha, Brianna; *ed:* Adelphi Univ (BA) His 1984; (MS) His 1994; *cr:* Bellmore-Merrick Soc Stud Tchr 1989-90; Wantagh HS Soc Stud Tchr 1990-; *ai:* Adelphi Univ Var Soccer Coach; Hope for Youth 1993-, Bd of Dirs; Mc Pham HS Tchr of Yr 1990; *office:* Wantagh HS Beltagh Ave Wantagh NY 11793*

RUBBO, LENA SANTOMENNO, HS Child Care Teacher; *b:* Hartford, CT; *m:* Robert Anthony; *c:* Steven M.; *ed:* Central Ct St Univ (BS) Bio 1971, (MS) Spec Ed Pre K-8 1977; 15 Credits Spec Ed Pre K-12 1980; 15 Credits Family, Consumer Scis St Joseph Coll 1993; *cr:* Southington HS Bio Tchr 1971-76; Naugatuck HS Child Care Tchr 1981-; *ai:* Frosh Class Adv; Schl Climate Comm Chprsn NEASC Evaluation; Sunshine Comm; NEA, CT Ed Assn, Naugatuck Tchrs League 1983-.

RUBCICH, NICHOLAS GEORGE, Fourth Grade Teacher; *b:* Staten Island, NY; *ed:* Wagner Coll (BS) Elem Ed 1969, (MA) Advanced Ed 1973; *cr:* Willowbrook St Schl Tchr of Educables, Trainables, Young Adults 1969; Pub Schl 30 6th Grd Tchr 1969-70; Pub Schls 11 & 20 4th-6th Grd Tchr 1970-71; Pub Schl 30 4th-5th Grd Tchr 1971-75; Pub Schl 60 4th Grd Tchr 1975-80, Dist 4th GTrd Tchr of GATE 1980-89, 4th Grd Hnrs Tchr 1989-93, 4th Grd Tchr 1993-94, 4th Grd Hnrs Tchr 1994-95, 4th Grd Tchr 1995-; *ai:* After Schl Ctr Gym Tchr 1975-; Coord Ecology Fair, NY City Interscholastic Math League, Track; Adv NY City Educl Olympiad; Judge Dist Soc Stud, Sci Fairs; Fourth Grd, Great Books Fnd Ldr; Staten Island Rdng Assn, NY St Rdng Assn 1969-; Staten Island Cncl of Soc Stud; Staten Island Sci Tchrs Assn; United Fed of Tchrs; NY St United Tchrs; PTA; Frank Murphy AM Bsbl League 1968-70, Coach; Twyford Muche Major League Bsbl 1970-83, Coach; Richmond Cty Twilight League 1970-83, Coach, All Star Coach; Friends of Alice Austen; Protectors of Pine Oaks Woods Inc; Staten Island Ballet Co; Outstdng Tchr 1986; Dist 32 Elem Schl Tchr of Yr 1992; *office:* PS 60 The Alice Austen Schl 55 Merrill Ave Staten Island NY 10314

RUBEN, NANCY STEPHENSON, Sixth Grade Teacher; *b:* Plainfield, NJ; *m:* H. Walter Jr.; *c:* Andrew, Wendy Smith; *ed:* Georgian Court Coll (BA) Ed 1980, (MA) Ed 1988; 33 Credit Hrs Jersey City St Coll Admin, Supervision; *cr:* St Peter Elem Schl Art Tchr 1970-77; Meml MS 7th Grd Soc Stud, Lang, 6th Grd Soc Stud, Rdng 1980-; *ai:* Grd 6 Team Ldr; Schl Planning, Pupil Asst Comms; NJEA, NEA, Pt Pleasant Tchrs Assn 1980-; Alpha Zeta Chptr, Corresponding Sec 1990-92, Pres Elect 1992-94; Alpha Delta Kappa 1987-, Pres 1994-; Governor's Awd 1988; Tchr of Yr Dist Nom 1994; *office:* Memorial MS Laura Herbert Dr Point Pleasant NJ 08742

RUBENSTEIN, DAVID M., English Teacher; *b:* New York, NY; *m:* Bonnie B.; *c:* Jennifer, Rebekah, Dov; *ed:* Sullivan Co Comm coll (AA) Liberal Arts 1965; SUNY New Paltz (BS) Scndry Ed 1967; SUNY at New Paltz (MS) Scndry Ed, Eng 1972; SUNY at New Paltz (MS) Elem Ed 1986; 18 Credits Post Grad Stud at SUNY; *cr:* Middletown HS Eng Tchr 1967-68; Plainview Old Bethpabe #4 Eng, Media Stud Tchr 1969-70; Sangerties Jr, Sr HS Eng Tchr 1971-; *ai:* Peer Mediation; Learning Strategies Comm; Gemini Project; Saugerties Tchrs Assn 1971-, Treas, Bldg Rep, Pub Relations; NYSUT 1967-; *home:* 16 Ingersoll Rd Mount Tremper NY 12457*

RUBERT-LOPEZ, LUZ E., Student Support Services Dir; *b:* Cayey, PR; *c:* Maria; *ed:* Inter-American Univ (BA) Soc Work 1973, (MA) Guidance, Cnslng 1975; Certfd Alchol, Drug Abuse, Mental Hlth Cnslr; *cr:* MA Dept of Corrections Soc Worker 1976-77; MA Parole Bd Parole Ofcr 1977-79; Quinsigamond Comm Coll Cnslr 1979-93, Stu Support Svc Dir 1993-; *ai:* Dram Club Adv; MTA, NCA 1979-, Del; Worcester Fights Back 1985-, Bd Mem; Multicultural Collaboration 1989-, Chair; New England Evangalical Luth Church 1988-, Synod Cncl; Distng Women in Field of Substance Abuse; Dev Peer Advocate Prgm; *office:* Quinsigamond Comm Coll 670 W Boylston St Worcester MA 01606

RUBIC, GLENN K., Sr Sci Tchr & Tech Specialist; *b:* Brooklyn, NY; *m:* Christina Kasaic; *c:* Alex, Larissa; *ed:* SUC New Paltz (BA) Geology 1984; NY Univ (MS) Sec Sci Ed; *cr:* Amer Museum of Naval His Curatorial Asst Dept Photographer, Invo Paleontology; Riverdale Cntry Schl Sci Tchr, Tech Specialist 1984-94; *ai:* New Tchr Mentor, Adv, Curr Dev; NAGT 1984-; ASCD 1988-; Summerbridge 1990-, Sci Tchr; Outstdng Tchr Awd 1988; Yrbk Dedication 1992; Who's Who Among Amer HS Stdnts 1975; NSF Tchr Collaborative; *office:* Riverdale Country Schl 5250 Fieldston Rd Bronx NY 10471*

RUBICCO, JOHN ANTHONY, 8th Grade English Teacher; *b:* Mount Vernon, NY; *m:* Claudia Kaufman; *c:* Melissa, Gabrielle; *ed:* Iona (MA) Eng 1970, (MS) Eng Ed 1975; Fordham at Tarreytown 9 Credit Hrs Admin; *cr:* NYC Bd of Ed 7th-8th Grd Eng Tchr 1969-73; Mamaroneck Bd of Ed 8th Grd Eng Tchr 1973-; *ai:* AFT 1969-, Tchr; NYSUT 1969-, Tchr Rep; MTA 1973-, Tchr; *office:* Hommocks MS 10 Hommocks Rd Larchmont NY 10538*

RUBIN, DOROTHEA R., Language Arts Teacher; *b:* Stamford, CT; *m:* Sheldon; *c:* Glen D.; *ed:* Kane Coll (BA) K-8 Elem Ed 1972; Minor Rdng K-12 1972; NJ St Cert Rdng & Lang Arts 1982; 18 Credit Hrs Exceptional Child; 12 Addtl Credit Hrs in Learning Styles & Strategies for the At-Risk Stu; *cr:* Jefferson Twp Spcl Ed Tchr 3 Yrs; Mount Olive Rndg, Gifted & Talented Tchr 26 Yrs; Pgm for 7th Grd 4 Yrs; *ai:* PEER Tutoring Coord & Pgm Developer in Schl Dist; NEA & NJEA 1972-; NCTE & IRA 1982-; First Recipient of Governors Recognition of Tchrs in NJ Awd; *office:* C. M. Stephens Mt Olive MS 99 Sunset Dr Budd Lake NJ 07828*

RUBIN, JUDITH HERMAN, Math Teacher; *b:* New York, NY; *m:* Norman S.; *c:* Joy Kupperstein, Cheri Fleisch, Sandra Schaeffer; *ed:* Hunter Coll (BA) Math 1962; Grad Credits Marywood Coll, Penn St, Beaver Coll; *cr:* Olinville Jr HS Math Tchr 1962-63; Council Rock HS Math Tchr 1972-73; Log Coll MS Math Tchr 1973-74; Eugene Klinger MS Math Tchr 1974-; *ai:* Challenge of 24 Team Coach; BCCTM 1973-, Mem at Large; NEA 1996; *office:* Eugene Klinger MS 1415 2nd Street Pike Southampton PA 18966

RUBIN, PHYLLIS LEVINE, Fourth Grade Teacher; *b:* Ellenville, NY; *m:* Stanley M.; *c:* Lesa, Danyel; *ed:* St Univ at New Paltz (BS) PreK - Common Branch 1961; 116 Addl Credit Hrs Post Grad; *cr:* Fallsburgh Cntrl Schl Spec Class Tchr 1961, Third Grd Tchr 1961-64; Monticello Cntrl Schl K-6th Grd Tchr 1964-; *ai:* Campaigning for Bd Mem Ellenvlle Pub Lib; AFT, NEA 1972-; Sullivan Cty Rdng Council 1988-; Auxiliary Ellenville Comm Hospital 1965-, Bd Mem 13 Yrs; Lit Vol 1990-; NY St Lib for the Blind 1987-, Read Books on Tape Vol; 4 Arts Sake & Yours 2; Adopt a Grandparent Prgm; *office:* Emma C Chase Elem Schl Pennsylvania Ave Wurtsboro NY 12790

RUBIN, PHYLLIS M., Mathematics Teacher; *b:* New York, NY; *m:* Milton; *c:* Michael, Scott; *ed:* City Coll of NY (BA) Soc Stud 1963; 60 Credit Hrs Temple Univ, Bucks Cty Comm Coll, Bloomsburg Univ, East Stroudsburg; *cr:* Philadelphia Schl Dist Math Tchr 1963-69; Beth Jacob Hebrew Acad Math Tchr 1977-79; Morrisville Schl Dist Math Tchr 1979-; *ai:* Tchr Mentoring Prgm; Grad Intern Tchrs Prgm Rider Coll; NHS Adv; NCTM 1963-; BCTM, NEA, PSEA, MEA 1979-; PCTM 1990-; *office:* Morrisville HS W Palmer Ave Morrisville PA 19067

RUBIN, ROBERT MARC, Asst Prin for Mrktg; *b:* New York, NY; *ed:* Adelphi Univ (BBA) Bus Ed 1966, (MA) Bus Ed 1968; Pace Univ (MS) Educl Admin 1972; *cr:* Grover Cleveland HS Tchr 8 Yrs; Harry S Truman HS Tchr 3 Yrs; NYC Bd of Ed Admin 5 Yrs; Norman Thomas HS Asst Prin Mrktng 15 Yrs; *ai:* DECA; NY Bd Ed Assn 1966-, Pres; NY St Bus Ed 1987-, Pres; *office:* Norman Thomas HS 111 E 33rd St New York NY 10016

RUBINS, MARLENE, Fourth Grade Teacher of GATE; *b:* Brooklyn, NY; *ed:* Queens Coll (MS) PE 1973; Adelphi Univ (MSW) Soc Work 1994; *cr:* PS 75 Schl Elem Ed Tchr 1970-76; PS 63 Schl Elem Ed Tchr 1976-86; PS 56 Schl Gifted Ed Tchr 1986-; *ai:* Rdng Remediation After Schl Prgm; UFT, AFT 1970-; NASW 1994-; Visiting Nurse Svc 1994-, Soc Worker; Tchr of Yr; *office:* PS 56 Harry Eichler 86-10 114th St Richmond Hill NY 11418*

RUBINSTEIN, HARRY, Professor of Chemistry; *b:* Cologne, Germany; *m:* Jean Rauch; *c:* Moira Maggio, Felicia Magida, Simone Horvitz; *ed:* Brooklyn Coll (BS) Chem 1953; Purdue Univ (PHD) Organic Chem 1958; *cr:* Wyandotte Chemicals Rsrch Chemist 1958-60; Keystone Chemurgic Asst Dir Rsrch 1960-61; Merk & Co Rsrch Chemist 1961-64; Springfield Coll Chem Prof 1964-65; Univ of MA Prof & Dean Grad Schl 1965-; *ai:* Univ Cncl; NE Regn Grad Schl Head of Deans; Sigma Xi 1958-, Pres; NEA 1972-, Del; AAUP; Jaycees 1959-64; Amer Chem Soc 1950-; Grants: Weizmann Inst, Brandeis Univ, Tufts Univ & Harvard Univ; *office:* Univ Of MA At Lowell Dept of Chem 1 University Ave Lowell MA 01854

RUBY, NANCY DUNLAP, Social Studies Teacher; *b:* Rutland, VT; *m:* Carl A.; *ed:* Castleton St Coll (BS) Ed & Soc Stud 1967, (MA) Ed 1978; 21 Credits; Trinity Coll 3 Credits; Coll of St Joseph 3 Credits; *cr:* Fair Haven Union HS Soc Stud Tchr 1968-; *ai:* Stdnts for Stdnts Peer Cnslrs Adv 1975-95; Head Adv Sr Class 1983-84 & 1995-; Dept Chair 19 AFT 1974-; Southern VT His Alliance 1987-; TOPSS-Amer Psyc 1995-; Natl Geographic Soc 1987-; Catholic Dirs of Amer Recording Sec; UVM Tchr of Yr 1984; Prins Crystal Apple Awd 19 Tchr of Yr Runner-Up 1989; General Electric Starr Awd 1986, 1994; *office:* Fair Haven Union HS Mechanic St Fair Haven VT 05

RUBY, SHAWN LEON, History Teacher; *b:* Staten Island, NY; *m:* Jane; *ed:* William Paterson Coll (BA) His 1992; *cr:* Netherlands Ref Chrstn Schl His Tchr 1992-; *ai:* Sr Planning Comm Adv; Act Nigh Reptile Club Adv; *office:* Nthrlnds Rfmd Christian HS 164 Jacksonv Pompton Plains NJ 07444

RUCH, CAROLYN MARY, Sixth Grade Teacher; *b:* Allentown, P Kutztown St Coll (BS) Elem Ed 1969, (MED) Ed 1972; 30 Addl Cre Ed; 27 Credits Elem Cnslng; *cr:* James W. Good Elem Schl 6th Gr 1969; Northwestern Lehigh Elem Schl 6th Grd Tchr 1969-71; Weis Elem Schl 6th, 4th Grd Tchr 1971-92; Northwestern Lehigh MS 6 Tchr 1992-; *ai:* Sixth Sense Acad Team Co-Adv; PSEA, NEA NMSA 1994-; Jessie K. Berlin Meml Order of Eastern Star 1981 Matron; *office:* Northwestern Lehigh MS 6636 Northwest Rd New PA 18066*

RUCH, JANICE SMITH, English Teacher; *b:* Geneca, NY; *m:* Fr *c:* Martin F.; *ed:* Roberts Wesleyan Coll (BA) Eng 1966; SU Brockport (MA) Eng 1975; *cr:* Spencerport Cntrl HS Eng Dept 1987-95, Eng Tchr 1966-; *ai:* Assessment Comm; NCTA 1987-; AF 1966-; ASCD 1993-95; RWC Alumni Cncl 1966-, Sec, Comm Pearce Mem Church1963-; Ed Comm; Rochester Inst of Tech Distng Awd 1992; *office:* Spencerport HS 2707 Spencerport Rd Spencerp 14559*

RUCH, MARGARET MINNICH, Music Teacher; *b:* Reading, Keith C.; *ed:* West Chester Univ (ME) Music Ed 1978; Penn St Cmp 1995-; *cr:* Exeter Schls Elem Music 1971-; *ai:* Musical Dir, Clu Instructional Support Team Mem; NEA, PSEA 1971-; MENC; Chur Womens Groups Church Cncl Choir 20 Yrs, Choir Dir, Jr Choir Local Choral Soc Solist, Chorus; Local Theatre Productions; Pl Comm Kinder Konzert; *office:* Exeter Twp Schl Dist 37th & Perkiom Reading PA 19606

RUCK, BYRON JAMES, High School Biology Teacher; *b:* Wapak OH; *m:* Lois J. Cornell; *c:* Christa J., Brady J.; *ed:* Wittenberg Univ Biological Sci & Math Ed 1964; Univ of Dayton (MS) Ed Admin Bowling Green St Univ 8 Hrs Post-Grad; OH Northern Univ 6 H Grad; Univ of Dayton 6 Hrs Project Discovery; *cr:* Wapakoneta Cit Bio & Math Tchr 1964-66 & 1973-; *ai:* Sci Day Coord; Driver Ed OH Acad of Sci 1978-; Wapak Ed Assn & OH NEA Ed Assn 1982 Lodge 1973-87, All Chair Offices; Wapakoneta VFW 1978-; Soil Conservation 1981-82, Bd Mem; *office:* Wapakoneta Sr HS 1 Reds Wapakoneta OH 45895

RUCKER, KENNETH HEWITT, Social Studies Teacher; *b:* Washi DC; *ed:* Bowie St Coll (BA) Soc Sci 1971; Loyola Coll (MMS) M Stud 1986; 30 Miscellaneous Grad Hrs; *cr:* St Mary's Schl Tchr 19 Atholton HS Tchr 1980-; *ai:* Harvard Model Congress Team Spon; MD ST Tchrs Assn 1980-; Howard Cty Ed Assn, Treas 1989-91 Capital Historical Museum of Transportation 1970-, Pres, Sec; MD of His Museums 1995-, Treas; Montgomery Cty His Consortium Pres; Railway Museums Assn, Treas; Articles Pub.

RUCKI, DEBRA STEPHANIE, Dean of Students; *b:* Pittsburgh, P IN Univ of PA (BS) Hlth, PE 1977; Univ of PIttsburgh (MED) Educl 1982; Elem Prin Cert 1985; *cr:* PIttsburgh Schl Sub Tchr, Dean of 1 Yr, Elem Tchr 5 Yrs, MS Tchr 16 Yrs; *ai:* Girl's Bsktbl Coach 1 Girl's Swim Coach 4 Yrs, Girl's Vlybl Coach 8 Yrs, Girl's Soccer C Yrs; AFT, PFT 1979-; Pgh Admin Assn 1995-; Phi Epsilon Kappa Treas 1976-77; Amer Red Cross 1979-, 15 YRS Svc; Grant Open Proposal Project Self-Esteem 1995; *office:* Arsenal MS 3900 Bu Pittsburgh PA 15201

RUDARI, DAVID JOSEPH, Vocal Music Dir & Spanish Tc Syracuse, NY; *ed:* SUNY at Fredonia (BM) Music Ed 1983; Univ (MM) Vocal Performance 1985; Span Coursework Jefferson Comr 1991-93; WV Univ DMA in Vocal Performance/Opera 1995-; *cr:* Fre Solo Singer, Conductor 1981-; Summer Schl of Arts Cnslr, Head 1981-85; Univ of WY Music Tchng Asst 1983-85; South Jefferson C HS Vocal Music Dir 1985-; WVU Tchng Asst in Music Ed 1995-, Methods & Stu Tchr Suprv; *ai:* Production, Musical Dir; Schl M Theatre Productions Vocal Coach, Conductor; Attendance, Sched Advy Cncl Comms; Dir Sr Choir St Mary's Church; MENC, NY 1980-; Phi Mu Alpha Sinfonia 1980-, VP 1982-83; NYSUT, SJTA 19 North Cntry Music Soc 1986-95, Asst Conductor 1991-95; Jefferson, Cty Music Tchrs Assn 1985-95, Treas 1993-95; Univ of WY Assistantship; NYSSMA Cert Vocal Adjudicator; Syracuse RC D Cert Cantor, Song Ldr; Guest Choral Festival Conductor; Concert S Recitalist; WVU Tchng Asst Scholarship; *office:* South Jefferson Schls Box 10 Adams NY 13605

RUDD, LANCE DAMON, Social Studies Teacher; *b:* Washington, D Natalie J.; *ed:* Hampton Univ (BA) His, Soc Stud 1993; Post Baccala Cert in Ed John Carroll Univ 1994; *cr:* Beachwood HS Soc Stud Tchr Cleveland Hghts HS Soc Stud Tchr 1995-; *ai:* Med Explorers Post 1995-; NAACP 1992-; *office:* Cleveland Heights High School 13263 Rd Cleveland Heights OH 44118

RUDD, SHARON B., Math Teacher; *b:* Watertown, NY; *m:* Calvin Lisa, Gregory, Michael; *ed:* William Smith Coll (BA) Math 1971; Classes at SUNY at Oswego; *cr:* South Jefferson Cntrl Schl Math 1983-; *ai:* NHS Adv; Lions Club 1976-; 4-H 1993-, Yth Issues C *office:* South Jefferson Cntrl Schl PO Box 10 Adams NY 13605

RUDDEK, RICKY CHARLES, Social Studies Instructor; *b:* Johns PA; *m:* Cathy Jean Straw; *c:* Charles, Lewis, Thomas; *ed:* Juniata Col His 1972; St Francis Coll Tchr Cert 1973; 12 Credit Hrs Univ of Pit at Johnstown; Post Grad Hrs IN Univ of PA; *cr:* Greater Johnstowr Voc Tech Schl Soc Stud Instr 1978-83; Forest Hills Jr HS Soc Stud 1983-86; Forest Hills Sr HS Soc Stud Instr 1986-; *ai:* NHS Fac Comm; LEO Club Adv 1987-89; Asst Coach Wrestling, Var Ftbl, Tr HS Head Ftbl Coach; NEA 1978-; PSEA 1978-, Local Commissione Rep; Jaycees 3 Yrs, Pres & Internal Dir; Adam's Twp Little League South Fork Yth Assn 3 Yrs; BSA 6 Yrs, Troop Comm Chm; Endowment for Hum Grant 1986; *office:* Forest Hills Sr HS 489 Loc PO Box 325 Sidman PA 15955

RUDDER, MARLENE JUDITH, Chemistry Teacher; *b:* Brooklyr *m:* Joel; *c:* Scott, Debra McNally; *ed:* Brooklyn Coll (BS) Chem Marywood Coll (MS) Integrative Ed 1982; 30 Credit Hrs; *cr:* C Gershwin Jr HS Tchr 1964-66; Morris Knolls HS Tchr 1974-; *ai:* For Adv; Staff Dev Steering Comm; NJEA 1974-; MHRDEA 1974-, NJSTA 1982-; ACSTA 1985-, Bd Mem, Edward J Merrill; White M Temple 1970-, Va'ad Mem; Morris Knolls HS Tchr of Yr 1985-8 Governors Tchr Awd; *office:* Morris Knolls HS 50 Knoll Dr Rockaw 07866

RUDDY, MARGARET, Academic Guidance Counselor; *b:* Brooklyr *ed:* Saint Joseph's Coll (BA) Bio 1966; Saint John's Univ (MS) Bio *cr:* Diocese of Brooklyn Elem Schl Tchr 1954-66; St Brendan's H

Tchr 1966-75; Sisters of Saint Joseph Vocation Dir 1972-81; Saint 's Coll Asst Prof of Bio 1978-87; Bishop Kearney HS Acad Guid 1987-; *ai:* Stud Svcs Comm Chprsn; Cath Scndry Schl Coun of NYC NY St Coll Admission Cnslrs 1990-; 2 NSF Grants; *office:* Bishop ey HS 2202 60th St Brooklyn NY 11204

Y, THOMAS A., Math Teacher; *b:* Scranton, PA; *m:* Lenore one; *c:* Thomas, Timothy, Jean Marie, Daniel, Kathy; *ed:* Univ of on (BS) Math Ed 1970; Marywood (MS) Math Ed 1977; *cr:* Dunmore th Tchr 1969-; *ai:* Stu Assistance Team; *office:* Dunmore H S Quincy Warren St Dunmore PA 18509

EN, DOROTHY J., French Teacher; *b:* Paterson, NJ; *ed:* Montclair (BA) Fr, Eng 1983; Middlebury Coll (MA) Fr 1984; Univ of Paris, orbonne Fr Lang & Civilization Diploma 1982; *cr:* TV World ine Translator 1984-86; Ecola Lang Schl Eng Tchr 1985-86; St Mary Eng Tchr 1986-87; Manchester Twp HS Fr Tchr 1987-; *ai:* Fr Club NEA 1987-; *office:* Manchester Township HS 101 S Colonial Dr urst NJ 08733

LL, FREDRICA, Associate Prof of Mrktg; *b:* New York, NY; *m:* w A. Beveridge; *c:* Sydney; *ed:* Vassar Coll (BA) Pol Sci 1968; nbia Univ (MBA) Mrktg 1975, (PHD) Mrktg 1978; *cr:* Baruch UNY Mrktg Asst Prof 1978-82; Iona Coll Mrktg Asst Prof 1982-85, Assoc Prof 1985-; *ai:* Chair Environmental Concerns, MBA ssions, Rank, Tenure, Awds, Advancment Comms; Amer Mrktg Assn Dissertation Awd 1978; Assn for Consumer Research 1977-; NY AAUP; AAUW; Envir Comm Yonkers 1992-, Chair; City Cncl ns Advy Group; Longvale Homeowners' Assn Bd; Dist Ldr, Yonkers cratic Patry; Steering Comm, Rep; New Rochelle Environemntal ership; Pub Book: Consumer Food Selection and Nutrition nation 1979, Various Articles, Conf Papers; Small Flwshps, Grants; Iona College 715 North Ave New Rochelle NY 10801

ELLA, MARY ANN (RODOSKY), Nursing Instructor; *b:* sburg, PA; *m:* Michael A.; *c:* Matthew, Mark; *ed:* PA St Univ (BS) Dev 1980; Cntrl PA Schl of Nrsng (RN) Nrsng 1985; PA St Univ Nrsng 1990; 13 Credits Post Grad Stud; *cr:* Philipsburg St Gen Hosp e, Staff Nurse 1985-88; Cntrl PA Schl of Nrsng Instr 1988-91; Lock Univ Nrsng Instr 1991-; Philipsburg Area Hosp Emergency Room 1992-; *ai:* Nrsng Dept Curr Comm; Fac Org; Inservice, Evaluation, Assessment Comms; Natl, PA Leagues of Nrsng 1993-; APHA 1992-; Theta Tau 1989-; Comm Nrsng Advy Bd; Tchr of Yr 1994; *office:* Haven Univ 119 Byers St Clearfield PA 16830

GERS, GREGORY BRUCE, Music Teacher; *b:* Leroy, NY; *c:* ynn, Sarah; *ed:* Ithaca Coll (BA) Music 1970; Elmira Coll (MS) Ed *cr:* Odessa Montour CS Music Tchr 1970-75; Southside HS Music 1975-; *ai:* Schl Literary Magazine; MENC 1970-; NYSSMA 1970-, Rep; Arnot Ogden Hosp 1994-, Vol; Northwestern Univ Flwshp; es Pub; *home:* 106 Lexington Ave Elmira NY 14905*

GER, LANCE WADE, Chemistry Tchr & Sci Dpt Chair; *b:* lyn, NY; *c:* Heidi L.; *ed:* SUNY at Albany (BS) Chem; St Lawrence MED) Ed 1982; Grad Hrs: Univ of CA at Berkeley, Univ of WI at on, WV Univ, Miami Univ, SUNY at Potsdam; *cr:* Potsdam Cntrl Tchr 1980-; *ai:* Sci Olympiad Coach; Ski Club; Cmptr Coord; St nce Vly Tchrs Cr, Treas; NSTA; STANYS, Bd of Dirs, Section Chair; TE, Bd of Dirs; Phi Delta Kappa, Rsrch Chair; Lions Club, Pres, Dir, Treas, Pres Awd; Kiwanis Club, Charter Mem; Dow Hnrs Tchr; row Wilson Dreyfuss Master Tchr; Natl Radio Astronomy vatory Mentor, Assoc Mem; Grants: Amer Chem Soc, Inst for ical Ed, Miami Univ, St Lawrence Vly Tchrs Cr; Co-Author istry in the Environment Book; *office:* Potsdam Cntrl Schl 29 Leroy sdam NY 13676*

N, SHERWOOD, Teacher; *b:* Passaic, NJ; *m:* Elise Winters; *ed:* IN BA) Jrnlsm; Fairleigh Dickinson Univ (MA) Eng 1975; *cr:* William on Coll Admin 1970-71; No Vly HS Tchr 1971-; *ai:* Lit Magazine & ve Writing Club Adv; *office:* Northern Valley Regional HS Central ld Tappan NJ 07675

SILL, DAVID A., 7th Grade Social Studies Tchr; *b:* Philadelphia, *m:* Donna Gross; *c:* Deeann Sherman, Darla, Debra, Danielle; *ed:* nsburg St Univ (BS) Geo 1967; 30 Credits Hrs in Geo Ed; *cr:* quoquallis High Tchr 1967-70; Cntrl MS Tchr 1970-76; Gauger MS 1976-; *ai:* Stu Cncl Adv; IM Coach; NEA 1967-; DE Cncl For Soc 1967-; DSEA 1970-; Gauger MS Tchr of Yr 1991; *office:* Gauger MS nder Rd Newark DE 19711

SIU, CLAIR MICHAEL, Physical Education Teacher; *b:* York, PA; nda Colby; *c:* Jamie, Corby; *ed:* Defiance (BS) Hlth & PE 1971; rn MD (MA) Hlth & PE 1977; *cr:* Northern York Cty Schl Dist PE 1971-; Northern HS Ftbl Team Defensive Coord 1971-88; Messiah Prof Movement in Elem PE Course 1984-90; *ai:* HS Wrestling Head n; Elem IM Coord; Dist Wrestling Coaches Rep; NYEA 1971-; PSEA ; NEA 1971-; Natl Wrestling Assn 1971-; Evaluating Team of Fellow in Cntrl PA; Mentor for PE Tchrs in Dist; Created Sat Morning Pgms lem Stdnts; *office:* Northern York Cty Schl Dist 202 Chestnut St burg PA 17019

NICK, ISIDORE LESLIE, Music Professor; *b:* Detroit, MI; *ed:* of North TX (BM) Jazz Stud 1986, (MM) Composition 1992; *cr:* ski St Music Schl Jazz Prgm Dir 1989-91; Univ of ME at Augusta rer in Music 1992-94; Intnl Summer Jazz Schl Dir 1994-; Univ of ME gusta Music Dept Chair 1994-; *ai:* Intnl Stdnts Club Fac Adv; Intnl of Jazz Edctrs 1992-, Pres-ME Chptr 1995-; Intnl Trombone Assn ; Lib Bd 1992-; Univ of ME System Intl Prgm Grant; Polish Natl nce of North Amer Prgm Grant; Koscuiszko Fnd Schlsp; Polish stry of Culture Medal of Hnr; *office:* Univ Of ME At Augusta 46 rsity Dr Augusta ME 04330*

OLPH, DOROTHY ELIA, Eighth Grade Teacher; *b:* Woburn, MA; dward P.; *c:* Edward, Keri; *ed:* Boston St Coll (BS) Ed 1972; ridge Coll (MED) Ed 1996; *cr:* St Francis of Assisi Tchr 1978-88; of Somerville Tchr 1988-; *ai:* Somerville Tchrs Assn 1988-; NEA; St is Womens Club 1978-; *office:* Winter Hill Schl 115 Sycamore St rville MA 02145

OLPH, MARK RAYMOND, Fifth Grade Teacher; *b:* Bridgeport, CT; ne E.; *c:* Elizabeth K., Peter R.; *ed:* Muhlenberg Coll at Allentown Ec 1970; Univ of Bridgeport (MS) Ed 1974; *cr:* Riverfield Schl Fifth Tchr 1974-95; Holland Hill Schl Fifth Grd Tchr 1995-; *ai:* Tech, Dist Steering Comms; CEA, NEA 1974-; ASCD 1990-; UCC Church, on, Trustee, Music Comm, Choir; Publishing; Wetland Awds; *home:* itchfield Tpke Bethany CT 06524

OLPH, MICHAEL SCOTT, High School Math Teacher; *b:* worth, OH; *ed:* Univ of Akron (BA) Scndry Ed, Math 1986; *cr:* erleaf HS Math Tchr, Coach 1986-87; London HS Math Tchr, Coach -91; N Royalton HS Math Tchr, Coach 1991-; *ai:* Asst Var Ftbl Coach; 1986-; NREA 1991-; *office:* North Royalton HS Royalton Rd North lton OH 44133

OLPH, ROBERT ARTHUR, Amer Govt Tchr & Dept Chm; *b:* town, NY; *m:* Marilyn Kling; *c:* David, Scott, John; *ed:* Gettysburg BA) His 1965; Morgan St Univ (MS) His 1973; 30 Hrs Beyond MS; aure De Grace HS Soc Stud Tchr, Dept Chair 1965-88; C. Milton ht HS Soc Stud Tchr, Dept Chair 1988-; *ai:* Bsbl Coach; PSAT, SAT Cty, Kids Voting Comms; Forest Hill Recreation Cncl 1986-, Coach, All-Star Coach Awd, 10 Yr Svc; Churchville Puritan Club 1986-; Coach of Yr 1974; 30 Yr Tchng Awd; Recreational Cncl 10 Yr Awd; *office:* C Milton Wright HS 1301 Fountain Green Rd Bel Air MD 21015

RUDOLPH, THOMAS E., Music Director; *b:* Upper Darby, PA; *m:* Tiiu Lutter; *c:* Liia, Gusten, Kalev; *ed:* Coll of Perf Arts (BMus) Music Perf, Ed 1977; West Chester Univ (MMus) Music 1983; Wipener Univ (EDD) Adult Learning 1993; *cr:* Kennett Cons Schl Dist Inst Music Instr 1977-79; Haverford Sch Dist Music Dir, MS Instrumental 1979-; Villanova Univ Adj Instr 1989-; *ai:* Band; Jazz Band; MENC 1977-; Natl Assn of Jazz 1977-; Numerous Articles Pub; Author Music, the Apple II, Teaching Music with Technology; *home:* 544 Glendale Cir Springfield PA 19064*

RUDOSKY, GEORGIA CATHERINE, Physics & Mathematics Teacher; *b:* Kittanning, PA; *m:* John A.; *c:* John M., Catherine, Andrew; *ed:* IN Univ of Pa (BSEd) Math 1983; 36 Post Grad Credits; Westminster Coll Physics Cert 1988; *cr:* Kittanning Sr HS Tchr 1983-84; Elderton HS Tchr 1984-89; Kittanning Sr HS Tchr 1989-90; Armstrong Cntrl Sr HS Tchr 1990-92; Ford City HS Tchr 1991-; *ai:* Helping All Through Sci Club Adv; Gray Matter Games Jr HS Coach; AAPT 1988-; HS Physics Tchr 1990-; Armstrong Ed Assn 1983-, Comm Chprsn; PSEA; NEA; Parks & Rec Bd 1994-; Church Lector 1992-; RCIA Instr 1995-; Chapel of Four Chaplains Project Lifesavers 1st Place Schlsp 6 Stdnts, Adv Prize; *office:* Ford City Jr Sr HS 1100 Fourth Ave Ford City PA 16226

RUDY, LINDA MAE, Mathematics Teacher; *b:* York, ME; *m:* Jacob W.; *ed:* Univ of South ME (BS) Math 1971; 9 Credit Hrs 1978-81; George Washington Univ 6 Credit Hrs 1983-86; *cr:* Cape Elizabeth MS Math Tchr 1971-78; Memorial Jr HS Math Tchr 1978-79; York HS Math Tchr 1979-81; La Plata HS Math Tchr 1983-; *ai:* MD Stu Assistance Team Chprsn; NEA & St Tchr Assn 1971-; Ed Assn of Charles Cty 1983-, Bldg Rep 1988-89; NCTM & MD Cncl Tchr of Math 1983-; Cobb Island Citizens Assn 1981-; Cobb Island Bapt Church 1985-, Treas; Co-Author "Challenging Choices" Teaming Prgm for 9th Grd; Cert of Recognition Charles Cty Bd of Ed 1988; Cert of Instructional Leadership MD St Dept of Ed 1989; Listed in 1994 Edition of Marquis "Whos Who in Amer Ed"; Nom for "Whos Who in the World"; *office:* La Plata HS PO Box 790ion Rd La Plata MD 20646

RUDY, PAMELA MENGES, Third Grade Teacher; *b:* PA; *m:* Kenneth C.; *c:* Nathaniel, Benjamin, Alexander; *ed:* Millersville Univ (BS) Early Chldhd, Elem Ed 1980; Millersville Univ, Penn St Univ (ME) Elem Ed 1991; *cr:* Millersburg Area Schl Dist First Grd Tchr 1980-91, Third Grd Tchr 1991-; *ai:* NEA, PSEA, Millersburg Ed Assn 1980-; *office:* Lenkerville Elem Schl 520 S Market St Millersburg PA 17061

RUDY, STACEY COLLEEN, Cosmetology Teacher; *b:* Reading, PA; *m:* Timothy A.; *ed:* Penn St Univ (BS) Voc Indstrl Ed 1993; *cr:* Berks Career & Tech Ctr Cosmetology Tchr 1994-; *ai:* Club Adv VICA; Iota Lambda Sigma 1993-; NEA, PSEA, Natl Cosmetologist Assn 1995-; PA Cosmetologist Assn, AVTECH 1995-; VICA Prof Mbrshp 1994-; *office:* Berks Career Tech West Schl RD 1 Box 1370 Leesport PA 19533

RUDZINSKI, JEANNE (MARION), Counselor; *b:* Hyannis, MA; *c:* Jonathan W.; *ed:* Keene St Coll (BS) Spec Ed & Elem Ed 1978; Plymouth St Coll (MED) Guidance & Counseling 1986; *cr:* Gilford Mid-HS Tchr of 6th-12th Grd Spec Ed 1979-81, 6th-8th Grd Tchr 1981-83; Twin City Spec Ed Consortium Tchr of 1st-5th Grd Spec Ed 1984-85; Plymouth St Coll Cnslr for Stdnts with Disabilities 1986-; *ai:* Introduction to Acad Comm Course Instr; Amers with Disabilities Act Steering Comm; Prof Dev & Trng-Dev Comms; NH Ed Opportunity Assn 1986-, Conf Comm; New England Assn Ed Opportunity 1986-, Conf Comm North Cntry Postsecondary Disabilities Consortium 1988-; Interlakes Day Care & Nursery 1992-, Treas, Bd of Dirs; Meredith Youth Soccer League 1994-, Vol Coach; Issues of Learning Disabilities & Amers with Disabilities Act at Postsecondary Level Wkshp Presenter at Saint Anselms Coll, NH Women in Higher Ed, Plymouth St Coll Fac-Staff Inservice Days, Univ of CT Postsecondary Inst on Learning Disabilities; *office:* Plymouth St Coll 17 High St Plymouth NH 03264*

RUEDA, NORMA G. (GRACIELA), Assistant Professor of Math; *ed:* FL St Univ Statistics (MS) 1983, (PHD) 1987; *cr:* St Lawrence Univ Asst Prof 1987-91; Merrimack Coll Asst Prof 1991-; *ai:* Salary & Benefits, Honorary Degree Comms; Soc for Industrial & Applied Math 1991-; Admin Sci Assn of Canada 1995-; 5 Fac Dev, 2 Assn for Women in Math Travel Grants; 13 Research Articles Pub.

RUESE, TIMOTHY L., Industrial Tech Teacher; *b:* St Marys, OH; *m:* Elizabeth B.; *c:* Caitlyn, Sara; *ed:* BGSU (BA) Ed 1984; Baldwin Wallace (MA) EA 1995; *cr:* Strongsville City Schls Ind Tech Tchr 1984-; *ai:* Head 8th Grd Ftbl Coach; *office:* Ctr Jr HS Strongsville 13200 Pearl Rd Strongsville OH 44136*

RUETH, HENRY GEORGE, Biology Teacher; *b:* Brooklyn, NY; *m:* Linda Riehl; *ed:* St Johns Univ (BA) Bio Ed 1972, (MS) Bio Ed 1974; 18 Credits in Supervision & Admin; *cr:* St Agnes Acad HS Bio Tchr 1972-75; Archbishop Molloy HS Bio Tchr 1975-79; St Agnes Cathedral HS Bio Tchr & Sci Chprsn 1979-85; Carle Place HS Bio Tchr 1985-; *ai:* NHS Adv; Effective Schls & Mid St Comms; AFT & NEA 1985-; *office:* Carle Place H S Cherry Ln Carle Place NY 11514

RUF, FREDERICK JOHN, Assoc Professor of Religion; *b:* New York, NY; *m:* Christine Anne Henry; *c:* Joanna V., Jesse Y.; *ed:* Williams Coll (BA) Rel 1973; Univ of Chicago (MA) Rel 1977; Harvard Univ (PHD) Rel 1988; *cr:* Harvard Univ Instr 1987-88; Georgetown Univ Asst Prof 1988-94, Assoc Prof 1994-; *ai:* Amer Acad of Rel 1984-; Books: The Creation of Chaos, Genie and the Religious Construction of the Self; *office:* Georgetown Univ 37th & O Sts NW Washington DC 20057*

RUF, MITCHELL CHARLES, English & Theater Arts Teacher; *b:* Passaic, NJ; *m:* Eileen; *c:* Mageen, Matthew; *ed:* Kean Coll of NJ (BA) Eng, Speech Theatre, Media 1976; Montclair St Univ (MA) Theatre Arts, Lit 1980; *cr:* Roselle Park HS Eng, Theatre, Speech, Media Tchr 1977-78; Chatham HS Eng, Theatre, Speech, Media Tchr 1978-79; Millburn HS Eng, Theatre, Speech, Media Tchr 1979-80; New Providence HS Eng, Theatre, Speech, Media Tchr 1980-82; Lenape Vly Regnl HS Eng, Theatre, Speech, Media Tchr 1982-; *ai:* Plays, Musicals, Lighting & Tech Dir; Schl Newspaper Adv; NEA, NJEA, ITS 1978-; STANJ 1982-, Best Play Festival 1989; Westbrook Tennis & Swim Club 1991-, VP; Adj Prof 1980-, Instr Kean Coll of NJ; North Edison Bsbl Coaches 1990-, Coach; Directorship Awds Bucks Cty Playhouse, Speech Theatre Assn of NJ, Surflight Theatre of NJ; Bravo Network Gilbert & Sullivan Theatre; 2nd Pl Natl Competition Contest; *office:* Lenape Valley Reg HS PO Box 578 Stanhope NJ 07874

RUFF, AMY FISCHER, 10th Grade Health Teacher; *b:* Flourtown, PA; *m:* Dean E.; *c:* Stephen, Sara, James; *ed:* West Chester Univ (BS) Hlth, PE 1981; *cr:* Oakcrest HS Hlth, PE Tchr 1981-83; Egg Harbor Twp HS Hlth, PE Tchr 1983-; *ai:* Asst Coach Girls Cross-CntryTeam; NJ Ed Assn, NEA, NJHPERD 1981-; NHS, Honorary Mem; Ocean City Arts Ctr, NJ St Yth Soccer Assn 1995-; WFPG AM Radio Station Guest to Speak on Intergenerational Movement, Tchr Subject in Classroom; Featured in NJEA Review 1995; Tchr Mentor 1994; *office:* Egg Harbor Twp HS 24 High School Dr Egg Harbor Townshi NJ 08234

RUFF, CHEREE LYNNE, First Grade Teacher; *b:* Oneonta, NY; *m:* Paul E.; *c:* Abigail, Trevor; *ed:* St Univ Coll at Oneonta (BA) Elem Ed 1977, (MS) Elem Ed 1982; Whole Lang Confs; Morning Prgm Trng; *cr:* Oneonta St Migrant Tutorial Prgm Tutor 1978-80; Laurens Schl 1st Grd Tchr 1980-; *ai:* Morning Prgm Coord; Scheduling, Discipline Comms; NYSUT 1987-; NEA 1980-87; NY St Rdng Assn 1987-93; Tchr of Yr 1995; Grant Awded to Work on Theme Based Curr; *office:* Laurens Central Schl PO Box 301 Laurens NY 13796

RUFF, DONALD RAYMOND, Literature Teacher; *b:* Cuyahoga Falls, OH; *m:* Deanna Marie Harris; *ed:* Univ of Akron (BA) Scndry Ed, Eng 1989; 3 Credit Hrs Child Psych; *cr:* First Bapt Chrstn Schl Lit, Eng Tchr 1990-; *ai:* Sr Class, Forensics Adv; Drama, Soccer Coach; ACSE 1990-; Church 1978-, Sunday Schl Tchr, Deacon, Sunday Schl Supt; Maternity, Family Help Ctr 1995-, Pantry Distributor.

RUFF, PATRICIA K., Chemistry Teacher; *b:* Cincinnati, OH; *c:* Jude, Philip, Karen Ruff-Noll; *ed:* OH St Univ (BS) Chem 1958; Rutger Univ (MED) Scndry Sci 1976; 6 Weeks Introductory Phys Sci Inst for Chemical Ed Chem Update; *cr:* Highland Pk MS 6th Grd Sci, Math Tchr 1973-75; Bridgewater West HS IPS Tchr 1975-77; Roselle Cath HS Sci, Math Tchr 1978-79; Watchung Hills Reg HS Chem Tchr 1979-; *ai:* Operation Chem Team Mem; Chem League Coach; Tchrs Affiliate ACS 1988-, Exec Comm; NJ Sci Tchrs Assn 1985-, Convention Presenter; Chem Tchrs Alliance 1991-, Demonstration Session Ldr; Kessler Rehab Ins 1987-, Prosthesis Demonstrator; Woodward Wilson Master Chem Tchr 1990; Rudolph Awd Sci Excl 1995; AP Chem Reader 1995; *office:* Watchung Hills Regional HS 108 Stirling Rd Warren NJ 07059

RUFFNER, ROBERT D., US His, Psych & Sociology Tchr; *b:* Greensburg, PA; *m:* Phyllis Watters; *c:* Sherri Holler, Kelly Grejtak, Robert Jr., Rebecca; *ed:* Clemson Univ (BA) His 1968; Post Grad Indiana Univ of PA; Cmptr Stud Westmoreland Cty Comm Coll; *cr:* Greater Latrobe Jr HS US His Tchr 1968-71; Greater Latrobe Sr HS US His, Psych, Sociology Tchr 1971-; *ai:* Ftbl, Tennis Coach; NEA 1968-; St Vincent Coll Cert of Hnr 1993; *office:* Greater Latrobe HS 131 Country Club Rd Latrobe PA 15650

RUFFOLO, ANGELA MARIE, Senior American Govt Teacher; *b:* Kettering, OH; *ed:* Univ of Dayton (BS) Scndry Ed, Soc Stud Comprehensive 1994; Stud for Masters in Ed Admin; *cr:* Chaminade-Julienne High Govt & Ec Tchr 1994-; *ai:* Var & Reserve Womens Asst Soccer Coach; LIFE Youth Group Moderator; Stu Cncl & Sr Trip Planner & Helper; OCEA 1994-; *office:* Chaminade-Julienne HS 505 S Ludlow St Dayton OH 45402

RUFINO, VINCENT J., Choral Activities Director; *b:* Hoboken, NJ; *m:* Jane O'Brien; *c:* Mark, Janine, Mary, David, John; *ed:* Jersey City St Coll (BA) Music Ed 1970, (MA) Clarinet Performance 1972; Attnd IN Univ, Westminster Choir Coll, Montclair St Coll, Univ of Cntrl CT, Mannes Coll of Music; *cr:* Univ of VT Summer Instr 1969-74; Hoboken HS Choral, Asst Band Dir 1970-72; West Morris Cntrl HS Choral Dir 1972-; Rutgers Univ Summer Curr Coord 1993; *ai:* Musical Dir; Concert Choir, Women's Ensemble, Men's Choir Dir; Gifted, Talented Adv; NEA, NJEA, MCCEA 1970-, Local VP; WMREA; MENC, NJ Music Educators 1970-; Intnl Clar Soc, Amer Choral Dir 1980-; St Virgil's RC Church 1979-, Chm PreCana Comm, Choir; Family Opera Co Orch 1969-, Prin Clar; Conductor: Iron Area Choir 1974, AA North Jersey Region I Jr HS Choir 1990, Messiah Sing Fisher Hall NYC 1992-93, Mozart Requiem Sing In 1995; All N Jersey Rgn Sr HS Chr; Fellow Natl Endowment Hum 1991; Messiah Sing In 92-; *office:* West Morris Central HS Bartley Rd Chester NJ 07930*

RUFO, GLORIA FRANCES, Math, Science & Religion Tchr; *b:* New York City, NY; *ed:* Hunter Coll (BA) Psych, Elem Ed 1976; Prof Dev 30 Hrs; *cr:* St Elizabeth Seton 4th Grd Tchr 10 Yrs, 6th Grd Tchr 7 Yrs; *ai:* Sci, Math Comms; *office:* St Elizabeth Seton Schl 751 Knickerbocker Ave Brooklyn NY 11221

RUFUS, NANCY GENTILE, AP European His Teacher; *b:* Cleveland, OH; *w:* Joseph (dec); *c:* Susan, Jodie; *ed:* Kent St Univ (BS) His, Pol Sci 1972; Attnd Notre Dame Coll; *cr:* Hudson Local Schsl Sub Tchr 8 Yrs; Woodridge Local Schls Sub Tchr 3 Yrs; Nodonia Hills Schls Sub Tchr 3 Yrs; Our Lady of the Elms HS Tchr 8 Yrs; *ai:* Moderation Stu Govt; Soc Stud Dept Chair; Close-Up Coord; NCEA 1986-; *office:* Our Lady of the Elms HS 1375 W Exchange Akron OH 44313

RUGGERI, JO ANN ZIPKO, High School Mathematics Tchr; *b:* Dover, NJ; *m:* Anthony S.; *c:* James, David; *ed:* Caldwell Coll (BA) Math, Scndry Ed 1965; Jersey St Coll 1 Credit; William Peterson Coll 2 Grad Credits; *cr:* Jefferson Twp HS Mat Tchr 1965-67; Dover MS Math Tchr 1968-69; Sacred Heart Schl Rockaway Math Tchr 1976-78; Morris Cath HS Math Tchr 1978-; *ai:* Natl Beta Club Spon; NCEA 1978-; NCTM; AMTNJ; William Paterson Coll, the Inst for Tech in Math Grants 1993-94; *office:* Morris Catholic HS Morris Ave Denville NJ 07834

RUGGIERI, ANTHONY GERALD, Secondary English Teacher; *b:* Rochester, NY; *m:* Sarabeth Lansing; *c:* Christopher, Jodi, Casey Elizabeth, Brendan Justine; *ed:* SUNY at Brockport (BS) Eng 1967, (MS) Eng 1971; *cr:* Hoover Dr Jr HS Eng Tchr 1967-72; Arcadia HS Eng Tchr 1973-; *ai:* Newspaper Adv 10 Yrs; Stu Cncl Adv 1 Yr; NHS Adv 2 Yrs; Lit Mag Adv 7 Yrs; NEA 1967-; Greece Tchrs Union 1967-; NCTE 1975-85; Arcadia Tchr of Yr 1989; Asst Team Ldr 1970-71; *office:* Greece Arcadia HS 120 Island Cottage Rd Rochester NY 14612

RUGGIERI, CHRISTOPHER LANE, 8th Grd Social Studies Teacher; *b:* Rochester, NY; *m:* Andrea Gail LeGro; *ed:* SUNY at Oswego (BS) Bus Admin 1988; Nazareth Coll (MS) Scndry Ed 1996; Cert in Scndry Soc Stud & Bus Ed 1991; *cr:* Greece Apollo MS 8th Grd Soc Stud Tchr 1992-93; Greece Arcadia MS 8th Grd Soc Stud Tchr 1993-; *ai:* Washinngton Trip Coord 1996; Frosh Bsbl Coach; 7th Grd Girls Bsktbl Coach; NEA 1992-; NY St Bowhunters Assn 1993-; Ducks Unlimited 1995-; *office:* Greece Arcadia MS 130 Island Cottage Rd Rochester NY 14612

RUGGIERI, THOMAS MICHAEL, Band Director; *b:* Rome, Italy; *m:* Patricia; *c:* Rachel; *ed:* Youngstown St Univ (BS) Music Ed 1988; 9 Hrs Toward MS in Ed; *cr:* Boardman HS Assoc Dir of Bands 1988-89; East HS Band Dir 1989-; *ai:* OMEA, NEA 1988-; Youngstown Area Arts Cncl Outstndg Arts Tchr Nom 1993; *office:* East HS 1544 E High Ave Youngstown OH 44505

RUGGIERO, DONNA ELIZABETH, Social Worker; *b:* Bethpage, NY; *m:* Ralph P.; *c:* Victoria; *ed:* Adelphi Univ (BSW) Soc Work 1983, (MS) Soc Work 1983; Pub Schl Tchng Cert; Certfd Conflict Mediator; Drug Abuse Cert; Child Abuse Identification & Reporting Cert; *cr:* US Peace Corps Yth Dev Specialist 1983-86; St Christophers-Ohilie Caseworker 1986-88; Berkshire Svcs for Yth Fam Svc Coord 1989-90; Hauppauge Pub Schls Soc Worker 1990-91; Islip Schl Dist Soc Worker 1991-; *ai:* STAR & Peer Ldrshp Adv; NYSUIT 1990-; US Peace Corps 1983-86, Vol; *office:* Islip HS 2508 Union Blvd Islip NY 11751*

RUGGIERO, GARY ALLEN, Guidance Counselor; *b:* Norwalk, OH; *m:* Juliet Romaine Breece; *c:* Jeffrey A., Stacey A.; *ed:* Bowling Green St Univ (BS) Ed 1963; Xavier Univ (MED) Guidance 1972; Addl 45 Hrs Univ Toledo; Certified in Schl Admin, Supervision & Ed Specialist; *cr:* Willard City Schls Tchr, Coach 1963-65; Urbana City Schls Tchr, Coach 1965-72; Fremont City Schls Guidance Cnslr 1972-; *ai:* Cnslr Jr Class Activities; Driver Ed Instr 32 Yrs; Ftbl, Bsktbl, Track & Golf Coach; Migrant Summer Schl Dir 11 Yrs; Peer Listener Coord; Fremont Ed Assn 1972-; OH Ed Assn, NEA 1963-; Campfire Inc 1975-, Pres 1987-; Runaway Safehouse 1991-, Pres 1991-; United Way Rep 1987-89; Village House Sandusky Cty, Founder & Pres 1995-; NDEA Grant 1965; Fremont Cty Schls "Excl in

Action" 1992; Sandusky Cty Chamber of Commerce Distinguished Serv Awd 1994; *office:* Fremont Ross HS 1100 North St Fremont OH 43420

RUGGIERO, LYNN MARIE, Kindergarten Teacher; *b:* Hazleton, PA; *ed:* Stroudsburg Univ (BS) Elem Ed 1975; Univ of Scranton (MS) Elem Ed 1982; 60 Credit Hrs; *cr:* Freeland Elem Schl Kndgtn Tchr 1978-; *ai:* Dev Appropriate Practices Mentor; Math Book Adoption, Kndgtn Comms; Hazleton Area Ed Assn 1975-, Fac Rep; NEA; PSEA; Hazleton Art League 1973-, Silver Smithing, 1995-, Stained Glass, BEst of Show; Dev Appropriat Practice 1993; Articles Pub; *office:* Freeland Elem Schl 400 Alvin St Freeland PA 18224

RUGGIERO, RENEE EVELYN, Mathematics Teacher; *b:* Paterson, NJ; *m:* Michael Anthony; *c:* Evan; *ed:* William Paterson Coll (BA) Math 1967; Monclaire St Coll (MA) Math 1987; 13Post Grad Credits; *cr:* Jefferson Twp HS Math Tchr 1967-69; Roxby Twp HS Math Tchr 1969-; Cty Coll of Morris Statistics Tchr 1980-83; Centinary Coll Tutor Govt Funded Program 1983-86; *ai:* NEA, NTEA, NCTM 1963-; MAMA 1990-; *office:* Roxbury HS 1 Bryant Dr Succasunna NJ 07876*

RUGGIERO, ROBERT F., Spanish & Latin Teacher; *b:* Pen Argyl, PA; *m:* Linda Lee Grupe; *c:* Karen Lynn, Melissa Ann; *ed:* LaSalle Univ (BA) Span 1972; Credit Hrs East Stroudsburg Univ; *cr:* Pocono Cntrl Cath HS Span Tchr 16 Yrs; Pocono Mountain HS Span Tchr 1 Yr; Pius X HS Span, Latin Tchr 6 Yrs; *ai:* Astronomy Club Adv; Homework Deficiency Monitor; Bsbl Coach; Schl Plays Coord; *office:* Pius X HS 580 3rd Ave Bangor PA 18013

RUGGIRELLO, MARGARET BOUCK, High School English Teacher; *b:* Albany, NY; *m:* Philip; *ed:* SUC at Oneonta (BA) Eng Ed 1984; SUNY at Albany (MA) Eng 1992; 15 Addl Credits Eng, Ed; *cr:* Greene Cntrl Schl Jr Sr HS Eng Tchr 1984-87; Cherry Vly Springfield Schl HS Eng Tchr 1989-; *ai:* HS Bldg Level Team; Chair NHS Fac Cncl; Principals Cabinet; Founder, Adv Line Open Line Poetry Rdngs; NYSUT, CATE 1989-; NCTE 1984-; Tchr of Yr, Tchrs Ctr Grant Clearwater Across the Curr 1992; Commencement Speaker, Arts Cncl Grant The Renaissance Modern Parallels, Presentor SUCO Conf Cross Curr Acts in Bio, Eng 1994; Hum Tchr Inst Amer Womens Lives Anthology 1995; Tchrs Ctr Grant Otsego Lake Across the Curr 1993; *office:* Cherry Valley Springfield Sch PO Box 485 Cherry Valley NY 13320*

RUGGLES, DIANE (VACIRCA), Business Education Dept Chprsn; *b:* Mount Kisco, NY; *m:* William; *c:* Jonathan, Jessica; *ed:* Dutchess Comm Coll (AAS) Secretarial Sci 1976; St Univ of NY at Albany (BS) Bus Ed 1978, (MS) Bus Ed 1981; St Univ of NY at New Paltz Post Grad Educl Admin; *cr:* John A Coleman HS Bus Tchr 1978-80; Kingston City Schl Adult Bus Tchr 1980-81; Pine Bush HS Bus Tchr 1981-82; Valley Cntrl HS Bus Dept Chprsn 1982-; *ai:* Comm as Schl Prgm Coord & Tchr; BEAM, NBEA 1981-; Mechanicstown Elem Schl PTO 1990-, Sec 1994-; *office:* Valley Central HS 1175 Rt 17k Montgomery NY 12549

RUGGLES, JEANNE-FRANCOISE PETER, French Teacher; *b:* New York City, NY; *m:* Thomas M.; *c:* Rebecca L., Mary Ann, D. Fairchild; *ed:* Harvard Univ (BA) Romance Langs-Magna Cum Laude 1967; Arch Stud Radcliffe Coll 1948-51; Extension, Cultural Stud 1970-80; *cr:* Tower Schl Fr Tchr 1959-66; Shore Cntry Day Schl Dept Chair Frgn Langs 1968-82; Beaver Cntry Day Schl Dept Chair 1983-90, Fr Tchr 1982-; *ai:* Coord Frgn Exch Prgms; Fr Prize 1967; Small Grants Rsrch Abroad Cultural Topics.

RUGGLES, KATHLEEN CORMANY, Fourth Grade Teacher; *b:* Kansas City, MO; *m:* Michael; *c:* Kristin Hall, Laurel White; *ed:* Beloit Coll (BS) Bio 1959; Eastern Ct St Univ (MA) Lang Arts 1973; *cr:* Northeast Schl Fourth Grd Tchr 1972-; *ai:* Co-Facilitator Schl Comm Annual Fun Fair; Schl Store Facilitator; Schl Rep Vernon Tech Comm; Mentor to 1st Yr Tchrs; Soc Stud Curr Revision Comm; NEA 1978-; Alpha Delta Kappa 1986-, Corresponding Sec; PTO; Sexual Assault Crisis in Hartford CT 1983-89, Crisis Cnslr, Hot Line Vol; Presentor Madeline Hunter Design for Effective Instruction 2 Yrs; Facilitator & Presentor of Instrl Wkshps at the Found Pub Schl Karachi Pakistan Intntl Friendship Tchng Exch; *home:* 81 Seneca Dr Vernon Rockville CT 06066

RUGH, W. DEAN, Psych Peer Helper & His Tchr; *b:* Lodi, OH; *m:* Jane Zimmer; *c:* Zohn; *ed:* Otterbein Coll (BA) Soc 1969; Univ of Dayton (MS) Cnslng 1987; United Theological Seminary MA in Divinity 1973; 6 Credit Hrs in Peer Cnslng, Mediation, Conflict Resolution; *cr:* Trotwood Madison Cty Schls Sociology, Human Relations Tchr 1973-74; Stebbins HS Peer Helping Class, Soc Stud, Psych Tchr 1975-; *ai:* Peer Helping Coord; Attendance Comm for HS Chprsn; 7th Grd Boys Bsktbl Team Coach; NEA, OEA, WOEA, MREA 1975-, Bldg Rep; OH Peer Helpers Assn 1990-, Pres, Harriet Leidhauser Awd; Natl Peer Helpers Assn 1987-; Schl Cnslrs Assn Grant to Promote Peer Helping; Dayton-Montgomery Cty Pub Ed Fund Excl in Tchng Awd 1990; Mad River Twp Tchr of Yr 1989; *office:* Stebbins HS 1900 Harshman Rd Dayton OH 45424

RUHL, F. MARCIA (MORAWICK), HS Mathematics Teacher; *b:* Bayonne, NJ; *m:* Harry Jay; *c:* Janice, Marcy; *ed:* Jersey City St Coll (BA) Sci, Math 1965; Attnd Rutgers Univ; *cr:* Plainfield HS Chem Tchr 1965-66; Hopewell Valley HS Chem, Algebra Tchr 1966-67; Allentown HS Algebra Tchr 1967-70; Hightstown HS Math Tchr 1981-; *ai:* Fac Senate Mem; NEA, NJEA, MCEA, 1981-; East Windsor Ed Assn 1981-, Rep; NCTM, AMTNJ 1982-; Delta Kappa Gamma 1990-, Membership Co-Chprsn; Princeton Plasma Physics Lab Intern; Princeton Univ Awded Fractals & Chaos Wkshp Schlsp 1993; *office:* Hightstown HS 25 Leshin Ln Hightstown NJ 08520

RUHL, ROBERT K., Physics Tchr & Sci Dept Coord; *b:* Carlisle, PA; *m:* Anna Marie Hershey; *c:* Stephanie, Lora; *ed:* Shippensburg Univ (BS) Physics 1970; 75 Grad Credits Penn St, La Salle, Shippensburg, Trenton St, East Stroudsburg, Bloomsburg, Carlow Coll, Marywood; *cr:* Quakertown Comm Schl Dist Tchr, Dept Coord 1970-; *ai:* QCEA, PSEA, NEA 1970-; AAPT 1984-; *office:* Quakertown Comm Sr HS 600 Park Ave Quakertown PA 18951

RUIZ, LILLIAN, Instructor of English; *b:* New York, NY; *ed:* Univ of Rochester (BA) Eng, Minor Psych 1989; UCLA (MA) Eng 1991; 30 Addl Hrs; *cr:* Mira Costa Comm Coll Eng Instr 1992-93; Palomar Comm Coll Eng Instr 1992-93; Greenfield Comm Coll Eng Instr 1993-; *ai:* Phi Theta Kappa Adv; MLA, NTE 1991-; *office:* Greenfield Comm Coll 1 College Dr Greenfield MA 01301

RUIZ, SONIA, Bilingual 3rd Grade Teacher; *b:* New York, NY; *m:* Carlos; *c:* Carlos R., Nancy Wich; *ed:* Lehman Coll (BA) Ed 1978, (MS) Ed 1980; 30 Credits Biling Ed, Cmptrs; *cr:* Pub Schl 32X Educl Asst 1968-78, Biling Tchr 1978-; *ai:* AFT, UFT 1968-; AFT, UFT 1968-; *home:* 4150 Boyd Ave Bronx NY 10466

RUKAVINA, MADALANA L., Language Arts Teacher; *b:* Canton, OH; *m:* Peter M.; *c:* Jennifer; *ed:* Kent St Univ (BA) Eng 1972; Univ of Akron (MA) Scdnry Ed Admin 1983; Comm Intervention; Assertive Discipline; Mentor Trng; *cr:* Perry Local Schls Eng Tchr 1973-; *ai:* Recognition Night, Outstdng Boy, Girl, Strategic Planning; Staff Dev, Lang Arts, Dist Levy Comms; NCTE 1973-; Malone Coll Tchr Advy Bd 1992-, Sec; Perry Alumanae Comm 1992-; Suzuki Assn of Canton 1985-; Jr League of Canton 1989-, Pres Provisional Class; Church of Svaior United Meth 1955-; *office:* Perry Local Schls 4201 Harsh Ave Massillon OH 44646*

RULAND, DONNA WHEELER, Third Grade Teacher; *b:* Albany, NY; *m:* Arthur L.; *c:* Michael, Marcy, Marc; *ed:* SUNY at Oneonta (BS) Elem Ed 1976; Grad Courses, In-Svc Stud, Prgms; *cr:* Schoharie Cntrl Schl Grd Three Tchr 1977-; *ai:* BEAC 1995-; NYSUT 1977-; *office:* Schoharie Central Schl Main St Schoharie NY 12157

RULE, VERNON CHARLES, 12th Grd English Teacher; *b:* Bigfork, MN; *m:* Walta Child; *c:* Heidi Nestor, Sean, Tom, Heather; *cr:* Littlestown HS Eng Tchr 1967-; *ai:* Stu Cncl Adv; Dept Chm; NEA 1967-, Pres 1974; Ed 2000 Task Force 1991-; Congressional Advy Bd on Ed; *home:* 3792 Baltimore Pike Littlestown PA 17340

RULIFFSON, MARY PATRICIA, Spanish Teacher; *b:* Rochester, NY; *m:* James; *ed:* Monroe Comm Coll (AA) Lbrl Arts 1967; SUNY at Brockport (BA) Scndry Span 1969; Permanent Span Cert SUNY at Geneseo 1973; 3 Credit hrs Iberian-Amer Univ 1966; *cr:* St Agnes HS Span Tchr 1969-73; Amer Scientific Products Receptionist 1976-84; Wayne Cntrl HS Span Tchr 1984-85; Fairport Schls Span Tchr 1985-86; Palmyra-Macedon HS Span Tchr 1987-; *ai:* New Block Scheduling Advy Comm; AFT, NYSUT 1984-; Palmyra-Macedon Tchrs Assn 1987-; *office:* Palmyra-Macedon HS 151 Hyde Pky Palmyra NY 14522

RULLI, JOSEPH, English & Music Teacher; *b:* Johnstown, PA; *ed:* Univ of Pittsburgh (BA) Eng & Comm 1982; IN Univ of PA (BA) Music 1986; *cr:* Forest Hills Jr High Eng & Music Tchr 1982-87; Forest Hills Sr High Eng Tchr 1988-93; Forest Hills MS Eng & Music Tchr 1994-; *ai:* Sr Class Adv 1990-93; PSEA 1982-, Bldg Rep; NEA 1982-; *office:* Forest Hills MS Frankstown Rd Sidman PA 15955

RUMBOLD, LYNN R., Third Grade Teacher; *b:* Buffalo, NY; *m:* Paul A. Jr.; *ed:* Medaille Coll (BS) Elem Ed, Rdng 1976; SUNY AB (EDM) Rdng Specialist 1988; 6 Hrs Post Grad Ed, Rdng Specialist; *cr:* St Paul Luth Schl Presch, 3-4 Grd Tchr 1976-88; Randolph Cntrl Schls Rdng Tchr 1988-90; North Tonawanda City Schls 3 Grd Tchr 1990-91; Williamsville Cntrl Schls 3 Grd Tchr 1991-; SUNY Ab Clinical Fac 1994-; *ai:* Lang Arts Literacy Assessment Comm; NYSET 1988-; WTA 1990-; N Presbyn Church 1995-, Bd of Chrstn Ed Co-Chair; Teach Grad Level Elem Methods Course 1994; *office:* Williamsville Cntrl Schls 250 N Forest Rd Williamsville NY 14221*

RUMBUTIS, JAN MERCURIO, Art Teacher; *b:* Utica, NY; *m:* William; *c:* Kimberly D'Auria, Lynel; *ed:* Mohawk Valley Comm Coll (AAS) Advertising Art Design 1970; Empire St Coll (BS) Fine Arts 1978; Cortland St Coll (MSE) Ed, Rdng 1980; Munson William Proctor Inst Schl of Art; Oneonta St Coll Watercolor; *cr:* BOCES Oneida Cty Art Tchr 1971-87; Whitesboro Cntrl HS Art Tchr 1987-; *ai:* Art Club Adv; Afterball Party, Block Scheduling, Bldg Grounds Comms; Medeation Comm Mediator; NYSATA 1990-, Pres; Utica Art Assoc 1970-, VP; Fabrique Craft Group 1970-, Sec; 1st-3rd Pl Awds Various Art Competitions; *office:* Whitesboro HS 6000 St Rd Rt 291 Marcy NY 13403*

RUMMEL, AMY BETH POWELL, Assoc Professor of Marketing; *b:* Washington, DC; *m:* Randal Thomas; *c:* Melissa Ashley, Emily Margaret; *ed:* Juniata Coll (BS) Psych 1980; Purdue Univ (MS) Consumer Sci 1984, (PHD) Consumer Sci 1984; *cr:* Walker Rsrch Market Analyst 1986-88; Univ of Otago Sr Lecturer 1988=91; Alfred Univ Assoc Prof 1991-; *ai:* Amer Mrktg Assn, Assn for Consumer Rsrch 1991-; Assn Retarded Citizens 1994-, Bd of Dir; J. Henry Smith Flwshp; *office:* Alfred Univ 26 N Main St Alfred NY 14802

RUMMEL, CATHY MARIE (FLYTE), Family & Consumer Sci Teacher; *b:* Scranton, PA; *m:* Jeffrey L.; *c:* Justin, Jeremey, Jordan; *ed:* Mansfield Univ (BS) Family & Consumer Sci, Home Ec 1979; 24 Credit Hrs; *cr:* Halifax Area Schl Dist Tchr 17 Yrs; *ai:* Prof Dev, Assessment, Scheduling Comms; FHA, Hero, Stu Cncl, Sr Class Adv; Food Svc Cncl; PSEA, NEA 1979-, Local Treas, VP; PA Assn of Family & Consumer Sci 1994-; Millersburg Civic Club, Chprsn; Millersburg Comm Task Force, Chprsn; Parish Cncl-Queen of Peace Cath Church, Chprsn; Various Booster Orgs; Cub Scout Ldr; Future Directions Task Force; FHA-HERO Bd of Dir, Treas, Chprsn; FHA Adv of Yr; Consumer, Homemaking Grant; Ag, Rural Yth Dev Grant; Yrbk Dedication; *office:* Halifax Area Schl Dist 3940 Peters Mountain Rd Halifax PA 17032

RUMPH, ROBERT ROY, Driver Education Teacher; *b:* Manhattan, NY; *m:* Marita T. Fitzpatrick; *ed:* Fresno St Coll (BA) PE & Hlth Ed 1964; IN Univ at Bloomington (MS) Hlth & Safety & Ath Trng 1970; Attnd Los Angeles St Coll, Cal State at Northride, Univ of CA at Santa Barbara, Pepperdine Univ, Plattsburgh Univ St Coll, Ithaca Coll; *cr:* Redwood Intermediate Schl 7th & 8th Remedial Math, Ind Arts, Gen Sci Tchr 1965-69; Plattsburgh St Univ Coll PE, Hlth Ed Instr & Ath Sports Trainer 1970-73; Peru HS Driver Ed & Hlth Ed Tchr 1973-; *ai:* Part-Time Tchr at Clinton Comm Coll 21 Yrs; Schlsp Comm Peru HS 23 Yrs; Phi Delta Kappa 1970-; Natl Ath Trainers Assn 1970-77; IN Univ Alumni Assn 1970-; NEA 1973-; Lions Club 1973-82; Numerous Articles Pub; Comm for Rewriting NYS Traffic Safety Ed Guide; *office:* Peru Central Schl School St Peru NY 12972*

RUMPOLO, CHRISTOPHER J., Biology Teacher; *ed:* Brooklyn Coll (BS) Bio 1992, (MS) Bio 1993; *cr:* Midwood HS Tchr of Bio 1995-; *ai:* ECO Enviromental Awareness, Action Club; Japenese Animation Soc; Westinghowse Mentor; UFT 1994-; NABT 1995-; *office:* Midwood HS At Brooklyn Coll Bedford Ave At Glenwood Ave Brooklyn NY 11210

RUNDEL, WENDY J., Guidance Counselor; *b:* Brookline, MA; *ed:* Bloomburg St Coll (BSEd) Elem Ed 1959; Wayne St Univ (MSEd) Psych Cnslng 1979; Addl 24 Credit Hrs Loyola Coll, 16 Credit Hrs Univ of HI, Supvr of Stu Cnslrs; *cr:* Perry Hall Elem Schl 3-5 Grd Tchr 7 Yrs; Hilo Union Elem Schl 3, 5 Grd Music Tchr 3 Yrs; Dept of Defense 3-4 Grd Tchr 6 Yrs; Powhatan Elem Schl 4-5 Grd Tchr 2 1/2 Yrs; Riverview Elem Schl Cnslr 3 Yrs; Owings Mills Elem Schl Cnslr 13 Yrs; *ai:* Parenting Groups; Supvr Stu Interns; NEA, TABCO 1959-; Balto Cty Cnslrs Assn 1980-; *office:* Owings Mills Elem Schl 10824 Reisterstown Rd Owings Mills MD 21117*

RUNFOLO-MC CORMACK, MARIA, Guidance Counselor; *b:* Newark, NJ; *m:* Joseph Mc Cormack; *ed:* Seton Hall Univ (BS) Ed 1986, (MA) Guid Cnslng, Stu Prsnl Svcs 1992; Working Towards Cnslng License Examination; *cr:* Union Ave Schl 1st Grd Tchr 1986-88; Hamilton MS Rdng Tchr 1989-93, Guid Cnslr 1993-; *ai:* 8th Grd Advy; Fund-Raising Adv; NEA 1986-; Kappa Delta Pi 1985-; *office:* Alexander Hamilton MS 310 Cherry St Elizabeth NJ 07208

RUNG-SLIWIAK, MEREDITH, Vocal Music Director; *b:* Elizabeth, NJ; *m:* George A. Sliwiak; *ed:* Westminster Choir Coll (BMEd) Music Ed 1970; 60 Addl Hrs Acad of Vocal Arts; *cr:* Tri-State Area Soprano Soloist 1963-71; Princeton Univ Chapel Soprano Soloist 1963-; St John the Divine Soprano Soloist 1963-; Carnegie Hall Soprano Soloist 1963-; Abraham Clark HS Vocal Music Dir 1973-; *ai:* Liason Comm Tchr, Admin; Liason, Grad, Scheduling, Renaissance Comms; REA, ACDA, MENC 1973-; NJEA; ACCOP; NCDA; NJCDA; First Presbyn Church 1963-, Session, Choir Mem; Elder; Governor's Tchrs Recognition Awd; Mayor's Proclamation; Cty, St, Natl Chorus Trophies, Placques; Prin Dedication Awd; *office:* Abraham Clark HS 122 E 6th Ave Roselle NJ 07203

RUNNALLS, ELIZABETH DENMARK, Frgn Lang Coord & Spanish Tchr; *b:* Elmira, NY; *m:* Lee; *c:* Amanda, Emily, Blake; *ed:* Caldwell Coll (BA) Span 1969; Univ of DE (MA) Span 1971; 102 Addl Credit Hrs Beyond a (BA) Degree; St Univ of NY at New Paltz Schl Dist Admin Educl Admin 1993; *cr:* Middletown Jr HS Span Tchr 1971-75; Middletown HS Span Tchr 1975-; *ai:* Tchr Rep Schl Improvement Team; Tchrs Union Bldg Rep; Tchr Rep Exec & Policy Bd of our Tchr Ctr; NY United Tchr, AFT, NYS Assn of Foreign Lang Tchrs 1971-; Middletown Tchrs Assn 1971-, Offic Rep; Woodrow Wilson Fellowship Nom; Awd Grad Tchng Asst S Univ of DE; Member of Delta Epsilon Sigma Natl Honor Soc 1969 Caldwell Coll & Univ of DE "Cum Laude"; Chprsn Middletown Comm Mentor/Intern Prgm; *office:* Middletown HS Gardne Middletown NY 10940

RUNNER, KATHLEEN KAHLE, Secondary Teacher; *b:* Lima, C Jack C.; *c:* Kristen, Kelly; *ed:* Bowling Green St Univ (BS) Ed, Lib, Media-Cum Laude 1977; Attnd Ashland Univ, Univ of Toledo; *cr.* Angel's Schl Tchr 1978-81; Sandusky Lib Children Svcs Librn 19 Erie Co Bd of Ed Instr Enrichment Prgm 1984-92; St Mary Cntrl Ca Tutor, Stu Asst Prgm Coord 1990-; *ai:* Safe & Drug Free Schls (Intervention Team Coord; Stu Svc Cncl; Adults Organized Kids; N OCEA 1978-; NEA, OEA 1990-; US Power Squadron 1984-; Erie Cc Free Grant Comm 1993; March of Dimes 1988; Outstdng Tchr of Cert Recognition OH Gov; *home:* 620 Marshall Ave Sandusky OH 4

RUNTON, KEITH L., Middle School Librarian; *b:* Philadephia, P. Millersville Univ (BS) Educl Media, Lib Sci 1974; K-12 Cert; Bloom Univ, Cntrl Susquehanna Intermediate Unit Masters Eqvival Villanova Univ 21 Grad Credits Lib Sci; *cr:* Margaret R. Grund Cataloging, Reference Librn 1974-77; Priestley-Forsyth Meml L 1977-79; Greenwood Area Schl Dist Elem Schl Librn 1979-80; Miffl Area Schl Dist MS Librn 1982-83, 1985-; Commonweath Correctional Facility Librn 1983-84; *ai:* 7th-8th Grd Lib Club Spon. 5th-8th Grd Ski Club Spon, Adv; Mifflinburg Area Schl Dist Sch Driver; Mifflinburg Area Ed Assn; NEA; PA Schl Librns Assn; Mifflinburg Area MS 151 E Market St Mifflinburg PA 17844*

RUNZO, DONNA STEVENSON, English & Reading Teacher; *b:* S OH; *m:* John Paul Jr.; *c:* Kamberlyn, Anthony; *ed:* Muskingun Col His & Govt 1972; Univ of Dayton Rdng; 54 Semester Hrs Above Ma *cr:* Maysville Jr High Tchr 1972-73; Kettering City Schls Tchr 197 Jr Class Cncl Adv; NEA; OEA; KEA; Fairmont Boosters 1987-; Ke Jr High PTA 1987-, Pres; Kettering Cncl of PTA 1988-, Pres; Fairmc PTA 1990-, Pres, Key Awd; *office:* Kettering Fairmont HS 3301 S Rd Kettering OH 45429

RUOF, BERNADETTE M., English & Journalism Teacher; *b:* Bu NY; *m:* Kenneth E.; *c:* Damian, Laura; *ed:* St Univ Coll at Buffalc Eng 1972, (MS) Eng Ed 1976; *cr:* Casey MS 8th Grd Tchr 1972-83 MS 8th Grd Tchr 1983-84; Williamsville East 9th-12th Grd Eng 1984-; *ai:* Schl Newspaper Co-Adv; Shared Decision Making Interview Comm Hiring Prin; NYSUT 1972-; WTA 1972-; ASCD Calvary Episcopal Church 1979-, Clerk & Vestry; Article Pub; Williamsville East H S 151 Paradise Rd East Amherst NY 14051

RUOFF, ELAINE NEUBRAND, Third Grade Teacher; *b:* Pittsburg *m:* Terry A.; *c:* Jamison M.; *ed:* Edinboro St Coll (BS) Elem Ed 1972, Elem Ed 1977; *cr:* Second Dist Schl 2-4 Grd Tchr 1972-90; West End Schl 3 Grd Tchr 1990-93; Cochranton Elem Chptr I Math Tchr 19 East End Elem Schl 3 Grd Tchr 1994-95, 6 Grd Tchr 1995-; West End Schl 3 Grd Tchr 1995-; *ai:* NEA, PSEA, CCEA 1972-; *home:* Forrest Dr Edinboro PA 16412

RUOPP, FAYE NISONOFF, Mathematics Educator; *b:* New Bruns NJ; *m:* Charles; *c:* Marcus; *ed:* Simmons Coll (BS) Math 1972, Math Ed 1973, (MS) Spcl Needs 1983; *cr:* Lincoln-Sudbury Reg Math Tchr 1972-87 & 1988-94; Polaroid Corp Tchr Intern 1987; E Ctr Project Dir 1987-; *ai:* NEA 1972-87; NCTM 1972-, Natl Mktg 1995; MAA 1987-; Lucretia Crocker Fellow 1986-87; Pub Article.

RUOZZI, GARY, Computer Programming Teacher; *b:* Mc Keespor *m:* Mary; *c:* Anthony, Nicholas; *ed:* IN Univ of PA (BSEd) Math 19 Hrs in Cmptr Sci; *cr:* Canon Mc Millan HS Math, Cmptr Tchr 197 Head Cross Cntry, Asst Track Coach; PSEA, NEA 1978-; *office:* Canc Millan HS Elm St Ext Canonsburg PA 15317

RUPERT, ANNE ELM, Retired Third Grade Teacher; *b:* Batavia, N Vernon G.; *c:* Vernon J. (dec); *ed:* NYSU at Brockport (BS) Ed NYSU at Buffalo; *cr:* Pembroke Cntrl Schls 6th Grd, 4-8, 5, 3 Grd Sc 37 Yrs 6thc; *ai:* Pembroke Tchrs Schlsp Selection Comm; 4-H Advy Tchrs; Sci Mentor for Intermediate Schl; Coach of Odyssey of Mind; OM on Local & St Levels; Pembroke Tchrs Fed 1955-, Correspondin Alexander Cobblestone Soc; Alexander Citizens Advy Bd of Sewers; of Eastern Star 1954-; Gamma Gamma 1985-, Pres; *home:* PO Bo Alexander NY 14005

RUPERT, ELLEN FENTON, Vocal Music Director; *b:* Harrisburg *m:* Larry J.; *c:* Cassandra Lee, Seth Fenton; *ed:* Indiana Univ of PA Music Ed 1973, (MED) Music Ed 1978; Seton Hill Coll Elem Ce Kiski Area Schl Dist Elem Gen Music, Jr HS Vocal Tchr 1974-90, HS Music Dir 1991-95; *ai:* Mixed Show Choir; Girls Show Choir; Jazz Ensemble; NEA, KAEA 1974-; MENC, PMEA 1974-, Dist One C Host 1996; WCMEA 1874-, Cty Chorus Host 1994; Eastern Star Scandinavian Soc of Western PA 1994-; St Vincents Coll Great Tch 1994; Amer Family Inst Gift of Time Tribute 1996; *office:* Kiski Ar 200 Poplar St Vandergrift PA 15690*

RUPERT, GARY LYNN, Director of Bands; *b:* Kittanning, PA; *m:* C Marie Altman; *c:* Chad, Jeremy; *ed:* Potomac St Coll (AA) Music Ed WV Univ (BA) Music Ed 1975; Indiana Univ of PA Masters Equi Music Ed; *cr:* East Brady HS Band Dir 1975-76; Kittanning HS Ban 1977-79; Knoch HS Band Dir 1979-88; Middletown HS Band Dir 1 *ai:* Marching Band, Concert Band, Percussion Ensemble & Jazz Ens Dir; Tech Comm Music Rep; NEA & MENC 1976-; MMEA 1989- Elect, Excl in Music Awd 1994; MBDA 1989-, Pres Elect; Cath Ministry Lifeteen Prgm 1993-, Music Dir; Outstanding Young Ame 1984 & 1985; Recognition for Excl in Tchng 1990; Article Pub ir Music Educators Journal; *home:* 20302 Barbara Dr Hagerstowr 21742*

RUPERT, KELLEY ESTADT, Second Grade Teacher; *b:* Clarion, P Jon David; *c:* Lindsey, Mark, Jacob; *ed:* Penn St Univ (BA) Adver 1981; Clarion Univ (BS) Elem Ed 1988, (MSEd) Sci Ed 1993; *cr:* Butler Cty Schl Dist 4th Grd Tchr 1988-89, 2nd Grd Tchr 1989-; *ai:* Comm; PSEA 1989-; NEA 1989-; PA MS Assn 1995-; Thanks to Tchrs Recognition Nom; *office:* Clinton Elem Schl 100 Deer Cree Saxonburg PA 16056*

RUPERT, LARRY JOSEPH, Sixth Grade Teacher; *b:* Natrona He PA; *m:* Ellen Fenton; *c:* Cassandra, Seth; *ed:* Univ of Pittsburgh Sociology 1971, (MED) Educl Admin 1984; Edinboro Univ Elem Ed Cert 1972; *cr:* Kiski Area Schl Dist 4th Grd Tchr 1974-76, 6th Grd 1976-, Head Tchr 13 Yrs; *ai:* Boys Var Bsktbl Head Coach 20 Yrs; Girls Track Head Coach 12 Yrs; Girls Soccer Asst Coach 3 Yrs; Bsktbl Asst Coach 1 Yr; NEA, PSEA 1974-; KAEA 1974-, Bldg Rep; of Italy #229 1976-; Kiski Area Kiwanis Elem Tchr of Yr 1984, 19 1995; *home:* 172 N Washington Rd Apollo PA 15613*

RUPINSKI, CHARLES ANTHONY, Mathematics Teacher; *b:* J City, NJ; *m:* Linda Ann Lembeck; *c:* Kyle, Kevin; *ed:* Seton Hall Univ Ed, Math 1963; Montclair St Coll (MA) Admin, Supervision 1968; *cr.* Brook Jr HS Math Tchr 1963-69; Hasbrouck Hgts HS Math Tchr 196 New Milford HS Math Tchr 1971-80; Leonia HS Math Tchr 198 Clifford Scott HS Math Tchr 1990-; *ai:* Asst Var Ftbl Coach; NEA, N ECEA, EOEA 1963-; NCTM, ANTNJ 1990-; NJ Wrestling Official

. Pres; Governors Tchr Recognition Awd Tchr of Yr 1993-94; *office:* rd J Scott H S 129 Renshaw Ave East Orange NJ 07017

', **GLENDA COOLEY,** Elem Prin & First Grade Tchr; *b:* Wauseon, : Ronald; *c:* Keri, Matthew; *ed:* Morehead St Univ (BA) HPER 1968; Toward Admin MA; *cr:* Mt Sterling Elem PE Tchr 1968-69; South ur PE, Hlth Tchr 1969-70; Sandcreek Elem South 3rd Grd Tchr 71; Living World Chrstn 1st-2nd Grd Tchr, Elem Prin 1985-; *office:* Word Chrstn Schl 2275 4 B 50 Stryker OH 43557

'**ERT, ANDREW C.,** Social Studies Teacher; *b:* Boyertown, PA; *m:* M. Stallone; *c:* Gina M., Anthony T.; *ed:* Albright Coll (BA) His Temple Univ (MED) Scndry Ed 1991; *cr:* Spring-Ford Area Sr HS tud Tchr 1989-; *ai:* Ftbl Asst Coach 1990-; NEA 1990-; Bsbl Asst 1989-95; *office:* Spring-Ford Area Sr HS 413 S Lewis Rd Royersford 468

', **REBECCA D.,** Mathematics Teacher; *b:* Amsterdam, NY; *m:* ry W.; *c:* Melissa, Kristin; *ed:* SUNY at Oswego (BS) Scndry Ed, 1974; Grad Hrs Coll of Saint Rose; *cr:* Jordan-Elbridge Jr-Sr HS Tchr 1974-; *ai:* Math, Sci Awds Night Chprsn; NYSUT, AFT, JETA

:HIN, MARY A., Second Grade Teacher; *b:* Brooklyn, NY; *w:* as Gerard (dec); *c:* Elizabeth Zalackas, Janine M. Gorline, Marianne, as; *ed:* Nassau Comm Coll (AAS) Lbrl Arts 1972; Adelphi Univ (BS) Ed Minor Soc Stud 1974; Adelphi Univ (MS) Elem Ed 1978; Post C. W. Post Univ; Cert Brittish Integrated Day Schl Stds; Visited nd Group Further Stud; 60 Post Grad Stud Soc Stud, Music, Art, Lang Concepts & Classroom Mngmt Wayne Univ; *cr:* Clear Stream nd Grd Tchr 1975-81; Willow Rd Schl 3rd Grd Tchr 1981-82; Forest chl Kndgtn, GATE Class Tchr 1982-87, 2nd Grd Tchr 1987-; *ai:* epoint Club Tchr 6 Yrs; Schls Annual Thanksgiving Day Breakfast rama Presentation; GATE Dist 30's; Report Card, Lang Art, Drama native Comms; Organized Fac 1995; NEA, AFT, IRA 1974-; Vly St Assn 1974-, Del Exec Cncl; New Hyde Park Columbiettes 1963-, Life Time Mem Awd; Fr Sq North Civic Assn 1972-, Sec; Girl Scouts 67, Brownie & Jr Ldr; Wash St Schl PTA 1960-74, Class Mother; old Assn of US Cert of Appreciation Outstdng Svc Introducing Good ion Stdnts 1995; Adelphi Univ Grant Continued Ed Adult Ldrshp nued Awd; Art Pub 1970; *home:* 1017 Maple Dr Franklin Square NY *

:INGNO, GERALD, Faculty Associate; *b:* Jersey City, NJ; *ed:* Saint s Coll (BS) Natural Sci 1980; NY Chiropractic Coll (DC) practic Stud 1990; Med Tech Metpath Lab 1994-96; Attnd Seton Hall *cr:* Met Path Lab Med Tech 1984-86; Dr of Chiropractic Employed Dr 1991-93; Seton Hall Univ Fac Assoc, Tchr Anatomy, ology Nurses, Pre-Phys Therapists, Bio Majors 1993-; *ai:* Adv 80 rof, Pre-Phys Therapy, Pre-Physician Asst Stdnts; *home:* 38 hawk Path Ringwood NJ 07456*

:ITO, STEVEN SILVA, Social Science Teacher; *b:* Providence, RI; a Iafrate; *c:* Rebecca; *ed:* RI Coll (BA) Ed, Soc Sci 1985; Cambridge MA) 1994; Army Ofcr Advance Course Infantry; Army Basic Ofcrs e Military Intelligence; Army Combined Arms Svc Support Schl; *cr:* native Ctr for Ed Soc Stud Tchr 1986; No Providence HS Soc Stud 1986-; *ai:* Boys Cross Cntry, Girls Indoor Track Coach; RI Model ature St Coord; Substance Abuse Trng Adv; AFT 1986-; RI Soc Stud 1990-, Exec Bd Mem; Received Key to Town 1992 for Substance Prgm; Citations from RI Gen Assembly for RI Model Legislature; : No Providence HS 1828 Mineral Spring Ave N Providence RI *

)EN, JOAN ZACKER, Third Grade Teacher; *b:* Bronx, NY; *m:* rd D. Jr.; *c:* James; *ed:* St Univ at Oswego (BS) Elem Ed 1963; 60 Credits; Attnd St John's Univ, Hunter Coll; *cr:* Commack Schls Fourth Grd Tchr 1963-; *ai:* SBM, Rsrch & Dev, Stu Handbook Dev n; Train Stu Tchrs; AFT, NEA, CTA 1963-; Port Washington ren's Ctr 1981-, Bd of Dirs; Schreiber HS Home & Schl Assn 4 Yrs; Comm Chest, Collect Funds; Tchr of Yr Nom 1996; *office:* Burr nediate Schl Burr Rd Commack NY 11725

I, DEBRA LOBAUGH, Teacher & Assistant Principal; *b:* Cleveland, *n:* Robert; *ed:* Kent St Univ (BS) Ed 1973; *cr:* St John Bosco 5th-6th Tchr 1974-79; Annunciation 5th-8th Grd Tchr, Asst Prin 1979-85; St lan 7th-8th Grd Tchr 1985-87; St Ignatius 7th-8th Grd Tchr, Asst Prin ; *ai:* Stu Cncl Adv.

I, J. MICHAEL, Building Principal; *b:* Laurinburg, NC; *m:* Frances Nikki Green, Michael, Mike; *ed:* Fayetteville St Univ (BS) Elem Ed Trenton St Coll (MA) Spec Ed 1974; Nova Southeastern Univ (EDD) Ldrshp 1992; *cr:* Franklin Twp Schls 5th Grd Tchr 1969-71; New swick Schls Spec Ed Tchr 1971-79; Toms River Schls Resource Room 1980-81, Instruction Supvr 1981-87, Prin 1987-; *ai:* NJPSA 1987-, et Mem; NAACP 1980-, Exec Bd, Outstdng Citizen; Omega Psi Phi ; Natl Confs of Chrstn & Jews 1990-, Bd of Mentor; *office:* South River Elem Schl 419 Dove Rd South Toms River NJ 08753*

H, JACQUELYN CHRISTINA, 6th Grade Teacher; *b:* Cleveland, *n:* Lawrence C. Sr.; *c:* Tiffany C. Rush-Wilson, Lawrence C. Jr.; *ed:* hoga Com Coll (AA) Ed 1977; Cleveland St Univ (BS) Ed 1980,)) Ed Curr, Inst 1988; Educl Law June 1995; *cr:* Operation Newstart e Mgr 1969-71; Cuyahoga Comm Coll Prof Asst 1975-77; Boulevard Schl PTA Pres 1978-79; City of Cleveland Civil Svc Tutor 1980; East Bd Ed Elem Tchr 1980-; *ai:* Black His Comm Co-Chm, Acad enge, Class Performance Schl Presentation; NEA 1980-; Phi Delta a, Rock & Roll Hall Fame 1995-; Natural His Musuem 1987-, G-Pac -; *home:* 2896 Woodbury Rd Shaker Heights OH 44120

H, KAREN MC CONAGHY, Physical Education Teacher; *b:* urgh, PA; *m:* John E.; *c:* Megan; *ed:* Slippery Rock Univ (BS) Hlth, 82; West Virginia Univ (MS) PE, Ath Trng 1992; *cr:* FT Cherry HS Grd PE Instr 1982-; *ai:* Schls Stu Support Team; Ath Trainer; Natl Ath ers Assn, NEA 1986-; *office:* Ft Cherry Jr Sr HS 110 Fort Cherry Rd onald PA 15057*

H, LINDA LEE, Elementary Guidance Counselor; *b:* Akron, OH; *m:* ey A.; *c:* Bryan, Bradley; *ed:* Capital Univ (BA) Elem Ed 1969; Kent (MS) Ed, Counseling 1987; Addl 15 Hrs Beyond Masters Cert in seling; *cr:* Sharon Ctr Elem 4th Grd Tchr 1969-70, 1st Grd Tchr -73, 2nd Grd Tchr 1973-83, 1st Grd Tchr 1983-89; Highland Local Elem Guidance 1989-; *ai:* Sharon Elem Pupil Evaluation Team Chem ndency Coord; NEA, OEA 1969-; HEA 1969-, Sec, Treas, Pres; Delta a Gamma; OH Schl Cnslrs Assn 1988-; Right to Read Dir 1974-76; *e:* Highland Local Schls 3880 Ridge Rd Medina OH 44256

H, LIONEL G., International Sales Director; *b:* Mobile, AL; *m:* e Moreno; *c:* Gina, Edward, Morris, Elizabeth; *ed:* URI (BA) Ec ; *ai:* J. F. Kennedy Schl of Intnl Stud Awd.

HATZ, TASHA JO, 10th Grade English Teacher; *b:* Allentown, PA; Working on Masters in Scndry Ed with Specification in Eng at own Univ; *cr:* Upper Perkiomen HS 10th Grd Eng Tchr 1992-; *ai:* Co-Adv; Adv of Poetics Club; PSU Scholars Pgm 1991-; Golden Key 1992-; Thesis in Cooperative Learning Pub by Penn St Scholars Pgm; *e:* Upper Perkiomen HS 2 Walt Rd Pennsburg PA 18073*

H-SLOAN, CHERYL LEE, Biology Teacher; *b:* Point Pleasant, NJ; ohn Kennedy; *c:* John Kennedy II, Ryan Christopher; *ed:* Georgian Court Coll (BS) Bio 1987; 16 Credit Hrs MS Bio Stud; Cert Elem Ed, Scndry Ed Comprehensive Sci; *cr:* Lacey Twp HS Chem Tchr 1989-90; Toms River HS Bio Tchr 1991-; *ai:* NEA 1994-; BSA 1995-, Tiger Cub Organizer; Tri Beta, Charter Mem; *office:* Toms River HS East Raider Way Toms River NJ 08753

RUSILOSKI, BENJAMIN EDWARD, Asst Professor of Chemistry; *b:* Bennington, VT; *m:* Josellen Frances Urbanski; *c:* Lauren Frances; *ed:* Kings Coll (BS) Chem 1990; Duke Univ (PHD) Phys Chem 1994; *cr:* DE Vly Coll Asst Prof 1994-; *ai:* Curr Comm; Acad Standards Comm; New Stu Orientation Fac Adv; Orientation Advy Comm; Fac Cncl; Fac-Stu Rsrch Comm; Amer Chemical Soc 1991-; Sigma Xi 1992-; AAUP 1994-; Bucks Cty Sci Tchrs Assn 1995-; *office:* Delaware Valley Coll 700 E Butler Ave Doylestown PA 18901

RUSIN, JOHN J., Instrumental Music Teacher; *b:* Shenandoah Heights, PA; *m:* Elizabeth M. Thomas; *c:* John D., Nicole M.; *ed:* West Chester St Univ (BS) Music Ed 1962, (MA) Music Ed 1967; 42 Grad Credit Hrs Villanova Univ Summer Prgm; *cr:* Quakertown Comm Schl Dist Jr HS, Elem Instrumental Music Tchr 1962-87, Elem Instrumental Music Tchr 1987-; *ai:* Concert, Rock, Polka Bands; Jazz Band, Quintet, Quartet; Amer Fed of Musicians 1954-; NEA, Pa Music Ed Assn 1962-; Kiwanis, Former Mem; PA Tchr of Yr Nom 1995-; *office:* Tohickon Valley Elem Schl 2360 Old Bethlehem Pike Quakertown PA 18951

RUSIN, RICHARD, Professor of Social Sciences; *b:* Yonkers, NY; *c:* Theresa J.; *ed:* St Univ of NY at Cortland (BA) Soc Sci 1965; St Univ of NY at Albany (MA) Govt 1968; 30 Grad Credits Fordham Univ; *cr:* Yonkers Pub Schls Tchr 1966-67; Hudson Valley Comm Coll Prof 1967-; *ai:* Huson Valley Comm Coll Fac Assn 1967-, Pres; Averill Park Fire Co 10 Yrs, VP; East Greenbush NY Town Supvr; *office:* Hudson Valley Comm Coll 80 Vandenburgh Ave Troy NY 12180

RUSNAK, MATTHEW FRANCIS, Professor; *b:* Trenton, NJ; *ed:* Temple Univ (BA) 1986; Attnd Univ of PA; Attnd Muhlenberg Coll 1984; *cr:* Bucks Cty Comm Coll Prof 1990-; *ai:* Phi Beta Kappa; *office:* Bucks County Comm Coll Swamp Road Newtown PA 18940

RUSSELAVAGE, RANDALL LEE, Reading Teacher & Athletic Dir; *b:* Lykens, PA; *ed:* PA St Univ Capilto Campus (BA) Elem Ed 1981; *cr:* William Vly HS Asst Ftbl Coach 1981-93, Asst Bsbl Coach 1983-, Rdng Tchr 1984-, Ath Dir 1996; *ai:* Asst Bsbl Coach; Williams Vly Tchrs Assn, NEA 1984-; Schuylkill Chptr #25 1992-; Ftbl Fnd, Hall of Fame; Schlr Ath, NHS 1977; *home:* 1703 E Grand Ave Tower City PA 17980

RUSSELL, CHRISTINE MARIE, Physics Teacher; *b:* Greensburg, PA; *ed:* Grove City Coll (BS) Applied Physics 1993; Manhatten Coll 4 Credit Hrs; *cr:* Souderton Area Schl Dist Physics Tchr 1993-; *ai:* HS Cabinet & SASD Strategic Planning Comms; SAEA Bldg Rep; Comm Stu Bible Stud Adv; NEA, PSEA & SAEA 1993-; MCSTA 1993-; AAPT 1993-; *office:* Souderton Area HS 41 N School Ln Souderton PA 18964

RUSSELL, DAVID GERALD, Science Teacher; *b:* Sayre, PA; *m:* Lisa Fraboni; *c:* Aubrie, Miranda; *ed:* SUNY at Oswego (BS) Scndry Ed, Earth Sci 1992; SUNY at Cortland (MSEd) Scndry Ed, Earth Sci 1995; *cr:* Owego Free Acad Sci Tchr 1993-; *ai:* Boys Bsktbl Coach; Stu Environmental Awareness Soc, Envirathon Team Adv; NYSUT 1993-; *office:* Owego Free Acad George St Owego NY 13827

RUSSELL, DEBORAH WAHLER, Global Studies Teacher; *b:* Lockport, NY; *m:* Jeffrey W.; *c:* Emmett, Karen, Andrew; *ed:* Canisius Coll (BA) Scndry Soc St Ed 1971; St Univ Coll at Buffalo (MS) Scndry Soc Stud Ed 1976; 15 Addl Hrs in Math courses; *cr:* Tonawanda Jr HS 7th-8th Grd Soc Stud Tchr 1971-75, 8th Grd Math Tchr 1977-79; St Paul's Kenmore 7th-8th Math Tchr 1985-89; Mt St Mary Acad Global Stud Tchr, Dept Chair 1989-; *ai:* NHS, Stu Cncl Moderator; Presented Wkshp at NCSS Convention; *office:* Mt St Mary Acad 3756 Delaware Ave Kenmore NY 14217

RUSSELL, DOROTHY B., Language Arts Teacher; *b:* Dayton, OH; *m:* Rodney L.; *c:* Brooke, Blair; *ed:* Univ of Cincinnati (BA) Eng 1973, (BS) Eng 1973; Wright St Univ (ME) Tchr Ldr 1983; Rdng K-12; *cr:* Little Miami JHS 7th Grd Lang Arts Tchr 1973-; *ai:* Newspaper Adv 1986; Power of the Pen Writing Team Coach 1991; OCTELA 1986-; Project Excl Nom 1992-93; *office:* Little Miami HS 605 Welch Rd Morrow OH 45152

RUSSELL, FRANCES ELEANOR,IHM, Assoc Professor of Education; *b:* Brooklyn, NY; *ed:* Marywood Coll (BA) Elem Ed 1964; Temple Univ (ME) Instr Tech 1970; Penn St Univ (PHD) Curr & Instr Rdng 1980; Temple Univ Rdng Specialist Cert; *cr:* Marywood Psy-Ed Clinic Rdng Tchr 1962-64; Northeastern PA Elem Tchr 1964-68; Diocese of Scranton Rdng & Media Specialist 1968-70; Marywood Coll Assoc Prof of Ed 1970-77; Penn St Univ Tchng Asst 1977-80; Marywood Coll Assoc Prof of Ed 1980-; *ai:* Kappa Delta Pi Cnslr; Rank & Tenure Comm; Curr Comm; Tchr Ed Advy Comm; KSRA 1981-, Pres, VP, Pres-Elect; NPRA 1981-, Pres, VP, Pres-Elect, Celebrate Literacy Awd; IRA 1984-; ASCD Assn for Supervision & Curr 1985-; Phi Delta Kappa 1978-; Kappa Delta Pi 1987-; Pi Lamda Theta 1978-94; Sisters. Servants of Immaculate Heart of Mary 1959-; *office:* Marywood Coll 2300 Adams Ave Scranton PA 18509

RUSSELL, GREGORY DEAN, American History Teacher; *b:* Neenah, WI; *m:* Elizabeth Weaver; *c:* Hannah, Andy; *ed:* Univ of WI at Stevens Point (BA) Asian Stud 1975; SUNY at Brockport (MA) Soc Stud Ed 1987; Univ of WA at Seattle 12 Credit Hrs; SUNY at Cortland 3 Credit Hrs; *cr:* Peace Corps S Korea Eng Tchr & Hlth Worker 1976-77; JFK Prep Schl His Tchr 1978-79; Port Byron HS His Tchr 1980-81; Palmyra-Macedon HS His Tchr 1981-; *ai:* AFT 1981-; Salvation Army Bd 1985-; Canadaigua Summer Soccer Coach 1989-; Univ of Rochester Excl in Tchng Awd 1987; *office:* Palmyra-Macedon H S 151 Hyde Parkway Palmyra NY 14522

RUSSELL, JIM GERVASE, 7th Grade Lang Arts Teacher; *b:* Akron, OH; *m:* Julie; *c:* Joseph, Anthony, Maria, Jim; *ed:* Bluffton Coll (BA) Hlth PE K-12 1981; Akron Univ (BA) Elem Ed 1985; *cr:* Field Jr HS Tchr 1984-; *ai:* HS Ftbl Coach; Flwshp Chrstn Ath 1993-; *office:* Field Jr HS 2900 St Rt 43 Mogadore OH 44260

RUSSELL, JOHN DAVID, Band Director; *b:* Troy, NY; *m:* Victoria A. Milanese; *c:* Rachel, Lauren; *ed:* SUNY at Albany (BA) Music 1978; SUNY at Potsam (MM) Music 1980; 15 Credits Rel Stud Providence Coll; *cr:* Bishop Hendricken HS Stage Band Dir 1980-86; Bishop Stang HS Music Dir 1986-87; Wadhams Hall Seminary Fine Arts Chair 1987-88; NYS Dept of Corrections Music Tchr 1988-91; Lisbon Cntrl Schl Band Dir 1991-; *ai:* Stage Band; Music Theory Course; Oswegatchie Music League; NY St Schl Music Assn Solo Festival; NYSSMA, NYSUT 1991-; *office:* Lisbon Central Schl 6866 Cty Rt 10 Main St Lisbon NY 13658*

RUSSELL, JOHN G., Business Education Teacher; *b:* Huntingdon, PA; *m:* Vickie Jean Heckman; *c:* Jacklyn; *ed:* Shippensburg Univ (BS) Bus Ed 1973; Completed Licensed Ministry Schl 1996; *cr:* Penn Cntrl Natl Bank Asst to Controller 1973-78; Broad Top Industries Office Mgr 1978-82; J & P Furniture Manufacturing Owner, Sec, Treas 1982-86 Tussey Mountain Schl Dist Bus Ed Tchr 1986-; *ai:* FBLA Adv; Stu Assistance Team for At-Risk Stdnts; Head Tennis Coach; Drug & Alcohol Advy Comm; PSEA, NEA 1986-; United Church Bd Homeland Missions 1996; *office:* Tussey Mountain Jr Sr HS PO Box 178A RD 1 Saxton PA 16678

RUSSELL, JUDITH,OP, Sixth Grade Teacher; *b:* Newark, NJ; *ed:* Caldwell Coll (BA) Elem Ed; Certfd Rel Ed; *cr:* St Aedan 2nd Grd Tchr 1972-73; St Ann 1st Grd Tchr 1976-77; St Mary 4th Grd Tchr 1978-87; St Catharine 6th Grd Tchr 1987-; *ai:* Computing Data, Schedules; NCEA 1967-; *home:* 211 Essex Ave Spring Lake NJ 07762

RUSSELL, LORNA SMITHERS, French Teacher; *b:* Boston, MA; *m:* Carlton T.; *ed:* Wheaton Coll (BA) Fr 1964; Harvard Univ (MA) Romance Lang & Literatures 1965; Many Ed & Career Related Courses; *cr:* King Philip Reg HS Fr Tchr 1965-69; Norton HS Fr Tchr 1972-; *ai:* Class of 1998 Adv; Adj Music Dept Accompanist on Piano; Phi Beta Kappa 1964-; NEA 1965-; Amer Assn Tchrs Fr 1972-; Trinity Episcopal Church Organist, Choir Dir 1972-; *home:* PO Box 382 Norton MA 02766

RUSSELL, NANCY VAN EENWYK, English Teacher; *b:* Sodus, NY; *m:* Laurence; *c:* Laurence J., Jennifer; *ed:* William Smith Coll (BA) Eng 1961; Univ of Rochester Ed; Syracuse Univ Leading to Permanent Cert; *cr:* Waterloo HS Eng Tchr 1966; Penn Yan Acad Eng Tchr 1978-86; Geneva HS Eng Tchr 1986-; *ai:* Lit Magazine Adv; Amnesty Intl; Dist Site Cncl; Tchrs Assn; NEA 1986-; Smith Opera House 1989-, Sec; Trinity Episcopal Church 1961-; NAACP Local Outstndng Tchr; *office:* Genevea HS Carter Rd Geneva NY 14456*

RUSSELL, PATRICIA JEAN, Dance Teacher; *b:* Miami, FL; *c:* Daena Grant, Marshall Grant; *ed:* Brooklyn Coll (BA) Dance Performance 1975; NY Univ (MA) Dance Choreography, Tchng 1995; Laura Norman & Assocs Reflexology Foot Massage; *cr:* Dane Friends Co Co-Founder 1978-82; June Lewis & Co Dancer 1976-78; John Dewey HS Dance Tchr 1983-91; *ai:* Dance Co Artistic Dir; Adv Modern Dance Club, Dewey Dance Ensemble Co-Dir; AAHPERD 1995-.*

RUSSELL, PEGGY,RSM, Principal; *b:* Riverside, NJ; *ed:* Georgian Ct Coll at Lakewood (BA) Elem Ed 1970, (MA) Admin 1978; *cr:* St Elizabeth Schl 4th Grd Tchr 1959-62; St Francis Schl 1st, 2nd Grd Tchr 1962-64; St Catherine Schl 2nd Grd Tchr 1964-66; St Joseph Schl 1st Grd Tchr 1966-71; St Charles Borromeo Prin 1971-88; St Frances Cabrini Prin 1989-; *ai:* NCEA 1962-; ASCD 1980-; NSTA, NCTE, IRA 1994-; NCTM 1992-; Catherine Mc Auley Ctr, Bd of Dirs; Mercy Ctr 1996, Bd Of Dirs; Edctr of Yr Diocese of Metuchen; *office:* Saint Francis Cabrini Schl 2300 Cooper St Piscataway NJ 08854

RUSSELL, ROBERT, Drama, Music & English Tchr; *b:* Staten Island, NY; *ed:* Rutgers Univ NCAS (BA) Theatre, Seech 1975; Univ of Denver (MA) Theatre 1983; *cr:* Kean Coll Adjunct Prof 1983-90; Montclair St Coll Adjunct Prof 1989-90; Queen of Peace HS Tchr 1990-; *ai:* Musical Theatre Productions Dir; Fine Arts, Liturgical Coord; NCEA 1990-; Actors Equity Assn, AFTRA 1979-; Natl Assoc of Pastoral Musicians; Article Tams Witmark Inc; *office:* Queen Of Peace HS 191 Rutherford Pl North Arlington NJ 07031*

RUSSELL, RODNEY BROOKS, French & Spanish Teacher; *b:* Washington, DC; *m:* Marva Delois Brown; *c:* Saamya Louvenia, Rodney Brooks II; *ed:* Dist of Columbia Tchrs Coll (BS) Span & Fr 1973; *cr:* Aviation HS & Newton D Baker Intermediate Schl Fr & Span Tchr 1987-88; Aviation HS & A B Hart Intermediate Schl Fr & Span Tchr 1988-89; Willson Intermediate Schl Span Tchr 1989-90; Collinwood HS Fr & Span Tchr 1990-; *ai:* Cross Country, Track & Field Head Coach at Benjamin O Davis JR HS 1980-; AFT 1973-; OHSAA 1980-; OHT 1980-; CCC 1980-; Martha Holden Jennings Scholar 1981-82; *office:* Collinwood HS 15210 Saint Clair Ave Cleveland OH 44110*

RUSSELL, SHARON LYNN, English Teacher; *b:* Ironton, OH; *m:* Douglas; *c:* Aysha Dennis, Tiffany, Mandi; *ed:* OH St Univ (BA) Eng 1984; Ashland Univ 24 Hrs Educl Supervision; *cr:* Lexington HS Eng Tchr 1984-; *ai:* Yth Coach 3rd-4th Grd Soccer; *office:* Lexington HS 103 Clever Ln Lexington OH 44904

RUSSELL, SHIRLEY DECK, Reading Teacher & CBC Chprsn; *b:* Bunn, NC; *m:* Ralph Augusta; *ed:* Federal City Coll (BS) Elem Ed 1970; George Washington Univ 3 Credit Hrs Spec Ed; Trinity Coll 9 Credit Hrs Rdng, Spec Ed; DC Tchrs Coll 6 Credit Hrs Rdng, Spec Ed; *cr:* River Terrace Elem Schl Spec Ed Tchr 1970-71; Birney Elem Annex Rdng Tchr 1971-75; Syphax Elem Schl Rdng, Math, Spec Tchr 1976-85; Shaw Jr HS Rdng, Lang Arts Tchr 1985-; *ai:* Stu Cncl Spon 1977-79; Bsktbl Coach 1980-82; S2P2 Transition Team Ldr; Rdng Dept Chprsn 1988; Compentency Based Curr Chprsn 1990-; Band Chaperone Marching Band 1989-; ASCD 1990-; AFT, WTU 1970-; DC Rdng Cncl 1992-; Hillcrest Hts Civic Assn 1992-; Mission Friends Southwest Assn 1991-93, Dir; Tutorial Vol Rdng Awd; Outstanding Coaching Awd; Speaking Awds 1 Kiwanis Club, Gethesemane HS Alumni Banquet; Outstanding Tchr 1975-76; 1987-90, 1994; Slctd Among 88 Outstdng Tchrs/ Edctrs in Metro Area; *office:* Shaw Jr HS 925 Rhode Island Ave Washington DC 20001*

RUSSELL, SHIRLEY KATHLEEN (BROWN), Mathematics Instructor; *b:* Baltimore, MD; *m:* Milton; *c:* Milton Lewis Jr., Shirlethea T. Holmes, Marcell M., Marlon L., Maurice L.; *ed:* Morgan St Univ (BS) Math 1975, (MA) Math 1988; 18 Hrs Post Grad Stud New Destiny Bible Inst; 6 Hrs Post Grad Stud Charles Mason Bible Coll; *cr:* Morgan St Univ Instr 1979-; Towson St Univ Instr 1982-83; Gwynn Lake Coll Preparatory Schl Univ Connection Instr 1995-; *ai:* Mu Alpha Tau Sr Adv; Math Ed Conf Comm; Mathematical Assn of Amer, Morgan St Univ Women 1985-; Alpha Mu Omega 1988-, Visionary Founder, Woman of Yr 1991-95; Pi Mu Epsilon 1974-; Glorious Church of Jesus Christ 1991-, Co-Pastor, Woman Among Women 1994; ECCO Outreach Ministries 1982-, VP; Pub Book: Polynomial Approximation and Interpolation 1988; Presidential Awds for Excl in Sci & Math Tchr; Outstdng Svc Awd for Career Dev 1987; Outstdng Svc Awd of Math 1996; *office:* Morgan State Univ Cold Spring Ln & Hillen Rd Baltimore MD 21239

RUSSELL, SUSAN MARGARET, Agent Cruelty Investigation; *b:* Worcester, MA; *m:* James J. Donison; *c:* Peter, Grace, Elizabeth; *ed:* Univ of MA (BA) Ed 1980; 15 Credits Post Grad Stud Fitchburg St Coll; *cr:* Horseback Riding Instr Self-Employed 1981-; Weare Elem Schl Tchr 1981-88; Russell Import Co Proprietor 1988-91; NH Equine Humane Assn Cruelty Investigation Agent 1995-; *ai:* Stu Adv; Drama Coach; Curr Dev Comm; Chrstn Ed Tchr; NEA 1981-88; NH Equine Humane Assn 1993-95, Sec; NH Hunter & Jumper Assn 1994-; Weare Congregational Church 1996; Certfd Amer Horse Protection Assn Equine Cruelty Investigator; *home:* 95 Quaker St Weare NH 03281*

RUSSELL, TERESA LUPOLI, Art Specialist; *b:* Boston, MA; *m:* Thomas R.; *ed:* MA Coll of Art (BSAE) Fine Arts 1967; RI Schl of Design (MAE) Art Ed 1975; Post-Grad Frgn Stud Italy, France, England, Holland 1970-95, Ed Univ of CA at Berkeley 1969-70; *cr:* Riverside CA Schl Dist Tchr 1967-71; Providence Schl Dept Flynn Art Specialist 1971-; RI Coll Adj Prof Art Ed 1971-; RI Schl of Design Adj Prof Art Ed 1971-; *ai:* Art Dev Team 1995-; Women, Infants Hosp Partners-in-Ed, Exec Dir 1985-95, Bd 1996; AFT 1967-; Prov Tchrs Union 1971-, Del; RIATA 1971-, Art Chm; NAEA 1971-; RI Alliance Arts 1988-; Soc Ed Through Arts 1975-85, Pres, VP, Bd Dir; Pub Ed Fund 1985-95, Adop-A-Schl Dir; Bristol Art Museum 1975-; Prudence Island Assns 1989-; Nom Tchr of Yr 1985; PTO Tchr of Month 1991; Art Grants RI St Cncl on Arts, NAEAPSD, RI Fnd. RI Comm Hum, Pub Ed Fund, Champlin Fnd 1971-; Flynn Outstdng Tchr Awd 1993; Women, Infants Hosp Svc Awd 1995-; Flynn 25 Yr Svc Awd 1996; Chamber Commerce Distngd Panelist 1988.

RUSSELL-RADER, KATHLEEN, English Teacher; *b:* Dayton, OH; *m:* Donald M.; *ed:* Bowling Green St Univ (BS) Ed 1975; Univ of Dayton (MS) Scndry Ed, Rdng 1987; *cr:* Wapakoneta HS Eng Tchr 1975-76; Sinclair Comm Coll Eng Tchr 1991-; Fairborn Baker Jr HS Eng Tchr 1976-; *ai:* Natl Jr Honor Soc, Stu Leadership Group Adv; Drama Club Co-Adv, Dir; Power of Pen Interscholastic Writing Team Coach; Phi Delta Kappa 1987-; HCTE 1986-, Judge Promising Young Writers; OH Cncl

Tchrs of Eng Lang Arts 1986-, Judge Writing Contest; IRA 1986-, Pres; Acad Cncl 1988-; Tchr of Yr; Very Schneider Tchng Grant 1988-92; OH Interscholastic Writing League Tchr Honor Roll; *office:* Fairborn Baker Jr HS 200 Lincoln Dr Fairborn OH 45324*

RUSSERT, MICHAEL TIMOTHY, 6th Grade Teacher; *b:* Buffalo, NY; *m:* Judith Buck; *c:* Cullen; *ed:* Buffalo St (BS) Elem Ed 1963; Empire St Coll (MALS) Civil War Stud 1996; 50 Addl Hrs at Buffalo St, Albany ST, Gettysburg Coll; *cr:* City of Buffalo Pub Schls 5-6 Grd Tchr 1963-72; Hoosick Falls Cntrl Schl 6 Grd Tchr 1972-; *ai:* AFT 1968-; Cambridge Lib Bd 1988-, VP; Capital Dist Civil War Round Table; Book Review Staff Civil War News; Edited, Introduction to Several Books; Participant Diversity in Documents Grant 1992; Outstdng Capital Region Tchr 1995.

RUSSMAN, DAVID WAYNE, Science Dept Chair & Teacher; *b:* Pittsburgh, PA; *m:* Kathy; *c:* Erika, Kurt, Colleen; *ed:* Penn St Univ (BS) Ed, Bio 1965; Addl 26 Hrs CA St Univ, Duquesna Univ, Univ of Pittsburgh; *cr:* Baldwin-Whitehalls Schls Tchr 1965-; *ai:* Sci Dept Chprsn; AV Media Coord.

RUSSO, ALISA, High School Science Teacher; *b:* Brooklyn, NY; *m:* Alex M. Migliozzi; *ed:* LIU-CW Post (BS) Medical Bio 1984, (MS) Bio Ed 1987; Seeking Cert in Earth Sci, Bio, Chem, & Elem Ed; *cr:* North Shore Univ Hosptial Med Bio I 1984-86; Baldwin Sr HS Sci Tchr 1986-; *ai:* Adv of Sci Clb, Chrldng JV, & Kickline; STANYS & AFT 1986-; NYSUT, NEA, ASMT; Asst Dir of Young People Day Camp 1988.

RUSSO, BARBARA CAIEZZA, Chemistry Teacher; *b:* Jersey City, NJ; *m:* Thomas John; *c:* Thomas Michael; *ed:* Jersey City St (BA) Sci Ed 1965, (MA) Sci Ed 1968; 18 Hrs Bio & Chem Seton Hall Univ; 24 Hrs Chem Simmons Coll; 12 Hrs Math St Peters Coll; *cr:* Ridgefield Pk HS Bio & Chem Tchr 1965-75; Bayonne Evening HS Bio & Chem Tchr 1975-80; Secaucus HS Bio & Physics Tchr 1980-88; Columbia HS Physics & Chem Tchr 1988-91; Ferris HS Chem Tchr 1991-; *ai:* Scholastic Bowl Dist Co-Chprsn; JCEA 1991-; NJEA, NEA, NJSTA 1965-; NSTA 1985-; *office:* James J Ferris HS 35 Colgate St Jersey City NJ 07302*

RUSSO, CHRISTOPHER, Physics & Physical Sci Teacher; *b:* Brooklyn, NY; *ed:* Carnegie-Mellon Univ (BS) Physics 1987; Univ of CA at Los Angeles (MED) Ed 1989; *cr:* Simi Vly HS Physics, Chem Tchr 1989-90; Berendo MS Phys Sci Tchr 1990-92; Northern Highlands RHS Physics, Astronomy, Phys Sci Tchr 1992-; *ai:* Planetarium Dir; NJAAPT 1992-; *office:* Northern Highlands Reg HS Hillside Ave Allendale NJ 07401

RUSSO, DONNA DANIEL, Assistant Principal; *b:* Hartford, CT; *m:* Richard Douglas; *ed:* Hofstra Univ (BS) Art Ed; Rutgers Univ (MA) Ed Admin; Fairfield Univ Sixth Yr Admin, Supervision; St Univ of NY; Univ of Bridgeport; *cr:* Division Ave HS 7-12th Grd Art Tchr; Hockanum Schl 5-8th Grd Tchr; Interim Jr HS 7-8th Grd Tchr; Ridge HS 9-12th Grd Tchr, Admin Asst; Bethel HS Art Tchr, Dept Coord, Asst Prin; *ai:* ASCD; Natl Assn of Sec Schl Prins; NAEA; Amer Assn of Univ Women; Amer Cancer, Leukemia Soc; Newcomes Club, VP; Womens Club, Pub Relations; St, Local Art Awds; CT Assn of Bds of Ed Awd of Excl for Educl Comms; *office:* Bethel HS Educational Park Bethel CT 06896

RUSSO, EMANUEL J., Physics Tchr & Dept Asst; *b:* Philadelphia, PA; *m:* Elizabeth A. Singer; *c:* Jessica, Elizabeth, Joseph; *ed:* Glassboro St (BA) Sci Ed 1968, (MA) Sci Ed 1981; *cr:* Sterling HS Tchr 1968-; *ai:* Boys Soccer Head Coach; Bsbl Asst Coach; Dept Asst; NEA, NJEA, SEA 1968-; NJAPT 1979-; NJSTA 1975-; Knights of Columbus 1982-; Rel Ed 1987-; Sterling HS Tchr of Yr 1989-90; *office:* Sterling HS 501 N Warwick Rd Somerdale NJ 08083*

RUSSO, JAQUELIN F., Fourth Grade Teacher; *b:* Cleveland, OH; *ed:* Akron Univ (BS) Elem Ed 1973; Ursuline Coll (MED) Ed Admin 1995; *cr:* St Michael Schl Head Start & Kndgtn Tchr; St Monica Schl Kndgtn Tchr 1976-80, 4th Grd Tchr 1980-; *ai:* Yrbk Adv; Intermediate Level & Rel Comm Coord; NCEA 1976-; Eastern Region Cleveland Cath Bd of Ed #1 Club 1989; *office:* St Monica Schl 13633 Rockside Rd Cleveland OH 44125

RUSSO, JOHN JOSEPH, Music Teacher; *b:* Worcester, MA; *m:* Kristina; *c:* Angela, Lynne, Joellen, Lisa; *ed:* Berklee Coll of Music (BA) Music Ed 1976; Post-Grad Stud Worcester St, Framingham St Coll; *cr:* Assabet Vly Regnl Voc HS Music Dir 1977-; *ai:* Chorus Dir; Music Adv; Drama Club; AFT 1977-; *office:* Assabet Valley Reg Voc HS 215 Fitchburg St Marlborough MA 01752

RUSSO, JOSEPH PHILIP, 9th Grade English Teacher; *b:* Buffalo, NY; *ed:* Columbia Univ (BA) Eng 1982; Univ Notre Dame Law Schl (JD) 1989; Buff St Coll (MA) Eng Lit 1996; *cr:* Wilson Central HS 9th Grd Eng Tchr 1993-; *ai:* Lit Magazine, SAT, Coll Writing Adv; NCTE, AFT, NYSTR 1993-; *office:* Wilson Central HS 374 Lake St #380 Wilson NY 14172

RUSSO, JOSEPHINE R., Art Teacher; *b:* Bayonne, NJ; *m:* James Lutrario; *ed:* Jersey City St Coll (BA) Art Ed 1964; 15 Addl Credits; Cert NY Schl of Interior Design; *cr:* Union City Schl System Tchr 31 Yrs; *ai:* Yrbk Adv; Art & Lit Steering Comm; Fac Cncl; NEA, NJEA 1964-; HCEA, UCEA 1965-; *office:* Emerson HS 318 18th St Union City NJ 07087

RUSSO, JUDITH, Home Economics Teacher; *b:* Bayonne, NJ; *m:* Jack; *c:* Christopher Carle, Matthew; *ed:* Kean Coll (BA) Elem Ed 1972; Univ Coll Rutgers Home Ec Cert 1976; 30 Credits Extra Toward Home Ec Cert; *cr:* Woodbridge HS Home Ec Tchr 1978-95; J F Kennedy HS Home Ec Tchr 1995-; *ai:* NEA 1980-; Womens Aglow 1980-, Metuchen Chapter Pres; *office:* J F Kennedy HS Washington Ave Iselin NJ 08830

RUSSO, LISA A., 9th-12th Grade English Teacher; *b:* Youngstown, OH; *ed:* OH Univ (BS) Sec Ed, Eng 1990; Xavier Univ Paideia 1991; *cr:* Gamble Jr HS Eng Tchr 1990-91; Hughes Center HS Eng Tchr 1991-; *ai:* Teen Inst Coord; Asst Chrldng Adv; Levy, UNCF Comm; CFT, UNCF 1990-; Black Achievers 1995-; Easter Seals Vol 1988-; Univ Cultural Crossroads 1990-; *office:* Hughes Ctr 2515 Clifton Ave Cincinnati OH 45219*

RUSSO, LORRAINE JOAN, English & ESL Teacher; *b:* New York City, NY; *ed:* Mills Coll of Ed (MS) Elem Ed 1971; NY Univ (MA) Elem Ed 1974; Hunter Coll (MS) Eng Scndry Schl Ed 1987; *cr:* St Bartholomews Schl Elem Schl Tchr 1978-83; Cathedral HS Eng Tchr 1983-85; JHS Arts & Crafts Tchr 1985-86; Newtown HS Eng & ESL Tchr 1986-; *ai:* SAT Supvr & Coord; NY Prsnl Comp Users Group 1994-; *home:* 2180 33rd Rd Long Island City NY 11106*

RUSSO, LOUIS HARRY, Social Studies Teacher; *b:* New Haven, CT; *m:* Paula C. Torniero; *c:* David, Jennifer; *ed:* Univ of CT (BA) Psych 1968; Southern CT St Univ (MA) Ed 1971; *cr:* Assumption Schl 4th-5th, 7th-8th Grd Tchr 1968-72; Elizabeth C. Adams MS 7th-8th Grd Soc Stud Tchr 1972-; *ai:* Yrbk; Tech, Fac Cncl, Dist Negotiations, Comm Comms; Curr Articulation Team; NEA, CT Ed Assn 1972-; Grant to Fund Colonial Living Unit; Pub of Instrl Tool The Immigration Game; *office:* Elizabeth C. Adams MS Church St Guilford CT 06437*

RUSSO, MARYANN JERBASI, American History Teacher; *b:* Orange, NJ; *m:* Jack; *ed:* Caldwell Coll (BA) His 1973; Fairleigh Dickinson Univ His; Jersey City St His & Ed; *cr:* Randolph Intermediate Schl 7th Grd Soc Stud Tchr 1973-83; Randolph HS 10th & 11th Grd Amer His Tchr 1983-; *ai:* Yrbk Adv; REA & NJEA 1973-; NJ 1983-; NCSS 1983-; Natl Historic Trust 1990-; Smithsonian Inst 1990-; Kennedy Ctr 1990-; Museum of Natural His 1990-; Lib of Congress 1993-; *office:* Randolph HS Millbrook Ave Randolph NJ 07869

RUSSO, MERLE ARDEN, French & Spanish Teacher; *b:* New Kinsington, PA; *m:* Karen Marie Donachy; *c:* Heather Marie, Elizabeth Marie; *ed:* Clarion Univ of PA (BS) Span, Fr 1975; Youngstown St Univ (MSEd) Span 1981; Universidad de Valencia Espana Span 1973; Post Grad Stud Univ of Dayton, Kent St Univ; *cr:* East Liverpool City Schls Span, Fr Tchr 1975-95; *ai:* French Club; ELEA, OEA, NEA, AATSP 1975-; *office:* East Liverpool HS 100 Maine Blvd East Liverpool OH 43920

RUSSO, PHILIP THOMAS, Social Studies Teacher; *b:* Pittston, PA; *m:* Barbara Menarick; *c:* Philip, Marcy, Matthew; *ed:* East Stroudsburg U (BS) Ed 1966, (MS) His; Wilkes U 30 Post Grad Credit Hrs; *cr:* WY Area Schl Dist Tchr 1966-; *ai:* Pub Relations Liaison; NEA 1966-; PA St Ed Assoc 1966-, Region Exec Bd & Resolutions Comm; WY Area Ed Assoc 1966-, Pres, VP & Comm Chairmanships; Exeter Hose Co #1 Life Mem; Councilman 4 Yrs; WA Key Club WY Area Tchr of the Yr 1996; *office:* Wyoming Area Schl Dist Memorial St Exeter PA 18643

RUSSO, PHYLLIS CAROL, Professor of Nursing; *b:* Newark, NJ; *ed:* Seton Hall (BS) Nrsng 1960; Columbia Univ (MA) Nrsng Ed 1964; Seton Hall (EDD) Admin, Supervision 1985; *cr:* St Mary's Hosp Staff Nurse, Educator 1955-64; Felician Coll Asst Prof 1964-68; Seton Hall Univ Assoc Prof 1968-; *ai:* Univ Rank, Tenure Comm Mem; Sigma Theta Tau 1976-, Chptr Pres; Co-investigator NIH Grant; *office:* Seton Hall Univ Coll of Nursing 400 S Orange Ave South Orange NJ 07079*

RUSSO, RICHARD A., Science Coordinator & Teacher; *b:* Clearwater, FL; *m:* Deborah Wolstein; *c:* Gina, Ron; *ed:* Fairleigh Dickinson Univ (BA) SciEd 1969; William Paterson Coll (MED) Sci Ed 1972; Univ Natl Peru (EDD) Archaed Astronomy 1989; Sabattical Yr Rsrch Columbia Univ 1980-81; Astronomy 29 Credits; *cr:* Bard Coll Adj Prof of Astronomy, Sci Ed 1982-87; Ramapo Coll Adj Prof of Astronomy, Sci Ed 1975-; Coll of New Rochelle Adj Prof of Astronomy, Sci Ed 1978-; Montvale Schls Sci Tchr 1969-; *ai:* Boys, Girls Track Coach 1969-; Rocketry Club Moderator 1969-; NSTA 1974-; NY Acad of Sci 1981-; NEA, NJEA 1969-; Bergen Cty Tchr of Yr 1987-88; Montvale Tchr of Yr 1991-92; Publications; *office:* Montvale Pub Schls Spring Valley Rd Montvale NJ 07645

RUSSO, RICHARD PAUL, English & Drama Teacher; *b:* Brooklyn, NY; *m:* Sandra Lee Woods; *c:* Joseph; *ed:* St Francis Coll (BA) Eng 1964; C. W. Post Univ (MA) Theatre 1985; 60 Addl Credit Hrs; *cr:* Brookside Jr HS Eng Tchr 1964-67; Valley Stream Cntrl HS Eng Tchr 1967-68; Hauppauge HS Eng Tchr 1968-69; Rocky Point Schls Eng, Drama Tchr 1969-; *ai:* Moderator Thespian Troupe; Schls Dramatics Productions Dir; NYSUT 1964-; Prof Ski Instrs of Amer 1983-; Appalachian Mountain Club 1995-; League of Amer Bicyclers 1992-; *office:* Rocky Point Jr Sr HS 82 Rocky Point Yaphank Rd Rocky Point NY 11778

RUSSO, STEPHEN S., Mathematics Teacher; *b:* Winthrop, MA; *m:* Maryann Maccaro; *c:* Kimberly, Jennifer, Stephen Jr.; *ed:* Salem St Coll (BS) Ed 1975; Boston Univ (MED) Math Ed 1989; *cr:* St John's Grammar Schl Tchr 1976-80; Mt St Joseph Acad Math Tchr 1980-81; St Dominic Savio HS Math Tchr 1981-93; Arlington Cath HS Math Tchr 1993-; *ai:* NCTM, MAST 1993-; St John's C.Y.O. 1990-, Dir; *home:* 15 Court Rd Winthrop MA 02152

RUSSO, THOMAS JOSEPH, Chemistry Teacher; *b:* East Meadow, NY; *m:* Pamela Arpino; *c:* Victoria, Louis; *ed:* Fordham Univ (BS) Chem 1973; St John's Univ (MS) Chem, Ed 1979, (PD) 1996; *cr:* Holy Cross HS Tchr 1973-86; H. F. Carey HS Tchr 1986-; *ai:* Alert; Var Sftbl Coach; JV Boys Bsktbl; NEA, NSA 1986-; PAL 1980-; Chem Lab Manual Author; *office:* H Frank Carey HS 230 Poppy Ave Franklin Square NY 11010*

RUSSO, VINCENT JOHN, Social Studies Teacher; *b:* Long Island City, NY; *m:* Laurie Hildebrandt; *c:* Vincent III, Kerrianne, Alex; *ed:* Hofstra Univ (BA) Pol Sci 1986, (MS) Scndry Ed 1988; *cr:* Mineola HS Soc Stud Tchr 1988-; *ai:* Regents Plus Prgm, Class Advisorships, Tchr of Driver Ed Coord; LICSS 1989-; Class of 1995 Favorite Tchr; *office:* Mineola HS 10 Armstrong Rd New Hyde Park NY 11040

RUSSO-BARON, FRANCES, Gifted & Talented Svcs Dir; *b:* Passaic, NJ; *m:* Gregory D.M.D.; *c:* Bradley, Tyler; *ed:* William Paterson Coll (BA) Eng 1974, (MED) Admin, Supervision 1982; *cr:* Garfield HS Eng Tchr 1974-, Dir Gifted, Talented Svcs 1991-; *ai:* Drama Club; HS Liaison Comm; Intnl Thespian Soc; AFT 1980-; PTSA 1974-; Mid Sts Steering Comm 1989-92; Tchr of Yr 1992-93; Dir Mentorship Prgm; *office:* Garfield HS 500 Palaside Ave Garfield NJ 07026*

RUSSO-HABER, VINCETTA R., English Teacher; *b:* Warren, OH; *m:* Jerold A.; *ed:* Kent St Univ (BS) Eng, Speech 1976, (MA) Rhetoric, Communicaton 1984; Attnd Youngstown St Univ, Univ Central FL, Walt Disney World Univ, WAlsh Coll, Kent St Univ; *cr:* Ursuline HS Eng, Speech Tchr 1976-91; Youngstown St Univ Speech Tchr 1982-91; Boardman HS Eng Tchr 1991-; *ai:* World of Words Essay Contest; NCTE, NEA, OEA 1991-; *office:* Boardman HS 7777 Glenwood Ave Boardman OH 44512*

RUSSOMAGNO, GABRIELLE, Barness Endowed Chair in Art; *b:* Summit, NJ; *m:* Paul Stephen Mezey; *ed:* Smith Coll (BA) Amer Stud, Art 1985; Yale Univ (MFA) Photography 1989; Filmmaking Univ of PA; Digital Imaging Ctr for Creative Imaging; *cr:* LaSelle Coll Photography Instr 1986-87; Brandeis Univ Photographer for Coll 1989-90; Yale Univ Photography Instr 1987-89; Germantown Acad Barness Endowed Chair in Art, Photography Instr, Upper Schl Tech Coord 1990-; *ai:* Comms Guid, Hlth Issues, Fac Concerns, Dean Girls Search; Sr Project Adv; Curr Tech Coord; IM Vlybl; Peer Cnslng; Soc Photographic Ed 1990-; Penn Art Edd Assn 1993-; Cnsl Women in Ind Schls 1992-; Alice Kimball Eng Flwshp; Kast Grants; Books Sexquake, Pleasure & Terror of Domestic Comfort 1991; Amheart Review; Exhibitions; Collections; *office:* Germantown Acad Morris Rd Fort Washington PA 19034

RUSSONIELLO, PAT, High School Math Teacher; *b:* Newark, NJ; *m:* Elaine Flesko; *c:* Lisa Sabatino; *ed:* William Paterson (BA) Math 1965; Montclair St (MA) Math Ed 1971; 30 Addl Hrs in Math & Comp Sci; *cr:* Morris Hills Regnl HS Math Tchr 1965-; *ai:* NJEA & NEA 1965-; *office:* Morris Hills Regl HS 520 W Main St Rockaway NJ 07866

RUST, PATRICIA, Third Grade Teacher; *b:* Hartford, CT; *m:* John E.; *c:* Robert, Sharon Rust Bottone, Cristie Rust Kitnick; *ed:* Eastern Ct St Univ (BA) Elem Ed 1960; 30 Grad Credits Central Ct St Univ 1980; *cr:* Park Ave Schl 5th Grd Tchr 1960-62; Center Schl 3rd Grd Rdng Tchr 1970-; Naubuc Schl 3rd Grd Rdng Tchr 1970-; *ai:* NEA 1970-; CEA; Yankee Gardeners 1980-, Sec, Pres; *office:* Naubuc Elem Schl 84 Griswold St Glastonbury CT 06033

RUTENBERG, LYNNE RAUCHBACH, Second Grade Teacher; *b:* Newark, NJ; *m:* Martin; *ed:* Univ of DE (BSEd) Elem Ed 1967; In-Svc Credits; *cr:* Nortvail Schl Third Grd Teacher 1967-83, Second Grd Tchr 1983-; *ai:* NEA, NJEA 1967-; MCCEA, PTHEA; Mineltill Bd of Ed 2 Yrs, Mem; A Plus for Kids Grant; NJ Ag Soc Grant; *office:* Northvail Elem Schl 10 Eileen Ct Parsippany NJ 07054*

RUTH, GEORGE ALLEN, Art Education & Drama Director; *b:* Chester, PA; *m:* Deborah Kaufman; *ed:* Kutztown Univ (BS) Art Ed 1961; Attnd Univ of DE; *cr:* Chichester Elem Schl Art Ed Tchr 1961-64; Dept of Defense Crafts Instr 1964-68; Upland Elem Schl 1968-69; Brandywine Schl Dist Art Ed & Drama Tchr 1969-; *ai:* Direct HS Musicals & Plays; Drama Dept Head; NEA 1961-; Brandywine Ed Assn 1961-, Bldg Rep; Upland Ed Assn 1968-, Pres; Claymont Ed Assn 1969-76, Pres; Illustrated 2 His Textbooks, Cook Book: Delaware Heritage Cook Book; *o* Mount Pleasant HS 5201 Washington St Ext Wilmington DE 19809*

RUTH, NANETTE EASTER, English Teacher; *b:* Fountain Hill, P John; *c:* Brandy, Robert Whitney; *ed:* Ursinus Coll (BA) Eng 1962; L Univ (MED) Rdng 1978, (EDD) Rdng; West Chester Univ Fello Writing Project 1986; Supvr, Rdng, Supvr Comms; *cr:* Springford Dist HS Eng, Alegebra, Geometry Tchr 1962-63; Bel aire Schl Dist Grd Tchr 1966-67; Souderton Schl Dist Eng, Soc Stud Tchr, D Presenter of Writing Wkshps 1981-87, Rdng Specialist, Eng Tchr, T Gifted 1987-, Eng Dept Chair 1981-93; *ai:* NEA 1974-; PA Cncl for of Eng, Presenter; IRA Natl Convention, Presenter; Fellow Present Writing Project; Dissertation: Applying Reliability, Validity Standa Writing Portfolio Assessment; *office:* Indian Valley MS 130 Mapl Harleysville PA 19438*

RUTH, THOMAS, Asst Prin & Phys Ed Teacher; *b:* Norristown, P Susan Deck; *c:* Jack, Molly; *ed:* West Chester Univ (BA) Hlth & PE (MED) Hlth & PE 1991f Kutztown Univ (MED) Elem Ed 1996; We Univ at Chester Working Toward Doctorate in Admin; *cr:* Owen J R HS PE Tchr 1982-83; Souderton HS PE Tchr 1983-84; Wilson Cntrl Jr PE Tchr & Asst Prin 1984-; *ai:* Swim, Water Polo, LaCrosse & Wre Coach; SAP; FCA; Phi Epsilon Kappa 1980-; AFT 1986-; Phi Delta K 1995-; Thesis Pub 1991; Natl Water Polo Coach of the Yr 1992; Kut Stu Advy Comm for Accreditation 1995; *office:* Wilson Central Jr HS Grandview Blvd West Lawn PA 19609*

RUTHBERG, EDWARD BRYAN, Math Teacher; *b:* Bronx, N Kristin A.; *c:* Matthew, Danielle; *ed:* Oswego Coll (BA) Sociology LIU (MS) Sec Ed, Math 1984; Lehman Coll Tchng Degree Math, S 1979; *cr:* White Plains HS Math Tchr 1979-81; A. Mac Arthur Ba Math Tchr 1981-92; Ramapo Ridge MS Math Tchr 1993-; *ai:* Swim C 14 Yrs; NEA 1993-; NYSUT 1981-92; Sussex III Condo Bd 1988-, Yrs; *home:* 113 Somerset Dr Suffern NY 10901

RUTHERFORD, FRANK A., Registrar & Chemistry Tch Philadelphia, PA; *m:* M. Deborah; *c:* Matthew, Paul; *ed:* Lebanon Coll (BS) Bio 1974; Univ of DE (MS) Marine Stud 1976; *cr:* Merce Acad Sci Tchr 1976-, Dept Head 1987-90, Registrar 1990-; *ai:* Inves Club, Outdoor Club & 11th Grd Class Adv; Asst Swim Coach; Prize & Comm; Amer Chemical Soc 1976-; Mercersburg Area Swim Club 1 Pres; Mercersburg Little League 1992-, Coach; Software Review i Tchr; Articles Pub; *office:* Mercersburg Acad 300 E Semina Mercersburg PA 17236*

RUTKOWSKI, MARY PAULECK, 4th-5th Grade Science Teach Granttown, WV; *m:* Cecil John; *c:* Lisa Marie Bonnet, Steven, Laur Waszil; *ed:* CA Univ (BS) Elem Ed 1973, (ME) Elem Ed 1983; IU; St; Univ of Pittsburgh 9 Addl Credit Hrs; WV Univ 6 Addl Credit Waynesburg Coll 6 Addl Credit Hrs; *cr:* Canon Mc Millan Schl Dist Tchrs 22 Yrs; *ai:* Girls Bsktbl, Swim Team; Ben Franklin Stamp PSEA, NEA, CMEA 1974-; Red Cross Vol, Sec Bd Mem; Girl S 1969-75, Ldr; Tchr of Yr 1988-89; Red Cross Vol for Swimming, Sa Canoeing.*

RUTLEDGE, JEFFERY L., Social Studies Teacher; *b:* Ft Belvoir, V Cynthia Gross; *c:* Kyle, Kristyn; *ed:* Corning Comm Coll (AS) So 1984; NY St Univ at Albany (BA) Pol Sci, His, Psych 1986; NY St at Cortland (MS) Soc Stud, His 1991; Post Grad Intnl Rela Northeastern Univ, His Univ of ND, Spec Ed Mansfield Univ, Cns Alfred Univ; *cr:* US Army Sgt. Officer Candidate Schl 1988-89; E City Schl Dist Sub Tchr 1990-91; Hammondsport Cntrl Schl Soc Stud 1991-92; Bradford Cntrl Schl 9, 11-12 Grd Soc Stud Tchr, Psych, Cri Justice Tchr 1993-; *ai:* Chess Team, Class of 1999, Military His Intra-Mural Fitness Club, SAAD Adv; Var Soccer Coach; Safety C NEA 1992-; NY St Cncl for Soc Stud 1993-; Phi Alpha Theta 1990-; 1994-, Vol; US Chess Fed Grant 1995; Natl Chess Championships Nation 1995; Tchr of Yr 1994; *office:* Bradford Central Schl 2820 R Bradford NY 14815*

RUTSTEIN, BARBARA A. (LERNER), Mathematics Teacher; *b:* MA; *ed:* Salem St Coll (BSEd) Math, Sci 1965; Cambridge Coll (ME 1991; *cr:* Kennedy Jr HS Grd 8 Math Classroom Tchr 1965-68; Robe HS Grd 8 Math Classroom Tchr 1978-; *ai:* NEA; NCTM; Medford L Women Votors, Pres; Medford Recycling, Conservation Commiss *office:* Roberts MS 35 Court St Medford MA 02155

RUTT, DAVID EARL, Vocal Music Teacher; *b:* Reading, PA; *m:* N Reitner; *c:* Chad, Travis; *ed:* Temple Univ (BA) Vocal, Gen Music Addl Hrs Music Ed, Vocal Performance; Alvernia Coll Elem Degre Glenside Elem Schl Choir Dir, Gen Music Tchr 1975-76; Northeas Choral Dir, Gen Music Tchr 1976-; *ai:* Northeast Choir Dir; 8th Grd Comm Spon; Disc Jockey Schl Dances; Yth Soccer Coach Muhlenberg 10 Yrs; BCME, REA, PSEA, NEA 1976-; Alsace Luth Church Choir 1 Choir Dir; Pvt Vocal Tchr 1974-; St Paul's Luth Church Fleet 1977-87, Choir Dir; Calvary Reformed Church Tenor Soloist; *o* Northeast MS 13th & Marion Sts Reading PA 19604*

RUTT, MELANIE BECK, K-8th Grd Teacher of Gifted; *b:* Gordon PA; *c:* Bryan E., Marcus I.; *ed:* Millersville Univ (BA) Sociology (MED) Gifted Ed 1984, (MED) Elem Ed 1985; Supervisory Cert Ele Elem Ed Cert; Preschool Cert; *cr:* Franklin & Marshall Coll Proj C Asst to Dir Dev of Intellectual Potential 1980-82; MIllerville Univ Frosh Rdng Tutor 1982; Jenkins Early Chlhd Ctr Millersville Univ Nursery Instr 1982-85; Lancaster #13 K-6 Grd Tchr of Gifted 198 Elanco Schl Dist K-8 Grd Tchr of Gifted 1993-; *ai:* Watercolor Works Rep in Private Collections; Pi Lambda Theta 1984-, Recording PA Assoc for Gifted Ed 1985-; Natl Assn for Ed of Young Children 1 NEA, PSEA 1991-; Capital Area Writing Project Advy Bd; MENSA 1 Sacred Heart Acad 1970-, Pres, VP, Recording Sec, Dir; Natl W Project Fellow; Daisy Spangler Awd; Meml Schlsp; Inaugural Fac Me Governor's Schl for Tchng 1990; *home:* 2000 Creek Hill Rd Lancast 17601*

RUTTER, CHARLES EDWARD, Soc Stud, PE Tchr & Ath Di Pittsburgh, PA; *m:* Cathrine Emanuele; *c:* Sean, Genna, Francesca; *ed* St U (BA) Soc Stud & PE 1962, (MA) PE 1966; Duquesne Univ Scndry Admin 1973; Ec 6 Credits; Comp Ed 6 Credits; PE 9 Credits Archmene Acad Tchr 1962-65; Shepherd HS Tchr & Ath Dir 196 Cntrl Cath Tchr & Ath Dir 1970-81; Seton LaSalle Tchr & Ath Dir 1 *ai:* Bsbl Coach; Ath Dir; Driver Ed Tchr; Schl Acad Cncl; Natl Cath Union 1973-, Union Negotiations; PA Ath Dirs 1975-; Coach of S LaSalle Western PA Bsbl Champions 1995; *office:* Seton-La Salle HS Mcneilly Rd Pittsburgh PA 15226

RUTZ, NANCY MILNER, 2nd Grade Teacher; *b:* Syracuse, N William; *c:* David, Steven; *ed:* SUNY at Cortland (BS) Elem Ed 196 Palmyra-Macedon Schl 2nd Grd Tchr 1964-65; Seneca Falls Schl 2n Tchr 1965-68, 6th Grd Tchr 1980-81, 2nd Grd Tchr 1982-; *ai:* Prof Bldg Cncl Rep for Comm Comms; Delta Kappa Gamma 1986; *hon* Stevenson St Seneca Falls NY 13148

RUYACK, ROBERT DAVID, Spanish Teacher; *b:* Yonkers, NY; *ed:* Coll (BA) Span, Philosophy, Theology 1965; St John's Univ (MA) Hispanic Stud 1973; Attnd Univ de Mexico, Fordham Univ; Uni Madrid Cert Espanol, Pedagogia 1969; *cr:* Mt St Michael Acad Frgn L Theology Tchr 1965-68; Iona Prep Frgn Lang, Theology Tchr 196 Byram Hills HS Frgn Lang Tchr 1970-; *ai:* Moderator of Club Los Am

ch Bi-lingual Prgm; Site Based Cncl; Tchr of Span, Pedagogy Tchrs ntrl Dist Observation, Evaluation Comm; AFT 1970-; NY St Assn of :hr 1970-, Lecturer; Hispana; Church of Annunciation 1995-, Choir Awd Grant Tchr of Yr; Awrd Grant Moderator of Club los Amigos; Ed; Tchr Mentor.*

A, PATRICIA ANN, Latin I-III Secondary Tchr; *b:* Ashtabula, OH; hard Jackson; *ed:* OH St Univ (BA) Classics 1974; Youngstown St MA) Amer His 1979, (MS) GATE Ed 1993; Tching Cert YSU 1977; A Work 1984-89 & MS Work 1993-, Enrolled Youngstown St Univ Pgm; *cr:* Seneca Valley Scndry Tchr 1980-; Youngstown St Univ d Svc Instr 1983-; *ai:* SVEA Schlsp & Room Assignment Comm; ang Dept Chair; SVEA 1980-; Ashtabula Co Humane Soc; Various nmental & Humane Orgs; Local Meth Church,; OSU Summa Awd Scholar; YSU Grad Assistantship; Nom PA Tchr of Yr 1994; All Star Awd 1995; *office:* Seneca Valley Schls Seneca Schl Rd Harmony PA

, ANGELA UDOVICH, Spanish & French Teacher; *b:* Waynesburg, Duane A.; *ed:* CA Univ of PA (BS) Span, Fr 1977; Kutztown Univ (MA) Span 1982; Credits Cooperative Learning, Diversity; Penn St ng Toward MS in Tchng & Curr; *cr:* Millersburg Area HS Span, Fr 977-90; Miltoh Hershey Schl Span, Fr Tchr 1990-; *ai:* Yrbk Adv; Fac ver; Cooperative Learning Support Grp Ldr; AATF, AATSP 1978-; NEA; ASCD, Interdscplnry Ntwrk Coord; Outstanding Tchr Awd 991; *office:* Milton Hershey Schl 300 Hotel Rd Hershey PA 17033*

, ANN MARIE SHIPMAN, English Teacher; *m:* Thomas P Jr.; *ed:* f Notre Dame (BA) Eng 1988; Montclair St Univ (MAT) Eng 1996; mpson Thacher & Bartlett Paralegal 1989-91; Marylawn Eng Tchr *office:* Marylawn Of The Oranges Schl 445 Scotland Rd South NJ 07079

, CAROLYN, High School English Teacher; *b:* Elizabeth, NJ; *ed:* Coll (BA) Writing, Pol Sci 1991; NJ Provisional Prgm; Eng, Elem *r:* Mt St Mary Acad Amer Lit Tchr 1994-; *ai:* Newspaper Adv; Dance *office:* Mount St Mary Acad 1645 US Highway 22 Watchung NJ

, CAROLYN ROYER, 7th Grd English Teacher; *m:* Charles J. Jr.; olyn R. Razo; *ed:* Mansfield Univ (BS) Comm 1970; *cr:* TAMS 7th ng Tchr 1970-94; Towanda HS 10th-12th Grd Eng Tchr 1994-; *ai:* Presenter Whole Lang Related Arts & Humanities; Interpersonal & Mngmt Skills for MS Stdnts Portfolio Assesment; Cheerleading Choreographer 16 Yrs; Yrbk Adv 12 Yrs; Calligraphy; Journalism; Pi Kappa Delta, Phi Delta Kappa, NEA & PSEA 1970-; a Theta Nu 1970-, Sec, VP, Founders Awd 1970; PA Spec St Schlsp, Coll for Related Arts; Lay Reader St Paul's; *office:* Towanda HS St & Western Ave Towanda PA 18848*

, DONNA CAROL, Elem Special Education Tchr; *b:* London, ad; *m:* Frank Charles; *c:* Eric Christian; *ed:* St Univ Coll at Buffalo xceptional, Elem Ed 1979, (MS) Exceptional Ed 1982; *cr:* Orleans ra BOCES Spec Ed Tchr, Self-Contained Class 1979-81; on-Porter Cntrl Schl Spec Ed Tchr, Self-Contained Class 1982-89; on Porter Cntrl Chl Spec Ed Tchrs, Resource Room, Integrated gs 1992-; *ai:* Child Stud Team; Bldg, Dist Comms; Cncl for tional Children 1980-, Orton Dyslexia Soc 1980-, NY St United 1979-; Ladies Sodality-St Mary's 1994-; Cath Church Byzantine Participated Establishing Guidelines fo Collaborative, Integrative Ed n Level 1992; *office:* Lewiston-Porter Sth Elem Schl 4061 Creek Rd stown NY 14174

, EDWARD WILLIAM, Professor of Economics; *b:* Plainfield, NJ; orgian Hurley; *c:* Sarah, Jennifer; *ed:* Univ of PA (BS) Fin 1955; Univ (MA) Ec 1957; Addl Grad Work Fordham Univ; *cr:* Fordham Instr 1956-57; Iona Coll Instr 1958-60; Manhattanville Coll Prof *ai:* Founder, Dir Ec Freedom Inst; Amer Ec Assn 1956-; EC His 1990-; Inaugural Distngd Sr Fac Alumni Awd; First Consumer ate, Intrdctn by William E Simon, Thomas Horton & Daughters *office:* Manhattanville Coll 2900 Purchase St Purchase NY 10577

, ELAINE TOSH, First Grade Teacher; *b:* Bethlehem, PA; *m:* *c:* Gail Tosh; *ed:* Churchman Bus Sch (AA) Sec Stud 1971; Univ sburgh (BS) Elem Ed 1976; St Univ of NY at Oswego (MS) Voc Ed *cr:* Univ of Pittsburg Admin Asst 1974-76; South Hills Bus Schl Fin r, Instr 1980-84; C. W. Baker HS Bus Ed Tchr 1988-95; Elden Elem irst Grd Tchr 1995-; *ai:* NEA 1988-; *office:* Baldwinsville Cntrl Schl 9 E Oneida St Baldwinsville NY 13027

, ELIZABETH FRICK, 2nd Grade Tchr, Asst Principal; *b:* Buffalo, : Kathleen Burroughs, Jennifer; *ed:* D'Youville Coll (BS) Elem m Laude 1964; *cr:* St Gerard's Schl 6th Grd Tchr 1961-63; Infant of Schl 4th, 2nd Grd, Rdng Enrichment Tchr 1964-67, 1980-, Asst Prin St James' Schl 4th Grd Tchr 1967-68; *ai:* Mid Sts Accreditation, Respect Life Comms; Annual Family Rdng Celebration Spon; Parish mm Past Chprsn; NCEA 1980-; D'Youville Coll Alumni 1964-; Rel of Yr Diocese of Buffalo; *office:* Infant Of Prague Schl 921 Cleveland eektowaga NY 14225

, GERALD JOSEPH, Mathematics Teacher; *b:* Waterbury, CT; *m:* C. S.; *c:* Megan E., Kara L.; *ed:* Western CT St Coll (BS) Elem Ed (MS) Ed 1979; *cr:* Oxford Schl System 8th Grd Math Tchr 1973-; *ai:* Coach; Audio Visual & Math Curr Coord; NEA 1973-; Nom for ential Awd for Excl in Math Tchng; *home:* 30 Dawn Cir Watertown 795*

, JEFFERY THOMAS, High School Science Teacher; *b:* El Paso, : Michelle Lee Macy; *c:* Brandon, Ashley; *ed:* Bob Jones Univ (BA) osite Sci 1991; 24 Hrs Toward 30 Hrs MA; *cr:* Emmanual Acad HS chr 1992-94; Riverdale Bapt Schl HS Sci Tchr 1994-; *ai:* Boys plinary Dean; Sci Dept Head; Sci Fair Coord; *office:* Riverdale st Schl 1133 Largo Rd Upper Marlboro MD 20774

, JOSEPH DENNIS, Learning Support Teacher; *b:* Coudersport, : Donna L. Hans; *c:* Bret; *ed:* Northern IL Univ (BS) Spec Ed 1973; Work Gannon Univ, PA St Univ; *cr:* Echlin Manufacturing Co Factory 965-67; Henry Pratt Co Analyist Indust Engr Dept 1967-70; North a Ctr Supervising Tchr 1970-73; Ridgway MS-HS Learning Support 1973-; *ai:* Girls Bsktbl Coach 15 Yrs; Seneca Highlands Ed Assn , VP, Pres; *office:* Ridgway MS-HS 1403 Hill St Ridgway PA 15853

, JOSEPH G., Math Chair; *b:* Dublin, Ireland; *m:* Julienne; *ed:* attan Coll (BS) Math 1981, (MBA) Finance 1986; *cr:* Cardinal Hayes ath Chair 1984-; *ai:* Chprsn; Manhattan Coll Track Coach; NCTM ; NCEA 1986-; ASTD 1992-; *home:* 105 Garth Rd Apt 6H Scarsdale 0583

, JOSEPH JEROME, Social Studies Teacher; *b:* Chateaugay, NY; aisy; *c:* Jeremiah, Jennifer, Leah Benson; *ed:* SUNY at Plattsburg Ed 1969; SUNY at New Paltz (MS) Ed 1974; Educl Admin Advanced Cert 1984; 67 Addl Grad Hrs; *cr:* Blue Mt MS Tchr, Team Ldr 1969-; of New Rochelle Adj Fac 1984-; *ai:* Living His Coord; NYSUT, AFT ; Co of Military Historians 1977-, Chm, Fellow; Verplarch Fire Co ; Outstdng Tchr of Amer His 1982; Freedoms Fnd Vly Forge Tchrs 1992; NBC TV Truth About Tchrs 1989.*

, JOSEPH P., Chemistry Teacher; *b:* New York, NY; *m:* Irene E. *c:* Kathleen, Pamela, Christopher; *ed:* St John's Univ (BS) Chem (MSE) Scndry Ed 1965; Univ of MS (MS) Combined Scis 1971; *cr:* Hicksville Sr HS Chem Tchr 1961-; St Univ of NY at Farmingdale Adjunct Chem Prof 1989-; *ai:* NEA, NYSTA, Hicksville Congress of Tchrs 1961-; United Univ Prof 1989-; PAL 1978-83, Pres 1980-83; East Meadow Soccer Club 1984-91, Coach; N Bellmore Bsktbl League 1983-87, Coach; Nassau Cty Soccer Ofcls Assn 1981-87, HS Soccer Referee; Natl Sci Fnd Grant 1970-71; Prin Advy Comm; *office:* Hicksville Sr HS Division Ave Hicksville NY 11801*

RYAN, KAREN LYNN, 8th Grade Writing Teacher; *b:* Coaldale, PA; *m:* Timothy P.; *c:* Christopher; *ed:* Kutztown Univ (BS) Ed 1987; 24 Addl Credits; *cr:* Tamaqua Area JHS 8th Grd Writing Tchr 1987-; *ai:* STOPP Comm Club Adv; *office:* Tamaqua Area Jr HS PO Box 90 Tamaqua PA 18252

RYAN, KATHLEEN MARIE, 8th Grade English Teacher; *b:* Syracuse, NY; *c:* Robert Bateman, Edward Bateman, Jason Bateman; *ed:* SUNY at Oswego (BS) Scndry Ed & Eng 1988, (MS) Scndry Ed & Curr Dev 1993; *cr:* Mexico MS 8th Grd Eng Tchr 1988-; *ai:* AFT 1988-; Saint Agnes CYO 1993-, Bd of Dirs; *office:* Mexico Acad & Cntrl Schls Fravor Rd Mexico NY 13114*

RYAN, LINDA MORIN, English & ESL Teacher; *b:* Providence, RI; *m:* William M.; *ed:* RI Coll (BA) Eng 1970, (MAT) Eng 1974; 55 Credit Hrs Beyond Masters; Cert for Eng, Soc Stud, His, Eng as Second Lang with MS Endorsement; Currently Enrolled in Cert of Advanced Grad Stud Prgm with Educl Admin Major; *cr:* Johnston HS Eng & Eng as Second Lang Tchr 1970-; *ai:* Stu Cncl Adv; Close Up Coord; RI Skills Commission; Schl Imprv Team Curr Coord Comm; AFT & JFT 1970-; *office:* Johnston Sr HS 345 Cherry Hill Rd Johnston RI 02919

RYAN, LORI JEANNE, School Counselor; *b:* Auburn, NY; *m:* Michael J.; *c:* Molly, Nicholas, Shannon; *ed:* SUNY at Brockport (BA) Sociology 1978, (MSEd) Cnslng 1981, (CAS) Cnslng 1985; *cr:* Monroe Cty Dept of Soc Svcs Income Maintenance 1978-79; NY St Division for Yth Therapist 1979; Ctr for Yth Svcs Data Collection Specialist 1979-83; Manchester-Shortsville Schl Dist Cnslr 1983-; *ai:* NHS Adv; NYSUT; NYSACAC; MCCA; TCCA; *office:* Manchester-Shortsville Schl 1506 Rt 21 Shortsville NY 14548

RYAN, LORRI LYNNE, Biology Teacher; *b:* Pittsburgh, PA; *ed:* Univ of Pittsburgh (BS) Biological Scis-Cum Laude 1993; Grad Schl of Ed 30 Post Grad Hrs 1994; *cr:* Bethel Park Sr HS Bio Tchr 1995-; *ai:* PA Jr Acad of Sci, Sci Club Spon; AFT 1995-; WPBTA 1993-; PSEA 1992-; Hand-n-Hand Festival 1992-, Vol with Physically & Mentally Challenged Children; Golden Key NHS; Hearst Merit Schlsp; Outstdng Stu Tchr Awd Nom; Univ of Pittsburgh Ed Schlsp; *office:* Bethel Park Sr HS 309 Church Rd Bethel Park PA 15102

RYAN, MARGARET R., Kindergarten Teacher; *b:* Allentown, PA; *ed:* Gwynedd Mercy Coll (BS) Elem Ed 1971; Lehigh Univ (MED) Elem Ed 1976; *cr:* Sacred Heart Schl 2nd Grd Tchr 1961-68; St Elizabeth Schl Kndgtn Tchr 1968-73; Whitehall-Coplay Schl Dist Kndgtn Tchr 1973-; *ai:* Co-Chprsn Action Team for Strategic Planning Comm Prgm, Elem Level Soc Stud Curr Revisal Team; NEA, Whitehall-Coplay Ed Assoc 1973-; *office:* C M Gockley Elem Schl 2932 Macarthur Rd Whitehall PA 18052

RYAN, MARGUERITE MASTRIANNI, Third Grade Teacher; *b:* Derby, CT; *m:* John Joseph; *c:* Elizabeth, Sean; *ed:* Southern CT St Univ (BS) Spec Ed, Elem Ed 1968; Lesley Coll (MED) Ed, Creative Arts in Ed 1991; *cr:* Irving Schl, Derby HS Spec Ed Tchr 1968-70; Peabody Schl 3-6 Grd Tchr 1972-; *ai:* Cncl on Schl Reform 1993-; Rdng Curr Comm; MA Rdng Assn 1993-; Peabody Fed of Tchrs 1972-; *office:* Center Schl 18 Irving St Peabody MA 01960*

RYAN, MARLENA CATHERINE, Seventh Grade English Teacher; *b:* Philadelphia, PA; *ed:* LaSAlle Univ (BA) Eng, Ed 1993; Scndry Cert, 28 Credit Hrs Fr; *cr:* Abington Jr HS Eng Tchr 1993-; *ai:* Lit Magazine, Diversity Club, Newspaper Adv; Multicultural Comm Mem; Costume Dir Guys, Dolls; Team Mem of Stu Asst Prgm, Keystone Integrated Framework; NEA 1995-; Phi Sigma Iota 1992-; *office:* Abington Jr HS 2056 Susquehanna Rd Abington PA 19001

RYAN, MELISSA O'DELL, French & Russian Teacher; *b:* Beckley, WV; *m:* Matthew; *ed:* WV Univ (BA) Frgn Langs 1990; *cr:* Bentworth HS Fr, Russian Tchr 1991-; *ai:* Fr Club Spon; PSMLA 1994-; *office:* Bentworth HS 500 Lincoln Ave Bentleyville PA 15314

RYAN, MICHAEL G., Mathematics Teacher; *b:* New York City, NY; *ed:* Don Bosco Coll (BA) Math, Philosophy 1980; Pontifical Coll Josepheniun (MA) Theology, Counseling 1995; Fordham Univ (MA) Ed 1987; Soc Work, Counseling Courses; *cr:* Salesian HS Math Tchr 1980-83; Lasalle HS Tchr, Cnslr 1985-86; Corpus Christi Schl & Youth Ctr Tchr, Cnslr 1989-95; East Orange Pub Schls Math Tchr 1995-; *ai:* Interact Club Adv; HSPT Prgm Coord; NEA 1986-; NCTM 1995-; Salesian Youth Ministry Bd 1991-; Port Chester Youth Bureau 1991-, Svc, Civic Awd; Westchester Cty Coilition on Homelessness 1991; Port Chester, Rye Brook Svc Awd; *office:* East Orange HS 14 N Walnut St East Orange NJ 07017*

RYAN, RICHARD GEORGE, Science Teacher & Swim Coach; *b:* Jersey City, NJ; *m:* Daren M. Twiford; *ed:* SUNY Stony Brook (BS) Bio 1983; NY Inst of Tech (MS) Human Resource Dev 1990; 15 Credit Hrs; *cr:* Sewanhanka Pub Schls Sci Tchr & Lab Technician 1983; LaSalle Military Acad Sci Tchr & Swim Coach 1984; Hicksville HS Sci & Math Tchr 1985; Lindenhurst MS Sci Tchr & Swim Coach 1986-; *ai:* Boys Head Var Swimming & Diving Coach 1989-; Tchrs Assn of Lindenhurst 1986-; Natl Interscholastic Swim Coach Assn 1990-; Amer Swim Coaches Assn 1990-; *office:* Lindenhurst Pub Schls 350 Wellwood Ave Lindenhurst NY 11757*

RYAN, ROSINA MC AVOY, English Teacher; *b:* Philadelphia, PA; *m:* Francis J.; *c:* Francis P., Maureen D., Sean B.; *ed:* Temple Univ (BA) His 1970; Villanova Univ (MA) Eng; Attnd La Salle Univ 1992; *cr:* Little Flower HS Soc Stud Tchr 1981-82; Archbishop Ryan HS Eng, Soc Stud Tchr 1982-83; Northeast Cath HS Span, Eng Tchr 1983-84; Mt St Joseph Acad Eng Tchr 1984-; *ai:* Irish Culture Club Moderator; Curr Comm Mem; Amer Educ Stud Assn 1994-; Mid Atlantic Sts Philosophy of Ed Soc 1990-; NEH Grant; *office:* Mt St Joseph Acad 120 W Wissahickon Ave Flourtown PA 19031

RYAN, SUSAN JEAN, Physics Teacher; *b:* Jersey Shore, NJ; *m:* Steven A.; *c:* Melissa, Madeline, Meghan; *ed:* Albright Coll (BS) Bio 1979; *cr:* Wall HS Sci Tchr 1979-80; Manasquan HS Chem Tchr 1980-82; Raritan HS Chem, Physics Tchr 1982-87; Lacey Twp HS Physics, AP Physics Tchr 1987-; *ai:* Physics Club Adv; NEA 1979-; LTEA 1987-; NJPTA 1988-; Outstdng Tchr of Math & Sci; Tandy Tchr of Yr; Supts Round Table 1992; *office:* Lacey Township HS PO Box 206 Haines St Lanoka Harbor NJ 08734*

RYAN, TAMMY (GUM), Vocal Music Director; *b:* Parkersburg, WV; *m:* Ronald; *c:* Rebecca; *ed:* Glenville St Coll (BA) Music Ed 1981; Grad Hrs WV Univ, Ashland Coll; *cr:* Vienna Elem 6th Grd & Music Tchr 1982-83; Bennerhassett Elem 4th Grd Tchr 1983-87; Lincoln Elem 6th Grd Tchr 1987-88; Mayfield Ctr Elem Chapter I Tutor 1988-89; Brooklyn City Schls Vocal Music Dir 1989-94; Brookridge Elem 4th Gr Tchr 1994-; *ai:* NEA 1982-, OH Music Ed Assn, MENC 1989-94; Amer Choral Dirs Assn 1993-94; *office:* Brookridge Elementary 4500 Ridge Rd Brooklyn OH 44144*

RYAN, THERESA M.,SC, Jr High Teacher; *b:* Brooklyn, NY; *ed:* Mt St Vincent at Halifax (BA) Elem Ed; *cr:* St Kevin Schl First Grd Tchr 1956-61; St Peter Schl First Grd Tchr 1961-67; St Sebastian Fifth Grd Tchr 1967-69; Sacred Heart Sixth Grd Tchr 1969-70; St Barnabas Fifth Grd Tchr 1970-73; St Sebastian Sixth-Eighth Grds Tchr 1973-; *ai:* Lang Arts Coord; Adv to Prin; LA Olympiad, Cath Daughters Contests; NCEA, Natl Eng Ed Assn 1973-; Bishop's Rel Ed & 25 Yrs of Svc Awds; St Elizabeth Ann Seton's Outstdng Tchr of Yr Awd; *office:* St Sebastian Schl 39-76 58th St Woodside NY 11377

RYAN, THOMAS, Social Studies Teacher; *b:* Warwick, NY; *m:* Janet Elizabeth Day; *ed:* SUNY at Plattsburgh (BA) Scndry Ed 1985; Jersey City St Coll (MA) Urban Ed & Principalship & Supervision 1989; 24 Addl Post-Grad Credits; *cr:* Camelot Child Care 1985; Saint Anne Inst Child Care 1985-86; High Point Regnl HS Soc Stud Tchr 1986-; *ai:* Var Soccer Head Coach; Var Ski Head Coach; Class Adv; NEA, NJEA & HPEA 1986-; 1st Yr Tchrs Mentor; *office:* High Point Regional HS 299 Pigeon Hill Rd Sussex NJ 07461*

RYAN, TIMOTHY FRANK, Art Teacher; *b:* Dayton, OH; *m:* Holly Elizabeth Wobbe; *c:* Taylor Beth; *ed:* Berea Coll (BA) Art, Ed 1983; *cr:* New Carlisle MS Art Tchr 1983-86; Greeneview HS Art Tchr 1988-; *ai:* Art Show Dir; Var Golf Coach; OHSGCA 1989-; *office:* Greeneview HS 53 N Limestone St Jamestown OH 45335*

RYAN, VICKI L., Math, Science & History Tchr; *b:* Johnstown, PA; *m:* John D.; *c:* Heather, Zachary; *ed:* Univ of Pittsburgh at Johnstown (BA) Elem Ed 1992; *cr:* Riverside Chrstn Acad Elem Tchr 1992-; *ai:* Yrbk, IM Adv; Pi Lambda Delta 1990-92; *office:* Riverside Christian Acad R D 4 Box 61a Johnstown PA 15905

RYAN, WILLIAM LAWRENCE, English Teacher; *b:* Holyoke, MA; *m:* Patricia Delisle; *c:* Helen F., Michael D.; *ed:* Boston Univ (AA) Liberal Arts 1957; DePauw Univ (BA) Eng Lit 1959; Amer Intl Coll (MA) Ed 1962; *cr:* Chicopee HS Eng Tchr 1960-62; Chicopee Comprehensive HS Eng Tchr 1962-68; West Springfield HS Eng Tchr 1968-; *ai:* Eng Dept Chm; WSEA, MTA, NEA 1968-; NCTE 1996; NDEA Univ of MA 1968; Newspaper Fellowship Univ of MO 1964; *office:* West Springfield HS 425 Piper Rd West Springfield MA 01089*

RYAN-HSU, MONIKA ELISABETH, Second Grade Teacher; *b:* Poland, Europe; *m:* Pete Hsu; *c:* Jason Ryan, Erik Ryan, Kelvin Hsu; *ed:* SUNY at Oneonta (BA) Ed, Ger 1972; Western CT (MS) Ed, Comm 1977; 50 Hrs Past Masters; *cr:* Ben Franklin 1st, 3rd Grd Tchr 1972-77; Van Cortlandtville 2nd-4th Grd Tchr 1977-80; G.W. 5th Grd Tchr 1980-83; Lakeland Schls 2nd Tchr 1983-; *ai:* Sci & Hlth Curr Comm; PTA; Character Bldg Comm; LFT 1972-, Rep; Tchr of Yr Local Newspaper Nom; *office:* George Washington Elem Schl Mohegan Lake NY 10547

RYANS, EDWARD O'NEAL, English Teacher; *b:* Cleveland, OH; *m:* Betty Dawson; *c:* Ricky; *ed:* Morehouse Coll (BA) Eng 1993; Attnd Trinity Coll; *cr:* Crossland Sr HS Eng Tchr 1993-; *ai:* Var Bsbl, Jr Var Bsktbl Head Coach; Class Spon; NCTE 1994-; *office:* Crossland Sr HS 6901 Temple Hill Rd Temple Hills MD 20748*

RYBACK, SUSAN KING, English & Humanities Teacher; *b:* Detroit, MI; *m:* Ralph; *c:* Dylan, Gregg, Kevin, Luke, Kurt, Jesse; *ed:* Univ of MI (BA) Eng 1963; Univ of PA (MA) Folklore 1968; Post Grad Stud Art, Philosophy, Cultures of New Western World; Univ of MI Tchng Cert; *cr:* East Jackson HS 1963-64; Saline HS 1964-65; Cherry Hill HS Tchr 1965-66, 1967-68; Lexington HS 1968-69; WA Intnl Ctr 1970-75; Univ of DC at NIH 1970-78; Montgomery Coll; Walt Whitman HS 1978-; *ai:* Founder Intervention Team Stdnts at Risk; MCEA, NEA, MCTELA 1978-; Channel Seven Awd Outstdng Tchng; Agnes Meyer Outstdng Tchr Awd; *office:* Walt Whitman HS 7100 Whittier Blvd Bethesda MD 20817

RYBAK, RONALD EDWARD, Physical Sci Teacher & Chair; *b:* Nanticoke, PA; *m:* Sandra Lee Demski; *c:* Ronald J., Randall C.; *ed:* King's Coll (BS) Biological Sci 1961; Univ of Scranton (MS) Sci 1968; 40 Credits Univ of MD, Wilkes Univ; *cr:* Mt Carmel HS Bio Tchr 1961-63; Freeland HS Bio, Earth Sci Tchr 1963-65; Dallas HS Phys & Earth Sci Tchr, Sci Chair 1965-; *ai:* Asst Bsktbl Coach 10 Yrs; PIAA Bsktbl Ofcl 14 Yrs; Sr HS Ftbl Coach; NEA, PSEA, DEA 1963-; Natl Sci Fnd Awd Univ of MD, Univ of Scranton, Wilkes Univ; Tchr of Yr 1984; Tchr Mentor Dallas Schl Dist; *home:* 24 Overlook Rd Nanticoke PA 18634

RYBAR, DONALD STEPHEN, Social Stud & Drivers Ed Tchr; *b:* Johnstown, PA; *m:* Linda Lee Pethtel; *ed:* Clarion Univ (BS) Soc Stud 1960; Edinboro Univ (MED) Soc Stud 1963; 45 Credits Beyond Masters at Duquesne Univ, IN Univ of PA & Gannon Univ; *cr:* Ft LeBoeuf HS Tchr 1960-; *ai:* Intensive Scheduling, Inclusion, Discipline, NHS & General Ed Diploma Comms; Activity Spon; Silent Rdng Club; Mentor Tchr; PSEA, NEA 1960-, Life Mem; PA Assn Environmental Ed, Inst for Earth Ed 1990-; Taft Inst for Tchrs 1989-; Outstanding Achvmt Awd for Excl in all Categories at PA Free Enterprise Week; Honorary Citizen of Erie for Participation in Taft Inst for 2 Party Govt; Duquesne Univ Ec Grad Stud Grants; PA Assn for Safety Ed Svc Awd; *office:* Fort Le Boeuf HS 931 N High St Waterford PA 16441*

RYBARCZYK, JAMES EDWIN, 7th Grade Math Teacher; *b:* Toledo, OH; *m:* Antoinette Zawierucha; *c:* Debra A. Pacer, Patrick J.; *ed:* Univ of Toledo (BA) Elem Ed 1968, (MA) Admin, Supervision 1973, (EDS) Admin, Supervision 1981; *cr:* Jefferson Jr HS 8th Grd Math Tchr 1969-81; Washington Jr HS 7th-8th Grd Math, Cmptr Tchr 1981-; *ai:* Jr HS Girls Bsktbl, Track; TAWLS 1969-, Outstdng Tchr 1993-94; OEA, NEA 1969-; *office:* Washington Jr HS 5700 Whitmer Dr Toledo OH 43613

RYBERG, MARGENE ROBERTA, Mathematics Teacher; *b:* Cincinnati, OH; *m:* David L.; *c:* Stacey, Stephanie; *ed:* Xavier Univ (BS) Math 1979; Univ of Cincinnati (MED) Curr & Instr 1984; *cr:* Northwest HS Tchr 1979-; *ai:* Tech Comm Bldg Pilot Group; Jr Engr Tech Soc Co-Spon; North Cntrl Evaluation Co-Chprsn; Phi Delta Kappa 1990-; OH Cncl Tchrs of Math, NEA, OEA, NAE 1979-; Charlotte Schmidlapp Fnd, Honeywell Corp Grants; Gen Electric Tchr Awd; *office:* Northwest HS 10761 Pippin Rd Cincinnati OH 45231*

RYDER, JEFFREY, Social Studies Teacher; *b:* Jersey City, NJ; *m:* Lynn Marie Wolfe; *ed:* Brandywine Coll (AS) Lbrl Arts 1979; West Chester Univ (BSEd) Scndry Ed, Soc Stud 1981; Jersey City St Coll (MS) Admin & Supervision 1993; *cr:* Lenape Vly Regnl Schl Tchr of Soc Stud 1984-85; Hopatcong MS 8th Grd Soc Stud Tchr 1985-94; Hopatcong HS Tchr of Soc Stud 1995-; *ai:* Asst Cross Cntry, Asst Wrestling, Asst Track & Field Coach; NEA, NJEA 1984-; HEA 1985-, VP Grievance; *home:* 107 W Baldwin St Hackettstown NJ 07840*

RYDER, RICHARD CARL, History Teacher; *b:* Union, NY; *ed:* Gettysburg Coll (BA) His 1969; Temple Univ (MA) His 1987; *cr:* Cherokee HS His Tchr 1987-; *ai:* Presidential Classroom, His, Star Trek Club Adv; NEA, NJEA 1987-; Fellow of Natl Stereoscopic Assn 1986; E. J. Berkowitz Awd for Best Articles Pub 1988; Articles Pub; *office:* Cherokee HS 120 Tomlinson Mill Rd Marlton NJ 08053

RYDER, THOMAS H., Mathematics Teacher; *b:* Massillon, OH; *m:* Brenda S.; *c:* Olivia Morgan; *ed:* Kent St Univ (BS) Math & Ed 1990; Working on Masters Ashland Univ; *cr:* Northwestern HS Math Tchr 1991-; *ai:* Head Girls Sftbl & Asst Var Bsktbl Coach; OCTM 1989-; NCTM 1989-; NEA 1990-; *office:* Northwestern HS 7569 N Elyria Rd West Salem OH 44287

RYERSON, MARJORIE GILMOUR, Journalism Professor; *b:* Germantown, PA; *c:* Nicholas G. Jones, Emily R. Jones; *ed:* Beloit Coll (BA) Eng & Sociology 1965; Univ of IA (MFA) Creative Writing & Poetry 1976; Attnd Parsons Schl of Design, Univ of Rochester & Philadelphia

Museum Coll of Art; *cr:* The Times Argus Ed in Chief of News Magazine 1986-90; Johnson St Coll Prof Writing & Lit Dept 1990-91; Middlebury Coll Poetry Fac 1991-; Castleton St Coll Prof of Comm 1991-; *ai:* Sr Class Mentor for Randolph Union HS 1993-; Poetry Rdngs at Colls, Univs & Lit Ctrs; Stu Newspaper Adv Johnson St Coll 1990-91; Stu Newspaper Adv 1991-; Big Br-Big Sr Vol; AFT 1990-, Del to Fed; The Image Coop 1976-, Pres of Bd 1980-; Randolph Comm Dev Corp 1991-, Bd of Dirs; Justice of the Peace, Orange Cty VT 1984-; Select Bd of Randolph 1995-, Selectperson; Arts-Medicine Prgm for Gilford Hospital 1996-, Dir; Gilford Hospital, Corporator 1983-; Outstanding New Fac Mem of Yr Castleton St Coll 1992; Phi Eta Sigma Scholar Castleton St Coll 1996; Journalist of Yr for Weekly Newspapers 1981; Numerous Articles & Photos Pub Since 1976; Marquis 1995-96 Whos Who in East; *office:* Castleton St Coll Leavenworth Hall Castleton VT 05735

RYGIEL, RANDY L., Eighth Grd Language Arts Tchr; *b:* Cleveland, OH; *ed:* Youngstown St Univ (MS) Spec Ed, GATE 1995; *cr:* Rialto Unified Schl HS Eng Tchr 1988-89; Sebring Local Schls HS eng Tchr 1990-91; Boardman Local Schls 8th Grd Lang Arts Tchr 1991-; *ai:* Play Dir; BEA, OEA, NEA, NCTE 1991-, Bldg Rep; IRA 1993-; Youngstown St Univ Eng Festival; Writing Awd for Tchrs; *office:* Boardman Glenwood MS 7635 Glenwood Ave Youngstown OH 44512*

RYKLIN, ELLA HADASSAH, French & Russian Teacher; *b:* Moscow, Russia; *c:* Edward Baruch, Jacqueline Esther; *ed:* St Univ of Moscow (BA) Frgn Langs; Masters Pol Sci; *cr:* New Utrecht HS Fr & Russian Tchr 6 Yrs; *ai:* Russian Club Adv; *office:* New Utrecht HS 1601 80th St Brooklyn NY 11214

RYKOSKEY, CAROL KLEBER, Fifth Grade Teacher; *b:* Pittsburgh, PA; *c:* Ron, Michael, Mark; *ed:* Duquesne Univ (BAE) Elem Ed 1958; Univ of Dayton (MS) Counseling 1976; *cr:* John F Kennedy Tchr; *ai:* KEA, OEA, NEA 1973-; *office:* John F Kennedy Elem Schl 5030 Polen Dr Dayton OH 45440

RYLKO, W. RUSSELL, Earth Science Instructor; *b:* Everett, MA; *m:* Theresa Ellen Conover; *ed:* Northeastern Univ (BSEd) Ed 1971; *cr:* Melrose Pub Schls Tchr Aide 1969-70; North End Union-ABCD Rdng Instr 1970; Natick Pub Schls Earth Sci Instr 1971-; *ai:* 900-R Team Ldr; Supply Coord; After Schl Activity Prgm; Mystic Valley Railway Soc 1970-, Pres; Hyde Park Dev Co 1983-86; Boston Comm Schls 1985-; Saint Adalberts Fin Com 1986-; Several Courses & Wkshps for Prof Dev Points; Boston Edison Grant for Energy Applications 1986; Mass Water Resources Authority Grant for Oceanographic Stud 1993; Hosted Several Stdnts From Framingham St Coll for Practicum; Assisted Several Field Stud Stdnts From Framingham St Coll; *office:* Wilson MS 24 Rutledge Rd Natick MA 01760*

RYNN, JOSEPH C., Social Studies Teacher; *b:* Brooklyn, NY; *m:* Rosemary L. Charas; *c:* Michael, Maura, Kathleen, Joseph; *ed:* Duquesne Univ (BSEd) Soc Stud 1971, (MSEd) Scndry Admin 1977; Grad Work Towards MA in His; *cr:* Montour HS Soc Stud Tchr 1973-; *ai:* NHS Adv; NEA, PSEA, Montour Ed Assn 1973-; Phi Alpha Theta; *home:* 45 S Grandview Ave Pittsburgh PA 15205

RYZNAR, MATTHEW THOMAS, 8th Grade English Teacher; *b:* Youngston, OH; *c:* Rahcelle M., Jeffrey A.; *ed:* Univ of Notre Dame (BA) Eng 1972; Youngstown St Univ (MSEd) Guid, Cnslng 1978; Addl Hrs Educl Theory & Methods, Psych, Curr Dev, Spec Ed; *cr:* West Jr HS 8th Grd Eng Tchr 1972-89; East Jr HS 8th Grd Eng Tchr 1989-90; Western Reserve Jr HS 8th Grd Eng Tchr 1990-; *ai:* Creative Writing Adv; Schl Improvement Comm; Spec Enrichment Class Tchr; Warren Ed Assn 1972-, Bldg Rep; NEOEA, NEA, OEA 1972-; Univ of Notre Dame Alumni Org, YSU Alumni Org 1972-; Jenings Scholar; Ashland Oil Tchr of Yr Nom; Tchr in Space Applicant; *office:* Warren Western Reserve Jr HS 200 Loveless Ave SW Warren OH 44485*

RZEZNIK, JOSEPH J., Chemistry Teacher; *b:* Amsterdam, NY; *m:* Shirley Anne Mruczek; *c:* George, Michael, Lawrence; *ed:* Villanova Univ (BS) Bio 1964; St Rose Coll (MS) Ed 1969; Union Coll (MS) Sci 1971; Attnd Atmospheric Sci Research Ctr 1977, Cntrl CT St Coll 1966, Mary Grove Coll; Natl Sci Fnd Grant 1967; *cr:* Amsterdam High Bio, Chem Tchr 1965-; St Johnsville High Tchr 1964-65; *ai:* Cross Cntry Team Coach 1985-; 4 Mile Runs 1982-; Bio Stud Winter Hiking 1974-78; Amsterdam Tchrs Assn 1965-; Fulmont Road Runners Club 1982, Pres 3 Yrs, Race Dir 5 Yrs; Hagaman Vol Fire Dept, 1978-, EMT, Trustee.

RZEZNIK, LAWRENCE DAVID, Biology Teacher; *b:* Amsterdam, NY; *m:* Deanna Mazurowski; *ed:* SUNY at Geneseo (BS) Bio & Ed 1991, (MS) Bio & Ed 1993; *cr:* Quincy Coll Chem Instr 1992-93; Laboure Coll Anatomy & Physiology Instr 1992-93; Mahopac HS Bio Tchr 1993-; *ai:* Club Adv for Interact; Asst Modified Wrestling & JV Bsbl Coach; *office:* Mahopac High School Baldwin Place Rd Mahopac NY 10541

S

SAAB, KIMBERLEE JULIA, 9th-11th Grade English Teacher; *b:* Allentown, PA; *ed:* LaSalle Univ (BA) Comm 1990; Kutztown Univ Scndry Eng Cert 1992; *cr:* WXTV Cntry 92 FM Pub Affairs Dir & Promotions Asst 1988-90; Thomaston HS Eng Tchr 1992-; *ai:* Grizzly Newspaper Adv 1994-; Prin Cncl Mem; Environmental Club Co-Adv 1992-94; Lit Magazine Adv 1994-; Stu Cncl Adv 1995-; CEA & NEA 1992-; NCTE 1994-; *office:* Thomaston HS Branch Rd Thomaston CT 06787

SAARI, KAREN CECILIA, Social Studies Teacher; *b:* Minneapolis, MN; *m:* William J.; *c:* Amanda, Adam, Aimee; *ed:* George Williams Coll at Downers Grove (BA) Soc Stud 1981; Univ of WI at Superior (BS) Scndry Ed 1989; Working Towards MED in Scndry Schl Cnslng West Chester Univ; *cr:* Ashland HS Soc Stud, Alternative Ed Tchr 3 1/2 Yrs; Pennridge HS Soc Stud Tchr 2 Yrs; *ai:* WI Tchrs Assn 1990-; NEA 1994-; *home:* 515 Lombard St Perkasie PA 18944

SABA, SIMON, Tech Resource Tchng Specialist; *b:* Wilkes-Barre, PA; *m:* Merry Hotalen; *c:* Matthew; *ed:* Lehigh Univ (BA) Psych 1964, (MED) Elem Ed 1976; EDD Candidate Educl Tech; *cr:* Hampton Twp Schl Dist Tchr 1975-; *ai:* NEA, NJEA, HTEA 1975-, Pres 1981-83; Hampton Twp Tchr of Yr 1994-95; Nom for NSF Math Tchr of Yr 1993, Sci Tchr of Yr 1992; *office:* M. E. Mc Keown Elem Schl 1 School Rd Newton NJ 07860

SABA, VIVIANNE A., Span Tchr & Frgn Lang Chair; *b:* Havana, Cuba; *m:* Michael; *c:* Elias, Suzanne; *ed:* SUNY at Cortland (BA) Scndry Ed 1977; Syracuse Univ 36 Grad Credit Hrs Toward MA in Span; Univerite de Neuchatel Cert d'Excl Fr 1976; *cr:* West Genesee Sr High Span Tchr 1978-79; Syracuse Univ Grad Tchng Asst 1980-81; Bristol Myers Prsnl Dept Sec 1981-89; Chrstn Bros Acad Frgn Lang Chair, Span Tchr 1990-; *ai:* Curr, Crisis Intervention Comms; Dance Club Adv; *office:* Christian Brothers Acad 6245 Randall Rd Syracuse NY 13214

SABABU, UMEME, History Professor; *b:* Greenville, MS; *m:* Renee Coates-Smith; *c:* Celeta, Aleta, Atiba, Angel; *ed:* Northern IL Univ (BS) Bus Mgmt 1982; Cornell Univ (MS) Africana Stud 1984; Attnd Syracuse Univ; *cr:* Cornell Univ Lecturer 1984-85; Syracuse Univ Lecturer 1985; Niagara Univ Black Family Ctr Execution Dir 1987-89; St Univ of NY at Fredonia Lecturer 1989-90; Edinboro Univ of PA Asst Prof 1989-; *ai:* Univ Senate; Curr & Planning & Assessment Comms; Syracuse Univ & Cornell Univ Flwshps; *office:* Edinboro Univ Of PA Dept of His Edinboro PA 16444

SABADAY, GAIL YOST, 6th Grade Language Arts Tchr; *b:* Pottsville, PA; *m:* Joseph Andrew; *c:* Zachary A.; *ed:* PA St Univ (BS) Elem Ed 1973; Post Grad Stud in Counseling at Kutztown Univ & Rdng at Bloomsburg Univ; *cr:* Minersville Area Schl Dist 1st Grd Tchr 1974-75, Lang Arts Tchr 1976-; *ai:* In Charge of Modern Woodmen Oratory & Creative Writing Contests; PSEA 1974-; Phoenix Park Union Church 1952-, Treas; *office:* Minersville Area Schl Dist PO Box 787 Minersville PA 17954

SABADAY, JOSEPH ANDREW, Math, Science & Reading Tchr; *b:* Pottsville, PA; *m:* Gail A. Yost; *c:* Zachary A.; *ed:* Kutztown St Univ (BS) Elem Ed 1977; Bloomsburg St Univ Rdng Specialist 1981; Post Grad Stud Penn St Univ; *cr:* Minersville Area Schl Dist 4th Grd Long Term Sub Tchr 1978-79; Saint Clair Area Schl Dist Rdng Specialist 1979-81; Good Shepherd Regnl Schl 5-8 Grd Math, Sci, Rdng Tchr 1984-; *ai:* Charge of Mathlete; Spelling Bee Coach; Mid Sts Evaluation Chaired Comm; Lay Tchr Assn Bldg Rep; ADLTA 1985-; Former Lions Club, Rescue Hook & Ladder; *home:* 106 Broad St Saint Clair PA 17970

SABAKA, JUDITH LOEHR, Second Grade Teacher; *b:* Reading, PA; *m:* Norman G.; *ed:* Kutztown Univ (BA) Elem Ed 1972; M Equiv Penn St, Elizabethtown, Millersville; *cr:* Paradise Elem First Grd Tchr 1972-93; Heidelburg Elem Second Grd Tchr 1993-; *ai:* Assateague St Park Camp Hostess 1989-91; NEA, PSEA 1972-; SGEA 1972-, Bldg Rep; Order of Eastern Star 1974-; Delta Kappa Gamma 1983-; *office:* Heidelberg Elementary School Rd 3 Box 3438 Spring Grove PA 17362

SABARI, JOYCE SHAPERO, Occupational Therapy Professor; *b:* New York, NY; *m:* Naftali; *c:* Michelle, Joshua, Benjamin; *ed:* Univ of PA (BS) Occupational Therapy 1973; NY Univ (MA) Physiological Psych 1978; NY Univ (PHD) Occupational Therapy 1992; *cr:* Goldwater Meml Hospital Clinical Supvr, Sr Occupational Therapist 1973-81; NY Univ Adjunct Asst Prof 1981-85; SUNY at Brooklyn Assoc Prof 1985-; NY Univ Adjunct Asst Prof 1992-; *ai:* Fac Adv Alpha Kappa Chapter, Pi Theta Epsilon Natl Occupational Therapy Honor Soc; Coll of Hlth Related Professions; Strategic Planning Comm; Tching Mentor; AM Occup Ther Assn 1974-, Stroke Resource Person; Am Ot Pol Action Com 1988-, Region I Rep to Bd of Dirs 1993-95; Multiple Articles Pub Amer Journal Occupational Therapy Chapter in Occupational Therapy Phys Dysfunction 4th Ed; *office:* Health Science Ctr at Brooklyn 450 Clarkson Ave PO Box 81 Brooklyn NY 11203

SABATINI, PATRICIA MALEC, Fifth Grade Teacher; *b:* Bridgeport, CT; *m:* Daniel J.; *c:* Jeffrey; *ed:* Eastern CT St Univ (BS) Elem Ed 1970; 30 Credit Hrs Southern CT St Univ; *cr:* Elizabeth Shelton Schl Fifth Grd Tchr 1970-75; Bungay Elem Schl Fifth Grd Tchr 1985-; *ai:* Mem of Bungay Schl PTA 1985-, Treas 1990-91; Sec of Parent Advsy Cncl Bungay Schl 1994-; NEA 1985-; Skokorat Civic Assn 1989-, Bd of Dirs; Math Wkshps for Tchrs; Math Curr Comm Mem; Erly Intrvntn Team Mem 1994-; *office:* Bungay Elem Schl 35 Bungay Rd Seymour CT 06483

SABATINI, SMERALDO JOSEPH,JR., Lang Arts & Soc Stud Tchr; *b:* Bryn Mawr, PA; *ed:* Villanova Univ (BA) His 1970, (MA) Ed Admin 1973; Elem, Sec Tchng Cert at Immaculata Coll 1970-73; *cr:* Our Lady of Perpetual Help 6th-7th Grd Tchr 1970-73; Haverford Jr HS 7th-9th Grd Tchr 1973-76; Brookline Elem Schl 6th Grd Tchr 1976-85; Haverford MS 6th Grd Tchr 1985-; *ai:* IM Sports Elem Schl; Bsktbl MS Girls; Track MS Boys; NEA 1973-; *office:* Haverford MS 1701 Darby Rd Havertown PA 19083

SABATINO, DEBRA O'BRIEN, Chemistry & Physics Teacher; *b:* Lompoc, CA; *m:* Paul A.; *c:* Paul, Steven; *ed:* Penn St Univ (BS) Ed & Chem 1983; West Chester Univ (MA) Physical Sci 1987; Indiana Univ of PA Cert Physics 1991; Cmptr Courses; *cr:* West Chester Area SD Sci Tchr 1983-; Johns Hopkins CTY Chem Instr Summers 1992, 1994-95; *ai:* Girls Spring Track; Viking Pride Comm & Fac Cncl; NEA, PSEA, WCAEA 1983-, Fac Rep; NSTA 1983-; *office:* West Chester East HS 450 Ellis Ln Westchester PA 19380*

SABATINO, JOYCE ANN, Kindergarten Teacher; *b:* Pen Argyl, PA; *ed:* Penn St Univ (BA) Soc Welfare 1966; Beaver Univ (MS) Early Chldhd 1985; Temple Univ Courses Cert 1967-70; Univ of Arts 60 Addl Hrs Master Tchr 1991; *cr:* Gideon Elem Schl Kndgtn Tchr 1967, Head Start Tchr 1970-76; E. A. Poe Elem Schl Tchr; Stephen Girard Elem Schl Kndgtn Tchr; *ai:* PFT 1967-; NAEYC 1995-; Tchr Flwshp 1969; Cooperating Tchr of Yr Awd Temple Univ 1991; Women in Ed Honoree 1996; *office:* Stephen Girard Elem Schl 18th & Passyunk Ave Philadelphia PA 19145

SABBETH, MARGERY J., Fourth Grade Teacher; *b:* Brooklyn, NY; *ed:* Southampton Coll (BA) Psych 1967; C. W. Post Coll (MS) Ed 1970, (PD) Educl Admin 1981; Addl 15 Credit Hrs Above PD; *cr:* William Floyd Schl Dist 1, 3-5 Tchr 1967-; *ai:* Peer Mediation, Dicipline Comms; Project Reach Out; NEA, UFT 1967-72; AFT 1972-80; NYSUT 1980-96 Blding VP; *office:* Moriches Elem Schl Montauk Hwy Moriches NY 11955

SABELLA, ROBERT MICHAEL, Mathematics Lead Teacher; *b:* Hoboken, NJ; *m:* Jean Phillips; *c:* Andrew, Mark; *ed:* Seton Hall Univ (BS) Math 1970, (MS) Math 1973; NJ St Supvr of Math Cert; *cr:* Paul VI Regnl HS Math Tchr 1973-79; Parsippany Hills HS Math Tchr 1979-85; Parsippany HS Math Dept Head 1985-; *ai:* Math Team Adv; NJ Math League Champs 1994-95; NCTM 1983-; AMTNJ 1983-, Editorial Bd; NEA, NJEA 1979-; PHTEA 1979-, Treas; AP Bd Awd; Mid Atlantic Sts Tchr of Yr 1996; *office:* Parsippany HS 309 Baldwin Rd Parsippany NJ 07054

SABIA, MICHAEL G., Mathematics Teacher; *b:* Philadelphia, PA; *m:* Sally Ann Mills; *c:* Michael Warren; *ed:* West Chester Univ (BA) Math 1968; Philadelphia Textiles, Scis (MS) Cmptr 1992; Numerous Credits at Penn St, West Chester Univ; *cr:* William Tennet HS Math Tchr 1966-69; Cntrl Chester Cty Vo Tech Math, Cmptr Sci Tchr 1969-72; Michael G. Sabia Jr. Inc Builder, Dev 1974-84; Wissahickon Schl Dist Math Tchr 1984-; *ai:* NEA, WEA 1984-; Won 4 Cmptr Prgm Contests 1972; Undefeated Bsktbl Teams 1985, 1992; *home:* 128 Holly Dr Lansdale PA 19446*

SABINA, FRANK J., French, Eng Tchr & Dept Chair; *b:* Scranton, PA; *m:* Veronica A. Griebel; *c:* Jeffrey, Lauren, Gregory; *ed:* E Stroudsburg Univ (BS) Scndry Ed & Fr 1973; Marywood Eng 1975; Masters Equivalancy Eng & Fr 48 Grad Credit Hrs; *cr:* Carbondale Area HS Eng & Fr Tchr 1973-; *ai:* Fr Club; Schl Newspaper & Lit Magazine; NEA, PSEA, CATA & NCTe 1973-; NE Writing Project 1988-; NE Writing Cncl 1980-, Sec 2 Yrs; AATF; PSMLA; Fellowship NE Writing Project; St Writing Assessment Comm; Writing Cncl Newsletter Ed; Whos Who Entry 1991; Whos Who Among Writers, Eds & Poets 1991; Short Story Articl *office:* Carbondale Area HS Rt 6 Carbondale PA 18407

SABLESKI, THOMAS LEE, Pub Speaking, Comm & Eng T Dayton, OH; *m:* Patricia Lee Gibbs; *c:* Amy, Matthew; *ed:* Wright S (BS) Scndry Ed 1968; Educl Admin Courses Univ of Dayton; Le Styles Course Antioch Univ; *cr:* Carroll HS Pub Speaking, Comm Tchr 1973-; Sinclair Coll Pub Speaking & Comm Tchr 1976-; *ai:* Adv; Dir of Sports Prgm; Pub Address Announcer at Home Sp Events; Rules Comm; Tchng Inmates at Dayton Correction Inst Archdiocese of Cincinnati Pension Plan Steering Comm; Optimus Awd of Gratitude; Prin Selection Comm; Mem Steering Comm to R Million For Church; *office:* Carroll HS 4524 Linden Ave Dayt 45432*

SABO, DANEEN COMUNALE, English & Reading Teach Wilkensburg, PA; *m:* Joseph W.; *c:* Joe, Nick; *ed:* Univ of Pittsburg Elem Ed 1976; OH St Univ Spec Ed Cert; *cr:* Buckeye Vly Schl L. D 1978-79; Big Walnut MS L. D. Tchr 1979-87, Eng, Rdng Tchr 198 Newspaper Adv 10 Yrs; Drug, Alcohol Abuse Intervention Tear Walnut Ed Assn 1978-, Pres 2 Yrs, VP 4 Yrs; IRA 1986-; OEA, NEA IRA 1990-; Martha Jennings Scholar 1993-94; Renaissance Magazin Jennings Fnd Scholar 1992-93; *home:* 7119 N State Route 61 Sunbu 43074

SABO, JUDITH M., Biology Teacher; *b:* Allentown, PA; *m:* Michael; *c:* Jenine, Mary Kathryn; *ed:* Kent St Univ (BS) Eng 197 Honors; Univ of Akron 20 Semester Credit Hrs Post Grad Sci; *cr:* R HS Eng, Bio Tchr 1972-77, Bio Tchr 1988-; *ai:* Stu Cncl Adv; Recycling, Environmental Awareness; OH Educ Assn, Rittman Edu 1988-; NEA; Three Arts Club, Pres 1984-85; Northeast OH Ensemble 1987-, Bd of Trustees; *office:* Rittman HS 100 Saurer St R OH 44270

SABO, MARY RAK, French Teacher; *b:* McKees Rocks, PA; *m:* Ga IN Univ of PA (BS) Fr Ed 1982; Rowan Coll of NJ (MA) Stu Prsr 1995; Univ of Rome France 1980; *cr:* Gateway Sr HS Fr Tchr 1982- Lebanon Sr HS Fr Tchr 1983-84; Woodbury Jr-Sr HS Fr Tchr 198 Class of 1999 Adv; NEA 1985-; FLENJ 1985-; *office:* Woodbury Jr 25 N Broad St Woodbury NJ 08096

SABOL, JACK JOSPEH, Algebra Teacher; *b:* Norristown, P Patricia Bondi; *c:* Kelly Anne, Jaclyn; *ed:* E Stroudsburg Univ (BS & Scndry Ed 1974; Wilkes Masters Equivalent in Ed 1992; *cr:* St P Elem Math & Sci Tchr Grds 6th-8th 1974-79; Plymouth Whitemar Math Tchr Grds 10th -12th 1979-80; Quakertown HS Math Tch 10th-12th 1980-; *ai:* Head Girls Cross Cntry Coach; Head Girls Track Coach; Asst Girls Outdoor Coach; NEA 1979-; QCEA 1980-; 1979-; *office:* Quakertown Community Sr HS 600 Park Ave Quak PA 18951

SABOL, JOHN ROBERT, Social Studies Tchr & Ath Dir; *b:* Clev OH; *m:* Denise Marie; *c:* Todd, Scott; *ed:* Walsh Univ (BA) His 19 Addl Hrs Scndry Admin & Prins Cert; *cr:* St Vincent-St Mary's H Stud Tchr 1989-, Ath Dir 1994-; *ai:* Head Var Soccer Coach; Mer Security Comms; Natl Soccer Coaches Assn of Amer, Greater Scholastic Socder Coaches Assn 1991-; Natl Fed Interscholastic C Assn, Natl Fed Interscholastic Ofcl Assn 1994-; Soccer Coaches Sportsmanship Awd 1995; *office:* Saint Vincent-Saint Mary Schl Maple St Akron OH 44303

SABOL, JUDITH MALENOWSKI, Fourth Grade Teacher; *b:* N NJ; *m:* Thomas P.; *c:* Joshua, Matthew; *ed:* Rider Univ (BA) Psych Marywood Coll (MS) Ed 1977; 60 Hrs Post-Grad Stud; *cr:* Hopatco Ed Tchr 1970-; *ai:* Hopatcong Ed Assn, NJEA, NEA 1970-; NJ Gove Hopatcong Mini Grants; 8 Eng Workbooks Pub; *office:* Durban A Elem Schl Box 1029 Durban Ave Hopatcong NJ 07843

SABOL, MICHAEL C., 9th Grd Earth & Space Sci Tchr; *b:* John PA; *m:* Melissa S. Batey; *ed:* California Univ of PA (BA) Scndry Ed *cr:* Richland Sr HS Sci Tchr 1991-; *ai:* Richland HS Ftbl Head C Track Asst Coach; NEA 1991-; PSFCA; REA; *office:* Richland Sch 340 Theatre Dr Johnstown PA 15904

SABOL, SUSAN, Biology Teacher; *b:* Brooklyn, NY; *ed:* Brentwo (BS) Ed 1968; Manhattan Coll (MS) Admin, Supervision 1980; 18 Credits; Sci NSF Grants IA St Univ, Southern OR Coll; *cr:* St Micha 1st Grd Tchr, 7th-8th Grd Sci Tchr 1968-70; St Camillus Schl 7th-8 Sci Tchr 1970-76; St Elizabeth Seton Elem Asst Prin 1976-84; St Queens Hospital Admin Coord Surgery 1984-91; St Joseph HS Bi 1992-; *ai:* Moderator of Stu Cncl; Schl Store Mgr; NY St Bio Tchrs 1993-; Cath Sci Cncl 1992-; Emergency Medical Technician for Pen Vol Ambulance Corp 1974-84, Crew Chief, Life Membership Gold Schl Consolidation in Bushwick Section Brooklyn; One of First M Peninsula Vol Ambulance Corp; Founder Ambulatory Surgery Uni Johns Queens Hospital 1984; NSF Grants in Sci NM, OR Coast; P Green Reach Brooklyn Botanical Garden Grant for HS Bio Stdnts; N Prin for Teach of Yr Sci Awd.

SABOURIN, EDGAR G., Accounting & Bus Mgmt Tchr; *b:* Sali VT; *m:* Carole C. Cauchon-Sabourin; *c:* Lisa, Bonnie, Craig, Kellie; Michael's Coll (BA) Bus Adm 1961; (MSA) Pending Thesis Comp Grad Stud Univ of VT; *cr:* Winooski Schl Dist Bus Tchr, Dept 1961-66; Burlington Schl Dist Bus Tchr 1966-; Burlington Te Acctng, Data Processing Tchr 1966-; *ai:* Acctng, Bus Mngmt Advsy Chprsn; Asst Ftbl Coach 1962-65; VEA, NEA, BEA 1961-, Cncl Rep; Prof Negiation 2 Yrs; Licensed Real Estate Broker 1978-; Tchrs C Realty Co 1978-, Owner, Mgr; *home:* 76 Audet St Winooski VT 054

SABOUSKY, RICHARD ANTHONY, Spcl Ed & Rehabilitation P Oil City, PA; *ed:* Clarion Univ (BS) Spec Ed 1984, (MS) Spec Ed Kent St Univ (ABD); *cr:* Keystone Elem Schl Spec Ed Tchr 19 1988-91; Riverview I U #6 Spec Ed Tchr 1985-88; Clarion Univ Sp Rehab Prof 1991-; *ai:* Fac Forum Chair; CEC 1993-; PDK 1991-; Grant; Co-Author 2 Articles; *office:* Clarion Univ Of PA Clarion PA

SABOW, RICHARD MICHAEL, Retired Fifth Grade Teach Creighton, PA; *m:* Roberta J.; *c:* Diane Szydlik, Debra E.; *ed:* Cali Univ of PA (BS) Elem Ed 1965; Penn St Univ Elem Cert 24 Credi Comm Coll of Alleg Co 6 Credit Hrs; Western MI Univ 3 Credit Hrs; Quest Int Cert; *cr:* Fairmount Elem 5th Grd Tchr 1965-95; *ai:* NEA, F HEA 1965-.

SABULIS, ANN HAWKESWORTH, English Teacher; *b:* Worcester, *m:* Ronald E.; *c:* Michael W.; *ed:* Fitchburg St Coll (BS) Eng & Ed Clark Univ (MALA) Lbrl Arts 1994; Univ Coll Galway Ireland 6 Gr *cr:* Providence St Jr High Eng Tchr 1968-69; Dennis-Yarmouth Reg Asst Librn 1970-79; Burncoat MS Eng Tchr 1984-; *ai:* Schl Governa Prins Advy Cncl; BMS Staff Assn VP; NEA 1984-; MTA 1984-; 1984-; Burncoat MS Tchr of the Yr 1991-92; *office:* Burncoat Stre 135 Burncoat St Worcester MA 01606

SABULIS, JOHN PAUL, History & Technology Ed Tchr; *b:* Derb *ed:* Sacred Heart Univ (BA) His 1972; Southern CT St Univ (M 1978, (MS) Elem Ed 1983; Cntrl CT St Univ (MS) Indstrl Arts Co-Operating Mentor Tchr; Tech Ed Enhancement Ctr; Auto-Desk The Tchr Prgm; Fire Instr I; *cr:* Ansonia HS His, Tech, Ed Tchr 197 Cultural Affairs Club Asst, Tech Stu Assn, Yrbk, Schl Newspaper Adv 1974-, Steward, VP, Pres 1989-; CTEA 1983-, Drafting Curr Chair,

; Ansonia Vol Fire Dept Instr; Knights of Lithuanian 1972-; St ny's Mens Club 1990-; Natl Scholastic Press Assn 1984-, Judge; Dev, Affirmitive Action, Best Selection, Staff Evaluation, HS ation Steering Comms; *office:* Ansonia HS 115 Howard Ave Ansonia 401

O, RICHARD N., Sixth Grade Teacher; *b:* Rockville Center, NY; U at Southampton (BS) Psych 1967, (MS) Ed 1969; LIU at CW Post ry Admin) Admin 1974; 75 Academic Hrs Beyond Masters; *cr:* n Cntrl Schl Dist 4th-6th Grd Tchr 1967-; *ai:* Grad Adv & Coord; Trip & Fund Raising Coord; Early Sports Pgm Instr; AFT 1964-; T 1964-; Sachem Cntrl Tchrs Assn 1964-, VP; NEA 1964-; *office:* m Cntrl Schl Dist 1 David Mello Dr Holtsville NY 11742*

O, ROBERT ANTHONY, Elementary Art Specialist; *b:* Boston, *m:* Constance DiGiulio; *c:* Gene, Frank, Carl, Stacy Dillon, Ann o, Robert M.; *ed:* Boston St Coll (BSEd) K-8th Elem Ed 1958; Salem l (MED) K-8th Elem Ed 1968; 15 Addl Hrs His, Art; *cr:* San Diego Schl 6th Grd Tchr 1958-59; Meriden Elem Schl 4th, 6th Grd Tchr 64; Saugus Elem Schl 5th-6th Grd Tchr 1964-88, Art Specialist 90, 1993-, Chapter I Tchr 1990-93; *ai:* Natl NEA, MA MTA 1964-; Saugus 1964-, Fac Rep 1976; Amer Legion 1992-, Adjutant 1993-; as Advertiser Newspaper 1977-; Cartooning; Written Articles; ated Curr Guides.

RDOTE, MARC, Teacher & Animation Prgm Dir; *b:* Mt Vernon, : Kim Lewis; *c:* Angelo, Marysa, Marguerite, Nicholas; *ed:* NY Univ Comm, Ed 1971; Post Grad Stud at NY Univ Media, New Schl for srch Writing Process; *cr:* IS 71 Brooklyn Schl Math Tchr 1972-82; er 167 Schl Math Tchr, Animation 1982-; *ai:* Animation Club After Animation Production Tchr-in-Charge; AFT 1967-; UFT 1967-,Chptr mpact II 1980-; Amnesty Intnl 1986-; Common Cause 1985-; ACLU ; Grants: WNET 13 for Animation 1994-95, Impact II 1983-84, 88; Challenger & Flwshp 1991-92; Citibank Success Fund Awd 1992; rous Articles Pub; *office:* Wagner MS 167 220 E 76th St New York 0021*

RDOTE, THOMAS JOSEPH, Social Ethics Teacher; *b:* Hartford, : Mary Lynn Hayes; *c:* Timothy, Thomas; *ed:* Saint Anselm Coll (BA) 976; Boston Coll (MA) Pastoral Ministry 1982; Fairfield Univ (CAS) n & Supervision 1990; *cr:* Trinity HS Tchr & Dept Chprsn 1976-80; t Saint Joseph Acad Tchr, Dir & Campus Ministry 1981-86; Fairfield Tchr, Dir of Comm Svc 1986-; *ai:* Amnesty Intl Adv; Fac Comm on sity Mem; NCEA 1990-; Eastern Region Comm Svc Dirs, Chprsn; Scndry Ed Assn; Saint James Church, Parish Cncl Mem 1990-; : Fairfield Coll Preparatory Sch 1073 N Benson Rd Fairfield CT)*

HDEVA, SARITA, Math Teacher; *b:* Lydhiana, Punjab; *m:* Ravinder; dha, Mala, Gopal; *ed:* Miranda House Delhi Univ (BA) Math 1965; phi Univ (MS) Spcl Ed 1989; St Johns Univ (PD) Admin & rvision 1991; 60 Credits Above MS; Doctral Pgm Candidate; *cr:* ns Voc & Tech HS Math Tchr 1985-92; Richmond Mill HS Math Tchr -; *ai:* Intnl Club, Math Rsrch Team & Math Hnr Soc Coord; ASCD -; Phi Delta Kappa 1991-; Peace Unity & Prosperty 1990-, Pres; India of Long Island 1990-; *office:* Richmond Hill HS 89-30 114th St mond Hill NY 11418*

HS, BURTON IRA, Band Director & Music Teacher; *b:* Brooklyn, *n:* Gail Husid; *c:* Robin; *ed:* Hofstra Coll (BS) Music Ed 1961; Boston 30 Grad Credits; Manhattan Schl of Music 30 Credits, Berkshire c Ctr 1955-59, Stu Orch; *cr:* Cliffside Park HS Instrumental Music 1965-66; Mineola HS Instrumental Music Tchr 1966-78; Ryan Jr HS umental Music Tchr 1985-87; Benjamin N. Cardozo HS Instrumental c Tchr 1987-; *ai:* Jewish Stu Union, Club Adv; Stud Promoting AIDS enes, Club Adv; UFT 1985-; NY St Schl Music Assn 1987-; Music ators NY City 1989-; NY Road Runners CLub 1985-; Big Apple atholon Club 1987-; Queens Symphonic Band, 1st Trumpet; Queens Brass Ensemble; *office:* Benjamin N Cardozo HS 57-00 223rd St ide NY 11364

HS, HAROLD, Assistant Principal; *b:* New York City, NY; *m:* Kyle noyer; *c:* Colin, Christopher; *ed:* Marietta Coll (BA) His & Ed 1976; r Coll (MS) Secondary Admin 1991; *cr:* Salem HS Hum Tchr -94; Woodburg MS 1994-; *ai:* Pitching Coach U Mass Lowell Womans ; NAT 1995-; *office:* Salem School District 206 Main St Salem NH 9

HS, MICHELLE MYKULYN, Mathematics Teacher; *b:* es-Bare, PA; *m:* Louis Brian; *c:* Rebecca; *ed:* Bloomsburg St Univ Elem Ed 1977; Western MD Coll (MS) Curr & Dev 1990; *cr:* St 's Cty Pub Schls Elem Tchr 1979-; *ai:* Dept Chprsn; SIT Team; NEA -; EASMC 1979-, Schl Rep.

HS, NED, Assistant Principal; *b:* Brooklyn, NY; *m:* Judith Adler; *c:* ard, Randi; *ed:* PACE (BBA) Finance 1966; CW Post (MS) Supervision ; *cr:* Franklin Deland Roosevelt HS Tchr 2 Yrs; Benjamin Cardozo HS 11 Yrs; Forest Hills HS Asst Prin, Bus Tchr 16 Yrs; *ai:* FBLA Adv; Ed Assn 1969-; *office:* Forest Hills HS 6701 110th St Flushing NY 5*

HSEL, GERARD RICHARD, History Teacher; *b:* Garwood, NJ; *m:* n Forcino; *c:* Richard, Gregory, Jonathan; *ed:* Univ of Notre Dame His 1960; Seton Hall Univ (MA) Constitutional His 1969; Attnd nell Univ; *cr:* Jonathan Dayton Regnl HS His Tchr 1960-65; Millburn S His Tchr 1965-94; Millburn HS His Tchr 1994-; *ai:* Boys & Girls s-Cntry, Wrestling & Girls Track Coach; NEA 1960-; NJEA 1960-; burn Ed Assn 1965-, Negotiations Chm; Bd of Ed 1966-70; Comcast Announcer for Wrestling 1979-; New Providence Recreation mission 1980-; Jaycee Man of Yr 1965; NJ Wrestling Coach of Yr ; Harry E Lake Awd 1988; NJSIAA Contributions to Wrestling 1988; CA Hall of Fame 1995; *home:* 37 Woodbine Cir New Providence NJ 74

HSON, THERESA, Religion Teacher; *b:* Sioux City, IA; *m:* Steven; raig, Kevin, Julie, Christopher; *ed:* Briar Cliff Coll (BA) Theology ; 6 Credit Hrs Theology St Charles Seminary; *cr:* Heelan HS Tchr 5-76; Camden Cath HS Tchr 1978-; *ai:* Liturgy, Mid St Steering ms; SCTO 1986-.

K, PATRICIA FRANCES, 7th-8th Grade English Teacher; *b:* adelphia, PA; *ed:* Temple Univ (BA) Jrnlsm 1986; Addl 15 Credits er Coll Eng, Ed; *cr:* St Luke the Evangelist Schl 7th-8th Grd Tchr 7-89; Ancillae Assumpta Acad 7th-8th Grd Tchr 1989-; *ai:* Forensics n Coord, Coach; Mt St Joseph Acad HS Forensic Team lerator-Coach; Project Outreach to Homeless Coord; Jr High Lang Arts rd; NCEA 1988-; ASCD; NCTE; *office:* Ancillae-Assumpta Acad 2025 rch Rd Wyncote PA 19095

KETT, JEFFREY ALLYN, Social Studies & English Tchr; *b:* oklyn, NY; *m:* Paulette Sheldon; *c:* Victoria, Elizabeth; *ed:* SUNY at z (BA) His, Eng-Cum Laude 1971; Queens Coll (MA) European His 4; NY Univ (MA) East Asian His 1976; Queens Coll Prof Diploma Ed nin 1983; History, Lit, Lang Courses Brooklyn Coll, New Schl for Soc h; *cr:* Martin Luther HS His, Eng, Rel Tchr 1973-75; Kings Park HS , Soc Stud Tchr 1975-; Suffolk Comm Coll Hum Tchr 1993-; *ai:* Pub Dir 1973-74; Jrnlsm Adv 1980-88; Kings Park Classroom Tchrs Assn 5-; Horror Writers of Amer 1988-, Nom for Stoker Awd 1990; NY St Cncl Hum 1992-, Local Seminar Coord; Natl Endowment Hum Flwshp 1992; Multicultural Intnl Schlsp Spon by NY St Ed Dept, Govt of Germany; Pub 5 Novels; *office:* Kings Park HS 200 Route 25a Kings Park NY 11754

SACKS, DEBORAH J., English Teacher; *b:* Toledo, OH; *m:* Bruce M.; *c:* Joelle; *ed:* Univ of Toledo (BED) Eng 1974, (ME) Scndry Ed 1982; *cr:* Toledo Pub Schls Eng Tchr 1975-; *ai:* Northwest OH Regnl Prof Dev Ctr 1991-, Exec Bd; Toledo Fed of Tchrs, Staff Rep, Sergeant-at-Arms; AFT; Phi Delta Kappa; Univ of Toledo Alumni Assn; Toledo Museum of Art; Toledo Area AFL-CIO Cncl Del; Martha Holden Jennings Scholar 1988-89; Amer Assn of Colls for Ed Tchrs Presenter 1986; *office:* Toledo Pub Schls 420 E Manhattan Toledo OH 43608

SACKS, PATRICIA ANN, Sixth Grd Tchr & Math Coord; *b:* Camden, NJ; *m:* Thomas J.; *c:* Kristin K., Amy N.; *ed:* Rutgers Univ (BA) Psych 1981; Georgian Court Coll Pursuing Masters in Educl Admin; *cr:* Sacred Heart Schl Sixth Grd Tchr 1988-; *ai:* NCEA 1988-; NCTM 1994-; ASCD 1995-; Sacred Heart PTA 1985-, Pres; *office:* Sacred Heart Schl 250 High St Mount Holly NJ 08060

SACKS, PAUL N., Theatre Magnet Dir & Eng Tchr; *b:* Baltimore, MD; *m:* Dawn; *c:* Andrew, Jennifer; *ed:* Loyola Coll (BA) Music Ed 1976; (BA) Elem Ed 1979; 30 Addl Hrs; *cr:* Sandalwood Elem Schl 5th-6th Grd Tchr 1979-81; Deep Creek MS 6th-8th Grd Eng Tchr 1981-91; Perry Hall MS 6th Grd Eng Tchr 1991-95; Loch Raven Acad Theatre Dir 1995-; *ai:* Wishing Star Theatre Productions Dir; NEA, MSTA 1979-; *office:* Loch Raven Acad 8101 LaSalle Rd Baltimore MD 21286

SADAR, TIMOTHY G., Mathematics Teacher; *b:* Cleveland, OH; *m:* Maria Szucs; *c:* Timothy John, Ashley; *ed:* Oberlin Coll (AB) Govt 1966; Temple Univ (MED) Ed 1969; *cr:* Cherry Hill West HS Math Tchr 1966-; *ai:* NEA, NJEA 1966-; AMTNJ, NCTM 1990-; Florence Twp Planning Bd 1986-, Vice Chm; Holy Assumption Parish Cncl 1994-, Pres; *office:* Cherry Hill West HS Chapel Ave Cherry Hill NJ 08002

SADD, THOMAS E., History Teacher; *b:* Pittsburgh, PA; *m:* Dean Acheson Smith; *c:* David A., Elizabeth B., Jonathan F.; *ed:* Geneva Coll (BA) His, Pol Sci 1967; *cr:* Peace Corps Afghanistan Tchng Eng Med Schl 1967-70; Intnl Schl of Rotterdam MS Math, Sci, His Tchr 1970-73; Sewickley Acad 5th Grd Tchr 1973-; *ai:* 8th Grd Corps Team Ldr; Orienteering Club Adv; WA DC Trip Dir; Sierra Club 1973-; Assn Protection of Civil War Battlefields 1993-; Western PA Conservancy 1973-; BSA 1975-, Asst Scoutmaster; Nichols-Benedum Fnd Grant Leningrad Arts Exchange 1990; *office:* Sewickley Acad 315 Academy Ave Sewickley PA 15143

SADDIK, ORLY EVON, English Teacher; *b:* Tel Aviv, Israel; *ed:* Montclair St Coll (BA) Eng 1980; Columbia Univ (MA) Eng Lit 1981, (MPhil) Phd Eng 1983; *cr:* Hudson Cty Comm Coll Bus Eng, Comm Instr 1984-85; Montclair St Coll Eng Instr 1984,-85, 1990; Fairleigh Dickinson Univ ESL Instr 1985; Lewis F. Cole MS Eng Tchr 1985-86; Christopher Columbus MS Eng Tchr 1986-92; Clifton HS Eng Tchr 1992-; *ai:* Mid St, Curr, Eng Dept Hospitality, Study Skills Comms; NEA, NJEA 1985-; NCTE 1979-; Phi Kappa Phi 1980-; Poetry Pub Literary Magazines Quarterly, Reflections, Snowy Egret, The Villager, The Eng Journal; *office:* Clifton H S 333 Colfax Ave Clifton NJ 07013

SADDLEMIRE, DAVID CHARLES, Social Studies Teacher; *b:* Cobleskill, NY; *m:* Diane E. Robbins; *c:* Geoffrey, Carin, Ann-Marie, Aileen; *ed:* Syracuse Univ (BS) Bus Admin 1963; SUNY (MS) Ed 1965; Addl Grad Credits in His, Pol Sci & Soc Sci; *cr:* Chester Jr-Sr HS Soc Stud Tchr 1965-; *ai:* AFT; NY St United Tchrs; NCSS; *office:* Chester Jr Sr HS 3 Maple Ave Chester NY 10918

SADDORIS, DANA J. KYLER, 5th Grade Teacher; *b:* Toledo, OH; *m:* Jon C.; *c:* Megan; *ed:* Univ of Toledo (BE) Elem Ed 1987; *cr:* Glendale Feilbach Elem Schl 1st Grd Tchr 1987-88; Riverside Elem Schl 4th Grd Tchr 1988-89, 1990-95; Sprin Elem Schl 4th Grd Tchr 1989-90; Old Orchard Elem Schl 5th Grd Tchr 1995-; *ai:* Natl Rdng Assn 1992-; Cats Cable Grants 1994-; *office:* Old Orchard Elem Schl 2402 Cheltenham Toledo OH 43606

SADETSKY, LAURIE BEHRMAN, Sixth Grade Special Ed Teacher; *b:* Brooklyn, NY; *m:* Steve; *c:* Karen M., David M.; *ed:* St Univ Coll at Oswega (BS) Elem Ed 1978; Long Island Univ at C. W. Post (MS) Spec Ed 1980; 17.3 Inservice Credits; *cr:* Plainview-Old Bethpage Schl Sub Tchr 1979-80; Cntrl Squar Cntrl Schl Resource Tchr 1980-86; Burns Ave Elem Schl Primary, Intermediate Self-Cont 1986-92; Lee Ave Elem Schl Intermediate Self-Contained Tchr 1992-95; Hicksville MS 6th Grd Self-Contained Tchr 1995-; *ai:* Spec Ed Curr Writing in Sci, Soc Stud; Taught Spec Ed Cmptr Classes Summer 1991; Sponsored VFW Essay Contest; NEA 1980-; Hicksville Congress of Tchrs 1986-; PTA, SEPTA 1986-; *office:* Hicksville MS 215 Jerusalem Ave Hicksville NY 11801

SADLON, ELTHEA WOOD, Latin Teacher; *b:* Glens Falls, NY; *m:* Jeffrey S.; *ed:* SUNY at Albany (BA) Latin, Fr 1979, (MA) Latin 1981; *cr:* Gowana Jr HS Latin, Span Tchr 1981-82; Albany HS Latin, Fr Tchr 1982-83; Saratoga Springs Sr HS Latin Tchr 1983-; *ai:* Latin Regents Examination Comm 1991-94; Natl Honor Soc Co-Adv 1993-; NYSAFLT, ACL, CAES 1978-; EZTLA 1986-; *office:* Saratoga Springs Sr H S 186 W Circular St Saratoga Spgs NY 12866

SADLON, KATHLEEN E., High School Earth Science Tchr; *b:* Little Falls, NY; *ed:* Herkimer Cty Comm Coll (AS) Math, Sci 1974; SUNY at Cortland (BSE) Earth Sci Ed 1977-; Attnd Northern IL Univ, Geneseo St Coll, Brockport St Coll; *cr:* Attica MS Math, Sci Tchr 1977-81; Attica HS Earth Sci Tchr 1981-; *ai:* Flwshp of Chrstn Aths Huddle Ldr; Class Adv; AFT, NYSUT 1977-; NY St Sci Tchrs 1990-; NY St Regents Exam in Earth Sci Item Writer 1989, 1992, 1994; *office:* Attica Sr HS 3338 E Main Street Rd Attica NY 14011

SADOWSKI, ANDREW JOHN, Social Studies Teacher; *b:* Mineola, NY; *m:* Rosemary Forrester; *c:* Emma, Abigail A.; *ed:* Marist Coll (BA) His 1986; Columbia Univ Tchrs Coll (MA) His & Ed 1993; Attnd Queens Coll, Fordham Univ, St Johns Univ, Nassau Comm Coll, Brooklyn Coll & Coll of St Rose; *cr:* NYS Historic Site Museum Asst 1986; Mudge Rose el al Litigation Legal Asst 1987-88; Patterson, Belknap et al Litigation Legal Asst 1988-89; Philippa Schulyer MS Soc Stud Tchr 1989-94; Southold HS 1994-; *ai:* AFT, NYSUT & UFT 1989-; Suffolk Cty Soccer Coaches Assn 1994-; Phi Alpha Theta 1985-; Glen Cove Soccer Club 1972-90, Player, Referee, Coach; Columbia Univ Tchr Coll Alumni Nentor Pgm; Taft Inst & The Catholic Univ of Amer Honors Seminar; Philippa Schuyler Leadership League Awd; Anti-Drug Video Project Consultant-Drug Prgm Grant; Southold Boys Var Soccer Coach 1994-; *home:* 17 Delaware Ave Commack NY 11725*

SADOWSKI, BETTY JO, Sixth Grade Teacher; *b:* Toledo, OH; *ed:* Univ of Toledo (BED) Elem Ed 1975; Grad Work Univ of Scranton, Heidelberg; *cr:* Swanton Local Schls Elem Tchr 1976-; *ai:* Outdoor Ed Dir; SCAPE Mem; Fulton Co Math Comm; Swanton Local Schl Sci Comm; Band Booster; Intervention Assistance Team; Mentor; Band & Ath Announcer; NEA, OEA 1975-; UniServe 1975-, Treas; Swanton Ed Assn 1975-, Pres, VP, Sec, Bldg Rep; NCTM 1985-; OCTM; Toledo Zoo; WGTE Channel 30 PBS; Trinity United Meth 1963-, Ad Cncl VP Worship Chair; Freedoms Fnd Am Legion Schlsp TaftInst; Jennings Scholar & Grant; NCREL, Eisenhower Grants; Classroom of Future; Outdoor Ed Presenter; *home:* 12815 Airport Hwy Swanton OH 43558

SAEX, LAWRENCE K., Algebra & Pre-Algebra Teacher; *b:* Springfield, MA; *ed:* Univ of VT (BA) Math 1973; Syracuse Univ (MA) Guid & Cnslng 1975; *cr:* Forest Park MS Math Tchr 1975-; *ai:* Comm Svc Adv for Stdnts Volunteering Riverdale Gardens Nrsng Home; Adv Math Team; Western MA Assn Umpires 1973-; Beth Israel Synagogue 1984-, Perform Svcs; WTCC Radio Disc Jockey 1984-, Oldies Show; Beacon Awd 1994-95; *home:* 94 Nassau Dr Springfield MA 01129*

SAFFORD, RICHARD WRIGHT, Retired Sixth Grade Teacher; *b:* Schnectady, NY; *m:* Marion Krapowicz; *c:* Richard Jr., Michael, Kathleen Joslin; *ed:* Hartwick Coll (BS) Bus Mngmt 1957; St Univ of NY (MS) Elem Ed 1863; Attnd SUNY At New Platz 1974, SUNY at Oneonta 1994; *cr:* Brinckerhoff Elem Schl 4th Grd Tchr 1963-65, 6th Grd Tchr 1966-91; Myers Corners Elem Schl 6th Grd Tchr 1992-95; *ai:* Dev Outdoor Ed Prgm at Sharpe Reservation Residental Prgm; Adv, Dir 6th Grd Plays; Coach; Coord Sci Curr; AFT, Wappingers Congress Tchrs 1970-; Lions Intnl 1975-; SPEBSQSA Barber Shop Singing, Golden Age Singers 1994-; BSA 1969-84, Scout Ldr; Distinguished Svc Adv For Tchng Excl 1993; *home:* Box 1292 Rt 82 Lagrangeville NY 12540

SAFRAN, HAL, Teacher; *b:* Bronx, NY; *m:* Diana; *c:* David, Jonathan, Rachel; *ed:* CCNY (BS) Math 1972, (MA) Tchng Math; NYU Post Grad; *cr:* MS180 Tchr 1972-; *ai:* Ftbl Coach Brooklyn Tech HS; CC Sports Network 1971-, VP, BD Mem; *office:* MS 180 700 Baychester Ave Bronx NY 10475*

SAFRAN, JOAN SCHULMAN, Assoc Prof Educational Psych; *b:* Jersey City, NJ; *m:* Stephen; *c:* adam, Elisa; *ed:* CT Coll (BA) Eng 1973; Rutgers Univ (MEd) Special Ed 1975; Univ of VA (PhD) Emotional Disturbance Learning Disabilities 1980; Attnd Univ of London Degree Prgm; *cr:* Highland Park HS Tchr 1975-77; OH Univ PT Asst Prof Coord Prgm 1984-93, Asst Prof 1993-95, Assoc Prof 1995-; *ai:* Varied Dept, Coll, Univ Comm Including Chair; APA (Div for Ed Psych) 1992-; CEC, CLD, CCBD 1978-; Childrens Trust Fund Bd 1993-; Athens Assoc for Gifted Children 1990-, Ed Newsletter 1991-92; CAP Prgm Vol 1990-93; 33 Articles from 1980-94; OH Univ Univ Prof Designation 1995-, for Outstanding Tchng; *office:* OH Univ Coll of Education Athens OH 45701

SAGAN, CATHERINE MEEHAN, Lang Arts Tchr & Dept Chprsn; *b:* New York, NY; *m:* John J.; *c:* John C., Paul, Michael; *ed:* Mount St Vincent (BA) Eng, Scndry Ed 1960; Fordham Univ (MA) Philosophical Psych 1967, (PHD) Philosophy, Philosophical Psych 1977, (PD) Admin, Supervision 1981; Western Comm Coll Labor, Personnel Cert Prgm 1977; Certs: Permanent 7-12 Eng, Permanent SAS, Permanent SDA; *cr:* David Farragut Jr HS Eng Tchr 1960-61; Commerce HS Eng Tchr 1961-62; NY Archdiocese Rel Ed Dir 1971-74;PACE Univ Extension Ctr Dir 1975-76; Mercy, Pace Colls A djunct Instr 1976-79; Northern Westchester, Putnam BOCES Curr Coord Asst, Gifted/Talented Specialist, Bay Area-Natl Writing Project Co-Dir 1977-80; Lakeland HS Eng Tchr 1980-81; Manhattanville Grad Schl of Ed Adjunct Instr 1980-84; North Salem HS Chprsn, Lang Arts, Eng Tchr 1981-; *ai:* K-12 Dist Leadership Team; Dist Inclusion Comm; Middle States Evaluation Team; AFT 1980-; NCTE 1993-; 9-12 MacMillan Lit Series Author, Ed; Northern Westchester, Putnam Tchr Ctr Guest Lecturer Annual Symposium & Tchr, Trainer of Westchester Eng Educators; Co-Semi Finalist: Christa Mc Auliff Fellowship 1990, Annual Dean's Awd Tchng Excl 1988, Regents Fellowship Doctoral Stud 1960; Reader's Digest Team Recipient; Westchester Coalition Grant 1995-; *office:* North Salem Mid, High Schl Old Rt 124 North Salem NY 10560*

SAGAR, JEFFERSON WILLIAM, 6th Grade Teacher; *b:* Wash CH, OH; *m:* Rhonda L.; *c:* Jordan, Donald; *ed:* OH Univ (BA) Elem Ed 1985; *cr:* Wayne Elem Schl 6th Grd Tchr 1985-; *ai:* Sci Fair Coord; Peer Mediation Adv; Kappa Delta Pi, Phi Delta Kappa 1985-; *office:* Wayne Elem Schl 3978 North St SE Washington Court H OH 43160

SAGE, CATHY DELAIR, 6th Grade Teacher; *b:* Glen Falls, NY; *m:* Lawrence; *c:* Catherine, Corey; *ed:* SUNY at Potsdam (BA) Elem Ed 1970; Nazareth Coll (MS) Elem Ed 1975; *cr:* Fairport Cntrl Schls Tchr 1970-80; Syracuse City Schls Tchr 1988-; *ai:* Tech Comm; AFT, NYSUT 1970-; *home:* 137 Robbins Ln De Witt NY 13214

SAGE, LAWRENCE T., 5th Grade Teacher; *ed:* Southern CT (BA) Elem Ed 1968, (MA) Rdng 1973; *cr:* Wallingford 5 Grd Elem Ed Tchr 1968-70; Regnl Dist #13 5 Grd Elem Ed Tchr 1970-; *ai:* NEA, CEA 1968-; REA 1970-.

SAGGESE, BETTYANN, English Teacher; *b:* Brooklyn, NY; *m:* Anthony; *c:* Anthony, James; *ed:* St Johns Univ (BA) Eng & Scndry Ed 1971; *cr:* OLPH HS Eng Tchr 1990-; *ai:* Stu Act Cncl Moderator; *office:* Our Lady of Perpetual Help HS 550 59th St Brooklyn NY 11220

SAGIANI, FREDERICA, Principal; *b:* Ponticates-Epirus, Greece; *m:* George; *c:* Stephan; *ed:* Hunter Coll (BA) Bio 1972, (MS) Guid 1978; Tchrs Coll (MS) Curr, Supervision 1984; Doctoral Prgm Bil Educ ABD; *cr:* St Demetrios Schl Guid Cnslr 1979-82; Fantis Parochial Schl Prin 1984-90; Archbishop Iakovos HS Prin 1990-; *ai:* Archdiocesan Bd of Ed Greek Orthodox Arch 1992-, Pub Relations, Curr; Documentation Project NYS Ed Dept St Archines 1994-; Title VII Grant; Deans List; Cum Laude; *home:* 4027 218th St Bayside NY 11361*

SAGINARIO, FRANCINE GAROFALO, High School Reading Specialist; *b:* Brooklyn, NY; *m:* Anthony; *c:* Anthony Jr.; *ed:* C. W. Post Ctr LIU (BA) Eng Ed 1974; Adelphi Univ (MS) Rdng, Spec Ed 1977; Hofstra Univ 6 Credits Fnds, Bilingual Ed; Computers in Classroom, Ed Admin; Nassau BOCES 10 Credit Hrs; Long Beach City Schl Dist Span I, II, III 9 Credit Hrs; *cr:* Adelphi Univ Grad Rdng Supvr 1978-81; Floral Park Memorial HS Rdng Specialist 1979; Long Beach HS Rdng Specialist 1979-; Adelphi Univ Grad Redng Supvr 1983-85; Nassau Comm Coll Adjunct Rdng Basic Ed 1995-; *ai:* Yrbk Adv; AFT, LB-Classroom Tchrs Assn 1979-; AAUP 1983-; Adj Fac Assn 1995-; Viceroy Civic Assn 1978-; Sigma Tau Delta 1973-; Columbia Scholastic Press Assn 3rd Place 1983, 2nd Place 1984; Empire St Schl Press Assn All NY Rating 1983-84; *office:* Long Beach HS 322 Lagoon Dr W Long Beach NY 11561*

SAHL, FRANK, Sixth Grade Teacher; *b:* Boston, MA; *m:* Shirley Peterson; *ed:* Boston Univ Coll of Gen Stud (AA) Gen Ed 1959; Boston Univ Schl of Ed (BS) Elem Ed 1962; Northeastern Univ (MED) Educl Admin 1965; 39 Addl Credits; *cr:* Easton Pub Schls 6-8th Grd Tchr 1962-80, Admin Intern 1980-81, Asst Prin 1981-83, Prin 1983-88, Admin Asst to Supt 1988-89, 6th Grd Tchr 1989-; *ai:* Easton Edctrs Assn, MA Tchrs Assn, NEA 1962-; Boston Univ Coll of Gen Stud Alumni Assn Bd 1975-, VP, Pres, Natl Alumni Cncl Awd, Alumni Awd Spec Distinction 1990; Article Ed; *office:* Lincoln St Intermediate Schl Lincoln St North Easton MA 02356

SAIA, PAUL ANTHONY, AP Biology & Regents Bio Tchr; *b:* Bronx, NY; *m:* Laurie Masterpole; *c:* Anthony, Christina, Joseph; *ed:* SUNY at Buffalo (BS) Bio, Geology 1981; SUNY at New Paltz (MS) Sci Ed 1986; 60 Addl Credits; *cr:* Pawling Cntrl Schl Dist Chem Tchr 1981-85; Somers Cntrl Schl Dist Bio Tchr 1986-; *ai:* Var Bsbl, Acad Challenge Coach; NYSUT, AFT, SFA 1981-.

SAID, JANE ANN WARBURTON, Instructional Support Teacher; *b:* Chester, PA; *m:* Camilo Jr.; *c:* Albert, Aaron; *ed:* West Chester Univ (BS) Elem Ed, Sp Ed 1980; Penn St Univ (MED) Spec Ed 1987; 3 Credits Assertive Discipline Lee Carter; 3 Credits Math; *cr:* Melmark Schl Tchr of Multiply Handicapped 1980-85; Haverford Schl Dist Homebound Instr

1985-86; Penn Delco Schl Dist 1st & 2nd Grd Sp Ed Tchr 1986-89; Interboro Schl Dist Resource Room Sp Ed Tchr 5 Yrs, IST Tchr 2 Yrs 1989-; *ai:* Behavior Advy Comm; NEA 1986-; Delta Kappa Gamma 1994-, Former Recording Sec; ASCD 1995-; Nether Providence Schl Goals Comm, Schoolwide Themes 1995-; Nether Providence Schl SAC 1996; Wallingford Presbyn Church 1995-, Sunday Schl Tchr; Impact Grant Partners in Amer 1990; *office:* Tinicum Schl 1st & Seneca Sts Essington PA 19029*

SAIL, MICHAEL ROBERT, Fifth Grade Teacher; *b:* New York City, NY; *m:* Ann Granger; *c:* Leah, Adam; *ed:* St Univ Coll at Oneonta (BS) Elem, Early Scndry Ed 1973; St Univ of NY at Albany (MS) Ed Comm 1976; Cert in Supervision of Stu Tchrs, Interns at St Univ Coll at Oneonta; Cert in Indstrl Labor Relations at Cornell Univ; *cr:* NY St Dept of Ed Consultant 1984-88; North Colonie Cntrl Schls Elem Tchr 1973-; *ai:* Stu Govt Adv; Math, Lang Arts, Soc Stud Curr Comms; Test Dev, Evaluation Comms; Tchrs Assn 1973-, VP, Negotiation; AFT 1973-, Del; NY St United Tchrs 1973-, Del; Temple Gates of Heaven 1982-, Brotherhood Bd; *office:* North Colonie Central Schls PO Box 708 Newtonville NY 12128*

SAILOR, BARBARA HART, Retired HS Art Teacher; *b:* Cleveland, OH; *m:* Ralph M.; *c:* Elizabeth Dianne Rockhold, Richard A., Marilyn Lea Kohler; *ed:* Bowling Green St Univ (BS) Art Ed 1960; Wright St Univ (MED) Curr, Supervision 1984; Certs Elem Ed 1970, Admin 1985; *cr:* Elyria Pub Schls Jr HS Art Tchr 1960-61; Wapakoneta City Schls 4th-12th Grd Art Tchr 1961-62; Jackson Ctr Elem 4th-6th Grd Tchr 1967-73; Jackson Ctr HS 7th-12th Grd Art Tchr 1973-; *ai:* Art, Drama Clubs Adv; NHS Adv, Fac Advis Cncl; Natl Art Honor Soc; Chrldr Adv; Yrbk Adv; OH Art Educ Assn 1980-; Jackson Ctr Educ Assn 1967-; Arts in Action 1989-, Pres; Sidney, Shelby Cty Art Tchrs Org 1991-94; Delta Phi Delta; Kappa Delta Pi; Pub Article 1987.

SAINATO, DIANE MARIE, Sixth Grade Teacher; *b:* Cleveland, OH; *m:* Aldo; *c:* Jodi, Keri; *ed:* Bowling Green St Univ (BS) Elem Ed 1973; *cr:* St Monica Schl 6th Grd Tchr 1988-; *ai:* Stu Adv, Safety Patrol Adv; *home:* 4811 Great Oaks Pkwy Independence OH 44131

ST CLAIR, HELAINE COLLINS, Spanish Teacher; *b:* Newark, NJ; *m:* Wayne; *c:* Craig, Alexis; *ed:* Adelphi Univ (BA) Span 1974; FL Atlantic Univ 30 Hrs Span Linguistics; Adirondack Comm Coll 6 Hrs Fr; Greater Tchr Ctr 3 Hrs Span Immersion; *cr:* FL Atlantic Univ Span Tchng Asst 1974-75; St Marys Acad Span Tchr 1976; Shenedehowa Cntrl Schl Span Tchr 1984-; *ai:* Mentor, Mentee Prgm for At-Risk Stud; NYSAFLT 1984-; COLT 1994-; Temple Sisterhood 1987-; Guilderland Ballet 1987-95, Sec 1992-95; Presenter at Regnl NYSAFLT Conf; *office:* Shenendehowa Central Schl Rt 146 Clifton Park NY 12065

ST CROIX, JEFFREY JAMES, 8th Grd Mathematics Teacher; *b:* Watertown, NY; *m:* Rosemarie T. Goss; *c:* Matthew, Monica, Michael, Mark; *ed:* Potsdam Coll (BA) Math & Ps 1977, (MAEd) Upper Elem & Early Scndry Ed 1983; *cr:* Holy Family Schl Jr HS Tchr 1977-80; General Brown 8th Grd Math Tchr 1980-; *ai:* Immaculate Heart Cntrl Boys Bsktbl Coach; NYSUT 1980-, VP; Knights of Columbus, 1972-; Northside Improvement League 1994-; *office:* General Brown Cntrl Schl Cemetary Rd Dexter NY 13634

ST JOHN, CATHERINE, Instr of Studio Arts & Hum; *b:* Bronx, NY; *ed:* William Paterson Coll (BA) Art Ed 1964, (MA) Art 1967; NY Univ (DA) Studio Art & Art Professions 1995; Schl of Visual Arts Cert, Studio & Agency Skills 1963; Art Stdnts League 1963; Vermont Studio Schl Residency 1989; *cr:* Mahwah HS Chprsn Art Dept 1966-79; Ramapo Coll Prof Art Methods 1973-78; Berkeley Coll Instr Studio Arts & Hum 1981-; *ai:* Creative Arts Soc Adv; NJ Art Edctrs 1994-; Museum of Modern Art 1983-; Artist's Network 2996; NEH Flwshp 1993; Outstdng Tchr of Yr 1986, 1992; Hecksher Museum Awd 1980; Emily Lowe Prize Natl Acad of Design 1977; Paterson Museum Invitational 1993; First Place Judges Awd Bergen Museum of Art 1985; Artlcle Pub; *office:* Berkeley Coll Garret Mountain Campus West Paterson NJ 07424

ST JOHN, FRAZE LEE, Assoc Prof of Zoology; *b:* Lebanon, OH; *m:* Mary Ellen Kindell; *c:* James, David; *ed:* Miami Univ (BSEd) Bio 1961; IN Univ (MA) Zoology 1963; OH St Univ (PHD) Zoology 1970; *cr:* Miami Univ Lecturer 1963-65; OH St Univ Rsrch Specialist 1969-70, Asst Zoology Prof 1970-77, Assoc Zoology Prof 1977-; *ai:* Club Adv; Fac Assembly Comms; Sigma Xi 1970-; AAUP 1985-; OH Acad of Sci 1968-, Zoology Section Chair; Newark Amateur Radio Assn 1986-; Newark Model Railroad Club 1990-, Pres, Sec; OH Acad of Sci Fellow; 4 Articles Pub; United Way Loaned Exec 1995; Tchng Excl Awd 1977; *office:* OH St Univ At Newark University Drive Newark OH 43055

ST JOHN, MARCY DOMERGUE, French Teacher; *b:* Sewickley, PA; *m:* Ralph; *c:* Matthew, Jessica; *ed:* Grove City Coll (BA) Fr, Ger 1968; Univ of WI at Madison (MA) Fr 1970; Attnd France, Bowling Green St Univ, Miami Univ; *cr:* Univ of WI Tchng Asst 1968-71; Lake Mills MS Tchr, Fr 1971-73; Sylvanis Mccord JR HS Tchr, FR 1973-78; Bowling Green HS Tchr, FR 1978-; *ai:* Fr Club; Amnesty Intnl; Travel Group Ldr; NEA, OEA 1973-; AATF 1971-; Ohio Frgn Lang Tchrs Assn 1978-; Cub Scouts, BSA 1993-94, Ldr; 1st Presbyn Church Ofcr, Tchr; Summer Travel Grant; *office:* Bowling Green HS 530 W Poe Rd Bowling Green OH 43402

ST JOHN, MICHAEL JOHN, Earth Science Teacher; *b:* Chelsea, MA; *ed:* Boston St Coll (BS) Earth Sci 1969; Antioch Univ (MS) Ed 1989; 32 Credits; *cr:* Stuart Jr HS Earth Sci Tchr 1969-70; Nashua Sr HS Earth Sci Tchr 1970-75; Elm St Jr HS Earth Sci Tchr 1975-; Antioch New Eng Grad Schl Critical Skills Master Tchr 1983-; *ai:* Ski Club; AFT 1970-; Nashua Solid Waste Advy 1992-, Vice-Chair; Hampshire Chemical Co 1991-, Citizens Advy Bd; NSF; Critical Skills Prgm Originator; The Critical Skills Classroom Manual Major Contributor.

ST JOHN, WILLIAM C., Accounting Professor; *b:* New York City, NY; *ed:* Siena Coll (BS) Acctng 1966; Union Coll (MS) Indstrl Admin 1972; Rensselaer Poly Tech (PHD) Urban Environmental Stud 1989; Attnd US Army War Coll 1989, US Army Command, Gen Staff Coll; *cr:* Capital Dist Transportation Athy Comptroller, Treas 1970-82; Rensselaer Cty Treas 1982-85; Rensselaer Poly Tech Prof 1990-; *ai:* Fac Adv Pi Kappa Phi; Fac Intervention Prgm; Co-Dir Internation Prgm; Inst of Man ACC, Amer Acctng Assn 1990-; Chamber of Commerce 1979-, Pres; Indstrl Dev Agency 1984-, Chm; Ec Dev Agency 1984-, Pres; *office:* Rensselaer Polytechnic Inst 110 8th St Troy NY 12180

ST JOHN, WILLIAM HUGH, English Teacher; *b:* New Haven, CT; *m:* Margot Joly; *c:* Matthew St. John; *ed:* Univ of CT (BA) Ger 1982; Univ of MA (MA) Ger 1987; Grad Schl, Univ of ME; Orono Schl of Ed C.A.S. Pgrm; *cr:* Averill HS Eng Tchr 1987-89; Dirigo HS Eng Tchr 1990-; *ai:* Odyssey of Mind; Drama Coach; Outing Club; NEATE, ME Ed Assn 1989-; *office:* Dirigo HS 99 Weld St Dixfield ME 04224

ST LAWRENCE, DIANE MARIE, Tchr of Deaf & Hard of Hearing; *b:* Brockton, MA; *m:* John H. Mac Donald; *ed:* Southeastern MA Univ (BA) His 1976; Gallaudet Univ (MA) Ed of Deaf 1980; Univ of Southern ME Interpreter Trng, Sign Lang; *cr:* MD Schl for the Deaf Tchr 1980-81; Schl Admin Dist #48 Tchr of Deaf, Hard of Hearing 1981-; *ai:* Division of Deafness Advy Bd; Sign Lang Club Adv; Accreditation, Tech Grant, Scheduling, Fac, Spec Ed Comms; Pilot Project Tchng ASL Interactive TV; Cncl Ed of Deaf 1980-; ME Ed Assn 1981-; Registry Interpreters for Deaf 1987-, Sec; Support Network Edctrs of Deaf, Hard of Hearing 1987-; *office:* Nokomis Regional HS Williams Rd Newport ME 04953

ST PETER, FLORENCE S., Librarian; *b:* Waterville, ME; *m:* Joseph E.; *c:* Anna Linn, Mary Hendricks, Janet Jordan; *ed:* Thomas Bus Coll (D) Secretarial 1955; *cr:* Philip W Sugg MS Librn 1973-; *ai:* NEA, MTA 1973-; *office:* Sugg MS Rt 196 Lisbon Falls ME 04252

ST PIERRE, JAMES FRANCIS, English Teacher; *b:* Pawtucket, RI; *ed:* Univ of MA at Lowell (BA) Eng 1990; Univ of S ME, Gorham 30 Credits Towards Masters of Ed Cert; Bread Loaf Schl of Eng 6 Credits Towards Masters; *cr:* Fryeburg Acad Eng Tchr 1993-; *ai:* Soccer, Track & Acad Decathlan Coach; One Act Play & All Schl Play Dir; Ed Newsletter for Tchng Shakespeare in Classroom; ME Youth Ctr Writing Workshop for Youth Offenders; *office:* Fryeburg Acad 152 Main St Fryeburg ME 04037

ST PIERRE, SUSAN WHITE, History Teacher; *b:* Melrose, MA; *m:* Roger; *c:* Jennifer, Andrea; *ed:* Univ of Lowell (BS) His 1978; Univ of ME at Orono (MEd) Ed 1991; *cr:* Buckfield Jr-Sr HS Soc Stud Tchr 1978-84; Livermore Falls MS Soc Stud Tchr 1984-91; Livermore Falls HS His Tchr 1991-; *ai:* Stu Cncl Adv; NCSS 1978-; ASCD 1989-; Washburn Norlands Fnd 1991-, Trustee; *office:* Livermore Falls HS 25 Cedar St Livermore Falls ME 04254

SAJDAK, CAROLE COTTER, Spanish & English Instructor; *b:* New York, NY; *m:* Robert; *c:* Aniella Marie, Richard John; *ed:* Marymount Coll at Tarrytown (BA) Span 1966; Fordham Univ (MS) Admin 1968; Manhattan Coll Post Grad Stud; *cr:* Sacred Heart HS Span Tchr 1966-67; Commerce HS Eng, Span, Algebra Tchr 1967-72; Pace Bus Schl Comm Dept Chprsn 1982-87; Mitchell Coll Span Instr 1985-; Sacred Heart HS Span, Eng Tchr 1987-; *ai:* Stu Cncl, Acad Team, Pub Speaking Competitions Moderator; NCTE, AATSP 1966-; Kappa Delta Pi 1970-, Charter Mem; TKKC Holding Corp 1972-; NDEA Summer Inst Hofstra Univ; Westchester Cty Veterans Assn Commendation; *office:* Sacred Heart HS 34 Convent Ave Yonkers NY 10703*

SAKELARIDES, JOHN, Art Teacher; *b:* Raway, NJ; *ed:* Kean St (BA) Art Ed 1990; Attnd Parsons Schl of Design, Haystack Mountain Schl of Art, Stocton St & Artist Tchr Inst; *cr:* North Hunterdon HS Art & AP His of Art Tchr 1990-; *ai:* Club Adv & Video Yrbk; NEA 1990-; NAEA 1990; Green Peace 1990-; Pohatcong Wildlife Refuge 1995-; Haystack Mountain Schl of Art Stud Grant; Thelma E Newman Excl in Art Awd; Kean St Stu Tchr of Yr Awd; *office:* North Hunterdon HS 1445 State Route 31 Annandale NJ 08801

SAKOWSKI, CATHERINE A., Second Grade Teacher; *b:* Greensburg, PA; *m:* Frank W.; *c:* Brian; *ed:* Penn State (BS) Elem Ed 1972; CA St Univ 9 Credits; IN Univ of PA 20 Credits; Univ of Pittsburgh 3 Credits; *ai:* Methods Class & Tchr Mentor; Cooperating Tchr; Rdng & Hop for Leukemia Chprsn; Progress Report, LA, Prof Evaluation & Report Card Comms; NEA 1972-; PTEA 1972-; PSEA 1972-.

SAKUSKY, WILLIAM A., Social Studies Teacher; *b:* Tamaqua, PA; *m:* Pamela Bixler; *c:* Steven, Amy; *ed:* Mansfield St Coll (BS) Soc Stud 1971; Temple Univ, Lehigh Univ, Wilkes Coll MS Equivalency; *cr:* St Josephs Schl Tchr 1971-73; Hamburg Area HS Tchr 1973-; *ai:* Ftbl Coach 19 Yrs; JV Bsktbl Coach 8 Yrs; Jr & JV Bsbl Coach 6 Yrs; Jr Class Adv 4 Yrs; PSEA 1973-; NEA 1973-; Berks Gold Leaf Club 1993-; Berks Cty Ftbl Coach of Yr 1985 & 1988; *office:* Hamburg Area HS Windsor St Hamburg PA 19526*

SALA, TRACY LEIGH, Applied Biology & Chem Teacher; *b:* Erie, PA; *m:* Massimo; *ed:* Gannon Univ (BS) Bio 1985; Slippery Rock Univ Cert Scndry Ed 1988; *cr:* Sacred Heart Grd Schl Sci Tchr 1989-90; East HS Bio Tchr 1993-95; Cntrl HS Bio Tchr 1995-; *ai:* Sr Class Adv; Alternative Ed Team Ldr; NEA 1993-; *office:* Erie Cntrl HS 3325 Cherry St Erie PA 16508

SALADINO, JEAN ELIZABETH, Director of Vocal Studies; *b:* Springfield, MO; *m:* David Andrew; *c:* Amy, Joel; *ed:* Wichita St Univ (BME) Music Ed 1968; FL St Univ (MM) Vocal Performance 1986; Univ of IL 18 Addl Hrs; *cr:* Univ of WI at Stevens Point Asst Prof Voice 1986-91; Cal St at San Bernardino Instr of Voice 1991-93; Univ of RI Coll of Continuing Ed, Artist in Residence 1993-94; Walnut Hill Schl Dir of Vocal Stud 1994-; *ai:* Natl Assn of Tchrs of Singing 1986-, VP Elect RI Chptr; Robert Shaw Chamber Chorale 1988; OR Bach Festival Choir 1991-92; *office:* Walnut Hill Schl 12 Highland St Natick MA 01760

SALAGAJ, DEBORAH D'ALESSIO, Computer Programming Teacher; *b:* Newark, NJ; *m:* Stanley; *c:* Robert, Alyssa; *ed:* Montclair St Coll (BA) Math 1973, (MA) Math Ed 1976; Cert in Stu Prsnl Svcs; *cr:* East Side HS Math Tchr 1974-; *ai:* NHS Adv; NAME 1975-; NASAA 1992-; *office:* East Side HS 238 Van Buren St Newark NJ 07105

SALAMON, GEORGE JOSEPH, Spanish Teacher; *b:* New York, NY; *m:* Sheila Cox; *c:* Christopher, Paul, Scott; *ed:* Iona Coll (BA) Span & Ed 1969; C. W. Post (MS) Biling-Bicultural Sp 1977; Attnd Hunter Coll & Adelphi Univ; *cr:* John Philip Sousa Jr HS Span Tchr 1968-; Sacred Heart Acad Span Tchr, Dean & Chprsn 1969-; Valley Stream Cntrl HS Summer Driver Ed Tchr 1983-; *ai:* LILT & ASCD 1979-; AATSP 1990-; ASCD 1985-; BSA 1986-, Fund Raiser & Scoutmaster, Pelican; Federal Grant Study of Biling Span; *office:* Sacred Heart Acad 47 Cathederal Ave Hempstead NY 11550*

SALATI, ORAZIO JOSEPH, Art Teacher; *b:* Arnara, Italy; *ed:* St Univ Coll at Buffalo (BS) Art Ed 1972; Istituto Statale d'Artem, Univ of Siena Painting, Ceramics, Art His, Italian Culture, Lang 1970; Post Grad SUNY at Oswego, New Paltz & Oneonta, Binghamton Univ, Elmira Coll; *cr:* Johnson City Schls K-12 Grd Art Tchr 1972-75; Union Endicott HS 9-12 Grd Art Tchr 1975-; *ai:* Art Chprsn 1979-83; Empire St Coll Tchr; Ger Exch Coord Goethe House; Attendance, Air Quality Comm; Curr Dev, Field Stud NYS Ed Dept; AFT, NYS Tchrs Assn 1972-; NYS Art Tchr Assn 1972-, Section 4 Pres 1995-, Art Edctr of Yr 1994-95; Endicott Tchr Assn 1975-; Buffalo St Alumni 1972-; Standing Rock Sioux Indian Reservations Guest Artist; Illustrated Book; Pub Article in Magazine; Exhibiting Artist Agory Gallery 1993; Natl TV Appearance 1994; Montserrat Gallery 1994; Prodigy Gallery Observed Art, Restoration of Sistien Chapel Vatican Italy 1988; *home:* 206 Hannah St Endicott NY 13760

SALCITO, CHRISTINE URBANK, Program Dir of Math Education; *b:* Maspeth, NY; *m:* Steven Nicholas; *c:* Alexa Christine; *ed:* Univ of Hartford (BA) Scndry Ed, Math 1974; Kean Coll (PBM) Acctng 1985, (MA) Admin 1990; *cr:* St Francis of Assissi Schl 8th Grd Math Tchr 1974-76; Woodbridge Jr HS MS 8th-9th Grd Math Tchr 1976-93; Rahway Pub Schls Prgm Dir of Math 1993-; *ai:* NCTM 1980-; AMTNJ 1993-; Kiwanis 1993-; *office:* Rahway Bd of Ed Kline Pl Rahway NJ 07065

SALDAN, DARLYNE YOUNG, 5th Grade Teacher; *b:* Philadelphia, PA; *m:* Alexander Jr.; *c:* Melissa Soldan Ames, Scott A.; *ed:* Masters Equivalency Plus 30 Credits; *cr:* Sol Feinstone Elem Schl Grd 4-5 Tchr 1967-; *ai:* Co-Ed Schl Newspaper; NEA, PSEA 1967-; CREA 1967-, Bldg Rep 4 Yrs; Juvenile Diabetes Found 1990-; Amer Diabetic Assn 1985-; Tchrs Mentor; *office:* Sol Feinstone Elem Schl 1090 Eagle Rd Newtown PA 18940

SALDIVAR, TONI J. WELLS, Assistant Professor of English; *b:* Jacksonville, FL; *m:* Samuel G.; *c:* Samuel M., Matthew; *ed:* FL St Univ (BA) Eng 1964; SUNY at New Paltz (MA) Eng 1975; NY Univ (PHD) Eng 1990; *cr:* Mount Saint Mary Coll Asst Prof of Eng 1991; *ai:* Alpha Chi Natl Honorary Adv; Phi Kappa Phi 1963-; Phi Beta Kappa 1964-; MLA 1980-; NEMLA 1980-; NEH Summer Seminar Grant 1993; Sylvia Plath Confessing The Fictive Self Pub 1992; *office:* Mount Saint Mary Coll 330 Powell Ave Newburgh NY 12550

SALEM, GEORGE GREGORY, Business Teacher; *b:* Akron, C Gail Balsavich; *c:* Ryan; *ed:* Univ of Akron (BA) Psych 1984, (B 1988; *cr:* North Olmsted HS Tchr 1988-92; Cloverleaf HS Acctng Tchr 1992-; *ai:* Head Var Boys Bsbl & Asst Boys Var Bsktbl Coach 1992-.

SALEM, TIMOTHY JOSEPH, History Teacher; *b:* Danbury, C Eastern CT St Univ (BA) Pol Sci 1991; Sacred Heart Univ (MS) Scn 1996; *cr:* Danbury HS His Tchr 1993-; *ai:* Class of 99 Adv; Coac Head Boys Bsktbl, Frosh Ftbl, JV Girls Soccer, Asst Track, Field Force 2000 Comm; NEA 1994-; Conn Coaches Assn 1993-; Danbu Meml 1987-; Danbury Jaycees Distngd Svc Awd Nom 1994; Danbury HS Clapboard Ridge Rd Danbury CT 06810*

SALEMI, JOSEPH SALVATORE, Classics Professor; *b:* New Yo NY; *m:* Helen Palma; *ed:* NY Univ (MA) Eng Lit 1970;, (PHD) E 1986; Grad Ctr CUNY MA Classcis; *cr:* Pace Univ Eng Prof 1977-8 Univ Hum Prof 1982-; Fordham Univ Eng Prof 1988-89; Hunte Classics Prof 1989-; Brooklyn Coll Classics Prof 1994-; *ai:* Natl A Scholars 1992; Assn Lit Scholars & Critics 1994-; Classical, Mod Awd; Lane Cooper Dissertation, NEH Summer Seminar Flwshps; F Musurillo Meml Schlsp; Articles Pub; *home:* 220 9th St Brookl 11215

SALEMSON, BETSY ANN, Foreign Lang Dept Head; *b:* Louisvil *m:* Eric C. Knuffke; *c:* David S. Knuffke; *ed:* Queens Coll (BA) Fr Antioch New England (MA) Ed 1972; LIU CW Post Campus Cert Admin 1991; 60 Hrs Cert in Psychotherapy Washington Square I Psychoanalytic Therapy; 30 Hrs Span Lang Immersion Courses from Immersion Inst at SUNY New Paltz; 30 Hrs Italian Lang Imm Courses From Lang Imm Inst SUNY New Paltz; *cr:* Great Neck Pub FLES Fr Tchr 1968-69; Mineola Pub Schls Fr Tchr 1970 Interdisciplinary Act Comm Chair; Stu Research Project Adv; Co Revise Constitution of Mineola Tchrs Assn Chair; Dist Comm on S Decision Making; Mineola Tchrs Assn 1970-, Bldg Rep, VP, NYSUT, AFT, ATF, LILT, FLACS, NYSAFLT 1970-; NOW, M LIAAC; Cinema Arts Cntr; *office:* Mineola HS 10 Armstrong Rd New Park NY 11040*

SALERNO, ADELE GOMBITA, Science Dept Chair & Teach Homestead, PA; *m:* Thomas L.; *ed:* Duquesne Univ (BS) Chem Villanova Univ (MA) Chem 1972; *cr:* Vincentian HS Sci Dept C 1956-70; Mt Notre Dame HS Sci Dept Chprsn 1970-; *ai:* Schl Music ACT & SAT Classes; Sci Fair; Acad Cncl; North Cntrl Co-Chm; 1970-; America Chemical Soc 1956-; Iota Sigma Pi 1990-; Parish 1991-, Pres 1992-93, Sec; Arch Diocesan Pastoral Cncl 1990-, Exe Vice Chm 1993-; ACS Chem Test Writing Comm 1981-, Chprsn 19 Cornell Univ Shell Fellowship; NSF Summer Math Grants; Spectro Soc Keivin Burns Awd; Miami Univ Sci Fair Chprsn & Spec Judge; & Local Conventions Presenter; Demonstration for Brownie T Outstanding Tchr Awd; Outstanding Scndry Educator of America Chem Ed Confs Presentor; Seminars & Summer Courses at Various Amer Chemical Soc Test Writing Comm Chm 1991-93; Receive Charlotte Schmidlapp Grant 1993; US Cath Bshps' Natl Advy Cncl Mem 1996-; *office:* Mount Notre Dame H S 711 E Columbia Cincinnati OH 45215*

SALERNO, JACQUELINE FESTA, Social Studies Teacher; *b:* Pa NJ; *m:* Michael; *ed:* William Paterson Coll (BA) Sociology, Comm Montclair St Univ (MA) Ed, Trng 1993; Rutgers Univ Drug, Al Cnslng, Trng Cert 1989; Belleville HS Drug Prevention Trng Ce Belleville HS Soc Stud Tchr 1988-90; Sylan Learning Ctr Dir 1991-92; Private Industry Cncl Adult Ed Instr 1992-93; Clifton H Stud, Amer His Tchr 1993-; *ai:* Morning Announcements Adv Belleville HS SADD Adv 1989; CAST Asst Adv 1993-; SASH 1995-; NEA 1993-; ASCD 1989-; Phi Kappa Delta 1985-; NACSS PIC Adult Ed Tchr Recognition 1993; Belleville HS Tchr of Month *office:* Clifton HS 333 Colfax Ave Clifton NJ 07013*

SALERNO, LETITIA, 6th Grade Teacher; *b:* Rome, NY; *m:* Micha Stephen; *ed:* SUNY at Oswego (BA) Elem 1963; 90 Credit Hr Bellamy 6th Grd Tchr 1963-69; Columbus Kndgtn, 2nd & 5th Grd 1970-85; Gifted & Talented Pgm 1st Grd Tchr 1985-86; Ft Stanwix 4t Tchr 1986-88; Lake Delta 6th Grd Tchr 1988-; *ai:* NEA 1963-; RTA NYSTA 1963-; St John the Bapt, Eucharist Minister; Rescue Mi Tchr; Rome Tchrs Ctr Grants for Local His, Bio Sci & Lang Humor.

SALETTA, RICHARD JOSEPH, Criminal Justice Teacher; *b:* Creek, NY; *m:* Anita Tabak; *c:* Michael, Jennifer; *ed:* Jamestown C coll (AA) Criminal Justice 1975; St Univ of NY at Fredonia (BA) Justice 1979; Buffalo St Coll (MS) Ed 1995; 16 Credit Hrs Univ of VA Natl Acad; *cr:* Chautouqua Cty Sheriffs Dept Sgt, Criminal Investi 1973-93; Hewes Educl Ctr Criminal Justice Tchr 1992-; Buffalo St Vo-Tech Ed Instr 1995-; *ai:* HS Hockey Coach; NYS Southern Tech-Prep Consortium; AVA 1995-; FBI Natl Acad Assn 1986-; NY 1992-; Loyal Order of Moose 1986-; VFW 1990-; Amer Legion 1 Jaycees 1971-, Treas; Deputy Sheriff of Yr NY St 1980; Chautauqu Sheriffs Bravery Awd 1991; Deans List Buffalo St Coll 1993-95; Out Young Lw Enforcement Officer Jaycees 1979; *home:* 54 Babcock Silver Creek NY 14136*

SALGADO, RAMONA MATOS, Prof Emeritus of Health Ed; *b:* Pl Tchrs Coll Columbia U (BS) Hlth Ed 1960, (MA) Family, Comm Ed (EDD) Ed Family, Comm 1974; Amer Inst Psychotherap Psychoanalysis Courses Psychotherapy, Family & Couples Therapy Therapy; *cr:* Comm & Mental & Pub Hlth Various Positions 196 Yeshiva Albert Einstein Coll Mental Hlth Prgm Instr 1968-69; Bx C Coll CUNY Adj Prof of Hlth Ed 1969-95; *ai:* Fac Adv Curr, Senate, Stud; Various Comms 26 Yrs; AFT; AAUP; PSC; Family Therapy Net Puerto Rican Family Inst 1983-, Pres Bd of Dirs, Treas; Women Caucus; NY Acad of Sci; Dissertation Awd Ford Fnd; Distngd Svc Articles Pub.

SALHANY, BERNADETTE, First Grade Teacher; *b:* Central Falls *ed:* William Paterson Coll (BA) Elem Ed 1974; 30 Addl Hrs; *cr:* S Title I Math, Rdng Tchr 1974-83, Fourth Grd Tchr 1983-90, Second Tchr 1994-95, First Grd Tchr 1993-94; Title I (BSI) Rdng, Math 1995-; *ai:* Chrldrs Co Adv; Rdng Incentive Goal Comm Co-Chprsn; Advy Group; T&E Schl comm; Schl Soc Fund; Schl Adv Group Team 1993-95, Team Alternate 1995-;Core Team Mem 1995; NEA 1974-; L. Sullivan Meml Comm 1988-, Sec; Peer Assistance; Tech for Chi Grant; *office:* Schl Number Two Mill & Passaic Sts Paterson NJ 075

SALIBA, AKHEE, Computer Science Teacher; *b:* Elizabeth, NJ; *m:* Grobes; *c:* Armando; *ed:* Rutgers Coll (BA) His 1972; Rutgers (EDM) Ed 1976, (PHD) Ed 1981; Attnd Pan Amer Univ Cmptr Sci *cr:* Rutgers Univ Asst Dean of Stdnts 1974-75, Asst to Provost 197 Southmost Coll Psych Tchr 1982-84; Elizabeth HS Cmptr Sci Tchr 19 *ai:* Roselle Chess Club Coord; NJEA 1985-; Optimist Club 19 Research Grant to Stud Acad Effects of Chess Games; Pub Researc Self Esteem & Achvmt in Children; *office:* Elizabeth HS 600 Pea Elizabeth NJ 07202

SALIBA, TONY ELIAS, Chem Engineering Assoc Prof; *b:* Be Lebanon; *m:* Susan Shappert; *c:* L. Joseph; *ed:* Univ of Dayton (BS) C Engineering 1981, (MS) Chem Engineering 1982, (PHD) Mate Engineering 1986; *cr:* Univ of Dayton Asst Prof 1986-91, Assoc

; Prof, Chmn 1994-; *ai:* Tau Beta Pi Adv; SAMPE 1986-, Chm, ler, Adv, Midwest Chapter Dir, Treas, Coll Composite Curr Chm, Stu osium Chair; ASC 1986-, Charter Mem; Sigma Xi 1987-; Michael Tchng Excl Awd 1988, 1992-93; Engineering Comm Distinguished Awd; Victor Emmanuel 15th Annual Meml Chem Engineering Excl 1981; *office:* Univ of Dayton KL 445-0246 Dayton OH 45469*

ICCE, LINDA ANN (BOROWSKI), Associate Professor of Biology; 'tsburgh, PA; *m:* Robert Louis; *c:* Adam Robert, Carla Maria, Eric el; *ed:* West Liberty St Coll (BS) Med Tech 1968; Univ of Pittsburgh D) Higher Ed 1974; *cr:* Univ of Pittsburgh Instr 1971-77; Comm Coll llegheny Cty Temporary Dept Chprsn Medical Lab Tech 1980, Time Instr Bio 1987-93, Assoc Prof Bio 1993-; *ai:* Aids Task Force n; Bio Clv Adv, Curr Comm; Acad Affairs Comm; Comm Service ning Comm; Distance Learning Comm; Str Adv; Women's Initiation n; AMer Soc of Clinical Pathologists 1968-; AFT 1968; Human omy of Physiology Soc 1996; PTA 1982-, Bd; Produced Medical Trng os at Univ of Pittsburgh; *office:* Comm Coll Allegheny County ogy Dept 595 Beatty Rd Monroeville PA 15146

INGER, STEPHANIE M., Program Support Teacher; *b:* delphia, PA; *m:* Ivan; *c:* Ashley; *ed:* Temple Univ (BS) Ed 1972; nova Univ MA Equiv Elem Ed 1976; Attnd Bloomsburg Univ, Univ of *cr:* Clymer Elem Schl Tchr 1973-89, Prgm Support Tchr 1989-; *ai:* hair Ldrshp Team; Home, Schl Assn Exec Bd Mem; Safety Patrol ; Mentor Tchr; AFT 1973-; PFT 1973-, Bldg Rep, Comm; 25th Police Advy Cncl 1993-; *office:* George Clymer Elem Schl 12th & Rush Sts delphia PA 19133*

IOLA, DEBORAH ANN, High School Science Teacher; *b:* Union, *ed:* Cook Coll at Rutgers (BS) Environmental Sci 1993; Biological g Cert 1994; *cr:* Rahway HS Sci Tchr 1994-; *ai:* Key Club Adv; 9th House Coord; Summer Inst Ldrshp Trng; NEA, NJEA, REA 1994-; 'A, NSTA 1993-; *office:* Rahway HS 1012 Madison Ave Rahway NJ 5*

ISBURY, GORDON THOMAS, English Teacher; *b:* Lancashire, and; *m:* Francince Alicia; *c:* Joseph; *ed:* SUNY at Buffalo (MA) Art, Music, (BA) Eng; *ai:* Tennis, Cross Cntry Coach; Drama Club Dir; bility Comm; New Tchr Mentor; NYSUT; St Paul's Cathedral Choir -; USAR, ISG 1985-, Drill Sgt of Yr; Participant Action Magna ers Univ; Dist Tchr of Yr 1995; *home:* 315 Hartford Ave Buffalo NY 3*

ISBURY, ROBERT EARL, 5th Grade Elementary Teacher; *b:* eland, OH; *m:* Carol Susan Williams; *c:* Brian Robert; *ed:* Akron Univ Elem Ed 1979; Cleveland St Univ Working on Exercise Sci; *cr:* eland St Univ Asst Swim Coach 1981-83; Brunswick City Schls 5th Tchr 1980-; Berea HS Head Swim Coach 1984-94; Cleveland St tius HS Head Swim Coach 1994-; *ai:* Swimming, Water Polo, hing, Soc, Cmptr, Fac Advy Comms; ASCA, NISCA 1990-; Coach of 995; *home:* 453 Lombardy Dr Berea OH 44017

ISBURY, RONALD DEAN, Science & Biology Teacher; *b:* nington, OH; *m:* Diana Cahall; *c:* Doug Otto, Michael; *ed:* OH St Univ Ag Ed, Bio 1975; Attnd Xavier Univ, Wright St Univ, Univ of Dayton; pper Scioto Vally HS Voc Ag Tchr 1975-77; Fairfield Local Schls Sci, Chem, Physics Tchr 1978-90; Eastern Local HS Sci, Bio, Chem, ics Tchr 1990-; *ai:* NHS Adv; SWOEA 1980-; *office:* Eastern Local s PO Drawer 500 Sardinia OH 45171

ISBURY BLAIR, DANA YVETTE, English Teacher; *b:* Annapolis, *ed:* Hampton Univ (BA) Eng Ed 1987; Howard Univ (MED) Curr & uction 1992; *cr:* James Madison MS Eng Tchr 1988-; *ai:* Co-Spon Natl onor Soc; Team Ldr; Schl Planning & Mngmt Team; Comer Steering m; Instrctnl Team; Eng Dept Chprsn; NEA, MSTA, PGCEA 1988-; a Kappa Alpha 1989-; *home:* 4346 Stockport Way Upper Marlboro 20772*

LADE, KATHLEEN, Title I Reading Specialist; *b:* Reading, PA; *ed:* town St Coll (BS) Elem, Early Chldhd Ed 1980; Kutztown Univ D) Rdng Specialist 1986; *cr:* Reading Schl Dist Elem Ed 1981-83, r Title I Rdng Specialist 1983-; *ai:* NEA, PSEA, REA 1981-; PA Assn ederal Prgm Coord 1988-; Jr Womans Club 1980-, Project, Welfare rsn, Treas; Advanced Instrl Methods Staff Dev Trainer; Instrl Support n; PA Dept Ed Division Federal Prgms Comm Practitioner, Former missioners Asst; Tchr Mentor; *office:* Tenth & Green Elem Schl 400 0th St Reading PA 19604

LAY, CHRISTINE GUTZEIT, Art Instructor; *b:* Elyria, OH; *c:* ffrey, Douglas; *ed:* OH Univ (BFA) Fine Arts & Ed 1971; Attnd ling Green St Univ, Kent St Univ, Cleveland Inst of Art, Lorain Comm ; 35+ Credit Hrs; *cr:* Firelands Local Schls 5th-12th Grd Art Instr 1 Yr; view Local Schls 4th-6th Grd Art Instr 6 Yrs; Keystone Local Schls 5th th Grd Art Instr 1 Yr; LCCC Spcl Instr for Gifted 1 Yr; Lorain City s K-12th Grd Art Instr 11 Yrs; *ai:* Mentor AKHS for Troubled Stdnts; Based Mgmt Team for 3 Schls Rep; Curr Comm; NEA, OEA & OAEA 4-; LEA 1984-, Bldg Rep; RASAP 1993-, Instr; Silver Awd; Grant to duce Stu Work to Card Format; *office:* Southview HS 2270 E 42nd St ain OH 44055*

MON, MARCIA (ZAPASNIK), Health Educator; *b:* New Castle, PA; Daniel J. Jr.; *c:* Elizabeth, Daniel J. III, Julie Salmon Chapman; *ed:* lgewater St Coll (BS) Hlth & PE 1972; 18 Credit Hrs Beyond Bachelors Related Areas of Hlth Ed Human Sexuality; *cr:* Bishop Cassidy HS PE r & Coach 1964-68; Somerset HS Hlth Educator 1972-; *ai:* Fac Advy nm; STA, MTA, NEA 1972-; Fall River CC 1975-, Exec Bd; CWGA 1975-, Pres, VP, Treas; Horace Mann Grant for Curr Dev & S Ed 1987; Chrldr Adv & Coach 1972-81; New England Assn of Schls 'olls Inc Visiting Comm Mem 3 Times; *office:* Somerset HS Grandview Ext Somerset MA 02726

LMON, MARGERY M., Biology & Chemistry Teacher; *b:* Duluth, ; *m:* Gary F.; *ed:* Univ MN at Duluth (BA) Bio, Chem Minor 1970; Grad rses Cmptrs, Ed, Hlth, Sci; *cr:* Vermont Achvmt Center Swimming r, Bio Tutor 1975-80; Rutland HS Bio Tchr 1980-82; Otter Valley UHS , Chem Tchr 1982-95; Black River HS Bio & Chem Tchr 1995; *ai:* NHS Chprsn; Act 230 Chprsn; Dist Cmptr Comm; VT Sci Tchrs Assn 1982-, wsletter Ed 3 Yrs; NSTA 1980-; Red Cross 1972-, Water Safety Chprsn Yrs, Water Safety Instr, Trainor 10 Yrs; Apple Awd; NABT Mem; China egation to Visit Chinese Bio Tchrs 1988; Learning Post Magazine icle; *home:* RR 1 Box 665 Cuttingsville VT 05738*

LO, ARNE ELLIS, 7th-8th Grd Soc Stud Teacher; *b:* Warren, OH; *m:* an M. Fondoulis; *c:* Bronwyn E., Evan K.; *ed:* Youngstown St Univ) Comprehensive Soc Stud 1975, (MS) Scndry Admin 1985; General Tchr Cert 1989; *cr:* Champion Local Schls 7th-8th Grd Soc Stud Tchr 76-; Howland Local Schls ABE Instr 1977-; *ai:* Coach 8th Grd Boys ktbl 1976-78, 8th Grd Ftbl 1976-78, Jr Var Boys Bsktbl 1978-85, Var sistance Bsktbl 1985-86, Head Var Bsktbl 1986-88, Frosh Ftbl 1980-85, 88-, Girls Track 1988-; Ftbl Coord 1978-80; Soc Stud Dept Chm 81-83; NEA 1976-; *office:* Champion MS 5435 Kaszmaul Warren OH 483

LPIETRA, NICHOLAS RICHARD, Mathematics Instructor; *b:* ungstown, OH; *ed:* Youngstown St Univ (BS) Math 1991; 40 Grad Hrs vard a Masters of Sci in Math; *cr:* Liberty Local Schls Math Sub Tchr 1988-92; Youngstown St Univ Grad Asst 1992-93, Math Instr 1993-; *office:* Youngstown St Univ 410 Wick Ave Youngstown OH 44555

SALSER, SCOTT ALAN, Choral Director; *b:* Oil City, PA; *m:* Karen Kreiner; *ed:* Indiana Univ of PA (BS) Music Ed 1984; PA St Univ Credits Toward a MED in Music Ed; *cr:* St Coll Area Schl Dist Elem & Jr HS General Music Tchr 1984-86; East Stroudsburg HS Choral Dir 1987-91; Indiana Sr HS Choral Dir 1991-; *ai:* Direct Mixed Chorus, Mens Chorus, Womens Chorus, Acappella Choir, Madrigal Singers & Annual Musical; House Mgr for Drama Productions; IN Area Ed Assn 1991-; PA Music Educators Assn 1982-; Music Educators Natl Conf 1982-; Amer Choral Dir Assn 1993-; Presbyn Church 1988-91, Directed Choirs, Led Youth Groups & Bible Stud; Meth Church 1974-87; Listed in Outstanding Young Men of Amer 1985, Whos Who Among Amer HS Stdnts 1984 & Whos Who in Music 1984; *office:* Indiana Sr HS 450 N 5th St Indiana PA 15701

SALTARELLI, GEORGE XAVIER, Mathematics Teacher & Dept Chm; *b:* Buffalo, NY; *m:* Betty Jane Trautman; *c:* Mark, Michael, Mary E. Knoerl, Monica, Marie T. Maziarz; *ed:* Canisius Coll (BA) Eng 1943; Univ of Notre Dame (MS) Math 1947; Addl 30 Credit Hrs; *cr:* Canisuis Coll Math Instr 1943-44; Carneigie Inst Dept of Terrestrial Magnetism Mathematician 1944-45; Univ of Notre Dame Tchng Fellow 1945-49; Bell Aircraft Corp Dynamics Engr 1950-53; Amherst Cntrl HS Tchr 1954-84; Univ of Bflo Evening DIvision, Math Lecturer 1954-86; Holy Angels Acad Math Chm 1984-; *ai:* NY St Tchr Assn, Western NY Tchrs 1954-; City of Tonawanda 1975-83, Alderman; Awded Carl Naish Awd of Excl Tchng Math By Millard Fillmore Coll ST Univ of NY at Bflo; *office:* Holy Angels Acad 24 Shoshone Dr Buffalo NY 14214*

SALTER, CAROL LYNN, Fifth Grade Teacher; *b:* Akron, OH; *m:* Glenn; *c:* Justin; *ed:* Kent St Univ (BFA) Art Ed 1978; John Carroll Univ; Quest; Bridge to Success; *cr:* Kent Roosevelt Schl Art Tchr 1979-80; Kent Davey Jr HS Art Tchr 1979-80; St John Bapt Schl 5th Grd Tchr 1981-86; Annuciation St John Schl 5th Grd, 5-8th Grd Math Tchr 1986-; *ai:* Stu Cncl, Safety Patrol Adv; Tchr of Yr 1989-90; St Vicent St Mary HS Frosh Favorite Tchr 1995.

SALTER, KEITH THEISS, Fourth Grade Teacher; *b:* Allentown, PA; *m:* Sharon M. Geesaman; *c:* Diane M.; *ed:* 57 Credit Hrs Post Grad Stud Allentown Coll, Millersville Univ, PSU & Temple Univ; *cr:* Cornwall Elem Schl Grd 4 Tchr 1970-76; Ebenezer Elem Schl Grd 4 Tchr 1976-; *ai:* CLASS Participating Tchr; NEA, PSEA 1970-; LCEC 1990-, Bike-A-Thon Co-Chair; CLEA 1970-, Bldg Rep; St John's UCC 1982-, Consistory Pres; Lebanon Cty Hnr Soc 1987-; *office:* Ebenezer Elem Schl 452 Ebenezer Rd Lebanon PA 17046

SALTMARSH, ALEXANDER WILLIAM, Educl Services Dir & Coach; *b:* Concord, NH; *m:* Hope Demarest; *c:* Jason B., Aaron A., Anthony J., Davis F.; *ed:* UNH (BA) Bio, Ed 1969; 30 Credit Hrs Guid, Occupational Ed; 40 Credit Hrs Sport Sci; 20 Credit Hrs Environmental Stud; *cr:* Winnacunnet HS Bio Tchr 1969-70; US Coast Guard Marine Sci Tech 1st Class 1970-74; St of NH Educl Consultant 1975-80; Fitness Resources Educl Svcs Dir, Presenter, Writer, Bsktbl & Track Coach 1980-; *ai:* AAU Bsktbl Club Dir & Coach; Fitness & Sports Medicine Groups Adv; ACSM Regnl Presenter; NEAAU Sports Medicine Comm, Championship Coach; RRCA Natl Sports Medicine Comm Chm; NH Governor's Cncl on Phys Fitness, Steering Comm; Presenter Several Non-Profit Prgsm; Coaches & Prgms Adv; Road Runners Club of Amer Rod Steele Awd; Numerous Articles Pub; *home:* 122 Bow Bog Rd Bow NH 03304*

SALTZ, SIMON E., Professor of Accounting; *b:* New York, NY; *m:* Susan; *c:* Naomi Saltz Vann, Rena Saltz Bak, Aaron, Dov Adina; *ed:* Brooklyn Coll (BS) Acctng 1972; Univ of St of NY Prof License CPA; *cr:* Touro Coll Prof of Acctng 1984-; NY St Office of Hlth Systems Mgmt Fiscal Analyst-Hlth Care 1984-; Simon Saltz CPA Pvt Practice 1985-; *ai:* Bus Dept Fac Adv; Stu Acctng Soc Adv; Touro Fac Outstdng Prof; *home:* 1343 E 8th St Brooklyn NY 11230

SALTZMAN, DALE ANDREW, Art Teacher; *b:* New York, NY; *m:* Ellen; *c:* Naomi, Kyle; *ed:* RI Schl of Design (BFA) Illustration, Painting 1965; Western CT St Coll (MA) Ed 1978; 36 Addl Credits City Coll of NY City; *cr:* Self-employed Art Svc Graphic Designer 1965-70; Case Worker NYC 11968-69; Commune Mem Worker, Father 1970-73; Briarcliff Pub Schls Indstrl Arts Tchr 1973-83; Fox Lane HS Art Tchr 1983-; *ai:* Art Club; Yth in Action; BSA; Earth Day Ritual 8 Yrs; AFT; NYSATA; NYSUT; Environmental Issues, Anti-Nuclear, Local Activist; Grants Art, Outdoor Prgms; Runner-Up NYS Tchr of Yr 1981; Several Pub Illustrated Books; *office:* Fox Lane HS PO Box 390 Bedford NY 10506

SALUDIS, WILLIAM CHRISTERPHOR, Chemistry Teacher; *b:* Sewickley, PA; *m:* Lisa Schweinsberg-Saludis; *c:* Anthony, Margarette; *ed:* CA St Coll (BS) Chem 1983; CA Univ (BED) Scndry Ed 1984, (MS) Math 1987, (MED) Cmptr Sci 1989; PA Chem Industry Ed Fnd; Woodrow Wilson Sci Fnd; Tchrs Ind ustry & Environment; PA St Cmptr Advancement, Computer Interface Seminar: Duquesne, Envrnmt studs SRUP; *cr:* CA Univ Gifted Tchr & Cnslr Summers 1982-88; Freedom Area HS Chem Tchr 1984-; *ai:* Asst Var Wrestling Coach; Timing Ofcl Track; Coord Sci Bowl; Gale Proj Coord; Tchr & Mentr GATE Prog; Coord PA Cross Curric Mngmt; NEA & PSEA 1984-, Grievance Chm; NSTA 1984-; AACE 1985-; FAEA Marching & Chowder 1984-, Pres, Man of Yr; ACS 1982; Holy Trinity Greek Orthodox Youth Cncl 1985-, Pres; Natl Rifle Assn 1986-; Natl Aududon Soc 1982-; VFW; FOE; *home:* 1805 Conway Wallrose Rd Freedom PA 15042*

SALUGA, MARY ANN (VACCARO), Drama & English Teacher; *b:* Uniontown, PA; *m:* Paul F.; *c:* Douglas P., Julie E.; *ed:* Tarkio Coll (BA) Drama, Sec Ed 1967; CA Univ of PA Grad Credits Sec Eng 1967-70; *cr:* German Twp Sr HS Grd 11 Eng Tchr 1967-70; German Twp Jr HS Grd 8 Eng Tchr 1971-87; Albert Gallatin Sr HS Grd 10 Drama, Eng Tchr 1987-; *ai:* Drama Coach; Schl Plays Dir; Video Production Coord; Albert Gallatin Schl Dist Writing Comm; Albert Gallatin Area Ed Assn, PA St Ed Assn, NEA 1967-; Greater Uniontown Heritage Consortium 1993-, Ed Comm Chprsn; Critical Reader; Participated in PA Writing Evaluation; *office:* Albert Gallatin Sr HS Rd 5 Box 175a Uniontown PA 15401

SALVATI, DIANA MARIA, Junior High Teacher; *b:* Philadelphia, PA; *ed:* Rosemont Coll (BA) Psych 1977; St Charles Seminary (MA) Theology 1996; *cr:* St Thomas Aquinas Schl 2nd, 5th & Jr High Tchr 1985-89; Holy Spirit Schl 6th Grd Tchr 1989-90; St Madeline-St Rose Schl Jr High Tchr 1991-; *ai:* Stu Cncl Moderator; Rel Coord; Liturgical Music Dir; NCEA 1985-, Tchr Assn; *office:* St Madeline-St Rose Schl Tome & Rodgers Sts Ridley Park PA 19078

SALVATO, JOHN A., 8th Grade Social Studies Tchr; *b:* NY; *ed:* St Univ Coll at Oneonta (BS) Sec Ed 1970; NY Univ (MA) Asian Stud 1977; 60 Credit Hrs Amer His, Multicultural Ed, Bio, Geology, Conflict Resolution; *cr:* Margaretville Cntrl Schl 9, 10, 12 Grd Soc Stud Tchr 1970-73; Wheatly Schl 9 Grd Soc Stud Tchr 1979-80; Southside MS 7-8 Grd Soc Stud, 7 Grd Human Relations Tc hr 1989-; *ai:* Track, Cross Cntry Coaches; Stu Cncl Adv; Conflict Resolution Facilitator; NYS Assn of Soc Stud Tchr; Long Island Assn Soc Stud Tchr, Edctr Soc Responsibility, Conflict Res Group; PTA Tchr of Yr Awd; Amer His Inst Grant Buffalo Univ; *office:* South Side MS Hillside Ave Rockville Center NY 11570*

SALVATO, SCOTT VINCENT, 10th-11th Grade Theology Tchr; *b:* Rockville, NY; *ed:* St Bonaventure Univ (BA) Theology 1993; *cr:* St Dominic's HS 12th Grd Theology Tchr 1993; Holy Trinity HS 10-11th Grd Theology Tchr 1994-; *ai:* Lay Tchrs Assn 1994-; *home:* 108 Washington Pl Massapequa NY 11758

SALVATO, VINCENT, Social Studies Teacher; *b:* Lexington, KY; *m:* Sonya J. Ferris; *c:* Anthony, Amy; *ed:* Williams Coll (BA) His 1967; Xavier Univ (MED) Eng 1971; *cr:* Lakemont Acad Tchr 1967-69; Glen Este Jr HS Tchr 1969-71; Sycamore HS Tchr 1971-; *ai:* Sycamore Dist Insurance, Evaluation, Career Ladder, & Staff Dev Comms; Negotiations Team; Independent Study Cls; Sycamore Ed Assn 1971-, Grievance Chm; OEA 1969-, Alphi Cncl Chm; NEA 1969-; OCSS 1984-; *office:* Sycamore HS 7400 Cornell Rd Cincinnati OH 45242

SALVATORIELLO, SANDRA L., 1st Grade Teacher; *b:* Jersey City, NJ; *m:* Douglas; *c:* Dan, Marc; *ed:* Trenton St Coll (BS) Early Chldhd Ed 1972; 15 Grad Credits Concentration Childrens Lit; *cr:* Robert L. Craig Schl 2nd Grd Tchr 1972-78, 1st Grd Tchr 1980-; *ai:* Curr Comm; Costume Dir Schl Play; NEA, NJEA 1972-; Moonachie Tchr of Yr 1992; *office:* Robert L Craig Elem Sch 20 W Park St Moonachie NJ 07074

SALVIA, ANTHONY, Biology & Chemistry Teacher; *m:* Zoe F. Strитt; *c:* Annasophia, Ralph, Julia, Zachary; *ed:* Marist Coll (BS) Bio 1980; Western CT St Univ (MA) Schl Cnslng 1986; *cr:* Anderson Schl HS Sci Tchr 1980-83; Dover Union Free Schl Bio, Chem Tchr 1983-88; Fox Lane HS Bio, Chem 1988-; *ai:* Site Base Mngmt Comm; 1998 Class Adv; NSTA; AFT; NYSTA; *office:* Fox Lane HS PO Box 390 Bedford NY 10506*

SALVIA, CAROLEE KAPNER, Spanish Teacher; *b:* Freeport, NY; *m:* Anthony; *c:* Charles, Amanda; *ed:* Univ of Miami (AB) Span 1970; Rutgers Univ (MA) Span Lit 1974; 30 Credits, Doctoral Exams in Span Lit; *cr:* Univ of Miami Tchng Fellow 1970-71; Bloomfield Coll Lecturer 1972-73; Westfield HS Scndry Tchr 1973; Rutgers Univ Tchng Asst, Lecturer 1973-76; Mt Sinai HS Scndry Tchr 1991-; *ai:* Site Based Mgmt Comm; AATSP, NYSAFLT 1989-; *office:* Mount Sinai HS Gertrude Goodman Dr Mount Sinai NY 11766

SALVIDIO, NANCI MAHONEY, Assoc Dir of Acad Advising; *b:* Boston, MA; *m:* Frank A. Jr.; *c:* Rachel Rhoda; *ed:* Westfield St Coll (BA) Soc Sci 1974, (MA) Psych 1984; Soc Work Credits U Conn Schl of Soc Work; *cr:* MA Dept Mental Hlth Client Prgm Coord 1975-77; Westfield St Coll Cnslr, Urban Ed Prgm 1980-90, Assoc Dir Acad Advising 1990-; *ai:* Open Gates; Natl Stu Exch; Search Comms; MA Tchrs Assn, NEA 1986-; FIPSE Grant; Westfield 150 Distngd Svc Awd; Nationally Certfd Cnslr; *office:* Westfield St Coll Western Avenue Westfield MA 01086

SALZGABER, BETTE YOUNG, Fourth Grade Teacher; *b:* Marion, OH; *m:* Gary Richard; *ed:* Capital Univ (BA) Music Ed 1968; Wright St Univ (MS) Ed, Rdng 1979; *cr:* Graham Local Schls Third Grd Tchr 1968-72; Urbana City Schls Fourth Grd Tchr 1972-; *ai:* Fac Admin Cncl; Graham Ed Assn 1968-72; Urbana Assn Classroom Tchrs 1972-, Bldg Rep; OH Ed Assn, NEA 1968-; Urbana United Meth Church 1970-, Choir; Awd of Merit 1989; *office:* Urbana City Schls 630 Washington Ave Urbana OH 43078

SALZGEBER, KAREN A., HS Mathematics Teacher; *b:* Cleveland, OH; *m:* Alan J.; *c:* Kristen, Kurt; *ed:* Kent St Univ (BSEd) Math 1976; Cleveland St Univ (MED) Curr & Instruction Cmptr Uses in Ed 1993; *cr:* Collinwood HS Math & Jrnlsm Tchr 1976-79; Parma Sr HS Math Tchr 1991-; *ai:* Parma Sr HS Ski Club Adv; NHS Tchr Comm Mem; NEA, OEA, NCTM 1991-; PTA 1991-; *office:* Parma Sr HS 6285 W 54th St Parma OH 44129

SAMAD, ABDOOL, Math Teacher; *b:* Guyana; *m:* Monica; *c:* Liselle, Vanessa; *ed:* Univ of Guyana (BED) Math Ed 1981; Lehman Coll (MS) Math 1990; *cr:* Stewartville Scndry Schl Math, Physics Tchr 1968-86; DeWitt Clinton HS Math Tchr 1988; Jr HS 82 Math Tchr 1988-90; A. Philip Randolph HS Math Tchr 1990-; *office:* A. Philip Randolph Campus HS 135 St & Convent Ave New York NY 10031*

SAMARAT, MARIE CERBONE, English Teacher; *b:* Bayonne, NJ; *m:* Mahmoud; *c:* Adam; *ed:* Jersey City St Coll (BA) Eng 1972; Montclair St Univ (MA) Admin & Supervision 1978; *cr:* Bayonne HS Eng Tchr 1972-81; Living Lang Coll-Cairo, Egypt Instr & Curr Dev 1981-82; Bayonne HS Eng Tchr 1982-; *ai:* Excl Comm; NCTE, NEA 1972-; *office:* Bayonne HS 29th St & Ave A Bayonne NJ 07002

SAMAROO, AMAR, Math Teacher; *b:* Georgetown, Guyana; *ed:* Univ of London (GCE) Arts 1976; Leningrad Univ (MS) Ec 1985; Adelphi Univ (MA) Ed 1995; *cr:* Ministry of Fin Accountant 1976-79; NYC Bd of Ed Tchr 1986-; *ai:* Soccer Coach; Soccer Club; AFT, UFT 1986-; Sr Schl Schlsp 1974; Govt Schlsp 1979; *office:* JHS 190 Russell Sage 6817 Austin St Flushing NY 11375*

SAMICH, JACQUELINE CATALANO, French Teacher; *b:* Lakehurst, NJ; *m:* Steven; *c:* Steven; *ed:* Montclair St U (BA) Fr, Eng, Speech, Drama 1969; *cr:* Woodbridge HS Fr, Eng Tchr 1969-79; John F. Kennedy HS Fr Tchr 1983-91; Woodbridge HS Fr Tchr 1991-95; Colonia HS Fr Tchr 1995-; *ai:* Fr Club Adv 1983-; FLENJ, AATF 1991-.*

SAMKO, PAUL GEORGE, Chemistry Teacher; *b:* McKees Rocks, PA; *m:* Nancy M. Lucas; *c:* Melanie, Amanda; *ed:* Edinboro Univ (BS) Chem & Ed 1972; Univ of Pittsburgh (MED) Scndry Ed 1976; Credit Hrs From Duquesne Univ & Carnegie Mellon Univ; *cr:* Allderdice HS Chem & Earth Sci Tchr 1972-73; Oliver HS Chem Tchr 1973-; *ai:* Ftbl Asst Coach; Hlth Tech Team; New Standards Comm Pittsburgh Bd of Ed; SEPA Outreach Prgm; AFT, PFT 1972-; NSTA 1985-; Robinson Twp Girls Sftbl 1990-, Coach; Spectroscopy Soc of Pittsburgh Equipment Grant; Soc of Analytical Chemists of Pittsburgh-Keivin Burns Awd; *office:* Oliver HS 2323 Brighton Rd Pittsburgh PA 15212

SAMMARTINO, LINDA SCHWERDTMANN, Business Teacher; *b:* Camden, NJ; *m:* Carmen John; *c:* Stacey Marie Bishop Allen, William Michael Bishop; *ed:* Camden Cty Coll (AAS) Exec Sec 1978; Trenton St Coll (BS) Bus Ed 1981; Cmptr Courses; *cr:* Collingswood HS Bus Ed Tchr 1981-82; Clayton HS Bus Ed Tchr 1982-; *ai:* NJEA 1981-; NJBEA 1980-; *office:* Clayton HS 350 E Clinton St Clayton NJ 08312

SAMMET, CLAUDIA CORBIT, English Teacher; *b:* Canton, OH; *m:* Dwight D.; *c:* Jessica, Katie; *ed:* Bowling Green St Univ (BSEd) Eng, Speech & Theatre 1974; Coll of Mount St Joseph (MAEd) Ed 1985; Working Towards Admin Cert at Ashland Univ; *cr:* Glen Oak HS Eng Tchr 1974-79; Walsh Coll Part-Time Theatre Instr 1980-85; Stark Tech Coll Part-Time Eng Instr 1980-85; Glen Oak HS Eng Tchr 1985-; *ai:* Eng Dept Team Ldr; Lang Arts Curr Comm Mem; Tchr Ldr Network Mem; PLTA Tchrs Union 1985-, Exec Comm; NCTE 1985-; OCTELA 1983-; *office:* Glen Oak HS West Campus 1015 44th St NW Canton OH 44709*

SAMMON, SCOTT JOSEPH, High School Biology Teacher; *b:* Bronx, NY; *m:* Lisa Marie; *c:* Laura Marie, Keara Elizabeth; *ed:* SUNY Coll at Cortland (BS) Bio 1986, (MAT) Scndry Sci Ed 1988; *cr:* Clarkstown North HS Bio, Physics Tchr 1987; Cicero-North Syracuse HS Bio Tchr 1988-; *ai:* Sci Olympiad Coach; Dist Sci Fair Steering, Bio Curr Comms; NY Sci Tchrs Assn 1989-; NYSUT 1988-; Empire St Challenger Flwshp; *office:* Cicero-North Syracuse HS Rt 31 Northstar Dr Cicero NY 13039

SAMMONS, KAREN R., Tutor, Sub Tchr, Testing Coord; *b:* Lancaster, OH; *m:* Jeffery D.; *c:* Jessica, Angela; *ed:* OH Univ (BA) Elem Ed 1978; 12 Grad Credit Hrs; *cr:* Allensville Elem Schl 1st Grd Tchr 1978-80; Madison Elem Schl 1st Grd Tchr 1980-86; Grace Chrstn Schl Testing Coord 1995-; *ai:* Tutor; Sunday Schl Tchr.

SAMOILA, FRANCES EVELYN, Vocal Music Instructor; *b:* Akron, OH; *m:* Bruce A.; *ed:* Univ of Akron (BME) Music Ed 1982; *cr:* Cedar,

Clarendon Elem Schl Instr 1987-; Lathrop Elem Schl Gen Music 1990; Shipley Ctr 1987-94; Timken Sr HS Vocal Music Instr 1982-; *ai:* Pep Club, Commencement Comm; NEA, OEA, ECOEA, CPEA, MENC, OMEA 1982-; Summit Cty Choral Soc 1990-93, Section Ldr; *office:* Timken Sr HS 521 Tuscarawas St W Canton OH 44702

SAMORDIC, MICHAEL GEORGE, Math & Computer Science Tchr; *b:* Washington, DC; *ed:* VPI & SU (BS) Math 1974; Cath Univ (MS) Math 1980; *cr:* DeMatha HS Math, Cmptr Sci Tchr 1975-88; Eleanor Roosevelt HS Math, Cmptr Sci Tchr 1988-; *ai:* Its Acad Coach; Cmptr Club, Operation Sweep Spon; Multicultural Comm; NEA, MAA, PCCEA 1988-; Knights of Columbus 1991-, 3rd Degree Awd; The Smithosonian Assn 1992-; Inducted in NHS as Tchr 1980; Tandys Cmptr Math, Cmptr Sci Tchr of Yr 1994-95; *office:* Eleanor Roosevelt HS 7601 Hanover Pky Greenbelt MD 20770

SAMOYEDNY, JOHN MICHAEL, High School English Teacher; *b:* New York, NY; *c:* Andrew John, Christian Michael; *ed:* Iona Coll (BA) Mktng, Comm 1982, (MS) Eng Ed 1985; Addl Hrd Wilkes Univ Eng, Ed, Bloomsburg Univ Rdng, Univ of Scranton Scndry Schl Cnslng Prgm; *cr:* Sacred Heart HS Eng Tchr 1983-87; Keystone Job Corps Ctr Rdng Inst 1987-88; Williams Vly HS Eng Tchr 1988-89; Upper Dauphin Area HS Eng Tchr 1989-91; Hazleton Area HS Eng Tchr 1991-; *ai:* Newspaper Pub Consultant; Stu Act Comm; NEA, PSEA 1988-; NCTE 1983-; Cunyngham Vly Civic Org 1995-; St John Bosco Church 1996; *office:* Hazelton Area HS 101 S Church St Hazleton PA 18201

SAMPLE, BARBARA F., Second Grade Teacher; *b:* Middleton, OH; *c:* Wendy Ann, Stephanie Jane; *ed:* Miami Univ (BS) Ed 1965; Xavier Univ (MS) Ed 1983; Grad Courses Univ of Cincinnati & Dayton & Fresno Pacific Univ; *cr:* W Carrollton City Schls 2nd Grd Tchr 1965-67; Franklin City Schls 2nd-3rd Grd Tchr 1976-; *ai:* Soc Stud Curr Comm; Alumni Treas for My HS Class; OEA, NEA 1976; FEA 1976-, Bldg Rep; Awded Grant to Improve Rdng Skills of Stdnts; *office:* Pennyroyal Elem Schl 4203 Pennyroyal Rd Franklin OH 45005

SAMPLE, BOBBI KLINGEL, Second Grade Teacher; *b:* Marion, OH; *m:* Gerald Herbert; *c:* Ebben, Aaron, Ian; *ed:* OH St Univ (BS) Elem Ed 1974; Attnd Robert Morris Coll, Ashland Univ; *cr:* Dublin Local Schls 3-4th Grd Tchr 1975-78; Mt Gilead Schls 2nd Grd 1978-; *ai:* Help Coord Mt Gilead Soccer Assn for Grds K-6; Cub Scout Den Asst 2 Yrs; NEA, OEA 1975-; MGTA 1978-; IRA Mem; *office:* Mt Gilead Exempted Village Sch N Cherry St Mount Gilead OH 43338

SAMPLE, DANIEL EDWARD, AP American History Teacher; *b:* Butler, PA; *m:* Pamela Sue Greynolds; *c:* Deanna, Lindsay; *ed:* Geneva Coll (BA) His 1973; Duquesne Univ (MS) Schl Admin 1979; Univ of Pittsburgh Amer His 1981; *cr:* Seneca Vly HS Tchr 1974-; *ai:* Track Coach; PSEA 1974-, Leg Rep; *office:* Seneca Valley Sr HS 126 Seneca Schl Rd Harmony PA 16037

SAMPSELLE, DAVID WILLIAM, Senior High English Teacher; *b:* Washington, DC; *m:* Kathy R. Spencer; *c:* Dirk Ryan; *ed:* Western MD Coll (BA) Eng 1970; Univ of PA (MA) Eng 1971; *cr:* Gaithersburg High Eng Tchr 1973-89; Watkins Mill Eng Tchr 1989-; *ai:* Sr Class Adv; NEA & NSTA 1973-; Yrbk Adv of Medalist & All-Amer Yrbks 1976, 1979-81, 1983, 1986-88; *office:* Watkins Mill HS 10301 Apple Ridge Rd Gaithersburg MD 20879

SAMPSON, SALLY ANN, French Teacher; *b:* Akron, OH; *m:* Donald T. Jr.; *c:* Donald III, Rhys; *ed:* Mount Union Coll (BA) Fr, Eng 1967; Kent St Univ (MA) Eng 1982; Attnd Laval Univ in Quebec, Central MI Univ, Northern MI Univ; *cr:* Marlington HS Fr, Eng Tchr 1967-69; Minerva HS Fr Tchr 1971-73; Republic-Michigamme Fr Tchr 1973-76; Boardman HS Fr, Eng Tchr 1976-; *ai:* Fr Club Adv; NEA, AATF 1967-; Order of Eastern Star 1966-; Deerfield United Meth Church 1957-, Music Dir 10 Yrs, Organist 10 Yrs, Jr Choir Dir 16 Yrs, Adult Choir Dir 10 Yrs; NACEC 1991-; BSA 1983-, Silver Beaver Awd; AATF Schlsp Winner Laval Univ in Quebec 1984; *home:* 2071 Bonner Rd Deerfield OH 44411

SAMPSON, VIRGINIA JANE, Counselor & French Teacher; *b:* Erie, PA; *ed:* Villamaria Coll (BA) Fr, Latin; Gannon Univ (MA) Fr, Guid, Ed; 18 Post Grad Credit Hrs in Fr Univ of Northern IA, L'Univ D'Anger; La Sorbonne Ctr Confs Experimental Hnr Cert; *cr:* Northwestern Schls Fr Tchr, Guid 26 Yrs; *ai:* MS Travel Club; NEA 26 Yrs; Frgn Lang Assn; Classical Assn of Atlantic St; Northwestern Ed Assn Tchrs Awd 1984; Lang Awds for Stdnts; Schlsps; Drama Presentations in Fr.

SAMS, PATRICIA A., Mathematics Teacher; *b:* Elmira, NY; *m:* William E.; *c:* Michael, Brian; *ed:* SUNY at Geneseo (BA) Math 1975; *cr:* Palmyra Macedon MS Math Tchr 1975-87; Palmyra Macedon HS Math Tchr 1987-; *ai:* NHS Advy Bd; 1994 Tchr of Yr; *office:* Palmyra Macedon HS 151 Hyde Parkway Palmyra NY 14522

SAMS, SANDRA BAILEY, Mathematics Teacher; *b:* Gary, IN; *m:* Joseph Mark; *c:* Kristin Rachel, Christopher Ryan, Karen Malinda, Kaylyn Rene; *ed:* Ozark Chrstn Coll (BCE) Ed 1982; Miami Univ (MED) Scndry Math 1993; Post Grad Univ of Cincinnati, Pittsburg St Univ; MO Southern St Coll Credit Hrs; *cr:* South Jr HS Tchr, Intervention Specialist 1985-91; Middletown HS Tchr 1991-; *ai:* Bldg Ldrshp Team Steering Comm, Facilitator; Cmptr, Math Clubs; Drama Dir; Bldg Advy Comm; Girls Head, Boys Asst Var Track & Field Coach; Current Act t; NEA, OEA, NCTM 1985-; OCTM 1990-; Middletown SAY Soccer 1993-, Bd Mem; BSA 1995-, Cub Master; Sallie Mae Tchr Awd Nom; *office:* Middletown H S 601 N Breiel Blvd Middletown OH 45042*

SAMSA, RICHARD ANTON, Chemistry Teacher; *b:* Youngstown, OH; *m:* Rebecca; *cr:* Purchase Line HS Chem, Physics Tchr 1985-86; Grove City HS Chem Tchr 1987-; *ai:* Bsktbl Coach; PSEA, NEA 1985-; Two Articles Pub in The Journal of Chemical Education; *office:* Grove City Sr HS 511 Highland Ave Grove City PA 16127

SAMSEL, JEANNIE N., Sixth Grade Teacher; *b:* Jersey City, NJ; *m:* Sandy; *c:* Jason, Carrie; *ed:* Mercer Cty Comm (AA) 1974; Trenton St Coll (BS) Elem Ed 1976; Working on Masters in Admin; *cr:* Melvin Kreps Schl 6th-8th Grd Eng & Math tchr 1977-79; Robert Stacy Schl Basic Skills Math Tchr 1979-80, 4th Grd Self Contained Tchr 1980-82; Captain James Lawrence Schl 5th Grd Self Contained Tchr 1983-84; Wilbur Watts MS 6th-8th Grd Math, Eng & Rdng Tchr 1984-89; Wilbur Watts Intermediate Schl 5th-6th Grd Self Contained Tchr 1990-; *ai:* Morning Intramurals; Cmptr, Text Selection, Progress Reports, Gym & Fields Dedication Comms; 6th Grd Lead Tchr; Articulation Comm; NEA, NJEA 1977-; BCEA 1979-; WWIS Tchr of Yr 1995; *office:* Wilbur Watts Intermediate Schl High St Burlington NJ 08016*

SAMSON, LINDA MARIE, Speech & Language Pathologist; *b:* Lockport, NY; *m:* Lee Douglas; *c:* Erika, Melanie; *ed:* St Univ of NY at NYC-FIT (AAS) Apparel Design 1970; St Univ Coll at Buffalo (BS) Commnctn Disorders 1980, (MS) Commnctn Disorders 1982; St Univ Coll at Buffalo (CAS) Schl Admin & Supvr 1996; Niagara Univ; Ed Admin; *cr:* Orleans Niagara BOCES Speech Therapist 1981-83 & 1985-86; Lewison Porter Cntrl Schl Dist Speech Therapist 1983-85; Hardin Cty Bd of Ed Speech Therapist 1986-88; Medina Cntrl Schl Dist Speech Therapist 1988-91; Williamsville Cntrl Schl Dist Speech & Lang Pathologist 1991-, Admin Intern 1995-; *ai:* Co-Adv SADD; Peer Partner Pgm Coord; Admin Internship; Speech Hearing Assn of Western NY 1991-, Treas; NY St Speech, Hearing & Lang Assn 1992-; Amer Speech, Hearing & Lang Assn 1992-; Williamsville T Assn; AFT; Phi Delta Kappa 1993-; Erie Cty Victim Impact Panel 5 Yrs, Presenter; Niagara Cty Historical Soc 8 Yrs; Grad Rsrch Awd; Grant from OH Dept of Ed; Consultant to Various Western NY Dists; Presenter to Colls, Univs & Orgs; *home:* 6025 McKee Rd Newfane NY 14108

SAMUELS, BONNIE ETTINGER, Fourth Grade Teacher; *b:* Brooklyn, NY; *m:* Norm; *c:* Sarah, Hava; *ed:* Queens Coll (BA) Elem Ed 1969; St Univ of NY at Stony Brook (MA) Lbrl Arts 1975; Post Grad & In-Svc Courses; *cr:* NYC Schls Dist 19 5th Grd Tchr 1969-70; Mt Sinai UFSD 3rd Grd Tchr 1970-71, 2nd Grd Tchr 1973-77, 4th Grd Tchr 1979-; *ai:* 4th Grd Math Olympiads Adv; NYSUT 1969-; Mt Sinai Tchrs Assn 1970-; AFT; N Shore Jewish Ctr Hebrew Schl Bd 1982-; *office:* Mt Sinai Elem Schl N Country Rd Mount Sinai NY 11766

SAMUELS, LINDA GARBER, Instructor in Science; *b:* Mansfield, OH; *m:* Martin A.; *c:* Marilyn, Charles; *ed:* Univ of Cincinnati (AB) Bio, Zoology 1969, (MS) Population Bio 1971; Tufts Univ Human Genethics, Bioethical Decisions 1994; Syracuse Univ Coll Credit, Advanced Placement Bio 1986; Boston Univ Grad Ed 1972; *cr:* Univ of Cincinnati Anatomy, Physiology Instr 1969-70; Cambridge Acad Bio, Chem, Physics, Algebra II Tchr 1971-72; Simmons Coll Frosh Bio Tchr 1972-73; Dana Hall Schl AP Bio, Adv Bio, Honors Bio, Life Sci Instr 1972-; *ai:* Access Excl 1996; Rap Around; Discussion Dissection in the Classroom; Liason Comm 1995-; Galapogos Islands, Ecuadorian Amazon, Machu Picchu Ed Travel 1996; NABT 1994-, Outstanding Bio Tchr; MA Assn of Sci Tchrs 1980-, Tchr of Yr 1994; NSTA 1975-; New England Sci Tchrs 1989-; Temple Israel-Sukkot Comm; Bar Bat Mitzvah Comm Parent Rep; Parking Comm; Condominium Trustee; H. Dudley Wright Fellowship Innovative Sci Ed 1996; Sabbatical Grant 1995; *office:* Dana Hall Schl 21 Dana Rd Wellesley Hills MA 02181

SAMUELS, PATRICIA LYNN, Cooperative Bus Ed Tchr, Coord; *b:* Indianapolis, IN; *m:* Steven; *c:* Scott; *ed:* Ball St Univ (BS) Bus 1967; Northern KY Univ (MED) Bus 1983; *cr:* Withrow HS Bus Tchr 1969-73; Merry Jr HS Hearing Impaired Bus Tchr 1975-79; Withrow HS Bus Tchr 1979-87, CBE Tchr, Coord 1987-; *ai:* Bus Prof of America; Voc Curr Cncl Chprsn; Delta Pi Epsilon 1988-89, VP, Sec; Swobta, Pres, VP; NBEA, AVA 1995-; WLW, CG&E Awd of Inspiration; Pub Svc Awd; OVELI; *office:* Withrow HS 2488 Madison Rd Cincinnati OH 45208

SAMUELSEN, MARGARET ROONEY, 7th Grade Teacher; *b:* Morristown, NJ; *m:* Anre; *ed:* Coll of St Elizabeth Convent (BA) Eng & Elem Ed 1960; Math, Span & Prof Dev Courses; *cr:* St Vincent Schl 5th & 6th Grd Tchr 1956-62; Immaculate Conception 7th & 8th Grd Tchr 1962-68; Our Lady of Sorrows 5th Grd Tchr 1968-69; St Charles Borromeo 8th Grd Tchr 1969-70; Dayton St Schl 5th Grd Tchr 1970-72; Bragaw Ave Annex 6th Grd Tchr 1972-79; George Washington Carver 7th Grd Tchr 1979-; *ai:* Newark Tchrs Union 1970-; Merck Pharmaceutical Grant for Math & Sci Through a Camera 1989; Newark Pub Schl Math Sci Fair 1st Place Awd for Correlative Math Sci & Soc Stud 1990.

SAMUELSON, KRISTEN MARIE, Spanish Teacher; *b:* Rhinebeck, NY; *m:* David; *c:* Hannah; *ed:* SUNY at Oswego (BA) Scndry Ed 1991; SUNY Empire St Coll Liberal Studies Major 8 Credit Hrs; *cr:* Clymer Cntrl Schl Long Term Sub & Span Tchr 1991-92; Pine Valley Cntrl Schl Long Term Sub & Span Tchr 1992; Jamestown Schls Span Tchr 1993-; *ai:* NEA 1993-; Cert of Recognition for Pioneering the Original Selborne Project; *office:* Jefferson MS 195 Martin Rd Jamestown NY 14701

SAMULSKI, GARY JOSEPH, Director of Bands; *b:* Buffalo, NY; *m:* Cynthia O'Brocta; *ed:* Daemen Coll (BS) Music Ed 1976; Grad Work At Niagara Univ in Educl Admin Permanent NY St Cert 1981; Addl Grad Work Music Ed at Berklee Schl of Music, SUNY at Buffalo & SUC at Fredonia; *cr:* Edward Town MS 7th & 8th Grd General Music Tchr 1976; Tonawanda Sr HS Music Tchr 1976-79; Honeoye Cntrl Schl Band Dir 1980-89; Greece Athena HS Band Dir 1989-; *ai:* Pit Orch Dir for Schl Musical; Show Choir Combo Dir; Pub Address Announcer for Ftbl & Bsktbl Gams; Acad Stans Comm Chm; Monroe Cty Schl Music Assn 1989-, Pres Elect; NY St Schl Music Assn 1976-; NY St Band Dirs 1993-; Greece Tchrs Assn & NEA 1989-; Section 5 Exec Ftbl Comm 1992-, Dir of Ceremonies; Monroe Cty Special Olympics 1991-, Public Address Announcer; NYS Ftbl; Nationally Registered Music Educator 1991 Music Educators Natl Con; Excl in Scndry Schl Tchng 1987 Univ of Rochester; Appointed an Adjudicator for NY St Schl Music Assn; Appointed An Adjudicator Natl Level Heritage Festivals; *office:* Greece Athena HS 800 Long Pond Rd Rochester NY 14612*

SAMWICK, ANDREW ALAN, Economics Professor; *b:* Manhasset, NY; *ed:* Harvard Coll (AB) Ec 1989; MA Inst Tech (PHD) Ec 1993; *cr:* Natl Bureau Ec Rsrch Aging, Hlth Care Ec Fellow 1993-94; Dartmouth Coll Asst Prof Ec 1994-; *ai:* Amer Ec Assn 1992-; Flwshps NSF Fnd Grad, Lynde, Harry Bradley Fnd; Natl Inst Aging Pre-Doctoral Trng Grant; Pub Natl Tax Journal; Brookings Papers Ec Act, Contemporary Ec Policy; *office:* Dartmouth Coll 6106 Rockefeller Hall Hanover NH 03755

SANACORE, VICKI R., Pupil Personnel Services Coord; *b:* Bronx, NY; *m:* Tony; *ed:* Hunter Coll (BA) Speech, Drama 1969; Lehman Coll (MA) Speech Ed 1974; *cr:* Morris HS Speech Tchr 1969-80; Bronx Regnl HS Pupil Prsnl Coord 1980-86; Grace Dodge HS Drama Tchr 1986-87; Hostos Lincoln Acad Pupil Prsnl Coord 1987-; *ai:* Annual Drama Performance Dir; Stu Cncl Adv; Stu Activities Coord; UFT 1969-, Del; AFT 1969-; NASSP 1990-; Base Grants 1993-94; Stop the Violence Grant; Team Up to Clean Up Grant; Alternative Tchr of Yr 1978; Pub Articles; *office:* Hostos-Lincoln Acad Of Science 475 Grand Concourse Bronx NY 10451

SANBORN, BRIAN ALBERT, Chemistry Teacher; *b:* Lewiston, ME; *m:* Pamela Jane Hoyt; *c:* Allana, Kristin; *ed:* Colby Coll (BA) Math, Chem 1982; *cr:* R. W. Traip Acad Chem Tchr 1982-; *ai:* Var Girls Bsktbl Coach; NEA 1982-; *office:* R. W. Traip Acad 12 Williams Ave Kittery ME 03904

SANBORN, JOHN NEWELL, Professor of English; *b:* Exeter, NH; *ed:* Univ of NH (BA) Sociology 1957, (MST) Eng 1966; Univ of WI (PHD) Medieval Eng 1973; Post-doctoral Stud Stanford Univ 1981; *cr:* Unity Coll Prof of Eng 1970-; *ai:* Fac Ath Rep; ME Medievalists Assn 1985-; Summer Fellow: Natl Endowment for Hum Stanford Univ 1981, Natl Defense Ed Act Simmons-Harvard 1965; Dissertation Directed by Profs; Numerous Articles Pub; *office:* Unity Coll Quaker Hill Unity ME 04988

SANBORN, PAUL JOSEPH, Dean of Social Studies; *b:* Philadelphia, PA; *m:* Therese Hopkins; *c:* Andrew Paul, Nathan Paul; *ed:* Villanova Univ (BA) Russian Stud 1968; West Chester Univ (MA) Philosophy 1972; St Joseph's Univ (MBA) Mngmt 1981; Cheney Univ Ad Cert Elem, Scndry Principalships 1983; 24 Credits MS Military Sci at Amer Military Univ; *cr:* US Govt Military Analyst Consultant 1966-;Southeast Delco Schl Dist 1980-90; Freedom Fnd Historian 1971-; Villanova Univ Mngmt Instr 1982-; Schl Dist Haverford Twp 1990-; *ai:* Head Cross Ctry Indoor, Outdoor Track Teams 12 Yrs; Hist Soc PA 1980-; Comp of ML Hist 1972-; ASCD 1985-; Naval Intllgnce Prof; Marine Corps Assoc; Contributing Ed, Lead Writer Pub Co 1993; Outstanding Alumnus Awd Philosophy Dept, West Chester Univ PA; Sports Hall of Fame Mem, Devon Prep Schl; Encyclopedia of The War of Revolution Assoc Editor 1994; Var Articles Pub; *office:* Schl Dist Haverford Twp 1801 E Darby Rd Havertown PA 19083*

SANCHES, CLEMENTE VAZ, Spanish Teacher; *b:* Chaves, Portugal; *ed:* Southern CA Univ (BA) Span 1974, (MS) Linguistics 1980; *cr:* Berlitz Schl of Lang Span, Portugese Tchr 1977-80; Danbury Bd of Ed Span, Portuguese Tchr 1981-; *ai:* New Haven Soccer Team Captain; *ho* Chestnut Hill Rd Sandy Hook CT 06482

SANCHEZ, ANA CRISTINA, Spanish Teacher; *b:* Heredia, Costa *m:* Alexander Arguedas; *c:* Alex Jr, Gaby, Alonso; *ed:* Unive Nacional at Costa Rica (BA) Eng as Second Lang 1985, (BA) Lingu Lit 1986; West Chester Univ (MA) Biling Ed 1990; Cert to Teach Eastern Coll; 20 Credits Towards Dr in Ed Immaculata Co Universidad Nacional at Costa Rica Eng Tchr 1984-88; Goshen F Schl Span Tchr 1990-91; West Chester Univ Span Tchr 1990-93; U DE Span Tchr 1992; Sun Vly HS Tchr 1993-; *ai:* NEA 1993-; Fu Schlsp to Purse Master's Degree 1988; Article Pub PENN TESO News 1990; Transaltion from Eng to Span a Tape Course 1991; Re for Pub lciation of Span III Course 1992; Paper Selected, Presented i Intnl Conf on Hispanic Humor Philadelphia 1995.

SANCHEZ, SANDRA DOLORES, Spanish Teacher; *b:* Newark, N Mercyhurst (BA) Span, Ed 1969; 3 Credits Translator NYU; 6 Cred Ed Kean Coll; *cr:* Sampson G. Smith Span Tchr 1970-80; Franklin HS Tchr 1980-; *ai:* Wheelchair Bsktbl; Var Men, Ladies Tennis Coach Club; Founder & Adv Ultimate Warriors; Mid Sts Evaluation; Co Resolution Improvment Comm; Chaperone; TQ Team; NJEA, NEA FLENJ 1992-95; NJ Coaches Assn; Span Club of Newark; Coach Girls, 1988, 1994-95, Boys 1991; Governor's Tchr of Yr 1994; Franklin HS 415 Francis St Somerset NJ 08873

SAND, JACQUELYN M., Frgn Lang Chprsn & French Tchr; *b:* Clev OH; *m:* Gustav H. Freedman; *c:* Lisette Sand-Freedman; *ed:* Univ (BA) Fr 1967; NY Univ (MAT) Fr 1968; *cr:* Baldwin Schl Fr Tchr 19 Speed Speaking ESL Tchr 1972-75; Highland Park HS Fr Tchr 19 Milton Acad Fr Tchr 1980-81; Walnut Hill Schl Fr Tchr, Frgn Lang C 1981-; *ai:* Acad Comm, Fac Affairs Adv 1995-; Fr Exchange Coord; 1980-, Bd Mem; MaFLA 1981-; NAIS, CWIS, AISNE 1981-, Bd Rockefeller Fnd Grant 1991; E. E. Ford Fnd Excl in Tchng Grant, 1991; E. E. Ford Fnd Summer Stud Grant 1994; Cncl Basic Ed Su Grant 1995; *office:* Walnut Hill Schl 12 Highland St Natick MA 01

SAND, JOHN WILLIAM, Social Studies Teacher; *b:* Madison, W Lauren Knies; *ed:* Univ of CT (BS) Ed 1990, (MA) Ed, Curr, Instru 1995; *cr:* E. O. Smith HS Tchr 1990-; *ai:* Curr, Assesment Act Tear Cncl for Soc Stud Bd Mem; Curr Comm; Prin Advy Bd Fac Rep; P Reach Coord; Natl His Day Adv; Ice Hockey Coach; BSA 1992 Skating Merit Badge Instr; *office:* E O Smith HS 1235 Storrs Rd Mansfield CT 06268*

SANDBERG, KAREN S., HS Social Studies Teacher; *b:* Bronx, N St Univ of NY at Albany (BA) His 1969; NY Univ (MA) Soc Stud Ed Attnd Various Univ & Coll 60 Addl Credit Hrs; *cr:* Commerce HS 1969-73; Gorton HS Tchr, Soc Stud Dept Chprsn 1985-; *ai:* Amer L Oratorial Contest, Gettysburg Contest in Yonkers, Citizens Bee Conte NYS, Bicentennial of the US Constitution Map Contest & HS Ad Coach; YFT, NYSUT & AFT 1969-; NCSS 1970-; Westchester Cncl o Stud 1980-; Taft Inst, Cert of Appreciation Encouraging Stu Particip in NYS Citizen Bee Contest; *office:* Gorton HS Shonnard Pl Yonke 10703

SANDELL, NANCY, Fifth & Sixth Grade Teacher; *b:* Burlingame *m:* Peter Labounty; *ed:* Univ of CA (BA) Eng Lit 1976; Univ of ID Elem Ed 1987; Sci Grad Work; *cr:* Piermont Village Schl Tchr 1987 Annual All Schl Dramatic Production Dir; Schl Newspaper Adv; GL Coord; Curr Advy, Sci Curr Comm; NSTA 1992-; NH Tchr c Semifinalist; Outstdng Sr of Yr Univ of ID Coll of Ed; Grolab Walker Fnd, Catamount Arts Grants; *office:* Piermont Village Schl P 98 Piermont NH 03779

SANDERS, CAROL, Social Studies Teacher; *ed:* Adelphi Univ (BA 1979; C. W. Post Univ at Long Island (MA) His 1990; *ai:* Stu Cncl Site Based Mngmt Comm; Long Island Cncl for Soc Stud; NCSS.

SANDERS, ELIZABETH WILDER, Vocational Home Economics *b:* Raleigh, NC; *c:* Crystal, Stephanie, Joycelyn Ware; *ed:* NC A&T Clothing & Textile 1963; Voc Home Ec 1964; Capitol Univ Elem Ed OH St Home Ec Ed 1974; *cr:* NC A&T Clothing Instr 1963; Sullivant 4th Grd Tchr 1966-75; South HS Home Ec Ed Tchr 1975-; *ai:* FHA OEA, CEA, NEA 1966-; PTA, Membership Drive Chm; Columbus Comm Awd; Educator of Yr; *office:* South HS 1160 Ann St Columbu 43206*

SANDERS, ESTELLE WATSON, English Department Head; *b:* Port ME; *m:* Charles; *c:* Noel Marie, Aimee Nicole; *ed:* Univ of ME (BA 1967; Tulane Univ (MA) Eng 1968; Caniscius Coll at Buffalo 7 Gra Credits; Univ of South ME 9 Grad Credits Gifted Ed, 3 Grad Cred Learning Disabilities, 3 Grad Credits Adolesc Lit; Univ of AP Inst, In Ed of GATE & Biblical Greek; St Josephs Coll 6 Credits in Latin; Francis Coll Eng Instr 1968-69; Mt Mercy Acad Eng Tchr 197 Windham Jr High Eng Tchr 1980-83; Windham High Eng Dept Head 1 Cen ME Tech Coll Adj Eng Instr; *ai:* Coord Stu Tchr Placement; C Grad Speakers, Contestants in Lions Club & Rotary Club Speech Con Liaison Person Cntrl ME Tech & Eng Dept for AP Prgm for Tech Stdnts; NCTE 1990-; MCELA 1989-, Exec Bd; Phi Beta Kappa & Kappa Phi 1967-; Citation From NE Regnl Office of Coll Bd Contributions to AP Prgm; Master Tchr Cert 1991; Nom MIT Stu as Influential Tchr 1991; Presidential Distinguished Tchr Awd 1991; Natl Awd From Kohl Intnl Tchng Awds 1991; Poems, Review, Biograp Sketch & Essay Pub 1989-93; Selected as Tchr Who Made Signif Contribution to His Ed By High Scores on ME Ed Assessment Test 1994; *office:* Windham HS 406 Gray Rd Windham ME 04062

SANDERS, FRED A.,JR., Clinical Instr of Radiography; *b:* Pahokee. *m:* Robyn Michelle Walker; *c:* Brittany; *ed:* 32 Credit Hrs Hlth Sci Univ of Med & Dentistry of NJ Clinical Instr 1993-; *ai:* Hosp B League; ASRT, AART 1992-; Hlth Sci Cert of Achvmt 1994.

SANDERS, LOIS BENTLEY, Fifth Grade Teacher; *b:* Fleming, KY Paul Leonard; *c:* Eric R., Cary M.; *ed:* Morehead St Univ (BA) Ele 1972; Wright St Univ (MS) Tchr Ldrshp & Curr 1995; Univ of Cinci Spcl Ed Cert; 6 Credit Hrs Ec; *cr:* Mt Orab Schls 1st-4th Grd Tchr 196 West Clermont Schls 1st-4th Grd Tchr 1967-72; Milford Exempted S Tutor of LD 1973-78; Clermont Northwestern Local Schls 3rd-5th Tchr 1978-; *ai:* NEA 1978-; OH Ed Assn 1978-; Clermont Northwe Ed Assn 1978-, Sec, Treas, VP, Outstdng Treas Awd (2 Times) From C OH Child Conservation League Local Chptr 1975-, Pres & Sec.

SANDERS, LOUIS EDWARD, Social Studies Teacher; *b:* Plymouth, *m:* Connie H.; *ed:* NC AT&T St Univ (BS) Soc Sci 1965; City Univ of (MA) Soc Sci; Union Theol Seminary (MDiv); Columbia Univ Cns Gen Theolo Seminary Theological Stud; *cr:* Marion Anderson HS Soc Tchr 1965-67; Camden Co HS Soc Stud Tchr 1967-68; Tuckahoe HS Chair, Tchr 1968-; St Charles AME Zion Church Pastor 1980-; US Chaplain 1980-; *ai:* Minority Coaliton, Model Congress, Jr Class Assembly Coord; AFT, NYSTA 1969-, VP, Distngd Svc; NCSS 19 NYSCSS 1969-; WCSS 1969-, Sec; Sparkill-Piermont Rotary 19 Chaplain; Alpha Phi Alpha 1985-, Chaplain; Prince Hall Masons 19 Chaplain; NAACP 1985-, Life Mem; Rockland Co COC 1995-, VP, Mem; Alpha Man of Yr Ed; VFW Man of Yr; Tchr of Yr 1969; NA Humanitarian Awd; Meritorious Svc Awd USAFR; *home:* 39 Van Sparkill NY 10976

ERS, MARY ANN BANKSTON, 7th Grd English & Reading Tchr; urel, MS; *m:* Robert C.; *c:* Darrell; *ed:* Univ of Southern MS (BS) Ed Univ of Houston 4 Hrs; Wright St Univ 16 Hrs; Ashland Coll 3 Hrs; loxi Pub Schls Elem Tchr 1965-72; Aldine IDS Elem Schl 1972-79; a City Schls Jr HS Tchr 1980-; *ai:* Adv News Bulletin, Spelling Bee , Tech Comm Rep; Team Newsletter Ed; NEA, OEA 1980-; paign Co Rdng Cncl 1990-; Strategic Planning Comm 1991-; Block Comm Rep 1990-; Block Grant 1993; Tchr of Yr 1979, 1989; Tech acement Trends Magazine Tech Advancement in Classroom 1992; a Jennings Awd 1983; Ashland Oil Tchr Achvmt Awd Nom 1995; : Urbana Jr HS 500 Washington Ave Urbana OH 43078*

DERS, PAMELA FLEET, Math Tchr & Asst Dir; *b:* Manchester, CT; borah, Peter; *ed:* Wilson Coll (BA) Math & Psych 1965; Univ of DE edit Hrs; Allegheny Coll 3 Credit Hrs; *cr:* The Baldwin Schl 7-12 Tchr 1965-68; The Tatnall Schl Geometry Tchr & Research 1974-76; ington Friends Schl Math & Cmptr Tchr 1976-78; The Harrisburg Math Tchr & Asst Dir at Upper Schl 1981-; *ai:* Act Coord & Comm oord; Quiz Bowl Coach; NCTM & PCTM 1984-; NAOAA 1989-; W 1977-, VP & Treas, Gift Awd; Harrisburg Bridge Club 1986-, Pres eas, Harold F Lanshe; Silverspring Presbyn Church 1988-, Deacon; olph St John Tchng Awd 1994; *office:* Harrisburg Acad 10 Erford Rd lesyburg PA 17043*

DERS, REBECCA BONNER, Physics Teacher; *b:* Bogota, nbia; *m:* Michael Wayne; *c:* Bridget; *ed:* LSU-S (BS) Bio, Chem 15 Hrs Middlesex Coll Physics; *cr:* South Brunswick HS Physics 4 Yrs; *ai:* Sci Bowl, Physics Olympics Coach; Pilot Test Tchr Active cs; NJEA 1990-; NAPT 1993-; *office:* South Brunswick HS Major Rd nouth Junction NJ 08852

DERS, SANDRA LEE, English Teacher; *b:* Patchogue, NY; *m:* Mark; MS); *cr:* Thomas Stone HS Eng Tchr 1992-; *ai:* Soph Class Spon; NEA -; *office:* Thomas Stone HS 3785 Leonardtown Rd Waldorf MD 20601

DERS, TAMMY J., Former Health & PE Teacher; *b:* Decatur, AL; *ed:* on St Coll (BS) Hlth, PE 1993; *cr:* Mt St Mary Acad Hlth, PE Tchr -94; *ai:* Field Hockey Coach; Aerobics Instr; Bowling Club; Driver Ed NJAHPERD 1993-; Sigma Phi Sigma 1991-; Amer Cancer Soc 1996, *home:* 1606 W Princeton Ave Brick NJ 08724

DERS, WILMA JOCELYN, Second Grade Teacher; *b:* Providence, : Matthew, Peter, Stephanie Ferris; *ed:* Univ of RI (BS) Home Ec ; Bridgewater St (MED) Learning Disabilities 1974; Addl 60 Credits; anover Pub Schls Grd 2 Tchr 1969-; *ai:* Multi-Comms; Hanover Tchrs 1969-, Sec; Plymouth Cty Ed Assn, MA Tchrs Assn, NEA 1969-; over Historical Soc 1975-; Stetson House 1975-, Bd of Dir, Corres Sec, stmas Show House; Patriot Ledger Golden Apple Awd; Tchr eciation Night Hingham Ward Church Latter Day Saints; *office:* Cedar Schl 265 Cedar St Hanover MA 02339*

DERSON, COLLEEN MCLAUGHLIN, English Teacher; *b:* na, PA; *m:* E. Ted; *c:* Sean, Ethan; *ed:* Lock Haven Univ (BS) Scndry 1969; Shippensburg Univ (MED) Scndry Eng 1974; *cr:* Cntrl Dauphin Dist Eng Tchr 1969-80; Susquehanna Twp Schl Dist Eng Tchr 1980-; ng Dept Chm; 8th Grd Team Ldr; Discipline Comm; Multicultural n; Gifted Ed Comm; NEA; PSEA; NCTE; Sigma Kappa; Selected Dist of Yr, Guest Lecturer Shippensburg Univ; Featured in Tchr TV, spaper Article; *office:* Susquehanna Twp Schl Dist 801 Wood St isburg PA 17109

DERSON, CYNTHIA A., French & English Teacher; *b:* Denver, CO; urt, Brett, Carrie; *ed:* Miami Univ (BS) Fr 1972; Bowling Green St Fr 1976; Post Grad Stud Universite d'Avignon; Calvin Coll Total ical Response Credits; *cr:* Lakeland Comm Coll Tutor & Sub 1972-83; ling Green St Univ Fr Instr 1974-75; Cuyahoga Comm Coll Fr Instr -79; Notre Dame Coll Fr Instr 1986-87; Willoughby-Eastlake City s Fr Instr 1983-88; John F Kennedy Schl Fr Instr 1988-90; Willoughby ake City Schls Fr Instr 1990-; *ai:* Fr Ed Intl Tour Coord; AATF 1972-; A 1972-; NEA 1972-; NEOTA 1972-; OMLTA Convention; Article Ambassade de France Schlshp; *home:* 23970 Effingham Blvd Euclid 44117

DERSON, JOHN M., 10th Grade Biology Teacher; *b:* Harrisburg, *m:* Jean R.; *c:* Karen Rosenberry, Jason, Sara; *ed:* Shippensburg (BS) 1962; IN Univ of PA (MS) Bio 1967; *cr:* Newport Schl Dist Sr High Ed Tchr 1962-63; Cumberland Vly schl Dist 8th Grd Bio Tchr 3-92, 10th Grd Bio Tchr 1992-; *ai:* 9th Grd Girls Bsktbl Coach; NEA 2-; PSEA 1962-; Fire Co 1973-; Lions Club 1973-; Cntrl Twp Planning m 1985-; Centre Twp Vacancy Bd 1985-, Chm; Cty-Wide Tchr of the hippensburg Univ; One of 64 Tchrs Selected for 2 Week Environment of Key Largo, Everglades, Coral Reefs & Florida Bay; *office:* berland Vly Schl Dist 6746 Carlisle Pike Mechanicsburg PA 17055

DERSON, JOHN MICHAEL, 6th-8th Grade Sci Dept Chm; *b:* Long nch, NJ; *m:* Ellen Perillo; *c:* Megan, Caitlin; *ed:* Belmont Abbey Coll) Elem Ed 1975; *cr:* Avon Elem Schl 6th Grd Tchr, 6th-8th Grd Sci r & Dept Chm; *ai:* Saint Rose HS Girls Soccer Prgm Head Coach; Saint e HS Girls Bsktbl Prgm Asst; Sci Fair Coord; Avon Ed Assn 1977-, s; NJSSA, NFIOA, NFICA 1985-; NEA 1977-; SSOA 1988-; Young onaut Prgm, Chprsn; Avon Sci Fair 1981-, Chprsn; *office:* Avon Elem 505 Lincoln Ave Avon By The Sea NJ 07717

NDERSON, RICHARD A.,SR., Business Teacher; *b:* Westfield, MA; acqueline L. Carll; *c:* Karen, Richard Jr., Justin, Julianna; *ed:* Amer l Coll (BS) Bus Admin 1964; Credit Hrs at Westfield St Coll, Syracuse v, OSwego St Coll, Utica Coll; *cr:* Canastota Jr-Sr HS Bus Tchr 1965-; NHS Comm; Canastota Tchrs Assn 1964-, Treas; NYSUT 1964-; AFT 4-; Clinton Swin Club 1990-, Treas; *home:* RR 5 Box 134 Canastota NY 32

NDHU, PARMINDER SINGH, Engineering & Tech Asst Prof; *b:* hbazpur, Punjab India; *m:* Navjot Kaur Tung; *c:* Baldev S., Manraj S.; Guru Nanak Engrng Coll (BS) Mechanical Engrng 1986; Boston Univ S) Mechanical Engrng 1990; *cr:* RI Comm Coll Instr 1989-93; nchester Comm Tech Coll Asst Prof 1993-; *ai:* Engrng Pathways Prgm ord; Tech-Prep Prgms Asst; Dev Customized Courses for Industry for raining Purposes; ASQC 1994-; Grant for Setting up Metrology Lab 5; Grant for Setting up Tech Interface with Math Dept 1994; Tchng shp, Schlsp at Boston Univ 1987-89; *office:* Manchester Comm-Tech l 60 Bidwell St Manchester CT 06045*

NDLAS, VALERIE DEPPA, English Teacher; *b:* Liberty, NY; *m:* James an; *ed:* SUNY at Oneonta (BA) Lit 1983, (MS) Scndry Eng Ed 1991; Sullivan Cty BOCES Asst Tchr 1984-85; Union Springs Cntrl Schl Eng ar 1986-; *ai:* Amnesty Intnl Adv, USTA Schlsp Comm Mem; NCTE 9-; *home:* 2207 Morris Dr Seneca Falls NY 13148

NDLER, MELVIN, Dept of Electrical Engrng Chm; *b:* Brooklyn, NY; Ruth F. Klarberg; *c:* Amy Gail Hymowech, Noah Ari, Benjamin Moshe; Polytechnic Univ of NY (BEE) Control 1958, (MEE) Cmptrs 1960, D) Electrophysics 1965; *cr:* Polytechnic Inst of NY & Microwave ch Inst Rsrch Assoc 1958-64; Airborne Inst Lab Group Ldr 1964-69; W Grace Sr Venture Capital Specialist 1969; Cooper Union Dept of Elec gr Chm 1969-; *ai:* Dir of Russian Retraining Prgm; IEE, TBH 1975-; N 1973-; Sigma Xi 1960-; NSF, Mellon Sloan Fnd; *office:* The Cooper ion Albert Nerken Schl Of Engrng 51 Astor Pl New York NY 10003

SANDO, CAROL RENEE, Nursing Instructor; *b:* Seattle, WA; *c:* Renee Codington, Marilu Coddington; *ed:* Widener Coll (BS) Nrsng 1978; St Josephs Univ (MS) Ed 1987; Widener Univ (MS) Nrsng 1990; DNSc Nrsng Ed; Post Grad Cert in Nrsng Ed 1990; *cr:* Jefferson Park Hospital Educl Consultant 1984-86; Meth Schl of Nrsng Fac 1987-; Neumann Coll Adj Fac 1988-89; Widener Univ Adj Fac 1993-94; *ai:* Meth Schl of Nrsng Sr Class Adv; Widener Univ Statistical Consultant; Collagen Corp Collagen Therapist; Natl League for Nrsng 1989-, Rsrch Forum; Sigma Theta Tau 1989-, Intnl Nrsng Hnr Soc; Belmont Hills Civic Assn 1986; Amer Heart Assn 1987-, CPR Instr; PA Nom for Item Writer for St Bd Licensing Exam for RN Excl in Nrsng Ed Awd by Natl Co-Alliance for Tchrs Excl 1992 & 1993; Whos Who in Amer Nrsng 1993-94; *office:* Methodist Hosp Schl Of Nursing 2301 S Broad St Philadelphia PA 19148*

SANDOMIR, LARRY PHILIP, General Studies Head Teacher; *b:* Bronx, NY; *m:* Mindy; *c:* Chelsea, Justin, Rachel; *ed:* Queens Coll (BA) Elem Ed 1972, (MA) Urban Stud, Admin 1973; *cr:* Leonardo Da Vinci Int Schl Grds 6-8 Eng Tchr 1972-74; Elizabeth Barrett Browning Jr HS Grd 8 Eng Tchr 1974-75; Churchill Schl Grd 5 Spec Ed Tchr 1975-76; Ramaz Lower Schl Grd 6 Head Tchr 1976-; *ai:* Yrbk Fac Adv; Lit Magazine; Stu Govt; Author; Articles Pub; Dev Curr on Tolerance Grd 6; *office:* Ramaz Lower Schl 125 E 85th St New York NY 10028*

SANDOVAL, DORIS SIMMONS, Chemistry Teacher; *b:* Cambridge, MD; *m:* Amado J.; *ed:* Western MD Coll (BA) Bio 1961; Amer Univ (MS) Chem, Earth Sci 1971; 36 Hrs PA St Univ; 24 Hrs Univ of MD; *cr:* Leland Jr HS 9th Grd Gen Sci Tchr 1961-64; Springbrook HS AP Chem, Bio Tchr 1964-86; Bethesda-Chevy Chase HS AP Chem Tchr 1986-92; Montgomery Blair HS MagnetTc hr 1992-; *ai:* Var Cross Cty Coach; Investment Club Spon; NEA, MD St Tchrs Assn, Montgomery Cty Ed Assn 1961-; NSTA; Howard Cty Striders 1976-; Leo Schubert Awd for Outstdng Chem Tchng 1988; MD Jr Sci & Hum Outstdng Tchr 1993; Semifinalist Pres Awd for Excl 1989; *office:* Montgomery Blair HS 313 Wayne Ave Silver Spring MD 20910*

SANDS, CAROL PAJOR, French Teacher; *b:* Nanticoke, PA; *m:* Allen; *c:* Jeffrey, Jill; *ed:* Wilkes Coll (BA) Fr 1967; Temple Univ (MS) Ed 1970; 42 Addl Credit Hrs Beyond Masters Degree; *cr:* Wyoming Valley W Schl Dist Scndry Fr Tchr 1967-; *ai:* Sr & Underclassman Awds Comm; Mid St Steering Comm; Wilkes Univ Ed Dept Advy Comm; NEA, PSEA & WVWEA 1967-; Delta Kappa Gamma Intnl & Alpha Rho 1982-; *office:* Wyoming Valley West HS Wadham St Plymouth PA 18651*

SANDS, FRANK JAMES, Head Crew Coach; *b:* Philadelphia, PA; *m:* Cynthia Lyn Balich; *c:* Candice, Justin; *ed:* Mercyhurst Coll (BA) His, Pol Sci 1976; Attnd Edinboro Univ, Univ of NE; *cr:* Univ of NE Head Crew Coach 1976-78; North Cath HS Head Crew Coach; *ai:* North Hills Jaycees; Cunnberg Lions; Girls Team Won Natl Championship 1994; *office:* North Catholic HS 1400 Troy Hill Rd Pittsburgh PA 15233

SANDS, LENORA TYLER, Secondary Mathematics Teacher; *b:* Batavia, NY; *m:* John F.; *c:* Jennifer, Rebecca; *ed:* SUNY at Albany (BA) Math, Psych 1968; SUNY at GEneseo (MS) Ed, Math 1972; *cr:* Pavilion CS Math Tchr 1968-69; Alisal HS Math Tchr 1969-71; Elba CS Scndry Math Tchr 1971-72, 1979-, Dept Chm 1979-; *ai:* Sr NHS, Future Tchrs club Advs; Sr HS Math Team Coach; NCTM, AMTNYS, NYSAMS 1979-; Church Choir 1970-; Delta Kappa Gamma 1985-, Treas; Univ of Rochester Tchr of Excl 1985, 1993; RIT Distinguished Tchr Awd 1989; *office:* Elba Central Schl 57 S Main Elba NY 14058*

SANDS, LOUISE FILTEAU, French Teacher; *b:* Berlin, NH; *c:* Patricia, Victoria; *ed:* Rivier Coll (BA) Fr 1969; Assumption Coll (MA) Fr 1971; Institut Catholique at Paris France Diploma in Fr Stud 1973; Attnd Univ of NH & Dartmouth Coll; *cr:* Winnisquam Regnl HS Fr Tchr 1971-76; Berlin HS Fr Tchr 1982-; *ai:* NHS Exec Comm; NEA, NHEA, BEA, AATF & NHATFL 1982-; Assn Canado-Americaine 1988-, Trustee; BPW Young Career Woman 1974; Outstanding Scndry Educator of Amer 1975; *office:* Berlin HS 550 Willard St Berlin NH 03570

SANDSTROM, ELLEN S., Family & Consumer Science Tchr; *b:* Providence, RI; *m:* Scott; *c:* Michael, Kristen; *ed:* Univ of RI (BS) Home Ec, Textiles 1975; Tchng Cert 1978; Working on Early Chldhd Ed; Cnslng Grad Stud; *cr:* Woonsocket Jr HS Home Ec Tchr 1979-81; Scituate HS Home Ec Tchr 1982-83; Burrillville HS Family, Consumer Life Tchr, Dept Chair 1983-; *ai:* Presch Coord; Child Care Advy Comm; RI Family, Consumer Sci Assn 1990-, NEA; *office:* Burrillville H S 425 East Ave Harrisville RI 02830

SANDUSKY, CANDYCE STEBBINS, 6th Grade Science Teacher; *b:* Erie, PA; *m:* Edward Paul; *c:* Christine Marie, Jon Paul Edward; *ed:* Edinboro Univ (BS) Elem Ed 1979; 7 Credits in a Grad Course of Rdng at Bowling Green St Univ; 9 Credits in a Grad Pgm for Cert of Elem Ed; *cr:* Sandusky City Schls Elem Ed Tchr 1980-81; ST Vincent Day Care Ctr Group Supvr & Asst Dir 1983-89; Millcreek Twp Schl Dist 5th Grd Tchr, 6th-8th Grd Geog Tchr, 7th Grd Lang Arts Tchr & 6th Grd Sci Tchr 1990-; *ai:* Environmental Action Club; Ski Club Adv; Schl Wide Budget Comm & Detention Tchr; Tchr Mentor; MEA 1991-; PSEA 1991-; NEA 1991-; 1st United Meth Church, Sunday Schl Tchr; PSEA Innovative Tchng Grant; Intnl Paper EDCORE Grant; *home:* 512 Wilshire Rd Erie PA 16509*

SANDY, MARY H., 7th Grade Math Teacher; *b:* Dover, OH; *ed:* Kent St Univ (BS) Ed 1984; Addl 18 Hrs; *cr:* New Phila Schls 7th Grd Math Tchr 4 Yrs, 6th Grd Tchr 7 Yrs; *ai:* New Phila Ed Assn, OH Ed Assn, NEA 1984-; *office:* Welty MS 315 4th St NW New Philadelphia OH 44663

SANECKI, DOUGLAS PETER, Social Science Teacher; *b:* Adams, MA; *m:* Lynda Marsac; *c:* Caren, Patrick; *ed:* Brooklyn Coll CUNY (BA) His 1973; Trenton St Coll (MSEd) Soc Sci 1978; Post Grad Credits MA plus 15 at LIU at St Peters; *cr:* Bishop Kearney HS Soc Sci Tchr 1973-75; Hopewell Valley Regnl HS Soc Sci Tchr 1975-77; Holmdel HS Soc Sci Tchr 1977-; *ai:* Girls Var Bsktbl Coach; Schl Renaissance Comm Mem; Holmdel Twp Ed Assn 1977-, Greivance Chm; Amer Psychological Assn 1985-, TOPPS; NJ Cncl of Soc Stud 1993-; Lions Club 1992-; Fair Haven Recreation Commission 1989-, VP; Coach of Yr 1985-86; HS Tchr of Month Nom; *office:* Holmdel HS 36 Crawfords Corner Rd Holmdel NJ 07733*

SANECKI, JUDITH ANN CUMBIA, Science Teacher; *b:* Rocky Mount, NC; *m:* Ronald Louis; *c:* Karen, Robin, Jamie; *ed:* Sacred Heart Coll (BS) Bio 1971; *cr:* St John Vianney Tchr of Sci & Bio 1973-; *ai:* NCEA; *office:* St John Vianney Reg HS Line Rd Holmdel NJ 07733

SANELLI, ANNE, Biology Teacher; *b:* Philadelphia, PA; *c:* Martin, Stephanie; *ed:* Rutger's Univ (MS) Zoology; Hartford Univ 4 Addl Credit Hrs Advanced Placement Bio Wkshp; *cr:* St Joseph's By The Sea HS Bio Tchr 1976-79; Trenton St Coll Bio Tchr 1979; Middlesex Cty Coll Bio Tchr 1991; St Cecilia Schl Jr HS Sci Tchr 1991-93; West Essex Sr HS Bio Tchr 1993-; *ai:* Sci League; Sci Olympiad; Indepedent Rsrch Project with Pub Schls; NJEA, NEA, NSTA, NABT 1993-; *office:* West Essex Sr Regnl HS W Greenbrook Rd North Caldwel NJ 07006*

SANFERRARO, JOANNE FRANCES, Mathematics Teacher; *b:* Camden, NJ; *ed:* Rutgers-Camden (AB) MAth 1963; Rutgers St Univ (EDM) MAth 1967; Trenton St Coll (EDM) Stu Prsnl Svcs 1971; *cr:* Audubon HS Math Tchr 1963-64; Lenape HS Math Tchr 1964-; *ai:* NJEA Cert, Ed, Tenure Comm; NEA, NJEA 1963-; BCEA 1963-, Treas 1988-; *office:* Lenape HS 235 Hartford Rd Medford NJ 08055*

SANFORD, ELINOR MINNICK, Home Economics Teacher; *b:* Brattleboro, VT; *m:* Timothy Fox; *c:* Jeffrey David, Jennifer Reese, David Hamilton, Emily Bridges; *ed:* Univ of CT (BS) Food, Nutrition 1973; Univ of Southern ME (BA) Tech Ed 1995; 15 Credits Toward Masters Tech Ed; *cr:* Calais Regnl Voc Schl Food Svc Instr 1989-94; Calais HS Home Ec Tchr 1991-95; St Croix Regnl Tech Ctr Food Svcs Instr 1994-; *ai:* Vica Adv; Relief Soc Pres; Amer Culinary Fed 1995-; ME Ed Assn 1991-; PTG Alexander Schl 1975-, Pres; *office:* St Croix Regnl Tech Ctr RR 1 Box 22A Calais ME 04619

SANFORD, JONATHAN MALCOLM, Third Grade Teacher; *b:* Albion, NY; *m:* BethAnn Abballe; *c:* Jonathan C., Kaitlin E.; *ed:* St Univ of NY Coll at Geneseo (BA) Anthropology 1983; St Univ of NY Coll at Brockport (MS) Rdng Tchr 1988; Elem Ed Cert 1983; *cr:* Carl I. Bergerson MS Chptr One Rdng Tchr 1983-85; Albion Primary Schl Kndgtn Tchr 1985-87, Third Grd Coord 1989-91, Third Grd Tchr 1987-; *ai:* Flag Day Act, Sanford's Rangers Incentive Prgm Coord; Hardware Assessment Comm; Phi Delta Kappa 1990-; NYSUT 1983-; Amer Radio Relay League 1994-; Rochester Amateur Radio Assn 1993-; Rochester Radio Repeater Assn 1994-; *office:* Albion Primary Schl 324 East Ave Albion NY 14411

SANFORD, KATANA KIMBERLY, English Teacher; *b:* Glen Cove, NY; *ed:* Univ of MD at College Park (BA) Eng, Speech Ed 1992; *cr:* Forestville HS Eng Tchr 3 1/2 Yrs; *ai:* Sr Class, Drama Club Spon; Television Production Instr; NEA 1993-; *office:* Forestville HS 7001 Beltz Dr Forestville MD 20747*

SANFORD, LISA STEPHENS, Social Studies Teacher; *b:* North Hornell, NY; *m:* Terry L.; *c:* Katharine; *ed:* SUNY Geneseo (BA) His 1977; SUNY Brockport (MA) His 1989; Addl Masters Coursework in Ed Completed at SUNY Buffalo, Coursework Completed Areas of Cooperative Learning, Peer Coaching, Multiple Intelligence; *cr:* Barker Cntrl Schl Soc Stud Tchr 1977-88; Hornell HS Soc Stud Tchr 1988-; *ai:* Model UN Adv; NHS Fac Comm; NEA, NEA-NY 1988-; NY St Cncl for Soc Stud 1982-; Delta Kappa Gamma 1989-; *office:* Hornell HS Maple City Park Hornell NY 14843

SANGER, JOSEPH M., Span Tchr & Foreign Lang Chm; *b:* Lebanon, PA; *m:* Rosa Lopes; *c:* Sharon Davis, Marcus, Michael; *ed:* Houghton Coll (BA) Scndry Ed 1965; Penn St Univ (MED) Scndry Ed, Span 1967; 62 Addl Credit Hrs; *cr:* Hershey HS Span Tchr 1965-; Voice of God Recordings Inc Translator 1987-; Harrisburg Area Comm Coll Span Prof 1990-; *ai:* Span Club; Span Honor Soc; NEA, PSEA, HEA 1965-; Poem in Span Pub; *office:* Hershey HS Homestead Rd Hershey PA 17033

SANGIACOMO, FAYE ANN, Career Planning & Dev Teacher; *b:* Orange, NJ; *m:* Joseph; *c:* Joseph, Camille, Leanne Carousis; *ed:* Kean Coll (BA) Early Chldhd Ed 1962; *cr:* Livingston HS Career Planner 5 Yrs; *ai:* ADVAB, SAT Testing; NJEA 1990-; *office:* Livingston H S Robert Harp Dr Livingston NJ 07039

SANGREY, CYNTHIA ELAINE, Soc Studies Tchr & Dept Chprsn; *b:* Lancaster, PA; *ed:* Millersville Univ (BS) Scndry Ed & Soc Stud 1984 & (MA) His 1990; *cr:* Conestoga Valley Jr HS Soc Stud Tchr 1985; Solanco HS Soc Stud Tchr 1986; George A. Smith MS Soc Stud Tchr 1987-; *ai:* Honor Society Adv; NCSS; *office:* George A Smith MS 645 Kirkwood Pike Quarryville PA 17566

SAN JOSE, BENILDA M., Science Teacher; *b:* Manila, Philippines; *ed:* Univ of Philippines (BSE) Phys Sci 1969; Univ of St Thomas (MS) Math 1971; *cr:* Women Tchrs Coll Math, Sci Tchr 1984-88; Sts Peter & Paul Schl Sci Tchr, Prgm Dir 1988-93; Marylawn of Oranges Schl Sci Tchr 1993-; *ai:* Modertor Cooking Club; NJAPT, ASCD 1994-; HS Physics IV Book for Philippines Stdnts; *office:* Marylawn Of The Oranges Schl 445 Scotland Rd South Orange NJ 07079

SANKES, HEIDI BELLING, 5th Grade Teacher; *b:* Niagara Falls, NY; *m:* Gary; *c:* Josh, Matthew; *ed:* SUC at Fredonia (BA) Elem Ed 1969; St Univ Coll at Buffalo (MS) Ed 1973; Valparaiso Univ; Univ at Antwerp Belgium; Univ of Buffalo; *cr:* Niagara Falls Schl System 4th Grd Tchr 1969; Duneland Schl System 4th-5th Grd Elem Ed 1970-71; South Elem & North Elem Schls K-6th Grd Tchr 1971-; *ai:* St Josephs Collegiate Inst Bsktbl Team, Parent Support Group; AFT 1973-; NEA 1973-; LPUT 1973-; Buffalo Hookbill Assoc; Regular Ed Tchr with Consultant Tchr Svcs; *office:* Lewiston Porter Sr HS 4061 Creek Rd Youngstown NY 14174*

SANKEY, CATHIE GREEN, Elementary Guidance Counselor; *b:* Woodville, OH; *m:* Robert J.; *ed:* Hillsdale Coll (BA) Fr & Music 1973; Heidelberg Coll (MA) Ed 1991; Schl Guid & Cnslng Cert; Post Grad Stud in Cnslng; *cr:* Clyde-Green Springs Schls Music & Fr Tchr 1973-95, Elem Guid Cnslr 1995-; *ai:* NEA & OEA 1973-; ASCA & OSCA 1995-; AAUW 1989-; *office:* Clyde-Green Springs Schls 108 S Main St Clyde OH 43410

SANKEY, THOMAS LEE, High School Math Teacher; *b:* Grove City, PA; *m:* Mary Ann Buchheit; *ed:* Grove City Coll (BA) Math 1975; Johns Hopkins Univ (MED) Ed 1979; *cr:* Waterloo MS Math Tchr 1976-80; Mt Hebron HS Math Tchr 1980-; *ai:* Schl Plays, Spring Musicals Dir; Schl Choir Accompaniest; NEA 1976-, NCTM 1980-; Howard Cty Summer Theatre 1984-, Dir; Howard Cty Tchr of Yr 1989 & 1994; PTSA Distinguished Tchr Awd 1987; *office:* Mount Hebron HS 9440 Rt 99 Ellicott City MD 21042

SANN, DEBORAH BALENTINE, Junior English Teacher; *b:* Greensburg, PA; *c:* Nathaniel, Bethany; *ed:* Grove City Coll (BA) Comm 1972; CA Univ of PA (MED) Eng 1976; Seton High Coll (BS) Soc Sci 1981; *cr:* Yough Sr HS Tchr 1973-; *ai:* Spon Stu Cncl, Comm Action Prgm, SADD; Co-Spon Yrbk; NEA 1973-; NCTE 1982-; *office:* Yough Sr HS 99 Lowber Rd Herminie PA 15637

SANNA, MARY TONRA, Theology Teacher; *b:* Bronx, NY; *c:* Ann Wisniewski, Eileen, Michael, Catherine; *ed:* St Joseph Coll (BA) Child Stud 1977; Attnd Immaculate Conception Seminary; *cr:* St John of God Schl 5th Grd Tchr 1977-83; St John the Bapt DHS 9th Grd Theology Tchr 1983-; *ai:* Stu Action League; Renaissance Tchr of the Yr; Jenkins Memrl Awd; *office:* St John the Bapt HS 1170 Montauk Hwy West Islip NY 11795

SANNER, ROBERT MICHAEL, Asst Prof of Aerospace Engrng; *b:* New Haven, CT; *ed:* MIT (BS) Aeronautics & Astronautics 1985, (MS) Aeronautics & Astronautics 1988, (PHD) Aeronautics & Astronautics 1993; *cr:* Univ of MD Asst Prof of Aerospace Engrng 1993-; *ai:* AIAA 1993-; NASA, NSF Rsrch Grants; 2 Journal Articles, 1 Book Chptr Pub; Tech Conf AIAA, IEEE Papers Pub; Outstdng Paper Awd IEEE 1992; *office:* Univ Of MD Coll Park College Park MD 20742

SANNER, ROY EUGENE, Supervisor of Transportation; *b:* Franklin, PA; *c:* Chad, Tiffany; *ed:* Westminster Coll (BA) Bus Admin 1976; *cr:* Valley Grove Schl Dist Trnsprttn Sprvsr, Athltc Dir; *ai:* Boys Var Bsktbl; Girls Var Sftbl; Girls Jr HS Bsktbl; PTAP 1991-; PASBO 1991-; *office:* Valley Grove Schl Dist 403 Rocky Grove Ave Franklin PA 16323

SANO, ANTHONY M., Assistant Professor; *b:* Albany, NY; *ed:* Schenectady Cty Comm Coll (AS) Music 1987; SUNY at Albany (BA) Music 1988; Hartt Schl U of Hartford (MM) Music Ed 1993; *cr:* Schenectady Cty Comm Coll Music Asst Prof 1989-; *ai:* Acad Affairs; Disability Advocate; Mid Sts Review; Comm, Cultural Events; Amer Fed Musicians 1972-; Guitar Fnd of Amer 1985-; Capital Dist Classical Guitar Soc 1987-, Pres; Performances Tippett Festival, Empire Jazz Orch, Solo Concerts, Aids Benefits, Pub Schl Concerts; *office:* Schenectady County Comm Coll 78 Washington Ave Schenectady NY 12305

SANO, MICHAELENE BARBARA, Social Studies Teacher; *b:* Riverhead, NY; *c:* Jennifer, John, Christina; *ed:* St Johns Univ (BA) Soc Sci 1973, (MSEd) Cnslng 1981; Suffolk Comm Coll Chemical Dependency Courses; *cr:* St John the Bapt HS Sub Tchr 1991-94; Brentwood Schl Dist Sub Tchr 1992-; East Islip HS SAT I Pgm Instr 1993-; Brentwood Evening HS Soc Stud Tchr 1994-; *office:* Brentwood HS 2 6th Ave Brentwood NY 11717*

SANSALONE, MARY C., Math Teacher; *b:* Little Rock, AR; *m:* John J.; *ed:* Chrstn Brothers Univ (BS) Math 1979; Univ of Cincinnati (MAT) 1994; *cr:* Immaculate Conception HS Math Tchr & Ath Coord 1979-81; Booker T. Washington HS Math Tchr 1981-83; Lakota HS Math Tchr 1983-89; Apex HS Math Tchr 1989-91; Lakota HS Math Tchr 1991-; *ai:* NHS Adv 1992-95; Girls JV Bsktbl Coach 1989-91; SB2 Comm 1989-91; Girls JV Soccer 1983-89 & Sftbl Coach 1985-88; NCTM 1984-; LEA 1983-89 & 1991-; *office:* Lakota HS 5050 Tylersville Rd West Chester OH 45069

SANSEVERE, MARY XAVIER,FMSC Retirement Club Director; *b:* Union City, NJ; *ed:* Ladycliff Coll (BA) Math 1964; 45 Hrs Archdiocese of NY Inservice Inst 1964; 3 Credits Ladycliff Coll Inter Comm Sci Inst 1967; 3 Credits Seton Hall Univ Aero Space Inst; *cr:* St Anthony 5-8 Grd Tchr 1950-58; Assumption 7-8 Grd Tchr 1958-65; O. L. Q. of Martyrs 7-8 Grd Tchr 1965-76; St Joseph 6-8 Grd Tchr 1976-91; Mt St Francis Retirement Dir 1991-; *ai:* St Joseph of the Palisades Sci Dept Chprsn 1976-91; NCEA 1975-.

SANSEVERE, SANDRA ANN, Literature & Math Teacher; *b:* Hoboken, NJ; *ed:* Jersey City St Coll (BA) Elem Ed 1974; *cr:* David E. Rue Schl BSIP Remedial Tchr 1976-77; Joseph F. Brandt BSIP Remedial Tchr 1977-84, 6th Grd Tchr 1984-91, 8th Grd Lit, Math Tchr 1991-; *ai:* 8th Grd Class, Yrbk, Natl Jr Hnr Soc Adv; Schl Site Mngmt; NEA, HEA 1976-; STEVENS, SSI 1994-; Hoboken Tchr of Yr 1995; *office:* Joseph F. Brandt MS 9th & Garden Sts Hoboken NJ 07030*

SANSING, LOUISE BERBRICH, Math Teacher; *b:* Hartford, CT; *m:* Charles E.; *c:* Chandler E.; *ed:* Cntrl CT St U (BS) Math, Eng 1969; (MA) Math 1973; 6th Yr Intermediate Supervision-Admin 1987; *cr:* East Hartford HS Math Tchr 1969-; *ai:* CT Best Prgm-Mentor Tchr for Beginning Tchr, Cooperating Tchr for Stu Tchrs; NEA, CEA 1986-; NCTM 1990-; EHEA 1972-; *office:* East Hartford HS 869 Forbes St East Hartford CT 06118*

SANSONE, RAMONA JEAN, Vocational & Substitute Tchr; *b:* Norwood, MA; *c:* David, Courtney, Terrance; *ed:* UMass Occupational Tchrs Approval; *cr:* Weymouth High Voc Tech HS Sub Tchr 1989-93, Long Term Sub 1993-94, Sub Tchr 1994-; South Shore Chrstn Acad Sub Tchr 1995-; *ai:* Class Play Helped Cosmetology Stdnts; *office:* Weymouth High Voc Tech HS Commercial St Weymouth MA 02188

SANSONE, VIRGINIA VANDUZER, Third Grade Teacher; *b:* Queens, NY; *m:* Mark A.; *c:* Robert, Kenneth; *ed:* SUNY at Oswego (BS) Elem Ed 1970; 30 Addl Hrs; *cr:* Weedsport Cntrl Schl Grd 5 Tchr 1970-77; Lancaster Cntrl Schl Grd 3 Tchr 1989-; *ai:* Schl Lit Magazine Chm; Schl Invention Convention Comm; NYSUT 1970-; AFT 1974-; Articles Pub; *office:* Como Park Elem Schl 1985 Como Park Blvd Lancaster NY 14086

SANTABARBARA, BARBARA CANTORE, Second Grade Teacher; *b:* West Haven, CT; *m:* James; *c:* James Jr.; *ed:* Southern CT St Univ (BS) 1969, (MS) 1974; 15 Addl Credits; *cr:* Live Oaks Schl 4th Grd Tchr 1969-73; Calf Pen Meadow Schl 1st, 2nd Grd Tchr 1984-; *ai:* NEA, CEA 1969-; Milford Ed Assn, Bldg Rep; Mini Grant Milford Bd Ed 1994 Ocean Stud, 1993 Nonfiction Rdng; *office:* Calf Pen Meadow Elem Schl 395 Welches Point Rd Milford CT 06460

SANTA LUCIA, GAETANO FRANCIS, English Teacher; *b:* Waterburg, CT; *ed:* St Francis Coll (BA) Eng 1966; Case Western Reserve Univ (MA) Eng 1968, (PHD) Eng 1974; *cr:* Univ of New England Tchr 1969-84; Deering HS Tchr 1984-; *ai:* Acad Decathlon; NEA; MLA; Italian Heritage Club; *home:* 23 First St Biddeford Pool ME 04006*

SANTAMARIA, WILLIAM, Science Teacher; *b:* Havanna, Cuba; *m:* Barbara; *c:* Josiah, Adam; *ed:* Bapt Bible Coll (BAR) Philosophy 1978; Westminster Theological Seminary (MAR) 1980; *cr:* William C McGinnis Schl; *ai:* Greek & Latin Classes Spon; Santamaria Music Composer; NEA 1995-; Music Production for Audio Cassette Books Robinson Crusoe & Pilgrims Progress; *office:* William C Mc Ginnis Schl 271 State St Perth Amboy NJ 08861

SANTANGELO, EDWARD WILLIAM, Physical Education Tchr & Dean; *b:* Bronx, NY; *m:* Andrea Carbonaro; *c:* Michelle; *ed:* Herbert H. Lehman Coll (MS) Hlth Ed 1975, (BA) Phys Ed 1969; C. W. Post Coll 18 Credits Ed Admin; *cr:* All Hallows Inst 3rd Grd Tchr 1969-70; CIS 22 Hlth & Phys Ed Tchr 1970-72; CIS 166 Hlth & Phys Ed Tchr 1972-85; August Martin HS Phys Ed Tchr, Dean 1985-; *ai:* Athl Dir; UFT 1969-; *home:* 2500 Bayview Ave Wantagh NY 11793

SANTANGELO, MEREDYTH J., English Teacher; *ed:* Kent St Univ (BA) Eng 1990; *cr:* Hoban HS Eng Tchr 1990-91; Diocese of Youngstown Schls Eng Tchr 1991-93; New Brighton HS Eng Tchr 1993-; *ai:* Ushers Clb; NCTE 1990-.

SANTARLAS, JOAN M., Spanish & SAT Prep Teacher; *b:* Madison, WI; *m:* Edward A.; *c:* Christina, Michael, Theresa; *ed:* Rutgers Univ (BA) Eng, Span 1965; Rowan Coll Cert ESL 1980; *cr:* Camden Cty Ed Commission ESL Tchr 1980-86; Haddon Heights HS Span, SAT Prep Tchr 1986-; Camden Cty Coll SAT Prep Tchr 1993-; Norristown HS Span, Eng Tchr 1993-; *ai:* AFS, Environmental Club Adv; NEA, NJEA 1985-; HHEA 1985-, Fac Rep; St Rose Parish Cncl 1993-, Rep; Mentor Tchr 1995-; Wkshp Presenter to Tchrs SAT Math, Verbal Stategies Max Scores; *office:* Haddon Heights HS 301 2nd Ave Haddon Heights NJ 08035

SANTAY, ROSLYN CAIAZZO, 9th & 10th Grade English Tchr; *b:* Easton, PA; *m:* Gregory; *c:* Christopher, Darrin; *ed:* East Stroudsburg Univ (BS) Eng 1968; Indiana-Wesleyan (MS) Ed 1996; *cr:* Pleasant Valley HS Sr Eng Tchr 1968-71; Gettysburg HS 9th Grd Eng Tchr 1972-73; Fairfield HS Sub 1973-82, 9th-10th Grd Eng Tchr 1982-; *ai:* HS Musical Co-Dir; Yrbk Lit Adv; SAP Team Mem; FEA 1982-, Sec; NECE 1993-; Lower March Creek Church; Spiritual Life team 1985-; Writing Awd-Natl Spon by Bristol Meyers Co.

SANTEE, MARCK N., English Teacher; *b:* Toronto, Canada; *w:* Andrea Blake (dec); *c:* Christopher Blake; *ed:* AZ St Univ (BS) Ed 1976; CA St (MA) Comm 1979; Univ of MD Educl Policy, Admin; *cr:* Mc Keesport HS Tchr 1980-82; Chapticon HS Tchr 1982-; *ai:* Lit Annual Spon; Mock Trail Coach; NEA 1980-; NTE 1982-; EASMC 1982-90, Bldg Rep; Human Rights Campaign 1979-; Philanthrofund Fnd 1986-; Brother Help Thyself 1989-; Whitman-Walker Clinic 1990-; *office:* Chopticon HS Rt 242 Morganza MD 20660*

SANTEE, WILLIAM L., A P English Teacher; *b:* Sewickley, PA; *ed:* Clarion St Coll (BS) Lang Arts 1970; PA St Univ (MA) Eng; *cr:* Northgate Schl Dist Scndry Eng 1970-; *ai:* Cum Laude Soc Spon; AP Coord; Mentor Tchr; PA St EA, NEA & NCTE 1970-; Greater Pittsburgh Prof Mens Soc; Pittsburgh Press All-Star Educator 1991; *office:* Northgate HS 589 Union Ave Pittsburgh PA 15202*

SANTELL, ANTHONY J., Fifth Grade Teacher; *b:* Sharon, PA; *m:* Marion E.; *c:* Paul, Gino; *ed:* Kent St Univ (BS) Ed; Bowling Green St Univ (BS) Liberal Arts, Bio Major, Recreation Minor; Westminster Coll (MS) Admin 1981; OH Prin Cert; *cr:* Joseph Badger Schl Dist 5th-8th Grd Tchr 1974-; *ai:* OEA, NEA, BEA 1974-; *home:* 2110 Timber Creek Dr E Cortland OH 44410

SANTERRE, PAUL ANTHONY, Dir of Bands & Music Tchr; *b:* Nashua, NH; *m:* Sophia Michael Blastos; *ed:* Keene St Coll (BM) Music Ed 1983-; *cr:* Manchester Schl System Instrumental & Gen Music Tchr Grds 5-8 1983-86; Manchester HS West Dir of Bands 1986-; *ai:* Asst Bsktbl Coach Hesser Coll; Pvt Music Instr; NH Music Edctrs, Exec Bd, Jazz Chm; NH Band Dirs Assn, Exec Bd; Intnl Assn of Jazz Edctrs; Son of Amer Legion, Svc Chm; NEA; Music Edctrs Natl Conf; Natl Band Assn; Superior Ratings Classic Music Festival for Concert Band, Jazz Ensemble 1994; Guest Conducted the Jazz Ensemble at Elm St Jr HS Nashua, NH 1994; Jazz Ensemble Selected to Perform on Mt Washington Cruise Ship on Lake Winnepesaukee 1993; Hosted the NH Jazz All-St Festival 1993; Jazz Ensemble Selected to Represent NH at Eastern Div Convention of Music Edctrs Natl Conf 1991; Conducted the All-City Jr HS Band 1991; Guest Conducted the Lin-Wood Schl Bank Lincoln NH 1991; Conducted the Univ of NH Wind Symphony at Conductors' Clinic 1991; *office:* Manchester West HS 9 Notre Dame Ave Manchester NH 03102*

SANTIAGO, ANN MARIE, Sixth Grade English Teacher; *b:* New York City, NY; *ed:* SUNY at Oswego (BS) Elem Ed 1967; SUNY at New Paltz (MS) Elem Ed 1972; SUNY at New Paltz In-Svc Courses; *cr:* Traver Road Elem Schl Sixth Grd Tchr 1967-70; West Road Intermediate Sixth Grd Tchr 1970-84; Arlington MS Sixth Grd Eng Tchr 1984; *ai:* NYSUT, AFT 1967-; *office:* Arlington MS 5 Dutchess Tpke Poughkeepsie NY 12603

SANTIAGO, CARL MICHAEL, English & Religion Teacher; *b:* New York, NY; *ed:* Seton Hall Univ (BA) Eng 1989; Hispanic Leadership Opportunity Prgm; (MEd) Candidate Substance Awareness; *cr:* Queen of Peace HS Eng, Rel Stud 1989-; *ai:* Forensics Speech & Debate; Model United Nations; C.O.R.E. Team; NCEA; *office:* Queen Of Peace H S 191 Rutherford Pl North Arlington NJ 07031

SANTIAGO, MAYRA C., Assoc Prof of Physi & Kinesio; *b:* San Juan, PR; *ed:* Hollins Coll (BA) Pre-Med 1974; Harvard Univ (MED) Educ Admin 1979; Univ of MN (MA) Exer Physiology 1985, (PHD) Exer Physiology 1990; *cr:* Baldwin Schl of PR Scndry Schl Tchr 1975-77; Univ of MN Grad Tchng Asst 1982-89; Temple Univ Assoc Prof 1989-; *ai:* Grad Stu Mentorship, Rsrch & Curricular Matters; Am Coll Sports Med, Am Alliance Hlth, PE, Rec & Dance 1982-; Pub Scientific Articles; *office:* Temple Univ Coll of HPERD 126 Pearson Hall 048-00 Philadelphia PA 19122

SANTIAGO-ALVAREZ, DIANA JADE, Crisis Intervention Teacher; *b:* New York City, NY; *m:* Felipe Alvarez; *c:* Carmelo, Edwin; *ed:* City Coll of NY (BS) Ed 1985, (MS) CRMD Ed 1990, (MS) Admin, Supervision 1994; *cr:* IS 184X Schl Resource Room Tchr 1986, Dance Drama Tchr 1987-, Career Edctr 1988-, Crisis Intervention Tchr 1995-; *ai:* Drama, Dance Instr; Dir, Coord, Chorographer, Stage Lights, Background; Bsktbl, Ftbl, Sftbl Coach; Hispanic Soc of Tchrs 1992-; AFT 1992-, Admin; Conscientious Musical Review 1989-, Exec Dir; *office:* IS 184 Rafael Cordero Y Molina 778 Forest Ave Bronx NY 10456*

SANTIAGO-DUNLOP, JUDITH, 7th-8th Grd Math Teacher; *b:* New York City, NY; *c:* Brian Charles II; *ed:* Hunter Coll (BA) Sociology, Ed 1989, (MS) Ed, Math Specialty 1995; 15 Credits Rel Cert; *cr:* St John Chrysostom Schl 1st, 4th-5th Grd Tchr 1982-90; Blessed Sacrament Schl 6th-8th Grd Math Tchr 1990-; *ai:* Fed Cath Tchrs 1984-, Del; Assn Tchrs Math 1995; Alpha Kappa Delta; Cath Schl Catechist Level 1 & 2; Who's Who Amer Ed 1992-; Ambassador Awd; Whole Lang Wkshp Speaker; Dean's List 1987; *office:* Blessed Sacrament Schl 1160 Beach Ave Bronx NY 10472*

SANTILLO, JACQUELINE BAKUHN, Fourth Grade Teacher; *b:* New Castle, PA; *m:* Thomas; *ed:* IN Univ of PA (BA) Elem Ed 1962; IN, Slippery Rock, & PA Post Grad Credits; *cr:* New Wilmington Area Schls 5th Grd Tchr 1962-1992, 4th Grd Tchr 1992-; *ai:* WAEA 1962-; PSEA 1962-; NEA 1962-.

SANTINI, ANNMARIE PRATT, Business Education Teacher; *b:* Ellwood City, PA; *m:* Pat Jr.; *c:* Nicholas P.; *ed:* Robert Morris Coll (BS) Bus Admin 1982, (MS) Bus Ed 1988; 24 Credit Hrs Sci Duquesne Univ; *cr:* One Mellon Bank Ctr Commercial Fin, Loan Admin 1983-85; Duff's Business Inst Bus Instr 1985-87; Laurel Schl Dist Bus Tchr 1988-; *ai:* Bus Dept Chprsn; FTLA Adv; PSEA, NEA 1988-; Tri-St Bus Ed Assn 1987-; Grad Asst Robert Morris Coll; *office:* Laurel Jr Sr HS R D 4 Box 30 New Castle PA 16101*

SANTNER, MARCIA CUNNINGHAM, Third-Fourth Grade teacher; *b:* Boston, MA; *m:* Lynn Edward; *c:* Elizabeth Santner Cuff, Susan Ross Borucki; *ed:* Univ of MA (BA) Elem Ed 1976; Lesley Coll (MED) Curr Instruction Specialization Creative Arts Learning; Attnd Allegheny Coll 1955-58; *cr:* Amherst Pub Schls Tchr Aide 1968-70; Wendell Ctr Schl Tchr Aide 1972-76; Swift River Schl Tchr Aide 1976-77, Tchr 1977-; *ai:* Safety Advy Comm Co-Chm; Math Frameworks Stud Comm; MA Tchrs Assn, NEA 1991-; Western Girls Scout Cncl Special Appreciation Tchr Awd in Celebration of Tchr Christa Mc Auliffes Life; Presented Wkshps Classroom Discipline, Problem solving Meetings Greenfield MA Pub Schls, MTA; Produced, Directed Ten Musicals Third Grd Children.

SANTO, DOROTHY E. WIATRAK, Elem & Jr High Teacher; *b:* Passaic, NJ; *m:* Dennis S.; *c:* William, John, Todd; *ed:* Lab Inst of Merchandising (AS) Merchandising 1957; Duquesne Univ (BS) Elem Ed 1983, (MS) Elem Ed, Rdng Spec 1986; *cr:* Allied Stores Asst Buyer 1957-60; R. Butler Schl Tchr Aide, Sub Tchr 1969-79; NH Sub-Svc Sub Tchr 1984-86; All Saints Schl Elem, Jr HS Tchr 1986-; *ai:* Jr Safety Patrol; Sacramental Catechist; Homecoming; NCEA 1986-.

SANTOMAURO, LIZABETH MARY (TOTH), 9th Grd Earth Science Teacher; *b:* Manhattan, NY; *c:* Anthony; *ed:* Ocean Cty Coll (AA) Liberal Arts 1985; Monmouth Coll (BS) Ed 1990; *cr:* Toms River HS North Earth Sci Tchr 1990-; *ai:* Asst Bus Mgr Drama Club; Co-Adv Peer Support Group; Peer Ldrshp Adv; NJ Sci Tcher Assn, NEA, NJEA 1990-; *office:* Toms River HS North Old Freehold Rd Toms River NJ 08753*

SANTORA, FRANK JOSEPH, Asst Pastor & Alegebra Teacher; *b:* Brooklyn, NY; *m:* Lisa M.; *ed:* Rutgers Univ (BA) Acctng, Bus 1993; *cr:* J. H. Cohn & Co Staff Accountant 1993; Bright Clouds Ministries Asst Pator, HS Algebra Tchr 1994-; New Hope Chrstn Acad Asst Pastor, HS Algebra Tchr 1994-; *ai:* Bsktbl Coach; Yth Pastor; *office:* New Hope Christian Acad 18 Clapboard Ridge Rd Danbury CT 06811

SANTORA, MARK DANIEL, Guidance Counselor; *b:* Port Chester, NY; *m:* Maria Bologna; *c:* Christine, Sara, Daniel; *ed:* Univ of Charleston (BA) His 1972; Univ of Bridgeport (BS) Guidance, Dev 1975; Educl Mngmt Prof Diploma 1989; *cr:* Port Chester HS Soc Stud Tchr 1972-86, Soc Stud Dept Chair 1983-86, Guidance Cnslr 1986-; *ai:* Mentoring Prgm Site Dir; Frosh Success Experience Coord; Block Scheduling, 9th Grd Interdisciplinary Stud, Wellness Day Comms; AFT 1972-; WRPCA 1986-; Kiwanis Club 1984-, Pres, Treas, Kiwanis of Yr 1994; Port Chester Youth Bd 1990-, Chprsn; Port Chester Youth Ftbl, Bsbl 1994-; Tchr of Yr 1995; *office:* Port Chester HS 1 Tamarack Rd Port Chester NY 10573

SANTORE, JONATHAN CONRAD, Asst Prof of Music Theory; *b:* Greeneville, TN; *m:* Marcia Lucinda Green; *ed:* Duke Univ (AB) Music 1985; Univ of TX at Austin (MM) Composition 1987; UCLA (PHD) Music 1994; *cr:* UCLA Dept of Music TA Consultant 1992-93; CA St Univ Adjunct Asst Music Prof 1992-93; U of MN Schl of Music Music Theory Lecturer 1993-94; Plymouth St Coll Asst Prof of Music T[illegible] Composition 1994-; *ai:* Amer Composers Forum; Amer Music Ctr; [illegible] Music Theory; Canterbury Westwood UCLA 1992-93, Bd Mem; [illegible] Campus Ministry 1995-, Bd Mem; Numerous Commis[illegible] Compositions; Presentations of Papers on Music Theory, An[illegible] Fellowships, Schlsps UCLA, U of TX, Duke; *office:* Plymouth St C[illegible] High St Plymouth NH 03264

SANTORE, SANDRA L. (FOX), English Teacher; *b:* Oswego, N[illegible] Joseph J.; *c:* Caitlin; *ed:* SUNY at Oswego (BS) Eng, Scndry Ed 19[illegible] Post-Grad Hrs; 18 Hrs CAS Degree; *cr:* St Paul's Acad Eng Tchr 19[illegible] Mexico HS Eng Tchr 1977-; *ai:* Var Vlybl Coach; Writing C[illegible] Negotiations Team; MACS Fac Assn 1977-, Pres, VP; NYSUT [illegible] AERC 1994-; ECTRA 1992-; Grad Honoree 1994, 1995; *home:* 218[illegible] St Mexico NY 13114*

SANTORINI, VICTORIA ANNE, English Teacher; *b:* LaMesa, C[illegible] Rutgers Coll of Rutgers Univ (BA) Eng 1993; Trenton St Coll Altern[illegible] Cert Pgm; *cr:* Stuart Cntry Day Schl 5th Grd Eng, SS Tchr 19[illegible] Howell HS Jr-Sr Eng, Jrnlsm Tchr 1995-; Freehold Borough HS Night Schl Jr-Sr Eng Tchr 1996; *ai:* Jrnlsm Newspaper; Schl [illegible] Releases; NJEA 1995-; NCTE 1995-.

SANTORO, FRANK, Computer Teacher & Tech Coord; *b:* Bridget[illegible] *m:* Nancy Katherine Logan; *c:* Mat, Andy, Tim, Jason; *ed:* Haverfor[illegible] (AB) Eng 1969; Rowan Coll of NJ (MA) Eng 1976; *cr:* Upper De[illegible] Schls Supplemental Instr for Learning Disabilities 1970-72; Bridget[illegible] Tchr 1973-83; Cumberland Regnl HS Tchr 1984-; *ai:* NEA, NJEA [illegible] NSCAA 1980-; US Soccer 1978-, Natl Cncl; *office:* Cumberland Re[illegible] HS Silver Lake Rd PO Box 5115 Seabrook NJ 08302

SANTORO, GEORGE F., Business Teacher; *b:* Buffalo, NY; *m:* [illegible] Wiltsie; *c:* Michelle, Michael; *ed:* Alfred St (AAS) Bus Admin [illegible] Buffalo St (BS) Bus & Mrktg 1974; Buffalo St (MS) Voc Ed 1976; Ca[illegible] Coll (MS) Cnslr Ed 1988; Fredonia St (CDS) Admin 1993; *cr:* Fr[illegible] Cntrl Tchr & Admin 1974-; *ai:* Yr Book Adv; Block Sched Comm[illegible] Schls Comm; Frontier Groups TD 1974-, VP; AFT 1974-; NYS U[illegible] Tchrs 1974-; NYS Bus Tchrs 1974-; Hamburg Town Yth Bd 1990-; M[illegible] Awd; Epsilon Delta Epsilon Hnr; *office:* Frontier Central Sr HS 443[illegible] View Rd Hamburg NY 14075

SANTORO, KAREN L., Business Teacher; *b:* Bronx, NY; *m:* Willi[illegible] *ed:* Suffolk Comm Coll (AAS) Exec Sec 1966; Hofstra Univ (BBA[illegible] Admin 1969, (MA) Scndry Ed 1974; C W Post Coll (PDSAS) Admin [illegible] Cooperative Work Exp; Attnd Nassau Comm Coll & NY Tech; *cr:* C[illegible] Bay HS, Katharine Gibbs Sec Schl, Sutton Sec Schl, Adelphi Bus [illegible] Canterbury Sec Schl & Gloria K Sec Schl Bus Tchr 1969-; *ai:* Dist [illegible] for All Extra Classroom Act; HS Fund & GO Schl Store Spon; Sch[illegible] Partnerships & Work Experience Pgm Coord; Mid Sts Comm; Nassa[illegible] Chm Assn 1969-; Nassau Cty Bus Ed Assoc 1969-, Pres Bus Tchrs of [illegible] 1984-; LI Bus Ed Chm Assoc 1985-; Work Exp Coord Assoc [illegible] NYOSSA 1989-; *office:* Oyster Bay-East Norwich HS 150 E Ma[illegible] Oyster Bay NY 11771

SANTORO, MARIA HALLAS, Home Economics Teache[illegible] Gloversville, NY; *m:* Anthony Nicholas; *c:* Alexis C., Anthony N., D[illegible] M.; *ed:* Univ of RI (BS) Early Chldhd Ed 1969; URI (MS) Home Ec [illegible] Food Sci, Nutrition's Home Ecs Tchr Cert; Course Mgrs in Food S[illegible] *cr:* No Providence Schl Kndgtn Tchr 1969-82, Home Ec Tchr 198[illegible] Discipline Comm; Family & Consumer Sci 1993-; Nanagansett Qu[illegible] Guid 1979-; RNQG Quilting Guid 1995-; Who's Who Among Bus [illegible] Awd Outstndg Home Ecs Tchr; Omicron Nu NHS; *home:* 23 Pine [illegible] Ave Lincoln RI 02865

SANTORO, YVONNE MICHELE, English Teacher; *b:* Paterson, N[illegible] Joseph Anthony; *c:* Jeannine; *ed:* Montclair St Coll (BA) Eng & [illegible] 1981, (MA) Drug & Alcohol Cnslng 1992; Credit Hrs Toward Cert Al[illegible] Cnslr; Curr Courses Learning Styles, Domestic Violence & Cmptr [illegible] *cr:* Nutley HS Eng Tchr 1981-88; Cedar Grove HS Eng Tchr 1988-; [illegible] 1988-1993; *ai:* Forensic Adv; Peer Cnslng Adv & Spon; Voi[illegible] Democracy Spon; Judge NJCTE Writing Contest 1995, Facilitate; [illegible] VFW Essay Writing Contest 1996; NEA, NJEA, NJCTE & NCTE [illegible] ASAP 1991-1993; Rep HS at NJ HS Proficiency Stand Setting C[illegible] Facilitate Parent Wkshps; Voted Fav Tchr 5 Yrs; Adj-Ctr of Pedago[illegible] Montclair St Univ, Critical Thinking/Mentoring Prgms 1994-; *o[illegible]* Cedar Grove HS Rugby Rd Cedar Grove NJ 07009*

SANTORSOLA, ALBERT JOSEPH, Theology Teacher; *b:* Philadel[illegible] PA; *ed:* Temple Univ (BS) Ed 1979; St Charles Seminary (MA) The[illegible] 1986; Villanova Univ (MS) Cnslng, Human Relations; *cr:* St D[illegible] CHurch Asst Parochial Vicar 1986-88; St John Neumann HS Fac 198[illegible] Margaret Church Resident 1988-95; St Justin Church Resident 1995[illegible] Comm Svc Corps Moderator; NEA, NART 1988-; *office:* Saint [illegible] Neumann HS 2600 Moore St Philadelphia PA 19145

SANTULLI, ANNMARIE, Floriculture Teacher; *b:* Peekskill, NY[illegible] Davis-Elkins Coll (BA) Ed 1971; Occupational Ed Univ St of N[illegible] Oswego; *cr:* Northwestern Elem Schl Grd 5 Tchr; Reeds Nu[illegible] Landscape, Floral Design Mgr 1984-91; PNW Boces Tech Ctr Floricu[illegible] Tchr 1991-; *ai:* Voc Indstrl Clubs of Amer Adv; AFT, NYSUT 1991-; [illegible] Boces Tchrs Ctr 1992-, Rep; Dirs Awd PNW Boces Tech Ctr 1994; *o[illegible]* Putnam-Nrtrn Wstchtr Boces Sch 200 Boces Dr Yorktown Heights [illegible] 10598*

SANZ, MICHAEL LEO, Biology Teacher; *b:* Lowell, MA; *m:* Kath[illegible] Casey; *c:* Keelin; *ed:* Univ of MA at Lowell (BS) Bus 1983; Univ o[illegible] Cert Sci Ed 1990; 30 Hrs Towards MA in Sci Ed; *cr:* St Thomas Aq[illegible] HS Sci Tchr 1990-; *ai:* Var Boys Tennis, JV Girls Bsktbl Coach; IM P[illegible] Comm Svc Coord; Class Adv; Admissions Comm; NSTA, NHSTA 1[illegible] NH Audubon 1988-; Accreditation Teams New England Assn of Sc[illegible] Colls 1993, 1995; *office:* St Thomas Aquinas HS 197 Dover Point Rd D[illegible] NH 03820*

SANZEN, PETER LANCE, Professor of Criminal Justice; *b:* Amster[illegible] NY; *m:* Sheila Mahan; *c:* Benjamin John; *ed:* Fulton-Montgomery C[illegible] Coll (AAS) Bus Admin 1968; Univ of WI at Superior (BA) Pol Sci [illegible] Wichita St Univ (MA) Pol Sci 1973; *cr:* Hudson Vly Comm Coll [illegible] 1974-80, Asst Prof 1980-87, Assoc Prof 1987-92, Criminal Justice [illegible] 1992-; *ai:* SUNY Fac Cncl of Comm Colls Del; Acad Senate; Fac Stu [illegible] Bd of Dirs; Criminal Justice Edctrs Assn of NY St 1980-, Pres 199[illegible] Acad of Criminal Justice Sci 1986-; Amer Soc of Criminology 1987-[illegible] for Law & Justice 1992-, Vice Chair; Troy Human Rights Comm 199[illegible] Articles Pub; *office:* Hudson Valley Comm Coll 80 Vandenburgh Ave [illegible] NY 12180

SANZENI, KENNETH ALAN, 9th-12th Grade Math Teacher; *b:* Br[illegible] NY; *m:* Mary Ellen Munch; *c:* Christopher, Rachel; *ed:* Western CT St [illegible] (BA) Math 1969, (MS) Ed 1974; 120 Hrs Prof Dev; *cr:* Danbury HS M[illegible] Tchr 1968-; *ai:* Little League Bsbl Coach 1982-86; BSA Adv 198[illegible] NEA, CEA 1968-; ATOMIC 1980-; *office:* Danbury HS Clapboard R[illegible] Rd Danbury CT 06811

SAPARA, LINDA HARRIS, Elementary Counselor; *b:* Berea, OH [illegible] Joseph Paul; *c:* Kyle, Colin; *ed:* Principia Coll (BA) Elem Ed 1982; [illegible] St Univ (MA) Elem Schl Cnslng 1987; *cr:* Strongsville City Schls S[illegible] Group Instr 1984-85, 5th Grd Tchr 1985-95, Elem Schl Cnslr 1995-; [illegible] OEA, NEA, SEA 1985-; NCECA, OCA, NCOCA 1995-.

RSTEIN, HERBERT, 7th-8th Grade Teacher; *b:* New York, NY; *m:* a Pijlman; *c:* Ariella; *ed:* Rutgers Univ (BA) Bus Admin 1968; Univ Grad Schl of Bus; NY Univ Film Schl; *cr:* Waldorf Schl of Princeton Grd Tchr 1986-; *ai:* Grd Schl Chm 1993-; Fac Mem for Schl Yrbk; Range Planning 1995-, Dev 1989-92, 1995-, Comms; Waldorf Schl Trustees 1989-91; *home:* 18 Shirley Ln Lawrenceville NJ 08648

ENZA, ALFRED,JR., Mathematics Teacher; *b:* Manchester, NH; *m:* a Anne Phelan; *c:* Linda Anthony, Phillips, Thomas, Edward; *ed:* of NH (BA) Elem Ed 1973; 30 Addl Hrs; *cr:* Varney Elem Schl 6th chr 1973-81; Manchester West Elem Schl 5th Grd Tchr 1981-85; side Jr HS 7th Grd Math Tchr 1985-; *ai:* Math Book Selection, Rep n Discussion Comms; Mentor to Stdnts Needing Guid; Kairos Inc VP of Natl Org, Chm of St Org; Fed Grant; Recommended for Tchr *office:* Southside Jr HS 140 S Jewett St Manchester NH 03103*

R, GARY, Teacher; *b:* Brooklyn, NY; *ed:* Monmouth Univ (BS) Bus Kean Coll (MS) Admin, Supervision; *cr:* Old Bridge Twp Pub Schls 967-; *ai:* Soccer Coach; Fitness Club Adv; Sftbl Team Dir; Bowling Adv; Former Wrestling Coach; NJEA 1967-; PTA Lifetime Mbrshp Tchr of Yr 1987; *office:* Carl Sandburg MS Rt 516 Old Bridge NJ

O, NANCY Y., Mathematics Teacher; *b:* Bradford, PA; *m:* Michael Michael T., Heather L., Sara J.; *ed:* Clarion Univ (BS) Scndry Ed & 1969; Penn St Univ Scndry Ed & Math; Robert Morris Cert Paralegal *cr:* Upper St Clair Schls Math Tchr 1969-75; Ringgold Schls Math 992-; *ai:* NEA 1992-; PSEA 1992-; Nottingham Twp Recreation Bd *office:* Ringgold HS 3645 Dry Run Rd Monongahela PA 15063

IN, ELIZABETH J., Sixth Grade Teacher; *b:* New York City, NY; Y Univ (BA) Fr, Music 1972; Bank Street Coll (MSEd) Elem Ed Manhattanville Coll Music Ed Cert 1972-74; *cr:* NY Gilbert & an Players Bass Musician 1979-84; Natl Orchestral Assn Bass ian 1979-84; PS 234 Tchr 1985-; *ai:* Needlework Club Ldr; UFT ; Natl Audubon Soc 1994-; Natl Audubon Wkshp Grant 1994; S-Team rg Guest Speaker 1995; *office:* P S 234 292 Greenwich St New York)007

AR, SUSAN CRAIG, English Teacher; *b:* Mount Pleasant, PA; *m:* rd; *c:* Megan; *ed:* Grove City Coll (BA) Eng 1966; Fairleigh nson Univ (MA) Human Dev 1979; Attnd Monmouth Univ, Jersey it, KEAN, Georgian Courst, Intnl Univ of LA, IN Univ at Edinburgh Total 50 Credit Hrs; *cr:* Peniciuk HS Fulbright Exchange 1983-84; Twp HS Eng Tchr 1966-; *ai:* Literary Magazine Adv; NCTE & E Writing Judge; Article Pub; TOEA 1966-, Bldg Rep; MCEA 1966-, Comm; NJEA 1994-; Amer Acad of Poets 1994-; NCTE 1966-; Kappa Gamma 1985-; Coord Shakespeare Festival 1989-92; NJ Cncl ırs of Eng 1990-; Dodge Poetry Group 1993-; 2 NEH Summer Insts chrs 1994 & 1995; 2 NEH Summer Seminars 1989 & 1993; NJ Inst Grants: Lifetime Rdng 1989, Bindings 1993 & BIO Cycles 1994; : Ocean Township HS 550 W Park Ave Oakhurst NJ 07755*

OZNIK, NORMAN, Film & Video Shop Tech Tchr; *b:* Linz, Austria; ffa Dueck; *c:* Dalia, Michelle, Steven; *ed:* Schl of Visual Arts (AA) Arts 1967; CA St Coll at Los Angeles 21 Credits in Industrial Arts Corps Trng Prgm in Malaysia Svc Tchr 1967-69; City Coll & Staten coll 62 Credits for New York City Tchr License Requirements leted 1995; *cr:* Sultan Ibrahim Malaysia Industrial Arts Tchr -69; Advertising Prof Art Dir & Television Producer 1971-85; bank Jr HS Media Arts Tchr 1985-86; IS 237 Media Arts Tchr 1986-; ideo Squad Adv; Chinese Stu Arts & Crafts Adv; Black His Month; Adv; Video & Photography For Schl Functions & Spec Projects s & Concerts; UFT, NYC 1985-; New York Newsday Person of -Tchr 1995; *office:* IS 237 Rachel Carson 4621 Colden St Flushing 1355

ACKI, IRVING J., Economics Teacher; *b:* Buffalo, NY; *m:* Elizabeth nnedy; *c:* Renee, Timothy, Christian; *ed:* Kent St Univ (BS) Soc Stud Univ of MI (MA) His 1959; 30 Credit Hrs Toward PHD; 10 Credit lis Univ of Buffalo; *cr:* Lafayette HS Soc Stud Tchr 1959-63; East HS Stud Tchr 1964-79; Hutch Tech HS Soc Stud Tchr 1979-; *ai:* Sr Class Debate Coach; Current Issues & Law Clubs; BTF & NEA 1995-.*

AFIN, MARION BUDNY, Chemistry & Physics Teacher; *b:* Glen , NY; *m:* Gregory Thomas; *c:* Christina, Gregory; *ed:* SUC at Geneseo Bio 1977; C W Post (MS) Bio & Ed 1987; *cr:* Beth Israel Med Ctr Tchr 1977-78; St Catharines Acad Chem Tchr 1978-86; Mercy HS & Physics Tchr, Sci Dept Head 1989-; *ai:* Girl Scout Ldr 6 Yrs; est Scientific Club 7 Yrs; NCEA 1977-; *office:* Mercy HS 1225 ander Ave Riverhead NY 11901

AZEN, DENNIS M., MS Math & Science Chair; *b:* West Islip, NY; hrista M.; *c:* Ashley N., Dominick J.; *ed:* SUNY at Oswego (BS) 1984; *cr:* Upper Room Chrstn Schl Learning Ctr Supvr 1986-92, MS Tchr 1992-94, MS Math & Sci Chair 1994-; *ai:* Stu Cncl Adv; Act Powerhouse Yth Ministry 1991-, Yth Pastor; *office:* Upper Room stian Schl 722 Deer Park Rd Dix Hills NY 11746*

BER, CAROLE BREUER, Academic Director; *b:* Pittsburg, PA; *m:* am; *c:* Carl, Kenneth; *ed:* Carnegie-Mellon Univ (BA) Eng 1966, Eng 1972; *cr:* Charleroi HS 1966-69; Belle Vernon Area HS 1969-73; n Hills Chrstn Eng Tchr 1988-89; Wilson Chrstn Acad Dir 1991-93; age Hills Chrstn Acad Principal 1993-95; Wilson Chrstn Acad Dir -; *ai:* NHS, Sr Class, Newspaper Spon; Amer Assn of Schl Dev, NCTE -; Order of Eastern Star 1981-, Drill Instr 2 Yrs; Andrew Carnegie Soc -; Pittsburgh Carnegie Institute; *office:* Wilson Christian Acad 2910 rty Way McKeesport PA 15133*

DINHA, MARY, Sr Class Adv & Amer His Tchr; *b:* Bristol, RI; *ed:* Tchrs Coll (BA) Ed 1964; Providence Coll (MA) Rel Stud 1974; 6 Credit Hrs; Geog 6 Credit Hrs; Guid 3 Credit Hrs; *cr:* Santa Maria Tchr; China Mission Tchr 1964-67; St Francis Xavier Prin 1967-70; na HS Tchr 1970-75; St Patrick Schl Tchr 1979-82; Fatima HS 9th Grd g, 12th Grd Rel Tchr 1982-; *ai:* Foundress, Dir Summer Camp 28 Yrs, Life Club 25 Yrs, Chess Club 3 Yrs; NCEA 1960-; NRL 1980-; cesan Respect Life, Bd Mem; Portuguese Fed, Bd Mem; Summer Camp nt; Introduce Geog in Curr 1986; *office:* Our Lady Of Fatima HS 360 ket St Warren RI 02885

RDO, SANFORD, Choral Music Teacher; *b:* New York, NY; *ed:* SUNY tony Brook (BA) Music 1992; Aaron Copland Schl of Music at Queens Post Grad Stud; *cr:* Grand Ave Jr HS Chorus Tchr 1993-; Sanford H. houn HS Choral Dir, Adv 1993-; *ai:* Show Choir, Barbershop Quartet, et Adelines, Chamber Choir Adv; Drama Club Lighting Designer; AFT, , NMEA 1993-; MENC, NYSSMA 1992-; Amer Choral Dirs Assn 2-; Long Island Musicians Assn Music Edctr of Yr 1995-; *office:* ford H. Calhoun HS 1786 State St Merrick NY 11566

RDONI, PHYLLIS LAMANNA, 8th Grade Teacher; *b:* New York City, *c:* Gene Jr., Craig; *ed:* Paterson St Tchrs (BS) Ed 1956; *cr:* Coolidge 5th Grd Tchr 1956-57; St Philip the Apostle 7th Grd Tchr 1964-79; hasquan Elem 8th Grd Tchr 1987-90; Avon Elem 8th Grd Tchr 1990-; Soc Stud & Jr High Chprsn; Yrbk Adv & Guid; NEA 1987-; NJEA 7-; AEA 1987-, Sec; Church Parish Cncl 1993-, Sec.*

RGENT, ALEXIS HELYNNE, French Teacher; *b:* Kingston, PA; *c:* tin C. Robertson, Roslyn H. Robertson; *ed:* Master's Equivalency; La bonne 6 Credit Hrs; Temple Univ 12 Credit Hrs Towards MA Liberal Arts; *cr:* Dover Area HS Fr Tchr 1968-69; Cntrl Dauphin East HS Fr Tchr 1979-80; Susquehanna Twp MS Fr Tchr 1982-85; Meade HS Fr Tchr 1985-; *ai:* Fac Cncl; Human Relations Comm; MSTA, NEA 1985-; Ulmstead Cove Assn 1990-; VP 1994-95; Fulbright Tchr Exch Applicant.*

SARGENT, CRAIG DEWARD, Social Studies & Math Teacher; *b:* Ithaca, NY; *m:* Barbara Henry; *c:* Kristin, Kathryn; *ed:* SUNY at Plattsburgh (BA) Soc Stud 1973; Russell Sage (MS) Elem Ed 1976; CPR Coaching Cert; *cr:* Town of Bethlehem Recreation Playground Supvr 1967-73; NY Racing Assn Parking Attendant 1981; Schalmont Cntrl Schls Tchr & Coach 1974-; *ai:* Girls Track Coach 1985-; Girls Modified Bsktbl Coach 1990-; Var Boys & Girls Cross Cntry Coach 1995-; Gifted & Talented K-12 Coord 1977-80; NYSUT 1973-; Altamont Reformed Church, Deacon 1985-89, Choir Mem 1986-, Soloist; Empire St Games 1993-, Soccer Ofcl, Semi Final Game, Competitor, 6th Pl Awd; Schalmont HS Tchr of the Yr 1993; Schalmont Sr Class Tchr of Yr 1994; Gifted & Talented Grant for Arts & Learning; *home:* 136 Lincoln Ave Altamont NY 12009*

SARGENT, LAURA WHITING, Mathematics Teacher; *b:* Somerville, NJ; *m:* Steven Bowers; *ed:* Rider Coll (BS) Math, Sec Ed 1993; *cr:* Scotch Plains Fanwood HS Math Tchr 1993-; *ai:* JV Chrldng Coach 1993-95; Var Chrldng Coach 1995-; NJEA, NEA 1993-; NCTM, ATMNJ 1995-; Tchr of Month; *office:* Scotch Plains Fanwood HS Westfield Rd Scotch Plains NJ 07076

SARGI, TERRIE ANDERSON, Fifth Grade Teacher; *b:* Youngstown, OH; *m:* Thomas L.; *c:* Trisha Schum, Tiffani; *ed:* Kent St Univ (BS) Elem Ed 1970, (MED) Master Tchr 1977; *cr:* Kent City Schls Tchr 1970-; Learning Ctr of Stow Owner of Tutoring BUs 1990-93; *ai:* Schl Improvement Team; Mentor Tchr; Safety Patrol Adv; Kent Ed Assn 1990-; Delta Kappa Gamma 1990-; *office:* Longcoy Elem Schl 1069 Elno Ave Kent OH 44240*

SARI, KATHLEEN, 10th-12th Grade English Tchr; *b:* Brooklyn, NY; *m:* Robert S.; *c:* Andrew; *ed:* St John's Univ (BA) Eng, Scndry Ed 1972; Coll of Staten Island (MS) Scndry Ed, Eng 1978; *cr:* St John the Bapt HS 9th-10th Grd Eng Tchr 1983-85; St Anthony of Pauda Schl 7th-8th Grd Eng Tchr 1991-92; Hewlett Schl Eng Tchr, Asst Dean 1992-95; East Islip HS 10th-12th Grd Eng Tchr 1995-; *ai:* Stu Cncl; NHS; East Islip Tchrs Assn 1995-; *office:* East Islip Schl Dist Craig B. Gariepy Ave Islip Terrace NY 11752*

SARI, MARION FAMA, Fourth Grade Teacher; *b:* Bayonne, NJ; *m:* John Americo; *c:* Giancarlo; *ed:* Caldwell Coll (AA) Soc Stud, Elem Ed 1968; Villanova Univ (MA) Pol Sci 1973; Bank St Schl of Ed 4 Credit Hrs; Bayonne Bd of Ed Inservice Trng 3 Credit Hrs; *cr:* Nativity Schl Second Grd Tchr 1962-63; St John the Apostle First-Second Grd Tchr 1963-67; St Catherine Schl First Grd Tchr 1967-68; St Boniface Schl Fifth Grd Tchr 1968-70; St Francis De Sales Schl Second Grd, Adult Ed Tchr 1970-73; Paul VI Regnl HS Amer His 1-2, Govt, World Cultures Tchr, Soc Stud Dept Chm 1973-76; Robinson Schl Comp Ed Tchr 1976-77; Vroom Learning Ctr Schl 7-8 Grd Tchr 1977-82, Grd 4 Tchr 1986-; *ai:* Lit Art Magazine Advis; Acad Challenge Coach; Peer Mediation Adv; Beyonne 2000 Clearner & Greener Schl Rep; Bayonne Tchrs Assn, NJEA 1977-; St Andrews Choir 1977-; St Andrews Catechist 1978-, Catechist of Yr 1995-; *office:* Vroom Learning Ctr 18 W 26th St Bayonne NJ 07002

SARIS, CHARLES J., Biology Teacher; *b:* Toledo, OH; *m:* Christine Bodnar; *c:* Mathew, Julie, Andrew; *ed:* Bowling Green St Univ (BS) Bio & PE 1976; Akron Univ (MS) Outdoor Ed 1987; *cr:* Manchester MS Tutor 1976-77; Smithville HS Bio Tchr, Ftbl & Track Coach 1977-; *ai:* Ftbl & Track Coach; NEA 1977-; *office:* Smithville HS 480 E Main Smithville OH 44677

SARLI, ROBERT SALVATORE, English Instructor; *b:* Brooklyn, NY; *m:* Kathleen Florence Barbera; *c:* Andrew; *ed:* St Francis Coll (BA) Eng 1967; Hofstra Univ (MA) Eng, Hum 1973; C. W. Post Coll Prof Diploma Admin 1991; *cr:* Bethpage HS Eng Instr 1967-; Adelphi Univ Adj Instr 1986-; *ai:* Sr Class, Audio-Visual Adv; NYSUT; Bethpage Congress of Tchrs; Natl Endowment for Hum Grant Colloquium on Creek Classics; *office:* Bethpage H S Cherry Ave Bethpage NY 11714*

SARNA, SHIRLEY F., Adjunct Professor of Law; *b:* Germany; *m:* Steven Nelson; *c:* Eric Nelson, Adam Nelson; *ed:* Cornell Univ (BA) Govt 1970; NY Univ (JD) Law 1974; Schl of Law (LLM) Corp 1995; *cr:* Federal Trade Commission Staff Atty, Asst Reg Dir, Acting Dir 1974-80; John Jay Coll Adj Law 1990-; NYS Attorney General Chief Bureau of Consumer Frauds, Protection 1995-; *office:* John Jay Coll of Criminal Jstc 899 10th Ave New York NY 10019

SARNACKI, ELEANOR, Advertising Design Instructor; *b:* Pittsfield, MA; *m:* Alexander Charles; *c:* Alexander; *ed:* SUNY at Oswego (BS) Ed 1992; Working Towards Masters; *cr:* Oneida BOCES Schl Advertising Design Instr 1990-; *ai:* Portfolio Dev Team; Vo Tech Hnr Soc Adv 1990-95; ASCD 1992-; AAUW 1995-; NYS Occ Ed Assn 1994-; Distinguished Voc Tech Tchr 1995; *office:* Oneida BOCES Schl 4747 Middle Settlement Rd New Hartford NY 13413

SARNO, JANE ELIZABETH, English Teacher; *b:* Gloversville, NY; *m:* John E. Browne; *ed:* Oh Wesleyan Univ (BA) Eng 1971; Unif of MN (MA) Amer Stud 1984; Addl Grad Courses; *cr:* Univ of VT Instr in Continuing Ed 1980-81, 1985-86, 1990-91; Otter Valley UHS Eng TChr 1971-; *ai:* Lit Magazine Adv; Mem of District Wide Assesment; Task Force; Judge for VT Honors Competition for Excl in Writing; Judge for NCTE Achvmt Awd in Writing; Stu Sen Adv; NCTE 1971-; Amer Stud Assn 1984-; Delta Kappa Gamma 1980-; VCTE 1973-; Received $3000 St Grant for Regnl Writing Center; Crystal Apple Awd; Appointed by Commissioner of Ed to Serve on Family Comm Involvement Working Group; Tchr of the Yr 1995; *office:* Otter Valley Union H S RD I Box 1115 Brandon VT 05733

SARNO, PATRICIA A., Science Dept Chair & Bio Tchr; *b:* Ashland, PA; *ed:* Penn St (BS) Bio 1967, (MED) Bio 1972; Post Grad Stud Bucknell Univ, Bloomsburg Univ; *cr:* Pottsville HS Planetarium Curr Coord 1967-72; Schuylkill Haven Bio, Chem, Physics Tchr 1972-76; *ai:* Bio Club; Lead Tchr 7-12 Sci; Adv Hrs AP Course Bio; NABT, NSTA, PSEA, SHEA 1970-; NY & PA Acad of Sci; Smithsonian Assn; Amer Mus of Natl HSI; Phi Sigma; Delta Kappa Gamma; Greenpeace Digit Fund; Penn St Alumni Fund; Arbor Soc; Heart Fnd, St Jude Fnd 1970-; Dow Chem Co Grant for Effects of Pesticides on Household Spiders; Pub PA Pesticide Quarterly; Numerous Curr Guides; New Guides Senior Honor Ind Stud; Discovered New Species of Spider in Northeastern PA, Only One of Its Species in N Amer; County Specialist in Laser Dish & Interactive Multimedia Tech; Listed in Who's Who Amer Women, Emerging Leaders, in the East, Outstanding Scndry Educators, Amer Ed; Women of Yr 1991; Five Thousand Personalities in the World; World's Who's Who of Women; Intnl Who's Who of Intellectuals; Two Thousand Notable Amer; *office:* Schuylkill Haven Area Schl E Main St Schuylkill Haven PA 17972*

SARNOWSKI, HELEN ANN, Business Teacher & Dept Chair; *b:* Stroudsburg, PA; *m:* Gary; *c:* Marian; *ed:* Marywood (BS) Bus 1966, (MS) Ed 1972; Adm Cert Scndry Ldrshp 1995; Post Grad at Temple Univ; *cr:* Pittston Area Achl Tchr 1967-, Dept Chair 1994-; *ai:* FBLA Adv; Bus Dept Chprsn; PAFT 1970-; PBEA 1968-; St Maria 1973-; Marywood Coll Alumni Assn 1967-; *office:* Pittston Area High School 5 Stout St Yatesville Pittston PA 18640

SAROSI, BRIDGET, English Teacher & Dept Head; *b:* Johnstown, PA; *ed:* Univ of Pittsburgh at Johnstown (BA) Eng Ed 1972; +30 Credit Hrs; *cr:* Diocese of Altoona Tchr 1974-78; Bishop McCort HS Tchr 1978-; *ai:* Forensics Coach; Newest Eng Tchr Mentor; Dept Head; Cath Schl Tchrs Assoc 1984-, Sec, VP & Bldg Rep; NCTE 1990-; NASAA 1995-; Log House Quilters Guild 1989-; *office:* Bishop Mc Cort HS 25 Osborne St Johnstown PA 15905*

SARRA, EVE GORHAM, Middle School Math Teacher; *b:* Norwalk, CT; *m:* John Bernard; *c:* Kyle Jonathon, Amanda Rose; *ed:* Central CT St Univ (BS) Elem Ed 1974; Sacred Heart Univ (MAT) Ed 1995; Fairfield Univ Cert Small Bus Mngmt 1985; *cr:* Our Lady of the Assumption Schl MS Math Tchr 1989-; *ai:* Math Counts Coach; Audio Visual Chprsn; Asst Stu Cncl Adv; Jr Women's Club of Monroe 1988-, Treas, Sec, Parliamentarian; Outstdng Thesis Ed AwdSacred Heart Univ 1996; *home:* 319 Pepper St Monroe CT 06468*

SARRA, MARIO, Spanish Teacher; *b:* Monte San Giovanni, Italy; *m:* Gail Whitbourne; *ed:* Monroe Comm Coll (AA) Liberal Arts Span 1975; SUNY at Brockport (BA) Lib Arts Span 1977; Univ of IL (AM) Comparative Lit 1981, (PHD) Comparative Lit 1986; *cr:* Univ of IL Span & Italian Tchr 1978-86; West Irondequoit HS Italian Tchr 1986-87; Aquinas Inst Span Tchr 1987-; *office:* Aquinas Inst Of Rochester 1127 Dewey Ave Rochester NY 14613

SARRATORE, ANTHONY A., Seventh Grade Teacher; *b:* Wheeling, WV; *ed:* OH Univ (BS) Elem Ed 1974; Dayton Univ (MS) Elem Prin 1981; *cr:* North Elem 6th-7th Grd Tchr 17 Yrs; Elm MS 7th Grd Tchr 5 Yrs; *ai:* Civics & Career Day at St Clairsville; Govt in Action; United Ed Profession 1973-; Martins Ferry Italian Club 1965-, Pres & Treas; Martins Ferry Vol Fire Dept 12 Yrs, Office Treas, Honorary Mem; Fraternal Order of Eagles 1988-; City Councilman, Cncl Pres; Belmont Cty Democratic Cntrl & Democratic Party Comm; *home:* 719 N Zane Hwy Martins Ferry OH 43935*

SARRATORI, MICHAEL ANTHONY, Physical Education Teacher; *b:* N Tonawanda, NY; *m:* Jeanne Marie; *c:* Michael; *ed:* Univ of Buffalo (BA) Soc Sci, Mental Hlth 1987; Canisius Coll (MS) PE 1993; *cr:* Autistic Svcs of Buffalo PE Tchr 1989; Dunkirk Sr HS PE Tchr 1990-, Ath Dir 1993-; *ai:* Var Club Adv; Section VI Division VI Chm; IM Track, Weightlifting Instr; Var Track, Var Ftbl Head Coach; Chautauqua Ath Dirs Assn; *office:* Dunkirk Sr HS 75 W Sixth St Dunkirk NY 14048*

SARRO, THOMAS JOHN, Professor; *b:* Far Rockaway, NY; *m:* Katherine Baker; *c:* Rebecca; *ed:* Fairleigh Dickinson Univ (BS) Bio 1973, (MS) Bio 1975; NY Univ (PHD) Bio 1992; *cr:* Mt St Mary Coll Assoc Prof & Prof 1975-; *ai:* Acad & Womens Bsktbl Team Adv; Outdoor Club; Torrey Bot Club 1976-; JBNHS 1993-, Trustee; Humana 1995-; *office:* Mount Saint Mary Coll 330 Powell Ave Newburgh NY 12550*

SARSAR, SALIBA, Associate Professor of Pol Sci; *b:* Jerusalem, Jordan; *ed:* Brookdale Comm Coll (AA) 1977; Monmouth Coll (BA) His & Pol Sci 1978; Rutgers Univ (PHD) Pol Sci 1984; *cr:* Monmouth Coll Ldrshp Initiatives Project Dir 1992-93; Monmouth Univ Pres for Ldrshp Spcl Asst 1993-95, Ctr for Stud of Pub Issues Exec Dir 1993-, Schl of Arts & Scis Assoc Dean 1994-; *ai:* Mid Sts Assn Self-Stud Steering Comm Co-Chair; Founders Day Comm; Task Force on Outcomes Assessment; Provosts Cncl; Model United Nations Co-Adv; Task Force on Class Capacities; Received W K Kellogg Fndtn Dissemination Grant 1995-; Received & Directed GTE Grant Lectureship Pgm in Sci, Tech & Human Values 1989-90; Pub Books: Ideology, Values and Technology in Political Life 1994 & World Politics, An Interdisciplinary Perspective 1995; Numerous Articles & Book Reviews Pub; *office:* Monmouth Univ Cedar & Norwood Aves West Long Branch NJ 07764

SARTIN, JEAN KOBOWSKI, English & French Teacher; *b:* Wilkes-Barre, PA; *m:* Edward Nelson; *c:* Heather J. Wickizer, Edward N., Thomas N.; *ed:* Coll of Misericordia (BA) Fr, Eng 1972; 8 Credits Fr Dijon Univ France 1970; 15 Credits Luzerne Intermediate Unit; Rel Ed Cert; 6 Credits Temple Univ; SAP Trng Wilkes Univ; *cr:* Wilkes-Barre Area Schl Dist Eng, Fr Tchr 1980-84; HOly Child Elem Schl Eng, Rdng, Math Tchr 1986-87; Bishop O'Reilly HS Eng, Fr Tchr 1988-; *ai:* Fr Club Moderator; Natl Fr Hnr Soc Spon; New Tchrs Mentor; AATF 1988-; NCTE 1992-; Blue & Gold Parents Club 1987-; *office:* Bishop O'Reilly HS 316 N Maple Ave Kingston PA 18704*

SARTY, MARY JANE (LAPARO), Second Grade Teacher; *b:* Bellevue, OH; *m:* August Thomas; *c:* Thomas August, Kimberlie Jo Sarty Tiedeken; *ed:* OH Dominican (BA) Elem Ed 1968; Attnd Bowling Green St Univ & Ashland Coll; *cr:* St Peters Cath Schl 3rd Grd Tchr 1965-66; York Schl Remedial Rdng 1967-76; Shumaker Schl 2nd Grd Tchr 1976-; *ai:* BEA 1967-; NEA 1967-; OEA 1967-; Club Amer-Ital 1965-; Daughters of Isabella 1983-; IAB Auxillary 1992-; *office:* Shumaker Elem Schl 1035 Castalia St Bellevue OH 44811

SARUBBI, JOSEPH THOMAS, Elec Constr & Maint Assoc Prof; *b:* Yonkers, NY; *m:* Colleen Mc Manus-Sarubbi; *c:* J. T., Alisha, Nicole, Brett; *ed:* SUNY Inst of Tech (BS) Voc Tech Ed 1983; 15 Addl Credits Educl Admin, Policy Stud SUNY at Albany; *cr:* IBEW Journeyman Electrician 1974-78; Hudson Vly Comm Coll Assoc Prof Electrical Construction, Maintenance 1979-; *ai:* ECM Club Adv; ECM Dept Prgm Coord; Stu Adv; Head Coach Pop Warner Ftbl; Mgr Girls Sftbl; Coach Little League Bsbl; Regnl VICA Competitions Judge; HVCC Fac Assn 1979-; Assn of 2 Yr Colls 1989-; ECM Stdnts Dedicated Svc Recognition Awd 1993; *home:* 17 Timberland Dr East Greenbush NY 12061

SARVER, BARBARA (CAMBETES), Math Tchr & Curriculum Coord; *b:* Mount Vernon, NY; *m:* Michael; *c:* Christine Barney; *ed:* Hunter Coll (BA) Math, Statistics 1962; Western CT St Univ (MS) Math, Ed 1976; Pace Univ (MS) Cmptr Sci 1986; *cr:* Archbishop Stepinac HS 9th-12th Grd Math Tch 1973-78; Hendrick Hudson HS 9th-12th Grd Math Tchr 1978-79; Croton Harmon HS 9th-12th Grd Math Tchr 1979-; *ai:* Grd 6-12 Curr Coord; Dev Alternative Assessment; NCTM 1986-; NY St Tchr of Yr Nom 1994; *home:* 34 Scenic Cir Croton On Hudson NY 10520

SARVER, PHYLLIS ANN, Kindergarten Teacher; *b:* Berlin, PA; *m:* Ronald T.; *c:* Michael R.; *ed:* CA Univ of PA (BA) Elem Ed 1971; Perm Cert CA Univ of PA; *cr:* Berlin Brothers Vly Schl Dist Kdg Tchr 1971-; *ai:* PSEA 1971-.*

SASO, MARY BETH, Kindergarten Teacher; *b:* Poughkeepsie, NY; *m:* Gregory T.; *c:* Katharine A., Gregory T.; *ed:* Russell Sage Coll (BS) Psych 1981; Attnd SUNY at New Paltz Elem Ed 1989; *cr:* Highland Elem Schl 5th Grd Tchr 1984-87, Kndgtn Tchr 1988-; *ai:* NYSUT 1984-; *office:* Highland Elem Schl Lockhart Ln Highland NY 12528

SASS, ANDREW RAYMOND, Physics Teacher; *b:* Budapest, Hungary; *m:* Geraldine Ragamata; *c:* Michael, Peter; *ed:* MIT (BS) Electr Eng 1958; Purdue Univ (MS) Electr Eng 1960, (PHD) Electr Eng 1962; *cr:* RCA Research Engr 1964-69; IBM Sr Engr 1969-76; General Instrument Dir, Product Plng 1976-83; Krell Software Dir Mrktng 1983-89; Island Trees HS Physics Tchr 1991-95; *ai:* NHS, Sci Olympiad Adv; AAPT, STANYS 1991-; cmptr Chapter Applied Superconductivity Acad Press; 15 Tech Articles & Presentations; David Sarnoff Team Achvmt in Sci, Two RCA Labs Outstanding Achvmt Awds; *office:* Island Trees HS 59 Straight Ln Levittown NY 11756*

SASSANO, SAMUEL J., Teacher; *b:* Philadelphia, PA; *ed:* Thomas Edison St Coll (BA) Rel & Elem Ed 1990; Boston Coll (MED) Educl

Admin 1993; 20 Grad Credit Hrs Theology; *cr:* Holy Name Schl 6th Grd Tchr 1981-84; St Gabriel Schl 8th Grd Tchr 1984-89; Sacred Heart Schl Prin 1991-94; Gloucester Cath Rel Tchr 1994-; *ai:* TEAMS & Assoc Yth Coord; NCEA 1981-; Prin Assn 1991-, VP; Diocese of Cander; Yth Minister 1985-; Yth Cty Coord for Diocese 1991-; Boston Coll Schlrshp; *office:* Gloucester Catholic HS 333 Ridgeway St Gloucester City NJ 08030*

SASSEVILLE, EUGENE HENRY, Electronics Teacher; *b:* New Bedford, MA; *m:* Jeanine Yvonne Barrett; *c:* Susan Saraiva, Richard; *ed:* Southeastern MA Tech Inst (ASEE) Electrical Engrng; Fitchburg St Coll (BS) Occupational Ed; Working Towards Masters Ed Admin 12 Credit Hrs; Currently Enrolled Diaconal Stud; *cr:* Aerovox Corp Tech 1661-66; Ratheon Corp Engr 1966-68; New Bedford Voc Schl Electronics Tchr 1968-; Greater New Bedford Regnl Voc HS Electronics Tchr 1968-; *ai:* Voc Indstrl Clubs of Amer Adv; Tech Prep Dept Chair; Dept Curr Ldr; Church, Parish, Coord of Rel Ed Lector, Eucharistic Minister, Diocesan Marian Medal; *office:* Greater New Bedford Reg Voc SD 1121 Ashley Blvd New Bedford MA 02745

SASSI, JOHN J., Advanced Placement Lit Tchr; *b:* Pittston, PA; *m:* Diane; *c:* Jill, Jonathan; *ed:* Kings Coll (BA) Eng 1967; Wilke Coll (MS) Eng Ed 1972; Post Grad at Penn St; *cr:* Pittston Area Tchr 29 Yrs; *ai:* Evaluating Comm for Lang Arts Related to Lit & Writing; AFT 1967-, Sec; *office:* Pittston Area Sr HS 5 Stout St Yatesville PA 18646

SASSO, DENNIS ANTHONY, Teacher & Coach; *b:* Newark, NJ; *c:* Dennis, Michael Dante; *ed:* St Peters Coll (CC) Classical Langs 1969; Fordham Univ (MA) Classical Lang & Lit 1970; Doctoral Pgm Classics; *cr:* Essex Cath HS Latin & Eng Tchr & Ftbl, Bsbl & Bsktbl Coach 1973-76; Middletown HS South Eng, Latin & Mythology Tchr & Bsbl & Bsktbl Coach 1977-81; Nutley HS Eng & Pub Speaking Debate Tchr & Bsbl & Bsktbl Coach 1981-; Fairleigh Dickinson Univ Eng & Myth Tchr & Bsbl Coach 1985-; *ai:* Sr Class, Forensics & Debate Adv; Head Bsbl Coach; NEA & NJEA 1976-; NCTE 1976-; Fordham Univ Grad Assistantship; US Army Military Police Capt; Commandants List Distngd Military Grad; NJ Bsbl Coach of Yr 1975, 1979, & 1983; Northwest Regnl Coach of Yr 1975, 1979, 1983, 1988-89, & 1993; *office:* Nutley HS 300 Franklin Ave Nutley NJ 07110

SASSO, LINDA BEECHER, Spanish Teacher; *b:* Chicopee, MA; *m:* John V.; *c:* Stacie Cote, Melissa Beecher, Allison Beecher; *ed:* Univ of MA (BA) Span 1971; Westfield St coll (MED) Educl Tech 1987; *cr:* Bowe Elem Schl BiLing Tchr 1972-74; East Longmeadow HS Span Tchr 1974-81; Agawam HS Span Tchr 1981-82; Agawam Jr HS Span Tchr 1982-91; Agawam HS Span Tchr 1991-; *ai:* Peer Leadership Adv; Renaissance Prgm Co-Chprsn; Mentor Tchr; NEA, MTA 1972-; Agawam Ed Assn 1982-; Frgn Lang Assoc 1994-; AAU Girls Bsktbl 1992-, Vol; Admin Asst 1995-; Chicopee High Bsktbl Boosters 1994-; Brown & Orange Extraordnry Svc Awd 1995; Horace Mann Grant Recipient 1986-87; *office:* Agawam HS 760 Cooper St Agawam MA 01001*

SATRIANO, ANITA GUARDO, Retired Kindergarten Teacher; *b:* Hartford, CT; *m:* Salvatore F.; *c:* Anne Satriano Tucker, Steven; *ed:* Hartford Coll for Women (AA) Lbrl Arts 1951; St Joseph Coll (BS) Child Dev 1953; Univ of CT (ME) Elem Educ 1966; *cr:* Goodwin Schl Kndgtn Tchr 1953-54; Vinton Schl 2nd Grd Tchr 1954-55; Southeast Schl 4th Grd Tchr1959-61; Vinton Schl Kndgtn Tchr 1966-91; *ai:* NEA, CEA Ret 1953-; Delta Kappa Gamma 1976-, Local Pres, St Progr Ch Fin; Mansfield Ed Assn Pres 2 Times, Sec; Republican Town Comm 1970's, Vice Chair; Delta Kappa Gamma 1976-, Planning Comm, Networking for Children 1993-, Caring for Our Planet 1990, 1996; Hospice Vol for Visiting Nurse of Eastern CT 1992; Mansfield Tchr of Yr 1986-87; Mainstreaming Inclusion Downs Syndrome, Physically Handicapped Since 1980; *home:* 14 Stafford Rd Mansfield Center CT 06250

SATYAL, LALITA BALI, Third Grade Teacher; *b:* Jullundhur, Punjab India; *m:* Vinay K.; *c:* Rajiv, Rakesh, Vikas; *ed:* Allahabad Univ (BA) Eng Lit 1968, (MA) Eng Lit 1970; Miami Univ (MAT) Elem Ed 1972; 12 Hrs of Educl Media for Another MA Degree; *cr:* Fillmore Elem Schl Fourth Grd Tchr 1972-80, Fifth Grd Tchr 1980-90, Fourth Grd Tchr 1991-94, Third Grd Tchr 1995-; *ai:* Chaperone for Field Trip; Judge for PTA Art Contest; Jr Achvmnt Chprsn for Grd Level; ATP Vol; OEA, NEA, NCTA 1972-; Delta Kappa Gamma First VP; HSGC 1980-, Childrens Comm; Grad Asst at Miami Univ Jury Duty; *home:* 1320 Hunter Ct Fairfield OH 45014*

SATYSHUR, ROSEMARIE FRANCES DIMAURO, Asst Prof & Child Hlth Nurse; *b:* Camden, NJ; *m:* Michael Peter; *c:* Matthew Valentino, Maria Francine; *ed:* Thomas Jefferson Univ (BSN) Nursing 1981; The Cath Univ of Amer (MSN) Nursing 1984, (DNSc) Nursing 1991; *cr:* W Jersey Hosp Hlth Care System Alternate Charge Nurse Neonatal ICU 1976-77; Thomas Jefferson Univ Hosp Infant Care Coord Neonatal ICU 1977-82; The Cath Univ of Amer Asst Prof Maternal Child Hlth Nursing 1984-; *ai:* Masters Curr, Deans Fac Advy, Admissions, Progression & Retention & Doctoral Proposal Acceptance Comms; Masters & Baccalaureate Stdnts Adv; CUA Nursing Alumni Chptr 1982-, Pres 1993-95; The Amer Assn of Univ Profs 1984-; Soc of Pediatric Nurses 1985-; Sigma Theata Tau Kappa Chptr 1988-, 1st VP 1993-95, Svc Awd; Natl League for Nursing 1994-; MD Nurses Assn 1988-; Amer Nurses Assn 1988-; DC League for Nursing 1994-; Natl League for Nursing 1994-; Archdiocesan Cath Schl Bd of Ed 1995-; CUA Grant in Aid for Comparison Adolescents with Cancer Nursing Care; Mary McCarthy Mem Fund for Doctoral Dissertation Completion; Whos Who in Amer Nursing; Whos Who of Amer Women; Alphy Delta Gamma Kappa Chptr Instr of the Month; *office:* The Catholic Univ Of America Brookland Ave Washington DC 20064

SATZMAN, PAUL, Professor of Music; *b:* New York City, NY; *m:* Sarah Wilkes; *c:* Rebecca, Rachel; *ed:* Adelphi Univ (BA) Music 1964; CUNY Queens Coll (MA) Music Ed 1972; SUNY at Stony Brook (MALS) Art His 1995; Attnd SUNY at Buffalo; *cr:* Harborfields HS Music Tchr 1964-65; Brentwood HS Choral Dir 1965-70; Locust Vly HS Choral Dir 1970-79; Suffolk Comm Coll Music Prof 1981-; *ai:* Wkshp Ldr SUNY at Stony Brook; Cadence Club Adv; Art Dept Prgm Review Comm Chair; Guest Lecturer Inservice Prgm for Classroom Tchrs; AFT, NYSUT 1965-; Piano Technicans Guild 1970-, Craftsman, Master; Newsday Tchr of Yr Locust Vly 1976; Excl in Tchng Chancellor's Awd 1995; Master Tchr Seminar 1990; Coord Interdisciplinary Stud Prgm; *office:* Suffolk Comm Coll Ammerman Cmp 533 College Rd Selden NY 11784*

SAUCIER, ROBERTA ANN, Math Tchr & Technology Mentor; *b:* Bristol, RI; *m:* Robert M.; *c:* Beth; *ed:* RI Coll (BED) Math, Elem Ed 1963, (MED) Math, Elem Ed 1968; 96 Addl Hrs Post Grad Stud Guid, Elem Admin, Scndry Math; *cr:* Bristol Schl Dept Math Tchr 1963-93; Salve Regina Univ Math Ed Tchr 1970-75; Bristol Cty Travel Consultant 1987-; Bristol Warren Regnl Schl Dept Math Tchr, Tech Mentor 1993-; *ai:* Trip Adv; IM Vlybl Ref; BWEA, RIEA, NEA, NCTM, RICTM 1963-; Delta Kappa Gamma 1980-; IATA 1986-; Univ of New Haven Parents Assn 1994-; Univ of IL Sci Flwshp; RI, Bristol Jaycee Tchr of Yr; Jamaica Travel, Disney Coll of Knowledge Specialist; *home:* 126 Berry Ln Bristol RI 02809*

SAUDER, ROBERT JAY, Spanish Teacher & Athletic Dir; *b:* Wauseon, OH; *m:* Pamela Ruffer; *c:* Mary, Kelly; *ed:* Hesston Jr Coll (AA) 1965; Goshen Coll (BA) Math Ed 1967; Univ of MT (MED) Guidance & Counseling 1973; Univ of Toledo (EDS) HS Admin 1990; *cr:* Fayette Local Schls Tchr, Coach 1967-72; North Cntrl Local Schls Tchr, Coach Guidance Cnslr 1972-79; Millcreek-West Unity Local Tchr, Coach, Ath Dir 1979-; *ai:* Ath Dir; OEA, NEA, OFLA 1967-; OHSAAA 1993-; Salem Mennonite Church 1972-, Elder; *home:* 14581 Cty Rd N-65 Pioneer OH 43554*

SAUER, JOHNOTHON A., Math Teacher; *b:* Columbus, OH; *m:* Theresa G. O'Neil; *c:* Jack, Michaelanne; *ed:* OH St Univ (BSED) Math 1990; *cr:* Newark Cath HS Math & Drama Dept Chair, Dean of Stdnts 1990-95; LaSalle HS Math Tchr 1995-; *ai:* Asst Dir, Production Coord Drama; TEA 1995-; *office:* La Salle HS 3091 W North Bend Rd Cincinnati OH 45239*

SAUERS, JAMIE L., Health & PE Teacher; *b:* Lewisburg, PA; *m:* Tracy Ann; *c:* Abby, Justin; *ed:* (BS) Hlth & PE 1975; Post Grad Stud at Penn St Univ, Bucknell & Villanova; *cr:* Mifflinburg Area HS Hlth & PE Tchr 1976-; *ai:* Ftbl & Bsbl Head Coach; Intramural Dir; Penn St Club 1985-; PA St Ftbl Assn 1976-; Sons of Amer Legion 1992-; 20 Yr Coach in PA.

SAUKAS, MARK W., Soc Stud Tchr & Dir Stu Act; *b:* Waterbury, CT; *m:* Frances Thompson; *c:* Robert Szantyr; *ed:* Providence Coll (BA) Soc Stud 1972; Southern CT St Univ & ND St Univ Grad Credits; *cr:* Sacred Heart High Soc Stud Tchr 1975-, Dir Stu Act 1994-; *ai:* Var Bsbl Coach; Stu Assistance Team; Stu Fund Raising Coord; NCEA 1976-; NHSACA 1976-; CHSCA 1976-; NASAA 1994-; Anderson Boys Club Hall of Fame; *office:* Sacred Heart HS 142 S Elm St Waterbury CT 06722

SAUL, ROBERT W., Science Dept Team Ldr & Instr; *b:* Millville, NJ; *m:* Linda Davies; *c:* Keith Alape; *ed:* Montclair St Univ (BA) Math, Phys Sci 1967; Rutgers Univ (MED) Admin, Supervision 1989; Bus Admin; Univ of AZ Sports Med; Univ of CO Ath Trng; *cr:* Abraham Clark HS Math, Sci Tchr 1967-69; Cedar Ridge HS Math Tchr 1969-70; Union Cty Coll Adj Prof of Math, Sci 1971-75; S Plainfield HS Math, Sci Tchr 1970-; *ai:* Physics Club 1981-; Head Winter Track, Spring Track Coach 1969-89; NEA, NJEA 1967-; SPEA 1967-, Pres, VP; NJTFOA 1972-, Pres, VP, Outstdng Ofcl; NJSIAA 1980-, Exec Bd, Achvmt of Hnr; S Plainfield Jaycees 1973-77, Treas; Millville Rotary Club 1967-69; Middlesex Cty Coaches 1969-81, Pres 1981, Track Coach of Yr; Alpha Phi Omega 1964-67, Treas; NJ St Schlsp; Merit Schlsp Finalist 1962; BSA Eagle Scout; *office:* South Plainfield HS 200 Lake St South Plainfield NJ 07080*

SAULINO, ALPHONSE F.,III, Fifth Grade Teacher; *b:* Fall River, MA; *m:* Leonora R. Botelho; *c:* Peter, Justin, Amanda; *ed:* Providence Coll (BA) His, Ed 1970, (MED) Cnslng 1974; Attnd RI Coll, Univ MA at Dartmouth; *cr:* Jerome Dwelly Schl Tchr 1970-78; Slade Schl Tchr 1978-; *ai:* Fall River Edctrs Assn, MA Tchrs Assn, NEA 1970-; Vol St Anne's Hosp; Cub Scout Ldr; Boy Scout Committeeman; PTO; St Thomas More Roman Cath Parish, Cncl, Eucharistic Minister, Rel Ed Tchr; *office:* Slade Elem Schl 200 Lewis St Fall River MA 02724

SAULL, MARGIE DIANE (SHEETS), Fourth Grade Teacher; *b:* Delaware, OH; *m:* Fredrick J. Jr.; *c:* Bradley, Brian; *ed:* OH St Univ (BS) K-8 Elem Ed 1974, (MA) Early Mid Chldhd Ed 1979; Rdng Cert; Cooperative Learning, Power Writing, Stress Mngmt, Integrated Lang Arts, Multi-Aged Grouping, Dev Responsible Behavior in Schls; *cr:* Buckeye Valley Local Schls Kndgtn Tchr 1974-75; Marion City Schls Rdng Resource Tchr 1975-76, Kndgtn Tchr 1976-77, 2-5th Grd Tchr 1977-; *ai:* Third Grd Spring Prgm Dir; Nursing Home Prgm-PR Coord; Dev Responsible Behavior Inservice Dir; MEA, OEA, NEA, IRA 1975-; Univ Women OSU Alumni Assn 1974-, Sec; Phi Delta Kappa 1986-; Wesley United Meth Church, Music Comm; Young Author's Prgm Chprsn 1991; *office:* George Washington Elem Schl 300 Pennsylvania Ave Marion OH 43302

SAUNDERS, CHRIS R., Social Studies Teacher; *b:* Syracuse, NY; *m:* Cathleen Burbee; *c:* Dylan; *ed:* (BA) His 1990; *cr:* East Lake HS Soc Stud Tchr 1990-91; Wellington HS Soc Stud Tchr 1991-92; Boothbay Region HS Soc Stud Tchr 1992-; *ai:* Model St, Jr Class & Stu Cncl Adv; Soccer Coach; AP His Club Adv; NEA, MEA; NEH Summer Seminar for Tchrs 1995 at Univ of AL; NEH Inst at Univ of Southern ME 1993; *home:* PO Box 424 Boothbay ME 04537*

SAUNDERS, CYNTHIA ANN, Cheerleader Coach; *b:* Washington, DC; *c:* Ottawa, Octavia, Antonio; *cr:* Eliot Jr HS Educl Aide, Office Asst; *ai:* AuxiliaryCoach; Band, Chorus Asst; Recieved Awds of Recoginition.

SAUNDERS, DONALD E., 9th-12th Grd Earth Sci Tchr; *b:* Charlerol, PA; *ed:* CA Univ of Penn (BA) Earth Sci, Geography 1971; MA Equivalent 45 Hrs; *cr:* Carlynton HS Tchr 1971-; *ai:* Ftbl Head Coach; Natl Earth Sci Tchrs Assn 1980-; Penn Ftbl Coaches Assn 1980-; *office:* Carlynton HS 435 Kings Hwy Carnegie PA 15106

SAUNDERS, EMILY E., Health Coordinator; *b:* New York, NY; *m:* Thomas M.; *c:* Elizabeth; *ed:* Mercy Coll (BS) Bio & Chem 1965; Univ of MA (MSPH) Pub Hlth 1968; NYU Adm Dip Admin 1976; New Rochelle Coll Staff Dev; *cr:* Sacred Heart HS Bio Tchr 1965-66; Univ of MA Hlth Instr 1966-68; Woodlands HS Health Ed Coord 1968-; *ai:* Var Ath Against Substance Abuse Adv; Past Adv NHS; Spirit Pgm Coord; NYSUT & GTF 1968-, Pres 1993; Westchester Putnam Pres Cncl; Darylea Nutrition & PDQ Grant; Hlth Net Adv; *office:* Woodlands HS 475 W Hartsdale Ave Hartsdale NY 10530

SAUNDERS, JANETTE, English Teacher; *b:* Taplin, WV; *m:* William C.; *c:* Michele Anderson, Angela, Lisa; *ed:* Bluefield St Coll (BS) Home Ec Ed, Eng 1965; 3 Credit Hrs Bowie St Coll; 15 Grad Credit Hrs Western MD Coll; *cr:* Office of Ec Opportunity Soc Worker 1965-66, Nutritionist Operation Head Start 1966-69; P. G. Cty Schls Sub Tchr 1983-85, Tchr 1985-; *ai:* Co-Chair Mid Sts Self Stud Comm; Co-Spon NHS; Lit Magazine Spon; NEA, MSTA, PGCEA 1986-; ASCD 1995; NCTE; *office:* Forestville HS 7001 Beltz Dr Forestville MD 20747*

SAUNDERS, LAURIE ANN, 3rd & 4th Grd Multiage Tchr; *b:* Laconia, NH; *cr:* Various Hlth Clubs Fitness Instr 1984-; Gilford Elem 5th Grd Tchrs Aide 1986-1987; Woodland Heights Elem 3rd & 4th Grd Multiage, 4th & 5th Grd Tchr 1987-; *ai:* Work with PSC Stu Tchr; *office:* Woodlands Heights Elem Schl 225 Winter St Laconia NH 03246*

SAUNDERS, SANDRA GRANT, Spanish Teacher; *b:* Houston, TX; *m:* Douglas J.; *c:* Ian Grant, Julie Elizabeth; *ed:* Alfred Univ (BA) Fr 1968; Elmira Coll (MS) Ed 1987; Attnd Univ of Salamonca in Spain, Univ of Hartford, SUNY at Plattsburg, Univ of Montreal, LAVAL Univ & St Rose Coll; *cr:* W Wilkes HS Fr Tchr 1 Yr; Cath Schls of Broome Cty Span Tchr 1 Yr; Whitney Point HS Fr & Span Tchr 3 Yrs; Newark Valley HS Span Tchr 6 Yrs; *ai:* Literacy Vols 1992-; AFT 1985-, Bldg Rep, Sec; NYSAFLT 1985; Project Neighbor, Sec; Church Cncl, Sec; Culture & Lang of Fr Canada Seminar & Grant; Fulbright-Hays Grant Applicant; *office:* Newark Valley HS PO Box 547 Newark Valley NY 13811

SAUNDERS, SHEILA MAE LEWIS, Special Education Teacher; *b:* Bethesda, MD; *m:* Paul Cyril; *c:* MaryAnn, Molly, Marjorie; *ed:* Marymount Univ (AA) Lbrl Arts 1982, (BA) Spec Ed, Emotional Dist 1983; Hood Coll (MA) Spec Ed 1987; 30 Credit Hrs Curr & Tchng Strategies; *cr:* Mark Twain Schl Spec Ed, 6th-9th Grd Math, Sci Tchr 1984-88; RICA Spec Ed, 6th-8th Grd Math Tchr 1988-91; Fox Chapel Elem Spec Ed Intensity Tchr 1991-; *ai:* Sci, Support Team Comms; NEA 1985-; Wesley Grove United Meth Church 1970-; Green Valley ES PTA; *office:* Montgomery Cty Pub Schls 850 Hungerford Dr Rockville MD 20850*

SAUNDERS, TIM R., Physical Education Teacher; *b:* Columbus, OH; *m:* Janie Armington; *c:* Shelby; *ed:* Univ of Rio Grande (BS) PE 1981, (BS) Spec Ed 1983; Ashland Univ (MA) Sports Sci 1984; *cr:* Meigs HS Spec Ed Tchr 1981-85; IN Univ Asst Bsbl Coach 1985-88; Dublin Coffman HS PE Tchr 1988-; *ai:* Outdoor Pursuit PE, Asst Ath Dir; Head Var Bsbl Coach; Cntrl Dist Bsbl C. A. 1988-, Pres 1992; OHSBCA 1981-, Pres 1996; Jennings Scholar 1996; Olympic Sports Festival Bsbl Coach, Nort 1995; *office:* Dublin HS 6780 Coffman Rd Dublin OH 43017

SAUNDERSON, PATRICK JOSEPH, World History Teacher; *b:* Spring, MD; *ed:* Univ of MD (BS) Scndry Ed 1991; Working on M in Admin, Supervision at Loyola Coll; *cr:* Atholton HS World Hi Cross Cntry & Track Coach 1992-; *ai:* It's Acad Coach; Schl Impro Team; Ninth Grd Team Ldr; NEA, MSTA, HCEA 1992-; Mt Zion Meth 1979-, Admin Bd, Staff Parish Relations Comm; AYRA, Bsbl Track Coach of Yr 3 Times; Black Stu Union Favorite Tchr Awd; Atholton HS 6520 Freetown Rd Columbia MD 21044*

SAUR, JANICE SNYDER, Family Life & Con Sci Tchr; *b:* Wayne PA; *m:* Robert Ross; *c:* Brenton, Bryan, Blythe Saur Davis; *ed:* A Univ (BS) Home Ec 1957; Univ of MD (MS) Ed 1963; *cr:* Longfe HS Clothing Tchr 1957-59; Clear Spring Jr-Sr HS Home Ec Tchr 19 Clear Spring Sr HS Family Life, Consumer Svc Tchr 1965-; *ai:* Adv Homemakers of Amer; Nutrition Sci Completer, Child Care Prof Schl Improvement Team, Hlth & Safety Comms; Extended Curr WCTA 1961-, Schl Rep; MSTA, NEA 1961-; Delta Kappa Gamma Kidney Fnd 1966-; Nom Tchr of Excl 1991; *home:* 12812 Oak Hi Hagerstown MD 21742

SAURO, ANN ROSSI, 8th Grade Mathematics Teacher; *b:* New Yo *w:* Joseph (dec); *c:* Barbara, Jo-Ann Corsillo, Lisa, Ann; *ed:* Fordhar (BS) Math 1948; *cr:* NY Telephone Co Budget Engr 10 Yrs; Saint T Aquinas Schl Tchr 1 Yr; Saint Benedict Tchr 25 Yrs; *ai:* Fed of Cath 1980-; Throggsneck Vol Ambulance Corps 1979-, Bd of Dirs, Eme Medical Technician-D; Comm Cncl 1972-, Sec, Past Exec Bd Womans Republican Club 1995-; RCIA 1990-, Team Mem; *offi* Benedict Schl 1016 Edison Ave Bronx NY 10465

SAUSELEN, ELWOOD LARRY, Visiting Asst Professor of A Springfield, OH; *ed:* OH St Univ (BFA) Drawing & Painting 1975, Drawing & Painting 1979; *cr:* OH St Univ Lecturer of Art 19 Visiting Asst Prof of Art 1995-; *ai:* Gallery Curator; Comp & Request Review Comms; Univ Classroom of Tomorrow Fac Mem; Prof Dev Tchng & OH Arts Cncl; Natl Endowment for the Arts Flws of OH Senate Recognition for Artists Books; *office:* OH St Univ At M 196 Morrill Hall Marion OH 43302*

SAUSVILLE, LINDA HAMBACHER, 7th Grade Language Arts T Plainfield, NJ; *c:* Kenneth, Gretchen; *ed:* Montclair St Univ (BA) E 1969; *cr:* South Plainfield MS 7th Grd Lang Arts Tchr 1969-; *ai:* 1992-; NEA, NJEA, MCEA, SPEA 1975-; *office:* South Plainfield MS Plainfield Ave South Plainfield NJ 07080*

SAUTER, CINDY ELISSA (BERG), Spanish Teacher; *b:* Bronx, N Joseph; *ed:* Cedar Crest Coll (BA) Span & Ed 1974; NY Univ (MA) & Scndry Ed 1977; Attnd Univ of Madrid 1977, Univ of Valencia 197 Middletown HS Span Tchr 1979-; *ai:* NY St United Tchrs 1979- 1979-; NY St Fed of Frgn Lang Tchrs 1979-; Middletown Tchrs 1979-; Mentor Middletown Intern Pgm 1988-89; *office:* City Schl D Middletown Gardner Ave Ext Middletown NY 10940

SAVAGE, JOHN DAVID, Assistant Professor of Science; *b:* Wilkes- PA; *ed:* Boston Coll (BS) Chem 1987; Univ MA at Amherst (PHD) Chem 1993; *cr:* Roxbury Comm Coll Instr 1992-94, Asst Prof 199 Sci Dept Chm; Roxbury Comm Coll Pgm Coord for RCC-MIT STEPP Several Articles Pub; *office:* Roxbury Comm Coll 1234 Columbu Boston MA 02120*

SAVAGE, MICHAEL VICTOR, Chemistry & Physics Teache Worcester, MA; *m:* Sandra L. Norrman; *c:* Erik, Mark; *ed:* Worces Coll (BA) Bio 1971, (MED) Leadership & Admin 1978; 36 Credit Hr Ed; 24 Credit Hrs Ed Courses; *cr:* Bay Path Voc HS Sci Dept Head *ai:* Peer Mediator Adv; Mentor Prgm; US First Competition Graphics 1996; Var Sftbl Coach 13 Yrs; Bay Path Tchrs Assn 1973-, Pres, Bd of MA Tchrs Assn, NEA 1973-; Auburn Bd of Hlth 1982-, Chm, Vice Auburn Elks Lodge 1981-; Auburn Little League 1978-89, Coach, Tobacco Initiative Grants; Horace Mann Grant; *office:* Bay Path Voc HS 57 Old Muggett Hill Rd Charlton MA 01507

SAVAGE, PEGGI BENNER, Explorer Teacher; *b:* Key West, FL; *m:* *ed:* Univ of Marie (BS) Elem Ed 1977; Working on MS in Sci & M Cntrl CT St Univ; *cr:* Union #47 Bath Schl System 1st & 2nd Grd 1979-84; Windsor Schl Dist K-2nd Grd Tchr 1984-87, Elem Specialist 1987-89, Kndgtn Tchr 1989-91, 4th Grd Explorer Pgm 1991-; *ai:* NEA 1979-; NSTA; Windsor Ed Assn 1984-; Harley O Group Hartford Chptr 1994-; ME Tchr of the Yr Finalist 1984; Edctr Yr at Roger Wolcott Schl 1990; Sci Tchr Summer Flwshp at Univ Hlth Ctr 1994; Edctr of the Yr at Oliver Ellsworth Schl 1994; *office:* C Ellsworth Elem Schl 730 Kennedy Rd Windsor CT 06095*

SAVAGE, VALERIE HARK, Art Teacher; *b:* Hornell, NY; *m:* Ga Peter, Abigail; *ed:* Roberts Wesleyan Coll (BS) Art Ed 1985; Nazareth of Rochester (MS) Art Ed 1991; *cr:* Wheatland-Chili HS Art Tchr 1 Roberts Wesleyan Coll Art Ed Adj Assoc Prof 1991-; *ai:* Art Club Curr Ldr; HS Curr Chm; NYSATA 1985-; AFT 1985-; NAEA 1995-; Wesleyan Church 1985-; *office:* Wheatland Chili HS 940 North Scottsville NY 14546

SAVASTANO, ANTHONY F., Middle School Guidance Cnslr; *b:* York City, NY; *m:* Gail Griffin; *c:* Nicole, Peter, Joseph, Brooke CCNY (BA) Scndry Ed 1970, (MA) Scndry Ed 1973; LIU (MS) Cnslng 1988; Post Grad Group Cnslng; *cr:* Longfellow Jr HS Tech 1968-72; Blue Mountain MS Tech Tchr 1972-88, Guid Cnslr 1988- Coord Stu Mediation Prgm; AFT 1968-, Grievence Comm Chm Patrick's Church 1980-, Eucharistic Minister, Fin Comm; *office:* Mountain MS 7 Furnace Woods Rd Montrose NY 10548*

SAVEL, BETH ROSE, HS Mathematics Teacher; *b:* Madison, OH Bowling Green St Univ (BS) Ed 1988; *cr:* North Olmstead HS Math 1988-; *ai:* Math Team 1990-, Stu Cncl Class 1992- Adv; Ldrshp C 1996; Frosh Mentor 1996; Sftbl Scorekeeper; North Olmsted Ed A OEA, NEA 1988-; NCTM, OCTM 1992-; *office:* North Olmsted HS Burns Rd North Olmsted OH 44070*

SAVERINO, PHILIP N., Social Studies Teacher; *b:* Washington, DC Belinda C. Scaldeferri; *c:* Joseph, Nicholas; *ed:* Bowie St (BS) Psych 1977; Grad Stud 27 Hrs; *cr:* Croom Voc HS Tchr 1977-84; Fred Douglass HS Tchr 1984-; *ai:* Coach Var Bsbl, Vlybl; NEA, PGCEA, M 1977-; *office:* Frederick Douglass HS 8000 Croom Rd Upper Marlboro 20772

SAVIDGE, DORIS HEETER, Kindergarten Teacher; *b:* Parker, PA Thomas Whitfield; *c:* Susan Savidge Israel, Jane Savidge Horetsky; East Stroudsburg Univ (BS) Elem Ed 1963; Edinboro Univ (MS) E Chldhd & Elem 1988; *cr:* Washington Twp Schl 1st Grd Tchr 1962 Pocono Mt Schl Dist Kndgtn & 4th Grd Tchr 1963-68; Northeast Pre Pre-School Tchr 1972-74; Ripley Cntrl Schl Dist Kndgtn Tchr 1980- Stu Assistance Team; Elem Discipline Comm; Math Textbook Sele Comm; NEA 1963-; NYEA 1963-; Ripley Ed Assn 1980-, VP Soc C Chautauqua Co Kndgtn Assn 1983-, Treas 1988-89, Pgm Dir 1996 Meth Church 1969-, Sunday Schl Tchr, Bible Schl Dir, Pastor P Chprsn; Jr Womens Club 1969-75, Dir; Brownie Ldr 1973-75; Pub Established Story Hr; Ripley Cntrl Schl HS Yrbk Dedication 1995; Ri Cntrl Schl Tchr of Yr 1995; *office:* Ripley Central Schl PO Box 688 Ri NY 14775

DGE, THOMAS K., 7th Grade Mathematics Teacher; *b:* Champaign, Martha L.; *c:* Kimberly A. Schwarz; *ed:* Shippensburg Univ (BS) Ed Attnd PA St Univ, Boston Coll; *cr:* West York Area Schl Dist 7th Grd Tchr 1965-; *ai:* Acad Awds Comm; NEA, PSEA 1965-; WYAEA , Bldg Rep; *office:* West York Area Jr HS 1700 Bannister St York PA

NI, JOANNE, Teacher & Business Dept Chair; *b:* Charleroi, PA; *m:* J. Jr.; *ed:* PA St Univ (BS) Bus Logistics 1981; Robert Morris Coll strl Cert 1991; 51 Credits Toward Permanent Cert, Masters; *cr:* Highlands Sr HS Bus Tchr 1994-; *ai:* Interact Club Spon; PSEA, , 1994-; *office:* Laurel Highlands Sr HS 300 Bailey Ave Uniontown 401

NI, MICHAEL ANGELO, Technology Teacher; *b:* Suffern, NY; *m:* ne Ann Fox; *ed:* SUNY at Oswego (BS) Tech 1987; SUNY at New (MA) Spec Ed 1992; *cr:* Washingtonville CSD Tech Tchr 1987-; *ai:* ngtonville Tchrs Assn; NY St Tech Ed Assn; *office:* Washingtonville W Main St Washingtonville NY 10992

NO, JILL SCHARER, Technology Teacher; *b:* Perth Amboy, NJ; *m:* J.; *c:* Suzanne, Randy; *ed:* George Washington Univ (BA) Elem Ed Georgian Court Coll Tech Cert 24 Credits; *cr:* Schl #1 2nd Grd Tchr 72; Pine Beach Elem Schl 6th Grd Tchr 1987-93, Tech Tchr 1993-; I-Servicing Tech Tchrs; 6th Grd Yrbk, Cmptr Club Adv; Schl Nwsp TREA, NJEA 1987-.

TSKI, JOHN WILLIAM, English Teacher; *b:* Wilkes-Barre, PA; *m:* Glennon; *c:* Leigh Ann, John, Jacob; *ed:* Kings Coll (BA) Eng 1973; s Univ (MS) Eng & Ed 1988; 48 Hrs Beyond MS; *cr:* Crestwood HS Tchr 1973-; *ai:* NEA 1973-; PSEA 1973-; CEA 1973-, Rep; wood Tchr of the Yr 1990; *office:* Crestwood HS 281 S Mountain Blvd tain Top PA 18707

TZ, FRED ROBERT, Professor of Education; *b:* Philadelphia, PA; ll; *c:* Ryan, Ian; *ed:* Ursinus Coll (BA) Pol Sci 1968; Temple Univ) Scndry Ed 1970, (EDD) Curr, Instruction 1977; *cr:* Saint Joseph's Asst Ed Prof 1979-86; Neumann Coll Ed Division Chair 1986-92, Ed Prof 1989-94, Ed Prof 1994-; *ai:* Fac Senate Sec; Fac Ath Rep; er Equity in Ed, PA Assn of Colls Tchr Educators Planning Comms; 1970-; ATE, PACTE 1986-; Elem Schl Soc Stud Curr; Articles Pub; Neumann Coll Concord Rd Aston PA 19014*

KO, JANET LYNN, First Grade Teacher; *b:* Corry, PA; *ed:* Univ of urgh (MS) Ed 1981; Gannon Univ, Edinboro Univ Masters Courses; naventure Univ Admin Courses; *cr:* Warren Cty Schl Dist Tchr 1976-; Warren Cty Ed Assn, NEA, PSEA 1976-; Delta Epsilon Sigma 1989-; olstein Assn 1986-; *home:* RR 1 Box 94 Sugar Grove PA 16350

NER, ELIZABETH MARY, Sci Dept Chair & Physics Instr; *b:* New swick, NJ; *ed:* Georgian Court Coll (BA) Physics 1976; NJ Inst of (MS) Applied Sci 1983; *cr:* Bishop George AHR HS Physics Instr & Chprsn 1976-; *ai:* Sci League Moderator; Asst Sftbl Coach; *office:* p George AHR HS 1 Tingley Ln Edison NJ 08820

, PHYLLIS, School Psychologist; *b:* New Haven, CT; *ed:* Cntrl CT iv (BA) Psych 1977; Southern CT St Univ (MS) Schl Psych 1980; 6th chl Psych 1982; Cert Spec Ed 1987; Cert Intermediate Supervision, in Fairfield Univ 1985; *cr:* Southington Bd Ed Schl Psychologist -80; Yale Univ Greater New Haven Child Hlth Stud Part-time Parent viewer 1983-85; Ctr for Human Potential Pvt Practice 1988-90; East n Summer Schl Prgm Dir 1992-93; East Haven Bd Ed Schl hologist 1980-; *ai:* After Schl Homework Prgm; CT Assn Sch Psy, Natl Sch Psy, NEA 1980-; *office:* Joseph Melillo MS 67 Hudson St East n CT 06512

OIE, RONALD EMERY, 8th Grade US History Teacher; *b:* hampton, MA; *m:* Linda J. Popielarczyk; *c:* Kelly, Ronelle; *ed:* mption Coll (BA) His 1970; Westfield St Coll (MED) His 1979; Attnd field Univ, U Conn; *cr:* St Michael's HS US His Tchr 1970-76; West ngfield HS US His Tchr 1976-77; Cowing Jr HS US His Tchr 1977-81; Alister MS US His Tchr 1981-; *ai:* Soc Stud Dept Coord 1989-91; St hael's HS Intramural Dir 1970-76, JV Bsbl Coach; West Springfield Cowing Jr HS Intramural Dir 1976-81, JV Bsbl Coach; Intramural Dir -86; Suffield HS Coach JV Bsbl 1983-87, Var Bsbl 1988-91; Suffield ssn, CEA, NEA 1981-; OAH Amer Historians Org 1986-; Ct Soc Stud ; NCSS; Southhampton Youth Ath Assn 1980-90, Coach; Hampshire al HS Booster Club 1992-, Pres; Pub Western New England Historical nal Article 1981; Who's Who in Amer Ed 1994-; *home:* 80 Line St thampton MA 01073

OY, DORIS JEAN HURD, Spanish Teacher; *b:* Mobile, AL; *m:* ney Purcell III; *c:* Sean Perrin, Scott Purcell, Courtney Maria; *ed:* ris Brown Coll (BA) Span & Ed 1967; Howard Univ 24 Credit Hrs ; Trinity Coll 15 Credit Hrs Ed; Georgetown Univ 3 Credit Hrs Span; v of FL 3 Credit Hrs Ed; *cr:* DC Pub Schl Span Tchr 1968-; tgomery Coll Span Tchr 1994-; *ai:* Jr, Sr Hnr Soc & Sr Class Trip n; Collidge Cultured Pearls Charm Club; Russian Exch & Yth for lerstanding Liaison; Intnl Day, Hospitality, Amer Ed Week, necoming, Sr Class, and Winter Holiday Comms; AFT 1968-; Amer n of Tchrs of Span & Portuguese 1982-; Greater WA Area Tchrs of Frgn gs 1984-; Alpha Kappa Alpha 1965-, Mbrshp Chprsn; Jack & Jill of er Inc 1987-, Corr Sec, Beautillion Chair; C&P Telephone Co Outstdng r Awd; Outstdng Young Woman of Amer; SECME Grant; *office:* olidge Sr HS 5th & Tuckerman Sts NW Washington DC 20011*

VOY, SARA, Sixth Grd Eng & Rdng Tchr; *b:* NYC, NY; *m:* Fred; *c:* c, Michelle Lyn Litt; *ed:* Amer Univ (BA) Eng Ed; Queens Coll (MS) 60 Post Grad Credits Brooklyn Coll, Coll of St Rose, TC at Columbia; East Meadow Pub Schls Tchr 1962-64; Hewlett Woodmere Pub Schls r 1964-69, Adult Ed Tchr 1965-86, Tchr 1986-; *ai:* Coaching Young iters; Poetry Club Facititator; Rdng, Writing Weaknesses Tutor; SUT, HWFA 1986-; NEA 1962-; ORT 1974-, Donor Chm; Sisterhood HERJC 1975-; *office:* Woodmere MS 1170 Peninsula Blvd Hewlett NY 557*

WAN, AMY J., Latin Teacher; *b:* Columbus, OH; *m:* Eugene D. Jr.; *ed:* nyon Coll (BA) Eng, Classics 1986; Univ of Akron (MA) Scndry Ed 92; Continuing Ed Courses Pompeii Life, Death, Love 1995, nversational Italian 1992-93, Body Sulphing, Golf; *cr:* Our Lady of ns HS Latin, Eng Tchr 1986-90; Medina Sr HS Latin Tchr 1990-; *ai:* Jr assical League Adv; Amer Classical League 1986-; OH Classical Conf 36-, Pres 1st-2nd VP; Archaeological Inst of Amer 1996; Excl in Tchng d; 3 Letters Pub; *office:* Medina Sr HS 777 E Union St Medina OH 313

WAYDA, MARLENE LANZI, Spanish & Social Studies Tchr; *b:* ownsville, PA; *m:* Michael; *c:* Michael, Rebecca; *ed:* Slippery Rock iv (BS) Span 1969; Seton Hill Coll (BS) Soc Stud 1988; Attnd Univ of tsburgh at Greensburg, CA Univ of PA; *cr:* Mt Pleasant Schl Dist Tchr 59-74; Penn-Trafford Schl Dist Tchr 1990-; *ai:* Span & Var Club Spon; A 1969-; PSMLA 1990-; *office:* Penn Trafford HS PO Box 530 Harrison y PA 15636

WICKI, MARY MURPHY, Retired Social Studies Teacher; *b:* anklin, NH; *m:* Edmund M.; *c:* Brian Lewis, Logan Page, Stephen, nes; *ed:* Mt St Mary (BS) Scndry 1953; Plymouth St Univ Several Grad edits; *cr:* Belmont HS Gen Scndry Tchr 1953-60; Nashua HS Gen Scndry hr 1953-60; St Mary Elem 6-7 Grd All Subject Tchr 1968-73; Franklin Schl System Soc Stud Tchr 1973-95; *ai:* NH Soc Stud 1975-95; Franklin Outing Club 1962-; Tchr of Yr; 7th Grd Team Ldr New MS 1989.*

SAWICKI, STEPHANIE, 8th Grd Language Arts Teacher; *b:* Detroit, MI; *ed:* Univ of MT at Missoula (BA) Eng 1971; Wroxton Coll-Fairleigh Dickinson Univ (MA) British Lit & Drama 1974; *cr:* Audubon Jr Sr HS Tchr 1972-73; Highland Regnl HS Tchr 1973-77; Amer Schl Tchr 1978-79; H. M. Phifer MS Tchr 1979-; Rowan Coll Adj Prof Comm Dept 1987-89; *ai:* NCTE 1985-; NJEA, PEA 1981-; NEA 1972-; Tchr of Yr 1991; *office:* H. M. Phifer MS 2801 Park Ave Pennsauken NJ 08109

SAWINSKI, ERNEST P., Technology Education Teacher; *b:* Greensburg, PA; *ed:* Point Park Coll (Assoc) Engrng Drafting 1966; CA Univ of PA (BSEd) Industrial Arts 1968, (MED) Industrial Arts 1974; 43 Addl Credit Hrs at Baldwin Wallace Coll & Kent St Univ; *cr:* Northwood Jr HS Industrial Arts Tchr 1968-79; Elyria HS Tech Ed Tchr 1979-; *ai:* Stu Cncl; NEA, OEA & EEA 1970-; ITEA; OTEA; ASCD; Elyria Elks; Elyria Jaycees Outstdng Young Edctr 1978; OH Assn of Stu Cncls 1986-90; *office:* Elyria HS 6th St Elyria OH 44035

SAWKA, PAUL, Math Department Chairman; *b:* Mayfield, PA; *m:* Corolla L. Rogers; *c:* Mary Jess Ford, W. Scott, Sean, Susan Halley; *ed:* Univ of Scranton (BS) Math Educ 1965, (MS) Math Educ 1974; 12 Credits East Stroudsburg Univ; 12 Credits LeHigh Univ; 3 Credits Wilkes Univ; 20 Credits Univ of Scranton; 27 Credits Wilkes Univ; *cr:* Elk Lake Schls Math Tchr 1965-67; Vestal Schls Math Tchr 1967-68; Lakeland Schl Math Dept Chm 1968-; PA St Univ at Dunmore Part Time Math 1979-; *ai:* Jr Class Adv; Co-Adv FHA; PA Math Assmnt Comm; AP Reader 1995-96; PSEA, NEA 1970-; Lakeland Educ Assn 1970-, Treas 4 Yrs, VP 2 Yrs; NCTM; PA Cncl Math Tchrs, Pres 15 Yrs; *home:* RR 5 Box 5902 Lake Ariel PA 18436

SAWYER, CAROL ROBELEN, French Teacher; *b:* Brooklyn, NY; *m:* Ricky J.; *ed:* King's Coll (BA) Fr 1978; SUNY at New Paltz (MS) Elem Ed 1983; 6 Addl Credit Hrs Russell Sage; *cr:* Monroe-Woodbury HS Perm Sub Tchr 1980-83; Argyle Cntrl Schl Fr Tchr 1984-87; Queensbury MS French Tchr 1987-; *ai:* Supts Advy Cncl; Advy Homerooms; NYSAFLT 1984-; *office:* Queensbury MS 99 Aviation Rd Queensbury NY 12804

SAWYER, JACQUELINE ANN, Dance Educator; *b:* New York City, NY; *ed:* Smith Coll (BA) Theater 1974; Columbia Univ Tchr Coll (MA) Dance Ed 1975; NY Univ (PHD) Dance & Dance Ed 1996; Attnd Amer Dance Festival, Laban Inst for Dance Edctrs, City Ctr Dance Ed Outreach; *cr:* Prof Theaters Dancer & Actress Edctr 1977-87; NY Univ Creative Arts Team Actor, Tchr 1984-88; Bd of Ed NYC Dance Edctr 1988-; *ai:* W. C. Bryant Dance Co Artistic Dir, Amer Unity Club Adv; Dance Edctrs Inst BOE; Amer Dance Guild 1991-, Co-Chair Schlsp Comm; NYSAHPERD 1992-; Screen Actors Guild 1982-; Actors Equity Assn 1981-; Women's Intnl Aglow 1988-; NY Univ Deans Rsrch Awd; Aaron Diamond Fnd Schlsp; Bank St Coll Tchr Incentive Grant; John W. Saunders Schlsp; *home:* 54 W 56th St New York NY 10019*

SAWYER, JOANNE JANDROWITZ, Tchr of Academically Talented; *b:* Passaic, NJ; *m:* John Samuel III; *c:* Keith, Kevin, John Samuel IV; *ed:* Wm Paterson (BA) Kndgtn Primary 1968; Kean Coll Ed; Fairfield Univ Psych; *cr:* Collegiate Schl Tchr 1968-75, Head Tchr 1975-79; Trumbull Rdng Specialist 1978-81; Colts Neck Cedar Dr Schl Resource Enrichment Prog Tchr 1981-84; Manalapan Tchr of Academically Talented 1984-; *ai:* Var Chrldng Coach 1968-75; NEA; NJEA; MEEA; Colts Neck Town Cncl, Schl & Town Liason; *office:* Taylor Mills Schl 77 Gordons Corner Rd Englishtown NJ 07726

SAWYER, NANCY MENANSON, English Teacher; *b:* Worcester, MA; *m:* Clifford R.; *c:* Marc, Leigh, Lindsay, Laura; *ed:* Worcester St Coll (BA) Eng 1974, (MED) Spec Ed 1977; 30 Credit Hrs 1996; *cr:* North Brookfield HS Tchr 1974-77; Tantasqua Rengl HS Tchr 1977-; *ai:* Commencement Coord; NEA, MA Tchrs Assn, IRA, MA Rdng Assn 1974-; NCTE, New England Assn Tchrs of Eng 1994-; Schl Cncl Midland St Elem Schl 1993-, Sec; Schl Cncl Forest Grove MS 1995-; MA Dept of Ed Rgnl Ed comm 1980-89, Chm 1983-89; *office:* Tantasqua Regnl Sr HS 319 Brookfield Rd Fiskdale MA 01518

SAWYER, ROBERT CARL, PE & Earth Science Teacher; *b:* Bridgeport, CT; *m:* Susan Mae Abbott; *c:* Caitlyn Mae, Nicole Marie; *ed:* Southern CT St Univ (BS) Bio 1975, (MS) Environmental Stud 1985; 6th Yr Sci Instruction 1987; *cr:* Adams MS Earth Sci, Bio Tchr 1981-91; Guilford HS Phy Sci, Earth Sci Tchr 1991-; Wallingford Gifted Prgm Tchr of Gifted & Talented 1987-; *ai:* Sr, Jr Class Adv; Phenomenology Clb, Pilgrim Flwshp Adv; NEA, CEA 1981-; NSTA 1995-; *office:* Guilford HS New England Rd Guilford CT 06437

SAWYER, SUSAN LUTWYLER, Guidance Counselor; *b:* Hackensack, NJ; *m:* Jeffrey R.; *c:* Brett; *ed:* OH Wesleyan Univ (BA) Fr 1969; Villanova Univ (MED) Guid, Cnslng 1975; *cr:* Easton Area Schls Elem Fr Tchr 1969-70; Hatboro-Horsham Schl Dist Scndry Fr Tchr 1970-75; Fair Lawn Schl Dist Guid Cnslr 1989-; *ai:* Interact Club Adv; NEA, NJEA, Bergen Co Prof Cnslrs Assn 1989-; Stdnts Taking a New Direction Cty Awd; *office:* Fair Lawn HS 14-00 Berdan Ave Fair Lawn NJ 07410

SAWYER, WILLIAM FREDERICK, 6th Grd Science & Health Tchr; *b:* Buffalo, NY; *m:* Marjory Lawler; *c:* Lisa Welfare, Michelle Napierella, Tammy; *ed:* St Coll at Buffalo (BS) Elem Ed 1963, (MS) Admin, Supervision 1968; 25 Hrs Grad Work in Elem & Conservation Ed, Admin Supervision; *cr:* Spruce Elem Grds 4-6 Tchr 1963-88; Lowry MS Grd 6 Math, Sci, Hlth Tchr 1988-; *ai:* Audio-Visual Comm Dir; IM Instr Grds 6-8; Trained To Teach; Just Say No Club Adv; JV Sftbl Coach; Adult Ed Instr HS Equivalency 1980-89; AFT, NEA, NY St United Tchr 1963-; North Tonawanda United Tchrs 1963-, Treas 1978-80, 1984-88; N Tonawanda Recreation, Sftbl Coach 1970-90; Police Ath League, Bsktbl Coach, Referee 1985-89; Sr Prom Breakfast Asst 1986-91; Yth Bd 1988-91; Young Edctr Tchr of Yr 1968; *home:* 850 Nash Rd N Tonawanda NY 14120

SAWYER, WINSLOW ALLEN, Director of Music & Tchr; *b:* Davenport, IA; *m:* Gloria A.; *c:* W. Allen III; *ed:* Univ of NH (BS) Music Ed 1965; Worcester St Coll (MED) Ed Admin 1979; Attnd Univ of MA at Amherst, Boston Univ; *cr:* Newmarket NH Schls Music Dir 1965; Doctor UT Schls Music Dir 1965-67; Quabbin Regnl Schl Dist Music Dir 1967-; *ai:* Elem Band Dir; MENC, NEA, MTA, QRTA1967-; QVMEA 1972-, Pres 1983-91; Mount Zion Lodge AF & AM 1973-, S Deacon; Articles Pub; *office:* Quabbin Regnl Schl Dist West Union St Barre MA 01005

SAWYER-HUDSON, SHEILA LORRAINE, High School English Teacher; *b:* Brooklyn, NY; *ed:* Lincoln Univ (BA) Eng 1971; Harvard Univ Grad Schl (MAT) Ed 1972; Cheyney Univ Prin Cert Pgrm; Immaculata Coll Doctorate Prgm Educl Ldrshp; *cr:* Lincoln Univ Instr of Eng 1972-77; Fugett MS 7th & 8th Grd Eng Tchr 1977-87; Pierce MS Asst Prin 1987-88; East HS 10th Grd Eng Tchr 1988-91; Henderson HS 9th & 10th Grd Eng Tchr 1991-; *ai:* Curr Cncl; Sited-Based Mngmt Team; Team Ldr; Dept Chm; WCEA 1979-; Alpha Kappa Alpha 1969-; West Chester Comm Performers 1995; Univ of Richmond Outstanding Tchr Awd; *office:* Henderson HS Montgomery & Penn Sts West Chester PA 19380

SAXBY, WILLIAM E., Middle School Soc Studies Tchr; *b:* Canandaigua, NY; *m:* Patricia Barrett; *c:* Andrew J.; *ed:* SUC at Geneseo (BS) Scndry Ed 1970, (MS) Soc Stud 1975; *cr:* Honeoye Cntrl Schl Soc Stud Tchr 1970-; *ai:* Ath Dir; Var Boys Bsktbl & Golf Coach; NYSUT 1970-; HTA 1970-, Pres 1973; NYS Coaches Assn 1975-; Tchr of Yr 1985; CAA Cert Ath Admin.

SAXBY, WILLIAM R., Psychology Professor; *b:* Burlington, VT; *m:* Patricia J.; *c:* Justin, Paige; *ed:* Univ of VT (BA) Psych 1972; Fuller Theological Seminary (MA) Theology 1978; Univ of VT (PHD) Psych 1981; *cr:* Affiliates in Psychotherapy Clinical Psychologist 1979-92; Nyack Coll Psych Prof 1992-, Head Dept of Psych 1994-, Chair Division of Soc & Natural Sci 1995-; *ai:* Pre-Doctoral Flwshp NIAAA; *office:* Nyack Coll 1 South Blvd Nyack NY 10960

SAXE, JEAN T. (MERANDA), HS Mathematics Teacher; *b:* Cambridge, MA; *m:* Michael B.; *c:* David, Richard; *ed:* Newton Coll of the Sacred Heart (BA) Math 1969; Northeastern Univ (MS) Math 1970; 75 Plus Credit Hrs in Math, Cmptrs & Ed Courses; *cr:* Burlington HS Math Tchr 1972-; *ai:* Math League Team Coach; NEA 1972-; *office:* Burlington HS 123 Cambridge St Burlington MA 01803

SAXON, BURT, Teacher of the Gifted; *b:* Aurora, IL; *m:* Myra Hamburg; *c:* Jeffrey, Rebekah; *ed:* Carleton Coll (BA) Ec 1969; Wesleyan Univ (MAT) His 1971; Columbia Univ (EDD) Family, Comm Ed 1977; Southern CT St Univ Schl Admin Cert 1992; *cr:* Lee HS Soc Stud Tchr 1970-75, 1977-80; Yale Univ Ed Instr 1976-; Hillhouse HS Tchr of Gifted 1980-; *ai:* Tennis Coach; Schl Accreditation Comm Co-Chair; New Haven-Yale Saturday Seminar, Summer HS Tchr, Facilitator; AFT 1970-; Orange Democratic Town Comm 1986-; Temple Emanuel 1983-; Co-Author of Books: Modern Human Sexuality, Invitation to Psychology; Articles Pub; Tchr of Yr 1982; *home:* 411 Richard Ln Orange CT 06477

SAXTON, JON C., 10th Grd World History Tchr; *b:* Columbus, OH; *m:* Angela Shoemaker; *c:* Taylor Lynne; *ed:* Capital Univ (BA) Soc Stud Ed & His 1989; OH Univ (MSS) Soc Stud 1996; *cr:* Logan Elm HS Tchr 1989-; *ai:* Stu Cncl Adv; Mock Trial Team Coach; FCA Adv; Var Golf & Bsktbl Coach; North Cntrl Evaluation & Cty Curr Comms; Peer Trng Comm for Cmptrs; LECTA, OEA, NEA 1989-; Ross Cty Genealogical Soc 1995-; Salem United Meth Church, Pastor-Parish Comm; Ashland Tchr Awd Nom 1995-96; *office:* Logan Elm HS 9575 Tarlton Rd Circleville OH 43113*

SAXTON, TIMOTHY LAWRENCE, Mathematics Teacher & Coach; *b:* Boardman, OH; *m:* Gina Diane Funari; *ed:* Grove City Coll (BS) Math, Sec Ed 1988; Assertive Discipline, 5 Qtr Hrs Baldwin-Wallace Coll; Tchr Expectations & Stu Achvmt Kent St Univ; *cr:* Bedford HS Math Tchr, Coach 1988-; *ai:* Ftbl, Track Asst Var Coach; OEA, NEA 1988-; OCTM 1990-; *home:* 1341 E Highland Ave Unit 3 Ravenna OH 44266*

SAYAGO, TERESA BORIO, English Teacher; *b:* Philadelphia, PA; *m:* Brian S.; *c:* Margaret, Joanna, Catherine; *ed:* PA St Univ Eng (BA) 1971, (MA) 1973; Lafayette Coll Scndry Ed Cert; *cr:* Sts Phillip & James Elem 3rd Grd Tchr 1973-75; Easton Area HS Eng Tchr, Writing Lab Instr 1976-; *ai:* Spring Challenge Adv; PSEA, NEA 1976-; *office:* Easton Area HS 2601 William Penn Hwy Easton PA 18045

SAYBOLT, ADRIENNE,IHM, Eighth Grade Teacher; *b:* Germantown, PA; *ed:* Immaculata Coll (BA) Theology; St John's Univ (MA) Liturgical Stu 1996; Cert Peer Coaching 1994; 24 Credit Hrs Rel Archdiocese of Philadelphia; 18 Credit Hrs Liturgical Stu Immaculate Coll 1987; Instrl II Permanent Tchng Cert St of PA 1983; *cr:* St Jane's Schl 5-6 Grd Tchr 1970-73; Holy Trinity Schl 7-8 Grd Tchr 1973-75; Immaculate Conception 8th Grd Tchr 1975-76; Holy Saviour Schl 7th Grd Tchr 1976-80; St Bartholomew Schl 7-8 Grd Tchr 1980-84; St Martin Schl 8th Grd Tchr 1984-85; St Joachim Schl 8th Grd Tchr 1985-87; Holy Spirit Schl 8th Grd Tchr 1987-88; St Monica Schl 8th Grd Tchr 1988-92; St Ephrem Schl 8th Grd Tchr 1992-; *ai:* Mid St Re-Accreditation, IHM Liturgy Comms; RCIA Team Mem; Math Contests Coach; STEP Mem; Schl Liturgy, World's Most Sesquicentennial Act Coor Involved Math Problem Coords; NCEA 1970-; NCTM 1991-; NPM 1986-; Ed Comm Awd Diocese of Metuchen 1984; Bucks Cty Intermediate Unit Grant 1995; PA Dept of Ed Awd Tchr Trng & Induction Plan 1988; Nom PAESMT Math 1992, Sci 1995; *office:* St Ephrem Schl 5340 Hulmeville Rd Bensalem PA 19020*

SAYER, DENNIS GARY, Chemistry Teacher; *b:* Brooklyn, NY; *c:* Mary Corbett, Theresa Kiwak, Carolyn Johnson; *ed:* Columbia Univ (BS) Pharmaceutical Scis 1972; Duke Univ (MA) Biological Scis 1973; Addl 30 Credits; Supervisory Cert Jersey City St Coll; *cr:* John Marshall HS Sci Tchr 1972-78; Passaic Valley HS Chem, Earth Sci Tchr 1979-79; Madison Boro HS Chem, Earth Sci Tchr 1979-82; Irvington HS Chem, Allied Hlth Tchr 1982-83; Montclair HS Chem Tchr 1983-86; Hasbrouck Heights HS Chem Tchr 1986-; *ai:* Head Coach Boys Var Soccer; Fac Adv SADD; Fac Stu Placement Comm; NHS Fac Comm; NJST, NJPTSA 1978-; ACS, NEA, NSCAA 1972-; Anti Drug Cncl 1986-, VP; *home:* 7 Cliffwood Ter East Rutherford NJ 07073*

SAYERS, THERESE MARIE RUDELLA, Asst Prof of Nrsng & Dept Chmn; *b:* Philipsburg, PA; *m:* Paul A.; *c:* Ryan Phillip, Aaron Paul; *ed:* Carlow Coll (BSN) Nrsng 1982; Penn St Univ (MS) Nrsng 1990; Post-Grad Credits Hlth Ed; *cr:* Allegheny Gen Hosp Staff Nurse 1982-85; Cntrl PA Schl Nrsng Instr 1985-90; Lock Haven Univ Asst Prof 1990-; *ai:* Univ Comms; Stu Adv; Certfd Schl Hlth Nurse 1978-; Sigma Theta Tau 1990-; Natl League Nrsng 1994-; Penn St Alumni Assn 1990-; Emergency Mngmt Coord Covington Twp 1988-; QCK Water Authority Bd 1994-; Pub Educator Amer Cancer Soc; *office:* Lock Haven Univ 119 Beyers St Clearfield PA 16830*

SAYRE, AARON LEE, Agricultural Education Teacher; *b:* Pomeroy, OH; *m:* Shirley Sue Congo; *c:* Stephanie, Jessica, Lori; *ed:* OH St Univ (BS) Ag Ed 1973, (MS) Ag Ed 1976; Paramedic, Fire Trng Hocking Tech; *cr:* Meigs Local Ag Tchr 1973-76; Eastern Local Ag Tchr 1973-76; Southern Local Ag Tchr 1976-; *ai:* Racine FFA Adv; Racine Alumni; Syracuse Fire Dept, Emergency Squad; Water Bd Pres; Vegetable Growers Assn; AVATA, OUA 1973-; Racine Masonic Lodge 1976-; Racine Grange 1966-, Trustee; Morse Chapel Church 1960-, Supt & Sunday Schl Tchr; Meigs Cty Farm Bureau 1976-, Pres of Meigs Bd; Received Several BOAC Grants; Constructed Shelter House, Signs for Racine Stav Mill Park; *office:* Southern Local HS Elm St Racine OH 45771*

SAYRE, CONNIE L., Legal Asst Program Instructor; *b:* Portsmouth, OH; *m:* Harold R.; *c:* Jodi R., Chadwick K.; *ed:* OH Univ (BAEd) Bus Ed 1979, (MA) Ec 1981; Course Work in Schl Admin, Curr & Instruction, Personnel Inservicing, Multi-Cultural Ed, Cmptr Sci; 30 Hrs at OH St Univ, Dayton Univ, OH Univ, Akron Univ; *cr:* Scioto Cty Joint Voc Schl Tchr 1979-; OH Univ Part-time Tchr 1993-; *ai:* Bus Prof of Amer Adv; Tchrs Assn Sec; NEA 1979-, Pres, Sec, Negotiator; Portsmouth Receiving Hosp, Vol, Outstdng Svc; Southern OH Med Ctr, Vol; Veterans of War, Vol, Outstdng Svc; *office:* Scioto Co Joint Voc Schl PO Box 766 Lucasville OH 45648*

SAYRE, NANCY RESSLER, Professor; *b:* Canton, OH; *m:* W. G.; *c:* Kirk D., Kelly D.; *ed:* Eastern MI Univ (BS) Eled 1967; Slippery Rock Univ (MED) Early Chldhd 1981; Univ of Pittsburgh (PHD) Eled, Ech 1987-; *cr:* Milan Schl Dist Tchr 1967-69; Slippery Rock Park Commission Aquatic, Early Chldhd Dir 1974-86; Clarion Univ Prof 1986-; *ai:* Adv Pittsburgh Assn for Ed of Young Children; Chair Internal Review Bd, Early Chldhd Comm; NAEYS 1984-; Phi Delta Kappa 1986-; Sec, Treas, Pres, VP, DDK Grant; PA Assn for Ed of Young Children 1984-, Treas; Jefferson-Clairon Head Start Bd of Dirs 1990-, Pres, VP; Amer Red Cross 1965-, Aquatic Instr; Articles Pub; Grants Fnd, Key Stone Univ Research Corp, NCCC, SSHE Chancellor, Soc Equity; *office:* Clarion Univ Of PA 120 Stevens Hall Clarion PA 16214

SAYYEAU, PAUL A., French Teacher; *b:* Watertown, NY; *ed:* Jefferson Comm Coll (AA) Lbrl Arts 1968; SUNY at Oswego (BA) Scndry Ed Fr

1970; Grad Work at SUNY at Potsdam; 48 Credit Hrs; *cr:* Alexandria Cntrl Fr Tchr 1970-; Jefferson Comm Coll Adj Fr Prof 1985-; *ai:* NHS Adv; Europe Chaperone; NYSAFLT 1970-, Distngd Frgn Lang Tchr Awd; *office:* Alexandria Cntrl Schl Bolton Ave Alexandria Bay NY 13607

SBARATTA, CHRISTINA (COUROUNIOTIS), Fourth Grade Teacher; *b:* Aticholos, Greece; *m:* Anthony; *c:* Christopher; *ed:* Jersey City St (BA) Elem Ed 1965, (MA) Ed 1978; Post Grad Stud Co-Operative Learning, Process Writing, Whole Lang, Quest; *cr:* Roosevelt Schl Sixth Grd Tchr 1965; Orange Ave Schl Sixth Grd Tchr; Livingston Ave Schl Sixth Grd Tchr 1981-95, Fourth Grd Tchr 1995-; *ai:* GATE; Soc Stud, Tech Comms; NEA, NJEA 1965-; Phi Delta Kappa 1977-; Suburban Rdng Cncl; Cranford River Comm 1989-; Clean Comms 1993-; Sierra Club 1996.

SCACALOSSI, JAMES JOSEPH, Theology Teacher; *b:* New York, NY; *m:* Leonor Perez; *c:* Allison Patricia; *ed:* St Johns Univ (BA) Psych 1986; Seminary of the Immaculate Conception (MA) Theology 1991; Attnd NEH Summer Inst for Tchrs 1995; *cr:* Amer Re-Insurance Asst Account Rep 1986-87; Regis HS Theology Tchr 1991-; *ai:* Yrbk, Darkroom, Asian Cultural Soc Moderator; Organize & Dir of Regis in Ecuador Summer Svc Prgm; *office:* Regis HS 55 E 84th St New York NY 10028

SCADDEN-REMIREZ, ELLEN ELIZABETH, Spanish Teacher; *b:* Water bury, CT; *c:* Kathleen; *ed:* CCSU (BS) Span 1969, (MA) Span 1972; UCONN, Bd Ed 24 Hrs Comptr Ed, Voc Guidance, Intensive Classrm Mgmt 6th Yr Degree 1996; Tunxis Comm Coll CT Brokers Real Estate License Cert 1972-; Cheshire Park, Rec Continuing Ed; 90 Hrs Americ Civl War; *cr:* J. A. DePaolo Jr HS (Dept Chm, Span Tchr 1969-94; Southington HS Span Tchr 1994-; *ai:* PTO 1994-; Design for Effective Instruction Trained by Ted Forte; Co8Adv Span Club 1994-; Q Plus CAT Ldr 1992-; Comms Sunshine 1994-, Mem Schlsp Fac Fundraising 1995-, For Lang Curr Revision 1995-; Ct Cncl of Lang Tchrs 1975-; SEA, CEA, NEA 1969-; Am Assn Tchrs of Span & Port 1990- Major; Alpha Mu Gamma 1968-; Alpha Delta Kappa 1995-; Friends of Cheshire Lib 1991-; Cheshire Jr Womans Club 1975-84, Philanthophy Chm; Statue of Liberty, Ellis Island Fund 1983-, Charter Mem; Intnl Cetecean Soc 1983-; No Amer Bluebird Soc 1982-, Charter Mem; Cheshire Historical Soc 25 Yrs; US Captiol Historical Soc 1990-, Charter Mem; *office:* Southington HS 720 Pleasant St Southington CT 06489

SCALA, JOHN CHARLES, Planetarium Director; *b:* Summit, NJ; *m:* Virginia Anne Ronen; *c:* Aubrey Lyn, Valerie Anne; *ed:* Lycoming Coll (BA) Astronomy 1980; Attnd Univ of AL at Huntsville; *cr:* Stetson MS Sci Tchr 1980-82; Mendham HS Sci Tchr 1982-83; Hopatcong MS Sci Tchr 1983; Cty Coll of Morris Adj Prof Astronomy 1983-89; Lenape Vly Regnl HS Planetarium Dir 1987-; *ai:* Intl, Mid Atl Planetarium Socs, NEA, NJEA, NJSTA 1987-; NJ Governor's Tchr Recognition Awd 1993; Dist Tchr of Yr 1994; Geraldine R. Dodge Fnd Grant 1993; A+ for Kids Tchr Network Inductee 1993; Amer Astron Soc Natl Astronomy Resource Tchr; *office:* Lenape Valley Reg HS PO Box 578 Sparta-Stanhope Rd Stanhope NJ 07874

SCALETTA, JUDITH PALMER, Secondary Mathematics Teacher; *b:* Ambridge, PA; *m:* Richard; *ed:* Edinboro Univ of PA (BS) Music 1981, Math 1986; Post Grad Stud; *cr:* General Mc Lane HS Math Tchr 1986-; *ai:* Tech Resource Person; Learning Strategies Resource Team; Bus, Ed Partnership Comm; Tchs Seminars on Using Graph Calculators in Clrm, Sem Speaker on Tchng in Longer Block of Time; NCTM 1986-; COMAP; PCTM; MAA; NPAECT; Tandy Tech Math Excl Ssholar Awd; Fac Awd 1991; Classroom Strategies, Techniques Profiles Pub in Book Quality of Tchng 1992; St Vincent Coll Great Tchr Recgntn Pgm for Exc in Tchng; *office:* General Mc Lane HS 11761 Edinboro Rd Edinboro PA 16412

SCALIA, JOSEPH E., Eng & Creative Writing Teacher; *b:* Brooklyn, NY; *c:* Janine DeLuca, Ian, Jesse, Mikki; *ed:* St Francis Coll (BA) Eng 1964; Brooklyn Coll (MA) Eng 1970; 60 Credit Hrs SUNY at Brockport, SUNY at Stony Brook; *cr:* Hicksville Jr HS Eng, Comm Tchr 23 Yrs; Hicksville Sr HS Eng, Cr Writing Tchr 8 Yrs; *ai:* Adult Ed Prgm; NEA 1970-; EPDA Eng Grants Brockport & KY; *office:* Hicksville Sr HS Division Ave Hicksville NY 11801

SCALISI, PAUL A., Bio, Cmptrs Tchr & Grd Adv; *b:* Brooklyn, NY; *m:* Linda F. Thommen; *c:* Paul, Bill, Frank; *ed:* Wagner Coll (BS) Bio 1965, Richmond Coll (MS) Guidance 1971; 30 Credits above Assorted Microbiology, Marine Sci, Psych; *cr:* New Dorp HS Tchr & Grd Adv 25 Yrs; Tottenville HS Tchr & Grd Adv 5 Yrs; *ai:* Sailing Club; Golf Coach; Cmptrs in Sci Curr Developer; Richmond Cty Yacht Club 1977-, Rear-Vice Commodore; *office:* Tottenville HS 100 Luten Ave Staten Island NY 10312

SCALLEAT, SAMUEL A., Supervisor Guidance; *b:* Hazleton, PA; *m:* Janine M. Zukovich; *c:* Stefan, Kimberly, Lindsay; *ed:* Bucknell Univ (BS) Scndry Ed 1967; Kutztown Univ (MED) Scndry Guid 1969; Univ of Scranton Supvr Guid Cert 1982; Penn St Univ Grad Credits; *cr:* Hazleton Area Schl Dist Scndry Tchr 1967-70, Supvr & Cnslr 1971-95, Supvr Guid & Title I 1995-; *ai:* HAEA, PSEA & NEA 1967-; PA Schl Cnslrs Assn 1971-; PA Assn Federal Pgm 1995-; YMCA-YWCA Bd 1985-88; United Charities Bd 1995-; Cancer Cnslng St Grant 1988; *office:* Hazleton Area Schl Dist 101 S Church St Hazleton PA 18201

SCALLERO, JULIA ANNETTE, 9th-12th Grd Soc Stud Teacher; *b:* Dobbs Ferry, NY; *ed:* Mercy Coll (BA) Liberal Arts 1974; Tona Coll (MS) Scndry Ed, His 1978; Addl 75 Credits; *cr:* North Salem Ctr Schls HS Soc Stud Tchr 1974-; *ai:* Model UN Club Fac Adv; Co-Sr Class Adv; Curr Innovation Team; AFT 1974-; Westchester Soc Stud Cncl 1985-, Outstanding Soc Stud Tchrs Awd 1987; NYS Soc Stud Cncl; Natl Cncl for Soc Stud; Metropolitan Museum of Art 1987-; N Salem Stu Cncl Outstanding Tchr of Yr 1987; Grant Awded Natl Endowment for Hum to Write Gender Stud Curr Sarah Lawrence Coll, NYS Bar Assn for Law Day Prgm; Deans Award for Excellence in Tchng by SUNY at New Paltz 1995; Excellence Award in Tchng in Mid-Hudson Regn by Mid-Hudson Schl Study Cncl 1995; *office:* North Salem Cntrl Schls Old Rt 124 North Salem NY 10560

SCALLY, GINGER HUTZELL, 6th Grd Social Studies Teacher; *b:* Hagerstown, MD; *m:* Daniel; *c:* J. Benjamin, Erin Carol; *ed:* Townson St Univ (BS) Elem Ed 1983; Hood Coll (MA) Psych 1991; *cr:* E. Russell Hicks MS Tchr 13 Yrs; Hagerstown Jr Coll Part-Time Instr; *ai:* Prof Dev Cncl; *office:* E Russell Hicks MS 1321 S Potomac St Hagerstown MD 21740

SCANLAN, JANE OVERTON, English Teacher; *b:* Washington, DC; *m:* Robert M.; *c:* Daniel; *ed:* WV Wesleyan Coll (BA) His & Anthropology 1981; Boston Coll (MA) Eng 1983; Univ of MD 30 Credit Hrs Ed; *cr:* Boston Coll Tchng Fellow 1981-83, Abstractor & Indexer 1983-84; Charles Cty Comm Coll Part-Time Eng Tchr 1984, 1990-92; McDonough HS Eng Tchr 1985-; *ai:* Four Period Day Stud Comm; NEA 1987-; *office:* McDonough HS 7165 Marshall Corner Rd Pomfret MD 20675

SCANLON, JEFFREY M., English Teacher; *b:* New Haven, CT; *m:* Victoria Lenkeit; *ed:* Middlebury Coll (BA) Sociology 1983; 24 Credit Hrs Trinity Coll; 12 Credit Hrs Middlebury Coll; *cr:* The Gunnery Tchr, Admissions Officer 1983-86; Loomis Chaffee Schl Alumni Annual Fund Dir 1986-89, Eng Tchr 1989-; *ai:* Intramural Soccer, Boys Var Hockey, Boys Var La Crosse Coach; Boys Dormhead; Soph Tchrs Coord; Austin Wicke Awd; *office:* Loomis Chaffee Schl Batchelder Rd Windsor CT 06095

SCANLON, MICHAEL JOSEPH, Physics Teacher & Sci Coord; *b:* Norwood, MA; *m:* Laura June Mann; *c:* Gregory, Andrea; *ed:* Northeastern Univ (BS) Mechanical Engrng 1971; Boston St Coll (MED) Ed 1972; Framingham St Coll (MA) Admin 1979; *cr:* Norwood Pub Schl Sci Tchr 1972-78; Hopkinton Pub Schl Jr High Coord 1978-82, HS Sci Tchr 1982-; *ai:* Cross Cntry, Track & Field Coach; MTA & NEA 1972-; MASS 1994-; *office:* Hopkinton Pub Schls 88 Hayden Rowe St Hopkinton MA 01748

SCANNELL, PATRICK E., Principal; *b:* Astoria, NY; *ed:* St Bonaventure Univ (BA) Philosophy 1966; Hunter Coll CUNY (MA) Scndry Ed 1973; Fordham Univ (PHD) Admin & Supervision 1987; 30 Credits Theology Christ The King Seminary; 6 Credits Admin; *cr:* St Mary Gate of Heaven 7th-8th Grd Tchr 1967-84, Prin 1984-; *ai:* NCEA 1970-; ASCD 1984-; St John Neumann Awd 1991; *office:* St Mary Gate Of Heaven Schl 10406 101st Ave Ozone Park NY 11416

SCANNELL, TIMOTHY F., Social Studies Teacher; *b:* Concord, NH; *c:* Timothy C, Tara C.; *ed:* Keene St Coll (BE) Scndry Ed & Soc Stud Tchr 1969; *cr:* Mastricola MS Soc Stud Tchr 1969-; *ai:* Mock Trial Competition Coord; 7th Grd Envirnomental Ed Pgm Dir; MS Evaluation Comm Past Mem; NEA Past Mem; NHEA Past Mem; MTA Pres 1971-73; NH 4H Camps Bd of Governors 1984-89, Asst Chprsn; *office:* Mastricola MS 26 Baboosic Lake Rd Merrimack NH 03054

SCANTLIN, EUPHEMIA EMANUEL, English Teacher; *b:* Boston, MA; *c:* Emilie; *ed:* Univ of FL (BA) Eng Ed 1981; 26 Credit Hrs in Post Grad Work Lit, Theatre Arts, Portfolio Assessment UNH, Breadloaf Schl of Eng Middleburg Coll 1983-95; *cr:* Beasley MS 7th Grd Eng Tchr 1981-84; Londonderry HS Eng Tchr 1984-85; Raymond HS Eng Tchr 1986-; *ai:* Co-Adv Stu Lit Magazine; Acad Challenge Team Coach; Lib Media, Assessent Performance Comms; NCTE 1981-; NHATE 1987-; 2 Wkshps Conducted Children's Lit Course Dev; *office:* Raymond HS 45 Harriman Hill Rd Raymond NH 03077

SCAPTURA, JAMES J., Global Stud Tchr & His Chm; *b:* Auburn, NY; *m:* Jean Smyder; *c:* Michael J., Christopher N., Sharron Holland, Joseph M.; *ed:* St Bonaventure Univ (BA) His 1958; Elmira Coll (MSEd) His 1970; Extensive Grad Work at Cornell Univ; *cr:* Odessa-Montour Cntrl Schl His Tchr 1958-; Elmira Coll Continuing Ed Instr 1990-; *ai:* Audio Visuals Co-Coord; His Dept Chprsn; NEA 1958-; Odessa-Montour Tchrs Assn 1958-, Past Pres; NY St Ed Assn 1968-; 5 Ctys Soc Stud Conference; Village of Watkins Glen 1975-81, Trustee; Schuyler Co United Fund 1987-, Assoc Dir; St Marys of the Lake Parish Cncl 1988-90, Past Pres; Watkins Glen Grand Prix Historic Comm 1988-, Sec & Treas; Watkins Glen Pub Lib 1989-, Past Pres; NY St Schlrsp Russian His 1966 & Iroquois His 1984; Jr High Tchr of the Yr 1990 & 1994.*

SCARAMUZZA, THERESA M., 6th Grade Teacher; *b:* Philadelphia, PA; *m:* Robert; *c:* Christine, Monica; *ed:* Rosemont Coll (BA) Eng & Elem Ed; Cabrini Coll Post Grad Stud for MA in Ed; *cr:* St Laurence Schl Tchr 8 Yrs; *ai:* Fac Mem in Charge of Schl Newspaper; Art & Eng Coord; In Charge of Lit Mag; NEA 10 Yrs; *office:* Saint Laurence Schl 8245 W Chester Pike Upper Darby PA 19082*

SCARANO, ANTHONY F., Social Studies Teacher; *b:* Saratoga Springs, NY; *m:* Madeline Mangini; *c:* Gina Osika, Beth, Michele; *ed:* St Bonaventure Univ (BA) His 1963; Siena Coll (MA) His 1969; Attnd SUNY at Albany, Coll of St Rose at Albany Grad His Courses; *cr:* Averill Park Jr High Soc Stud Tchr 1964-67; Shaker HS Soc Stud Tchr 1967-70; Saratoga HS Soc Stud Tchr 1971-; *ai:* NYSUTA 1964-; *office:* Saratoga Spgs Sr HS W Circular St Saratoga Springs NY 12866

SCARAVILLI, GAYLE L., Theology Teacher; *b:* Cleveland, OH; *ed:* John Carroll Univ (BA) Rel Stud 1975, (MA) Rel Stud 1979; Continuing Ed Seminars; *cr:* St Joseph HS Tchr 1979-88; Holy Name HS Tchr 1988-89; St Ignatius HS Tchr 1992-; *ai:* Chrstn Life Comms Group Ldr; Fac Assn, Treas; NCEA 1980-; Rel Tchrs Assn 1981-; *office:* St Ignatius HS 1911 W 30th St Cleveland OH 44113*

SCARBERRY, BARBARA HOHMAN, 7th-12th Grade Teacher; *b:* Pittsburgh, PA; *m:* Philip Jay; *c:* Linda Dillard, Timothy M., Daniel L.; *ed:* Tchng Courses 6 Hrs; Acctng 8 Hrs; Bible Courses 8 Hrs; Cmptr 2 Hrs; *cr:* Parma City Schls Dept Chm 6 Yrs, Tchr 9 Yrs; Elyria Chrstn Acad 3 Yrs; Northside Chrstn Schl 14 1/2 Yrs; *ai:* Schl Store; BCSA 1985-.*

SCARBOROUGH, CATHLEEN MARIE, English Teacher; *b:* Reading, PA; *m:* Michael J.; *c:* Jennifer Zeigler, Bethann Zeigler; *ed:* Alvernia Coll (BA) Scndry Eng & Elem Ed 1989; Kutztown Univ (MS) Curr & Instruction 1992; PA Writing Project 6 Credits; PA Assessment Test Scorer; 12 Credits Post Masters Degree Curr & Instruction; *cr:* Govenor Miffle Schl Dist 6th Grd Tchr 1989-92, 7th-8th Grd Eng Tchr 1992-; *ai:* KARE Adv & Founder; 8th Grd Field Trip & Alternative Scheduling Comms; NEA 1987-; NCTE 1987-; PSEA 1987-; Sigma Tau Delta 1987-; AAUW 1991-; Implemented & Founded Book Buddy Pgm 1989; STAIRS Grant Berks Ed Fndtn 1992; Newsweek & Amway Class Act Awd 1994; *office:* Governor Mifflin MS 10 S Waverly St PO Box C750 Shillington PA 19607*

SCARBROUGH, PHILIP E., Social Studies Teacher; *b:* Mt Vernon, OH; *m:* Karen; *c:* Christine, Michael; *ed:* OH St Univ (BA) Soc Stud 1965; Miami Univ (MA) Amer His 1966; Addl 90 Plus Hrs Doctoral Work 1969-72; *cr:* Mansfield Malabar HS Soc Stud Tchr 1966-69; Miami Univ His Instr 1971-72; Finneytown HS Soc Stud Tchr 1972-75; Oak Hills HS Soc Stud Tchr 1975-; *ai:* Stu Cncl Adv; NEA, OH Ed Assn 1975-; Oak Hills Ed Assn 1975-, Former VP; OH Cncl of Soc Stud 1993-; Oak Hills Levy Comm 1996; Pub TV Vol 1990-; Oak Hills Tchr of Yr 1988; Friend of Ed PTA Awd 1995; 4-H Adv Svc Awd; *office:* Oak Hills Sr HS 3200 Ebenezer Rd Cincinnati OH 45248

SCARELLA, MARY NICKENS, Soc Stud Tchr & Cnslr; *b:* Bronx, NY; *m:* Robert Anthony; *c:* Matthew, Timothy, Christopher; *ed:* Coll of New Rochelle (BA) Sociology 1975; Fordham Univ (MA) His 1979; Long Island Univ (MS) Guid, Human Dev 1988; Parent Ed Ldrshp Trng Prgm Archdiocese of NY, Parent Ed Ministry Cert 1989; *cr:* The Ursuline Schl Tchr 1976-85, Tchr, Cnslr 1990-; *ai:* WA Seminar HS Stdnts Coord; Alcohol Awareness & Ed Prgm Facilitator; Holy Rosary Home & Schl Assn 1990-, Sec 1993-95; BSA 1991-, Den Ldr; St Elizabeth Ann Seton Compassionate Edctr Awd 1995; *office:* Ursuline Jr Sr HS 1354 North Ave New Rochelle NY 10804

SCARFIA, JAMES M., European & Bio-Ethics Instr; *b:* Rochester, NY; *m:* Dr. Shirley B.; *c:* Jillian, Matthew; *ed:* John Fisher Coll (BA) Rel Stud 1978; Univ of Toronto (MDiv) Theology 1982; St Univ of NY at Brockport (MA) Liberal Stud 1995; 12 Hrs in Prof Ed at Nazareth Coll; *cr:* Andrean HS Rel Stud Tchr 1978-79; Aquinas Inst Advanced Placement European & Bio-Ethics Instr 1982-; *ai:* Saint Monicas Club Moderator; Var Bowling Head Coach; Fac Advy Cncl Mem; Human Resources Comm Mem; RACSS 1985-; NEA 1988-; RDUA 1986-; Mid Sts 1987-; Nom for Tchr of Yr Twice; *office:* Aquinas Inst 1127 Dewey Ave Rochester NY 14613*

SCARL, DONALD, Retired Professor of Physics; *b:* Easton, PA; *m:* Barbara S. Cohen; *c:* Judith; *ed:* Lehigh Univ (BA) Physics 1957; Princeton Univ (PHD) Physics 1963; *cr:* NYU Instr 1962-63; Cornell U Instr 1963-66; Polytechnic U Asst Prof to Prof 1966-65; *ai:* Amer Physical Soc; Optical Soc of Amer; Am Soc Engineering Ed; AAAS; Visiting Scientist Brookhaven Natl Lab, Lawrence Livermore Lab, Naval Research Lab; 1 Book, 30 Articles Pub; *home:* 8 Woodland Rd Glen Cove NY 11542

SCARLOTT, CHARLOTTE LEE CUSTER, 7th-8th Grd Literature Teacher; *b:* Canton, OH; *c:* Steven Glenn; *ed:* Malone Coll (BA) Eng 1970; 160 Addl Hrs Rdng Cert K-12 1986; Ashland Coll Cooperative Learning, Reflective Practitioner I, II, III, IV, V; *cr:* Carrolton Bell-Herron MS 8th Grd Lang Arts Tchr 1970-92, 7th-8th Grd Lit Tchr 1992-; *ai:* Chrldr, Club Adv; Play Dir; Odyssey of Mind Coach; Inservice Planning C Classroom of Future Team; Dance Line Instr; Venture Capital C NEA, ODEA, CEA 1970-, Exec Comm, Bldg Rep; Carroll Cty H Soc; Forest Audubon Club, Hike Ldr; Custer Mem Assn; Sunday Sch Foursquare Gospel Church; Girl Scout Ldr; OH Child Conser League; Carroll Cty Hot Stove League Girls' Sftlb Coach; B League; Women's Missionary Group, VP; Carroll Cty Spelling Bee Winner; *home:* 1196 Glory Rd NW Carrollton OH 44615

SCARPA, CAROL TRAMONTANO, Secondary English Teacher; *b* Haven, CT; *m:* Daniel; *c:* Jessica, Joseph; *ed:* Univ of New Haven Eng, Librl Arts 1969; Southern CT St Univ (MA) Eng, Ed 1971; 6 H Univ; 12 Hrs Wesleyan Univ; *cr:* West Haven HS Eng Tchr 19 Guilford HS Eng, Librl Arts 1984-; *ai:* Interact Club Adv; NEA 1984-; Comm Kitchen; *office:* Guilford HS New England Rd Guilfo 06437*

SCARSELLA, THERESA TYANNE, 6th Grade Teacher; *b:* Birmir AL; *m:* Michael A.; *c:* Michael, Amanda, Daniel; *ed:* East Strou Univ (BS) Early Child, Elem 1987, (MED) Elem Ed 1995; Lehig Writing Project Penn St at Allentown; Great Books Fdn Ldr Trng C Peer Coach Conf Lead Tchrs; *cr:* US Air Force Sergeant 198 Stroudsburg Schl 8th Grd Tchr Comm Skills 1987-94, 6th Grd Tchr *ai:* Yrbk Adv; Schl Newspaper; NEA 1988-; ASCD 1989-; Chrst Assembly 1984-, Tchr; Lehigh Vly Writing Project Fellow Presente Penn St Allentown Camps; Article Pub Lehigh Vly Writer's Book; *c* Stroudsburg MS 123 Linden St Stroudsburg PA 18360*

SCARTON, DINO W., Assistant Principal; *b:* Portage, PA; *m:* De R.; *c:* Nicole, Christopher; *ed:* WSU (BA) Ed; Duquesne (MS) Admi Richland Schl Dist Tchr; Johnstown Schl Dist Tchr & Admin; *ai:* S Comm; *office:* Greater Johnstown Schl Dist 222 Central Ave Johnstov 15902*

SCARZFAVA, LAWRENCE DOMINICK, Admin & World Lit Te *b:* Middletown, NY; *m:* Linda Marie Carus; *c:* Daryl, Aaron, Jorda SUNY at New Paltz (BA) Eng 1991; *cr:* Harmony Chrstn Schl Eng 1989-94, Admin 1995-; Stanley H Kaplan Ed Ctr SAT Prep Tchr 19 *ai:* Stu Cncl Adv 1991-93; Sr Class Adv 1993-95; NCTE 1995-; *o* Harmony Christian Schl RD 2 Box 730 Middletown NY 10940

SCASNY, TIMOTHY JAMES, Journalism & Publication Tc Savannah, GA; *m:* Lynne T. Hamill; *c:* Jason, Keith, Jenna-Rachel, *ed:* Bowling Green St Univ (BA) Photo Jrnlsm 1974; John Carroll (MED) Admin 1993; Black Hills St Coll Post Grad Scndry Cert; Clev St Univ, Kent St Univ Post Grad Ed; OH Univ Post Grad Cmptr Graphics; *cr:* Chateh MS Tchr 1975-76; Trail Cty Schl Multi Grd 1976-78; Hot Springs HS Tchr 1978-81; Lumen Cordium HS 1983-85; Cleveland Hghts Tchr 1985-; *ai:* Newspaper, Yrbk Adv Publisher Schl Newsletter; Alumni Assn Advy Comm; Natl Photographers Assn, Great Lakes Interscholastic Press Assn 1986-; 1985-; Lake Erie League, Publications Advs; New Convent Chrsth Inc 1994-, Bd; Mayfield Village Septic Homeowners Assn 1995- Progressive Insurance Co Grant; Introduced First Desk Top Publis One of First 2 Schls Pub Newspaper on Internet WWW Home Page; *o* Cleveland Heights HS 13263 Cedar Rd Cleveland Heights OH 44118

SCATENATO, PAUL, Choir Director; *b:* Port Chester, NY; *m:* Raffaele; *c:* Lisa, Ryan, Christopher, Lindsay; *ed:* Hofstra Univ Music Ed 1978; Coll of St Rose (MS) Music Ed 1984; Grad Stud Q Coll; SUNY at New Paltz 25 Post-Grad Credits; *cr:* M. Clifford Mil HS Vocal Music Tchr 1979-87; Kingston HS Choir Dir 1987-; *ai:* T Hnr Soc Chptr Spon; Musical Theatris; Mixed Chorus, Alumni C Vocal Dir; Ulster Co Music Ed 1980-; NYSSMA, MENC 1978-; UC Choral Festival Choir; NY St Schl Music Assn Cert Voacl Adjudic *office:* Kingston HS 403 Broadway Kingston NY 12401

SCAVONE, SARAH BAKER, Assistant Prof of Business; *b:* Hol MA; *ed:* Univ of MA at Amherst (BS) Bus 1976; Lesky Coll (MS) 1987; *cr:* J. C. Penney Co Sr Merchandise Mgr 1976-81; Mt Ida Coll 1981-82; Chamberlagne Jr Coll Instr 1982-86; Lasell Coll Asst Prof o 1986-; *ai:* Natl Soc for Experimental Ed Coll Mem; Blue Key Awd.*

SCEE, JOSEPH E., Third Grade Teacher; *b:* Lackawanna, NY; *e* Univ of NY at Oswego (BS) Ed 1965; St Univ of NY at Potsdam (MS) 1988; US Naval War Coll Trng & Curr Dev; *cr:* Watertown Schl Dis Grd Tchr 1968-91, 3rd Grd Tchr 1991-; *ai:* NYSUT 1974-, Newsletter Ed; *office:* Knickerbocker Schl 739 Knickerbocke Watertown NY 13601

SCELFO, TONIA PROFITA, Guidance Counselor; *b:* Paterson, NJ Joseph Leonard; *c:* Joseph Thomas, Tonia Jill; *ed:* Trenton St Coll Scndry Eng Ed 1968; Georgian Court Coll (MA) Ed 1991; Cert Stu Svcs; *cr:* Westwood HS Eng Tchr 1968-71; Wall Twp HS Eng 1971-75, 1983-91, Guid Cnslr 1991-; *ai:* Stdnts at Risk, Guid Qu Assurance, Grd Weighting Comms; Crisis Intervention Team; Newsletter Ed; NEA, NJEA 1968-; Monmouth Cty Ed Assn, Wall Tw Assn 1971-; NJ Schl Cnslrs Assn 1991-; Wall HS Boosters Assn 19 Acad Chair; *office:* Wall Twp HS 18th Ave Wall Township NJ 07719

SCERBO, GAIL L., Spanish Teacher; *b:* Torrington, CT; *m:* David Anthony, Sean; *ed:* Kutztown Univ (BS) Scndry Ed 1982; East Strouds Univ (MS) Scndry Ed 1990; *cr:* Stroudsburg HS Frgn Lang Tchr 1982- Stu Cncl, Class Adv; NEA 1982-; *office:* Stroudsburg HS 1100 W Ma Stroudsburg PA 18360*

SCHABEL, DIANE BURSON, 10th Grade Health Educator; *b:* Tol OH; *m:* Robert P. I; *ed:* Miami Univ (BS) Ed 1979; Univ of Toledo Ed 1995; *cr:* Toledo Pub Schls Bldg Sub Tchr 1979-80; Oregon City S Ed Hlth, PE Tchr 1980-; *ai:* Frosh Vlybl Team Coach; Vol Work at Nursing Homes; AFT 1979-; OFT 1980-; Currently Working on a Jou Article & a Book; *office:* Clay HS 5665 Seaman Rd Oregon OH 43616

SCHACH, CLAUDE HENRY, Retired Earth & Space Sci Tchr; *b:* Rav PA; *m:* Judith Elaine Bowman; *ed:* Kutztown St Univ (BSEd) Chem 1 West Chester St Univ 13 Credits; Luth Theological Seminary at Gettysl 52 Credits; *cr:* Kutztown Area HS Chem Tchr 1963-67; Northern Leba HS Earth, Space Sci Tchr 1967-93; Friedens UCC Pastor 1994-; *ai:* PS 1963-, NLEA Local Pres, Chief Negotiator; PSEA Awd PA Innovative T of Yr 1973; *home:* 147 S 6th St Tower City PA 17980

SCHACHTER, DOROTHY SEIDEL, Business Education Teacher Pittsburgh, PA; *c:* Susan Schachter Moore, David; *ed:* Westminster (BA) Bus Ed, Eng 1960; Attnd Univ of Pittsburgh, Univ of CO, Ro Morris Coll; Cmptr Specialist Cert; *cr:* Avalon HS Bus Tchr 1960- Comm Coll of Alleg Co Part-time Bus Instr 1965-; Northgate HS Bus T 1980-; *ai:* Pen & Key; Prins Advy Cncl; Tech Task Force; Strate Planning Comm; NEA, PSEA 1980-; N Suburban Planning Commiss 1965-85, Sec; Univ of Pgh, Pgh Post Gazette Star Edctrs Awd 1994; *off* Northgate HS 589 Union Ave Pittsburgh PA 15202

SCHACHTER, WILLIAM NORMAN, Band & Orchestra Director Washington, DC; *c:* Andrew; *ed:* Coll Conservatory of Cincinnati (B Music Ed 1970; Post Grad Work at Peabody, U of MD; *cr:* E Instrumental Tchr 1973-83; Crofton MS Orch Dir 1983-86; Old Mill Band, Orch Dir 1986-95; *ai:* MENC 1986-; ASTA 1982-, Mbrshp Ch NEA 1973-; *office:* Old Mill MS South 620 Patriot Ln Millersville 21108

DE, CHRISTINE ELIZABETH, High School Math Teacher; *b:* , NY; *m:* Thomas A.; *ed:* Ithaca Coll (BA) Math 1987; Dowling Coll cndry Ed 1995; *cr:* Southold HS Math Tchr 1992-; *ai:* Stu Cncl Adv; League Co-Adv; NCTM, AMTNYS 1992-; *office:* Southold Jr Sr HS aklawn Ave Southold NY 11971

DE, JERE ALLEN, 8th-9th Grade Science Teacher; *b:* Gettysburg, *:* Penn St Univ (BS) Scndry Ed 1980; West Chester 30 Credit Hrs ; *cr:* Radnor HS Sci Tchr 1980-81; Council Rock Schl Dist Sci Tchr 37; Beijing Tchrs Coll-Bejing Intnl Schl Eng, Sci Tchr 1988-89; il Rock Schl Sci Tchr 1989-; *ai:* Environmental Club 1992-95; NEA

DEGG, KIRA RUNION, Science Teacher; *b:* Bethesda, MD; *m:* David; *c:* Brenna Ashley, Kellan Robert; *ed:* Acad of New Church 1977; Univ of NC at Chapel Hill (BS) Sci Tchng 1979; Beaver Coll) Sci Illustration 1996; *cr:* Acad of New Church Tchr 1979-82; Holy mer Hospital Exercise Technician 1982-92; Acad of New Church 1992-; *ai:* Yrbk Adv; Alternate Scheduling Comm Mem; NSTA, A, NCTM, ATMOPAV 1992-; Bryn Athyn Fire Co 1979-, Sec of Bd Ambulance Captain; Pine Run Park Playground Assn 1984-, Pres Bryn Athyn Fire Co Womens Auxiliary 1979-, Pres 2 Yrs; *office:* Of The New Church 2815 Benade Cr Bryn Athyn PA 19009

AEFER, CAROL M., Earth Science Teacher; *b:* Bronx, NY; *m:* Barry witz; *c:* Richard Seckel; *ed:* St Univ of NY at Farmingdale (AA) Lbrl 983; Hofstra Univ (BA) Commnctns 1985; Long Island Univ at CW Campus (MS) Scndry Earth Sci Ed 1990; 60 Credits Post Grad es; *cr:* Mercy HS Earth Sci Tchr 1989-91; Cntrl HS Earth Sci Tchr 96; *ai:* Environmental Club Adv; NSTA 1989-; Natl Earth Sci Tchrs 1991-; ASCD 1991-; Numerous Environmental Orgs; *office:* Valley n Central HS 135 Fletcher Ave Valley Stream NY 11582

AEFER, EDWARD ANTHONY, Middle School Band Director; *b:* ort, NY; *m:* Lisa A. Mangels; *c:* Edward, Dylan, Rhiannon; *ed:* IN of PA (BA) Music 1977; C. W. Post Ctr of LI Univ (MS) Music Ed *cr:* Bay Shore Schls 4-6 Grd Band Dir 1984-86; Bay Shore HS Asst ning Band Dir 1984-93; Bay Shore MS Jazz Band Dir 1987-, 7-8 Grd Dir 1987-; *ai:* Tech Comm Consultant Bay Shore Schls; AFT, NYSUT ; MENC, SCMEA 1983-; Phi Mu Alpha 1973-; Another Color Album al Music Entirely Self Composed, Performed, Produced; Endorsed Drums, OpCode Software Co; *home:* 9 Hawthorne Rd Rocky Point 1778

AEFER, KENNETH W., Fifth Grade Teacher; *b:* Bay Shore, NY; *m:* C. Brown; *c:* Nancy, Paul, Meghan, Todd; *ed:* Adelphi Suffolk Coll Liberal Arts 1967; Adelphi Univ (MA) Ed 1972; *cr:* Brentwood Schls 1967-68; Cntrl Solis Schls Tchr 1968-70; Sayville Schls 5th Grd Tchr -; *ai:* Sci Mentor; Math & Sci Curr Comm; AFT 1972-; Tourist oad Assn 1982-; Railroad Museum of Long Island 1982-, Trustee & *home:* 51 Hamilton St Sayville NY 11782

AEFER, LINDA THOMPSON, Biology Teacher; *b:* Yonkers, NY; *m:* d C.; *c:* Brian; *ed:* SUNY at Oswego (BS) Bio 1966, (MS) Bio, Scndry 974; NYS Insurace Broker License; *cr:* Mohonasen HS Bio Tchr -; *ai:* Club Adv; Church Mem; Mini-Grants Bio Projects; *office:* rdam-Mohonasen Cntrl Schl 2072 Curry Rd Schenectady NY 12303

AEFER, MISSIE HODGES, Latin Teacher; *b:* Washington, DC; *m:* ard M. Jr.; *c:* Kristin S. Robertson, Jason A.; *ed:* Wake Forest Univ Latin 1966; Western MD (MLA); *cr:* Liberty HS Latin Tchr 1981-, rs; *ai:* PTSA Tchr Rep; Schl Improvement Comm Mem; NEA, Amer sical League 1984-; Fulbright Grant to Stud in Italy; *office:* Liberty 855 Bartholow Rd Sykesville MD 21784

AEFER, MYRNA L., Senior English Teacher; *b:* Scranton, PA; *m:* ence George; *c:* Stephanie, Renee; *ed:* Wilkes Univ (BA) Eng 1968; of Scranton (MA) Eng 1972; Supvr of Eng 1991; 60 Credit Hrs nd MA; *cr:* Meyers HS Eng Tchr 1968-; *ai:* Stand Tall Org for inence From Drugs & Alcohol; Grad Ceremony Dir; Eng Adv & d; Phi Delta Kappa 1983-; NCTE 1986-; NEA, PSEA & WBAEA; E Fed Credit Union 1984-, Bd of Dirs; St Peters Luth Church; Book *office:* Elmer L Meyers Jr Sr HS 341 Carey Ave Wilkes Barre PA 2

AEFFER, INGRID MARY, 7th & 8th Grade Drama Teacher; *b:* New en, CT; *m:* Emad Haerizadeh; *c:* Mytra Haerizadeh; *ed:* egie-Mellon Univ (BFA) Drama 1984; London Acad of Music & natic Art; *cr:* Educl Ctr for the Arts Theater Tchr 1986-95; Betsy Ross Magnet Schl Drama Tchr 1989-91; Creative Dramatics Dir of Pvt Schl -; Hopkins Schl Drama Tchr 1995-; *ai:* Direct Productions after Schl; rs Equity Assn 1987-; Amer Alliance for Theater in Ed; Educl Theater ; *office:* Hopkins Schl 986 Forest Rd New Haven CT 06515

AEFFER, JO ANN BLICKENSTAFF, Science Teacher; *b:* erstown, MD; *m:* Charles E. Jr.; *c:* Mary Jo Milligan, Kurt Alan; *ed:* tburg St Univ (BS) Bio; Master's Equivilancy Univ of MD at College , Towson St Univ, Loyola Coll; *cr:* Arundel Sr HS Bio Tchr 1965-67; othy River MS 6th Grd Sci Tchr 1980-95; Arundel Sr HS Sci Tchr -; *ai:* NEA, Tchrs Assn of Anne Arundel Co, MD St Tchrs Assn 1980-; ton Woods Homeowner's Assn 1985-, Bd of Dirs; *home:* 206 Mustang iambrills MD 21054

AEFFER, TERESA JOAN, Spanish Teacher; *b:* Glendale, CA; *m:* glas B.; *c:* Tricia, Mason, Tracie Pierce, Gryan, Heidi, Kelly; *ed:* ham Young Univ (BA) Span 1969; 40 Addl Hrs Span, Scndry Ed; *cr:* nite HS Span Levels 1-4 Tchr 1970-72; Calabasas HS Sub, Full-time Tchr 1982-92; Mc Nicholas HS Span Tchr 1994-; *ai:* Basque Stud; A 1993-; WISK-FLO 1990-; BSA 1987-, Bd of Review, Ldrshp, Svc; O Soccer 1982-, Division Dir; Short Stories, Articles Pub; *office:* Mc holas HS 6536 Beechmont Ave Cincinnati OH 45230

HAFER, ANNA MARIE GAUDIO, Fourth Grade Teacher; *b:* Jersey , NJ; *m:* William F.; *c:* Bill, Kevin; *ed:* Fairleigh Dickinson Univ (BA) n Ed 1970; *cr:* St Francis de Sales 4th Grd Tchr 1971-72; St Margaret Grd Tchr 1972-75; St Micheal Lang Arts 1979; St Mary 4th Grd Tchr -; *ai:* Talent Show Adv; Mid St Steering Comm; NCEA; Great Book.

HAFER, DAVID WILLIAM, Social Studies Teacher; *b:* Philadelphia, *m:* JoAnne B. Gallo; *c:* Natalie, Dana; *ed:* Coll of Steubenville (BA) np Soc Stud 1972; Beaver Coll 9 hrs; Temple Univ 3 Hrs; *cr:* St Michael Arch Soc Stud Tchr 1972-74; Melrose Acad Soc Stud Tchr 1974-75; hop Conwell HS Soc Stud Tchr 1976-93; St Hubert HS Soc Stud Tchr 3-; *ai:* Comm Svc Corps; Talent Show; ACT 1976-; *office:* St Hubert h HS for Girls 7320 Torresdale Ave Philadelphia PA 19136

HAFER, MARION BIERWEILER, Professor of English; *b:* lfeboro, NH; *m:* Guy T.; *c:* Peter Swett, David Swett; *ed:* Mount yoke Coll (AB) Eng Composition 1971; Univ of NH (MST) Eng 1972; rs on-Going Post Grad Work Linguistics at Harvard Univ; *cr:* NH HS g Tchr 1972-89; Saint Pauls Schl Advanced Stud Prgm Master Tchr nmers 1989-95; NH Tech Coll Eng Prof 1990-; *ai:* Phi Theta Kappa -Adv; Phi Beta Kappa 1970-, Mem; Assorted Poems & Essays; Feature ries Local Publications; Received Grant to Establish Stories of North ry Women an Annual Publication of Stu Writing; *home:* RR 2 Box 125 itefield NH 03598*

HAFER, WILLIAM PATRICK, Demonstration Teacher; *b:* tsburgh, PA; *ed:* Edinboro St Univ (BA) Elem Ed 1970; Univ of tsburgh (MS) Ed 1975; *cr:* Northview Elem Tchr 1970-75; Lincoln Elem Tchr 1975-76; Reizenstein Mid Math Tchr 1976-93; Pittsburgh Pub Schl Dist Demonstration Tchr 1993-; *ai:* Assessment Comm of Tchr Leadership Team; Core Curr Framework Team; AFT 1970-; NCMT 1990-; *office:* Pittsburgh Pub Schl Dist 129 Denniston Ave Pittsburgh PA 15206*

SCHAFF, ROBERT A., Assoc Prof Mrktg & Intnl Bus; *b:* New Haven, CT; *m:* Sandra; *c:* Robert III, Jana, Andrea; *ed:* Northeastern U (BS) Mrktg 1964, (MBH) Mrktg 1966; Baruch Coll CUNY (PHD) Mrktg 1974; *cr:* Univ of Bridgeport Asst Prof 1966-74, Dean 1974-89, Assoc Prof 1989-; *ai:* Univ Senate Moderator; Fac Cncl VP; Strategic Planning Task Force; Ethics Inst; Amer Mrktg Assoc 1963-; Beta Gamma Sigma 1964-; NHRHTA 1986-, Judge; Numerous Articles Pub; Journel Bd of Eds; Bus & Civic Orgs Bd of Dirs; *office:* Univ Of Bridgeport 230 Park Ave Bridgeport CT 06601

SCHAFFER, LYNDA L., HS Spanish Teacher; *b:* Columbus, OH; *c:* Tara; *ed:* OH St Univ (BA) Span & Eng 1971, (MS) Span Ed 1982; 45 Post Grad Work at Ashland Univ; *cr:* Pickerington HS Span Tchr 1971-; *ai:* Chrldng Coach 14 Yrs; *office:* Pickerington HS 300 Opportunity Way Pickerington OH 43147

SCHAFFER, THEODORE, Biology Teacher; *b:* Mc Keesport, PA; *m:* Jill Witmer; *c:* Cayla; *ed:* Penn St Univ (BS) Ag 1989; Temple Univ (MED) Ed 1995; *cr:* Perdue Farms Inc Supvr 1989-90; US Peace Corps Vol in Mali West Africa 1991-92; Girard Coll Bio, Chem Tchr 1993; Liberty HS Bio Tchr 1993-; *ai:* Frosh Class Adv; Comm Svc Environmental Liason; NEA 1993-; Church of Christ 1995-, Deacon; Wrote & Produced Educl Video on Fungus, Grants Provided; *office:* Liberty HS 1115 Linden St Bethlehem PA 18018*

SCHAFFNIT, MARK CHRISTOPHER, Middle School Band Director; *b:* Butler, PA; *m:* Laurie Pomerson; *ed:* Capital Univ (BA) Music Ed 1986, (BA) Music Performance 1986; *cr:* Westfall Local Schls Band Dir 1987-; *ai:* HS Marching Band Asst; HS Percussion Instr; Unified Arts Team Ldr; OMEA 1987-; Percussive Arts Soc 1982-; Amer Fed of Musicians Local 103 1983-; Percussion Judge Pickaway Cty Honors Band; Created Pickaway Cty Day of Percussion 1989-; *office:* Westfall MS 19545 Pherson Pike Williamsport OH 43164

SCHAFT, THEODORE E.,JR., Math & Physics Teacher; *b:* Philadelphia, PA; *c:* Trey, Trevor; *ed:* Castleton St Coll (BS) Ed, Math 1986; *cr:* Otter Vly UHS Math, Cmptr Tchr 1986; Mill River UHS Math Tchr 1987; Mt St Joseph Acad Math, Sci Tchr 1987-; *ai:* Golf, Scholar's Bowl Coach; Outing Club Spon; NCEA, NAAPT 1988-; USA Hockey 1991-, Referee; *home:* 8 Warner Ave Proctor VT 05765

SCHAGRIN, MORTON LOUIS, Philosophy Professor; *b:* Wilmington, DE; *m:* Shirley Ruston; *c:* Alissa Keene, Stuart, Kenneth; *ed:* U of Chicago (BA) Librl Arts 1951, (BS) Physics 1952, (MA) Philosophy 1953; U of CA at Berkeley (PHD) Philosophy 1965; *cr:* U of FL Asst Prof 1961-63; Denison Univ Asst & Assoc Prof 1963-70; SUNY Assoc & Full Prof 1970-; *ai:* Phil of Sci Soc 1953-; Amer Phil Assn 1961-; His of Sci Soc 1961-; NSF Flwshp; 2 Fulbright Tchng Awds to China; Kasling Lecturer Awd; Numerous Articles & Books Pub.

SCHAIPER, LEN LOUIS, Assoc Prof, Dept of Spec Ed; *b:* Cleveland, OH; *ed:* Kent St (BS) Scndry Ed 1968, (MS) Spec Ed 1972; Univ of TN (EDD) Curr & Instruction 1983; *cr:* Univ of TN Doctoral Stu 1980-81; Western Carlonia Univ Asst Spec Ed Prof 1981-83; Eastern NM Univ Asst Spec Ed Prof 1984-86; Youngstown St Univ Spec Ed Dept Assoc Prof 1987-; Pub Schl Tchng 9 Yrs; *ai:* CEC, Kappa Delta Pi 1982-; Phi Delta Kappa 1975-; Self Esteem, Learning Styles, Troubled Youth Natl Consultant, Speaker, Wkshp Ldr; *office:* Youngstown St Univ 410 Wick Ave Youngstown OH 44555*

SCHAIRER, ROBERT F., English Teacher & Supervisor; *b:* Galloway, NJ; *m:* Mary Schairer; *c:* Bonnie, Robin Rudole, Robert Jr., Kate DiVaccaro, Joseph; *ed:* Glassboro St Coll (BA) Tchng of Eng 1965, (MA) Tchng of Eng 1967; 15 Credits; NJ Supvrs, Prins Certs 1982; *cr:* Prof Musician Full, Part-time 1960-; Hammonton HS 8 Grd Eng Tchr 1965-66; Glassboro St Coll M A Grad Asst 1966-67, Comm 101 Part-time Instr 1967-69; Gloucester City Jr-Sr HS 11 Grd Eng Tchr 1967-82, Eng Supv, Tchr 1982-; *ai:* Hon Soc Selection, Schl-Based Planning Comms; Instrl Renewal Cncl; Eng, NJ HSPT-EWT Responsibilites, Dist SRA Coord; Supervision of Eng Dept's, Cmptr Lab, Tchr Scheduling, Curr Revision, Basic Skills; GCEA, NEA, NJEA 1967-82; GCAA, NJASSP, NASSP 1982-; Local 77-1 of A F of M 1968-; *office:* Gloucester City Jr Sr HS Rt 130 & Market St Gloucester City NJ 08030

SCHAKEL-TROOST, CAROL MARIE, English Teacher; *b:* Indianapolis, IN; *m:* Donald P.; *c:* Deborah, Matthew; *ed:* Hope Coll (BA) Eng 1968; Coll of St Rose (MA) Rdng 1985; *cr:* Creston JHS Eng Tchr 1968-69; Scotch Plains Fanwood HS Eng Tchr 1969-70; Shenendehowa HS Eng Tchr 1970-71f Galway Cntrl HS Eng Tchr 1972-75 1985-; *ai:* Schl Newspaper; NYSEC 1985-, Tchr Excl; NCTE, GTA 1985-; 1st Reformed Church of Scotia 1985-, Elder, Deacon, Church Schl Tchr; NHS Tchr of Yr 1993; *office:* Galway Cntrl HS 5317 Sacandaga Rd Galway NY 12074*

SCHALGE, DONNA ROCKCASTLE, Mathematics Teacher; *b:* Rochester, NY; *m:* Gary; *c:* Jennifer, Garett, Bryan; *ed:* Marietta Coll (BS) Math 1972; SUNY at Brockport (MS) Ed, Scndry Math 1976, (CAS) Educl Admin 1988; 18 Hrs Cmptr Sci; *cr:* Greece Cntrl Schl Dist Math Tchr 1972-; Nazareth Coll Adj Fac 1988-91; SUNY at Brockport Adj Fac 1994-; *ai:* Math Team Adv; Tech Prep Math Support; Soph Class Adv; NCTM 1992-; AMTNYS 1972-; NEA-NY 1972-, VP; Gerald L. Brown Pre-Svc Tchng Awd.*

SCHALL, JOY K., Math Teacher; *b:* Bowling Green, OH; *m:* James Kevin Sr.; *c:* James Jr., Jonna, Jalana; *ed:* Bowling Green St Univ (BS) Math 1993; 9 Post-Grad Hrs; *cr:* Whitmer HS Math Tchr 1993-; *ai:* Tech Prep Co-Chair Steering Comm; NEA 1993-; *office:* Whitmer HS 5719 Clegg Dr Toledo OH 43613

SCHALL, ROBERT B., Math & Cmptr Applications Tchr; *b:* Darby, PA; *m:* Georgene B.; *ed:* Millersville Univ (BS) Math 1972; Addl 30 Credit Hrs; *cr:* Wheatland Jr HS Math, Cmptr Tchr 1972-; *ai:* Ftbl, Boy, Girls Track Coach; Weightlifting Club Adv; PSEA, NEA, LEA, NCTM, PCTM 1972-; Maxwell Club 1985-; Lancaster Newspaper Tchr of Wk; *office:* Wheatland Jr HS 919 Hamilton Park Dr Lancaster PA 17603

SCHALLER, C. SUE, Humanities Teacher; *b:* Elgin, IL; *c:* Susanna, Jeremy; *ed:* Northwestern Univ (BA) Pol Sci 1960; Univ of Cologne (MA) Soc Sci, Eng 1981; Free Univ of Berlin Fulbright Pol Sci 1960-62; *cr:* Urban Planning Group Educl Consultant 1971-81; Stone Ridge Schl of Sacred Heart Eng, Jrnlsm Tchr 1988-89; Wilson Sr HS Eng Tchr, Intnl Stud Prgm 1989-94; Prof Performing Arts Schl Hum Tchr 1994-; *ai:* Stu Govt, Coll Adv; NY Tchrs Union 1994-; Washington Tchrs Union 1992-94; AFT 1994-; NEH Seminar Native Amer Lit Univ of TX 1994; Team Tchr Intnl Stud Prgm.

SCHALLEUR, MARYANN C., English Teacher; *b:* Philadelphia, PA; *c:* Ilona Haris; *ed:* Immaculata Coll (AB) Eng 1965; 15 Hrs Villanova; 30 Hrs In Svc; *cr:* Phila Schl Dist Eng Tchr 1968-72; Tredyffrin Eastown Schl Rdng Tchr 1972-73; Interboro HS Eng Tchr 1975-; *ai:* Class Spon; HS Chrldng Coach 1988-93; NEA 1975-; Interboro Educ Assn 1975-, Pres 1980-84; Springfield Yth Club 1980-85, Dir Chrldng; Mid Sts Curr Chm 1990; PA Goal 2000 Project Comm.*

SCHAMP, JAMIE S., 7th Grade English Teacher; *b:* Bronx, NY; *m:* Richard; *c:* Lucas Goetz, Rudy Goetz, Jacob; *ed:* Plattsburgh St (BA) Eng 1968; 90 Grad Hrs; *cr:* Chestnut Hill MS Eng Tchr 1968-; *ai:* UFLA 1968-; NEA 1968-; Cong Ner Tamid 1968-, Bd of Ed; Articles Pub.

SCHANTZ, SHARON SOPHIE, Business Teacher; *b:* Quakertown, PA; *c:* Lacy; *ed:* Gwynedd-Mercy Coll (BS) Bus Ed 1993; Attnd Holy Family Coll, Penn St, Temple, St Josephs Univ & IN Wesleyan Grad Credits; *cr:* Penn Stainless Products Asst to Controller 1988-93; Neshaminy HS Bus Tchr 1993-; *ai:* Assist FBLA; Participate in Grad Ceremony; Class Trip Chaperone; Spon PA Free Enterprise Week; AFT 1993-; Nom for Ed to Bus Partnership Awd; *office:* Neshaminy HS 2001 Old Lincoln Hwy Langhorne PA 19047

SCHARFSPITZ, MARJORIE WALLEN, Sixth Grade Teacher; *b:* Philadelphia, PA; *m:* Roland; *c:* Jason, Emily; *ed:* Univ of PA at Phildelphia (BA) Eng 1963; Tchr Cert Credits Hunter Coll; *cr:* Schl 10 6thGrd Tchr, Math 1986-; *ai:* NEA, PEA, NJEA 1986-; NCTM 1993-; U of P Club Metropolitan NJ 1983-, VP, Ben Franklin Awd; Governor's Tchr Recognition Awd, City Paterson Civic Awd 1992; *office:* Elem Schl 10 48 Mercer St Paterson NJ 07524*

SCHARNWEBER, LISA MARIE, Mathematics Teacher; *b:* Kenmore, NY; *ed:* St Univ of NY Coll at Buffalo (BS) Math Ed 1989, (MS) Gen Ed 1995; *cr:* Sweet Home MS 7th-8th Grd Math Tchr 1990-93; Sweet Home HS 9th-12th Grd Math Tchr 1993-; *ai:* Sr Class Cncl Co-Adv; Sweet Home Mathletes Coach; Sweet Home Edctrs Assn 1990-.

SCHATTLE, ARTHUR G., Technology Ed Department Head; *b:* Providence, RI; *m:* Shelia M.; *c:* Hans, Heidi, Erica, Ann; *ed:* RI Coll (BS) Indstrl Arts 1964; Cntrl Ct Univ (MS) Indstrl Ed 1966; Post Grad Stud Univ of HI, Boston Univ, Univ of RI; *cr:* Portsmouth HS Indstrl Art Tchr 1964-66; Bristol Adult Schl Prin 1968-80; Mt Hope HS Tech Ed Dept Head 1966-; *ai:* Perkins Grant, Prgm of Stud, Bldg Comms; ITEA 1988-; NEATT, RITE, BWEA, NEARI, NEA 1964-; East Providence Career & Tech Ctr 1986-, Advy Comm; Blithewold Mansion & Gardnes 1979-, Advy Comm; St Marys Church 1972-, Fin Comm; Tech Tchr of Yr, NEATT, RITE; Tech Tech Excl Awd ITEA; RI Coll Alumni Hnr Roll Awd; Outstdng Scndry Edctrs of Amer Awd; Outstdng Tech Prgm Awd, ITEA, WEATT, RITE; *office:* Mt Hope HS 199 Chestnut St Bristol RI 02809*

SCHATZ, JOAN CURRIER, Mathematics Teacher; *b:* Albany, NY; *m:* Bernd G.; *c:* Matthew, Patricia; *ed:* St Univ of NY at Albany (BA) Math 1967, (MA) Math 1971; *cr:* Albany HS Tchr 1969-71; Acad of Holy Names Tchr 1981-; *ai:* Math Club Adv; AMTNYS & NCTM 1991-; Cath War Veterans 1979-, 2nd VP; Columbiettes 1991-; Rosary Soc 1976-; *office:* Acad of the Holy Names 1075 New Scotland Rd Albany NY 12208

SCHATZ, JOHN R., Soc Studies Tchr & Dept Chair; *b:* Mc Keesport, PA; *m:* Joan Hungerford; *c:* Erica; *ed:* SUNY at Cortland (BA) Soc Stud 1972, (MSEd) Soc Stud 1980; SUNY at Oneonta (MSEd) Guidance, Counseling 1992; *cr:* Narrowsburg CSD Tchr 1973-80; Delaware Valley CSD Tchr, Dept Chair 1980-; Sullivan Cty Comm Coll Govt, Ec Instr 1992-95; *ai:* Grd 9 Class Adv; Curr Writing Group; NYSUT, NY Soc St Cncl 1973-; DVFA 1980-, Past Pres; Amer Counseling Assn 1990-; Town of Delaware Republican Comm 1995-, Chm; *office:* Delaware Valley Central Schl Rt 97 Callicoon NY 12723

SCHATZEL, PATRICIA AUDREY, Span Tchr & Fac Adv Amnesty; *b:* Ossining, NY; *ed:* Pace Univ (BA) Fr Ed 1964; Syracuse Univ (MS) Ed Cnslng 1982; 30 Credit Hrs; Span Instituto Fenix at Cuernavaca 1975-76; *cr:* Mount Carmel High Fr Tchr 1964-67; Jordan-Elbridge HS Fr & Span Tchr 1967-79; Easter Seal Soc Pgm Dir 1982-83; St Josephs Hosp Soc Worker 1983-85; North Syracuse Schls Fr & Span Tchr 1985-; Syracuse Univ Summer Inst Instr 1989-; *ai:* Chptr of Amnesty Intnl Spon; Stu Support Group Mem; AFT 1985-; NYSUT 1985-; Amnesty Intnl 1987-, Regnl Coord; Syracuse Chorale 1994-; Wrote & Received Grant Wegmans Corp; *office:* Cicero-North Syracuse HS Northstar Dr Cicero NY 13039

SCHAUB, TERRY BOBSIEN, American His & Geography Tchr; *b:* Cleveland, OH; *w:* William (dec); *c:* Amanda; *ed:* Hiram Coll (BA) His Ed 1972; Kent St Univ (MA) His Ed 1978; *cr:* Grand Valley Local Schl 6th-8th Grd Tchr 22 Yrs; *ai:* OEA & NEA 1972-; Orwell North Church 1964-; Eastern Stars 1969-, Colebrook Precinct Committeman 1990; Friends of Grand Valley Lib 1993-, Treas.

SCHAUBLE, BRUCE, K-12th Grd English Coordinator; *b:* Mt Kisco, NY; *m:* Barbara; *c:* Barney, Jason, Oren; *ed:* Univ of HI (MED) Elem Ed 1971; Harvard Flwshp; MA Flwshp Boston Writing Project 1989; *cr:* Dean Luce Schl Elem Tchr 1971-73; Galvin MS Eng Tchr 1973-84; Canton HS Eng Coord 1984-95; *ai:* Partnership for Educl Progress Faciliator; Frosh Bsktbl Coach; NCTE 1975-; NCATE MA Poet-of-the-Yr; *office:* Canton HS 900 Washington St Canton MA 02021*

SCHAUBLE, THOMAS J., Drafting & Design Teacher; *b:* Paterson, NJ; *m:* Sharon Stansfield; *c:* Argi, Shawn, Tina, Jamiee; *ed:* Montclair St (BA) Indstrl Arts, Tech 1968; Addl Studies African American Stud, Cmptr Aided Drafting; Multi Inteligence Ed, Portfolios in RD, Cmptr Programming, Automotive Comp Tech; *cr:* Montclair HS Auto-Tech Tchr 1969-70; Precison Inc Pres, Dir Personal 1970-82; Montclair HS Small Engine Repair, Gen Tech, Drafting, Robotics, Architecture, CAD, Engrng, Interior Design 1982-; *ai:* Curr Cncl; Design Comm; Co-Chair Indstrl Arts & Tech Review; VICA 1968-69, 1985-86; NEA, NJEA, Montclair EA, Ind Art Assn 1969-; Natl Kidney Fdn 1993-; Randolph Rec Assn 1981-; Montclair Assn Educl Excl, NHS, Robotics Grants; Featured in NJEA Commercial BILL Video 1995; Co-Author Technology Magnet High School; *office:* Montclair HS 100 Chestnut St Montclair NJ 07042

SCHAUER, CYNTHIA KNISLEY, German Teacher; *b:* Baltimore, MD; *m:* Jerry Emmert; *c:* Andrew, Amy, Julie; *ed:* Albright Coll (BA) Ger 1970; Villanova Univ (MA) Ger 1988; Inservice Trng Essential Elements of Ed, Stu Assistance Svc; *cr:* Neshaminy Schl Dist Ger & Music Tchr 1970-71; Great Valley Schl Dist Ger Tchr 1971-73; Villanova Univ Grad Asst, Tchr 1984-88; Tredyffrin-Easttown Schl Dist Ger Tchr 1986-87; Delaware Cty Comm Coll Ger Instr 1984-86; Eastern Coll Ger Instr 1986-87; Downingtown Area Schl Dist Ger Tchr 1988-; *ai:* Ger Club; Cultural Exch Comm; Ger-Amer Partnership Prgm; PSEA, AATG 1988-; GAPP 1993-; Church of the Good Samaritan, Church Choir; Albright Coll Gold "A" Awd 1970; *office:* Downingtown HS 445 Manor Ave Downingtown PA 19335

SCHAUER, RALF WILHELM, Associate Professor; *b:* Albany, NY; *m:* Linda L. Scharf; *c:* Lauren Simone; *ed:* St Univ of NY at Albany (BS) Physics, German 1981; Union Coll (MST) Natural Scis 1994; *cr:* Schdy Co Comm Coll Instr 1982-84, Asst Prof 1984-95; Assoc Prof 1995; *ai:* Electrical Tech Club Adv 1984-94; SCCC Envirl Clb Adv 1995; NEA 1982-; Astronomical Soc at Pacific 1987-; Natl Audubon Soc 1970-; Albany Area Amateur Astronomers 1982-; Schdy Co Environmental Advy Cncl 1991-93; Org for Action on Riverfront 1993-94; Captl Dist Maritime Cntr; Nom SCCC Fnd Tchng Excl Awd 1991, 1992, 1994, 1995; *office:* Schenectady County Comm Coll 78 Washington Ave Schenectady NY 12305

SCHAUER-WEBSTER, LYNN, High School Art Teacher; *b:* Syracuse, NY; *m:* Andrew Thomas II; *c:* Chandler D.; *ed:* St Univ Coll at Buffalo (BS) Art Ed 1990; Working Towards MS in Art Ed; *cr:* Genesee Vly BOCES Itinerant Art Tchr 1991-93; Stanley G. Falk Schl Spec Ed Work Stud, Summer Art Tchr 1992-93; Alexander Cntrl Schl HS Art Tchr 1993-; *ai:* Yrbk Adv; NHS Co-Adv; NYSUT 1991-; Albright-Knox Art Gallery 1993-; NASAA 1995-; St Paul's Episcopal Cathedral 1991-, Hunger Outreach, Communication Comms, Altar Guild, Usher, United Thank

Offering Chprsn; *office:* Alexander Central Schl 3314 Buffalo St Alexander NY 14005

SCHAUFFELE, SUSAN ANN, GED Teacher; *b:* Dayton, OH; *ed:* Wheaton Coll (BS) Eng 1989; *cr:* Rochester City Schl GED Tchr 1990-; *ai:* Jobs for Yth Acad Enrichment Tutor; *office:* Baden St GED Prog 152 Baden St Rochester NY 14605

SCHECHTMAN, KATHRYN TURONE, English Teacher; *b:* Buffalo, NY; *m:* Glenn S.; *c:* Daniel, Lara; *ed:* St Univ of NY at Albany (BA) Eng Lit 1975; Coll of St Rose (MS) Spec Ed, Learning Disabilites 1981; Addl 21 Credit Hrs; NY St Dept of Ed Testing Prgms; *cr:* Schenectady City Schl Dist Tchr Asst, Temporary Tchr 1976-77; North Colonie Cntrl Schl Dist Tchr Asst, Resource Room 1978; Saratoga Springs City Schl Dist Eng Tchr 1978-; *ai:* Movie Club Adv; AFT, NYSUT 1978-; NCTE 1993-; *office:* Saratoga Spgs Sr HS W Circular St Saratoga Springs NY 12866

SCHECTER, BARBARA, Acctg & HS Bus Law Teacher; *b:* New York City, NY; *m:* Martin; *c:* JEFFREY, Alison; *ed:* C. W. Post (MS) Spec Ed 1982; Addl 45 Credits Learning Styles; Stud Post MS Bus 1993; *cr:* Amityville HS Tchr 1980-; *ai:* Stu Govt Adv; Instituted Moot Court; NYSUT, NEA, NBTA 1980-; Suffolk Cty Bus Tchrs Assn 1985-; Sisterhood Mem Congregation Bethel; *office:* Amityville Memorial HS 250 Merrick Rd Amityville NY 11701*

SCHEDIN, STEVEN WILLIAM, 7th Grd Social Studies Teacher; *b:* Elizabeth, NJ; *m:* Julie R. Williams; *c:* Deirdre A.; *ed:* York Coll of PA (BA) Comprehensive Soc Stud 1973; 25 Post Grad Credits Penn St at York; *cr:* Northeastern MS 7th Grd Soc Stud Tchr 1976-; *ai:* Dist Weightlifting Supvr; Stu Cncl Adv; Discipline, Dist Tchr Evaluation Comms; WYBC Bsbl Coach; NEA, PSEA 1976-, Bldg Rep, Exec Comm 1984-90; VASA of Amer 1990-, Yth & Schlsp Chm, Inner Guard; Gift of Time Awd 1990, 1992; Northeastern Schl Dist Tchr Recognition Awd 1986; TV Channel HTM 27's Tchr in Spotlight 1995.

SCHEER, MARY C., Homeroom, Social Studies Tchr; *b:* Brooklyn, NY; *ed:* Queens Coll (BA) His, Scndry Ed 1983; St John's Univ (MS) Ed 1986; 15 Hrs Cath Diocese of Brooklyn; *cr:* Most Precious Blood Schl 8th Grd SS, Rel Tchr 1983-89; *ai:* Pub Relations Acts Sr Adv; 30 Hr Famine Coord; After Schl Prgm Supvr; Newsletter Writer, Ed; *office:* Mary's Nativity Schl 146-28 Jasmine Ave Flushing NY 11355

SCHEIBLING, BARBARA BROSI, Business Education Teacher; *b:* Cornwall, NY; *m:* Doug; *c:* Dustin, Kylie; *ed:* SUNY at Cobleskill (AS) Bus Mgt 1981; Pace Univ (BA) Bus Ed 1983, (MS) Ed 1988; Continuing Ed Classes in Bus & Comp Field; *cr:* Orange Uster Vo Tech Bus Tchr 1983-88; SS Seward Inst Bus Ed Tchr 1988-; *ai:* School-To-Work, Comm Svc, Schl Store Coord; DECA Adv; *office:* SS Seward Institution 53 N Main St Florida NY 10921

SCHEID, CONSTANCE A., 6th Grade Lang & Rdng Teacher; *b:* Hamilton, OH; *m:* Richard; *c:* Kimberly, Joseph, Kathryn; *ed:* Miami Univ (BS) Elem Ed 1987; Coll of Mt St Joseph (MA) Ed 1993; *cr:* Fairfield MS Tchr 1987-; *ai:* NEA; FCTA; OEA; *office:* Fairfield MS 255 Donald Dr Fairfield OH 45014

SCHEID, CYNTHIA LOUISE, Band Director; *b:* Warren, PA; *m:* Eric M.; *ed:* Westminister Coll (BM) Music 1985; Mansfield Univ (MS) Music 1986; *cr:* Charleroi HS Permanent Sub Choral Dir 1990-91; Youngsville Mid, Sr HS Band Dir 1991-; *ai:* Marching Band, Jazz Band Dir; NEA, PSEA, WLEA 1991-; PMEA 1990-; Order of the Eastern Star 1995-; *office:* Youngsville Mid, Sr HS 227 College St Youngsville PA 16371*

SCHEIDEMANN, PAUL JOSEPH, Social Studies Teacher; *b:* Bronx, NY; *m:* Elizabeth; *c:* Katilin, Caroline, Meghan, Claire; *ed:* Niagara Univ (BA) His 1981; St Univ Coll at Buffalo (MS) Soc Stud Ed 1992; *cr:* Tonawanda HS Soc Stud Tchr 1987-88; Williamsville South HS Soc Stud Tchr 1988-90; Mill MS Soc Stud Tchr 1990-; *ai:* 7th-8th Grd Boys Bsktbl Team Coach; Airband Snow Adv; Sr Bldg Rep; 7th-8th Grd Boys Soccer Team Coach; *office:* Mill MS 505 Mill St Williamsville NY 14221

SCHEIDET, ROBERT AUGUST, Science Chairman; *b:* Flushing, NY; *m:* Margery Rose Bernstein; *c:* Betsy, Heidi; *ed:* Stony Brook Univ (BS) Earth, Space Sci 1970; Queens Coll (MS) Sci Ed 1974; Hofstra Univ (MS) Ed Admin 1979; 12 Credits Performance Assessment 1994-95; 9 Credits NSF; *cr:* Jericho Pub Schls Sci Tchr 1970-73; Miller Place Schls Tchr, Admin 1973-; *ai:* Dist Expert Performance Assessment, Video Specialist; Sci Hnr Soc Adv; ASCD 1991-; ITEA, NBTA 1985-; STANYS, NSTA 1990-; Bahai' Faith, Dir Regnl Sunday Schl; NYNEX Cmptr Grant; *home:* 70 Broad View Cir Wading River NY 11792*

SCHEITHAUER, MARY M., Spanish Teacher; *b:* Akron, OH; *m:* David R.; *c:* Ross William, David Leach; *ed:* OH St Univ (BS) Ed 1975, (MS) Ed 1979; Univ of Akron Ed 1974; *cr:* Westland HS Span Tchr 1975-; *ai:* SWEA, OEA & NEA 1975-; *office:* Westland HS 146 Galloway Rd Galloway OH 43119*

SCHEIVERT, REBECCA E. (MALONEY), 9th-10th Grade English Teacher; *b:* Lancaster, PA; *m:* John E.; *c:* Jospeh, Stephanie; *ed:* Shippensburg Univ (BS) Lib Sci, Eng 1976, (MS) Eng Ed 1979; *cr:* Hanover HS 9 Grd Eng Tchr 1976-82; Spring Grove Area Schl Dist 7 Grd Eng Tchr 1983-86, 9-10 Grd Eng Tchr 1987-; *ai:* Frosh Class Avd; Tchr Mentor; Prof Dev, Strategic Planning Comms; PSEA, NEA 1976-; NCTE 1978-; PCTE 1995-; St Paul Luth Church 1977-, Sunday Schl Supt, Parish Ed Comm; *office:* Spring Grove Sr HS Hanover & Jackson St Spring Grove PA 17362

SCHEIWER, SUSAN ELLEN, HS Mathematics Teacher; *b:* Hornell, NY; *ed:* St Univ of NY at Geneseo (BA) Math 1988; Univ of NV at Las Vegas Prof Dev Cert Ed 1991; CA Univ of PA Math, Cmptr Sci; *cr:* Clark Cty Schl Dist MS Math Tchr 1991-93; Chartiers Vly Schl Dist HS Math Tchr 1993-94; Peters Twp Schl Dist HS Math Tchr 1994-; *ai:* Chrldng Coach; Grad Project Comm; Forensics Spon 1994-95; AFT 1993-; Natl Collegiate Math Awd; *office:* Peters Twp Schl Dist 264 E Mcmurray Rd Canonsburg PA 15317

SCHELL, BRIAN DUANE, Social Studies Teacher; *b:* Hazelton, PA; *m:* Sharon Remington; *c:* Erin, Allison; *ed:* Bloomsburg Univ (BS) Soc Stud 1979; Wilkes Univ (MS) 1992; Univ of VA 3 Credits Presential Classroom 1980; Shippensburg Univ 3 Credits Exec acad on Global Ed 1980; *cr:* Northern Lehigh Jr HS Tchr 1979-; *ai:* Sftbl 1979-89, Field Hockey 1985-87 Var Coach; Dept 1980-83, Boy Scout Career Prgm 1980-90 Coord; NEA 1979-; Outstanding Young Educator PA Jaycees 1985; Sftbl Team Won AA St Title 1988; *office:* Northern Lehigh Jr HS 600 Diamond St Slatington PA 18080

SCHELL, JESSIE ROSENBERG, Creative Writing Dept Chair; *b:* Greenville, MS; *m:* David; *c:* Susanna; *ed:* Univ of NC at Greensboro (BA) Eng 1963, (MFA) Creative Writing 1970; PHD Eng at Tulane Univ; *cr:* Univ of NC at Chapel Hill Eng & Writing Dept Instr 1971-76; Northeastern Univ Extension Eng & Writing Dept Instr 1987-94; Brandes Univ Eng Writing Dept Instr 1988-89; Walnut Hill Schl Eng Tchr & Creative Writing Head 1990-; *ai:* NEA Grant; Novel Pub 1968; Numerous Poems & Short Stories Pub; Summer Writing Grant 1994; E E Ford Awd 1993; *office:* Walnut Hill Schl 12 Highland St Natick MA 01760

SCHELL, RICHARD C., History Teacher; *b:* Booten, NJ; *ed:* Otterbein Coll (BA) His, Scndry Ed 1992; Ashland Coll Sport Sci; *cr:* Westerville South HS His Tchr, Ftbl, Track Coach 1992-96; *ai:* Head Frosh Ftbl, Asst Track Coachs; Globeplotter Adv; Soc Stud Curr; OEA, NEA 1992-; *office:* Westerville South HS 303 S Otterbein Ave Westerville OH 43081

SCHELL, WILLIAM ALAN, History & Sociology Teacher; *b:* Lakewood, OH; *m:* Cheryl Rose Coressel; *c:* Jessica; *ed:* Bowling Freen St Univ (BA) His 1989; 15 Hrs Grad Work; Cleveland St Univ Comprehensive Soc Stud Cert 1991; *cr:* Westlake City Schls Sub Tchr 1991-92; Fremont City Schls Tchr 1992-; *ai:* Frosh Ftbl, Boys JV Bsbl Coach; NEA 1992-; *office:* Fremont Ross HS 1100 North St Fremont OH 43420

SCHELLER, JEFF JAMES, Fourth Grade Teacher; *b:* Pittsburgh, PA; *m:* Carrie Ann Lucas; *c:* Dustin; *ed:* Point Park Coll (BA) Ed 1987; Masters Equivalency 39 Addl Hrs in Sci Ed; *cr:* Laurel Schl Dist 3rd Grd Tchr 1987-88; North Allecheny Schl Dist 4th Grd Tchr 1988-; *ai:* Bus Proctor; Sci Team; AFT 1987-; Gift of Time Awd 1989-; Teach Elem Sci Wkshps for Tchrs 1991-; Wolf Awd Nom 1992-; *home:* 324 Duff Rd Sewickley PA 15143

SCHELLHASE, KIMBERLY JEAN, 8th Grd American Cultures Tchr; *b:* Waynesboro, PA; *m:* Keith E.; *c:* Meredith J.; *ed:* Shippensburg Univ (BSEd) Comprehensive Soc Stud 1982; Post Grad 35 Credit Hrs; *cr:* Waynesboro Area Schl Dist 8th Grd Soc Stud Tchr 1983-; *ai:* NEA, PSEA, WAEA 1983-; Admin Bd, Sunday Schl Tchr Christ United Meth Church; *home:* 11431 Brookdale Dr Waynesboro PA 17268

SCHELLING, LINDA GORE, First Grade Teacher; *b:* Williamsport, PA; *m:* William; *c:* Jody Schelling Roupe, Julie; *ed:* Mansfield St Univ (BS) Elem Ed 1969; Frostburg St Univ (MA) Elem Ed 1977; *cr:* Funkstown Elem Schl 3rd Grd Tchr 1969-75, 2nd Grd Tchr 1977-1995; Paramount Elem Schl1st Grd Tchr 1995-; *ai:* Integrated Eng Lang Arts Liason; NEA, WCTA 1969-; NCTM 1995-; *office:* Paramount Elem Schl 19410 Longmeadow Rd Hagerstown MD 21742*

SCHELLINGER, THOMAS, 5th Grade Teacher; *b:* Philadelphia, PA; *m:* Sally Tracy; *c:* Tracy, Jill; *ed:* Cheyney Univ (BS) Elem Ed 1971, (MS) Elem Ed 1974; 55 Addl Credits Cmptr Tech; *cr:* Sharon Hill Schl 6th Grd Tchr 1971-93, 5th Grd Tchr 1993-; Ashland MS Asst Prin 1987-88; *ai:* Tech Steering Comm Chprsn; NEA, SDEA 1971-; Tchr of Yr Awd 1994; *office:* Sharon Hill Schl 701 Coates St Sharon Hill PA 19079*

SCHENCK, BARBARA JORDAN, Guidance Counselor; *b:* Camp Hill, PA; *c:* Clark, Scott; *ed:* Susquehanna Univ (BA) Eng, Soc Stud 1963; Shippensburg Univ (MED) Guid, Cnslng 1968; *cr:* Cumberland Vly Eng, Soc Stud Tchr 1963-68, Guid Cnslr 1976-; *ai:* Peer Helpers; Comm Bus Partnership; NEA; CVEA; PSEA; KCA, Sec; NLDA; NRTA; Civic Letort Quilters; AQS; NQA; MS Cnslr of Yr 1992; *office:* Eagle View MS 6746 Carlisle Pike Mechanicsburg PA 17055

SCHENCK, JANE LOUISE, English Teacher; *b:* York, PA; *ed:* Penn St Univ (BA) Eng 1973; Post-Grad Courses at York Campus; *cr:* York Cty Area Voc Tech Schl Eng Tchr 1974-; *ai:* NHS Adv; Steering Comms for Strategic Planning; Stu Orientation; Stu Portfolios; NEA, YCVTEA 1974-, Exec Comm; Historical Soc of York 1975-; Outstanding Tchr Shippensburg Univ 1994; Outstanding Voc Tchr Penn Coll of Tech 1995; Rep Schl at Bill Signing Ceremony at White House for Schl-to-Work Legislation 1994; *office:* York Co Area Voc Tech Sch 2179 S Queen St York PA 17402*

SCHENCK, SUSAN REIBIE, Foreign Language Dept Supvr; *b:* Pittsburgh, PA; *m:* Clark B. Jr.; *c:* Clark III, Scott, Kurt, Julianne; *ed:* Wilson Coll (AB) Classics 1972; Univ of Cincinnati (MA) Classics 1975; Shippensburg Univ Supervisory Cert in Foreign Langs; Cert in Ger Wilson Coll; *cr:* Cumberland Valley Schls Supvr for Lang 1973-80; Hamburg Area HS Supvr for Lang 1980-; *ai:* Adv Ger, Latin Club, Adv Ger NHS; Fac Adv Comm NHS; AATG 1978-; PCA 1972-; PSEA, NEA 1973-; Church Cncl 1993-; Own Daycare Ctr 1989-, Dir; Phi Beta Kappa; Tchr of Yr 1980; *office:* Hamburg Area HS Windsor St Hamburg PA 19526

SCHENK, EDWARD A., Fourth Grade Teacher; *b:* Canton, OH; *m:* Lilanne Bousquet; *ed:* Plattsburgh St (BS) Ed 1970; Cortland St (MS) Ed 1975; McGill Univ Diploma Lit 1968; Music Theory, Composition Bert Henry; *cr:* Huntington Acad Tchr 1968-69; Roberts Elem Schl Tchr 1970-; *ai:* Boys, Girls After Schl Bsktbl; Hockey After Schl; Music, Plays, Prgms; NEA 1970-; *home:* 100 Alanson Rd Syracuse NY 13207

SCHENKELBERG, SUSAN ROGERS, High School English Teacher; *b:* Albuquerque, NM; *m:* Charles J.; *c:* Katherine, Elizabeth, Ellen; *ed:* John Carroll Univ (MAT) Eng & Urban Stud 1969; 6 Post Grad Credit Hrs in Ed 1995; *cr:* Cleveland Pub Schls 7th-8th Grd Tchr 1969-72; Area Schls Sub Tchr 1982-90; St Ignatius HS 9th-12th Grd Eng Tchr 1991-; *ai:* CLC Moderator; Stu Prayer Group; NCTE 1991-; St Marys Alumni Club 1968-; Jr League of Cleveland 1976-; St Dominic Parish Cncl 1990-94; *office:* St Ignatius HS 1911 W 30th St Cleveland OH 44113*

SCHENKER, SHIRLEY ANNE (BLATZHEIM), Social Studies Teacher; *b:* Portsmouth, VA; *m:* Nathan M.; *c:* Rachel, Anna; *ed:* Univ of VA (BA) Political & Social Thought 1976; West Chester Univ Ed Cert in His; Attnd Immaculata Coll, Coll of William & Mary His; *cr:* Oxford MS Soc Stud Tchr 1988-89; Avon Grove HS Soc Stud Tchr 1989-; *ai:* Discipline Review Bd; Stu-Fac Sexual Harrassment Task Force; Topics Club Do-Adv; Graduation Monitor; NEA & PSEA 1989-, Phi Alpha Theta Intl; NCSS & PCSS 1990-, Honor Soc in His 1988; Avon Grove Ed Assn 1990-, Sec 1993-; Natl & PA Cncl for Soc Stud; PA Tchr of the Yr Nom 1995; *office:* Avon Grove HS 257 E State Rd West Grove PA 19390*

SCHER, HELENA ELLINGHAUS, Assistant Principal; *b:* Baltimore, MD; *m:* Joseph A.; *c:* Samantha; *ed:* Essex Comm Coll (AA) Elem Ed 1972; Towson St Univ (BA) Elem Ed 1977; Loyola Col (MED) Educl Mngmt, Admin, Supervision 1995; MD Advanced Prof Cert 1987; Archdiocese of Baltimreo Catechist Cert; Anne Arundel Outdoor Ed Cert, Initiative, Confidence Trng 1984, 1990; *cr:* St Rose of Lima Schl Tchr 1972-80; St Mary's Schl Tchr 1982-91, Asst Prin 1991-; *ai:* Stu Cncl Moderator; Yrbk Adv; After Schl Care Coord; Admin Funication Comm Co-Chprsn; Lang Arts coord; NCEA 1982-; ESTA 1988-; Tanager Forest Civic Assn 1977-, Welcoming Comm Chprsn; MD Acad of Scis NSF Wkshps 1985; *home:* 1811 Woodrail Dr Millersville MD 21108

SCHER, MARY GUSKIN, Movement Ed & Enrichment Tchr; *b:* New York, NY; *m:* Mark D.; *c:* Seth, Scot; *ed:* Queens Coll (BS) Elem Ed 1970; Brooklyn Coll (MS) ELem Ed 1973; 30 Post Grad Credits; *cr:* PS 225 K Grd 1, 6, 5 Tchr 1970-75; PS 139 Q Grd 6 Tchr 1982-87, Grd 2 GATE Tchr, Grd 1-6 Movement Ed Tchr, Grd 2, 4, 6 GATE Tchr 1988-; *ai:* Bsktbl Team Coach; Organizer of Intnl Dance Festival; Parent Tchr Liaison Chprsn; Compact for Learning Comm; Schl Improvement Prgm; UFT 1970-; NYSHPERD 1990-; Saunders House Tenants' Assn 1980-, Pres; Exec Bd of Townsend Harris HS 1993-, Recording Sec; Exec Bd of Forest Hills HS 1990-93; Angela Zirpiades PE Awd 1992; New York City Pub Ed Grant 1991; Article Pub; Amer Heart Assn NY Affiliate Plaque 1990; Outstdng Tchr Adv Bicentennial US Constitution Essa Contest 1987; Impact II Adaptor Grant 1986; *office:* Pub Schl 139Q 93-06 63rd Dr Rego Park NY 11374

SCHERER, SUZANNE KRONENBERGER, Senior High Schl Math Tchr; *b:* Columbus, OH; *m:* Philip Murray; *c:* Jennifer Ouweleen, Elizabeth Montazzoli, Joseph, Sarah Julian, Anna; *ed:* OH Dominican Coll (BA) Math, Eng 1963; LA St Univ (MED) Scndry Ed 1976; 9 Hrs Educl Ldrshp Doctoral Prgm Western MI Univ at Kalamazoo 1979-80; *cr:* St Francis De Sales HS Algebra, Geometry Tchr 1963-64; Jesuit HS Algebra, Eng Tchr 1975-77; Niagara Univ Bus Math Tchr 1981-83; Mt St Mary's Acad Sr HS Math Tchr 1983-85; Buffalo Acad of Sacred Heart Sr HS Math Tchr 1985-86; Diocesan Scndry Schl Math Coord 1985-86; Wilso Schl Dist Jr, Sr HS Math Tchr 1986-; *ai:* Niagara Frontier Math Adv; Wilson Staff Dev Stud Group; AFT 1986-; AMTNYS 1988 Rsrch Grant Stud Geometry, Islamic Art; *home:* 99 Lake St Wils 14172*

SCHERER, VIRGINIA LEE, Science Teacher & Dept Ch Cincinnati, OH; *ed:* Coll of Mt St Joseph (BA) Chem 1962; Univ o Dame (MS) Chem 1971; Attnd OH St Univ, Miami Univ of OH, Univ, Univ of Dayton, CO Schl of Mines; *cr:* St Louis HS Tchr 1 Alter HS Tchr 1966-68; Lehman HS Tchr 1968-77, 1987-; Marion C Tchr, Prin 1977-87; *ai:* Sci Olympiad, Chem Quiz Bowl, Sci Fair, Moderator; Substance Abuse Coord; Sr Class Adv; NSTA 1970-; 1977-, Bd of Dirs 3 Yrs; OH Sci Acad 1970-, Dist Rep 4 Yrs; AAPT Delta Kappa Gamma 1972-; Red Cross 1970-77, Bd of Dirs; OH Sc Outstanding Math, Sci Tchr; *office:* Lehman Cath HS 2400 St Mar Sidney OH 45365

SCHERER, WENDELL ALOYSIUS, English Teacher; *b:* Kingstc *m:* Nora Catherine Mc Carthy; *c:* Sara Catherine, Bettina Neal, W Fitzgerald; *ed:* Fordham Univ (BA) Eng 1971; SUNY at New Paltz 3 Hrs Permanant Cert; Attnd Bard Coll Writing Inst, Shakespeare Ins *cr:* Myron S. Michael Jr HS Eighth Grd Tchr 1971-76; Kingston City 7-12 Grd Tchr 1971-; Myron S. Michael Jr HS Ninth Grd Tchr 1 HS Tchr 1984-; GED Class 1986-92; *ai:* Theater Arts Dir, Tchr Coach House Players 1971-, Pres, VP, Sec, Treas, Dir, Actor, Li Directed 6 Childrens Theater Productions, 7 Dramas; *home:* 46 Lin Kingston NY 12401*

SCHERER-GOLDPAUGH, KATHRYN, 7th Grade English Teac Kingston, NY; *m:* Thomas W. Goldpaugh; *c:* Jamie Garvey, M Garvey, Matthew, John; *ed:* SUC at Oneonta (BA) Scndry Ed 1978; at New Paltz (MPS) Humanistic Ed 1982; *cr:* Kingston City Schls M Tchr 1974-79; SUNY Writing Skills Coord 1972-82, Acad Suppo EOP Prgm 1981-93; Haviland MS Eng Tchr 1989-; *ai:* Regnl Spellir Coord; AFT NYSUT 1980-; NCTE 1982-; Phi Delta Kappa 1987-; Fellow, Peer Tutoring 1982; NEH Women in Fiction 1991; *office:* Ha MS 20 Haviland Rd Hyde Park NY 12538

SCHERGER, MIRIAM YOUNG, Kindergarten Teacher; *b:* Lima, C Gregory; *c:* Stephanie, Nathan; *ed:* Bowling Green St Univ (BS) Chldhd Ed 1981; *cr:* Delphos St John Kndgtn Tchr 1981-82, Secor Tchr 1982-89; Kndgtn Tchr 1989-; *ai:* Sci Leadership Comm; 1981-; NDEA 1994-.

SCHERR, ARLENE COHN, Art Teacher & Yearbook Advis Baltimore, MD; *m:* Robert J.; *c:* Michael; *ed:* (BS) Fine Arts 1976 Cert Art K-12 1991; Attnd Loyola Coll of MD; *cr:* Advertising, Sales, Freelance Consultant 1977-87; Housecalls Magazine Publ Co-Owner 1987-89; Pikesville MS Art Tchr, Yrbk Adv 1991 Multi-Cultural Act Comm; NEA, MSTA, TABCO 1991-; Balto Muse Art 1989-; Smithsonian Inst 1991-; Jane Austen Soc 1995-; Pikesville MS 7701 7 Mile Ln Baltimore MD 21208*

SCHESSL, KEITH RICHARD, Instrumental Music Teacher; *b:* Bu NY; *m:* Lori D. Giaquinto; *c:* Eric, Brandon, Kayle; *ed:* SUNY at B (BFA) Music Ed 1978, (MFA) Music Ed 1980; *cr:* Kendal Cntrl Jr Music Instr 1980-82; Wilson Cntrl Mid & Sr High Music Instr 198 Stage Crew Adv; MENC 1980-; Niagara Cty Music Edctrs Assn 198 of Bands, Sec & Pres; AFT 1982-; Amer Fed of Musicians 1988-; Sa Fire Co Band 1982-, Asst Dir; Ontario Lodge 1995-; *office:* Wilson C Schl PO Box 648 Wilson NY 14172

SCHEUFLER, DAVID EARL, Band Director; *b:* Marraro, LA; *m:* J M. Wunderlich; *c:* Jacqueline, Daniel; *ed:* OH Northern U (BED) Music Ed 1982; Cleveland St U (MA) Schl Admin 1993; Elem Prin 1993, Renewal 1996; *cr:* Aizu-Wakamatsu Eng Acad Eng Instr 19 Lake Cath HS Band, Choir Dir 1984-86; Parma City Schls Band Dir *ai:* Marching, Jazz Band; 2 Elem Orch to Disney World Perform Competition Lead Dept; NEA, PEA 1986-; ASCDA 1993-; Bay V Meth Church 1993, Staff Relations Chm; Civic Orch 1982-84, Trombone; *office:* Normandy HS 2500 W Pleasant Valley Rd Parm 44134*

SCHIAN, KAREN SUE (PRICE), Home Economics Teacher; *b:* Hornell, NY; *m:* Robert Dale Jr.; *c:* Richard Fremont, Robert John, Mi Edward; *ed:* Adrian Coll (BS) Home Ec, Sec Educ 1984; SUNY C Buffalo (MSEd) Home Ec Ed 1989; Attnd MI St Univ, Long Island *cr:* Spartan Village Day Care Ctr Asst Tchr 1984-85; Barker Central Home Ec Tchr 1985-; *ai:* Schl Coord White Ribbon Month, Teen Pregn Awareness; FHA Adv 1985-; Hlth Advy Bd 1987-91; Teen Issue, Hlth Co-Chair 1990; Home Ec, Supts Day Cty Chair 1989; Var Chrldng C 1985-88; PTA Mem; Pre-K Parent Advy Bd 1991-92; Hnrs & Awds, Sc Cty AIDS Awareness, MS Planning, Block Scheduling Plannign Comm; HETA, NY St Home Ec Tchrs 1985-; Amer Home Ec Assn, K Omicron Phi, Kappa Delta Pi 1982-; *office:* Barker Central Schl Quaker Rd Barker NY 14012

SCHIANO, ELEANOR COONEY, Adjunct Prof Finance & Math; *b:* York City, NY; *m:* Ralph; *c:* Kristen; *ed:* William Paterson Coll (BA 1982; Fairleigh Dickinson Univ (MBA) Fin 1986; *cr:* Wayne Savings Group Fin Planner, Registered Securities Rep 1990-92; Life & Insurance Agent; William Paterson Coll Adj Prof, Master Tutor 1992- WPC, Alumni Bd; Wayne Bd of Ed, Long Range Planning Comm; *of* William Paterson Coll 300 Pompton Rd Wayne NJ 07470

SCHIAPPA, SUSAN (ZALEWSKI), Mathematics Teacher; *b:* Min NY; *m:* Vincent P.; *ed:* Dowling Coll (BA) Math 1987; C W Post Coll (Educl Tech 1991; 45 Addl Credit Hrs in Various Disciplines, Cooper Learning Pub Speaking; *cr:* Oakdale Bohemia Jr HS Math Tchr 198 Ronkonkoma Jr HS Math Tchr 1991-92; Connetquot HS Math Tchr 1 *ai:* Sr Class Adv; NCTM 1987-; Curr Dev Comm; *office:* Connetquo 7th St Bohemia NY 11716

SCHIAVO, MICHAEL SCOTT, History & Religion Teacher; *b:* So Point, NJ; *ed:* Colgate Univ (BA) His 1987; Villanova Univ MA in 1994; *cr:* Holy Spirit HS His, Religion 1992-; *ai:* Spirit Swimming H Coach; Renaissance Soc Moderator; St Bernadettes Church, Youth G Vol; Rotary Intnl Group Stud Exchange Team Mem to India 1990; C Atlantic League Natl Conf Swimming Coach of Yr 1994; *office:* H Spirit HS New Rd Absecon NJ 08201

SCHIAVO, WILLIAM ALAN, 12th Grade English Teacher; *b:* Brook NY; *m:* Veronica Bruno; *c:* Vincent Costa, Victoria Ocon; *ed:* St Jc Univ (BA) Eng 1967; C W Post Coll (MA) Eng 1971; 60 Credit Hrs C & In-Service Credits; *cr:* Cntrl Islip Pub Schls Eng Tchr 1967-; *ai:* N Adv; Prins Schlsp & Prins Awds Comm; Cntrl Islip Tchrs Assn 19 Schlsp Comm; AFT; Cornell Univ Cert of Recognition 1988; NY St Cncl Tchr of Excl Awd 1985; Commendation Letter From Sacred H Univ 1995; *office:* Cntrl Islip Pub Schls Wheeler Rd Central Islip 11792*

SCHIAVONE, COLLEEN KELLS, Physical Science Teacher; Allentown, PA; *m:* Mark; *c:* Mark Jr., Dominic, Stani; *ed:* Gettysburg C (BA) Bio 1972; Recertified General Sci; East Stroudsburg Univ Post G *cr:* Parkland HS Bio Tchr 1973-78; Bangor Jr High Phys Sci Tchr 19 *ai:* Sci Olympaid Coach; Operation Grad; NFIOA 1993-; *office:* Bango HS 5 Points & Richmond Rd Bangor PA 18013

:KLER, PATRICIA PALLOTTO, English Teacher; *b:* Waterbury, Mark A.; *c:* Matthew, Jason, Brianne; *ed:* Marietta Coll (BA) Eng, 9; Fordham Univ (MA) Amer Lit 1970; Attnd Sacred Heart Univ; rboro Jr HS 8th Grd Lang Arts Tchr 1970-74; St Catherine of Siena id Grds Eng Tchr 1987-; *ai:* Drama Club Coach; Schl Paper, Stu loderator; NEA, CTE 1987-; Amer Red Cross 1977-, Instr, Outstdng rls Scouts Amer 1985-, Ldr, Trainer Svc Unit Mgr, Outstdng Ldr; 72 Intervale Rd Bridgeport CT 06610*

:BEL, WAYNE R., English & Latin Teacher; *b:* Butler, PA; *m:* Mary Hilderdrand; *c:* Craig, Dana; *ed:* Duquesne Univ (BA) Eng 1969; *cr:* d Sacrament Elem Schl Tchr 1969-74; Prudential Insurance an 1974-77; St Joseph HS Eng, Latin Tchr 1977-; *office:* St Joseph) Montana Ave Natrona Heights PA 15065

:FER, GARY LEE, Assoc Prof of Bus; *b:* Bucyrus, OH; *m:* Jo Anne *ed:* Bowling Green St Univ (BS) Bus Admin 1981, (MA) Amer Stud (MBA) Mgmt 1989; *cr:* Oh St Univ Lecturer in Ec 1984-85; Oh rn Univ Instr of Ec & Fins 1985-88; Clarion Univ Instr of Admin Sci 0; Bluffton Coll Assoc Prof of Bus 1990-; *ai:* Fac Rep Bd of s; Fac Adv to Stu Investment Club; Fac Affairs Comm & Acad Adv; Fin Assoc 1990-; Oh Assoc of Ec & Pol Scientist 1994-; *office:* n Coll Bluffton OH 45817

EL, JOHN EDWARD, Mathematics Teacher; *b:* Bronx, NY; *m:* Mendelson; *c:* Melissa, Sarah, Emily; *ed:* Haverford Coll (BS) s 1974; Trenton St Coll Summer Grad Work; *cr:* The Lawrenceville 1ath Tchr 1974-, Housemaker 1980-92, Lower Schl Dir 1987-92; *ai:* tbl Head Coach; Day Stu Adv; *home:* PO Box 6207 Lawrenceville 548

ERING, JERALD, Bus Teacher & Activities Coord; *b:* Cincinnati, *l:* Miami Univ (BS) Ed 1970, (MED) Admin 1979; *cr:* Northwest HS & Coach 1972-80; Northwest Schls Asst Prin 1980-92; Colerain HS chr & Act Coord 1992-; *ai:* Act Coord; Stu Cncl Spon; OH Assn Stu 989-, Exec Bd; Natl Assn Stu Act Advs 1989-; NEA; Employees Fed Union 1993-, Bd of Dirs, Pres; Tchr of Yr Colerain HS 1996; *office:* ain HS 8801 Cheviot Rd Cincinnati OH 45251

FF, DEBRA GARDNER, Unified Mathematics Teacher; *b:* ville, NJ; *m:* Jorden D.; *c:* Tyler James; *ed:* Rutgers Univ (BA) Math Trenton St Coll (MED) Math 1994; *cr:* Hillside MS Unified Math, Tchr 1989-95; *ai:* Grds 6-7 NJ Math League Coach; Grds 7-8 Math s Coach; Grds 6-8 Knowledge Master Open Coach; NEA 1989-; 4-H Club Ldr; Paul Douglas Tchr Schlsp 1985-89; *office:* Bridgewater n MS PO Box 6933 Meriwood Dr White House Sta NJ 08807

FF, MARGO LYNN, Spanish & French Teacher; *b:* Bridgeport, CT; ark; *c:* Evan, Vanessa; *ed:* Simmons Coll (BA) Span 1970, (MAT) Ed 1972; Fairfield Univ Biling Multicultural Ed 7th Yr; *cr:* Medford an Tchr 1970-72; Weston HS Span Tchr 1972-74; Andrew Warde HS & Fr 1977-81; Fairfield Woods MS Span & Fr 1981-; *ai:* Stdnts ee Pgm Adv; COLT 1972-; NEA 1990-; FEA 1990-; Fairfield Univ al Grant for Biling Multicultural Ed Degree; Certfd St Mentor Tchr; Pgm St Assessor; *office:* Fairfield Woods MS 1115 Fairfield Woods irfield CT 06430

FF, MURRAY, K-8th Grd Health & PE Teacher; *b:* Philadephia, PA; irley; *c:* Matthew, Chayna; *ed:* Penn St Univ (BS) Hlth & PE 1977; dl Grad Credits Masters Equivalency; *cr:* Tinicum Schl K-8 Hlth & chr 1977-; *ai:* Intramural Dir; Bsbl Coach; Hlth & PE Area Coord; l Asst Jump Rope for Heart Amer Heart Assn; Jump Rope For Heart l, Amer Heart Assoc 1996; Interboro Ed Assn, Penn St Ed Assn & 1977-; PA Interscholastic Ath Assn 1980-, Ofcl Bsbl & Bsktbl; Grant er Impact Partners for Ed 1990; *office:* Tinicum Schl 1st & Seneca St gton PA 19029

FFMAN, AUDREY, Retired Teacher; *b:* New York, NY; *m:* Barnett Steven; *ed:* Queens Coll (BA) Ed 1959; *cr:* Seaford Manor Schl n Tchr 1960-62; Howell Rd Schl Kndgtn, 2nd Grd Tchr 1970-74; ler Ave Schl 2nd-3rd Grd Tchr 1974-95; *ai:* NYSUT 1960-; VS Tchrs 1970-; Rockville Ctr Guild for Arts 1996; *home:* 61 Kennedy Ave ville Centre NY 11570

FINI, PATRICIA MARIE,OSU, Religion Teacher; *b:* New York, *ed:* Coll of New Rochelle (BA) His 1982; Fordham Univ (MS) Rel 1985; Coll of New Rochelle (MS) Guid, Cnslng 1994; *cr:* Our Lady gels Tchr 1982-85; Acad of Mt St Ursula Tchr 1986-95; Ursuline Schl 1995-; *ai:* Peer Ministry; SOUP Kitchen Coord; NCEA 1986-; ES 1995-; *office:* Ursuline Schl 1354 North Ave New Rochelle NY 4

ILDKAMP, R. JOSEPH, HS Visual Arts Teacher; *b:* Greensburg, PA; atricia L. Lovell; *c:* Corey, Katie; *ed:* Indiana Univ of PA (BS) Fine Ed 1975, (MA) Drawing 1984; Art Inst of Pittsburg Diploma Layout, action Art 1990; *cr:* Hempfield Area Schl Dist Art, Visual Arts Edctr rs; *ai:* PSEA, NAEA 1978-; Greensburg Art Club 1976-, Treas; *office:* pfield Area Schl Dist RD 6 Box 77 Greensburg PA 15601

ILL, L. JANE J., Art Educator; *b:* Syracuse, NY; *c:* David J. I. tier; *ed:* St Univ of NY at New Paltz (BS) Art Ed 1960; Attnd Tokyo , Coll of St Rose, Rochester Inst of Tech, Syracuse Univ, St Univ of at Oswego, Idyllwild Schl of Music & the Arts; *cr:* Schenectady City Dist Elem Art Tchr 1960-62; USAF Dependent Schls 1-8th Grd Art 1962-64; Schenectady City Schl Dist 7-9th Grd Art Tchr 1964-68; Van verp MS 6-8 Grd Art Tchr 1968-70; Mont Pleasant HS, Schenectady Art Tchr 1975-; *ai:* Art Curr Comm 1982-94; NYS Tchrs Retirement, Art Tchrs Assn 1964-; Schenectady Fed of Tchrs 1975-; Southwestern for Indian Art, Iroquois Indian Museum 1987-; Schenectady Rose Soc -, Past Recording Sec; Human Concerns Comm St John the Evangelist ch 1988-; City Rescue Mission of Schenectady Vol 1980-, Vol Coord oliday Meals 1995-; *office:* Schenectady HS The Plaza Schenectady 12308

ILLACI, PATRICIA ANN, Mathematics & Spanish Teacher; *b:* ton, PA; *ed:* Wilkes Coll (BA) Math, Sci 1976; Univ of Scranton (MS) , Ed 1979; Supervisory Math Cert; Sec Schl Prin Cert; *cr:* Wyoming Schls Perm Sub 1976-79; Pittston Area Schls Math, Sp Tchr 1979-; Key Club, Sr Class Adv; AFT 1979-; NCTM 1976-; ASCD 1993-; M 1995-; NpCTM 1995-; *office:* Pittston Area SR HS 5 Stout St ston PA 18640

ILLING, EVA GRZELLA, English, ESL & German Teacher; *b:* taw, Poland; *m:* Ronald J.; *c:* Karl, Marla; *ed:* Cntrl CT St Coll (BS) TESOL 1978; Univ of MA (MA) Ger Lang, Lit 1981; Goethe Inst many Lang Spec Stud; Univ of Hartford Russian 9 Hrs, Work Related g Construction Courses; *cr:* Idioma Sprachschule Eng Tchr 1980; thington HS Ger Tchr 1981, 1983; Learning Skills Instr 1982; J. F. nedy Jr HS GT, Eng Tchr 1984-94; Southington HS Ger, Eng, ESL Tchr 4-; *ai:* GATE Mentor; CEA, SEA, PTO 1983-; NCTE 1984-; NCTG 4-; Mark R. Shedd Excl in Educating People About Law Awd 1994; r of Yr 1994-95; *office:* Southington HS 720 Pleasant St Southington 06489

HILTZ, MARY BETH, Fourth Grade Teacher; *b:* Syracuce, NY; *ed:* ondaga Comm Coll (AS) Applied Sci 1975; Brockport St Coll (BS) N-9 Stud Ed 1977; Syracuse Univ (MS) Urban Ed 1979; Grd Mgr; kway; Cmptr & Change in Classrroom; Coaching Cert; Bus Math & h; *cr:* Syracuse City Schl Dist Sixth Grd Tchr 17 Yrs; West Genesee Schl Dist Fourth Grd Tchr 1 Yr; *ai:* Stu Tchr Supv; Hnr, Ski Club Adv; Enrichment Instr; Site Base Planning Team; Tchng Ctr Directing Cncl; Lang Art Curr, Rdng Textbook Adoption, Preservice Instrl Comms; Schl Improvement Team; Syracuse Tchr Assn 1980-, Rep; West Genesee Tchr Assn 1995-; NY St Tchrs Assn 1980-; Natl DARE Ofcr 1990-; Critical Thinking, Cmptr, Cmptr Prgm Interactive Software Grants; *home:* 1537 Comstock Ave Syracuse NY 13210*

SCHIMPF, JERRY ALAN, Machine Shop Instructor; *b:* McKeesport, PA; *ed:* IN Univ of PA 60 Cr Tchr Cert Pgm; Tool & Die Maker 8000 Hr Apprenticeship; *cr:* Somerset Cty Area Voc Tech Machine Shop Instr; *ai:* NTMA Machine Apprenticeship Adult Evening Class Tchr 1990-; NEA 1994-; Trent Bakersville Lavansville Rod & Gun 1981-, Sec; NRA 1975-; *office:* Somerset Co Area Voc-Tech Sch RR 5 Somerset PA 15501

SCHIMPF, SHIRLEY J., Algebra Teacher; *b:* Abington, PA; *m:* Larry C.; *ed:* East Stroudsburg St (BS) Math & Scndry Ed 1969; Penn St Univ (Masters Equiv) Ed 1990; *cr:* Unami Jr HS 7th-9th Grd Math Tchr 1969-91; Tamanend MS 8th & 9th Grd Math Tchr 1991-; *ai:* Hockey, Bsktbl & Sftbl Coach; Stu Cncl 1982-; PA St Math Assessment Comm 1994-; NCTM; Church Choir 1981-; Church Cncl 1988-93, VP; Nom for Presidential Awd for Tchng Excl; *office:* Tamanend MS 1492 Stuckert Rd Warrington PA 18976*

SCHIOPPA, RALPH ANTHONY, High School Coach; *b:* Queens, NY; *m:* Catherine; *c:* Ryan, Anthony, Candice; *ed:* Attnd C. W. Post, Kansas Univ, Ottawa Univ PE, Hlth; *cr:* John H. Glenn HS Coach 1990-; *ai:* Soccer, Lacrosse, Bsktbl, Ftbl, Sftbl Coach; Coach of Yr Awds Soccer 1993-94, 1995-, Bsktbl 1990-91, 1993-94; *office:* Elwood-John Glenn HS 100 Kenneth Ave Elwood NY 11740

SCHIRTZ, JODI FRANCES, Owner & Instructor; *b:* Rochester, NY; *m:* Charles William; *c:* Alli Marie, Zachary, Blake; *ed:* Brockport St Univ Dance; Dance Tchrs Trng Prgm in Russian Tecnique; *cr:* NY Acad of Dance Owner, Tchr 1980-; *ai:* Dance Rochester Inc Mbrshp Comm; Dance Edctrs of Amer 1981-; Local Chptr PTA 1993-; Actively Organizes & Participates in Charitable Dance Events; Fundraisers; *office:* New York Acad Of Dance Schl 3800 Dewey Ave Rochester NY 14616

SCHLAACK, MARGARET LANDRY, 6th Grade Teacher; *b:* Detroit, MI; *m:* John G.; *c:* Tanya Lee, Erika Lynn; *ed:* Central MI Univ (BS) Soc Sci 1960; Univ of ME, Univ of NH 90 Grad Hrs 1975-; *cr:* Camp for Girls Field Dir 1960-63; Adak Schl 5-8 Grd Tchr 1963-65; Williams-Cons Schl 5th Grd Tchr 1976-88, 6th Grd Tchr 1989-; *ai:* Math, Soc Stud Curr Comms; NEA 1975-; NCTM 1991-; NERA 1992-; Elem Tchrs of MA St Awd; Presidential Awd Excl in Sci, Math Tchng 1993-94; *office:* Williams-Cone Elem Sch 19 Perkins St Topsham ME 04086*

SCHLACHTER, PAUL A., History Teacher; *b:* Pittsburgh, PA; *ed:* MI St Univ (BS) Soc Sci 1971, (MA) Soc, Philosophic Fnd Ed 1973; 18 Hrs Guid, CnslngDuquesne Univ; *cr:* Upper St Clair HS Soc Stud Tchr 1973-; *ai:* AFT 1981-; Outstdng Tchr Awd; *office:* Upper Saint Clair HS 1825 McLaughlin Run Rd Upper Saint Clair PA 15241

SCHLAGEL, JOSEPHINE REGAR, French Instructor; *b:* PA; *m:* Richard H.; *ed:* George Washington Univ (BA) Fr, Eng 1962, (MA) Fr 1970; Ecole Normale, Conservatoire de Paris Music Stud; *cr:* St Johns Coll HS Fr Instr 16 Yrs; *ai:* Fr Natl Honor Soc, Fr Club Moderator; Bd of Discipline; AATF, NCEA, Alliance Francaise 1980-; *office:* St John's College HS 2607 Military Rd NW Washington DC 20015*

SCHLAGETER, ROBERT LEO, Retired Math Tchr & Dept Chair; *b:* Rochester, NY; *m:* Karen Ann Leydecker; *c:* Ronald, Robert, Lidan Heselton, Sharon; *ed:* Ithaca Coll (BA) Math 1959; 20 Hrs Univ of Buffalo; 9 Hrs Canisius Coll; 12 Hrs Buffalo St Coll; 10 Hrs Univ of MT; 6 Hrs Syracuse Univ; 10 Hrs IA St Univ; *cr:* Springville-Griffith Inst Math Tchr 1959-95, Coach 1970-95, Dept Chair 1970-95; *ai:* Ftbl; Bsktbl; GIFA, NEA 1959-; AFT 1967-; Jaycees 1968-; Springville Ath Schlsp Comm 1975-, Treas; NY St Ed Dept Meritorious Achvmts for Cmptr Manuals; Tchr of Yr 1989, 1995; Pop Warner Hall of Fame 1995.

SCHLAIKJER, MARY O'LEARY, Social Studies Teacher; *b:* Brooklyn, NY; *m:* Dana C.; *c:* Christina; *ed:* Queens Coll (BA) His, Ed 1960, (MA) Ed 1963; OH Univ (MA) His 1966; Natl His His Hnr Soc; *cr:* West Islip Pub Schls Soc Stud Tchr 1960-; *ai:* Co-Adv Class of 1996; Extra Curr Treas; AFT, NYSTA, WITA 1960-; NDEA Grant 1965 GA Southern Univ; *office:* West Islip Sr HS 1 Lions Path West Islip NY 11795*

SCHLATTER, KAREN KAY, HS Guidance Counselor; *b:* Paulding, OH; *ed:* The Defiance Coll (BS) Elem ed 1979; Bowling Green SU (MED) Spec Ed 1983, (MED) GUidance 1987; *cr:* Paulding Exempted Village Schls Elem Tchr 1979-83, MS Math & Rdng Tchr 1983-89, HS Spec ed tchr 1989-91, HS Cnslr 1991-; *ai:* HS Yrbk & Scholastic Bowl Adv; NEA, OEA, PEA 1979-, Bldg Rep; Crippled Children's Soc 1980-, Treas 9 1\2 Yrs; *office:* Paulding Exempted Village Schl 405 N Water St Paulding OH 45879

SCHLEFSTEIN, MURIEL S., Science Teacher; *b:* Brooklyn, NY; *m:* Maurice; *c:* Michael, Linda, Corcoran, Dale Miller, Suzanne Patterson; *ed:* Long Island Univ (BS) Ed 1961; Richmond Coll (MS) Elem Ed 1970, (MS) Spec Ed 1974; *cr:* PS 23R Tchr 1965-70; IS 57 Tchr 1970-87; PS 36 Tchr 1987-; *ai:* Sci Fair Coord; Schl Fund Raiser; Trip Coord; Phi Delta Kappa 1995-; NYSTA 1990-; Liberty Sci 1995-; Amer Assoc of Univ Women 1995-, Bd; NY Dept of Parks Vol 1992-94; Girl Scouts of Amer, Ldr, Cookie Mgr 25 Yrs; Bd of Ed City of New York Imprest Grant Staten Island Assn Arts & Scis; *office:* PS 36R 255 Ionia Ave Staten Island NY 10312*

SCHLEGEL, AURORA RINI, French Teacher; *b:* Long Branch, NJ; *m:* Thomas Albert; *c:* Nicole Jeanne, Thomas Anthony, Lance; *ed:* Elizabethtown Coll (BS) Fr 1968; Seton Hall Univ (MA) Fr Lit 1973; TESA, AP Lit, AP Grammar; *cr:* Ocean Twp HS Fr Tchr 1969-78, Frgn Lang, World Lang, Art Dept 1979-88, Fr Tchr 1989-; *ai:* Var Chrldng Coach 8 Yrs; Var Girls Track Coach 4 Yrs; Fr Club Adv 20 Yrs; NHS Comm 12 Yrs; Instrl Cncl 4 Yrs; Liason Comm 4 Yrs; Cafeteria Comm Liaison 1 Yr; NEA 1968-; FLENJ 1990-, Cntrl Jersey Frgn Lang Acad Alliance 1993-; PTA 1994-, Corresponding Sec; *office:* Ocean Township HS 550 W Park Ave Oakhurst NJ 07755

SCHLEGEL, DIANE KAY, Spanish Teacher; *b:* Fremont, OH; *ed:* Bowling Green St Univ (BS) His 1975, (MEd) Admin, Supervision 1982; Post Grad Stud 1985-94; *cr:* Centerburg Local Schls Tchr 1975-77; Elyria Schls Tchr 1977-; *ai:* NEA 1975-; OFLA 1981-; Delta Kappa Gamma 1994-; Martha Holden Jennings Scholar; *office:* Elyria West HS 42101 Griswold Rd Elyria OH 44035

SCHLEGEL, ROBERT EDWARD, Mathematics Teacher; *b:* Rochester, NY; *m:* Joan Ballou; *c:* Jennifer; *ed:* Norwich Univ (BS) Math 1966; Post Grad Stud: SUC at Brockport-Philosophy & Math & Univ of Rochester-Math; *cr:* Greece Schl Dist Math Tchr 1968-69; SUC at Brockport Grad Asst Philosophy 1969-71; NY Life Insurance Co Agent 1971-73; Rochester City Schl Dist Math Tchr 1973-; *ai:* Girls Var Swim Team Coach; NISCA 1973-; SCANYS 1983-; ASCA 1991-; Prism Tchr of the Yr 1993-94.

SCHLEICH, JEFFREY DENNIS, Soc Stud Tchr & Asst Coach; *b:* Columbus, OH; *m:* Nancy A.; *c:* Sarah, J.D.; *ed:* Kenyon Coll (BA) Psych 1987; Eastern MI Univ (MS) Pe 1989; Tchr Cert College of Wooster; 8 Plus Hrs Ashland Univ Admin Cert; *cr:* Eastern MI Univ Ftbl Grad Asst, PE Tchg Asst 1987-89; Coll of Wooster Asst Ftbl Coach, Recruiting Coord, Strength & Conditioning Room Coord, PE Instr 1989-; Cloverleaf Schls Soc Stud Tchr, Ftbl Coach 1992-; *ai:* Emerald Key Adv; Asst HS Ftbl Coach; Schl Levy Steering, Cloverleaf Expansion, Attendance Hearings Comms; Selected Attnd Future Ldrs Forum; NEA, OEA, CEA 1992-; PTA 1992-; Church Admin Cncl, Amer Alliance Rights & Responsibilities 1994-; Tchr of Yr 1993-94; *office:* CloverLeaf Jr HS 8525 Friendsville Rd Lodi OH 44254*

SCHLEIFER, GERRIE SCHLEIFER, Physical Education Teacher; *b:* Buffalo, NY; *m:* Gerald Schneggenburger; *c:* Jill Schleifer Schneggenburger, Lindsay Schleifer Schneggenburger; *ed:* SUNYAB (BED) PE 1969, (MED) Spcl Ed & PE 1981; *cr:* West Seneca Schls Phys Edctr 1969-; *ai:* Art & Juggling Clubs; Reality Therapy Cnslng; Tchr-in-Charge in Absence of Prin; AFT 1969-; West Seneca Tchrs Assn 1969-; Habitat for Humanity 1991-; *office:* Winchester Elem Schl 650 Harlem Rd West Seneca NY 14224

SCHLEIFER, MARGENETT ROTH, Fourth Grade Teacher; *b:* Bethlehem, PA; *m:* Herman William Jr.; *ed:* Kutztown Univ (BS) Elem Ed 1971; Lehigh Univ (MED Elem Ed 1976; *cr:* Bushkill Elem Schl Third Grd Tchr 1971-73; Stockertown Elem Schl Fifth Grd Tchr 1973-76; Lower Nazareth Elem Schl Third-Fourth Grd Tchr 1976-93; Floyd R. Shafer Elem Schl Fourth Grd Tchr 1993-; *ai:* Dist Curr Ldr; 24 Challenge Adv; Koalaty Kid Team Mem; Drive for Ed Coord; Math Comm Co-Chair; New Tchr Mentor; NEA 1971-; *office:* Floyd R. Shafer Elem Schl 49 S Liberty St Nazareth PA 18064

SCHLEIN, JACK M., Professor of Biology; *b:* Brooklyn, NY; *m:* Gail Schweber; *c:* Kim, Barrie, Sylvie; *ed:* Brooklyn Coll (BS) Bio 1966; Lehigh Univ (MS) Bio 1969, (PHD) Bio 1971; *cr:* Penn St Extension at Allentown Adj Instr of Bio 1968-71; York Coll of CUNY Asst Prof Bio 1971-79, Assoc Prof Bio 1979-92, Prof Bio 1992-; *ai:* Pre-Med, Pre-Dental Advs; Amer Assoc for Advancement of Sci 1971-; Sci Tchr Enhancement Prgm in Phys Sci Grant Project Dir NY St Dept of Ed; Summer Sci Camp Project Dir NSF; MASTAP Project Dir NASA; *office:* City Univ Of NY York Coll 94-20 Guy Brewer Blvd Jamaica NY 11451*

SCHLEINING, MARJORIE A., French Teacher; *b:* Endicott, NY; *c:* Justin Smith; *ed:* St Univ of NY at Albany & Univ De Nice (BA) Fr 1976; SUCO (MS) Remedial Rdng 1984; Attnd Coll of Saint Rose & Saint Johnsbury AP Acad; *cr:* South Kortright Cntrl Schl Fr Tchr 1976-79; Cooperstown Cntrl Schl Fr Tchr 1979-; *ai:* 9th Grd Class Adv; Compact Team Task Force for Elem Foreign Lang Ed Mem; Spec Fac Comm Mem; NEA 1976-, Sec; NYSAFLT 1995-; *office:* Cooperstown Central Schl Linden Ave Cooperstown NY 13326

SCHLEITH, HELMUT JOHN, Science Teacher; *b:* Brooklyn, NY; *m:* Denise Anne Oliver; *ed:* Hofstra Univ (BA) Chem 1990; Adelphi Univ (MS) Inorganic Chem 1993; *cr:* Baldwin Sr HS Sci Tchr 1992-; *ai:* Sci Honor Soc Adv; *office:* Baldwin HS 841 High School Dr Baldwin NY 11510

SCHLENGER, GAIL SUSAN, Resource Room Teacher; *b:* New York, NY; *m:* Ernest; *c:* Alison, Lauren; *ed:* Boston Univ (BA) Psych 1972; Coll of New Rochelle (MS) Spec Ed 1975; Fordham Univ (PHD) Educl Psych 1994; *cr:* Ledgewood Residential Treatment Ctr Child Care Cnslr 1972-73; NY City Bd of Ed Spec Ed Tchr 1973-74; Lakeland HS Spec Ed Tchr 1974-78; Horace Greeley HS Resource Rm Tchr, Learning Specialist 1978-; *ai:* Edctrs, Parents Wkshps; Private Tutor; AFT, NYSUT 1974-; *office:* Horace Greeley HS 70 Roaring Brook Rd Chappaqua NY 10514

SCHLENKER, JON ARLIN, Sociology & Anthropology Prof; *b:* Takoma Park, MD; *m:* Barbara Tognoli; *c:* Lori, Jennifer, Jessica; *ed:* Muhlenberg Coll (AB) Sociology 1968; Univ of Southern MS (MA) Sociology 1972, (MA) Anthropology 1974; Univ of Southern ME (MS) Adult Ed 1980; Post Grad Univ of HI; *cr:* Jones Cty Jr Coll Instr 1970-74; Univ of ME at Augusta Prof 1975-; *ai:* Honors Prgm Dir; Phi Theta Kappa Fac Spon; Tchng Refinement Prgm Coord; Soccer Club; Natl Collegiate Honors Coun 1987-, Comm Chair 2 Yrs; NENCHC 1988-; UMS Honors Dirs Cncl 1987-; Sr Spectrum 1994-; Chamber of Commerce 1986-; 2 Annenberg Grant; Fac Dev Grant; Outstanding Tchr Awd; 3 Books; 12 Articles; *office:* Univ of Maine Augusta 46 University Dr Augusta ME 04330

SCHLESSINGER, FRANCES SCHULMAN, Mathematics Teacher; *b:* Brooklyn, NY; *m:* Arthur J; *c:* James Ryan, Caren Rachel; *ed:* Cortland St Coll (BS) Early Scndry ED, Math 1967; Adelphi Univ (MS) Ed 1970; 81 Credit Hrs Var of Schls, Courses; *cr:* Harriman Elem Schl Elem Tchr 1967-68; Larding Meadow Elem Schl Elem Tchr 1968-72, 1974-75; Comsewogue Schls Tchr Asst 1981-83; Three Village Jr HS, HS Math Tchr 1983-84; N Babyland HS Math Tchr 1984-87; Bellport HS Math Tchr 1987-; *ai:* NYSUT 1981-; NYS Math Tchrs Assn 1994-; Bellport Tchrs Assn 1987-, Crisis Chair, Soc Chair 2nd Yr; Bellport Parent Tchr Stud Assn 1996; *office:* Bellport HS Beaver Dam Rd Brookhaven NY 11719

SCHLICHER, ERICH WILLIAM, Music Teacher; *b:* Allentown, PA; *m:* Kim Lanae; *c:* Broghan E.; *ed:* Lebanon Vly Coll (BS) Music Ed 1982; *cr:* Perkiomen Vly Schl Dist Music Tchr 1983; Middletown Area Schl Dist Music Tchr 1983-; *ai:* 6th-8th Grd Chorus Dir; NEA 1983-; PSEA 1983-; MAEA 1983-; *office:* G W Feaser MS 214 Race St Middletown PA 17057

SCHLICK, JEROME FRANCIS, Govt Instructor; *b:* Cleveland, OH; *m:* Barbara Moyer; *c:* Amanda Kay, Kourtney Ann; *ed:* Bellarmine Coll (BA) Scndry Ed 1970; Bowling Green St Univ (MED) Curr & Inst 1987; *cr:* St Marys at Tiffin OH 5th-6th Grd Tchr 13 Yrs; Seneca East Elem 5th Grd Tchr 2 Yrs; Seneca East Jr HS 7th & 8th Grd Tchr 9 Yrs; Seneca East HS 12th Grd Tchr 1 Yr; *ai:* Ftbl Coach; Track Coach; Math Course of Study; OEA, NEA, SEEA 1983-, A R 1983-; OH HS Ftbl Asst Coach 1983-; Northwest OH Ftbl Asst Coach 1983-; Knights of Columbus 21 Yrs; Health Grant Seneca Cty Bd of Ed; Drug Use & Abuse; *office:* Seneca East Jr HS PO Box 462 Attica OH 44807

SCHLIE, JAMIE, Science Dept Chair & Teacher; *b:* Bay Shore, NY; *m:* Jeannine; *c:* Lynn, David; *ed:* SUNY at Oswego (BA) Zoology 1982; Oh St Univ (MS) Zoology 1985; Tchr Rsrch Flwshp Beltsville Agricultural Ctr; *cr:* Children's Hosp Rsrch Asst 1990-94; Newport Schl Sci Tchr 1985-90, Sci Dept Chair 1994-; *ai:* NSTA, Assoc Superv Curric Dev 1994-; *office:* The Newport Schl 11311 Newport Mill Rd Kensington MD 20895

SCHLIEF, MARILYN NAGANO, Senior Program Officer; *b:* Detroit, MI; *m:* Donald Richard; *ed:* WAyne St Univ (BS) Ed 1968, (MS) Ed 1972; Eastern MI Univ Tchng Certs Spec Ed 1978, Japanese 1990, Span 1977; *cr:* Garden City Pub Schls Gen Ed Tchr 1968-78, Spec Ed Tchr Consultant 1978-87; Exch Tchr 1987-88; Garden City Pub Schls Consultant, Soc Stud, Frgn Lang Tchr 1988-93; Cambridge Univ Frgn Lang Tchr 1993; Nat'l Fdn for the Improvement of Ed Sr Prgm Ofcr 1994-; *ai:* Japanese Club; NEA, SEA, LEA 1968-; Japanese Amer Citizens League 1960-, Pres, Ed Chair; MI St Dept of Ed Japan Exch Tchr 1987-88; NEA Christa Mc Auliffe Edctr 1992; *office:* Natl Fnd Improvement of Educ 1201 16th St NW 4615 N Park Ave Washington DC 20036*

SCHLIMGEN, DENISE MONN, Jrnlsm Instr & Kndgtn Tchr; *b:* Frederick, MD; *m:* James T.; *c:* Whitney M., James Adam; *ed:* Bob Jones Univ (BA) Print Jrnlsm 1986; Early Chldhd; Elem Ed; *cr:* Heritage Acad Tchr, Adv 1993-; *ai:* Newspaper, Yrbk Adv; Anniversary Comm; *office:* Heritage Acad 12215 Walnut Pt W Hagerstown MD 21740

SCHLINK, WILLIAM E., US History & Government Tchr; *b:* Newburgh, NY; *m:* Maggy Bauman; *c:* Meghan, William, David; *ed:* East Stroudsburg Univ (BS) Ed 1974; Western CT Univ (MS) Ed 1978; *cr:* Rombout Jr High Soc Stud Tchr 1974-75; Mount St Marys HS Soc Stud Tchr 1975-79; Van

Wyck Jr HS Soc Stud Tchr 1979-85; John Jay HS Soc Stud Tchr 1985-; *ai:* Head Var Ftbl Coach; WCT 1979-; AFT 1979-; *office:* John Jay HS PO Box 38 Hopewell Junction NY 12533

SCHLOSSBERG, ROBIN FLAX, First & Second Grade Teacher; *b:* Baltimore, MD; *m:* Mark S.; *c:* Jennifer A., Andrew R.; *ed:* Univ of MD (BS) Early Chldhd Ed 1970; Loyola Coll (MS 1982; 30 Addl Credits; *cr:* Mt Winans Elem Schl First, Second Grd Tchr 1970-72; Howard Cty Schl System Elem Sub Tchr 1979-82; Guilford Elem Schl Second Grd Tchr, Team Ldr 1983-95, First, Second Grd Resource Tchr 1995-; *ai:* Lang Arts, Math Curr Comms; Schl Improvement, Progress Teams; BTY 2000 Team; NEA, HCEA Tchrs Assn 1983-; Multiple Sclerosis Soc 1990-, Vol Svcs; US Against MS 1990-, MS Walkathon; Levindale Geriatric Home 1994-, Vol Svcs; Howard Cty Chamber of Commerce Outstdng Educator of Yr Awd 1990; *office:* Guilford Elem Schl 7335 Oakland Mills Rd Columbia MD 21046*

SCHLOSSER, BRUCE E., Middle School Teacher; *b:* Napoleon, OH; *m:* Sandra Lynn Dull; *c:* Collin, Tyler, Cole; *ed:* Bowling Green Univ (BS) Elem Ed 1977; *cr:* Liberty Ctr Local 6th Grd Tchr 1977-80; Holgate Local MS Tchr 1980-; *ai:* Boys Track Coach; Girls Var Bsktbl; Holgate Tchrs Assn; NEA; OEA; *office:* Holgate Schl 103 Frazier Ave Holgate OH 43527

SCHMAUS, LILLIAN MARIA, Social Studies Teacher; *b:* Newark, NJ; *m:* Anthony E.; *c:* Anthony J., Kristalynn; *ed:* Rutgers Univ (BA) Soc Stud 1975; Seton Hall Univ (MA) Ed 1977; *cr:* Our Lady of Lake Schl Soc Stud Tchr 1991; Montclair Kimberly Acad Soc Stud Tchr 1993; Immaculate Conception HS Soc Stud Tchr 1991-; Columbia HS Soc Stud Tchr 1994-; *ai:* Dir Immanculate Conception Gospel Choir; Jr Class Adv 1991-93; Core Team Mem; NEA 1994-; Natl Cncl of Soc Stu 1996-.*

SCHMEISSER, WILLIAM RICHARD, Social Studies Teacher; *b:* East Orange, NJ; *m:* Gail Purchase; *c:* Lori, Lisa, Amy; *ed:* Montclair St Univ (BA) His 1959; Addl 12 Credits Rutger Univ; *cr:* Warren Twp Schls Tchr 1959-; *ai:* Eighth Grd Adv; WTEA 1959-, Negotiations Chair; SCEA, NJEA, NEA 1959-; Governors Awd; Tchr of Yr 1990-91; Recreation Dir 1961-81; 20 Yrs Svc Awd; *office:* Warren MS 100 Old Stirling Rd Warren NJ 07059

SCHMERSAL, SUSAN A., Fifth Grade Teacher; *b:* New York City, NY; *m:* Douglas; *c:* Suzanne Distefano, Denise Zinczenko; *ed:* SUNY at New Paltz (BS) Early Chldhd 1962; Coll of New Rochelle (MS) Spec Ed 1983; Various Conferences; *cr:* Nassau Schl 2nd Grd Tchr 1962-66; Hagan Schl K-3, 5 Grd Tchr 1971-78; PSEN Math Tchr 1979-80; Evans Schl 4-5 Grds Tchr 1980-82; Hagan Schl K-2nd, 5th Grds Tchr 1982-; *ai:* AFT 1962-; *office:* Hagan Elem Schl 42 Hagan Dr Poughkeepsie NY 12603*

SCHMETZ, BETH SCHEFFLIN, Mathematics Teacher; *b:* New York City, NY; *m:* Edward; *c:* Jay Herbert, Stephanie Ellen; *ed:* City Coll of NY (BSEd) PE 1965; George Washington Univ (MSEd) Ed 1970; Univ of MD at College Park Stud Math; Montgomery Coll Germantown Campus Stud Cmptr Sci, Cmptr Applications; *cr:* St Joseph's Coll for Women Instr 1965-66; Lackey Jr Sr HS PE Tchr 1966-69; Seneca Valley HS Math Tchr 1983-; *ai:* TEAMS, Math Team Coach; Ftbl Ticket Mgr; NEA, Montgomery Cty Math Tchrs Assn 1966-, MCTA; *office:* Seneca Valley HS 12700 Middlebrook Rd Germantown MD 20874

SCHMIDLIN, GARY BRYON, Teacher & Coach; *b:* Bridgeport, CT; *m:* Sandi Kondrasko; *ed:* Southern CT St Univ (BS) His, Poli Sci 1971, (MS) Pol Sci 1972; Yale Hopkins Summer Stud 1989-; *cr:* Stratford HS Tchr, Coach 1971-; Yale-Hopkins Russian East European Staff Master Tchr 1995-; *ai:* Outdoor Track, Cross Cntry, Boys Bsktbl Head Coach; Model United Nations Adv; Mentor Tchr; BEST Prgm; CT HS Coaches Assn 1971-; Inst World Affairs 1989-; *office:* Stratford HS 45 N Parade St Stratford CT 06497*

SCHMIDLIN, SANDRA KONDRASKO, Language Arts Teacher; *b:* Bridgeport, CT; *m:* Gary; *ed:* Univ of CT (BA) Eng 1971; Southern CT St Coll (MA) Rdng; *cr:* Flood MS Schl Lang Arts Tchr 1972-; *ai:* Chrldng Coach; NEA & SEA 1972-; Celebration of Excl BEST; *office:* Flood MS 490 Chapel St Stratford CT 06497

SCHMIDT, CHARLES ARTHUR, Social Studies Teacher; *b:* Queens, NY; *ed:* Rider Coll (BA) His-Magna Cum Laude 1975; Trenton St Coll (MED) Soc Stud 1983; *cr:* North Hunterdon HS Soc Stud Tchr 1978-; *ai:* Mock Trial Team Coach 1995; Soc Stud Curr Review Comm; Pub Addr His Announcements; NJ Ed Assn 1978-; Kappa Delta Pi 1984-; Phi Alpha Theta 1973-; *office:* North Hunterdon HS 1445 State Route 31 Annandale NJ 08801

SCHMIDT, ELIZABETH MILNE, School Nurse; *b:* Cincinnati, OH; *m:* Lee H.; *c:* Gregory, Susanna Mechler, Margaret Hall, John, Eric, Lisa, Beth, Karl; *ed:* Mercy Schl of Nrsng (RN) Nrsng 1960; Thomas More (BES) Soc 1983; Miami Univ (MA) Hlth Ed 1993; Attnd Natl Louis Univ Affectiive Hlth Ed, Hlth Ed Update; Univ of Cinc Assesment of Young Children with Disabilities; *cr:* Childrens Hosp Staff Nurse 1962-64; Bethesda Hosp Surgery Staff Nurse 1964-68; Goodsam Hosp OB Delivery Room 1968-77; St James White Oak Schl Nurse 1977-86; Three Rivers Local Schl Dist Schl Nurse 1986-; *ai:* Facilitator of Teen Parenting Group; Intervention Asst Team; Bldg Led Team; Multi-Factor Evaluation Team; Natl Assn of Schl Nurs 1980-; Ohio Assn Schl Nurses 1980-, ASN Rep; Southwestors OH Schl Nurses Assn 1980-, Past Pres; Hamilton Cty Schl Nurses 1978-, Past Pres; Seruciolo Area Youth 1989-; Chm of Bd; Great Rivers Girl Scouts 1977-, Ldr, Ldrs Awd; St James Ed Commissions; Preceptor for Stu Nurses; FLorence Nightengale Awd; Poster Presentor at Wasn Convention 1994; Mem of Stragic PLanning Comm.

SCHMIDT, FRANKLIN THOMAS, Middle School Biology Teacher; *b:* Camden, NJ; *m:* Tami Oberparlieter; *ed:* Southern IL Univ (AS) Ed 1981, (BS) Biological Sci 1981; Rowan Coll (MS) Educl Admin 1995; *cr:* C. W. Lewis MS Phys Sci Tchr 1981-82; Glen Landing MS Phys, Biological Sci Tchr 1982-; Ann A. Mullen MS Asst Prin 1996; *ai:* Black Horse Pike Regnl BOE; Boys Sftbl Team Coach; Gloucester Twp Golf Schlsp Comm; Gloucester Twp Summer Schl Supvr 1994-; NEA; NJEA; ASCD; NJSBA; Glen Landing PAT Comm 1993-; Glen Landing Spirit Comm 1993-; Camden Cty Environment Com 1992-93; Blue Ribbon Panelist 1992-93; Bd of Chosen Freeholders; Greenhouse, Biosphere Project Grant 1991-92; *office:* Glen Landing MS 85 Little Gloucester Rd Blackwood NJ 08012

SCHMIDT, GLORIA PAOLINI, Second Grade Teacher; *b:* Baltimore, MD; *c:* Andrew V., Mary Maragaret Szymanski; *ed:* Coll of Notre Dame of MD (BS) Elem Ed 1979; *cr:* St Ursula Schl Second Grd Tchr 1959-; *ai:* Liturgy, Soc Stud Comm; ESTA; *office:* St Ursula Schl 8900 Harford Rd Baltimore MD 21234

SCHMIDT, GLORIA ROOK, Fourth Grade Teacher; *b:* Philadelphia, PA; *m:* Arthur F.; *c:* Christopher; *ed:* Immaculata Coll (BA) Math 1964; Temple Univ (MED) Ed 1967; Attnd Drexel Univ; *cr:* Springfield Schl Dist 4 Grd Tchr 1964-; *ai:* Springfield Ed Assn 1964-, Bldg Rep, Negotiations; PSEA, NEA 1964-; PSEA Innovative Tchng Awd; Ec Amer Awd; *office:* Harvey C. Sabold Elem Schl 468 E Thompson Ave Springfield PA 19064*

SCHMIDT, JEANNETTE COLONNA, 7th-10th Grd HS Band Director; *b:* Kittanning, PA; *m:* Martin Albert; *c:* Martin Anthony, Jana Maria, Rachel Victoria; *ed:* Seton Hill Coll at Greensburg (BM) Music Ed 1960; Duquesne Univ (MD) Music Ed 1965; *cr:* Butler Jr HS General Music Tchr & Band Orchestra Dir 1960- 70; Butler Jr HS Band Dir 1987-94; Butler Intermidate HS Band Dir 1985-; Butler HS Marching Band Dir 1994-; *ai:* Dir of Musicals for 8 Yrs; Butler Golden Tornado Fnd Mini- Grant Comm; Stu Scholarship Comm; Twirler & Color Guard Adv 9 Yrs; NEA 1960-; PSEA, Butler Ed Assoc 1960-, Soc Chm-Schl Rep; MENC; PMEA; Natl Band Assn; Natl Orchestra Assn; Percusive Arts Soc; Sigma Alpha Iota Honorary Music, Pres, VP; All-amer Judge Amer Schl Band of Amer Bd, Local Musicians Union; Butler Business & Prof Womans Club 1960-, Pres; Butler Soroptimist Club 1960-; Butler Comm Concert Assn 1960-, VP; Tuesday Music Club 1960-; Various Comm Chm; Outstanding Young Woman of Amer 1967; Guest Conductor Various HS Band Concerts; Mem Butler Cty Symphony Orchestra; Mem Butler Musicians Concert Band & IN MPTF Pops Concert Band; Flute Soloist for Various Church & Civic Groups in Comm; Church Organist; Meridian Comm Choir; Clark Music Scholarship, Slippery Rock Comm Concert Band; *office:* Butler Area Schl Dist 167 New Castle Rd Butler PA 16001*

SCHMIDT, JOAN A., Sixth Grade Teacher; *b:* Philadelphia, PA; *ed:* Holy Family Coll (BA) Elem Ed 1973; Beaver Coll (MED) K-12th Grd Rdng Specialist 1979; ITEC Micro-Cmptrs in Ed Cert; Prof Cert Dept of Rel Ed; *cr:* Saint Bartholomew Cath Schl 4th-6th Grd Tchr 1969-; *ai:* K-8th Grd Soc Stud Coord; Distinguished Cath Educator Dist Winner for the Archdiocese of Philadelphia 1988; Saint Bartholomew Tchr of Yr 1994; *office:* St Bartholomew Schl 5600 Jackson St Philadelphia PA 19124

SCHMIDT, JOY NELSON, Kindergarten Teacher; *b:* Brooklyn, NY; *m:* Richard P.; *c:* Andrew, Kristine; *ed:* Brooklyn Coll (BS) Early Chldhd Ed 1959; C W Post LIU (MS) Cnslng 1985; Attnd Elmira Coll & Adelphi Univ; *cr:* Pub Sch 92 Kndgtn Tchr 1959-60; Norwood Ave Schl 2nd Grd Tchr 1961-; Dickinson Ave Schl Kndgtn, 3rd & 6th Grd Tchr 1970-; *ai:* AFT & NEA; NYSUT; *home:* 3 Dawn Dr East Northport NY 11731*

SCHMIDT, MARIA E., Social Studies Teacher; *b:* Newark, NJ; *m:* Robert E.; *c:* Marjorie; *ed:* Montclair St Univ (BA) Tchr Ed 1972, (MA) Soc Sci, Tchr Ed 1975; Seton Hall Univ (JD) Law 1978; Eagleton Inst of Politics Tchr Assoc Rutger's Univ; Prin, Supvr Cert Credits; *cr:* Westfield HS Tchr 1972-; *ai:* Mock Trial Team Coach; Internship in Govt, Politics Supvr; Voter Registration Coord Yth in Cty Govt Day; Mentoring Prgm; NEA, NJEA 1972-; Westfield Ed Assn 1972-, Del Assembly; NJ Cncl for Soc Stud; Cnslng Ctr, Bd of Trustees; NJ St Bar Fnd, Pub Ed & Law Related Ed Comms; NJ Ctr for Law-Related Ed Advy Bd; Caucus in the Classroom Advy Bd; US Supreme Court Inst, NJ & the Constitution Flwshp; Book: Tchrs Guide to Courses in AP US Govt & Politics; *office:* Westfield HS 550 Dorian Rd Westfield NJ 07090*

SCHMIDT, MARY ELIZABETH, Mathematics Teacher; *b:* Hamilton, OH; *ed:* Currently Working on MAT Miami Univ at Oxford; *cr:* Lakota HS Math Tchr 1986-; *ai:* NCTM & OCTM 1985-; NEA 1986-; *office:* Lakota HS 5050 Tylersville Rd West Chester OH 45069*

SCHMIDT, PATRICIA ALLEN, Fifth Grade Teacher; *b:* Buffalo, NY; *m:* David Gordon; *c:* Alexander; *ed:* Rosary Hill Coll (BS) Elem Ed 1972; St Un Coll at Buffalo (MED) Elem Ed 1976; *cr:* Depew Pub Schls 5 Grd Tchr 1973-86, 5 Grd GATE Tchr 1986-91, 5 Grd Tchr 1991-; *ai:* NY St United Tchrs, Depwe Tchrs Org 1973-; Kappa Delta Pi; *office:* Depew MS 5201 Transit Rd Depew NY 14043

SCHMIDT, PAUL JOSEPH, Biology Instructor; *b:* Hoboken, NJ; *m:* Julianna Kraszewski; *ed:* Montclair St Coll (BS) Bio 1969; William Paterson Coll (MA) Admin & Supervision 1991; Working Towards Masters in Urban Ed; Currently Taking Courses in Cmptr Sci; *cr:* Passaic HS Bio Instr 1969-; *ai:* Sr Class Adv 1973-90; NJ Ed Assn & NEA 1969-; Ed Assn of Passaic 1969-, VP 1978-82; NJ Sci Tchrs 1982-; Pi Lambda Theta Natl Honor Soc 1989-; Hugh O'Brien Youth Org 1987-, Vol; Girl Scouts of America 1990-, Vol; Lincoln Park Jaycees 1988-89, Vol; Clifton Police Dept, Vol; Tchr of Yr Nom 1990; *office:* Passaic H S Paulison Ave Passaic NJ 07055*

SCHMIDT, PHILLIP HARRY, Professor of Mathematical Sci; *b:* Fort Benning, GA; *m:* Susan Melinda Maki; *c:* Kristen Marie, Karin Melinda; *ed:* Purdue (BS) Math 1967, (MS) Math 1969, (PHD) Applied Math 1972; *cr:* Purdue Univ Instr 1969-72; Univ of Akron Asst Prof 1972-77, Assoc Prof 1977-85, Prof 1985; CO St Univ Visting Assoc Prof 1982-83; *ai:* TIME Adv; Permanent Fac Correspondent; MAA 1967-; SIAM 1972-; Numerous Articles Pub; NASA Grants; *office:* Univ Of Akron Dept of Math Sci 302 Buchtel Mall Akron OH 44325*

SCHMIDT, REBECCA HAMMOND, Second Grade Teacher; *b:* Harrisburg, PA; *m:* Dennis J.; *c:* Ryan D., Tyler B.; *ed:* HACC (BA) Elem Ed 1971; Penn St Capital Campus (BAEd) Elem Ed 1973; Masters Equivalency; *cr:* Middletown Area Schl Dist Tchr 22 Yrs.

SCHMIDT, RENE ANN, Elementary Orchestra Teacher; *b:* Syracuse, NY; *m:* Robert Arthur; *c:* Alexandra Rae, Michael Francis; *ed:* Ithaca Coll (BA) Piano Performance 1983, (BA) Music Ed 1983, (MA) Music Ed 1988; *cr:* Vestal Schl Dist Elem Och Tchr 1983-85; ME Endwell Schls Elem Orch Tchr 1985-; *ai:* Prin Chair Violinist Binghamton Comm Orch; Dept Team Ldr Schl Music Fac; Private Tchr of Violin, Piano; MENC, NYSSMA, NEA 1983-; Broome Cty Music Edctrs Assn 1983-.*

SCHMIDT, RUTH L., Choral Teacher; *b:* Mc Keesport, PA; *ed:* Wheaton Coll (BME) Vocal Music 1962; Indiana Univ of PA Master Equivalancy; *cr:* Mc Keesport Jr HS Choral Tchr 1962-76; Mc Keesport Area HS Choral Tchr 1976-; *ai:* A Cappella Choir; Mixed Ensemble; MAEA, RSEA, NEA, PMEA, MENC 1962-; *office:* Mc Keesport Area HS 1960 Eden Park Blvd Mc Keesport PA 15132

SCHMIDT, VIRGINIA ALISON, Sixth Grade Teacher; *b:* Philadelphia, PA; *c:* Jason, Jeremy; *ed:* Adelphi Univ (BS) Ed, Sci 1969; Masters Equivalency; *cr:* West Jr HS 7th Grd Math Tchr 1970-71; Worrall Schl 5th-6th Grd Tchr 1971-75; East Ward Schl 6th Grd Tchr 1987; Brandywine Wallace Schl 6th Grd Tchr 1987-; *ai:* IST; Mentor New Staff; DAEA, PSEA, NEA 1987-; *office:* Brandywine Wallace Elem Schl 435 Dilworth Rd Downingtown PA 19335

SCHMIDT, WILLIAM HOWARD, Bus & Technology Dist Dept Chm; *b:* Derby, CT; *m:* Julie Gagliardi; *c:* Nicole, Catherine; *ed:* New Haven Coll (AS) Arts & Sciences 1967; Cntrl CT St U (BS) Industrial Arts 1969; Southern CT St U (MS) Safety Ed 1975; 6th Yr Intemediate Admin 1986; *cr:* Amity Regnl SD Tchr, Dept Chair 1969-; *ai:* Cmptr Tech Steering, Staff Dev, Adult Ed Tchr Comms; NEA 1969-; ITEA 1985-; CTEA 1969-; *office:* Amity RSD #5 Schl 25 Newton Rd Woodbridge CT 06525

SCHMIDT, WINIFRED VANPELL, Teacher & Volunteer Coord; *b:* Batavia, NY; *m:* John E.; *c:* Adam John, Catherine Ann; *ed:* SUNY at Geneseo (BS) Elem Ed 1966; Univ of Southern ME (MS) Educl Admin 1991; 21 Grad Hrs SUNY at Buffalo, Southern ME; *cr:* Medina Cntrl Schls 4th Grd Tchr 1966-67; Williamsville Cntrl Schls 5th Grd Tchr 1967-74; Pittsburgh Cath Schls 6th Grd Tchr 1975-76; M S A D #1 6th Grd Tchr, Vol Coord 1985-; *ai:* GATE, Goals 2000 Comms; Hockey, Ath Boosters; NEA, MEA 1966-, Area Rep; Presque Isle Tchrs Assn 1985-, Sec, Negotiations; Phi Delta Kappa 1991-, VP; Beta Sigma Phi 1988-, Pres, VP, Woman of Yr, Valentine Princess; Selected to Represent Area Tchrs ME Tchrs Summit to Write New Learning Results Reform Ed MI; Write, Advise Soc Stud Section ME Educl Assessent Statewide Achievement Test Given to Grds 4, 8, 11; *office:* ME Schl Administrative Dist #1 PO Box 1118 Presque Isle ME 04769*

SCHMIESING, JUDY A., Third Grade Teacher; *b:* Versailles, OH; *m:* Marvin; *c:* Andy; *ed:* Univ of Dayton (BS) Elem Ed 1968, (MS) Elem Ed 1985; *cr:* Russia Local Schl 3rd Grd Tchr 1963-65, 4th Grd Tchr 1965-69, 3rd Grd Tchr 1973-; Anna Local Schl 4th Grd Tchr 1969-71; *ai:* OEA; REA, Treas; *office:* Russia Local Schl 110 Main St Russia OH

SCHMITT, BARBARA ANN (SIEG), Fourth Grade Teacher; *b:* NY; *m:* Robert George; *c:* Diana L. Bryant, Marlene A.; *ed:* Geneseo (BS) Lib, Elem Ed 1960; SUNY Fredonia (MS) Sci Elem E Admin, Supervision 1985; 60 Addl Credits; *cr:* East View Jr H 1960-62; Lake Shore Cntrl SD Sixth Grd Tutor, Sub Tchr 1 1963-74; Highland Elem Schl Third Grd Tchr 1974-85, Fourth G 1985-; *ai:* Sci Team Ldr; NYS ESPET Mentor; Lake Shore Tch 1974-, RIF Project Coord; NYSUT, AFT 1974-, Bldg Rep, RA Re of Evans Recycling Comm; Sr Girl Scout Ldr; Evans Bus, Prof Pres; *office:* Highland Elem Schl 6745 Erie Rd Derby NY 14047

SCHMITT, CAROL DESILVA, Language Arts & Reading Tchr; York City, NY; *m:* Edward Wilfred; *c:* J. Scott Scholl, Kirsten Jessica Scholl; *ed:* Ursinus Coll (BA) Eng 1964; West Chester Un Rdng 1986; 60 Post-Grad Credits; Attnd Drexel Univ, St Joseph Gratz Coll; *cr:* Springford-Royersford HS His Tchr 1964; Upper M HS Eng Tchr 1964-67; Francis Scott Key HS Eng Tchr 1969-71; H Prep Schl for Learning Disabled Adolescents Eng Tchr 1985-86; Pe HS Eng & Rdng Tchr 1986-; *ai:* Class Spon 1986-94; Schl Newspap Spon 1994-; NEA 1986-; PSEA 1986-; NCTE 1986-; NRA 1995-; Lifetime Mem; Oratorio Soc 1996; Natl Bd Eng Tchrs Selecting Tchrs Evaluator 1995; Rose Tree Media Schl Dist Grants.*

SCHMITT, DONALD EUGENE, Math Tchr & Instrl Ldr; *b:* Buffa *m:* Patricia R. Wojciechowski; *c:* Julie J.; *ed:* Buffalo St Coll (BS) Ed 1967, (MS) Math, Ed 1972; 60 Addl Hrs; Canisius Coll 2 Yr Mat *cr:* Orchard park Cntrl Schl MS Math Tchr 1967-84, HS Math Tchr *ai:* Co-Curricular Funds Adv; HS Instrl Ldr Cncl; Dist Math Comm Dev; HS & Dist Curr Cncl; Orchard Park Tchrs Assn 1967-, Bldg R ST Assn of Math Tchrs 1972-; NCTM 1995-; NYS Assn of Math 1995-, Western NY Region Rep; Orchard Park Jaycees 1969-76, Tre Pres, Distngd Svc Awd; Queen of Heaven Carnival Exec Bd 1992- Chm; *office:* Orchard Park Cntrl Schl 4040 Baker Rd Orchard Pa 14127

SCHMITT, DOROTHY ANN, Resource Room Teacher; *b:* Bal MD; *ed:* Our Lady of Angels Coll (BA) Soc Sci 1973; Trenton (MED) Rdng, Ed 1980; Post Grad Trenton St, Riders Coll; Sacrament Schl, Holy Angels Schl, Immaculate Conception S Joseph's Schl, St Rose Schl, St Raphael Schl K-8th Grd Tchr 52 Y NCEA 1945-; IRA, Tri-Cnty Rdng 1980-; Garden St Storytellers Natl Storytelling League 1985-, Second VP; Kappa Delta Pi 1981- Art Magazine; *home:* 68 Lakeview Ct Yardville NJ 08620

SCHMITT, JOHN M., AP Psychology Teacher; *b:* Eric, PA; *m:* Kelly; *c:* Susann, Kellie, Jenna; *ed:* Mercyhurst Coll (BA) Soc 1978; Edinboro Univ (MED) Ed, Psych 1982; 21 Addl Hrs Grad C in Ed; *cr:* McDowell Sr HS Psych, AP Psych Tchr 1979-; Perfor Learning System Educl Consultant, Grad Ed Course Instr 1982-; *ai:* PSEA, MEA 1979-; Trained Over 2000 Tchrs in Series of Grad Ed Co *office:* Mc Dowell HS 3580 W 38th St Erie PA 16506

SCHMITT, KAREN ELLEN, 10th Grade English Teacher; *b:* E O NJ; *ed:* Douglass Coll (BA) His, Eng 1965; *cr:* Broadway Jr HS En 1965-67; Union HS 10th Grd Eng Tchr 1967-; *ai:* NEA, NJEA *office:* Union H S N 3rd St Union NJ 07083

SCHMITT, WARREN G., Language Arts Teacher; *b:* Dayton, O Vicky A.; *c:* Kara Brooks; *ed:* John Carroll Univ (MA) Psych 1966; St Univ (MA) Schl Admin 1977; Tchng Cert 1971; Various Cou Cmptr, Writing Process; *cr:* Saint Helens Parochial Schl Tchr 19 Tower Heights MS Eng Lang Arts Tchr 1973-; *ai:* NEA 1973-; Big B of America 1972-74, Vol; Amer Cancer Soc 1974-78, Vol; Heart 1976-80, Vol; PTO, Treas Schl Bd 1974-75; Wkshps in Lit & Dif Methods of Instructing Grammar & Creative Writing; Power of Pen & Judge 1985-87; Odyssey of Mind Competition Judge 1988-; Coach 1973-78; Vlybl Coach 1982-84; *office:* Tower Heights MS Johanna Dr Centerville OH 45459

SCHMITZ, GENEVIEVE RECLA, Business Education Teach Hazelton, PA; *m:* John S.; *c:* John Jr., Joseph; *ed:* Bloomsburg Univ Bus Ed Acctng 1968; Attnd St Univ at New Paltz, Marywood Coll, St at Oswego; *cr:* Marlboro HS Bus Ed Tchr & Work Stud Coord 2 Orange Comm Coll Bus Ed Tchr 13 Yrs; *ai:* BEAM 1968-; NYSTA MFA 1968-; *office:* Marlboro Central HS 50 Cross Rd Marlboro NY

SCHMOOK, JEFFREY CHARLES, Mathematics Teacher; *b* Pleasant, PA; *ed:* IN Univ of PA (BS) Math 1992; 18 Credit Hrs T (MED); *cr:* Yough Schl Dist Math Tchr 1993-; *ai:* Sftbl Coach; PSEA, NCTM, PCTM, MCWP, LHMA 1993-; Recieved Assistan Presented at PA Cncl of Tchrs of Math 1994-1995; *office:* Yough Sr Lowber Rd Herminie PA 15637

SCHMOYER, BRUCE CARL, Instrumental Music Tchr & Ch Allentown, PA; *m:* Jane Snyder; *c:* Lori, Brian; *ed:* West Chester St Music Ed 1973; Addl 24 Credit Hrs Grad Stud, 6 Credit Hrs Widener Supvr Cert; *cr:* Daniel Boone HS Sr High Band Dir 1973-76; Wilson Dist Instrumental Tchr 1976-; *ai:* Marching Band, Jazz Band Dir; M 1973-; AFT 1990-; Pottstown Band 1985-88 Dir; St Marks Brass Ense 1980-, Dir; St Marks Orch 1987-, Dir; *office:* Wilson Schl Dist Grandview Blvd West Lawn PA 19609

SCHMOYER, JEAN C., 6th Grade Teacher; *b:* Upper Darby, PA; *m:* R.; *c:* Janine M. Clarke, Todd M.; *ed:* Muhlenberg Coll (BA) Psych, Ed 1985; *cr:* Southern Lehigh Schl Dist Remedial Math, Co-op 1085-87; Hillside Schl Classroom Tchr of Children with Lea Disabilities 1987-; *home:* 805 N 2nd St Emmaus PA 18049

SCHMOYER, KATHRYN ANDERSON, Substitute Teacher & Volun *b:* Defiance, OH; *m:* Michael Scott; *c:* Brittany Nicole, Nicholas Scot CA Univ of PA (BS) Elem, Early Chldhd 1986; Working Towards Specialst Cert at PA St Univ; *cr:* Gonzales Union Schl Dist 4th Grd 1987-88; Dover Area Schl Dist Long Term Sub Tchr 1990-91, 4th Grd 1991-95; Medina City Schl Dist Vol, Sub Tchr 1995-; *ai:* Garfield Schl Yrbk, Math Night Comms; NEA 1991-; IRA 1995-; Medina Pre Church 1996, Sunday Schl Tchr; *home:* 4050 Stonegate Dr Medina 44256*

SCHMUCK, JOAN MARIE, Math & French Teacher; *b:* York, PA Steven A.; *c:* Amanda, Megan, Erica; *ed:* York Coll (BS) Sec Ed, 1993; *cr:* Red Lion Chrstn Schl K-4 Grd Tchr 1980-85; Trinity Chrstn K-4 Grd Tchr 1986-88; Red Lion Chrstn Schl Math, Fr Tchr 1990- Yrbk Adv; Organize Fr Stdnts Trip; Church Act; NCTM 1993-; Alpha Hnr Soc; *office:* Red Lion Christian Schl 105 Springvale Rd Red Lio 17356

SCHNABEL, SUSAN JANE, Social Studies Teacher; *b:* Philadelphia, *ed:* Ursinus Coll (BA) Soc Stud 1962; Attnd Abilene Chrstn Coll; V Forge Freedoms Fnd Seminar Grant; *cr:* Phoenixville Area J. T. Schl Soc Stud Tchr 1962-; *ai:* Former Dept Chprsn, Stu Tchr Supvr; Discip Acad Awds Comms; Supt Advy Comm 1969-70; Prin Advsy C 1995-96; NEA, PSEA 1962-; Phoenixville Area Ed Assn 1962-, 1963-64; Pi Gamma Mu, Pi Nu Epsilon 1962-; Trinity Luth Church; A Sigma Nu 1963-; Valley Forge Freedoms Fnd Natl Tchrs Medal; Ge Ditter Awd; Scndry Ed Outstanding Ldr; Pub Article; *office:* Phoenix Area MS 1330 S Main St Phoenixville PA 19460

ACKY, CELIA, Chemistry Teacher; *b:* Rochester, NY; *m:* Paul M. an; *c:* William; *ed:* Case Western Reserve Univ (BS) Elem Ed 1972; l (MAT) Phys Sci 1985; *cr:* Brockport Child Care Presch Tchr 3; Jewish Comm Ctr of RI Presch 1978-83; Lincoln Schl Chem Tchr *ai:* Admissions, Dorothy Gifford Awd Comms; Cum Laude Soc; ngland Assn of Chem Tchr 1993-; Astronomical Soc of Southern ngland 1995-; *office:* Lincoln Schl 301 Butler Ave Providence RI

AUFFER, ROBERT WILLIAM, Health & Physical Ed Instr; *b:* k, NJ; *m:* Sharon Lynn; *c:* Brett, Meagan; *ed:* East Stroudsburg Univ lth, PE 1965; Montclair Univ 16 Credit Hrs; *cr:* Nutley Bd of Ed E Instr 1965-67; West Essex HS Hlth & PE Instr 1967-; *ai:* Head oach 24 Yrs; Asst Soccer Coach 17 Yrs; Jr Class Adv 1988-1992; 965-; NJEA 1965-; AAHPERD 1967-; Coach of the Yr 1981; *home:* land Ave West Caldwell NJ 07006

EBERGER, WILLIAM, Fine Arts & Art History Tchr; *b:* Passaic, Nancy; *c:* Amy; *ed:* Wm Paterson Coll (BA) Art Ed 1966, (MA) Arts 1970; Currently Working Towards Doctorate at T. C. Columbia *cr:* Wm Paterson Coll Fine Arts Instr 1969-72; N Vly Reg HS Fine rt His Tchr, Coord of Gifted Prgms 1972-; *ai:* Acad Decathlon Adv; ; NJEA; NEA; NAEA; Fulbright Alumni Assn; INSEA; Fulbright ar; Natl Endowment for the Hum Scholar; Bard Fellow; RISD); Ramapo Coll Oxford Hnrs Awd; Presenter Inter Congress of val Stud; NJ Gov Tchng Awd; NJ Senate Citations; NVOT Tchr of d; Who's Who in NJ; *home:* 60 Lake Ave Midland Park NJ 07432*

ECK, DALE A., Journalism & English Teacher; *b:* Allentown, PA; oravian Coll (BA) Eng 1963; *cr:* Easton Area HS Eng, Film Making 1963-75; The Mornging Call Newspaper Film Arts Ed 1977-84; n Vly Schl Dist Jrnlsm, Eng Tchr 1987-; *ai:* Reflector Yrbk, Panther Newspaper Adv; Co-Curr Cncl; NEA, PSEA 1963-; Saucon Vly Ed 1987-; Amer Film Inst 1981-; Screenwriter of Feature Motion es 1996; *home:* 2863 Meadowbrook Cir S Allentown PA 18103

EDEKER, JOHN, Director of Guidance; *b:* Rockville Centre, NY; rbara Leigh; *c:* Lora, Bryan, Julie; *ed:* Princeton Univ (AB) Psych Trenton St Coll (MED) Stu Per Svcs 1977; Candidate for EDD g Psych Rutgers Univ; *cr:* Hightstown HS Math Tchr, Content alist 1973-80; Allentown HS Guid Chprsn 1980-85; Summit Schls Dir d 1985-; *ai:* Stu-to-Stu Peer Helping Adv; Schlsp Coord; Amer Coun 980-; NEA 1973-, Local Pres; NJACA 1980-, Rsrch Awd; NJASGW Pres; Family Serv Assn of Summit 1990-93, Svc Awd; Articles Pub; rious Book Reviews for Co Journals; *office:* Summit HS 125 Kent Pl Summit NJ 07901

EEHAGEN, RUTH GOREY, Second Grade Teacher; *b:* gfield, MA; *m:* William H.; *c:* Carol Evans, Colleen Reeb, Cynthia ore; *ed:* Catonsvill Comm Coll (AA) Ed 1970; Towson St (BS) Ed Western MD (MS) Admin & Supervision 1982; Attnd Loyola Univ, e Washington Univ, John Hopkins Univ; *cr:* Carroll Cty Bd of Ed 26 Yrs; *ai:* Odyssey of the Mind MD St Judge, World Judge; Team IEA, MSTA, CCEA 1975-; ASCD 1985-; Odyssey of the Mind 1984-, Dir, MD Bd of Dirs; MD Governors Salute to Excl 1989; Nom for chr of Yr 1991-.

EEWEISS, ERIN MURPHY, Eng, Theatre, Comm & Speech; *b:* York, NY; *m:* Fred; *c:* Caitlyn, Christopher; *ed:* Fordham Univ at ln Ctr (BA) Theatre, Eng 1985; Attnd Montclair St, Fairleigh nson; *cr:* Hasbrouck Heights HS Eng, Theatre, Comm, Speech Tchr *ai:* Jr HS Musical, HS Musical, Sr Play Drama Dir; Talent Show, a Club, Soph Class Adv; Teen Arts Coord; NEA, BCEA 1988-; Kappa Phi 1986-; HHEA Assn, Pub Relations; Pub Events Comm 1995-; : Hasbrouck Heights HS 365 Boulevard Hasbrouck Heights NJ *

NEIDER, ADELIA, Spanish & Italian Teacher; *b:* Italy; *m:* Gerry; n, Eric; *ed:* Brooklyn Coll (BA) Span, Italian 1961-65; Loyola Coll) Educl Psych 1980-84; Howard Comm Coll Art 1973-76; Towson St Advanced Prof Tchng Cert Scndry Ed 1977; *cr:* Pomezia Textiles g Office Mgr 1965-68; Howard Cty Bd of Ed Frgn Lang Tchr 1979-; mer Field Svc 1982-89; Intnl, Span, Italian Clubs; Staff Dev, Awds ns; NEA, MSTA 1979-; MFLA 1980-; AATSP 1980-89; HCEA; n Station Townhouse Assn 1995-, Bd of Dir; Howard Cty Jewish n Schl 1981-84, Bd of Dir; Cancer Assn 1985-89, Vol; Heart Assn 90, Vol; MD Frgn Lang Assn Achvmt & Excl of Performance Awd; Kappa Gamma; Authored, Implemented Italian Prgm Howard Cty Schls 1979; Dev Oral Proficiency Guidelines 1986; *office:* Oakland HS 9410 Kilimanjaro Rd Columbia MD 21045

NEIDER, CALVIN WILLIAM, Industrial Arts Teacher; *b:* ville, PA; *m:* Suzanne Paul; *c:* Douglas, Elizabeth; *ed:* Millersville (BSEd) Indstrl Arts 1967; Post Grad, Cert Penn St Univ, East dsburg Univ; *cr:* Nitschmann Jr HS Indstrl Arts Tchr 1967-83; om HS Indstrl Arts Tchr 1983-; Bethlehem Area Schl Tchr 1967-; *ai:* Publishing Dept; Prin Advy Team; Restructuring Staff Dev Mem; Coach Liberty HS 1973-85; Bethlehem Ectrs Assoc, PSEA, NEA -; Aid Assn for Luths 1986-, Branch Pres, Branch VP, Lamplighter; cy Coord of Vol, Fraternalist of Yr 1995; Tech Grant Lehigh Tech Curr *home:* 4542 Deerbrook Ct Walnutport PA 18088

NEIDER, CECELIA ANN (PETRZILKA), Mathematics Teacher; *b:* Brunswick, NJ; *m:* George David; *c:* Keith; *ed:* Trenton St Coll (BS) Ed, Minor in Math 1976; *cr:* Monmouth Regnl HS Math Tchr 1979-; SPT Testing Comm; NEA, NJEA, MREA 1979-; *office:* Monmouth onal HS 1 Norman J Field Way Eatontown NJ 07724

NEIDER, CHRISTINE (OTTINGER), English Teacher; *b:* delphia, PA; *m:* William P.; *c:* Michael, Scott; *ed:* Mount Saint Marys (BS) Eng Ed 1977; Rowan Eng Grad Course; *cr:* Vineland HS Eng 1978-; *ai:* Fac Communication Comm 1981-; Fac Commencement m 1981-91; Schl Spirit Club Co-Adv 1982-86; Sr Class Co-Adv 1986-; Newspaper Adv 1990-; Vineland Ed Assn 1978-, Bldg Rep 1980-; NJ ssn 1978-; NEA 1978-; NCTE 1978-; Jr Womans Club of Vineland -85, Trustee; Capri Swim Club 1986-, Trustee 1988-90, Pres 1990-92; & Implemented Local Newspaper Teen Page 1990; *office:* Vineland outh 2880 E Chestnut Ave Vineland NJ 08360*

NEIDER, DELORES CRYSTAL, Resource Room Teacher; *b:* klyn, NY; *m:* Edmund Lee; *c:* Jeffrey, Steven; *ed:* Brooklyn Coll (BA) 963, (MS) Spec Ed 1966; Cnslng; Guid; Psych; *cr:* PS 273 CRMD Ed Tchr 1970-71; PS 205 CRMD Spec Ed Tchr 1971-80; Pasteur MS esource Room Tchr 1980-95; Hawthorne MS 74 Resource Room Tchr -; *ai:* Newspaper Club, Drama Club Adv; AFT 1970-; *office:* Nathaniel thorne MS 74 61-15 Oceania St Bayside NY 11364

NEIDER, DOUGLAS RICHARD, Physical Education Teacher; *b:* hester, NY; *ed:* Herkimeiz Comm coll (AS) PE 1981; SUNY at kport (BS) PE 1983; 18 Masters Credit Hrs in PE; *cr:* St Charles omeo Schl PE Tchr 1985-; Spencerport Cntrl Schls Var Track & Cross y Coach 1982-; *ai:* Var Girls Track, Var Boys & Girls Indoor Track & Boys & Girls Cross Cntry Coach; NYSCA 1994-; ASCD 1991-; NCEA -; Spencerport Sports Boosters 1985-, VP, Pres; *office:* Spencerport l Schls 71 Lyell Rd Spencerport NY 14559*

NEIDER, EDITH LOUISE, Instrumental Music Teacher; *b:* hester, NY; *ed:* Univ of NC (BM) Music Ed 1966; Univ of MI (MM) Music Ed 1970; Attnd Eastman Schl of Music; *cr:* Greensboro Pub Schls Instrumental Music Tchr 1966-68; Rochester City Schl Dist Instrumental Music Tchr 1971-; *ai:* Spirit, Schl Climate Comms; NYSUT; MENC; NYSSMA; NYSBDA; League of Women Voters; Schl Violence Prevention Grant; *office:* Nathaniel Rochester Comm Schl 85 Adams St Rochester NY 14608

SCHNEIDER, EDWARD A., Vocal Music Teacher; *b:* Tampa, FL; *m:* Randi Lynn Drucker; *c:* Roger Troy, Brian Gregory; *ed:* NY Univ (BA) Psych 1965; Brooklyn Law Schl (JD) General Practice 1992; Manhattan Schl of Music B Mus Theory 1967, M Mus Theory 1968; *cr:* Intermediate Schl 155 Music Tchr 1968-69; Col. David Marcus Jr HS 263 Music Tchr 1969-71; Toscanini Jr HS 145 Music Tchr 1971-73; Bildersee Intermediate Schl 68 Music Tchr 1986-; *ai:* NEA, NYSUT, AFT, UFT 1986-; NY Bar Assn 1993-; *office:* IS 68 Bildersee Interm Schl 956 E 82nd St Brooklyn NY 11236

SCHNEIDER, EMIL J., Social Studies Teacher; *b:* Schenectady, NY; *m:* Edith; *c:* Kyle, Nicol; *ed:* Valparaiso Univ (BA) Ger & Soc Stud 1969; SUNY at Brockport, SUNY at Albany Ger, Scndry Ed; *cr:* Saranac Lake Cntrl Schl Dist Ger, Soc Stud 1970-; *ai:* Boys Var Asst Soccer Coach; NYSUT 1970-, Pres 3 Times; *office:* Saranac Lake Cntrl Schl Dist La Pan Hwy Saranac Lake NY 12983

SCHNEIDER, ESTELLE, Asst Professor of Phys Therapy; *b:* Bronx, NY; *ed:* Long Island Univ (MS) Phys Therapy 1986; *cr:* SUNY Hlth Sci Ctr at Brooklyn Asst Prof, Acad Coord of Clinical Ed 1994-; *ai:* Arthur Ashe Inst Hlth Sci Acad Liaison; NYS Consortium of Phys Therapy Clinical Edctrs; Amer PT Assn, Hlth Vols Overseas 1994-; Cross Cultural Intnl Interest Group 1987-; Comm for Hlth Rights in Amers 1987-; Prof Dev Quality of Life Term, Continuing Fac Dev Awd 1995.

SCHNEIDER, FERD MICHAEL, Math Teacher; *b:* Perth Amboy, NJ; *ed:* Miami Univ (BA) Math, Chem 1989; *cr:* Aiken HS Math Tchr 1990-; *ai:* AP Comm; Asst Coach Var Ftbl; Asst Coach Var Swimming; Weight Lifting Adv; Head Coach Var Track; AFT 1990-; Cincinnati Wolfhounds Rugby Ftbl Club 1989-, Soc Chm, MVP 1993; Tchr Ed Loan Prgm 1986-89; Stu Mentor 1993-; *office:* Aiken HS 5641 Belmont Ave Cincinnati OH 45224*

SCHNEIDER, HOLLY D., 6th Grade Teacher; *b:* Lorain, OH; *c:* Tom, Jeff; *ed:* Miami Univ (BA) Elem Ed 1974; Reading Inc John Carroll; Coop Learning Ashland; Alcohol Ed Akron Univ; Whole Lang Notre Dame, Comm Inst; Coop Lrng; *cr:* Amherst Bd of Ed Sub, LD Tutor 1976-80, Rdng Tchr 1981, 6th Grd Tchr 1982, LD Tutor, Chem Depending Tutor 1983, 6th Grd Tchr 1984-; *ai:* Drug Free Coord; Just Say No Club Adv; Math Contest Organizer; Collaboration Team; NEA; OEA; Amherst Tchrs Assn; Golden Apple Awd 1993, 1994; *office:* Shupe MS 600 Shute Ave Amherst OH 44001

SCHNEIDER, JACOB C., Instrumental Music Teacher; *b:* Pittsburgh, PA; *m:* Deborah Leasher; *c:* Gretchen E., Martin A.; *ed:* Clarion Univ of PA (BA) Music Ed 1972; Westchester Univ of PA (MMEd) Music Ed 1978; *cr:* Cecil Manor Elem Schl Choral & Instrumental Music Tchr 1972-90; Hill & Kenmore Elem Schl Choral & Instrumental Music Tchr 1972-90; Hill & Kenmore Elem Schl Instrumental Music Tchr 1990-; *ai:* NEA; Music Edctrs Natl Conf; MD Music Ed Assn Awd for Excl 1996; *office:* Cherry Hill MS 2535 Singerly Rd Elkton MD 21921

SCHNEIDER, JAMES WILLIAM, Social Studies Teacher; *b:* Cincinnati, OH; *m:* Eileen Ann Wietlisbach; *c:* Christina, Daniel, Benjamin; *ed:* Univ of Steubenville (BA) His 1970; Xavier Univ (MED) Scndry Admin 1979; Post Grad Stud His; *cr:* McAuley HS Soc Stud Tchr 1970-; Xavier Univ Adjunct Prof 1995-; *ai:* Prom Promise; Cincinnati Historical Soc; *office:* Mc Auley HS 6000 Oakwood Ave Cincinnati OH 45224

SCHNEIDER, JANE RUSSELL, Math Teacher; *b:* Binghamton, NY; *m:* Glenn E.; *ed:* SUNY at Brockport (BA) Math 1970; 30 Addl Hrs; *cr:* Hoover Drive Jr HS 7-8 Grd Math Tchr 1970-84; Olympia HS 9-10 Grd Math Tchr 1984-93; Odyssey Schl 8-10 Grd Math Tchr 1993-; *ai:* Fiscal Integrity, Scheduling, Back to Schl Day Comms; NEA, NY Ed Assn 1970-; AMTRA; NCTM 1994-; *office:* Greece Odyssey Schl 133 Hoover Dr Rochester NY 14615*

SCHNEIDER, JEFFREY W., Instrumental Music Teacher; *b:* Columbus, OH; *ed:* OH St Univ (BA) Music Ed 1976; VanderCook Schl of Music (MA) Music Ed 1993; *cr:* Lima City Schls Instrumental Music Tchr 1977-79; Bexley City Schls 5th-12th Grd Instrumental Music Tchr 1979-; *ai:* All Instrumental Music Act; HS Girls Track & Reserve Bsktbl Teams Coach; NEA, OEA, MENC, OMEA 1977-; Natl Band Assn 1979-; Bexley Music Parents 1979-, Bd Mem; Bexley Athletic Booster 1979-; Big Brothers Assn 1983-; *office:* Bexley City Schls 348 S Cassingham Rd Bexley OH 43209

SCHNEIDER, JENNIFER BETH, 7th & 8th Grd Science Teacher; *b:* Brystol, PA; *m:* Scott; *c:* Zachary; *ed:* Rutgers Univ (BS) Environmental Stud 1987; Marine Bio Prgm Northeastern Univ 1 Yr; Addl Sci Coursework Astronomy, Meteorology Rowan Coll; *cr:* Northern Burlington Cty Regnl Jr HS 7th-8th Grd Sci Tchr 1989-; *ai:* Sr HS Var Chrldng Coach; Jr HS Whale Watching Trip Co-Spon; Spec Ed In-Class Support Prgm Comm Mem; NJEA, NSTA 1989-; *office:* No Burlington Reg Jr-Sr HS 160 Mansfield Rd E Columbus NJ 08022

SCHNEIDER, LEE DAVID, Dean of Students; *b:* Rockville Ctr, NY; *m:* Pamela Rowe; *c:* Julie, Tracey; *ed:* CAES Rutgers Univ (BS) Env Bus Admin 1970; Rutgers Univ (MS) Agricultural Ec 1971, (EDD) Educl Admin 1988; *cr:* Rutgers Univ 1970-74; Cook Coll Rutgers Univ Ec Instr 1970-73, Assist, Assoc Dean Acad Svcs 1973-87, Dean of Stdnts 1988-; *ai:* Fac Acad, Sr Class Adv; Ldrshp Dev; Coaching; Recreational Sports; Parents, Alumni Assn; Natl Assn of Stu Prnsl Admin; ASCD; Scarlet R; Montgomery United Meth Church 1982-, Tchr Ed Comm Chair; Alpha Zeta; Golden Key; Cook-CAES Alumni Assn 1970-; Cook Parents Assn 1994-; Rutgers Ftbl Hall of Fame 1994; Rutgers Ftbl Capt 1969 Centennial Team; Baccalaureate Speaker Grad 1989; Nine Publications; Featured Speaker; Consultant; *office:* Cook Coll Cook Campus Ctr Box 231 Cook Office Bldg New Brunswick NJ 08903

SCHNEIDER, MARGARET DOYLE, Retired English Teacher; *b:* Bronx, NY; *m:* Richard; *c:* Bernard, Beth Coon, Christopher, John, Mary, Ellen Christiano; *ed:* Union Coll at Cranford (AS) Womens Stud 1976; Kean Coll at Union (BA) Eng 1980; Continuing Ed Courses; *cr:* Cranford Schl System Sub Tchr 1980-83; Garwood Pub Schl Elem Aide 1984; St Theresa Parochial 6-8 Grd Eng Tchr 1985-95; *ai:* Lit Vols of Amer; NJ Assn Eng Tchrs; NCTE; Wednesday Morning Club Cranford 1995-.

SCHNEIDER, MARVIN A., Assistant Principal; *b:* Brooklyn, NY; *m:* Roberta Sunshine; *c:* Mark, Melanie; *ed:* Brooklyn Coll (BA) Math 1960; NY Univ (MS) Math Ed 1965; Pace Univ (MS) Supervision & Admin 1977; *cr:* Lafayette HS Math Tchr 1964-74; Edward R. Murrow HS Math Tchr & Supvr 1974-; *ai:* NCTM 1964-; Two Textbooks Co-Authored; *office:* Edward R Murrow HS 1600 Ave L Brooklyn NY 11230

SCHNEIDER, SANDRA PARKER, Sixth Grade Teacher; *b:* Buffalo, NY; *m:* Daniel Charles Jr.; *c:* Jennifer, Matthew; *ed:* St Univ Coll at Geneseo (BS) Elem Ed, Deaf Ed 1970; St Univ Coll at Buffalo (MS) Elem Ed, Gifted Ed 1974; Canisius Coll Working Toward Admin Cert; *cr:* NY St Inst for Deaf Grd 2 Tchr 1970; West Seneca Schl System 3-6 Grd Tchr 1970-; *ai:* Pub Schl Newspaper 1980-90; Wrote, Directed Musicals; AFT, NYSUT, WSTA 1970-; Baker United Meth Church 1973-, Childrens Choir Dir 1985-94; Outstdng Tchr of Yr West Seneca Jaycees 1980; Pub Book Bamdoozle 1980; Books to be Pub Door, Colors, What Your Best Friend Won't Tell You, You'll Never Believe What David Did!; *office:* Allendale Elem Schl 1399 Orchard Park Rd West Seneca NY 14224

SCHNEIDER, SUSAN D., High School English Teacher; *b:* New York City, NY; *m:* Stephen Z.; *c:* Sam, William; *ed:* Boston Univ (BA) Eng 1969; Long Island Univ (MS) Eng, Ed 1974; 75 Addl Credits; *cr:* Farmingdale HS Eng Tchr 1969-; Suffolk Cty Comm Coll Asst Prof Adj 1983-; *ai:* Lit, Art Magazine Adv; AFT, NYSAT 1969-; NY St Eng Cncl, NCTE 1986-; *office:* Farmingdale HS 150 Lincoln St Farmingdale NY 11735*

SCHNEIDER, WILLIAM ARTHUR, Student Support Teacher; *b:* Bay Ridge Brooklyn, NY; *m:* Elaine Grossarth; *c:* Lynn; *ed:* SUNY at Oneonta (BS) K-9th Grd Ed, Soc Stud 1967; SUNY at New Paltz (MA) Elem ED 1972; 15 Addl Credits 1975; *cr:* East Ramapo Cntrl Schl Dist 6th Grd Tchr 26 Yrs, SST, Stu Support Tchr 2 Yrs; *ai:* Dir, Peer Mediation; Adv Stu Cncl, Schl Newspaper; Coord Schl Safety Patrol; Banana Splits Group Ldr; Spon Stu of Month Prgm; NEA, E Ramapo Tchrs Assn 1967-; PTA 1967-, Founder's Day Awd, Excl in Tchng; Town Woodstock 1978-, Dir Recreation; Overlook Meth Church 1978-, Pres Admin Bd, Sec Bd Trustees; Tchrs Cent Grant, Children, Lit; *office:* Lime Kiln Elem Schl 35 Lime Kiln Rd Suffern NY 10901

SCHNEIDER, SC, MARY DOLORES, Latin & World Cultures Teacher; *b:* Detroit, MI; *ed:* Coll of Mount St Joseph (BA) Eng 1960; Loyola Univ of Chicago (MA) Eng 1968; Xavier Univ 3 Credits Eng 1971; Purdue Univ 3 Credits Eng 1974; Coll of St Thomas 6 Credits Ed 1976 & 1978; St Xavier Coll 1 Credit Ed 1976; *cr:* St Joseph Commercial HS Tchr 1960-66; St Leo HS Tchr 1966-69; Elizabeth Seton HS Tchr 1969-83; Seton HS Tchr 1983-; *ai:* Dir of Stu Act Seton HS; Moderator of Stu Cncl, Latin Club; Amer Classical League 1978-; Cinc Tchrs of Classics, Pompeiana Soc 1983-; Cincinnati Assoc of Tchrs of Classics 1983; NASSAD 1990; *office:* Seton H S 3901 Glenway Ave Cincinnati OH 45205

SCHNELL, JOAN E., Language Arts Instructor; *b:* Philadelphia, PA; *m:* J. Michael; *c:* Jacob, Adam, Rebekka; *ed:* Trinity Coll (MAT) Eng 1971; Johns Hopkins Univ (CAS) Lbrl Arts 1975; Cath Univ of Amer 15 Hrs, Univ of VT 22 Hrs Post Grad Stud; *cr:* Essex Comm Coll Asst Prof of Eng 1970-79; Goucher Coll Consortium Lecturer Eng 1976-78; Johnson St Coll Instr Dev Eng 1978-79; Trinity Coll Coord Writing Ctr 1980-81; Comm Coll Basic Writing Skills, Lit Lecturer 1982-85; BFA Lang Arts Tchr 1993-; *ai:* Natl Thespian Soc, Newspaper Adv; Restructuring, Prof Dev, Tech Comms; ASCD, NCTE 1993-; Northeast Coalition of Educ Ldr1993-, Bd of Dirs; Jrnlsm Ed Assn, Educl Theatre Assn 1995-; NEA 1994-; St Albans Town Schl Bd 1988-92; Northwest Med Ctr 1986-, Schlsp Comm; Ldrshp Champlain Bd 1991-94; VT Ethics Network 1990-94, Bd; Just-Writing 1976-77, 1981, 1988; Ldrshp Champlain 1990-91; *office:* Bellows Free Acad Hunt St Fairfax VT 05454*

SCHNELLINGER, MICHAEL E., Mathematics Teacher; *b:* Norwalk, OH; *m:* Patricia J. Recktenwald; *c:* Erin, Rusty; *ed:* Kent St Univ (BA) Math 1986, (MA) Math 1991; Cmptrs in Math Ed 1 Credit Hr; *cr:* Hudson MS 7th, 8th Grd Math Tchr 1987-92; Kent St Univ Part0time Math Fac 1988-92; Hudson HS Math Tchr 1992-; *ai:* Var Boys Asst Track, 8th Grd Girls Bsktbl Coach; NEA, OEA, HEA, OH Cncl Tchrs Math 1987-; PTO 1987-; Eagles 1992-; *office:* Hudson HS 2400 Hudson-Aurora Rd Hudson OH 44236*

SCHNEPP, PRESENTATION MARY, Office Assistant; *b:* Philadelphia, PA; *ed:* Immaculata Coll (BA) Ed 1968; Theology 1976; Addl Post Bacalaureate 1973; Many Rel Ed Courses; *cr:* Holy Savior Schl 3rd-4th Grd Tchr 1949-57; St Gabriel Schl 6th Grd Tchr 1957-61; Our Lady of Grace Schl 6th Grd Tchr 1961-63; Annuciation Schl 5th Grd Tchr 1963-64; St Cecila Schl 6th Grd Tchr 1964-68; St Barnabas Schl 5th Grd Tchr 1968-70; St Clement Schl 5th Grd Tchr 1970-74; Assumption Schl 5th Grd Tchr 1974-76; Good Shepherd Schl 5th Grd Tchr 1976-78; St Monica Schl 5th Grd Tchr 1978-84; Our Lady of Grace Schl 4th Grd Tchr 1984-92, Hnrs Math Tchr 1992-94, Office Asst 1994-; *ai:* Teach Rel, Prepare Sacraments; NCEA 1960-; Title 1 Math Grant; *office:* Our Lady Of Grace Schl 300 Hulmeville Ave Penndel PA 19047*

SCHNIPPER, LINDA MARTIN, Physical Science Teacher; *b:* Cincinnati, OH; *m:* Michael L.; *ed:* Miami Univ (BSEd) Bio & General Sci 1982, (MAT) Bio Ed 1990; Working on PhD; *cr:* Wilson Jr HS Phys Sci Tchr 1984-; Miami Univ Resource Tchr & Project Discovery 1993-; *ai:* Supt Advy, Bldg Instruction & Improvement, Curr & Sci Fair Comms; SW OH Prof Dev Ctr; Champ Ldrshp Team; Dist Sci Olympiad Coord; NSTA, OEA, NEA & OAS 1984-; SECO 1990-; *office:* Wilson Jr HS 714 Eaton Ave Hamilton OH 45013*

SCHNIPPER, SYDRA, Mathematics Teacher; *b:* New York City, NY; *c:* Merritt, Deborah, Claudia; *ed:* Queens Coll (BA) Math 1965; Cambridge Coll (MA) Ed 1989; Attnd Boston Univ Admin, NY Univ Math & Brooklyn Coll Guidance; *cr:* Canarsie HS Tchr & Dean of Girls 1965-68; West Haven HS Tchr 1968-70; Brooklin HS Tchr 1974-; *ai:* Renovation Comm-Finance; BEA 1974-; Newton Bd of Aldermen 1994-, Vice Chair Pub Facilities; Newton Schl Comm 1985-93, Chair 1989-93; NSF Grant in Math for NY Univ; *office:* Brookline HS 115 Greenough St Brookline MA 02146*

SCHNIPPERT, DORI GLENN, Art Dept Chairperson & Teacher; *b:* Greensburg, PA; *m:* William; *c:* Kirsten, Gretchen Bittler, Meaghen; *ed:* Clarion Univ (BS) Art, Elem Ed 1962; Elmira Coll (MS) Art His 1986; Attnd Mansfield Univ, OH Weslayn, Elmira Coll; *cr:* Virgin Island Tchr 1962-65, NJ Tchr 1965-70; FL Ed Ed Sci Jr HS Tchr 1968-70; CT Schl Head of Ed Lab Pre Schl 1970-79; PA Schl Art Tchr 1980-85; Notre Dame HS Art Tchr 1986-; *ai:* Frosh Moderator; Art Club Spon; NEA 1962-; NYSATA 1986-; NAtl Endowment Arts Study in Italy Winner 1990; *office:* Notre Dame HS 1400 Maple Ave Elmira NY 14904

SCHNITZEL, FREDERICK RICHARD, Industrial Technology Teacher; *b:* Atlantic City, NJ; *m:* Theresa E. Mc Carthy; *c:* Jacob, Emily, Sara; *ed:* Glassboro St Coll (BA) Indstrl Tech 1972; *cr:* Pleasantville HS Tchr 1972-; *ai:* Indstrl Tech, Bus Ed Dept Chprsn; Bldg, Planning, Tech Comms; NEA 1972-, Tech Comm; *office:* Pleasantville HS 350 S Franklin Ave Pleasantville NJ 08232

SCHOENEGGE, PAUL WILLIAM, HS Spanish Teacher; *b:* Athens, OH; *m:* Christine A.; *ed:* Post Grad Educ Courses Akron Univ; *cr:* Margaretta HS Span, Amer His, World His Tchr 1981-; *ai:* Frgn Lang, Frgn Traveling, Drama Club Adv; Stu Govt, Frosh Clas Adv8th Grd Vlybl, 8-9 Grd Bsktbl, 7-8 Grd Track Coach; OAFLT, OEA, NEA, Margaretta Tchrs Assn 1981-; *office:* Margaretta HS 209 Lowell St Castalia OH 44824

SCHOENFELDT, SANDRA LEE, Fifth Grade Teacher; *b:* Worcester, MA; *m:* Douglas L.; *c:* Steven; *ed:* 30 Addl Hrs; *cr:* Auburn Schl System Grd 5 Tchr 23 1/2 Yrs; *ai:* Auburn Youth Cncl; Take On Stu Tchrs Yearly; AEA, NEA, MTA 1970-; Tchr of Excl Awd Auburn Chamber of Commerce 1992; *office:* Julia Bancroft Oxford & Vinal Sts Auburn MA 01501

SCHOENING, CAROLE ELIZABETH, Professor of Chemistry; *b:* Brooklyn, NY; *m:* William S. Rockett; *ed:* Elizabethtown Coll (BS) Chem 1964; Mt Holyoke Coll Univ of MA (PHD) Organic Chem 1969; TX Tech Univ Scndry Schl Tchng Cert 1971-72; *cr:* TX Tech Univ Post Doctoral Fellow 1969-71; Tahoka TX HS Chem Tchr 1971-75; Burlington Cty Coll Chem Prof 1975-; *ai:* Chemical Advy Comm; Barry Goldwater Schlsp Fac Rep; ACS Affiliate Chptr Adv; ACS 1964-; NJEA, NEA 1975-; Society of Symatic 1968-; NJ Synad Stewardship Comm; ELCA 1989-; NSF Loci Grant 1979-81; NJ Dept Higher Ed Tech, Eng Grant 1988-89; Union

CArbide Flwshp Mt Holyoke Coll 1968-69; Welch Post Doctoral Flwshp 1969-71; Fac Flwshp 1977, 1978, 1987; *office:* Burlington County Coll Rte 530 Pemberton NJ 08068

SCHOENINGER, WILLIAM F., Sixth Grade Teacher; *b:* Philadelphia, PA; *m:* Marybeth B. Weber; *c:* Kirstin, Brittan, William; *ed:* West Chester Univ (BS) Elem Ed 1973; Temple Univ (MS) Elem Ed 1977; Doctoral Prgm; Post Grad Stud Villanova Univ, Penn St Univ; *cr:* Folsom Elem Schl Sixth Grd Tchr 1974-82; Edgewood Elem Schl Sixth Grd Tchr 1982-89; Ridley MS Sixth Grd Tchr 1989-; *ai:* IM Dir; Kndgtn Juggling Spon; Prof Dev Comm Co-Chprsn; Impact Co-Dir; NEA 1973-; PSMA 1996; Brandywine Yth Club 1993-, Age Group Commissioner; Twp Hockey League 1992-, Coach; Impact Grant 1991; PECO Ec Ed Grant 1995; *office:* Ridley MS Free & Dupont Sts Ridley Park PA 19078*

SCHOENSTADT, BARBARA L., Teacher of Gifted Education; *b:* Philadelphia, PA; *m:* Steven E.; *c:* Scott, Bruce, Cori; *ed:* Temple Univ (BA) Ed 1962; Beaver Coll (MS) Ed 1979; 60 Addl Credits; *cr:* Faust Elem Schl Tchr of Gifted 1979-82; Struble Elem Schl 4th Grd Tchr 1982-87, Tchr of Gifted 1987-; *ai:* Rdng Comm 1988; Sci Fair Coord 1987-; Prof Clown; Sunshine Coord 1985-93; NEA, BTEA 1979-; NCTM 1993-; CEC 1990-; Congregation Beth Chaim 1974-; Clown R Us 1994-.

SCHOFF, MARCIA WENDELL, Kndgtn Tchr & Colorguard Dir; *b:* Gloversville, NY; *m:* Philip H.; *c:* Wendi, Caryn, Philip; *ed:* Fulton-Montgomery Comm Coll (AAS) Cmptr Programming 1972; Empire St Coll (BA) Educl, Bus Ed 1981; SUNY at Cortland (MS) N-6 Ed 1988; *cr:* GE-Knolls Atomic Power Lab Data Recorder Operator 1970-72; White Mop Wringer Mfg Co Cmptr Operator, Programmer 1972-77; Fulton-Montgomery Comm Coll Adj Cmptr Prof 1982-84; St Johnsville C S Kndgtn Tchr 1982-83; Oppenheim-Ephratah CS K, 2nd, 5th Grd Tchr 1983-; *ai:* Colorguard Dir; AFT, NEA 1982-; NYSUT 1982-, Sec, Union Rep; Parish Cncl 1990-, Sec; St Patrick's Church 1990-, Lector, Instr; *office:* Oppenheim Ephratah Ctl Schl 6486 State Highway 29 Saint Johnsville NY 13452*

SCHOFIELD, GERALD C., Humanities Dept Supervisor; *b:* Philadelphia, PA; *m:* Lorraine Joyce Klamer; *c:* Sean, Jennifer Oakley, Kristen; *ed:* St Francis Coll at Loretto (BA) His 1965; Trenton St Coll (MA) His 1973; 33 Post Grad Hrs; *cr:* Holy Cross HS His Tchr 1965-69; Lenape HS His Tchr 1969-77; Cherokee HS His Tchr 1977-94, Supvr Hum Dept 1994-; *ai:* NHS, Stu of Month, Dist Long-Range Planning, Schlsp Selection Comms; Tchr of 20th Century Us His Modern European Hist AP; NASSP, ASCD, NCSS 1994-; Natl Endowment for Hum Grant 1992; NEH Grant 1994; *office:* Cherokee HS Willow Bend Rd Marlton NJ 08053*

SCHOFIELD, MARY ALICE A., Health Teacher; *b:* Watertown, NY; *ed:* Monroe CC (AS) Lbrl Arts 1975; Cortland St (BS) Hlth Ed 1977; 30+ Credit Hrs for Permanent Cert; *cr:* Fairport HS Hlth Tchr 1977-; *ai:* Boys JV Vollybl Coach; Mem of Core & Shared Decision Making Teams; Adv of Core Wellness Team; NYSFPHE 1977-; NYSUT 1977-; FEA 1977-.

SCHOFIELD, TIMOTHY L., Instructor of Statistics; *b:* Haddonfield, NV; *m:* Lynne Englund; *c:* Sean; *ed:* Lafayette Coll (BS) Math 1973; Univ of PA (MA) Statistics 1976; *cr:* Merck & Co Assoc Dir Bionetrics Rsrch 1976-; *ai:* ASA 1976-; Bionetrics Soc 1976-; DIA 1976-; Course Dir Tchr; Scientific Articles Pub; Co-Author of Textbook Statistics for Researchers; *office:* Ursinus Coll PO Box 1000 Collegeville PA 19426

SCHOLL, JOHN NEWMAN, Associate Professor; *b:* Detroit, MI; *m:* Theresa Ovecka; *c:* Adam J.; *ed:* Alma Coll (BS) Bio 1961; Temple Univ (MED) Psych 1968, (EDD) Psych 1974; Post Doctoral Trng Prgm Univ of PA Dept of Psych Marriage Counsel; *cr:* USAF Capt 1962-68; Comm Coll of Phila PA Assoc Prof 1970-; *office:* Community Coll Of Philadelphia 1700 Spring Garden St Philadelphia PA 19130

SCHOLZ, JEAN LABRIOLA, Biomedical Editor; *b:* Summit, NJ; *m:* Karl W.; *ed:* Millersville Univ (BS) Biochem 1983; Univ of PA (PHD) Molecular Bio, Genetics 1990; Attnd Temple Univ; *cr:* DNA Plant Tech Corp Rsrch Scientist 1989-93; Univ of PA Adj Instr 1991-; Ursinus Coll Asst Prof Bio 1993-95; Millersville Univ Adj Instr 1993-; Information Ventures Inc Biomed Editor 1996; *ai:* Steering Comm; Native Plants in Landscape Conf; AAAS; Local Theatre Groups 1992-; Main Line Unitarian Church, Soc Action; NSF-ILI Grant Co-PI 1994-95; Article Pub.*

SCHON, GREGORY PAUL, Human Sexuality Educator; *b:* Trenton, NJ; *m:* Rita Pepper; *c:* Paul, Matthew, Rachel; *ed:* Trenton St Coll (BS) Hlth Ed 1973; Towson St Univ (MA) Hlth Sci 1974; Trenton St Coll (MA) Counseling, Psych 1982; NY Univ PHD Candidate Human Sexuality; *cr:* Towson St Univ Hlth Instr 1973-74; Sheppard Pratt Psych Hospital Hlth Instr 1973-74; Edison HS Hlth, Sexuality Educator 1973-; Trenton St Coll Adjunct Fac Hlth, Sexuality 1975-92; *ai:* Core Team; Therapy Group; Grief Grp Facilitator, Staff Coord; Peer Disc Grps; NEA 1973-; Edison Tchr Assn 1973-, Tchr of Yr 1989; Soc Scientific Stud of Sex, Sex Informational Ed Cncl of US 1988-; Doctoral Dissertation HS Dating Violence; *home:* 1 Moro Dr Mercerville NJ 08619

SCHONFELD, BELLA, Assistant Professor; *b:* Leipzig, Germany; *m:* Raymond Goldwater; *c:* Mark, Monica Grajower; *ed:* City Coll (BA) Fr Lit 1972; NYU (MA) Counseling 1974; Columbia Univ (EDD) Family, Comm Ed 1989; *cr:* Touro College Asst Prof 1974-; *ai:* AACD 1974-.

SCHOOF, JAMES DAVID, Industrial Education Teacher; *b:* Montclair, NJ; *m:* Renee F. Auditore; *c:* Dustin J., Jeremy F.; *ed:* Glassboro St Coll (BA) Indstrl Ed, Tech 1977; *cr:* Hillsborough MS Indstrl Ed Tchr 1977-87; Hillsborough HS Indstrl Ed Tchr 1987-; *ai:* NJ St Systemic Initiative Thrust II Team; NEA, NJ Ed Assn 1977-; Natl Yth Sports Coaches Assn 1993-; *office:* Hillsborough HS 466 Raider Blvd Belle Mead NJ 08502

SCHOONOVER, ROBERT ALAN, English Teacher; *b:* Wadsworth, OH; *m:* Carolyn; *c:* Mark, Katie; *ed:* Heidelberg Coll (BA) Eng, Educ 1973; Akron U (MA) Educ 1983; *cr:* Barberton City Schls Eng Tchr 1973-74; Norton Schls Eng Tchr 1974-83; Wadsworth City Schls Eng Tchr 1983-; *ai:* Drama Dir; OJ Work Renovation Comm 1994-; *office:* Wadsworth HS 625 Broad St Wadsworth OH 44281

SCHOPP, DAVID L., Music Teacher; *b:* Tyrone, PA; *ed:* PA St Univ (BS) Music Ed 1987; Attnd Villanova Univ; *cr:* Tredyffrin Easttown SD General Inst, Choral Music Tchr 1988; Norristown Area HS Band Dir 1988-; *ai:* Marching & Jazz Band Dir; Indoor Dir; MENC 1986-; NEA 1988-; AF of M 1992-; Gift of Time 1988-89, 1992-93; *office:* Norristown Area HS 1900 Eagle Dr Norristown PA 19403

SCHOPP, KENNETH DAVID, Social Studies Teacher; *b:* Hartford, CT; *m:* Cathy Kennedy; *c:* Caitlin, Matthew; *ed:* Springfield Coll (BA) His 1974; Montclair St Univ (MA) Admin & Supervision 1982, (MA) Curr & His 1985; 30+ Credit Hrs Curr & His; *cr:* Franklin Ave MS Soc Stu Tchr 1975-; *ai:* Natl Geographic Geog Bee Coord; Coached Bsktbl & Bsbl for 15 Yrs; PAL Coach; NCSS 1989-; NEA, NJEA, FLEA 1975-, Local Rep; PAL Bsktbl & Bsbl Coach 1994-; Lesson Plans Pub in Various Books; *office:* Franklin Avenue MS 755 Franklin Ave Franklin Lakes NJ 07417

SCHOPPMAN, SUSAN G., Mathematics Teacher; *b:* Rockville Center, NY; *m:* Stephen Schoppman; *c:* Stacie, Shannon; *ed:* St Univ Coll at Oneonta (BS) Elem Ed 1975; St Univ at Stony Brook (MALS) Lbrl Arts 1989-; *cr:* Bellport HS Math Tchr 1984-; *ai:* Var Girls Cross Cntry, Track & Field Coach; Assn of Math Tchrs of NY St 1990-; *office:* Bellport HS Beaver Dam Rd Brookhaven NY 11719

SCHOR, GAIL S., Grade Advisor & Guidance Cnslr; *b:* Brooklyn, NY; *m:* Mark; *c:* Jill, Michael; *ed:* (BS) Hlth PE 1971; (MED) PE 1973; (MED) Hlth1976; Provisional St Cert Guid 1994; *cr:* B N Cardozo HS Tchr, Grd Adv Cnslr 1971-; *ai:* Teen Outreach Preg Prev Prgm Adv; Project Best Biling Prgm, Evening Cnslrs; *office:* Benjamin N Cardozo HS 57-00 223 St Bayside NY 11753

SCHOR, TOBY, Administrative Assistant; *b:* New York City, NY; *ed:* Long Island Univ (BS) Elem Ed 1967; Boston Univ (MED) Elem Ed 1968; St John's Univ (PD) Supervision, Admin 1988; *cr:* PS 36 Tchr 1968-87, Admin Asst 1987-; *ai:* Dist Math Comm; Parent Wkshps Math; Chorus Coord; UFT, AFT 1968-; Phi Delta Kappa 1988-; *office:* PS 36 187-01 Foch Blvd Saint Albans NY 11412*

SCHORPP, JANICE FINKEY, 4th Grade Teacher; *b:* Carlisle, PA; *m:* Edward L.; *ed:* Slippery Rock Univ (BS) Elem Ed, Spec Ed 1971; Shippensburg Univ (MED) Elem Cnslng 1973; Temple Univ (DED) Elem Ed 1986; *cr:* Carlisle Area Schl Dist Spec Ed 1971-73, 4th Grd Tchr 1973-; *office:* Crestview Elem Schl 623 W Penn St Carlisle PA 17013

SCHOTT, KEVIN JOHN, High School Technology Teacher; *b:* Buffalo, NY; *m:* Elizabeth Grucela; *c:* Christopher, Nicholas, Erik; *ed:* Buffalo St (BS) Tech Ed 1977, (MS) Tech Ed 1984; Addl Hrs Cmptr Class; *cr:* Orchard Park HS Tech, Photography Tchr 1978-; *ai:* Sports Card Club, Schl Newspaper Adv; Video Tape Ftbl Games; Photographer Orchard Park Pride; Schl Play Photographer; AFT, NY St United Tchrs 1979-; Orchard Park Tchr Assn 1979-, Photographer Edctr 1990; World Univ Games Stu Press Corp 1993-94, Adv; Skating Assn for the Blind & Handicapped 1993-94, Adult Ed Tchr, Vol; Achvmt in Educl Jrnlsm Awd of Excl NY Schl Pub Relations Assn; Western NY Schl Press Assn Guest Speaker; Staff Photographer Buffalo Bills 1989-90; *office:* Orchard Park HS 4040 Baker Rd Orchard Park NY 14127

SCHOTT, LAWRENCE W., Mathematics Teacher; *b:* Mount Carmel, PA; *ed:* Bucknell Univ (BS) Ed & Math 1989, (MS) Ed 1996; *cr:* Bloomsburg Chrstn Schl Math Tchr 1990-91; Stephen Decatur HS Math Tchr 1992-; *ai:* Power Team; JV Bsbl Coach; FCA Adv; Amer Drug Free Powerlifting Assn 1988-, MD St Champion; *home:* 509 Bay St Apt 219 Berlin MD 21811

SCHOTTENFELD, DANIEL M., History Teacher; *b:* New York, NY; *m:* Marilyne Meier; *c:* Aaron, Noah; *ed:* SUNY Stonybrook (BA) Pol Sci 1967; NYU (MA) Phil of Ed 1970; U of ME at Orono (CAS) Curr 1980; *cr:* IS 88 Tchr 1967-71; Dexter Regnl HS Tchr 1972-; *office:* Dexter Regional HS 12 Abbott Hill Rd Dexter ME 04930

SCHRADE, SHERRY EGAN, Mathematics Teacher; *b:* New York, NY; *m:* Steven; *c:* Kelly, Amy, Kyle; *ed:* Russell Sage Coll (BA) Math 1972; Union Coll (MST) Math 1990; Post Grad Stud St Univ of NY at New Paltz; *cr:* Schoharie Cntrl Schl Math Tchr 1972-76; Duanesburg Cntrl Schl Math Tchr 1976-77 & 1985-87; Niskayuna HS Math Tchr 1979; Canajoharie HS Math Tchr 1988-; *ai:* Capital Dist HS Challenge Team Adv; AMTNYS 1986-; Sunday Schl Tchr 1992-; Church Construction Comm 1993-, Chprsn; NYS Dept of Ed Consultant; TANDY Tchr of Yr 1994-96; *office:* Canajoharie HS 10 Erie Blvd Canajoharie NY 13317*

SCHRADER, ERIC BYRON, Band Director; *b:* Washington, PA; *ed:* Duquesne Univ (BS) Music Ed 1993; Youngstown St Univ (MS) Music Ed; *cr:* Commodore Perry Schl Band Dir 1993-; *ai:* Concert, Jazz, Pep, Marching Bands 1993-; Stu Cncl 1994-; Jr High Bsktbl Coach 1994-95; MENC, PMEA, NEA, CPEA, MCBDA 1993-; F & AM 1995-; Lions Club 1996; 1993-94 Golden Apple Awd Winner; Tchr of Month March 1994; *office:* Commodore Perry Schl 3002 Perry Hwy Hadley PA 16130*

SCHRADER, JILL ELLEN (GEORGE), Surgical Technician Instructor; *b:* Lancaster, OH; *c:* Melissa Jean Compton, Theresa; *ed:* Grant Hospital Schl of Nursing 1967; Attnd OH St Univ; *cr:* Grant Medical Ctr Surgery Staff Nurse 1967-76; Anthony S. Neri Office, Hospital Nurse 1976-81; Ft Hayes MEC Sr Surgical Tech Instr 1981-; *ai:* VICA Adv; Co-Author of Voc Newsletter Locally; OH Ed Assn 1985-; OH Assn Voc Occupations Tchr of Yr 1987; St Staff Mem VIC Skill Olympia 1987-90; *home:* 26 E Oak St Canal Winchester OH 43110

SCHRAMM, PATRICIA A., French Teacher; *b:* Schnectady, NY; *m:* Frank E; *c:* Michelle Lynn, Michael Dwight; *ed:* Otterbein (BA) Fr 1971; OH Univ (MA) Fr 1988-89; Mc Gill Univ Montreal; *cr:* Whitehall HS Tchr 2 Yrs; DODDS Schls Phillippines Clark Air Base 10 Yrs; Licking Valley HS Tchr 10 Yrs; Heath HS Tchr 5 Yrs; *ai:* Sr Class, Fr Club Adv; HEA 1991-, Tchr of Yr 1992; OFLA; LINC; HOLA; Rockefeller Flwshps 1987; Honeywell Grant 1996; *office:* Heath HS 300 Licking View Dr Heath OH 43056

SCHRECENGOST, LAURIE ANN, Music Professor; *b:* Dallas, TX; *m:* Kevin D.; *ed:* Baptist Bible Coll (BS) Bible, Ed 1986, (BSM) Music 1986; St Univ of NY at Binghamton (MMS) Piano 1992; *cr:* Private Studio Tchr 1982-; SUNY at Binghamton Grad Asst, Tchng 1992-94, Staff Pianist 1994-95; Bapt Bible Coll Music Instr 1986-95; *ai:* Natl Guild of Piano Tchrs 1987-; Music Edctrs, MTNA 1993-; *home:* 718 Radio Rd Elizabethtown PA 17022

SCHRECK, MARY SCUDIERI, First Grade Teacher; *b:* Brooklyn, NY; *m:* Alfred O.; *c:* Alfred S., Mae L. Meoli, Michael J., Rose M. Marvel; *ed:* Hunter Coll (BA) Ed, Lang 1956, (MS) Ed 1965; 60 Addl Credits Whole Lang, Individual Instr, Solving Problems, Assertive Tchng, Tchr Effective Trng, Meeting with Parents, Reaching Underachiever Child; *cr:* Mac Levy Dance School Ballet, Tap Dance Instr 1951-53; Roxy Theatre & Radio City Prof Dancer 1951-53; *ai:* Hobbies are Traveling, Rdng, Dancing, Creative Art Work; NEA 1961-; Hicksville Cong of Tchr 1961; Hicksville Bd of Ed Tchng in Excl Achievement Awd 1989; PTA Lifetime Membership Awd 1988; 25 Yrs Dedicated Svc Hicks Congress of Tchrs Awd 1987; *home:* 170 Park Ave Williston Park NY 11596*

SCHRECK, THOMAS JOSEPH, Human Services Instr; *b:* Albany, NY; *ed:* Notre Dame Univ (BA) Psych & Bus 1983; Russell Sage Coll (MA) Addiction & Psych 1990; Hospital Admin Cert Saint Josephs Coll; Inst for Rational Emotive Therapy Cert; *cr:* Sage Coll Instr 1990-93; Hudson Valley Comm Coll Instr 1992-; *ai:* Amateur Boxing Coach-Referee; Nursing Home Vol; Prof Cnslr Magazine 2 Times; Books Thinking and Feeling, Never Say Relapse; *home:* 38 Niblock Ct Albany NY 12206*

SCHREIBER, MARIA DESILLAS, High School Counselor; *b:* Sanford, ME; *m:* Robert R.; *c:* Susan Cramer, Robert T.; *ed:* OH St Univ (BSEd) Speech & Eng 1961; Kent St Univ (MED) Cnslng 1967; Attnd Univ of Akron, Ashland 18 Hrs After MS; *cr:* Akron Pub Schls Eng & Speech Tchr 1961-67, Jr HS Cnslr 1967-69, Career Specialist 1978-81, Alternative Schl Tchr 1981-84, Eng Tchr 1984-86, HS Cnslr 1986-; *ai:* NHS Comm; Intnl Baccaubureate & Career & Coll Cnslr; OH Proficiency Tutor; Liaison Cnslr APS; Akron Cnslrs Assn 1978-, Exec Comm; Akron Ed Assn 1978-; OH Cnslrs Assn 1986-; OH Assn of Coll Admin Cnslrs 1986-; Siama Delta Iota 1960-, Sec; Sunday Schl 1984-87, Dir; Philoptodros Soc 1990-; Shining Apple Awd 1992; City-Wide Inservice Comm for Cnslrs; *office:* Firestone HS 333 Rampart Ave Akron OH 44313

SCHREIBER, PAUL G., Language Arts Teacher; *b:* Buffalo, NY; *ed:* Canisius Coll (AB) Eng 1969, (MS) Scndry Ed 1972; 9 Post Grad Psych Hrs; *cr:* Buffalo Pub Schl System Lang Arts Tchr 1971-; Intensive Eng Lang Inst Part Time Inst SUNYAB 1973-85; Saint Leo the Great Church Dir of Music 1989-; *ai:* Kappa Sigma Phi Adv; BTF, NEA 1970-; Church Musicians Guild, Natl Assn of Pastoral Musicians 1989-; Taught Eng in Iran for 3 Months 1976; Supervised Tchrs at Iran-Amer Soc Hutchinson Central Tech HS 256 S Elmwood Ave Buffalo NY 142

SCHREINER, DAWN MARIE, Special Education Teacher; *b:* B NJ; *c:* Caitlyn; *ed:* Kean Coll (BA) Tchr of Handicap 1992; *cr:* HS Tchr 1992-; *ai:* Sr Class Adv; NJEA 1992-; Teen Ctr 1996, Ad Articles Pub on Preventing Teen Pregnancy; *office:* Bayonne HS 2 Ave A Bayonne NJ 07002*

SCHREINER, LEE CHARLES, Elementary Enrichment Tea Lackawana, NY; *m:* Jane Ellen Blackburn; *c:* Damien, Sebast Urbana Coll (BA) Ed, Fine Arts 1975; OH St Univ (MA) Early, Mid Ed 1985, (MS) GATE Ed 1990; Addl Hrs Toward PHD 1990-; G Cert; *cr:* Southwestern City Schls 4-5th Grd Tchr 1975-85, Elem Ec Tchr 1985-; *ai:* Odyssey of the Mind Dist, St, World Judge, Write Soccer, Cmptr Team Coach; Essex, Governors SU Insts; Washing Ny Trip Adv; Soccer Clinician; SWEA, OEA, NEA 1975, Dist, Del; Phi Delta Kappa 1985-, PALS Dist Rep, Kappan Awd; OSU, Alumni Assoc 1975-; Southwest Pub Lib Levy Comm 1980-, SWC Comm 1980-, Strategic Planning, Tech Comm Dist 1980-; OH St Yr Southwestern City Schls 1992;OH PTSA Edctr of Yr 1992; Articles Pub; OH Soccer Hall of Fame Player, Coach; *home* Clayburn Dr E Grove City OH 43123

SCHRENK, JOHN R., Social Studies Teacher; *b:* Philadelphia, Cynthia D. Persia; *ed:* Holy Family Coll (BA) Ed 1989; His Grad St Leo the Great Schl 7th-8th Grd Tchr 1990-; *ai:* Yrbk Adv 1992- 1989-; PSEA 1988-; *office:* St Leo the Great Schl 6649 T Philadelphia PA 19135*

SCHRENKER, RICHARD ROBERT,JR., Principal; *b:* Cincinna *m:* Laurinda Diane Campbell; *c:* Jason, Julie; *ed:* Miami Univ (BS 1974, (MED) Scndry Ed 1981; *cr:* Talawanda HS Fr Tchr 19 Landmark Chrstn Schl Span & Fr Tchr 1975-, Prin 1981-; *office:* La Christian Schl 500 Oak Rd Evendale OH 45241*

SCHREYER, MARY BENAMATI, Home Ec & Food Service I Indiana, PA; *c:* Philip, Brian, Brady; *ed:* IN Univ of PA (BS) H 1972, (MED) Ed 1978; *cr:* Apollo-Ridge HS Tchr 1972-76; Penn S Home Economist 1982-86; Altoona Sr HS Tchr 1986-88; Tyrone H 1988-91; Hollidaysburg Area Sr HS Tchr 1991-; *ai:* Amer Home E *office:* Hollidaysburg Area Sr HS 1510 N Montgomery St Hollida PA 16648

SCHRIDER, PATRICIA RAINEY, Second Grade Teach Philadelphia, PA; *m:* Terence Powell; *c:* Carly B., Jackson Appalachian St Univ at Boone (BS) Early Chldhd Ed 1979; Spe Credit Hrs; *cr:* Saw Mills Elem Schl Rdng Remediation 19 Waterford Twp Schls 2nd Grd Tchr 1983-; *ai:* Fac Cncl; Sunshine NJEA, Home & Schl Assn, WTEA 1983-; Literacy Vol of Amer Governors Tchr Recognition Awd 1989; Acted as cooperating Tchr Tchr 1990; *office:* Atco Elem Schl 160 Cooper Rd Atco NJ 08004*

SCHRODER, VALERIE KATHERINE, Chemistry Teach Hackensack, NJ; *ed:* Fairleigh Dickinson Univ (BS) Sci 1960, (MA Prsnl Svcs 1972; Montclair Univ Supervisory Cert 1981; *cr:* Linc Sci Tchr 1960-70; Passaic HS Chem Tchr 1970-; *ai:* Phy-Chem Clu Sci Fair Organizer; NSTA 1970-; NJSTA 1975-; NEA, NJEA, Educl Assn 1960-; Rutherford Woman's Coll Club 1970-, Schlsp Chm; Organist, Choir Dir Local Church 1984-; NJ Outstdng Tchr Xi Scientific Rsrch Soc FDU 1982; Edward J Merrill Awd Amer Ch 1989; Homer J Hall Outstdng Chem Tchr Awd NJ Inst of Chemists *office:* Passaic HS 170 Paulison Ave Passaic NJ 07055*

SCHROECK, JOHN THOMAS, Computer Teacher; *b:* Erie, P Michele-Marie Iarussi; *ed:* Gannon Univ (BS) Elem & Early Chl 1987; Addl 24 Post Grad Credit Hrs in Elem Ed & Cmptr Sci; *cr:* George Schl Soc Stud, Math & Sci Tchr 1989-95, Cmptr Admin 199 Boys & Girls Cross Cntry Coach; Cmptr Club Adv; Intnl Schl to Sch Comm; Giant Eagle Golden Apple Tchrs Awd Winner; *office:* St C Schl 1612 Bryant St Erie PA 16509

SCHROEDEL-UGUR, HUBERTA WOLF, Coord for Deaf & Hearing; *b:* Philadelphia, PA; *m:* Serafettin Mehmet Ugur; *c:* Ken Ugur; *ed:* Daemen Coll (BA) Sociology 1967; Univ of AZ at Tucson Cnslng 1969; Bank St Coll (MS) Educl Ldrshp 1994; Amer I Psychotherapy & Psychoanalysis 170 Credit Hrs; NY Univ Deaf Credit Hrs; *cr:* Rockland St Hosp Transitional Ed Coord 1969-72; N for the Deaf Head Tchr for Eng as 2nd Lang 1972-83; NY Bd of E of Deaf Stdnts 1972-; NY Ctr for Law & Deaf Exec Dir 1980-; NY Asst Prof 1981-85; *ai:* Jr Natl Assn for the Deaf; Deaf Yth Adv; Unit of Tchrs Capably Disabled Tchrs Comm; United Fed of Tchrs 1974- 1978-; Natl Assn of Female Execs 1982-; Amer Women for Ec Dev Turkish-Amer Fed 1994-; NY Civic Assn for the Deaf 1981-; Natl A Notary Pub 1994-; Durfee Intnl Awd for Human Rights; Vincent Ast for Legal Ed Grant; NY Fnd for Legal Ed Grant; *office:* Middle Colle 45-35 VanDam St Long Island Cty NY 11101

SCHROEDER, CAROL ANN, Fourth Grade Teacher; *b:* Defiance *m:* Owen; *c:* Debra, Sandra Johnson, Steve; *ed:* Defiance Coll (BA) Ed 1971; Bowling Green St (MS) Elem Ed 1981; *cr:* Cntrl Local Elem Tchr 1961-65, 1967-69; Edgerton MS Tchr 1971-; Edgerton Schl Tchr 1971-; *ai:* NEA, OEA 1961-; Edgerton Ed Assn 1971-; Mu of Alpha Delta Kappa 1981-, Pres; *home:* 8563 Scott Rd Edgert 43517

SCHROEDER, DIANE LYNN, Third Grade Teacher; *b:* Elyria, O Baldwin-Wallace Coll (BS) Ed 1969; 10 Credit Hrs; *cr:* Windsor Elen 2nd Grd Tchr 1969-70, 1st Grd Tchr 1970-74, 2nd Grd Tchr 1974-7 Grd Tchr 1975-76, 1st, 2nd Grd Tchr 1976-77, 3rd Grd Tchr 1977 Family Sci Coord; Young Authors Comm; Delta Kappa Gamma 1977- VP, Publicity, Prof Affairs; Elyria Ed Assn, OEA, NEA, Kappa De 1969-; NESTELA 1994-; Elyria Endowment Grant Sci Satchels; Author Tchr Ldr; Lorain Journal Newspaper Former Stu; Partici NASA Lewis Rsrch Ctr Seminars; *office:* Windsor Elem Schl 264 Wi Dr Elyria OH 44035

SCHROEDER, DIANE MARIE, Music Teacher; *b:* Findlay, O Omer I.; *c:* Leslie, Sarah; *ed:* Bluffton Coll (BA) Music Ed 1984; W St Univ (ME) Curr & Supvervision 1993; *cr:* Leipsic Local Schl Tchr 1984-; *ai:* NEA 1984-, MENC, OMEA 1987-; *office:* Leipsic Schl 232 Oak St Leipsic OH 45856

SCHROEDER, FRANK RICHARD, Social Studies Teacher; *b:* Pu County, OH; *m:* Dorothy Jane Birkmeier; *c:* Wayne, Ryan, Suzanne, B *ed:* OH St Univ (BA) Soc Stud 1972; Voc Ag Tchr; *cr:* Miller City Soc Stud Tchr 1972-79, Voc Ag Tchr 1979-86; Kalida Local Schls Soc 1986-; *ai:* NEA, OEA 1972-; MCEA 1974-, Pres; Church Holy Name Pres 1975; AP-UPI OH Coach of Yr 1988, 1989; Girls Var Bsktbl 198

SCHROEDER, JUDITH FEATHERS, Kindergarten Teacher; *b:* I OH; *m:* Errol Thomas; *c:* Nathan, Kate, Peter, Jacquie; *ed:* Bowling Univ (BS) Ed 1969; 150 Addl Hrs; *cr:* Van Wert City Schl Home E Trng Tchr 1969-70; Ottoville Local Schl Home Ec Voc Tchr 197 Leipsic Local Schl Home Ec Voc Tchr 1973-74; Jennings Local Kndgtn Tchr 1974-; *ai:* Jr HS Vlybl Asst; Former Var Chrldng Adv; o Jennings Local Schls 130 W 2nd St Box 187 Fort Jennings OH 4584

SCHROEPFER, JOSEPH, Math, PE & Religion Teacher; *b:* Jersey NJ; *m:* Allison Roehrich; *c:* Jessica, Stephanie, Shannon; *ed:* Amer

S) Criminal Justice 1980; 21 Grad Credits in Cnslng at Southern CT l; Spec Ed Cert at Georgian Court Coll; *cr:* Calvary Acad Tchr, 1982-; *ai:* Boys Bsktbl, Soccer Coach; *home:* 209 Ronald Rd ood NJ 08701

OLL, BEVERLY LOHR, English Instructor; *b:* Mt Pleasant, PA; l J. Jr.; *c:* Jamey, B. J.; *ed:* Alderson Broaddus Coll (BA) Ed 1971; rad Stud at CA St Univ & Univ of PA; *cr:* Mt Pleasant Area Schl ng Instr 1971-; *ai:* SADD & Sr Six Speakers Adv; NEA & PSEA Mt Pleasant Borough Cncl 1978-81, Finance Chm 3 Yrs; Lib Bd 1, Cncl Rep; Seton Hill Coll Tchng Excl Awd.

OMME, JEAN BIBLER, Third Grade Teacher; *b:* Perry Cty, OH; illiam; *ed:* OH Univ (BS) Ed-Summa Cum Laude 1970, (MA) mma Cum Laude 1973; *cr:* Millersport Elem Schl Kndgtn Tchr 7; Cedar Hghts Elem Schl Third-Fourth Grd Tchr 1968-; *ai:* Cncl Site-Based Comm; Delta Kappa Gamma 1975-, Treas; NEA, OEA LEA 1970-; Jennings Scholar; *home:* 529 Forest Rose Ave Lancaster 130

ON, STEVEN I., 7th Grd Social Studies Teacher; *b:* Troy, NY; *m:* a Lois; *c:* Amy, Peter, Andrew; *ed:* Univ of VT (BA) His-Hnrs 1969; at Albany (MA) His 1976; Schl Admin, Supvr Cert 1977; *cr:* Troy ist Scndry Ed Tchr 1969-; *ai:* AFT, NYSUT 1969-; Troy Narcotics Dev, Team Taught Positive Attitudes Towards Learning Sections to 300 Elem, MS, HS Tchrs; Channel 6 Tchr Who Made Difference; ted Wkshp Arts Alive Skidmore Coll & NYS Cncl for Children.*

OTH, CAROLINE WARD, Tchr of Gifted & Talented Prgm; *b:* ngton, DE; *m:* Lawrence L. Jr.; *c:* Kate Collins; *ed:* Kutztown St BS) Art Ed 1965; Rutgers Univ (EDM) Elem Ed 1981; Supervisory 989; 21 Credit Hrs Gifted & Talented Ed; 9 Credit Hrs Staff Dev; *cr:* Alpine Schl K-6th Grd Art Tchr 1965-69; Sandyston Walpack Schl Grd Art Tchr 1973-81; Frankford Twp Schl Tchr & Coord of Gifted nted 1981-, Staff Dev Ldr 1990-; *ai:* Stu Cncl Adv; Schl & Comm, Problem Solving Comms; MS Task Force; Natl Jr Honor Soc Adv; 1981-, Advy Cncl Chrprsn; NJEA 1965-; NJAGC 1983-; NJSCD Sussex Cty Assn for Gifted & Talented 1982-, Pres; Sussex Cty Arts itage Cncl 1984-, Bd of Trustees Mem; Sussex Cty Tchr of Yr 1988; Across the Water Tchr Exch (Russia) 1991-92; NJ Commissioner of vy Cncl on Gifted & Talented Ed 1993-; Sussex Cty Celebration of Co-Spon 1990-; *office:* Frankford Township Schl Box 430 hville NJ 07826*

RUENDER, EDWARD, 7th Grade Math Teacher; *b:* Lawrence, MA; nne Bresnahan; *c:* Kathleen, Edward Jr, Mark; *ed:* Plymouth St Coll Phys Sci 1970; U of Lowell (MMT) Math 1978; *cr:* N. A. MS Math, chr 1970-; *ai:* Sftbl Coach; NEA, MTA 1970-; N And Tea Assn 1970-, *ffice:* North Andover MS 495 Main St North Andover MA 01845*

BAUER-HARTMAN, MARJORIE ANN, Science Teacher; *b:* sburg, PA; *m:* Michael Hartman; *c:* Alexandra; *ed:* Lebanon Valley BS) Bio 1988; *cr:* Red Land HS Sci Tchr 1989-; *ai:* Vol Adv; NEA; Red Land HS 560 Fishing Creek Rd Lewisberry PA 17339

JBERT, BLYTHE GALLAWAY, English Teacher; *b:* Elizabeth, NJ; bert J.; *c:* Robert L., Amy Farris; *ed:* Denison Univ (BA) Eng 1968; Coll Appalachian Lit, His; Breadloaf Schl of Eng African-Amer ; Kent St Univ Adult Basic Ed Courses; *cr:* Morgan HS Eng Tchr Adult Basic Ed Instr 1979-85; *ai:* NHS, Tech-Prep Adv; Early Eng Assessment Prgm; NEA 1977-; NCTE 1980-; Lib Bd 1994-, Sec; loaf Schl of Eng Flwshp; OH Univ Partial Schlsp; *office:* Morgan HS aider Dr Mc Connelsville OH 43756

JBERT, CHEY COSTELLO, Theatre Arts & English Teacher; *b:* n, OH; *m:* Frank; *c:* Briana; *ed:* Kent St Univ (BS) Speech Ed 1980, D) Theatre 1991; 18 Addl Hrs; *cr:* Sandy Vly Local Theatre, Speech, Tchr 1980-91; Kent St Univ Co Curr Speech Act 1989-91; Jackson Theatre, Eng Tchr 1991-; *ai:* Drama Dir; Formerly Speech, Debate of 4 Natl Qualifiers; NEA, OEA 1980-; Sandy Vly Tchr of Yr; t Comm Wkshp at Mt Union Coll; *office:* Jackson Local Schls 7600 n Dr Massillon OH 44646

JBERT, SHARON E., Fifth Grade Teacher; *b:* Stuttgart, Germany; ian L.; *c:* Tracy, Jeremy; *ed:* Univ of TX at El Paso (BS) Sociology, Ed 1970; St Univ of NY at Buffalo (MS) Cl Rdng, Ed 1976; *cr:* ce Hills Elem Schl 4-5th Grd Tchr 1970-71; Clarence Centerel 4-5th Tchr 1972-74; St Stan's Elem Schl 5th Grd Tchr 1983-89; Whitney Intermediate Schl 5th Grd Tchr 1989-; *ai:* Grd Chair Org of 5th Grd Philadelphia, Fund Raising; Share-A-Day Starlab, Related Act Dist ; Quality Circle; Sci, Soc Stud Curr Comm; Assessment, Framework n; BARC 1983-89, 1995-; AFT 1989-; Christ Church 1996, Warden; rnik Observatory, Vol Edctr; *office:* Whitney Point Intermediate Sch ox 249 Whitney Point NY 13862

UCHERT, ROBERT J., Counselor; *b:* Pittsburgh, PA; *m:* Nancy; *c:* Joseph; *ed:* Clarion Univ (BS) Sociology 1968; CA Univ of PA) Ed 1973; Univ of Pittsburgh Credits Toward Doctorate; Slippery Univ Counseling Cert; *cr:* West Mifflin Area Cnslr, Tchr 1968-; *ai:* 1970-, Natl Certified Cnslr 1981-; Certified Prevention Specialist -; *office:* West Mifflin Area HS 91 Commonwealth Ave West Mifflin 5122

UCKER, JOANN PASTRICK, Soc Stud & Soc Sci Teacher; *b:* ra, NY; *m:* Gerald D.; *c:* Harold Morse, Melissa L. Morse, Carrie M. e; *ed:* Elmira Coll (BA) Soc Stud 1982, (MS) Ed 1986; Addl Six Post Hrs; *cr:* Horseheads HS Soc Sci, Amer Stud, Psych, Sociology Tchr -; *ai:* NCSS; Amer Psychological Assn; Tchrs of HS Psych Assn.

UENEMANN, CAROL A. (NASIFE), Art Teacher; *b:* Camden, NJ; rancis X. Jr.; *c:* Tara, Nicholas; *ed:* Glassboro St Coll (BA) Art Ed ; *cr:* Palmyra HS Art Tchr 1983-94; Delran HS Art Tchr 1994-; *ai:* Art Adv; NJAE 1983-; Article Pub; *office:* Delran HS 50 Hartford Rd an NJ 08075

UETTE, LISA HOLDEN, Mathematics Teacher; *b:* Mansfield, OH; andy; *ed:* OH St Univ (BS) Bus Admin 1986; *cr:* Marion Cath HS Tchr 1993-; *ai:* Soph Class, NHS Adv 1994-95; Math Club Adv -; Math Dept Chprsn 1994-; *office:* Marion Catholic Schl 1001 Mount on Ave Marion OH 43302*

UETZ, ELMER DAVID, Social Studies Teacher; *b:* Pittsburgh, PA; ary Ann Pusateri; *c:* Shannon, Beau, Molly; *ed:* Clarion Univ (BS) p Soc Stud 1970, (MS) Comm 1973; Akron Univ (MS) Admin 1977; West Branch HS Tchr & Coach 1971-72; Jackson HS Tchr & Coach -78; Perry HS Tchr & Coach 1978-80; Canton South HS Tchr & Head Coach 1980-86; Northwest HS Ath Dir 1986-88; Jackson HS Tchr & Ftbl Coach 1988-; *ai:* Head Ftbl, Head & Asst Track & Golf Coach; Adv; Head After-Prom Comm; Drug-Alcohol Prgm Dir; Asst Ftbl h Malone Coll; JMEA, OEA & NEA 1971-; OH Ftbl Coaches Assn -, Dir of St Ftbl Clinic 5 Yrs; Stark Cty Ftbl Coach of the Yr 1990; c Spkr; *office:* Jackson HS 7600 Fulton Rd NW Massillon OH 44646

UHART, ARTHUR LOVIS, English Teacher; *b:* Manitowoc, WI; *m:* a Alison McCash; *c:* Seren Theodora; *ed:* Univ of MN (BA) Eng 1987; ge Washington Univ (MA) Eng Lit 1992; Teach for Amer Summer *cr:* IS 162 Lola Rodriguez del Tio 8th Grd Communication Arts Tchr -91; Prince Georges Comm Coll Adjunct Prof of Eng 1993-; Wilson S Eng Tchr 1994-; *ai:* Internet, Military Sci Rdng & Theatre Clubs; WTU 1996; *office:* Woodrow Wilson Sr HS Nebraska Chesapeake NW Washington DC 20016

SCHUHART, BENJAMIN A., Music Department Chairperson; *b:* Baltimore, MD; *m:* Karleen Yohe; *c:* Alexander; *ed:* Shenandoah Conservatory (BME) Music Ed 1981, (MME) Music Ed 1986; *cr:* Greensville Cty HS Instrumental Music Tchr 1981-83; Patrick Henry HS Instrumental Music Tchr 1983-84; Johnson-Williams Intermediate Instrumental Music Tchr 1985-86; Luray HS Instrumental Music Tchr 1986-90; Magnolia MS Instrumental Music Tchr 1990-; *ai:* Aquarium Club Adv; Instrl Ldrshp Team; Magnolia MS Jazz Festival Founder; IDRS 1976-; MENC 1981-; NAJE 1981-; Susquehanna Symphony Orch 1992-; Shenandoah Conservatory Grad Assistantship 1984; *office:* Magnolia MS 299 Fort Hoyle Rd Joppa MD 21085

SCHULLER, LINDA K., German Teacher; *b:* Natrona Heights, PA; *m:* Gary W.; *c:* Scott, Laura; *ed:* IN Univ of PA (BS) Ger 1970, (MED) Ger Ed 1975; Lessing-Kolleg Marburg Germany Credit Hrs, Cert Prgm; Calvin Coll Introduction to Use TPR in Lang Instruction; *cr:* Center Area Schl Dist Ger Tchr 1970-74; Hopewell Area Schl Dist Ger Tchr 1974-; *ai:* Spon Ger Club, Delta Epsilon Phi; Co-Instr New Tchr Induction Prgm; Stu Assistance Prgm Mem; NEA, PSEA 1970-; AATG; MLA; PSMLA, Delta Phi Alpha; Western PA Chapter of NFSG 1972-78; Conducted Wrkshps for NFSG & PAMLA 1976-77; *office:* Hopewell Area Sr HS 1215 Longvue Ave Aliquippa PA 15001

SCHULT, ANNE BOURGEOIS, Dept Chprsn & Guidance Cnslr; *b:* Cleveland, OH; *m:* Robert G.; *c:* Robert L., Marianne E., David W.; *ed:* Univ of Dayton (BS) Math Ed 1965; Johns Hopkins Univ (MS) Guid, Cnslng 1987; Towson St Univ 6 Grad Credits Ed; Johns Hopkins Univ 15 Grad Credits in Curr; *cr:* Carroll HS Dayton OH, Math Tchr 1965-67; Severna Park HS Math Tchr 1980-83; Anne Arundel Co GATE Office Resource Tchr 1983-86; Meade HS Guid Cnslr 1986-; *ai:* Schl Improvement Team; Staff Liason Schlsps for Scholars; Weighted Grading & Grad Requirement Comm; NEA 1976-; ACA, ASCA, MSCA 1986-; NBCC 1991-; St Andrew Parish 1987-; Edctr of Month Anne Arundel Cty Pub Schls 1994; *office:* Meade Sr HS 1100 Clark Rd Fort Meade MD 20755

SCHULTE, DAVID H.,JR., Science Teacher; *b:* Allentown, PA; *c:* David III, Robert, Lornah, Kenneth; *ed:* Moravian Coll (BS) Chem 1970; Kutztown Univ (MS) Bio 1974; Marywood Coll (MA) Tchng 1995; Grad Work Univ of KS Botany; Grad Work Lehigh Univ Biochemistry; CESTA Trng; Textile Processing Courses Univ of NC, Clemson Univ; *cr:* Raytex Chem Corp Dye Lab Supvr 1967-79; Jauty Textile Corp Tech Mgr, Finishing Supt 1979-89; Johnsonburg SD Chem Tchr 1990; Mountain View SD Sci Tchr 1993-; *ai:* Portfolio, Elem, Scndry Sci Curr Comms; U-12 Soccer Coach; Vol Fireman, EMT; Church Yth Group Adv; NEA 1993-; ACS 1968-; Clifford Twp Vol Fire Co 1980-, 6 Yrs Bd of Dir, Trng Ofcr, Pres 2 Terms; BSA 1960-, Asst Scout Master Troop 190; Harford Congregational Church 1991-, Bd of Dir, Deacon; Susquehanna Cty Historical Soc 1982-; NWF, PAWF 1975-; Hazardous Materials DOT, Fire Acad Instr; PA DER Grant 1994-95; Keystone Integrated Framework Grant Team 1995; Skills Scrant Grant Phys Chem Dyeing Textiles 1994; Adj Instr Bio Luzerne Cty Comm Coll; *office:* Mountain View Jr Sr HS RR 1 Box 339 Kingsley PA 18826

SCHULTE, ELLEN GESSER, 7th Grade Social Studies Tchr; *b:* New York, NY; *m:* Paul H.; *c:* Caroline Richardson, Paul E., Mark E., Thomas J., Martha L.; *ed:* St Johns Univ (BA) His & Soc Stud 1964, (MS) Scndry Ed 1966; *cr:* EL Vandermeulen HS 11th Grd Tchr 1965-68; Batavia City Schls Tchr 1969-; *ai:* 6th & 7th Grds Hand in Hand Comm Svc Org; ASCD 1992-; St Josephs Church 1986-, Rel Ed; St Nicholas Womens Auxiliary; Lioness Club; Staff Dev for Batavia City Schls & Genesee WY BOCES; *office:* Batavia MS 96 Ross St Batavia NY 14020*

SCHULTE, JOAN MARIE, 6th-10th Grade PE Teacher; *b:* Dayton, OH; *ed:* Sinclair Comm Coll (AAS) Phys Therapy Asst 1982; OH St Univ (BS) PE 1987, (MA) Outdoor Pursuits, Adaptive PE 1989; *ai:* Cofounder of Monday Creek Adventure Co; Berne Union Ed Assn, NEA, OEA 1989-; *office:* Berne Union HS 506 N Main St Sugar Grove OH 43155

SCHULTE, LYNNE C., Fine Arts Chair & Art Teacher; *b:* Rochester, NY; *c:* Lisa Ruyter, Daniel Ruyter, Kenneth Ruyter; *ed:* Nazareth Coll of Rochester (BS) Art Ed 1965; Antioch Univ (MFA) Ceramics 1981; Univ of S ME Printmaking 3 Credit Hrs 1994; MCPS 16 Credit Hrs Misc Subjects 1974-85; Univ of MD 6 Credit Hrs Ceramics, AV 1973; *cr:* Arlington Pub Schls K-8 Art Tchr 1965-68; Gaithersburg HS Art Tchr 1971-72; Sherwood HS Fine Arts Chair, Tchr 1973-92; Woodstock Union HS Fine Arts Chair 1992-; Univ of VT Adj Prof 1994-95; Coll of St Joseph Adj Prof 1994-95; Haystack Schl of Crafts Instr; *ai:* Prin Search, K-12 Curr Steering, Art K-12 Curr Comms; NAEA 1975-; VATA 1995-, St HS Rep; CAA 1992-; NEA; 2 Summer Flwshps Art Fellows Skidmore Coll; Prof Artist 5 Solo Shows 1990-; AAVW St Convention Main Speaker; Designed 2 Art Depts, Mid Sts Visiting Comm; Produced 12 Page Report for Schl Bd; UT Cncl on Arts Served to Select Artists Arts in Ed; Chose Pub Art; Laurel Art Guild 7 Group Art Shows 2nd Place Awd 1992; *home:* 13 W Woodstock Woodstock VT 05091*

SCHULTES, CARLA NELSON, Asst Professor of Mathematics; *b:* Livingston, NJ; *m:* Eric; *c:* Alan; *ed:* Muhlenberg Coll (BS) Math 1984; Lehigh Univ (MS) Math 1987, (PHD) Math 1991; *cr:* Salisbury St Univ Asst Prof 1991-; *ai:* MAA 1992-; *office:* Salisbury State Univ 1101 Camden Ave Salisbury MD 21801

SCHULTHEIS, PRISCILLA W., Sixth Grade Teacher; *b:* Cambridge, MA; *c:* Frankie; *ed:* Bridgewater St Coll (BS) Elem Ed 1978; Grad Courses Rowan Coll; *cr:* Farmington MS 6-7 Grd Tchr 1978-80; Galloway Schls Oceanville 2-3 Grd Tchr, Team Ldr 1983-86; Galloway Schls Pomona 5-6 Grd Tchr, Team Ldr 1986-93; Galloway Schls Arthur Ronn 6 Grd Tchr, Team Ldr 1993-; *ai:* Arthur Rann MSDrama Coach; NEA 1983-; Absecon Presbyn Church Elem Yth Group 1990-; Governors Tchr Recognition Recipient 1993; *home:* 325 W Church St Absecon NJ 08201*

SCHULTHEISS, LORRAINE TITOLO, 8th Grade Math Teacher; *b:* New York, NY; *m:* Peter A.; *c:* Peter; *ed:* Nassau Comm Coll (ASSC) Math 1967; Stonybrook Univ (BS) Math 1969, (MA) Math Ed 1972; Dowling Coll, Stonybrook, Boces-in-Svc Ed & Cmptr 30 Credit Hrs; *cr:* North Jr HS Math Tchr 7th & 9th Grd 1969-91; North MS Math Tchr 8th Grd and 8th Grd Honors Tchr 1991-; *ai:* Ftbl, Homecoming Float Adv; SIT, Sunshine Comm; wrote Interdisciplinary Project; Math Curr Dev Team Wrote Exams for Dist; AFT 1969-; NYSMTA 1967-; SCMTA 1995-; Amer Cancer Soc 1972-; Suffolk Cty Math Tchr of Yr Awd 1995; *home:* 20 Arlene St Farmingville NY 11738*

SCHULTZ, ANNA MARIE (WHITE), Seventh Grd Tchr & Asst Prin; *b:* Montgomery, WV; *m:* Albert A.; *c:* Charles Albert; *ed:* WV Inst of Tech (BS) Math 1973; 15 Credit Hrs Notre Dame Coll Doctrine, Morals, Scripture, Liturgy, Sacraments, Christology, Peaceful Response to Conflict; 4 Credit Hrs Ursuline Coll Tech in Curr, Software; *cr:* Whittier Jr HS 7th-8th Grd Math Tchr 1973-76; St John the Bapt Schl 6th-8th Grd Math Tchr 1976-78; St John the Bapt Schl 5th, 7th Grd Tchr 1981-; *ai:* Schl Newspaper Club, Math Counts Competition, Spelling Bee Adv; Pub Schl of Rel Tchr Grd 6; St Anthony Cath Church 1978-; Participant in PBS Mathline 1994-95, Maya Quest 1996; *office:* St John The Baptist Schl 2140 E 36th St Lorain OH 44055

SCHULTZ, DANA RICHELL, English Teacher; *b:* Pittsburgh, PA; *m:* George; *ed:* Univ of Pittsburgh (BA) Eng Lit 1993; Vanderbilt Univ (ME) Sec Ed 1994; *cr:* W.A. Bass MS Intern Tchr 1993-94; Southside HS Eng Tchr 1994-; *ai:* Yrbk Spon; Alternative Ed Comm; NEA, Southside Ed Assn 1994-; Theta Phi Alpha 1992-, Local Bd Mem; Eskind Mini-Grant 1993-94; *office:* South Side HS 4949 St Rt 151 Hookstown PA 15050

SCHULTZ, DONALD CARL, Social Studies Teacher; *b:* Moline, IL; *m:* Victoria Cummings; *c:* Michael, Kathleen; *ed:* Western IL Univ (BA) His 1978; Humboldt St Univ (MA) Soc Sci 1987; Univ of ME at Orono (MED) Ed 1991; *cr:* Mount View HS Soc Stud Tchr 1991-; *ai:* Jr Class Adv; Tech Comm; ME Tchrs Assn, NEA 1991-; *office:* Mount View HS RR 2 Box 180 Thorndike ME 04986

SCHULTZ, DONNA L., English Teacher; *b:* Cleveland, OH; *ed:* John Carroll Univ (BA) Eng 1974; Post-Grad Courses at Baldwin-Wallace, Ursuline Coll & Cleveland St; *cr:* St Joseph Acad Eng Tchr 1974-; *ai:* Eng Dept Chair; NCTE 1974-; Poetry Pub; *office:* Saint Joseph Acad 3430 Rocky River Dr Cleveland OH 44111

SCHULTZ, EILEEN SAULNIER, Social Studies Teacher; *b:* Jersey City, NJ; *m:* Richard Allen; *c:* Erin, Bridget; *ed:* Jersey City St Coll (BS) Ed 1970, (MA) Rdng 1972; Cert in Admin Supervision 1976; *cr:* Our Lady of Victory Schl Tchr 1967-68; Jersey City Pub Schl Tchr 1969-70; Bayonne Pub Schl Tchr 1970-; *ai:* Acad Challenge Adv; Geog-Comp Assistance Coach; NJ NEA 1970-; *office:* Woodrow Wilson Schl Avenue B & 56th St Bayonne NJ 07002*

SCHULTZ, FREDERICK V., Fifth Grade Teacher; *b:* Marion, OH; *m:* Alison Williams; *c:* Allison, Jeff, Jennifer; *ed:* OH Univ (BA) His & Govt 1967, (MS) Elem Ed 1971; 2 Quarters Grad Schl His 1967-68; 6th Yr Competency Cert Elem Ed 1972; OH St Univ 8 Credit Hrs Elem Ed; *cr:* Southwest Licking Schls 4th-5th Grd Tchr; Canandaigua City Schls 5th-6th Grd Tchr; *ai:* Hlth Comm; Prof Mgmt Cncl; Shared Decision Making Dist Comm; Schl Tchrs Assn Exec Comm; Prof Dist Comm; AFT, NYSUT 1972-; Canandaigua Tchrs Assn 1972-, VP, Exec Comm; BSA 1975-, Scoutmaster, Scouters Key, Order of Arrow; Explorer Scouts of Amer 1991-, Comm Chair; Ontario Cty Historical Soc 1980-, Bd of Dirs; US Govt Educl Dev Act; OH Univ Fellow 1968-70; *home:* 70 Gorham St Canandaigua NY 14424

SCHULTZ, GINA JANE, Business Professor; *b:* Brooklyn, NY; *m:* Bernard P.; *c:* Eugene, Marc, Melinda; *ed:* Queens Coll (BA) Acctng & Ec 1970; Post Grad Clark Univ; *cr:* Arthur Young & Co NY Coord of Acctng Rsrch 1970-75; Hlth Awareness Svcs of Cen MA Exec Dir 1975-76; Cntrl NE Coll Adj Asst Prof 1976-89; Fisher Coll Adj Prof 1989-; *ai:* Hlth Awareness Svcs of Cntrl MA, Treas; Jewish Comm Ctr, Bd Mem; Temple Emanuel, Lib Comm; Bancroft Schl; PFA; Outstdng Young Women of Amer 1979; Excl in Tchng Awd 1983; Whos Who Worldwide 1993-94; *office:* Fisher Coll 255 Main St Marlborough MA 01752

SCHULTZ, GRETCHEN RUTH, English Teacher; *b:* Buffalo, NY; *c:* Kellyn Roth, Amy Roth; *ed:* Washington Coll MD (BA) Hum 1972; Johns Hopkins Univ MD (MLA) His of Ideas 1978; 12 Hrs Toward Cert of Advanced Stud in Liberal Arts; *cr:* NE HS Eng Tchr 1972-75; Stevensville MS Rdng & Lang Arts Tchr 1980-81; Queen Annes Cty HS Eng Tchr 1981-; Prince Georges Comm Coll Adj Prof of Writing 1993-; *ai:* Comm Work Alternative Bldg Dir; Gifted & Talented Comm for Cty; Philosophy & Goals Comm Chprsn; Class Adv 10 Yrs; NCTE 1985-; 5 1st Pl Awds for Class Play Competitions; Cty Tchr of the Yr Nom by Stu; *home:* 7014 Bridgepointe Dr Chester MD 21619*

SCHULTZ, JACK ROBERT, Social Studies Instructor; *b:* Doylestown, PA; *m:* Marie A.; *c:* Leslie Hope; *ed:* Trenton St Coll (BA) Elem Ed 1968; Seton Hall Univ (MA) Educl Admin 1973; Six Credit Hrs Educl Admin at Univ of PA 1992; *cr:* Delaware Township Schl Dist Soc Stud, Sci Tchr 1968-70; Reading-Fleming MS Soc Stud Instr 1970-; *ai:* Debating Team Founder 1990; Bsktbl Coach 1988; Ewing Twp, NJ YMCA Prgm Dir 1981; NEA, NJ Ed Assn 1968-; Flemington-Raritan 1970-, VP; Regnl Ed Assn, NCSS 1987-; New-Hope Solebury Comm Assn 1975-; New-Hope Solebury PTA 1981-; Secton Hall Univ Recruiting Bd 1991-; Deborah Heart Lung Assn Fund Raising Bd 1990; *office:* Reading Fleming MS 50 Court St Flemington NJ 08822*

SCHULTZ, JAN D., Soc Studies Tchr & Dept Chprsn; *b:* Washington, DC; *m:* Aaron W. Dodek; *ed:* Univ of MD (BA) Ed 1976; UVA, GW Univ Ed MA Equiv 1989; Continuing Ed 15 Credit Hrs; *cr:* Julius West MS 8th Grd Soc Stud Tchr 1976-77; Paint Branch HS Soc Stud Tchr 1977-79; Poolesville HS Soc Stud Tchr 1979-88, Soc Stud Dept Chair 1993-; Quince Orchard HS Soc Stud Tchr 1088-93; *ai:* Quince Orchard HS Sr Citizen's Prom Spon 9 Yrs; NEA, MCEA 1976-; NCSS 1996; PTSA 1976-, Fac Rep; Article Pub; Montgomery Co PTSA Lifetime Mbrshp, The Celebrity Artists Assn of Washington DC, Univ of Richmond Svc Awds; *office:* Poolesville Jr Sr HS 17501 W Willard Rd Poolesville MD 20837

SCHULTZ, LOIS V., Gifted Ed Specialist; *b:* Wauseon, OH; *m:* W. Sam Ashworth; *c:* Cheryl Crowder, Heather Lambert, Lesley Hatfield, Shannon Lambert; *ed:* Olivet Nazarene Univ (BS) Elem Ed 1969; Miami Univ at Oxford (MS) Ed, Gifted Validation 1995; *cr:* Wyoming Bd of Ed 1st Grd Tchr 1967; Momence Bd of Ed 1st Grd Tchr 1969; Lakota Dist 4th Grd Tchr 1969-90, Gifted Ed, Enrichment Specialist; *ai:* Stu Cncl Adv; Lead Fac; Recycling Dir; NEA, OEA, LEA 1970-; Delta Kappa Gamma 1994-; Phi Delta Kappa 1993-; NAGC 1990-; Friends of Sorg Opera House 1981-, Sec; Middfest Intnl 1980-, Dir Yth Act, Recognition Awd; City Parks Bd 1988-, Bd Mem; Middletown Lyric Theatre 1975-, Production Asst; Articles Pub 1985; Produced Video 1992, Bicentennial Documentary 1991; *office:* Adena Elem Schl 9316 Minuteman Way West Chester OH 45069

SCHULTZ, PHYLLIS ANN, Eighth Grd Tchr & Asst Prin; *b:* Rome, NY; *m:* Melvin Ray; *cr:* St Clare Schl Tchr 1961-68; St Gabriel Schl Tchr 1968-75; St Andrew Apostle Schl Tchr, Asst Prin 1975-; *ai:* Mentor Tchr; *office:* St Andrew Apostle Schl 11602 Kemp Mill Rd Silver Spring MD 20902*

SCHULTZ, ROBERT ARTHUR, Elem Sci Methods Tchng Fellow; *b:* Bedford, OH; *m:* Cynthia Marie Uber; *ed:* Univ of Akron (BS) Biological Scis 1988, (BA) Scndry Ed 1988, (MAEd) Curr & Instruction 1993; Kent St Univ PHD Sci Ed in Progress; *cr:* Springfield HS Chemistry Tchr 1992-95; Kent St Univ Tchng Fellow 1995-; *ai:* Summit Cty Sci Curr Dev, Sci Assessment Teams; Regnl Sci Olympiad Event Supvr; Stu Svc Org Adv; NHS, Acad Challenge Co-Adv; Phi Delta Kappa 1992-, VP Mbrshp, Scndry Edctr of Yr 1995; Kappa Delta Pi 1987-, Pres; NSTA, NABT, SECO 1989-; NAGC, SENG 1995-; Tchng Flwshp; *office:* Kent St Univ 401 White Hall Kent OH 44242*

SCHULZ, LAWRENCE H., Business & Economics Teacher; *b:* Buffalo, NY; *m:* Susan D.; *c:* Jennifer, Renee; *ed:* St John Fisher Coll (BBA) Bus 1972; Nazareth Coll 30 Addl Credit Hrs Ed 1977; *cr:* Sutherland HS Bus Tchr 1982-84; Monroe Comm Coll Adjunct Prof 1985-93; Brighton HS Bus, Ec Tchr 1984-; *ai:* Bookstore Supv; FBL Adv; PAC; NEA, MCBEA, EBTA 1972-; Monroe Cty Bsbl Coach 1992; *home:* 27 Bernie Ln Rochester NY 14624

SCHULZE, HOLLY OSBORN, Kindergarten Tchr; *b:* Winona, MN; *m:* Paul G.; *c:* Joshua, Justin; *ed:* Concordia Coll (BA) Elem Ed 1976; Coll of New Rochelle (MS) Spec Ed 1980; *cr:* St Matthew Luth Schl 3rd Grd Tchr 1976-83; Concordia Coll Ed Staff 1983-89; *ai:* Ldr Soc Stud Resource, Banana Splits; Inculsion Planning Team; AFT, NYSUT 1990-; *office:* Big Cross St Schl 15 Big Cross St Glens Falls NY 12801

SCHULZE, JONATHAN BRUCE, English Teacher; *b:* Towanda, PA; *m:* Beth Spyker; *c:* Lindsay, Elesha; *ed:* Kenyon Coll (BA) Eng 1981; Grad Stud Marshall Univ, Mansfield Univ, Penn St Univ, Univ of Scranton; *cr:* Athens HS Eng Tchr 1984-88; Wyalusing Vly HS Eng Tchr 1988-; *ai:* Head Track, Field Coach; Adv Lit Magazine; *office:* Wyalusing Vly HS RR 2 Box 7 Wyalusing PA 18853

SCHUMACHER, CHRISTOPHER CLINTON, Mathematics Teacher; *b:* Dayton, OH; *m:* Linda; *c:* Tina, Kim, Chris; *ed:* Otterbein Coll (BSEd) Math, Chem 1966; Univ of Cincinnati (MAEd) 1972; 15 Addl Hrs; *cr:* Cutter Jr HS Math Tchr 1966-71; Taft HS Math Tchr 1972-79; White Oak Jr HS Math Tchr 1979-83; Northwest HS Math Tchr 1983-; *ai:* IM Dir; Cross Cntry, Track Coach 1966-71; Var T Club Adv 1971-80; Wrestling Coach 1981-; NEA, OEA 1966-; SWOWCA 1971-, Pres, Hall of Fame; Chevoit UMC 1966-, Ed Comm; Northwest Booster 1983-, 2nd VP, Booster of Team 1990; Ashland Oil Tchr of Yr Nomination 1996; *office:* Northwest HS 10761 Pippin Rd Cincinnati OH 45231

SCHUMACHER, ROXANNE LEA, Mathematics Teacher; *b:* Bluffton, OH; *m:* Randall J.; *ed:* Bowling Green St Univ (BS) Scndry Math 1991; Wright St Univ (MA) Ed 1995; *cr:* Kalida HS Math Tchr 1992-; *ai:* Var Vlybl Coach; Kalida Ed Assn 1992-; *office:* Kalida HS 301 N 3rd St Kalida OH 45853

SCHUMACHER, WILLIAM ROBERT, Mathematics Teacher; *b:* Mt Vernon, NY; *m:* Mary Mullan; *c:* Andrew, Suzanne; *ed:* Manhattan Coll (BS) Math 1964; Adelphi Univ (MS) Math 1968; C. W. Post LIU Cnslng 1994; *cr:* LaSalle Military Acad Math Instr 1964-74; Centereach HS Math Instr 1974-; *ai:* Math Team Coach; Grad Dir; NCTM 1964-; Jenkins Awd Tchr of Yr; *office:* Centereach HS 14 43rd St Centereach NY 11720

SCHUMAKER, RONALD C., Professor of English; *b:* Punxsutawney, PA; *m:* Marjorie C. Amblod; *c:* Thomas F.; *ed:* Clarion Univ (BSEd) Eng 1962; Purdue Univ (MA) Eng Lit 1965; Univ of Pittsburgh (PHD) Eng Lit 1974; Post-Doctoral Stud Stanford U, Univ of NM; *cr:* Chautauqua Inst Eng Tutor 1962; Fox Chapel Schls Tchr 1962-63; Purdue U Grad Asst 1963-64; U of Pittsburgh Grad Fellow 1967-68; Clarion U Eng Prof 1968-; *ai:* NEH Grants Stanford U, U of NM, Fac Resrch; Pub Articles; *office:* Clarion Univ English Dept Clarion PA 16214

SCHUMAN, EMILY GOODMAN, Multicultural Education Tchr; *b:* Cham, Germany; *m:* Herbert; *c:* Michael, Sheri; *ed:* William Paterson Coll (BA) Elem Ed 1967; Kean Coll of NJ (MA) ESL 1981; Supervision Cert 1986; Montclair St Univ Cnslng Cert; *cr:* Passaic Schl Dist Tchr 1967-68; St Dept of Ed Coord 1977-78; Passaic Bd of Ed Tchr 1979-; *ai:* Natl Jr Hnr Soc; Kids for Saving Earth, Poetry, Modeling, Newspaper Clubs; Comm to Write ESL Mngmt System; Phi Delta Kappa 1987-; NEA, NJEA, EAP 1979-; Congregation Ahavas Israel 1994-, Bd of Govenors; Sisterhood of Ahavas Israel 1987-92, VP, Man of Yr; Tchr of Yr; Passaic Cert of Achvmt; ETS Brainstorming Comm; *office:* Lincoln MS 291 Lafayette Ave Passaic NJ 07055

SCHUMANN, CHRISTOPHER SCOTT, History Teacher; *b:* Easton, PA; *ed:* Widener Univ (BA) His 1985; East Stroudsburg 30 Master Credits His, 15 Credits Cert Spec Ed; *cr:* North Hunterdon HS Tchr, Coach 1985-; *ai:* Head Bsktbl 6 Yrs, Asst Lacross 8 Yrs, Asst Field Hockey 3 Yrs Coach; MKEA 1985-; NCSS 1993-; Bsktbl Coach of Yr 1990-91.*

SCHUMANN, NANCY FATZINGER, Art Dept Chair & Teacher; *b:* Palmerton, PA; *c:* Jeffrey, Kathryn, Karlo K.; *ed:* RI Schl of Design (BFA) Illustration 1956; Springfield Coll (MED) Ed 1976; 36 Addl Credits; *cr:* Washington Schl Kndgtn Tchr 1967-75; Kensington Av Schl Kndgtn Tchr 1976-78; Kiley Jr HS Art Tchr 1978-80; HS of Commerce Art Tchr, Dept Chair 1980-; *ai:* Art Frameworks, Outcomes & Assessment Coord; Art Club Adv; NEA, MA TA, Spfld EA 1967-; NAEA, MAEA 1987-; Springfield Lib & Museum Assn 1980-; *office:* HS Of Commerce 415 State St Springfield MA 01105

SCHUPPIG, LOIS UMBERG, Math Instructor; *b:* Cincinnati, OH; *m:* Ron; *c:* Annie, Joe; *ed:* Edgecliff Coll (BA) Math 1965; Univ of Cincinnati (MAT) MAth 1971; Attnd Xavier Univ, IL Inst of Tech; *cr:* Mother of Mercy HS Math Tchr 1965-71; Our Lady of Victory Math Tchr 1972-78; Schwab Jr HS Math Tchr 1978-79; Mother of Mercy HS Math Tchr 1979-80; Coll of Mt St Joseph Math Tchr 1985-; *ai:* Math Counts Moderator at St Aloysius Grd Sch; NCTM 1965-70, 1990-; Ed Comm 1987-88, Elected; Parish Cncl 1992-94, Elected; Excl in Tchng Awd 1995; *office:* College of Mount St Joseph 5701 Delhi Rd Cincinnati OH 45233

SCHUR, JUDITH P., Eng Teacher & Curr Coordinator; *b:* Philadelphia, PA; *m:* William A.; *c:* Roberta S. Zeff, Neil C.; *ed:* Univ of PA (BA) Eng 1963; Penn St Univ Commnctn Cert 1992; 24 Credit Hrs Grad Courses Eng; *cr:* Elkins Park Jr High Tchr 1963-66; Springfield HS Tchr 1975-80; Lower Moreland HS Tchr 1980-; *ai:* Comm Action Pgm for Srs Co-Coord; PAASP 1994-; *office:* Lower Moreland HS 555 Red Lion Rd Huntingdon Valley PA 19006

SCHUREMAN, FRANK EUGENE, Music Teacher; *b:* Newark, NJ; *m:* Bonnie Willis; *c:* Shannon, Suzanne; *ed:* Glassboro St Coll (BA) Music Ed 1972; Georgian Court Coll (MA) Supervision 1986; *cr:* Little Egg Harbor Elem Music Tchr & Band Dir 1972-73; Brick Twp Schls Gen Music Tchr, Chorus & Band Dir 1973-80; Lacey Twp MS Instrumental Music Tchr 1980-; *ai:* Concert & Jazz Bands; Drama Club, Talent Show & Asst HS Marching Band Dir; Natl Ed Music Conf 1980-; NJ Music Edctrs Assn 1980-; Ocean Pops Band; Ocean Cty Coll Bank; Former Conductor of All South Jersey Jr HS Band.

SCHURGIN, AUDREY GRISHMAN, Dean of Students; *b:* New York, NY; *m:* Marvin; *c:* Paul, John; *ed:* CCNY (BS) Elem Ed 1956; Fordham Univ (MS) Admin, Supervision 1982; *cr:* P. S. 31 Schl 5th Grd Tchr 1956-58; Garnerville Schl 2nd Grd Tchr 1958-59; Hebrew Fnd Schl 3rd Grd Tchr 1970-72; SAR Acad 6th Grd Tchr 1974-77, Assoc Prin 1977-95, Dean of Stdnts 1995-; *ai:* Bd of Jewish Ed of Greater NY 1980-, Pres 1986-92, Co-Chair 1993-; Article Pub 1988; *office:* Salanter Akiba Riverdale Acad 655 W 254th St Riverdale NY 10471*

SCHUSTER, BEVERLY KAY BROWN, Fifth Grade Teacher; *b:* Galion, OH; *m:* Carroll D.; *c:* Tonnia E. Howard, Rodney D. (dec); *ed:* Ashland Univ (BSEd) Elem Ed 1965; OH St Univ (MA) Ed 1977; *cr:* Oakland Hghts Elem Schl Third-Fourth Grd Tchr 1963-86; Colonial Acres Elem Schl Fourth-Fifth Grd Tchr 1986-89; George Washington Elem Schl Third-Fifth Grd Tchr 1989-; *ai:* NEA, OEA, COTA, MEA 1963-; Delta Kappa Gamma 1976-, Sec; Philomen Gregg IRA 1964-, Pres; Jr Svc Guild 1968-; MAUW 1965-, Pres; Williamsport U M Church 1953-; Outstdng Young Women of Amer 1975; *home:* 603 Mount Vernon Ave Marion OH 43302

SCHUSTER, CARMEN, Professor; *b:* Bucharest, Romania; *m:* Victor; *c:* Richard; *ed:* Bucharest Univ (MA) Eng, Romanian 1975, (PHD) Linguistics 1980; *cr:* Various European Univs Lecturer 1975-78; HS for Hum Eng Tchr 1978-80; HS for Telecommunications Eng Tchr 1980-83; Touro Coll Prof, Resources Coord 1987-; *ai:* REBECA Inc ESL Adv; Dist Wide ESL Tchr Vol; Co-Author ESL Cmptr Software, VB Tenses Created Unique Methods of Tchng Eng to Frgn Stdnts; *home:* 5405 90th St Elmhurst NY 11373*

SCHUSTER, FRED J., 8th Grade Government Teacher; *b:* Allentown, PA; *m:* Alice C. Mitchell; *ed:* Moravian Coll (BA) His 1963; Attnd Penn St, Temple; *cr:* Wallenpaupack Area HS Tchr 1963-67; Nazareth Area Tchr 1967-; *ai:* NEA 1963-; PSEA 1963-; Nazareth Area Ed Assn 1967-, Past Pres, Negotiating Team; *office:* Nazareth Area MS 1 Education Plz Nazareth PA 18064

SCHUSTER, GEORGE HENRY, 8th Grade Teacher & Dept Chair; *b:* Binghamton, NY; *m:* Kathleen Kabanek; *c:* David, Mark; *ed:* SUNY at Cortland (BA) Soc Stud 1971, (MS) Soc Stud 1975; *cr:* Susquehanna Vly CSD 7-9, 11th Grd, AP Amer His Tchr 1971-; *ai:* Jr HS Ftbl, Wrestling Coach; Scndry, Dist Curr Comm; NEA, NEANY 1971-; NY Soc Stud Supvr Assn 1995-; Historical Assn 1988-; NY Historical Assn 1989-; DAR Tchr of Yr; *office:* Susquehanna Vly CSD Schl PO Box 200 Conklin NY 13748

SCHUSTER, HARRIETT SCERBAK, Retired Business Teacher; *b:* Clifton, NJ; *w:* Frank (dec); *c:* Kurt, Karen, Lori S. Calderone; *ed:* Montclair St (BA) Acctng 1952, (MA) Guid 1973; Inservice Cmptr Courses; *cr:* Clifton Elem Schl #5 Sixth Grd Tchr 1954-55; Clifton HS Acctng Tchr 1957-95, Stu Act Treas 1990-; *ai:* Clifton HS Fac Org, Treas; Clifton Tchrs Assn, Del; Passaic Cty Ret Ed 1995-; NJREA; NEA; Montclair St Univ Alumni Assn 1952-; Clifton Coll Women's Club Inc 1958-, Pres, VP, Sec, Treas, Comms Chair; 4 Stu Tchrs Cooperating Tchr; Clifton Adult Evening Schl Acctng Tchr.

SCHUSTER, JULIE A., 6th Grd Lang Arts & Rdng Tchr; *b:* Youngstown, OH; *ed:* Youngstown St Univ (BA) Elem Ed 1992; 34 Quarter Hrs; *cr:* Conneaut Schls 7th Grd Rdng & 8th Grd Lang Arts Tchr 1992-93, 6th Grd Rdng & Lang Arts & 7th Grd Rdng Tchr 1993-; *ai:* Head JV Vllybl Coach; Perform Flute & Piano at Weddings; Math Tutor Vol; Class Trips Chaperone; NEA 1992-; OEA 1992-; MS Assn 1992-; Miss Conneaut Pageant Comm 1993-; MS Advy Comm 1995-; *office:* Conneaut Area City Schls 263 Liberty St Conneaut OH 44030

SCHUTZ, DONALD E., Occupational Work Exp Coord; *b:* Painesville, OH; *m:* Vickie Ramer; *c:* Nicole, Tyler, Courtney; *ed:* Univ of Akron (BSEd) Ed 1982, (MSEd) Ed 1984; *cr:* Mentor Pub Schl SBH Coord 1982-83; Univ of Akron Grad Asst 1983-84; West Geauga HS OWE Coord 1984; *ai:* Head Coach of Ftbl, Gymnastics & Track; Pep Club Adv; OWE Club Adv; OWECA 1984-; OHSFCA 1985-; Geauga TD Club 1993-, Trustee Dir; WGRC Bd 1984-; *office:* West Geauga HS 13401 Chillicothe Rd Chesterland OH 44026

SCHUTZ, KALLI JOY, Adapted PE Teacher & Coach; *b:* Middletown, CT; *ed:* Keene St Coll (BS) PE 1984; Southern CT St Univ (MS) Hlth Ed 1994; Studied, Performed Clown City; *cr:* Prof Clown 1994-; *ai:* Var Field Hockey, JV Sftbl Coach; Juggling Club Adv; Morgan Stu Assistance Team; NEA, CAHPERD 1988-; *office:* Morgan HS Rt 81 Clinton CT 06413

SCHUYLER, B. KAY, Reading Specialist & Eng Tchr; *b:* Baltimore, MD; *m:* James C.; *c:* Matthew, Patrick; *ed:* Lehigh Univ (MED) Elem Ed 1976; John Hopkins Univ (CASe) Spec Ed 1989; Rdng Specialist Cert 1982 Towson St Univ; *cr:* Colonial Northampton I.U. #20 Rdng Specialist 1974-79; St James Acad Rdng Specialist 1979-80; St Paul's Schl for Girls Rdng Specialist 1980-; Boys Latin Schl Rdng Specialist 1994-; *ai:* Admissions Comm; Eng, His Dept Coord; MS Eng, His Dept Chair; Orton Dyslexia Soc 1979-; *office:* Boys' Latin Schl 822 W Lake Ave Baltimore MD 21022

SCHUYLER, JANE, Full Professor of Fine Arts; *b:* Flushing, NY; *ed:* Queens Coll of CUNY (BA) Anthropology, Sociology 1965; Hunter Coll of CUNY (MA) Art His 1967; Columbia Univ (PHD) Art His 1972; *cr:* Montclair St Coll Adj Asst Prof 1970; York Coll Full Prof of Fine Arts, Art His 1973-; C. W. Post Coll Adj Assoc Prof 1977-78; *ai:* Celebrating the Cultures of the Mid East, Commencement Comms; Presidential Scholar, Pipeline Prgm Mentor; Coll Art Assn 1968-; NAWE 1991-; PSC 1973-; United Comm Democrats 1987-89, Pres; Assn of Neighborhood Dems 1994-, VP; PSC-CUNY Rsrch Awd 1990; 2 Title III Grants of US Dept of Ed 1990-93, 1986-87; Book: Florentine Busts: Sculpted Portraiture in the Fifteenth Century; Numerous Articles Pub.*

SCHUYLER, KATHLEEN T., PE Teacher & Athletic Director; *b:* Baltimore, MD; *ed:* Comm Coll of Baltimore (AA) PE 1970; Salisbury St Univ (BS) PE 1972; Master's Equivalence; 30 Addl Credits Western MD Coll; *cr:* Catonsville HS PE Tchr 1972-, PE, Ath Co-Chm 1983-94, Ath Dir 1994-; *ai:* Var Field Hockey Coach 16 Yrs; Lacrosse Coach 16 Yrs; Soccer 10 Yrs; Sftbl 3 Yrs; Chrldng 4 Yrs; Var Club Adv 10 Yrs; NEA, MSTA, TABCO 1972-; MSADA 1984-; NIAAA NF 1994-; *office:* Catonsville HS 421 Bloomsbury Ave Baltimore MD 21228

SCHUYLER, RAY C., Psychology Teacher; *b:* Paterson, NJ; *ed:* Cty Coll of Morris (AA) Soc Scis 1987; Long Island Univ (BA) Soc Scis 1989; *cr:* St Farm Ins Co Underwriter 1989-90; Don Bosco Tech HS Tchr, Coach 1990-; *ai:* Sports in Season; Bsktbl Coach 1989-; Soc Sci Dept Head, Curr Comm; APA 1996; Article Pub; *home:* 292 Belmont Ave Haledon NJ 07508

SCHWAB, JOHN ALAN, Math Teacher; *b:* Wellsboro, PA; *m:* Kay Dry; *c:* Jennifer, Jane; *ed:* Mansfield St (BA) Math 1969; Attnd Penn St Univ; *cr:* Wellsboro Area Schls Math Tchr 1969-; *ai:* NEA, PSEA 1969-; *office:* Rock L Butler MS 9 Nichols St Wellsboro PA 16901*

SCHWAB, JOYCE BRYANT, Algebra Teacher; *b:* Sharon, PA; *m:* William A.; *c:* Bryan, Sara; *ed:* Clarion Univ (BS) Scndry Ed Math 1979, (MEd) Sci Ed 1982; *cr:* Keystone Schl Dist Algebra I & II Tchr 1979-; *ai:* 8th Grd Team Tchr; Title I Math; Co-Operating Tchr; NEA, PSEA 1979-; KEA 1979-, Treas 4 Yrs, Membership 2 Yrs, Fac Rep; Delta Kappa Gamma, PSI Chapter; Tchr Apple Awd; *office:* Keystone Jr & Sr HS 700 Beatty Ave Knox PA 16232*

SCHWAB, RICHARD, Teacher of Art Enrichment Prgm; *b:* Newark, NJ; *m:* Rael Jean; *ed:* Jersey City St Coll (BFA) Printmaking, Art Ed 1991; *cr:* Kearny HS Art Tchr 1992-95; Montville Twp HS Art Tchr 1995; Kearny Pub Schls Art Tchr 1996; *ai:* Boys, Girls JV Track Coach Asst; NJEA, NEA 1992-; Printmaking Wkshp 1989; *office:* Kearny Pub Schls 336 Devon St Kearny NJ 07032

SCHWAB, RICHARD A., Mathematics Teacher; *b:* Syracuse, NY; *m:* Barbara J. Savory; *c:* Robyn, Kristin, Kathryn; *ed:* SUC at Cortland (BS) Math 1972, (MS) Math 1977; 30 Credit Hrs at Syracuse Univ & SUC at Cortland; *cr:* East Syracuse Math Tchr 1972-; *ai:* Jr High Math Team; Bd Mem Bright Beginnings Nursery Schl; Lay Mem of Nurture; OCMTA, Former VP; ESMUT, Past Bldg Pres & Treas, Outstndng Svc Awd; NYSUT & AFT; AMTNYS, Past Jr High Rep & Dist Chair; Lions Club; Quadrillears, Treas; Faye Heville United Meth Church, Admin Cncl, Schlsp & Nom Comm, Chm Childrens Cncl; Tchr of Excl Awd; *office:* Pine Grove Jr HS Fremont Rd East Syracuse NY 13057*

SCHWALB, MARY L., Secondary Social Studies Tchr; *b:* Rochester, NY; *ed:* Nazareth Coll of Rochester (BA) His 1967; Syracuse Univ (MA) Anthropology 1970; Addl 56 Post Grad Hrs; NY St Schl Admin & Supvr Cert; Tchr Trng Ctr Hrs of Trng, Taft Inst, Amer Univ, SUNY Brockport, Miami Univ of OH, Summer Inst; *cr:* Nazareth Acad Soc Stud Tchr 1967-68; Rochester Schl Dist Soc Stud Tchr 1970-72; Greece Cntrl Schl Dist Soc Stud Tchr 1972-; *ai:* Instrl Prgm Advy Cncl; Tech Prep Prgm; Peer Mediation Adv; Schl Advy Comm; NEA; NEANY; NCSS; Greece Cntrl Tchrs Assn; NYSCSS; Rochester Area Cncl for Soc Stud; *office:* Greece Olympia HS 1139 Maiden Ln Rochester NY 14612

SCHWALM, RITA ADAM, Kindergarten Teacher; *b:* Reading, PA; *m:* Bruce Jerred; *c:* Andrea; *ed:* Kutztown Univ (BS) Elem Ed 1973, (MED) Elem Ed 1981; 30 Addl Hrs; *cr:* Hamburg Area Schls Sub Tchr 1973-77; Kutztown Area Schls Sub Tchr 1973-77, Kndgtn Tchr 1977-; *ai:* NEA, PSEA 1977-; Kutztown Area Tchrs Assn 1977-, VP 1991-93; Kutztown Women's Club 1972-, Prgm Chprsn; Eastern Star E PA Chptr 1972-, Worthy Matron 1977; Hunter Safety Instr 1972-; Frieden UCC; *home:* 1228 Lenhartsville PA 19534*

SCHWAN, MADELINE GRUNET, High School English Teacher; York City, NY; *m:* Robert J.; *c:* Wendy Elana, Julie Michelle; *ed:* Univ (BA) Eng 1969, (MA) Eng Ed 1972; *cr:* Where Magazine Wr 1969-70; Locust Vly HS Eng Tchr 1970-; *ai:* Lit Magazine Adv; Arts, Creative Writing, AP Eng II Writer Creator; Spring M Choreographer 1971-78; Dance Club 1971-73; NYSUT 1973-, Bl 1995-, Union Paper Co-Founder, Ed 1971-74, 1991-93; NCTE 197

SCHWANFELDER, JOHN MARTIN,III, Social Studies Teac New Haven, CT; *c:* Gretchen, Thomas; *ed:* Univ of CT (BS) Ed, Hi Southern CT St Univ (MS) 1977; *cr:* Walsh Intermediate Schl Sc Tchr 25 Yrs, Soc Stud Chm 12 Yrs; *ai:* East Shore Region A Continuing Ed; Summer Stud Prgm; NEA 1971-, VP; G Conservation Commission 1988-, Vice Chm; Guilford Sideline 1995-, Sec; Tchr of Yr 1987-88; *office:* Walsh Intermediate Sc Damascus Rd Branford CT 06405

SCHWARTZ, ANNETTE FRIED, High School English Teac Antwerp, Belgium; *m:* Stan; *c:* Stephanie Granot, Julia S. Fried, M F. Fried; *ed:* City Coll of NY (BA) Eng Lit 1961; Hunter Coll (M Lit 1963; *cr:* Columbus HS Eng Tchr 1961-64, 1974-; *ai:* UFT Union Bd; Meml SLoan Kettering Hosp 1987-, Vol; Amit Women Editorial Bd; Articles Pub; *office:* Christopher Columbus HS 925 As Bronx NY 10469

SCHWARTZ, CAROLYN COLGAN, Language Arts Teach Flemingsburg, KY; *m:* Eugene Bernard; *c:* Todd E., Kyle D.; *ed:* M Jr Coll (AA) 1962; Morehead St Univ (AB) His, Eng 1964, (ME) Ec *cr:* Maysville Jr HS His Tchr 1964-65; Ripley-Union-Lews-Hunting His, Eng Tchr 1965-; *ai:* Soph Class, Newspaper, Yrbk Spon; Pl NEA 1964-; OEA, SWOEA 1965-; RULEA 1973-, Pres Parliamentarian, Sec; Fleming Cty Woman's Club 1973-, Pres; Beta Phi 1976-, Pres; Jennings Scholar; Lee Awd; Tchr of Yr; Ripley-Union-Lewis-Hntngtn HS 1317 S Second St Ripley OH 451

SCHWARTZ, CHERYL PROWDA, Spcl Ed & Resource Room T Binghamton, NY; *m:* Mark R.; *c:* Sarah Elizabeth Nowicki; *ed:* Sy Univ (BS) Elem Ed, Spec Ed 1970, (MBA) Mngmt 1983; Attnd SU Binghamton, SUNY at Cortland; *cr:* Thomas J. Watson Sr Elem S Grd Tchr 1970-72; Pine Grove Jr HS 7th-8th Grd Math Tchr 19 Eagle Hill MS 5th-8th Grd Resource Room Tchr 1985-86; Liverp 9th-12th Grd Resource Room Tchr 1987-; *ai:* NYSUT, NEA, AFT, 1987-; *office:* Liverpool HS 4338 Wetzel Rd Liverpool NY 13090*

SCHWARTZ, DEANNE MANGOLD, English Teacher; *b:* Lockpo *m:* Donald Paul Sr.; *c:* Daniel, Aaron, DJ, Jordan; *ed:* Alfred Univ Eng, Ed, Coaching 1984, (MS) Rdng Ed 1988; *cr:* Greenwood Cnt Eng Tchr 1984-86; Wayland Cntrl Schl Eng Tchr 1986-88; Hornell H Tchr 1988-; *ai:* Bsktbl, Track Coach 1984-90; BCT; Jr Class Mediation Adv; 8th Grd Team Leader; NEA 1984-; Hillside Bapt C 1993-, Yth Dir, Sunday Schl Tchr; *office:* Hornell HS 14 Allen St H NY 14843*

SCHWARTZ, DEBORAH ANN (DIETRICH), Physical Edu Teacher; *b:* Montclair, NJ; *m:* Alfred Michael; *c:* Alex, Corey, Jacqu *ed:* Ocean Cty Coll (AS) Liberal 1980; Montclair St Coll (BS) PE Georgian Court Coll (MA) Admin 1991; *cr:* Toms River North HS P 1983-85; Toms River East HS PE Tchr 1985-; *ai:* Var Coach Field H 1991-95, Sftbl 1988-; Asst Var Coach Field Hockey 1983-91, 1984-87; NEA 1983-; *office:* Toms River HS East Raider Way Toms NJ 08753*

SCHWARTZ, ELAINE D., Guidance Counselor; *b:* Bronx, N Martin; *c:* Allyson, Michael; *ed:* Syracuse Univ (BA) Eng, Scnd 1972; Tchrs Coll (MA) Guid, Cnslng 1973, (EDM) Applied Huma 1974; *cr:* Pascack HS Guid Cnslr 1974-79; Newtown HS Guid Cnslr *ai:* Co-Adv Stu Govt, Peer Cnslng; CT Cnslng Assn 1985-; Natl As Act Adv 1991-; Tchr of Yr Awd; *office:* Newtown HS 12 Berkshi Sandy Hook CT 06482

SCHWARTZ, ELAINE M., Student Advisor; *b:* Bronx, NY; *c:* Jon Stefanie; *ed:* Skidmore Coll (BA) Psych 1962; NY Univ (MA) Ed Attnd Coll of Fin Planning 1984; *cr:* Nathan & Lewis Securities Inc M Recruiting Dir 1985-88; Self Employed Certfd Fin Planner 198 Westchester Bus Inst Full-time Instr 1991-94, Stu Adv 1994-; *ai:* Inst Evening Coll Orientation Prgm; Started Single Parent Support C Participated in SED, ACICS Reports; WCBEA 1991-; Women in 1988-, Treas; Coll of Fin Planners 1984-; West Assn of Women Bus O 1989-; Nom Employee of Yr; Cert of Gratitude; *office:* Westcheste Inst 325 Central Ave White Plains NY 10606

SCHWARTZ, ELLEN M., Health & Physical Ed Teacher; *b:* Broo NY; *m:* Robert; *c:* Rebecca, Stephanie; *ed:* Brooklyn Coll (MS) PE 30 Post Grad Stud; *cr:* Lafayette HS Hlth & PE Tchr 1965-72, 19 Clara Barton HS Hlth & PE Tchr 1983-86; Townsend Harris HS Hlth Tchr 1986-; *ai:* Publicity Coord; Girls Var Bowling & Tennis Coach & AIDS Ed Team Ldr; UFT, Inception; BASE Grant (2 times); Townsend Harris HS 149-11 Melbourne Ave Flushing NY 11367*

SCHWARTZ, GLORIA JEAN (RINGWALD), Fourth Grade Teach Van Wert, OH; *m:* Larry Edwin; *c:* Larry Edwin Jr., Jeffrey Lyn; *ed:* W St Univ (BA) Elem Ed 1974, (MS) Elem Ed 1989; *cr:* Mendon Union Schl Third Grd Tchr 1974-84, Fifth Grd Tchr 1984-92; Par Intermediate Schl Fifth Grd Tchr 1992-95, Fourth Grd Tchr 1995-; *ai:* Calendar Comm 1994-95, Soc Comm 1995-; NEA, OEA, PEA 1992-; OEA, MURA 1974-92, Sec, Treas 1987-89; *home:* 20076 Mont Spencerville Rd Spencerville OH 45887

SCHWARTZ, HARRIET M. (COHEN), 8th Grade Global Studies *b:* Philadelphia, PA; *w:* Edward (dec); *c:* Lisa Sharon Park, Elain Daniel; *ed:* Univ of PA (BSED) Soc Stud 1958; Univ of PA Asian Credit Hrs; Jersey City Coll Cert Tchr of Handicapped; *cr:* Col Bu US His Tchr 1958; West Phila HS US His Tchr 1959-62; Morris Ct Tchr 1971-78; Parsip HS Soc Stud Tchr 1978-88; Parsippany Hills H Stud Tchr 1988-90; Cntrl MS Soc Stud Tchr 1990-; *ai:* Stu Tchr Mentor Prgm 1994; NEA, NCSS, NJ SS Cncl, NJ & Morris Cty Ed 1978-; IL SS Cncl 1993-; Alpha Delta Kappa 1983-, Sgt of Arms Pub Chprsn; Georgetown Univ Constitution Conf; Pub Article; *office:* C MS Off Rt 46 Parsippany NJ 07054

SCHWARTZ, HELAINE SACKS, Telecommunications & Art Tch Brooklyn, NY; *m:* Arthur S.; *c:* Jodi, Mitchell; *ed:* Brooklyn Coll Rhetoric, Pub Address 1985, (MA) Pub Comm 1989, (MS) TV-R Mng Production 1992; *cr:* John Wilson IS 211 Telecommunications & Media, Drama & Art 1986-; Brooklyn Coll CUNY Adj Speech Instr 1 Medgar Evers Coll CUNY Adj Speech Instr 1993-; LIU Brooklyn Speech Asst Prof 1995-; *ai:* Compact Team; Discipline Comm Ch Buddy Tchr; UFT Innovations Comm Wkshp Conductor; UFT, NYSUT 1986-; NYSSCA 1984-; Edctrs of Media & Telecommunica Delta Sigma Rho 1985-; Womens Amer Ort 1975-, Pres 1979-81, Wo of Yr 1979-80; LaGuardian HS of Perf Arts 1986-, Pres 1993-94; Bay BBYO Parent Advy Bd; Ryan Repatory Theatre 1996, Bd of Dir M Temple Emanuel of Canarsie 1958-; Mem of Team who Produce 2 Shows for NYC Bd of Ed; Impact II Grant; Awd Winning Stu & V Productions Fac Adv; NYS Learning Tech Fair 1990-92; NYS M

Kkkking Jr 1st Place; Womens His Month 1990; *office:* John Wilson 1001 E 100 St Brooklyn NY 11236*

ARTZ, JEFFREY WAYNE, Secondary Math Teacher; *b:* Carlisle, · Messiah Coll (BA) Math 1992; Credit Hrs in Math; *cr:* Boiling s Jr Sr HS Scndry Math 1992-; *ai:* NHS & Yth Alive Club Adv; Asst Coach; Weight Room Monitor; CEAI 1994-.

'ARTZ, JODI KNOX, 10th & 12th Grd Biology Tchr; *b:* London, James Arnold; *ed:* Houghton Coll (BS) Bio 1992; Wright St Univ rated Prgm Tchrs Cert 1993; *cr:* Worthington Chrstn HS Bio Tchr 4; London HS Bio Tchr 1994-; *ai:* Jr Class & Stu Cncl Adv; *office:* 1 HS 336 Elm St London OH 43140

'ARTZ, JUDITH B., HS Mathematics Teacher; *b:* New York, NY; ooklyn Coll (BA) Art-Cum Laude 1968; Boro Manhattan Comm Coll Cmptr Sci-with Hnrs 1985; Brooklyn coll (MS) Math Ed-with Hnrs Post Grad Stud Schl of Visual Arts, Lehman Coll, Hunter Coll; *cr:* Robinson IS Fine Art Tchr, Dept Chm 1968-70; TGI, Haber, ot, Cardinal Fine Artist, Typographer 1970-89; John Jay HS Math 989-; *ai:* Centennial Comm; Yrbk Adv 1992-93; Comprehensive Sci Prgm Enhancement Tutoring; Prin Hnr Inst for Gifted Stdnts; yn Coll NTE Prep Course Tchr; Kappa Delta Pi 1991-; NCTM; el 13, Mem; Natl Museum of Women in Arts 1989-, Charter Mem; e St Challenger Flwshp; Lehman Coll 3rd Annual Math Edctrs Conf er; *office:* John Jay HS 237 7th Ave Brooklyn NY 11215

'ARTZ, KARLEEN TRANT, 3rd Grade Teacher; *b:* Bath, NY; *m:* s; *c:* Shannon, Megan; *ed:* SUNY at Cortland (MA) Elem Ed 1979, Elem Ed & Rdng 1980; *cr:* Corning East HS 10th Grd Eng Tchr 1 Yr; g MS 8th Grd Fr Tchr 2 Yrs; Campbell Cntrl Schl HS Fr & Jr HS Tchr 13 Yrs; Campbell-Savona Schl 3rd Grd Tchr 4 Yrs; *ai:* Fr Club r Class Adv (2 Times); Musical Dir 10 Yrs; *office:* Campbell Savona Schl 64 E Lamoka Ave Savona NY 14879

/ARTZ, KENNETH S., American History Teacher; *b:* Brooklyn, : Lois Zable; *c:* Lauren, Louis; *ed:* Brooklyn Coll (BA) His 1967; s Coll (MS) Ed 1970; St John Univ (PD) Ed Admin 1974; Attnd Bar niv, Yale Univ, NY St Historical Assn at Gettysburg; *cr:* Robert ock Jr HS Act AP, Tchr, Dean 1967-93; Midwood HS Tchr 1993-; *ai:* Magazine Co-Ed; Daily Tutor; ATSS 1975-, Exec Bd; NYS Historical 1991-; US Holocaust Museum, Charter Mem; John Bunzell Awd Outstanding Jr HS Soc Stud Tchr 1993; Prospect Cemetery ration 1976; Amer Soc His Project 1991 Hunter Coll, Iroquois s NY St Historical Assn, Gilder-Lehrman Amer His Inst at Yale Univ 95 Stud Grants; *office:* Midwood HS Glenwood Rd & Bedford Ave lyn NY 11210*

VARTZ, LARRY, Social Studies Teacher; *b:* Brooklyn, NY; *m:* e Kromnick; *c:* Eric, Lisa; *ed:* Dartmouth Coll (BA) His 1964; bia Univ (MA) Tchng & Soc Stud 1965; 9 Credit Hrs; Fordham Univ edit Hrs Educl Admin; *cr:* Spring Vly Sr HS Soc Stud Tchr 1965-; *ai:* ud Hnr Soc Adv; Liberty Partnership Pgm Co-Coord; NEA 1965-; Founders Day Awd for Tchng; *office:* Spring Valley Sr HS Rt 59 Valley NY 10977

VARTZ, LLOYD, English Professor; *b:* Brooklyn, NY; *ed:* CUNY Eng 1962; Harvard Univ (MA) Eng 1963, (PHD) Eng 1976; *cr:* 1 Phoenix Classical Mus Ed 1977-, Fresh Air NPR Classical Mus 1987-; Univ of MA at Boston Frederick S Troy Prof of Eng 1982-, r & Creative Writing 1982-; *ai:* Co-Dir Creative Writing Prgms; Exec motion Comms; PEN Amer 1983-, Exec Bd; Pulitzer Prize for sm 1994; Book: Goodnight Gracie 1992; NEA Creative Writing vship Grant for Poetry 1990; Numerous Poems Pub; *office:* Univ Of t Boston Harbor Campus 100 Morrisey Blvd Boston MA 02125

VARTZ, MARY MARINO, Mathematics Teacher; *b:* New Haven, : Hal; *c:* Tracy, Michael, Christine; *ed:* Richmond Coll (BS) Math (MS) Math Ed 1974; Rutgers Univ (EDD) Math Ed 1984; *cr:* FAA tions Research Analyst 1976-77; Burlington Cty Comm Coll Sr ct Math Tchr 1978-81; Rutgers Univ Math Lecturer 1982-88; m R Satz MS Math & Cmptr Tchr 1988-92; Holmdel HS Math Tchr ; *ai:* Bldg Instructional Cncl Rep; Math Curr Comm; NCTM 1970-; a Delta Pi 1985-; NJ Assn of Math Tchrs 1992-; NEA 1988-; *office:* del HS 32 Crawfords Corner Rd Holmdel NJ 07733*

VARTZ, NORMAN DAVID, Social Studies Teacher; *b:* New York NY; *ed:* Queens Coll (BA) His, Ed 1973; George Washington Univ Pol Sci 1980; *cr:* Fairmont Heights HS Soc Stud Tchr 1973-77; nsburg HS Soc Stud Tchr 1978-79; Parkdale HS Soc Stud Tchr 80; High Point HS Soc Stud Tchr 1980-; *ai:* Mock Trial Team Coach; 978-; NCSS; Grad Tchng Fellowship 1977-78; NEH Summer nar Lake Forest Coll 1989; NEH Summer Inst Carnegie Mellon Univ NEH Summer Inst P. G. Comm Coll 1993; *office:* High Point HS Powder Mill Rd Beltsville MD 20705

VARTZ, RICHARD JOSEPH, Band Director; *b:* Scranton, PA; *m:* ia Lane; *c:* Samantha, Sarah; *ed:* Penn St Univ (BS) Accounting Wilkes Univ (BS) Music Ed 1976; Ithaca Coll (MS) Music Ed 1978; orth Scranton Intermediate Schl Choral Tchr 1982-83; West Scranton horal Tchr 1983-84; Scranton Cntrl High Strings Tchr 1983-84; West ton HS Strings, Band Tchr 1984-91, Band Tchr 1984-; *ai:* Marching, Band; Small Ensembles; Orch; Scranton Fed of Tchrs 1982-; CIO Musicians Fed 1976-; Natl Flute Assn 1980-; *office:* West ton H S 1201 Luzerne St Scranton PA 18504*

VARTZ, ROCHELLE ANN, Science Department Chairperson; *b:* mond, IN; *m:* Keith; *c:* Alex, Devon; *ed:* Valparaiso Univ (BS) Bio & 1985; Cntrl CT St Univ (MS) Supervision & Admin 1992; Currently ing on 6th Yr Prgm to Obtain Admin Cert; *cr:* BioPolymers Inc arch Scientist 1987-90; Daniel Hand HS Sci Tchr 1990-91; ington HS Sci Tchr 1991-95, Dept Chprsn 1995-; *ai:* Environmental Adv; Schl Improvement Team on Scheduling; NEA, CEA, CSTA ; CSSA 1995-; *office:* Southington HS 720 Pleasant St Southington 6489

VARTZ, ROSE BOKSER, Mathematics Department Chm; *b:* New City, NY; *m:* Sheldon; *c:* Barbara Gold, Michael; *ed:* Hunter Coll Math 1959; Brown Univ (MS) Math 1961; Iona Coll (MA) rvision, Admin 1990; *cr:* Bronx HS of Sci Math Tchr 1960-63; stown N South HS Math Tchr 1974-85; Clarkstown South HS Math Chm 1985-; *ai:* Adv Schl Yrbk, Mu Alpha Theta, Rockland Cty Math ae; Assn of Math Tchrs NYS 1974-; NYSAMS, NCTM 1985-; Tew Cty Assn 1994-, Exec Bd; Phi Delta Kappa 1986-; Delta Kappa Gamma -; Brown Univ Math Flwshp 1959-60, Tuition Schlsp 1960; *office:* stown South HS 31 Demarest Mill Rd West Nyack NY 10994*

WARTZ, SHARON, HS English Teacher; *b:* New York City, NY; *m:* in; *c:* Todd; *ed:* CCNY (MA) Eng 1973; *cr:* Bayside HS Eng Tchr 10 *ai:* UFT 1969-; PTA 1985-; Hadassah 1978-; E Meadow Jewish Ctr -, Sisterhood Bd Mem; *office:* Bayside HS 3224 Corporal Kennedy St ide NY 11361

WARTZ, STEVEN KELMORE, Soc Stud Dept Chm & His Tchr; *b:* dia, NJ; *m:* Andrea Hayes; *c:* Claria, Faith, Steven Jr., Jared; *ed:* Univ E (BS) Pol Sci, Ed 1976; Attnd GA Court Coll, Jersey City St Coll; *cr:* asquan HS His Tchr 20 Yrs, Dept Chm 4 Yrs; *ai:* Boys Var Track, Girls Cross Cntry Coach; FCA Adv; NEA, NJEA, NCSS 1976-; Manasquan Ed Assn 1976-, Pres; Councilman Long Branch 1990-94; Housing Commissioner 1984-91; *home:* 44 Lippincott Ave Long Branch NJ 07740*

SCHWARTZEL, ROMAYNE ROHALY, Spanish & English Teacher; *b:* Latrobe, PA; *m:* Paul C.; *c:* Gretchen, Erich, Kirsten; *ed:* Edinboro Univ of PA (BS) Scndry Span 1974; IN Univ of PA (MED) Scndry Span 1984; St Vincent Coll Scndry Eng Cert; Univ of Valencia Spain; Scndry Guid & Cnslng Cert; *cr:* Fairfax Cty Tchr 1976-78; Ligonier Vly Schl Dist Tchr 1978-; *ai:* Stu Cncl, Stu Forum & CODE Adv; NEA 1976-; PA St Ed Assn 1978-; Ligonier Vly Ed Assn 1978-; Thoburn Fndtn Awd Excl in Ed; Seton Hill Coll Tchng Awd; *home:* 800 S Shenandoah Dr Latrobe PA 15650

SCHWARZ, ELIAKIM LEONARD YOSEF, Judaic Studies Tchr; *b:* Chicago, IL; *ed:* Yeshivat Bnai Tonah (BHL) Talmud 1975; Jerusalem Tonah Coll (BMT) 1976; *cr:* Hebrew Yth Acad Judaic Stud Instr; Yeshiunt Mizrachil Banim Judaic Stud Instr; Hillel Acad Judaic Stud Instr; *ai:* Prgm Coord Holocaust Meml, Israel Independence Day Celebration; Rel Zionists, Amcha, Yesha, Young Israel 1975-.*

SCHWARZ, GWENDOLYN ANNE, English Teacher; *b:* Des Moines, IA; *m:* William A.; *c:* William M.; *ed:* Rice Univ (BA) Psych 1964; The Johns Hopkins Univ (MAT) Eng 1965; Attnd Fordham Univ, Pace Coll, Columbia Univ, Tchrs Coll & Bennington Coll; *cr:* Westlake HS Eng Tchr 1965-69; Mamaroneck HS Eng Tchr & Designer of Schl Within a Schl 1969-74; Tamarac HS Eng Tchr 1974-; SUNYA Univ in HS Adj Prof of Eng 1995-; *ai:* Dist Wide Retention Comm Chair; Spelling Team Coach; Peer Mediation Advy Team Mem; Planning Comm Mem; NYSUT 1965-; Blackwood & Brower Book Group 1988-; *office:* Tamarac HS RR 3 Box 200A Troy NY 12180*

SCHWARZ, MARY LING, 8th Grade Language Arts Tchr; *b:* Cincinnati, OH; *ed:* Coll of Mount St Joseph (BA) Elem Ed 1971; Xavier Univ 47 Hrs Ed Admin; Wright St Univ Cultural Diversity Training; *cr:* Our Lady of Visitation Schl 4th Grd Tchr 1971-77, 8th Grd Lang Arts Tchr 1977-; *ai:* Textbook Review, Selection Comm; Stu Cncl Fac Adv; Acad Team, Speech Tournament Competition Coach; Stu Writing Competency Judge; Project Bus, Jr Achvmt Cooperating Tchr; Schl Field Day Organizer; Bldg Comm Mem; NCEA 1971-; NCTE 1978-; ASCD 1994-; OCTELA 1994; St Ursula Acad Alumnae Assn Bd, Sec 1992, Pres 1993-, Comm Mem; *office:* Our Lady Of Visitation Schl 3180 South Rd Cincinnati OH 45248*

SCHWARZ, TIMOTHY SEAN, English Teacher; *ed:* Westchester Univ (BSEd) Eng 1990; Candidate for MA in Eng; *cr:* Lincoln MS Chapter One Coop Tchr 1990-91; Westchester Univ Grad Tchng Asst 1991-93; Parkland HS Eng Tchr 1994-; *ai:* Asst Bsebl Coach; NCTE, NEA, PSEA; Great Tchr Recognition Awd Saint Vincent Coll; *office:* Parkland HS 2675 Rt 309 Orefield PA 18069

SCHWARZ, WALTER RONALD, Asst Prof of Mechanical Engrng; *b:* Pittsburgh, PA; *m:* Sarah Aronson; *c:* Rebecca, Elliot; *ed:* PA St Univ (BS) Engrng Sci 1978; Univ of Pittsburgh (MS) Mechanical Engrng 1980; Stanford Univ (PHD) Mechanical Engrng 1993; *cr:* Westinghouse Electric Corp Sr Engr 1980-89; Stanford Univ Rsrch Asst 1989-92; Stevens Inst of Tech Asst Prof 1992-; *ai:* ASME 1989-, Fac Adv; AIAA, APS 1993-; Soc of Experimental Test Pilots Schlsp 1991-92; NASA Summer Fac Flwshps 1993-94; NJ Space Grant Consortium & NASA, JOVE Prgm Grants 1994-; Articles Pub; *office:* Stevens Inst Of Tech Castle Point on Hudson Hoboken NJ 07030

SCHWARZE, HARRY THOMAS, PE Teacher & Coach; *b:* Flushing, NY; *m:* Beverly Tuttle; *c:* Heather, Andrew; *ed:* Cortland St Coll (BS) PE 1963; Syracuse Univ (MS) PE 1967; Cortland St Coll Admin Cert 1990; *cr:* Elmont HS PE Tchr, Coach 1966-68; St Univ NY PE Instr, Coach 1969; Pearl River HS PE Tchr, Coach 1969-70; Waterloo HS PE Tchr, Coach 1970-; *ai:* Dept Chm Hlth, PE 1991-92; Bldg Team for Schl Improvement, Graduation, Discipline Comms; Class Adv 1973, 1983; Ftbl Coach; JV Girls Bsktbl, Var Vlybl, Asst Track Coach Boys, Girls; Waterloo Tchrs Assn 1970-, Chm Prof Rights, Responsiblities Comm; NY St Tchr, NEA 1970-; NY St Assn Hlth PE Recreations & Dance 1964-; NY St Coaches Assn 1964-, Cert of Recognition 200 or More Wins 1996; Assoc for Retarded Citzens 1980-82, Bd of Trustees; Waterloo Presbyn Church Adult Sunday Schl Tchr 1978-84; Worship Comm 1996; Finger Lakes Ath League Appreciation, Svc Awd, 20 yrs Svc as Vlybl League Chm 1995, Coach of Yr 1987, 1991, 1992.

SCHWARZEL, JOHN C., Auto Body Teacher; *b:* Pittsburgh, PA; *m:* Elayne Deegan; *c:* Christine S. Born, J. Michael; *ed:* Univ of Pittsburgh (BA) Indstrl Arts 1980; Drug & Alcohol Prevention Trng; ICAR; *cr:* Penn Hills Schl Dist Auto Body Tchr 1970-75, Cooperative Ed Tchr 1975-90, Auto Body & Mechanic Tchr 1990-92, Auto Body Tchr 1992-; *ai:* VICA, Auto Body Club Spon; PHEA, PSEA 1970-, Bldg Rep; F & AM Export #783 1978-, Past Master; Universal LOOM #298 1975-; Natl Rifle Assn 1965-, Life Mem; Murrysville Sportsmen's club 1965-; *office:* Penn Hills HS 12200 Garland Dr Pittsburgh PA 15235

SCHWEGLER, ROBERT PATRICK, Science Teacher; *b:* San Diego, CA; *c:* Robbie; *ed:* SUNY at Geneseo (BA) Geog 1979; SUNY at Brockport (MS) Scndry Ed, Physics 1990; US Coast Guard Acad 50 Credits; *cr:* Keshequa Cntrl Schl Sci Tchr 1982-; Corning Comm Coll Adjunct Physics Prof 1991; Houghton Coll Adjunct Human Physiology Prof 1992; *ai:* NHS Adv 1988-93; JV Golf Coach 1992-; Class Adv 1986; JV Bsbl, Bsktbl Coach; NEA 1982-; Keshequa Cntrl Tchrs Assn 1982-, Pres 1990-93; Kiwanis Intnl 1985-, Sec 1987-90; Nunda Ambulance Corp 1992-, Appreciation Awd 1993; Univ of Rochester Excl Awd 1991; *office:* Keshequa Central Schl 8 Mill St Nunda NY 14517

SCHWEIDEL, RICHARD STANLEY, Social Studies Teacher; *b:* Bronx, NY; *m:* Joan Speier; *c:* Stuart, Caren; *ed:* City Coll of NY (BA) His 1963; NY Univ (MA) His 1968; *cr:* Jr HS #22 Tchr 1965-69; Bronx HS of Sci Tchr 1969-; Frisch Schl 1989-; *ai:* AFT & UFT 1964-, Chapter Chm; Paramus Bd of Ed 1985-, Pres 1991-93; *office:* Bronx H S Of Science 75 W 205th St Bronx NY 10468

SCHWEIGARD, SUSAN BRAY, 6th Grade Reading Teacher; *b:* Johnstown, NY; *m:* Kenneth John; *c:* Edward Harlo, Daniel Martin; *ed:* Fulton-Montgomery Comm Coll (AS) Lbrl Arts 1970; Castleton St Coll (BA) Elem Ed 1973; Coll of Saint Rose (MS) Rdng 1983; *cr:* Clara S. Baron Elem Schl 5 Grd Tchr 2 Yrs; Cobleskill Elem Schl 4 Grd Tchr 1 Yr; Schoharie Elem Schl Remedial Math Tchr 1 Yr, 1 Grd Tchr 1 Yr, 4 Grd Tchr 5 Yrs, 6 Grd Tchr 8 Yrs; *ai:* NYSUT 1972-; Schoharie Cty Mental Hlth Svcs Bd 1980-88; DARE Bd 1988-94; *office:* Schoharie Central HS Main St Schoharie NY 12157

SCHWEIKART, LARRY EARL, Professor of History; *b:* Mesa, AZ; *m:* Nadia Marvey Castelitz; *c:* Adam; *ed:* AZ St Univ (BA) Pol Sci 1972, (MA) & (BA) His & Ed 1980; Univ CA at Santa Barbara (PHD) His 1984; *cr:* Brophy Coll Prep Instr 1977-84; Univ of WI at Richland Instr 1984-85; Univ of Dayton Prof 1985-; *ai:* Bus & Ec; Historical Soc; Southbrook Chrstn Church, Svc Work; Far Hills Bapt Church 1985-92, Fin Comm; Numerous Books Co-Authored; Numerous Articles Pub; Awds: UD Alumni in Schlsp 1989, Natl Phi Alpha Theta Best Paper (Twice); *office:* Univ Of Dayton 300 College Park Ave Dayton OH 45469*

SCHWEINSBERG, SALLY MC KAY, English Teacher; *b:* Rochester, PA; *m:* Paul Richard; *c:* Leslie Smith, Shelley; *ed:* Geneva Coll (BA) Ed 1958; Slippery Rock Univ (MA) Eng 1972; *cr:* Baden-Economy Schls Eng Tchr 1958-62; Freedom Area Schls Eng Tchr 1962-; *ai:* Soph Class Spon; NHS Co-Spon; Mem of Goals 2000; FAEA 1962-; PSEA 1958-; NEA 1970-; New Sewickley Presbyn Church 1983-; *home:* RR 2 Box 194B New Brighton PA 15066

SCHWEITZER, JOHN H., Deputy Principal; *b:* Cleveland, OH; *m:* Debra Ann Perry; *c:* Brian, Brad; *ed:* Miami Univ (BSEd) Comp Soc Stud 1973; Kent St Univ (MED) Ed Admin 1978; Coll of Mt St Joseph 1983; Cleveland St Univ 1990; Kent St 1995; *cr:* Parma City Schls Soc Stud Tchr 1973-93, Deput Prin 1993-, Summer Schl Prin 1991-93, Night Schl Prin 1994-, Admin Intern 1993; *ai:* Parma HS Dec 84 & 88 Act Part, Dec 92 Coord, Mock Trial Coach 1986-88, V Sftbl Coach 1984, KEY Club Adv 1987-90, Acad Chllng Coach 1987-93, Acad Dcthln Asst 1988-91, Stu Cncl Adv 1990-93, Natl His Day Coord 1990-92, Ctzn Bee Asst 1989-91, Soc Stud Dept Chm 1990-93, Curr Wrtng Pilot 1992, N Cntrl Strng Comm Chprsn 1991-94, Summer Schl Rstrctrng Chprsn 1993, Spirit Comm Charter Mem; Fay JHS Cross Cntry Coach 1976-80, Asst Bsbl Coach 1976-80, IM Dir 1980-82, Cnteen Supvr 1976-;2Assn of Parma Admis 1993-, OH Assn Sec Schl Princ, NASSP 1993-95, Act 1990-93; NEA, OHEA, PEA 1973-93; Greater Cleveland Soc Stud Cncl 1982-92; OH Assn of Stu Cncls 1990-93; OASSA 1993-; ASCD 1991-; Phi Delta Kappa 1995-; Kiwanis Awd for Svc; Parma Hgts Kiwanis Outstdng Svc Awd 1988; Jr Achvmt Awd for Proj Bus 1978-80; Acad Chllng Winning Coach 1987 & 1993; Crss Cntry Jr HS Chmpns Coach 1976; KEY Club Mbrshp Awd 1990; *office:* Parma Sr HS 6285 W 54th St Parma OH 44129

SCHWEITZER, KATHY JO, High School English Teacher; *b:* Lancaster, OH; *c:* Stefanie Jo; *ed:* Bowling Green St U (BS) Ed, Eng 1971; Toledo Univ (MED) Ed 1984; Attnd Bowling Green St U, Akron Univ; *cr:* Port Clinton HS 9, 10, 12 Eng Tchr 1971-; *ai:* Key Club Adv 1988-92; Various Schl Related Comm; AFT 25 Yrs; Port Clinton Kiwanis 1988-, VP 1994-95, Pres Elec 1995-96, Pres 1996-97; Alcohol Drug Addiction & Mental Hlth Bd Ottawa Erie Cty; *office:* Port Clinton HS 821 S Jefferson St Port Clinton OH 43452

SCHWEITZER, PAULA ANN, French & Spanish Teacher; *b:* Hackensack, NJ; *ed:* Caldwell Coll (BS) Fr 1970; Seton Hall Univ (MA) Fr 1972; Addl 24 Credits Cert K-12; *cr:* Mt St Dominic Acad Span, Fr Tchr 1972-78; St Cecelia HS Span 2 Tchr 1979-80; Acad of St Aloysius Fr, Span Tchr 1981-93, Frgn Lang Chair 1985-91; Immaculate Conception Schl Eng, Fr, Span Tchr 1993-; *ai:* St Class Adv; Fr NHS; Curr, Discipline Comm; AATF; *office:* Immaculate Conception HS 258 S Main St Lodi NJ 07644

SCHWEIZER, JO ANN MERLI, Home Economics Teacher; *b:* Pittston, PA; *m:* Carl W.; *c:* Kristin, Amy; *ed:* Marywood Coll (BS) Home Ec 1961; *cr:* United Gas Improvement Co Home Svc Dir 1961-62; Piscataway Twp Pub Schls Tchr 1962-66; East Brunswick HS Tchr 1976-; *ai:* Kndgtn Task Force; NHS Screening, Grad Comms; NEA, NJEA, MCEA, EBEA 1976-; Runner-Up Nom Governor's Tchr Awd 3 Times; *office:* East Brunswick HS Cranbury Rd E Brunswick NJ 08816

SCHWEIZER, MARK ROBERT, Bio Psych Astronomy Tchr & Dir; *b:* Reading, PA; *ed:* Gettysburg Coll (BA) Psych & Bio 1983; West Chester Univ Instr Cert Sci & Bio 1985; 30 Credit Hrs Industrial & Org Psych; *cr:* West Chester East HS Bio Tchr 1986; Black Horse Pike Reg Summer Schl Bio Tchr 1988-91; Lower Camden Cty Reg Summer Schl Bio Tchr 1992-95; Edgewood Sr HS Psych, Bio & Sci Tchr 1986-; *ai:* Audio & Visual TV Studio Dir & Club Adv 1992-; Phi Delta Kappa 1985-; Kappa Delta Pi 1985-; NEA 1985-; NJEA 1986-; Alumni Assn Gettysburg Coll 1984-; WHYY TV 12 Public Broadcasting Svc 1990-; Philadelphia Museum of Art 1990-; World Wildlife Fund 1995-; *office:* Edgewood Sr HS 250 Cooper Folly Rd Atco NJ 08004*

SCHWELLER-SNYDE, ELAINE, Band Director; *b:* Dayton, OH; *m:* Chip Snyder; *ed:* Univ of Dayton (BS) Music Ed 1973; Bowling Green St Univ (MM) Music Ed 1978; *cr:* Fenwick HS Band Dir 1973-77; Lehman Cath HS Band Dir 1978-; *ai:* March, Pep Band; Musical; Variety Show; Yrbk Bus Mgr; MENC 1970-; OH Music Ed Assn 1970-, Pres; Women Band Dir natl Assoc 1974-, OH Rep; Natl CAth Bandmasters Assoc 1985-; Natl Band Assoc 1987-; Presentations at 1990 OMEA Conf, Conv 1989, 1991, 1993; Articles Pub; *office:* Lehman HS 2400 Saint Marys Rd Sidney OH 45365

SCHWELLER-SNYDER, ELAINE, Music Dept Chair & Band Dir; *b:* Dayton, OH; *m:* Chip; *ed:* Univ of Dayton (BSED) Mus Ed 1973; Bowling Green St Univ (MME) Music Ed 1978; *cr:* Fenwick HS Band Dir 1973-77; Lehman HS Band Dir 1978-; *ai:* Marching, Pep Band; Musicals; Music Educators Natl Conf, OH Music Ed Assn 1970-; Natl Band Assn 1985-, Women Band Dirs Natl Assn 1974-, Natl Cath Band Assn 1989-; OH Music Ed Assn Convention 1990, OH Cath Ed Assn Conventions 1989, 1991, 1993, Complete Band Dirs Wkshp at Capital Univ 1992 Presented Sessions; *office:* Lehman Catholic HS 2400 St Marys Ave Sidney OH 45365

SCHWENK, ERNEST, Chemistry & Physics Teacher; *b:* Norristown, PA; *c:* Christopher, Adam; *ed:* Drexel Univ (BS) Metallurgical Engr 1974; Widener Univ (MED) Math Ed 1992; Post Grad Credits Math Ed, Chem; *cr:* Various Metallurgical Engr 1974-91; Sun Vly HS Physics, Tech Tchr 1992-94; Marple Newtown Sr HS Chem, Physics Tchr 1995-; *ai:* NEA, PSEA 1991-; MNEA 1995-; New Brooklyn UMC 1995-, Chrmn, Fin Comm; *office:* Marple Newtown Sr HS 120 Media Line rd Newtown Square PA 19073

SCHWENK, SANDRA MATES, French Teacher; *b:* Pottsville, PA; *m:* Ray T. Jr.; *c:* Matthew T.; *ed:* Penn St Univ (BS) Scndry Ed Fr 1975; 16 Grad Credits; 4 Inservice Credits; *cr:* Saint Nicholas Ukrainian Cath Elem Schl 5th & 6th Grd Tchr 1975-77; Nativity BVM HS Fr Tchr 1983-; *ai:* Fr Club, Soph Class & New Liaison Natl & Fr Contest Adv; Stu-of-the-Month, Recruitment & Jr Ring Day Pgm Comms; ADLTA 1983-; NCEA 1983-; Penn St Alumni Assoc 1975-; Penn St Club of Sch Cty 1975-; Pottsville Republican Ed Svcs Advy Comm 1989-; Nativity BVM Green & Gold Booster Club 1990-; Summer Cnslr for Cultural Heritage Alliance Educl Frgn Stud Tours Since 1985; Pottsville Republican Info Connect Homework Helpline Tchr of Week; *office:* Nativity BVM HS 1 Lawtons Hl Pottsville PA 17901

SCHWER, PATRICIA SEDOR, Home Economics Teacher; *b:* Johnstown, PA; *m:* Edwin H. III; *c:* Evelyn, Natalie; *ed:* IN Univ of PA (BSEd) Home Ec, Chem 1983; Masters Equivalency; *cr:* Smethport Area Jr, Sr HS Home Ec Tchr 1983-87; Cameron Cty Jr, Sr HS Home Ec Tchr 1987-; *ai:* Class Adv; NEA, PSEA, Cameron Cty EA 1983-; Amer Assn of Family & Consumer Sci, PA Assn of Family & Consumer Sci 1979-; Elk-Cameron Cty Family Living Prgm Dev Comm 1990-, Chprsn; Natl Quilting Assn; *office:* Cameron Cty Jr, Sr HS 601 Woodland Ave Emporium PA 15834

SCHWEYER, PAUL B., Science Teacher; *b:* Lichtenfels, Germany; *m:* Deborah L. Heinecke; *c:* Thane; *ed:* SUNY at Stony Brook (BS) Bio 1973, (MA) Liberal Stud 1975; NY Chiropractic Coll (DC) Chiropractic 1982; *cr:* Holy Family Diocesan HS Sci Tchr 1973-80; Hicksville HS Sci Tchr 1983-; *ai:* Schl Improvement Team; Collegiality Comm; NSTA, Sci Tchrs Assn of NY 1984-; NEA 1983-; Kiwannis-Three Village 1988-, Bd 1989; Suffolk Lodge F&AM 1973-; Three Village Historical Soc 1990-; Setauket United Meth Church 1982-, Admin Bd Chm 1989-91, Trustee 1996-; Who's Who Among Rising Young Amer 1991-92; Outstanding Tchr Awd Tandy Tech Scholars 1990; Visiting Comm Mem Mid Sts Assn 1983; Long Island Sci Congress Outstanding Sci Tchr Awd 1978; Long Island Sci Congress Sr HS Division Dir 1979; *office:* Hicksville HS Division Ave Hicksville NY 11801*

SCHWIMMER, ELAINE D., Modern Languages Dept Chair; *b:* Brooklyn, NY; *m:* Enrico; *c:* Bradley, Laurence; *ed:* Yale Univ (BA) Span 1971; Boston Univ (MA) Span 1973; *cr:* Malden HS Span Tchr 1972-81; Dedham HS Span Tchr 1981-82; St Sebastian's Cntry Day Schl Chair Modern Languages Dept & Span Tchr 1982-; *ai:* Span Natl Hnr Soc, Intnl Club Advs; Amer Assn of Tchrs of Span & Portugese 1973-; AATF, Amer Cncl on Tchng of Frgn Langs 1975-; MA for Lang Assn 1973-; Pan Amer Soc of New England 1992-; Greater Boston for Lang Collaborative 1992-; Eastern MA for Lang Admins 1993-; *office:* St Sebastian's Schl 1191 Greendale Ave Needham MA 02192

SCHWIND, DAVID C., Music Supvr & Band Dir; *b:* Rochester, NY; *m:* Susan E.; *c:* Nicholas, Alexander; *ed:* Ithaca Coll (BM) Music Ed 1981, (MM) Music Ed 1986; *cr:* Mt Morris Cntrl Schl 4-12 Grd Band Dir 1981; Waterloo Jr HS 5-8 Grd Band Tchr 1981-86; Newark HS 9-12 Grd Band Dir 1986-, K-12 Music Supvr 1995-; *ai:* Jazz Ensemble, Marching Band Dir; NYSSMA, MENC 1981-; WCMEA 1986-; Lions Club 1994-; *office:* Newark HS 625 Peirson Ave Newark NY 14513

SCHWINNEN, DENNIS ANTHONY, Guidance Counselor; *b:* Landeck, OH; *m:* Barbara Hickey; *c:* Christopher, Sara, Robert; *ed:* OH St Univ (BS) Mrktg, Ed 1971; Univ of Dayton (MS) Schl Admin 1977; Cnslng 1980; *cr:* Elida HS Mrktg Ed 1971-95, Guid Cnslr 1995-; *ai:* HS Tennis Coach 1974-; Adv NHS 1995-, Jr Class, Deca Club 1971-95; HS Schl Cabinet; OH Tennis Coaches Assn 1975-, 200 Victories Awd, 20 Yr Awd; Elida Area Sertoma 1980-, Sgt of Arms; Lima Elks Club 1981-; Elida Village 1980-91, Mayor, Cncl; Outstdng Young Educator 1979; WBL Conf Coach of Yr 1978, 1979, 1982; *office:* Elida HS 101 E North St Elida OH 45807

SCHWOLOW, ERNA EMMA, Third Grade Teacher; *b:* Norwalk, CT; *m:* Thomas Joseph Lehmacher; *c:* Adam Thomas Schwolow-Lehmacher, Griffin Kyle Schwolow-Lehmacher; *ed:* Univ of CT (BA) Eng 1969; Southern CT St Univ (MS) Elem Ed 1972; *cr:* Tuttle Schl Third Grd Tchr 1970-76; Momauguin Schl Third-Fourth Grd Tchr 1976-77; Deer Run Schl Third Grd Tchr 1977-; *ai:* East Haven Ed Assn 1970-, Sec 1973-79; Delta Kappa Gamma 1989-, Pres 1989-; *office:* Deer Run Schl Rt 80 East Haven CT 06512*

SCHWORTZ, BENYONNE JOY LEE, Eng Tchr & Core Writing Coord; *b:* Chung King, China; *m:* Robert; *c:* Andria; *ed:* CCNY (BA) Lit & Langs 1966; Queens Coll (MS) Enl & Scndry Ed 1988; Attnd Lehman Coll, St Johns Univ, Dramatists Guild & Coll of Staten Island; *cr:* John Bowne HS Tchr 1985-86; Bryant HS Tchr 1986-87; Grover Cleveland HS Tchr 1987-87; St Johns Univ Instr 1987-; Bayside HS Tchr 1987-; Lehman Coll Instr 1989-;Eng Tchr, Core Wrtng Coord, Newspaper Adv, & Conflict Negotiation Specialist; *ai:* PTA Hunter Coll HS; Newspaper Adv; Writing Project Coord; Grad Speakers Comm; Bd of Dir, NYC Scholastic Press Assn; UFT & NCTE 1985-; Natl Writing Project 1989-; Romance Writers of Amer 1978-; Bus & Prof Advertising Assn 1972-; Kissenia Cycle Club 1970-, Sec; CCNY & Queens Coll Alumni Assn; Natl Honor Soc; Arista Tchr of Yr 1992; Bayside HS Tchr of Yr 1992; Articles & Poetry Pub; New Adv Award NYCSPA 1993; *office:* Bayside HS 32-24 Corporal Kennedy St Bayside NY 11361*

SCHWYER, ROBERT GLENN, History & Government Teacher; *b:* Canton, OH; *ed:* Kent St Univ (BS) Scndry Ed 1990; Ashland Univ K-12 Rdng Endorsement 1993; *cr:* Canton Local Schls Sub Tchr 1991-93; Tuslaw Local Schls Tchr 1993-; *ai:* Jr Class Co-Adv; Asst Var Bsbl Coach; NEA, OH Educ Assn 1993-; OH HS Bsbl Coaches Assn 1995-; Cert Total Quality Trng Prgm; Nom Sallie Mae First Class Tchr Awd 1993-94; *office:* Tuslaw HS 1723 Manchester Ave NW Massillon OH 44647

SCILEPPI, JOHN A., Dir & Prof of MA Psych Prgm; *b:* Brooklyn, NY; *m:* Lynn A. Ruggiero; *c:* Luke; *ed:* Marist Coll (BA) Psych 1967; Loyola Univ of Chicago (MA) Soc Psych 1969, (PHD) Soc Psych 1973; NSF Spon Chatauqua Courses on Prgm Evaluation, Sco Indicators; *cr:* St Xaviers Coll Asst Prof of Psych 1971-73; Marist Coll Asst Prof of Psych 1973-75; Oglala Sioux Comm Coll Acad VP 1975-76; Marist Coll Assoc Prof 1976, Prof 19880; Dir, MA Psych 1990-; *ai:* Psi Chi Adv; Rank & Tenure, Acad Affairs Comm Chair; Amer Psychological Assn 1974-; Eastern Psych Assn 1977-; Rehabilitation Prgms Inc 1982-, Exec Comm; Valedictioria 1967; NDEA Flwshp 1969-71; Book: A System's View of Education: A Model For Change 1984; Numerous Journal Articles Pub; NYS Licensed Psych 1983-; *office:* Marist Coll Psychology Dept Poughkeepsie NY 12601*

SCIORTINO, ANGELA RENEE, Math Teacher; *b:* York, PA; *ed:* Penn St Univ (BS) Math 1992; 15 Credit Hrs Towards MA Comm Cnslng at Shippensburg Univ; *cr:* William Penn Math Tchr 1993-; *ai:* Women's His Month Act Coord; Sr Class 3 Yrs, Peer Mediation Trnr 2 Yrs Adv; Stu Assistance Prgm 3 Yrs; Discussion Group Co-Facilitator; Take Our Daughters to Work Day Coord; NEA, PSEA, YCEA 1993-; ACCESS York Inc 1994-; Amer Assn of Schl Admin Nom for 1993-94 Sallie Mae First Class Tchr Awd; *office:* William Penn Sr HS 101 W College Ave York PA 17403

SCIPIONI, LUKE, Biology Tchr & Sci Dept Chm; *b:* Lebanon, PA; *m:* Marijane Smith; *c:* Luke TOdd; *ed:* Millersville Univ (BS) Bio Sci 1959; Temple Univ (MS) Ed 1968; Addl 60 Credit Hrs Millersburg Post Grad; *cr:* South Lebanon HS Bio Tchr 1959-64; Cedar Crest HS Bio Tchr 1965-; *ai:* Sci Dept Chm; Pep Club Organizer, Adv 19 Yrs; Bsktbl Coach, Asst 15 Yrs, Head Coach 8 Yrs; Sr Class Adv; Mid States Evaluation Comm; Sci Chm; CLEA, PSEA, NEA 1959-; Dev Innovative Summer Schl for Honor Stdnts in Sci, Summer In-Service Fac Who's Who in Scndry Ed; *home:* 406 E Evergreen Rd Lebanon PA 17042*

SCLAFANI, ELISABETH BELLE, English Teacher; *b:* Rockville Center, NY; *m:* Dominic Donald; *c:* Elisabeth Anne; *ed:* Adelphi Univ (BA) Eng 1968, (MA) Eng 1972; *cr:* John Glenn HS 9th Grd Eng Tchr 1968-70; Elwood MS 7th-9th Grd Eng Tchr 1970-; *office:* Elwood MS 478 Elwood Rd East Northport NY 11731

SCLAFANI, LORRAINE ANNE TORTI, Reading Teacher; *b:* Bronx, NY; *m:* Salvatore; *c:* Matthew P., Katherine V., Christopher D.; *ed:* Fordham Univ (MS) Ed 1977; Coll of St Rose TEACH; LIU Cooperative Learning; *cr:* Wm H. Taft HS Eng Tchr 1974-75; Olinville Jr HS 113 Eng, Rdng Tchr 1976-78; William W. Niles MS 118 Eng Tchr 1978-84; Thomas Giordano MS 45 Eng, Rdng Tchr 1990-92; William W. Niles MS 118 Eng, Rdng Tchr 1992-; *ai:* UFT, AFT 1974-; IRA 1995-; Friends of Muscoot 1986-, Bd Mem; Friends of Lasdon Park & Arboretum 1991-, Bd Mem, Newsletter Ed, Publicity; DARE Vol Yorktown Police Dept 1995-; *office:* William W. Niles MS 118 577 E 179th St Bronx NY 10457

SCOLES, PASCAL E., Mental Health Associate Prof; *b:* Philadelphia, PA; *m:* Joanne Ferrarelli; *c:* Pascal, Andy, Emily; *ed:* LaSalle Coll (BA) Psych, Sociology 1964; Rutgers Univ (MS) Cnslng 1966; Univ of PA (DSW) Addictions, Hlth 1974; *cr:* Psychotherapist Pvt Practice 1970-; PA Transportation Dept Sr Consultant 1974-84; Alcohol & Mental Hlth Assoc Exec Dir 1974-84; Comm Coll of Philadelphia Assoc Prof 1984-; *ai:* Plymouth Little League Exec Bd; Plymouth Soccer League VP, Exec Bd; Plymouth Twp Park, Recreation Bd Chprsn; Mental Hlth Club Adv; AFL, CIO 1970-; 50 Articles Pub; 2 Books Ed; *office:* Comm Coll Of Philadelphia 1700 Spring Garden St Philadelphia PA 19130

SCOLLIN, GEORGE F., Counselor; *b:* Lynn, MA; *m:* Maura E.; *c:* Shelagh, Terence, Kathleen; *ed:* Merrimack Coll (BA) Fr, Ed 1966; Salem St Coll (MED) Guid 1972; Boston Coll (CAES) Cnslng, Psych 1978; Attnd Georgetown Univ, Univ of Dijon France; *cr:* Natl Security Agency Intelligence Technician 1966-68; Bishop Fenwick HS Fr Tchr 1969-72; Whitefield Elem Schl Cnslr 1972-74; Amherst MS Cnslr 1974-87; Chelmsford HS Cnslr 1987-88; Cntrl HS Cnslr 1988-; *ai:* Asst Debate Coach; Teach Part-time at Local Coll; NEA-NH, AACD 1972-; NH Schl Couns Assn 1972-, Treas, Cnslr of Yr; Jaycees, Pres; Knights of Columbus 1962-; Pastoral Cncl, VP; BC Club of NH, Bd of Dirs; *office:* Manchester Central HS 207 Lowell St Manchester NH 03104

SCONONE, ROBERT LAWRENCE, PE Teacher; *b:* Brooklyn, NY; *m:* Maureen Ann Mc Neill; *c:* Robert Salvatore; *ed:* Suffolk Comm Coll (AA) Lbrl Arts 1987; Adelphi U (BA) 1989; Stony Brook (MAS) Lbrl Arts 1994; *ai:* Head Coach Var Ftbl, Bowling; Weight Room Supvr All Yr; Head Coach JV Lacrosse; Suffolk Cty Ftbl Assn 1993-; Suffolk Cty Bowling Assn 1990-; *office:* Patchogue-Medford HS 181 Buffalo Ave Medford NY 11763*

SCOPINO, ALDORIGO JOSEPH,JR., 8th Grade American His Teacher; *b:* Waterbury, CT; *m:* Jane Marie Pomerleau; *c:* Blake, Erika; *ed:* St Francis Coll (BA) His 1970; Brown Univ (MA) Amer His 1973; Univ of CT (PHD) Amer His 1993; Cert of Completion 1991-92; Tchr Educator Support & Trng Prgm; *cr:* St Thomas Schl Tchr 1970-71; Bethany Comm Schl Tchr 1974-75; Turaif Schl Tchr & Team Ldr 1975-77; Captain Nathan Hale Tchr, 8 Grd Coord 1977-; *ai:* St Christopher's Church Soc Action Comm; Advocacy & Empowerment Prgms for Poor; Adjunct Instr in Amer His Cntrl CT St Univ; Coventry Educl Assn 1977-; Amer Soc of Church His 1993-; Assn for Stud of CT His 1987-; Assn for Scientific Stud of Religion 1993-; Doctoral Fellowship Univ of CT; Stud & Research Grant NJ Historical Commission; *office:* Captain Nathan Hale MS 1776 Main St Coventry CT 06238

SCORESE, DIANNE MILLER, Latin Teacher; *b:* Northampton, MA; *m:* Joseph P.; *c:* Angela, Alison; *ed:* Smith Coll (AB) Classics, Music 1980; Univ of MA (MAT) Classical Hum 1982; Columbia Law Schl (JD) Law 1991; Amer Acad Summer Fellow 1982; Vergilian Soc Greece, Italy Stud Tour 1985; *cr:* Kent Schl Latin, Greek Tchr 1982-88; Mc Carter & English Assoc Attorney 1991-92; Northern Highlands RHS Latin Tchr 1994-; *ai:* NEA, NJEA, Amer Classical League 1995-; *office:* Northern Highlands Reg HS Hillside Ave Allendale NJ 07401

SCOTT, ALFRED ROBERT, Health Teacher; *b:* Woonsocket, RI; *m:* Avis I Forthun; *c:* Tanya, Erin; *ed:* RI Jr Coll (AA) Liberal Arts 1967; Dickinson St Univ (BS) Soc Sci & Ed 1971; Providence Coll (MED) Scndry Admin 1974; Attnd Univ of MA, Univ of RI & RI Coll; *cr:* Woonsocket HS Hlth & PE Tchr 1971-; *ai:* AFT Local 951 1971-, Sec, Financial Sec; *office:* Woonsocket HS 777 Cass Ave Woonsocket RI 02895

SCOTT, ANN ROSLYN (STIFANO), Retired 6th Grade Teacher; *b:* Providence, RI; *m:* Richard A.; *c:* Susan Desrosiers, Anne DeFaria, Richard C.; *ed:* RIC (BA) Elem Ed 1971; RIC (MAT) Elem 1975; *cr:* Anna McCabe Schl 4th-6th Grd Tchr 1971-88; R C LaPerche Schl 6th Grd Tchr 1988-94; *ai:* Sci Fair, Physics Fest & Energy Carnival Coords; Parent Univ Math-Sci Fest; NEA 1971-; RISTA & NSTA 1990-; RIEEA 1985-; NCTM 1993-; Audubon Soc of RI 1990-.*

SCOTT, ANNE HILLER, Clinical Assistant Professor; *b:* Queens, NY; *m:* Richard; *ed:* NYU Schl of Ed (BA) Occupational Therapy 1969, (MA) Occupational Therapy 1982, (PHD) Occupational Therapy 1995; *cr:* St Vincents Hosp NYC Sr Occupational Therapist 1969-82; SUNY at Brooklyn Clinical Asst Prof 1982-; *ai:* Amer OT Assn 1969-; World Fed of OT 1985-; Metropolitan NY Dist; Occupational Therapy Assn 1969-, Bd 1995-; Occupational Therapy Mental Hlth Journal 1995-, Bd; Downstate Mental Hlth Assoc, Bd 1991-; Fellow Amer Occupational Therapy Assn 1987; Merit of Practice NYS Occupational Therapy Assn 1986; Journal Allied Hlth 1995; Pub Article; *office:* St Univ of NY Hlth Sci Ctr Occupational Therapy Program Box 81 450 Clarkson Ave Brooklyn NY 11203*

SCOTT, AREE JACKSON, Testing Coordinator; *b:* Clairborne Parrish, LA; *m:* Tommie E.; *c:* Vivian Cobb, Toni Scott; *ed:* Univ of MD CP (BA) General Stud, Early Chldhd 1974; George Washington Univ (Ma) Elem Ed, Human Dev 1982; Attnd Ball St Univ,Cath Univ, Bowie St, Western MD Coll; *cr:* Dept of Defense Schls Tchr 1978-81; Prince George's Schl Tchr 1981-; *ai:* Multi-Cultural, Drama, Black His Prgm, Positive Role Model Prgm Spon; PG Cty Educators Assn 1978-, Bd of Dirs; MD St Tchrs Assn, NEA 1978-; Andrews AFB Protestant 1987-, Outstanding Tchr; Ebenezer AME Church 1987-, Tchr; *office:* Stephen Decatur MS 8200 Pinewood Dr Clinton MD 20735*

SCOTT, ARLENE J., English Instructor; *b:* Detroit, MI; *m:* Bernard; *ed:* Siena Hghts Coll (BA) Eng 1963; Univ of MI (MA) Eng 1969; *cr:* Blessed Sacrament Schl 7th-8th Grd Lang Arts Tchr 1963-67; Dominican HS Eng Tchr 1967-75; Sussex Cty Comm Coll Eng Tchr 1991-; *ai:* Sr Grad Adv; Coll Newspaper Adv; Eng Dept Chair; Full Time Fac Liaison to adj Fac; AFT 1991-, Sec; NCTE 1991-; NISOD Excl Awd 1996.*

SCOTT, BERNARD J., Agriscience Teacher; *b:* Zanesville, OH; *m:* Jean Ellen; *c:* Selene, Gary, Alan, Joyce, Jill, Dasa, Sara; *ed:* OH St Univ (BS) Ag Ed 1961, (MS) Supvr 1977; *cr:* Otsego HS Tchr 1962-; *ai:* FFA; Ed & Voc Ed 1962-; Vol Fire Dept 1964-; Numerous; *home:* 18577 Tontogany Rd Tontogany OH 43565

SCOTT, BETTY JO ANN, Heatlh & Physical Ed Tchr; *b:* Washington, DC; *ed:* Howard Univ (BS) PE 1975, (MS) Scndry PE, Counsel Sports Medicine 1977; Buzzard Bay Sports Medicine Acad Ath Trng Cert Sports Medicine 1977; *cr:* Georgetown Day HS Head Co-ed Track Coach 1986-89; Archbishop Carroll HS Head Var Vlybl Coach 1989-; Coolidge HS Asst Bsktbl Coach 1995-; *ai:* Ath Cnslr; The Padded Cell Pre-Production Studio Spon; Teen Club Adv, Chaperon; CYO Adv Aths; Video Tech; Musical Productions Dir & Film; AAHPERD, NTA, NEA 1978-; NCABVO 1968-, Certfd Ofcl; ACSM 1980-, Ath Trainer Cardholder; Metropolitan Bsbl Sftbl Assn, Certfd Umpire 1989-; Arlington Co, Bill Grey Bsktbl Assn, Certfd Umpire, Bsktbl Ofcl 1990-; Montgomery Co Chap NAACP 1992-; St Augustine Church 1994-, Sub Usher, Eucharistic Minister 1988-, Sub Minister; PVAC Champs 1986-89; Natl Strength & Conditioning Awd Cert ACSM; Metropolitan Bsbl Sftbl Assoc Cert Clinic Internet Trng 1996; Amer U Blue Chip Recruited Bsktbl; Gold Medal Vlybl Clinic; *home:* 16515 Brogden Rd Spencerville MD 20868*

SCOTT, CALVIN LLOYD,JR., Social Studies Teacher; *b:* Celina, OH; *m:* Ruth Ann Williams; *c:* Lizabeth, Nicholas; *ed:* Wright St Univ (BS) Soc Stud Comp 1975, (MED) Curr & Supervision 1985; Non-Degree Classes in Cmptr Areas-Wordprocessing, Spreadsheets; Periodic Class in Sports Medicine & Other Related Sports Updates; *cr:* Celina Immaculate Conception Jr HS Soc Stud Tchr 1975-86; Celina Jr HS DH Tchr of Spec Ed 1986-91; Celina Sr HS Soc Stud Tchr 1991-; *ai:* Var Soccer Coach; Jr HS Track Head Coach; Sr Ski Club Adv; Celina Ed Assn 1986-, Bldg Rep; OH Ed Assn, NEA 1986-; Mercer Cty Demo Cntrl Comm 1995-, Mem; Immaculate Conception Church 1952-, Mem; Mercer Cty Sportsmans Club 1980-, Mem; Immaculate Conception Guitar Group 1980-, Co-Founder; Immaculate Conception Bd of Ed, VP; Comm Chm for OH Cath Schls Conf in Cincinnati; Dept Rep for North Cntrl Evaluation Comm; *office:* Celina Sr HS 715 E Wayne St Celina OH 45822*

SCOTT, CLYDE EUGENE, Retired Band Director; *b:* Weatherly, PA; *m:* Jeannette Sitler; *c:* Deborah Hess, Clyde, Linda Rosati, Amy; *ed:* Penn St Univ (BS) Music Ed 1958; 6 Credit Hrs Lock Haven Univ; *cr:* Chief Logan HS Band Dir 1959-69; Berwick HS Band Dir 1969-79; Berwick MS Music Tchr, Band Dir 1980-93; *ai:* Chief Logan Cty, Dist, Band Host; Berwick Dist, Region Band Host; NEA, PSEA, MENC 1958-; MCBDA 19[illegible] Pres; CCBDA 1969-.

SCOTT, DEBORAH HOWARD (BELL), First Grade Teac[illegible] Cincinnati, OH; *m:* Ronald B.; *c:* Charles J. Bell; *ed:* Miami Ur[illegible] Elem Ed 1970, (MS) Elem Ed 1975; Wharton Schl of Fin, Univ [illegible] *cr:* Hamilton City Schl Kdgtn-1st Grd Tchr 1970-91; Finneytown [illegible] Grd Tchr 1991-; *ai:* Stu Cncl Adv; St Tchrs Retirement Syst[illegible] Trustee; Lobbied WA DC; OH Ed Assn 1970-, Pres, VP; NEA[illegible] Resolution Comm; Hambuco Fed Credit Union; Pilgrim Bapt [illegible] Schlsp Comm; Educator of Yr 1995; Elem Schl Hall of Fame; [illegible] Aspen Ct Cincinnati OH 45246

SCOTT, DENNIS BUZZ, Social Studies Teacher; *b:* New York C[illegible] *ed:* Thiel Coll (BA) His & Bus 1978; CA Univ of PA Admin 34 Hr[illegible] *ai:* Ftbl Coach, Def Coor; Head Track Coach; AFT 1985-; NEA [illegible] PA Coach Assn 1987-; Historical Soc of Western PA 1985-; Worl[illegible] Cncl 1988-; Allegheny Minority Cncl 1995-; Flwshps USAF Aca[illegible] Washington Ct Spec Olympics 1990-, Allegheny Cty Spec O[illegible] 1990-.*

SCOTT, DIANE E., 6th Grade Teacher; *b:* York, PA; *m:* Willia[illegible] Matthew D.; *ed:* Millersville Univ (BS) Elem Ed 1977; St of [illegible] Equivalency; 16 Credit Hrs Toward MA in Tchng & Curr; *cr:* South [illegible] MS 5-6 Grd Tchr 18 Yrs, Team Ldr 13 Yrs; *ai:* Girls Vlybl Coach[illegible] Girls Bsktbl Coach 3 Yrs; South Eastern Ed Assn 1978-; Fawn Unit[illegible] Church 1969-; First Capital Compact Mini Grant 1994-95; *office* [illegible] Eastern MS 417 Main St Fawn Grove PA 17321

SCOTT, HARRY G.,III, Mathematics Teacher; *b:* Canton, [illegible] Suzanne; *c:* Jennifer; *ed:* Malone Coll (BA) Elem Ed 1976; Univ of [illegible] (MS) Schl Admin 1987; *cr:* Osnaburg Local Schls 6th Grd Tchr 1[illegible] Louisville City Schls 7th Grd Math Tchr 1978-; *ai:* NEA, NCTM[illegible] *office:* Louisville MS 300 E Gorgas St Louisville OH 44641

SCOTT, IRVIN LEON, English Teacher; *b:* Chambersburg, [illegible] Lakisha Nicole Barnwell; *c:* Irvin L. I., Leon C., Nicholas [illegible] Millersville Univ (BS) Eng 1989; Manhattan Coll Advanced Placem[illegible] Cert; Univ of PA Grad Stu; Millersville Univ Elem Ed Cert S[illegible] Millersville Univ PA Governor's Schl Instr 1990-92; Mc Caskey [illegible] Instr, Gospel Choir Dir, 11th-12th Grd Advanced Placement L[illegible] 1989-; *ai:* Stu Assistance Prgm; McCaskey Gospel Choir Dir; NEA[illegible] PSEA; NCTE 1989-90; COGIC Denomination Ordained Elder; [illegible] Fellowship; Lanc Endowment for Ed Enrichment Recipient; Lesso[illegible] Monthly Articles; Allen Coleman Awd; WITF Graet Tchr Awd 1995; [illegible] J. P. Mc Caskey HS 445 N Reservoir St Lancaster PA 17603*

SCOTT, JAMES E., Air Traffic Control Instructor; *b:* Rochester, [illegible] Betty Lynn Conner; *c:* James R., Shannon L.; *ed:* Comm Coll Bea[illegible] (AS) Aerospace Mngmt 1987; Inst Security, Tech Telecommuni[illegible] Interconnect Technician 1985; *cr:* Jones & Laughlin Steel Corp [illegible] Equipment Mechanic 1972-82; Self-Employed Contractor 1982-87; Coll Beaver Cty Control Tower Supvr, Air Traffic Control Instr 19[illegible] EAP Rep; Stu, Fac Comm; Air Traffic Controllers Assn 1987-; [illegible] Comm College Of Beaver Co Aviation Sci Cntr 125 Cessna Dr Beav[illegible] PA 15060

SCOTT, JEANNE A., Dir of Campus Ministry, Cnslr; *b:* Natrona, [illegible] Duquesne Univ (BS) Eng, Latin 1964 & (mED) Guidance Cou[illegible] 1968; Jungian Stud; Family Systems; Prsnl Mgmt; *cr:* Commonwe[illegible] PA Prsnl Alalyst 1974-83; Cathedral HS Cnslr 1983-89; Oaklan[illegible] Cnslr 1989-90; North Cath Cnslr, Tchr & VP 1990-; *ai:* Stu Ass[illegible] Prgm; Allegheny Cty Cnslrs 1989-; Cert of Appreciation From US [illegible] Ed; Improvement & Reform of Schls & Tchng Outstanding Svc [illegible] *office:* North Catholic HS 1400 Troy Hill Rd Pittsburgh PA 15212

SCOTT, JOHN T., Assistant Principal; *b:* Buffalo, NY; *m:* Rita M. [illegible] *c:* Lauren C.; *ed:* St Univ of NY (BA) Eng 1969, (MED) Eng Ed[illegible] (EDD) Educl Admin 1992; *cr:* West Seneca Schls 9th-12th Grd En[illegible] 1971-92, Admin 1992-; *ai:* Bldg Shared Decision Making Team; [illegible] Dist Pub Relations, Dist GATE Comms; Phi Delta Kappa [illegible] Newsletter Ed; NY Assn of Schl Admins 1992-; Assn of Schl Bus [illegible] ASCD 1990-; West Seneca Tchr Ctr 1994-, Policy Bd; Phi Delta [illegible] SUNY at Buffalo Chapter Distinguished Dissertation Awd 1993; [illegible] Eng Tchr of Excl 1988; *office:* West Seneca West Sr HS 3330 Sen[illegible] West Seneca NY 14224

SCOTT, JONATHAN F., Associate Professor of Art; *b:* Boston, [illegible] Marie F.; *c:* Jonathan Jr., Malia, Joshua, Andrea, Nathaniel; *ed:* A[illegible] Coll (BA) Fine Arts 1962; Univ of KS (MA) Art His 1967; Univ [illegible] (PHD) Art His 1985; *cr:* Univ of HI Instr 1968-72; Univ of NM As[illegible] 1978-79; Gustavus Adolphus Coll Asst Prof 1980-81; Castleton S[illegible] Assoc Prof 1988-; *ai:* Art Dept Chm; Chairs Comm; Fac Fellows Sel[illegible] Comm; Frosh Advocate Prgm; Spon Art Consortium with Castleton S[illegible] Green Mountain Coll, Comm Coll UT; Phi Kappa Phi 1982-, Honora[illegible] for 4.0 GPA Un of MN; Coll Art Assn 1978-; AFT 1988-; Marthas Vi[illegible] Youth Soccer League 1982-87, Coach; Southeast MA Yth Soccer [illegible] 1985-, Co-Coach Team Won League Championship Un MA; Phi Kap[illegible] Honorary Soc 1982; Grad Flwshp Un of MN; Schlsp Amherst coll; [illegible] Awd for Excl Tchng Svc Un of HI 1971; Numerous Articles Pub; [illegible] Castleton St Coll Fine Arts Ctr Castleton VT 05735

SCOTT, JUANDA DAVIS, Mathematics Teacher; *b:* Salisbury, [illegible] Joseph B.; *c:* Jacquelyn; *ed:* Livingstone Coll (BS) Math & Ed [illegible] Western MD Coll (MS) Supervision & Admin 1994; *cr:* Westmorela[illegible] Schl Tchr 1973-74; Prince Georges Cty Schl Tchr & Coord 197[illegible] Female Coalition Spon; Sub Admin; Stu Svc Liaison; Facilitate C[illegible] Multicultural Ed Initiatives; Plan & Expand Mentoring Prgms; [illegible] Expand Prgms in HS & Cluster Area; NEA, PGCEA 1974-; PTSA [illegible] Bd; Antioch Bapt Church 1978-, Trustee, Choir Pres, Treas, Outst[illegible] Trustee Awd; Outstanding Educators Awd Presented by Prince C[illegible] Chamber of Commerce 1994; *home:* 10700 Tyrone Dr Upper Marlbo[illegible] 20772

SCOTT, KATHLEEN ELIZABETH, 7th Grade Mathematics Teac[illegible] Mountainside, NJ; *ed:* VA Wesleyan (BA) Ed 1974; Rider Univ [illegible] Counseling 1991; 30 Credits Toward Admin & Supervisor; *cr:* [illegible] Stephens Tchr 1974-75; Archdiocese of Seattle Tchr 1976-82; Bric[illegible] Bd of Ed Tchr 1986-87; Howell Twp Bd of Ed Tchr 1987-; *ai:* Mento[illegible] Dev & Fac Adv Comms; Peer Tutoring; Core Team; Stu Resource C[illegible] NJEA, NEA 1986-; HTEA 1987-, Legislative Chair; One Se[illegible] Sabbatical Awded by Bd of Ed to Research & Dev Math Softwa[illegible] Support of 7th & 8th Grd Prgm, Directory Will Be Written As Resou[illegible] Our Dist & Surrounding Dists; *office:* Howell Twp MS 501 Squa[illegible] Yellowbrook Rd Howell NJ 07727*

SCOTT, LINDA KANE, Instructor; *b:* Staten Island, NY; *m:* G[illegible] Wilkinson; *c:* Christian, Oliver; *ed:* Davis & Elkins Coll (BA) Eng [illegible] Univ of ME (MA) Eng Lit 1992; ME Tchng Cert; 15 Hrs Complete[illegible] Century Stud, Victorian Lit; *cr:* Deer Isle Stonington Jr Sr HS [illegible] 1984-95; Univ of ME Instr PHD Candidate 1995-; *ai:* Chm Accre[illegible] 1986-95; NHS Adv 1985-95; Sr Class Adv 1986095; Restructuring [illegible] 1989-95; Lang Arts Curr Comm 1992; AAO 1990-93, 1995; Delta [illegible] Gamma 1989-; Red Cross Disaster Svcs 1993-, Disaster Coord; [illegible] Mem Book Sale 190-95; Consultant Work Childrens Awarene[illegible] Harrassment K-12; Continuing Engagement ME St Lib Series [illegible] Publication 1994; Monograph Univ of ME; *office:* Univ of ME De[illegible] English Orono ME 04469*

', MARGARET CLAY, Second Grade Teacher; *b:* Oil City, PA; *m:* L.; *c:* Kristina Renee, Sue Anne, Kathleen Marie; *ed:* Mercyhurst A) Elem Ed 1966; 36 Grad Credit Hrs; *cr:* St Francis de Sales Schl l Tchr 1966-67; St Aloysius Schl 2nd Grd Tchr 1967-68; Oil City st 2nd Grd Tchr 1968-70, Kndgtn-2nd Grd Tchr 1986-; St Joseph ndgtn Tchr 1976-79; *ai:* Staff Dev, Curr Improvement Comms; Tchr; Stu Tchrs Clinical Supvr; NEA, PSEA 1986-; YWCA 1970-; 4 Scotts Ln Oil City PA 16301*

', MARION LISI, Asst Prof of Hlth & Med Sci; *b:* Boyers, PA; *m:* E.; *c:* Sondra Scott King, Susan M.; *ed:* St Elizabeth Med Ctr Schl g (RN) Nrsng 1961; Youngstown St Univ (BED) Hlth Ed 1982, Hlth Ed 1987; *cr:* St Elizabeth Hosp Registered Nurse 1961-78; St Schl Nurse 1978-87; Youngstown St Univ Asst Prof 1988-; *ai:* rievance, Stu Acad Stans, Fac Stans Comms; ASHA, AAHEPERD OAHPERD 1992-, Chair Schl Hlth Section; CHES 1990-; License al Nurses Bd 1993-, Bd of Dir; Safe Childs Coalition 1993-, Bicycle Div Chair; Sr Citizen Bd 1992-, Bd of Dir; OH Dept Of Hlth Grants 3; Distngd Prof for Tchng 1995; Phi Kappa Phi 1992; Childs Book 96; Articles Pub 1989-; *office:* Youngstown St Univ 410 Wick Ave town OH 44555

', MARJORIE DAVIS, Art & Photography Teacher; *b:* Norfolk, Sterling L. II; *ed:* Morgan St Univ (BS) Art Ed 1970; Trinity Coll Art Ed 1976; Math Credential at CA St Univ at Los Angeles & CA v at Fullerton 1985; *cr:* Montgomery Cty Pub Schls Art Tchr 6; Diversified Employment Office Mgr 1977-79; Norrell Svcs Inc Mgr 1979-81; Inglewood Unified Schls Math Tchr 1981-86; omery Cty Pub Schls Art & Math Tchr 1986-; *ai:* Stu Assistance eam; African Amer His Month Comm; Soc Comm; Art Dept Chprsn; , MSTA, NEA 1986-; MCAEA, WCP 1990-; Jack & Jill of Amer Inc Jr Teen Group Co-Chair, Membership Comm Mem; Rotary Club of ship Heights Travel Grant 1994; Montgomery Cty Schls Media l Awd of Spec Merit 1994-95; Scholastic Art & Writing Awds; 1995 f Recognition; *office:* Walt Whitman HS 7100 Whittier Blvd da MD 20817*

', NATHAN C., Social Studies Dept Supervisor; *b:* Upper Darby, Christine Gray; *ed:* Univ of PA (BA) His 1989, (MSEd) Soc Stud 9; Candidate for EDD Widener Univ; *cr:* Triton Regnl HS Soc Stud 990-95; *ai:* Asst Bsbl Coach; Adv Mock Trial Team; NEA, NJEA Participant Rutgers Univ Seminar, South Jersey Inst for Edctrs; Triton Regional HS 250 Schubert Ave Runnemede NJ 08078

T, PHYLLIS DIANE (HARVEY), Social Studies Teacher; *b:* ond, IN; *m:* Donald W.; *c:* Kristene Krohn, Korlin K.; *ed:* St Josephs S) Elem Ed 1967; Purdue Univ (MS) Ed Admin 1973; Southern IL Kent St Univ & Eastern MI Univ Post-Grad Stud; *cr:* Lansing Pub th Grd Tchr 1967-70; Thornton Fractional Area Educl Cooperative 70-73; Purdue Univ Instr & Asst to Dir Tchr Ed 1975-77; IN Dept of str Rdng Consultant 1977-78; Brighton Area Schls 2nd, 4th, & Grd Tchr 1979-87; Canton Cntry Day Schl MS Soc Stud Tchr *ai:* Jr Achvmt Project Bus; NCSS 1988-; Natl Cncl on His Ed 1994-; ncl for the Soc Stud; MI Head Injury Alliance 1981-, VP, Vol nition Awd; Natl Head injury Fndtn 1981-; Zion United Church of 1987-; OH Head Injury Assn 1990-, Bd of Dir; Valparaiso Univ, IN & Purdue Univ Deans List Stu; Purdue Univ at Calumet Grad antship; *office:* Canton Country Day Schl 3000 Demington Ave NW OH 44718*

T, RAYMOND L., 9th Grade History Teacher; *b:* Kenmore, NY; *m:* Sysol; *c:* Kelly, Kathleen, Gregory, Sarah; *ed:* SUNY at Fredonia d Soc Stud 1963; SUNY at Buffalo (MS) Soc Stud 1970; Univ of o Psych; *cr:* Boston Vly Schl 6th Grd Elem Tchr 1963-64; Hamburg 8th Grd His Tchr 1964-78, 9th Grd His Tchr 1995-; *ai:* Mrml Day Chm 31 Yrs; Black His Month Comm Chm; Hamburg Tchrs Assn Pres; NYSUT 1963-; AFT, NYCSS 1975-; Phi Delta Kappa 1971-; s of Columbus 1972-, Grand Knight; Amer Legion Post 527 1985-, nship Awd 1986; Buffalo Chptr Red Cross, 12 Gal Donor; Chm Soc 3 Yrs; *home:* 2750 Pleasant Ave Lake View NY 14085*

T, RICHARD J., Ind Arts Teacher; *b:* Greenfield, MA; *m:* Judith *c:* Robert, Lisa Madru; *ed:* Western New England Coll (BS & BA) 969; Amer Intnl Coll (MED) Ed 1973; *cr:* Holyoke High Ind Arts Tchr ; *ai:* MTA 1976-.

T, RITA KOPRA, Spanish Teacher; *b:* Buffalo, NY; *m:* John T.; *c:* ; *ed:* Buffalo St Univ Coll (BS) 7th-12th Grd Span 1969, (MS) Disciplinary 1983; Univ of Buffalo K-6th Grd Span 1986; Bureau of search TPR 1984, BETA C 1992, Cooperative Learning 1992; *cr:* 7th-8th Grd Span Tchr 1969-71; Allendale Jr 6th-9th Grd Span Tchr 78; East Sr 9th-12th Grd Span Tchr 1980-81; West Sr Sr 9th-12th Grd Tchr 1981-; *ai:* Cheerleading Coach; Schlsp Comm; Foreign Lang AATSP, AFT, HISPANIA, NEA, WYSTA 1969-; Amherst ssadors 1990-, Sec, Treas, Chaperone; Amer Youth on Parade 1990-, ator; Outstanding Natl Educator; 1st Intnl Foreign Lang Conf er; *office:* West Seneca West Sr HS 3330 Seneca St West Seneca NY *

'T, ROBERT EDWARD,JR., Business Instructor; *b:* Skowhegan, : Janet Christer Scott; *c:* Geoffrey, Lara; *ed:* London Schl of Mngmt s Post Grad; *cr:* PP Co E-A Mgr Internal Audit 1982-87; Phillips eum Co SNR Systems Coord 1987-88; Northern Me Tech Coll Instr ech 1989-; *ai:* Cmptr Utilization comm; Bus & Industry Classes Instr; 1976-, Qualified; Presque Isle CC 1991-, VP; Washburn Rotary , Treas; Planning Bd 1993-; Dev EDP Audit Tools for Use in United om; *office:* Northern ME Tech Coll 33 Edgemont Dr Presque Isle ME

'T, RUSSELL BERT, Professor; *b:* Jeannette, PA; *m:* Frances M.; *c:* y, Clifton; *ed:* Strayer Coll (MCS) Acctng 1954, (BCS) Acctng 1956,) Dr of Humane Letters 1994; MD Assoc of Pub Accounts CPA 1961; edit Hrs; *cr:* Strayer Coll Prof 31 Yrs; Self-Employed CPA Firm Head s; *ai:* MD Assn of CPA 1961-; *home:* 6806 Berkshire Dr Temple Hills 0748

'T, SANDRA HOWLEY, 7th Grade Soc Stud Teacher; *b:* Lowville, : John J.; *c:* Sharon, John, Caron, James; *ed:* SUNY at Farmingdale Dental Hygiene 1961; SUNY at Oswego (BA) Ed 1975; Attnd SUNY ffalo, Suffolk Comm Coll; *cr:* Mexico Acad & CS 7th Grd Soc St Tchr ; *ai:* Cmptr Hall of Fame & Arts Comms; Spring Musical Dir 17 Yrs; o Historical Soc 1976-; Oswego Cty Heritage Fnd 1995; NYSUT ; Charter Mem Mexico Historiacl Soc & Friends of Mexico Pt Pk; uthor Book: Mexico The Twentieth Town in the Twentieth Century; rours Articles Pub; *office:* Mexico Acad & Cntrl Schl Academy St o NY 13114

'T, SARAH CASSIDY, Secondary Science Teacher; *b:* Bayshore, n: Kevin Michael; *c:* Graham, Courtney, Owen; *ed:* SUNY at Stony (BS) Bio, Psych 1984, (MALS) Ed 1993; Prof Ed 1986; *cr:* wood HS Scndry Sci Tchr 1986-88; Port Jefferson Jr HS Scndry Sci 1988-90; Mt Sinai MS Scndry Sci Tchr 1990-; *ai:* Disabilities eness, Amer Ed Week, Adv, Advy Planning, Natl Jr Honor Soc tion Comms; Adv Sci Club, Spirit Week; PTO Tchr Laison; STANYS ; Suffolk Co Homemakers 1994-, Sec; *office:* Mt Sinai MS N Country O Box 398 Mount Sinai NY 11766

SCOTT, SHIRLEY E., German Teacher; *b:* Springfield, OH; *ed:* Otterbein Coll (BA) Ger, Eng Ed 1970; Attnd OH St Univ, Wright St Univ, Miami Univ; *cr:* Graham HS Ger & Eng Tchr 1970-; OH Hi-Point JVS Ger Tchr 1991; *ai:* Lang Arts Dept Head; Fac Adv; Yrbk Adv; NHS Adv; Ger Exchange Pgm Coord; NEA, OEA & GEA 1970-, Pres, Schlrshp Chair; AATG 1985-; 4-H 1989-, Adv; Graham Alumni Assn 1990-, Schshp Chair; Most Influential Tchr (3 Times); Martha Jennings Scholar; *office:* Graham HS 7800 W St Rt 36 Saint Paris OH 43072

SCOTT, SUSAN C. WINKLER, First Grade Teacher; *b:* Baltimore, MD; *m:* Michael Joseph; *c:* Adam, Sarah; *ed:* Edinboro St (BS) Elem Ed 1975; Youngstown St (MS) Elem Ed, Early Chldhd 1981; 21 Addl Hrs; *cr:* Neal MS Fifth Grd Tchr 1977-81, Seventh Grd Math Tchr 1981-82, Seventh Grd Math, Eighth Grd Rdng Tchr 1982-83; Currie Elem Schl First Grd Tchr 1985-; *ai:* Mathews Tech Comm; Jr HS Chrldng Adv 1977-79; Curr Comm 1979-80; Act Chm 1994-95; NEA 1977-; Mathews Tchrs Assn 1977-, Bldg Rep 2 Yrs; Case Ave PTO 1989-; 2 Soc Stud Mini-Grants 1979, 1986; *home:* 1013 Bechtol Ave Sharon PA 16146

SCOTT, SUZANNE GLASS, Math Teacher & Department Chr; *b:* Canton, OH; *m:* Harry G. III; *c:* Jennifer; *ed:* Malone Coll (BA) Math, Scndry Ed 1976; Univ of Dayton (MS) Admin 1987; *cr:* Louisville HS Math Tchr 19 Yrs, Dept Chr Math Dept 15 Yrs; Central Cath HS Math Tchr 1 Yr; *ai:* NEA, NCTM 1976-; Sigma Zeta 1975-; *office:* Louisville Sr HS 1201 S Nickelplate St Louisville OH 44641

SCOTT, VINCENT ARTHUR, Science Teacher; *b:* Jamaica, NY; *m:* Karen Irene Davis; *ed:* C. W. Post (MS) Bio Ed 1977; Working Toward MA in Dramatics at Queen Coll; *cr:* St Francis Prep Schl Chem Tchr 1974-75; Carey HS Sci Tchr 1975-77; New Hyde Park Schl Sci Tchr 1077-; *ai:* Key Club, Jr Class Adv; Musical Dir; JV Soccer Coach; NEA 1974-; STANYS 1990-; Kiwanis 1994-, Best Adv; PTSA 1974-, Tchr Rep, Life Mbrshp, Schlsp Awd; March of Dimes Birth Defect Schlsp; Sewanhana Mini Grant Theatre in Sewanakaka, Artist in Res; *office:* New Hyde Park HS 500 Leonard Blvd New Hyde Park NY 11040*

SCOTTALINE, MICHAEL E., Asst Prin & European His Tchr; *b:* New York, NY; *m:* Kathryn Russo; *c:* Eric, John; *ed:* Adelphi Univ (BA) His 1974; SUNY at Stony Brook (MA) Liberal Arts 1979; Dowling Coll (SAS) Educl Admin 1993; 90 Addl Credits; *cr:* North Babylon HS His Tchr 1974-, Dean of Stdnts 1989-93, Asst Prin 1993-; *ai:* Reader, Rater Advances Placement European His Exams; Fulbright Alumni, CAS 1993-; LICSS 1979-; NEH Fellowship 1993; Fulbright Scholar 1992; Fac Consultant Coll Bd for AP European His Exam 1990-; *office:* North Babylon HS 1 Phelps Ln North Babylon NY 11703

SCOTT-HUNTER, JUDITH, Communications Coord; *b:* Chester, PA; *m:* Alain E. Hunter; *c:* Juliane Mahrash Huntry, Alain S. J. Hunter; *ed:* Penn St (BA) Sec Ed, Eng 1966; Univ of IL (MAT) ESL Intnl Prgm 1969-72; Penn St Univ (MED) Rdng 1978; Univ of IL EdD Prgm 60 Addl Hrs; Attnd Wake Forest Univ, Trinity Coll; *cr:* Dept of Pub Instr Lang Arts Resource Specialist 1969-70; Tehran Univ Lang Arts Resource Specialist 1970-72; Stuart Hobson MS Eng Dept Chair 1987-88; Eastern Sr HS Pre-Law Comm Coord 1988-; *ai:* NHS Adv; Tennis Team Coach; Stu Tchr Mentor; Multicultural, Cmptr, Tech Comm; Mid Sts Comm Chair; AFT; NCTE; Stanton Park Neighborhood Assn, Schlsp Comm; Natl Inst Citizens Ed, Law, DC St Trainer; DC Am 2000 Goals, Comm Rep; Nom Agnes Meyer Outstdng Tchr Awd; Legacy Awd US Dept of Ed; Ctr Rsrch, Dev Law Related Ed; Text-Alive Scholar; *office:* Eastern Sr HS 17th & E Capitol Sts NE Washington DC 20003*

SCOTTI, ANDREW P., Mathematics Teacher; *b:* New York City, NY; *ed:* Fordham Univ (BS) Bus 1981; Adelphi Univ (MA) Ed & Math 1990; Queens Coll 36 Credit Hrs Masters Pgm for Schl Cnslng; *cr:* Christ The King Tchr 1983-; St Johns Univ Adj Spcl Univ Pgm & Math Instr 1990-; *ai:* Organized & Taught Stud Skills Course Math & Sci 1993; Math Club; Choir; Comm Theatre; NCTM 1986-; Nassau Cnslrs Assn 1995-; *office:* Christ The King Regional HS 6802 Metropolitan Ave Middle Village NY 11379*

SCOTTO, JOSEPH NICHOLAS, Science & German Teacher; *b:* New York City, NY; *m:* Donna Lauchle; *c:* Travis, Curtis; *ed:* Villanova Univ (BS) Bio 1978, (MS) Bio 1982; 6 Credit Hrs West Chester Univ; 4 Credit Hrs Mooby Bible Inst; 3 Credit Hrs Lancaster Bible Coll; *cr:* Villanova Univ Grad Asst 1981-82; Chrstn Schl of Yolk Tchr, Sci 1982-83; Bible Bapt Schl Tchr, Sci, Ger, Math 1983-; *ai:* Sci Fair Coord 1984-; Coach Var Bsbl 1984-93; Cnslr EF Educl Tours 1988, 1992; Eastern European Bible Mission; Missionary Prgm 1983-85; *office:* Bible Baptist Schl 201 W Main St Camp Hill PA 17011

SCOTTO CARANNANTE, ANGELA, Coordinator Foreign Lang Dept; *b:* Brooklyn, NY; *m:* Antonio; *c:* Anthony; *ed:* Brooklyn Coll (BA) Italian 1974; Fordham Univ (MS) Biling Stud, (MS) Curr, Tchng 1979; Supvrs Cert Admin Keane Coll 1991; *cr:* P S 86 K Biling Italian, Span Tchr 1974-85; New Dorp HS Chprsn, Coord Forgn Lang Dept 1992-, Italian, Span Tchr 1985-; *ai:* Adv NHS, Societa Onoraria Italica; African Amer Latino Ldrshp Club; Co-Adv Intl Club; SING Production; Schl Based Mngmt Comm; Tchr Liason PTA; AFT, UFT 1974-; NY St Assn of Frgn Lang Tchrs 1985-; Italian Tchrs Assn, Assn Lang Instrs of Staten Island 1985-; Manville HS PTA 1990-, Exec Bd; Awded Christa Mc Auliffe Tchng Awd 1996; *office:* New Dorp HS 465 New Dorp Ln Staten Island NY 10306

SCOTTON, MARK ALLAN, Theology Teacher; *b:* Cleveland, OH; *ed:* Borromeo Coll of OH (BA) His 1980; Completed Course Work for MA Systematic Theology St mary Theological Seminary; *cr:* Urban Region CYO Parish Prgm Facilitator 1984-86; Trinity HS Theology Tchr 1986-; *ai:* Ministry Team; Sr Class, Hockey Statisticians Moderator; Marching Band Asst Dir; Moderator of Black Awareness Group; Admissions Team; NCEA 1986-; Outstdng Edctr of Yr 1993; *office:* Trinity HS 12425 Granger Rd Garfield Hgts OH 44125

SCOTTO-PDADVANO, ELVIRA, Math Dept Chprsn & Teacher; *b:* NY; *m:* Ronald; *ed:* Mt St Mary Coll (BS) Math 1977; Plymouth St Coll (MED) Scndry Math Ed 1980; Addl Hrs Educl Admin; *cr:* Middletown HS Math Tchr 1978-95, Math Chprsn 1995-; *ai:* Sr Class, Math Team Adv; Schl Improvement Team; Sci Tech Entry Prgm; MTA 1978-, Union Rep; NCTM, AMTNYS 1978-; *office:* Middleton City Schl Dist Gardner Ave Ext Middletown NY 10940*

SCOTT RICCO, BRENDA JOY, Special Education Teacher; *b:* Norwalk, CT; *m:* Ernest George; *c:* Richard, Elizabeth, Lorraine, Emilie; *ed:* Southern CT St Univ (BS) Spcl Ed 1985; (MS) Learning Disablities Pending; *cr:* Elizabeth OHara Walsh Spcl Ed Tchr 1986-88; Villa Maria Ed Ctr Spcl Ed Tchr 1989-; *ai:* Selected Top 5 Outstdng Tchr by CAPSEF 1989; *home:* 74 Westport Rd Wilton CT 06897*

SCOULIOS, JOHN A., Mathematics Instructor; *b:* New York City, NY; *m:* Berthlyn Williams; *c:* Nicholas, Theodroe, Makarios; *ed:* The City Coll of NY (BS) Math 1987, (MS) Math 1989; Started PHD Pgm; *cr:* The City Coll of NY & Adam Clayton Powell Jr HS #43M Math Instr 1987-92; Bladensburg HS Math Instr 1992-; *ai:* Chess Coach; AFT 1987-; Natl Deans List.

SCOZZAFAVA, ROSE T., 9th-12th Grade Music Teacher; *b:* Norwich, NY; *m:* John G.; *c:* Kathryn, John C.; *ed:* Syracuse Univ (BM) Music Ed 1961; Cath Univ (MM) Music Ed 1969; 30 Credit Hrs Montgomery Cty Pub Schls 1973; *cr:* John West Jr HS Music Tchr 1961-63; Pyle Jr HS Music Tchr 1963-64; Broone Jr HS Music Tchr 1964-65; Wood Jr HS Music Tchr 1965-85; Wootton HS Music Tchr 1985-; *ai:* Choral Competitions; Chamber Singers; NEA 1965-; MSTA 1965-; Cath Coll Alumni, Choral Dir & Ofcr; Our Lady of Woods, Choral & Concert Dir, Fund Raising; Schlsp to Syracuse Univ; Grant for Summer Stud; *office:* Thomas S Wootton HS 2100 Wootton Pky Rockville MD 20850

SCRIBA, TOBY MARCUS, Art Teacher; *b:* Newark, NJ; *m:* Erich Peter; *ed:* Douglass Coll (BA) Art Ed 1964; Rutgers Univ (MA) Art Ed 1973; *cr:* Conackamack Jr HS Art Tchr 1964-71; Schor MS Art Tchr 1971-72; Piscataway HS Art Area Specialist 1987-91, Art Tchr 1973-; *ai:* NEA, NJEA, PTEA, AENJ 1964-; Mid Sts Evaluation Comm 1992, 1996; *office:* Piscataway HS 100 Behmer Rd Piscataway NJ 08854

SCRIBNER, DONNA E., Math Dept Coord & Teacher; *b:* Huntington, NY; *m:* Kenneth C. Jr.; *c:* Kevin, Melinda; *ed:* UNH (BS) Math Ed 1975; Antioch NE (MED) Ed 1992; *cr:* Bow Meml Schl 9th Grd Math Tchr; Bishop Brady HS Math Tchr; Hudson Meml Schl Math Tchr; *ai:* Class Adv; Acad Achvmt Awds Coord, Chprsn; Proficiency Diploma Comm; NEA, Local Tchrs; NH-ATMNE; NCTM; *office:* John Stark Regional HS 618 N Stark Hwy Weare NH 03281*

SCRIMA, JAMES V., Language Arts Teacher; *b:* Pittsburgh, PA; *m:* Delma Ann Vitina; *c:* James Anthony, Angela Leigh Scrima Porter; *ed:* Univ of Pittsburgh (BA) Eng 1968, (BS) Scndry Ed 1971, (MED) Scndry; Duquesne Univ (MS) Cnslng, Scndry; *cr:* US Army Ofcr 1968-70; Churchill Area HS Tchr 1971-80; Woodland Hills Area HS Tchr 1980-; *ai:* NEA 1971-; US Army, Reserve Status; Elks; Amer Legion; *office:* Woodland Hills HS 2550 Greensburg Pike Pittsburgh PA 15221

SCRIP, DIANE WEBB, Fifth Grade Teacher; *b:* Charleroi, PA; *m:* Charles Samuel Sr; *c:* Charles Jr., Chad, Shannon; *ed:* CA St Coll (BS) Speech Pathology & Audiology 1969, (BS) Elem Ed 1972; 3 Credit Hrs Univ of HI Sci; 3 Credit Hrs CA Univ of PA Sci; *cr:* Centerville Clinics Inc Mental Hlth Soc Worker 1983-85; Centerville Clinics Inc, Hlth Amer Market Rep 1985-88; CA Area Schl Dist K-12th Grd Sub Tchr 1969-83, Tchr 1988-; *ai:* PSEA, NEA 1988-; CAEA 1988-, Membership Chm; CA Pub Lib Bd 1994-; First Down Ftbl Club 1981-, Sec; Centennial Comm 1995-; Nom 1996 Thanks to Tchrs Spon by Westinghouse Electric Corp, Giant Eagle, KDKA-TV2; *home:* PO Box 511 Roscoe PA 15477*

SCRIVEN, PETER S., Guidance Counselor & Teacher; *b:* Cleveland, OH; *m:* Laurel Coffin; *c:* Elizabeth, James; *ed:* Denison Univ (BA) Pol Sci 1971; Cleveland St U (MED) Counseling, Guidance 1975; Grad Coursework Kent St Univ, Coll of Mt St Joseph, Ashland Univ, Baldwin Wallace Coll; *cr:* Center Jr HS Tchr, Cnslr 1971-; *ai:* Frosh Sftbl Coach 1980-83; Hon Soc Adv 1973-; Creative Writing Team Coach 1989-; NEA, OEA 1971-; OSCA 1983-; *office:* Center Jr HS 13200 Pearl Rd Strongsville OH 44136

SCRO, CHERYL MC DOWELL, First Grade Teacher; *b:* Franklin, PA; *m:* Andrew D.; *ed:* Clarion Univ (BS) Elem Ed 1964; 12 Addl Credit Hrs Penn St; *cr:* Sandycreek Elem Schl 2nd Grd Tchr 1964-67; Spruce St Schl 2nd Grd Tchr 1967-80, 1st Grd Tchr 1980-81, Kndgtn Tchr 1981-83, 2nd Grd Tchr 1984-92, Basic Skills Tchr 1992-94, 1st Grd Tchr 1994-; *ai:* Photography Enrichment Class; Read-a-thon Co-Chm; LEA 1967-, Comm; NJEA 1967-; NEA 1964-; Alpha Delta Kappa, Sec; Beta Sigma Phi 1962-, Pres, VP, Corres Sec, Treas, Liftime Mem Silver Circle; *office:* Spruce Street Schl 90 Spruce St Lakewood NJ 08701

SCRUGGS, ROXANNE KANE, Art Teacher; *b:* Brooklyn, NY; *m:* Douglas P.; *c:* Jessica, Patrick; *ed:* Queens Coll of City Univ of NY (BA) Fine Arts & Ed-Cum Laude 1973; *cr:* W C Bryant HS Art Tchr 1973-74; Lawrence Cntry Day Schl Art Tchr 1987-89; Our Lady of Perpetual Help Schl Art Tchr 1989-; *ai:* Kappa Delta Pi 1973-; Long Island Art Tchrs Assn; *office:* Our Lady Perpetual Help Schl 240 S Wellwood Ave Lindenhurst NY 11757

SCULLIN, LAURIE E., English Teacher; *b:* Bath, NY; *m:* Carl M.; *c:* Heather E. Sprague; *ed:* SUNY at Brockport (BS) Ed, Amer Studies 1970; Elmira Coll (MS) Ed 1976; NY St Admin Cert; *cr:* Horseheads Cntrl Schls Title I Home Schl Tchr 1970-71; Elmira Coll Fac Assoc 1974-76; Elmira Heights Cntrl Schls Kndgtn, 2nd Grd Tchr 1978-81; Elmira City Schls Alternative Ed 1983-84; Corning Painted Post Schls Scndry Eng Tchr, Drama, Speech 1985-, Dept Chair Eng 1993-95; *ai:* Writer Wkshp Presenter 1989; Dept Chair Eng 1993-94; Dist Wide Scheduling, Scndry Eng Comms; Set-Builder Masterworks Conjunction Drama Classes; Artist in Residence Prgm Coord 1986-88; CPP Tchrs Assn 1985-; NYSUT 1971-; ASCD 1991-; AAUW 1993-; Elmira Little Theatre 1984-87, Bd of Dirs; Elmira Heights Schl Bd 1976-77; Seven Lakes Girl Scout Cncl 1976-84, Appreciation Pin 1988; Elmira Little Theatre 1985-92, Producer, Dir; *office:* West HS Victory Hwy Painted Post NY 14870

SCULLION, DENNIS MICHAEL, 8th Grade English Teacher; *b:* Queens, NY; *m:* Una Shannon; *ed:* NY Univ (BA) Eng, Amer Lit 1988; Working on MS Ed, Eng Lehman Coll; *cr:* IS 74 8th Grd Eng Tchr 1991-, Instrl Specialist 1994-; *ai:* Acad Olympic Team Head Coach; Yrbk Staff Adv; Dist 8 Eng Curr Task Force; Organizer Shakespearean Soc; AFT 1991-; *office:* Hungs Point Peninsula Schl 730 Bryant Ave Bronx NY 10474*

SCULLY, JAMES ANDREW, Sixth Grade History Teacher; *b:* Ridgewood, NJ; *m:* Elizabeth Gass; *c:* Peter, Hannah; *ed:* Farleigh Dickinson Univ (BA) Sociology 1982; Boston Coll (MA) Amer Stud 1991; *cr:* Landmark Schl Tchr & Coach 1984-88; Wayland Acad Tchr & Coach 1991-94; Hawken Schl Tchr & Coach 1994-; *ai:* Var Boys Bsktbl Asst Coach; *office:* Hawken Schl 5000 Clubside Rd Lyndhurst OH 44124

SCULLY, LINDA LANESE, Kindergarten Teacher; *b:* Waterbury, CT; *m:* Martin J.; *c:* Lindsay Ann; *ed:* Southern CT St Univ (BS) Elem Ed 1973, (MS) Elem Ed 1976; St Josephs Coll 6th Yr Equivalency in Ed 1987; *cr:* Merriman Schl 1st Grd Tchr 1973-74; Wendell L Cross Schl 1st Grd Tchr 1974-92, Kndgtn Tchr 1992-; *ai:* Waterbury Tchrs Assn 1973-; CT Ed Assn 1973-; NEA 1973- 1973-; *office:* Wendell Cross Elem Schl 1255 Hamilton Ave Waterbury CT 06706

SCURRY, LENORA R., Science Teacher; *b:* Bronx, NY; *ed:* Widener Univ (BS) Sci Ed 1984, (MED) Cmptr Ed 1988; *cr:* Chester HS Sci Tchr, Adv 1984-88; Ashland MS Sci Tchr 1988-89; Pulaski MS Sci Tchr 1989-90; Smedley MS Sci Tchr, Adv Team Ldr 1990-93; Chester HS Sci Tchr 1993-; *ai:* PSEA, NEA 1983-; CUEA 1984-; Operation Chem Team 1991-; Immaculate Heart of Mary Church 1976-; Womens Intnl Bowling Congress 1988-; *office:* Chester HS 18th & Melrose Ave Chester PA 19013

SCURSATONE, JOYCE MARAVICH, Business Teacher; *b:* Aliquippa, PA; *m:* Clyde V.; *ed:* Westminster Coll Bus Ed 1966; Attnd Univ of Pitt, Penn St; *cr:* Robert Morris Coll Instr 1974-92; Hopewell HS Tchr 1966-; *ai:* NEA, PSEA, HEA 1966-; *office:* Hopewell HS 1215 Longvue Ave Aliquippa PA 15001

SEABRA, JAMES JOSEPH, Band Director; *b:* Providence, RI; *c:* Jonathan; *ed:* Berklee Coll of Music (BM) Music 1976; RI Coll (MM) Music 1995; Post Grad Stud at CA St Univ at Northridge, Univ of CA at Los Angeles; *cr:* Floster-Gloster Elem Schl Music Tchr 1989-90; Cranston Pub Schls Music Tchr 1989-90; The Music Schl Music Tchr 1995; *ai:* NEA 1990-; PAS, AF of M 1976-; *office:* Smithfield HS 90 Pleasant View Ave Esmond RI 02917

SEABURG, KYLE BRUCE, High School History Teacher; *b:* Norwalk, CT; *ed:* Gettysburg Coll (BS) Pol Sci; Southern CT St Univ (MS) His 1993; *cr:* Norwalk HS Soc Stud Tchr 1993-; *ai:* Var Field Hockey Coach; Drama

Club Adv; Life in The 90s Wkshp Ldr; Norwalk-Naragote Sister City Project; *office:* Norwalk HS 23 Calvin Murphy Dr Norwalk CT 06851*

SEADEEK, CAROLYN, 8th Grade Mathematics Teacher; *b:* Gloversville, NY; *c:* Thomas J.; *ed:* Daemon Coll (BS) Math & Ed 1970; *ai:* NEA 1980-; NCTM 1989-; Grant for Ldrshp Wkshp at Rutgers; *office:* South River MS Thomas St South River NJ 08882*

SEAGREAVES, PETER, Principal; *b:* Allentown, PA; *m:* Deborah Kochard; *c:* A. Peter; *ed:* Bloomsburg Univ (BS) Ed 1974, (MS) Rdng 1988; Doctoral Prgm Widener Univ; *cr:* Lehighton Schl Dist Rdng Spec 1979-88; Wilson Schl Dist Rdng Spec 1988-95, Prin 1996; *ai:* Stu Cncl Adv; Jr HS Wrestling Coach; Bldg Staff Ldr; AFT, KSRA 1988-; *office:* Wilson Central Jr HS 2601 Grandview Blvd West Lawn PA 19609

SEAMAN, MARY C. (MENALIS), Lit & Social Studies Teacher; *b:* Mahanoy City, PA; *m:* Donald J.; *c:* Donald J., Joseph F., Mary Michele; *ed:* Rider Univ (BA) Eng Lit 1982; *cr:* St Peter's Schl Lit, Soc Stud, Eng, Rel, Biblical Stud Tchr 1987-; *ai:* Moderator, Facilitator Stu Comm Awareness Adopt-a-Nrsng Home Resident, Adopt Spec Olympics; Moderator Stdnts Poetry Club, Classical Soc of Deceased Versifiers; Supervising, Creating, Dir, Producing Scripts as Vehicles for Classical Lit Prgm, Soc Stud Time-Ventures; Stu Intro to Frgn Langs Multi-Dimensional Approach; Creating Raps in Lit, Soc Stud, Grammar; NCEA 1987-; Chptr II Grant; *office:* St Peter Schl 101 Middleton St Riverside NJ 08075

SEAMAN, MICHAEL J., Eng Tchr & Lang Arts Dept Head; *b:* Philadelphia, PA; *m:* Gail Mary Sisak; *c:* Michael, Brian; *ed:* Widener Univ (BA) Eng, Ed 1970; Westchester Univ (MED) Eng, Ed 1976; 45 Addl Credits; *cr:* Southeast Delco Schl Dist Eng Tchr 1970-, Dept Head 1990-; *ai:* Jr Var Vlybl Coach; NEA, PSEA 1970-; Springdale Parks, Recreation Commission 1994-; *office:* Acad Park High School 300 Calcon Hook Rd Sharon Hill PA 19079

SEAMANS, JEFFREY DEAN, Technology Education Instr; *b:* New Castle, PA; *m:* Tammy Renee; *c:* Erin Renee; *ed:* Penn St Univ (BS) Ed, Industrial Arts 1980; Wilkes Univ (MS) Ed 1990; Addl Stud Millersville Univ: Sci, Tech Tchng Cert Prins of Tech; *cr:* Lake Station Schls Jr High Industrial Arts Tchr 1980-83; Pocono Mountain Schls Sr High Tech Ed Tchr 1983-84; Bangor Schl Dist Jr, Sr High Tech Ed Tchr 1984-95; State Coll Schl Dist 1995-; *ai:* Tech Stu Assn, Ski Club Adv; NEA; PSEA; Tech Ed Assn of PA, Tchr Rep; Tech Stu Assn 1980-, Bd of Dir; *office:* Park Forest MS 2180 School Dr State College PA 16801

SEAMANS, LOIS FRONCZEK, Nursing Instructor; *b:* Auburn, NY; *m:* Roy E.; *c:* Richard, William; *ed:* Auburn Meml Hospital Schl of Nursing (RN) Nursing 1972; Oswego Univ (BS) Hlth Occupations 1996; Certified Nurse Asst Evaluator; *cr:* Auburn Meml Hospital Registered Nurse Staff 1972-78, Nursing Supvr 1978-87; Cayuga Onondaga Boces Nursing Instr 1987-; *ai:* NYSUTA 1972-; NYSTA 1987-; Cub Scouts 1977-, Scout Ldr; Girl Scouts 1991-, Scout Ldr; *office:* Cayuga Onondag BOCES 5980 South St Rd Auburn NY 13021

SEARFOSS, BETH, English Teacher; *b:* Trenton, NJ; *ed:* Post Grad Courses Western MD Coll, Univ of Md; *cr:* Thomas Stone HS Eng Tchr 1976-81; Benjamin Stoddert MS Eng Tchr 1985-89; Mc Donough HS Eng Tchr 1989-; *ai:* Yrbk, SADD Spon; NEA, MSTA 1985-; Charles Cty Humane Soc 1992-, Vol; Super Svc Awd 1992; *office:* Mc Donough HS 7165 Marshall Corner Rd Pomfret MD 20675

SEARFOSS, DENISE DESTEFANO, Orchestra Director; *b:* Scranton, PA; *m:* Jonathan; *ed:* Marywood Coll (BM) Music Ed 1981, (MM) Music Ed 1989; Attnd Ithaca Coll, Cath Univ; *cr:* Abington Heights Schl Dist Orchestra Dir 1981-; *ai:* Chamber Ensemble Dir; NEA 1983-; PMEA, MENC 1981-, Spec Learner Rep; NSOA, AFM Local 120 1981-; *office:* Abington Heights Schl Dist E Grove St Clarks Summit PA 18411

SEARFOSS, DIANNE MIDTGARD, Eng Dept Chprsn & Soc Sci Tchr; *b:* Hillsdale, MI; *m:* Rick T.; *c:* Austin A., Audra A.; *ed:* Hillsdale Coll (BLS) Pol Ec, Ed Eng, Soc Sci 1979; Speech, Comm 1992; Univ of Toledo; Drake Univ; *cr:* North Cntrl HS Eng Dept Chprsn 1979-, Soc Sci Tchr 1992-; *ai:* Acad Cncl; Certfd Mentor; FTC Adv; NCEA, NEA 1979-; *office:* North Central HS 400 Baubice St Pioneer OH 43554*

SEARLE, BARBARA ALLEN, English Teacher; *b:* Morristown, NJ; *m:* Mark; *ed:* Ithaca Coll (BA) Eng 1974; SUNY at Albany (MS) Rdng 1979; 27 Addl Crdts Cooperative Learning; Portfolio Assessment; NY Cncl for Hum Inst; Intergrating the Curricula; Holocaust; Asrtv Dspln; Mltpl Intlgncs; *cr:* Sacred Heart Schl Eng Tchr; Washington HS Rdng Tchr 1979-80; Wappingers Cntrl Schls Eng Tchr 1981-; *ai:* HOPE, Ski Club Adv; Renaissance Comm; NYSUT 1984-; Phi Delta Kappa 1990-; NCTE 1980-; ASCD 1993-; NYSEC 1992-, Treas 1995, Ed of Excl 1995; 2 Pub Articles ERIC; Tchr of the Yr 1995; *office:* John Jay HS Rt 52 Hopewell Jct NY 12533

SEARLE, RONALD O., Honors Biology Teacher; *b:* Gloversville, NY; *m:* Barbara J. Sherman; *c:* Robert G., Rhonda M.; *ed:* Cornell Univ (BS) Sci Ed, Bio 1969; SUNY at Albany (MST) Advanced Classroom Tchng 1974; SUNY at Cortland (CAS) Admin 1980; Credit Hrs SUNY at Plattsburgh, SUNY at Oswego; *cr:* Cornell Univ Summer Sessions Bio Lab Instr 1969-70; Glens Falls Cntrl Schls Jr HS Tchr 1969-72; Cornell Univ Summer Sessions Head Bio Lab Instr 1971; Fayetteville-Manlius Cntrl Schls HS Bio, Earth Sci Tchr, Dept Head Instrl Specialist 1972-; *ai:* Sci Hnr Soc Founder & Adv; NYSUT, AFT, STANYS 1969-; NABT 1983-; NSTA 1984-; NYS Sci Hnr Soc 1992-, Bd of Governors 1995-; Head Writer & Ed Local Sci Curricula; Local Lab Manual for Regents Earth Sci; *office:* Fayetteville-Manlius HS E Seneca Turnpike Manlius NY 13104

SEARS, ANNE CRIBBY, First Grade Teacher; *b:* Portland, ME; *m:* Arthur W.; *ed:* Saint Josephs Coll (BA) Elem Ed 1969; *cr:* Nathan Clifford Schl 1st Grd Tchr 1969-; *ai:* NEA, MEA, PEA 1969-; *office:* Nathan Clifford Elem Schl 180 Falmouth St Portland ME 04102

SEARS, JOSEPHINE RYAN, Professor of Nursing; *b:* Springfield, MA; *m:* Paul J.; *c:* Josephine Rodriguez, Patrick, Paul B., Kevin, Brian, Kathryn; *ed:* Boston Coll Schl of Nrsng (BSN) Nrsng 1959; Westfield St (MA) Ed 1981; 24 Credits Post Grad Univ of MA; *cr:* Soc of Our Lady of Trinity Vol Nurse, Tchr 1960-65; Putnam Voc HS 10th Grd Hlth Careers 1971-72; Pvt Duty in Spfld Pvt Duty Nrsng 1972-76; Mercy Hosp Staff Nurse 1977-78; STCC Prof of Nrsng 1978-; *ai:* Nrsng Math, Lib, Hnrs, Nrsng Curr Comms; Visiting Nrsng 1995-, Bd Mem; Birthright of Pioneer Vly 1975-, Co-Founder, Bd Mem; Holy Name Choir 1985-; *office:* Springfield Tech Comm Coll 1 Armory Square Springfield MA 01105

SEARS, KATHLEEN LAVALLEE, Counselor; *b:* Worcestor, MA; *c:* Katherine T., Shauna J.; *ed:* Northeast MO St Univ (BS) PE 1968; Appalachian St Univ (MA) PE 1975; Bridgewater St Coll (MED) Cnslng 1991; 12 Credits Johns Hopkins Univ; 15 Credits Univ of San Diego; Attnd Univ of MN, Univ of South Fl, MI St, Panama Canal Coll, Loyola Univ, Penn St Univ, Cal Poly SLO; *cr:* Canal Zone Schls PE Tchr 1968-79; Dept of Defense Schls PE Tchr 1979-84, Hlth Tchr 1984-90; Panama Canal Coll Cnslr 1990-91; Curundu Jr HS Cnslr 1991-; *ai:* Schl-Based Mngmt Cncl, Sec; Ath Coord; Tech, Schl Svcs, Schl Soc Comms; Panama Canal Fed Tchrs 1968-, Past Pres; Comm Mayors 1993-, Vice-Mayor, Outstdng Svc; Exceptional Performance 1992-95; *home:* PSC Box 2 Box 1022 APO AA 34002*

SEAS, RICHARD ANDREW, HS Assistant Principal; *b:* Piqua, OH; *m:* Lorna Marie Eyink; *c:* Ryan, Michael, Christina; *ed:* OH Univ (BSEd) Earth Sci Ed 1986; Wright St Univ (MED) Admin 1989; Addl 18 Hrs Principalship, Asst Supt; *cr:* Frederick HS Sci Tchr 1989-90; Springfield South HS Sci Tchr 1990-91; St Charles Schl Sci Tchr 1991-94; River View HS Asst HS Prin 1994-; *ai:* Stu Cncl Adv; OASSA 1994-; Knights of Columbus 1985-, Recorder; Educl Ldrshp Awd; *office:* River View HS 26496 Sr 60 N Warsaw OH 43844*

SEATON, KATHLEEN MARIE, Retired 5th Grade Teacher; *b:* Jamestown, NY; *ed:* St Univ Coll at Buffalo (BS) Elem Ed 1961; Tchrs Coll Columbia Univ (MA) Guid, Stu Prsnl Admin 1964; Post Masters Stud St Univ of NY at Albany Cnslng; *cr:* Kenmore Pub Schls 4th Grd Tchr 1961-63; St Univ of NY Asst Dean of Stdnts 1964-68; Guilderland Cntrl Schls 4th-6th Grd Tchr 1968-94; *ai:* NY St Ret Tchrs 1984-; Albany Region Ret Tchrs 1994-; NYSUT 1961-; *home:* 28 Chestnut Rd Delmar NY 12054

SEAVER, JONATHAN DAVID, 4th Grade Teacher; *b:* Utica, NY; *m:* Diana Plamadon; *ed:* Univ of Southern ME (BS) Elem Ed 1975; Eng as 2nd Lang Univ of Sydney NSW Australia; *cr:* Wollonyong Elem ESL Tchr 1976-78; Alfred Elem 5th Grd Tchr 1979-84; Shapleigh Elem Multi Age Tchr 1985-88; Alfred Elem Multi Age Tchr 1988-; *ai:* Cub Scout Master; Head Tchr; Parents Club Treas; Parents Club Co Pres; NEA, ME Tchrs Assn 1978-; Massabesic T A 1978-, Pres, VP; Boy Scouts, Master; Nora Grace Grant; DAV Commanders Club; Featured in Several Books; Co-Authored Several Grants; *office:* Schl Admin Dist 57 West Rd Waterboro ME 04083*

SEAVY, GERALD L., US History & Amer Govt Teacher; *b:* Warren, PA; *m:* Beth A.; *c:* Megan, Katie; *ed:* Bowling Green St Univ (BS) His, Pol Sci, Eng 1971; Akron Univ (MA) Latin Amer His, Russian His 1990; *cr:* Alliance HS His, Amer Govt, World His, Eng, Hum Tchr 1972-; *ai:* Golf Coach; Ralph Regula Stu Congressional Comm Adv; NEA; *office:* Alliance HS 400 Glamorgan St Alliance OH 44601

SEBASTIAN, LINDA ANN, Teacher of Gifted & Talented; *b:* Pittsburgh, PA; *m:* Raymond; *c:* James, Marcy; *ed:* OH Univ (BS) Elem Ed 1970; LD Tutor Cert; Gifted Ed Cert; 30+ Grad Hrs; Working on MA Econ & Entrepreneurship at Univ DE; *cr:* Waterloo Elem Spcl Rdng Tchr 1970-72; Milford Exempted Village 6th Grd & LD Tchr 1972-73, 1981-82; Great Oaks Voc Schls Adult Basic Ed Instr 1980-83, 1983-; *ai:* Strategic Planning, Commnctn & Comm Involvement & Tech Comms; Comp Lab Coord; Mind Match Coach; OAGC 1985-; PTO Mini-Grant Recipient 2 Yrs; Clermont Cty Edctr of the Yr Nom; *office:* Clermont Northeastern HS 5327 Hutchinson Rd Batavia OH 45103

SEBASTIANI, AURORA MORELLI, Assoc Prof of Biological Sci; *b:* Youngstown, OH; *m:* Loreto; *c:* Anthony, Loreto Mark; *ed:* Youngstown Univ (BS) Bio 1963; Tulane Univ (MS) Zoology 1965; *cr:* Youngstown St Univ Instr 1965-74, Asst Prof 1974-83, Assoc Prof 1983-; *ai:* Omicron Lambda Fac, Univ Chief Hlth Professions Adv; Dept Assessment, Dept Pre-Prof Evaluation Comm; Institutional Review Bd Western Reserve Care System; AAAS, OH Acad of Sci 1966-; Rsrch Grant 1982; Exploring Life 1972, 1978, 1983; *office:* Youngstown St Univ 410 Wick Ave Youngstown OH 44555

SEBEKOS, PETER J., Mathematics Instructor; *b:* Jamaica, NY; *ed:* Vassar Coll (BA) Lib Arts, Psych 1978; Brooklyn Law Schl (JD) Law 1989; *cr:* Hudson Vly OIC Lang Arts, Math Instr 1979-80; Law Office of Peter Chen Attorney 1989-91; Law Office of P. Sebekos Attorney 1991-, Inst of Design, Construction Math Instr 1994-.

SEBER, ANNETTE, Fourth Grade Teacher; *b:* Carbondale, PA; *ed:* Marywood Coll (AB) Elem Ed 1976; Rdng Specialist, Masters Equivalency 1981; Univ of CA Diagnostic Prescriptive Math Cert; Wilkes Univ Regnl Cmptr Resource Ctr; *cr:* Forest City Regnl Elem Tchr 1976-; *ai:* Tchr Mentor; Nutrition Fair Coord; Detention Supvr; Elem Support Group Cnslr; NEA, PSEA 1976-; KSRA; NPRA; Calligrapher's Guild 1994-; TRI-Boro Vision 2000, Old Home Week Parade Signs 1993-; NE PA Audubon Soc 1996-; *office:* Forest City Regional Elem Schl 100 Susquehanna St Forest City PA 18421*

SEBUYIRA, ANNETTE N., Chemistry Teacher; *b:* Kampala Uganda, East Africa; *c:* Enaw; *ed:* Elmira Coll (BS) Biochemistry 1986; SUNY at Albany (MS) Tchng Sci 1991; *cr:* Guilderlands HS Chem Tchr 5 Yrs; *ai:* Club Adv; Reach Group; Act Achieving Cultural Togetherness; Intnl Club; Sci Mentor; AICHEM-E, NSTA 1991-; Dwight D. Eisenhower Sci Flwshp 1991-93; *office:* Guilderland HS PO Box 37 Guilderland Center NY 12085*

SECAUR, ROBERT MICHAEL, Chem, Gen Sci & Math Teacher; *b:* Pittsburgh, PA; *ed:* Duquesne Univ (BS) Chem 1985, (MS) Scndry Ed 1988; 13 Post Masters Credits; *cr:* Elderton Jr & Sr HS Chem, Math & Sci Tchr 1989-90, 1992-; *ai:* Newspaper & Sci Olympiad Adv; Fac Steering Comm; PSTA 1994-; NCTM 1994-; PSEA & NEA 1994-; Grants: Spectroscopy Soc of Pittsburgh & Rural Scholars of PA; *office:* Elderton Jr Sr HS PO Box 124 Elderton PA 15736

SECHRIST, SARA JANE, Third Grade Teacher; *b:* Reading, PA; *ed:* Kutztown Univ (BA) Elem Ed 1968; Post Grad Course Work Berks Campus of PA St; *cr:* Exeter Twp Schl Dist Grds 3/4, 2-3 Tchr 1968-; *ai:* NEA, PSEA 1968-; Exeter Tchrs Assn 1968-, Recording Sec, Bldg Rep; Exeter Crime Watch, Active Patrol Mem; Natl Campers & Hikers Assn 1969-, Emphasis on Conservation Act.

SECODA, MARGARET MARY FOWLER, Bio & Environmental Sci Tchr; *b:* Philadelphia, PA; *m:* Joseph B.; *c:* Kathleen Olshefski, Kristine Rountree, Joseph B. Jr., Michael, Karen, Joshua; *ed:* Holy Family Coll (BA) Elem Ed 1979; Beaver Coll (MA) Sci Ed 1989; *cr:* Immaculate Conception Schl 5th Grd All Subjects Tchr 1966-68, 7th-8th Grd Math Tchr 1982-85; Holy Trinity Schl 7th-8th Grd Sci, Math Tchr 1985-88; St Michael the Archangel Schl 7th-8th Grd Sci, Math Tchr 1988-92; Nazareth Acad Bio, Environmental Sci Tchr 1992-; *ai:* Moderator To Respect Everyone's Environment Club; Spon, Judge PA Jr Acad of Sci; NSTA 1989-; NCEA 1980-; TANDY Scholars Recognition Awd 1994; Eisenhower Grant 1995; *office:* Nazareth Acad HS 4001 Grant Ave Philadelphia PA 19114*

SECZAWINSKI, MARY FARINELLA, Retired HS Span & Fr Tchr; *b:* Passaic, NJ; *c:* Joseph; *ed:* Upsala Coll (BA) Span, Fr 1954; 15 Addl Credits; *cr:* St Lukes HS Tchr 1955-56; Passaic HS Tchr 1957-59, 1966-94; *ai:* Adv Fr Club; EAP 1966-; NJEA; NEA; Passaic Republican Club 1967; NJ Governors Awd 1991; Wm Paterson Tchr Recognition Awd 1993; Nom Paterson Tchr Recog Awrd 1993; Nom Princeton Awd.*

SEDLAK, RONALD FRANK, Campus Minister & Sr Rel Tchr; *b:* Tarrytown, NY; *m:* Mary Theresa Foehlinger; *c:* David, Jonathan, Katrina, Angela, Marc, Maria; *ed:* St Marys Coll (BA) Philosophy 1969; Mt St Marys (MDiv) Theology 1991; *cr:* Paterson Cath HS Tchr 1974-77; Lancaster Cath HS Tchr, Campus Minster 1990-; *ai:* Respect Life Club; NHS; *office:* Lancaster Catholic HS 650 Juliette Ave Lancaster PA 17601*

SEDLAK, VALERIE FRANCES, Associate Professor of English; *b:* Baltimore, MD; *c:* Barry V. Bowen Jr.; *ed:* Coll of Notre Dame of MD (BA) Eng 1955; Univ of HI (MA) Eng 1962; Univ of PA (PHD) Eng 1992; *cr:* Univ of HI Grad Tchng Asst 1960-61; Boyertown Sr HS Eng, His Tchr 1962-64; Univ of Baltimore Asst Prof of Eng 1964-69; Dulaney Sr HS Eng Tchr 1969-70; Morgan St Univ Assoc Prof of Eng, Asst Dean Coll of Arts & Scis 1970-; *ai:* Writing for Television Prgm Coord; MLA, SAMLA, CLA 1970-; CEA 1980-, Pres, VP, Exec Bd, Liaison Ofcr; MD Cncl Tchrs of Eng, Lang Arts 1985-, MD Eng Journal Assoc Ed; Mid-Atlantic Writers Assn 1978-, MAWA Review Asst Ed; Delta Epsilon Sigma 1989-, P MD Hum Cncl 1992-, Consultant, Evaluator; Amer Cancer So Consultant, Socio-Economically Disadvantaged Comm; Morgan-F Fellow in Eng Univ of PA 1977-79; Natl Endowment for Hum F Study Flwshp 1984; Morgan Fac Rsrch Scholar 1982-83, Outstdng Tchng Prof Awd Coll of Lib Arts Univ of Baltimore 19 Chms Awd for Fac Tchng 1986-87; 18 Articles Pub; *office:* Morgan 1700 E Cold Spring Ln Baltimore MD 21239

SEDORE, TOM, 9th-12th Grd English Teacher; *b:* Englewood, Lisa; *c:* Katie, Jessie, Megan, Lindsay; *ed:* Montclair St Coll (E 1980; 23 Credit Hrs Eng & Psych; *cr:* Lakeland Regnl HS E 1980-81; Embroidery Designer Draftsman, 1981-86; Spaulding Tchr 1987-; *ai:* Adv, Writing Tchr Lit Magazine; Asst, Head Ftb 1986-91; NEA 1991-; Connections Rdng Grant 1989-94.

SEDOTA, G. ELIZABETH, English Teacher; *b:* Rochester, NY; *m* M.; *c:* Lisa Reinhardt, John, Marie, James P.; *ed:* SUNY at Fredon Eng 1968, (MSEd) Dev Rdng 1973; Post Grad Work in Ed; *cr:* F HS Eng Tchr 1980-85; Brocton HS Eng Tchr 1985-; *ai:* HS Ne Adv; NCTE 1995-; Brocton Dist Level Team 1994-; Numerous Pub; Stdnts have Won Over 500 Awds in Writing, Photography Brocton Central Schl 138 W Main St Brocton NY 14716

SEEDS, LAUREL HINES, Voice Teacher; *b:* Canton, OH; Edward; *c:* Christopher E., Matthew L.; *ed:* Kent St Univ (BM) Vocal Ed 1980, (MM) Voice Performance 1986; *cr:* Home Studi Tchr 1980-; Orchard Hill Schl Elem Music Tchr 1983-84; Coll of Ldrshp Prgm Coord 1985-87, Chorus, Band Tour Coord 1987-90; HS Staff Voice Coach 1991-; *ai:* OMEA 1991-; Delta Omicron 198 Stud Grant Awd; Cleveland Orch's Blossom Festival Chorus 198 United Church of Christ 1973-; Canton Civic Opera Adult Schls *home:* 1409 Salway Ave SW North Canton OH 44720

SEEGER, LINDA J., Second Grade Teacher; *b:* Buffalo, NY; *m:* *c:* Amanda, Alane; *ed:* SUC at Fredonia (BA) Early Chldhd Ed 19 at Buffalo (MS) Elem Ed 1973; *cr:* West Seneca Cntrl Schls Tchr *ai:* West Seneca Dist Lang Arts Comm; Tchrs Assoc, NYSUT 1971- Northwood Elem Schl 250 Northwood Ave West Seneca NY 1422

SEEGER, ROBERT PAUL, US History & Government Tchr; *b:* NY; *ed:* Broome Comm Coll (AA) Lbrl Arts 1964; Binghampton Un His 1967, (MAT) His 1968; Syracuse Maxwell Schl 20 Credit Vestal Cntrl Schls Tchr 1967-; *ai:* Vestal Tchrs Assoc 1967-, Bld Grievance Chair; NEA-NY 1967-, Del; NEA 1967-; *office:* Vesta 205 Woodlawn Dr Vestal NY 13850

SEEL, NANCY KOUBIK, Choral & Voice Director; *b:* St Paul, Donald W.; *c:* Donald J.; *ed:* Mount Mary Coll at Milwaukee (B 1969; Buffalo St Coll (MA) Ed 1979; Cargegie Hall Robert Shaw Singer 1992, 1994-96; *cr:* Pvt Schls Eng & Music Tchr 1960-70; Pub Schl Adult Ed Rdng Tchr 1970-74; Niagara Falls Adult Ed Rd 1974-75; West Seneca Pub Schls Vocal, Choral, Gen Music, Th Music His Tchr; *ai:* Schl Musical Dir & Producer; Wellness Comm Erie Cty Music Ed 1976-; MENC 1976-; WSTA & AFT 1976-; NY 1976-; ACDA 1985-; Freudig Singers 1984-; Buffalo Choral A 1985-; Aurora Players 1986-; Buffalo Philharmonic Chorus 1990 Seneca Tchr of the Yr 1994; East Srs Tchr of the Yr 1995; Choru Gold with Distinction NYSSMA Festival 1995; Erie Cty Music Assn Guest Conductor; *office:* West Seneca East Sr HS 4760 Se West Seneca NY 14224

SEELEY, GEORGE WHEELER, History Teacher; *b:* Bridgeport, Susan Skymaker; *c:* Shastin, Samantha; *ed:* Yale Univ (BA) Hi Northwestern Univ (JD) Law 1965; *cr:* Belmont Hill Schl His Tch Chm, Summer Prgms Dir 1965-; Cumberwell Grammar Schl His Tchr 1977-78; Bentley Coll Govt Adj Prof 1991-; *ai:* Mock Tr Debate, Var Squash Coach; Election Prgms Organizer; NCSS 197 Cncl of His Edctrs 1980-; Town of Lincoln 1980-92, Recreation Summer HS Tchr Internship 1975; Summer Flwshp for Ind Stud 19 Endowment for Hum; *office:* Belmont Hill Schl 350 Prospect St B MA 02178

SEELEY, JAMES LEO, Honors English Teacher; *b:* Leominster, Linda D. Fisher; *c:* Gretel, Amy; *ed:* Worecester St Coll (BA) Hi Fitchburg St Coll (MED) Eng 1972; Various Courses Writing, Lit MA, Salem St, Fitchburg St; *cr:* Groton Jr-Sr HS Eng Tchr 1967-69 MS Eng Tchr 1969-78; Salem HS Eng Tchr 1978-; *ai:* Adv Jr, Sr 1994-95; AFT, NCTE 1969-; *office:* Salem HS 77 Wilson St Sal 01970

SEELEY, MARY BETH CAVANAUGH, Kindergarten Teac Akron, OH; *m:* George; *ed:* Akron Univ (BSEd) Ed 1974; Attnd B Walloca, Kent St, Ashland, Mt Union +18 Hrs Post Grad; *cr:* Rime Schl Kndgtn Tchr 1975; McEbright Elem Schl Kndgtn Tchr 1 David Hill Elem Schl Kndgtn Tchr 1975-77; Betty Jane Elem Schl Tchr 1977-78; Hotchkiss Elem Schl Kndgtn Tchr 1978-; *ai:* AEA Hotchkiss Tchr of Yr & PTA Tchr of Yr; *home:* 123 W Barlow Rd OH 44236

SEELEY, VALERIE A., Dept of Biological Sci Prof; *b:* Brooklyn, Robert J.; *ed:* NYU (AB) Bio 1963, (MS) Bio 1965, (PHD) Bio 19 Brooklyn Coll Instr 1968-70; Queensborough Comm Coll As 1970-78, Assoc Prof 1978-82, Prof 1982-, Chprsn 1987-; Queensborough Community Coll 22205 56th Ave Flushing NY 11

SEELHORST, WAYNE JOHN, Mathematics Teacher; *b:* Pittsbur *m:* Barbara Charolette Majoka; *c:* Cynthia Shristine Schad, Wayne; *ed:* IN Univ of PA (BS) Scndry Math 1964; Univ of Pitt (MED) Scndry Ed 1967; 60 Addl Credit Hrs CCAC, Penn St; *cr:* Mills Sr HS Scndry Math Tchr 1964-; *ai:* Security Boys, Birls Vlybl Ticket Seller; Ftbl Tem Statistician 22 Yrs; SAT Prep Tchr; PSEA 1964-; NHEA 1964-, Chm 24 Yrs; St Andrews BC Church 19 Trustee 12 Yrs; Own SAT Preparation Bus Strategies For Success Taught Project Learning SAT Preparation 1980-92; *office:* North H HS 53 Rochester Rd Pittsburgh PA 15229*

SEELY, BRIAN L., Mathematics Teacher; *b:* Hazleton, PA; *m:* Ch E. Maslo; *c:* Brandon, Derek; *ed:* Penn St Univ (BS) Math Bloomsburg Univ (BS) Ed 1987; *cr:* Tamaqua Jr HS Chptr 1, Re Math Tchr 1988; East Stroudsburg HS Math Tchr 1988-; *ai:* Var Wr Asst Coach; NCTM, NEA, PSEA 1989-; Little League Bsbl 1992-, *office:* East Stroudsburg Sr HS 279 N Courtland St East Stroudsb 18301

SEELY, MARIBETH WALSH, 5th Grade Teacher; *b:* Lawrence, Thomas P.; *c:* Tim Francis, Keribeth Francis; *ed:* Lowell Univ (BS Ed 1966; 18 Credit Hrs; *cr:* Methuen 1st-3rd Grd Tchr 1966-71; La Rdng Tchr 1981-84; Montague Basic Skills Tchr 19 Sandyston-Walpack 5th Grd Tchr 1985-; *ai:* Environmental Club Tech Comm; Manna House Soup Kitchen 1989-, Exec Bd; Right t 1980-; Greenpeace 1985-; Nom NJ Tchr of the Yr 1993; Governor Recognition Winner 1994; Lenni Lenape Woman of Distinction 19 Herald Woman of the 90s 1995; *office:* Sandyston-Walpack Cons S Box 128 Layton NJ 07851*

SEELY, STEVEN ALAN, English Teacher; *b:* Mineola, NY; *m:* Martin; *c:* Kristin, Eric; *ed:* Allegheny Coll (BA) Eng 1969, (MAE Ed 1970; Cooperative Learning Methodologies; *cr:* South HS Eng

›9; Cold Spring Harbor HS Eng Tchr 1969-71; Sewanhaka Pub Schls :hr 1972-; *ai:* Accelerated Reader Prgm Head; NEA 1989-; *office:* HS 555 Ridge Rd Elmont NY 11003

E, DEBORA ZIGERELL, MS Social Studies Teacher; *b:* Beaver PA; *m:* Wayne D.; *c:* Megan, Amanda; *ed:* Clarion Univ (BS) Soc Sci 24 Post-Grad Credits; *cr:* Seneca Valley Sr HS Soc Stud Tchr '7; Forest Hills MS Soc Stud Tchr 1977-; *ai:* Instructional Support SWATT Tutoring Club Adv; Geography Bee Dir; NHS Fac Review EA, PSEA 1976-; Forest Hills Ed Assn 1977-; Girls Scouts Amer Troop Ldr; Bethel UM Church 1987-; *office:* Forest Hills MS RD 1 6 Sidman PA 15955

E, DONANNE PARKHURST, Spanish Teacher; *b:* Greensburg, PA; ey James; *c:* Joshua Todd, Caleb James; *ed:* Geneva Coll (BA) Span (BSEd) Elem Ed 1992; *cr:* Seneca Vly Jr HS Span Tchr 1992-94; r Cty Chrstn Schl Span Tchr 1992-; Geneva Coll Part-time Span er; *office:* Beaver Cty Chrstn Schl 601 Penn Ave New Brighton PA

E, WAYNE D., Mathematics Teacher; *b:* Shirley, MA; *m:* Debora C. ll; *c:* Megan I., Amanda J.; *ed:* Clarion Univ (BS) Scndry Ed & Math St Francis Coll (MED) Ed 1981; *cr:* Forest Hills Jr HS Math Tchr 77; Conemaugh Valley Jr HS Math Tchr 1977-78; Forest Hills Sr HS Tchr 1978-; *ai:* Jr HS Head Ftbl Coach; Asst Var Ftbl Coach; NHS eview Bd; NEA & PA St Ed Assn 1976-; Forest Hills Ed Assn 1978-, 981-85; Bethel United Meth Church 1987-, Admin Bd; Sallie Mae Tribute Awd 1993; *office:* Forest Hills Sr H S P O Box 158 Sidman 955

VER, MICHAEL L., AP History & Literature Tchr; *b:* Lima, OH; *m:* een P. Seewer; *ed:* OH St Univ (BSEd) His, Eng 1967; Wright St Univ His 1971; Columbia Pacific Univ (PHD) His, Lit 1983; OH Wesleyan His 1963-64; Life Cert His, Eng; Scndry Cert St of OH; *cr:* Fairborn 's, Eng Tchr 1967-71; Fairborn Park Hills HS His, Lit AP Tchr 32, Wright St Univ Adjunct Instr of His 1972; Fairborn HS His, Lit 82-; *ai:* Chm Dept of Soc Stud 1977-81; AP Coord 1981-85; Acad 986-89; Scndry Standards Comm 1986-89; Fairborn Ed Assn, OH Ed NEA, Western OH Ed Assn 1967-; Assn Amer Historians 1971-92; 1980-; Ordained Elder Presbyn Church Session Mem 1987-91; Chm Ed Comm 1988-89; Steering Comm Long Range Planning First yn Church 1991-92; Amer Civil Liberites Union; First presbyterian n Mem 1993-; mission Interpretation & Stewardship Chm 1993; ian Ed 1994; OH Historical Soc 1993-; Sierra Club 1993-; Chrstn Ed 995; Comm on Cert Edctrs 1994; DAR Outstanding Hist Tchr St of 984; Daughters of Colonial Wars Natl Outstanding Tchr 1984; gnition OH Legislature Tchng Excl 1986; OH Univ Recognition Excl 1988; Who's Who Amer Ed 1990; Greene Co Excl Ed Awd 1991, 1993; Outstanding Tchr Awd Univ of Chicago Honors 1991; Fairborn HS 900 E Dayton Yellow Springs Rd Fairborn OH 45324*

AS, JOHN, Speech & Theatre Teacher; *b:* Charleroi, PA; *m:* Janet ; *c:* Sharon, Douglas; *ed:* CA St (BA) Eng 1963; Attnd Penn St Univ, r Rock Univ; *cr:* Ledgemont HS Eng Tchr 1963-66; Pine-Richland ng, Speech, Theatre Tchr 1966-; *ai:* Forensic Speech, Debate Dir; NEA 1970-; PA HS Speech League, Natl Forensic League; Apple chr Awd; Tchr of Yr Finalist; *office:* Pine Richland HS 4300 ndale Rd Gibsonia PA 15044

IC, EVA YANZETICH, First Grade Teacher; *b:* Johnstown, PA; *m:* ; *ed:* Univ of Pittsburgh at Johnstown (BS) Elem Ed 1982; *cr:* St dict Schl First Grd Tchr 1982-; *ai:* NCEA 1982-; St Benedict emporary 1995-; St Benedict Church Cantor 1994-; *office:* St dicts Schl 2306 Bedford St Johnstown PA 15904

, DENISE ANNE, High School English Teacher; *b:* Pittsburgh, PA; ippery Rock Univ of PA (BS) Scndry Ed Eng 1993; Northeastern Working on MA Writing; *cr:* New Brighton Area Sr HS Eng Tchr; *ai:* a Club Stage Crew Supvr; NCTE 1992-; NEA 1993-; PA St Ed Assn ; IRA 1995-; Natl Collegiate End Awd USAA Recipient 1993; US nt Acad All Amer Scholar Recipient 1993; NBHS Tchr of Month Whos Who of Amer Women; Whos Who in Amer Ed; *home:* 846 St Apt 70 Sewickley PA 15143*

AL, INA M., 3rd Grade Teacher; *b:* Newark, NJ; *m:* Larry; *c:* Jeremy; esley Coll at Cambridge (BS) Ed 1967; 15 Grad Credits; *cr:* Joshua Schl 3rd Rdng Tchr 1967-70, 1973-; *ai:* Soc Stud Curr Comm; RTA, NEA 1967-70, 1973-.

AL, JEFFREY BARRY, High School Biology Teacher; *b:* New York, *d:* CCNY (BS) Bio 1972, (MA) Sci Ed 1977; 30 Credit Hrs Beyond n Bio, Chem, Physics, & Ed; *cr:* Far Rockway HS, Truman HS, Morris io & Gen Sci Tchr 1972-75; Great Neck North Jr HS Gen Sci Tchr 76; Evander Childs HS Bio & Gen Sci Tchr 1976-82; Bronx HS of io & Jr-Sr Genetics & Evolution Tchr 1983-; *ai:* Bio Tutor; Lab ical Comm; Exam Comm: Mentor; NABT, UFT 1972-; Museum of al His 1990-; NCPA 1995-; Eisenhower Grant; Ecology Trng Inst Demonstrator of Audio Visual Techniques at Meetings; Mentor for Stu Tchrs; *office:* Bronx HS Of Science 75 W 205th St New York NY 3*

ATTI, LAURA KRATZER, Adj Instr of Early Chldhd Ed; *b:* Easton, *n:* Christopher A.; *c:* Damien, Ellen; *ed:* Northampton Comm Coll) Early Chldhd 1973; East Stroudsburg Univ (BS) Elem Ed 1975, Ed 1991; *cr:* Various Other Affiliations Tchr 1975-83; Palmr vian Day Schl Admin, Dir 1983-88; Wind Gap Children's Schl ultant 1988-92; Northampton Comm Coll Adj Instr 1992-; *ai:* YC, Assoc Chldhd Ed Intnl 1992-.

BERS, DENA L., Cheerleading Coach; *b:* Newark, NY; *m:* Michael Shana, Mitchel; *ed:* Rochester Inst of Tech (BFA) Graphic Design ; *cr:* Canandaigua Acad Cheer Coach 1985-; Natl Spirit Group Sales 988-91; Var Spirit Corp Sales Rep 1991-; *ai:* Coach of Yr Seven Yrs; sification Championship Two Yrs; League Championship Four Yrs; *:* Canandaigua Acad HS 1 Academy Cr Canandaigua NY 14424

ELSKI, ANTHONY JAMES, Social Studies Teacher; *b:* Jamaica, *n:* Susan Marie Henze; *ed:* St John's Univ (BA) Pol Sci 1965, (MS) ry Ed 1967; SUNY Stony Brook (MA) Lbrl Stud 1977; 60 Addl its; *cr:* Patchogue-Medford Pub Schls Soc Stud Tchr 1967-; *ai:* Mock Team Adv; Site Based Mngmt, Pol Action Comms; HS Bldg Captain; S, NYSCSS, NCSS 1967-; PFT, PMCT, NYSUT, AFT 1967-, PFT 1968-70, PMCT Pres 1970-72; Kappa Delta Pi 1967-; South Cty Lib 995-, Trustee; Global Stud, Criminal Justice, Coll Transition Course, H Metropolitan Museum of Art Tour Guide; *home:* 79 Bieselin Rd port NY 11713*

URA, JOSE D., Spanish & Literature Teacher; *b:* Dominican Rep; *m:* yn Reyes; *c:* Betty, Evelyn, Jose Jr., Xavier; *ed:* LIU (MS) Ed 1978; ham Univ (MS) Ed Supervision 1982; Post Grad Stud Universidad De manca, Universidada Alcala De Henares, Spain; *cr:* JFK HS Math Tchr -81; Barringer HS Math Tchr 1981-83; DeWitt Clinton HS Span Tchr -; *ai:* AFT, UFT 1983-; NEA 1981-83; Latin Amer Writers Assn -; Ibero Amer Writers & Poets Guild 1992-; NEA Grant 1994; Ibero r Culture Inst Schlsp 1992; Pub Poetry Book 1995; *office:* Dewitt ton HS 100 W Mosholu Pky S Bronx NY 10468*

BERT, LEE MARTIN, Social Studies Teacher; *b:* Altoona, PA; *c:* Hunter, Heidi Nichole; *ed:* VA Military Inst (BA) His 1972; Central St Univ (MED) Higher Ed Jr Coll 1976, (MA) Southwestern Stud 1984; 166 Undergraduate Credit Hrs; 106 Grad Credit Hrs; *cr:* Midwest City-Del City Schl Dist 9th Grd Eng, 7th Grd Soc Stud Tchr 1976-77; Mustang Schl Dist 9th, 11th Grd Soc Stud Tchr 1977-84; East Pennsboro Area Schl Dist 9th, 12th Grd Soc Stud Tchr 1985-; *ai:* Facilitator Svc Learning Pgrm; Sr Class Adv; OK Tchr Cert Testing Comm 1982-83; Title IV-C Grant 1981-82; Pen-Heinz Svc Learning Grant 1983-84; Learn & Serve Amer Grant 1984-87; *office:* East Pennsboro Area HS 425 W Shady Ln Enola PA 17025*

SEIBERT, MARGARET ARMBRUST, Professor of Art History; *b:* Cincinnati, OH; *m:* C. J. Jr.; *ed:* Univ of Cincinnati (BS) Advertising Design 1967; OH St Univ (MA) His of Art 1972, (PHD) His of Art 1986; *cr:* Gibson Greetings Artist, Copywriter 1963-66; Stewart & Tassian Advertising Artist 1967-68; Ron Starbuck Advertising Artist 1971-72; Columbus Coll of Art & Design Prof 1972-; *ai:* Fac Cncl Mem at Large; Exhibition Comm; Art His Subject Area Comm; Coll Art Assn 1980-; Mid-Amer Art His Soc 1980-, Paper Presented 1980; Amer Assn of Univ Profs 1984-; Natl Museum of Women in Arts 1990-; Friends of OH St Univ Libs 1986-94, Bd of Trustees; Artwork Exhibited Cincinnati Art Dirs Club Annual Exhibition 1968; Columbus Comm Soc 1972; OH Exposition Purchase Prize 1980; Articles Pub; *office:* Columbus Coll Of Art & Design 107 N 9th St Columbus OH 43215*

SEIDEL, BONITA MARIE, Second Grade Teacher; *b:* Queens, NY; *ed:* Adelphi Suffolk Coll at Oakdale (BA) Hum, Elem Ed 1968; Adelphi Univ at Garden City (MA) Ed, Psych 1970; Elem Rdng 1973 at Mt Vernon Coll; Hum Southampton Coll 1977-83; Lit Hertfordshire Coll 1987; *cr:* Wheeler Rd Schl 4th Grd Tchr 1968-70; Cordello Ave Schl 3rd Grd Tchr 1971-79; Charles A. Mulligan Schl 2nd Grd Tchr 1979-; *ai:* Suffolk Rdng Cncl 1982-83; NYSUT, AFT, PTA 1968-; Cntrl Islip Tchrs Assn 1968-, Bldg Rep 1978; Neighborhood Kids tutorial Prgm 1979-81; See Saw Magazine Staff 1983-86; Sharing in Our Libraries 1984; Comm Merchants 1984-94; Doll Club of Huntington 1989-; Parkdale Civic Assn 1987-; Long Island Keepsakers Club 1993-; AFT Intnl Womens Yr Awd 1976; NYSUT Pol Action Awd 1978; Citation Educl Staff 1980-83; Poems Pub; *office:* Charles A. Mulligan Elem Schl Broadway & Suffolk Ave Central Islip NY 11722

SEIDELL, DONNA FUIMARA, Reading Consultant; *b:* Bridgeport, CT; *m:* John Edward; *c:* Nathan Tecca, Taylor Thomas; *ed:* Southern CT St Univ (BS) Early Chldhd Ed 1971, (MS) Rdng 1977; 6th Yr Supervision, Admin 1991; *cr:* Jane Ryan Elem Schl 2nd-3rd Grd Tchr 1971-91, K-5th Grd Rdng Consultant 1991-; *ai:* Schl Testing Coord; Stu Cncl Adv 1988-90; NEA, Trumbull Ed Assn 1972-; Pinewood Lake Assn 1983-, Lake Preservation Comm; Mentor Tchr; *office:* Jane Ryan Elem Schl 190 Park Ln Trumbull CT 06611*

SEIF, MARY JOAN, Fourth Grade Teacher; *b:* Bucyrus, OH; *m:* Robert M.; *c:* Tracy J. Reitzel, Darcy L. Barber, Hilary R.; *ed:* OH St Univ (BS) Elem Ed 1969; Ashland Univ (MED) Curr & Instruction 1990; 22 Grad Hrs Beyond Masters; *cr:* Galion City Schls 1st Grd Tchr 1969-70; Colonel Crawford Elem Art Tchr 1982-84, 3rd Grd Tchr 1984-88, 1st Grd Tchr 1988-89, 4th Grd Tchr 1989-; *ai:* NEA, Crawford Cty Rdng Assn; *office:* Sulphur Springs Elem State Route 602 North Robinson OH 44856

SEIFARTH, LINDA RITCHIE, Art Teacher; *b:* Reading, PA; *m:* Arvid K.; *c:* Martha Seifarth Beachley, Jana Briana; *ed:* Kutztown St Coll (BS) Art Ed 1968, (MS) Art Ed 1972; 24 Credits Pass Masters Degree; Museum of Art; *cr:* Reading Schl Dist Elem Art Tchr 1968-70; Boyertown Schl Dist Jr HS Art Tchr 1971-74, 1977-; *ai:* Set Design for Schl Musical; NEA; PSEA; PA Coalition for Arts in Ed; Phila Museum of Art; Good Shepherd United Church of Christ 1975-, Art Auctions, Music, Art Comm, Consistory; Artist in Residence Prgm; *office:* Boyertown Schl Dist Montgomery Ave Boyertown PA 19512

SEIFERT, MARILYN F., English Teacher; *b:* Erie, PA; *m:* Frederick A.; *ed:* Gannon Univ (BA) Eng 1966, (MA) Eng 1972; *cr:* Dunkirk Jr HS Tchr 1966-67; Roosevelt MS Tchr 1967-80; Strong Vincent HS Tchr 1980-81; Roosevelt MS Tchr 1981-; *ai:* NEA, PSEA, Erie Ed Assn 1967-; Tchr of Yr 1995; *office:* Roosevelt MS 2300 Cranberry St Erie PA 16502

SEIFERT, WILLIAM NORMAN, Director of Spiritual Act; *b:* Philadelphia, PA; *ed:* Univ of Scranton (BA) Philosophy, Theology 1977; Mary Immaculate Seminary (MDiv) Theology 1980; Pope John Paul II Inst STL Cand Marriage & Family Stud; *cr:* Allentown Cntrl Cath HS Theology Dept Chprsn, Yth Minister, Sr Theology Tchr 1981-87; Bethlehem Cath HS Sr Theology Prof, Spiritual Act Dir 1987-; *ai:* Wrestling Coach; Chess Club; Band Chaplain; Spiritual Life, Spiritual Life Steering Comms; Diocesan Yth Ldrshp Prgm Facilitator; NCEA 1987-; NCOD 1979-; Diocesan Bd of Ed 1986-, Consultant; Yth Ministry Adv Bd 1986-, Consultant Natl Yth Ministry Awd; Diocesan Liturg Comm 1996; Deaf Apostolate 1977-, Dir; Diocesan Family Life Ed Comm 1983-; Co-Author On Life & Love: A Summary of Catholic Teaching on Marriage, Touching the Truth: A Study Guide of Veritatis Splendor, Proclaiming the Gospel of Life; Who's Who in Rel 1993; Who's Who in the East 1995; *office:* Bethlehem Catholic HS 2133 Madison Ave Bethlehem PA 18017*

SEIGEL, ANDREW MARK, Music Teacher; *b:* Phillipsburg, NY; *m:* Felicia R. Weiss; *c:* Jessica Mariah; *ed:* West Chester Univ (BS) Music Ed 1987; Rowan Coll of NJ (MA) Curr Dev & Supervision 1993; Orff Level I Cert West Chester Univ; NJ St Cert Music, Elem Tchr & Curr Coord, Supvr; *cr:* Wm Davies MS Band & Choir Dir, Gen Music Tchr 1988-; Delsea Regnl HS Drum Line Instr, Arranger, Composer 1993-; *ai:* Concert Band, Choir Dir; NJHS, Grad, Inter-Dist Music Articulation, Chm Tchr Recognition Comms Adv; Instrument & Voice Lessons Instr; HTPS Tech Comm; HTEA, KOP, NJEA, MENC, NJMEA 1988-; ASCD, PAS 1993-; SGM, SRME 1989-; West Chester Univ Alumni Assn 1988-, Exec Ofcr, Treas; South Jersey Choral Dirs Assn 1988-, Adjudicator, Region 3 Chorus Mgr, Dir; South Jersey Band, Orch, Dir Assn 1988-, Adjudicator, Dir; HTEF Ed Grant 1995; Hamilton Township Pub Schls Music Tech SPARK Grant 1994; Delsea Regnl HS Percussion Seminars 1996; Clinician; Multi-Dist Music Tech & Percussian Clinician; Tchr Mentor 1994-95; Stu Composers Project 1993-; *office:* William Davies MS 1876 Vienna Ave Mays Landing NJ 08330

SEILER, MICHAEL, Science Teacher; *b:* Newark, NJ; *c:* Michael; *ed:* William Paterson Coll (BA) Bio, Chem 1974, (MA) Bio 1978; 40 Post-Grad Stud Seton Hay Univ, Kean Coll, Jersey City St Coll; *cr:* Westfield HS Sci Tchr 1974-; *ai:* Key Club, Class Advs; Schl Cntrl Treas; Westfield Ed Assn 1990-, Pres; Union Cty Ed Assn; NJ Ed Assn 1992-, Consumer Svcs; NEA; Kiwanis Intnl; 10 Articles Pub; *home:* 896 Anderson Rd Jackson NJ 08527

SEILHAMER, WILLIAM BUZZ, Sci Instr & Athletic Coach; *b:* Xenia, OH; *m:* Christine Ann Luttrell; *c:* Aric, Adam, Ashley; *ed:* Heidelberg Coll (BS) Bio 1965; Univ of WA Oceanography; Wright St Univ Geology; Univ of Dayton PE; *cr:* Wright St Univ Sci & Aviation Tchr 1986-; Beavercreek HS Sci Tchr & Coach 1965-; *ai:* Asst Bsktbl Coach 30 Yrs; Boys & Girls Track & Field Coach 30 Yrs; Aths Video Specialist 16 Yrs; Track Ofcl 25 Yrs; NEA, WOEA 1965; OEA 1965-, Life Mem; NSTA 1968-, Life Mem; OATCCC 1966-, Dist Rep, Dist Coach of Yr; OHSBCA 1970-; K of P Lodge 1973-, 25 Yr Pin; WCOT, CCOA 1970-; Track & Field WOL Coach of Yr 4 Times; Conditioning & Track & Field Clinic Speaker; FTA Tchr of Yr 1972; 300 Bsktbl Victories; Dist Track & Field Coach of Yr; *office:* Beavercreek HS 2660 Dayton-Xenia Rd Beavercreek OH 45434*

SEILING, WILLIAM W., Mathematics Teacher; *b:* Lima, OH; *m:* Jane Galloway; *c:* Terri Jones, Stacy; *ed:* OH St Univ (BA) Math 1962; Western MI Univ (MA) Math Ed 1970; *cr:* Mohawk HS Math Tchr 1962-67; Shawnee HS Math Tchr 1967-; *ai:* After Schl Acad Coach; NCTM, OCTM 1962-; Lions Club 1971-, Newsletter Editor; Jennings Schola; NSF Grant; *office:* Shawnee HS 3333 Zurmehly Rd Lima OH 45806

SEIPLE, REBECCA DURIG, Spanish Teacher; *b:* Youngstown, OH; *m:* Lee R.; *c:* Scott, Leigh Ann; *ed:* Edinboro St Univ (BS) Span, Eng S Ed 1972, (ME) Rdng 1978; Credit Hrs at Kent St Univ, Westminster Coll, Span at Univ of Valencio; *cr:* Bloomfield-Mespo Local Schl HS Span, Eng Tchr 1973-74; West Middlesex Local Schl Span I, Grds 7-8 Eng Tchr 1974-76; Maplewood Local Schls Span I-IV, Grds 7-12 Rdng, Grds 7-8, 12 Eng Tchr 1978-82; Joseph Badger Local Schls Span I-II, Grds 11-12 Eng Tchr 1986-87; Lakeview Local Schls Span I-II, IV, Grd 8 Rdng, Grds 9, 11 Eng, Basic Eng 9 Tchr 1987-; Trumbull Cty Schls GATE Span Classes; *ai:* 8th Grd Chrldr Advy; OEA, NEA 1973-, Bldg Rep; Trumbull Cty A Plus Tchr Awd 1995; Mentor Prgm Representing Lakeview HS in Trumbull Cty Prgm.

SEITH, NANCY L., 4th Grade Teacher; *b:* Shaker Heights, OH; *ed:* Univ of IL (BA) Landscape Arch 1952; Case Western Reserve Univ (MA) Ed 1968; Cleveland St Univ, Ashland Coll, John Carol Univ 36 Credit Hrs; *cr:* Richard Hawley Cutting Arch, Engr Designer 1952-54; Tkach, Wunderlich Consulting Engrs Partner 1954-57; Hargett, Yanda, Barber Consulting Engrs Head Hwy Design Dept 1957-62; NLS Assocs Prin 1962-; West GA Schls Elem Tchr 1966-; *ai:* Audio-Visual Dir; NEA, OEA 1966-; WGEA 1966-, Negotiator; Phi Kappa Phi; Alpah Alpha Gamma; Educl Cmptr Consortium of OH 1986-91, Bd of Dirs; US Govt Patents on Orthopedic Device 1 Patent, Automotive Device 2 Patents, Personal Flotation Device 2 Patents; Adj Prof Kent St Univ; *home:* 8800 Carmichael Dr Chesterland OH 44026

SEITHER, FRED S., HS Physical Education Teacher; *b:* Ithaca, NY; *m:* Christine Clum; *c:* Michelle, Patrick, David; *ed:* Orange Cty Comm Coll (AA) PE 1967; Ithaca Coll (BS) PE 1969; Permant Tchng Degree; Attnd Cortland St, Elmira Coll; *cr:* Watkins Glen CS Elem, HS PE Tchr 1969-79; Horseheads CS Elem, HS PE Tchr 1979-; *ai:* Coach Ftbl 1969-79, Track 1969-88, Swimming 1969-; Driver Ed 1972-95; Site Base Team 1993-; NYSCA, 100 Win Club 2 Sports; NFICA, NFIOA 10 Yrs; NYSSOA 15 Yrs; NYSTOA 5 Yrs; USS Ofcl 15 Yrs; USS Glen Gator Swim Club 16 Yrs, Pres; Church Cncl 3 Yrs; *home:* 126 Durland Ave Watkins Glen NY 14891

SEITZ, CAROLYN WALTERS, Social Studies Teacher; *b:* Circleville, OH; *m:* Merlyn E.; *c:* Jodi, Joel; *ed:* Capital Univ (BA) Speech, His, Govt 1967; Univ of Dayton (ME) Tchr Ed, Intnl Ed 1990; Amharic Cooperative Lang Inst Amharic Lang Cert 1968; Attnd OH St Univ at Columbus, Miami Univ at Oxford, Wright St Univ at Dayton; *cr:* Good Shepard Schl Tchr 1968-70; Brown Local Schls Sub Tchr 1974-79; Westerville City Schls Sub Tchr 1980-83; Columbus Pub Schls ESL Tutor 1981-83; The Eng Lang Inst Dir, Tchr of ESL 1983-86; Oakwood City Schls Tchr 1986-; *ai:* Intnl Club Adv; Oakwood HS Fall Play Dir; NEA 1988-; OEA 1988-, Peace, Understanding Awd; Oakwood Tchrs Assn 1988-, VP; OCSS 1986-, Mbrshp Chair; Dayton Cncl of World Affairs Global Connection 1983-, Task Force; St Paul Luth Church 1983-, Bd Mem, Tchr, Choirs; Montgomery Cntry Pub Edctrs Grants; OSU, OH Univ Summer Inst on Africa 1995; OH Geographic Alliance Summer Inst 1994; *office:* Oakwood Jr HS 1200 Far Hills Ave Dayton OH 45419*

SEITZ, GRAYCE ROSSO, Guidance Counselor; *b:* Passaic, NJ; *c:* David Allocca, Jeffrey; *ed:* William Paterson Coll (BA) Elem Ed 1961; Seton Hall Univ (MA) Psych 1977; Jersey City St 30 Credits Above MA; *cr:* Fairlawn Bd of Ed Elem Tchr 1961-64; New City Bd of Ed Elem Tchr 1967-69; Mt Olive Bd of Educ Elem Tchr 1970-71; Randolph Bd of Ed MS Lang Arts Tchr 1971-80, MS Guid Cnslr 1980-83, HS Guid Cnslr 1983-; *ai:* Pupil Assistance Comm; Coll Fair, Career Fair & Challengers Coord; Team Mem Suicide & Violent Loss Revised Policy Mem; REA 1970-; NEA 1970-; NJEA 1970-; MCPCA 1970-; MCEA 1970-; Randolph Ed Assn 1971-, Chm of Bd; NCTE 1963-; *office:* Randolph HS Millbrook Ave Randolph NJ 07869*

SEJBA, DONNA MARIE (BASTIAN), Jr High Tchr & Pastoral Min; *b:* Cleveland, OH; *m:* Frank J. III; *c:* Rebecca, Stephen; *ed:* St John Coll (BSE) Ed 1973; Ursuline Coll (MA) Ed Admin 1996; Attnd Baldwin-Wallace Coll; *cr:* PSR Schl 1-8 Grd Tchr 1969-; St Angela Merici Schl 2&3 Grd Tchr 1973-75; St Therese Schl 5 Grd Tchr 1975-76; Bedford YWCA Presch Tchr 1982-85; ST Wenceslas 2, 5, 7 & 8 Grd Tchr 1985-; *ai:* Yth Group; NCEA 1985-, Tchr Assoc; Lay Assoc of Sisters of Incarnate Word 1984-, Mentor; Awd for Excl, Outstdng Tchr Awd Diocesan 1991; WJW TV 8 Nomination Thanks to Tchrs Awd 1993-94; *office:* St Wenceslas Parish Schl 5250 Arch St Maple Heights OH 44137

SEKERES, EUGENE A., Prof of Adv, PR & Marketing; *b:* New Brighton, PA; *m:* Blanche Ratay-Antal; *c:* Robert Antal, Judiann Antal Donallow; *ed:* Geneva coll (BA) Eng 1950; Univ of Pittsburgh (ML) Mrktg, Advertising 1957; Syracuse Univ (MS) Radio, TV CAdv, PR, Comm 1972; Addl Hrs Doctoral Stud; *cr:* Various Businesses Advertising, Pub Relations, Sales, Promotion, Mrktg 1950-65; Military 1951-53; Geneva Coll Comm, Speech Instr 1966-67; Youngstown St Univ Prof of Advertising, Pub Relations, Mrktg 1967-; *ai:* Fac Senate; AAF Stu Chptr Co-Adv; First Yr Stu Mentor; Campus Coord Natl, Regnl Stu Advertising, Pub Relations Competitions; Many Comms; NEA, OEA 1971-; Amer Acad of Advertising 1970-, Indstry Flwshp; soc for Prof Journalists 1974-; Amer Assn of Advertising Agencies 1985-; Bus Mrktg Assn 1987-; Point of Purchase Advertising Inst 1988-; Vol Svcs Agency 1988-, Bd Mem; PR Comm, Prsnl Comm, Cnslr; Svc Corps of Retired Execs 1980-; Refugee Resettlement Bd 1985-, Bd Mem; Mahoning Vly Historical Soc 1990-; Natl Arbor Day Fnd 1993-; Jaycees 1955-60, Various Ofcs, Outstdng First Yr Mem; Univ Speakers Bureau 1985-, Speaker; Manuscript Reviewer, Contributor; Dir Mrktg Assn Seminar Flwshp; *office:* Youngstown St Univ Williamson Coll of Bus Admin 410 Wick Ave Youngstown OH 44555

SEKERES, MARK WILLIAM, Instr of Engineering Tech; *b:* Leechburg, PA; *m:* Kathryn Virginia Wolf; *c:* Carrie Elizabeth; *ed:* Clarion Univ of PA (BS) Bio 1990, (BS) Ed Sci 1990, (MED) Sci Ed 1995; Penn St Univ (BS) Elec Engrng; Engrng Tech Certs IN Univ of PA, CA Univ of PA, Wilkes Univ; *cr:* Penn St Univ Elec Engrng, Store Room Clerk 1984-85, Asst to Admin Aide, E E Dept 1984-88; J. W. Sekres Land Surveying, Engrng Assoc 1990-92; Saint Marys Area Schl Dist Instr Engrng Tech 1992-; *ai:* PRIDE, Engrng Related Tech Occupational Advy Comms; Distance Learning Project; NEA, PSEA 1990-; SMEA 1992-; BSA 1973-, Asst Scout master, Eagle Scout, God & Cntry; Explorers 1980-, Pres of Post; Saint Marys Sportsmans Assn, Beta Beta Beta 1990-; Presented Biological Rsrch Results 66th Annual Meeting PA Acad of Sci; Asst Instr PA Hunter's Ed Prgm; *office:* St Marys Area HS 977 S Saint Marys Rd Saint Marys PA 15857*

SEKINGER, ROXAN HENK, English Teacher; *b:* Pittsburgh, PA; *m:* John C. Sekinger; *ed:* Edinboro Univ (BA) Ed 1966; Univ of Pittsburgh MA Equivilant Ed; *cr:* Langley HS Eng Tchr 1966-70; Carrick HS Eng Tchr 1970-; *ai:* Mentoring; Young Writers Club; Curr & Assessment Svc; NCTE; AFT 1967-; Delta Kappa Gamma; Gold Wing Rd Runners Assn 1986-; All Star Edctr 1994; *office:* Carrick HS 125 Parkfield St Pittsburgh PA 15210

SELANDER, MARY ANN COPLEY, Science Teacher; *b:* Newark, NJ; *c:* Brian, Kelly; *ed:* Rutgers Univ (BS) Pharmacy 1973; Cook Coll, Rutgers Tchrs Cert 1990; *cr:* Towne Pharmacy Pharmacist 1973-89; Cranford,

Orange Ave Schl Sci Tchr 1990-91; Piscataway HS Sci Tchr 1991-; *ai:* Sci Club Adv; Drama Club Treas; Project Grad Tchr Contact; NJ Sci Tchrs Assn, NSTA, NEA, PTEA 1990-; NJ BISEC 1992-; Unitarian Church 1992-; NJ BISEC Summer Residential Inst Co-Chprsn, General Mgr, NJSTA Convention Presenter 1993, 1995; *office:* Piscataway HS 100 Behmer Rd Piscataway NJ 08854

SELDEN, MARY BETH, Third Grade Teacher; *b:* Akron, OH; *c:* Heather; *ed:* KSU (BS) Elem Ed 1970; 23 Grad Hrs Gifted Ed at Malone; *cr:* Springfield Schls Kndgtn Tchr 1970-75; Avon Schls 1st Grd Tchr 1974-75; Lake Local 3rd Grd Tchr 1981-; *ai:* 4-H Adv; SEEDS; NEA 1970-.

SELINGER, ADELE CORRIN, Biology & Ecology Teacher; *b:* Mononeahela, PA; *m:* Erik L.; *c:* Ian; *ed:* Slippery Rock Univ of PA (BS) Med Tech 1981; Univ of Pittsburgh Tchng Cert; *cr:* West Penn Hosp Med Tech 1981-85; Fox Chapel Area HS Tchr 1987-; *ai:* Yrbk Adv; SADD Spon; Coord of Camp Cnslr Prgm; NEA, PSEA 1990-; *office:* Fox Chapel Area HS 611 Field Club Rd Pittsburgh PA 15238*

SELINGER, ERIK L., Chemistry Teacher; *b:* Pittsburgh, PA; *m:* Adele L.; *c:* Ian; *ed:* Univ of Pittsburgh (BS) Scndry Ed 1987; *cr:* Slippery Rock Area HS Chem Tchr 1985-; *ai:* NHS, Chess Club Adv; NEA, PSEA 1988-; Amer Chem Soc 1996-; Scholors in Ed Awd; Sci Tchrs Enhancement Inst; *office:* Slipper Rock Area HS Kiester Rd Slippery Rock PA 16057*

SELL, BONNIE J., Business Teacher; *b:* Brooklyn, NY; *m:* Arthur A.; *c:* Jennifer, Corey; *ed:* Bloomsburg Univ (BS) Bus Ed 1970; Penn St at Bloomsburg (MA) Bus Ed 1991; *cr:* Souderton Area HS Bus Tchr 1970-; *ai:* Dept Coord; Stu Assistance Prgm 6 Yrs; Bsktbl, Cheerleading & Sftbl Coach; PSEA, NEA 1970-; Class Adv 1985, 1992; *office:* Souderton Area HS 41 N School Ln Souderton PA 18964

SELLERS, JAMES ALLEN, Mathematics Professor; *b:* San Antonio, TX; *m:* Mary Leigh Bressler; *c:* Nathaniel, David, Elizabeth; *ed:* Univ of TX at San Antonio (BS) Math 1987; PA St Univ (PHD) Math 1992; *cr:* Cedarville Coll Math Prof 1992-; Univ of Tx at San Antonio Prefreshman Engrng Prgm Math Instr 1994-95; *ai:* Amer Math Soc 1987-; Math Assn of Amer 1992-; Michael & Margaretha Sattler Fnd Math Software Grant; Numerous Articles Pub; *office:* Cedarville Coll PO Box 601 Cedarville OH 45314

SELLNER, LINDA M., High School Counselor; *b:* Paterson, NJ; *m:* Richard William; *c:* Megan L., Erin A.; *ed:* Montclair St Univ (BA) Family Cnslng, Psych 1981; Notre Dame Coll (MED Schl Cnslng 1990, Psychotherapy 1991; *cr:* Easter Seals Placement Cnslr 1987; Cath Med Ctr Clinical Soc Worker 1987-91; Pinkerton Acad Cnslr 1991-; *ai:* Nationally Certfd Instr Aerobics; Schl to Careers, Schl to Work Coord; Gender Equity, Sexual Harassment Comm; Voc Guid Coords 1991-, Sec; NH Schl Cnslrs Assn 1990-; NH Voc Assn 1991-; Career Cnslrs Assn 1990-93; *office:* Pinkerton Acad 5A Pinkerton St Derry NH 03038

SELLS, LINDA WILSON, Title I Reading & Math Teacher; *b:* Columbus, OH; *m:* Stanley; *c:* Tyler, Sarah; *ed:* Asbury Coll (BS) Elem Ed 1979; Georgetown Coll (MA) Elem Ed 1985; OH Univ 15 Credit Hrs; *cr:* Jessamine Cty Second Grd Tchr 1979-82; Barnesville Exempted Schls third Grd Tchr 1982-89, Second Grd Tchr 1989-95, Title I Rdng, Math Tchr 1995-; *ai:* NEA, OEA, BEA 1982-; NEA, KEA 1979-; Canvassed Comm Amer Cancer Soc; Awded Barnesville Area Fnd 2 Grants; *home:* 106 Shady Ln Barnesville OH 43713*

SELMAN, CAROL, History Teacher; *b:* New York, NY; *m:* Jules Schneider; *c:* Karen Schneider Dellaripa, Nancy Schneider; *ed:* Cornell Univ (BA) His 1969; St Univ of NY at Stony Brook (MA) Amer Stud 1981; SUNY at Stony Brook Doctoral Prgm on Amer Cultural His; *cr:* Millburn Sr HS Advanced Placement, US His, Soc & Culture Amer His, European Intellectual & Art His Tchr 1969-; *ai:* Amnesty Intnl Adv; NJEA 1969-; Millburn Ed Assn 1969-, Legislative Action Team & Chair; Org of Amer Hist; Phi Beta Kappa; NJ Historical Commission 1992-, Gubernational Appointment Pub Mem; Natl Endowment of the Hum Fellowship; *office:* Millburn Sr HS 462 Millburn Ave Millburn NJ 07041*

SELSKI, WILLIAM E., Architectural Drafting Teacher; *b:* Bridgeport, CT; *m:* Deborah Rick; *ed:* Syracuse Univ (BAE) Architecture 1975; Cntrl CT St Univ Ed 1982; Attnd Univ of WI at Madison; *cr:* Bullard-Havens Dept Head 1977-; Univ of Bridgeport Adj Prof 1982-93; *ai:* Yrbk Adv; Natl Hnr Soc Adv; Class of 98 Adv; AFT 1978-, Bldg Rep; Construction Specifications Inst 1987-, Chptr Pres, Treas; Licensed Architect; *office:* Bullard-Havens Regnl Vo-Tech 500 Palisade Ave Bridgeport CT 06610*

SELTUN, ELIZABETH MADDICKS, Social Studies Coord & Teacher; *b:* New York City, NY; *m:* Semre; *c:* Ahlem, Amare, Aman; *ed:* Coll of New Rochelle (BA) Amer Lit 1996; *ai:* Alumnae Assn; *office:* Mt Carmel-Holy Rosary Schl 371 Pleasant Ave New York NY 10035

SELTZ, NANCY STRIKMAN, Latin Teacher & Dept Chprsn; *b:* Cincinnati, OH; *m:* Donald A.; *c:* Claire Eichner, Amy Jo; *ed:* Univ of Cincinnati (BA) Classics 1962, (BS) Ed 1962; Xavier Univ (MS) Educl Admin & Latin 1980; *cr:* Walnut Hills HS Latin Tchr 1962-64, Latin Tchr 1974-, Dept Chair 1993-; *ai:* Cum Laude Soc Spon; Fac Soc Comm; Amer Classical League; Cincinnati Assn Tchrs of Classics, Elect Pres; AFT; OH Classical Conf; Vergilian Soc; Lead Tchr; CAMWS Tchr of Yr; *office:* Walnut Hills HS 3201 Victory Pkwy Cincinnati OH 45207*

SELTZER, FELICE ELLEN (SIMON), Early Childhood Specialist; *b:* Brooklyn, NY; *m:* Ivan; *c:* Michael, Randi; *ed:* Brooklyn Coll (MS) Early Chldhd Ed 1970; 30 Credit Hrs Above Masters Kingsborough Coll 1987; *cr:* PS 128 Bensonhurst Schl Early Chldhd K-2nd Grd Tchr 1967-; NY City Bd Of Ed Curr Writing & Staff Dev Citiwide Trainer 2nd Grd Math Curr 1985; Comm Schl Dist 21 Staff Dev & Tchr Trng 1985-88, Curr Writing 4th Grd Math 1988; *ai:* Chprsn & Ed of PS 128 & Brooklyn Studio Schl Newsletter; Pre-K & Kndgtn Parent Orientation Wkshp Chprsn; UFT & AFT 1967-; E Midwood Neighborhood Assn 1978-; Impact II Grant 1984 & 1988; PS 128 Tchr of the Yr 1985; *office:* The Bensonhurst Schl 2075 84th St Brooklyn NY 11214*

SELVAGE, THOMAS ALLEN, Secondary Teacher; *b:* Ashland, OH; *ed:* The OH St Univ (BSEd) Soc Stud Ed-Cum Laude 1987; *cr:* Hillsdale HS Scndry Tchr 1988-; *ai:* Yrbk, NHS, Mock Trl Team, Acad Team Adv; Ticket Mgr; NCOEA Exec Comm 1990-, Regnl Rep; *office:* Hillsdale HS 485 Township Road 1902 Jeromesville OH 44840

SEMBER, J. ELIZABETH SHOEMAKER, Retired First Grade Teacher; *b:* Scottdale, PA; *m:* Eugene; *ed:* Eastern Mennonite Coll (BS) Elem Ed 1957; Columbia Univ Elem Lang & Lit 1958; WV Univ Summer Evenings Elem Rdng 1960-61; Also Amer Univ Summer Elem Courses 1962; *cr:* Cross Roads Private Schl 1-6 Grd Tchr 1953-55; Connellsville City Pub Schls Grd 5 Tchr 1957-58, Grd Two Tchr 1958-66; Connellsville Area Pub Schls Grd One Tchr 1966-92; *ai:* Stu Tchr Mentoring; Classroom Vol; PSEA 1957-92, Local Treas 1958-; Delta Kappa Gamma 1968-, Local Pres, Recording Sec; Past Prof & Bus Women 1966-, Local Pres 1968-70; Delta Kappa Gamma 1968-, Local Pres 1976-78; Pub Numerous Articles; *home:* 1125 Pittsburgh St Scottdale PA 15683

SEMBER, JOHN MICHAEL, Social Studies Teacher; *b:* Johnstown, PA; *m:* Shirley Scott; *c:* Keli Ann Rollinger, Amy R. Mc Kee; *ed:* Indiana Univ of PA (BS) Soc Stud 1961; St Bonaventure Univ (MS) Schl Admin 1970; Attnd Penn St, Fredonia SUNY; Clinical Field Trng; *cr:* Baltimore MD Cty Tchr 1961-62d; Jamestown NY Bd Ed Tchr 1962-; *ai:* Clinical Field Supvr; Stu Tchrs; Dist Compact Learning, Schl to Work, Yth Apprentice Comms; NEA 1962-, Life Mem; NYEA 1969-; Jamestown Tchrs Assn 1962-; ASCD 1970-, Cty VP; Mayor's Citizens Advy Comm, Chm; Chautauqua Cty Yth Bureau; WCA Auxilary Vol, Taste of Senson Treas; Jamestown Democratic Party, Chm; Tchrs Pub Svc Awd; Co-Author Labor Mngmt Curr; *home:* 612 Prospect St Jamestown NY 14701*

SEMBER, SHIRLEY SCOTT, Third Grade Teacher; *b:* Bradford, PA; *m:* John M.; *c:* Keli Ann Rollinger, Amy R Mc Kee; *ed:* Villa Maria Coll (BA) Elem Ed 1966; 30 Hrs Rdng SUNY at Fredonia 1971; Guid St Bonaventure Univ; Clinical FIeld Supvr Stu Tchrs; Post-Grad Stud Ithaca Coll; *cr:* Blessed Sacrament Schl Practice Tchr 1963-64; Persell Schl, Bush, Ring Schl 3rd Grd Tchr 1966-; *ai:* After Schl Stu Prgm; Summer Tutor; NEA, NYEA 1966-; JTA 1966-, Bldg Rep; AAUW 1966-92; Jamestown Women's Club 1990-, Pres, VP, Newsletter; A Children's Place 1993-, Bd; WCA Auxiliary1984-, Taste of Season Treas, Chicken Barbeque Chprsn; Creche In c 1990-, Tag Days Chprsn; Pub Svc Vol Tutor; *home:* 612 Prospect St Jamestown NY 14701

SEMCHAK, JANET L., 6th Grade English Teacher; *b:* Mc Keesport, PA; *ed:* CA Univ of PA (BS) Elem Ed 1972; 3 Grad Credits; 30 Grad Credits PA St Univ; 4 Grad Credits Chapman Univ; 14 In-Svc Credits Allegheny Co, Washington Co Intermediate Units #1, #3, Mon Yough Cncl on Drug Abuse; Masters Equivalency Ed 1992; *cr:* William Penn Elem Schl 4th Grd Tchr 1972-91, 6th Grd Tchr 1991-92; Elizabeth Forward MS 6th Grde Eng Tchr 1992-; *ai:* PSEA, NEA 1972-78; Elizabeth Forward Fed of Tchrs, AFT 1981-; William Penn PTA 1972-92; Elisabeth Forward MS PTSA 1992-; Cousteau Soc 1983-; Ctr for Marine Conservation 1982-; William Penn Elem Schl PTA Cert of Appreciation 1987; Amer Family Inst at Vly Forge Gift of Time Tribute 1990; Thanks to Tchrs Partnerships Excl Awd Nom 1992; Stu Cncl Tchr of Month 1995; *office:* Elizabeth Forward MS 401 Rock Run Rd Elizabeth PA 15037

SEMEGEN, LINDA COULTER, Fourth Grade Teacher; *b:* Mineola LI, NY; *m:* Alex L. Jr.; *c:* Kristin; *ed:* Kent St Univ (BS) Spec, Elem Ed 1972; Credit Hrs Ashland Univ, Univ of Akron; *cr:* Lake Local Schls Tchr of Developmentally Handicapped 1973-86, First Grd Tchr 1986-87, Fourth Grd Tchr 1987-; *ai:* Comms Comm; PTO Rep; Chair Stu of Month Awd; Lake Local Ed Assn 1973-, VP, Pres; NEA 1973-; US Pony Club 1993-, Co Dist Commissioner; Spec Ed Tchr of Yr 1979; *office:* Lake Elem Sch 225 Lincoln St SW Hartville OH 44632

SEMENDINGER, PAUL RUSSELL, History Teacher; *b:* Ridgewood, NJ; *m:* Laurie Erickson; *c:* Ryan Paul; *ed:* Kings Coll (BA) His 1990; William Paterson Coll (MA) Educl Admin 1995; *cr:* Memorial MS His Tchr 1990-; Fair Lawn HS His Tchr 1994-; *ai:* Stu Cncl Adv; Outdoor Ed Staff; MS IMs; Site-Based Mngmt Team; A+ for Kids, Dist MS Steering, Observation & Evaluation Comms; NJ Assn for Mid Level Ed 1993-, Regnl Dir; NMSA 1994-; ASCD 1995-; NEA, NJEA 1990-; Governors Tchr Recognition 1994; A+ for Kids Awd 1993; Phi Alpha Theta 1989; Kappa Delta Pi 1993; Pi Lambda Theta 1994; *office:* Memorial MS 12-00 1st St Fair Lawn NJ 07410*

SEMENJUK, VICTOR GEORGE, Science Teacher; *b:* Detroit, MI; *ed:* SUNY at New Paltz (BA) Bio 1975, (MS) Scndry Ed Sci 1982; *cr:* St Denis, St Columba Sci Tchr 1978-; *ai:* Yrbk Adv; NCEA 1978-; Cath Yth Orgs Yth Ministry Awd 1987; *office:* St Denis, St Columba MS PO Box 368 Rt 82 Hopewell Junction NY 12533

SEMENZA, ROBERT A., Assistant Prof of Accounting; *b:* New Rochelle, NY; *m:* Marie Ann Vaccaru; *c:* Barbara Welch, Karen, Robert Jr.; *ed:* Iona Coll (BBA) Acctng 1956; St of NY Certified Pub Accountant; *cr:* Price Waterhouse & Co Acting Mgr 1956-64; Dorr-Oliver Inc Asst Controller 1964-69; KMG Main Hurdman Partner 1969-89; KMG Peat Marwick Partner 1969-89; Quinnipiac Coll Asst Prof 1989-; *ai:* Inst of Mgmt Accountants, Natl Dir, Hnr Soc; Amer Inst of Certified Pub Accountants 1960-, Various Comms; NY St Soc of Certified Pub Accountants 1960-, Various Comms; Boys Club of New Rochelle, Hall of Fame; *office:* Quinnipiac Coll Mount Carmel Avenue Hamden CT 06518

SEMINARA, JANE C., Theology Teacher; *b:* Mt Vernon, NY; *ed:* Manhattanville Coll (BA) Religion 1983; Harvard Univ (MTS) Theological Stud 1985; Emerson Coll (MA) Comm 1986; *cr:* Stuart Cntry Day Schl Theology Tchr & Campus Minister 1986-88; Newton Cntry Day Schl Theology Tchr 1988-90; Fontbonne Acad Theology Tchr 1990-91; Governors Schl of NJ Fac Summers 1985-; Arlington Cath HS Theologyd Tchr 1991-; *ai:* Multicultural Comm Chair; *office:* Arlington Catholic HS 16 Medford St Arlington MA 02174

SEMPER, FRANK VICTOR, 5th Grade Science Teacher; *b:* Pittsburgh, PA; *c:* Jennifer Alison; *ed:* Edinboro Univ (BS) Elem Ed 1967; Univ of Pittsburgh (MS) Elem Ed 1971; *cr:* Oakmont Schl Dist 3rd & 4th Grd Tchr 1967-70, Resource Tchr 1969-71; Riverview Schl Dist 5th & 6th Grd Tchr 1971-; *ai:* HS Drama Club; 5th & 6th Grd Musical Co-Dir; Strategic Planning Comm; PSEA 1967-; REA 1971-; Riverview Fndtn for the Arts 1994-; *home:* 138 Venango Ct New Kensington PA 15068*

SENA, MARY LEE T., French Teacher; *b:* Jersey City, NJ; *m:* James J.; *c:* Dina, James G.; *ed:* Caldwell Coll (BA) Fr Lang, Lit 1962; Montcair St Coll (MA) Fr Lang, Lit 1969; *cr:* Benjamin Franklin Jr HS Fr Tchr 1962-69, Dept Chm 1966-69; Madison HS Fr Tchr 1981-82; Mountain View Jr HS Fr Tchr 1982-83; Madison HS Fr Tchr 1983-; *ai:* Fr Natl Hnr Soc Adv; NEA, NJEA 1962-; AATF 1984-; NJ Frn Lang Tchrs Assn; Madison TA 1983-; *office:* Madison HS 170 Ridgedale Ave Madison NJ 07940

SENATORE, WILLIAM J., Teacher; *b:* Philadelphia, PA; *m:* Joanna Marie Belza; *c:* Michelle, Kimberly, William; *ed:* Philadelphia Coll of Performing Arts (BM) Music 1977, (BME) Music 1977; Chestnut Hill Coll (MS) Elem 1991; Temple Univ 18 Credits Math; *cr:* Hopkinson Grd Tchr 1989-90; Harding MS Grd Tchr 1990-; *ai:* North Cath HS Bsbl; Liberty Bell Yth Org; AFT 1990-; Paths-Prism 1992-; *office:* Harding MS Torresdale & Wakeling Philadelphia PA 19135

SENDRY, ANDREA ELIZABETH, Mathematics Teacher; *b:* New Kensington, PA; *ed:* IN Univ of PA (BS) Math 1969, (MS) Math 1973; Topology 3 Credits 1974; Intro to Cmptr Sci 3 Credits 1981; Intro to Cmptrs 3 Credits 1982; Appl Cmptr Prgm 3 Credits 1983; *cr:* Knoch Jr-Sr HS Math Tchr 1969-; *ai:* Kappa Delta Pi, NCTM 1968-; PSEA, NEA 1969-; Gray Stone Presbyn Church 1957-; *home:* 374 Beale Ave Leechburg PA 15656

SENECAL, LEN DEAN, English & Journalism Teacher; *b:* Alexandria Bay, NY; *m:* Debra A. Dunham; *c:* Mariah; *ed:* SUNY at Potsdam (BA) Eng 1980; SUNY at Oswego (MS) Ed 1992; *cr:* WPDM Radio Sports Broadcaster 1978-87; Watertown Daily Times Sports Reporter 1980-87; G. Ray Bodley HS Eng, Jrnlsm Tchr 1989-; Image Comics Ed, Writer 1993-95; *ai:* Jrnlsm Club Adv; Stu Radio Prgm Producer, Adv; Empire St Schl Press Assn Adv of Yr 1993; Syracuse Newspaper Golden Apple Awd 1995; Fulton Tchrs Assn Achvmt Awd 1994; Stdnts Have Won Numerous Awds in Print & Broadcast Jrnlsm; Pub Several Comic Books Image Comics; *office:* G Ray Bodley HS 6 William Gillard Dr Fulton NY 13069

SENESKY, LINDA GROW, Spanish Teacher; *b:* Rome, NY; *m:* John Stephen; *c:* Alexandra Gonzalez, Alan Gonzalez; *ed:* St Lawrence Univ (BA) Span 1968; Middlebury Coll (MA) Span 1969; *cr:* La Escuela Nautica Eng Tchr 1969-70; Bound Brook HS Span Tchr 1972-73; Bound Brook Adult Schl Facilitator, ESL Tchr 1974-75; Hillsborough HS Span Tchr 1976-; *ai:* Stu Adv; NEA, NJEA 1976-; Tuy Twig 1992-, VP; Reader Span Advanced Placement Exam; *home:* 126 N Doughty Ave Somerville NJ 08876*

SENGER, GEORGE J.,JR., 8th Grade Social Studies Tchr; *b:* Long Island, NY; *m:* Joyce A. Malik-Senger; *c:* George III, M Matthew; *ed:* Fairleigh Dickinson Univ (BA) His 1972; Attnd Univ Georgian Court Coll; *cr:* Glen Ridge MS 5th-8th Grd Soc Stu 1972-88; Toms River Int West Schl 8th Grd Soc Stud Tchr 1988-; *ai.* Boys Bsktbl; Curr Comm; NEA, NJEA 1972-; Toms River E A *office:* Toms River Intermediate Schl W Intermediate West Way Tom NJ 08753

SENGES, MARSHA WEBB, 5th Grade Teacher; *b:* Oakridge, Richard A.; *c:* Lara R. Graham, Charles A.; *ed:* Allegheny Coll (BA Ed 1965; Nazareth Coll (MS) Elem Ed 1979; Intensive Courses Dist; *cr:* Norcross Elem Schl 3rd Grd Tchr 1965-66; Hilton Centr Sub Tchr 1968-70; Fairport Central Schls Sub Tchr 1972-79; Nc Schl 6th Grd Tchr 1980-83; Brooks Hill Schl 4th Grd Tchr 19 Northside Schl 4th Grd Tchr 1989-; *ai:* Redistricting Comm; Past S Adv, PTA Rep; AFT 1968-; Perinton Vol Ambulance Corps 4 Yrs, M Dispatcher; Pub Articles, Parent Adv Awd for Spec Ed 1994; Northside Schl 181 Hamilton Rd Fairport NY 14450

SENKO, WILLIAM, High School & Jr HS Teacher; *b:* Brooklyn, Paula Ann Tagliabue; *c:* Susan, Michael; *ed:* Fairleigh Dickinso (BA) Soc Stud 1972; Tchr of Soc Stud Fairleigh Dickinson Univ Tchr of Handicapped Georgian Court 1992; Tchr of Driver Ed Row 1994; *cr:* US Postal Svc Lettercarrier, Supvr 15 Yrs; Hometown Truck Driver 3 Yrs; Pinelands Regnl Schl Dist Tchr 6 Yrs; *ai:* Ass Coach of Winter & Spring; Track & Field Ofcl; Bsbl Umpire; NTEA NTSIAA 1992-; NtSIAA 1989-; Natl Fed Interscholastic Ofcls Assn BPO Elks 1994-; Tchr of Month 1994; *home:* 803 Hazelton Ave Harbor NJ 08734

SENKOWSKY, LORRAINE JEAN, Third Grade Teacher; *b:* River, NJ; *m:* Robert; *c:* Lynn Bonner, Kim; *ed:* Kean Coll (BA) K- Ed, Early Chldhd & Nursery Schl 1966; *cr:* South Plainfield Bd of E 28 Yrs; Sayreville NJ Tchr 2 Yrs; *ai:* Chaperoning Schl Cultural Ov Trips; Feeding Homeless; S Plainfield Tchrs Assn Comms; NEA NJEA 1966-, Rep for Tchrs Pension & Annuity; SPEA 1966-, Bl Negotiator; Veterans of Foreign War Loyalty Day Grand Marshal 1

SENOS, ROSA MARIA, Spanish Teacher; *b:* Newark, NJ; *ed:* Mc St Univ (BA) Span 1990; Working Toward MA in ESL; Cert in E Paramus HS Span Stu Tchr 1990; Abraham Clark HS Span Tchr 19 Marine Acad of Sci & Tech Span Tchr 1992-; *ai:* Span Club Adv; Sp Soc Founder of Chptr & Adv; Jr Class Adv; NEA, NJEA 1990-; 1994-; *office:* Marine Acad Of Sci & Tech 305 Gunnison Rd Sandy NJ 07732*

SENSOR, ROBERT LOUIS, Mathematics Teacher; *b:* Erie, PA; *m:* Ann Staebler; *c:* Michael, Joseph, Chad; *ed:* Clarion St Univ (BS 1967; Edinboro St Univ (MED) Math 1974; Attnd Penn St at Behren Edinboro St Univ; *cr:* Ft LeBoeuf HS Math Tchr 1967-; Penn St B Math Lecturer 1992-; *ai:* Var Ftbl Asst Coach; Intensive Sche Comm; Math Dept Chm; Curr Cncl; NEA, PA St Ed Assn, LeBoeuf E 1967-; Gen City Track Ofcls 1970-, Pres; PA Track Coaches Assn PA Ftbl Coaches Assn 1995-; Erie Yth Soccer Coach; Theta Xi, Adv; Presenter at Tech Seminar; Mentor Tchr Awd 1989; *off* LeBoeuf HS 931 N High St Waterford PA 16441*

SEPI, THOMAS JOSEPH, Soc Studies, Sci & Rel Tchr; *b:* New Yor *m:* Marianne J. DiMeo; *c:* Juliane; *ed:* Bronx Comm Coll (AA) His Herbert H Lehman Coll (BA) Soc Sci & Scndry Ed 1972, (MA) S 1978; Archiocese of NY Level I Rel Ed & Rel Media; *cr:* Mizii Iron Mgr 1968-70; Sears Roebuck & Co Sales & Credit 1969-70; Michel IS 144 Soc Stud Tchr 1972; CYO Day Camp Section Ldr 1981-82; Heart Grd Schl Soc Stud, Sci & Rel Tchr 1972-; *ai:* Confir Sacramental Prgm; Admin Responsibilities for Prin & Pastor; Desig & Tests; Trip Planner & Coord; NCEA 1972-; Fed of Cath Tchrs Amer Heritage Historical Soc 1970-; Knights of Columbus, Chan Holy Name Soc, Pres; Archdiocese of NY & Cathechist for Archd Elem Schl Prin Candidate; *office:* Sacred Heart Elem Schl 108 Sh Pl Yonkers NY 10703*

SEPINSKI-RICCI, BONNIE, English Teacher; *b:* Nyack, N Donald; *c:* Brian Sepinski, Jon Sepinski, Elizabeth Sepinski, Adrien SUNY at Albany (BA) Fr 1968; SUNY at New Paltz (MA) Eng 197 Coll (MBA) Mgmt Info Syst 1988; Attnd Columbia Univ Datab Credits Spcl Ed; *cr:* Westchester Comm Coll Adj Eng Tchr 1974-9 Coll Weekend Coll Dir 1982-86; Radio Expenditure Reports Rsrch A 1986-89; IS 131X Albert Einst Int Schl Comp Tchr 1989-93; Jacq Kennedy Onassis Eng Tchr & Coll Adv 1993-; *ai:* Coll Adv; Sr Cns Coord; NHS Adv; NCTE 1993-; NACAC 1995-; Dobbs Ferry Luth C Flower Chair.

SEPLAVY, STEPHANIE, Speech Pathologist; *b:* Norwich N England; *c:* Paul Mazzuca, Edward, Michael, Deborah; *ed:* SUNY New Paltz (BA) Speech, Hearing Handicapped 1979; Coll of St Rose Comm Disorders 1982; *cr:* Questar III Speech Pathologist 1980-; C Comm Coll Adj Fac 1987-; *ai:* NY St License Pvt Practice; *hom* Montross St Saugerties NY 12477*

SEPPENTINO, ROBERT JOHN, 5th Grade Elem Teache HAckensack, NJ; *m:* Madeline Gerardi; *c:* Christopher; *ed:* W Paterson Coll (BA) Elem Ed 1964; *cr:* Schl #1 5th Grd Tchr 19 1994-; Schl #2 5th Grd Gifted & Talented Tchr 1990-94; *ai:* Piloting for Rdng & Lang Arts in Elem Schl; Mentor Supvr of a Novice Advncmnt Tchng & Mgmt Wrkshps Participant; CTA Delegate; Coord; Stu Tchrs Suprv; Conf Cultural Awareness & Biases Rep; NEA, CTA 1964-; Recipient of Governor of NJ 1st Recognition Prg Outstanding Tchrs; Nom for Educator of Yr for Clifton Pub Schls Clifton Edctr YR 1996; *office:* Schl #1 158 Park Slope Clifton NJ 0

SEPRISH, MARY JO (SPAGNOLO), 5th Grade Teacher; *b:* Clea PA; *m:* Robert; *c:* Stacy, Scott; *cr:* Goshen Elem 6th Grd Tchr 1973-7 Grd Tchr 1976-79; Bradford Elem 3rd Grd Tchr 1979-80, 5th Gr 1980-; *ai:* Lang Arts Comm; Soc Comm Chprsn; NEA 1973-; Bradford Township Elem Schl Bigler PO Bigler PA 16825

SERAFIN, JAMES T., High School English Teacher; *b:* Greensbur *m:* M. Maureen Super; *c:* Leanne M., Kristin E., Kaitlin E.; *ed:* Clar Coll (BA) Scndry Eng 1969; Duquesne Univ (MS) Scndry Admin 197 Norwin Jr HS West Eng Tchr 1969-73; Norwin Sixth Street Schl Eng 1973-80; Norwin Jr HS West Eng Tchr 1980-93; Norwin Sr HS Eng 1993-; *ai:* Boys Bsktbl Asst Coach; Norwin Educl Support Team; 1969-; *office:* Norwin Sr HS 251 Mcmahon Dr North Huntingdon PA

SERAFINI, ANTHONY L., Assoc Professor of Philosophy; *b:* Gler NJ; *m:* Tina; *c:* Alina; *ed:* Cornell Univ (BA) Zoology 1965; Syracuse (MA) Philosophy 1970, (PHD) Philosophy 1972; Post Grad Stud Ha Univ; *cr:* Boston St Coll Assoc Prof 1970-86; Centenary Coll Assoc 1986-; *ai:* Fac Rsrch & Dev Comm; APA 1988-; ACPA 1991-; Articles *office:* Centenary Coll 400 Jefferson St Hackettstown NJ 07840*

SERAPIGLIA, KARLA KRULL, English Teacher; *b:* New York NY; *m:* James; *ed:* Kent St Univ (BS) Eng Ed 1969; SUNY at Stony (MA) Liberal Stud 1973; 59 Post Grad Credits Eng, Photogr Sociology, Psych, Comm; *cr:* Half Hollow Hills Cntrl Schl Eng 1969-83; Akron Cntrl Schl Eng Tchr 1985-; *ai:* NY St Bldg Level ompact for Learning; NYSUT 1969-; Manual Editor; *home:* 203 ood Dr Getzville NY 14068*

DICK, MICHAEL JOHN, Choral Director; *b:* Cleveland, OH; *m:* Ann Visher; *c:* Amy, Andrew; *ed:* Kent St Univ (BSEd) Music Ed MA Organ Performance 1976; *cr:* Parma City Schls Choral Dir *ai:* OMEA, ACDA 1967-; Orch Youth Chorus Asst Dir; Asst ctor Orch Chorus 1984-90; *home:* 4064 Diana Dr Broadview Heights 47

KA, MERCEDES, 1st Grade Bilingual Teacher; *b:* Gurabo, PR; *c:* l, Enrique Ramos; *ed:* Univ of PR (BA) Sci; City Univ of NY (MA) Univ of South FL 16 Grad Hrs Ed 1993; Herbert H. Lehman Coll 30 Hrs Ed 1986; *cr:* PS 114 Biling Tchr 1971-78; PR Dept Ed Curr ist 1978-82; Weigard Elem Schl 3rd Grd Biling Tchr 1982-83; PS Grd, ESL Tchr 1983-90; PS 198M 2-3rd Grd Biling Tchr 1990-92; 1st Grd Biling Tchr 1993-; *ai:* AFT, NEA, UFT 1972-; *office:* PS 0 Fox St Bronx NY 10455

MBUS, JOHN HERMAN, Philosophy Professor; *b:* Philadelphia, Saint Josephs Univ (BA) Philosophy 1972; Villanova Univ (MA) ophy 1975; Temple Univ (PHD) Philosophy 1987; *cr:* Saint Josephs rof 1977-89; Widener Univ Prof 1989-; *ai:* Kappa Sigma Adv; Assn nbolic Logic 1980-; Amer Phil Assn 1980-; Articles Pub; *office:* er Univ 1 University Pl Chester PA 19013*

NE, JANET YEANY, Kindergarten Teacher; *b:* Mayport, PA; *m:* ; *c:* Shanelle Hawk, Cherie; *ed:* Clarion St Tchrs Coll (BS) Elem Ed *cr:* Cornerstone Chrstn Schl K-6 Grd Tchr 1978-79; Redbank Vly Grd Tchr 1954-56, Combination 1 & 2 Grd Tchr 1962-64, Kndgtn, Tchr 1964-78, Kndgtn, 2 Grd Tchr 1979-; Coffee House Mgr; *ai:* VP CEAI 1975-; NACE, CEE 1985-; Clarion Gun Owners VP; ption Lib Svcs Owner; Childrens Church, Sunday Sunday, Adult Stud Tchr; Street Ministry; *home:* RR 1 Box 247 Mayport PA 16240*

NO, EDGEL E., Mathematics Professor; *b:* Hutton, MD; *c:* Andrea; ostburg St Univ (BS) Math 1962; San Diego St Univ (MA) Math Univ of MD (PHD) Math 1974; *cr:* James Madison Univ Math Prof 9; Prince Georges Comm Coll Math Prof 1969-80; Dept of Defense Dist Mathematician, Comptr Spec 1980-83; Montgomery Coll Math 983-; *ai:* Speaker's Bureau Fac Cncl; Curr Comm; AAWP; MAA; rants for Grad Work at Duke Univ, Yale; *office:* Montgomery Coll mantown 20200 Observation Dr Germantown MD 20876*

ATY, JUDITH CHESTER, English Teacher; *b:* Brooklyn, NY; *ed:* iv (BS) Eng 1965, (MA) Eng 1967; Hunter Coll Admin, Superv Cert Guid Cnslng 18 Credits; Eng, Sociology 12 Credits; Spec Ed 6 s; *cr:* Eastern Dist HS Eng Tchr 1965-68; Downs Sec Schl for Girls 9; Julia Richman HS Tchr, Acting Asst Prin 1970-93; August Martin hr 1993-; *ai:* Peer Mediation; Yrbk; Newspaper; Chrldrs; NCTE, 965-; NYCATE 1970-80; ORT 1972-; NEH Seminar 1996; Curricula g; Mentor; *office:* August Martin HS 156-10 Baisley Blvd Jamaica 434*

I, ROSE ANNE, Journalism Professor; *b:* Somerville, MA; *c:* Guy , Matthew Doyon; *ed:* Northeastern Univ (BA) Eng 1968, (MA) Eng *cr:* Bryant Mc Intosh Jr Coll Asst Prof 1970-72; Daniel Webster Jr nstr 1971-74; Northeastern Univ Sr Lecturer 1971-; Billerica Meml chr 1972-75; Univ of Lowell Instr 1975-77; Lowell Sun Gen nment, Investigative Reporter 1985-87; Regis Coll Instr 1987-88; esex Comm Coll Prof Jrnlsm 1988-; *ai:* Coll Newspaper Adv; NEA; chrs Assn; Northeastern Univ Jrnlsm Alumni Assn, Pres 1990-; nted Svc Acad Review Bd 1983; Who's Who in the East 1993; nking Nwspr Awd; Middlesex Comm Coll 1st Pl with Hnr 1993-94; Mem of the Yr 1990; Outstanding Young Woman of Amer 1980; eastern Univ Woman of the Yr 1968; *office:* Middlesex Community prings Rd Bedford MA 01730

NO, VERONICA IZBICKI, High School English Teacher; *b:* Jersey NJ; *m:* Joseph A.; *c:* Anthony; *ed:* Jersey City St Coll (BA) Eng & Ed (MA) Ed & Urban Stud 1977; Tchr of Rdng Cert 1978; Stu Prsnl Svcs 983; 33 Addl Credit Hrs; *cr:* Montclair HS Tchng Fellow & Rdng 976-77; Secaucus HS Eng Tchr 1977-83, Tchr of Eng & Basic Skills Clarendon Schl & Huber Street Schl Guid Cnslr 1983-84; *ai:* NEA A 1977-; NCTE 1992-; Jersey City St Coll Urban Stud Flwshp Pgm; Secaucus HS Mill Ridge Rd Secaucus NJ 07094

MARINI, LYNNE T., 6th Grade Teacher; *b:* Bryn Mawr, PA; *m:* Tony; Ann, Todd, Ron; *ed:* Ursinus Coll (BA) Span 1965; Georgian Ct Coll Elem Ed 1975; *cr:* Wrightstown Elem 2nd Grd Tchr 1965-66; ngton St Elem 2nd Grd Tchr 1966-68; Silver Bay Elem 4th Grd Tchr 89; West Dover Elem 6th Grd Tchr 1989-; *ai:* Invention Convention NEA, NJEA & TREA 1965-; Alpha Delta Kappa; *office:* West Dover Schl Blue Jay Dr Toms River NJ 08755

A, LEWIS, High School Spanish Teacher; *b:* NYC, NY; *ed:* Iona BA) Peninsula Literatura 1969, (MS) Ed, Span 1975; Attnd Univ of d, Univ of Salamanca; 75 Addl Credit Hrs; *cr:* Holy Trinity HS Adult an Tchr 1972-81; Worcester Pub Schls Adult Ed Span Tchr 1981-90; ssett Regnl HS Dept Chair 1986-90; Bellmore-Merrick CHSD Span 1990-; *ai:* Foreign Lang Asst to Chair; Sr Class, LA Sociedad raria Hispanica Adv; Site-Based Mgmt Team; Co-Chair of Meyham Cncl; AATSP, NYSAFLT, MLA, ACTFL 1969-; LILT 1990-; Flwshps Carlos, NYS, Writer as Witness of His-Her Time; NEA Grant; *office:* ngton C. Mepham HS Camp Ave Bellmore NY 11710*

RA, PAUL THOMAS, Retired Mathematics Teacher; *b:* Baltimore, *ed:* Kent St Univ (BA) Math 1962; *cr:* Euclid Shore Jr HS Math Tchr, 1962-71; Euclid HS Math Tchr, Coach 1972-92; *ai:* Head Bsebl Ret 1992; NEA, NCTM 1962-; Euclid Tchrs Assoc 1962-, Tchr of 82; BPO Elks 1972-; *home:* 19770 Monterey Ave Euclid OH 44119

RANO, RAMONITA, Computer Science Teacher; *b:* Bristol, PA; *ed:* an Coll (BA) PE 1978; Hunter Coll (MSED) Elem Ed Bilgl 1996; Cert ronic Data Processing; *cr:* St Joseph Schl Sixth Grd Tchr 1981-84, Sub HS Tchr 1984; NYC Bd of Ed Lib, Sub HS Tchr 1984; Wm W. JHS 118 Sci, Math Biling Tchr 1985-92; Pace Acad Cmptr Sci Tchr ; Wm W. Niles MS 118 Cmptr Sci Tchr 1992-; *ai:* Biling Cmptr Tchr Comm Schls Prgm Tchng Parents; Adult Spon Manice Ed Ctr onmental Stud Prgm Pace Acad; AFT, UFT, NYSUT 1987-; ASCD ; *office:* William W. Niles MS 118 577 E 179th St Bronx NY 10457

RANO, RAYMOND, Social Studies Teacher; *b:* New York, NY; *m:* Luz; *c:* Adalberto, Lolita; *ed:* Queens Coll CUNY (BA) Puerto Rican 1973; NYU (MA) Politics 1975; *cr:* Queens Coll Lecturer 1974-79; at Old Westbury Instr 1979-80; NYC Comm on Human Rights Human s Specialist 1981-86; Long Island HS Tchr 1987-; *ai:* Soccer Coach; Club Adv; Danforth & Ford Flwshps 1973; *office:* Long Island City 430 Broadway Astoria NY 11101

SON, NANCY OLMSTED, Media Specialist; *b:* Amsterdam, NY; *m:* an; *c:* Joseph, Matthew; *ed:* SUNY at Albany (BA) Eng Ed 1977, S) Lib Sci 1980; Hudson Vly Comm Coll 7 Hrs Cmptr; NERIC ses; *cr:* Troy Schls Media Specialist 1980-81, 8 Grd Lang Arts Tchr -91, Media Specialist 1992-; *ai:* NYSUT 1980-; ALA 1990-; Tech n 1994-; Grant for Writing 8th Grd Lang Arts Skills Curr; *office:* ged City Schl Dist Troy 1976 Burdett Ave Troy NY 12180

URE, DANA FAYE, Social Studies Teacher; *b:* Buffalo, NY; *ed:* a Coll (BA) Soc Stud Ed 1991; Buffalo St Coll (MS) Soc Stud Ed 1993; NY St Coaching Cert; *cr:* Kids Play Yth Sports Pgm Coach 1992-94; Randolph Cntrl HS Tchr 1994-; *ai:* Stu Cncl Adv; JV Vllybl Coach; Comm Svc Projects; NCSS 1992-; AFT 1994-; *office:* Randolph Jr Sr HS Main St Randolph NY 14221

SERVIDIO, BARBARA (LAURENZI), HS Math Teacher; *b:* Cleveland, OH; *m:* Carmine F.; *c:* Carmine R., John A.; *ed:* Kent St Univ (BA) Math, Physics 1972; Fairleigh Dickinson Univ (MS) Physics 1975; *cr:* Grover Cleveland Jr HS Math Tchr 1972-77; James Caldwell HS Math Tchr 1977-79; Stuart Cntry Day Schl Math, Physics 1988-90; Montgomery HS Math, Physics 1979-81, 1990-; *ai:* Math League Adv; ETS Reader; NEA, NJEA 1972-; MTEA 1979-; AMTNJ 1995-; Hillsborough MS HSA 1993-; PTSA 1990-; Delta Kappa Gamma; *office:* Montgomery HS Burnt Hill Rd Skillman NJ 08558

SESSA, SANDRA ANN, Associate Professor of Psych; *b:* Trenton, NJ; *c:* Tiffany Elias, Jonathan Smith, Jessica Mc Lean; *ed:* Ocean Cty Coll (AAS) Nrsng 1975; Georgian Ct Coll (BA) Psych 1977; Kean Coll of NJ (MA) Ed, Schl Psych 1979-81; Seton Hall Univ (PHD) Cnslng Psych 1992; Hypnotherapy Cert; *cr:* Georgian Ct Coll Assoc Prof of Psych 1978-; Advent Cnslng Ctr Clinical Assoc 1985-95; The Stress Ctr Clinical Assoc 1993-; Ocean Cty Police Acad Instr 1995-; *ai:* Retention Comm Chprsn; Admissions, Outcomes & Assessment Comms; Acad Standing Comm Adv; Amer Psychological Assn, NJ Psychological Assn 1982-; Intnl Assn of Cnslrs & Therapists 1994; Ocean Cty Domestic Violence Comm, Garden St Philharmonic Chorus 1994-; Garden St Philharmonic League 1995-; Fac Dev Comm Grant; Article Pub; *office:* Georgian Court Coll 900 Lakewood Ave Lakewood NJ 08701

SESSLER, HARRIET MCNAMARA, ESL Teacher; *b:* Middlebury, VT; *c:* Trisha, Maria; *ed:* Utica Coll (BA) Eng 1969; Colgate Univ (MAT) Eng Tchng 1992; *cr:* Sauquoit HS Eng Tchr 1981-84; Proctor HS ESL Tchr 1988-95; Refugee Ctr Schl 1995-; *ai:* WCNY TV Syracuse NY Video Project Grant; Educators Moscow, St Petersburg Educl Tour Coord 1992; *home:* 9388 Mallory Rd New Hartford NY 13413*

SESSO, CAROL ANN, Jr HS Teacher; *b:* Cleveland, OH; *ed:* Cleveland St Univ (BSE) Grd 1-8 1971, (MED) Cnslng 1985; Art Therapy; Dimension in Learning; *cr:* St Ann Schl 3, 4th Grd Tchr 1958-62; Nativity 3rd Grd Tchr 1962-65; St Benedict 5th Grd Tchr 1968-80; St Pius X 5, 6, 7, 8 Grd Tchr 1965-80; St Catherine 7, 8 Grd Tchr 1980-91; St Ann Schl 7, 8 Grd Tchr 1991-; Ursuline Coll Curr II ED 315 Adj Tchr 1992-; *ai:* Jr HS Level Coord; NCEA 1965-; ASCD 1995-; Excl Awd Tchr Cleveland Diocese 1990; Class Act Tchr Awd 1991; *home:* 102 Talbot Dr Bedford OH 44146*

SETTICASE, MARY JO, French Teacher; *b:* Utica, NY; *m:* Alphonso J. Jr.; *c:* Rick; *ed:* Utica Coll of SU (BA) Lbrl Arts, Fr 1966; SUNY at Cortland (MS) Fr, Rdng 1991; 6 Addl Hrs; 12 Addl Hrs Syracuse Univ; *cr:* Canastota Cntrl Schl 7-12 Grd Fr Tchr 1966-71, 1987-; Madison Cty Soc Svcs Caseworker 1983-87; *ai:* EAP Shared Decision, 7th-8th Grd Orientation Comms; Model Schls, Alumni Awds Night Participants; NYSAFLT, NYSUT 1987-; Mohican Model A Club 1985-; Amer Cancer Soc, Vol; St Agathas Church; Local Sports Boosters; Madison Oneida BOCES Mini Grant.

SETTLE, SHARON E., Language Arts Teacher; *b:* Charleston, WV; *m:* Russell J.; *c:* Jamie, Matthew; *ed:* Glenville St Coll (BA) Elem 1972; WV Coll of Grad Stud (MA) Elem 1977; *cr:* Spencer Elem 1st Grd Tchr 1972-77; Accident Elem K-3rd Grd Tchr 1978-91; Northern Mid 8th Grd Lang Arts Tchr 1991-; *ai:* Stu Cncl Adv; Yrbk Adv Asst; NEA 1972-; *home:* 202 S Main St Accident MD 21520*

SEVERNS, BEVERLY DANCHISIN, Reading Teacher; *b:* Cleveland, OH; *m:* Gerald; *ed:* Cuyahoga Comm Coll (AA) Elem Ed 1966; Bowling Green St Univ (BS) Elem Ed 1968; Baldwin Wallace (MAEd) Rdng 1980; Addl 15 Hrs; *cr:* Parma City Schls First Grd Tchr 1968-69; Brooklyn City Schls First Grd Tchr 1969-89, Grd 4-6 Remedial Rdng Tchr 1989-90, 7-8 Grd Rdng Tchr 1990-; *ai:* MS Stu Cncl Adv, Advy Comm; Schl Comms; Mentor; North East OH Educ Assn, OH Educ Assn, NEA 1968-; IRA 1970-, Pres; Delta Kappa Gamma 1979-, VP; *home:* 3747 Kings Mill Run Rocky River OH 44116*

SEVERSON, CHRISTINE K., Eng Instr, Learning Specialist; *b:* Austin, MN; *m:* Richard Wenck; *ed:* Buena Vista Univ (BA) Eng 1990; Univ of RI (MA) Eng 1993; *cr:* Univ of RI Writing Tutor 1991; Southern VT Coll Writing Instr Summers 1991-93; Bristol Comm Coll Writing Instr 1993; NH Tech Coll Writing Instr, Learning Specialist 1993-; *ai:* Staff Dev, Title 3 Grant Writing, Schl-to-Work Transition Team; Outreach Comm; AAUW 1995-; Americorps Mngmt Team 1995-, Comm; Comm Theater 1994-, Actor; *office:* NH Tech Coll At Berlin 2020 Riverside Dr Berlin NH 03570*

SEVIGNY, SCOTT DANA, Social Studies Teacher; *b:* Biddeford, ME; *ed:* Univ of ME at Farmington (BS) Scndry Ed & Soc Stud 1992; *cr:* Fort Kent Comm HS Soc Stud Tchr 1992-; *ai:* Stu Cncl, Youth LEAD Adv; NEA 1992-, VP, Bldg Rep; Lions Intnl 1995-; *office:* Fort Kent Community HS 51 Pleasant St Fort Kent ME 04743

SEWARD, ALAN BRUCE, Guidance Counseling Svc Dir; *b:* Baltimore, MD; *m:* Diane Marie Eagan; *c:* Brent, Brooke; *ed:* Towson St Univ (BS) Eng 1968; Johns Hopkins Univ (MED) Guid & Cnslng 1976; 60 Addl Post Grad Hrs Guid & Related Field; *cr:* Perry Hall Jr HS 8-9 Grd Eng Tchr 1968-71; Perry Hall HS 10, 12th Grd Eng Tchr 1971-75, Guid Cnslr 1975-79, Dir of Guid 1979-; *ai:* Multi-Cultural, Tech Ed Comms; Prins Advy Cncl; Peer Cnslng Prgms Spon; Schlsp Comm Co-Chair; NEA, MSTA, TABCO 1968-, BCCA 1976-, Pres 1987-88; Amer Cnslng Assn 1980-; Natl Bd of Certfd Cnslrs 1988-; Kingsville Rotary Club 1977-91, VP, Paul Harris Fellow; Dev Peer Cnslng Prgm; *home:* 12100 Jerusalem Rd Kingsville MD 21087*

SEWARD, DAVID B., Latin Teacher; *b:* Kansas City, MO; *ed:* Univ of NE (BA) Latin 1980-; Univ of Pittsburgh (MA) Classics 1988, (PHD) Classics 1990; *cr:* NY Harlem Opera Violinist 1980-81; Stadttheater Giesseu Violinist 1982-86; Univ of Pgh at Greensburg Classics Instr 1991-; Winchester Thurston Latin, Fr, Span & His Tchr; *office:* Winchester Thurston Schl 555 Morewood Ave Pittsburgh PA 15213

SEWARD, JAY, Social Studies Teacher; *b:* Albany, NY; *m:* Darby Whalen; *c:* Molly, Kevin; *ed:* NH (BA) His 1971; North Adams St (MS) Ed 1993; Addl 30 Grad Credit Hrs Russel Sage Coll, 3 Grad Hrs Columbia Univ; *cr:* City of Albany Recreation Dir 1971-; Albany Schls Tchr 1973-, Var Bsbl Coach 1985-; *ai:* Schl Newspaper Adv; Schedule Comm; AFT, NYSUT, APSTA 1973-; Albany Pop Warner 1973-79 Pres; Amer Legion Bsbl 1975-85 Bd of Dir; Babe Ruth Bsbl 1989-94 Bd of Dir; Honored by Proclamation of Albany; Cty Legislature GEP Prgm Cty Jail 1982; Honored by Jr Achvmt; *home:* 218 S Manning Blvd Albany NY 12208

SEWARD, MARY ANN RANALLI, Foreign Language Teacher; *b:* Syracuse, NY; *m:* Arthur James; *c:* James David; *ed:* SUNY Coll of Fredonia (BA) Bio, Chem 1971; Univ of the St of NY Elem Ed, Corrective, Remedial Instruction Rdng 1978; Univ of St of NY Ger 1976; Univ of Bonn Germany; 30 Grd Hrs Univ of the St of NY; 24 Credit Hrs Ger 1976; Permanent Certification Bio, Chem, Gen Sci, Ger, Elem Ed; *cr:* Camillus Jr HS Gen Sci Tchr 1971-72; Auburn HS Bio, Gen Sci Tchr 1979-80; Onondaga Comm Coll Bio, Ger Tutor 1975-78; Auburn Enlarged City Schl Dist 8th Grd Ger, Fr Tchr 1980-84; Ger Tchr 1993-95, Latin, Fr Tchr 1995-; *ai:* AFT, NY St United Tchrs 1993-; Jehovah Witness 1972-; *home:* 285 Clark Street Rd Auburn NY 13021

SEWARD, ROBIN DUKERICH, Fourth Grade Teacher; *b:* Johnson City, NY; *m:* Darryl L.; *ed:* SUC at Cortland (BS) Elem Ed 1974; Elmira Coll (MS) Ed 1976; 30 Addl Hrs 1976-; *cr:* Apalachin MS 5th Grd Tchr 1974-82, Drama Club Adv 1977-79; Apalachin Elem Schl 4th Grd Tchr 1982-, 4th Grd Dept Chm 1983-86, 1989-91; *ai:* AFT, NYSUT, Owego-Apalachin Tchrs Assn 1974-; *office:* Apalachin Elem Schl 405 Pennsylvania Ave Apalachin NY 13732

SEWELL, FAY BARBARA, Mathematics Professor; *b:* Jamaica, West Indies; *m:* Trevor; *c:* Duane, Andrea; *ed:* Univ of West Indies (BA) Math 1965; Univ of WI (MS) Math 1970; Temple Univ (MS) Statistics 1978; *cr:* Glenmuir HS Math Tchr 1965-70; Univ of WI Learning Skills Specialist 1972-73; Temple Univ Part-time Math Tchr 1973-75; Montgomery Cty Comm Coll Math Prof 1976-; *ai:* AFT 1990-; NCTM 1988-; *office:* Montgomery County Comm Coll 340 DeKalb Pike Blue Bell PA 19422

SEXTON, COLLEEN LINDA MOORE, Jr & Sr Coll Prep Eng Teacher; *b:* Pittsburgh, PA; *m:* Jim D.; *c:* Heather; *ed:* Marshall Univ (AB) Speech, Eng 1975; 21 Grad Hrs in Speech; 1 1 /2 Yrs Sign Lang; 10 Graduate Hrs in Eng; *cr:* Marshall Univ Speech Instr 1976-77; Lawrence Co Voc Schl Eng Tchr 1978-82; Chesapeake MS Eng Tchr 1983-92; Chesapeake HS Eng Tchr 1992-; *ai:* Spelling Bee Judge; Schl Newspaper & Drama Club Spon; Schl TV Station Co-Adv; Writer-of-the-Month Originator; Lang Arts Comm Chprsn 1989; Dist Lit Magazine Co-Ed; St Comm BLT; Pupil Performance Objectives Comm 1988; Scores Co-Adv 1992-; NEA, CEA & OEA; YMCA 1988-89; Spirit of Victory Church; Young Authors Leadership Awd; OH St Outstanding Young Author Citation 1991; Martha Jennings Holden Schlsp Awd 1991-92; Ashland Oils Outstanding Tchr Awd Nom; Sign For Deaf Comm 1989-; New Tchr Cert Testing Comm Mem; Pub Poet; Pub Articles, Ed; *office:* Chesapeake HS PO Box 10 Chesapeake OH 45619*

SEXTON, GINA DUTEY, Teacher of Learning Disabled; *b:* Gallipolis, OH; *m:* Timothy Wayne; *c:* Tyler Scott, Taylor Brooke; *ed:* Morehead St Univ (BA) Ed 1983; Bowling Green St Univ (MS) Ed 1995; OH Univ LD Cert 1986; *cr:* Adena Local Schls DH Tchr 1984; Fairland Schl System DH Tchr 1984; Open Door Schl MRDD Tchr 1985; Ironton City Schls LD Tchr 1985-; *ai:* Intervention Assistance Team; NEA 1991-; Republican Women's Club 1990-; *office:* Ironton MS 302 Delaware St Ironton OH 45638*

SEXTON, PATRICIA STROHMAIER, Learning Support Teacher; *b:* Coatesville, PA; *m:* Raymond Charles; *c:* Nicole D. Lupinetti, Anna M. Lupinetti; *ed:* Millersville Univ (BSED) Spec Ed 1979; Indiana Univ of PA (MED) Ele Ed 1988; 63 Hrs Univ of CT; Trng of Parents of Excpetional CHildren Acad for Effective Instr; Keystone Hlth Promotion Conf Penn Star; *cr:* Elkton Jr-Sr HS Spec Ed Tchr 1980; United Elem Schl Spec Ed Tchr 1982-94; United MS Spec Ed Tchr, Gifted Coord 1994-; *ai:* Dev Inclusion, Enrichment, Mentorship Prgms Schl Dist; Spon His Day, Stu Competitions; Mentor Tchr; Assist Gifted Stdnts Grant Writing; UEA, PSEA, NEA 1982-, ASCD 1992-; ACLD 1983-88, Advy Bd; Penn Star Trainer; Stu Tchrs Coop Tchr; *home:* RR 1 Box 534 Homer City PA 15748

SEYDEWITZ, LINDA RANCOURT, Chemistry & Phys Science Tchr; *b:* Providence, RI; *m:* Thomas U.; *c:* Lauren, Lisa; *ed:* Univ of RI (BA) Scndry Ed & Bio 1973; Wesleyan Univ (MA) Sci 1976; Stu Committment with CT Dept of Environmental Protection for SEARCH Pgm; *cr:* Platt HS Earth Sci Tchr 1974-75; Newington HS Phys Sci & Chem Tchr 1975-79; East Hampton HS Homebound Tutoring 1986-89, Phys Sci & Chem Tchr 1989-; Middletown Adult Ed GED Pgm Tchr 1986-89; *ai:* Head Class Adv for Class of 1996; NEASC Comm Chair; Rsrch Team for Block Scheduling; NEA & CEA 19740-; CT Sci Tchrs Assoc 1974-; NSTA 1989-; Amer Chem Soc-Div of Chem Ed 1993-; East Hampton Jr Women 1984-, Mem Chm; CT Girl Scouts Org 1988-, Jr Consultant, GS USA Outstdng Ldr Awd; East Hampton Parent Tchr Stu Org 1992-; *office:* East Hampton HS 15 N Maple St East Hampton CT 06424

SEYEDKHALILI, SAIEDEH, Physical Sci & Chemistry Tchr; *b:* Tehran, Iran; *m:* Hassan Tajick; *ed:* TX Southern Univ at Houston (BS) Chem, Math 1980, (MS) Phys Anal Chem 1982; Cath Univ at Washington DC Chem Ed Cert 1992, Chem Fundamentals; Amer Univ at Washington DC PHD Candidate 1983-; *cr:* St Thomas Apostle Homeroom, All Subjects 7th Grd Tchr 1985-86; Our Lady of Lourdes 7th-8th Grd Math, Sci Tchr 1986-87; Holy Spirit HS Chprsn, Chem, Bio, Phys, Math Tchr 1987-89; La Reine HS Chem Instr 1990-92; Bishop Mc Namara HS Chem Instr 1992-; *ai:* Calendar Comm; Sci Fair Judge, Coord; Jr Class, Jr, Sr Prom, SADD Moderator; Ring Ceremony Coord; Newsletter Article Submitted 1992; *office:* Bishop Mc Namara HS 6800 Marlboro Pike Forestville MD 20747

SEYFARTH, ROBERT ERNST, Professor of Management; *b:* Cambridge, MA; *ed:* US Naval Acad (BS) Naval Sci 1961; Golden Gate Univ (MBA) Mgmt 1973; Univ of NV at Reno (EDD) Ed Admin 1980; Post Grad Stud at PA St Univ; *cr:* US Navy Officer 1961-81; Lock Haven Univ Prof 1981-; *ai:* TIMS 1984-.

SEYFERT, WAYNE G., Science Teacher & Rsrch Coord; *b:* Roslyn, NY; *c:* Sean, Kerry, Adam; *ed:* SUNY at Cortland (BS) Bio 1969; LI Univ at C. W. Post (MS) Bio, Ecology 1973; Queens Coll Cert School Admin & Supversion 1988; *cr:* Port Washington Schls Sci Tchr 1969-70; Sci Museum of LI Instr, Summer Prgm Dir 1973-86; Nassau Comm Coll Adj Prof 1975-; Lawrence Pub Schls Sci Tchr, Sci Rsrch Coord 1970-; *ai:* Sci Ind Rsrch; Lawrence Tchrs Assn 1970-, 1st VP 1983-; NYSUT 1969-; Adj Fac Assn 1975-, Dept Rep 1982-; AFDCS 1982-; Amer Philatelic Soc 1995-; CS & CSS soc 1984-; Precanal Soc 1988-; LI Course Soc 1982-; Pub Articles; Educator of Yr Hokstra Univ Chan 12 1995; *home:* PO Box 116 Woodmere NY 11598*

SEYLER, MARY DOLSON, Math Teacher; *b:* Hoboken, NJ; *m:* Edward W. III; *c:* Edward W. IV, Robert C.; *ed:* Coll of Mt St Vincent (BA) Math 1962; *cr:* Robert Fulton Schl 4th Grd Math Tchr 1962-65, 5th Grd Tchr 1965-68, 7th & 8th Grd Math Tchr 1968-79; NB HS Math Tchr 1979-; *ai:* Curr Comm; Tchr Inservice Comm; NEA, NJEA & HCEA 1962-, Del Assembly & Assembly Rep; NBEA 1962-, Pres, VP, Sec, Treas, Chair Philanthropic Fund; NBEA Philanthropic Fund 1990-, Chrpsn; *office:* North Bergen HS 7417 Kennedy Blvd North Bergen NJ 07047

SEYLER, SCOTT ALAN, German Teacher; *b:* Williamsport, PA; *m:* Alexandra; *c:* Celina; *ed:* Bucknell Univ (BA) Ger 1992; Univ of Pittsburgh 15 Grad Credits Ger; *cr:* MMI Prep Schl Ger Tchr, Cross-Country Coach 1993-; *ai:* NHS Adv; AATG, PFA 1993-; MMI Ath Assn 1993-; *home:* 135 Ridge St Freeland PA 18224*

SEYMOUR, LINDA JANDREAU, Career Pathways, Hlth Svc Tchr; *b:* Plattsburgh, NY; *m:* Raymond J.; *c:* Eric, Meredith, Jane; *ed:* St Univ Coll at Plattsburgh (BS) Schl Nurse Tchr 1958; Sage Grad Sch (MS) Hlth Serv Admin 1990; SUNY at Albany 12 Grad Hrs Ed; *cr:* Niskayuna Sch Sys Schl Nurse Tchr 1968-71; East Greenbush Sch Sys Schl Nurse Tchr 1987-92; Albany Med Sch of Nrsg Nrsng Instr 1971-74; Meml Sch of Nrsg Nrsng Instr 1971-74; Troy Schl Syst Career Pathway Tchr 1993-; *ai:* NYSUT 1968-; Troy Tchrs Assoc 1993-; NYS Schl Nurses Assoc 1987-; Helping Hands Presch for Disabled Children 1990-, Pres 1994-; Shenendehowa Bd of Ed 1980-89; Hatcher Awd, Outstdng Hlth Serv Admin Stu Sage Grad Schl 1990; Phi Kappa Phi 1990-; *office:* Troy HS 1948 Burdett Ave Troy NY 12180*

SEYMOUR, ROBERT JOSEPH, Science Teacher & Dept Chair; *b:* Marlborough, MA; *m:* Marie-Anne Bergeron; *c:* Cynthia Lapean, Rebecca, Jonathan; *ed:* St Anselm Coll (BA) Sci 1963-; Worcester St Coll (MED) Sci 1972; *cr:* Worcester Fdn for Experimental Bio Rsrch Tech 1963-67;

Algonquin Regnl HS Sci Tchr 1967-; *ai:* Sci Dept Chair 1988-; K-12 Sci, Sr Independant Projects Comm; Arta Negotiating Team; NEA, MTA 1957-; ARTA 1967-, Mem at Large; NSTA 1982-; *office:* Algonquin Regnl HS 79 Bartlett St Northborough MA 01532

SEYMOUR, STEVEN PAUL, Third Grade Teacher; *b:* Waverly, NY; *m:* Meredith Nestle; *c:* Matthew, Carolyn; *ed:* SUNY at Fredonia (BS) Elem Ed 1972, (MS) Elem Ed 1975, (CAS) Ed Admin 1988; *cr:* Westfield Cntrl Schl 3-6 Grd Tchr 1972-; *ai:* Westfield Olympic Torch Comm Liason; Aides Awareness Action Co-Chprsn; NEA, NYEA 1972-, Previously VP; Westfield Dev Corp 1994-, Schl Rep; Patterson Lib Bd 1992-, Sec; *office:* Westfield Acad & Central Schl 203 E Main St Westfield NY 14787

SFAYER, JAMES STEPHEN, Senior Marine Instructor; *b:* Brooklyn, NY; *m:* Sharon F.; *c:* Kathryn, Lauren; *ed:* St Francis Coll (BA) Soc Stud 1972; Long Island Univ (MBA) MNGMT 1986; Covey Ldrshp Instr 1994; *cr:* US Marine Corps Active Duty Ofcr 1973-94; US Navl Acad Cadet Summer Trng Instr 1974; US Military Acad Military Sci Instr 1984-87; Tottenville HS Sr Marine Instr, ROTC 1994-; *ai:* Cadet Drill Team; UFT 1994-; Intl Soc for Performance Instr 1991-, Chapter Pres; Rotary Club; Clements Award West Point 1987; *office:* Tottenville HS 100 Luten Ave Staten Island NY 10312*

SFERRA, DIANNA MARIE, Mathematics Teacher; *b:* New Brunswick, NJ; *m:* Ralph; *ed:* Rider Coll (BA) Math Ed 1983; Kean Coll (MA) Admin, Supervision 1989; *ai:* NJEA.*

SFRISI, JOHN J., Social Studies Dept Chprsn; *b:* Philadelphia, PA; *m:* Crystal Csacsko; *c:* Tina M.; *ed:* Villanova Univ (BA) His 1968; St Joseph's Univ (MA) Ed 1979; Temple Univ Tchng Cert 1970; St Joseph's Univ Instrl II Cert 1979; *cr:* Roman Cath HS Tchr of Math 1968-81, Coord of Govt Prgms 1975-81, Math Dept Chprsn 1979-81, Schl Admin in Charge of Supervision of Inst, Curr, Staff, Rostering 1981-90, Tchr of His 1969-, Soc Stud Chprsn 1990-; *ai:* Moderator of World Affairs Club; Assoc for Supervision & Curr Dev 1981-; NCEA 1968-; NCSS 1990-; Democratic Ward Exec Comm of Phila 1970-; Who's Who in Amer Ed 1987-88; Men of Achvmt; Distngd Cath Educator 1991; Senatorial Proclamation of Achvmt from St Senate of PA 1991; *home:* 2843 S Marvine St Philadelphia PA 19148

SGAMBATI, PATRICIA M., College Preschool Lab Instr; *b:* Youngstown, OH; *m:* Anthony P. II; *c:* Tony, Judy; *ed:* Youngstown St (BA) Elem Ed 1966, (MS) Counseling 1975; Pre-K Cert 1990; *cr:* Lowellville Elem Schl K Tchr 1964-66; Laird Ave Elem Schl 1 Grd Tchr 1966-68; Summit Co Bd of Ed Work Stud Coord 1968-70; Bath Elem Schl 1, 2 Grd Tchr 1970-72; Canfield United Meth Pre-Schl Tchr 1990-93; Youngstown St Univ Instr, Dir 1993-; *ai:* SAEYC Comm; NEA, OEA 1966-; NAEYC, TRU-MAH-COL 1990-; Diocesan Bd of Rel Ed 1990-94; *office:* Youngstown State Univ 410 Wick Ave Youngstown OH 44503

SGANGA, THERESA JOSEPHINE, Social Studies & Business Tchr; *b:* Brooklyn, NY; *m:* Joseph J.; *c:* Nancy Krupka, Joanna Rivard; *ed:* Hofstra Univ (BA) Psych 1978; St Johns Univ (MS) Soc Stud 1986; *cr:* Dominican Comm HS Bus & Soc Stud Tchr 1981-; Sewanhaka HS Part-Time Continuing Ed Tchr 1986-; *ai:* NCEA 1981-; Sons of Italy 1987-; Catholic HS Comm Teach Awd Recipient 1986-87; *office:* Dominican Commercial HS 161-06 89th Ave Jamaica NY 11432

SHABAZ, CATERINA PETROLITO, French & Italian Assoc Prof; *b:* Porto Empedocle, Italy; *m:* Zalmai; *c:* Nadia, Omar, Adriano; *ed:* Univ De Caen France (MA) 18th Century Fr Lit 1975, (PHD)20th Century Fr Lit 1978; Licence Es Lettres Fr 1974; *cr:* St Univ of NY Fr, Italian Asst Prof 1982-87; Univ of Rochester Sr Lecturer 1987-90; St John Fisher Coll Fr, Italian Assoc Prof 1990-; *ai:* Fr, Italian Clubs Adv; Alpha Mu Gamma; Campus Comms; Modern Langs Assn, Fac Adv; NYSAFLT 1983-, Svc Awd; MLA 1990-; ISCOR; RAUN; Rochester Sisters' Cities; NY St Assn of Frgn Langs Tchrs Svc Awd; Grant Awd; 4 Articles Pub; *office:* Saint John Fisher Coll 3690 East Ave Rochester NY 14618*

SHACK, JOAN ELIZABETH, Associate Professor; *b:* Flint, MI; *ed:* WMU (BA) Chem, Math 1971; MSU (MA) Math 1975; SUNYA Microcomputer in Math Classroom I & II 1983-84; *cr:* Mason Cty Cntrl HS Math, Chem Instr 1971-73; Concordia Luth Coll Math, Chem Instr Part-Time 1976-79; Washtenaw Comm Coll Part Time Math Instr 1976-79; Hudson Vly Comm Coll Math Instr 1979-; *ai:* Math Contest Coach; NY St Math Assn of Two Yr Colls 1979-, Math League Coord; NVCC Tchrs Assn 1979-, Sec; Nationwide Nonprofit Org 1992-, Pres 1992; Excl Tchng Awd 1987; Chancellors Awd Tchng Excl 1992; Articles Pub; Fac Dev Grant SUNY Capital Region Consortium of Two Yr Colls 1990-91; *office:* Hudson Valley Comm Coll 80 Vandenburgh Ave Troy NY 12180

SHACKELTON, GEORGE WILLIAM, Business Education Teacher; *b:* Walton, NY; *ed:* Suny at Cobleskill (AAS) Bus Admin 1967; Mc Neese St Univ (BS) Bus Admin 1971; Grad Course Work SUNY at Oneonta, Marywood Coll, Coll of St Rose; Cert Traffic, Saftey Ed SUNY at Cortland; *cr:* Walotn Cntrl Schl Bus Ed Tchr 1973-; *ai:* NHS Fac Cncl; NAE 1973-; Walton Tchrs Assn 1973-, Treas 1975-76; *home:* RR 2 Box 98 Walton NY 13856

SHACOCHIS, NORMAN F., History & Soc Sci Dept Chm; *b:* Newport, RI; *m:* Eileen Driscoll; *c:* David, Brian; *ed:* Bridgewater St (BA) His 1969, (MED) Guidance 1974; Addl 50 Hrs in Admin at CAGS; *cr:* Gates MS Soc Stud Tchr 1969-90; Bsktbl Coach 1969-86; Scituate Pub Schls Soc Stud Dept Chair 1990-; *ai:* Natl His Day Competition Chief Judge; Curr Review & MA Assessment Review Comms; Stu Govt Adv; South Shore Cncl for Soc Stud 1985-, Exec Bd; MA Cncl, NCSS 1972-; ASCD 1990-; *office:* Scituate High School 606 Chief Justice Cushing Hwy Scituate MA 02066*

SHADE, JILL SCHAEFFER, Spanish Teacher; *b:* Allentown, PA; *m:* Vern Henry; *c:* Katie M., Matthew J.; *ed:* Kutztown St Coll (BS) Scndry Ed, Span 1982; PA Dept of Ed Master's Equivalency 1995; 30 Grad Credits Kutztown Univ; 3 Grad Credits PA St Univ; 3 Inservice Credits Berks Cty Intermediate Unit; *cr:* Reading Cntrl Cath HS Span Tchr 1982-88; Fleetwood Area HS Span Tchr 1988-; *ai:* HS Spirit Club Co-Adv; Served as Mentor for Two New Tchrs 1994-; Fleetwood Ed Assn 1988-, Bldg Rep; PSEA, NEA 1988-; PA St Modern Lang Assn 1991-; Soc Outreach Comm Church 1994-, Sunday Schl Supt, Chprsn; Mini-Grant Pub Ed Fnd of Berks Cty 1994; *office:* Fleetwood Area HS 409 N Richmond St Fleetwood PA 19522*

SHADE, JON L., 6th Grd Science & Health Tchr; *b:* Bloomsburg, PA; *m:* Mary Beth Walewski; *c:* Justin; *ed:* Bloomsburg Univ (BS) Elem, Hlth & PE 1974, (MED) Elem Sci 1978; Sports Medicine; IA Univ Unit 16 Sci Consortium Classes; Sci Tech & Soc Ed Penn St; *cr:* Greenwood Elem 4th-6th Grd Sci & Hlth Tchr 1974-81; Millville Elem 6th Grd Sci & Hlth Tchr, Sci & Hlth Dept Chair 1981-; *ai:* Safety Prgm; NEA 1974-; Natl Corvette Restorers Soc 1992-; Natl Down Syndrome Congress 1991-; 4 Star Sci Tchr Amer Chemical Soc; Instr Magazine Pub of 4 Star Sci Activity in Astronomy; *office:* Millville Area Elem Schl PO Box 300 Millville PA 17846*

SHADE, THOMAS EARL, 9th Grade History Teacher; *b:* Erie, PA; *m:* Nancy Louise Proesl; *c:* Rachael, Paul; *ed:* Edinboro St Coll (BS) Scndry Ed 1978, (MS) Scndry Guid 1982; *cr:* Northwestern HS Alternative Ed Dir 1979; Brockway Area Schl Dis Soc Stud Tchr 1979-83; Du Bois Area Schl Dist Soc Stud Tchr 1983-; *ai:* Chess Club Adv; Ftbl, Wrestling, Track Asst Coach; NEA 1979-, Bldg Rep; Knights of Columbus 1981-, Trustee; *office:* Dubois Area Sr HS 400 Orient Ave Du Bois PA 15801*

SHADLER, DONALD L., Sixth Grade Teacher; *b:* Pottstown, PA; *m:* Barbara Gordon; *c:* Drew; *ed:* Shippensburg Univ (BA) Elem Ed 1977; Post Grad Credits; *cr:* Tchng Experience Grds 4-6 20 Yrs; *ai:* Cnty Sci Fair Responsibilities; Summer Sci Camp Penn St Univ; WAEA, PSEA, NEA Tchr Assns 1980-; PA Sci Tchrs Assn 1990-; Elks 1985-; Local Bus Partner Grant; Computer Tech Fellowship.

SHADRICK, DAVID G.,SR., Social Studies Dept Head; *b:* Providence, RI; *m:* Mary Eliabeth Cronan; *c:* Kelley, David Jr; *ed:* Providence Coll (BA) His 1971, (MA) Scndry Admin 1977; 30 Credit Hrs; *cr:* Orchard St Schl Eng, Soc Stud Tchr 1974-77; Martin Jr HS Soc Stud Tchr 1977-82; East Providence HS Dept Head 1983-; *ai:* Boys Tennis Coach; NHS Fac Comm; Friends of Athl Bd of Dir; Curr Coord Comm; RI Soc Stud Assn 1988-; RI Geog Assn 1994-; Natl Cncl His Ed 1992-; RIEA, NEA; Lions 1990-; Parents Assn 1974-; *office:* East Providence Sr HS 2000 Pawtucket Ave East Providence RI 02914

SHADROUI, JANET THERESA, English & Social Studies Tchr; *b:* Springfield, MA; *ed:* Univ of VT (BSEd) Eng-Cum Laude 1969; Northern AZ Univ (MAT) Ed, Eng 1972; 36 Post Grad Hrs UVM at Burlington, Cane Inst at Dartmouth Coll, Bradloaf Schl at Middlebury Coll; *cr:* Camp Verde HS Eng, Soc Stud Tchr 1969-72; Spaulding HS Eng, Soc Stud Tchr 1972-; *ai:* Arts Adv Comm; Tchng Intro Lit Class Comm Coll of Vt1993-95; BEA, NEA 1972-; Phi Beta Kappa, Kappa Delta Pi, Phi Kappa Phi; *office:* Spaulding HS 155 Ayers St Barre VT 05641

SHAFER, DIANE LOUISE, Mathematics Teacher; *b:* Mansfield, OH; *m:* Alan W.; *c:* Jenna M., Zackary A.; *cr:* Athens HS Math Tchr 1985-; *ai:* NEA, OEA, Athens Ed Assn 1985-; *office:* Athens HS PO Box 68 The Plains OH 45780

SHAFER, DONALD MARION, Eng Tchr & Dept Chair; *b:* Bellefontaine, OH; *ed:* Bowling Green St Univ (BA) Eng 1967; Wright St Univ (MED) Curr 1972; Bowling Green St Univ (PHD) Admin 1988; Attnd Akron Univ, Cleveland St, St Univ of NY at Buffalo & Univ of WI at Oshkosh; *cr:* Sidney City Schls Tchr 1968-73; Fairview Park City Schls Tchr 1974-; *ai:* Eng Dept Chair; NHS; Many Comms; NCTE 1968-, Corresponding Sec; OEA, NEA 1968-, Pres; Phi Delta Kappa 1984-; Optimists 1972-; Habitat for Humanity; Natl Endowment for Hum Hawthorne 1990 & Psalms 1994; Articles on Introducing New Tchrs to Profession; Tchr Evaluation; Ed for Grammer Holt Rinehart; Article on Using Poetry in Classroom; Received Tchr Awd from Local Bus Group; *office:* Fairview HS 4507 W 213th St Fairview Park OH 44126

SHAFER, LOUIS R., Vocal Music Teacher; *b:* Rochester, NY; *ed:* Fredonia Schl of Music (BM, BM) Music Ed, Vocal Performance 1993; *cr:* Clarence HS Vocal Music Tchr 1994-95; Williamsville North HS Vocal, Music Tchr 1995-; *ai:* Guy's, Select Chorus Musical Dir; NYSSMA, ECMEA 1994-; ACDA 1996; WTA 1995-; *home:* 2967 Town Line Rd Alden NY 14004

SHAFER, THOMAS RUSSELL,JR., English Teacher; *b:* Dayton, OH; *m:* Jane Elizabeth Seifried; *ed:* Wright St Univ (BS) Eng Ed 1984; *cr:* West Carrollton Jr High Eng Tchr 1984-88; West Carrollton Sr High Eng Tchr 1988-; *ai:* C-Team Peer Mediation & SADD Adv; Soph Class Adv & Chair; Var Girls Sftbl Coach; Chair of Learninng Commitment & Fac Liaison to WC After Prom Comms; NEA 1984-; OEA 1984-; West Carrollton Ed Assn 1984-, Bldg Rep & Soc Chair; WcEF 1993-, Exec Comm; Significant Tchr Awd from ERA 1987-; Piratan Tchr of Yr Awd 1991; Grand Marshall of WC Homecoming Parade 1991; Co-Authored Workbook for Jr Eng Classes 1994-; *office:* West Carrollton Comm Schls 5833 Student St Dayton OH 45449*

SHAFFER, CONNIE HARRISON, French Teacher; *b:* Philadelphia, PA; *m:* William B.; *c:* Kevin, Stephanie; *ed:* Bucknell Univ (BA) Fr 1969; Rutgers Univ (MA) Fr Lit 1977, (EDD) Lang Ed 1989; *cr:* Roland Park Cntry Schl Fr Tchr 1970-74; Fine Berlitz Schl of Lang Fr, ESL Tchr 1979-85; YWCA of Princeton ESL Prgm Coord, Tchr 1981-85; Hun Schl of Princeton Fr Tchr, Foreign Lang Dept Head, Summer Schl ESL Tchr 1991-; *ai:* Cheerleading Coach; Fr Club; Bd of Trustees Fac Rep; FLENJ, AATF 1994-; Cntrl Penn Jersey Acad Alliance for Lang Tchrs 1992-, Bd; Princeton Skating Club 1980-, Corresp, Rec Sec, Youth Group Adv; Publications Modern Lang Jl, Northeast Conf Newsletter; Presentations Bridging Theory & Practice in Foreign Langs, NJAIS Foreign Lang Tchrs Wkshp, Cntrl PA Jersey Acad Alliance, Northeast Conf on Tchng Foreign Langs, FLENJ Conf; *office:* Hun Schl Of Princeton 176 Edgerstoune Rd Princeton NJ 08540*

SHAFFER, CYNTHIA N., Elementary Reading Specialist; *b:* Johnstown, PA; *m:* Kevin R.; *c:* Jennifer Alis, Bethany Lynn, Travis John, Katy Marie; *ed:* IN Univ of PA (BA) Speech & Hearing 1981; Seton Hill Coll Elem Ed Cert; Duquesne Univ Rdng Specialist Cert; *cr:* Laurel Vly Elem Schl Rdng Specialist 8 Yrs; Fairfield Elem Schl Kndgtn Tchr 1 Yr; *ai:* Strategic Planning Comm; Tech Team Ldr; NEA, PSEA 1984-; Great Lakes Collaborative Tech Grant Awd; BRIDGES Grant Awd; *home:* 642 Hillside Ave Ligonier PA 15658*

SHAFFER, DAN M., Development Dir & Teacher; *b:* Erie, PA; *m:* Sheri J. Hardy; *c:* Brock; *ed:* Cntrl Bible Coll (BA) Ed 1985; Grad Stud Trinity Evangelical Divinity Schl 3 Hrs, Grand Rapids Bapt Seminary 3 Hrs; *cr:* Girard Alliance Chrstn Acad HS His Tchr 1988-; *ai:* Stu Ldrshp Comm Adv; *office:* Girard Alliance Chrn Acad 229 Rice Ave Girard PA 16417

SHAFFER, DAVID ROBERT, Mathematics Teacher; *b:* Blackwell, OK; *m:* Deborah Woodworth; *c:* Robert, Courtney; *ed:* Univ of NH (BA) Math 1966; Boston Univ (MED) Math & Ed 1967; Univ of Denver (MA) Schl Admin 1970; *cr:* US Air Force Acad Preporatory Schl Math Tchr 1967-71; Kent Schl Math Tchr 1971-84; New Milford HS Math Tchr 1984-; *ai:* Fac Senate; Scheduling Comm; Nea, CT Ed Assn 1984-; NCTM, ATOMIC 1979-; First Congregational Church of Kent 1980-, Treas, Chm of Prudential Comm; HBJ Algebra 1 & 2 Books Editorial Adv; Clarkson Awd for Inspirational Tchng 1993; Cert of Recognition Univ of Richmond 1994; Worcester Polytechnic Inst Recognition for Outstanding Tchng 1995; *office:* New Milford HS 25 Sunny Valley Rd New Milford CT 06776

SHAFFER, DIANE J., 8th Grade Teacher; *b:* Adrian, MI; *m:* Robert M.; *c:* Scott, Matt; *ed:* OH St Univ (BS) Elem Ed 1969; Grad Courses Performance Learning Systems & Bowling Green Univ; Credit Hrs Eng Lit OH St Univ Adult Ed Prgm; *cr:* Hamilton MS 5th-8th Grd Tchr 1969-; *ai:* Choir & Band Concerts Narrator; Hamilton Future Tchrs of Amer Adv; Asst Drama Dir; Testing Comm; Rdng, Lang Arts Stud Comm; Soc Stu Course of Stduy Com; Career Comm; Groveport Zion Luth Church; ELCA Women 1980-, Pres, VP; Sarah Cir 1980-, Pres, Sec; Martha Jennings Scholar; *office:* Hamilton Township MS 775 Rathmell Rd Columbus OH 43207*

SHAFFER, FREYA WEISTER, Mathematics Teacher; *b:* Tarentum, PA; *m:* Roy Martin; *c:* Brett, Tracy, Kyle, Tara, Ryan; *ed:* PA St Univ (BS) Math 1962; IN Univ of PA 12 Grad Credit Hrs; Intermediate Unit 8 4 Credits; *cr:* Westmont Hill Top Schls Jr HS Math Tchr 1962-66; Portage Area HS Math Tchr 1983-; *ai:* Mathcounts Coach; Algebra I Competition Team Coach; PSEA, NEA 1983-; PAEA 1983-, Fac Rep; Schl Bd 8+ Yrs; *office:* Portage Area HS 800 High St Portage PA 15946*

SHAFFER, JAMES, Principal; *b:* Cleveland, OH; *m:* Marcia Wilkins; *c:* James Jr.; *ed:* Lee Coll (BS) Ed 1976; Ashland (MA) Rel Ed 1993; *cr:* Parma Park Chrstn Life Acad Prin 1985-; *ai:* Stu Cncl Spon; Ski Club & Speech Meet Adv; Spelling Bee Coord; ACSI 1985-; Parma Schl [illegible] Fame Mem; *home:* 8218 Liberty Ave Parma OH 44129

SHAFFER, JEFFREY D., Spanish Teacher; *b:* Scranton, PA; *m:* S[illegible] Elizabeth Murphy; *ed:* Wilkes Univ (BA) Span, Scndry Ed 1991; Gr[illegible] Univ of Scranton; *cr:* Elk Lake HS Span, Spec Ed Tchr 1991-92; W[illegible] Wayne HS Span Tchr 1992-; *ai:* Boys Frosh Bsktbl coach 1992-; Prgm Supvr 1994-; Karate Club Adv 1994-; NEA, Amer Assn of Tch[illegible] & Portuguese 1992-; Penns St Modern Lang Assn; *office:* Western HS RD 2 Lake Ariel PA 18436*

SHAFFER, KEITH LAVERNE, English Teacher; *b:* York, P[illegible] Margaret Mary Lena Berbach; *ed:* Clarion St Coll (BS) Comm Arts[illegible] WA Coll Writing Project 6 Credits; Western MA Coll 3 Credits; U[illegible] MA Inst for Hum 3 Credits; Univ of UT 2 Credits; Loyola Coll 12 C[illegible] *cr:* North Caroline HS Eng Tchr 1979-; *ai:* Asst Vlybl, Drama Coach[illegible] Thespian Soc, Intramural Vlybl Spon; Ftbl, Bsktbl Running C[illegible] Scoreboard; Summer Teen Drama Wkshp 16 Yrs; *office:* North Carol[illegible] 10990 River Rd Ridgely MD 21660

SHAFFER, PAUL ALLEN,JR., 7th Grade Mathematics Teach[illegible] Philadephia, PA; *m:* Joanne Cooper; *c:* Stefanie, Christopher; *ed:* [illegible] Univ (BA) K-8 Elem Ed 1973; 39 Post Grad Credits; *cr:* Hatboro-H[illegible] Pub Schls 6 Grd MS Tchr 1973-83; Phila Pub Schls 4-5, 7 Grd Tchr [illegible] *ai:* 7-8 Grd Girls Field Hockey Adv, Spon; Kearny Elem 4-5 Gr[illegible] Bsktbl, Trck Adv, Spon; Geog City Wide Contest, Phila 76ers Stay I[illegible] Prgm Adv, Spon; Phila Fed Tchr 1985-; Penn St Ed Assn 1973-; AFT [illegible] Hatboro-Horsham Comm Yth Bsktbl, PA St Bskbtl 2 Yrs, Coach, R[illegible] Police Ath League Bsbl 2 Yrs, Spon, Coach; *home:* 1107 Tysc[illegible] Philadelphia PA 19111

SHAFFER, RICHARD ALLEN, Sixth Grade Teacher; *b:* Homestea[illegible] *ed:* WV St Coll (BSEd) Elem Ed 1968; IN Univ of PA 24 Grad Credi[illegible] Army Armored & Transportation Ofcr Basic Course; *cr:* US Army A[illegible] Transportation Corps Capt 1969-75; Kiski Area Schl Dist Permane[illegible] Tchr 1976-77; B&P Motor Freight Dispatcher 1978; Blairsville-Sa[illegible] Schl Dist Elem Tchr 1979-; *ai:* HS Track Coach 1980-86; HS Ftbl [illegible] 1981-92; Elem Flag Ftbl Coach 1993-; Natl Military Hnr Soc Scab[illegible] Blade 1967-, Lt; WV St Coll ROTC 1968-, Distngd Military Grad, [illegible] Commission; Bell Twp Vol Fire Dept 1968-, Asst Chief, Honorar[illegible] Mem; Twp of Loyalhanna 1993-, Emergency Mgmt Coord; Marg[illegible] McNamara Awd 1992; Blairsville-Saltsburg Schl Dist Edctr of Yr [illegible] ARIN Intermediate Unit Excl Fndtn Edctr of Yr 1994; Commonwe[illegible] PA Exemplary Elem Edctr 1994; Numerous Army Awds & Medals[illegible] Lexington Fire Equipment Appreciation Awd 1994; *office:* Saltsburg[illegible] Schl 250 3rd St Saltsburg PA 15681

SHAFFER, ROBERT JOHN, Spanish Teacher; *b:* Warren, PA; *ed:* [illegible] Haven Univ (BA) Scndry Ed & Span 1969; Edinboro Univ (MED)[illegible] 1977; Attnd Univ of Valladolid Spain & Eng Ctr madrid Spain; El[illegible] Cert 1974; *cr:* Lacy Elem Schl 6th Grd Tchr 1969-76; Clarendon Sh[illegible] Elem Schls Rdng Specialist 1976-85; Warren HS Span Tchr 198[illegible] Boys & Girls Cross Cntry & Girls Track Coach; Span Club Adv; [illegible] Cty Historical Soc; Museum 100 Club; *office:* Warren Area H S 345[illegible] Ave Warren PA 16365

SHAFFER, RONALD CHARLES, Business Teacher; *b:* Philade[illegible] PA; *ed:* PA St Univ (BS) Bus Ed 1972; Trenton St Coll (M) Bus Ed [illegible] Post-Grad Stud West Chester; *cr:* Neshaminy Schls Tchr 1972-; *ai:* [illegible] PAFT, NFT 1980-; *office:* Neshaminy HS 2001 Old Lincoln [illegible] Langhorne PA 19047*

SHAFFER, STANLEY JOHN, Art Teacher; *b:* Sharon, PA; *m:* Bor[illegible] Murphy; *ed:* Youngstown Univ (BS) Ed 1968; Edinboro Univ (ME[illegible] 1973; Sign Lang Penn St Univ, Intermediate Unit IV at Grove City; I[illegible] Design Mercer Co Vo Tech; *cr:* Sharon City Schls Art Tchr 1987-; A[illegible] Schl of Arts Visual Fine Arts Tchr 1992-; Thiel Coll Sign Lang Instr [illegible] *ai:* Dept Chprsn; Bible Club, Art Club, Prom Adv; STA, PSEA, NEA [illegible] PA Coalition for Arts 1993-; AHA Grant Sharon Lifelong Learning [illegible] PA Cncl on Arts, Vira I Heinz Endowment Grants; Cert Contri[illegible] Sharon city Schl Bd; *office:* Sharon City Schls 1129 E State St Shar[illegible] 16146

SHAFFER, TIMOTHY D., Criminal Justice Instructor; *b:* Dover, D[illegible] Kathryn M. Schrom; *ed:* Univ of So FL (BA) Criminal Justice 197[illegible] Northern Univ (JD) Law 1990; Ed Stud DE St Univ; *cr:* Tampa FL [illegible] Ofcr 1979-87; Cramer, Haber, MC Donald P.A. Assoc Attorney 19[illegible] Polytech HS Criminal Justice Instr 1993-; *ai:* Coach Mock Trial [illegible] 1995-96, VICA 1994-96; Crime Stoppers Fac Adv 1994-96; Hiring C[illegible] Amer Bar Assn, The FL Bar 1990-; NEA 1993-; *office:* Polytech H[illegible] Box 97 Woodside DE 19980*

SHAFFNER, VICKIE ANNE, 6th Grade Language Arts Tc[illegible] Wilmington, DE; *cr:* Redding MS Tchr 1977-; *ai:* Appoquinimin[illegible] 1978-, Pres; *office:* Lewis L. Redding MS 201 New St Middletow[illegible] 19709

SHAFFO, JOSEPH L., Physical Therapist Assoc Prof; *b:* Pittsburg[illegible] *m:* Diane Belechak; *c:* Maria, Joey, Anthony; *ed:* Univ of Pittsburg [illegible] Phys Therapy 1986, (MS) Orthopedic Phys Therapy 1989; *cr:* Bra[illegible] Med Cntrl Phys Therapist 1986-87; Univ of Pittsburg Sports Med[illegible] Physic Therapist 1987-92; Shaffo Physical Therapy Clinic Owner [illegible] Comm Coll of Alleghony Cty Assoc Prof, PTA Pgrm 1993-; *ai:* [illegible] Therapist Consultant 1983-; ICAA Coach Soccer, Little League; [illegible] Phys Therapist Ftbl Team 1983-; AFT 1993-; APTA 1984-; PPTA [illegible] Ed Comm 1986-89; Victoria L. Green Meml Schlrsp 1988-89; Who's [illegible] Among Amer Jr Coll Stdnts 1983; *office:* Comm Coll Algny Co [illegible] Cmps 595 Beatty Rd Monroeville PA 15146

SHAFNER, BETSY WALKER, Math Teacher; *b:* Beverly, MA; *m:* [illegible] L.; *c:* Jamie, Joey, Abby; *ed:* Merrimack Coll (BA) Math Tchng [illegible] Lesley Coll (MED) Integrating Arts into Curr 1994; *cr:* St Ma[illegible] Annunciation Math Tchr; Higgins Jr HS Math Tchr; Kennett HS [illegible] Thcr; Bishop Fenwick Math Tchr; *ai:* BATA, NCEA 1984-; *office:* B[illegible] Fenwick HS 99 Margin St Peabody MA 01923

SHAGAWAT, DIANA SOKASITS, Seventh Grade Teacher; *b:* Pa[illegible] NJ; *m:* Jeffrey J.; *c:* Patricia, David; *ed:* Mt St Mary Coll at New[illegible] (BA) Scndry Ed, Soc Stud 1969; *cr:* St Mary 6th-8th Grd Tchr 1969-[illegible] Paul 7th Grd, Tchr 1988-; *ai:* Home, Schl Exec Bd Tchr Rep; NCEA 1[illegible] St Paul Parish 1971-, Rel Ed Tchr 1974-77, RCIA Coord 1978-88, L[illegible] 1988-, Eucharistic Minister 1991-; *office:* St Paul Schl 1255 Mai[illegible] Clifton NJ 07011

SHAH, LALIT JAMNADAS, Asst Prof of Occup Therapy; *b:* Bor[illegible] India; *m:* Shakun L. Advani; *c:* Gunjan, Paurush; *ed:* Bombay Univ ([illegible] Occupational Therapy 1978; Coll Misericordia (MS) Occupat[illegible] Therapy 1989; Certified in Sensory Intergratin, Advanced Trng; Do[illegible] Candidate Higher Ed; *cr:* St Joseph's Ctr Dir OT Dept 1984-94; Misericrodia Adj Prof 1989-93, Asst Prof 1993-; *ai:* Fac Clinical Pra[illegible] Stu Adv; Mentor; AOTA 1978-; POTA 1993-; NE PA Indo-Amer Soc [illegible] Rsrch Flwshp 1987-89; *office:* Coll Misericordia 301 Lake St Dall[illegible] 18612

SHAHEEN, ROSEMARY LICATA, Second Grade Teacher; *b:* Met[illegible] MA; *m:* David G.; *c:* Matthew D., Alyson L.; *ed:* MA St Coll at L[illegible] (BS) Elem Ed 1968; 18 Credit Hrs; *cr:* Hampstead Cntrl Schl 1st Grd [illegible] 1968-71; Glen Forest Schl 1st Grd Tchr 1971-80; Stephen Barker Sc[illegible] Grd Tchr 1980-85, 2nd Grd Tchr 1985-90; CGS 2nd Grd Tchr 1990-

ıcl; Addison-Wesley Train the Trainer Prgm; 2nd Grd Team Liaison; v Survey Team; PTO; NEA 1968-; MA Tchrs Assn, Methuen Educ 971-; Edctr of Month 1985; Pub Several Articles; *office:* hensive Grammar Schl 100 Howe St Methuen MA 01844

D, LISA GROSS, Global Studies Teacher; *b:* York, PA; *m:* Ikram York Coll of PA (BA) Pol Sci, Govt Stud 1984; Millersville Univ Scndry Ed Cert 1987; Temple Univ of PA Working on ME; *cr:* ɔwn Area SD Sub Tchr 1988-89; Elizabethtown Area SD Soc Stud 89-; *ai:* Grad Reguirements Comm; NEA, PSEA 1990-; Cncl of Soc 92-; Young Democrats of York Cty 1987-; DAR Awd; Soc Stud YCP nental Awd; Alphi Chi Natl Coll Hnr Soc; *office:* Elizabethtown S 600 E High St Elizabethtown PA 17022

ER, CHARLES NASIB, K-12th Grade Computer Director; *b:* Fall IA; *m:* Darlene Caddick; *c:* Matthew Charles; *ed:* Providence Coll ɔ 1985; Lesley Coll (MED) Ed 1985; 500 Hrs Post Scndry Stud; *cr:* S K-12th Grd Cmptr Dir 1977-; Fisher Coll Prof 1980-; *ai:* Cmptr ED Premed Honor Soc; *office:* Joseph Case HS 70 School St a MA 02777*

ER, KATHLEEN N., Spanish Teacher; *b:* Philadelphia, PA; *m:* : Kori Rebecca; *ed:* Kings Coll (BA) Psych, Span 1967; 12 Post ud Univ of Bridgeport; 3 Post Grad Stud Western CT Univ; 3 Post ud Temple Univ; 6 Post Grad Stud Wilkes Univ; 6 Post Grad Stud t of Ed Wkshp; Numerous Prof Dev Wkshps; *cr:* Brookfield HS :hr 1967-70; Carlisle Intermediate HS Span Tchr 1970-71; Messiah an Tchr 1971-74; Filey's Schl Early chldhd Tchr 1980-89; Big HS Span Tchr 1990-; *ai:* Bus Yrbk Co Adv 1993-94; Frgn Educl Experience Coord 1994-; Ninth Grd Tchng Team Facilitator 1992-; :hr 1993-; NEA, PSEA, BSEA 1990-; PA Modern Lang Assn 1993-; Big Spring HS 45 Mount Rock Rd Newville PA 17241

ES, GAYA ROBINSON, English Teacher; *b:* Orlando, FL; *m:* *ed:* Vanderbilt Univ (BA) Eng Lit 1973; Colgato Rochester Divinity IA) Rel Stud 1977; Univ of Rochester (EDD) Ed 1995; *cr:* St Univ Tchr 1973-74; Rochester City Schl Dist Tchr 1974-; *ai:* African lis Comm; Univ of Rochester Prof Dev Advy Comm; Rochester ssn 1974-, Distinguished Tchrs Fellow; AFT, NYSUT 1974-; Amer Univ Women 1995-; Rochester Tchrs Assn 1974-, Multicultural Ed, ev & Instructional Svcs Comms Chprsn; Natl Endowment for Hum Todd Scholar at Univ of Rochester; Elizabeth Wright Scholar Assn k Women in Higher Ed; Multicultural Ways of Knowing Journal of 990; Stu Input- An Occasional Paper of Career in Tchng Prgm 1993; Response as Emancipatory Pedagogy-Raising Stans Journal of ter Tchrs Assn 1993; *office:* Edison Tech HS 655 Colfax St ter NY 14606*

KOVICH, TATYANA IVANOVNA, Adj Assoc Prof of Philosophy; egorsk Sakhalin, Russia; *ed:* St Petersburg Univ (BA) Russian gy 1973, (MA) Russian Philology 1975; SUNY at Stony Brook Comparative Lit 1991; St Petersburg Pedagogical Vacational Schl Tchr 3 Yrs; Fashion Schl Modeling, Designing of Woman's g 2 Yrs; *cr:* SUNY Asst Tchr 1986-89; Alexandra Tolstoy Russian r Inst Instr 1987-88; Dowling Coll Adj Assoc Prof 1991-; St s Coll Instr 1994-; *ai:* Coaching Ping-Pong Players at SUNY, St s Coll; Hagiography Soc 1991-; AATSEEL, MLA1986-; Articles rticipant of Med Forum at NH Plymouth Coll; *home:* 7 Burgess Ln Brook NY 11790

Y, ROBERT, Teacher & Museum Director; *b:* New Brunswick, NJ; gers Univ (MA) Ed 1974; 56 Addl Credits Educl Anthropology, gy, Philosophy; *cr:* Woodland Elem Schl Tchr 1968-74; Monroe S Tchr, Museum Dir 1974-; *ai:* Sr Class Adv; Museum Dir; NJEA, 968-; NJ Cncl for Soc Stud, Pres 1992; Fulbright Scholar China Middlesex Cty Tchr of Yr 1989; Governors Outstdng Tchr 1986-; s Publications.*

ACK, SHELDON MARVIN, Physics Teacher; *b:* Bronx, NY; *ed:* st of Tech (SB) Physics 1956; NM St Univ (MS) Physics 1959; NY HD) Physics 1970; *cr:* City Univ of NY Adj Asst Prof 1974-78; St NY Asst Prof 1976-77; NYC Pub Schls Sci &Math Tchr 1978-86; sant HS Physics Tchr 1986-; *ai:* Adv & Coach for Stu Competition Physics Team for the Intnl Physics Olympiad; AAPT 1974-, endations for US Physics Team; Physics Club of NY 1986-; AFT Articles Pub; *office:* Stuyvesant HS 345 Chambers St New York NY

AGHER, JOHN MICHAEL, US History Teacher; *b:* Montclair, NJ; en Arnold; *c:* Linda, Coleen, Jack, Timothy; *ed:* Jersey City St Coll is 1978, (MA) Urban Studies, Scndry Ed 1979; *cr:* North Jr HS 8-9 s Tchr 1981-87; Bloomfield MS 8 Grd Hist Tchr, Team Ldr 1987-; mer Yrbk Adv, Talent Show Coord; Asst Soccer Coach; Stu Cncl ield Trip Comm Chprsn; NEA, NJEA 1981-, BEA 1981-, Treas, Asst; Masters Grad Flwshp.

AHAN, MARY GRIFFIN, Chemistry & Physics Teacher; *b:* , NJ; *ed:* Coll of St Elizabeth (BS) Chem 1952; Univ of Notre Dame Chem 1967; Kean Coll (MA) Admin, Supervision 1977; Seton Hall Chem, Math, Electronics; NCE NJIT Physics & Math; Montclair St Ed, Bio; TX A&I Physics; Union Co Coll Bio, Cmptr Sci; Taft Schl ysics, Cmptrs Ed; Manhattan Coll AP Chem; *cr:* Air Reduction Labs Jr Chemist 1952-54, 1960; Arch Bishop Walsh HS Tchr, Dept Sci 1961-73; Jonathan Dayton Regl HS Tchr, Tchr Ldr, Supv, AP, s Level Chem & Physics Tchr 1973-; *ai:* Chem I, Chem II, Physics I AFT, NJSTA; ACS 1952-; NSTA 1975-; Schlsp Awd Grad Schl Stud hemists Club; NSF Grant for Stud; *office:* Jonathan Dayton Reg HS ountain Ave Springfield NJ 07081

AHAN, MICHAEL, Instr of Anatomy & Pathology; *b:* N Adams, *ed:* Bershire Comm Coll (AA) Bio-High Hnrs 1985; Univ of ster (AA) Bio, Molecular Genetics-Magna Cum Laude 1987; Attnd Med Coll for 2 Yrs; *cr:* Univ of Rochester Vol in Radiology Dept 37; Berkshire Med Ctr Vol in Pathology Dept 1992; *office:* Hudson Comm Coll 80 Vandenburgh Ave Troy NY 12180*

AHAN, THOMAS G., Legal Studies Instructor; *b:* Columbus, OH; iel, Brendan; *ed:* OH St Univ (BS) Soc Welfare 1977; Capital Univ aw 1982; *cr:* Private Practice of Law Attorney 1984-; Columbus St Coll Instr 1993-; *ai:* Stu Org of Legal Assts & Stu Newsletter Adv; ssessment Comm; OH St Bar Assn 1982-; Columbus Bar Assn 1982-, m Juvenile Law Comm 1990-91; *office:* Columbus St Comm Coll Spring St Columbus OH 43215*

E, ELIZABETH HARRIGAN, 6th Grade Teacher; *b:* Houlton, ME; ady; *c:* Dylan, Adam; *ed:* St Joseph's Coll (BA) Elem Ed 1985; Univ thern ME (MS) Lit 1990; 12 Addl Hrs; *cr:* SAD 61 6th Grd Tchr *ai:* Head Tchr; LA Curr Comm; MEA, NEA 1985-; Work with Lakes Environmental Assns; Lib Mini Grants; *office:* Stevens Brook Schl 18b Depot St Bridgton ME 04009*

E, JEFFREY S., Physics Teacher; *b:* Akron, OH; *m:* Traci; *c:* h; *ed:* OH Northern Univ (BS) Electrical Engrng 1987; Kent St Univ Scndry Ed 1990; *cr:* Revere HS Physics Tchr 1990-; *ai:* Jr Class Auditorium Coord.

E, MARY KATHLEEN, 8th Grade Social Studies Tchr; *b:* Olean, *d:* St Bonaventure Univ (BA) His 1992, (MSEd) Rdng 1994; *cr:* City Schl Dist 7th Grd Soc Stud Tchr 1992-94, 8th Grd Soc Stud Tchr 1994-; *ai:* OMS Whale Watch Club Adv; OMS Ski Club Co-Adv; His Curr Comm; Winterfest Comm; Peer Helpers Org; Springboard Comm; NEA-NY 1992-; Olean Tchrs Assn 1992-; *office:* Olean MS 420 N 7th St Olean NY 14760

SHANE, NANCY LEE PERUZZINI, Remedial Specialist; *b:* Buffalo, NY; *c:* Scott, Randall; *ed:* SUNY at Buffalo (BS) Elem Ed 1965, (MS) Rdng 1975; Nrsng Trocaire Coll 1983; Cmptr Sci Erie Comm Coll 1985; *cr:* Maryvale East Elem Schl Kndgtn & Primary 1 Tchr 1965-67; Union East Elem Schl Pre First & First Grd Tchr 1972-76, Rdng Tchr, Remedial Specialist 1976-; Medaille Coll Evening Fac, Rdng Prgm 1994-; *ai:* Lessons From Children Conf; Tchr Ctr of Cheektowaga; Schl Improvment, Dist Improvement Team; Cmptr Coord; Inservice Trainer; CLIC Whole Lang Group; Curr, Grnat Writing; Project TIME; Comm of Outstdng Learners Chprsn; Tutor; ASCD 1990-; Phi Delta Kappa 1992-; NY St Rdng Assn 1976-; Millard Suburban Hosp 1992-, Vol; Studio Arena Theater 1990-, Vol, Usher; Shea's Performing Arts Ctr 1993-, Vol, Usher; Philharmonic Soc 1985-; Tchr Ctr Grant; Using Video Tech in Classroom Grant; *office:* Union East Elem Schl 3550 Union Rd Cheektowaga NY 14225*

SHANECK, CHRISTINE TSCHERNE, Third Grade Teacher; *b:* Toledo, OH; *m:* Randy; *c:* Randy J., Michael M., Allison M.; *ed:* Univ of Toledo (BA) Elem 1974; *cr:* Sacred Heart Schl Third Grd Tchr 1974-82, Fifth Grd Tchr 1982-83; Third Grd Tchr 1983-; *ai:* Notre Dame Ed Assn; *office:* Sacred Heart Schl 824 6th St Toledo OH 43605

SHANER, JUDY ANN, Biology Teacher; *b:* Wildwood Crest, NJ; *m:* Bryan John; *c:* Mykal, Krystina; *ed:* Stockton St Coll (BS) Bio 1985; *cr:* Holy Spirit MS Bio Tchr 1985; Hammonton MS Bio Tchr 1986-; *ai:* Mock Trial; Tchr, Boys Bsbl Coach; NEA 1986-; NJEA 1986-; MEA 1986-; Zion Luth Church Cncl & Dir Educl Ministry 1990-, Cncl Mem; *home:* 3738 Moores Ave Hammonton NJ 08037

SHANEYFELT, SAMUEL R., Elementary Principal; *b:* Greensburg, PA; *m:* Shelley L. O'Keane; *c:* Kristin M., Erin L.; *ed:* CA Univ of PA (BS) Elem Ed 1970, (MED) Elem Ed 1976; Univ of Pittsburgh Admin Cert 1978; *cr:* Franklin Regnl Schl Dist Elem Tchr 1970-81; Various Schls Written Composition Instr 1978-; Franklin Regnl Sch Dist Elem Prin 1980-; Seton Hill Coll Instr 1991-93; Various Schls Cooperative Learning Instr 1991-; *ai:* Schl Dist Restructuring, Tech Comm; PAESP, NAESP 1991-; PSBA 1985-; Presbyn Church of Plum Creek 1989-, Sunday Schl Supt, Chrstn Ed Comm, Ldr Clown, Puppet Ministry; HAUW Murrysville Branch Educl Fnd Honoree; FRSD, Homer P. Kline Awd Dedicated Svc to Children; *office:* Sloan Elem Schl 4121 Sardis Rd Murrysville PA 15668*

SHANHOLTZ, MELINDA MAIN, Third Grade Teacher; *b:* Frederick, MD; *m:* Shane Hiett; *c:* David Hiett, Heather Elizabeth; *ed:* Frostburg Univ (BS) Elem Ed 1977; Shippensburg Univ & Hood Coll Grad Stud; *cr:* Liberty Elem Classroom Tchr 1977-95; *ai:* Home-Schl Relations Comm; Big Buddy & Little Buddy Pgm; NEA 1977-; MD Tchrs Assn 1977-; Frederick Cty Rdng Cncl 1995-; *office:* Liberty Elem Schl 11820 Liberty Rd Libertytown MD 21762

SHANHOLTZ, SHIRLEY DAY, First Grade Teacher; *b:* Harrisonburg, VA; *m:* Ronald; *c:* Julie; *ed:* Frostburg St (BA) Elem Ed 1972, (MED) Elem Ed 1976; *cr:* Mt Lena Elem Second Grd Tchr 1963-65; Broadway Third Grd Tchr 1965-66; Quincy Spec Ed Tchr 1966-67; Smithsburg Elem First Grd Tchr 1967-; *ai:* Dev First Grd Hans on Sci Curr; Tchr Rep Citizen Adv; First Grd SIT Com, Mentor; Train Stu Tchrs; NEA, MSTA, WCTA 1963-; Smithsburg Elem PTA 1967-; Mason Dixon Canoe Cruisers 1973-; *office:* Smithsburg Elem Schl 67 N Main St Smithsburg MD 21783*

SHANK, CHARLENE RYDER, Health, PE Tchr & Ath Trainer; *b:* York, PA; *m:* Robert Hyatt; *ed:* Lock Haven Univ (BS) Hlth, PE 1973; PA St Univ (MS) Comm Psych 1980; Natl Ath Trainers Assn Cert as Ath Trainer 1995 at West Chester Univ; *cr:* Manchester Elem Schl PE Tchr 1973-82; Mt Wolf Elem Schl PE Tchr 1973-82; Northeastern MS Hlth, PE Tchr 1983-91; Northeastern HS Hlth, PE Tchr, Ath Trainer 1991-; *ai:* Ath Trainer; NATA 1989-; PATS 1990-; NEA, PSEA 1973-; PA Journal of Hlth, PE, Recreation, Dance; Jaycees Young Edctr Awd 1976; *office:* Northeastern Sr HS 300 High St Manchester PA 17345

SHANK, HELEN HILLEARY, 2nd Grade Teacher; *b:* Baltimore, MD; *ed:* Towson St Univ (BS) Elem Ed 1967, (MA) Early Chldhd Ed 1974; Loyola Coll of MD Admin & Supervision Cert; *cr:* Towson Elem Schl Tchr 1967-79; Hampton Elem Schl Tchr 1979-; Hillendale Elem Schl Summer Schl Tchr; *ai:* Maps Comm 1991-92; Schl Based Mgmt Team 1995; Achvmt Comm Chprsn; Multi-Cultural Comm; NEA 1967-; PTA 1985-, Exec Bd; Elem Math Curr Advy Cncl 1985-; MSPAP 1990-; Pi Lambda Theta; Ashland Presbyn Church 1958-, Dir Rel Ed; Chamber of Commerce Excl in Ed Awd 1987-88, 1988-89; *office:* Hampton Elem Schl 1115 Charmuth Rd Lutherville Timoni MD 21093*

SHANK, JULIE, 10th Grade Biology Teacher; *b:* Pittsburgh, PA; *m:* Julia A. Balochko; *c:* Blair, Brett; *ed:* Univ of Pittsburgh (MS) Sci 1986; Addl Credit Hrs; Bio, Earth Space, Gen Sci, Phys Sci Certs; *cr:* Brandon Acad Sci, Bio, Chem Tchr 1978-81, Physic Tchr 1980-82; Franklin Regnl Bio, Earth Space Tchr 1985-; *ai:* Chrldr Spon 1985-90; NEA, FREA, PSEA 1977-; Tchr of the Yr 1982; *office:* Franklin Regnl Schl Dist 3200 School Rd Murrysville PA 15668*

SHANK, LACYE KOONS, English & Speech Teacher; *b:* Waynesboro, PA; *m:* James Owen; *c:* Wade T., Nathan B., Jayna L.; *ed:* Shippensburg Univ (BS) Eng 1971; Attn Western MD Coll; 30 Addl Credits; *cr:* South Carroll HS Eng, Speech Tchr 1990-; *ai:* Schl Improvement Team; Class Adv; Restucturing 4-Mod Day Comm Co-Chair; Evaluation Comm Chair; Grad, Attendance Comm; NEA, MD St Tchrs Assoc, NCTE 1990-; Juvenile Diabetes Assoc, Am Diabetes Assoc 1986-; Cty Curr Writing Eng; *office:* South Carroll HS 1300 W Old Liberty Rd Sykesville MD 21784

SHANK, TRACY SUZANNE, 6th-12th Grd Dir of Bands; *b:* Gettysburg, PA; *ed:* Lebanon Vly Coll (BS) Music Ed 1989, (BS) Psych 1989; Temple Univ 45 Grd Credit Hrs Concentration Educl Admin; *cr:* Southern York Cty SD Bands Dir 1989-; *ai:* Marching Band; Woodwind Quintet, Pit Orchestra, Brass Quintet, Jazz Band Dir; MENC, NEA 1989-; ASCD 1994-; NAFE, NASSP, AAUW 1995-; Who's Who Among Young Prof 1992-93; Fullbright Exch Schlsp 1993; Who's Who in Ed 1995; *office:* Southern York Cty Schl Dist PO Box 128 Glen Rock PA 17327*

SHANKS, MARILYNE E., Chemistry Tchr & Sci Coord; *b:* Cleveland, OH; *m:* Wayne C.; *c:* Tanya, Stephen; *ed:* Bowling Green St Univ (BS) Sci, Bio, Chem 1965; Hope Coll Advanced Chem; Ashland Curr; Youngstown His of Ed; *cr:* South Euclid Lyndhurst Tchr, Coord 1965-71, 1977; Cleveland Hts Univ Tchr, Coord 1978-80; Carrollton HS Tchr, Coord 1985-; *ai:* Dept Chair; Sci, EPA Club Adv; OEA, NEA 1965-; Jr OH Acad Sci, Battelle Awd 1990; NSTA 1990-; Civil Air Patrol 1989-, Major, Local & St Aerospace office; *office:* Carrollton HS 252 3rd St NE Carrollton OH 44615*

SHANKS, RICHARD EDWIN, High School Mathematics Tchr; *b:* Richmond Hill, NY; *m:* Janet H. Muller; *c:* Catherine A., Jennifer H., Ryan W., Daniel R.; *ed:* SUNY at Stony Brook (BS) Math 1970; C. W. Post Coll (MS) Math & Ed 1973; 30 Addl Credit Hrs; *cr:* Kings Park Jr High Math Tchr 1970-82; Kings Park Sr High Math Tchr 1982-; *ai:* Stu Cncl Adv 1970-75; Var Tennis Coach Girls & Boys 1972-86; AFT, NY St Tchrs Assn; NY St Math Tchrs Assn; Suffolk Cty Math Tchrs Assn; *home:* 41 Beacon Dr Sound Beach NY 11789

SHANNAHAN, KATHLEEN WINIFRED, English Teacher; *b:* Putnam, CT; *c:* Brendan P. Murcko; *ed:* SUNY at Oneonta (BA) Eng, Sec Ed 1973; SUNY at New Paltz (MA) Eng 1990; Lang Arts Permanent Cert 7-12; SUNY at Oneonta 30 Credits 1976; Permanent Cert N-6; Drake Univ 6 Ed Credits; Coll of St Rose 3 Ed Credits; *cr:* Margaretville Cntrl Schls 6th-8th Grd Lang Arts Tchr 1977-79; Hyde Park Schls 7th-8th Grd Lang Arts Tchr 1979-; *ai:* NYSUT, AFT 1977-; NY St Tchr Flwshp 1986; Honerable Mention Stone Ridge Poetry Soc Contest 1984; Pub in As If The World Had Not Known Sorrow 1985; *office:* Hyde Park Cntrl Schls Haviland Rd Hyde Park NY 12538

SHANNON, ANNE MC CONNELL, English Teacher; *b:* Warren, OH; *m:* Michael R.; *ed:* Allegheny Coll (BA) Eng 1988; Columbia Univ Tchrs Coll (MA) Eng 1991; Eng, Rel at Univ St Andrews at Scotland; *cr:* Spackenkill Jr HS P-T Grd 8 Eng Tchr 1991-92; Pawling HS Grd 12 Eng Tchr 1992-93, Grd 9 Eng Tchr 1994-; *ai:* Newspaper Adv; Trinity Church 1993-, Vestry; Blodgett Meml Lib 1992-; *home:* 505 Somerset Ct Fishkill NY 12524

SHANNON, DAVID KEVIN, Physical Education Teacher; *b:* Portsmouth, NH; *m:* Donna Ellen Keefe; *c:* Timothy, Megan; *ed:* Plymouth St Coll (BS) PE 1981; Univ of NH (MS) PE 1993; *cr:* Gilmanton Elem Schl PE Tchr 1981-83; Exeter Area HS PE Tchr 1983-; *ai:* Girls Soccer, Winter Track Coach; Officiate HS, Prep Schl, Coll LaCrosse; NEA, NHEA 1981-; NELOA 1985-; NHLOA 1985-, Exec Bd; BYBA 1995-; *office:* Exeter Area HS 30 Linden St Exeter NH 03833

SHANNON, ELIZABETH J., English Teacher; *b:* Pittston, PA; *m:* Robert E.; *c:* Amy Beth, Timothy Robert; *ed:* Kutztown Univ (BS) Ed & Eng 1971; Masters Equivalency 1988; *cr:* Daniel Boone HS Eng Tchr 1971-; *ai:* PSEA & NEA 1971-; *office:* Daniel Boone H S Chestnut St Birdsboro PA 19508

SHANNON, HILMA WILLIAMS, Bilingual Guidance Counselor; *b:* City of Colon, Panama; *c:* Gaviana Yadizmir; *ed:* New Rochelle Coll (BA) Psych, Ed 1989; Brooklyn Coll (MS) Guidance & Counseling 1991, (AC) Guidance & Counseling 1992; Univ of Panama Ed & Philosophy Stud; Hunter Coll Spec Ed Stud; *cr:* Walt Whitman Jr HS Family Asst 4 Yrs, Foreign Lang Tchr 3 Yrs; Abraham Lincoln HS Biling Guidance Cnslr 4 Yrs; Brooklyn Coll Adjunct Instr 2 Yrs; *ai:* Co-Coord Herencia Hispana Span Club; Site Supvr Brooklyn Coll After Schl Prgm at Jr HS; Kappa Delta Pi 1992-; NYC Assn Coun Dev 1992-, Prof Service VP; NYS United Tchrs 1993-; Southern Diaspora 1995-, Decorator; Leslie Crow Achvmt Awd Brooklyn Coll 1991-92; NYC Bd of Ed Biling Schlsp Grad Stud; *office:* Abraham Lincoln HS Ocean Pkwy & West Ave Brooklyn NY 11235*

SHANNON, MARY SUING, 7th-8th Grd Lang Arts Tchr; *b:* Yankton, SD; *m:* Peter E.; *c:* Leigh Marie, Alexa Melanie; *ed:* SD St Univ (BA) Speech & Jrnlsm 1982; Attnd Amer Univ; *cr:* Watertown Jr HS 8th Grd Lang Arts Tchr 1982-87; Holy Trinity Schl 7th & 8th Grd Lang Arts & Math Tchr 1989-; *ai:* Upper Schl Coord; *office:* Holy Trinity Grade Schl 1325 36th St NW Washington DC 20007*

SHANNON, TRACY JANE, Mathematics Teacher; *b:* Warwick, RI; *m:* Michael; *ed:* RI Coll (BA) Math Ed 1992; Providence Coll (MA) Admin 1996; *cr:* Exeter-West Greenwich HS Math Tchr 1992-; *ai:* Sr Class & Prom Promise Adv; Chrldng Coach; RIMTA 1990-, Exec Bd; ATMNE 1990-; NCTM 1990-; NEA 1992-; Admin Internship; Designer Math Chprsn; Numerous Articles Pub; *office:* Exeter-West Greenwich HS 930 Nooseneck Hill Rd West Greenwich RI 02817*

SHAO, LAWRENCE PETER, Assoc Prof Business Admin; *b:* Norfolk, VA; *ed:* Old Dominion Univ (BS) Gen Bus 1980-, (MBA) Finance 1982; Univ of TN (PHD) Finance 1989; *cr:* Univ of TN Instr Finance 1988-89; Fordham Univ Asst Prof of Finance 1989-95; Fitchburg St Coll Assoc Prof Bus 1995-; *ai:* Financial Mgmt Assn 1987-; Eastern Fin Assn 1989-; Acad of Intl Bus 1990-; Assn of Global Bus 1990-; Southern Fin Assn 1990-; Asia Soc 1993-; Financial Exec Inst 1994-; Books; Math for Mgmt & Fin, 6th & 7th Editions; Numerous Articles Pub; Managerial Fin Journal Guest Ed; Ad Hoc Reviewer; *office:* Fitchburg St Coll 160 Pearl St Fitchburg MA 01452

SHAPIRO, ANITA BENNETT, Fifth Grade Teacher; *b:* Brooklyn, NY; *m:* Eugene; *ed:* Cortland (BS) Elem Ed 1962; Hofstra (MA) Elem Ed 1969; *cr:* Massapequa Park 5th Grd Tchr 1962-64; Oceanside Pub Schls 4th & 5th Grd Tchr 1964-; *ai:* OFT; PTA, Honorary Lifetime Membership.

SHAPIRO, CAREN KNIGHT, Professor of Biology; *b:* Berkeley, CA; *m:* Stuart C.; *ed:* Univ of CA at Davis (BA) Microbiology 1967; Univ of WI (MS) Med Microbiology 1971, (PHD) Med Microbiology 1972; *cr:* IN Univ Rsrch Assoc 1973-74; IN Univ Med Schl Rsrch Assoc 1975-76; Roswell Park Meml Schl Rsrch Affiliate 1977; D'Youville Coll Asst Prof 1977-82, Assoc Prof 1982-; *ai:* Chm Undergraduate Curr Comm; VP Fac Cncl; Institutional Planning Comm; AAUP 1977-, Local Chptr Pres, VP, Treas; Assn for Women in Sci 1980-, Local Chptr Sec; AAAS 1977-; Sigma Xi 1972-; Amer Soc Microbiology 1982-; NY Acad Sci 1984-; AAUW 1978-, Asst Treas Local Branch; *office:* D'Youville Coll 320 Porter Ave Buffalo NY 14201*

SHAPIRO, CRAIG SCOTT, High School ESL Teacher; *b:* Bronx, NY; *m:* Loira Ortiz-Santiago; *ed:* Pace Univ (BBA) Acctng 1992; 40 Credits ESL Ed Fordham Unit; *cr:* Christopher Columbus HS ESL Tchr 1992; Dewitt Clinton HS ESL Tchr 1992-; *ai:* Close Up Fnd Coord; Paul Douglas, Empire St Schlsps; Univ Distngd Awd; Chncellor's Roll of Honor Ldrshp; *office:* De Witt Clinton HS 100 W Mosholu Pkwy S Bronx NY 10461

SHAPIRO, DENISE DECARLO, Art Teacher; *b:* Waterbury, CT; *m:* Alan; *ed:* Southern CT St Univ (BS) Art Ed 1980; Central CT St Univ (MS) Art Ed 1988; Cert Elem Ed 1994; *cr:* East Cath Art Tchr 1980-87; Naugatuck Schls K-5th Grd Art Tchr 1987-90; Hillside Schl 6th-8th Grd Art Tchr 1990-; *ai:* NEA, CEA, CAEA 1987-; One-Woman Art Show; S Windsor Group Art Show; Pastel Assn Group Show Winner; *office:* Hillside MS 51 Hillside Ave Naugatuck CT 06770*

SHAPIRO, EVELYN ISRAEL, Fourth Grade Teacher; *b:* Far Rockaway, NY; *m:* Aaron; *ed:* Brooklyn Coll (BA) Elem Ed, Art His 1967, (MA) Elem Ed, Rdng-Cum Laude 1970; *cr:* Center St Schl 4th Grd Tchr 1967-71, 3rd-4th Grd Inter-Age Tchr Open Classrm 1971-86, 4th Grd Tchr 1986-; *ai:* Stu Cncl Adv; GATE Advy, Schl Site Based Decision Making, Budget Site Based Comms; Herricks Tchrs Assn Rep; Mentoring Comm Tchr Consortium; NYSUT 1967-; Herricks Tchrs Assn 1967-, Schl Rep; PTA 1967-, Human Relations Chprsn, Jenkins Meml Lifetime Svc Awd; Natl Cncl Chrstn & Jews Cert of Recognition 1981; Soc Stud Mentor Dist 1-5 1986-88; *office:* Center Street Schl 240 Center St Williston Park NY 11596*

SHAPIRO, JOAN ARONSON, Spanish Teacher; *b:* Jersey City, NJ; *c:* Ellen Gail, Gary Israel; *ed:* Douglas Coll Rutgers Univ (BA) Span, Scndry Ed 1961; Iona Coll (MSEd) Span, Biling Ed 1978; *cr:* Bergenfield HS Span Tchr 1961-64; East Ramapo Schl Dist Per Diem Sub Tchr 1974-76; Highland Schl Span Tchr 1976-85; Leonia HS Span Tchr 1985-87; James I. O'Neill HS Span Tchr 1988-; *ai:* NHS, Jr Class, Span Club Adv; Stu Act Account Treas; Mid Sts Evaluation Team; AATSP, VFT 1976-; NEA 1961-; New City Jewish Ctr 1969-, Treas; B'Nai B'rith 1969-, VP; *office:* James I O'Neill HS Rt 9-W Highland Falls NY 10928*

SHAPIRO, MICHAEL CHARLES, Health Education Teacher; *b:* Washington, DC; *m:* Janice; *c:* Amy, Marc; *ed:* Penn St (BS) Hlth, PE 1957, (MED) Cnslng 1961, (EDD) Hlth Ed 1971; *cr:* St Coll Area Schls Tchr &

Coach 1958-; *ai:* Tennis Coach Boys 37 Yrs, Girls 14 Yrs; Jr HS Coach Ftbl 22 Yrs, Bsktbl 23 Yrs; NEA 1958-; Mid St USTA 1970-; Natl Fed Interscholastic Coaches 1993-; Coach of Yr 1973, 1987; Coach of Yr Section II & PA 1995; *home:* 1501 W Branch Rd State College PA 16801

SHAPIRO, SHARON R., Seventh Grade English Teacher; *b:* Los Angeles, CA; *c:* David, Laura; *ed:* Fairleigh Dickinson Univ (AA) Retail Merchandising 1961, (BA) Lbrl Arts & Eng 1963; Attnd Breadloaf Schl of Eng; Middlebury Coll 7 Grad Credits; *cr:* Grover Cleveland Jr HS 7th-8th Grd Eng 1963-64; Belleville MS 7th-9th Grd Eng 1964-; *ai:* Bedside Tutoring; NEA 1963-; NJEA 1963-; BEA 1964-; *home:* 95 Belmount Ave North Arlington NJ 07031

SHAPIRO, SHEILA ARONSON, Spanish Teacher; *b:* Miami, FL; *m:* Ira George; *c:* David, Adam; *ed:* Univ of NC at Chapel Hill (BA) Span 1969; 60 Grad Stud Credits Eng, Frgn Lang Temple Univ; *cr:* Chapel Hill Sr HS Span Tchr 1969-70; Huntingdon Jr HS Span, Eng Tchr, Dept Chair 1970-; Abington Jr HS Span, Eng Tchr, Dept Chair 1970-; *ai:* Natl Jr Hnr Soc Spon 1982-; Chaperone; Textbook Selection, Curr Dev, Discipline, Spec Events, Re-Org of Jr HS, Instrl Sequence, Gifted Ed, Long-Range Planning Comms; NEA, PSEA 1970-; Montgomery Cty Assn of Tchrs of Frgn Langs, Recording Sec 1995-; MLAPV; AATSP; PSMLA; MLA; Women's Amer ORT 1973-, Pres, VP, Treas, Angel of Yr; Old York Rd Temple Beth Am 1980-; *office:* Abington Jr HS 2056 Susquehanna Rd Abington PA 19001*

SHAPIRO, YEHOSHUA, HS Assistant Principal; *b:* Baltimore, MD; *m:* Sarah Rivkah Possick; *c:* Zev Nochum, Shoshana, Yitzchok David, Yaakov, Elisheva, Brocha Chana, Shira, Ephraim, Miriam; *ed:* Loyola Coll (BA) Acctng 1977; John Hopkins Univ (MED) Supervision, Curr 1980; NER Israel Rabbinical Coll Rabbinic Ordination 1982; *cr:* Beth Tfiloh Day Schl Tchr 1980-91; Talmudical Acad Tchr 1982-91; Bais Yaakov Schl for Girls Asst Prin, Tchr 1991-; *ai:* Stu Cnslng; Scheduling; Curr; NAASP 1991-94; ASCD 1992-94; Tchr of Yr 1987; *office:* Bais Yaakov Girls Schl 11111 Park Heights Ave Owings Mills MD 21117*

SHARE, DIANE LIEBERMAN, Early Childhood Educator; *b:* Bangor, ME; *m:* Barney; *c:* Andrew, Samuel; *ed:* Boston Univ (BS) Early Chldhd Ed 1971; *cr:* Maude H. Trefethen Schl 1st-2nd Grd Tchr 15 Yrs; Sherburne Schl 1st Grd Tchr 1 Yr; D. J. Bakie Schl 3rd Grd Tchr 1 Yr; Dow Lane Schl 3rd Grd Tchr 1 Yr; *ai:* Staff Dev Rep; Contract Negotiator; Portsmouth Coll Club 1980-, Mbrshp chm; Temple Israel 1972-, VP Ed; Portsmouth Schl Bd 1976-92, Vice Chm 4 Yrs, Chm 4 Yrs, Curr Comm Chm 8 Yrs; *home:* 38 Thaxter Rd Portsmouth NH 03801*

SHARICK, BRIAN ADAM, Secondary Mathematics Teacher; *b:* New Kensington, PA; *m:* Stacie Lynn Aftanas; *c:* Jacob, Morgan, Alexandria; *ed:* Edinboro Univ of PA (BA) Math 1984; 24 Addl Credits Penn St Univ Cmptr Application Areas; *cr:* Knoch MS Math Tchr 1985-; *ai:* Jr High Stu Cncl Adv; Tutoring Prgm; MS Transition Team; NEA 1985-; Gift of Time Awd 1993; *office:* Knoch MS Dinnerbell Rd Saxonburg PA 16056*

SHARK, DIANE MARIE, Spanish Teacher; *b:* Windber, PA; *ed:* St Francis Coll (BA) Span 1967; Millersville Univ (MA) Span 1985; Attnd Universidad Internacional at Saltillo; Span Lang Inst at Cuernavaca; *cr:* Berlin Brothers Vly Span Tchr 1967-; *ai:* Berlin Brothers Vly EA 1967-, Pres; PSEA 1967-, PACE, Legislative Chprsn; WEA; PSMLA; *office:* Berlin Brothers Valley Schl 1025 E Main St Berlin PA 15530

SHARLIN, JONATHAN, Photography Adj Prof; *b:* Hackensack, NJ; *m:* Olivia B. Mc Cullough; *ed:* Goddard Coll (BA) Music, Photo 1972; SUNY at Buffalo (MFA) Photography 1978; *cr:* Comm Coll of RI Adj Fac, Photography Tchr; Tufts Univ Adj Fac, Photography 1989-90; Univ of CT at Storrs Adj Fac, Photography 1990; RI Schl of Design Adj Fac, Photography 1991-94; RI Coll Adj Fac, Photography 1993-; *ai:* One Person Exhibitions Houston Ctr for Photography 1996, Duke Univ, Gallery One 1995; Gallery One 1992-, Bd; Individual Flwshp New England Fnd for Arts 1995; Artist Project Grant RI St Cncl for Arts 1992, 1994; Flwshp Individual Artist RI St Cncl for Arts 1989; *home:* 166 Lancaster St Providence RI 02906

SHARMA, SUSHMA, 7th-8th Grade Science Teacher; *b:* Nangal Twp, Punjab India; *m:* Kewal Krishan; *c:* Manisha; *ed:* Punjab Univ of India (BS) Bio, Chem 1973, (BED) Ed 1974, (MA) Hindi 1977; Tchr Cert Credits Kean Coll; *cr:* Our Lady of Mt Carmel Schl Sci Tchr 1985-86; Holy Trinity Schl Sci Tchr 1987-94; Hazlet Bd of Ed Sci Tchr 1994-; *ai:* Sci Fair Organizer; NEA 1994-; *office:* Union Ave MS 1639 Union Ave Hazlet NJ 07730*

SHARP, KATHRYN MALLET, French & Spanish Teacher; *b:* Williamsport, PA; *c:* Katrina M., Alexander V.; *ed:* Bluffton Coll (BA) Fr 1977; *cr:* Indian Lake HS Span, Eng Tchr 1977-78; Tecumseh HS Fr, Span Tchr 1978-; *ai:* Fr Club Adv; NEA 1977-; Church Bell Choir 1986-; *office:* Tecumseh HS 9830 W National Rd New Carlisle OH 45344

SHARP, KIMBERLEE ANNE, American History Teacher; *b:* Huntsville, AL; *m:* Kevin W.; *c:* Alex, Andrea; *ed:* Wright St Univ (BSEd) Soc Stud, Comprehensive Ed 1989, (MED) Educ Ldrshp 1995; Univ of Dayton Assertive Discipline Trng 1991 3 Hrs, Alcohol & Drug Intervention Trng 1990 3 Hrs; OH Mock Trial Trng OH Ctr for Law Related Ed 1990 5 Hrs; *cr:* Northmont HS World His, Black Amer His Tchr 9th-12th Grd 1990-94; Northmont Jr HS Amer His 8th Grd Tchr 1994-; *ai:* NEA, OEA, NDEA, OH Cncl Soc Stud 1990-; Faith Presbyn Church, 5th-6th Grd Sunday Schl Tchr 1994-95; Outstdng Achvmt Awd Sylvan Learning Ctr 1993; *office:* Northmont Jr HS 4918 National Rd Clayton OH 45315*

SHARP, MELVIN JAMES, Soc Stud Tchr & Stu Senate Adv; *b:* Salem, NJ; *m:* Cynthia Runkle; *c:* Sonya; *ed:* Rutgers (BS) Ec 1976; SUNY at New Paltz (MS) Soc Stud Ed 1987; Columbia Univ (MA) Amer Stud; *cr:* Goshen HS Tchr, Adv 5 Yrs; *ai:* Stu Senate Adv; Stu Activities Dir; AFT, NYSUT 1988-; NY Historical Assn 1991-; Mental Hlth Assn Vol 1987-, Cty Supvr's Vol Awd; COE Fellowship 1989-90; NY Historical Assoc Fellowship 1991; James Madison Meml Fellowship to Columbia Univ 1993-96; Book Vietnam War & Public Policy; Articles in Natl Journals; *office:* Goshen HS Scotchtown Ave Goshen NY 10924*

SHARP, REGINA DAWN, Asst Principal; *b:* Parsons, WV; *m:* Gary David; *ed:* WV Univ (BS) Ed, Soc Stud 1982, (MS) Ed Admin 1990; Instructional Strategies, Leadership Evaluation Courses; *cr:* Univ HS Soc Stud Tchr, Girls Bsktbl & Girls Tennis Coach 1983-87; RESA VIII Your Best Prgm Instr 1987-88; Jefferson HS Soc Stud Tchr 1989-95; Asst Prin Hagerstown North 1995-; *ai:* Schl Improvement Cncl Fac Rep; Soc Stud Dept Chprsn; Project Teach Comm Fac Chprsn; Alumni Assn Coord; Coed-Hi-Y Club Adv; Cty Curr Comm Soc Stud Rep; WVEA, NEA 1983-; Jaycees, Harpers Ferry Historical Soc 1988-; Camp Hill United Meth Church 1987-; Outstanding Young Educator Monongahelia Cty 1986-87; *home:* PO Box 1063 Harpers Ferry WV 25425*

SHARP, SHARON ANN (WASHKO), Second Grade Teacher; *b:* Hazleton, PA; *m:* Peter; *c:* Alexis; *ed:* Luzerne CC Coll (AA) General Stud 1977; Bloomsburg (BS) Elem Ed 1979; Scranton Univ (MED) Elem Ed 1984; Addl 60 Ed Courses, Grad Courses, Art Ed Kutztown Univ; *office:* Hazle Elem Schl 23rd & Mc Kinley Sts Hazleton PA 18201

SHARP, WILLIAM, Psychology Teacher; *b:* Philadelphia, PA; *ed:* Rider Univ (BA) Psych, Soc Stud 1993; Addl 6 Credit Hrs Tchng of Psych MA Rowan Coll; *cr:* Cherry Hill HS East Tchr of Psych 1994-; *ai:* Asian Culture Soc, Culture Newsletter Adv; Tech Comm; APA, TOPPS 1993-; NEA, CHEA, NJEA, CEA 1994-; Mid Sts Cncl for Soc Stud, NCSS 1992-; *office:* Cherry Hill HS East 1750 Kresson Rd Cherry Hill NJ 08003

SHARPE, AUDREY SESSOMS, Multicultural Writing Teacher; *b:* Lewiston, NC; *m:* Richard Earl; *c:* Chevonne, Richard Jr.; *ed:* St Augustines Coll (BA) Elem Ed 1967; City Univ (MS) Spec Ed 1976, (MS) Admin, Supervision 1995; *cr:* Pub Schl 67X 2nd Grd Tchr 1967-71; Comm Schl 234X 2nd Grd Tchr 1971-76; Comm Schl 152X 6th Grd Tchr 1976-; *ai:* Schl Planning Comm; Parental Involvement Comm; Parent, Tchr Assn; NC St Comm Pres; United Fed of Tchrs 1968-; Amer Tchrs 1970-; Burke Ave Bapt Church 1981-; Cora L. Banks Schlsp Comm 1985-, Pres; Star of Hope Gr 1982-, Dist Deputy; 3300 Bouck Ave Block Assn 1980-, VP; Banks Bible Inst 1984-, Class Pres; Natl Congress Parents, Tchrs Awd 1982; PAPEC Svc Awd 1984; *home:* 3320 Bouck Ave Bronx NY 10469*

SHARPE, CARL M., English Teacher; *b:* Worcester, MA; *c:* Heather L.; *ed:* Univ of MA at Amherst (BA) Eng 1966; St univ of NY at Albany (MA) Ed 1972; 40 Post Grad Credits; *cr:* Schuyler Prep Schl Eng Tchr 1966-71; Westborough HS Eng Tchr 1972-; *ai:* Schl Weekly Newspaper Aed; Tech Curr Writing Comm; Peer Partnerships; NEA, MA Tchrs Assn 1972-; Westborough Tchrs Assn 1972-, 2nd VP; NCTE 1985-; MA Cncl Tchrs of Eng, NECTE 1990-; Congregational Church 1979-, Deacon; Exch Club Cert of Recognition 1995; Data Gen Corp Exceptional Tchr Awd 1989; *office:* Westborough HS 90 W Main St Westborough MA 01581

SHARPE, CHARLES E., HS Tech Education Instructor; *b:* Jamestoww, OH; *m:* Jayne Linn Williamson; *c:* Kyle, Adam, Dustin, Phylicia; *ed:* Cntrl St Univ (BS) Indstrl Arts 1976; Bowling Green St Univ (MS) Tech Ed 1992; Univ of Dayton Acad Bus Advy Ldrshp Cncl, ICP Ldrshp; *cr:* Bellbrook HS Indstrl Arts, Tech Ed Tchr 1976-; *ai:* Dept Head Tech Ed; Frosh Baskbl, Cross Cntry, 5th & 6th Grd Bsktbl Coach; OTEA Schl Exhibits Mgr; Pres WOTEA; ICP Ldrshp Sci Olympia; OTEA 1976-, WOTEA Pres, Tchr Excellent; ITEA 1990-, Tchr Excellent; ICP Ldrshp 1996, Dir; Tec-Prep Steering Comm 1994-, W O Chprsn; OTEA Tchr Excl Awd 1994; Numerous Articles Pub BGSU 1992; *office:* Bellbrook HS 3491 Upper Bellbrook Rd Bellbrook OH 45305*

SHARPE, KATHLEEN, Social Stud Dept Chprsn & Tchr; *b:* New Haven, CT; *ed:* Albertus Magnus Coll (BA) Ec 1972; Wesleyan Univ (MALS) Soc Stud 1980; Southern CT St Univ 6th Yr Supervision, Admin 1989; *cr:* Guilford HS Soc Stud Tchr 1972-, Soc Stud Dept Chprsn 1990-; *ai:* Dist, Schl Prof Dev Comm; Soc Stud Curr Articulation Team; Guilford Ed Assn 1975-; CT Cncl for Soc Stud, NCSS 1973-; Delta Kappa Gamma 1992-; VFW Voice Democracy Cert Merit; BEST Prgm; *office:* Guilford HS 605 New England Rd Guilford CT 06437

SHARPE, KEVIN E., High School Math Teacher; *b:* Hamilton, NY; *m:* Sherry Raymong; *ed:* SUNY at Morrisville (AAS) Electrical Engrng Tech 1981; SUNY at Cortland (BS) Math Ed 1990; Syracuse Univ (MS) Instrl Design, Dev, Evaluation; *cr:* Auburn HS Math Tchr 1992-93; Fabius Jr\Sr HS Math Tchr 1993-; *ai:* Stu Act Account Mgr; Math League Team Co-Coach; NEA 1992-; NCTM 1994-; *office:* Fabius-Pompey Jr Sr HS South St Fabius NY 13063*

SHARPE, PEGGY A., Early Childhood Dir & Prof; *b:* Woodsfield, OH; *m:* Tom; *c:* Toby, Aaron, Travis; *ed:* Harding Univ (BS) Home Ec 1967; OH Univ (Ms) Child Dev 1989; *cr:* St Clairsville HS Home Ec Tchr 1967-1972; Self Employed 1972-1988; WA St Comm Coll Assoc Prof 1988-; Miss Peggys House Dir 1994-; *ai:* Club Adv; ACEI 1994-; NAEYC 1989-; Capnet 1988-; Church Of Christ 1962-; *office:* Washington State Comm Coll 710 Colegate Dr Marietta OH 45750

SHARPE, RUDOLPH,JR., English Teacher; *b:* Philadelphia, PA; *m:* Marcia Spangler; *c:* Amy Rebecca, Jeremy Warren; *ed:* Susquehanna Univ (BA) British Lit 1969; Shippensburg Univ (MED) Eng Lit 1972; IN Univ of PA (PHD) Rhetoric & Linguistics 1995; Supervisory Cert; Scndry Prins Cert; Curr Supervision K-12; Fellow PA Writing Project; *cr:* Lower Dauphin Schl Dist Tchr 1969-; *ai:* Frosh & Sr Class Adv; Dir Spring Musical; Yrbk Adv; PA Cncl Tchrs of Eng 1970-, Pres 2 Yrs; NCTE 1972-, Bd of Dirs 2 Yrs; PA Scholastic Writing Awds 1976-, Pres 3 Yrs; Natl St Tchr of the Yr; PA Tchr of Yr 1992; *office:* Lower Dauphin Sr HS 291 E Main St Hummelstown PA 17036*

SHARPLES, DOUGLAS B., Anatomy, Physiology & PE Tchr; *b:* Norwich, CT; *m:* Helene Debartolo; *c:* Brian Douglas, David Jon; *ed:* Georgetown Coll (BA) Bio & PE 1964; Eastern CT Univ (MA) Sec Ed & Psyc 1970; Southern CT Univ 6th Yr Admin 1986; Wilkes & NY Univ NSF Grant Molecular Bio 1968, Animal Behavior 1969; *cr:* St Bernard Bio, A&P & Molecular Biochem 1964-79, Asst Ath Dir 1976-78, Assoc Dean of Stdnts 1978-86, Dean of Stdnts 1986-94, PE & Anatomy Tchr 1994-; *ai:* Natl HS Cross Country Chair 1992-; New England HS Exec Bd 1990-; NASSP 1979-; Natl HS Ath Coaches Assn 1968-, Chair CC, Natl Coach of Yr 1986; New England Coaches Assn 1968-, New England Coach of Yr 1981 & 1986; CT Coach of Yr 1968; Natl Horwich Sports Hall of Fame 1990-; Natl Sci Fed Grant in Bio & Behavior; Articles for Harrier Magazine & Natl Coach.

SHARPS, HOWARD EDWARD, Fine Arts & Mathematics Tchr; *b:* Baltimore, MD; *m:* Lynn Martin; *c:* H. Nicholas, Nicole Dawson; *ed:* Morgan St Univ (BS) Art Ed 1969; Cntrl MI Univ (MS) Prsnl Mgmt 1983; Grad Stud Univ of DE, Temple Univ & Lincoln Univ; *cr:* Wilmington HS Fine Arts Tchr 1969-94; Thomas McKean HS Fine Arts & Math Tchr 1994-; *ai:* Dept Chm 1975-93; Creative & Performing Arts Magnet Schl Advy & Project Expansion Adv Cncls; Re-Learning Concept Adv & Schlsp Comms; Wilmington Parks & Rec & New Castle Cty Parks & Rec Art Dir; Stu Arts Exhibitions Co-Chair; Photo Club, Art Club, Yrbk & Class Adv; Adult Ed Instr; Track, Soccer & Vllybl Coach; Omega Psi Phi 1985-, Chptr VP; AFT; Civic Assn 1980-85, Pres; Tchr of Yr Nom 1985; *office:* Thomas Mckean HS 301 Mckennans Church Rd Wilmington DE 19808

SHARRER, RUTH WALTERS, Language Arts Teacher; *b:* Marietta, OH; *m:* Ralph E.; *c:* Debbie Ansel, John, Dean; *ed:* Marietta Coll (BA) Comprehensive Soc Stud 1963; OH Univ (MA) Eng Lit; 45 Credit Hrs Beyond Masters; *cr:* Grover Cleveland 7th-9th Grd Geog, Amer His & Eng Tchr 1963-84, 7th Grd Eng & Lang Arts Tchr 1987-; Zanesville HS 9th Grd Eng Tchr 1984-87; *ai:* Chrldng Coach 1964-84; Book Club Adv 1965-84 & 1987-; Odyssey of Mind Coach 1988-; NCTE 1965-; Delta Kappa Gamma 1976-, 1st, Pres & Corresponding Sec; Southeast OH Cncl of Tchrs of Eng 1978-, Mbrshp Chr & Pres; *office:* Grover Cleveland MS 714 Pershing Rd Zanesville OH 43701

SHATTUCK, BLAINE DE VERE, History Teacher; *b:* Toledo, OH; *m:* Ann Louisa Hess; *ed:* No. MI Univ (BS) Soc Stud 1985, (MA) His 1987; Post Masters Stud Western MD Coll, NM Highlands Univ, Univ of MD at College Park; *cr:* US Navy Ship Operations 1974-82; Samuel Ogle MS 8th Grd His Tchr 1985-86; Benjamin Tasker MS 8th Grd His Tchr 1986-87; Chas. Carroll MS 8th Grd His Tchr 1987-90; Central HS Testing Coord, His Tchr 1990-; *ai:* Schl-Based Instrl Decision Making Team; Prince George's Cty Ed Assn, MD St Tchrs Assn, NEA 1985-; Natl Endowment for Humanities Scholar 1990, Summer Seminar 1993; *home:* 7 Tuscarora Trl Taneytown MD 21787 *

SHAUGHNESSY, FRANCEEN LANZILLO, English Teacher; *b:* Troy, NY; *m:* Daniel N.; *ed:* Russell Sage Coll (BA) Eng, Sec Ed 1971; Coll of St Rose (MA) Eng 1976; Attnd SUNY at Albany; NY Univ 18 Hrs Hum; *cr:* Troy HS Eng Tchr 1972-; *ai:* Tchrs Assn Sec 1992-, Contract Negotiation Team, Exec Bd; Union Newsletter Ed; NYSUT 1972-, RA Del 1991-; AFT 1972-, Del 1994 Convention, 1996 Convention; Friends Troy Pub Lib 1991-; Rensselaer Cty Historical Soc 1982-; ED #10 1991-, Del; Troy Area Labor Cncl 1994-, Del; Phi Delta Kappa; Who's Who Amer Ed 1989-90; Who's Who Amer Coll & Univ; *office:* Troy HS 1950 Bur[e] Troy NY 12180*

SHAUGHNESSY, WILLIAM F.,JR., Hlth & Physical Education [T] Bronx, NY; *m:* Rosemary Cerreto; *c:* Jamie, Michael; *ed:* Rowan C[o] Hlth, PE 1972; 30 Grad Credits; *cr:* Millville HS Hlth, PE Tchr 1973-; *ai:* Head Coach Girls Cross Cntry; NEA, NJEA Championship Team Awds; *office:* Millville Mem HS 5th & Br Millville NJ 08332*

SHAUL, WILLIAM ROBERT, HS Math Teacher & Bsktbl Co Amsterdam, NY; *ed:* Syracuse Univ (BA) Math 1969, (MS) Ed 199 Univ of Lavane, US Sports Acad, St Univ of NY at Oneonta Coaching Effertneness Prgm; *cr:* Cherry Valley-Springfield Cn Math Tchr, Bsktbl Coach 1969-; *ai:* Var Boys Bsktbl Coach; Nat Soc Adv; Assn of Math Tchrs of NY St 1969-; NCTM 1973-; NY S Coachs Assn 1980-; Natl Assn of Bsktbl Coaches 1983-; Natl Coaches Assn; Natl Strength & Conditioning Assn; Who's Who Amer Edctrs; *office:* Cherry Vly-Springfield Schl PO Box 485 Valley NY 13320

SHAVER, HAROLD D., Physics Teacher; *b:* New York City, Antoinette; *c:* Christopher, Catherine; *ed:* SUNY at Stonybroo Psych 1968, (MA) Sci Ed 1969; Seminary (MA) Theology 1991; Po Cert in Spirtuality; *cr:* Half Hollow Hills HS Physics Tchr 1979-; Sci Rsrch; AFT, HHHTA, LIPTA, SCSTA 1971-; Regnl Indstrl T Comm of Long Island Forum for Tech Awd; *office:* Half Hollow H West 375 Wolf Hill Rd Dix Hills NY 11746

SHAVER, RICHARD CLAYTON, Third Grade Teacher; *b:* Wash DC; *ed:* Univ of MD (BS) Elem Ed 1973, (MED) Human Dev 19 Riverdale Hills Elem 1-3, 6 Grd Tchr 1974-82; William Wirt MS 7 Soc Stud Tchr 1982-85; Cooper Lane Elem Schl 6 Grd Tchr 19 Thomas S. Stone Elem Schl 3-5 Grd Tchr 1986-; *ai:* Schl Mngm Awds Comm Chm; Grd Level Chair; NEA 1974-, Assn Rep; Outstd Ldrshp Awd 1989; *office:* Thomas S. Stone Elem Schl 4500 34th St Rainier MD 20712

SHAW, CHERYL SMITH, Vocational Evaluator; *b:* Chillicothe, Keith R.; *c:* Abby M., Ally M.; *ed:* Rio Grande Coll 9BS) PE 198 of Dayton (MS) Cnslr 1987; Voc Evaluation Cert Kent St 1989; *cr:* HS PE, Hlth, Gen Sci Tchr, Vlybl, Sftbl Coach 1980-87; Pike Cty Jo Schl Voc Evaluator 1987-; *ai:* Voc Indstrl Clubs Amer; Speech 1987-; Vlybl Coach 1994-, Final Four St 1980-85; HS Sftbl 1980-85, Coach of Yr 1985; OVA, AVA, OVASNP 1987-; 4-H 1988 *office:* Pike County Joint Voc Schl 23365 St Rt 124 Piketon OH 45

SHAW, DANIEL CHARLES, Assoc Prof of Philosophy; *b:* Aur *m:* Vera Marie Shaw; *c:* Patrick; *ed:* Northern IL Univ (BA) Phil 1972, (MA) Philosophy 1975; OH St Univ (PHD) Philosophy 19 Gettysburg Coll Asst Philosophy Prof 1981-86; Lock Haven Univ Philosophy Prof 1986-; *ai:* Radio Station Fac Adv; Phi Beta Delta N of Intnl Stud Pres; Amer Philosophical 1981-; North Amer Nietzsc 1984-; Soc for Philosophic; Stud of Contemporary Arts 1991-; Schlsp; 2 NEH Summer Seminars; Articles Pub; *office:* Lock Have Raub Hall Rm 412 Lock Haven PA 17745*

SHAW, DENNIS DANIEL, Social Studies & Science Tchr; *b:* E MA; *m:* Christine Dankese; *ed:* Bunker Hill Comm Coll (AA) Lb 1986; Suffolk Univ (BS) Elem Ed 1988; Attending Salem St Col Schl Admin; *cr:* Project Explore Prgm Coord 1986-94; Everett Pub Tchr 1988-; *ai:* Everett Pub Schls Comm for Systemic Change; Stud Convener Sci Curr Revision; Stu Code Conduct Comm; NEA, MTA Pi Lambda Theta 1996-; HOG, AMA 1988-; *office:* Devens Schl Ch Everett MA 02149

SHAW, DOUGLAS ARDEN, Sixth Grade Teacher; *b:* Manheim, Susan M. Williams; *c:* Elizabeth Hill, Seth A.; *ed:* Elizabethtow (BA) Math 1965; 30 Plus Post Grad Credits for Elem Cert; *cr:* Wes Nigeria, W Africa Math, Lit Tchr 1965-67; Bauchi Gov HS, N N Upper Forms Math Tchr 1967-68; Stiegel Elem 6th Grd Tchr 196 Safety Patrol Supvr; NEA, PSEA 1968-; Manheim Ctr Ed Assn Negotiation Team, Head of Fac Concerns; Stiegel PTO 1968-, Pre Manheim Historical Soc; Natl Woodcarvers Assn; *office:* Stiegel Ele 3 S Hazel St Manheim PA 17545

SHAW, FLORENCE L., Third Grade Teacher; *b:* Upper Darby, P Chestnut Hill Coll (BS) Grad Stud, Cnslng 1976; Cath Univ of Cnslng Cert 1977; *cr:* Marywood Coll Grad Stud, Cnslng 1978; St C Seminary Grad Stud, Rel 1981-82; St Joseph Univ Grad Stud, Ed 19 Diocese of Trenton 2nd Grd Tchr 1967-69; Archdiocese of WA 2r Tchr 1978; Archdiocese of Philadelphia 1, 3, 5, 6, 7 Grd Tchr 19 1979-95; Integrated Lang Arts Coord; Cooperating Tchr for Stud NCEA 1986-; *office:* St Andrews Schl 535 Mason Ave Drexel H 19026

SHAW, FRANCES C., Social Studies Teacher; *b:* Baltimore, M Timothy L. Sr.; *c:* Timothy L. Jr., Todd, David, Daniel; *ed:* 30 Pos Credit Hrs Univ of MD at Baltimore Cty 1993; *cr:* Ellicott City Eler Tchr 1967-68; St Agnes Schl Soc St Tchr 1980-; *ai:* Soc Stud Dept Mid Sts Steering Comm Chprsn; Natl Geog Bee Schl Coord; NCEA *office:* St Agnes Schl 603 Saint Agnes Ln Baltimore MD 21229

SHAW, FRANK DAVID,JR., English Teacher; *b:* Mc Keesport, Renee Salloum; *c:* Christina, Jamie; *ed:* Univ of TX at El Paso (1970; Univ of CA (MA) Eng 1975; *cr:* Mc Keesport Area Schl Dist Soc Stud Tchr 26 Yrs; *ai:* Asst Var Ftbl Coach; Girls Sftbl Team PSEA, NEA 1971-; Mc Keesport Area Ed Assn 1971-, Bldg Rep; Mc Keesport Area Schl Dist 1960 Eden Park Blvd Mc Keesport PA

SHAW, GORDON ROBERT, Elementary Guidance Counsel McKeesport, PA; *m:* Anita Lynn Porter; *c:* Matthew, Rebecca, Jerem Westminster Coll (BA) His 1974, (MA) Cnslr Ed 1978; 30 Semest Beyond Masters; *cr:* Leetonia Village Schls 9th-12th Grd Scndry So Tchr 1974-76; Warren City Schls 7th-12th Grd Scndry Soc Stud 1977-91, Elem Guidance Cnslr 1992-; *ai:* Lakevew HS Var Ftb Coach; NEA, OEA, WEA 1974-; Cub Scouts 1989-, Treas; *office:* W City Schls 261 Monroe St Warren OH 44482*

SHAW, JAY M., 7th Grade Math Teacher; *b:* Camden, NJ; *m:* Judi *c:* Kaitlyn, Kyle; *ed:* St Francis Coll at Lorretto (BS) Elem Ed, Math Attending Rowan Coll Masters Degree Cnslng; *cr:* Bells Elem Sc Grd Tchr 1980-82, 5th Grd Tchr 1983-87, 6th Grd Tchr 1988-89; Ch Ridge MS 7th Grd Math Tchr 1989-; *ai:* Var Sftbl Washington T 1986-, MS Girls Bsktbl 1991- Coach; WTEA 1980-; NCTM, A 1993-; St Peter & Paul Parish 1987-; HS Coach of YR 1990.*

SHAW, JOAN WALLACE, Math & Social Studies Teacher; *b:* F ME; *m:* John; *c:* Suzanne Undergust, Melinda Campbell, Sharon Steven Greeley, Kevin Greeley; *ed:* Univ of ME (BS) Soc Stud 1981, Scndry Ed 1984; *cr:* Washburn HS Tchr 1981-; *ai:* NHS Adv; *hom* Box 207 Fort Fairfield ME 04742

SHAW, JOSEPH T., High School English Teacher; *b:* Auburn, N Susan Reuter; *c:* Joseph, Elizabeth; *ed:* NY St U Coll at Oswego (BA Ed, Eng 1972, (MS) K-12 Rdng Ed 1985; *cr:* Mexico Acad & Cs H Tchr, Coach 1972-; Dist Eng Dept Chr; *ai:* Stu Newspaper Co-Ad Bsbl Coach; Mexico Fac Assoc 1972-, Treas; Elected Grad Marshal Golden Apple Achvmt Awd; *office:* Mexico Acad & Cntrl Schl M Mexico NY 13114

LEWIS, Acctng & Bus Admin Prof; *ed:* NH Coll (BS) Acctng Bentley Coll (MS) Fin 1983; Addl Hours Univ of NH; *cr:* Univ of unct Prof 1981-87; Bay St Coll Prof 1989-; Dean Coll Adjunct Prof 3; Nichols Coll Adjunct Prof 1992-93; Suffolk Univ Adjunct Prof : Income Tax Prgm, Acctng Adv; Curr Comm Mem; Inst of Mngmt 1990-, CMA; Amer Acctng Assn 1990-, Comm Chair; NBEA 1990-; ngmt Accountants; *office:* Bay St Coll 122 Commonwealth Ave MA 02116

MARILYN L., 4th Grade Teacher; *b:* Lima, OH; *m:* Craig M.; *c:* Amy, Erin, Jason; *ed:* OH St Univ (BS) Elem Ed 1975; Wright St MS) Gifted Ed 1989; Talents Unlimited; Outcome Based Ed; Math e Level I, II; Make it Take it Econ 516; AIMS Math Sci; *cr:* field-Goshen Schl 5-6 Grd Lang Art, Art Tchr 1976-77, 5-6 Grd rts, Home Arts Tchr 1977-79; Wapakoneto City Schls Gifted Prgm), 4th Grd Classroom Tchr 1990-; *ai:* NEA, OH Ed Assn, oneta Ed Assn 1985-; 4-H Comm Adv 11 Yrs; 4-H Cty Comm, Sec; Club Girls Ath; Apollo Career Infusion Awd; OH Young Farmers, Farm Wives Outstdng Svc; OH Young Farm Wives Past Pres; Farm St Young Farm Couples Comm; *office:* Northridge Elem 3 N Pine oneta OH 45895

MICHAELLE HOLMAN, English Teacher; *b:* Elmira, NY; *m:* P. Jr.; *c:* Mitchell; *ed:* Corning Comm Coll (AA) Lbrl Arts 1984; th Coll (BA) Eng with Writing Concentration 1986, (MSEd) Scndry 91; *cr:* Waverly Jr HS 8-9 Grd Eng Tchr 1987-88; Waverly Sr HS Eng Tchr 1988-; *ai:* Asst Coach Chrldng 1988-93; Soph Class Adv NHS Adv 1992-94; NEA 1987-; Nazareth Alum Schlsp Comm 1989; Waverly Jr-Sr HS 1 Frederick St Waverly NY 14892

NEVA SCAROMIZZINO, Kindergarten Teacher; *b:* Johnstown, Saint Francis (BS) Elem Ed 1976; Master Equiv; *cr:* Visitation 964-66; Head Start Tchr 1966-76; Portage Area Schl Tchr 1976-; *ai:* PSEA 1976-; *office:* Portage Area Schl 84 Mountain Ave Portage PA

, PAMELA ANN, Biology Teacher; *b:* Fairfield, CA; *ed:* Frostburg (BS) Bio 1974; 30 Post Grad Credit Hrs Hood Coll, Western MD : Governor Thomas Johnson HS Tchr 1974-; *ai:* NHS Adv 1982-95; ck Cty Tchrs Assn, MD St Tchrs Assn, NEA 1974-; NABT 1976-; ssn Bio Tchr 1974-, Bd Mem 1995; Inst Biosafety Comm 1987-; Governor Thomas Johnson HS 1501 N Market St Frederick MD

, PAULINE HOLLAND, Chemistry Teacher; *b:* Portsmouth, OH; k H.; *c:* Christopher, Derek; *ed:* Oh Univ (BS) Chem 1975; OH St MS) Ed & Sci 1992; *cr:* Logan HS Chem Tchr 1975-81; Jackson HS Tchr 1982-83; Worthington HS Chem Tchr 1983-; *ai:* OEA & NEA OH Univ Chem Tchr of Yr 1995; ACS Chem Olympiad Coord: bus Secton; *office:* Thomas Worthington HS 300 W -Granville Rd Worthington OH 43085

, R. DOUGLAS, Social Studies Teacher; *b:* Sayville, NY; *ed:* on Coll (BA) Govt, Ec 1989; Addl Stud Coll of St Rose, 1R1 ative Ed, EncouragingStu Responsibility; *cr:* George Watsons Coll on Fellow 1989-91; LaSalle Sr Tchr, Prefect 1991-; *ai:* Sr Prefect; d Act Coord; Ski Club; European Travel Adv; *office:* La Salle Ctr ontauk Hwy Oakdale NY 11769*

, ROSALIE P., Chem Tchr & Sci Dept Chprsn; *b:* Philadelphia, PA; id L.; *c:* David J., Virginia Hearn, Angela Mc Keown, Charles A.; estnut Hill Coll (AB) Chem 1963; OH St Univ (MSC) Organic Chem Widener Univ Tchr Cert 1980; Grad Courses in Ed, Sci Ed, nmental Sci La Salle Univ 1995; *cr:* Little Flower HS Sci Tchr 1979; field HS Chem Tchr 1981; Cardinal O'Hara HS Chem Tchr 1981-, hair 1993-; Widener Univ Adj Instr 1981-; *ai:* Moderator Sci Fair; DE Cty, DE Valley Sci Fairs; ACS 1961-; NCEA 1981-; *office:* al O'Hara HS 1701 S Sproul Rd Springfield PA 19064

, SCOTT P., 11th Grade Math Teacher; *b:* Elmhurst, IL; *m:* Dottie; n L.; *ed:* St Univ Coll at Buffalo (MS) Ed 1975; 6 Credit Hrs Above s; *cr:* Sweet Home Jr HS 7th & 8th Grd Math Tchr 1973-74; towaga Cntrl Schl 8th-11th Grd Math Tchr 1974-; *ai:* Cheektowaga Tchrs Assn 1974-, Negotiator; NYSUT & AFT 1974-; ommissioned Ofcrs Assn 1985-; US Army Reserves 1971-, and SGM; Lord of Life Luth Church 1988-, Fund Raising Chm; Commendation Medal; Army Achvmnt Medal; Army Reserve nents Achvmnt Medal; Natl Defense Svc Medal; NCO Prof Dev n; Army Svc Ribbon; Armed Forces Reserve Medal; Expert ymans Badge; Drill Sargents Badge; Phys Fitness Badge; *office:* towaga Central H S 3600 Union Rd Cheektowaga NY 14227

, WILLIAM HARRY, Professor of Biology; *b:* Brooklyn, NY; *m:* o Quigley; *c:* Kathi, Mary Beth, Edward, Maureen, Amelia; *ed:* St enture Univ (BS) Bio 1966; St John's Univ (MS) Bio, Physiology SUNY at Binghamton (PHD) Bio, Ecology 1978; *cr:* NY Med Coll ologist 1968-69; Sullivan Cty Comm Coll Bio Prof 1969-; Inst of ystem Stud Visiting Scientist 1992-95; *ai:* Former Adv Sci Alliance 4; Amer Soc of Limnology & Oceonog 1972-; Ecological Soc of 1991-; North Amer Lake Mngmt Soc 1980-; Hudson River Env Soc Empire St Assn of Two Yr Col Biologists 1980-, Pres 1993-, etter Ed 1995-; Cary Summer Rsrch Flwshp Inst Ecosystem Stud NSF ROA 1993; EPA Acid Rain Stud 1994-; *office:* Sullivan County Coll PO Box 4002 Loch Sheldrake NY 12759

AKER, CAROLYN HECKERT, Social Studies Teacher; *b:* yville, IL; *m:* Edward; *c:* Winifred; *ed:* IL St Univ (BA) Soc Sci 1962; S) Sociology 1964; *cr:* Taylorsville HS Tchr 1962-63; De Kalb HS 964-65; Federal Bureau Prisons Case Worker, Ed Rsrch 1965-66; Whitman HS Tchr 1966-; *ai:* Spon Chinese Club; NEA 1966-; Asia 987-; Japan-Amer Soc 1984-; Korea Soc 1988-; Garrett Park Women's 969-; Garrett Park Garden Club 1969-, VP; Fulbright Schlsp; Flwshp MI East, Asia Ctr; Natl Endowment Hum Japanese Philosophy, Japan Cncl Basic Ed Flwshp; Author East & Asia His HS; *office:* Walt nan HS 7100 Whittier Blvd Bethesda MD 20817*

VEN, DEBORAH A., Dir of Lower School Admissions; *ed:* Hood BA) Early Chldhd Ed, Psych 1975; Johns Hopkins Univ (MS) Ed *cr:* Samuel Ready Schl Tchr 1975-77; Gilman Schl Tchr 1977-92; rt Schl Video Project Tchr, Writer 1987-; Gilman Schl Dir of Lower Admissions 1992-; *ai:* Stu Prgms Comm Chair; Tchr Mentor; Admin ance Comm; Samuel Ready Schlsps Bd 1994-; Dunn Flwshp; Reese Grant; *office:* Gilman Schl 5407 Roland Ave Baltimore MD 21210

WLEY, HAROLD LEE, 7th Grade Social Studies Tchr; *b:* Export, : Louise Perfetta; *ed:* CA Univ (BA) Soc Stud 1971, (MS) Soc Stud 15 Hrs Admin Prgm; *cr:* US Army Vietnam Veteran 1965-67; nghouse Rsrch 1967-71; Franklin Regnl Schl Dist Soc Stud Tchr ; *ai:* Site Based Cncl; Site Based Decision Group; Var Ftbl Coach 17 Var Bsktbl Coach 18 Yrs; NEA 1975-; Amer Legion 1985-; smen's Club 1975-; St Sylvester Church 1990-; *office:* Franklin nal Jr HS 4660 Old William Penn Hwy Murrysville PA 15668*

VVER, ROBERT LANCE, Mathematics Teacher; *b:* Lorain, OH; *m:* a Marie Snyder; *c:* Robert II, Reuben; *ed:* Cedarville Coll (BA) Math *cr:* Emmanuel Bapt Chrstn Schl Math & Sci Tchr 1982-; *ai:* Sr Class Instructional & Curr Comm; Emmanuel Bapt Church 1982-, Awana Club Dir; *office:* Emmanuel Bapt Christian Schl 4207 Laskey Toledo OH 43623*

SHAY, DANIEL BRANDT, Art Instructor; *b:* Charlotte, NC; *m:* Loretta Madeline Russo; *c:* Ginevra R., Dante B.; *ed:* East Carolina Univ (BFA) Studio Art, Painting 1975; Univ of MD (MFA) Studio Art, Painting 1981; Udornthani Tchrs Coll Cert Fine Arts 1972; *cr:* Prince George's Comm Coll Art Instr 1981-94; Smithsonian RAP Drawing Instr 1984-94; Natl Gallery of Art Svcs Mgr 1984-; MD Coll of Art & Design Art Instr 1989-; *ai:* Art Portfolio Review Comm; Judge for Stu Art Exhibit; WA Project for the Arts 1981-; MD Arts Pl 1993-; Intnl Artist's Support Group 1995-; Lectures Given St Pushkin Museum of Fine Arts in Moscow, Prince George's Art Guilt, Intnl Artist's Support Group in WA DC; *office:* Maryland Coll Of Art & Design 10500 Georgia Ave Silver Spring MD 20902*

SHAY, SUSAN MARIE, Third Grade Teacher & Coach; *b:* Lebanonn, PA; *ed:* St Bonaventure Univ (BS) Elem Ed 1992; Working on MS Spec Ed Millersville Univ; *cr:* Lebanon Schl Dist Third Grd Tchr, Lang Areas Multi-Age Grouping Setting 1992-; *ai:* Asst HS Girls Bsktbl Coach 1992-; Strategic Plan Assessment, Report Card, Lang Arts Comms; Children's Lit Cncl of Pa, Keystate Rdng Assn, PSEA, NEA 1992-; Full Bsktbl Schlsp, All Time leading Scorer & Rebounder at St Bonaventure Univ; Four Time All Conf Selection Atlantic 10 Conf; Inducted into Lebanon Cty & Palmyra Hall of Fames.

SHAYLOR, KAREN ANN, Art Dept Chair & Teacher; *b:* East Liverpool, OH; *ed:* Bowling Green St Univ (BSEd) Art, Prints 1974; Washington Univ (MFA) Prints 1979; Attnd Bowling Green Univ, Miami Univ Craftsummer, Univ of Cincinnati; Getty Ctr DBAE Tchr Wkshp; *cr:* Fostoria Pub Schls Tchr 1974-75; South Euclid-Lyndhurst Schls Tchr 1975-77; Univ of WI at Eau Claire Adj Instr 1979-80; Washington Univ Instr 1980; OH univ at Chillicothe Instr 1990-93; Sandusky St Mary Cntrl Cath Schl Instr, Tchr, Art Dept Chair 1985-; *ai:* Jr Class Adv; Curr Comm; Intervention Team; Delta Kappa Gamma 1993-; NAEA, OAEA 1990-; Sandusky Cultural Ctr 1995-, Bd Mem; OH Arts Cncl Arts in Ed Tchr Flwshp; Drawing Exhibit; Artists Who Make Books Exhibit; *office:* St Mary's Cntrl Cath HS 410 W Jefferson St Sandusky OH 44870

SHEA, DONNA PAPINI, Sixth Grade Teacher; *b:* New Britain, CT; *m:* William J.; *c:* Tyler, Matthew; *ed:* Cntrl CT St Univ (BS) Elem Ed 1978, (MS) Early Chldhd Ed 1984; *cr:* Hatton Elem Schl Sixth Grd Tchr 1980; Flanders Elem Schl First Grd Tchr 1980-82; North Ctr Elem Schl Transitional Tchr 1982-84, Fifth Grd Tchr 1984-85, Sixth Grd Tchr 1985-94; DePaolo MS Sixth Grd Tchr 1994-; *ai:* Schl, Bus Partnership Schl Coord; Sci Comm; Peer Advocate Asst; Quality Plus COmm, Ed Chprsn; PTO Liason; Natl Jr Honor Soc Asst Adv; Southington Ed Assn, CT Ed Assn, NEA 1980-; Kappa Delta Pi 1979-; First Annual Schl, Bus Partnership Awd; 1991 Nom Governors' Laurel Awd; 1992 Presenter Inservice Wkshps; Incentive Pay Recipient 1989; Mini Grant 1990; Southington Assn Retarded Citizens Integration Awd 1991; Tchr of Yr 1991; Interviewed, Photographed Fortune Magazine 1991; Team Ldr MS 1994-; *office:* DePaolo MS 385 Pleasant St Southington CT 06489*

SHEA, JEFF A., Math Teacher; *b:* Batavia, NY; *m:* Lorie R.; *c:* Jacob Adam; *ed:* Potsdam Coll (BS) Math & Ed 1990, (MS) Math & Ed 1992; *cr:* Malone Cntrl Schls Math Tchr 1993-; *ai:* Epsilon Hnr Soc, Stu Cncl, Malone Vllybl Club, Massena Vllybl Club & Games Club Adv; Vllybl Coach; Schl Improvement Comm; Tchr of Month Awd; *office:* Franklin Acad State St Malone NY 12953*

SHEA, JOANNE ST. MARTIN, First Grade Teacher; *b:* Norwick, CT; *m:* Dennis M.; *c:* Jill, Timothy, Erin; *ed:* Eastern CT St Univ (BS) Early Chldhd Ed 1973-, (MS) Early Chldhd Ed 1981; *cr:* Dr Helen Baldwin Schl 2nd Grd Tchr 1973-77, Chptr I Tchr 1978-80, 1st Grd Tchr 1980-90; Canterbury Elem Schl 1st Grd Tchr 1990-; *ai:* Canterbury Ed Assn 1973-77, 1980-; CT Ed Assn 1973-77, 1980-; NEA 1973-77, 1980-; *office:* Canterbury Elem Schl 67 Kitt Rd Canterbury CT 06331

SHEA, JOHN JAMES, Eighth Grade Lang Arts Tchr; *b:* Boston, MA; *m:* Ann; *ed:* St John's Univ (BA) Ed 1964; George Washington Univ (MA) Scndry Ed 1975; 15 Credits; *cr:* Holy Cross Grammar Schl Tchr 1957-63; Don Bosco Hall Soc Worker & Guidance Cnslr 1963-65; Leonard Hall Jr Naval Acad Eng Tchr & Guidance Cnslr 1965-70; Leonardtown MS Lang Arts Tchr & Dept Chm 1970-; *ai:* St Mary's Cty Ed Assn, MD St Tchrs Assn, NEA 1970-; Knights of Columbus 1970-, Treas 4 Yr; Cmptr Text Pub 1991; *office:* Leonardtown MS RR 1 Box 49-1 Leonardtown MD 20650

SHEA, MARIA ANNA, Biology Teacher; *b:* Syracuse, NY; *m:* Timothy John; *ed:* St Lawrence Univ (BS) Bio 1986; SUNY at Albany (MS) Curr Dev & Instrl Tech 1995; *cr:* Guilderland HS Bio Tchr 1989-; *ai:* Stu Govt Adv; Stu Asst Team Mem; Acting Dir for Schl Musicals; *office:* Guilderland Central HS School Rd Guilderland Center NY 12085*

SHEA, MARY A., Ancient Language Teacher; *b:* Malden, MA; *ed:* Boston Coll (BS) Ed, Latin 1962; Tufts Univ (MA) Classics 1968; 45 Addl Hrs Classics, His, Ed; *cr:* East Boston HS Tchr 1962-63; Medford HS Tchr 1963-70; Boston latin Schl Tchr 1970-; *ai:* NHS Comm; Open House Guides Coord; AFT 1970-; Classical Assn of MA 1978-, Sec-Treas 1986-90; Classical Assn of New England 1965-; Lead, Mentor Tchr Boston Pub Schls; Nat Endowment Hum Flwshp 1988; NEH Inst 1990-91; *office:* Boston Latin Schl 78 Avenue Louis Pasteur Boston MA 02115*

SHEA, MICHAEL PATRICK,III, English Dept Head & Instr; *b:* Taunton, MA; *c:* Molly Luisa, Michael P.G.; *ed:* St Michaels Coll (AB) Eng-Cum Laude 1971; Bridgewater St Coll (MA) Eng 1984; 12 Credit Hrs Towards Masters in Celtic Lang & Lit at Harvard Univ; *cr:* Sacred Heart HS Dir of Theater & Eng Tchr 1980-84; Thayer Acad Eng Instr 1984-; *ai:* Contra Adv; Declamation & Voices from the Mid; MS Bsbl Coach; Admissions Comm Adjutant; Co-Designer of Interdisciplinary Unit; NCTE 1986-, Awd for Excel 1995; Patriot Ledger Golden Apple Awd 1992; Tchr Seminar at Oxford Grant 1996; *office:* Thayer Academy MS 745 Washington St Braintree MA 02184

SHEA, REMEE HAUSMANN, English Professor; *b:* St Louis, MO; *m:* Michael; *c:* Christopher, Meredith; *ed:* WA Univ (BA) Eng 1969; Northwestern Univ (MA) Eng 1970; Univ of PA (PHD) Eng Ed 1987; Yeats Intnl Schl Sligo Ireland; *cr:* Federal City Coll Eng Asst Prof 1970-73; Madeira Schl Eng Tchr 1973-75; Univ of DC Prof Eng, Composition, Rhetoric Dir 1975-; Fordham Univ Adj Prof 1989-; Manhattan Coll Adj Prof 1989-; Univ of Cntrl FL Adj Prof 1989-; LaSalle Univ Adj Prof 1989-; Camosun Coll Adj Prof 1989-; *ai:* Contributing Ed; Wkshp Ldr for AP Eng Prgm; Dev, Evaluator GED Exam, LSAT, Grad Mngmt Exam; Consultant on Stans Dev & Curr Design to I C Pub Schls; NCTE 1975-, Comm on World, Comparative Lit, Network of Edctrs on Amers Bd of Dir 1994, DC Writing Project Advy Bd 1995, Coll Bd Guid, Admission Assembly 1993, Coll Bd Recognition Outstdng Svc 1996; NEA; 2 Books, Reading with the Writer's Eye, A Practical Rhetoric for College Writers; Grants from Natl Endowment for Hum, DC Comm Hum Cncl Univ of PA; Articles Pub; *office:* Univ Of The Dist Of Columbia 4200 Connecticut Ave NW Washington DC 20008*

SHEA, SANDRA BARNES, Soc Stud Tchr & Dept Chair; *b:* Austin, TX; *m:* Al; *c:* Kelly Shea Wade; *ed:* Univ of TX (MA) His 1960; Attnd PA St, Angelo St, Univ of HI & TX Tech; *cr:* Austin Public Schl Tchr 1961-62; Overseas Schl Spain Tchr 1962-65; Cleghorne Schl Tchr 1965; Pennsbury Schls Tchr 1967-; *ai:* Mock Trial Team, World Affairs & Environmental Clubs Spon; PHS Site Based Team 1993-95; NEA, PSEA & PEA 1967-; Delta Kappa Gamma Intnl 86-, 2nd VP 1990-92, Pres 1992-94; PA Tchr of Yr 2X Nom; Rider Coll Deans Citation 1990; Outstanding Scndry Educator; *office:* Pennsbury HS 705 Hood Blvd Fairless Hills PA 19030

SHEA, SHIRLEY PALMER, Bio Tchr & Sci Dept Chair; *b:* Upper Darby, PA; *m:* Raymond J.; *c:* Raymond J., Thomas A., Dianne L. Zaayenga; *ed:* West Chester Univ (BS) Ed 1972, (MA) Bio 1977; Penn St Univ (Instrl II) Sci Supervision 1992; 60 Credits Beyond Masters Degree; *cr:* Downingtown Sr High Sci Tchr 1972-, Sci Dept Chair 1994-; *ai:* Strategic Planning Comms; NEA, PSEA & DAEA 1972-; ASCD 1992-; Chester Cty Sci Tchr Assn 1995-; Named to Whos Who in Amer Ed 1994; *office:* Downingtown Sr HS 445 Manor Ave Downingtown PA 19335*

SHEA, SUSAN MC MORROW, Fifth Grade Teacher; *b:* St Albans, NY; *m:* Brian J.; *c:* Kathleen, Lindsay, Michael; *ed:* St Univ of NY at Plattsburgh (BS) Elem Ed 1974; St Univ of NY at Albany (MS) Curr, Instruction 1979; *cr:* Turnpike Elem Schl K, 1, 2, 4, 5 Grds Elem Tchr 1976-; *ai:* Stu Cncl Adv; Ski Club; Math Comm; NY St United Tchrs, AFT, Lansingburgh Tchrs Assn 1976-; WLAK TV Grant; RIF Grant Star Lab.

SHEAFFER, JOEL C., English Teacher; *b:* Harrisburg, PA; *ed:* Indiana Univ of PA (BS) Scndry Eng Ed 1991; Penn St Univ 6 Cr Hrs; Millersville Univ 3 Cr Hrs; *cr:* Alling & Cory Paper Dist Paper Cutter 1983-89; Milton Hershey Schl Scndry Eng Tchr 1992-; *ai:* Yrbk Adv; Var Bsbl Coach; NCTE 1991-; ASCD 1992-; PSEA, MHEA 1993-, Soc Comm; *office:* Milton Hershey Schl 300 Hotel Rd Hershey PA 17033

SHEAFFER, JOHN CLARENCE, Middle School Science Teacher; *b:* Ephrata, PA; *m:* Shelly Ann Lafferty; *c:* Jared Brent, Caleb Patrick; *ed:* Millersville Univ (BSEd) Sci & Bio 1982; Millersville Univ Penn St (MS) Sci & Bio 1990; *cr:* Upper Dauphin Area HS 10th Grd Bio 1982-83; Millersville Univ MD Sci 1983-; *ai:* Head Soccer Coach; NEA, PSEA, MAE 1985-, Pres 2 Yrs; NSTA 1982-; BSA 1973-; *home:* 140 Stence Ln Millersburg PA 17061*

SHEAFFER, KIMBERLY PHILLIPS, Advanced Mathematics Teacher; *b:* Trenton, NJ; *m:* Danial R.; *c:* Timothy; *ed:* Moravian Coll (BA) Elem Ed & Art 1985; Trenton St Coll (MA) Elem Ed 1992; *cr:* Pennsbury Schl Dist TELLS Instr 1985-87, Advanced Math Tchr 1987-; *ai:* NEA 1987-; NCTM 1995-; Nom Presidential Awds for Excl in Sci & Math Tchng 1990; *office:* Edgewood Elem Schl Edgewood & Oxford Vly Rds Yardley PA 19067

SHEAFFER, LLOYD E., English Teacher; *b:* Carlisle, PA; *m:* Caroline J. Smith; *c:* Laura K. Wills, Scott A.; *ed:* Dickinson Coll (AB) Psych 1970; Attnd Penn St Univ, Western Mary Coll; *cr:* Cumberland Vly Schl Dist Eng, Hum Tchr 1970-; *ai:* Shakespeare Troupe Adv, Dir; NEA, PSEA, CVEA 1970-; NCTE 1990-; Carlisle Arts Magnet Schl 1992-, Dean; Article Pub Eng Journal; *office:* Cumberland Valley HS 6746 Carlisle Pike Mechanicsburg PA 17055

SHEAHAN, PATRICIA ANN PENNETT, Principal; *b:* Oswego, NY; *m:* James; *c:* Greg, Kelly Dadich, Jonathan; *ed:* SUNY at Potsdam (BA) Elem Ed 1967; Univ of Pittsburgh (MA) Admin 1992; Working Toward EDD Duquesne Univ on Dissertation; Univ of Pittsburgh Spec Ed-Deaf, Comm; Point Park Coll Comm; *cr:* Mother of Sorrows Schl Tchr 1980-89; Seton Hill Coll Adj Prof 1985-89; Mother of Sorrows Schl Admin Educl Ldr 1989-; *ai:* Curr Writing for Diocese of Greensburg; Mid Sts Comm; Parish Cncl; Phi Delta Kappa, NCEA 1995-; ASCD 1992-; Fine Arts Chprsn 1993-; Young Astronauts 1990-; ALPHA Music Group 1980-; NCEA Prin of the Yr 1996 Nom; Oxfords Who's Who of Extraordinary Profs 1992-93; 2000 Notable Amer Women 1994; Thanks to Tchrs Finalist 1991; *office:* Mother Of Sorrows Schl 3264 Evergreen Dr Murrysville PA 15668*

SHEALER, BRENDA NORMAN, Eng, Jrnlsm Tchr & Dept Chprsn; *b:* Beaver Springs, PA; *m:* Dennis G.; *c:* Brent W., Kimberly D.; *ed:* Bloomsburg Univ (BS) Scndry Ed, Eng, Comm 1976; Various Grad & Non-Degree Credits; *cr:* Williamsport Schl Dist Jr HS Eng Tchr 1976-77; Philipsburg-Osceola HS Eng & Jrnlsm Tchr 1980-, Eng Dept Chprsn 1992-; *ai:* P-O Yth in Ed Assn, Schl Newspaper Adv; Assessment Comm Co-Chprsn; Mentor Tchr; NEA, PSEA 1980-; P-OEA; Rowland Theater, Vol; *office:* Philipsburg-Osceola HS Philips St Philipsburg PA 16866

SHEALER, MICHAEL L., Health Teacher; *b:* Gettysburg, PA; *m:* Ruth-Lin Sarver; *c:* Hayley; *ed:* Slippery Rock Univ (BS) Hlth Sci 1980; Frostburg St Univ 24 Post Grad Hrs; *cr:* Berlin-Brothersvalley HS Hlth, Driver Ed & Television Production Tchr 1983-; *ai:* Somerset Area HS Asst Track Coach; Shade Cntrl City HS Asst Ftbl Coach; PSEA 1983-; NEA 1983-; St Vincent Univ Great Tchr Awd; *office:* Berlin Brothers Valley Schl 1025 Main St Berlin PA 15530

SHEAR, JANE WISE, French Teacher; *b:* Bronx, NY; *m:* Dennis Leipold; *c:* John, Jeff; *ed:* St Univ of NY at Binghamton (BA) Fr 1964; St Univ of NY at Cortland (MS) Ed 1972; Attnd L'Universite de Grenoble France 22 Undergrad Credits 1963 1963; LhUniversite de Neuchatel Switzerland 6 Grad Credits 1972; *cr:* Chenango Forks Cntrl Schl Fr Tchr & Dept Chair 1965-74; Experiment in Intnl Living Site Dir & Group Ldr 1975-81; Susquehanna Schl & Hillel Acad Fr Tchr 1975-81; Windsor HS Fr Tchr 1981-; Binghamton Univ Ed Det Adjunct Ldr 1989-92 & 1994; Cont at Binghamton Univ 1995-; *ai:* Peer Tutoring Club & Peer Counseling Org Adv; Tchrs Assn Schlsp Comm; Crisis Response Team; Foreign Lang Club Co-Adv; AATF 1974-; NYSAFLT 1974-, James E Allen Awd Chair; Windsor Tchrs Assn & NYSUT 1981-; Binghamton Sister Cities 1992-, Sec, Treas, Choral Exch Chprsn; Binghamton Univ Chorus 1972-; Confluences 1989-; NYSAFLT Tchrs Project Grant; Item Writer for NY St Fr Regent Exams 1972-92; James E Allen Excl Foreign Lang Tchr Awd; *office:* Windsor HS 1191 Rt 79 Windsor NY 13865*

SHEAR, JIM, Physics Teacher; *b:* Brooklyn, NY; *c:* John, Jeff; *ed:* Binghamton Univ (BA) Bio 1962; Miami Univ (MAT) Botany 1968; 30 Addl Hrs, Dance, Theatre; Cert de Botanique Univ at Grenoble; *cr:* Maine-Endwell HS Tchr 1962-63; Chenango Forks HS Tchr, Dir 1963-; *ai:* Desinger Upstagers; Brain Brawl; NYSUT; AFT; NYSSTA; STANYS; Sro Productions 1984-, Pres; Applause Unlimited 1988-, Owner; NDEA Flwshp; *office:* Chenango Forks HS 1 Gordon Dr Binghamton NY 13901

SHEARD, LOU ANN SOMES, Guidance Counselor; *b:* Philadelphia, PA; *c:* Garry Jr., Thad, Paige; *ed:* East Stroudsburg Univ (BS) Elem Ed 1964; Marywood coll (MA) Cnslng 1979; 64 Addl Hrs; *cr:* Eldred Cntrl Schl Classroom Tchr 1964-66; Jeffersonville Cntrl Schl Classroom Tchr 1966-69; Delaware Vly Job Corps Cnslr 1979-81; Eldred Cntrl Schl Guid Cnslr 1981-83; Fallsburg Cntrl Schl Guid Cnslr 1983-; *ai:* Crisis Intervention Team; Sullivan Cty Guid Assn 1981-, Pres 1994-, VP 1991-94; Beach Lake Singles Group 1991-, Coord, Ldr; Habitat for Humanity 1990-91, Bd Mem; *office:* Fallsburg Cntrl Schl PO Box Ah Fallsburg NY 12733*

SHEARER, JOHN W., Mathematics Teacher & Ath Dir; *b:* Harrisburg, PA; *m:* Cathy B.; *c:* Angela, Anthony; *ed:* Shipponsburg St Coll (BSEd) Math 1965, (MED) Math 1968; Natl Sci Fnd Grant Knox Coll & MI St; *cr:* West York HS Tchr 1965-; *ai:* Track Coach 1966-81; Asst Ath Dir 1968-88; Ath Dir 1988-; NEA, PSEA, WYAEA 31 Yrs; PA St Truck Ofcl 27 Yrs; PA St Ath Dir Assn 9 Yrs; *office:* West York Area Sr H S 1800 Bannister St York PA 17404

SHEARER, LESLIE WIAN, French & Spanish Teacher; *b:* Carlisle, PA; *m:* Thomas P.; *c:* Jessica, Rachel; *ed:* West Chester Univ (BS) Fr, Span Educat 1974; West Chester & Wilkes & East Stroudsburg (MS) Ed 1991; 30 Addl Hrs; *cr:* Marple Newtown Fr, Span Tchr 1 1/2 Yrs; Cumberland Valley Fr, Span Tchr 8 Yrs; Lower Dauphin Fr, Span Tchr 1 Yr; Derry Twp

Fr, Span Tchr 11 Yrs; *ai:* Ski Club Adv HS; 8th Grd Awds Assembly Chair; 8th Grd Trip Comm; Assembly Comm; Intl Ed Week Chair; Prejudice & Dscrmntn Wkshp Chair; AATF 1991-; NEA, PSEA, HEA 1974-; ACTFL, PSMLA 1990-; Sunday Schl Tchr 1983-; Dev Inservice Prgm 19 Schl Dist; Mentor Tchr; Presenter Eastern Region Mid Schl Conf; Career Incentive Prgm; Peer Partnership Prgm; Cooperating Tchr for Stu Tchrs; Create, Dev New Mid Schl Foreign Lang Prgm; Intnl Ed Weekly Act Developer; *office:* Derry Twp Schl Dist Homestead Rd Hershey PA 17033*

SHEARER, MARY RUTH, Sci Dept Chprsn & Chem Tchr; *b:* Dayton, OH; *m:* Mark; *c:* Josh; *ed:* Wright St Univ (BS) Med Tech 1977; Univ of Dayton (MCLT) Clinical Lab 1982; *cr:* MVH Schl of Med Tech Clinical Chem Tchr 1980-83; St Albert the Great Cmptr Lab Coord 1988-90; Alter HS Chem Tchr, Sci Dept Chair 1990-; *ai:* Co-Moderator Stu Cncl; Acad, Vocal Musical Coach; SECO 1991-; NSTA 1992-; OCEA 1988-; *office:* Alter HS 940 E David Rd Kettering OH 45429

SHEARER, NANCY YOCUM, Sixth Grade Teacher; *b:* Danville, PA; *m:* Scidell C.; *c:* Michael S., Mark A.; *ed:* Bloomsburg Univ (BS) Elem Ed 1978; Masters Equivalent 5 Addl Credit Hrs; *cr:* Milton Area Elem Schl 3rd-4th Grd Tchr 1978-81, 2nd, 5th-6th Grd Tchr 1987-; *ai:* NEA, PSEA, MAEA 1978-; St Andrews United Meth Church 1957-, Admin Cncl, SS Tchr, Pianist; *office:* Milton Area Elem Schl Limestone Rd Milton PA 17847

SHEARER, STEVEN EDWARD, Math Teacher; *b:* Alexandria, VA; *m:* Cindy Lee Weidler; *c:* Christiana, Chelsea, Alexis, Madison; *ed:* Wilkes Coll (BS) Math, Cmptr Sci 1987; Lycoming Coll Tchr Cert Tchng 1988; *cr:* East Lycoming Schl Dist Math Tchr & Soccer Coach 1 Yr; Montoursville Area Schl Dist Math Tchr & Ftbl, Bsktbl & Track Coach 7 Yrs; *ai:* Ftbl, Girls Bsktbl, Track Asst Coach; CWA 1993-; *office:* Montoursville Area Sr HS 100 N Arch St Montoursville PA 17754

SHEARER-BICANOVSKY, DEBORAH JEAN, Art Teacher; *b:* Pittsburgh, PA; *m:* James; *ed:* Edinboro (BS) Art Ed 1974; Edinboro Univ (MS) Art Ed, Supervision 1981; Attnd Touchstone Ctr for Arts, Harlan Butt 1989, Cloisonne Vessels 1990, Doug Zaruba 1994, Bob Anderson 1995 Wheel Thrown Ceramics; *cr:* Brentwood Elem Schl Kdgtn-6th Grd Art Tchr 1975-85; Brentwood Elem MS HS Kndgtn-12th Grd Art Tchr 1986-92; Brentwood MS HS Jr-Sr High Art Tchr 1993-; *ai:* PSEA, NEA 1975-; Ed ASSN 1975, Pres 1980-82, 1993-95, Treas 1988-90; NAEA 1996; John Mc Millian Presbyn Church 1993-; Iris, Daylily Soc 1995-; Scholastic Art Comm, Shipment to NY 1994-; 1st Alumni Invitational Exhibition 1990; Art Edctrs Exhibit 1991; *office:* Brentwood Middle HS 3601 Brownsville Rd Pittsburgh PA 15227

SHEARS, GAIL M., 6th Grade Teacher; *b:* Malden, MA; *m:* Ted; *c:* Kim; *ed:* Univ of Denver (BA) Elem Ed 1971; Univ of Rochester (EDM) Ed Admin 1977; Attnd Westfield St Coll, Glassboro St Coll & Nazareth Coll at Pittsford NY; *cr:* Suffield Pub Schls 4th Grd Tchr 1971-73; Gibbsboro Pub Schl 4th Grd Tchr 1973-75; Pittsford Cntrl Schl 3rd-6th Grd Tchr 1975-; *ai:* Ski Club Head Adv; Scheduling & Tech Comms; Team Ldr; AFT 1975-; PDTA 1975-; Kappa Delta 1968-, Natl Coll Province Pres, Natl Alumnae Advy Chair, Outstndng Greek Alumnae & Order of Omega; Natl Panhelenic Conference 1968-; Hellenic Alumni Cncl 1980-; Featured on CBS Kidsworld; Ganett Newspaper Guest Speaker; *office:* Pittsford MS Barker Rd Pittsford NY 14534

SHEARSON, NANCY (WATERS), Sixth Grade Teacher; *b:* Ft Smith, AR; *m:* Steve; *c:* Stephen, Gregory, Amy; *ed:* CA Univ of PA (BS) Elem & Spcl Ed 1963; Carnegie Mellon Univ Comp Pgm; Grad Classes; *cr:* Charleroi Area Schls Tchr 1972-, Spcl Ed Tchr 1972-81, 4th Grd Tchr 1981-85, 3rd Grd tchr 1985-89, 6th Grd Tchr 1989-; *ai:* Charleroi Area Ed Assn 1972-, Bldg Rep; NEA 1972-; *office:* Charleroi Area Schl Dist 100 Fescen Dr Charleroi PA 15022

SHEATS, AUDREY HATHAWAY, English Teacher; *b:* Fall River, MA; *c:* Alice, Paul William; *ed:* Wellesley Coll (BA) Eng 1959; Radcliffe Coll (MA) Eng 1960; Harvard Univ (ABD) Eng 1960-67; *cr:* Harvard Schl Tchng Fellow 1963-67; St Univ of CA Northridge Lecturer 1967-68; UCLA Assoc 1968-72; Northfield Mt Hermon Schl Tchr 1975-; *ai:* Yrbk Adv; Coord Womens Group; *office:* Northfield Mount Hermon Schl 206 Main St Northfield MA 01360*

SHEATS, JOHN EUGENE, Professor of Chemistry; *b:* Atlanta, GA; *m:* Margaret Lee; *c:* David; *ed:* MIT (PHD) Chem 1966; *cr:* Bowdoin Coll Asst Prof 1965-70; Rider Univ Assoc Prof 1970-78, Prof 1978-; *ai:* Premedical & General Lbrl Arts Stdnts Adv; Dir; ACS Project SEED; Amer Chemical Soc 1961-, Emmett Reid Awd; Sigma Xi 1961-, Pres & Treas; Phi Beta Kappa 1961-; Cncl on Undergrad Rsrch 1961-; Presbytn Church 1975-, Elder, Deacon; Gideons Intnl 1980-; 5 Books on Oganometallic Polymers; Numerous Journal Articles; NSF Grad Fellow 1961-65; Woodrow Wilson Fellow 1961; NSF Sci Fac Fellow 1985-86; *office:* Rider Univ 2083 Lawrenceville Rd Lawrenceville NJ 08648*

SHEATZ, FRANCES EILEEN, French Teacher; *b:* Saginaw, MI; *m:* Chris A.; *c:* Christopher, Joelle; *ed:* Clarion Univ of PA (BA) Scndry Fr 1987; Univ Paul Valery BA Equivalent Modern Fr Lang & Lit 1977; Western KY Univ 2 Yrs Undergrad Credits Pre-Vet, Fr; 30 Grad Credits Toward Eng MA Prgm; *cr:* Language Studies Eng Tchr 1978-80; IBM Eng Tchr 1980-81; Chamber of Commerce Eng Tchr 1980-82; IU 6 Spec Ed Aide SED 1986-88; Keystone HS Fr Tchr 1988-; *ai:* Fr Club to Europe, Jr Class Adv; SADA Co-Adv; PSMLA 1994-; *office:* Keystone Jr Sr HS RR 2 Box 3b Knox PA 16232

SHEDD, CYNTHIA COLLOM, Fourth & Fifth Grade Teacher; *b:* Burlington, VT; *m:* Jeffrey Brian; *c:* Clarke Jonathon, Christopher Lee; *ed:* The Univ of VT (BS) Elem Ed 1979; 30 Grad Credit Hrs; *cr:* Ferrisburg Cntrl Schl 6th Grd Classroom Tchr 1979-91; Shelburne Comm Schl 4th-5th Grd Classroom Tchr 1991-; *ai:* Multi-Cultural Comm; CSEA 1991-, 4-5 Level Rep; NEA, VEA 1979-; ANTA 1971-91, Chief Negotiator, Treas; Presidential Awd Excl Sci, Math Tchng 1990, 1991; PTO Awds; *office:* Shelburne Cmty Schl Harbor Rd Shelburne VT 05482*

SHEEDY, PATRICIA CWYNAR, Second Grade Teacher; *b:* Pinconning, MI; *m:* John M.; *c:* Brian; *ed:* Buffalo St Coll (BS) Elem Ed 1962; Buffalo Tchr Ctr 30 Credit Hrs; *cr:* Centralia Schls Grd 2 Tchr 1962-63; Williamsville Pub Schls Grd 2 Tchr 1963-65, 1969-71; Buffalo Parochial Schls Grd 2, Grd 5 Tchr 1972-75; Buffalo Schl #59 Grd 5 Tchr 1975-77; Buffalo Schl #39 Grd 5 Tchr 1975-77; Buffalo Schl #11 Kndgtn Tchr 1977-78; Buffalo Schl #53 Kndgtn Tchr 1981-82; Buffalo Schl #17 Second Grd Tchr 1984-; *ai:* NEA, BTF 1975-; Women's Tchrs Assn 1985-; *office:* Buffalo Pub Schl #17 1045 W Delavan Ave Buffalo NY 14209*

SHEEHAN, CAROL JANICKI, 2nd Grade Teacher; *b:* Buffalo, NY; *m:* Joseph P.; *c:* Todd Janicki; *ed:* Daemen Coll (BS) Elem Ed 1969; Buffalo St Coll (MS) Elem Ed 1972; *cr:* Potters Road Elem Schl 2nd, 3rd Grd Tchr 1969-; *ai:* Schl Bookstore Adv; Shared Decision Making Team Co-Chm; Telethon, Sr Citizen Vol, Schl Spirit Comms; AFT, NY St, West Seneca Tchrs Assn 1969-; Phi Delta Kappa 1989-; Queen of Heaven Parish Carnival Comm 1985, Parish Cncl 1994, Bdlg Comm 1995, Sec; *office:* Potters Road Elem Schl 675 Potters Rd West Seneca NY 14224*

SHEEHAN, CHERYL DARRAH, 7th Grade Science Teacher; *b:* Greensboro, NC; *m:* Francis Robert; *c:* F. Robert, Corinne Joan; *ed:* Middlesex Comm Coll (AAS) Lab Tech 1969; C W Post Coll (BS) Bio 1971; Long Island Univ (MS) Bio 1973; St Univ of NY at Albany (MS) Ed 1984; *cr:* Draper & Mohonasen Schl Dist Sci Tchr 12 Yrs; Hacket MS Sci Tchr 1 Yr; *ai:* Sci Tchr Assoc of NY 1985-; NYSUT 1985-; *office:* Draper MS 2070 Curry Rd Schenectady NY 12303

SHEEHAN, DENNIS PATRICK, US History & Civil War Teacher; *b:* Boston, MA; *m:* Judith Joy Fonzi; *c:* Erin Robin; *ed:* Boston St Coll (BS) His 1974, (MED) Instrl Media 1977; Over 100 Credit Hrs in His at Penn St, Loyola Marymount, Brown & Gettysburg Coll; *cr:* Everett HS His, Eng Tchr 1974-81; Londonderry HS His, Eng Tchr 1982-; *ai:* Ftbl, Bsbl Coach; Class Adv; Fac Cncl NHS; NEA 1974-; NHEA, LEA 1982-; Lincoln Group of Boston 1983-, Advy Bd; Abraham Lincoln Assn, Lincoln Flwshp of Penn 1983-; NH Civil War Round Table 1995-; Pub Book Reviews on Lincoln Books; Yrbk Dedication 1987; *office:* Londonderry HS 295 Mammoth Rd Londonderry NH 03053

SHEEHAN, JANET FRANCES, Office Technology & Bus Tchr; *b:* Taunton, MA; *ed:* Boston St Coll (BS) Ed 1976; Boston Univ (MA) Bus & Career Ed 1978; Secretarial Katharine Gibbs Schl; *cr:* Quincy Coll Bus Tchr 1976-, Coord Cmptr Operations Prgm Displaced Homemaker Grant 1987-94; *ai:* Fac Sub-Comm; Acad Policies, Curr Comms; MTA, NEA, QEA 1976-; Tchr of Yr Quincy Coll 1995; *office:* Quincy Coll 34 Coddington St Quincy MA 02169*

SHEEHAN, JEREMIAH F., Social Studies Teacher; *b:* Stamford, CT; *m:* Patricia Emery; *c:* Kevin M., Kathryn M.; *ed:* Marist Coll (BA) His 1965; St Univ of NY at New Paltz (MS) Ed 1971; Addl 15 Credit Hrs at St of NY at Albany; *cr:* Cardinal Farley Military Acad Tchr 1965-69; Red Hook Cntrl HS Tchr 1969-; *ai:* Ftbl Coach; Acad Awds Comm Chm; AFT 1969-; NYSUT 1969-, Bldg Rep, Retirement Del; Red Hook Booster Club 1990-, Spon an Athl Awd; Natl Safety Cncl 1977-, Instr-Trainer; US Marine Corps Reserve 1963-69; Yrbk Dedications 1975 & 1983; *office:* Red Hook Central HS W Market St Red Hook NY 12571

SHEEHAN, KRISTINA K. (KRAFFT), French Teacher; *b:* Buffalo, NY; *m:* Paul F.; *c:* Megan A., Patrick P.; *ed:* Rosary Hill Coll (BA) Fr Ed 1971; Canisius Coll (MS) Ed 1976; *cr:* Nardin Acad Elem Schl Span, Fr Tchr 1972-; Nardin Acad HS Fr Tchr 1972-; *ai:* Stu Cncl Adv; Sr Class Dean; Mid Sts Steering Comm; AATF, WNYFLEC 1986-; NEA 1971-; Albright-Knox Art Gallery 1980-; Buffalo Zoo 1985-; Bd of Trustees 20 Yrs Svc Awd; *office:* Nardin Acad 135 Cleveland Ave Buffalo NY 14222

SHEEHAN, LYNN CAMPBELL, Health Teacher; *b:* New York City, NJ; *m:* James J.; *ed:* Trenton St Coll (BS) Hlth, PE 1975; *cr:* Colonia HS Hlth Tchr 1975-; *ai:* Sr Class, Interact Club Adv; Schlsp, Fac Advy Comms; NEA 1975-; Amer Red Cross 1980-, CPR Instr; Woodbridge PBA Outstdng Citizen Awd 1984; *office:* Colonia HS East St Colonia NJ 07067

SHEEHAN, MARY JANE M., Sixth Grade Teacher; *b:* Springfield, MA; *m:* Jere A.; *ed:* Our Lady of the ELMS (BA) Ed 1961; Westfield St; *cr:* Town of Ludlow 3rd-6th Grd Tchr 1961-; *ai:* MA Tchrs, NEA 1961-; Ludlow Tchrs Assn 1961-, Treas; *office:* Paul R Baird MS 109 Sportsmans Rd Ludlow MA 01056

SHEEHAN, MICHAEL FRANCIS, AP English Teacher; *b:* Philadelphia, PA; *m:* Rossana I Avelino; *c:* Ana Elana; *ed:* Temple Univ (BA) Eng 1979; Drexel Univ (MLS) Lib Sci 1981; *cr:* West Cath HS for Boys Librn 1982-83; St John Neumann HS AP Eng Tchr & Librn 1983-; *ai:* Stu Assistance Prgm Coord; Pirates Quill-Stu Lit Magazine Fac Moderator; JV Mathletes Moderator; Cath Lib Assn 1982-, VP; PA Lib Assn & Amer Lib Assn 1982-; FLPL 1975-, VP; *office:* Saint John Neumann HS 2600 Moore St Philadelphia PA 19045

SHEEHAN, PAULINE WALSH, Third Grade Teacher; *b:* Boston, MA; *m:* Paul J.; *ed:* Emmanuel Coll (BSBA) Bus Admin 1954; Boston St (MED) Elem Ed 1960; Addl 15 Credits; *cr:* South Elem Schl Third Grd Tchr 1960-61; Meadowbrook Schl Third Grd Tchr 1961-64; Oakdale Schl Third Grd Tchr 1964-; *ai:* Tchrs Supporting Tchrs; Mass Tchrs, NEA 1960-; *office:* Oakdale Elem Schl 91 Cedar St Dedham MA 02026

SHEEHAN, SUSAN MC GILLOWAY, 6th Grade Teacher; *b:* Bronx, NY; *m:* Michael; *ed:* Adelphi Univ (BA) Ed 1968, (MA) Ed 1969; Certfd NY St Rdng Tchr 1989; *cr:* Commack Schl Dist Tchr 1968-78; Eaton AIL Buyer 1979-81; Dept of Defense DCAS Buyer 1982-85; Commack MS Tchr 1986-; *ai:* Classroom Tchrs Assn 1986-; PTA, VP; League Women Voters 1978-, Pres, Human Resource Chair; Nom Tchr of Yr; Lifetime Mbrshp Honor Parent Tchr Org; *office:* Commack MS PO Box 150 Commack NY 11725

SHEEHY, KEVIN L., Science Institute Program Tchr; *b:* Staten Island, NY; *m:* Elaine Capelli; *c:* Kevin Jr.; *ed:* Wagner Coll (BS) Bio 1967, (MS) Sci 1971, (MBA) Fin, Mngmt 1990; Long Island Univ (MPA) Human Res Mngmt 1996; NY Inst of Fin Cert 30 Hrs 1962; Post Grad Stud Queens Coll, New Schl for Soc Rsrch; *cr:* Dean Witter & Co Mutual Fund Sales 1960-70; Tottenville HS Tchr 1970-; *ai:* Multicultural Coord; SBM, SDM Comm, Young Democrats, Indian Girls Dance Ensemble Adv; BRIO TRIO NYC Chm; Greenbelt Naturally Photo Competition Chm; UFT 1971-, Chptr Del, PAC Comm, Emerald Soc 1996; AFT, NYSUT 1971-, Del; Wagner Coll 1989-, Bd Sec, Exec Comm, Trustee; Johnn Noble Collection 1987-, Treas, Trustee; Snug Harbor Cultural Ctr 1987-93, Pef Arts Ch, Dir; Greenbelt Conservancy 1990-, Dir; Harbor Repertory Theatre 1985-, Dir; Phi Delta Kappa Tchr of Yr 1994; Staten Island Continuum Maurice Wollin Awd 1993; Brooklyn, Staten Island HS Outstdng Tchr 1993; Outstdng Tchr 1980; *office:* Tottenville HS 100 Luten Ave Staten Island NY 10312

SHEEHY, MIDGE, MS Language Arts Teacher; *b:* New York City, NY; *m:* Edward J. Duffy Jr.; *c:* Erin Sheehy Duffy; Mairead Sheehy Duffy; *ed:* Fordham Univ (BA) Eng 1973; Manhattan Coll (MS) Admnin in Progress; Southern CT St Univ, St Joseph Coll 12 Grad Credits Each; UConn 3 Grad Credits; *cr:* St Anthony Schl Tchr Grd 7-8 1973-75; Meml Hospital Unit Svc Coord 1975-77; St Margaret Schl Tchr 1985-94; Prin 1994-; *ai:* Testing Coord; Lit Magazine Adv; CCTE 1993-; NCEA 1985-; ASCD 1990-; Co-Recipient 2 Carnegie Grants MS Tchrs; *office:* Saint Margaret Schl 289 Willow St Waterbury CT 06710

SHEEKS, DONNA M., Computer & Accounting Teacher; *b:* Mc Comb, OH; *m:* C. James; *c:* Jill K. Konen, Angela K. Hines; *ed:* Defiance Coll (BS) Comprehensive Bus Ed 1978; 20 Addl Hrs OH St Univ, Univ of Toledo, Bowling Green St Univ, Miami Univ, Akron Univ; *cr:* Four Cty Voc Schl Tchr 18 Yrs; *ai:* Bus Profs of Amer Adv; Natl Bus Edctrs 1982-; NW OH Bus Edctrs 1978-, Pres; NEA 1978-, Pres Elect, Pres; OH Conservation League 1970-, Pres, Sec, VP; *office:* Four Cty Voc Schl 22-900 SR 34 Archbold OH 43502

SHEERAN, JOAN GARNER, Foreign Languages Teacher; *b:* New York, NY; *ed:* SUNY at Albany (BA) Ger, Fr 1968, (MA) Ger, Ed 1969; Univ of MN (PHD) Ger, Fr 1976; Span, Fr, Ger Tchng Certs; Attnd Julius Maxmilion Univ, Ruhr Univ, Siene Coll Span; *cr:* North Colonie CSD Jr HS Tchr of FLEX, Level I 1975-76; Hopewell Vly HS Frgn Lang Tchr 1977-79; Catskill CSD HS Frgn Lang Tchr 1979-80; Pomfret Schl HS Frgn Lang Tchr 1980-81; Stamford CSD HS Frgn Lang Tchr 1981-83; Lansingburgh CSD MS Tchr of FLEX, HS All Levels Tchr 1983-; *ai:* Tennis Club, Chrldr Team, Fr, Ger Clubs Adv; LHS Tour of Germany Trip Coord, Chaparone 1992; AFT; AATG, Pres; AATF; AATSP; ACTFL; NYSFLT; Troy German Hall Assn; Goethe House NYSFLT Awd Outstdng Tchr of Ger 1992; Designed Lansingurgh Model Flex Curr at Knickerbacher MS; Written Series of Introductory Frgn Lang Textbooks; *office:* Lansingburgh Cntrl Schl Dist 320 7th Ave Troy NY 12182

SHEERAN, MAUREEN FLYNN, Guidance Counselor; *b:* Lewiston, NY; *m:* Thomas; *c:* Meaghan, Brendan; *ed:* Niagara Univ (BA) Eng 1968, (MSEd) Cnslng 1976, (MSEd) Admin & Supervision 1991; Sp Admin 1978; *cr:* Niagara Falls Bd Ed Eng Tchr 1968-86, 1989-9 Assign Tchr 1986-89, Guid Cnslr 1995-; *ai:* NY United Tchrs 1968 1968-; Phi Delta Kappa 1989-; Lewiston Historic Preservation 1992-, Vice Chr; Articles Pub; Prof Present at Conf (4 Times); Niagara Falls City Schl Dist Buffalo Ave Niagara Falls NY 14304*

SHEETS, GEORGE WILLIAM, Lang Arts Tchr & Dept Chair; *b:* OH; *m:* Kathleen Sue Walker; *c:* Brannon; *ed:* Bowling Green St Un Eng 1972; Addl Credit Hrs; *cr:* Wynford Local Schls Lang A 1972-75; Ridgedale Local Schls Lang Arts 11-12 1975-; *ai:* Asst Girls Bsktbl; RTA Schlsp Comm Chair; NCTE, OEA, NEA OCTELA 1985-; RTA 1975-; Ridgedale Tchr of Yr 1983; *home:* I 74 Star Rt 98 Sulphur Springs OH 44881

SHEETS, STEPHEN LEE, Social Studies Dept Chm & T Huntington, WV; *m:* Clara Jane Bernardino; *ed:* Marshall Univ (A 1971, (MA) His 1974; OH Univ Tchr Cert 1975; *cr:* Chesapeake Stud Tchr 1975-; *ai:* Stu Assistance Team Mem; Peer Assistanc Co-Spon; NEA & OEA 1980-; NCSS & OCSS 1988-; Phi Alpha T Pi Sigma Alpha; *office:* Chesapeake H S P O Box 458 Chesapea 45619

SHEFFIELD, CHARLOTTE ANNE, English Social Studies Teac New Brighton, PA; *ed:* CA Univ (BA) Spcl Ed 1967, (MED) Spcl E Pittsburgh Inst of Mortuary Sci Diploma in Funeral Svc; Licensed I Dir; *cr:* Pittsburgh Tchr 1967-70; Boces of Rockland Cty Tchr 1 Pittsburgh Pub Schls Tchr 1974-80; Cleveland Pub Schls Work Stud 1980-87; Beaver Vly Intermediate Univ Tchr 1989-91; Ambridge L Support Tchr 1991-; *ai:* African Amer Club; Quippettes; AFT; NEA; NFD; Alpha Kappa Alpha 1967-, Grad Adv, Outstdng Gra Womens Rape Crisis Ctr 1994-, Bd; Children Advocacy Ctr 1995-,

SHEFTALL, BARBARA J., English Teacher; *b:* Vineland, NJ; *m:* (H. Jr.; *c:* Michael, Meredith, Adam, Alexis, Cody; *ed:* Glassboro (BA) Eng 1965, (MA) Tchng Eng 1971; *cr:* Vineland HS South E 1965-95; *ai:* Stu Assistance Publication Ed; Stu Newspaper Adv 19 Vineland Ed Assn, NJ Ed Assn 1965-; Hadassah 1993-, Ed Chair, P 1993-; Canine Hearing Companions 1994-, Bd of Dirs; Cumberla Child Placement Review Bd 1995-; Friends of Vineland Historic Pub Relations; Chamber of Commerce Tchr of Yr Awd 1991; Vineland HS South 2880 E Chestnut Ave Vineland NJ 08360

SHEIKH, SOHAIL, Associate Professor; *b:* Lahore, Pakistan; *m:* Sohail; *c:* Wasiq; *ed:* Govt Coll Lahore Pakistan (MS) Physics Syracuse Univ (MS) Cmptr Engrng 1985, (MS) Electrical Engrng (PHD) Electrical Engrng 1989; *cr:* Syracuse Univ Tchng Asst 1 Widener Univ Asst Prof 1989-95, Assoc Prof 1995-; *ai:* Supe Masters Thesis Stdnts; Stdnts Comm on Master's Thesis; IEEE 199 Kappa Phi; Tau Beta Pi; Rsrch Papers Pub; *office:* Widener University Pl Chester PA 19013

SHELBY, JAMES ELBERT, Prof of Ceramic Engineering; *b:* Me TN; *c:* Stephanie R.; *ed:* Univ of MS at Rolla (BS) Ceramic Engrng (MS) Ceramic Engrng 1967, (PHD) Ceramic Engrng 1968; C Engrng Honorary Degree; *cr:* Sandia Natl Lab Staff Mem 1968-8 Coll of Ceramics at AU Ceramics Engr Prof 1982-; *ai:* Mem Curr & Revisions, Schlsp Selection, Grad Stans; Chair Glass Sci Prgm for B PHD Degrees; Soc Glass Tech 1990-; Amer Ceramic Soc 1965-9 Morey Awd for Research; Author Glass Diffusion in Solids & Me Rare Elements in Glasses; *office:* NY St Coll of Ceramics 2 Pine St NY 14802

SHELDON, CINDA KAY, High School Science Teach Bellefontaine, OH; *m:* Sherman Rodney; *c:* Cinnamon Anne, Michael; *ed:* OH St Univ (BS) Comp Bio Educat 1972; Kent S (MED) Educl Media 1984; 22 Post Grad Hrs Curr Stud, Earth Sci, SEABASE; *cr:* Hudson HS Sci Tchr 1981-; *ai:* Camp Invention In Olympiad Judge; Adv Key Club, SADD, Envirnomental Club; S Chprsn; Vlybl Coach; Dist Curr Cncl; Directed Mystery Plays; S Coord; Natl Amer Bio Tchr 1993-; ASCD 1990-; Church in Falls Specialist 1978-; Kiwanis 1994; Jennings Scholar; Key Club Int Citation; Distngd Tchr Awd 1988; Summit Cty Clean Comms Sh Example Awd 1993; Wrote ACT Units; Exams Tchr Mentor; *office:* H HS 2500 Hudson Aurora Rd Hudson OH 44236*

SHELDON, ERIC, Physics Professor & Honors Dir; *b:* Pilsen, Bo *m:* Sheila Elizabeth Harter; *c:* Adrian; *ed:* Univ of London (BS) P Chem, Math 1951, Physics 1952, (PHD) Sci 1955, (D Sci) Sci 1972; Federal Inst of Tech; *cr:* Univ of London Lecturer & Demon 1952-55; Royal AF Tech Ed Ofcr 1955-57; IBM Rsrch Lab Assoc Ph 1957-59; Swiss Federal Inst of Tech Prof 1959-69; Univ of MA Lowe 1970-; *ai:* Hnrs Pgm Dir; Dept of Physics & Coll of Arts & Sci Comm; Royal Inst of GB Mem, Fellow, MRI; Inst of Physics Fellow F Inst P; Royal Soc of Chem Fellow, FRSC; Royal Astronomic Fellow, FRAS; Amer Phys Soc Fellow APS Fellow; Amer As Advancement of Sci Fellow, AAAS Fellow; AAPT Mem; MENSA; Soc Rsrch Grant 1954; US Natl Sci Fndtn, Sr Frgn Sci Fellow 1968 Prof 1985 & 1988; Order of Merit 1988; Hnrs Dir 1994; Nu Textbooks, Papers, Conf Abstracts.

SHELDON, JAMES EDMUND, Biology & Chemistry Teach Queens, NY; *ed:* Queens Coll of City Univ NY (BA) Bio, Scndry Ed St Joh's Univ (MS) Sci Scndry Ed 1996; *cr:* Archbishop Molloy HS Sci Tchr 1992-; *ai:* JV Soccer Moderator; Retreat, Stdnts Against Driving Coord; IM Sports Moderator; IAABO 1990-,; *office:* Arch Molloy HS 83-53 Manton St Jamaica NY 11435

SHELDON, JOSEPH FRANCIS, Professor; *b:* Philadelphia, P Joyce Rosamilia; *c:* Mary Frances, Emily, Joseph Jr., Jesse; *ed:* (MSW) Soc Work 1970; *cr:* Chester Cty Welfare Dept Exec Dir 3 West Chester Univ Prof 1992; Cheyney Univ Prof 1993-; *ai:* Behavioral Svc Majors Internship Prgm; NASW 1969-; Alum Bd 1992-, Treas; Westchester Univ Advy Bd 1990-, Treas; Bryn Mawr Hosp 1995-, Bd.

SHELDON, PENN, Math Teacher; *b:* Canandaigua, NY; *ed:* Unio (BS) Math 1973; Univ of Rochester (MS) Scndry Math Ed 198 Fairport HS Math Tchr 1976-; *ai:* Modified & Var Ftbl Coach; Ski C Soph Class Adv; Assist Math Team; Acad Decathelon; Selection Co Dist Math Textbooks; NYSUT 1979-; Masons 1978-, Master of I *office:* Fairport HS 1358 Ayrault Rd Fairport NY 14450

SHELLENBERGER, RICHARD L., American History Teach Indianapolis, IN; *m:* Kayla Chambers; *c:* Kim Gahring, Jill Mdin Tonya Yoder, Logan, Ryan; *ed:* Earlham Coll (BA) Geology 1952; IN (MS) Recreation 1954, (MA) Geography & His 1959; Univ of Akro Cnslr Cert 1981; Moody Bible Inst Bible Summers of 1968-69; *cr* Park Svc Ranger, Naturalist & Historian Summers of 1958-59, 1961, 1966, 1969, 1976-77; South Side HS Phys Geography Tchr 19 Scottsbluff HS Amer His & Intnl Relations Tchr 1961-72; Cuyahoga Chrstn Acad Amer His, Climatology, Geography, Conservation & Tchr & Cnslr 1972-; *ai:* Chess Teams Coach 35 Yrs; Vlybl Referee 1 Toastmasters, Dist Speech Champion in Western NE-WY Dist T Neighborhood Bible Stud 1980-, Tchr; Chess Teams Placed 2nd in N in OH & 4th in HS Natl Jr Var Division; *office:* Cuyahoga Valley Ch Acad 4687 Wyoga Lake Rd Cuyahoga Falls OH 44224

LEY, AMANDA MARGARET (JONES), Music Teacher; *b:* , MA; *m:* Robson William; *c:* Robson William Jr., Elizabeth Anne; estfield St (BA) Music Ed 1987; Univ of MA at Lowell (MM) mance & Conducting 1992; 8 Semesters Post Grad Conducting ndent Stud; *cr:* Ashland HS Music Tchr 1987-88; Raymond HS Tchr 1992-; *ai:* Pvt Lessons Tchr; Mosiacs Woodwind Quartet ng Mem; MENC 1987-; NEA 1992-, Del; Natl Band Dir Assoc IAJE 1992-; *office:* Raymond HS 45 Harriman Hill Rd Raymond NH

LEY, ELLEN W., Eng Tchr & Jrnlsm Pub Adv; *b:* Jacksonville Bch, Kent A.; *ed:* Wright St Univ (BS) Eng Ed; Attnd Univ of Dayton, iv, Ball St Univ Jrnlsm & Comm Post Grad; *cr:* Fairborn HS Eng 973-, Publications Adv 1977-; *ai:* Yrbk & Quill & Scroll Adv; ; SPIRITS; NEA 1975-, Newsletter Ed; Jrnlsm Assn of OH Schls Bd; NCTE 1980-; Jrnlsm Ed Assn; Tchr of Yr 1993-94; Yrbk Top wd Columbia Scholastic Press Assn, Nathl Schlastic Press Assn & ner Awds; Ashland Tchr Achievement Awd Nom 1995-96; *office:* n HS 900 E Dayton-Yellow Springs Rd Fairborn OH 45324*

LEY, MICHAEL ARTHUR, High School English Teacher; *b:* lle Ctr, NY; *m:* Gail Carson; *c:* Cassie, Chris; *ed:* LeMoyne Coll ng, Ed 1971; Stony Brook (MA) Ed 1975; *cr:* Accompsett Jr HS Eng 971-75; Smithtown HS West Eng Tchr 1975-91; Smithtown HS Campus Eng Tchr 1991-; *ai:* NYSUT 1971-.

LEY, SCOTT JOSEPH, 10th Grd World Cultures Tchr; *b:* ourg, PA; *m:* Deborah; *c:* Megan, Douglas; *ed:* Clarion Univ (BS) ud 1979; Shippensburg Univ (MED) Educl Admin 1990; Scndry Cert; *cr:* Mechanicsburg HS Soc Stud Tchr 1979-91; Camp Hill HS in 1991-93, World Cultures Tchr 1993-; *ai:* Ftbl, Bsbl Coaches; Stu eam; Stage Crew Adv; Lions Pride Coord; Bsktbl Club Adv; Dept ; 7th & 8th Grd Team Ldr; NEA 1979-; Allendale Assn 1990-; Camp Hill HS 100 S 24th St Camp Hill PA 17011

LHAMMER, JEFFREY DEL, Band Director; *b:* Ashtabula, OH; ly Lee Hayman; *c:* Jena, Taylor; *ed:* Bowling Green St Univ (BM) Ed 1975; Vonder Cook Coll of Music (MM) Music Ed 1984; Post tud FL St Univ 1984-85; *cr:* Berne Union Schls Band Dir 1975-78; nt City Schls Band Dir 1978-84; FL St Univ Grad Asst 1984-85; na-Jefferson Schls Band Dir 1985-; *ai:* Marching, Pep Bands, Schl l Orch Dir; OEA, NEA, GJEA 1985-; OH Music Ed Assn 1975-, ffairs Chair; Natl Band Assn 1975-, Citation of Excl 1992; Amer and Dir Assn 1981-, St Chair 2 Yrs, Stanbury Awd 1984; Stonybrook Choir 1985-, Dir 1986-95; Gahanna Comm Theater 1985-, Music Dir 4; Citation of Excl Natl Band Assn 1992; Stanbury Awd Amer Schl ir 1984; Mid West Intnl Band Performed 1992; *home:* 143 Brookhill anna OH 43230

LY, RUTH ANN BYERS, Home Economics Teacher; *b:* ersburg, PA; *m:* Roy D.; *c:* Tonya, Tiffany; *ed:* Messiah Coll (BS) Ec 1970; Addl 24 Hrs Master's Equivalency Ed; *cr:* Scotland Schl Ec Tchr 1970-; *ai:* Independent Living Prgm Adv; NEA, PSEA SSEA 1970-, Bldg Rep; Brethren in Christ Church 1975-, Deacon, ng & Dev Comm; *office:* Scotland Sch For Vet Children 3583 nd Rd Scotland PA 17254

TON, CINDY NELSON, Family & Consumer Sci Teacher; *b:* ukee, WI; *m:* David J.; *c:* Michelle Flanagan, Brian D.; *ed:* Stout St BS) Home Ec 1970; Grad Work Masters Equivalent from Millersville Temple Univ; *cr:* Menomonee Falls East HS Home Ec Tchr 1971-72; MS Home Ec Tchr 1983-84; Downingtown Jr HS Home Ec Tchr *ai:* Dist Staff Dev, Dist Strategic Planning Comms; Career ness Team; Before Schl Homework Club; Bowling Club Adv; NEA PHEA, AHEA, PHEA 1987-; Chester Cty Home Ec Assn 1987-, /P, Mbrshp; Newcomers Club 1978-, VP, Pres; Friends of Lib 1982-, p, Pres; Grant Awarded for Using Tech in Classroom; Awd Natl Fnd for Comm Svc Project with Stdnts; Pub Article What's New in Ec; *office:* Downingtown Jr HS 335 Manor Ave Downingtown PA

TON, CURTIS L., Middle School Art Teacher; *b:* Wadsworth, OH; orehead St Univ (BA) Art Ed 1974; Attnd Akron Univ, Ashland Univ sh Univ Post Grad Stud; *cr:* Chippewa MS Art Tchr 1974-; *ai:* NEA, DEA 1974-; OAEA 1987-; *office:* Chippewa Local Schls 257 High lestown OH 44230

TON, FRANCES M., Language Art Teacher; *b:* Jersey City, NJ; *m:* ; *c:* Christopher, Stephen; *ed:* Jersey City St C (BA) Elem 1966, Ed 1994; Continuing Educating in Childrens Lit, Supvrs Cert; *cr:* City B of E Elem Tchr 1966-; *ai:* Camp Frannie, the Read-In Camp r, Tchr; NEA, NJEA 1966-; NJRA 1995-; NJ Governor's Tchr nition Awd 1994-95, Excl Initiative Spurt St Peter's Coll; Columbia Mentor Prgm; Merrill Lynch Ldrshp Awd 1995; *office:* J. W. Wakeman 00 Saint Pauls Ave Jersey City NJ 07306

TON, GLORIA GORDON, Art Teacher; *b:* Richmond, VA; *m:* m Q. O.; *c:* William Jr., Andrea Berg, David; *ed:* Univ of MD (BA) 91, (MED) Curr, Instr 1994; African Amer Stud Cert; *cr:* Du Val HS hr 1994-; *ai:* Art Club, Stu with Pride & Dignity Spon; Schl Mngmt Dept Chair; PGCEA; Seabrook Rec Cncl 1980-, Pres 1991-, St & Vol of Yr 1992-; Prince George's Cty Pk, Recreation Advy Bd 1991-, Chair 1995-; Sallie Mae Awd Nom as Outstdng First Yr Tchr; 2 or's Citations for Outstdmg Svc to Comm; *office:* DuVal HS 9880 Luck Rd Lanham Seabrook MD 20706

TON, LILLIAN WEEKLEY, Physical Education Teacher; *b:* a, GA; *m:* Blackford Vincent; *c:* Lorie Hankins, Boots, Gary, Glenn; niv of AL (BS) PE 1952; Univ of Richmond (MED) Cnslng 1975; s Instrl Classes; *cr:* City of Dothan PE Tchr 1952-54; City of ond PE Tchr 1955-57; Anne Arundel Cty B of Ed PE Tchr 1973-; *ai:* Hockey Coach; A A Co Indoor League, Field Hockey Jr League; , NEA, MSTA 1973-; MSHSFHCA 1990-, Past Pres, Founder; A 1993-, Bd Mem; Nat HS FH Coaches Assn 1993-, Pres; A A Co nission for Phys Fitness, Promoting Fitness 1981; Governors Fitness 1982; A A Co Exec Citation for Svc 1984; Bob Pascal Awd for Ath 1989; Coaches Care Awd 1992; Scholastic Magazine Awd 1989; Pub e Scholastic Magazine 1982.

BERGER, GERALD R., HS Industrial Technology Tchr; *b:* lelphia, PA; *m:* Susan; *c:* Stacy; *ed:* Millersville Univ (BS) Industrial Ed 1972, (MS) 1977; Supervisory Cert Industrial Arts Ed; Scndry Cert; 50 Credits Past Masters; *cr:* Upper Moreland Schl Dist Ind Arts 1972; Upper Dublin Schl Dist Ind Arts Tchr 1973-74; Central Bucks Dist Ind Arts Tchr 1975-; *ai:* Prins Advy Cncl; PSEA, NEA 1973-; 1975-; PSEA 1973-; NEA 1973-; CBEA 1975-; *office:* Central -West HS 375 W Court St Doylestown PA 18901*

NKMAN, SUSAN FISCHER, Mathematics Teacher; *b:* Brooklyn, *n:* Sidney; *c:* Adam, Amy; *ed:* Queens Coll (BA) Math & Ed 1970; C W Post (MS) Math Ed 1995; 30 Credit Hrs Beyond Masters; *cr:* vin Jr HS Math Tchr 1970-82; Baldwin HS Math Tchr 1982-; *ai:* AFT, Nassau Cty Math Tchrs 1970-; Former Key Club Adv; Pub CD for Learning Fractions; *office:* Baldwin HS 841 High School Dr vin NY 11566*

PARD, BION, Sixth Grade Soc Stud Tchr; *b:* New Haven, CT; *m:* L.; *c:* Tracy Shiring, Kathleen Tessman, Kerry Laray; *ed:* Univ of Ct (BS) Elem Ed 1965; SCSU (MS) Elem Ed 1970; *cr:* Eliot Schl Tchr 1965-69; East Haddam Elem Tchr 1971-94; Hale Ray MS Schl Tchr 1994-; *office:* Nathan Hale-Ray Middle School Plains Rd Moodus CT 06469

SHEPARD, DARREN LEROY, Math Teacher & Coach; *b:* Nyack, NY; *m:* Eileen Mc Linsky; *c:* Kate, Dyan, Andrew; *ed:* Albany St (BS) Math 1974; 33 Grad Credits; *cr:* Albertus Magnus HS Math Tchr 1975-84; Nyack HS Math Tchr 1984-; *ai:* Var Girls Bsktbl, Sftbl Coach; NEA 1984-; RWSOA 1986-; RCSOA 1980-; *office:* Nyack Sr HS 361 Christian Herald Rd Upper Nyack NY 10960

SHEPARD, LEONARD DOUGLAS, Asst Professor of Education; *b:* Coudersport, PA; *m:* Mary Natzle; *c:* Scott, Steve, Jason; *ed:* Block Haven Univ (BS) Elem Ed 1971; Penn St Univ (MED) Ed Admin 1985; 20 Hrs Principalship Cert 1985; *cr:* Keystone Cntrl Schl Dist 6th Grd Tchr 1971-74, 5th Grd Gifted Tchr 1974-87; Lock Haven Univ Dir Summer Prgm Gifted Ed 1979-82; Keystone Cntrl Schl Dist Elem Schl Head Tchr 1979-86; Lock Haven Univ Asst Prof Elem Ed 1986-, Dir of Testing 1994-; *ai:* Admissions & Acad Regulations, Stu Minority & Retention Comms; APSCUF Local Negotiations; APSCUF 1986-, Assn of Curr & Supervision Dev 1992-; YMCA Board 1995-; Dir; Yth Bsktbl 1973-, Chair of Prgms, Founder & Coach; Yth Bsbl 1984-, Coach; Outstdng Elem Tchrs of Amer 1973; Outstdng Young Edctr Awd 1985-86 Jaycee Awd; Heritage Days Grant in Collaborationwith Keystone Cntrl Schl Dist & Lock Haven U niv.*

SHEPARD, SUZANNE VICTORIA, Assistant Professor of English; *b:* Montour Falls, NY; *m:* Tredwell Burch Jr.; *ed:* Eisenhower Coll (BA) Music, Lit 1980; Binghampton Uinv (MA) Eng 1983, (PHD) Eng 1995; *ai:* Written Expression, Lib Holdings Stud Comms; NCTE 1981-; Phi Kappa Phi 1980-; Presbyn Church USA, Lay Preacher 1993-; Writing Ctr Tutor; Presenter at Successful Tchng Conf, Cntrl NY Conf on Lang, Lit; Artic Pub in Center Stage; Dicussion Questions for Use with Cmptrs Pub in Norton Intro to Literature; *office:* Broome Comm Coll PO Box 1017 Binghamton NY 13902

SHEPARDSON, RICHARD P., Government Teacher; *b:* Holyoke, MA; *m:* Elizabeth Bray; *c:* Melanie Murray, Rob Murray, Bridget Murray, Colin Murray; *ed:* Springfield Coll (MS) Gen Sci 1966; Univ of MA (MAT) Ed 1968, (CAGS) Media 1975; *cr:* Juniper Park Schl 6th Grd Tchr 1968-69; Westfield Jr HS Soc Stud Tchr 1969-71; Westfield HS Soc Stud Tchr 1971-; *ai:* Adv Boys, Girls St; Model Congress; Close-Up; We the People Competition; NEA, MA Tchrs Assoc 1968-; NCSS 1985-; Tchr of Yr Continental Cable Co; *home:* 8 Pidgeon Dr Wilbraham MA 01095

SHEPHERD, ALICE J., English Teacher; *b:* Mercer, PA; *m:* James; *c:* Craig, Leslie, Courtney; *ed:* Slippery Rock Univ (BS) Eng 1971; *cr:* Mercer HS Eng, Writing Tchr 21 Yrs; *ai:* Jr Class Adv; *office:* Mercer Area HS 545 W Butler St Mercer PA 16137

SHEPHERD, GLORIA ANN, Guidance Counselor; *b:* Washington, DC; *ed:* Colby Coll (BA) Span 1964; Hunter Coll (MA) Span 1971, (MS) Cnslng 1982; *cr:* JHS 120 Span Tchr 1966-81; JHS 101 Span Tchr 1981-84; DeWitt Clinton HS Guid Cnslr 1984-; *ai:* AFT 1966-; ACA 1983-; AATSP 1970-; Bronx Alum Delta Sigma Theta 1974-, Recording Sec, Historian; *office:* Dewitt Clinton HS 100 W Mosholu Pkwy S Bronx NY 10468

SHEPHERD, KIM CHARLES, Creative Writing Teacher; *b:* Shelby, OH; *m:* Bonnie Mischka; *c:* Amy, Matt, Stacey; *ed:* OH St Univ (BSE) Eng 1970; 150 Addl Hrs Eng Ed Grad Prgm; *cr:* Hilliard HS Eng Tchr 1970-; *ai:* Mens, Womens Var Tennis Coach; NCTE 1975-; OH Tennis Coaches Assn 1980-, Exec Bd, 200 Victories Plaque; NCTE Natl Convention Creative Writing Lecture Presenter 1983; *office:* Hilliard HS 5100 Davidson Rd Hilliard OH 43026

SHEPHERD, ROBERT LEE, Science Teacher; *b:* Camden, NJ; *ed:* Glassboro St Coll (BA) Scndry Sci Ed 1970; Luth Theological Seminary (MA) Rel 1985; Rowan Coll Admin Ed, Supervision 33 Credits; Enrolled Doctor Ministry Prgm Carolina Univ of Theology; *cr:* DCA Educl Products Inc Sales, Regnl-Sales Mgr 1970-79; NTD Sales, Mrktg 1979-80; Lower Camden Cty Reg BE Dist Sub Tchr 1981-82; City Wide Interdenominational Bible Inst Instr 1985-92; NJ Conf Bd of Ministerial Trng Schl Instr 1985-92; Edgewood Jr HS Tchr 1982-93, Supvr 1992-94; Mt Zion AME Church Summer Admin Pastor 1992, 1995-; *ai:* Mentor; CYF Club; NJEA, NEA, LCCR Tchrs Assn 1983-; NASSP 1992-94; UTI Aluminae 1985-, Pres 1992; C-T Ministers Assn 1980-, Sec 1995; Conf Bd Ministerial Trng 1985-92, Bd Mem; Edgewood Jr & Overbrook Jr HS Summer Schl Prin 1995-; Awd Svc First Dist Women's Missionary Soc AMEC 1995; Awd Outstdng Svc Macedonia AME Church; *office:* Edgewood Jr HS 200 Cooper Folly Rd Atco NJ 08004

SHEPHERD, VALENCIA RADCLIFF, Diversified Med Tech Instr; *b:* Cleveland, OH; *m:* Mark; *c:* Mark William, Tyrell, Marshall; *ed:* Luth Med Ctr Nrsng Diploma 1983; 32 Credit Hrs Provisional Voc Tchng Cert Kent St Univ & Univ of Toledo; *cr:* Drs Kase & Speelman Med Asst 1978-82; St Lukes Hosp Staff Nurse 1983-95; Medina Cty Career Ctr Voc Instr 1992-; *ai:* VICA Chptr Adv; NEA 1992-; *office:* Medina County Career Ctr 1101 W Liberty St Medina OH 44256

SHEPPARD, AMI HOLLAND, Secondary English Teacher; *b:* Wilmington, DE; *m:* Michael Leroy; *ed:* Univ of DE (BA) Eng Ed 1994; *cr:* Newark High Eng Tchr 1994-; *ai:* Asst Ath Dir; Blue-Gold Club, Acad Bowl Adv; Bldg Renovations Comm; Ath Cncl; Pathways Process; NEA, DSEA 1994-; NCTE 1996-.

SHEPPARD, BETTIE HALL, Business Educator; *b:* Montgomery, AL; *m:* Taylor; *c:* Telford, Terrell L., Torrey; *ed:* AL St Univ (BS) Bus Ed 1960; The Cath Univ of AM (MS) Bus Ed 1972; Attnd Trinity Coll; *cr:* Veterans Admin Admin Asst 1960-65; DC Pub Schl System Tchr 1965-; *ai:* Bus Ed Dept Chprsn; NBEA; Voc Ed; Delta Pi Epsilon; Matthews Meml Bapt Church 1964-, Yth Dept Supt, Deaconess Ministry Chprsn; *home:* 517 Rosier Rd Fort MD 20744

SHEPPARD, CHARLENE ANN, Fifth Grade Teacher; *b:* Kane, PA; *m:* C. Russell; *c:* Chara, Rustene; *ed:* Edinboro St Univ (BS) Elem Ed 1970, (MS) Elem Ed 1994; *cr:* Kane Area Schl Dist Second Grd Tchr 1970-78, Third Grd Tchr 1978-86, Fifth Grd Tchr 1986-; *ai:* NEA, PSEA, KATA 1970-, Fac Rep; Mt Jewett Library Bd 1986-, Pres, VP; Presenter Mastery Learning & Outcome Based Ed; Conducted in Svc Prgms; *home:* 1 Chestnut St Ext Mt Jewett PA 16740

SHEPPARD, HAROLD, High School Science Teacher; *b:* Pittsburgh, PA; *m:* Gail Anne Sagenich; *c:* Nichole, Tyler; *ed:* Penn St Univ (BS) Plant Sci 1977; 45 Credits Post-Bal for Tchr Cert Slippery Rock Univ; 6 Grad Credits Penn St; 3 Grad Credits Slippery Rock; *cr:* Sheppard Intnl Inc Mrktg Mgr 1980-90; Marion Ctr HS Sci Tchr 190-91; Hickory HS Sci, Bio, Anatomy & Physiology Tchr 1991-; *ai:* PSEA 1990-; NEA 1990-; HEA 1991-; *office:* Hickory High School 640 N Hermitage Rd Hermitage PA 16148

SHEPPARD, KENNETH P., Kindergarten Teacher; *b:* Akron, OH; *m:* Mary Ellen Sharpe; *c:* Daniel, Elizabeth; *ed:* Kent St Univ (BS) 1-8 Elem Ed 1981, (ME) K-8 Elem Ed 1987; *cr:* Zion Luth Schl 5th-6th Grd Instr 1981-83, 3rd-4th Grd Instr 1984-85; Kent City Schls Central Kndgtn-First Grd Instr 1985-93; Kent City Schls Walls Kndgtn Grd Instr 1993-; *ai:* Kent Ed Assn 1985-; Kappa Delta Pi; The Chapel Sunday Schl Tchr; Tchr of Month 1996; Children's Hands-On Museum Storyteller; *office:* Walls Schl 900 Doramor St Kent OH 44240*

SHEPPARD, THOMAS WHITTIER, Asst Soc Stud Dept Chrmn; *b:* Honakar, HI; *ed:* Washington & Lee Univ (BA) His 1991; Lehigh Univ (MED) Ed Ldrshp 1995; Columbia Univ Klingenstein Summer Inst 1995; *cr:* Perkiomen Schl His Tchr 1991-; *ai:* Var Swim & Asst Var Bsbl Coach; Class Adv; Dormparent; ASCD 1994-; Kiwanis 1992-; Amer Red Cross 1992-; Upper Perkiomen Vly Outstndg Young Ed 1994; *office:* Perkiomen Schl PO Box 130 Pennsburg PA 18073

SHEPPARD, WILLIAM, Middle School Math Teacher; *b:* Williamston, NC; *m:* Maggie Mae Yates; *ed:* Elizabeth City St Univ (BS) Ed 1970; Attnd Univ of MD, Coll Park MD, Western MD Coll; *cr:* Bd of Ed Elem Tchr 1972-88; Prince George's Cty MS Tchr 1988-; Oxon Hill MS Tchr 1988-; *ai:* Drill Team; Tutor; NEA, MSTA, AFT 1984-; Masonic Lodge 1974-; St Paul Chrstn Comm Church 1984-, Deacon; *office:* Oxon Hill MS 9570 Fort Foote Rd Fort Washington MD 20744*

SHERANKO, FRANK, Gifted Ed Coord & Biology Tchr; *b:* Cleveland, OH; *m:* Mary Ann Gaydos; *ed:* Western Reserve Univ (BA) Bio 1956, (MA) Ed 1962; The OH St Univ (MS) Zoology 1974; St Cert Gifted Ed; *cr:* Collinwood HS Sci Tchr 1962; C. F. Brush HS Bio Tchr 1962-, Gifted Ed Tchr 1984-, Gifted Ed Coord 1989-; *ai:* NEA 1962-; Natl Assn of Bio 1965-; OH Assn of Gifted Children 1984-; *office:* Charles F Brush H S 4875 Glenlyn Rd Lyndhurst OH 44124

SHEREMETA, GREGORY, History, Law & Economics Tchr; *b:* Jersey City, NJ; *m:* Ingrid; *c:* Nicole, Amanda; *ed:* Seton Hall Univ (BS) Soc Stud 1974; Univ of SC (MAT) Russian, East European His 1976; *cr:* Teaneck HS Soc Stud Tchr 1977-78; Waldwick HS Soc Stud Tchr 1978-70; Copeland MS Soc Stud Tchr 1979-80; West Milford HS Soc Stud, Russian Tchr 1980-; *ai:* 1999 Class Adv; Mock Trial Coach; NEA, NJEA 1978-; Saint Barnabas Spirit of Excl 1995; *office:* West Milford Twp HS 67 Highlander Dr West Milford NJ 07480

SHERER, MAUREEN ALEXA, Chemistry Professor; *b:* Indianapolis, IN; *c:* Marguerite Ratz, Paul Ratz, Peter Ratz, Laura Ratz; *ed:* Purdue Univ (BS) Chem 1971; OH St Univ (MS) Phys Chem 1973; *cr:* Northern VA Comm Coll Instr of Chem 1974-78; Anne Arundel Comm Coll Asst Prof of Chem 1982-; *ai:* Educl Policies, Curr Comm; Amer Chemical Soc 1974-; OH St Univ Flwshp; *office:* Anne Arundel Comm Coll 101 College Pky Arnold MD 21012

SHERICK, PHILIP L., German Teacher; *b:* Fremont, OH; *ed:* Bowling Green St Univ (BS) Ger Ed 1981, (MA) Ger Linguistics & Lit 1983; Acad Yr Abroad in Salzburg Austria 1979-80 & 1981-82; Course Participant Goethe Inst W Berlin Summer 1988; Intnl Ferienkurse at Zellamsee Austria Summer 1982 & Salzburg Austria Summer 1991; *cr:* Bowling Green St Univ Grad Tchng Asst 1981-83; Westland HS Ger & eng Tchr 1983-85; Port Clinton HS Ger Tchr 1985-; *ai:* Ger Club Adv; AATG 1980-; AFT Local 1985-; *office:* Port Clinton HS 821 S Jefferson St Port Clinton OH 43452

SHERIDAN, BEVERLY KARANOVICH, Gen Music Tchr & Choral Dir; *b:* Detroit, MI; *m:* David Carl; *c:* David, Sara, Adam, Molly, Julie; *ed:* Univ of MI (BM) Music Ed 1964; 30 Addl Gad Hrs Univ of MI, Wright St Univ; Univ of Dayton; *cr:* Warren Consolidated Schls Elem & Jr High General Music, & Soc Stud Tchr 1964-68; Lake Orion Schls MS & Elem Music 1986-88; Centerville Schls MS General Music 1989-; *ai:* 6th Grd Girls Chorus; 7th-8th Grd Combined Choruses; Watts Singers Select Choir; Adv & Spon of Muse Machine; Classroom Adv; Bldg Comm; PTO; NEA, OEA, CCTA 1989-, CCTA Bldg Rep; MENC, OMEA 1989-; New Neighbors League 1988-, 3rd VP, Outstanding Mem; Fairhaven Church 1992-, Choir Singer; Natl Sci Fnd, OH St Univ, WA Twp Fnd Grants; Outstanding Tchr Awd WA Twp Fnd; *home:* 9531 Bridlewood Trl Dayton OH 45458*

SHERIDAN, DONNA DOWLING, English Department Chair; *b:* Oakland, CA; *w:* James J. (dec); *c:* Anne Flick, Kathleen Sheridan-Dotson, Maureen, Sheila; *ed:* Seton Hill Coll (BA) in Honors Eng 1965; Cleveland St Univ (MA) Eng 1981; Grad Credits Oberlin Coll Tchrs Acad; *cr:* St Augustine Acad Eng Tchr 1965-66; Magnificat HS Eng Tchr 1977-, Eng Dept Chm 1985-; Cuyahoga Comm Coll Adjunct Eng Fac 1982-; *ai:* Curr, Inservice Comms; Retreat Team; NCTE 1977-; GCCTE 1980-; CBE Network of Fellows 1991-; St Christopher Parish, Eucharistic Minister 1985-; Oberlin Coll Tchrs Acad Fellow; Ind Stud in Humanities Basic Ed NEH Fellowship Cncl; Distinguished Tchr Presidential Scholars Prgm 1993; *office:* Magnificat H S 20770 Hilliard Rd Rocky River OH 44116*

SHERIDAN, ELAINE S., Spanish Teacher; *b:* Lima, OH; *m:* Ray; *ed:* Bowling Green St Univ (BS) Span & His Ed 1976, (MA) Span 1980; Extra Courses at Univ of Dayton & Wright St Univ; Seattle-Pacific Univ Correspondence Course; *cr:* Riverdale HS Span & Amer His Tchr 1976-78; Bowling Green St Univ Grad Asst 1978-79; Greenon HS Span Tchr 1980-; *ai:* AFT, OH Fed of Tchrs 1985-; Mad River Green Fed of Tchrs 1985-, Chapter Pres 1984-86; *office:* Greenon HS 1215 Old Mill Rd Springfield OH 45502

SHERIDAN, GERRY RADER, English Teacher; *b:* Chicago, IL; *m:* Thomas E.; *c:* Timothy, Julie, Lorie, Edward; *ed:* Univ of IL (BA) Eng 1959; Bowling Green St Univ (MEd) 1994; *cr:* East Leyden HS Eng Tchr 1959-63; St Patrick Schl Eng, Rdng, Rel Tchr 1977-82; Bryan MS Eng 1985-95; Bryan HS 1995-; *ai:* NEA, OCTELA, BEA 1985-; Delta Kappa Gamma Honorary 1991-; WMS Cty Playhouse 1980-, Secy 1984-86, Best Actress 1987, Best Supporting 1987, 1991; St Patricks Church 1977-, CCD Coord 1989; Finalist OH Tchr of Yr 1988; *office:* Bryan HS 150 Portland Bryan OH 43506

SHERIDAN, JOAN EILEEN, Spanish Teacher; *b:* Youngstown, OH; *m:* Richard; *c:* Ryan, Erika; *ed:* Youngstown St Univ (BA) Span 1975; *cr:* Western Reserve HS Span Tchr 1981-; *ai:* Stu Cncl Adv; OEA, NEA, TOWR 1981-; *office:* Western Reserve HS 13850 W Akron Canfield Rd Berlin Center OH 44401

SHERIDAN, MARIANNE, Religion Teacher; *b:* Bronx, NY; *ed:* Queens Coll (BA) Eng, Elem Ed 1984; St Joseph's Seminary (MA) Rel Stud 1991; *cr:* Our Lady of Angels Schl Math Sci, Rel, Rdng, SS Tchr 1984-88; St Joseph's Schl 6-8 GRd Math, Sci, SS Tchr 1988-91; Sacred Heart MS 8 Grd Eng, Math, Read Tchr 1991-92; Msgr Scanlon HS 9-12 Grd Rel Tchr 1991-; *ai:* HS Coach Sftbl; Moderator Yrbk; Amnesty Intnl; Elem Coach Sftbl, Bsktbl, Bowling; Moderator Forensics; FCT 1988-; NCEA 1991-; *office:* Monsignor Scanlan H S 915 Hutchinson River Pky Bronx NY 10465*

SHERIDAN, MICHAEL J., English Instructor; *b:* Jersey City, NJ; *m:* Irene Knipe; *c:* Kerri, Amy, Michael; *ed:* Bloomfield Coll (BA) Bus Admin 1972; Montclair St Univ (MA) Admin & Supervision 1983; *cr:* Saddle Brook HS Bus, Soc Stud & Eng Tchr & Distributive Ed Coord 1978-; *ai:* Girls Indoor & Outdoor Track Coach 1980-; Graduating Class Adv 1989; Math, Sci Industrial Arts & Home Ec Dept Chm 1992-94; Stdnts Organized Against Rape 1 Yr; Past Key Club Adv; NEA 1978-; NJBEA 1978-; SB PTA 1978-; Secaucus PTA 1987-; Saddle Brook Booster Club 1980-; Listed in Bus Ed Index 1983; *office:* Saddle Brook HS 355 Mayhill St Saddle Brook NJ 07663

SHERIDAN, THOMAS MICHAEL, 9th-12th Grade Math Teacher; *b:* Manchester, CT; *c:* Timothy M., Jessica E.; *ed:* Curry Coll (BA) Sociology, Math 1969; 33 Addl Hrs in Ed Eastern CT St Univ; *cr:* New London Jr HS 7-8 Grd Math Tchr 1969-71; Bolton MS 7-8 Grd Math Tchr 1971-83; Claremont Jr HS 7-8 Grd Math Tchr 1984-86; Raymond HS 9-12 Grd Math Tchr 1986-; *ai:* Math Team Coach; Peer Outreach Adv; Internet-on Line Comm; K-8 Grd Math Dept Chm 1975-83; Odyssey of Mind Coach; Schl

Prof Improvement Comm; NEA, NHEA, REA 1969-, Local Pres; NHMTA 1987-; *office:* Raymond HS 45 Harriman Hill Rd Raymond NH 03077

SHERK, DEAN E., Mathematics Teacher; *b:* North Tonowanda, NY; *m:* Marie W. Winkley; *c:* Brian Scott, Heather Lynn; *ed:* Buffalo St Coll (BSEd) Elem Ed 1962, (MSEd) Elem Admin 1966; *cr:* Green Acres Elem 6th Grd Tchr 1962-80; Hamilton Elem 4th Grd Tchr 1980-90; Hoover Elem K-5th Grd Title I Math Tchr 1990-; *ai:* Kenmore Tchrs Assn 1962-, Sr Bldg Rep; NYSUT 1962-; AFT 1962-; Payne Ave Chrstn Church 1951-, Trustee, Chm of Fin & Stewardship; *home:* 1370 Westwood Ave North Tonawanda NY 14120

SHERLINSKI, MARK, Fifth Grade Science Teacher; *b:* Wilkes-Barre, PA; *m:* Carol Lynn Booth; *ed:* Bloomsburg Univ (BS) Elem Ed 1975; Bloomsburg Univ & Marywood Coll (MS) Elem Ed & Humanistic Stud 1981; Certified Alcohol-Drug Prevention Instr; PA Certified Environmental Ed Instr; *cr:* Millville Area Schl Dist 5th Grd Tchr 1975-; *ai:* Alcohol-Drug Coord; Environmental Ed Coord; PSEA, NEA 1975-; Millville Ed Assn 1975-, VP; Amer Cancer Soc, Bd of Dirs; Amer Trauma Soc, Pres; Columbia Cty Environmental Ed Tchr of Yr 1990; *office:* Millville Area Elem Schl PO Box 300 Millville PA 17846*

SHERLOCK-ROBSON, NANCY, Mathematics Teacher; *b:* Lewistown, PA; *m:* Keith C.; *c:* Nathaniel W., Gwendelyn C.; *ed:* Bloomsburg St Coll (BSEd) Psych 1971; Beaver Coll (MAEd) Math 1986; Attnd Penn St Univ, Temple Univ; *cr:* Montgomery Elem Schl 2nd Grd Tchr 1973-76; Gen Nash Elem Schl 2nd & 4th Grd Tchr 1976-86; North Penn Jr HS Math Tchr 1986-94; Pennbrook MS Math Tchr 1994-; *ai:* Math Counts Coach; NCTM 1985-; ATMOPAV 1986-; *office:* Pennbrook MS 1201 E Walnut St North Wales PA 19454

SHERMAN, DORIS EDITH WEAVER, Retired Third Grade Teacher; *b:* Palmerton, PA; *m:* Richard R.; *c:* Donald Kevin, Richard Douglas; *ed:* Mansfield Univ (BA) Elem 1964; 24 Credit Hrs PA St Univ; *cr:* Williamsport Schl Dist 3rd Grd Tchr 1964-65; Montoursville Schl Dist 2nd Grd Tchr 1965-81, 3rd Grd Tchr 1982-95; *ai:* NEA, PSEA 1964-; *home:* 325 Allen St Montoursville PA 17754

SHERMAN, GEORGE W., Economics & Government Teacher; *b:* Albany, NY; *m:* Nancy; *ed:* SUNY at Plattsburgh (BA) Soc Stud Ed 1986, (MS) Soc Stud Ed 1972; 36 Post Grad Credit Hrs; *cr:* Chateaugay Cntrl Schl Scndry Soc Stud Tchr 1968-71; Beekmantown Cntrl Schl Scndry Soc Stud Tchr 1972-; *ai:* AFT 1972-; NY St Cncl for Soc Stud 1982-; Natl Consortium for Tchng Canada 1990-; Books: The Canada Connection in American History, The Canadian Parlimentay Video and Teachers Guide, O Canada: Its Geography, History and People Who Call it Home; *office:* Beekmantown Cntrl Schl PO Box 829 Plattsburgh NY 12901

SHERMAN, HELEN STEELE, Physical Education Teacher; *b:* Biddiford, ME; *m:* James; *c:* Adam, Michael, Christopher; *cr:* Oak Hill HS PE Tchr, Coach 1978-; *ai:* Coach Field Hockey 16 Yrs, Bsktbl 5 Yrs, Sftbl 2 Yrs; Curr Comm; Variety Show 18 Yrs; Class Adv; New Tchrs Peer Support Team; Outing Club 15 Yrs; AAPER, Dance 1978-; Challenge Fnd 1992-, Chprsn; 2 Currs Pub; ME Stud Curr; *office:* Oak Hill HS PO Box 400 Sabattus ME 04280*

SHERMAN, LARRY RAY, Chemistry Professor; *b:* Easton, PA; *m:* Irene Helen Price; *ed:* Lafayette Coll (BS) Chem 1956; UT St Univ (MS) Chem 1961; Univ of WY (PHD) Analytical Chem 1969; Attnd Western Reserve Univ 9 Credits 1957-58, Univ of WA 6 Credits 1962-64, Univ of MS 3 Credits 1977; *cr:* NC A&T St Univ Fac Mem 1969-74; Univ of MS Fac Mem 1976-78; Akron Univ Fac Mem 1978-81; Univ of Scranton Fac Mem 1981-; *ai:* Amer Chem Soc 1955-, Numerous Comms; Royal Soc for Chem 1965-; PA Acad 1984-, Treas, Life Mem; Fed Russian Orthodox Clubs 1988-, Lieutenant Governor, Citation Awd; BSA 1947-, Asst Scoutmaster for 3 Troops, Silver Beaver Awd; USAF Office Scientific Research Summer Fellowship 1988, 1992-1995; NATO Fellowship 1989; NASA Fellowship 1968-69 & 1984; Russian Orthodox Journal Assoc Ed; Eastern Orthodox Comm on Scouting Exec Bd; Main Group Metal Chem Journal Editorial Bd; *office:* Univ Of Scranton Monroe St Scranton PA 18510

SHERMAN, LORRAINE PILGER, Preschool Teacher; *b:* Goodland, KS; *m:* Robert F.M.; *c:* Amanda Nicole, David Robert; *ed:* KS Wesleyan Univ (BA) Home Ec, Scndry Ed 1969; (BA) Elem Ed 1970; Attnd Gessell Inst; *cr:* Long Beach Island Schl Dist Prefirst, Kndgtn, 1st, 3rd Tchr 1971-87; Lighthouse Chrstn Acad Preschl, Kndgtn Tchr 1990-; *ai:* Early Ed Dept Head; Intnl Flwshp of Chrstn Schl Tchr 1995-; *home:* 1093 Prospect Ave Manahawkin NJ 08050

SHERMAN, MADELINE SCHNABEL, Librarian & History Teacher; *b:* Monticello, NY; *m:* Jacob R.; *c:* Deborah, Rebecca; *ed:* SUNY at Albany (BA) His 1968, (MLS) Lib Sci 1971; 30 Credit Hrs beyond MLS in His, Tech & Eng; *cr:* Mechanicsville Pub Lib Asst librn 1970-71; Coll of St Rose Acquisitions Asst 1968-70; Bethlehem Pub Lib Referance & Young Adult Librn 1971-73; Proctor Jr-Sr HS Tchr & Librn 1973-; *ai:* Sr Class & Yrbk Adv; Curr & Pub Engagement Comms; VEMA 1974-; VT Cncl for Soc Stud 1974-; ALA 1975-; VT NEA 1978-; AASL 1980-; NCSS 1980-; Org of Amer His 1990-; Rutland Jewish Ctr Sisterhood 1973-; Rutland City Schl Bd 1993-; *office:* Proctor Jr-Sr HS 4 Park St Proctor VT 05765

SHERMAN, MARY E., Retired Mathematics Teacher; *b:* Warsaw, NY; *ed:* SUNY at Geneseo (BS) Math Ed 1962, (MS) Math Ed 1967; *cr:* Penn yan Cntrl Jr HS Math Tchr 1962-65; Greece Cntrl Jr HS Math Tchr 1965-66; Hammondsport Cntrl Scndry Math Tchr 1966-95; Corning Comm Coll Visiting Lecturer I 1988; *ai:* Scndry Schlsp Chr, Class A Pass Comm Chair; Class & NHS Adv; NEA, NEA-NY 1962-; Assn of Math Tchrs of NYS; Rochester Philharmonic Orch; Yates County Cncl of Arts; Natl Womens Hall of Fame; WWF; NWA; AS; NGS; Downstairs Cabaret Theatre, Opera Theatre of Rochester, Glimmerglass Opera Mem; Lit Vols of Amer; Kappa Delta Pi Honrary Soc 1961-.

SHERMAN, NANCY CAROL, First Grade Teacher; *b:* Wellsboro, PA; *m:* Larry G.; *c:* James Alan; *ed:* Mansfield Univ (BS) Elem Ed 1971, (MED) Elem Ed 1981; *cr:* Northern Potter Schl Dist 1st & 2nd Grd Tchr 1971-72, 2nd Grd Tchr 1972-77, 1st Grd Tchr 1977-; *ai:* Schl Dist Prof Dev Comm; NEA, PSEA 1971-; Northern Potter Ed Assn 1971-, Pres, VP, Sec; NSDAR 1984-; Middle Ridge Church 1957-; Middle Ridge Grange 1964-; *home:* RR 1 Box 575 Westfield PA 16950*

SHERMAN, PAMELA NOREEN, Fifth Grade Teacher; *b:* River Falls, WI; *m:* Winchester Jr.; *c:* Christopher, Jennifer; *ed:* Univ of WI at River Falls (BS) Elem Ed 1966; Hood Coll (MA) Spec Ed Learning Disabilities 1981; *cr:* Lowell Schl 4th Grd Tchr 1966-69; DOD Schls Germany 2nd-4th Grd Tchr 1969-75; Washington Cty Schls 5th Grd Tchr 1975-78, 1981-; *ai:* NEA; *office:* Conococheague Elem Schl 12408 Learning Ln Hagerstown MD 21740

SHERMAN, RICHARD DAVID, Instrumental Music Teacher; *b:* Fostoria, OH; *m:* Susan Schriever; *c:* Katherine Elaine; *ed:* Bowling Green St Univ (BA) Music Ed 1976; Ashland Univ (MS) Ed Curr, Instruction 1992; *cr:* Zane Trace Local Schls Instrumental Music Tchr 1976-; *ai:* 5-12 Grd Marching, Concert, Jazz, Pep Bands; Solo, Ensembles; OMEA, MENC, OEA, NEA 1976-; *office:* Zane Trace Local Schls 946 St Rt 180 Chillicothe OH 45601

SHERMAN, RICHARD LEWIS, 8th Grade Language Arts Tchr; *b:* Syracuse, NY; *m:* Leslie Mack; *c:* Christen, Jeffrey; *ed:* Geneseo St (BA) Eng 1975; 30 Post-Grad Hrs Oswego St; *cr:* Mexico Acad, Cntrl Tchrs Asst 1975-76; Altmar Elem Schl 3rd Grd Tchr 1976-77; Altmar-Par- Wil MS8th Grd Lang Arts 1977-; *ai:* Offensive Coord Var Ftbl; Strength Coach; Weightlifting Club Coach, Adv; Fac Schlsp Comm; NYSUT 1975-; *office:* Altmar-Parish-Williamstown HS Rt 22 Parish NY 13131

SHERMAN, RICK, Physical Education Teacher; *b:* Bronx, NY; *ed:* William Jewell Coll (BS) PE, His 1970; So CT St Univ PE 30 Addl Hrs 1986; *cr:* Polo HS Soc Stud Tchr, Coach 1970-71; Plattsburg Elem Schl PE Tchr 1971-73; Flanders Elem Schl PE Tchr 1973-; *ai:* HS Head Wrestling Coach; CT Coaches Assn 1973-, Nom 9 Wr Coach of Yr; NEA, CEA, Natl Wr Coaches Assn 1973-; 2 Wrestling Articles Pub.

SHERMAN, SARAH MARIE, French Teacher; *b:* Glen Falls, NY; *ed:* SUNY at Cortland (BA) Fr Scndry Ed 1994; Attnd SUNY at Potsdam; *cr:* Carthage HS Scndry Fr Tchr 1994-; *ai:* Fr Club; Stu at Risk Comm; Mentoring Prgm; *home:* 703 West St Carthage NY 13619*

SHERRICK, RICHARD HUGH, Music Teacher; *b:* Lima, OH; *m:* Susan Cook; *c:* Katherine; *ed:* Ohio St Univ (BS) Music 1970; Wright St Univ (MS) Ed 1985; *cr:* Parkway Local Schls Music Tchr 1971-; Ohio Northern Univ Lecturer in Percussion 1972-; *ai:* NEA, MENC, NBA 1971-; OMEA 1971-, Dist Pres; ASBDA 1980-; Percussive Arts SOc AFM 1972-; Lions Club Intern 1985-, Past Pres; Amer Legion 1980-; Citizen of Yr 1974; *office:* Parkway Local Schls 401 S Franklin St Rockford OH 45882*

SHERRILL, EDMUND KNOX, Dean of Chapel & Hum Teacher; *b:* Dickinson, ND; *m:* Elizabeth Evans; *c:* Hannah, Goldthwaite, Samuel; *ed:* Macalester Coll (BA) Pol Sci, His 1979; Yale Divinity Schl (MDiv) 1983; Attnd Inst for Schl Ministry 1990; *cr:* St Paul's Schl Rel, His Tchr 1983-86; Wooster Schl Chaplain, Rel Dept Chair 1986-90; St Paul's Schl Dean of Chapel, Rel Dept Chair, Hum Tchr 1990-; *ai:* Missionary Soc Adv; Coach; Pastoral Care; Hlth, Scholastic Comms; Curr Planning; AAR, SBL 1993-; Episcopal Church Diocese of NH 1986-, Priest Ordained 1986, Commission on Ministry.*

SHERROD, MARGARET, PE & Health Teacher; *b:* Washington, DC; *m:* Lowell Anthony; *c:* U'tonna; *ed:* Univ of MD (BS) E 1977; U of M, SF Uni (APC) General 1987; *cr:* John Hanson MS Chprsn 1980-87, PE & Hlth Tchr 1977-87; Benjamin Stoddert MS Chprsn 1995-, PE & Hlth Tchr 1987-; *ai:* Pom Pon Squad Dir 1989-94, Natl Champions 1990-94; Tchr & Stu Mentor; Vllybl & Karate Clb Spnsr; Fitness Cncl Spnsr; MSTA Minority Affairs Comm Mem; NEA 1978-; MAHPERD 1977-, Simon McNeely Awd 1994; PTSA 1990-; *office:* Benjamin Stoddert MS 2040 St Thomas Dr Waldorf MD 20602*

SHERROW, DOUGLAS BARNES, AP Economics & Business Instr; *b:* Hackensack, NJ; *m:* Theresa Marie Edelmann; *c:* Leighanne, Jessica; *ed:* SUNY at Stony Brook (MLS) Liberal Arts 1975; Army Command & Staff Coll (MS) Military Sci 1989; US Army Quality Mngmt; *cr:* Commack HS South Soc Sci Tchr 1972-86; Commack HS Soc Sci Tchr 1986-89, AP Instr 1993-; Empire St Military Acad Deputy Commandant 1989-93; *ai:* Bookstore Adv; Fencing Coach; NY St United Tchrs 1972-, Chief Del; AFT 1972-; US Fencing Coaches Assn 1976-; Knights of Columbus 1995-, 3rd Degree; Militia Assn of NY 1972-, VP, Life Mem; Natl Guard Assn 1972-; Army of US Assn 1989-; Tchr of Yr Nom; *office:* Commack HS Scholar Ln Commack NY 11725

SHERTZER, MICHAEL JAMES, Agricultural Education Instr; *b:* Fremont, OH; *m:* Mary Lou; *c:* Jim, John, Stephanie; *ed:* OH St Univ (BS) Ag Ed 1970, (MS) Ag Ed 1977; Masters Plus 45 in Ed at Univ of Toledo; *cr:* Margaretta Schls Tchr 1970-71; Bowling Green Ag Ed Tchr 1971-; *ai:* Adult Ed; FFA Adv; NEA, OUATA-NAUATA 1970-; Farm Bureau 1980-; 4-H 1972-, Adv, Outstanding Adv Awd 1995; Little League 1975-85, Coach; Extension & 4-H Advy Comm; Gamma Sigma Delta Ag Honorary; 30 Minute Club-Articles Pub out of St; St of OH Outstanding Tchr 1984; Bowling Green City Schls Tchr of Yr 1993; *office:* Bowling Green HS 530 W Poe Rd Bowling Green OH 43402

SHERWIN, ALICE, Third Grade Teacher; *b:* Upper Darby, PA; *ed:* St Michael's Coll (BA) Elem Ed 1986; Project Wild; *cr:* St Ambrose Schl 4th Grd Tchr 1987-92, Kndgtn Tchr 1993, Third Grd Tchr 1993-, Fifth Grd Tchr 1994-95; *ai:* Schl Publicity; Home Schl Assn; NCEA 1988-; DETA 1995-; St Ambrose Church, Eucharistic Minister 1993-95; *office:* St Ambrose Schl 260 Okell St Buffalo NY 14220

SHERWIN, RENE DIBARTOLA, Former 3rd Grade Teacher; *b:* Pittsburgh, PA; *m:* Todd James; *c:* Ashley E., Amanda M.; *cr:* St Agnes Elem Schl 3rd Tchr 1986-92; *ai:* JV, Var Chrldng Spon 1986-91; *home:* 111 Shag Bark Ln Venetia PA 15367

SHERWOOD, BRUCE ARTHUR, Social Studies Teacher; *b:* Utica, NY; *m:* Beth; *c:* Emily; *ed:* Hartwick Coll (BA) His, Coaching 1977; Cortland St (MA) His 1985; Oswego St Driver Ed NYS Cirt 1990; *cr:* Morrisville-Eaton Schl Tchr 1980-; *ai:* B & G Cross Cntry, Boys Track, Indoor Track Coach; Frosh Class Adv; NEA 1980-; Lions Club 1980-, Tres 11 Yrs; Taft, Colgate Seminar Fellow; *office:* Morrisville-Eaton Schl P O Box 990 Fearon Rd Morrisville NY 13408

SHERWOOD, LINDA HOLLAND, English Teacher; *b:* Mamaroneck, NY; *m:* Steven T.; *c:* Steven Jr., Kayla; *ed:* Pace Univ (BA) Eng 1986; Columbia Univ (MA) Eng 1991; *cr:* Cardinal Spellman HS Eng Tchr 1988-90; Mamaroneck HS Eng Tchr 1992-; *ai:* Interdisciplinary Team Dev; Transitions Course Dev for ESL Stu; *office:* Mamaroneck HS 1000 W Boston Post Rd Mamaroneck NY 10543

SHERWOOD, ROSANNE EVANS, 5th Grade Teacher; *b:* Oakmont, WV; *m:* Richard; *ed:* Frostburg St Coll (BA) 1971, (MEd) 1974; 73 Hrs Over Masters; *cr:* Accident Elem 5th Grd Tchr 1971-; *ai:* Garrett Cty Tchrs Assn, MD St Tchrs Assn, NEA 1971-, Schl Rep; PTA; Alpha Alpha; Delta Kappa Gamma Intnl; NS DAR; Accident Cultural & Historical Society; Accident Concert Band; *home:* PO Box 26 Accident MD 21520

SHESMAN, MATTHEW MARK, Mathematics Teacher; *b:* Meadville, PA; *m:* Sharon Maryott; *c:* Danielle, Clay, Rachel, Samuel; *ed:* Slippery Rock Univ (BS) Ed & Math 1981; 24 Post Grad Hrs Permanent Cert; *cr:* Union City Area HS Math Tchr 1982; Northeast HS Math Tchr 1982-90; Iroquois HS Math Tchr 1990-; *ai:* Var Ftbl Coach; FCA 1991-; PSEA; First Bapt Church 1990-; *office:* Iroquois Jr Sr HS 4301 Main St Erie PA 16511

SHETH, SONAL B., High School Science Teacher; *b:* Umreth, India; *ed:* Miami Univ (BA) Sci Ed, Zoology 1992; OH St Univ 36 Hrs Earned Towards Masters in Sci Ed; *cr:* The Oxford Motel Desk Clerk, Mgmt 1988-92; Thomas Worthington HS Sci Tchr 1992-; *ai:* Braded Course of Stud Curr Comm; Mulitcultural Coord; Dance, Indian Dance, Culture Coord, Choreographer; MC for Columbus Comm Hindu Soc; NEA, OEA, WEA 1992-; Outstdng Woman of Amer 1991; Natl Awd Prof Indian Dance Competition; *home:* 1234 Bunker Hill Blvd Apt A Columbus OH 43220*

SHETLER, CURTIS BARRETT, Choral Director; *b:* Brunswick, GA; *m:* Donna; *c:* Anna, Kayla; *ed:* Eastern Nazanence Coll (BS) Music Ed 1975; Towson St Univ (BS) Music Ed 1983; Addl 30 Hrs in Music Ed; Bowie St Tchrs Coll Cert 1976; *cr:* Prince Georges Cty Schl Vocal Tchr 1976-83; Washington Cty Schl Vocal Tchr 1983-; *ai:* Bsktbl Asst Coach; Track Coach; Madrigal Show Choir; Theatre; Accompanist & Coord Washington Cty All-Cty Chorus Jr & Sr; ACDA 1990-; MENC 1980-; NEA 1976-; Rekobeth UM Church 1990-, Organist, Choral Dir; *office:* North Hagerstown HS 1200 Pennsylvania Ave Hagerstown MD 21742*

SHETROM, RICHARD DAVID, Amer History & US Govt Teacher; *b:* Huntingdon, PA; *m:* Amy Peet; *c:* Ian, Jesse; *ed:* Thiel Coll (BA) Pol Sci, His 1977; Grad Class at Penn St Univ; *cr:* Philipsburg Osceola Schl Tchr 1979-, Bsktbl Coach 1981-93, Bsbl Coach 1982-90, Ftbl Coach 19[illegible] *ai:* Stu Assistance Team; Discipline, Writing Assesment, Alternate [illegible] Comm; Scndry Instruction Support Team; PSEA, NEA 1979-; Hunt[illegible] City Bsbl League 1973-, Coach, Player, Mgr; Peter B. Haas Fnd [illegible] Trustee; Trinity United Meth Church 1979-, PPR, Nominations [illegible] *office:* Philipsburg Osceola Area Sr HS 502 Philips St Philipsbu[illegible] 16866*

SHEVALIER, MARY ELLEN KALIL, Art & Dance Teach[illegible] Syracuse, NY; *m:* Mark T.; *ed:* Onondaga Comm Coll (AAS) Graph[illegible] 1979; St Univ of NY at Oswego (MFA) Fine Arts 1987; Syracus[illegible] (BA) Art Ed, Visual & Performing Arts 1992; *cr:* Copenhagen Cnt[illegible] K-12 Grd Art Tchr 1982-85; South Jefferson Cntrl Schl Art & Danc[illegible] 1985-; Jefferson Comm Coll Adj Prof in Art 1989; *ai:* Art Club Adv[illegible] Dance Co Founder & Dir 5 Yrs; NYSATA 1996; Tri-Cty Art Tchr[illegible] 1982-, Chprsn 1 Yr; NYSUT 1982-; North Cty Artist Guild[illegible] Scholastics Art Advy Cncl 1985-; Amnesty Intnl, Natl Museum [illegible] ARTS 1995-; Disney Salutes the Amer Tchr Awd 1994; Stu Cncl O[illegible] Tchr Awd 1995; Publication in FYI Chalkboard, NY Fnd for the Arts[illegible] *office:* South Jefferson Central Schl PO Box 10 Rt 11 Adams NY 1[illegible]

SHEVCHIK, STEPHANIE S., Drama Teacher; *b:* Sewickley, [illegible] Robert V.; *c:* Corinne; *ed:* Edinboro Univ (BS) Lang Arts, Eng 19[illegible] Hopewell Jr HS Eng Tchr 1964-70; Hopewell Sr HS Drama Tchr 19[illegible] Thespian Troupe 4109 Spon; PSEA, NEA 1964-; Alpha Delta Kappa [illegible] Corresponding Sec; ETA 1995-; *office:* Hopewell Sr HS 1215 Longv[illegible] Aliquippa PA 15001

SHEVEL, WILLIAM ROBERT, English Teacher; *b:* Long Branch, [illegible] Steven Edward, Jonathan Mathew; *ed:* OH Univ (BSED) Eng 19[illegible] Athens HS Eng Tchr 1980-; *ai:* Stage Adv; NEA, OEA, NCTE [illegible] *office:* Athens HS 1 High School Rd The Plains OH 45780*

SHEVER, DORIS V., English Teacher; *b:* Ellwood City, PA; *ed:* C[illegible] Univ (BS) Comp Eng 1968; UPJ, Penn St (BS) Eng 1980; *cr:* Fores[illegible] Schl Spec Ed Tchr 1969-70; Conemaugh Vly HS Eng Tchr 1970-; *ai.*[illegible] Spelling Bee, Co-Sr Class Adv; Lang Arts Dept Chprsn; [illegible] Interscholastic Rdng Team Adv; NEA, PSEA, CVEA 1969-; *hom*[illegible] Lamberd Ave Johnstown PA 15904*

SHEW, NANCY CAROL, English Teacher; *b:* Detroit, MI; *m:* [illegible] Robert; *c:* Melissa, Maryanne; *ed:* Oakland Cty Comm Coll (ALA) I[illegible] Arts 1980; Wayne St Univ (BA) Eng, Ed 1983; Oakland Univ (MA[illegible] Stud 1988; *cr:* Troy Schls Long Term Substitute; Our Lady of Lake[illegible] Soc Stud Tchr 1988-, Jr Class Moderator 1990-91, Soph Class Mod[illegible] 1992; St Frances Desale HS Eng Tchr 1993-95; Westervi[illegible] Gahanna-Jefferson Sub 1996-; *ai:* Jrnlsm Club Adv; Created News[illegible] SADD Adv; Soph Class Co-Adv; Jr Class Adv; Stu Act & Banquets [illegible] NCTE; WSU Acad Schlsp Awds to Further Ed; *home:* 956 Woodse[illegible] Westerville OH 43081*

SHIDEMANTLE, DONNA PRICE, First Grade Teacher; *b:* New [illegible] PA; *m:* James I.; *c:* Curtis Scott, Polly A. Way, Amy, Tim; *ed:* Sl[illegible] Rock Univ (BS) Elem Ed 1964, (ME) Elem Ed 1969; 30 Credit H[illegible] Grad Stud; *cr:* Union Area Schl Dist 4th Grd Tchr 1964-65; Ellwoo[illegible] Area Schl Dist 1st & 3rd Grd Tchr 1965-67; Slippery Rock Area Sc[illegible] 1st Grd Tchr 1979-; *ai:* Elem Testint Comm; Mentor Tchr; Porte[illegible] Presbytn Church 1973-, Choir & Sunday Schl Tchr; *office:* Morain[illegible] Schl 350 Main St Prospect PA 16052

SHIELDS, BETSY A. MC CORMICK, 4th Grade Teacher; *b:* Scr[illegible] PA; *m:* Robert T.; *c:* Mary Shields Driebe, Thomas, Martin X., Terer[illegible] *ed:* Marywood Coll (BA) Elem Ed 1958; Univ of Scranton 6 Cred[illegible] Rutgers Univ 3 Credit Hrs; 3 Credit Hrs; *cr:* Lehigh Parkway Schl 1[illegible] Grd Tchr 1958-61; Clayton Avon Schl 1st, 5-6th Grd Tchr 1961-6[illegible] Lady of Sorrows Schl 6th Grd Tchr 1983-91; St James MS 4th Gr[illegible] 1991-; *ai:* Natl Spelling Bee Contest Schl Coord; Chprsn of Su[illegible] Fund, Comm; Cath Tchrs Assn; Schl Rep to Tchrs Assn 1983-[illegible] Endwell Comm Choir 1983-88. Pub Newsletter for Parish Yr of [illegible] Coord; *office:* St James MS 143 Main St Johnson City NY 13790

SHIELDS, GALE LEWIS, Health & PE Teacher; *b:* Indiana, P[illegible] Donna Jean Filler; *c:* Kimberly Kimmel, Brent; *ed:* Slippery Rock[illegible] Hlth & PE 1969; IUP Penn St (MS) 1985; *ai:* Coaching; AD; PSEA [illegible] NEA 1969-; *office:* Punxsutawney Area Sr HS N Findley St Punxsut[illegible] PA 15767

SHIELDS, JEFFREY FRANKLIN,SR., Assistant Professor of Acc[illegible] Seattle, WA; *m:* Joyce M. Shelleman; *c:* Amy, Jeffrey Jr.; *ed:* WA S[illegible] (BS) Psych 1978; Univ of Pittsburgh (MBA) Acctng 1991, (PHD) A[illegible] 1991; *cr:* Naval Post Grad Schl Visiting Asst Prof 1991; Univ of Bal[illegible] Asst Prof 1991-; *ai:* Amer Acctng Assn 1985-; Inst of Mngmt A[illegible] 1991-; Phi Beta Kappa; Editorial Bd Journal of Mngmt Acctng [illegible] *office:* Univ Of Baltimore 1420 N Charles St Baltimore MD 21201

SHIELDS, KIMBERLY, Scndry Learning Support Tchr; *b:* Harri[illegible] PA; *ed:* Millersville Univ (BS) Spec Ed 1993; Working Toward MA[illegible] Ed & Cert for Supervision in Spec Ed; *cr:* Harrisburg Area Sch[illegible] 7th-8th Grd Learning Support Tchr 1993-94; East Pennsboro Are[illegible] Dist Scndry Grd Learning Support Tchr 1994-; *ai:* Ftbl, Wrestl[illegible] Competition Squads Var Chrldng Coach; Pep Club, Jr Class Adv[illegible] Mediation Co-Adv; Staff Dev, Project Independence, Prof Dev C[illegible] PSEA, NEA 1993-; ASCD 1994-; CEC 1996; *office:* East Pennsbor[illegible] HS 425 W Shady Ln Enola PA 17025*

SHIELDS, LAMARR DARNELL, Spanish & History Teach[illegible] Chicago, IL; *ed:* Grambling St Univ (BA) Pol Sci 1993, (BA) Span [illegible] Universidad de Cohulia Saltillo Mexico; *cr:* LaPetite Acad After Sch[illegible] 1994; Glodal Works Yth Org, Cnslr 1994; Baltimore City Coll HS [illegible] 1994-; *ai:* UMOJa Stu Org, Class of 1998 Advs; Sons of Rob[illegible] Mentoring; NAACP 1993-; LOC 1995-, Comm Chair; Arena Play[illegible] 1995-; Nom New Tchr of Yr, Golden Apple Awd; Articles; [illegible] Baltimore City College HS 480 3220 The Alameda Baltimore MD 2[illegible]

SHIELDS, SANDRA G., English Teacher; *b:* Lynn, MA; *m:* Thom[illegible] *c:* Anastasia; *ed:* Grad Work PA St Univ Instrl Systems; *cr:* St Mary[illegible] Schl Speech Tchr 1 Yr; Austin Area Schl Eng 7-12 Grd, Tech Tchr 1[illegible] *ai:* PSEA 1984-; PAECT, CPAECT 1994-; Potter Cty Ed Cncl 1995-, [illegible] Comm; PA Serve Fellow; PA Writing Assessment Advy Comm; *hom*[illegible] 1 Box 376 Emporium PA 15834

SHIFFLETT, MARIE GEISWEIDT, Physics & Math Teach[illegible] Somerset, PA; *m:* George F.; *c:* Joseph F., John E., Jason C.; *ed:* IN[illegible] of PA (BS) Math Ed 1975; Frostburg St Univ Physics Cert; *cr:* So[illegible] Cty Area Voc-Tech Schl Math Tchr 1977-79; North Star HS Phys[illegible] Math Tchr 1983-; *ai:* Sr Class Adv; NEA 1983-; North Star Ed Assn [illegible] PSEA 1983-; Jenners Grace Brethren Church 1960-, Sec; *office:* Nort[illegible] HS 400 Ohio St Boswell PA 15531

SHIFFNER, SCOTT LAWRENCE, Social Studies Teacher; *b:* Syr[illegible] NY; *m:* Deborah Markowitz; *c:* Daniel, Jonathan; *ed:* Cornell Univ [illegible] Govt 1971; Harvard Univ (MAT) Soc Stud 1972; Attnd Stratford[illegible] Monticello Summer Prgm; *cr:* Orchard Park HS Soc Stud Tchr 1973-[illegible] AFT, NYSUT & OPTA 1973-, VP; NCSS 1975-; Western NY W[illegible] Project 1988-; NEH Summer Seminars 1983, 1986 & 1989 & Summe[illegible] 1992; *office:* Orchard Park HS 4040 Baker Rd Orchard Park NY 141[illegible]

SHIFFRIN, LAWRENCE L., Physics Teacher; *b:* New Haven, C[illegible] Amy; *ed:* Souther CT ST Univ (MS) Sci Ed 1976, (MS) Environmen[illegible] 1981; 6th Yr Admin Supervision 1982; *cr:* Fairfield Coll Prep Schl

3; North Beufrod HS Tchr 1978-80; Milford HS Tchr 1980-83; A Foran HS Tchr 1983-; *ai:* Var Tennis Coach; JETS Teams Coach, EA, CEA 1978-; *office:* Joseph A Foran HS 80 Foran Rd Milford 60

IN, STUART D., Science Resource Teacher; *b:* Baltimore, MD; *m:* erson; *c:* Victoria, William; *ed:* Univ of MD (BS) Scndry Ed 1980; MD Coll (MS) Curr & Inst 1994; *cr:* John F. Kennedy HS Sci Tchr 2; Redland MS Sci Resource Tchr 1992-94; Walt Whitman HS Sci e Tchr 1994-; *ai:* Sci Dept Chprsn; Howard Hughes Tchr Scholar ip; *office:* Walt Whitman HS 7100 Whittier Blvd Bethesda MD

MBA, MADELINE, Program Coordinator & Teacher; *b:* lphia, PA; *m:* Sakaria; *c:* Nankali, Tweendeni; *ed:* Cheyney St Univ ndry Ed 1964; San Francisco St (MA) Scndry Ed 1968; Credit Hrs of PA, Temple, Widener Univ, Kutztown Univ, Univ de Las Amers *cr:* Redwood High Tchr 1969-70; Kibaba Ed Ofcr 1972-76; Schl Philadelphia Tchr 1977-; *ai:* Ec, Entrepreneurship & Commerce Pgm Coord; World Affairs Spon; Phila Fed of Tchrs 1977-, Bldg 88-89; AFT 1977-; Phila Soc Stud Cncl 1988-92 & 1994-; World His 92-; PA Cncl of Soc Stud 1993-; Mid Sts Soc Stud Cncl 1992-; PA phic Alliance 1993-; Point Breeze Civic Assoc 1978-92, Treas, Svc 1984-86 & 1990; St Philips Episcopal Church 1982-, Sec of & Fin Chprsn; Comm Legal Svcs 1985-, South Branch Advy Bd Pres Advy Bd Mem; North of Washington Ave Coalition 1989-, Pres, Svc; Pierce Coll 1990-, Act 101 Advy Bd; Peace Action Group Awds: Freedoms Fndtn Stud Summer 1986, South Phila Partnership pport Group Comm Svc 1990; Area Cncl for Ec Ed Summer 1987; rother of Teamsters Labor Stud at UC at Berkeley 1988; Temple EC Schlsp 1988; Fulbright & Hays Summer Seminar 1990 & 1995; w Wilson Natl Flwshp & World His Summer Inst 1991; Frgn Policy nst 1991 & 1995; NEH Summer Inst 1992; PA Natl Geographic e Insts 1993; Numerous Publications & Articles.*

ING, THOMAS LEE, 8th Grd Social Studies Teacher; *b:* Ravenna, Kent St Univ (BS) Comprehensive Soc Stud 1972-; Univ of Dayton Educl Admin 1991; *cr:* St Mary MS 8th Grd Soc Stud Tchr 1974-95; in 1995; Soc Stu Tchr 1996-; *ai:* Soc Stud, Soc Justice Depts Chms; oord; Spec Evens Chprsn; *office:* Saint Mary MS 261 Elm Rd N E OH 44483

ORSKE, KAREN MORRIS, Spanish Teacher; *b:* Warren, OH; *m:* Jr.; *c:* Edward III, Micah; *ed:* Youngstown St (BS) Span, Ed; Univ on (ME) Counseling; *cr:* Lakeviwe HS Span Tchr 1976-; *ai:* Span AP; NEA, OEA, LTA 1976-; *office:* Lakeview HS 300 Hillman Dr d OH 44410

ONY, ROBERT JOSEPH, Biology Teacher; *b:* Brooklyn, NY; *m:* Kramer; *c:* Marna A., Jennifer M.; *ed:* Brooklyn Coll (BA) Bio 1968, d 1972; Attnd SUNY at Albany, NJ Inst of Tech, Univ of CO at r, CUNY at Staten Island; *cr:* John Jay HS Tchr 1968-72; Tottenville ir 1972-; CUNY Adj Tchr 1995-; *ai:* Med Tech Club, Sci Tchr hip Prgm Adv; Med Tech Prgm, Sci Rsrch Co-Coord; AFT 1968-; 1972-; NYSSTA 1976-; Hazlet Yth Advy Bd 1981-; Temple Beth, m; Mens Club 1980-; Contributing Author Interdisciplinary Sci Seminar; Curr Dev, Author Tech Grant; *office:* Tottenville HS 100 Ave Staten Island NY 10312*

JUNG GIL, Assoc Prof Electrical Engrng; *b:* Seoul, Korea; *m:* Kim; *c:* Sang Ok, Gina Nigel; *ed:* Seoul Natl Univ (BS) Elec 1965; Univ of PA (MSE) Systems Engrng 1976, (PHD) Systems 1979; *cr:* Hyundai Heavy Indstries Electrical Engr 1969-75; Inst of Tech Assoc Prof 1979-95; Sunkyong CPG Inc VP, Tech Adv *ai:* Advanced Tech Research Inst Dir; IEEE 1976-; KSEA 1979-, ASA 1988-, VP NY Chapter; Eta Kappa Nu 1984-; Sigma Xi 1979-; 1994-; Numerous Rsrch Grants SDIO, AFOSR, ONR,NRL; SIT Assoc Outstndng Tchr Awd 1988; *office:* Stevens Inst Of Tech Point Station Hoboken NJ 07030

L, PAUL J., Certified Public Accountant; *b:* Waterloo, NY; *ed:* ter Inst of Tech (BS) Accounting 1975; 9 Grad Hrs at James n Univ; 3 Grad Hrs at Robert Morris Coll; 3 Grd Hrs at St Univ of Oswego; *cr:* Cayuga Comm Coll Instr & Assoc Prof 1976-; Dermody, Brown Certified Pub Accountants PC Sr Staff Accountant & Office 977-90; *ai:* Accounting Curr Comm Chair; Coll-Wide Evaluation Sec; Accounting Banquet Comm Adv; AICPA, NYSSCPA 1982-; 981-; Saint Marys Church 1988-, Liturgy Comm Chair; *office:* Comm Coll 197 Franklin St Auburn NY 13021

LEDECKER, ELIZABETH MORRIS, Fourth Grade Teacher; *b:* rgh, PA; *m:* Neil A.; *c:* Jennifer Ann, Robert Neil; *ed:* Lincoln Univ lem Ed 1976; Working Toward MED Clarion Univ; *cr:* Jefferson b Schls 1-6 Grd Sci Tchr 1976; DuBois Area Pub Schls 1-6 Grd Tchr *ai:* Prof Dev Comm; Lead Tchr, Mentor Prgms; NEA, PSEA 1977-; 1996; Laurel Rdng Cncl 1993-, Bd Mem; Texas Lake Recreation 1995-; AEBC Media Tchr of Yr 1992; Insvc Cooperative Learning Presenter; *office:* Oklahoma Elem Schl Chestnut Ave Du Bois PA

, MARGARET EILEEN, Retired Teacher; *b:* Methuen, MA; *ed:* St Vincent Coll (BA) Eng 1960; Manhattan Coll (MA) Theology *cr:* St Peter's 7 Grd Math, Eng, Sci, Music Art Tchr 1946-50; St 3 Grd All Subjects Tchr 1950-57; St Anne's 7-9 Grd Math, Eng, Soc Tchr 1957-62; Mt St Joseph 7-9 Grd Math, Eng, Soc Stud Tchr 4; St Aidan's 6-8 Grd Math, Eng, Soc Stud, Music, Art Tchr 9; Cath Schls & Parishes Area Coord, Adult Ed Admin 1969-79; St l Schl 5-6 Grd Math, Eng, Sci, Soc Stud, Music, Art Tchr 1979-90; EA; *home:* 30 Merrimack St North Andover MA 01845

, MARY QUIN, Practical Nursing Teacher; *b:* Bronx, NY; *m:* Frank Phoebe Elisabeth; *ed:* Mount St Mary Coll (BSN) Nrsng 1988; Iona MS) Ed & Bio 1995; *cr:* Memrl Sloan Kettering Cancer Ctr ered Nurse 1988-90; Nyack Hosp Comm Hlth Nurse 1990-91; FOJP rg Med Malpractice Investigator 1991-92; Rockland Tech Ctr al Nrsng Tchr 1991-; *ai:* Practical Nrsng Stdnts VICA Adv; VICA Competition Chprsn 1994 & 1995; NYSNA 1992-; NYSHOEA NCLEX 1995- Panel Mem; *office:* Rockland Tech Center Schl 65 Rd West Nyack NY 10994

HOUSE, E. JANE, Prof of Biology; *b:* Chestnut Hill, PA; *m:* R.; *c:* Linda A. Saupe, Patricia G., James, Lisa Pupo; *ed:* Ursinus BS) Bio 1952; Univ of PA Phys Therapy 1953; *cr:* Ursinus Coll Asst me Instr 1960-77, Asst Prof 1977-84, Assoc Prof 1984-92, Bio Prof *ai:* Premed Credentials Comm; Allied Hlth, Premedical Adv; NABT PAS 1988-; Sigma Xi Assoc 1981-; Natl Assn of Advs for Hlth sions; Lindback Awd for Distngd Tchng 1981; Summer Rsrch Curr Dev 1988; Sabbitcal Leave for Curr Dev 1986; Glenmeade Grant Summer 1984; Articles Pub; *home:* 1747 S Collegeville Rd eville PA 19426

GLE, ZONIE S., English Teacher; *b:* Washington, PA; *ed:* West y St Coll (BA) Eng Ed 1991; *cr:* Mc Guffey HS Eng Tchr 1994-; *ai:* Club Spon; NEA, PSEA, MEA, ACUWPET 1994-; *office:* Mc H S 86 Mc Guffey Dr Claysville PA 15323

, SHELBY LYNN, French Teacher; *b:* Harrisburg, PA; *ed:* sville Univ (BSE) Fr 1990; Millersville Grad Fr Summerschl 14 Cr; Wilson Univ 6 Cr; Carlow Coll 3 Cr; *cr:* Cumberland Valley Fr Tchr 1990-; *ai:* PSEA & CVEA 1990-; NEA 1990-; AATF 1991-; *office:* Cumberland Valley HS 6746 Carlisle Pike Mechanicsburg PA 17055

SHIPENGROVER, WILLIAM L., Business Education Chair; *b:* Herkimer, NY; *m:* Judith A. Moyes; *c:* Joanna D.; *ed:* St Univ of NY at Albany (BS) Bus Ed 1956, (MS) Bus Ed 1962; Columbia Univ (MS) Higher Ed 1968; 30 Addl Credit Hrs; Univ of Buffalo Grad Courses; *cr:* Clarence HS Tchr & Dept Chair 1956-; Buffalo St Coll Adj Prof of Tchng & Supvr Stu Tchrs 1996-; *ai:* Mock Trial Adv, Championship Teams; Future Tchrs Adv; AFT, NEA & Clarence TA; Bus Tchrs Assn, Western NY Pre 1972; Sabbatical Leave-1st at Clarence HS 1967; Article Pub on Mock Trials; Cty Bar Assn Recipient of Liberty Bell Awd 1990; Prof Improvement Prgm NYU; *office:* Clarence Central HS 9625 Main St Clarence NY 14031

SHIPLEY, JANE A., Secondary English Teacher; *b:* Cumberland, MD; *c:* Dorothy Embry, Nathan; *ed:* Millersville Univ (BS) Scndry Eng 1985; Perm Cert; 26 Credit Hrs Various Insts; *cr:* Harrisburg Schl Dist Scndry Eng Tchr 11 Yrs; *ai:* Forensic Coach & Judge, Local, St & Natl; HEA, PSEA 1985-; *office:* Harrisburg Schl Dist 1201 N 6th St Harrisburg PA 17103*

SHIPLEY, JANET ELAINE, Fourth Grade Teacher; *b:* Pittsburgh, PA; *ed:* CA Univ of PA (BS) Elem Ed 1966; 28 Credit Hrs Elem Ed; 30 Credit Hrs ME; *cr:* Arlington Elem Schl 3-6 Grd Art, Acad 1966-67; Sunnyside Elem Schl 3-8 Grd Acad Tchr 1967-; *ai:* Organize Schl Incentive Prgm for Honor Roll, Citizenship Honor Roll; Operate Coupon Incentive Store for Classroom; Pgh Fed of Tchrs, PA Fed of Tchrs, Natl Fed of Tchrs 1969-; Monroeville Chrstn Church Photographer, Former Librn, Jr Choir Asst Dir, Choir Mem; Natl Rifle Assn 1994-95; PA Bowlers 1967-90; *office:* Sunnyside Elem Schl 4801 Stanton Ave Pittsburgh PA 15201

SHIPMAN, JANET VANZOEST, 8th Grade Language Arts Tchr; *b:* Willard, OH; *m:* Gregory S.; *c:* Andrew; *ed:* OH St Univ (BS) Elem Ed 1987; Western MD Coll (MS) Counseling 1996; *cr:* New Market Mid 6th Grd Lang Arts, Math Tchr 1987-88, 6th Grd Lang Arts, Soc Stud 1988-90, 7th Grd Lang Arts Tchr 1990-91, 8th Grd Lang Arts Tchr 1991-; *ai:* Team Ldr; Peer Mediation Adv; Svc Learning Group Ldr; NEA 1987-; ACA 1996; FCTA 1987-; Nom Chamber of Commerce Tchr of Yr; *home:* 5610 Doubs Rd Adamstown MD 21710*

SHIPP, RUSSELL E., 8th Grade English Teacher; *b:* Hartford, CT; *m:* Miriam Kilgore; *c:* John, Eric, Jeremy; *ed:* Earlham Coll (BA) Eng 1965; 70 Post Grad Hrs; *cr:* Boys Tech Schl Milwauee WI Eng Tchr 10th & 11th Grd 1 Yr; Shenendehower Schl Eng Tchr 9th & 10th Grd 2 Yrs; Iroquois MS Eng Tchr 8th Grd 26 Yrs; *ai:* NEA 1968-; NTA 1970-; Miscellaneous Poetry; *office:* Iroquois MS 2495 Rosendale Rd Niskayuna NY 12309

SHIPTENKO, ELLEN MARIE MALACKY, French Teacher; *b:* Warren, OH; *m:* Paul Elias; *c:* Paula Ann, Peter John; *ed:* Kent St Univ (BSEd) Fr & Russian 1961; Indiana Univ (MAT) Tchng of Russian 1964; Wright St Univ 9 Quarter Hrs 1977-78; Attnd NDEA Russian Lang Inst Acad Yr 1963-64 & Temple Univ Summer Prgm Univesite de Paris; *cr:* Mayfield HS Fr Tchr 1961-63; Thorntont Fractional S Fr & Russian Tchr 1964-65; Edison Comm Coll Fr Tchr 1979-80; Troy HS Fr Tchr 1980-; *ai:* Fr Club Adv; Tchr Cnslr & Stu Educl Travel; NEA, OEA, OFLA & TCEA 1980-; AATF 1988-93; ACTR 1987-; Miami Cty Democratic Woman 1988-, Exec Comm 1993-95; Troy City Bd of Hlth 1978-83; Candidate City Cncl Troy 1978 & 1980; FISH; Annunciation Greek Orthodox Choir; *home:* 1141 Maplecrest Dr Troy OH 45373*

SHIPTON, SHARON PEARL, Associate Professor of Nursing; *b:* Beaver Falls, PA; *m:* Larry K.; *c:* Michael, Matthew; *ed:* Comm Coll Beaver Cty (AS) Nrsng 1973; Slippery ROck Univ (BSN) Nrsng 1976; Edinboro Univ (MSN) Nrsng 1982; Univ of Pittsburgh (PHD) Nrsng 1994; Attnd Youngstown St Univ; *cr:* Mercer Cty Home & Hosp Head Nurse 1974-75; Grove City Hosp Acting Nrsng Dir 1976-77; Sharon Gen Hosp Schl of Nrsng Nrsng Instr 1978-82; Youngstown St Univ Assoc Prof 1982-; *ai:* Univ Curr, Coll Cmptr Dev, Dept Search Comm; NEA 1982-; PA Schl Bds Assn 1993-; Natl Schl Bds Assn 1994-; Grove City Area Schl Bd 1993-, Chprsn Educl Svcs Comm, Svc Awd; Midwestern Intermediate Unit Bd 1994-, Svc Awd; Sigma Theta Tau 1990-, Chprsn By-Law Comm; Awded Grad Fac Status 1996; *office:* Youngstown St Univ 410 Wick Ave Youngstown OH 44555

SHIRE, MARIA GALLACCIO, French & Spanish Teacher; *b:* Philadelphia, PA; *m:* Donald Steven; *c:* Norah J., John D.; *ed:* PA St Univ at Coll Park (BA) Fr 1963; Univ of PA (MA) Rom Lang, Fr 1964; 30 Addl Hrs; *cr:* Peirce Jr Coll Fr, Span Tchr 1965-67; Rutgers Univ Fr Asst Prof 1965-66; Univ of MD Fr Asst Prof 1967-68; ELS Lang Schl Eng as for Lang Tchr 1968; Winston Churchill HS Fr Tchr 1968-69; Bethesda Chevy Chase HS Fr, Span Tchr 1984-91; Thomas Sprigg Wootton HS Fr, Span Tchr 1991-; *ai:* Peirce Jr Coll Art Club Spon; Soc Comm; Fr Club Co-Spon; Bethesda Chevy Chase HS Mentor; NBA 1984-; AATF 1984-93; GWATFL 1993-94; *office:* Thomas S Wootton HS 2100 Wootton Pky Rockville MD 20850

SHIRES, JUDITH REDCLIFT, English Teacher & Dept Rep; *b:* Harrisburg, PA; *m:* Richard N.; *c:* Cooper, Wyatt; *ed:* Shippensburg Univ (BA) Eng Ed 1974; Addl 30 Hrs Gifted Ed; *cr:* Harrisburg Schl Dist Eng Tchr 1977-; *ai:* Eng Dept Rep; Textbook Adoption, Integration, Acad, Voc Comm; New Tchrs Mentor Prgm; PA Assn for Gifted Ed 1987-; Natl Assn Gifted Ed 1993-; NEA, HEA, PSEA 1977-; NCRVE 1992-; *office:* Harrisburg HS 2915 N 3rd St Harrisburg PA 17110

SHIREY, CONNIE MAE, English Teacher; *b:* Cleveland, OH; *m:* Kenneth W.; *ed:* Cleveland St (BA) Eng 1970; Ashland Univ (MA) Curr & Instr 1995; Attnd Akron Univ 18 Hrs; *cr:* Hillside Jr HS Eng Tchr 1970-82; Normandy HS Eng Tchr 1982-; *ai:* Academician Adv; Parma Tchr of Yr Nom; Jennings Scholar; PEA; OEA; NEA; NCTE 1970-; Alpha Delta Kappa; PTA OH St Life Mem; *office:* Normany HS 2500 W Pleasant Valley Rd Parma OH 44134

SHIRING, PAUL H., Chem Tchr & Sci Dept Chairman; *b:* Kittanning, PA; *ed:* Indiana Univ of PA (BS) Chem Ed 1961, (MED) Phys Sci in Ed 1965; Grad Stud at MA Inst of Tech & Univ of Pittsburgh; *cr:* Turtle Creek HS Chem Tchr 1961-65; Burrell HS Chem Tchr & Sci Dept Chm 1965-; *ai:* Tennis Coach; Burrell Ed Assn 1965-, Pres; PA Ed Assn, Natl PA Sci Tchrs Assn & NSTA 1961-; Amer Nuclear Sci Tchrs Assn 1970-, Charter Mem & Sec; Jaycees 1962-79, Pres, Outstanding Local Mem & St Pres Round Table Awds; Natl Sci Fnd Grants at Adelphi Univ, Univ of AR, PA St Univ, Hope Coll & Indiana Univ of PA; PA Outstanding Tchr 1976; Pittsburgh Spectroscopy Soc Awd for Excl in Sci Tchng 1970 & 1980; Co-Author Nuclear Sci for HS & Supplementary Materials for Nuclear Sci Pub by PA Dept of Ed; *office:* Burrell HS Puckety Church Rd Lower Burrell PA 15068

SHIRING, STEPHEN BOYD, Hospitality Mgmt Program Dir; *b:* Kittanning, PA; *m:* Tamara M Galzerano; *c:* Stephen Jr., Samantha, Elizabeth; *ed:* IN Univ of PA (BS) Restaurant-Hotel Mgmt 1981, (MBA) Bus 1985; Univ of Pittsburgh (EdD) Higher Ed Admin 1995; *cr:* Bob Evans Farms Inc Restaurant Mgr 1981-83; IN Univ of PA Bus Instr 1985-87; Butler Cty Comm Coll Hospitality Mgmt Prgm Dir 1987-; *ai:* Hospitality Club Adv; Little League Coach; Cncl on Hotel, Restaurant, Institutional Ed 1989-; Natl Rest Assn 1988-; Lions Club 1983-; Eagles 1981-; Butler Cty Prof Home Ec Grant; Stu Adv & Club Adv Awd; Charles W Nicholas Fac Enhancement Awd; Perkins Fac Externship; Articles Pub; *office:* Butler County Comm Coll Oak Hills Colleg Dr Butler PA 16001

SHIRK, RENEE HUNSBERGER, Social Science Teacher; *b:* Chambersburg, PA; *m:* Andrew E.; *ed:* Messiah Coll (BA) Behavioral Sci & Soc Stud 1988; Pursuing MS; *cr:* Camp Hill HS Soc Stud Tchr 1988-89; James Buchanan MS Soc Stud Tchr 1989-90; Chesire HS Soc Stud Tchr 1993-; *ai:* Yrbk Adv; Yth in Govt Co-Chprsn; SAM Intervention Team Mem; CT BEST Pgm Participant; NEA 1994-; Local Church 1992-, Yth Ldr; *office:* Cheshire HS 525 S Main St Cheshire CT 06410*

SHIRK, WANDA (GEHRET), English Teacher; *b:* Lewistown, PA; *m:* William K.; *c:* Dawn, Shawn; *ed:* Wheaton Coll (BA) Bible, Speech Comm 1971; Kutztown Univ (MED) Eng 1974; Addl 20 Credit Hrs; *cr:* Warwick HS Eng Tchr 1971-77; Northern Potter HS Eng Tchr 1983-95; *ai:* Past Yrbk, Newspaper, NHS Adv; Speech Team Coach; Attendance Comm; Timing Ofcl for All Ath Events; PTA 1985-, Pres 2 Terms; VCA Parent-Tchr Flwshp 1985-, Pres 4 Terms; PA Cncl of Tchrs of Eng 1991.*

SHIRLEY, DONALD R., English Teacher; *b:* Chambersburg, PA; *m:* Joyce Rinehart; *c:* Scott, Todd, Allison; *ed:* Shippensburg Univ (BED) Eng 1971, (MA) Eng 1976; Over 45 Hrs Beyond Masters; Supervisory Cert; *cr:* Mechanicsburg Area Sr Eng Tchr 1971-, Eng Dept Supvr 1987-; *ai:* Var Bsbl Head Coach 1971-; NEA 1971-; Phi Delta Kappa 1990-; Amer Bsbl Coaches Assn 1971-; Outstanding Svc to Stdnts 1979; *office:* Mechanicsburg Area HS 500 S Broad St Mechanicsburg PA 17055

SHIRLEY, ELEANOR MIRARCHI, College Professor; *b:* Philadelphia, PA; *m:* Francis J.; *c:* Brian F., Daniel V.; *ed:* Temple Univ (BS) Ed 1975; Natl Court Reporters Assn Cert Court Reporting Instr 1993; Philadelphia Coll of Textiles & Sci, Rider Coll; Marywood Coll Grad Credits Towards Masters; *cr:* St Hubert HS Bus Tchr 1975-80; Cardinal Dougherty HS Bus Tchr 1980-81; Katharine Gibbs Schl Instr 1984-87; Manor Jr Coll Adj Fac 1993-94; Peirce Coll Dept Coord, Coll Prof, Acad Adv 1987-; *ai:* Examiner of Registered Prof Reporters Exam of the Natl Court Reporters Assn; Dean's Cncl, Outcomes Assessment Comms; Natl Court Reporters Assn 1988-; Natl Bus Ed Assn; PA Bus Ed Assn; Pi Omega Pi 1975; *home:* 8628 Belfry Dr Philadelphia PA 19128

SHISLER, DALE, Algebra II & Calculus Teacher; *b:* Barberton, OH; *c:* E. Ray, Michael D., Jennifer M. Horst; *ed:* Univ of Akron (BA) Math Ed 1985; *cr:* Black River HS Math Tchr 1986-; Univ of Akron Math Instr 1986-; *ai:* Chess Club, Class Adv; NCTM; Math Assn of Amer; Zion Luth Church 1953-, Councilmen; *home:* 8 Greenwood Dr Doylestown OH 44230

SHIVELEY, M. SCOTT, Biology Teacher; *b:* Rochester, PA; *ed:* Geneva Coll (BS) Bio 1965; Miami of OH (MAT) Zoology, Physiology; Attnd Kent St, Walsh, Univ of Pittsburgh; *cr:* Sandusky HS Bio Tchr 1965-66; Boardman HS Bio Tchr; *ai:* NEA; OEA; BEA; *office:* Boardman Local Schls 7777 Glenwood Ave Boardman OH 44512

SHIVELY, LAIRD D., German Teacher; *b:* Danville, PA; *m:* Linda R.; *c:* Eric D., Karin E.; *ed:* Bloomsburg Univ (BS) Scndry Ed, Ger 1967; Villanova Univ (MA) Ger Lit 1972; Cert Comprehensive Soc Stud; *cr:* Chichester HS Ger, Eng Tchr 1967-69; Haverford Twp Sr HS Ger Tchr 1969-; *ai:* Ger Exch Prgm Coord; Ger Club Spon; Wrestling Announcer, Scorer; PSEA, NEA 1967-; AATG 1969-; Greenpeace, WWF, NWF, Natl Parks, Conservation Assn, Nature Conservancy, Defender of Wildlife Environmental Groups; *office:* Haverford Twp Sr HS 200 Mill Rd Havertown PA 19083

SHIVELY, PATRICIA COPPINGER, English Teacher; *b:* Youngstown, OH; *m:* David L.; *c:* Julie Anne; *ed:* Youngstown St Univ (BS) Comprehensive Comm 1990; Candidate for Masters Degree in Eng; *cr:* Liberty HS Jrnlsm Adv 1987-91; Youngstown St Univ Limited Svc Rdng, Stud Skills Tchr 1990-92; Mineral Ridge HS Eng Tchr 1992-; *ai:* Literary Magazine, Newspaper Tech Adv; Ldrshp Team; BLAT Team; Jrnlsm Ed Assn 1987-, Certfd Jour Ed; NCTE 1989-; OCTELA 1990-; WROTE 1994-, Mbrshp Sec; Tri-Cty Jrnlsm Assn 1988-, Dir; NEA, OEA 1992-; NSPA 1990-; Weathersfield Tchrs Assn 1992-, Publicity Chair; Grad Schl Schlsp; Dow Jones Advs Schls at OH Univ; Outstdng Stu Tchr at Youngstown St Univ; Numerous Articles, Photography Pub; *office:* Mineral Ridge HS 1334 Seaborn St Mineral Ridge OH 44440*

SHIVELY, PHYLLIS ANN, Retired Kindergarten Teacher; *b:* Piqua, OH; *ed:* Miami (BA) Ed 1962; Wright St (MS) Ed 1972; *cr:* Versailles Elem Kndgtn Tchr 1960-1995; *ai:* Soc Stud, Math & Nutrition Ed Comms; NEA & OEA 1960-; VEA 1960-, Pres; Library Friends Bd & Cncl of Churches; Mem of Nutrition Grant Comm.*

SHIVELY, TERRY WILLIAM, Fourth Grade Teacher; *b:* Lewisburg, PA; *m:* Cheryl Marie Lehman; *c:* Dion; *ed:* Williamsport Area Comm Coll (AS) Liberal Arts 1968; Lockhaven Univ (BS) Elem Ed 1971; Attnd Penn St Univ; *cr:* Bellfonte Area Schl Dist 5th Grd Tchr 1971-72; Bellefonte Area Schl Dist 3rd Grd Tchr 1972-73; Bellefonte Area Schl Dist 4th Grd Tchr 1973-; *ai:* NEA, PSEA & BAEA 1971-; *office:* Benner Elem Schl Buffalo Run Rd Bellefonte PA 16823

SHOAF, RUTH ANN, Vocational Instructor; *b:* Greensburg, PA; *m:* William G.; *c:* W Robert, Lee M. Ament; *ed:* Univ of Pittsburgh (BA) Ed 1989; IN Univ of PA Grad Work; *cr:* Perfection Photo Co Data Entry 1972-75; Overly Mfg Co Programmer 1975-80; Northern Westmoreland CTC Instructor 1980-81; Cntrl Westmoreland CTC Instructor, Programmer 1981-; *ai:* VICA Adv; Parlimentary Procedure Coach; PSEA, NEA 1980-; PBEA 1993-; VICA 1981-; PA Dept Ed Ememplary Prgm; *office:* Ctl Westmoreland Vo Tech Schl 240 Arona Rd New Stanton PA 15672

SHOALES, MICHAEL ALAN, Instrumental Music Teacher; *b:* Norwich, NY; *m:* Colleen Kelly; *c:* Chadrick, Kayla; *ed:* Onondaga Coll (AAS) Applied Music 1980; Murray S U (BME) Music Ed 1982; Alfred Univ (MSE) Ele Ed 1987; Addl Perm Cert Music Ed; SUNY at Geneseo 12 Cr Hrs Ele Ed; *cr:* Morris CS Instrumental Music Tchr 1982-84; Andover CS Instrumental Music Tchr 1984-; *ai:* Marching, Jazz, Pep Bands; NYSSMA Chm; Jr Hi All-County Band Dir; NEA 1982-, Gen Mem; MENC 1980-; GATE 1995-, Comm; Alfred Vlg Band 1986-, Asst Dir; Dir All-County Jr Hi, Sr Hi Band Events; Accompanist All-County 6th Grd, Sr H Chorus, Jazz Band; Adjudicator Ithica Coll Area-All-State Band; *office:* Andover Central Schl 31 Elm St Andover NY 14806

SHOBE, CHARLES WILLIAM, Art Teacher; *b:* Petersburg, WV; *m:* Susan Delaney; *c:* Joh, Ted, David; *ed:* Shepherd Coll (BA) Art & Eng 1963; 36 Grad Hrs Art & Ed; *cr:* US Marine Corps Vietnam War, Instr at Trng Base 1966-69; Frederick Cty Schls Art Tchr 1969-72; Dependent Schls Mainz Germany Tchr 1972-73; Frederick Cty Schls Art Tchr 1973-; *ai:* NEA 1975-; Vietnam Veterans Arts Group 1983-, Artist; Shown Paintings in Chicago, WA, NY, Houston, Albany, & Burlington; Written About in NY Times, New Art Examiner; *office:* Spring Ridge Elem Schl 9051 Ridgefield Dr Frederick MD 21701

SHOBY, SUSAN K., 6th Grade Teacher; *b:* Cleveland, OH; *m:* Richard A.; *c:* Elizabeth A., Stephanie M.; *ed:* Kent St Univ (BSEd) Ed, Hearing Impaired 1976; John Carroll Univ (MAEd) Cmptr Tech 1995; Cleveland St Univ Elem Ed 1980; 6 Addl Hrs; *cr:* Millridge Ctr for Hearing Impaired Tchr of Deaf, Presch 1976-78; St Margaret Mary Schl 6th Grd Tchr 1980-85; St Francis of Assissi Schl 4th Grd Tchr 1986-87; Orchard MS 6th Grd Tchr 1987-; *ai:* Cmptr Tech Comm; SEA Tchrs Assn 1987-; ASCD 1994-95; Knights of Columbus Immaculata Guild 1985-.

SHOCKEY, DAVID MATTHEW, Associate Professor of Voice; *b:* Sandy Spring, MD; *m:* Eleanor Frances Jane Kirk; *c:* Kirsten Melissa, Mark Henry IV, Kirk Nathaniel, Kevin Matthew; *ed:* Roberts Wesleyan Coll (BS) Music Ed, Voice 1974; Univ of Rochester, Eastman Schl of Music (MM)

Perf, Lit 1980; OH St Univ (DMA) Perf 1991; Attnd Graz Austria at Amer Inst of Musical Stud 1985; *cr:* E. J. Wilson HS Choral Dir 1974-78; Philadelphia Coll of Bible Voice Tchr, Choral Dir 1978-; *ai:* Coll Calendar Comm Chm; Coll Awds Comm; NATS, ACDA 1995-; PMEA Dist II HS Guest Dir 1996; *office:* Philadelphia Coll Of Bible 200 Manor Ave Langhorne PA 19047

SHOEMAKER, ANNE W., English as a Second Lang Tchr; *b:* Wilmington, DE; *ed:* Carleton Coll (BA) Russian Lang, Lit 1990; Pending MA Eng as Second Lang Univ of DE; *cr:* Newark HS Eng as Second Lang Tchr 1993-; *ai:* ACTR 1988-; *office:* Newark HS E Delaware Ave Newark DE 19711

SHOEMAKER, ELLEN RIVERS, HS Mathematics Teacher; *b:* Rochester, NY; *m:* James R.; *c:* Chelsea, Emily; *ed:* SUC at Potsdam (BA) Math & Scndry Ed 1984; SUNY at Brockport (MS) Math Ed 1989; *cr:* Greece Athena HS Math Tchr 1984-87, 1991-; Greece Athena MS Math Tchr 1987-91; *ai:* Stu Cncl Co-Adv; Math Assessment & HS Curr Comms; NEA 1984-; NY NEA 1984-; GTA 1984-; *home:* 103 Crosby Ln Rochester NY 14612*

SHOEMAKER, LINDA L., Director of Bands; *b:* Bell, CA; *ed:* Univ of NV at Reno (BS) Music 1965; CW Post Ctr of Long Island Univ (MS) Music Ed 1973; Attnd George Mason Univ, St Univ of NY at Stonybrook Post-Grad Music; *cr:* Woodbury Ave Schl Elem Band Dir 1967-71; Flower Hill Schls Elem Band Dir 1967-71; Huntington HS Asst Dir 1969-79; J. Taylor Finley Jr HS Band Dir 1971-82; Huntington HS Band Dir 1982-; *ai:* Marching Band; Jazz, Wind Ensemble; Pit Orch Spring Musical; Shared Decision Making Comm Re Scheduling 1995; MENC, NYSSMA, SCMEA, AFT, NYSUT 1967-; NBA 1973-; Long Island Sunrisers Sr Drum, Bugle Corp 1979-88; Cert Adjudicator NYSSMA Woodwinds 1980-; Tournament of Bands Outstdng Dir Awd 1990; MENC Nationally Registered Music Edctr, Honored by Town of Huntington for Outstdng Contributions to Comm Field of Ed 1991; *office:* Huntington HS Oakdwood & Mc Kay Roads Huntington NY 11743

SHOEMAKER, SHERRY LYNN LUNDY, Language Arts Teacher; *b:* Sidney, OH; *m:* William B.; *ed:* Bluffton Coll (BA) Elem Ed 1993; 12 Sem Hrs; *cr:* Fairlawn Local Schls MS Lang Arts Tchr 1993-; *ai:* Jr High Vllybl, Power of Pen, Var Chrldng & Head Boys & Girls Track Coach; Chrstn Ed Assn Intnl 1995-; AAE 1995-; Shelby Cty Intnl Rdng Assn 1995-; Schl Strategic Planning Team 1994-; Copeland Grant for Character Ed Pgm; *office:* Fairlawn Local Schls 18800 Johnston Rd Sidney OH 45365

SHOEMAKER, SUSAN MILROY, Mathematics Teacher; *b:* Sidney, NY; *m:* Dennis M.; *c:* Christopher; *ed:* Mansfield Univ (BS) Math & Ed 1987; Penn St Univ (MA) Math 1991; *cr:* Montoursville Area HS Math Tchr 1987-; *ai:* Class Adv; *office:* Montoursville Area Sr HS 100 N Arch St Montoursville PA 17754

SHOFF, VIRGINIA SUTTON, English Teacher; *b:* Philadelphia, PA; *c:* Stephen; *ed:* Dickinson Coll (BA) Fr 1964; Beaver Coll (MA) Comp Ed 1995; 30 Credits Eng, 18 Addl Credits Cmptr Sci Beaver Coll; 30 Credits Fr SUNY at New Platz; *cr:* Cheltenham Schl Dist Fr Tchr 1964; New Trier HS Fr Tchr 1964-65; Rondout Valley HS Fr Tchr 1966-68; Lower Moreland HS Eng, Fr Tchr 1965-66, 1974-; *ai:* Drug, Alcohol, Mental Hlth Intervention Stu Asst Prgm; Tech, NHS Comm; NEA, PSEA 1974-; LMTEA 1974-, Cncl of Rep; Article Pub; *office:* Lower Moreland HS 555 Red Lion Rd Huntingdon Vly PA 19006

SHOLLENBERGER, CHERYLENE TRACE, Fr Teacher & Foreign Lang Chm; *b:* Pottstown, PA; *m:* Barry P.; *c:* Beth A., Kristi L., Brian L.; *ed:* West Chester Univ (BS) Fr, Scndry Ed 1971; Univ of Montpellier France 1 Yr Abroad; Kutztown Univ 24 Grad Credits in Fr; Millersville Univ 32 Credits in Span for St Cert; *cr:* Daniel Boone Jr Sr HS Fr Tchr 1971-74; Reading Schl Dist Fr Tchr MS 1987-91; Reading HS Fr Tchr 1991-; *ai:* Dist Induction,Ger Exch Coord; Fr Club Spon; Frgn Lang Strategic Planning, Grad Requirement Comms; Intensive Scheduling Task Force; REA, PSEA, NEA, AATF 1991-; ACTFL 1992-; Nativity Luth Learning Ministry 1985-, Adult Forum Ldr; Steering Comm of Church 1987-; Church Lector 1986-; Bell Ringer 1991-; YWCA Woman's Trendsetter Awd 1985; *office:* Reading Sr HS 801 N 13th St Reading PA 19604

SHOLTANIS, CATHERINE KEEFE, First Grade Teacher; *b:* Boston, MA; *m:* Richard C.; *c:* Debra Dunlap, Richard J. (dec); *ed:* St Coll at Bridgewater (BS) Ed 1964; Lesley Coll (MS) Ed 1989; 12 Addl Credits Ed; *cr:* Clapp Schl Kndgtn-1st Grd Tchr 1964-70; South Elem Schl Kndgtn-1st Grd Tchr 1978-; *ai:* Schl Cncl; Co-Chair Playground Comm; Union Rep; MA Tchrs Assn 1978-, Bd Governor's; NEA 1978-; West Wind Shores Civic Assn 1976-, Sec, Mbrshp, Svc Awds; *office:* South Elem Schl Bourne Rd Plymouth MA 02360

SHONEBARGER, JAMES ALAN, Sixth Grade Teacher; *b:* Lancaster, OH; *m:* Judy Ellen Krile; *c:* Julie Ann, Erin Denise; *ed:* OH Univ (BSEd) Social Stud Comp 1971, (MED) Elem Ed 1991; *cr:* Lancaster City Schls Title I Tchr 1971-74; Amanda-Clearcreek Schls 6th Grd Tchr 1974-; *ai:* Hosler Sci, St Advisory Comms; Presidential Acad Fitness Awd, Elem DRama, AV Accounts Adv; Planning Hands-on Sci Teleconf; Elem Drama Presentations Dir; Arbory Day Comm Chm; NEA, OEA 1982-; ACEA 1980-; Knights of Columbus 1978-; Martha Holden Jennings Scholar 1985-86; *office:* Amanda-Clearcreek Schls Box 188 N School St Amanda OH 43102

SHONEBARGER, JULIE ANN, Band Director; *b:* Lancaster, OH; *ed:* Miami Univ (BM) Music Ed 1993; *cr:* Liberty Union-Thurston Band Dir 1993-; *ai:* Baltimore Correspondent for Lancaster Eagle Gazette; Chair of Fairfield All-Cty Music Festival; OH Music Edctrs Assn 1990-, Collegiate Triad Ed; ONEA; Intnl Trumpet Guild 1990-; *office:* Liberty Union-Thurston Schls 500 W Washington St Baltimore OH 43105*

SHONKWILER, MARK ALAN, Title I Reading & Math Tchr; *b:* Portsmouth, OH; *m:* Julie Ann Stewart; *c:* Hilary; *ed:* OH Univ (BS) Elem Ed 1987; Univ of Dayton (MS) Admin 1992; *cr:* Minford MS 6th Grd Tchr 1988-93, 4th-8th Grd Title I Rdng & Math Tchr 1993-94, Title I Rdng & Math Tchr & Dean of Stdnts 1994-; *ai:* NEA 1988-; *office:* Minford MS PO Box 204 Minford OH 45653

SHOOK, REBECCA ANN, Fourth Grade & Spec Ed Tchr; *b:* Westernport, MD; *m:* Paul Robert; *c:* Stacey Lynn; *ed:* Potomac St Coll (AA) Ed 1963; Fairmont St Coll (BA) Elem Ed Lang Arts, Math, Sci 1965; WV Univ & Frostburg St Univ (BA) Elem Ed K-8 & Special Ed; *cr:* Suitland Elem Schl Fifth Grd Tchr 1965-66; Bloomington Elem Schl Second, Third Grd Tchr 1966-70, Spec Ed Tchr 1975-80, Third-Fifth Grd Regular Classroom, Spec Ed Tchr 1980-; *ai:* Tutoring, Hometeaching, Tchng Adults for HS Diplomas, Supervising Tchr for Stu Tchrs, Mentoring New Tchrs and Stdnts; Phi Delta Kappa 1987-88; Former Mem Garrett Cty Tchrs Assn, MD Tchrs Assn, NEA; Former Mem Keyser Branch AAUW; Jaycettes, Former Pres, Jaycette of Yr; Apple Alley Players; Schl, Cty Adult Basic Educators Presented Inservice Wkshps; Will Present Math Stragegy Wkshp Frostburg St Univ 1994.*

SHOOP, LESLIE JAMES, American History Teacher; *b:* Kittanning, PA; *m:* Marsha Mc Minn; *c:* Aaron, Josh, Lindsay, Anthony, Jordan; *ed:* IN Univ of PA (BS) Soc Scis 1969; 30 Grad Credits; *cr:* Punxsutawney Area Schl Tchr, Coach 1969-82; Knoch HS Tchr, Coach 1982-; *ai:* Head Boys Bsktbl Coach; Head Boys, Girls Cross Cntry Coach; Asst Track Coach; NEA, PSEA 1969-; Coach Pittsburg Dapper Dan Rainball Classic 1991; *home:* 102 Janice Ln Saxonburg PA 16056

SHOPE, KEVIN RAY, Director of Bands; *b:* Ironton, OH; *m:* Kathryn Sandrock; *ed:* Marshall Univ (BA) Music Ed 1982, (MA) Music Ed 1990; *cr:* Zwick Music Co Instrumental Sales Mgr 1986-88; Marshall Univ Asst to Dir 1988-89; Cntrl Cath HS Dir of Bands 1991-; *ai:* Marching, Pep Band, Orch Musical Conductor; NCEA 1991-; MENC 1988-; Ambassador of Goodwill St of WV; *office:* Central Catholic HS 2550 Cherry St Toledo OH 43608

SHOPIS, NICOLINA, 6th Grade Rdng, Lang Arts Tchr; *b:* New York City, NY; *m:* Jorge; *c:* Adam, Crista; *ed:* St Johns Univ (BS) Ed 1966; Fairfield Univ (MA) Ed 1987; Sacred Heart Univ (CAS) Ed 1990; *cr:* NYC Schl System Grd 3 Tchr 1966-67; Bellmawr Park Schls Grd 3 Tchr 1967-68; Highland Park Schls Grd 2 Tchr 1968-71; St Emerys Schl Grd 4 Tchr 1983-84; Tomlinson MS Grd 6 Tchr 1985-; *ai:* Grd 6 Eng, Lang Arts, Comm Liaison; Schl Newspaper Adv; NEA, CEA, FEA 1985-; NCTE 1986-; Best Prgm of CT Tchr Mentor; Listening to Learn Lit, Mayan Math, Tchng of Grammar Through Writing Process Grant; *office:* Tomlinson MS 200 Unquowa Rd Fairfield CT 06430

SHORE, MARK ANDREW, Mathematics Professor; *b:* Cumberland, MD; *m:* JoAnna Burley; *c:* Harrison, Christopher; *ed:* Frostburg St Coll (BS) Math 1984, (MS) Math Ed 1986; WV Univ (ABD) Math Ed 1996; *cr:* Frostburg St Coll Prof of Math 1986-88; Potomac St Coll Prof of Math 1988-94; Allegany Coll Prof of Math 1994-; *ai:* Multimedia, Distance Learning Comm; NCTM 1986-; Heart Assn 1994-, Vol; *office:* Allegany Comm Coll Willow Brook Road Cumberland MD 21502*

SHORE, MEREDITH MANN, Math Teacher; *b:* Lewiston, ME; *ed:* Colby Coll (BA) Philosophy, Rel 1968; Univ of Southern ME (MED) Ed 1984; *cr:* Poland Comm Schl 6-8 Grd Math, His, Lang Arts Tchr 1976-94; Edward Little HS Math Tchr 1994-; *ai:* Bsbl Coach 1985-94; *office:* Edward Little HS Auburn Hts Auburn ME 04210

SHORE, SHIRLEY WALTHER, English Teacher; *b:* Wheeling, WV; *m:* Curtis H.; *c:* Laura Ann Shore Mack, Lisa Ann Shore Chorle; *ed:* CA Univ of PA (BSEd) Speech, Eng 1957; 6 Credit Hrs, CA Univ of PA; 12 Credit Hrs Penn St Univ; *cr:* Monongahela Jr HS 7th Grd Eng Tchr 1957-58; Phillipsburg Osceola Sr HS Speech, Drama Tchr 1958-63; Penn St Philipsburg Hosp Speech, Comm 1966-72; Philipsburg Osceola 9th Grd Eng Tchr 1975-91; Philipsburg Osceola Sr HS Eng Tchr IV 1991-; *ai:* Co-Spon Newspaper 1980-91; Drama Coach 1958-63; NEA, PSEA, Philipsburg Osceola Tchrs Assn 1975-; Moshannon Chap, DAR 1978-; Treas 3 Yrsk Registrar 3 Yrs; Indiana Paths CAR 1978-, Sr Pres 6 Yrs, Honorary Service Awd 1984; Daughters of Amer Colonists 1988-; Colonial Dames 17th C, 1991; Order of Eastern Star 1988-; Columnist Centre Daily Times 1982-90; *office:* Philipsburg-Osceola Area Sr HS 502 Phillips St Philipsburg PA 16866

SHORR, SANDRA B., Health Education Chairperson; *b:* Brooklyn, NY; *c:* Lindsay; *ed:* Boston Univ (MA) Hlth Ed 1972; Amer Univ (MA) Mngmt Information Systems 1983; *cr:* East Boston HS Hlth Edctr 1970-81; Samuel Ogle MS Hlth Edctr 1985-86; Wm Wirt HS Hlth Edctr 1986-87; Fairmont Hghts HS Hlth Ed Chprsn 1987-90; Parkdale HS Hlth Ed Chprsn 1990-; *office:* Parkdale HS 6001 Good Luck Rd Riverdale MD 20737

SHORT, BRENDA FIGGS, Math Teacher; *b:* Salisbury, MD; *m:* Shawn C.; *ed:* Salisbury St Univ (BS) Math & Comp Sci 1990, (MS) Ed 1995; *cr:* Stephen Decatur HS Math Tchr 1990-; *ai:* Marching Band Color Guard Instr; WCTA 1990-; MSTA 1990-; *office:* Stephen Decatur HS 9913 Seahawk Rd Berlin MD 21811

SHORT, CHERIE SALISBURY, English Teacher & Dept Chair; *b:* Hillsdale, MI; *m:* Keith E.; *c:* Kelly Short Tesar, Erin; *ed:* Defiance Coll (BA) Eng 1962; Toledo Univ (MS) Ed 1968; Addl 15 Post Masters Hrs Gifted Spec Ed; *cr:* Bryan HS Eng Tchr 1962-66; Archbold HS Eng Tchr 1966-; *ai:* Schl Newspaper, Jr Class Adv; Stu Cncl; Archbold Ed Assn 1966-; Archbold All Sports 1966-; *office:* Archbold HS 600 Lafayette St Archbold OH 43502

SHORT, DORIS DALE, Third Grade Teacher; *b:* Rome, NY; *m:* Ronald K.; *c:* Scott, Katie; *ed:* SUNY at Oswego (BS) Elem Ed 1961, (MS) Elem Ed 1970; *cr:* Liverpool Cntrl Schl 5th-6th Grd Tchr 1961-63; Camden Cntrl Schl 6th Grd Tchr 1963-65; Fayetteville-Manilius Cntrl Schl 3rd, 5th Grd Tchr 1965-69; Pinellas Cty Schls 4-6th Grd Tchr 1969-73; East Syracuse Cntrl Schl 2nd-3rd Grd Tchr 1973-75; Faith Heritage Schl 3rd Grd Tchr 1985-; *ai:* Church Responsibilities; *office:* Faith Heritage Schl 3740 Midland Ave Syracuse NY 13205

SHORT, FRANCIS THOMAS, English Teacher; *b:* Brooklyn, NY; *ed:* Niagara Univ (BA) Eng, Ed 1968; Seton Hall Univ (MA) Ed 1996; 30 Grad Courses Eng, Amer Lit Manhattan Coll 1968-72; *cr:* Jefferson Twp HS Eng Tchr 1968-72; Maple Shade HS Eng Tchr 1974-77; Green Hills Schl Eng Tchr 1977-; *ai:* Grad Coord; Lang Arts Curr Comm Chm; Sftbl Coach; NCTE 1980-; NEA, NJEA 1968-; Jefferson Twp Adult Sports League 1974-; Tchr of Yr 1994; *office:* Green Hills Schl Mackerly Rd Greendell NJ 07839

SHORT, FRANK J., Professor of Fine Arts; *b:* Philadelphia, PA; *m:* Lynne Myers; *c:* Kevin, Alex, Anna; *ed:* Temple Univ Tyler Schl of Art (BFA) Graphic Design 1977, (MFA) Graphic Design 1983; *cr:* Art Inst of Philadelphia Instr 1979; Tyler Schl of Art Instr 1979-81; Montgomery Cty Comm Coll Prof 1981-; Finland Art & Design Creative Dir 1989-; *ai:* Design & Dev Electronic Kiosk; Design Multimedia Software; Fine Arts Dept Coord; AFT 1981-; North PA Arts Alliance 1992-, Bd Mem; Free-Lance Designer, Illustrator; *office:* Montgomery County Comm Coll 340 Dekalb Pike Blue Bell PA 19422*

SHORT, GREGORY GORDON, Sixth Grade Teacher; *b:* Sidney, OH; *m:* Belinda E.; *c:* Ryan, Olivia; *ed:* Heidelberg Coll (BA) Hlth & PE 1973; Univ of Dayton (MA) Ed; *cr:* Possum MS 6th Grd Tchr 1975-; *ai:* NEA 1975-; *office:* Possum Elem Schl 2589 S Yellow Springs St Springfield OH 45506

SHORT, LEONARD DEAN, Science Teacher; *b:* Archbold, OH; *ed:* Bowling Green St Univ (BS) Comprehensive Sci Ed 1986; Xavier Univ (MED) Schl Cnslng 1991; Nature Photography Courses Miami Univ; *cr:* Oak Hills HS Sci Tchr 1986-; *ai:* Mock Trial; Sci Club; SADD; Stage Crew, Mgr; Speech Club Judge; Inclusion Comm; NEA, OHEA 1986-; SECO 1988-; *office:* Oak Hills Sr HS 3200 Ebenezer Rd Cincinnati OH 45248

SHORT, LOIS E., Mathematics Teacher; *b:* Providence, RI; *m:* John J.; *c:* Michael, Steven, Christina; *ed:* RI Coll (BA) Math, Scndry Ed 1971; Bryant Coll (MBA) Cmptr Information Systems 1990; 30 Addl Credits; *cr:* Burrillville HS Math Tchr 1983-, Math Dept Chair 1993-; *ai:* Math League, Comp Prgm Team Adv; NCTM 1995-; RI Math Tchrs Assn 1985-; Delta Kappa Gamma 1993-; *office:* Burrillville H S 425 East Ave Harrisville RI 02830

SHORT, MARK DAVIS, Math Teacher; *b:* Wauseon, OH; *m:* Cheryl Smith; *c:* Lindsey, Kendra; *ed:* Bowling Green St Univ (BS) Math Ed 1979; Univ of Dayton (MS) Schl Admin 1985; Coll St Joseph Post-Masters Stud; *cr:* Wapakoneta CIty Shoals Math Tchr 1979-; *ai:* NEA, OEA, WEA 1979-.

SHORT, MICHAEL PATRICK, English & Video Teacher; *b:* Detroit, MI; *m:* Susan Martishius; *c:* Patrick; *ed:* Univ of Detroit (BA) Comm 1985; Wayne St Univ (MA) Eng Ed 1996; *cr:* Springfield HS Eng Tchr 1992-; Univ of Toledo Composition Instr 1993-; *ai:* Drama Asst Dir; Theat Golf Coach; NEA 1992-; Hum 2000 Mem; *office:* Springfield HS Mccord Rd Holland OH 43528

SHORTEN, WILIAM M., French Teacher; *b:* Scranton, PA; *m* Charlene Grimes; *ed:* Univ of Scranton (BA) Fr 1966; 30 Credit Owego Jr HS Fr Tchr 1966-69; Owego Free Acad Fr Tchr 1969-; Lang Dept Chm; K-12 Lang Coord; AFT, OATA 1966-; Owego Elk *office:* Owego Free Acad George St Owego NY 13827

SHORTER, BRENDA WILLIE, Eng & Creative Writing Teac Ahoskie, NC; *m:* Bruce Tyrone; *c:* Tyra Elizabeth, Landon Tyrc Elizabeth City St U (BS) Eng 1982; Univ of DE 37 Hrs Eng Lit; V 9 Hrs Eng Lit; *cr:* Kent Co Pub Schls Tchr 1982-; *ai:* NEA, KCTA 1982-; Delta Sigma Theta 1981-; *office:* Kent Cty HS 25302 Meadow Rd Worton MD 21678*

SHOVLIN, GERALD, English Teacher; *b:* Pottsville, PA; *ed:* F (BS) Ed 1967; Masters Equivalency +30 Credits Marywood C Abington Schl Dist Tchr 1967-; *ai:* Eng Curr; 8th & 9th Gr Newspaper; Mentor of Eng 1993-; NEA 1967-; PSEA 1967-; AEA NCTE; *office:* Abington Jr HS 2056 Susquehanna Rd Abington PA

SHOWALTER, CHRISTINE LUBERTO, Forensic Science & Bi *b:* Queens, NY; *c:* Michael; *ed:* St Joseph Coll (BA) Bio 1969; Grad Hrs SUNY Binghamton 1974; *cr:* JFK Jr Sr HS Bio & Gen Tchr 1969-70; Vestal Cntrl Jr HS General Sci Tchr 1970-71; Africa HS Vestal General Sci Tchr 1971-78; Vestal Sr HS Forensic Sci & B 1978-; *ai:* Jr & Sr Class Adv 2 Yrs; Soph Class Adv 1 Yr; Var Tennis 2 Yrs; Scheduling & Cmptr Comm 2 Yrs; NEA & JFK Tchrs Assn Vestal Tchrs Assn 1970-; Forensic Seminar Presenter at ST Generated Forensic Sci Prgm; *office:* Vestal Sr HS 205 Woodl Vestal NY 13850

SHOWERS, RUSSELL T.,JR., English Teacher; *b:* Lebanon, Eileen Skarbek; *c:* Christopher, Daniel; *ed:* Elizabethtown Coll (B 1962; Attnd Drew Univ, IN Univ of PA Eng; *cr:* Annville-Cleona Sc Eng Tchr 1963-67; Spring Cove Schl Dist Eng Tchr 1967-71; Ca Schl Dist Eng Tchr 1971-; *ai:* Spelling Bee Coord; Keystone Tchr NCTE; Knights of Columbus; Fraternal Order of Eagles; Eagle Sco *office:* Camp Hill Jr Sr HS 100 S 24th St Camp Hill PA 17011

SHRADER, LINDA BARNETT, Business Education Teach Johnstown, PA; *m:* Douglas W.; *ed:* Robert Morris Coll (BS) Bus E *cr:* Forest Hills Schl Dist Bus Ed Tchr 1976-; *ai:* FBLA Adv; Tech Comm; Forest Hills Ed Assn 1976-, Treas 3 Yrs; PSEA, NEA 19 David's Luth Church 1986-, Church Cncl 1995-, Cncl Sec 1996, Schl Tchr, Lector; Who's Who Amoung Stdnts in Amer Colls, Uni Outstdng Young Women of Amer 1982; *office:* Forest Hills Schl D Locust St PO Box 325 Sidman PA 15955

SHREINER, GAIL FREDERICKS, Tchr & Coord of Gifted Stu Lafayette, IN; *m:* Robert G.; *c:* Todd, Matt, Jeff; *ed:* OH st Univ (BS Ed 1968; Ashland Univ (MS) Elem Ed & Gifted Ed 1996; Cert Gi 1995; Addl Grad Work Bowling Green St Univ, Heidelberg Coll & Toledo; *cr:* Linden Elem Tchr 1968-69; Travis Elem Tchr 19 Simpson St Elem Tchr 1970-73; Krout Elem Tchr 1974-79; Tiff Schls Tchr of Gifted & Talented 1988-94, Coord of Gifted & T 1994-; *ai:* Acad Challenge Quiz Bowl, Young Astronauts Pgm & L Career Mentorship Adv; Knowledge Master Open Coach; NEA, NWOEA & TEA 1968-; COCG, OAGC & NWOCCG 1995-; Merc Lay Advy Bd; YMCA, Bd of Dirs; Krout Elem PTO, Treas; Y-Wiv Pres, Y Wife of Yr; Swim Team Parents, Pres; Jr Womens League Pres; Welcome Wagon 1970-, Pres; St Josephs Church 1970-; Alumni Assoc 1970-; Columbia HS Ath Booster 1970-; Mercy Ho Comm, Awd Chprsn Comm Appeal; 2 Martha Holden Jennings Jaycee Outstdng Young Edctr; VFW Outstdng Tchr of Yr; *office:* Tiff Schls 217 S Washington Tiffin OH 44883*

SHREVE, ANGELA POLLARD, Early Childhood Ed Profes Flemington, WV; *m:* Charles; *c:* David, Kevin, John; *ed:* Fairmont (BA) Ed, Home Ec 1959; LA St Univ (MS) Human Ecology, Chi 1979; Univ of MD (PHD) Voc, Occupational Ed 1989; *ai:* Adj Fac i Chldhd Ed Mentor; ECE Prgms Coord; Supervise Stu Pra Experience; AVA 1978-; NAEYC, DAEYC 1986-; Family Relation 1977-82; Presented Papers AVA Natl Meetings, Family Relations Meetings; 2 Carl Perkins Grants; *office:* Delaware Tech & Comm C N Shipley St Wilmington DE 19801

SHRIBER, LINDA DUDEK, Occupational Therapy Asst Prof; *b:* E NY; *m:* Christopher; *ed:* St Univ of NY at Buffalo (BS) Occup Therapy 1975; St Univ of Coll at Buffalo (MS) Exceptional Ed 1 Univ of NY at Buffalo (EDD) Educl Admin 1995; Admin, Interpreta Southern CA Sensory Integration Tests, Neurodevelopmental T Certfd; *cr:* United Cerebral Palsy Assn Occupational Therapist 19 Lang Dev Prgm Admin Coord of Dev Svcs 1979-88; St Univ of Buffalo Asst Clinical Prof, Occupational Therapy 1988-90; D'Y Coll Asst Prof, Occupational Therapy 1990-; *ai:* Amer Occup Therapy Assn, NY St OT Assn 1975-, Niagara Frontier Dist OT Assn Sec; Neurodevelopmental Therapy Assn 1980-; Sensory Integratio 1978-; Bd of Dirs Lang Dev Prgm 1995-, Bd Mem; Niagara Fronti OT Assn 1975-, Sec; Niagara Frontier Dist OT Assn 1994, Appreciation; *office:* D'Youville Coll OT Dept 320 Porter Ave Buffa 14201

SHRIEVES, SANDRA GRUBB, Computerized Accounting T Athens, OH; *m:* John R.; *c:* Tammy Carsey, Connie Wallace; *ed:* O (BSEd) Comprehensive Bus 1983; OH St Univ Grad Hrs Voc Ed & Supervision; *cr:* Athens Cty CETA Prgm Asst Dir 1979; HAVAR I Admin 1979-81; Tri-Cty Voc Schl Adult Office Service Tchr 19 Placement Coord & Adult Bus Tchr 1985-89, Tchr of Compu Accounting 1989-; *ai:* Bus Profs of America Club Adv; Hockir Accounting Dept Advisory Comm Mem; Tri-Cty Voc Schl Applied MAPP Comm Mem; OVA & AVA 1985-; OEA & NEA 1989-; Chan Commerce 1987-89, Ed Comm; Athens Cty Comm Service Cncl 19 Treas 1 Yr; SE OH Placement Network 1985-89, Co-Chprsn 1 Yr; Tri-Cty Voc Schl 15676 St Rt 691 Nelsonville OH 45764

SHRIMPLIN, JO, English Teacher; *b:* Millersburg, OH; *m:* Micha Capital Univ (BA) Eng 1972; Ashland Univ (MED) Sports Sci 19 Mohican Yth Camp Rdng, Eng Tchr 1972-74; Wooster HS Eng Tch Loudonville-Perrysville Exempted Village Schls Rdng 1-6 Grd, H Grd Rdng Tchr 1975-; *ai:* Bsktbl 3-6th Grd Coach; NCTE 1994- 1982-; Boosters, Fin Bd; *office:* Loudonville HS 421 Campu Loudonville OH 44842

SHRIMPLIN, JOYCE THOMPSON, English Teacher; *b:* Lodi, C Don; *c:* Aaron, Kristin; *ed:* Muskingom Coll (BA) Hlth & PE 1967 of Akron (MA) Eng 1981; Post Grad Stud in Composition; Composition Cert; *cr:* St Coll Area Schls 1967-68; Parma City Sch Tchr 1968-70; Univ of Akron Composition Tchr 1981-86; Wadswor Schls Eng Tchr 1986-; *ai:* Writing Ctr Coord; NEA; OEA; WEA OCTELA & NCTE; *office:* Wadsworth HS 625 Broad St Wadswor 44281

SHRIVER, NORMA PRATT, English Teacher; *b:* Rochester, F Robert H.; *c:* Rob, Melinda; *ed:* Northampton Comm Coll (AA) Eng Moravian Coll (BA) Eng, Comm 1980; Kutztown Univ (MA) Eng 19

Area MS Eng Tchr 1987-89; Shawnee Intermediate Eng Tchr, Yrbk 3; Easton Area HS Eng Tchr 1993-; *ai:* Coll Bound Coord; NEA *office:* Easton Area HS 2601 William Penn Hwy Easton PA 18045*

ER, WILLIAM RUSSELL, History Teacher; *b:* Garfield Hghts, Karen; *c:* Lauren, Matthew; *ed:* Coll of Wooster (BA) His 1972; Chicago (MA) His 1973; Cleveland St Coll Tchng Credentials; Coll Credit Hrs; *cr:* Mount Vernon MS His Tchr 1974-77; Mount Sr High His Tchr 1977-; *ai:* MVSH Venture Capital Advy Comm; SCAP Amer His; MVSH Partnership; NEA 1974-; Ohio EA 1974-, Comm; North Cntrl OH EA 1974-, Past Pres, Exec Sec; Mount EA 1974-, Past Pres; First Presbyn Church 1977-, Elder; Mount Sr High Tchr of Yr 1990; OH Tchr Ed Cert Advy Commission NCATE Bd of Examiners 1993-; *office:* Mount Vernon HS 302 burg Rd Mount Vernon OH 43050

CK, TAMARA ANN, Third Grade Teacher; *b:* Greenville, OH; *m:* Jr.; *ed:* Wright St Univ (BA) Elem Ed 1982; Rdng Recovery at OH; *cr:* Ansonia Elem 5th Grd Tchr 5 Yrs, 4th Grd Tchr 2 Yrs, 3rd Grd Yr, Chapter I Rdng, Rdng Recovery Tchr 4 Yrs; *ai:* Past 5th Grd r Ed; NEA 1981-; Phi Delta Kappa 1987-; ESEA Ch 2 Grant 1994 *office:* Ansonia Elem Schl West Cross St Ansonia OH 45303*

CK, WENDOLYN T., History & Classics Teacher; *b:* Boston, MA; e A. Dominguez; *c:* Alexandra; *ed:* IN Univ (BA) His, Span 1967; d Univ (AM) His 1968; Univ of MA (MED) Ed 1982; 6 Grad Hrs ultural Ed 1991-92; 3 Grad Hrs ESL 1992; *cr:* MA Inst of Tech Lib 965; Northfield Schl for Girls His Tchr 1969-71; Northfield Mount n Schl His, Span, Classics Tchr 1971-; *ai:* Class Tchr 1991; 5th Yr n June; Northfield Elem Schl Chaplains' Outreach, Vol; NMH ins' Outreach, Vol; Woodrow Wilson Flwshp 1968; Acad Dean's Awd chng 1980; AP Prgm Citation 1994; Univ of Chicago Outstdng Tchr 995; Co-Authored Article Pub Amer Assn Petrol Geologists 1994; er New England Tchrs Conf 1995; *office:* Northfield Mt Hermon 6 Main St Northfield MA 01360

DEK, MICHAEL ANTHONY, English Teacher; *b:* Warren, OH; land Univ (BS), (BA) Comprehensive Comm 1985; 6 Addtl Hrs; *cr:* eld HS Eng Tchr 1985-87; Niles Mc Henry HS Eng Tchr 1987-; *ai:* dv; Track, Cross Cntry Coach; Track Ofcl; OCTELA; NEA; NCTA; ; MVCA; TCCC; *office:* Niles Mc Kinley HS 616 Dragon Dr Niles 446

PSHIRE, JACQUELYN ANN BOND, Business Teacher; *b:* gton, NC; *c:* Deltonia Nicole, Delonia, II; *ed:* NC Cntrl Univ (BS) rce 1970, (MS) Bus 1972; Johns Hopkins Univ (MS) Ec 1990; Post tud Include Courses for Children with Spec Needs; *cr:* Chapel Hill hr 1970-71; Martin Cty Pub Schls Bus Tchr 1971-72; East Granby hr 1972-74; Montgomery Cty Bus Tchr 1974-; *ai:* Liaison Comm lairs Best & Mentor Prgm Coords; Cooperative Office Ed Coord; mery Co Ed Assn 1974-; NEA 1970-; Delta Sigma Theta Inc 1981-, ist, Delta Great Tchr 1990; NAACP, Life Mem; Article Pub 1973; ized by Prin & Admins for Going Beyond the Call of Duty Awd St ition; *office:* Montgomery Blair HS 313 Wayne Ave Silver Spring 910*

YER, VIRGINIA C., Third Grade Teacher; *b:* Johnstown, PA; *m:* ; *c:* Melanie; *ed:* Univ of Pittsburgh (BS) Elem Ed 1971; *cr:* augh Twp Area Schls Elem Instr 1971-; *ai:* Elem Sci Instrl Ldr; upport Team; CT Area Ed Assn 1971-, Sec 1973; PSEA, NEA 1971-; 409 Palliser St Johnstown PA 15905

MP, BARBARA ANN, English Teacher; *b:* Braddock, PA; *m:* s W.; *c:* Thomas, Kristin, Megan; *ed:* CA Univ (BS) Eng; attnd Penn ; *cr:* Beaver Falls HS Eng Tchr; Norwin HS Eng Tchr 1979-; *ai:* Lit Arts Mag Adv; Ldrshp Trng; Penna Ed Assoc 1979-; NEA PA Schl Press 1990-, Exec Bd; Jrnslm Ed Assoc 1992-; Norwin cal Soc 1994-; *office:* Norwin Sr HS 251 McMahon Rd North g PA 15642*

HOB, 8th Grd Math Tchr & Team Ldr; *b:* Frederick, MD; *m:* Joan der; *c:* Jeremy; *ed:* Towson St Univ (BA) Ed, Math 1972; Johns s Univ (MS) Ed 1978; *cr:* Hammond MS Math Tchr 1972-; *ai:* NEA *office:* Hammond MS 8110 Aladdin Dr Laurel MD 20723

ERT, JONELLE M., Business Education Teacher; *b:* Bridgeport, Kevin; *ed:* Trenton St Coll (BS) Bus Ed 1992; Math Certfd; d Univ Working on Cmptrs in Ed MA; *cr:* Masuk HS Bus Ed Tchr *ai:* FBLA Adv 1992-; NEA, NBEA, CBEA 1992-; Kappa Delta Pi; Outstdng Achvmt, Potential as Tchr Awd 1992; *office:* Masuk HS Monroe Tpke Monroe CT 06468

IN, JOANNA SPAMPANATO, 6th Grade Science Teacher; *b:* Long City, NY; *m:* Jonathan; *ed:* Queens Coll (BA) His 1967, (BS) His, 2; Attnd Univ of WI, Univ of Northern CO, CCNY, Univ of CO, Univ Hofstra Univ, Univ of Southeastern MA, St. John's Univ, Hunter W. Post 45 Sci Credit Hrs; *cr:* St. Stan's Sci Tchr 1969-71; Most s Blood Sci Tchr 1971-81; Garden Schl Sci Tchr 1981-90; Roslyn i Tchr 1992-; *ai:* Young Astronaut Chapter Ldr; NSTA 1976-; YS 1994-; AFT 1992-; North Shore Univ Hosp 1992-; Schneider en's Hosp 1988-; Articles Pub; PTA Jenkins Awd; Grants Awded; Roslyn MS Locust Ln Roslyn Heights NY 11577

A, LYNNE GARVER, Seventh Grade Lang Arts Tchr; *b:* gboro, NJ; *m:* Lester; *ed:* Univ of DE (BA) Sociology, Psych 1983; ph's Univ Ed Cert I 1986; *cr:* Penn's Grove MS 6th, 7th Grd Lang Math Tchr 1986-; *ai:* Mentor Tchr; New Staff Induction; Staff Dev; vy Cncl; Report Card Revision; Multi-Disciplinary Team; Stdnts At Field Trip Coord; NEA, PSEA, OAEA 1986-; *office:* Penn's Grove 02 Garfield St Oxford PA 19363*

Y, LORRAINE J., 4th Grade Teacher; *b:* Greensburg, PA; *ed:* IN f PA (BA) Elem Ed 1970; 31 Addl Credits; *cr:* Willard Elem Schl d Tchr 1971-80, 4th Grd Tchr 1980-83; Saltsburg Elem Schl 4th Grd 983-; *ai:* Blairsville-Saltsburg Ed Assn 1970-, Bldg Rep; PSEA, 1970-; Saltsburg-Conemaugh-Loyalhanna Recreation Bd Adult Vlybl Ldr 1975-77; Rdng is Fundamental Co-Chm 1978; *office:* urg Elem Schl 250 3rd St Saltsburg PA 15681

RO, PAMELA REED, Special Education Teacher; *b:* Chicago, IL; ven M.; *c:* Matthew, Gwendulyn; *ed:* Mary Grove Coll (BA) Eng Columbia Univ (MA) Ed 1973; Harvard Univ (EDD) Ed 1995; Attnd f MI, Terysh Univ, Boston Univ, Boston Coll; *cr:* MI Paruchiu Schls MA Paruchiu Schls Tchr; Phila Pub Schls Tchr; Waltan Pub Schls Harvard Grad Schl of Ed Supvr, Tchng Fellow; Arlington HS Spec ır 1976-; *ai:* Diversity Comm; Safe Schl Comm; Task Force on Time ning; NEA, MTA, NCTE, IRA, ASCD, NECEL 1973-; Arlington Enrichment Fnd, Bd Mem; Cabat After Schl Prgm, Fnd mem, Bd Soc Contect of HS Eng; Several Grants Improvement of Learning.

ARTS, E. DAYTON, Math Teacher; *b:* Newton Hamilton, PA; *m:* . Dinardi; *c:* John M.; *ed:* Shippensburg Univ (BS) Math 1961; OH MS) Math 1973; 6 Addl Credit Hrs Univ of Pa; 5 Addl Credit Hrs m Young Univ; 1 Addl Credit Hr Univ of WI; *cr:* Quincy HS Math, chr 1961; Cedar Cliff HS Math Tchr 1961-62; Mt Union Area HS Sci Tchr 1962-; *ai:* NHS Adv; PSEA, NEA 1980-, Pres; Knights of bus 1983-; *home:* 601 Nolan Rd Mount Union PA 17066*

ARTS, WILLIAM BLAKE,JR., High School Math Teacher; *b:* sburg, PA; *m:* Amy G. Carr; *c:* Angela S., Sarah B.; *ed:* Lockhaven St Coll (BS) Scndry Ed 1972; 27 Credit Hrs; *cr:* West Branch Area HS Math Tchr 1982-; *ai:* NEA, PSEA & WBEA 1982-; *office:* West Branch Area Jr-Sr HS R 2 Box 194 Morrisdale PA 16858

SHUGERT, JULIA REED, Language Arts Teacher; *b:* New Castle, PA; *m:* Guy S. Jr.; *c:* Guy IV, Douglas; *ed:* Penn St Univ (BS) Se Ed 1977; Westminster Coll (MED) Rdng 1984; Attnd U of PItt Rdng Supvr 1990; *cr:* Equitable Life Insurance Salesperson 1978; Geneva Coll Part-time Span Instr 1981; Beaver Area Schls 7-8th Grd Sub, Lang Arts, Eng, Span Tchr 1979-; *ai:* Lit Club Co-Spon; PSEA, BAEA 1988-; IRA 1985-; League of Women Voters 1979-, Pres; Dr Leotta Hawthorne Rdng Cncl 1989-, Corr Sec; PAGE 1989-; Former BPW Beaver Falls 1979-, Pres, Women of Yr; Two Grants 1994-, to Have Holocaust Survivors Speak; *office:* Beaver Area MS Gypsy Glen Rd Beaver PA 15009

SHULER, HERBERT F., Social Studies Teacher; *b:* Norristown, PA; *ed:* Kutztown St Coll (BS) Soc Stud 1963; Johns Hopkins Univ (MLA) Lbrl Arts 1970; *cr:* Susquehannock High Tchr 1963-70; Cato-Meridian High Tchr 1970-; *ai:* AFT 1970-.

SHULINS, SUSAN SOULE, English Instructor; *b:* Sanford, ME; *m:* Paul S.; *ed:* Plymouth St Coll (BA) Eng 1979; Univ of NH (MA) Eng 1981; Simmons Coll (MA) Ed 1988; *cr:* CT Mutual Life Insurance Co Research Asst 1982-84; Champion Products Inc Exec Asst 1984-85; Bain & Co Case Mgr 1984-86; Greater Lawrence Tech Schl Eng Instr 1988-; *ai:* Mentoring Prgm Participant; Walk for Walden Woods Organizer; Literacy Vol; AFT 1988-; *office:* Greater Lawrence Technical Sch 57 River Rd Andover MA 01810

SHULL, LAUREL A., Reading & English Teacher; *b:* Camden, NJ; *m:* Walter C.; *c:* Kathryn, Amanda, Jeffrey; *ed:* Glassboro St (BA) Elem Ed 1968, (MA) Rdng 1976; Cmptr Courses; *cr:* Bellmawr Pub Schls 2nd Grd Tchr 1968-72; Eastern HS Rdng Tchr 1972-; *ai:* Vars Club, Class of 1996 Adv; Stu Alliance, Peer Mediation Fac Mem; Eastern Ed Assn 1976-, Tchr of Yr 1991; NJ Ed Assn, NEA 1976-; St Peter's Episcopal Alter Guild 1984-; *office:* Eastern HS Laurel Oak Rd Box 2500 Voorhees NJ 08043

SHULL, MICHAEL, Fifth Grade Teacher; *b:* Harrisburg, PA; *m:* Rosalie Nadine Brandt; *c:* Amy L., Matthew G.; *ed:* Bloomsburg Univ (BS) Elem Ed 1971; Millersville Univ (MED) Elem Ed 1974; 15 Post-Grad Credit Hrs; *cr:* Manheim Twp MS 6th Grd Tchr 1971-93; Reidenbaugh Elem Schl 5th Grd Tchr 1993-; *ai:* Asst HS Bsbl Coach 1981-95; Elem Knowledge Master Open Coach; Elem Math Curr Comm; MTEA 1971-; PSEA 1971-; NEA 1971-; BSA 1990-, Scout Master, Wood Badge Awd; *home:* 443 W Marion St Lititz PA 17543

SHULTZ, CAROLYN L., 10th Grade World Cultures Tchr; *b:* York, PA; *c:* Shelby L. Knapper, Brian L., Jody L. Brown; *ed:* York Coll of PA (BS) Scndry Ed, Soc Stud 1972; Millersville Univ (MS) Ed 1980; 41 Post Grad Credit Hrs; *cr:* Dallastown Area Schl Dist Tchr 1974-; *ai:* NES, PSEA 1976-; NCSS, PCSS 1981-; MCDSS 1990-, Bd Mem; Phi Delta Kappa 1991-; Fulbright Hays Schlsp Pub; Amer Schl of Classical Stud Schlsp; *office:* Dallastown Area Schl Dist 700 New School Ln Dallastown PA 17313

SHULTZ, CHRIS ANN (CASE), Secondary Mathematics Teacher; *b:* Bloomsburg, PA; *m:* Mark B.; *ed:* Bloomsburg Univ (BSEd) Math Ed 1990; 21 Post-Baccalaureate Credits; *cr:* Millville Area Schl Dist Scndry Math Tchr 1990-; *ai:* Jr High Stu Cncl & Soph Class Co-Adv; PSEA & NEA 1990-; *office:* Millville Area Schl Dist PO Box 260 Millville PA 17846

SHULTZ, EDWARD DANE, Band Director; *b:* Connellsville, PA; *m:* Deborah Houser; *c:* Brenna, David, April, Barbara; *ed:* IN Univ of PA (BS) Music Ed 1978, (MA) Music Ed 1982; *cr:* Bradwell Inst HS Band Dir 1981; Dubois HS Asst Band Dir 1982; Allegheny Clarion Vly Jr-Sr H S Band Dir 1983-88; Connellsville Area HS Band Dir 1988-; *ai:* Marching Band; Jazz Club & Ensemble; PA Music Edctrs Assn 1983-; *office:* Connellsville Area Sr HS 201 Falcon Dr Connellsville PA 15425

SHULTZ, ELLEN L., English & Theater Teacher; *b:* Jamestown, NY; *m:* Charles H.; *c:* David, Christina; *ed:* Alfred Univ (BA) Eng 1954, (MS) Ed, Rdng; Syracuse Univ Theatre; *cr:* West Irondequoit Jr HS Eng Tchr; Jamestown HS Eng, Theatre; Alfred Almond Schl Eng, Theatre; *ai:* Stage Crew, Drama Club, Thespians Adv; Theatre Prgm; NYSUT; NY St Eng Cncl; Habitat for Hum; Union Univ Church, Deacon; *office:* Alfred Almond Central School 6795 State Route 21 Almond NY 14804

SHULTZ, ROBIN EUGENE, Sixth Grade Teacher; *b:* Toledo, OH; *m:* Christine Dominique; *ed:* U of Toledo (BED) El Ed 1977, (MS) Admin 1988; Attnd Bowling Green; *cr:* Lake Local Schls 6th Grd Tchr 1977-; *ai:* NEA, OEA, LEA 1977-; *office:* Lake Elem Schl 28150 Lemoyne Rd Millbury OH 43447

SHULTZ, STEPHEN A., Asst Prin & Soc Stud Teacher; *b:* New York, NY; *m:* Dorothy A. Fischer; *c:* Jason R., Edward A.; *ed:* NY Univ (BS) Soc Stud Ed 1972, (MS) Soc Stud Ed 1976; Brooklyn Coll Prof Degree Educl Admin, Supervision 1992; Yale Univ New World Slavery Origins; Rockefeller Fellow Global Stud; *cr:* Franklin K. Lane HS Tchr, Boys Track Coach 1979-83; Boys & Girls HS Tchr, Asst Chm, Soc Stud Coord 1983-93, Asst Prin 1993-; *ai:* Cncl of Supvrs & Admins, Soc Stud Supvsrs Assn 1993-; Assn of Tchrs of Soc Stud 1978-, John Bunzel HS Soc Stud Tchr of Yr 1987-88; Impact II; *office:* Boys & Girls HS 1700 Fulton St Brooklyn NY 11213*

SHULTZMAN, BONNIE REEVES, Third Grade Teacher; *b:* Smile, KY; *m:* Terrence; *c:* Kendra, Aaron; *ed:* Grace Coll (BS) Elem Ed 1967; IN Univ (MS) Elem Ed 1971; 24 Addl Hrs Walsh Univ, Ashland Univ; Fr Stud Diploma Bethel Bible Inst at Lennoxville Quebec; *cr:* Cntrl Noble Comm Schl Corp 3rd Grd Tchr 1967-68; Tippecanoe Vly Schl Corp 3rd Grd Tchr 1968-71; Brethren Frgn Missionary Soc Bible Inst Tchr 1974-78; Southeast Local Schls 2nd-3rd Grd Tchr 1985-; *ai:* OEA, NEA, SELEA 1985-; Eisenhower, Arts Grants; Poetry Pub; *home:* 3288 Batdorf Rd Wooster OH 44691

SHUMAN, SHERRY L., Mathematics Teacher; *b:* Madison, OH; *m:* Michael R. Jr.; *c:* Nicholas; *ed:* Univ of Bowling Green (BS) Arts, Sci, Math & Cmptrs 1990, (BS) Scndry Math Ed 1990; Univ of Dayton (MS) Cmptrs in Ed 1993; *cr:* Stebbins HS Math Tchr 1990-; *ai:* Class & SADD Adv; Acad Team Coach; MREA, OEA, NEA 1990-; WSUACTM 1991-, Newsletter Ed; Tech Grant; *office:* Walter E Stebbins HS 1900 Harshman Rd Dayton OH 45424

SHUMAN, SUSAN EVANCHO, French Teacher; *b:* Hazleton, PA; *m:* Timothy E.; *c:* Daniel, Lorianne; *ed:* Lock Haven Univ (BS) Scndry Fr 1971; York Coll (BA) Comm 1990; Penn St Ed Courses; Universite of Dijon Fr; *cr:* Austin Schl Dist Fr, Eng Tchr 1970-71; *ai:* Transition Mngmt, Strategic Planning Teams; ACTFUL; Girl Scouts of Am 20 Yrs; *office:* Dover HS W Canal St Dover PA 17315*

SHUMWAY, ROBERT LANE, Band Director; *b:* Wellsboro, PA; *m:* Diane Clark; *c:* Louise, Sara, Noah, Daniel; *ed:* Mansfield Univ (BS) Music Ed 1977; *cr:* Wyalusing HS Band Dir 1979-90, Jr HS Band Dir 1990-; *ai:* Marching Band Asst Dir; Musical Theatre Dir; *office:* Wyalusing Valley Jr-Sr HS RR 2 Box 7 Wyalusing PA 18853

SHUPP, RICHARD C.,JR., Spanish Teacher; *b:* Easton, PA; *m:* Zenaida Miguel; *c:* Trixie Argente, Paula Bubulka, Jennifer Argente, Richard C. III, Leandro Miguel, Christopher, Angela, Cristina, Milagros; *ed:* Lafayette coll (BA) Span 1967; Lehigh Univ (MA) Modern Foreign Lang, Lit 1977; Post Grad Stud Maya Archaeology, Cultural Anthropology, Latin Amer Civilization, Mexican Folklore; *cr:* Easton Area HS Span Tchr 1967-; Northampton Comm Coll Span Tchr 1988-90; Lafayette Coll Span Instr 1992-; *ai:* Latin Amer Cultural Assn Dir; Amer Assn Tchrs of Span & Portuguese 1967-, Treas, MidEast PA Chapter; NEA, PSEA 1967-; Easton Area Ed Assn 1967-, Exec Bd; Hispanic Affairs Commission 1993-, Pres; Cncl of Span Speaking Assn 1991-, Delegate; Easton Span Ctr Bd 1990-, Delegate; Easton Hogar Crea Bd 1992-, VP; Yful Kellogg Fnd Grant Mexico US Project 1993; Comm Svc Awds Hispanic Bus Cncl 1992, Hogar Crea 1993; Two Books, Numerous Articles & Editorials Pub; *office:* Easton Area HS 2601 William Penn Hwy Easton PA 18045

SHUST, RICHARD B., English Teacher & Chairman; *b:* Bronx, NY; *ed:* Fordham (BA) 1961; Iona (MA) Ed, Eng 1984; Post Grad Stud at Monclair St, Fairleigh Dickinson, Univ of NH, Wesleyan Univ, St Univ of NY, Seton Hall Univ; *cr:* St Andrews Schl Tchr of Eng 1961-63; Dominican Coll of Blairvelt Lecturer in Eng 1985, 1992; Orange Cty Comm Coll Lecturer in Eng 1987; St Joseph Regnl, Asst Prin, Eng Dept Chm 1963-; *ai:* Mid Sts Steering Comm Chm; Mission Statement Comm Chm; Act Adv; NCTE 1995-; Assn for Supervision & Curr Dev 1985-; Bd of Ed Chester Union Free Schl Dist Pres 1992-1994, Mem 1981-83; Eucharistic Minister St Columba Church 1973-; Hum Schlsp Dodge Fnd; Federal Grant Cmptr Sci; Outstdng Scndry Edctrs of Amer Awd 1974; Archdiocese of Newark Tchr of Yr 1994; Pub by Assembly on Lit NCTE; *office:* Saint Josephs Regional HS 40 Chestnut Ridge Rd Montvale NJ 07645*

SHUSTA, DENISE ROSE, English Teacher; *b:* Monongahela, PA; *m:* John; *c:* Nicole, Joel; *ed:* CA (BA) Comm 1973; 24 Credit Hrs; *cr:* Belle Vernon Schl Dist Eng Tchr 1978-; *ai:* NEA 1978-; *home:* 1618 Irey St Monongahela PA 15063

SHUSTER, DOUGLAS, Fourth Grade Teacher; *b:* Allentown, PA; *m:* Neida Louise Krick; *ed:* East Stroudsburg Univ (MS) Elem Ed 1991; *cr:* Fredom Schl 4th, 5th, 6th Grd Tchr 1977-; *ai:* Ski Club; Safety Patrol Adv; Bsktbl, Sftbl Coach; Chess Club Adv; Environmental Ed Staff; Adventure Based Prgm Staff; NEA 1977-; Fredon Ed Assn 1977-, Pres, Treas; *home:* 585 Belfast Rd Nazareth PA 18064

SHUSTER, HY, Television Studio Coordinator; *b:* Montreal, canada; *c:* Mitchell; *ed:* Hunter Coll (BS) Comm 1973; Brooklyn Coll (MS) Television & Radio 1975; Pratt Inst (MLS) Schl Media Specialist 1976; Cert Advanced Stud in Ed Admin & supvn St Univ of New York at New Paltz 1985; *cr:* Rsrch Libs of NY Pub Lib Various Positions 1968-76; Bd of Jewish Ed of Greater NY Media Librn 1976-82; Finkelstein Memrl Lib Media Librn 1980-81; Clarkstown Cntrl Schl Dist Television Studio Coord 1981-; *ai:* CCSD-TV Coord; Dist Tech Comm; Alliance for Comm Media 1976-; Media Arts Tchrs Assn 1984-; AFT 1980-; Rockland Ctr for Holocaust Stud 1995-, Bd of Dir; TKR Cable-Cable in the Classroom Acad Awd; NSPRA 1995 Publications & Electronic Media Awd; *office:* Clarkstown South HS 31 Demarest Mill Rd West Nyack NY 10994

SHUSTER, SANDRA GARBER, Spanish Teacher; *b:* Philadelphia, PA; *m:* Todd L.; *ed:* Rider Coll (BA) Scndry Ed, Span 1977; Temple Univ (MED) Foreign Lang Educ 1986; *cr:* Collingswood HS Span Tchr 1977-79; Audubon HS Span Tchr 1980-82; Lower Moreland HS Span, Eng, ESL Tchr 1985-; *ai:* Participant Stu Assistance Prgm Team 1986-; Policy & Practice Review, Prof Supervision & Evaluation Comms; NEA, PSEA, Lower Moreland EA 1985-; Sigma Delta Pi 1977-; Demonstration Lessons for Foreign Lang Instruction; Designed Foreign Lang Placement Tests; Created, Implemented ESL Curr; Cert Eng; *office:* Lower Moreland HS 555 Red Lion Rd Huntingdon Vly PA 19006

SHUTA, BARBARA SPELLMAN, Speech & Drama Teacher; *b:* Scranton, PA; *m:* James M.; *c:* Jeffrey; *ed:* Marywood Coll (BA) Drama 1968; Univ of Scranton (MA) Eng 1978; *cr:* PA Ballet Co Asst Pub Relations 1971-75; Temple Univ Music Festival Pub Relations Dir 1971-75; Metropolitan Life Cmptr Programmer 1980-86; West Scranton HS Honors & Regular Eng Tchr 1986-91; Cranton HS Speech & Drama Tchr 1991-; *ai:* Drama Club Adv; AFT 1986-; Marywood Coll, Alumni Bd Mem 1991-95, Recruiting Network 1994- 1994-; *office:* Scranton HS 721 Adams Ave Scranton PA 18510

SHUTER, DAVID H., Spanish & French Teacher; *b:* Portsmouth, OH; *ed:* OH St Univ (BSED) Span 1982; Univ of Dayton (MSEd) Sncdry Ed 1990; Doctoral Candidate at OH Univ; *cr:* Amanda Clearcreek Local Schl Dist Tchr 1982-85; Vinton Cty Local Schl Dist Tchr 1986-91; OH Univ Instr 1991-93; Vinton Cty Local Schl Dist Tchr 1993-; *ai:* Fr Club Adv; Educl Excl Grant Writer; Phi Delta Kappa 1992-; Assn for Supervision, Curr Dev; OH Univ Grad Associateship; OH Coal Co Grant; Who's Who Among Amer Edctrs 1994-95; *home:* PO Box 116 Minford OH 45653*

SHUTOK, CYNTHIA MARIE, First Grade Teacher; *b:* Uniontown, PA; *ed:* CA St Coll (BS) Elem Ed 1972; WV Univ Grad Schl Elem Ed; *cr:* Laurel Highlands Schl Dist 4-6 Grd Rdng, K-1, 6 Grd Tchr 1972-; *ai:* LHEA, PSEA, NEA 1972-; Delta Zeta 1971-; *office:* Robert W. Clark Elem Schl 200 Water St Uniontown PA 15401

SHUTTLESWORTH, LYNN ELLEN, Second Grade Teacher; *b:* Pottsville, PA; *ed:* Bloomsburg Univ (BS) Elem Ed 1973; *cr:* Blue Mountain Schl Dist Second Grd Tchr 23 Yrs; *ai:* PSEA, NEA 1973-; BMEA 1973-, Sec; *office:* Blue Mountain Schl Dist 675 Reddale Rd Orwigsburg PA 17961

SHY, TERRI RAWLS, 10th Grade Science Teacher; *b:* Cleveland, OH; *m:* Philbert; *c:* Tiffany; *ed:* Univ of Cincinnati (BS) Bio 1980; *cr:* Shaw HS Bio Tchr 1986-92; Bedford HS Bio, Geo Physical Sci Tchr 1992-; *ai:* Venture Capitol Comm; Peer Mediation; Prof Dev Cncl; Delta Sigma Theta 1977-; Eliza Bryant 1996; *office:* Bedford HS 481 Northfield Rd Bedford OH 44146

SIANNI, MARY ANN C., English Teacher; *b:* Wilmington, DE; *m:* Anthony J.; *c:* Alex, Kate; *ed:* Univ of DE (BA) Eng Ed 1973; 30 Addl Hrs Linguistics, Lit; *cr:* Caesar Rodney HS Eng, Fr Tchr 1973-78; Salesianum Schl Eng, Fr Tchr 1978-; *ai:* Stu Assistance Team; Spirituality Comm; NCTE 1978-; NEA 1973-78; Christina Dist PTA 1985-, Legislative Rep; *office:* Salesianum Schl 1801 N Broom St Wilmington DE 19802*

SIANO, DENISE SMITH, Physical Education Teacher; *b:* Springfield, MO; *m:* David; *c:* Andrew M., Steven A.; *ed:* Springfield Coll (BA) PE, (MS) Athletic Admin 1990; *cr:* Town of Newington PE Tchr 1984-; *ai:* Stu Cncl Adv; NEA, CT Ed Assn 1984-; *office:* Martin Kellogg MS 155 Harding Ave Newington CT 06111

SIBERT, JOHN, Third Grade Teacher; *b:* Hastings, PA; *m:* Mary Beth Toth; *ed:* Lock Haven St Coll (BS) Elem Ed 1970; 15 Addl Credits Ed; *cr:* Northern Cambria Schl 1970-73, Third Grd Tchr 1973-; *ai:* NEA, PSEA, NEA 1970-; *home:* PO Box 186 Nicktown PA 15762

SIBERT, JOHN WINSTON, Social Studies Teacher; *b:* Takoma Park, MD; *m:* Suzanne Marie Brinks; *c:* Daniel, Christine; *ed:* Univ of TN (BS) Scndry Ed 1972; Bowie St Univ (MED) Scndry Admin 1975; Addl Credits Beyond Masters in Ed & Ec; *cr:* High Point HS Soc Stud Tchr 1974-; *ai:* Jr Class Adv; NEA, MSTA, PGCEA 1974-; Washington Post Excl in Ed Grant.

SIBICKY, MARK E., Asst Professor of Psychology; *b:* Norwich, CT; *ed:* Univ of CT (BA) Psych 1980; Colgate Univ (MA) cnslng 1984; Univ of AR (PHD) Soc Psych 1990; *cr:* Marietta Coll Asst Prof 1990-; *ai:* Psych Club, Psi-Chi Adv; APA 1990-; APS 1993-; NSF-ILI Grant; 5 Articles Pub; *office:* Marietta Coll Dept of Psychology Marietta OH 45750

SICA, JOANN, Mathematics Teacher; *b:* Jersey City, NJ; *m:* John Pappalardo; *c:* Jonathan, Jarrod, Marc; *ed:* Jersey City St Coll (BA) Math, Scndry 1971; Cmptr Sci; St Peter's Coll Manipulatives Math; CCNY Cmptr Sci in Classroom; *cr:* Snyder HS Math Tchr 1971-77; Acad HS Math Tchr 1977-87; Terri's HS Math Tchr 1987-; *ai:* NEA, NJEA, JCEA 1971-; *office:* James J Ferris HS 35 Colgate St Jersey City NJ 07302*

SICILIANO, GINA, Math Teacher & Guidance Cnslr; *b:* Philadelphia, PA; *ed:* St Josephs Univ (BS) Chem 1985, (MSEd) 1994; *cr:* Paul VI HS Math Tchr 1985-; *ai:* Stu Cncl Adv; NEA 1985-; *office:* Paul VI H S Hopkins Rd Haddonfield NJ 08033

SICILIANO, NITA HARRIS, Chemistry Instructor; *b:* Troy, NY; *m:* George R.; *c:* Peter G., Mark R.; *ed:* Russell Sage Coll (BA) Chem 1964; 36 Credit Hrs in Sci, Math & Ed; *cr:* Sterling-Winthrop Research Inst Asst Research Chemist 1964-69; Russell Sage Coll Lab Coord 1969-78; Swarthmore Coll Lab Instr 1979-86; Downingtown Sr HS Chem Instr 1986-; *ai:* Chem Tutor; Amer Chem Soc 1964-; NEA 1986-; Russell Sage Coll Alumnae 1964-, Sec; Lab Manual Contributor; Bridging the Gap Intern with Smith Kline Beecham; Domestic-Foreign Patents for SWRI; *office:* Downington Sr HS 445 Manor Ave Downingtown PA 19335

SICOLA, PIERINA CAPETOLA, French Teacher; *b:* Rapino, Italy; *m:* Joseph; *c:* Melissa Ann, Corinne Marie; *ed:* NY Univ (BS) Fr Ed 1971; *cr:* Maxcon MA Fr Tchr 1971-75; South Plainfield MS Fr Tchr 1984-86; South Plainfield HS Fr Tchr 1986-; *ai:* Fr Club, Fr Honor Soc; Coord Fr Elem Schl Prgm; NEA, NJEA, South Plainfield Ed Sssn, AATF, Foreign Lang Ed of NJ 1984-; *office:* South Plainfield HS 200 Lake St South Plainfield NJ 07080

SICOLI, M. L. CORBIN, Professor of Psychology; *m:* Thomas; *c:* Michael, Kathryn; *ed:* Westchester Univ (BS, MS) Music Ed, Educl Research 1966, 1973; Univ of WI (MS) Educl Admin 1967; Bryn Mawr (PHD) Dev, Educl Psych 1977; Clinical Psych Post Doctoral Stud; *cr:* Unionville Chadds Ford Schl Dist Music Supvr 1967-70; Rosemary Coll Prof Mid 1970; Cabrini Coll Prof 1977-; Self Employed Licensed Psychologist 1978-; *ai:* Psi Chi Founder, Adv; Psy Dept Co-Op Coord; Fac Dev, Evaluation Comms Chair; APA 1978-; EPA 1990-; CAB-TV 1980-, Stu Research Forum Coord; PCA 1980-, Psycological Aspects of Popular Culture Forum Area Chair; PTO Hillsdale Elem 1991-, Schl Newspaper Ed; Consultant to Agencies That Care for Children; Contribute Articles; Distinguished Coll Tchng Chrstn & Mary Lindback Fnd Awd; Chapel of Four Chaplains Honoree; *office:* Cabrini Coll 610 King Of Prussia Rd Radnor PA 19087

SICURANZA, LINDA MACHELL, Science Teacher; *b:* Exeter, NH; *m:* Leo; *c:* Evan, Jenna; *ed:* UNH (BA) Psych 1975; RIC (MAT) Phys Sci 1988; 30 Credit Hrs Post MS; *cr:* RIC Gen Chem Lab Instr 1985-88; Seekonk HS Chem & Physics Tchr 1988-90; Dedham HS Chem & Physics Tchr 1990-; *ai:* AMD Sci & Nature Club, Sci Olympiad & JETS Teams, Physics Olympics & Class of 1999 Adv; NEACT 1988-, Sec & Hosp Chair; Sigma Xi 1988-; NEST & MIT 1989-, Nominations Comm, Tchr of Yr; Mother Brook Coalition Treas; Nep RWA TAG Mem, Environmental Ed; Grants: Dedham Schl Dept 1992-93, Dedham Ed Fndtn 1992-95, Eisenhower Grant 1994, MWRA Enviro Lab 1994-95; Article Pub; *office:* Dedham HS 140 Whiting Ave Dedham MA 02026*

SIDDIQUI, ABDUL MAJEED, Assoc Professor of Mathematics; *b:* Rawalpindi, Pakistan; *m:* Tazeem; *c:* Aqsa; *ed:* Islamabad Pakistan (MS) Math 1975; Quaide Azam Univ (MPhil) Math 1976; Univ of Windsor at Ontario (MS) Applied Math 1982, (PHD) Fluid Mechanics 1986; *cr:* Aviation Dept Pakistan Aerodrome Ofcr 1975-81; Univ of Windsor Post Doc Rsrch Asst 1981-86; Penn St Univ Assoc Prof 1987-; *ai:* Amer Math Soc 1984-; Amer Acad of Mechanics 1988-; Soc for Industrial & Applied Math 1991-; *office:* PA St Univ York Cmps 1031 Edgecomb Ave York PA 17403

SIDELINGER, DEBRA DAY, English Teacher; *b:* Ridgway, PA; *m:* Randolph P.; *c:* Amanda; *ed:* Villa Maria Coll (BA) Eng 1977; 32 Credits Post Grad Stud; 6 Credit Real Estate; *cr:* St Marys Parochial Eng Tchr 20 Yrs; *ai:* Enrichment Rep 1993; Curr Coord Lang Arts 1987; Laurel Rdng Cncl 1994-; NCEA 1977-; Article Pub; *office:* St Mary's Parochial Schl 325 Church St Saint Marys PA 15857*

SIDER, HEIDI ANNE, School Counselor; *b:* Holyoke, MA; *m:* Ken; *ed:* Johnson & Wales Univ (AS) Fashion Merchandising 1985; SUNY at Oneonta (BS) Home Ec 1987, (MS) Schl Cnslng 1993; Working Toward CAS Schl Cnslng; *cr:* Kelly Svcs Sr Supvr 1989-91; W. L. Taylor & Son Inc Office Mgr 1991-94; Onatego HS Sub Schl Cnslr 1994; Laurens Cntrl Schl Schl Cnslr 1994-; *ai:* Dev, Instituted Stu Motivational Prgm; Peer Mediation Primary Screener; Instituted Stu Agendas Prgm; Supervised Schl Cnslng Intern; Grant for Cmptr Guid System; Invited to Speak to SUNY-Oneonta; Created Guide to Coll Planning, Application Booklet; *office:* Laurens Central Schl 64 Main St Laurens NY 13796

SIDERI, EVELYN ACEVEDO, English Teacher; *b:* Patchogue, NY; *m:* David; *ed:* SUNY at StonyBrook (BA) Eng, Scndry Ed 1990, (MA-LS) Lbrl Stud 1996; *cr:* William Floyd Schls Eng Tchr 1990-91; Westbury MS Eng Tchr 1991-; *ai:* Chrldng Coach; Honor Soc, Yrbk Adv; Crisis Intervention, Peer Mediation; AFT 1990-; NCTE, NYSEC 1992-; *office:* Westbury MS 455 Rockland St Westbury NY 11590*

SIDERIO, VINCENT JOSEPH, English Teacher; *b:* Philadelphia, PA; *m:* Michelle Krauss; *ed:* St Josephs Univ (AB) Eng, Philosophy 1965; Villanova Univ (MA) Eng 1983; SUNY at Binghamton Eng, Philosophy 42 Credits; *cr:* Paul VI HS Eng Tchr 1967-70; Eastern HS Eng Tchr 1970-; *ai:* Track Coach; NEA, EEA, NJEA 1970-, Pres & VP; *office:* Eastern HS Laurel Oak Rd Box 2500 Voorhees NJ 08043*

SIDES, BARBARA A., Second Grade Teacher; *b:* Winchester, MA; *ed:* North Adams St Coll (BSEd) Elem Ed 1965; Bridgewater St Coll (MA) Cmptr Ed 1985; *cr:* Billerica Schls 1st Grd Tchr 1965-67; Waltham Schls 1st Grd Tchr 1967-69; Hyannis West Schl 2nd Grd Tchr 1970-; *ai:* NEA, MTA, BTA 1965-; *office:* Hyannis West Elem Schl 549 W Main St Hyannis MA 02601

SIDNER, ANNE C., English Teacher; *b:* Springfield, OH; *ed:* Univ of Toledo (MA) Eng 1975; *cr:* Bishop Ready HS Sr AP, Soph, Frosh Eng Tchr; *ai:* Prins Advy Comm; NCTE 1985-; COESRA 1996; CDEA; *office:* Bishop Ready HS 707 Salisbury Rd Columbus OH 43204

SIDOTI, MARY ANGELA (SVIK), Coord of Dev Edctrs; *b:* Canton, OH; *m:* Roger; *c:* Ann, Elizabeth, Regina, Joseph; *ed:* Univ of Akron (BS) Scndry Ed 1971; Kent St Univ (MED) Curr, Instr 1990; 5 Hrs Schl Psych, Educl Rsrch; *cr:* Ravenna City Schls 8th Grd Soc Stud Tchr 1972-76; *ai:* Stu Act Budget, Schlsp Comms; Fac Advy Dev Svcs; Transitions, Comm 1994-, Learning Disabilities; OH Assn of Dev Edctrs 1990-; Kent Jr Mothers Club 1978-, Past Pres; Nom Distngd Tchr Awd; *office:* Kent St Univ Stark Cmps 6000 Frank Ave NW North Canton OH 44720*

SIDUN, ANN KEEFER, Third Grade Teacher; *b:* Steubenville, OH; *m:* James Andrew; *c:* Jennifer; *ed:* OH Univ (BSEd) Elem Ed 1973; Cleveland St Univ (MA) Early Chldhd 1983; Addl 4 Hrs in Cmptr Sci; *cr:* Murray City 4th Grd Tchr 1972-73; Cleveland Bd of Ed Elem Tchr 1973-78; Falls-Lenox Primary 1st-3rd Grd Tchr 1978-; *ai:* NEA 1973-, Bldg Rep; ADK 1980-, Sec; Girls Scouts of Amer, Ldr; PTA; Bible Schl, Tchr; Cancer Soc, Vol; *office:* Falls-Lennox Primary Schl 26450 Bagley Rd Olmsted Falls OH 44138

SIEFKE, NANCY LYNN (SHIPAN), Science Teacher; *b:* Cleveland, OH; *m:* Wayne E.; *c:* Erin, Adam, Amy; *ed:* Univ of Toledo (MS) Ed 1993; Stud of Great Lakes 1994; Bowling Green St Univ Sci, Tech 1995; *cr:* Oak Harbor Jr High Tchr 1986-; *ai:* Acad, Ath Boosters; OEA, Treas, Sec; NSTA, OH Earth Sci Tchrs; Delta Kappa Gamma; *office:* Oak Harbor Jr HS 315 Church St Oak Harbor OH 43449

SIEGEL, BARBARA GITLIN, French Teacher; *b:* Phila, PA; *m:* Burton; *c:* Leah Siegel Taylor, Sarah, Joshua; *ed:* Univ of PA (BA) Fr 1964, (MA) Fr 1969; 60 Addl Credit Hrs Jewish & Holocaust Stud Cnslng Psych; *cr:* George WA HS Fr Tchr 1964-77, Tchr, Mentor of Gifted Prgm 1977-; World Learning AU Pair Homestay USA Comm Coord Frgn Exchange Childcare Prgm 1990-; *ai:* Fr Club, Fr Hnr Soc, Ivy League Model United Nations Delegation, M. G. Energy Annual Publication of Gifted Prgm Spons; Mid St Evaluation Comm Chprsn; Frgn Lang Comm; AATF, AFT, MLA, PFT 1960-; Congregation Orhadash 1983-, Ritual Chprsn, VP, Israel Chair, Ira Silverman Awd of Jewish Reconstructionist Movement; Phila Alliance Tchng Hum in Schls Grant 1986; Chapel of Four Chaplains Awd for Comm Svc; *office:* George Washington HS 11000 Bustleton Ave Philadelphia PA 19116*

SIEGEL, CAROL NICI, Special Education Teacher; *b:* New York City, NY; *m:* William Reed; *c:* Regina Caroline; *ed:* SUNY at Stony Brook (BA) Theatre Arts 1984; LIU CW Post (MS) Spec Ed 1988; 23 Addl Credits; NY St Cert Spec Ed K-12, Elem Ed K-6, Speech, Lang; *cr:* Longwood Jr HS Spec Ed Tchr 1988-89; Great Neck South HS Spec Ed Tchr 1989-90; Lynbrook HS Spec Ed Tchr 1990-91; Island Trees HS Spec Ed Tchr 1991-; *ai:* Stu of Month Comm; Fac Music Concert Singer; Schlsps, Special Trips for Music Stdnts; AFT 1988-; UTIT 1991-; Sacred Hearts Church 1994-; Excl Ed Awd 1990-91; Directed 4 Major Productions; *office:* Island Trees HS 100 Owl Pl Levittown NY 11756*

SIEGEL, FREDERIC RICHARD, Professor of Geochemistry; *b:* Chelsea, MA; *m:* Felisa M. Pus; *c:* Gabriela Siegel-Benveniste, Galia; *ed:* Harvard Univ (BA) Geology 1954; Univ of KS (MS) Geology 1958, (PHD) Geology 1961; *cr:* Miguel Lillo Inst Tucuman Argentina Prof Titular-Investigador 1961-63; KS Geological Survey Geochem Division Head 1963-65; George Washington Univ Assoc Prof Geochem 1965-69, Prof Geochem 1969-; *ai:* Fulbright Scholar Colombia; 60 Refered Publications; 11 Sponsored Research Grants; Natural & Anthropogenic Hazards in Dev Planning 1996; Applied Geochem 1974; Geoquimica Aplicada 1992; *office:* George Washington Univ 2029 G St NW Washington DC 20006

SIEGEL, JAN ROSENTHAL, 8th Grade Mathematics Teacher; *b:* Hempstead, NY; *m:* Steven; *c:* Rachel; *ed:* Skidmore Coll (BA) EC 1985; Hofstra UNiv (MS) Scndry Ed 1988; *ai:* NEA, NCMTA 1988-; NCTM 1986-; *office:* Hicksville MS Jerusalem Ave Hicksville NY 11801

SIEGEL, JEROME, Professor of Psych Dept; *b:* New York City, NY; *m:* Marion Dachinger; *c:* Wayne, Terri; *ed:* City College of NY (BBA) Psych 1955; NY Univ (MA) Indstrl Psych 1957, (PHD) Indstrl Psych 1963; *cr:* Electronics Rsrch Labs Rsrch Psychologist 1957-63; Kollsman Instrument Corp Mgr, Human Factors 1963-67; Riverside Rsrch Inst Mgr, Psych Svcs 1967-71; City Coll of NY Prof, Dept of Psych Prof 1971-; *ai:* Mngmt Consultant; Dir BA, MA Prgm Psych; Dean Div Soc Sci 1980-84; Acad Adv; APA 1963-; SIOP-APA 1985-; METRO 1970-; Books: Psychological Testing; Numerous Articles Pub; *office:* City Coll of NY 137 St & Convent Ave New York NY 10031

SIEGENTHALER, EILEEN CUBON, Mathematics Teacher; *b:* Ravenna, OH; *m:* Calvin L.; *c:* Erica, Stehen; *ed:* Kent St Univ (BSE) Math, Elem Ed 1966; Kent St Univ (MED) Math Supervision 1969; *cr:* Rootstown Local Schl Dist HS Math Tchr 1966-78; Crestwood Local Schl Dist HS Math Tchr 1982-; *ai:* Portage Cty Curr Dev Comms; NEA, NEOTA, OCTM 1966-; NCTM 1991-;CEA 1982-; Eisenhower, KSU Grant Participant 1995-; Jennings Scholar 1990-91; *office:* Crestwood HS 10919 Main St Mantua OH 44255

SIEGERMAN, BRAD ALLEN, Social Studies Teacher; *b:* Long Island, NY; *m:* Julie Bye; *ed:* Widener Univ (BA) His 1984, (MED) Elem Ed 1985; Various Univs 42 Grad Credits; *cr:* Unionville HS Soc Stud Tchr 1985-90; Haverford HS Soc Stud Tchr 1990-; *ai:* Girls Tennis Coach; Sr Class Spon; Future Tchrs of Amer; NEA & PSEA 1985-; Loyal Order of the Moose 1986-, Treas; Fellowship in Ed; *office:* Haverford Sr HS 200 Mill Rd Havertown PA 19083*

SIEGFRIED, CHRISTINE L., Business Education Teacher; *b:* Easton, PA; *m:* David P.; *ed:* Bloomsburg Univ (BS) Bus Ed & Accounting 1989; East Stroudsburg Univ (MED) Prof & Scndry Ed 1995; Addl 30 Credits in Scndry Schl Guidance at Kutztown Univ; *cr:* Chubb-Keystone Bus Schl Instr 1989-90; Easton Area HS Bus Ed Tchr 1990-; *ai:* 7th & 8th Grd Field Hockey Coach; FBLA Adv; SAT Prgm Testing Admin; NBEA, PBEA 1989-; NEA, PSEA 1990-; Direct Selling Assn 1993-; Natl Bus Ed Assn Awd of Merit 1990; *office:* Easton Area Sr HS 2601 William Penn Hwy Easton PA 18045*

SIEGLE, MARY ANN, Fifth Grade Teacher; *b:* Nesquehoning, PA; *m:* James R.; *c:* Tara, Lindsay; *ed:* Kutztown Univ (BS) Elem Ed 1974, (ME) Elem Ed 1986; *cr:* Muhlenberg Elem Schl 4th Grd Tchr 1974-82; Cleveland Elem Schl 5th Grd Tchr 1982-91; Trexler MS 5th Grd Tchr 1991-; *ai:* Cncl; NEA 1976-; Allentown Women Tchrs 1994-; Allentown Hosp 1982-, Treas, Sec; NICU Parent's Support Group; *home:* 5832 Holiday Dr Allentown PA 18104

SIEGRIST, DAVID HARNISH, Former Administrator; *b:* Lancaster, PA; *m:* Dorothy Mast; *c:* Anthony, Jeffery; *ed:* Malone Coll (BS) Elem Ed 1978; MED Degree Candidate Millersville Univ; *cr:* Northern Yth Prgms Tchr 1978-88; New Danville Mennonite Schl Tchr 1988-92, Admin 1992-95; *home:* 1166 W Penn Grant Rd Lancaster PA 17603

SIEGRIST, SANDRA CAMERON, Mathematics Instructor; *b:* Cleveland, OH; *m:* Howard J.; *c:* Sarah Jane; *ed:* Cedarville Coll (BA) Math 1976; OH St Univ (MA) Math 1986; *cr:* Cntrl Bapt Schls Math Tchr 1976-79; OH St Univ Grad Tchng Asst 1984-86; Cntrl OH Tech Coll Math Instr 1986-; *ai:* Phi Theta Kappa Adv 1993-; COTC Fac Dev Comm 1992-; COTC Tchng Excl Awd 1992; *office:* Central OH Tech Coll 1179 University Dr Newark OH 43055*

SIEMBOR, ANNE M. SCHAEFER, Biology Teacher; *b:* Cleveland, OH; *m:* Jonathan; *ed:* Kent St Univ (BS) Ed & Comprehensive Sci 1992; Addl Credit Hrs Math; *cr:* Pymatuning Vly Local Schls Bio Tchr 1993-; *ai:* Chrldng Coach; Land Lab Comm; NEA, OEA 1993-; Order of Eastern Star 1992-, Electa, Ruth & Martha; Ashtabula Cty Soil & Water Conservation Dist Conservation Tchr of Yr 1995; *home:* 5900 Beach St Andover OH 44003*

SIEMERS, JENNIFER, 7th-8th Grade Math Teacher; *b:* Cincinnati, OH; *ed:* Univ of Cincinnati (BS) Scndry Math, Elem Ed 1982; Geog Stud OH St Univ; Environmental Ed Stud Miami Univ; *cr:* Pvt Svc Tutor 1983-87; St Francis Seraph Schl 7th-8th Grd Math, Sci Tchr 1988-94, 5th-6th Grd Tchr 1994-95; *ai:* Archdioscesen Soc Stud, Sci Curr Writing comms; OH Geographic Alliance 1991-, Tchr Consultant; Girl Scout Ldr; *office:* St Francis Seraph Schl 14 E Liberty St Cincinnati OH 45210

SIEMONEIT, REGINA PALIULIS, Professor of Psychology; *b:* Kaunas, Lithuania; *m:* Martin A.; *c:* Martin, Lelyte; *ed:* Univ of CT (BA) Psych 1963; Univ of Bridgeport (MS) Psych 1968; New Schl for Soc Rsrch (MA) Psych 1974; PHD Course Work Completed at Cognitive Inst at Rutgers Univ; *cr:* Staples HS Psych Tchr 1965-70; Union Cty Coll Psy 1971-; *ai:* Higher Ed Consortium for Drug Abuse Prevention in Office of Volunteerism; AAUP 1975-; Amer Assn of Baltic Psych 1992-; Westfield Sharing Talents & Skills 1990-, Storyteller Elem Mid Career Flwshp Princeton Univ; Post Doc Seminar Eng Lit 1 Article Pub; Stu Svc Awd for Outstdng Svc 1987-88; *office:* Union Coll 1033 Springfield Ave Cranford NJ 07016

SIENKO, JOHN W., Retired Principal; *b:* Pawtucket, RI; *m* Grimes; *c:* J. David, Sharon A. Burton; *ed:* Emerson Coll (BS) En RI Coll (MED) Elem Admin 1963; Addl 30 Credit Hrs; *cr:* Falls Sc Tchr 1959-62; Woodcock Schl Gr 5 Tchr 1962-63; Allen Avenue S 1963-93; *ai:* Timer N Attleboro High Bsktbl Games 30 Yrs; Pub Announcer N A Bstkbl 30 Yrs; Annual Flag Day Ceremonies Al Schl 30 Yrs; NA Admin Assn 1963-, Pres 1973; NA Tchrs Assn 195 1962; CYO-Blackstone Vly 1959-, Pres 1970, Man of Yr 1974.

SIEROTNIK, ANNE GAFFNEY, English Teacher; *b:* Syracuse, John; *c:* John, Daniel, Elizabeth, Brian; *ed:* LeMoyne Coll (BA) En IN St Univ (MS) Ed 1980; LeMoyne Coll 18 Hrs Cert; *cr:* LeMoy Stu Life Area Coord 1980-83; West Genesee MS Sub Tchr 1990-9 Genesee HS Tchr Eng 1993-; *ai:* Class of 1997 Adv; Prof Dev NEA, AFT 1993-; Holy Family Schl Bd 1995-, Chprsn; LeMoyne of Governors 1988-; Holy Family Schl Assn 1988-, Pres; *office* Genesee HS 5201 W Genesee St Camillus NY 13031

SIERS, RICHARD ARTHUR, Math Teacher; *b:* Middletown, Janet Mary Tuthill; *c:* scott, Beth; *ed:* Union Coll (BS) Math 1966 SUC at New Paltz, CCNY, OCCC; *cr:* Albany Acad Math, Physi 1966-68; Valley Cntrl MS General Sci Tchr 1968-70; Middletown H Tchr 1970-; *office:* Middletown HS Gardner Ave Ext Middleto 10940

SIGGINS, MICHAEL JOHN, Mathematics Teacher; *b:* Erie, Penn St Univ (BS) Ed, Math 1988; 36 Grad Hrs Master's Equivalenc *cr:* East Penn Schl Dist Jr HS Math Tchr 1989-90; Souderton Ar Dist Sr HS Math Tchr 1990-; *ai:* Head Var Girl's Bsktbl, Head Va Vlybl Coach; Jr Var Boy's Vlybl Coach Quakertown HS; NEA, PEA 1990-; PA Vlybl Coaches Assn 1992-; *office:* Souderton Area H School Ln Souderton PA 18964

SIGLER, GERALD P., Elem PE Teacher; *b:* Toledo, OH; *m:* Davids; *c:* Gerald Jr., Gretchen; *ed:* BGSU (BS) PE 1970, (MED) 1974; *cr:* Sylvania City Schls Elem PE Tchr 1970-; *ai:* Girls Var Sftbl Head Coach; Sylvania Ed Assn, NWOEA, OEA, NEA, AA 1970-; St Coaches Assn 1977-; Associated Press OH Coach of Northwest OH Coach of Yr 1978-79; Dist 7 Coaches Hnrs 1978-80 Bsktbl League Coach of Yr 1977-80, 1982-83, 1985-89; Sftbl Coach of Yr 1988-91.*

SIGMUND, MARY JOAN, Fourth Grade Teacher; *b:* Clairton, Thomas Francis; *c:* Thomas, Kevin, Kristin; *ed:* IN Univ of PA (BS Ed 1962; Univ of Pgh at Johnstown Post Grad Stud; *cr:* Gateway S Grd Tchr 1962-63; Richland Schls 5th Grd Tchr 1963-65; Geneva Nursery Schl Head Tchr 1980-86; Our Mother of Sorrows 4th G 1987-95; *ai:* Head Book Buddy Pgm; *office:* Our Mother Of Sorrov 430 Tioga St Johnstown PA 15905

SIGNORE, ANGELA C., Mathematics Teacher; *b:* Bayonne, Montclair St Coll (BA) Math 1958; Grad Courses in Math; *cr:* Be HS Math Tchr 1958-61; Bayonne HS Math Tchr 1961-; *ai:* Bayo Math Team, Club Adv; NEA, NJEA 1958-; BTA, HCTA; AFT 196 of Yr Bayonne Dist 1985; *office:* Bayonne H S Avenue A & Bayonne NJ 07002

SIGNORELLA, MICKEY, 5th Grade Teacher; *b:* Roselle Park, Arline Signorella; *c:* Gina Arlen, Michael, Maria; *ed:* Kean Co Elem Ed 1966, (MA) Elem Ed 1970; *cr:* Cntrl Six-Schl 6th G 1966-91; Cntrl Five Schl 5th Grd Tchr 1991-; *ai:* Affirmative Officer; Annual UNICEF Drive, Annual Clothing Drive Sioux Rosebud SD Chm; NEA, NJEA 1966-; Grant Novel Rdgn Outstanding Tchr Cert Appreciation NHS Glenora E. Feuchter 1988-90, 1993; *office:* Central-5 Schl Hilton Ave Union NJ 07083

SIGNORINI, DANIEL ALBERT, US History Teacher; *b:* Martin OH; *ed:* OH Univ (BA) Elem Ed 1975; Univ of Dayton (MS) Admi *cr:* Dillonvale Elem 4th-6th Grd Math Tchr 1975-77; Adena Elem Grd Soc Stud Tchr 1977-85; Buckeye South Jr High 7th-8th Grd Er 1985-90; Buckeye Southwest MS US His Tchr 1990-; *ai:* 8th Gr Bsktbl Coach; 7th, 8th Grd Ftbl; Buckeye Local Classroom Tch 1975-,; Holy Name Soc 1975-; Greyhound Pets of Amer 1988-; Buckeye Southwest MS 100 Walden Ave Tiltonsville OH 43963

SIKORA, GLORIA DIMARCO, Social Studies Teacher; *b:* Gl PA; *m:* David J.; *c:* Craig; *ed:* IN Univ of PA (BS) Scndry Soc Stu Grad Work Allegheny Cty Intermediate Unit, Comm Coll of Alleghe *cr:* West Mifflin Area Schls Soc Stud Tchr 1963-69; Levelle-Diocese of Pittsburgh Soc Stud Tchr 1984-87; Carlo Campus Schl Soc Stud Tchr 1987-; *ai:* Soc Stud Curr Coord; P CSEA 1987-; PA Cncl for Soc Stud 1990-; Historical Soc of West 1987-; Golden Apple Awd Nom 1992; Thanks to Tchrs Nom 1994-; Carlow College Campus Schl 3333 5th Ave Pittsburgh PA 15213

SIKOSKI, KAREN WELLS, Second Grade Teacher; *b:* Hartford, Robert A.; *c:* Erica, Ethan; *ed:* Salve Regina Coll (BS) Spec, E 1982; Cntrl CT St Univ (MS) Curr, Supervision 1988; *cr:* Tolland Grd Spec Ed Tchr 1983-84; Parker Meml Schl Kndgtn Tchr 1984- Grd Tchr 1985-94, 2nd Grd Tchr 1994-; *ai:* Sci Curr Comm; Tc Team; Stu Tchrs Cooperating Tchr; CEA, NEA 1983-; *office:* Memorial Primary Schl 104 Old Post Rd Tolland CT 06084

SILANO, PAUL EDWARD, 6th Grade English Teacher; *b:* Bro NY; *ed:* SUNY at Oswego (BS) Elem Ed, Eng 1985; Manhattanvil (MAT); 15 Addl Credit Hrs; *cr:* Harrison Children's Ctr Children's 1985-86; St Anthony's Schl 4th Grd Tchr 1986-88; Columbus Av Schl 6th Grd Tchr 1988-91; Valhalla MS 6th Grd Tchr, Lang Arts Sp 1992-; *ai:* Columbus Avenue Elem Yrbk Adv; Valhalla Jr Vol Amb Corp, Compact Learning Comm, Site-Based Mngmt Comm Tch Newspaper Tchr Coord; Tutor; *office:* Valhalla MS 300 Columb Valhalla NY 10595

SILBERG, DOROTHY DRAPER, Science Teacher; *b:* Nome, Ala Scott; *c:* Andrew, Hannah; *ed:* SUNY Coll at New Paltz (BS) Bio (MA) Scndry Ed & Chem 1987; *cr:* Roy C Ketcham HS Bio Tchr Replacement 1984; Syosset Cntrl Schls Sci Tchr 1984-85; Sougerti Schls Sci Tchr 1985-; *ai:* NYSUT 1984-; STANYS 1984-; Sau Tchrs Assn 1985-, Rep; New Paltz Rescue Squad 1983-90; PEO Treas Chapter CD 1991-92, Pres 1992-93; First Presbyn Church *office:* Saugerties Jr Sr HS Call Box A Saugerties NY 12477

SILBERMAN, SYDELLE BARON, HS Math Teacher; *b:* New Yo *m:* Irwin H.; *c:* Amy Rein, Beth Winograd, Ian; *ed:* Brooklyn Co Ed, Math 1960, (MA) Math 1965; Math, Math Ed, Cmptr Courses Univ, NYU, Brooklyn Coll, OR St; *cr:* Brooklyn Coll 1960; NY Part-time Instr 1967; NYC Pub Schls Math Tchr 1961-67; Charles E. Day Schl Math Tchr 1980-81; Bethesda-Chevy Chase HS Math Tchr *ai:* Montgomery Cty Pub Schls Graphing Calculator for Tchr 1992-93; Intnl Baccalaureate Prgm Comm; NCTM 1982-; Co- Book: Graphing Calculator Activities 1992; Outstdng Tchr Awd

₃o 1993; Outstdng Tchr, Tandy Designated Tchr Hewlett Packard Co ʾrgm 1994; *office:* Bethesda-Chevy Chase HS 4301 E West Hwy da MD 20814*

:RNAGEL, ROBERT A., English Teacher; *b:* Paterson, NJ; *m:* Traficante; *c:* Robert J., Rod, Leigh, Stephen, Michael; *ed:* Upsala 3A) Eng 1969; Seton Hall (MA) Prof Ed 1973; *cr:* Wayne Bd of Ed :hr 1969-; *ai:* Class Adv; NEA, NJEA 1969-; WEA 1969-, 25 Yrs Svc

-FLOWERS, JOYCE B., Chairperson of Management; *b:* Silver IC; *m:* Lloyd G.; *c:* Lloyd Rashal; *ed:* NC Cntrl Univ (BS) Bus 1963; r Coll (MSEd) Bus Ed; Manhattan Coll (MBA) Mgmt 1983; bia Univ TC (EDD) Higher Ed Ad 1991; *cr:* Barnard Coll Sec ;9; NY City Housing Authority Housing Dir 1968-70; NY City Prin Specialist 1970-74; Medgar Evers Coll Asst Prof 1983-; *ai:* Chptr ta Lambda & FBLA Adv; NY St Chprsn; Phi Beta Lambda Trustee; Zeller Schlsp Trust Fund; Alpha Xi Chptr; Delta Pi Epsila 1980-; 1980-; Amer Mgmt Assoc 1993-; ML Wilson Boy & Girls Club of ı, Corresponding Sec; PSC-CUNY Rsrch Awd 1992; *office:* Medgar Coll 1650 Bedford Ave Brooklyn NY 11225

ES, SHERI PAULETTE, Asst Prof of Phys Therapy; *b:* Bethlehem, : Univ of Scranton (BS) Phys Therapy 1987; IN Univ of PA (MS) :d Physiology & Adult Ed 1994; Doctoral Stu Medical Coll of PA & ɛmann Univ in Orthopedic Phys Therapy; *cr:* East Hills ilitation & Fitness Ctr Phys Therapist 1987-88; Allegheny & peak Phys Therapist Inc Phys Therapist 1988-92; Coll Misericordia ʾrof 1992-; *ai:* Fac Dev Comm; Pocono Susquehanna Clinical Ed rtium; Amer Phys Therapy Assn 1985-; Bd Certified Orthopedic al Specialist; Contributor to Clinical Cases in Phys Therapy; *office:* 1isericordia 301 Lake St Dallas PA 18612

ANEK, ANDA M., Latin Teacher; *b:* Riga, Latvia; *m:* David K.; *c:* Alison D.; *ed:* Western MI Univ (BA) Latin, Eng 1960; Univ of MI Latin 1966; Attnd Lehigh Univ, Amer Acad of Fine Arts at Rome; *cr:* velt HS Latin, Eng Tchr 1960-63; Concord HS Latin, Eng Tchr 56; Easton Area HS Latin Tchr, Japanese, Russian Facilitator 1964-; velt HS Latin, Eng Tchr 1966-68; ETS Consultant, AP Exams Reader)2; *ai:* Teach Home-Bound Stdnts 13 Yrs; Italy, Greece Tour Guide ;; NEA 1960-; Classical Assn of Atlantic Sts, PA Classical Assn of ic Sts 1968-; Unitarian Church 1972-; Fulbright Grant to Amer Acad e Arts at Rome; Rockefeller Grant for Ind Stud; Photographic ry Work; Numerous Papers Presented to Classical Orgs; *office:* Area HS 2601 William Penn Hwy Easton PA 18045*

ANEK, DOUGLAS MARK, Amer His, Govt & Ecnmcs Tchr; *b:* mer, PA; *m:* Paula; *c:* Joe; *ed:* Univ of Pittsburgh (BA) His, Pol Sci Youngstown St Univ (MA) His 1988; 15 Addl Hrs; *cr:* Beaver Local Permanent Sub Tchr 1978-79; East Palestine City Schls Tchr, Dist ud Coord 1979-; Youngstown St Univ Limited Svc His Instr 1988-92; Amer Legion Voice of Democracy Contest, Buckeye Boys, Girls St, & Blood Drives, Veterans Day Assembly; NEA, OH Ed Assn, East ıne Ed Assn 1979-; Mohawk Ath Assn 1980-, Coach; Mohawk Bsktbl ɛrs 1989-, VP; Youngstown St Univ Marion E. Blum Grad Essay Awd B'nai B'rith His Awd 1988; *office:* East Palestine City Schl Dist 360 ınt St East Palestine OH 44413

NOFF, MICHAEL, Mathematics Teacher; *b:* Wilmerding, PA; *ed:* ıinster Coll (BS) Math 1982, (BA) Ed 1984; St of Penna Masters alency Ed 1996; Westminster Soc Stud Cert 1989; *cr:* Norwin Schl Aath Tchr 1984-90; Baldwin-Whitehall Math Tchr 1990-; *ai:* Asst Ftbl Coach; Strength Coach; Defensive Coord; Sr Class Spon; ıtion Team; Caring Pgm Dir; NEA 1984-; St Nicholas Serbian ıdox Church 1960-, Auditor, Fin Sec for Sunday Schl; *office:* in-Whitehall Schl 4653 Clairton Blvd Pittsburgh PA 15236*

OWSKI, LILLIAN MARY,SC, 8th Grd Tchr & Vice Principal; *b:* c, NJ; *ed:* Coll of St Elizabeth (BA) His, Ed 1963; UC at Berkeley ɾea Writing Project 1981; MS Symposium St John Univ 1993-94; *cr:* f the Sea Schl Tchr 1952-53; Mt Carmel Schl 6th Grd Tchr 1954-55; :ulate Conception Schl 1st-2nd Grd Tchr 1055-62; Epiphany Schl th Grd Tchr 1962-73; Holy Cross Schl 5th, 7th Grd Tchr 1973-80; St Schl 7th-8th Grd Tchr, Vice Prin 1980-; *ai:* Moderator CYO Bsktbl, Teams, Schl, CYO Chess Club; Rainbows for God's Children Prgm ; Parish Yth Minister; NCEA 1980-; Jersey City Joint Act Advy Bd ; Archdiocesan Tchr of Yr 1994; *office:* St Mary Elem Schl 209 3rd sey City NJ 07302

WORTH, SANDRA J., Business Education Teacher; *b:* Jackson, MI; entral MI Univ (BS) Bus Ed 1969; Eastern MI Univ (MS) Bus Ed The Johns Hopkins Univ (MS) Cmptr Sci 1989; *cr:* Napoleon HS Bus hr 1969-79; Anne Arundel Cty Schls Bus Ed Tchr 1979-88; Charles ıb Schls Bus Ed Tchr 1988-; *ai:* MICCA 1987-; EACC 1988-; NEA ; Xi Alpha Delta of Beta Sigma Phi 1981-, Pres, Woman of Yr ɛss, Queen; Cmptr Tchr of Yr 1994-95; *office:* Thomas Stone HS 3785 ırdtown Rd Waldorf MD 20601

MAN, KATHLEEN ANDERSON, REAL Teacher; *b:* Philipsburg, ı: Dr. Carl Edwin; *ed:* PA St Univ (BS) Animal Sci 1977, (MS) bio 1982; Polyclinic Medical Ctr Schl of Medical Tech, Diploma in :al Tech; Instr i Cert Completed for Bio, General Sci, Chem 1985, ii Doctoral Candidate in Curr & Instr; *cr:* PA St Univ Research ologist 1982-83, Chem Tchr for Project Upward Bound 1989-93; Branch Area HS 7-12th Grd Sci & Cmptr Sci Tchr 1986-91; Lock ı Univ Microbio Instr 1991-; Bellefonte Area MS 6th Grd REAL Tchr ; *ai:* Sci Olympiad Team Coach 1993-94; Stu Assistance Team 1994-; 1995-; NEA, PSEA 1986-; ASCD 1993-; Amer Soc for Clinical gosts 1978-; Presbyn Church 1966-, Clerk, Elder & Tchr; *office:* fonte Area MS 100 N School St Bellefonte PA 16823

UP, ANN WALSH, Mathematics Teacher; *b:* Pittsburgh, PA; *m:* ond M.; *ed:* Duquesne Univ (MBs) Ed 1965; Johns Hopkins Univ Ed 1974; *cr:* Parole Elem Rdng Specialist 1971-83; A Leo Weil Elem Specialist 1979-83; Sterrett Classical Acad Math Tchr 1983-; *ai:* Count Coach 11 Yrs; Yrbk Spon 4 Yrs; Act Coord 5 Yrs; NEA 79, Schl Rep; AFT & PAFT 1979-, Schl Rep; NCTM & PCTM 1985-, gnition Outstdng Tchr; *office:* Sterret Classical Acad 7100 Reynolds sburgh PA 15208

, EDWARD P.,JR., Portuguese & Spanish Teacher; *b:* New Bedford, *m:* Cynthia J. Bettencourt; *c:* Matthew, Erin; *ed:* Univ of MA at nouth (BA) Portuguese-Ed 1972, (MA) Biling, BiCultural Ed 1978; sed Real Estate Agent MA; *cr:* Tiverton HS Portuguese, Sp Tchr , Foreign Lang Dept Chm 1985-; Bristol Cty House of Corrections 1991-; *ai:* Foreign Lang Club Adv; New Bedford Festival Theatre Bd Steering comm Chm; MAFLA, RIFLA 1985-; RINEA, Tiverton Assn 1972-; Coimbra Club 1985-, Treas.

, JACK P., Social Studies Teacher; *b:* Bethlehem, PA; *m:* Kathleen *l:* Penn St Univ (BS) Scndry Ed 1986; Kutztown Univ (MED) Curr & 1989; Lehigh Univ Cert of Supervision 1992 & PHD Curr & Instr; 30 Grad Credits; *cr:* Holicong Jr HS Tchr 1986-88; Central Bucks HS E 1986-89; Souderton Area HS Tchr 1989-; *ai:* US His Advanced ment Tchr; Mock Elections Coord; Secondary Soc Stu Coord; gic Planning Leader; NEA, PSEA & SAEA 1986-; PA Cncl of Soc 1987-; ASCD 1990-; NCSS 1994-; St Ursula's Cath Church 1968-; A 1991-; Penn St Univ Coll of Ed Outstanding Stu Tchr 1986; Penn St Univ Alumni Assn Honorary Lifetime Mem; Kutztown Univ Honor Grad Summa Cum Laude.*

SILVA, JANICE LYNN, English Teacher; *b:* Lowell, MA; *m:* David John; *c:* Amanda Leigh; *ed:* Rivier Coll (BA) Eng 1969; U MA (MA) Curr Design 1974; U MA at Boston (CAGS) Admin 1976; *cr:* Atkinson Acad Grd 4-6 Tchr 1969-70; West Jr HS Eng Tchr Grd 9 1970-72; Mc Carthy Jr HS Eng Tchr Grd 9 1972-80; Chelmsford HS Eng Tchr Grd 9-12 1980-; *ai:* Yrbk Adv 10 Yrs; Chelmsford Fed of Tchrs, Natl Fed of Tchrs 1980-; NEA 1970-80; Amer Cancer Soc Fundraiser 4 Yrs, Chairwoman; *home:* 470 Groton Rd Westford MA 01886

SILVA, JOHN, Physics Department Instructor; *b:* New Bedford, MA; *ed:* Capecod Comm Coll (AA) Ed; Fitchburg St Coll (BS) Ed; Bridgewater St Coll (MS) Eart Sci, Astronomy; Attnd Southeastern MA Univ; *cr:* Old Rochester Regnl HS Tchr 1976-77; Southeastern MA Univ Tchr 1977-90; Bristol Comm Coll Instr 1978-95; UMass Dartmouth Instr 1990-; *ai:* Dev Hands-on Sci Prgm for Pub, Pvt Schls; MTA 1988-; Distngd Fac Awd 1993, 1995; *office:* Univ Of MA At Dartmouth Old Westport Road N Dartmouth MA 02747

SILVA, RALPH E., PE Teacher & Coach; *b:* Gloucester, MA; *m:* Constance G. Jackson; *c:* Kenneth, Paul, Tony, Keith, Jeff, Cynthia Gould, Kristi Brown; *ed:* Springfield Coll (BS) PE 1959; Attnd Univ of MD, Keene St; *cr:* Charlestown HS AD, Tchr, Coach 1959-65; Fall Mountain Regnl AD, Tchr, Coach 1966-71; Claremont Jr HS Sci Tchr, Coach 1972-80; Claremont HS Tchr, Coach 1981-; Stevens HS Tchr, Coach 1981-; *ai:* NEA, NHCA 1959-; SREA 1971-; Claremont Yth Hockey Pres; Claremont Yth Bsbl, Sr Babe Ruth 1985 St Champs; Windsor VT Legion, Mgr, 1994 St Champs; *home:* RR 2 Box 673 Claremont NH 03743

SILVEIRA, AUGUSTINE,JR., Prof & Chemistry Dept Chprsn; *b:* New Bedford, MA; *m:* Beverly Ann Washburn; *c:* Linda Ann, Karen Silveira Moore; *ed:* Univ of MA Dartmouth (BS) 1957; Univ of MA at Amherst (PHD) Chem 1962; *cr:* Acushnet Process Co Rsrch Chemist 1957-62; Univ of MA at Amherst Instr 1960-62; Rutgers Univ Asst Prof 1962-63; Inst Chemical Ed ICE Tchng Assoc 1991; Univ of CA at Irvine Visiting Prof 1976-77, Sabbatical 1984, 1991; SUNY at Oswego Assoc Prof 1963-64, Prof Chem 1964-76, Chprsn Dept Chem 1967, Distngd Tchng Prof 1976-; *ai:* Amer Chemical Soc; Amer Assn Advancement Sci; Amer Inst Chemists; Sigma Xi; United Unv Professions; Oswego Intnl Rotary Club, Chair Meals-on-Wheels Prgm, Intnl Yth Projects Comm, Schlsp Comm; Numerous Articles Pub; Rep Awds Honorary Doctor of Sci 1975 Outstdng Tchrn, Rsrch, Admin, Perosnal Achvmt Awd 1973 Outstdng Accomplishment; Appt Lifetime SUNY Fac Exch Scholar 1981; First Co-Recipient Pres Awd 1983 Recognition Outstdng Schlsp; Amer Chem Soc Syracuse Section Awd 1988 Outstdng Contributions Chem, Chemical Ed; NY St, United Univ Professions Excl Awd 1990 Sustained Outstdng Perf, Superior Svc St Univ, St NY; *office:* S U N Y Coll At Oswego Chemistry Dept 219A Snygg Hall Oswego NY 13126*

SILVER, EDITH TICKNER, Professor of Mathematics; *b:* Norwalk, CT; *m:* James F.; *c:* Pamela Silver Botts, Lorna Jean Elliot, Frank James; *ed:* Trenton St Coll (BA) Math, Sci Ed 1952, (MS) Math Ed 1966; *cr:* Morris Plains Elem Schl 6-8 Grds Math, Sci Tchr 1952-53; Bernards Twp Schls 6-8 Grds Math, Sci Tchr 1953-54; Trenton Jr Coll Math Instr 1966-67; Trenton St Coll Elem Ed 1966-67; Mercer Cty Comm Coll Math Instr 1967-; *ai:* Teach 7 Stu Bag Piping; NEA, NJEA 1970-; NCTM 1992-; Co-Authored Books Unravelling Mathematical Concepts & Topics in Math; Authored Textbook Experiencing Algebra; *office:* Mercer County Comm Coll 1200 Old Trenton Rd Trenton NJ 08690

SILVER, JEFFREY YEHUDA, Instructor; *b:* Brooklyn, NY; *ed:* Yeshiva Univ (BA) Math 1971, (MA) Math 19971; NY Univ (MS) Cmptr Sci 1981; Yeshiva Rabbi Soloveitchik Ordination Rabbinics 1968; Rabbinical Judge Ordination; Rabbis Solovetchik & Rabbi Feinstein; *cr:* Bronx Comm Coll CUNY Lecturer 1980-84; Touro Coll Math, Cmptr Sci, Talmudano, Jewish Law Instr 1985-; Congregation Beth-Medragh Ha Gadol Rabbi, Tchr 1994-; Congregation Cherra Stard Rabbi, Tchr 1994-; *ai:* Rabbi Adv; Authentic Judaism Lector Cncl; Assn of Orthodox Jewish Scientist Bd; Jewish Family Law Comm; HA Pardes, Kavod Ha Rav Columnist; *office:* Touro Coll 240 W 23rd St 27 W 23rd St New York NY 10033

SILVERBERG, MITCHEL AARON, American History Teacher; *b:* Staten Island, NY; *m:* Lisa Kiss; *c:* Elizabeth J., Paul B.; *ed:* Syracuse Univ (BA) Amer His 1979, (BS) Scndry Ed 1979, (MS) Soc Sci & Scndry Ed 1980; *cr:* Altmar-Parish-Williamstown Schls Soc Stud Tchr & Coach 1980-85; Pine Bush HS Soc Stud Tchr & Coach 1985-; *ai:* Ftbl 1980-, Tennis 1981-84 & 1989-, Sftbl 1985-88 & Bsktbl 1983-85 Coach; NYSUT 1980-; Natl Historical Soc 1978-; *office:* Pine Bush HS Maple Ave Pine Bush NY 12566*

SILVERBERG, SANDRA S., Prof of Mathematics & French; *b:* New York, NY; *ed:* NY Univ (MA) Fr Lang & Ed 1971, (ABD) Fr Lang & Lit 1976; Post Grad Stud in Math at Rutgers Univ, Farleigh Dickinson Univ & Montclair Univ; *cr:* Cours Victor Hugo Admin 1969-71; Bergen Comm Coll Prof 1971-; *ai:* Fac Senate; NEA, NJEA 1971-; NYCLSA 1990-; AATF 1971-, NJ Pres; Womens Rights Information Ctr 1985-; Fr Club Spon 1971-84; Integration Project Hum Grant Chair 1989-93; Recipient Distinguished Fac Scholar Bergen Comm Coll 1995; Eng in Two Yr Coll; TETYC Ed; *office:* Bergen Comm Coll 400 Paramus Rd Paramus NJ 07652*

SILVERMAN, CATHY LEFFLER, English Teacher; *b:* Olean, NY; *m:* Michael B.; *c:* Paul, Lauren, James; *ed:* East Stroudsburg Univ (BS) Eng, Scndry Ed 1969; *cr:* North Brunswick-Linwood Jr HS Eng, Lang Arts Tchr 1969-72; Mt Pleasant HS Eng, Lang Arts Tchr 1974-78, 1986-89; Jackson Meml HS Eng, Lang Arts Tchr 1989-; *ai:* NJ St Testing Writing, NHS Selection Comms; Dist HS Writing Comm Rep; NEA, NJEA, NCTE 1969-; Manchester Twp NJ PTA 1980-; Manchester Twp HS Touchdown Club 1996; *office:* Jackson Memorial HS Don Conner Blvd Jackson NJ 08527

SILVERMAN, FRANCINE DIANNE, English Teacher; *b:* Philadelphia, PA; *m:* Roy; *c:* Heather, Joshua; *ed:* Temple Univ (BS) Scndry Ed 1969, (MS) Eng Ed 1971; 30 Credit Hrs Comp Coursed Ed Methods & Materials; 30 Credit Hrs of Cultural & Religious Enrichment of Adult Ed; *cr:* Philadelphia Schls Sub Tchr 1969-70; Delhaas HS Eng Tchr 1970-80; Truman HS Eng Tchr 1980-; *ai:* 11th Grd Curr Comm Chprsn; NEA 1970-; PSEA 1970-; BTEA 1970-, Bldg Rep; Womens Amer ORT 1972-, Ed VP Mother of Another; Ohev Shalom of Bucks Co 1978-, Ritual VP 5 Yrs; Certs of Svc Recognition from Bristol Twshp Bd of Schl Dir; *office:* Harry S Truman HS 3001 Green Ln Levittown PA 19057*

SILVERMAN, JAY HARRY, Math Teacher; *b:* Baltimore, MD; *m:* Janis; *c:* Melissa; *ed:* Univ of MD (BS) Math, Ed 1972, (MA) Measurement & Statistics 1975; 30 Credits Measurement & Statistics; *cr:* Laurel HS Math Tchr 1971-88, Magnet Acad Coord 1988-95, Math Tchr 1995-; *ai:* NEA, MSTA, PGCEA 1971-; NCTM 1989-; Spec Ed Advy Cncl 1984-; Natl Down Sydrome Cngress, Natl Down Syndrome Soc 1982-; Chesapeake Down Syndrome Parent Group 1982-, Founder, Pres; Intnl Brotherhood of Magicians 1977; *office:* Laurel HS 8000 Cherry Ln Laurel MD 20707

SILVERMAN, LAWRENCE I., Band Director; *b:* New York, NY; *m:* Leslie Dawn Dixon; *ed:* Hunter Coll (BS) Music Ed 1978, (MA) Music Ed 1985; *cr:* Yonkers Schl System Band Dir 1978-84; Rye City Schl Dist HS MS Band Dir 1984-86; Leonia HS Music Dir 1986-; *ai:* Jazz Ensemble Dir; Pit Orch; Wind Ensemble; Marching Band; Front, Talent Show Adv; Mentor Tchr; MENC 1986-; BCSMA 1986-; Yonkers All-City Band 1976-78, Asst Dir; Bergen Cty Band, Dir; Original Musicals Percussion Scores; *office:* Leonia HS 100 Christie Heights St Leonia NJ 07605*

SILVERMAN, LINDA GERHARDT, HS Mathematics Teacher; *b:* New York City, NY; *m:* Steven; *c:* Jennifer, Andrew; *ed:* City Coll (BS) Math, (MS) Math Ed; 50 Credits Ed & Grad Courses; *cr:* Julia Richman HS Math Tchr 1972-80; St John's Univ Math Adjunct Lecturer 1983-85; Francis Lewis HS Math Tchr 1985-; *ai:* Mentor New Tchr; Tutoring; Curr Writing; AFT, UFT 1972-; Rocky Hill Civic Assn 1977-; *office:* Francis Lewis HS 58-20 Utopia Pkwy Flushing NY 11365*

SILVERMAN, MYRON, A P American Government Tchr; *b:* Chicago, IL; *m:* Elaine Ballaban; *c:* Joshua; *ed:* St Univ of NY at Oswego (BS) Soc Stud Ed 1967; St Univ of NY at Albany (MS) Soc Stud Ed 1968; St Univ of NY at Stony Brook (MA) Liberal Stud 1974; 30 Addl Yrs in Pol Sci, Govt, His; *cr:* Patchogue-Medford Pub Schls Tchr 1967-, Lead Tchr 1990-; *ai:* AFT, NYSUt, LICSS 1967-; NYSCSS 1970-; APIC 1991-; NCSS 1975-; North Shore Jewish Ctr 1974-; Who's Who Among Univ Stdnts 1968-; Alpha Psi Omega, Kappa Delta Pi, Pi Gamma Mu 1967-; Summer Grant SUNY Stony Brook 1971 & 1972; *office:* Patchogue-Medford HS Buffalo Ave Medford NY 11763

SILVERMAN, PHYLLIS WEITZ, Coordinator of the Gifted Pgm; *b:* New York, NY; *m:* Jay; *c:* Brian, Tracy, Jill; *ed:* Univ of Chicago (BA) Eng 1956; Western CT Univ (MS) Psych & Elem Ed 1969; 60 Credit Hrs Beyond Masters Various Inst including Univ of PA, Univ of CA & Univ of WI at Widener; *cr:* Chicago & Markham Schl Dist 5-6th & 10-12th Grd Tchr 1956-58; Peekskill & Lakeland Schl Dist 2-4th Grd Tchr 1963-70; Turner Schl Dist 6th-8th Tchr of Self Contained & Gifted 1970-77; Norristown Area Schls Tchr of the Gifted & Scndry Gifted Coord 1977-; *ai:* Mock Trial Tchr & Coach; Co-Chm Underclass Awd Comm; HS Gifted Pgm Comm; Comm Mentorship Dir; EANA; PSEA; NEA; PAGE; WI Cncl for the Gifted & Talented Charter Mem; WI Assn for Edctrs of Gifted & Talented Founding Mem & Newsletter Ed; Presenter at Several PAGE Conf & WCGT Conf; Guest Lecturer on Gifted Univ of WI & West Chester Univ; Wrote Curr & Stud Guides 1966; Designed & Coord Team Tchng Pgms 1968; Best Tchr of the Schl Citation 1974; Outstdng Ldr in Elem & Scndry Ed Awd 1976; Subject of Numerous Feature Newspaper Articles 1776; *office:* Norristown Area HS 1900 Eagle Dr Norristown PA 19403

SILVERSMITH, ERNEST FRANK, Chemistry Professor; *b:* NuernbergBavaria, Germany; *m:* Eva Perlman; *c:* Ann, Ruth, Edward, Daniel; *ed:* Harvard Univ (AB) Chem 1952; Univ of WI at Madison (PHD) Organic Chem 1955; *cr:* CA Inst of Tech Research Fellow 1955-56; Mt Holyoke Coll Asst Prof of Chem 1956-58; E. I. Du Pont Co Research Chemist 1958-67; Morgan St Univ Prof of Chem 1967-; *ai:* Chem Club, Pre-Pharmacy Stdnts Adv; Amer Chem Soc 1952-, Chm, Sec, Treas, MD Chemist of Yr Svc Awd; Tchng E. Emmet Reid Awd; Author, Co-Author Tech Papers, Patents, Book; *office:* Morgan State Univ Coldspring Lane & Hillen Rds Baltimore MD 21239

SILVERSON, MERRILY ALBERTI, Kindergarten Teacher; *b:* New York City, NY; *m:* Robert M. Jr.; *c:* Samantha, Meredith; *ed:* Fordham Univ (BS) Elem Ed 1965, (MS) Elem Ed 1967; *cr:* St Gabriel Schl Kndgtn Tchr 1979-; *home:* 3515 Henry Hudson Pkwy Bronx NY 10463

SILVERSTEIN, RONALD M., 10th-11th Grade Chemistry Tchr; *b:* Philadelphia, PA; *c:* Alan R.; *ed:* Drexel Inst (BS) Chemical Engrng 1958; Tempel Univ Bus Admin; Engineering Mgmt; West Chester Univ Ed; *cr:* Betz Laboratories Research 1955-65; Drew Chemical Corp Research Mrktng & mgmt VP 1965-80; Philadelphia Schl Dist Sci Tchr 1985-; *ai:* Basic Skills Tutoring; AFT 1985-; NEA 1985-; ACS 1958-; CTI 1966-; Patents, Book Articles; Regognized as Corrosion Specialist by Natl Assn of Corrosion Engrs; *office:* Saul HS 7100 Henry Ave Philadelphia PA 19128

SILVERSTRIM, C. ELAINE, 3rd Grade Elementary Teacher; *b:* Sayre, PA; *m:* Nelson T.; *c:* Bart M.; *ed:* Mansfield (BS) Elem Ed 1972; Addl 27 Credit Hrs; *cr:* Towanda Area Schl Dist 3rd Grd Tchr 1972-; *ai:* PSEA & NEA 1972-; Fr Aslum United Meth Church, Sunday Schl Tchr, Organist; *office:* Wysox Elem Schl RR 2 Box 131 Wysox PA 18854

SILVESTRI, ANTOINETTE GRACE, HS Business Education Teacher; *b:* Queens Astoria, NY; *m:* Gino; *c:* Dawn, Erica, Cynthia; *ed:* City Coll & Baruch Coll (BBA) Accty & Ed 1966, (MS) Ed 1970; LI Univ (CW Post Prof) Admin 1995; Numerous Credits in Bus, Comps, Ed Commnctns & Mrktg; *cr:* NY Inst of Tech Cooperating Inst with Coll & HS Course 3 Yrs; Glen Cove HS Bus Ed Tchr 15 Yrs; William Cullen Bryant HS Bus Ed Tchr 2 Yrs; *ai:* HS DECA Chptr & HS Yrbk Bus Adv; Mem of the Glen Cove Dist Tech Comm; Long Island Assn of Supervision & Curr Dev 3 Yrs; NCBEA 1983-; NBEA 1993-; Glen Cove Lions Club 1995-; Glen Cove HS PTSA 15 Yrs; DECA NY St Honorary Life Awd 1995; 5 Yr Svc Awd Glen Cove Beautification Commission; Nom for the Long Island Univ Tchr of the Yr Awd 1996; *office:* Glen Cove HS 150 Dosoris Ln Glen Cove NY 11542

SILVESTRI, JOHN E., Math Teacher; *b:* Providence, RI; *m:* Virginia; *c:* John P., Anthony D.; *ed:* Providence Coll (BA) Math, Ed 1964; Scndry Principalship RI Coll; *cr:* East Providence HS Math Tchr 1965-; *ai:* NEA, RI, RI Math Tchrs, East Providence Ed 1965-; Reserve Ofcrs 1968-; *office:* East Providence Sr HS 2000 Pawtucket Ave East Providence RI 02914

SILVIA, EDWARD J., Fifth Grade Teacher; *b:* North Dighton, MA; *m:* Cathy G. Rollins; *c:* Chris E., Susan L.; *ed:* Bridgewater St Coll (BA) His 1970, (MA) His 1976; *cr:* South MS Fifth-Sixth Grd Tchr 1971-89; North Elem Schl Fifth Grd Tchr 1989-; *ai:* Somerset Tchrs Assn 1971-, Fin Comm Chm, Bldg Rep; MA Tchrs Assn, NEA 1971-; BSA 1982-, Asst Scout Master; Golden Apple Awd; *office:* North Elem Schl 580 Whetstone Hill Rd Somerset MA 02726

SILVIA, GAIL MARIE, HS Social Studies Teacher; *b:* Fall River, MA; *ed:* Southeastern MA Univ (BA) Pol Sci 1976; Bridgewater St Coll (MAT) Ed, His 1983; *cr:* Westport HS Soc Stud Tchr 1977-; *ai:* Field Hockey Var Coach; Westport Fed of Tchrs 1977-; MSSFHA 1987-; *office:* Westport HS 19 Main Rd Westport MA 02790

SILVIA, MARY JANE, Youth Minister; *b:* Fall River, MA; *ed:* St Marys Coll (BA) Rel Stud & Eng 1976; 24 Credit Hrs toward MA in Pastoral Ministry; *cr:* St Marys Coll Residence Dir 1979-81; St Michael Schl Jr HS Tchr 1981-83; Bishop Eustace Prep Schl Yth Minister 1983-; *ai:* Drama Club & Show Band Dir; NCEA 1981-; *office:* Bishop Eustace Prep Schl 5552 Rt 70 Pennsauken NJ 08109

SILVIA, SUSAN GREGORY, Foreign Language Dept Chprsn; *b:* Providence, RI; *m:* Frank M. III; *c:* Jennifer; *ed:* Newton Coll of Sacred Heart (BA) Fr 1972; RI Coll (MAT) Fr 1980; Providence Coll 12 Credit Hrs Guidance, 18 Credit Hrs Span; *cr:* St Raphael Acad Fr Tchr, Chair 1972-79; Bishop Connolly HS Fr Tchr, Chair 1983-; *ai:* Foreign Lang Club Adv; Moderator Societe Honoraire de Francais; MAFLA 1983-; AATF 1994; *office:* Bishop Connolly HS 373 Elsbree St Fall River MA 02720

SILVIDI, ALAN CHARLES, English Teacher; *b:* Ravenna, OH; *ed:* Univ of Notre Dame (BA) Eng 1990; Kent St Univ (MAT) Scndry Ed 1993; *cr:* Archbishop Hoban HS Eng Tchr 1993-; *ai:* Stu Cncl, Lit Magazine, Spirit Comm Adv; NCTE 1993-; Sigma Tau Delta 1990-; *home:* 5065 Portland Cv Stow OH 44224

SILVIO, NANCY SCHAPP, Tchr & Frgn Lang Dept Chair; *b:* Freeport, NY; *m:* Joseph R.; *c:* Teri J., Jay B.; *ed:* Boston Univ (BA) Romance Lang & Lit 1967, (MED) Scndry Ed & Span 1969; Attnd Cornell Univ Romance

Lang & Lit 1962-65; 30 Grad Credits Montgomery Cty Pub Schl System; *cr:* Centro Colombo-Amer Eng Tchr 1967; Brooklin Pub Schls Span & Fr Tchr 1970-73; E Brooke Lee Jr HS Fr, Span & ESOL Tchr 1973; Northwood HS Span Tchr 1975-76; Montgomery Vill Jr HS Span Fr, Orientation to Lang Tchr 1976-81; Herbert Hoover Jr HS Span & Fr Tchr & Dept Head 1981-89; M L King Jr MS Span & Fr Tchr & Dept Head; Damascus HS Span Tchr & Dept Head 1993-; *ai:* Intl Club Spon; Mentoring Pgm for at Risk Stus; Mentor Univ GA Grad Stus; Textbook Evaluation & Selection Comm; Montgomery Cty Ed Assn 1973-; MD St & Natl Ed Assn 1973-; MD Frgn Lang Assn 1980-; AATSP; FLAMCO; Audubon Naturalist Soc 1978-, Comm Mem; *office:* Damascus HS 25921 Ridge Rd Damascus MD 20872*

SILVIS, SUSAN A., 5th Grade Teacher & Mentor; *b:* Brooklyn NYC, NY; *m:* John Charles; *c:* Mark Charles, Suaanne Lynn; *ed:* Brooklyn Coll (BA) Elem Ed 1961; 15 Hours Grad Classes Elem Ed; In Svc Courses; NYSUT Mentor-Tchr Internship Cert Prgm; *cr:* PS 116 NYC Bd of Ed 5th Grd Tchr, Mentor 1992-; *ai:* CYO Coaching Girls Track & Field; Young Astronaut Prgm Tchr; Afterschool Remediation Math Classes; Olympic Trng Camp Coach; Tchr of the Yr 1993; *office:* PS 116 Elizabeth L Farrell 515 Knickerbocker Ave Brooklyn NY 11237*

SIMAN, JOHN ANDREW, Fifth Grade Teacher; *b:* Ravenna, OH; *m:* Joan Warwick Olton; *c:* John Jr., Kelly E., Jennifer L.; *ed:* Hiram Coll (BA) Elem Ed 1973; John Carroll Univ (MA) Ed 1988; Natl Sci Fnd Grant 7 Hrs; Kent St Univ 18 Hrs; *cr:* Crestwood Local Schls 5th Grd Tchr 1973-, 7-8th Grd Girls Bsktbl Coach 1978-95, 7-8th Grd Boys Track Coach 1978-, Athl Dir 1995-; *ai:* 7-8th Grd Boys Track Coach; Ath Dir; Crestwood Ed Assn 1973-, Pres; OH Ed Assn 1973-; NEA 1973-; 7 Prin Awds; *office:* Crestwood MS 10880 John Edward Dr Mantua OH 44255*

SIMARI, M. COLEEN DRISCOLL, 8th Grade Language Arts Tchr; *b:* Lawrence, MA; *m:* Rocco; *c:* Gregory, Catherine; *ed:* Plymouth St Coll (BS) Scndry Ed, Eng 1978; Fitchburg St Coll (MA) Scndry Ed 1993; *cr:* St Joseph's Schl 7-8th Grd Soc Stud Tchr 1979-85; Salem NH Adult Ed Tchr 1979-89; Woodbury MS 7-8th Grd Lang Arts Tchr 1985-; *ai:* Salem HS Jr Var Field Hockey Coach; Jr HS Chrldng Coach; NEA 1985-; ADK 1992-.*

SIMAS, JOSEPH C., Latin & French Teacher; *b:* Providence, RI; *ed:* St Michaels (BA) Eng 1959, (MAT) His 1961; *cr:* Tchng 1954; Taught in England 1960-74; *ai:* Various Comm; RIFLA 1991-; AATF 1994-; *office:* Lasalle Acad 612 Academy Ave Providence RI 02908

SIMBOLI, GARY J., Special Education Teacher; *b:* Albion, NY; *m:* Laura M. Condoluci; *ed:* SUNY at Geneseo (BA) Music Theory, His & Voice 1985; Certs in K-12th Grd Spec Ed, K-12th Grd Music & K-6th Grd Elem Ed; *cr:* Albion HS Spec Ed Tchr 1990-91, Instrumental Music Tchr 1991; Albion Primary Schl Vocal Music Tchr 1992-93, Spec Ed Tchr 1993-; *ai:* Dir of All HS Plays & Musicals; Drama Club Adv; Dir of Annual Talent Competition & Annual Speaking Competition; Adv to Annual Black His Presentation.

SIMCOE, ALISON LEIGH, First Grade Teacher; *b:* Buffalo, NY; *ed:* West Chester Univ (BS) Elem Ed 1981; NY Institude of Tech (MS) Instrl Tech 1995; Attnd Univ of VA, West Chester Univ Post Grad Stud; *cr:* Totaro Elem Schl Tchr 1982-88; Roscoe Cntrl Schl Tchr 1989-; *ai:* Jr Class Adv; Bldg Ldrshp Team; Interdisciplinary Projects Coord; Grade Level Chprsn; Coordinating Tchr for Stu Tchrs; Girls Sftbl, Girls Bsktbl Coach; Roscoe Tchrs Assn 1989-; NEA 1982-; Zeta Tau Alpha 1973-, Chprsn; *office:* Roscoe Central Schl Academy St Roscoe NY 12776*

SIMEINDINGER, GARY L., Art & Computer Graphics Instr; *b:* Kettering, OH; *m:* Connie; *c:* Rozie; *ed:* Univ of Cincinati (BA) Art Ed, Fine Arts 1980; Cincinati Grad Stud; *cr:* Lebanon HS Art Instr 1990-96; *ai:* Art Portfolio Club; Bridges; NEA, NAEA, OEA 1990-; Lebanon Fine Arts Soc; Elk; Eagles; Schlsp Renewable Cincy Art Acad; Various Art Competition Awds; *office:* Lebanon HS 25 Oakwood Ave Lebanon OH 45036

SIMEONE, WENDY MATHESON, English Teacher; *b:* Middleboro, MA; *m:* Robert; *c:* Paul, Adam, Matthew; *ed:* SMU (BA) Eng, Ed 1973; Grad Writing Pgm U MA at Boston; *cr:* Plymouth-Carver Region Schls Eng, Scndry Tchr 1975-92; Carver HS Eng Tchr 1993-; *ai:* Fac Senate Pres; Stud Skills Comm; Stu Writing Spon; Tchr Mentor; NCTE, MCTE 1992-; ASCD 1994-; NEA, MTA 1973-; United Church of Christ Yth Ed, Comm Outreach; Plympton Garden Club 1991-; BSA, Former Mem; Soccer Coach; Plympton Historical; South of Boston's Best Tchr 1993; Natl Fnd for Advancement in Arts 1994; Tufts Univ Tchr Who Inspires 1995; Simmons Coll Tchr Who Inspires 1993; Pub in NCTE 1995; *office:* Carver HS 60 S Meadow Rd Carver MA 02330*

SIMI, RICHARD ANDREW, PE Tchr & Athletic Director; *b:* Worcester, MA; *m:* Jeanne Louise Langevin; *ed:* Pursuing Undergraduate Degree Worcester St Coll; *cr:* First Assembly Chrstn Acad PE Tchr, Ath Dir, Coach 1994-; *ai:* Soccer, Bsktbl Coach; Class Adv; *home:* 412 Harding St Worcester MA 01610

SIMINGTON, MICHAEL WILLIAM, High School English Teacher; *b:* Youngstown, OH; *m:* Kimberly K. Pierce; *c:* Philip, Meredith, Stephen; *ed:* Kent St (MA) Eng 1972; Youngstown St (MS) Ed 1985; *cr:* Kent St Tchng Fellow 1970-73; Poland Seminary Schl Eng Tchr 1974-; *ai:* Ftbl, Track Coach; NHS Control Bd; Ath Hall of Fame Comm; NEA, OEA, PEA 1974-, Bldg Rep; OH HS Coaches Assn; Presbyn Church 1978-, Elder, Sunday Schl Tchr; *home:* 6685 Shawbutte St Poland OH 44514

SIMISON, ANNE M., Computerized Accounting Tchr; *b:* Columbus, OH; *c:* Jill Sagraves, Robert Jr.; *ed:* OH St Univ (BS) Prsnl Mgmt 1970; Wright St Univ (MED) Bus Ed 1985; Post Grad Hrs Univ of Cincinnati; *cr:* Warren Cty Career Ctr Jr Computerized Accounting Tchr 1977-; *ai:* Bus Prof of Amer Adv & Classroom Educators Advy Cncl; OVA, AVA, OBTA, WCCC Tchrs Assn 1977-; AFT 1986-; OH St Univ Alumni Assn 1970-; Warren Cty Progress Cncl Tchrs Excl, Tchr of Yr & Five Star Tchr Awds.

SIMKO, JOHN JOSEPH, Alternative Educator; *b:* Philadelphia, PA; *m:* Veronica Valz; *ed:* Univ of VT (BA) Psych 1986, (MEd) Spec Ed 1989-90; 15 Addl Post Grad Credit Hrs Various Seminars Trng Drug, Alcohol, Motivation, Behavioral Stud; *cr:* Edmunds MS Educl Asst 1987-88; Burlington HS Alternative Edctr 1988-; *ai:* Coach JV Boys Bsktbl, Asst Var Boys B-ball, Asst Boys Var Golf; ASCD, Harvard Edcl Letter 1994-; *office:* Burlington H S 52 Institute Rd Burlington VT 05401

SIMKO, JOSEPH MICHAEL, Tech Dept Chairman & Teacher; *b:* Greensburg, PA; *c:* Troy, Kipp, Kristi; *ed:* Oswego St Univ (BA) Ind Arts Ed 1965; 32 Addl Hrs 1968; Inservice Hrs Syracuse City Courses; *cr:* Henninger HS Tech Tchr 1965-; *ai:* Grasshopper, Little League Bsbl Coach; 36 Stu Tchrs During Past Yrs; Syr Tchrs Assn 1965-; *office:* Henninger HS 600 Robinson St Syracuse NY 13206

SIMMERER, JULIA LYNN BRESNAHAN, 5th Grade Teacher; *b:* Winston Salem, NC; *m:* Bradley Alan; *ed:* OH Univ (BS) Elem Ed 1990; Univ of Akron (MS) Elem Ed 1995; *cr:* Brunswick City, Strongsville, N Royalton Schls Sub Tchr 1990-91; Crestview Elem Schl 5th Grd Tchr 1991-92, 5th Grd Tchr 1992-; *ai:* Marching Band Flag Instr; Sci, Soc Stud Curr Comms; Future Ldrs in Ed Cty Comm; Brunswick Ed Assn, OH Ed Assn, NEA 1991-; *office:* Crestview Elem Schl 300 W 130th St Brunswick OH 44212*

SIMMONS, BERNARD DEAN, Social Studies Teacher; *b:* Medina, OH; *m:* Shirley Jean Thomas; *c:* Audra Bester, Sherria Bester, Victoria, Bernard; *ed:* Baldwin Wallace (BA) His 1969; Cleveland St (MED) Curr 1984; *cr:* Addison Jr HS Soc Stud Tchr, Coach 1969-75; East HS Soc Stud Tchr, Coach 1975-; *ai:* Head Ftbl Coach; Team Tchng Prgm for 9th Grd Realignment; Tutoring For Citizenship; Proficiency Exams; Weightlifting Coach; AFT 1969-; GCFCA 1993-; Bethlehem Luth Church 1993-; B-P Inspirational Tchr of Yr 1992; Senate League Coach of Yr Girl's Bsktbl 1987, 1990-91; *office:* Cleveland East HS 1349 E 79th St Cleveland OH 44103

SIMMONS, BRUCE F., HS Choral Music Teacher; *b:* Danbury, CT; *m:* Arlene Gould; *c:* Brian, Mark; *ed:* Houghton Coll (BMUS) Ed 1964; 55 Addl Credit Hrs; *cr:* Warwick Vly Cntrl Schls Jr, Sr HS Music Tchr 1964-66; Monroe Cty Schl Corp Elem, Jr HS Music Tchr 1969-81; ARAMCO Schls Jr HS Music Tchr 1981-86; Beacon City HS Choral Tchr 1987-; *ai:* NEA 1964-; MENC 1981-; NY St Schl Music Assn 1987-; Music Wkshp Listen-Up for Better Singing, Near East South Asia Tchrs Assn Athens Greece 1985; *home:* 19 Dogwood Ct Goldens Bridge NY 10526

SIMMONS, BRYAN KEITH, Math Teacher; *b:* Baltimore, MD; *ed:* Robert Morris Coll (BA) Cmptr Info Systems, Quan Bus Analysis 1988; Coppin St (MS) Math 1996; *cr:* Household Fin Account Exec 1988-89; Cellular Directory Sales Rep 1989-90; Booker T. Washington Schl Scndry Math 1990-; *ai:* Bethel AME Mentorship Prgm; Balto Tchr Union 1990-; *office:* Booker T Washington MS 130 1301 Mcculloh St Baltimore MD 21217

SIMMONS, DEBORAH YVETTE, Grade Coordinator & Teacher; *b:* New York, NY; *ed:* City Coll of NY (BS) Math 1971; City Coll of NY (MA) Math Ed 1979; Bank Street Coll (MED) Educl Ldrshp 1994; 30 Addl Grad Credits; *cr:* Elijah D. Clark JHS 149 Grad Coord, Tchr 1971-; *ai:* Schoolwide Prgm Chprsn; Schl Choice Comm Mem; Testing Coord; Math Dept Chprsn; ARISTA Hon Soc Adv; Prins Cabinet Mem; UFT 1971-; Bank Street Coll Prins Inst Schlsp; *office:* Elijah D. Clark JHS 149 360 E 145th St Bronx NY 10454*

SIMMONS, DEL, Mathematics Teacher; *b:* Detroit, MI; *m:* Janet E. Fleet; *c:* David M., Brian L.; *ed:* Slippery Rock (BS) Math 1968; Univ of Pittsburgh (MS) Math Ed 1972; *cr:* Mount Lebanon Schls Tchr 28 Yrs; *ai:* Golf Coach; Wrestling Asst Coach; Boys Intramural Dir; NEA, PSEA, MLEA 1968-; Recreation Comm 1985-; Mentored 7 Stu Tchrs; *office:* Mt Lebanon Sr H S 7 Horsman Dr Pittsburgh PA 15228*

SIMMONS, FAYE W., Assoc Professor of CIS; *b:* Gouverneur, NY; *m:* William A.; *c:* Jay A., Daniel S.; *ed:* SUNY at Potsdam (BA) Comp Sci 1968, (MS) Ed 1985; 30 Credit Hrs Beyond Masters; *cr:* SUNY at Potsdam Programmer & Analyst 1968-79, Inst Rsrch Dir 1979-88; SUNY at Canton Assoc Prof 1988-; *ai:* Advising Curr Coord; ACM 3C; *office:* Canton Coll of Tech Cornell Dr Canton NY 13617

SIMMONS, KATHERINE SMITH, Sixth Grade Teacher; *b:* Sewickley, PA; *m:* Douglas James; *ed:* Marietta Coll (BA) Elem Ed 1990; Slippery Rock Univ (MS) Elem Ed 1992; Various Univ, Colls 15 Addl Credit Hrs; *cr:* Evans City Elem Schl 6th Grd Tchr 1990-; *ai:* Rdng, Writing Wkshps Intermediate Units Presenter; NEA, PSEA 1990-; *office:* Evans City Elem Schl 345 W Main St Evans City PA 16033*

SIMMONS, MARGARET (FLYNN), Business Education Teacher; *b:* New Haven, CT; *m:* Larry R.; *ed:* Cntrl CT St Univ (BS) Scndry, Bus Ed, Eng-Acad Hnrs 1971, (MS) Curr, Rsrch, Supervision 1977; *cr:* Milford HS Bus Ed Tchr 1971-73; Foran HS Bus Ed Tchr 1973-91, Rdng Tchr 1991-92, Bus Ed Tchr 1993-; *ai:* Prin Advy, Prof Dev, Grad Comms; Schl Mngmt Team; Yrbk Adv, Sr Act; NEA, CT Ed Assn, Milford Ed Assn 1971-; Northhaven Lib Friends 1995-; Pub Posters; *office:* Joseph A Foran HS 80 Foran Rd Milford CT 06460

SIMMONS, MARY ANN, 5th Grade Teacher; *b:* Atlantic, IA; *c:* Chris, Samantha; *ed:* Dakota Wesleyan Univ (BA) Sociology, Ed 1961; IA St Univ (MS) Ed, Cnslng 1979; 30 Addl Hrs Ed; *cr:* Rapid City Pub Schl System Jr HS Tchr 1979-89; Belmont Elem Schl Tchr 1989-; *home:* PO Box 546 Tilton NH 03276

SIMMONS, PHYLLIS KEEZER, Fourth Grade Teacher; *b:* Haverhill, MA; *c:* Lorice Simmons Sadewicz, Bradford R., Douglas W.; *ed:* Middlebury Coll (BA) Bio, Chem 1954; Univ NH Grad Credits; *cr:* Harvard Med Schl Rsrch Technician 1954-57; Timberlane Regnl Schl Dist Permanent SUb 1963-67; Pollard Elem Schl Second Grd Tchr 1967-80, Fourth Grd Tchr 1980-; *ai:* Coord, Adv Ski Club 1976-; Enrichment Team 1987-; Dist Sci Curr 1994-; Odyssey of Mind Coach 1985-; Timberlane Tchrs Assn 1974-, Treas 1987-89, Sec 1989-91; TTA, AFT 1992-, Bldg Rep, Exec Bd 1992-93; Plaistow Bast Church 1958-, Diaconate 1980-86; PTA 1964-; Plaistow Woman of Achvmnt 1984; Middlebury HS Hall of Fame Inductee 1995; *office:* Pollard Elem Schl 120 Main St Plaistow NH 03865

SIMMONS, TIMOTHY JOHN, Sixth Grade Science Teacher; *b:* Port Jervis, NY; *m:* Jeanne Ellen Kugler; *c:* Ryan, Matthew; *ed:* Univ of Bridgeport (BS) Elem Ed 1976; SUNY at New Paltz Grad Credits; *cr:* Eldred Cntrl Schl Tchr 1977-79; Minisink Vly Cntrl Schl Tchr 1979-; *ai:* Asst Var Ftbl Coach 1979-; Asst Wrestling Coach 1979-95; Port Jervis Fire Dept 1976-, Co Pres, Co 1st Lieutenant, Dive Team Ldr, High Angle Rescue Team Pres; *office:* Minisink Vly Cntrl Schl PO Box 217 Rt 6 Slate Hill NY 10973

SIMMS, DEBBIE L., Math Teacher; *b:* Marietta, OH; *m:* Thomas M.; *c:* Craig, Katie, Carrie; *ed:* OH Univ (BA) Elem Ed 1983; *cr:* Fort Frye Elem Schl 1st, 2nd Grd Tchr 1983-84; Watertown Elem Schl 1st, 2nd Grd Tchr 1984-85; Waterford Jr HS 7th, 8th Grd Math, Hlth Tchr 1985-; *ai:* NCTM 1994-; Sunday Schl Tchr; *office:* Wolf Creek Schl PO Box 45 Waterford OH 45786

SIMON, ABRAHAM JOSEPH, Mathematics Teacher; *b:* Wilkes-Barre, PA; *m:* Corrine Liska; *c:* Rachel Ann; *ed:* Bloomsburg Univ (BA) His 1983, (MS) Ed; Over 50 Credit Hrs in Post Grad Stud; *cr:* Gate of Heaven Schl 6th-8th Grd Math Tchr 1983-; *ai:* Bishop O'Reilly HS Boys Bsktbl Head Coach; Cmptr Room Specialist; PA Jr Acad of Sci Judge; Knights of Columbus 1985-; Scranton Diocese Distinguished Svc Awd; St House of Reps & Senate Letters of Accommodation; *office:* Gate Of Heaven Schl 40 Machell Ave Dallas PA 18612*

SIMON, GINA ANN, Second Grade Teacher; *b:* Washington, DC; *m:* H. Dale II; *c:* Todd Franklin, Shawn Anthony; *ed:* Univ of MD (BS) Elem, Spec Ed 1980; 45 Addl Credit Hrs Educl Cnslng Wilmington Coll; *cr:* Indian Queen Elem Schl 4th, 5th Grd Tchr 1980-82; East Dover Elem Schl Spec Ed, Basic Skills Tchr 1982-83, Spec Ed, Resource Rm 1983-84, 1st Grd Tchr 1984-93, 2nd Grd Tchr 1994-; *ai:* Talent Show Producer Grds 2-4; Positive Action, Drug Free Schls, Hlth Ed Curr Prgm Evaluation Comms; Family Rdng, Math Night; Diamond St Rdng Assn 1995-; Capital Edctrs Assn 1982-; Tchr of Yr 1991-92; *office:* East Dover Elem Schl 852 S Little Creek Rd Dover DE 19901

SIMON, JOAN DINEEN, Student Activities Dean; *b:* Jersey City, NJ; *m:* Frederick III; *c:* Shaun, Jenny; *ed:* St Peter's Coll (BA) Urban Stud 1975; Seton Hall Univ (MA) Theology 1993; *cr:* Sacred Heart Clifton Yth Minister, Intern Prin 1983-90; Mary Help of Chrstn Acad Dept Chair, Tchr, Yth Minister 1990-92; Don Bosco Tech HS Dean of Act 1992-; Caldwell Coll Adj Prof 1995-; *ai:* Stu Cncl Moderator; NASAA, NCEA 1992-; Pub Article 1995; *home:* 14 Whitmore Pl Clifton NJ 07011

SIMON, LINDA ONDRUS, Work & Family Life Teacher; *ed:* Adrian Coll (BS) Ed & Home Ec & Bus 1977; Univ of Toledo, Bowling Green St Univ Hrs Toward Masters in Ed; *cr:* Lasalle's Asst Fashion Dir 1977; C[illegible] Work & Family Life Tchr 1977-; *ai:* OR Adult Ed Pgm Fitness Tchr[illegible] Toledo Area Home Ec Assoc 1980-; Wrote 1 Grant in 1995 & 2 i[illegible] Accepted by Work & Family Life Pgm; *office:* Clay HS 5665 Sea[illegible] Oregon OH 43616

SIMON, MARCIA SHEDROFSKY, Retired Third Grade Teac[illegible] Brooklyn, NY; *m:* Howard; *c:* Andrew, Julie; *ed:* Brooklyn Coll (B[illegible] 1959, (MS) Ed 1963; *cr:* Mark Twain Jr HS 6th Grd Tchr 1959-6[illegible] Schls 205K 4th-5th Grd Tchr 1960-66; Pub Schl 200K 3rd-5th Gr[illegible] 1976-95; *ai:* Guy M. Stewart Cancer Fnd Inc 1974-, Financial Sec, [illegible]

SIMON, MICHAEL ALAN, Physics & Math Professor; *b:* New Yo[illegible] *m:* Bonnie Helene Lebenson; *c:* Laurie Jill Friedmann, Pamela Ga[illegible] Cooper Union (BS) Elect Engr 1965; NY Univ (MS) Elect Engr 1[illegible] Post Grad Credits; *cr:* Housatonic Comm Tech Coll Sci & Math Prof[illegible] Fairfield Univ Adj Math & Physics Prof 1983-; Southern CT St Ur[illegible] Math Prof 1990-; St Vincents Coll Adj Math Prof 1995-; *ai:* AAPT[illegible] *home:* 65 Primrose Dr Trumbull CT 06611

SIMON, MICHAEL C., Government Professor; *b:* Brooklyn, N[illegible] Andrea L.; *c:* Samantha, Jason; *ed:* Pace Univ (BA) Pol Sci 1981; Fo[illegible] Univ Schl of Law (JD) Law 1984; Rutgers Univ Schl of Criminal [illegible] PHD Candidate; *cr:* NY Cty Dist Attorney Asst Dist Attorney 1984-[illegible] Division of Criminal Justice Deputy Attorney General 1988-90; M[illegible] C. Simon Attorney at Law, Attorney 1990-94; John Jay Coll of Cr[illegible] Justice Adj Assoc Prof 1994-; *ai:* East Brunswick Bd of Ed 1995-; [illegible] John Jay Coll of Crim Justice 445 W 59th St Ofc New York NY 100[illegible]

SIMON, ROSE TEMKIN, Retired Teacher; *b:* New York, NY; *m:* H[illegible] *c:* Eric; *ed:* Hunter Coll (BA) Eng 1951; Queens Coll (MS) Ed; Undergraduate, Prof Level Courses; *cr:* PS 31 Queens Schl 6th, 5[illegible] Tchr of Gifted 4 Yrs; Dist 26 Schl All Grds Tchr; *ai:* AFT, De[illegible] Assembly; NYSUT, Del St Assembly; UFT, Del to Del Ass[illegible] Trachtenberg, Chptr Ldr, Pol Action Chprsn Dist 26; Comm Bd, [illegible] Housing Comm; Hollis Ct Tenants Assn, Pres; Hollis Court Owner[illegible] Coop Bd.

SIMON, SHIRLEY COHEN, Resource Teacher of the Bli[illegible] Brooklyn, NY; *m:* Jacob; *c:* Ilene J., Bertram H.; *ed:* Brooklyn Col[illegible] Ed 1956, (MS) Ed 1959; Hunter Coll (MS) Spec Ed 1982; *cr:* PS 20[illegible] Schl Tchr 1956-59; PS 286 Elem Schl Tchr 1959-61; PS 238 Resourc[illegible] of Visually Limited 1978-81; Edward R. Murrow HS Resource T[illegible] Blind, Visually Limited 1981-; *ai:* AFT, UFT 1978-; Phi Beta [illegible] Magna Cum Laude with Hnrs Ed Brooklyn Coll; *office:* Edward R M[illegible] HS 1600 Avenue L Brooklyn NY 11230*

SIMONDS, RODNEY GENE, Social Studies Teacher; *b:* Glove[illegible] NY; *m:* Lori Knowlton; *c:* Kaitlyn Amy; *ed:* Hudson Vly Comm Col[illegible] Lbrl Arts 1968; St Univ Coll at Oneonta (BS) Soc Sci 1978, (MS) S[illegible] 1984; Schl Admin Cert; *cr:* Fonda-Fultonville Cntrl Tchr 1978-; *a[illegible]* St United Tchr, Fonda Fultonville Tchrs Assoc 1978-; VFW 1978-; [illegible] Fonda-Fultonville Cntrl Schl 112 Old Johnstown Rd Fonda NY 120[illegible]

SIMONE, ROSEMARY E., Spanish Teacher; *b:* Newark, N[illegible] Montclair St Coll (BA) Span K-12 1971; Stony Brook Univ (MS) Lb[illegible] 1992; 75 Addl In-Svc, Grad Credits Long Island Inst for Prof Stu[illegible] Canter, South Cntry Tchr's Ctr, Univ of MO; *cr:* Frelinghuysen Jr HS[illegible] Tchr 1987; Randolph HS Span Tchr; Connetquot Schl Dist Spar[illegible] 1987-89; Bellport MS Span Tchr 1989-; *ai:* Intnl Club Adv; Hom[illegible] Clinic Adv, Tutor; Bus, Publicity Renaissance Comm; NEA [illegible] Bellport Tchrs Assn 1989-; PTA 1989-; NY Frgn Lang Tchrs 1990-[illegible] Schlsp; *office:* Bellport MS Kreamer St Bellport NY 11713

SIMONELLI, PASQUALE J., History Professor; *b:* San Paolo B[illegible] Naples Italy; *m:* Maria GIovanna Sarappa; *c:* Emilia, Julius; *ed:* U[illegible] Napoli Italy (DR) Philosophy 1970, (DR) His, Philosophy, Or[illegible] Stud-Summa Cum Laude 1980; Coll De Merode at Rome Maturita Cl[illegible] 1962; Dottorato Di Ricerca Univ Orientale Napoli; Flwshp Univ Ori[illegible] Napoli; *cr:* Univ Napoli Ricercatore 1973-, Asst Prof Philosophy [illegible] Asst Prof 1987-; Monmouth Univ His Prof 1988-; *ai:* Stu Adv; Acca[illegible] Tiberina Rome 1974-; Soc Filosofica Italiana 1972-; ISMEO Rome [illegible] APA 1989-; Grants Indian Govt; Numerous Articles Pub; P[illegible] Dissertation; *office:* Monmouth Univ Cedar Ave West Long Bran[illegible] 07764

SIMONETTA, STEFANIE GASBARRE, French Teacher; *b:* B[illegible] NY; *m:* Anthony; *c:* Daniella, Dante; *ed:* SUNY at Buffalo (BA) Ita[illegible] Fr 1985, (MAH) Italian & Fr 1990; *cr:* SUNY at Buffalo Tchng A[illegible] Italian 1983-84; Cheek-Sloan Schl Dist Fr Tchr 1985-; *ai:* Fr Club[illegible] Bldg Goals Comm; Values Comm Co-Chair; Cheek-Sloan Tchrs [illegible] 1985-, Bldg Rep; NYSFLT 1987-; San Pio Italian Club 1991-, VP; [illegible] John F Kennedy Jr Sr HS 305 Cayuga Creek Rd Cheektowaga NY 1[illegible]

SIMONS, KAREN MARTIN, Computer Sci & Busniess Tc[illegible] Covington, KY; *m:* Philip M.; *c:* Brian M., Mary Kathryn; *ed:* U[illegible] Cincinnati (BA) Scndry Ed, Voc 1974; Attnd Univ of Dayton, Wri[illegible] Univ; *cr:* Wyoming HS Bus Tchr 1975; Northridge Bd of Ed Adu[illegible] Cmptr Instr 1992-94; Northridge HS Voc Coord, Bus, Cmptr Sci[illegible] 1975-; *ai:* Adv Class, CBE Club; Mentor; Voc Liasion MVCTC; Vo[illegible] Dev Comm; Passport-For-All Pilot Prgm Staff; NEA; OH Ed [illegible] Northridge Tchrs Assn; OH Bus Tchrs Assn; *office:* Northridge HS[illegible] Timber Ln Dayton OH 45414

SIMONS, KENNETH J., English Teacher; *b:* New York City, N[illegible] Barbara Leeds; *ed:* Stony Brook (BA) Eng 1971; WI (MA) Eng [illegible] Columbia Univ (PHD) Eng & Comp Lit 1980; Post LIU SDA 19[illegible] LILCO Corporate Media Spokesperson 1981-85; NY Law Schl [illegible] Comm 1985-90; Syosset HS Eng Tchr 1990-; *ai:* Yrbk Adv 19[illegible] Scndry Curr Cncl 1995; Ind Stud Mentor 1995-; NCTE & NYSUT [illegible] The Ludic Imagination A Reading of Joseph Conrad; Marlow Ed H[illegible] Bloom Article on Conrads Narrativity; Article on Intern-Mentor [illegible] NCTE Monographs.

SIMONS, PENNY PASCALE, 7th-12th Grd Tech & Sci Tchr; *b:* A[illegible] NY; *c:* Lindsey, Delton J.; *ed:* St Univ of NY at Morrisville (AAS) A[illegible] Sci 1978; MI St Univ (BS) Animal Sci 1980; Potsdam Coll (MS) S[illegible] Sci Ed 1989; 3 Post Grad Hrs Each Project River & Project Learning [illegible] *cr:* Hammond Cntrl Schl 7th-12th Grd Tech & Sci Tchr 1982-; *ai:* Sr[illegible] & Whiz Quiz Adv; Audio-Visual & Cmptr Network Coord; WNP[illegible] Rep; Hammond Tchrs Assn 1982-, Pres 1989-90, Grievance & Soc Co[illegible] AFT, AFL-CIO, NYSUT 1982-; Kappa Delta Pi 1989-; TOPS #N[illegible] 1989-, Ldr 1994-; *home:* PO Box 53 Hammond NY 13646

SIMONS, ROBERT LAWRENCE, English Teacher; *b:* Easton, P[illegible] Margaret Diggs; *c:* Florence, Benjamin; *ed:* Wittenberg Univ (BA[illegible] 1968; 100 Plus Post Grad Credit Hrs at Luth Theological Semin[illegible] Philadelphia, Temple Univ & Other Colls; *cr:* Honesdale HS Eng [illegible] 1970-; *ai:* NEA, PSEA 1970-; WHEA 1970-, VP, Treas, Bldg [illegible] Grievance Chprsn, Negotiator; NCTE 1970-; Maple City Band 1974-, Wayne Choralaires 1973-, Pres, Bd Mem; St Johns Luth Church [illegible] 1980-; Photographs Pub in Two Psych Textbooks; *office:* Honesda[illegible] 459 Terrace St Honesdale PA 18431

SIMONS, THOMAS CLAY, Elementary Principal; *b:* Painesville, [illegible] *ed:* Pensacola Chrsn Coll (BA) Elem Ed 1980; 9 Credit Hrs Liberty [illegible] *cr:* Grace Chrstn Schl 5th Grd Tchr 1980-82; Faith Bapt Schl 4th Grd[illegible] 1982-87; Chrstn Life Acad 4th Grd Tchr 1987-89; Bethel Chrstn Aca[illegible] Grd Tchr, Prin 1989-; *ai:* Tchng Affective Parenting Prgm; Created &[illegible]

geous Olympics; Working With Grant Comm Cmptr Networking Pub 4th Grd Spelling Book, 1st Grd Short Stories; *office:* Bethel ian Acad 12901 W Pleasant Valley Rd Parma OH 44130

NSEN, JANETTE MAGENHEIMER, 4th Grade Teacher; *b:* ss, NY; *m:* Paul; *c:* Bridget Marie; *ed:* GW Post Coll (BA) Elem Ed Stonybrook Univ (MS) Lbrl Arts & Ed 1987; *cr:* Forest Park Elem th Grd Tchr 1985-.

NSEN, MARY GARTNER, French Teacher; *b:* Independence, KS; gust H.; *c:* Heidi, Erik, Kristi; *ed:* Univ of KS (BS) Fr Ed 1964; One er Stud Sorbonne in Paris; *cr:* Martin Luther HS Fr Tchr 1964-68; noreland Cty Comm Coll Adult Ed Fr Tchr 1978-79; Southmoreland Dist Vietnam Children ESL Tchr 1980-82; Connellsville Jr HS West hr 1983-; *ai:* Natl Jr Hnr Soc Adv; New Tchrs Mentor; *office:* llsville Jr HS West 215 Falls Ave Connellsville PA 15425

NSON, CAROL, 4th Grade Teacher; *b:* Cleveland, OH; *ed:* Bowling St U (BED) Elem & Spcl Ed 1974; Cleveland St U (MED) Curr & 1980; Post Grad Admin; *cr:* Midview Bd of Ed Tchr 1974-; *ai:* NEA ; OEA 1974-; MEA 1974-; Transitional Housing 1992-; St Joseph ni Bd 1994-; Fulbright Scholar; Martha Holding Jenning Scholar; lng Tchr Rep 1995; *office:* East Carlisle Schl 1959 Grafton Rd Elyria 4035*

NSON, TRUDY B., Lower School Principal; *b:* Pasco, WA; *m:* n D.; *c:* Betsy; *ed:* Eastern WA Univ (BED) Lang Arts 1968; Univ of MED) Cnslr Ed 1973; *cr:* Little Friends Nursery Schl Dir, Tchr 79; Lincoln Schl Tchr 1980-90, Prin 1990-; *ai:* Embry-Riddle nautical Univ Grant 1994; *office:* Lincoln Schl 301 Butler Ave dence RI 02906

RELLIS, CHRISTOS, Social Studies Department Head; *b:* Lowell, *m:* Ellen; *c:* Victoria, Alana; *ed:* Suffolk Univ (BA) His 1960, (BED) Ed 1962; 27 Grad Hrs Comps Lowell Univ, Voice of Diction Emerson & Harvard Univ; *cr:* Chelmsford Pub Schls Soc Stud Tchr 1962, Dept Soc Stud Tchr 1975; *ai:* Soc Stud Curr for Curr Frameworks; Dist Cncl; Chelmsford Fed Of Tchrs 1962-, Barganing Team 12 Times gnition Awd for Svc; NEA; Chelmsford Cultural Cncl, ONE of ling Mems 1975; 4th of July Comm 1968-70; Democratic Town n 1990-; Television Grant 1970; *office:* Mc Carthy MS 250 North Rd nsford MA 01824*

KINS, JOHN AUDREN, Music Tchr & Theatre Dir; *b:* Columbia, *ed:* Miami Univ (BM) Music Ed 1992; *cr:* Anderson HS Music Tchr, e Dir 1993-; *ai:* Adv Theatre Prgm, Thespian Troupe; Teach Ind e Stud; MENC, OH Music Edctrs Assn 1992-; Amer Choral Dirs 1993-; Educl Theatre Assn 1995-, St Bd Mem; OH Theatre Alliance ; Awded PTA Mini-Grant Theatre; Nom Forest Hills Schl Dist Edctrs 1995; PTA Friends of Children Awd 1995; Awded Host of St OH ian Conf 1996; *office:* Anderson HS 7560 Forest Rd Cincinnati OH *

KINS, MARY ELLEN (SIEGENTHALER), Third Grade Teacher; ssillon, OH; *m:* Jerry Lee; *c:* Travis Lee; *ed:* Kent St Univ (BS) Elem 66; 150 Credit Hrs; *cr:* Orrvile City Schls Third Grd Tchr 1966-; *ai:* OH Ed Assn, EAO Tchrs Assn Dist 1966-; Martha Holden Jennings; lng Tchr; *office:* Orrville City Schls 815 N Ella St Orrville OH 44667

SON, AMY TAYLOR, 6th Grade Teacher; *b:* Exeter, NH; *m:* d; *c:* Diana, Christopher; *ed:* Keene St (BED) Home Ec 1956; Attnd ewater St Elem 1980; *cr:* NH Schls Home Ec & Bio 4 YRS; Plymouth Elem 14 Yrs; *ai:* NEA 1980-; *office:* Plymouth Comm Intermedite 25 Long Pond Rd Plymouth MA 02360

SON, CRAIG BONHAM, Interdisciplinary Teacher; *b:* Springfield, *ed:* Univ of MS (BS) Ed 1972; Providence Coll (MA) Asian His 1977; ndover HS Tchr 1978-; *ai:* Adv to Amnesty Intnl Club; Liason to tion of Essential Schls; *office:* Andover HS Shawsheen Rd Andover 1810*

SON, DEBORAH M., Assoc Prof & Learning Ctr Coor; *b:* land, OH; *m:* Richard H.; *c:* Erik, Thomas; *ed:* Hiram Coll (BA) Eng Kent St Univ (MA) Eng 1966; 39 Credits Post Masters St venture Univ, Univ of CA at Long Beach, Jamestown Comm Coll, at Regents, Adams St Coll; *cr:* Montessi Childrens House Tchr Asst 79; Jamestown Comm Coll Assoc Prof 1980-; *ai:* Co-Dir Tchng, ing Ctr; Numerous Coll Sub Comms; Human Svcs Adv; Editorial Bd n-House Newsletters; NY St Union of Tchrs 1995-; Kappa Delta Pi; Rdng, Learning Assoc; Natl Cert Tutor Trng Prgm; First Presbyn ch; Bd of Literacy Vols Sec; Fac Excl Awd 1985; Enchanted tains Bus, Prof Women Woman of Yr 1987; Scandinavian Fac Exch p 1992; Chancellors Awd Prof Svc 1995; Natl Inst Staff, Orgnl Dev of TX at Austin 1996; Excl Tchng, Ldrshp Awd; *office:* Jamestown n Coll 312 N Barry St Olean NY 14760

SON, ERNEST GENE, Physical Ed Teacher; *b:* Chicago, IL; *m:* Jane; *c:* Debbie Sandlin, Jeff; *ed:* Otterbein Coll at Westerville (BS) 59; Attnd OH Northern Univ at Ada, Wright St Univ at Dayton, Univ ayton; *cr:* Bradford HS Tchr, Head Ftbl Coach, Ath Dir 1977-82; am HS Tchr, Head Ftbl Coach 1982-86; Riverside HS Tchr, Head Ftbl 1986-88; Triad HS Tchr, Head Track, Ftbl 1988-; *ai:* OH HS Ftbl hes Assn 1959-; Natl Fed Interscholastic Coaches Assn; *office:* Triad 941 Brush Lake Rd North Lewisburg OH 43060

SON, GLENN THOMAS, Biology Teacher; *b:* Rochester, NY; *m:* n M. Hosler; *ed:* SUNY at Brockport (BS) Bio 1973; SUNY at seo (MS) Ed 1977; NSF Honors Sci Univ of Rochester 1985; Attnd inade Univ 1987, Rochester Inst of Tech 1982-91, Cornell Univ -91; *cr:* Rush-Henrietta HS Bio, Ecology, Physics Tchr 1974-80; equoit HS Bio, Chem Tchr 1980-81; Victor HS Bio, AP Bio, Microbio 1981-; *ai:* Bio Club, Stage Technicians Advs; Theatre Tech Dir; Sci pration Days Exhibit Coord; Sci Olympiad Adv; AFT 1974-; Sci Tchrs 1976-; NABT 1993-; Pub Know Your Beer; Cornell Univ Inst of Bio Fellowship Extension Assoc; Cornell Inst of Bio Tchrs Lab Instr; : Victor HS 953 High St Victor NY 14564*

SON, HOWARD T., 6th Grade Teacher; *b:* Mineville, NY; *m:* een Kelly; *c:* Kelly breason, Howard, Kristie Jaakkola; *ed:* St Univ At Plattsburg (BS) Ed 1967, (MS) Ed 1970; *cr:* Glens Falls City Schl 5th Grd Tchr 1967-69; Greenwich Cntrl Schl 6th Grd Tchr 1970-; NY th Dept Camp Sanitary Aide 1991-; *home:* RR 1 Box 1059 Salem NY 5

SON, JUDITH GARNER, Social Studies Teacher; *b:* Washington, : Andrew, Megan; *ed:* High Point Coll (BA) His 1969; 30 Hrs Bowie niv; *cr:* Dr Brown Elem Schl Tchrs Aid 1978-80; Gen Smallwood MS Aid 1980-81; Thomas Stone HS Soc Stud Tchr 1981-83; LaPlata HS Stud Tchr 1983-; *ai:* Co-Spon Renaissance Prgm; Collects Tickets Girls Bsktbl Games, Wrestling Matches; NEA, MSTA, EACC 1981-; ed Heart Church 1972-; Nom by Local Chptr DAR as Amer His Tchr ; *office:* La Plata HS PO Box 790 La Plata MD 20646

PSON, KENYON RAY, 6th Grade Teacher; *b:* Greene, NY; *m:* cia Burris; *c:* Ira, Kaleb, Jason Sevigny, Jacqueline Sevigny; *ed:* eton St Coll (BS) Elem Ed 1970; 32 Grad Hrs NY St Cert; *cr:* Fair n Grd Schls 1st Grd Tchr 1970-71; Bolton Cntrl Schl Title I Rdg Tchr -72, 3rd Grd Tchr 1972-73, 2nd Grd Tchr 1973-88, 1st Grd Tchr -92, 6th Grd Tchr 1993-; *ai:* Chess Club; Bolton Tchrs Assn 1971-; n Free Lib 1984-86, Sec; Parents Tchrs Stdnts Assn 1983-, Charter, VP; Stony Creek Rod & Gun Club 1974-82, Sec, Pres, Trustee; Warren Co Conservation Cncl 1974-82, Del Sec; Gold 4-H Clover, Natl 4-H Wildlife, Fisheries Recognition Awds; Awd of Merit NY St Assn Cooperative Extension 4-H Agents 1989; *office:* Bolton Central Schl Horicon Ave Bolton Landing NY 12814

SIMPSON, PEGGY ANN, English & Language Arts Tchr; *b:* Vicksburg, MS; *m:* Ronald; *c:* Ronald, Fred, Shelba Van-Lierop, Darian, Martin; *ed:* Coll of New Rochelle Rosa Park Campus (BA) Early Chldhd Dev, Psych 1988; *cr:* NY Schl of Pratical Nrsng LPN 1971-73; Meml Sloane-Kettering Cancer Ctr Unit Sec 1979-90; IS 275 7th-8th Grd Eng, Lang Arts Tchr; *ai:* UFT 1989-; Order of Eastern Star Daughters of Amina #441 1990-, Worthy Matron; *office:* I S 275 Schl 134 Bet Lex & 7th Ave New York NY 10037*

SIMPSON, ROSEMARY, English & Journalism Teacher; *b:* Northampton, PA; *m:* Terry L.; *ed:* Moravian Coll (BA) Eng, Jrnlsm 1972; Lehigh Univ (MA) Ed 1984; *cr:* Allentown Schl Dist Eng Tchr 1972-; PA Power & Light Co Writing Consultant 1986-; *ai:* Newspaper, Class Adv; Allentown Ed Assn 1972-; Outstdng Tchr of Yr 1987; Exemplary Tchr Awd Cedar Crest Coll 1990; Pub Writing Manual; *office:* Louis E. Dieruff HS 815 N Irving St Allentown PA 18103

SIMPSON, YVETTE LASHON, Scndry Social Studies Teacher; *b:* Washington, DC; *c:* Mya, Michael, Darrell; *ed:* Univ of DC (BA) His, Ed 1986; Howard Univ 15 Grad hrs; Trinity Coll 9 Grad Hrs; *cr:* Greater Mt Zion Day Schl Tchr 1986-87; DC Dept of Recreation Tchr 1987; DC Pub Schls Tchr 1987-; *ai:* Media Tech & Soc Rsrch Charter Schl Co-Author, Ldr; Washington Tchrs Union 1987-; NCSS 1990-; DC Alliance Natl Geographical Soc 1993-; 12th St Chrstn Church 1990-, Deaconess; Natl Geographic Soc Summer Inst Flwshp 1993; *office:* MTSR Acad at Kelly Miller 49th & Brooks St NE Washington DC 20019*

SIMPSON-CHANEY, EVETTE R., 9th-12th Grade Spanish Teacher; *b:* Galveston, TX; *m:* Claude H.; *c:* Joy Elizabeth; *ed:* Whitman Coll (BA) Fr & Span 1973; Middlebury Coll (MA) Span Lang & Lit 1975; 19 Credit Hrs Pace Univ Post-Grad Stud Bus 1979; *cr:* Irvington HS Sub Tchr 1984; Summit HS Span Tchr 1984-85; Seton Hall Univ Upward Bound Fr & Span Tchr 1991-94; Clifford J Scott HS Span Tchr 1991-; *ai:* NJ Tchrs Assoc 1991-; Frgn Lang Tchrs of NJ Assoc 1994-; *office:* Clifford J Scott H S 129 Renshaw Ave East Orange NJ 07017*

SIMPSON-LEVI, KELLEY JO, Music Teacher & Band Director; *b:* Lorain, OH; *m:* Steve Levi; *c:* Lori, Sam; *ed:* Kent St Univ (BA), (BME) Music 1978; Post-Grad Stud Vandercook Schl of Music, Univ of HI, OH St Univ; *cr:* Ind Day Schl Gen Music, Orch Tchr 1978-82; Gulfside Elem Schl Gen Music, Band Dir 1982-88; West Franklin Elem Schl Gen Music Tchr 1988-95; Finland Elem Gen Music Tchr, Band Dir 1995-; Finland MS Gen Music Tchr, Band Dir 1995-; *ai:* 5th Grd Choir Dir; MENCA, NEA 1984-; Kent St Univ Schlsp; Guest Soloist Cleveland Orch; Author Childrens Musicals; *office:* Finland Elem & MS 2975 Kingston Ave Grove City OH 43123*

SIMS, EDWARD FREDERICK, Director of Bands; *b:* Rootstown, OH; *m:* Karen Sue Morgan; *ed:* Kent St Univ (BA) Music Ed 1975; Univ of Akron (MS) Music Ed 1987; Addl Post Grad Stud; *cr:* Cleveland City Schls Tchr 1975-80; Cuyahoga Falls City Schls Tchr 1980-83; Rittman Exempted Village Schls Tchr 1984-; *ai:* Dir Band, Marching, Concert, Pep, Jazz; OH Music Ed Assn; Music Educators Natl Conf; NEA; OH Ed Assn; East Cntrl OH Educators Assn; Rittman Ed Assn, Pres 7 Yrs; Wayne Co Council of Educators; Tri Cnty Cncl of Edctrs Pres 2 Yr; *office:* Rittman H S 100 Saurer St Rittman OH 44270*

SIMS, JOANNE MAGALDI, Associate Prof of Textiles; *b:* Brockton, MA; *m:* Norman V.; *ed:* MA Coll of Art (BFA) Fashion Design 1972; Southeastern MA Univ (MFA) Visual Design 1979; 40 Credit Hrs Sci, Psych; *cr:* Fisher Jr Coll Fac Mem 1974-75; Chamberlayne Jr Coll Fac Mem 1974-76, Dept Head 1976-88; Mt Ida Coll Prgm Dir, Fac Mem 1988-1989, Fac Mem 1989-; *ai:* Yearly Fashion Shows; Rank & Status Sec; Handbook Comm Sec; Knitting Guild of Amer 1986-; Amer Guilters Soc 1989-; MA Coll of Art Alumni Assn 1972-; Southeastern MA Univ Alumni Assn 1979-; Designs Pub: McCalls Needlework, Crafts, McCalls Design Ideas Vol II, Womans Day Magazine; Quilt Shoow Surface Design Assn Intnl Conf; 4 Book Reviews Prentice Hall Publishing; *office:* Mount Ida Coll 777 Dedham St Newton MA 02159*

SIMS, PATRICIA S. TAYLOR, English Tchr & Dept Chprsn; *b:* Hastings, NE; *c:* Kristin Leigh, Cory Edward; *ed:* Monmouth Univ Coll (BA) Speech, Drama, Eng 1972; Parkway Playhouse Univ NC at Burnsville Theatre Stud; USM Prof Stud; *cr:* Oakhurst Twp HS Eng Tchr 1972-73; Wiscasset HS Eng Tchr, Drama Chair 1975-80; Lincoln Acad Eng Tchr, Chprsn 1987-; *ai:* 1997 Team Adv; Governance, Scheduling Comms Chprsn; NCTE 1989-; Midcoast Children Theatre 1994-; Theatre Mentor 1995-.*

SIMS, THOMAS RAY, Psychology Professor; *b:* Pensacola, FL; *m:* Kathy Phillips; *c:* Brian Geary, Steven Howell; *ed:* Troy St Univ (BS) Eng, Sociology 1968; Univ of GA (MED) Counseling, Stu Prsnl 1972; Vanderbilt Univ (EDD) Human Dev Counsling 1986; Post Grad Stud at Univ of New Orleans; *cr:* US Army Infantry Platoon Ldr 1968-70; Warm Springs Rehabilitation Hospital Lead Cnslr 1972-74; Veterans Admin Counseling Psychologist 1974-82; Belmont Univ Psych Prof, Doctoral Candidate 1983-85; Prestonsburg Comm Coll Cnslr 1985-86; Univ of Southern ME Grad Schl Prof 1986-87; St of ME Ed Unit 1988-89; Stress Research & Dev Corporate VP 1989-90; Jefferson Comm Coll Psych Prof 1990-; *ai:* APA Psych Tchrs 1995-; Amer Legion Compassionate Friends; AAMFT Clinical Mem; Whos Who in South & Southwest Personality of Amer, Distinguished Amers; NCC Cert; Copyrighted Stress Survey; Developing Personality Theory; *office:* Jefferson Comm Coll Outer Coffeen Street Watertown NY 13601

SIMS, VERNA CRAYTON, Title I Teacher; *b:* Omaha, GA; *m:* Alvin Eugene Weber; *c:* Jeremy, Todd; *ed:* Jersey City St Coll (BA) Ed 1966; Seton Hall Univ Cert Early Chldhd 1968; Incomplete Masters in Guid; *cr:* Mt Pisgah Schl Dir 1966-82; PS #8 Tchr 1966-; *ai:* NEA 1966-; NJEA 1966-; HCTA 1966-; NAACP 1960-; Coll Women, Inc 1967-, Pres, 1st & 2nd VP; Mt Pisgah AME Church 1970-; Faith Van Vorst Nursery 1978-, Sec; Greenville Natl Little League 1987-, Treas; Outstdng Young Women in Amer 1979; Awd for Comm Work 1989; Awd for Church Work 1992; *office:* Public Schl No 8 96 Franklin St Jersey City NJ 07307

SIMS, YVETTE PATRICIA, Kindergarten Teacher; *b:* Newark, NJ; *ed:* Kean Coll Union (BA) Early Chldhd Ed 1983; *cr:* Jefferson Park Day Care Ctr Tchr 1983-88; Marquis De Lafayette Sixth Grd Tchr 1988-93, Kndgtn Tchr 1993-; *office:* Marquis de Lafayette Schl 1071 Julia St Elizabeth NJ 07201*

SINAGUGLIA, JOSEPHINE ANNE, Music Teacher; *b:* Buffalo, NY; *ed:* Nazareth Coll (BS) Music Ed 1955; Univ of Buffalo (MED) Music Ed 1965; *cr:* Bd of Ed Vocal & Instrumental Tchr 1955-; *ai:* NEA, NYSSMA 1955-; *home:* 92 Harrogate Sq Williamsville NY 14221

SINCLAIR, THEO ANN (FOGAN), Kindergarten Teacher; *b:* Irvona, PA; *m:* Ronald Clair; *c:* Lyncola Clair; *ed:* Penn St Univ (BS) Elem & Kndgtn 1966, (MSEd) Elem Ed 1971; *cr:* Glendale Schl Dist 1st Grd Tchr 1967-76, Kndgtn Tchr 1977-; *ai:* GEA 1967-, Treas 1970; PSEA 1967-; NEA 1967-; Glendale PTO; Gift of Time Awd 1995; *home:* PO Box 1 Flinton PA 16640

SINDALL, ROBERT ST CLAIR, 5th Grade Teacher; *b:* Baltimore, MD; *m:* Marilyn Darrall; *c:* Christine, Colleen, Carleigh; *ed:* Wheeling Jesuit Coll (BS) Psych 1970; Western MD (MED) Elem Ed 1980; Univ of MD Elem Ed Cert 1972; 60+ Hrs Post Grad Work; *cr:* Cold Spring Elem 3rd-6th Grd Tchr 24 yrs; *ai:* 8th Grd Girls Sftbl Coach & Mgr; Advy & Liaison Comms; MSTA 1972-; MCEA 1972-, Schl Del & Union Rep; NEA 1972-; MD Geog Alliance 1991-; Nom for Agnes Myers Tchr of Yr Awd 1987; *office:* Cold Spring Elem Schl 9201 Falls Chapel Way Rockville MD 20854

SINFORD, ROBERT FRED, PE Teacher & Athletic Director; *b:* Ellsworth, ME; *ed:* Univ ME at Presque Isle (BS) PE 1984; 6 Grad Hrs; *cr:* Rose M. Gaffney Schl PE Tchr 1985-; Machias HS Ath Dir 1995-; *ai:* Coach Var BOys Soccer, Frosh Boys Bsktbl; Machias Ed Assn, NEA 1984-; AAHPERD 1994-; ME Ath Admins Assn 1996; Machias Vly Little League 1992-, Pres; Coach of Yr Boys Soccer 1990, 1991, 1993; *office:* Rose M Gaffney Elem Schl 109 Court St Machias ME 04654

SINGER, DONNA ANNE, Band Director; *b:* Ridgewood, NJ; *ed:* St Univ of NY at Potsdam (BS) Music Ed 1986; NY Univ in Performance Toward Masters; *cr:* Sherburne Schl Elem Music Tchr 1986-87; Earlville Schl Jr HS Music Tchr 1986-87; Glen Ridge HS Band Dir 1989; Ramsey HS Woodwind, Marching Band, Lessons Instr 1988-; Cliffside Park HS Band Dir 1990-; *ai:* Marching, Concert Bands; Wind, Jazz Ensembles; Drama Club & Productions; NEA 1987-; MENC 1988-; Bergen Cty Music Educators 1990-; Church of Nativity Musician 1993-; Conductor & Musician in Pit Orchs; Distngsd Schlr Recgntn Awd Wnnr 1993, WPC; *office:* Cliffside Park HS Palisade And Riverview Aves Cliffside Park NJ 07010*

SINGER, GWENDOLYN K., Second Grade Teacher; *ed:* PA St Univ (BS) Ed 1971; Lehigh Univ (MED) Ed 1973; 30 Grad Credit Hrs; *cr:* Saucon Vly Schl Dist 1st-2nd Grd Tchr 25 Yrs; *ai:* NEA, PSEA & SVEA 1971-, PR Chair & Bldg Rep; Saucon Vly Comm Ctr, Bd of Dirs 6 Yrs; Delta Kappa Gamma 1980-, Chptr Pres, St Prof Affairs Chair & Protocol Chair 1988-95; Storytime in Park 1990-94, Dir & Coord; *office:* Reinhard Elem Schl 301 Magnolia Rd Hellertown PA 18055*

SINGER, HELENE, 4th Grade Teacher; *b:* Brooklyn, NY; *ed:* Suny at Stony Brook (BA) Pol Sci 1968, (MA) Librl Stud 1973; Addl 90 Credits; *cr:* Holbrook Rd Schl 1, 2, 3, 4 & 5 Grd Tchr 1968-; Mid Cntry Tchrs Assn Union VP 1984-; Coll of New Rochelle Inservice Edctr 1980-; *ai:* Report Card, Redistricting, Dist Discipline, Interview, Schrshp Comm; AFT, NYSUT 1971-, Del; Mid Cntry Tchrs Assn 1968-, Bldg Rep; Mid Cnty Tchr Ctr 1985-, Policy Bd, Chair, VP; NY Civil Liberties Union 1970-, Suffolk Mem; PTA 1968-, VP, Cncl Del; MCTA Line Ed; Union Newsletter; Winner Many Awds in NYSUT Jrnslm Competition; PTA Jenkins Awd, Natl Lifetime Mbrshp Awd; *office:* Holbrook Road Elem Schl 170 Holbrook Rd Centereach NY 11720*

SINGER, JOAN, Spanish Teacher; *b:* New York City, NY; *c:* Jonathan, Jacqueline; *ed:* The City Coll of NY (BA) Art, Span 1967, (MA) Comm-Cum Laude 1969; 60 Credits Forrester Inst, Domine; *cr:* Christopher Columbus HS Art Tchr 1968-70; Newfield HS Art Tchr 1970-74; Ward Melville HS Art tchr 1980-92, Span Tchr 1992-; *ai:* Ldr Schl Trips 1992-; Muralist, Organizer Frgn Lang Wing Hall, Classroom, Painting Project; TVTA 1980-; Phi Beta Kappa; NYSFLT, LILT 1992-; Article Pub 1992; Outstdng Tchr Awd 1985, 1986; Distngd Tchng Awd 1994; *home:* 8 Bucknell Ln Stony Brook NY 11790

SINGER, KATHLEEN MARIE, English & Reading Tchr; *b:* Hoboken, NJ; *m:* Bruce I.; *c:* Ian, Kelly, Kirk, Ryan; *ed:* Felician Coll (BA) Ed, Eng 1970; Seton Hall Univ (MA) Prof Ed 1973; *cr:* Glen Ridge Cntrl Schl 2nd Grd Nongraded Prgm Tchr 1970-72; St Phillips Lrng Ctr Coord of Curr, Act Dev Dept Prgms 1-3 Grd, 1-3 Grd Tchr, Coord; Toms River Intermediate East 8th Grd Eng, Rdng Tchr 1987-; *ai:* High Risk Children Tutor; Lending Lib Eng, Rdng Tchrs 1989; NJEA 1970-; TREA 1987-; NEA 1970-72, 1982-; Jr Womens Club 1972-75, Rookie of Yr; Local Theatre Groups 1964-86, Head Publicity, Pres; Womans Bowling League 1993-95, VP, Pres; Mixed Bowling League 1994-; Local Chorus, Glee Clubs 1966-87, Pres, VP, Publicity Dev, Conflict Mgrs; Peer Ldrshp Tchr Adv; Pupil Assitance Prgm; Schl Play Dir 1988-92; Numerous Articles Pub 1981-94; *office:* Toms River Intermediate E Schl Hooper Ave Toms River NJ 08753*

SINGER, LARRY D., Mathematics Teacher; *b:* Johnston City, NY; *m:* Patricia Heier; *c:* Andrea, Emily, Matthew; *ed:* Montclair St Univ (MA) Math 1972; Pace Univ Schl of Law (JD) Law 1982; Addl Stud Natl Sci Fnd Scholar, NYU Grad, Fairfield Univ Grad; *cr:* N Rockland HS Math Tchr 1968-; *ai:* Stu Govt, Math League, Mu Alpha Theta Advs; Graduation, Math Regents Competency Test Coords; Acad Comm Chm; N Rockland TA, NYSUT, AFT 1968-; Rockland Cty assn of Math Tchrs 1971-, Pres; Park Evangelical Free Church 1971-, Chm, Choir Dir; Cty Math Tchr of Yr; Assoc of Math Tchrs of NYS Seminar Speacker; Rockland Cty Math League Founder; *office:* North Rockland HS 106 Hammond Rd Thiells NY 10984

SINGER, MARK D., Criminal Justice Professor; *b:* Newark, NJ; *m:* Geri Riemer; *c:* Lindsey, Mallory, Brian; *ed:* John Jay Coll (BS) Criminal Justice 1986; Seton Hall (MA) Ed Admin 1990; Rutgers (EDD) Psych 1996; *cr:* West Orange Police Sergeant 1984-94; Union Cty Coll Prof 1992-; *ai:* Amer Psychological Assn 1991-; AAUP 1992-, NJ Assn of Criminal Justice Edctrs 1993-.

SINGER, MARY O. DOUGLAS, English Teacher; *b:* Bridgeport, CT; *m:* Neil Robert; *c:* Jessica Lynn, Douglass Jacob; *ed:* William Smith Coll (BA) Eng 1972; Univ of NH (MED) Rdng Ed 1981; Addl Hrs Ed; *cr:* East Lyme Jr HS Grd 6 Lang Arts Tchr 1972-72; Derryfield Schl 7-12 Grds Eng, Lang Arts Tchr 1974-77; Franklin Jr, Sr HS Eng Dept Head 1077-79; Cntrl HS Eng, Rdng Coord 1979-83; St Anselm Coll Instr 1983-88; Goffstown Area HS Eng Tchr 1988-; *ai:* NEAS&C Reaccreditation Self-Stud Co-Chair; NEA 1988-; Articles Pub; *home:* 22 Tanager Rd Goffstown NH 03045*

SINGER, MARY THERESA, School Administrator; *b:* Brooklyn, NY; *m:* Joel; *ed:* St Joseph Coll (BA) Child Stud, His 1971; CUNY Richmond Coll (MS) Ed 1974; Iona Coll (MS) Schl Admin; Iona, Fordham Univ; *cr:* PS 105K Brooklyn Early Chldhd Tchr 1971-76; Visitation Acad Soc Stud Tchr 1977-79; Annunciation Schl Tchr 1979-81; St Augustine's Soc Stud Tchr 1981-82; Our Lady Victory Acad HS Soc Stud Tchr 1982-95; Sacred Heart Schl, Prin 1995; *ai:* Westchester Cncl for Soc Stud; Westchester Cnty Holocaust Comm Educl Out-Reach Comm 1994; Intnl Cat Assn 1983-; Straight & Curl of It Cat Club 1988-; Educator of Yr 1985, Assoc of Tchrs of NY; 1991 Fellowship to Stud The Holocaust & Jewish Resistance in Poland & Israel, Spon by Jewish Labor Bd NYC; Hum Focus Grant-Natl Endowmnt for Hum; *office:* Our Lady of Victory Acad HS 565 N Broadway Dobbs Ferry NY 10522*

SINGER, MICKIE RUTH, English Teacher; *b:* Cincinnati, OH; *c:* David B. Werner; *ed:* Univ of Cincinnati Coll of Ed (BS) Scndry Ed & Eng 1975; Univ of Cincinnati Coll of Arts & Scis (MA) Lang, Lit & Pedagogy 1980; *cr:* Cincinnati Pub Schls Jr High & HS Eng Tchr 1973-78; Univ of Cincinnati Eng Instr 1978-85; PA St at York Lecturer 1985-86; Spring Grove HS Eng Tchr 1990-; Lebanon Valley Coll Adjunct Eng Comp & World Lit Tchr 1993-; *ai:* Schl Newspaper Adv; Professional Storytelling; Free-lance Writing; Southcentral PA Storytellers Guild 1984-, Pres 1984-86; PA Hum Cncl Grant 1986-87; Univ of Cincinnati Departmental Tchng Awd 1982, Tchng Incentive Awd 1985; Articles Pub Amer Baby Magazine 1989, Apprise Magazine 1986-91; Starlog Magazine 1988; Book Reviewer Cincinnati Enquirer 1982-83, Feature Articles The York Dispatch 1986-90; *office:* Spring Grove HS 220 W Jackson Spring Grove PA 17362

SINGER, VERA TEUTONICO, Retired Math Teacher; *b:* Brooklyn, NY; *m:* Edward J.; *c:* Gerard, Paul, Annette, John; *ed:* St John's Univ (BA) Math 1948, (MS) Ed, Adm 1950; GATE, New Methods in Tchng Math, Cmptrs, Using Manipulatives in Tchng In-Svc Courses; *cr:* George Washington Schl Tchr Grd 1 1948-56; Assumption Schl Sub Tchr 1963-70; Emerson Bd of Ed Individual Home Instruction Tchr 1978-80; Assumption Schl Math Tchr, Math Coord 1970-81; St Mathias Math Tchr, Math Coord 1982-94; *ai:* Math Tutor; NJ Tchrs of Math; NEA, WH Tchrs Assn; PTA; NJ Right to Life 1995-.

SINGLETON, DOROTHY, Fifth Grade Teacher; *b:* Kingstree, SC; *c:* William; *ed:* Wilberforce Univ (BS) Bus Admin 1956; Temple Univ Credit Hrs Elem Ed Cert 1958-60; Kean Coll Credits Elem Ed NJ Cert 1967-69; Montclair Univ 6 Post Grad Hrs Tchng Philosophy to Children; *cr:* Philadelphia Schl System 3rd-5th Grd Tchr 1956-66; Red Bank Schl System 4th-6th Grd Tchr 1968-; *ai:* Discipline Comm; Remedial Tutoring Club; MCEA, NEA, NJEA 1969-; Christ Church Unity Bd of Dirs 1980-, Sec; Asbury Park Lib Vol 1980-; Delta Sigma Theta 1954-; Tchr of Yr 1984; Governor's Grant 1993; NJ City Schls of Excl Awd, 25 Yrs Dedication 1990; *office:* Red Bank MS 101 Harding Rd Red Bank NJ 07701

SINGLETON, JOANNE K., Associate Professor; *b:* New York, NY; *ed:* St Clares Schl on NSG (DIPL) Nursing 1973; Marymount (BA) Psych 1982; New Schl (MA) Mngmt 1986; Regents Coll of NYS (BS) Nursing 1989; Adelphi Univ (PHD) Nursing 1993, Post Masters Cert Family Nurse Practitioner; *cr:* Hosp of Albert Einstein Coll of Medicine Staff Nurse 1973-80; Beth Abraham Hosp Nurse Recruiter 1980-81; Montefiore Med Ctr Dir Nurse Recruitment 1981-82; Mt Sinai Coord Nurse Recruitment 1982-86; Mt Sinai Med Ctr Clinical Nsg Supvr 1986-89; SUNY HSCB 1989-, Assoc Prof, Chrprsn Nurse Practitioner Prgrms; *ai:* ANA; NLN; Sigma Theta Tau; NYSNA; *office:* SUNY Health Science Ctr 450 Clarkson Ave # 22 Brooklyn NY 11203

SINGLEY, JUDITH GREENE, Recreation Coordinator; *b:* Bridgeport, CT; *m:* Gary; *c:* Joel Greene, Kirsten Elizabeth; *ed:* Univ of MA at Amherst (BS) Leisure Stud & Resources 1982, (MED) Higher Ed 1992; *cr:* Elder Day Ctr Activity Dir 1985-86; Greenfield Comm Coll Adj RLS Pgm 1987-93, Emerging Careers Pgm Coord 1993-94, RLS Pgm Coord & Asst Prof 1993-; Farren Care Ctr Therapeutic Recreation Dir 1991-93; *ai:* Brownie Troop Ldr, Classroom Vol; Cncl of Activity Profs MA Longterm Care Fed 1991-; Natl Assn of Activity Profs 1992-; Natl Recreation & Park Assn 1993-; Book: The Professional Activity Consulant 1996; *office:* Greenfield Comm Coll 1 College Dr Greenfield MA 01301*

SINGURA, LYDIA, Home Economics Teacher; *b:* Schweinfurt, Germany; *m:* Zenon; *c:* Sophia, Tanya; *ed:* James Madison Univ (BS) Home Ec Ed 1968; Kean Coll (MS) Early Chldhd Ed 1995; *cr:* St Elias Schl Elem Tchr 1968-70; Engelhard Corp Clerk, Typist 1970-71; Carteret Bd of Ed Sub Tchr 1980-83; Carteret HS Home Ec Tchr 1983-; *ai:* FHA Adv, Home Ec Related Occupations Club 1986-; Assn of Family & Consumer Sci 1976-, Treas; Middlesex Co F&C Sci 1976-, Pres; NJEA Middlesex Co Ed Assn, Carteret Ed Assn 1983-, Bldg Rep; Ukrainian Womens League of Amer 1980-, Pres, VP; Carl Perkins Voc Consumer & Homemaking Grant; A Plus for Kids Tchr Grant; Tchr of Yr; Dist Tchr of Yr; Article Pub; *office:* Carteret HS 199 Washington Ave Carteret NJ 07008

SINIBALDI, CAROL CHASE, Retired 5th Grade Teacher; *b:* Lawrence, MA; *m:* Robert John; *c:* Gayle Sinibaldi Merrill, Robert Stephen; *ed:* Keene Tchrs St (BEd) Elem Ed 1956; 30 Addl Post Grad Credit Hrs; *cr:* Fisk Schl 5 Grd Tchr 1963-64; Robert Frost Schl 5 Grd Tchr 1964-65; Woodbury Schl 5 Grd Tchr 1965-66; Pleasant St Schl 5 Grd Tchr 1966-67; W. E. Lancaster 5 Grd Tchr 1967-70, 5 Grd Tchr 1972-95; *ai:* Chic Team 8 Yrs; Curr Dev 3 Yrs; Cmptr Software Comm 5 Yrs; NEA, NHEA, SEA 1963-; Salem Jr Women's Club 1956-70, Pres 1960-62; *home:* 218 North St Georgetown MA 01833

SINISCARCO, LORRAINE BONO, Asst Prof of Occup Therapy; *b:* Utica, NY; *m:* Joseph; *c:* Krista, Nicole; *ed:* Utica Coll (BS) Occupational Therapy 1975; SUNY at Cortland (MS) Hlth Ed 1993; *cr:* St Joseph Nrsng Home Occupational Therapy Dir 1975-78; Masonic Home of Utica Occupational Therapy Dir 1978-82; United Cerebral Palsy Ctr Occupational Therapist 1982-89; Hertimer Co Comm Coll Occupational Therapy Asst Prof 1989-; *ai:* Occupational Therapy Asst Club Co-Adv; Curr Comm; Amer Occ Therapy Assn, NY St Occ Therapy Assn 1995; NY St Assn for Woman in Ed 1996; Shared Decision Making Team 1994-, Parent Coach for Fays Drug Quiz Team 1994-; Sci Fair Judge Donovan Jr HS 1944-; *home:* 806 Mildred Ave Utica NY 13502

SINK, CLAY V., Management Professor & Chair; *b:* Winston-Salem, NC; *ed:* Pfeiffer Coll (BS) Bus Ed 1958; Univ of TN at Knoxville (MS) Bus Ed 1964; OH St Univ (PHD) Bus Ed 1967; Attnd Univ of MD Fr, MI St Univ Mrktg; Cert Admin Mgr CAM 1988; *cr:* Morehead St Univ Assoc Prof 1964-69; Univ of RI Prof 1969-; *ai:* Beta Gamma Sigma Tchng Awd; Delta Pi Epsilon Adv; NBEA 1958-; Acad of Mngmt 1981-, Assn of Bus Comm 1975-; New England Bus Edctrs 1983-, Pres; Vol Svcs for Animals 1989-92, Treas; Journal of Ed for Bus Editor; Taught Univ of Grenoble, Intnl Inst of MGT at New Dehli; *office:* Univ Of RI Coll of Bus Admin Kingston RI 02881

SINKEY, HENRY ANTHONY,JR., Fifth Grade Teacher; *b:* Wellsville, NY; *ed:* Washington & Jefferson Coll (BA) His 1971; Duquesne Univ (MS) Elem Ed 1973; Attnd Winona St 1974, Charles Cty Comm Coll, Univ of MD Cert in Admin; *cr:* Port Tobacco Elem Schl Grds 3-5 Tchr 1973-77; Walter J. Mitchell Elem Schl Fifth Grd Tchr 1977-91; Mary H. Matala Elem Schl GATE, Fifth Grd Tchr 1993-; *ai:* Fifth Grd Math Team Supvr; NEA, MD St Tchrs Assn, Educl Assn of Charles Cty 1973-; Agnes Meyer Awd Nom 1982-83; *office:* Mary H. Matula Elem Schl 6025 Radio Station Rd La Plata MD 20646

SINN, KEITH MICHAEL, 8th Grade Science Teacher; *b:* Abington, PA; *m:* Sandy Margaret Graf; *c:* Emily Margaret; *ed:* Kutztown Univ (BS) Ed, Chem 1989; Beaver Coll (MED) Ed, Sci 1995; 9 Credit Hrs Computer Ed; 11 Credit Hrs Chem Ed; *cr:* Quakertown Comm HS Chem Tchr 1990-91; Amer Resource Consultants Environmental Chemist 1991-92; Tamanend MS Sci Tchr 1992-; *ai:* Track 1993-, Cross Cntry Asst 1994- Coach; NEA 1992-; Cntrl Bucks Ed Assn 1992-, Fac Rep; *office:* Tamanend MS 1492 Stuckert Rd Warrington PA 18976*

SINNAMON, ROBERT HUME,JR., Chemistry Teacher; *b:* Philadelphia, PA; *m:* Karen Anne Kasmarik; *c:* Rob, Anne, Katherine, Andrew, Noelle; *ed:* PA St Univ (MS) Scndry Ed, Chem 1974; West Chester Univ (MA) Phys Sci 1980; 10 Addl Credits; *cr:* Main-Line Day Schl Phys Sci, 9th Grd Spec Ed Tchr 1974-75; Upper Moreland Jr HS Phys, Earth Sci Tchr 1975-78; CB West AP & Regular Chem Tchr 1978-; DE Valley Coll Adjunct Chem Instr PT 1992-; *ai:* Sci Olympiad Team Coach; Chem Lab Supervisor; NEA 1974-; NSTA 1990-; Lenape Valley Rec Cncl 1990-, Coaching; Ed Testing Service 1994-; Reader Praxis 2; SAT Task Force Acad Stans Comm Chair; *office:* Central Bucks HS West Lafayette & W Ct Sts Doylestown PA 18901*

SINNEMA, JEFFREY WARREN, Industrial Arts Teacher; *b:* Cleveland, OH; *m:* Donna Jean; *c:* Jeffrey, Jean; *ed:* Kent St Univ (BS) Ind Arts Ed 1964; Univ of Akron (MS) Admin 1972; Attnd Kent St, Univ of Akron, OH St Univ-Martha Holden Jenning Scholar, Otho Dominican Coll, ND St; *cr:* Berea City Schls Tchr, Coach 1964-66; Maple Hts City Schls Tchr, Coach, Class Adv 1966-70; Mayfield City Schls Tchr, Coach, Club Adv 1970-72; Rocky River City Schls Tchr, Coach, Class Adv, Dept Head, Ath Coord 1972-; *ai:* Head Tennis Coach; NEA, OEA, RRTA, OITA 1964-; NIAAA 1992-; OH Tennis Coaches Assn 1972-, Exec Bd Mem; Masonic Lodge 1976-; OH Tennis Coaches Hall of Fame.

SINNING, KAREN M., 8th Grade English Teacher; *b:* Pittsburgh, PA; *m:* William H.; *c:* Craig W., Steven R.; *ed:* John Carroll Univ (BA) Hum 1975; Univ of Pittsburgh (MEd) Eng Inst 1992; Additional Grad at IN Univ at Bloomington, Kent St Univ, Cleveland St Univ; *cr:* Beachwood HS Eng, Hum Tchr 1975-78; Upper St Clair HS Gifted Prgm, Eng Tchr 1978-81; Ich Schl of Bus Bus, Eng Tchr 1983-89; Univ of Pittsburgh Tchng Asst, Stu Tchr Supvr 1989-92; Franklin Regnl JHS Eng Tchr 1992-; *ai:* NCTE 1975-81, 1989-; NEA, PSEA 1992-; Panel Presenter, NCTE Spring Conf 1992; *office:* Franklin Regional Jr HS 4660 Old William Penn Hwy Murrysville PA 15668

SINOFSKY, DORIS HANSSEN, Retired Teacher; *b:* Roseville, CA; *m:* Kenneth; *c:* Francine, Steven, Karen, Linda, Paul; *ed:* Univ of NV (BA) Jrnlsm 1949; Wm Paterson Coll (MA) Rdng; *cr:* Robt Mitchell Schl 4th Grd Tchr 1949-51; Union Schl 4th Grd Tchr 1951-55; Kennedy Schl 1967-92; *ai:* NEA; *home:* 27 Rillo Dr Wayne NJ 07470

SINTROS, THOMAS MICHAEL, Biology Teacher; *b:* Lowell, MA; *m:* Amy Byrnes-Sintros; *c:* Michael, Nicholas; *ed:* Lowell St Coll (BA) Bio 1971; 70 Hrs Keene St Coll Spec Ed; 12 Credits Antioch, NE Grad Schl Environmental Sci; 12 Credits Fitchburg St Coll; *cr:* Daly Jr HS Phys Sci Tchr 1971-76; Lowell HS Bio, ACE Tchr 1977-79; Athol-Royalston RHS AP Bio, Chem, Bio Tchr 1979-86; Monadnock RHS Bio, Envir Sci Tchr 1986-90; TNT Collaborative E H Stdnts Head Tchr 1990-93; Keene HS Bio, Envir Sci, Anati-Physio Tchr 1993-; *ai:* Sierra Club, Peer Mediation Adv; Co-Adv Envirothon Team; Staff Advy Cncl; Aids Awareness Comm; Improve Schl Advy Cncl; Monadnock Waldorf Schl 1984-87, Bd of Dir; Monadnock Childrens Museum 1986-88, Founding Bd; Governors Awd Volunteerism 1992; *home:* 31 Boston Pl Keene NH 03431*

SIPKA, ANN MACLEAN, Mathematics Professor; *b:* Poarland, ME; *c:* Todd, Tracy; *ed:* Marietta Coll (BA) Math 1970; 18 Hrs Grad Credits Math at Rivier Coll at Nashua; *cr:* Hood Meml Jr High 9th Grd Math 1973-74; Fairgrounds Jr HS Substitute Tchr 1982-85, Special Needs Aid 1985-86; NHTC Nashua Math Prof 1986-; *ai:* Girls Cross Cntry Coach; Boys Winter, Girls Spring Track Asst Coach; NCTM 1994-; Booster Club 1989-; *home:* 19 Biscayne Pkwy Nashua NH 03060

SIPP, ANTHONY FRED HOOKER, English & Journalism Teacher; *b:* Philadelphia, PA; *m:* Nancy Elaine; *c:* Kim Bailey-Granor, Larry Paige Bayley, Kathryn Theresa, Douglas Arthur, Gregory Bernard, Zachary David, Ashlie, Keli, Genevieve; *ed:* Catawba Coll (AB) Eng, His & Psych 1960; Midalebury Coll (MA) Eng 1968; Univ of GA 45 Hrs Grad Stud in Eng; Wharton 1980; *cr:* Sterling HS Eng Tchr, Coach & Adv 1961-65; Marie H Katzenbach Schl for Deaf Acad Stud Tchr 1965-66; Encinal HS Tchr & Coach 1966-68; Cherry Hill HS Eng Tchr, Coach & Adv 1968-, Eng Dept Chm 1970-75; *ai:* Eastside (Newspaper), Levendis (Review Magazine) & Cougars Den (Newsletter) Adv 1986-; Girls Cross Cntry & Track Head Coach 1981-83; Boys Track Head Coach 1968-76, Asst Coach 1984-90; NJEA & NEA 1961-; Delaware Valley Jrnlsm Faculty Adv of Yr From Temple Univ Press Tournament 1993; Courier Post Cross Cntry Coach of Yr 1993; Cherry Hill East Honored Tchr 1993; Session Ldr at Temple Press Tournament 1994-; *office:* Cherry Hill HS East Kresson Rd Cherry Hill NJ 08003*

SIRACUSA, PHYLLIS FREEMAN, Learning Specialist; *b:* Brooklyn, NY; *m:* John G. Jr.; *c:* Benjamin, Tamar; *ed:* SUNY at Buffalo (BA) Eng 1973; Columbia Univ Tchrs Coll (EDM) Cnslr Ed 1976; Post Masters Work John Hopkins Univ; *cr:* Hewlett HS Set UP Resource Room Tchr 1976-78; Montgomery Cty Pub Schls Rdng, Eng Tchr 1978-80; Rippswam Cisqua Schl Eng Tchr 1982-83; Niagara Cty Comm Coll Rdng, Writing Instr 1991-93; Elmwood Franklin Schl Learning Specialist 1993-; *ai:* Stu Adv; Work With Schls on How to Accommodate Learning Styles; Give Wkshps; Conduct Stud Groups; Orten Dyslekia Soc, Ed of Newsletter; Paretn Cncl Pres 1989-90; Search Comm Mem for Headmaster; Active Vol at Childrens Schl; Phi Beta Kappa; *office:* Elmwood Franklin Schl 104 New Amsterdam Ave Buffalo NY 14216*

SIRAGUSA, JAMES J., English Teacher; *b:* Williamstown, MA; *m:* Linda M.; *c:* Barry, Louise; *ed:* Dickinson Coll (BA) Eng 1979; Univ of Southern ME MS Ed 1991; *cr:* Lewiston HS Eng Tchr 1984-; *ai:* Speech Coach; NEA 1984-; MEA 1984-; LTA 1984-; BSA 1995-, Ldr; *office:* Lewiston HS 156 East Ave Lewiston ME 04240*

SIRI, WALTER ALAN, Science Teacher & Chairperson; *b:* Carlstadt, NJ; *m:* Joyce E. Meyers; *c:* Walter Jr., John S.; *ed:* Montclair St Coll (BA) Sci 1963, (MA) Sci 1968; Univ of MD Overseas Prgm; Attnd Pace Univ, Fairleigh Dickenson Univ, Rutgers Univ, Univ of PA, LaSalle Univ; *cr:* East Rutherford HS Sci Tchr, Chprsn 1963-71; H. P. Becton Regnl HS Sci Tchr, Chprsn 1971-; *ai:* Adv: Key Club 33 Yrs, NJ Sci League; NEA, NJEA 1963-; NJ Sci Sup Assn 1980-; ACS Tchrs Sect; Carlstadt Bd of Ed 1968-84, Pres 1971; Kiwanis Club 1992-; 1st Presbyn Church 1971-, Elder, Session Clerk; Boys St Chm Amer Legion 1986-; Adjutant 1995; USAF in Europe Educl, Conspicuous Educl Achvmt Awds; Fairleigh Dickenson Univ Sigma Xi Devotion, Promotion Sci Research Recognition Cert; Edison Sci, Youth Day Sci Ed Distinguished Svc Citation; Who's Who in Amer Ed; *office:* Henry P. Becton Regnl HS Paterson Ave & Cornelia St East Rutherford NJ 07073

SIRICO, ROSETTA AUSTIN, English Teacher; *b:* Brooklyn, NY; *c:* Sandy Massaquooi; *ed:* Queen Coll (BA) Eng 1977; Tchr coll at Columbia (MA) Spec Ed 1978; New York Univ (MA) Eng & Coll Ed 1979; Tchr Coll at Columia Univ (MEd) Eng & Spec Ed 1981; *cr:* Francis Lewis HS Tchr 1991-; Queens Coll Adjunct Prof 1993-; *ai:* Indian Club Adv; African Heritage Clb; United Kingdom Tchr 1994 CIE; *home:* 15272 Melbourne Ave Apt 1P Flushing NY 11367*

SIRIGNANO, JENNIFER, Art Teacher; *b:* NY; *ed:* Saint John's Univ (BFA) Graphic Design 1993; Adelphi Univ (MS) K-12 Art Ed 1996; *cr:* St Mary's HS Art Tchr, Yrbk Moderator 1993-94; Mary Louis Acad Art Tchr 1994-; *ai:* Ring Day, Open House Comms; Irish Club Moderator; *office:* The Mary Louis Acad 17621 Wexford Ter Jamaica NY 11432

SIRMAN, MARSHA STEIN, German & ESL Teacher; *b:* Bergen Belsen, Germany; *m:* Laurence E.; *c:* Sara Lynn, Jacob David; *ed:* Univ of DE (BA) Ger, Eng 1971, (MI) Instr 1989; 60 Credits Post Grad Work Frgn Lang, ESL Stud; *cr:* Woodbridge HS Eng Tchr 1971-73; Seaford HS Ger Tchr 1979-, ESL Tchr 1991-; *ai:* Ger Club Adv; Frgn Lang Dept Chprsn; Acad Cncl; DE Cncl Tchng Frgn Lang 1971-, Pres Elect, Tchr of Yr 1986; Am Assn Tchrs of Ger 1971-, Ger Tchr Aws 1990; NEA; SEA; DE Framework Comm 1995-97; St of DE Content Stan Writer Ger 1989-; Tchr of Yr 1985-86; DE Elem Tchr of Yr 1986-87; Frgn Lang Tchr Trainer St of DE; Conf Speaker FL, ESL Tchrs; *office:* Seaford HS N Market St Seaford DE 19973*

SIROIS, BARBARA J., Mathematics Teacher; *b:* Brooklyn, NY; *m:* Lee; *c:* Michael, Kenneth; *ed:* Amer Intnl Coll (BS) Math 1964; AIC (MA) Ed & Physics 1972; CAGS in Ed 1982; *cr:* Perry HS Math Tchr 1 Yr; East Hampton HS Math Tchr 2 Yrs; Wilbraham Jr HS Math Tchr 1 Yr; MRHS Physics & Math Tchr 22 Yrs; *ai:* Mathletes Team Coach; Tchrs Union VP; Math West 1990-; NCTM 1994-; Article Pub; *office:* Minnechaug Reg HS 621 Main St Wilbraham MA 01095

SISCA, RODGER FRANKLIN, Anatomy & Physiology Professor; *b:* Allison Park, PA; *ed:* Univ of Pittsburgh (BS) Natural Sci 1955, (MS) Natural Sci 1963, (DDS) Dentistry 1962; Univ of MD (PHD) Anatc Physiology 1967; *cr:* Univ of Pittsburgh Asst Prof of Dentistry 19 Univ of MD Assoc Prof of Dentistry 1964-75; Univ of TX at San A Prof of Dentistry 1975-85; Allegany Comm Coll Prof of Anato Physiology 1992-; *ai:* St Adv; Several Comms; ADA, AAUP, AADS AADR, IADR 1980-; *office:* Allegany Comm Coll Willow Brook Cumberland MD 21502*

SISKA, KATHYLENE FRANCES, Social Work Assoc Professor; *b* Jefferson, NY; *c:* Morgan; *ed:* Corning Comm Coll (AA) Liberal Arts Elmira Coll (BA) Foreign Langs 1968; Marywood Coll (MSW) Soc 1988; Columbia Univ (PHD) Soc Welfare 1995; *cr:* St Univ of NY Coll of Med Sr Research Specialist 1989-; Marywood Coll Asst Prof Saint Ambrose Univ Dir Schl of Soc Work 1996; *ai:* CSWE 1993-; N 1987-; Approximately 9 Articles; Chapter in Book; *office:* Marywoo 2300 Adams Ave Scranton PA 18509*

SISKA, PETER EMIL, Chemistry Professor; *b:* Evergreen Park, Jeanne Cathy Artman; *c:* David P., Sarah J.; *ed:* DePaul Univ (BS) 1965; Harvard Univ (AM) Chem 1966, (PHD) Phys Chem 1970; *cr:* of Chicago Rsrch Assoc 1970-71; Univ of Pittsburgh Chem Fac 197 Provosts' Adv Comm Undergrad Prgms; Senate Educl Policy Comm Exec, Lib, Promotion Review Comm; Amer Chem Soc, Amer Phy 1972-; Alfred P. Sloan Rsrch Flwshp 1975-79; Chancellor;s Distngd Awd 1987; 70 Articles Pub; 6 NSF Rsrch Grants; *office:* Univ Of Pitts Department of Chemistry Pittsburgh PA 15260

SISTO, LINDA, Spanish Teacher; *b:* Kearny, NJ; *m:* John J.; *ed:* Stroudsburg St Coll (BS) Scndry Ed, Span 1979; East Stroudsburg (MED) Scndry Ed, Admin 1983; HS Morris Hills Regnl Rockaw 1975; Stud Exchange St Judes Blingual HS San Jose, Costa Rica, Amer 1973; *cr:* Pocono Mountain HS Span Tchr 1979-89, Foreign Dept Head 1982-89; Hillside HS Span Tchr 1989-90; Mt Olive HS Tchr 1990-; *ai:* Ed Assn of Mt Olive 1990-; NJ Ed Assn, NJ For La Assn 1989-; NEA, Amer Cncl on Tchng For Lang 1979-; Phi Delta 1985-; Presenter at Northeast Conf of Tchng of For Lang; Ins Planner Pocono Mt For Lang Group; *office:* Mount Olive HS Co Flanders NJ 07836*

SIT, WILLIAM Y., Mathematics Professor; *b:* Hong Kong; *m:* Kwa Claire Law; *c:* Emil Meng-Chi, Eugene Meng Wei; *ed:* Hong Kong (BA) Math 1967; Columbia Univ (MA) Math 1969; Columbia Univ Math 1972; City Coll of NY (MS) Cmptr Sci 1978; *cr:* City Coll Part-time Lecturer, Instr 1971-73, Asst Prof 1973-80, Assoc Prof 19 Prof 1993-; *ai:* Math Assn of Amer 1969-; Assn Comp Mach Manhattan Schl of Music PreparationDivision 1995-, Bd of Dirs; NSA, CUNY Grants; Math Post Awd; Publications Pub; *office:* City Of NY City Coll Convent Ave At 138th St New York NY 10031

SITES, KIMBERLY ANN, English Teacher; *b:* Ironton, OH; *ed:* X Univ (BA) Eng 1990; OH Univ Grad Credit Hrs; *cr:* Rockhill HS 9t Eng Tchr 6 Yrs; *ai:* Prom Adv 3 Yrs; Soph Class Spon; *office:* Roc HS 2171 Cty Rd 7-C Ironton OH 45638*

SITLER, MICHAEL RALPH, Associate Professor; *b:* Harrisburg, P Kathleen; *ed:* East Stroudsburg Univ (BS) PE, Ath Trng 1976, (MS Ath Trng 1977; NY Univ (EDD) Admin, Sports Medicine 1989; Na Trainers Assn Certfd 1977; *cr:* Kean Coll of NJ Ath Trainer, Ad 1977-82; US Military Acad Asst Prof 1982-88; Temple Univ Asso 1988-; *ai:* Natl Ath Trainers Assn, EATA 1976-; PATS 1988-; A O'Donoghue Awd 1989; Henry Albert Scientific Awd 1993; Com Awd for Svc 1988; Phi Kappa Phi Schlsp Awd 1987; *office:* Temple 125 Pearson Philadelphia PA 19122

SITLER, ROBERTA CAROLINE, Language Arts Teache Bloomsburg, PA; *m:* Larry I.; *c:* Amy J., Adam R.; *ed:* Bloomsburg S (BS) Ger 1965; Millersville St Coll (MED) Elem Ed 1970; Addl 50 Credits Beyond Masters Degree; *cr:* Tulpehocken Area Schl Dist Ger Spring 1965, Kndgtn Tchr 1965-66, 3rd Grd Tchr 1966-71; ELCO Sch Chptr I Rdng Tutor 1979-81, 7th-8th Grd Lang Arts Tchr 1981-; *ai:* N Hnr Soc Adv; ELCEA, PSEA, NEA 1981-; Friedens Luth Church Cncl Mem, Worship & Music Chm; Falco Families of Cntrl PA 1992 Pres; Lebanon Cty Educl Hnr Soc; *office:* Eastern Lebanon Cty Sch 60 Evergreen Dr Myerstown PA 17067*

SIVERTS, RODNEY D., Math Teacher; *b:* Pasco, WA; *m:* Ann Thomas M., Scott B.; *ed:* Edinboro St Coll (BS) Math 1970; Ur Pittsburgh (MED) Ed 1974; *cr:* Bethel Park HS Math Tchr; *ai:* E 1981-93 9th Grd; Ftbl 1975 Coach 9th Grd; Bsktbl 1996 7th Grd Bethel Park Fed Tchrs AFT 1971-, VP 1973; *office:* Bethel Park HS Church Rd Bethel Park PA 15102

SIVERTSON, ANITA KOLINOFSKY, Seventh Grade Teacher; *b:* T PA; *m:* John N. Jr.; *ed:* East Stroudsburg St Univ (BS) Elem Ed Rutgers Univ (EDM) 1981; *cr:* Middlesex Bd of Ed 4th Grd Tchr 196 6th Grd Tchr 1975-80, 8th Grd Tchr 1981-82, 7th Grd Tchr 1983-; *ai:* to Academically Talented Adv; SIP; MEA 1968-, Bldg Rep, Negoti Team & Grievance Comm; NJEA 1968-; NEA 1968-; NJSTA 1 Governors Awd for Excl in Ed 1994-95; *office:* Von E Mauger MS Ave Middlesex NJ 08846*

SIVIGLIA, ANNE KLOTZ, Eng & Creative Writing Teacher; *b:* York, NY; *m:* Peter; *c:* Ellen, Judy; *ed:* Brown Univ (BA) Eng Columbia Univ Tchrs Coll (MA) Eng 1963; *cr:* Rye HS Eng Tchr 196 New Rochelle Acad Eng Tchr 1983-86; The Hackley Schl Eng Tchr 1 *ai:* Yrbk Adv; Alumni Oscar Kimelman Awd; *office:* The Hackley Sch Benedict Ave Tarrytown NY 10591*

SIZELOVE, COLEEN M., English Teacher; *b:* Greenville, OH Kenneth A.; *c:* Joshua, Annamaria, Chloe; *ed:* Wright St Univ (BS) E Theatre 1980; Miami Univ (MA) Theatre Arts 1986; *cr:* National Tra Eng Tchr 1985-; *office:* National Trail HS 6940 Oxford Gettysburg Rd Paris OH 45347

SIZER, CLARA ROBINSON, Business Teacher; *b:* Franklinton, L Vernon C.; *c:* Hayward Jones III, Kevin R.; *ed:* Southern Univ (BS) Soc Stud 1965; Nazareth Coll (MS) Ed 1976; *cr:* Terresbone Parish HS Ed Tchr 1966-67; Jefferson HS Bus Ed Tchr 1967-88; Benjamin Fra HS Bus Ed Tchr 1988-; *ai:* Ldrshp Club Adv; IBM Cmptr Lab Adv; Examination Comm; Rochester Tchr Assn 1968-; AFT; Inhu Meht Stu 1989-, Historian; *office:* Benjamin Franklin HS 950 Norton St Roch NY 14621*

SKALA, TODD JAMES, Social Studies Teacher; *b:* LaConia, NH Gina Pellegrino; *ed:* Wagner Coll (BA) His 1990; Univ at Stony B (MS) Lbrl Stud 1992; *cr:* Eastport Schl Dist Tchr & Coach 1994-; *a* Bsbl Coach; Jr HS Boys Bsktbl Coach; JV Boys Soccer Coach; Long I Cncl for the Soc Stud 1990-; NYSUT 1994-; *office:* Eastport Sch Montauk Hwy Eastport NY 11941

SKALET, LINDA H., History of Art Profesor; *b:* Port Chester, NY Steven A.; *c:* Jason H., Matthew H.; *ed:* Bryn Mawr Coll (BA) His o 1970; Univ of PA (MA) His of Art 1972; Johns Hopkins Univ (PHD of Art 1980; *cr:* Johns Hospkins Univ Schl of Continuing Stud Adj 1993-; Montgomery Coll Adj Prof His of Art 1981-; *ai:* Coll Art 1980-; *home:* 5207 Wehawken Rd Bethesda MD 20816

SKANE, MARIE A., Second Grade Teacher; *b:* Boston, MA; *ed:* Bo St Coll (BSEd) Elem 1968; Mass General Hospital Phonetic Rdng Substance Abuse Awareness, Abnormal Psych Courses; Tufts ial Rdng Course; *cr:* Osgood Elem Schl 1st Grd Tchr 1968-84; ort Elem Schl 2nd Grd Tchr 1985-; *ai:* Schl Cncl Mem; Medford Jnion 1968-, Union Rep; MTA, NEA 1968-; Ortman Gillingham ch to Rdng Peer Instruction Prgm Ldr; *office:* G Davenport Elem Horne Ave Medford MA 02155

OUPKA, NORMAN J., Art Tchr & Fine Arts Dept Chm; *b:* ind, OH; *m:* Mary Andrews; *c:* Laura S. Woolf, Scott, Michelle S. ; *ed:* OH Northern (BS) Fine Arts 1966; Attnd IN U East, Wright St Dayton Univ; *cr:* Northmont Sr HS Art Tchr, Adv Art Instr, Dept 966-; *ai:* Coach Ftbl Var, Wrestling, Track Reserves; NEA, OEA, 1966-; NDEA 1966-, Bldg Rep; Outstdng Educator; Nom Excl Awd Fac Bldg; *office:* Northmont Sr H S 4916 National Rd Clayton 315

EDMUND G., French Teacher; *b:* Saco, ME; *m:* Suzanne R. ; *c:* Gretchen, Andrew; *ed:* Univ of MA (BA) Fr 1966; St Michaels MEd) Ed 1972; 6 Addl Credit Hrs Span; *cr:* Montpelier HS Fr Tchr ign Lang Chair 1966-; *ai:* Soph Class Adv; Strategic Action Comm; VEA 1966-; MEA 1966-, Pres 1979-81; AATF & UFLA; *office:* elier HS Memorial Dr Montpelier VT 05602

EY, DEBRA MALONEY, Social Studies Teacher; *b:* Northampton, Richard, William; *ed:* SUNY at Albany (BA) His 1978; Elmira Coll) Scndry Ed 1987; Attnd Cornell Univ 1993, NYS Hum Inst at Univ 1991, Adelphi Univ Summer Inst 1978; *cr:* Horseheads Jr HS oc Stud Tchr 1984-86; Elmira Southside HS Soc Stud, Eng Tchr 2; Horseheads HS Soc Stud Tchr 1992-; *ai:* Updating Global Stud riteria NYS Compact for Learning 10th Grd; NYSUT 1984-; NYS r the Soc Stud 1987-; Friends of the Horseheads Free Lib 1987-, VP, *ffice:* Horseheads HS 415 Fletcher St Horseheads NY 14845

DING, JAMES EDWARD, Fifth Grade Teacher; *b:* Toledo, OH; *m:* Kuron; *c:* BRIAN J., Jennifer L.; *ed:* Univ of Toledo (BED) Elem ec Ed 1974; 36 Post Grad Hrs; *cr:* Dorr Elem Schl Tchr 1974-; *ai:* icl, Quiz Bowl Adv; Schl TV Station Mgr, ADv; AV Coord; rsonal Relations Cadre Chm; Schl Steering, Dist Tech, Sci Comm; OEH, SEA 1974-; NSTA 1995-; BSA 1972-; Blessed Sac Parents 987-, Pres; Tchr of Yr 1995; Jennings Scholar 1994-95; *office:* Dorr Elem Schl 1205 King Rd Toledo OH 43615

LEY, DYMPNA,OSF, Latin Teacher & Media Director; *b:* Alexis, Coll of St Teresa (BA) Latin, Math, Lib 1941; Cath Univ of Amer Greek, Latin 1953; Creighton Univ 12 Grad Credit Hrs in Ed; *cr:* St ine HS Latin, Math Tchr, Librn; Cotter HS Latin, Eng Tchr, Schl Yrbk; Sacred Heart & Later Burns HS Math Tchr, Librn; Notre HS Latin, Eng Tchr, Media Ctr Dir 1965-67, 1969-; *ai:* NEA; OH ibrns Assn 1975-; *office:* Notre Dame HS 2220 Sunrise Ave outh OH 45662

LY, KATHLEEN M., Chemistry Tchr & Sci Dept Head; *b:* Boston, Robert A.; *c:* Paul A., Christopher A.; *ed:* Emmanuel Coll (BA) 1965; Northeastern Univ (MS) Chem 1972; U of MA at Lowell Sci Ed 1994; *cr:* Randolph HS Chem Tchr 1965-66; Charleston Cath Tchr 1966-67; Chelmsford HS Chem Tchr 1977-74; Amer Schl of Chem Tchr 1974-79; Chelmsford HS Chem Tchr 1980-81; Beverly em HS 1980-82; Dana Hall Schl Chem Tchr, Dept Head 1982-; *ai:* on, Hiking Club; One Trustee Comm; Sci Tchrs & Resource Swap NSTA 1982-, Pres 1990-94; MA Assn of Sci Tchrs 1982-; Amer Soc 1988-; AAAS 1987-; CO PI 3 Yr NSF Grant; *office:* Dana Hall Dana Rd Wellesley MA 02181

LY, MARYLEE, English Teacher; *b:* Rochester, NY; *m:* Wade *ed:* Nazareth Coll (BA) Eng 1974; SUNY at Brockport (MA) Eng 6; *cr:* Elba Eng Tchr 1974-76; Nazareth Acad Eng Tchr 1976-85, hr & Project Asst Artist in Residence 1992-; Nazareth Coll RLSD of & Writing Resource Tchr 1986-92; *ai:* Jr Class Moderator; Lit ine Moderator; Project UNIQUE 1989-, Pres; Mary Cariola Charity Chprsn & Registration; Golf Tournament Bd Chm; *office:* Nazareth ny HS 1001 Lake Ave Rochester NY 14613

LY, MICHAEL JOHN, Biology Teacher; *b:* Schenectady, NY; *m:* en; *ed:* Hobart Coll (BA) Bio 1973; Syracuse Univ (MS) Ed 1977; SUNY ESF; *cr:* Fayetteville Manlius Schl Dist Bio Tchr 1977-; *ai:* ympiad, Environment Conscious Organized Stdnts, Character Ed, ts Comm Past; Bldg Comm Rep; NYSUT; NYSTA; AFT; *office:* eville-Manlius HS E Seneca Turnpike Manlius NY 13104

LY, SUSAN J., Fifth Grade Teacher; *b:* Harrisburg, PA; *ed:* nsburg St Coll (BSED) Elem Ed 1972; Millersville St Coll (MED) Ed 1977; Millersville Univ (MS) Psych 1991; *cr:* St Francis of Assisi Third Grd Tchr 1972-73, Grad Stu 1973-75; Halifax Elem Schl , Fourth, Fifth Grd Tchr 1975-; *ai:* PSEA, NEA 1975-; Prof Hospice 986-, Vol, Bereavement Svcs; *office:* Halifax Area Elem Schl 3940 Mountain Rd Halifax PA 17032

RY, HELENE HICKEY, Principal; *b:* Cambridge, MA; *ed:* Salem (BSEd) Ed 1965, (MED) Rdng 1969; Northeast Consortium, Salem (CAGS) Innovations in Ed 1995; 45 Credits Beyond CAGS; Attnd Coll, Tufts Univ, Boston Univ; Cath Univ; Univ of Lowell, nac Coll, Lesley Coll, Harvard Univ; *cr:* Burk Schl Tchr, Rdng alist 1965-88; St Dept of Ed Migrant Division Staff Asst, Ed list 1078-88; South Schl Asst Prin 1988-94; Center Schl Principal *ai:* Law Day Prgm, Kndgtn Review Comm Chprsn; Harvest Festival enter Schl Cncl; NEA; MA Tchrs Assn; Intnl Rdng Assn; ASCD; d Prins Ctr:; Cultural Clearinghouse; League of Women Voters; Rdrs Presenter; Exemplary Prgms Contributor; Migrant Ed Prgm on Reference Testing Series in Rdng, Math; Amer Bar Assn Law Day nition Awd; CAGS Action Rsrch Author; *office:* Center Elem Schl 18 St Peabody MA 01960*

EL, AMIE LYNN, Mathematics Teacher; *b:* Wheeling, WV; *m:* d Martin Jr.; *c:* Whitney, Kelsey; *ed:* OH Univ (BA) Elem Ed 1983; Minor & General Sci Validation; *cr:* Union Local Schls HS Math 983-; *ai:* Math Dept Chprsn; NHS Co-Adv; NEA 1983-; Delta Kappa a 1989-; Eastern Star 1978-; *office:* Union Local HS Rt 1 Belmont 718

MORE, HELEN L., Retired Elementary Teacher; *b:* Montrose, WV; nald L.; *c:* David, Derry, Beth; *ed:* Univ of Akron (MS) Elem Ed *cr:* Norton City Schls Elem Tchr 1972-93; *ai:* OEA, NE OH Tchrs Norton City Tchrs Assn 1972-; Jennings Scholar Awd; *home:* PO Box Iinton OH 44216

MORE, RONALD KEITH, Professor of Art; *b:* Cumberland, MD; ostburg St Univ (BS) Art Ed 1976; WV Univ (MFA) Printmaking *cr:* Garrett Comm Coll Prof of Art 1981-; *ai:* Art Gallery Dir 1986-; al Events Coord 1995-; Stu Motivation Comm 1994-; Garrett Cty Cncl 1981-, Bd Mem, 1993-, Pres; MD St Arts Cncl 1993-, Grants st; Freelance Artist; *office:* Garrett Comm Coll 687 Mosser Rd Mc MD 21541*

RSKI, LINDA SUSAN, Assistant Principal & Teacher; *b:* port, CT; *ed:* Marywood Coll (BS) Elem Ed 1977; Rdng Specialist, ert; *cr:* St Mary's Visitation Schl 5th Grd Tchr 1977-83, 3rd Grd Tchr 89, 6-8 Grd Tchr 1989-95; La Salle Acad Asst Prin, 6th & 8th Grd 995-; *ai:* Curr Comm; Stu Adv; NCEA 1985-; ASCD 1990-; *office:* le Acad 309 First Ave Jessup PA 18434*

SKIFF, STEVEN DOUGLAS, 11th Grade History Teacher; *b:* Tupper Lake, NY; *m:* Jean Marie Arleo; *c:* Jesse, Christopher; *ed:* SUNY at Plattsburgh (BS) Sec Ed 1985; SUNY at Plattsburgh (MS) His 1978; *cr:* Tupper Lake HS His Tchr 16 Yrs; *ai:* Boys Var Bsktbl Coach 15 Yrs; Sr Class Adv; NYSUT 1980-; *office:* Tupper Lake HS 25 Cheney Ave Tupper Lake NY 12986

SKILTON, KENNETH DOUGLAS, Mathematics Teacher; *b:* Painesville, OH; *m:* Christina Lynne Spisak; *c:* Michael, Rachel; *ed:* John Carroll Univ (BA) Tchng Math 1992; Working on Curr, Instruction MA Ashland Univ; *cr:* Orange City Schls Spec Ed Aide 1992; Mentor Exempted Schls Math Tchr 1992-; *ai:* Head Frosh Wrestling, JV Soccer Coach; Weight Lifting Supvr; Sr Project Adv; Proficiency Math Tchr, Tutor; MTA, OEA, NEA 1992-; 1994 St Soccer Champions; *office:* Mentor HS 6451 Center St Mentor OH 44060*

SKINNER, AMY WOO, Jr HS Language Arts Teacher; *b:* Boston, MA; *m:* Liam; *ed:* Wellesley Coll (BA) Eng 1989; Univ of MA at Lowell (mED) Curr & ESL Specialization 1994; Stanford Univ Chinese Stud 1984-87; *cr:* Saint Patricks Schl 7th-8th Grd Lang Arts Tchr & 8th Grd Hmrm Tchr 1989-94; Agassiz Schl Lang Arts Tchr 1994-; *ai:* Edward Kalesa Terrific Tchrs Making a Difference Awd 1993; *home:* 245 Mount Hope St Lowell MA 01854*

SKINNER, CHRISTOPHER JAMES, Physical Education Teacher; *b:* Lancaster, OH; *ed:* Muskingum Coll (BA) Scndry Hlth, PE 1988; *cr:* Maysville HS Gen Sci, Hlth, PE Tchr 1990-93; Maysville MS Phys Sci Tchr 1990-93, PE Tchr 1993-; *ai:* Intervention Homeroom; IM Dir; OAHPERD 1993-; NEA, MEA 1990-; NORBA 1993-, Expert; Y City Cycling 1988-; *office:* Maysville MS 2725 Pinkerton Ln Zanesville OH 43701

SKINNER, DEBRA, Instrumental Music Teacher; *b:* Buffalo, NY; *m:* Stephen; *c:* Amanda, Zachary; *ed:* Fredonia St (BM) Music Ed 1986; Univ of Buffalo (MA) Elem Ed 1992; *cr:* Attica Cntrl Schl Instrumental Music Tchr 1987-; *ai:* Jazz Band; NYSUT 1987-; United Way 1993-; *office:* Attica Cntrl Schl Main St Attica NY 14011*

SKINNER, KATHLEEN ANN, Special Education Teacher; *b:* Worcester, MA; *ed:* Univ of Hartford (BA) Psych 1968, (MA) Spec Ed 1971; 30 Addl Credits; *cr:* Wethersfield Schl System Learning Disabilities, Spec Ed Tchr 1968-; *ai:* AFT, WFT 1980-, Sec, Mbrshp Chm; CSFT 1980-, Hnr Roll; *office:* Wethersfield Pub Schl System 95 Highcrest Rd Wethersfield CT 06109

SKINNER, MICHAEL MARK, Mathematics Teacher; *b:* Crediton, England; *m:* Susan Patricia; *c:* Jennifer E., Jessica L., Jillian N.; *ed:* St Univ of NY at Buffalo (BA) Anthropology 1971; Carisius Coll (MA) Scndry Ed 1996; MA Equiv Anthropology at Univ of NC at Chapel Hill 1973; Math Cert 1978-79, Hlth Cert 1981-82 St Univ of NY at Buffalo; *cr:* Williamsville North HS Soc Stud Tchr 1974-79, Math Tchr 1980-; *ai:* Stu Cncl Adv 1975-; Ldrshp Camp Facilitator; Intervention Network Drug & Alcohol Cnslr 1986-88; Homecoming Act Dir 1975-; NASAA 1975-; SEPTSA 1975-, VP 1975; AFT, NYSUT 1974-; NCTM, AMTNYS 1991-; PTSA 1974-; Co-Founder Stu Indep Learning Ctr 1974-79; St Lawrence Master Tchr Citation 1986; HS Stu Pursuing Career in Scndry Ed-Math Internship Prgm Founder 1991-; *home:* 2370 Dodge Rd East Amherst NY 14051*

SKINNER, PHILLIP R., Business Education Teacher; *b:* DuBois, PA; *ed:* Penn St Univ (BS) Bus Ed 1970, (MED) Educl Admin 1974; Prins Cert 1975; IN Univ of PA 21 Grad Credits; Clarion Univ of PA Acctng Credits; *cr:* Ridgway Schl Dist Bus Ed Tchr 1970-; Jeff-Tech Adult Ed Bus Instr 1972-84; *ai:* Peer Tutor Spon; Perkins Advy & Curr Comms; Ridgway Area Tchrs Assn 1970-, Pres, Sec, Treas; NEA 1970-; PSEA 1970-; Penn St Univ Alumni Assn 1971-, Life Mem; *office:* Ridgway Area Schl Dist PO Box 447 Ridgway PA 15853

SKINNER, ROBERT GEORGE, Physics Teacher; *b:* Buffalo, NY; *m:* Jacqueline Kay; *ed:* SUNY Coll at Buffalo (BS) Physics 1990, Embry-Riddle Aero Univ (AAS) Prof Aeronautics 1991; SUNY Coll at Buffalo (MS) Educl Computing 1993; Commercial Pilots License FFA Rating 1989; Radiation Physics Course Sponsored by Sci Fnd, Los Almos Natl Labs; *cr:* US Army Aviation Logistics Command Avionics Tech 1985-87; Holland Cntrl HS Physics Tchr 1990-95; Frontier Cntrl HS Physics Tchr 1995-; *ai:* Sci Club; Tech Comm Bldg, Dist Level; Frontier Block Scheduling, Tech Prep Comm, Physics Club Adv; NEA 1990-95; NY United Tchrs 1995-; AAPT 1995-; US hang Gliding Assn 1992-, Hang II Rating; South Towns Amateur Radio Soc 1993-; *office:* Frontier Cntrl HS S-4432 Bay View Rd Hamburg NY 14219

SKIPWORTH, KELLY OAKES, English Teacher; *b:* Portsmouth, OH; *m:* James G.; *ed:* Capital Univ (BA) Soc Stud, His, Eng 1992; Univ of Rio Grande (MA) Ed 1995; *cr:* Portsmouth West HS Eng Tchr 1992-96; *ai:* Peer Facilitator Adv; OEA 1992-; Chuch Choir 1983-; Sunday Schl Tchr 1992-; Church Choir 1983-; *office:* Portsmouth West HS 1420 13th St Portsmouth OH 45663

SKIRCHAK, CAROL JANINE, Spanish & English Teacher; *b:* Washington, PA; *ed:* CA Univ (BS) Ed, Span 1974; Geneva Coll Ed, Eng 1978; Univ of Valencia Spain 15 Credits Span 1973; 3 Credits 1989-90; *cr:* Washington HS Stu Tchr, Sub 1974-78; Bentworth HS Span Tchr 1975-76; Blue Ridge MS Span, Eng Tchr 1978; Jefferson-Morgan HS Span, Eng Tchr 1978-; *ai:* Negotiating Comm; Bldg Rep; Span Tutor; HS Stdnts Pen-Pal Coord; Frgn Lang Week Coord; Jr HS NHS Comm; JMPA, PSEA, NEA 1978-; PSMLA 1995-; CFU 1953-; All-St Edctr Awd 1990; Thanks to Tchrs, Great Expectations Hnr Roll, Daily Point of Light Nom 1991; Pub Article 1991; *office:* Jefferson-Morgan Jr Sr HS PO Box 158 Jefferson PA 15344*

SKISCIM, STEPHEN J., Instrumental Music Teacher; *b:* Dearborn, MI; *m:* Gina P. Palladino; *c:* Stephen P.; *ed:* Mansfield (BS) Music Ed 1978; Elem Ed K-8 Cert; 30 Grad Credits; *cr:* Upper Twp Music Tchr 1978-; *ai:* 3 Concert, 1 Jazz Band Dir; Honor, All South Jersey & All South Jersey Band Stud Spon; MENC 1978-, Nationally Certified Music Educator Awd; NJEA & NJMEA 1978-; UTEA VP; Governors Tchr Recognition Prgm Tchr of Yr 1986; *office:* Upper Township MS 525 Perry Rd PO Box 158 Tuckahoe NJ 08250

SKITT, KENNETH A., Principal; *b:* Providence, RI; *m:* Beverly Marcoccio; *c:* Tara Elizabeth, Lianne Beverly; *ed:* Bryant Coll (BS) Bus Admin 1966; RI Coll (MS) Elem Schl Admin 1973; Attnd RI Coll, Providence Coll, Bridgewater St Coll, URI; Natl Assn of Underwater Instr; *cr:* Johnson Wales Univ Bus Dept Instr 1 Yr; Barnes Schl 5th Grd Tchr 1 Yr; Thornton Schl Annex 5-6 Grd Tchr 8 Yrs; H. A. Ferri Schl 6 Grd Tchr 3 Yrs; G. C. Calef Schl 5-6 Grd Tchr 15 Yrs; Graniteville Schl Tchr, Prin 1 Yr; *ai:* RI Coll Head Scuba, Clinical Instr; Smithfield Youth Soccer League Coach; Johnston Curr Cncl; NAIU 1974-, RI Chptr Ldr, Svc Awd 1988, Continuing Ed Awd 1991; AFT 1968-, VP 1978; RI Assn Schl Prins 1995-; Smithfield HS Parent Cncl 1991-, Sec; Amer Red Cross 1991-, First Aid Instr; St of RI Honor for Contributions Made to Scuba Diving Through Ed, Safety, Promotion of Diving 1991; MAH Beneath the Sea Dive Show Speaker 1990; *office:* Graniteville Elem Schl 6 Collins Ave Johnston RI 02919*

SKIVINGTON, LYNNE ANN, Sixth Grade Teacher; *b:* Rochester, NY; *m:* Michael; *c:* Jill, Steven; *ed:* Hiram Coll (BA) Elem Ed 1973; SUNY at Brockport (MA) Ed; Attnd SUNY at Geneseo; *cr:* Wheatland-Chili CS 2nd, 5th & 6th Grd Tchr 1973-; *ai:* Musical Dir; 5th & 6th Grd Instrumental Accompanist; Fine Arts Chprsn; Site-Based Shared Decision Making Team; CORE Team; AFT 1973-; NYSUT 1973-; Wheatland-Chili Fed of Tchrs 1973-, Sec 1975; Friends of Lib 1991-; Wheatland Historical Assn 1991-; PTA 1993-; *home:* 347 Stewart Rd Scottsville NY 14546

SKLAR, KENNETH ALAN, Head of HS Gifted Program; *b:* Philadelphia, PA; *m:* Claudia McBride; *c:* Jason, Benjamin; *ed:* PA St Univ (BA) Rel Stud & Philosophy 1971; Univ of PA (MS) Ed 1975; *cr:* Radnor HS Soc Stud Tchr 1975-; PA Governors Schl for Intnl Stud Instr 1985; Radnor HS Dept Head of Gifted Pgm 1991-; *ai:* Model United Nations, Global Awareness Comm, Comp Club & Stu Publications & Jrnl Adv; NEA 1975-; Radnor Tchrs Ed Assn 1975-, Pres 1987-89; PACIE 1985-; PAGE 1991-; World Affairs Cncl of Philadelphia 1985-; *office:* Radnor HS 130 King of Prussia Rd Radnor PA 19087*

SKLAR, LIVIA EDITH, Guidance Counselor; *b:* Oradea, RUmania; *m:* Mike; *c:* Lisa, Akiva, Ilan, Orit; *ed:* City Coll of NY (BA) Writing 1969; Jewish Theological Seminary (BHL) Hebrew Lit 1969; Long Island Univ (MSE) Cnslng 1992; *cr:* Progressive Grocer Magazine Editorial Asst 1969-71; Esquire Magazine Editorial Asst 1972-73; Cosmopolitan Editorial Asst, Freelance Writer 1973-75; Evander Childs HS Guid Cnslr 1993-; *ai:* Westchester Putnam Rockland Assn for Cnslng, Dev 1992-; *office:* Evander Childs HS 800 E Gun Hill Rd Bronx NY 10467

SKOLER, NAOMI NASON, Reading Teacher; *b:* Boston, MA; *m:* Maurice Joseph; *c:* Michael Joseph; *ed:* Lesley Coll (BSEd) Ed 1963; Boston Univ (MED) Ed & Eng 1964; 31 Credits Beyond Masters at Univ of MA at Boston & Emmanuel Coll; *cr:* Medway Pub Schls 4th Grd Tchr 1964-65; Dedham Pub Schls 4th Grd Tchr 1965-68; Israel 6th-8th Grd Advanced Work Exch Pgm 1968-69; Boston Pub Schls Title I Coord & 1st-5th Grd Rdng Tchr 1970-84, Rdng Tchr 1984-; *ai:* Boston Tchrs Union 1970-; AFT; NEA; Brookline MA Pub Lib 1982-84, Vol; Lesley Coll 1989-95, Trustee, 1995-, Corporator; Babson Coll Alumni Assn 1990-, Honorary Mem; *home:* 73 Levbert Rd Newton Center MA 02159*

SKOLNIK, SHERRY ZUCKMAN, English Teacher; *b:* Brooklyn, NY; *m:* Richard; *c:* Jeffrey, Frann; *ed:* Univ of RI (BA) Eng Ed 1966; Hofstra Univ (MS) Guid, Cnslng 1970; 60 Addl Credits; Post Grad Work at Tchrs Coll of Columbia Univ; *cr:* Wantagh HS Eng Tchr 1966-; *ai:* Ldrshp Skills Club Adv; Scndry Curr Cncl; AFT; NYSUT; NCTE; Natl Assn Gifted Children; Bellmore Bd of Ed 1988-, Pres, VP; Bellmore-Merrick Cntrl HS Dist Bd of Ed 1991-; Yth Commission, Schlsp Comm Metropolitan Region 15 Yrs; Bellmore Jewish Ctr Bd of Trustees 10 Yrs; Women's Amer ORT 20 Yrs, Chptr VP; Hadassah, Lifetime Mbrshp; Nassau Suffolk Schl Bd, NY St Schl Bd Assns; *office:* Wantagh HS Beltagh Ave Wantagh NY 11793

SKOMRA KUSKOWSK, ANN, Executive Producer; *b:* Uniontown, PA; *m:* David M.; *ed:* Penn St Univ (BS) Jrnlsm 1988; California Univ of Pa (MA) Comm 1991; *cr:* WPXI-TV Pittsburgh On-Air Talent Producer 1988-92; Lock Haven Univ Jrnlsm Instr 1992-95; WFMJ-TV Exec Producer; *ai:* Loch Haven Advised Student-Run TV Station, Created Televised News Magazine, Stu Radio Station, Soc Collegiate Jrnlsts Fac Adv.

SKOOG, BONNIE LUAN, English Teacher; *b:* Rochester, PA; *ed:* Clarion Univ (BS) Eng, Rdng 1968; SUNY at Fredonia (MSEd) Rdng Specialist 1971; Attnd Jamestown Comm Coll Real Estate License 1993, SUNY at Buffalo 6 Hrs, Chapman Coll 3 Hrs, Univ of KY 3 Hrs, SUNY at Fredonia 3 Hrs, Edinboro Univ 6 Hrs, Jamestown Comm Coll 15 Hrs; *cr:* Chambersburg Sr HS Rdng Specialist 1968; Panama Cntrl Sch Eng, Rdng 1968-72; DOD Okinawa Japan Eng, Rdng Specialist 1972-73; Panama Cntrl Schl Eng, Rdng, Pub Speaking 1974-; *ai:* Sr Class Adv; Effective Schls Chair; Panama Task Force; Chautauqua Co Tchrs, NEA 1968-; Delta Kappa Gamma 1973-, Prof Advancement Chair, Indian Affairs Chair; US Defense Dept Tchr 1972-73 Letter of Commendation; *home:* 4993 Route 474 Ashville NY 14710*

SKOOG, WILLIAM ELLIOTT, High School English Teacher; *b:* Manchester, CT; *m:* Pamela Bonafine; *c:* Jessica, Travis; *ed:* Springfield Coll (BS) Eng 1965; Univ of CT (MA) Eng 1972; *cr:* Springfield Coll All Amer Swimming Champion 1964; Windham HS Eng Tchr 1965-; *ai:* Stu Philosopher Ed Which Won Natl Bronze Awd 1995; AFT & CSFT 1966-; WFT 1966-, Pres, Plaque for Excl in Ldrshp; NCTE; Mentor & Cooperating Tchr; Newsletter Publisher; *home:* 233 Route 87 Columbia CT 06237*

SKORA, DENNIS JOHN, 8th Grd Social Studies Tchr; *b:* Binghamton, NY; *m:* Maureen Murphy; *c:* Karen, Kevin; *ed:* SU Coll at Cortland (BS) Soc Stud 1965; SU Coll at New Paltz (MS) Soc Stud 1972; Cert Advanced Stud Admin; *cr:* Wappingers Falls Jr HS 6th Grd Tchr 1965-66, 7th-8th Grd Soc Stud Tchr 1966-; *ai:* Schl Newspaper, IM Sports Adv; Wappingers Congress of Tchrs 1970-; Career Ed, GATE Grants.*

SKOUG, REED STEVENS, Spanish Language Teacher; *b:* Alexandria, VA; *m:* Michael George Roller; *ed:* Bryn Mawr Coll (BA) Russian 1986; Villanova Univ Tchrs Cert 1992; *cr:* Germantown Acad Russian & Span Tchr 1986-; *ai:* Animal Issues Club; Foreign Lang Coord 1995-; Montgomery Cty Tchrs of Foreign Lang; Amer Cncl of Tchrs of Russian; Humane Soc of US; Amer Anti-Vivisection Soc; Natl Wildlife Fed; Girls Cross Cntry Asst Coach 1995; Natl Endowment for Hum; Grant for Russian Stud; Kast Grant for Stud of Cooperative Learning; Wissahickon Grant for Educl Opportunities; *home:* 317 Stormfield Dr Harleysville PA 19438

SKOVIRA, ROBERT JOSEPH, Computer & Systems Professor; *b:* Mt Pleasant, PA; *m:* Mary Elizabeth Machuga; *c:* Suzanne Marie; *ed:* St Vincent Coll (BA) Philosophy 1966; U of Pittsburgh (MA) Classics 1973, (PHD) Philosophy, Anthro of Ed 1977, (MS) Information Sci 1986; Cert Cmptr Programming; *cr:* Greensburg Cntrl Cath HS Latin Tchr 1967-75; Univ of VA Asst Prof 1972-78; Univ of Houstan Asst Prof 1980-81; Robert Morris Coll Full Prof 1983-; *ai:* Curr Coord Comm & Information Systems; Chair Subcommittee for RMC WEB Site Dev; Data Processing Mngmt Assn Stu Chptr Adv; ACM 1989-; ASIS 1986-, SIG Steering Comm; AIS 1994-; PES 1977-; Arthritis FDS 1993-, Governing Bd; Hollow Oakland Trust 1993-, Dir; Chptrs Pub in 2 Books; Distngd Mentor Awd 1992; Cert of Appreciation; *office:* Robert Morris Coll Narrows Run Road Coraopolis PA 15108*

SKOWRONEK, PATRICIA ANN, Math, Cmptr & Sci Teacher; *b:* Pittsburgh, PA; *ed:* Carlow Coll (BS) Elem Ed 1963; Clarion St Univ (MS) Elem Math 1973; Carnegie Sci Ctr Weather Station Credits; Theology, Art Credits; *cr:* St Clare 1-8 Grd Tchr 1956-70; St Coleman 1-8 Grd Tchr 1956-70; St Xavier 1-8 Grd Tchr 1956-70; Epiphany Tchr, VP 1970-73; Carlow Coll Tchng Tchrs Math & Grad Courses 1973-80; St Agnes Schl Vice Prin, Tchr 1973-; *ai:* Tchrs Mentor; Natl Tchrs of Math 1980-; Carnegie Sci Ctrs 1993-; Dio of Pittsburgh Golden Apple Awd 1993; *office:* St Agnes Schl 120 Robinson St Pittsburgh PA 15213

SKOWRONSKI, JOYCE M., First Grade Teacher; *b:* Waterbury, CT; *m:* William; *c:* Fred, Joe, Bill Lockwood, Deena; *ed:* SCSu (BA) Ed 1974; WCSC (MA) Rdng 1978; 36 Credit Hrs Beyond Masters; *cr:* RSD #15 1st Grd Tchr 22 Yrs; *ai:* PTO Tchr Rep; NEA 1974-; CEA 1974-; Celebration of Excl Winner; *office:* Gainfield HS Old Field Rd Southbury CT 06488

SKOWRONSKI, RICHARD MICHAEL, 6th Grade Teacher; *b:* Brooklyn, NY; *m:* Marian Grace Cullen; *c:* Nicholas, Alison; *ed:* Cntrl CT St Univ (MS) Admin & Supervision 1988; Univ of Hartford (6th Yr) Admin & Supvr 1992; Comp Sci PASCAL, Appleworks & Hypercard 11 Hrs;

Bilingual Spcl Ed 3 Hrs; *cr:* Our Lady of Mercy Schl Comp Sci & Math Tchr 1982-84; Noah Webster Schl 6th Grd Tchr 1984-; Equal Pgm Sci Tchr 1989; *ai:* 6th Grd Tchr Trng Educl Dir; Schl Based Mgmt Comm Mem; Chm Admin Comm; AFT 1985-; ASCD 1993-; Little League 1995-, Coach; CT Pub Television Outstdng CT Tchr; Celebration of Excl Honorable Mention; CT Hum Alliance Mem; *office:* Noah Webster Elem Schl 5 Cone St Hartford CT 06105*

SKRABONJA, JOHN MICHAEL, English Creative Writing Tchr; *b:* Philadelphia, PA; *m:* Jean E. McGovern; *c:* Catherine, John M. Jr; *ed:* Glassboro St (BA) Magna Cum Laude Scndry Ed 1975; Grad Work at Rutgers Univ; *cr:* Audubon HS Eng, Creative Writing & Jrnlsm Tchr 1977-; Johnnycake Jr High Eng & Soc Stud Tchr 1975-77; *ai:* Dir 1 Act Plays; Schl Newspaper Adv; Instructional Cncl Mem; Lit Magazine Adv; Comm Newsletter Adv; NEA 1975-; NJEA 1977-; AEA 1977-; Kappa Delta Pi 1974-; Cherry Hill Soccer Club 1993-95, Asst Coach; Nom S Jersey Soccer Coach Yr 1983; Nom Governors Tchr Recognition Awd 1992; *office:* Audubon HS 350 Edgewood Ave Audubon NJ 08106

SKRADSKI, ELLEN M., Mathematics Teacher; *b:* Pittsburgh, PA; *m:* Richard K.; *c:* Richard, Angela, Thomas, Daniel; *ed:* Slippery Rock Univ (BS) Scndry Ed, Math 1988; Attnd Carlow Coll, IN Univ of PA; *cr:* Freeport HS Math Tchr 1989-; *ai:* Strongland Math Competition Spon; Freeport Area Care Team; Math Evening Tutoring; NEA, PSEA 1988-; NCTM 1994-.

SKRALY, JANICE KUZAK, Chemistry & Computer Sci Tchr; *b:* Blue Island, IL; *m:* Richard L.; *c:* Monica, Frank; *ed:* Alliance Coll (BS) Chem 1963; Univ of Pittsburgh (MED) Sci Ed, Sec 1973, (PHD) Sci Ed, Sec 1983; *cr:* St Josephs Schl 5th Grd tchr 1963-64; Colton HS Chem Tchr 1964-66; St Angela Merici Schl Sci, Math Tchr 6-8 1971-77; Univ of Pittsburgh Tchng Asst 1977-78; South Allegheny Jr Sr HS Chem, Cmptr Sci Tchr 1978-; Adjuct Fac CCAC; *ai:* Staff Dev; Cmptr Instr Fac; Cmptr, Sci, Future Tchrs Club Spon; Earth Day Act, Sci Fair Act; PSEA, NEA 1978-, Rep 13 Yrs; W PA Assn Cmptr Sci Tchrs 1989-, Rep 3 Yrs; ASCD 10 Yrs; Kappa Delta Pi 9 Yrs; NSTA 6 Yrs; Sierra Club 2 Yrs; Greenpeace 1 Yr; 7 Pub Articles; Supt Awd Excl Tchng; Outstanding Tchr Awd Assn Sci Tech Centers; Recipient Grants Spectroscopy Soc of Pittsburgh, Mon Yough Consortium; 1989 Who's Who Amer Ed; *office:* South Allegheny Jr-Sr H S 2743 Washington Blvd Mc Keesport PA 15133*

SKROCK, PATRICK J., Philosophy Teacher; *b:* Youngstown, OH; *m:* Eileen Munnelly; *c:* Alicia, Jason; *ed:* OH Univ (BS) His 1962; Fairfield Univ (MA) Ec 1971; Univ of Bridgeport (CAS) Ed 1987; *cr:* Jefferson HS His Tchr 1962-63; Wilson HS Ec Tchr 1963-67; Stanford HS Philosophy Tchr 1967-; *ai:* AFT 1963-, Sec; Greater Bridgeport Jr Hockey Assn 1979-83, Bd of Dir; Celebration of Excl Awd St of CT; Tchr of Excl Univ of Chicago & Tufts Univ; Stamford Pub Schls Tchr of Excl; *office:* Stamford HS 55 Strawberry Hill Ave Stamford CT 06902

SKROCKI, JODY E., 5th Grade Teacher; *b:* Pittsfield, MA; *ed:* Cntrl CT St (BS) Elem Ed 1974; 36 Credit Hrs Mstrs Eqvlnt; *cr:* Tyringham Schl 5th & 6th Grd Tchr 1974-76; Otis Schl 5th Grd Tchr 1976-,4th Grd Soc Stud, Rdng Tchr 1994-; *office:* Farmington River Regnl Schl Di Main St Rt 8 Otis MA 01253

SKRYPZAK, STANLEY ROBERT, English Teacher; *b:* Erie, PA; *m:* Audyne Marie Wolbert; *c:* Mary Elizabeth, Amy Martino, S. Robert; *ed:* Gannon Univ (BA) Eng 1959, (MA) Eng 1968; 6 Credits NDEA Project Eng; *cr:* Erie Schl Dist Tchr 1962-67; Gannon Univ Instr 1965-70; Mercyhurst Coll Instr 1967-69; Millcreek Twp Schl Dist Tchr 1969-, Eng Dept Chair 1986-94; *ai:* NEA, SEA, MEA 1969-; NCTE; Amer Red Cross, Vol Life Saving, Swimming 1958-76; NDEA Study Grant Project Eng 1965; Emloyee of Month 1987; *office:* Millcreek Twp Schl Dist 3740 W 26th St Erie PA 16506*

SKRZYSZOWSKI, CLAIRE JEAN, Italian & Spanish Teacher; *b:* Torrington, CT; *m:* Jon; *c:* Lauren, Mark; *ed:* Southern CT St Univ (BS) Italian, Scndry Ed 1970, (MS) Biling Ed 1975; *cr:* Hillhouse HS Italian, Span Tchr 1970-71; Michael Whalen Jr HS Italian, Span Tchr 1972-80; Hamden MS Italian, Span Tchr 1987-; *ai:* Coord HUGSS Prgm; NEA, CEA 1987-; CT Org Lang Tchrs 1970-; Cheshire Jr Women's Club 1982-87; St Thomas Becket Women's Club 1980-; Tchr of Yr 1992; Hartford Courant Vol Recognition Awd 1993; Governor's Yth Action, Vol Action Ctr Awds 1993; *office:* Hamden MS 550 Newhall St Hamden CT 06517

SKUDAR, MICHAEL D., Seventh Grade Teacher; *b:* Philadelphia, PA; *ed:* La Salle Univ (BA) Eng Ed 1975; Prof Cert for Tchng Religion; *cr:* Ancillae Assumpta Acad 5th, 7th & 8th Grd Tchr 1975-76; Epiphany of our Lord Schl 5th & 7th Grd Tchr 1975-86; St Timothy Schl 7th Grd Tchr 1986-; *ai:* Coord of Schl Wide Acad Awds Assembly in June; Spirit Day Team Moderator; NCEA; *office:* St Timothy Schl 3033 Levick St Philadelphia PA 19149

SKUDLAREK, CHAD EDWARD, 8th Grade Science Teacher; *b:* Salamanca, NY; *m:* Nanette Archer; *c:* Samantha, Jacob; *ed:* SUNY at Fredonia (BA) Sci Ed 1988, (MS) Rdng 1992; *cr:* New Directions Alternative Schl Alternative Ed Tchr Sci, His 1988-90; Salamanca City Cntrl Schl 8th Grd Sci Tchr 1990-; *ai:* HS Bsbl Coach; Class Adv; Dist Tech Comm; NEA 1988-; Cum Laude Grad; Awd for Excl in Stu Tchng 1988; Honored by Seneca Nation of Indians, City of Salamanca; *home:* 79 Larkin St Randolph NY 14772*

SKUMMY, ROBERT W., Music Teacher; *b:* Kittanning, PA; *m:* Marguerite Anne Palilla; *c:* Bobby, Kathryn, David, Tommy; *ed:* IN Univ of PA (BS) Music 1974; 20 Addl Post Grad Credits; Duquesne Univ Music Learning Theory 6 Credit hrs; *cr:* Shannock Vly HS Music Tchr 1981-82; Kittanning HS Band, Choral Dir 1982-83; Lenape Elem Schl Instrumenta Music Tchr 1984-; *ai:* NEA, PMEA 1981-; Intnl Trumpet Guild 1990-; St Mary's Church Choir 1975-, Dir; ARIN Mini-Grant; Elem Band Performed PA Music Edctrs Assn St Convention 1993, 1996; Who's Who Outstdng Young Men of Amer 1987; *home:* RR 5 Box 187E Kittanning PA 16201

SKUNDA, KATHLEEN MYERS, 1st Grade Teacher; *b:* Baltimore, MD; *m:* James Alexander; *c:* Ellen, Kathleen, Amy; *ed:* Towson St Univ (BS) Elem Ed 1966; Addl 60 Credit Hrs Beyong Masters Equivalency; Post Grad Stud Morgan St Univ, Johns Hopkins Univ, Loyola Coll; Early Chldhd Ed, Spec Ed-Learning Disabilities Cert; *cr:* Colgate Elem Schl Kndgtn-1st Grd Tchr 1966-83; Sussex Elem Schl Kndgtn-1st Grd Tchr 1983-; *ai:* Arts, Crafts club Spon; Mentor; Stu Tchr Supvr; Climate Comm; United Way Rep; K-2 Primary Talent Identification Comm; NEA, MSTA, TABCO 1966-; Peach Orchard Civic Assn Mem; Big Brothers, Big Sisters 1976-86 Svc Awd; Arthur Slade Regnl Cath Schl Bd, Chm of Acad Comm; Sci Fnd Grant; *office:* Sussex Elem Schl 515 S Woodward Dr Baltimore MD 21221*

SKURICH, MONICA MARY SABULA, Mathematics Teacher; *b:* Youngstown, OH; *m:* Michael J.; *c:* Mari E., Michael S., Matthew J.; *ed:* Youngstown St (AB) Dual Ed 1964; Kent State (ME) Ed 1968; *cr:* Manor Ave Elem Math & Art Tchr 1964-67; Struthers HS Math Tchr 1967-; *ai:* NEA, OEA, SE Assn 1964-; NCTM 1985-; Delta Kappa Gamma 1980-, Corresponding Sec; YSU Womens Club 1980-; Kent St Mothers 1991-; Goodwill Jr Vols 1994-; *home:* 2486 Timothy Knoll Ln Poland OH 44514

SKURKA, KATHLEEN MARIE, Spanish Teacher; *b:* Passaic, NJ; *ed:* Mt St Mary Coll at Newbugh (BA) Elem Ed 1964; Middlebury Coll (MA) Span 1971; Fondham Univ, Iona Coll Seton Hall Univ Assumption Coll Undergrad; Dayton Univ, Georgetown Univ, Saltillo 1972 Grad Credits Hrs; *cr:* St Augustine Grd Schl 4th Grd Tchr 1961-63; St Mary HS Rel, Span Tchr 1963-69; Msgr Donovan HS Span Tchr 1969-; *ai:* Var Boys Bsktbl Scorekeeper; AATSP Hispania 1969-; Tchr of Yr 1993-94; Rotary Club Awds; Tchng, Soc Work Peru 14 Summers; *office:* Msgr Donovan HS 711 Hooper Ave Toms River NJ 08753

SKUTNIK, MARY JO, Religion Dept Chprsn & Teacher; *b:* Newark, NJ; *m:* Janek A.; *c:* Jonathan, Peter; *ed:* Coll of St Elizabeth (AB) His 1968; Drew Univ Masters of Letters Interdisciplinary Hum 1994; *cr:* Manfacturers Hanover Bank Intnl Banking 1968-69; East Orange Catholic HS His, Eng Tchr 1969-71; Signode Corp Office Mgr 1978-88; Union Cath HS His, Religion Tchr 1987-88; Mount Saint Mary Acad Religion Tchr, Chair 1988-; *ai:* Liturg Coord; Jr Retreat Coord; Acad Cncl; Cheerleading Coach; Coord for Food Drives; MSEA, NAIS, NJAIS 1988-; NCEA 1987-; St Bartholomew the Apostle Parish 1979-, Vol Svc Areas; *office:* Mount Saint Mary Acad 1645 US Rt 22 W Watchung NJ 07060

SLAAEN, JUDITH L., Math, Science & Tech Supvr; *b:* Jersey City, NJ; *m:* Harold T.; *c:* Craig T., Kari L.; *ed:* Montclair St Univ (BA) Math Ed 1969, (MA) Math Ed 1975; Attnd Jersey City St Coll, Rutgers Univ, Montclair St Univ, William Paterson St COll; *cr:* Palisades Park Jr Sr HS Math Tchr-; Fairleigh Dickinson Univ Adj Fac 1975-77; Essex Connly Coll Adj Fac 1977-79; Palisades Pk Jr Sr HS Supvr of Instr 1993-; *ai:* NHS Adv; NEA 1969-; NAASP 1993; Booster CLub; PTA; Mountaintop Soccer League; NSF Grant; Star Tchr Awd; *office:* Palisades Pk Jr Sr HS 1 Veterans Plz Palisades Park NJ 07650

SLABE, RONALD S., 4th & 5th Grd, Geog & His Tchr; *b:* New Kingston, PA; *m:* Mende Baehl; *c:* Mackenzie; *ed:* IN Univ of PA (BS) Scndry Ed, Soc Sci 1969; Duquesne Univ (MED) Elem Ed 1970; 30 Credit Hrs Duquesne Univ, Univ of Pittsburgh; 30 Credit Hrs Elem, Scndry Admin Dual Cert; *cr:* Regent Square Elem Schl Tchr 1969-82; Dilworth Elem Schl Tchr 1982-83; Minadeo Elem Schl Tchr 1983-; *ai:* Schl Instrl Cabinet; AFT 1969-; Pgh Fed of Tchrs 1969-, PFT Bldg Rep; Pi Gamma Mu, Phi Alpha Theta 1970-; Amer Alliance for Hlth, PE, Recreation, Dance 1981-.*

SLACK, MARJORIE A., English Teacher & Guid Cnslr; *b:* Denver, CO; *m:* Garth W.; *c:* Darrel, Amy; *ed:* Alma White Coll (BA) His 1961; *cr:* Belleview Schls Tchr; Sycamore Grove Tchr; Zarephath Chrstn Schl Tchr 1960-; *ai:* Yrbk Fund Raising.

SLACUM, ROSEMARY EHLINGER, 10th Grade English Teacher; *b:* Wabeno, WI; *m:* James Randolph; *ed:* WI St Univ at Oshkosh (BS) Scndry Ed 1965; Salisbury St Univ (MA) Ed 1985; *cr:* Sparrows Point HS 9th Grd Eng Tchr 1965-67; Bennett Jr HS 7th Grd Eng Tchr 1967-68; Washington Intermediate 8th Grd Eng Tchr 1968-69; Wicomi Cty Bd of Ed Adult GED Tchr 1970-80; Worcester Cty Bd of Ed GED Tchr 1980-85; Pocomoke HS 11th Grd Eng Tchr 1985-86; Snow Hill HS 10th Grd Tchr 1986-; *ai:* Soph Class & Yrbk Adv; Schl Improvement Team; MAPSCE 1972-85, Sec, Pres, Ed of Newsletter, Adult Ed Tchr of Yr; NEA, MSTA & WCTE 1985-; NCTE 1986-; MCTELA 1987-; GFWC & MFWC; Jr Wicomi Cty Womans Club 1977-, Sec; *office:* Snow Hill HS 305 S Church St Snow Hill MD 21863

SLADE, FARLINA WILSON, Social Studies Teacher; *b:* Reidsville, NC; *m:* Floyd E.; *c:* Kalonji S.; *ed:* Greater Hartford Comm (AS) Lbrl Arts 1973; Cntrl CT St (BS) Elem Ed 1977, (MA) Admin, Supervision 1990; 9 Hrs 6th Yr Prgm Admin; *cr:* Pratte & Whitney Aircraft Machine Operator 1964-69; Aetna Life & Casualty Tech Clerk 1972-75; Lewis Fox MS Tchr 1978-; Oak Hill for the Blind Asst Tchr 1980-93; *ai:* Sci, Tech Prgm Planning; CMT Comm Planning; AFT 1978-; Natl Geographic Assn 1995-; MCET 1994-; Articles & Booklet Pub; *office:* Lewis Fox MS 305 Greenfield St Hartford CT 06112

SLAGEL, JAMES GERARD, Physics Instructor; *b:* Findlay, OH; *ed:* Findlay Coll (BS) Natural Sci 1977; Wright St Univ (MED) Classroom Sci Tchng 1988; *cr:* Wayne Trace HS Chem, Physics, Phys Sci & Earth Sci Tchr 1977-80; Oakwood HS Physics & Phys Sci Tchr 1981-94; Jr HS Sci Tchr 1994-; *ai:* Chem Bowl Team Adv; Scholastic & Sci Team; Cross Cntry Coach; Chess Adv; 9th Grd Bsktbl Coach; Wright Patteson AFB Summer Fellowship Prgm; *office:* Oakwood HS 1200 Far Hills Ave Dayton OH 45419

SLAGLE, ELSIE SISLER, Allied Health Teacher; *b:* Friendsville, MD; *m:* Bill L.; *c:* Ronald, Randall, Cheryl, April; *ed:* Hocking Tech Coll (AA) Nursing 1983; WV Tech Masters Cert Voc Ed 1985; *cr:* Garrett Cty Bd of Ed 1979-95; Garrett Meml Hospital 1984-85; *ai:* Allied Hlth Stdnts Adv; GTA 1985-; *office:* Southern HS 1100 E Oak St Oakland MD 21531

SLAK, MARY DONNA, English Teacher; *b:* Cleveland, OH; *ed:* Cleveland St Univ (BA) Eng 1975; Scndry Ed Cert; Elem Ed Cert; *cr:* St Mary Schl Lang Arts Tchr 1976-84; Villa Angela Acad Eng Tchr 1984-90; Villa Angela St Joseph Schl Eng Tchr 1990-; *ai:* Drama Club Moderator; Play Dir; Eng Dept Chprsn; NCEA 1984-; St Vitus Parish Cncl 1994-; Drama Soc Lilija 1974-; Diocese Cleveland Outstdng Tchr 1990; *office:* Villa Angela-St Joseph HS 18491 Lake Shore Blvd Cleveland OH 44119*

SLANCHIK, JOANNE DECESARE, Business & History Teacher; *b:* Steubenville, OH; *m:* George J.; *c:* Rob, Georgie; *ed:* West Liberty St Coll (BA) Scndry Ed 1990; 18 Credit Hrs Franciscan Univ of Steubnville; 5 Credit Hrs OH Univ Eastern; 3 Credit Hrs Youngstown St Univ; *cr:* Steubenville HS Typing Tchr 1990-91; New Cumberland Jr HS Typing Tchr 1991-92; Martins Ferry HS His & Bus Tchr 1992-; *ai:* NHS Fac Comm; OH Ed Assn 1992-; NBEA 1990-; *office:* Martins Ferry HS 810 Hanover St Martins Ferry OH 43935

SLANINA, DONALD R., Electrical Engrng Tech Instr; *b:* Youngstown, OH; *ed:* Youngstown Univ (BE) Electrical Engrng 1967; Univ of Pittsburgh (MS) Electrical Engrng 1968; Westinghouse Electric Corporate Headquarters Trng Prgms in Engrng Mgmt, Quality Assurance; *cr:* Westinghouse Electric Corp Sr Engr 1967-83; Control Transformer Corp Sr Engr 1985-86; Kent St Univ Asst Prof 1986-87; Youngstown St Univ Instr 1987-; *ai:* Historical Preservation of Antique Bicycles & Automobiles; IEEE 1966-; NEA, OEA 1987-; ASEE 1995-; Antique Automobile Club of Amer 1971-, Regnl Dir, Vehicle Preservation Awds; Horseless Carriage Club of Amer 1974-; Wheelmen 1984-, Century Ride Awds; Sigma Tau Outstanding Scholar Awd; US Patent 3783426 1974; Several Papers Related to Design & Manufacture of Transformers for Electric Utility Industry; Registered Prof Engr OH; *office:* Youngstown St Univ 410 Wick Ave Youngstown OH 44555

SLAPIN, JANN A., Art Teacher; *b:* Orange, NJ; *m:* Harold D.; *c:* Jonathan, Emily; *ed:* Pratt Inst (BFA) Graphic Design & Ed 1971; Kean Coll (MA) Art 1975; Various Grad Courses Beyond Masters; *cr:* Flemington-Raritan MS Art Tchr 1972-79; Cedar Hill Elem Schl Art Tchr 1990-; *ai:* NJ Art Ed Assn, Bernards Twp Tchrs Assn, NAEA 1990- 1990-; Basking Ridge Presbyn Church 1987-, Deacon, Church Schl Tchr; Cedar Hill PTA 1990-, Pres; Garden St Quilters Guild 1980-, Quilt Show Chm; Various Wkshps; *office:* Cedar Hill Schl 100 Peach Tree Rd Basking Ridge NJ 07920

SLATER, ELIZABETH A., English Teacher; *b:* Elkton, MD; *m:* Thomas H.; *c:* Mary, Kathy, Ann; *ed:* Univ of DE (BA) Eng 1971; *cr:* DE Tech & Comm Coll Eng Tchr 1979-; Padua Acad Eng Tchr 1981-; *ai:* Shakespeare Festival; NCTE 1994-; DE Cncl of Tchrs of Eng, NCCE 1985-; Wrkshps on Portfolia Assessments DE, MD, PA; *office:* Padua Acad 905 N Broom St Wilmington DE 19806

SLATER, LINDA J., Span Tchr & Publications Adv; *b:* Youngstown, OH; *m:* Jeffrey W.; *c:* Jason, Jarrod; *ed:* Youngstown St Univ (BA) Eng & Span 1974; Grad Work Done at Kent St Univs Main Campus & Trumbull Campus; *cr:* Springfield Local HS Span & Eng Tchr 1974-77; Hubbard Exempted Village Schls Sub Tchr 1988-94; Hubbard HS S[illegible] Publications Tchr 1994-; *ai:* Intervention Assistance & Schl Ldrshp [illegible] Parent Advy Bd Rep; HS Newspaper Adv; Dance Chaperone; TriCty [illegible] Assn Bd Mem; NEA 1995-; OEA 1995-; HEA 1995-; HS Bsbl B[illegible] 1995-, Treas; *office:* Hubbard HS 350 Hall Ave Hubbard OH 4442[illegible]

SLATER, MARION CALDARA, English Teacher; *b:* Schenectad[illegible] *m:* Donald; *c:* Tricia Lynn Ballato; *ed:* Georgian Court Coll (BA) [illegible] 1963; The Cath Univ (MA) Eng Lit 1965; Columbia Univ (EDM) [illegible] Curr 1996; 3 Addl Hrs Eng Ed St Univ of NY at Albany; 6 Addl Hrs [illegible] Pace Univ; 3 Addl Hrs Eng Ed NYU; 6 Addl Hrs Long Island Univ; [illegible] Hrs Coll of New Rochelle; Attnd Tisch Schl of Arts; NY St Cert [illegible] Admin, Schl Admin, Supvr; NY St Cert to Teach Scndry Level E[illegible] Ballston Lake HS Eng Tchr 1965-66; Newburgh Free Acad En[illegible] 1967-70; Ardsley HS Eng Tchr 1972-73; Gorton HS Eng Tchr 1974-[illegible] Lane HS Eng Tchr 1976-86; Fox Lane MS Eng Tchr 1986-92; Fox L[illegible] Eng Tchr 1992-; *ai:* Stu Govt Adv 1992-; Class Adv 4 Yrs; AF[illegible] 1965-; Bedford Tchrs Assn 1976-; Westchester Cncl of Eng Edctrs; [illegible] Eng Cncl; NCTE; Natl Soc for the Study of Ed; ASCD; Natl [illegible] Restructuring Ed, Schls & Tchng; Natl Assn of Multicultural Ed; S[illegible] for NY St Bureau of Eng Lang Arts 1992, 1993; NY St Eng Cncl P[illegible] Excl Awd 1991; Kappa Delta Pi; Phi Delta Kappa; *home:* 35 Sagam[illegible] Bronxville NY 10708*

SLATER, NANCY LYNNE, Special Education Teacher; *b:* Brookly[illegible] *m:* Barry Erenburg; *c:* Adam Saslow; *ed:* Hofstra Univ (BA) Com[illegible] 1978; Long Island Univ (MS) Spec Ed 1980; *cr:* New York Ci[illegible] System Spec Ed Tchr 1979-81, 1992; Harold Katz Advertising A[illegible] Exec 1986-88; Seaford Mid, HS Spec Ed Tchr 1989-91; Garden C[illegible] Spec Ed Tchr 1993-; *ai:* Ed Spec Edition Newsletter Parents of Cl[illegible] Stdnts; Hlth Awaress Day Planning Comm; AFT, NEA 1979-; [illegible] Scroll Soc 1974-; West Hills Day Camp 1989-, Girls Div Ldr; Clu[illegible] 2nd Place Winner Newsday Scholastic Publications Awd Outstdng [illegible] Mid Schl Newspaper 1989; *office:* Garden City Sr HS 170 Rockaw[illegible] Garden City NY 11530

SLATTERY, MARILYN MURRAY, Mathematics Dept Chair & T[illegible] New York, NY; *m:* David J.; *ed:* St Thomas Aquinas Coll (BS) Ed, [illegible] Sci 1964; Manhattan Coll (MA) Rel Stud 1971; 15 Credits Beyond [illegible] Various Subjects; *cr:* St Theresa Schl 2nd Grd Tchr 1963-65; St A[illegible] Schl 4th-6th Grd Tchr 1965-67; St Anns Schl 4th, 6th & 7th Gr[illegible] 1967-71; Visitation Schl 8th Grd Tchr 1971-73; St Marys Schl 8th G[illegible] 1973-83; Monsignor Scanlan HS Math & Rel Tchr & Math Dept [illegible] 1983-; *ai:* Math Peer Tutoring Prgm Spon, Coord & Supvr; Fed [illegible] Tchrs 1974-; NCEA; *office:* Monsignor Scanlan H S 915 Hutchinso[illegible] Pkwy Bronx NY 10465

SLAUGHTER, EARLETTE EARNESTINE, English Dept Rep T[illegible] *b:* Harrisburg, PA; *ed:* Harrisburg Area Comm Coll (AFA) Hum, E[illegible] PA St Univ (BH) Linguistics, Scndry Ed 1981; Shippensburg Univ [illegible] Publication; PA St Univ Sci & Sci Engrng; Clarion Univ Cmptr Tec[illegible] Stroudsburg Univ Spec Ed Issues; NY Univ Cmptr Ed; *cr:* Harrisb[illegible] Eng Tchr 1988-90; John Harris HS Eng Tchr 1990-, Eng Dept Rep [illegible] *ai:* Multicultural Writers Conf; Faire; Comm Tutorial Svcs; PSEA [illegible] NEA 1989-; Minority Caucus 1993-; Bethel AME CHurch 1979-, L[illegible] Choir; Second Bapt Church 1996-, Choir, Trustee Aide; Harrisburg [illegible] League PP&L Schlsp 1980-81; Clarion Univ Letters of Recog Gr[illegible] Avg; PA St Univ Deans List; *office:* Harrisburg HS 2451 Martin [illegible] King Blvd Harrisburg PA 17103

SLAUGHTER, GLENN O. B., Fourth Grade Math Teacher; *b:* Bal[illegible] MD; *c:* Brooks; *ed:* 30 Addl Grad Hrs; *cr:* Wicomico Cty Bd of E[illegible] 1974-; *ai:* Schl Mentoring Prgm Coord; Schl Improvement Team; [illegible] Market Game Adv; NEA, MSTA, WCTA 1974-; Elks Lodge 817; Na[illegible] Festival Awd 1st Place 1980-81; *home:* 610 Bowman Dr Salisbu[illegible] 21804*

SLAUGHTER, JANICE, Elementary Teacher; *b:* Atlanta, GA; *e[illegible]* Tchrs Coll Elem Ed 1970; Attnd Howard Univ, Trinity Coll; *cr:* [illegible] Schls Tchr 26 Yrs; *ai:* Rdng is Fundamental Comm; Schl Mo[illegible] Oratorical Co-Chair; AFT 1971-; African Amer Historical & Genea[illegible] Soc 1985-; Friends of Lamond Riggs Lib.*

SLAUTTERBACK, LOU M., Elementary PE Teacher; *b:* Pittsbu[illegible] *m:* Mary Susan Robb; *c:* Bethany; *ed:* Slippery Rock St Coll (BS) [illegible] Phys Ed 1968, (MED) Hlth & Phys Ed 1972; Penn St Univ & Vil[illegible] Univ; *cr:* Franklin Area Schl Dist Tchr 1968-; *ai:* Coord & Coach F[illegible] Elem Girls Bsktbl League; Coord Elem PE Pgm-Cntrl Elem [illegible] AAHPERD EDA 1979-, Pub Relations Chair, Pa St AAHPERD [illegible] Pres, 1995, Tchr of Yr; Franklin Pub Lib Treas 1990-94; Venango C[illegible] Asst Office Chm 1982-94; Key note Speaker for many Prof Conf & [illegible] Both in-out of the Hlth & Phys Ed Field; Pub at Least 20 Prof A[illegible] *office:* Central Elem Schl 1276 Otter St Franklin PA 16323*

SLAWINSKI, BARBARA PESANELLO, 6th Grade Math Teac[illegible] Jersey City, NJ; *m:* Kenneth; *c:* Kristin, David; *ed:* JerseyCity St Co[illegible] K-8 Ed 1966; *cr:* PS #40 5th-6th Grd Tchr 25 Yrs; *ai:* Math Tutor-M[illegible] Pgm; Basic Skills Tchr; Jersey City Ed Assoc 1966-; NJ Ed Assoc[illegible] Tchrs of Amer; Friends of the Lib 1975-; East Bruns Soccer Club, [illegible] NJ Tchrs Governors Awd; *office:* Ezra L Nolan Schl 40 88 Gates Ave [illegible] City NJ 07305

SLAYTON, JEANETTE VIVIAN, Instructor of the Gifted; *b:* Bro[illegible] NY; *m:* John Walton; *c:* Suzanne Marie Vanover, David Scott; *ed:* R[illegible] Coll (BSEd) Elem Ed 1964; Post-Grad Stud Univ of VA; *cr:* London[illegible] Elem Schl 3-6 Grd Tchr 1967-74; Brownell Elem Schl Grds 1, 4, [illegible] 1975-84; Highland Elem Schl Grd 5 Tchr 1984-89; New Cumberla[illegible] Gifted Support Instr 1989-; *ai:* Yrbk Adv; Spelling Bee Coord; Acad [illegible] Knowledge Master Open, Thinking Caps Coach; AFT; NEA; [illegible] WSSDSC 1990-; Marriage Encounter 1980-, Regnl Coord; St Ther[illegible] C. Church 1984-, Parishoner; Gilroy Garlic Festival 1982-83, [illegible] Chprsn; West Shore Schl Dist ACCLAIM Awd 1995; WSSD[illegible] Recognition Awds 1992; Mentor Tchr 5 Times; *office:* New Cumb[illegible] MS 331 8th St New Cumberland PA 17070*

SLAYTON, ROBERT GARY, Latin Teacher; *b:* Morrisville, VT; *m:* [illegible] Ann Vanesse; *c:* Steven, Julie; *ed:* Univ of VT (BA) Latin 1969; 36 [illegible] Hrs; Lesley Coll 3 Credit Hrs; *cr:* Hardwick Acad Latin, Eng[illegible] 1969-70; Hazen union Latin, Eng Tchr 1970-74; Mt Mansfield Uni[illegible] Latin Tchr 1974-; *ai:* Var Bsbl Coach 23 Yrs; VT NEA 1983-, V[illegible] Coaches Assn 1984-, Sec, Treas; VT Classical Lang Assn [illegible] Chittenden East Schl Dist Tchr of Yr 1983; USA Bsbl's Golden Di[illegible] Vol Amateur Bsbl Coach of Yr 1995; Metro League Bsbl Coach of Yr [illegible] 1991, 1993-94; Coach of Yr 1994; *office:* Mt Mansfield Union HS B[illegible] Trace Rd Jericho VT 05465

SLECHTA, HENRY M., Music Dept Chair & Band Dir; *b:* Plainfie[illegible] *c:* John C., Ann S. Denney; *ed:* Ithaca Coll (BS) Music Ed 1964, [illegible] Music Ed 1967; *cr:* Bordentown Pub Schls Band Dir 1964-66; [illegible] Endicott Jr HS Band Dir 1967-74; Union-Endicott HS Band As[illegible] 1974-78, Bands Dir 1978-80; Chenango Forks HS Bands Dir, Music [illegible] Chair 1980-; *ai:* Alternative Scheduling, Bicentennial Comms; Broo[illegible] Music Ed Assn 1967-, VP, Treas; NY St Schl Music Assn 1967-; Natl [illegible] Assn 1969-, NY St Chm 1977-80; MENC 1964-; AFT 1974-; Articl[illegible] Guest Conductor, Clinician in NY, NJ, DE; Dir NY St Yth Jazz [illegible] European Tour 1978; *office:* Chenango Forks Cntrl Schls 1 Gord[illegible] Binghamton NY 13901

PER, MARK DAVID, Physical Therapy Asst Prof; *b:* Kenmore, NY; borah Ann Manna; *c:* Nichole Ann, Jon Mark; *ed:* Geneseo St Coll Bio 1984; Ball St Univ (MS) Exercise Physiology 1987; Univ at o (BS) Phys Therapy 1990; Addl Hrs Orthopedic Phys Therapy; *cr:* d Fillmore Hosp Part-time Phys Therapist 1990-; Daemen Coll Asst 993-; *ai:* Hlth Day Act Coord; Acad Standards Comm Chair; Bus s Trustee, Enrollment Comms; Amer Phys Therapy Assn 1990-; n Yth Flwshp 1987-, Ldr; Camp Duffield Comm 1993-, Bd of Dirs; te for Humanity 1987-; Numerous Articles; *office:* Daemen Coll Main St Amherst NY 14226*

H, BURNETTA, Professor; *b:* Cairo, IL; *m:* George Percell way; *c:* Constance Jackson, Gregory; *ed:* Fordham Univ (BA) ogy, Psych 1973, (MS) Ed 1975; 15 Credit Hrs; *cr:* Manhattan Comm dng Dept Supvr 1976-; The Modern Schl Classroom Tchr 1984-93; Coll Prof 1985-; *ai:* Prof Dev Prgm; Diagnostic Tchng of Rdng; ing, Crediting Materials in Open Classroom; IRA, NCSS 1973-; e of Women Voters 1972- Chprsn; Democratic Club, Order of Eastern 947-; Natl Tchrs Corp Fordham Univ; Permanent Cert Rdng, Spec c Stud; Manhattan Comm Coll Spec Svc Project Cert of Excl; *home:* onvent Ave New York NY 10031

KER, JAMES GERVAIS, Social Studies Teacher; *b:* Niagara Falls, Susan Annette Tefft; *c:* Margaret Slenker Lake, James III; *ed:* St of NY at Albany (BA) His 1965, (MA) Soc Stud 1966; AP Ec Cert at e Univ; Grad Stud at Syracuse Univ, SUNY at Oswego; NEH Fellow Marys Coll; Attnd Colonial Williamsburg Tchr Inst; *cr:* Liverpool HS ud Tchr 1966-; LeMoyne Coll Adj Ed Tchr 1990-; *ai:* AFT 1966-; SS, NYSCSS 1970-; Ctr for Ec Educ 1988-, Co-Dir; Pugh Fndtn; Liverpool HS 4338 Wetzel Rd Liverpool NY 13090*

NSKI, RICHARD E., Physics Teacher; *b:* Goshen, NY; *m:* ne Marie Bissinger; *ed:* Oneonta St Coll (BS) Physics & Math 1987; altz St Coll (MS) Physics 1992; *cr:* Dover Free Union Schl Physics 988-91; Pine Bush Cntrl Schls Physics Tchr 1991-; *ai:* Sci Club; Sci bics, Paper Recycling Adv; NHS Physics Stdnts 1987-; Empire nger Schlsp Sci Grad Stud 1990; Flwshp Industry Ed Partner's t 1990; Grant Dutchess Cty Sci Grant 1991; Tandy Tech Scholars ng Tchr Awd 1993; *office:* Pine Bush HS Rt 302 Pine Bush NY *

AK, SOPHIE LUKOWSKI, English & Reading Teacher; *b:* nsack, NJ; *m:* Thomas L. Slezak; *c:* Matthew; *ed:* Jersey City St Coll Eng 1973, (MA) Uban Ed 1974; 30 Post Grad Hrs Ed, Rdng, Eng; *cr:* rford Jr HS Rdng Tchr, Consultant 1974-75; Rutherford HS Rdng 975-77; Union Schl Eng, Rdng Tchr 1971-; *ai:* NEA, NJEA 1974-, p Chair; NCTE 1989-; *office:* Union Schl 359 Union Ave Rutherford 070*

K, GREGORY EDWARD, Physical Ed & Health Teacher; *b:* stown, MD; *m:* Nona Beatrice Kelly; *c:* Jeb, Luke; *ed:* Frostburg St BS) PE 1976; Frostburg St Univ (MED) PE 1988; Rockaway Flwshp Washington Cty Alternative Schl Tchr 1977-78; North Hagerstown hr 1979-; *ai:* 9th Grd Ftbl, Var Wrestling Coach; Ski, Lacrosse Clubs; line, Attendance, Mid Sts Comms; NEA, MSTA, WCTE 1977-; Cty Recreation 1983-; Rock City Reds Rugby 1978-, Pres; *office:* North stown HS 1200 Pennsylvania Ave Hagerstown MD 21740*

K, KIM JOEL, Chemistry & Computer Sci Tchr; *b:* Altoona, PA; *m:* E. Fegely; *c:* Jason W.; *ed:* PA St Univ (BS) Scndry Sci Ed 1978; of Pittsburg (MS) Chemistry 1981; Lehigh Univ (EDD) Educl Tech *cr:* PA St Univ Instructional Systems Lecturer 1988-; Brandywine ts Ara HS Chem & Cmptr Sci Tchr 1978-; *ai:* NEA 1978-; Phi Delta 1990-; Brandywine Hts Ed Assn Pres; *office:* Brandywine Heights HS 200 W Weiss St Topton PA 19562*

K, NANCY CORLE, Remedial Math Teacher; *b:* Queen, PA; *m:* d B.; *c:* Mark G.; *ed:* Penn St Univ (BS) Kndgtn, Elem Ed 1963; 12 Credit Hrs; *cr:* Claysburg-Kimmel Schl Dist First Grd Tchr 1963-78, d Grd Tchr 1978-95, Remedial Math Tchr 1995-; *ai:* Fourth Grds Enrichment Club; Grange 1967-, Lady Asst Steward; Gift of Time e Awd 1994-95; *home:* RR 1 Box 172 Roaring Spring PA 16673*

ER, MARY KATHRYN, English Teacher; *b:* Binghamton, NY; *m:* ; *c:* Eileen, Randy, Molly; *ed:* SUNY at Binghamton (BA) Eng Lit, ric 1991; Attnd Coll of St Rose Scndry Ed; *cr:* Seton Cath Cntrl HS Tchr 1993-; *ai:* Dean of Soph Class 1995-96; Yrbk Adv 1993-; STI ar Org 1994-; Comm Involvement Alliance 1993-; Southern Tier Inst ts 1994-, Coöp Tchng with Artists; *office:* Seton Catholic Central HS minary Ave Binghamton NY 13905

KO, JOSEPH G.,JR., Instructor; *b:* Philadelphia, PA; *m:* Laura Ann sky; *c:* Cecilia, R. J.; *ed:* Univ of Pittsburgh at Johnstown (BA) Bus 86; St Francis Coll (MA) Indstrl Relations, Prsnl Admin 1988; *cr:* ria-Rowe Bus Coll Instr 1991-; *ai:* PA Bus Ed Assn 1995-; *office:* ria-Rowe Business College 221 Central Ave Johnstown PA 15902*

E, WILLIAM W.,JR., Spanish Teacher; *b:* Lebanon, PA; *m:* Fay H. umbine; *c:* William W. III; *ed:* Lebanon Vly Coll (BA) Span 1962; Millersville Univ; *cr:* Elco HS Span Tchr 1962-; *ai:* NHS Selection, Requirement Comms; NEA, PSEA 1962-; ELGEA 1962-, Mbrshp Covenant U M Church 1952-; Goodwill Fire CO #5 1961-; Lebanon Bowling Assn 1961-, Hall of Fame; Tchr of Yr 1991-92; Lebanon Cty Hnr Soc; Excl in Ed Awds 3 Yrs.

ER, TRENT W., Agriculture Teacher; *b:* Somerville, NJ; *m:* Donna *c:* Bryan, Joseph; *ed:* DE Vly Coll (BS) Dairy 1975; Rutgers Univ) Ed 1981; *cr:* Phillipsburg HS Ag Tchr 1976-85; Newton Schl Dist hr 1985-91; North Warren Regnl Ag Tchr 1991-; *ai:* FFA Adv; NJ Ed 1976-; NEA 1976-; North Warren Ed Assn 1991-; Warren Cty Ed Assn ; NJ FFA Adv of the Yr 1981 & 1995; North Warren Regnl Tchr of r 1995; *office:* North Warren Regional HS 410 Lambert Rd Blairstown 825

VINSKI, STEVEN T., Art Teacher; *b:* Philadelphia, PA; *m:* Susan er; *c:* Melece, Melanie, Nicholas; *ed:* Kutztown Univ (BS) Art Ed Addl 30 Post Grad Hrs; *cr:* Methacton Schl Dist Art Tchr 1974-75; Area Schl Dist Tchr 1975-; *ai:* Golf, Art Club; NEA, PSEA 1974-, Area EA 1974-, Pres 1985-86; Claverack Rural Electric Co-op 1975-, Natl Soc of Mural Painters, Exhibitions in US, Europe; *home:* RR 2 52 Troy PA 16947

VINSKI, SUSAN J., English & Journalism Teacher; *b:* Reading, PA; even Theodore; *c:* Melece, Melanie, Nicholas; *ed:* Kutztown Univ Eng & Scndry Ed 1972; 3 Grad Credits Susquehanna Univ; 6 Grad ts Mansfield Univ; *cr:* Governor Mifflin Jr HS 9th Grd Eng Tchr 75; Canton Jr-Sr HS 7th Grd Eng & HS Jrnlsm 1975-; *ai:* 8th Grd ition Outcomes Comm Chm; 7th Grd Orientation Comm; CAEA, NEA 1975-; PTA 1976-, Treas; *office:* Canton Area Jr Sr HS 139 E St Canton PA 17724

AN, ANNETTE MARIE, English Instructor; *b:* Clark's Summit, PA; cholas, Blake, Jessica Perry; *ed:* Univ of IA (MFA) Poetry 1963; 18 t Hrs; *cr:* Univ of PR Instr 1963-65; NYC Bd of Ed Latin, Eng Tchr 90; Marywood Coll Instr 1990-; *ai:* UFT 1995-; Mulberry Poets, rs 1995-, VP; PA Cncl on Arts Flwshp Poetry 1995; Bus Week Awd nnovative Tchng 1989; Articles Pub; *home:* RR 1 Gouldsboro PA 4

SLOAN, IRVING JOSEPH, Social Studies Teacher; *b:* New York, NY; *m:* Esther Gendelman; *c:* Philip; *ed:* Univ of WI (BA) Amer Insts 1946; Harvard Law Schl (JD) Law 1950; Yeshiva Univ Grad Schl of Ed (MS) Scndry Soc Stud 1959; 45 Addl Credits Tchrs Coll Columbia Univ; *cr:* Yellin & Levy Law Assoc 1950-52; L. L. Poses Law Assoc 1952-54; British Book Centre Ltd Exec VP 1954-57; Wm J. Gaynor JHS 9th Grd Eng Tchr 1957-61; Scarsdale MS 7th-8th Grd Soc Stud Tchr 1961-; *ai:* AFT, NCSS, Westchester Cncl Soc Stud 1961-; Amer Historical Assn 1950-; Scarsdale Pub Lib 1987-91, VP, Trustees Bd; Village Historian 1991-; Scarsdale Tchrs Assn 1963-, Exec Comm; Ford Fnd Tchng Fellowship 1958-59; Ed Press Amer Awd; Pub in Books 1992-93; Columnist; *office:* Scarsdale MS Mamaroneck Rd Scarsdale NY 10583*

SLOAN, JAMES ALAN, World Cultures Teacher; *b:* Philadelphia, PA; *m:* Catharine Cline; *c:* Suzi, Dave, Stacie; *ed:* Westminster Coll (BA) His 1967; Slippery Rock Univ (MED) Ed 1971; *cr:* North Allegheny Intermediate HS World Cultures Tchr 29 Yrs; *ai:* Girls Var Tennis Coach 22 Yrs; "Just Say No" Spon; AFT, NAFT, PAFT 1980-; Jaycees 1973-78, Sec 1 Yr; Allegheny North Swim Club Bd 1979-87, Pres 1980, VP 1981-91; Ingomar North Swim Club Bd 1975-79, 1990-, VP 1990-91, Pres 1992 & 1993; JISEA Fellowship Japan 1981; Japan Internship Coord & Host Family 1989; Pitt Asian Stud Inservice Speaker Japan 1992; Outstanding Innovative Soc Stud Tchr PA 1974; *office:* North Allegheny Intermdte H S 350 Cumberland Rd Pittsburgh PA 15237

SLOCUM, KAREN HOWMAN, High School Art Teacher; *b:* Ashland, OH; *m:* Gary A.; *c:* Melissa S., Zakary A.; *ed:* Ashland Coll (BS) Comprehensive Art Ed 1972; Working on Masters Kent St; *cr:* Field MS Art Tchr 1973; Streetsboro Elem Art Tchr 1973-78; Rootstown HS Art Tchr 1985-; *ai:* Jr Class Adv 5 Yrs; NEA 1985-; Jr Womens Guild 1978-, Pres; Laura Cirjak Schlrshp Fund 1993-, Head; *home:* 4111 Marks Ave Rootstown OH 44272

SLOCUM, STUART W., Biology & Anatomy Instructor; *b:* Jackson, PA; *m:* Carolee P.; *ed:* East Stroudsburg Univ (BA) Bio 1970; Post Grad; Univ of Scranton Bio, Math Cert; *cr:* US Air Force Enlisted 1971-73; Mountain View HS Instr 1976-; Luzerne Co Comm Coll Itinerant Instr, Sci Chair 1992-; *ai:* Middle States Steering Comm; Sci Fair Coord; Mentor Tchr; PSEA, MVEA, NEA 1976- Pol Chair; Florance Shelby Preserve of Nature Conservancy 1980-, Educl Chair; Forest Landowners Ed, Mt View Open Forum Apprec Awds; *office:* Mountain View Jr Sr HS RR 1 Box 339 Kingsley PA 18826*

SLOCUMB-BRADFORD, ALESIA B., Geometry & Algebra Teacher; *b:* Buffalo, NY; *m:* William Bradford; *ed:* Daemen Coll (BS) Cmptr Sci & Math 1987; Univ of DC (MS) Bus Ed 1990; Bowie St Univ (MS) Mgmt Information Systems 1994; Currently Pursuing Doctoral Degree in Mgmt Engrng at George Washington Univ; *cr:* Louis Charles Rabaut Jr HS Math Tchr 1987-89; Thomas Jefferson Jr HS Cmptr Sci & Bus Tchr 1989-; Univ of DC Cmptr Sci Tchr Part-Time; Strayer Coll Math Tchr Part-Time; *ai:* Stock Market Club Spon; The Robotomania Project Co-Partner; DC Cmptr Sci Conf Coach; AFT 1993-; NCTM 1987-; DC TM, Delta Pi Epsilon 1987-; Phi Delta Kappa 1991-; Recipient of GTE Fnd Grant; *office:* Jefferson Jr HS 8th & H Sts SW Washington DC 20024*

SLOGGATT WOLF, CONSTANCE, Art Educator; *b:* Merrick, NY; *m:* Charles Robert; *c:* Amelia; *ed:* Pratt Inst (BFA) Painting & Fine Arts 1982; Long Island Univ (MFA) Painting & Fine Arts 1987; Molloy Coll at Rockville Ctr Comp Art; *cr:* Long Island Univ at Greenvale Painting Tchng Asst 1985-87; Fine Arts Museum of LI Asst to Dir 1987-89; Huntington Twp Art League Fac Part-Time 1990, 1994 & 1995; Northport & East Northport Schls Art Edctr 1991-; *ai:* Co-Spon Natl Art Hnr Soc Northport Chptr 1992-; NYSATA; NAEA; AFT; Huntington Twp Art League; NOW; Northport E Northport Bd Ed Prof Achvmt Awd 1995; Western Suffolk Tchrs Ctr Grants Women Artists Visual Resource Ctr & Stu Portfolio on CD Rom; NYSATA Presenter 1994; *office:* Northport HS Laurel Hill Rd Northport NY 11768*

SLONAC, HELEN, Kindergarten Teacher; *b:* Windber, PA; *c:* Paul Joseph, Tiffany Marie; *ed:* Lock Haven Univ (BS) Elem Ed 1969; IN Univ of PA (MED) Elem Ed 1972; 30 Addl Credit Hrs; *cr:* Forest Hills Schl Dist Tchr 27 Yrs; *ai:* Stu Cncl, Humanitarian Club & CYO Adv; Parenting Classes Tchr; NEA & PSEA 1969-; Forest Hills Ed Assn 1969-, Bldg Rep; Delta Kappa Gamma 1975-, VP; Keystsone St Rdng Cncl; Johnstown Rdng Cncl; Amer Legion Aux 1969-, Pres, VP, Sec, Treas, Chaplain & Historian; Adams-Croyle Recreation Authority 1991-, VP; Local Historical Soc 1990-; *home:* PO Box 198 Saint Michael PA 15951*

SLONIM, MICHELE JOY, Foreign Language Teacher; *b:* St Louis, MO; *ed:* Univ of MD (BS) Span, Fr, Eng 1969; Marywood Coll (MS) Humanistic, Integrative Ed 1981; *cr:* Cherry Hill West HS Fr, Span Tchr 1969-72; Maple Shade HS Span, Fr, Eng Tchr 1974-; *ai:* Interact, Span Clubs Spon; NEA, NJEA 1969-; MSEA 1974-; Alpha Lambda Delta; Diadem Mortar Bd; Kappa Delta Pi; Dean's List; Who's Who MD Univ Stdnts; Woodrow Wilson Flwshp Candidate; Firemen-Policemen Banquet Civic Duty Recognition; *home:* 25 S Church #13 Barclay Maple Shade NJ 08052*

SLOSS, HENRY E., Associate Professor of English; *b:* San Francisco, CA; *m:* Geralyn Marie; *c:* Noah, Nicole, Leo, Lily, Sophia; *ed:* Univ of CA at Berkeley (BA) Eng 1962; Univ of MN (MA) Eng 1965; Univ of VA 1967-68; *cr:* WA & Lee Univ Instr 1965-66, Asst Prof 1968-72; Univ of MD Instr 1975-85; Anne Arundel Comm Coll Asst Prof & Assoc Prof 1988-; *ai:* Articles & Poetry Pub.

SLOTER, WAYNE, Mathematics Teacher; *b:* Cutler, OH; *m:* Rebecca Ruth McGraw; *c:* Kenneth, Donna Sloter Little, Lisa Sloter Beswick, Eddie; *ed:* Glenville St Coll (BA) Ed 1964; Post Grad OH Univ; *cr:* Doylestown HS Math Tchr 1964-65; Waterford HS Math Tchr 1965-; *ai:* Soph Class Adv; NEA, OEA, SEOEA 1964-; WCLEA 1965-, Pres; First Bapt Church of Belpre 1987-; Beverly Waterford Jaycees Outstdng Edctr 1971; *home:* RR 1 Box 373 Vincent OH 45784

SLOZAK, LINDA SKIDMORE, US History Teacher; *b:* Bayshore, NY; *m:* Robert W.; *c:* Erika Anne, Rebeka Marion; *ed:* Univ of Rochester (BA) His 1969; American Intnl Coll (MAT) Soc Stud 1973; Attnd Univ of London Schl of Oriental & African Stud; *cr:* Chestnut Jr High Soc Stud Tchr 1970-80; Collingwood Schl Tchr 1973-74; Kiley Jr High Tchr 1980-86; Sprinfgfield Cntrl HS Tchr 1986-; *ai:* Soc Stud Assessment Wkshp; NEA & MTA 1970-; Westfield Little League 1989-, Umpire in Chief for Sftbl; Alpha Delta Kappa 1991-, Corres Sec; *office:* Springfield Central HS 1840 Roosevelt Ave Springfield MA 01109*

SLUGA, CRAIG CHARLES, Sixth Grade Teacher; *b:* Kane, PA; *m:* Ann Marie Clark; *c:* Felicity, Rachel, Emily; *ed:* Edinboro Univ (BS) Elem Ed 1972, (MS) Guid, Coun 1975; *cr:* Iroquois Schl Dist Classroom Tchr 1972-; *ai:* Var Boys, Girls Track & Field Coach 22 Yrs; Former Jr HS, Jr Var Ftbl; Former Elem Boys Bsktbl; PSEA, NEA 1972-; Iroquois Ed Assn 1972-, PR & R Chprsn; *office:* Lawrence Park Elem Schl 4231 Morse St Erie PA 16511

SMABY, BEVERLY PRIOR, Assoc Professor of History; *b:* Denver, CO; *m:* Richard; *c:* Niels, Kristin; *ed:* Univ of WA (BA) Ger Lit 1962; Yale Univ (MAT) Ger Lang Tchng 1963; U of PA (MA) Ger Lit 1967, (MA) Amer Civilization 1971, (PHD) Amer Civilization 1986; *cr:* Clarion Univ Assoc Prof 1991-95, Asst Prof 1995-; *ai:* Pres Commission on Status of Women; Womens Stud Advy Comm; Amer Historical Assn, Org of Amer Historians 1991-; Jefferson Cty Historical Soc 1995-; Book The Transformation of Moravian Bethlehem From Communal Mission to Family Economy 1988; *office:* Clarion Univ Of PA History Dept Clarion PA 16214

SMAIL, IAN E. V., English Teacher; *b:* Paoning Sechnan, China; *c:* Margaret, Douglas, Charles, Deborah; *ed:* SUNY Coll at Cortland (BS) Eng 1962, (MS) Eng 1966; Attnd Wheaton Coll IL, Syracuse Univ, Ithaca Coll; *cr:* DeWitt Jr HS Eng Tchr 22 Yrs; Ithaca HS Eng Tchr 12 Yrs; *ai:* Elizabethan Soc Club Adv; Ithaca Tchrs Assn 1962-, Rep; NYSUT, NEA 1962-; United Way 1962-, Town of Ulysses Pres; Pub in St Unions Magazine, Newspaper; *home:* 108 E Seneca Rd Trumansburg NY 14886*

SMALES, SANDRA L., Coordinator of Paralegal Prgm; *b:* Pittsburgh, PA; *ed:* Univ of Pittsburgh (BA) Eng, Sociology 1973, (JD) Law 1976; 3 Credit Hrs CIMTE Univ of NM 1994; *cr:* Fisher Jr Coll Adj Fac 1983-87; Middlesex Comm Coll Adj Fac 1985-90; Quincy Coll Fac & Coord of Paralegal Prgm 1988-; *ai:* Prgms & Instruction Accreditation Sub, Curr Comm Chair; Quincy Educl Assn 1988-, Exec Bd, Negotiating Team; MTA, NEA 1986-; Mass Bar Assn 1982-; *office:* Quincy Coll 34 Coddington St Quincy MA 02169

SMALL, JAMES, Black Studies Adjunct Lecturer; *b:* Georgetown, SC; *m:* Carol Tondu; *c:* Madeline, Chanmoni, Najah, Malik, Akhenaton, Oneka; *ed:* City Coll of NY (BA) His 1975; *cr:* Org of African-Amer Unity Eastern Regnl Dir 1968-80; Muslim Mosque Inc Imam 1968-; City Coll Stu Ctr Managing Dir 1982-92; City Coll NY Black Stud Dept Adj Lecturer 1983-; *ai:* Caribbean Stu Assn, Black Stud Stu Org, Young Witnesses for Christ Fac Adv; City Univ Black Fac, Staff Rep; Black Stud Study Abroad Prgm Chprsn; ASCAC 1984-, Pres, Eastern Region; KM-WR Sci Consortium 1986-, Exec Bd Mem; People of African Ancestry 1991-, Bd of Ed, Exec Bd; MLK Jr Democratic Club 1980-; CCNY Black Alumni 1975-, Pres, VP; The Prevention Prgm Trust Inc 1996-, Chprsn; African Pilgrimage Project 1995-, VP; Kuperman-Helms Awd; Outstdng Tchrs Awds; Pub Articles; *office:* City Coll of NY 138 St at Convent Ave New York NY 10031*

SMALL, RITA, Latin Teacher; *b:* Morrisville, PA; *ed:* Villanova Univ (BA) Latin 1958; Cath Univ (MA) Latin 1967; 3 Credits Theology; 3 Credits Schl Law; *cr:* PA Parochial Schls Tchr 1948-56; Diocesan HS Latin Tchr 1956-69, Admin 1969-85; Merion Mercy Acad Latin Tchr 1985-; *ai:* Latin Club Moderator; KATES GIRLS Moderator; NCEA 1970-; PCS; PACS; ACL; PA Classical Soc & Philadelphia Classical Soc 1985-; *office:* Merion Mercy Acad 511 Montgomery Ave Merion Station PA 19066

SMALL, WYLIE JAMESON, English Teacher; *b:* Rochester, NY; *m:* Stuart P.; *c:* Rudy; *ed:* Sweet Briar Coll (BA) Eng, Creative Writing 1983; Univ of Rochester (MSE) Scndry Ed 1985; *cr:* Allendale Columbia Schl Eng Tchr 1987-88; Pittsford Sutherland HS Eng Tchr 1988-91; Webster HS Eng Tchr 1991-; *ai:* Webster Tchrs Assn 1992-; *office:* Webster HS 875 Ridge Rd Webster NY 14580

SMALLEY, RICHARD LEE, Science Teacher; *b:* West Union, OH; *m:* Alison Dick; *c:* Aislinn; *ed:* OH Univ (BA) Scndry Ed, Sci 1989; Shawnee St Univ Scndry Ed, Sci; Xavier Univ Masters Prgm Scndry Ed Emphasis in Physics; *cr:* Portsmouth HS 9-12 Grds Sci Tchr 1992-; *ai:* Girls Bsktbl Var Head Coach; Boys Bsktbl Var Asst Coach; Scholastic Coach; *office:* Portsmouth HS 1149 Gallia St Portsmouth OH 45662

SMALLEY, ROGER BENN, 5th Grade Teacher; *b:* Cleveland, OH; *m:* Linda K. Hamilton; *ed:* Muskingum Coll (BA) His 1970; Univ of Akron (MA) Ed Admin 1976; Chinese Stud at Oberlin Coll; NASA Ed at Baldwin-Wallace Coll; 30 Addl Post Grad Hrs; *cr:* Medina Cty Schls Sub 1970; Walter Kidder Elem 5th Grd Tchr 1970-; *ai:* Venture Capital Mission Statement, Outdoor Ed Comm; Parent Tchr Guild Parlimentarian; Brunswick Ed Assn 1970- Pres, Treas, Distinguished Svc; OH EA 1970- Outstanding Local Treas; NEA, NEOEA 1970-; Medina City Cncl 1988, Cnclman Reelected Twice; First Chrstn Church 1959- Bd, Finance Chair; Project Munch 1990- Bd Mem; Ldrship Medina Cty 1993-; OEA Human Relations Awd Nom; Contributing Author to Modern Curr Press Math Series 1-6; Tchr Magazine Contributer; Guest Writer for Medina Cty Gazette; Tchr of Yr 1989-90; Citizen of the Day; *office:* Kidder Elem Schl 3650 Grafton Rd Brunswick OH 44212

SMALLING, BARBARA WASHINGTON, High School Teacher; *b:* Fairmount, MD; *ed:* Univ of MD at Eastern Shore (BA) Eng Ed-Magna Cum Laude 1982; Univ (MA) African & Afro-Amer-summa Cum Laude Lit 1983; *cr:* Univ of MD Tutor & Upward Bound Pgm Tutor & Tchr 1981; Benjamin Stoddert MS Eng Tchr 1983-85; Forestville HS Eng Tchr 1985-; *ai:* Whos Who Among Stdnts in Amer Univs & Colls 1980-81; Natl Deans List 1981-82; Natl Register of Outstdng Coll Grads 1983; OH St Univ Flwshp; Article Pub; *home:* 701 Trenary Cir Fort MD 20744

SMARDON, CAROLYN CARDEN, History Teacher; *b:* Knoxville, TN; *m:* Kenneth A.; *c:* Abigail; *ed:* Univ of TN (BS) Ed 1971; Univ of North FL (MED) Soc Stud Ed 1976; 9 Hrs Ec Ed Columbus Coll 1978; 3 Hrs TX His Harris Cty Comm Coll 1986; 9 Hrs Ed Univ of Dayton 1992; Wright St 6 Hrs; *cr:* Sandalwood Jr, Sr HS Soc Stud Tchr 1971-76; Jordan Voc Soc Stud Tchr 1976-78; Shaw Sr HS Soc Stud Tchr 1978-80; Sandalwood Jr, Sr HS Soc Stud Tchr 1981-84; Spring HS Soc Stud Tchr 1985-88; Lakota HS Soc Stud Tchr 1990-; *ai:* Sandalwood Prom Spon, Jordan JV CHrldr Spons; Sandalwood Keyette Club, Girls Swim Coach, Anchor Svc Club; NCSS 1980-; NEA, OEA 1990-; AFT 1983-84; Habitat for Humanity 1993-, Food Coord; PTA 1980-; Tchr of Yr; *home:* 5459 Oldgate Dr West Chester OH 45069*

SMART, JUDITH DECKER, Mathematics Instructor; *b:* Fremont, OH; *m:* Philip A.; *ed:* Otterbein Coll (BS) Math, Ed 1970; Heidelberg Coll MS Math in Progress; *cr:* Lakota Local HS Math Tchr 1969-70; Upper Arlington HS Math Tchr 1970-71; Newport News HS Math Tchr 1971-73; Clyde Old Fort Schl Sub Tchr 1973-82; Terra Comm Coll Math Instr 1982-; *ai:* OMATYC 1994-; 4-H Adv 1989-; Church Fin Sec 1976-; *home:* 1455 County Road 31 Fremont OH 43420

SMART, THOMAS JOHN, Physics Teacher; *b:* Geneva, NY; *m:* Denise G. Doglione; *c:* MacKenzie, Andrew, Trevor; *ed:* Hobart Coll (BA) Physics 1968; Attnd SUNY at Geneseo, Elmira Coll, SUNY at Brockport; *cr:* Penn Yan MS Sci Tchr 1968-85; Penn Yan Acad Physics Tchr 1985-; *ai:* Cross Cntry & Asst Track Coach; NHS Adv; NEA 1970-; Penn Yan Tchrs Assn 1970-, Pres 1993-94; AAPT; Penn Yan Lions 1986-; Woodrow Wilson Wkshps; Multiple Coach of the Yr Awds-X-Cntry; *office:* Penn Yan Acad 305 Court St Penn Yan NY 14527*

SMARTSCHAN, CARL ERNEST, Biology Teacher; *b:* Allentown, PA; *m:* Nancy Leinbach; *c:* Adam, Neil; *ed:* Millersville St Coll (BS) Bio Ed 1974; Kutztown Univ (MA) Ed, Bio 1989; *cr:* Bensalem Twp Schl Dist Life Sci Tchr 1974-75; Allentown Schl Dist Bio Tchr 1975-88; East Penn Schl Dist Bio Tchr 1988-; *ai:* Coach Head Boys' Bsktbl, Bio Olympics Team; NEA 1974-; *office:* Emmaus HS 851 North St Emmaus PA 18049*

SMEATON, WILLIAM ANDREW, Fourth Grade Teacher; *b:* Pittsburgh, PA; *ed:* Indiana Univ of PA (BS) Elem Ed 1972; Duquesne Univ (MS) Elem Admin 1976; *cr:* Penn Hills Schl Dist Tchr 24 Yrs; *ai:* Stipend & Schl of Focus Comms; Penn Hills Ed Assn 1972-, Pres, VP 1976-82; Penn Hills Cizizen of Yr 1976; US Jaycees Young Men of Amer 1980; Penn Hebron Tchr of Yr 1987; Penn Hills Tchr of Yr 1981; *office:* Penn Hebron Elem Schl 102 Duff Rd Pittsburgh PA 15235

SMELAS, THOMAS WILLIAM, Business Education Teacher; *b:* Allentown, PA; *m:* Tracy L. Hartenstine; *ed:* Bloomsburg Univ (BS) Bus Ed & Accounting 1987; Post Grad Stud at Horavian Coll, E Stroudsburg Univ, & Cedar Crest Coll; *cr:* Palmerton Area Schl Dist Bus Ed 1987-; *ai:*

FBLA Adv; Asst Var Bsbl Coach; Palmerton Area EA 1993-, Treas; NEA, PSEA, & PBEA 1987; *office:* Palmerton Area HS 3525 Fireline Rd Palmerton PA 18071

SMELTZ, TODD BRIAN, Chemistry & Mathematics Tchr; *b:* Harrisburg, PA; *m:* Melanie Marie Jenks; *ed:* Mansfield Univ of PA (BS) Chem & Math Ed 1989; Masters Equivalency 36 Grad Credit Hrs; *cr:* York City Schl Dist General Sci & Math Tchr 1989-90; Upper Dauphin Area HS Chem & Math Tchr 1990-; *ai:* Soph Class Adv 1990-; Ski Club Adv 1992-; Photography club 1994-; Strategic Planning Comm; Stu Assistance Team; NEA, PSEA 1990-; Upper Dauphin Area EA 1990-, VP 1994-, St Del 1992-; Partners Sci Research Prgm 1992-94; *office:* Upper Dauphin Area HS 220 N Church St Elizabethville PA 17023

SMELTZER, DEBORAH RHOADS, Chemistry Teacher; *b:* Shamokin, PA; *m:* Thomas Terry; *c:* Audrey Denise, Thomas Darryl; *ed:* Bloomsburg Univ (BS) Chem 1971; & (MA) Gen Sci 1976; 17 Credits Beyond Masters Equivalency; *cr:* Milton Schl Dist Gen Sci & Bio 1971-88 & Chem 1988-; *ai:* Discipline Comm; NEA 1971-; PSEA 1971-; MAEA 1971-; Ralpho Womens Club 1987-; Chem Industry Conf 1993; Mentor 1993-94; Stu Tchrs from Bucknell Univ 1993-95; *office:* Milton Area Sr HS 700 Mahoning St Milton PA 17847*

SMERCANSKY, MARY LYNN, Social Studies Teacher; *b:* Youngstown, OH; *m:* David J.; *ed:* Youngstown St Univ (BA) Anthropology 1978, (BS) Comp Soc Stud 1991; Working on MA Guidance, Counseling Westminster Coll; *cr:* Springfield Local HS Soc Stud Tchr 1992-; *ai:* Curr Cncl; Discipline Comm; NEA, OEA, SLCTA 1992-; Delta Zeta Alumnae 1975-; Stu Tchr of Yr 1991 at Youngstown St Univ; *office:* Springfield Local HS 11335 Yngstn Pittsburgh Rd New Middletown OH 44442

SMERDEL, JO DESIMONE, Zoology Teacher & Sci Chair; *b:* Pittsburgh, PA; *m:* Joseph; *c:* Kristine, Paul, Joi; *ed:* Carlow Coll (BA) Bio 1965; Univ of Pittsburgh (MED) Sci Ed 1975; Addl 20 Credits Ed, Cmptrs; Duquesne Univ 12 Credits Towards MA Bio, Ed; *cr:* Edgewood HS Bio Tchr 4 Yrs; Cntrl Cath HS Bio Tchr 8 Yrs; Univ of Pittsburgh Rsrch Coord 4 Yrs; Comm Coll of Allegheny Ant, Physics Instr 12 Yrs; Woodland Hills HS Zoology Tchr, Sci Dept Chair 17 Yrs; *ai:* Hlth Quest Challenge, Lad Aids Coord; Curr, Fac Advy Comm; W H Tchrs Assn 17 Yrs; ABT 5 Yrs; Women in Sci 10 Yrs, Guest Speaker, Wkshp Presenter; STAR Awd Outstdng Tchr Cornell Univ; Outstdng Women in Sci Ed Chatham Coll; Alumnae of Yr Ed Carlow Coll; Rsrch Grants Prof Enrichment Prgm 6 Yrs; *office:* Woodland Hills HS 2550 Greensburg Pike Pittsburgh PA 15221*

SMERECZNIAK, JERILYN M., Vocational & Tech School Tchr; *b:* Connellsville, PA; *m:* David Afton; *c:* Karyn Lee Thompson, Scott Steven, Jeffrey David; *ed:* WA Hospital Schl of Nursing (RN) Nursing 1965; CA Univ of PA (BSE) Pub Schl Nursing 1991; IN Univ of PA Voc I Degree Voc Ed 1993; *cr:* St. Clair Hospital Medical Surgical Nurse 1965-66; Norfolk General Hospital Medical Surgical Nurse 1966-67; Prince Georges Pub Schl Schl Nurse 1980-82; Curry Meml Home Nursing Supvr 1985-90; Greene Cty AVTS Tchr 1990-; *ai:* Hlth Occupations Stdnts of Amer Adv; Tech-Prep Consortium Comm Mem; Hlth Occupations Advy Comm Spon; St. Oliver Plunkett Parish Folk Group 1989-, Guitar Player, Ldr; River of Life Prayer Group 1991-, Ldr & Co-Ldr; *office:* Green Co Area Voc Tech Schl RR 2 Box 40 Waynesburg PA 15370

SMERICK, JACQUELINE ELIZABETH, First Grade Teacher; *b:* Lakewood, OH; *ed:* Valparaiso Univ (BS) Elem Ed 1970; 80 Addl Semester Hrs; Attnd Baldwin Wallace Coll, Kent St Univ, Cleveland St Univ, Ashland Univ, Notre Dame Coll; *cr:* Roosevelt Schl Elem Tchr 1970-84; Hayes Schl Elem Tchr 1984-94; Taft Schl Elem Tchr 1994-; *ai:* Right to Read Week Illustrator 1979-95; Lakewood Tchrs Assn 1970-, Pres 1984-85, 1988-89, 1996-; NEOTA, NEOEA, OEA, NEA 1970-; PTA Cncl Tchr of Yr 1981; Jennings Scholar 1990-91; *office:* Taft Elem Schl 13701 Lake Ave Lakewood OH 44107

SMERLING, ROCHELLE, 8th Grade Social Studies Tchr; *b:* Brooklyn, NY; *m:* Sheldon; *c:* Barry, Jill, Elliot; *ed:* Queens Coll (BA) Ed 1960; St Univ at Stony Brook (MA) Soc Studs 1983; Adelphi Univ (MA) Spec Ed 1983; CW Post Univ His Courses; *cr:* New York City Bd of Ed Kndgtn & 6th Grd Tchr 5 Yrs; Elwood Pub Schls 8th Grd Soc Stud Tchr 2 Yrs; MS 67 Queens 8th Grd Soc Stud Tchr 15 Yrs; *ai:* Fundraising; Soc Studs Lead Tchr; AFT 1960-; UFT 1960-, Union Rep; Long Island Cncl Soc Stud; PTA, Liaison; Law Grant; NY St Soc Stud Tchr of Yr; NYC MS Soc Stud Tchr of Yr; Bnai Brith Holocaust Tchng Awd; *office:* Louis Pasteur MS #67 Queens 51-60 Marathon Pkwy Little Neck NY 11362*

SMERNOFF, INA KAPLAN, Teacher of GATE & Pgm Leader; *b:* Hartford, CT; *m:* Marvin; *c:* Robert; *ed:* Univ of CT (MA) Eng Ed 1968, (MA) Eng Ed 1971; *cr:* East Hartford MS Eng & Tchr of GATE 1968-; *ai:* Newspaper Adv; Team Ldr of GATE Prgm; Prof Improvement, Evaluation Comms; NEA 1968-; CEA 1968-, Bd, Salute Svc Awd; East Hartford EA 1968-, Pres; Phi Delta Kappa; Pi Lambda Phi; Jewish Children Svc Org; Milken Edctr, CT Edctr Awds; Wkshp Presenter; *office:* East Hartford MS 777 Burnside Ave East Hartford CT 06108

SMIELECKI, KELLY J., Spanish Teacher; *b:* Buffalo, NY; *m:* Michael; *c:* Jessica K.; *ed:* SUNY Coll at Buffalo (BSEd) Span Scndry Ed 1987; SUNY at Geneseo (MSEd) Span Scndry Ed 1993; Credit Hrs; *cr:* Batavia City Schls Span Tchr 1987-; *ai:* Class of 1997 Adv; Interim Report Comm; *office:* Batavia HS 260 State St Batavia NY 14020

SMILEY, BILLIE JO (FERRARI), Kindergarten Teacher; *b:* Brownsville, PA; *m:* Terry Lee; *c:* Shawn C. D.; *ed:* CA Univ of PA (BS) Elem Ed 1969; *cr:* Mc Guffey 4th Grd Tchr 1968-70, Kndgtn Tchr 1971-80, 2nd Grd Tchr 1980-84, 3rd Grd Tchr 1984-86, 2nd Grd Tchr 1986-93, Kndgtn Tchr 1993-; *ai:* MEA, PSEA, NEA 1970-; BPW, Treas, Pres, Local Correspondent; PTG, Treas; *home:* PO Box 308 West Alexander PA 15376

SMIRCICH, JANICE MONTALBANO, Eng, Lit & Rel Tchr; *b:* Queens, NY; *m:* John Paul; *c:* Mary Ellen, Susanne Mary; *ed:* Fordham Univ (BS) Elem Ed 1962, (MS) Elem Ed 1969; *cr:* St Fortunata Schl First Grd Tchr 4 Yrs; St Patrick's Military Acad Fifth Grd Tchr 5 Yrs; St Christopher's Schl Sixth Grd Eng, Soc Stud Tchr 3 Yrs; St Margaret Mary's Schl Rel Coord 8 Yrs; St Teresa of Avila Dir of Rel Ed 5 Yrs; Holy Cross Schl 5-8 Grd Eng Tchr 8 Yrs; *ai:* Campfire Girls Ldr 5 Yrs; Schl Newspaper 8 Yrs; Stu Spectrum Television Pgrm 6 Yrs; Western Turnpike Rescue Squad 1979-, Mem of Membership Comm; Parish Cncl 1986-, Trustee, Mem; Teresian House Nrsng Home 1992-, Vol, Pin of Svc; *home:* 60 Highland Dr Albany NY 12203*

SMIT, NANCY JEAN, Science Teacher; *b:* Erie, PA; *m:* Cees; *c:* Mark; *ed:* Edinboro Univ (BS) Sec Ed, Bio 1972; Earth Sci CertGannon Unvi; 30 Addl Hrs Masters Degree Equivalency; *cr:* Erie Schl Dist 6th-12th Grd Sci, 9th Grd Earth Sci, 10 Grd Bio Tchr 1973-; *ai:* NEA, PSEA, EEA 1974-; *office:* East HS 1151 Atkins St Erie PA 16503

SMITH, ALEXANDER JOHN, Teacher; *b:* Wilkesbarre, PA; *m:* Ann Deburi; *c:* Alex; *ed:* Montclair (BA) Psych 1973; Newark St (BA) Psych, Elem Ed 1973; Kean Coll (MA) Psych 1976; *cr:* Roselle Park MS Math, Soc Stud Tchr 22 Yrs; *ai:* MS, Town League Wrestling Coach; NJEA 1973-; NJ Governor's Outstdng Tchr Awd; *office:* Roselle Park MS Webster Ave Roselle Park NJ 07204*

SMITH, ALVA N., Retired Professor of Education; *b:* Lock Haven, PA; *m:* Carrie C.; *c:* Linda Stillings, Karen Shaffer, David, Dorothy Gibbs; *ed:* Lock Haven Univ (BS) Biological Sci 1955; Penn St Univ (MED) Biological Sci 1963, (DED) Scndry Ed 1971; *cr:* Lock Haven HS Bio Tchr 1957-73; Thiel Coll Ed Prof 1973-95; US Fish & Wildlife Asst Regnl Dir for Yth Prgms 1971-80; *ai:* Ed Dept Chprsn 9 Yrs; NASTA, PDK 1973-; NSF Flwshp; Pub Several Sci Articles; *home:* 3 Williamson Rd Greenville PA 16125*

SMITH, ALYCE M., Spanish & Speech Teacher; *b:* Gallipolis, OH; *ed:* Capital Univ (BA) Span, Ed 1969; OH Univ (MED) Educl Admin 1980; Post Grad Hrs Ed, Admin Univ of Louisville, Univ of MO, Coll of Mt St Joseph, Univ of Dayton, OH Univ; Paramedic Cert OH SEOEM Trng Prgm; *cr:* Jackson City Schls Tchr 1969-; SEOEMS Part-time Paramedic 1985-; *ai:* Pub Rel, Marshall Univ SCORES Coord; NEA, OEA, JCEA 1969-; OH Frgn Lang Assn; Eastern Star 1969-; Emblem Club 1970-, Organist; Garden Lovers Too 1994-, Sec; *office:* Jackson HS 21 Tropic St Jackson OH 45640

SMITH, AMY K., English Teacher; *b:* Englewood, NJ; *c:* Samantha, Alison; *ed:* Fairleigh Dickinson Univ (BS) Eng 1965; Long Island Univ (MS) Tech 1990; Attnd Univ of CA; *cr:* Ackerly HS Eng Tchr 1966-67; Ackerly Jr HS Eng, His Tchr 1968-69; Franklin Ave Jr HS Eng Tchr 1981; Mahwah HS Eng Tchr 1982-83; Ramapo HS Eng Tchr 1985-; *ai:* Tech, Lib Renovation Comm; Pvt Tutor; Acad Decathlon Tutor; Tennis Coach; NEA, NJEA 1985-; NCTE 1993-94; Dow Jones Flwshp in Jrnlsm Mentor Practice Tchrs; *office:* Ramapo HS George St Franklin Lakes NJ 07417

SMITH, ANIECE ODELIA, Business Teacher; *b:* New Orleans, LA; *c:* Michelle Lee, Michael Lee; *ed:* Southern Univ (BS) Bus 1963; 18 Addl Credit Hrs St Joseph Univ; *cr:* Southern Univ Sec to Dean 1963-64; Berean Inst Tchr 1964-68; J. W. Hallahan HS Tchr 1968-91; Archbishop Prendergast HS Tchr 1991-; *ai:* Coord VITA Prgm; NBEA; PBEA; NCEA; Urban Leabue, NAACP 1963-; Philadelphia Literacy Prgm 1990-; *office:* Archbishop Prendergast HS 1401 N Lansdowne Ave Drexel Hill PA 19026

SMITH, ANNE REIDELL, Eighth Grade Latin Teacher; *b:* Philadelphia, PA; *m:* Steven L; *ed:* Dickinson Coll (BA) Latin & Eng 1987; Villanova Univ (MA) Classical Stud 1989; Stanford Univ Intercollegiate Ctr Classical Stud Rome Italy 1985; Coll of Holy Cross Natl Endowment of Hum Summer Inst Polis & Res Publica, Classical Pol Theory & US Constitution 1990; *cr:* Notre Dame Acad 9th-12th Grd Latin, Greek & Archaeology Tchr 1987-94; The Shipley Schl 8th & 9th Grd Latin Tchr 1994-; *ai:* 8th Grd Adv; Tapes for Blind Svc & Buck Lane Day Care Svc Act; Field Hockey & Vlybl Coach; Philadelphia Classical Soc 1987-; Classical Assn of Atlantic Sts 1987-, E Adelaide Hahn Athens Schlsp 1991; Amer Classical League, Philadelphia Classical Assn, Ind Schl Tchrs Assn 1987-; Saint Josephs Univ Summer Classical Prgm Assoc Dir 1989, 1990, 1992 & 1994; Notre Dame Acad Yrbk, Newspaper, Soph Class & classical Club Moderator; *office:* The Shipley Schl 814 Yarrow St Bryn Mawr PA 19010

SMITH, ANNE TENNEY, Senior HS English Teacher; *b:* Jamestown, NY; *m:* James G.; *c:* David S. Tenney; *ed:* Edinboro St Univ (BS) Eng 1973, (MS) Eng 1977; *cr:* Southwestern Cntrl HS Eng Tchr 1973-; *ai:* Boys & Girls Var Tennis Coach; NEA & Southwestern Tchrs Assn 1973-; NY St Coaches Assn 1985-; Marvin Comm House 1990-; Vikings Diana Lodge 1989-; US Tennis Assn 1975-; Buffalo WKBW Channel 7 Coach of Yr Awd 1987; Scholastic Coach Magazine Natl HS Coaching Gold Awd 1988; NY St Coaches Assn Outstanding Achvmt Honor Awd 1993; Pub Poetry Bk 1988, 1994; *office:* Southwestern Central H S 600 Hunt Rd Jamestown NY 14701

SMITH, ANTHONY J., Heat, Vent & AC Dept Head; *b:* Brooklyn, NY; *m:* Nancy L.R.; *c:* Alicia; *ed:* Prof Tchng Cert; Attnd IBR Inst, Tech Careers Inst; *cr:* T&R Refrigeration Inc Owner 1975-80; Tech Careers Inst HVAC Dept Instr 1980-87; Platt Reg-Voc Tech Schl HVAC Dept Head 1987-; *ai:* AFT 1980-; KOFC 1986-, Treas, 4th Degree Awd; *office:* Platt Reg Voc-Tech Schl 600 Orange Ave Milford CT 06460

SMITH, ARTHUR J., Retired Biology Teacher; *b:* Buffalo, NY; *m:* Mary Eileen McMahon; *c:* Michael, Thomas, Sharon Vinett Madonna, Gregory; *ed:* St Bona Univ (BS) Bio 1960; Canisius Coll (MSEd) Sci Ed 1965; Attnd Buffalo St Coll; *cr:* South Park HS Tchr 1/2 Yr; Hamburg HS Tchr 2 Yrs; West Seneca West HS Tchr 32 Yrs; *ai:* 12 Yrs Sci Dept Chm; NHS Bookstore Adv 1965-; Golf Coach 1968-1970; Building Rep 1964-65; AP Bios Tchr 25 Yrs; AFT, NYSUT 1960-; NABT 1985-; West Seneca Tchr Assn 1963-; St Martins Church 1970; Usher Society; Holy Name Society; Nom Tchr of Yr; Honorary Induction NHS; Yrbk Dedicatee 1986, 1995.

SMITH, BARBARA SIMPSON, Spanish Teacher; *b:* Syracuse, NY; *c:* Peter; *ed:* Smith Coll at Northampton (BA) Sciology 1952; Attnd Syracuse Univ; Univ AZ at Guadalajara Post Grad Stud; *cr:* Amer Friends Svc Comm Workcamp Nayarit 1954; Childrens Court Probation Officer 1955; Canastota Cntrl Schl Span, Fr Tchr 1964-; *ai:* AFT, NY St Foreign Lang Tchrs Assn 1964-; *office:* Canastota Cntrl Jr Sr HS Robert St Canastota NY 13032

SMITH, BEN, Physics Teacher; *b:* Baltimore, MD; *m:* Lottie A.; *ed:* Lebanon Vly Coll (BS) Physics 1989; Pa St Univ (MED) Tchng & Curr 1996; *cr:* Red Lion HS Physics Tchr & Soccer Coach 1989-; *ai:* Soccer Coach; AAPT 1987; NSTA 1989; NEA 1989; 3 Yr Grant from Olin Flinchbaugh Charitable Trust; Participant Topics in Modern Physics Fermilab 1992; *office:* Red Lion Area Sr HS 200 Horace Mann Ave Red Lion PA 17356*

SMITH, BETTY PARKER, Fifth Grade Teacher; *b:* Honga, MD; *m:* Bruce C.; *c:* Jeremy; *ed:* Frostburg St Coll (BS) Elem Ed 1972; Frostburg St Univ (MA) Elem Ed, Rdng Specialist 1977; Addl 21 Credit Hrs; *cr:* Rt 40 Elem Schl 5th Grd Tchr 1972-; *ai:* Garrett Co Tchrs Assn, MD St Tchrs Assn, NEA 1972-; Western MD Rdng Cncl 1990-; Delta Kappa Gamma Womens Soc Women Educators 1978-, Treas 1979-84; *office:* Rt 40 Elem Schl 17764 National Pike Frostburg MD 21532

SMITH, BONNIE GERALYN, 4th Grd Teacher & Elem Coord; *b:* Portsmouth, VA; *ed:* SUNY Coll at Cortland (BS) PE, Elem Ed 1978; SUNY Coll at Buffalo (MS) Elem Curr 1983; CAS, Admin; *cr:* West Vly Cntrl Schl Vlybl, Sftbl Coach 1979-94, Elem Coord 1982-, Elem Tchr Grd 4 1979-; *ai:* Tech Team; Stu Achvmt for Excl Comm; Shared Decision Making Plng Team; Section VI Vlybl Chprsn; Delta Kappa Gamma 1992-; West Vly Tchr Assn, NYSUT, AFT 1979-, Local VP; World Univ Games Buffalo NY 1993, Vol, Chair Vlybl Statis; Atlanta Summer Olympics 1996, Vol; Thanks to Tchr Apple Cmptr Awd 1992; *office:* West Valley Cntrl HS PO Box 290 School St West Valley NY 14171*

SMITH, BONNIE WILSON, English Teacher; *b:* Steubenville, OH; *c:* David, Peggy; *ed:* Steubenville Univ (BA) Eng 1973; Univ of Dayton (MST) Tchng, Ed 1981; Youngstown St Univ Towards MA in Eng; *cr:* Indian Creek HS Eng Instr 21 Yrs; *ai:* Prins Advy Comm; AP Eng Adv; NHS Selection, Schlsp Comms; NEA 1985-; Phi Alpha Kappa; Baconian Soc; *office:* Indian Creek HS 200 Park Dr Wintersville OH 43952

SMITH, BRIAN THOMAS, Soc Stud, World His, Geog Tchr; *b:* Cleveland, OH; *m:* Kriste DeAnna; *c:* Jacob; *ed:* Bowling Green St Univ (BA) Pol Sci 1989; Cleveland St Univ Comprehensive Soc Stud Tchng Cert 1991; 32 Addl Quarter Hrs in Ed Soc Stud Curr & Instruction; *cr:* North Royalton HS Soc Stud Tchr 1992-93; Brecksville-Broadview Heights HS Soc Stud Tchr 1993-; *ai:* Var Asst Ft, Head JV Ftbl, Head 9th Grd Girls Sftbl Coach; *office:* Brecksville-Broadview Hts HS 6376 Mill Rd Broadview Heights OH 44147*

SMITH, C. KENDALL, Elementary Social Studies Tchr; *b:* Cleveland, OH; *m:* Dot Ann; *ed:* Heidelberg Coll (BA) Elem Ed 1961; Bowling Green St Univ Rdng Specialist 1975; Univ of Toledo Post Grad Work; *cr:* Thompson Local Schls Tchr 1959-65; Monroeville Schls Tchr 19 EHOVE Career Ctr Admin 1971-89; St Paul Elem Schl Tchr 199 North Cntrl Sci Soc; Soc Stud Curr Comm; NDEA, HCRTA 1990- 1959-; Monroeville Teach 1966-, Pres; Monroeville Bd of Pub 1978-82; Milan Chamber of Commerce 1981-; BSA 1972-74, Ldr; 12 Fairoaks Dr Milan OH 44846

SMITH, C. WAYNE, World History Teacher; *b:* East Orange, NJ; *m* Douglas; *c:* Scott, Christopher, Brett; *ed:* Muskingum Coll (BA) His Ashland Univ (MED) Ed 1991; Attnd John Carrol Univ, Bostor Cleveland St; *cr:* Euclid Sr HS His Tchr 1962-; *ai:* Close Up Clu Close Up Comm Coord; OEA, NEA 1962-; NEOCA; ETA; South Recreation Comm 1986-, Pres 1988-95; Euclid Mens Bowling 1978-84, Pres; Civic Citation for Saving Family in Fire 1985-; Holding Jennings 1974; Cncl on Human Relations Schlsp 1968; Cl Japan Participant 1993; *office:* Euclid Sr HS 711 E 222nd St Eucl 44123

SMITH, CARL D., Math Instr & Department Chair; *b:* Mifflintow *c:* Grace A., Carri A.; *ed:* Shippensburg Univ (BS) Math 1969, (MS 1974; Grad Credits at PA St Univ; *cr:* West Perry HS Math Instr & Chair 27 Yrs; *ai:* Math Competition Team Adv; NEA, PSEA, WPEA NCTM, PCTM 1985-; Lions Club 1975-, Sec, Treas; Shermans Heritage Assn 1985-; *office:* West Perry HS Rd 1 Box 7 Elliottsb 17024

SMITH, CAROL S., Health, PE Teacher & Ath Dir; *b:* Frederick, M Jerome Wilcom; *c:* Kami Culb; *ed:* Frostburg St Coll (BA) Hlth, PE Western MD Coll (MA) Ed 1974; 3 Credit Hrs Aides & Teens; 3 Cre Juvenile Delinquency; 3 Credit Hrs First Aid Instr; 3 Credit Hrs CP Trainer; *cr:* Brunswick HS Dept Head Tchr 28 Yrs, Ath Dir 12 Yrs; Boys & Girls Golf Coach; Var Girls Track & Field; NEA 1966-; 1966-, St Hnrs, Awds; FCAHPER 1966-, Dist Awd 1974; Kappa Kap 1968-; Red Cross 1966-; Amer Heart Assn 1966-; YMCA Local Bd Dist Outstdng Tchr 1974; Inducted into Fred Co Hall of Fame of Sp Ath Dir 1996; *office:* Brunswick HS 101 Cummings Dr Brunswic 21716*

SMITH, CAROL ANN BARONE, Business Education Teach Sandusky, OH; *m:* Richard A.; *c:* Angela Edith Kurtz, Rosalyn Lee Scot Allen, Richard John, Christopher Paul; *ed:* Bowling Green Univ Ed 1972, (MA) Bus Ed 1976; 30 Hrs Post Grad Stud Educl Tech, Cor Trng Univ of Toledo; *cr:* St Paul HS Bus Tchr 1972-75; Sandusky HS Ed Tchr 1972-80; Perkins HS Bus, Soc Stud Tchr 1976-; Norwalk HS Ed Tchr 1974-75; *ai:* Tennis Coach 1972-80; Sr, Jr, Frosh Class Ac Dir; Mat Maid Adv; PEA, OEA, NEA 1976-; Pi Omega Pi 1970-; Ph Kappa 1988-, Newsletter Ed 1988-94; Kiwanis 1990-; St Theate 1988-; Italian-Amer Beneficial Club 1986-, Pres 1995-; Awded Write Stu Act Handbook; *office:* Perkins HS 3714 S Campbell Sa OH 44870*

SMITH, CATHERINE D., Dean of Students; *b:* Columbus, OH; *ed* of Toledo Ath Admin 1989; Post Grad Work Ed Admin Toward Prin & Specialist Degree; *cr:* DeVillaiss HS Hlth Ed Tchr 1983-84; N Hale Elem PE Tchr 1984-88; Leverette Jr High Hlth & PE Tchr 19 McTigue Jr High Dean of Stdnts 1994-; *ai:* Conflict Mediation Pgr Character Counts Trainer for Dist; Ath Trainer; NATA 1981-; TAAP Phi Delta Kappa 1996; Toledo Ski Club 1988-.

SMITH, CHARLES RICHARD, Advanced Biology Teache Kittanning, PA; *m:* Elaine L. Busofsky; *c:* Carolyn, Elizabeth, Ma Daniel; *ed:* IUP (MED) Bio 1978; Penn St 24 Credit Hrs; Westmo Comm Coll 6 Credit Hrs; Univ of IA 12 Credit Hrs; *cr:* Ford City H Tchr 1970-90; Kiski Area Summer Schl Tchr 1976-; Kittannin Advanced Bio Tchr 1990-; *ai:* Soph Class Adv; Spon Sci Olympic Asst Ftbl Coach; Ticket Salesman; PSEA 1970-, Treas 2 Yrs; NEA Knights of Columbus 1986-, Deputy Grand Knight, Recorder; League 1985-, Asst Coach, Scorekeeper; NSF Grant 1974 Univ *office:* Kittanning Sr HS 1200 Orr Ave Kittanning PA 16201

SMITH, CHERYL CANFIELD, Science & Photography Teach Wellsboro, PA; *m:* Mark A.; *c:* Kimberly J., Krista J.; *ed:* Lycomin (BA) Cum Laude 1973; Divine Providence Hospital (ASCP) Medica 1973; Lycoming Coll Post BA Tchng Cert 1986; Mid-Mgmt Course Robert Packer Hospital Medical Technician & Hematology Supvr 19 Williamsport Hospital Medical Technician 1981-84; Montgomery Schls Phys Sci & Envronmental Sci Tchr 1987; S Williamsport Are HS Bio II, Research Bio & Physiology Tchr 1987-; Penn Coll of Adjunct Fac 1992-; *ai:* Sr Class Adv, Yrbk Co-Adv; SCUBA; PSEA & 1987-; MTASCP 1973-; Habitat for Humanity 1992; Audubon Soc & Wildlife 1990-; SADD Prgms Hwy Safety Awds; Several Credit Hematology Seminars; Penn Coll Adjunct Fac Excl in Tchng Awd *office:* S Williamsport Area Jr Sr HS 700 Percy St South Williamsp 17701

SMITH, CHERYL LORENA, Third Grade Teacher; *b:* Oakland, M Frostburg St Univ (BS) Early Childhood Ed 1978, (MS) Ed, Adn Supervision 1984; *cr:* Friendsville Elem Schl First Grd Tchr 1978-7 House Elem Schl 1-3 Grd Tchr 1979-90; Dennett Rd Elem Schl Thi Tchr 1990-; *ai:* Garrett Co Tchrs Assn 1978-, Exec Bd; MD St Tchr NEA 1978-; Crellin Assembly of God 1994-; *office:* Dennett Road Schl 1217 Dennett Rd Oakland MD 21550

SMITH, CLAIRE D., Religion Dept Chairperson; *b:* Staten Island *m:* Harold J.; *c:* Douglas, Brian; *ed:* Pace Univ (BBA) Mngmt, Fi 1965; St Joseph's Coll (MA) Rel Ed 1986; *cr:* Our Lady Star of Sea C Dir of Rel Ed 1983-93; Msgr Farrell HS Tchr 1990-; *ai:* NCEA *office:* Monsignor Farrell HS 2900 Amboy Rd Staten Island NY 103

SMITH, CLAIRE F., Fourth Grade Teacher; *b:* Yonkers, NY; *c:* Mi Megan; *ed:* Brooklyn Coll (BA) Psych 1964; Long Island Univ Counseling & Guidance 1996; *cr:* Saint Jeromes Elem 4th Grd Tchr Our Lady of Peace Elem 3rd Grd Tchr 1965; Pub Schl 114 Ryder 1966; *office:* PS 114 Ryder 1077 Remsen Ave Brooklyn NY 11236

SMITH, COLLEEN JONES, Special Education Teacher; *b:* Montgo AL; *m:* Edward Charles; *c:* Yvette Selene Jones; *ed:* Univ of Cinc (BS) Criminal Justice, Hlth Care Admin 1978, (MS) Ed 1985; Ec Gra Career Ed CEV; Educl Confs; *cr:* Comm Mutual Sr Claims Pro 1967-75; Intnl Halfway House Admin Asst 1978-79; Cincinnati Co for People with Disabilities Supvr Advocate 1979-80; Cincinnati Pub Career Tchr 1980-; *ai:* Career Ed Specialist; Write to Read C Parent-Stu Mentor, Cnslr; AFT, OH Career Ed Assn 1986-; Alumni Univ of Cincinnati 1979-; Cincinnati Museum Ctr 1993-, Tour Guide of Cincinnati 1991-, Mayor's Summit on Ed, Adv; Young Scholar 1990-, Spon, Mentor; Local Schl Advy 1987-88, Schl Rep; Hamilto Municipal Ct 1982-, Vol, Probation, Ct Ofcr; Grad Minority Fellow Consultant Greater Cincinnati Ctr Ec Ed; Panelist Career Ed Task F Presentor Wkshps; Article Pub; Served on US Dept Ed Blue Ribbon Excl Prgm; *home:* 10666 Gloria Ave Cincinnati OH 45231*

SMITH, CORINNE ISAAC, English Teacher; *b:* Cleveland, OH; *m:* Raymond; *c:* Heather; *ed:* BLSU (BAEd) Eng 1969; Xavier Univ Scndry Ed 1992; Mentor Prgm 9 Hrs 1991; *cr:* Waukegan HS Eng 1969-71; Montourseville HS Eng Tchr 1971-72; Kings HS Eng Tchr 1 *ai:* Lit Magazine Adv 1988-; NCET 1988-; OCET; KEA; Miami Uni Writing Project Fellowship 1990; Project Excl in Tchng Warren Cty

H, CURTIS ALAN, Fifth Grade Teacher; b: Akron, OH; m: Sharon ing; c: Stephanie, Chad; ed: Univ of Akron (BS) Elem Ed 1979; Attnd nd Univ; cr: Akron Pub Schls Auxiliary Svcs Tutor 1972-82; na Chrstn Acad Tchr 1982-86; Akron Pub Schls ECIA Tutor 1986-87, 1987-; ai: Cmptr Network Admn; Peer Mediation Supvr; Sci Coord; doption Comm; Tchr of Yr 1992; PTA Outstdng Edctr 1992; rship Fnd Grant 1993-94, 1995-; office: Essex Elem Schl 1160 irst Dr Akron OH 44313

H, DANA FREDERICK, History Teacher; b: Burbank, CA; m: Perez; c: Analisa, Alex, Adam; ed: Sacramento St Univ (BA) His, Park Admin 1977; Boston Coll (MAT) His 1985; Minor in Rec, Park n 1977; ai: Asst Track Coach; Harvard Model Congress Prgm oderator; NHS Selection Comm; Schl of Ed Guest Speaker; office: Johns Prep Schl 72 Spring St Danvers MA 01923*

H, DANIEL J., 6th Grd Soc Stud & Rdng Tchr; b: Rochester, NY; aron; c: Bradley, Trevor; ed: SUNY at Oswego (BS) Scndry Ed 1986; at Brockport (MA) Lbrl Stud 1990; cr: Churchville Chili MS 6th chr 1986-; ai: Ski Club Co-Adv; Ashokan Outdoor Environment Adv; 1986-.*

H, DARRELL WAYNE, History & Bible Teacher; b: Pontiac, MI; tricia Ann Cook; c: Christopher, Paul; ed: Bob Jones Univ (BA) His 1979; cr: Heritage Bapt Church Pastor 1979-; Heritage Chrstn His, Bible Tchr 1988-; ai: AACS 1988-; Garden St Assn Chrstn Schls , VP; office: Heritage Christian Acad 530 Union Mill Rd Mount NJ 08054

H, DARRYL J., English Teacher; b: Allentown, PA; m: Bonnie Smith; c: Daniel, Laura, Erin; ed: Kutztown St Coll (BA) Eng 1965; own Univ (MS) Eng 1972; Post Grad Stud Univ of AK 6 Credits, sburg St Coll 9 Credits; cr: Souderton Area HS Eng Tchr 1966-; ai: Ftbl Coach; Russell Galt Awd for Excl in Tchng; Chprsn Eng Dept 93; office: Souderton Area HS 41 N School Ln Souderton PA 18964

H, DAVID ALBERT, Retired Teacher; b: Brockton, MA; m: Joyce es; c: Susan Forbes, David A. Jr.; ed: Fitchburg St Coll (BS) Elem 83; cr: US Army Spec Forces, Battalion SGM 28 Yrs; ai: Assoc of rmy 1955-; VFW, Amer Legion 1955-; home: 142 Townsend St rell MA 01463

H, DAVID ALLEN, Chemistry Tchr & Sci Dept Chm; b: Reading, : Nancy A. Hess; c: Lauren C.; ed: Alvernia Coll (BS) Chem & y Ed 1980; Wilkes Coll Post Grad Credits; Berks Co Intermediate A Dept of Ed In Service Credits; cr: Schuylkill Valley HS Chem Instr , Sci Dept Chm & Chem Tchr 1989-; ai: Coord SSIP 1982-84; NEA, 1980-; NSTA 1982-92; office: Schuylkill Valley H S RR #2 Box 2165 ort PA 19533

H, DAVID ARTHUR, Biology Teacher; b: Troy, NY; m: Barbara ; c: Dane Andrew, Bradley Cooper; ed: SUNY at Albany (BS) Bio & 1971, (MS) Bio & Ed 1976; Union Coll 6 Grad Hrs; cr: WK Doyle ife Sci Tchr 1971-82; Troy HS Bio Tchr 1983-; Russell Sage Coll nct Prof of Ed 1995; ai: Authorship Bio Variance & Final ination; AFT, NYSUT 1971-; Natl Bio Tchrs Assn 1988-, Book wer; BSA 1996-, Den Ldr; Christ Comm Reformed Church 1990-, Ministries Comm; Natl Sci Tchrs Assn Natl Cert in Bio, Gen Sci for Tchr in Research Fellowship Union Coll NSF; Fellowship from cular Bio & Cell Bio Assn, Fellowship from Amer Physiology Assn, wship from General Electric Corp, 2 Patents Pending; office: Troy HS Burdett Ave Troy NY 12180

H, DAVID B., Pgm Leader of Soc Stud Dept; b: Melrose, MA; m: Hoyt-Smith; c: Kevin D., Thomas, Timothy, Gerald; ed: Univ of ME ono (BED) His, PE 1968, (MED) His 1969; 15 Hrs Admin, Soc Stud St, Univ Southern ME; cr: Stearns HS Var Bsktbl, PE Tchr 1972-74; ley Jr HS Hlth Tchr, Var Bsktbl 1974-86; Winchester HS Var Bsktbl 90; Gloucester HS His Tchr 1986-; ai: Stu Cncl, Coll Bowl Adv; Soc Prgm Ldr; NEA 1972-; Gloucester Tchrs Assn 1974-; office: ester HS Leslie O. Johnson Rd Gloucester MA 01930*

H, DAVID C.,JR., Sci Dept Chair & Biology Tchr; b: Lancaster, PA; ay; c: Nicole, David n.; ed: Gettysburg Coll (BA) Bio 1962; ensburg Univ (MED) Bio 1976; Attnd Lebanon Coll, Elizabethtown cr: Lower Dauphin Sr HS Bio Tchr 1963-, Sci Dept Chair 1967-; ai: Cncl Intnl Stud For Travel Coord 1969-; NEA; PSEA; AIFS, ACIS ; Scndry Classroom Tchng Awd 1981; Pub Work Contributions to mmended Sci Competency Continuum of PA Schls 1987; PA Dept of Ct Dept Consultant Re Learning Project Coalition of Essential Schls 90; St of CT Dept of Ed Consultants Common Core of Learning rmance Assessment Project 1990-91; office: Lower Dauphin Sr HS Hanover St Hummelstown PA 17036

H, DAVID JEFFERY, Social Studies Teacher; b: Logan, OH; m: Marie Christian; ed: Univ of Toledo (MS) Ed 1994; cr: Anthony e Elem Schl 3rd Grd Tchr 1975-76; Shoreland Elem Schl 7th Grd 1976-80; Wernert Elem Schl 6th Grd Tchr 1984-90; Jefferson Jr HS rd Tchr 1980-84, 1990-; ai: Asst Coach Ftbl 16 Yrs, Girls Track 18 Frosh Girls Bsktbl 10 Yrs; NEA, OEA, TAWLS 1976-; ASCD 1993-; : Jefferson Jr HS 5530 Whitmer Dr Toledo OH 43613*

H, DAVID JOSEPH, Asst Prof of Paralegal Stud; b: Baltimore, MD; na Thea Choudhary; c: Lorenzo Joseph; ed: The Amer Univ (BA) Pol & Urban Affairs 1982; Univ Baltimore (JD) Law 1984; Natl Ctr caton Ed 1989; cr: Villa Julie Coll Asst Prof & Lecturer 1989-93; on St Univ Lecturer 1989-90, Atty At Law 1985-, Mediator 1993-; rd Comm Coll Asst Prof 1992-; ai: Paralegal Stud Assn Adv; AAFPE ; MSBA 1985-; AFM 1992-; Legal Research & Writing Book Delmar , MD Family Law Monthly 1991 Article; office: Harford Comm Coll Thomas Run Rd Bel Air MD 21015

H, DEBORAH VERPLANCK, English Teacher; b: Norwich, NY; aniel R. Abbasi; c: Jordan V.; ed: Wellesley Coll (BA) Pol Sci, Fr Harvard Grad Schl of Ed (EDM) Ed 1991; Bread Loaf Schl of Eng Eng 1994; cr: Hamlin Schl Fr, Eng Tchr, Dir of Publications -90; Aspect Intnl Lang Schl ESL Tchr 1991-92; Bryn Mawr Schl 9-12 Eng Tchr 1992-; ai: Pol Awareness Club Fac Adv; Scheduling, Gender xuality, Summer Rdng Comms; office: Bryn Mawr Schl 109 W ose Ave Baltimore MD 21210

H, DEBORAH Y., Reading Specialist; b: Bristol, VA; m: Charles; c: r Phillips, Eric Phillips; ed: Wilberforce Univ (BSEd) Elem Ed 1963; eland St Univ (MSEd) Rdng Curr, Instruction; cr: Wade Park Elem Grd 2 Tchr 1963-68; Mary B. Martin Elem Schl Follow Through -71; Paul L. Dunbar Elem Schl Grd 3 Tchr 1972-82, Listening Tchr -90, Rdng Specialist Title I Tchr 1990-; ai: Vol Tutor Transitional ing 1995; Asst Fin Sec Shaker Hghts Comm Church 1995-, Exec Bd -94; AFT, Cleveland Fed of Tchrs 1963-; Delta Sigma Theta 1961-; eland Bd of Ed Title I Rep in Wash DC Natl Recognition Prgm Title I olwide Svc; office: Paul L Dunbar Elem Schl 2200 W 28th St eland OH 44113

H, DELORES JANE HADDEN, Special Education Teacher; b: klyn, NY; m: Lawrence Howard; c: La Chaune Eulaique Tinsley; ed: Comm Coll (AA) Lbrl Arts; Brooklyn Coll (BA) Elem Ed 1991; vioral Mngmt 6 Credits; Working on Spec Ed MS; Coll of St Rose CH, Cooperative Learning 6 Credits; cr: Family Planning Ctr Dr Asst, ptionist 1967-69; Nathan Hale MS 293 Para 1969; Bethel Day Care Ctr Group Tchr 1985-92; Nathan Hale MS 293 Spec Ed Tchr 1991-; ai: Gen Org, Modeling Group Coord; Choir Directress; Retirement Comm; Chrldrs, UNICEF Adv; Day Care Ctr Toy Drive; Cobble Hill Nrsng Home Supplies Drive; AFT 1991-; Colony House, Adv; Yth United 1991- Advy Bd; SNAP 1993-; Yth Ministry 1990-, Advy Bd; Bethel BC 1985-, Bd of Trustees, Recording Sec; Mass Choir 1972; Mothers Club; office: Nathan Hale MS 293 284 Baltic St Brooklyn NY 11201

SMITH, DELVER B., English Teacher; b: Weymouth, England; m: Jeanne L. Steele; c: Felicia Fosmire, Tain Schlesman, Melissa; ed: CA Univ of PA (BS) Eng 1967; IN Univ of PA (MS) Eng 1973; PHD Eng Prgm; cr: Hempfield Area Schl Dist Eng Tchr 1967-; ai: NEA 1967-.

SMITH, DENISE ARRIGO, Spanish Teacher; b: Millville, NJ; m: Ronald W.; c: Jared, Amanda; ed: Cumberland Cnty Coll (AA) Lbrl Arts 1972; Montclair St Coll (BA) Span 1974; Post-Grad Studs Rutgers Univ, Glassboro St Coll & Jersey City St Coll; cr: Millville Elem Schls Biling & ESL Tchr 1975-91; Millville Sr HS Span Tchr 1992-; ai: Span Club Adv; Natural Helpers Ldr; Dist Bldg Rep Planning Comm; NEA & Local Affiliates 1975-; ACTFL 1996; Millville 1st Church of the Nazarene 1985-, Sec of Bd; NJ Governors Awd for Excl in Tchng 1977-79; Served on NJ Commisioner of Ed; Advy Comm on Biling Ed; home: 203 Kenyon Ave Millville NJ 08332*

SMITH, DENISE DARROW, High Schl Mathematics Teacher; b: Schenectady, NY; m: Keith H.; c: Jeremy James, Jennifer Lynne; ed: St Univ Coll at Oneonta (BS) Elem Ed & Early Scndry Ed 1977; 30 Grad Hrs at Manhatten Coll, Coll of St Rose, Univ of Albany; cr: Highland Chrstn Mission Tchr & Missionary 1977-79; Averill Park HS Math Tchr 1979-; ai: Soph Class Adv; Drug & Alcohol Abuse Comm; PTO Comm; NYSUT 1979-; AFT 1979-; AMTNYS 1993-; office: Averill Park HS 16 Gettle Rd Averill Park NY 12018

SMITH, DENNIS GREYLING, Music Teacher; b: Bethlehem, PA; m: Joanne Jordan; c: Jordan; ed: West Chester St Coll (BS) Music Ed 1976; West Chester Univ (MS) Music Theory 1990; Attnd Berklee Coll of Music, Hartt Schl of Music, Westminster Choir Coll; cr: Saucon Vly Schl Dist Music Ed Tchr 1977-; ai: SVHS Jazz & Show Ensemble Dir; Saucon Vly Educ Assn 1977-; NEA, MENC & PMEA 1977-; Pi Kappa Lambda 1991-; office: Saucon Vly Schl Dist 1050 Main St Hellertown PA 18055

SMITH, DIANA MASSON, English Teacher; b: Grove City, PA; m: Frank Fred; c: Jennifer, Adam; ed: IN Univ of PA (BS) Eng Ed 1971; Slippery Rock Univ 9 Hrs; Edithboro Univ 9 Hrs; cr: Cochranton HS Eng Tchr 1971-85; Meadville HS Eng Tchr 1985-; ai: Newspaper, Key Club Adv; NEA, PSEA 1971-; NCTE; NEH Lit Inst 1985; home: RR 8 Box 676 Meadville PA 16335

SMITH, DIANE B. (VINCI), Second Grade Teacher; b: New York City, NY; m: Arthur J.; c: Jennifer, Shannon; ed: Hunter Coll (BA) Sociology, Ed 1964; C. W. Post Univ (BS) Spec Ed 1982; 30 Credit Hrs Post Grad Work; cr: Gardiner Manor Elem Tchr 1965-71; Mary G. Clarkson Elem Schl Tchr 1984-; ai: Schl Improvement Team; Stu Activity Fund for Stony Brook Unitarian Universalists; Nassau Cty Rdng Assn; Phi Beta Kappa; Little Shelter Animal Rescue, Vol.

SMITH, DONALD F., Science Teacher; b: New York City, NY; ed: NY Univ (BFA) Film & Television 1982; St Univ of NY at Cortland (MSEd) Sci Ed 1991; cr: Pablo Casals Intermediate Schl Sci Tchr 1986-90; Newfield Central Schl Sci Tchr 1992-; ai: NYSUT 1992-; STANYS 1993-; office: Newfield Elem Schl 247 Main St Newfield NY 14867

SMITH, DOUGLAS WILLIAM, Science Teacher; b: Johnstown, PA; m: Janet Johnson; c: Erik, Jonathan, Todd; ed: Slippery Rock (BS) Elem Ed 1975; 28 Hrs Ed; cr: Forest Hills Summerhill Elem Schl 3 Grd Tchr 1975-76; Forest Hills Elem Schl 3 Grd Tchr 1976-88; Forest Hills MS 6-7 Grd Sci Tchr 1988-; ai: Sr HS Ski Club Adv; Stu Assistance, Instrl Support Team; FHEA 1975-, Past Pres; PSEA 1975-; PA Stu Assistance Profs 1991-; Church Cncl, Past Pres; Cub Scout Ldr; Little League Coach; office: Forest Hills MS 1427 Frankstown Rd Sidman PA 15955

SMITH, DUELLA, Substance Abuse Counselor; b: Raleigh, NC; m: Duella Lewis; c: Geneva, Michael, Bianca Washington, Ababach J.; cr: Dist 23 Substance Abuse Prevention Specialist & Cnslr 1982-85; Attendance Imp Pgm Cnslr 1985-90; SPINS Dist 23 Credential St Cnslr 1990-95; ai: Cntrl Bklyn Mobilization 1975-, Sec & Bookkeeper, Congressmen Owens; home: 1371 Linden Blvd Apt 6A Brooklyn NY 11212

SMITH, ELAINE SPRAGUE, Home Ec, Fam & Cnsumr Sci Tchr; b: Jamestown, NY; m: Kenneth M.; c: Michael B.C.; ed: Buffalo St Coll (BS) Home Ec Ed 1985; SUNY Oneonta (MS) Home Ec Ed 1993; Courses in Amer Sign Lang; cr: Deer Run Resort Condo Mgr 1985-87; Charlotte Vly Cntrl Schl Home Ec Tchr Long Term Sub 1986-87; Stamford Cntrl Schl Home Ec, FCS Tchr 1987-; ai: FHA, HERO Adv; Team Prep; STA Prof Stan Comm; Prom Adv; Stamford Tchrs Assn 1987-, Comm Chair; NY St Assn of Family, Consumers Sci Edctrs 1988-; Phi Upsilon Omicron 1983-; Delta Kappa Gamma 1990-; Stamford United Meth Church 1988-; Admin Cncl; Grange 1977-, Various Local, Cntry; Young Granger of Yr; 4H Local Ldr 1994-, Local Ldr; SHARE Food Coop 1992-; office: Stamford Central Schl 1 River St Stamford NY 12167

SMITH, ELVIRA MARIA, French & Spanish Teacher; b: West Chester, PA; m: Dwight S. Jr.; c: Christopher, Matthew; ed: Millersville Univ (BS) Fr; Masters Equivalenc Cert 1986; Jr Yr Abroad West Chester Univ 1976-77; Summer Grad Prgm Millersville Univ 1982, 1st Yr Stu Awd 1982; cr: Great Vly HS Fr Tchr 1978-86; Northeast HS Fr, Span Tchr 1988-89; Harford Comm Coll Fr Tchr 1992-; C Milton Wright HS Fr, Span, Eng Tchr 1992-; ai: NEA 1994-; St Ignacious Church CCD Kndgtn Tchr 1995-; office: C Milton Wright HS 1301 N Fountain Green Rd Bel Air MD 21015*

SMITH, EMMA L., Global Studies Teacher; b: Savanac Lake, NY; ed: LeMoyne Coll (BS) His 1964; St Univ of NY at Potsdam (MS) Scndry His 1973; Cornell Univ 30 Inservice Credits; Univ of HI at Honolulu 24 Credits; Elmira Coll 3 Credits; SUNY at Oneonta 3 Credits; cr: Hounsfield Cntrl Schl 7th-8th Grd US His & Eng Tchr 1964-66; Watkins Glen MS 8th Grd US His Tchr 1966-81; Watkins Glen HS US His & Global Stud I Tchr 1981-; ai: HS & Dist Excl Comms 1986-94; Dist Planning Comm for Shared Decision-Making 1994-; HS Shared Decision-Making Bldg Team 1995-: NHS Co-Adv; US His & Global Stud RCT Remediation; NYSUT 1966-; 5 Counties Soc Stud Cncl 1970-; NY Geographic Alliance 1991-; Cath Daughters of Amer 1966-, Treas; office: Watkins Glen HS 301 12th St Watkins Glen NY 14891

SMITH, ERNESTINE, Teacher; b: Gallispolis, OH; m: Keith; c: Shelly, Carita; ed: Rio Grande Coll (BS) Math 1970; Univ of Dayton Masters Cnslng 1991; cr: Kyger Creek HS Tchr 1970-92; River Valley HS Tchr 1992-; ai: Frosh Class Adv; NEA, OEA 1975-; 4-H Adv; Scndry Tch of Yr by Gallia Cty 1989; Acad Excl Fnd 1991-92 Jennings Scholar; office: River Valley HS 1482 Little Kyger Rd Cheshire OH 45620

SMITH, ESTHER RUTH (HORST), Math & Chemistry Teacher; b: Hagerstown, MD; m: William Wayne; c: Timothy, Daniel, Rachel; ed: Eastern Mennonite Coll (BS) Bio 1973; Addl 27 Credit Hrs at Western MD coll; cr: Heritage Chrstn Acad Sci Tchr 1972-73; Mt Airy Mennonite Schl Prin, Tchr 1986-87; Mt Airy Full Gospel Chrstn Schl Sci, Math Tchr 1988-91; New life Chrstn Schl Math, Chem Tchr 1991-; ai: NCTM 1990-; Goshen Mennonite Church 1963-, Sunday Schl Tchr; office: New Life Christian Schl 5913 Jefferson Pike Frederick MD 21702

SMITH, EVELYN M., Fourth Grade Teacher; b: Rehrersburg, PA; ed: Kutztown Univ (BS) Elem Ed 1957; Temple Univ (MED) Elem Ed 1961; Admin Cert Elem Prin 1986; 60 Grad Credits Above Masters Penn St Univ, West Chester, Millersville; Lancaster Real Estate Inst Grad 1984; cr: Tulpehocken Elem Schl Third, Fourth Grd Tchr 1957-58, Fourth Grd Tchr 1958-85, Prin 1965-75; Bethel Elem Ctr Fourth Grd Tchr 1985-; ai: Career Ed, Assembly Comm; Tulpehocken Ed Assn 1957-; PSEA 1957-, Cty, St, NEA 1957-, Del; Bethel-Tulpehocken Lib 1960-, Trustee; Church Cncl 1990-; Tulpehocken Settlement Historical Soc 1960-; Outstdng Tchrs of Amer 1973; Red Cross Spon 1965-75; home: PO Box 125 Lancaster Ave Mount Aetna PA 19544*

SMITH, FORREST JOSEPH, Biology & Anthropology Prof; b: Barberton, OH; m: Monica Harrison; c: Jacob, Joseph; ed: Hiram Coll (BA) Bio 1973; Purdue Univ (MS) Bio 1974; Kent St Univ (MA) Anthropology 1982; Degree Candidate Biological Anthropology; cr: Wayne Coll Instr 1975-; Univ of Akron Instr 1975-; ai: Co-Adv Phi Theta Kappa Coord Bio, Geology, Anthropology; Amer Anthro Assn 1988-, Exec Bd; Soc Anthropology Comm 1988-, Pres; OH Acad Col Sci 1988-93, Area VP Soc, Anth; Clinton Canal Comm 1995-; Medina Writers Club 1979-; Internal Grants; Presentations Bio & Anthro Local, St, Natl Levels; Numerous Articles Pub; Recd Intnl Notice Co-Discovery Fossil Mastadon with Stone Tools Nearby; office: Univ Of Akron-Wayne Coll 1901 Smucker Rd Orrville OH 44667*

SMITH, FREDERICK C. J., Dir of PE & Athletics Coach; b: Glen Cove, NY; m: Virginia Wunsch; c: Holly Kromer, Kim, Kevin; ed: Cortland St Coll (BS) Hlth & PE 1959; Hofstra Univ (MS) Guidance & Counseling 1966; NY Univ Dir of PE & Ath in PE & Ath 1966; cr: Friends Acad Dir of PE & Ath & Ftbl, Wrestling & Track Head Coach 1959-67; Cold Spring Harbor Schl Dist PE Tchr & Ftbl Head Coach 1967-69; Locust Valley Cntrl Schl Dist PE Tchr & Ftbl Head Coach 1969-80, Dir of PE & Ath & Ftbl Head Coach 1980-; ai: 50 Athletic Teams Admin; Intramural Prgm Dist Admin; AAHPRD, NYSAHPERD 1967-; NYSAAA 1987-, Section VIII Athletic Admin of Yr Awd 1992; Nassau Cty HS Ftbl Coaches Assn, Pres 1973, Coach of Yr Awd 1985; Conf IV Ftbl Coach of Yr 1984, 1986, 1987 & 1988; Newsday Ftbl Coach of Yr 1985; Journal Amer Metropolitan NY Private Schl Ftbl Coach of Yr 1965; office: Locust Valley Jr-Sr HS Horse Hollow Rd Locust Valley NY 11560

SMITH, FREDERICK STANTON, English Teacher; b: Jersey City, NJ; m: Elizabeth J. Baker; c: Matthew, Rebecca, Bethany, Geoffrey; ed: Canisius Coll (BA) Eng 1968; Univ of CT (MA) Eng Ed 1984; Sacred Heart Univ; cr: St Bernard Girls Schl Eng Tchr 1968-72; St Bernard HS Eng Tchr 1972-; Mitchell Coll Adj Eng Prof 1972-75; ai: Var Sftbl Coach; Steering & Curr & Schedule Comms; NHSACA & CHSCA 1972-; NCTE 1980-; CCTE 1992-; Covenant Shelter Bd of Dir Chair, Svc Awd; CT Fed of Stu Cncls Bd, Merit Awd; St James Church Sr Warden 1991-93; CT Spcl Olympics Clinician; New London Day Girls Bsktbl Coach of Yr 1986; Eastern CT Bd ASA Umpires Sportsmanship Awd 1988; Ocean Spray Grant Winner for Supporting Womens Sports Pgms; office: Saint Bernard HS 1593 Norwich New London Tpke Uncasville CT 06382

SMITH, GARY SCOTT, Professor of Sociology; b: Franklin, PA; c: Gregory Scott, Joel Andrew; ed: Grove City Coll (BA) Psych 1972; Gordon-Conwell Theological Seminary (MDiv) 1977; Johns Hopkins Univ (MA) Amer His 1979, (PHD) Amer His 1981; Attnd Barrington Coll 1984, Princeton Univ 1988; Stud Grant 1994; cr: Grove City Coll Religion & Philosophy Instr 1978-80, Sociology Instr 1980-81, Asst Prof of Sociology 1981-85, Assoc Prof of Sociology 1986-90, Sociology Prof 1990-; ai: Pi Gamma Mu, Circle K, New Life Adv; Chrstn Sociological Soc 1983-; Conf on Faith & His 1986-, Exec Bd 1995-; Presbyn Church, Interim Pastor; Jubilee Chrstn Schl Bd 1980-90, Bd Pres 1986-90; Author & Ed; Over 50 Articles Pub; office: Grove City Coll 100 Campus Dr Grove City PA 16127

SMITH, GERALD E., Professor of Marketing; b: Salt Lake City, UT; m: Elizabeth; ed: Brandeis Univ (BA) Ec 1978; Harvard Bus Schl (MBA) Mrktg 1981; Boston Univ (DBA) Mrktg 1992; cr: Arthur D Little Consultant 1981-83; General Mills Product Mgr 1983-84; Kurzweil Inc Dir of Mrktg 1984-88; ai: Mrktg Acad Adv; Univ Acad Cncl; Educl Policy Comm; AMA, ACR 1989-; 20 Articles Book Chapters; office: Boston College Chestnut Hill MA 02167

SMITH, GERALD MICHAEL, Mathematics Professor; b: Middletown, NY; m: Juliana Bullock; c: Susan Hogan, Michael, Jennifer; ed: St Univ of NY at Cortland (BS) Math Ed 1964, (MS) Math Ed 1968; 39 Hrs Post Grad Work in Math; 9 Hrs Post Grad Work in Jr Coll Admin; cr: North Syracuse CS Math Tchr 1964-65; Southern Cayuga HS Math Tchr 1969-67; Cato-Meridian HS Math Tchr 1967-68; Cayuga Comm Coll Math Prof 1968-; ai: NYSMATYC 1973-, Pres; AMATYC 1985-; MAA 1993-, 2nd Vice Chair; NSF Grant 1970 & 1992; AMATYC Grant 1985; Pres St Univ of NY Fac Cncl of Comm Colls 1983-85; Pub Book Statistical Process Control & Quality Improvement 1991, 2nd Edition 1995; office: Cayuga County Comm Coll Franklin Street Auburn NY 13021

SMITH, GLEN ALLEN, Biology Teacher; b: Toledo, OH; m: Olive M. Hostutler; c: Christopher A., Monica S.; ed: Olivet Nazarene Univ (BA) Bio 1967; Bowling St Univ 4 Hrs; Heidelberg Coll 8 Hrs; cr: Wynford HS Gen Sci Tchr 1967-82; Wynford MS 6-8th Sci 1982-89; Wynford HS Bio Tchr 1989-; ai: Track, Cross Cntry Coach 1967-84; Wrestling Coach 1974-76; Key Club Adv 1967-69, 1994-95; NHS Adv 1993-; Wynford Ed Asso 1967-, Pres; OEA, NEA, NCOEA 1967-; SECO 1976-; North Cntrl Sci Soc 1967-, Pres, Sci Ed Awd; OH Track & Cntry Officials Assoc 1985-, Pres, Contributors Awd; Martha Holden Jenning Awd; home: 1430 Linwood Dr Bucyrus OH 44820

SMITH, GREGORY LEE, 8th Grade Math Teacher; b: York, PA; m: Janice Elaine Patches; c: Jennifer E., Jeremy R.; ed: Millersville Univ (BS) Math 1972; York Coll of PA (BS) Acctng 1981; cr: South Western SD 8th Grd Math Tchr 1973-; ai: Mathcounts Coach; NEA, PSEA, SWEA 1973-; NCTM 1986-; Christs Amer Bapt Church 1993-, Asst Treas; office: Emory H Markle Intrmdt Schl 225 Bowman Rd Hanover PA 17331

SMITH, GROVER,III, Social Studies Teacher; b: Pittsburgh, PA; m: Sue; c: Brandon, Aaron, Garrett; ed: Univ of PA (BA) Comprehensive Soc Stud 1971; 36 Cert; cr: Richland HS Tchr 1971-72; Carlyton HS Tchr 1972-; ai: Wrestling Coach; Stu Cncl.

SMITH, HANK E., Scndry Physical Ed Instr; b: Saugerties, NY; m: Ellen Tucker; c: Stephanie Carlson, Brian, Allison Scherer; ed: Mid TN St Univ (BS) PE 1965, (MED) PE-Magna Cum Laude 1972; cr: Baltimore Cty Pub Schls PE Instr 1965-69; Saugerties Cntrl Schls PE Instr 1969-; ai: IM Ftbl Head, JV Coach, Var Asst; Head Wrestling Coach; Demonstration Tchr; NY St Assn Fed Tchrs 1969-; St Mary's Church 1969-, Parish Cncl Chm; BSA 1979-, Phy Fitness Chair; Champions of Christ 1990-, Facilitator; Viacrafe Rep St Mary's 1987-, Chm; Amer Assn Hlth PE Outstdng Edctr of Amer 1972; Assistantship for Masters Degree; Accepted into Archdiocese of NY St Joseph's Seminary Diaconate Formation Ordination; home: 23 Glenerie Ln Saugerties NY 12477*

SMITH, HAROLD EDWARD,JR., Fine Arts Department Chairman; b: Glyndon, MD; m: Elizabeth A.; c: Jennifer Smith Miller, Peter Thalmadge; ed: MD Inst Coll of Art (BFA) Art Tchr Ed 1965, (MFA) Art Ed Printmaking 1969; Over 60 Hrs Beyond Masters at Loyola Coll, Towson Univ & Johns Hopkins; cr: Franklin HS Art Tchr 1965-68; Randallstown HS Art Dept Chair 1969-84; Dulaney HS Art Dept Chair 1985-; ai: Arts Collective Spon; Badminton Coach; Antiquities & Art Foreman Travel with

Stdnts to Italy; Comparative Architecture Stud with Stdnts to Spain & France; MD Printmakers 1987-, Past Pres, Newsletter Publisher; Project Basic Outstanding Artist Educator 1988; Outstanding Tchr 1991; Baltimore Museum of Art Docent Trng; Modern Dutch Poster BMA Speaker; Curr Writing in Film, Architecture & Advanced Placement Art His; *home:* 41 E Henrietta St Baltimore MD 21230

SMITH, HAROLD H., Scndry Math & Physics Teacher; *b:* Dunkirk, NY; *m:* Lois Rosina Ognibene; *c:* Robert H., Kirk A., Kathleen D.; *ed:* Gannon Univ (BS) Scndry Maths 1971; SUNY at Fredonia (MS) Scndry Maths 1976; Attnd SUNY at Buffalo; *cr:* RIpley Cntrl Schl Schdry Math, Sci 1971-72; Brockton Cntrl Schl Scndry Math & Physics 1972-; *ai:* Scndry Scheduling Comm; NYSUT, AFT 1971-; Brocton Tchrs Assn 1972-, Treas; Chautauqua Cty Farm Bureau 1974-; Chautauqua Comwlth Coop Ext; Portland Town Supvr 1981-93; Bd Dirs Natl Grape Coop 1994-; Pres Chautaqua Cty Town Supvr Assn; *office:* Brocton Central Schl 138 W Main St Brocton NY 14716

SMITH, HARRY E., Allied Human Svcs Dept Chm; *b:* Rocky Mount, NC; *c:* Harry II, Leslie; *ed:* NC Cntrl Univ (BA) Soc Sci, Psych 1957; Howard Univ Schl of Soc Work (MSW) Comm Org 1960; 38 Addl Credits Union Grad Schl Ed Admin; *cr:* Bureau of Recreation Street Club Dir 1961-67; Westinghouse Electrical Corp Sr Soc Scientific 1967-74; Souvner Douglas Coll Adj Prof 1979-; Baltimore City Comm Coll Prof, Chprsn Human Svc Dept 1975-; *ai:* Allied Human Svcs Dir; MD St Bd of Occupational Therapy; Investment Vehicle Task Group; Comm Fitness Prgm Adv; Nat Assn of Soc Work 1961-, St Pres, St Soc Worker of Yr 1995; Natl Org Human Svc Ed 1989-, Chair Prof Dev, Majors Citation; BTW Assn 1980-, Natl Pres; Certfd Soc Worker 1978-; Mayors Office Children & Yth 1985-, Bd Chm of Kidsline; Liberty Hlth System 1991-, Advy Bd; Justice, Unity, Generosity & Svc Inc Comm Svc; Baltimore City Comm Coll Fac Excl Awd; MAHE Outstdng Edctr of Yr Awd; Dev Two Retention Strategies; Grant; *office:* Baltimore City Comm Coll 2901 Liberty Heights Ave Baltimore MD 21215*

SMITH, HEATHER ANNE, Secondary English Teacher; *b:* Paterson, NJ; *ed:* Johns Hopkins Univ Working on MA Tchng Scndry Eng; *cr:* J A Assocs Pub Relations Acct Exec 1993-95; *ai:* Schl Newspaper Facilitator; Chrldng Coach; NCEA 1995-; Elem Schl Tchrs Assn of Archdiocese of Baltimore; Univ Church 1983-, Pub Relations Chair; *office:* Our Lady Of Mt Carmel HS 1706 Old Eastern Ave Baltimore MD 21221

SMITH, HELEN GEARY, Kindergarten Teacher; *b:* Ogdensburg, NY; *m:* Lowell J.; *c:* Carole Degenford, Calvin; *ed:* SUNY at Potsdam (BS) Elem Ed 1960, (MS) Elem Ed 1972; *cr:* Ogdensburg Lincoln Schl Third Grd Tchr 1960-64; Lisbon Cntrl Schl Third Grd Tchr 1964-67, Kndgtn Tchr 1984-; *ai:* AFT, NYSUT 1984-.

SMITH, HERBERT JAMES, Fifth Grade Teacher; *b:* Glen Falls, NY; *m:* Ann Marie Prevost; *c:* Lara Denise, Jiniel Diane; *ed:* Adirondack Comm Coll (AA) Liberal Arts 1969; Brockport St Coll (BS) Art, Elem Ed 1971; Castleton St Coll, St Joseph the Provider Grad Work Toward NY Permanent Cert; *cr:* Granville Cntrl Schl 5th Grd Tchr 1971-; *ai:* NEA, NYSUT 1971_; *office:* Granville Cntrl Schl Quaker St Granville NY 12832

SMITH, IRENE TUTTLE, Latin Teacher; *b:* Hornell, NY; *m:* Ray L.; *c:* Ray Jeremy, Jacob; *ed:* Elmira Coll (BA) Classical Lang 1983; SUNY at Brockport (MA) Lbrl Stud 1988; *cr:* Albion HS Latin Tchr 1983-; *ai:* Latin Club Adv; *office:* Albion HS 302 East Ave Albion NY 14411*

SMITH, JACQUELYN SMITH, First Grade Teacher; *b:* Philadelphia, PA; *m:* Levan P.; *ed:* Cntrl St Univ (BS) Elem Ed 1967; Temple Univ (MS) Elem Ed 1995; Attnd West Chester Univ; *cr:* Wynnewood Rd Elem Schl Tchr 1967-78; Penn Vly Elem Schl Tchr 1978-; *ai:* Instrl Curr Cncl; Assessment, Testing Comm; NEA 1967-; PSEA 1967-, Chprsn Integroup Relations Commission; NABSE 1992-; NAACP 1967-; NEA Journal Article Pub; Integroup Relations Awd; *office:* Penn Valley Elem Schl Righters Mill & Hagysford Rds Narberth PA 19072*

SMITH, JAMES F., English & Drama Teacher; *b:* Wilmington, DE; *m:* Diana K. Bjornson; *c:* Jennifer, Amy; *ed:* Univ of DE (BA) Drama 1967; 30 Credit Hrs in Eng; *cr:* Oak Grove Jr HS Eng Tchr 1971-73; Brandywine HS Eng Tchr 1973-; *ai:* Drama & Morning Announcer Clubs Spon; Commencement Ceremony Dir; NEA 1971-; NCTE 1978-; The Brandywiners 1973-; Cert of Tchng Excl Selected by Colleagues 1990; *office:* Brandywine HS 1400 Foulk Rd Wilmington DE 19803*

SMITH, JAMES HOWARD, Student Services Facilitator; *b:* Portsmouth, OH; *m:* Janice A. Shephard; *c:* Jennifer; *ed:* OH Univ (BSEd) Phys Scis & Math 1963, (MED) Admin & Guid 1967; Univ of Cincinnati Voc Guid 1974; *cr:* McKinley Jr HS Sci Tchr & Coach 1963-67; Portsmouth East HS Tchr, Coach & Stu Svcs Facilitator 1967-; *ai:* Stu Tutorial Svcs; NHS & Sr Class Adv; Var Girls Bsktbl Coach; Proficiency Tutoring Comm; Portsmouth City Tchrs 1963-; OH Ed Assoc 1967-; NEA 1967-; MCT 1974-; Sciotoville United Meth Church 1959-; OH HS Ath Assn Register Ofcl 1962-, Bsktbl 32 Yrs & Track 20 Yrs; Order of Masons 1970-, 25 Yr Pin; Shawnee St Univ Tchr & Coach Honoree; Scioto Fndtn 1st Annual Tchr of Yr; *office:* Portsmouth East HS 224 Marshall Ave Sciotoville OH 45662*

SMITH, JAMES MICHAEL, Drama Director; *b:* Waterbury, CT; *ed:* Bentley Coll (BS) Mrktg, Mgt 1982; *cr:* Sacred Heart HS Bus Tchr 1983-84; ITT Hartford Insurance Consultant 1984-; Bristol Cntrl HS Drama Dir 1994-; *ai:* Alpha Psi Omega 1980-, Pres; *office:* Bristol Central HS 480 Wolcott St Bristol CT 06010

SMITH, JAMES R., Asst Prin & Jr HS Math Teacher; *b:* Mansfield, OH; *ed:* OH St Univ (BS) Bus Admin 1983; Ashland Univ (MA) Admin 1995; Bachelors Plus Prgm 1991; *cr:* Galion St Josephs Schl Tchr 1983-88; Mansfield St Peters Schl Tchr 1988-92, Asst Prin, Tchr 1992-; *ai:* Ath Dir; Math Counts Coach; Acad Challenge; Quiz Bowl Adv; Math Dept Chprsn; Toledo Diocesan Math Ldrshp Cncl Mem; OCTM, NCTM, NCEA 1983-; *office:* Mansfield St Peters Elem Schl 63 S Mulberry St Mansfield OH 44902

SMITH, JAMES RICHARD, Instrumental Music Teacher; *b:* East Stroudbug, PA; *m:* Kathryn Wickstrom; *ed:* Mansfield St Coll (BS) Music Ed 1976; Univ of Hartford; East Stroudsburg Univ; West Chester Univ Currently Working Towards Masters; *cr:* Oppenheim-Ephratch Cntrl Schl 4-12th Grd Instrumental Music Tchr 1977-78; Lehighton Area Schls 4-8th Grd Instrumental Music Tchr 1982-84; Lackawanna Trail Jr, Sr HS 7-12th Grd Instrumental Music Tchr 1984-; *ai:* Marching, Concert Band; Jazz, Small Ensembles; Lackawanna Trail Ed Assn, PA Music Edctrs Assn, Music Edctrs Natl Conf 1984-; NEA 1982-; *office:* Lackawanna Trail Jr/Sr HS PO Box 85 Factoryville PA 18419*

SMITH, JAMES WILLIAM, TV Studio Director; *b:* Orange, NJ; *m:* Lana; *c:* Matthew, Devin, Amy; *ed:* Fairleigh Dickinson Univ (BA) Fine Arts 1970; Montclair St Univ (MA) Fine Arts 1976; *cr:* Schl #3 Art Tchr 1970-71; Mt Pleasant MS Art Tchr 1971-79; Livingston HS Graphics, Drawing & Ceramics Tchr 1979-83, TV Studio Dir & Television Production Tchr 1984-; Wm Snyder Design 18th St Designer & Graphic Artist 1983-84; *ai:* Cable TV Shows Exec Producer; Television Production Club & AM Wired Adv; NEA, NJEA, Essex Cty Ed Assn & Livingston Ed Assn 1971-; ACM 1988-; NJTEC 1990-, Founding Mem; Livingston Pub Broadcast Comm 1988-, Bd of Dirs Mem; Recipient of Livingston HS Tchr of Yr Awd 1992; Recipient of Governors Recognition Awd 1992; *office:* Livingston H S Robert Harp Dr Livingston NJ 07039

SMITH, JANE COYLE, 11th Grd Eng & Amer Stud Tchr; *b:* Ashley, PA; *m:* John E.; *c:* Coyle, James, Michael; *ed:* Coll Misericordia (BA) Eng 1974; Wilkes Univ (MS) Ed 1989; 54 Addl Credit Hrs; *cr:* Dallas Schl Dist Sub Tchr 1974-80; Lake Lehman Schl Dist Sub Tchr 1974-80; Lake Lehman Jr HS 7th Grd Tchr 1980-93; Lake Lehman Sr HS 11th Grd Tchr 1993-; *ai:* Past 7th Grd Class, Honor Soc Adv; NEA, PSEA, LLEA 1980-; *office:* Lake Lehman Schl Dist Old Rt 115 Lehman PA 18627

SMITH, JANE MCDANIEL, School Nurse; *b:* Troy, OH; *m:* Ted A.; *c:* Robert Anson, Daniel Brock, Nancy Jane; *ed:* OH St Univ (BSN) Nrsng 1963, (MA) Hlth Ed 1982; *cr:* Church Home Hosp RN Team Ldr 1963; Columbus Pub Hlth Nrsng Svc Pub Hlth Nurse 1964-66; Lancaster City Schls Schl Nurse 1978-; *ai:* Peer Advocates Adv; Baird Front Moderator; COSN, OSN, NASN & NEA 1983-; Natl Schl Hlth Assn 1983-; AAHPERD 1983-; Friends of Libs; Columbus Museum of Art.

SMITH, JANET M., Physical Education Teacher; *b:* Sunbury, PA; *m:* David L; *c:* Shelly M.; *ed:* Lock Haven Univ (BA) Hlth & PE 1969; Credit Hrs at Shidponsburg Univ & Penn St Univ; Attnd Harrisburg Area Comm Coll 1966; *cr:* Juniata Cty Schl Dist PE Tchr 1969-; *ai:* Var Field Hockey, Jr Var Girls Bsktbl & Var Sftbl Coach.

SMITH, JANICE KOSHAK, Med Lab Tech Instr & Ed Coord; *b:* Portage, PA; *m:* Ronald John; *c:* Ronald Jon, Christian, Jennifer; *ed:* MT Aloysius Jr Coll (AS) Lab Tech 1965; PA St Univ (BS) Med Tech 1967; St Francis Coll (MED) Ed 1990; Scndry Tchng Cert Bio, Gen Sci St Francis Coll 1988; *cr:* Mercy Hosp Immunology Dept Head 1968-80; Portage Area HS Bio Tchr 1987-90; Clinical Pathology Facility Med Technologist 1990-91; Mt Aloysius Coll Instr & Ed Coord 1991-; *ai:* Curr, Core Requirement, Fac Dev Comms; Amer Soc of Cl Path 1967-; PSMT 1970-; PTO 1975-; Provide Acad Tutoring to Troubled Yth Through Probation Office Vol; *office:* Mount Aloysius College 7373 Admiral Peary Hwy Cresson PA 16630

SMITH, JAY MAC ARTHUR, Eng, Rdng & Soc Stud Tchr; *b:* San Francisco, CA; *m:* Bonnie Lee Herder; *c:* Jessica Ann, Brian Mac Arthur; *ed:* CA St Univ at San Francisco (BA) Elem Ed 1965; Attnd Kean Coll Holocaust Stud, Seton Hall Univ Elem Ed, Saint Elizabeth Coll Hlth Ed & Holocaust; *cr:* Jedidiah Smith Schl 3rd-4th Grd Tchr 1966-67; Chowchilla Elem Schl 5th Grd Tchr 1967-68; Lester C Noecker Schl 6th Grd Tchr 1968-; *ai:* NEA, NJ Ed Assn 1968-; Roseland Ed Assn 1968-, Chief Negotiator; Verona Ftbl 5th Downers 1993-, Pres; Verona Sports Boosters 1993-, Bd Mem; Verona Bsbl League, Coach; Verona Recreation, Coach; *home:* 8 Whitney Ter Verona NJ 07044

SMITH, JEAN BABINEC, Fifth Grade Teacher; *b:* Little Falls, NY; *m:* Barry J.; *c:* Quintin, Mitchell; *ed:* Siena Coll (BS) Cmptr Sci 1984; SUNY at Cortland (MS) Elem Ed 1987; *cr:* Little Falls City Schl Dist Elem Tchr 1987-; *ai:* Drama Club Adv; *office:* Monroe Street Elem Schl 156 W Monroe St Little Falls NY 13365

SMITH, JEAN V., English Teacher; *b:* Wilmington, NC; *ed:* Duke Univ (MAT) Eng 1968; Villanova Univ Scndry Cnslng Cert; Addl Hrs Cornell, Univ of PA Women's Stud; *cr:* Gettysburg Coll Asst Dean of Women 1967069; Upper Darby HS Eng Tchr 1969-; *ai:* Peer Mediation Mentor 1995-; Girl's Swimming Coach 1969076; JV Girl's LaCrosse Coach 1975-81; Dist Chprsn Women's His Month 1990-95; Equity Issues Comm 1975-95; PSEA, NEA 1969-; Impact Awd Innovative Tchng Idea; Tchr of Month; *office:* Upper Darby HS 601 N Lansdowne Ave Upper Darby PA 19082*

SMITH, JEANETTE M., Special Educator; *m:* Joseph J.; *ed:* Ocean Cty Coll (AA) Gen Ed 1975; William Paterson Coll (BA) Spec Ed, Elem Ed 1978; *cr:* Noah's Arck Day Schl Pre Schl Tchr 1978-79; Stafford Intermediate Schl Spec Ed Tchr, Resource Ctr 1980-; *ai:* Stafford Tchng Assn, Sec; Soc Comm, Chprsn; Stafford Sr Assn Rep 6 Yrs; Assn Rep 6 Yrs; Head Coach 1980-86; Spec Ed Mentor; Tchr of Enrichment Prgm; Task Force Comm Chprsn; Prof Imprvement Prgms Wkshps; Stafford Parents Wkshps; Annual Clothing Drive For Needy Founder; Toy, Food Drive Asst; NTEA; Extended Arms; PTA; Municipal Alliance Mem.*

SMITH, JEANNE M., 9th Grd Language Arts Teacher; *b:* Hanover, PA; *ed:* Shippensburg Univ (BS) Eng Ed 1971, (MED) Eng 1979; 90 Credit Hrs; *cr:* Shippensburg Jr High 9th Grd Tchr 1975-; *ai:* Play Adv 1975-; Chrldng Adv 10 yrs; Curr Comms; PSEA & NEA 1975-; NEH Shakespeare Seminar; *office:* Shippensburg Area Jr HS 317 N Morris St Shippensburg PA 17257*

SMITH, JOAN BOTNICK, Teacher; *b:* Cleveland, OH; *m:* Robert N.; *c:* Kevin, Keith, Jennifer; *ed:* Cleveland St (BS) Elem Ed 1963, (MS) LD, BD 1980; Addl Hrs, CEU Offered by OH; *cr:* Almira Schl Tchr 1963-67; St Ignatius Schl Tchr 1983-88; St Mary Scnl Tchr 1980-83; *ai:* Yrbk; Newspaper; Stu Cncl; Spelling, Acad Challenge Adv; Jr Women, League of Women Voters 1970-; PTA 1973-.

SMITH, JOAN FUSARO, Title 1 Reading Teacher; *b:* Jamaica, NY; *m:* Victor George; *c:* Diane Gottfried, Pamela Holschuh, Matthew, Michael; *ed:* OH Univ (BS) Ed 1987; Grad Hrs in Rdng Instruction; *cr:* Watertown Elem Schl 3rd-4th Grd Tchr 1987-90, Title 1 Rdng Tchr 1990-; *ai:* Spelling Bee Coord 1987-92; WCLEA, NEA 1987-; Heritage Rdng Cncl, OCIRA 1988-; IRA 1989-; St Ambrose Parish 1975-, Rel Ed Coord 1985-, Basic & Advanced Cert; *office:* Waterford Elem Schl PO Box 45 Waterford OH 45786

SMITH, JOANNA E., Special Education Teacher; *b:* Jackson, MS; *c:* Jade Berry; *ed:* Jackson St Univ (BSE) Hlth, PE 1978; USM, MC, William Carey Coll Spec Ed Cert 1984; *cr:* New Method R-1 Enlarged Schl Hlth, PE Tchr 1978-80; East Main HS Spec Ed Tchr 1981-84; Prentiss MS Spec Ed Tchr 1986-90; Washington MS Spec Ed Tchr 1990-91; Forest Hill HS Spec Ed Tchr 1991-93; Bowie HS Spec Ed Tchr 1993-; *ai:* Multicultural, Mentoring Prgms Coord; Gospel Choir, Young Enterprising Stus Multicultural Club Spon; Sr Class Co-Spon; NEA 1978-; PGCEA, MSTA 1993-; Alpha Kappa Alpha 1986-; Dev Summer Yth Involvement Prgm for Prince George's Hosp Ctr; Achvmt Awd 1995; Concerned Black Men Washington DC.*

SMITH, JOANNE M. AUSTIN, English Teacher; *b:* Albion, NY; *m:* Robert; *c:* Michael; *ed:* Keuka Coll (BS) Eng, Ed 1979; SUNY Brockport (MS) Ed 1985; *cr:* Red Jacket Cntrl Schl 9th, 12th Grd Eng Tchr 1980; Hilton Cntrl Schl 10th, 12th Grd Eng Tchr 1980-81; Lyndonville Cntrl Schl 10th-12th Grd Eng Tchr 1981-; *office:* L A Webber Jr Sr HS PO Box 250 Lyndonville NY 14098

SMITH, JOHN CLIFFORD, Supervisor of Social Studies; *b:* East Stroudsburg, PA; *m:* Michelle L. Decker; *c:* Christa, Stephen, Matthew, Jeffrey; *ed:* East Stroudsburg Univ (BS) Scndry Ed & Soc Stud 1974, (MED) Scndry Ed 1983; Attnd Rider Univ 6 Credits & LaVerne Univ 9 Credits; *cr:* North Hunterdon HS Soc Stud Tchr & Ftbl Head Coach 1974-76; Pius X HS Vice Prin & Ftbl Head Coach 1976-78; North Hunterdon HS Soc Stud Tchr & Ftbl Head Coach 1978-82; Pius X Vice Prin & Ftbl Head Coach 1980-82; Wallkill Valley HS Soc Stud Tchr & Ftbl Head Coach 1983-84; Pleasant Valley HS Soc Stud Tchr & Ftbl Head Coach 1984-87; Delaware Valley Regnl HS Supvr of Soc Stud & Ftbl Head Coach 1987-; *ai:* Equipment Mgr 5 Yrs; NJ Prins & Supvrs Assn 1994-; NJ Cncl for Soc Stud, NCSS 1985-; Knights of Columbus 1972-; Comm Park Bd 1987-; Youth Wrestling Org 1985-, Pres; Certified Bsktbl Referee & Bsbl Umpire in PA & NJ 25 Yrs; *office:* Delaware Valley Regnl HS 19 Senator Stout Rd Frenchtown NJ 08825

SMITH, JOHN F., Scndry Physical Education Tchr; *b:* Punxsutawney, PA; *ed:* Slippery Rock Univ (BS) Hlth, PE, Recreation 1971; Attnd Wilkes Coll, Duquesne; *cr:* Punxsutawney Area Schls PE Tchr 1971-; *ai:* Boys, Girls Cross Cntry, Indoor Track, Field, Head Outdoor Boys Field Coach; PSEA, NEA 1971-; PTFCA 1987-; Eagles 1994-; Jef Cty Assn for Retarded Citizens, Past Mem; St, Natl Level Recog Cross Cntry, Track, Field Coach; Track, Field Clinics Guest Lecturer Track, Field Certfd Level I Coach; *office:* Punxsutawney Area Sc Findley St Punxsutawney PA 15767

SMITH, JOHN H.,JR., Professor & Director; *b:* Salem, NJ; *m:* Ali Begley; *c:* Megan, David; *ed:* Univ of Denver (BS)(BA) Hotel, Rest. Mngmt 1972; East Stroudsburg Univ (MED) Educl Admin 1987; Ce Hotel Admin, Food Mngmt Prof; *cr:* East Stroudsburg Univ Ass 1983-87; Sheration Crossgate General Mgr; HolidayInn General Drexel Univ Prof, Dir Enrollment, Industry Relation 1987-; *ai:* Eta Delta, Hospitality Sales & Mrktg, Minority Hoteliers Soc Adv; Cncl Restaurant & Institutional Educator 1978-; Club Mgr Assn 1991- Restaurant Assn, Soc Foodservice Mngmt 1993-; Pennsville Pub 1993-, Bd Mem; Rotary 1979-; Pennsville Historical Soc 1990-; G AHEED Handicapped Employment, Fac Internship ARAMARK Ma Kings Dominion, Natl Restaurant Assn; Instr City-Wide Sanitation *office:* Drexel Univ 33rd & Market St Philadelphia PA 19104

SMITH, JOHN S., Mechanical Engrng Tech Instr; *b:* Mysore, Karn India; *m:* Neela; *c:* Susan, Bharathi, Amar; *ed:* Univ of Mysore (B Mechanical 1969; Worcester Poly Inst (MSME) Mechanical 197 Point Park Coll Asst Prof in Mechanical Engrng Tech 1993-; *ai:* ASM Adv; *home:* 827 N Lincoln Ave Pittsburgh PA 15233

SMITH, JOLENE DELEATH, Admin Asst & Choral Direct Harrisburg, PA; *m:* David Alan; *c:* Dylan Thomas; *ed:* West Chester S (BS) Music Ed 1977; *cr:* Avon Grove Schl Dist MS Gen, Vocal 1977-78; Williams Vly Schl Dist Jr, Sr HS Gen, Vocal Music 197 Williams Vly Schl Dist 7-12 Grd Choral Music Tchr, Admin Asst *ai:* Choral Dir; Sr Class Adv; Sr HS Drama Coach; MENC 1977-; PA PSBA, ACAPA 1987-; Lykens Liberty Hose Co #2 1985-; Porter- Rotary Club 1989-; Jaycees Outstdng Young Educator Awd; Williams Vly Schl Dist Rt 209 Tower City PA 17980

SMITH, J. OTIS, Professor of Psychology; *b:* Wilmington, N Theresa Hill; *c:* J. Otis III, Karen, J. Ryan; *ed:* Oberlin Coll (BA) 1963; Temple Univ (MA) Psych 1965, (EDD) Cnslng Psych & Cns 1971; *cr:* Temple Univ Asst Dean of Men, Temple Opportunity P Upward Bound Dir 1965-71; Stand By Systems II Inc Sr Consultant Cheyney Univ Acting Pres 1993, Psych Prof; *ai:* Stu Affairs Advy Chprsn 1992-94; Stu Govt Cooperative Assn Adv 1994; Strategic Range Planning Cncl Co-Chprsn; APSCUF Exec Comm & Meet & D Team Mem; Assn of Multicultural Cnslng & Dev 1971-, Treas, Pres 1979, 1984 & 1992; Amer Cnslng Assn 1971-, Treas 1986; PA A 1975-, Pres 1988; PA Lib Bd 1985-87; Awds: Cheyney Univ Excl Fac 1987, PA Black Conf on Higher Ed Mary D Baltimore 1988, Hum Schlsp Fac Motivator 1994; *office:* Cheyney Univ Of PA Box 532 Ch PA 19319

SMITH, JOY S., English Teacher; *b:* Danville, VA; *c:* Chad R. Red Northeastern Univ (BS) Ed 1974; Cambridge Coll Post Grad Stu Boston Tech HS Eng Tchr 1974-77; Solomon Lewenberg MS Ass 1978-80; Madison Park HS Lang & Drama Tchr 1981-88; Wentworth Upward Bound Prgm 1989; Boston Latin Acad HS 1989-; *ai:* Housem for Jrs; Responsible for Discipline Matters Relating to Jrs; Bu Portfolio Mem; Fin Inv Clb; Black Educators Alliance of MA 1975- 1974-; Boston Pub Schls Peer Leadership Awd; *office:* Boston Latin HS 205 Townsend St Boston MA 02119*

SMITH, JOYCE EMILY, Fourth Grade Teacher; *b:* Pittsburgh, P Todd A. Kalsey; *ed:* Slippery Rock Univ (BA) Ed 1969, (MA) Ed 197 Post Grad Credits; *cr:* Perryville Elem Schl 4th-5th Grd Tchr 1969-9 Intyre Elem Schl 4th Grd Tchr 1992-; *ai:* Playground Aide; Have Stu from Duquesne; PSEA; NEA; PACE; PTA 1969-, Lifetime Mbrshp *office:* Mc Intyre Elem Schl 200 Mcintyre Rd Pittsburgh PA 15237

SMITH, JUDITH LYNN, Mathematics Teacher; *b:* Slame, OH Douglas R.; *c:* Wendy Smith Roller, Rebecca, Kelly; *ed:* Kent St U Elem Ed & Scndry Ed Math 1966; Youngstown St U (MS) Curr 1985; Univ Post Grad Studies; *ai:* Schl Improvement & Negotiations Co NEA 1966-; OEA 1966-; NCTM 1993-; OCTM 1993-; Leetoni Boosters 1990-; Leetonia Bd of Ed Grant; Leetonia Schls Tchr Month; *office:* Leetonia Exempted Village Schl 181 Walnut St Leeton 44431*

SMITH, JULIE GRUN, Mathematics Teacher; *b:* Bay Shore, N David Scott; *c:* David, Jacqueline; *ed:* Coll of New Rochelle (BA) 1976; Stony Brook Univ (MS) Ed 1977; *cr:* Sachem Schl Dist Math 1976-; *office:* Sachem Schl Dist 850 Main St Holbrook NY 11741

SMITH, JULIE LOE, Seventh Grade Teacher; *b:* Springfield, OH Joseph Gregory; *ed:* Univ of TN (BS) Elem Ed 1985; Univ of Dayt Grad Credit Hrs; Cambridge Coll 3 Grad Credit Hrs; Wright St Univ 1 Credit Hr; *cr:* Roosevelt MS 6th Grd Tchr 1985-94, 7th Grd Tchr 1 *ai:* Schl-Bus Partnership, Math, Lang Arts, Math Textbook Ado Comms; Math Bldg, 6th Grd Team Coord; Right to Read Rep; Track, Cntry Coach; Odyssey of Mind, City Spelling Bee Rep; Phi Delta K 1985-; NEA 1994-; *office:* Roosevelt MS 1600 N Limestone St Spring OH 45503

SMITH, KAREN BURGESS, Art Dept Chair & Gallery Dir; *b:* Ki ME; *m:* Randall P. Raymond; *c:* Nathaniel, Megan, Erin; *ed:* Univ o (BS) Art Ed 1974; Dartmouth Coll (MA) Hum 1983; Tufts Univ Mu Stud Cert 1994; *cr:* Concord HS Art Dept Tchr 1974-85; St Pauls Mass Media Master Tchr 1984-88, Gallery Dir, Art Dept Chair 198 Anselm Coll Art Dept Lecturer 1985-89; *ai:* Photo Svc, Video Yrb Advs; Fitness Instr; 5th-6th Grd Form Hum Design Team, Proctor Co Heads of Houses; NAEA 1975-; Ind Schls Art Edctrs Assn 1993-; Assn of Museums 1991-; Cartebury Straker Village 1994-, Bd Capitol Ctr for Arts 1993-, Visual Arts Adv; Cncl Cable TV Access C 1989-, Policy Comm Chair; Natl Gallery of Art Summer Flwshp 199 Museum Assn Publications Design Awd Second Place 1995; Amer A Museums Publications Designs Awd Honorable Mention 1994; NEA Media Awd 1984; Natl Endowment for Hum Fellow 1981; *office:* Pauls Schl 325 Pleasant St Concord NH 03301

SMITH, KAREN CARROCCIA, Evening Instr of Bus Admi Wilmington, DE; *c:* Kathleen C., Sarah N.; *ed:* Brandywine Jr Coll Legal Secretarial 1969; Salisbury St Univ (BS) Bus Admin Wilmington Coll (MBA) Bus Admin 1986; *cr:* Nanticoke Meml Ho Dir of General Accounting 1981-87; Beebe Medical Ctr Cont 1988-91; DE Tech & Comm Coll Evening Instr & Sr Financial Specialist 1991-; *ai:* Coll Senate Vice-Chair & Senator 1991-; St o Certified Pub Accountant 1993; *office:* DE Tech & Comm Coll At Gr PO Box 610 Georgetown DE 19947

SMITH, KAREN JEAN, Child Dev Coordinator & Tchr; *b:* Indiana *m:* Davis Lee; *c:* Matthew; *ed:* IN Univ of PA (BS) Home Ec 1972, (M Home Ec 1980; Post grad Stud at Penn St Univ; *cr:* Penn-Trafford Schl Tchr 1972-; *ai:* Stu Assistance Pgm; Parent Ed Classes; Career Prep NEA & PSEA 1972-; AAFCS & PAFCS 1972-; Delta Kappa Gamma 1 VP, Mbrshp Chair & Project Chair; Red Cross Day Chprsn, Svc Church 1976-, Numerous Offices Held Yth Ldr Recognition; PA Hom f the Yr 1978; Pride Awd for Excl in Tchng 1986 & 1992; *office:* rafford HS Box 366 Harrison City PA 15636

I, KAREN M., Business Education Teacher; *b:* Syracuse, NY; *m: l:* SUNY at Cobleskill (AAS) Bus Admin 1987; SUNY at Oswego us Dist Ed 1989, (MS) Rdng 1995; *cr:* Jordan-Elbridge HS Bus Ed 993-; *ai:* Schl Store Adv; NBEA 1993-; IRA 1995-; *office:* Jordan ge JR/SR HS 5721 Hamilton Rd Jordan NY 13080

I, KAREN MC DONALD, Family & Consumer Sci Teacher; *b:* Mt , OH; *ed:* OH St Univ Voc Home Ec 1977; *cr:* Mt Vernon MS Hlth 979-80; East Knox HS Voc Home Ec Tchr 1982-; *ai:* FHA, HERO, dvs; Jr Act Dir 4 Yrs; Tchrs Assn 1981-; Questers 1970-, Pres; Knox torical Soc 1990-; Knox Co Home Ec Assn 1977-, Past Pres; *office:* nox HS 23227 Coshocton Rd Howard OH 43028

I, KAREN REICHEL, Instructor of Nursing; *b:* Waltham, MA; *m:* s; *c:* Jason, Jennifer, Julie; *ed:* Wagner Coll (BS) Nrsng 1978; Sage Coll (Ms) Nrsng 1983; *cr:* Muhlenburg Hosp Registered 1978-80; Memrl Hosp Registered Nurse 1980-81; Univ Hghts ered Nurse 1981-82; Sage JCA Assoc Prof 1980-90; Samaritan Hosp Nrsng Nurse Fac 1990-; *ai:* Sunday Schl Coord; Yth Group & Yth Dir; Girl Scout Ldr; Soccer Coach; Sigma Theta Tau 1992-; PTA Numerous Articles Pub.

I, KATHLEEN ANN, Professor of Education; *b:* Punxsutawney, : IN Univ of PA (BS) Elem Ed 1966; Clarion St Coll (MED) Elem 9; Clarion Univ of PA (MS) Spec Ed 1981; PA St Univ (PHD) Instrl s, Design & Tech 1986; *cr:* Punxsutawney Area Schls Elem Tchr 3; Clarion St Coll Elem Tchr, Instr 1973-80; Clarion Univ of PA rof Spec Ed Dept 1980-87, Assoc, Full Prof Ed Dept 1987-89, Ed hair 1989-95, Full Prof of Ed 1995-; *ai:* Fac Senate; Stu Affairs Chair; NCATE Liaison; PA Assn for Educl Comm & Tech 1981-, vc Awd 1990; Phi Delta Kappa 1976-, Pres 1982-83, Svc Awd 1989; Delta Pi 1984-, Co-Cnslr; Clarion Cty MH & MR 1984-86, Bd; rs in Human Svc 1980-87, Bd; Alumni Bd 1992-; Book: You Can Do gether 1986; Numerous Articles Pub; *office:* Clarion Univ Of PA PA 16214*

H, KATHLEEN FRANCIS, Fourth Grade Teacher; *b:* Bethlehem, Seton Hall Univ (BS) Elem Ed 1976; *cr:* Parochial Schls 1-4th Grd 962-72; St John's Schl 3-4th, 6-8th Grd Tchr 1972-82; St Joseph's h Grd Tchr 1982-; *ai:* Earth Day, Rel Coord; NCEA 1982-; Tchr of hdiocese of Newark 1995; *office:* St Joseph Schl 131 E Fort Lee Rd NJ 07603

H, KRISTE DEANNA, Business Teacher; *b:* N Royalton, OH; *m: c:* Jacob; *ed:* OH St Univ (BS) Bus Ed 1990; Cleveland St Univ (MS) Learning, Dev 1995; *cr:* Cuyahoga Comm Coll Office Admin Instr Parma Sr HS Bus Tchr 1992-; N Royalton HS Bus Tchr 1992-; *ai:* Trail Teen Inst; SADD; JV Soccer, 8th Grd Vlybl, Swim Coach; g, Class Adv; OH Bus Tchrs Assn 1990-; Cleveland Area Bus Tchrs Sec; *office:* North Royalton HS 14713 Ridge Rd North Royalton OH

H, LARRY JOHN, Social Studies Teacher; *b:* Cumberland, MD; *m:* Lynn Heauner; *ed:* Frostburg St Univ (BS) Pol Sci, Philosophy Addtl Grad Stud Pol Sci, Guid, Cnslng, Ed; Frostburg St Univ MED , Supervision 1996; *cr:* Calvert Cty Pub Schls Amer Govt, World sych Tchr 1991-92; Allegany Cty Pub Schls US His, Amer Govt Tchr *ai:* Schl Improvement Team; Allegany Cty Pub Schls Strategic ng Comm; Schl Safety Comm; Soc Stud Cncl; Phi Delta Kappa, NEA, ACTA 1992-; Natl St Tchrs of Yr 1996; Knights of Columbus 3rd Degree Knight; MD Dept Disabled Amer Veterans St endation; Allegany Cty Tchr of Yr 1995; Soc of Socrates, Hypatia; ept Higher Ed Chms Awd for Excl; Commendation MD Bus table; Key to City of Cumberland; Motivational Speaker; Senatorial p; Lalitta Nash Mc Kaig Schlsp; *home:* 824 Shriver Ave Cumberland 502*

H, LAURENCE MARTIN, Physics Teacher; *b:* Lowell, MA; *ed:* st of Tech (BA) Chem 1972; Boston Univ (MED) Sci Tchng 1988; nchester HS Sci Tchr 1974-; *ai:* NEA 1974-; MTA 1974-; AAPT *office:* Winchester HS 80 Skillings Rd Winchester MA 01890

H, LAWRENCE M., Chemistry & Physics Teacher; *b:* Albany, NY; zabeth T. Hogan; *c:* Meghan, Erin, Colleen, Patrick; *ed:* Siena Coll Chem 1972; Coll of St Rose (MS) Ed Philosophy 1975, (MS) Admin *cr:* St Casmirs Schl Sci Tchr 1972-76; Albany HS Sci Tchr 1976-88; HS Asst Prin 1988-90; Thomas O'Brien Acad Sci Tchr, Prin)1; Albany HS Sci Tchr 1991-; *ai:* Ski Club Adv; Yrbk Bookkeeper; Comms; STANYS, AFT 1976-; Cub Scout Ldr, Den Ldr; Little Coach, Mgr; *office:* Albany HS 700 Washington Ave Albany NY

H, LEE E., High School Counselor; *b:* Dayton, OH; *ed:* Miami Univ (BS) Ed & Sci 1962, (MED) Sci 1966; 40 Hrs in Counseling & ; *cr:* Dayton Pub Schls Sci Tchr 1962-68, Schl Cnslr 1968-; *ai:* Lead Cnslr; Dayton Ed Assn 1962-; NEA 1962-; Dayton Pub Schl Org 1968-; Ohio Schl Cnslrs Assoc 1993-; Former Mem Church ; Lions Club, Sec for 2 Yrs; Belmont HS Tchr of Yr Nom; Licensed Cnslr; *office:* Belmont H S 2323 Mapleview Ave Dayton OH 45420

H, LENORE, Social Studies Teacher; *b:* New York City, NY; *m:* d; *c:* Barbara Smith Stolfe, Nancy Susan; *ed:* CCNY (BA) Soc Sci Hunter Coll (MA) Soc Stud Ed 1964; Addl 44 Credits Post Grad vice Courses, Ec, Labor Relations, Remedial Rdng, Cmptrs; *cr:* JHS chr 1960-64; Newburgh Schl Sub Tchng 1965-71; South Jr HS Tchr 36; Newburgh Free Acad Tchr 1986-; *ai:* Advanced Placement Stdnts Write Coll Recommendations; AFT 1961-; Mid Hudson Soc Stud Hunter Coll Flwshp; Honor Soc Keynote Speaker 1995; *office:* urgh Free Acad 201 Fullerton Ave Newburgh NY 12550

H, LEON R., 4th Grade Teacher; *b:* Memphis, TN; *m:* Mary Marlene -Smith; *c:* Ericca J.; *ed:* St Univ at Onconta (BA) Ed, Soc Stud 1965; y at Cortland (MS) Ed, Curr 1981; 36 Addl Hrs; *cr:* Broadalbin Cntrl th Grd Tchr 1966-67; Oppenheim Schl 7-9 Grd Soc St Tchr 1967-69; ch Schl 7-9 Grd Soc St Tchr 1967-69; Richfield Springs Cntrl 4th Grd 1969-71; Herkimer Cntrl Schl 4th-5th Grd Tchr 1971-; *ai:* Curr Advy ; Bowling, Trach, Ftbl Coach; NYSUT 1966-; AFT 1971-; HFA , VP; *home:* 822 W German St Herkimer NY 13350

H, LEONARD C., Fifth Grade Teacher; *b:* Reading, PA; *m:* Lana er; *c:* Kristin, Brad; *ed:* Kutztown St Coll (BS) Elem Ed 1973; rsville St Coll (MED) Ed 1975; *cr:* Amity Elem Ctr 5th Grd Tchr ; *ai:* DBEA, PSEA & NEA; *office:* Daniel Boone Area Schl Dist 1445 n St Douglassville PA 19518

H, LEVAN PRETZMAN, Art Teacher & Coordinator; *b:* Reading, : Jacquelyn; *ed:* Penn St Univ (BA) Art 1970; Tyler (MFA) Art 1972; Kutztown Art 1975; Chestnut Hill Coll ASID 1985; *cr:* Ardmore Jr HS chr 1970-78; Bala Cynwyd MS Art Tchr 1978-; Lower Merion Schl Art Curr Coord 1996-; *ai:* Soccer Coach; Evaluations Comm; ction Curr Cncl; Arts Dept Chm; NEA, PSEA 1970-; LMEA 1970-, Pub Relations Chair; Narberth Improvement Civic Endeavor 1992-; Pub Relations Awd; *office:* Lower Merion Schl Dist Montgomery Ardmore PA 19003*

'H, LINDA SPRINGER, Learning Support Teacher; *b:* Rochester, : Joseph Eric; *c:* Amanda Jo, Thomas Michael, Katherine Ann; *ed:* Slippery Rock Univ (BS) Ed Spec & Elem 1987; Classes Taken at Various Univs; *cr:* United Cerebral Palsy Tchr Preschool 1987; Northern York Schl Dist EMR Tchr Grds 6, 7, 8 1987-89; Norfolk Pub Schls Spec Ed Tchr Grds 1-6 1989-90; Northern York Schl Dist Learning Support Tchr Grds 9-12 1993-; *ai:* Northern MS spec Olympics Coach; Northern HS Class Adv; VFW Auxiliary 1993-; *office:* Northern York HS 655 S Baltimore St Dillsburg PA 17019

SMITH, LOIS KIME, Retired Third Grade Teacher; *b:* Willard, OH; *m:* Gerald Lawrence; *c:* Melody Sue Sweet, Joni Joy Durham, Barry Lee; *ed:* OH Wesleyan Univ (BA) Ed 1953; Ashland Univ (MA) Ed 1980; Attnd Univ of WI at Madison, Ottenben Coll at Westerville, La Verne Coll CA, Oh St Univ at Columbus, Univ of Dayton, OH Univ at Athens; *cr:* DE City Schls Home Ec Tchr 1953-54; Buckeye Valley Schl 4th Grd Tchr 1965-68; DE City Schls K-5th Grd Elem Tchr 1969-94, Pre-Kndgtn Tchr 1970-79, Pre-Kndgtn Dir 1979-81; *ai:* OH Wesleyan Univ Stu Tchr; NEA; OEA; OCTA; DCRT; Delta Kappa Gamma Women Tchrs Honory 1969-, Pres 1986-88; United Way, Pres 1984-85, Bd 9 Yrs; People In Need, Bd, Pres, Advy Bd 1986-' Cntrl OH Diabetes DE Chapter Bd 1988-95; First Presbyn Church 1954-, Elder, Deacon Trustee; Grandy Hsptl Vol 1994-; Delwood Chldrn's Home Bd Mem 1994-; Tchr of Yr 1984-85; Martha Holden Jennings Scholar 1980-81; Ashland Oil Golden Apple Achiever Awd 1987; St of OH Tchr Ldr Network Rep 1989-1993.

SMITH, LOIS SHROYER, Sixth Grade Teacher; *b:* Lebanon, PA; *m:* Richard Henry; *c:* Frances MecKley, Ritt S., Anne L., Erin K.; *ed:* Lebanon Valley Coll (BA) Elem Ed 1964; Attnd Penn St & Clarion Post Grad Courses; *cr:* Kane Chestnut St Elem Schl 5th Grd Tchr 1976-84; Kane MS 6th Grd Tchr 1984-; *ai:* Kane Wolves Cry Newspaper, Birthday Club, Pop in Poems & Spelling Bee Adv; Musical Dir; Stu Self-Esteem & Tchr Self-Esteem Comms; KATA & NEA 1990-; Kane First Meth Church, Admin Bd 1985-; Kane Comm Players 1981-; Tchng Excl Awd 1986; PA Eng Convention, Natl MS Convention & St MS Convention Presenter & Prgm Inciting Writing Author; Various Schl Dist Inservice Presenter; *office:* Kane Area M S W Hemlock Ave Kane PA 16735

SMITH, LORRAINE (KUTZ), Mathematics Teacher; *b:* Jamaica, NY; *m:* Gilbert John; *c:* Marissa, Kelly; *ed:* ST Johns Univ (BS) Ed & Math 1979; Adelphi Univ (MS) Spec Ed 1981; *cr:* St Francis Prep Schl Math Tchr 1979-; *ai:* Peer Mediator, REACH; AMTNYS 1992-; *home:* 157 W 19th St Huntingtn Sta NY 11746

SMITH, LOUANNE WALKLING, Latin Teacher; *b:* Philadelphia, PA; *m:* Randolph N.; *c:* Troy W.; *ed:* Dickinson Coll (BA) Latin 1975; Univ of MO at Columbia (MA) Classical Lang 1978; Attnd Intercollegiate Ctr for Classical Stud in Rome 1973, NY St Regents Coll Ed Courses 1984-86; *cr:* Univ of MO Latin TA 1976-78; Chapin Schl Latin Tchr 1976-80; Friends Acad Latin Tchr 1980-83; Garrison Forest Schl Latin Tchr 1986-; *ai:* Frgn Lang Dept Chair, Club Adv; Curr Comm; Amer Classical League; MD Frgn Lang Assn; Williams Coll Assn of MD Outstdng Scndry Schl Tchr Awd 1991; Grad Tchng Awd Unvi of MO 1978; *office:* Garrison Forest Schl 300 Garrison Forest Rd Owings Mills MD 21117

SMITH, LYNETTE CUTHBERTSON, Reading Specialist; *b:* Allentown, PA; *m:* Mark; *c:* Lauren, Alexander; *ed:* Lehigh Univ (MED) Rdng Ed 1983; Hood Coll (BA) Early Chldhd Ed 1978; Rdng Specialist Cert 1983; Rdng Supvr Cert 1993; Currently Enrolled in Admin Cert Prgm; *cr:* Parkland Schl Dist First Grd Tchr 1978-83, Third Grd Tchr 1983-91, Elem Rdng Specialist 1991-; *ai:* Kutztown Univ Tchr Advy Cncl; Parkland Schl Dist Strategic Planning, Report Card, Land Arts Comms; IRA; Phi Delta Kappa; ASCD; NEA, Parkland Ed Assn; Colonial Assn of Rdng Edctrs; Keystone St Rdng Assn; Parkland Comm Lib 1993-, Corresponding Sec; Nativity Luth Church Sunday Schl Tchr; *office:* Schnecksville Elem Schl 4260 Sand Spring Rd Schnecksville PA 18078*

SMITH, LYNN MONTGOMERY, Associate Professor of Math; *b:* Lawrence, MA; *m:* Joseph E.; *c:* Sarah K.; *ed:* PA St Univ (BA) Math 1970; Merrimack Coll (MA) Math 1972; 12 Addl Credits; *cr:* Gloucester Cty Coll Math Tchr 1972-; *ai:* Curr Comm; Cmptr Liason; AFT 1973-; NCTM 1972-; Assn Math Tchrs NJ 1972-, Mem at Large; ASQC 1990-; Precalculus Solutions Manual Pub; *office:* Gloucester County Coll 1400 Tanyard Rd Sewell NJ 08080

SMITH, MABEL ANNE, Soc Studies & English Teacher; *b:* Oneida, NY; *m:* Edward; *c:* Edward, Kevin, Pamela, Michelle; *ed:* SUNY at Albany (BA) His & Eng 1963, (MA) His 1965; Fairfield Univ 15 Credit Hrs Guid; Wesconn Univ 18 Credit Hrs Guid; Syracuse Univ 15 Credit Hrs Guid; *cr:* Holland Patent Cntrl Tchr 1963-65; Chittenango Cntrl Schl Guid Cnslr 1965-68; Brewster CS Sub Tchr 1974-80; Pawling CS Soc Stud & Eng Tchr 1980-, Guid 2 Yrs; *ai:* Soc Stud Club; Mock Trial; Model Congress; Geog Bee; NEA 1980-; Pawling Tchrs Assn 1980-, Sec; Eastern Star Chptr 21 1964-, Starpoint, Ruth; Patterson Recreation 1975-78; Brewster Schl Bd 1989-91, VP; Local Paper & Schl News Column Writer 2 Yrs; *office:* Pawling Jr Sr HS Reservoir Rd Pawling NY 12564

SMITH, MARCIA BABCOCK, Business Education Teacher; *b:* Frostburg, MD; *m:* Harry Paul; *c:* Kelly Riahin, Heather Chaney, Corey; *ed:* Frostburg St Univ (BS) Bus Ed 1986, (MS) Guid & Cnlsng 1995; *cr:* Westmar HS Bus Ed Tchr 1986-95; Ft Hill HS Bus Ed Tchr 1995-; *ai:* Peer Mediation Coord; SHOP Adv; NEA, MSTA, ACTA 1986-; *office:* Fort Hill HS 500 Greenway Ave Cumberland MD 21502

SMITH, MARCIA ZAHN, English Teacher; *b:* Carthage, NY; *c:* Patrick B.; *ed:* Syracuse Univ (BA) Eng Ed 1958; Middlebury Coll (MA) Amer, British Lit 1962; Addl Credit Hrs Lit Syracuse Univ, St Lawrence Univ, St Univ of NY at Potsdam; *cr:* South Jefferson Cntrl Schl Scndry Eng Tchr 1958-; *ai:* Future Tchrs Club Adv; NY St Eng Cncl 1988-; NCTE 1983-; Coll Women's Club Jefferson Co 1960-, Corresponding Sec 1989; Alpha Delta Kappa; HS Tchr of Excl 1989 NYS Eng Cncl; *home:* 26836 Ridge Rd Watertown NY 13601

SMITH, MARGARET MOLINARO, Third Grade Teacher; *b:* Cleveland, OH; *m:* James; *c:* Matthew Matko, Michael Matko, Anrew Matko, Jamie; *ed:* Kent St Univ (BS) Ed 1968; OH St UNiv (MA) Ed, Rdng, Eng 1981; *cr:* Euclid Schl System Tchr 1968-69; Worthington Bd Ed Tchr 1969-71; OH St Univ Writing Instr 1978-80; Columbus St Univ Writing Instr 1978-80; Franklin Univ Writing Instr 1978-; Worthington Bd Ed Tchr 1987-; *ai:* Textbook Selection Comm; Schl Bus Partnership; Integrated Units Comms; WEA 1987-; 2 Innovation Awds Creative Projects; Written, Produced 5 Original Play Scripts; Written, Directed Musical Original 6 Educl Songs; *office:* Evening Street Schl 885 Evening St Worthington OH 43214*

SMITH, MARK FRANCIS, Soc Stud, Psych & US His Tchr; *b:* New Britain, CT; *m:* Patricia Vogel; *ed:* Boston Univ (BS) Ed & Soc Stud 1972; Grad Credits in Psych, US His, Art His, Photography & Cnslng; *cr:* Acton Boxborough HS Soc Stud, Psych & US His 1972-; *ai:* Schl Counsel; Schl Climate; Ftbl Staff & Fitness Instr Vol; NEA & AEA 1972-, AEA Assorted Offices; Berlin Lions Club 1982-, Assorted Including Pres; *office:* Acton Boxborough Regnl HS 96 Hayward Rd Acton MA 01720*

SMITH, MARK JOHN, Sixth Grade Teacher; *b:* Wilkes-Barre, PA; *m:* Carol Ann Colantuono; *c:* Sara, Adam, Emily; *ed:* East Stroudsburg (BS) Elem Ed 1974; Addl Course Work at Wilkes Univ, Bloomsburg Univ & Penn St; Attnd Marywood Coll Grad Prgm; *cr:* Cotton Avenue Schl 5th Grd Tchr 1974-88, 6th Grd Tchr 1989-; *ai:* Fundraiser Chprsn; Act Dir; NEA, PSEA, WBAEA 1974-; Cotton Avenue Schl PTG 1974-, Treas, Co-founder; Ballet Northeast 1990-, VP; Plains Bsbl 1990-92, Coach; Plains Field Day 20 Yrs, Founder, Chprsn; *home:* 31 Hilldale Ave Wilkes Barre PA 18705

SMITH, MARK MC CALLUM, 8th Grade US History Teacher; *b:* Sendai, Japan; *m:* Terri Ann Cornuelle; *c:* Kimberly, Megan; *ed:* MI Univ (MA) His 1981, (MED) Scndry Admin 1984; 6 Credit Hrs Miami Univ; 2 Credith Hrs Coll of Mount St Joseph; *cr:* Amelia MS His Tchr 1974-; *ai:* Soc Stud Curr Comm West Clermont Local Schls; Schl Fac Liason Comm; OH Ed Assn 1993-; NCSS 1992-; Chancel Choir St John's UCC 1987-; Pres 1994-, Coach of Yr 1990; Clermont Cty Ec Educator of Yr 1991; Who's Who Amer Ed 1993; *office:* Amelia MS 1341 Clough Pike Batavia OH 45103*

SMITH, MARTHA WARD, Middle Schl Vocal Music Tchr; *b:* Sewickley, PA; *ed:* Findlay Univ (BA) Music Ed 1969; Bowling Green St Univ (MM) Music Ed 1988; Earned PHD; *cr:* BGSU Summer Theater Music Dir 1988-95; Huron City Schls Tchr 1970-; *ai:* OMEA 1973-, Adjucator; NEA 1970-; OCDA 1985; Tchr of Yr 1993; *office:* Mc Cormick MS 325 Ohio St Huron OH 44839

SMITH, MARY DONOHUE, Special Education Teacher; *b:* Albany, NY; *m:* Victor H. Jr.; *c:* Jesse, Leda; *ed:* Nazareth Coll (BA) Sociology 1972; Coll of St Rose (MA) Spec Ed 1975; *cr:* CCHS Spec Ed Tchr 1974-; *ai:* AS Ldr 11 Yrs; Doane Stuart Schl, Parents Assn Pres, Trustee Bd; *office:* Colonie Central HS 100 Loralee Dr Albany NY 12205

SMITH, MARY F. (REDDY), Spanish Teacher; *b:* Kalamazoo, MI; *m:* Bruce D.; *c:* Hilary; *ed:* Western MI Univ (BA) Span 1965, (MA) Span 1971; Univ of Southern MO-Certfd Trainer of Span of Law Enforcement Prsnl, Span for Bus, Prof People; Univ of Cinti-Rdng Cert; Coll of Mt St Joseph 9 Credit Hrs; Madeline Hunter Assocs-Mastery Tchng I; *cr:* Portage Pub Schls Span Tchr 1965-68; Wyoming Pub Schls Span Tchr 1968-70; Latin Amer Cncl Outreach-Span 1970-72; Kentwood Pub Schls Span Tchr 1972-73; IN Univ Visiting Lecturer 1973-77; Oak Hills Pub Schls Span Tchr 1979-; *ai:* Bldg FL Coord; Dist Dept Chair; Lang Club, Natl Jr Hnr Soc, Ski Club Adv; North Cntrl Steering, Prins Advy Comms; NEA 1965-; OEA 1977-; OHEA 1977-, Bldg Rep; OH For Lang Tchrs Assn 1977-, Comms; NATSP 1965-; Phi Delta Kappa 1976-; ACTFL; Sayler Park Village Cncl 1985-, VP, Sec; Sayler Park Historical Soc 1985-; Fernbank Garden Club 1988-, Pres; Neighborhood Support Prog, Chair Review Comm; Pan Amer Games-Interpreter; Articles Pub; *office:* Bridgetown Jr HS 3900 Race Rd Cincinnati OH 45211*

SMITH, MARY JANE, Fourth Grade Teacher; *b:* Lancaster, PA; *m:* David H.; *c:* Benjamin D., Jason H.; *ed:* Elizabethtown Coll (BS) Elem Ed 1975; Attnd Millersville Univ; *cr:* Kraybill Mennonite Schl 4th Grd Tchr 1984-95; *ai:* Ed Comm; Steering Comm for Accreditation MSA; West Green Tree Church of the Brethren, Moderator; *office:* Kraybill Mennonite Schl 598 Kraybill Church Rd Mount Joy PA 17552

SMITH, MARY ANNE,RSM, Admissions Dir & Span Tchr; *b:* Havana, Cuba; *ed:* Mt St Agnes Coll (BA) Span 1966; Tulane Univ (MS) Latin Amer Stud 1976; *cr:* Mt De Sales Acad Lang Tchr 1966-67; Mercy HS Span Tchr 1967-71; San Vincente De Paul Rel Tchr 1971; Mercy HS Dir of Admissions, Span Tchr 1972-; *ai:* Sr Class Coord; AATSP 1970-; ACTFL 1976-; Schl Bd St Pius X 1988-; *office:* Mercy HS 1300 E Northern Pkwy Baltimore MD 21239

SMITH, MARY SUE, 4th Grade Teacher; *b:* Penn Yan, NY; *m:* Robert H.; *c:* Vanessa, Andrew\; *ed:* St Univ of Oswego (BS) Soc Sci 1969; St Univ of Cortland (MS) Ed 1974; *cr:* Whitney Point Cntrl Schl 4th-5th Grd Tchr 24 Yrs; *ai:* Young Yorker Club Adv; Campbell's Labels for Ed, UNICEF Schl Coord; Co-Chprsn Bldg Team; Math Curr Comm; AFT; NY St United Tchrs; *office:* Whitney Point Intermediate Sch Rt 11 Whitney Point NY 13862

SMITH, MAUREEN ANNE, Second Grade Teacher; *b:* Newark, NJ; *ed:* Kean Coll (BA) Early Chldhd Ed 1974; William Paterson Coll (MED) Learning Disabilities 1981; 18 Credit Hrs Beyond my Masters; *cr:* Cedar Knolls Schl 1st-5th Grd Remedial & Enrichment Tchr 1974-75; Franklin Schl 3rd Grd Tchr 1975-90, 2nd Grd Tchr 1990-; *ai:* Odyssey of Mind Judge; Project Grad Vol; NEA 1975-; NJEA 1975-; REA 1975-, Sr Bldg Rep 1975-; PTA 1975-; *office:* Franklin Schl 8 Meeker St Succasunna NJ 07876*

SMITH, MELODY LOUISE, Global Studies Teacher; *b:* Oswego, NY; *m:* Richard; *c:* Megan; *ed:* The Amer Univ (BA) Intnl Stud 1976; SUNY at Oswego (MS) Soc Stud Ed 1990; Cornell Univ Post Grad Ag Ec; *cr:* Liverpool HS Global Stud Tchr 1986-; *ai:* NCSS 1986-; Fulbright Exch Tchr Hungary 1990-91; *office:* Liverpool HS 4338 Wetzel Rd Liverpool NY 13090

SMITH, MERELYN ELIZABETH, Mathematics Teacher; *b:* Providence, RI; *ed:* Gordon Coll (BS) Elem Ed 1979; Univ of NH (MST) Math 1993; *cr:* Glen Urquhart Schl 5th-6th Grd Combination Tchr 1979-80, 4th-5th Grd Combination Tchr 1980-81, 5th Grd Tchr 1981-87, 6th-9th Grd Math, Cmptr Tchr 1987-90, 6th-8th Grd Math, Cmptr Tchr 1990-95; PRIME-NH Staff Mem 1995-; Inst Learning, Dev Intern 1995-; Gordon Coll Instr Math Ed 1996; Univ of NH Instr Math Ed 1996; *ai:* Act Period Tchr; Adv, Chair Prof Growth, Dev Comm; Fin Comm; mS Team Ldr; NCTM 1979-; ATMIM, ATMNE 1989-; Beverly Group Home Flwshp 1982-, Co-Founder, Vol Svc Awd 1987, 1995; North Shore Comm Bapt 1980-, World Focus Comm, Choir, Spec Projects Comm, Auditor; Finalist Christa Mac Auliffe Flwshp 1995; Who's Who Amer Ed 1992-; *office:* Glen Urquhart Schl 74 Hart St Beverly MA 01915*

SMITH, MICHAEL H., Bio, Anatomy & Physiology Tchr; *b:* Oak Hill, OH; *m:* Helen Jo Wimer; *c:* Rebecca, Rachel, Carey; *ed:* OH Univ (BS) Bio, Sci Ed 1971, (MEd) Stu Prsnl 1975; Univ of Dayton Elem, Scndry Prin Cert 1992, Asst Supt Cert 1996; *cr:* Minford MS Sci Tchr 1972-92; Shawnee St Univ Southern OH Correctional Facility Bio Adj 1990-91; Minford HS Bio, Sci Tchr 1992-; *ai:* Dist Comm Ed Dir; Tech, Sciota Cty Sci Curr, Dist Sci Fair Comms; NEA, OH EA 1971-; NABT 1990-; Minford Ed Assn 1971-, VP; Martha Holden Jennings Awd; *office:* Minford HS 125 Falcon Rd Minford OH 45653*

SMITH, MICHAEL WALTER,SR., Physical Education & Hlth Tchr; *b:* Elizabeth, NJ; *m:* Vanessa Roberta Silvera; *c:* Alacie Michelle Smith Bennett, Michael Walter Jr., Malcolm Corey, Alexis Marie; *ed:* William Paterson Coll (BA) PE, Hlth 1976; *cr:* Abraham Clark HS Tchr, Coach 1976-; *ai:* Frosh Ftbl, JV Bsktbl, Tennis Club Coach; Yth Flwshp Adv; Staff Flwshp; Core Team, Aids Assembly Comms; NEA, Roselle Ed Assn 1976-; Bethlehem Bapt Church 1975-, Deacon, Sunday Schl Tchr, Yth Dir; William Paterson Coll Alumni 1976-; Tchr of Yr Awd 1989-90; Union Cty Tournament JV Bsktbl Champions 1995-; *office:* Abraham Clark HS 122 E 6th Ave Roselle NJ 07203*

SMITH, MICHELE MCLOUGHLIN, Spanish Teacher; *b:* Troy, NY; *m:* Gordon B.; *c:* Megan, Gregory, Peter; *ed:* The Coll of St Rose at Albany (BA) Span His & Eng Ed 1972; Addl Courses in His & Pol Sci; *cr:* Granville Cntrl Schl Span I & II 1972-74, 7th-8th Soc Stud Tchr 1974-86, Span 7th-9th Grds Tchr 1987-; *ai:* Co-Senior Class Adv; Modern Lang Club; Sunshine Comm; Frosh Class Adv; Elem Youth at Risk Comm; NYSUT, Granville Tchrs Assn 1972-; *office:* Granville Cntrl Jr-Sr HS Quaker St Granville NY 12832

SMITH, NANNETTE BOYD, English Teacher; *b:* Cambridge, OH; *m:* Jack; *c:* Colleen; *ed:* Grad Work Kent St, Baldwin Wallace; *cr:* Brooklyn

HS Eng Dept Tchr 1960-; *ai:* Var Chrldng Coach; Team Cnslng; NEA; OEA; GCTE; OCTELA; BEA, Sec; Fairview Hosp Auxiliary Bd.

SMITH, PAGE ANDREW, AP His, Govt & Ec Instructor; *b:* St Marys, OH; *m:* Patricia Adele Tangeman; *c:* Adam B., Tara S.; *ed:* Wright St Univ (BS) Soc Stud Comprehensive 1978; Univ of Dayton (MS) Educl Admin 1983; Post Grad Stud; Mentor Prgm; ICS Industrial Mechanics & St of OH Journeyman Cert 1976; St of OH Stationary Engrs License 1984; *cr:* Celina Sr HS Instr & Dept Chm 1978-84; Wapakoneta Sr HS Instr 1985-87; Wright St Univ Instr 1983-; Celina Sr HS Instr 1988-; *ai:* Mercer Cty Teenage Republican Spon; Wright St Univ Scholastic Bowl Judge & Adv; North Central Evaluation Comm Faculty Rep; NCSS, Univ of Dayton Alumini & Wright St Univ Alumni; Asst Cty Bd Elections; Legislator Asst Auglaize Right to Life; Small Bus Fed of America; Outstanding Stu Tchr of NW OH; Natl Jrnlsm Ctr Ed & Research Inst Internship Awd; Sec St of OH Instr of Politics Awd; OH Hum Cncl Grant; Pub Articles; *office:* Celina Sr HS 715 E Wayne St Saint Marys OH 45822*

SMITH, PAMELA S., 6th Grade Social Studies Tchr; *b:* Greensburg, PA; *ed:* PA St Univ (BS) Elem Ed 1974, (MED) Developmental & Remedial Rdng 1974; Clarion Univ 6 Credits; Univ of HI 1 Credit; *cr:* Yough Schl Dist 1st Grd Tchr 1974-78, Remedial Rdng Tchr 1978-82, 1st Grd Tchr 1982-94; Yough MS 6th Grd Soc Stud Tchr 1994-; *ai:* NEA 1974-; PSEA 1974-; Crabapple Park & Pool 1989-, Bd Mem Pres; St Charles Borromeo Cath Church 1992-, Parish Cncl Mem & Choir; *office:* Yough MS Rd 1 Box 574 Ruffs Dale PA 15679

SMITH, PATRICE, Eighth Grade English Teacher; *b:* McSherrystown, PA; *c:* Caroline, Gideon; *ed:* Indiana Univ of PA (BA) Jrnlsm 1975; Shippensburg Univ of PA (MED) Eng 1989; Real Estate Sales Cert 1978; Classical Piano Stud 1958-69; *cr:* Hanover Evening Sun Reporter, Photographer & Ed 1975-79; PA Cncl on Arts Pub Information Officer 1977-78; Evansville Courier Entertainment Ed 1980-86; Littlestown HS Writing Coach 1986-88; Maple Ave MS 8th Grd Eng Tchr 1988-; The Gettysburgian & Coll Nwsp Adv 1992; *ai:* Drama Dir; Newspaper Adv; Theme Comm Chprsn; Local Union Newsletter Ed; Speech Tournament Judge; Stud Assistance Team; NCTE, NEA & PA St Ed Assn 1988-; Littlestown Area Ed Assn 1988-, Cncl Rep; Soc of Prof Journalists 1975-, Numerous Writing Awds 1976-86; Interfaith Ctr for Peace & Justice 1989-; Local PTA & Parent Tchr Org 1981-, Prgm Dir 2 Yrs; Adams Comm Television 1988-, Bd 2 Yrs; Publicist, Adams Cnty Arts Cncl Publicist; Bloomington IN Playwrights Project 1985; Gettysburg PA Rainbow Theatre Project Composer & Lyricist 1990; Amer Assn of Univ Women Schlsp Awd 1987; Gettysburg Deja Vu Music Dir 1988-; Evansville WTVW Channel 7 Movie Critic 1983-85; *office:* Maple Avenue M S Maple Ave Littlestown PA 17340*

SMITH, PATRICIA, English Teacher; *b:* South Amboy, NJ; *m:* Wayne Howard; *c:* Marc; *ed:* 30 Addl Grad Credits; *cr:* Matawan Regnl HS Fr, Eng Tchr 1965-67; Lloyd Rd MS Eng Tchr 1968-80; Matawan Ave MS Eng, Performing Arts Tchr 1980-85; Matawan Regnl HS Eng Tchr 1985-; *ai:* SADD, Chess Club Adv; Co-Adv Lit, Art Journal; Asst Band Dir; NEA, NJEA, MCEA, MRTA 1964-; Aberdeen Zoning Bd 1994-; ATMVA 1995-, Commissioner; Aberdeen Republican Club 1994-, Treas; Performing Arts Dir 1980-84; Fac Cmptr Trainer; 9th Grd Eng Tech Prgm Creator 1994; Dir Summer Theatre, HS, MS Musicals, Childrens' Theatre Wkshps 1976-85; *office:* Matawan-Aberdeen Regnl HS 450 Atlantic Ave Aberdeen NJ 07747

SMITH, PATRICIA ANN, Science Teacher; *b:* Vineland, NJ; *ed:* Cumberland Cty Coll (AA) PE 1976; Columbia Pacific Univ Sci & Guidance; *cr:* Sacred Heart Rgnl Schl PE Tchr 1976-81; Sacred Heart HS Algebra Tchr 1981-82; Sacred Heart Rgnl 5th-8th Grd Sci Tchr 1982-; *ai:* Yrbk Co Adv; Intramural Prgm Adv; Sci Fair; Sci Dept Chair; Spirit Club; Drug Ed & Spelling Bee Coord; Boys Bsktbl Gate; Day Care Dir; NCEA 1980-; NSTA 1990-; Sacred Heart Parish Cncl 1980-82, Sec; CYO Bsktbl 1974-80, City Champs 1976-80; *office:* Sacred Heart Rgnl Schl 922 E. Landis Ave Vineland NJ 08360

SMITH, PATRICK SEAN JAMES, Eng Tchr & Basketball Coach; *b:* Bangor, ME; *m:* Elizabeth Ann Zouzalik; *c:* Joseph, Maria, Sean, Nathan, Matthew; *ed:* Harvard Univ (BA) Ec 1986; *cr:* DeMatha Cath HS Eng Tchr 1987-; *ai:* Asst Var Mens Bsktbl Coach; Edited & Co-Authored DeMatha Offensive Notebook; Assisted in Writing Coaching Bsktbl Successfully; Fr James Day OSST Awd for Outstndng Tchr of Yr 1996; *office:* De Matha Catholic HS 4313 Madison St Hyattsville MD 20781

SMITH, PAUL A., Business Technology Instructor; *b:* Lynn, MA; *m:* Barbara A. Graves; *c:* Paul, Holly, Jill, Karen, Scott; *ed:* Salem St Coll (BS) Bus Ed 1965; Worcester St Coll (MED) Admin 1970; Court Reporting; *cr:* Nipmuc Regnl HS Tchr 1965-67; Bellingham Meml HS Dept Head Tchr 1967-69; Holliston Jr Coll Dean of Stdnts 1969-75; Shawsheen Voc Tech Tchr 1975-; *ai:* VICA Coord; Stu Cncl Adv; Dir of Schl Accts; Adult Ed Dir; Shawseen Tchrs 1975-, Treas; MA Tchrs Assn, NEA 1975-; Amer Voc Assn; MA Voc Assn; Natl Assn Tax Prac 1979-; Natl Soc Pub Acct, Natl Soc Tax Prep, NH Assn Pub Acct 1994-; Elks 1989-; Amer Legion 1994-; Yearbook Dedication; *office:* Shawsheen Voc Tech HS 100 Cook St Billerica MA 01821*

SMITH, PAUL EDGAR, English Prof & Dept Chprsn; *b:* Mkar, Nigeria; *m:* Romaine R. Jesky-Smith; *c:* Amy R. Fattibene, Sara M. Locke, Christopher P.; *ed:* Calvin Coll (AB) Eng 1960; Bowling Green St Univ (MA) Eng 1963; Univ of Pittsburgh (PHD) Eng 1981; Univ of WI at Madison Post Masters Stud; *cr:* Calvin Coll Lecturer 1961-63; Appleton HS Eng Tchr 1964-66; Geneva Coll Prof 1966-; *ai:* Dept Chprsn; Core Curr Commission; Ombuds Person for Coll Employees; Academic Prgm, Prof Ed Comms; NCTE 1966-; Conf Christianity & Lit 1972-; Modern Lang Assn 1982-; Presbyn Church 1964-, Deacon, Elder; Natl Endowment for Humanities Stud Awd 1985; *office:* Geneva Coll 3200 College Ave Beaver Falls PA 15010

SMITH, PAUL MICHAEL, Biology Teacher; *b:* Allentown, PA; *m:* Susan Eyer; *c:* James, Alison; *ed:* Millerville U of PA (BS) Bio & Comprehensive Sci 1965; Kutztown U of PA (MED) Bio 1968; 33 Credit Hrs: Millersville U, Kutztown U, U of MD & UAL at Huntsville; *cr:* Emmaus Jr HS Sci & Bio Tchr 1965-; *ai:* PSEA & NEA 1965-; Amer Bio Tchr 1975-; Macungie Shade Tree Com 1993-, VP; Space Camp Schlsp; Outstndng Tchr; *office:* Emmaus Jr HS 660 Macungie Ave Emmaus PA 18049

SMITH, PAUL R., Health Ed Tchr & Dept Chprsn; *b:* Wellsville, NY; *m:* Darrah Dusenbury; *c:* Kimberly, Steven, Eric; *ed:* St Univ of NY at Brockport (BS) Hlth, PE & Recreation 1967, (MS) Hlth Ed & PE 1969; *cr:* Wayland Cntrl Schl PE Tchr & Coach 1967-69; Lancaster Cntrl Schls Hlth Ed Tchr 1970-; *ai:* K-12th Grd Hlth Dept Chprsn; Girls Var Bsktbl & Boys Jr Var Soccer Coach; Adv of Drug & Alcohol Awareness Day Prgm Facilitators & AIDS Awareness Day Prgm; Stu Schlsp Comm; AID Advy Bd Chprsn; Drug Free Schl Grant Coord; NYSTA, AFT 1967-; NYSPHE 1990-; *office:* Lancaster Cntrl Schls 1 Forton Dr Lancaster NY 14086

SMITH, PAULA SANFORD, Art Teacher; *b:* Hamilton, OH; *ed:* Miami Univ at Oxford (BFA) Drawing & Painting 1963, (MA) Art Ed 1984; *cr:* Lazarus Cols Q Asst Prod Mgr, Retoucher, Home Artist, Supvr Fashion, Layout 1963-74; Saillitos Illustrator 1974-76; US Shoe Corp Stylist 1976-79; WKRC WLW-TV Co-Exec Prod, Art Dir, Co Music Prod 1976-78; Collage Free Lance Artist 1977-; *ai:* Drawing; Ceramics; Painting; Sculpture; Singing; NAEA 1986-; Alpha Kappa Alpha 1962-, Adv 1980-84; Artisan Emporium Gallery 1988-90, Partner; Bethel AME Church 1958-, Choir, Young People's Group; Lectures; *office:* Princeton HS 11080 Chester Rd Cincinnati OH 45246

SMITH, PEGGY A., Spanish Teacher; *b:* Logan, OH; *m:* David; *c:* Katy, Mark; *ed:* Miami Univ (BS) Span Ed 1975; Mount St Joseph (MA) Ed 1990; Addl Hrs at OH Univ, OH St Univ, Drake Univ, Ashland Univ; *cr:* Liberty Union HS Span, Eng Tchr 1975-85; Watkins Meml HS Span Tchr 1986-; *ai:* Coord of Bi-annual Stu Trips to Span Speaking Countries; OEA, NEA 1975-; *office:* Watkins Memorial HS 8868 Watkins Rd SW Pataskala OH 43062

SMITH, PETER R., Social Studies Teacher; *b:* Mount Pleasant, MI; *m:* Melissa S. McFarlane; *c:* Andrew, Jared, Patrick, Kyle; *ed:* Cntrl MI Univ (BS) His 1983, (MS) Hist 1989; *cr:* Springfield City Schls-South HS Soc Stud Tchr 1984-; *ai:* Girls Track Head Coach; Class of 1988 adv; OH Dist 9 Girls Track Coach of Yr 1995; *home:* 136 S Kensington Pl Springfield OH 45504

SMITH, RAYMOND JOSEPH, Dept Lead Tchr & Latin Istr; *b:* Cambridge, MA; *m:* Marie A. Beninati; *c:* Carolyn, Jacquelyn; *ed:* Boston Coll (BA) Latin, Scndry Ed 1970; OH St Univ (MA) Latin, Greek 1972, (PHD) Classics 1977; Intro to Data Processing 3 Credits; COBAL Programming 6 Credits; Basic Programming 3 Credits; *cr:* OH St Univ Grad Tchng Assoc 1970-75; Arlington Pub Schls Latin Tchr 1975-, Lead Tchr Dept of Frgn Lang 1992-; *ai:* Latin Club 1975-78 Adv; Frgn Lang Dept Re-Accreditation Comm Chm 1982, 1992; Sftbl Coach Girls Yth League 1989-94; Document Storage Admin for BBN Inc; Arlington Educ Assn, MA Tchrs Assn, NEA 1976-; Amer Classical League; Classical Assn of New Eng; *office:* Arlington HS 869 Massachusetts Ave Arlington MA 02174*

SMITH, RICHARD C., Retired Teacher; *b:* Dover, PA; *m:* Marie Rebecca Wallace; *c:* Cynthia K. Mc Coy, Brenda J., Pamela D. Ruppert; *ed:* Shippensburg Univ (BS) Elem Ed 1959; Western MD Coll (MED) Admin 1967; 15 Credit Hrs Post Grad Courses; *cr:* Centrl York Schl Dist 6 Grd Tchr 1959-78, 5 Grd Tchr 1978-89, Head Tchr 1966-84; *ai:* York Cty Chptr PA Assn of Schl Retirees 1989-; AARP 1990-; Pigeon Hills Snowmobile Club, PSSA 1989-; EAA 1995-; 2 PA Cmptr Equipment Grants.

SMITH, RICHARD C., Social Studies Teacher; *b:* Philadelphia, PA; *m:* Teresa; *c:* Christina; *ed:* Widener Univ (BA) Bus 1984, (MED) Ed 1992; *cr:* Beverly Hills MS Tchr 1990-; *ai:* Ftbl, Wrestling, Bsbl Coach; NEA 1990-.

SMITH, RICHARD GRANVILLE, Chemistry Teacher; *b:* Montgomery, AL; *m:* Donna J. Squire; *c:* Eric, Mark; *ed:* OH Univ (BSEd) Comprehensive Sci 1966; IN Univ (MAT) Chem 1970; Addl Stud Chem; *cr:* Lancaster HS Chem Tchr 1966-69; OH Univ Chem Tchr 1967-69; Bexley HS Chem Tchr 1969-; *ai:* Seiko Youth Challenge I, II Schlsp Judge; Bexley Educ Assn, OEA, NEA 1966-; NSTA 1968-; ACS 1978-, Regnl Outstanding Chem Tchr 1978; Worthington Chrstn Village Bd 1988-, Trustee 8 Yrs; Fairfield Church of Christ 1970-, Elder 26 Yrs; Amateur Radio Operator 1966-; Vol Firefighter & Emt; Natl Sci Fnd Grants 1967-70; Co-author Merrill Phys Sci, Merrill Chem, Solving Problems Chem, Tchr Resource Book Chem; *office:* Bexley H S 326 S Cassingham Bexley OH 43209

SMITH, RICHARD MOUNT, Retired Choral Activities Dir; *b:* Philadelphia, PA; *ed:* West Chester Univ (BS) Music Ed 1960; Temple Univ (MM) Choral Conducting-Hnr 1971; *cr:* Audubon HS Music Tchr, Dir of Choral Act 1960-95; *ai:* Musical Dir Concert Choir, Madrigal Singers, Alumni Chorus; Fine, Performing Arts Chm 1965-88; NJ Ed Assn, MENC 1960-; NJ Music Edctrs 1960-, Exec Sec; South Jersey Choral Dirs Assn 1961-, Pres, Treas; NJ Music Edctrs Distngd Svc Awd 1991; NJ St Governor's Music Ed Distngd Svc & Ldrshp Awd 1995; Conductor NJ All-St Chorus 1970, 1979, All-South Jersey Chorus 1968, 1978, 1988; *home:* 215 Pine Run Dr Blackwood NJ 08012

SMITH, RICHARD ROBERT, French & Mathematics Teacher; *b:* Chicago, IL; *ed:* Univ of Chicago (BA) Span 1952; Middlebury Coll (MA) Fr 1966; Attnd Temple Univ Italian 24 Credit Hrs, George Washington Univ 18 Credit Hrs, San Francisco St Coll 7 Credit Hrs & Univ of VA 6 Credit Hrs; *cr:* South Shore HS Schl Tutor 1948-54; US Navy 2nd Class Yeoman 1954-57; Wilbraham Univ Dean of Acad & Lang & Math Depts Head 1957-74; William Penn Charter Schl Lang Dept Head & Fr & Math Tchr 1974-; *ai:* Acad Detention Coord; Curr Comm; Attendance Coord; Admin Search Comm; Acad Adv; Homeroom Tchr; AATF 1960-, Pres, VP, Contest Chm, Treas; GLSTN 1994-; Les Amis 1988-, Exec Sec; Allegro 1985-, Exec Sec; John F Gummere Distinguished Tchr Awd 1989; *office:* William Penn Charter Schl 3000 W School House Ln Philadelphia PA 19144

SMITH, RICHARD STEPHEN, Special Education Teacher; *b:* Plattsburgh, NY; *m:* Therese C. Brady; *c:* Sean Patrick; *ed:* Castleton St Coll (BS) Spec Ed 1984; Plattsburgh St Univ (MS) Spec Ed 1987; *cr:* Ticonderoga Cntrl Schl Spec Ed Tchr 1987-; *ai:* Jr Var Ftbl Coach; Girls Var Bsktbl Coach; NY St United Tchrs 1987-; Ticonderoga Tchrs Assn 1987-, Treas; Westport Chapter Bsbl Umpires 1993-; Bsktbl Coach of Yr 1988 & 1995; *office:* Ticonderoga Cntrl Schl 351 Amherst Ave Ticonderoga NY 12883

SMITH, ROBERT DONALD, Mathematics Teacher; *b:* Wilkes-Barre, PA; *m:* Veronica Joan Sharkus; *c:* Tammy Ann, Charles; *ed:* Wilkes Coll (BS) Math Scndry Ed 1963; Univ of SC (MM) Math 1972; Attnd Univ of S FL, Univ of Cincinatti; *cr:* Wilkes-Barre Area Schl Dist Math Tchr 1965-; *ai:* Math Team Coach; NEA, PSEA, W-BAEA 1965-; NCTM 1990-; First Bapt Church 1980-, Chm; Irim Temple 1975-; NSF Flwshp Univ SC; *office:* James M Coughlin Sr HS 80 N Washington St Wilkes Barre PA 18701*

SMITH, ROBERT ELLIOTT, Mathematics Teacher; *b:* Elmira, NY; *m:* Janis Marie Moss; *c:* Betsy; *ed:* Mansfield Univ (BS) Math 1966; Elmira Coll (MS) Math Ed 1970; Rutgers Univ NSF Grant 1969 8 Credits; Post Grad Cornell, OH St, 18 Credits Syracuse Univ; *cr:* Ernie Davis Jr HS Math Tchr 1966-70; Southside HS Math Tchr 1970-; *ai:* Schl at Work, Fac Convocation Comms; Boys Var Soccer Coach; AFT, NYSUT 1966-; AMTNYS 1985-; NCTM 1989-; Speaker AMTNYS Annual Meetings; *office:* Southside HS 777 S Main St Elmira NY 14904

SMITH, ROBERT FRANCIS, English Teacher; *b:* Northampton, MA; *m:* Mary Ellen Potyrala; *c:* Nathan, Geoffrey; *ed:* Wesleyan Univ (BA) Eng, Russian 1975; Univ of MA at Amherst Tchr Preparation Prgm, Western MA Writing Project Participant; *cr:* Pioneer Vly Regnl Schl Eng, His Tchr 1977; Middleton HS Eng, Alternative Schl Tchr 1977-78; Frontier Regnl Schl Grd 8 Eng Tchr 1978-; *ai:* Girls Var Track, Boys, Girls Var Cross Cntry, MS Boys Bsktbl Coach; NCTE 1980-; MA Tchrs Assn 1978-; Whately Schl Bldg Comm 1989-, Chair; *office:* Frontier Regional Schl 113 N Main St South Deerfield MA 01373

SMITH, ROBERT OAKFORD, Seventh Grd Language Arts Tchr; *b:* Bridgeton, NJ; *m:* Joann Dekatch; *c:* Kelli, Deborah, Stephen; *ed:* Austin Peay St Univ (BA) Eng, Psych 1971; 6 Credit Hrs Psych Rowan Univ; *cr:* Bridgeton HS Spec Ed Tchr 1973-74; Fairfield MS Lang Arts Tchr 1974-88; Woodruff Schl Lang Arts Tchr 1988-; *ai:* Soccer, Bsktbl Coaches; Ath Dir; NEA, NJEA 1974-; *office:* Woodruff Schl Hwy 77 Seabrook NJ 08302*

SMITH, ROBERT REED, Retired 7th Grade Math Teacher; *b:* Jersey City, NJ; *m:* Marilyn F. Wardell; *c:* Heather; *ed:* 25 Credit Hrs Post Grad Stud; *cr:* West Belmar Schl 4th Grd Tchr 1970-83, 6th Grd Tchr 19
Wall Intermediate Schl 6th Grd Math Tchr 1987-88, 7th Grd Ma
1989-94; *ai:* Safety Patrol Adv; Wall Tchrs Assn 1970-, Negotiator
Monmouth Cty Ed Assn 1970-; NJ Ed Assn, NEA 1970-; St of NJ D
of Fish & Game Vol Instr 1975-85.

SMITH, ROBIN W., Business Teacher; *b:* Knoxville, TN; *m:* E. Fr
ed: Meredith Coll (BS) Bus Admin 1977; Wilmington Coll (MB
Admin 1988; 55 Addl Hrs Cmptr, Bus Tech, Ed, Career Guid; *cr:*
DE Admin Asst 1977-79; Middletown HS Bus Tchr 1979-80; Wooc
HS Bus Tchr 1980-91; Smyrna HS Acctng, W Processing Instr 19
Bus Prof of Amer Club Adv; Co-Chair Mid Sts Comm; Bd of Dir
Prof of Amer; Frameworks Comm for Bus, Mrktg Ed; NBEA, DBEA
VP, Bd of Dir, DE Bus Edctr of Yr; NEA, WEA, SEA 1979-, Loc
Bldg & Dist Tchr of Yr; Amm Assn of Univ Women 1977-, Sec, Nev
Chair; *office:* Smyrna HS 85 Duck Creek Hwy Smyrna DE 19977

SMITH, RODNEY RAY, American History Teacher; *b:* Sharples,
Marcia Lynne Huffman; *c:* Kara Leigh, Nathan Andrew; *ed:* Glen
Coll (AB) PE, His 1974; Ashland Univ (MA) Sports Sci 1994; *cr:* C
Co Schls 8th Grd His Tchr, Coach 1974-76; Logan Elem Schls 8th C
Tchr, Coach 1977-; *ai:* Var Ftbl, Jr HS Track Asst Coach; Var Wr
Head Coach; NEA 1974-; OEA 1977-, Past Local Pres; Mid St Girl
Coach of Yr 1983; Tchr of Month 1994; OH Cntrl Dist Wrestling
Sportsmanship 1995; *office:* George Mcdowell-Exchange Sch 9575
Rd Circleville OH 43113

SMITH, RONALD D., Spanish Teacher & Athletic Dir; *b:* Midd
OH; *m:* Sandra J. Helton; *c:* Tyler, Stacey; *ed:* Miami Univ (B
Admin, Minor Span 1983; 8 Post Grad Credit Hrs Univ of Dayt
Cincinnati Chrstn Schl Tchr 1985-; *ai:* Girls Var Vlybl, Boys, Girls
Field Coach; Stu Affairs Comm; Hunter Yth Recreation Assoc 199
office: Cincinnati Christian Schools 825 Waycross Forest City OH

SMITH, RONALD L., Sixth Grade Teacher; *b:* DuBois, PA; *m:*
Marie Bonaventure; *c:* Nicole Christine, Brian Douglas; *ed:* Shippe
St Coll (BS) Elem Ed 1969; PA St Univ (MED) Elem Ed 1972; Tu
Intermediate Unit #11 In-Svc; *cr:* Mount Union Area Schl Dist 6
Tchr 1969-; Huntingdon St Correctional Inst Adult Basic Ed Tchr 19
Altoona Area Schl Dist Adult Basic Ed Tchr 1980-85; *ai:* Museu
Girls Vllybl & Bsktbl Game Mgr; Inservice Advy Cncl Mem; M
PSEA & NEA 1969-, VP & Negotiations Comm; BSA 1974-, Cub
Dist Awd of Merit, Silver Beaver & Saint George; Tchr Adv Weekly
Magazine; *office:* Mount Union Elem Schl Mt Union Area Schl Dis
Market St Mount Union PA 17066*

SMITH, ROSEMARIE KING, Science Teacher; *b:* Westbrook,
Clifton D.; *c:* Patrick, Katie, Daniel; *ed:* Bates Coll (BS) Bio 197
of VT (MED) Classroom Tchr Ed 1981; 5 Credit Hrs Woodrow
Chem Inst; 4 Credit Hrs Summer Physics Inst at Bates Coll; 12 Cre
Howard Hughes Grant Colby Coll Oceanography, Geology, Sci &
Women in Ed; *cr:* ME Med Ctr Rsrch Asst 1974-76; Univ of VT Me
Rsrch Asst 1977-81; Catherine Mc Auley HS Sci Tchr 1982-84;
Hills HS Math & Sci Tchr 1985-87; Waterville HS Sci Tchr 1987-; *a*
Adv; Sci Olympiad Team Coach; Curr Comm; NSTA, NEA 1985-
1987-; AAPT 1989-; Numerous Articles Pub; Presented at ME Sci
Assn Convention 1993-95; Presented at PRISMS Conf 1994-95;
Waterville HS 1 Brooklyn Ave Waterville ME 04901

SMITH, ROSEMARY TERESA, Associate Professor of Lit; *b:* Eva
IL; *c:* Jamal Davis; *ed:* CA St Univ at Los Angeles (BA) Eng 1967,
Educl Admin 1989; Post Grad Credit at Univ of CA at Los Angel
John C. Fremont HS Eng Tchr 1 Yr; Eliot Jr High Schl Spec Ed Tch
1 Yr; Washington Jr HS Eng, Music, Drama Tchr 2 Yrs; John Muir
Tchr 19 Yrs; Howard Univ Eng Instr 3 Yrs; Prince Georges Com
Assoc Prof of Lit & Writing 3 Yrs; *ai:* Staff Dev, Cross Cultural Ed
Coord; Mrktg Comm; Black Heritage Project, Prince Georges Cty
Cultural Ed Advy Cncl; Staff Dev Advy Cncl; Mentor in ALANA
Club Adv; NEA 1970-; MLA 1994-; CLA 1991-; NAACP 1983-;
Sigma Theta 1967-; Tchr of Yr Svc Awd 1983; *office:* Prince G
Comm Coll 301 Largo Rd Largo MD 20772*

SMITH, RUTH LYNETTE, Assoc Prof of Religion; *b:* Chicago,
East TN St Univ (BA) Lit 1969; OH Univ (MA) Linguistics 1971; H
Divinity Schl (MTS) Theology 1976; Boston Univ (PHD) Soc Ethic
cr: Berea Coll Eng Instr 1971-74; OH Wesleyan Univ Asst R
1982-83; Worcester Polytechnic Inst Assoc Rel Prof 1983-; *ai:* SCE
AAR 1983-; APA 1983-; SSSR 1986-; Soc for North Amer Soc Phil
1987-; MA Fndtn for the Hum, 1988-95, Bd Mem, Exec Comm 19
VP 1993-95; Roothbert Fellow for Grad Stud 1980-81; Numerous A
Pub, Lectures & Presentations.

SMITH, STANLEY, HS Social Studies Teacher; *b:* Savannah, G
Marda Ann Westenhoefer; *c:* Jason, April; *ed:* Millersville Univ (
1975; Kutztown Univ (MS) Ed 1981; +30 Credit Hrs; *cr:* Souderto
Dist Tchr 1975-; *ai:* Wrestling Coach; NEA 1975-; *office:* Souderto
HS 41 N School Ln Souderton PA 18964

SMITH, STEPHEN CHARLES, Reading Workshop Teacher; *b:* G
NY; *m:* Kathleen Mary Hanford; *c:* Julia, Bryant T., Adam C.,
Molly, S. Michael; *ed:* SUC at Oswego (BS) Elem Ed 1967, (MS) Ed
Soc Stud 7-12, Math 7-9 Post Grad Stud; *cr:* Waterloo Cntrl Schl 5
Tchr 1967-70, MS Math Tchr 1970-89, MS Rdng Wkshp Tchr 199
MS Summer Session Head Tchr; MS Bldg Team; Yorker Club Adv
Arts-In-Ed Coord; NEA 1967-; *home:* 14 S Seneca St Waterloo NY

SMITH, STEPHEN D., Chemistry & Biology Teacher; *b:* Washi
DC; *m:* Mary E.; *c:* Rebecca, Alex; *ed:* Univ of MD (BS) Microb
1980; Univ of Pittsburgh (MAT) Ed 1992; *cr:* Greensburg Salem HS
& Bio Tchr 1992-; *ai:* Division of Chemical Ed & Amer Chemic
1995-; *office:* Greensburg Salem HS 65 Mennel Dr Greensburg PA

SMITH, SUSAN B., English Teacher; *b:* Jersey City, NJ; *ed:* Montc
Coll (BA) Eng Ed 1982; Jersey City St Coll (MA) Arts 1993;
Pleasant Boro HS Eng Tchr 1983; Pt Pleasant Beach HS Eng Tchr 19
Brick Meml HS Eng Tchr 1985-; *ai:* Asst Cheerleading & Girls
Track Coach; Class of 1994 Adv; Acad Competition Squad; NEA
BTEA; New Jersey Cncl of Tchrs of Eng; Brick Meml HS Tchr
Governors Tchr Recognition Prgm; Brick Meml HS Natl
Champions Coach 1992; NJ Family Life Curr 10 Yr Review & Re
Book Tech & Curr Consultant; *office:* Brick Meml HS 2001 Lanes M
Brick NJ 08724*

SMITH, SUSAN BETH, 7th Grade Mathematics Teacher; *b:* Malden
ed: (MED) Cnslng 1981; (BS) Elem, Math 1973; Courses in MS
Cooperative Tchng & Learning, Cmptrs; *cr:* Shawsheen Elem Schl 5
Tchr 1973-83; West Intermediate Schl Math Tchr 1983-; *ai:* Coope
Prgm Marshall's Inc for Stdnts; NEA 1973-; NCTM 1984-; WTA
Bldg Rep, Bargaining Rep; *office:* West Intermediate Schl Cart
Wilmington MA 01887*

SMITH, SUSAN CHARLOTTE, French & Spanish Teache
Manchester, NH; *ed:* Bates Coll (BA) Fr 1969; Univ of MN (MA) Fr
cr: Oyster River HS Tchr 1971-; *ai:* Granite St Challenge, Fr Club
Stu, Fac Senate; Comm Svc Prgm Soup Kitchen; AATF, Treas; A
NEA; First Parish Congregational Church; Outstdng Svc HS 1986,
office: Oyster River HS 55 Coe Dr Durham NH 03824

H, SUSAN TAYLOR, American Literature Teacher; b: Ahoskie, Fred Richard III; ed: East Caroline Univ (BS) Eng Ed 1993; Attnd ulie Coll; AP Cert Lang & Composition Pembroke St Univ; cr: St l's Schl Tchrs Asst 1994; Cath HS of Baltimore Tenth Grd Eng Tchr ai: Stu Cncl Moderator; Lit Club Adv; office: Catholic H S Of ore 2800 Edison Hwy Baltimore MD 21213

H, SUZANNE CHOMKA, Eight Grade English Teacher; b: Utica, James F.; c: Travis, Ashley; ed: SUNY at Geneseo (BA) Eng, Elem SUNY at Cortland (MS) Rdng 1984; 45 Addl Credit Hrs; cr: Auburn Schl 10th Grd Eng Tchr 1980-81; Sauquoit Vly Cntrl Schl 8th Grd chr 1981-; ai: Writers' Club Adv; Chrldng Coach; NYSUT 1980-; Sauquoit Vly Cntrl Schl Sulphur Springs Rd Sauquoit NY 13456*

H, TAMMY ANN, Health & Physical Ed Teacher; b: Hazleton, PA; st Stroudsburg Univ (BS) Hlth, PE 1982; cr: North Warren Regnl HS PE Tchr 1983-; ai: Coach Bsktbl Girls 1984-94, Womens 1995-; 1984-; Tchr of Yr 1994; office: North Warren Regional HS Lambert Box 410 Blairstown NJ 07825*

H, TERRI LEFFLER, Soc Studies Teacher; b: Pottsville, PA; m: ed: Messiah Coll (BA) Soc Stud 1973; cr: Pine Grove Area HS Soc chr 1992-; ai: SADD Adv; office: Pine Grove Area HS 101 School e Grove PA 17963

H, TERRY SELDON, Occptnl Work Experience Coord; b: Louisa, : Beverly Ann Zanchetti; c: Debra Dean Thompson, Kimberly Ann; orehead St Univ (BA) 1973; Attnd Miami Univ Ed, Wright St Univ d, Kent St Univ Voc Ed; cr: Clermont Northeastern Schls HS Indstrl chr 1973-79, MS Indstrl Ed Tchr 1979-92, HS Indstrl Ed Tchr 95, OWE Coord 1995-; ai: Clermont NE Tchrs Assn 1975-; ational Work Exp Coord Assn; Rep St Comm to Review Tchr Cert; Comm.

H, THELMA CHERYL (CROMARTIE), Assistant Principal; b: gee, AL; m: Pierce A.; c: Cheri, Dawn, Pierce; ed: Univ of Dayton Pre-Medicine 1975; Hood Coll (MS) Educl Ldrshp 1996; Univ of NC ieville Ed Cert; Hood Coll Admin; cr: South Fr Broad Jr HS Math 1982-83; Seneca Valley HS Sci Tchr 1983-; ai: Minority Achvmt & ipation Prgm Coord; Models & Mentors; Self-Esteem Enhancement; n Acad Plus Tchr; NEA 1983-; Church Youth Group 1990-93, Ldr, of Ed; Acad Plus Prgm Successful Prgm Awd; Inroads Cnslr Awd Germantown Kiawanas Tchr of Yr 1993; office: Martin Luther King, 11700 Neelsville Church Rd Germantown MD 20874

H, THERESA CLAIR, Former Prof of Intnl Relations; b: Anderson, : Bruce Edward Auerbach; c: Benjamin George; ed: IN Univ (BA) Relations 1972; Univ of MN (PHD) IR, Frgn & Pub Policy 1977; Doc Columbia Univ, Harriman Inst Soviet Stud 1982-83; Attnd rsidad de Guadalajara, Friends World Coll; cr: Rutgers Univ Intnl ons Asst Prof 1978-82; IN Univ Visting Asst Prof 1983-84; Russian Visting Asst Prof 1983-84; Mac Alester Coll Visting Asst Prof 85; Mankato St Univ Intnl Relations Prof 1985-; ai: Intnl Stud Assn; Assn of Univ Women; No Asylum 1996; Security V. Survival 1985; n Peace Univ of Denver 1982; home: 3 Sheffield Ln Pottstown PA

H, THOMAS CARL, 7th Grade Science Teacher; b: Panama Ancon, Zone; m: Luz Nereida Pellot; ed: Hocking Tech Coll (AA) ation & Wildlife 1979; OH Univ (BS) Outdoor Ed, Sec Ed Bio 1984; land St Univ (MS) Sci Curr, Instruct 1989; Kent St Univ Biological r: Northwood Jr HS 7th Grd Sci Tchr 1984-; ai: 8th Grd Ftbl Coach; NABT, NEA, OEA, EEA, EECO 1984-; office: Northwood Jr HS Gulf Rd Elyria OH 44035*

TH, THOMAS GORDON, Teacher; b: Hartford, CT; ed: Cntrl CT St (BA) Eng 1970, (MS) Ed 1979; Trinity Coll (MA) Amer Stud; 27 t Hrs Univ of MA; Fairfield Univ; Harvard Univ; Univ of CT; cr: ord Pub HS Tchr 1970-74; Thomas Snell Weaver High Tchr & disciplinary Stud Pgm Facilitator 1974-; ai: WQTQ-FM Radio Station Operator & Mgr; Weaver Chptr NHS Asst Adv; High Drama Adv; n CT Scholars Pgm; AFT 1970-; Alpha Phi Alpha Inc 1988-, Corres Hartford Pub Lib 1995-, Second Century Fund Comm; office: Thomas Weaver HS 415 Granby St Hartford CT 06112

TH, THOMAS JOHN, Social Studies Teacher; b: Scranton, PA; c: Maloney, Sherri; ed: Penn St (BS) Ed & Scndry 1971; cr: Cntrl HS 1973-75; Tech HS Tchr 1979-90; West Scranton HS Tchr 1990-92; nton HS Tchr 1992-93; ai: Asst Var Girls Bkstbl Coach; 8th Grd Girls l; AFT 1973-; office: West Scranton HS 1201 Luzerne St Scranton PA 4

TH, THOMAS NEIL, Jr High Math Teacher; b: Montpelier, OH; m: Nelson; c: Adam, Calah, Ty; ed: Bowling Green St Univ (BS) Elem 977; Univ of Toledo (MA) Admin, Supervision 1994; cr: Bowling n City Schls Fourth, Fifth Grd Tchr 1977-79; Gorham-Fayette Local Third Grd Tchr 1979-90; Millcreek-West Unity Local Schls Seventh, h Grd Math Tchr 1990-; ai: HS Girls Var Softbl Coach; NEA, OEA ; Local Tchrs Assn 1977-, Pres 1987-88; Friends of Lib Bd 1992-, VP; n Little League Bd 1995-, Trustee; office: Millcreek West Unity Local 13 S Defiance St West Unity OH 43570

TH, THORTON, World Civilization Teacher; b: Erwin, NC; m: ara Stanley; ed: Univ of Pittsburgh (BA) His & Fr 1957; Goddard Coll US His 1974; 39 Credits in Pub Admin at Nova Univ 1977-84; Attnd ra Coll 6 Credits Fr, City Coll of NY 12 Credits Fr, William Paterson 18 Credits Schl Admin; cr: Ferris HS US His Tchr 1960-62; Raritan r Tchr & Supvr for Lang 1962-70; Teaneck HS US His Tchr 1970-72; on Cty Voc Tech Schls Prin 1984-87; Elizabeth HS World Civilization lture Tchr 1987-; ai: Coll & Univs Stu Adv; Union Cty Ed Assn 1987-; d Assn, NEA 1984-; Kiwanis Club of Jersey City, Pres, Distinguished Awd; Kappa Alpha Psi, Pres, Pres Awd; Salvation Army, Bd of Dirs, Awd; Jersey City Bd of Ed, VP, Svc Awd; Wrote Book on Historical rpretation of Reconstruction 1865-1877 for HS Stdnts to be Pub; home: Arlington Ave Jersey City NJ 07304*

TH, TIMOTHY MACK, Social Studies Teacher; b: Athens, OH; m: ry Norene Grooms; c: Alexis Ann, Nicholas Alexander; ed: OH leyan Univ (BA) His 1972; Post Grad Stud OH Univ at Athens Elem Educl Remediation Cooperative Ed, Tchr Trng, Mentorship; cr: River HS Soc Stud Tchr 1973-77; Athens City Schls Soc Stud, Elem Tchr -; ai: Girls Var Bsktbl Coach; OH Univ, The Plains Elem Partnership, Stud Curr Comms; NEA, OHSBCA, OEA 1973-; Sons of Union rans, Sons of Amer Revolution 1994-; OH HS Bsktbl Coaches Assn of Fame; Federal Hocking HS Hall of Fame; River View HS Hall of e; Red Apple Awd from Athens Spec Ed Parents; home: 16790 mpson Rdg Athens OH 45701

TH, TRINA LUANN, Mathematics Teacher; b: Olean, NY; m: Nelson : Jared, Katie; ed: Clarion Univ of PA (BS) Ed & Math 1978; Attnd ana Univ of PA, Penn St Univ, Gannon Univ; cr: Brookville Area Math 1978-; ai: Math Contests Adv; SADD Co-Adv; Eligibility, Discipline urr Comms; NEA, PSEA 1979-; Brookville Area Ed Assn 1979-, VP; M 1993-; Zion Luth Church 1978-, Cncl Mem, Congregation Treas; 1990-, Ldr; office: Brookville Area HS Jenks St Brookville PA 15825*

TH, TROND L., Social Studies Teacher; b: Circleville, OH; m: Carrie n; ed: Bowling Green St Univ (BS) Soc Stud Ed 1992; cr: Licking ghts HS Soc Stud Tchr 1993-; ai: JV Boys Bsktbl & Bsbl Coach; Licking Cty Soc Stud Curr Comm; NCSS 1993-; OH Cncl of Soc Stud 1993-; NEA 1993-; Licking Heights Ed Assn 1993-; sigma Chi Alumni 1992-; BPOE 1993-; home: 6537 Warriner Way Canal Winchester OH 43110

SMITH, VALERIA ANN LOMAX, 8th Grade Science Teacher; b: Washington, DC; m: Bernard Addison; c: Dajando, Che; ed: Bowie St Univ (MS) Gen Ed 1979; 18-21 Credit Hrs; cr: Benjamin Tasker MS 7th-8th Grd Math & Sci Tchr 15 Yrs; Montpelier Elem 3rd-6th Grd Tchr 10 Yrs; Margaret Edmonston Elem 2nd Grd Tchr 1 Yr; ai: Mentor; NEA 1968-; PGCEA 1968-; MSTA Curr Dev Assn; Queens Chapel United Meth Church 1960-, Pres Higher Ed & Mass Choir; Oakcrest Civic Assn 1976-; Outstdng Sci Tchr Prince Georges Cty Nom; Outstdng Work for Mentoring Pgm Cert; Article Pub; office: Benjamin Tasker MS 4901 Collington Rd Bowie MD 20715*

SMITH, VERN J., Fifth Grade Teacher; b: Kingston, PA; m: Robert; c: Chipper, Tammy; ed: Coll Misericordia (BS) Elem Ed, SS 1964; Master Equivalency 1994; ai: NEA, WVW 1973-; office: Wyoming Valley West HS Maple Ave Kingston PA 18704*

SMITH, VICKEY D. (JORNOD), Social Studies Teacher; b: Boise, ID; m: Douglas W.; c: Kirsten, Morgan; ed: IN Univ at Bloomington (BS) Soc Stud 1967; CA St Univ at Long Beach (MA) His 1974; Addl Credit Hrs in Eng for Eng Tchng Credential; cr: Lakeside Union Schl Dist Tchr on Spec Assignment Curr, Soc Stud, Eng, Resource Tchr 1977-82; Northern MS Soc Stud Tchr 1983-85; Tierra del Sol MS Lang Arts, Soc Stud Tchr 1985-89; Lorain HS Soc Stud Tchr 1989-; Lorain Admiral King Schl Soc Stud Tchr 1989-; ai: Unity Spon; LAK Site Based Decision Making Comm Sec; NEA 1977-, Tchr of Yr Lakeside Union 1989; NCSS, ASCD 1983-; Bay Presbyn Orch 1995-; Erie Shores Girl Scouts 1993-; Soc Stud Curr for Mentally Gifted; His, Soc Sci Curr Lakeside Union Schl Dist; Lit Units for CA Lnag Arts Curr; Poetry Booklet Pub: Our Thoughts are Straight From the Heart; office: Lorain Admiral King HS 2600 Ashland Ave Lorain OH 44052

SMITH, VIRGINIA BAER, English Professor; b: Chattanooga, TN; c: Courtney L., H. Granville, Thomas E.; ed: Univ of TN at Knoxville (BS) Ed 1969; Hood Coll (MA) Human Sci 1993; cr: Montgomery Cty Pub Schls Eng Tchr 1969-71; Visual Systems Co Educl Seminar Coord, Presenter 1978-88; Montgomery Coll Eng Prof 1993-; Southeastern Univ at Rockville Eng Prof 1994-; ai: NCTE 1969-; Women in Advertising, Mrktg 1991; Assn of Fac for Advancement of Comm Coll Tchng 1994-; Bullis Schl Bd of Trustees 1988-; office: Montgomery Coll At Rockville English Dept 52 Mannakee St Rockville MD 20850*

SMITH, WAYNE HOWARD, Mathematics Teacher; b: Red Bank, NJ; m: Patricia Ann Rutter; c: Marc; ed: Monmouth Coll (BS) Math Ed 1969; Montclair St (MA) Math Ed 1979; 30 Addl Credits; cr: Matawan Regnl HS Tchr 1969-; ai: Cmptr Club; Staff Cmptr Trainer; NEA, NJEA 1969-; NJBA 1987-; Aberdeen Town Cncl 1994-, Councilman; Republican Club 1994-; Tchr of Yr 1986; Founder Local Comm Scholar Prgm; Adv Explorer Post 278; home: 2 3rd St Matawan NJ 07747*

SMITH, W. BARRY, Registrar; b: Buffalo, NY; m: Barbara Ann McNamara; c: Deirdre M.; ed: Saint Bernard Coll (BA) Philosophy 1959; Cath Univ (MA) His 1968, (PHD) His 1969; cr: Saint John Vianney Seminary Asst Prof 1968-74; Christ the King Seminary Asst Prof & Dean 1974-77; R C Diocese of Buffalo Continuing & Adult Ed Dir 1977-84; DYouville Coll Lecturer 1984, Registrar 1991-; ai: Amer Historical Assn 1968-; Amer Cath Historical Soc 1967-; Cath Theological Soc 1970-; Parish Schl Bd Chair 1992-95; DYouville Coll Admin of Yr 1994-95; office: D'Youville Coll 320 Porter Ave Buffalo NY 14201

SMITH, WHENDOLYN, Reading Recovery Teacher; b: Waterville, ME; m: William; c: Miles; ed: Univ of ME (BS) Elem Ed 1982, (MS) Ed 1987, (CAS) Lang Arts 1991; Rdng Recovery Trng; cr: Lawrence MS 4th Grd Tchr 1983-88; Clinton Schl Chapter I Rdng Tchr 1988-93; Benton Schl Chapter I Rdng & Rdng Recovery Tchr 1993-; ai: NEA, MEA 1983-; ME Rdng Assn 1988-, Exec Bd; IRA 1988-; ME Rdng Assn Grant; office: Benton Elem Schl Old Benton Neck Benton ME 04901

SMITH, WILIAM, Biology Teacher; b: Clarion, PA; m: Rose M. Niederriter; c: Bret A., Dawn M. Zimmerman, Tina M. Conrad; cr: Brookville HS Bio Tchr 1964-.

SMITH, WILLIAM DAVID, Education Professor; b: Coaldale, PA; m: Maryann; c: Patricia Ann Gonzalez, Lori Hill, William D.; ed: E Stroudsburg St Coll (BS) Elem Ed 1960; Kean Coll (MA) Supervision, Admin 1968; Doctoral Candidate Schl Admin Widener Univ; 30 Hrs Schl Admin Newark St Coll, Fairleigh Dickinson Univ, Glassboro St Coll, William Paterson Coll; cr: Caldwell, Bristol, Palmerton Schls Elem Tchr 1960-68; Toms River Bd Ed Prin, Asst Supt, Dist Curr Supvr 1968-92; Silver Burdett & Ginn Pub Co Educl Consultant 1992-93; Monmouth Univ Adj Fac Instr 1970-; ai: Conduct Reader Response Journal Project; ASCD; Poetry Collective Ocean Cty; 1992 Panelist New Amer Schls Dec Corp; 1991 Contributor Natl Conf Lang Arts, 1992 Natl Math, Sci Symposium, 1989 NJ Dept of Ed St Curr Strategic Planning Document; home: 1968 Sweetwood Dr Forked River NJ 08731

SMITH, WILLIAM E., Economics & Sociology Teacher; b: Des Moines, IA; c: Darby; ed: Lehigh Univ (MA) His, Ed 1968; 80 Addl Hrs His, Ec, Tchng Strategies; cr: Neshaminy HS Hum Dir, Tchr 1971-73, Soc Stud Tchr 1967-; ai: Golf Coach, Bldg Comm AFT; Strategic Planning Comm; AFT 1968-, VP, Treas; NCSS, PCSS 1969-; Jaycees 1970-; PIAA Track 1990, Ofcl; Rotary Group Stud Exch Japan 1977; office: Neshaminy HS 2001 Old Lincoln Hwy Langhorne PA 19047*

SMITH, WILLIAM PAUL, Social Studies Teacher; b: Boston, MA; m: Joan Rollo; c: Amy, Jill, Thomas, Peter; ed: St Coll of Boston (BS) Ed 1970; 30 Post Grad Credit Hrs; cr: East Bridgewater Schls Soc Stud Tchr 1970-; ai: Soc Stud Awareness Adv; NEA, MTA 1970-; East Bridgewater Ed Assn 1970-, Bldg Rep; Saint Johns, Youth Ministry 1987-87, Youth Minister, CCD Rel Ed Tchr 1975-95; office: East Bridgewater HS 11 Plymouth St East Bridgewater MA 02333

SMITH, WILLIAM PRESTON,III, Music & Drama Teacher; b: Washington, DC; ed: Western CT St Univ (MS) Music Ed 1978; cr: Carmel Schl Dist Music Tchr 1973-; ai: Music Production Wkshp Dir 12 Yrs; Tour of Wizard 1980; Summer Stock 1981-86; One Man Show 1992; MENC 1973-; NYSSMA 1995-; CT Opera House Mem 1983-87; office: Carmel HS 30 Fair St Carmel NY 10512

SMITH, WILLIAM STEPHEN, Language Arts Teacher; b: Bremerhaven, Germany; m: Dorothea Tomassoni; c: Christopher, Erin, Kelly; ed: Univ of Scranton (BA) Eng, Philosophy 1969; 30+ Credits Lit, Ed, St Univ of NY at binghamton; cr: Bishop Hannon HS Soc Stud, Ec 1970; Maine-Endwell MS Lang Arts 1971-; ai: Coach Modified Girls Soccer 9 Yrs; Dir of Musical 1990-93, Dir of Drama 9 Yrs; Adv Yrbk 14 Yrs; Maine-Endwell Tchrs Assn 1988-; Amer Quarter Horse Assoc; Empire St Quarter Horse Assoc; US Power Squadron 1988-; Cornell Cooperative Ext St 4H Competitive Horse Events Comm, Chm 4H Comm Div; Prof Horse Trainer, Instr 25 Yrs; Prof Horse Show Judge 12 Yrs; Chosen Judge North Amer Intnl Livestock Exposition 1990 4H Div; 5 Articles Pub in Assorted St 4H Magazines; office: Maine-Endwell HS 750 Farm to Market Rd Endicott NY 13760*

SMITH, WILLIAM THOMAS, English Teacher; b: Madison, NJ; ed: Bucknell Univ (BA) Eng 1993; cr: Point Pleasant Beach HS Eng Tchr 1994-; ai: Peer Cnslng; Soccer Coach; NEA & NJEA 1994-; office: Pt Pleasant Beach HS 700 Trenton Ave Point Pleasant Bea NJ 08742

SMITHINSKY, ANDREA NOEL, Special Ed Teacher; b: Fostoria, OH; m: Steve; c: Carter Nixon, Elizabeth Nixon; ed: Randolph-Macon Woman's Coll (BA) Ger 1965; Univ of NC (MA) Ger 1968; cr: Phillips Jr HS Eng Tchr 1968-69; North Kingstown HS Eng Tchr 1970-71, Eng, Ger Tchr 1978-; ai: Past Drama Club Adv; Skills Commission Comm for Stu Success; Schlsp, Curr Comms; NEA, RI Frgn Lang Assn 1978-; AATG 1981-; South Cty Coalition Against Racism 1980-, Pres, VP; Westminster Unitarian Church 1984-, Soc Action Comm; Flwshps from Goethe Inst, AATG to Attnd Tchr Trng Seminars at Martin Luther Univ, Halle, East Germany 1987, Berlin 1990, Pol Stud Wiesneck 1993, Haus Rissen Hamburg 1995; office: Maholm Elem Schl 96 Maholm St Newark OH 43055*

SMITHSON, DAVID G., Fifth Grade Teacher; b: Ilion, NY; m: Mary Anne (Young); c: Sarah, Peter; ed: SUNY Oswego (BS) Ed 1970, (MS) Counseling 1986; Post Grad Work; cr: West Genesee Schl Dist 5th Grd Tchr 1970-71; US Navy GED Tchr 1971-72; West Genesee Schl Dist 5th Grd Tchr 1972-; ai: Syracuse Univ Mem; Tchng Ctr Bd of Dirs, Prof Dev Schl Master Tchr; AFT, NYSUT 1972-; West Genesee Tchrs Assn 1972-, Bldg Pres 5 Yrs; Knights of Columbus 1980-; BPOE 1972-, Schlsp Chair 1975-93; Camillus Optimist Tchr of Yr 1989; office: Stonehedge Elem Schl 400 Sanderson Rd Camillus NY 13031

SMITH-TALBOTT, MONICA ALICE, Art Professor; b: Rochester, NY; m: Ron; c: Sean; ed: Rochester Inst of Tech (AA) Painting 1977, (BFA) Painting 1979, (MFA) Painting 1982; Light Impressions Framer & Sales Clerk 1982-83; Washington Times Graphic Artist 1983-84; Harrisburg Area Comm Coll Art Instr 1984-; cr: Gallery Comm; Transfer Stdnts Adv; ai: Coll Art Assn; Artwork in Local & Fac Exhibits; Juried Local Art Exhibits.

SMITH WAGNER, LISA REXANN, Bus Ed Instr & Tech Coord; b: Parkersburg, WV; m: Kevin Allen; ed: Glenville St Coll (BA) Bus Ed 1981; WV Univ (MS) Comm Stud 1988; Addl Hrs West VA Univ, OH Univ; Kent St Univ, Univ of Akron Voc Certs; cr: Tri-Cty Joint Voc Schl Bus Instr 1982-83; Washington Cty Career Ctr Bus Instr 1983-; ai: Tech Coord; Bus Profs of Amer Adv; Delta Kappa Gamma 1987-, Second VP; OEA, NEA 1983-, Treas; WCCC Tchrs Assn 1982-, Treas; Bus & Prof Women 1987-, Sec, Young Careerist; Tri-Sigma Alumni 1982-, Outstanding Alumnus; Martha Holden Jennings Scholar; Ashland Oil Golden Apple Achiever Awd; Cmptr & Classroom Learning Nom Outstanding Tchr; Tandy Tech Scholar Nom; office: Washington County Career Ctr Rt 2 Marietta OH 45750*

SMITTLE, HARRY E., Coordinator of Gifted Ed; b: Hillsboro, OH; m: Janet E. Core; c: Scott, Debbie; ed: Morehead St Univ (AB) Eng, PE, Hlth 1965; Xavier Univ (MED) Admin, Hlth, PE 1972; OH Univ (MED) Gifted Ed 1985; cr: Pickaway-Ross JVS Adult Ed Tchr 2 Yrs; Lynchburg-Clay Tchr, Coach 4 Yrs; Ripley-Union-Lewis Tchr, Coach 3 Yrs; Zanetrace Schls Gifted Ed, Eng Tchr 19 Yrs; Fairfield Cty Schls Gifted Ed Coord 1 Yr; ai: Amanda-Clearcreek Curr Comm, Var Boys Bsktbl Coach; Right to Read 1980-, Ross Co Tchr Awd; NEA; OEA; AARP; Gifted St Funded Grants; Power of the Pen Winning Stu Participants; Odyssey of the Mind Dist Winning Teams; Kodak Photography Contest St Stu Winner; Right to Read Poster Contest Stu Winners; office: Fairfield Cty Schls N School St Amanda OH 43102*

SMOKER, JOANNE M. (ALTHOUSE), Bio, Adv Bio & Genetics Tchr; b: Reading, PA; m: James R.; ed: Kutztown Univ (BS) Bio 1966; Grad work Millersville 1978; Coll of Williams, Mary NSF Summer Inst 1968-69; cr: Governor Mifflin Schl Tchr 1966-, Sci Dept Staff Ldr 1993-95, Mentor 1995-; ai: Sftbl Coach 1967-69; Stu Asst Team 1991-95; NEA, PSEA 1966-; Who's Who Among Coll, Univ Stdnts 1966; Dev Genetics Mini Course Tech Grant 1987-88; office: Governor Mifflin Sr HS 101 S Waverly St Shillington PA 19607

SMOLA, DANIEL JOHN, Environmental Technology Prof; b: Ludlow, MA; m: Rachelle Marie Louise; c: Emily Brittain, Matthew Brittain; ed: Univ of MA at Amherst (BS) Mechanical Engineering 1967, (MS) Environmental Engineering 1969; 15 Credits Toward MS in Pub Hlth & Industrial Hygiene Specialty; cr: US Army Sanitary Engr & Capt 1969-70; Camp Dresser & McKee Consulting Engr 1970-71; Dufresne & Henry Consulting Engr 1972; Hamilton Standard Engr 1973-74; Springfield Tech Comm Coll Prof & Dept Chair 1975-; ai: MA Water Pollution Control Assn 1980-; MA Water Works Assn 1985-; Western MA Am Industrial Assn 1986-; MA: Prof Engr Sanitary Engineering, Certfd Wastewater Oper, Certfd Water Treatment Plant Operator; office: Springfield Tech Comm Coll 1 Armory Square Springfield MA 01101

SMOLKO, MARIE BREZNAI, Spanish Teacher; b: Warren, OH; m: Joseph S. Jr.; c: Lori Smolko Smith, Carrie, Isaac; ed: Youngstown St Univ (BA) Span 1970, (MSEd) Cnslng 1995; cr: Boardman HS Span Tchr 1970-72; Villa Maria Coll Prep Span Tchr 1988-89; Cardinal Mooney HS Span Tchr 1989-91; Wilmington Area HS Span Tchr 1991-; ai: Local Assn, NEA & PSEA 1991-; Chi Sigma Iota, Kappa Delta Pi, Phi Kappa Phi 1994-; Former Foster Parent; New Life Assembly of God; Bd of Pub Affairs, Former Clerk; Gould Soc; Youngstown St Outstdng Woman Scholar 1970; 4.0 GPA for Masters; 3.96 GPA Undergraduate.

SMOLNYCKI, DANIEL HARRY, Guid Cnslr & District Coord; b: Syracuse, NY; m: Jill Ann Stanislay; c: Kristen L., Kara E.; ed: Hartwick Coll (BS) Music Ed 1972; SUNY at Oswego (MS) Ed 1980, (CAS) Cnslng Svcs 1990; cr: Unatego Cntrl Schls Instrumental Music Tchr 1972-73; Chittenango Cntrl Schl Instrumental Music Tchr 1973-87, Guid Cnslr 1987-; ai: Guid Dept Chprsn; Curr Cncl; Schlsp Comm; Test Supvr; NY St United Tchrs, AFT 1972-; Chittenango Tchrs Assn 1973-; NY St Schl Cnslrs Assn, Mohawk Vly Cnslrs Assn, NY Cnslrs Assn 1987-; Dirs of Guid Svcs for Onondaga & Madison Ctys 1994-; NY St Assn of Coll Admissions Cnslrs 1995-; Chittenango Lions Club 1973-, Eye Sight Chm; Zoning Bd of Appeals 1979-, Past Chm; Knights of Columbus 1993-, Trustee; Dollars for Scholars 1984-, Past Chm; SUNY Morrisville Admission Advy Comm; Onondaga Comm Coll Cnslng Advy Comm; office: Chittenango Cntrl Schl 150 Genesee St Chittenango NY 13037

SMOLTER, MARY CATHERINE CYNKAR, 5th Grade Teacher; b: Pittsburgh, PA; m: Pres; c: Nicole, Katie, Valerie, Melanie; ed: Slippery Rock Univ (BA) Elem Ed, Lib Sci 1977; Univ of Pittsburgh 15 Credits; Wilkes Coll 6 Credits; Penn St Beaver Campus 3 Credits; cr: St Mary's Elem Schl 6th Grd Tchr 1977-80; St Alexis Elem 5-6th Grd Tchr 1981-; ai: Stu Cncl Moderator; Girls JV Bsktbl Coach St Bonaventure; NCEA; Chrstn Mothers St Bonaventure 1984-, Various Comms; Golden Apple Tchr 1990-91; office: Saint Alexis Schl 10090 Old Perry Hwy Wexford PA 15090*

SMOOT, ROBERT CLARENCE,IV, Science Teacher; b: Baltimore, MD; m: Elizabeth Lynn; c: Brielle, Brandy, Hunter; ed: Duke Univ (BS) Botany 1981; Penn St Univ (MS) Botany 1989; cr: Mc Donogh Schl Sci Tchr, Coach 1981-; ai: Asst Ftbl, Head MS Wrestling Coach; Flwshp of Chrstns in Univs & Schls Adv, Ldr; MABT; NABT; Abstract Pub in Phycology Symposium; Talk Given at Phycology Symposium; office: Mc Donogh Schl 8600 Mc Donogh Rd Bowie 380 Owings Mills MD 21117

SMORE, THOMAS J., HS Social Studies Teacher; b: Uniontown, PA; m: Carol (Ammirato) A.; c: Megan, Greg; ed: Indiana Univ of PA (BS) Soc Sci Ed 1973; Penn St (MA) Amer Stud 1977; Wilkes Coll 15 Credits; cr:

Cumberland Valley HS Soc Stud Tchr 1973-; *ai:* NEA, PA St Ed Assn & Cumberland Valley Ed Assn 1973-; St Theresa Cath Church 1975-, Area rep; Consultant Hershey Museum of Amer Life; Coll Evaluator PA Dept of Ed; HS Evaluator; Cooperating Tchr Shippensburg Univ & Dickinson Coll; *office:* Cumerland Valley HS 6746 Carlisle Pike Mechanicsburg PA 17055

SMORRA, MARYANN, Professor of Education; *b:* West Long Branch, NJ; *m:* William J. Robertson; *ed:* Monmouth Coll (BS) Elem Ed, Music 1970; Rutgers Univ (EDM) Creative Arts Ed 1977, (EDD) Elem Ed, Supervision, Curr 1981; Rdng Ed Johns Hopkins Univ; Music Ed Univ of MD; *cr:* Eatontown Schls 4th Grd Tchr 1970-72; Baltimore Cty Schls Vocal Music Tchr 1972-74; Freehold Twp Schls 3rd GATE Tchr, Coord 1974-81; Tinton Falls Schls Dir Gifted Prgms, Acting Prin 1981-84; Bridgewater-Raritan Schls Supvr Curr, Instruction 1984-88; Creative Dimensions Constultant, Performer 1988-90; NJ St Dept Ed Consultant 1990-; Georgian Ct Coll Prof Ed 1990-; *ai:* Moderator De La Salle Ed Club; Undergraduate Curr Comm; Project Dir Stu Tchng Multiple Intelligences Project; ASCD 1984-, Presenter Mem Natl Confs; ATE 1990-, Presenting Mem Natl Conf; Kappa Delta Pi 1977-, Honor Soc; Phi Delta Kappa 1980-, Honor Soc; Joyful Spirit Music Ministry 1992-, Vocalist, Spokesperson, Liturgical Dancer; Creative Ed Fnd 1982-, Presenter, Colleague; Grants NJ Collegiate Consortium Hlth Ed, NJ St Arts Cncl, Metropolitan Opera; Numerous Articles Pub; Who's Who Amer Women; *office:* Georgian Court Coll 900 Lakewood Ave Lakewood NJ 08701*

SMOSKY, DONNA FINGAR, Third Grade Teacher; *b:* Newark, NJ; *m:* Robert; *c:* Richard, Mark, Kevin; *ed:* SUC Cortland (BS) PE 1968; Hofstra (MA) Spec Ed 1981; 75 Addl Grad Hrs; Cert PE, Spec Ed, Elem Ed, Rdng Specialist; *cr:* Wenonah Elem Schl PE Tchr 1968-71; Leeway Schl Spec Ed Tchr 1979-91; Coram Elem Schl Spec Ed Tchr 1981-85, 2nd, 3rd Grd Classroom Tchr 1985-; *ai:* PTA Liaison; Head Start Christmas Gift Coord; Hlth, Safety Comm; AFT; NEA; MITA; Friends of Mid Cty Pub Lib 1994-, VP; Mid Cty Booster Club 1994-; Del to Russia, Hungary 1992; Mid East Suffolk Tchrs Grant 1990; Participant Natl Tchr Trng Inst 1994; Model Tchr for Tchng Video 1989-; *office:* Coram Elem Schl Mt Sinai Rd Coram NY 11727

SMREK, RICHARD MICHAEL, Orchestra Teacher; *b:* Youngstown, OH; *m:* Linda M. Gustinella; *c:* Michael, Anne, Mary; *ed:* Youngstown St (BM) Music Ed 1984, (MS) Ed 1989; *cr:* Alliance City Schls Orch Tchr 1984-85; Youngstown St Univ Cnslr, Acad Adv 1985-87; Boardman Pub Schls Orch Tchr 1987-; *ai:* After Schl Rehearsal String Coach; Pvt Violin Tchr; OMEA, MENC 1987-; NSOA 1992-; OSOA 1992-, VP 1993, Pres 1994; St Luke Parish Cncl 1993-, Pres 1994-; Younstown Symphony Violinist 1981-87; Canton Symphony Violinist 1983-87; Warren Chamber of Commerce Violinist 1982-87; *office:* Boardman Schls 7777 Glenwood Ave Boardman OH 44512*

SMRTIC, SHARON PALOMBI, Spanish Teacher; *b:* Amsterdam, NY; *m:* Gerald; *c:* Kristin, John; *ed:* Fulton Montgomery CC (AH) Lbrl Arts 1970; SUNY at Albany (BA) Eng 1972, (MA) Ed 1988; *cr:* Bishop Scully High Span & Eng Tchr 1982-86; Amsterdam HS Span Tchr 1986-; *ai:* NY SAFLT 1986-; COLT 1990-; St Marys Hosp Auxiliary 1976-.

SMUCKER, LINDA L. (ZIMMERMAN), Advocate Coordinator; *b:* Wooster, OH; *m:* Larry J.; *c:* Matthew J., Amy L. Smucker Baker; *ed:* Kent St Univ (BS) Bus Ed 1964; IN Univ (MS) Bus Ed 1971; *cr:* Peru HS Bus Ed Tchr 1964-67; Wayne Cty Schls Career Ctr Bus Ed Instr 1971-; *ai:* Bus Prof of Amer Yth Org Adv 25 Yrs; OH Voc Ed Assn & Amer Voc Ed Assn 1971-; Unified Ed Assn 1985-, Pres & Treas; OH Ed Assn 1985-; NEA 1985-; Wooster Swim Club Parents 1974-, Co-Pres; Wooster Womans Guild 1993-, VP; Delta Pi Epsilon; *home:* 409 Mather Hill Dr Wooster OH 44691

SMULLEN, JUDITH EISENHART, English Teacher; *b:* Oneonta, NY; *m:* David E.; *ed:* Muhlenberg Coll (BA) Eng 1971; Lehigh Univ (MA) Eng 1983; *cr:* Liberty HS Eng Tchr 1971-; Moravion Coll Adjunct Prof 1990; Allentown Coll Adjunct Prof 1993; *ai:* BEA, PSEA, NEA 1972-, VP, Rep; NCTE 1985-; Rugby East Referees 1987-; Maulie Maguires Women's Rugby Ftbl Club 1977-; First Presbyn Church Chancel Choir 1973-; Amnesty Intnl; Designing Writing Prgm BASD HS; Curr Dev: Honors Prgm 9th Grd Curr; II Applied Curr Restructuring Team Chair; *office:* Liberty HS 1115 Linden St Bethlehem PA 18018

SMUTKO, PATRICIA LEE WEBER, Asst Prof of Nursing; *b:* Spangler, PA; *m:* Kevin; *ed:* Sharon Gen Hosp (RN) Nrsng 1982; Slippery Rock Univ (BSN) Nrsng 1988; LaRoche Coll (MSN) Nrsng 1995; Numerous Inservice Credit Hrs; *cr:* Sharon Gen Hosp Staff Nurse, Critical Care Instr 1982-89; Jameson Meml Hosp Nrsng Instr 1989-91; Comm Coll of Allegheny Co Asst Prof of Nrsng 1991-; Kent St Univ Part-time Asst Prof 1996-; *ai:* Coll Comms; Sigma Theta Tau 1996-; *home:* 108 Buttercup Dr Cranberry Twp PA 16066

SMYTH, NANCY JEAN, Social Work Asst Professor; *b:* Tarrytown, NY; *m:* Dennis G. Mike; *ed:* Univ at Albany (BA) Psych 1981, (MSW) Soc Work, Mental Hlth 1986, (PHD) Soc Welfare 1991; Credential Alcoholism Cnslr; *cr:* Leonard Hosp Outpatient Clinic Soc Worker 1987-89, Clinical Dir 1989-91; Rsrch Inst on Addictions Assoc Rsrch Scientist 1991-; Univ at Buffalo Asst Prof 1991-; *ai:* Chair MSW Concentration Alcohol, Other Drug Problems; Adv Soc WOrk Grad Stu Assn; Cncl Soc Work Ed1988-; Natl Assn Soc Workers 1983-; Greater Buffalo Cncl Alcoholism, Substance Abuse 1993-, VP; Inst Addiction Stud, Trng 1991-; Numerous Articles, Book Chptrs Pub; Presidential Flwshp; *office:* Univ at Buffalo 359 Baldy Hall Buffalo NY 14260*

SNEAD, LALA F., Mathematics Teacher; *b:* Washington, DC; *m:* Robert L. Jr.; *c:* Anthony; *ed:* DC Tchrs Coll (BA) Math 1971; George Washington Univ (MA) Art of Tchng Math 1974; *cr:* Alice Deal Jr High Math Tchr 1971-83; Anacostia High Math Tchr 1983-90; Duke Ellington Math Tchr 1990-; *ai:* Integrated Curr Dev Mem; ICDP Project; NCTM, WA Tchrs Union 1971-; DCTM; MCTM; AFT; *office:* Duke Ellington Schl Of Arts 3500 R Street NW Washington DC 20007

SNEED, BARRY GRAY, 1st Grade Teacher; *b:* Cleveland, OH; *ed:* Cleveland St Univ (BA) Elem Ed 1991, (MA) Curr, Instruction 1994; Cert Elem Admin, OH Elem Prin Cert; *cr:* Euclid Pub Schls 1st Grd Tchr 1991-92; Perry Pub Schls 1st Grd Tchr 1992-; *ai:* Staff Dev, Bldg Advy, Portfolio Asessment Comms; Paideia Grant Writing Comm Co-Chair; Play Ground Construction Comm Gen Coord; Phi Delta Kappa, Assn Supervision & Curr Dev, IRA 1995-; NEA 1991-; Wildwood Singers 1989-; 2 Time Presenter OH Kndgtn, Primary Conf 1995; Presenter, Speaker John Carrol Univ Be Tomorrows Tchr; TV-8 Thanks to Tchrs Awd 1994; *home:* 4905 Glenn Lodge Rd Mentor OH 44060*

SNEED, DENISE LYNN, Health & Physical Ed Teacher; *b:* Wilmington, OH; *c:* Curtis; *ed:* Coll of Mt St Joseph (BA) Hlth, PE 1989; *cr:* Pleasant Run MS Hlth, PE Tchr 1989-; *office:* Pleasant Run MS 11770 Pippin Rd Cincinnati OH 45231

SNEIDER, PATRICIA WELTER, Bio & Human Physiology Teacher; *b:* Fremont, OH; *m:* Herbert Richard; *c:* Barbara Jones, Brian, Kevin, Mark, Stephen; *ed:* Bowling Green St Univ (BS) Eng 1958, (MS) Guid, Cnslng 1987; Addl 20 Hrs, 1 CEU; IN Univ 3 Hrs; *cr:* Fremont Ross HS Eng Tchr 1958-59; Gibsonburg HS Sub Tchr 1960-74, Bio, Eng Tchr 1974-; *ai:* Red Cross Stu-Operated Bloodmobile Adv; Ind Stud Marine Bio Class Spon Tchr; NEA, OH Tchrs Assn, NW OH Tchrs Assn 1958-; Local Tchrs Assn 1974-, Bldg Rep; Gibsonburg Women's Fed 1969-, Past Pres; Gibsonburg Sorosis 1988-, Pres; Cty Bd MRDD, Past Mem; Gibsonburg Area His Group; Good Apple Awd 1987; Jennings Scholar 1982-83; *office:* Gibsonburg HS 300 S Harrison St Gibsonburg OH 43431

SNELL, GERTRUDE PANNELL, Fourth Grade Teacher; *b:* Lynchburg, VA; *m:* Lee; *c:* David; *ed:* Queens Coll (BA) Elem Ed 1973, (MS) Early Chldhd Ed 1975; 30 Addl Credit Hrs; *cr:* Queensbridge Day Care Ctr Tchr, Dir 1973-79; Bethel at Weeksville Head Start Dir 1979-84; Pub Schl 38 Q Tchr 1984-; *ai:* PTA Advy Bd; Sharp After Schl Prgm; United Fed of Tchrs 1985-, Chptr Ldr; Phi Delta Kappa 1987-, Publicity Dir; Phi Delta Kappa Early Chldhd Ctr Bd of Dirs 1990-, Chprsn; Grace UM Church 1978-, Fin Comm, Trease, Fin Sec; Tchr of Yr 1988; *home:* 206-05 Lori Dr Bayside NY 11360

SNELL, LINDA HARNER, Nursing Professor; *b:* Brockport, NY; *m:* Alden H.; *c:* Alden II, Christopher; *ed:* Roberts Wesleyan Coll (BS) Nrsng 1975; SUNY at Buffalo (MS) Women's Hlth Nurse Practitioner 1985; Doctoral Prgm Schl of Nrsng; *cr:* SUC Nurse Practitioner 1985-90; SUNY Clinical Instr 1985-88; Hlth Care Plan Nurse Practitioner 1990-; D'Youville Coll Asst Prof 1992-; *ai:* Acad Resources, Stu Affairs, Curr Congruence Comms; AWHONN 1976-, Chprsn 1990-; Nurse Practitioner Assn of Western NY 1986-; Sigma Theta Tau 1985-, Rsrch Awd 1992; 1st Bapt Church of Lancaster NY 1991-, Sunday Schl Supt; Article Pub 1992; Wrote Chapter Nursing in the Community 1989; *office:* D'Youville Coll 320 Porter Ave Buffalo NY 14201*

SNELL, NINA LANNING, 4th Grade Teacher; *b:* Barberton, OH; *m:* James A. Jr.; *c:* Jennifer; *ed:* Univ of Akron (BS) Elem Ed 1985; Ashland Univ (MED) Supervision 1990; *cr:* West Holmes Local Schl 4th Grd Tchr 1985-; Ashland Univ Adj Prof, Grad Stud Cmptrs 1991-; *ai:* Tech Comm W Holmes Schls Schl Rep; Delta Kappa Gamma 1990-, Pres; West Holmes Ed Assn 1985-; Handweaving & Spinning Guild of Wooster 1992-, Treas, Pres; OH Child Conservation League 1992-, Sec, VP, Pres; Martha Holden Jennings Grant Soc Stud 1995-; *office:* Millersburg Elem Schl 430 E Jackson St Millersburg OH 44654*

SNELL, SHAWN ANITA, French & Spanish Tchr; *b:* Osaka, Japan; *ed:* Ricker Coll (BA) Fr, Span 1973; Univ of Southern ME (MA) Admin 1988; Mainstreaming Course, Word Processing Course; *cr:* Houlton HS Fr Tchr 1973-, Fr, Span Tchr 1977-, Dept Chprsn 1989-92, Modern Lang Subject Coodr 1995-; *ai:* Curr Comm; Modern Lang Subject Coord; NEA, AATF, Flame 1973-; Phi Delta Kappa 1986-, Initiation Ldr; St Marys Church 1959-; Democratic Party 1969; Mem of Right to Read Task Force Helped Dev Prgm in MSAD #29 in 1977; *office:* Houlton HS 5 Bird St Houlton ME 04730

SNIDER, MARY BETH, Sixth Grade Social Sci Tchr; *b:* Defiance, OH; *ed:* Bowling Green St Univ (BS) Elem Ed 1975; IN Wesleyan Univ (MS) Ed 1995; Attnd Univ of Toledo, Bowling Green St Univ, Drake Univ & Dayton Univ Post Grad Stud; *cr:* St Augustine Schl 7th & 8th Grd Tchr 1975-76; Bryan MS 6th Grd Tchr 1978-; *ai:* 8th Grd Vlybl Coach; Insight Facilitator; NEA & OEA 1978-; BEA 1978-, Treas 2 Yrs; Delta Kappa Gamma 1988-; OH Geo Alliance; Williams Cty Playhouse 1978-, Production Bd, Pres 3 Yrs; Girl Scouts 1961-; OH Comm Theater Assn, NW Reg Rep 1993-; NW OH Episcopal Shared Ministry Bd Pres; *office:* Bryan MS 1301 Center St Bryan OH 43506

SNIDER, NANCY S., US History Teacher; *b:* Winston-Salem, NC; *m:* A. Monroe Jr.; *c:* Alicia Elizabeth, Eric Brandon; *ed:* Pfeiffer Coll (BA) European & Amer 1965; ASU (MA) European His 1969; UNC Addl Credit Hrs His; *cr:* Jackson HS His, Eng Tchr 1965-67; ASU Pol Sci Tchr 1968-69; Elizabeth Forward HS His Tchr 1969-70; Cntrl Cath HS His Tchr 1970-; *ai:* World Affairs Cncl 1990-; Fed of Diocesan Tchrs, VP; *office:* Central Catholic HS 4720 5th Ave Pittsburgh PA 15213

SNIFFIN, ALLAN D., English Teacher; *b:* Danbury, CT; *m:* Deanne L. Engstrom; *c:* Timothy, Tricia; *ed:* Univ of Bridgeport (MS) Scndry Ed; Rutgers Univ (BA) Eng 1964; 6th Yr in Admin, Guidance, Counseling; *cr:* Danbury HS Eng Tchr 1964-, Dept Chprsn Dist 1981-82, Counseling Tchr, Eng Dept 1987-89; Danbury Pub Schls Adult Ed Cnslr 1975-81; *ai:* CAPT Test Supvr; Stu Performance Assessment Comm; NEA 1964-, Life Mem; Coun Ed Assn, Danbury Ed Assn 1964-; Bd of Selectmen 1983-, 1st Selectman Pro Team; Lions Club 1994-, Tail Twister; Zoning Comm 1974-83, Chm; Church Cncl, Prince of Peace Luth Church 1970-76; *home:* 10 N Beech Tree Rd Brookfield CT 06804

SNINSKI, FRANK G., Social Studies Teacher; *b:* Linden, NJ; *ed:* Penn St Univ (BA) Soc Stud, Scndry Ed 1972; J. P. Stevens HS Soc Stud Tchr 1974; Manalapan HS Soc Stud Tchr 1975-78; Howell HS Soc Stud Tchr 1978-; *cr:* Pub Address Announcer Ftbl Games; Var Ftbl Coach 12 Yrs; *ai:* NEA, NJEA,MCEA, FRHSDEA 1975-; Rotary Club 1986-; Rotary Intnl Stu Exch Prgm 1990-, Exec Comm St of NJ; *office:* Howell HS Squankum-Yellowbrook Rd Farmingdale NJ 07727*

SNITZER, HOLLY STEMPIEN, Elementary Music Teacher; *b:* Lewistown, PA; *m:* Andrew; *c:* Mark; *ed:* Mansfield St Univ (BA) Music Ed 1973; 25 Extra Credit Hrs; *cr:* Blue Ridge Schl Dist Music Tchr 1973-; *ai:* Elem Select Choir; PSEA, NEA, PMEA, MEA 1974-; BREA 1974-, VP; Parents of Friends fo BSA Troop 1989-, VP 1994, Pres 1996; Choir Dir 1986-; Note a Bells 1990-; Parents of Gifted Stdnts 1995-; Susquehanma Comm Band 1990-.

SNIVELY, JOHN THOMAS, Occupational Teacher; *b:* Bellaire, OH; *m:* Marilyn Korner; *c:* Ben, Jodi, Julie, Dan, Zac; *ed:* OH Northern Univ (BS) Hlth, PE 1971; OH Univ Masters PE 1985; Post Grad Occupational Work Experience Voc Degree; *cr:* Bellaire HS Spec Ed Tchr 1971-74; Bellaire St John Cntrl HS Hlth, PE Tchr 1974-76; John Marshall Sr HS Hlth Ed Tchr 1977-88; North Union HS Hlth, OWE Tchr 1988-93; Lancaster Sr HS Occupational Work Experience Tchr 1993-; *ai:* Head Sftbl, Asst Ftbl Coach; OEA, LEA, NEA 1988-; OVA-AVA 1995-; Cntrl Dist Sftbl Coaches Assn 1988-, 100 Wins; *office:* Lancaster HS 1312 Granville Pike Lancaster OH 43130

SNIVLEY, RETA MC LAUCHLIN, 7th Grade Teacher; *b:* Dowagiac, MI; *m:* Richard L.; *c:* Jon Watts, Jacqueline Watts Weaver, Patty Watts, Paul Watts; *ed:* Western MI Univ (BS) Elem Ed 1958; Addl 6 Hrs; Univ of Notre Dame 6 Hrs; Bowling Green St Univ 9 Hrs; *cr:* Niles Pub Schls 3rd Grd Tchr 1958-61; Climax-Scotts Schls 6th Grd Tchr 1966-67; St Patrick Schl 6th-8th Grd Tchr 1972-74, 3rd, 7th Grd Tchr 1978-; *ai:* Spelling Bee Coord; Stu Cncl Adv; Soc Stud Advy Comm; NCEA 1979-; Bryan Bus & Prof Women 1972-, Sec, Treas, VP, Pres; Church Circle 1994-; Dist I Funeral Dirs 1976-; *office:* Saint Patricks Schl 610 S Portland St Bryan OH 43506

SNODDY, CHARLES WILLIAM, Accounting Professor; *b:* Memphis, TN; *ed:* Oklahoma City Univ (MSA) Accounting 1978; *cr:* Huntingdon Coll Accounting Prof 1987-88; Finger Lakes Comm Coll Accounting Prof 1988-; *ai:* Affirmative Action Comm Co-Chair; Financial Strategies Comm Chair; Acad Policies Comm; OK Soc of CPA, AICPA 1980-; *home:* 107 Yacht Club Dr Canandaigua NY 14424

SNODGRASS, FRANCIS THOMAS, Social Studies Teacher; *b:* Martins Ferry, OH; *m:* Gretchen Ann Holland; *ed:* OH Univ (BSEd) Ed 1990; *cr:* Shadyside HS Soc Stud Tchr 1994-; *ai:* FTA Chprsn; Educl Hnr Soc, Historical Hnr Soc 1990-; Temple Shalom Trustee Bd 1994-; *office:* Shadyside HS 3890 Lincoln Ave Shadyside OH 43947

SNODGRASS, GRETCHEN ANN, English Teacher; *b:* Martins Ferry, OH; *m:* Francis T.; *c:* Jacob; *ed:* OH Univ (BS) Ed, Eng 1981; Fort Hays St Univ (MA) Eng 1991; *cr:* Martins Ferry HS Eng Tchr 1982-; *ai:* Soph Class Adv; NEA, OEA, MFEA 1982-; *office:* Martins Ferry Hanover St Martins Ferry OH 43935

SNOOK, JOANN PIERCE, English Teacher; *b:* Camden, NJ; *m* *ed:* Trenton St Coll (BA) Eng & Scndry Ed 1977, (MA) Eng 1983; Prin Cert; *cr:* Mercer Cty Comm Coll Adj Instr of Eng 1985-92; All HS Vice Prin & Supvr of Eng 1988-89 & 1993-95, Eng Tchr 1977 Schl Newspaper Adv; Comm Svc Club; NJNEA 1977-; NJ Prin Assn 1994-; NCTE 1994-; NJ Governors Tchr Awd 1982; Poen *office:* Allentown HS 27 High St Allentown NJ 08501

SNOUFFER, JOHN I., Social Studies Teacher; *b:* Dover, OH; *m* Hartsook; *ed:* OH St Univ (BS) Ed & Soc Stud Comp 1974; Ashlar (MS) Sports Sci 1983; Addl Hrs in Distant Learning Fiber Optics Methods Tech; *cr:* Walnut Springs MS 8th Grd His Tchr 1974-84 HS Soc Stud Tchr 1985-; *ai:* Jr Achvmt Adv & Tchr; NEA, C Westerville EA 1974-; Jr Achvmt of Cntrl OH Tchr of Yr 1995; No Jr Achvmt Tchr of Yr 1995; *office:* Westerville North HS 950 Coun Rd Westerville OH 43081*

SNOVITCH, ELAINE, Mathematics & Cmptr Sci Tchr; *b:* Alle PA; *m:* Michael; *c:* Nicholas; *ed:* Allentown Coll (BS) Cmptr Sci-Cum Laude 1990, (BS) Math-Summa Cum Laude 1991; Post Grad Cmptr Sci, Tchng & Ed Discipline; *cr:* PA Power & Light Co Positions 1968-79; Bethlehem Cath HS Tchr 1990-; *ai:* NCTM *office:* Bethlehem Catholic HS 2133 Madison Ave Bethlehem PA 1

SNOW, LINDA COOPER, Family & Consumer Science Chm; *b:* B PA; *m:* James R.; *c:* Kevin, Bradley; *ed:* Messiah Coll (BS) Home 1980; *cr:* Greencastle Antrim Schl Dist Home Ec Tchr 1980-81; Hy HS Home Ec Tchr 1981-82; Everett Area Schl Dist Home Ec Tchr 1 Home Ec Dept Chair 1984-; *ai:* Renaissanc Discipline Comm; Rena Trustee; Grad Project Comm; PSEA 1980-, Bldg Rep, Pace Office Troop #444 1991-, Treas; *office:* Everett Area HS 12 N River Ln PA 15537

SNOW, MARION R., English Teacher; *b:* Kahnawake QC, Canada; Joseph Coll (BA) Eng 1966; Brooklyn Coll (MA) Eng 1971; 18 Addl Hrs Towards Second MA; 9 Addl Credits Post Grad Fordham Enric *cr:* Sacred Heart Acad Eng Tchr 1973-83; Universidad Catolica de Rico Eng Instr 1983-86; Sacred Heart Acad Eng Tchr 1986-; Acaden Ignacio Prin 1989-90; *ai:* Alumnae Newsletter Ed; NCTE, NCEA CEA 1984-; TESOL 1983-86, Bd Mem; *office:* Sacred Heart A Cathedral Ave Hempstead NY 11550

SNYDER, ANITA DYE, 2nd Grade & Head Teacher; *b:* Columbu *m:* C. Mark; *c:* Megan; *ed:* Miami Univ (BSEd) El Ed 1968, (ME Media 1975; Continuing Educl Units; *cr:* Project Head Start Aid Hamilton City Schls Tchr 1969-; *ai:* NEA, OEA 1972-; HCTA 1969 Rep; Delta Kappa Gamma 1995-; Friends of Lane Lib 1996; *office:* M Elem Schl 951 Carriage Hill Ln Hamilton OH 45013

SNYDER, ANNE H., Third Grade Teacher; *b:* Massillon, OH; *m:* D.; *c:* Steven, Sandy; *ed:* Muskingum Coll (BS) Ed 1961; Attnd Univ, Eastern MI Univ, Ashland Univ, Akron Univ; *cr:* Columbus Pu Sixth Grd Tchr 1961-63; Dearborn Pub Schls Second Grd Tchr 19 Montgomery Schls Non Graded 4-6 Grd Tchr 1964-66; Orrville Pub Third Fourth Grd Tchr 1980-; *ai:* Sci Curr Comm; NEA 1980-; Admin Bd 1993, Tchr; Tchr of Yr North Schl 1982; Martha Je Scholar 1986; *office:* Oak Street Schl 209 W Oak Orrville OH 4466

SNYDER, CAROL K., Mathematics Teacher; *b:* Celina, OH; *e* Northern Univ (BS) Math 1991; Grad Work Univ of Dayton; *cr:* V Sub Tchr 1991-92; OH Hi-Point JVS Applied Math Instr 19 Waynesfield-Goshen HS Math Instr & Chair 1994-; *ai:* BLC Comm Class Adv; OH Cncl of Tchrs of Math 1991-; NCTM 1991-; AVA NEA & OEA 1994-; Wright Connection; *home:* 401 Hamilton Rd Wapakoneta OH 45895

SNYDER, CAROL LYNN, Seventh Grade English Teacher; *b:* C OH; *ed:* Malone Coll (BS) Elem Ed 1977; Walsh Coll (MA) Spec Ed Cooperative Learning Ashland Univ; *cr:* Pleasantview Elem Grd 5 1977-80; Louisville Jr HS 7 & 8 Grd Tchr 1980-91; Louisville MS Eng Tchr 1991-; *ai:* Inservice Comm; Spelling Bee Comm; NEA, LEA 1980-; Westbrook Park United Meth Church 1967-, Choir, Bell Comms; Louisville Lions Club Tchr of Month; *office:* Louisville M E Gorgas St Louisville OH 44641

SNYDER, CAROL STANEK, 5th Grade Teacher; *b:* Charleroi, P Herb; *c:* Kurt; *ed:* CA Univ of PA (BS) Elem Ed 1968; Univ of Pitts (ME) Safety Ed 1971; *cr:* Atlastburg Elem Intermediate Tchr 196 Labor Union Poster Contest Spon; Tech Comm; NEA 1968-; PSEA BAEA 1968-; NCTE 1985-; WA Cty Historical Soc 1988-, Ed C Jefferson Historical Soc 1992-; Gift of Time; *office:* Atlasburg Elen Box 295 Main St Atlasburg PA 15004

SNYDER, CURTIS W., 9th Grade Earth Science Tchr; *b:* Albany, N Stacey S.; *c:* Sydney; *ed:* SUNY at Geneseo (BA) Earth Sci 1991; Gra for Masters SUNY at Albany; *cr:* Lansingburgh HS Earth Sci Tchr *ai:* 8th Grd Boys Soccer Coach; AFT 1993-.

SNYDER, DAVID LEE, Small Animal Tech Teacher; *b:* Philadelphi *m:* Pamela Taylor; *c:* Victoria; *ed:* Pa St Univ (BS) Ag Ed, (BS) A Bio Sci 1980; Beaver Coll (BS) Enviromental Sci 1990; 60 Credits Masters; *cr:* W.B. Saul Tchr 1980-; *ai:* Run Indoor Hockey, Lacrosse FFA Adv; AALAS, PFT 1980-; *office:* Walter Bittle Saul HS Ag Sci Henry Ave Philadelphia PA 19128*

SNYDER, DONNA GIESELMAN, Third Grade Teacher; *b:* Jacobus *m:* Gene A.; *c:* Brenda Jane Hostetler, Brian Eugene; *ed:* Millersville (BS) Elem Ed 1971; Commonwealth of PA Masters Equiv Elem Ed *cr:* York Twp Elem Schl Second Grd Tchr 1971-80, Fifth Grd 1980-83, Fourth Grd Tchr 1983-93, Third Grd Tchr 1993-; *ai:* Dallas Schl Dist Curr Dev Comm; Soc Stud, Career Dev; PSEA, NEA 1972-; Symphony Chorus 1962-, Sec; Amer Guild of Organists 1990-, Exe York Chamber Singers 1983-, Bd of Dir; Christ United Meth Church Music, Organist; *office:* York Twp Elem Schl 2500 S Queen St Yo 17402*

SNYDER, GARY FREDERICK, 6th Grade Teacher; *b:* Ashland St PA; *m:* Sharon A.; *c:* Melissa Greiner, Michelle; *ed:* Bloomsburg St (BA) Elem 1966, (MS) Elem Ed 1973; *cr:* Tri-Valley Schl Dist 3rd-6t Tchr 1966-; *ai:* Asst Ath Dir 22 Yrs; NEA, PSEA, TVEA 1966-; N NCTM, IRA 1985-; United Meth 1969-, Choir; Speaker NCTM Conve 1995; *home:* RR 2 Box 143 Hegins PA 17938

SNYDER, GREGORY LYNN, Band Director; *b:* Canton, OH; *m:* S Kay Skaggs; *c:* Alexander, Adam; *ed:* Bowling Green St Univ (BA) 1980; Vander Cook Coll of Music (MS) Music 1986; Attnd Conservatory of Music; Univ of Cincinnati Credit Hrs; *cr:* Clyde-C Springs Schls Band Dir 1980-88; Lakota Schls Band Dir 1988- Concert, Jazz Marching & Pep Bands; Ohio Music Ed Assn, NEA 1 Lakota Ed Assn 1988-; Amer Schl Bd Dir Assn 1988-; Phi Beta Mu *office:* Lakota HS 5050 Tylersville Rd West Chester OH 45069

SNYDER, JAYNE SILFIES, Substitute Teacher; *b:* Rochester, NY Dennis Claude; *c:* Chad, Marc, Elisabeth; *cr:* Pavilion Bapt Schl S Math Tchr 1988-91; Pavilion Cntrl Schl Sub Tchr 1992-; *home:* 1 Creek Rd Pavilion NY 14525

ER, JEAN FISTER, 9th-12th Grade Math Teacher; *b:* Reading, PA; hn A.; *c:* Emily J., Jessica L.; *ed:* Albright Coll (BS) Math 1967; h Univ (MA) Ed 1968; Probability & Statistics PA st; Calculus for Lafayette; Leadership Courses Marywood; Basic amming-Pascal Programming Villanova; *cr:* Radio Shack Ed Ctr Tchr 84; Pennridge Schl Dist Tchr 1967-; *ai:* Summer Theatre, Yrbk Bus SAT Wkshp Coord & Author; Commencement Awd Chprsn; Unified PSEA, PEA 1967-, Local Treas; NCTM 1967-; ATMOPAV 1989-; h Choir 1967-; Outstanding Tchr of Yr Jaycees 1968-70; Co-Author Courses, SAT Wkshp; *office:* Pennridge HS 1228 N 5th St Perkasie 944*

ER, JEANNETTE S., Kindergarten Teacher; *ed:* Univ of DE (BS) Chldhd 1970; Millersville & Penn St 45 Grad Credits; *cr:* Red Lion Schls Kndgtn Tchr 1971-; *office:* Windsor Manor Elem Schl 2110 or Rd Windsor PA 17366

ER, JEFFREY LYNN, Fine Arts Dept Chr, Music Tchr; *b:* York, Lisa Kay Leiphart; *ed:* West Chester St Coll (BS) Music Ed 1968; rn MD Coll (MED) Music Ed 1971; Adm Supervision of Music Cert Attnd East Stroudsburg St Univ, Amer Univ, PA St Univ, IN Univ of owson St Univ, Wilkes Coll; *cr:* Dover Area Intermediate Schl Music 1968-71; Dover Area HS Fine Arts Dept Chair 1971-; Dover Area Schl Supvr of Music 1984-94; *ai:* Select Choral Group; NEA, PSEA, 1968-; PA Music Ed Assn, MENC 1971-; ASCD 1984-; Dover es Outstdng Young Educator 1981; Renaissance Performed for C, PMEA Convention 1991, White House Staff 1995, Recorded act Disc 1994.

ER, JOAN BOTSCHNER, Adult Education Teacher; *b:* Massillon, *w:* Robert (dec); *c:* Scott, Randall, Danton; *ed:* Heidelberg Coll (BA) d, Eng 1951; Akron Univ Addl Credits Cmptr Sci, Eng; *cr:* Coventry us Ed Tchr 1951-59; Manchester HS Voc Bus Tchr 1973-78; Portage Career Ctr Voc Bus, Cmptr Tchr 1978-95, Adult Ed, GED Cmptr 1995-; *ai:* BPLA Adv; NEA; OEA; St John's Schl 1993-, Sec, Bd of lorence Daugherty Awd; Tchr of Yr; Course in Stud; *home:* 2013 Dan nal Fulton OH 44614

ER, JOHN ARTHUR, Science & Physics Teacher; *b:* Lima, OH; *m:* beth Marie Malczewski; *c:* Luke, Joseph, Martha, Ruth, Issac; *ed:* of Toledo (BA) Comprehensive Sci 1976; Summer Courses in Cmptr & Environmental Physics at Kent St, Bowling Green St & OH St *cr:* Maumee City Schl Math Tchr 1976; OH City Schl Sci Tchr -84; Otsego HS Sci Tchr 1984-; *ai:* OEA, NEA 1990-; Local League l, Bsbl, Track & Cross Cntry Coach; *home:* 1006 Michigan Ave rville OH 43566

ER, JOYCE ANN, Second Grade Teacher; *b:* London, England; *m:* D.; *c:* Jennifer, David; *ed:* Univ Of Cincinnati (BS) Ed 1975; Univ incinnati Cert for Elem Fr; Xavier Univ Grad Courses; *cr:* St ninus Tchr 1975-, Primary Coord 1979-; *ai:* Primary Coord; OEA -; Kappa Delta Phi 1975-77; Girl Scouts 1992-, Cookie Coord & er; Nom for Ashland Oil Tchr Awd; *office:* Saint Antoninus Schl 5425 ar Dr Cincinnati OH 45238*

ER, JUDY JOHNSON, 1st Grade Teacher; *b:* Portsmouth, OH; *m:* L.; *ed:* OH Univ (BS) Elem 1975; Addl Credit Hrs Ashland Coll, OR *cr:* South Webster Elem Tchrs Aide 1972-75; Scioto Furnace Elem rd Tchr 1975-77; Frey Elem 1st, 5th Grd Tchr 1977-81; Norwood 1st Grd Tchr 1981-; *ai:* NEA, OEA, WJ Tchrs Assn 1979-; *office:* wood Elem Schl 899 Norwood Dr West Jefferson OH 43162

DER, KAREN STEIN, Spanish Teacher; *b:* York, PA; *m:* Michael K.; lia K.; *ed:* Bloomsburg Univ (BS) Span, Scndry Ed 1989; Millersville (MS) Elem Ed 1994; *cr:* Kennard Dale HS Span Tchr 1991-; *ai:* Adv Class, Key Club; Girls' Jr HS Bsktbl Coach; SEEA, NEA, AATSP -; Kiwanis Club 1994-; *office:* Kennard Dale HS RD 1 Box 26 Fawn e PA 17321

ER, KATHRYN ANN, Sixth Grade Teacher; *b:* Detroit, MI; *m:* ael L.; *ed:* Bowling Green St Univ (BS) Elem Ed 1969; Univ of Toledo Elem Ed 1985; 21 Credit Hrs Beyond Masters; *cr:* Central Elem 4th Tchr 1969-76; Napoleon MS 6th Grd Tchr 1976-; *ai:* Acad Boosters & PTO Staff Adv; Steering Comm; NEA, OEA 1969-; Delta Kappa ma 1989-; *office:* Napoleon MS 303 W Main St Napoleon OH 43545

ER, KENNETH R., Physics Dept Chair & Prof; *b:* Amsterdam, NY; atrice Cacciatore; *ed:* Rensselaer Poly Inst (BS) Physics 1961; Univ E (MS) Physics 1964; Univ of FL (MS) Nuclear Engrng 1973; TX Univ 6 Grad Hrs; *cr:* Univ of NE Tchng Asst 1961-64; SUNY at risville Physics Prof 1964-; Univ of FL Rsrch Asst 1972-73; *ai:* Dept r; Fac Congress; Acad Affairs Comm Chair; Schlsp Comm; Engrng Sci Long-Time Adv; UUP, AFT & NYSUT 1987-; Univ of TX at Austin D Excl Awd Winner 1996; Article Pub; *office:* S U N Y Coll Of A & rrisvl Morrisville NY 13408

ER, LINDA CLYMER, 5th Grade Teacher; *b:* Phillipsburg, NJ; *m:* iam D.; *ed:* Trenton St Coll (BS) Elem Ed 1971; 15 Addl Credits; *cr:* man Schl 5th-6th Grd Tchr 1971-89; Phillipsburg MS 5th Grd Tchr -91; Andover Morris Schl 5th Grd Tchr 1991-; *ai:* Field Hockey Asst h; Variety Show, Schl TV Station Advs; Site Based Mngmt Team Ldr; Negotiating Team; Curr, Act Comms; Phillipsburg Ed Assn 1971-, esponding Sec; NJEA, NEA 1971-; NJ Tchr Recognition Awd 1989, ; Phillipsburg Tchr of Yr 1993.*

DER, LISA KAY, Family & Consumer Sci Tchr; *b:* Columbia, PA; *m:* rey L.; *ed:* IN Univ of PA (BS) Home Ec 1976, (MED) Family, sumer Scis 1980; *cr:* Dover Area HS Family, Cons Sci Tchr 1976-; *ai:* Home Ec Club 1976-86, Chrldng 1976-78, Class 1978-81, 1993-94; A, PSEA, NEA, York Cty Home Ec 1976-; Phi Delta Kappa; Started ourses; *home:* 1124 Laurel Dr York PA 17404

DER, MARION TEBO, Retired Fourth Grade Teacher; *b:* Blandford, *m:* Vernon E.; *c:* Amy B., Paul V.; *ed:* Westfield St Tchr Coll (BS) Ed ; 15 Credit Hrs Rdng Courses; *cr:* Leeds Schl 3rd Grd Tchr 1953-54; son Street Schl 3rd Grd Tchr 1954-56; Southampton Road Schl 3rd Grd 1956-58; Ft Meadow Schl 4th Grd Tchr 1965-82, Southampton Road 4th Grd Tchr 1982-95; *ai:* Westfield Tchrs Assn, MA Tchrs Assn -; NEA 1953-, Life Mem; Organized Giving to Westfield Food Bank, ing Ornaments for Milton Bradley Giving Tree 1987; Chm Westfield System Bicentennial of the US Constitution 5 Yr Natl Project; ibited Quilts Made by Class 1987, 3 Blue Ribbons 1988; Dist npetion 3rd Place 1989, 1st Place, St Competion 1991 Natl Historical oral Map Contest.

DER, MARK, High School Guidance Counselor; *b:* Lebanon, PA; *m:* ron Beth Faust; *c:* Laurie Sauder, Todd Walter, Betsy; *ed:* Gettysburg (BS) Hlth, PE 1965; West Chester Univ (MED) Ed 1970; Millersburg Cnslr Ed Cert 1985; *cr:* Reading HS Hlth, PE Tchr, Asst Ftbl & Track ch 1967-71; Schuylill Vly HS Hlth, PE Tchr, Head Ftbl Coach 1971-74; Mifflin HS Hlth, PE Tchr, Head Ftbl Coach 1974-76; Warwick HS , PE Tchr, Head Ftbl Coach 1976-86, 1986-; Franklin & Marshall Coll Ftbl Coach, Offensive Coord 1991-; *ai:* Coll Ftbl Coaching; NEA, A 1965-; Warwick Ed Assn 1976-; HS Ftbl Coach of Yr 4 Times in 15 ; *office:* Warwick HS 301 W Orange St Lititz PA 17543

DER, MARY JANE MISSMER, Third Grade Teacher; *b:* Allentown, *m:* Roy G.; *c:* Michael R., Alison; *ed:* Alvernia Coll (BA) Elem Ed, e Arts 1975; 30 Credits Penn St Univ at Millersville; *cr:* Conrad Weiser Schl Dist Third Grd Tchr 23 Yrs; *ai:* Rdng, Math, Report Card Comm; Mentor Prgm; CWEA 1975-, Bldg Rep; NEA 1975-; Women's Club, Various Comm Chprsn.

SNYDER, NANCY ANN OLEWINSKI, Spanish Teacher; *b:* Kearny, NJ; *c:* Matthew, Jennifer; *ed:* Glassboro St (BA) Span 1976; 15 Grad Credits; *cr:* Hillsborough MS Span Tchr 1977; Eastern Intermediate, Sr HS Span Tchr 1977-; *ai:* Stu Alliance Prgm; Stud Skills Comm; Coord Schl-to-Schl Prgm with Spain; NJEA, NEA, EEA 1977-; Gibbsboro HSA 1986-, Pres; *office:* Eastern Intermediate HS Laurel Oak Rd Box 2500 Voorhees NJ 08043*

SNYDER, PATRICK SHERDELL, Health & PE Teacher; *b:* York, PA; *m:* Erin Mc Donel; *c:* Kevin; *ed:* IN Univ of PA (BA) Hlth, PE 1979; PA St Univ (MS) Hlth Ed 1991; *cr:* Indiana Area Sr HS 10th Grd Hlth, PE Tchr 1980-; *ai:* Asst Var Ftbl 16 Yrs, Bsktbl 14 Yrs, Head Track & Field 17 Yrs Coach; IM Dir; Fac Wellness Coord; PAHPERD 1986-; NEA, PSEA 1980-; Compiled HS His Ftbl, Track, Field; Coached 49 Straight Sports Seasons; Spoke St HPERD, ARIN Conventions, Baldwin Track, Field Clinics; *office:* Indiana Area Sr HS 450 N 5th St Indiana PA 15701*

SNYDER, PAULETTE R., Professor; *b:* Buffalo, NY; *m:* Kenneth J.; *c:* Kenneth V., Samantha C.; *ed:* SUNY at Buffalo (BA) Bio 1968, (MED) Sci Ed 1981; *cr:* Buffalo Pub, No Tonawanda Pub Scndry Schls Sci Tchr 1966-78; Erie Comm Coll Bio Instr, Prof 1979-; *ai:* Stu Life, Cultural Diversity, Orientation, Grad Comm Mem; NEA 10 Yrs; NY St Org, 10 Yrs, Mem; Org for Retarded, Handicapped; West Seneca DC Chapter NYARC Inc; Infusing Cultural Diversity Into Curr 1992-93 Mini Grant; AAHE Conference Co-Presenter 1993; ECC Pres Recognition Awd 1992; NISOD Excellence Awd 1993; Chancellors Awd for Excellence in Tchng 1995; *office:* Erie Comm Coll North Cmps 6205 Main St Williamsville NY 14221

SNYDER, RICHARD WILSON,II, 1st-12th Grade Art Teacher; *b:* Clearfield, PA; *m:* Lori Jolene Peacock; *ed:* PA St Univ (BS) Art Ed 1976; 30 Post Grad Hrs; *cr:* Glendale Schl Dist Art Tchr 1977-; *ai:* Fine Arts Dept, Dist Technology Comm & Dist Sr Project Comm Chmn; NEA 1977-; PA Coalition For Arts in Ed 1988-; Assocs for Supervision & Curr Dev 1989-; Clearfield Cty Historical Soc 1990-; PHEAA-ITECH Grant & Numerous other Grants; Outstdng Youngman of Amer; *office:* Glendale Jr Sr High School 1466 Beaver Valley Rd Flinton PA 16640

SNYDER, SALLY ANN, Retired 5th Grade Teacher; *b:* Sunbury, PA; *m:* Oscar Lee; *c:* Terri Martin, Tracy Moyer, Ted; *ed:* Kutztown Univ (BA) Elem 1970; *cr:* Kutztown Elem Schl 5th Grd Tchr 21 Yrs; *ai:* PSEA, NEA, KATA 1971-; Quilt Guild 1995-.

SNYDER, SALLY JEANNE (RHOADES), Third Grade Teacher; *b:* Hicksville, OH; *m:* Michael; *c:* Kimberly, Kelly Schroeder, Kristin, Scott; *ed:* Defiance Coll (BA) Elem Ed 1962; *cr:* Mason Consolidated First Grd Tchr 1962-63; Quincy Elem Schl Second Grd Tchr 1963-64; Defiance City Schls Third Grd Tchr 1977-; *ai:* OEA, NEA 1977-; Defiance City Ed Assn, Bldg Rep; Alpha Delta Kappa 1994-; *home:* 1234 Fallen Timbers Dr Defiance OH 43512

SNYDER, SARAH JANE, Special Education Teacher; *b:* Rochester, NY; *ed:* SUNY at Cortland (BS) Elem Ed, Math 1980; Nazareth Coll (MS) Spec Ed 1985; 15 Addl Grad Credit Hrs; *cr:* Bradford Cntrl Schl Jr HS Math Tchr 1981-84; Monroe Cty BOCES I HS Spec Ed Sub Tchr 1984-86; Marion Jr Sr HS MS Spec Ed Tchr 1986-; *ai:* Earth Shuttle Club Adv; 7th Grd Stu of Week Coord; Tech-Prep Comm; Negotiator Marion Tchrs Assn; CEC 1993-; NYSUT, Marion Tchrs Assn 1986-; *office:* Marion Jr Sr HS 4034 Warner Rd Marion NY 14505

SNYDER, SHELLEY F., Science Teacher; *ed:* Univ of VT (BA) Geology 1978; St Michaels Coll (MED) Ed 1987; Addl Courses; *cr:* Univ of VT Water Quality Technician 1979-81; Mt Abraham HS Math, Sci Tchr 1988-; UVM Adj Instr 1995-; *ai:* Odyssey of the Mind Coord, Coach; Adv for Thin Budget Productions Theater Group; Curr Assessment Comm; Schl Dev Cncl; VT Geological Soc 1974-, Pres, Ed Chair; VT Sci Tchr Assoc 1990-; Natural Resources Comm 1976-, Current Chair; Articles Pub; Eisenhauer Funds for Projects; Local Standards Bd 1993-95; *office:* Mt Abraham Union HS 7 Airport Dr Bristol VT 05443*

SNYDER, STANLEY ROBERT, Biology Teacher; *b:* Kempton, PA; *m:* Helen Louise Shelhamer; *c:* Ross A., Alison J.; *ed:* East Stroudsburg Univ (BA) Bio 1967; 36 Credit Hrs 1976; 30 Credit Hrs; *cr:* Hamburg Area HS Bio Tchr 1967-; *ai:* 8th Grd Girls Bsktbl, JV Boys Bsktbl, Head Soccer & Jr High Bsbl Coach; Wilderness Club Adv 26 Yrs; Soph Class Adv; NEA, PSEa & HAEA 1967-, Pre Local; Jaycees 1967-73, Different Chairmanship; NSF Grants 3 Yrs; Outstdng Conservation Tchr 1995; *home:* RR 1 Box 406-A Bernville PA 19506

SNYDER, SUSAN NOON, 5th Grade Math Teacher; *b:* Johnstown, PA; *m:* Paul D.; *c:* Dustin M.; *ed:* Slipperty Rock St Coll (BS) Elem Ed 1975; 25 Credit Hrs; *cr:* Forest HIlls Elem Schl 1st Grd Tchr 1975-81, 3rd Grd Tchr 1981-87, 5th Grd Tchr 1987-; *ai:* Portfolio Comm; NEA, PSEA, FHEA 1975-; St Josephs Church 19860, CCD Tchr; Motivational Manipulatives Wkshp; *office:* Forest HIlls Schl Dist 547 Locust St Sidman PA 15955

SNYDER, THOMAS JAMES, Instrumental Music Teacher; *b:* Punxsutawney, PA; *m:* Sara Wuenchel; *c:* Krista, Bradley; *ed:* Clarion St Coll (BS) Music Ed 1980; Duquesne Univ (MM) Music Ed; 30 Addl Credit Hrs; *cr:* North Allegheny Schl Dist HS Instrumental Music Tchr 1980-83; Woodland Hills Sch Dist HS Instrumental Music Tchr 1983-84; West Allegheny Schl Dist HS Instrumental Music Tchr 1984-; *ai:* Marching Band; Jazz, Percussion, Small Ensembles; Pit Orch Musical Theatre; PMEA, PSEA 1980-; TRMBA 1984-, Sec, Treas; PFCJ 1988-, Judge; Musicians Concert Band 1986-, Performer; Prgm Consultant; Curr Dev Presentations; All-Star Educator Awd; *office:* West Allegheny HS 205 W Allegheny Rd Imperial PA 15126

SNYDER, THOMAS MICHAEL, Native Amer & World Hist Tchr; *b:* Highland Cty, OH; *m:* Janis Marie Porter; *c:* Clinton Robert Oney, Paul Justice; *ed:* Cntrl St Univ (BS) His, PE 1979; Kent St Univ (MA) Admin Higher Ed 1986; *cr:* Wilmington HS Tchr; Coll of Wooster Admin Asst 1983-86; Kent St Univ Dir Ath, Asst Prof PE 1986-92; Hillsboro HS Tchr 1992-; *ai:* Var Boys, Girls Cross Cntry Coach; Ath Cncl; Lions Club; *office:* Hillsboro HS 358 W Main St Hillsboro OH 45133

SNYDER, WAYNE, Physics Teacher & Dept Chair; *c:* Sabrina, Justin; *ed:* Grove City Coll (BS) Bio 1974; Univ of Rochester (MS) Environmental Stud, Toxicology 1978; SUNY at Brockport Cert Scndry Physics, Chem, Bio Cert 1976; Admin Courses; *cr:* Wayne Cntrl HS Physics, Chem Tchr 1977-91; SUNY Dept of Ed Instr 1991-92, Dept of Ed Adj 1989-; Spencerport HS Physics Tchr, Dept Chair 1992-; *ai:* Odyssey of Mind; Dist Sci Comms; STANYS; NSTA; AAPT; AP Physics Test Dev Comm; AFT; AAUP; ETS-AP Physics Consultant; Physics Tchng Resource Agent; Operation Physics Ldr; Presidential Awd Finialist 1991; Tchr of Yr 1986, 1989; Keynote Address NHST 1994; WXXI Innovative Tchr Awd 1994; Excl in Tchng Awd 1995; Eisenhower Grant 1992-93; *office:* Spencerport HS 2707 Spencerport Rd Spencerport NY 14559*

SNYDER, WILLIAM BIRCH, 9th Grade Language Arts Tchr; *b:* Philadelphia, PA; *m:* Jennifer Sue; *ed:* Millersville Univ (BA) Eng & Soc Stud 1964, (MA) Eng 1972; *cr:* Palmyra MS Lang Arts Tchr 1964-91; Palmyra HS Lang Arts Tchr 1991-; *ai:* Patriot News Scholastic Awds Judge 1992-; NEA & PAEA 1964-; PSEA, Life Mem; MHS Alumni, PA Trappers Assn & USCF, Life Mem; PA Three Mem 1975-, Lebanon Cty Ed Honor Soc 1988-; LVCC Excl in Ed 1991-93,95; Tchr of the Yr 1995; *office:* Palmyra Area HS Park Dr Palmyra PA 17078

SNYDER, WILLIAM JOSEPH, Social Stud Dept Chair & Tchr; *b:* Philadelphia, PA; *ed:* La Salle Univ (BA) His 1968; Temple Univ (MEd) US His 1972; Cert Tchr of Hearing Impaired; His and World Film Grad Stud; *cr:* Holy Spirit HS Tchr 1968-71; St John Neumann HS Tchr 1972-74; Masterman Lab & Demonstration Schl AP His Tchr, Soc Stud Dept Chair 1975-; *ai:* NHS Adv; Mock Trial Coach; Stu Govt Assn Moderator; PA Cncl for Soc Stud 1989-; Squirrel Hill Civic Assn 1985-; Natl Fac Acad for PA Tchrs; Advanced Placement US His Fac Consultant; Mellow Fellow Advanced Placement; Minority Enrollment in Coll Bd Advanced Placement Prgm Consultant; *office:* Masterman Demonstration Schl 17th & Spring Garden Sts Philadelphia PA 19130

SNYDER, YOLANDA K., English & Speech Teacher; *b:* Lewisburg, PA; *c:* Kristen Seitz, David Andrew; *ed:* Millersville U (BA) Eng 1979; Penn St U (MA) Amer Stud 1987; Completion Ed Curr Wilson Coll; *cr:* Harrisburg Area Comm Coll Fac Tchr 1990-; Millersville U Fac Tchr 1994-; *ai:* Co-Chair Career Day; Coord Spec Event; Liaison Tech Prep; Tutor ESL; Exec Producer Musical; Campus Cncl; Delta Tau Kappa 1987-; NCTE 1991-; PADE 1993-; MACCRA 1995-; CRLA 1996-; Lancaster Lebanon Literacy Cncl, Lebanon Arts Cncl 1993-; Susquehanna Folk Music Soc 1987-; Prof Dev Prgm; Mid-Amer Folklife; Thoughts Lit Magazine; Lebanon Daily News; *home:* 308 Canal St Lebanon PA 17046

SNYDER-LEIBY, TERESA EILEEN, Assistant Professor of Biology; *b:* Harrisburg, PA; *m:* Mark W. Leiby; *ed:* Juniata Coll (BS) Plant Ecology & Environmental Sci 1981; ND St Univ (MS) Plant Pathology 1983; PA St Univ (PHD) Plant Pathology 1994; Post-Doctoral Research with Mark Guiltinan at PSU Summer 1993; *cr:* US Army Corp of Engrs Seasonal Ranger Summers 1979-80; ND St Univ Research Asst 1981-83; Hershey Medical Ctr Research Technologist & TEM 1984-86; PA St Univ Research Technician 1986-93; Marist Coll Asst Prof of Bio 1993-; *ai:* Greenhouse & Arboretum Dir; Class of 1996 Adv; Internal Review Bd Mem; ASPP 1987-; 1987 Recieved US-AID Grant to Support Research in Disease Resistance of Cacao in Costa Rica; 1995 Pub in Plant Physiology; 1995 Registered DNA Sequence for Cacao in Gen Bank U30324 on World Wide Web; *office:* Marist Coll 101 Donnelly Hall Poughkeepsie NY 12601

SOARES, DEBORAH HONHAN, Fourth Grade Teacher; *b:* New Bedford, MA; *m:* Kenneth; *c:* Terel K., Kyla M.; *ed:* Bridgewater St Coll (BS) Spec Needs El Ed 1972; Southeastern MA Univ Rdng Courses; *cr:* Acushnet Schl Tchr 1977-78; Nortn Schl Tchr 1978-; *ai:* PALMS Change Team; Sci Fair Chprsn; MA Foster Parents, CCD Tchr 1994-; Nom Sci Tchr of Yr; *home:* 88 Acushnet Rd Mattapoisett MA 02739*

SOAVE, I., HS Mathematics Teacher; *b:* Bronx, NY; *ed:* Pace Univ (BBA) Mrktg 1982; Lehman Coll (MS) Bus Ed 1991; *cr:* IS 192 7th Grd Italian Tchr 1989-91; Harry S Truman HS Math Tchr 1991-; Bronx Comm Coll Adj Math Instr 1993-; *ai:* Fieri-Long Island Chptr Mem & Schlsp Chprsn; Amer Tchrs of Italian 1988-; NBEA 1990-; Delta Pi Epsilon 1991-; Assn of Math Tchrs in NYS 1992-; Forum of Italian-Amer Edctrs 1989-; NYS Multicultural Schlsp; Studied in Siena Italy 1991; AP Calculus Mellon Grant 1995; *office:* Harry S. Truman HS 750 Baychester Ave Bronx NY 10475*

SOBEL, KENNETH MARK, Electrical Engineering Prof; *b:* Brooklyn, NY; *ed:* City Coll of NY (BEE) Electrical Engrng 1976; Rensselaer Polytechnic Inst (ME) Electrical Engrng 1978, (PHD) Electrical Engrng 1980; *cr:* Lockheed CA Co Sr Rsrch Specialist 1980-87; City Coll of NY Assoc Prof 1987-93, Prof 1993-; *ai:* Electrical Engrng Dept Exec Comm; PHD Prgm Engrng Exec Comm; Fac Senatre; AIAA, Assoc Fellow; IEEE, Sr Mem; Sigma Xi; Amer Radio Relay League; Alpha Phi Omega; NASA Summer Fac Fellow 1987; USAF Summer Fac Fellow 1988, 1990; Articles, Book Chptrs Pub; Co-Author Direct Adaptive Control Theory & Applications 1994; Prof of Yr; *office:* City Coll of NY Dept of Electrical Engineering New York NY 10031

SOBEL, SANDRA GAIL, English Teacher; *b:* Newark, NJ; *m:* Clifford; *c:* Steven, Laurie; *ed:* Monmouth Coll (AA) Speech & Drama 1973; Kean Coll (BA) Eng 1975; Addl 12 Credit Hrs Rutgers Univ; *cr:* Colonia Jr HS Eng Tchr 1976-81; Colonia Sr HS Eng Tchr 1981-; *ai:* Voice of Democracy Speech Contest Adv; Pupil Assistance Comm Mem; NEA 1976-; *office:* Colonia HS East St Colonia NJ 07080

SOBEL, STANLEY ALLEN, High School Science Teacher; *b:* Columbus, OH; *ed:* OH St Univ (AD) Pre-Medicine 1966; Rio Grande Coll (BS) Bio 1969; Northern AZ Univ (MS) Bio & Genetics 1976; Attnd OH Univ 12 Credit Hrs Sci & Bowling Green Univ 6 Credit Hrs Sci; *cr:* Southwestern Schls Govt & Bio Tchr 4 Yrs; Northwestern Schl Dist Bio & Physiology Tchr 2 Yrs; Union Local Schl Dist Bio, General Sci, Anatomy & Physiology Tchr 19 Yrs; *ai:* Stu Cncl & Frosh Class Adv; Belmont Cty In-Svc Coord; Sci Chprsn, Sci Fair Coord; OEA & NEA 1969-; ULACT 1977-, Pres, Pres Elect; Ohio Hills Uniserv 1988-, Sec; Belmont EMT Squard 1990-; Belmont Meth 1978-; Rotary 1995; Jennings Scholar 1991-92.*

SOBER, SALLY WILSON, 8th Grade Math Teacher; *b:* Brockport, NY; *m:* John R.; *c:* Kenneth, Kevin, April; *ed:* SUNY at Oswego (BA) Eng Lit 1970; SUNY at New Paltz (MS) Ed & Math 1985; Coll of St Rose Fordham; Permanet NY St Cert Math & Eng 7th-12th Grd; Courses in Both Eng & Math as Wess as Guid, Careers & Cnslng; *cr:* SUNY Eng Grad Asst 1970-71; Red Hook Cntrl Schl Eng & Math Tchr 1977-; *ai:* Adv: HS Drama, MS Drama & 8th Grd Class; Comms on Math, Sci & Tech Integration; Liaison with Chamber of Commerce; MST Goals 2000 Curr Comm; NYSUY & AFT 1977-; Scndry Schl Assn 1977-, Pres, VP, Sec & Treas; Mem Hudson Valley Portfolio Project 3 Yrs; *office:* Red Hook Cntrl Schl Linden Ave Red Hook NY 12571

SOBERG, CYNTHIA ANN, Counselor; *b:* Mitchel, SD; *m:* Fred; *c:* Jonathan, David, Joshua, Nathanael; *ed:* Univ of Pittsburgh (BS) Psych, Eng 1989, (MA) Schl Counseling 1992; *cr:* West Mifflin HS Cnslr 1993-94; East Alleghany HS Cnslr 1994-95; Keystone Oaks HS Cnslr 1995-; *ai:* NEA 1994-; Allegheny Co Cnslrs 1993-; Mon Valley Ed Consortium Grant 1994; *office:* Keystone Oaks High School 1000 Kelton Ave Pittsburgh PA 15216

SOBNOSKY, CAROL ANN (FRANTZ), Fifth Grade GATE Teacher; *b:* Youngstown, OH; *m:* Joseph V.; *c:* Joseph V. IV; *ed:* Univ of MD (BS) Elem Ed 1974; Post Grad Univ of VA; *cr:* Henry G. Ferguson Elem Schl Grd 5 Tchr 1975-76; Clinton Grove Elem Schl Grd 4-5 Tchr 1976-81; Apple Grove Elem Schl Grd 5-6 Tchr 1981-; Henry G. Gerguson Elem Grd 4-5 Tchr 1988-; *ai:* NEA, MSTA, PGCEA 1975-; Tchr Most Remembered Awd 1992; *office:* Henry G Ferguson Elem Schl 14600 Berry Rd Accokeek MD 20607

SOBOLESKI, MELVIN, Science Teacher; *b:* Baltimore, MD; *m:* Doris Cwiek; *c:* Dennis, Kathleen Baer, John, Mary Frost, Teresa Stromberg; *ed:* Towson St Univ (BS) Ed 1957; Univ of MD (MED) Ed & Admin 1971; 6 Credit Hrs at US Naval Flight Schl, Morgan St Coll, Loyola Coll & Univ of MD; 8 Credit Hrs Johns Hopkins Univ; *cr:* Baltimore City Pub Schls Sci Tchr, Dept Head, Admin, Supv & Curr Writer 1957-80; The Lamb of God Schl Prin & Sci Tchr 1980-; *ai:* Summer & Fall Camp & Sci Fair Coord; Univ of MD Flwshp; *office:* Lamb Of God Cmty Schl 1815 Woodside Ave Baltimore MD 21227

SOBOLEWSKI, CHARLES S., Guidance Counselor; *b:* Bridgeport, CT; *m:* Jo-Anne; *ed:* Alliance Coll (BS) Bio 1964; Fairfield Univ (MA) Scndry Ed 1965; 6th Yr Cert in Guidance 1968; Addl 21 Hrs Grad Stud in Scndry Admin; *cr:* New Milford HS Chem & General Sci Tchr 1 Yr; David Wooster Jr HS Phys Scis Tchr 6 Yrs; H B Flood Jr HS Phys Scis Tchr 10 Yrs; F S Bunnell HS Chem & General Sci Tchr 4 Yrs, Guidance Cnslr 10 Yrs; *ai:* Interact Club Adv; Assessment Team Chm; Blood Drive Coord; NEA 1965-; *office:* Bunnell HS 1 Bulldog Blvd Stratford CT 06497

SOBOLEWSKI, RONALD, Ceramics Instr & Fine Arts Chm; *b:* Pittsburgh, PA; *ed:* Univ of Pittsburgh Studio Art 1971, Art Ed 1974; *cr:* Homewood Elem Schl Tchr 1974-80; Latimer Jr HS Tchr 1980-82; Allderdice HS Tchr, Dept Chair 1982-; *ai:* Instrl Cabinet Mem; Conflict Resolution Mediator; Schl-Wide Musical; Scenery; PFT 1974-; PA-AFT; Bsbl Boosters, Pres; Grad Schl Flwshp; *office:* Taylor Allderdice HS 2409 Shady Ave Pittsburgh PA 15217

SOBRINSKI, JOSEPH WILLIAM, Third Grade Teacher; *b:* East Stroudsburg, PA; *m:* Diane Evelyn Sopper; *c:* Joseph, Marcella; *ed:* E Stroudsburg St (BS) Elem Ed 1971; 51 Grad Credits Master's Equivalency; *cr:* Whiteham-Coplay Schl Dist Third Grd Tchr 1971-; *ai:* Little League, Chess Coach; NEA 1971-; Whitehall-Coplay Ed Assn 1971-, Pres 1984, VP 1985, Negotiations Team 1980-95, Rep Cncl 1980-, Bldg Rep 1995; *office:* Whitehall-Coplay Schl Dist 2928 MacArthur Rd Whitehall PA 18052

SOCCIO, MARY FRANCES, Guidance Cnslr & Psych Teacher; *b:* Dover, NJ; *ed:* Trenton St Coll (BA) Eng 1974, (MEd) Stu Prsnl Services 1982; Post Grad Courses Jersey City St Coll Supervision & Admin; East Stroudsburg Univ, Seton Hall Univ, Montclair St Univ; *cr:* Lenape Valley Reg HS Eng Tchr 1974-80, Chapter I Rdng Dev & Eng Tchr 1980-88, Guidance Cnslr & Psych Tchr 1988-; *ai:* Key Club Adv; Admin & Fac Roundtable; Schlsp Selection Comm; NHS Fac Cncl; NEA, NJEA, LVEA 1974-, Treas 1978-81, Pres 1984-86; Kappa Delta Pi Honor Society 1982-; APA Scndry Schl Affiliate 1991-; NJSCA 1990; St Michaels RC Church 1954-, Eucharistic Minister 1982, Renew Chprsn 1985-87; Grad Asst Trenton St Coll 1981-82; NJ Governors Tchr Grant 1986; Kappa Delta Pi Honor Society; Advancement of Tchng Acad 1985; *office:* Lenape Valley Reg H S Stanhope/Sparta Rd Stanhope NJ 07874*

SOCHA, BEATRICE L. (PION), Math Dept Chairperson; *b:* Webster, MA; *m:* Francis A.; *c:* Edward F., Elizabeth Rekowski, Luann Quaiel, Catherine A.; *ed:* Anna Maria Coll (BA) Elem Ed 1962; Attnd Worcester St Coll; *cr:* Webster Pub Schl 6th Grd Tchr 1962-63; Saint Anne Schl 4th-8th Grd Tchr 1970-73, 5th-8th Grd Tchr 1974-, Math Dept Chprsn 1975-; *ai:* NCEA 1970-; Schl Assn 1968-, Pres, VP, Sec; *office:* St Anne Schl 12 Day St Webster MA 01570

SOCHOR, MARY ELLEN DOYLE, Math Teacher & Dept Chprsn; *b:* Troy, NY; *m:* Robert G.; *c:* Kenneth J., Paula Marie; *ed:* Coll of St. Rose at Albany (BS) Math 1968; SUNY at Binghamton (MST) Math; Addl Credits Manhattan Coll, Fordham Univ for Admin & Supervision Cert; *cr:* St. Mary's Acad Math Tchr 1967-70; Cath Cntrl HS Math Tchr 1970-76; Seton Cath Cntrl HS Assoc Prin 1976-79; Bishop George Ahr HS Math Tchr & Dept Chair 1984-; *ai:* Moderator for Math League, Mission Club, Summer Vol Prgm with Poor; Math Peer-Tutoring Prgm Dir; NCTM, AMTNJ 1992-; Delta Epsilon Sigma 1970-; *office:* Bishop George Ahr HS 1 Tingley Ln Edison NJ 08820*

SODEN, IRVING W., Earth Science Instructor; *b:* Deposit, NY; *m:* Marie A. Sinicki; *c:* Sarah M.; *ed:* SUC at Oneonta (BA) Geography 1970; Grad Work at SUC at Cortland, Coll of St Rose; *cr:* Windsor HS Earth Sci Instr 1970-; *ai:* AFT, NYSUT, STANYS 1970-; Windsor TA 1970-, Pres 1995; Madrigal Choir of Binghampton 1995-, Bd of Dir; Broome Cty Fire Advy Bd 1995-, Bd of Dir; BC Fire Chiefs Assn 1990-, comm Comm Chm; Ouaquaga Fire Co 1976-, current Chief; Safety Comm WCS 1990-; NSTA Awd 1978; Articles Pub; *office:* Windsor HS 1191 Rt 79 Windsor NY 13865

SODIKOW, RICHARD B., Dir of Forensics & Debate Tchr; *b:* Brooklyn, NY; *ed:* NY Univ (BS) Eng 1959; City Univ of NY (MA) Eng 1962; Univ of Birmingham UK Cert Shakespeare Stud & Paleography 1982; Grad Studs in Admin, Eng, Speech, Supervision at The City Coll, Hebrew Union Coll, Hunter Coll, Long Island Univ & Yeshiva Univ; *cr:* Evander Childs HS Eng Tchr 1959-68; Columbus-Evander Adult Ctr Creative Writing & Theater Tchr 1963-70; Bronx Comm Coll Adjunct Eng Instr 1965-70; Bronx HS of Sci Eng & Debate Tchr 1968-; Hebrew Acad HS Eng & Chem Tchr 1972-82; Univ of Pittsburgh Debate Instr 1976-77; Northwestern Univ Debate Instr 1978-87; Univ of IA Instr & Dir of Debate Tchrs inst 1994-; *ai:* Debate-Speech Team, Founder & Coach 1969-; AFT 1962-, Relaince Awd in Ed; Amer Forensic Assn 1960-, Assoc ed, Journal; BSA 1949-, Dist Chair, Cncl Camping Chair, Natl Rep, Scoutmaster, Silver Beaver Awd, Shofar Awd, Vigil Honor; Univ of Chicago, Outstanding Tchr Cert 1984, 1994, 1995; Natl Forensic League Hall of Fame 1995; Natl Forensic League Diamond Key Awds 1975, 1980, 1985, 1990, 1995; Emory Univ Gold Key Awd 1978; VA Independence Bicentennial Commission Awd for Debate 1975, 1976, 1980, 1982; MA Bicentennial Commission Awd for Debate 1976; NYC Bd of Ed Tchr of Yr Recognition 1979, 1991; *office:* Bronx HS Of Science 75 W 205th St Bronx NY 10468*

SODOMA, KAREN GOODWIN, Math Teacher; *b:* Rochester, NY; *m:* Ronald L.; *c:* Amanda J., Rebecca L.; *ed:* SUNY at Brockport (BS) Math Ed 1966, (MS) Math Ed 1971; *cr:* Pittsford Cntrl Schl 8th-9th Grd Math Tchr 1966-68; Albion Cntrl Schl 7th Grd Math 1968-; *ai:* Team 7; Discipline, Awds Comms; Intnl Delta Kappa Gamma Soc, Pres 1982-84; Delta Kappa Gamma Pi, Awds St Comm 1983-87; NY St United Tchrs; Albion Tchrs Assn; Girl Scouts 1980-, Asst Ldr, Svc Awd; Albion Swim Team Booster, Svc Awd; Albion Cntrl Schl 25 Yrs Svc Cert; Yrbk Dedication 1986-87; *office:* Albion Cntrl Schl 254 East Ave Albion NY 14411

SOFFIN, BARRY RONALD, HS Mathematics Teacher; *b:* Brooklyn, NY; *m:* Rosemary Searcy; *c:* Rachel, Deborah, Jonathan, Daniel; *ed:* SUNY at Buffalo (BS) Psych, Math, Ed 1968, (MS) Interdisciplinary Stud 1984; 30 Addl Hrs; *cr:* East HS Math Tchr 1968-71; South Park HS Math Tchr 1971-74; Interdisciplinary, Ethnic Stud Math Specialist 1974-75; City Honors Schl Math Tchr 1975-; *ai:* Math Team Coach; City Honors, Buffalo St Coll SAT Prep Coords; NEA, NY Ed Assn 1969-, Del; Buffalo Tchrs Fed 1969-, Exec Comm, Del Chm; Buffalo Pub HS Math League Founder, Chm; *office:* City Honors Schl Masten & North Sts Buffalo NY 14204

SOFKA, KATHLEEN, First Grade Teacher; *b:* Johnson City, NY; *ed:* Saint John's Univ (BS) Ed 1976; St Univ of NY at Binghamton (MS) Ed 1979; *cr:* Broome Cty Cath Schls Sixth Grd Tchr 1981-90; Whitney Point Cntrl Schls Sub, First Grd Tchr 1990-; *ai:* CEA Bldg Team; Inservice, Rdng, Family Fun Carnival Comms; *office:* C. E. Adams Elem PO Box 249 Keibel Rd Whitney Point NY 13862

SOFRANKO, EDWARD ROGER, Professor of Psychology; *b:* Detroit, MI; *m:* Judy Wickline; *c:* Tony Garlic, David, Jean, Tracy Garlic; *ed:* Univ of Detroit (BA) Comm 1967; Ball St Univ (MA) Cnslng Psych 1971, (EDD) Cnslng Psych 1978; *cr:* USAF Supply Svcs Ofcr 1967-71; Ctr for Healthy Living Owner, Dir, Therapist 1985-; Univ of Rio Grande Prof 1971-; *ai:* Founder, Dir of Rid Early Action Prgm, Summer Retention Prgm, Univ Hnrs Prgm; Supvr Univ Cnslng Ctr; Amer Cnslr Assn, Assn for Humanistic Ed & Dev 1971-; Natl Collegiate Hnrs Cncl, Mid-East Hnrs Assn 1988-; Big Brothers, Big Sisters 1985-, Bd Mem, Cert of Appreciation; Outstdng Young Amer; Outstdng Edctrs of Amer; Alumni Fac Citation Awd; Soc of Hnr Stdnts Awd of Appreciation; *office:* Univ Of Rio Grande 1 Atwood Dr Rio Grande OH 45674

SOHONYAY, ANNA MARIE HUSSAR, Social Studies Teacher; *b:* Allentown, PA; *m:* Stephen E.; *c:* Stephen R., Simon P.; *ed:* St Joseph Coll at Emmitsburg (BA) His 1965; *cr:* Sacred Heart Schl Tchr 1978-; *ai:* His Day, Geog Bee Coord; Tchr of St His Day Grp 2nd Place; Tchr Natl His Day Group 8th Place; *office:* Sacred Heart Schl 235 Nevin St Lancaster PA 17603

SOKOL, LISA ROBIN, Industrial Arts Tech Teacher; *b:* Brooklyn, NY; *m:* Barry Steven; *c:* Emily, Peri, Ithan; *ed:* St U at Oswego (BS) Indstrl Arts Ed 1978; Bowling Green St U (MS) Career Tech Ed 1979; *cr:* Visicorp Cmptr Software Natl Sales Trainer 5 Yrs; Ctr for Stragetic Mgmt Sr Trainer 6 Yrs; South Brunswick HS Indstrl Arts Tech Tchr 2 Yrs; *ai:* NEA 1994-; TEANJ 1995-; NJEA 1994-; Flwshp Masters in Career Tech Ed; *office:* South Brunswick HS PO Box 183 Major Rd Monmouth Junction NJ 08852

SOKOL, MARY, Physical Education Teacher; *b:* Worcester, MA; *ed:* Salem St Coll (BS) Sport Fitness Leisure 1986; Springfield Coll (MED) Ath Admin 1987; *cr:* St Marys Reg Jr HS 7th Grd Tchr; Salem Pub Schls Substance Abuse Tchr 1992-93; Douglas Mid Sr High Ath Dir, PE Tchr, Sftbl & Bsktbl Coach 1993-; *ai:* Ath Dir, Good Grief Team Mem; WBCA 1987-; MTA 1993-; *office:* Douglas Middle Sr HS 21 Davis St East Douglas MA 01516

SOKOLL, CARL ANTON, Adjunct Professor of History; *b:* Pittsburgh, PA; *m:* Dr. Jane Vakiener; *c:* Walter A.; *ed:* Fairleigh Dickinson Univ (BA) His 1951; Columbia Univ (MA) His 1965, (EDD) His 1974; *cr:* New Rochelle Schl System Adjunct Prof of His; *ai:* Org of Amer Historians 1964-; NJ Lions 1970-, Chm for Blind Childrens Camp; Pub The NJ Camp for Blind Children A Brief His.

SOLAK, IVAN, Math Teacher; *b:* Warren, OH; *m:* Gina Hvisdak; *c:* Kaye Louise; *ed:* Youngstown St Univ (BA) Ed 1988; 30 Hrs Admin; *cr:* Lowellville Local Schls Math Tchr 1991-; *ai:* Ftbo Coach; Dept Chair; *office:* Lowellville Local Schls 2 E Grant St Lowellville OH 44436

SOLAR, NEIL S., Mathematics Teacher; *b:* Queens, NY; *m:* Paulla Kolnaski; *c:* Tiffany, Brittany, Kasey; *ed:* Assumption Coll (BS) Math 1981; Eastern CT St Univ (MA) Human Relations 1986; *cr:* St Thomas More Prep Schl Math Tchr 1981-83; Cutler MS Math Tchr 1983-; *ai:* Math Counts Coach; Math Curr Comm; Knights of Columbus 1990-; St Michaels Schl Advy Bd 1995-; Pawcatuck Neighborhood Ctr 1992-; *office:* Cutler MS 160 Fishtown Rd Mystic CT 06355

SOLASKI, PAUL, English Teacher; *b:* Richmond Hill, NY; *m:* Myrill Elise Armstrong; *c:* Myrill Jean, Ariel Elizabeth, Robert Arthur, Lorienne Elysia; *ed:* Adelphi Univ (BA) Eng 1972; Stonybrook Univ (MA) Drama 1974; 60 Credits Cmptr, Ed; Attnd Cathedral Coll; *cr:* Cntrl Islip HS Eng Tchr 1973-; *ai:* Auditorium Mgr; Lighting & Sound Mgr; ERU Writing Club Adv; NYSUT 1973-; PTA 1973-, Jenkins Awd; *office:* Cntrl Islip HS 85 Wheeler Rd Central Islip NY 11722

SOLBERG, ROGER LEE, Assistant Professor of English; *b:* Staten Island, NY; *m:* Mary Frances Benson; *c:* David; *ed:* Upsala Coll (BA) Eng 1975; IN Univ (MS) Ed 1977; Univ of IA (MA) Eng, Writing 1985; IN Univ of PA ABD Rhetoric & Linguistics 1995; Courses in Writing & Film at New Schl for Soc Rsrch 1980-81; *cr:* Wagner Coll Union Dir 1978-82; Univ of IA Rhetoric Tchng Asst 1983-85; Univ of TX Eng Adj Instr 1987-88; Edinboro Univ Eng Asst Prof 1989-; *ai:* Edinboro Peace Ctr Adv; Univ & Comm Theatre Actor; Host of Weekly Radio Prgm; Inst for Ethics & Values Ed Mem; NCTE, Eng Assn of PA St Univ 1989-; Presented Papers at Natl Confs 1993, 1995; Essays Pub; *office:* Edinboro Univ Of PA 240 Centennial Hall Edinboro PA 16444

SOLBERG, RONA (BERNSTEIN), Sixth Grd Language Arts Tchr; *b:* Fall River, MA; *m:* Myron; *c:* Sarah S., Julie S., Laurence M.; *ed:* Simmons Coll (BS) Soc Sci 1956; Boston Univ (EDM) Ed, Rdng 1958; 50 Credit Hrs; *cr:* Malden Schl Sixth Grd Tchr 1956-61; Highland Pk Schl Title I Tchr, Suppl Tutor 1970-73, Sixth Grd Tchr 1974-; *ai:* NEA, NJEA, HPEA 1974-; *office:* Bartle Schl Mansfield St Highland Park NJ 08904

SOLE, MARILOUISE ANNE, English Instructor; *b:* Youngstown, OH; *ed:* Youngstown St Univ (BA) Eng-Summa Cum Laude 1990, (MA) English 1995; Walsh Coll, Kent St Univ Post Grad Work; *cr:* News Svc Jrnlsm Internship 1988-90; Eng Ctr ESL Tutor 1988-90; YSU Rsrch Asst 1989-90; Freelance Ed 1990-92; Boardman HS Eng Instr 1992-; *ai:* OCTELA 1990-, Fall Conf Presenter 1995; NEA, BEA 1992-; Sigma Tau Delta 1995-; Phi Kappa Phi 1990-; Cross Talk 1995-; Kappa Delta Pi 1990; Gamma Pi Delta, Golden Key NHS 1989-; Poem Pub 1995; Ashland's Tchr of Yr Nom 1992; Who's Who Among Stdnts in Amer Colls & Univs 1990; *office:* Boardman Sr HS 7777 Glenwood Ave Youngstown OH 44512

SOLEM, BERMINNA WHITE, Hum Dev & Spec Ed Assoc Prof; *b:* Philadelphia, PA; *m:* Kenneth; *c:* Ken C., Signe Solem Stubits, Jon Erik; *ed:* Beaver Coll (BEA) Fine Arts 1958; Rowan Coll (MA) Learning Disabilities 1972; 35 Grad Credit Hrs Trenton St Coll Spec Ed, Deaf Ed 1958-62; *cr:* Marie Katzenbach Schl for the Deaf Tchr 1958-60; Barrington Pub Schls Multiple Handicapped, Deaf Tchr 1960-62; Clarksboro Presch for Deaf Dev Prgm Tchr 1968-71; Deptford Pub Schls Learning Disabilities Consultant 1971-72; Gloucester Cty Coll Assoc Prof 1972-; *ai:* Acad Standing Comm; Learning Consultant; AFT, CEC 1972-; Assn for Retarded Citizens 1976-; Coll Prgm Coord 1972-90; Adult Staff Trng Contract Project Dir 1979-93; US Office of Spec Ed & Rehabilitative Svc Project Dir 1979-91; Comm Coll Cooperation for Staff Dev of Workers with Deaf Children 1974; *office:* Gloucester County Coll 1400 Tanyard Rd Sewell NJ 08080

SOLENSKI, BRUCE MITCHELL, 6th Grade Teacher; *ed:* St Univ at Plattsburgh (MS) Ed 1969; Addl Hrs & Inservice Hrs; *ai:* Eng Expectations 6th Grd Comm; AFT; NEA; Shenendehowa Tchrs Assn; Saratoga Springs Historical Soc, Bd of Trustee; *office:* Shenendehowa Cntrl Schl Acadia 970 Route 146 Clifton Park NY 12065

SOLEY, EDITH BLADES, Assistant Principal; *b:* Woburn, MA; *m:* Robert Daniel; *c:* Kirk, Erin, Drew; *ed:* Lowell St Coll (BS) Elem Ed 1970; UMASS at Lowell (MA) Admin 1995; Post Grad Courses Salem St, Fitchburg St, Univ of NH; *cr:* Soule Schl 4-5 Grd Tchr 1970-75; Barron Schl 5 Grd Tchr 1975-87; Haigh Schl 6 Grd Tchr 1987-88; Soule Schl 5 Grd Tchr 1988-94; Woodbury Schl Asst Prin 1994-; *ai:* Math Club Adv; Natl Geo Bee Coord; Collaborative Team Comm; NASP, NHASP 1995-; PTSA 1994-; Woman of Decade; *office:* Woodbury MS 206 Main St Salem NH 03079

SOLIMANDO, JOHN M., Intermediate Schl English Tchr; *b:* Brooklyn, NY; *ed:* St John's Univ (BS) Eng 1988; Coll of Staten Island (MA) Eng Lang, Lit 1991, (MS) Admin & Supervision 1993; Inst of Childrens Lit 1989; *cr:* E. B. Shallow IS 227 Eng Tchr, Mentor 1988-; *ai:* Yrbk Fac Adv; Parent Liason PTA; UFT 1988-; NCTE 1989-; ASCD 1991-; FIERI 1994-; Articles Pub; Evaluator Tchng Products for Learning; *office:* Edward B. Shallow IS 227 6500 16th Ave Brooklyn NY 11204

SOLIWODA, PAMELA JANE (TONTY), Spanish Teacher; *b:* Erie, PA; *m:* Timothy; *c:* Timothy James; *ed:* Univ of Dayton (BS) Scndry Ed 1991; Edinboro Univ Schl Admin; *cr:* Mercyhurst Prep Span Tchr 1991-; *ai:* Teenage Action Club Adv; Cheerleading Coach; Jaycees 1992-; Duquesne Univ Honor; *office:* Mercyhurst Prep Schl 538 E Grandview Blvd Erie PA 16504*

SOLLANO, ROSEMARIE, Spanish & Italian Teacher; *b:* Brookly
ed: Fordham Univ (BA) Span Lit 1984; Univ of VA (MA) Span Li
cr: St Philip Neri Schl Span Tchr 1987; Herricks MS Span & Italia
1988-; *ai:* Span Club Adv; AATSP 1988-; *office:* Herricks MS 7 H
Rd 7 Hilldale Dr Albertson NY 11507

SOLLARS, REBECCA ELLEN, Adv Biology & Physiology Tc
Columbus, OH; *ed:* Miami Univ (BS) Bio Sci 1970; *cr:* Eastside El
Grd Tchr 1970-71; Miami Trace HS Sci Tchr 1971-; *ai:* Sci Curr C
Amer Quarter Horse Assn 1988-; *office:* Miami Trace HS 3722 State
41 NW Washington Court H OH 43160

SOLLENBERGER, MICHAEL GEORGE, Assoc Prof of Class &
Lang; *b:* Philadelphia, PA; *m:* Merril Anne Evans; *ed:* Rutgers Univ
Classics 1979, (PHD) Classics 1984; Andrew W. Mellon Post-D
Flwshp Washington Univ 1985-86; *cr:* Rutgers Univ Asst Prof of C
1986-88; Mount Saint Mary's Coll Asst Prof of Classics, For
1988-94, Assoc Prof of Classics, For Langs 1994-; *ai:*
Environmental, Capital Improvements Comms; Moderator Intnl
Assn; Co-Moderator Campus Ministry Club; Coord Latin Rdng Gro
Choices; Stu Adv; AIA, APA 1979-; So. PA AIA Chptr VP; Soc for A
Greek Philosophy 1981-; AATG 1989-; Carroll Vly Citizen Co
1995-; Articles Pub; Presidential Pride Grants 1989-91, 1993;
Mount Saint Marys Coll Emmitsburg MD 21727*

SOLOBAY, AMELIA FANTINI, World Cultures Teacher; *b:*
Vernon, PA; *m:* Joseph A.; *c:* Timothy J., Miriam Jo Miller, Mark
CA Univ of PA (BS) Soc Stud 1963, (MA) Soc Stud 197
Chartiers-Houston Jr Sr HS Supts Advy Cncl 1984-88, Soc Stud Dept
1976-88, Tchr 1963-; *ai:* Scndry Instructional Support, Stu Assis
NCATE Teams; Served Mid Sts Evaluating Comms; Mem Long
Planning Comm, Curr Dept; NEA, PSEA 1964-, Instructional, Pro
Cncl; CHEA 1964-, Chief Negotiator, Grievance Chair; Vol Natl
Assn, Natl Kidney Fnd; St Patrick's Parish Cncl Lector; Grants
Westminster Coll, Univ of Pittsburgh, Wake Forest Univ, Frank
Marshall Coll, CA Univ of PA, Natl Environment for the Hum;
Chartiers Houston HS 2080 W Pike St Houston PA 15342*

SOLOMITO, MARK, 6th Grade Mathematics Teacher; *b:* Waterbur
m: Margaret Walesky; *c:* Matthew; *ed:* Cntrl CT St Univ (BS) El
1976, (MS) Admin 1981; *cr:* Saint Francis Xavier Schl 6th-8th Gr
1977-78; City Hill MS 6th Grd Math Tchr 1978-; *ai:* Recreational L
Soccer Coach; Mentor Tchr; NEA, CEA, NTL 1978-; *home:* 169 Pa
St Oakville CT 06779

SOLOMON, ALLEN D., Mathematics Teacher; *b:* Patton, PA; *m:*
Marie; *c:* Jill Wysocki, Patrick; *ed:* Indiana Univ of PA (BS) Math
(MS) Math 1966; *cr:* Warren Jr HS Arithmetic Tchr 1962-63;
Cambria Sr HS Math Tchr 1963-; *ai:* NEA, PSEA 1963-; *office:*
Cambria Sr HS 208 Schoolhouse Rd Ebensburg PA 15931*

SOLOMON, CATHERINE F., Program Dir of Human Servic
Chicago, IL; *m:* Margaret M. Magraw; *c:* Madeleine Solomon-Magra
Macalester Coll (BA) 1979; Smith Coll (MSW) Soc Wk 1982; Br
Univ (PHD) Soc Policy 1993; *cr:* MA Mental Soc Wkr 1982-83; C
Memrl HCC Soc Wkr 1983-87; Smith Coll Adj Prof 1990-; Boston
Field Adv 1991-; RI Coll Prof 1993-94; Lasell Coll Pgm Dir 1995-
NASW 1982-; NEOHSE 1995-; Pub Chptr 1995; *office:* Lasell Coll
Commonwealth Ave Newton MA 02166

SOLOMON, CYNTHIA SHERMAN, Spanish Teacher; *b:* Harris
PA; *m:* Arthur B.; *c:* Brian J.; *ed:* PA St Univ (BS) Ed 1970; Fairfield
(MS) Ed 1980; Univ of Salamanca Spain; *cr:* Stamford HS Span
1970-77; Rippowam HS Span Tchr 1977-87; Westhill HS Span Tchr 1
ai: Class Adv; NEASC Steering, Frgn Lang Curr & Dist Schl
Comms; BEST Tchr; NEA, CEA & SEA 1970-, Rep; NCTFL 1
AATSP 1970-; JCC 1970-.*

SOLOMON, DEBRA AIMIS, 5th Grade Teacher; *b:* Jersey City, N
David; *c:* George, Beth Frede, Paul; *ed:* New Paltz (BS) Ed 1958; 30
Credits Rdng; *cr:* Pearl River Pub Schl Kndgtn Tchr 1958-65; Ch
Elem Schl K-3, 5-6th Grd Tchr 1975-; *ai:* Dist Prof Performance R
Task Force; Amy Bull Crist Rdng Assoc 1991-; *office:* Chester Elem
2 Herbert Dr Chester NY 10918*

SOLOMON, ELIZABETH KRAUS, Fifth Grade Teacher; *b:* New
NY; *ed:* U of Rochester (BA) Psych 1970, (MA) Elem Ed 1972; 30
Credits; *cr:* Mid Hudson Hebrew Day Schl Classroom Tchr 198
Wappingers Cntrl Schls Classroom Tchr 1987-; *ai:* Peer Mediation
Mem Schl Crisis Team, Dist Sci Trainer; WCT, AFT 1987-; *o*
Wappingers Cntrl Schl Dist Hollowbrook Park Wappingers Fls NY 1

SOLOMON, HATTIE BENNETT, Guidance Counselor; *b:* Edisto Is
SC; *ed:* Barber Scotia Coll (BS) Bus Ed 1967; Kean Coll (MA) Stu P
Svcs 1980; *cr:* Charleston Cty Schl Dist Bus Tchr 1967-71; East Sid
Bus Tchr 1971-86, Guid Cnslr 1986-; *ai:* AFT, Newark Tchrs Union 1
NEA, NJEA, NTA 1980-; Newark Guid Assn, Essex Cty Schl Coun
1986-; NJ Schl Coun Assn 1990-; Phi Delta Kappa 1983-, T
Morristown Area WMS 1985-, Treas; Alumni Assn of NJ 1972-,
office: East Side HS 238 Van Buren St Newark NJ 07105

SOLOMON, JAMES, Guidance Counselor; *b:* Sayre, PA; *m:* Susa
Wendy, Dana; *ed:* Mansfield Univ (BSEd) Soc Stud 1966; Millers
Univ (MSEd) Cnslng Guid; Post Grad Potsdam, Marywood; *cr:* O
Apalachin Schls Guid Cnslr 1969-; *ai:* AP, Fin, Aid Coord; AFT, NY
1969-; OATA 1969-, Chief Negotiator, Retirement Del; Waverly Muni
Water Bd 1977-, Commissioner; Waverly Village Bd 1980-84; Hart
Coll Excl in Coll Cnslng Awd 1992; *office:* Owego Free Acad Geor
Owego NY 13827

SOLOMON, MYRAH SMITH, Global Studies Teacher; *b:* Char
Amalie, St Thomas VI; *m:* Raphael Augustine; *c:* Raphael Ali; *ed:* Bo
Univ (BS) His 1971, (MA) Ed 1973; Cmptr & Tech in Ed 6 Post
Credits; *cr:* West Park Union Free Schl Dist Soc Stud Tchr 197
Kingston City Schls Consolidated Soc Stud Tchr 1974-; *ai:* Fencing
Adv; Ebony Club Adv; AFT-NYSUT 1974-; *office:* Kingston City S
Consolidat 403 Broadway Kingston NY 12401

SOLOMON, ROBIN MILLAR, English Teacher; *b:* Wilmington, D
Simon M., Alexander M.; *ed:* Fairleigh Dickinson Univ (BA) Eng 1
Colgate Univ (MA) Eng 1992; *cr:* St Univ of NY at Morrisville Adj
Prof of Eng 1992-; New Berlin HS Eng Tchr 1992-; *ai:* Sr & Soph C
Adv; AAUP, AFT 1992-; *office:* New Berlin HS 1 School St New B
NY 13411

SOLOMON, STEPHANIE GAIL, Biology & Gen Science Teache
Brooklyn, NY; *ed:* Brooklyn Coll (BA) Anthropology, Scndry Ed 1
Queens Coll (MSEd) Couple, Marriage, Family Cnslng 1991; 36 Cr
Scis, EMT; *cr:* JASA Case, Group Worker 1980-82; NYC Bd Ed
1982-; *ai:* UFT, AFT, NYSUT 1982-; *office:* Abraham Lincoln HS O
Pkwy & West Ave Brooklyn NY 11235*

SOLOMOND, FRANK A., American Cultures Teacher; *b:* Pittsburg,
m: Darlene Postupack; *c:* Michelle, Christopher, Laurie, Jonathon;
Clarion St Univ (BS) Soc Sci 1963; IN Univ (MS) His 1968; Uni
Pittsburg 6 Grad Credit Hrs; IN Univ of PA Grad Stud; *cr:* New Kensin
Jr High 8th-9th Grd His Tchr 1963; Penn Hills Jr HS 7th-8th Grd His
1963-65; Burrell Schl HS 10th Grd Amer Culture Tchr 1965-; *ai:*
1963-; PSEA 1963-; BEA 1965-; PIAA 1974-, Chptr Rules Interpreter;
Ftbl Ofcl 1974-; EAIFO Ftbl Ofcl 1978-, Rules Interpreter; AK Bs

AK Bsbl Ofcl; Head Ftbl Coach-Won WPIAL Title 1968; Officiated rous Playoff & St Championship Games in Ftbl; *office:* Burrell HS ty Church Rd Lower Burrell PA 15068

DMONIC, SUZANNE ORLOW, Art Teacher; *b:* New York, NY; *m:* rd; *c:* Danielle, Jordan, Michael; *ed:* SUNY Coll at Purchase (BFA) graphy & Drawing 1984; Brooklyn Coll (MS) Art Ed 1988; *cr:* Beach nel HS Tchr 1984-86; Grover Cleveland HS Art Tchr 1986-; *ai:* Yrbk oto Club Adv; Art Dir Schl Play; PLEA 1993-; AFT & VFT.

DMOS, RHODA, Director; *b:* New York City, NY; *c:* Jill R., Fern, ., Adina; *ed:* NY Univ (BS) Ed 1960; Trenton St Ed; *cr:* South River chl Tchr 1965; Jamesburg Pub Schl Tchr 1966; Old Bridge Pub Schl 1967-69; Robin Jay Nursery Schl & Kndgtn Dir 1969-; *office:* Robin ursery Schl 110 Charles St Old Bridge NJ 08857*

DSKY, DONNA MARIE, Chemistry Teacher; *b:* Rockville Centre, *n:* William R. Proctor Jr.; *c:* Edward W., Elizabeth A.; *ed:* Fairfield (BS) Chem 1982; Hofstra Univ (MS) Scndry Ed 1984; *cr:* Herricks Sci Tchr 1985-; *office:* Herricks HS 100 Shelter Rock Rd New Hyde NY 11040

DWEY, STEPHEN MILES, Global History Teacher; *b:* Brooklyn, *d:* Hofstra Univ (BA) Pol Sci 1972; NYU (MA) Soc Stud 1981; *cr:* tt Clinton HS Global His Tchr 1983-88; Brooklyn Tech HS Global Tchr 1988-; *ai:* Club Adv; *office:* Brooklyn Tech HS 29 Fort Greene Pl klyn NY 11217

YS, STEPHEN ROBERT, Mathematics Teacher; *b:* Sellersville, *n:* Delma Jean High; *c:* Erinn B., Adam P., Emily B.; *ed:* Messiah Coll Math 1987; Millersville Univ (MED) Math Ed 1993; Attnd Villanova ; *cr:* Manheim Cntrl HS Math Tchr 1987-; *ai:* Var Boys Soccer Coach; , PSEA, Manheim Cntrl Ed Assn 1987-; NCTM 1996-; Akron nonite Church 1991-, Congregational Cncl; PA Soccer Coach's Assn -; *office:* Manheim Central HS 400 Adele Ave Manheim PA 17545*

Y, PAUL WILHELM, Social Studies Teacher; *b:* Munich, Germany; heryl Farmer; *c:* Kelly, Brian; *ed:* Bethany Coll (BA) His 1973; WV (MA) Ed Admin 1988; Geog Bee, Sci Olympiad Coord; *ai:* Geog Bee, Olympiad Coord; Family Planning 1991-, Bd, VP; OH Ofcl Vlybl, ; WV Ofcl Vlybl; *office:* Harding MS 1928 Sunset Blvd Steubenville 3952

MARY, JOHANNES FELIX, Arts & Music Dept Chairman; *b:* Zurich, zerland; *m:* Anne Van Zandt; *c:* Stephen, Geoffrey, Karen Romano; *ed:* Univ (BA) Music Theory 1957, (MMus)Music Composition 59; *cr:* klyn Coll Music Instr 1960-61; Schl of Sacred Arts Instr 1984-91; Yale Visiting Music Prof 1984-85; Horace Mann Schl Arts & Music Dept 1961-; *ai:* Glee Club Conductor; Chamber Music Club, Young ublicans Club, Stu Advs, Fac Guidance Prgm; Schls Instruction Comm; ce Mann Chapter Pres; Cum Laude Soc 198794; Riverdale Chapter 1963-77, Prgm Dir; Amer Guild Organists NY Chapter 1960-, Exec Mem; Friendship Ambassadors Inc 1982-, Bd of Dirs Mem; NY diocesan Music Commission 1980-90; Amor Artis Inc 1962-, ding Mem, Music Dir; Fairfield Cty Chorale 1975-, Conductor, Music Taghkanic Chorale 1993-, Conductor, Music Dir; St Jean Bapt Church -; Fr Baroque Music Stud Grant 1982; Tchng Cert of Merit Chicago 1981; Cert of Merit Yale Schl of Music Alumni Assn 1982; Stereo ew Record of Yr Awds 1969, 1970, 1975, 1978; Madeira Bach Festival al Dir 1985; Dist Orch Festival Conductor; Univ of British Columbia Festival Conductor 1986; Choral Inst of Jefferson Music Festival al Dir, Clinician; *home:* 620 W 254th St Bronx NY 10471*

MBAR, ROSE, Nursing Instructor; *b:* Philadelphia, PA; *m:* S. Thomas; ott Grenoble Sipple Jr., Jonathan Gray Sipple, Christina Faith Sennett; Wesley Coll (BS) Nrsng 1987; Salisbury St Univ (MS) Nrsng 1996; 46 Hrs Perinatal Nrsng; *cr:* Correctional Med Systems Staff Dev, QA -93; Polytech HS Nrsng Instr 1993-; *ai:* Clinical Rotation Supvr; r Master of Tech Diploma Comms; VICA Adv; Acad Mgr; DE Nurses ; DEA; NEA; Sigma Theta Tau; Who's Who in Amer Nrsng; Amer ses Assn in Staff Dev & Continuing Ed, Amer Nurses Assn in Nrsng in Certs; *office:* Polytech HS PO Box 97 Woodside DE 19980

MERSCALES, EUAN FRANCIS CUTHBERT, Assoc Prof of Mech ng; *b:* London, England; *m:* Patricia Ann; *c:* Susan, David; *ed:* Univ ondon (BSC) Mech Engrng 1953; Rensselaer Polytechnic Inst (MME) h Engrng 1961; Cornell Univ (PHD) 1964; *cr:* North British omotive Co Grad Apprentice1953-55; British Army 2nd Lieutenant 5-57; Rensselaer Polytechnic Inst Instr 1958-60; Cornell Univ rsrch 196 0-64; Rensselaer Polytechnic Inst Fac 1964-; *ai:* Fac Adv; nula SAE; RPI; Amer Soc of Mech Engrs 1965-, His, Heritage Comm, ow; Natl Assn of Corrosion Engrs 1983-; Hall of His Fnd 1985-, stee; Amer Assn of Univ Prof 1964-, Sec RPI Chptr; Pi Tau Sigma 1959; na XI 1960; Sr Visiting Fellow Manchester Univ 1975-76; Sr Visiting entist Natl Phy Lab 1983; Ben Gough Medal Inst of Metals 1988; hor 62 Papers, 2 Monographs; Ed 2 Books; *office:* Rensselaer ytechnic Inst 110 8th St Troy NY 12180

MERVILLE, WESLEY DAVID, Physical Education Teacher; *b:* eca Falls, NY; *m:* R. Lorraine Knittle; *c:* David Wesley, Shawna Marie age, Leesa Ann Yates; *ed:* Ithaca Coll (BS) PE, Hlth, Rec 1963; 6 Credit Univ of Geisson Germany; 24 Grad Hrs; *cr:* Trumansberg Cntrl Schl PE Tchr 1963-67; Charles O. Dickerson HS PE Tchr 1967-; *ai:* Var o Adv; Var Boys Bsktbl, Var Girls Sftbl Coach; Bsktbl Coaches Assn of St, Exec Comm; NEA, Trumansburg Tchrs Assn 1970-; Who's Who of er HS Bsktbl Coaches 1988-89; Bsktbl Coach of Yr Sect IV 1995; Coach of Yr Ithaca Journal 1982; Trumansburg Rotary Club Outstdng zen of Yr 1982; *office:* Charles O Dickerson HS 100 Whig St mansburg NY 14886*

MMA, MICHAEL, Art History Teacher; *b:* New York, NY; *m:* Ruth S. lbeau; *c:* Akintunji, Pilar, Frederico; *ed:* Trinity Coll (BA) Fine Arts 55; Hartford Art Schl (MA) Arts, Sculpture 1970; 75 Addl Credits; *cr:* nity-Pawling Schl Art Dept Head 1965-67; Hartford Pub HS Art Dept ad 1967-; *ai:* Designers Club; ERASE Prgm; AFT 1965-; CT Acad of e Arts 1968-; Comm Ctr Bd 1985-; CT Acad Sculpture Prize; *office:* rtford Public HS 55 Forest St Hartford CT 06105

MMER, SUSAN WOLF, 8th Grade Amer His & Eng Tchr; *b:* Paterson, *m:* Roland; *c:* Kristen; *ed:* William Paterson Coll (BA) Early Chldhd, m Ed 1980; Long Island Univ MS 27 Credit Hrs; *cr:* Saddle Brook Elem ls 1, 6, 7 Grd Tchr 1982-93; Saddle Brook MS 8th Grd Tchr 1993-; *ai:* ddle Brook Educ Assn, NJEA, NEA 1982-; Citizens Against Substance use 1984-, Pres; Amer Legion Outstanding Educator Awd 1988; NJ vernor's Tchr Recognition Awd 1987; Franklin Schl Outstanding Tchr d 1992, 1993; *office:* Saddle Brook MS Mayhill St Saddle Brook NJ 62*

MMER, WILLIAM FREDERICK, English Teacher; *b:* Mexico City, xico; *m:* Mary Elizabeth Plessinger; *c:* William F., Thomas A., Stephen Timothy E.; *ed:* Miami Univ (BA) Eng 1975; Grad Stud Kent St, wling Green, OH St, Antioch Coll; Trng Strategic Planning Cambridge oup; *cr:* West Carrollton Jr HS Classroom Tchr 1976-; *ai:* Head Girls ck Coach; Frosh Class Adv; NEA, OEA 1976-; West Carrollton Tchrs sn 1976-, VP; Jaycees 1977-, Pres; Presidential Citation Vietnam Era erans 1978; *office:* W Carrollton Jr HS 424 E Main St West Carrollton 45449*

SOMMERS, ANN MARGARET, Special Education Teacher; *b:* Brooklyn, NY; *m:* Kenneth; *c:* Catherine Diamond, Andrew Diamond; *ed:* Brooklyn Coll (BA) Eng 1964; Hunter Coll (MA) Eng 1967; Prof Cert Admin, Supervision 1988; *cr:* Bushwick HS Eng Tchr 1964-65; Mepham HS Eng Tchr 1965-67; Francis Lewis HS Spec Ed Tchr 1979-80; Beach Channel HS Resource Room Tchr 1980-; *ai:* AFT 1964-; Cert of Appreciation1991; *office:* Beach Channel HS 100-00 Beach Cannel Dr Far Rockaway NY 11694*

SOMMERS, BEVERLY MERYL, Fourth Grade Teacher; *b:* Orange, NJ; *ed:* Trenton St Coll (BA) Kndgtn, Primary Ed 1964; Monmouth Univ (MS) Stu Prsnl Svc 1974; 45 Post Grad Hrs Seton Hall Univ & Montclair St Coll; *cr:* River Plaza Schl 2-6 Grd Tchr 1964-; *ai:* Middletown Twp Ed Assn, Monmouth Cty Ed Assn, NJEA, NEA 1964-; Governor Recognition Tchr of Yr 1988, 1992; Governor Recognition for Enhancing NJ Stud 1987.

SOMMERS, DANIELLE D'EVEGNEE, Second Grade Teacher; *b:* Ogden, UT; *c:* Katherine; *ed:* UT St Univ (BS) Elem Ed 1972; Bowling Green St Univ (MA) Admin 1979; Ashland Univ 30 Hrs; *cr:* Willard City Schl 1st Grd Tchr 1972-73; South Cntrl Local Schl K-4gh grd Prin 1989-90, 2nd Grd Tchr 1974-; *ai:* Chrldng Adv; SCEA 1974-, Bldg Rep, Sec, Pres; OEA, NEA 1974-.

SOMMERS, JUDY BROWN, Kindergarten Teacher; *b:* Warren, OH; *m:* Frederick A. Jr.; *c:* Kelsey, Ricky; *ed:* Asbury Coll (BA) Elem Ed 1977; Attnd Lake Erie Coll, Kent St Univ; *cr:* Maplewood Local Schl Dist Kndgtn Tchr 1977-; *ai:* Dist Philosophy, Prins Advy, Rdng, Sci Curr Comms; MEA 1977-; OEA; NEA; Johnston Fed U M Church 1969-, Organist, Choir Dir; NEOSERRC Grant 1993; *office:* Maplewood East Elem Schl 4174 Greenville Rd Cortland OH 44410*

SOMMERVILLE, ROBERT J., Government Teacher; *b:* Clarksburg, WV; *m:* Helena; *c:* Robert, Antionette; *ed:* Fairmont St Coll (BA) Ed & Soc Stud 1969; Bowie St Univ (MA) Ed & Admin Supvr 1975; Attnd Salisbury St Univ, Univ of VA, Cath Univ, MD Univ; *cr:* Glenridge Jr HS Tchr 1970-76; Eleanor Roosevelt HS Tchr 1976-; *ai:* NCSS; MD City Civic Assn; Whos Who in Ed Intl Bio; Bell Atlantic Scholar-Ldrshp Forum; *office:* Eleanor Roosevelt HS 7601 Hanover Pky Greenbelt MD 20770*

SON, SOOK HEE, Bilingual Ed Teacher; *b:* Chung Chung Nam Do, Korea; *m:* Jung Hoon; *c:* Harry, Philip; *ed:* Sook Myung Womens Univ (BA) Pedagogy 1972; NY Univ (MA) Biling Spec Ed 1990; Attnd Queens Coll, Yeon Sei Univ, Sang Hai Tchrs Univ, Itsbon Tchrs Univ; *cr:* Chan An MS Soc Stud Tchr 1972-73; Korean Schl of NY Tchr 1982-90; Queens NY Sub Tchr 1989-90; PS 32 Spec Ed Resource Room Tchr 1991-92; Francis Lewis HS Biling Tchr 1992-; *ai:* Korean Club, Magazine Adv; UFT 1992-; Korean Pub Schl Tchr Assn 1992-; Queen Child Guide Ctr 1991-, Bd Mem; SUNY at Stonybrook Korean Stud Bd Mem; NY Univ Masters Prgm Grants; Yeon Sei Univ Flwshp Tchrs Wkshp; *home:* 9 Talbot Dr Great Neck NY 11020

SONCUYA, MARLENE, Science Teacher; *b:* Elizabeth, NJ; *m:* Robert; *c:* Robert; *ed:* Kean Coll (BA) Elem Ed 1974; 24 Addl Grad Credits; *cr:* St Theresa's Schl 5th Grd, Sci Tchr 1986-92; Bishop George Ahr HS Sci Tchr 1992-; *ai:* Hope 4 Animals Club Adv; NCEA 1986-; *office:* Bishop George AHR HS 1 Tingley Ln Edison NJ 08820

SONDAK, ABBEY RONALD, Math Teacher; *b:* Philadelphia, PA; *c:* David L., Jean E.; *ed:* Bucks Cty Comm Coll (AA) Individual Stud 1973; Trenton St Coll (BS) Elem Ed 1975; George Washington Univ (MA) Ed 1981; Univ of MD Math; *cr:* Tayac Elem Schl 4th-6th Grd Tchr 1977-82; Shadyside Elem Schl 4-5 Grd Tchr 1982-83; Clinton Grove Elem Schl 6th Grd Tchr 1983-85; Frederick Comm Coll Math Instr 1989-; High Point HS Math Tchr 1985-; *ai:* NCTM 1994-; NEA, MSTA 1977-; *home:* 18051 Wagonwheel Ct Olney MD 20832

SONERSON, PAUL, Language Arts Teacher; *b:* Pittsburgh, PA; *m:* Mary Ramsay; *c:* Dustin, Calla; *ed:* Univ of Pittsburgh (BA) Eng Ed 1974, MED) Ed Comm 1979; 30 Credit Hrs; *cr:* Neil Armstrong MS 8th Grd Lang Arts Tchr 1974-80; Tri Cty Yth Pgms Mental Hlth Cnsl 1982-84; Williston Northampton Schl 7th & 9th Grd Eng & Lang Arts Tchr 1984-; *ai:* Frisbee Club Adv; Fitness & Aerobics Pgm Coach; Spcl Assemblies Coord; AFT 1974-80; Vol Librn 1995-; Received Numerous Stud Grants; *office:* The Williston Northampton Schl 19 Payson Ave Easthampton MA 01027

SONGSTER, CHARLES E., Associate Professor of Ed; *b:* Springfield, PA; *ed:* Villanova Univ (BS) Soc Sci 1958; Temple Univ (MED) Ed Admin 1965; Spec Ed Credits Penn St Univ; Elem Ed Cert Westchester Univ; *cr:* Morton Boro Schl Dist Elem Tchr 1960-65; Cheyney Univ Assoc Prof 1960-; *ai:* Spec Ed Undergraduage Majors, CEC Adv; Promotion, Evaluation, Selection Comms; Men's Bsktbl Coach 1982-89; CEC 1976-; Assn St Coll & Univ Facs; Natl Assn Bsktbl Coaches 1971-; *office:* Cheyney Univ Of PA Creek Rd Cheyney PA 19319

SONNE, KENNETH J., 7th-12th Grade Technology Tchr; *b:* Jamestown, NY; *m:* Rhonda; *c:* Julie, Jenna, Jill; *ed:* Buffalo St (BS) Indstrl Arts Ed 1970, (MS) Indstrl Arts Ed 1971; 6 Addl Credits; *cr:* Elba Cntrl Schl Indstrl Arts, Driver Ed Tchr 1971-74, 7th-12th Grd Cmptr, Tech Tchr 1971-; *ai:* Tech, Safety Comms; Geneseo, Orleans Tech Assn; NYS Tech Ed Assn; NYS United Tchrs 1970-; Epsilon Pi Tau 1969-; First United Meth Church 1985-; Buffalo St Alumnae Assn; *office:* Elba Cntrl Schl PO Box 370 Elba NY 14058

SONNEBORN, SYLVIA HOTT, English Teacher & Dept Chm; *b:* Johnstown, PA; *m:* Jackson; *c:* Patshal Landis; *ed:* Shippensburg Univ (BS) Eng 1963, (MED) Eng 1967; 30 Post Grad Hrs PSV Writing Consultant, Essential Instruction Elements, Learning Dimensions, Cooperative Learning, Coherent Curr, ADAPT Brigham Young Univ, Shippensburg Univ, PA St Univ; *cr:* Dallastown Area HS Eng Tchr, Eng Dept Chair 1963-67; Eastern York HS Eng Tchr, Eng Dept Chair 1967-, Eastern Dept Chair 1993-; Antique Shop Co-Owner; *ai:* Tchr Mentor 1994-; Stu Cncl Co-Adv 1995-; Voice of Democracy, Amer Legion Essay Contest Adv 1967-; Eastern York Ed Assn 1967-, Pres 1982, Pub Relations Chair 15 Yrs, PSEA Comm Awd 1983; NEA, PSEA 1963-; Alpha Delta Kappa 1986-90, Chaplain; Strategic Planning Comm 1994-; Sunday Schl Tchr; AARP; Model A Restorers Antique Automobile Club; Model A Ford of Canada; Fostoria Soc; Lancaster Antique Car Club; Greater Baltimore Antique Car Club; Gettysburg Antique Car Club; Poetry Pub; Awd Gift of Time Cert Poen; VFW Distngd Svc Org Awd contest Adv 20 Yrs; *office:* Eastern York HS PO Box 2002 Cool Creek Rd Wrightsville PA 17368*

SONNIE, WALLACE H., Math Teacher; *b:* East Cleveland, OH; *m:* Elaine LaMonica; *c:* Wally Jr., Catherine, William, Kevin; *ed:* OH Univ (BSEd) Math 1976; Case Western Reserve (MA) Ec 1978; John Carroll Univ (MA) Ed 1994; *cr:* Centerior Energy Statistician, Analyst 1978-85; Pru Bache Broker 1985-86; Prescoll Ball Turban Municipal Bond Trader 1986-87; Shaker Bd of Ed Tchr 1988-; *ai:* Ftbl Coach; *office:* Shaker Heights MS 20600 Shaker Blvd Shaker Heights OH 44122

SONSIRE, FRANCIS JAMES, Fifth Grade Teacher; *b:* Brooklyn, NY; *m:* Teresa Steers; *c:* Cari Francis Daniels, Craig Francis, Tricia Francis; *ed:* Brooklyn Coll (BA) Elem Ed 1967; St Univ of NY at Stonybrook (MA) 1972; Stud Classroom Discipline & Rdng Instruction at Ithaca Coll, Traditional African Soc at St Univ of NY at New Paltz & Curr Dev at Dowling Coll; Received Elem Prin Cert from Hofstra Univ; Sub Saharan African Music; *cr:* NY City Bd of Ed 5th Grd Tchr 1961-62, Elem PE Tchr 1966-67; E Islip HS Girls Bsktbl Coach 1979-85; East Islip Schls Elem Tchr 1967-; *ai:* Schl Photographer; Bsktbl Coach; Soccer & Bsktbl Referee; AFT 1967-; E Islip Tchrs Assn 1967-, Bldg Rep 1987-92; Intnl Ctr of Photography 1991-; NYSUT 1967-; UFT 1961-66; Natl Federation of Sports Officials; Nature Conservancy & Sierra Club 1980-; Natl Wildlife Fed 1982-; Greenpeace 1981-; *home:* 4 Stanley Pl Hauppauge NY 11788*

SONSKY, SIDNEY NATHAN, Elec & Cmptr Engrng Tech Prof; *b:* New York, NY; *ed:* City Coll of NY (BEE) Electrical Engrng-Cum Laude 1958; NY Univ (MEE) Electrical Engrng 1964; Prof Engr's License NY St 1968; FCC Radio Telephone Lifetime License US 1985; Univ of CO Electromagnetic Measurements; *cr:* Polarad Electronics Corp Electrical Engr 1958-59; ITT Federal Labs Electronic Engr 1959-61; FXR Division Amphenol Borg Electronics Sr Electronic Engr 1961-64; US Naval Applied Sci Lab Task Ldr 1964-69; Queensborough Comm Coll of CUNY Asst Prof 1969-74, Assoc Prof 1974-78, Full Prof 1978-; *ai:* Electric Circuits, Electronics Courses Notes, Manuals Writing; Tech-Prep Prgm; Eta Kappa Nu 1957-, Sr Mem; IEEE 1958-; Sigma Xi, NSPE 1966-; ASEE, AFT, AAUP,PSC 1969-; NY St Assn of Jr Colls 1972-; Tau Beta Pi 1974-; Tau Alpha Pi 1976-; Natl Assn Bus, Educl Radio 1984-; US Marine Corps Reserves 1966-74; 3 IEEE Appreciation Certs 1979-81; NY Chptr NSPE 4 Schlsp Comm Chm Dedicated Svc Appreciation Plaques 1984, 1987, 1989, 1994; Sci & Tech Entry Prgrm Dedication Appreciation Plaque 1991; Books: Theory and Experiments in Basic Electric Circuits 1978, Introduction to Technical Mathematics with Computing 1979; 3 VEA Grants NY St Ed Dept; Contributed Articles to Prof Journals; *office:* City Univ of NY Queensborough Comm Coll 222-05 56th Ave Bayside NY 11364

SONTUM, LYNN O., Physics Teacher; *b:* Tarentum, PA; *m:* Susan; *ed:* Mount Union Coll (BS) Physics 1964; Univ of Pittsburgh (MED) Math Ed 1968; 33 Plus Credits Beyond Masters in Ed; *cr:* Knoch HS Math, Sci & Physics Tchr 1964-; Butler Cty Comm Coll Math & Physics Tchr 1968-; *ai:* AAPT 1968-; PA Acad Sci 1970-82; PA Jr Acad Sci, Regnl Dir 1978-81, Chairing St Meeting Awd 1980; PSEA 1964-; Friends of Saxonburg Area Lib 1989-93, Treas; Saxonburg Planning Commission 1989-, Sec; Saxonburg Historical Commission 1989-94, Sec; *office:* Knoch HS Dinnerbell Rd PO Box 628 Saxonburg PA 16056

SOOHY, DAVID, Middle School Science Teacher; *b:* Johnstown, PA; *m:* Karen Ohler; *c:* Nicole, Kayla; *ed:* PA St (BS) Elem Ed 1976; Indiana Univ of PA (MA) Elem Ed 1980; 8 Credit Hrs; *cr:* Windber Area Schl Dist Tchr 1976-; *ai:* Chess Club Adv; Sci Olympiad Coach; Windber Area Ed Assn 1976-, Treas 1986-; NEA, PSEA 1976-; Weaver Mennonite Church 1980-, Treas 1990-; *office:* Windber Area Schl Dist 2301 Graham Ave Windber PA 15963

SOOPPERSAND, SAMNARAIN, 6th Grade Teacher; *b:* Canje Berbice, Guyana SA; *m:* Sevika; *c:* Vaneshnee, Vashti, Neemwattee, Vashram; *ed:* Borough of Manhattan CC (AA) Bus 1974; Baruch Coll (BBA) Insurance 1976; Queens Coll (MS) Childrens Lit 1992; *cr:* United Artist Corp Sales Rep 1970-82; PS 42 Q 6th Grd Tchr 1985-; *ai:* Eastern Amer Cricket League Coach; Queens & Jamaica Cricket Club Player; AFT 1985-; Christ Luth Church 1983-, Pres & Councilman; *office:* PS 42 Robert Vernam 488 Beach 66th St Far Rockaway NY 11692

SOPER, CYNTHIA CHEESEMAN, Third Grade Teacher; *b:* Malone, NY; *m:* John; *c:* Cory, Jeffrey; *ed:* SUNY at Potsdam (BA) Psych & Elem Ed 1973, (MS) Elem Ed 1978; 40 Hrs Inservice; *cr:* Flanders Elem 2nd Grd Tchr 1973-80, Kndgtn Tchr 1981-84, 3rd Grd Tchr 1985-95; *ai:* Master Tchr for Malone Cntrl Elem Schls; Rep for Flanders; NYSUT 1973-; Malone Federation of Tchrs 1973-; Malone Coll Club 1973-80 & 1994-, Treas; Alpha Delta Kappa 1975-, Historian, Recording Sec; Malone Music Boosters 1990-, Sec; *office:* Malone Cntrl Schl-Flanders Ele 221 E Main St Malone NY 12953

SOPKO, JOHN ANTHONY, Social Studies Teacher; *b:* Buffalo, NY; *ed:* Canisius COll (BA) His, Pol Sci 1982, (MS) Scndry Ed 1986; NY St Coaching Cert; *cr:* Alden Cntrl MS 7th, 8th Grd Soc Stud Tchr 1986; Alden Cntrl HS 9th-12th Grd Soc Stud Tchr 1987-89; Springville 9th, 11th, 12th Grd Soc Stud Tchr 1989-; *ai:* Ftbl Head Coach; IM Weight Lifting Inst; NYSUT 1986-; NHS Tchr of Yr 1994; Tchr of Month Alden Cntrl; Tchr, Mentor Prgm 1995-; *office:* Springville Griffith Inst HS 240 N Buffalo St Springville NY 14141*

SOPRANO, KATHLEEN COOMBS, Math, Reading & Soc Stud Tchr; *b:* Sayre, PA; *m:* John; *c:* John, Mary Clink, Courtney, Travis; *ed:* Mansfield Univ (BS) Elem & Eng 1973; Post Grad Credits at Penn St; *cr:* Main Elem 1st & 3rd-5th Grd Sci Tchr 1973-90; Rowe MS 7th Grd Eng, Math, Social Stud & Rdg Tchr 1990-; *ai:* Drama Coach; NEA 1973-; PSEA 1973-; AAEA 1973-; Jayncees 1975-80; *office:* Harlan Rowe MS 0 Pennsylvania Ave Athens PA 18810

SORBER, BARBARA, Computer Coordinator & Teacher; *ed:* Bloomsburg Univ (BS) Math, Scndry Ed 1975; 60 Addl Credit Hrs Cmptr, Math; *cr:* Northwest HS Tchr & Cmptr Coord 1975-; *ai:* Video Club; AP Classes; NEA, PSEA 1975-.*

SORBER, WALTER, HS Social Studies Teacher; *b:* Kingston, PA; *m:* Vera; *c:* Becky, Jesse, Chad; *ed:* Mansfield (BA) Soc Stud 1970; 48 Hrs Soc Stud; *cr:* Lake-Lehman HS Tchr 1970-; *ai:* Head Bsbl Coach; NEA 1970-; NRA 1975-; Penn St Wilkes-Barre Spec Svcs Awd; Coach of Several Championship Bsbl Teams; *office:* Lake-Lehman HS PO Box 38 Lehman PA 18627

SORCHIK, SCOTT WILLIAM, Industrial Arts Teacher; *b:* Sussex, NJ; *m:* Betty Ann Davis; *c:* Joshua, Annie; *ed:* Univ of NE Lincoln (BSEd) Industrial Arts 1977; Attnd Univ of NV, Temple Univ; *cr:* Vernon Twp Schl Dist IA Tchr 1977-79; Titanium Metals Corp Rsrch & Dev 1980-84; Childrens Svc Ctr IA Tchr 1984-87; Wilkes-Barre Vo-Tech Schl 9th Grd IA Tchr 1987-; *ai:* NEA 1987-; PSEA 1987-; Loyalville United Meth Church 1990-, Admin Comm Mem; Harveys Lake Little League 1993-, Coach; Back Mt Yth Soccer League 1994-, Coach; BSA Pack 241 1994-, Comm Mem; *home:* RR 2 Box 82A Harveys Lake PA 18618

SORENSEN, ERL, Business Statistics Professor; *b:* White Plains, NY; *m:* Cilla Rice; *c:* Kristin, Erik; *ed:* Syracuse Univ (BA) Math 1970, (MBA) Bus Statistics 1972, (PHD) Quantitative Methods for Bus Admin 1983; *cr:* Syracuse Univ Instr & Asst Prof 1975-80; Bentley Coll Assoc Prof 1985-92; Northeastern Univ Visiting Prof & Lecturer 1980-85, 1992-; *ai:* Amer Statistical Assn 1975-; Syracuse Univ Outstdng Prof Awd 1980; Northeastern Univ Excl in Tchng Awd 1984; *office:* Northeastern Univ 219 Hayden Hall Boston MA 02115

SORENSEN, KELLY BONZO, English Teacher; *b:* Corning, NY; *m:* Kirk; *c:* Nicholas; *ed:* SUNY at Fredonia (BA) Eng 1991; Pursuing MS in Ed Elmira Coll; *cr:* Watkins Glen Schl Dist Summer Schl Eng Tchr 1991-92; Bradford Cntrl Schl Eng Tchr 1992-; *ai:* Theater; Chrldng Coach; NEA 1992-; *home:* 1990 County Road 10 Alpine NY 14805

SORENSEN, ROBERT G., Science Chm & Physics Tchr; *b:* Rockville Center, NY; *m:* Susan Anea Courtney; *c:* Karn Anea, Nils John; *ed:* SUNY at Buffalo (BA) Physics Ed 1966, (MA) Physics 1969; *cr:* West Vly C. Schl Sci Tchr 1966-67; Springville Cntrl Schl Physics Tchr, Sci Dept Chm 1970-; Gravesend Boys Schl Fulbright Exch Tchr 1976-77; Doon Acad Fulbright Exch Tchr 1989-90; *ai:* STANYS 1970-; AAPT 1980-; NFSSA 1985-, Pres; Presbyn Church 1970-, Elder; Church Choir 1970-; Springville Players 1969-, Pres; Fulbright Exch Scotland 1989-90,

England 1976-77; Tchr of Yr 1979; *home:* 292 E Main St Springville NY 14141

SORKIN, STEVEN BRUCE, Mathematics Teacher; *b:* Brooklyn, NY; *ed:* Univ of VA (BA) Bio 1966, (MED) Cnslng Psych 1972; Attnd Univ of North Cardenia at Chapel HIll, Univ of St Andrews in Scotland, Univ of Alberta in Canada; *cr:* Woodberry Forest Schl Math Tchr 1968-71; Landon Schl Math Tchr 1977-; Governors Schl Epistemology Instr 1983-; *ai:* Kappa Delta Pi; Fulbright Assn; Schl Tchr Flwshp Univ of St Andrews 1989; Agnes Meyer Outstdng Tchr Awd 1994; Fulbright Schlr 1980-81; *office:* Landon Schl 6101 Wilson Ln Bethesda MD 20817

SOROCHIN, RONALD F., Associate Professor; *b:* Buffalo, NY; *m:* Catherine M. Beazley; *c:* Adam Christopher, Craig Alexander; *ed:* Rochester Inst of Tech (BS) Bio 1968; Alfred Univ (MS) Bio Ed 1990; *cr:* Olean Gen Hosp Sr Technologist 1972-76; Bethesda Comm Hosp Chief Technologist 1976-80; Jones Memrl Hosp Clinical Lab Mgr 1980-86; Alfred St Coll Assoc Prof & MLT Pgm Dir 1986-; *ai:* ASCP 1975-; Alfred St Coll Allied Hlth Dept Tchr of Yr 1992; Manuals Pub: Hematology & Coagulation Lab Manual 1995 & Laboratory Manual for Urinalysis & Body Fluids 1995; Numerous Articles Pub; *office:* S U N Y Coll Of Tech At Alfred Room 214 Allied Health Alfred NY 14802

SOROKA, RONALD T., Computer Science Teacher; *b:* Key West, FL; *m:* Ann B. Curran; *c:* Ronald T. Jr., Brian T., Stacey A.; *ed:* Glassboro St Coll (BA) Math Ed 1972, (MA) Math Ed 1977; 60 Addl Credit Hrs; 6 Credit Hrs Cmptr Sci AP Tchrs; Supvr Cert; *cr:* Ocean City HS Math, Cmptr Sci Tchr 1972-; *ai:* Cmptr Tech Comm; Cmptr Competition Team Adv; NEA, NJEA 1972-; AMTNJ 1971-; Eucharistic Minister St Joseph Church 1994-; Mid Sts Evaluation Adj Instr; *office:* Ocean City HS 6th & Atlantic Ave Ocean City NJ 08226

SORRENTINO, ELAINE, Biology Teacher; *b:* Paterson, NJ; *ed:* Keuka Coll (BA) Bio 1968; Glassboro St Coll Early Ed Cert; Rutgers Univ Behavioral Bio; *cr:* Burlington Cty Coll Asst Instr 1979-82; Rutgers Univ Research Asst 1985-86; Egg Harbor Twp HS Tchr 1986-; *ai:* Cooperating Tchr for Stu Tchrs from Candidates for Scndry Ed Cert Stockton St; NEA, NJEA 1979-; NASTA; Written Numerous Articles, Trng Manual, Lectured in US, Canada & England-Topics Include Psych of Learning, Trng & Instructing; *office:* Egg Harbor Twp HS 24 High School Dr Egg Harbor Townshi NJ 08234

SORRENTINO, JOSEPH CARMAN,JR., Athletic Coach; *b:* Rockaway Beach, NY; *m:* Donna M.; *ed:* Sullivan Co Comm Coll (AA) Lbrl Arts, Sci 1975; Univ of Buffalo (BS) PE 1977; *cr:* Brookside Jr HS PE Tchr, Ath Coach 1977-82; Unatego Jr Sr HS Track, Field Coach 1982-84; Laurens Cntrl Schl PE Tchr, Ath Coach 1982-87, 1992-; *ai:* Soccer, Bsktbl, Track, Field Coach; NY St Pub HS Ath Assn 1983-86, Section IV Modified Ath Rep; *office:* Laurens Central Schl PO Box 301 Laurens NY 13796

SORRENTINO-SUTTON, ERICA, English Teacher; *b:* Toms River, NJ; *m:* Robert D.; *c:* Zackary; *ed:* Univ of DE (BA) Eng Ed 1986; *cr:* The Windsor Schl Eng Tchr 1987; Downington HS Eng Tchr 1987-89 & 1991-; West Chester East HS 1989-90; *ai:* NEA 1988-; *office:* Downingtown Sr HS 445 Manor Ave Downingtown PA 19335

SORTMAN, FRANCES HELEN FERNAN, Elementary Teacher; *b:* Buffalo, NY; *m:* Francis Eugene; *c:* Francis Scott, Suzanne McCarthy, Jeffery Robert, Mark James, Amy Eliz Dashnaw, Jennifer Helen (dec); *ed:* LeMoyne Coll at Syracuse (BS) Hum, Eng 1963; Attnd SUNY at Oswego, Syracuse Univ, Coll of St Rose; *cr:* Altmar Elem 5th Grd Tchr 1963-64; St Charles Schl 4th Grd Tchr 1964-66; Parish Elem 4th-5th Grd Tchr 1968-71; A-PW HS 9th Grd Soc Stud, Eng Tchr 1976-78; Altmar-Elem 4th-5th Grd Tchr, Librn 1979-; *ai:* Shared Decision Making Team; Effective Schls; Parent Activity Group; Curr Cncl; AFT, NYSUT 1970-; *home:* 34 Dean Dr Parish NY 13131

SOSA, ALBERT ANTHONY, Career & Vocational Guid Cnslr; *b:* New York City, NY; *ed:* Air Univ (AAS) Police Sci 1964; Holy Apostle Coll (BA) Eng Lit, Philosophy 1973; Niagara Univ (MS) Ed, Cnslng Psych 1976; St of NJ Bd of Soc Work Examiners Cert; Judeo-Chrstn Theological Stud 131 Credit Hrs; Nova Southeastern Univ EdD Stud Prgm; *cr:* USAF Aerospace Sec Police Dept 1964-68; Archdiocesan Cath HS Edctr, Cnslr 1975-85; WNY Dist Affirmative Action Dis Chprsn, Officer 1989-93; WNY Police Dept, Juvenile Div Cnslr 1986-; Memorial HS Career, Voc Guid Cnslr 1985-; *ai:* St NJ Superior Court Conf Comm Co-Chair; WNY Juvenile Div Cnslng Staff; WNY Rent Control Bd Vice Chair; WNY Affordable Housing Commission; NJ Tenant Assn; Natl Eagle Scout Assn BSA; Phi Delta Kappa 1980-, Pres, Past Pres, Svc Key Awd, Edctr of Yr; Knights of Columbus 1985-, Fourth Degree Svc to Other Awd; NEA, WNYEA 1985-, Ex Bd; Natl Ed Assn Hispanic Caucus; NJ Ed Assn; NJ Career Cnslr Assn; Hudson Cty Prsnl, Guid Assn; Amer Prsnl, Guid Assn; NCEA; Welfare Advocacy 1977-, Pres, Pres Awd; Jr Chamber of Commerce 1967-, VP, Comm Awd; BSA 1960-, Asst Cncl Comm Eagle Scout; WNY Tenant Assn 1980-, Pres, Comm Awd; John A. Shedd Meml Awd; *office:* Memorial HS 5501 Park Ave West New York NJ 07093*

SOSA, ARLENE, St Certfd Biling Guid Cnslr; *b:* Brooklyn, NY; *m:* Mariano Arroyo; *ed:* Long Island Univ Brooklyn Campus (MS) Guid & Cnslng 1992; Inter-Amer Univ of PR San Ger Campus (BA) Secreterial Scis; *cr:* IS 49 Keyboarding Tchr 1987-92; Eastern Dist HS Biling Guid Cnslr 1992-; *ai:* Project Smile Coord; United Fed of Tchrs 1987-; NYSUT 1987-; AFT 1987-; Eastern Dist HS Outstdng Guid Cnslr Awd for Basis Recogniton Ceremony 1995; *office:* Eastern District HS 850 Grand St Brooklyn NY 11211

SOSIK, CARM A., Ger, Latin Tchr & Dept Chair; *b:* Brooklyn, NY; *m:* Nick; *c:* Nick III, Mark, Nicole; *ed:* Wilkes Univ (MS) Ed 1991; 30 Post-Grad Credits; *cr:* WY Vly West Ger & Rdng Tchr 1970-72; Kutztown HS Long-Term Sub Eng Tchr 1980; Fleetwood HS Eng, Ger & Latin Tchr 1981-; *ai:* Strategic Planning Comm; Mentor for New Tchrs; Dept Chprsn; PSEA; NEA; PSMLA; Amer Classical League; Womans Club of Kutztown 1975-, Sec; St Marys Womens Aux 1980-, Pres, Sec; *home:* 713 Luella Dr Kutztown PA 19530

SOSLAND, DAVID N., Secondary English Teacher; *b:* Hartford, CT; *m:* Shirley Schreiber; *c:* Jessica Sosland Katz, Matthew; *ed:* Univ of CT (BA) Eng 1967; Univ of Hartford (MA) Eng 1968; 32 Addl Credits at Columbia Tchrs Coll; *cr:* Reynolds Jr HS Tchr 1968-69; Thomas Jefferson Jr HS Eng Tchr 1969-82; Teaneck HS Eng Tchr 1982-; *ai:* Lang Arts Consulting Tchr; NEA, NJEA 1968-; NCTE Journal Article on Tchng Moral Dilemmas in Death of a Salesman; *office:* Teaneck HS 100 Elizabeth Ave Teaneck NJ 07666

SOSTRE, OLGA IRIS, Exercise Physiology, Hlth Tchr; *b:* New York, NY; *ed:* Long Island Univ at Brooklyn (BS) PE, Dance 1987; Long Island Univ at Brooklyn Campus (MS) Exercise Physiology 1990; 18 Credit Hrs Towards EDD PE, Movement Sci; *cr:* Flatbush YMCA Sports & Fitness Dir 1984-89; Prospect Park YMCA Sports & Fitness Dir 1989-90; Bridge School PE, Hlth Tchr 1990-; *ai:* Boys & Girls Bsktbl Coach; Fitness Club, Peer Mediator Advs; Conflict Resolution Tchr, Stress Mngmt Trainers; Ala-Teen Adv & Cnslr; AFT, UFT 1990-; NYSHPERD, AAHPERD 1994-; Natl Museum Amer Indian 1994-; Angela Zirpiades PE Tchr of Yr Awd Dist & City Wide 1992-93; LIU Exercise Physiology Grad Asst Awd 1987-90; *office:* Bridge Schl 141 E 111th St New York NY 10029*

SOTO, RITA, Spanish Teacher; *b:* Brooklyn, NY; *m:* Monico; *c:* Bernadette; *ed:* SUNY at Oswego (BA) Scndry Ed, Span 1969, (MS) Ed 1974; *cr:* Mexico HS Span Tchr 1969-; *ai:* Span Club, Sociedad Honoraria Hispanica Adv; NYSUT 1969-; NYSAFLT, FLACNY; AATSP 1974-; *office:* Mexico HS Main St Mexico NY 13114

SOTTOLANO, MATTHEW JOSEPH, Driver & Physical Ed Tchr; *b:* Doylestown, PA; *ed:* Lock Haven Univ (BS) Hlth & PE 1993; 6 Credits Toward Masters in Spec Ed at Mansfield Univ; *cr:* Williamson Jr-Sr HS Tchr 1993-; *ai:* Athletic Dir; SADD Adv; Bsktbl Asst Coach; Track Head Coach; NEA, PSEA 1993-; PSADA 1995-; PSHPERD 1990-; Natl Eagle Scout Assn 1989-; *home:* PO Box 21 Middlebury Center PA 16935

SOUDERS, BUD, General Science Teacher; *b:* Allentown, PA; *m:* Susan M.; *c:* Craig M.; *ed:* Kutztown Univ (BS) Bio 1965, (MED) Sci, Ed 1967; *cr:* Emmaus Jr HS 7th Grd Sci Tchr 1965-69; East Penn Schl Dist Elem Environmental Ed 1970-81; Emmaus Jr HS 8th Grd Gen Sci Tchr 1982-; *ai:* Outdoor Ed Club, Schl Envirothon Team Adv; NEA, PSEA 1965-; Wildlands Conservancy 1975-, Bd Mem; Lehigh Vly Audubon Soc 1965-, Pres; Articles Pub; Naturalist PA St Park System; *home:* 3950 Azalea Rd Allentown PA 18103

SOUDERS, CAROL ANN (MAUER), Fourth Grade Teacher; *b:* Pottsville, PA; *m:* Henry W.; *c:* Jennifer, William; *ed:* Messiah Coll (BA) Behavioral Sci 1970; Post Grad Hrs at Shippensburg Univ; *cr:* Southrn Fulton Schl Dist 3rd & 4th Grd Tchr 1970-78, 1984-; *ai:* Act & Power of Positive Stdnts Comms Mem; NEA, PSEA 1970-; Band Boosters 1990-, Treas; Athletic Assn 1990-, Bd of Dirs; *office:* Southern Fulton Elem Schl HCR 80 Box 116 Warfordsburg PA 17267

SOULE, GARDNER NORTHUP,JR., Air Transportation Teacher; *b:* Chicago, IL; *m:* Sally Elizabeth Fitzgerald; *c:* Peter F., Heidi A., Molly R.; *ed:* Stetson Univ (BA) Geog 1966; SUNY at Oswego 30 Credit Hrs-Permanent NYS Cert 1972; Airline Transport Pilot Cert 1973; Multi Engine Flight Instr 1985; FAA Control Tower Written Exam 1995; *cr:* Page Airways Chief Flight Instr & Aircraft Salesman 1967-69; Whitney St HS Annex Air Transportation Tchr 1969-79; Edison Tech & Occupational Ed Ctr Air Transportation Tchr 1979-; *ai:* Sailing Club Adv; After Schl Flying Pgm Instr; Adult Ed Flight Simulator Instr; AOPA 1966-; AFT 1969-; NYSUT 1969-; Farmington Friends Church 1975-, Clerk, Ministry of Counsel & Choir Mem; Rochester Sailboard Club 1989-, Regatta Comm & Several 1st Prizes; Canaltown Chorale 1990-, Soloist & Bass; FAA Appointment as Accident Prevention Cnslr; Wrote NY St Competency Based Aviation Curr; Wrote FAA Part 141 Curr for Edisons Flight Pgm; Dev Partnership with Amer Airlines to Help Our Stdnts; *office:* Edison Tech & Occupational Ctr 655 Colfax St Rochester NY 14606

SOUNTIS, JOAN MARIE, Business Education Teacher; *b:* Jersey City, NJ; *ed:* Montclair St (BA) Bus Ed, Secretarial 1973; Grad Bus; Crisis Mgmt; Psych Evaluations I, II; Suicide Awareness I, II; Mulitcultural Stu Body I, II; Russia Cultural Exch; Pupil Asst Comm; Interpreting Test Results for Parents; Preparing Stu of EWT, HSPT; *cr:* Ft Lee Adult Ed Keyboarding Tchr 1979-80; Cliffside Park High Bus Ed Tchr 1993-; *ai:* Bergen Cty Tech Schls 1993-, Mid St 1991-91 Advy Bd Comm; Bus Ed Curr Appraisal Comm Chprsn 1992-94; Cliffside Park Ed Assn Schlsp Comm Mem; Cliffside Park Ed Assn, NEA, Bergen Cty Ed Assn, NJ Ed Assn 1973-; NJ Bus Ed Assn Convention Recorder; *office:* Cliffside Park HS Palisade and Riverview Aves Cliffside Park NJ 07010

SOUSA, JUDITH INTEGLIA, 5th Grade Teacher; *b:* Providence, RI; *m:* Edward A.; *c:* Matthew, Gregory; *ed:* RI Coll (BS) Elem, Spec 1973, (MED) Spec Ed 1975; *cr:* La Perche El Tchr 1972-73; Cook Schl Sp Ed Tchr 1973-77; Old Cty Rd El Tchr 1977-; *ai:* Skills Commission; Negotiations Team; NEA 1973-, Negotiations 1977-, Nominating Comm; *office:* Old County Road Schl 200 Old County Rd Smithfield RI 02917*

SOUSA, NANCY ANN (WROBEL), Kindergarten Teacher; *b:* Fall River, MA; *m:* Anthony W.; *ed:* RI Coll, Bridgewater St Coll 18 Credit Hrs Post Grad Stud; *cr:* Brayton Ave Schl Kndgtn Tchr 1970-; *ai:* 4th-6th Grd Chrstn Living Class Tchr; MTA, NEA, Fall River Edctrs Assn 1970-.*

SOUTH, CYNTHIA KALLOS, French Teacher; *b:* Columbus, OH; *m:* Roderick V.; *c:* Christopher, Crystal; *ed:* Capital Univ (BAEd) Fr 1969; Univ of Paris Degre Elementaire Fr 1967; Addl 150 Hrs; *cr:* Reynoldsburg Sr HS Fr Tchr 1969-; *ai:* REA, OEA, NEA 1969-; Captial Area Humane Soc 1987-; Friends of Lib 1982-; *home:* 9627 Shalemar Dr Pickerington OH 43147

SOUTH, E. WAYNE, Sci & Environmental Ed Teacher; *b:* Easton, PA; *m:* Anita Emerick-South; *ed:* Maryville Coll (BS) Bio, Chem 1967; 54 Addl Hrs; *cr:* Harmony Twp Schl 6th Grd Tchr 1967-68; Elkton MS Sci Tchr 1968-69; White Twp Schl Sci, Environmental Ed Tchr 1969-; *ai:* Hawk Watch Prgm; Environmental Ed Project Organizer, Fundraiser; Pub Relations Comm; NEA, NJ Ed Assn 1967-; White Twp Ed Assn 1969-, Negotiations Chprsn; NSTA 1993-; NJ Governors Tchr Recognition Recipient; Warren Cty Conservation Educator of Yr; NJ Natl Energy Fnd; Outstanding Tchr Awd; NJ Sci Tchrs, Supvrs Awd; Natl Sci Fnd Publication Grant Co-Recipient; Schl Bd Commendations; *office:* White Twp Consolidated Schl RR 03 Box 580 Belvidere NJ 07823

SOUTH, GARY PAUL, Global Studies Teacher; *b:* Malone, NY; *m:* Marion O'Donnell; *c:* Jody; *ed:* Jefferson Comm Coll (AA) Liberal Arts 1967; SUC at Plattsburgh (BA) Scndry Ed, Soc Stud 7-12 1969; 33 Grad Hrs SUC at Potsdam; *cr:* St Regis Falls Cntrl Schl 8-10 Grd Soc Stud Tchr, Bsktbl, Bsbl Coach 1969-86; Brushton Moira Cntrl Schl 9-10 Grd Soc Stud Tchr, Soccer, Bsktbl, Sftbl Coach 1986-; *ai:* Boys Var Bsktbl, Soccer, Girls Modified Sftbl Coach; Tchr Schlsp Comm; NYSUT, AFT 1969-; BM United Tchrs Assn 1986-; NFICA 1974-; Sons of Amer Legion 1984-; Var Bsktbl Coach of Yr Awd; *home:* 17 Cherry St Malone NY 12953*

SOUTH, TED JOHNSON, Assistant Professor of History; *b:* Heidelberg, Germany; *m:* Frances Johnson; *c:* Katherine Tyler; *ed:* CO Coll (BA) Medieval Stud 1980; Cornell Univ (MA) Medieval Stud 1986, (PHD) Medieval His 1990; Durham Univ at England (MA) Early Medieval Archaeology 1987; *cr:* Bowdoin Coll His Instr 1990-; Univ of RI His Instr 1990-91; Western New England Coll Asst His Prof 1991-; *ai:* WNEC Medieval Feast Co-Spon; Phi Beta Kappa 1980-; Bethell Prize Charles Homer Haskins Soc 1990; Papers Pub; *office:* Western New England Coll 1215 Wilbraham Rd Springfield MA 01119*

SOUTHALL, SHELIA YVONNE, Fifth Grade Teacher; *b:* Port Lavaca, TX; *m:* Robert L.; *c:* Tysha, Robert Jr.; *ed:* Prairie A&M Univ (BS) Elem Ed 1972; 14 Hrs Xavier Univ; *cr:* Princeton City Schls Tchr 1975-84; Cincinnati Pub Schls Tchr 1986-; *ai:* Frosh Girls Chrldng Coach; Bsktbl Team Mother; Co-Ed Vlybl Team; Earn & Learn Prgm Tchr; AFT; NEA.

SOUTHARD, DON MC CORMICK, Science Department Head; *b:* Atlantic City, NJ; *m:* Deborah Dressell; *ed:* Marietta Coll (BS) Chem 1979; John Carroll Univ (MED) Admin, Supervision 1986; *cr:* Hathaway Brown Schl Asst Upper Schl Head Sci Dept Chair 1981-; *ai:* Summer Schl Dir; Scheduler; Schl Evaluations Coord; New Fac, Mentor Prgm Dir; NSTA 1981-; Phi Beta Kappa 1979-; ACS; *office:* Hathaway Brown Schl 19600 N Park Blvd Shaker Heights OH 44122

SOUTHERTON, JAMES PATRICK, 7th-8th Grade English Teacher; *b:* Honesdale, PA; *m:* Maria Yatsonsky; *c:* Jennifer; *ed:* Bloomsburg Univ (BA) Scndry Eng Ed 1988; Attnd Wilkes & Millersville 27 Grad Credits; *cr:* Mifflinburg Area Schl Dist Eng Tchr, Quest, Stu Cncl & Bldg Club Adv 1988-; *ai:* Discipline & Sick Leave Bank Comm; MAEA 1988-; PSEA 1988-; NEA 1988-; Sacred Heart Roman Cath Church 1988-; Mifflinburg Area Jaycees Outstdng Young Edctr Awd 1994-95; *home:* 302 Mel Lewisburg PA 17837

SOUTHWOOD, NANCY E., Senior High English Teacher; *b:* W Canada; *m:* Richard T.; *c:* Richard, Meghan; *ed:* Niagara Univ (B 1969, (MAT) Eng, Ed 1981; *cr:* Lewiston-Porter Sr HS Eng Instr Caskill MS Eng Instr 2 Yrs; Niagara Falls Sr HS Eng Instr 1 Yr; N Univ Eng Instr 4 Yrs; *ai:* Staff Dev, Standards Comms; NHS Ad Club Niagara Falls 1980-, Pres; Cayuga Island Garden Club Corresponding Sec; St Francis Guild of Mt St Mary's Hosp 1971- One of Fifty Participants Nationwide Harvard Univ Inst Writing, Civic Ed 1990; *office:* Lewiston Porter Sr HS 4061 Creek Rd Youn NY 14174

SOUTHWORTH, WILSON MAIN, Fourth Grade Teacher; *b:* M NY; *m:* Claudia Jean Amos; *c:* Courtney Lynne; *ed:* Brockport St El (BS) 1969, (MS) 1976; *cr:* Towne Elem Second Grd Tchr 1969-80, Grd Tchr 1980-; *ai:* Elem Math Dept Chairmanship; AFT-NYSUT *office:* Warren P Towne Elem Schl 181 Bates Rd Medina NY 14103

SOUTRA, MARCUS STANFORD,JR., Sociology & Psych Teacher; *b:* Springfield, MA; *m:* Carol Fagan; *c:* Marcus III, Matthe Holyoke Comm Coll (AS) Lbrl Art 1968; Amer Intnl Coll (BA) Soc 1970, (MA) Sociology, Anthropology 1972; 30 Addl Credits 6th Yr *cr:* East Windsor HS Soc Sci Tchr 24 Yrs; Springfield Tech Comr Prof of Sociology, Psych, Soc Psych, Human Relations, Soc Proble Yrs; *ai:* Stu Cncl Adv; Cross Cntry Coach; Newspaper Adv; Po Comms; Goals, Objectives for 10 Yr Evaluations Chm; Model Co Adv; NEA, CT Ed Assn 1972-, E Windsor Ed Assn 1972-, Pres; NE Cncl for Soc Stud 1972-, Planning comm; Chrstn Ed Comm 1994-; T Yr 1988, 1990, 1993; NSF Grant 1986; Univ of CT Excl Tchng Awd Tchng Awd; Dev grant 1995-; Prin Awd 1988, 1990; *office:* East W Jr Sr HS 74 S Main St East Windsor CT 06088

SOUZA, DONNA L., Mathematics Specialist; *b:* Newport, R Syracuse Univ (BA) Math Ed 1988, (MS) Math Ed 1990; *cr:* Ft Plain Schl Math Tchr 1990-91; Southern VT Coll Math Specialist 1991-; *a* Fac Assn; Acad Standing, Fac Dev Comms; Acad Probation, Yrbk NCTM 1990-; *office:* Southern Vermont College Monument Bennington VT 05201

SOUZA, TERESA ANN, Third Grade Teacher; *b:* New Bedford, M Timothy; *ed:* Univ of MA at Dartmouth (BA) Sociology 1979; Ed Cert 1980; *cr:* Holy Family-Holy Name Schl 4th Grd Tchr 1987-9 Grd Tchr 1991-; *ai:* Bee Buddies Spelling League, Standard Spelling Bee Coord; Sci Fair Judge; Spelling Bee Coach; *office:* Family-Holy Name Schl 91 Summer St New Bedford MA 02740

SOVA, JOYCE SPRAGUE, 5th Grade Teacher; *b:* Malone, NY; *w:* (dec); *c:* Greg, Jeff, Alan, Kerry; *ed:* SUNY at Plattsburgh (BS) Ele 1962; Russell Sage Coll 35.5 Credit Hrs; *cr:* North Syracuse Schls 4t Tchr 1962-63; Salmon River Schl Dist 2nd Grd Tchr 1963-64; M Schls Kndgtn Tchr 1966-67; Saratoga Spr City Schls 5th Grd Tchr *ai:* SSTA 1968-; NYSUT 1962-; *office:* Caroline Street Elem Sch Caroline St Saratoga Springs NY 12866

SOVCHIK, ANDY, Asst Principal; *b:* Cleveland, OH; *m:* Lia; *c:* Lir Tyler; *ed:* Kent St Univ (BA) K-12th Ed & Industrial Tech 1981, Scndry Admin 1985; Addl Post Grad Studs in Admin; *cr:* Parm Industrial Tech Tchr 1981-82; Bedford HS Industrial Tech Tchr 198 Stow-Munroe Falls HS Drafting & Design Tchr 1983-94; Stow HS Prin 1994-94; Streetsboro HS Asst Prin 1995-; *ai:* OASSP; Street Parks & Rec Safety Land Course Instr; Stow Bd of Ed Tchr of Yr Stow Munroe Falls HS PTSA Educator of Yr 1993; *office:* Streetsbo 1900 Annalane Dr Streetsbore OH 44241*

SOWARDS, KENNETH R., Social Studies Department Chr Middletown, OH; *m:* Monica L.; *ed:* Univ OH Miami (BA) His 1973; Dayton (MSEd) Ed 1990; *cr:* Fort Loramie Local Schls Soc Stud 1975-; *ai:* NEA, OEA 1975-; FLEA 1975-, Treas 3 Yrs; OH Cncl fo Stud 1986-; Miami, Shelby Ctys Daughters of Amer Revolu Outstanding Tchr of Amer His 1992; Jennings Scholar 1986-87.

SOWDERS, SHAWN GREGORY, 8th Grade History Teache Cincinnati, OH; *m:* Misty Lee Lane; *c:* Lacey Lane, Lincoln Lee, Lee; *ed:* Hanover Coll (BA) His 1989; 3 Credit Hrs Mount Saint Jose Succeeding with Difficult Stdnts; Wrkng Twds Maters in Scndry Tch Miami Univ; *cr:* Harrison Jr HS Tchr 1990-; *ai:* Jr HS Ftbl & Bsktbl C HS Bsbl Coach; Dir of JTM Summer Bsbl Prgm Ages 13-18; NE SLCTA 1990-; PTA 1990-, Friend of Stdnts Awd 1993; Harrison Jr HS of Yr 1992-93; *home:* 125 Etta Ave Harrison OH 45030*

SOWERBROWER, SHIRLEY J., 5th Grade Teacher; *b:* Somerset *m:* Donald; *c:* Amanda, Jessica; *ed:* Shippensburg St Coll (BA) Ele 1972; *cr:* Rockwood Elem 3rd Grd Tchr 1972-78, 1st Grd Tchr 197 6th Grd Tchr 1985-86, 5th Grd Tchr 1987-; *ai:* Tech, Book Selecti Curr Comms; Amer Heart Jump A Thon Chm; PSEA & NEA 1972-, Rep, Neg Comm & PACE Chm; *home:* 362 White Oak St Rockwoo 15557

SOWERBY, JAMES A., Instructional Support Teacher; *b:* McKees PA; *m:* Maureen J.; *c:* James A. III, Patrick M.; *ed:* Edinboro St Coll Elem Ed 1970; Duquesne Univ (ME) Elem Ed 1975; Elem Guidance *cr:* South Allegheny Schl Dist 4th-6th Grd Elem Tchr 197 Instructional Support Tchr 1993-; *ai:* Southwestern PA Ctr for Leadership; NEA, PSEA 1972-; SAEA 1972-, Pres 1990-92; Glas Lions Club 1989-; Amer Legion, Glassport Ath Assn, Glassport Elem 1972-; *office:* Glassport Central Elem Schl 3rd & Ohio Ave Glasspor 15045*

SOWERS, AMY RAWLINS, High School English Teacher; *b:* Clevel OH; *m:* Edward M.; *ed:* OH Univ (BS) Comm, Eng 1990; Clevelan Univ (MA) Rdng 1994; Admin Cert Summer 1996; *cr:* Garfield Hei City Schl 9-12 Grd Eng Tchr 1990-91, 7-8 Grd Rdng Tchr 1991-92, Eng Tchr 1992-; *ai:* Yrbk Adv; Renaissance Co-Coord; OEA, NEA 1 Tchrs Assn 1990-, Rep 1992-95, VP 1995-, OEA Del 1994-; Nom Edc Yr; Ashland Tchr Awd; *office:* Garfield Heights City Schls 12000 M Leaf Dr Garfield Heights OH 44125

SOWRI, DOSS, Physics Teacher; *b:* Bhavanisagar, India; *m:* P Graham; *c:* Anand, Rakesh; *ed:* Univ of Madras India (BSC) Physics 1 Annamalai Univ India (MSC) Physics 1977; St Joseph's Uni Philadelphia (MS) Ed 1995; *cr:* St Maria Goretti HS Physics, Chem 1987-; *ai:* AAPT-SEPENNA 1989-.

SOWRY, GINGER LA FAYE, Spanish & Reading Teacher; *b:* Union IN; *m:* Claude D.; *c:* Nikki, Robert; *ed:* Ball State Univ (BA) Span 1 Wright State Univ (MA) Scndry Curr & Super 1983; Attnd Univ of Day Univ of WA at Seattle, Wright St Univ; *cr:* Westmont HS Span 1969-72; Ansonia Local Schls Migrant Tchr 1976-82; Ansonia HS S Rdng Tchr 1982-; *ai:* Span Club, Sr Class Adv; Lang Arts Comm; Stu Adv Mexico Trips 1984, 86, 89, 90 & 96; FL Dept Chprsn; Congrsnl A Adv; Frgn Excch Stdnt Adv; Tech Comm; Restructuring Steering Co Darke Cnty Tchr of Yr Judge 1993-; NEA, OEA, WOEA 1969-; OF AATSP 1982-; Founder Darke Co Foreign Lang Tchrs Assn 1993; Phi D Kappa 1990-; Beta Sigma Phi 1973-; WSU Schlshp 1982; TX OH Mig Fellowship 1982; WSU Outstanding Grad Stu 1983; Exchange Tchr C Rica 1988; Staff Dev Awds 1988-; JVS Cert Excl 1991; Ansonia Tchr o

Darke Co Tchr of Yr 1993; Ashland Oil Tchr Achvmnt Awd 1995; 730 Primrose Dr Greenville OH 45331*

RS, NANCY, Fourth Grade Teacher; *b:* Martins Ferry, OH; *c:* James, *d:* Heidelberg Coll (BS) Elem Ed 1963; Youngstown St Univ (MA) nce & Counseling 1977; *cr:* Prairie-Lincoln North Elem Tchr 5; Millersburg Elem Tchr 1965-67; Salem City Schls Elem Tchr 8, 1974-; *ai:* NEA, OEA 1963-; SEA 1974-, Negotiating Team Sec; Holden Jennings Scholar; Mount Union Coll Ed Dept Advy Bd 2 *fice:* Prospect Elem Schl 838 Prospect St Salem OH 44460

A, TONI DIANE, Geometry Teacher; *b:* Washington, PA; *ed:* ro St Coll (BS) Math 1974; 24 Grad Credits; *cr:* Ft Cherry Schl Dist Tchr 1974-; *ai:* NEA 1974-; PSEA 1974-.

ACCINO, SANDRA ROMANO, Music Teacher; *b:* Bridgeport, CT; cy Spadaccino Vaine; *ed:* Univ Bridgeport (BS) Music Ed 1965; Heart Univ (MAT) Tchng 1988, 6th Yr Advanced Admin 1989; 90 Hrs Prof Dev; *cr:* Samuel Staples Schl, Redding Schl Music Tchr 7; Blackham Schl Music Tchr 1972-74; Flood MS Music Tchr *ai:* Tchr-Coordr of Trips to America Sings in Washington DC 8th horus; Tchr-Coord Yearly Trips to Broadway Enhancement Act for d Chorus Lessons; NEA, CEA, SEA, CMEA 1965-; GMLT 1990-; Heart Univ ADvy BD 1988-; Omega Phi Alpha Svc 1962-, Pres; ation of Excl 1991; 8th Grd Tchr Appreciation Awd 1992; Winner nergy Ed Day 1987; *office:* Flood MS 490 Chapel St Stratford CT

AFORA, VINCENT LOUIS,JR., Assistant Professor; *b:* Oneida, Elaine M. Sorbello; *c:* Vincent III, Anthony, Jill Megan; *ed:* SUNY St Coll (BS) Cultural Stud 1977; US Army Defense Information Certs: Broadcast Jrnlsm, Jrnlsm & Still Photography & Film ction; *cr:* Onondaga Comm Coll Asst Prof & Chprsn 1974-; *ai:* Curr & Proctor; OCC Fac Union; Gen Ed, Chprsns, Acad Discipline, ce Learning & OCC Budget Comm; NAB 1972-; NAEB 1974-; T 1974-; Canastota Lions Club 1990-; NYS Golden Gloves 1990-; Boxing Hall of Fame 1990-; OCC Outstdng Alumni Awd 1986; SUNY e St Alumni Awd 1990; OCC Tchng Excl Awd 1993; *home:* 106 Arthur Pl Canastota NY 13032

TH, BARBARA J., Second Grade Teacher; *b:* Gloversville, NY; *m:* *c:* Philip, Sarah; *ed:* Oswego St (BS) Elem Ed 1972; 30 Addl Hrs; *cr:* ville Central Schl Elem Tchr 1972-; *ai:* AFT 1972-; Zoning Bd Sec; *home:* PO Box 673 Northville NY 12134

NOLA, NATALIE JOAN, Mathematics Teacher; *b:* Cleveland, OH; eveland St (BA) Eng 1970, (MA) ENg; 8 Addl Hrs Certs Math, Eng; dubon Jr HS Math Tchr 1970-86; John Hay HS Math Tchr 1986-; *ai:* 2 Yrs, Prof Days 3 Yrs, Flower, Gift 6 Yrs Comm Chprsn; CTU Bldg 6 Yrs; SLT Chprsn 3 Yrs; CTU 1970-, Exec Bd; AFT, OFT, GCCTM ; *home:* 13488 Clifton Blvd Lakewood OH 44107

NOLA, SANDRA DEBERNARDI, High School Art Teacher; *b:* um, PA; *m:* Dominick J.; *c:* Consylvia, Steven; *ed:* Penn St Univ Art Ed 1972; 24 Grad Credits Seton Hill Coll; *cr:* St Gertrude Elem Art Tchr 1972-73; Apollo Elem Schl Art Tchr 1986-87; Kiski-Area heny Jr HS Art Tchr 1988; Saltsburg HS Art Tchr 1988-89; Freeport rt Tchr 1989-; *ai:* Jr Class Spon; Yellow Jacket Newspaper Spon; Ski Co-Spon; PSEA 1989-; NEA 1989-; FEA 1989-; *office:* Freeport Area O Drawer H Freeport PA 16229

NOLETTI, PAULA ANN, 8th Grade Math Teacher; *b:* Jersey City, Maurice; *c:* Paul, Lauren; *ed:* St Peter's Coll (BS) Mrktg Mngmt (MA) Ed 1988; 9 Addl Credit Hrs; *cr:* St Anthony HS Tchr 1984-88, Prin 1988-90; PS #27 7th Grd Tchr 1990-93, 8th Grd Tchr 1993-; *ai:* Schl Math Club; NEA, NJEA, JCEA 1990-; *office:* PS 27 201 North sey City NJ 07307

NOLO, SHIRLEY BALLARD, English Teacher; *b:* Tyler, TX; *c:* nt James Nystrom, Jennifer Paysse Rosen, Laurie Spagnolo Cipriani; outhwestern Univ at Georgetown (BFA) Eng, Speech Drama 1967; of TX at Austin (MA) Eng 1969; Duquesne Univ Cert Elem Ed 1989; iloxi HS Tchr 1969-70; Ball HS Tchr 1970-71; Crocket HS Tchr 77; Edgewood HS Tchr 1978-81; Woodland Hills Schls Tchr 1981-; urr, Intensive Scheduling Comms; Mentor Tchr Prgm; Scorer-PA St ssment Tests; NEA, PSEA, WCTE, NCTE 1978-; *office:* Woodland Sr HS 2550 Greensburg Pike Pittsburgh PA 15221

NUOLO, JOHN RALPH, Biology Teacher; *b:* Wilkes Barre, PA; *m:* E. Corcoran; *c:* John, Deborah; *ed:* Kings Coll (BS) Bio, General Sci Univ of Scranton (MS) Scndry Ed 1969; Kings Coll 9 Addl Hrs; s Univ 20 Hrs; PA St Univ 20 Hrs; Temple Univ 6 Hrs; Bucknell Univ s; Univ of Rochester Schl of Medicine & Dentistry 6 Hrs; Univ of aton 3 Hrs; *cr:* High Bridge Schl Sci Tchr 1964-65; E. L. Meyers HS Tchr 1965-; *ai:* NEA, PSEA 1965-; WBAEA 1965-, Mem Chm -69; *office:* Elmer L. Meyers HS 341 Carey Ave Wilkes Barre PA 2

HR, BERTHA E., Chemistry Teacher; *b:* York, PA; *c:* Michael, hew; *ed:* Elizabethtown Coll (BS) Chem 1965; Shippensburg Univ D) Chem 1969; Penn St Univ 3 Credits; Wilkes Coll 6 Credits; *cr:* r Area HS Chem Tchr 1966-69, 1971-; Lincoln Intermediate Unit ner Acad Chem Tchr 1987-; Sci Dept Chprsn 1994-; *ai:* Tchr Mentor; rleading, Stu Cncl, Foreign Exchange Club, Class Adv, Meet & ass Comm Chprsn, Fac Advy Cncl; DAEA, PSEA, NEA 1965-, Schlsp r; NSTA 1985-; Alpha Delta Kappa 1986-, Pledge & Membership r; Spring Grove Ambulance Club 1980-87, Emergency Medical nician; York Hosp vol 1980-87, EMT; York Cty Jr Miss, Judge; baugh Alumni Awd Elizabethtown Coll for Excl Chem 1st Pub Schl of HS Stdnts to Receive Awd; Candidate Whalen Meml Awd Tchng ; TIE Wrkshp 1993; *office:* Dover Area H S W Canal St Dover PA 5*

HR, SUSAN JEAN, Family Studies Teacher; *b:* York, PA; *m:* Todd hew; *ed:* VA Tech (BS) Home Ec Ed 1994; *cr:* Perry Hall HS Family Tchr 1994-; *ai:* Class of 1998 Co-Spon; Schl Improvement Team n; Tech Prep Comm Rep; Interdisciplinary Multicultural Comm Rep; , 1994-; MSTA 1994-; AAFCS 1991-; Co-Write Curr for Residential rior Design Class & Fashion Strategies Class; Created Career pleter; *office:* Perry Hall HS 4601 Ebenezer Rd Baltimore MD 21236*

LLA, LAWRENCE ANTHONY, Social Studies Instructor; *b:* ongahela, PA; *ed:* West Liberty St Coll (BA) Soc Stud Comp & Elem 970; Duquesne Univ (MA) Early Modern European His 1980; Univ of burgh (PHD) Soc Stud Ed 1992; Attnd OH St Univ, AZ St Univ & hington & Jefferrson Coll; *cr:* Windsor Elem Elem Instr 1970-72; e Ave Elem Elem Instr 1972-80; Trinity HS Soc Stud Inst 1980-; *ai:* y Bd for Scndry Ed California Univ of PA; Curr Cncl; NEA 1970-; S 1975-; Natl Cncl for Hist Edu; SAR 1990-; Grad Fellowship Univ ittsburgh; Disseration "Herbert Baxter Adams A Pioneer in His Ed"; *e:* 510 Fairway St Washington PA 15301*

LLA, THOMAS WILLIAM, Biology Teacher; *b:* McKeesport, PA; Francene M.; *c:* Laura M., Thomas C., Kenneth W.; *ed:* Univ Duquesne Bio, Sci Ed 1968; Univ of Pittsburgh (MED) Bio, Sci Ed 1975; Attnd St Univ, Carlow Coll, Point Park Coll, Wilkes Univ, Allegheny rmediate Unit; 42 Credits; *cr:* South Park HS Bio Tchr 1970-; Thomas erson HS Bio, Chem Tutor 1980-94; Allegheny Intermediate Unit thern Shelter 1983-86; *ai:* Ind Stud Tchr; Sport Video Taker; Curr Dev Regnl & Dist; Pleasant Hill Soccer Coach, Sftbl Team; Attendance Comm Person; Chess Coach, league Pres; Bsktbl Scout; Schl Play Actor; PSEA 1969-; AARP 1991-; MTA 1965-; WPBTA 1996-; Pleasant View Soccer Vol Spec Olympics Asst 1995-; Pittsburgh South Hill Soccer Assn 1986-, Schedule Coord, Asst Commissioner; Juraville Diabetes Vol 1993-; Mumon Comm 1993-; Patent on Umpire Counter; Lab Manual; NSF Grant; Honorable Tchr of Year 1987; *office:* South Park HS 2178 Ridge Rd Library PA 15129*

SPALLONE, BARBARA NOLIA (SOPER), Third Grade Teacher; *b:* Cleveland, OH; *m:* Michael Anthony Carl; *c:* Rebecca J. Balcer, Tamara M., Daniel M.; *ed:* Cuyahoga Comm Coll (AA) Math, Sci 1966; Cleveland St Univ (BS) Ed 1969, (MED) Ed 1973; 11 Addl Semester Hrs; 2 Semester Hrs John Carroll Univ; 20 Semester Hrs Kent St Univ; 30 Semester Hrs Ashland Univ; *cr:* Maple Hghts Bd of Ed Third Grd Tchr 1969-; *ai:* United Way Chm; Beautification, Curr, Staff Dev, Soc Climate, Pub Relations, Career Ed, Soc, Schl Levy, Young Authors Conf Comms; MHTA, NEOEA, OEA, NEA 1969-; Amer Legion Aux 1958-, Pub Relations; Elks Club 1970-; Eagles Club 1985-; Awds 15 Yrs, 25 Yrs Tchng; Helped Write Grant Venture Capital Schl; *home:* 1691 Sunview Rd Lyndhurst OH 44124

SPALLONE, SHARON LEE, Eng, Comm Instr & Dept Chr; *b:* Hazleton, PA; *m:* Robert C.; *ed:* Bloomsburg St Coll (BS) Scndry Ed 1968; PA St Univ (MA) Theatre Certs 1970; Addl 41 Credits at 4 Colleges; *cr:* Bloomsburg St Coll Tempory Instr 1970; Weatherly Area HS Instr, Comm Adv, Speech, Oratory, NHS 1970-; Luzerne Cty Comm Coll Adjunct Instr 1978; *ai:* NHS Adv; Curr, Dept Chprsn; Past Coach Gratory, Dramatic Rdng; Past Ed Creative Writing Booklet; NEA, PSEA, NT E 1970-; Poetry Pub Collegiate, Prof, Other Works; Poem Pub Collectible Mag; Who's Who in Amer Coll, Univ; Mentor PA St Master Tchr New Tchrs; Charter Mem Natl Museum of Women in the Arts; Curr Author; *office:* Weatherly Area HS 6th St Weatherly PA 18255

SPALTER, SHEILA, Retired French & ESL Teacher; *b:* Brooklyn, NY; *ed:* Brooklyn Coll (BA) Fr 1960; Univ of WI (MA) Fr 1961; Addl Courses New Schl, Hunter Coll, NYU, Ulpan; *cr:* Brooklyn Coll Lecturer 1961; Long Island City HS Fr Tchr 1961-64; Abraham Lincoln HS Fr & ESL Tchr 1964-95, Mentor 1989-93; *ai:* UFT, AATF 1961-; Womens Circle 1995-, Chorus Mem; Magna Cum Laude with Hnrs; Tchng Assistantship Univ of WI; NYS Grant in Russian; NDEA, Fr Govt, NYS Grants; Gideon Hawley Tchr Recognition Awd; Pi Delta Phi; Phi Beta Kappa; *home:* 2330 Voorhies Ave Apt 4M Brooklyn NY 11235*

SPANG, DEBRA REEPING, Chemistry Teacher; *b:* Des Moines, IA; *m:* Bryan D.; *ed:* Grove City Coll (BS) Biochemistry 1989; Tchng Cert in Chem 1993; Addl 6 Grad Credits, 2 Credit Hrs; *cr:* Amer Red Cross Sailing Instr 1988-89; Pennex Products Co Inc Quality Control Chemist 1989-91; Comm Coll of Allegheny Cty Chem, Physics, Ed Technician Adj Tchng 1991-93; Butler Area Sr HS Hnrs Chem Tchr 1993-; *ai:* Coach 5 Odyssey of Mind Teams; IM Bowling Adv; NEA, PSEA, Butler Ed Assn 1993-; Odyssey of Mind 1988-, Regnl Problem Captain Bd of Dir SWPA; *office:* Butler Area Sr HS 167 New Castle Rd Butler PA 16001

SPANGLER, DAVID LEE, Fifth Grade Teacher; *b:* Shelby, OH; *m:* Linda Kay Thurman; *c:* Kellie, Kyle; *ed:* OH St Univ (BA) Ed 1971; Post-Grad Hrs; Attnd Bowling Green St Univ; *cr:* Shelby City Schls 5th Grd Tchr 1971-; *ai:* Tech & Staff Evaluation Comms; NEA, OEA, SEA 1971-; Martha Holden Jennings Scholar; Coached St Champion Team for Odyssey of Mind, 10th Place Finish in World Finals; *office:* Auburn Elem Schl 109 Auburn St Shelby OH 44875

SPANGLER, FAYE S., English Teacher; *b:* Youngstown, OH; *m:* Darrell L.; *c:* Kristin H., Brooke M.; *ed:* OH Northern Univ (BA) Eng 1969; Wright St Univ (MA) Eng 1985; Addl Credit Hrs; *cr:* Newport Schl 8th Grd Lang Arts Block Tchr 1969-70; Versailles HS 9th-12th Grd Eng Tchr 1970-; *ai:* Future Tchrs of Amer Adv; North Cntrl Steering Comm; Staff Dev Dir; Versailles Ero Assn 1970-, Sec 1980; OCTELA, WOCTELA 1995-; NCTE 1990-; SHS Vlybl Boosters 1990-, Pres 1994-95; Selection Pilot Project Change Course; *office:* Versailles HS 459 S Center St Versailles OH 45380*

SPANGLER, GLENN LEWIS, Agriculture Education Teacher; *b:* Lewisburg, PA; *m:* Patricia Swank; *c:* Lindsay M., Alicia J.; *ed:* PA St Univ (BS) Ag Ed 1974, (MED) Ag Ed 1978; 12 Hrs Agronomy; 3 Hrs Ag Ed; 9 Hrs Animal Scis; 3 Credit Hrs Ag Ec; 12 Addl Hrs; Briggs & Stratton Svc Schl Voc Ed Tchrs; *cr:* Manheim Cntrl Schl Dist Ag Tchr 1974-77; PA St Univ Ag Mechanics Tchng Asst 1977-78; Mifflinburg Area HS Ag Tchr 1978-; *ai:* FFA Chapter Adv; PA Envirothon Tchr Steering Comm; PA FFA Agronomy Contest Chm; Earth Day Pgm, Forestry Sec 1994-; PA Ag Mech Team Coach, 1st Pl Eastern St Expo 1995; PA Farm Business Mgt Team Coach, Nat FFA Conv 1994; PA Crops Team Coach, Nat Crops Inventional Purdue Univ 1995; NEA, PSEA 1974-; PVATA 1974-, Regnl VP 1990-92; NVATA 1988-; Christ United Luth 1968-, Cncl Mem; Union Cty West End Fair 1979-, Swine & Sale Chm; Mifflinburg Young Farmers 1978-, Past Adv; Union Cty Extension Advy Comm 1985-91, Treas; Central Dist Dairy Show Trea 1993-, Comm Mem 95-; PA Ag Mechanics Team Coach at Natl FFA Convention 1988, 1990, 1992; PA Ag Mechanics Team Coach at Springfield 1991; PA Farm Mngmt Team Coach at Natl FFA Convention 1978; PA FFA Honorary Keystone Degree; *office:* Mifflinburg Area HS 1st & Market Sts Mifflinburg PA 17844

SPANGLER, LINDA R., Fifth Grade Teacher; *b:* York, PA; *m:* Thomas T.; *c:* Benjamin, Emily; *ed:* York Jr Coll (AS) Elem Ed 1967; Millersville St Coll (BS) Elem Ed 1969, (MS) Remedial Rdng 1973; *cr:* Romulus Cntrl Schl 5th Grd Tchr 1969-70; Dover Area Schl Dist 2nd Through 5th Grd Tchr 1970-; *ai:* DAEA, NEA 1970-; *office:* Dover Elem Schl 109 E Canal Rd Dover PA 17315

SPANGLER, VIRGINIA MARIE, Second Grade Teacher; *b:* Alger, OH; *m:* Roger Jacob; *c:* Jeffrey, Mark, Rhonda Church; *ed:* Gods Bible Coll (AB) Tchng 1960; Defiance Coll (BA) Tchng 1974; Mt St Joseph (MA) Tchng 1989; IN Purdue at Ft Wayne 15 Hrs; *cr:* Paulding Exp Village Schls 2nd Grd Tchr 21 Yrs; *ai:* NEA, OEA, PEA 1975-; Church 1955-, Sunday Schl Tchr, Bible Schl Dir, Yth Dir, Jr Church Dir; *home:* 24548 Rd 207 Oakwood OH 45873

SPANIER, MARK RICHARD, English Teacher; *b:* New York, NY; *m:* Shari Gross; *ed:* Univ of Hartford (BA) Eng 1977; Adelphi Univ (MA) Eng 1986; *cr:* Freeport HS Eng Tchr 1987-; *ai:* Yrbk Adv.

SPANNER-MORROW, MINERVA, Spanish Teacher; *b:* Aruba Antilles, Netherlands; *m:* Todd A. Morrow; *c:* Alaun Morrow, Etienne Morrow; *ed:* Franciscan Univ of Steubenville (BA) Span Theology 1989, (MS) Educl Admin 1996; 7-12 Span Sec Teach Cert; *cr:* Jefferson Cty Mental Hlth Ctr Drug, Alcohol Awareness, Act Coord 1989; Franciscan Univ of Steubenville Admissions Cnslr 1990-91, Span Lecturer 1994; Steubenville HS Span Tchr 1992-; *ai:* Span Club, Y Teens Fac Adv; Black His Comm; NEA, OEA, NAATSP 1992-; AKA 1990-, VP; *office:* Steubenville HS 420 N 4th St Steubenville OH 43952*

SPANOS, JOE JAMES, Business & Technology Teacher; *b:* Hartford, CT; *ed:* Univ of Lowell (BS) Bus Admin 1976; Simmons Coll (MS) Ed 1983; 60 Credits Beyond Masters Degree in Bus & Tech Field; *cr:* Greater Lowell Regnl Bus Tchr 1976-77; Hesser Coll Bus Instr 1985-87; Unique Gifts & Jewelry By Joe N. Andy Jewelry & Gift Shop Owner 1985-94; Andover HS Bus, Tech Tchr 1977-; *ai:* TV Production Coord; Radio Club, Business Club, ABC Adv; Mrktg Club Adv 1977-; Jr Var & Var Hockey Coach; Hlth & Fitness Instr; Co-Adv for Schl Store; Building Rep for Fac; Faciliator of Concerts & Shows; MTA 1977-; AEA 1977-, Clerical; Tchr of Yr 1989; *office:* Andover HS Shawsheen Rd Andover MA 01810

SPARACCIO, KATHLEEN MALONE, English Teacher; *b:* Rockville Centre, NY; *m:* Salvatore P.; *c:* Salvatore, Nicholas, Luke; *ed:* Molloy Coll (BA) Eng, Ed 1981; Adelphi Univ (MS) Rdng 1988; *cr:* Maria Regina DHS Eng Tchr 1984-; Nassau Comm Coll Rdng Tchr 1986-; *office:* Holy Trinity HS 98 Cherry Ln Hicksville NY 11801

SPARE, MARGARET ANN, Sixth Grade Teacher; *b:* Cincinnati, OH; *ed:* Beaver Coll (BA) Eng 1956; 15 Grad Credits Ed Temple Univ, Glassboro St Tchrs Coll; *cr:* Millville MS 6th Grd Tchr 1961; Troy Ave MS 6th Grd Tchr 1962-71; Mullica MS 6th Grd Tchr 1978-; *ai:* Various Curr Dev Comms; NEA, NJEA 1961-; MTEA 1978-; Alateen Groups Spon; NJ Governors Tchr Recognition Awd 1991; William Carlos Williams Poetry Awd 1978.

SPARGO, ROBERT BROOK, Ret Instrumental Music Teacher; *b:* Westerly, RI; *m:* Carol A. Hutchings; *c:* Stephen R., Brian T., Sherrie A.; *ed:* Boston Univ (BM) Music Ed 1959; Univ of RI (ME) Ed 1971; *cr:* Rochester NH Schls Instrumental Music Tchr 1959-60; Charitto Regnl Schl Vocal, Instrumental Music Tchr 1960-66; Westerly Pub Schls Instrumental Music Tchr 1966-69; Grotom Ct Pub Schls Instrumental Music Tchr 1969-95; *ai:* Cutler MS Adv, Advisee Comm; Curr Review Comm; NEA; CEA; GEA; MENC; Dunn's Corners Church, Bldg & Grounds Comm; Professionally Performed & Produced Rel & Original Trumpet Music Album to Raise Money for Local Shelter; *home:* 16 Plateau Rd Westerly RI 02891

SPARHAWK, HELEN SUSANNE, Second Grade Teacher; *b:* Akron, OH; *c:* Theresa Hockett, Judy Di Mascio, Cynthia Hannold; *ed:* Akron Univ (BA) Ed 1972; 155 Addl Post-Grad Hrs Ed Univ of Akron; *cr:* Lincoln Elem First & Second Grd Tchr 1972-77; Richardson Elem Schl First, Second, Third Grd Tchr 1977-; *ai:* Rdng, Soc Stud Selection Comms; Fac Advy; CFEA Rep; NEA, OEA 1972-; CFEA 1972-, Personal Growth, Svc; DKT Tchng Honorary 1977-; Kappa Kappa Gamma 1948-, Pres; 25 Yrs Tchng; *home:* 3423 E Prescott Cir Cuyahoga Falls OH 44223*

SPARKE, KAREN H., History Teacher; *b:* Cincinnati, OH; *m:* Greg; *c:* Paul; *ed:* (BS) Elem Ed 1972; 18 Addl Hrs; *cr:* Lockland Schl Tchr 1972-; *ai:* NEA 1972-, Bldg Rep.

SPARKS, CAROL COWDEN, English & Theater Teacher; *b:* Warren, OH; *m:* William Franklin; *c:* Bradley, Sharon, Brenda Fisher; *ed:* Muskingum Coll (BA) Speech, Theater 1957; Univ of Dayton 14 Quarter Hrs; Miami Univ 26 Semester Hrs; *cr:* Oakmont HS Speech, Eng Tchr 1959-61; New Carlisle MS Eng Tchr 1975-84; Tecumseh HS Eng, Theater Tchr 1984-; *ai:* Adv NHS; Mentor New Tchrs; NEA, OEA, TEA 1975-; Delta Kappa Gamma 1980-; Outstanding Clark Cty Tchr 1990; Martha Holden Jennings Scholar 1980; *home:* 1629 E Mile Rd Springfield OH 45503*

SPARKS, JOHN A., Bus Adm, Ec & Intnl Mngmt Chm; *b:* San Francisco, CA; *m:* Marion Malarkey; *c:* John Andrew, Elizabeth Lee; *ed:* Grove City Coll (BA) Ec 1966; Univ of MI Law Schl (JD) 1969; *cr:* HIllsdale Coll Chr Division of Eco & Bus Adm 1969-76; Grove City Coll 1976-; *ai:* Mercer Cty Bar, PA St Bar 1981-; St Bar MI 1969-; Grove City Area Schl 1994-, Bd Dir; Covenant Presbyn Church 1980-, Elder; Chavanne Fellow Baylor Univ; Freedoms Fnd Medal; *office:* Grove City Coll 100 Campus Dr Grove City PA 16127

SPARKS, JUDITH LENZE, 4th Grade Teacher; *b:* St Marys, PA; *m:* Bob L.; *ed:* OH St Univ (BS) Elem Ed 1975, (MA) Ed Admin 1982; *cr:* Queen of the World Schl 4th Grd Tchr 1959-62; St Mary's Parochial Schl 4th Grd Tchr 1964-65; St Gabriel Schl 7th Grd Tchr 1966-68; Our Lady of Perpetual Help Schl 3rd Grd Tchr 1968-69, 7th Grd Tchr 1969-72, 8th Grd Tchr 1972-82; Notre Dame Elem Schl Admin 1982-84; Our Lady of Perpetual Help Schl 5th Grd Tchr 1984-92, 4th Grd Tchr 1992-; *ai:* Chrldng Adv; CCD Tchr; CDEA 1968-, Pres; Diocese of Columbus 1968-, Outstdng Tchr of Yr 1985; OH St Alumni Assn 1975-.

SPARKS, MARIA CONSUELO, Professor of History; *b:* Lima, Peru; *ed:* Universidad Catolica (EDD) Philosphy 1968, (MA) Biling Ed 1971; Univ of Pittsburgh (PHD) His 1972; Universidad de Lima (MA) Ed Admin 1975; Univ of Pittsburg Cert Latin Amer Stud 1970; Amherst Hampshire Coll 5 Summers Peace & Security Stud; *cr:* Tchng & Admin Positions 1960-; Colegio F. A. P. Quiones Prin 1970-72; Colegio Villa Maria Peru Prin 1972-76; Cardinal Dougherty HS Tchr, Soc Stud Chair 1976-8 1; Immaculata Coll Prof 1981-; *ai:* Moderator Alpha Alpha Rho, Intnl Relations Soc; Tchr Ed Comm; LAAS 1969-; MACLAS 1977-, Bd; AAS 1990-; PSSC 1969-, Pres, Plaque; Consorcio Colegios Catolicos 1963-, Pres, Diploma; PACIE 1983-, Sec; Chester Cty Children Youth & Family 1990-, Bd; Fulbright Stud, Woodrow Wilson Fnd Rsrch Grant; Rep of Cath Church to Ed Law Reform Commission Peru 1974-76; Numerous Articles Pub; *office:* Immaculata Coll PO Box 726 Immaculata PA 19345

SPARNECHT, CHARLES ARTHUR, History Teacher; *b:* Freeport, NY; *m:* Camilla Hartwig; *c:* Michael, Katheryn; *ed:* SUNY Coll at Potsdam (BA) Pol Sci 1971; SUNY Coll at Brockport (MS) Ed Admin 1985; *cr:* Penfield HS Tchr 1974-; *ai:* Citizen Bee Adv; JV Golf Coach; Penfield Bapt Church, Bd of Deacons Chm, Pastoral Relations; Penfield Village Nursery Schl Bd of Dir Sec; Rockfeller Scholar; *office:* Penfield HS 25 High School Dr Penfield NY 14526

SPARROW, JAMES, History Teacher; *b:* Syracuse, NY; *m:* Kristin Bickley; *c:* Sara Bickley; *ed:* Hiram Coll (BA) His 1980; Case Western Reserve Univ (MA) His 1982; Courses to Receive Gifted Validation; *cr:* West Carrollton Schls His Tchr 1985-90, 1991-; US Army Soldier Desert Storm 1990-91; *ai:* Mock Trial; Acad Challenge; Speech & Debate; Jennings Scholar; Governors Awd OH Distinguished Citizen; Pres, West Carrollton Ed Assn; *office:* West Carrollton Sr HS 5833 Student St West Carrollton OH 45449*

SPARROW, SALLY WILSON, English Teacher; *b:* Bethlehem, PA; *m:* Ronald J.; *c:* Stacy, Rachel; *ed:* East Stroudsburg Univ (BS) Scndry Ed Eng 1966; PA Dept of Ed Masters Equivalency 1991; *cr:* Pleasant Vly Sr HS Eng Tchr 1966-68; Pocono Mountain Sr HS Eng Tchr 1968-70, 1981-; *ai:* Schlsp, Intensive Scheduling, Grading, Grad Comms; Stu Assistance TEam; NCTE; NEA; PA St Ed Assn; Pocono Mountain Ed Assn; Mountain Home Meth Church; Amer Heart Assn, Vol; Barrett Friendly Lib; PA Dept of Ed Bureau of Curr, Acad Svcs Recognition for New Stans Project; Gift of Time Tribute, PA Stu Assistance Prgm Awds; *office:* Pocono Mountain Sr HS Box 200 School Rd Swiftwater PA 18370

SPATARO, OLIMPIA, Chemistry & Phys Sci Teacher; *b:* New York ; *c:* Joseph, Linda Dorniteim, Diana Irizorry, Cristina; *ed:* Hunter Coll (BA) Pre Mid, Biochemistry, Ed 1958; Adelphi Univ (MS) Bio 1972; NY Univ)MS) Chem 1973; Post Grad Bio 1973-75; *cr:* Aviation HS Chem, Phys Sci Tchr 1959-63; Elander Childs HS Chem, Phys, Bio Tchr 1964-; *office:* Evander Childs HS 800 E Gun Hill Rd New York NY 10467

SPATZ, ROBERT ALAN, Mathematics Teacher; *b:* Reading, PA; *m:* Rochelle Myers; *c:* Karen, Lisa, James; *ed:* Kutztown St (BS) Math, Sec Ed 1974; West Chester Univ (MA) Math 1978; 30 Post Grad Hrs Math, Cmptrs; *cr:* Upper Dublin HS Math Tchr 1974-; *ai:* Math Team Spon; UDEA, PSEA, NEA 1974-; Medal Winner Top Tchr; Philadelphia Sci Cncl Awd Winner; *office:* Upper Dublin HS 800 Loch Alsh Ave Fort Washington PA 19034

SPAZIANO, CAROL ANN, Math Teacher; *b:* Warwick, RI; *m:* John G.; *c:* Carrie; *ed:* RI Coll (BA) Math 1974, (MED) Instrl Tech 1979; 16 Misc Post Grad Credit Hrs; *cr:* Comm Coll of RI Math Technician 1974-77, Math Instr 1980-; Coventry HS Math Tchr 1977-; *ai:* AFT 1977-, Bldg Rep; RI Math Tchrs 1995-; *home:* 1167 Greenwich Ave Warwick RI 02886*

SPEAR, SUSAN H., Fourth Grade Teacher; *b:* Norwalk, CT; *m:* George P.; *c:* Susan S. Sneathen, William D.; *ed:* Cntrl CT St Univ (BS) Elem Ed 1956; Southern CT St Univ (MA) Elem Ed 1980; Addl 50 CEU's; Univ of AZ Mid Winter Conf; *cr:* Walnut Beach Schl Kndgtn Tchr 1956-57; Kay Ave Schl 1st Grd Tchr 19575-8; Sliney Schl 5th Grd Tchr 1980-82, 4th Grd Tchr 1983-90; Branford Hills Schl 1st Grd Tchr 1982-83; Mary T. Murphy Schl 3-4th Grd Tchr 1990-93; *ai:* Lang Arts Curr & Authentic Assessment Comms; Math Cadre; Interview Team; Goals 2000 Team; Schl Imprvmnt Cncl; Soc Stud Curr Team; NEA, CEA, BEA, IRA, CRA, NCTE, CCTE 1980-; NCTM 1990-; WLU 1990-, Ambassador Corps Chair; Blackstone Lib 1963-, Trustee; Br D. Cong Church 1965-, Schlsp Comm, Sec; IRA Publication Article Pub; BFD Bd of Ed 3 RAH Awds; St Dept of Ed & SNET Celeb of Excl, Awd of Merit; Presenter at Confs & Wkshps; *home:* 41 Brookhills Rd Branford CT 06405*

SPEAR, SYLVIA NILES, English Teacher; *b:* Lewiston, ME; *m:* Charles E. Jr.; *c:* Christopher Scott, Keith Allan; *ed:* Univ of ME (BSEd) Eng, Speech 1964; 12 Credit Hrs Toward MFA Vermont Coll; *cr:* Northampton Schl System Jr HS Eng Tchr 1964-66; US Army GED Instr 1966-67; Clinton Elem Schl Rdng Tchr 1976-85; Lawrence HS Eng Tchr 1985-; *ai:* Amnesty Intnl Adv; 7-12 Grd AIDS Comm; PEER Mediation Comm; NEA, ME Ed Assn 1985-, Exec Bd Mem, Bldg Rep; Order of Eastern Star 1965-, Organist, 25 Yr Pin; Universalist, Unitarian of Waterville 1990-; Cert of Recognition for Contribution to Tri-St Chptr I Practioners Sourcebook of Effective Educl Practices; *office:* Lawrence HS MSAD #49 School St Fairfield ME 04937

SPEARRY, ALBERTA, Retired Teacher; *b:* Scioto Cty, OH; *w:* Vaughn (dec); *c:* Marci S. Smith, Deena A. Crinnion; *ed:* OH Univ (BS) His, Govt, Eng 1965; 32 Addl Sem Hrs; *cr:* Vly Intermediate 7th Grd Eng 1964-69; Vly HS 9th, 11th Grd Eng Tchr 1969-70; Nauvoo Elem 7th-8th Grd Soc Stud, Eng Tchr 1970-92; *ai:* OH Retired Tchrs Assoc 1992-; AARP 1990-; *home:* 2545 Argonne Rd Portsmouth OH 45662

SPEARS, JEFFREY WILLIAM, High School Art Teacher; *b:* Xenia, OH; *m:* Connie Lynne Hughes; *c:* Nicholas, Erin, Jenna; *ed:* Morehead St (BA) PE, Art 1977; Wright St (ME) Admin 1991; Addl 30 Hrs Hold Prin, Asst Prin, Asst Supt, Supt Cert; *cr:* Miami Trace HS Art Tchr 1977-95; *ai:* Art Club, Sr Class Adv; *office:* Miami Trace HS 3722 State Route 41 NW Washington Court H OH 43160*

SPEARS, PAMELA ANN, 4th Grade Teacher; *b:* Columbus, OH; *m:* Herschel Allen; *c:* Jennifer Lynn Davis; *cr:* OH Dept of Ed Sec 1971-76; OH Bureau of Workers Compensation Sec 1977-78; OH Dept of Mental Hlth Admin Asst 1979-86; South-Western City Schls Tchr 1987-; *ai:* Bldg Curr Comm; Schl Bell Awd 1989-91, 1994-95; Cert of Excl 1993-94; Ambassador Awd 1994-95; *office:* Stiles Elem Schl 4700 Stiles Ave Columbus OH 43228

SPECIALE, LAURIE, English Teacher; *ed:* Geneseo St Univ (BA) Eng, Amer Civilization 1977; Elmira Coll (MA) Eng Ed 1983; *cr:* Notre Dame HS Eng Tchr 1978-92; Thomas A. Edison HS Eng Tchr 1992-; *ai:* Goals 2000 Participant; Schl to Work Comm; NEA 1992-; *office:* Thomas A. Edison HS 2083 College Ave Elmira Heights NY 14903

SPECK, MARILYN PIERCE, Sixth Grade Teacher; *b:* Cleveland, OH; *w:* Joseph E. (dec); *c:* Kelly S. Neumeister, Stacy S. Vigh; *ed:* Bowling Green St Univ (BSED) Elem Ed 1958; Baldwin Wallace Grad Stud; *cr:* Brookridge Elem Schl Fourth Grd Tchr 1958-62, Sixth Grd Tchr 1969-, Lang Arts Specialist; *ai:* Schl Newspaper, Lit Magazine Adv; WVIZ-TV Poetry-Cmptr Forum Co-Adv; Co-Tchr Inclusion Prgm; Outdoor Ed Prgm Supvr; Bldg Cncl; NEA, OEA 1958-; BEA 1958-, Sec; Delta Kappa Gamma 1972-, Sec, 2nd VP; Kappa Delta 1955-, Sec; St Bd of Ed Bicentennial Awd; Martha Holden Jennings Gifted, Talented Prgm Awd; Mohican Schl in Out-of-Doors Achvmt Awd; *office:* Brookridge Elem Schl 4500 Ridge Rd Brooklyn OH 44144

SPECTOR, JOYCE ANN, 4th Grade Teacher; *b:* Brooklyn, NY; *m:* Stanley; *c:* Caroline, Stephanie; *ed:* Brooklyn Coll (BA) ED 1973, (MS) Spec Ed 1977; 30 Addl Hrs; *cr:* PS 5R Tchr 1986-; *ai:* Bowling League; AFT, UFT 1986-.

SPEDDING, RICHARD DAVID, 6th Grade Teacher; *b:* Worcester, MA; *m:* Carol Ann Comeau; *c:* Daniel M., Christine J. Stratton; *ed:* Worcester St Coll (BS) Elem Ed 1965, (MS) Elem Ed 1973, (CAGS) Pub Achl Admn 1976; Harvard Univ Summer Institute 1990 12 Hrs; *cr:* Woodland St Schl 5th Grd Tchr 1965-66; USAF Capt 1966-70; St Nicholas Ave Schl 6th Grd Tchr 1970-87; MIllbury St Schl 6th Grd Tchr 1987-; *ai:* Dir Schl, Comm Garden; NEA, Ed Assoc of Worcester 1965-; Thomas Jefferson Awd for Outstdng Svc 1995; Worcester Alliance for Ed Grant 1993; Worcester Hiatt Grant 1993 for Schl Comm Garden; *office:* Millbury Street Elem Schl 389 Millbury St Worcester MA 01610*

SPEED, CAROLYN WHITE, English Teacher; *b:* Tallahassee, FL; *m:* Samuel G.; *c:* Erinn C., Michael A.; *ed:* Bowling Green St Univ (BS) Scndry Ed Eng 1973; Cleveland St Univ (MED) Curr, Instr 1987; *cr:* Addison Jr HS Eng Tchr 1973-75; Patrick Henry Jr HS Eng Tchr 1976-79; Charles Mooney Jr HS Eng Tchr 1980, 1984; Collinwood HS Eng Tchr 1982-; *ai:* Jr Class, Yrbk Adv; Fellow Chrstn Assn Co-Adv; AFT 1973-; NAACP; Delta Sigma Theta 1969-, Chaplain 1993-; Metro-Cabse Inspirational Tchr 1995; *office:* Collinwood HS 15210 Saint Clair Ave Cleveland OH 44110

SPEER, SHARON ELIZABETH, Univ & Comprehensive Eng Tchr; *b:* Washington, DC; *ed:* Frostburg St Coll (BA) Psych, Eng 1973; Bowie St Coll (MED) Psych, Guid, Cnslng 1976; Attnd WA Schl Psychiatry 1990; *cr:* Westernport Elem Schl Spec Ed Tchr 1973; Suitland HS Soc Stud, Eng Tchr 1973-91; Prince George's Comm Coll Part-time Psych Instr 1981-91; Laurel HS Univ, Comprehensive Eng Tchr 1991-; *ai:* Spon Frosh Class 1991-92; Co-Coached It's Acad Team 1993-94; Chaperoned NY Hair Show Field Trip 1994-95; Proofread Mid Sts Evaluation 1983-84; Psych Curr Guide 1975; NEA, MSTA, PGCEA 1985-; PTSA, APA, APA Division II 1973-; Cancer Soc Collector 1967-; *office:* Laurel HS 8000 Cherry Ln Laurel MD 20707*

SPEICHER, DENISE CULVER, English Teacher; *b:* Seaford, DE; *m:* Daryl Everett; *c:* Danielle, Joanna; *ed:* Salisbury St Univ (BA) Eng Ed 1987; Univ of DE 30 Addl Hrs Toward MA; *cr:* Delmar Jr Sr HS 7th Grd Eng Tchr 1987-91, 10th Grd Eng Tchr 1991-; *ai:* Drama Coach; St Comms; Gen Regulations Review; Revocation Review, Ldrshp Acad Mentoring, Tchr Standards, Embedded Assessment Comms; NEA, DSEA, DEA 1987-; Phi Kappa Phi 1984-; Lombda Iota Tau 1986-; Delmars Tchr of Yr 1992-93; DE Eng, Lang Arts Curr Frameworks Comm 1992-95.*

SPEICHER, JUDY L., Home Economics Teacher; *b:* Massillon, OH; *m:* Loren Matey; *c:* Jacob Matey; *ed:* Ashland Univ (BS) Fashion Merch & Home Ec 1984, (MED) Curr & Instruction 1992; *cr:* DeVry Inst of Tech Stu Svcs 1988-90; Plymouth Local Schls MS Home Ec Tchr 1990-91; Buckeye Joint Voc Schl Child Care Instr 1991-92; Tuslaw Jr & Sr High Home Ec Tchr 1992-; *ai:* Yrbk Co-Adv; FHA; NEA & OEA 1987-; Stark Cty Home Ec Assn 1992-; *office:* Tuslaw HS 1723 Manchester Ave NW Massillon OH 44647

SPEIDEL, BYRON D., Science Tchr & Dept Coord; *b:* Philadelphia, PA; *m:* Lizabeth R. Williams; *c:* Kimberly R.; *ed:* East Stroudsburg Univ (BS) Bio, Ed 1964; Glassboro St Coll (MA) Environmental Ed 1975; Supervision Cert 1980; Trenton St Coll Addl Grad Stud; *cr:* Tunkhanneck HS Bio Tchr 1964-66; Marlton MS Life Sci Tchr 1966-69; T. E. Harrington MS Life Sci Tchr, Dept Head 1969-; *ai:* NEA 1964-; NJEA 1966-; Nom Governors Recognition Prgm 1989-91; *office:* Thomas E Harrington MS 514 Mount Laurel Rd Mount Laurel NJ 08054

SPEIGHT, MARTHA M., US History Teacher; *b:* Walstonburg, NC; *ed:* Fayetteville St Univ (BS) Soc Sci 1979; *ai:* Yrbk Spon; Served on Numerous Comms; Female Mentoring Odssesy of the Mind, Team Ldr 6 Yrs; Schl Ldr; NEA 1979-; PGCEA 1979-; MSTA 1983-; Lib Asst, Lib Awd; Adult Ed Coord 1985-93, Comm Coord; 4-H Club 1975-79, Pres, Presidential Awd; Church Treas 1970-75, Meth Awd; *office:* Thurgood Marshall MS 4909 Brinkley Rd Temple Hills MD 20748

SPELLMAN, KATHLEEN ANN, Social Stud Dept Chairperson; *b:* New York, NY; *m:* John M.; *c:* Kathleen, Christine; *ed:* St Johns Univ (BS) Soc Stud 1969; Queen Coll (MS) Soc Stud 1972; *ai:* Prom Moderator; NCA 1980-.

SPELLMAN, MARLIN JAMES, Business Ed & Soc Stud Teacher; *b:* Meadville, PA; *m:* Barbara L. Beitler; *c:* Amy Blanford, Kirstin Kennedy Poling, Mark, Matthew, Erika Kennedy; *ed:* Kent St Univ (BS) Soc Stud & Bus Ed 1965, (MA) Bus Ed 1971; Attnd Univ of Dayton, Edinboro Univ of PA; *cr:* Shaw HS Bus Ed 1965-66, Pymatuning Valley HS Bus Ed & Soc Stud Tchr 1966-; Kent St Univ Asst Prof Office Mgmt & Related Tech 1971-; *ai:* Sr Class, Stu cncl Advs; Phi Alpha Theta, Kappa Delta Pi, Pi Omega Pi 1965-, Ed Honoraries; Pymatuning Valley Ed Assn 1966-, Pres, Sec & Treas; Ashtabula Cty Ed Assn 1966-, Pres, Sec, Del to NEA; OEA, NEA 1965-; Chapel in Marlboro 1993-; Pathfinders 4-H Club 1979-, Adv; Andover Church of Christ 1983-, Deacon, Tchr, Choir; Singles Together Acheiving Faith & Fellowship 1983-, Exec Comm Tchr; Golden Apple Awd; Instr A Presidentail Classroom for Young Amer; Tchr Gifted Stdnts Prgm; Curr Dev Comm Bus Ed; Prgm Asst Ashtabula Cty 4-H Clubs; OH Rep on Alumni Bd of Presidentl Classroom for Young Amers; *office:* Pymatuning Valley Schl US Rt 6 W Andover OH 44003*

SPELMAN, KEVIN LANE, Advanced Placement Ec Tchr; *b:* Bayshore, NY; *m:* Laurie K. Burke-Spelman; *c:* Vanessa, Corey, Matthew; *ed:* Villanova Univ (BA) Ed 1971; Adelphi Univ (MBA) Mngmt 1987; Fin Planning Cert 1990; *cr:* Sachem HS North Soc Stud Tchr 1972-; *ai:* Boys Var Track, Cross Cntry Coach 1972-80; Girls Var Track Asst Coach 1984-86; Black His Month Coord; Sachem Cntrl Tchrs Org 1980-93, Bldg Rep; Yth Soccer Coach 1989-; Little League Mgr 1993-; Selected as Reader for AP Ec Exam by Coll Bd.

SPENCE, ANN, High School English Teacher; *b:* Bronx, NY; *c:* William, Robert, MIchael, Laura; *ed:* St Johns Univ (MA) Eng 1990; 6 Credits Non Matriculataed PHD SUNY at Stonybrook; *cr:* NY Bd of Ed PS 42 5th Grd Tchr 1 Yr; NY Bd of Ed PS 162 5th Grd Tchr 1 Yr; NY Bd of Ed Francis Lewis HS Eng Tchr 6 Months; NY Bd of Ed Far Rockaway HS Eng Tchr 6 Yrs; *ai:* AFT 1990-; Bayville Chamber of Commerce 1971-90 Chprsn of Various Comms, Adhvmt Awd; Village of Bayville Awd for Comm Svcs; Hospice of Westbury Awd for Vol Work; *office:* Far Rockaway HS Carnaga Ave Far Rockaway NY 11961

SPENCE, ANN HARKRIDER, 6th Grade Teacher; *b:* Chicago, IL; *m:* Steven D.; *c:* Jay Harkrider, Brad Harkrider; *ed:* Univ of Houston (BS) Elem Ed & Psych 1977; *cr:* Big Walnut MS 6th Grd Tchr 6 Yrs; Spring Branch Elem 5th Grd Tchr 2 Yrs; Ridgecrest Elem 3rd Grd Tchr 2 Yrs; *ai:* Stu Cncl Adv; NEA 1989-; BWEA 1989-; Ruth Jennings Scholar 1995; *home:* 4940 Dublin Rd Dublin OH 43017

SPENCE, CORINNE LAFRENIER, Computer Facilitator; *b:* Lawrence, MA; *m:* Richard M.; *c:* Christopher; *ed:* Bridgewater St Coll (BA) Chemical Physics 1966; Lowell St Coll (MED) Scndry Admin 1971; 60 Grad Credits; *cr:* Methuen Jr HS Sci Tchr 1967-75; Tenney MS Sci Tchr 1975-91; Methuen MS Cmptr Facilitator 1991-; MA St Coll Grad Schl Cmptr Sci Instr 1991-95; *ai:* Tech Comm; Schl Cncl; Schl Newspaper Ed; PTO; In-Svc Instr; NEA 1967-; Methuen Ed Assn 1967-, Sick Leave Pool Chprsn; Boston Cmptr Soc 1991-; ASCD 1990-; Order of Eastern Star 1967-, Worthy Matron; Rainbow Girls 1967-, Advy Bd; Salem Strategic Planner 1988-; Horace Mann Grant; Outstdng Scndry Edctr of Amer 1973; Tchr of Month 1984; *office:* Methuen Schl Dist 75 Pleasant St Methuen MA 01844

SPENCE, GERRY, Technology Ed Teacher; *b:* Trenton, NJ; *c:* Sarah; *ed:* Trenton St Coll (BA) Industrial Ed 1968, (MED) Ind Ed & Supervison 1972; Rider Coll (MA) Admin 1980; *cr:* Northern Burl Cty Regnl HS Tchr & Stu Adv 28 Yrs; *ai:* Stu Cncl, Drama Stage Set Dir & Tech & Musical Stage Dir & Tech Adv; NEA & NJEA 1968-; TEANJ 1989-; Crosswicks Comm Assn 1987-, Trustee; Free Masons of NJ 1989-, Worshipful Master 1996; Scottish Rite Of N Amer 1990-, Production Staff; Shriners 1990-, Dirs Staf; York Rite of N Amer 1993-, Sec; Ch, Cncl & Commandery; Sciots 1995; Chesterfield Twp Comm Svc Awd 1984; *office:* N Burlington Co Reg Jr/Sr HS Mansfield Rd Columbus NJ 08022*

SPENCE, JOANNE FRANCES, Fifth Grade Teacher; *b:* Lynn, MA; *ed:* Salem St Coll (BS) Elem Ed 1967; Cntrl CT St Univ (MS) Gen Elem ED 1975; Addl 60 Credit Hrs; *cr:* Smith Schl 4th Grd Tchr 1967-68, 5th Grd Tchr 1967-86; Gaffney Schl 3rd Grd Tchr 1986-94, 4-5th Grd Tchr 1994-95, 5th Grd Tchr 1995-, 1986-; *ai:* Report Card Revision, Soc Stud Curr, Sci Curr, Search Comms; Math, Sci Coord; Math Ldrshp Inst; AFT 1967-; Farmington Democratic Town Comm 1991-, Habitat for Hum 1993; Charter Revision Commission 1996; *home:* 24 Farmington Chase Cres Farmington CT 06032

SPENCE, LINDA SAMUELSON, 7th Grd Health & PE Ed Teacher; *b:* Jamestown, NY; *m:* Robert A.; *c:* Crystal Spence-Lewis, Erik; *ed:* E Stroudsburg Univ (BS) Hlth, PE 1967; *cr:* Hazleton Area Schl Dist Tchr 1967-; *ai:* Jr, Sr HS Cheerleading Coach; Jr HS Bsktbl Coach; Act 78 Comm; Stud Assistance Prgm; Individual Support Team; PSEA, NEA 1967-; *office:* Hazleton Jr HS 700 N Wyoming St Hazleton PA 18201

SPENCER, ALLISON BLAIR, Science Teacher; *b:* Cincinnati, OH; *m:* Eugene; *c:* Kelsey, Keith; *ed:* Bucknell Univ (BS) Bio 1979; 24 Grad Credits in Ed; *cr:* Berwick Jr High Sci Tchr 1979-88; Berwick HS Sci Tchr 1989-; *ai:* NEA 1979-; Danville LWV 1992-, Treas; Danville 4-H 1993-, Entomology Ldr; Cub Scouts 1994-, Asst Den Ldr; Trinity Univte Meth Church 1990-, Sunday Schl Supt; Berwick Jaycees Outstanding Young Educator 1992; Nom for Natl PTA Outstanding Educator 1993; *office:* Berwick Area Sr HS 1100 Fowler Ave Berwick PA 18603

SPENCER, JILL, Teacher; *b:* Newton, MA; *ed:* Univ of ME (BA) Pol Sci 1968, (MED) Mid Level Ed 1991; Drake Univ Grad Hrs in His; Univ of Southern ME Grad Hrs in Eng & Ed; *cr:* MT Ararat Schl Tchr 1973-; *ai:* Odyssey of the Mind Coach; Facilitator Curr Design Team; ME Assn of Mid Level Ed 1988-, Bd of Dir, Mid Level Ldr of the Yr 1992; NMSA 1990-; NEA, ASCD & ME Cncl for Eng Lang Arts; Articles Pub; Tchr Consultant Prof Dev Ctr Univ of S ME; Presenter at St & Natl Mid Level Confs; *office:* MT Ararat MS Spring St Brunswick ME 04011

SPENCER, JO ANN JONES, Guidance Counselor; *b:* Hampstead, NC; *m:* Richard Edward; *ed:* Fayetteville St Univ (BS) Elem Ed 1968; Univ of WI (MS) Guid, Cnslng 1973; Attnd Loyola Univ, Johns Hopkins Univ; *cr:* Perryville Elem Schl Tchr 1968-72; Univ of WI Dormitory Dir 1973; Southampton MS Resource Tchr 1973-75; Bakerfield Elem Scl Cnslr 1975-81; Edgewood MS 1981-86; *ai:* Minority Stu Suppo Spon; Pupil Svc Team Chprsn; Eligibility, Schl Ldrshp, SBDIM United Tchng Assn 1964-; MD Assn of Cnslng & Dev 1973-; Harf Assn of Cnslng & Dev 1973-, Pres; NAACP 1968-, Treas; *office:* H Grace HS 700 Congress Ave Havre De Grace MD 21078

SPENCER, KAREN ALLEN, 5-6th Grade Elementary Teac Brookline, MA; *m:* David A.; *ed:* Univ of VT (BSEd) Elem ed K- Miami Univ (MED) Elem K-8 Rdng Concent 1980; Attnd Univ of Wright St Univ; *cr:* Mc Guffey Lab Schl Grad Tchr 3-6 Grd 1 Broadmoor Acad 5-6 Grd Tchr 1980-; *ai:* Hlth Bk Adoption Comm Bd Mem; NEA, OEA 1980-; Sylvan Learning Ctr, Asst Dir; Tchr of *office:* Broadmoor Acad 701 E Main St Trotwood OH 45426

SPENCER, KATHLEEN RACZKA, Cheerleading Coach; *b:* Man NH; *m:* Troy Laberton; *ed:* Univ of NH (BS) Bus Admin 19 Automatic Data Processing Sales Rep 1993-95; US Healthcare Mrk 1995-; *ai:* Chrldng Coach; *home:* 28 Golfview Dr Manchester NH

SPENCER, MARCIA CARPENTER, Social Studies Teacher; *b:* CO; *m:* Edward L.; *c:* Dorothy; *ed:* CO Coll (BA) His 1971; Ya (MA) His 1973; Tchr Cert Notre Dame Coll; Plymouth St Coll, Univ at Farmington Ed Courses; *cr:* Mountain House Schl Soc Stu 1980-82; Newport Jr, Sr HS 7th Grd Tchr 1989-90; Stevens HS S Tchr 1990-95; Sunapee Mid HS Soc Stud Tchr 1995-; *ai:* Dist S Curr Comm; NH Soc Stud Content Comm; Soph Class Ad Geographic Alliance 1990-, Tchr, Consultant, NHEA 1990-; NEA Natl Cnl for Geog Ed 1994-; NCSS, Natl Cncl for His Ed 199 Historical Soc 1995-; Instrl Ldrshp Inst, Natl Geog Soc 1995; ARGJ Exch Hiroshima Japan 1995; St Farm Awd winner 1995; Governor Merrill Awd 1993; Author Two Soc Sci Articles; *office:* Sunapee M 10 North St Sunapee NH 03782

SPENCER, RALPH S., Fifth Grade Teacher; *b:* Springfield, Lachelle D.; *ed:* Norfolk St Coll (BS) Elem Ed 1973; *cr:* East Linde Schl Tchr 1973-; *ai:* Cols Recreation Dept; Safety Patrol Adv; Fi Chprsn; NEA, OEA, COTA, CEA 1973-; Masons 1977-; Shriners Elks 1981-; *office:* East Linden Elem Schl 2500 Perdue Ave Columb 43211*

SPENCER, REX LEROY, Social Studies Tchr & Dept C Kendallville, IN; *m:* Diana Carole Land; *c:* Katie Jo, Emily Pai Defiance Coll (BS) Soc Stud Comprehensive 1966; Ball St Univ Amer His 1970; Post Grad Hrs in Amer His & Anthropology 1980- Ansonia HS Soc Stud Tchr 1966-80; Ansonia MS Soc Stud Tchr 19 Edison St Comm Coll Adjunct Fac 1983-88; Ansonia HS Soc Stu 1986-; Defiance Coll Adjunct Fac 1989-92; *ai:* Staff Dev Comm M Hoc Comm for Restructuring the Curr Prgms Mem; Lands End U Cncl Mem; NEA, OH Cncl for Soc Stu & NCSS 1982-; OH Ed Assn AEA Treas 1986-; Barber Shop Harmony Soc 1990-, Chapter Church Admin Board 1981-; Whos Who Amer Ed 1993; Dar Outstanding Amer His Tchr 1992; Dist Tchr of Yr 1989; 2nd Pl BP Prgm for Ec Ed 1988; 4th Pl in Natl Joint Cncl for Ec Ed Prgm 1988; Who in the World 1994; *office:* Ansonia HS 200 W Canal Anson 45303*

SPENCER, RITA A., High School Science Teacher; *b:* Youngstow *ed:* Gallaudet Univ (BA) Bio 1971; Western MD Coll (MED) Deafness 1975; Attnd Sangamon St Univ, OK St Univ; *cr:* MD Schl Deaf MS Sci Tchr 1972-80, HS Sci Tchr 1980-; *ai:* NHS Adv; Astronauts; Space Camp Coord; NSTA; AFT; MAST; NFSD Outstdng Mem Aed 1983; GUAA 1973-; NEWMAST 1992 Goddard Flight Ctr Summer Inst; *office:* Maryland Schl For The Deaf 101 Cl PO Box 250 Frederick MD 21705

SPERANZA, EUGENE A., Drafting Teacher; *b:* McDonald, PA; *m:* R. Mountain; *ed:* PA St Univ (BS) Landscape Architecture 1968; U Pittsburgh (ME) Voc Ed 1983; *cr:* Gateway Inst of Tech Drafting, Tchr 1968-71; Triangle Inst of Tech Drafting, Math Tchr 1975-81; Pa West AVTS Drafting Tchr 1981-; Comm Coll of Allegheny Cty Part CAD Tchr 1985-; *ai:* Parkway West Fed of Tchrs 1981-, Sec, VP, AFT 1981-; McDonald Lions Club 1976-, Pres, Treas, VP; *office:* Pa West Area Voc Tech Sch 7101 Steubenville Pike Oakdale PA 15071

SPERGEL, MARTIN, Physics Professor; *b:* New York, NY; *m:* Ro Leffert; *c:* David, Jonathan, Lauren; *ed:* Rensselear Polytechnic Physics 1959; Univ of Rochester (MA) Physics 1960, (PHD) Physics *cr:* Grumman Aerospace Corp Rsrch Scientist 1963-67; York Coll P Physics 1967-; Brookhaven Nat Lab Visiting Scientist 1975-; Regen Prof of Physics 1990-; *ai:* Amer Phys Soc 1957-; Prof Staff Union 1964-; Amer Geophy Union 1969-; Amer Assoc for Adv of Sci 1975- Coll Spirit Awd & Outstdng Achvmt Awd; Grants From NSF, NASA Inst of Hlth, Sloan Fndtn & Dept of Ed; Numerous Articles, Report Numerous Prof Presentations; *office:* City Univ Of NY York Coll Guy Brewer Blvd Jamaica NY 11451

SPERINO, DAVID MICHAEL, English Teacher; *b:* Fairport, N Nora D.; *c:* Kelli Pease, Traci, Michael; *ed:* SUNY at Geneseo (B 1970; Permanent Cert in 7-12 Grd Eng; Grad Hrs in Drug & Al Cnslng; *cr:* York Cntrl Schl Eng Dept Chm 1970-; *ai:* Asst Var Ftbl C Co-Adv Schl Newspaper; Co-chair Stu Support Team; Eng Dept NYSUT; AFT; Univ of Rochester Excl in Scndry Tchng Awd 19 1992.*

SPERLING, ELISABETH ESTHER, History Teacher; *b:* New York *ed:* Harvard & Radcliffe Colls (BA) Russian & Soviet Stud 1987; Colu Univ Tchrs Coll (MA) Soc Stud Ed 1992; Pushkin Inst Moscow US Semester Cert 1985; *cr:* Scarsdale HS Stu Tchr & Sub Tchr 1989; H Mann Schl His Tchr & Assoc Dean 1990-; *ai:* Union to Amnesty In 10th Grd Class Adv; Valuing Differences Comm; ASCD 1996; ATIS Amnesty Intnl 1994-; Woodrow Wilson Natl Flwshp Fndtn Summer I World His; Klingenstein Flwshp for Acad Yr 1996-97; *office:* Horace Schl 231 W 246th St Bronx NY 10471

SPERO, ANN SHALOUM, Retired Elem Computer Teacher; *b:* New City, NY; *m:* Victor E.; *c:* Eric, Bryan; *ed:* Hunter (BA) Sci, Ed 1959, Sci, Ed 1963; Admin, Supervision St John's Univ 1970; Rdng Manh Coll 1965; Cmptr Queens TAC, IS 74 Summer Schl; *cr:* PS 18 Classroom Tchr 1960-64; PS 57 Schl Classroom, Rdng Tchr 1964-6 21 Schl Classroom Tchr 1978-83, 1983-95.*

SPERRAZZA, MICHAEL JAMES, Drama Director; *b:* Bronx, NY Univ of Evansville (BS) Commnctn 1987; New Schl (MFA) Media *cr:* Passaic Vly Regnl HS Drama Dir 1989-; Bergan Comm Coll Ad 1995-; *ai:* Drama Club Adv; Field Trips to Theatre & Overseas Travel; Ace Productions Film Dir, Writer & Producer; *office:* Passaic Valle 100 E Main St Little Falls NJ 07424

SPESSARD, CAROL SUE (ANDREWS), French Teacher; *b:* Colum OH; *m:* Ronald Miles; *c:* Heather Anne, Heidi Alison, Richard Andr *ed:* Otterbein Coll of OH (BA) Fr, Ed 1968; Wright St of OH (MA 1988; Jr Yr Abroad At Univ of Strasbourg France 1966-67; 1 Credit Ashland Coll Summer 1995; 1-2 CEU Every Yr 1988-; *cr:* Masson J Fr, Eng Tchr 1968-69; Providence HS Eng Tchr 1969-70; Benjamin L HS Fr, Eng, Latin 1970-72; Fairbanks HS Sub Tchr 1979-85; Triad H II Survey 1985-86; Benjamin Logan HS Fr I-V 1988-; *ai:* Fr Club, Club Adv; Take STus to France for Homestay, Travel tour; NEA, C

, 1968-; BLEA 1968-, Bldg Rep; Kappa Delta Pi 1988-; ASCD 1994-; n Homemakers 1979-, Sec, Treas, VP; Girl Scout Ldr 1979-85; Benjamin Logan HS 6609 St Rt 47 E Bellefontaine OH 43311*

ALE, A. JOSEPH, Physical Education Teacher; *b:* Brooklyn, NY; ricia Canfield; *c:* Loren, Kimberly; *ed:* Athens Coll (BS) PE 1969, PE 1970; *cr:* Green Hills Schl PE Tchr 1970-; *ai:* Sports Coord; Girls l, Sftbl Coach; NEA 1970-; Tchrs Assn 1970-, Pres 1975; *office:* Hills MS PO Box 14 Greendell NJ 07839

E, PAMELA ANN (MITCHELL), Eng & Creative Writing Tchr; *b:* e, AL; *m:* Robert E.; *c:* Rob; *ed:* Univ of DE (BAEd) Eng Ed 1972; n Coll (MA) Eng Ed 1982; 15 Addl Credits; *cr:* Caesar Rodney HS chr 1972-75; Eastern Regnl HS Eng, Creative Writing Tchr 1975-; JEA, NEA 1975-; *office:* Eastern Regnl HS Laurel Oak Rd Voorhees 055

HER, KATHLEEN LOUISE, World Cultures Tchr; *b:* Bellefonte, *d:* Penn St (BS) Ed 1972, (MED) Liberal Arts 1976, (DED) Curr & ction 1984; *cr:* St Coll Area Schl Dist Tchrs Aide in Soc Stud, Sci & 1971-72; Bellefonte Area Schl Dist Amer His & Ancient His Tchr 84, Amer His & World Cultures Tchr 1984-; PA St Univ Asst Prof in tud Methods 1990-92; *ai:* Bellefonte Area Ed Assn, PSEA & NEA ; PCSS; 10 Poems Pub; *home:* PO Box 353 Lemont PA 16851*

GEL, DENNIS D., Training Specialist; *b:* Bucyrus, OH; *m:* Ann ria Mc Leish; *c:* Katrina M., Christopher D., Kyle D., Karen V.; *ed:* ni Univ (BA) Chem 1977, (BS) Scndry Ed 1977; Wright St Univ (MA) lassroom Tchng 1992; Thesis Completed 1992; *cr:* Little Miami HS , Physics Tchr 1978-79; Tippecanoe HS Chem, Gen Sci Tchr 81; Sinclair Comm Coll Chem Lab Mgr, Instr 1981-86; New Carlisle ighth Grd Sci Tchr 1986-93; TAMSCO Trng Specialist, DOD 1993-; ower of the Pen Cmptr Scorer; Bsktbl, Track, Cross Cntry Coach; Sci , Chess Club, Homeroom Adv; Sci Dept Chair; Employee Friendship m; Jump Rope for Your Heart Spon; Employee Morale & Welfare -, Treas; St John's Luth Church 1990-, Catechism Instr; Nom Tchr of WOEA 1989, Ashland Oil 1990; Power of the Pen Outstdng Svc Awd ; Clark Cty Excl in Ed Awd 1993.*

GELBERG, KRISTIN JEANNE, Mathematics Teacher; *b:* Parma, *ed:* Wittenberg Univ at Springfield (BA) Math 1993; 15 Grad Credits rd (MA) Math at John Carroll Univ; *cr:* Vly Forge HS Math Tchr -; *ai:* Ftbl, Bsktbl & JV Chrldng Coach; Marching Band Asst Dir; N Outcomes Accreditation Steering Comm Mem; NEA 1993-; ematical Assn of Amer 1990-; NCTM 1993-; Amer Mathematical Soc -; Parma Symphony Orch 1993-, Librn & Bd of Dirs; *office:* Valley e HS 9999 Independence Blvd Cleveland OH 44130

SMAN, SARAH J., Spanish Teacher; *b:* Geneva, OH; *ed:* Bowling n St Univ (BA) Span Ed 1988; 9 Addl Credit Hrs in Guid, Cnslng; *cr:* mer HS Span Tchr 1988-; *ai:* Span Club Adv; NEA, TAWLS, OFLA -; Lucas Cty I Make Difference Awd 1994; *office:* Whitmer HS 5601 g Dr Toledo OH 43613

SS, DENISE CAROL, Soc Stud & Lang Arts Tchr; *b:* Bryan, OH; *c:* Jordan; *ed:* Bowling Green St Univ (BS) Soc Stud 1978; Post Grad fted Ed; *cr:* Williams Cty Schls Tchr of Gifted 1982-86; Bryan City s Tchr of Gifted 1986-; *ai:* Jr High Newspaper Adv; Power of the Pen, Bowl Tm Coach; BEA, OEA, NEA 1987-; OH Assn for Gifted dren 1983-; Friends of Bryan Public Lib 1989-; Acad Booster Club -, Advy Bd; Bryan Athletic & Music Boosters; *office:* Bryan City s 1301 Center St Bryan OH 43506

SS, TIMOTHY L., High School Mathematics Tchr; *b:* Napoleon, *m:* Lee Ann LaBuda; *c:* Quentin Dane; *ed:* The Defiance Coll (BA) h 1984; *cr:* Delta HS Math Tchr 1984-87; Edgerton Local Schls Math Head, Tchr 1987-93; Napoleon HS Math Tchr 1993-; *ai:* LCHS Asst Coach, Weight-Room Coord; Asst Track Coach; NEA, OEA 1984-; 1993-; Liberty Ctr Ath Booster 1991-, VP, Pres; St Paul Luth Church , VP, Pres; Westgate Chapel 1994-, Jr HS Yth Ldr; Tchr of Yr 1990; *e:* 1620 Wildwood Rd Toledo OH 43614*

ETH, ELIZABETH SCHALL, 3rd Grade Teacher; *b:* Wauseon, OH; obert C. III, Scott C.; *ed:* OH Univ (BSEd) Elem Ed 1983; Univ of ton (MEA) Admin 1993; Demings Quality Classroom; Cooperative rning; Dimensions of Learning; *cr:* Fairfield Cty Bd of MRDD reation Supvr 1984-87; Lancaster City Schls 3rd Grd Tchr 1987-; *ai:* r Revision Dist Support Team; Coord a Schl Comm Partnership; Bldg for Assn; Negotiation Comm; Facilitate Site Cncl; *home:* 357 awha Rd Lancaster OH 43130*

KER, ROBIN JEAN, English Teacher; *b:* Oakland, MD; *ed:* Garrett nm Coll (AA) Liberal Arts 1985; Frostburg St Univ (BS) Eng 1986; r Cert MD; *cr:* Southern HS Tchr 1986-; *ai:* Jr Class Adv; Prom Spon; Jr Class Play Dir; Tutor; SAT Prep Class; AFT 1991-; *office:* Southern 345 Oakland Dr Oakland MD 21550

LLANE, KATHLEEN KELLY, English Teacher; *b:* London, England; ristin, Honora, Brendan; *ed:* Le Moyne Coll (BA) Eng 1971; Grad Stud acuse Univ & SUNY at Oswego; *cr:* Jamesville DeWitt HS Tchr 1971-; Newspaper Adv; AFT 1971-; *office:* Jamesville-Dewitt HS Edinger Dr Witt NY 13214

NA, BERNADETTE ALELI, Religion Teacher; *b:* Philadelphia, PA; Anthony; *c:* Laura Marie, Monica; *ed:* Glassboro St Coll (BA) Eng 7; *cr:* Mill Road Schl Jr High Eng Tchr 1967-69; Absecon Pub Schls Tchr 1982-83; Holy Spirit HS Rel Tchr 1983-; *ai:* Dept Chair; Spirit ganizer & Adv; Awds Night Coord; SCTO 1985-; NCEA 1989-; Absecon storical Soc 1988-, VP; *office:* Holy Spirit HS New Rd Absecon NJ 01

NA, VINCENT, Associate Professor of Spanish; *b:* Brooklyn, NY; *c:* n Carlos; *ed:* Fordham Univ (BA) Eng 1966; NY Univ (MA) Span 1978, HD) Span 1982; *cr:* NY Univ Instr 1980-83; Boricua Coll Instr 1983-84; ger Univ Asst Prof 1985-87; Clarion Univ Span Assoc Prof 1987-; *ai:* ha Mu Gamma Adv; Clarion Historical Soc 1995-; Articles, Poetry Pub; bright Argentina 1988; *office:* Clarion Univ Of PA Modern Languages Cultures Clarion PA 16214

NAVARIA, JOANNE MARINO, Eighth Grade Teacher; *b:* lmington, DE; *m:* Vincent; *c:* Stacy, Stephen; *ed:* Southern CT St Univ) His, Scndry Ed 1968; William Paterson Coll 7 Credits Ed; *cr:* hwah HS His Tchr 1968-70; St Catherine Schl Eighth Grd Tchr 1981-; Stu Cncl Adv 1992-; Yrbk Coord 1981-94; Rdng Coord 1994-; Soc Stud ord 1981-93; Grad Adv 1981-; Natl His Hnr Soc; Mid Sts Evaluation ering Comm Co-Chair; NCEA 1981-; TASC 1992-; Certfd Catechist 4-; *home:* 91 Timber Ln Newfoundland NJ 07435*

INELLA, LINDA MARIE, Instrumental Music Teacher; *b:* Syracuse, *ed:* SUNY at Potsdam (BM) Music Ed 1980; Syracuse Univ (MM) rformance 1985; *cr:* Dundee Cntrl Schl Instrumental Music Tchr 80-86; Onondaga Cntrl Schl Instrumental Music Tchr 1987-; *ai:* AFT 80-86; Onondaga Cty Music Edctrs 1987-; Syracuse Oratorio Singers 86-; *office:* Onondaga Cntrl Schls 4479 S Onondaga Rd Nedrow NY 120

INELLI, GEORGETTE F., Fourth Grade Teacher; *b:* Jersey City, NJ; Richard G.; *c:* Kevin, Kimberly, Sandra; *ed:* Univ of MD (BS) Elem Ed 65; 47 Grad Hrs Rdng Ed; *cr:* Ridgefield Elem Schl 3rd Grd Tchr 65-66; Montgomery Co Pub Schl 4-6 Grd Tchr 1967-73; Prince George Co Pub Schl 406 Grd Tchr 1967-73; South Jefferson Cntrl Schl Gifted 12 Yrs, 3-4 Grd Rdng Tchr 1973; *ai:* NYSTA.

SPINELLI, JACK, Earth Science Teacher; *b:* Erie, PA; *m:* Carol L. Saxton; *c:* Matthew T., Jennifer M.; *ed:* Penn St Univ (BS) Earth Sci 1977; Addl 60 Post Grad Hrs in Natural Sci for Master's Degree Equivalency Cert from PA Dept of Ed; *cr:* Conneaut Vly HS Sci Tchr 1977-93; Mc Dowell Intermediate HS Sci Tchr 1993-; *ai:* PA St Ed Assn, NEA 1977-; Crawford Cty Conservation Edctr of Yr 1983, 1990; *office:* Mc Dowell Intermediate HS 3320 Caughey Rd Erie PA 16506

SPINELLI, PAUL F., Social Studies Teacher; *b:* Vineland, NY; *m:* Josephine Orlando-Spinelli; *c:* Paul Angelo; *ed:* Mt St Mary's Coll (BS) Soc Stud Ed 1975; 15 Grad Credits Cmptr Sci, 6 Grad Credits Soc Sci, 3 Grad Credits Behavioral Scis Rowan Coll; *cr:* Williamston Jr HS Tchr 1975-76; Assumption Regnl Schl Tchr 1976-79; Cumberland Regnl HS Tchr 1979-80; Atlantic City HS Tchr 1980-82; Chelsea Jr HS Tchr 1982-; *ai:* Liaison Comm; Chess, Soc Stud Club; Know Bowl, Bsbl 1980-84 Coach; NEA, NJEA, ACEA 1975-; ACEA 1980-, Sr VP; Natl Assn Soc Stud Tchrs 1982-; Vineland Jaycees 1975-, VP, Treas, Bd of Dirs, Keyman of Yr; Natl Assn of Sports Ofcls 1985-; Com-Cape Bsktbl Ofcls 1975-, Sec, Treas, Interpretor; NJ St Bd of Bsktbl 1985-, Pres, VP; Jaycee of Month 6 Times; 3 Times NJ St Bsktbl Finals Ofcl; Run Ofcls Camp for Yng Bsktbl Ofcls; Mentor Tchr Twice; *home:* 2284 Baywood Dr Vineland NJ 08360*

SPINGLER, ROSE ANTHONY, Chemistry Teacher; *b:* Philadelphia, PA; *ed:* Immaculata (BA) Theology, Bio 1968; Villanova (MSSS) Scndry Sci 1972; Immaculata (MA) Cnslng Psych 1995; Schl Psychologist Cert 18 Hrs; *cr:* Archbishop Prendergast HS Phys Sci Tchr 1969-72; Villa Maria Acad Chem, Physics Tchr 1972-78; Bishop Mc Devitt HS Chem Tchr 1978-84; Marian HS Chem Tchr 1984-88; Cardinal Dougherty HS Chem Tchr 1988-; *ai:* Moderator of Comm Svc Corps; Sr Prom; Stu Assistance Prgm Team; NCEA 1961-; Distngd Cath Edctr Awd; *office:* Cardinal Dougherty HS 6301 N 2nd St Philadelphia PA 19120*

SPINKS, CLOYCE ISAAC, Social Studies Teacher; *b:* Greensboro, NC; *m:* Josephine Cecelia; *c:* Anthony, Steven; *ed:* NC A&T Univ (BS) Soc Stud 1969; Geo Washington (MS) Ed 1982; Grad Work Trinity Coll; *cr:* Oxon Hill Sr HS Soc Stud Tchr 11 Yrs; Walker Mill MS Soc Stud Tchr 11 Yrs; Chopticon HS Soc Stud Tchr 4 Yrs; *ai:* Spon Black Pursuits Team, Jr Class 1991, Soph Class 1990; NEA 1970-; MD Real Estate Salesman 1973-; Prince Hall Masons 1988-; IBPOEW 1980-, First Scribe; Brothers Unlimited 1994-, HS Dir; Ldrs Amer Outstdng Scndry Tchrs Awd 1972; *home:* 4368 Rock Ct Waldorf MD 20602*

SPINNER, BARBARA, Mathematics Teacher; *b:* Cleveland, OH; *m:* George J. III; *c:* Christine, George, Jeffrey; *ed:* Kent St Univ (BS) Ed, Math 1970; Cleveland St Univ (MED) Curr & Instruction 1989; Lake Erie Coll Ec; *cr:* Willoughby-Eastlake Schl Adult Ed Tchr 1980-84; Eastlake MS Math Tchr 1984-85; Willowick MS Math Tchr 1985-91; North HS Math Tchr 1970-77, 1991-; *ai:* Sr Class Adv; Math Counts, Acad Decathlon Math Coach; Core Team; NEA 1970-, Convention Del 1976; OEA, NEOEA 1970-; WETA 1970-, Bldg Rep, 1970-; NCTM; OH Cncl of Tchrs of Math; Tri-County Cncl of Tchrs of Math; *office:* North HS 34041 Stevens Blvd Eastlake OH 44095

SPINNER, CHARLES MICHAEL, Social Studies Instructor; *b:* Naperville, IL; *m:* Patrice Supik; *c:* Scott Lee; *ed:* Conception Seminary Coll (BA) Philosophy 1968; WV Univ (MA) Sociology 1973; Northwest MO St Coll Soc Stud Tchr Cert 1968; Numerous Grad Courses; *cr:* Parma Sr HS Soc Stud Instr 1968-71; Normandy HS Soc Stud Instr 1972-91; Shaker Hghts HS Soc Stud Instr 1991-; *ai:* Co-Chprsn of Schl & Comm Relations Comm; Hum Team; Fac Steering Comm Mem; Greater Cleveland Cncl for Soc Stud 1975-, Pres 1982; OH Cncl for Soc Stud; Shaker Hghts Tchrs Assn 1991-; Shaker Hghts PTO 1991-; St John Bosco Church 1973-; Parma Hghts Charter Review Commission; Martha Holden Jennings Master Tchr Awd Recipient 1979; Pub Article; Kent St Univ Read Scholar 1982; Biographical Article Pub 1984; Rockefellar Scholar 1986; Speaker at Various Confs; *office:* Shaker Heights HS 15911 Aldersyde Dr Cleveland OH 44120

SPINNEY, ANNE AVARD, Mathematics Department Head; *b:* Moncton NB, Canada; *m:* Craig; *c:* Colin, Heather; *ed:* Mt Allison Univ (BSC) Chem-Honors 1971, (BED) Scndry Schl Ed 1972; Attending Univ de Moncton; *cr:* Moncton HS Math, Chem Tchr 1972-77; Three Oaks HS Math Tchr 1978-79; Moncton HS Math Dept Head 1983-; *ai:* Founder Schl Enrichment Comm; Staff Adv Knight, Knightlette Comms; Ticket Sales Schl Musical; NB Tchrs Assn Math Cncl 1972-; NCTM; Guest Lectures Ed Dept; Co-Author Mathematics, Principles & Process 10; Author Portims of the Teachers Resource for Principles Process 10 and 11; Inservice to Tchrs; Prime Minesters Awd for Excl in Tchng Math, Sci & Tech; Math Tchr of Yr 1994; Schl Dist Distgd Svc Awd 1995; Author of 4 Major Curr Documents for 10-12th Grds; *office:* Moncton HS 207 Church St Moncton NB E1C 5A3 Canada CN*

SPINNEY, CHARLOTTE C., Social Studies Teacher; *b:* Worcester, MA; *ed:* Worcester St Coll (BSEd) Soc Stud 1958, (MSEd) Sociology 1961; 100 Addl Credits; *cr:* Westborough HS Soc Stud Tchr 1958-; *ai:* Pub Relations; Stud Group; Soc Stud Review, Steering Comm Evaluation Chair; Westborough Tchrs Assn 1958-, Pres 1968-70, Negotiations Chair; MA Tchrs Assn, NEA 1958-; United Way 1975-, VP Exec Bd 1991; Contribution to United Way 1990; Habitat for Hum; Soc Stud, Cultural Stud Tchr of Yr; Nom MA Tchr of Yr; Contribution to Cntrl MA Ftbl; Booster of Yr; *office:* Westborough HS 90 W Main St Westborough MA 01581*

SPINO, DIANE DIMODUGNO, 7th & 8th Grd Soc Stud Teacher; *b:* Bronx, NY; *m:* Charles; *c:* Steven, Christina; *ed:* Jersey City State (BA) Spec Ed 1976; Boston Coll (MED) Spec Needs 1978; *cr:* Gaebler Schl Spec Ed Tchr 1977-80; Clifton Pub Schl Supplemental Instr 1980-81; Corpus Christi Schl Tchr 1988-; *ai:* Stu Cncl, Yrbk Adv; Schl Cnslr; CCD Tchr OLMC; NCEA 1989-; *home:* 801 Newcomb Rd Ridgewood NJ 07450

SPIRLET, ALAN FRANCIS, Anatomy & Physiology Tchr; *b:* New Bedford, MA; *m:* Paula; *c:* Kevin; *ed:* Fitchburg St (ME) Ed; Univ Mae Dart (BS) Bio 1970; Cert in Bio, Chem, Scndry Math, Scndry, Eng; *cr:* Bishop Stang High Bio, Chem, Math Tchr 1970-79; Voc Tech in New Bedford Bio, Chem, Math Tchr 1979-; Fisher Coll A, P I, II Algebra I, II Stud of Diseases Tchr 1980-; *ai:* Class Notating Yearly Adv; Math Team Coach; *home:* 933 Surrey Ln New Bedford MA 02745

SPIRO, LOUIS MARSHALL, Fifth Grade Teacher; *b:* New London, CT; *m:* Barbara Temkin; *c:* Lori; *ed:* Holyoke Comm Coll (AA) Elem Ed 1973; Univ of MA (BA) Elem Ed 1974; Westfield St Coll (ME) Educl Admin 1981; *cr:* Danaby Schl Tchr of 5th Grd & Gifted & Talented 1974-79; Phelps Schl Tchr of 4th-5th Grd & Gifted & Talented 1979-87; Agawam MS 5th Grd Tchr 1987-; *ai:* Drama Club; After Schl Fun Clubs; Comm Svc Grant to Work with Elderly; Pub Article for Parents: A Perscription to Homework; Pub Book: Tchng for Success-A Practical Guide.*

SPITLER, CHRISTOPHER SCOTT, Industrial Arts Instructor; *b:* Piqua, OH; *m:* Margaret Ruth Boyce; *ed:* OH Northern Univ (BS) Industrial Tech & Ed 1993; *cr:* Vinton Cty HS Industrial Arts Instr 1993-; *ai:* Frosh Ftbl, JV Girls Bsktbl & Var Girls Track Coach; Arts Dept Chprsn; OEA 1993-; NEA 1993-; VLTA 1993-; *home:* 158 N Mulberry St Chillicothe OH 45601

SPITLER, GERALD LOUIS, English Teacher; *b:* Weehawken, NJ; *m:* Kathleen O'Brien; *c:* Scott, Stephanie, Valerie; *ed:* Seton Hall Univ (BS) Eng Ed 1969; Jersey City St Coll (MA) Rdng 1973; Attnd Penn St Univ; *cr:* Don Bosco Tech HS Eng, His Tchr 1969-73; Dowingtown Jr HS Eng, Rdng Tchr 1973-; *ai:* Play Dir; Yrbk Photographer; NEA 1973-; St Cecelia's Church 1988-; *office:* Downingtown Jr HS 335 Manor Ave Downingtown PA 19335*

SPITLER, JOHN EDWARD, Law Enforcement Coord & Instr; *b:* Dayton, OH; *m:* Lee Cerney; *c:* Andrew, Amy, Adam; *ed:* Sinclair Comm Coll Criminal Justice; Northwestern Univ Mgmt; Bowling Green St Univ Criminal Justice; Univ of Toledo Voc Ed; *cr:* OH St Hwy Patrol Patrolman, Sgt, Lt 1967-93; Case Western Reserve Univ Law Enforcement Instr 1979-92; Sandusky Police Acad Law Enforcement Instr 1985-; Ehove Career Ctr, JVS Law Enforcement Coord, Instr 1993-; *ai:* Erie Cty Enhanced 911 Comm, Advy Comm Chm; Voc Industrial Clubs of Amer Adv; NEA, OVA, AVA 1993-; OH Chiefs of Police Assn 1995-; Sandusky Area Safety Cncl 1982-, VP; Several Law Enforcement Awds; *office:* Ehove Career Ctr, JVS 316 Mason Rd W Milan OH 44857

SPITTAL, DAN SCOTT, Ftbl Coach & Weight Trng Instr; *b:* Johnstown, PA; *m:* Kathie Rufolo; *c:* Matthew, Meghan; *ed:* Lock Haven St Coll (BS) Elem Ed 1979; Temple Univ (MS) Sports Admin 1986; *cr:* Woodbury HS Tchr & Coach 1981-83; Temple Univ Coach 1983-85; Pemberton HS Tchr & Coach 1985-92; Eastern HS Tchr & Coach 1992-; *ai:* Asst Ftbl, Weight Trng Coach; NEA 1981-; Amer Ftbl Coaches Assn 1983-; Natl Strength & Conditioning Assn 1987-, CSCS Awd 1992; Winslow Twp Youth Ath Assn Vol; *office:* Eastern HS Laural Oak Rd Voorhees NJ 08043

SPITZ, ROBERT MICHAEL, HS Mathematics Teacher; *b:* Munich, Germany; *m:* Susan Argiro; *c:* Michael A.; *ed:* Rutgers-Camden (BA) Math 1984; *cr:* Lenape HS Math Tchr 1984-; *ai:* Environmental Club Co-Adv; Bridge a Stu Support Group Co-Adv; NJEA 1984-; Pi Mu Epsilon; *office:* Lenape HS Church & Hartford Rd Medford NJ 08055

SPITZMESSER, ANA MARIA, Assistant Professor of Spanish; *b:* Vigo, Spain; *m:* Donovan James; *c:* Sofia M. Stachel; *ed:* Cal St Univ San Bernardino (BA) Span 1986; Univ of CA Riverside (MA) Span 1988, (PHD) Span 1992; Fr, Portuguese; Certfd Span Interpreter; Ag Labor Bd Interpreter; *cr:* Univ of CA Riverside Tchrs Asst 1986-88, Assoc Span 1989-92; Niagara Univ Asst Prof Span 1992-; *ai:* Faith, Intellectual Life, Intnl Stud, MS Ath Commission Rules Comms; Conductor Stud Ahead Prgm; Levante la Raza Adv; Hispanic Stdnts Assn; AATSP 1990-; AAUW, AAUP, Phi Sigma Iota 1992-; Amer Red Cross 1992-, Vol Translator; Rsrch Flwshp 1994; Excl Tchng 1995 Awd; Books, Articles Pub; *office:* Niagara Univ Dept of Foreign Languages Niagara University NY 14109

SPIVACK, ROBERTA FRANK, Reading Specialist; *b:* Brooklyn, NY; *c:* Alycia B., Gregg Steven; *ed:* SCSC (BS) Elem Ed & Rdng 1966; Grad Work in Rdng at Worcester St & Framingham St; Addl Grad Work in Elem Ed & Rdng; Project Read all 4 Segments; Wilson Prgm Therapy for Specific Rdng Disability, Inclusion & Whole Lang Courses; DAP; Childrens Lit; Rdng in Content Areas; *cr:* Baldwin Schl 1st Grd Tchr 1962-66; Milford Bd of Ed Rdng Specialist 1972-; Various Schls After Schl & Summer Prgms Tchr 1984-92; *ai:* Rdng Comm; Woodland Schl SAT Comm 3 Yrs; Report Card Comm; MRA, Nobscot Rdng Comm, NEA 1972-; IRA 1994-; Hadassah 1958-, Many Offices Including Pres, Chapter VP in Charge of Programming; Bnai Brith 1962-, Many Offices Including Pres; ORT 1964-, VP; Jewish Family Svc 1990-, Bd of Dir, Food for Seas Gala Co-Chair, Adoption Comm; Madeline Hunter Observing Tchr 1988-90; Dev Deductive & Inductive Thinking Course for Gifted; *office:* Woodland-Brookside Schls N Vine St Milford MA 01757

SPIVEY, NATASHA, Mathematics Teacher; *b:* Norfolk, VA; *c:* Keyon R., Morgan T.; *ed:* Norfolk St Univ (BS) Math 1994; *cr:* Babcock & Wilcox Comp Programmer 1992-93; Navy Pub Works Ctr Pgm Analysis 1994; Suitland HS Math Instr 1994-; *ai:* NEA 1994-; Prince Georges Cty Ed Assn 1994-; *office:* Suitland HS 5200 Silver Hill Rd Forestville MD 20747*

SPODNIK, JASON KENT, American History Teacher; *b:* Westfield, OH; *m:* Lisa Dawn Mac Phee; *ed:* Messiah Coll (BA) His, Ed 1992; *cr:* Pequea Vly HS Tchr, Coach 1992-; Messiah Coll Asst Coach 1994-; *ai:* Var Club Adv; Boys Var Soccer Coach; Character Ed Comm; PSEA, NEA 1992-; Soccer Coach of Yr 1993, 1995.*

SPOEHR, LUTHER WILLIAM, History Teacher; *b:* Pittsburgh, PA; *m:* Kathryn Troyer; *c:* Matthew, Richard; *ed:* Haverford Coll (BA) His 1969; Stanford Univ (MA) His 1970, (PHD) His 1975; *cr:* Univ of RI His Dept Instr 1975-77; Lincoln Schl His Dept Instr 1977-, Chair 1987-90, Dean of Stud 1990-93; *ai:* Sr Internship Prgm Adv; Natl Cncl His Ed 1991-; Org of Amer Historians, Amer Historical Assn 1970-; Barrington Little League 1989-, Bd of Dirs Sec; AP Recognition Awd 1991; Articles Pub Co-Author 1994-95; Modern Red Schoolhouse His Consultant 1993-; AP Prgm His Consultant 1984-; *home:* 4 Windward Dr Barrington RI 02806*

SPOERLEIN, ROGER LEE, 6th Grade Teacher; *b:* Somerset, PA; *m:* Linda Reeves; *c:* Jason, Jenny, Jared; *ed:* Potomac St (BA) Elem Ed 1969; Fairmont St Coll (BA) Elem Ed 1971; 6 Grad Credits Millersville Univ; 9 Grad Credits Penn St Univ; 9 Grad Credits Univ of Pittsburgh; *cr:* Marion Cty Schls Elem Tchr 1971-73; Meyersdale Schl Dist Elem Tchr 1973-; *ai:* Elem Math Dept Head; PSEA, NEA, MAFA 1973-, Pres 1986; Church Choir 1976-; Church Band 1991-; Sunday Schl Tchr; Chrstn Ed Bd Mem; Church Bd Mem Past Treas & Pres; *office:* Meyersdale Area Schls Rd 3 Meyersdale PA 15552*

SPOHN, SUSAN SHIELDS, High School Math Teacher; *b:* Abington, PA; *ed:* Ursinus Coll (BS) Math 1968; 36 Addl Credit Hrs Villanova Univ, Beaver Coll, Marywood Coll; *cr:* Cheltenham Schl Dist Jr HS Math Tchr 1968-69, HS Math Tchr 1970; *ai:* Spon Schl Bank; CEA, PSEA, NEA 1968-; NCTM 1970-; North Penn Singers 1986-; *office:* Cheltenham HS Rices Mill Rd & Carlton Dr Wyncote PA 19095

SPONDER, HARRY, Naval Science Instructor; *b:* Bacoa, Romania; *m:* Linda Cowart; *c:* Jeffrey, Chad, Jennifer, Andrew; *ed:* NY Inst of Tech (BS) Comm Mental Hlth 1981; Barry Univ (MS) Cnslng 1986; Western Kennery Univ; *cr:* US Coast Guard Ofcr 1973-93; Passaic HS Naval Sci Instr 1993-; *ai:* Little League Coach, Umpire; Adult-Ed Tchr; NEA 1993-; Psi Chi 1981-; *office:* Passaic HS 170 Paulison Ave Passaic NJ 07055

SPONENBERG, CARL G., High School Band Director; *b:* Berwick, PA; *m:* Jean Dunn; *c:* Krista, Rebecca, Carrie; *ed:* Wilkes Coll (BS) Music Ed 1968; Eastman Schl of Music (MM) Music Ed 1972; *cr:* Canastota Schl Dist Jr HS Music Tchr 1968-69; Big Spring Schl Dist Elem Instrumental Music Tchr 1969-75, MS Instrumental Music Tchr 1975-88, HS Instrumental Music Tchr 1988-; *ai:* HS Marching Band; HS Pit Band for Various Musicals; HS Bsbl Asst Coach; HS Jazz Band Dir; CU Schl Comm Band; BSHS Winter Percussion Dir; NEA & MENC 1968-; PMEA 1968-; BSEA 1969-; West Hill United Meth Church 1972-; Big Spring Lodge #361 F&AM 1972-; Music Dept Chm 1984-; Cumberland Cnty Music Edctr VP 1995-; *office:* Big Spring HS 45 Mount Rock Rd Newville PA 17241*

SPONZO, ELAINE DINEEN, Mathematics & Science Teacher; *b:* Hartford, CT; *m:* Michael; *c:* Gregory, Kevin; *ed:* St Joseph Coll (BS) Chem; (MS) Ed 1985; 30 Addl Credits; *cr:* Hartford Hosp Med Tech 1963-67; Hardford Bd of Ed Tchr 1966-67; E Granby Schl BOE Sub Tchr 1970-82, Tchr 1982-; *ai:* Class Adv 1998; JETS Teams Coach; Sci, Pathways Chprsn; NECT; CSTA; ACS; Tchr Flwshp 3 Yrs CBIA; *office:* East Granby MS HS 95 S Main St East Granby CT 06026

SPOONER, RICK STEPHEN, Assistant Headmaster; *b:* Hartford, CT; *m:* Celine Pelletier; *c:* Jason, Allison, Stephen; *ed:* Bates Coll (BA) His 1969; Saint Josephs Coll (MA) Counseling; *cr:* Rumsey Hall Schl Tchr, Dorm Parent, His Dept Chm, Dean of Stdnts Asst Head 1969-; *ai:* Vlybl Coach; Schl Cnslr; *office:* Rumsey Hall Schl 201 Romford Rd Washington Depot CT 06794*

SPORE, KAY A., Gifted & Talented Coordinator; *b:* Ashland, OH; *w:* Barry L. (dec); *c:* Rebecca, Molly; *ed:* Ashland Coll (BA) Ed, Curr Supervision 1969, (MS) Ed, Curr Supervision 1986; 20 Grad Hrs; *cr:* Mt Hlthy Schls 3rd, 6th Grd Tchr 4 Yrs; Pinellas Cty Schls Home Instruction, Comp Ed 1 Yr; Madison Local Schls SBH Tchr 1 Yrs; Ashland City Schls K-12 Grd Gifted Coord, 3, 4, 6, 8th Grd Tchr 6 Yrs; *ai:* Venture Capital Subcommitties; Soc Stud Curr Study; OEA, NEA 1985-; Beta Sigma Phi 1985-, Pres, Sec; Delta Kappa Gamma 1990-, Schlsp Comms; Altrusa 1995-; Written Citizenship Manuel for St of OH; *office:* Ashland City Schls 730 Grant St Ashland OH 44805*

SPOSET, BARBARA ANN, Spanish Teacher & Dist Coord; *b:* Cleveland, OH; *m:* Raymond W.; *c:* Michael; *ed:* Kent State (BA) Span & Jrnlsm 1968; Millersville St (MED) Span & Curr Instr 1992; *cr:* Brooklyn City Schls Tchr & Coord 1968-; *ai:* Newspaper; Dept Chair Frgn Lang; Pub Relations; Grant Writer; Coord Commisary Svc; Span Club; BEA, NEA, & OEA 1970-, Sec; OFLA 1970-, Exec Recorder; Phi Delta Kappa 1991-, Publications Editor; ASCD 1990-; Rockefeller Fellow; Jennings Fellow; AFS Exchange Tchr; Presentation & Womens Prof Groups; Whos Who of Women in World; *office:* Brooklyn City Schls 9200 Biddulph Rd Brooklyn OH 44144*

SPOTWOOD, JOSEPH BENSON, Spanish Teacher; *b:* Pittsburgh, PA; *ed:* York Coll of PA (AS) Behavioral Sci 1969; Millersville Univ (BA) Span 1972; Temple Univ (MS) Gen Ed Tchrs 1975; Span Basic Diploma; Minstry of Ed & Sci Kingdom of Spain; West Chester Univ 19 Credit Hrs; Marywood Coll Grad Schl 9 Credits; Forrester Inst Intnl San Jose Costa Rica 6 Weeks; CEMANAHUAC Cuernavaca Mexico 6 Grad Credits Nicholls St Univ at Thibodaux LA; *cr:* Bishop Mc Devitt HS Span Tchr 1985-86; West Cath HS Span Tchr 1986-91; Archbishop Prendergast HS Span Tchr 1991-; *ai:* Span Club, Moderator; NACST Local 1776, AATSP 1986-; Penn St Modrn Lang Assoc; Permanent Prof Cert Commonwealth of PA; *office:* Archbishop Prendergast HS 401 N Lansdowne Ave Drexel Hill PA 19026

SPRADLEY, GAREY BRITTON, Philosophy Professor; *b:* Corpus Christi, TX; *m:* Judy Gerault; *c:* Paul, Laurel, David; *ed:* Univ of TX Austin (BBA) Accounting 1967, (JD) Law 1971; Southwestern Bapt Seminary (MDIV) 1983 |(*#: Syracuse Univ (MA), (PHD) Philosophy 1990; Univ of Houston 27 Hrs of Philosophy, 6 Hrs Ger; *cr:* US Court of Appeals Law Clerk 1971-72; Butter & Binion Trial Attorney 1972-78; Univ of Houston Law Ctr Assoc Prof 1978-83; Grove City Coll Assoc Prof 1991-; *ai:* Bd Elders Grove City Alliance Church; Team Mgr Grove City Little League; Evangelical Philosophical Soc 1978-; Soc Chrstn Philosophers 1983-; Outstanding Young Man in Amer 1981; Law Schl Honors TX Law Review; Order of the Coil; Pub Book Reviews, Articles in Faith, Philosophy; Chrstn Scholars Review Western Journal of Law; Houston Law Review; MN Law Review; Journal of Law, Religion; *office:* Grove City Coll 100 Campus Dr Grove City PA 16127

SPRADLIN, PAT, English & Art Teacher; *b:* Chicago, IL; *m:* Rod; *c:* Andrew; *ed:* Marshall Univ (BA) Eng, Visual Art 1984, (MA) Fine Art 1989; Undergraduate Work in Cmptr GraphicsShawnee St; Summer Media Inst Cmptr Imaging OH Univ at Athens 1995; *cr:* Green HS Eng, Art Tchr 1984-87; OH Univ Visiting Fac, Eng Dept 1987-89; Shawnee St Univ Eng Adj Fac 1989-91, Portsmouth East HS Eng, Art Tchr 1990-; OH Univ Eng Tchr 1992-; *ai:* Var Vlybl Coach; Eng Dept Chair; HS Newspaper Staff Spon; Natl Hnr, Art Club, Video Broadcast Spon; NEA; OH Cncl Eng Lang Arts; OH Art Ed Assn; Phi Delta Kappa, Tchr of Yr 1991; Wheelersburg Meth Church 1993-; Portsnet Tech for City Schls; Ports City Schls Tchr of Yr Awd 1992; Ashland Oil Golden Apple Tchr Achvmt Awd 1990; *office:* Portsmouth East HS Marshall & Farney Ave Sciotoville OH 45662*

SPRAFKA, MARIA DINARDO, English & Humanities Teacher; *b:* East Cleveland, OH; *m:* Kenneth J.; *ed:* Lake Erie Coll (BA) Eng, Italian 1970; Attnd OH Univ Renaissance Art, Arch, Univ of Pisa, John Carroll Univ Rdng Cert; *cr:* Charles F. Brush HS Eng Tchr 1971-82; Beachwood MS Eng Tchr 1982-83; Charles F. Brush HS Eng, Hum Tchr 1983-; *ai:* Environmental Club Adv; Sunshine Comm Co-Chm; Whole Lang Dist Comm, Scndry Mem; Acad Decathlon Team Coach; S Euclid-Lindhurst Tchr Assn 1970-, Sec, Bldg Rep; OEA, NEA 1970-; Italian-Amer Cultural Fnd 1994-, Bd of Trustees; Rock & Roll Hall of Fame 1995-; Mini Grant Ventur Capital; Hum Tchr of Yr 1977; *office:* Charles F. Brush HS 4875 Glenlyn Rd Lyndhst-Mayfld OH 44124

SPRAGUE, CATHY L., Senior English & Drama Teacher; *b:* Waukegan, IL; *m:* Stevan J.; *c:* Catie, Cristopher; *ed:* Miami Univ (BS) Comm, Eng 1977; Attending Marietta Coll; *cr:* Bellevue HS Eng, Drama Tchr 1978-80; Hemet HS Eng Tchr 1980-81; Ft Frye HS Sr Eng, Drama Tchr 1982-; *ai:* Jr Class, Prom Adv; Drama Dir; NEA, OEA 1982-; Educl Theatre Assn 1986-; 4-H Advy Bd 1995-; 4-H Ldr 1991-; Local Tchrs Assoc FFTA Pres Extra Mile Awd; *office:* Ft Frye HS 5th St Beverly OH 45715

SPRAGUE, CHARLOTTE HIMES, English Teacher; *b:* Punxsutawney, PA; *m:* Royce; *c:* Kimberly Hand, Jeff; *ed:* Clarion St Coll (BA) Eng, Soc Stud 1967; 6 Post Grad Credit Hrs; *cr:* Brockway Area Jr Sr HS Bus, Eng, Composition, Cmptr Instr, Eng Tchr 1967-; *ai:* NEA, PSEA 1967-; Cultural Arts, Spelling Bee Judge.

SPRAGUE, LOIS VITELLI, Music Teacher; *b:* New Haven, CT; *m:* Paul; *c:* Lauren; *ed:* Western CT St Univ (BS) Music Ed 1978; Cntrl CT St Univ (MS) Ed 1987; *cr:* St Paul Jr HS Gen, Instrumental Music Tchr 1978; Music in Amer Inc Pvt Band Dir 1979; Center Schl Gen, Instrumental Music Tchr 1980-; *ai:* Stu Assistance Team; Music Booster Club; MENC 1976-; NEA 1980-; PTA 1994-, Cultural Arts; Good Apple Awd; *office:* East Hampton Center Schl 7 Summit St East Hampton CT 06424

SPRANCE, ROBERT M., Teacher & Dean; *b:* Brooklyn, NY; *m:* Elaine M. Mc Kay; *c:* Jennifer, Kelly, Robin, Jaclyn, Steven; *ed:* Queens Coll (BS) PE 1972; Queens Coll (MS) Ed 1977; LaVerne Univ 15 Credits, Mc Pherson Univ 15 Credits Toward PHD; *cr:* IS 93 Tchr, Dean 21 Yrs; *ai:* Robeson Var Boys Soccer, Forest Hills Girls Soccer Coach; Pomonok Supvr ASC Ctr; *office:* IS 93 66-56 Forest Ave Ridgewood NY 11385

SPRAU, SANDRA GORDON, Mathematics Teacher; *b:* Danbury, CT; *m:* Duane; *c:* Duane, Keith, Brett; *ed:* Coll Misericordia (BS) Math Ed 1975; *cr:* Elk Lake Schl Math Instr 1978-80; Coll Misericordia Math Instr 1990-92; Dallas Schl Dist Math Instr 1993-; *ai:* NEA, PSEA 1993-; PTO 1987-, Treas; *office:* Dallas Sr HS PO Box 2000 Dallas PA 18612

SPREEN, JUDITH A., Fourth Grade Teacher; *b:* paterson, NJ; *c:* Carol Anne Spreen-Sprigman, Lynne Sreen Raffo; *ed:* William Paterson Coll (BA) Elem Ed 1963; Jersey City St Coll, Monmouth Coll 45 Addl Hrs; *cr:* Meml Schl Elem Tchr 1963-67; Jefferson Schl Elem Tchr 1974-; *ai:* Hawthorne Tchrs Assn 1974-, VP; NJEA 1963-, Negot Consultant; NEA 1963-; Friends of Lib 1980-, Dir Art, Photo; Amer Labor Museum 1985-; Municipal Ct of Passaic Cty 1992-, Vol Mediator, Coord; Haw Democ Club 1980-; Governors Tchrs Recognition Awd for Excl 1985-86; *office:* Thomas Jefferson Elem Schl Goffle Hill Rd Hawthorne NJ 07506*

SPREIREGEN, HAROLD M., Accounting Professor; *b:* New York, NY; *m:* Eleanor Wallace; *c:* Mark Alan, Daniel Paul; *ed:* Bernard Baruch Schl of Bus Admin (BBA) Acctng 1955; Brooklyn Law Schl (JD) Law 1960; *cr:* Bergen Comm Coll Adj Prof 1969-; Maritime Coll-SUNY Prof 1993-; *ai:* NY Bar; CPA NY St; *office:* Bergen Comm Coll 400 Paramus Rd Paramus NJ 07652

SPRENKLE, FRANCES EVELYN, Fifth Grade Teacher; *b:* Philadelphia, PA; *m:* William A.; *ed:* Holy Family Coll (BA) Elem Ed 1976; Provisional Rel Cert Theology 1982; Prof Rel Cert Theology 1994; Post Grad Work Theology St Charles Borromeo Seminary, Continuing Credit Hrs Rdng, Soc Stud, Sci, Math; *cr:* Salvation Army Mbrshp Summer Bible Studies, Arts, Crafts Aide 1967-69; St Ambrose Schl Elem Edctr 1971-; *ai:* Coord Rdng Intermediate, Jr High Levels, Drama; Yrbk Staff-Photographer; Mid Sts Comm; Extraordinary Minister; NCEA 1971-; Natl Geographic Soc 1982-; Natl Museum of Amer Indian, Charter Mem; Inst of Amer Indian Arts; Wolf Ed, Research Ctr, Friends of Forest; Archdiocese of Philadelphia Tchr of Month 1993; Distngd Svc Cath Ed Awd 1996; *office:* St Ambrose Schl 405 E Roosevelt Blvd Philadelphia PA 19120

SPRIEGEL, SHIRLEY (BOMMER), Lecturer; *b:* Buffalo, NY; *m:* Clyde L.; *c:* Jeffrey E., Andrew R., Charlotte Huebschmann, Craig E.; *ed:* Buffalo St Coll (BS) Elem Ed 1953, (MS) Elem Ed 1963; Buffalo St Coll Post Grad Hrs in Learning Disabilities; *cr:* Williamsville Schls First Grd Tchr 1953-54; Kenmore Town of Tonawanda Schls Pre-First & First Grd Tchr 1959-94; Buffalo St Coll Lecturer Part-time 1996-; *ai:* Schl Vol; Niagara Frontier Watercolor Soc; NYSUT 1959-; Kenmore Retired, Tchrs 1994-; Distinguished Svc Awd 1991; Tchr of Yr 1990; Outstanding Svc to Youth Awd 1983; Life Mem for Svc to PTA 1975; *office:* St Univ Coll at Buffalo 1300 Elmwood Ave Buffalo NY 14222

SPRIGGS, GLORIA CAPPON, Middle School French Teacher; *b:* Rochester, NY; *w:* Timothy (dec); *c:* Jason, Bradley; *ed:* Bryant & Statton (AOS) Secretarial Sci 1979; Lemoyne Coll (BA) Fr 1990; *cr:* Security NY St Corp Sec 1979-81; NTID-RIT Sec 1981-83; Lemoyne Coll Sec 1983-84; Greece Chrstn Schl Fr Tchr 1990-; *ai:* NYSFLT & RAFTA 1990-; *office:* Greece Christian Schl 750 Long Pond Rd Rochester NY 14612

SPRINER, ESTHER, Guidance Counselor & Coll Adv; *b:* Brooklyn, NY; *ed:* Brooklyn Coll (BA) Sociology 1978, (MSEd) Ed 1980; Adv Cert Guid & Cnslng 1992; *cr:* NYC Dept of Housing Neighborhood Aid 1978-80; Soc for Seamens Children Social Worker 1980-83; NYC Dept of Hlth Resource Coord 1983-86; NYC Dept of Probation Probation Offcr 1986-87; NYC Bd of Ed Guid Cnslr, Coll Adv 1988-; *ai:* Amer Cnslng Assn 1990-; United Federation of Tchrs 1987-; Positive Force Awd Medgar Evers Coll Talent Search Prgm; *office:* Prospect Heights HS 883 Classon Ave Brooklyn NY 11225

SPRINGER, JOSEPHINE FRANZONE, Third Grade Teacher; *b:* Philadelphia, PA; *m:* Richard V.; *c:* Richard J., Christine Springer-Velicer, Andrew V.; *ed:* 2 In-Svc Credits Tchng Integrated Lang 1995; 3 Post-Grad Credits Cmptrs Ed 1988; 5 In-Svc Credits Music in Elem Schl 1963; 1 In-Svc Credit Tchng Rdng to Slow Learner 1964; *cr:* Camden Pub Schls Elem Tchr 1962-63; Phila Pub Schls Elem Tchr 1963-65; St Luke the Evangelist Schl Third Grd Tchr 1978-; *ai:* NCEA.

SPRINGFIELD, REBECCA BLAKELEY, Social Studies Teacher; *b:* Philadelphia, PA; *m:* Dennis R.; *c:* Sekou T., D. Omar; *ed:* Lake Forest Coll (BA) Sociology 1971; Univ of MA (MED) Urban Ed 1973; *cr:* Newrak Bd of Ed Soc Stud Tchr, Team Ldr 1973-75, 1986-87; Orange Bd of Ed 5th-6th Grd Tchr 1978-80; NJ Bell Telephone Co Asst Mgr, Bus Office 1980-86; Montclair Bd of Ed 6-8th Grd Soc STud Tchr 1990-; Seton Hall Univ Upward Bound Instr 1992-; *ai:* Family Life Group New Parent Orientation 1996; NEA 1989-, MEA 1990-; Delta Sigma Theta 1986-, Schlsp Chm, Soc Action, Regnl Conv Comm; CPOC South Orange Maplewood Schl Dist 1995-, Exec Bd; Adult Correctional Inst Awd in Tchng Cert; *office:* Glenfield MS 25 Maple Ave Montclair NJ 07042

SPRINGLE, TERRY WADE, Mathematics Teacher; *b:* Norfolk, VA; *m:* Mary Blossom; *c:* Robert M., Gregory R., Katherine E., Clara L., Martha A.; *ed:* Old Dominion Univ (BA) Pol Sci 1972; Norfolk St Univ (MA) Communication 1978; *cr:* Northampton MS Math Tchr 1973-77; Northampton HS Math & Speech Tchr 1977-83; Pocomoke MS Math Tchr 1984-86; Pocomoke HS Math Tchr 1986-; *ai:* Stu Cncl & Regnl Stu Cncl Adv; Tennis Asst Coach; MSTA 1983-; NEA 1972-; NCTM 1984-; MD St Stu Cncl Adv of Yr; *office:* Pocomoke H S 1817 Old Virginia Rd Pocomoke City MD 21851

SPRINGSTEAD, EDWIN A., Retired PE Teacher; *b:* Nyack, NY; *m:* Florence Pettograsso; *c:* Edwin Jr., Michael; *ed:* SUNY at Brockport (BS) Hlth, PE 1954; Ithaca Coll (MA) PE; NY St Dir of Hlth, PE Cert; *cr:* Saugerties HS PE Tchr 1956-58; South Colonie Cntrl Schls PE Tchr, Coach 1958-66; North Colonie Cntrl Schls PE Tchr, Coach 1966-89; *ai:* Var Boys Cross Cntry Coach; Chm Boys Cross Cntry; Asst Boys Track Coach; Albany Curling Club 1983-, Pres 1993-95; *home:* 6 Davis Pl Latham NY 12110

SPRINGSTEEN, KATHRYN ROSE M., Chemistry Professor; *b:* Logan, WV; *m:* Arthur W.; *c:* Anne E.; *ed:* WV Univ (PHD) Inorganic Chem 1977; *cr:* Colby-Sawyer Coll Instr 1977-78, Asst Prof 1978-84, Assoc Prof 1984-93, Prof 1993-, Dept Chair 1986-; *ai:* Alpha Chi Spon; Fac Ath, Bd Trustees Rep; Acad Policies, Standing, Prsnl Chair, Safety, Benefits Comms; Amer Chem Soc 1977-; NSTA, NE Chem Tchrs 1990-; Visiting Scholar Harvard Schl of Pub Hlth; *office:* Colby Sawyer Coll 100 Main St New London NH 03257*

SPRINKLE, MAGGIE, Business, Computer & Math Tchr; *b:* Johnstown, PA; *c:* Erin; *ed:* Lynchburg Coll (BS) Bus Admin 1970; 24 Credit Hrs Ed, Math; *cr:* Cambria Rowe Bus Coll Tchr 1971-75; The Stratford Schl Tchr 1987-91; Good Shepherd Schl Tchr 1991-93; Catholic Hs of Baltimore Tchr 1993-; *ai:* Adult Ed Cmptr Applications Tchr; Math Club Adv; NCEA 1993-; *office:* Catholic H S Of Baltimore 2800 Edison Hwy Baltimore MD 21213

SPROSS, MICHAEL DILLARD, 9th-12th Grade Art Teacher; *b:* Poughkeepsie, NY; *ed:* Edinboro St Coll (BFA) Painting 1979; SUNY at New Paltz (MA) Painting 1991; K-12th Art Ed Cert 1986; *cr:* Millbrook Cntrl Schl HS Art Tchr 1986-; *ai:* Art Club Adv 1986-; Art Shows Dir 1986-; NY St Tchr Assn 1993-; Town Washington Bi-Centennial, Village Millbrook Centennial Pub Svc; *office:* Millbrook Cntrl Schl Box AA Alden Pl Millbrook NY 12545

SPROUL, DAVID WALTER, Science Teacher; *b:* Kodiak, AK; *ed:* Univ of ME (BE) Animal Sci 1983; Univ of Southern ME (MS) Ed 1990; *cr:* Deering HS Sci Tchr 1983-; *ai:* Sr Class Adv; Implementation Comm for New Block Schedule; NABT; *office:* Deering HS 370 Stevens Ave Portland ME 04103*

SPROUL, MAUREEN S., Spanish Teacher; *b:* Philadelphia, PA; *m:* Thomas J.; *c:* Kari, Matthew, Alison, Terri Marie; *ed:* Temple Univ (BS) Scndry Ed, Span 1970; Addl Hrs at: Univ of Valencia Spain, Univ of Madrid Spain 6 Credit Each, Temple Univ 18 Post Grad, Kutztown Univ 18 Post Grad; *cr:* Archbishop Ryan HS Span Tchr 1970-75; Cntrl Cath HS Span Tchr, Dept Chair 1983-; *ai:* Dept Chprsn; Advy Bd; NEA; PSMLA; ACTFL; AATSP 1985-; Assoc Sprvsn & Curr 1995; Parkland Lib Bd 1986-89, Twp Rep.

SPROULL, KATHLEEN (KELLY), Second Grade Teacher; *b:* Johnstown, PA; *m:* Thomas J.; *c:* Colleen; *ed:* Indiana Univ of PA (BA) Sociology 1969; Elem Ed Credits for PA I & PA II Cert Seton Hil *cr:* St Joseph Schl Second Grd Tchr 1983-; *ai:* Parish Ed Comm Fa Stu Support Team Mem; Schl Dev Core Group Rep; NCEA 1983-; St Joseph Schl 1129 Leishman Ave New Kensington PA 15068

SPRUEL-THOMPSON, MOLLYE E., Fourth Grade Teach Moorestown, NJ; *m:* Roddy M.; *ed:* Bennett Coll at Greensboro (BA Ed 1967; Wm Paterson Coll (MA) Urban Ed, Comm Svcs 1982; Montclair St Coll; Tchg Chld Philos Think I 1984, Tchg Chld Philos II 1985, Wm Patterson Coll Admin & Super 1979-80 12 Credit Hrs *cr:* Hawkins Street Schl Grd 2 Tchr 1967-84, Grd 4 Tchr 1984-90, Skills Project Tchr Grds 2-4 1990-93; Louise A. Spencer Elem Schl Tchr 1993-94; Hawkins Street Schl Grd 4 Tchr 1994-; *ai:* Dis Comm; NTA; NJEA; NEA; United Prof 1967-; Phi Delta Kappa Former Episoleus; North Jersey Chpt Bennett Coll Alumnae 1986-, Parliamentarian; NAACP 1988-; Montclair Juvenile Conf Comm Christ Church Montclair 1995-.

SPRUILL, WILLIAM L., Band & Orchestra Director; *b:* Columbi *m:* Sherrill Marie; *ed:* NC Cntrl Univ (BA) Music 1963, (MA) Music Attnd Ashland Univ, Bowling Green Univ, Cleveland St Univ; 3 Masters Further Stud; *cr:* NC Schls Band Dir 1963-71; Admiral Ki Band & Orch Dir 1971-; *ai:* Jazz Band, Marching Band, Concert Orch & Photo Club Dir; Stage Mgr; Intnl Assn of Jazz Edctrs 1986-; Phi Alpha 1961-; NAACP 1970-; *office:* Admiral King HS 2600 A Ave Lorain OH 44052

SPRUNGER, JONATHAN S., Social Studies Teacher; *b:* Wheaton, Jacqueline Susan Manley; *ed:* Taylor Univ (BS) Soc Stud Ed 1990; Sociology Capital Univ; 25 Hrs His, Pol Sci OH St Univ at Columbu Worthington Kilbourne HS Soc Stud Tchr 1990-; *ai:* Var, Yth Bo Soccer Coach; Ski Club Coord; NEA, OH Ed Asns, Worthington Ed 1993-; *office:* Worthington Kilbourne HS 1499 Hard Rd Columbu 43235

SPRY, JANET DENISE (RICHBURG), Assistant Professo Baltimore, MD; *m:* Michael Rennie; *c:* Amber Denise, Aryn Mika Univ of MD in Baltimore Cty (BA) Sociology 1977; Coppin St Coll Voc Rehab Cnslng 1979; George Washington Univ (EDS) Voc Evalu (EDD) Ed & Rsrch 1993; *cr:* St of MD Div Rehab Supvr & Cnslr 19 Coppin St Coll Asst Prof 1995-; *ai:* Natl Rehab Assoc 1996-; Voc Work Adj Assoc 1996-; Natl Assoc of Svc Providers in Pvt Rehab Anne Arundel Cty Bd of Ed Human Relations Comm 1995-; Rehabilitation Cnslr; Certfd Voc Evaluation & Work Adjus Specialist; Certfd Prof Cnslr St of MD; *office:* Coppin St Coll 25 North Ave Baltimore MD 21216*

SPURGEON, LARRY D., 9th-12th Grd Art Instructor; *b:* Canton, O Sandra K.; *c:* Christopher Todd, Chad Dayton; *ed:* Kent St Univ (BA Ed 1966, (MA) Painting 1976; *cr:* Canton Local Schls Elem, Jr HS Tchr 30 Yrs; *ai:* Art Club Adv; Var Boys Tennis, Jr HS Ftbl; OH Ed NEA 1966-; Martha Jennings Awd 1985; *office:* Canton South HS Faircrest St SE Canton OH 44707

SPURLOCK, CONNIE KAISER, Media Specialist; *b:* Cincinnati *m:* Ronald J.; *c:* Alyson, Eric; *ed:* Eastern KY Univ (BS) Math 1976; Work 32 Hrs; 3 Cred Hrs Xavier Univ; 3 Cred Hrs East Wright St Uni Wilson Jr HS Math Tchr 1977-84; Wm H Harrison High Math 1984-93, Media Specialist 1993-; *ai:* Stu Cncl & Friendship Fund Co- Dist Internet Tech Coord; Discipline Comm; OELMA 1993-; ALA 1 OEA & NEA 1976-; CASLA 1993-; Hamilton Booster Org 1994-, Exe Grants for Media Ctr Art Gallery, Renaissance Festival & Mentor *office:* Wm Henry Harrison HS 9860 West Rd Harrison OH 45030

SQUADRITO, WILLIAM JAMES, 7th Grade Teacher; *b:* Philadel PA; *m:* Maureen Christine Saraceni; *c:* James, Nicole; *ed:* Temple (BS) PE, Comm Rec 1980; *cr:* Stella Maris Schl Tchr 1980-86; Our of Loreto Schl Tchr 1986-; *ai:* Stu Cncl Moderator; After Schl Prgm Stud, PE Coord; NCEA 1980-, Finalist NCEA Tchr of Yr Awd Elmwood Park Ath Assn 1988-, Coach, City of Phila Coaches Awd; *h* 2548 S Bellford St Philadelphia PA 19153

SQUARESKY, MARTHA SLATER, Spanish & French Teache Lancaster, PA; *m:* Jay; *c:* Adam, Gregory; *ed:* Millersville St Univ Span 1974; Villanova Univ (MA) Span 1989; *cr:* Conestoga Vly HS Tchr 1974-75; Overbrook Schl for the Blind Span Tchr 1975-78; D HS Span & Fr Tchr 1978-85; Milton Hershey Schl Span & Fr Tchr 19 *ai:* Peer Observer; AAFT 1992-; AATSP 1992-; PSEA & NEA 19 ASCD 1995-; *office:* Milton Hershey Schl 300 Hotel Rd Hershey PA 1

SQUEGLIA, BERNADETTE WASKO, French Teacher; *b:* McKees PA; *m:* Carl E.; *ed:* PA St Univ (BS) Scndry Ed French 1972; 50 Hou St Univ; *cr:* S Allegheny Jr & Sr HS Fr Tchr 1972-; *ai:* Intnl Lang Spon; NEA, PSEA & SAEA 1972-; PSMLA 1976-; *office:* South Alleg Jr/Sr H S 2743 Washington Blvd Mc Keesport PA 15133

SQUIRES, DEENA LABEL, 4th Grade Elementary Teacher Philadelphia, PA; *m:* Melvin; *c:* Deborah, David; *ed:* Temple Univ Elem Ed 1967, (MS) Elem Ed 1972; 30 Credits; *cr:* Meade Elem Sch Grd Tchr 1967-70; Bustleton Elem Schl 4th Grd Tchr 1970-71; Rhawnh Elem Schl 4th & 5th Grd Tchr 1971-; *ai:* Rdng & Lang Arts Tuto *office:* Rhawnhurst Elem Schl Castor Ave & Borbeck St Philadelphi 19152

SQUIRES, SYLVIA CUNNINGHAM, 8th Grd English Teacher Presque Isle, ME; *m:* Richard Walter; *c:* Tracy Squires LaPointe, Ro F.; *ed:* Bates Coll (AB) Eng 1953; Attnd Bradford Jr Coll; Post Grad Univ of NH; *cr:* Madison HS Eng Tchr 1953-54; Presque Isle HS Eng 1954-55; Maine Cntrl Inst Eng Tchr 1955-56; Portsmouth HS Eng 1956-62; Porsmsoth MS Eng Tchr 1970-; *ai:* Foley Team Ldr; C Devising Interdisciplinary Units; NEA 1953-; Assn Portsmouth T 1953-, Sec; Beta Sigam Phi 1954-, Past Pres, Sec; Alpha Delta K 1981-, Sec; Bates Key Club 1981-; *office:* Portsmouth MS 155 Parrott Portsmouth NH 03801

SQUITIERI, JOANNE MARIE (SMYTH), Social Studies Teacher Jersey City, NJ; *m:* Mark D.; *c:* Mark Thomas; *ed:* Jersey City St Coll (Elem Ed-Summa Cum Laude 1980; Post Grad Stud Rdng; *cr:* W Robinson Schl PS #3 Compensatory Ed Rdng & Math 1980-81; Vr Learning Ctr GATE Prgm, 7 & 8 Grd Soc Stud, Rdng Tchr 1982-; *ai:* G 7th Grd Soc Act Chprsn; Yrbk, Acad Team Advs; Halloween Act, C Responsibility, Bayonne 2000 Cleaner & Greener Comms; NEA, NJ BTA 1980-; Bergen Point Comm Church 1995-, Sunday Schl Presch In Governors Tchr Recognition Awd 1987; Mini Grant Received Bayonne of Ed 1988, 1989, 1994; Cert of Commendation Senator Bill Bradleys G Awareness Recognition Prgm 1988.

SRACIC, PAUL ALBERT, Asst Prof of Political Science; *b:* Morristo NJ; *m:* Susan Yvonne Mark; *c:* Katya; *ed:* Albright Coll (AB) Pol Sci & 1984; Rutgers Univ (MA) Pol Sci 1990, (PHD) Pol Sci 1993; Youngstown St Univ Instr 1992-94, Asst Prof 1994-; *ai:* Prelaw, Po Legal Thought Soc Adv; APSA 1988-; OEA 1992-, EPAC Rep; Master T Awd Youngstown St Univ 1995; Numerous Articles Pub; *off* Youngstown St Univ 410 Wick Ave Youngstown OH 44555*

SRIRAM, VEN, Associate Prof of Marketing; *b:* Madras, India; *m:* Ang L. Cox; *ed:* Univ of Madras (BA) Ec 1978; Univ of Bombay (MMS) Mr 1980; Univ of MD (PHD) Mrktg 1987; *cr:* Richardson-Hindustan Ltd P Exec 1980-82; Univ of Baltimore Asst Prof 1986-87; Hofstra Univ A

987-91; Morgan St Univ Assoc Prof 1991-; *ai:* Departmental, Schl, omms; Acad Intnl bus; Acad Mrktg Sci; Assn Asian Stud; 14 Journal s, 15 Conf Proceedings Pub; Several Natl, Intnl Presentations; Univ Amer Mrktg Assn Grants; Univ of MD Outstdng Tchr Awd; *office:* n St Univ Dept of Business Admin Cold Spring Ln-Hillen Rd ore MD 21239

FE, SHELLEY H., 8th Grade Math Teacher; *b:* Toledo, OH; *m:* 1 L.; *c:* Elizabeth D., Matthew L.; *ed:* Univ of Toledo (BEd) Elem Ed Univ of Cincinnati (MEd) Spec Ed 1979; *cr:* -Union-Lewis-Huntington Schls Tchr 1973-; *ai:* Its Acad, Spelling oon; Math Dept Chprsn; NEA, OEA 1973-; RULHEA 1973-, Pres, P, BR, Parliamentarian; Concerned Citizens for Youth 1993-; Venture l Grant; *office:* Ripley Union-Lewis Huntington 1317 S 2nd St OH 45167*

TS, FRANK DAYTON, Biology Teacher; *b:* Phillipsburg, NJ; *m:* *c:* Nina; *ed:* Univ of MT (BA) Scndry Ed, (BA) Resource rvation; Minor Geology; *cr:* Hammond Acad Tchr Earth Sci & al Sci 1987-88; Peace Corps Environmental Ed, Natl Parks Vol in uay 1988-90; Boyertown Area Schl Dist Tchr Earth & Space Sci 93, Bio, AP, Acad, General 1993-; *ai:* NEA 1993-; Track Coach of 88; Published Photographer; *office:* Boyertown Area Sr HS 4th & e St Boyertown PA 19512

ILE, DONALD ROBERT, Economics Professor; *b:* New York, NY; niv of FL (BSBA) Bus 1966; Univ of MA (MA) Ec 1972, (PHD) Ec *cr:* Natl Assn of Accountants Assoc Ed 1972-74; Drury Coll Asst 978-80; St Mary's Coll Prof, Assoc Prof, Asst Prof 1980-; *ai:* Fac Ath NCAA; Editorial Bd Mem Journal of Ec Issues; Assoc Ed Bus Lib w; Amer Ec Assn 1981-; Ec Amer 1981-, Ctr Dir; Books: Activist ism 1993, The Pub Debt of US 1991, Propherts of Order 1984, Work lfare 1996; Wrote Articles; Dir NEH Summer Seminar for Schl Tchrs 93; *office:* Saint Marys Coll of Maryland St Marys City St Marys City 0686

ILE, MARYANN OHALEK, English Teacher; *b:* Bayonne, NJ; *m:* y R. Sr.; *c:* Jeffrey Jr., Joelle Marice; *ed:* Notre Dame Coll of Staten (BA) Eng 1962; *cr:* Bayonne HS Eng Tchr 1962-68; Holy Family Eng & His Tchr 1983-88; Bayonne HS Eng Tchr 1988-; *ai:* NHS Adv; Bayonne Tchrs Assn & NJEA 1988-; *office:* Bayonne HS 29th St & enue Bayonne NJ 07002

LUM, ROBERT J., Political Sci & Economics Tchr; *b:* Pottsville, : Susanne; *c:* Nicole, Jason; *ed:* Bloomsburg Univ (BS) Pol Sci 1970,) Pol Sci 1973; *cr:* Minersville Area Jr Sr HS Tchr 1970-; *ai:* Stu NHS & Quiz Bowl Adv; PA Cncl on Ec Ed 1989-, Tchr Consultant; aster Pack 100; Ec Summit Scholar 1989; Excl in Ed Awd 1995; egic Planning Coord 1995; *office:* Minersville Jr Sr HS PO Box 787 rsville PA 17954*

CK, ELIZABETH ANNE, English Teacher; *b:* Brooklyn, NY; *m:* Josh osenblum; *c:* Zachary Stack Rosenblum; *ed:* Univ Ctr at Binghamton Gen Lit 1984; Univ Ctr at Binghamton (MA) Philosophy 1990; 4 ts Brooklyn Coll Writing, Rdng in Scndry Schls, Ed; 6 Credits City Western Lit, Summer Sub for HS Tchrs; 6 Credits Long Island Univ Spec Ed; 3 Credits Kingsborough Comm Coll Spec Ed, Human ions; *cr:* Sarah J. Hale HS Eng, ESL Tchr 1987; Abraham Lincoln HS Tchr, Fac Adv 1987-94; Brooklyn Coll Adj Eng Dept 1994; sborough Comm Coll Adj, Eng Dept 1994-; *ai:* Lincoln Log HS Fac 1988-93; Mentor to Several Former Stdnts; Tchr Trainer to Stu Tchrs; e Press Releases for Schl; Attnd Writers Confs for Schl; ASPCA -; Wildlife Conservation Soc 1993-; NY Pub Lib, Amer Museum Nat 995-; Brooklyn Museum 1996; Humane Soc of US 1994-; Flwshp to Philosophy for MA Degree; Articles Pub; Grant by NEH to Stud ern Lit Summer Inst.

CK, KATHLEEN MARIE (KLUBERT), Assistant Principal; *b:* wood, OH; *m:* Raymond G.; *c:* Steven J., Christina H.; *ed:* Baldwin ace Coll (BSE) Elem Ed 1985, (MAEd) Admin & Supervision 1992; leveland Cath Diocese 5th, 7th & 8th Grd Tchr All Subjects 1985-87; wood City Schls Sub Tchr 1987-89; Horace Mann MS 7th Grd Rdng c Stud Tchr 1989-93, Asst Prin 1993-; *office:* Horace Mann MS 1215 lifton Blvd Lakewood OH 44107

CK, SUSAN A., Kindergarten Teacher; *b:* St Paul, MN; *m:* Thomas; aura, Monica; *ed:* Coll of St Catherine (BS) Ed 1966; Eastern CT St (MS) Ed 1983; *cr:* St Rose of Lima Schl Grd 2 Tchr 1966-74; Parents' Nursery Schl Head Tchr, Dir 1974-79; Crystal Lake Schl Grd 1 Tchr)-95; Windermere Schl Kndgtn Tchr 1995-; *ai:* Child Care Ct Ctr for d Abuse Prevention; Prof Dev & Evaluation Comm; EEA, CEA, NEA)-, Pub Relations; Human Svcs Commission 1996; St Luke Folk Group -; BEST Contributions to Beginning Tchrs Awd.

CKPOLE, PETER, Science Dept Head; *b:* Fall River, MA; *m:* olyn; *c:* Lynne Anne, Amy Beth; *ed:* Bowdoin Coll (BA) Chem 1967; oy Coll (MST) Chem & Physics 1972; Clark Univ Candidate for PHD; ynnfield HS Sci Tchr 1967-88; Univ of MA Visiting Lecturer 1988-89; berlane RHS Sci Dept Head 1989-; *ai:* ACS 1991-, Aula Laudis.

CY, BARBARA ELLEN (WIRE), Voc Home Economics Tchr; *b:* ngstown, OH; *c:* Gary L., James H., Stacy; *ed:* Youngstown St Univ) Home Ec 1970, (MS) Early Chldhd 1984, (MS) Home Ec 1992; Voc) Home Ec 1977; 30-40 Hrs Post Grad Stud; *cr:* Hubbard MS Grds 5-8 ds Tchr 1970-72; Stuttgart HS Grds 9-12 Home Ec Tchr 1972-74; Reed Grd 5-8 Foods Tchr 1974-77; Roosevelt Jr HS Voc Home Ec Tchr 7-79; Poland HS Voc Home Ec Tchr 1980-; *ai:* FHA Adv; Sr Class Adv; plied Arts Dept Head; PACT Comm; NEA, OEA, PEA, YHEA, AHEA 0-; AVA, OVA 1979-; YSU Home Ec Advy Comm 1984-,; Daffodil Sales cer Soc; Tods Childrens Hosp Donator Ronald Mc Donald House; land Oil Golden Apple Awd 1995; Jaycees Woman of YR Nom 1978; stndg Home Ec Alumni Awd 1993; OH Voc Outstdng Edctr of Yr Nom 5; *office:* Poland Seminary H S 3199 Dobbins Rd Poland OH 44514*

ADTMILLER, MARILYNN BURDICK, English Teacher; *b:* Erie, PA; Rupert James; *c:* James, Michael, William; *ed:* St Mary of the Woods l (BA) Eng 1957; Western Reserve Univ (MA) Eng 1962; NEH Summer ms Allegheny Coll 1985, TX Chrstn Univ 1986; *cr:* Meml Jr HS 7th-8th Eng Tchr 1957-62; Acad HS 10th-12th Grd Eng Tchr 1962-63; Erie l Dist 7-12 Grd Sub Tchng 1972-80; Villa Maria Acad 9th, 11th-12th Eng Tchr 1980-; *ai:* Yrbk Copy Reader; Acad Sports League Coach; H Commonwealth Partnership 1985; NEH Grant for Stud in Plato, stotle, Machiavilli at TX Chrstn Univ 1986.

ADULIS, JANET KLIMASZ, Assistant Professor of English; *b:* ooklyn, NY; *m:* Robert Eugene; *c:* Daniel Joseph, Michael Robert, hrine Aniela; *ed:* St Univ of NY (BA) Early Scndry Eng 1968; Mankato Univ (MA) Eng 1973; Kent St Univ (PHD) Curr & Instruction 1991; *cr:* ndlewood Jr HS 9th Grd Eng Tchr 1968-69; Univ of Akron Part-Time mposition Instr 1979-81; Kent St Univ Part-Time Eng Instr 1979-93; keland Comm Coll Prof of Eng 1993-; *ai:* Dev Writing Specialist; Ad c Dev Ed Comm Mem; Affirmative Action Comm; Cultural Diversity in rr Stud Group; NCTE 1986-; Natl Assn of Developmental Ed 1986-, Coll mposition & Communication 1986-; IRA, Coll Rdng Assn 1986-; wman Ctr Parish Cncl 1995-, Sec; Lakeland Comm Coll Lib 1995-, Advy ; Presentations at Coll Rdng Assn, Natl Assn of Developmental Ed, CCC & IRA; Invited Panelist on Developmental Ed at 4th Annual Intnl nf on Adolescent & Adult Literacy; Publications in Annual Proceedings of Coll Rdng Assn; *office:* Lakeland Comm Coll 7700 Clocktower Dr Mentor OH 44060*

STAERKER, EUGENIA MARIE, Department Chairperson; *b:* Lackawana, NY; *m:* Raymond; *c:* John, Lisa Ansadorian, Laura; *ed:* Medaille Coll (BS) Ed 1964; Russell Sage Coll (MS) Ed 1971; NYS Cert Admin 1988; 30 Credits Above MS; *cr:* St Augustine Schl 8th Grd Tchr 1972-78; Hudson Vly Comm Coord Rdng Lab 1978-83, Acad Adv 1983-95, Dept Chair 1995-; *ai:* Enrollment & Planning Comm; Waiver Comm; Natl Acad Advs Assn 1987-; Dept Chprsns Assn; Troy City Cncl 1978-82; Well Spouse Fndtn 1991-94, Bd of Dir; Disabled Stdnts Svcs Awd 1982-94; Pres Awd HVCC 1990; *office:* Hudson Valley Comm Coll 80 Vandenburgh Ave Troy NY 12180

STAFFORD, CARL JAY, Hotel, Food Svc Mgmt Asst Prof; *b:* Manchester, CT; *m:* Brenda Mathewson; *c:* Natalie; *ed:* Manchester Comm Tech (AS) Restaurant Mngmt 1986; Univ of New Haven (BS) Hotel, Restaurant, Travel Admin 1993; *cr:* Hotel, Food Svc, Restaurant Industry 1978-86; Manchester Comm Tech Coll Asst Prof 1987-; *ai:* Hospitality Industry Assn Club Adv; CBEA 1992-; HSMAI 1990-; Article Pub 1996; *office:* Manchester Comm Coll PO Box 1046 60 Bidnell St Manchester CT 06040

STAFFORD, JOSEPH JOHN, Teacher & Coord of Gifted; *b:* Well Tannery, PA; *m:* Virginia C. Cunningham; *c:* Joseph J. III; *ed:* Shippensburg Univ (BS) Earth Sci 1969; West Chester Univ (MA) Phys Sci 1973; Univ of CT, Millersville Univ, Univ of DE for Gifted Ed; *cr:* Colonial Schl Dist Jr HS Sci Tchr 4 Yrs, HS Sci Tchr 4 Yrs; Gettysburg Area Schl Dist Sci Tchr 9 Yrs, Tchr & Coord for Gifted 9 Yrs; *office:* Gettysburg Jr HS Lefever St Gettysburg PA 17325

STAFFORD, MARCIA JONES, Kindergarten Teacher; *b:* Jamestown, NY; *w:* Jack Wendel (dec); *c:* Jennifer C. Lachajczyk, Trever W.; *ed:* Syracuse Univ (BA) Ed 1962; *cr:* Rochester City Schls Kndgtn Tchr 1962-65; Parker Schl Kndgtn Tchr 1965-67; Jamestown City Schls Kndgtn Tchr 1979-; *ai:* Site Base Decision Making Team; JTA 1979-, Past Schl Rep; NEA 1979-; Church Choir 1984-; Trained in Multiple Talents Approach to Tchng; *home:* 3334 Moon Rd Jamestown NY 14701

STAGGER, ANITA E., Geography Teacher & Admin Asst; *b:* Chicago, IL; *c:* Phillip Thompson, Yosef Thompson, Arnold, Symiel; *ed:* Rust Coll (BA) Soc Stud 1972; Attnd NYU at Buffalo, Univ of PA, Carlow Coll & STEP; *cr:* Penn Hills Sr HS US His & Afro Amer His Tchr, Soc Stud Curr 1972-79; Linton MS Geog & World Cultures Tchr 1980-, Soc Stud Tchr 1983-90, Afro Amer His & Geog Tchr 1990-, Admin Asst 1995-; *ai:* Positively Linton Club Spon; Variety Show Coord; Connection Club Spon; Afro-Amer Gifted Bowl 1993-94; PHEA & NEA 1972-; ACIS 1995-; Church Yth Dir; Multi Purpose Ctr Bd; NYU at Buffalow Flwshp; Afro Amer Gifted Bowl 1st Pl (2 Times); *office:* Linton MS 12200 Garland Dr Penn Hills PA 15235*

STAHL, BARBARA DEVITA, Senior High English Teacher; *b:* Washington, DC; *m:* Gerald; *c:* Kathryn M.; *ed:* (BS) Sec Ed Tchng 1976; Cnslng Masters Equivalent 1982; *cr:* Mifflin Cty Schls Eng Tchr 1976-81; Cntrl Daupin Schls Eng Tchr 1986-; *ai:* Newspaper Adv 1989-95; Yrbk Adv 1987-91; PSEA, NEA 1986-; *office:* Central Dauphin East Sr HS 626 Rutherford Rd Harrisburg PA 17109

STAHL, DEBRA DAWN, English Teacher; *b:* Columbus, NE; *m:* Paul Eugene; *c:* Lauren Nicole, Kolbi Paxton; *ed:* Concordia Coll (BA) Scndry Ed 1979; Bowie St Univ (MS) Rdng Specialist 1986; 3 Credit Hrs Newspaper Advs at Amer Univ; 3 Credit Hrs William & Mary Yrbk Advs; In-Svc Credits at MD St Dept of Ed, Cmptr Trng; *cr:* Capital Luth HS Eng Dept Chprsn 1979-86; Queen Anne's Cty HS Rdng Specialist, St Comp Ed, Eng Tchr 1986-; *ai:* Cmptr Tech Aid, After Schl Workshop Coord; Focus Groups Schl Improvement Comm; NEA, MSTA 1979-, Del; 4-H Vol 1990-; Stewardship Bd of Immanuel Luth Church 1994-; Women,s Club 1988-, Pres; IBM Educl Specialist; Natl Transportation Agency, MD BD of Ed, FL Bd of Ed Curr Specialist; *office:* Queen Anne's Co HS 125 Ruthsburg Rd Centreville MD 21617*

STAHL, DIANE MARIE, Tchr of Behavioral Disorders; *b:* Waynesboro, PA; *ed:* Salisbury St Coll (BS) PE 1977; The Johns Hopkins Univ (MS) Emotional Disturbances 1987; *cr:* Wash Co Alternative Schl 7th-12 Grd Hlth, Sci Tchr; Boonsboro MS 6th-8th Grd PE Tchr 1988-92; Wash Co Bd of Ed Tchr of K-6 Behavioral Disorders 1992-; *ai:* Boonsboro HS Sftbl 1983-, Bsktbl 1987-90 Coach; North Hagerstown HS Bsktbl, Sftbl Coach 1977-81; Johns Hopkins Univ Alumni Assn 1987-; Natl Sftbl Coaches Assn 1993-; Am Assn of Univ Women 1995-; NEA, MD STA 1987-; WA Cty Tchrs Assn 1987-, Bd of Dirs 1990-91; Natl Org for Women 1994-; Amer Legion Ladies Auxilliary 1988-; Head Coach Girls Bsktbl MD St Champions 1980-81; Alternative Schl Tchr of Yr 1985; *office:* Washington Cty Pub Schls PO Box 730 Hagerstown MD 21740

STAHL, DONALD L., Geography Professor; *b:* Gallatin Cty, KY; *c:* Eric, Julie, Kurt; *ed:* Eastern KY St (BA) Geography 1951; Univ of Cincinnati (MEd) Ed 1957; Miami Univ (MA) Geography 1967; *cr:* Boone Co Schls HS Tchr 1954-60; Three Rivers Schl Jr High Tchr 1962-63; Edinboro St College Geography Prof 1966-69; Essex Comm Coll Geography Prof 1969-; *ai:* Fac Appeals, Division Review Comms; Sierra Club 1970-; ACLU, Potomac Appalachian Trl Comm 1980-; *office:* Essex Comm Coll 7201 Rossville Blvd Baltimore MD 21237

STAHL, MICHAEL E., High School Counselor; *b:* Brooklyn, NY; *m:* Polly; *c:* Jeremy, Jerusha; *ed:* SUNY at Albany (BS) Bio 1973, (MS) Advanced Classroom Tchng 1977, (CAS) Cnslng, Psych 1985; *cr:* Oneida Jr HS Sci Tchr 1973-74; Woodlawn MS Sci, Math, Hlth Tchr 1974-84; Linton HS Bio Tchr 1984-86; Woodlawn MS Cnslr 1986-88; Steinmetz MS Cnslr 1988-90; Schenectady HS Cnslr 1990-; *ai:* Odyssey of Mind Coach; NYSUT 1973-; CDCA 1985-; Saratoga Schl Bds Assn 1987-; Galway Bd of Ed 1987-, Bd Mem; *office:* Schenectady HS 1401 The Plz Schenectady NY 12308

STAHL, REBECCA J., First Grade Teacher; *b:* Lima, OH; *m:* William W.; *c:* Christopher; *ed:* Bowling Green St Univ (BS) Elem Ed 1976; Univ of Findlay (MA) Tesol 1992; *cr:* C. R. Coblentz Schl Kndgtn-First Grd Tchr 1976-78; McComb Local Schl First Grd Tchr 1978-; *ai:* McComb Tchrs Assn 1978-, Elem Rep, Sec; L. Dale Dorney Fund Hancock Cty Grant 1992; Co-Presented "Teaching Basic Skills Through Literature" in Canada, Univ of Findlay Summer Inst & OH Migrant Tchrs Trng; *home:* 6243 County Road 139 Findlay OH 45840

STAHL, SHARON ANN, English Teacher; *b:* Brooklyn, NY; *ed:* Hunter Coll of City Univ of NY (BA) Eng 1969; Duke Univ (MA) Eng 1970; *cr:* Vly Stream South HS Eng Tchr 1970-73; George W. Hewlett HS Eng Tchr 1973-; *ai:* AFT 1970-; NCTE Tchr of Excl 1990; Natl Endowment for Hum Summer Inst 1988; *office:* George W Hewlett HS 60 Everit Ave Hewlett NY 11557

STAHLER, JERALD W., Bible Teacher & Counselor; *b:* Danville, PA; *m:* Lynn Wilson; *c:* Kent Mathew, Kevin Michael; *ed:* Bapt Bible Coll (BRE) Ed 1975; Attnd Pensacola Chrstn Coll & Liberty Univ Schl of Life Long Learning; *cr:* Bible Bapt Schl Tchr & Head Tchr 1975-81; IBM Admin Analyst 1981-92; Harrisburg Chrstn Schl Tchr & Cnslr 1992-; *ai:* Stu Life Adv 1994-; Ed Policies & Finance Comms; Discipleship Group Ldr; AACC 1995-; Grace Bible Fellowship Church 1994-; *office:* Harrisburg Chrstn Schl PO Box 6464 Harrisburg PA 17112*

STAHLMAN, MARY BADERTSCHER, Retired 3rd Grade Teacher; *b:* Bluffton, OH; *c:* Jeffrey; *ed:* Bluffton Coll (BSEd) Elem Ed 1963; Xavier Coll (MED) Ed 1978; Attnd Defiance Coll, IN Univ Extension at Ft Wayne; *cr:* Cory-Rawson Schls 5th Grd Tchr 1957-58; Grover Hill Schls 4th Grd Tchr 1958-61; New London Schls 4th Grd Tchr 1963-66; Sidney City Schls 3rd-4th Grd Tchr 1966-95; *ai:* ORTA 1995-; NEA, OEA, SEA 1975-95; Northwood Home Owners Assn 1992-, Sec; 1st United Meth Praise Choir 1992-; 1st United Meth Music Comm 1988-94, Sec; Martha Jennings Scholar 1980-81; Outstdng Elem Tchr of Amer 1974; *home:* 128 Leisure Ct Sidney OH 45365

STAHLMAN, MARY BUTLER, Softball Coach; *b:* DuBois, PA; *m:* Steven; *c:* Sarah, Elizabeth, Rachel; *cr:* St Rose of Lima Schl Sftbl Coach; *ai:* St Rose Home & Schl Assn Pres; Cath Yth Org Treas; North York Borough Schl Newsletter Publisher; Book Fair Chprsn; Schl Spring Sports Coord; *home:* 924 N Duke St York PA 17404

STAHURA, MARGARET MARY, Mathematics Teacher; *b:* Hazleton, PA; *ed:* Cabrini Coll (BA) Math 1965; Villanova Univ (MATM) Math 1973; *cr:* Sacred Heart Schl 6th Grd Tchr 1965-67; St Cyril Acad 9th-12th Grd Math Tchr 1967-78; Lebanon Cath HS 9th-11th Grd Math Tchr 1978-80; Bishop Hafey HS 10th-11th Grd Math Tchr 1981; Morristown HS 9th-11th Grd Math Tchr 1982-83; PA St Univ Tech Math, Calculus 1983-91; Nazareth Acad HS 9th-12th Grd Math Tchr 1991-; *ai:* Adv,Coach Sr Mathletes; NCEA 1965-; PA Cncl Tchrs Math 1992-; St Cyril Acad Alumnae Assn 1960-, VP; St Joseph Church Choir 1982-, Choir Dir 1990-; Natl Assn Pastoral Musicians 1987-.

STAIGER, BRIAN EDWARD, Science Teacher; *b:* Valdosta, GA; *m:* Therese Harding; *c:* Michelle, Colin; *ed:* Broome Comm Coll (AS) Liberal Arts, Criminal Justice 1979; St Univ Coll at Oneonta (BA) Elem, Early Sec Sci 1982; St Univ Coll at Cortland (MS) Scndry Bio 1991; *cr:* Vestal HS 9th Grd Earth Sci Tchr 1983-84; Cedarhurst Elem 4th Grd Tchr 1984-86; Susquehanna Valley Jr High 7th Grd Life Sci Tchr 1986-; *ai:* Boys, Girls Var Cross Cntry 1990-; Stu Cncl Adv 1987-; Bldg Improvement Team 1995-, Mem; NEA 1987-; *office:* Susquehanna Valley Jr HS PO Box 225 Conklin Rd Conklin NY 13748

STAIR, PEGGY DEROSA, Former Teacher; *b:* Indianapolis, IN; *m:* Stephen Von; *c:* Cameron; *ed:* Miami Univ (BA) Zoology 1987, (MAT) Biological Sci 1989; Cleveland St Univ 6 Grad Hrs; Notre Dame Coll Ctr for Prof Advanement 4 Grd Hrs; *cr:* Miami Univ Asst Tchr 1988-89; Metro Cath Parish Schl Jr High Sci, Hlth Tchr 1990-92; *ai:* Phi Sigma, Omicion Delta Kappa 1986-; *home:* 962 Dark Shadow Ct Westerville OH 43081

STAITI, JO ANN JOHNSON, Chemistry & Biology Teacher; *b:* Wareham, MA; *m:* Richard; *c:* Gregory, Scott, Katherine, Steven, Andrew; *ed:* Stonehill Coll (BS) Bio 1973; Suffolk U Schl of Law (JD) Law 1984; Attnd George Washington U Schl of Medicine, Bridgewater St Coll; *cr:* Chelmsford HS Chem Tchr 1978-80; Archbishop Williams HS Chem, Bio Tchr 1984-85; Rudin & Herzog PC Assoc Attorney 1986-87; Westwood HS Chem, Bio Tchr 1987-; Canton Citizen Sports Writer, Ed 1982-; *ai:* Ecolibrium Adv; Co-Mod Jud Cncl 1994-; WTA 1987-; MTA, NEA 1978-; Canton Schl Comm 1989-94, Chm, Sec, Vice Chm; Canton Arts Lottery Cncl 1989-; Enable Inc Bd of Trustees 1996-; Grant Recipient Westwood Educl Fnd; *office:* Westwood HS 200 Nathan St Westwood MA 02090*

STAITI, RICHARD ROBERT, Science Teacher; *b:* Boston, MA; *m:* Jo Ann Johnson; *c:* Greg, Scott, Katherine, Steven, Andrew; *ed:* Stonehill Coll (BS) Bio 1973; Bridgewater St (MED) Admin 1975; Suffolk Law Univ (JD) Law 1989; *cr:* Galvin MS Tchr 1973-75; Canton HS Tchr 1975-; *ai:* Ath Trainer; EMT; Stu Cncl, Stu Advy Comm Adv; NEA, CTA 1973-; ATOM 1985-; MBA 1990-; Bd of Selectmen 1980-89, Chm 1981, 1984, 1987; Bd of Lib Trustee 1978-80; Norfolk Cty Adv Bd 1980, Chm; MA Resp Hosp Trustee 1989-, Vice-Chm; Canton Lions Clubs 1978-; *office:* Canton HS 900 Washington St Canton MA 02021

STAKER, PATRICIA SPARKS, Teacher; *b:* Portsmouth, OH; *m:* Martin; *c:* Michael, Katelyn; *ed:* Western IL Univ (BS) Elem Ed 1987; OH Univ (MS) Micro Comps in Ed 1995; *cr:* Wheelersburg Elem Tchr 1989-; *ai:* Kappa Delta Pi 1987-; NE A 1989-; Outstdng Pre-Svc Tchng Awd 1987; *office:* Wheelersburg Elem Schl 1760 Dogwood Ridge Rd Wheelersburg OH 45694*

STALBAUM, BERNARDINE VASEL, English Tchr & Rdng Specialist; *b:* Passaic, NJ; *ed:* Montclair St Coll (AB) Eng 1964, (MA) Eng 1969; Rdng Spec, Prin & Supvr Cert 1981; Clifton Bd of Ed Cmptr Programming Courses; *cr:* Christopher Columbus Jr HS Lang Arts Tchr 1964-82; Clifton Evening Schl GED Instr 1984-; Clifton HS Rdng Specialist 1982-, Eng Tchr 1991-; *ai:* Acad Decathlon Coach; NEA 1964-, Local Del; NCTE 1964-; NJCTE 1993-; IRA 1981-; NJRA 1982-; Montclair St Coll Alumni Assn 1968-, VP; Fac Org 1982-, Welfare Chprsn; Clifton Tchrs Assn 1964-, Various Comms, 25 Yr Svc Awd; Co-Authored Assessment & Skills Tests for Schl; Who's Who in Amer Ed 1989-90, 1992-93; Lang Arts-Eng Dept Resource Person; *home:* 279 Pershing Rd Clifton NJ 07013*

STALEY, ALENE, Business Admin Dept Chair; *b:* Chicago, IL; *ed:* Univ of IL at Chicago (BS) Acctng 1970; Southeastern Univ (MS) Acctng 1979; *cr:* Arthur Young & Co Staff Auditor 1970-72; Fed Govt Budget Ofcr, Other Positions 1972-82; Saint Joseph's Coll Chair Also Asst Prof 1987-; *ai:* Adv to Coll Democrats; AICPA 1988-; ME Soc of CPA's 1983-; *office:* Saint Josephs Coll 278 White's Bridge Rd Standish ME 04084*

STALEY, LINDA LUCREZI, 6th Grd English Teacher; *b:* Painesville, OH; *m:* Bruce Franklin; *c:* Brandon, Jason, Michael; *ed:* West Liberty St Coll (BA) Elem Ed 1979; Lee Canter Courses Quest Intnl; TESA Outdoor Ed; *cr:* Meml MS 5th Grd Tchr 1979-82, 8th Grd Rdng Tchr 1983-86; Madison MS 7th Grd Eng, 8th Grd Rdng Tchr 1987-88, 6th Grd Eng Tchr 1988-; *ai:* NEA, OEA, MEA 1979-; *office:* Madison MS 1941 Red Bird Rd Madison OH 44057

STALEY, RICHARD RAY, 5th Grade Teacher; *b:* Tuscarawas, OH; *m:* Carol Ann Ronald; *c:* Stephanie, Bethanie; *ed:* Malone Coll (BSEd) Elem Ed 1967; Ashland Univ (MAEd) Curr, Instruction 1989; *cr:* Dover Pub Schls 6th Grd Tchr 1966-79; Dover Pub Schls 5th Grd Tchr 1980-; *ai:* Coach 5th, 6th Grd Girls Bsktbl; Head Coach Dover HS Girls Track; NEA, OEA, DEA 1966-; Dover Elks 1968-, Past Exalted Ruler, All OH; Free & Accepted Masons 1965-; Dover First Morivana Church 19730, Past Trustee; Dist Coach of Yr 1990-92, 1994-95; *office:* Dover Pub Schls 219 W 6th St Dover OH 44622*

STALL, DONALD LLOYD,JR., 5th Grade Teacher; *b:* Marshallville, OH; *ed:* Ashland Univ (BA) Elem Ed 1988; Working on Masters Multiple Intelligences, Admin; *cr:* Elyria City Schls 5th Grd Tchr 1988-; *ai:* Stu Cncl Adv; HS, Cath HS Var Chrldng Coach; Site Base Comm; Multiple Intelligences, Schl Wide Teams; Drama Club Tri Coach; ESC Tchr Assn 1988-; NEA 1984-, Treas; Jennings Scholars Awd Martha Holden Jennings Fnd; *office:* Franklin Elem Schl 446 W 11th Elyria OH 44035*

STALLINGS, SUSAN F., Coordinator of the Gifted; *b:* Canton, OH; *m:* Richard H. III; *c:* Laurel, Sharon, Kathryn; *ed:* Malone Coll (BS) Fr, Eng 1971; Millersville Univ (MA) Gifted Ed 1990; Quality Team Leading Roadway Express; Increasing Human Potential Sprint United Telephone; *cr:* Northwest HS Fr, Eng Tchr 1983-84; Mechanicsburg Intermediate Schl Fr, Eng Tchr 1985-86; Good Hope MS Tchr of Gifted 1986-87; Big Spring Schl Dist Scndry Tchr of Gifted 1987-90; Boiling Springs Jr Sr HS Coord, Scndry Tchr of Gifted 1990-; *ai:* SADD Club Adv; Quiz Bowl, Debate, Mock Trial Coach; PDK 1990-; Tchrs of Gifted Assn 1989-, Pres; PA Assn for Gifted Ed 1987-; ACES Outstdng Ed Awd; Governor's Hwy Safety in Ed Awd; *office:* Boiling Springs HS 4 Forge Rd Boiling Springs PA 17007

STALNAKER, TAMMY ADAMS, Sixth Grade Teacher; *b:* Columbus, OH; *m:* Michael O.; *c:* Adam; *ed:* Otterbein Coll (BS) Elem Ed 1985; Wright St Univ (MED) Tchr Ldr 1995; *cr:* Jonathan Alder Local Classroom Tchr 1986-; *ai:* Canaan Bldg Advy Comm; Cntrl OH Regnl Prof Dev Math Tchr Ldr; NEA 1981-; OH Ed Assn 1981-, Stu Prgm St Pres; Jonathan Elder Ed Assn 1986-, Pres, Mbrshp Chair, Bldg Rep; Plain City United Meth Church 1975-; *office:* Canaan MS 7055 US Highway 42 S Plain City OH 43064*

STALONAS, GERALDINE GRUSON, English Teacher; *b:* Cheverly, MD; *m:* Bernard Dornbusch; *c:* Kerry, Ellen; *ed:* SUNY at Buffalo (BA) Eng 1967; Hunter Coll (MA) Eng 1976; 30 Addl Post Grad Credit Hrs; *cr:* Jerusalem Ave Jr HS Eng Tchr 1967-70; Boody Jr HS Eng Tchr 1977-83; Kingsborough Comm Coll Adjunct Lecturer in Basic Writing Skills for Coll NOW Prgm 1989-; New Utrecht HS Eng, Creative Writing Teacher & Lit Magazine Adv 1983-; *ai:* Hlth Information & Condom Availability Prgm Facilitator; Site Writing Coord; NYC Bd of Ed; United Fed of Tchrs, AFT 1977-; NCTE, NY City Writing Project 1985-; Natl Writing Proect & Ctr for Study of Writing & Literacy 1990-; Poetry Fellow by Tchrs & Writers Collaborative NYC to Participate in Series of Poetry Seminars; Elected 1992 Tchr Honorarily Inducted into ARISTA; *office:* New Utrecht HS 1601 80th St Brooklyn NY 11214

STALTER, RICHARD, Professor of Biology; *b:* Montvale, NJ; *c:* Laurie; *ed:* Rutgers Univ (BS) Bio 1963; Univ of SC (PHD) Bio 1968; *cr:* High Point Coll Asst Prof of Bio 1968-69; Pfeiffer Coll Asst Prof of Bio 1969-70; St Johns Univ Prof of Bio 1971-; *ai:* Roger Bacon Sci Soc & Delta Sigma Phi Moderator; Rugby Coach; Assn of Southeastern Biologists 1967-; SC Acad of Sci 1968-; Southern Appalachian Bot Club 1969-; Torrey Bot Club 1971-; Northeastern Weed Sci Soc 1971-, 2nd Best Paper Awd 1980; Numerous Grants; Numeorus Articles Pub; 3 Books Pub; Honorable Mention for Best Tchr Awd at St Johns 1995.

STAMBAUGH, DAVID ALLEN, English Teacher; *b:* Reading, PA; *m:* Suzanne Louise Fritch; *c:* Paige S. Jarecki, Chad D., Shannon A.; *ed:* Wesley Coll (AA) Lbrl Arts 1965; WV Wesleyan Coll (BA) Fr & Eng 1967; PA St Univ 30 Credits Post Grad Stud; *cr:* Susquenita HS 10th-12th Grd Fr Tchr 1967-68; Hamburg Area HS Jr High Eng Tchr 1968-; *ai:* Var Bsbl & Var Soccer Coach; Life Skills Club Adv; NEA 1970-; PSEA 1970-; Williamson Lodge #37 1968-; Rajah Shrine 1969-; Tall Cedars of Lebanon 1969-; Stu Cncl Tchr of Yr 1981; Annie Sullivan Awd Nom 1995; *home:* Main St Strausstown PA 19559

STAMBORSKY, PHILLIP, Assoc Prof of Eng & Dept Chm; *b:* Springfield, MA; *m:* Linda Karen Perlman; *c:* Daniel; *ed:* Univ of MA at Amherst (BA) Eng 1977, (MA) Eng 1979, (PHD) Eng 1987; Post Doctoral Stud Philosophy, Intellectual His Yale Univ 1988-93; *cr:* Albertus Magnus Coll Eng Prof 1987-; *ai:* Fac Status, Lbrl Stud Advy Comms; ALSC 1995-; Yale-Mellon Visiting Fac Flwshp; Books: The Depictive Image Metaphor and Literary Experience, Myth and the Limits of Reason, Poetic Work of Emily Dickinson A Readers' Text; *office:* Albertus Magnus Coll 700 Prospect St New Haven CT 06511

STAMER, ERICH DETLEF, German Teacher; *b:* Bremerhaven, Germany; *m:* Marilyn Adams; *c:* Erich Adam; *ed:* Westminster Coll (BA) Ger, Soc Stud 1971; Fairleigh Dickinson U, Slippery Rock 1972; Montclair St Coll 1973; Westminster Coll 1974; Beaver Valley Intermediate Unit 77; *cr:* Blackhawk HS Ger, Soc Stud Tchr 1971-; *ai:* HS Soccer Coach 1978-; Beaver Valley Acad Summer Prgm; NEA 1971-; Ger Smer Partnership Prgm 1988-; Teutonia mannerchor 1991-; Goethe House GAPP Prgm Contributor; *office:* Blackhawk HS 500 Blackhawk Rd Beaver Falls PA 15010

STAMM, K. BRAD, Asst Prof of Economics & Bus; *m:* Tami; *c:* Sara; *ed:* Bowling Green St Univ (BS) Bus, Ec 1975; Eastern Coll (MBA) Bus, Ec 1987; Ec Fordham Univ; Attnd Gordon Coll, FL St Univ; *cr:* Glassboro St Univ Ec Prof 1988; Eastern Coll Ec Prof 1988; Nyack Coll Bus, Ec Prof 1989-; *ai:* Bus Club, Stu Mrktg Adv; Amer Ec Assn, Amer Mngmt Assn 1992-; Chrstn Bus Fac Assn 1989-; Fac Grant; *office:* Nyack Coll 1 S Boulevard Nyack NY 10960*

STAMMER, CHRISTINE L., English Teacher; *b:* New York, NY; *m:* Donald; *c:* Kirsten, Judson, Kimberly, Christopher; *ed:* Mount Saint Mary Coll (BA) Eng 1971; 33 Grad Credit Hrs in Eng & Ed; *ai:* Site-Base Mgmt Team; NYSUT 1973-; *office:* Spackenkill HS 112 Spackenkill Rd Poughkeepsie NY 12603

STAMP, AUDREY FINNELL, German Teacher; *b:* Omaha, NE; *m:* Donn; *c:* Andrew, Zachary, Trevor; *ed:* Univ of NE at Lincoln (BS) Ger & Eng 1971; Grad Work at Xavier Univ & Univ of Dayton; Spec Stud at Goethe Inst in Germany; *cr:* Crown HS Ger & Eng Tchr 1971-72; Lakota HS Ger Tchr 1972-77 & 1990-; *ai:* Ger Club Spon; Curr Comm; OFLA 1990-; AATG 1990-; Scouting 1987-, Various Ldrshp; PTO 1983-, Various Offices; Hope Evangelical Free Church 1990-, Various Act; Ashland Oil Tchr Achvmt Awd Nom; AATG Awd for Outstdng Achvmt of Ger; *office:* Lakota HS 5050 Tylersville Rd West Chester OH 45069*

STAMPFEL, WALTER F., Math Teacher; *b:* New York, NY; *ed:* St John's (BS) Ath Admin 1986, (MS) Scndry Ed 1994; *cr:* LIC YMCA Asst to Prgm Dir 1986-87; Msgr McClancy HS Tchr & Coach 1987-; *ai:* NHS Adv; Jr Var Bsbl Coach; Alumni Relations Dir; Yrbk Bus Adv.

STANCIL, DANIEL DEAN, Prof of Electrical & Comp Engr; *b:* Raleigh, NC; *m:* Katherine Elaine Campbell; *c:* Brian Alan, Michael Adam; *ed:* Tenn Tech Univ (BSEE) Electrical Engrng 1976; MIT (SM) Electrical Engrng 1978, (EE) Electrical Engrng 1979, (PHD) Electrical Engrng 1981; *cr:* NASA Langley Rsrch Ctr Engrng Trainee 1974-75; MIT Lincoln Lab Part-Time Staff Mem 1980-81; NC St Univ Asst Prof 1981-86; Carnegie Mellon Univ Assoc Prof & Prof 1986-, Assoc Dept Head 1992-94; *ai:* CMU Amateur Radio Club; Fac Adv & Station Trustee; CMU Chptr of the Order of the Engr; Fac Adv; Sigma Xi, NC St Rsrch Awd 1985; Phi Kappa Phi; IEEE Sec & Treas, VP Sr Mem Magnetics Soc; Am Phys Soc; Tau Beta Pi; Eta Kappa Nu; Georgetown Coll 1996, Bd ofTrustees; IBM Applied Rsrch Flwshp 180-81; Book: Theory of Magnetostatic Waves 1993; Numerous Articles Pub; Smithsonian Computerworld Awd Finalist 1996; *office:* Carnegie Mellon Univ 5000 Forbes Ave Pittsburgh PA 15213

STANCLIFF, MELANIE DEITZ, Cosmetology Teacher; *b:* Chincotigue, VA; *m:* Robert; *c:* Christina, Charles; *ed:* Attnd Washington DC Beauty 1968, MDU 1989-93, PGCC 1973-95; *cr:* Dominic Hair Stylists 1968-73; Mel's Hair Designs Owner, Stylist 1973-86; MD Schl of Hair Design Owner, Tchr 1979-88; Laurel HS Cosmetology Tchr 1988-; *ai:* VICA Adv, Bd of Dirs; Dept Chair; Perkins Comm; MD Cosmetology Task Force; Cosmetology By Laws Comm; NCA 1990-; AVA 1988-; VICA 1994-, Bd of Dir Sec; FOPA 1979-83; PG Cty Sci Credit for Cosmetology; *office:* Laurel HS 8000 Cherry Ln Laurel MD 20707

STANCO, REGINA FITZGERALD, 5th Grade Teacher; *b:* Kew Gardens, NY; *m:* Rocco; *ed:* St Josephs Coll (BA) Child Stud & Spcl Ed 1985; Queens Coll (MS) Elem Ed 1988; *cr:* Polk St Schl 5th Grd Tchr 1985-; *office:* Polk Street Elem Schl 960 Polk Ave Franklin Square NY 11010*

STANDERA, STAN, Social Studies Teacher; *b:* Dunkirk, NY; *m:* Rachel Wood; *c:* Keith, Renee, Jessica; *ed:* SUC at Fredonia (BA) Soc Stud & His 1965; SUC at Geneseo Grad Hrs; *cr:* Letchworth Cntrl Schl Soc Stud Tchr 1965-; *ai:* Class & Var Club Adv; Past Soccer, Ftbl & Bsktbl Coach; NYSTA 1965-71; Letchworth Cntrl Tchrs Assn 1965-, Pres 3 Yrs; NEA & NYEA 1971-; Gainesville Fire Dept 1984-; Univ of Rochester & Letchworth Hnr Soc Tchr of Yr Awd 1986 & 1994; *office:* Letchworth Cntrl Schl School Rd Gainesville NY 14066

STANDLEY, DENISE JANOWIECKI, 7th Grd Language Arts Teacher; *b:* Toledo, OH; *c:* Christopher, Sara, Rachel, Jessica; *ed:* Univ of Toledo (BE) Elem, Primary Ed 1971; 20 Grad Hrs Counseling; 8 Grad Hrs Elem Writing Courses; *cr:* St Vincent de Paul Schl 6th Grd Tchr 1972-76; Bellevue City Schls Sub Tchr 1980-82; Queen of Peace Schl 7th-8th Grd Tchr 1984-92; Toledo Pub Schls 7th Grd Lang Arts Tchr 1992-; *ai:* CARES; Toledo Fed Tchrs 1992-; Articles Pub; *office:* Jones Jr HS 550 Walbridge Ave Toledo OH 43609

STANEK, MICHAEL FRANCIS, Math & Science Teacher; *b:* Wilkes-Barre, PA; *m:* Cynthia Louise Okuniewski; *c:* Michael, Joseph; *ed:* Wilkes Univ (BS) Bio 1975; Bloomsburg Univ (MS) Bio 1979; Wilkes Univ Scndry Tchng Cert Bio 1977, Math 1992; *cr:* Coll Misericordia Adj Fac Mem, Sci Dept 1989-91; Luzerne Cty Comm Coll Adj Fac Mem, Sci Dept 1991-93; Crestwood Schl Dist Math, Sci Tchr 1985-; *ai:* Sci Fair 7th Grd Class Adv; Luzern Cty Chptr Mathcounts Competition Team Coach; Natl Sci Olympiad Amer Jr HS Math Examination 7th Grd Class COord; PA Math League, Continental Math League Contests; Crestwood Ed Assn, PA St Ed Assn, NEA 1985-; NSTA 1996; Hanover Area Yth Soccer League 1995-; Ashley-Newtown Minor League Bsbl Coach 1992-; Saint Aloysius Schl 3rd, 4th Grd Bsktbl Coach 1994-; Ashley-Newtown Little League Player Agent 1995-; Presenter Project Learn Wilkes Univ 1992; Presentation Macintosh Cmptr & Application; Recipient Family of Yr Awd 1991; *office:* Rice Elem Schl RR 8 Nuangola PA 18637

STANEK, SHARON MOYNIHAN, English Teacher; *b:* Yonkers, NY; *m:* Michael; *c:* Kerri, Chris; *ed:* SUNY at Albany (BA) Eng 1972; SUNY at Stonybrook (MA) Lbrl Stud 1976; 75 Addl Credit Hrs; *cr:* Sachem South HS Eng Tchr 1973-; *ai:* AFT, NYSUT, Sachem Cntrl Tchrs Assn 1973-; Improved Schl Svc Limited Eng Proficient Stdnts ISS Grant 1990-91; Mid East Suffolk Tchrs Mini Grant 1989-92.

STANFIELD, WILLIAM FREDERICK, Art Teacher; *b:* Hillsdale, MI; *m:* Marta Vestfals; *c:* Heidi, Darek; *ed:* Adrian Coll (BA) Art 1966; Youngstown St Univ (MBA) Scndry Admin 1976; Credits at OH Univ, Geneva Coll; *cr:* Beaver Local Schl Grds 5-12 Art Tchr, Coached Bsbl HS 1968-72; Beaver Local MS Art Tchr 1987-; Columbiana HS Asst Coach Girl's Softbl; *ai:* Tri-Hi-Y 1966-67, Art Club 1968-75 Adv; Prof Tchrs Org Pres 1977-; Negotiater Tchr's Org 1990; Head Bsbl 1977-, Asst Girl's Sftbl Columbiana HS Coach; BLEA 1966-; Pres, Negotiater; NEA 1972-; NEOTA 1966-; Columbiana Bsbl Assoc 1990-; Beaver Local Boosters 1968-; Columbiana Boosters 1986-; Zion Luth Church 1972-, Pres, VP, Trustee; *office:* Beaver Local HS 13052 SR 7 Lisbon OH 44432

STANFORD, CINDY GEARNER, Family Advocacy Outreach Mgr; *b:* Mt Pleasant, TX; *m:* Andrew B.; *c:* Lauren E.; *ed:* Univ of TX at Austin (BS) Tchr of Hearing Impaired 1976; Trinity Univ (MED) Guid, Cnslng 1981; *cr:* San Antonio ISD Tchr of Hearing Impaired 1976-78; TX St Schl for Deaf Tchr of Hearing Impaired 1978-80; San Antonio ISD Tchr of Hearing Impaired 1990-91, Guid Cnslr 1991-94; USAF Family Advocacy Outreach Mgr 1995-; *ai:* Coordinate Big Brothers, Big Sisters Prgm; Red Cross HIV, AIDS, Babysitting Instr; After Schl Care Comm; Amer Cnslng Assn; Alpha Delta Kappa; Joan Orr 17th Air Force Spouse of Yr 1995.

STANFORD, CURTIS TILLERSON, Third Grade Teacher; *b:* Spartanburg, SC; *m:* Lorenzo; *c:* Sheri Lynn; *ed:* Morris Coll (BS) Elem Ed 1958; Attnd Hunter Coll, Kean Coll; *ai:* Crimson Queen Production Travel Consultant; Sci Curr Dev Mem; NEA 1968-; NJ Ed Assn 1977-; Second Bapt Church, Schlsp Comm Chprsn & Cresent Club Mem; *home:* 727 John Ter Neptune NJ 07753*

STANGE, GILBERT WILLIAM,III, Social Studies Teacher; *b:* Baltimore, MD; *m:* Mary Louise Thompson; *ed:* Towson St Univ (BS) Soc Sci 1990; Johns Hopkins Univ 12 Credits Towards Lbrl Arts MA; *cr:* Towson HS Soc Stud Tchr 1991-; *ai:* Head Coach Mens' Cross Cntry, Indoor, Outdoor Track, Field; Sons of Amer Revolution 1988-; *office:* Towson HS 69 Cedar Ave Baltimore MD 21286

STANGEL, JO ANN, Amer Lit & SAT Prep Teacher; *b:* Cumberland, MD; *ed:* WV Univ (BS) Eng, Speech 1954; Masters Equivalency Jrnlsm WV Univ 1969; *cr:* Allegany HS Tchr 1963-72; Carrick HS Tchr 1972-90; Bishop Walsh MS Tchr 1990-; Walsh HS Tchr 1990-; *ai:* Newspaper; Yrbk; Schl Musical; Lit Magazine; Sr Class Spon; Chrldrs; Drill Team;Allegany Comm Coll Frosh Eng Tchr; Grad Stud in Jrnlsm Wall Street Journal Fellowship; Pittsburgh Steelers Girls Dance Drill Teams Dir; Middle State Evaluating Team for HS Eng; *office:* Biship Walsh MS, HS Bishop Walsh Dr Cumberland MD 21502*

STANGHELLINI, MARY ELLEN (TOWER), Chemistry Teacher; *b:* Weymath, MA; *m:* Robert; *ed:* St Joseph's Coll (BA) Bio, Chem 1986; Bridgewater St (MAT) Chem 1989; 24 Credit Hrs Post Grad Stud Bridgewater & Fitchburg St; *cr:* Cardinal Spellman HS Chem Tchr 1986-91; Quincy Coll Chem Tchr 1990-93; Coyle-Cassidy HS Chem Tchr 1991-93; Silver Lake Regnl HS Chem Tchr 1993-; *ai:* Stu Cncl Adv; MAST, NEA, PCEA 1993-; LPGA 1996-; Ed Grant; Eastern Edison Awd; *office:* Silver Lake Reg HS 132 Pembroke St Kingston MA 02364

STANIEC, JOANNE MONACO, High School Religion Teacher; *b:* Philadelphia, PA; *m:* Victor G.; *c:* Alycia Bischof, Rusty, Stephen, Christian; *ed:* Gwynedd Mercy (BS) Elem Ed 1980; Trenton St 21 Post Grad Credits Towards MA, Prgm in Guidance & Cnslng; St Charles Seminary 24 Post Grad Credits in Theology; *cr:* Our Lady of Calvary 3rd-4th & 6th Grd Elem Tchr 1971-81; Archbishop Ryan Hs for Boys 9th & 12th Grd Theology Tchr 1981-84, Archbishop Wood HS for Boys 9th-11th Grd Theology Tchr 1984-88; Paul VI Hs 9th-11th Grd Theology Tchr 1988-; *ai:* Comm Svc Corp Prolife Moderator; NEA 1981-; ACT 1981-; Cherry Hl Civic Assn 1988-, Sec; Parents Booster Club 1992-, Pres; Parents Booster Club 1993-95; Sec & Pres; S Jersey Hotel-Motel Assn 1986-, VP; Nom & Chosen by Sdnts at S Jersey Best Tchr 1992 & 1993; *office:* Paul VI HS Hopkins Rd Haddonfield NJ 08033

STANIK, LEOKADIA STAWICK, Art Teacher; *b:* Brooklyn, NY; *m:* Theodore; *c:* Dana, Laura; *ed:* Glassboro St (BA) Art Ed 1969; Newark St (MA) Art Ed; *cr:* Terrill Jr High Art Edctr 1969-72; David Brearley Regnl HS Art Edctr 1972-77; Hillsborough HS Art Edctr 1988-; *ai:* Natl Art Hnr Soc Adv; Fine Arts Calendar Coord; Set Designer & Art Dir for Musical; Mid Sts Eval & Dist Staff Dev Comms; Art Edctrs of NJ 1969-, 2nd VP 1973; NAEA 1988-; Brachburg Womans Club 1985-; *office:* Hillsborough HS 466 Raider Blvd Belle Mead NJ 08502

STANILKA, CATHY M., Physical Education Teacher; *b:* Ticonderoga, NY; *m:* Edward B.; *ed:* Lyndon St Coll (BA) PE 1976; 30 Addl Hrs Ed 1979; Cmptr Trng; Discipline Courses, Trng Models; *cr:* Hartford Cntrl Schl K-12 Grd PE Tchr 1976-77; Bolton Cntrl Schl K-12th Grd PE Tchr 1977-81; Lake George Jr Sr HS 7th-12th Grd PE Tchr 1981-; *ai:* Var Coach Vlybl, Sftbl; Var Club Adv; Post Prom Comm; Stu Advy Cncl; AFT, NYSUT 1977-; LGEA 1981-; NYSSCDG 1990-; PTSA Yth Commission 1984-; Coach of Yr All Area Vlybl 1993, 1994; NYS Class C Sftbl Champions 1992; Team NYS Sportsmanship Awd Sftbl 1992, Vlybl 1993, 1994; NYSPHSAA Scholar, Team Ath Awds; *office:* Lake George Jr/Sr HS 425 Canada St Lake George NY 12845*

STANISCI, TINA BOTTALICO, Second Language Eng Teac Brooklyn, NY; *m:* Franco; *c:* Carlo, Gian Vito, Rosanna; *ed:* Long Univ (BA) Span, Ital 1973, (MA) Biling Ed 1978, (MA) Schl Admir *cr:* I. S. 281 Schl Biling Ital Tchr 1973-77; P. S. 58 Schl Biling I Tchr 1977-81, 5th Grd Tchr 1981-83, Math, Sci, SS for GAT 1983-91, ESL Tchr 1991-; *ai:* UFT, AFT 1973-; Flwshp Schl Adm Kawnus Recognition Awd for Working with Immigrant Stdnts.

STANISLAUS, YOLANDA, HS Earth Science Teacher; *b:* Brookly *ed:* 3 Hrs Fordham Univ, Coll of St Rose; Full Time Stu Horstra Ur John Jay HS Tchr 1994-; *ai:* Dance Instr Multicultural Dance Club; Choreographer Yth United Change World; *office:* John Jay HS 347 St Brooklyn NY 11201

STANKEWICZ, MARY CHRISTINE, Seventh Grade Geography *b:* Perth Amboy, NJ; *ed:* Trenton St Coll (BA) Soc Stud 1971; Pos Stud Geography, Amer His; *cr:* Avenel Jr HS Soc Stud Tchr 19 Woodbridge MS Geography Tchr 1981-; *ai:* Soc Stud Staff Ldr; 1978-; NJ Cncl for Soc Stud, NJ Geographic Alliance 1987-; Alpha Kappa 1982-, Chapter Historian 1984-86, Chapter Correspondir 1986-88, Chapter Pres 1988-90, St Bylaws Chm 1990-94; Amer Post 471 Tchr of Yr 1988; Governor Kean's Tchr Recognition Awd *office:* Woodbridge MS 525 Barron Ave Woodbridge NJ 07095

STANKO, DIANNE DANKA, Biology Teacher; *b:* Cleveland, O James J.; *ed:* OH St UNiv (BS) Bio Ed 1960; Univ of TX at Austin (Bio 1965, (PHD) Bio 1967; *cr:* Beachwood HS Bio Tchr 1960-63; U OK Asst Prof 1968-70; Upper St Clair HS Bio Tchr 1974-; *ai:* 1960-; AFT 1982-; Natl Sci Fnd Flwshp; Articles Pub; *office:* Upper Clair HS 1825 Mclaughlin Run Rd Pittsburgh PA 15241

STANLEY, BETH A., Social Studies Teacher; *b:* Canton, OH; *ed:* K Univ (BS) Soc Stud 1974; 17 Grad Hrs; *cr:* Canton City Schls Sub 1971-79; Stark Cty Schls Sub Tchr 1974-79; St Pauls Schl Soc Stuc 1979-; *ai:* St Paul's Church Sesquicentennial Celebration Schl (Hoover HS Fnd of Excl Honored Edctr 1994.

STANLEY, MARY MONTGOMERY, Business Dept Chairpers Cambridge, MD; *m:* Waddell B.; *c:* Angela Chinelle Stanley Hamilto DE St Univ (BS) Bus Ed 1965; United Chrstn Coll (BTH) Theology Wilmington Coll (MS) Human Resource Mngmt 1992; *ai:* Bus Pr Amer, Peer Cnslng Adv; Schl to Work Advy Comm; Gospel Choir; DSEA 1980-; DBSEA 1988-; Prison Flwshp 1982-, Comm Coor Awd; NAACP 1989-; Prison Flwshp Area Cncl 1995-; Peter Spencer Awds.

STANLEY, NORMAN, Assistant Principal; *b:* Bayonne, NJ; *m:* Ar Cofield; *c:* Norman III; *ed:* Kean Coll-Cum Laude (BA) Elem Ed (MA) Educ Admin 1983; *cr:* Lincoln Schl Tchr 1976-88; Ashland Sch Prin 1988-; Essex Cty Coll Part-time GED Tchr 1995; *ai:* Span Imm Unique Schl Comm; Safety Patrol, Kndgtn Kops Parent Vol Group Adv; East Orange Ed Assn 1976-, Negotiations Chprsn; NJEA, NEA Union Rep; E O Admin Assn 1988-; Iselin Ath Assn 1996-, Coach; NJ Day Recognition Awd 1988; Lincoln Schl Tchr of Yr Nom 1988 Selected East Orange Stdnts to Intnl Future Problem Solvers of Amer 1st Place 1988; *office:* Ashland Elem Schl 180 Lincoln St E Oran 07018*

STANLEY, PERRY, English Teacher; *b:* Spring Valley, NY; *ed:* Ru Univ (BA) Eng 1987; *cr:* Willingboro HS Eng Tchr 1987-88; Brunswick HS Eng Tchr 1988-90; Fair Lawn HS Eng Tchr 1992 Newspaper Adv; *office:* Fair Lawn HS Berdan Ave Fair Lawn NJ 074

STANLEY, ROBERT EDWARD, Social Studies Tchr & Dept Ch Chicago, IL; *m:* Nancy; *c:* Matt, Melissa; *ed:* Mac Murray Coll (B 1971; Cleveland St Univ (MED) Ed; Attnd John Carroll Univ, Kent St Toledo Univ, Univ of FL; *cr:* Lee Burneson Jr HS Soc Stud Tchr 197 Westlake HS Dept Chm 1985-; *ai:* Wrestling Coach; Close-Up Adv; 1971-; Natl Assn of Scndry Supvrs; Town Criers 1985-; Jr Achvmt B Ldrshp Awd; Taft Flwshp; Applied Ec Tchr Flwshp.

STANLEY, THOMAS E., English Teacher; *b:* Toledo, OH; *m:* Klopping; *c:* Aaron, Sarah; *ed:* Univ of Toledo (BED) Eng, Geo (MED) Guid 1981; 12 Post Grad Hrs Ed; *cr:* NSW Dept of Ed 1973-74; Genoa Area HS Tchr 1975-; *ai:* Coaching Ftbl 16 Yrs, Girls 17 Yrs; Career Ed Comm 20 Yrs; NHS Comm 5 Yrs; AFT 1975-; Past Schlsp Fnd 1990-, Pres; *office:* Genoa Area HS 2980 N Genoa Clay C Rd Genoa OH 43430

STANLEY, VERA M. MOORE, Level 2 Teacher; *b:* Kansas City, K Gerald W.; *c:* Jeffrey, Andrea Stanley Baker; *ed:* Central MO St Univ Ed 1958, (MS) Ed, Admin 1961; 15 Semester Hrs Univ of Toledo Independence MO Schl Tchr 1958-61; Kansas City MO Tchr 196 Center Schl Dist Tchr 1971-72; Anthony Wayne Schls Tchr 1972-; *ai:* Tchr; Grd Level Chm; Supvr of Stu Tchrs; NEA 1958-; OEA 1972-; A 1972-, Exec, Welfare Comms; IRA 1972; Church Svc 1972-, Tchr, Group Coord, Dir of Bible Schl, Co-Ldr of Visitation & Greeting Min Care Group Ldr; Scouting Prgm 1975-; Alanon 1985-; Jennings Sc 1985; Ashland Tchr Awd Nom 1991; Tchr of the Yr 1993; OH Math M Facilitator; Trained Other Tchrs in Area; *home:* 861 Cherry Ln Water OH 43566*

STANSBURY, CLAYTON C., Honors Program Director; *b:* Havr Grace, MD; *m:* Catherine P.; *ed:* Morgan St Univ (BS) Psych 1955; Ho Univ (MS) Psych 1962; Univ of MD (PHD) Soc Psych 1972; *cr:* Ho Univ Psych Instgr 1965-67; Morgan St Univ Psych Cnslr & chm 197 Frosh Prgm Dir 1975-77, Stu Affairs VP 1977-80, Honors Prgm Dir 19 *ai:* Epworth United Meth Chapel Mens Pres; Howard Cornish MSU Alu Chapter Schlsp Chm; Md Collegiate Honors Cncl; Md Psychological A Treas; Alpha Phi Alpha 1952-, Chapter Pres, Eastern Man of Year & of Merit 1988; NAACP; Urban League; Morgan St Alumni Assn, Bd M Alumnus of Yr; Portrait of Colored Man Clayton C. Stansbury Sr. 1 NAFEO Awd; Morgan St Gala Star; *office:* Morgan State Univ Cold Sp Ln & Hillen Rd Baltimore MD 21239

STANSBURY, KEVIN BRADLEY, Engish Literature Teacher Morristown, NJ; *ed:* Coll of Saint Elizabeth (BA) Eng-Cum Laude 1 Grad Schl Working Towards MA in Urban Ed; *cr:* Long Branch HS Eng Tchr 1994-; *ai:* 1998 Class Adv; Frosh Ftbl Coach; Boys Bsktbl, Girls Asst Coach; NJEA 1994-; Sigma Tau Delta; Kappa Gamma Pi; NA 1989-; Created Mentor Prgm at Red Bank MS 1994; Met US Pres 1 Who's Who in Amer Colls & Univs 1994; *office:* Long Branch HS Westwood Ave Long Branch NJ 07740*

STANSBURY, LORRAINE S., School Counselor; *b:* Philadelphia, PA Robert; *c:* Laura, Rob; *ed:* Fitzgerald Mercy Hosp Schl of Nrsng (Nrsng 1969; Neumann Coll (BA) 1985; Villanova Univ (MS) 1990; Acad of Notre Dame Schl Cnslr 1989-; *ai:* Stu Assistance Team; Wom Ldrshp Comm; ACT 1989-; PSCT 1989-; Amer Cancer Soc 1990-, Re to Recovery; *office:* Acad of Notre Dame de Namur 560 Sproul Villanova PA 19085

STANSKI, SHARON ROWNY, Math & Computer Teacher; *b:* Wi Barre, PA; *m:* Charles Stanski; *c:* Charles, Ann, Suzanne, Stanley; *ed:* Misericordia (BA) Math 1969; 33 Credit Hrs in Comp & Math Ed Marywood Coll; *ai:* SADD Club Adv & Helper; Math Club; NCTM 19 PCTM 1994-; LCCTM 1994-; *home:* 24 Spruce St Wilkes Barre PA 18

STANTON, ALEX WILLIAM, Human Anatomy & Health Teacher Canton, OH; *m:* Yvonne Valle; *ed:* Bowling Green St Univ (BS) Hlth 19

Hlth 1977; *cr:* Bowling Green St Univ Grad Asst 1976-77; Defiance r, Ath Trainer 1977-; *ai:* NEA, OEA 1977-; Natl Ath Trainers Assn OH Ath Trainers Assn 1986-; *office:* Defiance HS 1755 Palmer Dr e OH 43512

ON, ALEXA TWEEDIE, Fourth Grade Teacher; *b:* Walton, NY; ard; *c:* Amy, Jeffrey, Paul, Julie-Jo; *ed:* SUNY at Cobleskill (AAS) Ed 1969; SUC at Oneonta (BS) Elem Ed 1971; 30 Post Grad Hrs; Upton Cntrl Schl 1-2, 5-6 Grd Tchr 1971-89; Gilbertsville-Mt Upton chl 4 Grd Tchr 1990-; *ai:* 2nd Bapt Church; *office:* Gilbertsville-Mt Schl RR 1 Box 10a Gilbertsville NY 13776

ON, ANN FOGARTY, Chem & Environmental Sci Tchr; *b:* New Y; *m:* Mark Kevin; *c:* Siobhan Noel; *ed:* Russell Sage Coll (BS) 985; Columbia Univ Tchrs Coll (MA) Scndry Ed 1991; *cr:* Troy HS Tchr 1986; Wilburcross HS Chem Tchr 1986-88; Dobbs Ferry HS Environmental Sci, Forensics Tchr 1988-; *ai:* Class Adv; Co-Chair ompact Comm; DFUT 1988-, Bldg Rep; Alliance of Chem Educators Bd Mem; ACS, STANYS 1988-, Mem; Yale Univ Fellowship to Stud Quality & Curr Planning 1987; Woodrow Wilson Inst for Chem Tchrs rs 1990-95; *office:* Dobbs Ferry HS 505 Broadway Dobbs Ferry NY

TON, BEVERLY SAY, Spanish & Computer Teacher; *b:* Franklin, David Allen; *ed:* Houghton Coll (BA) Span 1969; Addl 30 Hrs; *cr:* Cntrl Schl Elem Tchr 1969-71; Richburg Cntrl Schl Home Ec Tchr 2; Bolivar Cntrl Schl Asst Librn 1983-84; Friendship Cntrl Schl Cmptr Tchr 1984-; *ai:* NHS, Span Club, Class of 2001 Adv; ine Policy Comm; AFT 1985-, Local VP, Sec; 1991 Cncl Hum Conf Photojournalism Travel Grant NY St Foreign Lang Tchrs Assn; Friendship Central Schl 46 W Main St Friendship NY 14739

TON, BRADLEY JOHN, Reading & Cmptr Applctns Tchr; *b:* own, NY; *m:* Annette; *c:* Ryan, Matthew; *ed:* Edinboro Univ (BS) 1974, (MS) Rdng Specialist 1977, (MS) Elem 1977; IBM Cmptr rk System Operator Trng; Cmptr Applications Stud; *cr:* Eisenhower ing Specialist 1974-, Network Systems Operator 1991-, Cmptr ations Tchr 1995-; *ai:* Soph Class Adv; NEA, PSEA, WCEA 1974-; rove Twp 1979-, Auditor; *home:* RR 2 Box 2111 Russell PA 16345

TON, ELIZABETH MATKO, Educl Media Spec & Librn; *b:* k, NJ; *m:* Frank J. Jr.; *c:* David C., Paul G., Bryan K.; *ed:* water Coll (BA) Sociology, Elem Ed 1975; Fairleigh Dickinso Univ Learning Disabilities 1978; Montclair St Univ Post MA Assoc Media list 1985, Advanced Post MA Educl Media Specialist 1989; 65 Addl Hrs Post Grad Stud Jersey City St Coll, Seton Hall Univ, Monmouth *r:* Rockingham Cty Schls 2-3 Grd Tchr 1974-75; Riverview Schl 4-6 chr 1975-82; Valleyview Schl 7-8 Grd Rdng Tchr 1982-83; Riverview Grd, 6 Grd Eng Tchr 1983-85; Valleyview Schl 6-8 Grd Educl Media list, Librn 1985-; *ai:* Lib Club Adv; Tech, Author Day Comm; Lib ation Project; Book Fair Comm; NEA, NJEA 1975-; Amer Lib Assn Educl Media Assn of NJ 1989-; Phi Kappa PHi 1985-; *office:* view MS 320 Diamond Spring Rd Denville NJ 07834

TON, GRACE S., Learning Disabilities Teacher; *b:* Menominee, Lori Stanton Dubetz, Leslie Stanton White; *ed:* Auburn Univ (BA) Ed 1955; Mount St Joseph (MS) Rdng 1987; *cr:* Sturgis Elem 6th Grd 955-56; Smith MS Learning Disabilities Tchr 1978-; *ai:* Bus Supvr; Discipline Comms; Spec Ed Team Ldr; Parent Mentor, CEA Rep; Kappa Gamma 1982-; Ortella 1992-; CEA 1978-, Schl Rep; OEA PEO 1969-, Pres, Corr Sec, VP; Friends of Lib 1990-; Walnut St Church 1968-; Spokesperson for Ed; Charles A. Smart Awd; Mentor Martha Holden Jennings Schlr; *office:* Smith MS 345 Arch St cothe OH 45601

TON, MARLA ULLRICH, Spanish & French Teacher; *b:* New NY; *m:* Robert M Sr.; *c:* Robert M. Jr.; *ed:* Coll of Notre Dame (BA) 1973; Masters Equivalency Fr, Span Towson St Univ; *cr:* Maryvale Schl Frgn Lang Tchr, Dept Chprsn 1973-; *ai:* Fr NHS Moderator; 1973-; *office:* Maryvale Prep Schl 11300 Falls Rd Brooklandville 1022

TON, SUSAN JEANETTE, Home Economics Teacher; *b:* New NY; *c:* Kelly, Kimberly, Gregory; *ed:* Ashland Univ (BS) Voc Home 74; *cr:* M.J. Ryerson MS Home Ec Tchr 1990-91; West Essex Reg Jr ome Ec Tchr 1991-92; New Milford HS Home Ec Tchr 1993-; *ai:* Peer ation Adv; NEA 1990-; Carl Perkins Homemaking Grant 1994-95; rs Univ Significant Tchr Appreciation; *office:* New Milford HS 1 r Cir New Milford NJ 07646*

NTON, TERRY LAING, Second Grade Teacher; *b:* Teaneck, NJ; *m:* eth A.; *c:* Tracy Stanton Smith; *ed:* Montclair St Coll (BA) Acctng Cert Courses in Elem Ed; 10 Credits In-Service Courses; *cr:* ers Schl 3rd Grd Tchr 1967-69; Mt View Schl 3rd Grd Tchr 1969-70; r Elem Schl Rdng Tchr 1970-71; Sandshore Schl 4th Grd Tchr 1976; iew Schl 2nd Grd Tchr 1976-; *ai:* Spelling, Report Card Revision n; NEA, NJEA, EAMO 1967-; *office:* Mountain View Schl Clover Hill anders NJ 07836

NTON, TIMOTHY JAMES, Assoc Professor of Economics; *b:* stown, PA; *m:* Kathleen Burke; *c:* Burke; *ed:* Edinboro St Coll (BS) 978; Univ of KY (MA) Ec 1983, (PHD) Ec 1988; *cr:* Centre Coll Instr -89; Mount Saint Mary's Coll Prof 1989-; *ai:* Moderator of Ec Soc; speake Assn of Ed Ec 1994-, Governor; Amer Ec Assn 1986-; Eastern ssn 1992-; 8 Articles Pub; Various Presentations for Ec Assn; *office:* nt Saint Marys Coll Rt 15 Emmitsburg MD 21727

NZIALE, CHRISTINE TORRE, 8th Grade English Teacher; *b:* New City, NY; *ed:* Jersey City St Coll (BA) Elem Ed 1973; Montclair St Working on MS Degree in Cnslng & Human Svcs; *cr:* Roosevelt Schl th Grd Tchr 1974-85; Mt Olive MS 8th Grd Eng Tchr 1985-; *ai:* is Cty Cncl of Ed Assn Newsletter Ed; Dodge Grant to Stud Rain sts in HI 1990; Amer Express Geog Competition 3rd Prize 1990; Rand ally Geog Tchr Awd 1st Prize 1991; *office:* Mount Olive MS 10 Sunset udd Lake NJ 07828

PLES, PAULA HOWE, 3rd Grade Teacher; *b:* Windsor, VT; *m:* Gary; ler; *ed:* Univ of VT (BA) Elem Ed & Psych 1971; 30 Addl Credit Hrs; eace Corps Tchr 1971-72; Hartford Head Start Tchr 1972-74; Hartland Tchr 1974-; *ai:* Staff Dev Comm; Enrichment Comm; Winter Activity r; VEA & NEA 1972-; NSDC 1993-, Comm Mem; ASCD 1995-; PTA -, Liaison.

PLETON, ELIZABETH ROSE, Social Studies Teacher; *b:* Astoria, *ed:* St John's Univ (BBA) Mrktg 1958; Long Island Univ (MS) Ed ; *cr:* St Nicholas of Tolentine3rd Grd Tchr 1964-69, 7th Grd Lang Arts 1969-70; St Mary Schl 7th-8th Grd Lang Arts Tchr 1970-86, 8th Grd chr 1993-94, 7th-8th Grd Soc Stud Tchr 1986-; *ai:* Coord Soc Stud, e, Career Skills; Stu Cncl Moderator; NCEA 1970-; AAUW 1990-; *e:* St Mary Schl 16 Harrison Ave East Islip NY 11730

PLETON, JAMES MICHAEL, Social Studies Teacher; *b:* Norwood, *m:* Adele Lillian Enos; *c:* Tess; *ed:* Curry Coll (BA) Eng & His 1985; mons Coll (MAT) Ed 1986; *cr:* Prouty JHS Soc Stud Tchr 1986-87; veton HS Eng Tchr 1987-88; Johnson MS Soc Stud Tchr 1988-; *ai:* d Boys Soccer & JV Girls Bsktbl Coach; NEA 1987-; Ash St ground Comm 1994-, VP; *office:* Johnson MS 111 Robbins Rd Walpole 02081

STAPLETON, LEANNE PETICCA, Mathematics Teacher; *b:* Marcus Hook, PA; *m:* Christopher; *ed:* Kutztown Univ (BS) Ed, Math 1992; MA Prgm West Chester Univ; *cr:* Oxford Area Schls Math Tchr 1992-; *ai:* Girls Tennis Coach, Math Club Mu Alpha Theta Spon, Adv; NCTM 1992-; *office:* Oxford Area HS 301 5th Street Rd Oxford PA 19367*

STARCHER, LOIS AGUE, Art Teacher; *b:* Pittsburgh, PA; *m:* Rev. Ronald L.; *c:* Sara, Evan; *ed:* TN Temple Univ (BS) Art Ed 1974; *cr:* Howland Chrstn Schl 1st-12th Grd Art Tchr 1974-; *ai:* Yrbk Adv; ACSI 1994-; Freelance Artwork for Pub Lib; Logo Design for Area Businesses & Clubs; *office:* Howland Christian Schl 8957 E Market St Warren OH 44484

STARCHER, MARYANNE HORACK, 3rd Grade Teacher; *b:* Middlefield, OH; *m:* Paul; *c:* Paula Starcher Cooley; *ed:* Kent St Univ (BS) Early Chldhd 1975, (MS) Gifted Ed 1986; 25 Grad Credit Hrs 1987-92; *cr:* Katherine Thomas Elem Schl 1st-3rd Grd Tchr 1976-; *ai:* March for Parks Main Organizer & Benefactor; Eagle Creek Preserve Save The Rainforest Benefactor; Nature Conservancy KT Annual Food Dr for Sr Citizens; Earth Day Tree Distribution; Windham Tchrs Assoc 1976-, Bldg Rep; Womens Army Corp 1959-61, Clerical, Honorable Discharge; Army Reserves 1979-; East OH Gas Grants 1985-91; VoEd Schl Grant 1986; OH Edison Mini Grant 1987 & 1994; OH St Univ Mini Grant 1995; Served in Desert Storm; *office:* Katherine Thomas Elem Schl 9600 Community Rd Windham OH 44288

STARK, FREDERIC L., Chemistry & Physics Teacher; *b:* New York City, NY; *m:* Dawn Siegel; *ed:* SUNY at Albany (BS) Chem 1990; SUNY at Stony Brook (MA) Lbrl Stud & Sci Ed 1992; Coll of St Rose 9 Credit Hrs; *ai:* Hewlett Woodmere Fac Assn Bldg Rep & Newsletter Ed; Long Island Sci Congress 1993 & 1995 Judge & Adv; Hewlett Woodmere Fac Assn 1990-, Bldg Rep & Newsletter Ed; AFT 1990-; Amer Inst of Chemists 1990-92; Sigma Lambda Sigma Alumni Assn 1991-, Sec; Oceanside Jewish Ctr 1995; *office:* George W Hewlett HS 60 Everit Ave Hewlett NY 11557

STARK, JANE BRANDT, Substitute Teacher; *b:* Greenville, OH; *m:* Raymond Stark; *ed:* OH St Univ (BS) Elem Ed 1984; *cr:* Dallas ISD Migrant Tchr 1985; Amer Schl of Puebla 5th Grd Eng as a Second Lang 1985-87; Pleasant View MS 6th- 8th Grd Lang Arts & Soc Stud 1987-95; *ai:* Cert of Excl 1990 & 1993; Schl Bell Awd 1993; Ambassador Awd 1993; *home:* 2500 London Groveport Rd Grove City OH 43123

STARK, MICHAEL D., Fifth Grade Teacher; *b:* Buffalo, NY; *m:* Susan Muranyi; *c:* Michael G., Gregory S.; *ed:* SUNY at Fredonia (BS) Elem Ed 1973; Niagara Univ (MS) Elem Ed 1977; 24 Post Grad Hrs Various Univs; *cr:* Grand Island Cntrl Schls 3rd Grd Tchr 1973-87, 5th Grd Tchr 1987-; *ai:* Tech Comm; GITA, NYSUT, AFT 1973-; Western Niagara Frontier Bd of Ofcls for Women's Soccer 1974-, Pres 1982-; Inspiration to Ed Awd, Grand Island Cntrl Schls 1995; *office:* Kaegebein Elem Schl 1690 Love Rd Grand Island NY 14072

STARK, NORMA JEAN, Music Specialist; *b:* Toledo, OH; *m:* James; *ed:* OH St Univ (BSEd) Music Ed 1969; Bowling Green St Univ (MED) Elem Ed 1975; *cr:* Lakota Local Schls Vocal & Instrumental Music Tchr 1969-72; Fremont City Schls Instrumental & General Music Tchr 1972-78; USD 471 Instrumental & Vocal Music Tchr 1978-80; Rossford Exempted Village Instrumental & Vocal Music Tchr 1980-88; Eastwood Local Schls Instrumental & Vocal Music Tchr 1988-; *ai:* Amer Orff Schulwerk Assn 1982-; OMEA, MENC, OEA, NEA 1969-; Eastwood Ed Assn 1988-, Jennings Scholar; Northwest OH Orff Chapter 1982-, Past VP, Past Prgm Chair; Holland United Meth Church 1980-, Music Dir, Admin Bd, Worship Comm; Sr Orff Ensemble Was Selected to Perform at AOSA Conf in Indianapolis IN 1993; 1 of 3 Runners Up in OH Tchr of Yr 1987; Rossford Jennings Scholar; Rossford Outstanding Educator 1986; Wrote for 99er Magazine CAI Articles Cmptr Magazine; 6th Grd Choir was Selected to Perform at OMEA Conf in Cleveland 1986; Given Speeches & Demos on CAI at OMEA Conf in Dayton OH & San Francisco CA; Wkshps at Bowling Green St Univ, Capital Univ, IN Univ, Newark NJ, Grove City PA & Terre Haute IN; *office:* Eastwood Local Schls 4800 Sugar Ridge Rd Pemberville OH 43450*

STARK, THOMAS DANIEL, HS Tech & Indstrl Arts Teacher; *b:* Red Bank, NJ; *m:* Lynda Lupia; *c:* Taylor; *ed:* Trenton St Coll (BS) Indstrl Arts 1981, (MED) Indstrl Tech 1985; 65 Addl Credits, Supvr, Prin, Schl Bus Admin Certs; *cr:* Keansburg HS Indstrl Arts, Tech Ed Tchr 1981-; *ai:* Soph Class, Tech Club Adv; Strategic Planning, Schlsp, Pupil Assistance, Alumni, Discipline Comms; Teen Night, Bsktbl Camp Supvr; Cross Cntry, IM Track, Head Var Bsktbl Coach; NJEA, NEA 1981-; NASSP 1991-; AAU Bsktbl Local 1990-, Pres; St Tech Grants to Improve Tech in Drafting Lab; *office:* Keansburg HS 140 Port Monmouth Rd Keansburg NJ 07734*

STARKE, RICHARD CARL, Fifth Grade Tchr; *b:* Philadelphia, PA; *m:* Arlene Mane Scavo; *c:* Matthew R., Michael C.; *ed:* State Univ of NY at Brockport (BS) 1986, (MS) 1993; *cr:* Schl Dist 7 3rd, 5th Grd Tchr 1987-; *ai:* Curr & Standards Comm; NYSUT, RTA 1987-; *home:* 9 Miller Dr North Chili NY 14514

STARKEY, KAY CASPER, Middle Schl Lang Arts Teacher; *b:* Canton, OH; *m:* Milton Eugene; *c:* Daniel Lee, David Eugene, Dale Edward; *ed:* 12 CEU's Malone Coll; 6 Grad Semester TEACH, PRIDE Courses Mt St Joseph Coll; *cr:* Carrollton Ex Village Seventh Grd Self-Cont, Sixth Grd Rdng Tchr 1965-66, Sub Tchr 1966-71; Alliance City Schls 6th Grd Self Cont Tchr 1961-65, Sub Tchr 1073-75; West Branch Schls Sub Tchr 1974-76, 1979-87; Real Life Chrstn Acad MS Lang Arts Tchr 1987-; *ai:* Jr HS Speech Meet Coord; Yrbk Adv 1989-95; OEA 1964-, Life Mem; PTO Pres 3 Yrs; PTF 1987-; Israel Luth Church 1963-, Sec Church Cncl, VBS Dir 5 Yrs, Church Camp Lay Staff, Sunday Schl, Catechism Tchr; BSA, Sec Troop 147 5 Yrs; *home:* 26316 Georgetown Rd Homeworth OH 44634

STARKEY, ROXANE MARIE, Math & Science Teacher; *b:* Steubenville, OH; *m:* George Daniel Jr.; *c:* Cole Brandon, Shay Morgan; *ed:* OH Univ at Belmont (BS) Elem Ed 1991; Associate of Sci 1990; Jefferson Tech Coll EMT-Paramedic 1986; *cr:* St John Cntrl Grade Schl Sci & Math Tchr 1991-; *ai:* Acad Fair Chprsn; Stu Cncl Adv; Tech Coord; Spelling Bee Comm; Girls Bsktbl Coach; Jr High Tack Coach; Wintersvill Vol Fire Dept 1984-, Parmedic & Firefighter; *home:* 166 Parkview Dr Wintersville OH 43952

STARKMAN, PHYLLIS, Spanish Teacher; *b:* Perth Amboy, NJ; *ed:* Douglass Coll (AB) Lbrl Ed, Span Ed 1960; *cr:* St Peters Cath HS Span Tchr 1979-83; St James Elem Schl Span Tchr 1983-92; Red Bank Cath HS Span Tchr 1983-; *ai:* Span Club Co-Adv; RBC Ministry Team; Frgn Lang Edctrs of NJ 1987-; Natl Cath Edctrs Assn 1983-; *office:* Red Bank Catholic HS 10 Peters Pl Red Bank NJ 07701

STARKS, CAROLE BRAGG, 8th Grd Amer History Teacher; *b:* Birmingham, AL; *m:* Joe; *c:* Wm Kent II, Lauren Kimm; *ed:* Bowling Green St Univ (BA) Elem Ed 1963; Ashland Coll, Akron Univ (MS) Ed 1979; *cr:* Margaret Park Elem 1st & 2nd Grd Tchr 1963-72, 5th & 6th Grd Tchr 1973-87; Perkins MS 8th Grd Amer His, Lang Arts Tchr 1988-89, 8th Grd Amer His Tchr 1990-; *ai:* Activity Supvr; Drama Coach; Teen Lift Adv; African-Amer His Comm Adv; UNCF Rep; Ski Club Chaperone; Stu Cncl Adv; Teen ed Dev Drug Free Youth, Prevent & Neutralize Drug, Alcohol Abuse; HS European Summer Trips Chaperone; AEA, OEA, NEA 1963-, Comm Work; UNCF Core Comm 1982-, Ticket Chair; UNCF Leadership Tm 1989-,; Delta Sigma Theta 1966-, Sgt at Arms Svc Awd; UNCF Core Comm 1982-, Ticket Chair Svc Awd; UNCF Leadership Team 1989-, Youth Group Awd; NABSE 1987-; Outstanding Tchr of Amer Awd; Ashland Inc Indvdl Tchr Achvmnt Awd; Featured in Jrnl; *office:* Simon Perkins MS 630 Mull Ave Akron OH 44313

STARKS, MARION REDMOND, Pre K Teacher & Coordinator; *b:* Baltimore, MD; *ed:* Coppin St Coll (BA) Elem Ed 1957; Johns Hopkins Univ (MS) Ed 1975; *cr:* Columbus Elem Schl Classroom Tchr 1957-63, Demonstration Tchr 1963-75; Harford Hghts Elem Schl Supplemental Tchr 1975-80, Tchr, Coord Pre-K, Head Start 1993-; *ai:* Handwriting Coach Beginning Tchrs; Staff Dev; Instrl Support Team; Grd Chprsn; AFT 1957-; Phi Delta Kappa 1992-; Natl Asson Negro Bus, Prof Women's Clubs 1987-, Treas, Recording Sec, Sgt-at-Arms; NAACP 1957-; Tchr of Yr 1990.

STARKWEATHER, JOHN EARL, English Professor; *b:* Watertown, NY; *ed:* Jefferson Comm Coll (AA) Hum 1971; St Univ of NY at Geneseo (BA) Eng 1973; Syracuse Univ (MA) Eng 1975; Completed Doctorate Coursework 1977; *cr:* Onondaga Comm Coll Eng & Comm Instr 1987-; Syracuse Univ Instr of Prof Writing 1988-; Onondaga Comm Coll Learning Disabilities Assistance Prgm Asst Coord 1990-93, Learning Disabilities Assistance Prgm Coord 1993-95; *office:* Onondaga Comm Coll Onondaga Hill Road Syracuse NY 13215

STARKWEATHER, PAUL DOUGLAS, Social Studies Teacher; *b:* Batavia, NY; *ed:* Alfred Univ (BA) His & Ed 1958; Attnd St Univ of NY at Geneseo, St Univ of NY at Buffalo, Univ of Rochester, Univ of VT & St Univ of Brockport for Grad Hrs; *cr:* Leroy HS Soc Stud Tchr 1959-63, prin 1963-66; Batavia HS Soc Stud Tchr 1966-, HS & MS Soc Stud Dept Chm 1992-; *ai:* Yrbk, Class, Stu Cncl, Its Acad & Honor Soc Adv; Batavia Tchrs Assn 1966-, Rep 5 Yrs, Past Pres; NY St Tchrs Assn & AFT 1970-; Robert Morris Soc Stud Cncl; Town of Batavia Planning Bd 1960-; Oakfield Meth Church 1960-, Ed Chm; Genesee Cty Comm Services Bd 1965-, Past Pres; Buffalo Psychiatric Ctr 1981-91, Bd of Visitors; Batavia United Nations Chm; Univ of VT Natl Inst 1967; Univ of Rochester Excl in Scndry Schl Tchng Awd 1985; Appointed to Mental Hlth Bd; Outstanding Secondary Ed of Amer, 1973 Edition; Batavia HS Outstanding Educator 1973; *home:* 3522 W Main St Batavia NY 14020

STARN, NANCY GEIGER, Biology Teacher; *b:* Findlay, OH; *c:* Lori Ann, Eric Alan; *ed:* Capital Univ (BS) Bio 1970; OH St Univ (MA) Sci Ed 1973; Attnd Ashland Univ & Drake Univ; *cr:* Reynoldsburg MS 7th Grd Sci Tchr 1971-76; Liberty Union- Thurston HS 8th & 9th Grd Sci & Bio Tchr 1979-85; Watkins Meml HS Bio Tchr 1985-; *ai:* Swim Team Spon; Sci Ed Cncl of OH 1986-; Dow Tchng Excl Awd; *office:* Watkins Memorial HS 8868 Watkins Rd SW Pataskala OH 43062*

STARNER, FRANCIS EUGENE,JR., Industrial Technology Teacher; *b:* Zanesville, OH; *m:* Kahty M. Bradford; *c:* Sarah, Hannah; *ed:* Mukkingum Tech Coll (BA) Engrng 1971; OH Univ (BA) Engrng 1976; Xavier Univ (MS) Educl Admin 1986; Command General Staff Coll 25 Grad Hrs; *cr:* Zanesville City Schls Industrial Tech Tchr 1976-80; River View Local Schls Industrial Tech Tchr 1981-; *ai:* Rocket Club Adv; NEA, OEA, RVEA 1995-; Licking Twp Vol Fire & EMS 1984-, Asst Chief; Frazeysburg Masonic Lodge 1972-, Past Master; US Army Reserves 1977-, Major, Army Commendation Medal; Nom For Ashland Tchr Awd; *office:* Riverview Jr HS 26546 SR 60N Warsaw OH 43844*

STAROSTA, WILLIAM J., Human Comm Studies Professor; *b:* Oconomowoc, WI; *m:* Kiran Wadhera; *c:* Aron Navine; *ed:* WI Univ at Oshkosh (BA) Speech & Eng 1968; IN Univ (AM) Rhetoric & Intercultural Comm 1971, (PHD) Intercultural Corr, Asian Stud 1973; Yr in India Schlrsp 1967; Schlsp Univ of Chicago 1966; NDFL Fellowship Univ of MI 1970; Fellowship Indian Inst of Advanced Stud 1976; *cr:* IN Univ Debate Coach 1968-71; Univ of VA Prof of Comm 1972-77; Howard Univ Prof of Comm 1978-; *ai:* Howard Journal of Comm Ed; Chinese Comm Stud Assn Adv; Natl Indian Amer Chamber of Commerce Bd Mem; Intnl Intercultural Comm SCA Div Chair; Speech Comm Assn 1968-, Div Chair; Eastern Comm Assn 1968-, Div Chairs; US Chess Fed 1972-; Howard Univ Grad Schl 1978-, Outstanding Achvmt; Fulbright Hays Fellowship 1971-; Rhodes Schlsp Evaluator; Canadian Indo-Shasta Fdn Evaluator; Henry Luce Schlsp Comm; Natl Ctr on Post Consultant; Scndry Tchng, Learning & Assessment; *office:* Howard University Box 471 Washington DC 20059

STAROWITZ, ANNE MARIE PECA, Fourth Grade Teacher; *b:* Batavia, NY; *m:* Richard; *c:* Jennifer, Jessica; *ed:* D'Youville Coll (BS) Elem Ed 1972; SUC at Buffalo (MS) Ed 1989; SUC at Brockport; *cr:* Wolcott Street Schl 3rd Grd Tchr 1972-78; YWCA Nursery Schl Presch Tchr 1980-83; Jackson Schl 2nd Grd Tchr 1984-85; Robert Morris Schl 4th Grd Tchr 1985-; *ai:* Stdnt Cncl, Schl Newspaper Adv; NYSUT 1972-; Batavia Cemetery Assn 1992-, Bd Mem, 1994 Recognition Awd; Landmark Soc, Paola Busti Soc 1992-; Pub Childrens Book The Day We Met Cindy 1988.

STARR, KEVIN J., High School Teacher; *b:* Buffalo, NY; *m:* Mary Anne; *c:* Andy, Shana, Katie; *ed:* SUC of NY at Buffalo (BS) Scndry Engl Ed 1979, (MA) Engl 1984; Empire St Coll NYS Cert His 1989; *cr:* Amherst Cntrl HS Eng Tchr 1979-81; Williamsville South HS Eng Tchr 1981-82; East Aurora HS Eng Tchr 1982-83; Frontier Cntrl HS Eng Tchr 1983-89; Clarence Cntrl HS Eng Tchr 1989-; *ai:* Stu Cncl Adv; Boys Var Vlybl Coach; AFT-NYSUT 1979-; Clarence TA 1989-, Exec Comm; WNY Vlybl Coaches Assn 1980-, Schlsp Comm; Holocaust Resource Ctr of Buffalo 1994-, Bd of Dir; WNY Vlybl Coach of Yr 1988; Article Pub 1989; *office:* Clarence Cntrl Sr HS 9625 Main St Clarence NY 14031

STARR, MADELINE BETH, Core Teacher; *b:* Brooklyn, NY; *m:* Howard; *c:* Holly Jill; *ed:* Mills Coll (BA) Elem Ed; Adelphi Univ (MS) Elem Ed 1987; *cr:* PS 31 Schl 4th Grd Tchr 1983-90; Marie Curie MS 158 Core Tchr 1990-; *ai:* Schl Cncl; Soc Comm; Grants Bd of Ed Schl; *office:* Marie Currie MS 158 46-35 Oceania St Bayside NY 11361*

STARR, PATRICIA VAN HARKEN, Sixth Grade Teacher; *b:* Patterson, NJ; *m:* Douglas L.; *c:* Christopher L., Kelley A.; *ed:* Western CT (BA) Elem Ed 1966; Working Towards Masters of Education Univ of Toledo; *cr:* Ridgefield CT Elem 3rd Grd Tchr 1966-68; Paxton MA Elem 4th Trd Tchr 1968-69; Washington Local Schls K-6th Grd Tchr 1976-; *ai:* Safety Patrol & Stu Cncl Adv; NEA 1976-; Toledo Edison Grant; Cable Television Grant; Venture Capital Grant St of OH; *office:* Hiawatha Elem Schl 3020 Photos Dr Toledo OH 43613

STARR, RICHARD, Physics Teacher; *b:* Olean, NY; *m:* Marlene A.; *c:* R. Jeffre, Jennifer L., R. Jeremy; *ed:* SUNY Coll at Cortland (BS) Sci Ed 1964; Univ of Rochester (MED) Ed Admin 1967; SUNY Coll at Brockport (CAS) Ed Admin 1981; *cr:* Penfield Cntrl Schls Sci, Gen Sci, Earth Sci & Physics Tchr 1966-; *ai:* Comp & Attendance Comms; NEA 1966-; NYSUT & Penfield Ed Assn 1966-, Bldg Rep; STANYS 1980-87, CWS Exec Sec, Svc Awd 1984; Sci Edctrs Assn 1984-, Bd Dirs; Perinton Comm Church 1972-, Church Bd; Finger Lakes Trl Conf 1990-, Trl Spon; 4 NSF Grants; 5 Pub Articles; Summer Staff Ithaca Coll NSF Computer Project; *office:* Penfield HS 1 Highschool Dr Penfield NY 14526

STARR, ROBYN J., Social Studies Teacher; *b:* Buffalo, NY; *ed:* SUC at Fredonia (BS) Sociology, Psych 1984; Buffalo St Coll (MS) Scndry Soc Stud Ed 1996; Daemen Coll Ed Cert 1991; *cr:* Alden HS Psych Tchr 1992-94; Alden MS 7-8 Grd Soc Stud Tchr 1994-; *ai:* Bldg Improvement Team 2 Yrs; Spec Event Comms Chprsn, Co-Chprsn; Local Educl Theatre Dir, Choreographer; NCSS 1994-; NYSUT 1992-; *office:* Alden MS 1648 Crittenden Rd Alden NY 14004*

STARR, SUSAN DUNN, Education Specialist; *b:* New Haven, CT; *c:* Beth, Jonathan; *ed:* Clark Univ (BA) Sociology 1969; Worcester St Coll (MED) Ed 1971; *cr:* Millbury Pub Schls Elem Schl Tchr 1969-73; Clark

Univ Dept of Ed Clin Prof 1977-94; Univ of MA Med Ctr Pediatrics Dept Educl Specialist; *ai:* Clark Univ Stu Tchng Prgms Coord; Clark Univ Jewish Stu Coalition Adv; Clark Univ Natl Alumni Assn Pres 1986-87; Natl Cncl of Jewish Women 1976-, Past Pres; Wor Jewish Fed 1973-, Past VP Women's Division, Young Ldrshp Awd 1980; Presentations Amer Pediatric Assn 1995-; Article Pub 1995; *home:* 27 Dick Dr Worcester MA 01609

STARRETT, WILLIAM GRANT, Eighth Grade Teacher; *b:* Dayton, OH; *m:* Patricia A. Adcock; *c:* William, Trisha Wade, J. Matthew, Julie; *ed:* Grace Coll (BA) Soc Stud Comprehensive 1964; Miami Univ of OH (MED) Curr, Supervision 1970; Attnd Univ of Dayton, Cntrl St Univ, Wright St Univ; *cr:* Ferguson Jr HS Classroom Tchr 1964-; *ai:* Dept Chair; Curr Revision, Schlsp Comms; Assn Amer Edctrs 1996-; Civil War Inst Tchr Scholar; Howard L. Post Ed Excl Awd 1995; *home:* 1678 Sioux Dr Xenia OH 45385

STARUCH, JEFFREY NICHOLAS, Math & Computer Science Tchr; *b:* Buffalo, NY; *ed:* SUNY Coll at Brockport (BS) 7-12 Math Ed 1987; SUNY Coll at Buffalo (MS) Educational Computing 1995; *cr:* Frontier Sr HS Math, Cmptr Sci Tchr 1992-; *ai:* Math Dept Co-Chm; NYSMTA 1992-; Cadral T A 1990-; ASCD 1995-; *office:* Frontier Sr HS S-4432 Bay View Rd Hamburg NY 14075

STARUCH, KORINA, Option I Teacher; *b:* Brookville, PA; *m:* Michael; *c:* Tyler, Jenessa; *ed:* Slippery Rock Univ (BA) N-K 1-6 Grd 1984; Oswego (MS) Spec Ed 1989; *cr:* Salina Jefferson Schl Spec Ed Tchr 1984-85; Webster Schl Intermediate Opt I Tchr 1985-91, Primary Option I Tchr 1991-; *office:* Webster Elem Schl 500 Wadsworth St Syracuse NY 13208

STARZ, KENNETH J., Social Studies & Reading Tchr; *b:* Pittsburgh, PA; *m:* Carole M.; *ed:* Edinboro St Coll (BA) Elem Ed 1970; Masters Equivalency 1976 at Slippery Rock Univ; *cr:* Slippery Rock Area Schls 4th Grd Tchr 1 Yr, 6th Grd Math Tchr 8 Yrs, 7th-8th Grd Math Tchr 9 Yrs, 6th Grd Soc Stud, Rdng Tchr 6 Yrs; *ai:* Stu Assistence Prgm; PSEA, NEA 1970-; *office:* Slippery Rock Area MS Kiester Rd Slippery Rock PA 16057

STASHIS, SUZANNE BELL, Counselor; *b:* Audubon, NJ; *c:* Alfred J. Jr., Timothy J.; *ed:* Temple Univ (BSEd) Hlth, PE 1960, (MED) PHys Therapy 1964; Glassboro St Coll (MA) Stu Personnel Svc 1972; Jersey City St Prins Admin Cert 1973; *cr:* Cherry Hill HS W Hlth, PE Tchr 1960-81; Eastern Reg HS Supvr 1981-92; Bishop Eustace Prep Schl Assoc Dean, Cnslr 1992-; *ai:* NACAC 1992-; AAHPER 1960-; NJAHPERD 1980-; NJWBOA 1996; Al Larino, Temple Univ Hall of Fame; *office:* Bishop Eustace Prep Schl Rt 70 Pennsauken NJ 08109*

STASZAK, MARCI ANN, Social Studies Teacher; *b:* Dover, NJ; *c:* Todd Joseph; *ed:* Cty Coll of Morris (AAS) Hum, Soc Stud 1985; Millersville Univ (BSE) Scndry Ed, Soc Stud, Sociology 1987; 18 Addl Credit Hrs Psych & Sociology; *cr:* Dover HS Sub Tchr 1987-88; Jefferson Twp HS Soc Stud Tchr 1988-; *ai:* Conflict Meditation Coord; Peer Dev Prgm Fac Adv; Stu Cncl; NEA, NJEA Jefferson Twp Ed Assn 1988-; Ledgewood Bapt Church 1976-; *office:* Jefferson Township H S Weldon Rd Oak Ridge NJ 07438*

STATHES, DEBORAH DEEMS, English Teacher; *b:* Columbia, SC; *m:* Christopher Thomas; *c:* Hilary, Alexander, Gregory; *ed:* Washington Coll (BA) Eng Lit 1971; Amer Univ (BA) Lit 1974; Univ of Gottingen 1972-73; Cath Univ 3 Hrs; Trinity Coll 3 Hrs; *cr:* Northern VA Comm Coll Instr 1974-75; Acad of the Holy Cross Tchr 1975-; *ai:* Curr Coord; Admissions Comm; Amnesty Intnl Fac Moderator; Level Adv; NCTE; AISGW, ASCD 1993-; *office:* Acad Of The Holy Cross 4920 Strathmore Ave Kensington MD 20895*

STATON, COLLEEN QUINN, Health & PE Teacher; *b:* Philadelphia, PA; *m:* Joseph R.; *ed:* PA St Univ (BS) Exercise, Sports Sci 1987, (MED) Hlth Ed 1993; *cr:* PA St Univ Instr 1995; Cumberland Vly Schl Dist Hlth, PE Tchr 1987-; *ai:* Unified Bowling Coach; Stu Assistance Team Mem; Coord Employee Wellness, Pub Relations, Cmptr Advy Comm; Mentor; NEA 1987-; AAHPERD 1992-; Article Pub; *office:* Cumberland Valley HS 6746 Carlisle Pike Mechanicsburg PA 17055*

STATTEL, PHILIP JAMES, Vocal Music Teacher; *b:* Jamaica, NY; *m:* Cynthia Fay Miller; *ed:* IN Univ (BME) Music Ed 1986; 12 Grad Credits; 12 Grad Credits Western CT St Univ; Attnd Shenandoah Univ; *cr:* John Glenn HS Vocal Music Tchr 1986-88; New Paltz HS Vocal Music Tchr 1988-89; Poughkeepsie MS Vocal Music Tchr 1989-90; Maurice J. Mc Donough HS Vocal Music Tchr 1990-; *ai:* Music Dept Chm; Drama Dir, Asst-Dir; MENC, ACDA 1984-; NEA 1991-; Port Tobacco Players 1992-; Charles Cty Bd of Ed 1995, Curr Comm; *office:* Maurice Mcdonough HS 7165 Marshall Corner Rd Pomfret MD 20675

STATUTO, TONI MARIE, 6th Grade Teacher; *b:* Ridgewood, NJ; *m:* Dino Romano; *ed:* Elon Coll (BA) Math 1990; *cr:* Manchester MS 7th Grd Tchr 1993, 6th, 8th GrdTchr 1993-94, 6th Grd Tchr 1994-; *ai:* NEA 1992-; *office:* Manchester Twp MS 2759 Ridgeway Rd Lakehurst NJ 08733*

STATUTO, WENDY RAND, Business & Technology Teacher; *b:* Queens, NY; *m:* Mark A.; *c:* Amy, Erika, Sean; *ed:* Boston Univ (BS) Bus 1970; Long Island Univ Enrolled in K-12th Educl Tech 2 Yr Grad Prgm; 36 Addl Credit Hrs; *cr:* Cresskill HS Bus Tchr 7 Yrs, Tech Coord 2 Yrs; *ai:* Interact Club Adv, Dist Tech Comm, Schl Stud & Curr Cncl; NEA, NJEA, NJBEA, CEA 1989-; Rotary Club 1991-, Honorary Mem; Rotary Service Awds 1993-95; *office:* Cresskill HS 1 Lincoln Dr Cresskill NJ 07626

STAUB, CARROLL JOSEPH, Assistant Principal; *b:* Hanover, PA; *m:* Cheryl A. Goshkey; *c:* Jarod, Matthew, Christopher; *ed:* Millersville Univ (BS) Soc Stud 1972, (MED) Guid 1990; Cert Spec Ed 1973; Penn St Cert Principalship, Ed Admin 1994; Cert Soc Stud, Guid, Admin; *cr:* Schl Dist of Lancaster Spec Ed Tchr 1972-73, Soc Stud Tchr 1973-93; York Suburban SD Guid Cnslr 1993-94; Schl Dist of Lancaster Asst Prin 1994-; *ai:* Sr Class House Prin; Homecoming; Prom; Post Prom; Grad; Sr Comm Svc Project; PSEA, NEA 1972-76, 1992-94; PASSP, NASSP 1994-; Church Festival Vol 1990-; Vol MU 1987-91; Coord Stu Tchrs 1994-; Rotary Ldrshp Camp Cnslr 1979-93; *office:* Schl Dist of Lancaster 1001 LeHigh Ave Lancaster PA 17602

STAUB, MICHAEL J., Mathematics Teacher; *b:* Paterson, NJ; *m:* Sandra Scheren; *ed:* William Paterson Coll (BA) Math 1969, (MED) Stu Prsnl Svcs 1973; Addl 60 Credits Math, Ed; *cr:* Ben Franklin Jr HS Math Tchr 1969-85; Ridgewood HS Math Tchr 1985-; *ai:* NEA, NCTM 1969-; *office:* Ridgewood HS 627 E Ridgewood Ave Ridgewood NJ 07450

STAUBER, JOHN MICHAEL, High School Math Teacher; *b:* St Charles, MO; *m:* Rosemarie A.; *ed:* St John's Univ (BS) Acctng 1983, (MBA) Tax Acctng 1985; Attnd SUNY Old Westbury, SUNY Stony Brook, SUNY Farmingdale, NassauComm Coll; *cr:* Alfred E. Smith HS Math Tchr 1990-; *ai:* Attendance Coord 1994-; Vol Math Tutor 1990-; UFT 1990-; St Killian's Church 1992-, Rel Ed Tchr; Young Adult Ministry 1986-, Comm Chprsn; *office:* Alfred E Smith HS 333 E 151st St Bronx NY 10451*

STAUFFENEGER, PATRICIA, French Teacher; *b:* Ashtabula, OH; *m:* Carl Richard; *c:* Scott Joseph; *ed:* Kent St Univ (BS) Scndry Ed, Eng & Fr 1974; Mount Saint Joseph (MA) Ed 1987; *cr:* Mount Carmel Schl Jr HS Lang Arts Tchr 1974-77; Columbus Jr HS Lang Arts Tchr 1981-83; Ashtabula HS Fr & Eng Tchr 1983-; *ai:* NHS Adv; NEA 1981-; Saint John Independent 1992-95, Bd Mem; Zonta Intnl 1993-95.

STAUFFER, ANNE E., Fourth Grade Teacher; *b:* Worcester, MA; *ed:* Bates Coll (BA) His 1967; Springfield Coll (MED) Elem Ed 1972; Univ of ME 6 Credit Hrs in Eng as Second Lang; *cr:* Oak Grove Schl 7th-12th Grd Tchr 1968-69; Gordon Schl Tchr 1969-71; Webster Schl 4th-6th Tchr 1972-; Huaibei Tchrs Coll China Eng Tchr 1987-88; *ai:* Lit Assessment Comm; Schl Bank Partnership Prgm; Roadside Theater Adv; Hospice Vol 1985-; Auburn Lib Friends; Historical Novels for Young Adults-Friendly Rebels, Return of the Redcoats & Redcoats Return.*

STAUFFER, BRENDA GARRETT, English Teacher & Dept Head; *b:* Mansfield, OH; *m:* Gene; *c:* Carolyn; *ed:* Grace Coll (BA) Eng Ed 1965; OSU (MA) Eng Ed 1976; *cr:* West Jefferson HS Eng Tchr; *ai:* Class Play; WJEA, OEA 1971-; *office:* West Jefferson HS 561 W Jefferson Kiousville Rd West Jefferson OH 43162

STAUFFER, DEBORAH SWARTLEY, First Grade Teacher; *b:* Quakertown, PA; *m:* Russell W.; *c:* Matthew; *ed:* Bluffton Coll (BA) Elem Ed 1973; OH St Univ (MS) 1995; *cr:* 1st Grd Tchr 1973-; *office:* Waynesfield-Goshen Sch PO Box 370 Waynesfield OH 45896

STAUFFER, JUD FIX, English Teacher; *b:* York, PA; *m:* Kelly Sue Krout; *c:* Maggie Rae, Sara Ann; *ed:* Lebanon Vly Coll (BA) Eng 1982; Temple Univ (MSEd) Ed 1987; PA Dept of Ed Performance Learning Systems; Attnd Penn St Univ; *cr:* Dallastown HS Eng Tchr 1982-; *ai:* Act 178 Comm; Career Integration Comm Chm; Phi Delta Kappa 1993-, Mbrshp VP; Dallastown Area Ed Assn 1982-; Grace Luth Church Cncl 1991-93, Pres; Red Lion Redevelopment Comm 1991-93, VP; York Cty Planning comm 1994-; Grace Luth Church 1995-, Adult Sunday Schl; Red Lion Lodge #649 F & AM 1994-; Rdng, Writing Wkshps; Peer Coaching; Integrating the Curricula; Parent to Parent; Dimensions of Learning; First Capital Compact Grant Career Integration 1995; Article Pub; Dev Lit of sports, Recreation Class; PA Framework Chcl, ACT Presenter; *office:* Dallastown HS 700 New School Ln Dallastown PA 17313

STAUFFER, KATHY SUE, Mathematics Teacher; *b:* Lancaster, PA; *ed:* Grace Coll (BA) Math Ed 1981; *cr:* Elkhart Bapt Chrstn Schl Math Tchr 1981-84; Latham Chrstn Acad Math Tchr 1984-88; First Bapt Chrstn Schl Math Tchr 1988-; *ai:* Litchfield Town Band 1991-.

STAUFFER, MARIE CARUSO, Music Teacher; *b:* Brooklyn, NY; *m:* George B.; *c:* Matthew; *ed:* City Coll (BA) Music 1972; Tchrs Coll at Columbia Univ (MA) Music Ed 1977; Hunter Coll Grad Seminars in Music 9 Credits 1983-85; Kodaly Summer Cert Pgm; NY Univ 1994; Handbells at Westminster Choir Coll 1995; *cr:* Columbia Univ Admin Asst 1972-78; St Vincent Ferrer HS Music Tchr 1978-; *ai:* Chorus & Handbell Choir Dir; *office:* St Vincent Ferrer HS 151 E 65th St New York NY 10021

STAUFFER, ROBERT J., Mathematics Teacher; *b:* Philadelphia, PA; *m:* Jane Adams; *c:* Jeffrey, Christopher; *ed:* Millersville Univ (BS) Math & Physics 1965, (MS) Math 1968; Attnd Bucknell Univ; *cr:* Oxford Area HS Math Instr 1966-67; Ardmore Jr HS Math Instr 1967-73; Lower Merion HS Math Instr 1973-; Villanova Univ Math Instr 1987-; *ai:* Theatre Spon; NEA, PSEA 1966-; LMEA 1968-; John Fritz Brennan Awd for Svc to Schl & Comm 1992; Interschool Cncl Grant for Calculus Project; Isaac F Seiverling Awd for Math; Hamilton Watch Awd for Math, Sci & the Arts; *office:* Lower Merion HS 245 E Montgomery Ave Ardmore PA 19003

STAUFFER, ROY ALLEN, Social Studies Teacher; *b:* Allentown, PA; *m:* Marla Bennicoff; *c:* Jayme, Robert; *ed:* Edinboro Univ (BS) 1974, (MS) His 1982; Post Grad Credits East Stroudsburg Univ, Univ of KY; *cr:* Emmans HS Tchr 1974-75; Cambridge Springs HS Tchr 1976-81; Gen Mc Lane HS Tchr 1981-; *ai:* Bsktbl, Bsbl Coach 22 Yrs; Negotiating Team Union Rep; NEA, PSEA 1974-; EMEA 1981-, Bldg Rep, Negotiating Team; 2 Ath Hall of Fames Le High Vly & Edinboro Univ; Coll Bsktbl, Bsbl All Amer Performer; *office:* General Mclane HS 11761 Edinboro Rd Edinboro PA 16412

STAUFFER, SALLY ANNE, English Teacher; *b:* Greensburg, PA; *ed:* Thiel Coll (BA) Eng 1963; (MA) Eng 1979; Post Grad Stud Manhattan Coll at NYC; IN Univ at IND Wall St Journal Flwshp; *cr:* Southmoreland Schls Eng Tchr 1963-67; Southwestern Cntrl Schls Eng Tchr 1967-; *ai:* Trojan Newspaper Adv; Past Pres Tchr Assn; Dist Compact Comm; Past Eng Dept Chprsn; NEA, STA 1963-, Pres, Sec, Curr Chr; Fortnightly 1980-, VP, Sec, Treas; Thiel Coll Alumni Assn; Fenton His Soc 1990-; World Wildlife; Natl Humane Soc; *home:* 8 Beverly Pl Jamestown NY 14701*

STAUL, DENNIS RICHARD, Assistant Principal; *b:* Farrell, PA; *m:* Andrea; *c:* Cara, Andrew John; *ed:* Westminister Coll Scndry Ed 1990; Masters Plus 24 Credit Hrs; *cr:* Kennedy Chrstn HS Tchr, Coach 1974-79; Sharon HS Tchr, Coach 1979-82; Meadville HS Tchr, Coach 1982-84; Kennedy Christina HS Tchr, Coach 1984-86; New Wilmington HS Tchr, Coach 1986-88; Sharon HS Tchr, Coach, Asst Prin 1988-; *ai:* Ftbl Coach 18 Yrs; Bsbl Coach 12 Yrs; Bsktbl Coach 4 Yrs; Track Coach 3 Yrs; NEA 1988-; STA 1988-, Greivance Chm; Bsbl Coach of Yr 1978, 1981; *office:* Sharon Jr-Sr HS 1129 E State St Sharon PA 16146*

STAULTERS, HAROLD JAY, Soc Stud & Global Studies Tchr; *b:* Ballston Spa, NY; *m:* Suzanne Marie Dumas; *c:* Katherine, Christine; *ed:* Univ at Albany (BA) Pol Sci 1985, (MA) Soc Stud Ed 1986; *cr:* Ballston Spa Cntrl Schls Scndry Soc Stud Tchr 1987-; *ai:* Jr Var Wrestling, Sftbl Coach; *office:* Ballston Spa HS 480 Garrett Rd Ballston Spa NY 12020

STAUSS, CAROL WOHLTMAN, Photography & Art Teacher; *b:* Bayonne, NJ; *m:* Albert Raymond Jr.; *c:* Jason, Ryan; *ed:* Montclair St Univ (BA) Art Tchr Ed 1971, (MA) Textiles 1973; 45 Addl Credits Cmptrs, Bus Admin, Schl Law; *cr:* Saddle Brook HS Art, Photography Tchr 1971-; *ai:* Photography, Art Shows Local, Cty, St, Natl Level; Photography Club; Yrbk Adv; NEA, NVEA 1971-; Belleville Music Parents 1992-, Corresponding Sec; Tchr of Yr 1988; *office:* Saddle Brook HS 355 Mayhill St Saddle Brook NJ 07663

STAVOLA, STEPHEN PETER, History Teacher; *b:* Middle Village, NY; *ed:* Fordham Univ (BA) His 1986; Fordham Grad Schl (MA) His 1989; *cr:* Fordham Prep Schl His Tchr 1986-90; Intermediate Schl 77 His Tchr 1990-91; Benjamin N Cardozo HS His Tchr 1991-; *ai:* Key Club Fac Adv 1992-95; After Schl Tchr 1995-; Stu Tchr Mentor; Raised Money for UNICEF, AIDS Rsrch, Cancer Rsrch & Muscular Dystrophy Assn.*

STAWASZ, MARYANN WILLIS, Reading Specialist; *b:* Malden, MA; *m:* Thomas P.; *c:* Kevin; *ed:* Keene St Coll (BED) Eng 1968; Univ of NH (MS) Rdng 1974; Univ of MA at Lowell Post Grad Work in Span; Rivierc Coll Rdng, ESL; *cr:* Pelham MS Eng Tchr 1968-70; Milford MS Rdng Tchr 1970-73; Spring St Jr HS Rdng Specialist 1973-87; Pennichuck Jr High Rdng Specialist 1987-; *ai:* Bldg Level Staffing Team; Lang Arts Curr Comm; AFT, Granite Rock Rdng Cncl 1973-; NCTE 1968-; League of NH 1973-, Bd of Dirs; Craftsmen, Pres; Herbs at Homestead 1992-; Nashua Boys Club Adopt-A-Duck Comm; Project Springboard Federal Grant; Adopt-A-Schl Regognition Cert; *office:* Pennichuck Jr HS 207 Manchester St Nashua NH 03060

STAYER, JANE FREY, Substitute Teacher; *b:* Lancaster, PA; *m:* George Edward; *c:* Jonathan, Thomas, Philip; *ed:* Elizabethtown Coll (BA) Eng 1949; PA St Univ 6 Post Grad Credits; *cr:* Denver HS Eng & Ger Tchr 1949-55; Lancaster & York Counties All Subjects Sub Tchr 1970-89 & 1994-; Chrstn Schl of York Sr High Eng Tchr 1989-94; *ai:* CSY Sr Class Play Coach 1995; Grace Bapt Church 1971-, SS Tchr, Fin Sec & Womens Missionary Soc Pres; *home:* 499 Kirkham Dr York PA 17402*

STEA, MARY LUCILLE (DEFELICE), Visual Art Teacher; *b:* Brooklyn, NY; *m:* Daniel Jr.; *c:* Daniel III; *ed:* NY Inst of Tech (BA) Fine Arts 1969; C. W. Post (MA) Fine Arts 1974; 30 Addl Grad Credits; Adelphi Credits in Ed; *cr:* Hicksville Jr HS Visual Art Tchr 1969-87; International Offset Commercial Artist 1969-70; Hicksville Sr HS Visual Arts Tchr 1987-; *ai:* Collegiality Comm; NEA 1969-, Delegate; NYSATA, LIATA 198 Enviromental 1987-; Special Olympics, MADD 1993-; Yrbk Dec 60 Hrs as Drug, Alcohol Facilatator for Tchrs Grad Course by *office:* Hicksville Sr HS Division Ave Hicksville NY 11801*

STEAD, DONNA LYNN, Mathematics Teacher; *b:* Amsterdam, Jon R.; *c:* Samantha, Courtney; *ed:* Siena Coll (BA) Math, Ed 1984 at Albany (MA) Math 1989; *cr:* Watervliet Jr Sr HS Math Tchr Fonda-Fultonville Cntrl Schl Math Tchr 1985-87; Good Counsel H Tchr 1987-91; Fonda-Fultonville Cntrl Schl Math Tchr 1991-; *ai* Tchrs Assn 1991-; Fulton Cty Republican Club 1992-; *office* Fultonville Central Schl 112 Old Johnstown Rd PO Box 1501 Fo 12068

STEARNS, ANN KAISER, Professor Dept of Psychology; *b:* OK; *c:* Amanda, Ashley; *ed:* OK City Univ (BA) Philosophy, Re Duke Univ (MDIV) Pastoral Cnslng 1967; Union Inst (PHD) Psyc Jerusalem, George Washington Univs Amer Schl Oriental Rsrch; *c* Univ Assoc Chaplain 1967-69; Essex Comm Coll Prof of Psych 19 Amer Psychological Assn; Amer Assn Pastoral Cnslrs; Author's (Amer; Articles Pub 1995; *home:* 614 Lake Dr Baltimore MD 2128

STEARNS, DAVID ALLEN, Instrumental Music Teacher; *b:* B OH; *ed:* Simpson Coll (BM) Music Ed 1977; 4 Hrs Akron Univ; *cr:* Heart Schl Elem Music Tchr 1978-81; Patrick Henry Schls Elem Sub Tchr 1982; Delphos City Schls Instrumental Music Tchr 19 Marching Band Asst; Pep Band, HS Musical, Pit Orch, Elem Musi Pvt Piano Lessons; Piano Accompanist; OMEA 1982-; Eagels 1996 Delphos City Schls 227 N Jefferson St Delphos OH 45833

STEARNS, PETER N., Dean of Humanities & Soc Sci; *b:* I England; *m:* Carol Zisowitz; *c:* Duncan, Deborah, Clio, Corde Harvard (BA) His 1957, (MA) His 1959, (PHD) His 1963; *cr:* V. J. C Instr to Assoc Prof 1962-68; Rutgers Univ Prof, Chm His Dept 1 Carnegie Mellon His Prof 1974-, Dean 1992-; *ai:* Amer Historic 1965-, Various Comm Chairs, VP 1995; NCSS 1982-; Journal of S 1967-, Ed-in-Chief; Editorial Bd; His Tchr; Nat Bd; Prof Tchng Editor, Co-Editor Various Prof Journals, Series, Books; Author, Co- Numerous Soc His Books; Various Funded Projects Co-Dir; Nu Consultancies; Television, Radio Appearances; Phi Beta Kappa; F Soc Sci Research Cncl 1956, 1960-61, 1967-68, Guggenheim 1 Amer Philosophical Soc Grant 1967-68; Fr Historical Stud Soc Prize 1964; Newcomen Spec Awd Bus His Review 1965; Elliott Smith Tchng Awd Hum, Soc Sci Coll Carnegie Mellon 1992; Doberty Prz; Ed Ldrshp Carnegie Mellan 1995; *office:* Carnegie University Baker 260 Pittsburgh PA 15213

STEBBINS, ALLEN H., History & Social Studies Tchr; *b:* Brid CT; *ed:* C. W. Post Coll (BA) His 1970; 30 Addl Post Grad Stud; *cr.* Mc Mahan HS Tchr 1973-74; Maynard HS Tchr 1975-; *ai:* Stu Gov NCSS, NEA 1975-; Amer Alpine Club 1983-; Appalachian Mounta 1972-, Boston Chptr Mountaineering Comm Chm; Ed of News *office:* Maynard HS 1 Tiger Dr Maynard MA 01754

STEBBINS, BARRY STEVEN, Biology & Physics Teacher; *b:* D OH; *m:* Cynthia K. Shouto; *c:* Christopher, Jenna; *ed:* OH St Uni Comprehensive Biological Sci in Ed 1971, (MA) Environmental Ed Voc Course Work Hyper Card & Multimedia, Apple Cmptr Inc, In Consultant Trng, Pasco Scientific; *cr:* Roosevelt Jr HS Sci Tchr 19 Wedgewood Jr HS Voc Coord 1979-80; West HS Voc Coord 1980-86; Classrooms of Tomorrow Sci Tchr 1986-; *ai:* Girls Jr Bsktbl 1979-82; Vlybl Asst Vlybl Coach 1980-82; Vlybl Var Coach 198 Vlybl Coaches Assn 1986-; NEA, OEA, CEA, COTA 1972-; OH 1986-; Sigma Xi 1989-; Phi Kappa Phi 1994-; Westerville Judo Club IBF Black Bar Bd 1981-; Testified Before Congress Improving Sci Ec Acad of Sci Comm Hearing; Sigma Xi Tchr of Yr; Lazarus Writing Articles Pub; Presentation of Many Educl Conf; Natl Sci Fnd Tchr D Tchr; *office:* West HS 179 S Powell Ave Columbus OH 43204*

STEBBINS, RICHARD VAUGHN, Social Studies Teacher; *b* Angeles, CA; *c:* Amani, Vaughn, Lauren; *ed:* Grambling St Univ (B 1967; Howard Univ (MA) Personel Admin 1973; Univ of MD 24 Hr Cert; *cr:* Howard Univ Asst Ftbl Coach, Head Recruiter; Xerox Corp Rep 1980-84;Washington Post Advertising Rep 1984-88; Howard Ct System Tchr 1991-; *ai:* Head Track Coach Columbia Express Elite; Prof Ftbl Player 1967-69; Olympic Gold Medalist 1964; Master T *home:* 5672 Stevens Forest Rd Apt 93 Columbia MD 21045

STEBBINS, TIMOTHY PAUL, Social Science Teacher; *b:* Bidd ME; *m:* Karen Maire Labonte; *c:* Brady Maie, Noah; *ed:* Univ of Sou ME (BS) ECs, Pol Sci 1985; Beginning Stages Grad Degree Educl A 12 Hrs Completed; *cr:* Biddeford HS Soc Stud Tchr 1986-; *ai:* As Ftbl, AAU 18 Yr Olds Bsktbl Coach; Scheduling & Disciplinary C Girls Bsktbl Coach; Stud Performance Comm; Involved in Rewritin Scis Curr; Served on Steering Comm That Restructured BHS; Natl S Excel 1996; Implemented School-to work Pgm for Gr 12 Econ Currently Reviewing Credit & Weighted Avgs for stu; *office:* Biddefor Maplewood Ave Biddeford ME 04005*

STEBER, JACK, Bio, Sci Dept Instrl Rsch Tchr; *b:* Coaldale, P Rebecca; *ed:* East Strounsburg St (BS) Bio 1964; Masters Equivanlac John F Kennedy HS Bio Tchr 1964-70; Jim Thorpe Area Schl Bio Tch Instr 1970-; *ai:* NHS, Class Adv; Sci Dept Chair; Head Wresting C Asst Ftbl Coach; NEA, NSTA 1970-; Conservation Tchr Yr; *office* Thorpe Area Schl Dist 1100 Center St Jim Thorpe PA 18229

STEBER, RONALD JOHN, Power Technology Instructor; *b:* Haz PA; *m:* Jacqueline McGovern; *c:* Melissa, Noelle, Jeffrey; *ed:* Penn St (BS) Ed, Industrial Arts 1974; St of PA (ME) Ed, Industrial Arts 1982; in Trng 20 Hrs; Working Toward FAA Airframe & Powerplant Mainte License 3000 Hrs; *cr:* Hazleton HS Power Tech Instr 1974-92; Haz Area HS Power Tech Instr 1992-; *ai:* NEA, PSEA 1974-; Experim Aircraft Assn 1992-; Hazleton Hghts Vol Fire Co 1970-, Pres, VP, Del Atlantic Air Museum 1986-; Restored 3 Aircraft as Schl Project Museum; Received Numerous Recognitions for Stdnts & Schl; Air Displayed at Numerous East Coast Air Shows; *office:* Hazelton Are 1601 W 23rd St Hazleton PA 18201

STEBLE, ROSE ANNINA, Second Grade Teacher; *b:* Amityville, NY Mt St Vincent Univ of Halifax (BA) Psych 1962; Boston Coll at Che Hill (MA) Elem Ed 1970; Growing Healthy Prgm, Recognition of Al Drug, Child Abuse, Certs; Credit Hrs Multi-Cultural Stud; *cr:* St Patr Girls Schl 2-4 Grds Tchr 1954-62; St Michael's Schl 1st Grd Tchr 196 Acad of the Assumption 4th Grd Tchr 1965-70; Our Lady of Angels 2-3 Grd Tchr 1970-79; St Aidan Schl 2-3 Grd Tchr 1979-; St Aidan's Enrichment Class Tchr, Remedial Math, Rdng Tchr 1986-93; *ai:* Mission Coord; Cath Schls' Week Comm; NEA; *office:* Saint Aidan 525 WIllis Ave Williston Park NY 11596

STECK, CALVIN KINGSLEY, Senior Spanish Teacher; *b:* Buffalo, *m:* Gail Ann Kelch; *c:* Marcus Kelch, Abigail Kingsley, Rachel Kins *ed:* Westminster Coll (BA) Greek-Latin & Classical Hum 1968; Co Rochester (MDiv) Semitics & Theology 1971; Union Theolo Seminary (STM) Patristics & Hellenistics 1972; Working Toward Sa Music & Sacred Lit Degree; *cr:* Lakemont-Rock Stream Presbyn Ch Presbyn Tchr 1972-77; Westminster Presbyn Church Presbyn 1977-88; Saint Peters Episcopal Church Rector 1988-92; Buffalo Schls Biling Sub Tchr 1993-94; O'Hara HS Sr Span Tchr & Lang I

94-; *ai:* Span Club & Jr Class Adv; Phi Mu Alpha Sinphonia 1966-; riential Soc, Amer Church Hist Soc 1970-; Optimist Club 1978-88, /S Newsletter; Jamestown Youth Bur 1977-79, Pres; Chaut Co r Singers 1980-85, Pres; Jamestown General Hospital 1979-88, VP.

, PETER CHARLES, Principal; *b:* New York City, NY; *m:* Alice aro; *c:* Alison C. Hain, Melissa A., Peter C. Jr., Jennifer M., Dara t Francis Coll at Brooklyn (BA) Psych 1969; SUNY at Stony Brook brl Stud 1976; Long Island Univ Prof Diploma Educl Admin 1984; r Park Ave Elem Schl Tchr 1969-89; Robert Moses MS Tchr ; Marion G. Vedder Elem Schl Prin 1993-; *ai:* CAS, AFSA 1993-; Marion G Vedder Elem Schl 794 Deer Park Ave North Babylon NY

EL, TOM, Assoc Professor of Chemistry; *b:* Bryn Mawr, PA; *ed:* ard Coll (BS) Chem 1972; TX A&M Univ (PHD) Chem 1978, Ed 1984; *cr:* TX A&M Univ Lecturer Chem 1980-84; Temple Univ st Prof Chem 1985-91, Adj Prof Chem 1991-92; WA St Comm Coll Prof Chem 1992-; *ai:* Sci Club Adv; Amer Chem Soc 1972-; OH cal Soc 1991-; WA Cty Natl His Soc 1993-; Sr Acad Cncl OH Acad I Great TchrsWkshp; *office:* Washington State Comm Coll 710 e Dr Marietta OH 45750*

EL, TRICIA R., Math, Computer Science Teacher; *b:* Allentown, David Steckel; *ed:* Bloomsburg Univ (BS) Scndry Ed, Math 1993; tehall-Coplay SD Sub Tchr 1994; Bellefonte Area SD Math, Cmptr r 1994-; *ai:* Yrbk Adv; Asst Chrldng Coach; Kappa Delta Pi 1993-; NEA 1991-; *office:* Bellefonte Area HS 830 E Bishop St Bellefonte 23

IAN, MARY FITZGERALD, Associate Professor of Nursing; *b:* le Centre, NY; *m:* Kenneth J.; *c:* James, Erin; *ed:* Molloy Coll (BS) 1974; Adelphi Univ (MS) Nrsng 1978; *cr:* Mary Immaculate Hosp N 1970-72; Winthrop Univ Hosp Staff RN & Head Nurse 1972-77; of NY Assoc Prof of Nrsng 1977-; *ai:* Stu Nurse Assn Adv; United rofessions Exec Bd Mem & Hlth & Safety Rep; NYSUT 1979-; Suffolk Cncl 1990-, Corresponding Sec & Bd Mem; Nassau Cty ep 1994-, Steering Comm; Adv of the Yr at SUNY at Farmingdale *office:* S U N Y Coll Of Tech At Frmgdl Melville Road Farmingdale 735

RONSKY FERNANDEZ, LOUISE E., Sixth Grd Mathematics r; *b:* Brooklyn, NY; *m:* Frank M.; *c:* Michelle Elizabeth, Steven Michael Joseph; *ed:* Attnd Kean Coll Math; *cr:* Herbert Hoover Jr -9th Grd Math Tchr 1969-91, 6th-7th Grd Math Tchr 1991-; *ai:* Schl Tchr; Twirling Adv; Cook for Elderly in Inclement Weather; ce Classes in Cmptrs, Math Related Topics; Amer Sign Lang Club; Math Tchrs of NJ; NCTM; Edison Twp Ed Assn; NJ Ed Assn; NEA; outs of Amer 1955, Ldr & Camp Vol 1982; BSA 1986-, Resource ; Edison HS Band Parents 1988-, Comm Vol; Rescue Squad Cravet 1993-; PTO; Sport Eams; Speaker for Inroads; *office:* Herbert MS 174 Jackson Ave Edison NJ 08837

OLE, JOHN, Architectural Design Teacher; *b:* Rockville Ctr, NY; quelyn Boehm; *ed:* St Univ Coll at Oswego (BS) Indstrl Arts 1982; IL Univ (MS) Tech Ed 1983; *cr:* Mc Graw Cntrl Schls Tech Ed Tchr 8; homer Cntrl Schl Dist Arch Tchr, Engrng Prin 1988-; *ai:* Dist Planning, Steering Comms; NEA 1983-; Cortland Cty Historical Soc Trustee; Natl Trust for Historic Preservation 1989-; Stdnts Won se Univ Arch Design Competition Schlsps; *office:* Homer Cntrl HS Vest Rd Homer NY 13077

L, DIANA (DICKERSON), English & Reading Teacher; *b:* ette, IN; *m:* A. Jeffrey; *c:* Adam A., Sarah A.; *ed:* Ball St Univ (BA) Ed 1974; Xavier Univ (MS) Ed 1977; Wright St Univ (MS) Gifted Ed *cr:* Oak Hills Schls 5th Grd Tchr 1974-80; Northwest Schls 8th Grd 988-; *ai:* Power of Pen Writing Team Coach; Hnrs, Awds Comm; ual Career Planning Team; NEA, OHEA 1974-; Greater Cincinnati earning Links Grant; *office:* White Oak MS 3130 Jessup Rd nati OH 45239

LE, ALAN CARL, Physical Education Teacher; *b:* Herkimer, NY; an; *ed:* SUNY at Cortland (BSE) PE 1988, (MSE) Hlth Ed 1993; *cr:* ner HS PE Tchr 1989-; *ai:* Var Ftbl, Wrestling Coach; Girls Var *home:* 634 Maple Grove Ave Herkimer NY 13350*

LE, FRANK, Alternative Program Director; *b:* New York City, NY; ary Jo Koehler-Steele; *c:* Jean Nora, Mary Kate, Meghan Therese; *ed:* s Coll (BA) Pol Sci 1977; Long Island Univ (MS) Ed 1978; *cr:* NYC Ed Tchr Trainer 1980, Tchr Mentor 1984, Brooklyn North Coord Alternative Prgm Dir 1993; *ai:* Dist 14K Bsktbl Coach; Cath Tchrs 1977-, Exec Bd, Edctr of Yr 1991; NY St Tchrs 1983-, Tchr of Yr John Bowne Regular Democratic Club 1983-, Pres, Dist Ldr; Began rive for Orphans & Foster Children for Holidays & Birthdays; *office:* Hopkins Jr HS #33 70 Tompkins Ave Brooklyn NY 11206

LE, HELEN READ, Chemistry Teacher; *b:* Conway, NH; *m:* niel Allen; *c:* Henry, Eliot; *ed:* Chatham Coll (BS) Chem 1966; 30 Credits Chem, Physics, Ed & Research Design; *cr:* Univ of Pgh cal Schl Research Asst 1966-67; Sinclair- Koppers Co Asst Chemist 68; Ashland HS 7th-12th Grd Sci Tchr 1968-71; Kingswood Regional chr & Sci Dept Head 1972-86; Kennett HS Chem Tchr 1986-; *ai:* NHS ty Advorory Bd; Stud as Research Scientists; Poetry Club; Amer ical Society, NEA 1966-; AEA, Pres 1967; Tamworth Rescue Squad, Officer 1978-91; Barnstormers Summer Theatre 1969-, Sec Bd of Tamworth Outing Club 1965, Dir 1968-; Wonalancet Chapel 1970, Minister; Fellowship Smith, Kline & French Immunology; Dev & mentation Sr Honors Prgm in Humanities Kingswood HS; Sabbatical Self Directed Research on Epidemiology of Multiple Sclerosis 1981 6; Alumnae Tchr of Yr 1996; *office:* Kennett HS Main St Conway NH 3*

LE, IRIS CLARKE, Assistant Principal; *b:* Rustburg, VA; *m:* ice I.; *c:* Jonathan, Jade; *ed:* VA St Univ (BS) Elem Ed 1971; Johns ins Univ (MED) Admin, Supervision 1978; attnd Loyola Coll, Towson iv; *cr:* Balto City Schls Tchr 1971-87; Balto Cty Schls Tchr 1987-91, Asst Prin 1991-93, MS Asst Prin 1994-; *ai:* New Tchr Comm; A;Cheerleading Spon; Bldg Leadership; ARD Chprsn; SBMT; JCDA; elta Kappa 1990-; ASCD 1992-; NABE, NAEP; Delta Sigma Theta , Historian; St Bernardine RCC Womens Club Sec; Cath Daughters Amer; Project Mounting Stu Possibilities; Project Enhance; *office:* llawn MS 3033 Saint Lukes Ln Baltimore MD 21207*

ELE, JAMES RAYMOND, Mathematics Teacher; *b:* Lewes, DE; *ed:* of DE (BA) Math Ed 1976; Salisbury St Univ (MA) Ed & Scndry in 1995; *cr:* Indian River Schl Dist Math Tchr 1976-; *ai:* Sr Class & League Adv; Fac Liaison & Schl Attendance Comms; NHS Fac Cncl; IREA 1976-, Bldg Rep; NCTM, DCTM 1976-; Lower Sussex Little ue 1976-, Pres, Player Agent, Bd of Dirs; Selected Bldg Tchr of Yr & 1995; Supts Awd for Excl 1991; *office:* Indian River HS Clayton Frankford DE 19945

ELE, JOANNE, Fourth Grade Teacher; *b:* New York City, NY; *c:* d, Jonathan; *ed:* 30 Post Grad Credit Hrs Rowan Coll; 6 Credit Hrs den Cty Coll; *cr:* Gloucester Twp Pub Schls 1st Grd Tchr 1978-82, 4th Tchr 1982-; *ai:* NEA 1978-; Tchr of Yr; *home:* 20 Bently Dr Sewell 8080

STEELE, KATHLEEN PATRICIA, Science Teacher; *b:* Staten Island, NY; *ed:* Caldwell Coll (BA) Bio 1972; WV Univ (PHD) Bio 1977; Allentown Coll Stu Assistance Prgm; Boston Univ Tchng Physics; Gwyneod Coll Bio Scholars Course; *cr:* Inst for Cancer Research Post Doctoral Fellow 1977-79; Moravian Coll Bio Prof 1979-86; Pius X HS Sci Tchr 1986-; *ai:* Honor Soc Adv; Sftbl, Scholastic Scrimmage Team & Forensics Club Coach; Chess Club Moderator; ASM & Sigma XI 1976-; GSA & Natl Historical Soc 1980-; AAAS 1973-; NABT, AAPT, NSTA & ACS 1986-; Hawk Mt Sanctuary 1983-; Great Books Club 1978-, Co-Ldr; Woodrow Wilson Fnd Fellowship-Phys Sci; Commonwealth Partnership Fellowship-Bio; Lindback Awd for Outstanding Coll Tchng; *office:* Pius X HS 580 3rd Ave Bangor PA 18013

STEELE, MARY KOPP, English & Computers Teacher; *b:* St Marys, PA; *m:* Stephen A. Sr.; *c:* T. J., Stephen, Patrick; *ed:* Lock Haven St Univ (BS) Comm, Eng 1976; *cr:* Spotsylvania Area HS Eng Tchr 1977-84; Queen of the World Schl Jr High Eng, Cmptrs Tchr 1984-; *ai:* PTFA Treas; Awesome Apple Cmptr Club Coord; Laurel Rdng Cncl Mbrshp Chm; Eng Dept, Cmptr Dept Chm; Odyssey of the Mind Judge; *home:* 376 Rock St Saint Marys PA 15857*

STEELE, SUSAN JANE, 8th Grade Science Teacher; *b:* Baltimore, MD; *m:* John R.; *c:* Scott, Sarah; *ed:* Towson St Univ (BS) Bio 1977; Masters Degree Equivilance from Baltimore 1985; Cty Tchr Insvc; *cr:* Stemmers Run MS Sci Tchr 1977-; *ai:* Dimensions of Learning Comm; NEA 1977-; MSTA 1977-; PTA 1977-; BSA 1986-; Geology Mentor; Sci Tchr of the Yr 1990; Appeared on 60 Minutes in 1993 Dealing with Exxon Valdez Oil Spill & Clean-Up; *office:* Stemmers Run MS 201 Stemmers Run Rd Baltimore MD 21221

STEELE, TERESA ANN, Social Studies Teacher; *b:* Newark, NJ; *ed:* Kean Coll of NJ (BA) Sociology 1981; Elem Ed Cert 1985; Working on MA in Educl Admin, Supervision, Principalship; *cr:* Irvington Bd of Ed Sub Tchr 1981-86; Onyx Sales, Mrktg Inc Office Mgr 1990-91; Irvington Bd of Ed Soc Stud Tchr 1986-; *ai:* Peer Leadership Adv; Solid Rock Bapt Church Ed, Schlsp Comms; NJEA, NEA, ASCD, NCSS, NJABSE, IEA 1986-; Mayor Michael G. Steele Civic Assn 1990-, Corresponding Sec; Irvington Town Cncl Pub Svc Awd, Excl in Ed Awd 1992; Golden Apple Tchr 1993; *office:* Chancellor Ave Elem Schl 844 Chancellor Ave Irvington NJ 07111

STEELMAN, ANN MARGARET SULLIVAN, 9th Grd Earth Sci & Bio Tchr; *b:* Baltimore, MD; *m:* Carey Douglas; *ed:* Salisbury St Univ (BS) Bio 1993; BA Equivalency Earth Sci; 18 Credits Grad Hrs at Johns Hopkins Univ Working Toward a Degree in Environmental Sci; *cr:* Hammond HS Ninth Grd Earth Sci, Bio Tchr 1993-; *ai:* Sr Class Spon; New Tchr Support Team; NSTA, NEA 1993-; Sallie Mae New Tchr of Yr; Conservation Ed Cncl Flwshp; Washington Post Ed Grant; *office:* Hammond HS 8800 Guilford Rd Columbia MD 21046

STEEN, KAREN KEISTER, Business Education Teacher; *b:* New Lexington, OH; *m:* John Richard; *c:* Amanda Katherine, Angela Louise; *ed:* OH Vly Coll (AA) Gen Stud 1980, (BS) Ed 1982, (MS) Ed 1989; Intensive Office, Cooperative Ed Kent St Univ; Acctng, Cmptr Sci Hocking Tech Coll; Cmptr Sci Muskingum Area Tech Coll, Cntrl OH Tech Coll; Cmptr Sci, Lib Sci OH St Univ; *cr:* New Lexington City Schls Exec Sec 1982-83; Guernsey-Noble Career Ctr Jr Clerical Instr 1983-84; Sheridan HS Bus Instr 1984-; Cntrl OH Tech Coll Part-time Instr 1987-94; *ai:* Bus Profs of Amer 1983-; OH Bus Tchrs 1982-, Sect 4 Chm; Amer & OH Voc Assn, Delta Phi Epsilon 1989-; Amer Red Cross 1975-, Swimming Instr; *office:* Sheridan HS 8660 Sheridan Rd NW Thornville OH 43076

STEEN, MICHAEL ALAN, English Teacher; *b:* East Stroudsburg, PA; *m:* Margaret Mary Mannhaupt; *c:* Jeremy, Janette; *ed:* East Stroudsburg St Coll (BS) Eng Ed 1973; Marywood Coll (MA) Eng 1980; Addl 24 Credit Hrs in Cnslng; *cr:* Stroudsburg HS Eng Tchr 1973-; *ai:* Chess Coach; Mock Trial Adv; NEA, PSEA 1973-, Local Pres; *office:* Stroudsburg HS 1100 W Main St Stroudsburg PA 18360

STEENBERG, MATTHEW ALAN, PE Teacher & Ftbl Coach; *b:* Sidney, NY; *m:* Lynn Bacon; *c:* Chrysa, Ryan, Sara; *ed:* Ithaca Coll (BS) PE 1977, (MS) Sports Psych 1979; *cr:* Ithaca Coll Grad Asst, Ftbl Coach 1977-78; Chenango Forks HS Driver Ed Tchr, Ftbl Coach 1978-79; Lansing HS Hlth, PE, Driver Ed Tchr, Ftbl Coach 1979-84; SUNY at Cortland PE Instr, Ftbl Coach 1984-86; Christian Brothers Acad Ath Dir, Ftbl Coach 1986-89; Fayetteville-Manlius Schls PE, Ftbl Coach 1989-; *ai:* Head Ftbl, Strength, Conditioning Coach; AFCA 1984-; NYSFBA, AAPERD 1994-; NSCA 1990-; Coach of Yr Ithaca Journal for Var Ftbl 1983; *home:* 116 Cooper Ln De Witt NY 13214

STEENSTRUP, MELANIE ZIMMER, High School Math Teacher; *b:* Endicott, NY; *m:* Christian; *c:* Caitlin, Mallory; *ed:* SUNY at Binghamton (MS) Ed 1981; SUNY at Cortland (BS) Math Ed 1978; *cr:* Vestal HS Math Tchr 1979-; Broome Comm Coll Adj Prof 1982-91; *ai:* NEA, VTA 1979-, PTA 1993-; Vestal United Meth Church 1992; *office:* Vestal Sr HS 205 Woodlawn Dr Vestal NY 13850

STEERE, DANIEL EDWARDS, Assistant Professor; *b:* Providence, RI; *m:* Kathleen Anne Marsters; *c:* Zachary, Brendan; *ed:* Southern CT St Coll (BS) Spec Ed 1977; Rutgers Univ (MED) Spec Ed 1978; Univ of CT (PHD) Spec Ed 1988; *cr:* Inst for Human Resource Dev Sr VP 1987-92; MT St Univ Asst Prof 1993-95; East Stroudsburg Univ Asst Prof 1995-; *ai:* Stu Tchr Supvr; Spec Ed Hnrs Soc Fac Adv; TASH 1984-; CEC 1985-; NCRE, Natl Rehabilitation Assn 1993-; Co-Authored Articles, Textbook, 4 Book Chptrs; *office:* East Stroudsburg Univ Dept of Spec Ed & Rehab 200 Prospect ST E Stroudsburg PA 18301

STEFANELLI, ELLEN MCFADDEN, Seventh Grd Social Stud Tchr; *b:* Orange, NJ; *m:* John; *c:* Suzanne Bodeep Rauso, Thomas Michael Bodeep, John III; *ed:* Monmouth Univ (AA) Liberal Arts 1961; Kean Coll (BA) Elem Ed 1967, (MA) Interdisciplinary Ed 1989; 36 Hrs Post Grad Work in Psych, Classroom Mgmt, Supervision, Prejudice Reduction; *cr:* Clifton MS Tchr of Gifted 1983-89; Woodrow Wilson MS Soc Stud Tchr 1989-; *ai:* Knowledge Bowl Competition Fac Adv; NEA, NJEA, CTA 1979-; Oakside Bloomfield Cultrual Ctr, Trustee.

STEFANELLI, LISANDRA ANNE MONETTI, Accounting & Bus Law Tchr; *b:* Newark, NJ; *c:* Donald, David; *ed:* Montclair St (BA) Eng, Scndry Ed 1964; Rutgers Schl of Law (JD) Law 1993; Bus Ed Cert Montclair St 1987; Licensed to Prac Law in NY & LA; *cr:* Hillside HS Eng Tchr 1967-70; Bloomfield Bd of Ed Home Instr, Adult Ed 1970-82; Belleville Bd of Ed Jr HS, 8th Grd Eng Tchr 1977-78; Essex Cty Voc Bd of Ed Eng, Bus, Accounting, Law Tchr 1978-; *ai:* FBLA Adv 1993-; Mediation Project Stdnts Against Violence; Court Appt Mediator; NEA, NJEA 1977-; NJBEA 1989-; Phi Delta Phi 1992-; NJSBA 1994-; Spec Ed 1973-76, Co-Pres; Parents & Profs Part of Founding Group; Essex Cty Disabled Young Adult Group 1987-90, Bd Mem; Cncl for Lrng Disabled Young Adult Group, Inc.; *office:* Essex Co Vo Tech HC 91 W Market St Newark NJ 07103*

STEFANIK, CHARLOTTE KATHLEEN, 6th Grd Rdng & Lang Arts Tchr; *b:* Walnutport, PA; *m:* Robert; *ed:* Bloomsburg St Coll (BS) Elem Ed 1966, (MED) Elem Ed 1971; 60 Grad Credit Hrs Beyond Masters; *cr:* Arthur Street Elem Schl Classroom Tchr 1968-; *ai:* HAEA 1968-, Fac Rep, Exec Bd Mem 1992-93; PSEA, NEA 1968-, Fac Rep; PTA 1972-; *office:* Arthur Street Elem Schl 424 E 9th St Hazleton PA 18201

STEFFANINA, RON, Band Director; *b:* Tarentum, PA; *m:* Kimberle E.; *c:* Amante, Mario; *ed:* Indiana Univ of PA (BS) Music Ed 1976; Attnd Univ of MN, Carlow Coll; *cr:* Wakpala Schl K-12 Grd Music Tchr 1977-79; Hot Springs HS 5-12 Grd Band Dir 1979-81; Wall HS 5-12 Grd Band Dir 1982-84; Western Beaver HS 5-12 Grd Band Dir 1989-; *ai:* Gymnastics, Little League Bsbl Coach; Jazz Band Musical Theatre Dir; Chrldng Adv; PA Music Edctrs Assn 1987-, CItation of Excl; Hopewell Bsbl 1992-, League Dir, Championship Team 1995; Rapid City Symphony 1979-81; Festival Band Host 1990, 1996; PA St Band Flutist Pvt Flute Tchr 1991; *office:* Western Beaver Co Jr Sr HS 216 Engle Rd Industry PA 15052*

STEFFEL, VLADIMIR, History Professor; *b:* New York, NY; *m:* Margaret Jennings; *ed:* Case Western Reserve (AB) Pol Sci 1957; OH St Univ (MA) His 1959, (BSEd) Ed 1961, (PHD) His 1969; Clarkson Univ ACM-MAA Inst for Retraining in Cmptr Sci 1985-86; *cr:* Strongsville HS Tchr 1961-62; OH St Univ Instr 1965; Dalhousie Univ Asst Prof 1966-67; OH St Univ Instr 1968-70, Asst Prof 1970-74, Assoc Prof 1974-; *ai:* Griffin Soc, Dir of Honors Prgm; Chair Cmptr Comm; AHA, APSA, AAASS 1955-; NCSS, OCSS, CBS; OAH 1968-, Sec & Treas, Dist Svc Awd; Delaware Recyclers 1978-, Pres, Sec & Treas; Delaware & Omutninsk; Friendship Project 1985-, Pres; Natl Endowment of Hum Fellowship 1974-75; Articles Pub; *office:* OH St Univ at Marion Campos 1465 Mount Vernon Ave Marion OH 43302

STEFFEN, PATRICIA JO, Third Grade Teacher; *b:* Altoona, PA; *ed:* Glassboro St (BA) Elem Ed 1984; *cr:* Oaklyn Pub Schl 3rd & 5th Grd Tchr 1985-; *ai:* Chrldng Coach; Stu Cncl Co-Advisor; Peer Mediation Coord; NJEA 1985-; Haddon Hts Drug Commission 1991-, Sec; *office:* Oaklyn Public Schl 136 Kendall Blvd Oaklyn NJ 08107

STEFFEN, RHONDA BUTLER, 5th Grade Teacher; *b:* Brockport, NY; *m:* Douglas W.; *c:* Rachael Blair, Tiffany; *ed:* St Univ Coll at Brockport (BS) Dance, Elem Ed 1983, (MA) Dance, Kinesiology 1986; *cr:* Spotlight Studio Owner, Instr, Dir of Dance 1977-; SUNY Brockport Kinesiology Instr 1990; Brockport Cntrl Schl 3rd Grd Tchr 1984-86, 5th Grd Tchr 1986-; *ai:* Spec Ed Task Force; Shared Decision Making Team; Dance Rochester 1995-; Stdnts Perform an Annual Spring Show; *office:* Brockport Hill Schl 40 Allen St Brockport NY 14420

STEFFENSMEIER, BRUCE MICHAEL, Physical Education Teacher; *b:* Sleepy Eye, MN; *ed:* Dakota St Univ (BS) PE 1973; Univ of SD (MA) PE 1982; 50 Addl Hrs AZ St Univ, Univ of South FL, Mankato St Univ, SD St Univ, Boston Coll; Univ of MD; *cr:* Edgemont Schls Math Tchr, Coach 1973-74; Hauff Sporting Goods Sales 1974-76; Jefferson Schls Math, PE Tchr 1976-81; Univ of SD Grad Asst 1981-82; Ramstein Jr HS PE Tchr 1982-; *ai:* HS Var Boys, Girls Vlybl, Track, Field Coach; Natl Jr Honor Soc Adv; Practical Arts Dept Chprsn; Intramural Coord; Dodds Europe Track & Field Comm; European Alliance AAPERD 1992-, Pres Awd; AAHPERD 1992-, Fndr; European Coaches Assoc Pres, Fndr; Spec Olympics Outstanding Comm Svc, Citizen 1982; DoDDS Dist Tchr of Yr 1995; *home:* PSC Box 2 Box 7805 APO AE 09012*

STEGER, DONALD JOSEPH, Math Teacher; *b:* Cortland, NY; *m:* Bonnie Phillips; *c:* Greg, Eric, Lindsey, Corey; *ed:* SUNY at Cortland (BS) Elem, Early Sec Ed 1986, (MS) Elem Math 1989; 14 Credits; *cr:* Whitney Point MS Math Tchr 1986-; *ai:* Bsbl Coach 1988-92; Team Tchng, Ldr; 7th Grd Chprsn; Bd of Dirs MS book Store; WP Tchrs Assn 1986-, Bldg Rep; NYSUT Assn 1986-; Cub Scouts 1994-, Blue & Gold Dinner Chair 1995-; Newman Foundation Church 1978-, Dinner Dance Comm 1988-; 6th Grd Oddessy of Mind Team World Competition Championship Coach 1988; Tchr of Yr 1993; *office:* Whitney Point MS Rt 11 S Whitney Point NY 13862

STEGGERDA, RICHARD JOHN, HS English Teacher; *b:* Denver, CO; *m:* Margaret Mary; *c:* William, Katherine, Elizabeth, Alicia; *ed:* Cntrl MI Univ (BSE) Dramatic Arts 1970; Univ of VT (MED) Admin 1977; Middlebury Coll (MA) Eng 1990; *cr:* Essex Jct HS Eng Tchr 1970-79; Linden Hall Eng Tchr 1981-82; Mt Abraham Union HS Eng Tchr 1982-; *ai:* Bsbl, Bsktbl, Tnns, Drama Coach; NEA 1982-; Alpha Psi Omega; Fellowship Bread Loaf Schl Eng Rural Tchr Schlsp; Chm Eng Dept, Mt Abraham Union HS 1987-90; Pub Poet, 3rd Pl Wnnr, Natl Poets Wrtng Cont, Ed Awd; *home:* 122 Mountain St Bristol VT 05443*

STEGMAIER, ANNE MARIE, 7th Grd Tchr & Pastoral Cnslr; *b:* Washington, DC; *ed:* Immaculata Coll (BA) Theology, Soc Stud 1978; Neumann Coll (MS) Pastoral Cnslng 1992; *cr:* St Bartholomew Schl 5th-6th Grd Tchr 1972-75; St Gabriel Schl 8th Grd Tchr 1975; Immaculate Conception Schl 7th-8th Grd Tchr 1976-78; St Piux X Schl 7th-8th Grd Tchr 1978-82; St James Schl 8th Grd Tchr 1982-87; St Louis Schl 7th-8th Grd Tchr 1987-92; Our Lady of Grace Schl 8th Grd Tchr 1992-94; St Dominic Schl 7th Grd Tchr 1994-; *ai:* Yrbk Adv; Psi Chi, Amer Cnslng Assn 1990-; Amer Schl Cnslr Assn 1992-; NCEA 1972-; PA Instrl II Cert; *office:* St Dominic Schl 8510 Frankford Ave Philadelphia PA 19136

STEGMAN, RONALD R., Religion Teacher; *b:* Dayton, KY; *m:* Michele Holbrook; *c:* Kira, Shana; *ed:* St Paul Seminary (BA) Philosophy 1959; Xavier Univ (MED) 1969; St Paul Seminry (MDiv) Rel 1985; Post Grad Stud Educl Psych, Drama, Theology, Span; *cr:* Cincinnati Pub Schls Eng, Latin Tchr 1967-78; Mt St Joseph Coll Speech, Drama Tchr 1976-77; St Xavier HS Rel, Tchr of Soc Justice, Relationships 1979-; *ai:* Amnesty Intnl Moderator; Dir Mission Collection 3rd World Projects; Bread for World 1976-, Regnl Dir; Greenpeace 1987-; Pub Book: Families, Reflections from the Heart; CGE Awd Excl Tchng; Golden Apple Awd OH; Univ of Chicago Awd; *office:* St Xavier HS 600 N Bend Cincinnati OH 45224*

STEHLE, NORMA CALDERON, Gifted & Talented Teacher; *b:* Portsmouth, VA; *m:* Karl J.; *c:* Dennis, Rae Lyn, Caryn Fogel; *ed:* Wm Paterson Coll (BA) Elem Ed 1976; Montclair St Univ (MA) Environmental Ed 1985; 12 Credit Hrs in Fiber Arts; Post Grad Stud in Educl Philosophy & Methodology; *cr:* Macopin Schl MS Tchr 1977-; Camp Wapalance Naturalist 1985-; *ai:* Environmental Club Adv; Coord of Environmental Ed Residence Prgm 7th Grd; Union Rep; NEA, NJEA & WMEA 1976-; NJ Peace Action 1989-; Geraldine R Dodge Rainforest Fellow 2 Times; Tchr of Yr Runner-Up for Dist & Nom Twice for Schl; *home:* PO Box 431 Hewitt NJ 07421

STEHLIK-BAKER, WENDY KNIGHT, Asst Principal & 5th Grd Tchr; *b:* Lincoln, NE; *m:* John David Baker; *c:* Liate Stehlik, Jennife Stehlik, Brent Stehlik, Marta Stehlik; *ed:* Baldwin Wallace Coll (BS) Elem Ed 1976; Cleveland St Univ (MED) Curr & Instruction 1990; Elem Prin Cert; *cr:* Grant Schl Elem Tchr 1984-90; Lakewood City Schls Gifted Ed Coord 1990-93, Curr Coord 1993-94; Brecksville-Broadview Hts City Schls 5 Grd Tchr, Asst Prin 1994-; *ai:* Sci, Hlth Course of Stud Writing Comm Chair; Venture Capital Grant Comm; Strategic Plan Action Team Ldr; PDK Cuyahoga Vly Chptr 1994-, VP Prgm; OH Assn for Gifted Children 1983-, Treas; ASCD 1986-; PEO Sisterhood 1966-; Martha Holden Jennings Grant to Tchrs 1986; George Gund Fnd Grant 1987; CEC Bill Geer Grant 1988; Joint Cncl for Ec Ed Natl Awd 1988; ODE Grant for Bus, Schl Partnerships 1990; ODE Grant for Gifted Stdnts 1992; Articles Pub 1988; *office:* Oakes Rd Intermediate Schl 4450 Oakes Rd Brecksville OH 44141

STEHMAN, ROSE MARY, Guidance Counseling Chprsn; *b:* Walsenburg, CO; *m:* Lance; *c:* Lance; *ed:* Univ of Tulsa (BA) Eng 1972; Kent St Univ (MA) Guidance & Cnslng 1976; 25 Hrs Post Grad Kent St Univ; *cr:* Stow Schls Eng Tchr 1972-76, Guid Cnslr 1976-84, Guid & Cnslng Chprsn 1984-; *ai:* Interact Adv; Rotary; Schl Fndtn Trustee; OEA 1972-; NEA 1972-; STA 1972-; OSCA 1976-; Summit Cty Cnslrs 1976-; Lib Bd 1972-75; City Charter Commission 1973-74; PTSA 1974-, Outstdng Edctr; Rotary 1995-; Preserve Planet Earth 1996; *office:* Stow-Munroe Falls HS 3227 Graham Rd Stow OH 44224*

STEIDER, JUDITH HARTZLER, English, Jrnlsm & Rdng Teacher; *b:* Bellefontaine, OH; *m:* Larry E.; *c:* Jason, Beth; *ed:* Hesston Coll (AA) Eng 1970; Goshen Coll (BA) Eng 1972; Wright St Univ (MA) Eng 1991; *cr:* Cardington-Lincoln Jr HS Eng Tchr 1973-78; West Liberty-Salem HS Eng Tchr 1980-; *ai:* Stu Publications, Soph Class Adv; OEA, NEA 1973-, Negotiations Team; NCTE 1990-; Gemeinschaft Chamber Singers 1987-95; *office:* West Liberty-Salem HS 7208 US Hwy 68 N West Liberty OH 43357*

STEIER, GARY L., 4th Grade Teacher; *b:* Scranton, PA; *m:* Nadia Sanchuk; *c:* Christy Ware, Jamie D.; *ed:* East Stroudsburg St Univ (BS) Elem Ed 1967; Univ of Scranton (MS) Elem Ed 1972; 43 Credit Hrs; *cr:* Abington Hghts Schl Dist Grd 4 Tchr 1967-; *ai:* Soc Stud, Portfolio Assessment, Process Writing Comms; NEA, PSEA 1967-; *office:* Abington Heights MS 1555 Newton Ransom Blvd Clarks Summit PA 18411*

STEIGER, GARY, Sixth Grade Teacher; *b:* Westfield, MA; *m:* Linda Smith; *ed:* Westfield St Coll (BS) Ed 1965, (MA) Ed 1967; Univ of MA Cert of Grad Stud 1969; *cr:* Hazardville Meml 5th Grd Tchr 1965-70, Head Tchr 1967-, 6th Grd Tchr 1970-; *ai:* Floor Hockey Coach; CEA, NEA 1965-; *office:* Hazardville Memorial Schl 68 N Maple St Enfield CT 06082

STEIN, CHARLES ROBERT, American History Teacher; *b:* Brooklyn, NY; *m:* Susan K. Price; *ed:* SUNY at New Paltz (BS) Eng, Sec Ed 1972; CUNY Brooklyn Coll (MA) His 1995; *cr:* Reynolds IS 43 SS, Eng, Debate Tchr 6 Yrs; *ai:* Lincoln-Douglas Debate Team Coach; Natl Jr Hnr Soc; Fac Senate; Compact for Learning Achieved Schl Success Comm; UFT 1990-; NY Historical Soc Summer Inst Scndry Schl Tchrs 1989; *office:* Reynolds IS 43 1401 Emmons Ave Brooklyn NY 11235*

STEIN, HANNAH KOPLOWITZ, English Teacher; *b:* New York, NY; *m:* Zvi Martin; *c:* David B., Jeffrey M., Aaron N., Stuart J., Benjamin; *ed:* Yeshiva Univ (BRE) 1963; City Coll of NY (BA) Eng 1965; 33 Credit Hrs at Brookly Coll Grad Schl; *cr:* NY City Bd of Ed HS Eng Tchr 1965-69; NY City Bd of Ed Title II Rdng Tchr 1969-71; John Adams HS Eng Tchr 1986-; *ai:* AFT & UFT 1986-; Young Israel Adult Ed Comm 1980-, Study Group Ldr & Tchr; Comm Burial Soc 1982-; The Phoenix Lit Magazine Fac Adv; *office:* John Adams HS 101-01 Rocksaway Blvd Ozone Park NY 11417

STEIN, MARILYN HOPMANN, 7th & 8th Grd Mathematics Tchr; *b:* Franklin Square, NY; *m:* Philip; *c:* Kimberly, Sharon; *ed:* St Univ of NY at Oneonta (BS) Scndry Ed 1973; St Univ of NY at Stony Brook (MALS) Liberal Stud 1976; *cr:* Holy Angels Regnl Schl Math Tchr 1975-81, 1985-; *ai:* Math Dept Chprsn; Yrbk Adv; NCEA 1975-; Nassau Cty Math Tchr Assn 1995-; *office:* Holy Angels Regnl Schl Division St Patchogue NY 11772

STEIN, MARSHA E., Associate Prof of Marketing; *b:* New York, NY; *m:* Alan H.; *c:* Audrey Beth; *ed:* Queens Coll (BA) Home Ec 1969; NY Univ (MA) Fashion Merchandising 1972; 30 Addl Grad Credits Mrktg & Behavioral Sci; *cr:* Parsons Jr HS Home Ec Tchr 1969; Macmillan Co Home Ec Ed 1969-71; Fawcett Publications Managing Ed 1971-73; Simplicity Pattern Co Managing Ed 1973; Stacy Fabrics Corp Educl Coord 1973-75; Teikyo Post Univ Assoc Prof 1975-; *ai:* Fashion Merchandising Dir; Curr Comm Chprsn; Coop Educ Advsy Bd; Fashion Club Adv; Amer Mrktg Assn 1983-; Intnl Textile & Apparel Assn 1989-; AAUP 1980-; Assn of Retail Educators 1992-; Hadassah, Jewish Fed of Waterbury 1977-; Mag Ed 1971-73; Comm Newspaper Contributor 1981-88; *office:* Teikyo Post Univ 800 Country Club Rd Box 2540 Waterbury CT 06723

STEIN, MARY CHARITY, English Teacher & Dept Head; *b:* Chicago, IL; *m:* Irwin M.; *c:* Billy J. Xerxes; *ed:* NY Univ (BA) Eng-Cum Laude 1967; Goddard Coll (MA) Lit, The Novel 1980; MI St Univ (MA) Curr & Tchng 1989; Attnd AP Summer Inst; *cr:* Anatolia Coll 9-12 Grd Eng, ESL Tchr 1979-81; Cairo Amer Coll AP Eng Grd 12, Hon Eng 10-12 Grd, Speech & Debate Tchr 1981-91; Colegio Internacional de Caracas IB Eng 11-12 Grd Tchr, ESL Dept Head 1991-93; Intnl Schl of Beijing IB, Hnrs Eng 10-12 Grd Tchr, Dept Head 1993-; *ai:* Model United Nations Co-Adv; BEIMUN III Organizer; MUNITY Chief Fac Adv; Phi Beta Kappa 1967-; CERCOS 1993-; NE, SA 1981-91; THIMUN 1986-; Selected 3 Times for NEH Summer Seminars Stanford Greek Tragedy Milton's Poetry 1984, 1987; Univ of Arts Beckett; Amer Ctr in Cairo Lectured on Hawthorne; Helped Organize MUN Confs in Cairo & Caracas; NE-SA ECIS, CERCOS Confs Presenter; Co-Authored Countdown to College Admissions; *office:* The Intl Schl Of Beijing ISB Amer Embassy PSC 461 Box 50 FPO AP 96521*

STEIN, MARY ALICE, English & Latin Teacher; *b:* Tiffin, OH; *ed:* Mount St Joseph (BA) Eng, Latin 1963; John Carroll Univ (MA) Eng 1972; *cr:* Queen Martyrs 7th Grd Tchr 1963-64; St Marys Eng, Latin Tchr 1964-67; Carroll HS Dayton Eng, Latin Tchr 1967-; *ai:* Sr Class, Latin Club Adv; Amer Classical League 1988-; OH Classical League 1989-; Sisters of Charity 1959-; Carroll Tchr of Yr 1975, 1976, 1978; *office:* Carroll H S 4524 Linden Ave Dayton OH 45432

STEIN, SANDRA MCKEAN, Special Education Master Tchr; *b:* Pittsburg, PA; *m:* Robert M.; *c:* Mark, Matthew, Alicia; *ed:* Univ of Dayton (BS) Elem Ed & Spcl Ed 1975; Univ of Pittsburg (MS) Spcl Ed 1980; *cr:* Allegheny Intermediate Unit Tchr 1976-92; North Allegheny Schl Dist Tchr 1992-; *ai:* Conflict Resolution Comm; Grad Requirements Comm; Spcl Ed Advy Comm; Instrl Support Team; AFT 1976-; Presenter for Scndry Support Initiative; *office:* N Allegheny Schl Dist 350 Cumberland Rd Pittsburgh PA 15237

STEINBACH, RICHARD ADAM, Soc Studies Tchr & Ath Coach; *b:* New York City, NY; *m:* Pamela Katz; *c:* Bobby, Rae; *ed:* OH Wesleyan Univ (BA) Politics, Govt 1983; Columbia Univ (MA) His 1988; *cr:* US Peace Corps Comm Extension Agent 1984-87; N Colonie Cntrl Schls Ath Coach, Sub Tchr 1989; Troy City Schls Soc Stud Tchr Ath Coach 1989-; *ai:* Boys JV Soccer Team, Head Boys Track Coach; *office:* Troy HS 1950 Burdett Ave Troy NY 12180

STEINBAUM, MARTIN JAY, Physics & Natural Sci Teacher; *b:* New York City, NY; *m:* Kathryn Elise Spitzer; *ed:* Adelphi Univ (BA) Bio 1966, (MA) Ed 1968; Columbia Univ (PHD) Astronomy 1978; NSF Grant Spec Cert Astronomy Cornell Univ; Addl Post Grad Stud Astronomy; *cr:* Hayden Planetarium Assoc Astronomer 1966-69; New Rochelle City Schl Dist Astronomy, Space Sci Dir 1969-91, Planetarium, Astronomy Consultant 1991-; Iona Coll AsSoc Prof Physics, Natural Sci 1987-; *ai:* Admin, Supervision of Planetarium Trng Prgm; Natl Rifle Assn 1981-; Pub Astronomy, Educl Articles; *office:* Iona College North Ave New Rochelle NY 10801

STEINBECK, RITA PATRICE, 5th Grade Language Arts Tchr; *b:* Cleveland, OH; *m:* Robert; *c:* Michelle, Eric; *ed:* Coll of Mount Saint Joseph (BSEd) Elem Ed 1966; Addl Credit Hrs Miami Univ; *cr:* Oxler Elem Schl 4th Grd Lang Arts Tchr 1966-69; Oak Hills Schls K-8th Grd Sub Tchr 1980-87; Saint Aloysius Schl 5th & 6th Grd Tchr 1987-; *ai:* Schl Mission Dir; PTC Bd Rep; Girl Scouts & Brownies, Troop Ldr; *office:* St Aloysius On The Ohio Sch 6207 Portage St Cincinnati OH 45233

STEINBERG, SANDRA LEBOWITZ, Learning Support Teacher; *b:* Scranton, PA; *m:* Michael J.; *c:* Hilary, Jaimee; *ed:* West Chester St Coll (BS) Elem Ed 1970; Marywood Coll Grad Stud, Spec Ed; *cr:* Prince Georges Cty Montpelier Schl 3rd Grd Tchr 1970-72; Childrens Learning Wkshp Primary Tchr 1983-91; JCC Pre Schl Transitional Tchr; Abington Heights Schl Dist Learning Support Tchr 1991-; *ai:* AHEA 1991-; Temple Hesed CRE 1994-, Comm Mem; Temple Hesed Yth Adv 1992-; *office:* Abington Hghts Schl Dist Grove St Clarks Summit PA 18411

STEINBERG, THEODORE LOUIS, English Professor; *b:* Baltimore, MD; *m:* Phyllis Kenshur; *c:* Gillian, Daniel, Miriam; *ed:* Univ of IL (AM) Eng 1969, (PHD) Eng 1971; *cr:* SUNY Asst Assoc Prof 1971-; *ai:* Hnrs Pgm Dir; Medieval Acad 1968-; AFT 1971-; Intnl Porlock Soc 1978-; Das Puppenspiel 1994-, Bd of Dir; Books: Mendele Moucher Seforim, Piers Plowman & Prophecy; Numerous Articles Pub.

STEINBROOK, RUSETTA LYNN, Fourth Grade Teacher; *b:* Columbus, OH; *ed:* Bob Jones Univ (BA) Rel 1976; Pensecola Chrstn Coll (MA) Ed 1990; *cr:* Dade Chrstn 4th Grd Tchr 1976-80; Licking Cty Chrstn 4th Grd Tchr 1980-89 & 1991-; *ai:* Heart of OH Quilters Guild 1995-; *home:* 19 Licking View Dr Apt B Heath OH 43056

STEINDEL, RICHARD GALLENTINE, Mathematics Teacher of Gifted; *b:* Altoona, PA; *m:* Doris Long; *c:* Joel, John, Janice; *ed:* Penn St Univ (BA) Commerce 1954; 18 Addl Hrs IN Univ of PA; *cr:* Kittanning Jr HS Tchr 1961-90; Armstrong Cntrl Jr HS Tchr 1990-; *ai:* PA Jr Acad of Sci Spon; Adult Basic Ed Tchr; NEA, PSEA 1962-; Armstrong Ed Assn 1975-; Church 20 Yrs; Planning & Zoning Commission 12 Yrs; Excl Fnd 2 Yrs; US Army 1954-56; Tchr of Yr Jr Chamber of Commerce 1966.

STEINER, BARBARA JANUS, French Teacher; *b:* Pittsburgh, PA; *m:* Dennis Aaron; *c:* Matthew, Marc; *ed:* IN Univ of PA (BS) Fr 1971; Shippensburg Univ of PA (MED) Scndry Cnslng 1977; Univ of Guadalajara Summer Schl Prgm Span Cert; Hood Coll Stud to Complete Admin & Supervision Cert; *cr:* Washington Cty Bd of Ed 6-8 Grd Fr Tchr 1971-74; North Potomac MS 6-8 Grd Fr Tchr 1974-76; Boonsboro HS Fr Tchr, Dept Chair 1977-; *ai:* Odyssey of Mind Competition Coach; Sr Class Adv; NHS Fac Cncl; Schl Improvement Team; NEA, MSTA, WCTA 1978-; ACTFL, MD Frgn Lang Assn 1982-; Frederick HS Safe & Sane Grad Comm 1995-; *office:* Boonsboro HS 10 Campus Ave Boonsboro MD 21713

STEINER, CAROL J. (ERZEH), Instr, Basic Math Concpt Coord; *b:* Akron, OH; *m:* John; *c:* Emily; *ed:* Univ of Akron (BS) Scndry Ed, Math 1971; Kent St Univ (MED) Curr & Instruction 1974; Cmptr Sci Programming Courses, Post Grad Credit Tech in Ed; *cr:* St Peter HS Math, Typing Tchr 1972-73; Mogadore HS Math Tchr 1974-77; Kent St Univ Part-time Math Instr 1983-89, Instr Coll of Ed 1989-90, Instr & Coord Math Dept 1990-, Adv for Coll Arts & Scis 1995-; *ai:* Math Club Vol Adv Norton MS; NCAA Internal Review of Kent St Univ; Fiscal Integrity Comm; NCTM 1990-; Strikes & Spares Tchrs Bowling League 1990-, Sec, Treas, High Game 232; Natl Sci Grant for Scndry Math Tchrs Summer 1973; Grad Asst Coll of Ed Kent St 1973-74; Norton Schl Bd 1990-93; Del OH Schl Bd Assn 1990-93; Presider at NCTM 1994-95 Annual Convention; Speaker for OCTM; *office:* Kent St Univ 233 MSB Kent OH 44242

STEINER, VIRGINIA M., 6th Grade Teacher; *b:* Dover, OH; *m:* Marlin; *c:* Jeremy; *ed:* Kent St Univ (BS) Elem Ed 1979; Ashland Univ (MED) Educl Admin 1991; *cr:* St Joseph of Mantoa 5th-8th Grd Tchr 1979-81; East Holmes Local Schls 7th-8th Grd Tchr 1981-86, 6th Grd Tchr 1986-; *ai:* OEA & NEA, Pres 1995-; OH Cncl Tchrs of Math; *office:* Berlin Elem Schl PO Box 310 Berlin OH 44610

STEINFORT, FAITH SANDERSON, Language Arts Teacher; *b:* Philadelphia, PA; *m:* Robert Edwin; *c:* Kurt, Matthew; *ed:* Montclair St Coll (BA) Eng 1968; *cr:* Memorial Jr HS Eng Tchr 1968-74; Cinnaminson MS Lang Arts Tchr 1984-; *ai:* Bldg Advy, Discipline, Bd Liaison Comms; CEA, BCEA, NJEA, NEA 1984-, Bldg Rep, Crisis Chm; Delta Kappa Gamma Intnl 1974-, Chptr Pres, St Chm, St Rose Awd for Distngd Svc, Achvmt; St Matthew Luth Church 1990-, Stewardship Comm; Concerned Citizens Against Asbestos 1978-81, Co-Fnd, PTA Awd Svc to Schls; Tchr of Yr 1992; *office:* Cinnaminson MS Forklanding Rd Riverton NJ 08077*

STEINHOFF, PATRICIA CRAFT, Fifth Grade Teacher; *b:* Ellenville, NY; *m:* Mark; *ed:* Amer Intnl (BS) Elem Ed 1974; SUNY at New Paltz (MS) Elem Ed 1988; *cr:* Ellenville Cntrl Schl Grds 3,4,6 Tchr 1975-; *ai:* Field Hockey & Track Coach; Treas Stu Accounts; Sr Class Adv, Dist Level Team; Ellenville Tchrs Assn, VP; AFT, NYSUT 1974-; ETA 1974-, Treas, VP; *home:* PO Box 453 Ellenville NY 12428*

STEINLAGE, RALPH CLETUS, Professor of Mathematics; *b:* St Henry, OH; *m:* Mary Margaret Rammel; *c:* Cindy Kulikowski, Viki Kroeger, Laara Doorley; *ed:* Univ of Dayton (BS) Math 1962; OH St Univ (MS) Math 1963, (PHD) Math 1966; *cr:* Univ of Dayton Prof Math 1966-; *ai:* Math Modeling Competition Adv; Math Assn of Amer 1962-; Amer Math Soc 1966-; Intnl Fuzzy Systems Assn1970-; Woodrow Wilson Fellowship 1962-63, Grant 1982; *office:* Univ of Dayton 300 College Park St Dayton OH 45469

STEINMAN, DAVID WARREN, Professor of Psychology; *b:* Orleans, France; *m:* Rachel Glatzer; *c:* Deborah, Akiua, Auigayel, Benyamin Yoel, Chann; *ed:* Univ of Pittsburgh (BA) Philosophy & Eng Lit 1976; Ner Isreal Rabbinical Coll (BTL) Ordained Rabbinics 1981; Adelphi Univ (PHD) Clinical Psych 1994; *cr:* Pvt Practice Psych 1984-; Touro Coll Prof 1992-; Coney Island Hosp Pgm Dir 1994-; Lumina Inc Psych 1995-; *ai:* ACHPA 1995-; JACS 1982-, Rabbinic Bd; 2 Articles Pub; Addressed EPA Convention 1995 & 1996; *home:* 1616 E 24th St Brooklyn NY 11229*

STEINMETZ, DONNA HUBSCH, Counselor; *b:* Allentown, NJ; *m:* Robert G.; *c:* Robert G. Jr., Kristin D.; *ed:* Trenton St Coll (BS) Ed 1974, (MA) Cnslng, Personnel Svc 1991; NJ Substance Awareness Coord Cert 1991; *cr:* Alfred Reed Elem Schl 2nd-4th Grd Tchr 1975-91; Antheil Elem Schl 2nd-4th Grd Tchr 1975-91, Jr Prof Experience Stdnts Cooperating Tchr 1986-91, Stu Assistance, Guid Cnslr 1991-; Parkway Elem Schl Stu Assistance, Guid Cnslr 1991-93; Lanning Elem Schl Stu Assistance, Guid Cnslr 1991-93; Trenton St Coll Adj Prof Cnslng Dept 1994; *ai:* Trenton St Coll, Rider Univ Site Supvr Cnslr 1993-; NEA, NJEA, ETEA 1974-; ACA, MCPCA 1991-; Chi Sigma Iota 1991-; Kappa Delta Pi 1992-; Contact Intnl 1984-94, Vol, Trainer of Vols; Governors Tchrs Recognition Prgm Tchr of Yr 1990-91; Ewing Twp Bd of Ed & Supt of Schls Recognition Awd 1992; *office:* Anthell Elem Schl 339 Ewingville Rd Trenton NJ 08638

STEINMETZ, SHIRLEY WENNING, English as Second Lang Tchr; *b:* Waterbury, CT; *m:* George; *c:* Susan Steinmetz Hoskins, John, Christine; *ed:* Univ of CT (BA) Home Ec 1953; 30 Credits in Ed at Cntrl CT St Univ 1979; *cr:* Waterbury Bd of Ed Kndgtn Tchr 1954-65; Wethersfield Bd of Ed Eng as Second Lang Tchr 1978-; *ai:* Prof Dev Comm; Parents Meetings; CEA, NEA 1954-65, 1978-; CT TESOL 1978-; CAPSEA 1995-; Zoning Bd of Appeals 1980-82; Planning & Zoning 1982-87, Clerk; Wethersfield Democratic Town Com, Captain 1978, Chair 1987; Hartford Chms Club 1987-, Chair; Intnl Stdnts as Cultural Resources CT TESOL Presenter & Panel 1983; Distinguished Svc Awd 1986; Wethersfield Tchr of Yr 1987-88; St Tchr of Yr Finalist 1988; Wethersfield Bd of Ed Congratulations 1988; Wethersfield Bd of Ed Resolution of Appreciation 1993; *home:* 375 Brimfield Rd Wethersfield CT 06109

STEINMILLER, JANET LYNNE, Elementary Librarian; *b:* Pittsburgh, PA; *m:* Elio Arturo Ingala; *c:* Justin, Kevin; *ed:* Univ of Pittsburgh (BA) Lang Commnctn 1976; Working on +18 Credits Lib Info Sci Univ of Pittsburgh; 36 Credits Ed at Assorted Univs; *cr:* Escuela Campo Alegre 7th-9th Grd Eng Tchr, 7th-8th Grd Thinking Skills, Librn Pre-K-5th Grd 15 Yrs; W Forest Schls 7th-12th Grd Eng 3 Yrs; Booker Washington Inst of Tech 9th-12th Grd Eng Tchr 1 Yr; *ai:* Curr Dev; Ldrshp Team; MS Act; Yrbk; Detention Supvr; TIE 1990-; *home:* PO Box 521308 Miami FL 33152*

STELLA, JAMES MICHAEL, Art Teacher; *b:* Philadelphia, Temple Univ (BS) Art Ed 1976; 24 Credits in Comp Art; *cr:* Neumann HS Art Tchr 1977-90; John W Hallahan HS Art Tchr & 1990-; *ai:* Schl Television Production; NAEA 1990-; Solo & G Exhibits; *office:* John W Hallahan HS 311 N 19th St Philadelphia P

STELLABUTO, DAVID L., Mathematics & Reading Tea Punxsutawney, PA; *m:* Sherry Sloniger; *c:* Noah; *ed:* IN Univ of Elem Ed 1973; 24 Post Grad Clarion Univ of PA; *cr:* Manstella 1973-74; Oklahoma Elem Schl Tchr 1976-86; Juniata Elem S 1974-76, 1986-95; DuBois MS 6th Grd Tchr 1995-; *ai:* NEA, PSE *office:* DuBois MS Liberty Blvd Du Bois PA 15801

STELLER, ROBERT EDWARD, Social Studies Instructor; *b* Lake, NJ; *m:* Patricia Louise Gibson; *ed:* Villanova Univ (BS) H 1969; Grad Work Seton Hall Univ 1969-70; *cr:* Middletown HS Stud 1969-; Brookdale Comm Coll Adjunct Instr of Comm Division 1984-; *ai:* Pol Sci Club, Cultural Affairs Club, Monmo Govt Inst, Princeton Model United Nations & Harvard Model C Adv; NJ Ed Assn & Middletown Twp Ed Assn 1975-; NJ Cncl Eductrs 1993; Borough of Spring Lake, Councilman 1974-80; Plar of Borough Spring Lake Mem, 1975-81, Vice-Chm 1980-81; Spri Historical Soc 1975-, Pres 1981-82, VP 1982-83, Trustee Monmouth Cty Rep Comm 1990; Spg Lk Hts Rep, Treas 1995; Grad Schl of Ed Fellowship 1990; Rdng, Writing, & Civic E Governors Excl in Tchng Awd 1988; Tchr of Yr; Consultant to De for Statewide Scndry Level Soc Stud Proficiencies 1990-; Middletown HS South 501 Nutswamp Rd Middletown NJ 07748

STELLRECHT, SUSAN MARIE (FELSER), Second Grade Tea Buffalo, NY; *m:* John William; *c:* Eric, Laura, Marc, Joseph; Brockport (BS) Elem Ed N-6 1970; Fine Arts Degree Dance 1970; Grad Hrs SUC Buffalo 1974; *cr:* E Aurora Schls Kndgtn Tchr 1970- 1 Tchr 1979-85, Grd 2 Tchr 1986-; *ai:* Tech, Kids Kit Comm NYSUT; *office:* Parkdale Elem Schl 80 Parkdale Ave East Au 14052

STELLUTE, DANIEL J., Social Studies Teacher; *b:* Pittsburgh, Euphemia Hamrock; *ed:* Clarion Univ (BS) Geog, Soc Stud 1968; Park Schl Dist Soc Stud Tchr 1968-; *ai:* Ftbl Coach; PSEA; SPEA

STELZER, KARL ALAN, Bible & Art Teacher; *b:* Indianapolis, Deborah Ann Jenkins; *c:* David Hans, Suzannah Lynn, Daniel Jam William; *ed:* Bluffton Coll (BA) Rel, Art 1972; Grace Theo Seminary (MDiv) Theology 1977, (THM) Theology 1982; Worki Pensacola Chrstn Coll; *cr:* Grace Coll Art Instr 1973-75; Flwsl Church Asst Pastor 1975-80; Bible Bapt Schl Pastor 1982-89; Lick Chrstn Acad Bible, Art Tchr 1983-; *ai:* Soccer, Bstkbl, Track C Class Adv; St Fine Arts Commp Judge; OH Designer Craftsman 19 Arts & Crafts Guild 1990-; Evangelical Bapt Missions 1988-; Seve Ceramic, Pottery Awds; *home:* 61 Pierce Ave Newark OH 43055

STEM, CLARK A., World Cultures Instructor; *b:* E Stroudsburg, Barbara J. Stem Clark; *ed:* ESU (BA) His 1963; 24 Credit H Palmerton HS Soc Stud Tchr 1967-69; North HS Soc Stud Tchr 1 East Stroudsburg Area HS Soc Stud Tchr 1972-; *ai:* Former H Wrestling Coach; Former Var Asst Ftbl Coach; NEA, PSEA, MSCSS; Elks; Moose; *office:* East Stroudsburg HS N Courtland Stroudsburg PA 18301

STEM, DARLA, 3rd Grade Teacher; *b:* Jacksonville, NC; *c:* Barb East Stroudsburg Univ (BS) Elem Ed 1968; Masters Equivalency 1992; IU 20 Credit Hrs; *cr:* Moore Twp Schl 2nd Grd Tchr 19 Smithfield Schl 3rd Grd Tchr 1976-1995; Resica Elem Schl 199 PSEA & ESEA 1976-; Amer Family Inst Positive Tchng Awd 1987; 1989-90; *office:* Resica Elem Schl 1 Gravel Ridge Rd East Stroudsb 18301

STEMMLER, CATHERINE CONSIDINE, Fourth Grade Teac Erie, PA; *m:* David; *c:* Shaun, Chad; *ed:* Mercy Hurst Coll (BA) E 1968; Gannon Univ (MA) Elem Ed; Edinboro Univ Masters Equiv Elem Ed 1990; IU #5 at Edinboro In-Svc Credits; *cr:* Jo Anna Conne Schl 4th Grd Tchr 1968-; *ai:* Dists Acad Sports League Judge; Lea EEA, PSEA, NEA 1968-, Bldg Rep; Delta Kappa Gamma 1988 1992-94; GMEA Triathalon, Vol; Tchr of Yr 1994; *office:* Jo Anna C Elem Schl 1820 E 38th St Erie PA 16510

STEMNISKI, MICHAEL ANDREW, Chemistry Teache Wilkes-Barre, PA; *m:* Anne Marie Philippon; *c:* Paul M.; *ed:* Vi Univ (BS) Chem 1962; Fordham Univ (PHD) Organic Chem 1967; F Cert Univ of DE 1972; *cr:* Brandywine Springs Jr HS Sci Tchr 19 Univ of DE Part-time Lecturer 1972-; Thomas Mc Kean HS Cher 1972-; DE Tech Part-time Instr 1982-; *ai:* Hnr Soc Selection Comm Chem Soc 1962-, DE Section Chm 1990; Chemical Soc London NSTA 1984-; DE Tchrs of Sci 1970-; NEA; DSEA; North Mill Cree 1978-, Pres 1995; DE Chem Tchr 1984; Tillmanns-Skolnick Soc Aw 1995; *office:* Thomas Mc Kean HS 301 Mc Kennan's Chur Wilmington DE 19808

STEMPIEN, SHARON KAY, 5th Grade Teacher; *b:* Wilmington, Matthew; *ed:* Bloomsburg Univ (BS) Elem Ed 1981, (MED) Elem Ed 30 Credits Beyond Masters 1990; *cr:* Edgewood Schl 5th Gr 1982-83, 4th Grd Tchr 1983-84, Kndgtn Tchr 1984-91, 5th Grd Tchr *ai:* PSEA 1982-; NEA 1982-; *office:* Edgewood Elem Schl 899 C Valley Rd Yardley PA 19067

STENCE, DEBORAH C., English Teacher; *b:* Schenectady, N Robert, Tammy; *ed:* Charter Oak Coll (BA) Hum 1987; Eastern CT S Eng 7-12 Tchr Cert 1990; 6 Hrs Wesleyan Univ; 6 Hrs Univ CT W Project; Working Towards MA in Writing Manhattanville Co WERACE Adult Evening Ed HS Eng Completion and GED Tchr Conard HS 10-12 Grd Eng Tchr 1991; Danbury HS 9-12 Grd Eng 1991-; *ai:* Class Adv; MS After Schl Prgm Tutor 1993-95; Variety Producer 1994; Schl Play 1992; NEA, NEATE, CCTE 1990-; M Gleason Awd for New England Assn of Tchrs of Eng Most Promisin Eng Tchr 1991; *office:* Danbury HS 47 Clapboard Ridge Rd Danbu 06811

STENDARDI, EDWARD JOHN, Assoc Professor of Manageme Brooklyn, NY; *m:* Deborah M.; *c:* Bridget, Matthew; *ed:* SUNY at Co (BA) Scndry Soc Stud 1972; SUNY at Albany (MS) Scndry Soc Stud (MBA) Fin 1979; Completed Requirements for CFP Designatio Scotia-Glenville HS Amer Stud Tchr & Bsbl Coach 1972-78; SUNY Tchng Asst 1978-79; St John Fisher Coll Mgmt Assoc Prof 1979 Strategic Review & Fac Welfare Comm; Trustee Comm on Fin Via IAFP 1975-; Fin Mgmt Assn 1985-; Midwest Fin Assn 1991-; C 1988-, Fin Comm; Numerous Articles Pub; *office:* Saint John Fishe 3690 East Ave Rochester NY 14618

STENDARDO, JEANNE M., English Teacher; *b:* New Hyde Park, N Anthony; *c:* Amy, Richard; *ed:* College of St Rose (BA) Eng, (MA 1993; 9 Credit Hrs; *cr:* Colonie HS 9-12 Grd Eng Tchr 1990-92; S HS 9-13 Eng Tchr 1992-; *ai:* Stu Awareness & Ed About Aides Adv Skills, Eng Lang Arts Comms; Wellness Week; Mentor; NCTE, NY 1990-; Pub Articles; *office:* Shaker HS 445 Watervliet Shaker Rd La NY 12110*

STENDER, CAROL J., English Teacher; *b:* Upper Darby, PA; *m:* J P.; *c:* Tracy, Michael, Jeffrey; *ed:* Millersville St Univ (BS) Eng wn St Univ (MS) Rdng 1974; Lehigh Univ (MA) Eng Lit 1986; *cr:* rg Area Schl Dist Rdng & Eng 23 Yrs; *ai:* Lit Magazine Adv; NEA A 1971-; NCTE & NASSP 1990-; *office:* Hamburg Area Jr-Sr HS or St Hamburg PA 19526*

ERSON-REYNOLDS, MARGARET, Chemistry Master Teacher; York City, NY; *m:* Francis E. Reynolds Jr.; *c:* Michael Reynolds; Thomas Aquinas Coll (BSE) Sci 1965; City Univ of NY (MSEd) ci 1971; Boston Coll CAGS Scndry SCi 1975; Fiber Optics 6 Credit ducl Ldrshp 3 Credit Hrs; Spectroscopy-Audit; *cr:* Brockton HS Tchr 1980-88; Oliver Ames HS AP Chem, Organic Sci Tchr 1988-93; chusetts Acad of Math & Sci Master Tchr 1993-95; Abington HS Tchr 1995-; *ai:* Massasoit Comm Coll Adj Fac; NEA, MTA 1971-; ACS Ed Div 1988-; Children's Museum 1992-, Bd of Dirs; Woodrow Flwshp Bates Coll 1985; 3M Transparencies 1st Place Awd 1965; Abington HS Lincoln Blvd Ext 106 Newcomb St Abington MA

G, JOHN P., Sixth Grade Teacher; *b:* Brooklyn, NY; *ed:* OH St Univ Ed 1986, (BSEd) Mid Chldhd Ed 1987; Ashland Univ (MED) Sports 94; *cr:* Edison MS Tchr 1987-89; Mark St Elem 5th Grd Tchr 93; Taft MS 6th Grd Tchr 1994-; *ai:* Math Curr Dev; Strategic ng Comm; USA Jr Olympic Vllybl Coach; NEA; OSU Alumni Assn; Club Adv; Kiwanis Club; *office:* Taft MS 474 N State Marion OH

GER, JAMES A., 8th Grade Teacher; *b:* Pittsburgh, PA; *m:* Brenda ack; *ed:* John Carroll Univ (BS) His 1962; *cr:* St Michaels Schl 8th chr 1962-68; St John Bosco Schl 8th Grd Tchr 1968-75; J & R age Inc Co-Owner & Pres 1976-84; St Michaels Schl 8th Grd Tchr *ai:* Yrbk & HS Selection Adv; Soc Stud Dept Head; NCEA 1987-; 1988-; *office:* St Michaels Schl 6906 Chestnut Rd Independence OH

ZLER, WILLIAM MARK, Computer Science Magnet Tchr; *b:* lyn, NY; *ed:* St Univ of NY at Albany (BS) Math 1970, (MS) Math 72; Hofstra Univ Completed Coursework PHD Educl Rsrch; *cr:* ack HS South Project CAL Co-Dir, Assoc Rsrch Dir, Math, Cmptr chr 1971-84; Maternity & Infant Care-Family Planning Systems, ns & Programming Mgr, Consultant 1980-89; Mineola HS Math, Sci Tchr, Lab Dir 1984-85; NY Inst of Tech Assoc Prof 1984-; s E. Gorton HS Cmptr Sci Magnet Tchr 1989-; Westchester Hebrew mptr Tchr 1993-; *ai:* Cmptr Contests Co-Adv; Schl Improvement Redesign Comms; Strategic Thinking, Related Software Club Spon; 1979-; ACM 1975-; NCTM 1971-; Suffolk Cty Math Tchrs Assn , Mbrshp Chm, Svc Awd 1976; AMTNYS 1974-; NEA, AFT 1971-; Noteworthy Amers 1976; *office:* Charles E Gorton HS Shonnard Pl rs NY 10703*

ANSKI, ALEXANDER ROY, Mathematics Teacher; *b:* Nanticoke, : Joyce Lorraine Moot; *c:* Eric D., Scott A., Jennifer L. Mills; *ed:* nsburg St Coll (BS) Math Ed 1963; Cntrl MI Univ (MA) Math 1969; SUNY at Cortland, Colgate Univ & Syracuse Univ Math & Cmptr es; BOCES In-Service Prgms; *cr:* Stockbridge Valley Cntrl Schl Tchr 1963-68; Morrisville-Eaton Cntrl Schl Math Tchr 1968-70; bridge Valley Cntrl Schl Math Tchr 1971-; *ai:* Jr HS Bsktbl Coach; etics Adv; Senior Class Adv; Stockbridge Valley Tchrs Assn 1963-, & Negotiator; NY Ed Assn & NEA 1963-; AMTNYS 1987-; AMTOC ; Colgate Univ Seminar Prgm Coord & Math Tchrs Conf 1968; use Univ Tchng Asst 1970-71; Attnd NSF Institutes; Pres of alley League Ath Dir; *office:* Stockbridge Valley Cntrl Schl Main St sville NY 13409

HAN, DONALD L., English Department Chairman; *b:* Gallion, OH; thenaeum of OH (AB) Philosophy 1960; Xavier Univ (MED) Eng, Ed Univ of Dayton (EDS) Ed Admin 1995; Attnd Purdue Univ, Ball St Wright St Univ; *cr:* St Mary's Schl Lang Arts Tchr 1963-66; Sidney ng Tchr 1966-73; Peace Corps Njala Univ Eng, Ed Instr 1973-75; y HS Eng Dept Chair, Tchr 1975-; *ai:* NHS Adv; NCTE 1976-, Chair Eng; OH Cncl Tchr of Eng 1976-, Ldrshp; NEA, OEA, WOEA, SEA ; Western OH Cncl Tchrs of Eng 1976-, Pres; Gateway Arts Cncl , Bd; 1984 Sidney Ed Tchr of Yr; Ctr Learning Advanced Writing, Lit; *office:* Sidney HS 1215 Campbell Rd Sidney OH 45365*

HAN, JOSEPH FRANCIS, Global Studies Teacher; *b:* Syracuse, *m:* Patricia M. Halloran; *c:* Therese Warguleski, Michael, James, en, Anne Marie, John; *ed:* Lemoyne Coll (BS) His 1964; Syracuse (MS) His, Ed 1972; *cr:* Chrstn Brothers Acad Tchr 1964-68; pool HS Tchr 1968-; *ai:* Curr Dev Comm; NYS United Tchrs 1968-; A Grant for Grad Stud; *office:* Liverpool Cntrl Schls 4338 Wetzel Rd pool NY 13090*

PHAN, NANCY ROBINSON, Tchr of the Gifted & Talented; *b:* clair, NJ; *c:* Courtney C., Maggie E.; *ed:* Susquehanna Univ (BA) Eng ; Univ of CT (MA) Ed 1995; *cr:* Southern Regnl MS Eng, Tchr of E 1972-; *ai:* Adv Lit Magazine, Instrl Cncl; Assessment Comm; NJEA ; NCTE 1988-; NAGC 1992-; Fed Grants; NJASCD Awd Outstdng ices Curr Dev; Pub Journals, Lit Magazines; *office:* Southern Regnl 5 Cedar Bridge Rd Manahawkin NJ 08050

PHAN, RICHARD A., Professor of Music; *b:* Buffalo, NY; *m:* Doris Fleming; *c:* Cheryl Burton, James, Timothy, Michelle; *ed:* St Univ at BS) Music Ed 1952; Eastman Schl of Music (MM) Music Ed 1953; Univ of Buffalo, Brigham Young Univ; *cr:* Buffalo Pub Schls Music 1956-57; Hamburg Cntrl Schls Coord of Music, String Tchr 1957-68; e Schl of Music Prof, Conductor 1968-; *ai:* Advising; NY St Schl c Assn 1956-, Orch Chair; MENC 1956-; United Univ Profs 1968-; Ward Choir 1968-, Choir Dir; LDS Stake Choir 1994-, Choir Dir; right Sr Scholar Awd 1984; Natl Schl Orch Assn Composition Contest ner 1986; Conductor Opening Ceremonies Orch, Chorus, Olympics ; *office:* Crane Schl of Music Pierrepont Avenue Potsdam NY 13676

PHEN, WILLIAM H., Biology Teacher; *b:* Olean, NY; *m:* Marlene A. ett; *c:* Bill, Melissa; *ed:* Earlham Coll (BA) Bio 1973; St Bonaventure) Ed 1994; Attnd Gannon Univ, Elmira Coll; *cr:* Bradford Area High Tchr 1974-75; Salamanca Jr-Sr High Sci Tchr 1975-76; Smethport Bio Tchr 1976-; *ai:* Track, Wrestling & Little League Bsbl Coach; ss Club; *office:* Smethport Area Jr Sr HS 412 S Mechanic St Smethport 6749

PHENS, BARBARA, High School English Teacher; *b:* Odessa, TX; Univ of TX at Austin (BS) Eng & Comm Ed 1984, (MS) Theatre Ed); Amer Acad of Dramatic Arts 1985-86; *cr:* Killeen ISD 6th-8th Grd atre Arts Tchr 1984-85; Falmouth Pub Schls Spec Ed Asst 1987-88, HS Tchr 1988-; *ai:* Sr Class Play Dir; Television-Jrnlsm Adv & Tchr; nouth Theatre Guild, Woods Hole Theatre; MTA & NEA 1987-; West nstable Sftbl League 1991-; Falmouth Recreation Ctr Womens Bsktbl 0-; Hambridge Ctr GA Writer In Residence 1992; Edward F Albee Fnd ter In Residence 1993; Whos Who-Rising Amers; *office:* Falmouth HS Gifford St Falmouth MA 02540

PHENS, BETH ANN, Second Grade Teacher; *b:* Tiffin, OH; *m:* Brian ott; *ed:* Miami Univ (BS) Elem Ed 1973; Wright St Univ (MS) Intnl Lit 7; Currently Enrolled in Doctoral Prgm in Ed Leadership; *cr:* Palmer n Tchr 1973-; Univ of Dayton Adjunct Tchr 1990-95; *ai:* NEA 1973-; 1990-; ASCD 1995-; Outstanding Stu Wright St Univ 1987; Tchr of 1988; *home:* 7250 Whitetail Trl Centerville OH 45459

STEPHENS, BRIAN D., Science Teacher; *b:* Camden, NJ; *m:* Sherrie L. Kaufman; *c:* Daniel, Katie; *ed:* Trenton St Coll (BA) Bio 1977; Rutgers Univ (PHD) Microbio 1984; *cr:* Dickinson Coll Asst Prof 1983-85; Triton Reg HS Sci Tchr 1985-; *ai:* Sci League & Bible Study Club Adv; NJEA 1985-; NABT 1991-; DVBTN 1994-; *office:* Triton Regional HS 250 Schubert Ave Runnemede NJ 08078

STEPHENS, HARRY, Science Teacher; *b:* Pittsburgh, PA; *m:* Geraldine J.; *c:* Emily, Craig; *ed:* Clarion Coll (BS) Bio Ed 1967; Purdue Univ (MS) Molecular Bio 1973; 40 Addl Credits; Addl Stud Univ of Pittsburgh, Carlow Coll, Edinboro Coll, Penn St Univ; *cr:* Perry Traditional Acad Sci Tchr 1967-; *ai:* Dept Chprsn; Ath Dir; Jr Science Acad Coord; AFT, PAFT 1967-; PSADA 1985-; *office:* Perry Traditional Acad 3875 Perrysville Ave Pittsburgh PA 15214

STEPHENS, JAMI LEIGH, Social Studies Teacher; *b:* Amiston, AL; *m:* Anthony Williams; *c:* Annie, Jessie; *ed:* Middlebury Coll (BA) His & Fr Tchr 1976; Rhema Bible Trng Ctr; *cr:* Alexis I duPont HS Soc Stud & Eng Tchr 1977-80; Faith Chrstn Acad His, Eng & Fr Tchr 1980-82; Wilmington Chrstn Schl World His & Geo 1992-; *ai:* Ski Club; Stu Senate Adv; Sr High Bible Stud; Jr Class Adv; DE Cncl Soc Stud 1992; Middle States Cncl Soc Stud 1996; Cornerstone Presbyn Church 1996, Jr Church Coord; Winterthur Tchrs Adv Bd.

STEPHENS, KIMBERLY SHERWOOD, Nursing Instructor; *b:* Pittsburgh, PA; *m:* Bruce D.; *c:* Benjamin, David, Luke; *ed:* CCAC Allegheny Campus (ADN) Nrsng 1981; Duquesne Univ (BSN) Nrsng 1988; Working on MSN & MBA Cert; *cr:* Allegheny Gen Hosp Staff RN 2 Yrs; South Hills Hlth System Home Care RN 8 Yrs; CCAC Boyce Campus Nrsng Instr 6 Yrs; *ai:* Stu Nrsng Assn Adv; Sigma Theta Tau Intnl 1988-; Good Thinking-Test Taking, Problem Solving & Study Skills for Nursing Stdnts 1994.

STEPHENS, MARK LLOYD, Wrestling Coach; *b:* Takoma Park, MD; *m:* Rhonda Lee Cooper; *c:* Sally, Gracie; *ed:* Salisbury St Univ (BS) Cmptr Sci 1985; *cr:* Bowie Sr HS Wrestling Coach 1987-; *ai:* FCA Spon 1994-; Natl Wrestling Coaches Assn 1994-; Bowie Baysox 1994-, Chaplain; Bowie St Ftbl Div II 1994-, Chaplain; *office:* Bowie HS 15200 Annapolis Rd Bowie MD 20715

STEPHENS, MARK W., Tchr & Lower Schl Wrtng Coord; *b:* Mt Kisco, NY; *m:* Janet N.; *c:* Laurie, Mindy; *ed:* Franklin & Marshall Coll (BA) Anthropology 1974; Cntrl St Univ (MED) Ed 1984; Cert Tchng El Ed Millersville Univ 1976; *cr:* Casady Schl 5th & 6th Grd Tchr 1976-84; Germantown Acad 6th Grd Tchr & Math Coord 1984-85, 4th Grd Tchr 1985-95, 6th Grd Tchr & Writing Coord 1995-; Eastern Coll Part-time Grad Course Instr 1994-; Chestnut Hill Coll Part-time Children's Lit Instr 1996; *ai:* Writing Comm Lower Schl Chair 1992-; Soc St Comm Lower Schl Chair 1988-90; Math Comm Lower Schl Chair 1984-85; MS Tennis Coach 1990-92; Upper Schl Jv & MS Girls Soccer Coach 1984-86; IRA 1993-; PCTM, PA Prof Storytelling Guild 1989-; First Presbyn Church 1984-, Deacon 1989-91; Whitpain Coaches Assn 1993-, Soccer Coach; Level IV Master Tchr; Elem Tchr Writing NAEP; Natl Fellow Ind Stud in Hum 1990; Edward R. Kat Fellow 1987, 1989, 1994; Natl Assessment of Ed Progress in Math for Congress; Wkshps Children's Lit IRA Natl Conf 1993-94; Authored & Co-Authored 6 Books; Outstdng Tchr Awd 1986, 1993; *office:* Germantown Acad PO Box 287 Fort Washington PA 19034

STEPHENSON, E. ROGER, Professor of English; *b:* Needham, MA; *m:* Betsy M. Delle Bovi; *c:* Edward R. Jr., Sean P.; *ed:* Boston Coll (BA) Eng 1965, (MA) Amer Stud 1966; Brown Univ (PHD) Amer Civilization 1972; *cr:* RI JC Instr 1966-67; Canisius Coll Instr, Asst Prof, Prof 1970-; *ai:* Little Theatre Adv; 12 Articles Pub; *office:* Canisius Coll 2001 Main St Buffalo NY 14208

STEPHENSON, HOLLY WINSLOW, English Teacher; *b:* Ithaca, NY; *m:* David Baldwin; *c:* Christopher, Kelly Stephenson Zola, Sean W.; *ed:* Univ of RI (BA) Eng 1966; 70 Credit Hrs; *cr:* South Kingstown HS 9th-12th Eng Tchr 1974-; *ai:* Dir & Adv Annual Jr Class Var Show; Adv & Coach Speech & Debate Team; Class Adv; TASK Mem; RI NEA 1974-; *home:* 3629 Tower Hill Rd Wakefield RI 02879

STEPHENSON, JEFFREY EARL, Former Teacher; *b:* St Petersburg, FL; *m:* Tracy L. Glisson; *ed:* Univ of South FL (BA) Lbrl Stud 1990; Georgetown Univ (MA) Lbrl Stud 1996; *cr:* Thom Howard Acad 9th-12th Grd Eng, Lang Arts Tchr 1993-94; Diplomatic Lang Svcs Ed 1995-; *home:* 101 4th St NE Washington DC 20002

STEPHENSON, MARY BRADLEY, Math & Health Teacher; *b:* Cincinnati, OH; *m:* Robert D.; *ed:* Morehead St Univ (BA) Elem Ed 1985; Working Towards Masters Degree in Ed; *cr:* St Andrews MS 5th-6th Grd Tchr 1985-87; Whittier Elem Schl 5th-6th Grd Tchr 1988-; *ai:* Yth Mentor for Cincinnati Pub Schls; Past Grd Schl, HS Vlybl Coach; Discipline Comm; AFT, CFT 1988-; *office:* Whittier Elem Schl 945 Hawthorne Ave Cincinnati OH 45205*

STEPIEN, CAROL FLESHER, Second Grade Teacher; *b:* Somerville, NJ; *m:* Robert; *c:* Laura, Lisa; *ed:* Kean Coll of NJ (BA) Elem Ed, Rdng 1975; *cr:* Our Lady of Mount Virgin Schl Seventh Grd Tchr 1975-77; Our Lady of Fatima SchlSecond Grd Tchr 1985-; *ai:* K-8th Grd Tutor 6 Yrs; Mid Sts Comm 1 Yr; Various Admin Duties Attendance Records, First Penance, First Communion Coord 9 Yrs, Eucharistic Minister 5 Yrs, Cnslng, Schl Publicity 2 Yrs, Mentor 2 Yrs; NCEA 1985-; Diocese of metuchen Tchr of Yr 1990; *office:* Our Lady Of Fatima Schl 499 New Market Rd Piscataway NJ 08854*

STEPLER, PATRICIA FINEGAN, Second Grade Teacher; *b:* Atlantic City, NJ; *c:* Jessica; *ed:* Glassboro St (BA) Elem Ed 1967; Addl 4 Hrs Univ of DE; *cr:* Penn Beach Schl Elem Tchr 1967-; *ai:* NEA, NJEA 1967-; *home:* 47 W Grant St Woodstown NJ 08098

STEPP, BARBARA MALIS, Retired First Grade Teacher; *b:* Butler, PA; *w:* Eugene L. (dec); *ed:* Slippery Rock Univ (BS) Elem Ed 1964; 24 Credits Lib Sci Cert; *cr:* Clearfield Area Schls First Grd Tchr 1964-66; Shaler Area Schls First Grd Tchr 1967-95; *ai:* NEA, PSEA 1964-; SAEA 1967-.

STEPPELLO, ELEANOR STAMBOLY, Retired Kindergarten Teacher; *b:* Utica, NY; *m:* James Jr.; *c:* Laura Tehan, James V. III; *ed:* MVCC Lbrl Arts 1970; *cr:* St Agnes Schl Kndgtn Tchr 1968-94; *ai:* CYO Dir; Re Ed; Vol St Lukes Hosp; Sub Tchr; *home:* 2200 Portal Rd Utica NY 13501

STERBER, JOANN H., 3rd Grade Teacher; *b:* Amityville, NY; *ed:* Adelphia Univ (BS) Elem Ed 1969, (MS) Spec Ed 1972, (MBA) Bus, Fin 1981; C W Post Educl Admin Prof Diploma 1981; *cr:* Beverly Hill Elem 4th Grd Tchr 1969-80; Maplewood Intermediate Schl 1st-3rd Grd Tchr 1980-; *ai:* Inservice Review Bd; Curr, PTA Dist Cncl; South Huntington Educl Fnd; AFT, NYSUT 1969-, Del; Orton Soc 1972-; PTA 1969-, Tchr Rep; South Huntington Tchrs Assn 1969-, Bldg Rep, Treas, Pres; Townwide Fund of Huntington 1973-, Bd of Dir; Republican Club of Huntington Women 1973-; Meals on Wheels 1970-, Vol; St Peter's Luth Church, Nursery Vol; Salvation Army of East Northport, Nursery Vol; Delta Mu Delta; Ed South Huntington Tchrs Assn Newsletter; *home:* 6 Patrician Dr East Northport NY 11731

STERE, ATHLEEN JACOBS, Associate Professor of Biology; *b:* Boston, MA; *m:* Hassell L. Jr.; *c:* David W. Bishop II, Deborah Bishop Crist, Robert H.; *ed:* Bryn Mawr Coll (BA) Bio 1941; Harvard & Radcliffe (MA) Bio 1942; PA St Univ (PHD) Bio 1971; *cr:* Harvard Univ Bio Tchng Fellow 1942-44; Boston Univ Schl of Medicine Immunology Rsrch Asst 1944-46; Einstein Med Ctr Microbiology Rsrch Asst 1959-63; PA St Univ Rsrch Asst, Asst Prof & Assoc Prof 1963-; *ai:* Fac Senate; Disciplinary Bd; Numerous Comms; Biological Scis Coord; Amer Assn for Advancement of Sci; PA Acad of Sci; Sigma Xi; Iota Sigma Pi; Phi Kappa Phi; Lindback Awd for Distngd Tchng Univ-Wide; Altoona Campus Long Awd for Fac Excl & SGA Awd for Tchng Excl; Rsrch Grants: NIH, NSF, Am Heart Assoc; Numerous Articles Pub; *office:* PA St Univ Altoona Cmps Altoona Campus Altoona PA 16601

STERIO, ANTHONY ANGELO, HS Mathematics Teacher; *b:* Elizabeth, NJ; *ed:* Seton Hall Univ (BA) Math 1989; *cr:* Santillos Pizza Pizza Maker & Delivery 1981-91; Atlantic Alloy Health & Equip Corp Sales Asst 1989-91; Elizabeth HS Math Tchr 1991-; *ai:* NEA 1992-; NJEA 1992-; St Anthonys RC Church Lecturer & Usher; *home:* PO Box 9005 Elizabeth NJ 07201

STERLING, C. GALE, English Teacher; *b:* Indiana, PA; *ed:* Montclair St Coll (BA) Scndry Eng Ed 1972; Fairleigh Dickinson Univ (MA) Human Relations 1981; Jersey City St Coll (MA) Ed 1990; 30 Addl Hrs; *cr:* Keansburg HS Eng Tchr 1972-; *ai:* Pupil Assistance Comm; Ret Sftbl Coach; Ret Lit Magazine, Class Adv; Keansburg TA 1972-, VP 1980; NJEA, NEA 1972-, Pres 1981-83, Bldg Rep 1983-; NCTE 1972-; Juvenile Conf 1989-, Court Appointee; *office:* Keansburg HS 140 Port Monmouth Rd Keansburg NJ 07734

STERLING, DONNA MILLS, Language Arts Teacher; *b:* Crisfield, MD; *m:* Royce S.; *c:* Steve, David; *ed:* Salisbury St Univ (BS) ELem Ed 1985; Attnd Western Maryland Coll; *cr:* Princess Anne ELem Schl Tchr 1985-88; Westover Elem Schl Tchr 1988-89; Woodson MS Tchr 1989-; *ai:* Summer Schl Tchr; Spelling Bee Comm; Schl Improvement Team; MS Adv Team; Monster Squad Team Sec; PTA Sec; NEA; MSTA; Immanuel Meth Church; Retired Sunday Schl Tchr 16 Yrs; Little League Equipment, Canteen Mgr 9 Yrs; *office:* Woodson MS 281a Woodson School Rd Crisfield MD 21817*

STERLING, JUDYTH OCSHIER, 2nd Grade Teacher; *b:* Conneaut, OH; *m:* Roger L.; *c:* Lisa L., Kelsey E., Sarah M.; *ed:* Kent St Univ (BS) Early Chldhd 1971; Edinboro Univ, Ashland Coll Credit Hrs; *cr:* Lakeview El Schl 2nd Grd Tchr 1971-; *ai:* CEA, OEA, NEA 1971-; *office:* Lakeview Elem Schl 670 Lakeview Ave Conneaut OH 44030

STERN, ISABEL, Russian & Art Teacher; *b:* Rosin, Russia; *m:* Harry; *c:* Steven, Tamara; *ed:* Brooklyn Coll (BA) Elem Ed, Art 1974; Staten Island Coll (MS) Spec Ed 1995; Columbia Univ Tchrs Coll Conflict Mediation Trng; *cr:* Morgan Guaranty Trust Co Personnel, Payroll 1974-80; Staten Island Tech HS Tchr, Mediation Coord 1990-; *ai:* After Schl Art Club Adv; Conflict Mediation Specialist; *office:* Staten Island Tech HS 485 Clawson St Staten Island NY 10306*

STERN, MARTIN RICHARD, US History Teacher; *b:* Pittsburgh, PA; *ed:* Univ of Toledo (BED) Soc Scis 1972; OH St Univ (MA) His 1977, (MA) Ed 1984; *cr:* Medina MS 8th Grd Soc Stud Tchr 1973-92; Brookhaven HS 11th Grd US His Tchr 1992-; *ai:* Chess Club Adv; NEA, OEA, CEA, COTA 1973-; Jennings Scholar 1983-84; *office:* Brookhaven H S 4077 Karl Rd Columbus OH 43224

STERN, MEL ALAN, Sixth Grade Teacher; *b:* New York City, NY; *m:* Lynn Jackson; *c:* Steven, Larry; *ed:* Queens Coll (BA) Ed; SUNY at Stony Brook MPS Mngmt, Labor 1996; C. W. Post Coll 30 Grad Credits Elem Ed; Univ of Buffalo Philosphy, Psych; *cr:* IS 148 5-6th Grd Tchr 1968-70; PS 53 5-6th Grd Tchr 1968-70; Vanderbilt Elem Schl 6th Grd Tchr 1970-78; Synquam Elem Schl 6th Grd Tchr 1978-91; West Hollow MS 6th Grd Tchr 1991-; *ai:* Staff Dev, Shared Decision Making, MS Reorganzation, Professional Standards Comms; AFT, NYSUT 1968-, Pol Action Comm, Svc Awds, Del 1984-; Half Hollow Hills Tchrs Assoc 1970-, VP, Pol Action Chair; Pol Action Awds; Coord for Congressman Mrazek, Negot, Grievances, Ldrshp Awds; Walfare Trust Officer Newsletter; Commack Neighborhood Assc 1980-, VP, Pres; Commack Little League, Mgr, Bd, VP; Tchr Fed Credit Union 1994-, Mktng Comm; Western Suffolk Tchrs Ctr Bd Chm, Vice Chair; NYSUT Comm of 100; PTA Lifetime, Jenkins Awd; Prof Cert Harriman Schl Mngmt & Labor Relations; *office:* West Hollow MS 250 Old East Neck Rd Melville NY 11747*

STERN, NAN L., Reading Consultant; *b:* New York, NY; *m:* Stewart H.; *c:* Alan; *ed:* St Univ Coll at Buffalo (BS) Elem Ed 1967; Univ of Bridgeport (MS) Rdg 1973; *cr:* Nyack Pub Schls 3rd Grd Tchr 1967-68; Rochester Pub Schls 1st Grd Tchr 1968-70; Fairfield Pub Schls 1st Grd Tchr 1970-73; Trumbull Pub Schl Rdg Consultant 1973-; *ai:* Cert CRISS Trainer; NEA; CEA; IRA; TEA; BSA 1986-, Advancement Chm Woodbadge; Trumbull HS Marching Band Parent Org 1993-, Class Rep, Uniforms; Sea Scouts 1994-, Mate Advancement; Project DARE After-School Grant; *office:* Daniels Farm Schl 710 Daniels Farm Rd Trumbull CT 06611*

STERN, SHEILA B., Sixth Grade Teacher; *b:* New York, NY; *m:* Lee; *c:* Scott, Joshua; *ed:* Queens Coll at CUNY (BA) Elem Ed 1967, (MS) Ed 1970; 30 Post Grad Credits; *cr:* PS 32 1st-3rd Grd Tchr 1967-85, Sci Coord 1985-92, 6th Grd Tchr 1993-; *ai:* Stu Cncl Adv; Bd of Examiners; Planetarium Coord; Wkshp Presenter; Various Act; AFT 1967-; NSTA 1985-; *office:* PS 32 Queens 171-11 35th Ave Flushing NY 11358

STERN, SUSANNA BURGER, History Teacher; *b:* Bloomington, IN; *m:* Martin L.; *ed:* Bates Coll (BA) His 1984; Univ of PA (MA) His 1985; Holy Cross NEH Inst on Constitutional Theory 1990; Univ of NH NEH Inst on Women in 19th C Amer; *cr:* Oxford Hills Schl Dist Sub Tchr 1986; Rotary Intnl Admin Asst 1986-87; The Bryn Mawr Schl His Tchr 1987-; *ai:* 7th Grd, MS Film Club Adv; Scheduling Comm; St Peter's Episc Church 1992-; Cncl for Basic Ed Ind Stud in Hum Grant 1994; Plutarch, Athens NEH Seminar 1993; His Merrick Chair 1995; *office:* Bryn Mawr Schl 109 W Melrose Ave Baltimore MD 21210*

STERN, VERONIQUE SHULTZ, French Teacher; *b:* Altoona, PA; *m:* Kevin L.; *c:* Kristopher, Erik; *ed:* PA St Univ (BS) Ed, Fr 1985; 24 Post Grad Credits Toward Cert; *cr:* Hollidaysburg Area Sr High Fr Tchr 1986-; *ai:* Fr Club Adv; PA St Ed Assn 1986-; *home:* 12 Cochran Dr Duncansville PA 16635*

STERNER, HARRY S.,III, Biology Teacher; *b:* Harrisburg, PA; *m:* Mary Ann Vilk; *c:* Andrea, Deanna, Melissa; *ed:* Shippensburg St Coll (BS) Bio, Chem Educl 1968, (MED) Chem 1971; 9 Addl Credit Hrs Sci; *cr:* Cedar Cliff HS Chem Tchr 1968-72, Bio Tchr 1972-; *ai:* WSEA, PSEA, NEA 1968-; *home:* 6211 Warren Ave Harrisburg PA 17112

STERNLIEB, ROSLYN PHYLLIS, College Counselor; *b:* New York, NY; *c:* Scott, Mitchell; *ed:* Herbert H. Lehman Coll (BA) Bus Ed 1990; Queens Coll (MS) Cnslr Ed 1993; *cr:* Adlai E. Stevenson HS Coll Coord 1978-93; Grover Cleveland HS Coll Cnslr 1993-; *ai:* Arista Adv; Key Club Co-Adv; NYSCA 1993-; SUNY at Plattsburgh Educl Opportunity Prgm Distinguished Svc Awd; *office:* Grover Cleveland HS 2127 Himrod St Ridgewood NY 11385

STESLOW, LOUIS S., Art & Humanities Teacher; *b:* Shenandoah, PA; *m:* Elaine D.; *c:* Andrew R.; *ed:* Kutztown St Univ (BS) Art Ed 1965, (MED) Art Ed 1968; 6 Cr Penn St Univ; 2 Cr Allentown Coll; 6 Cr Wilkes Coll; *cr:* Cumberland Vly HS Art, Hum Tchr 1965-; *ai:* Adult Ed Tchr; Elem, MS Art Prgm; Cumberland Vly Ed Assn, PA St Ed Assn, NEA 1965-; Exemplary Tchr of Hnrs Stdnts Penn St Univ 1990; *home:* 121 Sunset Dr New Cumberland PA 17070

STEVENS, ANITA ALTIERI, 5th Grade Teacher; *b:* Allentown, PA; *m:* John S. Jr.; *c:* Jonathan, Lisa, Marisa; *ed:* Kutztown Univ (BS) 1967; Grad Courses Kutztown Univ, Penn St Univ, Temple Univ; *cr:* Allentown Schl

2nd Grd Tchr 1967-68; Abington Schl Dist 2nd Grd Tchr 1968-71; Allentown Schl 3-5th Grd Tchr 1986-; *ai:* PTA 1986-, Parky's Ldrshp; NEA, AEA, Allentown Women Tchr Assn 1986-; Lehigh Vly Ostopathic Hosp Auxiliary 1978-, Treas; *home:* 3864 Sunrise Ave Allentown PA 18103*

STEVENS, CHRISTOPHER DENVER, History Department Chair; *b:* Brooklyn, NY; *m:* Carolyn; *c:* Megan; *ed:* Slippery Rock Univ (BA) His 1987; Fordham Univ (MA) Amer His 1993; *cr:* Bank of NY Mutual Fund Specialist 1987-88; Xavier HS Alumni Affairs Coord 1988-89, His Tchr, Ftbl Coach 1989-, His Dept Chair 1993-; *ai:* Asst Var Ftbl Coach; NHS Review Bd; Disciplinary Review Bd; Pres Budget Comm; Assn of Supervision of Curr Dev 1993-; Amer Historical Assn 1995-; Phi Alpha Theta 1986-; Phi Sigma Kappa 1983-, Sentinal; Tenored Mem Xavier Fac 1995; *office:* Xavier HS 30 W 16th St New York NY 10011

STEVENS, DAVE, Social Studies Teacher; *b:* Columbus, OH; *m:* Rebecca Price Maloney-Stevens; *c:* David Jr., Andrew; *ed:* OH Northern Univ (BA) His 1970; OH St Univ (BS) Ed 1987; Working on Master of Soc Sci; *cr:* Unioto HS Soc Stud Tchr 1988-; *ai:* Var Boys Track Coach; NHS Fac Comm; NEA, OEA, NCSS 1988-; OH Cncl for Soc Stud; Ross Cty Curr Comm; Pickaway Residential Assn 1990-, Bd, VP; Masons 1988-; *office:* Unioto HS 1432 Egypt Pike Chillicothe OH 45601*

STEVENS, DOUGLAS A., 8th Grade Science Teacher; *b:* Troy, OH; *m:* Marta A. Moser; *c:* Nicole, Christian, Christopher, Alexi, Dan Goodwin; *ed:* OH Univ (BSEd) PE, Sci 1973; Attnd Kent St, Ashland Univ; *cr:* Miami East Local Schls PE Tchr 1973-74; Kast Metals Corp Radio Grapher 1974-76; Fairborn HS Industrial Arts, PE Tchr 1976; Wellington Schls Sci, PE Tchr 1977-; *ai:* 8th Grd Ftbl; Boys Asst Var Bkstbl; 7th Grd Bsktbl; Jr High Track; OH MS 1991-; Penfield Comm Church 1982, Youth Ldr, Trustee, Deacon, Bldg Comm, Sunday Schl Tchr; *office:* Mc Cormick MS 201 S Main St Wellington OH 44090

STEVENS, DOUGLAS M., Communication Arts Teacher; *b:* Columbus, OH; *ed:* Miami Univ (BA) Eng, Ed 1990, (MA) Curr, Supervision 1996; *cr:* Woodward HS Tchr 1990; White Oak MS Tchr 1991; Schwab MS Tchr 1991-; *ai:* Quality Schls, Mid Grds Cert Prgm Comm; NMSA 1991, Conf Chair; AFT 1991-; Miami Univ Grad Stud Grant; Natl MS Assn Conf Presenter; Author: Project V.I.P. Violence Is Preventable; *home:* 273 Millville Oxford Rd Hamilton OH 45013

STEVENS, GIFFORD MAXIM, English Teacher; *b:* Danbury, CT; *m:* Annabelle Lawrence LaBree; *c:* Jonathan; *ed:* Univ of ME (BA) Eng 1966, (MA) Eng 1968; Over 20 Post Grad Hrs in Folklore & Eng; *cr:* Univ of ME at Orono Instr 1968-69; Ricker Coll Assoc Prof 1969-78; Bowdoin Coll Upward Bound Tchr 1978-80; Hampden Acad Eng Tchr 1980-; *ai:* Weight Room Coach; Outdoor Club Adv; Fly-Tying Tchr; Folk Music Club; Dulcimer Luthier Club; St Hum Grant-Folklore; Books Pub Insite & Our ME Lore; DECMA Folk Artist of Yr 1985, Dulcimer Player of Yr 1985, 1986 & 1987; Kellogg Grant to Stud Allagash Waterway Insect Life; *office:* Hampden Acad Main St Hampden ME 04444*

STEVENS, GLENN L., Biology & Physical Sci Teacher; *b:* Altoona, PA; *m:* Linda M. Delbaggio; *c:* Terry, Ben, Leah; *ed:* PA St Univ (BS) Scndry Ed 1972; Attnd Univ of KY, Univ of Detroit; *cr:* Hollidaysburg Area Jr HS Bio, Phy Sci Tchr 24 Yrs; *ai:* Mid Level Chprsn 1990-; Bsktbl Coach 1975-88; Supts Advy Cncl Chm 1984-90; NEA, PSEA 1972-; ASCD 1985-; NSTA, NBTA 1973-; Sinking Valley Cntry Club 1977-, VP; *office:* Hollidaysburg Area Jr HS Hart & Hewit Sts Hollidaysburg PA 16648*

STEVENS, GRETCHEN JANE, Fourth Grade Teacher; *b:* Lewiston, ME; *m:* Mark I.; *c:* Amanda, Makayla; *ed:* Univ of ME at Presque Isle (BA) Behavioral Sci 1986; K-8 Tchng Cert 1987; *cr:* Caribou MS Home & Schl Coord 1986-87; New Life Chrstn Schl 2nd & 3rd Grd Tchr 1987-89; Sugg MS 6th Grd Tchr 1989-95; Lisbon Elem Schl 4th Grd Tchr 1995-; *ai:* Var Field Hockey Coach 1994-; Jr Var Field Hockey Coach 1992-94; *office:* Lisbon Elem Schl School Dr Lisbon ME 04250

STEVENS, HEATHER CRAPSER, Chemistry Teacher; *b:* Rochester, NY; *m:* John Andrew; *ed:* Russell Sage Coll (BA) Bio, Sec Ed 1990; SUNY at Potsdam (MS) Ed, Chem-with Hnrs 1994; *cr:* SUNY at Canton Bio, Chem Lab Instr 1991-94; South Jefferson Cntrl Schl Chem Tchr 1994-; *ai:* Sr Class Adv; Clarke Compact Comm; Natl Bio Hnr Soc 1990-; *office:* South Jefferson Jr Sr HS PO Box 10 Adams NY 13605

STEVENS, JAY ARTHUR, Social Studies Teacher; *b:* Cumberland, MD; *m:* Janet Marie Martens; *c:* Alexander, Tristan; *ed:* Frostburg St Univ (BS) Pol Sci & Music 1978, (MED) Admin & Supervision 1981; Georgetown Univ (MA) Govt 1980; Towson St Univ 21 Credit Hrs Soc Sci Cert; Johns Hopkins Univ 12 Credit Hrs; *cr:* WV Schl for the Blind K-12th Grd Music Tchr 1979; Braddock MS 7th-8th Grd Music & Soc Stud Tchr 1979-83, 7th Grd Soc Stud Tchr 1988-; Bruce HS 8th, 10th & 12th Grd Soc Stud Tchr 1984-86; Bruce MS 8th Grd Soc Stud Tchr 1986-88; *ai:* Stu Govt Adv; Ski Club Coord; NEA 1978-; MSTA 1978-; Allegany Cty Tchrs Assoc 1979-, Schl Rep; Rotary 1986-, Pres; Frostburg Lib Bd 1995-; 1st Tchr of Yr Bruce HS 1986; *office:* Braddock MS 909 Holland St Cumberland MD 21502

STEVENS, JAY G., Science Teacher; *b:* Towanda, PA; *c:* Shannon Stevens Bagnaturo; *ed:* E Stroudsburg Univ (BS) Bio, Scndry Ed 1966; Natl Sci Fnd Summer Inst at Wilkes Coll 1969; *cr:* Tunkhannock Area MS 7th Grd Sci Tchr 1966-95; *home:* RR 7 Box 413 Tunkhannock PA 18657

STEVENS, JERRY LYNN, Mathematics & English Teacher; *b:* Defiance, OH; *m:* Janet Kay; *c:* Julie Waldron, Jina Flory, Jon; *ed:* Anderson Univ (BA) Soc Stud 1966; Defiance Coll Elem Cert 1975; 15 Grad Hrs in Guidance; *cr:* Adrian Madison Local Jr HS Eng & His Tchr 1966-72; Ayersville Jr HS Eng & Math Tchr 1973-; *ai:* Jr HS Girls Bsktbl Asst Coach; Var & Jr HS Boys Bsktbl Timer; OEA 1972-; NEA 1972-; PATH 1993-; McDowell MISSION 1992-; *office:* Ayersville MS Rt 7 Defiance OH 43512

STEVENS, JOHN ALLEN, 3rd Grade Teacher; *b:* Bronx, NY; *m:* Patricia Guttman; *c:* April Lynn, Alison Lynn; *ed:* SUNY at Geneseo (BS) Ed 1974; SUNY at Stony Brook (MALS) Lbrl Stud 1978; 75 Post Grad Stud in Ed; *cr:* Mid Cty Schl Dist Elem Sub, Grd 6 Tchr 1974-77; Most Holy Trinity Elem 5th, 8th Grd Tchr 1977-78; St John Nepomucene 7th & 8th Grd Tchr 1978-79; LOngwood Cntrl Schl Dist 3rd Grd Tchr 1979-; *office:* C E Walters Elem Schl 15 Everret Dr Yaphank NY 11980

STEVENS, KATHY, English Teacher; *b:* Cleveland, OH; *m:* Jesse Moore; *ed:* Mary Baldwin Coll (BA) Lbrl Arts 1980; Tufts Univ (MA) Educl Policy 1989; Addl 30 Credit Hrs Staff Dev; Attnd Univ of Bath in England; *cr:* Stoneham HS Eng Tchr 1987-90; Harvard Univ MIT Various Rsrch, Ed Related Positions 1987-95; Attleboro HS Eng Tchr 1993-; *ai:* Newspaper Adv; Fac Senate; Supt Schl Improvement Team; NEA 1990-; NCTE 1994-; Yankee Pen 1996; *office:* Attleboro HS Rathbun Willard Dr Attleboro MA 02703*

STEVENS, LINDA, 7th Grd Language Arts Teacher; *b:* Philipsburg, PA; *m:* Glenn L.; *c:* Terry DelBaggio, Benny Delbaggio, Leach DelBaggio; *ed:* PA St Univ (BS) Scndry Ed 1984; Attnd Univ Pittsburgh at Johnstown; Wilkes Coll; *cr:* Hollidaysburg Area Schl Dist Tchr 1985-; *ai:* Team Ldr; Stu Cncl Adv; PSEA, NEA 1985-; NCTE 1995-; Cath Daughters 1990-; Sinking Valley Cty Club 1995-; St Matthews Church 1969-, youth Adv, tchr; Phi Beta Kappa 1981-1985; *office:* Hollidaysburg Area Jr HS 501 Hart St Hollidaysburg PA 16648*

STEVENS, LOUISE DOERING, Math Teacher & Dept Chair; *b:* Piittsburgh, PA; *m:* Peter B; *c:* Shannon, Sean C., Erin E. Connors, Brady B.; *ed:* Acad of the New Church (BS) Ed 1959; Beaver Coll (MEd) Ed 1990; 39 Addl Grad Hrs Math; *cr:* Bryn Athyn Church Schl 2nd, 4-5th Grd Tchr 1958-65, 8th Grd Tchr 1978-90; Acad of the New Church Math Tchr 1990-; *ai:* Alpha Kappa Mu Club Adv; Media Ctr Comm; Asst Producer Schl Play; ATMOPAV 1987-; NCTM 1989-; Theta Alpha Intnl 1957-, Exec Comm; Theta Alpha Local Chapter 1958-; *office:* Acad Of The New Church PO Box 707 Bryn Athyn PA 19009

STEVENS, MARK B., 5th Grade Teacher; *b:* Canton, OH; *ed:* Kent St Univ (BS) Elem Ed 1979, (BS) Scndry Eng Ed 1979; OH St Univ (MS) Soc Stud Ed 1983; *cr:* Westerville City Schls 5th Grd Tchr 1979-; *ai:* Westerville Ed Assn 1979-, Fac Rep at Large 13 Yrs, Negotiations Comm 15 Yrs; BEA, NEA 1979-; *home:* 8442 Juniper Dr Lewis Center OH 43035

STEVENS, MARY BROWN, Teacher & Staff Developer; *b:* Wilmington, NC; *m:* LLoyd H.; *c:* Kelly, David H.; *ed:* Brooklyn Coll (BS) Psych 1964; City Univ (MS) Ed 1984; 21 Credit Hrs Queens Coll; 6 Credit Hrs New Schl Soc Rsrch; 27 Credit Hrs City Univ; *cr:* IS 70 M Coord AIDP 1988-90; Crossroads Schl Tchr, Staff Dev 1990-93; UU Schl for Soc Change Dir 1993-95; The Renaissance Schl Tchr, Staff Dev 1995-; *ai:* Yrbk Staff, Math Team Adv; New Tchrs Mentor; AFT, UFT 1980-; NY Assn Black Schl Edctrs 1985-; ASCD 1986-; Impact II 1983-, Dev Awd 1990, 1992; Schomburg Lib 1985-.*

STEVENS, PATRICIA A., Sixth Grade Teacher; *b:* Worcester, MA; *m:* David Sr.; *c:* Ann Louise Santos, Karen Grunberg, David Jr., Kathryn Walker; *ed:* Worcester St Coll (BS) Ed 1962; Johnson St Coll (MED) Ed of Gifted 1982; Univ of VT (CAS) Mid Level Ed 1990; 18 Credits Sci in Elem Schl; 3 Credits Spec Stud, 3 Credits Literacy Assessment St Michaels Coll; *cr:* New Bloomfield Elem Tchr 1962-63; Lamoille South Supervisory Union Sub Tchr 1973-77; Morristown Elem 6th Grd Tchr 1977-; *ai:* Spelling Team Adv; Literacy Comm; NEA 1977-; MEA 1977-, Sec; VAMLE; Holy Cross Parish Cncl, Sec; Numerous Articles Pub; Outstanding Tchr Awd 1985; Chapter in Book Dancing Thru Walls for Mid Level Educators; *office:* Morristown Elem Schl Rt 15A Morrisville VT 05661

STEVENS, REBECCA A., Sociology Professor; *b:* Bedford, OH; *ed:* Mt Union Coll (BA) Psych, Sociology 1980; Univ of Akron (MA) Sociology 1988; Univ of Akron (PHD) Sociology 1991; *cr:* Notre Dame Coll Dept Chair, Sociology Tchr 1988-94; Kent St Univ Asst Prof Criminal Justice 1994-95; Univ of Akron Adj Asst Prof, Sociology; *ai:* ASA 1987-; AKD 1981-; *office:* Univ Of Akron Olin Hall 302 Buchtel Mall Akron OH 44325

STEVENS, RONALD L., Mathematics Teacher; *b:* Dayton, OH; *m:* Janet E. Mabry; *c:* Susan Ci. Imel, Sheryl D.; *ed:* OH Univ (BS) Math 1965; Ruters St Univ of NJ (MST) Math 1971; Post Grad Stud Comptrs, Math Ed Univ of Dayton; *cr:* Northeastern HS Math Tchr 1965-; Clark St Univ Math Instr 1974-87, 1996; *ai:* OH Math League Team; NEA 1965-, Local Pres 1978, Negotiations Chair 1979-82; NSF Grant; Clark Cty Bd of ED Excl in Ed Hnrs.

STEVENS, SHIRLEY S., English Coordinator; *b:* New Orleans, LA; *ed:* Indiana Univ of PA (BS) Ed; Univ of Pittsburgh (MA); *cr:* Quaker Vly Sr HS Eng Coord, Instr 1962-; *ai:* Lit Magazine Spon; Delta Kappa Gamma 1967-, VP; Pub Poetry Book; *office:* Quaker Valley Sr HS Beaver Rd Leetsdale PA 15056*

STEVENS, WALTON CRAIG, Asst Professor of Kinesiology; *b:* Gettysburg, PA; *m:* Suzanne Mangan; *c:* Walton Bryan, Brendan Grady; *ed:* Johns Hopkins Univ (BA) Psych 1974; Springfield Coll (MS) Exercise Physiology 1982; Temple Univ (PHD) Exercise Physiology 1989; Post Doctoral Rsrch Assoc Inst Environmental Med Univ of PA 1988-92; *cr:* Temple Univ Grad Asst, Tchng Asst 1980-88; Univ of PA Post Doc Rsrch Assoc 1988-92; West Chester Univ Asst Prof 1992-; *ai:* Kinesiology Dept Curr, Stu Fitness Ctr, Acad Festival Comms; Wellness Project Team; ACSM 1977-, Regnl Past Pres; NAPEHE 1993-; APSCUF 1992-, Hlth & Welfare Specialist; AAHPERD; APS; NSCA; Southern Chester Co Soccer Assn 1994-, Commissioner; DE Vly Sci Fair Judge; Pan Hellenic Cncl Tchng Awd Temple Univ 1987; Who's Who in Amer Ed 1993; 5 Grants; 2 Book Chptrs, 3 Articles, 29 Abstracts Pub; *office:* West Chester Univ Dept of Kinesiology Coll Ave\S High St West Chester PA 19383

STEVENS, WILMA BROWN, Fourth Grade Teacher; *b:* Old Town, ME; *m:* Forrest S.; *c:* Daniel, Kerry Roderick, Julie Mc Carthy; *ed:* Univ of ME (BS) Elem Ed 1968; *cr:* Alton Grammar Schl 4th-6th Grd Prin 1966-67; Viola Rand Schl Fifth Grd Tchr 1968-70; Dr. Lewis Libby Schl Fourth Grd Tchr 1970-77; Mainstreet Elem Schl Fourth Grd Tchr 1977-; *ai:* Tchr Recertification Chair; Madison Area Tchrs Assn 1977-, Pres, Sec; ME Tchrs Assn, NEA 1968-; Amer Cancer Soc 1990-, Pres, Commitment Awd; Skowhegan Madison Elks Aux 1978-, Sec; Skowhegan Federated Church 1996, Deaconess.

STEVENS-GLEASON, HELEN ELIZABETH, Fourth Grade Teacher; *b:* Middletown, OH; *m:* Richard Louis; *c:* Aggy Elizabeth, Anny Valentine; *ed:* William Woods Coll (BA) Elem Ed, Eng, Soc Stud 1970; Post Grad Stud Wright St Univ, Miami Univ, Xavier Univ; *cr:* Hunter Elem Schl 3-6 Grd Intermediate Tchr 1970-; *ai:* Odyssey of Mind Coach, Third Place, Second Place, Creativity Winner; NEA; Phi Beta Psi 1980-, Historian; Middletown Historical Soc, Lifetime Mem; Colonial Dames of 17th Century 1975-; Daughters of Amer Colonists 1975-, Golden Acorn; Musical PROMISES Mission Group Toured Japan & Alaska 1972-95; Middletown Music Club 1975-; Church of Ascension, Choir Dir, Sunday Schl Tchr; Sorg Opera Co; Wildwood Golf Club; Cincinnati Art Museum, Cincinnati Natural His Museum 1979-; Pro Musica Prof Singing Group 1980-95; Middletown Comm Fnd; Stevens Fnd; *office:* Hunter Elem Schl 4418 W State Rt 122 Franklin OH 45005

STEVENSON, ALLAN CHARLES, Psychology Teacher; *b:* Baltimore, MD; *m:* Deborah Ann Reick; *c:* Jody Lynn, Ryan Charles; *ed:* Univ of MD at Baltimore Cty (BS) Psych & Ed 1974; Univ of MD at College Park (MA) Human Dev 1979; Biosystems Inst (AA) Respiratory Therapy 1985; *cr:* Arundel Sr HS Psych Tchr 1979-80; Anne Arundel Medical Ctr Respiratory Therapist 1980-85; Annapolis Sr HS Psych Tchr 1985-; *ai:* SADD Fac Adv; NEA, MD St Tchrs Assn, Tchr Assn of Anne Arundel Cty 1985-; Eastern Shore Hockey Assn 1989-, Exec Bd, Coach; Kent Island Youth Soccer League, 1989-, Coach; Kent Island Youth Lacrosse League 1995-, Coach; Amer Lung Assn of MD Vol of Yr 1985; *office:* Annapolis Sr HS 2700 Riva Rd Annapolis MD 21401

STEVENSON, BARBARA PITTS, 5th Grade Teacher; *b:* Philadelphia, PA; *m:* Milton Edward; *c:* Bailey Alysa; *ed:* Westchester St Univ (BS) Elem Ed 1979; Temple Univ (MS) Educl Admin 1983; 45 Credit Hrs Elem Ed Millersville Univ; 9 Credit Hrs Elem Ed St Joseph's Univ; 6 Credit Hrs Elem Ed Univ of AK; *cr:* Beaver Creek Elem Schl 5th Grd Tchr 1979-; *ai:* Downingtown Area Ed Assn Negotiating Team; Kappa Delta Pi, Downingtown Area Ed Assn 1979-; *office:* Beaver Creek Elem Schl 601 Pennsylvania Ave Downingtown PA 19335

STEVENSON, BETH, Physical Education Teacher; *b:* Columbus, OH; *ed:* OH St Univ (BS) PE 1986; *cr:* St Barnabas Schl K-8th Grd PE Tchr 1988-90; Glendening Elem K-5th Grd PE Tchr 1990-95; Madison Elem K-5th Grd PE Tchr 1995-; *ai:* JV Sftbl Coach; Franklin Cty Acad of Phys Edctrs PDS Comm; Quest for Excl Adv 1988-89; NEA 1990-; AAHPERD 1990-; OAHPERD 1990-; *office:* Madison Elem Schl 4600 Madison Schl Dr Columbus OH 43232

STEVENSON, JIM, Fifth Grade Teacher; *b:* Philadelphia, PA; Ehrhardt; *c:* Luke, Matthew; *ed:* Gettysburg Coll (BA) Sociolog Temple Univ (MED) Ed Admin 1976; *cr:* Enfield Elem Schl 5th G 1971-73; Arcola Intermediate Schl 6th Grd Tchr 1973-83; Worcest Schl 3rd Grd Tchr 1983-84; Eagleville Elem Schl 3rd, 5th Gr 1984-95; Audbon Elem Schl 5th Gr Tchr 1995-; *ai:* AFT 1980-, Lo Appalachian Svc Proj 1991-; Habitat for Hum 1990-; Towamencir Auth 1989-, Youth Coach; *office:* Audobon Elem Schl 2765 Eg Norristown PA 19403

STEVENSON, ROBERT GEORGE, High School Psych & His I Del Rio, TX; *m:* Eileen Patricia Casey; *c:* Robert Louis, Sean Cas Coll of Holy Cross (BA) His 1967; Fairleigh Dickinson Univ (MA 1968; Montclair St Univ (MA) Amer His 1970; Fairleigh Dickinsc (EDD) Death Ed 1984; Assn for Death Ed & Counseling Cert Grie Death Educator; *cr:* Bengen Cath HS Soc Stud Instr, Ath Dir 19 River Dell Reg HS Soc Stu Instr, Coach 1970-; Columbia Univ S Co-Chair 1985-; *ai:* Bowling Coach; Spec Olympics; Jr Hockey B Pres; Assn of Death Ed & Counseling 1987-, Bd of Dir, Natl Educ Yr 1991; NJ Track & Field Officials 1976-, Rules Interpretor, Off Yr 1992; River Dell Ed Assn 1970-, Pres, Governors Awd; NJ Ches 1968-, VP, Man of Yr; Pawlings Levies 1986-, Living His Awd; Pu Will We Do Preparing a Schl Comm to Cope with Crisis & Death Schls an Educators Resource Guide.*

STEVENSON, SUSAN YORK, English & Journalism Teach Houlton, ME; *m:* Ford; *c:* Tyler, Thomas, Joseph; *ed:* Univ of ME at (BA) Eng Lit 1972, (MED) Scndry Ed 1992; *cr:* Livermore Falls H 1989-; *ai:* Yrbk, Newspaper, Class Adv; NCTE 1990-; Yrbk Ded 1995; *office:* Livermore Falls HS 25 Cedar St Livermore Falls ME

STEVENSON, VICTORIA E., Mathematics Teacher; *b:* Baltimore *m:* James; *c:* Jamie; *ed:* Morgan St Coll (BS) Math 1972; Morgan S (MS) Math 1974; 6 Credit Hrs Loyola Coll; 3 Credit Hrs Alleghen 3 Credit Hrs OR St Coll; *cr:* Western HS Math Tchr 1973-; *ai:* Curr Balto City Pub Schls Calculus; Advanced Placement, Curr Baltimore Children Museum Youth Adv Bd; Schl Imprvmt Team; 1987-; MCTM 1975-; ASCD 1992-; AFL-CIO, BTU 1989-; Mellon AP Calculus Inst; Hewlett Packard Calculator Donation Prgm W Kurt L Schmoke Tchr of the Year Awd.*

STEVER, DEBORAH J., Supvr & Assistant Principal; *b:* Hancock *ed:* Valley Forge Chrstn Acad (BA) Chrstn Ed 1979; *cr:* Deposit Acad Supv & Asst Prin 1979-; *ai:* Maple Lane Assembly of God Bd Mem.

STEWARD, SABRA CORBIN, Choral & General Music Teach Baltimore, MD; *m:* Frederick Henry; *c:* Ryan Thomas Mavity, Corbin Mavity; *ed:* Frostburg St (BS) Music Ed 1973; Peabody Inst Loyola 18 Hrs; *cr:* Carroll Cty Schl Elem Music Tchr 1973-78; Dorc Cty Schl Choral, Gen Music Tchr 1987-; *ai:* Chorus, Ski Trip Coord; DE; Music Edctrs; Eastern Shore Choral Dirs; Dorchester, Wor Counties Chorus Dir; MMEA Eastern Region Pres; *home:* 7270 Fran Easton MD 21601

STEWART, CAROL MARIA, German Teacher; *b:* Lowville, N Edson F.; *c:* E. Jerrad; *ed:* Oswego (BA) Scndry Ger Ed 1968; Perm Cert; *office:* Dolgeville Central Schl Slawson St Ext Dolgeville NY

STEWART, CAROL WENDT, Mathematics Instructor; *b:* Rome, N Gilbert R.; *ed:* Clarkson Coll of Tech (BS) Math 1971; Canisius Coll Ed 1985; 13 Addl Hrs Critical ThinkingLong Island Univ; 13 Add Learning Disabilities Alfred Univ; 28 Addl Hrs Statistical Sci SU Buffalo; *cr:* Trocaire Coll Cmptr Stud Dir 1983-86; SUNY Coll In Mgmt Adjunct Instr 1987; Alfred Univ Math Adjunct Instr 1987-89; S Coll of Tech Math Adjunct Instr 1988-90; Inst 1990-94 Asst Prof 199 Acad Affairs, VP-Search Comms; Gender Equity Project; Budget & Ldr Seminar, Tech Prep, Mid St Adv Tm, Comp Ctr Dir Search Comm New Stu Con; NYSMATC 1994-; UUP, NYSUT, AFT 1988-; *office:* S Coll of Tech at Alfred Math Dept Alfred NY 14802*

STEWART, CONSTANCE CORSO, 8th Grade Reading Teacher; *b:* Mawr, PA; *m:* Edward A.; *c:* Ryan, Brandon, Dustin; *ed:* Penn St Univ Early Chldhd & Elem Ed 1977, (MEd) Curr & Instr 1993; *cr:* Altoona Schl Dist Sub Tchr & At Risk Coord 1981-88; Bellwood-Antis Sch 8th Grd Rdng Tchr 1988-; *ai:* Rdng Competition Coach; Yrbk Adv Assistance Team; NEA 1988-, Fac Rep; *office:* Bellwood-Antis MS M St Bellwood PA 16617*

STEWART, DAVID WILLIAM, Recreation Pgm Supvr & Coac Philadelphia, PA; *ed:* Eastern Coll (BS) Hlth, PE 1993; Plymouth-Whitemarsh HS Instructional Aide 1993-; Whitemarsh Prgm Supvr 1995-; *ai:* Girls Vlybl, Girls & Boys Diving Head Coach; & Boys Swimming Asst Coach; Germantown Acad Girls & Boys D Head Coach; PA Recreation & Park Soc 1995-; Certfd Pool Spa Oper Diving Coaches Assn 1994-; Achvmt Cert Colonial Schl Dist 199 *home:* 403 Revere Rd Lafayette Hill PA 19444

STEWART, DEBORA JEAN (RAMBONE), Special Education Tea *b:* NJ; *m:* Robert L.; *c:* Robert M., Kimberly Jean; *ed:* FL Atlantic (BA) Tchr of the Handicapped; *ai:* Drama Dir 5 Yrs; NJEA; NEA; *h* PO Box 4 Newfield NJ 08344

STEWART, DENISE BOSWORTH, Math Teacher; *b:* Washington, *m:* Harry; *ed:* Johns Hopkins Univ (MS) Ec 1993; *cr:* Eleanor Roos HS Math Tchr 1987-88; High Point HS Math Tchr 1988-; *ai:* Cheerleading; P G Cty Pub TV; Homecoming Chprsn; PGCEA, MSTA 1988-; *office:* High Point HS 3601 Powder Mill Rd Beltsville 20705

STEWART, ELEANOR YEAGER, English Teacher; *b:* Middletown, *m:* Phillip; *c:* Katherine; *ed:* Miami Univ (AB) Eng 1972, (MA) Eng Post Grad Ed, His; *cr:* Middletown City Schls Geog, TAP, ABE 1976-94; Miami Univ Visiting Instr 1988-93; Middletown City Schls Tchr 1973-; *ai:* Mercury, Various Act, FTA Spon; Various Schl Cor MTA, OEA, NEA 1973-; Alpha Delta Kappa 1982-, VP; Phi Delta Ka Progressive Animal Welfare Soc 1984-, Bd, Auxiliary Mem, Vol; Essay Judge for MENSA; Phi Beta Kappa; Freen Lance Writer; *of* Lemon Monroe HS 101 W Elm St Monroe OH 45050*

STEWART, ELLEN HICKMAN, Guidance Counselor; *b:* Springf OH; *ed:* KY St Univ (BA) Elem Ed 1970; Univ of Dayton (MS) Cnsln 1989; Grad Hrs Cnslr Ed; *cr:* Springfield City Schls 5-6 Grd Tchr 197 3-4 Grd Tchr 1974-81, 4 Grd Tchr 1981-91, Cnslr 1991-; *ai:* I Care Adv; NEA, OEA 1972-; OH Schl Cnslr Assn 1991-; *home:* 235 Limestone St Springfield OH 45503

STEWART, FITZROY ANTHONY, Director of Choral Activities Kingston Jamaica, West Indies; *m:* Ghislaine Kubica; *ed:* Ithaca Coll Music Ed 1966, (MS) Music Ed 1967; Attnd Frankfurt Hochsc Diploma Conducting 1982, Crane Schl of Music 1971-72, Manhattan of Music 1968; *cr:* Vestal Schl System Choral Music Tchr 1965 Maine-Endwell HS Choral Music Tchr 1970-75; Jugend Musikschule 1982-87; Binghamton Comm Orch Conductor 1987-94; Maine-Endwel Choral Music Tchr 1989-; *ai:* Corning Philharmonic Yth Orch, Music 1988-; NEA, MENC 1989-; Fulbright Hays Schlsp 1979-81; Founde Directed Neue Oberurseler-Kammer Orch in Oberursel, West Germ 1982-87; Franz-Grothe-Stiftung Awd for Conducting 1981; *home:* Hooper Rd # 271 Endicott NY 13760*

RT, JAMES E., English Teacher; *b:* Birmingham, AL; *m:* Brenda *c:* Jennie, Megan; *ed:* OH St Univ (BS) Eng Comm 1975; Ashland 1A) Scndry Admin 1994; *cr:* East HS Tchr 1975-81; Mifflin HS)82-; *ai:* Instrl Support Team; Self Governance Comm; Grant ; Interdisciplinary Comm; Frosh Class Admin; CEA, OEA, NEA East HS Tchr of Yr 1977; Cntrl OH Tchr of Yr 1988; Pacesetter Capitol Grant 1996.

ART, JAMES JOSEPH, Former Teacher & Coach; *b:* Bradford, PA; eton Univ (BA) Class CIV-Hnrs 1982; Univ of Glasgow (MA)-Phil ; 1983; *cr:* Darlington Schl Tchr, Dorm Parent, Coach 1983-87; eld Schl Tchr, Coach 1988-94; *ai:* Scholar Bowl Prgm.

ART, JANE HILDNER, Business Educator; *b:* Kearny, NJ; *m:* *d:* Fairleigh Dickinson Univ (BS) Bus 1970; Grad Hrs From Marist ern CT St; *cr:* Wayne Valley HS Cooperative Work Coord & Bus 70-74; Roy C Ketcham Cooperative Work Coord & Bus Tchr 1974-; k & Jr Class Co-Adv; Wappingers Congress of Tchrs 1970-; BTA Former Cheerleading Coach; *office:* Roy C Ketcham HS 99 Myers s Rd Wappingers Falls NY 12590

ART, JENNIFER KIRBY, Tchr & Coordinator of Gifted; *b:* town, OH; *m:* Terry W.; *c:* Sara, Alison, Kevin; *ed:* Miami Univ ors) Elem Ed 1984; Wright St Univ (Masters) Gifted 1991; *cr:* Elem 5th Grd Tchr 1984-85; Schenck Elem 5th & 6th Grd Tchr ; Franklin Jr HS Hnrs Eng & Soc Stud Tchr 1987-90; Franklin City chr of Gifted & Coord 1990-; *ai:* HS Girls Tennis Coach; Play Dir; y of the Mind Coord; WCOCG 1991-; Jennings Grant for Gifted ch Pgm; *office:* Franklin City Schls 150 E 6th St Franklin OH 45005

ART, JERRY EDWIN, Admissions Director; *b:* Chambersburg, Marian Strange; *c:* Mary Vasquez, David, Nancy Welker; *ed:* nsburg Univ (BSEd) Eng 1961, (MSEd) Eng 1966; Attnd Centre annon Univ 9 Credits; *cr:* Chambersburg Central Jr HS Civics & ır 1961-63; Scotland Schl for Veterans Children Eng, His & Speech)63-74, Dir of Admissions 1974-; *ai:* Schl Newspaper Ed; NDEA *office:* Scotland Sch For Vet Children 3583 Scotland Rd Scotland 54

ART, JUDITH CHOLEWA, Teacher; *b:* Chicago, IL; *m:* Robert; *c:* r, Emily; *ed:* Loyola Univ at Chicago (BS) Bio 1968; SUNY at (MA) Biochemistry 1971; *cr:* Eastman Kodak Clinical Chemist 8; St Helen's Schl Jr HS Tchr 1981-83; Cardmooney HS Physics & Tchr 1983-89; Spencerport HS Chem Tchr 1989-; Forensics Coach; S; STANYS; NSTA; NFL; *office:* Spencerport HS 2707 Spencerport ncerport NY 14559

ART, JUDITH E., HS Social Studies Teacher; *b:* New Britain, CT; ert G. Orbacz; *c:* Frances Orbacz; *ed:* Trinity Coll of VT (BA) Sec c Sci 1989; 12 Credit Hrs; *cr:* Milton HS Part-time Soc Stud Tchr Bellows Free Acad HS Soc Stud Tchr 1990-; *ai:* Peer Support, Jr Adv; Svc Comm Mem; NCSS 1989-; OAH, NEA 1990-; Southern y Law Ctr 1993-; Amer Diabetes Assn 1989-; Amnesty Intnl 1995-; t Applicant James Madison Flwshp; *office:* Bellows Free Acad PO Hunt St Fairfax VT 05454

ART, KELLY LYNN, 7th Grd Language Arts Teacher; *b:* ore, MD; *ed:* Univ of MD (BA) Eng 1990; Loyola Coll 5 Post Grad s Admin; *cr:* Mac Arthur MS Seventh Grd Lang Arts Tchr 1990-; *ai:* Planning, Instruction Materials Comms; MSPAP Presenter; MD ment Consortium; New Tchr Prgm Mentor; NEA 1990-; Parent Tchr g 1994-; NHS, Amer Legion Schlsps; *office:* Macarthur MS 3500 nbach Rd Fort Meade MD 20755*

ART, LYNN ALOUISE, English & Drama Teacher; *b:* Pittsburgh, Stephen R.; *c:* Jarod, Shay, Kasey; *ed:* Geneva Coll (BA) Eng 1973; of Pittsburgh Grad Schl; *cr:* Burgettstown HS Eng Tchr 1973-74; a Valley HS Eng & Drama Tchr 1974-; *ai:* Musical Dir; SH Stage Thespian Spon; NEA 1975-; NCTE 1990-; *office:* Seneca Valley Sr 8 Seneca School Rd Harmony PA 16037*

VART, MARGENE A., Piano Professor; *b:* Holmes Cty, OH; *m:* *c:* Garrick; *ed:* Capital Univ (MMus) Piano 1964; OH Univ (MFA) 1966; *cr:* OH Univ Piano Prof 1966-; *ai:* Society of Alumni & s Exec Sec; Tau Beta Sigma Alpa Chptr Adv; *office:* OH Univ s OH 45701

VART, PAMELA WIDDUP, Middle School Counselor; *b:* esburg, PA; *m:* William R. Jr.; *c:* Sean, Christopher, Patrick; *ed:* IN of PA (BS) Ger 1973; Univ of Dayton (MS) Scndry Schl Cnslng 1979; Credit Hrs WV Univ, West Liberty St Coll; *cr:* Brooke HS Ger, Eng 1974-79; Trinity HS Ger Tchr 1986-87; Mc Guffey MS Scl Cnslr ; *ai:* Act 178, Strategic Plan, Grading Comms; Alpha Delta Kappa , Schlsp Chm; Washington-Greene Cty Assn 1987-, NEA, PSEA, Mc y Ed Assn 1987-; Faith United Presbyn Church 1991-, Bd of Deacons; ance Musician; *home:* 788 RR Valley Rd Washington PA 15301*

VART, PAUL MICHAEL, Health & PE Teacher; *b:* Lebanon, PA; *m:* .; *c:* Paul, Jeff, Mike, Jessica; *ed:* East Stroudsburg Univ (BS) Hlth, 80; Penn St Univ 25 Credit Hrs; *cr:* Parkland Schl Dist Asst Bsktbl 1983-93, Asst Ftbl Coach 1988-94. Soccer Head Coach 1982-87, r Asst Coach 1994-, Asst Track & Field Coach 1983-, Hlth PE Tchr ; *ai:* NEA, PSEA; *office:* Parkway Manor Schl Parkway Rd town PA 18104

VART, PEGGY WATSON, Guidance Counselor; *b:* Nelsonia, VA; *m:* ge A.; *c:* Tricia O'Neal; *ed:* Univ of MD Eastern Shore (BS) Home Ec 970; Salisbury St Univ (MED) Scndry Ed, Guid 1982; Certfd Home Ec *cr:* Pocomoke HS Home Ec Tchr 1971-95; Pocomoke MS Guid Cnslr ; Snow Hill MS Guid Cnslr 1995-; *ai:* FHA, Master Adv; FHA Natl p Conf; Region 6 Chptr Excl, Amer Home Ec Assn Prof Certs; Adv v Awd 1988; Amer Assn Family & Consumer Sci 1975-; MD Home sn 1975-, MD Chair Intnl Yr of Family; NEA 1973-; Worcester Co Assn 1973-; Schl Improvement Team 1990-; Pupil Svc Team 1995-; h of Dimes Svc 1990-, Plaque; Holly Ctr, Vol Awd; *office:* Pocomoke 00 8th St Pocomoke City MD 21851

VART, RICKIE LYNN, English Teacher; *b:* East Liverpool, OH; *c:* a Lynette; *ed:* Kent St (BA) Eng, Soc Stud 1972; In-Svc Courses 24 Temple Univ 10 Hrs; *cr:* Stetson MS Eng Tchr 19 Yrs; Saul HS Eng 3 Yrs; *ai:* Phila Fed of Tchrs, AFT 1972-; Work Study; *office:* Walter ıl HS 7100 Henry Ave Philadelphia PA 19128

VART, SALLY ANNE, 7th & 8th Grade Math Teacher; *b:* Portland, *m:* Wilson W.; *c:* Michael, William; *ed:* Univ of ME at Orono (BS) Ed 1978; Masters Courses in Schl Law, Tchng Math Problem Solving, stics & Probability, Introduction to Cmptr Literacy & Mainstreaming ptional Stdnts in Classroom; *cr:* Kingswood Regnl MS Math Tchr -, Team Ldr 1980-83, Tchr of Alternative Ed 1983-85; *ai:* Private r for HS Math Courses & SAT Preparations; Summer Math Tutor; rnor Wentworth Regnl Schl Dist Dir; NELMS 1985-, Guest Speaker NH-ATMNE, NCTM 1989-; Dev Scope & Sequence for Governor worth Regnl Schl Dist Summer 1982 & 1984; Governor Wentworth al Schl Dist Math Task Force 1980-; Bsktbl Coach 1978-85; Lesley Guest Lecturer 1984; *office:* Kingswood Regnl MS S Main St eboro NH 03894

VART, STEVEN BRIAN, History Teacher; *b:* Philadelphia, PA; *m:* na G. Harris; *c:* Gregory; *ed:* Eastern Bapt Coll (BA) His 1968; Temple 15 Credit Hrs; *cr:* Devereaux Fndtn Tchr 1968-69; Harrisburg Acad His Tchr 1969-, Ath Dir 1970-94, Asst Dir of MS 1995-; *ai:* Var Soccer Coach 1969-83; Ath Dir 1970-94; Var Sftbl Coach 1973-87; Acad Day Camp Dir 1976-89; MS Soccer, Bsktbl & Sftbl Coach 1987-1994 Touch Ftbl & Bsktbl Club; NCSS; PA Cncl for the Soc Stud; Lewisberry United Meth Church 1972-, Sunday Schl Supt; Harrisburg Acad Spcl Tchng Awd 1994; *office:* Harrisburg Acad 10 Erford Rd Wormleysburg PA 17043

STEWART, TEBBIE WILLIS, ESOL Teacher; *b:* Macon, GA; *m:* Paul D. Sr.; *c:* Paul Jr., Dia; *ed:* Howard Univ (BM) Music 1966; Cath Univ of Amer (MM) Music 1972; Johns Hopkins Univ (MED) Rdng, Elem Ed 1979; 26 Credit Hrs ESL UMBC; *cr:* Wilde Lake MS ESL Tchr 1983-; *ai:* NEA, HCEA 1987-; *office:* Wilde Lake MS 10481 Cross Fox Ln Columbia MD 21044

STEWART, VICKI DENNISON, Title I Reading Teacher; *b:* Huntington, WV; *m:* Richard L.; *c:* Kimberly, James; *ed:* OH St Univ (BS) Elem Ed 1974; 17 Addl Hrs; *cr:* Kalida Local Schls 3rd Grd Tchr 1967-69; Clear Fork Vly Local Schls 3rd-5th Grd Tchr 1969-; *ai:* IAT Comm; Bsktbl, Bsbl Moms; OFT, AFT 1982-; OEA, NEA 1967-; CFVEA 1969-, Bldg Rep, Treas, Linda Sharp Awd 1994; Ath Boosters 1990-, Reporter; Band Boosters 1991-; Cub Scout Ldr; Girl Scout Ldr; Martha Holden Jennings Scholar; Good Apple Awd; Clear Fork Vly Fnd Grant; Clear Fork Bd of Ed Grant 1992, 1995; *office:* Bellville, Butler Elem Schls 125 School St Butler OH 44822

STEWART-BARRETT, DIANNE M., Chemistry Instructor; *b:* Panama Canal Zone, Panama; *m:* Michael Garrett; *c:* Stephen A. Stewart-Williams, Michael Jr.; *ed:* Wesleyan Univ (BA) Bio, Psych 1985; Columbia Univ 30 Credit Hrs; Woodrow Wilson Flwshp Scholar at Princeton; *cr:* Garden Schl Sci, Math Instr 1985-86; Prep for Prep Inc Sci Instr, Coord 1986-94; Brooklyn Friends Schl MX-US Sci, Math Instr, Sci Coord 1986-90; St Ann's Schl US Sci Instr 1990-91; Brooklyn Friends Schl Sci Chprsn, US Sci Instr 1991-93, Head of Upper Schl 1993-; *ai:* Diversity Coord; Dewitt Wallace Diversity Conf Facilitator; Packer Collegiate Diversity Collaborative; Natl Assn of Indep Schls, Assn Tchrs Indep Schls, Natl Assn Scndry Schl Sci Tchrs 1986-; Chemical Bank Schlsp; *office:* Brooklyn Friends Schl 375 Pearl St Brooklyn NY 11201*

STIANCHE, ROBERT MICHAEL, Science Teacher; *b:* Hauto, PA; *m:* Joan H. Cipko; *c:* Joann Chenet, Robert, David; *ed:* Columbia Univ (MS) Microbiology 1959; *cr:* VA Medical Ctr Chief Clinical Microbiologist 20 Yrs; Saint Joseph Hospital Clinical Lab Supvr 19 Yrs; *ai:* Future Medical Prof Club; MB ASCP 1963-; Amer Soc of Microbiology 1963-.

STICCO, PATRICIA CARACCIO, English & Theology Teacher; *b:* Philadelphia, PA; *m:* Thomas; *c:* Philip, Angela, Teresa; *ed:* W Chester Univ (BS) Eng 1976; Attd St Charles Seminary Working Toward Masters in Theology; *cr:* Sharon Hill HS 10th-12th Grd Eng Tchr 1976-77; St Martin of Tours Schl 6th Grd Tchr 1979-80, 5th Grd Tchr 1981-82, 8th Grd Lang Arts Tchr 1983-84 & 1987-; St Maria Goretti 9th Grd Eng & 12th Grd Theology Tchr; *office:* St Maria Goretti HS 1736 S 10th St Philadelphia PA 19148

STICK, LOIS MARIE, Music Teacher & Choral Dir; *b:* Petoskey, MI; *m:* Harvey William Jr.; *ed:* Spring Arbor Coll (BA) Soc Sci, Music 1971; Trenton St Univ (MA) Music 1979; *cr:* Howard M. Phifer MS Music Tchr, Choral Dir 1972-; *ai:* MENC 1972-; South Jersey Choral Dirs Assn 1987-95, VP, Jr HS Festival Guest Conductor; Walnut Street Theatre 1995-, Vol Usher; NJ Governors Awd-Tchr of Yr 1986; *office:* Howard M. Phifer MS 8201 Park Ave Pennsauken NJ 08109

STICK, RICHARD CLAUDE,SR., High School Math Teacher; *b:* Lebanon, PA; *m:* Trudy Lee Bullock; *c:* Richard Claude Jr.; *ed:* Millersville Univ (BS) Math 1970, (MED) 1976; Millersville Univ Safe Living Cert 1974, Schl Prgm Specialst Cert 1985; *cr:* Harrisburg Area Comm Col Adjunct Fac, Math 1988-; ELCO HS Math Tchr 1970-, Dept Head 1976-92; *ai:* NHS Selection Comm; NEA 1970-; PA ST Ed Assn 1970-; NCTM 1969-; Eastern Lebanon Cty Educators Assn 1970-; Math Assn of Amer 1990-; PA Cncl of Tchrs of Math 1990-; Lebanon Cty Educl Honor Soc 1992-; *office:* Eastern Lebanon Cty HS 180 Elco Dr Myerstown PA 17067*

STICKA, GLORIA MORRIS, Sixth Grade Teacher; *b:* Hartford, CT; *m:* Charles C.; *c:* Gregory, William; *ed:* Cntrl CT St Univ (BS) Elem Ed 1959; Univ of Hartford (MED) Ed 1969; Fairfield Univ 30 Credits 1982; *cr:* Park Avenue Schl 5th Grd Tchr 1959-1963; Fuller Schl 5-6th Grd Tchr 1973-; A W Hanmer Schl 6th Grd Tchr 1982-; Emerson William 6th Grd Tchr 1995-; *ai:* Math Olympiad Club Tchr Adv; Math Curr Comm; Cooperating Mentor Tchr; EAW & NEA 1959-1963, 1973-; St George Philoptichos 1960-; *office:* Emerson-Williams Elem Schl 462 Wells Rd Wethersfield CT 06109*

STICKLES, PETER L., Regents Earth Science Teacher; *b:* Hudson, NY; *m:* Sarah Irene Karg; *c:* Peter Jr., Jeffrey, Elizabeth; *ed:* Brockport St (BS) Bio & Earth Sci 1971; 30 Hrs Toward Permanent NYS Cert; *cr:* Gouverneur HS Sci Tchr 1971-73; Cheektowaga HS Sci Tchr 1973-75; Mexico HS Regents Earth Sci Tchr 1975-; *ai:* AFT 1971-; NY St United Tchrs 1971-; Cntrl NY Soccer Ofcls 1975-, Pres & VP; Natl Intracollegiate Soccer Ofcl 1978-; Cntrl NY Lacrosse Ofcls 1987-; NY Power Authority Tchr on Loan 1988 & 1989; *office:* Mexico Acad & Cntrl Schls Main St Mexico NY 13114

STICKLEY, STEVEN ALAN, Chem Physics & Math Teacher; *b:* Urbana, OH; *m:* Paula Ethel Imhoff; *c:* Shaun, Craig; *ed:* Urbane Univ (BS) Comprehensive Sci 1973; Attnd Wright St Univ for Math Cert; *cr:* Fort Loramie Local Schl Chem, Physics & Math Tchr 1974-; *ai:* Cross Cntry & Track Coach, Jets Team Adv; NEA & OEA 1974-; FLEA 1974-, Pres, VP, Sec; 4-H Adv 11 Yrs; *office:* Fort Loramie Local Schls PO Box 26 Fort Loramie OH 45845

STIDHAM, BEVERLY DAVIS, Sixth Grd Rdng & Lang Teacher; *b:* Marion, OH; *m:* Kenneth E.; *c:* Aaron G., Sarah E.; *ed:* OH St Univ (BS) Elem Ed 1969; Addl Credit Hrs Drake Univ, Ashland Coll; *cr:* Marion City Schls 2nd Grd Tchr 1969-73; North Union Schls 6th Grd Tchr 1979-; *ai:* North Union Task Force on Svcs for Pupils with Disabilities; NCTE 1990-; *office:* North Union MS 16 Norris St Richwood OH 43344

STIDHAM, MARY BIHL, Title I Math Teacher; *b:* Hamilton, OH; *c:* Amy Michelle, Lafe Mitchell; *ed:* Morehead St Univ (BA) Elem 1973; Marshall Univ 5th Yr; *cr:* Mason Cty Schls Kndgtn Tchr 1973-75; Fleming Cty Schls Kndgtn Tchr 1975-79; Green Local Schls Kndgtn, Second Grd, Title I Math Tchr 1980-; *ai:* Chrldng Boosters Treas 1 Yr; PTO: Tech Plan Comm; Track, Field Booster; NEA 1980-; OEA 1980-, Local Treas 2 Yrs; Natl Right to Life; Martha Jennings-Holden Scholar.

STIETZEL, RONALD D., Sixth Grade Teacher; *b:* Norwalk, CT; *m:* Barbara Ann Rogers; *ed:* Springfield Coll (BS) Recreation 1960; 48 Credit Hrs Cmptr, Guid, Sci, Math; *cr:* Worcester YMCA Yth, Camp Dir 1960-66; Southbridge YMCA Yth, Camp Dir 1966068; Charlton Schl Dept 6 Grd Tchr 1968-72; Dudley-Charlton Rengl Schl Dist 6 Grd Tchr 1972-84, Cmptr Resource Tchr K-6, 6 Grd Tchr 1987-; *ai:* Schl Cncl 1993-95, Tchr Rep; MA Tchr Assn 1966-; Charlton Tchrs Assn 1968-, Pres 1970-72; Dudley-Charlton Tchrs Assn 1972-; Starbridge Fed 1966-; Church Cncl; Diaconate;Trustees; Aucion; Auction Comm 1995-, Chm; *office:* Heritage Schl 34 Oxford Rd Charlton MA 01507

STIFFLER, DALE TURNER, Teacher of the Gifted; *b:* White Plains, NY; *m:* Richard; *c:* Leigh; *ed:* Monmouth Univ (BS) Ed 1977, (MS) Stu Prsnl Svcs 1992; *cr:* Nut Swamp Schl Elem Tchr 1977-86; Bayshore MS Tchr of Gifted 1986-; *ai:* Peer Mediation Adv; NJEA, NEA 1977-; Kappa Delta Pi NHS; Governors Recognition Awd; Withycombe Tchr Grant 1989, 1990, 1993; *office:* Bayshore MS 36 Leonardville Rd Leonardo NJ 07737*

STIFFLER, MARY LOU, Algebra Teacher; *b:* Clarence, PA; *m:* Jacob W.; *c:* Jacob W. Jr., Jeffrey, Danielle; *ed:* PA St Univ (BS) Scndry Ed, Math 1968; Rutgers Univ (EdM) Math Ed 1973; *cr:* Forest Hills HS Math Tchr 1993-; *ai:* Math Tutors Prgm 1995-; SADD Adv 1993-94; Sr Project Comm; FHEA 1993-; LHMA 1994-; *office:* Forest Hills HS PO Box 290 Sidman PA 15955

STIFFLER, ROBERT BLAND, Retired Middle Schl Math Tchr; *b:* Altoona, PA; *m:* JoAnn Gurgovits; *c:* Mark A., Craig R.; *ed:* IN Univ of PA (BS) Math 1956; Addl 6 Post Grad Credits; 6 Post Grad Credits Seton Hill Coll; 12 Post Grad Credits Notre Dame Univ; *cr:* Penn Hills Schl Dist Math Tchr 1956-65; Shady Side Acad Math Tchr, Ath Dir, Coach 1965-93; *ai:* Natl & St & Local Tchrs of Math 1972-; Paul G. Benedum Tchng Fellow 1981; Kenneth M. Vasko Awd Exemplery Tchng 1992; Ruth & F. Walter Jones Svc Prize 1993; Robert B. Stiffler Ath Awd; *home:* 497 Kerrwood Dr Pittsburgh PA 15215

STILES, BRUCE EDWARD, Physical Science Teacher; *b:* Barnesville, OH; *m:* Leslie Kay Zollars; *c:* Zak J., Carlee Justin; *ed:* Salem Coll (BS) Scndry Ed 1986; Dayton Univ (MS) Guid Cnslng 1991; *cr:* Barnesville Schl Sub Tchr 1986-88; Union Local Schls Sub Tchr 1987-88; St Clairsville Schls Sci Tchr 1988-; *ai:* Sci Club Adv; Ftbl, Bsktbl, Track Coach; Weightlifting Adv; United Ed Assn 1989-; NEA 1988-; Nation Arbor Day Fnd 1990-; Natl Park & Svcs, Natural Wildlife Assn 1992-; Harley Owners Group 1991-, VP Upper OH Vly Chptr; Pres Environmental Yth Awds; US Environmental Protection Agency Awd; *home:* 108 Westminster Dr Saint Clairsville OH 43950

STILES, LORI HOBBS, Science Department Chairperson; *b:* Olney, MD; *m:* Christopher Remus; *c:* Devin Ellen, Taylor Riggs; *ed:* Hood Coll (BA) Environmental Stud, Bio 1983, (MA) Environmental Bio 1992; Tchng Cert Western MD Coll 1985; *cr:* Brunswick HS Bio, Physical Sci Scndry Tchr 1986-89, Dept Chair, Bio Tchr 1990-; *ai:* NHS Comm; Stud Asst Prgm; Frederick Cty Tchrs Assn, NEA, MD Assn of Bio Tchrs 1985-; Master Thesis Pub 1992; Allelopathy Article Pub 1985; *office:* Brunswick HS 101 Cummings Dr Brunswick MD 21716

STILES, RUTH HULL, Kindergarten Teacher; *b:* Waterford, PA; *m:* Louis L.; *ed:* Mercyhurst Coll (BA) Elem Ed 1966; Edinboro Coll (ME) Elem Ed 1970; 34 Post Grad Credits Beyond Masters Level; *cr:* Erie Schl Dist Kndgtn Tchr 1966-; *ai:* EEA 1966-; PSEA PA 1966-; NEA Natl 1966-; PA Congress of PTA 1966-, Honorary Life Mem Awd; Erie Sq & Round Dance Assn 1962-, Sec & Treas, Honorary Life Mem Awd; Tchr of Yr 1995; *office:* Joanna Connell Elem Schl 1820 E 38th St Erie PA 16510

STILKEY, STEWART R., Biology Teacher; *b:* Brunswick, ME; *m:* Lynda Hart; *c:* Amy, Susan, Rebekah; *ed:* Eastern Coll (BA) Bio 1968; Univ of ME (MS) Sci Ed 1992; Attnd West Chester Univ; *cr:* Brookhaven Jr HS Sci Tchr 1968-73; Mount Ararat HS Bio Tchr 1973-; *ai:* NEASC Comm; War Bd; NEA 1968-; ME St Tchrs Assn, Merry Meeting Ed Assn 1973-; NSF Fellowship in Immunology; *office:* Mt Ararat HS RR 201 Topsham ME 04086

STILLER, CONNIE KREIDER, Pastor; *b:* Upland, PA; *m:* David W.; *c:* Erich, Sonja Martin, Geoffrey; *ed:* Eastern Coll (BA) Math, Scndry Ed 1966; Univ of ME at Orono (MED) Spec Ed 1972; Drew Theological Schl (MDiv) Ministry 1994; *cr:* Haz-Nanticoke MH MR Psychotherapist, Svc Dir 1981-85; Immanuel Chrstn Schl Tchr 1985-90; Diamond UMC Assoc Pastor 1992-94; St Paul's UMC Pastor 1994-; *ai:* Teach Parenting Class; Supervise Church Choir; Write Material & Supervise Challenger's Club; Amer Assn of Chrstn Cnslrs 1994-; Circuit Rider's 1996; Various Women's Groups Speaker; Devotionals Pub; Deah Meml Schlsp Evangelical Schl of Theology.

STILLER, DAVID W., Teacher & Science Dept Chprsn; *b:* Orange, NJ; *m:* Rev. Connie Kreider; *c:* Erich Paul, Dr. Sonja, Dr. Geoffrey; *ed:* Eastern Coll (BA) Bio 1965; Univ of ME (MS) Biochemistry 1970, (PHD) Nutrition 1976; *cr:* Univ of ME Instr 1968-74; John Bapt HS Chem Tchr 1974-78; Mining & Mechanical Inst Chem Tchr 1978-; *ai:* PAIS, NAIS, PSTA 1978-; LCSTA 1978-, Past Pres; Laurel Lodge F&AM 1980-, PM; Tandy Scholars; ACS Recognition for Outstanding Tchng; *office:* Mining & Mechanical Inst 154 Center St Freeland PA 18224*

STILLMAN, ANN ALLEN, English Teacher & Dept Chair; *b:* Utica, NY; *c:* Katherine Ross, Julia Ross, Jonathan Ross, Nicholas Ross; *ed:* Northwestern Univ (BS) Speech 1953; Univ of WI (MS) Rdng 1979; Attnd Yale Univ Frgn Lang Schl, San Diego St Univ, Utical Coll of Syracuse Univ; *cr:* Leyden HS Eng Tchr 1953-56; Univ of WI Eng 101 Tchr 1970-73; New Hartford Sr HS Eng Tchr 1978-, Eng Dept Chair 1992-; *ai:* NYSEC 1985-; NCTE 1992-; Hospice 1979-, Bd Sec; Hospice Vol 1979-; *office:* New Hartford Sr HS 33 Oxford Rd New Hartford NY 13413

STILLMAN, DYANE ALAINE, Sub Teacher & Drama Ensmbl Adv; *b:* Pequannock, NJ; *ed:* Lycoming Coll (BA) Eng, Philosophy 1988; Scndry Ed Cert 1991; *cr:* Frew Mill Schl Sub Tchr 1992-93; Seneca Vly Jr Sr HS Sub Tchr 1992-93; Northwest Area Jr Sr HS Sub Tchr, Theatre Ensemble, Class Advs 1993-; *ai:* NEA, PSEA, Northwest Area Ed Assn 1994-; *office:* Northwest Area Jr Sr HS RR 2 Box 2271 Shickshinny PA 18655

STILLWAGON, JOANNA PIETROPAOLI, Sr HS Art Teacher; *b:* Mt Pleasant, PA; *m:* Richard Allen; *c:* Jason, Stephanie; *ed:* Seton Hill Coll (BA) Art 1969; Penn St Extension Cert Credits; *cr:* Norwin Schl Dist Jr High Art 1969-74; Gby Salem Schl Dist Elem Art 1977; Ligonier Valley Schl Dist Jr, Sr High Art 1990-; *ai:* Art & Display Coord & Club, Do Little Club; Stu Asst Prgm; Fac Advy Bd; Tchr Mentor Prgm; NEA 1969-74, 1990-; High Acres Civic Asso 1983-, Children's Act Coord; Gby Cntrl Cath HS Alumni Cncl 1978-, Bd Mem; Gby Cntrl Cath HS 1990-, Parents Bd; Seton Hill Alumni Asso 1979-, Co-Chm; Featured Artist/Craftsman in Gbg Tribune Reviews Home & Hobby; Co-Dev Jr High Curr 1972; *home:* 2939 Seminary Dr Greensburg PA 15601*

STILSON, JENNIFER PALMER, Former Fifth Grade Teacher; *b:* Cleveland, OH; *m:* William C. Jr.; *c:* Samantha, Ryan; *ed:* Bowling Green St Univ (BS) Elem Ed 1986; Cleveland St Univ (MA) Ed Gifted, Talented 1992; *cr:* Various Schls Sub Tchr 1986-89; Bedford City Schls Fifth Grd Tchr 1989-92; *ai:* Celebration Luth Church 1992-; Comm Chair, Ed; *home:* 32840 Woodsdale Ln Solon OH 44139

STIMMEL, KATHLEEN MCFADDEN, Bus Ed Dept Chprsn & Teacher; *b:* Allentown, PA; *m:* William P.; *c:* William P. III, Robert W.; *ed:* Bloomsburg Univ (BS) Bus Ed 1970, (MEd) Ed 1974; *cr:* Randallstown Sr HS Tchr 1970-71; Allen HS Chprsn, Tchr 1971-; *ai:* Chprsn; NBEA, PBEA, PSEA 1971-; NEA 1970-; BSA 1985-, Comm Person; *office:* Allen HS 126 N 17th St Allentown PA 18104

STIMMEL, ROBERT BRYAN, Science Teacher; *b:* Cumberland, MD; *ed:* Frostburg St Univ (BS) Gen Sci & Earth Sci 1994; Working Towards Masters in Ed 3 Credits; *cr:* Bishop Walsh MS & HS Sci Tchr 1994-; *ai:* Ecology Club Adv; Girls Vllybl Fac Moderator; NSTA 1995-; Paul Douglas St Tchrs Schlsp 1990-94; Gamma Theta Upsilon; *office:* Bishop Walsh Schl 700 Bishop Walsh Rd Cumberland MD 21502

STIMPSON, JUDY K., Mathematics Teacher; *b:* Munich, Germany; *m:* Wayne A.; *c:* Jonathan, Alexander; *ed:* Trinity Coll (BA) Eng 1977; Univ of VT (MAT) Math 1980; Attnd Wright St Univ Ed & Math Several Credits; *cr:* Sinclair Comm Coll Full & Part Time Lecturer 1980-84; TX Luth Coll Part Time Lecturer 1985; Fairfax Cty Schls Part Time Instr 1986-87;

Sinclair Comm Coll Full & Part Time Lecturer 1987-89; Carroll HS Math Tchr 1989-; *ai:* OH Math League Moderator; NCTM 1991-; *office:* Carroll HS 4524 Linden Ave Dayton OH 45432

STINE, JUDY ANN, Fifth Grade Teacher; *b:* Toledo, OH; *m:* Rand; *c:* Scott Loomis, Nicole Yarnell, Kelly Loomis; *ed:* Univ of Toledo (MED) Rdng 1993; *cr:* Riverside Elem Schl 4-5 Grd Tchr 1985-86; Navarre Elem Schl 6 Grd Tchr 1986-87; Hawkins Elem Schl 2 Grd Tchr 1987-88, 3 Grd Tchr 1988-89, 5 Grd Tchr 1989-; *ai:* Conflict Mediation Facilitator; Impact II Network, IRA 1992-; AFT 1985-; Phi Kappa Phi, Kappa Delta Pi, Pi Lambda Theta 1984-; Natl Cert Candidate; Impact II Grants 1992-95; NEED Awds 1992, 1994; Envirosafe Grant 1994; Cablevision Awd 1994; Eisenhower Sci Grants 1986, 1990, 1993; Drug Prevention Awd 1992; Libbey Schlshp 1993; Eisenhower Math Grant 1994; Experienced Tchrs Handbook Article 1993; *office:* Hawkins Elem Schl 5550 W Bancroft St Toledo OH 43615

STINE, ROBERT NELSON, Physics Teacher; *b:* East Stroudsburg, PA; *m:* Carmella Jean Ninno; *c:* Julie, April; *ed:* East Stroudsburg Univ (BA) Physics 1987; Montclair St Univ 12 Credit Hrs Statistics; *cr:* US Army 1st Lt 1988-93; Hasbrouck Hghts HS Physics Tchr 1994-; *ai:* Acad Decathlon & Chess Club Adv; NEA 1993-; *office:* Hasbrouck Heights Jr Sr HS 365 Boulevard Hasbrouck Heights NJ 07604

STINEBAUGH, MARILYN MADISON, 9th Grade English Teacher; *b:* St Louis, MO; *m:* William H. Jr.; *ed:* Kutztown Univ (BA) Ed, Comm 1984; Comm, Radio, TV Univ of MO; Grad Stud Eng Rutgers Univ; *cr:* Nativity BVM HS 10th Grd Eng Tchr 1985-86; Springhouse Jr HS 9th Grd Eng Tchr 1986-; *ai:* Yrbk Adv; Kutztown Univ Deitriech Schlsp Awd 1984; *office:* Springhouse Jr HS 1200 Springhouse Rd Allentown PA 18104*

STINEMAN, JAMES M., Technology Education Teacher; *b:* Indiana, PA; *m:* Dawn L. Phillips; *c:* Hanna, Kendra; *ed:* CA Univ of PA (BS) Tech Ed 1985; *cr:* Dover Area HS Tech Ed Tchr 1985-; *ai:* NEA, PSEA 1985-; York Cty Tech Ed Assn 1985-, Pres; Make-a-Wish 1995-, Wish Granter; *home:* 3426 Essex Rd Dover PA 17315

STINER, SHERRY ANN, Fifth Grade Teacher; *b:* Wellsboro, PA; *m:* Steve C.; *c:* Mackey, Skye; *ed:* Mansfield Univ (BS) Soc Work 1982, (BS) Elem Ed 1987; 29 Addl Hrs; *cr:* Covington Comm Daycare Ctr Tchr 1982-87; Canton Elem Schl Tchr 1987-; *ai:* ACT 178 Comm; Prof Dev; NEA, PSEA, CAEA 1987-; First United Meth Church 1983-; *home:* RR 1 Box 284B Blossburg PA 16912

STINSON, ANNE D'ANTONIO, Teaching Asst; *b:* Long Branch, NJ; *m:* Julian Lee; *ed:* Brookdale Comm Coll (AA) 1988; Monmouth Univ (BA) Eng, Fr 1990, (MAT) Ed 1992; Collecting Data for Dissertation Study; *cr:* Henry Hudson Regnl Schl Eng, LA Tchr 1992-94; Rutgers St Univ Tchng Asst 1994-; *ai:* GSE DEpt of Learning & Tchng Stu Grievance Comm; AAUP 1994-; Phi Delta Kappa 1996; NCTE 1992-; Sigma Tau Delta 1989-, Pres; Edward Fry Endowed Schlsp for Rdng Rsrch 1995; *office:* Rutgers St Univ Grad Schl of Ed 10 Seminary Pl New Brunswick NJ 08903*

STIO, PERRY DOMINICK, Whole Language Teacher; *b:* Newark, NJ; *c:* Stacy, Gina, Vincenzo; *ed:* Jersey City St (BA) Elem Ed 1974, 9MA) Elem Ed 1976; Kean Coll (MA) Admin, Supervision 1980; *cr:* Piscataway Twp Schls 1-5 Grd Tchr 1974-; *ai:* Whole Lang Coord; Conflict Resolutin Tchr; Kids' Book Talk Club; NEA, NJ Ed Assn, Local Ed Assn 1974-; Middlesex Rdng Cncl 1983-, Treas; Phi Delta Kappa 1996-; NJ Rdng Assn Tech Chair; St Andrews 1972-, CCD Tchr; Woodbridge HS PTA, Fifth Quarter Club 1993-; Avenel MS PTA 1990-; IRA Exemplary Svc; Governor's Tchr of Yr Awd; Articles Pub; *office:* Martin Luther King Schl 5205 Ludlow St Piscataway NJ 08854*

STIRNEMAN, DAWN KIDD, Kindergarten Teacher; *b:* Baltimore, MD; *m:* John; *c:* Scott, Elyse S. Crabtree; *ed:* Towson St Univ (BS) Early Chldhd 1955; Johns Hopkins Univ (MED) Elem Ed 1963; Post Grad Work W Chester Univ, PA Bible Coll; Attnd Balto Sch of Bible, Gesell Inst at New Haven CT; *cr:* Thomas Johnson Schl Kndgtn, 1st Grd Tchr 1955-63; Dela Co Chrstn Schl Kndgtn-2nd Grd Tchr 1963-; *ai:* Fac Adv; Kiononia, HELP Parent Ed; NAEYC 1980's-; ACSI 1970's-, Early Chldhd Conf Organizer; Church of Saviour; Mid Atlantic Chrstn Schl Conventions Wkshps; Assn Chrstn Schl Conf Seminars; Commission Elem Schls for Mid Sts Accreditation; ACSI Accreditation Team Mem; *office:* Delaware County Christian Schl Bishop Hollow Rd Newtown Square PA 19073*

STITSINGER, JOELLE MUNSON, Spanish Teacher; *b:* Indianapolis, IN; *m:* Glenn W.; *c:* Matt, Elizabeth; *cr:* Wilson Jr HS Eng Tchr 1969-74, Span Tchr 1986-; *ai:* Club Pride Adv; NEA 1986-; Pride Parents 1991-; *office:* Wilson Jr HS 704 Eaton Ave Hamilton OH 45013

STITT, ROBERT KEITH, Woodworking & Drafting Teacher; *b:* Kittanning, PA; *m:* Alice Cavanaugh; *c:* Rebecca, Joshua; *ed:* CA Univ of PA (BS) Industrial Arts Ed 1982; IN Univ of PA 24 Post-Grad Credit Hrs; *cr:* Purchase Line Schl Dist Power Tech Inst 1982-86; Sharon City Schl Dist Wood & Metal Instr 1986; Middletown Schl Dist Wood & Metal Instr 1987-; *ai:* Var Girls & Var Boys Soccer Coach; Flwshp of Chrstn Aths Adv; Tech Ed Club Adv; NEA 1982-; NSCAA 1989-; Tech Ed Assn of PA 1993-; Elizabethtown Grace Brethren Church 1988-, Church Cncl; *office:* Middletown Area HS 1155 N Union St Middletown PA 17057*

STJEAN, CHRISTINE M., Social Studies Teacher; *b:* Evanston, IL; *m:* Paul R.; *c:* Nicole E., Justin R.; *ed:* CT Coll (BA) Govt 1967; Univ of NH (MA) US His 1976; 30 Grad Credit Hrs at Boston Coll; 6 Grad Credit Hrs Georgetown Univ; *cr:* Exeter Area HS Soc Stud Tchr 1971-, Soc Stud Dept Head 1982-92; *ai:* NEA 1971-; NH Cncl for Soc Stud 1982-; Exeter Civic Index Comm 1985-; Natl Bicentennial Competition on the Constitution & Bill of Rights Tchr of Class Winning NH Title 1989, NH RE 1988; *office:* Exeter Area HS 30 Linden St Exeter NH 03833*

STOCK, ROBERT E., Physics Teacher; *b:* Rosedale, NY; *m:* Katharine Davey; *c:* Wendy, Penny; *ed:* Cornell Univ (BS) Sci Ed 1968, (MS) Sci Ed 1972; Franklin & Marshall Univ (MA) Earth, Space Sci 1973; Brookhaven Natl Lab; *ai:* Physics, Sci Olympiads; Long Island Physics Tchrs Assn; NYSUT; AFT; Grants NSF, Dept of Energy Tchr Research; *office:* Smithtown H S 100 Central Rd Smithtown NY 11787

STOCK, ROSEMARY DILLING, Math & Social Studies Teacher; *b:* Nanty-Glo, PA; *m:* Richard A.; *c:* Clarion Univ (BS) Scndry Soc Stud 1967; Univ of Pittsburgh (BS) elem Ed 1972; *ed:* Clarion Univ (BS) Scndry Soc Stud 1967; Univ of Pittsburgh (BS) Elem Ed 1972; Univ of Pittsburgh Post Grad Stud; St Vincent Coll Drug Prevention Prgm; Univ of Pittsburgh Information Tech Trng; *cr:* Jenner Boswell HS Soc Stud Tchr 1967-68; Harrison Pk Elem Fifth Grd Schl 1968-69; Sunrise Ests Elem Schl Third, Fourth, Fifth Grd Tchr 1969-93; Penn MS Sixth Grd Math, 7th Grd Soc Stud Tchr 1993-94, Sixth Grd Math, Soc Stud Tchr 1994-; *ai:* PSEA, NEA 1967-; PTEA 1968-, Exec Bd 1976-84, Mbrshp Chprsn 11981-84, Negotiations 1976-77; Plum Food Pantry 1995-, Appalachian Work Missions Team 1988-, Asst Crew Ldr; Holiday Park United Meth Church 1969-, Music, Ed Ministries; Six Time Nom for Penn Trafford Pride Awd for Tchng Excl; *home:* 638 Blue Ridge Rd Pittsburgh PA 15239*

STOCK, SANDY, Science Teacher; *b:* Milwaukee, WI; *m:* Reuben Yeager; *c:* Melanie, Ashley Yeager; *ed:* AZ St (BA) Scndry Ed 1970; CT St (MS) Sci 1974; Attnd Clarion, Penn St; *cr:* Grant Joint Union Tchr; Peace Corps West Africa; Sarah Siddons; Correctional Inst; Dallastown Area HS Tchr; *ai:* Coach Cumberland Vly Aquatic Club USS Swim Team; NEA 1980-; PSEA; PSTA; *home:* 303 Stumpstown Rd Mechanicsburg PA 17055

STOCKER, BRADLEY DENNIS, Teacher of the Gifted; *b:* Phillipsburg, NJ; *m:* Laura Baker; *ed:* Lebanon Vly Coll (BS) Elem Ed 1973; St of PA M Equivalency 1995; Attnd Millersville Univ, Marywood Coll, IN Wesleyan; *cr:* Annville-Cleona Schls 5th Grd Tchr 1973-83, Tchr of Gifted 1983-91, 1995-, 6th Grd Tchr 1991-95; *ai:* Schl Musical; 4th-6th Grd Math Clubs; IMS; NEA, PSEA, A-CEA 1973-; Encore Musical Productions 1987-, Sec; Annville Comm Theatre 1991-, Bd Mem; Jaycees Outstdng Young Edctr 1985; *office:* Annville-Cleona Schl Dist 205 S White Oak St Annville PA 17003

STOCKL, SANDRA LYNN, Mathematics Teacher; *b:* Camden, NJ; *ed:* Trenton St (BA) Math Ed 1988; Rowan Coll (MA) Cnslng 1994; *cr:* Washington Twp Math Tchr 1989-; *ai:* Head Lacrosse, Frosh Bsktbl & JV Field Hockey Coach; NEA & NJEA 1989-; *office:* Washington Twp HS 509 Hurrffville Cross Keys Sewell NJ 08080*

STOCKMAN, MAUREEN DILAURA, Mathematics Teacher; *b:* Baltimore, MD; *m:* Franklin David; *ed:* Loyola Coll (BS) Math 1992; Attnd Salisbury St Univ; *cr:* NC HS Math Tchr 1992-; *ai:* Adj Fac Chesapeake Coll; NCTM; *office:* North Caroline HS 10990 River Rd Ridgely MD 21660

STOCZ, SHIRLEY L., 6th Grade Language Arts Tchr; *b:* Sharon, PA; *c:* Kimberly Jean Aubel, Kelly Lynn Ferguson; *ed:* Youngstown St Univ (BS) Elem Ed 1972, (MA) Elem Ed Admin 1976; Post Grad 1980; Univ of Dayton Post Grad 1978; *cr:* Champion Local Schls 5th Grd Tchr 1972-73, 3rd Grd Tchr 1973-85, 6th Grd Tchr 1985-; Dale Carnegie Instr 1988-; John Roberts Powers Fashion Modeling 1988-; Dee Trentel Fashion Modeling 1988-; *ai:* Supt's Advy Cncl; Prin's Advy Cncl; Howland, Lakeview, Warren Sub Tchr; Career Ed Week, Right to Read Week Chm; Right to Read Prgm Spec Recognition; Elem Admin Practicum; Spec Grant Recipient; Trumbull Cty St Rep as St Level Input Person; Trumbull Co Schls Tchr Mentor; Spelling Bee Coord; Schl Newsletter Ed; Soc Comm for Ed Assn, Bldg Rep; Champion Ed Assn; Trumbull Cty Ed Assn; OH Ed Assn; NEA; Dale Carnegie 1984-, VP, Highest Achvmt; John Roberts Powers 1989-, Model, Model of Month; Dee Trantel Models 1990-, Model, Model of Month; *home:* 2331 Westview Rd Cortland OH 44410

STODDARD, BERYL BOESHORE, Science Teacher; *b:* Lebanon, PA; *c:* Daniel; *ed:* Millersville Univ (BS) Elem Ed 1989; Gifted Ed 1991; Working Toward Doctorate in Sci Curr & Instruction at Penn St; *cr:* Milton Hershey Schls Summer of Opportunities Prgm Sci Tchr 2 Yrs; Cedar Crest MS Sci Tchr 1989-; *ai:* Odyssey of Mind Adv & Coach; IU Sci Steering Comm; Rocket Club Adv; NEA, NSTA; PSTA, LLSTA; Delta Kappa Gamma; Woodrow Wilson Fellowship; Anne E Beyers Outstanding Stu Tchng Awd; *office:* Cedar Crest MS 101 E Evergreen Rd Lebanon PA 17042*

STODDARD, RAYMOND MICHAEL, Social Studies Dept Chprsn; *b:* Elmira, NY; *ed:* Coll of Notre Dame of MD (BA) His, Pol Sci 1991; Webster Univ at St Louis Theatre Arts, His 80 Hrs; Loyola Coll of MD at Baltimore Modern Stud MA Candidate; *cr:* Baltimore Polytechnic Inst Soc Stud Tchr 1991-92; Frederick Douglass Sr HS Soc Stud Tchr 1992-93; Mercy HS Soc Stud Tchr 1994-95, Soc Stud Dept Chair 1995-; *ai:* Model Org of Amer Sts Moderator; Oakland Mills HS Set Designer; Mid Sts, MD Cncls on Soc Stud, NCSS 1994-; *office:* Mercy HS 1300 E Northern Pky Baltimore MD 21239

STOECKICHT, CHARLENE LEWIS, Director & Kdg Teacher; *b:* Dayton, OH; *c:* Anna Maria Conard, Erika; *ed:* Smith Coll (BA) Ed 1953; Attnd Miami Univ, Univ of Dayton, Sinclair Coll, Wright St Univ, Fairfield Univ; *cr:* Dorothy Lane Schl 1st Grd Tchr 1953-55; Hightstown Elem Schl 1st Grd Tchr 1955-56; Fairview Elem Schl Kdg Tchr 1957-60; First Schl Dir, Kdg Tchr 1971-, LD Class Tchr 1975; *ai:* Le Club Sec; Gourmet Pres; Sustainer Cncl of Jr League of Dayton OH; NEA 1975-; DAYC 1975-, Sec; Jr League of Dayton OH Inc 1953-; Speech, Hearing Bd 1960-; Vol Svc Bureau Bd 1954; *office:* First Schl 7659 Mcewen Rd Dayton OH 45459

STOFFER, ROSS W., American Government Teacher; *b:* Salem, OH; *ed:* Univ of Akron (BS) Scndry Ed 1991; 20 Post Baccalaureate Hrs; Kent St Univ 4 Grad Ed Hrs; *cr:* Hubbard HS Soc Stud Tchr 3 Yrs; *ai:* Sr Class Adv; Frosh Ftbl Head Coach; Var Track Asst Coach; 8th-9th Grd Bsktbl Coach; Leadership Comm; NEA, OEA, HEA 1993-; Alpha Delta Pi 1990-; *home:* 1375 S 12th St Beloit OH 44609

STOFFER, WILLIAM E., Earth & Space Science Teacher; *b:* Harrisburg, PA; *m:* Carol Ann Smith; *c:* Autumn, Tara, Logan; *ed:* Harrisburg Area Cty CC (AS) Sci 1967; Shippensburg St (BS) Earth & Spec Sci 1969; Penn St Univ (MED) Scndry Ed 1971; Temple Univ (EDD) Adult & Continuning Ed 1996; Prin Cert Western MD Coll At Westminster 1975; *cr:* Middletown Area Schl Dist Tchr 25 Yrs, Admin 1 Yr; Middletown Area HS Coach 9 Yrs, Dept Chair 3 Yrs; *ai:* Dept Chair Sci Dept; Environmental Sci Club Adv; NEA, PSEA, MAEA 1970-; AAACE, PAACE 1986-; BSA 1990-, Ablicity Comm; *office:* Middletown Area HS 1155 W Union St Middletown PA 17057*

STOHLER, THOMAS CLYDE, 8th Grade American His Teacher; *b:* Lebanon, PA; *m:* Terrell Grundon; *c:* Meredith Lynn, Shannon Dietrick, Adrienne C.; *ed:* Lebanon Vly Coll (BA) Pol Sci 1966; Shippensburg Univ (MA) Guid & Cnslng 1971; Penn St Univ Guid & Prsnl; *cr:* Susquehanna Jr HS Tchr & Cnslr 1966-75; Susquehanna Twp HS Tchr & Coach 1976-80; Susquehanna M S Tchr & Dept Chair 1981-; Susquehanna Twp Recreation Dir 1990-95; *ai:* Ath Dir; Bsbl, Sftbl & Wrestling Coach; Class 1979, Model UN & Stu Cncl Adv; Soc Stud Dept Chair; Curr Cncl; Natl Geog Bee Coord; NEA & PSEA 1968-, Pres & Negotiator; NCSS 1980-; Rutherford Yth Club Bd 1972-, VP; St Marks Luth Church 1980-, Cncl Pres; Sinatara Twp Rec Commission 1990-; Harrisburg Jayces Tchr of Yr 1968; GEM NET Global Edctr Presenter 1988; Japanese Cultural Exch Japan 1989; *office:* Susquehanna Twp MS 801 Wood St Harrisburg PA 17109*

STOICOVY, CHRISTOPHER GEORGE, Social Science Teacher; *b:* Pittsburgh, PA; *m:* Michelle Lynn Pilot; *ed:* Grove City Coll (BA) Scndry Ed, Soc Sci 1991; IN Univ of PA (MA) Scndry Schl Cnslng 1995; *cr:* IN Area Jr HS Permanent Sub Geog 1991-92; Johnstown HS Soc Sci Tchr World Cultures, Pol Sci 1992-; *ai:* Mock Trial, Trojan Pride Club Adv; Prof Dev, Soc Sci Curr Comms; Sftbl Coach; Gifted Support Tchr; PSEA, NEA 1992-; ASCA 1995-; *office:* Greater Johnstown Schl Dist 222 Central Ave Johnstown PA 15902

STOKER, KENNETH R., German Teacher; *b:* Philadelphia, PA; *m:* Claudia Hance; *c:* Colleen, Andrew; *ed:* Susquehanna Univ (BA) Ger & Eng 1968; Nazareth Coll of Rochester (MS) Ed 1975; Course Work at Univ of Salzburg Austria 1971; Gocthe Inst 1972, 1974, 1978 & 1986; *cr:* Bd of Coop Ed Svcs Ger Tchr 1968-69; Marion Cntrl Schl Ger & Eng Tchr 1969-71; Fulbright Commission Germany Eng Tchr 1971-72; Marion Cntrl Schl Ger Tchr 1972-; *ai:* Ger-Amer Partnership Pgm & Marion Ski Club Adv; WAFFLE 1969-; NYSAFLT 1975-, Regnl Dir, Outstdng Tchr 1986; Fulbright Tchr 1971-73; Rockerfeller Awd for Lang Tchng 1988; Article Pub; *office:* Marion Jr Sr HS 4034 Warner Rd Marion NY 14505*

STOKES, BELINDA E., Math Teacher & Dept Chair; *b:* Jersey City, NJ; *m:* Anthony; *c:* Angela, Antwanette; *ed:* St Peter's Coll (BS) Math 1981; Jersey City St Coll (MA) Math Ed 1993; *cr:* J. C. Pub Schls Tchr 14 Yrs; *ai:* Math Club Adv; JCEA, NJEA 1982-; AMTNJ 1990-; NCTM 1989-; Governors Tchrs Recognition Prgm; *office:* Lincoln HS 60 Crescent Ave Jersey City NJ 07304

STOKES, CATHERINE ANN COFFEY, 6th Grade Teacher; *b:* N City, NY; *m:* Edward; *c:* Michael, Matthew; *ed:* Suffolk Comm C 1970; Potsdam SUNY (BA) Ed, Psych 1972; New Paltz SUNY (M 1974; Post Grad LIU 1988; *cr:* Rombout Jr HS 6th Grd Tchr South Ave Elem Schl 6th Grd Tchr 1978-91; Rombout MS 6th C 1991-; *ai:* Curr Comm; NEA 1972-; Mid Hudson Sci Cncl; Natl Edn Day Com 1987; Outstdng Sci Tchrs Awd; Natl Sci Fnd Grant Eisenhower Grant 1994; *office:* Rombout MS Mattewan Rd Bea 12508

STOKES, GARY LEE, Biology Teacher; *b:* Punxsutawney, PA; *m* Penoplus; *c:* Steven, Nicole; *ed:* IN Univ of PA (BS) Bio Ed 1969; (MS) Instrl Media Tech 1970; 20 Hrs Instrl Media Specialist Cert; Univ 3 Hrs; *cr:* IN Area Schl Dist Bio, Gen Sci Tchr 1970-; *ai:* B Adv; NEA; PSEA; IAEA; *office:* Indiana Sr HS 450 N 5th St Ind 15701

STOKES, JANNIE MYRICK, Keyboarding Teacher; *b:* Williston Marshall J.; *c:* Andre, Geoffrey; *ed:* Winston-Salem St Univ (BS) 1974; *ai:* Keyboarding Club.*

STOKES, NINA O., Biology & Anatomy Teacher; *b:* Mobile, Michaeline, Kathryn, Jaclyn; *ed:* Bluffton Coll (BA) Hlth, Bio 197 of Dayton (MS) Sci Ed 1990; Attnd IN Univ, Bowling Green S Duquesne Univ; *cr:* Ottoville HS Bio, Anatomy Tchr 1985-95; *ai.* NEA; Sci Edctrs of OH; NABT; *office:* Ottoville HS PO Box 248 O OH 45876*

STOKUM, SONDRA LYNNETTE, Learning Support Teac Washington, PA; *m:* Gary Alan; *c:* Jesse Alan, Christopher Jacob; St Coll (BS) Speech Correction 1976; CA Univ of PA (MS) Spcl E *cr:* Intermediate Unit I Speech Clinician 1978-83, Learning Suppo 1983-; *ai:* NEA 1978-; PSEA 1978-; *office:* Burgettstown Area J Bavington Rd Burgettstown PA 15021

STOLA, ALFRED J.,JR., Art Teacher; *b:* Berwick, PA; *m:* Lynn *ed:* Kutztown St Coll (BS) Art Ed 1977; Bloomsburg Univ (MS) Ins 1989; *cr:* Sullivan Cty Schl Dist Art Tchr 1987-92; Montgomery A Sr High Art Tchr 1992-; *ai:* Stu Cncl Adv; PAEA 1992-, Regio Outstdng Rep 1993-95; NAEA 1992-; St Boniface Liturgy Comm *office:* Montgomery Area H S 120 Penn St Montgomery PA 17752

STOLARICK, CATHERINE RUTH, IST Support Teach Wilkes-Barre, PA; *ed:* Bloomsburg Univ (BS) Elem Ed 1974, (MS Ed 1978; *cr:* Pine Grove Area Schl Dist Remedial Math Tchr 1 5th-6th Grd Math Tchr 1976-79, 3rd Grd Tchr 1979-92, K-4th G Support Tchr 1992-; *ai:* SCEA VP; PGAEA, PSEA & NEA 1974-, Sec; Delta Kappa Gamma 1982-, Recording Sec; SCEA 1982-, Pr Sec & Treas; Eastern Star 1976-; Pine Grove Historical Soc 1995- RD 3 Box 1064-D Schuylkill Havn PA 17972*

STOLL, CONSTANCE DARNOWSKI, Guidance Counse Brooklyn, NY; *m:* Charles G.; *c:* Gerard, Elizabeth Hubert, Ma Murphy, Constance Crameri, Margaret Lageman; *ed:* St Johns Un Math, Ed 1956; Worchester (MS) Cnslng 1986; Sacred Heart Univ Cert 1995; 12 Credit Hrs Queens Coll NY; *cr:* New Hyde Park H Tchr 1956-59; Maria Regina HS Math Tchr 1972-79; Plainfield HS Tchr 1979-86; Plainfield Cntrl MS Guid Cnslr 1986-; *ai:* Afte Tutoring; Coord Adv Groups; Dist Curr Co-Coord; NEA, CEA CASC 1986-; Thompson Historic Soc 1980-; St Annes Soc 1980- Mem US Olympic Womens Track & Field Team 1952, 1956; *home:* F 93 195 Thompson Rd Thompson CT 06277*

STOLL, KIMBERLY HVARRE, Music Teacher; *b:* North Ston CT; *m:* Douglas E.; *ed:* Westminster Choir Coll (BM) Music Ed 199 Roberts Univ 24 Credits Hrs Towards Masters in Chrstn Ed Adm Kent Place Schl N-7th Grd Music Tchr 1991-92; Full Gospel Chrst 1st-12th Grd Music Tchr 1992-; *ai:* 7th-12th Grd Vocal Ensemble Dir; MS Band Dir; Yrbk Adv; MENC 1987-; Full Gospel Assemblies of God 1992-; *office:* Full Gospel Chrstn Schl Northfield Rd Livingston NJ 07039

STOLL, MATTHEW EDWARD, Life Science Teacher; *b:* Norwal *m:* Lisa Joan Haswell; *ed:* Baldwin-Wallace (BA) Bio 1981; Attnd K *cr:* Black River HS Bio Tchr 1981-89; *ai:* Head Var Ftbl Coach 1981-; Lorain Cty Coaches Assn 1990-; Coach of Yr 1984-85, 1 1991; *office:* Mc Cormick MS 201 S Main St Wellington OH 44090

STOLLE, NANCY SIEGEL, French & English Teacher; *b:* Young OH; *c:* Susan Stolle Jauche; James William; *ed:* Westminster Coll (& Eng 1963; Youngstown St Univ (MS) Ed & Rdng 1993; *cr:* Boa HS Fr & Eng Tchr 1963-69; Youngstown Pub Schls Fr & Eng Tchr 19 Ursuline HS Fr & Eng Tchr 1983-; *ai:* Foreign Lang Dept Chprsn; F & Ski Club Adv; OCEA 1983-; Chi Omega Alumni 1963-; *office:* U HS 750 Wick Ave Youngstown OH 44505

STOLLER, RITA LINDA, Title I Mathematics Teacher; *b:* Brookly *m:* Joel; *c:* Fran Tepper, Daniel; *ed:* Brooklyn Coll (BA) Ed 1964; C (MS) Spec Ed 1983; 30 Credits Beyond Masters; *cr:* Pub Schl 124 3rd Grd Tchr 1964-67; Temple Beth-El Nursery Schl Tchr 1976-7 Schl 166 Tchr 1978-; *ai:* Math Competitions Adv; New York Interscholastic Math League; NCTM 1992-; Conducted Family Wkshps; *office:* Public Schl No 166 33-09 35th Ave Long Island C 11106*

STOLLINGS, LESLIE L., English & Home Ec Teacher; *b:* Hunti WV; *c:* Marc Andrew, Matthew David; *ed:* WV Univ (BS) Home Ed Ohio Univ Rdng, Composition; Miami Univ OH Writing Project; St Univ Creative Writing Process; *cr:* Hayes Consolidated Schl Dis 1979-80; Lawrence Cty Voc Schl Food Svc Instr, Co-op Coord 19 Chesapeake Union Exempted Schl Dist Lang Arts, Home Ec Tchr *ai:* Stu Cncl Exec Adv; Safe Schls Comm Chprsn; Power of Pen Adv; Rep, Negotiations; Venture Capital Grant Comm; NEA, OEA 1990 Cncl for Tchrs of Eng & Lang Arts 1991-; Fifth Ave Bapt Church Ronald Mc Donald House 1995-, Vol; Amer Quarter Horse Assn 1995 Writing Project Flwshp Miami Univ of OH; Exec Producer Gun *office:* Chesapeake MS 10255 Cty Rd 1 Chesapeake OH 45619

STOLOFF, HELEN ARCURI, Professor; *b:* Glens Falls, NY; *m:* No *c:* David, Stephen; *ed:* SUNY at Albany (BS) Bus Ed 1962; Coll of St (MS) Ed 1965; *cr:* Rensselaer Schl 3 First, Third Grd Tchr 3 Yrs Greenbush Elem Schl First Grd Tchr 1 Yr; Hudson Vly Comm Co Division Prof 30 Yrs; *ai:* SUNY at Albany Class of 62 Alumni Cnsl Assn; SUNY Amni Cncl.

STOLT, RUTH ALLEN, Science & Computer Teacher; *b:* Plainfiel *m:* Robert Allen; *c:* Meg, Barbara; *ed:* Newark St Coll (BA) Math 1967; Trenton St Coll (MED) Sci Ed 1980; Shenandoah Univ (MS) Ed 1990; 15 Post Grad Hrs at Rutgers Univ & NJ Inst of Tech; *cr:* Adams MS Tchr 1968-; NJIT Instr Summers 1992 & 1993; *ai:* 1970-; ETEA 1968-; Pioneer Girls Guide; NJ Statewide Systemic Init 1995-; HazTox Wkshp Summers 1992 & 1993; *office:* John Adams MS Dover Rd Edison NJ 08820

STOLTZ, SHELLEY H., Dance & Drama Director; *b:* Brooklyn, N Marc; *c:* Adam, Melissa, Lauren; *ed:* Brooklyn Coll (BA) Dance 197 Credits Toward Masters in Hlth; *cr:* James Madison HS Dance 1972-77; Private Dance Studios Dance Tchr 1977-93; Our Lady of Acad Dance & Drama Dir 1985-; *ai:* Mercy Dance Co & Mercy P Dir; PDTA 1990-; NEDT 1994-; Womens Amer Ort 1975-, Pres Plair

)82-84; CW Post HS Dance Competition Best Choreography Awd YS Martin Luther King Jr Performing Arts Competition 3rd Pl assau Cty Martin Luther King Jr Performing Arts Competition 2nd 1st Pl 1995 & 1996; *office:* Our Lady Of Mercy Acad 815 Convent set NY 11791

Z, THOMAS PAUL, Soc Stud & Economics Tchr; *b:* Somerset, Sandra Lee Sandusky; *c:* Hillary, Nicholas; *ed:* Univ of Pittsburgh em Ed 1983; Syracuse Univ (BA) Ec 1992, (MA) Ec; *cr:* Oriskany Sr High 7th-8th & 12th Grd Soc Stud Tchr 1985-; *ai:* Key Club ross Cntry & Track Coach; Oriskany Tchrs Assn 1985-, Pension); AFT 1985-; The Federalist Soc 1991-; Oneida Civic Coral 1989-, r; Kiwanis 1992-, Hnr Mem; St Patricks Choir 1993-; Took Group s to MO Flood Clean Up; *office:* Oriskany Jr Sr HS PO Box 539 Oriskany NY 13424

AUGH, MELISSA LEE, English Teacher; *b:* Johnstown, PA; *ed:* Pitts at Johnstown (BA) Eng & Comm 1992; *cr:* Forest Hills Eng Drama Adv 1993-; *ai:* Drama, NHS, SADD, Forensics Adv; Stu sst Adv; Strategic Planning Comm; PSEA & NEA 1993-; *office:* Hills Sr HS PO Box 325 Sidman PA 15955

'S, STEPHEN A., Director of Choirs; *b:* Hamilton, OH; *m:* Carole eri; *c:* Sybil, Kathleen; *ed:* Ball St Univ (BS) Music Ed 1970; estern Univ (MM) Conducting 1978; Defense Lang Inst at ey Ger Lang Cert; Ball St Univ Doctoral Candidate Conducting, erformance; *cr:* Shortridge HS Dir of Choirs 1970-72; Ball St Univ nstr, Dir of Choirs 1978-83; MO Western St Coll Voice Instr, Choral ting 1983-84; SUNY Asst Prof, Dir of Choirs, Orch 1984-85; HS Dir of Choirs 1986-; *ai:* Concert Choir, Chamber Singers, 's Chorale Dir; NYSSMA, ACDA, MENC 1986-; Oswego Opera Bd Mem; Music Therapy Journal; *office:* Auburn HS Lake Ave Ext NY 13021*

:, ANNETTE GRODECKI, Music Teacher; *b:* Ravenna, OH; *c:* s, Matthew; *ed:* KSU (MS) Music Ed; *cr:* Springfield Local Schls 86-89; Akron Pub Schls Tchr 1989-92; Painesville Twp Schls Tchr 3; Chardon Local Schls Tchr 1993-; *ai:* Spring Musical Dir; , Ski Club Adv; Vlybl coach; Drama Club; Choral Fest; OMEA Delta Omicron 1984-, VP, Treas; Alpha Gamma Delta 1977-, Pres, tstdng Sister, Tchr Awds; Miss OH, Miss Amer Padgent top 10 Winner 1979; Cleveland Porthouse Opera 1979-; Amer Yth Concert Ravenna Comm Choir 1979-; *office:* Chardon Local Schls 424 North don OH 44024*

, CAROLE KOWALLIS, Social Studies Teacher; *b:* Pittsburgh, Lynn Clark, Wm, David, Virginia Caruso; *ed:* PA St (BS) Hlth, PE niv of Pgh Grad Credits; *cr:* Duquesne Schls PED Tchr 1954-61; Schls Sub Tchr 1965-79, Hlth, Soc Stud, Sci Tchr 1980-; *ai:* Stu dv; NEST Team; Drug, Alcohol Comm; Team Ldr; Mentor; NEA, 980-; Westmoreland Girl Scouts 1961-, 1st VP, Bd Mem, Camp nance Chm, Capital Fund Steering Comm; Penn's Woods Civic Assn Bd Mem; *home:* 711 Pettigrew Rd Irwin PA 15642

:, COLLEEN MC NEVIN, Guidance Counselor; *b:* Pittston, PA; ald; *c:* Courtney, Kyle; *ed:* East Stroudsburg Univ (BA) Sociology, oology 1973; Univ of Scranton (MS) Cnslr Ed 1977; Lehigh Univ lits Cnslr Ed; *cr:* St Michael's Schl for Boys Cnslr 1974-75; PA Dept r & Industry Employment Cnslr, Admin 1975-84; Bethlehem Area ist Guid Cnslr 1992-; *ai:* Adv Peer Helper SADD Club, Class of Chprsn Restructuring Comm; PA Schl Cnslr Assoc 1993-; *home:* Madison Dr Bethlehem PA 18017

:, EDWARD GEORGE, Assoc Prof Information Systems; *b:* , OH; *m:* Diane Patrecilli; *c:* Marilou, Brian; *ed:* Kent St Univ Ec 1968, (MAT) Bus Ed 1970; Herkimer Cty Comm Coll Cert Data sing 1982; SUNY Inst of Tech Telecommunications; *cr:* Norwayne ar 1970-72; Berne Knox Westerlo Cntrl Tchr 1972-77; Herkimer Cty Coll Tchr 1977-; *ai:* Stu Senate Adv; Fac Stu Assn Bd Mem; Phi ambda St Adv; NYSUT 1972-; NYSATYC, Herkimer Cty Chamber merce 1992-; United Way 1980-, Bd of Dir; Boy Scouts 1983-, Cub , Den Ldr, Asst Scoutmaster; Mohawk Little League 1 Yr, Asst Rsrch Proj Discovery, Tech Support Ctr; Distance Learning Coord Audio; *office:* Herkimer County Comm Coll Reservoir Road ner NY 13350

E, FRANCES ADAMS, Retired Fourth Grade Teacher; *b:* Barton, Richard Norman; *c:* Lee Ann, Terry Stone Porreca, Richard G., .; *ed:* Lyndon St Coll (BS) Elem Ed 1952; 30 Addl Hrs; *cr:* So e Elem Schl 3rd-5th Grd Tchr 1948-49; Derby Ctr Elem Schl 3rd-4th hr 1949-51; Meadow Schl 4th Grd Tchr 1952-53; E Hartford Schl Grd Tchr 1953-55; Norwich-Marion Cross Schl 4th-8th Grd Tchr 1; *ai:* Prof Ethics Comm Chm 10 Hrs; Beginning Tchrs Mentor; 952-; VEA, NTA 1955-; *home:* 60 Lebanon St Hanover NH 03755

E, JO, Assistant Professor of Art; *b:* Lexington, KY; *ed:* San Diego v (MFA) Art, Studio Furniture 1994; Murray St Univ (BFA) Art, onal Wood, Drawing Design 1985; *cr:* San Diego Museum of Art ng, Sculpture Instr 1992-94; San Diego St Univ Tchng Assoc ng I, II, 2D 1991-93, Instr Adj, Furnitire & 3D Design 1994; SUNY rof of Furniture, Sculpture, Drawing Art 1994-; *ai:* Stu Art Assn; Fac Fac Senate, Policy Comm; Occasional HS Wkshps; Coll Art Assn, AUP 1994-; Visiting Artist Flwshp Anderson Ranch Arts Ctr 1996; Grant KY Fnd for Women 1989; *office:* S U N Y Coll At Geneseo ege Cir Geneseo NY 14454*

E, JOYCE CALMEISE, Seventh Grade Mathematics Tchr; *b:* nati, OH; *m:* Nelson M. Sr.; *c:* Nelson Jr.; *ed:* Cntrl St Univ (BS) Ed 1972; Xavier Univ (MED) Educl Admin 1986; MS Math Cert St Univ; *cr:* Belle Haven Elem Schl 7th Grd Math Tchr 1971-82; ew MS 7th Grd Math Tchr 1982-, Math Dept Chprsn 1994-; *ai:* sment Comm of Tchrs Project Lead Tchr; Math Course of Stud g Team Mem; NEA, WOEA 1972-; NCTM, OCTM 1982-; Benjamin ker Assn 1995-; Dayton Contemporary Dance Company Out Reach 1984-; Delta Sigma Theta 1964-; Summer Wkshp 1995; Fnd Scholar 93; Tchr of Yr 1993-94; *office:* Fairview MS 2408 Philadelphia Dr OH 45406

E, LAWRENCE HARVEY, Social Studies Teacher; *b:* Pittsburgh, Carole Joy Mervis; *c:* Edyce Jean Ochoa, Susannah Levy-Shoen, Benjamin, Rachel Lindhome, Robin Levy; *ed:* Mc Neese St Univ Scndry Ed 1971, (MA) His 1972; ABD Doctoral Candidate Univ of western LA 1975; *cr:* Univ of Southwestern LA His Instr 1977-81; view Prep Inst Head Master 1977-84; Knoxville MS Rdng Tchr 93; Schl of Advanced Jewish Stud Hnrs Instr 1987-; Taylor dice HS Soc Stud Tchr 1993-; *ai:* Asst Ftbl Coach; Wrestling Coach; n-Amer Action Soc, Gaming Club Adv; US His Overview Russian grant Citizenship Preperation Classes Instr; Pittsburgh Fed of Tchrs , Bldg Rep; *office:* Taylor Allderdice HS 2409 Shady Ave Pittsburgh 217

E, MICHAEL, 6th Grade Teacher; *b:* Levittown, PA; *m:* Pamela; *c:* n; *ed:* Juanita Coll (BS) Early Chldhd Ed 1979; Penn St Univ (BS) Ed 1981, (MS) Ed Admin 1983; *cr:* Bellefonte Area Schl Dist Tchr ; *ai:* Ftbl & Wrestling Coach; Stu Cncl Adv; Little League Bsbl; M 1979-; Transformations Project 1994-; *office:* Bellefonte Area MS School St Bellefonte PA 16823*

STONE, MICHAEL CHARLES, Earth Science Teacher; *b:* Gowanda, NY; *m:* Dianne L. Meyers; *c:* Aaron M.; *ed:* Fredonia St Coll (BS) Geology 1986; Buffalo St Coll (MS) Earth Sci 1991; *cr:* Brocton Cntrl Schl Earth & Gen Sci, Phys Sci Tchr 1986-; *ai:* Trap & Field, Ski Clubs Adv; Class Adv; Envirothon Coach; Prin Advy Comm; NSTA 1993-; Brocton Tchrs Assn, NYSUT 1986-; Jaycees 1990-; *office:* Brocton Central Schl 138 W Main St Brocton NY 14716

STONE, MICHELLE DIANE, Asst Prof of Social Grntolgy; *b:* Lansing, MI; *ed:* Western MI Univ (BA) Psych 1977, (MA) Applied Behavior Analysis 1985, (PHD) Sociology 1994; Specialist Gerontology 1985; Post-Doctoral Flwshp Natl Inst of Aging with the Schl of Soc Work Univ of MI 1993-94; *cr:* MI St Univ Geriatric Clerkship Coord 193-85; Western MI Univ Adj Instr 1985-93; St Cloud St Univ Asst Prof 1987-92; Youngstown St Univ Asst Prof 1994-; *ai:* Chair Multidisciplinary Gerontology Comm; Nrsng Home Admin Comm; Gerontological Soc of Amer 1978-, Co-Chair Women's Spec Interest Group 1993-94; Assn for Humanist Soc 1986-, Ed, Humanity & Soc; Amer Sociological Assn 1993-; OH Network of Educl Consultants in the Field of Aging 1994-; Alzheimer's Disease Family Support Group 1979-85, Convienor; Alzheimer's Assn SW MI Chptr 1985-87, Pres; Del to White House Conf on Aging 1994; St Cloud St Univ Achvmt Awd 1989, Distngd Tchng Awd 1988-89; Western MI Univ Rsrch & Creative Scholar Awd 1987, Dept of Sociology Rsrch & Creative Scholar Awd 1987; *office:* Youngstown St Univ Dept of Sociology & Antaropolo 410 Wick Ave Youngstown OH 44555*

STONE, PATRICIA T., Tech Div Chr, Ec & Mngmt Tchr; *b:* Easthampton, MA; *m:* James E.; *c:* Scott, Wendy Malette, Kerry Wentworth; *ed:* Holyoke Jr Coll (ABS) Bus 1958 New Hampshire Coll (BS) Bus Ed 1976, (MS) Bus Ed 1985; *cr:* St of MA Soc Worker 1958-60; Timberlane Schl Dist Bus Ed Tchr 1973-88, Tech Division Chair, Ec, Mngmt Tchr 1988-; *ai:* 5 Yr Tech Planning Dist, Action, Early Graduation, Schlsp, TQM Comms; Shadowing, Mentorship Prgm; Schl Bus Partnerships; NBEA, NEBEA, NHBEA, ASCD 1974-; Delta Pi Epsilon; NASSP; Friends of Kimball Lib 1965-; Mealey's Meals 1987-, Tchr of Yr in Bus Ed NH 1995; Ec Article Pub; *office:* Timberlane Regional HS 36 Greenough Rd Plaistow NH 03865*

STONE, PHILIP D., English, History Tchr & Chair; *b:* New York, NY; *ed:* Coll of Wooster (BA) Speech, Ed 1970; Univ of NE at Lincoln (MFA) Directing, Theatre 1982; Doctoral Stud Univ of NE at Lincoln ABD; Theatre Arts Brooklyn Coll; Oral Interpretation, Comm Hunter Coll; *cr:* Adelphi Acad Speech, Eng Tchr 1971-76; Univ of NE Grad Asst 1982-83; Devonshire Acad Chair Eng Dept 1984-86; Adelphi Acad Chair Eng, His, Coord US 1986-; *ai:* Fac, Curr Comm; Drama Supvr; Newspaper Adv; Liason Coalition Essential Schls; Alumni Assn Rep; Coll Guid; Adelphian Players 1971-, Pres, Artistic Dir; *office:* Adelphi Acad 8515 Ridge Blvd Brooklyn NY 11209*

STONE, ROGER F., Foreign Languages Dept Chm; *b:* Oklahoma City, OK; *c:* Justin, Jennifer; *ed:* Holy Cross Coll (BA) Classics 1969; Trinity Coll (MA) Classics 1976; Attnd Harvard Unif, Tufts Univ, Univ of NH & Merrimae Coll; Salem St Coll; *cr:* Austin Prep Schl Forgein Lang Dept, Chm, Latin Tchr 1969-; *ai:* Jr Classical League; Classical Assn of New England 1969-; Amer Classical League; *office:* Austin Preparatory Schl 101 Willow St Reading MA 01867*

STONEBRAKER, ROBERT J., Professor of Economics; *b:* Hagerstown, MD; *m:* Annie Laurie Wheat; *c:* John C., Stephen R.; *ed:* U MD (BA) Ec 1967; Princeton U (PHD) Ec 1973; *cr:* IN U of PA Asst Prof 1971-75, Assoc Prof 1975-78, Prof 1978-, Interim Assoc Provost 1994-95; *ai:* Univ Senate & Acad Affairs & Univ Admissions Comm; Alumni Newsletter Ed; Non Profit Org Consultant; Amer Ec Assn 1970-; Soc for Scientific Stud of Rel 1992-; Zion Luth Church 1971-, Treas, Cncl Mem & Financial Sec; IUP Distngd Tchng Awds 1977-89; Numerous Articles Pub; *office:* Indiana Univ Of PA Dept of Ec IVP Indiana PA 15705

STONEBRIDGE, ROBERT, Technology Teacher; *b:* Valley Stream, NY; *ed:* St Univ of NY at Delhi (AAS) Construction Mngmt; St Univ of NY at Buffalo (BS) Tech 1970; St Univ of NY at Albany (MS) Educl Admin 1972; 24 Addl Credit Hrs; North Adams St Coll 6 Credit Hrs Internship; *cr:* South Glens Falls HS Tech Instr 1970-; Adirondack Comm Coll Engineering Adj Prof 1989-; *ai:* Dist Citizens' Advy, Curr, Tech Comms; Chm Prof Growth, Dist Hlth, Safety Comms; South Glens Falls Fac Assn 1970-, VP; NY St United Tchrs 1970-; NY St Tech Tchrs Assn 1980-; Intnl Tech Ed Assn 1992-; South Glens Falls Fed Credit Union 1990-, Bd of Dirs; Supt's Advy Cncl 1993-; Staff Dev Day Presenter; Pilot Prgm Curr Dev; *office:* Sou Glens Falls HS 42 Merritt Rd S Glens Falls NY 12803*

STONEHAM, ELLEN, English & Math Teacher; *b:* Bronx, NY; *m:* Donald; *c:* June; *ed:* St Thomas Aquinas (BA) His 1969; Iona Coll (MSEd) His 1990; *cr:* Immaculate Heart His Tchr 1981-85; *ai:* NCEA; *office:* Notre Dame Interparochial Schl 312 1st St Palisades Park NJ 07650

STONEHAM, LISA HIPP, Eng, Drama, Speech & Rdng Tchr; *b:* Sandusky, OH; *c:* Sara; *ed:* Bowling Green St U (BS) Speech & Drama 1979; Ashland Univ Eng Cert 1990, Rdng Endorsement 1995; *cr:* South Cntrl Tchr 1992-; *ai:* Drama Club & Sr Class Adv; Play Dir; Firelands Acad Challenge Co-Adv; NEA 1994-; SCEA 1995-, Sec; *office:* South Central HS 3305 S Angling Rd Greenwich OH 44837

STONE MARTIN, JACQUELINE EILEEN, Orchestra Teacher; *b:* Queens, NY; *m:* Stephen W. Martin; *c:* Emma Rose, Alexandra Grace; *ed:* James Madison Univ (BA) Instrumental Music 1988; Queens Coll (MS) Instrumental Music 1992; Hartt Schl of Music Cert of String Repair 1992; Prof Diploma Prgm in Educl Admin 1994-; *cr:* Lawrence Schl Dist Gen Music Tchr 1988-89; West Babylon Schl Dist HS Orchestra Dir, Elem String Tchr 1989-; *ai:* HS String Ensemble Conductor; Orch Violinist; NSOA 1988-; Long Island String Festival Assn 1988-, Adjudication Chprsn 1991-; Music Edctrs Natl Conf 1988-, NYSSMA Adjudicator; Suffolk Cty Music Ed Assn 1989-, Chprsn, Adjudicator; Sigma Alpha Iota 1986-; Orch Asst Flwshp, Schlsp to James Madison Univ; *home:* 18 Baylis Pl Syosset NY 11791

STONER, JOHN BLAINE, 7th Grd Language Arts Teacher; *b:* Mt Pleasant, PA; *m:* Linda Cheryl; *c:* Miriam, Thomas; *ed:* OH Univ (BSEd) Eng Comprehensive 1979; Univ of Toledo (MA) Eng 1983; OH St Univ (MA) 1993; 18 Credit Hrs; *cr:* Northeastern HS Hnrs Eng 11 1984-86; Bellefontaine HS Hnrs Eng 9 & 11 1986-95; Bellefontaine MS Lang Arts 7 1995-; Grad Tchng Asst Univ of Toledo; *ai:* Future Tchr Pgm Spon; HS Girls Cross Cntry, Drama, Wrestling & Track Coach; Newspaper, Yrbk & Sr Class Adv; Intervention Team; Peer Mediator; Schlsp Recipient: OH Univ Intensive Jrnlsm Inst 1992, OH Wesleyan Writing Inst 1991; *office:* Bellefontaine MS 509 Park Rd Bellefontaine OH 43311*

STONER, MARY KRAUSS, World Cultures Teacher; *b:* Reading, PA; *m:* Herbert L.; *c:* Victoria, Susan; *ed:* Penn St Univ (BA) His, Govt 1966; Shippensburg Univ (MED) His 1972; *cr:* James Buchanan HS Govt, World Cultures Tchr 1968-; *ai:* Intnl Stu Exch Club, His Competition Adv; TEA, PSEA, NEA, NCSS, PCSS, 1966-; *office:* James Buchanan H S 4773 Ft Louden Rd Mercersburg PA 17236

STONER, MARY SUE, Second Grade Teacher; *ed:* Penn St Univ, West Chester Univ (MS) Ed 1990; *office:* Shamona Creek Elem Schl 501 Dorlans Mill Rd Downingtown PA 19335

STONER, PAULA SMITH, Biology Teacher; *b:* Canton, OH; *m:* Ken; *c:* Alicia, Chelsea, Kirsten; *ed:* Kent St Univ (BS) Bio, Hlth 1974; Post Grad Hrs Elem Cert, Sci; *cr:* Streetsboro MS Life Sci, Sci, Hlth Tchr 1977-92; Streetsboro HS Bio, Advanced Bio Tchr 1992-; *ai:* Ski Club Adv 5 Yrs; 7th Grd Girls Bsktbl Coach 1 Yr; North Cntrl Assn Schl Improvement Plan Steering Comm; Streetsboro Edctr Assn, NEA 1976-; Jennings Scholar 1990-91; *office:* Streetsboro HS 1900 Annalane Dr Streetsboro OH 44241*

STONER, SARAH LISA (MAUPIN), Business Education Teacher; *b:* Wheeling, WV; *m:* Jeffrey G.; *c:* Jacob; *ed:* West Liberty St Coll (BS) Bus Admin, Specialization in Cmptr Information Systems 1986; 30 Under & Grad Hrs to Complete DE Tchr of Bus Ed Cert; Hrs in Voc Ed, Continuing Ed; *cr:* Kent Cty Voc Tech HS Data Processing Tchr 1989-91; Polytech HS Bus Ed Tchr 1991-; *ai:* Bus Profs of Amer Adv; DE Bd of Dirs; New Tchrs Mentor; Schl to Work Planning, Sr Project, Schl Climate & Grad Comms; Co-Chair DE Bus Mrktg & Fin Ed Frameworks Commission; DE Bus Ed Assn 1992-, Rep St Exec Bd; Bus Prof of Amer 1989-, St Bd Former Sec; DE St Ed Assn, NEA 1990-; Polytech Ed Assn 1990-, Sec; DE Olympic Comm 1993-; Asbury United Meth Church 1988-, Various Comms; *office:* Polytech HS PO Box 97 Woodside DE 19980

STONER, STEVEN REYNOLDS, Sixth Grade Teacher; *b:* Gary, IN; *m:* Christine Lusardi; *ed:* Kutztown Univ (BED) Elem, Spec Ed 1977; Univ of Pittsburgh (MED) Curr, Supervision 1980; *cr:* Western PA Schl for Blind Children Tchr, Supvr 1977-84; Altoona Area Schl Dist Gifted Prgm Tchr 1984-85; Grier Schl Tchr 1985-88; Tyrone Area Schl Dist Tchr 1988-; *ai:* Stu Store Adv; Tyrone Ed Assn 1988-, Pres, VP; NEA 1978-; PA St Ed Assn 1988-; Tyrone Regnl Arts Cncl, Allegheny Chorale 1989-, Pres; Tyrone Comm Players 1990-, Bd of Dirs; Tyrone Area YMCA 1991-, Bd of Dirs; Western PA Flwshp; *office:* Warriors Mark Elem Schl General Delivery Warriors Mark PA 16877*

STONEY, GEORGE CASHEL, Goddard Professor of Cinema; *b:* Winston-Salem, NC; *c:* Mary Louise, James Bruce; *ed:* UNC at Chapel HIll (BA) Eng, Jrnlsm 1937; Cert AV Ed U of London 1948; Attnd Balliol Coll 1945; Grad Courses New Schl & NYU 1938-39; *cr:* Univ of Sou CA Summer Schls Production Instr 1953, 1956; City Coll of NY Inst of Film Prgm Chair 1956-57; Columbia Univ Adj Instr in Film 1958-63; Stanford Uni v Filmmaker in Residence 1965-67; Univ of Ibaden Lecturer Short Term 1967; Natl Film Schl Documentary Instr 1967; Intnl Schl of Amer Film Prof 1967-68; Natl Film Bd of Canada Exec Producer Challenge for Change 1968-70; Tisch Schl of the Arts NYU Film, TV Prof 1970-; Univ of Sou CA Schl of Cinema Visiting Prof 1984, 1 988; Fulbright Prof of Film Cath Univ 1989; *ai:* Filmaking; Production, Grad Degree Candidates in Documentary Films Adv; Assn of IN Video & Filmakers 1971-, Bd Mem, Eye Beam Awd; Alliance Com Media, 1st Recipient Stoney Awd 1982, Bd Mem, Founding Mem 1978; Univ Film, Video Assn 1975-; Dirs Guild 1953-; Manhattan Neigh Network 1993-, Bd Mem; Written, Directed, Produced 80 Documentaries; Articles Pub; Currently Producing a Series; *office:* NY Univ 721 Broadway #944 New York NY 10003

STOPERA, MICHELLE STEELE, Business Education Teacher; *b:* Troy, NY; *m:* Daniel; *c:* Christopher, Matthew, David; *ed:* Maria Coll (AAS) General Stud 1978; Coll of Saint Rose (BS) Bus 1980; St Univ of NY at Albany (MS) Bus Ed 1982; 6 Grd Hrs in Cooperative Ed Now a Certified Diversified Cooperative Ed Coord; *cr:* Maria Coll Tchr 1980-81; Albany HS Tchr 1981-82; Cohoes HS Tchr 1982-86; Niskayuna HS Tchr 1986-; *ai:* Key Club & Schl Store Adv; Mock Trial Team Coach; MS Restructuring Comm; Tech CORE Team; NYSUT 1981-; Delta Pi Epsilon 1982-; Niskayuna Tchrs Assn 1986-; Capital Dist Bus Ed Assn 1990-; Saint Helens 1990-, Rel Ed Instr; *office:* Niskayuna HS 1626 Balltown Rd Niskayuna NY 12309*

STORCH, JEROME ELLIOTT, Deputy Chair; *b:* Bronx, NY; *c:* Allysen Mary, Aaron David; *ed:* Seton Hall Univ (AAS) Police Sci 1959; Mercy Coll (BS) Soc Sci 1971; John Jay Coll of Criminal Justice (MA) Criminal Justice 1975; Tchrs Coll Columbia Univ (MED) Higher & Adult Ed 1989, (EDD) Higher & Adult Ed 1991; *cr:* Port Authority of NY & NJ Police Ofcr 1956-62; NY St Police Investigator & Trooper 1962-81; John Jay Coll of CJ Deputy Chm & Asst Prof 1981-; *ai:* Gamma Sigma Hon Soc Safety & Security Club Fac Adv; Curr Comm Dept Chair; Stu Grd Appeals Comm; Temple Sinai 1972-, Pres & Bd of Trustees; Commission on Human Rights Orange Cty NY 1987-92; Numerous Articles Pub; *office:* John Jay Coll of Criminal Just 889 10th Ave New York NY 10019

STORIE, SINA PROCACCINI, 4th Grade Teacher; *b:* Princeton, NJ; *m:* Wayne F.; *c:* Steven; *ed:* Elizabeth Seton Coll (AA) Lbrl Arts 1969; Felician Coll (BA) Elem Ed 1971; *cr:* Saint Paul Schl 4th Grd Tchr 1971-; *ai:* NCEA 1971-; Brier Crest Woods Civic Assn 1985-; Hillwood Manor Civic Assn 1971-; Golden Apple Awd; Tchr of Yr; *office:* St Paul Schl 218 Nassau St Princeton NJ 08542

STORM, BRUCE JAMES, Art Department Head; *b:* Palmerton, PA; *m:* Nella Lynn Godbey; *ed:* Penn St Univ (BS) Art Ed 1965, (MED) Art Ed 1969; *cr:* Lahabra City Schls Art Tchr 1965-68; Pennsbury Schls Art Coord 1969-74; Springfield Twp Art Tchr, Set Design 1974-72; East Lycombing Schls Dept Head Art 1974-; *ai:* Set Designer CIWC & Scholastic Production; Art Club Adv; Animation Film Wkshps; Taught Adult Ed Craft Courses Penn St Univ; Nation Art Ed Assn, Penn St Ed Assn 1969-; Phi Delta Kappa 1979-, Outstndng Tchr Awd St of PA; Munley Historical Soc 1974-; Prof Exhibiting Artist in Galleries East Coast; Written Articles; Restoration Artist Historic Church & Pub Bldg Restorations; *home:* 106 N Main St Muncy PA 17756

STORMER, KIMBERLEE MALAH, Chemistry Teacher; *ed:* Clarion Univ PA (BS) Chem Sec Ed 1991; Masters in Sci Ed Prgm 26 Hrs; *cr:* Portage Area HS Chem Tchr 1991-92; Allegheny-Clarion Valley HS Chem Tchr 1992-; *ai:* Stu Cncl, Olympiad Adv; Girls Var Track & Field Coach; NSTA, PSTA, PSEAA 1991-; TIE Wkshp Awardee; *office:* Allegheny-Clarion Vly Jr Sr HS PO Box 345 Foxburg PA 16036

STORMS, PATRICIA A. SANDBLOOM, Comp Ed & Math Tchr; *b:* Jamestown, NY; *c:* William, Robert, Ronald Jr., Richard; *ed:* SUNY Fredonia (BA) Elem Ed 1970, (MS) Early Chldhd 1975; 12 Post-Grad Hrs Learning Disabilities Univ of Edinboro; *cr:* R. R. Rogers Schl Kndgtn Tchr 1970-72; C. C. Ring Schl Kndgtn Tchr 1972-84, 1st Grd Tchr 1984-93; C. V. Bush Schl Comp Ed Math Tchr 1993-; *ai:* Labor Mngmt Cncl; Admin Liason, Terminal Leave Comms; JTA Bldg Rep, Constitutional Comm Rep; Jamestown Tchrs Assn 1970-, Chprsn Curr Cncl; NEA 1970-; Lakewood Zoning Bd Appeals 1986-, Vice Chprsn; *office:* C. V. Bush Schl 150 Pardee Ave Jamestown NY 14701

STORRY, JAMES DOUGLAS, Music Teacher; *b:* Warren, OH; *ed:* Baldwin-Wallace Coll (BME) Music Ed 1969; Kent St Univ (MM) Music Ed 1980; *cr:* Mentor Pub Schls Music Tchr 1969-70; Nordonia Hills City Schls Music Tchr 1970-; *ai:* Choir Dir; Handchime Dir Lee Eaton Schl; NHEA, DEA, NEA 1970-; MENC 1969-; American Guild of Organists 1967-; Cleveland Orch Chorus 1969-; Church in Aurora 1981-, Organist; *home:* 1105 Canyon View Rd Apt 505 Sagamore Hills OH 44067

STORSBERG, NANCY J., Guidance Director; *b:* Elizabeth, NJ; *ed:* Philadelphia Coll of Bible (BS) Bible & Chrstn Ed 1971; Kean Coll of NJ (MA) Stu Personal Svcs 1982; Luther Ride Seminary (MA) Cnslng 1986; *cr:* Timothy Chrstn Schl 3rd Grd Tchr 1971-76, Guid Dir 1976-; *ai:* NHS Adv; Jr Homeroom Tchr; *office:* Timothy Christian Schl 2008 Ethel Rd Piscataway NJ 08854

STOSAK, PATRICIA ANN, Elem Language Arts Teacher; *b:* Bridgeport, CT; *ed:* Southern CT St Univ (BS) Ed 1963; Univ of Bridgeport (MS) Ed 1965; St Joseph's Coll 6th Yr Cert 1987; *cr:* Eli Whitney Schl Sixth Grd

Lang Arts Tchr 1963-; *ai:* Schl Spirit Comm, Chprsn; Yrbk Spon; Greek Day Coord; Musical, Drama Presentations; SEA, CEA, NEA 1963-; Bethany C&MA Church 1959-, Dir Children's Ministries; PTA 1963-, Second VP; Cooperative Tchr; Nom Tchr of Yr 1983, 1989; *office:* Eli Whitney Elem Schl 1130 Huntington Rd Stratford CT 06497

STOTZ, JUDITH ESTHER (SPENCER), Seventh Grade English Teacher; *b:* Buffalo, NY; *m:* Thomas Lee; *c:* Marc Thomas, Paul Spencer, Matthew Lawrence; *ed:* St Univ of NY at Buffalo (BS) Ed 1965, (MS) Ed 1967; Addl 30 Hrs Beyond Masters; *cr:* Holland Cntrl 8th & 9th Grd Eng Tchr 1965; West Seneca Cntrl 7th & 8th Grd Eng Tchr 1965-75, 1981-; *ai:* West Seneca Tchrs Assn, NYSUT, AFT 1965-; Ebenezer United Church of Christ 1956-; *office:* East MS 1445 Center Rd West Seneca NY 14224

STOUDER, WILLIAM DENNIS, Jr HS Lang Arts, Soc Stud Tchr; *b:* Cincinnati, OH; *ed:* Miami Univ (BSE) Soc Stud 1971, (MED) Scndry Admin 1981; 6 Hrs Post Grad Eng; 6 Hrs Post Grad Am His; *cr:* St Columban Schl Jr HS Soc Stud Tchr 1964-66; St Michael Schl Jr HighSoc Stud, Eng Tchr 1966-; *ai:* Eng Dept Chair 1976-; Soc Stud Chair 1966-; Spelling Bee Coord 1990-; EECAP 1988-; NCEA 1968-; Democratic Club 1972-; Big Brothers of Amer 1986-; Vly Forge Flwshp 1971; OWP Flwshp, Jr HS Play Patented 1987; *office:* Saint Michaels Schl Oak St & Creek Rd Sharonville OH 45241

STOUDT, MICHAEL DOUIE, 6th Grade Teacher; *b:* Utica, NY; *m:* Christine Amelia Johnson; *c:* Peggy Weaver, Michael; *ed:* Parsons Coll (BA) Elem Ed 1961; *cr:* Cornwell-Lebanon Schl Dist 6th Grd Elem Tchr 1965-; *ai:* NEA, PSEA & CLEA 1961-; Lebanon Valley Chamber of Commerce Excl in Ed Awd; *office:* Cedar Crest MS 101 E Evergreen Rd Lebanon PA 17042*

STOUGH, SCOTT DAVID, Drafting & Technology Teacher; *b:* Harrisburg, PA; *m:* Terry JO; *c:* Dustin, Cara; *ed:* Millersville Univ (BS) Indstrl Arts 1981, (MED) Indstrl Arts 1986; *cr:* Caesar Rodney HS Indstrl Arts Tchr 1982-84; Rdng Schl Dist Indstrl Arts Tchr 1984-86; Northern Garrett HS Drafting, Tech Ed Tchr 1986-; *ai:* Wrestling Coach; Class Adv; AFT 1986-; Natl HS Wrestling Coaches Assn; Natl Wrestling Coaches Assn; *office:* Northern Garrett HS 86 Pride Pkwy Accident MD 21520

STOUT, PATRICIA, Junior High History Teacher; *b:* Bidwell, OH; *m:* Patrick; *c:* Brian, Jason; *ed:* Univ of Rio Grande (BS) Elem Ed 1980; Univ of Dayton (MS) Guidance Counseling 1985; *cr:* Cheshire-Kyger Elem Schl Kndgtn Tchr 1980-82; Addaville Elem Schl Kndgtn & 2nd-4th Grd Tchr 1982-92; Bidwell-Porter Elem Schl Jr HS His Tchr 1992-; *ai:* 8th Grd Adv; Var Cheerleading Coach; NEA 1983-; Cradle to Coll Mothers Club 1984-, Sec; Martha Holden Jennings Scholar 1995; *home:* PO Box 185 Bidwell OH 45614

STOUT, THOMAS MICHAEL, Accounting Instructor; *b:* Fremont, OH; *m:* Alix T. Foust; *c:* Theresa, Lisa, Danielle; *ed:* Bowling Green St Univ (BS) Acctng, Mrktg 1971, (MBA) Acctng 1980; IBM I Clas Trng Schl; *cr:* Apollo Career Ctr Instr 1976-; *ai:* Bus Prof of Amer Adv; NEA, OEA 1995-; Bus Prof Amer 1979-, Regnl Adv, 10 Yr Adv Awd; *office:* Apollo Career Ctr 3325 Shawnee Rd Lima OH 45806

STOUTER, MAURA OLGA, Physical Education Teacher; *b:* Pittsfield, MA; *ed:* SUNY at Cortland (BSE) PE 1970; SUNY at Stony Brook (MALS) Lbrl Stud 1975; 45 Addl Hrs; *cr:* Smithtown HS Tchr, Coach 1970-; *ai:* Var Vlybl Coach; NEA, NYSUIT, AAHPERD 1971-; NYSAAPERD 1971-, Coaching Hnr Awd Excl in Coaching 1990; Am Vlybl Coaches Assn 1987-; Suffolk Cty VB; SCVCA Coaches Assn 1976-, Pres, Past Pres, Jdr Dev Dir Excl in Coaching 1987; Suffolk Cty Vlybl Coaches Assn Coach of Yr 1990, Fall Coach of Yr 1990-95; Natl HS Coaches Awd Gold Awd Excl in Coaches 1988; Stony Brook Univ Women in Sport Hnr Awd 1992; *office:* Smithtown HS 100 Central Rd Smithtown NY 11787

STOVALL, SHERRY INGRAM, 5th Grade Teacher; *b:* Cleveland, OH; *m:* Howard; *ed:* Kent St Univ (BS) Elem Ed 1971; Cleve St Univ Masters Degree Curr, Instr 1990, Rdng Cert 1982; *cr:* Douglas Mac Arthur El Schl Classroom Tchr 1971-77; St Funded Prgm Rdng Tchr 1977-80; Forest Hill Parkway El Schl Classroom Tchr 1980-85; Watterson-Lake El Schl Classroom Tchr 1985-; *ai:* Musical Plays; Stage Designs; Awd Comm; *office:* Watterson Lake Elem Schl 1422 W 74th St Cleveland OH 44102

STOVER, GERALD I., Biology & Env Biology Teacher; *b:* Lebanon, PA; *m:* Grace Marie Mase; *c:* Adrienne Marie, Matthew Michael; *ed:* Hofstra Univ (BA) Bio 1974; Masters Equivalency 60 Credit Hrs Post Grad Work PA St Univ & Millersville Univ; *cr:* St Pauls Episcopalian Schl 5th, 8th-9th Grd Sci, Bio, Geology Tchr 1975-79; Cornwall-Lebanon Earth, Space Sci, Bio, Environmental Bio Tchr 1980-; *ai:* Environmental Club, Soph Class Adv; Girls Var Sftbl, Palmyra Civic Bsbl, Midget Ftbl, Rec League Bsktbl Coach; Cub Scouts 1991-, Comm Chm, Den Ldr, Cubmaster; St Johns EC Church 1951-, Sunday Schl Supt, Tchr; *office:* Cornwall-Lebanon School Dist 115 E Evergreen Rd Lebanon PA 17042

STOVER, KELLIE BOOZER, Biology Teacher; *b:* Elizabethtown, PA; *m:* Kevin; *ed:* Millersville Univ (BS) Bio Scndry Ed 1991; AP Cert Bio; Gen Sci Cert; Shippensburg Univ Working on (MS) Guid; *cr:* Elizabethtown MS Life Sci Tchr 1991-92; Hempfield Sr HS Bio Tchr 1992-93; South Western Sr HS Bio Tchr 1993-; *ai:* Cross Cntry, Track & Field Asst Coach; NEA 1991-; PSEA 1992-; Natl Wildlife Fed 1992-; Earth Day Celebration Act; Nixon Cty Park Guest Speaker; 3-Time All-Amer Cross Cntry & Track & Field; *office:* South Western Sr HS 200 Bowman Rd Hanover PA 17331*

STOVER, MICHAEL R., American Civics Teacher; *b:* Williamsport, PA; *m:* Gail P.; *c:* Brian, Michelle; *ed:* Mansfield St Coll (BA) His, Soc Stud 1964; Bloomsburg St Coll (MS) Ed 1972; *cr:* Wyalusing Area Schl Soc Stud Tchr 1964-66; Hughesville HS Soc Stud Tchr 1966-; *ai:* PSEA, NEA 1964-; *office:* Hughesville HS 349 Cemetery St Hughesville PA 17737

STOVER, RONALD HOWARD, Secondary Teacher; *b:* Brockton, MA; *m:* Isabelle Ann Kerrwood; *c:* Ryan, Ashlyn, Shawn; *ed:* SUNY at Fredonia (BA) His 1979; Western CT St Unv (MA) His 1990; Participant Robert Taft Inst for Two Party System, Pace Univ 1983; *cr:* JFK HS Soc Stud Tchr 1980-90; George F. Baker HS Soc Stud Tchr 1990-; *ai:* Coach Ftbl, Girls Bsktbl, Sftbl; Yth in Govt Adv; NYSUT 1990-; Vol Yth Coach Kiwanis 1994-; *office:* George F Baker HS Rt 17 Tuxedo Park NY 10987

STOWELL, MATTHEW H., 8th Grade Social Studies Tchr; *b:* Columbus, OH; *ed:* Miami Univ (BS) Scndry Soc Stud 1991; mA Prgm in Curr & Instr at OH St Univ; *cr:* Dublin City Schls Tchr 1991-; *ai:* MS Track Coach; NEA 1991-, Local Grievance Chair; NCSS 1990-; OH Cnclf for Soc Stud 1989-, Exec Bd, Pres Awd; Cnty Democrat Party 1993-, Word Committeeman; Article Pub; Stratford Hall-Monticello Summer Stud Seminar 1995; OCSS Conf Presentations 1990-91; *office:* Ann Simpson Davis MS 2400 Sutter Pky Dublin OH 43016

STOWELL, WILLIAM CHARLES, Agriculture Teacher; *b:* Albany, NY; *m:* Jean M. Lopata; *ed:* SUNY at Cobleskill (AAS) Ag Engrng 1980; Cornell Univ (BS) Ag Ed 1983; SUNY at Oswego (MS) Voc Ed 1983; *cr:* Cobleskill HS Ag Tchr 1983-84; South Jefferson HS Ag Tchr 1984-; Jefferson Cty Comm Coll Part Time Cmptr Instr 1992; SUNY at Oswego Part Time Ed Instr 1994-; *ai:* FFA Adv; NY St FFA Bd of Trustees Chm & Sec; NY St FFA Leadership Trng Fnd Bd Mem; Tchrs Assn Comms; Negotiating Team; Assn of Tchrs of Ag & NYSUT 1983-; Mem of AVA, NVATA; Chamber of Commerce 1990-; NY St Ed Grant for Tchrs; *office:* South Jefferson HS PO Box 10 Adams NY 13605*

STOWERS, CHARLOTTE W., Business Teacher; *b:* Chambersburg, PA; *m:* Robert H.; *c:* Leah, Rebecca, Gregory; *ed:* Ricks Coll (AS) Clerical Arts Trng 1979; Brigham Young Univ (BS) Bus 1983; Kent St Univ (MED) Ed, Bus 1988; Attnd Ashland Univ; *cr:* Payson HS Bus Instr 1983-84; Minneapolis Bus Instr 1984-85; Rootstown HS Bus Instr 1986-; Elgin Comm Coll Bus Instr 1991-92; Coll of DuPage Bus Instr 1991-92; *ai:* Bus Profs of Amer Stu Adv; Comms Bus Ed Dept Advy Chair, Schl Dist Tech; Akron Area Bus Tchrs Assn 1986-, Pres; OH Bus Tchrs 1992-; PTA 1993-; Relief Soc Women's Org 1976-, Sec, Tchr; Nom Ricks Coll Outstdng Tchr Awd, Ashland Inc Tchr; Shippensburg Univ Grad Assistantship; *office:* Rootstown HS 4190 St Rt 44 Rootstown OH 44272

STOY, SANDRA KEENE, Health, Home & Careers Teacher; *b:* Gilbertsville, NY; *m:* David F.; *c:* Vickie Udden, Michelle Havens, Joann; *ed:* St Univ NY at Oneonta (BS) Home Ed 1954, (MS) Ed 1974; Hlth Ed Cert; *cr:* Oneonta HS Sub Tchr 1965-69; Gilbertsville Schl Sub Tchr 1965-69, Tchr 1969-91; Gilbertsville Mt Upton Schl Tchr 1991-; *ai:* HIV, AIDS, Hnrs Comms; Delta Kappa Gamma 1987-; NYEA 1975-, Pres; Woman's Cr Church 1991-, Moderator; Fireman's Auxiliary 1970-, Pres; Grandes Dames 1985-, Chprsn; *home:* RR 1 Box 27N Otego NY 13825*

STRACHAN, DAVID GORHAM, Mathematics Teacher; *b:* Buffalo, NY; *m:* Joan Rieckelman; *c:* Alice Barr, Charles, James, Edward, David Jr.; *ed:* Middlebury Coll (BA) Math 1955; Harvard Univ (MAT) Math Ed 1957; Bowdoin Coll (MA) Math 1970; Post Grad St Andrews Univ Scotland; *cr:* Belmont Schls Math Tchr 1955-56; Ridgewood Schls Math Tchr 1956-57; Nichols Schl Math Tchr 1957-83; Cmptr Instruction Bus Owner 1983-88; Nichols Schl Math Tchr 1988-; *ai:* Adv; Coach; Publications; NCTM 1970-; The Cabinet 1988-; Olive R. Ringo Fac Achvmt Awd 1992; *office:* Nichols Schl 1250 Amherst St Buffalo NY 14216

STRACHAN, GEORGE HUGH, Physics & Earth Science Tchr; *b:* Kitzmiller, MD; *w:* Virginia (dec); *c:* Kevin Hickey, Gina Wyatt, George; *ed:* Frostburg St Coll (BS) Sci, Ed 1962; Univ of Northern IA (MA) Sci 1968; Univ of MD 30 Addl Hrs Sci Ed; Univ of Northern IA, Univ of MD, Portland St Univ 30 Addl Hrs Sci, Sci Ed; *cr:* Hyattsville Jr HS Math Tchr 1962-63; Nicholas Orem Jr HS Math, Sci Tchr 1963-64; Greenbelt Jr HS Math, Sci Tchr, Dept Chair 1964-78; Project Upgrade Summer Schl Sci, Sci Skills Tchr 1969-91; Night Schl Basic Ed, GED, Sci Tchr, Prin 1969-74; Eleanor Roosevelt HS Physics, Geology Tchr 1978-86, Tchr, Sci Coord 1986-93; Towson St Univ Physics Adj Prof 1991; Eleanor Roosevelt HS Physics, Earth Sci Tchr 1993-; NASA Goddard Space Flight Ctr Consultant, Visiting Scientist 1993-; *ai:* Nethered Satellites, Networking ERHS Spon Stu Team Coop NASA GSFC; NEA 1962-; MSTA 1962-, Rep Assembly; PGCEA 1962-, Chair Greenbelt, Bldg Reps 1968-78; NSTA; Masonic Lodge 1969-; Scottish Rite 1993-, 32 Degree; Masonic Shrine, Eastern Star 1993-; Presenter Prince George's Cty Sci Trek 1987-93; NSF Acad Yr Inst 1967-68 U of N IA; NSF Hnrs Wkshp Geology of MD 1976; Mt St Helens Cascade Range Hnrs Wkshp NSF, Portland St U 1986; Physics Resources & Instrl Strategies Motivate Stdnts Natl Wkshp U of N IA, NSF 1988-89; Presenter Regnl NSTA, MD Assn Sci Tchrs; Citizen Ambassador Prgm Intnl Delegation Physics Vietnam, Natl DelegationGeology Russia 1993; Tchr of Yr Greenbelt Jr HS 1974; Outstdng Tchr of Sci Joint Bd Sci & Engr ng Ed Greater WA Area; *home:* 485 Kenora Dr Millersville MD 21108*

STRACK, RICHARD NICHOLAS, English Teacher; *b:* New Brunswick, NJ; *m:* Sharon Ann Mc Cann; *ed:* Rutgers Univ (BA) Lang Arts Ed 1973; *cr:* Avenel Jr HS Eng, Modern Comm Tchr 1973-80; Colonia HS Eng Tchr 1981-; *ai:* Asst Var Ftbl, Bsbl Coach; Head Frosh Ftbl Coach; Stu Peer Educator Selection Adv; First Yr Tchr Mentor; Fac Advy Comm Chr; Stu-Ath Code of Conduct Comm Mem; NTEA 1979-, Bargaining Cncl; NJEA 1979-; Metuchen Cath Diocese Family Life Bureau 1985-, Engaged Encounter Facilitator; Newspaper & Newsletter Articles Pub; Most Influential Tchr; *home:* 106 Anita Dr Piscataway NJ 08854*

STRACQUATANIO, VINCENT, Physics Teacher; *b:* Jersey City, NJ; *m:* Patricia Mele; *c:* Rose Ann, Joseph; *ed:* Univ of PA (BS) Mechnical Engrng 1972, (MS) Math Ed 1973; NY Univ Cert Math Supervision; *cr:* Univ City HS Sci Tchr 1972-73; NY City Pub Schls Math Tchr 1973-76; Teaneck HS Physics Tchr 1976-77; Midland Park HS Sci, Math Tchr 1977-80; Vernon Twp HS Physics, Math Tchr 1980-; Sussex Cty Comm Coll Math Adj Instr 1988-; *ai:* Asst Ftbl Coach; AAPT 1993-; NCTM 1972-; Nat Fed Int Coach A 1995-; OLF Carnival Comm 1988-, Comm Chprsn; Summer Scholar Residence; *office:* Vernon Township HS PO Box 800 Vernon NJ 07462

STRACZYNSKI, THOMAS S., Sixth Grd & Foreign Lang Tchr; *b:* Brooklyn, NY; *ed:* Manhattan Coll (BA) Govt 1968; 6 Credits; *cr:* Holy Cross Schl Tchr 1969-74; St Bartholomew Schl Tchr 1974-; *ai:* Soc Stud Dept, Frgn Lang Dept Chm; Polish Amer Cncl for Civil Rights 1978-, Founder, Chm; Polish Amer Museum; Queens Historical Soc; Jacques Marchais Museum of Tibetan Art; Cath Near East Welfare Assn; Articles Pub; *office:* St Bartholomew Schl 44-15 Judge St Elmhurst NY 11373*

STRADER, ARLENE M., Physics Teacher; *b:* Rockville Center, NY; *m:* Ronald P.; *c:* Heidi, Brad; *ed:* SUNY at Albany (BS) Bio 1961, (MS) Bio 1966; *cr:* Saratoga Springs Jr HS Sci Tchr 1961-67; Saratoga Springs HS Bio Tchr 1967-71; Wise Owl Nursery Schl Owner 1978-84; Saratoga Springs HS Physics Tchr 1985-; *ai:* Key Club Adv 1986-; BSA Troop Comm; Girls Scout Cncl; NYSTA; AAPT; STANYS; *office:* Saratoga Springs HS 186 West Ave Saratoga Springs NY 12866

STRADER, ELIZABETH SAUNDERS, Social Studies Teacher; *b:* Glens Falls, NY; *m:* Scott Sheldon; *ed:* Univ of CO at Boulder (BA) Anthropology & His 1984; St Univ of NY at Albany (MA) Ed 1986; *cr:* Hudson Falls Sr HS Soc Stud Tchr 1987-89; St Farm Insurance Agent 1989-91; Glens Falls Sr HS Soc Stud Tchr 1991-; *ai:* 6th Grade Intramural Field Hockey Coach; NYS Cncl for Soc Stud 1994-, Mem; Glens Falls Kiwanis Club 1989-, Bd of Dirs, Distinguished Kiwanian Awd; Glens Falls Sr Citizens 1990-, Bd of Dirs; *office:* Glens Falls HS 10 Quade St Glens Falls NY 12801

STRADFORD, GEORGIA A., 5th-8th Grade APOGEE Teacher; *b:* Lancaster, SC; *ed:* Benedict Coll (BA) Elem Ed 1963; 3 Hrs Ed Monmouth Coll NJ Cert; 6 Hrs Ed Courses Kean Coll; *cr:* WA DC Schl System Tchr 1966-68; Asbury Park MS Acad Prgms for Gifted, Equity, Excl, Rdngy Tchr 1969-; *ai:* Site Mgr for Cmptr Lab; Steering Comm; NEA 1969-; NJEA 1969-, Del Assembly; MCEA 1969-, Bd of Trustees; APEA 1969-, VP, Pres; St Stephen AMEZ Church, Bd of Stewards; *office:* Asbury Park MS 1200 Bangs Ave Asbury Park NJ 07712

STRAIGHT, DONALD CHARLES, High School Math Teacher; *b:* Massena, NY; *m:* Wendy Sue Mac Kinnon; *ed:* SUNY at Potsdam (BA) Math 1988, (MA) Math 1988; NYS Tchng Cert Sec Math 1888; Novell Cmptr Network Trng 1995; *cr:* Massena Cntrl Schl HS Math Tchr Summer 1988; Brasher Falls Cntrl Schl HS Math Tchr 1988-; *ai:* NHS Adv; AFT, NYSUT 1988-; Northern Zone Yth 1982-, Treas, Advy; Brushton Holiness Camp 1982-, Treas; *home:* 14823 State Highway 37 Massena NY 13662

STRAIN, SHERRY SHYLENE, Associate Professor of Comm; *b:* Canyon, TX; *ed:* West TX St Univ (BA) Theatre 1983; Univ of Denver (MA) Theatre, Directing Emphasis 1985; Southern IL Univ (PHD) Speech, Comm, Theatre 1993; *cr:* West TX St Univ Stu Theatre Staff 1981-83; Univ of Denver Grad Tech Asst 1983-84; Southern IL Univ Grad Tchng Asst 1985-88; Keystone Coll Dir of Theatre 1988-; *ai:* Comm Guild, Lit Magazine Adv; General Ed Review, Concerts, Lectures Chair; Keystone Players Dir; Fac Senate VP; NCTE 1995-; ECTC 1993-; ATHE 1990-; Mulberry Poets & Writers 1988-, VP; Dissertion Research Awd; Article Pub; Notable Women of TX 1985; Outstanding Young Women 1984; *office:* Keystone Jr Coll PO Box 50 La Plume PA 18440

STRAIT, GENE MARTIN, Biology Teacher; *b:* Chambersburg Karel Anne Martin; *c:* Megan; *ed:* Millersville Univ (BSEd) Bio & Ed 1989; 15 Plus Hrs Masters Equivalency; 18 Credits Toward M Biblical Stud; *cr:* Cedar Crest HS Bio Tchr 1989-; *ai:* Stdnts for Class of 1996 Adv; Tech-Prep Team Mem; Millersville Bible 1990-, Elder; *office:* Cedar Crest HS 115 E Evergreen Rd Leb 17042

STRAIT, PEGGY TANG, Professor Emerita; *b:* Canton, China; *m* *c:* Pawl, David; *ed:* Univ of CA at Berkeley (BA) Math 1953; M Math 1957; NYU (PHD) Math 1965; *cr:* U C Radiation Lab Pro 1954-55; G. C. Dewey Corp Rsrch Asso 1957-63; Queens Coll o Prof 1964-; *ai:* AMS 1964-; NSF Flwshp; Book: A First Course And Stat with Applications; Articles Pub; *office:* Queens Coll of C of NY 6530 Kissena Blvd Flushing NY 11367*

STRAITS, SHELLEY ANN, English & Journalism Teacher; *b:* OH; *ed:* OH St Univ (BS) Eng, Jrnlsm 1989; Grad Work Ashla Drake Univ, OH St Univ; *cr:* Buckeye Vly HS Eng, Jrnlsm Tchr 1 Newspaper, Magazine Adv; Schlsp Comm; Newsletter Chm; NCT OSU Alumni, Young Bucks 1990-, VP, Sec, Newsletter; Delta Zeta Columbus Musuem of Art 1995-; *office:* Buckeye Valley HS 901 Rd Delaware OH 43015

STRAKA, DEBRA LYNN, Science Teacher; *b:* Steubenville, William L.; *c:* Daniel L., Casey T., Jamie M.; *ed:* Franciscan Steubenville (BS)-Magna Cum Laude Elem Ed & Sci 1993; *cr:* Cntrl Elem 6th-8th Grd Sci Tchr 1993-; *ai:* Archeological Fie NCEA 1993-; Alpha Chi Natl Hnr Schlsp; Franciscan Univ Schlsp; Governors Awd for Excl in Yth Sci Opportunites 1995; H Resolution From Steubenville City Cncl.

STRAKA, MARY KAISER, Business Ed Tchr & Dept H Huntingburg, IN; *m:* Joseph Frank Jr.; *c:* Amy Elizabeth, Ryan Jos IN Univ (BS) Mngmt 1974; Univ of Toledo (BE) Comp Bus E (MED) Bus Ed 1995; *cr:* St Ursula Acad Bus Ed Dept Head, Tch Stautzenberger Coll Bus Ed Fac 1995-; *ai:* Sr Class Adv; Advy B Comm; NBEA, NW OH Bus Ed Assn, OH Bus Tchrs Assn 1991-; Jr 1984-; Kappa Kappa Gamma 1974-, Pres, Treas; *office:* St Ursu 4025 Indian Rd Toledo OH 43606

STRAKER, LYNDA V. TAITT, Mathematics Tchr & Vice Trinidad, West Indies; *m:* Louis Hilton Sr.; *c:* Louis Jr., Lyndon, *ed:* Baruch Coll (BBA) Mngmt 1980; Brooklyn Coll (MS) Math, E *cr:* Hanson Pl SDA Schl Tchr 1984-, Vice Prin 1993-; *ai:* NADOF Tchrs Rep; Black Achievers Awd Hanson PL AJY Soc 1996; *office:* Place Sda Schl 38 Lafayette Ave Brooklyn NY 11217

STRALEY, LINDA RADKEY, Fifth Grade Teacher; *b:* Fostoria, Bernard Lee; *c:* Tracy L. Mays, John A., Michael N.; *ed:* Bowlin St Univ (BS) Elem Ed 1979; *cr:* North Baltimore Schl 8th G 1979-80; St Michael Schl 5th Grd Tchr 1980-; *ai:* Just Say No Adv; of Lib 1986-; Hancock Historical Soc 1993-; Ashland Oil Natl Apple Achiever Awd 1993; *home:* 305 W State St North Baltim 45872

STRAND, CARL KEVIN, High School Art Teacher; *b:* Hollywo *m:* Susan Faith (Green); *c:* Sarah, Joshua; *ed:* San Diego St Univ (1979; Univ of S CA (MFA) Visual Art 1982; Columbia Univ Tc (MED) Art Ed 1987; *cr:* Univ of S CA Tchng Asst 1980-82; Columb Tchrs Coll Art Tchr, Saturday Morning Prgm 1986-87; E Meadow Free Schl Dist Art Tchr 1988-; Queens Coll-CUNY Cartoonin Childrens Summer Prgm 1993; *ai:* E Meadow HS Art Club Adv; In & Curr Comm Mem; Natl Art Ed Assn 1986-; Kappa Delta P NYSUT, & EMTA 1988-; *office:* East Meadow HS 100 Carmen A Meadow NY 11554*

STRANDBERG, BETH A., Vocal Music & World Hum Tchr; *b:* OH; *ed:* OH St Univ (BA) Music Ed 1994; 12 Hrs Music Ed in Kodaly Cert, Educl Philosophies, Univ Choir; *cr:* Columbus Alt HS Vocal Music, World Hum Tchr 1994-; *ai:* Praxis Testin Evaluation Music Portion Tchrs Exam, Tchr Retreat Comms; Musical Dir; Tchr with All City Choir, Accompanist, Voice Coach OEA 1994-; OMEA 1992-; Broad St Presbyn Church, Toddlers, Music Tchr; Summa Cum Laude; Co-Lecturer OMEA; St Con Tchng Strategies HS Music; Co-Presenter OH St Summer Wkshp M High Schls; *office:* Columbus Alternative HS 2632 Mcguffey Rd Col OH 43211*

STRANG, MARILYN HUGHES, English & Journalism Teac Pittsburgh, PA; *m:* David William; *c:* Douglas, Bonnie; *ed:* U Pittsburgh (BA) Ed 1988; *cr:* Bentworth HS Eng 10, Jrnlsm Tchr 19 Schl Newspaper; Creative Writing; NEA, BEA 1988-; *home:* 199 Se Rd Avella PA 15312*

STRANGE, BONNIE L., 6th Grade Teacher; *b:* North Adams, William P.; *c:* Wade, Leigh; *ed:* North Adams St Coll (BA) Elem Ed (MS) Admin 1988; Addl Hrs Castleton St Coll Behavior Mngmt, Learning Disabilities; Univ of VT Issues in Contemporary Ed, Sp Cmptrs in Ed; North Adams St Coll Children with Spec Problems Classroom, Schl Law, Rdng & Lang Arts, Schl Fin; *cr:* Pownal Ele Title I Tchr 1975-76, 1st Grd Tchr 1977-79, 3rd Grd Tchr 1980-81, Tchr 1982-, Sub in Prins Absence 1987-; *ai:* Tchr Evaluation Comm Expectation & Stu Achvmt Trainer; Stu Tchr Supvr; NEA 1977-95, Rep 1991-93; Soccer, Little League Bsbl Coach; *office:* Pownal Ele RR 2 Box 97 Pownal VT 05261*

STRANGE, JOHN SEBASTIAN, Accounting Chprsn & Instruc Port Chester, NY; *ed:* Iona Coll (BA) Pol Sci 1975, (MBA) Acctng 15 Credits Orgnl Behavior Cert 1989; 8 Credits Soc Sci SUNY at Pu 1983; *cr:* Columbus HS Math Instr 1986-87; St Univ of NY Bus Inst Westchester Bus Inst Acctng, Mngmt Instr 1987-, Acctng Chprsn 19 Conduct Prep Course for Accreditation Accountancy Exam; Natl S Accountants 1995-; Smithsonian Inst 1983-, Natl Assoc; Accredit Preparer 1994; Permanent Cert St NY Scndry Ed, Bus Ed, Soc Stud *office:* Westchester Bus Inst 325 Central Ave White Plains NY 106

STRANGIS, DANIEL ANTHONY, Band Director; *b:* Mc Keespo *m:* Jill Ann Crum; *ed:* WV Univ (BM) Music Ed 1988; Post Gra Duquesne Univ; *cr:* Bentworth HS Band Dir 1988-; *ai:* Musical C PMEA, NEA, MENC 1988-; PA Fed Contest Judges 1977-; Artic New Ways; *office:* Bentworth Sr HS 500 Lincoln Ave Bentleyvi 15314

STRAPP, NANCY ELLEN, Fifth Grade Teacher; *b:* Urbana, O Edgecliff Coll of Xavier Univ (BS) Ed 1971; Post Grad Credit Hrs; Marys Schl 7th Grd Tchr 1967-69; St Dominic Schl 5th Grd Tchr 19 St Margaret of Cortona 7th Grd Tchr 1973-84, 5th Grd Tchr 1984-; *a* Stud Curr Coord; Up Downtowners 1980-; Archdiocesan Pension 1986-92; Share the Spirit Awd for Outstdng Svc to Cath Schls 1988; Saint Margaret Of Cortona HS 4100 Simpson Cincinnati OH 45227

STRASSER RUSH, MONA DIANE, English Teacher; *b:* Pittsburg *c:* Matthew J., Michael E.; *ed:* Univ of Pittsburgh (BA) Eng 1963, (Admin 1992; Cert Scndry, Elem Admin 1992; Completing Doctoral in Educl Admin 1996; *cr:* Langley HS Tchr 1963-70, 1975-87; L Educl Med Ctr Tchr 1987-91; Langley HS Tchr 1991-; *ai:* Jr Class t Mediator; Stu Tchrs Mentor; Sr Class Spon; Yrbk; NHS; Play Dir; asting Club; NCTE; ASCD; AFT; WPTE; Pittsburgh Diocesan l Cncl; Theresa Burke Irish Dances, Chprsn; Pittsburgh Ceili Club; ance Play Dir; Guardian Angels Parish, Eucharistic Minister; ıny Conf Grant; Voice of Democracy Contest Judge; Article Pub; Conventions Presenter; Kappa Delta Pi; *office:* Langley HS 2940 en Blvd Pittsburgh PA 15204*

TTON, GARY DAVID, Dean of the Chapel; *b:* Seattle, WA; *m:* Lynn Jordan; *c:* Ashley, Jordan, Joshua, Selah; *ed:* Wheaton Coll 'hrstn Ed 1980; Talbot Schl of Tech (MA) Theology 1991; Fuller gical Seminary Phd Stud in Process in Historical Theology; *cr:* s Crusade for Christ Campus Dir 1980-85; Whittier Chrstn HS Tchr, al Life Dir 1985-89; AMI Pres 1989-91; Biola Univ Theology Instr 4; Gordon Coll Dean of Chapel 1994-; *ai:* Svc Learning Comm; orce on Stu Volunteerism; Evangelical Theological Soc 1992-; Amer CHurch His, Amer Historical Assn 1994-; Articles Pub; Keynote r for Vision Ministries 1994; Natl Conf for Japanese-Amer Stdnts ts for Christ 1993; West Coast Conf for Korean-Amer Stdnts; Tchr y Class of 1993; *office:* Gordon Coll 255 Grapevine Rd Wenham MA

TTON, RICHARD G., English Teacher; *b:* Portland, ME; *ed:* Colby A) Eng 1957; Wesleyan Univ (MALS) Lit 1970; Attnd Cornell Univ, d Univ, Wesleyan Univ, IN Univ, SUNY at Geneseo; *cr:* Hebron Eng, His Tchr 1960-73; Nichols Schl Eng, His Tchr 1973-; *ai:* al Information Test; Fac Adv Levithan; Amnesty Intl; Cum Laude Project Comm; Chm Nichols Schl Eng Dept 1984-91, Hebron Acad ept 1972-73; Phi Beta Kappa 1957-; Woodrow Wilson Fellowship NEH Fellowship IN Univ 1989, SUNY at Geneseo 1993; *office:* s Schl 1250 Amherst St Buffalo NY 14216*

UB, DONNA JEAN, Science Teacher; *b:* Woodbury, NJ; *m:* Fred III; wan St Coll (BA) PE & Chem 1989; *cr:* Woodbury HS Sci Tchr 1990; nstown HS Sci Tchr 1990-; *ai:* Weather Club & Stage Crew Club Achvmt Night & Expo Comm; AFT 1990-; NEA 1990-; *office:* nstown HS 561 Clayton Rd Williamstown NJ 08094

UB, ELSIE L., English Teacher; *b:* Danville, PA; *ed:* Bloomsburg BS) Scndry Eng 1964, (MED) Ed 1967; 6 Addl Grad Credit Hrs sville Univ & Wilkes Coll; 18 Addl Hrs; *cr:* West Snyder HS Eng 964-, Dept Head 1985-, Mem WS Discipline Comm; *ai:* Drama Club Musical Drama Dir; 7th & 9th Grd Co-Adv; Curr Coord Cncl; Play a Dir; Mid-west Ed 1964-, Pres; PSEA, Chprsn Several Comm; taville Wesleyan Church, Tchr, Sunday Schl Supt, PA- Jersey Cert of it;Seminar Presentor Christian Life & Ministries Convtn PA-Jersey Vesleyan Church; LAY Speaker; *office:* West Snyder HS RR 1 Box eaver Sprgs PA 17812*

UB, MARYBOB HOGENKAMP, Spanish Teacher; *b:* Lima, OH; nes Joseph; *c:* Kelly, Lara Rose; *ed:* John Carroll Univ (BA) Span 30 Grad Hrs Bowling Green St Univ; 12 Hrs Madrid Spain; 15 Hrs stituto Techologico y de Estudios Superiores de Monterrey Nuevo Mexico; *cr:* Leipsic HS Span & ESL Tchr 1979-80; Lima Central HS Span Tchr 1980-85; Ada HS Span Tchr 1985-90; Shawnee HS Tchr 1990-; *ai:* Spirit Club Asst Adv; Values & Ethics Cmte Co Chair; e Bio; Mexican Archeology Co Instr; OH Fgn Lang Assn 1980-; P 1980-; Lima Sister Cities Comm 1994-, Charter & Bd Mem; Lima Circles 1994-, Group Ldr; Article Pub; *office:* Shawnee Schls 3333 ehly Rd Lima OH 45806*

UCH, DAWN, Mathematics Teacher; *b:* Redbank, NJ; *cr:* St Mary's ath Tchr 1982-85; Keansburg HS Math Tchr 1985-; *ai:* NJEA 1985-; NJ 1989-; *office:* Keansburg HS 140 Port Monmouth Rd Keansburg 734

US, JOSEPH, Social Studies Teacher; *b:* Brooklyn, NY; *ed:* SUNY ts Coll (BS) Lbrl Arts 1989; CUNY Lehman Coll (MA) Soc Stud Post Grad Stud Ed Manhattan Coll; *cr:* USAF Logistics, Intell, ity 1965-88; Dewitt-Clinton HS ROTC Tchr 1988-94, His Tchr ; *ai:* UFT, AFT 1989-; Air Force Assn 1985-; Letters Awd; Articles *home:* 2600 Netherland Ave Apt 1802 Bronx NY 10463

USER, GEORGE J., General Music Teacher; *b:* Philadelphia, PA; san Knapp Parkyn; *c:* G. Andrew; *ed:* West Chester Univ (BS) Music 64, (MS) Music Ed; IN UNiv (MS) Music Opera; Post Grad Stud lair St Coll, Univ of IL, Oberlin Coll Conservatory; *cr:* Oley Valley horal Dir 1964-67; Wayne HS Choral Dir 1967-68; NOrthern Valley horal Dir 1968-75, 1978-83;Wallkill HS Choral Dir, Drama Tchr 95; Lept ondale Elem Schl Gen Music 1995-; *ai:* 5-6 Grd Dir Wide s; MENC 1964-; NYSSMA, AFT, WTA, NYSUT 1984-; Study at in Rockefeller Grant 1973; NHS Tchr of Yr 1974; Numerous Festivals Conductor; *office:* Leptondale Elem Schl 94 Mill St Wallkill NY

USER, NED C., Counselor; *b:* Lewistown, PA; *c:* Eric, Aaron; *ed:* ta Coll (BS) Psych 1967; PA St Univ (MED) Cnslng 1969; *cr:* amsport Area Comm Coll Cnslr 1970-74; Muncy St Correctional Fac ctions Cnslr 1974; White Deer Run Treatment Ctr Therapist 1974-75; Drug & Alcohol Agency Addictions Cnslr 1976-83; Corning Comm Cnslr 1983-; *ai:* Stu Ldrshp Prgm; Peer Helping Prgm; Fac Assn; Corning Comm Coll 1 Academic Dr Corning NY 14830*

AUSS, ANDREW M., Chemistry Teacher; *b:* Dexter, MO; *m:* Noelle nger; *c:* Heidi, Benjamin; *ed:* New England Coll (BS) Chem 1966; eyon Univ (MALS) Chem, Physics 1972; *cr:* Berlin HS Sci Tchr 67; Pelham HS Chem Tchr 1967-70; Somers HS Chem Tchr 1970-; oys & Girls Var Soccer Coach; Varsity Ath Against Substance Abuse; SFA; The Coll Bd Chem Consultant; Chem AP Grader; *office:* Somers t 139 Lincolndale NY 10540*

AUSS, JANICE LITTLE, Spanish Teacher; *b:* Pittsburgh, PA; *m:* frey; *c:* Micah, Alicia; *ed:* SUNY at Binghampton (BA) Span 1968, T) Span 1970; Post Grad Stud Nazareth Coll ESOL Cert; *cr:* uehanna Valley HS Span Tchr 1969-70; Union-Endicott Schls eteacher, Span Tchr 1970-88; Vestal Schls Hometeacher 1970-86; ego-Apalachin Schls Span Tchr 1988-; *ai:* Span Club Adv; Shared sion Making Team Chrprsn; NYSUT 1986-, Bldg Rep; NYSAFLT -, St Grant Chair; Delta Kappa Gamma 1994-; PTA 1979-, Pres, ime Membership, Distinguished Svc Awd; BSA 1989-, Merit Badge r; Union-Endicott Schls 1993-, Schl Bd Trustee; Hum Tchr Inst owship 1991; Tchr Recognition Awd; NYSAFLT Tchr Incentive Grant ; Article Pub 1996; *office:* Owego-Apalachin MS 100 Elm St Owego 13827*

AUSS, LINDA BROWER, Science Teacher; *b:* Rahway, NJ; *m:* Mark k; *c:* Samantha, Spencer, Tyler; *ed:* Douglass Coll (BS) Med Tech ; Rutgers Univ (MED) Sci Ed 1995; Addl 30 Credits Grad Work obiology; *cr:* Ortho Diagnostics Rsrch Scientist 1974-82; Hunterdon HS Sci Tchr 1990-; *ai:* Adv Sci Olympiad Team; NSTA, NABT -; ASCP 1974-, MT; Neshamic Church Consistory 1995-, Chprsn; Girl ts of Amer 1985-, Ldr; Geraldine R. Dodge Grant; Rudolph Awd Excl Tchng; Coaches Awd NJ Sci Olympiad; *office:* Huntedon Central onal HS 84 State Route 31 Flemington NJ 08822

AUSS, M. JOANNE, Mathematics Teacher; *b:* Bronx, NY; *ed:* nan Coll (BA) Math 1970, (MA) Math 1973; Post-Grad Stud Fordham , Wagner Coll & Mount St Vincent Coll; *cr:* Bronx HS of Sci Math Tchr 1970-; *ai:* Backgammon, Table Tennis & Thai Club; Ultimate Team; Earth Day Festival Coord; Frosh Math Team & NYC Math Team Coach; AFT & UFT 1971-; NCTM 1979-; Amer Bapt Womens Ministries of Metro 1980-, Love Gift Chprsn & Pres; Bapt Peace Flwshp 1989-, Regnl Coord for Metro; Oxfam Amer 1990-; LI Soundwatch 1992-; Governor Morris Awd for Environmental Ed 1996; *office:* Bronx HS Of Science 75 W 205th St Bronx NY 10468

STRAUSS, SARAH ANN, Former Social Studies Teacher; *b:* Washington, DC; *ed:* Amherst Coll (BA) Amer Stud 1988; Tufts Univ (MAT) Soc Stud 1993; Brandeis Univ PHD Candidate Soc Policy 1995-; *cr:* Newbury Coll Adj Eng Tchr 1993-94; Framingham HS Soc Stud Tchr 1994-95; *ai:* Gay, Straight Alliance Adv; MTA, NEA 1994-; Fulbright Grant Alternative Candidate 1993.

STRAWN, REGINA G., Math Teacher; *b:* Atlantic City, NJ; *m:* Jeffrey R.; *c:* Amanda; *ed:* Glassboro (BA) Ed 1980; *cr:* Mulica Twp MS 7th-8th Grd Math Tchr 1980-; *ai:* PAC Helper; Dance Coord; NEA 1980-; *office:* Mullica Township Primary Sch PO Box 318 Elwood NJ 08217*

STRAZZA, BRIAN ANTHONY, Science Teacher & Dept Chprsn; *b:* New York city, NY; *m:* Joan Marie; *c:* Jennifer Knill, Thomas; *ed:* Sprinfield Coll (BA) Bio 1968; SUNY at Stony Brook (MS) Ed 1973; 75 Addl Grad Credits; *cr:* Sachem Cntrl Schls Sci Tchr 1968, Dept Chprsn 1984-; *ai:* Vlybl Referee; NEA, SCTA 1968-; *office:* Sagamore Jr HS 57 Division St Holtsville NY 11742

STRAZZA, JOAN M., Math Teacher; *b:* New Rochelle, NY; *m:* Brian A.; *c:* Jennifer Strazza Knill, Thomas B.; *ed:* St Lawrence Univ (BS) Math 1967; SUNY at Stony Brook (MLS) Soc Stud 1980; 75 Addl Credit Hrs; *cr:* Lindenhurst Pub Schls Math Tchr 1967-69; Sachem Cntrl Schls Math Tchr 1969-78, 1980-; *ai:* Math Team Adv; Renaissance, Natl Jr Hnr Soc Comms; Girl Scout Ldr; Little League Sftbl Coach; *office:* Sagamore Jr HS 57 Division St Holtsville NY 11742*

STREET, ERIC P., Keyboard Studies Director; *b:* Newton, IA; *ed:* Cornell Coll (BM) Piano Performance 1975; IN Univ Schl of Music (MM) Piano Performance 1977, (DM) Piano Performance 1985; Post-Doctoral Stud Hochschule fur Musik at Vienna; *cr:* IN Univ Assoc Piano Instr 1977-81; Bethany Coll Distngd Prof of Music 1981-92; Univ of Dayton Keyboard Stud Dir 1992-; *ai:* MTNA 1981-; OMEA 1992-; Coll Music Society 1989-; OH Arts Cncl 1993-, Touring Artist; KS Arts Commission 1986-, Touring Artist; ISPE 1987-; Carnegie Recital Hall 1991; Japan Tour 1990; Russian Tour 1992; Egypt Tour 1994; Central Asian Tour 1995; Concerts in Paris, London, Florence, Rome, Salzburg, Prague, Brussels, Berlin 1995; Numerous Articles Pub; Book Chptr Pub; Music Tchrs Natl Assoc Master Tchr Cert; *office:* Univ Of Dayton 300 College Park Ave Dayton OH 45469*

STREETER, LINDA ELEANORE, High School English Teacher; *b:* Randolph, VT; *m:* Jonathan L. Harris; *c:* Alexandra Streeter Harris; *ed:* Bates Coll (BA) Eng 1974; Univ of VT Eng & Ed 30 Plus Grad Hrs 1975-; Saint Michaels Coll Eng & Ed 30 Plus Grad Hrs 1975-; *cr:* Milton HS Eng Tchr 1975-77; South Royalton Schl Jr HS Eng Tchr 1977-78; Mount Mansfield HS Eng Tchr 1978-; *ai:* Restructuring Comm; K-12th Grd Lang Arts Curr Dev Comm; Learning Lab Grant Steering Comm; VT-NEA 1976-; Green Mountain NEA 1977-; Friends of Brownell Lib, Dir; Tchr of Yr 1994-95.*

STREIBIG, JEAN C.,RSM, Math Teacher; *b:* Philadelphia, PA; *ed:* Villanova Univ (BA) Hum; St Louis Univ (MA) Math; *cr:* Merion Mercy Acad 5th Grd Tchr 1957-59; St Johns Schl 7th Grd Tchr 1959-60; St Pauls Schl 8th Grd Tchr 1960-62; Little Flower HS Math Tchr 1962-72; Merion Mercy Acad HS Math Tchr 1972-76; Archbishop Prendergast HS Math Tchr 1976-; *ai:* Asst Ath Dir; Cheerleading Coach; Archdiocesan HS Math Curr Comm; Archdiocesan Joint Elem Scndry Math Curr Comm; Math Dept Chrprsn 1977-85; NCEA, ATMOPAV; Archdio Charismatic Music Ministry; *office:* Archbishop Prendergast HS 401 N Lansdowne Ave Drexel Hill PA 19026

STREIFF, JEAN ANN CAPIZZI, English Teacher & Dept Chair; *b:* Philadelphia, PA; *m:* Charles J.; *c:* Matthew P.; *ed:* Duquesne Univ (BA) Eng 1965; Univ of Pittsburgh (MA) Rhetoric, Comm 1990; *cr:* Sumter HS Eng Tchr 1969; Sacred Heart HS Eng & Theatre Tchr 1971-89; Oakland Cath HS Eng & Theatre Tchr 1989-, Dept Chair 1993-; *ai:* Stu Cncl Moderator 1989-; NCTE 1990-; Speech Comm Assn 1986-, ECA Rep SCA Legislative Cncl; Eastern Comm Assn 1993-, ECA Rep Legislative Cncl; Speech Comm Assn of PA 1971-, Pres, VP, Carroll Arnold Distngd Svc Awd; Speech Comm Assn of PA Founding Mem Speech Comm Ed Comm; *office:* Oakland Catholic HS 144 N Craig St Pittsburgh PA 15213*

STREJECK, DONALD F., History, Govt Tchr & Dept Chm; *b:* Greensburg, PA; *m:* Rose; *c:* Karen Lucas, Donald, David, Douglas; *ed:* CA St Univ of PA (BS) Soc Stud 1959; CA St Univ of PA (MEd) Soc Stud 1968; Prins Cert; Govt Grant Asian Stud Western MD; Overseas Stud India; IN Univ of PA 14 Addl Credits; WV Univ Doctoral Prgm; *cr:* West Newton HS Prin 1 Yr & Tchr 1959-75; Yough Schl Dist Tchr & Dept Chm 1976-; *ai:* Local PSEA & NEA 1959-, Pres of Local; Local, St & Natl Realtors Assn 1984-; Stu Tchrs Dir & Mentor from CA Univ & IN Univ of PA; *office:* Yough Sr HS 99 Lowber Rd Herminie PA 15637*

STREKO, JOHN A., Environmental & Physics Tchr; *b:* Newark, NJ; *m:* Kathy Koetsch; *c:* Jason, Melanie; *ed:* Fairleigh Dickinson Univ (BS) Bio 1971; Montclair St Univ (MS) Environmental Sci 1979; *cr:* Upper Elem Schl 6-8th Grd Sci Tchr 1971-75; Long Vly MS 7-8th Grd Sci Tchr 1975-87; West Morris Cntrl HS Environmental Issues, Physics Tchr 1987-; *ai:* Girls Bsktbl Head Coach; La Crosse Asst Coach; Whale Watch Dir; Recycling Coord; NEA, NJEA 1971-; Regnl E. A. 1987-; Mine Hill Twp Planning Bd 1981-, Sec; Mine Hill Env Commission 1992-; Dodge Fnd Grant; Earth Ed Partnership, Tchr, Consultant; Unitarian EcoAction '95 Speaker, Panelist; Cause for Cause for Concern Bd of Dirs; *office:* West Morris Central H S Bartley Rd Chester NJ 07930*

STRELAU, NANCY PETTERSEN, Orchestra Director; *b:* Oak Park, IL; *m:* G. Paul; *ed:* Syracuse Univ (BM) Music Ed 1977; Univ of Miami (MM) Music Ed 1985; 1 Yr Towards DMA in Violin Performance; *cr:* Pocatello Schl Dist Tchr 1977-79; Comm Music Ctr Tchr 1980-83; Philharmonic Orch of FL Violinist 1984-86; Penfield HS Orch Dir 1986-; Fingerlakes Symphony Orch Music Dir & Conductor 1993-; *ai:* ASTA, MENC, NSOA & NEA; Rochester Philharmonic Awds Comm & Rochester Philharmonic Youth Orch Comm 1991-; Rochester Philharmonic Orch Outstanding Music Educators Awd 1991; Cndctr of Finger Lakes Symphny, Hochstein Yth Orch, Greater Rochester Women's Philharmonic; *office:* Penfield H S High School Dr Penfield NY 14526

STRELSER, JENNIFER JACOBS, Chemistry & AP Biology Teacher; *b:* Silver Spring, MD; *m:* Marc E.; *ed:* Franklin Marshall (BA) Bio 1988; Colgate Univ (MAT) Bio, Ed 1990; 18 Credit Hrs Chem; *cr:* Williamsport HS Chem, Bio Tchr 1992-; *ai:* Soc Comm; Class Adv; NSTA, NEA, WCTA 1992-; UNCF Grant Reader; *office:* Williamsport HS 5 S Clifton Dr Williamsport MD 21795*

STREMBA, M. RITA,OSBM Religious Studies Teacher; *b:* Reading, PA; *ed:* Immaculata Coll (BA) Ed 1958; Villanova Univ (MA) Theology 1968; LaSalle Univ (MA) Religious Stud, Scripture 1975; 6 Credit Hrs St Cert; *cr:* Thomas Ford Elem Schl 2nd Grd Tchr 1958-60; St Basil HS Acad 9th Grd Tchr 1964-65; St Peter & Paul Elem Schl First Grd Tchr 1965; St Basil Acad 9th-12th Grd Tchr, Dept Chprsn 1965-; *ai:* Frosh Class Moderator; Yth Minister; Philosophy Comm Chprsn; Rel Stud Chprsn; Act Comm; Eng Comm; NCEA 1975-; Eastern Cath Diocesan Dir of Rel Ed 1980-82; Manor Jr Coll 1989-, Bd of Trustees.

STRIANESE, ANTHONY JOHN, Culinary Arts Chprsn & Prof; *b:* Troy, NY; *m:* Pamela Phillips; *c:* Michael, Lawrence; *ed:* Bryant (BS) Mrktg 1967; Coll of Saint Rose (MS) Educl Psych 1980; Walt Disney World Coll Pgrm Ducktorate Degree; *cr:* Dewitt Clinton Hotel Banquet Mgr 1968-72; Rowntowner Motor Inn Food & Beverage Mgr 1972-74; Schenectady Cnty Coll Prof, Hotel & Tourism 1971-; *ai:* Walt Disney World, Inn at Shelbourne Farms Coord; Soc of Wine Edctrs,Cncl of Hotel, Restaurant Institutional Edctrs 1976-; NEA CADA Unit 1976-, Pres; Clifton Park Soccer Club 1979-, Sec; Albany Cty Convention & Visitors Bd of Dir 1993-; Schenectady Cty Tourism Bd 1991-; Text Author; Software; Video's Author; *office:* Schenectady County Comm Coll 78 Washington Ave Schenectady NY 12305

STRICKBERGER, FRANCES EVANS, English Teacher; *b:* Wilmington, DE; *m:* Harold Paul; *c:* Daniel, Matthew, Adam; *ed:* Univ of DE (BA) Theatre Arts & Eng 1953; Rider Univ (MA) Lang Arts & Rdng Specialist 1981; 6 Post Grad Hrs at Univ of PA; 6 Post Grad Hrs at Rutgers Univ; Attnd Trenton St; *cr:* Newspaper Reporter Part-Time 1948-52; New Castle Spcl Schl Dist Eng Tchr 1953-56; Morrisville Schl Dist Eng Tchr 1969-; *ai:* Spon Class of 1976; PYEA Adv 1972-; DSEA 1953-56; NEA 1969-; PSEA 1969-; Ymca; Synogogue; Morrisville HS Tchr of the Yr 1985; *office:* Morrisville Middle Sr HS Palmer Ave Morrisville PA 19067*

STRICKER, KATHLEEN KAPICA, 4th Grade Teacher; *b:* S Amboy, NJ; *m:* Gerald; *c:* Gregory, Glen, Gary; *ed:* Glassboro St Coll (BA) Ed, Home Ec 1976, Elem Ed 1987, Tchr of Nursery Schl 1987; *cr:* Sayerville HS Home Ec Tchr 1977-78; Matawan Regnl HS Home Ec Tchr 1978-79; Eisenhower Schl Math Basic Skills Tchr 1988-89; Truman Schl 4th Grd Tchr 1989-; *ai:* NEA 1987-; SEA 1987-; AMTNJ 1995-; SWMHS Band Parents Assn 1992-, E-Bd, By-Laws; *office:* Harry S Truman Schl 1 Taft Pl Parlin NJ 08859

STRICKHART, ROBERT ALAN, Environmental Science Teacher; *b:* Jersey City, NJ; *m:* Sandra L. Ogg; *c:* Peggy, James, Robert Jr.; *ed:* Jersey City St (BA) Geology, Earth Scis 1973; *cr:* Keansburg Jr Sr HS Earth Sci Tchr 1973-82; Franklin HS Envir Scis Tchr 1982-; *ai:* NJEA, NEA 1973-; FOHBCC 1985-; AT&T Tech Grant 1995-; Author of WED Rutgers Univ Curr Dev; *office:* Franklin HS 415 Francis St Somerset NJ 08873

STRICKLAND, BRIDGET FRANCES, Math Teacher; *b:* Quonset Point, RI; *ed:* Univ of RI (BS) Applied Math 1981; Post Grad 6 Credit Hrs Univ of Southern ME Exceptionality; *cr:* New Market HS Math Tchr 1984-86; Kennebunk HS Math Tchr 1986-; *ai:* NHS Selection Comm; NEA, MTA, KKEA 1986-; *office:* Kennebunk HS 89 Fletcher St Kennebunk ME 04043

STRICKLAND, DEBORAH ANN COVER, First Grade Teacher; *b:* Marietta, OH; *c:* Stephanie M., Richard L. II; *ed:* Lynchburg Coll (BS) Hlth, PE 1970; Bowie St Univ (APC) Early Chldhd Ed 1988; Attnd Trinity Coll at Washington, Troy St Univ; *cr:* Guam Pub Schls 10th-12th Grd PE Tchr 1970-71; Montgomery Co Bd of Ed 5th-6th Grd, 8th-9th Grd Eng Tchr, 7th-9th Grd PE Tchr 1971-74; Newton Co Bd of Ed 1st-5th Grd Elem PE Tchr 1974-75; Big Bend Comm Coll Mth, Eng, Rdng Tchr 1978-79; GBCS Private Schl Dir, Prsnl Dir, K Tchr 1983-87; Charles Co Pub Schls Kndgtn, 1st Grd Tchr 1987-; *ai:* Rdng Task Force Chprsn; Team Ldr; Chrldng Coach; Children of NATO Forces in Belgium Swim Team Coach; Soc Comm; Union Rep; NEA, MSTA, EACC 1988-; Grace Bapt Church 1982-, Sunday Schl Tchr; 5th Grd Grad Guest Speaker; Pilot Open Ed Prgm; *office:* C. Paul Barnhart Elem Schl 5800 Lancaster Cir Waldorf MD 20603

STRICKLIN, REBECCA ELLEN, Chemistry Teacher; *b:* New Albany, IN; *ed:* OH Univ (BS) Chem, Math Ed 1974, (MS) Inorganic Chem 1976; Univ of Cincinnati (EDD) Sci Ed 1993; OH St Univ Hydrobiology Field Stud 1983; Princeton Univ Woodrow Wilson Fellow Dreyfus Master Tchr 1985; Miami Univ Indstrl Partnerships 1988-; Univ of Cinnati Curr & Supervision Cert 1990; *cr:* Cincinnati Tech Coll Visiting Instr 1978-82; Miami Univ Visiting Instr 1989-; Oak Hill HS Chem Tchr 1976-; *ai:* Sci Club Adv; JETS, Sci Bowl, Sci Olympical, OESPER Coach; Venture Capital Gain, Bldg Renovation, Sci Curr Comms; Amer Chemical Soc 1974-, Ed Comm Chair, 2nd VP, Sec, Tchr Awd at Sectional, Regnl Level; NSTA, St SECO 1976-, Local Safety Comm Chair; OH Acad of Sci 1976-, VP, Chair SW Cncl, Krecher Awd, Achvmt Awd; NEA, OEA, OHEA 1976-; Westwood First Presbyn 1976-, Elder, Deacon, Circle Chair, Comms; Presbynt of Cincinnati 1976-, G A Comm, Comms; Oak Hill PTA 1976-, 2nd VP; Tandy Tech Scholar; Chemical Man Assoc Catalyst Awd; Dreyfus Outreach Grants; Amer Chemical Soc Grants; *office:* Oak Hills HS 3200 Ebenezer Rd Cincinnati OH 45248*

STRICKMAN, LEO, Drama Director; *b:* New York, NY; *m:* Marjorie Newmark; *c:* Michael (dec), Peter, Bonnie; *ed:* Loyola Univ at New Orleans 2 Yrs; Rutgers Univ at New Brunseick 2 Yrs; *cr:* Elbe File Binder Co Inc Sec of Corp 1935-70; Union Bookbinding Co Inc VP Sales 1970-90; Little Theatre of Fall River Actor, Dir 1945-95; Sacred Heart Acad Drama Coach 1960-62; Somerset HS Drama Dir 1962-67; Biship Connolly HS Drama Dir 1990-; Bristol Comm Coll Tennis Coach 1989-; *ai:* YMCA 1952-, Bd of Dir; Mental Hlth Ctr 1986-, Bd of Dir; Park Commissioner, 2 Mayors; Comm Svc Awd 1992 Chamber of Comm; Person of the Month Awd, Mayor's Office; *office:* Bishop Connolly HS 373 Elsbree St Fall River MA 02720

STRIDACCHIO, DONNA MARIE, Mathematics Teacher; *b:* Newark, NJ; *ed:* Seton Hall (BS) Accounting 1979; Montclair St Coll (MA) Admin & Supervision 1992; *cr:* First Natl St Bank Trust & Estate Accountant 1979-82; Nivingston HS Math Tchr 1982-83; Barringer HS Math Tchr 1983-; *ai:* Math Club, Acad Decathlon & NHS Adv; Beautification Club; Schl Mentor; AFT, Newark Assn of Math Educators 1983-; *office:* Barringer HS 90 Parker St Newark NJ 07104*

STRIETBECK, ELIZABETH, French Teacher; *b:* Cumberland, MD; *m:* Arthur III; *c:* Daniel; *ed:* Frostburg St Univ (BA) Frgn Lang, Ed 1991; 6 Credit Hrs Toward MA; *cr:* Mt Savage Schl Fr Tchr 1991-; *ai:* NHS, Fr Club Adv; NEA, ACTA, ACTFL 1991-; Ray Kroc Tchr Awd; *office:* Mt Savage Schl 13201 New School Rd NW Mount Savage MD 21545

STRIEWSKI, EDWARD P., Fifth Grade Teacher; *b:* Camden, NJ; *m:* Lois A.; *ed:* Morris Harvey Coll (BA) Ed, Music & His 1974; Western CT St Coll (MS) Ed & His 1976; Eng Writing, Spec Ed & His Courses; *cr:* New Milford Pub Schls 3rd, 5th Grd & K-3rd Grd Music Tchr 1974-1986; Woolwich Cntrl Schl 7th & 8th Grd Lang Arts & Soc Stud Tchr 1988-95, 5th Grd Tchr 1995-; *ai:* Yrbk Adv; Chorus Accompanist; Tchr Assn Pres; NEA 1974-; MEA, Woolwich Tchrs Assn 1987-; Local Church, Organist 9 Yrs; CT Tchr of Yr; *home:* RR 1 Box 535 Woolwich ME 04579

STRIFE, DAVID, Biology Teacher; *b:* Owensboro, KY; *m:* Nancy Ralston; *c:* Emily; *ed:* Dartmouth Coll (AB) Bio 1969; Montclair St Univ (MA) Bio 1980; Supervision & Admin 24 Credits; Methods of Tchng 8 Credits; *cr:* South Royalton HS Bio, Chem, Physics Tchr 1969-70; Port Hacking HS Bio Tchr 1970-72; Paterson Cath HS Bio, Physics Tchr, Dept Chair 1972-75; Tenafly HS Bio, Chem, Phys Sci Tchr, Dept Chair 1975-; *ai:* Schl Newspaper Adv; NEA, BEA, TEA, NSTA 1975-; AAAS, NJSSA 1993-; Dartmouth Club of Northern NJ 1975-, Pres 1993-95; Fulbright Tchr Exch Scotland 1985; Article Pub 1982; Governor's Awd for Excl in Tchng 1987; Outstdng Tchng Awd MIT, Univ of Chicago, Dartmouth, Brown, Princeton,

John Hopkins, Tafts; *office:* Tenafly HS 500 Columbus Dr Tenafly NJ 07670*

STRINE, HARRY CORNELIUS,III, Communication Professor; *b:* Danville, PA; *m:* Mary Ann Bolig; *c:* Harry C. IV, Sean Bolig; *ed:* Susquehanna Univ (BA) Eng 1964; Ohio Univ (MA) Speech 1969; *cr:* Shamokin Area HS Speech & Eng Tchr 1966-70; Bloomsburg Univ Instr, Asst & Assoc Prof 1970-; *ai:* Dir of Forensics; Pi Kappa Delta Adv; Pi Kappa Delta 1970-, Governor of Province of Colonies; SCAP 1970-; SCA 1975-; NFA 1976-; CFA 1980-, Pres, Coach of Yr; Elks 1964-; *office:* Bloomsburg Univ Of PA Dept of Commnctn Stud 400 E 2nd St Bloomsburg PA 17815

STRINE, JAMES ARTHUR,II, Biology Teacher; *b:* Carlisle, PA; *m:* Trudy Jean; *c:* Nadeen Jeanette; *ed:* Dickinson Coll (BS) Bio 1971; Shippensburg Univ (MS) Bio 1975; Attnd Various Colls & Univs Numerous Courses; *cr:* Mechanicsburg HS Bio I & Electronics Tchr 1971-72; Carlisle Area Schl Dist 10th-12th Grd Bio II & Chem Tchr 1972-73, 7th Grd Life Sci Tchr 1973-79, 10th-12th Grd Bio I & Bio II Tchr 1979-; *ai:* NHS Faculty Cncl & Local Chapter Chm; Natl Network for Implementing Human Genetics & Bioethics into Scndry Bio; Carlisle Area Sci Advisory Comm 1978-, Schlsp Comm Chm 1986, Prgm Comm Chm 1983; Area Newspaper Tchr of Yr Awd Finalist 1986; Shippensburg Univ Schl Stud Cncl Outstanding Tchr Guest Lecturer Awd 1991-92; Mem of Writing Team Awarded St Cmptr Grant; One of Sr Class Top 5 Favorite Tchrs; *office:* Carlisle West H S 723 W Penn St Carlisle PA 17013

STRITTMATTER, CHRISTINE MARIE, Second-Third Grade Tchrs Aid; *b:* Syracuse, NY; *m:* David Richard; *c:* Samuel David, Alison Joy; *ed:* Cumberland Cty Coll (AA) Liberal Arts General 1983; Glassboro St Coll (BA) Home Ec 1988; *cr:* Fairton Chrstn Ctr Acad Kndgtn Tchr & Jr & Sr High Vlybl Coach 1981-83; Childcare in my Home, Caretaker of my own Child & others 1991-93; Fairton Chrstn Ctr Acad Second & Third Grd Tchrs Aid 1993-94; Kndgtn & First Grd Tchr 1994-; Jr & Sr High Vllybl Coach; *ai:* Vlybl Referee; Church Ministries Prayer Chain & Sub Sunday Schl Tchr; *home:* 216 W Butler Ave Vineland NJ 08360

STRITTMATTER, JOHN, Chemistry Teacher; *b:* New Bedford, MA; *m:* Rosalie L. Peirce; *c:* Robin L. Soares, Gayle E.; *ed:* Bridgewater St Coll (BA) Bio 1967; Worcester Polytechnical Inst (MNS) Natural Sci 1974; Univ of MA at Darmouth 6 Hrs; Brigewater St Coll 26 Hrs; *cr:* Keith Jr HS Tchr 1967-69; New Bedford HS Tchr 1970-; *ai:* MEA, MTA 1967-; NBEA 1967-, Pres; *office:* New Bedford HS 230 Hathaway Blvd New Bedford MA 02745

STROH, DAVID A., Mathematics Teacher; *b:* Saint Marys, OH; *m:* Lisa M. Ferguson; *ed:* Miami Univ (BS) Ed 1985; The OH St Univ (MA) Math 1990; *cr:* Fairbanks Schls Math & Cmptr Tchr 1986-88; OH St Univ Tchng Asst 1988-89; Covington Exempted Illage Math Tchr 1990-; *ai:* Jr HS Cross Cntry Coach; HS Jr Var Girls Bsktbl Coach; HS Track Asst Coach; Jr Class Adv 1996; NCTM 1993-; NEA & OEA 1986-; CEA 1990-, Pres; *office:* Covington HS 807 Chestnut Covington OH 45318

STROHM, GLENDA KAY (LOUIS), Fourth Grade Teacher; *b:* Bucyrus, OH; *ed:* OH St Univ (BS) Elem Ed 1980; Ashland Univ, Bowling Green Univ, Univ of Toledo Addl Grad Courses; *cr:* Surrounding Schls Sub Tchr 4 Yrs; Wynford Local Schls 3rd Grd Tchr 1 Yr, 4th Grd Tchr 11 Yrs; *ai:* Labor-Mngmt Comm; NEA, OEA 1984-; WEA 1984-, Pres 1992-94, Schlsp Comm; Grace United Meth Church 1993-; Wynford Acad Boosters 1990-; Crawford Cty Intnl Rdng Assn 1984-, Treas 1987-88; *office:* Wynford Intermediate Schl 4401 State Route 19 Bucyrus OH 44820

STROHM, JANE PENNYBAKER, Mathematics Teacher; *b:* Frankfort, Germany; *m:* James Lee; *c:* James Jonathan, Joshua David, Jeffrey Jacob; *ed:* Millerville Univ (BS) 1969, (MED) 1973; Grad Credits Wilkes Coll, Lehigh Univ; Other Courses Muhlenburg, Beaver Colls; *cr:* William Penn Sr HS Math Tchr 1969-70; Conestoga Valley HS Math Tchr 1970-73; Central Bucks East HS Math, Cmptr, Sci Tchr 1973-; *ai:* NCTM 1972-; NEA, PSEA, CBEA 1973-; South Jr Comm Network 1990-, Vol Coord; West Rockhill PTO 1990-93, Pres 1990-92; Deibler PTO 1983-90, Pres 1986-89; St Stephen's UCC Consistory 1994-, Chm Flwshp, Svc Div; *office:* Central Bucks-East HS PO Box 405 Buckingham PA 18912

STROLLO, MICHAEL ANGELO, Social Studies Teacher; *b:* Batavia, NY; *m:* Flora Jeanne Mari; *c:* Christina Strollo Amendina, Michael III, Danielle; *ed:* SUNY at Brockport (BA) Pol Sci 1970; Georgian Court Coll (MA) Ed 1993; 12 Hrs in Admin; *cr:* Asbury Park MS 5th Grd Tchr 1992; Ramtown Elem 7th-8th Grd Soc Stud Tchr 1992-94; Howell Township MS Soc Stud Tchr 1994-; *ai:* Cross Cntry Coach; Stock Market Club Adv; Soc Stud Curr Comm; NEA 1992-; TORCH Inst; *office:* Howell Township MS 501 Squankum Yellowbrook Rd Farmingdale NJ 07727

STROM, GREGORY LAWRENCE, Fine Arts Dept Head & Instr; *b:* Camden, ME; *ed:* Univ of ME at Farmington (BS) Spec Ed 1984; Cert Hlth; Post Grad Photo; Working on Fine Arts Degree; *cr:* Bonum Eagle HS Spec Ed Tchr 1984; Hope Elem Schl Spec Ed Tchr 1985; Fryeburg Acad Tchr 1986-; *ai:* Yrbk; Musical Dir; Fine Arts Dept Head; Dorm Parent; *office:* Fryeburg Acad 152 Main St Fryeburg ME 04037

STROMAN, CLYDE BRADLEY, Art Teacher; *b:* Harrisburg, PA; *m:* Patricia Ellen Gruber; *c:* David Bradley; *ed:* Kutztown Univ (BS) Art Ed 1972-; 30 Hrs Post Grad Millersville Univ & Penn St Univ; *cr:* Lower Dauphin Schl Dist Elem Art Tchr 1972-80, Scndry Art Tchr 1980-; *ai:* Past Natl Art Honor Soc Chapter Co-Adv 1983-91, Dept Coord 1994-95; NEA, PSEA 1980-; NAEA, PAEA 1983-; Freemasonry 1980-; Art Assoc of Harrisburg, Colored Pencil Soc of Amer 1990-; Natl Recipient Marie Walsh Sharpe Art Fnd & Natl Art Ed Assn Artist-Tchr Awd 1990; Artwork Pub for Natl Dist; *home:* 2086 Rhoda Ave Mount Joy PA 17552

STROMAN, ROGER JOE, 8th Grade Civics Teacher; *b:* Garrett, IN; *m:* Kathleen M. Slater; *c:* Michele, Tricia, David; *ed:* IN Univ (BA) Soc Stud & Amer His 1967, (MAT) Amer His 1971; *cr:* Lorain Cty Schls Amer His, Map Skills, Geography & Civics Tchr 1968-; *ai:* Site-Based Core Decision Making Comm; NEA, OEA, NEOEA, LEA 1968-; BSA, Learning for Life; *office:* Lorain MS 602 Washington Ave Lorain OH 44052

STROMGREN, DIANE COMPEAU, Third Grade Teacher; *b:* Ogdensburg, NY; *m:* Daniel Robert; *c:* Kristen, Jason; *ed:* SUC at Potsdam (BA) Psych 1974, (MS) Elem Ed 1981; 20 Addl Hrs; *cr:* Lisbon Cntrl Schl K-5th Grd PSEN Math Tchr, K-3rd Grd Integraded Classroom Tchr 1974-; *ai:* NYSUT, AFT 1974-; *office:* Lisbon Central Schl 6866 Cty Rt 10 Lisbon NY 13658

STRONACH, MARY SAPORETTI, Spanish Teacher; *b:* Italy; *m:* Robert; *c:* Rondi, Tere-Jeanne, James, Alexander, Anthony; *ed:* Coll of St Rose (BA) Span, Ed 1971; 40 Addl Hrs; *cr:* Sauquoit Vly HS Span Tchr 1971-84; Mohawk Vly Comm Coll Adj, Span Tchr 1979-93; Utica's John F. Kennedy HS Span Tchr 1986-87; Whitesboro HS Span Tchr 1987-; *ai:* Teen AIDS Task Force Adv; Intnl Club Co-Adv; Design, Layout, Writer Schl Publications; Discipline Comm; Conflict Mediator; AFT, NEA, NYSUT, 1971-; Whitesboro Tchrs Assn 1987-; Frgn Lang Hnr Soc 1985-; NYS Frgn Lang Tchrs Assn 1971-; Amer Cncl of Tchng of Frgn Langs 1995-; Rel Tchr 1993-; Salvation Army Advy Bd 1986-; Woman of Merit in Mohawk Vly 1986; 1 of Top 5 All-Star Tchrs Mohawk Vly 1992; Extra Mile Awd Cooperative Extension 1995; Writing Awds Articles, Videos; *office:* Whitesboro HS 6000 State Rt 291 Marcy NY 13403*

STRONG, J. ANTHONY, Assistant Professor; *b:* Calgary Alberta, Canada; *ed:* Univ of Calgary (BM) Piano Performance 1970; IN Univ (MM) Piano Performance 1974; 2 Yrs Towards Piano DM 1974-76; *cr:* Montserrat Schl of Music & the Arts Founder, Dir, Instr 1976-87; Raritan Valley Comm Coll Adj Prof 1985-95, Asst Prof 1996; *ai:* Music Area Coord; Adj Mentor; Fac, Stu Recital Coord; Accompanying; Coaching; AFT 1991-; *office:* Raritan Valley Comm Coll PO Box 3300 Somerville NJ 08876

STRONG, RAYMOND WILLIAM, Biology Teacher; *b:* Indiana, PA; *m:* Lois M. Shontz; *c:* Mark, Todd, David; *ed:* Edinboro St Coll (BS) Ed 1964; St Univ Coll at Buffalo (MS) Ed, Bio 1967; 6 Credit Hrs Canisius Coll; 21 Credit Hrs Niagara Univ; *cr:* Lewiston-Porter Cntrl Schl Tchr 1964-; *ai:* Hnr Soc; Key Club; Lewiston-Porter United Tchrs, NYSUT, AFT 1964-; Sci Tchr Assn of NY St 1970-; Kiwanis Club 1983-, Pres 1996; Lew-Port All Sports Boosters 1985-, Pres, Treas; *office:* Lewiston Porter Sr HS 4061 Creek Rd Youngstown NY 14174

STROUD, DIANA WIECHMAN, Mathematics Teacher; *b:* Cincinnati, OH; *m:* James B. III; *ed:* OH St Univ (BS) Math Ed 1992; Grad of OH Math-Sci Project Discovery; *cr:* Mason MS Math Tchr 1992-; *ai:* Advy Cncl Mem for Highter Ability Stdnts; Miami Univ Clinical Fac Comm; NCTM 1991-; NEA, MEA 1992-; *office:* Mason MS 707 Mason-Montgomery Rd Mason OH 45040

STROUD, JUDY GRAVES, Mathematics Teacher; *b:* Mount Clemens, MI; *m:* David; *c:* Brian, Jesse; *ed:* MI Chrstn Coll (AA) Liberal Arts 1973; OK Chrstn Coll (BSE) Math Ed 1975; Bowling Green St Univ (ME) Scndry Ed 1991; *cr:* Choctaw HS Math Tchr 1977-80; Lakota HS Math Tchr 1986-93; Northwood HS Math Tchr 1994-; *ai:* Discipline & Right to Read Comms; OCTM; NCTM; NEA; Perrysburg Church of Christ 1989-, Teen adv, Ladies Group Comm; *office:* Northwood HS 700 Lemoyne Northwood OH 43619

STROUT, DAVID CARROLL, Anatomy & Physiology Teacher; *b:* Lorain, OH; *m:* P. Sidney Houck; *ed:* Wilmington Coll (BS) Botany 1976; Bowling Green St Univ (MED) Scndry Ed 1978; Univ of MI Cryptogammic Botany; *cr:* San Joaquin Outdoor Schl 1976-77; Abington Friends Schl HS Sci Tchr 1980-86; Warren Hills Regnl SD HS Anatomy & Physiology AP Bio 1986-; *ai:* Master Stained Glass Craftsman; Olympic-Style Weightlifter, Highland Games Ath; NEA, NJEA, WHREA 1980-; Amer Bryological & Lichenological Soc 1977-; Rel Soc of Friends 1972-; Loyal Order of Moose 1978-; Mosses of Lake Erie Islands; Pres Environmental Yth Awd; Stu Tchr Mentor; *office:* Warren Hills Regnl Schl Dist 41 Jackson Vly Rd Washington NJ 07882*

STRUBBE, JON SCOTT, Mathematics Teacher; *b:* Cleveland, OH; *m:* Betsy Reed; *c:* David, Andy; *ed:* Mt Union Coll (BS) Math 1969; *cr:* Roberts Jr High Math Tchr 1969-84; Cuyahoga Falls HS Math Tchr 1984-; *ai:* CFEA, OEA & NEA 1969-; Cuyahoga Fallas Jaycees 1981-83; Cuyahoga Falls Tchr of Month September 1989 & Educator of Yr 1991-92; Tchr of Yr 1994-95; *home:* 2341 N Haven Blvd Cuyahoga Falls OH 44223

STRUBEL, ELIZABETH BRILL, Assistant Principal; *b:* Rockville Center, NY; *m:* James Robert; *ed:* Marywood Coll (BA) Art Ed 1969; Antioch Univ (MFA) Ceramics 1981; John Hopkins Univ Admin, Supervision Cert; *cr:* Sligo Jr HS Art Tchr, Chprsn 1969-73; John F. Kennedy HS Art Tchr 1973-87; Quince Orchard HS Arts Resource Tchr 1987-92, Asst Prin 1992-; *ai:* Founded Bus Partnership; Mentoring, Peer Mediation Prgm; Arts, Sci dept Supv Fine, Practical Arts; NEA, MCEA, MSTA 1969-; NCASSP, SSAA, NASSP 1992-; Hewlett Packard 1992-, Natl Schlshp Review Bd; Staff Mem of Yr 1989; Outstndng Tchr Summer Schlsp RI Schl of Design; Ceramic Work Galleries Ny, MD; One Man Show MD 1981; *office:* Quince Orchard HS 15800 Quince Orchard Rd Gaithersburg MD 20878*

STRUBLE, TERRY W., Physics Teacher; *b:* Latrobe, PA; *ed:* Grove City Coll (BS) Physics, Sec Ed 1991; 33 Credits Admin Westminster Coll; *cr:* Grove City HS Physics Tchr 1992-; *ai:* PSEA 1992-, Bldg Rep; NEA 1992-; *office:* Grove City HS 511 Highland Ave Grove City PA 16127

STRUCKMAN, ELIZABETH ZINK, English Teacher; *b:* Dayton, OH; *m:* Steven P.; *ed:* Wright St Univ (BS) Eng 1975; Univ of Dayton (ME) Rdng Specialist 1981; Prof Writing Cert Wright St 1986; OH Writing Project 1990; *cr:* Ferguson Jr HS Eng, Rdng Tchr 1976-86; Digital Tech Inc Tech Writer 1986-88; Bridgetown Jr HS Eng, Rdng Tchr 1988-; *ai:* Vlybl Coach 1976-77; Drill Team Adv 1977-78; Chrldr Adv 1978-81; Hnr Roll Comm 1978-86; Wrestlerette Adv 1988-90; Natl Jr Hnr Soc Adv 1988-93; Just Say No Adv 1991-94; BEA 1976-86; OHEA 1988-96; *office:* Bridgetown Jr HS 3900 Race Rd Cincinnati OH 45211

STRUMBEL, BARBARA ANN, English Teacher & Dept Chair; *b:* Cleveland, OH; *ed:* Bowling Green St Univ (BS) Eng 1961; Post BA Ed 1968; Purdue Grad Credit Eng 1970; *cr:* Willoughby Jr HS Tchr 1965-73; Eastlake North HS Tchr 1973-; *ai:* Acad Decathlon Coach; NHS Adv; NCTE, WETA, OEA, NEA 1965-; Jennings Scholr; Tchr of Yr 1978; Composition Lesson Plans BGSU Publication; *office:* Eastlake North HS 34041 Stevens Blvd Eastlake OH 44095

STRUNK, BRUCE RICHARD, HS Physical Education Teacher; *b:* Abington, PA; *m:* Lee Marie Bacon; *ed:* West Chester Univ (BS) Hlth, PE 1989; Working on Masters Towson St Univ; *cr:* Patterson HS Head Wrestling Coach 1989-90; Polytechnic Inst Tchr, Ftbl, Wrestling Coach 1990-95; Northern HS Head Ftbl Coach 1995-; *ai:* Weight Trng; AFT 1989-; MA St Ftbl Coachs Assn 1990-; Balto Touchdown Club 1996, Admin Comm; *office:* Baltimore Polytechnic Inst 1400 W Cold Spring Ln Baltimore MD 21209*

STRZYZ, RONALD EDWARD, English Instructor; *b:* Buffalo, NY; *m:* Barbara Warren; *c:* Karen, Mark, Brian; *ed:* Canisius Coll (BA) Eng 1965, (MS) Ed 1969; Buffalo St Coll (SDS) Admin 1989; Driver Ed Certfd; 60 Addl Grad Hrs; *cr:* Bishop Fallon Instr 1965-75; Bishop Turner Instr 1975-80; St Josephs CI Instr 1980-; *ai:* IM Moderator; NCET 1965-; Phi Delta Kappa 1989-; Outstdng Scndry Edctr of Amer; Outstdng Diocesan Tchr; *office:* Saint Josephs Coll Inst 845 Kenmore Ave Buffalo NY 14223

STUART, KENNETH PELHAM, Dept of History Head; *b:* Knoxville, TN; *m:* Mary June Gillilan; *c:* Margaret June Flood, Douglas Guy; *ed:* Furman Univ (BA) His, Pol Sci 1946; Penn St Univ (MA) His, Pol Sci; Univ of SC His, Pol Sci 30 Hrs; *cr:* Fishburne Military Acad Tchr, Coach 1949-51; Carson Long Military Inst Tchr, Coach, Soc Stud Dept Head, Commantant of Cadets, Asst to Pres 1951-; *ai:* Org of Amer Historians 1952-; Alpha Kappa Phi; Phi Beta Kappa; Phi Alpha Gamma; VFW 1946-; Seven Articles Pub; Envel Awd for His; *office:* Carson Long Military Inst 200 N Carlisle New Bloomfld PA 17068

STUART, WENDY BROSS, Musician & Ethnomusicologist; *b:* Yonkers, NY; *m:* Ronald C.; *c:* Fiona, Jessica; *ed:* Mc Gill Univ (AM) Piano Performance 1966, (BA) Fr, Music 1969; Univ of BC (MMUS) Ethnomusicology 1972; Prof Tchng Cert 1980; Advanced Tchng License; *cr:* Comm Music Schl of Vancouver Music Tchr 1972-74; YMCA Coll of Langs Eng Tchr 1974-76; Convent of Sacred Heart Music Dir 1976-79; Saku HS Eng Tchr 1988-89; York House Sr Schl Music Dir 1980-94; *ai:* BC Coll of Tchrs 1990-; Judith Marcuse Dance Co 1995-, Bd Mem; Holocaust Ed Assn 1995-, Mem; Canada Cncl Grant; Book: Gambling Music of the Coast Salish Indians 1972, Northern Haida Songs 1996; Choral Arrangements Pub; *home:* 411 W 49th Ave Vancouver BC V5Y 2Z9 Canada CN

STUBER, ANN MARCHIONDA, Spanish Teacher; *b:* Pacentro, Italy; *m:* Ronald; *c:* Jennifer Lynn, Amanda Marie; *ed:* Youngstown St Univ (AB) Span, Italian, Scndry Ed 1971, (MS) Span, Scndry Ed 1976; Attnc Univ, FL St Univ; 30 Addl Hrs; *cr:* Hamilton Local Schls Su 1971-72; Youngstown St Univ Frgn Lang Lab Supvr 1972-73; Aus Fitch HS Span Tchr 1973-, Italian Tchr 1973-91; *ai:* Italian Cl 1973-91; NEA, OEA, AEA 1973-; *office:* Fitch HS 225 Id Austintown OH 44515

STUBER, KRISTINA JANE, First Grade Teacher; *b:* Coatesville, Bucknell Univ (BS) Elem Ed, Music 1976; MA Equivalency +1 Cr Kings Hwy Elem Schl 2nd Grd Tchr 1977-78; Caln Elem Schl 1st G 1978-; *ai:* Schoolwide Theme Comm Chprsn 1995-; Piano Accor Elem 4th-5th Grd Choruses; Grd Level Chprsn 1990-95; PSEA 1976-; Olivet United Meth Church, Childrens Choir Dir; West Ch Barley Sheaf Players Theatre 1986-, Recording Sec, Music Dir Accompanist; Pvt Piano Instr; Positive Tchr Awd; Outstdng Svc Aw Chester & Barley Sheaf Players Outstdng Music Svc Awd; *ho* Winterberry Dr Downingtown PA 19335

STUBINSKI, JULIA A., Science Teacher & Dept Chair; *b:* Phoen PA; *ed:* West Chester U (BS) Scndry Ed, Earth, Space Sci 1974, Phys Sci 1994; 6 Hrs FL Inst of Tech; 6 Hrs Penn St Univ; 30 Ad *cr:* Coatesville Schl Dist Sci, Earth, Space Tchr 20 Yrs, Dept Chair *ai:* Sci Chair; NEA, PSEA, CATA 1975-, Pres, Adv Bd; NSTA 1978- 1990-; Phila Zoological Soc 1980-; Pilot Prgm Pub 1982; Honored Bd for PA Sci Olympiad Work; *office:* Coatesville Area School Di E Lincoln Hwy Coatesville PA 19320

STUCK, MARK KEVIN, PE Teacher & Drivers Ed Instr; *b:* St OH; *m:* Lisa Ann Mc Michael; *c:* Jared, Gabriel, Julia; *ed:* Olivet Na Univ (BS) PE 1982; Started MS Wright St Univ; *cr:* Paulding Ex Schls PE Tchr 1987-; *ai:* HS Ftbl, Head Boys Track Coach; NE Paulding Ed Assns 1987-; Nazarene Church 1970-; Natl Outstdn Awd Nom 1993; *home:* 151 Lakeview Dr Defiance OH 43512

STUCKEY, DAVE BRUCE, Social Studies Teacher; *b:* Van Wert, Brenda Lee Downend; *c:* Jared, Jenna; *ed:* Wright St (BA) Soc Stuc Attnd Hanover Coll & Univ of Cincinnati; *cr:* Franklin HS Tchr 19 Springboro HS Tchr 1979-; *ai:* Golf Coach 2 Yrs; Ftbl 18 Yrs; Bs Yrs; Jr Class Spon 5 Yrs; NEA & OEA 1984-; *office:* Springboro H S Main St Springboro OH 45066

STUCKEY, EMAGENE K., Third Grade Teacher; *b:* Wauseon, Robert Eugene; *c:* Jared, Gregory, Tanya; *ed:* Eastern Mennonite Co Elem Ed 1970; Univ of Toledo (MED) Elem Ed 1989; Grad, Post Gr of Children's Lit; *cr:* Waldron Area Schls 3rd Grd Tchr 1970-76; Cntrl Schls 1st Grd Tchr 1978-79; Hilltop Elem Schl 1st Grd Tchr 19 3rd Grd Tchr 1992-; *ai:* Sci Curr Dev, Tech Grant Comms; NEA 1983-; WUEA 1983-, VP, Pres; Article Pub; *office:* Hilltop Elem Sc S Defiance St West Unity OH 43570

STUCKEY, RONALD W., Guidance Dir & Dean of Acad; *b:* Mc LA; *m:* Theresa Cardenas; *c:* Robert, Patricia; *ed:* LA Tech Univ (Eng Ed 1972, (MAEd) Guidance & Counseling 1988; Attnd Sq Officer's Schl, Air Command & Staff Schl USAF; Attnd Marine Cor & Staff Schl US Marines; *cr:* USAF Command Pilot 1972-92; Riv Bapt Schl Dir of Guidance, AP U.S. His Tchr 1992-; *ai:* JV Bsbl 1992, 1993; Girls Var Bsktbl Coach 1993-; Fellowship of Chrstn Ath 1993-95; Women's Bsktbl Coaches Assn 1993-; MD St Bsbl Coache 1991-; Marlboro Boys & Girls Club 1988-; Prince George's Babe Ru 1991-; Mattaponi PTA 1988-93; Boosters Club 1991-; *office:* Riv Baptist Schl 1133 Largo Rd Upper Marlboro MD 20774

STUCKI, DANIEL ROBERT, Social Studies Teacher; *b:* Clevelan *c:* Megan Marie; *ed:* Cleveland St Univ (BA) Comprehensive So 1976; Ashland Univ (EG) Curr & Instruction; *cr:* Various Cath Sch & 8th Grd Tchr 19660; *ai:* Head Ftbl, Bsbl Coach; US Slo-Pitch Sftb 1985-; Eastern Cuyahuga Cty Umpires Assn, OH HS Ath Assn, Intn of Approved Bsktbl Officials Inc 1976-; Euclid Pony League Coach *home:* 20651 S Lake Shore Blvd Euclid OH 44123

STUCKWISCH, WILLIAM ELDO, Chemistry Teacher; *b:* Cedar R IA; *m:* Nancy DeVantier; *c:* Erica, Wade; *ed:* NM Highlands Univ Chem 1966; SUNY at Buffalo (MED) Sci Ed 1968; City Coll Bowdoin Coll, Niagara Univ, Canisius Coll 60 Hrs Past Masters; *cr:* Island HS Chem Tchr 1968-; *ai:* Wrestling Coach 1971-85; Solar House Adv 1986-89; Odyssey of the Mind 3rd in NY St 1990; AFT Union Rep Assembly; *office:* Grand Island HS 1100 Ransom Rd Island NY 14072

STUDER, MELANIE WEST, Work & Family Life Teacher; *b:* Colu OH; *m:* Andrew; *ed:* OH St Univ (BS) Home Ec Ed 1989, (MS) Ho Ed 1990; *cr:* Cardington Lincoln HS Work & Family Life Tchr 199 FHA, HERO Club Adv; HS Fac Advy Comm; Peace Luth Church Sunday Schl Tchr, Youth Comm; *office:* Cardington-Lincoln H Chesterville Ave Cardington OH 43315

STUEBE, DAVID F., Junior HS Social Studies Tchr; *b:* Portland, C Patricia Gathmann; *c:* Michael, Jennifer; *ed:* Concordia Univ at S (BS) Soc Stud 1968; Attnd Bowling Green St Univ, Eastern MI Un Evergreen Luth Schl Soc Stud Tchr 1968-79; St Paul Luth Schl Soc Tchr 1979-; *ai:* Eighth Grd Girls Bsktbl, Seventh-Eighth Grd Track C OHSAA Vlybl Ofcls 1987-, Assn Rule Interpreter; *office:* St Paul Lu Schl 1075 Glenwood Ave Napoleon OH 43545

STUHLDREHER, THOMAS JOHN, Professor of Finance; *b:* A OH; *m:* Wendy Louisa Weagraff; *c:* Thomas, Timothy, Peter; *ed:* Bor Coll of OH (BA) Scholastic Philosophy 1969; Univ of Notre Dame Philosophy 1971; Kent St Univ (MBA) Bus Admin 1975, (DBA) Fi 1979; *cr:* Kent St Univ Asst Dean 1976-79; Shippensburg Univ of PA Prof of Finance 1979-84; Clarion Univ of PA Prof of Finance 1984-; Clarion Univ Of PA 317 Still Hall Clarion PA 16214

STUKES-MAURICE, JOAN, English Teacher; *b:* Clarendon, SC; *m.* J. Maurice; *c:* Alexandra, Malcolm; *ed:* Morgan St Coll (BA) Eng Morgan St Univ (MA) Eng Lit 1979; Coppin-Hopkins Classical 1989; Ed Credits Towson St Coll, Morgan St Coll 1976; *cr:* Patterso Eng, Hlth Tchr 1976-80; Morgan St Univ Remedial Eng Tchr 197 Eastern HS Eng Tchr 1980-86; Baltimore City Coll Eng Tchr 1986 1998 Class Adv; Schl Wellness Coord; Arts, Curr Comms; NCTE Ebenezer AME Church 1975-, Steward; Melvin L. Stukes Pol Cam 1980-, Election Day Coord; Unselds Schl Assn 1991-, Parent Class C NAACP 1980-; Morgan Alumni Assn 1975-; Eastern HS Tchr of Yr *office:* Baltimore City Coll HS 3220 The Alameda Baltimore MD 21

STULMAKER, RICHARD M., Social Science Teacher; *b:* Brooklyn *c:* Alissa A., Jeffrey M., Kenneth L.; *ed:* SUNY (BA) Soc Sci 1962, Soc Sci 1964; *cr:* Herkimer HS Soc Sci Tchr 1964-; Mohawk Vly C Coll Adj Sociology 1971; Utica Coll Sociology Adj Prof 1988-; *ai:* U Nations Club; 8th Grd Class Spon; Supervising Cooperating Tchr fo Tchrs Utica Coll; NEA, AFT 1980's; Crop Walk, Local Food Pantry Recruiter; VFW Voice of Democ 1980-, Essay Comm Coord, Citizen 1986; Temple Beth Joseph 1960's, Adult Ed, House Comms; Hnrs Se Lecturer BOCES 1970's; Conducted Grant Project Sociology Investi Marriage Cnslng Techniques.

STULTS, TAYLOR, Professor of History; *b:* Evanston, IL; *m:* Campbell; *c:* David, Eric, Evan; *ed:* Antioch Coll (BA) His, 1959; Ur MO (MA) His 1960, (PHD) His 1970; *cr:* Muskingum Coll His 1962-65, His Asst Prof 1965-71, His Assoc Prof 1971-75, His Prof 1

ıer Histocial Assn; Assn for Advancement of Slavic Stud; Assn for ın Stud in US; OH Acad of His; Pub Book, The Course of Russian , Articles, Essays; *office:* Muskingum Coll New Concord OH

'Z, **LARRY THOMAS,** Teacher; *b:* Canonsburg, PA; *m:* Barbara Matthew L., Eric T.; *ed:* CA St Coll (BSEd) Scndry Math 1973, (MS) 7; Addl 30 Credits; Univ of CA Coll Cert Scndry Prin Papers; *cr:* rs-Houston Schl Dist Tchr, Scndry Prin, Admin Asst 23 Yrs; *ai:* Club; Acad Olympics; AFT 1974-, VP; PAFT; CHFT; Sports Arena s Union 1981-, 1993 Employee of Yr; Acting Prin, Asst to Supt.

P, KRISTA HURLEY, First Grade Teacher; *b:* Union City, IN; *m:* Alan; *c:* Cory S., Katie N.; *ed:* OH Northern Univ (BA) Elem Ed Wright St Univ (ME) Tchr Ldr 1991; 15 Semester Hrs Beyond s in Math, Rdng, Writing, Gifted Ed & Phonic at Portland St Univ of Dayton; *cr:* Mississinawa Vly Title I Rdng & Math Tchr 1978; Cty Local Schls Kndgtn-8th Grd Sub Tchr 1980-86; Ansonia Local Kndgtn Chptr I Rdng Tchr 1986-87; Greenville City Schls 3rd Grd 987-88, 1st Grd Tchr 1988-; *ai:* Phi Delta Kappa 1983-, VP Pgms NEA, OEA & GEA 1987-, Bldg Rep 1993 & Mbrshp Pacesetter; d Church of the Brethren, Womens Choir; Awded: Flwshps from St Univ 1989 & 1990 & 3 Local Grants from My Schl Dist; Bldg the Yr 1995; Article Pub; *office:* Gettysburg Elem Schl 260 E Main ourg OH 45328*

P, ROSANNA M., Second Grade Teacher; *b:* Shelby, OH; *m:* ; *c:* Tom, Chris, Steve, Chad, Stasi Stump Ulmer; *ed:* OH St (BS) d 1972; *cr:* Buckeye East 1st Grd Tchr 1973; St Bernard 2nd Grd 973-; *ai:* Jump-A-Thon For Heart Assn Chr; CCIRA 1985-; NCEA Rosary Altar Soc 1952-, Pres, Sec; Tots to Teens Mothers Club Pres, Sec, Treas; Home Schl 1993-; OSU Educ Honorary; OSU eld Charter Mem; *office:* St Bernard Schl 320 W Mansfield St New gton OH 44854

PF, CARL RICHARD, Cmptr Information System Instr; *b:* and, OH; *m:* Constance Coppers; *c:* Carl Wayne, Elizabeth; *ed:* nd Comm Coll (AAB) Cmptr Sci 1968; Univ of Akron (BS) Bus Ed, Post Scndry Tech Ed 1978; John Carroll Univ Cleveland Ctr for Ec st Grad Ec; *cr:* Willoughby-Eastlake City Schls Tchr 1971-; nd Comm Coll Instr 1979-86, 1988-89, 1996-; *ai:* OH Scndry Rep oom Advy for Bus Prof of Amer; NE OH, OH CEAC Rep Bus Prof er OH Delegation; Regnl Bus Prof of Amer Adv; Career Ed Coord; NEA 1971-, Classroom Rep; Career Ed Assn 1987-, Coord; Bus Prof er 1980-, Rep, Star Adv; Mentor Chrstn Church 1978-, Asst Chair of VIZ Cmptr Sci Scndry Tchr of Yr; 1991 Express Info Svcs ship for Writing Springboard Exercise; 1994 Jennings Scholar ent; *office:* Willoughby-Eastlake Tech Ctr 25 Public Sq Willoughby 094*

PF, JOSEPH R., Technology Education Instr; *b:* Pittsburgh, PA; *m:* A. Cypher; *c:* Daniel, Michael, Curtis; *ed:* CA Univ of PA (BS) Ed St Univ of NY (MS) Ed 1970; *cr:* Allegheny-Clarion HS Ind Arts 966-67; Knoch Jr-Sr HS Ind Arts Tech Ed Instr 1967-; *ai:* SBCEA, NEA 1966-, Fac Svcs Rep, Schlsp Comm Chm; Knights of bus 1990-; BSA 1988-, Scoutmaster; Se-Jong Tae Kwon Do 1986-, Belt; Chrstn Black Belt Assn 1993-; Natl Rifle Assn 1967-; Natl o Life 1980-; *home:* PO Box 32 Herman PA 16039

PF, RICHARD DAWSON, Agriculture Teacher; *b:* Greensburg, Deborah Weinschenker; *c:* Rebecca, Jennifer; *ed:* PA St Univ (BS) 1967; MA Equivalent; *cr:* Port Allegany HS Ag Tchr 1967-68; HS Ag Tchr 1968-69, 1995-; *ai:* United FFA Adv; United Ed Assn, 1968-; PA Voc Ag Tchr Assn 1986-, Reg VP; IN Co Ag Extension Bd of Dirs; PA Assn of Conservation Dist Tchr of Yr; *office:* United ist PO Box 168 Armagh PA 15920*

DEVANT, SANDRA L., Reading Specialist; *b:* Union City, PA; *m:* ert; *c:* Sharon, Adelbert II, Sandell; *ed:* Edinboro Univ (BS) Elem Ed (MED) Rdng Specialist 1987; Mercyhurst Coll Spec Ed; *cr:* Mount aedict Presch Tchr 1985-86; Harborcreek Yth Svcs Rdng Specialist *ai:* Church; PSEA 1983-; IRA, Erie Rdng Cncl 1985-; Girl Scouts Ldr, Troop Comm, Ldrshp; PTA 1974-, Pres, Life Mbrshp; Grad antship; Erie Area Citizen Svc Cncl Comm Svc Mini Grant 1990-; Harborcreek Yth Svcs Schl 5712 Iroquois Ave Harborcreek PA

GEON, SUE WINEGARDNER, First Grade Teacher; *b:* ville, OH; *m:* James Lee; *c:* Lori, Jason, Jeffery; *ed:* OH Univ (BSEd) Ed 1984, (MSEd) Elem Ed 1994; *cr:* Glenford Elem Math Tutor 1983, Grd Chapter I Tchr 1984-85, Grd One Tchr 1986-; *ai:* Northern Local Assn Rep; Lang Arts, Sci Course of Stud Comms; venture Capital ning Bd; Mentorship Prgm; Delta Kappa Gamma 1994-; Hopewell Church 1970-; Shared Integrated Curr Practices with OH, IN Schl Tchrs; Several Presentations OH Children's Lit Conf, OCTELA ; *office:* Glenford Elem Schl 8700 Sheridan Rd NW Thornville OH

IALE, GEORGE I., English Teacher; *b:* Rockeville Centre, NY; *m:* ra Gelsey; *c:* Stephanie Gelsey; *ed:* St Univ of NY at Fredonia (BA) 975, (MA) Eng 1977; Attnd Columbia Univ, Syracuse Univ, Univ of n; *cr:* Bishop Ludden HS Eng Tchr 1978-83; Syracuse Univ Adjunct Prof 1983-87; Skaneoteles Cntrl Schl Eng Tchr 1983-; *ai:* NYSUT ; NEH Grant; Shakespeare Soc Eng Speaking Union; Tchr of Yr 80, 1987-88; Fac Marshall 1991, 1995; *office:* Skaneateles Cntrl 49 E Elizabeth St Skaneateles NY 13152*

M, FREDERICK IVAN, Jazz Stud & Contemp Media Prof; *b:* stock, IL; *m:* Susan; *c:* Ivan, Madeline; *ed:* Lawrence Univ (BM) Ed 1973; Eastman Schl of Music (MM) Composition & Arranging Grad Stu in Music Performance Univ of N TX 1973-74; *cr:* Lawrence Dir of Jazz Stud 1977-91; Eastman Schl of Music Chair Jazz Stud emporary Media 1991-; *ai:* Composer, Arranger, Producer & uctor; Visiting Music Artist & Clinician; Intnl Assn of Jazz Educators ; NEA 1994 Composition Grant, 1995 Music Research Grant; AS 1995 Music Recording Grant; Text & CD Pub by Adv Music any; *office:* Eastman Schl Of Music 26 Gibbs St Rochester NY *

RNIOLO, GARY F., Mathematics Teacher; *b:* Altoona, PA; *m:* Janice ieder; *c:* Gregory, Todd; *ed:* PA St Univ (BS) Scndry Ed 1972; burg St Univ, Western MD Coll 40 Addl Credit Hrs; *cr:* Clear Spring ath Tchr 1972-86; Penn St Univ Math Tchr 1980-82; Boonsboro HS Tchr 1986-; *ai:* Tech Advy Comm; Cmptr Club Adv; Inter Active ision Tchr; NCTM 1978-; NEA, MSTA, Wash Cty Tchrs Assn 1993-, Rep; Hewlett Packard Calculator Grant Winner; *office:* Boonsboro) Campus Ave Boonsboro MD 21713

RTEVANT, JAYE W., Mathematics Teacher; *b:* Cleveland, OH; *m:* la; *c:* Carrie, Heidi, Asa; *ed:* Buffalo St (BS) Ed 1971, (MS) Ed 1989; rongsville HS Tchr 1971-72; Niagara Luth Jr Sr HS Tchr 1980-83; St Luth Tchr & Prin 1983-85; Niagara Falls Bd of Ed Math Tchr 1986-; Rochester DX Assn, Ham Radio AA2TX; Niagara Falls 1978-, Pres; rican Red Cross, Co-Chair Disaster Team; *office:* Niagara MS ara Falls NY 14304

RTEVANT, VIRGINIA ANN, Learning Specialist; *b:* Worcester, *c:* Corinne Spezeski, Deidre Spezeski, Kara Spezeski; *ed:* Univ of MA (BA) Fr, Elem Ed 1963; Cntrl MI Univ (MA) Spec Ed, Voc Ed 1980; *cr:* Northern Berkshire Assn Retarded Citizens Evaluation, Trng Dir 1981-84; Southern VT Coll Coord Lrng Disabilities Prgm 1985-95; Southern VT Coll Instr 1989-92; Holyoke Comm Coll Learning Specialist 1995-; *ai:* Acad Support, Stu Dev, ADA Comms; Assn on Higher Ed & Disability 1990-; NEA 1963-64, 1995-; Outstdng Dedication as Learning Disabilities Coord Southern VT Coll 1989; *home:* 139 Bridges Rd Williamstown MA 01267

STURTZ, AGNES LEONARD, Librarian & Admin Assistant; *b:* Cambridge, MD; *ed:* Salisbury St Coll (BS) Elem Ed 1966, (MS) Elem Ed 1990; Educl Media Assoc 1996; *cr:* Hurlock Elem Schl Tchr Grds 2, 4, 5 1966-68; Denton Elem Scho Tchr Grd 6 1968-69; Preston Elem Schl Tchr Grd 6 1969-90, Librn 1990-; *ai:* NEA; MSTA; CCTA; *office:* Preston Elem Schl PO Box 69 Preston MD 21655

STURTZ, MARTHA SEARLES, Fifth Grade Teacher; *b:* Oswego, NY; *m:* Russell E III; *c:* Russell IV, Kenneth; *ed:* St Univ at Oswego (BS) Ed Art 1979, (MS) Curr Dev Ed 1985; *cr:* Eddies Big M-Mexico Head Cashier 1975-79; Mexico Cntrl Schls Permanent Sub Tchr 1979-80, 3rd Grd Elem Tchr 1980-81, 6th Grd MS Tchr 1981-92, 5th Grd MS Tchr 1992-; *ai:* 4-H Ldr, Adv; Heidi Allen Search Ctr Bd of Dir; Higsteaks 4-H Club Ldr; Oswego Cty Fair Chaperone; Comm Mem to Elect Cty Legislator; NYSUT Mexico F Assn 1979-, Co-Pres & Negoigator; Delta Kappa Gamma 1993-, Leg Comm, Historian; NSTA 1984-; St Sci Tchrs Assn 1984-; NY St Rdng Assn 1980-; Oswego Cty 4-H 1990-, Ldr; Oswego Cty Beef Producers 1990-, Pub Relations; Girl Scouts of Amer 1964-, Ldr & Adv; *office:* Mexico Cntrl Schls Fravor Rd Mexico NY 13114

STUTZ, PAUL LAWRENCE, English Teacher & Dept Chprsn; *b:* Pittsburgh, PA; *m:* Gail Evans; *c:* Kathleen; *ed:* IN Univ of PA (BS) Eng Ed 1975; Univ of Pittsburgh (MED) Curr & Supervision 1979; *cr:* Holy Ghost HS Tchr 1975-77; North Cath HS Tchr & Coach 1978-; *ai:* Boys & Girls Cross Cntry Coach; IM Sports Dir; Newspaper Adv; WPCTE 1988-; *office:* North Catholic HS 1400 Troy Hill Rd Pittsburgh PA 15212

STUYVESANT, KATHERINE FENNELL, Kindergarten Teacher; *b:* Butler, PA; *m:* Richard; *c:* Tyler, Kimberly; *ed:* Edinboro Univ (BS) Elem Ed 1973; Masters Equivalency Commonwealth of PA 1986; 30 Credits Plus Educl Prof Growth; *cr:* General McLane Schl Dist 1st Grd Tchr 1973-78, 4th Grd Tchr 1978-92, 3rd Grd Tchr 1992-93, Kndgtn & Rdng Recovery Tchr 1993-; *ai:* NEA 1974-.

STUYVESANT, MARY ANN, Consumer & Family Science Tchr; *b:* Meadville, PA; *m:* Phillip Wayne; *c:* Eric, Nathan; *ed:* Univ of Akron (BAFA) Clothing & Textiles 1980; 55 Hrs Post Grad Stud; *cr:* Akron Pub Schls Consumer & Family Sciences Tchr 1981-; *ai:* Sr Class Adv 9 Yrs; Prom Adv 10 Yrs; FHA Adv; Akron Ed Assn 1982-; Akron Area Home Ec Assn 1981-; PTA Buchtel HS 1983-; *office:* Buchtel HS 1040 Copley Rd Akron OH 44320

STYER, TIMOTHY L., Biology Teacher; *b:* Upper Darby, PA; *m:* Dana DiProspero; *ed:* Bloomsburg Univ (BS) Scndry Ed, Bio 1990; 36 Post-Grad Credits; *cr:* Strath Haven HS Bio Tchr 1990-; *ai:* Coach Head Wrestling 1990, Asst Track 1993-; Ski Club Adv 1992-; Environmental Club Assoc 1992-; PSEA 1990-; Swarthmore Rec Assn 1991-; Rsrch Asst Coll Grant 1993; Coach of Yr 1995; *office:* Strath Haven HS 205 S Providence Rd Wallingford PA 19086

STYERS, NANCY HAIFLEIGH, Second Grade Teacher; *b:* Frederick, MD; *m:* Daniel Kit; *ed:* Frederick Comm Coll (AA) 1972; Hood Coll (AB) Early Chldhd Ed 1974, (MA) Rdng Specialization 1980; Addl 15 Hrs; *cr:* Thurmont Elem Schl Second Grd Tchr 1974-; *ai:* Second Grd Team Ldr; Former SIT Team Mem; FCTA, MSTA, NEA 1974-; Chapel Luth Church 1952-, Cncl Mem; *office:* Thurmont Elem Schl 805 E Main St Thurmont MD 21788

STYPULA, AMY LYNN, Spanish Teacher; *b:* Pittsburgh, PA; *ed:* Slippery Rock Univ (BS) Span 1993; *cr:* Mt Alvernia HS Span Tchr 1993-; *ai:* Windows of the World & NHS Moderator; NEA 1993-; Phi Sigma Pi 1992-; Sigma Delta Pi 1992-; Kappa Delta Pi 1993-; *office:* Mount Alvernia HS 146 Hawthorne Rd Pittsburgh PA 15209

SUAREZ, CARMEN MARIA, Spanish Teacher; *b:* Havana, Cuba; *m:* Michael Wachter; *ed:* Kutztown St Coll (BS) Scndry Ed Fr, Span 1982; Kutztown Univ (MS) Curr, Instruction 1994; Masters, 30 Addl Grad Credits; *cr:* Lenape Jr HS Fr, Span Tchr 1982-83; Devereaux Fnd Fr, Span Tchr 1985-86; Boyertown Area Sr HS Span Tchr 1986-; *ai:* Chaperone Frgn Lang Trips Abroad; NEA, PSEA 1986-.

SUAREZ, RUBEN, Adult Christian Education Tchr; *b:* Brooklyn, NY; *m:* Annette A. Amaro; *c:* Ruben Jr., Rebecca Eve; *ed:* Univ of Turabo at Puerto Rico (BA) Criminology 1986; Assemblies of God Bible Inst 4 Yr Diploma Chrstn Ed, Theology 1991; Gordon Conwell Seminary Cnslng, Chrstn Ed; *cr:* New Bedford Pub Schl Biling Sub Tchr 1993-95; Assemblies of God Bible Inst Tchr of Theology, Pastoral Stud, Admin, Cnslng 1988-; *ai:* Bapt Convention of New England 1995-, Licensed Minister; MA Bapt Assn 1994-, Licensed Minister; New Dawn Bapt Church, Pastor, Pres Bd of Trustees; Project Vida 1994-; Latino Access Ctr 1994-, Trustee; Tchr of Yr 1992; Honorary 4th Yr Degree 1991; 1990 Awded Chrstn Worker Cert; 1992 License to Preach by Gen Cncl of Assemblies of God; *home:* 952 Geraldine St New Bedford MA 02740*

SUAZO, GABY MONTOYA, ESOL Teacher; *b:* Santa Fe, NM; *m:* Peter A. Jr.; *c:* Peter, Ramon; *ed:* Coll of Santa Fe (BA) Elem Ed 1968; Univ of NM (MS) Elem Ed, Eng & Rdng 1972; Univ of WA (PHD) Elem Ed & Biling Ed 1979; *cr:* NM St Employment Svc Employment Cnslr 1959-68; Santa Fe Pub Schls Biling Tchr 1968-71; Seattle Pub Schls Tchr 1971-73; Univ of Miami Prgm Mgr 1973-80; Prince Georges Pub Schls ESOL Tchr 1980-; *ai:* Rdng & Soc Stud Comms; Effective Schls Team; Tchr-in-Charge; Hispanic Comm Liaison; Admin Team; Tutoring Prgm Coord; NEA, MSTA, PGCEA 1980-; Mexican Amer Womens Natl Assn 1975-; NABE 1970-; Howard Cty Human Rights Commission 1980-, Chprsn; Prof Bus Womens Assn Schlsp; US Title VII Fellowship; Dissertation; *office:* Ridgecrest Elem Schl 6120 Riggs Rd Hyattsville MD 20783

SUBERI, NAOMI, 6th-8th Grades Bible Teacher; *b:* Brooklyn, NY; *ed:* Brooklyn Coll (BA) Area Stud of Mid East 1981; Yeshiva Univ Tchrs Inst for Women Hebrew Tchrs Degree Judaic Stud 1979; *cr:* Bialik Schl 1st-8th Grd Tchr 1981-89; Yeshivah of Flatbush HS Bible, Hebrew Lit Tchr 1986-88; Magen David Yeshiva 4th Grd Tchr 1989-90; Yeshivah of Flatbush HS Bible Teacher 1990-; *ai:* Prepare Stdnts for Regnl, Natl, Intnl Bible Contests; Joseph S. & Caroline Gruss Excellent Tchrs Fund Grant 1988-89.

SUBERS, RICHARD C., Social Studies Teacher; *b:* Norristown, PA; *m:* Patricia A.; *ed:* Millersville Univ (BS) Soc Stud 1966; West Chester Univ (ME) His 1975; Cheney Univ Admin Cert 1979; *cr:* Methacton Schl Dist Tchr 30 Yrs, Comm Svc Coord 6 Yrs; Inst at Neumann Coll 1994-95; *ai:* Jr High Track & HS Var Ftbl Coach; Methacton Help Fund & Class of 1988 Adv; Methacton Aquatics Prgm Supvr; Interim Asst & Summer Schl Prin; NEA 1966-; PA Geographic Soc 1980-; Natl Comm Education Assn 1992-; NSEE; Youth Serve Amer Affiliate; Upper Salford Historical Soc 1990-, Pres; Uppper Salford Citizens Group 1990-, Planning Bd; DVA-DVP 1992-; PA Assn of Vol 1993-; Penn Serve Fellow 1994-95, Heinze-Pew & NJ Serve Amer Grant; Article Pub in PA Pride, Natl Youth Leadership Cncl Magazine Generator & Svc Learning in Soc Stud Portofolio; Co-Wrote & Produced Svc Learning Video; NSEE Fellow 1994-; Kellogg Peer Consultant 1994-; PA Dept of Ed Advy Bd for Learn and Serve Grants 1994-95; *office:* Methacton HS 1001 Kriebel Mill Rd Norristown PA 19408*

SUBRAMANIAN, E. V., 12th Grade Teacher; *b:* Madurai, India; *ed:* IN Inst of Tech (BS) Metallurgical Engrng 1981; Univ of TX at Austin (MS) Materials Sci, Engrng 1983, (PHD) 1988; *cr:* Cooper Union Schl of Engrng Visiting Asst Prof 1989-90; Luth HS Tchr 1992-; *ai:* Sr Adv; Numerous Articles Pub; *office:* Lutheran HS 6101 W Oxford St Philadelphia PA 19151

SUCH, MICHAEL, Asst Prof of Criminal Justice; *b:* Troy, NY; *ed:* Hudson Valley Comm Coll (AAS) Criminal Justice 1977; St Univ of NY (BA) Pub Justice 1979, (MA) Pub Admin 1983; Post Grad Cert Policy Analysis & Planning SUNY 1983; La Salle Univ PHD Candidate Criminal Justice Mngmt; *cr:* Loss Prevention Consultants VP, Gen Mgr 1984-89; Security & Such Pres 1992-; Hudson Valley Comm Coll Instr 1989-; *ai:* Acad Advisement; Criminal Justice Stu Assn Fac Adv; Comm Assignments; CJEANYS 1990-; NBFAA 1984-; ASIS 1985-; BPOE; Policy Impacts, Privitization, Admin Issues Writings; Security Consulting; *office:* Hudson Valley Community Coll 80 Vandenburgh Ave Troy NY 12180

SUCHANEK, DAVID PAUL, Chemistry & Physics Instructor; *b:* Youngstown, OH; *m:* Rita Mc Daniel; *c:* Heather; *ed:* Youngstown St Univ (BA) Bio 1969; Morgan St Univ (MS) Chem 1973; Attnd Univ of Akron, Case Western Reserve Univ; *cr:* Aberdeen HS Chem, Physics Tchr 1969-76; Dept of Army Chem Instr 1976-77; Hudson HS Chem, Physics Instr 1977-; *ai:* Ed Assn Bldg Rep; Tech Comm; Chess Team Adv; NEA 1969-; HEA 1977-, Bldg Rep; OEA; *office:* Hudson HS 2500 Hudson Aurora Rd Hudson OH 44236

SUCHAR, EVELYN ROWLEY, English Teacher; *b:* Jamestown, NY; *m:* Alphonse A.; *c:* Stephen, Mary; *ed:* Jamestown Comm (AA) Eng 1965; SUNY at Fredonia (BA) Eng 1967, (MA) Eng 1984; Addl 10 Hrs Post Grad; *cr:* Frewsburg Cntrl Schl 9-12 Grd Eng Tchr 1967-68; Monroe HS 8-9 Grd Eng Tchr 1969; Southwestern Cntrl Schl 9, 11 Grd Eng Tchr 1971; Frewsburg Cntrl Schl 8-12 Grd Eng Tchr 1972-; *ai:* Schl Publication Adv; Fac Assoc Exec Bd; AFT 1967-; Kappa Delta Gamma 1986-, Mbrshp Chair; Chautauqua Cty Tchrs Ctr 1988-95, Policy Bd Chair; *office:* Frewsburg Central Schl 26 Institute St Frewsburg NY 14738

SUCHARZSKI, LOIS PARKS, English Teacher; *b:* Bayonne, NJ; *m:* Robert; *ed:* JCSC (BA) Eng 1964; JCSC (MA) Eng 1968; Bayonne Bd of Ed In-Services Courses; *cr:* Bayonne Bd of Ed Eng Tchr 1964-; *ai:* Beacon Newspaper, Literary-Art Magazine & Acad Bowl Adv; NJEA 1964-; NEA 1964-; NCTE 1964-; Awds for Excl in Tchng 1987; Judge for Columbia Schlstc Press 1989; Judge & Timekeeper for Local & St Knights of Pythias Pub Speaking Contests 1984-92; *office:* Bayonne HS 669 Ave A Bayonne NJ 07002

SUCHECKI, WAYNE, Social Studies Teacher; *b:* Medford, MA; *m:* Virginia Olson; *c:* David, Michael; *ed:* Merrimack Coll (BS) Mrktg & Ed 1969; 45 Addl Credits; *cr:* Woburn Schl System Tchr 1970-; *ai:* Jr Class Adv; Former HS Hockey & Jr High Sftbl Coach; NEA, MTA & WTA 1970-; US Army Reserve 14 Yrs, Staff Sergeant; *office:* Woburn HS 88 Montvale Ave Woburn MA 01801

SUCHORA, DANIEL H., Professor of Mechanical Engrng; *b:* Youngstown, OH; *m:* Patricia A.; *c:* Kevin, Sherri, Matthew; *ed:* Youngstown St (BE) Mech Engr 1968, (MS) Mech Engr 1970; Case Western Reserve Union (PHD) Mech Engr 1973; *cr:* Cntrl OH Tech Coll Instr & Chair Engr Tech 1973-75; Youngstown St Univ Asst Prof Engr Tech 1975-79; Prof of Mech Engrng 1979-; *ai:* Lib Comm; Comp Comm; ASME 1973-, Chm & Vice Chair; Sigma Xi 1975-, Treas; Boardman Comm Bsbl 1985-, Bd Mem; Tri-T Bsbl 1991-, Bd Mem; Pub Numerous Articles; Kinematics & Stress Analysis Tech Confs; *office:* Youngstown St Univ 410 Wick Ave Youngstown OH 44555*

SUCHY, JAMES R., Soc Studies Dept Chairperson; *b:* Bronx, NY; *ed:* Fordham Coll (BA) His 1971, (MA) Amer His 1974; SUNY at New Paltz (CAS) Supervision 1987; 30 Addl Hrs Amer His, Medieval His Fordham Univ 1974-77; *cr:* Clarkstown HS North Soc Stud Tchr 1971-, Soc Stud Dept Chprsn 1987-; SUNY at New Paltz Adjunct Clinical Prof of Ed 1993-; *ai:* Stu Cncl Adv; Model Congress Adv; Natl His Day Adv; PTSA 1980-, Treas; NYSUT, CTA 1971-; ASCD, NYSCSS, RCSS 1987-; St Augustine Church 1965-, Usher, Past Pres, Parish Cncl; Mid Hudson Stud Cncl; Excl in Tchg Awd SUNY At New Paltz 1993; CHSN PTSA Life Mem; *office:* Clarkstown HS North Congers Rd New City NY 10956

SUCHY, ROBERT L., 6th-7th Grade Math Teacher; *b:* Charleroi, PA; *m:* Saundra Jo; *c:* Joelle Lee; *ed:* CA Univ of PA (BS) Elem, Math 1969, (MS) Elem 1970; *cr:* Castner Schl 6th Grd Tchr 1969-74; 6th Street Schl 6th Grd Tchr 1974-79; Carroll Jr HS 6th Grd Tchr 1979-80; Gastonville Elem Schl 6th Grd Tchr 1980-85; Carroll MS 6th Grd Tchr 1985-; *ai:* Ftbl 1975-79, Vlybl 1989-, Sftbl 1986-89, Gymnastics 9 Yrs Coach; REA, PSEA, NEA 1969-; Presented Thesis to NCTM in West PA; *office:* Carroll MS 120 Alexander Ave Monongahela PA 15063

SUCHY, SAUNDRA TRONA, Guidance Counselor; *b:* Charleroi, PA; *m:* Robert Lee; *c:* Joelle; *ed:* California Univ of PA (BS) Elem Spec Ed 1969, (MA) Elem 1971; Pub Schl Psychologist Cert 1980, Scndry Schl Counseling cert 1984; *cr:* Ringgold Itinerate Remedial Rdng 1969-70; Ringgold Gastonville 3rd Grd Tchr 1970-85; Ringgold Carroll Finley Tells Rdng Tchr 1985-86; Ringgold HS Guidance Cnslr 1986-; *ai:* NHS Spon; REA, PSEA, NEA 1969-; Washington Cty Cnslr Assn 1986-; Tech Prep Advy Bd 1994-; *office:* Ringgold HS 3645 Dry Run Rd Monongahela PA 15063

SUCKARIEH, GEORGE G., Professor; *b:* Damascus, syria; *m:* Nancy E. Woodall; *c:* Melanie A., Andrew G.; *ed:* Univ of Damascus (BS) Civil Engrng 1971; Univ of Cincinnati (MS) Civil Engrng 1973; OH St Univ (PHD) Civil Engrng 1976, (MBA) Bus Admin 1976; *cr:* Resource Intl Assoc Researcher 1973-76; A M Kenney Inc Construction Mgmt 1977-78; Univ of Cincinnati Prof 1978-, Dept Head 1988-91; *ai:* Tchng; Research; Amer Soc Civil Engrs 1984-, Local Chapter MgGrp; Amer Inst of Construction 1988-, Local Bd Chm; Madeira Schls Planning Commission 1988-; Articles in Natl & Intnl Publications; CIOB Confs; *office:* Univ Of Cincinnati 2220 Victory Pkwy Cincinnati OH 45206

SUDALL, DANA D., Math & Physics Teacher; *b:* Philadelphia, PA; *m:* Kevin P.; *cr:* Bensalem Twp Schl Dist Long-Term Sub Tchr 1992-93; Neshaminy Schl Dist Daily Sub Tchr 1993-94; Wardlaw-Hartridge Schl Math & Physics Tchr 1994-; *ai:* Chrldng, Jr Swim Team Coach; Jr Tennis Asst Coach; *home:* 1040 Plainfield Ave Plainfield NJ 07060

SUDMYER, RONALD PAUL, Social Studies Teacher; *b:* Schenectady, NY; *m:* Marjorie Cleveland; *c:* Jeffrey, Todd, Stephanie, Katrina Hart; *ed:* Hobart Coll (BA) Pol Sci 1971; Framingham St Coll (MA) Educl Leadership 1994; 36 Semester Hrs in Soc Sci Related Courses; *cr:* Framingham North Hs Soc Stud Tchr 1972-75; Framingham South HS Soc Stud Tchr 1975-91; Framingham HS Soc Stud Tchr 1991-; Framingham Pub Schls Admin Intern 1993-94; *ai:* Fac Forum Mem; ASCD 1993-; NEA, FTA 1972-; Coll Bsbl Umpires Assn 1985-; HS Bsbl Umpire 1975-; Intnl Assn of Bsktbl Ofcls 1982-; Nobscot Valley Ftbl Ofcls Assn 1978-; Jiffy Lube-Middlesex News Salute to Excl Awd 1995; *office:* Framingham HS 115 A St Framingham MA 01701*

SUDOCK, EILEEN M., 4th Grade Teacher; *b:* Hazleton, PA; *c:* Jeff, Sharon Sudock Brown; *ed:* St Univ at Bloomsburg PA (BS) Elem Ed 1965; Rutgers Univ NJ (MA) Admin, Supervision 1972; Attnd Plymouth Plantation, NJ Geographic Alliance at Rowan Coll, WNET Natl Tchr Trng Inst Math, Sci, Tech; *cr:* Clara Barton Schl Tchr 1966-71; Rutgers Univ Sabbatical Tchr 1972; WA Schl Tchr 1973-; *ai:* Ed Strategic Planning Comm 1996; NEA, NJEA, ETEA, Kappa Delta Pi, NJ Geographic Alliance, Tchr Consultant Natl Geographic Soc; WA Schl PTO; St Third Place Winner Mock Trial Competition NJ St Bar Fdn; Agricultural Soc NJ Grant; Edison Ed Fdn Grants; *office:* Washington Elem Schl 153 Winthrop Rd Edison NJ 08817

SUDOL, BEVERLY J., Art Teacher; *b:* Paterson, NJ; *m:* Eugene J.; *c:* Alexandra; *ed:* William Patterson coll (BA) Art Ed 1969, (MA) Art 1975; *cr:* Pequonnock HS Art Tchr 1969-70; Wayne Valley HS Art Tchr 1970-84; George Washington Jr HS Art Tchr 1984-; *ai:* NEA 1969-; NJEA 1969-; NJAEA 1970-; NJAEA Mini Grant Recipient; Hunterdon Printmaking Competition Exhibitor.

SUEDKAMP, LORI ELIZABETH IMHOFF, 9th Grade Math Teacher; *b:* Hamilton, OH; *m:* Gerald Dean; *c:* Steven Mark; *ed:* Miami Univ (BS) Scndry Ed Math 1990; 3 Hrs Grad Schl; *cr:* Stephen T Badin HS Math Tchr 1991-; *ai:* Spirit Club Moderator; *office:* Stephen T Badin HS 571 Hamilton New London Rd Hamilton OH 45013

SUEVER, SANDY STALLKAMP, First Grade Teacher; *b:* Lima, OH; *m:* Criag L.; *c:* Sara, Allison; *ed:* Bowling Green St Univ (BS) Elem Ed 1974; OH St Univ (MA) Early Mid Chldhd Ed 1996; *cr:* Delphos St Johns Kndgtn Tchr 1975-89; Franklin Elem 1st Grd Tchr 1989-; *ai:* DARE, Crisis Intervention Team; NEA 1976-; Delta Kappa Gamma 1993-; Phi Kappa Phi 1995-; OCCL 1978-, All; *home:* 668 E 7th St Delphos OH 45833

SUGRA, JOSEPH J., Sixth Grade Teacher; *b:* Allentown, PA; *m:* Debora S. Drosnock; *c:* Matthew P., Allison E.; *ed:* West Chester Univ (BS) Elem Ed 1972; *cr:* Pottsgrove Schl Dist 5th Grd Tchr 1972-74; Colonial Northampton IU #20 Jr HS Rdng Tchr 1974-75; Moore Elem 6th Grd Tchr 1976-; *ai:* PSEA 1974-; NEA 1976-; *home:* 585 E 11th St Northampton PA 18067

SUHALLA, VIRGINIA C., Asst Professor of Education; *b:* Buffalo, NY; *m:* Michael J.; *ed:* St Univ of NY (BS) Elem Ed 1961, (MS) Elem Ed 1964; *cr:* Daemen Coll Asst Prof of Ed 28 Yrs; *ai:* Admissions & Fin Aid, Acad Stans, Lib Comms; Fac Adv for Ed Club; Trustee Comm for Stu Affairs; NYS Tchrs Assn 1968-; Comm on Tchr Ed 1969-75; Kappa Delta Pi; Who's Who for Amer Coll & Univ; *office:* Daemen Coll 4380 Main St Amherst NY 14226

SUHR, LOIS ELLA (WALTERS), Supervisor & Teacher; *b:* Harrisburg, PA; *m:* Earl Martin Sr.; *c:* Earl Jr., Diane, Ronny, Carl, Tami; *ed:* Trng Cert in Essential Learning Inst; Cert Accelerated Chrstn Ed Supvr; *cr:* Armstrong Valley Chrstn Schl Supvr & Tchr 7 Yrs; *ai:* Armstrong Valley Chrstn Schl, Schl Bd Mem, Sec; Armstrong Valley Bible Church, Ladies Fellowship Treas; *home:* 1511 Rutter Rd Halifax PA 17032

SUKENIK, JOHN K., Teacher & Coach; *b:* Johnstown, PA; *m:* Carole A. Swanger; *ed:* Mansfield Univ (BS) Soc Stud 1963; Shippensburg Univ (MED) Ed SS 1968; Attnd Temple Univ, Wilkes Coll; *cr:* Big Spring HS Tchr, Fbl & BB Coach 1963-66; Solanco HS Tchr, Fbl Coach 1966-70; Warwick HS Tchr, FBL & Golf Coach 1970-; *ai:* PSAP Mem; PSEA 1963-; PSAP 1991-; USGA 1983-; *office:* Warwick HS 301 W Orange St Lititz PA 17543

SULCOSKI, MICHAEL STEPHEN, Science Teacher; *b:* Wilkes-Barre, PA; *m:* Linda Mary Skurla; *c:* Stephen, Michael; *ed:* Wilkes Univ (BA) Physics 1984; 93 Credit Hrs; *cr:* Plains Jr HS Sci Tchr 1984-; *ai:* Book Selection Comm; Ski Club Adv; PSEA, NEA 1984-; NSTA 1995-; Luzerne Cty Civil Defense 1984-, Radiation Monitor; *office:* Plains Jr HS 33 W Carey St Wilkes Barre PA 18705

SULINSKI, DENNIS JOHN, Health Ed Dept Chm & Ath Dir; *b:* Brooklyn, NY; *m:* Hilda Umger; *c:* John, Linda, Stephen, Karen; *ed:* Long Island Univ (BS) Hlth Ed, PE 1969; Queens Coll (MS) PE 1971; 60 Addl Credit Hrs St John's Univ; *cr:* Brooklyn Automotive HS Hlth, PE, Spec Ed 1969; PS 250 Schl PE, Spec Ed 1969; Great Neck South Jr HS MS Hlth Educator, Dept Head, Ath Dir 1970-; *ai:* Stu Org Fac Spon; PASS Adv; Schl Hlth Cncl; Substance Abuse Task Force; Alcohol Valuing Project; Nutrition Comm; Ath Coach Bsktbl, Ftbl, LaCrosse, Soccer, Wrestling; NYSUT; AFT; Great Neck Tchrs Assn 1970-; Great Neck Credit Union, Bd Dirs; Tchr Selection Comm; Great Neck Pub Schls 25 Yr Svc Awd; Natl Assn Sports, PE; Knights of Columbus 1978-, Grant Knight 1985-86, NY St Deputy Cert of Commendation, All Local Offices, Bd Dirs, Trustee, PGK, Dist Warden 1987-89, Supreme Cncl Awds, GK, PGK, Trustee Awds; Cold Spring Harbor Comm Soccer, LaCrosse Clubs, Coach, Prgm Org, Comm Svc; Cath Yth Org, St John Cansius, St Patrick's; Amer Red Cross, First Aid, CPR Instr 1975-; Comm Local Pub Svc Awds; Indstrl Home for Blind; United Cerebral Palsy; Autism Soc; AHRC; Coaching Awds; *office:* Great Neck South MS 349 Lakeville Rd Great Neck Estates NY 11021

SULLENBERGER, ROGER W., Mathematics Teacher; *b:* North Charleroi, PA; *m:* Deborah L. Misutka; *c:* Maureen G., Roger W. Jr., Neil S., Lindsey J.; *ed:* Univ of CA at PA (BSEd) Scndry Ed & Math 1967, (MED) Scndry Ed & Math 1972; Univ of Pittsburgh (PHD) Scndry Ed & Math 1982; NSF Summer Inst at Kent Univ 1968; *cr:* Monessen HS Math Instr 1967; Hempfield Area HS Math Instr 1967-; PA St Univ Monroeville Beaver Continuing Ed Fac 1975-77; Univ of Pittsburgh at Greensburg Adjunct Fac 1990-; *ai:* Track & Ftbl Coach; Natl, St & Local Levels Math Tchrs Speaker; NEA, PSEA, HAEA 1967-; NCTM 1972-; MCWP 1975-, Pres, Exec Bd; PCTM 1975-, Pres, Exec Bd, Outstanding Svc Awd 1995; *office:* Hempfield Area Sr HS Rd 6 Box 77 Greensburg PA 15601

SULLIVAN, CARL G., President of Consulting; *b:* Memphis, TN; *m:* Towanda; *c:* Amir, Jaleel; *ed:* Univ of Memphis (BA) Philosophy, Psych 1974, (MS) Psych 1976; Univ of WI at Milwaukee (PHD) Psych, Testing 1982; LL Thurstone Psychometric Lab Univ of NC Post Doctoral Fellow; *cr:* NC Cntrl Univ Assoc Prof 1987-88; Educl Testing Svc Prgm Dir GRE Gen Test 1988-91; Fayetteville St Univ Asst Prof 1992-95; Sullivan & Assoc Pres, Psych Prof 1991-; *ai:* Prof Svcs Group NJ Consultant; Intnl Educl Rsrch Ctr; Little League Bsbl Coach; Amer Psychological Assn 1975-; Assn Black Psychologists 1976-, Chair, Testing Comm; AAUP 1995-; Amer Ed Rsrch Assn 1979-; PTA 1989-; Fellow Natl Inst Mental Hlth; Congressman Harold Ford Pub Svc Awd; Univ of WI at Milwaukee Acad Achvmt Awd; *office:* Sullivan & Associates 16 Hampshire Dr Plainsboro NJ 08536

SULLIVAN, CAROL BENJAMIN, French Teacher; *b:* Cumberland, MD; *m:* Larry Patrick; *ed:* Univ of NC at Chapel Hill (AB) Ed 1966; Univ of MD at Coll Park (MED) Foreign Lang Ed 1980; Univ of NC at Greensboro Ed; *cr:* Annapolis Jr High Fr Dept Chprsn, Eng Tchr 1968-79; Old Mill MS North Fr Tchr, Dept Chprsn 1980-83; Crofton MS Fr Tchr, Dept Chprsn 1983-86; Anne Arundel Comm Coll Part-Time Fr, Lecturer IV Instr 1984-94; Annapolis Sr HS Fr Tchr 1986-; *ai:* Intnl Club Spon; NEA, Anne Arundel Cty Tchrs Assn 1968-; Phi Beta Kappa 1966-; Delta Kappa Gamma Soc Rho Chapter 1995-; AATF Travel, Stud Schlsp to France 1976; Univ of Aix-en Province Fr Govt Stud Grant 1984.*

SULLIVAN, CAROL P., Psychology & History Teacher; *b:* Long Island, NY; *c:* Jennifer; *ed:* Fisk Univ (BA) Sociology 1970; Univ of Hartford (MED) Urban Ed 1971; Attnd Univ of MA, Springfield Coll, Cambridge Coll & Fitchburg for 15 Addl Hrs Psych; *cr:* Occupational Voc Dev Ctr Rehabilitation Cnslr 1970-71; Van Sickle Jr HS Soc Stud Tchr 1971-78; Springfield Schl Dept Youth Employment Job Cnslr 1978-79; Classical HS Soc Stud Tchr 1979 -86; Central HS Psych & Afro Amer Tchr 1986-; *ai:* Yrbk Bus & Peer Counseling Adv; NEA 1972-; *office:* Springfield Central H S 1840 Roosevelt Ave Springfield MA 01109

SULLIVAN, CHARLES EDWARD,JR., 5th Grade Teacher; *b:* Boston, MA; *m:* Maria Rosa; *c:* Nicole; *ed:* Bridgewater St (MS) Schl Admin 1995; *cr:* Wilmington Schl System 4th Grd Tchr 1974-78; Quincy Pub Schls 6th Grd Tchr 1978-80; Palm Beach Cty Schls 6th Grd Tchr 1980-85; Canton Pub Schls 5th Grd Tchr 1986-; *ai:* NEA 1974-; MTA 1986-; *home:* 159 Bittersweet Ln Apt 126 Randolph MA 02368*

SULLIVAN, CHRISTOPHER FRANCIS, English Teacher; *b:* Lawrence, MA; *m:* Joyce K. Ryan; *c:* Liam P.; *ed:* Merrimack Coll (MA) Eng 1985; Rivier Coll (MA) Eng Tchng 1991; *cr:* Central Cath HS 1985-; *ai:* Bsbl & Ftbl Asst Coach; Stu Cncl Moderator, Stu Ambassadors Dir of Admissions; NCTE 1989-; NCEA 1985-; St Thomas Acquinas Parish; *office:* Central Catholic HS 300 Hampshire St Lawrence MA 01841

SULLIVAN, CYNTHIA PELGER, Instructional Support Teacher; *b:* Lancaster, PA; *m:* Terry J.; *c:* Terry II, Alaina, Abby; *ed:* Shippensburg Univ (BS) Elem Ed 1973, (MA) Early Chldhd Ed 1978; Addl 36 Credit Hrs Penn St Univ, Western MD Coll; *cr:* Mowrey Elem Schl 1st, 2nd, 5th Grd, IST Tchr 1992-; *ai:* Stu Cncl Adv; Stu Enhancement Comm; NEA, PSEA, WAEA 1974-, Sec, Bldg Rep, Comm Co-Chprsn, Cty Coordinating Cncl; *office:* Mowery Elem Schl 210 Clayton Ave Quincy PA 17247

SULLIVAN, DONALD DAYNE, Band & Orchestra Director; *b:* Ellwood City, PA; *m:* Nancy Rogers; *c:* Sean, Adam, Jaimie, Alyssa; *ed:* Grove City Coll (BM) Music Ed 1973; Grad Stud Bowling Green St Univ, Slippery Rock St Univ & Akron St Univ; *cr:* Cntrl Fulton HS Elem & Jr High Dir 1973-74; Perkins HS Elem & HS Asst Dir 1974-77; West Middlesex HS Band Dir 1977-79; Bedford HS Dir & Music Coord 1979-; *ai:* Marching Band; Jazz Ensemble; Musical Dir; Time Restructuring Comm; Music Coord; Dept Chm; OH Ed Assn 1975-; OH Music Ed Assn 1975-; Intnl Assn of Jazz Ed 1980-; *home:* 14617 Tabor Ave Maple Heights OH 44137

SULLIVAN, EILEEN MARY, First Grade Teacher; *b:* Cincinnati, OH; *ed:* Mt St Joseph Coll (BA) Elem Ed 1972; 2 Credit Hrs Math; 2 Credit Hrs Earth, Phys Sci; *cr:* Our Lady of Visitation Schl First Grd Tchr 1972-; *ai:* Curr Comm; NCEA 1972-; *office:* Our Lady Of Visitation Schl 3180 South Rd Cincinnati OH 45248

SULLIVAN, ELENA NEGMATULLAEVA, Former Lecturer; *b:* Dushanbe, Tajikistan; *m:* Richard E.; *c:* Natalie Landman, Joseph Richard; *ed:* Music Coll Tajik (BA) Music His 1972; Moscow Univ Russia (MA) Art His 1981; Inst of Art Uzb (PHD) Art His 1989; Silk Painting, Ceramic, Jewellery Classes; *cr:* Acad of Sci Sr Researcher 1981-91; Haifa Univ Israel Lecturer 1991-93; *ai:* Adult Silk Painting Class at BAEC at Boston Tchr Instr; Tour Guide of New England; Acting in Non-Prof Theater in Brookline; Prof Articles Pub.

SULLIVAN, F. PATRICK, Lang Arts & TeleComm Teacher; *b:* Pittsburgh, PA; *m:* Roberta F. Jefferson; *c:* Casey Ann; *ed:* Slippery Rock Univ (BSEd) Scndry Eng 1967; Post Grad Stud PA St Univ; *cr:* Pittsburgh Pub Schls Tchr 1967; Verona Pub Schls Tchr 1968-71; Riverview Schl Dist Tchr 1971-; *ai:* Telecomm, Television Productions Dir; Riverview Ed Assn 1971-, Chief Negotiator; PA St Ed Assn, NEA 1967-; *office:* Riverview HS 100 Hulton Rd Oakmont PA 15139

SULLIVAN, F. RUSSELL,JR., Professor of Philosophy & Math; *b:* Lynn, MA; *m:* Judith Ann Grant; *c:* F. Russell III, Scott; *ed:* Holy Cross Coll (BA) Philosophy, Classics 1955; Boston Coll (MA) Philosophy 1965; Boston Univ (PHD) Philosophy 1973; Tufts Univ (MA) Classics 1979; *cr:* Cntrl Cath HS Latin, Eng Instr 1963; New Prep Schl Greek, Latin, Eng Instr 1963-67; North Shore Comm Coll Prof Math, Philosophy 1967-; *ai:* NEA 1967-; Books Pub; *office:* North Shore Comm Coll 1 Ferncroft Rd Danvers MA 01923

SULLIVAN, GERALD JOSEPH, English & Latin Teacher; *b:* Chelsea, MS; *ed:* St Anselm Coll (BA) Eng 1970; Univ of IA (MA) Eng 1973; *cr:* Boston Pub Schls Eng Tchr 1976-80; Savio Prep HS Eng, Latin Tchr 1981-; *ai:* NHS, Lit Magazine Moderator; Acad Amer Poets 1994-; 14 Poems Pub; *office:* Savio Prep HS 145 Byron St East Boston MA 02128

SULLIVAN, HAROLD JOSEPH, Associate Prof of Govt Dept; *b:* Boston, MA; *ed:* Univ MA at Boston (BA) Politics 1969; City Univ Of NY (PHD) Pol Sci 1978; *cr:* Vassar Coll Visiting Prof 1983; Mt Holyoke Coll Visiting Prof 1983-84; John Jay Coll CUNY Assoc Prof & Chair 1984-; *ai:* Prsnl & Budget Comm; Cncl of Chairs; PSC-CUNY, NYSUT, AFL-CIO 1984-; Several Articles & Book Chapters on Constitutional Rights, Privatization of Govt Svcs, Racial Discrimination; *office:* John Jay Coll of Criminal Just 445 W 59th St Ofc New York NY 10019

SULLIVAN, J. BRYAN, Mathematics Teacher; *b:* Worcester, MA; *m:* Joan C. Sundin; *c:* Jeffrey Robert, Kristen Marie; *ed:* Worcester St Coll Math Ed (BSEd) 1965, (MED) 1968; 45 Addl Credit Hrs Beyond Masters; *cr:* Hudson HS Math Tchr 1965-; Mid Pacific Inst Math Tchr 1995; *ai:* WOCOMAL 1972-; ARML Coach, Exec Bd; Comm Chm, Speaker Local, Regnl & Natl Math Confs; Past ATMIM Spring Conf Chm 1990-94; ATMIM 1965-, Pres 1985-87; MAML 1976-, Content Dir, Pres 1976-79; WOCOMAL 1972-, Sec 1993; HEA, NEA, MTA, ATMNE, NCTM, NCSM; Math Coord 1969-89; NSF Fellow Univ DE 1985; Al Kulfus Founders Awd ARML 1993; Tandy Tech Scholar 1993; Spec Tchrs Are Recognized Cornell Um 1994; Featured Video NCTM Dreams Count; Presidential Awd Winner MA-NCTM Math, Sci; NCTM Conf Chm 1988; *office:* Hudson HS 69 Brigham St Hudson MA 01749*

SULLIVAN, JAMES E., English & Social Studies Tchr; *b:* Cleveland, OH; *m:* Kathleen M. Ward; *c:* Daniel W., Stephen J.; *ed:* Univ of MA at Boston (BA) Anthropology 1975; Boston St Coll (MED) Media 1982; 45 Addl Hrs Bridgewater St, Fitchburg St; Enrolled in CAGS Prgm in Educl Ldrshp Bridgewater St Coll; *cr:* Scituate HS Eng Tchr 1977-88; Newport HS Eng Tchr, Ath Dir 1988-89; Norwell HS Eng, Soc Stud Tchr 1989-; *ai:* Head Ftbl, Wrestling, Golf Coach; Fin Comm; Restructuring Comm Chair; NEA, MA Tchrs Assn 1977-; Norwell Ed Assn 1989-; Scituate Tchrs Assn 1977-88; Knights of Columbus 1988-; Scituate Yth Ftbl 1991-, Announcer; Scituate Little League 1992-, Asst Coach; Horace Mann Tchr Grant 1987; MA Shriner's All Star Ftbl Game Asst Coach 1994; South Shore League Ftbl Coach of Yr 1993, Ftbl Sportsmanship Awd 1992, Wrestling Sportsmanship Awd 1995; *office:* Norwell HS 18 South St Norwell MA 02061*

SULLIVAN, JAMES F., Professor of Physics; *b:* Cincinnati, OH; *m:* Sylvia J. Kasselmann; *c:* Robert L.; *ed:* Xavier Univ at Cincinnati (BS) Physics 1965, (MS) Physics 1969; Attnd Marion Coll, Butler Univ, Univ of Cincinnati; *cr:* Brebeuf Preparatory Schl Physics Instr 1965-68; Univ of Cincinnati Physics Prof 1968-; *ai:* Decanal Review Comm Chair; AAPT, Instrl Media Comms; Fac Senate Action Comm on Merit Grievances; Amer Assn of Univ Profs Negotiating Team Chief Negotiator; Southern OH Section AAPT 1983-, First Pres, VP, Section Rep, Sec, Assoc Sec; AAPT 1965-; Amer Assn Univ Profs 1992-; Univ of Cincinnati Chapter Amer Assn Univ Profs 1992-, VP; Amer Soc Engrng Ed 1978-; OH Acad of Sci 1990-; Amer Radio Relay League 1978-; Aircraft Owners, Pilots Assn, Dayton Pilots Club 1988-; OH Vly Amateur Radio Assn 1980-, Pres, VP; Greater Cincinnati Amateur Radio Assn; Author: Tech Physics; Co Author: Lab Manual for Gen Physics, Physics for Tech Lab Manual; O Educator of Amer 1973; Tau Alpha Phi Tchr of Yr Awd 1983; *offic* Of Cincinnati 2220 Victory Pky Cincinnati OH 45206

SULLIVAN, JAMES MICHAEL, 8th Grade US History Teac Holyoke, MA; *ed:* Westfield St Coll (BA) His & Ed 1987; Attnd F Univ; *cr:* Holyoke Pub Schls MS Tchr 1987-; *ai:* Bsktbl Coach; Adv; NEA & MA Tchrs Assn 1987-; Holyoke Tchrs Assoc 1987 *office:* John Lynch MS 1575 Northampton St Holyoke MA 01040

SULLIVAN, JANICE C., Sixth Grade Teacher; *b:* Taunton, M William; *c:* William Jr., Tammi L., Kathleen L.; *ed:* Barrington Co Elem Ed 1969; Fitchburg St Coll (MED) Educl Tech 1989; *cr.* Beckwith MS 6th Grd Tchr 1970-, 6th Grd Coord 1991-; *ai:* Sund Tchr; NEA, MTA 1970-; Dighton Rehoboth Regnl Tchrs Assn 197 Cue Inc 1989-; Bennett Schl PTO 1990-94, Pres, Treas; Mulcahey M 1994-, VP; Mulcahey MS Cncl 1994-, Co-Chm; SERRC 1992-; *off* L. Beckwith MS 330r Winthrop St Rehoboth MA 02769

SULLIVAN, JOHN WILLIAM, Math Teacher; *m:* Terry; *c:* Jason, *ed:* Univ of ME at Orono (BS) Math 1965; Univ of ME at Portland Ed 1974; *cr:* Noble HS Math Tchr 1965-; *ai:* Var Bsbl Coach 12 Yrs Team Coach 10 Yrs; MTA, MEA, ATONIN 1975-.

SULLIVAN, JOYCE ANN, Jr High Mathematics & Sci T Lawrence, MA; *m:* Philip S.; *c:* Michael, Tara Sullivan Dolan, E Merrimack Coll (BA) Hum, Ed 1964; Salem St Summer Course; C Religion; *cr:* Newton Meml Schl Jr High Eng, Sci Tchr 1964-66; Jr High Grd 9 Sci Tchr 1966-68; Sacred Heart Schl Jr High Math, S 1980-; Danvers HS Summer Schl Math, Eng Tchr 1988; Private T SSAT Prep Math Stud Skills Tchr 1989; *ai:* Dir Sci Fair; Coord H Grds 6-8; Chprsn Grad Ceremony; Grd 8 Placement Cnslr Gra Class; Math, Sci Chprsn, Lead Tchr; NCEA 1980-; North Andover Assn 12 Yrs; Andover Choral Soc 3 Yrs; *home:* 66 Jay Rd North A MA 01845*

SULLIVAN, KATHLEEN, Vice Prin & Jr HS Math Teacher; *b:* Pal PA; *ed:* St Peter's Coll (BS) Eng 1971; *cr:* Immaculate Conception 7 Tchr 1965-68; St Fortunata 8th Grd Tchr 1968-69; St Augustine Vic 8th Grd Tchr 1969-; St Joseph Summer HS Eng Tchr 1977-; *ai:* CYO; After Schl Prgm; Chprsn Math Dept; NCEA 1969-; ATMNJ, 1992-; Weehawken Lib Bd 1976-; CYO Bd Advs 1971-; St Elizabe Ed Dept Advy Bd 1986-92; *home:* 23 King Ave Weehawken NJ 070

SULLIVAN, KATHLEEN MARIE, Science Teacher; *b:* Frami MA; *ed:* VA Intermont Coll (BA) Hlth, PE 1972; *cr:* Our L Assumption Sci, PE, Hlth Tchr 1973-; Winchester HS Chrldng 1986-; *ai:* Natl Cath Edctrs Assn 1973-; *office:* Our Lady The Assu Schl 40 Grove St Lynnfield MA 01940

SULLIVAN, LENORE SAVELKOUL, Sixth Grade Teacher; *b:* ND; *m:* Michael John Bourke; *c:* Susan Sullivan Tullar, John Michael Daniel, Anne Sullivan Hudepohl; *ed:* Creighton Univ (BS Ed 1959; Attnd Univ of CA, CA St, Univ of Toledo; *cr:* Henry Ya Grd Tchr 1959-60; MT View 2nd Grd Tchr 1960-61; Indian Hill 2 Tchr 1961-62; Betterton 3rd Grd Tchr 1967; Kennedyville 56th 6 Tchr 1967; Riverside NJ 2nd Grd Tchr 1967-69; Modesto CA 2nd Gr 1969-74; Sacramento CA Pre-Schl 1974-76; Darien Il 4th Gr 1976-80; Napoleon OH 1981-; *ai:* NEA 1959-; Napoleon Fac 19 Augustines Church 1981-; Alpha Lit Club 1981-; Outstdng Tchr A 1972; *home:* 450 Briarcliff Dr Napoleon OH 43545

SULLIVAN, LINDA D., Social Studies Teacher; *b:* Troy, NY; *m:* M P.; *c:* Megan E.; *ed:* St Univ of NY at Oswego (BA) Ed 1969; *cr:* Cntrl Schl 7th Grd Soc Stud Tchr 1970-; *ai:* Sr Class & Jr HS St Adv; Team 7 Ldr; NEA 1970-; NYNEA 1970-, Del to Dels Assembl 1970-, Rep, NEA Del; Girl Scouts 1986-, Treas; *office:* Sodus Centr Mill St Ext Box 220 Sodus NY 14551

SULLIVAN, LOLA BLANK, English Teacher; *b:* New York City, James F.; *c:* Lola Reynolds, James Jr., Timothy, Sheila Jackson, Brian, Dennis, Mark, Aline; *ed:* Trinity Coll (BA) Eng 1951; Col Univ (MA) Eng Tchng 1952; *cr:* Pelham Meml HS Eng Tchr 19 1972-; Pelham MS Eng Tchr 1972-; *ai:* Fac Cncl Team Ldr; Pelham Assn 1972-, Pres 1976-82; Delta Kappa Gamma 1976-; *office:* Pelha Colonial & Corlies Aves Pelham NY 10803

SULLIVAN, LOUISE FRANCES, Chair Dept of Foreign Langua Norwood, MA; *ed:* Saint Joseph's Coll (BS) Ed 1956; Cath Univ of (MA) Fr Lang, Lit 1966; Univ of Paris at Sorbonne (PHD) Comparat 1972; Cert Inst of Phonetics & Linguistics 1970; Cert Sc Interpretation; *cr:* Holy Cross Schl Frgn Lang Dept Chair, Fr, Lati 1955-65; Coll St-Jean-Viannay Comparative Lit Prof 1973-74; N Univ Frgn Lang Dept Chair, Prof of Fr 1977-; *ai:* Phi Sigma Iota Daughters of Charity Comms; MLA, NYSAFLT 1977-; AATF 1977-, Pres; Rsrch Grants; Flwshp Mc Gill Univ; Fr Govt Grant; Nu Articles 1993-95; *office:* Niagara Univ Dept of Foreign Language N University NY 14109

SULLIVAN, MARGARET B., Counselor; *b:* Buffalo, NY; *m:* Jos Podgorski; *ed:* St Coll at Buffalo (BS) Scndry Soc Stud 1978; Ca Coll (MS) Cnslng 1981, (MS) Admin 1988; *cr:* Villa Maria Acad 1979-84; Amherst Cntrl HS Cnslr 1984-87; Orchard Park HS Cnslr *ai:* Sr Class Adv 1995-; Stu Govt, NHS Adv; Coord Co-Curricula OPTA 1988-; Bldg Rep; Canisius Coll Di Gamma Hnr Soc; Canisiu Alumnea Assn 1980-, Treas; *office:* Orchard Park HS 4040 Bak Orchard Park NY 14127

SULLIVAN, MARILYN MURPHY, English Teacher; *b:* Kansas Cit *m:* John L.; *c:* Megan, Kathleen, Erin; *ed:* KS St Univ (BS) Ed 1972, Scndry Ed 1974; 30 Addl Grad Hrs Beyond Masters; *cr:* Linn HS Eng 1972-74; Drouin HS Eng Tchr 1974-75; Atchison HS Eng Tchr 19 Wurzburg HS Eng Tchr 1979-; *ai:* Eng Dept Chair; NHS Adv; NEA, 1972-; NCTE 1989-; *office:* Wuerzburg HS Cmr 475 Box 297 AP 09036*

SULLIVAN, MARY DOLAN, Third Grade Teacher; *b:* New York NY; *m:* Gerard J.; *c:* Gerard T., John W., Paul C., Peter J., Elizabe Claire Blaise, Mary Davis; *ed:* Fordham Univ (BS) Elem Ed 1955; H Coll (MA) His 1978; *cr:* PS 9 First Grd Tchr 1955-59; St Catharine's Third Grd Tchr 1978-; *office:* Saint Catherines Catholic Schl Perkiomen Ave Reading PA 19606

SULLIVAN, MARY MARINAN, 2nd Grade Teacher; *b:* Elmira, N Thomas J.; *c:* John M., Daniel J., Kathleen A., Thomas; *ed:* Chestnu Coll (BS) Sci 1948; Elmira Coll Grad Stud; *cr:* Holy Family Cath K-2nd Grd Tchr 33 Yrs; *ai:* Chemung Area Rdng Cncl 1993-.

SULLIVAN, MARY BETH, English Teacher & Jrnlsm Adv; *b:* Broo MA; *m:* Mark J.; *c:* Brett, Kendra; *ed:* Bridgewater St Coll (BA) Eng Univ of Denver (MA) Theatre 1971; *cr:* Brockton HS Tchr 197 Bridgewater St Coll Tchr 1984; Stone Hill Coll Tchr 1984-90; East High Tchr 1991-92; Walpole HS Tchr 1993-; *ai:* The Rebellion Newspaper Adv; The Edctrs Exch Ed; *office:* Walpole HS 275 Comm Walpole MA 02081

SULLIVAN, NOREEN YEE, English as a Second Lang Tchr; *b:* Bo MA; *m:* Paul F.; *c:* Pamela, Marguerite, Susan; *ed:* Boston Univ (B 1971; Post Grad Stud in Eng as a Second Lang Univ of MA at Bosto Braintree Pub Schls K-12 Grd Eng as a Second Lang Instr 1986-, P ng Ed Eng as a Second Lang Tchr 1993-; Urbanistics Inc Eng as a Lang Tchr Summer Prgm 1994; *ai:* Cultural Awareness Club Adv; ok Bus Mgr; MA Assn Tchrs to Spekers of Other Langs 1993-; S Cncl 1993-95; SouthMS PTO 1989-92, VP, Pres; St Clare's Rel , 1985, 1989, CCD Tchr; Girls Scouts 1987-88, Troop Ldr; NHS Who Influenced a Mems Life Awd; *office:* Braintree HS 128 Town tree MA 02184

/AN, PATRICIA, Biology & Physiology Teacher; *b:* Holyoke, Eugene J.; *c:* Anne, Beth; *ed:* Elmo Coll (BA) Bio; Univ of MA Counseling & Guidance; Stud Providence Hospital Schl of *cr:* Providence Hospital Schl of Nursing Instr 1975-78; Holyoke Sci Dept Head, Tchr 1978-; *ai:* Acad, Discipline Bd; Lab Asst atl Honor Soc Comm Adv; Peer Edctrs Adv; Mass Sci Tchr, Cath ssn 1980-; Assn for Supervision & Curr Dev.

/AN, PAULINE F., Theological Tchr & Dept Chair; *b:* Providence, Anna Maria Coll (BA) Eng, Ed 1975; Providence Coll (MED) Guid, 1979; Boston Coll (AM) Theology 1989; Fordham Univ PHD Cand y; Capt MBTI Prof Prgm; *cr:* Providence Diocese Tchr 1976-79; lan Schl Prin 1979-82; Prout Meml Schl Guid Dir 1986-87; Msgr Schl Tchr 1983-86; St Mary Acad Tchr, Dept Chair 1992-; nce Coll Visiting Lecturer 1993, 1996; *ai:* Soph Class Adv; Acad rategic Planning Comm; Fac, Stu Advy Bd; Comm Task Force; 976-; APT 1985-; Court Appointed Spec Advocate; Regnl Adult Ed sh Cncl VP; Presidential Schlsp; Journal Tchrs Grant; Project Bus Recognition; *office:* St Mary Acad Bayview 3070 Pawtucket Ave e RI 02915*

VAN, REBECCA JEANNE, Assoc Prof of Allied Dental Ed; *b:* St MO; *m:* Daniel; *c:* Jessica, Lyndsay; *ed:* Bergen Comm Coll (AAS) Hygiene 1980; Columbia Univ (BS) Dental Hygiene Ed 1982; Univ (EDM) Ed 1985; *cr:* Univ of Medical & Dental of NJ Instr ; Union Cty Coll Instr 1984-85; Tunxis Comm-Tech Coll Assoc 85-; *ai:* Stu Am Dental Hygiene Assn Adv; Stu Affairs Comm; DH ons Comm; ADHA 1980-, Stu Adv Awd; CT Nutrition Assn 1994-; out Ldr 1993-; Nutrition Speaker Vol; TCTC Fnd Awd; UCONN Tchng Fac Awd; NISOD Outstanding Tchr Awd; *office:* Tunxis Tech Coll 271 Scott Swamp Rd Farmington CT 06032

VAN, RICHARD J., Athletic Dir & PE Teacher; *b:* Buffalo, NY; e; *c:* Penny, Dawn, Mark, Sandy; *ed:* Houghton Coll (BS) PE 1974; Hrs Various Colls; *cr:* Belfast Cntrl Schl Ath Dir, PE Tchr 1974-; Var Boys Soccer, Bsbl; NYSUT 1974-; Fire Dept Rescue Squad *office:* Belfast Central Schl PO Box 336 King St Belfast NY 14711

VAN, RONALD JOHN, High School Guidance Counselor; *b:* n, NY; *m:* Dorothy; *c:* Jennifer, Susan, Elizabeth; *ed:* Fairfield SS) Ed, His 1962; Queen Coll (MS) Ed 1972; CW Post (MS) e 1980; 42 Grad Hrs Hofstra, St Joseph, St John Univ, Azusa Nassau Comm Coll, Adelphi Univ, NYU; *cr:* Seaforth HS Soc Stud Guidance Cnslr 1962-; Cathage Group RNC Certified Financial 1987-; *ai:* Class Adv 1965-92; Var Coach Cross Cntry 1966-94, Track 1965-94; NEA 1968-; AFT 1965-; ICFP 1988-; NY St s Assn 1970-; NY St Track Coach of Yr 1982; Finalist as Natl Track of Yr 1982; Nassau Cty Sportsmanship Awd 1983; *home:* 35 Meade erport NY 11721

VAN, ROSEMARIE TRINCHERE, First Grade Teacher; *b:* PA; *m:* Thomas E.; *ed:* East Stroudsburg St Coll at Millersville em Ed 1977, (MS) Gen Ed 1992; *cr:* Ada B. Cheston Schl Grd K-1 984-; *ai:* Lang Arts, Rdngs Fun, Fac Fund Comms; PSEA, NEA PTA 1991-, Gril Tchr Rep; Lower Nazareth Womens Club 1992-94, ng Sec; Easton Area Schl Rep IBM Cmptr Magazine; *home:* 4629 Ln Nazareth PA 18064*

VAN, SEAN JOSEPH, Calculus Teacher; *b:* Castletownbere, *ed:* Iona Coll (BA) Math 1977; Manhattan Coll (MSEd) Ed 1983; Hallows HS Math Chm 1981-86, Vice Prin Discipline 1986-91, ing Dir 1991-92; Television Studio Moderator 1993; All Hallows cruiting Dir 1995-; *ai:* Cath HS Hockey League Commissioner 3; Inner-City Jobs Coord 1985-; Math Club Coord 1983-; Var Coach 1973-90; Vars, JV Bsbl Coach 1980-; Cath HS Ath Assn -Fame 1995; *office:* All Hallows HS 111 E 164th St Bronx NY

VAN, STEPHANIE SAMEN, Former Teacher; *b:* New Rochelle, Patrick; *c:* Haleigh; *ed:* Monmouth Coll (BA) Elem Ed 1988, (BA) 988; *cr:* Vetter Schl 3 Grd Tchr 1993-94; Woodmere Schl 5, 6 Grds 990-92, 3-6 Grds Basic Skills Tchr 1994-95.

VAN, SUSAN L., Health & Biology Educator; *b:* Baltimore, MD; v of MD at Coll Park (BS) Hlth Ed 1993; *cr:* Bladensburg HS Hlth, hr 1994-; *ai:* NEA 1994-; *office:* Bladensburg HS 5610 Tilden Rd sburg MD 20710

VAN, TIMOTHY LEE, Fifth Grade Teacher; *b:* Baltimore, MD; *m:* Brocklehurst; *c:* Katie Lee, Meghan Marie; *ed:* Bridgewater St Coll Elem Ed 1979; Lesley Coll (MED) Creative Arts, Learning 1989; Providence Coll, Univ of New England; *cr:* Dighton Elem Schl Fifth hr Aide, Permanent Sub Tchr 1979, Fifth Grd Tchr 1979-; *ai:* g Coach 1984-93; 5th Grd Acad Knowledge Open Coach 1990-93; d Team Ldr 1994-; MA Tchrs Assn, NEA, DRRTA 1979-; *office:* n MS 1250-R Somerset Ave Dighton MA 02715

VAN, WAYNE HARRIS, Amer History & Lang Arts Tchr; *b:* , NY; *m:* Barbara June Crouch; *c:* Brent, Sean; *ed:* MI St (BA) Ed, 59; OH St (MA) Ed 1980; Post Grad Work in Learning Style; *cr:* C. Wilson HS Tchr, Coach 1969-70; Georgesville Schl Tchr 1970-83; n Hghts HS Var Soccer Coach 1984-85, Girls Var Bsktbl Coach 3; Pleasant View MS Tchr, Track Coach 1984-, 7th Grd Girls Bsktbl *ai:* Washington DC Chaperone; SWEA 1970-, Rep; OEA, NEA Schl Bell Tchng Awd; *office:* Pleasant View MS 7255 Kropp Rd City OH 43123

VAN, WILLIAM JOSEPH, Assoc Prof of Religious Stud; *b:* on, MA; *m:* JeAnne Verliac; *c:* Pierre, William, Jeanne O'Brien, Kathleen, Siobain; *ed:* Saint Pauls Coll (BA) Philosophy 1953; Inst ique (STL) Theology 1963, (sTD) Theology 1967; Lang Courses Fr rance, Ger Ulm Germany; *cr:* OEO-Job Corps Admin 1967-1969; ohn Fisher Coll Assoc Prof 1969-; *ai:* Rochester Educl Access orative; Martin Luther King Day Comm; Coll Theology Soc 1969-; oorhood Assn 1980-, Pres; Reconciliation 1988-, Pres; Book s in Journal of Ecumenical Studs; Chapters Pub in The Capuchin 1970; Why Priests Marry 1970; Co-Author Crime & Comm in al Perspective 1980; *office:* Saint John Fisher Coll 3690 East Ave ster NY 14618

VAN-CARR, KATHLEEN MARY, Social Studies Teacher; *b:* yn, NY; *m:* Edward Carr; *ed:* SUNY at Albany (BA) His Ed 1987; Staten Island (MS) His Ed 1994; *cr:* Bishop Kearney Schl Soc Stud, chr 1987-88; Our Lady of Perpetual Help Schl Soc Stud Tchr 0; St Edmund Prep Schl Soc Stud Tchr, Coord 1990-; *ai:* Chm Mid m Acts, Soc Stud; NCEA 1987-; *office:* St Edmund Prep HS 2474 Ave Brooklyn NY 11229*

ER, JAYNE RYBAR, English Teacher; *b:* Mc Keesport, PA; *m:* : Melissa, Meridith; *ed:* Kent St Univ (BS) Eng 1969; *cr:* Kiski Area th Grd Eng, Speech Tchr 1969-70; Wesley Elem Schl 6th Grd Team Ldr 1970-76; St Brendan Schl 6th-8th Grd Gifted, Sci Tchr 1982-85; Dublin Mid Schls 6th-8th Grd Gifted Tchr 1987-90; Dublin Coffman HS 9th-12th Grd Eng, Speech Tchr 1990-; *ai:* NHS, Comm Club Adv; JV Tennis Team Coach; Steering Comms: Excl in Ed, Literacy Conf, Challenge of Choices; North Cntrl Assn Acad Achvmt Clyear; Coll Testing, Assessment; PTO Bd Rep; NEA 1987-; NASSP, NAGC 1988-; Dublin Arts Cncl 1995-; OSU Excl in Tchng Profession 1993; *office:* Dublin Coffman HS 6780 Coffman Rd Dublin OH 43017

SULSKY, JUDY, Mathematics Teacher; *b:* Elmira, NY; *m:* Leonard; *c:* Benjamin, Jessica; *ed:* SUNYA Cortland (BA) Psych & Math 1970, (MS) Ed 1972; Johns Hopkins Univ Post Grad Stud; *cr:* Peekskill HS Math Tchr 1972-73; Andover HS Math Tchr 1973-75; Arlington HS Math Tchr 1984-; *ai:* NYSUT 1984-; Arlington Tchrs Assn 1984-; AFT 1984-; MENSA 1989-; *office:* Arlington HS-N Campus 110 Stringham Rd Lagrangeville NY 12540

SULTAN, STANLEY, Professor of English; *b:* Brooklyn, NY; *m:* Betty Ann Hill; *c:* James Lehman, Sonia Elizabeth; *ed:* Cornell Univ (AB) Eng 1949; Boston Univ (MA) Eng Lit 1950; Yale Univ (PHD) Eng Lang & Lit 1955; *cr:* Smith Coll Instr 1955-59; Clark Univ Asst Prof to Prof 1959-; *ai:* AAUP 1960-; Natl Writers Union 1981-, Book Contracts Consultant; PEN Amer Ctr 1988-; NAACP 1948-; ACLU 1968-; Democratic Socialists of Amer 1973-; Amnesty Intnl 1975-; Books: Argument of Ulysses, Ulysses, The Waste Land and Modernism, Yeats at His Last & Rabbi; Numerous Articles & Short Stories Pub; *office:* Clark Univ 950 Main St Worcester MA 01610*

SULTANIK, HELEN MENCHE, Science Coordinator & Teacher; *b:* Wetzlar, Germany; *m:* Abraham; *c:* Edina, Joshua, Shana; *ed:* Brooklyn Coll (BS) Ed 1968, (MA) Sci Ed 1971; Advanced Cert in Supervision & Admin 1991; NYU & Tchrs Coll Doctoral Credits; *cr:* PS 138 Sci Tchr 1968-70; Yeshivah Of Flatbush K-8th Grd Sci Coord & 6th-8th Grd Sci Tchr 1976-; Brooklyn Coll Sci Ed Lecturer 1995; *ai:* Sci Club; Sci Rsrch Group; 7th Grd Play Choreographer; Understanding Adolescence Classes; NSTA; NY Acad of Scis; AAAS; STANYS; NY St Sci Mentor to Bd of Jewish Ed.*

SULZBACH, TRACY LYNN, Mathematics Teacher; *b:* Willoughby, OH; *ed:* Kent St Univ (BA) Math Scndry Ed 1989; *cr:* Grand Vly HS Math Tchr 1990-; *ai:* Var Vlybl, Girls Frosh Bsktbl Coach; *office:* Grand Valley HS 44 N School St Orwell OH 44076

SUMEREAU, MARIA BURANOVSKY, Science Teacher; *b:* Washington, DC; *m:* Timothy; *c:* Danielle M, Timothy Jr., Lauren A; *ed:* George Washington Univ (BS) Sci, Bio 1986; 15 Credit Hrs; *cr:* Queenot Apostles Schl Sci Tchr 1986-88; Randolph MS 8th Grd Sci Tchr 1988-91; West Morris Cntrl HS SCi Tchr 1991-; *ai:* Chrldng Adv 1991-; NEA, NJEA, NJSTA 1988-; PTA 1993-; Rosary Soc 1992-; *office:* West Morris Cntrl HS Four Bridges Rd Chester NJ 07930

SUMI, MARY LOU JERMAN, French & Spanish Teacher; *b:* Greenwich, CT; *m:* David A.; *c:* Karen, David, Carl; *ed:* St Joseph Coll (BA) Fr 1965; Fordham Univ (MA) Fr 1970; 6th Yr Guidance 1983 Univ of Bridgeport; *cr:* Westhill HS Fr, Span Tchr 1965-; Rippowam HS Fr, Span Tchr 1965-; Stamford HS Fr, Span Tchr 1965-; *office:* Westhill HS 125 Roxbury Rd Stamford CT 06902

SUMINSKI, DOLORES LASKO, English Teacher; *b:* South Amboy, NJ; *m:* Robert; *c:* Stephanie, Thomas; *ed:* Montclair Univ (BA) Eng 1966; *cr:* Sayreville HS Eng Tchr 1966-68; Escambia HS Eng Tchr 1968-69; Sayreville HS Eng Tchr 1969-72, 1984-; *ai:* Procedures, PLAID Comms; Mid Sts Evaluation Comm Chprsn; NEA; NJEA; SEA; Tchr of Yr 1995; *office:* Sayreville War Memorial HS 820 Washington Rd Parlin NJ 08859

SUMME, RACHAEL MARIE, Social Studies Teacher; *b:* Melrose, MA; *m:* Gregory Leonard; *ed:* Keene St Coll (BA) Soc Sci 1991; Yale Hopkins Summer Inst Russian Stud; *cr:* Keene HS Pol Sci, Ecs & Russian His Tchr 1991-; *ai:* Var Field Hockey Coach 1992-; Frosh Girls Bsktbl 1991-; NEA 1991-; *office:* Keene HS 42 Arch St Keene NH 03431

SUMMERS, BARBARA LEVETT, Family & Consumer Science Tchr; *b:* New Kensington, PA; *m:* David J.; *c:* Scott Thomas, Kaitlin Brenna; *ed:* Penn St Univ (BS) Home Ec 1979; Attnd Robert Morris, Pitt Univ; *cr:* Highland HS Family & Consumer Sci Tchr 1981-; *ai:* Co-Spon of Human Relations Comm; Attendance Comm; PSEA 1979-; HEA 1979-; *office:* Highlands Sr HS Idaho At Pacific Natrona Heights PA 15065

SUMMERS, BONNITA STEEN, First Grade Teacher; *b:* Warren, OH; *m:* Robert D.; *c:* R. Scott; *ed:* Youngstown Univ (BS) Elem Ed 1967; Kent St 6 Credit Hrs; Ashland Univ 3 Credit Hrs; Youngstown St 18 Credit Hrs; *cr:* Lisbom Schl 2nd Grd Tchr 1964-65; Southington Schls 1-2 Grd Tchr 1965-67; Warren City Schls 3rd-1st Grd Tchr 1972-; *ai:* Sunshine Social Textbook Selection; Grd Level Ldr; Stu Achvmt Comm; Parent, Tchr cncl; NEA, OEA, NEOEA, WEA 1964-; Trumbull Area Rdng Cncl 1985-; Kent St Mentor 1986-88; Bus & Prof Women 1970-; *office:* Warren City Schls 625 Roosevelt Warren OH 44483*

SUMMERS, NANCY, Coord of Hum Svc Pgm; *b:* Columbus, OH; *m:* Martin O. Yespy; *ed:* Wilmington Coll (BA) Sociology & Psychology 1965; Penn St Univ (MA) Amer Stud 1981; Loyola Coll in MD (MA) Clinical Psychology 1988; *cr:* Harrisburg Hosp Ment Hlth Ctr Caseworker 1968-71; Harrisburg Area Comm Coll Adjunct Fac 1971-; N Dan MH & MR Caseworker 1972-74; Handler Ctr Dir of Consultation & Educ 1974-90; Dan Co MH & MR Dir of Consultation & Ed 1990-; Instr & Coord of Socialogy; *ai:* PA Turnpike His, Heritage Comm 1990-, Techical Adv' Michway Forest Assn 1992-, VP; Upper Allen Twnshp Architectural Review 1993-; Pub The Silver Lining, The unexpected Advantage of Divorced Women; *office:* Harrisburg Area Comm College One HACC DR. Harrisburg PA 17110

SUMMERS, NANCY JOAN, Vocal Music Instr; *b:* Montrose, PA; *m:* Kenneth Ketchum; *ed:* Crane Schl of Music SUNY Potsdam (BSME) 1975; SUNY New Paltz, Coll of St Rose 30 Grad Hrs; *cr:* DE Valley Cntrl Schl K-12th Grd Vocal Music 1978-84; Susquehanna Valley HS 7th-12th Grd Vocal Music 1984-87; Whitney Point HS Singer & Keyboards 1988-; *ai:* Concert & Mixed Select Chorus; Phoenix Club; Preparation of Solos for Auditions; MENC 1978-; NYSSMA 1978-; ACDA 1994-; Whitney Point Music Boosters 1989-, Past Sec; WP Schl Comm Theatre 1991-; *office:* Whitney Point HS Keibel Rd Whitney Point NY 13862

SUMMERSON, ANN MC ANENY, Art Teacher; *b:* Johnstown, PA; *m:* Richard A.; *c:* James Lyle; *ed:* Coll of Notre Dame of MD (BA) Art Ed 1974; Masters Equivalency Towson St Univ at Loyola; *cr:* Stemmers Run Jr HS Art Tchr 1974-79; Mid River MS Art Tchr, Dept Chair 1984-89; Dumbarton MS Art Tchr, Art Team Ldr 1989-; *ai:* Art Svc Club Spon, Ldr; Spon for Stdnts Helping Armacost Nrsng Home & Jospeh Richey Hospice; Schl Liason Kids Helping Hopkins; GATE Art Curr; Amer Ed Wk Comm; SIT Comm; NEA, Tchrs of Baltimore Co 1974-; MAEA 1995-, Outstdng Visual Arts Edctr 1995; St Piux X 1976-, CCD Tchr; Chamber of Commerce Outstdng MS Tchr Awd 1992; Wrote Portfolio's An Art Tchrs Resources Chaired Comm; MS Schl Curr Guide Curr Comm; *home:* 634 Regester Ave Baltimore MD 21212*

SUMMONTE, MARY THERESE O'GRADY, First Grade Teacher; *b:* Staten Island, NY; *m:* John Michael; *c:* Kevin Francis; John Michael; *ed:* Georgian Court Coll (BA) Elem, Nursery Schl 1979, (MED) 1984; *cr:* Freehold Twp Schls Kndgtn-4th Grd Tchr 1979-; *ai:* Early Intervention Comm Pre-Kndgtn Children; Mentor Tchr New 1st Grd Tchrs; Teach Summer Prgm Pre-Kndgtn Children Need Help; NJ Ed, Freehold Township Ed Assn 1979-; *home:* 229 Plymouth Dr Freehold NJ 07728*

SUMNER, ALTON ELLIOT, History & Government Teacher; *b:* Enfield, NC; *m:* Betty Jean DeBerry; *c:* Jonathan E., Nichelle J.; *ed:* NC Cntrl Univ (BA) His 1976, (MA) His 1982; 24 Credit Hrs in Schl Admin; *cr:* Hillside HS His & Soc Stud Tchr 1976-89; Durham Extended Day Schl His Tchr 192-85; Walt Whitman HS His & Govt Tchr 1990-; Mt Vernon Coll Adj His Prof 1993-94; *ai:* Fac Cncl Chm; Montgomery Cty Employees Charity Campaign for Whitman Coord; NEA 1976-; MSTA 1990-; MCEA 1990-; Durham NC Mayors Key Vol Awd; Durham Comm on the Affairs of Black People Comm Svc Awd 1982 & 1983; UNCF Meritorious Svc Awd 1989; *office:* Walt Whitman HS 7100 Whittier Blvd Bethesda MD 20817

SUMNER, DAVID MASON, Design Technology Teacher; *b:* Attleboro, MA; *ed:* Wentworth Inst (Diploma) Machine Design 1959; Northeastern Univ (BS) Ed 1962; *cr:* King Philip HS Tech Drawing Tchr 1962-; Lincoln Coll Engrng Graphics Lecturer 1964-68; *ai:* Schl Cncl; Acad Stans Comm; NEA 1962-, Longevity; KPTA 1962-; New England Tech Drawing Tchrs Assn 1964-, VP; *office:* King Philip HS 201 Franklin St Wrentham MA 02093

SUMNER, DONNA CELLUCCI, Mathematics Dept Chprsn & Tchr; *b:* Newton, MA; *m:* George Laurence; *ed:* Regis Coll (BA) Math 1977; Cambridge Coll (MEd) 1994; *cr:* Matignon HS Math Tchr & Dept Chprsn 1977-; *ai:* Math Club Moderator; Sr Grad, Sr Awds & SAT Prep Course Adv; NHS Bd; Acad Cncl; NCEA 1977-; NCTM 1980-; ASCD 1990-; Tandy Tech Scholar Awd; Tufts Univ & MS Inst of Tech Letters of Commendation; NHS Tchr of Yr Awd; Boston Coll Math Tchr Ctr Math Inst Seminar Series & Math Forum; *office:* Matignon HS 1 Matignon Rd Cambridge MA 02140

SUNDAY, NANCY JO, Special Education Teacher; *b:* Defiance, OH; *ed:* Eastern NM Univ (BS) PE 1975; IN Univ (MS) Elem Ed 1987; *cr:* Ray of Hope Schl Tchr 1977-79; Hicksville Elem Schl Tchr of Spec Ed 1979-; *ai:* Elem Stu Cnslr Adv; Hicksville Ed Assn 1979-, Treas, Pres; OH Ed Assn, NEA 1979-; Delta Kappa Gamma 1988-, World Fellowship Chprsn; *office:* Hicksville Elem Schl W Arthur St Hicksville OH 43526

SUNDAY-LEFKOWITZ, LISA, Asst Prof of Occuptnl Therapy; *b:* Wilkes Barre, PA; *m:* Jay Lefkowitz; *c:* Noah; *ed:* Coll Misericordia (BS) Occupational Therapy 1987; Coll Misericordia (MSEd) Educ 1994; 2 Grd Credits School-Based Practice for Related Svcs 1992; 2 Grad Credits Classroom Application for Schl-Based Practice 1993; Working on MED; *cr:* Allied Svcs Occupational Therapist 1987-88; Luzerne Intermediate Unit Occupational Therapist 1988-92; Complete Home Care Occupational Therapist 1991-; Coll Misericordia Fieldwork Coord, Instr 1992-; Hazleton Area Schl Dist O. T. Consultant 1993-; Cnsltnt to Lksde Nrsng Cntr 1994-; *ai:* Dev of New O. T. Curr Contributor; Pi Theta Epsilon, Psi Chapter Adv; MIT, Fac Dev, Tech Integration Task Force Comms; Honors Stu Mentor; AOTA 1987-; POTA 1992-, Prgm Chair Dist III; COE of AOTA, POTA 1992-; PSEA, NEA 1988-92; *office:* College Misericordia 301 Lake St Dallas PA 18612*

SUNDBERG, ARNOLD PETER, Amer History & Govt Educator; *b:* Jersey Shore, PA; *m:* Maureen Pastrick; *c:* Arnold; *ed:* Lock Haven Univ (BS) Scndry Ed, Soc Sci 1973; PA Dept of Ed Master's Equivalency 1991; *cr:* Jersey Shore Area Schl Dist HS Amer His, Govt Tchr 1973-; *ai:* Adv: Stu Cncl 1975-82, HS Class 1982-87, Model United Nations 1986-; NEA 1973-; PA St Ed Assn 1973-, Cntrl Region Exec Comm; Jersey Shore Area Ed Assn 1973-, VP; Jersey Shore Borough Planning Commission 1986; Intl Stud Inst Schlsp 1974; Young Amers Inst Presidential Classroom 1982; Dist Prof Dev Comm Chprsn; *office:* Jersey Shore Area Sr HS 701 Cemetery St Jersey Shore PA 17740*

SUNDERMAN, MARILYN A.,RSM, Religious Studies Asst Prof; *b:* Warner Robins, GA; *ed:* Edgecliff Coll (BA) Span, Eng-Summa Cum Laude 1970; Univ of Cinti (MA) Span 1972; Aquinas Coll (MA) Rel Ed 1983; Fordham Univ (PHD) Theology 1995; *cr:* Lourdes Coll Span & Rel Stud Instr 1982-86; St Mary's Seminary & Univ Asst Prof, Systematic Theology 1992-94; St Joseph's Coll Asst Prof, Rel Stud 1994-; *ai:* Rel Ed Commission of St Edmund's Parish, Stu Svcs Comm Mem; CTSA, AAR, MHEC, Intnl Merton Soc 1995-; MAST 1990-; Coll Theology Soc 1982-; Kappa Gamma Pi 1970-; Charles Fleischman, Instituto de Estudios Ibero Americanos, Univ of Cinti Grad Schlsps; Articles Pub 1996; *office:* Saint Josephs Coll 278 Whites Bridge Rd Standish ME 04062

SUNUNU, ALEXANDRA E., Foreign Language Teacher; *b:* New York City, NY; *c:* Nicole, John, James, Thomas; *ed:* Manhattanville Coll of Sacred Heart (BA) Span Lit 1964; St John's Univ (MA) Span Lit 1967; Grad Ctr CUNY (PHD) Hispanic, Luso Brazilian Lit 1993; Studied at Universita De Toulon, L'Universite de Caen; Cathedral Coll; *cr:* Delehanty HS Tchr 1964-65; West Hempstead HS Tchr 1976-; *ai:* Class 1998, Fr Club Adv; AATSP, AATF 1976-; AATI 1979-; LILT 1988-; Church Orz; Lang Clubs; Article Pub; *office:* West Hempstead HS 400 Nassau Blvd West Hempstead NY 11552

SUPON, PATRICIA REDENBACH, Math & American History Tchr; *b:* Wooster, OH; *m:* John F.; *c:* Aaron F.; *ed:* OH St Univ (BA) Elem Ed 1975, (MS) Early & Mid Chldhd Ed 1984; Cert in Music 1975; Prin & Supvrs Cert 1984; 15 Plus Semester Hrs Past Masters Degree; *cr:* Crestline Exempted Village Schl 3rd Grd Tchr 1975-79, 7th & 8th Grd Tchr 1979-; 1st United Meth Church Choir Dir 1978-, Handbell Dir 1985-, Organist 1993-94; Math & Amer His Tchr 1995-; *ai:* MS Vlybl Coach 5 Yrs; Choreographer, Pianist & Musical Dir for HS Plays 8 Yrs; Acompanianist & Piano MS & HS Choirs 6 Yrs; Coord for MS Discipline & Reward Prgm 7 Yrs; OH Ed Assn 1975-, Bldg Rep 11 Yrs, Treas 2 Yrs, VP 5 Yrs & Pres 2 Yrs; 1st United Meth Church 1978-, Choir Dir, Handbell Dir, Organist; You Made a Difference Awd 1995 Given by 8th Grd Class; Recognition by Crestline Music Booster for Contributions Made as Choir Accompianist 1994-95; *office:* Crestline MS 215 N Columbus St Crestline OH 44827*

SUPPA, VERONICA PETRUSKY, Music Dept Chair & Eng Tchr; *b:* Shenandoah, PA; *m:* Carl M.; *c:* Carl Joseph, Regina Grabey, Elizabeth; *ed:* Chestnut Hill Coll (MusB) Music 1950; West Chester Univ Music Cert 1974; Temple Univ Music Cert 1974; Private Vocal Stud in New York City, Philadelphia PA & Milan Italy; *cr:* Opera Company of Philadelphia, Philadelphia Grand Opera & Springfield Symphony Performing Artist 1952-80; Notre Dame Acad Eng & Music Tchr & Music Dept Chprsn; *ai:* Glee Club Moderator; Curr Comm; Faculty Adv; MENC & NEA 1970-; NCEA 1980-; *office:* Notre Dame Acad 560 Sproul Rd Villanova PA 19085

SUPPELSA, SUZANNE MARIE, Biology Teacher; *b:* Cudahy, WI; *m:* George Zilvetti; *ed:* Boston Coll (BA) Bio, Sec Ed 1988, (MST) Scndry Ed 1989; *cr:* Benjamin Franklin MS Sci Tchr 1989-94; Teaneck HS Bio Tchr 1994-; *ai:* Class Spon Class of 1998; Womens Issues Group Spon; NABT, NJSTA 1989-; Dodge Fnd Grant Recipient; *office:* Teaneck HS 100 Elizabeth Ave Teaneck NJ 07666*

SURACE, MICHELE MARIE, Business Education Teacher; *b:* Atlantic City, NJ; *ed:* SUNY Coll at Oswego (BA) Bus Ed 1989; SUNY Coll at Cortland (MS) Rdng Ed 1996; 6 Post Grad Hrs; *cr:* Norrell Svcs Human Resource Mgr 4 Yrs; Westmoreland HS Bus Tchr 3 Yrs; *ai:* Comm Trng on Cmptrs; Chrldng Coach 3 Yrs; Coord Annual Career Days 3 Yrs; Adult Trng Local Coll; WTA 3 Yrs; FBLA 2 Yrs; Prsnl Bus Mgrs Assn 4 Yrs; *home:* 556 S Jay St Rome NY 13440

SURASH, BARBARA CELENTANO, High School English Teacher; *b:* Bronx, NY; *m:* Robert; *c:* Rebecca, William; *ed:* SUNY at Binghamton (BS) Eng & His 1982; SUNY at Brockport (MSEd) Scndry Eng 1991; *cr:* Hilton Cntrl Schl HS Eng Tchr 1992-; *ai:* Class of 1996 Adv; AFT; NYSUT; Natural Family Planning 1985-, Instr, Instr of Yr 1988; Craig Hill PTA 1992-; The Cyril & Gertrude Hare Awd; Baline M DeLancey Awd; *office:* Hilton HS 400 East Ave Hilton NY 14468

SUREAU, JAMES P., Leadership Education Teacher; *b:* Bronx, NY; *c:* Thom, Tim; *ed:* Marist Coll (BA) Bus 1969; National Univ (MBA) Bus 1982; DOD Comptroller Air Univ at Montgomery 1985; *cr:* USMC Ofcr 1969-90; DOD USMC Fin Analyst 1991-93; Lindenhurst HS JROTC Instr 1993-; *ai:* MC JROTC Drill Team; JV Soccer, Var Asst Girls Sftbl Coach; Backstage Dir Thespians; Amer Soc Military Comptrollers 1985-, Budget Ofcr of Yr 1990; Retired Ofcrs Assn 1989-; 1st Yr Unit Awd Pride of Lindenhurst Comm Svc 1993-94.

SURETTE, RICHARD JAMES, Eng & Creative Writing Tchr; *b:* Chelsea, MA; *m:* Lorraine Jean Umhoefer; *c:* Andrew Raymond; *ed:* Univ of MD (BA) Eng Ed, (BA) Latin 1977; Masters Equivalency Degree Montgomery Cty Pub Schls 1989; 21 Credits Counseling, Gerontology, Hood Coll; *cr:* Poolesville HS Spec Ed Aide, Sub Tchr 1978-79; Montgomery Village Jr HS Spec Ed, Learning Disabilities Aide 1979-81; Tilden MS Learning Disabilities, Eng Tchr 1981-83; M. L. King MS 7-8 Grd Eng, Creative Writing Tchr 1983-; *ai:* Domescus HS Coach Girls JV Vlybl; Intramurals Dir, Spon; Gifted & Talented Selection Comm Chprsn; NEA, MCEA 1991-; NCTE 1984-; Amer Vlybl Coaches 1989-; US Vlybl Assn 1988-, Level II Accreditation; Supts Writing Awds Spon 1989, 1991; *home:* PO Box 485 3318 Paprika Ct Buckeystown MD 21717

SURIANO, THOMAS MICHAEL, High School Guidance Counselor; *b:* Martines Ferry, OH; *m:* Kimberly Ann Gdula; *c:* Susan, Stephanie; *ed:* West Liberty St Coll (BA) PE, Spec Ed 1977-; Dayton Univ (MS) Gud, Cnslng 1984-; *ai:* Var Ftbl Coach; Underclass Coord; NEA, MFEA, OEA 1977-; *office:* Martins Ferry HS 810 Hanover St Martins Ferry OH 43935

SURIEL, REGINA L., Earth Science Teacher; *b:* Santo Domingo, Dominican Repub; *m:* Chris Papadopoulos; *ed:* City Univ of NY (BS) Scndry Ed, Sci 1992; 18 Post Grad Credits; Cert Bronx Zoo Wildlife Through Zoological Ed Prgm; *cr:* Theodore Roosevelt HS Tchr, Cluster Coord 1992-; *ai:* Sci Club Dir; Feminists in Search of Reaching Excl Spon, Collaborator; Authentic Sci Rsrch Prgm Facilitator; UFT 1992-; *office:* Theodore Roosevelt HS 500 E Fordham Rd Bronx NY 10458

SURON, SANDRA LEE, English & Social Studies Tchr; *b:* Kittanning, PA; *c:* J. Paul, Adam; *ed:* Glenville St Coll (BA) Eng & Soc Stud 1973; Working on Masters in Lit at IN Univ of PA; *cr:* Armstrong Schl Dist Eng & Soc Stud Scndry Educator 1976-; *ai:* Gothic Lit Club Adv; Drama, Newspaper & Class Spon; Vlybl Coach, SADD Adv; Puppetry Club; NCTE 1995-; PSEA 1976-, NEA 1976-; Armstrong Cty Hosp 1990-91, Vol; Compassion Intnl 1987-; Amer Sign Lang Club Adv; Yrbk Dedication; Poetic Voices of Amer 1988; Armstrong Schl Dist Educl Grant; *office:* Armstrong Schl Dist Main St Ford City PA 16226

SUROWITZ, BONITA ROSE, 6th Grd Sci & Lang Arts Tchr; *b:* Johnson City, NY; *ed:* Oneonta (BS) Elem Ed 1963; *cr:* Vestal Cntrl Schls Tchr 1963-; *ai:* Bldg Planning Dist Group; NEA, Vestal Tchr Assn 1963-; *home:* 74 Cook St Johnson City NY 13790*

SUSI, KATHERINE C., First Grade Teacher; *b:* Dexter, ME; *m:* Ted; *c:* Christie E., John Dominic; *ed:* Wheelock Coll (BS) Early Chldhd 1974; Rich Classroom Comp Tech, Rdng & Writing Connection; *cr:* Bloomfield Elem 2nd Grd Tchr 1981-89; Norridgewock Elem Kndgtn Tchr 1991-93; North Elem 1st Grd Tchr 1993-; *ai:* Pride of North Elem; MEA 1974-; NEA 1974-; ME Rdng Assn 1992-; Grants: Writing & Sci Connection, Recycling Elem Grds; *office:* North Elem Schl Reed St Skowhegan ME 04976

SUSLA, JEFFREY J., English Teacher; *b:* Bridgeport, CT; *m:* Patricia Anne Plumb; *ed:* Wesleyan Univ (BA) Eng, His 1982; Dartmouth Coll (MALS) Hum 1991; Post Grad Stud Wesleyan Univ CT St Cert 1992-93; *cr:* Woodhall Schl Eng, His Tchr 1986; US Peace Corps Vol Eng Tchr 1988-89; Woodstock Acad Eng Tchr 1993-; *ai:* Stu Cncl, Natural Helper Advs; NEA, NCTE, CCTE 1993-; CT Writing Project Fellowship 1994; *office:* Woodstock Academy Academy Rd Woodstock CT 06281*

SUSTER, ZELJAN E., Economics Professor; *b:* Split, Yugoslavia; *m:* Sanja Grubacic; *ed:* Univ of Belgrade (BA) Ec, Fin 1981, (MA) Intnl Ec 1984, (PHD) Ec 1988; Visiting Fac Yale, Mellon Prgm Yale Univ; *cr:* Inst of Ec Sci Rsrch Fellow 1983-89; Univ of CT Visiting Lecturer 1989-90; Univ of New Haven Asst Prof 1990-95, Assoc Prof 1995-; *ai:* AAASS, NASSS 1993-; North Amer Soc for Serbian Stud 1993-, Governing, Editorial Bds; Mellon Flwshp Univ of IL at Urbana Champaign; Ester Botwinik Awd; Numerous Articles Pub; *office:* Univ Of New Haven 300 Orange Ave West Haven CT 06516

SUSZYNSKI, JOHN VINCENT, High School English Teacher; *b:* Mc Kees Rocks, PA; *m:* Karen Ann Kuchta; *c:* Julia; *ed:* IN Univ of PA (BS) Scndry Eng 1972; Univ of Southwestern LA (MA) Eng, Creative Writing 1976; US Merchant Marine Acad 1968-69; *cr:* Sto-Roy HS Scndry Eng Tchr 1972-78; The Resume Writer Proprietor 1979-86; Peters Twp HS Scndry Eng Tchr 1986-; *ai:* Acad Cncl Charter Mem; Stu Cncl, Sr Class Spon; Grad Project Ad Hoc, Ineligibility Policy Revision, Blue Ribbon Writing Comms; AFT 1986-; Articles Pub; Movie Critic; *office:* Peters Twp HS 264 E Mcmurray Rd Mc Murray PA 15317

SUTCLIFFE, GEORGE DOUGLASS,JR., Chemistry Teacher & Coll Cnslr; *b:* Boston, MA; *m:* Jannine Praetsch; *c:* Kent, Heather; *ed:* Univ of ME (BS) Natural Resource Mgmt 1974; Worcester Polytechnic Inst (MNS) Natural Scis 1986; *cr:* Tilton Schl Math Chair Sci Division & Tchr 1974-; *ai:* Cycling, LaCrosse & Soccer Coach; Woodworking Instr; Outdoor Wilderness Ldr; NSTA 1978-; NSSA 1988; Fred Andrew Smart Chair for Distngd Tchng 1990-; Dean Jeffries Awd 1987; *office:* Tilton Schl 30 School St Tilton NH 03276*

SUTER, GRACE, Physical Science Teacher; *b:* Yellow Springs, PA; *m:* Donald; *c:* Brian, Jeffrey; *ed:* Bloomsburg St Coll (BS) Earth, Space Sci, Gen Sci 1966; MS Equivalency; Grad Credits PA St Univ, Temple Univ, Trenton St Univ; *cr:* F. D. Roosevelt Jr HS Sci Tchr 1966-, Sci Dept Chprsn 1970-; *ai:* BTEA, PSEA, NEA 1966-; Sci Advy Cncl of Bucks Cty 1995-; ASA 1991-, ACSI 1991-, VP; Planetary Soc Aut Com 1993-; St Stephen's Luth Church 1979-; Amer Legion Auxilliary 1973-, Philadelphia 200, Acad Natl Sci; Bristol Twp Strategic Planning Comm 1993-94; Eisenhower Grant 1992-93; *office:* F D Roosevelt Jr HS 1001 New Rodgers Rd Bristol PA 19007

SUTER, STEVEN MATTHEW, Social Studies Teacher; *b:* Findlay, OH; *ed:* Muskingum Coll (BA) His 1992; *cr:* Arlington HS Soc Stud Tchr 1992-; *ai:* Asst Ftbl, Bsktbl Coach; AFT 1992-; *office:* Arlington Local Schl 336 S Main Arlington OH 45814

SUTER, THOMAS EDWIN,JR., Art Instructor; *b:* Portsmouth, OH; *m:* Lori Lynn; *c:* Tyler Edwin; *ed:* Univ of Cincinnati (BFA) Art Ed 1984; Miami Univ at Oxford (MA) Art Ed 1989; Post Grad Courses at OH St Univ; *cr:* Wheelersburg Local Schls Grd 6-12 Art Instr 1984-; OH Univ Adj Art Ed, Painting Instr 1990-; Shawnee St Univ Adj Cmptr Art Instr 1995-; *ai:* Jr HS Boys Bsktbl Coach; Home PAGE Team Ldr, Creator; Tech Comm Chprsn; NAEA, OAEA 1984-; Univ of Cincinnati Summer Grad Flwshp 1989; Miami Univ Top Grad Stu Awd 1990; OH Dept of Ed Art Tchrs Are Stars Awd 1992; GTE, Cncl of Great Lakes Governors Educl Tech Awd 1992; *home:* 8712 Avalon St Wheelersburg OH 45694

SUTER, VALERIE JACKSON, Physics & Chemistry Teacher; *b:* Jersey Shore, PA; *m:* Robert B.; *c:* Nathaniel, Katherine; *ed:* Univ of Pittsburgh (BS) Bio 1968; Univ of MI (MS) Zoology 1969; RPI Grad Courses in Physics 1990-91; *cr:* Univ of MI Tchng Asst 1968-69; St Marys Acad Chem Tchr 1969-71; IUPUI Lecturer 1974-77; Vassar Coll Lecturer 1977-78, Dir of Natural His Ed Pgm 1983-88; Wappingers Schls Physics & Chem Tchr 1989-92; Arlington Schls Physics & Chem Tchr 1992-; *ai:* NHS Adv; STANYS 1989-, Physics Sar 1992-95; NSTA; STANYS Outstdng Tchr of Sci 1992; *office:* Arlington HS-N Campus 263 State Route 55 Lagrangeville NY 12540

SUTERA, STEPHEN ANTHONY,SR., English Teacher; *b:* Boston, MA; *c:* Stephen Jr., LIsa Lucido, Michael, Scott; *ed:* Univ of MA (BA) Eng, Ed 1966; Salem St (MAEd) Eng 1972; *cr:* Gloucester HS Eng Tchr 1966-87; Bishop Fenwich HS Eng Tchr 1987-; *ai:* Cross Cntry, Winter & Spring Track Coach; NCEA, NCET 1987-; *home:* 8 Harvard St Gloucester MA 01930*

SUTHERLAND, CATHERINE ELIZABETH, Vocal Music Teacher; *b:* Jamestown, NY; *m:* Ronald Anthony; *ed:* St Univ NY at Fredonia (BS) Music Ed 1977; SUNY at Fredonia (MS) Music Ed 1983; Hertfordshire England, Northern IL Univ Choral Music Experience Inst for Choral Tchr Ed; Voice Ed in Real World Sponsored by Hartt Coll Voice Care Network; *cr:* Portville Cntrl Schl Vocal Music Tchr 1977-81; Depew Cntrl Schl Vocal Music Tchr 1981-82; Williamsville Cntrl Schl Vocal Music Tchr 1982-; *ai:* Western NY Childrens Chorus Accompanist; Steering Comm Chprsn, Adv, Advisee; Mentor, Mentee Comm; Private Piano Instr; NY St Schl Music Assn Chprsn; Amer Choral Dirs Assn; NY St Schl Music Assn, Winter Conf Head Chaperone; MENC; Erie Cty Music Edctrs Assn, Sec; NY St United Tchrs; Williamsville Tchrs Assn, Bldg Rep; Cty, NYSSMA Choral Music Festivals Active Guest Conductor.

SUTHERLAND, LINDA, Art Teacher; *b:* Hudson, NY; *m:* Fred J.; *c:* Frederick; *ed:* Columbia Greene Comm Coll (AA) Lbrl Arts-Hnrs 1978; SUNY at Albany (BA) Art-Summa Cum Laude 1980; Coll of St Rose (MS) Art Ed 1983; *cr:* Red Hook Cntrl Schl Dist Continuing Ed Instr 1981, Sub Tchr 1982-85; Vincentian Ed Ctr 1st Grd Art Lab Tchr 1981; Columbia Greene Comm Coll Sub Instr Continuing Ed Pgm 1982-85; Schodack Cntrl Schl Dist Sub Tchr 1982-85; Germantown Cntrl Schl Dist Sub Tchr 1982-85; Hudson City Schl Dist Sub Tchr 1982-85; Taconic Hills Cntrl Schl Dist Elem Art Sub Tchr 1985-86; Onteora Cntrl Schl Dist Jr Sr HS Art Tchr 1986-; *ai:* Attendance, Discipline & Tech Comms; Past Mid Sts & Bldg Site Comms; *office:* Onteora Jr & Sr HS Rt 28 Boiceville NY 12412

SUTHERLAND, LINDA ARMSTRONG, Mathematics Teacher; *b:* Cooperstown, NY; *m:* Gary; *c:* Sarah; *ed:* Colgate Univ (BA) Math 1971; Syracuse Univ (MS) ELem Ed 1976; Post Grad Stud Syracuse Univ; *cr:* New Berlin Cntrl Schl Math Tchr 1975-78; SUNY at Cortland Math Ed Prof 1980; Syracuse Univ Math, Ed Prof 1978-80; Jamesville Dewitt Cntrl Schl Math Tchr 1980-81; Rhinebeck Cntrl Schl Math Tchr 1981-; *ai:* Choral, Solo Accompanist; Fac Rep PTSO; Parent Rep To Dist Insvc COmm; Tchr Rep Dist Planning Team; BLdg Planning Team; NCTM, AFT, Phi Delta Kappa 1975-; NY St Assn of Math 1975-, Cty Chm; Girl Scout Ldr 1992-; Phi Beta Kappa 1974-; Pub Articles NSF Publications, Elem Schl Journal, AMNYS Journal; *office:* Rhinebeck Cntrl Schl PO Box 351 Rhinebeck NY 12572

SUTLA, GORDON D., High School History Teacher; *b:* Lockport, NY; *m:* Barbara Daigle; *c:* David; *ed:* Hudson Vly Comm Coll (AAS) Bus Admin 1967; Syracuse Univ (BA) His 1969; St Univ of NY at Albany Ed Admin 1981; 15 Hrs Ed Univ of Miami 1970-71; *cr:* Monsgr pace HS His Tchr 1970-75; Saratoga Cath HS His Tchr 1975-81, Prin 1981-85; LaSalle Inst His Tchr 1985-; *ai:* Moderator NHS; Dept Supvr, Bsbl Coach; NCTA 1975-; SHSPA 1981-; *office:* La Salle Inst 174 Williams Rd Troy NY 12180

SUTLIFF, NADINE B., American History Teacher; *b:* NYC, NY; *m:* William D.; *c:* Craig, Todd; *ed:* Univ at Albany (BA) His, Sociology 1970, (MA) Ed 1973; *cr:* Burnt Hills His Tchr 1970-81, Sub Tchr 1984-90; Ballston Lake Schls His Tchr 1970-81, Sub Tchr 1984-90; Tewksbury Meml HS His Tchr 1994-; *ai:* Yrbk Adv; Mass Curr Frameworks Comm; MTA 1994-; *home:* 11 Starr Ave E Andover MA 01810

SUTLIFF, WILLIAM FRANCIS,III, English Professor; *b:* Karne City, PA; *m:* Dolores Faye Green; *c:* William, Julie; *ed:* Clarion Univ (BS) Bio & Eng 1962; IN Univ of PA (MED) Concentration in Eng 1965; Univ of Pittsburgh & Carnegie Mellon Univ 36 Addl Credit Hrs Grad Work; *cr:* Karns City HS Bio & Eng Tchr 1962-66; Butler Cty Comm Coll Eng Asst Prof 1966-67; Allegheny Cty Comm Coll Eng Prof 1967-; *office:* Comm Coll Algny Co Boyce Cmps 595 Beatty Rd Monroeville PA 15146

SUTPHEN, MARK ALBERT, 8th Grade Physical Sci Teacher; *b:* Abington, PA; *m:* Blair Horton; *ed:* Westchester Univ (BS) Earth Sci 1984; *cr:* Millbury HS Grds 8-12 Tchr 10 Yrs; *ai:* Fr Ftbl Coach 9 Yrs; Boys Track Coach 9 Yrs; Ski Club Adv 9 Yrs; Cable Club Adv 5 Yrs; *office:* Millbury Memorial Jr Sr HS 12 Martin St Millbury MA 01527*

SUTTER, JUDITH ANNE, Academic Dean & Professor; *b:* Springfield, MA; *m:* Edward J. Mc Caul; *ed:* Vermont Coll (AS) Mental Hlth 1974; Lee Coll (BA) Psych 1976; Springfield Coll (MED) Psych 1980; Univ of ME (EDD) Cnslr Ed 1991; Guest Rsrch Univ of Lund Sweden 1990; *cr:* Hosp & Comm Mental Hlth Therapist 1977-87; Univ of ME Rsrch Asst, Adj Prof 1987-92; Strayer Coll Dean 1992-; *ai:* Intnl Stu Affairs; AERA 1988-; AAUW, NAFE 1992-; Amer Red Cross 1982-; Sterling Who's Who; *home:* 144 Huntington Rd Worthington MA 01098*

SUTTLE, JOHN L., World Cultures Teacher; *b:* Ellwood City, PA; *m:* Susan Louise; *c:* John; *ed:* OH St Univ (BS) Ed, Soc Stud 1969; OH Univ (MED) Scndry Admin 1972; *cr:* Belpre MS 6th Grd Tchr 1969-71, 7th, 8th Grd His Tchr 16 Yrs; Belpre HS World His Tchr 7 Yrs; *ai:* OEA 1969-, Life Mem; NEA 1969-; Fellowship Church of Nazarene 1989-.

SUTTON, AUGUSTUS, English Teacher; *b:* Elizabeth City, NC; *m:* Janice Yvonne Perry; *c:* Augustus Jr., Bobby, Ebony; *ed:* Elizabeth City St Univ (BS) Eng 1974; Eng Ed VA St Univ; Grad Course Work Trinity Coll, American Univ, CAthalic Univ; *cr:* Petersburg HS Eng Tchr 1974-83; Eastern SHS Eng, Fr Tchr 1984-; *ai:* Home-Schl, Prins Retirement, Hospitality Comms; NCTE 1985-; ASCD 1993-; DCCTE 1984-; WTU 1983-; Knights for Christ Singers 1985-, Sec, Treas; Prince Hall Mason 1988-; Tchr of Yr 1993; *office:* Eastern HS 17th & E Capitol Sts NE Washington DC 20003

SUTTON, IVAN CLARK, Chemistry Teacher; *b:* Arbovale, WV; *m:* Bessie; *c:* Vivenne Mc Ginnis, Susan Day; *ed:* WV Univ (BS) Sci Ed 1960, Morgan St Univ (MS) Sci Ed 1966; Univ MD at College Park 40 Credit Hrs; Towson St Univ 8 Credit Hrs; *cr:* Glenelg HS Chem Tchr, Sci Dept Chair 1960-; Howard Comm Coll Adjunct Fac, Part-time Chem & Sci Instr 1972-; *ai:* Sr Class Adv; Howard Co Teach Assn, MSTA, NEA 1960-; MD Assn of Sci Tchr 1980-; Howard Cty Chamber of Commerce 1988; MD Chapter Amer Chem Soc MD 1993 Tchr of Yr; Life Membership MS Congress PTA; *office:* Glenelg HS 14025 Burnt Woods Rd Glenelg MD 21737

SUTTON, JACQUELYN FAGOURI, Teacher; *b:* Olean, NY; *c:* Kristin, Amy, Beau; *ed:* St Univ of NY at Cortland (BS) Soc Stud 1963; Syracuse Univ (MA) Soc Sci 1964; Attnd Taft Inst, SUNY at Albany; *cr:* Yonkers Schl System Scndry Schl Tchr 1964-; *ai:* AFT; *office:* Museum S Warburton Yonkers NY 10701

SUTTON, JAMES R., Retired Mathematics Teacher; *b:* Roches *m:* Ann A.; *c:* Heather; *ed:* St Univ of NY at Brockport (BS) Ed 19 Ed 1965; 18 Hrs Past Masters; *cr:* Brockport Cntrl Schl 8th Grd M 1961-95, Team Ldr 1974-74, Subject Area Ldr 1969-73; *ai:* NY S Tchrs, AFT, NY St Math Tchrs, Area Math Tchrs 1961-; St Luke's 1940-, Vestry Mem 1971-77; Brockport Fire Dept 1968-, Pres Active Svc; Brockport Exempts 1995-; Jaycees 1962-, VP 1963; T 1977; *home:* 72 Westwood Dr Brockport NY 14420

SUTTON, LINDA MASIELLO, Mathematics Teacher; *b:* Jersey *m:* Robert J.; *c:* Robert, Jeffrey, Michael; *ed:* St Peter's Coll (B 1973; *cr:* Acad of St Aloysius Tchr 1973-75; Union Cath Girl's Dept Chprsn 1975-78; Thompson Jr HS Tchr 1978-80; Keyport 1990-; *ai:* Soph Class Adv; NHS Selection, Fac Adv Comm; Stu NEA, NJEA 1990-; Governors Recognition Awd Tchr of Yr 1992 Keyport HS 351 Broad St Keyport NJ 07735*

SUTTON, ROBERT H., Dept of Ed Supvr; *b:* Ridgewood, NJ; *m* Hufnal; *c:* Robert J., Jill E.; *ed:* Glassboro St Coll (BA) Ed 1962; M St Coll (MA) Stu Prsnl Svcs 1979; Georgian Court Coll Substanc Cnslng; Monmouth Univ Prin, Supvr Cert; Jersey City St Coll Handicapped; *cr:* Neptune Twp Pub Schls Tchr 1962-69; Wall T Schls Head Guid Cnslr 1969-94; Georgian Court Coll Dept of E 1994-; *ai:* Brookdale Comm Coll Mens Soccer Coach; NEA; WTEA; WA Vol Fire Co 1961-, Pres; Wall Soccer Club 1966-, T James Episcople Church 1978-, Treas; *home:* 1116 Hillcre Manasquan NJ 08736

SUVER, SARA L., Principal; *b:* Dayton, OH; *m:* R. James; *c:* Ba Amy, Lisa; *ed:* OH St Univ (BA) Elem Ed 1968; Wright St Univ (M Superv 1985; PHD Prgm Univ of Dayton; *cr:* Grove City Sch 1968-69; Licking Hts Schls Tchr 1973-78; Tecumseh Schls Tchr 1 Prin 1991-; *ai:* Sci Curr Coord; Dist PR Comm; Dist Newsle OAESA, ASCD 1991-; NSTA 1985-; OH Pacesetter, Tecumseh Grants 1996; *office:* Donnelsville Elem Schl 150 E Main St Donn OH 45319

SUWALSKI, JULIE ANNE, Mathematics Teacher; *b:* Edwards A *ed:* Univ of Dayton (BA) Math 1992; 15 Credit Hrs Wright St Univ Discovery; *cr:* Toronto HS Math Tchr 1992-93; Tri-Cty North H Tchr 1993-; *ai:* Acad Quiz Team, Stu Cncl, Soph Class Adv; Ment *office:* Tri-County North HS 500 Panther Way Lewisburg OH 4533

SUWINSKI, WILLIAM S., Fifth Grade Teacher; *b:* Spangler, PA Univ of PA (MS) Elem Ed 1974, (MED) Rdng 1978; Addl 30 Cre *cr:* Northern Cambria Schl Dist Elem Tchr 1976-; *ai:* NEA, NCEA St Stanislaus Church 1967-, Lector; Area Little League Coach 1 NC Parks & Rec Bd; Outstdng Tchr Awd 1987; *office:* Northern C Schl Dist 600 Joseph St Barnesboro PA 15714

SUZZI VALLI, SOPHIA BRACCIOFORTE, Italian Teach Palermo, Italy; *m:* Angelo; *c:* Robert, Anthony, Michael; *ed:* Brookl (BA) His, Italian 1969; St John's Univ (MS) Scndry Ed 1974; Addl Grad Stud ESL, Italian Adelphi Univ, Finch Coll; *cr:* JHS 171 His, Tchr 1969-75; Ravenna Elem Schl Tchr 1975-76; Cavallaro JHS S Tchr 1977-78; Berlitz Lang Schls Tchr of Italian 1988-91; H. Fran HS Tchr of Italian, ESL 1991-; *ai:* Coord Schl Spon Trip to Italy, R San Marino; LILI, AATI, NYSAFLT 1991-; Order Sons of Ital Sicula 1994-; Tchr of Yr 1994; Ed Sammarinese Journal USA; Adv, Articles; *office:* H Frank Carey HS 230 Poppy Ave Franklin Squ 11010

SVEC, J. C., Comm, Performance Instructor; *b:* Bayonne, NJ; *ed:* Univ (BA) Theatre 1978; William Paterson Coll (MA) Comm 19 Rutgers Univ Dir Theatre Operations, Instr 1978-88; Kean Co 1985-89; William Paterson Coll Instr, Producer 1989-95; Mo Kimberley Acad Instr, Dic 1989-; *ai:* Fall, Spring Play Dir; Spring Producer, Dir; Lighting Designer Winter Musical; Coord Weiss A Off-Off Broadway Prof Production Designer, Art Dir; 4 Feature Numerous NJ Theatrical Scene, Assorted Acad Scenic, Costume Designs, NJ Corperate, Cable TV Art Dir Design Credits.

SVENSEN, DIANE D., English & French Teacher; *b:* Fall River, Arthur T.; *c:* Alan, Andrea, Alex; *ed:* Bridgewater St Coll (BS) Eng Fr Course at Harvard Univ 1991; Univ of North IA Fr Prgm in Franc *cr:* Falls Village Schl Tchr 1965-66; Campion Coll at Kingston J Eng Tchr 1973-74; Temple Univ Extension at Berlin Germany Er 1982-83; Sacred Heart HS Fr Tchr 1986-87; Archbishop Williams H Eng Tchr 1987-; *ai:* NHS Adv; Boston Archdiocese Tchrs Assn 1988 *office:* Archbishop Williams HS 80 Independence Ave Braintree MA

SVIDRON, KEVIN JOSEPH, 8th Grd American Cultures Tchr; *b:* City, MO; *ed:* IN Univ of PA (BS) Scndry Soc Sci 1989; Westmoreland Cty Comm Coll 1990, WV Univ 1985-86; *cr:* Latrobe Sr HS US His Tchr 1994-95; Greater Latrobe Jr HS Amer C Tchr 1996; *ai:* 7-8 Hr HS Head Ftbl, Var Vol Asst Wrestling Coach Veterans Recognition; *home:* 50 Joanne Dr Latrobe PA 15650*

SVILAR, LORRAINE EVA, English & Journalism Teacher; *b:* Br NY; *c:* Daniel W. Smith III, Mathew Livingston Smith; *ed:* Gouch (BA) Eng 1985; Western MD Coll (MS) Ed 1991; *cr:* Bel Air H Jrnlsm Tchr 1985-; *ai:* Schl Newspaper Adv; Women's Mentoring Adv; NTE 1994-; Voluntary Action Ctr of Cntrl MD Vol Awd; *offi* Air HS 100 Hieghe St Bel Air MD 21014*

SVOBODA, WILLIAM JOESPH, Computer & Business Chp Garfield Hghts, OH; *m:* Kathleen M.; *c:* William Jr., Kelly An Cleveland St Univ (BBA) Bus Ed 1986; 30 Hrs Cmptr Sci Ed; *cr:* HS Cmptr-Bus Chairperson 1986-; *ai:* Head Boys Bsktbl Coach Ministry Team; Retreat Ldr; NCEA, NBEA, GCBEA, OBCA Presenter Tech Exchange II Cleveland St Univ; *office:* Trinity HS Granger Rd Cleveland OH 44125*

SVORONOS, PARIS, Professor of Chemistry; *m:* Soraya Gh Manesh; *c:* Alexandra, Theodore; *ed:* Amer Univ in Cairo (BS) Cl Physics 1973; Georgetown Univ (PHD) Organic Chem 1979; *cr:* Coll Asst Prof 1979-81; QCC of CUNY Asst Prof 1981-86, Asso 1986-91, Prof 1991-; Georgetown Univ Vis Prof 1981-; *ai:* Chair 2YC3 Two Yr Coll Chem Conf Spon by Amer Chem Soc 1995; 1979-; ACS 1979-; AFT 1991-; Amer Univ in Cairo Tuition Schlsp & List 1968-73; Georgetown Univ Rsrch & Tchng Fellow 1973-79; Dept Nom for Two Yr Coll Chem Tchr Awd 1987; *office:* QCC of 22205 56th Ave Flushing NY 11364*

SWAIKO, NANCY MARIE, Reading & English Teacher; *b:* New City, NY; *ed:* Coll of Notre Dame (BA) Elem Ed 1972; Western M (MEd) Deaf Ed 1975; Addl Post Grad Credit Hrs Gallaudet Univ; *c* Schl for Deaf Tchr 1973-; *ai:* Rsrch Review Comm; Mentor Tchr i Project Achieve Gallaudet Univ; SoMIRAC St MS Intnl Rdng Assn Co-Authored Children's Book A Christmas Carol; Contributor Books Deaf Ed; Co-Presented Regnl Conf; Co-Dir Summer Rdng 1985-91; Taught Grad Level Course; Authored Articles Pub Amer A of Deaf; Editorial Consultant; Tchr of Yr 1984; *office:* Maryland Sc The Deaf 101 Clark Pl Box 250 Frederick MD 21705

SWAILES, ALICE LEGER, Sixth Grade Science Teache Chambersburg, PA; *m:* William M.; *c:* Jami Michelle, Billie Jo

Coll (BA) Soc Stud 1962; Shippensburg Univ (MED) Elem Ed ttnd Wake Forest Univ, East Carolina Univ, Millersville Univ & Coll; *cr:* West Snyder HS Soc Stud & Eng Tchr 1962-64; stle Antrim HS Eng Tchr 1965-66; Tuscarora Schl Dist 6th Grd 57-; *ai:* Games Club Adv; Prins Advy Comm; TEA, PSEA, NEA, NSTA; Mercersburg Womens Club; Mercersburg Lib Assn; burg VFW; Girl Souts, Life Mem; Numerous Wkshps Sponsored Federal & Private Concerns; Much Was Also Learned From e Travels Throughout the 50 Sts, Europe, Mexico & Canada; 07 E Seminary St Mercersburg PA 17236*

ES, JAMES EDWARD, 8th Grd Social Studies Teacher; *b:* rsburg, PA; *m:* Kathy L. Brant; *c:* Diron, Rebecca, Jenna; *ed:* sburg Univ (BA) Soc Stud 1974; *ai:* HS Soccer Coach; PSEA, NEA *ffice:* James Buchanan M S 5191 Fort Loudon Rd Mercersburg PA

, CAROL MURPHY, 1st Grade Teacher; *b:* Cochrane ON, *m:* Robert Joseph; *c:* Michael J., Karen U.; *ed:* North Adams St Elem Ed 1957; 40 Addl Credit Hrs; *cr:* Conway St Schl Grd 1 Tchr ; Greylock Elem Schl Grd 1 Tchr 1965-; *ai:* NEA, MTA 1965-; 965-, Exec Bd; *office:* Greylock Elem Schl 100 Phelps Ave North MA 01247

OW, RICHARD KENNETH,JR., Elementary Music Dept Supvr; nd, PA; *m:* Alice; *c:* Richard III, Christopher Michael; *ed:* West Univ (BS) Music 1971, (MED) Music 1975; 66 Hrs Beyond ; *cr:* Ridley HS Band Dir & Dept Head 1971-93; Ridley Elem Schls tr & Dept Head 1993-; *ai:* Dist & Symphonic Bands; PMEA, NEA & REA 1971-; Natl Judges Assn 1980-93; Tournament of 976-93, Chapter Chief; *office:* Ridley Schl Dist 1001 Morton Ave PA 19033*

ANDREA SPESHOCK, Second Grade Teacher; *b:* Connellsville, William H. Jr.; *c:* William III, Kelly Fuchs, Amy, Timothy; *ed:* IN PA (BS) Elem Ed 1962; Masters Equivalency Penn St 1980; *ai:* SEA 1962-; Delta Kappa Gamma 1984-, VP 1992; Eastern Star

STEVEN R., Social Studies Teacher; *b:* Columbus, OH; *m:* Cheryl s; *c:* Amy Swan Parke; *ed:* OH Univ (BSEd) Soc Stud Comp 1970; oto HS Tchr 1971-; *ai:* NEA 1971-; OH Ed Assn 1971-, Exec Cntral OEA, NEA Inc 1971-, Area Rep; *home:* 1252 Nelson Dr the OH 45601

, CHARLES F., Science Teacher; *b:* Erie, PA; *m:* Davileen M. *c:* Kristina, Rachel; *ed:* Edinboro St Coll (BA) Ed 1963; Post Grad ppery Rock St Coll; *cr:* Lockport Sr HS Tchr 1963-64; Moniteau HS Tchr 1964-; *ai:* Act Spon, Adv; Drama, MUsical Theater ions Tech Dir, Adv; NEA, PSEA 1964-; Moniteau Ed Assn 1964-, P, Treas, Mbrshp Chm, Rep Cncl, Cty Coordinating Cncl; *office:* u Jr Sr HS RD 1 West Sunbury PA 16061

, BEVERLY MITCHELL, Business Teacher; *b:* Dover, DE; *m:* *c:* Pedro Jr., Darius; *ed:* DE St Univ (BS) Bus Ed 1992, (MS) Ed *r:* Dupont Co Relocation Information Spec 1971-91; Newark HS r 1991-; DE St Univ Adj Instr 1993-; *ai:* Bus Profs of Amer Club EA, DBEA, DSEA 1993-; Alpha Kappa Alpha 1993-; Dupont Night the Town, Section, Superstar in Ed Awds; *office:* Newark HS E re Ave Newark DE 19711*

SON, CONNIE LABBADIA, Music Teacher; *b:* Stamford, CT; *c:* *ed:* Western CT St Univ (BS) Music Ed 1976, (MS) Music Ed 1983; g on 6th Yr Degree Ed at Trinity Coll of VT; *cr:* Park Ave Elem Schl rd Vocal, Gen Music Tchr 1976-79; Mill Ridge Primary Schl K-2nd cal, Gen Music Tchr 1976-79; Broadview Jr HS 7-9th Grd Choral 9-92; Broadview MS 6-8th Grd Choral Dir, Gen Music Tchr 1992-; w Choir 1980, Concert Choir Format Comm 1982; Act Period mittee 1992; 8th Grd Awds Presentation Spec Areas Comm 1992-; Music Comm 1985; MENC 1976-; Amer Choral Dirs Assn 1988-; anbury Ed Assn 1976-; Jr Women's Club Greater Danbury 1979-80; Club Danbury 1993-94; Choral Clinician Ridgefield 1986; Guest Conductor Southern CT MS Festival 1987; Choral Chm, Piano panist Western CT Region Jr HS Festival 1983; Outstdng Tchr ition Union Carbide, Western CT Supt Assn 1988; Music in Parks Lakewood NJ 1st Place Awds, Concert, Pop Choir, Best Overall wd 1983-84, 1st Place Awd Concert Choir 1985, 1988, 2nd Pl Awd Choir, 1st Place Awd Pop Choir 1990, 1st Place Awds Concert, Pop Best Overall Choir Awd 1992, 1st Place Concert Choir, 2nd Place oir 1994; Six Flags Music Festival 1st Runner-up Concert Choir; l Carousel Festival Agawam MA Ratings of Superior Concert, Pop 991; Great East Festival Agawam MA Superior Rating Concert 993; *office:* Broadview MS 76 Hospital Ave Danbury CT 06810

SON, JOHN T., Graphic Arts & Drafting Tchr; *b:* Morristown, NJ; y L.; *c:* Eric, Peder; *ed:* Trenton St Coll (MA) Industrial Ed 1969; ll Grad Credits; *cr:* Rancocas Valley Reg HS Graphic Arts Tchr 9; Montgomery hS Graphic Arts, Drafting & CAD Tchr 1969-; n St Coll Co- adjunct & graphic Arts Tchr 1970-77; *ai:* Printing Tech EA & NJEA 1965-; IGEA 1976-; Carl Perkins Voc Grant to Build a Lab; *office:* Montgomery HS 375 Burnt Hill Rd Skillman NJ 08558*

SON, NANCY E. (POVLOCK), High School Art Teacher; *b:* nca, NY; *m:* Duane; *c:* Christopher, Jacob; *ed:* Rochester Inst of BFA) Graphic Design 1987; Brockport St (MS) Ed 1992; Buffalo St hng Cert 1989; *cr:* Hilton HS AA Tchr 1990-91; Gates Chili HS AA 91-; *ai:* Frosh Class & Svc Club Adv; NYSATA 1986-; *office:* Gates S 910 Wegman Rd Rochester NY 14624

SON, SEAN ARTHUR, High School English Teacher; *b:* ence, RI; *ed:* Loyola Coll MD (BA) Eng Lit & Writing 1988; Johns ns Univ (MAT) 1989; Addl 12 Credit Hrs Including Gifted & d Cert; *cr:* Dunbar HS Hopkins-Dunbar Fellow 1988-89; Old Mill Eng Tchr 1989-; *ai:* NEA, MSTA, TAAAC 1990-; Hopkins-Dunbar ship; *office:* Old Mill Sr HS 600 Patriot Ln Millersville MD 21108

SON, STEVEN JON, Womens Soccer Coach; *b:* Biloxi, MS; *m:* olakowski; *c:* Alexis, Kelsey; *ed:* MI St Univ (BA) Bus Admin 1984; f IA (MA) Ath Admin & Coaching 1989; *cr:* West HS Head Boys Coach 1987-89; Dartmouth Coll Asst Ath Dir 1989-, Womens Coach 1990-; *ai:* Upper Vly Lighting Soccer Assn Coach & Dir; A 1987-; US Coaches Pgms 1993-; ISAA, NW Regnl Chair; Upper ghting Soccer Assn 1990-, Dir; B-License USSF 1987; A-License 1991; New England Coach of Yr 1993; *office:* Dartmouth Coll 6083 i Gym-W Soccer Hanover NH 03755

D, ROSS ANDREW, Music Director; *b:* Willimantic, CT; *m:* LaBelle; *ed:* Univ of CT (bS) Music Ed 1988, (MS) Music Ed 1994; swold HS Band Dir 1988-89; Putnam HS Dir of Music 1989-; *ai:* Sr Co Adv; Steering CMTE for Re Accredidation; MENC & NEMFA CMEA 1989-, Eastern Regnl Chm Elect & Band Chm; Educator of d 1990-91; *office:* Putnam HS 152 Woodstock Ave Putnam CT *

R, FREDERICK DEAN, Designer & Graphic Coord; *b:* Manheim, : Valerie Elaine Kaufman; *c:* Amanda, Gabriel, Zachary; *ed:* sville Univ (BS) Art Ed 1969; PA St Univ (MA) Art Ed 1975; Attnd own Univ, Tyler Schl of Art Temple Univ Art Ed; *cr:* Hatfield Elem Art Tchr 1969-73; North Penn HS Art Tchr 1973-78; Weinstock Conestoga Screen Printing Supvr 1978-85; All-Size Corr Packaging Designer 1985-; *ai:* Pvt Art Classes 1980-; PTO, Baron Stage Parents Org Manheim Cntrl Schl Dist; NEA 1969-78; Oasis Yth Svc 1989-, Bd Mem 1991-95; Artwork in Permanent Collections; Juried Art Shows; Gallery Exhibitions; Donated Artwork for Benefits; *home:* 539 E Elizabethtown Rd Manheim PA 17545

SWART, MARILYN LONG, Fifth Grade Teacher; *b:* Pottstown, PA; *c:* Elizabeth J. Zlotowski, Stephanid J. Stamy; *ed:* PA St Univ (BS) Elem Ed 1957; Attnd Whittier Univ, Marywood Coll, AZ St Univ; *cr:* Pottstown Schl Dist Fourth Grd Tchr 1957-60; Cypress Schl Dist Fourth-Fifth Grd Tchr 1960-64; Owen J. Roberts Schl Dist Fourth-Fifth Grd Tchr 1968-; *ai:* Schl Stu Store Spon; Math Olympiad Elem Stdnts Coach; Soc Stud Curr Comm; REA, PSEA, NEA 1968-; Order of Eastern Star 1958-; Keeshond Club of Amer 1974-; Amer Cat Fanciers Assn 1991-.

SWARTS, EVELYN MILLER, Science Teacher & Dept Chm; *b:* Buffalo, NY; *m:* Donald; *c:* Gregg, Kevin, Cathy; *ed:* Gettysburg Coll (BA) Bio 1963; Brown Univ (MAT) Genetics 1967; 30 Hrs Post Grad Boston Univ, Amer Univ; *cr:* DuVale Sr HS Bio Tchr 1963-66; Kenmore West HS Bio Tchr 1967-86; Kenmore MS Sci Tchr 1986-, Dept Chair 1991-; *ai:* Sci Fair Chm; Curr Revision Comm; Mentoring Wkshp; NSTA 1967-, NY St Sci Tchrs Assn 1967-; Amer Assn of Univ Women 1991-; Buffalo Museum of Sci 1986-; Acad Yr Inst 1966-67; Distngd HS Sci Tchr; Amer Chem Soc Awd 1986; *home:* 2535 W River Rd Grand Island NY 14072*

SWARTZ, BEVERLY J. (WRAY), Child Care Specialist; *b:* Johnstown, PA; *m:* Richard L.; *c:* Michael, David, Laura Frank; *ed:* Indiana of PA (BA) Home Ec 1959; 36 Credit Hrs Masters Equivilency PA St Univ, IA St Univ, Elmira Coll at Millersville, Wilkes Coll; *cr:* Beatty Jr HS Home Ec Tchr 1959-62; Altoona Area HS Home Ec 1976-; *ai:* FHA, Hero Club Adv; Ed Assn Dept Rep; PSEA, VPAE Cntrl Region Rep to St; NEA, PSEA, AAEA, PHEA 1976-; NAEYC, KAEYC 1993-; Delphi Chptr #65 Order Eastern Star 1985-, Past Matron, Grand Chptr Page; Dorcus Chptr Daughters of Nile 1986-; Jaggard Meth Church 1970-, Worship Comm; AARP19 88-; Spec Tchr Awd 15 Yrs Spec Ed, Home Ec; Altoona Pride Awd; *office:* Altoona Area HS 1415 6th Ave Altoona PA 16602

SWARTZ, EUGENE ROBERT,JR., Director of Choral Activities; *b:* Cleveland, OH; *m:* Vicki Masters; *c:* Sarah, Amanda; *ed:* DS Lancaster Comm Coll (AAS) Engr Tech 1977; Univ of TN (BS) Vocal Music 1987, (MS) Vocal Music Choral 1989; *cr:* TN Vly Auth Engr Tech 1978-87; FBC Minister Music, Yth 1989-91; Springhill Lake Elem Schl Vocal, Gen Music Tchr 1991-93; Centennial HS Choral Act Dir 1993-; WA Bible Coll Voice Tchr 1993-; *ai:* Class Spon 1996; Scheduling, Awds Comms; ACDA 1986-, Pres UT Chptr; MENC 1986-, St Pres Stu Chptr; MMEC 1991-; Adult Literacy 1990-91, Bd of Dirs; Hamiton Conducting Schlsp 1988-89; UT Choral Arts Chair Stu Conductor 1988-89; Articles Pub; *office:* Centennial HS 4300 Centennial Ln Ellicott City MD 21042

SWARTZ, GARY L., Literature Teacher; *b:* Fremont, OH; *m:* Kimberly S.; *c:* Morganne B., Garrison M.; *ed:* Bowling Green St Univ (BS) Ed (End) 1993; *cr:* Sylvania Southview HS Lit Tchr 1993-; *ai:* Bsbl Coach; Sylvania Ed Assn, NEA 1993-; NCTE 1992-; *office:* Sylvania Southview HS 7225 Sylvania Ave Sylvania OH 43560*

SWARTZ, JANE LEE, Spanish & English Teacher; *b:* Martins Ferry, OH; *ed:* West Liberty St Coll (BA) Span 1975; Franciscan Univ of Steubenvill (MS) Edtl Adm 1995; WV Univ, Univ of Dayton, Mt St Joseph's; *cr:* Pleasants Cty MS Tchr 1975-77; Cadiz HS Tchr 1977-; *ai:* Sociedad Honoraria Hispanica Adv; Odyssey of Mind Judge; NEA; OEA; HHTA; OH Foreign Lang Assn; Amer Assn Tchrs of Span, Portuguese; *home:* PO Box 402 Dillonvale OH 43917

SWARTZ, JUNE ANN FRATTAROLA, English Teacher; *b:* NY; *m:* Gerald Neal; *c:* Jennifer; *ed:* Skidmore Coll (BA) Eng 1973; SUNY at Albany (MS) Ed 1976; Post Masters Sarah Lawrence Coll, LIU, NY Univ, Northeastern U, Lit, Writing, SUNY Purchase Tchrs Ctr Methods of Tchng; *cr:* Russell Sage Coll Instrl Svcs Ctr, Asst to Dir 1975-77; Lansingburgh Schls Rdng Tchr 1977-78; Harrison HS Eng Tchr 1978-; *ai:* Tchr of GATE Local Consortium; Tech, NHS Selection, Shared Decision Making Comm; Lang Arts Stans 1993-94; NCTE 1972-; ASCD 1980-; AFT; NYSUT; Harrison Assn of Tchrs 1978-, Rep Cncl Alternate 1995-; Harrison Children's Ctr 1990-, Bd of Dirs, VP; Emelin Theatre 1991-; Rye Arts Ctr 1992-; Harrison Cncl for Arts 1993-; Natl Endowment for Hum Grant; *office:* Harrison HS Union Ave Harrison NY 10528*

SWARTZ, RODNEY EUGENE,JR., Retired English Teacher; *b:* York, PA; *ed:* Ashland Coll (BS) eng 1960; Western MD (MLA) Eng 1976; Attnd Univ of NC, Penn St Univ; *cr:* Hayesville HS Eng Tchr 1960-61; West York HS Eng Tchr 1962-93, Dept Chair 1966-93; *ai:* Play Dir; PSEA, NEA, WYAEA 1962-; Northwest Civic Assn 1970-, Treas 10 Yrs; *home:* 420 Roosevelt Ave York PA 17404

SWARTZ, TERRY HOWARD, Mathematics Teacher; *b:* Buffalo, NY; *m:* Lana M. Ruth; *c:* Terry H. II; *ed:* St Univ of NY at Fredonia (BS) Elem Ed 1963; St Univ of NY at Buffalo (EDM) Elem Ed 1967; 60 Addl Hrs of Grad Stud; *cr:* Grand Island Schls 5th Grd Tchr 1963-89, 6th Grd Math Tchr 1990-; *ai:* Schlsp Fund Raiser Chprsn; Matters of the Mind Creator & Coord Intellectual Competition Prgm for 4th-6th Grds; NY St United Tchrs 1967-, Local Del, Leadership Awd; Grand Island Tchrs Assn 1963-, Local Pres, VP, Grievance Chprsn; *home:* 86 Montfort Dr Buffalo NY 14225

SWATLING, JAN DELILLI, French Teacher; *b:* Gloversville, NY; *m:* Charles F.; *c:* Pamela Mormando, Eric; *ed:* Fulton-Montgomery CC (AA) LA 1966; SUNY at Albany (BA) Fr Ed 1969; 32 Grad Hrs New Paltz Oneonta; *cr:* Broadalbin Perth HS Fr Tchr 1969-; *ai:* Fr Club Adv; Curr Coord Foreign Lang Dept Cncl; Mentor Tchr; NEA, NYSUT, BPTA 1969-; *office:* Broadalbin-Perth Cntrl Schl 100 Bridge St Broadalbin NY 12025

SWAUGER, JAMES EDWARD,SR., Sixth Grade Teacher; *b:* New Germany, MD; *m:* Margaret Ann Wills; *c:* James E., Karen Renae; *ed:* Frostburg St Tchrs Col (AA) 1960, (BS) Jr HS 1962; WV Univ (MA) Soc Stud, Scndry Ed 1967; 15 Addl Credit Hrs; *cr:* Oldtown HS Sixth Grd Tchr 30 Yrs; *ai:* ACTA, MSTA, NEA 1964-; DAV 1984-; VFW 1966-; Woodmen of World 1956-; George's Creek Valley Lodge 1969-; Scottish Rite & Ali Ghan Temple; *home:* 26 Harold St Cumberland MD 21502

SWAYNE, JANET M., Math Teacher; *b:* Philadelphia, PA; *m:* Thomas C.; *c:* Mary Beth, Kerry; *ed:* PA St Univ (BS) Math Ed 1976; Temple Univ (MED) Math Ed 1979; *cr:* Hopkinson Schl 7th-8th Grd Math Tchr 1976-90; Edison HS Math Tchr 1990-; *ai:* After Schl Acad Prgm Mentor; NCTM, Pi Lambda, Theta, ATMOPAV 1976-; Camp Fire Girls 1991-, Ldr; Nom Rose Lindenbaum Awd; *office:* Thomas A. Edison HS 151 W Luzerne St Philadelphia PA 19140

SWEARS, STANLEY B., Science Teacher; *b:* Johnstown, NY; *m:* Wendy Cashman; *c:* Benjamin, Channing; *ed:* SUC at Oneonta (BS) Bio 1970; Addl Hrs; Univ of VT Intensive Tchr Trng; *cr:* Underhill Schl Sci Tchr 1970-71; Franklin Cntrl Schl Sci Tchr 1971-; *ai:* 8th Grd Class Adv; Soccer, Wrestling, Bsbl Coach; Length of Schl Day, Safety Comms; NEA, NYSUT; Town Planning Bd, Pres; Rsrch Pub in Journal; *office:* Franklin Central Schl 1 Institute St Franklin NY 13775

SWEATMAN, JON SCOTT, Biology & Ecology Teacher; *b:* Fitchburg, MA; *m:* Diane; *c:* Marci, Jody; *ed:* Fitchburg St Coll (BS) Bio 1973, (MS) Sci Ed 1979; *cr:* North Middlesex Reg HS Sci Tchr 1973-; *ai:* Earth Action Adv; NEA, MTA 1973-; MAST 1990-; Jaycees Cleominster 1980-, Pres; *office:* North Middlesex Regional HS 19 Main St Townsend MA 01469*

SWEATT, RONALD B., Jr HS Dept Chair & Team Leader; *b:* Concord, MA; *m:* Ermelinda Espinola; *c:* Tanya, Jason; *ed:* Leicester Jr Coll (AA) 1967; Nasson Coll (BA) Soc Stud 1969; Univ of CT (MA) Elem Ed 1973; *cr:* L P Wilson Jr HS Soc Stud Tchr 1969-71; Plainfield Cntrl Schl Soc Stud Tchr & Dept Head 1971-; Private Businesr-Bustins Builders; *ai:* Little League, Girls Var Soccer & Bsktbl Coach; Schl DJ; Newspaper Club; Tchr of Yr & Curr Reasearch Comm; Landscape Comm Chprsn; NEA & CEA 1972-; PEA & NCSS 1971-; Little League 1985-, Pres 2 Yrs; Bustins island Overseas 1984-90; Bustins Island Fire Chief 1990-95; ME Trip Learning Adventure Grant; Plainfield Cntrl Schl Tchr of Yr 1990; Bustins Island Landscape Comm Chprsn; Curr Research Comm; Cooperating Tchr 1975-; Pomfret Boosters Club VP; *office:* Plainfield Central Schl 75 Canterbury Rd Plainfield CT 06374*

SWECKER, ELIZABETH ANN, Intermediate Lvl Tchr of Deaf; *b:* Tiffin, OH; *m:* Dennis E.; *ed:* Bowling Green St Univ (BS) Ed 1982; Heidelberg Coll (MA) Ed 1992; Post Grad Stud in Ed; *cr:* Lincoln Schl Tchr of the Deaf 1983-84; Chamberlin Hill Tchr of the Deaf 1984-93, Cross Categorical Resource Tchr 1993-95, Tchr of the Deaf 1995-; *ai:* IEP Trng Team; Tech Comm; Regnl Prof Dev Ctr; NEA 1982-; Natl Machinery Co & North West OH Regnl Resource Ctr Grants; NWO SERRC Spcl Edctr Awd; St Marys Church Interpret Mass; Teach Sign Lang.

SWEDENBURG, JAMES KENT, Social Studies Teacher; *b:* Salina, KS; *ed:* Emporia St Univ (BS) Soc Sci 1975, (MS) Soc Sci 1981; Xavier Univ Grad Cert Hrs; *cr:* Emporia St Univ Grad Asst 1975-76; Burlington HS Tchr 1976-78; Our Lady of Angels HS Tchr 1978-84; Roger Bacon HS Tchr 1984-; *ai:* Pub Relations Coord; Acad Team; Recycling Club; Prin's Advy Bd; Schl Photographer; NCEA 1978-; Laubach Literacy Action 1991-, Tutor; Natl Audubon Soc, World Wildlife Fund 1980; Sierra Club 1982-; Nature Conservancy 1984-; Amer Newspaper Pub Assn Fnd, Amer Scholastic Press Assn Jrnlsm Awds; Track Coach of Yr 1985; Press of Amer Best Adv Jrnlsm Awd; *office:* Roger Bacon HS 4320 Vine St Cincinnati OH 45217*

SWEENEY, GRETCHEN BRUCE, English Teacher; *b:* Harrisburg, PA; *m:* Mark; *ed:* CCAC at Boyce Campus (AA) Lbrl Arts 1987; IN Univ of PA (BS) Eng Ed 1990; 22 Credit Hrs Allegheny Intermediate Unit; *cr:* St Therese Schl Eng Tchr 6 Yrs; *ai:* Stu Cncl; Schl Newspaper; Oraborical Contest; Pittsburgh Post Gazette Natl Spelling Bee Spon; NCTE 1991-; Adult Literacy Vol 1991-; *office:* St Therese Schl 3 Saint Therese Ct Munhall PA 15120

SWEENEY, MARILYN L., Math, Sci Tchr & Dept Chr; *b:* Yonkers, NY; *m:* Paul G.; *c:* Kara, Lisa, Laura, Kristina; *ed:* The Kings Coll (BA) Math 1979; *cr:* Howland Chrstn Schl Algebra I & II, Geometry, Trig, Chem, Physics Tchr 1979-; *ai:* MathCounts Coach; Soph Class Adv; Vlybl, Bsktbl Scorer; Ladies Missionary Fellowship 1980-, Treas 1983-; AWANA Sparks Dir 1989-; 4-H Vol 1992-95; *office:* Howland Christian Schl 8957 E Market St Warren OH 44484

SWEENEY, MARY SHEILA, Dept Chair & Teacher; *b:* Cleveland, OH; *ed:* Ursuline Coll (BA) Latin 1944; Univ of Notre Dame (MA) Latin 1956; St Louis Univ (PHD) Latin 1968; *cr:* St Joseph Acad Latin, Eng Tchr 1944-59, 1961-63; Nazareth Acad Prin 1963-69; Diocese of Cleveland Ed Office Asst Supt 1969-75; Nazareth Acad Latn, Eng Tchr 1975-77; St Joseph Acad Latin, Eng, Math Tchr 1977-; *ai:* Classical Langs Dept Chair; Moderator Jr Classical League; Amer Classical League 1977-; St Joseph Congregation 1944-; *home:* 3430 Rocky River Dr Cleveland OH 44111

SWEENY, JOSEPH E., Social Studies Teacher; *b:* Erie, PA; *c:* Caitlin, Robert, Patrick; *ed:* Edinboro Univ (BSEd) Soc Stud 1969; Attnd St Univ of NY at Fredonia; *cr:* Dunkirk City Schl Dist Soc Stud Tchr 1969-; *ai:* Co-Chair to Labor, Mgmt, Inservice & Discipline Comms; Supervisory Practices & Compact Comms; Dunkirk Tchrs Assoc 1969-, Pres 1979-; NY St United Tchrs 1972-, Dist Dir 1986-; AFT 1972-; Democratic Party Comm 1979-95, Chm, Vice Chair, Ward Chair; *office:* Dunkirk HS W 6th St Dunkirk NY 14048

SWEET, LARRY F., HS Social Studies Teacher; *b:* Ilion, NY; *m:* Sandra K.; *c:* Lynn C. Terry Jr., Bryan L.; *ed:* Herkimer Cty Comm Coll (AA) Soc Sci 1974; St Univ of NY at Fredonia (BA) His, Scndry Ed 1976; Syracuse Univ (MA) His 1983; *cr:* Clymer Cntrl Schl HS Soc Stud Tchr 1977-; *ai:* Court of Conduct Adv; NEA 1984-, Second VP; Lakewood Rod, Gun Club 1994-; *office:* Clymer Central Schl Main St Clymer NY 14474*

SWEET, MARCIA S. (CLAY), English Teacher; *b:* Columbus, OH; *m:* Kevin B.; *ed:* Mt Vernon Nazarene Coll (BA) Eng Ed 1985; Working Towards Master's Degree in Eng Ed OH St Univ; *cr:* Independence HS Eng Tchr 1987-; *ai:* NCTE 1994-; CEA, OEA, NEA 1987-; *office:* Independence HS 5175 Refugee Rd Columbus OH 43232*

SWEET, SHARON SNYDER, Health Teacher & Vlybl Coach; *b:* Hicksville, OH; *m:* Robert W.; *c:* Jacob W.; *ed:* The Defiance Coll (BS) PE & Hlth Ed 1979; Hamline Univ Advanced Techniques of Coaching Vlybl; Youth & Sports & Death & Dying Courses; Advanced Hlth & Wellness Fit Defiance Coll; *cr:* DeKalb Eastern Comm Schl Elem PE Tchr 1979-80; Hicksville Exempted Village Schl Hlth Tchr 1981-; *ai:* Var Vlybl Coach; Drug Prevention Coord; NEA & HEA 1990-; OAHPERD 1993-; OHSAA 1991-; *office:* Hicksville Exempted Vlg Schl 109 Smith St Hicksville OH 43526

SWEETLAND, RAYMOND DAVID, History Teacher; *b:* Pawtucket, RI; *m:* Katherine Blanchette; *c:* Raymond, Michael, Kevin; *ed:* Cntrl CT St (BS) His 1971, (MS) Guid 1977; *cr:* Alfred Plant Jr High His Tchr & Coach 1971-79; King Philip MS His Tchr & Coach 1979-82; William H Hall HS His Tchr & Coach 1982-; *ai:* Common Ground Adv; Mens Track 1981-85, Soccer 1981-94 & Asst Bsktbl 1980-93 Coach; WHEA 1971-; CEA 1971-; NEA 1971-; *office:* William H Hall HS 975 N Main St W Hartford CT 06117*

SWEIGART, JEAN REBECCA (HORNING), Sixth Grade Teacher; *b:* West Reading, PA; *m:* Richard John; *c:* Rebecca Jean, Matthew Richard; *ed:* Kutztown St Coll (BS) Elem Ed 1968, (MED) Elem Ed 1972; *cr:* Governor Mifflin Schl Dist 5th Grd Tchr 1968-72; Berks Cty Intermediate Unit Schl Substitute Tchr 1982-86; Berks Cty Pub Schls Substitute Tchr 1982-86; Kutztown Area Schl Dist Kndgtn & Long-Term Substitute Tchr 1986; Hamburg Area Schl Dist 4th Grd & 6th Grd Tchr 1986-; *ai:* NEA & PSEA 1968-72 & 1988-; HASD Ed Assn 1988-; Hamburg Area Schl Dist Tchr of Yr 1990-91; Berks Cty Intermediate Unit Courses Seminars & Conf; *office:* Hamburg Elem Schl Hamburg Area Schl Dist 680 E State St Hamburg PA 19526

SWEITZER, JACK JOSEPH, Sr HS Art Teacher; *b:* Dover, OH; *m:* Pamela A.; *c:* Troy Furbay, Trevor Furbay, Pete; *ed:* Dakota St Coll (BS) Art 1973; SD St Univ (MS) Guid, Cnslng 1974; Addl Grad Hrs Cmptr, Educl Courses; *cr:* New Philadelphia HS Tchr 1975-; *ai:* Art Club Adv; NEA 1975-; NPEA 1975-, Tchr Rep; OEA 1975-; Elk 1980-,; *office:* New Philadelphia HS 343 Ray Ave NW New Philadelphia OH 44663

SWEITZER, MELODY M. FOSTER, Fourth Grade Teacher; *b:* Dover, OH; *m:* Robert S.; *c:* Michelle, Dawn, Tara; *ed:* Mount Union Coll (BA) Elem Ed 1983; Kent St Univ (MA) Rdng Specialization 1991; Masters Plus Stud Walsh Univ, Ashland Univ; *cr:* Claymont HS Spec Ed Tchr 1983-84; Claymont Jr HS Seventh Grd Tchr 1984-85; Eastport Ave Elem Schl Sixth Grd Tchr 1985-90, Fourth Grd Tchr 1990-; *ai:* Claymont Educ Assn 1983-, Rep; First Chrstn Church of New Philadelphia 1991-; Venture Capital Grant Goverance Bd; Acadimically Talented Tchr Educ Pgrm Mentor;

Ashland Tchr Achvmnt Awd Nom; Tchr of Yr Nom 1996; Amer Tchr Awds Nom; Pres Awds for Excl in Sci, Math Nom; *office:* Claymont City Schls 1200 Eastport Ave Uhrichsville OH 44683*

SWEITZER, RICHARD, Social Studies Teacher; *b:* Pittsburgh, PA; *ed:* Grove City Coll (BA) His 1966; Bowling Green St Univ (MA) His 1967; *cr:* North Hills HS Tchr 1967-; *ai:* NHEA, PSEA, NEA 1967-; NCSS 1980-; MSCSS 1987-; *office:* North Hills Sr HS 53 Rochester Rd Pittsburgh PA 15229

SWENGOSH, MICHAEL EDWARD, Chemistry Teacher; *b:* Wilkes-Barre, PA; *m:* Clara May Bollias; *c:* Elizabeth; *ed:* Wilkes Univ (BA) Bio 1965; Morgan St Univ (MS) Sci 1970, (MS) Admin, Supervision 1977; Environmental Stud Cert Johns Hopkins Univ; *cr:* North Point Jr HS Tchr 1965-81; Morgan St Univ Asst Bio Prof 1974-81; Overlea HS Tchr 1981-; *ai:* Class of 1984 Spon; Sci, Outdoor Club; Bio Lecturer Essex Comm Coll; Adult Ed Prin 1985-90; NEA, MSTA, TABCO 1965-; Jaycees, Ret Sec, Spoke, 2 Spark Plugs, Outstdng Jaycee of Month; Girl Scout, Ret Asst Ldr; Sunday Schl Tchr 1985-; NSF Grants; Physics Project; GATE Chem Curr in Writing Comm; Passed Natl Tchrs Exam for Bio & Chem; *office:* Overlea HS 5401 Kenwood Ave Baltimore MD 21206

SWENSON, BARBARA, 5th Grade Teacher; *b:* Philadelphia, PA; *m:* Gerald A.; *c:* Anne, Jill; *ed:* North Park Coll (BA) 1968; Western CT St Univ (MS) 1985; Masters 60 Credit Hrs 1995; *cr:* Ryerson Elem 3rd Grd Tchr 1968-69; Flower Voc HS Eng Tchr 1970-72; Little Brown Schlhouse 5th Grd Tchr 1972-74; Compound Elem 5th Grd Tchr 1981-; *ai:* Rdng, Soc & Dist Spelling Curr Comm; Schoolwide Enrichment; NYSRA 1990-; ASCD 1994-; Fndtn for Excl in Yorktown Ed 1995-; *office:* Crompond Elem Schl 2901 Manor St Yorktown Heights NY 10598*

SWENSON, IDA B., Life Science Teacher; *b:* Madison, WI; *m:* John; *c:* Paul; *ed:* OH St Univ (BSE) Bio Sci 1969; Attnd Wright St Univ; *cr:* Linmoor Jr High Phys Sci Tchr 1969-70; Iroquois Mid Phys Sci Tchr 1970-71; Whittier Mid Phys Sci Tchr 1971-73; Greene Cntrl Chem Tchr 1973-80; Binghamton Cntrl HS Chem Tchr 1981; East MS Life Sci Tchr 1983-; *ai:* Eclgy Clb Adv; Prof Dev Schl Steering Comm; 7th Grd Adv; Natl Sci Tchrs 1973-; Sci Tchr Assn of NY St 1989-, Mid Level Subject Area Rep, Newsletter Ed & Southern Section Vice Chm; Greene Cntrl Bd of Ed 1986-89; Performing Arts Forum 1983-, Sec & Artistic Dir; Berean Bible Church; BEST Inst Co-Dir & Resource Tchr; Pub Journal of Pediatric Gastrochtenology & Nutrition; Michael Faraday Competition Finalist 1994; *office:* East MS 167 E Fredrick St Binghamton NY 13904

SWERDLOFF, MARGARET TAUB, English Teacher; *b:* New York, NY; *m:* Daniel; *ed:* Hunter Coll (BA) Eng, Speech & Debate 1967, (MA) Eng & Ed 1982; 30 Addl Grad Credits in Developmental & Remedial Rdng; *cr:* Margaret Knox Jr HS Eng Tchr 1967-76; Jackie Robinson Jr HS Eng & Rdng Tchr 1976-87; Williamson HS Eng Tchr 1987-; *ai:* Lit Magazine Co-Adv; Delta Kappa Gamma 1995-; NTEA 1987-; *office:* Williamson Jr Sr HS RD 2 Box 205 Tioga PA 16946

SWERSEY, BURT L., Senior Lecturer; *b:* Bronx, NY; *m:* Alice Shapiro; *c:* Bill, Sarah, Rachel; *ed:* Cornell Univ (BSME) Mechanical Engrng 1959; *cr:* Polaroid Corp Design Engr 1959-60; Sylvania Electric Systems Design Engr 1960-62; Brookline Instrument Co Founder, Pres 1962-72; Amer Scale Corp Founder, Pres 1972-88; Rensselaer Polytechnic Inst Sr Lecturer 1989-; *ai:* Innovation in Engrng Conf, Prgm Co-Ldr; Fac Intervention Prgm; Taconic Vly Bus Cncl 1989-, Founder, Pres; Northeast NY Nursery, Landscape Assn 1989-, VP; 12 US Patents for Scales; Hesburgh Awd Innovation in Undergraduate Ed 1995; Amer Soc of Mechanical Engrs Design Ed Curr Innovation Awd for Sr Design Course 1994; *office:* Rensselaer Polytechnic Inst Dept of Mechanical Engrng Troy NY 12180*

SWESTYN, ROBERT L., Mathematics Teacher; *b:* Carmichaels, PA; *ed:* Grove City Coll (BS) Electrical Engrng 1963; Math Tchng Cert 1987; Engrng Related Tech Tchng Cert 1992; *cr:* I-T-E Circuit Breaker Co Test Engr 1965-75; BBC Brown Bovers Inc Sr Design Engr 1975-85; Western Area Vo-Tech Engrng Related Tech Tchr 1991-95, Math Tchr 1995-; *ai:* PSEA, NEA 1991-; Knights of Columbus 1963-, Fin Sec.

SWETKOWSKI, EDWARD JOSEPH, American Government Teacher; *b:* Norristown, PA; *m:* Rosalie Mandracchia; *c:* Edward, Sam, Katy; *ed:* West Chester Univ (BS) Soc Sci 1968, (MEd) Soc Sci 1973; PA St Univ Comprehensive, Spec Ed; *cr:* Plymouth Jr High Soc Stud Tchr 1968-70; Norristown High Soc Stud Tchr 1970-71; Whitemarsh Jr High Soc Stud, Spec Ed Tchr 1971-81; Colonial MS Spec Ed Tchr 1981-91; Plymouth Whitemarsh HS Soc Stud, 12th Grd AP, Heterogeneous Tchr 1991-; *ai:* Asst Ath Dir; Stu Cncl Spon; NEA, PSEA 1968-; Plymouth His Assn 1992-; Excellence in Ed Awd; Tchr of Yr 1993; *office:* Plymouth Whitemarsh HS Germantown Pike Plymouth Meeting PA 19462

SWETON, EVA J., Fourth Grade Teacher; *b:* Canonsburg, PA; *ed:* Indiana Univ of PA (BS) Elem Ed 1967; Univ of Pittsburgh (MED) Elem Ed 1971; *cr:* Canon-Mc Millan Schl Dist 4th Grd Tchr 1967-; *ai:* PSEA, NEA 1967-; United We Stand Amer 1993-; Canon-Mc Millan Tchr of Yr 1988.

SWIATEK, MARY ANN, Asst Prof of Psychology; *b:* S Plainfield, NJ; *ed:* Oberlin Coll (BA) Psych 1988; IA St Univ (MS) Psych 1990, (PHD) Psych 1993; *cr:* Suny Coll at Fredonia Asst Prof of Psych 1993-; *ai:* Psych Club Co-Adv; Psi Chi Co-Adv; Various Dept, Campus Comms; Amer Psychological Assn, Amer Psychological Soc, Amer Ed Rsrch Assn 1994-; Natl Assn Gifted Children 1990-; Sigma Xi 1994-; AAUP 1993-; Amer Mensa Ed, Rsrch Fnd Awd Excl Rsrch 1992; NY ULIP PDQWL Awd 1994-95; Scholarly Incentive Awd 1994-95; Amy Everett Meml Awd 1995; Pub Articles 1991-95; *office:* S U N Y Coll At Fredonia W353 Thompson Hall Fredonia NY 14063

SWICKARD, ELLEN RUTH (GRAFTON), Chem Tchr & Science Dept Chair; *b:* Fort Knox, KY; *m:* Patrick Dale; *ed:* Univ of Dayton (MSEd) Scndry Ed 1990; Mt Vernon Nazarene Coll (BA) Chem 1984; Credit Hrs Career Ed Univ of Dayton, Ashland Univ, Seattle Pacific Univ; *cr:* Edison Local Schl Dist Chem, Physics, Phys Sci Tchr 1984-; *ai:* Jr Sr Class Spons 1984-86, 1988; Girls Reserved Bsktbl Coach 1984-88; Teens for Christ Spon 1984-89; Beta Club Spon 1987-; Cty Sci Curr, Textbook Comms; Dev Tech Prep Prgm in Jeff Cty; NSTA 1984-86; ACS 1984-88; SECO 1991; Steubenville 1st Church of Nazarene 1977-, Sec of Bd; Toronto Comm Concert Band 1984-; Outstanding Young Women of America 1991; *office:* Edison H S P O Box 308 Richmond OH 43944

SWIDER, LOUISE PICTROWSKI, Fourth Grade Teacher; *b:* Pittsfield, MA; *m:* Alan C.; *ed:* Coll of Our Lady of Elms (BA) Math, Elem Ed 1973; Cambridge Coll (MED) Mngmt 1989; 56 Credit Hrs Lesley Coll, Univ of MA, Holyoke Comm Coll; *cr:* Kittredge Elem Schl Tchr 1973-80; Berkshire Trl Elem Schl Tchr 1980-; *ai:* CBTRA Bldg, Prof Dev Rep; Head Tchr 1991-94; Water Safety Instr; Asst Swim Team Coach; LA, Math, TASC Comm; Olympic Stu Prgm, Philatelist Club Adv; Cummington, WIndsor Schl Improvement Cncl; MTA, NEA 1973-, Bldg Rep; CHADD 1994-; MA Audubon Soc 1992-, Aquatic Project Wild Awd; Amer Red Cross 1973-, Vol, 20 Yr Svc Awd; Girl Scouts of Amer, 20 Yr Svc Awd; Cooley Dickinson Hosp 1992-, Vol; NAUI, PADI 1987-; Initiated, Created Olympic Stu Prgm 1992; Tchr of Yr Nom; Berkshire Cty Real Women; Thanks to Tchrs Excl Awd Nom 1990; Ag in Classroom 1989; *office:* Berkshire Trail Elem Schl 2 Main St Cummington MA 01026*

SWIFT, DOUG, English Professor; *b:* Bridgeport, CT; *m:* Michile Emoigrard; *ed:* Univ of Bridgeport (BA) Eng, Cinema 1985-; Johns Hopkins Univ (MA) Creative Writing 1986-; Univ of IA (MFA) Creative Writing 1988; *cr:* Muskingum Coll Eng Prof 1988-; *ai:* First Cir Lit Magazine Adv; Numberous Poems Pub; Yaddo, VA Ctr for Creative Arts Fellow; Mack Grant; 2 Green Flwshps; *office:* Muskingum Coll New Concord OH 43762*

SWIFT, MELISSA MC KAY, English Teacher; *b:* Latrobe, PA; *m:* Eric P.; *ed:* Duquesne Univ (BS) Eng Ed 1994; 12 Grad Credits in Cnslr Ed Indiana Univ of PA; *cr:* Pine-Richland Schl Dist Eng Tchr 1994-; *ai:* Asst Forensics Coach 1995-; AP Cncl; Lang Arts Performance Assessment Comm; Portfolio Pianist for Stu-Dir Musical 1994-95; NEA, PSEA, PREA, NCTE 1994-; St Sylvester Church 1991-, Organist, Music Dir; Gift of Time Recipient 1994-95; *office:* Pine-Richland HS 4300 Warrendale Rd Gibsonia PA 15044

SWIFT, PATRICK MICHAEL, Dean; *b:* Bronxville, NY; *ed:* SUNY at Plattsburgh (BA) Ec 1988; Lehman Coll (MA) Scndry Soc Stud 1996; *cr:* Ma Combs Intermediate Schl 7th-8th Grd Tchr 1991-93, Dean 1993-; *ai:* Coach Swim, LaCrosse; Stu Spon Partnership Adv; AFT 1991-; United Fed Tchr; *home:* 1956 Palmer Ave Larchmont NY 10538*

SWIFT, STEPHEN E., English Teacher; *b:* Bryn Mawr, PA; *m:* Candace R. Thurman; *c:* Taylor; *ed:* Denison Univ (BA) Ed Theory & Learning Process 1972; Univ of Pittsburgh (MED) Scndry Ed 1981; 42 Hrs of Post Grad Work at Univ of Pitt & Montgomery Cty In-Service Courses; *cr:* Penn Circle Comm HS Tchr & Dir 1973-81; Comm Coll of Allegeny Cty Tchr 1982-85; Conservation Consultants Dir 1984-85; Montgomery Cty Pub Schls Eng, & Psych Tchr 1985-; *ai:* Var Field Hockey & JV Girls Soccer Coach Guid Adv Comm; NEA 1985-; NCTE 1986-; Numerous Articles Pub; Humanities Cncl Flwshp.

SWIGART, MARTHA HUNTER, English Teacher; *b:* Lewistown, PA; *m:* John Workman Jr.; *c:* Anne Hunter, Katherine Wells; *ed:* Wilson Coll (BA) Fr 1961; PA St Univ, Juniata Coll Post Grad Stud Educating Exceptional Child, Great Epochs of World Culture & 20th Century Fr Lit; *cr:* Huntingdon Area HS Fr, Eng Tchr 1962-65; Juniata Coll Writing Instr 1970; Huntingdon Area HS Fr, Eng Tchr 1982-; *ai:* Table Games Club Adv; HAHS Action Teams Steering Comm; NEA, PSEA; HAEA, Exec Comm Bldg Rep; Amer Assn of University Women, Friends of Huntingdon Cty Lib, Friends of Juniata Coll Lib, Stone Church of the Brethren; *office:* Huntingdon Area HS 2400 Cassady Ave Huntingdon PA 16652

SWINARSKI, WANDA JOANN (LARSON), Fourth Grade Teacher; *b:* Dawson, MN; *m:* Gerald Walter; *ed:* Moorhead St Coll (BS) Elem Ed, Music 1963; Ball St Univ (MA); 30 Addl Hrs; *cr:* Mound Pub Schls Sixth Grd Tchr, Elem Music 3 Yrs; Orono Pub Schls Sixth Grd Tchr 1 Yr; Lafayette Jr HS Music Tchr 2 Yrs; Dept of Defense Dependent Schls HS Music Tchr 1 Yr, Fourth Grd Tchr 25 Yrs; *ai:* Fourth Grd Level Chprsn; Strategic Plan Comm; Federal Ed Assn 1975-; AARP 1992-; NEA 1988-, Lifetime; Sunanon 1978-68; Oakland Symphony Chamber Chorus 1967-68; Exceptional Performance Ratings 1975, 1977, 1979, 1985, 1991, 1993-95; Who's Who in Amer Coll & Univ 1963; *home:* Dodds PSC Box 118 Box 478 APO AE 09137

SWINFORD, DENNIS D., Critical Lang Coord, Eng Instr; *b:* Canton, OH; *ed:* Kent St Univ Eng (BA) 1988, (MA) 1991, (PhD); ABD in Ed Admin 1996; Planned Dissertation in Intnl Ed; *cr:* USAF Morse Systems Operator, Analyst 1982-86; Kent St Univ Eng Instr 1987-88, Coord Critical Langs 1990-, Eng Instr 1991-; *ai:* Working with Stu Groups; NASILP 1990-; NAFSA 1994-; GLSTN Cleveland 1995- Bd Mem; Grad Stu Senate Outstanding Tchr Awd 1988; Fulbright Grantee to Finland, Finnish Folklore 1988-89; Air Force Outstanding Achvmt Awd, Meritorious Svc Medal 1986; *office:* Kent St Univ 119 Bowman Hall Kent OH 44242*

SWINGLE, HERBERT HYATT,JR., History Teacher; *b:* Rochester, NY; *m:* Kathleen Griffin; *c:* Sarah, Matthew; *ed:* Western MI Univ (BS), (MS) His & Pol Sci 1967; Attnd Oxford Univ at England British Stud, Cornell Univ Black Stud, Univ of Rochester Hindu Stud, Harvard Univ China Stud; *ai:* Asst Ftbl Coach; Head Wrestling Coach; Mock Trial Adv; Peer Mediation Adv; NEA 1967-; Western MI Univ Alumni; Nom for NY St Law Related Educator of Yr; Teach for Amer Wkshp Presenter, Natl Coalition for Safe Schls Conf Prsntr in FL & CA; NEA Natl Safe Schl Conf Attendant; *office:* Greece Olympia HS 1139 Maiden Ln Rochester NY 14615*

SWINK, LAURA ALICE, Third Grade Teacher; *b:* Rockingham, NC; *ed:* Appalachian St Univ (BS) K-6th Grd Elem Ed 1986; Pembroke St Univv (MA) K-6th Grd Elem Ed 1988; Eurocentre Florence Italy; 12 Hrs Toward Admin Degree; *cr:* L. J. Bell Elem Schl Third Grd Tchr 1986-92; Amer Intnl Schl Third Grd Tchr 1992-; *ai:* Tchng Eng as a Second Frgn Lang; Dir Choral Music; NCAE, NEA 1986-; MAIS 1992-; ECIS 1993-; Group Stud Exch Osaka Japan 1992; NC Ctr for Advancement of Tchrs; Grd Level Chprsn; Tchr of the Yr L. J. Bell Elem Schl 1991-92; Hnr Tchr for Graduating Class at ASU 1986; Delta Kappa Gamma Tchrs Schlsp; *office:* Amer Intnl Schl Genoa Italy Via Quarto 131c Genoa Italy XX*

SWINTON, JILL ELIZABETH, 3rd Grade Teacher; *b:* North Creek, NY; *ed:* St Univ of NY at Plattsburgh (BS) Elem Ed 1981, (MS) Elem Ed 1987; *cr:* Cold Spring Elem Schl Kndgtn Tchr 1982-85, 3rd Grd Tchr 1985-; *ai:* Intnl Pen Pal, Rain Forest Prgms; 3rd Grd Musical; Kappa Delta Pi 1981-; AFT, NYSUT 1982-; Literacy Vols 1993-; Amnesty Intnl 1989-; *office:* Cold Spring Elem Schl RR 1 Box 487 Homan Rd Stanfordville NY 12581

SWISHER, PAUL LEO, HS Science Teacher; *b:* Kenmore, NY; *m:* Candy L. Sweet; *ed:* Buffalo St Coll (BA) Psych 1982, (MS) Ed 1990; *cr:* North Tonawanda HS Earth Sci & Environmental Sci Tchr 1985-; *ai:* Envirothon Team Adv; Crisis Intervention Team Comm; AFT 1985-; Musicians for Kids 1994-, Pres; Empire St Grad Flwshp 1988; *office:* North Tonawanda Sr HS 405 Meadow Dr North Tonawanda NY 14120

SWITALA, WILLIAM J.,JR., Social Studies Teacher; *b:* Pittsburg, PA; *ed:* St Vincent Coll (BA) His 1992; 30 Credit Hrs Bloomsburg Univ; Working on MA in Curr, Instruction; *cr:* Selingsgrove Area HS Soc Stud Tchr 1992-; *ai:* Men & Womens Vlybl Coach; Soph Class Adv; Tech Comm; PCSS 1990-, His Day SIG Chair; PSEA 1992-; Phi Alpha Theta 1991-, Xi Nu Chptr VP; PAC-TE 1992-, Stu Tchr of Yr; St Co-Coord PA His Day 1994; *office:* Selinsgrove Area HS N Broad St Selinsgrove PA 17870*

SWITZER, ALAN ALEXANDER, Physical Education Teacher; *b:* New Rochelle, NY; *m:* Betsy Joan Kline; *c:* Joy Carr, Derek Husson, Gretchen Hucks, Debra Husson, Jeffrey, Alan III; *ed:* Harvard Coll (AB) Sociology, Math 1952, (EDM) Ed 1958; *cr:* Hebrow Acad Head Ftbl, Swimming, Bsbl Coach, Instr in Math 1955-62; the Hill Schl Swimming Coach, Instr in Math 1962-71; Univ ME Head Swimming Coach, Pool Coord, Lecturer 1971-90; Plymouth St Coll Women's Swimming, Diving Coach, Pool Coord, Lecturer 1990-; *office:* Plymouth St Coll P. E Center Plymouth NH 03264

SWITZER, DANIEL LELAND, Associate Principal; *b:* Johnson City, NY; *m:* Silvia Cristina Bendana; *ed:* Messiah Coll (BA) Eng 1987; 28 Credits Regent Univ; *cr:* Montgomery Cty Convenant Acad Tchr, Coach 1987-91, Ath Dir 1990-91; Lanham Chrstn Schl Tchr, Coach 1991-94, Ath Dir 1992-94; Camp Courage Dir 1993-95; Ets Chaiyim Tree of Life Schl Tchr, Assoc Prin 1994-; *ai:* Coached Athletics; *office:* Ets Chaiyim Tree of Life Schl 215 W Montgomery Ave Rockville MD 20850*

SWOGER, MARK STEPHEN, Language & Theology Teacher; *b:* Erie, PA; *ed:* Gannon Univ (BA) His 1982; Christ the King Seminary (MDiv) Theology 1986; Performance Learning Systems 12 Credits; Gannon Univ Ed Courses; *cr:* Elk Cty Chrstn Part-time Tchr 1988; DuBois Cntr Schl Tchr, Theology Dept Chm 1989-; *ai:* Dev, Bing, Jr Class Pro Stu Asst Prgm; NCEA 1989-; Rotary Interact 1990-, Monito Vincent Great Tchr Recognition Prgm 1992; *office:* Central Chrn 204 Hospital Ave Du Bois PA 15801*

SWYERS, SUSAN LEHNING, Social Studies Teacher; *b:* Buffa *m:* Gifford; *c:* Tracy, Christopher; *ed:* SUNY at Fredonia (BA) 197 Ed, Soc Stud 1975; 60 Addl Grad Hrs; *cr:* Lake Shore Cntrl Schl Soc Stud Tchr 1971-; *ai:* Big Brother, Big Sister Prgm Participa GOALS Prgm; NYSUT 1971-; First Congregational United Ch Christ 1962-; *office:* Lake Shore Cntrl MS 8855 Erie Rd Angola N

SYCHTERZ, TERESA A., First Grade Teacher; *b:* Reading, Kutztown Univ (BS) Elem Ed 1974; Univ of Scranton (MS) Sch 1991; Allentown Coll of St Francis de Sales Campus Ministry Ce 13 Grad Credits PA St Coll; *cr:* St Catharine of Siena Tchr 19 Religion Coord 1980-; Report Card Revision Comm 1995; Fac R Bd 1995-; Cooperating Tchr to Stu Tchrs 1990-; Mrktg Comm 19 Dev Comm 1990; NCEA 1974-; NCTE, IRA 1994-; Sacred Dan 1978-, Pres Chapter; Pub Book The Bible & Me; Articles Pub in C Todays Cath Tchr; Fatima Ctr Vol of Yr 1984; NASA Tchr i Participation Cert 1986; Whos Who in Amer Ed 1989-91, 1995-9 Who in the East 1991-92; Prof Best Leadership Awd Honorable 1989; *office:* St Catherine Of Siena Schl 2330 Perkiomen Ave Rea 19606*

SYDEN, JEFFREY, Earth Science Teacher; *b:* Queens, NY; *m:* Leeds; *c:* Benjamin, Deborah; *ed:* C. W. Post Coll (BA) Bio, Ed 196 Bio, Marine Sci 1972; SUNY at Stony Brook (MLS) Earth Sci 197 of WA Grad Stud Oceanography; SUNY at Oneonta Grad Stud Ea *cr:* Woodland Jr HS Sci Tchr 1968-88; East Meadow HS Sci Tch *ai:* Mens Var Vlybl Coach; AFT, NYSUT, East Meadow Tchrs Ass STANYS; Oceanography, Earth Sci NSF Grants; *office:* East Mea 100 Clymer St East Meadow NY 11554*

SYDESKI, RANDAL T., Social Studies Teacher; *b:* Rochester, Univ of Pittsburgh (BS) Bus Mngmt 1989; St Vincent Coll Tchr C Stud 1994; Pursuing MED; Prins Papers; 4 Credits California Uni *cr:* Ligonier Vly HS Soc Stud Tchr 1994-; *ai:* SADD Adv; Interac Co-Spon 1995; Var Sftbl Coach 1995; Jr HS Bsktbl Coach 1994 PSEA 1994-; PIAA Bsktbl Ofcl 1987-; Amer Legion 1995-.

SYDOW, HOLLY NELSON, Music Teacher; *b:* Chattanooga, Larry Roy; *c:* Cindy Lyn Stockhouse, Jan D. Stockhouse (dec); *ed:* (BME) Flute 1960; St Univ of NY at Fredonia (MM) Flute 1982; Day Schl Music Dir 1976-78; Mercyhurst Coll Flute Instr 1 Chautaugue Inst Flute Instr 1980-82; Gannon Univ Flute Instr & C 1980-; Fairview HS Music Dir 1984-; *ai:* PMEA Dist Regnl & St in Band, Chorus & Orch; Adopt an Artist Prgm; MS Music Enric MENC 1984-; PMEA 1984-; EMTA 1976-; AF of M 1962-; Zon 1994-, Dir; St Johns Luth Church 1984-, Music & Worship Chair; Grenadilla Recording Cos & Discography; *office:* Fairview H Mccray Rd Fairview PA 16415

SYGAR, JANET E., Enrichment Resource Teacher; *b:* Detroit, Richard S.; *ed:* Univ of MI (BA) Elem Ed 1967; Hunter Coll (MS Early Chldhd 1974; 30 Addl Credits Lit, Arts; *cr:* PS Detroit Tchr 1 PS 140 Tchr 1969-81; PS 110 Tchr 1981-87, Enrichment Res Tchr *ai:* Detroit Pub Schl Tchr 1967-69; PS 140 Tchr 1969-81; Intellectually GATE Tchr 1981-87, Enrichment Resource Tchr 198 In-Svc Course 1992-; Staff Dev Dist #1, Consultant Schl Dists US Appointed to Write Curr NYC Arts, Hum 1994; Coach Tchrs Licensing Exams Arts, Soc Stud 1995-; UFT 1969-; NYFA Gra Prgm; Dist #1 DIG, NYSCA Grants; Awd Flwshp 1994; Awd Natl 1 Awd Arch Prgm Designs by Children Urban Network Univ of MI; PS 110 Florence Nightingale 285 Delancey St New York NY 1000

SYKES, LINDA EPPS, Social Stud & Humanities Tchr; *b:* Raymo *c:* Nicholas; *ed:* Jackson St Univ (MAT) Soc Stud 1975; Attnd Bosto Univ of MD, MS St Univ; *cr:* Lanier HS Soc Stud Tchr 1975-83; HS Soc Stud Tchr 1983-84; Nuernberg MS HS Soc Stud Tchr 1 Ansbach MS HS Soc Stud Tchr 1994-; *ai:* NHS, Natl Jr Honor So of 97 Spon; Track Team Coach; Schl Improvement Comm; OEA Red Cross Aids Awareness Awds; MS Acad Cert; Stud of Tchng Cert Trng Cert; *office:* Ansbach HS Cmr 454 Box 2762 APO AE 09250

SYKES, TODD PHILIP, Art Educator; *b:* Scranton, PA; *m:* M Piersimond; *c:* Lindsay, Loren; *ed:* Keystone Coll (AA) Fine Ar Kutztown Univ (BS) Art Ed 1983; Maryland Coll MA Painting St Scranton Prep HS Art Eductr 1987-; *ai:* Art club Adv; Open Gyp Co NAEA 1992-; Presbyn Church 1993-, Deacon.

SYLAK, ROBERT STANLEY, Science Teacher; *b:* Youngstown, Maureen M.; *c:* Benjamen, Jonathan; *ed:* 60 Addl Hrs; *cr:* O Natural Resources Water Division 1973; OH St Univ Sci Lab Dir 1 Shaker Hghts Bd of Ed Tchr 1976-; *ai:* Tutoring Ctr Dir; Enviro Club Adv; Debate Coach; Natl Forensic League; North Am Env Ed Shaker Hghts Tchrs Org 1976-; Doan Creek Watershed 1976-, Bd Chagrin River Watershed Inst, Founding Mem; Pub Svc Duschier A Dept of Ed Presidential Distinguished Tchr 1994-95; PTO, C Watershed Inst Fellowships; *office:* Shaker Heights HS 15911 Al Dr Shaker Heights OH 44120*

SYLVESTER, DAVID JOHN, 10th Grd Social Studies Tchr; *b:* Per *m:* Tisha Ann; *c:* Natalie Marie, David Michael; *ed:* Geneseo St Un Scndry Ed & His 1985, (MA) Ed 1989; *cr:* Wellsville Cntrl 7th & Soc Stud Tchr 1985-86; Alexander Cntrl 8th-11th Grd Soc Stu 1986-88; Perry Cntrl Schl 10th & 12th Grd Soc Stud Tchr 1988-; & Sftbl Coach; Stu Govt Adv; Peer Mediator; AFT 1987-; U Rochester Excl in Scndry Schl Tchng Awd 1995; *office:* Perry Cntrl Watkins Ave Perry NY 14530*

SYLVESTER, SUZANNE TOMPKINS, English Teacher; *b:* Cle OH; *m:* Brian A. Tomkins; *c:* Zephyr Tompkins; *ed:* Amherst Co Eng 1982; Antioch Univ (MED) Ed 1992; *cr:* Lebanon Jr High 7th- Eng Tchr 1987-95; Francis Richmond MS 6th Grd Eng Tchr 1995-; Comm; Quiz Bowl Coach; Lit Magazine Coord; Open Rdng, Recita & Trip Organizer; Arts Day Organizer & Guest Artist; NCTE 1989- 1990-; NELMS 1991-; Presenter at NH MS Inst & NELMS Convention; Parent Wkshps on Writing with Adolescents; *office:* Richmond MS Lebanon St Hanover NH 03766

SYMANSKY, LEONARD L., Professor of Foreign Languages; *b:* A NY; *m:* Selma Cohen; *ed:* Middlebury Coll (BA) Fr 1964, (DML) F Attnd Siena Coll at Loudonville, George Washington Univ; *cr:* Saint Rose Assoc Prof of Frgn Langs 1964-75; Columbia-Greene Coll Prof of Frgn Langs 1977-; *ai:* Stu Life Comm; Sigma Delta Alpha Chi Omega Campus Coord; NY St Assn Frgn Lang Tchrs 196 of Dirs 3 Yrs, Ruth E Wasley Awd; NYSAFLT; AATF; AATSP; AA Theta Kappa Honorary Mem; Sigma Delta Mu & Alpha Chi Ome Mem; Fulbright Seminar Grant 1980; Pres Awd for Excl 1982-83; Columbia Greene Comm Coll P O Box 1000 Hudson NY 12534*

SYMISTER-DAVID, CATHALENE ELIZABETH, Fourth Teacher; *b:* Manhattan, NY; *m:* Patrick Albert David; *c:* S Christopher; *ed:* Coll of Mt St Vincent (BS) Psych 1976; Trinity Col Rdng, Ed 1982; NY St Tchng Cert N-8 1976; *cr:* P S 104 New Yor al Second & Third Grd Tchr 1976-79; Capitol Hill Day Schl Third :hr 1984-87; Green Acres Schl Fourth Grd Tchr 1987-; *ai:* alture Alliance Tchrs Mentor; After-Schl Enrichment Prgm, :d Day Prgm Green Acres Camp Dir; Tutor; Black Stu Fund 1984-; Alumni Assn 1982-; Mount Saint Vincent Alumni Assn 1976-; Assn Schl; MD Sts Arts Cncl Grant; *office:* Green Acres Schl 11701 e Dr Rockville MD 20852*

NDS, DAVID MARSHALL, Seventh Grade Math Teacher; *b:* ille, MA; *m:* Patricia Marie Lobb; *c:* Douglas Marshall, David ; *ed:* Olivet Coll (BA) Math 1970; Temple Univ at Phila (MA) Ed, 975; *cr:* Upper Merion MS Seventh Grd Math Tchr 1970-; *ai:* Asst Head Cross Cntry & Track Coach; Ursinus Coll Head Cross Cntry, ack Coach; Head Girls Cross Cntry, Spring & Winter Track Coach; A, NEA 1970-; Track & Field Coaches Assn 1970-, Svc Awd; n 3 T & F Coaches Assn; PA T & F Coaches Assn; DE Vly Girls Coaches Assn; Natl Cross-Cntry Coaches Assn; *office:* Upper MS 435 Crossfield Rd King Of Prussia PA 19406

LA, DAVID STANLEY, Mathematics Teacher; *b:* East Bloomfield, Rosemarie DeGregorio; *c:* David Jr., Andrew, Rebecca; *ed:* St Univ at Albany (BS) Math 1962, (MS) Math 1963; Post Grad Credit Hrs a Coll & Saint Rose Coll; NSF Inst Univ of DE 1985; *cr:* Bethlehem IS Math Tchr 1962-; St Univ of NY at Albany Adjunct Prof 1986-; ra-Classroom Accounts Treas; Bethlehem Cntrl Tchrs Assn 1962-, Bldg Rep; NYEA, NYSUT, NEA 1962-; Guilderland Pop Warner 5, Pres, Commissioner; New Scotland Pop Warner 1986-, Founding Mendolssohn Club of Albany 1995-; Capital Hill Choral Soc 8; NYS Certified Swim Ofcl 1962-87, Pres, Treas, NYSPHSAA ionships Ofcl; Price-Chopper Gelub Fnd Tchr & Scholar Awd 4 Nom for Presidential Awd for Excl in Math Tchng 1988; *home:* 218 Ct Voorheesville NY 12186

OINOS, MARIA, ESL Teacher; *b:* Athens, Greece; *ed:* Bradford A) Western European Lit 1976; Salem St Coll (MED) Rdng, Lang Univ of MA (MBA) Mrktg, Mngmt 1983; 30 Addl Credit Hrs Ed; ne Paris Frances Cert of Fr Lang, Civilization; *cr:* Winter Street -4 Grd Greek Biling Tchr 1977-78; St James Schl 5-8 Grd Greek Tchr 1978-79; Hunking Schl 5-8 Grd ESL Tchr 1979-80; Consentino -8 Grd ESL Tchr 1980-; *ai:* Adult Ed Night Schl ESL, Greek Lang ure Tchrs; ESL Mentor for TOEFOL Examination; Sat Schl Tchr for Boarderline Stdnts; NEA 1980-; MABE, NABE 1976-; *office:* atino Schl 685 Washington St Haverhill MA 01832

ILAS, RITA KOLETTI, Jr High & HS Greek Teacher; *b:* kastroy-Kard, Greece; *m:* Dennis C.; *c:* Vayia D.; *ed:* Univ of Athens Philosophy, Ancient Greek & Modern Greek Stud 1972; Addl Stud niv Eng Lang 1973-75, Huyter Coll Eng Lit 1976-77; *cr:* St rios HS Tchr 1973-; *ai:* Cultural Coord; Choir Lady of Educl Comm; Amer Tchrs Assn 1978-; Fed of Hellanic-Amer 1994-; Assn of NY Soc 1972-, Bd Mem, Sec, Auditor; South Demetrios HS Awd 1990; Organizer of Greek Dept 1979-85; Greek Archdiocese of North & Amer Awd 1988; *home:* 2201 29th St Astoria NY 11105*

CA, SUSAN W., First Grade Teacher; *b:* Johnson City, NY; *m:* d J.; *c:* Jeffrey J., Thomas E.; *ed:* St Univ of NY Coll at Brockport lem Ed 1971; St Univ Coll at Cortland (MA) Rdng 1976; *cr:* Harry nson Elem Schl 2-4 Grd Multiaged Tchr 1971-82, Kndgtn Tchr 0, K-1 Grd Tchr 1990-92, First Grd Tchr 1992-; *ai:* NEA 1971-; l Pub Articles; *office:* Harry L Johnson Elem Schl 235 Harry L Dr n City NY 13790

CK, NICHOLAS GEORGE, 7th-8th Grd US History Teacher; *b:* y, NJ; *ed:* VA Military Inst (BA) His 1981; Kean Coll (MA) Lbrl His 1990; 50 Undergraduate Credits Soc Stud Cert; 30 Addl Credits dmin; *cr:* Elizabeth Pub Schls Soc Stud Tchr 1988-90; Carteret Pub Soc Stud Tchr 1990-; *ai:* Audio Visual Coord; Supvr Schl Safety ; *office:* Pvt Nicholas Minue Elem Schl 83 Post Blvd Carteret NJ *

O, CAROL ANN, Second Grade Teacher; *b:* Camden, NJ; *m:* Joseph Beth Ann, Douglas, Mark, Janine; *ed:* Trenton St (BA) Kdgn Primary 55; *cr:* Willingboro Schl Dist 1st Grd Tchr 1965-69; Clementon Schl nd Grd Tchr 1977-79; Berlin Twp Schl Dist K-2nd Grd Tchr 1979-; th, Sci Comm; Berlin Twp Tchrs Assn 1990-, Sec; PTA 1975-; Tchr 1994; *office:* John F. Kennedy Schl Mt Vernon Ave West Berlin NJ *

O, PRISCILLA E., First Grade Teacher; *b:* Syracuse, NY; *m:* t W.; *c:* Robert W. Jr., Daniel Scott; *ed:* LeMoyne Coll (BS) ogy 1963; St Univ of NY Coll at Oswego (MS) Ed, (CAS) Instrl 1989; 24 Hrs Grad Ed Boston Coll; 12 Hrs Grad Ed Syracuse Univ; racuse City Schls 1st-3rd Grd Tchr 1965-69; Liverpool Cntrl Schl st-3rd, 5th Grd Tchr, Admin Intern 1969-; *ai:* United Liverpool Fac 1969-; Phi Delta Kappa 1988-; NY St United Tchrs; AFT; Liverpool er, Liverpool Mat Clubs 1978-84; Who's Who Among Human Svc 1988; *office:* Willow Field Elem Schl 3900 State Route 31 Liverpool 3090*

EWSKI, MARY (MARSHALL), Eng, Jrnlsm Tchr & Dept Chprsn; mbridge, MD; *m:* Joseph T.; *ed:* DE St Univ (BA) Eng 1973; Post Work Univ of DE; *cr:* DE Adolescent Prgm Inc Eng Tchr 1974-78; Forest HS Eng, Jrnlsm Tchr 1978-; *ai:* Schl Newspaper Adv 18 Yrs; & Scroll Adv; Lang Arts Curr Revision Comm; Eng Dept Chprsn; 1978-, LFHS Eng Tchr of Yr; DSPA 1978-, St Treas; DSRA 1980-; , DSEA, NEA 1978-; *office:* Lake Forest HS RD 1 Box 847 Felton 943

KMARY, LINDA E., 2nd Grade Teacher; *b:* New York City, NY; *m:* J.; *c:* Jared; *ed:* SUC at New Paltz (BA) Elem Ed 1974; SUNY at y (MS) Rdng 1977; *cr:* Catskill Cntrl Schls Tchr 1974-; *ai:* Dist K-12 Arts, Bldg Level Shared Decision Making Comm; NYSUT, IRA, ill Tchrs Assn 1974-; NYS Whole Lang Conf Presenter 1993, Rdng nter 1994; Dist-Wide Improvement Grant 1984, 1988-93; *office:* g Primary Schl 2 Academy St Catskill NY 12414

LAI, PATRICIA SIRANOVIC, Library & Media Specialist; *b:* gstown, OH; *m:* Gene; *c:* David, Jennifer, Jonathan; *ed:* Youngstown iv (BSEd) Eng, Spec Ed 1972; Kent St Univ (MS) Lib Media 1991; gstown St Univ Elem Ed 1980; 45 Addl Hrs Ashland, Drake, e-Pacific, Walsh; *cr:* Hubbard Local Schls Spec Ed Tchr 1972-77; d City Schls Spec Ed Tchr 1985-86, Lang Arts, Elem Tchr 1986-90, Wide Lib Media Specialist 1990-; *ai:* English Festival; NEA 1972-; d Assn 1972-, Bldg Rep; Girard Jr Women's; Delta Kappa Gamma; Commendation Dept Ed Columbus; *home:* 510 E Broadway Ave d OH 44420*

ZEPANSKI, CAROL LEE KOZAK, Science Teacher; *b:* Niskayuna, n: Ronald; *c:* Amy, Michael; *ed:* Univ of Rochester (BA) General Sci SUNY at Albany (MA) Ed 1965; Union Coll Grad Chem Course; *cr:* Y at Plattsburgh Asst Dean of Stdnts 1965; Schalmont Cntrl Schls Sci 1965-66; Fonda-Fultonville Cntrl Sci Tchr 1966-67; Schenectady Schl Sci Tchr 1967-; Schenectady Cty Comm Coll Adjunct Sci Instr -75 Part Time; Union Coll Adjunct Instr in MAT Prgm; *ai:* Team Ldr Scholar Team; AFT, NYSUT, SFT 1970-; STANYS Intermittently; ch of Our Lady of Fatima 1971-, Lector Team Chair 1989-, Liturgy , Parish Cncl; Tchr of Yr 1991 Sigma Chi Iota Union Coll Chapter; Influential Tchr 1993 & 1995; Mentor to Union Coll Interns; Univ of Notre Dame NSF Grant Chem 1970; *office:* Schenectady HS 1401 The Plz Schenectady NY 12308*

SZCZESNY, ANNE T., Foreign Language Dept Chprsn; *b:* Tel Aviv, Israel; *m:* Leonard; *c:* Antoinette, Gregory; *ed:* St Univ of NY at Buffalo (MA) Fr, Polish & Ger 1965; Attnd Various Insts Over Yrs; *cr:* Frontier Cntrl Foreign Lang Tchr & Dept Chprsn 1962-; *ai:* Dist Dev Cncl; Lang Clubs; Mentor for Tchrs & Stdnts; Scorer for Natl Evalaution Systems; St & Natl Tchrs Orgs 1962-; NYS Lang Tchrs 1962-, Several Offices, 1982 Outstanding Lang Tchr NYS; WNY Lang Tchrs 1962-, Several Offices, 1990 Outstanding Tchr WNY; Polish Arts Club 1965-, Bd of Dirs, 1982 Outstanding Awd for Polish Culture; Koscuiszko Fnd 1975-; Blue Army 1985-; PTSA; Amer-Polish Eagle Outstanding Educator Western NY 1986; Canisius Coll Outstanding Educator Western NY 1993; Writer for NYS Regents Examination; *office:* Frontier Central HS S-4432 Bay View Rd Hamburg NY 14075*

SZEGEDY, PAMELA MARIE (HILL), Fifth Grade Teacher; *b:* Cleveland, OH; *m:* Allen Thomas; *c:* Allen, Amy-Marie, Amanda, Allison-Ann; *ed:* OH Univ (BA) Elem Ed 1971; Cleveland St Univ (MS) Curr, Instruction 1982; Elem Admin Cert 1994; *cr:* Cleveland Pub Schls Elem Tchr 1971-76; Vermilion City Schls Elem Tchr 1977-79; Avon Lake City Schls Elem Tchr 1981-; *ai:* Report Card Revision, Testing Results Needs Comms, Math Curr Coord, Staff Dev Day Comm, Curr Magazine Comm; NEA, OEA 1981-; Pi Lambda Theta 1982-; West Shore Rdng Cncl 1989-; OH Univ Alumni Assn 1971-; Avon Lake Tchrs Assn 1981-; Little League Bsbl Fed 1993-, Coach; Avon Lake Boosters Club 1990-; Tchr of Yr 1991; Articles Pub on Book Reporting, Nutrition Awareness, Parental Involvement, Self-Esteem 1987-1994, Journal Wrtng; *office:* Troy Intermediate Schl 237 Belmar Blvd Avon Lake OH 44012*

SZELIGA, CHRISTINE ANN, Special Education Teacher; *b:* Perth Amboy, NJ; *ed:* Kean Coll (BA) Spec Ed & K-12th Grd Tchr of Handicapped 1982, (MA) Spec Ed & Phys Act for Handicapped 1987; *cr:* Samuel E Shull Schl Tchr of Spec Ed & PI 1982-85; Perth Amboy HS Tchr of Spec Ed & RR 1985-; *ai:* Var Ftbl, Bsktbl & Competition Cheerleading Coach; Mentor; Peak Performance Team Co-Adv; Tennis Intramural Adv; AFT 1982-; *office:* Perth Amboy HS Eagle Ave & Francis St Perth Amboy NJ 08861*

SZELONG, RICHARD JOSEPH, English Teacher & Yrbk Advisor; *b:* Alexandria, VA; *m:* Brenda Irene Frank; *c:* Joshua, Sarah; *ed:* Univ of Pittsburgh at Johnstown (BA) Jrnlsm 1982, (BA) Scndry Ed Commnctn 1985; *cr:* United Jr-Sr HS 9th Grd Eng Tchr & Yrbk Adv 1985-; *ai:* Writing Steering Comm; NEA 1985-; PSEA 1985-; UEA 1985-; St Benedict Church 1972-; Arbutus Bsbl League 1994-, 2nd VP; Pub Newspaper Sports Column; *office:* United Jr Sr HS PO Box 168 Armagh PA 15920

SZENTE, CHRISTOPHER JON, 5th Grade Teacher; *b:* Elyria, OH; *m:* Kathy; *c:* Angela, Kelli, Chris, Rick, Michael, Tristan; *ed:* Lorain Comm Coll (AA) Ed 1973; Univ of ME at Presque Isle (BS) Elem Ed 1985; *cr:* SAD #44 Woodstock Schl 6th Grd Tchr 1985-91, 2nd Grd Tchr 1982-95, 5th Grd Tchr 1995-; *ai:* Soc Stud Comm; NEA, MTA 1993-; *home:* 1348 Intervale Rd Bethel ME 04217

SZEREG, SONIA, English Teacher; *b:* New York, NY; *ed:* St John's Univ (BA) Eng 1981, (MA) Eng 1983; NEH Renaissance Inst 1992; *cr:* St George Acad Eng Chprsn 1987-; *ai:* 11th Grd Homeroom; Stu Cncl; Co-Organizer: Sr Trip 1990, 1992, 1994, Spec Events; Newsletter, Lit Magazine Moderator; Stu Contests Coord; NCTE 1992-; NGPT 1989-; Ukrainian Music Inst 1987-, Piano Instr; Vocal Ensemble 1985-; Ukrainian Amer Youth Assn 1965-, Summer Cnslr, Instr 1980-90; NYSCSS, NYS4A Conf Co-Presenter 1994; Fulbright Summer Pgm in Poland & Hungary 1995; *office:* St George Acad 215 E 6th St New York NY 10003

SZILAGYI, TAMAS, History Teacher; *b:* Szatmarnemet, Hungary; *m:* Brigitta Rischer; *c:* Steven; *ed:* Budapest Tchrs Coll (BA) His, Geog 1954; Pittsburgh Univ (MA) Russian His 1968; *cr:* HS Tchr, Coach 1953-56; Kiski Schl Tchr, Coach 1963-; *ai:* Tennis; MEH Seminar 1992 Canisius Coll; *home:* 1888 Brett Ln Saltsburg PA 15681

SZOKOLI, DARREN ROBERT, Health & Phys Education Tchr; *b:* Huntington, NY; *ed:* Univ of Dayton (BS) Hlth, PE 1992; SUNY at Stony Brook (MA) Lbrl Stud 1996; *cr:* Elwood-John H. Glenn HS Hlth, PE Tchr 1992-; *ai:* Var Ftbl, JV Wrestling, Bsbl Coach; *office:* Elwood-John H. Glenn HS 478 Elwood Rd East Northport NY 11731

SZUCH, ANNETTE E., Vocal Music Teacher; *b:* Vandergrift, PA; *c:* James Michael, Stacey Hodits; *ed:* Carnegie Mellon Univ (BFA) Music 1958; Seton Hill Coll (EDB) Music Ed 1979; 2 Addl Hrs Opera Carngegie Mellon; 24 Addl Hrs Ed; *cr:* Kiski Area Schl Dist Music Tchr 1967-69; St Gertrude Parochial Schl 7th Grd Music Tchr 1975-81; Freeport Schl Dist Scndry Vocal Music Tchr 1981-; *ai:* Annual Musical Prod Producer, Dir; NEA, PMEA, FEA, MENC, PMEA 1981-; Cath Daughters of Amer 1965; *home:* 520 Franklin Ave Vandergrift PA 15690

SZYMANSKI, ELLEN M., Social Studies Teacher; *b:* Dayton, OH; *m:* Robert; *c:* David, Rebecca; *ed:* SUNY at Buffalo (BA) His 1973; Hofstra Univ (MA) Soc Stud 1976; Addl 45 Credits; *cr:* Center Moriches HS Soc Stud Tchr 1973-; *ai:* NYSUT, LICSS 1973-; *office:* Ctr Moriches HS 311 Frowein Rd Center Moriches NY 11934

SZYMANSKI, FRANK T., Retention Specialist & Cnslr; *b:* Baltimore, MD; *m:* Colleen Kirby; *c:* Mike, Allison; *ed:* Salisbury St Univ (BS) Lbrl Stud 1992, (MED) Admin Ed 1994; *cr:* Salisbury St Univ Asst Bsbl Coach 1992-94; Baltimore City Comm Coll Retention Specialist, Cnslr & Head Bsbl Coach 1994-; *ai:* Ath Cnslr; Natl Assn of Acad Advs for Ath 1995-; *office:* Baltimore City Comm Coll 2901 Liberty Heights Ave Baltimore MD 21215*

SZYMCZAK, BARBARA K., High School Math Teacher; *b:* Bayonne, NJ; *ed:* Jersey City St Coll (BA) Spec Ed Cert 1973, Elem Ed 1978 & Scndry Math 1985; 32 Credits in Cmptrs, Word Perfect, Ed & Children in Need; Post Grad Stud Jagiellonski Univ in Krakow, Poland 1987; 12 Grad Credits in Urban Ed St Peters Coll; Conflict Resolution Trng; *cr:* Philp Baker Schl Resource Room Tchr 1973-78; Our Lady of Victory Schl 6th Grd Tchr 1978-81; Bayonne HS Resource Room Tchr 1981-84, Math Tchr 1984-; *ai:* Curr Revisions; HSPT & EWT Interpretations; Math Tutorial Svc; St Peters Prgm for Srs; NJEA 1980-; NCTM 1986-; AMTNJ 1989-; Mini Grant for Cmptr for Resource Room; Tchr of the Month 1993-94; *office:* Bayonne HS 28th & Avenue A Bayonne NJ 07002

T

TABACHNICK, MICHAEL NEIL, Associate Professor of Physics; *b:* New York, NY; *m:* Naomi Berlin Weisberg; *c:* Lawrence Weisberg, Michael Weisburg, Susan Juliano, Robert C., Susan A.; *ed:* Temple Univ (AB) Physics 1965; Columbia Univ (MA) Physics 1967; PHD Level Courses Solid St Physcis Rutgers U 1967-68; *cr:* Temple U Grad Tchng Asst 1964-65; Columbia U Grad Tchng Asst 1965-67; Rutgers U Grad Tchng Asst 1967-68; DE Vly Coll Assoc Prof of Physics 1968-; *ai:* Sexual Harassment Onbudsperson; Hillet Adv; Fac Cncl Chm; Instrl Resources Comm; AAUP Chptr Union Pres; AAUP 1994-, Pres; Alpha Phi Omega 1965-, Lifetime Honorary Mem; Columbia Univ Spec Awd Distngd Tchng 1967; NSF Flwshp Honorable Mention 1965; Grad Magna Cum Laude 1965; *office:* Delaware Valley Coll 700 E Butler Ave Doylestown PA 18901

TABACHNICK, PATRICIA ANN, English Resource Teacher; *b:* Nanticoke, PA; *c:* Jill Susan, Beth; *ed:* Wilkes Coll (BA) Eng 1969; Post Grad Stud Ed, Eng, Psych PA St Univ, Montgomery Cty MD, Tchr Inservice Courses, George Washington Univ; *cr:* Bensalem Twp Schl Dist 9th-12th Grd Eng, Spec Ed Tchr 1969-75; Holy Ghost Schl 6th-8th Grd Lang Arts, Soc Stud, Religion Tchr 1984-85; Montgomery Cty Pub Schls 7th-8th, 10th-12th Grd Eng Tchr 1986-; *ai:* NHS, Lit Mag Advs; NEA, MCEA 1986-; Hospital, Nursing Home Vols 1986-; *office:* Poolesville Jr/Sr HS 17501 W Willard Rd Poolesville MD 20837*

TABACINSKI, ELAINE BIGELOW, Chemisty & Physics Teacher; *b:* Lynn, MA; *m:* William G.; *ed:* Univ of MA (BS) Bio, Chem 1967; Univ of CT (MS) Dev Bio 1970; 30 Addl Hrs; Bio, Chem Tchng Cert 1971; *cr:* E Hampton HS Tchr 1973-; *ai:* Class Adv; Prins Advy Comm; E Hampton Ed Assn 1973-, Rep; ACS 1996-; C2T 1996-; *office:* East Hampton HS 9 N Maple St E Hampton CT 06424

TABACINSKI, WILLIAM GEORGE, Agriscience Instructor; *b:* Bronx, NY; *m:* Elaine Bigelow; *ed:* Univ of CT (BS) Plant Sci 1970; Tchng Cert & 33 Credits; *cr:* Nathan Hale-Ray HS Tchr 1972-; *ai:* FFA Adv; NEASC Schl Comm, Honor Soc Selection, Class Levels & Weights Comms; CVATA 1971-, Sec, VP, Outstanding Young Tchr of Yr; E Haddam EA 1971-, Pres; Moodus Sportsmens Club 1974-, Pres; CT DEP Conservation Ed Firearms Safety Instr 1982-; Assisted in Dev of CT DEP Firearms Safety and CT Natural Resources Currs; Dev Wildlife Bio & Aquatic Resources Curr; *office:* Nathan Hale-Ray HS School Dr Moodus CT 06469

TABASCO, DENISE, Mathematics Teacher; *b:* Philadelphia, PA; *ed:* Rowan Coll of NJ (BA) Math 1989, (MA) Math Ed 1991; *cr:* Rowan Coll of NJ Grad Asst 1989-90; Camden Cty Coll Math Instr 1989-92; Gloucester Cath HS Math Tchr 1991-; *ai:* Math Club Adv; Cheerleading Coach; *office:* Gloucester Catholic HS 333 Ridgeway St Gloucester City NJ 08030

TABER, DAVID WM, Retired 7th Grd Soc Sci Tchr; *b:* Town of Perinton, NY; *ed:* Franklin Coll of IN (BA) His, Math 1957; 30 Hrs Univ of Rochester, SUNY at Brockport, SUNY at Genseo, SUNY at Oswego Permanent Cert; *cr:* Palmyra-Macedon Cntrl Schl 7th Grd Soc Stud Tchr 1960-94; *ai:* Stu Cncl Adv; Yorker Club Spon; Pal-Mac Fac Assn 1960-, Treas; Wayne Cty Tchrs Assn 1960-, Treas; NYS United Tchrs 1960-, Comm Svc; Wayne Cty Ret Tchrs 1994-, VP; Freemasons 1960-, Master, Mason of Yr; Pevinton Recreation Comm 1964-70; Historical Soc Wayne Cty, Pres; First Bapt Church 1947-, Moderator, Deacon, Trustee; Historian Village of Fairport 1995-.*

TABER, JANE C., English Teacher; *b:* New Rochelle, NY; *m:* Michael J.; *ed:* SUCC at Cortland (BA) Sec Eng Ed 1971; SUNY at Albany (MA) Sec Eng Ed 1972; Concentration in Gifted Ed 75 Credit Hrs; *cr:* Sayville HS Eng, Creative Writing, Hum SAT Tchr 1974-; *ai:* Lit Magazine, Quiz Bowl Team, Theater Crew Adv; NCTE 1970-; NEA, AFT 1973-; *office:* Sayville HS 20 Brook St West Sayville NY 11796*

TABER, SHARON FOWLER, Sixth Grade Teacher; *b:* New Berlin, NY; *c:* Margaret, Frederick, Steven; *ed:* SUNY at Oswego (BS) Elem Ed 1962; 45 Grad Hrs; *cr:* Union Endicott Cntrl 1st Grd Tchr 1962-64; Marion Cntrl Schl Sub Migrant Ed Tchr 1964-70; NYS Bureau of Migrant Ed 1970; Sodus Cntrl Schl 5th & 6th Grd Tchr 1971-; Butler Shock Camp Night GED Tchr 1992-94; *ai:* Team Ldr; Intermediate Rep to SFA; Mem of Dist Shared Decision Team; Chrldng Coach; Employer & Employee Rep; NEA 1962; Wayne Cty Tchr Assn 1962-, Tchr Rep; Sodus Cntrl Fac Assn 1971-Intermediate Rep; Victim Resource Ctr 1984-, Bd Of Dir; Eastern Star 1973-, Past Matron; *office:* Sodus Jr Sr HS PO Box 220 Sodus NY 14551*

TABER, THOMAS JAY, English Dept Chair & Teacher; *b:* Sidney, NY; *m:* Inge N. Schwede; *c:* Thomas Jay II; *ed:* Bloomsburg St Univ (BS) Scndry Ed, Eng 1968; Keane Coll of NJ (MA) Stu Prsnl Svcs 1980; 66 Addl Grad Credits Beyond MA Seton Hall Univ Driver Ed, Penn St Univ Psych, Jersey City St Coll Ed, Monclair St Coll Ed; *cr:* Bernards HS Eng Tchr 1968-, Head Var Golf Goach, 1970-89, Eng Dept Chair 1988-; *ai:* Advy Panel to Prin; Dist Instructional Cncl Mem; Dist Strategic Planning Comm; Yr 2000 Mem; Honorary Mem of NHS; Bernardsville Ed Assn 1968-, VP; NJ Ed Assn, NEA 1968-; ASC, NCTE 1988-; Tewksbury Youth Athl Assn 1987-, Officer, Coach, Admin; Coach of Yr 1985; *office:* Bernards HS 25 Olcott Ave Bernardsville NJ 07924*

TABLER, DEBRA (GRIFFITH), Math Teacher & Dept Head; *b:* Fukuoka, Japan; *m:* James Stephen Sr.; *c:* James Jr., Jeremy, John; *ed:* Shepherd Coll (BA) Math Ed 1978; WV Univ (MA) Rdng Ed 1986; Research Math Mt St Marys Coll; Modeling with Natl Sci Fnc; *cr:* Clear Spring HS Tchr 1978-82, Tchr, Dept Head 1985-; *ai:* Jr Class Spon; Prom Adv; Computer Lab Coord; Schl Improvement Team; MCTM, NCTM 1991-; MSTA, NEA, WCTA 1978-; Berkeley Co Youth Fair Bd 1991-; 4-H Ldr 1987-; Church Trustee 1980-, Bd Mem, Pres; Tandy Cmptr Tchr of Yr Semifinalist; *office:* Clear Spring HS 12630 Broadfording Rd Clear Spring MD 21722*

TABOR, DENISE LYNNE (OSTROW), English Instructor; *b:* Berkely, CA; *m:* Gary Martin; *ed:* Skidmore Coll (BA) Eng, Arts 1984; Oxford Univ-Lincoln Coll Breadloaf Schl of Eng (MA) Eng Lit 1988; Attnd New Schl, St Marks Place Poetry Project; *cr:* Friends Seminary Permanent Eng, Art Sub Tchr 1984-86; Tchrs & Writers Collaborative Writer-in-Residence 1988-90; Prep for Prep-Broad Jump Eng Tchr 1988-90; Phillips Acad Eng Instr 1990-; *ai:* Search & Rescue Coach; House Cnslr; Potpourri Yrbk Adv; Writer-in-Residence Search Comm; Kenon Grant; Numerous Poems Pub; *office:* Phillips Acad S. Main St Andover MA 01810*

TABOROSI, MARY-JULIANNE, Sixth Grade Teacher; *b:* Rahway, NJ; *ed:* Kean Coll (BS) Elem Ed 1967; NY Univ (MA) Anthropology, Sociology 1970; Cert Color Analysis Look Consulting Intnl 1992; Coll Tchng Japanese, Cmptr Tech; 100 Hrs Japanese Lang, Culture; *cr:* Woodbridge Bd Ed 6th Grd Tchr 1967-; Color Consulting Bus Owner 1995-; *ai:* Math, Sci Curr Guide Comms; Run own Bus; Teach Eng Intnl Ctr Vol; NEA, WTEA 1967-; Amer Entrepreneurs Assn 1996; Assn Image Consultants Intnl 1996; Marble Collegiate Church 1978-, Vol; Jpana Soc 1970-; NY Univ Alumni Assn 1995-; Kappa Delta Pi Honorary 1969-; *home:* PO Box 20 Metuchen NJ 08840*

TACKETT, MICHELLE RENE (SHOVER), First Grade Teacher; *b:* Portsmouth, OH; *m:* Stephen Shon; *c:* Stephen Craig; *ed:* OH Univ (BA)

Elem Ed 1989; *cr:* Minford MS Fifth Grd Tchr 1990-91, 7th Grd Rdng, 8th Grd Art Tchr 1991-92, Fifth Grd Tchr 1991-95, First Grd Tchr 1995-; *ai:* Dist Tech, Software Selection Comms; NEA 1990-.

TACY, STEPHEN A., Vocal & General Music Tchr; *b:* Rochester, NY; *m:* Ellen B.; *ed:* Nazareth Coll of Rochester (BS) Music Ed 1981, (MS) Ed 1986; *cr:* Byron Berben Jr, Sr HS Vocal, Gen Music Tchr 1981-89; H. W. Schroeder MS Vocal, Music Tchr 1989-94; Thomas MS Vocal, Gen Music Tchr 1994-; *ai:* Swing Choir, Jazz Vocal Group; AFT 1981-; Webster Tchrs Assn 1989-; NYSTU 1981-, Head Bldg Rep; *office:* R L Thomas MS 800 Five Mile Line Rd Webster NY 14580

TADAL, PACKETA GAYLE, English Teacher; *b:* Jamaica, West Indies; *m:* Rene; *c:* Teran; *ed:* St Univ Coll at Brockport (BS) Eng 1975, (MS) Ed 1978; 15 Hrs Cert of Advanced Stud; *cr:* Edison Tech & Occupational Ed Ctr Eng Tchr 1977-, Writing Resource Tchr 1994-; *ai:* Class Adv; Bldg Comm; AFT, NYSUT 1977-; Rochester Tchrs Assn 1977-, Bldg Rep; NCTE 1990-; CASA, Urban League 1995-; Club Caribbean Edctr of Yr; Dr Freddie Thomas Learning Ctr Vol Awd; PRISM Edctr of Yr; *office:* Edison Tech & Occupational Ctr 655 Colfax St Rochester NY 14606*

TADDESSE, MELLESSE AMOSSA, Assistant Professor; *b:* Addis Ababa, Ethiopia; *m:* Erlin Ibreck; *c:* M. Yonas, M. Sahra, M. Fasil; *ed:* Columbia Univ (MIA) 1982, (EDM) 1984, (EDD) 1990; *cr:* City Univ of NY Hostos Coll Asst Prof 1990-; Baruch Coll Asst Prof 1990-93; Iona Coll Asst Prof 1991-93; Mercy Coll Asst Prof 1993-94; *ai:* Ethiopian Sport, Cultural Org Pres; Auditor Ethiopian Fed North Amer; NY African Stud Assn 1990-; Omicron Delta Epsilon 1976-; Oneonta St Distngd Comm Svc Awd; *office:* City Univ Of NY Hostos Coll 475 Grand Concourse Bronx NY 10451

TAFROW, THERESANN C., Third Grade Teacher; *b:* Trenton, NJ; *ed:* Glassboro St Coll (BA) Kndgtn, Primary Ed 1967; Post Grad Stud Trenton St Coll 15 Credit Hrs; Rutgers 3 Credit Hrs; *cr:* Peter Muschal Schl First-Fourth Grd Tchr 1967-; *ai:* Dist Environmental Coord 1991-; Innovative Recycling, Earth Day Celebratio Prgms, Act; NEA, NJEA 1967-; BREA 1967-, Parlimentarian 1973-74, Treas 4 Terms; United Fe dDoll Club 1980-, Del; DE Vly Doll Club 1980-, Treas, Parliemnt; Bordentown Historical Soc 1980-; Ryan's Hope A Child's Dream Inc 1985-, Bd of Trustees; NJ St Grants 1971-72, 1974, 1991-95; Environmental Clean Comms Grants; Bordentown Bd of Ed Grants 1970-71; *office:* Peter Muschal Schl 323 Ward Ave Bordentown NJ 08505

TAFT, CAROL SCOTT, First Grade Teacher; *b:* Warsaw, NY; *m:* Henry G.; *ed:* Roberts Wesleyan Coll (BS) His, Psych 1965; Brockport in Ed 1965-66; 53 Addl Hrs; *cr:* Williamson Elem Schl First Grd Tchr 1966-; *ai:* Lang Arts Comm; Schl Security Comm; AFT, NEA 1966-; Penfield Wesleyan Church Dir of Tots Prgm.

TAFT, MARILEE BOBIAN, Social Studies Teacher; *b:* Essex Junction, VT; *m:* Jeffrey William; *c:* Brooke, Heather; *ed:* Univ of VT (BA) His 1968; 30 Addl Hrs His, Sociology, Ed, Cmptr Tech; *cr:* Essex HS Soc Stud Tchr 1988-; *ai:* Close Up Coord; Attendance Review Bd; Track, Field Hockey, Gymnastics Ofcl; NEA, VT EJEA 1988-; Columbia Univ Book Awd; Phi Beta Kappa; Woodrow Wilson Scholar; Danforth Flwshp; Sr Hnrs Thesis; *office:* Essex HS 2 Educational Dr Essex Junction VT 05452

TAFT, RAYMOND FRANCIS, High School Science Teacher; *b:* Springfield, MA; *m:* Debbie Ellen Taylor; *c:* Aaron; *ed:* Westfield St coll (BA) Music Ed 1979; Inst for Creative Rsrch (MS) Sci Ed 1992; *cr:* Pioneer Vly Chrstn Schl Sci Tchr 1980-; *ai:* Sci Fair Coord; *office:* Pioneer Valley Christian Schl 965 Plumtree Rd Springfield MA 01119

TAGGART, JULIE ANNE, Fine Arts Instructor; *b:* Pittsburgh, PA; *ed:* Columbus Coll of Art & Design (BFA) Painting 1991; Syracuse Univ (MFA) Painting 1994; *cr:* Columbus Coll of Art & Design Instr 1994-; *ai:* BFA Review Comm; Rep by Allex Les Filles Gallery; *office:* Columbus Coll Of Art & Design 107 N 9th St Columbus OH 43215

TAGGART, NANCY, Former Teacher; *b:* Philadelphia, PA; *ed:* Chestnut Hill Coll (BS) Pol Philosophy 1987; Indiana Univ of PA Working on MS in Geog, Cartography; Univ of Oxford St Edmund Hall Master Stud Geog 1994; Univ of Poona Cultural & Regnl Geog 1992; *cr:* City of Philadelphia Soc Worker 1972-80; St Vincent de Paul Tchr 1981-85; Waldron Mercy Acad Tchr 1987-90; Norwood-Fontbonne Acad Tchr 1991-95; *ai:* Gamma Theat Upsilon, Treas; NCEA 1981-; Natl Cncl for Geographic Ed 1990-; PA Geographic Alliance 1990-, Tchr Consultant; Chestnut Hill Women's Vlybl League 1978-, Founder, Mentor's Awd; Newcomb Scholar Flwshp Newcomb Fnd 1985; Fulbright-Hays Schlsp for Advance Stud Univ of Poona 1992; Tchr Recognition Awd PA Geographical Soc 1993.

TAIBE, SALLY ANNE, Home Economics Teacher; *b:* Brooklyn, NY; *m:* John J. Jr.; *c:* Kathleen, John, Elizabeth, Victoria; *ed:* Brooklyn Coll (BA) Home Ec 1974; Queens Coll (MS) Ed 1989; 3 Credits Rdng SUNY at Plattsburgh; *cr:* Amer Hlth Fnd Home Economist, Hlth Cnslr 1974-75; A. C. Nielsen Market Rsrch Analyst 1976; Queens Coll Grad, Tchng Asst, Adj Lecturer 1987-89; Warrensburg HS Home Ec Tchr 1989-; *ai:* Career Connection Network Team Ldr; Item Writing for NY St Home Ec Proficiency Exams; SADD Adv; Amer Assn Family, Consumer Scis, NYSOEA, AVA 1989-; NY St Family, Consumer Sci Edctrs 1989-, Legislative Liaison; Phi Upsilon Omicron 1987-; Bus, Prof Women's Club 1990-, Fashion Show Coord; Empire St Flwshp for Tchrs 1986-90; Queens Coll Rsrch Grant 1988-89; *office:* Warrensburg HS 1 James St Warrensburg NY 12885

TAILER, THOMAS LORILLARD, Physics Teacher; *b:* New York City, NY; *m:* Beth; *c:* Kelly, Alexandra, Kate, Emily; *ed:* Darmouth Coll (BS) Earth Sci 1978; Masters of Ed Sci Methods 1984; *cr:* Windfarm Museum Ed Coord 1978-83; U-32 HS Physics Tchr 1984- 88; Mount Abraham UHS Physic Tchr 1989-; *ai:* Schl to Work Transition Bd Co-Chair; NEA 1983-; Essex Comm Historical Soc 1992-, Pres; *office:* Mt Abraham Union HS 7 Airport Dr Bristol VT 05443

TAKACS, AUDREY PUMILIA, 6th Grade Educator; *b:* Dayton, OH; *c:* Megan, Alana; *ed:* Univ of Dayton (BSEd) Lang Arts 1969; 12 Hrs Photography OH Univ; Sci Wright St; 12 Hrs Drug Substance Abuse; 12 Hrs Muse Machine Arts; *cr:* Broadmoor Acad Edctr, Unit Ldr, Schl Advy Cncl 1993-; *ai:* Photographer Schl Advy Cncl; Unit Ldr; Ldr Six Adv; Ed Week, Right to Read Comms; NEA, OEA 1982-; Ed Ldrshp 1992-; Martha Jennings Scholar; 2 Stan Foght Grants; Publication Muse Machine 1993; *home:* 315 Rockwood Ave Dayton OH 45405*

TAKAHASHI, LEO H., Assistant Professor of Physics; *b:* Liberty, MO; *ed:* William Jewell Coll (BA) Physics 1962; Southern IL Univ (MA) Physics 1964; Grad Work at Univ of MO at Rolla 1964-65; *cr:* IL St Univ Visiting Instr 1965-66; Kenyon Coll Visiting Instr 1966-67; Penn St Univ Instr & Asst Prof of Physics 1967-; *ai:* Ebedey Coll of Sci Deans Rep; Campus Schlsp Coord; Campus Honors Prgm Coord; AAPT 1967-; Pub in Journal of General Ed The Physics Tchr; *office:* Penn St Univ Beaver Campus Monaca PA 15061*

TAKAMORI, CRAIG K., 5th Grade Teacher; *b:* Wahiawa, HI; *m:* Deborah Krystowiak; *c:* Krysti, Stephanie; *ed:* Bob Jones Univ (BS) Elem Ed 1979; *cr:* Marquette Manor Bapt Acad 4th Grd Tchr 1979-80; Hanalani Schls 5th Grd Tchr 1980-81; High Point Bapt Acad 5th & 6th Grd Tchr 1981-95; *office:* High Point Baptist Acad Chapel & Furnace Rds Geigertown PA 19523

TALAMO, LAURA ANN, Eighth Grade Teacher; *b:* Astoria, NY; *ed:* Queens Coll (BA) His 1988, (MS) Scndry Ed & Soc Stud 1992; St Johns Univ; *cr:* St Stanislaus Kostka 8th Grd Tchr 1988-; *ai:* Moderator of Stu Cncl; *office:* St Stanislaus Kostka Schl 61-17 Grand Ave Maspeth NY 11378*

TALBOOM, SANDRA MAKUH, Fourth Grade Teacher; *b:* Van Wert, OH; *m:* C. Edward; *c:* Shane; *ed:* Bowling Green St Univ (BAEd) Elem Ed 1962; *cr:* Van Wert City Schls Kndgtn Tchr 1959-60; Hialeah 3rd Grd Tchr 1962-64; Van Wert City Schls 2nd & 4th Grd Tchr 1965-70; Delphos City Schls 4th Grd Tchr 1971-; *ai:* NEA, OEA, NWOEA, DEA; *home:* 19472 Rd 22 Fort Jennings OH 45844

TALBOT, DEBORAH JOHNSTONE, Spanish Teacher; *b:* Nyack, NY; *m:* Joseph P.; *c:* Jessica, Joseph; *ed:* Iona Coll (MS) Urban Ed 1989; *cr:* Sacred Heart HS Span Tchr 1988-90; Mahopac HS Span Tchr 1990-; *ai:* Frosh Cheerleading Coach; Span Club Adv; Youth Leadership Cncl Adv; Sen Class Adv; NYSUT 1990-; Tchr of Yr Sacred Heart HS 1990; Favorite Tchr 1995, 1996; *office:* Mahopac H S Baldwin Place Rd Mahopac NY 10541*

TALBOT, THOMAS E., Choral Music Director; *b:* Earlville, NY; *ed:* Alfred Univ (BA) Music 1969; SUC Potsdam Crane Schl of Music 50 Grad Hrs; *cr:* Sauquoit Valley C S Dir of Choral Music 1970-; *ai:* Select Music Ensemble Dir; AFT, NYSUT 1970-; MENC, NYSSMA 1965-; NAWCC 1976-, Local Bd Dirs 1986-88, Regnl Mart Chair 3 Yrs; Exec Comm, Cty Music Educators 1980-91; Guest Conductor All-Cty Music Festivals 3 Yrs; Lecturer in Music Hamilton Coll Fall Semester 1993; Hamilton Coll Choir Conductor; *office:* Sauquoit Valley Cntrl Schl 2601 Oneida St Sauquoit NY 13456

TALBOTT, LINDA MULLENS, US His & AP Tchr; *b:* Dunbar, WV; *m:* William M. II; *c:* Wm. III, Kimberly Arnold, Justin; *ed:* Univ of Charleston (BA) His 1965; Permmanent Tchng Cert Ed SUNY at Brockport 1975; *cr:* Spencerport Cntrl Schls Soc Stud Tchr 1965-73; Churchville-Chili Cntrl Schls Soc Stud Tchr 1985-; *ai:* Stu Action for Ed; NEA 1983-; RACSS 1987-; NYSCSS 1990-; PEO Sisterhood 1987-, Pres 1993-95; Western Mon Co Historical Soc 1989-, Docent; Spencerport Wesley Church 1967-, Organist, Choir Dir, Chrstn Ed; DAR His Awd Charleston WV; *home:* 17 Adams Trl Spencerport NY 14559

TALBOTT-SEMONIN, NANCY J., 5th-8th Grade Eng, Health Tchr; *b:* Phillippi, WV; *m:* Joseph E.; *ed:* Ashland Univ (NSEd) Eng 1973; Akron Univ 20 Post Grad Hrs; *cr:* Switzeland of OH Local Schl 7th Grd Homeroom, Eng, Lang Arts Tchr 1973-75; Arthur G. Mc Kee Asst Buyer 1975-78; Mayer China Expediter, Scheduler 1978-80; Chemtrol Adhesives Inc Mrktg Coord 1980-82; Sacks Electrical Supply Expediter, Receiving Clerk 1982-88; St Marys Schl 5-8 Grd Lang Arts, Hlth, Rdng Tchr 1988-; *ai:* Spelling Bee Tchr Spon; RCIA 1995-, Team Mem; Ldrshp Akron 1992, Rep; *office:* St Mary Schl 750 S Main St Akron OH 44311

TALERO, EDUARDO, Science Teacher; *b:* Sagamoso, Colombia; *m:* Rocio Del Pilar Gutierrez; *c:* Eduardo Andres, Jean-Paul; *ed:* Univ Nacional De Colombia (MD) Med 1983; Attnd Hofstra Univ Hlth Ed; *cr:* Ctrs Med Andes Physician 1984-85; Total Hlth Med Insurance Adv 1986-87; Liberty Lab Testing Inc Lab Technologist 1986-87; Equifax Med Examiner 1991-95; NYC Bd Ed Tchr 1989-; *ai:* Hispanic Club Adv; WFT, AFT 1989-; APC 1987-; Curr Review Bd Bio 1994; *office:* F D Roosevelt HS 5800 20th Ave Brooklyn NY 11204*

TALIANI, CRAIG LOUIS, Global Studies Teacher; *b:* Russellton, PA; *m:* Lisa Ann Dean; *ed:* Indiana Univ of PA (BS) Scndry Ed, Soc Stud 1989; 90 Credit Hrs Soc Sci Univ of Pittsburgh 1984-87; *cr:* Mount St Peters Schl 7th-8th Grd Soc Stud Tchr 1990-91; Springdale Jr-Sr HS Sub Tchr, Homebound Tutor 1991-93; Grove City Sr HS 9th Grd Global Stud Tchr 1993-; *ai:* Archery Club Spon; 9th Grd Theme Days Coord; PSEA, NEA, Univ of Pittsburgh 1993-; Frgn Stud Outreach Prgrm; YMCA 1995-; *office:* Grove City HS 511 Highland Ave Grove City PA 16127

TALIANI, LISA DEAN, English Teacher; *b:* Butler, PA; *m:* Craig L.; *ed:* Clarion Univ of PA (BS) Eng & Scndry Ed 1988; 26 Credit Hrs Middlebury Coll, Slippery Rock Univ of PA; *cr:* Butler Sr HS 12th Grd Eng Tchr 1989-90; Deer Lakes Jr & Sr High 7th, 9th & 12th Grd Eng Tchr 1990-; *ai:* Girls Vllybl Coach 1991-93; NEA 1991-; *office:* Deer Lakes Jr Sr HS PO Box 10 East Union Rd Russellton PA 15076*

TALL, GORDON F., Physics & Physical Sci Teacher; *b:* Auburn, NY; *m:* Mary J. Johnstone; *c:* Allison, Christine, Gregory; *ed:* Oswego St SUNY (BA) Chem & Physics 1963; 70 Grad Hrs Cortland SUNY, Syracuse Univ & Univ of PA; *cr:* Sauquoit Vly Cntrl Tchr 1963-64; Weedsport Cntrl Tchr 1964-; *ai:* Cross Cntry, JV Wrestling & Var Golf Coach; AFT 1963-; Weedsport Tchr Assoc 1964-, Tchr Rep & Negotiator; SWOA Wrestling Ofcl 1974-, Exect Comm; OSHL League Cross Cntry & Wrestling Chm; Grants to Stud at U of PA 1967, Syracuse U 1971-74, Cortland SUNY 1991-92, Oswego SUNY 1995; *office:* Weedsport Cntrl Schl Box 3000 E Brutus St Weedsport NY 13166

TALLAN, JOAN HARNETT, Art Teacher; *b:* Brooklyn, NY; *m:* Norman; *c:* Mitchell, Eric, Mark, Daniel; *ed:* SUNY Alfred Univ (BFA) Ceramic Design 1958; Wright St Univ (MED) Art Ed 1972; George Washington Univ (MA) Art Therapy 1984; Attnd Schl Art Inst of Chicago Oxbow, VT Studio Ctr, Arrowmont Schl of Crafts; *cr:* Stivers HS Art Tchr 2 Yrs; Alternative HS Art Tchr 7 Yrs; Fairview ISD Art Tchr 4 Yrs; Colonel White HS Art Tchr 9 Yrs; *ai:* Video Crew; OH Ed Assn 1972-, Outstdng Tchr; NAEA 1985-, Presenter; Dayton Art Inst Print Co-op 1985-; OH Art Ed Summer Flwshp for Tchrs of Fine Art 1994, 1990; Culture Works Grants to Artists 1995; Numerous Prizes Print Making; *office:* Colonel White HS For The Arts 501 Niagara Ave Dayton OH 45405

TALLARITA, DIANE T., Adj Instr of Paralegal Studies; *b:* Queens, NY; *m:* Gary; *c:* Annemarie, Michele, Patrice; *ed:* St Johns Univ (BS) Paralegal Stud 1984; 12 Credit Hrs Pub Admin Kutztown Univ; *cr:* Star Tech Inst Paralegal Instr 1991-93; Lehigh Carbon Comm Coll Adj Instr Paralegal Stud 1993-; *ai:* Club Advy Paralegal Club; Paralegal Stud Prgm Curr Consultant; Philadelphia Assn of Paralegals 1995-.

TALLCOUCH, TIM D., Chemistry Teacher; *b:* Bridgeport, CT; *ed:* Fairfield Univ (BS) Chem 1986; MAT Sacred Heart Univ 1991; *cr:* Star of Sea Schl 7th-8th Grd Sci, Math Tchr 1987-88; Univ Schl HS Sci, Math Tchr 1988-91; Westhill HS Chem Tchr 1992-; *ai:* Boys Frosh Asst Var Bsktbl Coach; Class of 1996 Adv; NEA, CEA 1992-; *office:* Westhill HS 125 Roxbury Rd Stamford CT 06902

TALLENT, ROBERT D., Chemistry Teacher; *b:* Newport News, VA; *m:* Marlene A.; *c:* Sara Juliana; *ed:* UMASS at Amherst (BA) Psych 1987, (MED) Chem Tchng 1993; 33 Addl Hrs Chem; 36 Addl Hrs Pharmacy; *cr:* Northampton HS Chem Tchr 1991-95; Deerfield Acad Private Chem Tutor 1991-; *ai:* Photography Club, Stu Cncl Adv; Schl Amnesty Intnl Founder, Adv; *home:* 2 Vernon Rd Enfield CT 06082

TALLEY, DAN R., Art His Instr & Dir of Ctr; *b:* Hogansville, GA; *ed:* Atlanta Coll of Art (BFA) Painting 1973; Univ of Hartford (MFA) Video, Photo 1976; *cr:* Art Papers Ed 1977-81; Nexus Contemporary Art Ctr Curator 1987-89; Jamestown Comm Coll Gallery Dir 1989-; *ai:* Huntington Beach, Atlanta Art Ctr Curator 1995; *office:* Jamestown Comm Coll 525 Falconer St Jamestown NY 14701

TALLEY, GLINDA, Tchr of GATE & Enrichment; *b:* Hart County, KY; *c:* Michael, Diane LaViano; *ed:* Fairleigh Dickinson (BA) Elem Ed 1974, (MA) Human Dev 1979; Credits Instrl Tech, Gifted Ed, Space Sci, Aerospace, Ldrshp; *cr:* Montvale Bd of Ed Kndgtn Tchr 1974-79, 1st Grd Tchr 1979-84, 3rd Grd Tchr 1984-85, 2nd Grd Tchr 1985-88, GATE, Enrichment, Cmptr Lab Tchr 1988-; *ai:* Tech Trng; Cmptr Courses; Stu Press; IMs; Essay Judge Acad Decathlon Regnl St Level 1987-9 Level 1994; Dist Staff, Curr Dev Comm; Dist Philosophy Comm Se NEA 1974-; MTA 1974-, VP; Local Soc Concerns Cncl 1991-, Chai West Side Presbyn Church, Deacon; Tchr in Space; Book in Fifth Re Articles Pub; Fellow Grad Stud Hum Dev Ctr; *office:* Memorial Ele 53 W Grand Ave Montvale NJ 07645*

TALLEY, MARTHA LYNN, English Teacher; *b:* Syracuse, N SUNY at Oswego (BA) Eng 1978, (MS) Rdng Ed 1994; Cert Ed 19 P. V. Moore HS Eng Tchr 1991-; *ai:* Adv Drama Club, Newspaper; C Writing Ed; NYSUT 1991-; *office:* Paul V Moore HS Caughde County Rt 12 Central Square NY 13036

TALLEY, PHYLLIS, Asst Prof & Prgm Chair Art Ed; *b:* Danville, Christa L. Cook; *ed:* Univ of AL (BS) Art Ed 1969; Univ of Greensboro (MFA) Painting 1990, (EDD) Curr, Instruction 1994; Univ, Daytona Beach Comm Coll Undergraduate; *cr:* Ch Mecklenburg Schls Art Tchr 1969-86; Univ of NC Tchng Ass 1988-93; OH Univ Asst Prof, Prgm Chair 1993-; *ai:* NAEA 1988-, Chptr OU; Phi Delta Kappa 1990-; OH Art Ed Assn 1993-; Tchr F 1993-; St of OH Grant for Arts in Ed Inst; OH Arts Cncl Grant Artists; Who's Who in Amer Edctrs 1992; *office:* OH Univ 413 S Hall Athens OH 45701

TALLMAN, CHERYL ANN, Eighth Grade Math & Sci Tchr; *b:* OH; *m:* Mark A.; *ed:* OH St Univ (BS) Elem Ed 1979; Attnd U Cincinnati 42 Grad Credit Hrs Math 1980-82 & Xavier Univ 6 Grad Hrs Math & Physics 1990-91; *cr:* Our Lady of Visitation Cmptr Cam 1987-91; Our Lady of Visitation Schl 8th Grd Math & Sci Tchr Xavier Univ Probability & Statistics Wkshps Co-Tchr 1993; *ai:* S Moderator; Acad Competition Team & Math & Sci Olympic Team Math Dept Chprsn; Schl Olympic Day Organizer; 8th Grd Sci Fair 4 Yrs; Greater Cincinnati Cncl of Tchrs of Math 1986-, Treas Presidential Awd for Excl in Math Tchng Nom; Outstanding Young Ldr Nom; Ashland Oil Co Gldn Apple Achvmnt Awd; *office:* Our L Visitation Schl 3180 South Rd Cincinnati OH 45248

TALLMAN, TERRY ANN (RANDALL), Fifth Grade Teach Southampton, NY; *m:* Alan Van; *c:* Lauren; *ed:* SUNY at Cortlan Elem Ed 1979, (MS) Elem Ed, Rdng 1983; *cr:* Schls Sub Tchr 19 Newfield Elem Schl Sixth Grd Tchr 1980-84, Third Grd Tchr 19 Newfield MS Fifth Grd Tchr 1987-; *ai:* Focus Team; NYSUT 19 Paul's United Meth Chur 1990-; SED Sci Mentor; Sciencenter Tch *office:* Newfield MS 247 Main St Newfield NY 14867

TALLON, BRUCE C., Asst Prof of Secretarial Stud; *b:* Malone, Rose Cooney; *c:* Cameron; *ed:* Cobleskill Coll (AAS) Acctng Castleton St (BS) Bus Ed 1969; Permanent Cert NYS; 60 Grad Cre Albany St, Plattsburgh St, US Sports Acad; *cr:* Long Lake Cntrl Sc Tchr 1969-82; Mater Dei Coll Asst Prof, Ath Dir 1982-; *ai:* Wome Bsktbl Coach; Mrktg Comm; Ath Dir; Yth Camp Dir; Picquet Club Coach of Yr NJCAA Division II Region III 1995; *office:* Mater D 5428 St Hwy 37 Ogdensburg NY 13669*

TAMBERINO, PHILIP, Fifth Grade Teacher; *b:* Flushing, NY; *m:* Rienzo; *c:* Philip, Michael; *ed:* St John's Univ (BS) Ed 1972; SU Stonybrook (MA) Liberal Stud 1974; 75 Ed Post Grad Credits; *cr:* Rd Schl 6th Grd Tchr 1972-84, 5th Grd Tchr 1985-; *ai:* Math, Writing Textbook Selection Comms; Gifted Prgm Bldg Coord; In Spec Ed Comm; Stud Cncl Coord; Initiated Schl Store, Sfty Ptrl; C Mediation, & Peer Tutor Prgms; Port Jefferson Station Tchr Assn Bldg Rep 1992-94; PTA Jenkins Meml Awd 1987; *office:* Boyle R Boyle Rd Port Jefferson Sta NY 11776*

TAMBERRINO, JEANNE HAFFNER, Physical Education Teac Brooklyn, NY; *m:* Richard A.; *c:* Thomas, Joseph, David, Kathle Univ of MD (BS) PE 1974; Towson St Univ (MED) Scndry Ed Emphasis 1980; Masters +60 Credits Through Balto Cty Bd of Ed, T St, Loyola Coll & Goucher Coll; *cr:* Balto Cty Pub Schl System P 1974-; *ai:* Girls Sports Referee; IM Chm; SADD Adv; NEA 1974-; T 1974-; MAHPERD 1974-80; Stu Against Drugs 1994-, Fac Adv; S Curr Wkshp on MS Enrichment Act Balto Cty Bd of Ed Chm & Parti 1995; MAHPERD Convention on Disability Awareness Asse Speaker; *office:* Pine Grove MS 9200 Old Harford Rd Baltimore MD

TAMBURRO, BARBARA J. BOSCAINO, Conductor & Strings Te *b:* Maplewood, NJ; *m:* Ronald R.; *ed:* Montclair St Coll (BA) Mu 1976; Jersey City St Coll (MA) Music Ed 1978; Attnd Univ of Urbino 60 Addl Hrs; *cr:* Livingston HS Conductor, Strings Tchr 17 Y Auditions Chair; MENC Sponsored Region Orch; Hnrs String Q Music Coach; Dist Elem, Combined MS, String Orchs Conductor; 1979-; Local 16, Amer Fed Musicians 1976-; Livingston Symphony Trustee; Article Pub; Prof Violinist; *office:* Livingston H S 30 Rober Dr Livingston NJ 07039

TANALSKI, ADAM JOHN, Earth Science & Biology Tchr; *b:* New City, NY; *m:* Linda Sarrantonio; *c:* Adam Thor, Lindsey Rose; *ed:* Coll (BS) Bio & Chem 1976; Queens Coll (MSEd) Bio 1988; *cr:* Demetrios Schl Tchr & Coach 1976-82; Richmond Hill HS Tchr Boys & Girls HS Tchr 1982-85; Bryant HS-LaGuardia Comm Coll Earth Sci, Bio & Animal Behavior Tchr, Security Coord & Coll Now 1985-95; *ai:* HS Track & Cross Cntry, 6th-8th Grd Bsktbl, Soccer & Coach; *office:* W C Bryant HS 4810 31st Ave Long Island City NY 1

TANCHICK, SUSAN E., French Teacher; *b:* Johnstown, PA; *m:* G.; *ed:* Univ of Pittsburgh (BA) His, Fr 1964, (MED) Scndry Ed 196 Cochran Jr HS Fr, His Tchr 1964-84; Garfield Jr HS Fr, His Tchr 19 Johnstown HS Fr Tchr 1985-; *ai:* Spon Fr Natl Hnr Soc; Jennifer Chptr; 9th Grd Orientation Comm; GJEA, PSEA, NEA 1964-; ACTFL 1988-; Ladies Auxiliary CWV, Pi Lambda Theta Democractic Party 1965-, Precinct Comm Person; Outstdng Young 1967; Project Bus Tchr 1980-81; Outstdng Tchr 1992-93.

TANFANI, ROBERT R., 8th Grade Social Studies Tchr; *b:* Woons RI; *m:* Linda Vetri; *c:* Jessica, Erica; *ed:* RI Coll (BA) Soc Stud (Masters) Ed 1973; *cr:* Woonsocket MS Tchr 1970-; Woonsocket 8th-9th Grd Soc Stud Tchr 1970-; *ai:* Mid Schl Boys Bsktbl Coach AFT, Woonsocket Tchrs Guild 1970-; RI His Assn 1980-; I Workingmen's Club 1990-; YWCA 1991-; *home:* 10 Pleasa Bellingham MA 02019*

TANGNEY, PATRICIA AMY, English Teacher; *b:* Meriden, C Western CT St Univ (BA) Eng 1976; Quinnipiac Coll (MAT) Eng Southern CT St Univ Eng Cert 1979; *cr:* North Haven HS Eng 1980-83, Adult Educator 1981-90; Stone Acad Placement Dir 198 Univ of New Haven Cooperative Ed Asst Dir 1986-90; North Have Eng Tchr 1990-; *ai:* Lit Magazine Adv; Future Prob Solvers Wrtng C NEA, CEA 1980-; CT Bus Assn 1983-, Women in Leadership Awd Amer Assn of Univ Women 1986-90, Leadership Awd 1988; De Rotondo Tchr of Yr Awd 1993; *office:* North Haven HS 222 Mapl North Haven CT 06473*

TANN, CARRIE MARIE, Fine Arts Dept Chprsn & Tchr; *b:* Erie, P Gannon Univ (BS) Art Ed 1984; Edinboro Univ of PA (MA) Art Hist *cr:* Holy Rosary Schl Art Tchr K-8 1984-87; Villa Maria Acad Fine Dept Chm & Art Tchr 1987-; Northwest Tri-Cty Intermediate Un History Part-Time 1990-; *ai:* Sr Class Adv; Racquetball Club Adv; Comm; Fine Arts Dept Chprsn; Curr Comm; NAHS Adv; Admin

NAEA, PA Art Ed Assn, NCEA 1984-; Villa Maria Acad Alumni -93, Pres 1984-86; NHS Villa Chapter Fac Honor Awd 1991; Most al Sr Tchr Awd 1992 & 1995; Who's Who Among Amers Edctrs; illa Maria Acad 2403 W 8th St Erie PA 16505

NBAUM, AUDREY, Athletic Trainer; *b:* Philadelphia, PA; *ed:* PA (Assoc) Recreation & Parks 1979, (BS) Admin of Justics 1981; Univ (MED) Ath Trng 1990; Continuing Ed Credits to Maintain Certfd Ath Trainer & Strenght Coach; *cr:* Holy Cross HS Asst Ath 986-88; Temple Univ Sports Med Ctr Grad Asst Ath Trainer 1988; erford Schl Grad Asst Ath Trainer 1988-89; Florence HS Head Ath 989-; *ai:* Strength & Conditioning Coach, Weight Room Supv; Stu ners Club & Environmental Club Adv; Hands On Strength Clinic peaker & Instr; Natl Ath Trainer Assn 1986-, Cert; Natl Strength tion Assn 1991-, CSCS; ATSNJ 1992-; US Triathlon Fed 1991-; ng Fed 1993-; Florence HS Svc Awd; Prof Adv & Ed Book Fitness a Diving; Articles Pub; *office:* Florence Twp Mem HS 500 E Front nce NJ 08518

NBAUM, CHANA GOLDSTEIN, HS Judaic Studies Teacher; *b:* Y; *m:* M. David; *c:* Yitzchak, Tehillah, Miriam, Tzui; *ed:* Stern Coll wish Stud; Bernard Revel Grad Schl (MS) Ancient Jewish His ern Coll Tchng Diploma; Doctoral Candidate Azrielli Grad Inst Supervision; *cr:* Stern Coll for Women Tchr 1995-; Yeshiva Univ 1986-; *ai:* Stu, Club Adv; Baumel Awd Excl Tchng Judaic Stud *fice:* Yeshiva Univ HS 8686 Palo Alto St Hollis NY 11423*

R, CHARLENE RAE, Fifth Grade Teacher; *b:* Lakewood, OH; *m:* : Rob, Mike; *ed:* Miami Univ Working on BS in Elem Ed; Attnd Dayton; *cr:* Germantown Elem 5th Grd Tchr 1975-; Monroe Elem Tchr; *ai:* NEA; VVTA.

R, CHERYL FELTS, 3rd Grade Teacher; *b:* Philadelphia, PA; *m:* c: Megan, David; *ed:* Millersville Univ (BS) Elem, DH 1966; Post s Bowling Green Univ; *cr:* East Union Schl 2nd Grd Tchr 1966-68; ontgomery Schl Dist Spec Ed DH 1968-71; Brunner Schl Spec Ed 71-75, 3rd Grd Tchr 1975-; Camper Schl 3rd Grd Tchr 1975-; *ai:* rbk; Genoa Area Ed Assn 1971-, Bldg Rep, Sec; AFT, DEA 1980-; ivic Theatre 1975-, Sec, Trustee; Lake HS Hockey Assn 1992-, VP; 127 Waltham Rd Northwood OH 43619

R, LYNNE R., Social Studies Teacher; *b:* Manhattan, NY; *c:* *ed:* Wilmington Coll (BS) Behavorial Sci 1972; LIU (MS) Ed : Kings Point Cntry Day Schl 6th Grd Tchr 1972-78; LB Schl Dist r 1981-85; Lbrl Jewish Day Schl Permanent Sub Tchr 1986-87; IS n Grd Soc Stud Tchr 1987-; *ai:* Debate Team & Chrldng Coach; Wkshp Ldr; Re-Org Comm; Kings Pt Newspaper Adv; AFT 1987-; 87-; BBYO 1991-, Field Adv; *office:* IS 218 370 Fountain Ave n NY 11208*

RY, CHARLES N.,JR., 7th Grade English Teacher; *b:* Ithaca, NY; Holmes; *c:* Eve H., Brooke E.; *ed:* Lehigh Univ (MED) Eng & Ed tnd Susquehanna Univ; *cr:* Springhouse Jr HS Eng Tchr 1971-; *ai:* m; NEA 1971-; Pennridge Summer Theatre Advisory Comm 1991-; l Jaycees Outstanding Young Educator; Cedar Crest Coll Howard p Awd for Excl in Tchng; *office:* Springhouse Jr HS 1200 ouse Rd Allentown PA 18104

RY, GAIL HOLMES, Mathematics Tchr & Dept Coord; *b:* MA; *m:* Charles N. Jr.; *c:* Eve, Brooke; *ed:* Susquehanna Univ ath 1973; Kutztown Univ (MED) Math Ed 1977; *cr:* Shicke Math 72-73; Cntrl Bucks HS E Math Tchr, Coord 1973-; *ai:* Math Coord; T Comm; CBEA, PSEA, NEA 1973-; NCTM; TLC Child Care Ctr Treas; *office:* Central Bucks HS East Box 405 Buckingham PA

INA, REBECCA DEBRA, Kindergarten Teacher; *b:* Passaic, NJ; les; *c:* Eryn, Charles; *ed:* Kean Coll (BA) Elem Ed 1973, (MA) hldhd 1981; William Paterson Coll Nursery Cert 1979; 6 Credits h Dickinson Univ; 9 Credits St Peter's Coll; *cr:* Garfield Bd of Ed Tchr 1973-80, 1983-84, 1986-; *ai:* Schl Base Mngmt, Citizen of Full Day Kndgtn Curr Comms; GEA, NJEA 1973-; GFT, AFT GEA, NJEA 1995-; Tchr of Yr 1994; *home:* 43 Eleron Pl Wayne NJ

Y, LARRY RAY, French & US History Teacher; *b:* Kansas City, Univ of MO (BA) His, Fr 1977; Temple Univ Fr Cert, Grad Credits ng Ed; Rutgers Univ Soc Stud Cert; *cr:* Phila Schl Dist Fr Tchr ; Florence Twp Schl Fr, US His Tchr 1982-; *ai:* Steering Comm d Sts Assn Coll & Schls; NJEA 1982-; FTEA 1982-, Grievance ec Ofcr; NJ Governor's Tchr Recognition Tchr of Yr 1990; *office:* Twp Meml HS 500 E Front St Florence NJ 08518*

N, RICHARD CHARLES, English Teacher; *b:* Lynn, MA; *m:* anock; *c:* Melissa, Amanda, Richard Jr.; *ed:* Univ of NH (BA) Pol 7, (MST) Ed 1982; Addl 30 Credits Writing, Photography; *cr:* HS Eng Tchr 1968-69; Rochester Jr HS Eng, Soc Stud Tchr ; Oyster River MS Eng Tchr 1972-81; Oyster River HS Eng Tchr, Dir 1981-; *ai:* Newspaper Adv 1968-69, 1986-; Drama Dir 1973-80, , 1988-93; Yrbk Adv 1977-78; NEA MA 1968-69; NEA NH 1969-; River Tchrs Guild 1972-, Pres 1976-77; City Councilor 1971-73, hair, Planing Bd 1981, Chair; Republican St Convention Del 1990-; Presidential Awd 1989; Articles Pub; *office:* Oyster River HS 55 Durham NH 03824

R, JILL M., 1st Grade Teacher; *b:* Freehold, NJ; *ed:* Glassboro St A) Elem 1976, (MA) Rdng 1990; *cr:* Pomona Schl Tchr 1977-78; gg Harbor Schl Tchr 1978-83; Pomona Schl Tchr 1983-; *ai:* NEA, 976-; GTEA 1976-, Recording Sec; Southern NJ Rdng Cncl 1990-, n; Phi Delta Kappa 1994-; Alpha Delta Kappa 1990-; Governors ecognition Awd; *office:* Pomona Schl Genoa Ave Pomona NJ 08240

R, LOUISE CONNOR, First Grade Teacher; *b:* New Bedford, Charles Joseph; *c:* Elizabeth, Caitlin, Matthew; *ed:* Bridgewater (BS) Elem Ed 1976; *cr:* Acushnet Elem 1st Grd Tchr 1976-; *ai:* Schl lath Curr Dev Comm; NEA, MA Tchrs Assn, Acushnet Tchrs Assn Delta Kappa Gamma-Eta Chapter 1993-, Corresponding Sec; Mann Grant for Developing & Instructing Tchr Math Wkshps; Courses & Wkshps for Rdng, Whole Lang, Math & Sci; *office:* et Elem Schl 800 Middle Rd Acushnet MA 02743*

ICAK, STEPHANIE J., Religious Education Parish Dir; *b:* town, OH; *ed:* Youngstown St Univ (BSE) Elem Ed & Kndgtn 1982; Univ (MRE) Rel Ed 1995; *cr:* Holy Name Schl First Grd Tchr 3; Holy Trinity Schl Second & Third Grds Tchr 1983-91; Holy Church Parish Dir of Rel Ed 1991-; *ai:* Altar Server Trainer; cio of Holy Trinity Parish Cncl; NPCD, NCEA 1994-; ODREO Cath Collegiate Assn 1993-; Kappa Delta Pi 1981-; Diocese of town Bd of Rel Ed 1990-93; *office:* Holy Trinity Church Schl 250 ge St Struthers OH 44471*

NTELLO, GUY, Earth Science & Physics Tchr; *b:* Waterbury, CT; e Cruess; *c:* Patricia, Robert, Joseph; *ed:* Seton Hall Univ (BS) Sci ehensive 1974; Central CT St Univ (MS) Admin & Supervision outhern CT St Univ Cert Admin & Supervision 1980; *cr:* Naugatuck Tchr 1974-; *ai:* Var Girls Sftbl, Asst Girls Bsktbl Coach; NEA, CT n, Naugatuck Tchrs Assn 1974-; NSTA, CT Sci Tchrs Assn 1976-; sn of Physics Tchrs 1987-; Natl Sftbl Coaches Assn 1992-; CT HS Coaches Assn 1980-; *office:* Naugatuck HS 543 Rubber Ave Naugatuck CT 06770

TARANTINI, MARY JEAN DELYCURE, Social Studies Teacher; *b:* Wilkes-Barre, PA; *m:* David; *c:* David M., Maria E.; *ed:* Coll of Misericordia (BA) Soc Stud 1964; Univ of Scranton (MS) Soc Stud 1972; 60 Addl Post Grad Hrs; *cr:* Swoyersville HS Tchr 1964-66; Wyoming Valley West Schl Soc Stud Tchr 1966-; *ai:* Wyoming Valley West HS Delegation to PA & Natl His Day Adv 1980-; Awds Comm; PA St Ed Assn 1964-; PA Soc Stud Cncl 1980-; Wyoming Valley West Ed Assn on Soc Stud 1966-; NEA; Wyoming Historical Soc 1988-; Plymouth Historical Soc 1988-; Slovak Heritage Soc of NE PA 1988-; WY Geological & Historical Soc Board of Dir 1993-; Boy Scout Merit Cnslr 1995-; Article Pub 1978; Wilkes Univ Ed Dept Advisory Comm; Kings Coll Ed Dept Source Person; PA St Dept of Ed Framework Comm; PA His Day Outstanding Tchr Awd 1992, 2nd Pl 1995; PA His Day Outstanding HS 1988-89 & 1992-93, 1995; Natl His Day Champions 1988; PA Historical Murgas Monument Comm 1990; *office:* Wyoming Valley West Schl 150 Wadham St Plymouth PA 18651

TARASKO, BASIL PAUL, Mathematics Teacher; *b:* Ansbach, Germany; *m:* Alexandra Bazylewsky; *c:* Andrei, Michael; *ed:* Hunter Coll (BA) Math 1970; City Coll of NY (MS) Math 1975; *cr:* JHS MU Math Tchr 1970-78; IS MO Math Tchr 1978-; *ai:* Tchr Mentor, Math Team Fac Adv; Bsbl Coach John Jay Coll; Assoc Bsbl Scout Atlanta Braves; NCTM 1988-; US Rep Ukraine Bsbl 1993-; Ukrainain Sports Fed of USA & Canada 1994-, Bsbl & Sftbl Rep; Dist Admin of Little Leagues in Ukraine 1995; Head Bsbl Coach Natl Bsbl Teams of Ukraine; Regular Columnist Intnl Bsbl Rundown Magazine; *office:* IS 73 William Cowper 70-02 54th Ave Maspeth NY 11378*

TARASOVIC, GEORGE M., Social Studies Teacher; *b:* Pittsburgh, PA; *ed:* California Univ of PA (BS) Comp Soc Stud 1969; Duquesne Univ of PA (MA) Counseling & Scndry Ed 1972; Admin & Scndry Ed Cert 1974; Masters +40 Credits in Ed, Soc Stud & Lang; *cr:* George Westinghouse HS Soc Stud Tchr 1971-76; John A Brashear HS Soc Stud Tchr 1976-81, Admin Staff Asst 1981-82, Soc Stud Tchr 1982-; *ai:* Bsbl Asst Coach; Intramural Bsktbl; AFT 1969-, Del Natl & St Conventions, Bldg Rep; West PA Cncl of Soc Stud 1972-; West PA Historical Soc 1989-; PA Amer Legion 1966-, Post Comm & Dist Commander, Chm St PA, Essay Comm; Saint Stephens Elem Schl Bd 1989-; Saint Vincent DePaul Soc (Saint Stephen Church) 1982-, Treas; Democratic Party Allegheny Co 1974-76, Committeman; 35th Dist Amer Legion Cert of Appreciation; Earth Wtch Expedidition 1994.*

TARBOX, ANNE W., Art Teacher; *b:* Portland, ME; *m:* Brian; *c:* Nat, Jon; *ed:* Univ of ME at Orono (BS) Art Ed 1974; Attnd ME Coll of Art & Antioch Coll; *cr:* Portland Schl Dept K-6th Grd Art Tchr 1975-83; Yormouth HS 9th-12th Grd Art Tchr 1983-; *ai:* Stu Cncl Adv; Art Club Adv; ME Ed Assoc 1983-, ME Art Tchr of the Yr 1991; ME Art Ed Assoc 1983-, Pres (3 Times); *office:* Yarmouth H S W Elm St Yarmouth ME 04096

TARBOX, PATRICIA (STANSFIELD), 9th-12th Grade English Teacher; *b:* Ipswich, MA; *m:* William F.; *c:* Richard P., Cheri A., William F.; *ed:* Salem St Coll (BA) Eng 1971, (MA) British & Amer Lit 1982; 15 Addl Credit Hrs; *cr:* Whitefield Elem Schl 5th-8th Grd Eng Tchr 1972-74; Winnacunnet HS Eng Tchr 1974-; *ai:* Lit Magazine Adv; Lang Arts Comm for Supervisory; Union #21 Winnacunnet Rep; NH Assn of Tchrs of Eng 1990-; Seacoast Ed Assn 1974-; New England Assn of Tchrs of Eng 1990-, NH Poet & Tchr of Yr 1992; NEA 1974-; NCTE 1995-; BU Ctr of Advancement of Character & Ethics NH Tchrs Acad 1990; Published Poet.

TARBOX, SUSAN JOYCE, First Grade Teacher; *b:* New York, NY; *m:* Glen; *c:* Amy; *ed:* Barrington Coll (BS) Elem Ed 1969; 36 Grad Hrs RI Coll, Univ of RI; *cr:* Somerset Schl First Grd Tchr 1969-71; Hamilton Schl Kndgtn Tchr 1972-73; Davisville MS Grd 7 Rdng Tchr 1975-76; Hamilton Schl First Grd Tchr 1973-75, 1976-; *ai:* Schl Improvement Team; Budget, Mathathon Comms; NEA RI 1972-, Exec Bd; NKPTSO 1991-, Sec; Cooperative Rsrch Projects, Improving Children's Experiental Backgrouns Grants; *office:* Hamilton Schl 25 Salisbury Ave North Kingstown RI 02852

TARDIF, DONALD OSCAR, Math Teacher; *b:* Biddeford, ME; *ed:* St Michael Coll (BA) Math 1969; Boston Coll (MA) Ed 1989; Cambridge Univ Examinations Syndicate Examiner 1978-84; *cr:* Tchrs Coll Math Lecturer 1977-85; St Dominic Regnl HS Math Tchr 1985-86, Asst Prin 1986-89; Bishop Gertin HS Asst Prin 1989-91, Math Tchr 1991-; *ai:* Math Dept Chm; NCTM 1995-; Schl Bd 1990-; NHS 1995; *home:* 194 Lund Rd Nashua NH 03060*

TARDIO, ROSEMARY MATARAZZO, Family & Consumer Sci Tchr; *b:* McKeesport, PA; *m:* Angelo A.; *c:* Nicole, Michael; *ed:* Seton Hill Coll (BS) Home Ec 1976; Penn St; IN Univ of PA Credits for Permanent Cert; *cr:* Plum Sr HS Home Ec Tchr 1976-78, Family & Consumer Sci Tchr 1981-; Riverview HS Home Ec Tchr 1978-81; *ai:* Pre-Schl Pgm Dir; NEA 1976-; PBEA 1976-; *office:* Plum Sr HS 900 Elicker Rd Pittsburgh PA 15239

TARGAN, ERIC GABRIEL, English & History Teacher; *b:* Syracuse, NY; *m:* Dollene Coolidge; *ed:* Oneonta St (BA) Lit 1985; 9 Grad Credit Hrs Towards Master Degree; *cr:* Perry Hall Chrstn Schl HS Eng Tchr & Bsktbl Coach 1988-89; Mt Airy Chrstn Schl HS Eng Tchr, Bsktbl & Sftbl Coach 1989-90; New Life Chrstn Schl HS Eng Tchr 1990-92; Lanham Chrstn Schl HS Eng, His Tchr & Bsktbl Coach 1992-; *ai:* Asst Bsbl & Sftbl Coach; Organized Chess Club; Helped Run Chapel Misc Pgm; Baltimore Musicians Union 1992-95; Recorded an album of Original Music 1986; *office:* Lanham Chrstn Schl 8400 Good Luck Rd Lanham Seabrook MD 20706*

TARINO, JANET Z., Assoc Professor of Chemistry; *b:* Jersey City, NJ; *m:* Charles A.; *c:* Michael, Steven; *ed:* Douglass Coll at Rutgers (BA) Chem 1961; Harvard Univ (MAT) Natural Resources 1962; Univ of Pittsburgh (PHD) Chem 1972; *ai:* Chem Olympiad & Pub Outreach Admin for Local Section of Amer Chemical Soc; Univ & Campus Comms; American Chemical Soc; Natl Soc of Sci Tchrs; Sigma Xi; Soc of Coll Sci Tchrs, St Membership Coord OH; Chemical Manufacturers Assn Regnl Catalyst Awd 1994; OSU Alumni Distinguished Tchng Awd 1990; Mansfield Campus Distinguished Tchng Awd 1981, 1989 & 1995; Sci Is Fun Hands on Sci Prgm for MS Supported By Grants; *office:* OH St Univ At Mansfield 1680 University Dr Mansfield OH 44906

TARLO, DAVID, Mathematics Teacher; *b:* Montreal, Canada; *m:* Judith; *c:* Howard, Joseph; *ed:* MC Gill (BS) Math, Physiological Psych 1967; LIU (MA) Educl Tech 1990; *cr:* FDR HS Math Tchr 1986-; *ai:* Vlybl Team; FDR Singers; UFT 1985-, Del; *office:* Franklin Delano Roosevelt HS 5800 20th Ave Brooklyn NY 11204

TARNACKI, MARY ELLEN LAUX, Teacher & Vice Principal; *b:* Jersey City, NJ; *m:* Richard; *c:* George Leonard, Mary Grace; *ed:* Coll of St Elizabeth (BS) Home Ec 1969; 27 Credit Hrs for Cert & Towards Masters; *cr:* Sacred Heart Schl 5th-8th Grd Math Tchr 1980-, Vice Prin 1989-; *ai:* Yrbk Adv; Dance Organizer; After Schl Prgm Directress; St Jude Math-A-Thom Coord 15 Yrs; NCEA 1981-; AMTNJ; NCTM; Archdiocese of Newark Outstanding Educator 1992; St Cecilia's Knight of Columbus Tchr of the Yr 1995.*

TARNER, LAURIE ANN(DESCH), Eighth Grade English Teacher; *b:* Lancaster, PA; *m:* Dax V.; *c:* Lindsay Megan, Zachary Young, Camille Cree, McKenzie Ciara, Cassidy Alyse; *ed:* Bowling Green St Univ (BA) Eng 1983; Post Grad Work Counseling in Schls at Johns Hopkins Univ; *cr:* Takoma Park MS Eng Tchr 1983-93; Briggs Chaney MS Eng Tchr 1993-; *ai:* Spelling Bee; Dramatic Arts Festival; NEA 1983-; *office:* Briggs Chaney MS 1901 Rainbow Dr Silver Spring MD 20904

TARNOWSKI, ANN MARIE, HS Social Studies Teacher; *b:* Somerville, NJ; *ed:* Villanova Univ (BS) Scndry Ed 1991; Currently Working Toward Masters in Grad Tchr Ed; *cr:* Brick Meml HS Soc Stud Tchr 1992-; *ai:* Key Club Adv; Girls Bsktbl Coach; Acad Team Coach; Pupil Assistance Comm Mem; Cmptr Dept System Operator; NJEA 1992-, Bldg Rep; Most Distinguished Key Club Adv-NJ Dist 1993-94.

TARONE, MARION, Principal; *b:* Hazelton, PA; *ed:* Marywood (MS) Elem Ed 1957, (BA) Elem Ed, Eng 1967; Scranton, Bridgeport, Pittsburg Dioceses Rel Cert; NY, PA Tchng Certs; *cr:* Saint John Schl Intermediate Grds Tchr 1961-63; Saint Rosalia Schl Primary Grds Tchr 1963-82; Saint Leo Schl Primary Grds Tchr 1963-82; Saint John Schl Primary Grds Tchr 1963-82; Saint Agnes Schl Primary Grds Tchr 1963-82; Saint Ambrose Schl Primary Grds Tchr 1963-82; Saint Ephrem Schl Intermediate Grds Tchr 1982-84; WY Area Cath Schl Primary Grds Tchr 1984-86, Intermediate Grds Tchr 1986-91, Jr HS Tchr 1991-95, Prin 1995-; *ai:* Parent Tchr Guild; Booster Club; Schl Advy Bd; NCEA; *office:* Wyoming Area Catholic Schl 1690 Wyoming Ave Exeter PA 18643

TARPEY, DANIEL JAMES, Principal; *b:* Columbus, OH; *c:* Danielle, Elissa; *ed:* Univ of Dayton (BA) Soc Stud, Ed 1987, (MS) Ed Admin 1993; OH Admin Cert 1995; 25 Hrs Beyond Masters; *cr:* Centerville HS Soc Stud Tchr, Coach 1987-95, East Unit Prin 1995-; *ai:* Prior Asst Var Ftbl, Head Frosh Bsbl Coach; NASSP 1995-; *office:* Centerville HS 500 E Franklin St Centerville OH 45459

TARQUINI, PATRICIA CASHIN, 6th Grade Science Teacher; *b:* Beacon, NY; *m:* Donald; *c:* Jamie, Sarah; *ed:* Univ of MA (BA) Elem Ed 1972; SUNY at New Paltz (MS) Elem Ed 1988; *cr:* Rombout Schl 5th Grd Tchr 1972-75; South Ave Schl 5th-6th Grd Eng, Lang Arts Tchr 1988-91; Rombout Schl 6th Grd Sci Tchr 1991-; *ai:* Site Based Mngmt Team; Supts Reorganization Comm; NEA 1988-; BTA 1989-91, Bldg Rep; STANYS 1991-; *office:* Rombout MS Matteawan Rd Beacon NY 12508

TARR, JENNIFER HOOVER, Third Grade Teacher; *b:* Radford, VA; *m:* Robert D. Jr.; *ed:* (BS) Early Chldhd ECE-MR 1985; Fourteen Hrs Toward Masters Early Chldhd Ed; *cr:* New River Vly Adult Wkshp Functional Acad Tchr 1985-86; Sacred Heart of Mary Schl 2nd Grd Long Term Sub Tchr 1987; Priv Tutor 1986-; Our Lady of Pompei Elem Schl Third Grd Tchr 1987-; *ai:* Coord RAINBOWS, Lang Arts; Steering Comm Mid St Acreditation; Tchr of Yr 1993; *office:* Our Lady of Pompei Elem Schl 201 S Conkling St Baltimore MD 21224*

TARR, WAYNE S., Sixth Grade Teacher; *b:* St Albans, VT; *m:* Sally V. Smith; *c:* Katheryn, Nicholas; *ed:* Univ of VT (BS) Ed 1976; 30 Addl Credit Hrs; *cr:* Alburg Educl Ctr 7-8 Grade Math, Sci Tchr 1978-80; Highgate Elem Schl 6th Grd Tchr 1980-; *ai:* Highlights Ed 1984-86; NEA, VT NEA 1978-; Franklin Northwest SU NEA 1980-, VP; Owner, Operator Photography Bus.

TARSA, BARBARA J., 9th-12th Grd Bus Info Sys Tchr; *b:* Pittsfield, MA; *m:* John J.; *c:* Christopher J., Robert J.; *ed:* Berkshire Comm Coll (AS) Selected Stud 1970; North Adams St Coll (BA) Math 1978; Voc Cert in Data Processing 1982; *cr:* Berkshire Comm Coll Programmer 1970-71; North Adams MS 6th Grd Math Tchr 1978-80; C.H. McCann Tech Schl 9th-12th Grd Data Processing Tchr 1980-; *ai:* Class Adv 1985, 1993; NHS Selection Comm; BIS Dept Chprsn 1990; Maintain Stud Masterfile of Grds, Schedules, & Attnd; NEA, MTA 1978-; McCann Faculty Assn 1980-; *office:* C H Mccann Tech HS Hodges Cross Rd North Adams MA 01247

TART, STEPHEN MORTIMER, High School English Teacher; *b:* Chicago, IL; *ed:* Amherst Coll (BA) Eng 1983; Columbia Univ (MA) Eng, Comparative Lit 1986; *cr:* Western Jr HS Instrl Aide, Spec Ed 1983-85; St Dunstar's Day Schl HS Eng Tchr 1986-88; Milton HS 1988-; *ai:* Stu Newspaper Adv.

TARTAGLIONE, LOUIS C., Full Prof of Civil Engineering; *b:* New York, NY; *ed:* Manhattan Coll (BSCE) Civil Engrng 1956; Univ of CT (MSCE) Civil Engrng 1959; Post Grad & Doctorate Stud at Univ of NH 1973-75; *cr:* Combustion Engrng Inc Engr 1956-59; Thiokol Chemical Corp Engr 1959-62; Auco Corp Head Engr 1962-67; Itek Corp Sr Staff Engr 1967-69; Univ of MA at Lowell Civil Engrng Prof 1970-; *ai:* Chi Epsilon Civil Engrng Honor Soc & Tau Beta Pi Natl Engrng Honor Soc Fac Adv; New England Dist Cnslr of Chi Epsilon; ASCE 1954-, Fellow Mem Status 1983; ACI; Commonwealth of MA Bldg Code Commission 1975-, Engrng Comm Adv; Structural Analysis Text McGraw-Hill Book Co 1991; Three Univ Grants; Five Outstanding Tchng & Svc Awds from Univ of MA at Lowell; Over 90 Tech Papers & Publications; *office:* Univ Of MA At Lowell 1 University Ave Lowell MA 01854

TARTAGLIONE, NANCY V., Basic Skills Teacher; *b:* Hackensack, NJ; *m:* Philip J.; *c:* Christine, Keith; *ed:* Rowan Coll (BA) Elem Ed 1972; 9 Grad Hrs Elem Math; *cr:* Parkview-Westville Schls 4th Grd Tchr 1972-76, Compensatory Ed Tchr 1976-79, 5-6th Grd Math Tchr 1982-92, Basic Skills Tchr `992-; *ai:* 4th, 6th Grd Math Asessment, Math Curr, Schl Based Planning, Tchrs Recognition Comms; NEA, NJEA 1972-; Westville Ed Assn 1972-, Pres; AMTNJ 1992-; Tchr Recognitin Awd 1993-; *office:* Parkview Elem Schl Birch & High Sts Westville NJ 08093

TARTARILLA, SUSANNE M., English & Public Speaking Tchr; *b:* Houlton, ME; *m:* Paul; *c:* Ashley, Brittany; *ed:* Univ of ME (BS) Eng, Drama 1983; Univ of NH (MST) Eng, Writing 1993; 8 Addl Credit Hrs Cambridge Univ England Hum 1982; *cr:* Brewer HS Internship 1982; Spaulding Jr High Eng Tchr 1983-84; Mt View Jr High Lang Arts Tchr 1984-86; Pinkerton Acad Eng, Pub Speaking Tchr 1986-; *ai:* Odyssey of Mind Coach; Talent Show, 1995 Fac Play Dir; Stu Writing Group Adv; Stu Assistance Comm; Stu Mentor; 5 Fac Play Productions Performer; NNATE 1986-; Stu Cncls Tchr of Day; Poetry Pub in Eng Journal; Non-Fiction Pub in Local Newspapers; *office:* Pinkerton Acad Pinkerton St Derry NH 03038*

TARTIVITA, PATRICIA CHRISTINA, English Teacher; *b:* Cleveland, OH; *m:* Carmelo; *ed:* King's Coll (BA) Eng, Scndry Ed 1990; Seton Hall Univ (MA) Eng 1992; *cr:* Seton Hall Univ Adj Prof 1991-93; Pequannock HS Eng Tchr 1993; Linden HS Eng Tchr 1993-; *ai:* Stud Cncl Adv; Accelerated Prgm Instr Seton Hall; Alternative Prgm Instr; NJEA, NEA 1993-; *office:* Linden HS 121 W Saint Georges Ave Linden NJ 07036

TASCOE, SUE DEBORAH, Second Grade Teacher; *b:* Montclair, NJ; *m:* Robert; *c:* Ria, Misty, Tolan; *ed:* Dillard Univ (BA) Elem Ed 1963; 9 Credit Hrs Kean Coll; *cr:* Lincoln Schl First Grd, Head Start Tchr 1964-70; Kentopp Schl Second Grd Tchr 1973-75; Elmwood Schl Second Grd Tchr 1976-87, GATE, Second Grd Tchr 1986-; *ai:* Educl Improvement Planning; NEA, NJEA, EOEA 1963-; Tchr of Yr 1981, 1982, 1992; *office:* Elmwood Elem Schl 181 Elmwood Ave East Orange NJ 07018

TASHJIAN, MATILDA DONABEDIAN, Mathematics Teacher; *b:* New York, NY; *m:* M. George; *c:* Louise, Richard, Carol, Joseph; *ed:* City Coll of NY (BSCHE) Chemical Engineering 1950; St John's Univ (MA) Ed 1980; 33 Credit Hrs Ed; *cr:* Eagle Pencil Co Research & Dev 1950-53; NY City Cath Schls Tchr 1970-78; Manhasset HS Sub Tchr 1978-80; Forest Hills HS Math, Cmptr Tchr 1980-; *ai:* Armenian Cultural Club Adv; *office:* Forest Hills HS 67-01 110th St Forest Hills NY 11375

TASHMAN, BARBARA ANN, Principal; *b:* Brooklyn, NY; *c:* Jodi Lynn, Stacey Beth; *ed:* Brooklyn Coll (BA) Elem Ed 1961; Queens Coll (MS) Elem Ed, Childrens Lit 1981; Prof Cert Supervision, Admin Dist, Schl Level 1987; *cr:* PS 201 Queens 3 Grd Tchr 1961-64; PS 219 Queens GATE, AP Tchr 1978-87; PS 107 Queens Asst Prin 1988-95; PS 209 Prin 1996; Queens Coll Grad Ed Adj Instr 1996; *ai:* Dist Wkshps Childrens Lit Presenter; Classroom Mngmt; Conflict Resolution Staff Dev; AFT, UFT 1961-; CSA 1987-; Tchrs of GATE 1978-; Contributing Writer Creative Classroom Mag Chldrens Television Wkshp 1993-; *home:* 1815 215th St Bayside NY 11360

TATAKIS, TIMOTHY A., Assistant Professor of Biology; *b:* Buffalo, NY; *ed:* SUNY Coll of Environmental Sci & Forestry (BS) Forest Bio 1980; Slippery Rock St Coll (MS) Bio 1982; Kent St Univ (PHD) Ecology 1992; *cr:* Monroe Comm Coll Asst Prof 1989-; *ai:* Fac Senate; Departmental Comms: Curr, Prsnl, Comp; Acad Adv Bio & Lbrl Arts; ESATYCB 1991-; Sigma Xi 1995-; Amer Heart Assn, Neighborhood Solicitor; Slippery Rock St Coll Outstdng Grad Stu Awd Bio 1982; NY St Rsrch Grant 1989; Kent St Grad Stu Senate Dissertation Awd 1993; *office:* Monroe Comm Coll 1000 E Henrietta Rd Rochester NY 14623

TATE, RICHARD JOHN, Guidance Counselor; *b:* Warren, OH; *m:* M. Patricia Thomas; *c:* Mary Denise Schindell, Gregory Kenneth; *ed:* Youngstown St Univ (BS) Bus Ed 1967; Westminster Coll (MA Ed) Guid 1972; Attnd Kent St Univ; *cr:* New Castle HS Bus Tchr 1966-67; Hubbard HS Bus Tchr 1967-74, Cnslr 1974-95; Reed MS Cnslr 1995-; *ai:* Var Girls Golf Coach; Intervention Asst Team Mem; Schl Dist Improvement Team Mem; HEA, OEA & NEA 1967-; OH Cnslrs Assn 1978-; Coalburg UM Church 1955-, Pastor Parish Comm, Sunday Schl Supt & Tchr, Fin Comm; Industrial Information Inst for Ed Distngd Edctr; *office:* Reed MS 150 Hall Ave Hubbard OH 44425

TATE, RICHARD ROBERT, Senior English Teacher; *b:* Altoona, PA; *m:* Donna Marie Mingle; *c:* Robert; *ed:* Lock Haven Univ (BS) Eng Ed 1971; PA St Univ (MEd) Scndry Ed 1974; *cr:* Bellwood Antis HS Eng Tchr 1971-; *ai:* Peer Cnslng; Peer Mediation; Stu Assistance Team; PSEA & NEA 1971-, Pres 1973-74; POWA 1981-; Trunt Unlimited 1970-; Outstndg Young Men of Amer 1983-, Listing; Distngd Tchr of Hnr Studnts 1994-, Awd; Book: The Trunt at the Walnut Tree 1991; Numerous Articles Pub; *home:* 715 W 3rd St Williamsburg PA 16693

TATISTCHEFF, MICHAEL, Mathematics Teacher; *b:* New York, NY; *m:* Patricia K. Larson; *c:* Lee, Nick, Tim, Becca; *ed:* Boston Univ (BS) Jrnlsm 1963; Univ of NH (MAT) Math 1969; *cr:* Bridgton Acad Tchr & Coach 1964-70; Hebron Acad Tchr & Coach 1970-79; Northfield Mt Hermon Tchr & Coach 1979-; *ai:* Var Tennis Coach; GTE Fellow; Stu Choice Awd & Fac Flwshp Recipient; AP Reader & Consultant; *office:* Northfield Mt Hermon Schl Main St Northfield MA 01360*

TATLOW, PATRICIA WHISKEMAN, Fourth Grade Teacher; *b:* Hollywood, CA; *m:* Richard H. IV; *c:* Leslie, Chip; *ed:* Univ of AZ (BA) Elem Ed 1966; Pepperdine Univ (MS) Schl Mngmt, Admin 1977, (MS) Spec Ed 1979; Columbia Univ Tech in the Classroom; *cr:* Fountain Vly Schl Dist Classroom Tchr, K-4th Grd Prgm Coord 1966-85, New Tchr Seminars Trainer 1968-74; CA St Dept of Ed Spec Ed Consultant 1980-82; Ardsley Schl Dist Classroom Tchr 1985-; *ai:* Planning & Performance Ldrshp Team; New Tchr Interview Comm; Rdng, Writing, Math Tutor; NYSUT, NEA, ACT 1985-; Fountain Vly Tchrs Assn Tchr of Yr 1971-72; Fountain Vly Jaycees Outstdng Young Edctr 1969-70; Westchester Gannett Tchr Hnr Roll 1994; *home:* 3 Brooklands Cir Apt 3H Bronxville NY 10708*

TATMAN, MICHAEL JON, Instrumental Music Teacher; *b:* Vincennes, IN; *m:* Annette Marie; *c:* Jennifer; *ed:* IN St Univ (BS) Music Ed 1987; PA St Univ (MS) Curr & Instruction 1995; Armed Forces Schl of Music 1982; *cr:* Coatesville Area Schl Dist Instrumental & Gen Music Tchr 1987-89; Harry S Truman HS Instrumental Music Tchr 1993-; *ai:* Marching Band & Musical Asst Dir; PA St Ed Assn 1987-; Percussive Arts Soc 1989-; *home:* 3855 Lukens Ln Hatboro PA 19040*

TATOR, ADRIENNE MARIA, French & English Teacher; *b:* Jersey City, NJ; *m:* David; *c:* Brennan, Andre, Kevin, Michaela; *ed:* Coll of St Elizabeth (BA) Fr, Eng 1968; Attending Kean Coll MA Educl Admin; *cr:* Frankfort Army HS Tchr 1 Yr; Lyndhust HS Tchr 1 Yr; St Pius X HS Supvr, Prin Summer Schl 10 Yrs; Scotch-Plains Fanwood HS Tchr 6 Mos; Rahway HS Tchr 2 Yrs; *ai:* NHS, Fr NHS, Fr Club Adv; NJEA; NEA; AAFT; NJTFLA; Pub Article 1995; *office:* Rahway HS 1012 Madison Ave Rahway NJ 07065

TATULIS, EDITH E., Fifth Grade Teacher; *b:* Washington, DC; *m:* William; *c:* Dana, Rachel, Gretchen; *ed:* UNH (BS) Sci 1975, (MED) Ed 1988; *cr:* Deerfield Comm Schl 7th-8th Grd Sci Tchr 1986-94, 5th Grd Tchr 1994-; *ai:* DEA 1986-, Treas; *office:* Deerfield Comm Schl 66 North Rd Deerfield NH 03037

TATUM, GREGORY A., Vice Principal; *b:* Newark, NJ; *ed:* Kean Coll of NJ (BA) Elem Ed 1983, (MA) Educl Admin 1990; *cr:* Hillside Pub Schls Basic Skills Tchr 1983-84, Second Grd Tchr 1984-88, Fifth Grd Tchr 1988-91, Admin Asst 1991-95, Vice Prin 1995-; *ai:* Stu Safety Patrol, Stu Cncl Adv; NJPSA 1995-; *office:* George Washington Schl 1530 Leslie St Hillside NJ 07205

TAUBITZ, RONALD MARSHALL, Language, Lit & Speech Prof; *b:* Detroit, MI; *m:* Liselotte Winkler; *c:* Monica, Eric; *ed:* AZ St Univ (BA) Eng 1966, (MA) Eng, Lang & Lit 1968, (PHD) Eng, Lang & Lit 1975; *cr:* AZ St Univ Instr 1968-70; Univ of Oviedo Visiting Prof 1970-72; Univ of Madrid Asst Prof 1972-83; Univ of MD Adj Fac 1983-; *ai:* Culture Club Spon; TEFL Comm; Stu Adv; Fulbright Lectureship 1970-72; Numerous Articles Pub; *office:* Univ Of Maryland-Munich Campus Unit 24560 APO AE 09183

TAUBMAN, NANCY BETH, English Teacher; *b:* White Plains, NY; *m:* Edward; *c:* Michele, Brendan; *ed:* SUNY at Albany (BA) Eng 1973; Fairfield Univ (MA) Eng Ed 1975; Various Courses in Post-Scndry Pursuits; Holocaust Course Vol Tchr 1993; *cr:* Westlake HS Eng Dept Tchr 1973-76; Springbrook HS Eng Dept Tchr 1976-84; Rockville HS Eng Dept Tchr 1985-; *ai:* Lit, Arts Magazine Spon; Social Comm; NEA, MCEA 1973-; Hadassah 1984-, VP Mbrshp 2 Yrs, Svc Awd; Article Pub; *office:* Rockville HS 2100 Baltimore Rd Rockville MD 20851*

TAVANO, LOURDES VIVIANA, HS ESL Teacher; *b:* Havana, Cuba; *m:* Guiseppe; *ed:* ST Peters Coll (BA) Span 1976; William Paterson Coll ESL 1977; Extra Credits at Columbia Univ Tchrs Coll in Comp Sci; *cr:* P&S #5 ESL Tchr 4 Yrs; Memorial HS ESL Tchr 1980-; *ai:* Intnl Club Adv; WNY Educl 1976-, Tchr Mem; NJEA 1976-, Tchr Mem; Cert of Merit from the St of NJ; *office:* Memorial HS 5501 Park Ave West NJ 07093

TAVELLA, BONNIE BARNO, High School English Teacher; *b:* Palmerton, PA; *m:* Anthony C. Jr.; *ed:* Bloomsburg St Univ (BS) Scndry Ed & Eng 1984; Bloomsburg Univ of Pa (MA) Speech Commnctn 1987; 54 Credits beyond Masters Degree; *cr:* Palmerton Area HS Eng Tchr 1984-; Penn St Univ Schuylkill Haven Campus Adj Prof of Speech Commnctn 1987-; *ai:* Frosh Class Adv; 7th-12th Grd Curr Coord of Eng; PYEA 1984-; NEA 1984-; PSEA 1984-; *office:* Palmerton HS Rd 3 Box 3681 Palmerton PA 18071*

TAVELLA, LORETTA STRUBE, Eng & Social Studies Teacher; *b:* New York, NY; *ed:* Adelphi Univ (BA) Eng & Soc Stud 1977, (MS) Spcl Ed 1978; Columbia (MA) Eng 1983; 30 Post Grad Credits; *cr:* St Marys Tchr 1978-79; Kings Park High Eng & SS Tchr 1979-; *ai:* AFT 1979-; *office:* Kings Park Sr HS 200 Route 25A Kings Park NY 11754

TAVENNER, JOY JEAN LEUGERS, Learning Disabilities Teacher; *b:* Belle Fontaine, OH; *c:* Chet; *ed:* Urbana Univ (BS) Ed 1985; Wright St Univ (MS) Ed 1992; *cr:* Indian Lake HS LD Tutor 1984-86; William K. Willis LD Tchr 1987-88; Triad HS LD Tchr 1988-; *ai:* Asst Vlybl & Girls Bsktbl Coach; Prin Advy Comm; Triad Ed Assn 1989-; NEA & OEA 1986-; OHSAA 1976-; ASA 1984-, Sec & VP; Kappa Delta Pi 1991-; OFT-AFT 1995-; VFW Auxilliary 1980-, Guard; *home:* 526A Mill St North Lewisburg OH 43060

TAVERNA, ANTHONY, Mathematics & Cmptr Sci Tchr; *b:* New York City, NY; *c:* Theresa; *ed:* NY Univ (BEE) Electrical Engrng 1967, (MSE) Electrical Engrng 1968; Hofstra Univ (MSEd) Scndry Ed, Math 1973; Numerous Grad Math, Ed, Inservice Courses; *cr:* Sperry Systems Mngmt Div Electronics Engr Navdal Cmptr 1968-69; Grumman Aerospace Corp Electronics Engr, LM Prgm, F14 Test Equip Design 1969-72; Vly Stream Cntrl HS Dist Math, Cmptr Tchr 1972-; *ai:* Prof Staff Dev, NHS Comms; Sportfishing Club; AFT, Vly Stream Tchrs Assn 1972-; ASCD 1995-; NY Sportfishing Fed 1991-; Natl Assn of Charterboat Operators 1992-; Three Village Civic Assn, Stony Brook Civic Assn 1985-; Apollo Achvmt Awd for Excl; NY Joint Industry Bd Flwshpl NSF Sponsored Stud in Lbrl Arts Math Curr; *home:* 16 Bayberry Ln Stony Brook NY 11790

TAYEK, JON GERARD, Choral & General Music Tchr; *b:* Cleveland, OH; *m:* Bonnie Hartman; *c:* George, Ian; *ed:* OH Univ (BMed) Music Ed 1981; Cleveland St Univ (MMUS) Choral Stud 1989; *cr:* St Wenceslas Elem Schl Music Tchr 1982-86; Willowick MS Choral Dir, Gen Music Tchr, Music Dept Chair 1986-; *ai:* Trng Voice Solo, Ensemble Participants; NEA, OEA 1986-; MENC 1981-; ACDA 1987-; AGO 1992-; Knights of Columbus 1990-; Cuyahoga Vly Civil War Round Table 1993-.

TAYLOR, ALBERT J.,JR., English Teacher; *b:* Philadelphia, PA; *c:* Darren, Linsey, Kathleen; *ed:* Lebanon Vly Coll (BA) Eng 1965; Commonwealth of PA (ME) Ed 1973; 100 Credit Hrs Grad Work; *cr:* William Tennent HS Eng Tchr 1965-; *ai:* Boys & Girls Asst Soccer Coach; 31 Yrs Coaching; NEA 1965-; Centennial Ed Assn 1965-, VP; *office:* William Tennent HS 333 Centennial Rd Warminster PA 18974*

TAYLOR, ALFRED OVERTON,JR., Assistant Dean; *b:* Arlington, VA; *m:* Delores Smith; *c:* Kenneth M., Karen D.; *ed:* Washington Tech Inst (BS) Tech Tchr Trng 1973; Federal City Coll (MA) Adm & Supv Adult Ed 1976; VPI St Univ (EDD) Higher Ed Adm 1994; *cr:* Assoc Prof, Chprsn 1969-79; Univ of DC Assoc Dean, Col Phy Sci Engr, Tech 1979-, Acting Asst Provost 1988-91, Asst Dean, Coll of Prof Stud 1994-; *ai:* Fac Adv Omicron Gamma Chptr; Project Dir Alliance of Minority Partners NSF; Natl Ctr for Rsrch in Voc Ed Presentor; Univ Cncl SECME; Advy Mem Transtech, IDEA Acads DC Pub Schl; DC Voc Ed Adv Comm 1969-, Former Chprsn; Arl VA Citizen Com Voc Ed 1993-, Chprsn; Omega Psi Phi 1974-; NAACP 1950-; Nauck Comm Father of Yr; *home:* 1924 S Lowell St Arlington VA 22204

TAYLOR, ANN I., Dept Chair & Associate Prof; *b:* Rochester, NH; *m:* Dennis Ciotti; *c:* Melissa Ciotti; *ed:* Mc Intosh Coll (ABS) Secretarial Sci 1982; Franklin Pierce Coll (BS) Bus Mngmt 1985; Notre Dame Coll (MED) Ed 1991; *cr:* Univ System of NJ Ex Asst 1985-91; NH Tech Coll Tchr 1991-94; Mc Intosh Coll Dept Chair, Tchr 1994-; *ai:* Founder, Adv Collegiate Secretaries Intnl; Field Hockey Coach 1991-94; Lib Comm; Delta Pi Epsilon 1994-; PSI 1993-; NBEA 1991-; Dover Chamber of Commence, Dover Bs & Prof Women 1995-; *office:* Mc Intosh Coll 23 Cataract Ave Dover NH 03820*

TAYLOR, ANN MANUEL, Professor & Academic Advisor; *b:* Atlanta, TX; *c:* Lia Rachel; *ed:* Union Inst (BA) Soc Welfare Admin 1979; Univ of Cincinnati (MED) Educl Admin 1983; Union Inst (PHD) Higher Ed Admin 1989; *cr:* The Union Inst Cnslr, Instr 1980-, Coord of Acad Svcs 1980-83, Prof 1983-; *ai:* Fac Appeals Comm; Fac Waiver Comm; AAUP 1994-, Urban League 1995-; YMCA Greater Cincinnati 1993-, Black Achiever; Cncl of Chrstn Communions 1989-, Chair-Ed Comm, Charles P Taft; Touching Kids Lives-Not-For-Profit Educl Svc for Children & Yth Dir; Hamilton Cty Dept of Human Svc for the Family to Family Project Respite Svc Grant; Back on the Block Career Symposium for Yth Grant 1993; Greater Cincinnati Fnd Summer Time Fun Grant 1993-94; City of Cincinnati TKL Teens Behind the Scenes Grant 1996; *office:* Union Inst 440 E Mcmillan St Cincinnati OH 45206

TAYLOR, ANNE THOMAS, High School Music Teacher; *b:* Philadelphia, PA; *ed:* Chestnut Hill Coll (BS) Music Ed 1987; Beaver Coll (MAH) Music, Fine Arts, Theater 1993; *cr:* Holy Cross Elem Schl 4th-8th Grd Music Tchr 1978-81; Nativity of Our Lord Elem Schl 4th Grd, 4th-8th Grd Music Tchr 1981-85; West Cath HS Music Tchr; *ai:* Gospel Choir Moderator; Stage Mgr for Shows; Steering Comm Schls of Excl, World Affairs; Cmptr Lab Aide; MENC 1985-; TAP 1992-; NCEA 1978-; *office:* West Catholic H S 4501 Chestnut St Philadelphia PA 19139

TAYLOR, ATHENA L., Business Education Teacher; *b:* Oakland, MD; *c:* Christopher, Nicholas; *ed:* Frostburg St Univ (BS) Bus Ed; Working on MBA; *cr:* H&R Block Tax Consultant; Mineral Co Bd Ed Instr; Burlington Family Svc Family Edctr; Garrett Co Bd of Ed Tchr; *ai:* FBLA, Soph Class Adv; GCTA; NEA; Beta Sigma Phi; *office:* Southern Garrett HS 345 Oakland Dr Oakland MD 21550

TAYLOR, B. JANE, Fourth Grade Teacher; *b:* Ashland, OH; *m:* Kent E.; *c:* Kent Jr., Julie Taylor Given; *ed:* Kent St Univ (BS) Elem Ed 1964; Attnd Kent St, Akron Univs; *cr:* Cuyahoga Falls 4th Grd Tchr 1964-67, Learning Disability Class 1967-69; Kent City Schls 4th Grd Tchr 1979-83, 5th Grd Tchr 1983-84, 4th Grd Tchr 1984-; *ai:* Kent Ed Assn 1979-, Bldg Rep; Delta Kappa Gamma 1987-; Alpha Chi Omega 1961-; *office:* Longoy Schl-Kent City Schls 1069 Elno Ave Kent OH 44240

TAYLOR, BARB, Kindergarten Teacher; *b:* Cincinnati, OH; *c:* Ken Jr., Dana; *ed:* Miami Univ (BS) Ed 19663; *cr:* Grand Blanc Schls 1st Grd Tchr 1965-66; *ai:* Prent Involvement Comm; NEA 1970-; OEA 1970-; Cov United Church of Christ 1970-, Bd of Chrstn Ed; Avocation Club 1973-, Rec Sec, Sec, Treas, VP & Pres; Delta Kappa Gamma 1980-; *office:* Covington Elem Schl 707 Chestnut St Covington OH 45318*

TAYLOR, BARBARA POTTS, Sixth Grade Teacher; *b:* Syracuse, NY; *m:* William George; *c:* Megan; *ed:* SUNY Delhi (AAS) Lbrl Arts 1980; SUCO Oneonta (BA) Elem Ed 1982, (MS) Elem Ed 1988; *cr:* Childrens Pl Tchr 1982; Sub Tchr 1983-86; Margaretville Cntrl Schl Sixth Grd Tchr 1986-; *ai:* Class 1997 Adv; Sec Tech Comm; NEA 1986-; *home:* HC 2 Margaretville NY 12455

TAYLOR, BARBARA SLAYBAUGH, First Grade Teacher; *b:* Canton, OH; *c:* Craig; *ed:* Bowling Green St Univ (BS) Elem Ed 1964; *ai:* OEA; NEA; TVTA; *office:* Bolivar Elem PO Box 196 Park Ave Bolivar OH 44612

TAYLOR, BENITA ESPINOZA, Special Education Teacher; *b:* Basco Batanes, Philippines; *m:* Lynn H.; *c:* Jennifer Sparico, Kristine, Melissa, Darrell; *ed:* CA St Univ at LA (BA) Lbrl Stud 1979; Clarion Univ of PA (MS) Sci Ed 1992; Spec Ed 1987; *cr:* Bassett USD 5th Grd Tchr 1979-83; Austin Schl Dist Spec Ed Tchr 1987-88; Kane Area HS Spec Ed Tchr 1988-89; St Marys Area Schl Dist Spec Ed Tchr 1989-; *ai:* Natl Sci Olympiad; Sci Olympiad; PSTA 1990-, Bd of Dirs; PSEA 1987-; SMEA 1989-, Bldg Rep; Kappa Delta Pi 1987-; *office:* St Marys Area MS 979 South St Marys St St Marys PA 15857

TAYLOR, BEVERLY SUE, 6th Grade Teacher; *b:* Dayton, OH; *c:* Lauree Lee Cox, Larry Lee Cox Jr., Paul Bryan cox, Mary Elizabeth Cox; *ed:* (BS) Elem Ed 1987; *cr:* E. Dayton Chrstn Schl 4th Grd Tchr 1987-90, 7 Tchr 1990-91, 6th Grd Tchr 1991-; *ai:* Schl Newspaper; Nom Math, Sci Tchr Awd; *office:* East Dayton Christian Schl 999 Spir Dayton OH 45431

TAYLOR, CAROL MCGUIRE, Gifted Program Seminar Tea Philadelphia, PA; *m:* Dr. Lee G.; *c:* Kristin, Lee, Lindsay; *ed:* East Coll (BA) Elem Ed 1972; Beaver Coll (MA) Rdng 1979; *cr:* Da Area SD 5th Grd Tchr 1972-74; Haverford Twp SD 3rd, 5th & 6th 1974-80, Tchr of Gifted 1980-; *ai:* Assessment & Strategic Comms; STEP Parenting Prgm Co-Ldr; Soc Stud Comm Environmetal Club Adv; PAGE 1988-; Bethany Collegiate Presby 1980-, Sunday Schl Co-Chair; Haverford HS Parent Advy Com Co-Chair Acad Group; *office:* Oakmont Elem Schl 50 E E Havertown PA 19083*

TAYLOR, CHRISTINE TILLINGHAST, Seventh Grade Teacher; *b:* Providence, RI; *m:* Kenneth; *c:* Greg, Emmy; *ed:* RI C Eng Ed 1975, (MED) Eng Ed 1995; *cr:* Freelance Pub Writer 1974 Coll Rsrchr & Editing Asst 1988-89; RI Dept of Ed GED Reader Cranston Dept of Sr Svcs Creative Writing Tchr 1989-; Johnston Tchr 1990-95; N A Ferri MS Eng Tchr 1995-; *ai:* AFT 1990-; NCT NEATE 1991-; *office:* N.A. Ferri MS 10 Memorial Dr Johnston R

TAYLOR, CLARENCE LEROY,JR., High School Chemistry Baton Rouge, LA; *m:* Sandra G. Pitre; *ed:* Southern Univ (BS) P Chem 1972, (MA) Admin & Supervision 1983, (MS+30) Comp S Amer Univ 3 Credit Hrs 1985-86; George Washington Univ 6 C 1987-89; Johns Hopkins Univ 3 Credit Hrs 1995; *cr:* Dist Pub Sch Tchr & Soccer Coach 1984-; US Naval Rsrch Lab Mentor-Tchr Pgm 1988-92, Pgm Adv SEAP 1995; *ai:* FCA; 3-T Mentors Pgm; of the Minds; Metro Soccer Coaches; NEA 1996; WA Tchrs Uni NSTA 1996; DCIAA Soccer Coaches Comm 1986-92; Gideons Int Chaplain; Deacon 1989-, Sec; Project IMPACT 1990; 4-Winds Project 1992; *office:* Ballou Sr HS 3401 4th St SE Washington D

TAYLOR, DARYL L., Physics Teacher; *b:* Lewistown, PA; *m:* M Lillie; *c:* Brandon, Jeffrey, Brian; *ed:* Shippensburg St Coll (BS) & Math Dual 1975; Salem Coll (MSQ) Interdisciplinary Stud 1 JFK HS Math, Bio & Physics Tchr 1976-79; Palmyra HS Math & Tchr 1979-82; Delran HS Math & Physics Tchr 1982-90; Willing Physics Tchr 1990-; *ai:* Chess Club Adv; Sci League Adv; Sci O Adv; NEA 1976-; NSTA 1976-; AAPT 1984-; NSF Grant for MS BISEC Grant to Work At Princeton Plasma Physics Lab-1992 Willingboro HS John F Kennedy Way Willingboro NJ 08046*

TAYLOR, DEBORAH A., Psychology Professor; *b:* Knoxville, Laurence I; *c:* Daniel, Johanna; *ed:* Cornell Univ (AB) Sociolog Rutgers Univ (MS) Soc, Pers Psych 1974, (PHD) Soc, Pers Psych Colby-Sawyer Coll Instr, Asst Prof, Assoc Prof 1976-86, Dean o VP Stu Dev 1986-90, Assoc Prof, Prof, Dept Chair 1990-; *ai:* Out Fac Mem 1986; Articles 1974-90; Grnt Funded 1993-; Colby-Sawyer Coll 100 Main St New London NH 03257

TAYLOR, ELIAS L., Sociology Professor; *ed:* Rollins Coll (BA) Soc Athropology 1962; Univ of CA at Berkeley 1962-63; Grad Schl (MA) Sociology 1966, (PHD) Sociology 1974; *cr:* Clarkson U 1967-70; Salisbury St Assoc 1970-75; Goucher Coll Asst 1975-79 St Prof 1978-; *ai:* Pgm Adv & Spon; Hnr Soc-Soc Sci; Coppin Senate; ODK Mem-Hnr Soc; AAVP 1980-, Cntrl MD Comm MANECCS 1982-; Soc Sci Dept Coppin St 1979-89, Chm; McNair 1992-; *office:* Coppin St Coll 2500 W North Ave Baltimore MD 2

TAYLOR, ELIZABETH MARY, Second Grade Teacher; *b:* Ha PA; *ed:* Immaculata Coll Elem Ed 1969, Eng 1972; *cr:* Incarnation Tchr 1972-77; Our Lady of Charity 1st Grd Tchr 1977-79; Saint J Grd Tchr 1979-82; St Bernadette 2nd Grd Tchr 1982-; *ai:* Rel, Unit Coord; NCEA 1972-; *office:* St Bernadette Schl 1015 Tur Drexel Hill PA 19026

TAYLOR, ELLIE (SCHOBEL), Kndgtn & Instrl Support T Pittsburgh, PA; *m:* Donald A.; *ed:* Clarion Univ of PA (BS) Elem E Masters Equivalency in Elem Ed; Penn St Univ 24 Grad Credit Forbes Elem Schl 3rd Grd Tchr 1972-74; Hebron Elem Schl 2nd & Tchr 1974-84; Penn Hebron Elem Schl Kndgtn, 1st & 2nd Grd Tch *ai:* NEA 1972-; PSEA 1972-; PHEA 1972-, Bldg Rep; PTA 197 Rep; Penn Hebron Tchr of the Yr 1990-91; *office:* Penn Hebron El 102 Duff Rd Pittsburgh PA 15235

TAYLOR, ELWOOD ALBERT, Seventh Grade Social Stud T Camden, NJ; *m:* Paula Louise Smith; *c:* Anna Page; *ed:* Gwynedd Coll (BS) Sociology 1986; *cr:* Pottsgrove Intermediate Schl 7th Stud Tchr 1987-; *ai:* Interdisciplinary Team Ldr; Schl Dist S Planning, New Mid Schl Bldg Comms; Pottsgrove Fed of Tchrs 198 1992; PSEA, NEA 1987-; Upper Pottsgrove Twp Planning Com 1992-, Vice Chm 1996; *office:* Pottsgrove Intermediate Schl 1329 Rd Pottstown PA 19464

TAYLOR, GLADYS COOLEY, 9th Grade History Teacher; *b:* R NC; *m:* Edward R.; *c:* Edward, Anthony, Dwayne, Erin; *ed:* Uni (BA); Rutgers Univ (MA); Working on JD Law Seton Hall Schl Attnd Stillman Coll; *cr:* Model Cities Prgm Coord 1976-79; Bd of 1980-; *ai:* Stu Govt Adv; Debate Coach; Jr Achvmnt Tchr; Blck Assn; Tchrs Assn; Thelma Burke Guild 1980-; The GIFT Club 197 Treas; Mike Amato Tlnt Agency; Model; Actress.

TAYLOR, GORDON S., Math & Science Teacher; *b:* Pittsburgh, Elaine Ruth Huemmrich; *c:* Christopher, Jonathan; *ed:* Penn St (B 1962; 20 Credits Univ of Pittsburgh; 6 Credits Slippery Rock Credits Grove City Coll; *cr:* Etna HS Math, Sci/Math Tchr 1962-66 HS Math, Sci/Math Tchr 1966-67; Grove City HS Math, Sci Tchr *ai:* Previously Ski Club Adv; PSEA 1992-; FFA Honorary; K Farmer; Harrisville Bus Assn; *office:* Grove City Sr HS 511 Highl Grove City PA 16127

TAYLOR, GREGORY SPENCE, Band Director; *b:* Winterhaven, Diana Lee; *ed:* OH St Univ (BME) Music Ed 1985; *cr:* Wyoming Ci Band Dir 1985-87; Carey Exempted Vlg Schl Band Dir 1987-89; H Local Schls Band Dir 1989-90; Worthington Schls Band Dir 1990-; Music Ed Assn 1985-, Region Sec, Treas; Music Edcts Natl Co 1985-; Pi Kappa Lambda; Deans List OSU; *office:* Worthington Ki HS 1499 Hard Rd Columbus OH 43235

TAYLOR, GRETCHEN CELESTE, Teacher & Athletic Direc Philadelphia, PA; *c:* Tamika, Jerome Doc; *ed:* Cntrl St Univ (BS) H Recreation 1970; Cleveland St Univ (MAEd) Curr, Instruction 19 Bettye Robinson Dance Schl Dance Instr 1965-71; Glenville Sc 1970-, Bsktbl Coach 1975-, Ath Dir 1995-; *ai:* Sr Act Adv; Girls Vlybl, Sftbl Coach; Boys, Girls Ath Act Dir; AFT; Delta Sigma 1972-; Phi Delta Kappa 1995-; Greater Cleveland Bsktbl Assn Auxilary Bd; OH HS Ath Assn 1978-; Key to City of Cleveland; Yr; Bsktbl Coach of Yr; Jennings Scholar; *office:* Glenville HS 650 St Cleveland OH 44108

TAYLOR, JACKIE LEE (PELTON), Sixth Grade Teacher; *b:* F OH; *m:* James Monroe; *c:* Jennifer Lee, Matthew Monroe; *ed:* U Findlay (BS) Elem Ed 1972; Univ of Dayton Post Grad Stud; *ai:* Advy; Riverdale Extracurricular Planning Com; NEA, OEA & REA First Chrstn Church 1986-; Martha Holden Jennings Schlr 1976-77

R, JAMES E., English Teacher & Counselor; *b:* North Sydney, *m:* Karen; *ed:* Messiah Coll (BA) Eng Ed 1992; Seminary of East *cr:* New Testament Chrstn Schl Eng Tchr 1992-; *ai:* Coll Adv; Yth 'oll Evening Instr; ACSI 1996; PTEA 1992-, Stu Tchr of Yr; New nt Church 1993-, Yth Pastor; Adj Instr Bay St Coll 1 1/2 Yrs; *office:* stament Christian Schl 1 New Taunton Ave Norton MA 02766*

R, JAMES FRANKLIN, Mathematics Teacher; *b:* Wolfeboro, Ricker Coll (BA) Math 1972; Notre Dame Coll (MED) Curr, Ed *r:* Gov. Wentworth Classroom Tchr 1972-76; Kingswood Schl om Tchr 1972-76; Southern Aroostook HS Classroom Tchr ; Farmington HS Classroom Tchr 1979-; *ai:* NHS, Math Team Adv; v Rep; Dept Chair Math, Sci; NEA, NEA-NH 1989-, St Comms; 1990-; Local Tchrs Assn 1979-, Treas; Regnl Tchrs Assn, Treas; : Lodge 1974-, Various Offices; Scottish Rite-Masons 1975-; 'armington HS Memorial Dr Farmington NH 03835*

R, JAMES MONROE, American History Teacher; *b:* Findlay, Jackie L.; *c:* Jennifer L., Matthew M.; *ed:* Univ of Findlay (BS) 2; Univ of Dayton (MA) Amer His 1982; *cr:* Hardin Northern HS mer Govt Tchr 1972-78; Riverdale HS Amer His Tchr 1978-; *ai:* oys Bsktbl Coach; NEA & OEA 1972-; REA 1978-; First Chrstn 1960-; APIC 1978-; Phi Alpha Theta Honorary His; Martha Holden s Scholar; Nom as OH Tchr of Yr 1986; US Postal Awd to Historic rservation 1994; *home:* 308 Wells Rd Forest OH 45843

R, JEFFREY MATTHEW, HS Mathematics Teacher; *b:* phia, PA; *m:* Elizabeth Ann Burnell; *ed:* La Salle Univ (MA) Sndry ; *cr:* Archbishop Ryan Cath HS for Boys Math Tchr 1983-84; Dougherty Cath HS Math Tchr 1987-89; St Hubert Cath HS for lath Tchr 1989-; *ai:* Video Yearbook Moderator; Stage Crew or; NCTM 1993-; ATMOPAV 1989-.

R, JOAN IDA, Retired Fourth Grade Teacher; *b:* Massena, NY; *ed:* t Potsdam (BS) Elem Ed 1955; St Lawrence Univ (MS) Ed 1962; Irondequist Schl 4th Grd Tchr 1955-61; Massena Cntrl Schls 4th r 1962-88; *ai:* Delta Kappa Gamma 1965-; *home:* 38 Ransom Ave a NY 13662

R, JOAN PATTERSON, English Instr & Program Dir; *b:* re, MD; *m:* Joseph Phillip; *c:* Roland, Raymond; *ed:* Morgan St 3S) Ed 1966; Masters Equivalent Ed 1978; Working Toward y MA St Mary's Seminary; Coppin St Coll Guid 12 Hrs; Attnd Hopkins Univ 1978; *cr:* Samuel Coleridge Taylor Elem Schl om Tchr 1966-89; James Monroe Elem Schl Classroom Tchr ; West Baltimore MS Demonstration, 8th Grd Eng Tchr 1989-, sing Tchr 1990-91; Johns Hopkins Univ Curr Writer 1991-92; 'urr Writer 1991-92; *ai:* Teach for Amer Newcomers Mentor; After Alternative, Tutorial Prgm Designer, Dir; Numerous Schl ment Teams; Wkshp Presenter; James Monroe Elem Schl Fac Advy Natl Assn Female Execs; NAACP; Delta Sigma Theta; NAFE 3TU Reform Comm 1996; MD ASCD 1995-; YWCA; Summer Yth Dance Instr; Park Heights Comm Life Theatre, Co-organizer, ader; United Negro Coll Fund, Reception Comm; St Ambrose Planner, Coord Cultural Arts Project, Artistic Dir; Mount Zion hurch Recreational Prgm Dance, Dramatic Instr; Adams Chapel icentiate Preacher, Assoc Minister; St Steven AME Church Assoc r; Agape Flwshp AME Church Assoc Minister; Initiated Creative nning James Monroe Elem Schl 1966; Human Relations Wkshp Dir reated James Monroe Modern Dance Troupe 1972; Individualized om Instruction Prgm Founder 1975; Published Work: Free To Be utstdng Svc Plaque Natl Summer Yth Corps 1973; Distngd Svc United Negro Coll Fund 1974; Souther Regnl Cncl; BCPS Career nities Prgm Appreciation Cert 1974; Elem, Scndry Ed Outstdng timore City Ed Dept 1976; Outstndg oung Women of Amer; Distngd 'larylander Awd Towson St Univ 1992; *office:* West Baltimore MS N Bend Rd Baltimore MD 21229*

R, JOHN HENDERSON, Social Studies & English Tchr; *b:* ville, TX; *m:* Linda C.; *c:* Chris H., J. Michael; *ed:* TX A&M (BS) 5, (MED) His 1967; Cert Scndcry Rdng Univ of TX at Austin; *cr:* son HS Eng & Soc Stud Tchr 1967-69; DODDS 1969-; *ai:* Soccer Sr Class Spon; Local OFT Rep; AFT, OFT, IFT, Lnr & Pres; The of Torrey; Inst of Natuical Archacology; *home:* PSC Box 88 Box PO AE 09821*

R, JOHN MICHAEL, Fourth Grade Teacher; *b:* Waterbury, CT; v of CT (BA) Eng 1965; Cntrl CT St Univ Working Towards Masters d 9 Credit Hrs; *cr:* Assumption Schl 7-8th Grd Tchr 1965-71; St Jr HS 7-8th Grd Tchr 1971-80; Travelers Insurance Contract 1980-89; St Thomas Schl 7-8th, 4th Grd Tchr 1989-; *ai:* Test Stu Cncl Aid; Drug Awareness Comm 1991-93, Mem; Spec cs Comm 1995-, Mem.

R, JOHN WILLIAM, Cosmetology Instructor; *b:* Lowell, MA; *m:* Ann Digilio; *c:* Christopher, John, Sarah; *ed:* Wilfred Acad re Cosmetologust 1981; Fitchburgh St Coll Cert Cosmetology Instr Jniv Lowell 3 Yrs Corp Ed, Lbrl Arts Pending; *cr:* Greater Lowell Schl Cosmetology Instr 9 Yrs; Fashions for Hair Cosmetologist 11 idgets Hair Design Cosmetologist 4 Yrs; *ai:* Statewide Integration; Adv; GLRTO Exec Bd, Former Ofcr; MA Tchrs Org 1987-; NEA; atent for Color Coordination Cone Granted by Fed Govt 1988.*

R, JOYCE V., 4th Grade Teacher; *b:* McKeesport, PA; *m:* William; Univ at PA (BS) Elem Ed 1969; *cr:* White Oak Elem Schl 4th Grd 969-; *ai:* Supts Liason Advy Comm 1994-; PTA Tchr Rep 1996-; 1969-; PSEA 1969-; NEA 1969-; Natl PTA Outstdng Edctr Awd 986; Local PTA Outstdng Edctr 1986; Creator of TLC 1993; Readers Amer Heroes in Ed Nom 1994; *office:* White Oak Elem Schl 1415 nia Ave Mc Keesport PA 15131

R, KAREN, Eng & Creative Writing Tchr; *b:* Salem, OH; *m:* Paul ; *c:* Meghan, Clayton; *ed:* Kent St Univ (BSEd) Eng 1968; MS d Univ 1992; *cr:* West Branch Local Eng Tchr 1968-72, 1976-; *ai:* Jr Sr Class, Pep Club, Mem Book Selection Comm Adv; Former on Comm WBEA Golden Apple Awd; Yearbook Adv; NEA, OEA WBEA 1968-72, 1984-, Publicity Chprsn 3 Yrs, Bldng Rep 3 Yrs; 1984-86, 1991-93; One of Top Three Educators WBEA Chosen Apple Awd 1987; Chosen 1991, 92-95, One of WBEA Top Tchrs by ting Srs; Ch 21 Tchr of Month 1995d; *office:* West Branch H S Main St Beloit OH 44609

)R, KEITH DAVID, English, Speech & Jrnlsm Tchr; *b:* ville, PA; *m:* Cynthia Pelloni; *c:* Jared, Caled; *ed:* Bob Jones Univ peech Ed 1985; *cr:* Augusta Chrstn Schl HS Eng, Speech Tchr 9; Augusta Coll continueing Ed, Eng Tchr 1986-89; Wilson Chrstn Eng, Speech Tchr 1989-90; Beaver Vly Chrstn Acad Eng, Speech, Tchr 1990-; Rhema Chrstn Schl Drama Dir 1991-; *ai:* Drama; ions; Jr Class Adv; Sr Banquet Coord; Fine Arts Dir; Chrstns in Arts 1989-; Various Comm, Church Theatre Prgms; *office:* Beaver Christian Acad 350 Adams St Rochester PA 15074

)R, KELLY (MC ADOO), Journalism Teacher; *b:* Findlay, OH; *m:* s J.; *c:* Meredith A., Kyle W.; *ed:* Bowling Green St Univ (BS) 1984, (MED) Guid, Cnslng 1986; *cr:* Mc Auley HS Eng Tchr 8; Sylvania Southview HS Jrnlsm Tchr 1988-; Bowling Green St Adj Jrnlsm Instr 1994-; *ai:* Yrbk, Newspaper, Lit Magazine Adv; Ed Assn 1990-; Great Lakes Interscholastic Press Assn 1986-, Bd 1991-93, Sec 1994-; Sylvania Ed Assn 1988-, Bldg Rep 1992-93, 1995; Certfd Jrnlsm Edctr; Articles Pub; *office:* Sylvania Southview HS 7225 Sylvania Ave Sylvania OH 43560

TAYLOR, LAURA GASSLER, Fourth Grade Teacher; *b:* Woodbury, NJ; *c:* Stephen, Gregory; *ed:* Glassboro St Coll (BA) Elem Ed 1973, (MA) Curr Dev, Supervision 1985; Gifted, Talented Ed Cert Coll of New Rochelle; *cr:* H. L. Reber Schl 4th-5th Grd, Tchr of Gifted, Talented 1973-83; Meml MS 5th Grd Soc Stud Tchr 1984-87; Marie Durand Elem Schl 4th Grd, Tchr of Gifted, Talented 1987-; *ai:* 1st Grd Tutor Coord; Schl Improvement Team; Young Authors Grant Coord 1994-; NEA, NJEA, VEA 1973-; Bethel Chrstn Ctr Sunday Schl Tchr 1991-, Woman's Ministry Chprsn; SS Supt Asst; Tchr of Yr, Attnd Symposium Governor's Awd 1990; Scott Foresman & Houghton Mifflin Cos Presenter, Consultant; Cooperative Learning, Whole Lang, Integrated Lang ARts Presenter; *office:* Marie Durand Elem Schl 371 W Forest Grove Rd Vineland NJ 08360*

TAYLOR, LESLIE M., English Teacher; *b:* New York City, NY; *m:* Peter E.; *c:* Matthew, Evan; *ed:* OH Wesleyan Univ (BA) Eng 1967; Curry Coll 3 Credits Ed; Bridgewater St Coll 3 Credits Ed; Univ of MA Masters Degree Prgm Spec Ed; *cr:* Samuel B. Ogle Jr High Lang Arts Tchr 1968; Elm Place MS Eng Tchr 1969-70; Valley MS Eng, Rdng Tchr 1971; Woodward Schl Eng Tchr 1982-; *ai:* Past Yrbk Ed 1988-94; Accreditation, Discipline Comms; New England Assn of Tchrs of Eng; NCTE; PTO Exec Bd 1994-95, Schlsp Comm; Hingham Ed Fnd 1994-; Golden Apple Awd; *office:* Woodward Schl For Girls 1102 Hancock St Quincy MA 02169

TAYLOR, LINDA O'DONNELL, English Teacher; *b:* Washington, PA; *w:* Franklin L. (dec); *c:* Tiffany L.; *ed:* CA Univ of PA (BSEd) Eng 1963; Post Grad Hrs at West VA Univ, Penn St Univ, Otterbein Coll; *cr:* Trinity Jr Sr HS Eng Tchr 1963-70; Northland HS Eng Tchr 1971-95; *ai:* Valkyrie Drill Team Adv 1992-95; Instrl Tchr Ldr Eng Dept 1987-95; NEA, OEA, NCTE 1963-; CEA 1971-; Honoray Hnr Soc Elected by Stdnts Harold Eibling Chptr; *office:* Northland HS 1919 Northcliff Dr Columbus OH 43229

TAYLOR, LINDA SUE, Teacher of Deaf Students; *b:* Fairbanks, AK; *ed:* Middlebury Coll (BA) Eng Lit-Cum Laude 1983; Gallaudet Univ (MA) Ed of Deaf Stdnts 1986; Boston Univ Doctorate Stud in Literacy, Lang & Cultural Stud 1992-; *cr:* MD Schl for the Deaf MS & HS His & Lang Arts Tchr 1986-92; Gallaudet Univ Manually Coded Eng by Sign Lang Instr 1988-91; Natl Sign Lang Consultant 1990-; Beverly Schl for the Deaf HS His & Lang Arts Tchr 1994-; *ai:* Sr Class Adv; Stu Newspaper Co-Ed; Curr Advy Comm; Extra- Curricular Sign Lang Tchr; Outdoor Schls Ldr; Convention of Amer Instrs Of the Deaf, Natl Assn of the Deaf, Alexander Graham Bell Assn of the Deaf 1986-; Frederick Cty Svcs for the Hearing Impaired 1988-, Bd Mem; Mid-MD Folk Arts Cncl 1990-, Bd Mem; MD Schl for Deaf Tchr of Yr Awd 1989; Rotary Intnl Schlsp 1985; Lang Intervention Project Fellowship 1992-94; Gallaudet Univ Alumar Fellowships 1992-96; Office of Spec Ed & Rehabilitative Svcs US Dept of Ed Grant 1995-96; *home:* 578 Old County Rd S Francestown NH 03043*

TAYLOR, LORI LYN, History Teacher; *b:* Ravena, OH; *ed:* Miami OH (BP) 1988; Brown Univ (MAT) Tchng; Working on MA in Womens Stud at George Washington Univ; *cr:* The Cambridge Schl of Weston His Tchr 1993-; *office:* Cambridge Schl Georgian Rd Weston MA 02193

TAYLOR, LUCINDA ELEVENA HODGES, Fifth Grade Teacher; *b:* Jamaica, West Indies; *m:* William Benjamin; *c:* Peter D., Wendy O., Paul D.; *ed:* City Coll (MS) Ed 1990, (BS) Ed 1993; *cr:* Balaclava Primary Schl K-3rd Grd Tchr 1953-56; Boston Primary Schl 1st-3rd Grd Tchr 1957-60; Trench Town Primary Schl 3rd-6th Grd Tchr 1960-69; Norman Manley Scndry Schl 7th-9th Grd Eng Lang Tchr 1969-84; All Saints Cath Schl 5th-6th & 8th Grd Tchr 1984-; *home:* 205 Dekalb Ave Brooklyn NY 11205

TAYLOR, MARTHA CATE MIDDENDORF, 6th Grade Teacher; *b:* Nashville, TN; *m:* Robert Lewis; *ed:* Kent St Univ (BS) Ed 1972; Rdng 1990; Attnd Trevecca Nazarene Univ, Univ of TN; *cr:* Geneoa Elem Schl First-Second, Fifth Grd Tchr 1966-76; Austinburg Elem Schl First, Sixth Grd Tchr 1976-; *ai:* Sci Fair Spon; CESAC Sec; Math, Textbook Evaluation Comms; Career Ed Coord; Grd Level Chm; NEA, NEOEA 1966-; OH Ed Assn 1966-, Instrl Advocate; Geneva Area Tchrs Assn 1966-, Negotiations Sec; Intnl Recycling Assn; Right to Read, Geneoa Rep; 99's Intnl 1996; Geneva Womens Club 1979-, Past Pres; Geneva Stud Club 1980-, Past Pres; Delta Kappa Gamma, Past Recording Sec; Fan Assn of North Amer 1996-; Cherokee Pilots Assn; Airplane Owners & Pilots Assn; Pvt Pilot, Commercial, Instrument Ratings; Martha Holden Jennings Fnd Nom; Master Tchr Awd 1973; *home:* 1701 State Route 307 Austinburg OH 44010

TAYLOR, MARY ANNE, English Teacher; *b:* Denver, CO; *ed:* Kutztown Univ (BS) Comm, Theatre 1976; Merrywood Grad Work; *cr:* Bangor Sr HS Tchr, Dir, Adv 16 Yrs; *ai:* Fall, Spring Drama Productions Dir; Class Adv; PSEA, NEA 1978-; NCTE 1980-; *office:* Bangor Area Sr HS 187 Five Points Richmond Rd Bangor PA 18013

TAYLOR, MICHAEL BROOKS, Professor of Mgmt & Ldrshp; *b:* Ann Arbor, MI; *m:* Cynthia Wieboldt; *c:* William, Catherine; *ed:* Carleton Coll (BA) Rel Stud 1966; Harvard Divinity Schl (STB) 1969; Harvard Univ (PHD) Rel Stud 1976; OH Univ (MBA) Mrktg 1984; *cr:* Occidental Coll Asst Prof of Rel 1974-76; Berea Coll Visiting Prof 1976-77; Marietta Coll Prof of Mngmt 1977-; Southwestern Univ Visiting Prof 1986-87; *ai:* Mc Coy Distinguished Prof; *office:* Marietta Coll Marietta OH 45750

TAYLOR, NANCY K., Book Store Owner; *b:* Red Lion, PA; *m:* W. Eugene; *c:* John, Jennifer Small; *ed:* Millersville Univ (BS) Early Elem Ed 1958; PA St 24 Credit IN-Svc Credits, Post Coll Credits; *cr:* Ore Vly Elem Schl 1st Grd Tchr 1958-93; Treasured Tales Paperback Trade 1993-; *ai:* PSERS, YCARSE 1993-; DAEA 1958-, Sec, Bd Mem; PSEA, NEA 1958-; St John's UCC, Choir; Mobile Food Svc 1980-, Bd Mem, Sec; Red Lion Area Women's Club 1975-, VP, Pres, Sec, Treas; Kaltreider Meml Lib 1994-, Sec, Bd Mem; Nom Jefferson Awd, Excl in Ed Awd; *home:* 131 Blymire Rd Dallastown PA 17313

TAYLOR, NANCY KELLY, Secondary Math Teacher; *b:* Syracuse, NY; *ed:* SUNY at Cortland (BA) Math Ed 1965; SUNY at Cortland Permanent Cert; Comp Stud at Various Colls; *cr:* Skaneateles HS Math Tchr 1965-; *ai:* Schl Improvement Team; NHS Selection Comm; Tchr Ctr Rep; NCTM; NYSTA; AMTNYS; St Marys Church 1965-; *office:* Skaneateles Sr HS 49 E Elizabeth St Skaneateles NY 13152

TAYLOR, NORMA SUE, Amer History & Sr Govt Teacher; *b:* Wadsworth, OH; *m:* William M.; *ed:* Kent St Univ (BS) His, Eng 1967; Univ of Akron 20 Grad Hrs; Ashland Univ 3 Grad Hrs; *cr:* Brunswick Schls Elem Tchr 1962-65; Green Local Schls Tchr 1967-; *ai:* Soc Stud Dept Chm; OEA, NEA 1967-; GEA 1967-, Pres 4 Yrs; Jennings Scholar; Tchr of Yr; *office:* Green HS PO Box 218 1737 Steese Greensburg OH 44232*

TAYLOR, PAUL M., Soc Stud, Jrnlsm & Eng Tchr; *b:* Ludlow, MA; *m:* Elaine Bourben; *cr:* Valley Cntrl HS Soc Stud Tchr 1986-87; Frontier Regnl Schl Soc Stud Tchr 1987-; *ai:* Var Bsbl Coach; Frontier Daily Sentinel, Frontier Amnesty Intnl, Frontier as Schls Match Wits; Frontier Tchrs Assn & NEA 1987-; Springfield Union News (Writer) 1989-; *home:* 19 Old Post Rd Worthington MA 01098

TAYLOR, PHYLLIS A., Instructor; *b:* Crystal, WV; *ed:* Berea Coll (BS) Bus 1971; George Washington (BS), (MS) Ed 1977; Western MD 6 Credit Hrs; *cr:* Chopticon HS Tchr 1971-78; Leonardtown HS Instr 1978-82; St Marys Cty Tech Ctr Instr 1982-; *ai:* NVTHS Spon; Charles Cty Comm Coll Part-Time Instr; SMLTA 1971-; MSTA 1972-; MD Bus Tchrs 1975-; NEA 1977-; Hospice 1991-, Treas; Articles Pub; *office:* Saint Mary's Tech Ctr RR 1 Box 49-2 Leonardtown MD 20650*

TAYLOR, PHYLLIS ULRICH, Physical Education Teacher; *b:* Lancaster, PA; *m:* Thomas W.; *ed:* West Chester St (BS) PE 1969; Towson St Univ (MED) PE 1976; 30 Addl Hrs; *cr:* Baltimore Cty Schls PE Instr 1969-; *ai:* Values Comm Chprsn; Stu Tchr Cooperating Tchr; Fac Cncl; *office:* 5th Dist Elem Schl 3725 Mount Carmel Rd Upperco MD 21155*

TAYLOR, RAYMOND L., Sixth Grade Science Teacher; *b:* Rochester, NY; *m:* Wilma Phelps; *c:* Christopher, Steven; *ed:* SUNY at Cortland (BS) Elem Ed 1966; Cooperative Learning Stud; MS Philosophy & Study Team 22 Yrs; Class Size Forum 8 Yrs; *cr:* Medina CS 6th Grd Tchr 1966-67; Lancaster CSD 6th Grd Tchr 1967-; *ai:* Drama Coach AMS 27 Yrs; Voice of Redskins Announcer for Ftbl & Wrestling; Co-chair Class Size Task Force; Lanc Cent Teach 1967-, VP & Grievance; AFT & UNION, Ed; Bowmansville Meth Church 1968-, Cert Lay Speaker & Finance Chm; *office:* Aurora MS 148 Aurora St Lancaster NY 14086

TAYLOR, ROBERT GREGORY, History, Math & Reading Tchr; *b:* Lancaster, OH; *m:* Miriam Ann Cox; *ed:* Salem Coll (BS) Elem Ed 1980; OH Univ Pursuing Masters; *cr:* Switzerland of OH Schls Jr HS Eng Tchr 1980-; *ai:* Coach: Jr HS Vllybl & Var Vllybl, Jr High Bsktbl, Frosh Bsktbl, JV Bsktbl; NEA, OEA & SOEA 1980-; Farm Bureau 1988-; Amer Simmental Assn 1994-; OH Simmental Assn 1994-; Midway Comm Ctr Bd 1995-; Eisenhower Grant Participant; Jennings Scholar; Ashland Tchr of the Yr Finalist; Mentor Pgm Trainee; *home:* 43777 Dogskin Rd Sardis OH 43946

TAYLOR, ROBERT M., Science Teacher; *b:* Needham, MA; *m:* Julie; *ed:* Univ of ME at Farmington (BS) Bio 1989; *cr:* Livermore Falls MS Sci, Math Tchr 1989-; Jay HS Sci Tchr 1990-; *ai:* Var Girls Bsktbl Coach; Jay Tchrs Assn 1990-, Pres; Conservation Tchr of Yr Franklin Cty, St of ME, US Northeast Region 1995; *office:* Jay HS 4 School St Jay ME 04239

TAYLOR, SHEILA SMITHERS, 8th Grade Science Teacher; *b:* Columbus, OH; *m:* Troy; *ed:* OH St Univ (BS) Ed, Hlth 1990; *cr:* Everett MS 8th Grd Sci Tchr 1990-; *ai:* East HS Frosh Track Coach; Drug Free After Schl Prgm Instr 1992-93; UNCF Fundraiser; NEA, OEA, CEA 1990-; Top Ladies of Distinction Comm Chm 1993-; *office:* Everett MS 100 W 4th Ave Columbus OH 43201*

TAYLOR, SKIP, Band Director; *b:* Buffalo, NY; *m:* Lin Bartlett; *c:* Scott, Joel; *ed:* SUNY at Fredonia (BM) Music Ed 1971; Grad Hrs SUNY at Brockport; *cr:* Pembroke Schls Band Dir 1971-; *ai:* Marching & Comm Bands; Jazz Ensemble; Ski Club; PTF 1971-; NYSSMA & MENC 1971-; GWMEA 1971; NYSBDA 1984-; *home:* 2395 Main Rd Corfu NY 14036*

TAYLOR, SUSAN E., Science Teacher; *b:* Woonsocket, RI; *m:* Charles W. Jr.; *ed:* Saint Joseph Coll (BA) Bio 1968; 15 Hrs Grad Work in Ed Admin at Western MD Coll; *cr:* Norwich Free Acad 10th-12th Grd Bio Tchr 1968-70; Catonsville MS 7th-9th Grd Sci Tchr 1970-; *ai:* MESA Adv; Acting Team Ldr; NEA, TABCO, MSTA 1970-; Eisenhower Grants to Attend Sci & Math Confs; Presented 5 MD MS Confs; Natl MS Conf Planning Comm 1996; *office:* Catonsville MS 2301 Edmondson Ave Baltimore MD 21228*

TAYLOR, SYLVIA PAULOO, Photography Teacher; *b:* Los Angeles, CA; *c:* Hadley, Geoffrey; *ed:* Pasadena City Coll (AA) Eng, Art 1955; Pomona Coll (BA) Lbrl Arts, Fine Arts 1957; Claremont Grad Schl (MFA) Fine Arts 1959; 30 Addl Post-Grad Credits; *cr:* The Usdan Ctr for Creative, Performing Arts Painting 6th-9th Grd 1971-75; UFSD #3 Adult Ed Ceramics, Drawing, Painting Tchr 1971-75, 1985; Harborfields UFSD #6 7th-9th Grd Art Tchr 1974-83; North Shore Schls K-8th Grd Art Tchr, 9th-12th Grd Mechanical Drawing Tchr 1983-85; Suffolk Comm Coll Adj Prof Drawing, Painting, Photography 1975-; Huntington HS Art, Photography Tchr 1985-; *ai:* HS Fac-Wide Bldg Comm; Assn Tchrs of Huntington Exec Cncl Cair; Morgioni Meml Photography Awd Comm 19 Yrs; HS Soc Comm; AFT,ATH 1974- Exec Comm; Natl Museum Women in Arts; Womens Caucus for Art; Huntington Twp Art League; Hickscher Museum; Smithtown Arts Cncl; Northport Running Club, Cow Harbor Race Comm Vol; Harbor Hghts Assn; Schlsps Ruth Estes Bissiri Meml Art 4 Yrs, Pasadena Chptr AAUW, Pomona Coll Full Tuiiton; Amer Legion Awd Outstdng Woman Grad; Rembrandt Club Art Prize; Numerous Undergraduate Honorary Groups; Numerous Undergraduate Elective, Appointive Positions; HarshMeml Grad Flwshp; Undergraduate Comprehensive Examination, Distinction, Cum Laude Grad; Grad Resident, Tchng Assistantship; Nom Most Outstdng tchr on Long Island 1993; Tchr of Yr 1993; Model Prgm Wkshp Presenter; Artist-in-Residence 1985, 1986, 1993, 1995; *home:* 87 Glenna Little Trl Huntington NY 11743*

TAYLOR, TIMOTHY ALAN, 5th & 6th Grade Science Tchr; *b:* Newark, OH; *ed:* OH St Univ (BS) Elem Ed 1979, (MS) Environmental Ed 1986; 3 Quarter Hrs; 8 Semester Hrs Ashland Univ; 5 Quarter Hrs MI St Univ; 9 Quarter Hrs OH Univ; 6 Semester Hrs Muskingum Coll; *cr:* North Elem Schl Learning Disabilities Tutor1980; Roseville MS Learning Disabilities Resource Room Tchr 1980-86, 5th Grd Math, Sci Tchr 1986-88, 5-6 Grd Sci Tch r 1988-; *ai:* Sci Olympiad, ECO Meets, Vlybl Coaches; Scorekeeper; Spelling Bee Coord; Scholastic Achvmt Prgm; Muskingum Cty Sci Course of Stud Comm; EECO 1978-, Treas, Findlay-Johnson; SECO 1989-, Friends of SECO; NSTA 1986-; Coshocton 4-H 1988-, Adult Camp Staff; Muskingum SWCD 1988-, Chprsn, Treas, Tchr of Yr Twice; Envirothon 1989-, Chrpsn, Treas; Sci Olympiad St Dir; Sci St & Natl Event Supvr; Buckeye Assn of Schl Admin; Ldrshp Ed Awd Prgm; GTE Growth Initiatives for Tchrs Grant; OH Bd of Regents Grant for Math & Sci Integration; *office:* Roseville MS 76 W Athens Rd Roseville OH 43777

TAYLOR, TINA M., Admission Dir & Eng Teacher; *b:* Barberton, OH; *ed:* Univ of Akron (BA) Scndry Ed & Comm 1991; 9 Credits Toward Soc Ed Masters; *cr:* Hoban HS Eng 9 & Amer Lit Tchr 1991-93, Speech Tchr 1993-95, Rdng Tchr 1994-95, Yrbk Adv 1991- & Dir of Admissions 1995-; *ai:* Ambassador Pgm; Yrbk; Alpha Delta Pi 1986-, Adv; *office:* Archbishop Hoban HS 400 Elbon Ave Akron OH 44306

TAYLOR, WILMA P., English & Drama Teacher; *b:* Cortland, NY; *m:* Raymond L.; *c:* Christopher, Steven; *ed:* SUNY at Cortland (BA) Sec Eng 1966; SUNY at Buffalo (MSEd) Ed 1978; *cr:* Lancaster Central Schl Tchr 1966-68; Clarence HS Tchr 1980-84; Lancaster CS Tchr 1984-; *ai:* Asst Marching Band Dir; Attendance Comm; Mid Schl Drama Dept Costumes, Make-Up; NYSUT 1966-; Lanc Cent Teach Assn 1978-; Lancaster Band Boosters 1984-; Bowmansville United Meth Church 1967-; *office:* Lancaster Central HS 1 Forton Dr Lancaster NY 14086

TAYLOR CHEVALIER, FAYTHE M., Third Grade Teacher; *b:* Erie, PA; *ed:* Indiana Univ of PA (ME) Rdng 1991; *cr:* Chestnut Elem Schl Third Grd Tchr 8 Yrs; *ai:* NEA 1986-; Fairview UM Bell Choir 1986-, Dir; *office:* Chesnut Elem Schl 7554 Chestnut St Fairview PA 16415

TEABO-SANDOE, GLENDA PATTERSON, Retired Teacher; *b:* Otisville, NY; *m:* William L.Sandoe; *c:* Geoffrey Teabo, laura Teabo-Sale; *ed:* Seton Hall Univ (BS) Elem Ed 1970; Canisius Coll (MS) Ed 1977; Addl 27 Post Grad Courses; *cr:* Minisink Vly Cntrl Schl Fifth Grd Tchr 1973-74, First Grd Tchr 1974-95; *ai:* NYSUT, NYS Rdng Assn, ABC Rdng Cncl 1973-; SA Comm Person Church 1970-71, SS Tchr, Deacon, Bible Schl Dir; GSA 1957-, Troop Ldr Brownies; Gifted Comm; Effective Schls Rep; NYS Rdng Assn Mini Grant; Who's Who Amer Ed 1992-93; *home:* 162 South St Middletown NY 10940

TEACH, KAREN L. (MAY), Business Education Instructor; *b:* Hagerstown, MD; *m:* William J.; *c:* Jennifer, Jamie; *ed:* Univ of MD at Coll Park (BS) Secretarial Ed 1973; Shippensburg Univ (MED) Bus Ed 1978; Work Study Coord Cert for Cooperative Office Ed Loyola Coll 1991; *cr:* North Hagerstown HS Bus Ed Instr, Dept Chair 1975-94; Clear Spring HS Bus Ed Instr, Dept Chair 1994-; *ai:* Adv FBLA; Trustee Blazer Band Booster Org; Liaison Rep; Career, Tech Ed Comm; NEA, MSTA, WCTA 1975-; AVA 1990-; Top 5 Tchr of Yr WA Co 1991; *office:* Clear Spring HS 12630 Broadfording Rd Clear Spring MD 21722

TEACH, NANCY, Director of Academic Advising; *b:* Buffalo, NY; *c:* Jessica; *ed:* Colby Sawyer Coll (BS) Bus Admin 1984; Plymouth St Coll (MBA) Mngmt 1993; *cr:* Colby Sawyer Coll Residential Life Dir 1984-89, Admissions Assoc Dir 1989-91, Acad Advising Dir 1991-; *ai:* Club Adv; Ski Tchng; Numerous Comms; NACADA 1994-; NASFA; Staff Employee of Yr; Town Gown Awd; Grad Awd; *office:* Colby Sawyer Coll 100 Main St New London NH 03257

TEACHEY, WINIFRED YVONNE, Kindergarten Teacher; *b:* Jamaica, West Indies; *m:* Robert L.; *c:* Robert D., Rochelle C., Roderick W., Roelan F.; *ed:* Hunter Coll (BA) Music 1957; Adelphi Univ (MS) Rdng, Learning Disabilities 1978; 24 Credits Music Ed Hunter Coll 1958-62, 6 Credits Instrumental Music Tchrs Coll Columbia Univ 1964-65; *cr:* Pvt Nursery Schl Tchr 1957-59; Pub Schl #56 Tchr 1959-73; Pub Schl #59 Tchr 1959-73; Clara H. Carlson Schl 1st Grd Tchr 1973-85; Stewart Manor Schl Kndgtn Tchr 1985-; *ai:* NYSUT 1973-; PTA NY St Congress 1973-, Honorary Life Mem.*

TEAF, LOUISE SPITZNER, 7th Grade Mathematics Teacher; *b:* Brooklyn, NY; *m:* Adrian Randall; *c:* Shane B. Reilly, Erin Reilly White; *ed:* West Chester Univ (BS) Elem Ed 1969; Widener Univ (MS) Ed 1988; Attnd Univ of DE; *cr:* Alexis I duPont Schl Dist 3rd Grd Tchr 1969-70, 7th Grd Tchr 1970-81; Anna P. Mote Elem Schl 5th-6th Grd Tchr 1982-86; Red Clay Consolidated Schl Dist Stu Relations Specialist 1994-95; Stanton MS 6th-7th Grd Math Tchr 1986-94, 7th Grd Math Tchr 1995-; *ai:* Reach Team Ldr; Math Dept Chprsn; New Standards Comm 1988-93; DSEA, NEA 1970-, New Tchr Orientation; NCTM, DCTM 1988-; Phi Delta Kappa 1989-; Amer Orchid Soc 1980-, Horticultural Judge 1993-; Tchr of Yr 1991; *office:* Stanton MS 1800 Limestone Rd Wilmington DE 19804

TEAGARDEN, VONNIE MARIE, Community Service Coordinator; *b:* Pittsburgh, PA; *m:* Robert V.; *c:* Robert J., Sarah, Michael J.; *ed:* Carlow Coll (BS) Psych 1969; WV Univ MSW) Soc Work 1974; *cr:* Youth Dev Ctr Cottage Supv 1970-78; Vision Comprehnsive Prevention Svcs Prevention Specialist 1985-89; Southeastern Greene Schl Dropout Prevention Coord 1989-; Vonnie Teagarden Cnslng Svcs Therapist 1990-; *ai:* Kids That Care Spon; Cert Prevention Specialist 1989; Licensed Soc Worker 1990-; NASW 1995-; Soc Svc League 1980-, Pres; Human Svc Advy Cncl 1993-; Wrote Grant & Coord Dropout Prevention & Comm Svc Programs for Dist & Drug Free Schls Program 1989-92; *office:* Southeastern Greene Schl RD 1 Greensboro PA 15338

TEAGNO, MARJORIE, Sixth Grade Teacher; *b:* Jersey City, NJ; *m:* Dante; *c:* Danielle, Rebecca; *ed:* Glassboro St (BA) Elem Ed 1968; 18 Addl Credits; Attnd Acad for Advancement of Tchng, Mgmt; *cr:* West Ridge Elem Schl 2nd Grd Tchr 1968-70, 4th Grd Tchr 1970-71, 3rd Grd Tchr 1971-77, 6th Grd Tchr 1979-; *ai:* Safety Patrol Adv; PAC, Tech, Sci, Site Based Mgmt Comm; NEA, NJEA, PREA 1968-; Tchr Mentor 1992; NJ Governor's Tchr Recognition Awd 1988; *office:* West Ridge Elem Schl 18 S 1st St Park Ridge NJ 07656

TEAGUE, PETER WESLEY, Superintendent; *b:* Gary, IN; *m:* Paulette Joan Neymeyer; *c:* Robert, Angela, Jessica, Nicole; *ed:* Sterling Coll (BS) Bus Admin & Psych 1973; Luther Rice Seminary (MA) Chrstn Ed 1987; Nova Southeastern Univ (EDD) Ed 1995; *cr:* Skaggs Drug Co Mgmt Trainee 1973-74; Grace & Truth Evangelical Assn Spec Asst to Dir 1974-75; Chrstn Schl of York Dir of Dev 1975-79, Supt 1975-; *ai:* Assn of Chrstn Schl Intnl 20 Yrs; Mid-Atlantic Chrstn Schls Assn, 20 Yrs, Convention Dir; Natl Assn of Todays Prins 15 Yrs; Lancaster Bible Coll 1989, Corp Bd; York Gospel Ctr, Adult Sunday Schl Tchr; Co-Ed Manuar for Chrstn Schl Admins 1988; Workshop Speaker Various Orgs; *office:* Christian Schl Of York 907 Greenbriar Rd York PA 17404*

TEAHAN, KATHLEEN MARY, Teacher; *b:* Brockton, MA; *m:* Robert S.; *c:* Anne Berry, Jean, Robert J., John; *ed:* Bridgewater St Coll (BA) Eng 1969; 30 Addl Credit Hrs; *cr:* Whitman-Hanson Reg HS Tchr; Holy Ghost Parish Rel Ed Coord; E Bridgewater MS Tchr; *ai:* NCTE 1987-; Whitman-Hanson Citizens Schl Fnd 1976-, Pres 1978, School Comm 1978-84, Habitat for Humanity 1995-, Family Selection Comm, Democratic town Comm 1976-; *office:* East Bridgewater MS 435 Central St East Bridgewater MA 02333

TEAMAN, LINDA KAY, 6th Grade Teacher; *b:* Fort Worth, TX; *m:* Robert John; *c:* Juliet Aulisio, Clayton Baird; *ed:* Blue Mountain Coll (BS) Elem Ed 1969; 4 Grad Hrs; *cr:* Palm River Elem Schl 5th-6th Grd Tchr 1969-70; Dayton Chrstn Schls 5-6 Grd Tchr 1979-80; Elyria Chrstn Acad 5-6 Grd Tchr, 12th Bible Tchr 1983-86; North Coast Chrstn Acad 6th Grd Tchr 1987-89, Jr HS Eng Tchr 1989-95, 6th Grd Tchr 1995-; *ai:* Jr HS & Var Squads Chrldng Adv; Stu Cncl Adv; Tutor; *home:* 4003 Oak Point Rd Lorain OH 44053

TEAR, HOWARD H., Science Teacher; *b:* Westbury, NY; *m:* Jayne; *ed:* Purdue Univ (BS) Bio Ed 1963; Hofstra Univ (MS) Bio Ed 1967; *cr:* Herricks Pub Schls Tchr 1963-95; *ai:* MS Boys Soccer Coach; Var Womens Track; Herricks Yth Pgm of Excel Adv; First Yr Sci Tchrs Mentor; AFT & NEA 1963-; Herricks Tchrs Assn 1963-; Masons 1965-; 30 Yrs Svc Pin; *home:* 310 W 72nd St New York NY 10023

TEARS, ELAINE KAYE, Latin Teacher; *b:* Penn Yan, NY; *ed:* SUNY at Albany (BA) Latin 1970; Elmira Coll (MS) Ed, Eng 1975; 6 Post Grad Hrs; Univ of NC at Greensboro 1 Semester; *cr:* Oneida City Schl Dist Latin Tchr 1970-71; Avoca Cntrl Schl Dist Latin Tchr 1971-; *ai:* Jr Classical League Co-Chr Contest; JCL Spon; Classical Assn Empire State 1970-, Past Treas; Amer Classical League 1970-, Natl Comm JCL; NYS Jr Class League 1970-, Past Co-Chair, Treas, Pres Awd 1978, 1983, 1989; ATA; NYSUT; AFT; Alpha Theta Mu; Outstdng Ldr Elem, Scqdry Ed; Amer Biographical Inst; Notable Amers; Delta Kappa Gamma; Article Pub; Testing Adv, Rev Comms; NYS Ed Dept Latin Regents; *office:* Avoca Central Schl Oliver St Avoca NY 14809

TEASDALE, GEORGE F., History & Italian Teacher; *b:* Brockton, MA; *ed:* St Univ of NY at Albany (BA) Italian & His 1990; IONA Coll (MS) Multicultural Ed 1993; *cr:* IONA Preparatory Schl Tchr 1990-; *ai:* Hockey & Forensics Coach; Bookstore Dir; Stu Fac Cncl Mem; Stu Leadership Comm Mem; Natl Forensic League 1982-, Coach, Degree of Distinction; *office:* Iona Prep Schl 255 Wilmot Rd New Rochelle NY 10804

TEBBEN, MARC F., 12th Grd Psychology Teacher; *b:* Lima, OH; *m:* Judy L. Jakes; *c:* Jason, Stacy, Molly; *ed:* Wright St Univ (BS) Comprehensive Soc Stud 1974; Univ of Dayton (MA) Admin 1982; *cr:* Cedarville HS Soc Stud Tchr 1975-78; Centerville HS Soc Stud Tchr 1978-; *ai:* NHS Asst Adv; Racquetball Club Spon; OEA, NEA, OHESS 1975-; Tchrs of Psych 1995-; *office:* Centerville HS 500 E Franklin St Centerville OH 45459*

TEBESCEFF, SERGIO F., Spanish Teacher; *b:* Olbia, Italy; *m:* Andrea Combs; *ed:* Montclair St Univ (BA) Span 1970; Univ of Southern CA (MSEd) Admin 1972; Courses in Counseling at Bridgport Univ; *cr:* E A Cavallini Schl Span Tchr 1972-; *ai:* NJEA 1972-; NJ Foreign Lang Ed Assn 1980-; Former Yrbk Assoc Adv; *office:* Emil A Cavallini MS 395 W Saddle River Rd Upper Saddle River NJ 07458

TEBO, GARY ROBERT, Science Teacher & Dept Chm; *b:* Tampa, FL; *m:* Nancy Lynn Pumphrey; *c:* Ryan, Lindsay; *ed:* Elmhurst Coll (BA) Bio 1968; Western MI Univ (MA) Sci Ed 1973; St Univ of NY at Buffalo Diploma in Cmptr Ed 1988; Buffalo St Univ Coll Schl Dist Admin 1990, Natl Sci Fnd 9 Hrs; Canisius Coll Natl Sci Fnd 8 Hrs; *cr:* Jimtown HS Physics, Chem, Bio & Phys Sci Tchr 1968-73; West Seneca Schls Sci & Cmptr Tchr 1973-; *ai:* Sci Olympiad Coach; Sci Chair; Stock Market Game Spon; Budget, Scheduling & Dist Tech Comms; Prgm Instruction Curr & Assessment Dist Comm; AFT, STANYS, NSTA 1973-; NY St Sci Supvrs Assn 1981-; Ebenezer Church 1973-, Consistory Pres 12 Yrs, Chrstn Ed Bd VP 7 Yrs; CETA Grant for Nature Ctr 1978; West Seneca Schls Tchr of Yr 1978; Nom by Dist as NY St Tchr of Yr 1986; *office:* West Seneca West MS 395 Center Rd West Seneca NY 14224

TEDESCHI, BEVERLY A., Science Teacher; *b:* Bangor, ME; *m:* Frank R.; *ed:* Colby Coll (BA) Bio 1985; Boston Univ (MAT) Sci Eduration 1991; Plymouth St Coll 8 Credit Hrs; Tuft Univ 8 Credit Hrs; Harvard Univ 8 Credit Hrs; *cr:* MA Eye, Ear Infirmary Sr Rsrch Asst 1985-90; Plymouth Regnl HS Sci Tchr 1991-; *ai:* Enviromental Club Co-Adv; Sr Class Adv; FAc Stu Talent Show; Fac Hankbook, Hlth Occupations Comma; NSTA, NHSTA 1991-; NABT, NEA 1992-; Hudson Comm Church 1978-, Deacon; Hudson Post 48 Band 1981-, Prin Flute; Quincy Bog Nature Ctr Rumney 1995-, Naturalist; Amer Red Cross Instr 1991-; Micrcusmos Regnl Wkshp Coord 1993; Finalist for New Outstdng Bio Tchr 1994; Articles Pub; *office:* Plymouth Regional HS 1 Old Wardbridge Rd Plymouth NH 03264*

TEDESCO, JOAN BLACK, English Teacher; *b:* Philadelphia, PA; *m:* Joseph; *c:* Kyle Bronwyn; *ed:* Temple Univ (BA) Eng 1970; Beaver Coll (MED) Eng Ed 1977; Supervision Cert Ed 1993; *cr:* Sulzberger Jr HS Eng Tchr 1970-71; South Philadelphia HS Eng Tchr 1971-82; Masterman Schl Eng Tchr 1982-; *ai:* AFT 1970-; *office:* Masterman Demonstration Schl 17th & Spring Garden Sts Philadelphia PA 19130

TEDESCO, LAURA MISTRETTA, Special Education Teacher; *b:* Oceanside, CA; *m:* Frank Joseph; *c:* Frank Vincent; *ed:* Kean Coll of NJ (BA) Spec Ed 1975, (MA) Spec Ed 1985; *cr:* Newton St Schl Spec Ed Tchr 1975; Monroe Twp HS Spec Ed Tchr 1975-87; Kennedy Park Schl Spec Ed Tchr 1991-; *ai:* Wee Deliver Schl Postal System; Peer Tutor Club; Family Writing; NJ Ed Assn 1975-; Governor's Tchr Recognition Awd Recipient; *office:* Kennedy Park Schl 24 Goodrich St Iselin NJ 08830

TEDRICK, KATHLEEN ANN, Biology Teacher; *b:* Akron, OH; *ed:* Kent St Univ (BS) Hlth, PE 1980; Univ of Akron Bio 1982; 20 Addl Hrs Bio & Cnslng; Cleveland St Univ Masters Comm Hlth Ed 1989; *cr:* Bay HS PE Tchr 1980-81, Bio Tchr 1983-; *ai:* Fac Mgr; Mentor Tchng Prgm; The Natl Fed Interscholastic Coaches Ed Prgm & the Amer Coaching Effectiveness Prgm; Instr N Cntrl Comm Svc Comm; OH Ed Assn, NEA 1980-; NFICEP, ACEP 1991-; Cleveland Regnl Assn of Biological Scis 1992; Amer Red Cross 1990-; *office:* Bay HS 29230 Wolf Rd Bay Village OH 44140*

TEETER, JEFFREY PAUL, Science Teacher; *b:* New Haven, CT; *m:* Jeanne O'Malley; *c:* Grace, Elizabeth; *ed:* Case Western Reserve Univ (BS) Biochemistry 1984; John Carroll Univ (MED) Ed 1990; Case Western Reserve Univ (MS) Biomedical Engrng 1992; Grad Credit Hrs for Validation in Tchng GATE Stdnts; *cr:* Charles F Brush HS Sci Tchr 1990-; *ai:* Stdnts for Soc Responsibility, Silent Sports Club Spon; Tech & Vision Comms; Venture Capital Grant Governance Bd; NEA 1990-; NSTA, ASCD 1991-; *office:* Charles F Brush HS 4875 Glenlyn Rd Cleveland OH 44124

TEGAN, ROBERT FRANCIS, Guidance Counselor; *b:* Cambridge, MA; *m:* Susan Giagrando; *c:* Christa, Tara, Shannon; *ed:* Northeastern Univ (BA) Span 1974; Bridgewater St Coll (MED) Cnslng 1994; *cr:* Cath Meml Schl Tchr, Cnslr 1974-; *ai:* Outdoor Club Adv; After Schl Stud Prgm Coord; Stu Asst Team; NEACAC, MSCA, CSCA 1994-; *office:* Catholic Memorial HS 235 Baker St West Roxbury MA 02132

TEHRANI, ALEX, Science Teacher; *b:* Tehran, Iran; *m:* Maribel; *c:* Andrew; *ed:* Jersey City St Coll (BA) Math 1981; City Coll of NY (BS) Electrical Engr 1984; City Coll of NY (MS) Electrical Engr 1986; *cr:* Bayonne HS Sci Tchr 1984-; Jersey City St Coll Physics Prof 1986-95; Husdon Cty Comm Coll Math Prof 1987-90; NJ Inst of Tech Physics Prof 1992-; *ai:* Physics Club & Sci League Teams Adv; JEEE, NEA, NJEA 1984-; *office:* Bayonne HS 28th St & Avenue A Bayonne NJ 07002

TEITELBAUM, CATALINA MARIE (CINELLI), Second Grade Teacher; *b:* New York City, NY; *c:* Edmond Blanc, Pierre Blanc; *ed:* Marymount Manhattan Coll (BA) Sociology Ed 1955; *cr:* Pelham Pub Schls 2nd, 3rd Grd Tchr 1968-; *ai:* Active Alumnae Assn; League for Svc Pres; NY St Tchrs Assn; Nom Miracle Tchr of Westchester; Pub Newspaper; *home:* 116 Kensington Oval New Rochelle NY 10805

TEIXEIRA, ANN M. MONTAGANO, Graphic Design Teacher; *b:* Brockton, MA; *m:* Joseph H.; *ed:* Univ MA at Dartmouth (BFA) Graphic Design 1985; MA Coll of Art Tchr Cert 1993; Voc Tchr Cert; *cr:* Morse Shoe Inc Graphic Designer 1985-92; J Baker Inc Art Dir 1992-93; Attleboro HS Tchr 1994-; *ai:* NAEA 1991-; MA Tchrs Assn 1994-; Museum of Fine Arts Boston 1988-, Mbrshp; *office:* Attleboro HS Rathbun Willard Dr Attleboro MA 02703

TEJADA, MARIA C., School Social Worker; *b:* Harlingen, TX; *m:* Mario; *c:* Sunshine, Adrian; *ed:* Evergreen St Coll (BA) Soc Work 1975; Univ of WA (MSW) Soc Work 1977; CA St U at Northridge (MPA) Pub Admin All Course Finished Except Thesis; Ventura Coll Admin of Justice Degree 1989; *cr:* Dept of Soc & Hlth Svcs Comm Outreach Worker 1977-79; Continuing Care Svc Branch Social Worker 1978-80; Ventura Cty Mental Hlth Social Worker 1980-81; Ventura Coll Instr 1983-89; Camarillo St Hosp Soc Worker 1981-86, Asst Gov Prog Analyst 1986-89, Asst to Exec Dir 1989-92; Dept of Defense Dependent Schls Schl Soc Worker 1991-; *ai:* 8th Grd Enrichment Stud Hall, PRIDE No to Drugs Club, Peer Mediation Spon; Crisis Mngmt Team Facilitator; NASW 1978-; Future Ldrs of Amer 1988-; Regnl Dir, Exceptional Merit; Na Edctrs of Amer 1992-; Adelante Latina 1991-, Co-Founder, Exceptional Svc; El Concilio 1989-, Bd of Dirs, Exceptional Svc; Future Ldrs of Amer 1986-, Bd of Dirs, Exceptional Svc; Pleasant Vly Schl 1989-, Bd of Trustees; Elected Official Bd of Trustees PVSD 1988-92; Exceptional Svc Awd Escuela de los Estados Unidos Chorillo, Panama; Exceptional Svc Awd Policia Technica Judicial, Ancon, Panama; Merit Awd Future Ldrs of Amer; *office:* Dept of Defnse Dependents Schl Unit 0925 APO AA 34002*

TELFORD, ALTHEA ADAMS, Eighth Grade Lang Arts Teacher; *b:* Providence, RI; *m:* R. Scott; *c:* Adam Wightman, Blaire Chapman; *ed:* RI Coll (BA) Eng, Scndry Ed 1971, (MED) Rdng 1976; *cr:* Barrington MS Lang Arts Tchr 1971-; *ai:* NEA 1971-; Barrington NEA 1971-, Bldg Rep; RI League of MS 1993-94; Wee Care Child Care Ctr 1990-, Bd of Dir; First Bapt Church 1978-, Var Bds, Comms; Champlin Fnd Grant Co-Author; Interdisciplinary Curr Co-Author; Presenter on Various Topics at RI League of MS, New England League of MS, RI Geography Alliance & Barrington Chrstn Acad; *office:* Barrington MS Middle Hwy Barrington RI 02806

TELICKI, DIANNE GALIPEAU, High School English Teacher; *b:* Rome, NY; *m:* Thomas David; *ed:* Stonehill Coll (BA) Eng Stud 1989; Northeastern Univ (MA) Lit & Writing 1991; Addl Grad Credits Fitchburg St; Cert Course Work Salem St Coll; *cr:* Northeastern Univ Tchng Asst 1989-91; Landmark Schl Tchr & Tutor 1991-93; St Bernard Cntrl Cath HS Eng Tchr 1993-; *ai:* Yrbk Adv; *office:* St Bernards HS 45 Ha[...] Fitchburg MA 01420

TELICKI, THOMAS DAVID, High School English Teac[...] Springfield, MA; *m:* Dianne Galipeau; *ed:* Stonehill Coll (BA) E[...] 1990; Univ of MA (MED) Tchng Eng 1992; Addl Grad Credits F[...] St Coll; *cr:* Athol HS Eng & Yrbk Tchr 1992-; *ai:* Track & Field[...] *office:* Athol HS 2363 Main St Athol MA 01331

TELIGA, DARLENE ANNETTE, English & Applied Comm [...] Martins Ferry, OH; *ed:* OH Univ (BS) Eng 1978; *cr:* St Mary Cn[...] Tchr 1978-88, Acting Prin 1987-88; Belmont Tech Coll Inst[...] Belmont Career Center Eng & Comm Tchr 1988-; *ai:* OEA, NE[...] NCTE 1988-; OCTELA 1991-; Iota Lambda Sigma Fraternity 199[...] NASAA; Jennings Scholar 1990-91; OEA Exec Comm 1991-; Di[...] Steubenville Tchng Service Awd; *office:* Belmont Career Center [...] Shannon Saint Clairsville OH 43950

TELL, MAVIS M., Teacher of Talented & Gifted; *b:* Turlock, [...] North Park Coll (AA) 1956; San Jose St Univ (BA) Ed 1958; Na[...] Univ (MA) 1990; Grad Work Univ of CT Summers 1990-95; *cr:* H[...] Elem Schl 4th Grd Tchr 1958-62; Dept of Defense Dependent[...] Germany, Okinawa, Tokyo, Germany 3rd-6th Grd, GATE Tchr 19[...] Stu Cncl Adv, Ldr; Elem Television Station Co-Dir Weekly, Stu-P[...] In-Schl Broadcasts; NEA 1958-; Fed Ed Assn 1962-.

TELLER, SUZANNE DODD, Elementary Vocal Music Teac[...] Skaneateles, NY; *m:* Arthur M.; *c:* Pam C. Bobick, Arthur Max[...] Stetson Univ at De Land (BME) Music Ed 1960; St Univ of NY at [...] (MMEd) Music Ed 1966; 10 Addl Grad Hrs; *cr:* YWCA Y-Teen P[...] 1960-61; Niagara Falls Bd of Ed Music Tchr 1961-; *ai:* Drama C[...] Tchr; AFT, NYSTA, NFT, NYSRS 1961-; AFM 1960-; Delta[...] Gamma 1986-; Western NY Orff-Schulwerk Assn 1973-; Coll Clu[...] 1960-, Past Sec, NF Philharmonic; Music Schl of Niagara 19[...] Trumpet 25 Yrs; Niagara Falls Little Theater Conductor 1994 [...] Church of Christ Scientist 1963-, Vocal Soloist, Lay Reader; Ar[...] Cross Vol Swim Instr; YMCA; Girl Scouts; SPCA; Niag Syn[...] Choruses Performed for Bd of Ed, Sr Citizen Ctrs & Apt Complexes[...] Homes, Local Soc Clubs, Comm Coll; 5 Stdnts Sang on Stage with[...] Rogers; *office:* Harry F Abate Elem Schl 1625 Lockport St Niaga[...] NY 14305

TEMLIN, DENNIS L., English Teacher; *b:* Bethlehem, PA; *m[...]* Liebig; *ed:* Moravian Coll (BA) Eng 1970; Lehigh Univ (MAT) E[...] *cr:* Centennial Schl Eng Tchr, Cnslr 1970-71; Liberty HS Eng Tch[...] *ai:* Curr Revision Project Renaissance, BASD Biling Ed Comms[...] NEA 1971-; US Eng 1991-; Lehigh Valley Chamber Orch 1980-; Al[...] Symphony Orch 1982-; PA Sinfonia 1992-; *office:* Liberty HS 111[...] St Bethlehem PA 18018

TEMONS, MARK J., Science Teacher; *b:* Lock Haven, PA; *m:* Pa[...] Haines; *c:* Mark J. II, Colleen M., Sean G., Laura F., Daniel P.; *e[...]* Haven Univ (BS) Comprehensive Soc Sci, (BS) Bio, General Sc[...] Bloomsburg Univ (MS) Bio 1994; Univ of Rochester 2 Hrs Immu[...] Univ of Eastern WA 3 Hrs Russian Geo; Bloomsburg Univ 24 Hrs M[...] Clarion Univ 3 Hrs Cmptrs in Classroom; Commonwealth Partne[...] Credit Hrs Cell Bio; Univ Rochester 2 Hrs Envir Bio; Penn St Uni[...] Indiv & Family Studies, 2 Hrs Microbiology; *cr:* Millville A[...] Permanent Substitute 1986-87; Bloomsburg Univ Bio Grad Asst 1[...] Bishop Neumann HS Sci Tchr, Dept Chair 1987-92; PA Coll o[...] Parttime Anat & Phys Instr 1991-93; Muncy HS Sci Tchr 1993-[...] Club Adv; Boys & Girls Vars Swim Coach; Var Bsbl Coach; Cla[...] Girls Var Tennis Coach; Girls Var Sftbl Coach; NABT, NSTA[...] Knights of Columbus 1989-; Alumni Choir 1992-; NABT 199[...] In-Service DNA FIngerprinting Gel Electrophoresis; Named Mast[...] by Univ of Rochester; Recognized by Dolores Kohl Ed Fnd for Exc[...] Tchng; Presented Ind Research to PA Acad of Sci & Commonwealt[...] Univ Biologists; PSTA Prsntr; Seiko Yth Chllng Phase I & II Jdg[...] L Envrnmntl Sci Ed Grant; Sci Co-op Prgm to Russia Tchr Ldr; D[...] Cndct Elem & MS Lab Wkshp; *office:* Muncy H S W Penn St Mu[...] 17756*

TEMONS, PAMELA, Science & Technology Teacher; *b:* Olean, [...] Mark Joseph; *c:* Mark II, Colleen, Sean, Laura, Daniel; *ed:* Lock[...] Univ (BSE) Bio & General Sci 1986; Bloomsburg Univ MS Prgm [...] Hrs, Clarion Univ 7 Credits, Lycoming Coll 3 Inservice Program[...] Haven Univ BS in Ed, Houghton Coll Bio; *cr:* Bishop Neumann H[...] & Life Sci Tchr 1987-92; Bald Eagle-Nittany HS Sci & Tech Tch[...] *ai:* Adv & Founder of BENS Environmental Club; Bishop Neum[...] Adv Schl Folk Group, Var Chrldng, Flute Choir, Environmental S[...] NHS Selection Comm; NABT 1986-; NSTA 1988-; St Boniface Folk[...] 1988-; St Boniface Parish Cncl 1992-; NSTA; PSTA; NABT; P[...] Educational Partnership; Seiko Youth Challenge Judge, Phi Beta [...] Statewide Initiative to Scndry Ed, Developed Plant Behavi[...] Response, Bishop Neumann Expo and Sci Fair, Presenter at [...] Meeting of Commonwealth of PA Univ, Conducted Study at W[...] Island Marine Sci Consortium, Beta Beta Beta Natl Honor Soci[...] Kappa Phi Natl Honor Society, Member of President's Comm [...] Retention at Lock Haven Univ, Kappa Delta Phi Natl Ed Honor S[...] *office:* Bald Eagle Nittany HS Ben Ave Mill Hall PA 17751*

TEMPLAR, JUDITH ELLEN, Second Grade Teacher; *b:* Syracus[...] *ed:* Onondaga Comm Coll (AA) Lbrl Arts 1964; St Univ of NY at C[...] (BS) Elem Ed 1966; *cr:* La Fayette Cntrl Schls 2nd-4th Grd Tchr[...] *ai:* Many Comms; NEA 1966-; La Fayette Tchrs Assn 1966-; Exec [...] *office:* C Grant Grimshaw Schl Rt 20 La Fayette NY 13084

TEMPLETON, ANNE L., Mathematics Teacher; *b:* Meadowbro[...] *m:* James V. Jr.; *c:* Mary Elizabeth, Victoria; *ed:* La Salle Univ (BA[...] Mngmt 1983; Beaver Coll (MED) Scndry Ed, Math 1993; *cr:* Hugg[...] Svcs Acturial Asst 1983-84; Bishop Conwell HS Math Tchr 19[...] Conwell-Egan Cath HS Math Tchr 1993-; *ai:* Cross Cntry Coach; JV[...] Mathletes Moderator; Arithmaletes Coord; Arithmaletes Coord; N[...] Cncl; NCEA 1984-; ATMOPAV 1986-; Lawncrest Recreation C[...] Camp Dir 1991-, Asst Dir 1989-; PA Grant to Attend Beaver Coll T[...] Math Cert 1989-92; *office:* Conwell-Egan Cath HS 611 Wistar Rd F[...] Hills PA 19030

TEMPLETON, WILLIAM L., Instructor of Biology; *b:* Wadswort[...] *c:* Jeremy; *ed:* Union Coll (AA) Life Sci 1969; CO St Univ (BS) Z[...] 1970; Rutgers Univ (MS) Zoology 1977; Georgian Court Coll Ed [...] Hrs; *cr:* Brookdale Comm Coll Anatomy Preceptor 1971-92; G[...] Court Coll Bio Lecturer 1991-; Brookdale Comm Coll Bio Instr 19[...] Vol Connection; NJEA, NEA 1974-, Area Rep, Grievance Cha[...] *office:* Brookdale Comm Coll Newman Springs Road Lincroft NJ 0[...]

TEMPLIN, STANTON A.,JR., Earth Science & Astronomy T[...] Lebanon, PA; *m:* Catherine L. Paul; *c:* Stanton III; *ed:* Millersvill[...] (BS) Cmptr Sci with Bio Emphasis 1967; Grad Work Earth & Spa[...] *cr:* Cedar Crest HS Sci Tchr 1967-; *ai:* Track Coach; NEA, PSEA, [...] 1967-; NSTA 1968-; Jaycees 1968-76, Pres 1972; *office:* Cedar Cr[...] 115 E Evergreen Rd Lebanon PA 17042

TENAGLIA, ROBERT C., Spanish Teacher; *b:* New York, N[...] Binghampton Univ (BS) Span & Bio; Middlebury Coll (MA) Span; [...] Work in Authentic Assessment & Comps; *cr:* St John the Bapt Di[...] HS Span Tchr 1987-88; Valley Stream Cntrl HS Span Tchr 198[...]

nd Lang Club & Hnr Socs Adv; LUT 1987-; NYSAFLT 1993-; *office:* ral HS 135 Fletcher Ave Valley Stream NY 11580

CZA, CAROL ESSEX, Fourth Grade Teacher; *b:* Mt Vernon, OH; *m:* Stephen; *ed:* Kent St Univ (BS) Elem Ed 1972; OH St Univ (MA) /, Mid Chldhd 1978; Credit Hrs Towards Masters 30 Plus Lit, spaper Ed, Drug Ed, Cnslng, Rdng; *cr:* Finland MS 6th Grd Tchr -82; East Franklin Elem Schl 3rd Grd Tchr 1982-83; Alton Hall Elem 4th Grd Tchr 1983-; *ai:* Tutor; Soc, BIT, Scheduling Comms; NEA -; OEA, SWEA 1975-; Columbus Ski Club 1978-, Vlybl, Sftbl; 3 Schl Awds; *home:* 4124 Leitrim Ct Dublin OH 43016*

CZA, JAMES A., Mathematics Teacher; *b:* Meriden, CT; *m:* Patricia; ian, Lindsay; *ed:* Cntrl CT St Univ (BS) Ind Arts 1975, (MS) Ind Arts , Middlesex Comm Tech Coll, Weslyan Univ Math Cert 26 Hrs; *cr:* erine Mc Gee MS Tech Ed Tchr 1975-76; Lyme-Old Lyme HS Tech Ed 1976-86; Pratt & Whitney Aircraft Sr Trades Instr 1986-88; Terryville Machine Shop Tchr 1988-89; Haddam-Killingworth HS Tech Ed, Math 1989-; *ai:* Ftbl Coach; Weight Room Asst; Schlsp Comm Co-Chm; , CEA 1975-; H-K EA, CT HS Coaches Assn 1989-; *office:* lam-Killingworth HS Little City Rd Higganum CT 06441

CZAR, MARGARET MARY, Sixth Grade Teacher; *b:* Providence, *ed:* Towson St Univ (BS) Elem Ed 1974; Providence Coll (MS) Elem in 1979; Attnd Univ of RI 6 Post Grad Credits, RI Coll 36 Post Grad its; 6 Addl Post Grad Credits; *cr:* George Street Schl 5th Grd Tchr -88; Bernon Heights Schl 4th Grd Tchr 1989-90; Soc Street Schl 5th Tchr 1990-91; Woonsocket MS 6th Grd Sci & Rdng Tchr 1991-, Sub -Prin 1992-; *ai:* SMART Tchr Trainer of Cmptr Tech Wkshps; nsocket Schl System K-12th Grd GESA, Gender & Ethnic ctations & Stu Achvmt Wkshps Facilitator; Curr Cncl Comm; SAC m Sec; Schl Assessment Curr Comms in Hlth, Sci & PE; NECEL -; AFT 1974-, Former RA Mem; Delta Kappa Gamma Soc 1985-93; r Assn of Univ Women 1980-84, RI St VP; RI Heritage Commission, h Subcommittee 1983-, Pres 1985-87; Quota Intnl 1990-93, Publicity sn; AFT, AFL-CIO Tchrs Guild Outstanding Tchr Awd 1993; RI Elem :ndry Ed Honors for Outstanding Achvmt Awd for Collaborative g; Candidate for Presidential Awd for Excl in Sci & Math Tchr 1995; *e:* Woonsocket MS 357 Park Pl Woonsocket RI 02895*

CZAR, MAUREEN ST MARTIN, Teacher; *b:* Northampton, MA; *m:* ory J.; *c:* Andrew, Jeffrey; *ed:* Univ of MA (BA) Elem Ed 1970; sework Career Ed 1970; Prof Dev Course Literacy Learning, ianship, Navigation, Math; *cr:* Easthampton Pub Schls 5th-8th Grd 1970-76; MA Migrant Prgm 1979-80; Easthampton Pub Schls 5th-8th Tchr 1981-; *ai:* AJHSME Prepare Stdnts; Math Curr Comm; Literacy ; NEA, MTA, EEA 1995-; Citizens Schlsp Fnd 1994-, Bd of Dirs; er Ed Article Co-Author 1970; *office:* White Brook MS 200 Park St iampton MA 01027

OLER FRIED, RUTH, Sci Dept Chprsn & Bio Tchr; *b:* New York, *m:* Sholom Fried; *c:* Leah, Yosef, Yitzchak, Sima; *ed:* Stern Coll for en (BS) Bio Summa Cum Laude 1985; NY Univ (MS) Neurobiology, iology, Dev, Cell Bio 1989; Attnd Michlala Jerusalem Coll for Women -83; *cr:* Nazareth Shaar Amo Educl Leader; Ethiopian Immigrants 1985; Bio Lab Instr 1985-87; Bio Tchng Asst, Lab Instr -87;Samuel H. Wang Yeshiva Univ HS For Gi rls Sci Dept Chprsn, AP Bio Tchr 1989-; *ai:* Life Sci Excl Feldman Awd; Jewish Ethics Lamport Meml Awd; Dean List; Belkin Scholar; *office:* Yeshiva Univ or Girls 86-86 Palo Alto St Hollis NY 11423

EROWICZ, ELAINE FRYDRYK, 11th Grd Social Studies Tchr; *b:* ow, MA; *m:* Stan F. Jr.; *ed:* Elm Coll (BA) His 1972; Amer Intnl Coll Criminal Justice 1977; *cr:* Notre Dame HS Soc Stud Ed Tchr -76; Cathedral HS Soc Stud Ed Tchr 1976-; *ai:* NCEA; Daniel Shays nar Amherst Coll Spon by Five Coll Inc.

NEY, CATHERINE WILLIAMSON, Media Specialist; *b:* sfield, OH; *m:* Robert W.; *c:* Megan, David; *ed:* Miami Univ (BS) Bus 975; Univ of Dayton (MS) Scndry Ed 1988; Wright St Univ Grad ; *cr:* Lehman Cath HS Bus Tchr 1975-84; Jackson Ctr HS Bus Tchr -91, Media Specialist 1991-; *ai:* Jr Class, Prom, Yrbk Adv; Chrldng h; Delta Kappa Gamma 1980-, Pres; JCEA Tchr Assn 1984-, Pres; MA 1991-; Lay Distributor-Holy Angels 1992-; Lehman Music ter 1994-, Sec; *office:* Jackson Ctr Jr-Sr HS 204 S Linden St Jackson er OH 45334*

NEY, CINDY ANSEL, Kindergarten Teacher; *b:* Logan, OH; *m:* glas S.; *ed:* otterbein Coll (BSEd) Ed & Spec Ed 1975; Univ of Dayton Ed) Ed & Rdng 1988; Attnd OH univ, OH St Univ, Ashland Univ, Drake Post Grad Hrs; *cr:* Talmadge Schl 4th Grd Tchr 1975-77, K Tchr -; *ai:* Staff Treas; OEA, NEA, LEA 1975-; Mills Meml U M Church -, Financial Sec; Jennings Scholar; Ashland Oil Achvmt Golden Apple *office:* Tallmadge Elem Schl 611 Lewis Ave Lancaster OH 43130

NEY, CYNTHIA A., Spanish Teacher; *b:* Ft Smith, AK; *m:* Leslie D. ; Jill, Jennifer; *ed:* Houghton Coll (BA) Span, Scndry Ed 1978; Alfred (MA) Ed, Rdng 1983; Attnd Inst Fenix Cuernavaca, Inst de Filologia anica Saltillo Mexico; *cr:* Ansonia HS Math Tchr 1978-79; Allegany Schls Sub Tchr 1979-80; Allegany BOCES Itinerant Span Tchr -84; Belmont Cntrl Schl Span Tchr 1984-; *ai:* Travel Club, Ski Club NHS Selection Comm Fac Mbr; NEA 1984-; NYSUT 1980-84; iont Tchrs Assn 1980-, Past VP; NYS Lang Tchrs 1980-93; *home:* 213 St Wellsville NY 14895

NEY, PAUL J., History Teacher; *b:* Boston, MA; *ed:* Northeastern (AB) His 1964; Tufts Univ (MA) US His 1966; Univ of MA at erst 30 Credits Doctoral 1981-91; *cr:* Brighton HS Tchr 1968-74; son Park HS Tchr 1974-90; Boston HS Tchr 1990-; *ai:* Schl Site Cncl -; Fac Senate Mem 1970-; Boston Tchrs Union 1968-, Bldg Rep 1970-; Fed of Tchrs 1975-, St Convention Del; Org of Amer Historians 1968-; : 281 Belgrade Ave # 1 Boston MA 02131*

NEY, VERNON S.,JR., High School Math Teacher; *b:* Meadville, *m:* Brenda L. Stevens; *c:* Mary Elizabeth, Vernon s Trey, Lewis A. n; *ed:* Edinboro St (BS) Math 1968; Clarkson Coll of Tech (MS) Math ; *cr:* Hornell Schls Math Tchr 1969-; NYSDOT Inspector 1989; Suny d Schl Math Tutor 1985-91, Tech Prep Design Team 1993-; *ai:* NEA; ell Tchrs; Natl Tech Prep Network; AMTNYS; *home:* 7 Maplewood Hornell NY 14843*

LI, JUDITH LADD, 8th Grade Reading & Lit Tchr; *b:* Ft enworth, KS; *m:* Anthony J.; *c:* Tripp Keister, Kristin Keister; *ed:* of DE (BS) Eng, Elem Ed 1967, (MED) Admin 1977; Post Grad; West ter Univ; Temple Univ Doctoral Candidate; *cr:* Baumholder Germany ird Tchr 1970-71; Chesapeake City Elem Schl 6th Grd Tchr 1971-75; n East Elem Schl 2nd Grd, 4th Grd Tchr 1976-83; Cecil Cty Pub Schls E Tchr 1983-86; Elkton MS 8th Grd Rdng, Lit Tchr 1986-; *ai:* Stu Cncl ; AAUW 1994-; Ed Alumni Assn 1993-, Treas; NEA 1967-; Cath ch; Coll of Ed Univ of DE Bd Mem 1993-; Commitment to Ed 1991 Univ of DE; *office:* Elkton MS 615 North St Elkton MD 21921*

FENHARDT, ALICE M., Guidance Counselor; *b:* Jersey City, NJ; *m:* nond; *c:* Jason, Kristen; *ed:* Jersey City St Coll (BA) Elem Ed 1969; d Felician Coll Pre-Sch Cert 1986; Monclair St Coll 21 Credits ards Major Cnslng; *cr:* St Aloysius HS Guidance Dir 1969-70; Our of Victories Grammer Schl Tchr 1970-72; Queen of Peace Grammer 5th Grd Tchr 1980-85; Paramus Cath Boys HS Guidance Cnslr 1986-; *ai:* Advy Cncl Mem; ESL Coord; Bergon Cty Cnslrs Assn; *home:* 119 Wheaton Pl Rutherford NJ 07070*

TERBUSH, MARIBEL, Spanish Teacher; *b:* Madrid, Spain; *m:* Gary Brian; *c:* Tyler, Maria; *ed:* SUNY at New Paltz (BA) Span Second Ed, Psych 1988, (MS) Spec Ed, Migrant Ed 1995; *cr:* Mountain Laurel Schl 1-3rd Grd Span Tchr 1985-86; Arlingtn Schl 8-12th Grd Span Tchr 1988-89; Tri Vly Cntrl Schl 7-12 Grd Span, Eng Second Lang Tchr 1989-; *ai:* NYSUT, AFT 1989-; NHHS, SDP 1986-; Sojourner Truth, Migrant Ed Flwshp.

TERCEK, BETH ANNE, Assoc Prof of Economics; *b:* Cleveland, OH; *ed:* Notre Dame Coll (BA) Soc Sci Ed 1972; Univ of MN (MA) His 1976; Boston Coll (PHD) Ec 1993; John Carroll Univ, Cleveland St Univ, Kent St Univ Postbaccaulaureate Work; Hamline Univ Grad Level; *cr:* St Anselm Schl 7th-8th Grd Tchr 1968-69; St Michael Schl 5th Grd Tchr 1969-73; Notre Dame Coll His, Pol Sci Instr 1973-79, Asst His Prof 1979-85; Boston Coll Tchng Fellow in Ec 1988-90, Notre Dame Coll Asst Ec Prof 1990-93, Assoc Prof of Ec 1994-, Bus Admin Div Head 1995-; *ai:* Frosh Adv; Fac Dev Comm; Reader for AP Ec Exam; Reader for GMAT Wrtng Assessment; Amer Ec Assn; OH Assn Of Ec, Pol Scientists; Economists Allied for Arms Reduction; GESU Parish Choir; Alpha Sigma Nu; North-South Tech Transfer in Context of Intnl Returns to Scale Dissertation; *office:* Notre Dame Coll of Ohio 4545 College Rd Cleveland OH 44121

TERENZIO, MARION ANN, Associate Professor; *b:* Stamford, CT; *ed:* Vassar Coll (AB) Music 1976; TX Womens Univ (MA) Music Therapy 1979; The Sage Grad Schl (MA) Comm Psych 1989; MI St Univ (PHD) Comm Psych 1991; *cr:* Russell Sage Coll Practicing Music Therapist 1977-, Assoc Prof, Asst Prof & Instr 1979-; *ai:* Club Adv; Creative Arts Therapy Pgm Coord; Coll Comm Chorus Dir; Sage Grad Schl Comm Chair; Natl Assoc for Music Therapy 1979-; Soc for Comm Rsrch & Action 1991-, Chair Comm Women; Wosthamerican Assoc for Masters in Psych 1993-, Ed Of Newsletter; Troy Area United Ministries 1994-, Bd Mem, Chair & Advy Comm; Comm Dispute Settlement Pgm Chair; Ethics in Giaber in City of Troy, Mem of Planning Comm; Rensselear Cty Anal of Arts; Distngd Fac Svc Awd 1992; *office:* Russell Sage Coll At Troy Fine Arts Ctr Troy NY 12180

TERESI, RICHARD ANTHONY, Biology Teacher; *b:* Cleveland, OH; *m:* Frances Ann Hruby; *c:* Scott, Johanna; *ed:* Hiram Coll (BA) Bio 1969; Kent St U (MA) Bio 1987; 15 Hrs Bio Credit; *cr:* James A Garfield HS Bio Tchr 1969-; *ai:* OEA & NEA 1969-, Pres; Garrettsville Vol Fire Dept 1972-, Asst Chief, Fireman of Yr (Twice); Stu Body Tchr of Yr Awd; Outstndg Schl Sci Awds; *home:* 7979 State St Garrettsville OH 44231*

TEREZAKIS, EMANUEL GEORGE, Professor of Chemistry; *b:* Waterbury, CT; *m:* Anneken L. Resch; *c:* Erik, Heidi; *ed:* MIT (BS) Chem 1962; Brown Univ (PHD) Inorganic Chem 1967; *cr:* Owens-Corning Corp Advanced Technologist 1967-73; Roxbury Comm Coll Assoc Chem Prof 1973-77; Comm Coll of RI Chem Prof 1977-; *ai:* Mem Advy Bd of Access to Opportunity Prgm, Schlsp, Environmental, Safety Comms; Amer Chem Sco 1963-; Northeast Partnership for Environmental Tech Ed 1994-; *office:* Community College Of RI 1762 Louisquisset Pike Lincoln RI 02865

TERLECKY, DOLORES ANDRES, Language Arts Teacher; *b:* La Coruna, Spain; *m:* Michael; *c:* Michael, Gregory; *ed:* Marymount Manhattan (BA) His, Eng 1972; SUNY at Albany (MA) His 1980; Course Work Completed Doctoral Work; *cr:* Boces Adult Ed Schl Tchr 1984-87; Empire St Coll Tchr, Instr 1986-88; Marist Coll Adj Prof 1986-87; Monroe Woodbury Schl Dist Tchr 1987-; *ai:* Odyssey of Mind Coach 1987-89; Bldg Comm 1993-94; NYS United Tchrs 1987-; Wallkill Wolves Soccer Club 1990-, VP; Friends of Pub Lib, VP; Republican Party Orange Cty 1995-, Comm Person; Fellow SUNY at Albany 1985-87; Noicc Gender Equity Grant 1994-; Project Wild 1995; *office:* Monroe-Woodbury MS Rt 32 Central Valley NY 10917

TERLECKY, PAULA SOOY, English & German Teacher; *b:* Elyria, OH; *m:* Jeffrey P.; *c:* Jared, Seth; *ed:* Baldwin-Wallace Coll (BA) Ger 1972; Youngstown St Univ (MS) Master Tchr 1979; *cr:* Liberty HS Ger Tchr 1974-75; Champion HS Ger, Eng Tchr 1975-; *ai:* Eng Festival Coord; OEA, NEA 1975-; *office:* Champion HS 5976 Mahoning Ave NW Warren OH 44483

TERLIZZI, JAMES VINCENT,JR., Science Department Head; *b:* Malden, MA; *m:* Marianne E.; *c:* James III, Eric; *ed:* Norwich Univ (BS) Bio 1962; Northeastern Univ (MS) Bio 1970; 90 Hrs Post Grad Stud Salem St Coll; *cr:* Kimberly Hall Schl Sci Tchr 1965-67; Seeglitz Schl Sci Tchr 1967-69; Peabody HS Bio & Chem Tchr 1969-71; Peabody Veterans Memrl HS Sci Dept Head 1971-; *ai:* Salem St Coll Collaborative Wkshp Coord; Orienteering Club Adv; AFT 1967-; MA Assn of Sci Supvrs 1973-, Pres 1985, Outstdng Edctr 1987; North Shore Sci Supvrs Assn 1973-, Sec-Treas; Natl Sci Ed Ldrshp Assn 1985-, Membership Chair; NSTA 1987-; New England Orienteering Club 1973-, Bd of Dirs; MA Fulbright Assn 1991-, Bd of Dirs; Fulbright Exchange Tchr 1990-91; *office:* Peabody Veterans Memorial HS 485 Lowell St Peabody MA 01960

TERNASKY, NANCY, School Nurse; *b:* Redlands, CA; *m:* Lance; *c:* Chad, Brooke; *ed:* Crafton Coll (AS) Nrsng 1971; Univ of Redlands (BS) Hlth Sci 1986; Sierra Univ (MS) Psych 1988; *cr:* Alternative Comm Schl Schl Nurse 1988-; *ai:* Women's Hlth & Human Sexuality Courses Tchr; NEA 1988-; *office:* Alternative Comm Schl 332 Chestnut Ave Ithaca NY 14850

TERRACCIANO, BARBARA CLARKE, Social Studies Teacher; *b:* Yonkers, NY; *m:* Joseph M.; *c:* Liane, Joseph R.; *ed:* Herbert H Lehman Coll (BA) Psych 1985; Iona Coll Grad Schl of Ed (MS) Elem Ed 1996; *cr:* St Eugene Schl K-8th Grd Comp Tchr 1985-87, 6th-8th Grd Soc Stud Tchr 1987-; *ai:* Moderator of Stu Cncl; Yrbk Comm Adv; After Schl Pgm Coord; *home:* 25 Hearthstone Rd Yonkers NY 10710*

TERRANA, SUSAN, Choral Director; *b:* Bronx, NY; *m:* Joseph; *c:* Stacey, Robyn; *ed:* Manhattan Schl of Music (BMus) Voice 1965, (MMus) Voice Ed 1967; Addl 60 Credits Beyond Bachelors Degree; *cr:* Bronx Pub Schl 4 Elem Instrumental & Vocal Tchr 1967-73; Reed Jr HS General & Choral Music Tchr; 1973-93; Central Islip HS Choral Dir 1993-; *ai:* Vocal Club; Show Choir; Rhythm Marchers; AFT, NEA, CITA, SCMEA; *office:* Central Islip HS 85 Wheeler Rd Central Islip NY 11722

TERRANO, ROBERT JOHN, Science Teacher; *b:* Medford, MA; *m:* Mary Ellen; *c:* Christine, Robert Jr., Andrew; *ed:* Boston St Coll (BS) Psych 1976; Grad Stud CO Schl of Mines, Univ of MA at Boston; *cr:* Lincoln MS 8th Grd Sci Tchr 1987-; *ai:* Sci Club, 8th Grd Peer Adv; Banquet Chm; NEA, MA Tchrs Assn, NSTA 1987-; *office:* Lincoln MS 215 Harvard St Medford MA 02155

TERRANOVA, LAURA WILSON, Eng, Speech Arts & Drama Tchr; *b:* Jersey City, NJ; *m:* John Joseph; *c:* Raymond Joseph, Elizabeth Theresa; *ed:* Montclair St Coll (BA) Speech, Theatre Ed 1984; *cr:* Jackson Meml HS Eng, Speech Arts, Dramatics Tchr 1985-; *ai:* Lucy N. Holman Theatre Co Exec Bd; Drama Club Adv; NEA, JEA 1985-; *office:* Jackson Memorial High School 101 Don Connor Blvd Jackson NJ 08527

TERRANOVA, ROSE ANTOINETTE, Eighth Grade Math Teacher; *b:* Brooklyn, NY; *ed:* Marymount Manhattan (BA) Math 1971; St Johns Univ Grad Courses; *cr:* Dry Dock Savings Bank Asst Banking Mgr 1970-75, Checking Dept Mgr 1976-78; Harcourt Brace & Jovanovich Bookstore Admin Asst 1979-82; St Adalbert Schl 7th-8th Grd Math Tchr 1983-; *ai:* Afterschl Pgm & Black Friars Theater Group Dir; Pvt Voice Tchr; *office:* St Adalbert Schl 5217 83rd St Elmhurst NY 11373

TERRELL, HENRY ROSS, Calculus Teacher; *b:* Manhattan, NY; *m:* Sandra Troy; *c:* LaShaunda Tania, Corey John Thomas; *ed:* Fayetteville St Univ (BS) Math, Scndry Ed 1969; 45 Hrs Advanced Math, 12 Hrs Micro Cmptrs Trenton St Coll; *cr:* Franklin HS Math, Cmptr Tchr 1969-; *ai:* Head Girls Track, Bsktbl 1974-80 Coach; Video of All Teams in Schl Sports Prgm; Coach of Yr 1990, 1992; Tchr of Marking Period 1990-91; NEA, NJEA, FTEA 1969-; 10 Tape Video Math Series with Work Books 1986; *office:* Franklin HS Amwell Rd & Charles St Somerset NJ 08873

TERRELL, SANDRA TROY, Business Education Teacher; *b:* Whiteville, NC; *m:* Henry Ross; *c:* LaShaunda, Corey; *ed:* Fayetteville St Univ (BS) Bus Ed 1972; *cr:* New Brunswick HS Bus Ed Tchr 1974; Franklin Alternative HS Bus Ed Tchr 1974-77; Franklin HS Bus Ed Tchr 1977-; *ai:* Readmissions & Appeals, FTEA Soc, 1994-95 Mid Sts Evaluation Comms; FTEA, NJEA, NEA 1972-; North Stelton AME Church Pisc 1983-, Stewardess, Schlsp Pres, Edna Morgan Svc Awd; *office:* Franklin HS 415 Francis St Somerset NJ 08873

TERRIEN, GERTRUDE SCHWAB, Computer Coordinator; *b:* Bridgeport, CT; *m:* William R. Sr.; *c:* William R. Jr, Kerry; *ed:* Johnson St Coll (BS) Ed 1967; 9 Credit Hrs St Michael's Coll; *cr:* Lawrence Barnes Schl Tchr 1967-70; Mater Christi Schl Tchr 1973-90, Cmptr Coord 1990-; *ai:* 8th Grd Class Adv; Drug & Alcohol Coord; Tech Task Force Comm; Home & Schl Assn; Organize Spirit Week; VSTC 1991-, Mbrshp Comm; NEA, BEA 1968-; Lib Trustee 1970-; *office:* Mater Christi Schl 50 Mansfield Ave Burlington VT 05401*

TERRILE, PAUL EDWARD, Mathematics Teacher; *b:* Boston, MA; *m:* Laura M.; *ed:* Boston Coll (BA) Math 1985; Univ of Lowell (MEd) Curr & Instr 1990; Natl Sci Fnd Washington DC 1992-94; *cr:* MA Bay Comm Coll Part-Time Instr 1990; Westminster City Schl Math Tchr 1990-91; Andover HS Math Tchr 1991-; Cape Cod Comm Coll Part-Time Inst 1995; *ai:* Amer Field Svcs Club Adv; Broadcaster & Timekeeper for Boys & Girls Var & JV Bsktbl; Broadcaster & Announcer for Var Ftbl; Ofcl at Track & Field Meets; Proctor for S AT Examinations; NCTM 1990-; NEA 1991-; MTA 1991-; *office:* Andover MS Shawsheen Rd Andover MA 01810

TERRITO, CHARLES JAEMS, Math Teacher; *b:* Rochester, NY; *m:* Lesley Hylas; *c:* Keri C., Kristy M.; *ed:* Brockport St (BA) Math 1968, (MS) Scndry Admin 1975; *cr:* Britton Rd Jr HS Math Tchr 1968-79, Dept Coord 1973-79; Greece Athena Jr HS Math Tchr 1979-88, Dept Coord 1981-83; Greece Arcadia MS Math Tchr 1988-90, Dept Coord 1984-90; Greece Apollo MS Math Tchr 1990-93, Temporary Vice Prin; Greece Arcadia MS Math Tchr 1993-; *ai:* Frosh Mens Bsbl, Womens Sftbl Coach; Greece Tchrs Assn 1968-, Bldg Rep, Negotiations Team 1973; NEA, Lifetime Mbrshp; *office:* Greece Arcadia MS 130 Island Cottage Rd Rochester NY 14612

TERRITO, LESLEY HYLAS, Math Teacher; *b:* Teaneck, NJ; *m:* Charles J.; *c:* Keri C., Kristy M.; *ed:* Douglass Coll at Rutgers (BA) Math 1964; St Univ at Brockport (MS) Math Ed 1973; Post Grad Stud Univ of Rochester; *cr:* Britton Rd Jr HS Math Tchr 1966-68; Greece Arcadia HS Math Tchr 1968-79, 1981-; *ai:* HS Math League; Cite-Based Mngmt Team; Cite-Based Schl Comms Crisis, Restructuring, Sexual Harrassment; Greece Tchrs Assn 1967-; NEA, Lifetime Mbrshp; Grad Schl of Ed & Human Dev Awd for Excl in Scndry Schl Tchng 1990; Tchr Most Available for Help Awd 1995; *office:* Greece Athena HS 800 Long Pond Rd Rochester NY 14612

TERRY, JOSEPH BRIGGS, Sixth Grade Teacher; *b:* Troy, NY; *m:* Lois Dogrenier; *c:* Natalie, Alexander; *ed:* HVCC (AS) Lbrl Arts 1973; SUNY at Plattsburgh (BS) Ed 1975; Coll of St Rose (MS) Ed & Rdng 1984; NYSUT Effective Tchng & Discipline with Dignity; *cr:* Lansingburgh Schl Dist Tchr Asst 1975-77, 6th Grd Tchr 1977-; *ai:* Positive Reward Comm; NYSUT 1977-; NYS Historical Assn 1985-; Capital Dist Cncl for Soc Stud 1993-; Knights of Columbus 1978-, Grand Knight 1981; Lansingburgh Elem PTO, Pres 1979-81; Wynantskill PTO 1993-, Pres 1996; Monsignor Mulqueen Memrl Fund Drive (CCHS) Chair 1989; *office:* Knickerbacker MS 320 7th Ave Troy NY 12182

TERRY, MAUREEN YVONNE, Mathematics Teacher; *b:* Williamsport, PA; *m:* Kenneth Eugene; *c:* Kent Eugene, Kurtis James, Brent Allen, Brian Andrew; *ed:* Lock Haven Univ (BA) Scndry Math 1970; Penn St Univ (MS) Ed 1994; *cr:* Spring Ford Area Sec Math Tchr 1970; Delmar Sec Math Tchr 1970-71; Jersey Shore Area Sec Math Tchr 1972-; *ai:* Facilitatotor for SERC Satelite Prgm; SAT Edge After Schl Course; NEA 1972-; NCPCTM 1987-; PCTM 1985-; Tiadaghton Vly Grace Brethren Church 1982-, Spec Music Coord; Jersey Shore Little League 1985-; *home:* RR 4 Box 106H Jersey Shore PA 17740

TERRY, RICHARD MILTON, Asst Professor & Coordinator; *b:* Baltimore, MD; *c:* Christina A.; *ed:* Baltimore City Comm Coll (AA) Legal Asst 1986; Univ of Baltimore (BA) Jurisprudence 1989, (MA) Legal, Ethical Stud 1991; *cr:* Baltimore City Comm Coll Adjunct Fac 1989-92; Morgan St Univ Lecturer 1991-93; Baltimore City Comm Coll Asst Prof 1992-; *ai:* Educl Testing Svc, Cmptr Curr Corp Consultant; AAFPE 1992-; Alpha Phi Omega 1992-, Sec; Encyclopedia Sports Law Article Pub; *office:* Baltimore City Comm Coll 2901 Liberty Heights Baltimore MD 21202*

TERRY, RICHARD ROBERT, Science Department Chairperson; *b:* Ware, MA; *m:* Rita Maiorano; *c:* Richard A., Robert M., Ritalynne M.; *ed:* Worcester St Coll (BS) Scndry Ed 1958; Worcester Polytechnic Inst (MS) Natural Sci 1982; *cr:* Mahar Regnl HS Sci Tchr 1958-59; Marlborough HS Sci Chm 1959-; *ai:* Bd Mem Worcester Regnl Sci Fair; MASS Eductrs Assn 1958-; Marlborough Edctrs Assn 1959-; MASS-Suburban Section 1962-; NSF Grant Georgetown Univ, St Lawrence Univ, Univ or Portland.

TERRY, VICKI (SAAS), Fourth Grade Teacher; *b:* Chicago, IL; *m:* John; *c:* John Jr., Scott, David; *ed:* Northern IL Univ (BS) Ed 1970; Grad Courses; *cr:* Gary Schl 4th Grd Tchr 1970-72; Willowbrook Schl 5th Grd Tchr 1972-73; Marshall Hill Schl Basic Skills Instru 1983-85; West Milford HS Basic Skills Instru 1983-85; Hillside Elem Schl 4th Grd Tchr 1986-; *ai:* Inside Hillside Lit Magazine & Newspaper in Ed Rep; PTO Fac Rep; Tchr Mentor & Cooperating Tchr Rider Univ; Soc Stud Curr Comm; NEA, NJEA, Mt Laurel Ed Assn 1986-; IRA 1991-; NJ Rdng Assn 1993-; West Jersey Rdng Cncl 1991-, Bd of Dirs, Sec, VP, Pres-Elect; First Presbyn Church 1990-; Hand Bell Choir 1990-; Moorestown Home Schl Assn 1986-; Distngd Svc Awd Burlington Cty Times & West Jersey Rdng Cncl 1989; Nom Governor's Tchr Recognition Awd 1989, 1990; *office:* Hillside Elem Schl 1370 Hainesport Rd Mount Laurel NJ 08054*

TERWILLIGER, ALLEN WARD, 5th Grade Team Teacher; *b:* Sussex, NJ; *ed:* William Paterson Coll (BS) Elem Ed 1980; Jersey City St Admin; *cr:* Wantage Elem Schl 4 Grd Tchr 1980, 5 Grd Tchr 1981, 3 Grd Tchr 1982, 5 Grd Tchr 1983-; *ai:* Yrbk Coord Pre-Gr 5; Adv Gr 5 Bowling Club, Art Club, After Care Latchkey Prgm; NEA 1981-; SWEA 1981-, VP 2 Terms; NJEA 1981-; Wantage Grange 1989-; NJ Christmas Tree Growers 1987-; Wantage PTO 1980-, Vice Pres; Gov Recognition Awd NJ 1989; Videotaped Lesson-Dodge Grants for NJ Tchrs Acad; *office:* Wantage Elem Schl 815 State Route 23 Sussex NJ 07461*

TERWILLIGER, CONNIE ANN, Music Director; *b:* Endicott, NY; *m:* Stephen; *ed:* Moody Bible Inst 3 Yr Diploma Frgn Mission 1978; Broome Comm Coll 9 Cr Hrs Gen Stud; Bapt Bible Coll 40 Credit Hrs Music Ed;

cr: Doris Todd Meml Chrstn Schls Music Tchr 1978-82; Cntrl Bapt Chrstn Acad Music Dir 1982-; *ai:* Choir Dir; Girls Var Soccer Coach; Music Comm; *office:* Central Baptist Christian Acad 1606 NY Rt 12 Binghamton NY 13901

TERZINO, JUEI-NI SUNG, Bilingual Social Studies Tchr; *b:* Taipei, Taiwan; *c:* Anthony E., Caroline A.; *ed:* Natl Taiwan Normal Univ (BA) Ed 1978; Brooklyn Coll (MA) Soc Stud 1993; *cr:* Lafayette HS Tchr 1987-; *ai:* Adv of Chinese; UFT, AFT, NYSUT 1987-; *office:* Lafayette HS 2630 Benson Ave Brooklyn NY 11214*

TESLUK, MYRA, Elementary Principal; *b:* Oldham, England; *ed:* Kent St Univ (BS) Elem Ed 1972; Cleveland St Univ (MS) Elem Ed 1979; OH Certs in Elem Supervision & Elem Admin; *cr:* Parma City Schl Dist Elem Tchr 1972-92, Elem Prin 1993-; *ai:* Parma Elem Prins Assn 1993-, Pres; APA, OAESA, NAESP 1993-; *office:* Ridge-Brook Elem Schl 7915 Manhattan Ave Parma OH 44129

TESMER, FLOYD STEPHEN, Social Science Professor; *b:* Grand Island, NE; *ed:* Univ of NB (BA) Psych & Sociology 1971, (MA) Ed Psych 1972, (PHD) Soc Fnds of Ed 1976; Attnd Southeastern Univ, Strayer Coll at Washington DC for Computer Classes; Intensive Practicum Rational Emotive Behavioral Therapy; *cr:* Univ of NB Grad Fac 1974-76; Nat Inst Alcow Ab Alcoh Prin Investigator 1978-80; Shenandoah Coll Asst Prof 1980-83; Southeastern Univ Adjunct Fac 1976-88; Strayer Coll Grad Fac 1985-; *ai:* Fac Spons; Alpha Chi Schlsp Honor Soc; Natl Dean's List Chair; ESOL/HILT Comm Arlington Pub Schls; Univ of NB Alumni Assn; Phi Delta Kappa Sec, Srv Awd; Soc for Advancement of Amer Philosophy 1993-; WN Philosophy Club Pres, VP 1978-; Amer Russian Cult Assoc 1995-; Panel Mem Cable TV Series-No Dogs or Philosophers Allowed; Edited and Revised Works; *office:* Strayer Coll 1025 15th St Washington DC 20005

TESSIER, MARC JOHN, English Teacher; *b:* Manchester, NH; *m:* Diane Courteau; *ed:* St Ancelns Coll (MA) Eng 1976; Antioch (MA) Eng 1986; *cr:* Cntrl HS Eng Tchr 1979-86; West HS Eng Tchr 1986-91; Meml HS Eng Tchr 1991-; *ai:* Drama Club Adv; NEA 1979-, Exec Bd Mem.*

TESTA, JIM, 6th Grd Teacher; *b:* Endicott, NY; *m:* Kendra; *c:* Jacinta, Jeremy, Emily, Nicholas; *ed:* Cortland St (BA) Scndry Soc Stud 1974; 30 Addl Hrs Elem Ed; *cr:* Henry B. Endicott 3rd, 6th Grd Tchr 1977-79; Our Lady of Good Counsel 5th Grd Tchr 1980-83; Seton Cath MS 5th, 6th Grd Tchr 1983-85; Thomas J. Watson 5th Grd Tchr 1985-92; Jennie F. Snapp 6th Grd Tchr 1992-; *ai:* Coach Frosh Bsbl 13 Yrs, Modified Bsktl 4 Yrs, Modified Soccer 1 Yr; NYSUT 1985-; Endicott Teener Leag 1972-80, VP; Endicott Yth Bsbl 1986-89, Bd Mem; Lifetime PTA Mem; *home:* 418 Firth St Endicott NY 13760*

TESTA, LAUREN TUNG, English Teacher; *b:* New York, NY; *m:* Keith L.; *c:* Nicole; *ed:* Queens Coll CUNY (BA) Eng, Drama 1990, (MS) Scndry Ed, Eng 1993; Multiculturalism Classroom Courses; *cr:* B. N. Cardozo HS Eng Tchr 1992-, Advanced Placement Eng Lit Tchr 1995-; *ai:* Research Contest Coach; Dir, Coord Martin Luther King Annual Assembly; Stu Tchrs Cooperating Tchr, Trainer; NCTE 1990-; *office:* Benjamin Cardozo HS 57-00 223rd St Bayside NY 11357*

TESTA, RONALD M., Fifth Grade Teacher; *b:* Boston, MA; *ed:* Salem St Coll (BS) Elem Ed 1973, (MS) Elem Ed 1976; Credit Hrs Rdng Dev Courses, Shore Collaborative ESL Ed, Whole Lang Dev; *cr:* Abraham Lincoln Schl 5th Grd Tchr; *ai:* Adv 5th Grd Afterschool Italian Lang & Culture Club; NEA 1972-, Bldg Rep; RTA 1972-, Bldg Rep; Schl Improvement Cncl 1992-, Tchr Mem; Bldg Based Support Team 1993-, Chprsn; Horace Mann Grant Tchr 1988-90; *office:* Abraham Lincoln Schl 68 Tuckerman St Revere MA 02151*

TESTA, VINCENT SAMUEL, Health & Phys Ed Teacher; *b:* Greensburg, PA; *m:* Diane Joan Byrne; *c:* Domenic, Catrina; *ed:* Lock Haven St Coll (BS) Hlth, PE 1983; 25 Grad Credits Penn St Hlth Sci; *cr:* Clearview Jr HS Hlth, PE Tchr 1983-89; Trafford MS Hlth, PE Tchr 1989-; *ai:* Head Wrestling Coach 7 Yrs; Penn Trafford Ed Assn, PA St Ed Assn 1989-; NJ Ed Assn 1983-; NEA; PA Wrestling Coaches Assn 1989-, Coach of Yr 1995, Section & WPIAL; Westmoreland Cty Coaches Assn 1989-; Section I-AAA Coach of Yr 1995; WPIAL-AAA Coach of Yr 1995; Nom PA Coach of Yr 1995; *office:* Trafford MS 100 E Brinton Ave Trafford PA 15085

TESTAGROSSA, PETER MICHAEL, Mathematics Teacher; *b:* New London, CT; *m:* Eileen F.; *c:* Mark, Kerry; *ed:* Northeastern Univ (BS) Math Ed 1971; Fairfield Univ (MA) Ed Admin 1975; Southern CT St Univ CAGS Ed Admin 1981; *cr:* Stoughton Jr HS Math Tchr 1971-72; Jonathan Law HS Math Tchr 1972-74; Central CT St Univ Adjunct Math Instr; Foran HS Math Tchr 1974-; *ai:* Head Girls Soccer, Asst Golf Coach; Soph Class Adv; NEA 1975-; *office:* Joseph A Foran HS 80 Foran Rd Milford CT 06460*

TESTO, PATRICIA LOONAN, Art Teacher; *b:* Albany, NY; *m:* Michael J.; *c:* Zachary; *ed:* Sage Jr Coll of Albany (AAS) Fine Arts & Painting 1980; Coll of St Rose (BS) Fine Arts & Painting 1982; St Univ of NY at Albany (MFA) Fine Arts & Painting 1985; 15 Credit Hrs of Ed Courses Cert; *cr:* Albany Acad for Girls Mid & Upper Grd Art Tchr 1985-86; Sage JCA Summer HS Art Waterbase Painting Tchr 1995-; Doane Stuart Schl Pre K-12th Grd Art Tchr 1991-; *ai:* Co-Chair of HS Art Exhibit; Troy Riverfront Arts Fest Sponsored by Rensselaer Cty Cncl for the Arts; Sage Jca Alumni Assn 1993-, VP & Distngd Alumni Awd 1994; Federated Bd Womans Caucus for Art Albany Chptr 1994-, Vice Co-Chair Mbrshp Chair 2 Yr; Sunshine Golob Awd from Mohawk Hudson Regnl 1995; RCCA Fence Show Merit Prize 1995; Landscape Exhibit 1st Prize at Cantebury Gallery 1995; Mrs T Awd 1995 Stu Awded Pgm; RCCA Spcl Opportunity Stipend 1991; Street Painting Festival 1989, 1990, & 1993; SUNYA Benevolant Awd; CSR Outstdng Scholar Awd; JCA Fine Arts Awd; *office:* Doane Stuart Schl Rt 9 W Albany NY 12202

TESTO, ROBERT MICHAEL, Third Grade Teacher; *b:* Bridgeport, CT; *ed:* (BSBA) Bus Admin 1970; (MS) Elem Ed 1973;(CAS) Elem Ed 1975; (CAS0 Gen Ed 1976; Univ of Bridgeport (MS) Scndry Ed 1978, (CAS) Scndry Ed 1979; Dowling Coll (MS) Ed Asmin 1988; Working on PHD Berne Univ Elem Ed, Early Chldhd; Univ of Bridgeport 8th Yr Inststruction 1980; 7th Yr Open Ed Curr 1977; *cr:* Fairfield Pub Schls Elem Tchr 1975-; Greens Farm Acad Elem Tchr 1977-79; *ai:* Stu Cncl Adv Grds 3, 4 & 5 1993-; FEA, CEA, NEA 1975-; Fairfield Hlth Dept First Aid Trng, Elem Schl Level 1994-; British Ed 1975-79; St of CT Tchng Certs; *home:* 171 Fulling Mill Ln S Fairfield CT 06430*

TETLAK, JOHN CHARLES, Science Teacher; *b:* Pittston, PA; *m:* Marion Roseanne Monteforte; *c:* Jesse, Joy, John O.; *ed:* Kings Coll (BS) Bio 1967; East Stroudsburg (MS) Ecology 1971; *cr:* Pittston Area HS Bio, Ecology & Zoology Tchr 1967-; *ai:* Var Cross Cntry Coach; Environmental Awareness Club Adv; 9th Grd Bsbl Coach; NSTA 1976-; Luzerne Cty Sci Tchrs 1976-; Pittston Area Fed of Tchrs 1973-; Dupont Little League 1977-, Sec, Coach; 4 League Championships; Elm Street Sportsmens Club 1989-, Bd of Dirs; Duryea Veterans of Foreign Wars 1993-; Polish Amer Citizens Club 1977-; *home:* 99 Florence St DuPont PA 18641

TETRAULT, WENDY L. (SCHMID), Fifth Grade Teacher; *b:* Hartford, CT; *m:* Gerald E.; *c:* Michael J., Kristaine A., Matthew J.; *ed:* Plymouth St Coll (BSE) Elem Ed-Summa Cum Laude 1991; 3 Grad Credits Tchr Effectivenes Training; 1 Grad Credit Lesley Coll Math; 3 Grad Credits UNH Improvement of Classroom Instruction; *cr:* Highland Goffes Falls 4th-6th Grd Intermediate Tchr 1971-; NH Marine Patrol 1st Female Boat Inspector, Dispatcher, Admin Asst to Chief & Dist Supvrs 1974-; *ai:* NEA 1971-; Kappa Delta Pi 1970-; Apple Manchester Users 1987-, VP, Sec; Poem Pub in Natl Lib of Poetry 1996; *office:* Highland-Goffes Falls Elem Sch 2021 Goffs Falls Rd Manchester NH 03103

TEUFEL, JEAN DOUGLAS, Retired Fourth Grade Teacher; *b:* Orange, NJ; *m:* Albert L.; *c:* Lynn Lucas, Albert J., Robin Samoilow; *ed:* Keane Coll (BA) Elem Ed 1967; *cr:* Franklin Schl Fourth, Fifth Grd Tchr 1967-93; *ai:* NEA, NJEA 1967-; Alpha Delta Kappa 1975-; *home:* 989 Roosevelt Ave Union NJ 07083

TEUKOLSKY, ROSELYN, Math & Cmptr Sci Teacher; *b:* Johannesburg, South Africa; *m:* Saul; *c:* Rachel, Lauren; *ed:* Univ of Witwatersrand at Johannesburg (BS) Math & Chem 1969; Cornell Univ (MS) Math Ed 1976; *cr:* Waverley Girls HS Math Tchr 1970-71; San Gabriel HS Math Tchr & Dept Chair 1971-74; Ithaca HS Math Tchr 1979-; *ai:* Math Team Coach 1985-; NEA 1974-; NCTM 1971-; Co-Author NCTM Math Yrbk 1987; Edith May Sliffe Awd 1988; *office:* Ithaca HS 1401 N Cayuga St Ithaca NY 14850

TEWANGER, BONNIE LOU, Third Grade Teacher; *b:* Canton, OH; *ed:* Kent St Univ (BS) Elem Ed 1970; 18 Hrs Past BS; *cr:* Plain Center Schl 2nd-3rd Grd Tchr 1970-78; Avondale Elem Schl 3rd Grd Tchr 1978-; *ai:* NEA, OH Ed Assn, Plain Local Tchrs Assn 1970-; North Canton Alumni Assn 1990-, Historian; Community Christn Church 1947-, Various Jobs; *office:* Avondale Elem Schl 3933 Eaton Rd NW Canton OH 44708*

TEXTER, LYNNE A., Assoc Prof Comm, Asst Dept Chm; *b:* Rochester, NY; *ed:* Ithaca Coll (BS) Television, Radio 1984; Syracuse univ (MS) Pub Relations 1985; St Univ NY at Buffalo (PHD) Comm 1990; *cr:* LaSalle Univ Assoc Prof of Comm, Asst Dept Chair 1989-; *ai:* Comms; WEXP-AM Adv; Speech Comm Assn 1987-; Habitat for Humanity; Rails to Trails Assn; Book: Advanced Interpersonal Communication 1995; Articles Pub; *office:* La Salle Univ 1900 W Olney Ave Philadelphia PA 19141*

THAINE, MICHAEL J., Instrumental Music Teacher; *b:* Albion, NY; *m:* Susan E. Collins; *c:* Abigail Grace; *ed:* SUNY at Fredonia (BM) Music Ed 1990; SUNY Coll at Brockport (MA) Lbrl Stud 1996; *cr:* Greenwood Cntrl Schl Dist Instrumental Music Tchr 1991-92; Prattsburgh Cntrl Schl Dist Instrumental Music Tchr, Dir of Music Dept 1992-; *ai:* Marching Band, Jazz Ensemble; Tchrs Assn Fund Raising Comm; Coord, Dir of Pageant of Bands; Music Edctrs Natl Conf 1987-; NY St Schl Music Assn 1990-; NY St Band Dirs Assn 1995; NEA 1992-; Naples First Bapt Church; Greenwood Cntrl Schl Tchr of Yr 1991-92; *home:* PO Box 620 Naples NY 14512

THAISZ, LESIA PRIME, Physics & Chemistry Teacher; *b:* Amsterdam, NY; *m:* Robert F.; *c:* Peter M., Jill M.; *ed:* Syracuse Univ (BA) Chem 1974, (BA) Ed 1974; Elmira Coll (MS) Ed 1977; *cr:* Stratford Central Schl 7-12 Grd Sci Tchr 1976-80; Tryon Residential Ctr Soc Stud Tchr 1990-92; Gloversville Schl Sci Tchr 1992-; *ai:* Adv Bio Club; Co-Coach Sci Team; Natl Sci Supvrs 1976-; NYSSTA 1992-; Lib Bd 1982-; YMCA 1980-; Amer Univ Women 1995-; *office:* Gloversville HS 199 Lincoln St Ext Gloversville NY 12078*

THANGAM, SIVA, Professor of Mechanical Engrng; *b:* Erode, TN; *ed:* Univ of Madras India (BE) Mechanical Engrng 1971; Rutgers Univ (PHD) Mechanical Engrng 1980; Indian Inst of Tech MTech Mechanical Engrng 1973; *cr:* Stevens Inst of Tech Asst Prof 1980-84, Assoc Prof 1984-90, Prof 1990-; NJ Space Grant Consortium Dir 1993-; *ai:* ASHRAE Stu Chptr Adv; AIAA Stu Chptr Co-Adv; ASME 1980-; Sigma Xi 1980-, Life Mem; APS 1980-, Life Mem; ASHRAE 1985-; AIAA 1986-; ASEE 1986-; NJ Space Grant Consortium 1992-; Numerous Rsrch Publications, Awds, Rsrch Grants & Contracts; *office:* Stevens Inst Of Tech Castle Point on Hudson Hoboken NJ 07030

THANOPOULOS, ANTHONY NICHOLAS, Chemistry Teacher; *b:* Troy, NY; *ed:* SUNY at Albany (BS) Bio & Chem, (MS) Rdng; *cr:* Watervliet Elem Schl Sci Tchr 5 Yrs; Averill Park HS Chem Tchr 2 Yrs; *ai:* NHS Dir; Scheduling, Risk Safety & Mgmt & Combat Stu Drugs & Alcohol Comm; Chem Hygiene & Safety Ofcr; NSTA 1992-; NYSUT 1993-; AFT 1994-; Watervliet Elks Club 1993-, Esteemed Leading Knight; *office:* Averill Park HS 146 Gettle Rd Averill Park NY 12018

THARP, SUSAN DUFOUR, Title 1 Teacher; *b:* Conneault, OH; *m:* Stephen P.; *c:* Ashley, Mackenzie; *ed:* Edinboro St Coll (BA) Elem Ed 1983; Youngstown St Univ Masters Early Chldhd 1996; *cr:* Conneaut Area City Schls Elem Tchr 1983-; *ai:* Parent Tchr Cncl; NEA, OEA 1984-; *office:* Conneaut Area City Schls 836 Main St Conneaut OH 44030

THATCHER, BONNIE L., Mathematics Teacher; *b:* Van Wert, OH; *m:* Brett; *c:* Bryn, Brock; *ed:* Saint Francis Coll at Ft Wayne (BS) Elem Ed 1978, (MS) Elem & Spec Ed 1983; Less Canter Courses Math & the Minds Eyes at Portland St Coll; *cr:* Pleasant Elem Schl 1st Grd Tchr 1978-90; Anthony Wayne Elem Schl 6th Grd Tchr 1990-95; Lincoln Jr HS Math Tchr 1995-; *ai:* Renaissance & Intervention Assistance Teams; Mentor for New Tchrs; Van Wert City Ed Assn 1978-, VP; OH Fed of Tchrs 1980-, St Standing Comm, Educl Issues & Civil Rights; AFT 1980-, Mem; NCTM 1994-, Mem; First United Meth Church 1966-, Admin Bd; YMCA, YWCA 1986-, Mem; OH Governors Comm on Inservice Ed 1983-, OFT Rep; Martha Holden Jennings Fnd Grant for Tchrs of Math; Roger K Thompson Self-reliance Awd Winner; *home:* 819 State St Van Wert OH 45891

THATCHER, CAROLEE MARY, Developmental Reading Teacher; *b:* Pittston, PA; *m:* Richard Lee; *c:* Chad; *ed:* Mansfield Univ (BS) Elem Ed 1964; Post Grad Stud Towson St Coll, Univ of MD 1965-75; MA Equivalency, MD Advanced Prof Cert 1975; Post Grad Stud Rdng Mansfield Univ 1975-77; PA St Cert Rdng Specialist 1977; *cr:* Anne Arundel Cty Schls 5th, 6th Grd Classroom Tchr, 2nd Grd Rdng Tchr 1964-75; Williamsport Area Schl Dist Elem Rdng Specialist 1975-77; Lycoming Cty Schls Sub Tchr 1979-84; Jeresey Shore Schl Dist 8th Grd Dev Rdng Tchr 1985-; *ai:* Yth Experiencing Success Adv; Young Environmentalists Adv; Schl Decorating Club Adv; Acad Awds Comm; Drug, Alcohol Awareness Cncl; Stu Cncl Adv; Odyssey of Mind Comm; Majorette, Silks, Color Guard Adv; Natl Tchr Day Comm; Pepper Awds Comm; NEA; Psea; Laubach Literacy Project; Lycoming Audubon Soc, Wetlands Chair, Bd of Dir; Lycoming Cty Police Camp Cadet Dir, Pub Relations, Bd of Dir; Lycoming Cty Brotherhood, Holocaust Remembrance Chair, Bd of Dir; *home:* RR 2 Box 349 Cogan Station PA 17728*

THATCHER, CYNTHIA MACQUAIDE, High School English Teacher; *b:* Orange, NJ; *m:* Joseph R.; *ed:* Georgian Court Coll (BA) Eng Ed 1985; State Cert Lib Media Specialist Jersey City Coll & Montclair St Coll 1992; *cr:* Cntrl Rgnl HS Eng Tchr 1985-; *ai:* NJEA 1985-; CREA 1985-; Superior Tchr Awd 1994-95; *office:* Central Regional H S Forest Hills Pkwy Bayville NJ 08721

THAYER, ADRIENNE B., World Languages Teacher; *b:* Newark, NJ; *m:* Richard; *c:* Eric, Kimberly; *ed:* Rutgers Univ (BA) Span 1964; Coll of St Elizabeth (MA) Ed 1995; *cr:* Cartenet HS World Lang Tchr 1964-68, 1969-70; Upward Bound Schl Span Tchr 1968-70; Montville Twshp World Lang Tchr 1977-; *ai:* Adv World Lang Club; Core Team; Schl Site Mngmt Comm; HS Mentoring Prgm; NEA, NJEA, FLTNJ 1964-; Presidential Tchr Awd 1986; *office:* Montville Township HS 100 Horseneck Rd Montville NJ 07045*

THAYER, ALLAN RICHARD, Drafting & Design Tech Tchr; *b:* Erie, PA; *m:* Shelley Owens; *c:* Kristen, Laura, Kimberly; *ed:* CA St Coll (BA) Industrial Art Tech 1974; Edinboro St Coll (M) Schl Admin 1981; Elem Prin Cert 1988; Scndry Prin Cert 1989; IN St Voc Cert Drafting Tech *cr:* Wilson MS Industrial Arts & Drafting 1974-75; Strong Vincent Sr Industrial Arts & Comm Tech Tchr 1975-89; Cntrl Sr High Vocati Drafting & Design Tech Tchr 1989, Acting Asst Prin Temporory 199 PSEA & NEA 1974-, Fac Rep; Prof Photographers of Amer 1984-, Merit Awd 1989 & 1990; Phi Delta Kappa 1990-, Historian & Alte Del; Article Pub; *office:* Central H S 3325 Cherry St Erie PA 16508

THAYER, GEORGE HOWARD, Band Director; *b:* Conneaut, OH Debra Lee Zappitelli; *c:* James, Tony; *ed:* OH Univ (BME) Music Ed Ashland Univ (MA) Admin 1995; *cr:* Fredericktown HS Band Dir 197 Lexington HS Band Dir 1983-84; Fairfield Union HS Band Dir 198 Highland HS Band Dir 1987-; *ai:* Marching, Pep, Jazz Bands Dir; 1977-, Local Pres; MENC 1977-; *office:* Highland HS 6506 St R Sparta OH 43350

THAYER, JOAN STEWART, Retired Third Grade Teacher; *b:* Pittsb PA; *m:* Lester C.; *c:* Pamela Thayer Smith, Daniel L.; *ed:* Un Pittsburgh (BS) Elem Ed 1958; Addl 6 Post Grad Credits; CA Univ 6 Credits; *cr:* Locust Grove Elem Schl First, Second Grd Tchr 195 Whitaker Elem Schl Third Grd Tchr 1975-78; Walnut Grove Elem Second Grd Tchr 1979-80; Clara Barton Third Grd Tchr 1980-93; *ai:* PSEA 1958-69, Rec Sec; WMFT 1975-93, Sec; Delta Kappa Ga 1989-, Corresponding Sec; Mon Valley Consortium Grants; *home:* Fleetwood Dr West Mifflin PA 15122

THAYER, M. SUSAN, Fourth Grade Teacher; *b:* E Liverpool, OH Thomas F.; *c:* Tena A., Julie A.; *ed:* West Liberty St Coll (BA) Scndr Soc Stud Comprehensive 1973, (BA) Elem Ed 1986; WV Univ Grad 24 Hrs; St of OH 12 Continuing Ed Hrs; *cr:* Hancock Cty Bd of Ed Tchr 1973-86; St Aloysius Schl 7th Grd Tchr 1986-94, 4th Grd Tchr 1 *ai:* In Charge of Schl Spelling Bee, 8th Grd Schl Newspaper Publica NCEA 1986-; Columbiana Cty Rdng Assn 1993-; Alpha Delta K 1992-; *office:* St Aloysius Schl 355 W 5th St East Liverpool OH 439

THAYER, MARILYN M., German Teacher; *b:* Cortland, NY; *m:* R J.; *c:* Erik, Scott; *ed:* SUNY at Oswego (BA) Ger 1969, (MS) Ed 1972; Grad Work in Elem Ed & Jrnlsm; Fl Ed; *cr:* Mexico HS Schl Ger 1969-; *ai:* GAPP Coord 1980-; Variety Show Adv 1980-; Ger Club 1969-; Ger Folk Dance Instr 1975-91; Indoor Soccer Coach 1993-; Adv 1978-82; AATG 1969-, Pres, VP, Sec; NYSAFLT 1972-, Distingui Tchrs Awd 1989, Goethe House Cert of Merit 1985; FLACNY 1 Mexico Youth Soccer Assn 1986-, Pres 1989-91; Delta Epsilon Phi 1 Adv; NYSAFLT, Tchr Ctr & AATG Grants; AASG Service Awd; o Mexico H S Main St Mexico NY 13114

THEEMAN, SUSAN S., Math & Computer Literacy Instr; *b:* Buffalo, *m:* Frank C.; *c:* Michael, Carolyn, Mark; *ed:* Canisius Coll (BA) Ma Math Ed 1975; Erie Comm Coll N (AAS) Ophthalmic Dispensing SUNY at Buffalo (MA) Math Instruction 1982; 15 Grad Credit Hrs Robert Optical Opthalmic Dispenser, Contact Lens Practitioner 197 Villa Maria Coll Math Instr 1976-77; Sacred Heart Acad Math 1978-79; Hamburg Jr High Math Tchr 1979-80; SUNY Gifted Pgm Instr 1983-90; Erie Comm Coll N Opthalmic Dispensing Instr 198 Math & Comp Literacy Instr 1989-; *ai:* AMTNYS; NYS Soc of Opti 1976-, Treas; Contact Lens Soc of NYS 1976-, Dir, Treas; YMCA 1 St Benedict Home & Schl Assn 1985-, Sec & Bd Mem; St Ben Extended Day Pgm 1988-, Pres & Dir; St Josephs Collegiate Inst Pa Guild 1994-; *office:* Erie Comm Coll North Cmps 6205 Mai Williamsville NY 14221

THEILEMANN, RUTH MORRIS, K-5th Grd Music Teacher; *b:* Bal Spa, NY; *m:* Peter J.; *c:* Megan E.; *ed:* SUNY at Fredonia (BS) Musi 1974; 35.5 Hrs Music Grad Stud; *cr:* Private Clarinet Instruction 197 Univ of VT at Burlington Music Cnslr, Librn, Band Mgr 1971-74; Rd Elem Schl K-5 Vocal, General Music Tchr, Chorus Dir 1974-; *ai:* NYSUT, NEA 1974-; Saratoga All Cty Music Educators 197 Saratoga-Potsdam Chorus Performing with Philadelphia Orch Eu Ormandy Dir 1975-80; *office:* Wood Road Elem Schl Wood Rd Bal Spa NY 12020

THEILLE, ANTHONY, English Teacher; *b:* New York, NY; *ed:* H Coll (BA) Eng 1968; Univ of ME (MS) Rdng & learning Disabilities Boston Univ (EDD) Eng Ed 1990; Univ of NH Post-Grad Stud Theor Linguistics & Math Logic; *cr:* Whitefield Schl 6th Grd Tchr 197 Westbrook Jr High 8th Grd Eng Tchr 1972-74; Westbrook HS Lea Disabilities Tchr 1974-76; Portsmouth MS 7th Grd Eng Tchr 1977- Schl Wide Comm on Discipline; Tchrs Negotiating Team; NEA 1 NCTE 1973-; IRA 1974-; Fund for Excl in Ed Grant & Excl in Ed Av

THEISEN, SUZANNE PETRELLA, English Teacher; *b:* Youngst OH; *m:* David; *c:* Steven, Jennifer Cherilyn; *ed:* Youngstown St Univ Eng, Speech & Theater 1971; Post Grad Stud at Kent St Univ, Wrig Univ; *cr:* Mentor HS Eng Tchr & Lit Magazine Adv 1971-72; St Jos HS Eng Tchr & Newspaper Adv 1972-74; Stow-Munroe Falls HS Eng Speech & Debate Coach 1990-; *ai:* Speech & Debate; Chess; Natl For League 1991-, Diamond Coach; Stow Tchrs Org 1991-; PTO 1 Outstdng Edctr; Natl Endowment of the Arts Grant; Natl Forensic Le Single Diamond 1996; *office:* Stow HS 3227 E Graham Rd Stow OH 4

THEISS, SHEILA TILBROOK, County Schl Bd Mem & Sub Tch Warren, OH; *m:* John Samuel; *c:* Laura Theiss Goodyear; John T., Jo E., Jay S., Rebecca Theiss Acheson; *ed:* Ohio St Univ (BS) Hlth, 1956; Attnd Ohio Univ 1978-79, Miami Univ 1990; *cr:* Edenton Schls First Elem Phys Ed Prgm Tchr 1962-63; Athen City Schls H Tchr 1973; Alexander Local Schls 5, 6, 7, 8th Grd Tchr 1979-95; C Svc Ctr Bd Mem, Area Sub; *ai:* Working as Elected Ofcl; Natl Assn o Stud 1985-; Ohio Geographic Alliance 1991-; Alexander Future Fnd 1 Eisenhower Grant; Martha Holden Jennings Scholar 1982-83; Ex Tchng of Ec Awd 1983-84; *home:* 1351 Grim Rd Athens OH 45701*

THELEN, JAMES M., Mathematics Professor; *b:* Brooklyn, NY Barbara Deevy; *c:* Kathleen, Kristin, Michael, Matthew; *ed:* Iona Coll Math 1966; Univ of Notre Dame (MS) Math 1969; Fordham Univ 36 Grad Hrs Math; *cr:* St Thomas Aquinas Coll Math Instr 1969-71; Rock Comm Coll Math Prof 1973-; *ai:* Fac Senate; Mentor, Instr M-TS Prgm; Gen Ed Task Force; AFT; MAA; NY St Mathematical Assn of Colls; Co-Author A Game of Numbers; Recipient Chancellor's Aw Excl for Tchng; *office:* Rockland Comm Coll 145 College Rd Sufferr 10901*

THELEN, KARL E., English Tchr & Yearbook Co-Adv; *b:* Schenec NY; *m:* Mary; *c:* Tamara, Shane, Joshua, Jeffrey; *ed:* Hiram Scott (BA Ed 1970; Plattsburgh St (MS) Admin, Supervision 1990; 18 Grad C Hrs Toward CAS Degree; *cr:* Moriah Cntrl Schl Eng Tchr 1970-80; M Abraham UHS Eng Tchr, Yrbk Adv 1980-; *ai:* Newspaper; VEA, 1980-; MAEA 1980-, Pres 1995-; Yrbk Dedication 1974, 1983, 1991 Outstdng Tchr Awd 1983; Edctr of Month 1995; Moriah Chamb Commerce Citizen of Yr 1980; *home:* 115 Bartlett Pond Rd Minevill 12956*

THELLER, KIMBERLY KAY, Elem Prin & Dist Test Coord; *b:* Fren OH; *m:* Eric; *c:* Megan, Eric; *ed:* Bowling Green St Univ (BS) Elem LBD 1982; Univ of Toledo (MA) Educl Admin 1986, (EDS) Educl A 1989, (PHD) Educl Adim 1995; *cr:* Fremont City Schls DPPF, Migra Auxiliary Svcs 1982-86, 4th Grd Tchr 1986-94, Elem Prin 1994- Testing Coord; Soc Stud Elem Comm Chprsn; Phi Delta Kappa 1 ASCD 1994-; Soroptimist Intnl 1995-; Article Pub in OH Assn vision & Curr Dev Inc Journal 1994; *office:* Fremont City Schls 109 ncoln St Lindsey OH 43442*

N, ARLENE M., Honors Biology Teacher; *b:* Pittsburgh, PA; *m:* *c:* Matthew, Megan; *ed:* DuQuesne Univ (BS) Bio 1972, (MS) Bio *cr:* North Allegheny Intermediate HS Bio Tchr 1973-; *ai:* AFT ; Delta Kappa Gamma 1994-; Weimaraner Assn of Greater Pittsburgh ; Greater Pittsburgh Dahlia Soc 1990-; Amer Family Inst Awd; *office:* egheny Intermediate HS 350 Cumberland Rd Pittsburgh PA 15237

DORE, MICHAEL, Mathematics Teacher; *b:* Akron, OH; *m:* n (Snyder); *ed:* Kent St Univ (BS) Elem, Sp Ed 1972, (MED) Curr, ction 1985; *cr:* Walls Elem Fifth-Sixth Grd Tchr 1972-86; Davey MS Grd, 7th-8th Grd Math Tchr 1986-; *ai:* Stock Market Club Adv; KEA ; NMSA 1994-; Phi Delta Kappa 1986-; OH Edison Grant 1986; A Convention Presenter 1994; Outstdng Cooperating Tchr Awd 1995; Davey MS 196 N Prospect St Kent OH 44240*

RIAULT, CARYL ANN, First Grade Teacher; *b:* Broxted, England; chael S., Stephanie; *ed:* Bridgewater St Coll (BS) Elem Ed 1967,) Rdng 1974; *ai:* Natl Women's Iniative Stu; MTA, NEA 1967-; Hector L Belisle Elem Schl 40 Clarkson St Fall River MA 02724

ROS, JOAN, Second Grade Teacher; *b:* Boston, MA; *ed:* Anna Maria BA) Elem Ed 1969; Worcester St Coll (MA) Elem Ed 1975; Cert Elem *ai:* NEA, MA Ed Assn, Oxford Ed Assn 1969-; *office:* Clara Barton 5 Depot Rd Oxford MA 01540

RRIEN, JEAN RANDALL, Middle School Teacher; *b:* Pittsfield, *m:* John William; *ed:* North Adams St Coll (BS) Elem Ed & Eng 1983; Grad Stud in Rdng & Diagnostic Tst; Addl Credit Hrs in Rdng, ng & Whole Lang, Process Wrtng; *cr:* Lenox Pub Schl Spec Ed Asst 84; Hoosac Valley HS Eng Tchr & Tutor 1984-85; Highcroft Schl n Lit & ESL Tchr 1985-88; St Joan of Arc Schl MS Tchr 1988-94; va Acad 1995-; *ai:* Yrbk & Tutorial Network Adv; NCTA 1988-; 420 Amherst Rd Belchertown MA 01007*

AULT, PHYLLIS S., Latin Teacher; *b:* Barrington, RI; *m:* Roger J.; T Coll (BA) Classics 1971; Post Grad Stud RI Coll, Providence Coll; orth Attleboro HS Latin Tchr 1971-; *ai:* Schl Jr Classical League Adv; Latin Hnr Soc Spon; Natl Latin Exam Spon; ACL, CANE 1975-; NEA, 972-; Town Lib 1983-, Vol; Helen Day Art Ctr 1990-; Green Mt Club ; Articles Pub in CANE Journals.*

AULT, STEPHANIE CARBONE, English Teacher; *b:* Massena, *n:* Ralph; *c:* Brook, Jordan; *ed:* SUNY at Potsdam (BA) Scndry Eng (MS) Eng 1976; *cr:* SUNY Tutor, Coord, EOP Prgm 1971-72; na Cntrl HS Eng Tchr 1972-; *ai:* Tech Prep Schl to Work Comm; AFT ; *home:* 12 Garvin Ave Massena NY 13662

EAULT, ROBERT H., English Teacher; *b:* Pawtucket, RI; *ed:* eis Univ (BA) Psych 1970; Boston Coll (MA) Ed 1981; Attnd rd Univ; *cr:* Phillips Schl Spcl Needs Tchr 1972-79; Salem High Spcl Tchr 1979-81, Eng Tchr 1981-; *ai:* Coll Bowl Team Adv & Coach ; Tech Integration Comm; NCTE 1981-; MCTE 1981-; NEATE 1983-; Madora Chorale 1980-; *office:* Salem HS 77 Wilson St Salem MA

ODEAU, CAROL H., Biology Teacher; *b:* Caribou, ME; *m:* rd; *c:* Robyn, Renee, Cara; *ed:* Univ of ME at Presque Isle (BS) Life Chem 1975; Univ of Southern ME (MS) Ed 1990; Attnd Simmons Boston Univ, Bates Coll with 6 Credit Hrs Each; *cr:* Limestone HS chr 1976-80; Caribou HS Bio & Chem Tchr 1980-; Northern ME Tech Nursing Prgm Anatomy, Physiology & Bio Tchr 1990-95; *ai:* Class Restructuring, Accreditation & Stdnts Assistance Team Comms; , NABT 1986-; ME Sci Tchrs Assn 1988-, Northern ME Rep; MEA ; Beta Sigma Phi 1968-, Pres, Sec, Woman of Yr Awd; Church Cncl ; Girl Scouts, Ldr 1975 & 1978; Started a Northern ME Bio Tchrs 1988-; Adult Educator of Yr 1994; Human Genome Project 1995-; & NABT Fieldtester; Software Review NABT; Present Wkshps ghout St; Sci Dept Head 1990-94; *office:* Caribou HS 410 Sweden St ou ME 04736

ODEAU, CATHERINE ELLEN (MAZZOLA), Eighth Grade er; *b:* Weymouth, MA; *m:* Allen F.; *c:* Michael, Judi; *ed:* eastern Univ (BS) Elem Ed 1968; Plymouth St Coll (MED) Mid Level 95; Foxfire Level I Trng & Facilitator; *cr:* Deerhill Elem Schl Tchr 69; Bicentennial Schl Tchr 1974-83; Jaffrey Rindge MS Tchr 1985-; M Coach; Crunch Niche Adv; Dists Curr Cncl Mem; Negotiating Mem; NEA 1985-; NHAMLE 1990-, Pres Elect; NELMS 1992-, Bd & Current Publications Comm; NHOM Regnl Comm 1993-; Schl vement Team; Staff Dev Comm; Articles Pub; Schl Improvement Now Defunct; ACT Participant; NHGIGE Participant; Pub in MLE Monographs on Integrated Curr.*

BAUD, SANDRA ROBINSON, 4th Grade Teacher; *b:* Pittsburgh, *r:* John P.; *c:* Rachel, Sarah, Justine, Ashley; *ed:* Univ of Pittsburgh Educl Comm, Tech 1984; Duquesne Univ (BS) Ed; *cr:* Diocese of urgh Tchr 1978-84; Seneca Vly Schl Tchr 1986-; *ai:* NEA, PSEA ; Thanks to Tchrs Awd KDKA Television; *office:* Evans City Elem 345 W Main St Evans City PA 16033

L, CAROLYN, Fourth Grade Teacher; *b:* Lockport, NY; *ed:* port St Coll (BS) Ed 1960; Univ of Buffalo (MS) Ed 1965; 32 Credit Post Grad Work; *cr:* Lewiston-Porter Schls 5th Grd Tchr 1960-64; ard Park Schls 4th-6th Grd Tchr 1965-; *ai:* NEA 1960-; NYSUT ; OPTA 1965-; Orchard Pk Presbyn Church 1980-, Choir Mem, er Session Mem, Church Elder; Outstdng Young Edctr Nom; *office:* Davis Elem S Davis St Orchard Park NY 14127

L, PAMELA B., Orchestra Director; *b:* Mechanicsburg, PA; *m:* ; *c:* Kristen, Kevin; *ed:* Wilkes Coll (BMus) Music Ed 1985; Bowling St Univ (MMus) Music 1987; *cr:* Bowling Green St Univ Grad Asst 87; Bowling Green City Schls Orch Dir 1987-; *ai:* NEA, OMEA ; MENC 1981-; ASTA 1991-; Perrysburg Symphony Orch 1993-, Bd ustees; Outstdng Grad Asst Bowling Green St Univ 1987; *office:* ng Green City Schls 530 W Poe Rd Bowling Green OH 43402*

LE, LAUREN FLANNERY, School Psychologist; *b:* Pittsburgh, PA; ic; *ed:* Allegheny Coll (BA) Psych 1991; The OH St Univ (MA) Schl 1993; *cr:* DE City Schls Schl Psych Intern 1 Yr; Union Local Schl Schl Psych 1 Yr; Bellaire City Schl Dist Schl Psych 1 Yr; *ai:* Natl of Schl Psychs 1992-; OH Schl Psych Assn 1992-.

ME, VICKI LYNN, High School German Teacher; *b:* Blackstone, *n:* Thomas J.; *c:* Megan, Caitlin; *ed:* Millersville Univ (BS) Scndry Ger 1974, (MA) Ger 1983; Shippensburg Univ Eng Cert; 30 Hrs Post ers in Ger; *cr:* Foust Jr HS Ger Tchr 1975-82; Chambersburg HS Ger 1982-; *ai:* Ger Club Adv; Forensics Team Coach; PYEA Future ators; *office:* Chambersburg Area Sr HS 511 S 6th St Chambersburg 201*

VON, JAY, Biology Teacher; *b:* Belleville, NJ; *m:* Kathleen anik; *ed:* East Stroudsburg Univ (BS) Bio 1987; Georgian Court Coll Bio 1996; *cr:* Pfizer Pharmaceutical Rsrch Chemist 1989-91; Seton Univ Tchng Asst 1991-92; Cntrl Regnl Schl Dist Tchr 1992-; *ai:* Asst Coach; NJEA, CREA, NJBTA, NJSTA 1991-.

LBERG, CHARLOTTE J., 6th Grade Teacher; *b:* Sharon, PA; *c:* Ryan; *ed:* PA St (BS) Elem Ed 1971; Attnd Youngstown St Univ, at St Joseph, Ashland Univ; *cr:* New Castle Union Schl 6th Grd Lang Tchr 1971-73; Crestview MS 6th Grd Lang, Rdng Tchr 1982-; *ai:* Aerobics Instr; NEA, OEA 1982-; Republican Women 1972-, Sec, Comm Person 1981; Rdng Assn 1989-.

THIMONS, JIM F., World Cultures Teacher; *b:* Tarentum, PA; *m:* Julie L.; *ed:* Indiana Univ of PA (BA) Scndry Ed Soc Sci 1989; PA Dept of Ed (MS) Ed 1993; Indiana Univ of PA Prins Cert to be Completed 1997; *cr:* Urban League of Pittsburgh Career, Job Specialist 1991-93; Robert Thimons & Son Construction Foreman 1981-; Freeport Schl Dist World Cultures Tchr 1993-; *ai:* SADD Spon; Ftbl Coach; Stu Assistance; Scndry Instructional Support; Homebound Tutor; Track Scorekeeper; Bsktbl Game Mgr; NEA, PSEA, FEA 1993-; PA St Constable 1992-; Tarentum Borough Civil Svc Commission 1991-; PA Chief's of Police Assn Lay Person of Yr Awd; Outstdng Achvmt Awd; *office:* Freeport Sr HS 625 S Pike Rd Sarver PA 16055

THISSELL, MERRILEE ANN, 1st Grade Teacher & Asst Prin; *b:* Manchester, NH; *m:* Richard R.; *c:* Jameson G., Joshua A., Jeremiah D.; *ed:* Mt Holyoke Coll (BA) Rel 1970; Lesley Coll (MA) Ed 1985; *cr:* Highland Schl Primary Tchr 1 Yr; Highland-Goffsfalls Schl Kndgtn Tchr 1 Yr; Hallsville Elem Schl 2nd Grd Tchr 3 Yrs, 1st Grd Tchr 21 Yrs; *ai:* Co-Dir Drama Group; MEA, NEA-NH 1970-; *office:* Hallsville Elem Schl 275 Jewett St Manchester NH 03103*

THIVIERGE, AMY SEAGO, English Teacher; *b:* Syracuse, NY; *m:* Kevin; *c:* Benjamin, Abaigeal; *ed:* Coll of St Rose (BA) Eng, Sec Ed 1988, (MA) Eng 1994; 6 Grad Credit Hrs Toward Mid Level Cert; *cr:* Charlton Schl Eng Tchr 1989-90; Coll of St Rose Writing Lab Grad Asst 1990-91; Poultney HS Eng Tchr 1991-; *ai:* Class Adv; Stu Cncl Co-Adv; NCTE 1994-.

THODEN, MICHELLE ELLEN, Science Teacher; *b:* Bayport, NY; *m:* Edmund Tallman; *ed:* St Univ of NY at Stony Brook (BS) Bio 1989; (MA) Sci Ed 1993; *cr:* Brentwood HS Summer Schl Bio Tchr 1989-; Patchogue-Medford HS Bio, Chem Tchr 1989-; *ai:* Sporting Events Chaperone; AFT, NYSUT 1989-; PMCT 1992-, Bldg Rep; Awd from Brookhaven Town for SADD Club Achvmts; *office:* Patchogue-Medford HS Buffalo Ave Medford NY 11763

THOM, BINNIE J., Fifth Grade Teacher; *b:* Manhattan, NY; *m:* Martin Vaccaro Jr.; *ed:* Douglas Coll (BA) Span 1973; Rutgers Univ (MED) Elem Ed 1979; *cr:* Livingston Schl Kndgtn Tchr 1973-77; Nathan Hale Schl Kndgtn-1st Grd Tchr 1977-79; Walter C Black Schl 2nd Grd, Biling Tchr1979-86; Melvin H Kreps Schl 5th-6th Grd Tchr 1986-92; Walter C Black Schl 5th Grd Tchr 1992-; *ai:* NEA, NJEA 1973-; Better Beginnings Child Care Ctr 1985-, Bd of Dir Mem; Tchr in Space Prgm St Finalist 1985.

THOMA, JOYCE ELIZABETH (SHIPMAN), Kindergarten Teacher; *b:* Sidney, OH; *m:* John Joseph; *c:* Travis, Kara; *ed:* Eastern KY Univ (BS) Elem Ed; Univ of Dayton (MED) Early Chldhd 1983; Eastern KY Univ Kndgtn Endorsement 1973; Tchng Cert 1984; Math Their Way Prgm; GATE Prgm; *cr:* Longvellow Elem Schl First Grd Tchr 1973-74, Kndgtn Tchr 1974-; *ai:* Bldg Rep 1974-75; Curr Cncl 1978-79; Lang Arts Course Stud Comm 1973-; Bowling Rep for Big Brothers, Big Sisters Soc Comm 1973-78; Honored Certified Staff 1994;Hall of Fame Staff Runners Up 1994; Chrldng Adv 1976; Foothall Moms 1992; Sidney Booster Club 1994-; OEA, NEA, EKU Alumni 1973-; SEA 1973-, Soc Comm; Univ of Dayton Alumni 1983-; Holy Angels Cath Church 1984-; March of Dimes 1987-93, Vol; Women of Moose 1978-; Women's Intnl Bowling Congress 1995-; Writing To Read Lab 1990; Tchr for Bus Advy Cncl Hnr 1993-94; Who'sWho in Amer Ed 1996; *office:* Longfellow Elem Schl 1250 Park St Sidney OH 45365

THOMAN, ANTHONY C., Social Studies Teacher; *b:* Berkeley, CA; *ed:* Bates Coll (BA) His 1984; Tchrs Coll, Columia Univ (MA) Tchng of Soc Stud 1989; *cr:* Mabel Dean Bacon HS Soc Stud Tchr 1986-92; John F. Kennedy HS Soc Stud Tchr 1992-; *ai:* Environmental, Chinese Club Fac Adv; UFT 1986-, Schl Rep; Bronx Comm Bd Parks, Rec Comm 1994-; Van Cortlandt Track Club 1990-, Exec Comm; Tchr of Yr 1990; Natl Endowment for Hum 1992; *office:* John F Kennedy HS 99 Terrace View Ave Bronx NY 10463

THOMAN, JANE FITZSIMMONDS, Fifth Grade Teacher; *b:* Washington, DC; *m:* Timothy Alan; *c:* Ian; *ed:* Frostburg St Univ (BA) Elem Ed 1979; Univ of MD 18 Credits Towards Masters; 15 St Dept Credits; *cr:* Arthur Middleton Elem Schl 4th Grd Tchr 1979-83; Eva Turner Elem Schl 4th-5th Grd Tchr 1983-87; Jenifer Elem Schl 5th Grd Tchr 1987-; *ai:* Odyssey of Mind, Math Team Coach; Site-Based Mngmt Team; NEA 1979-; *office:* Daniel St Thomas Jenifer Elem 2820 Jenifer Schl Ln Waldorf MD 20603

THOMAS, ALAN EDWARD, Chaplain & Religion Teacher; *b:* Meyersdale, PA; *ed:* Juniata Coll (BS) Bio 1986; Mount St Mary's Coll (MA) Theology 1991; *cr:* Bishop Carroll HS Chaplain, Tchr 1993-; *ai:* Stu Assistance Team; Forensics Competition Judge; *office:* Bishop Carroll HS 728 Ben Franklin Hwy Ebensburg PA 15931

THOMAS, ALFREDO CORREA, Principal; *b:* New York, NY; *m:* Lillian R.; *c:* Aisha, Aura; *ed:* Hunter Coll of NY (BA) Eng 1966; City Coll of NY (MA) Ed 1970; Ed Admin, Supvr Cert Ed 1972; *cr:* Arturo Toscanini JHS Eng Tchr, Asst Prin 1966-80; Diana Sands Intermediate Schl Asst, Acting Prin 1980-90; Artoro Toscanini JHS Asst Prin 1990; John Philip Sousa MS Prin 1991-; *ai:* Dir Ethical Cultures Fieldston Enrichment Prgm; Fraternity of Emile 1990-; Williamsbridge Woman's Club Man of Yr 1989; *office:* MS 142 John Philip Sousa 3750 Baychester Ave New York NY 10466

THOMAS, ANNE S., English Teacher; *b:* Philadelphia, PA; *m:* Harold Hobor; *c:* Hal, Sue, Melissa; *ed:* Immaculata Coll (BA) Eng 1965; Attnd Univ of PA, Univ of CO; *cr:* Marple Newtown Jr HS Eng Tchr 1966-70; Burr D. Coe Voc-Tech HS Eng Tchr 1970-71; Avon Grove HS Eng Tchr 1986-; *ai:* NEA, PSEA, AGEA 1986-; *office:* Avon Grove HS 257 E State Rd West Grove PA 19390

THOMAS, BENJAMIN L., Language Arts Teacher; *b:* Philadelphia, PA; *m:* Carol L.; *c:* Sally Tollens; *ed:* West Chester St (BS) Eng 1964; *cr:* Avon-Grove Area Schl Eng Tchr 1964-71; New Ipswich Regnl Schl Hum Chm, Tchr 1971-73; Alexis I Dupont MS Lang Arts 1973-; *ai:* Yrbk; Newspaper; Bsktbl, Var Bsbl Coach; Team Ldr; NEA, NCTE 1964-; West Grove Ath Assn 1971-; Designed Cooperative Learning Materials; Team Taught with William Moore 15 Yrs.*

THOMAS, BETH HALL, English Teacher; *b:* Rochester, NY; *m:* Seth M.; *c:* Jordyn, Natalie; *ed:* Nazareth Coll (BA) Eng 1984; Nazareth Coll at Rochester (MS) Ed 1988; *cr:* Victor HS 9th-12th Grd Eng Tchr 1983-; *ai:* Hlth Curr Review Comm; Musical Asst Dir; Dollars for Scholars Mem; Rochester Area Tchrs Assn Excl in Stu Tchng 1984; Univ of Rochester Tchr of Yr Awd-VCS 1988; *office:* Victor HS 953 High St Victor NY 14564

THOMAS, BRENDA RAY, Second Grade Teacher; *b:* Bar Harbor, ME; *m:* Donald Jesse; *c:* David, J. Chad; *ed:* Univ of ME (BS) Elem Ed 1973, (MED) Ed 1990; *cr:* Dr Charles C. Knowlton Schl Second Grd Tchr 1973-; *ai:* Ellsworth Tchr Recertification Comm Co-Chprsn; ME Ed Assn, NEA 1973-; Delta Kappa Gamma 1982-; Beta Sigma Phi 1979-.

THOMAS, BRIAN ALAN, Professor & Prgm Coordinator; *b:* Plainfield, NJ; *m:* Sharon Ann Reck; *c:* Samantha, Kelly, Craig, Dean; *ed:* Essex Comm Coll (AAS) Ophthalmic Sci-High Hnrs 1980; Union Coll (AA) Bus Admin-High Hnrs 1981; Montclair St Univ (BS) Allied Hlth Svcs 1985; Seton Hall Univ (MA) Hlth Professions Ed-Magna Cum Laude 1994; 9 Credit Hrs Towards EDS; Optician's Assn of Amer Certfd Refracting Optician; Amer Bd of Opticianry Master in Ophthalmic Optics; *cr:* SAFT Opticians Mgr, Optician 1981-90; Essex Cty Coll Adj Prof of Optics 1981-84; Raritan Vly Comm Coll Adj Prof, Prgm Coord 1984-89, Prof, Ophthalmic Sci Prgm Coord 1990-; *ai:* Stu Alumni Assn Fac Adv; Vehicle Violations Comm; Ophthalmic Sci Advy Bd; Ophthalmic Sci Schlsp Awd; Fac Fed Exec Cncl; Grievance, Holiday Party Comms; Opticians Assn of NJ 1990-, Bd of Dir, Ed Chair; Natl Acad of Opticianry 1980-, Acad Ed Ambassador, Cert of Recognition; Cert Optician 1980-, Amer Bd of Opticianry; Registered Contact Lens Filter 1989-, Natl Contact Lens Examiners; Philadelphia Regnl Ophthalamic Soc; Kappa Delta Pi 1995-, Intnl Hnr Soc for Ed; Natl Dean's List 1979-; Phi Theata Kappa Nom 1980-; Who's Who Among Rising Young Amer 1993-; Articles Pub; Natl Acad of Opticianry 1980, Educl Ambassador for NJ; Licensed Optician, NJ St Bd of Ophthalmic Dispensers 1980; *office:* Raritan Valley Comm Coll PO Box 3300 Somerville NJ 08876*

THOMAS, BRIAN ROBERT, 8th Grade Amer History Teacher; *b:* Trenton, OH; *ed:* Miami Univ (BS) Comprehensive Scndry Soc Stud 1992; *cr:* Hopewell Jr Schl Amer His Tchr 1992-, Co Dept Chair & Soc Stud Tchr 1995-; *ai:* 8th Grd Head Ftbl; 7th Grd Boys Bsktbl; Bible Stud Spon; Tech Comm Mem; North Cntrl Steering Comm; West Chester Chuch of Nazareth 1995-, Yth Spon; *office:* Hopewell Jr Schl 8200 Cox Rd West Chester OH 45069*

THOMAS, CATHEREE CHAMBERS, Communications Skills Teacher; *b:* Columbus, GA; *m:* LeRoy R.; *c:* Leonard Kevin, Melinda Kay, Sherice Monique; *ed:* Cntrl St Univ (BSEd) Bus Ed 1965; Cleveland St Univ Rdng K-12th 1987 15 Hrs; Info Res Guid Case Western Reserve 3 Hrs; Ashland Univ Stress Mngmt 6 Hrs; *cr:* Standard Oil Co Clerk Engrng Dept 1965-67; Glenville SYEP Prgm Coord 1968-71; Glenville HS Bus Tchr 1970-72; Empire MS Bus Tchr 1972-85; John Marshall HS Rdng Tchr 1985-; *ai:* Chrldrs Spon; Natl City Bank Mentor Prgm Adv; OBTA 1973-; GCCET 1990-; CABSE 1992-; *office:* John Marshall HS 3952 W 140th St Cleveland OH 44111*

THOMAS, CINDY HARLAN, First Grade Teacher; *b:* East Stroudsburg, PA; *m:* Matthew A.; *ed:* East Stroudsburg Univ (BS) Elem Ed 1988; *cr:* Child Dev Cncl Presch Tchr 1988-89; Susquehanna Prepatory Schl Fifth Grd Tchr 1989-90; Apple Tree Nursery, Primary Schl Nursery Tchr 1990-91, First Grd Tchr 1991-; *ai:* Tutor Stdnts K-6th Grd; *home:* 627 Tioga Ave Kingston PA 18704

THOMAS, CLAYTON, Geometry Teacher; *b:* Philadelphia, PA; *m:* Donna Ruth Willits; *c:* Kirstie, Kari, Kami, Kori; *ed:* Lycoming Coll (AB) Math; 40 Grad Credits Beyond PA Masters Equivalency; *cr:* Poquesing MS Math Tchr 1968-83; Neshaminy HS Geometry Tchr 1983-; *ai:* AFT 1970-; Borough Cncl 1989-, VP; *office:* Neshaminy HS 2001 Old Lincoln Hwy Langhorne PA 19047

THOMAS, DAVID ALAN, Chemistry & Physics Teacher; *b:* Cleveland, OH; *m:* Beth Dakes; *ed:* WV Univ (BS) Scndry Ed 1981; 30 Plus Hrs; *cr:* Park View HS Chem Tchr 1981-90; Catoctin HS Chem & Physics Tchr 1990-; *ai:* tennis Coach 1982-95; Bsktbl Coach 1981-83; Worked wigh Marching Band 1981-84; NEA 1981-; Took 2 Stdnts Intl Sci Fair 1 Week 1989; *office:* Catoctin H S 14745 Sabillasville Rd Thurmont MD 21788

THOMAS, DEB KUHLMAN, 1st Grade Teacher; *b:* Findlay, OH; *m:* Mike; *c:* Lynne Anne, Brad; *ed:* Univ of FL (BA) Elem Ed 1979; Univ of Dayton (MS) Elem Admin 1992; Prin's Cert 1996; *cr:* Van Buren Schl 5th Grd Tchr 1980-83, 3rd Grd Tchr 1983-85, 1st Grd Tchr 1985-; *ai:* 4-H Adv; NEA, OEA 1980-; Sunday Schl Tchr 1980-; Church Women's Assn 1994-, Pres; *home:* PO Box 252 Van Buren OH 45889*

THOMAS, DEBORAH ANN, Assistant Professor of Psych; *b:* Charleston, WV; *ed:* WV Univ (BA) Psych 1976, (MA) Cnslng & Guid 1978; 30 Hrs Post Grad Stud Towards EDD Educl Psych; *cr:* Summit Ctr Child Therapist 1978-83; Western Dist Mental Hlth Ctr Dir of Mental Hlth, Cnslr 1984-91; Fred J. Krieg PHD & Assoc Cnslr, Soc Worker 1991-93; WA St Comm Coll Instr, Learning Specialist 1993-; *ai:* Licensed Prof Cnslr, Certfd Soc Worker; *office:* Washington State Comm Coll 710 Colegate Dr Marietta OH 45750

THOMAS, DENNIS A., English Teacher; *b:* Mason City, IA; *ed:* St Joseph's Coll (BA) Speech 1968; Univ of Dayton (MA) Eng 1994; Addl Courses Wright St Univ; *cr:* St Helen Schl Eng Tchr 1968-71; Precious Blood Schl Eng Tchr 1972-75; Dayton Pub Schls Rdng Specialist 1977-79; Chaminade-Julienne Eng Tchr 1979-; *ai:* Yrbk Adv 15 Yrs; NCTE; NCEA; Dayton Arts Inst; Presenter Natl Convention NCTE 1994; Presenter Natl Convention NCEA 1995; *office:* Chaminade-Julienne HS 505 S Ludlow St Dayton OH 45402

THOMAS, DIANA JONES, Assistant Professor; *b:* Paris, France; *m:* Brett Lee; *ed:* Cath Univ (BM) Cello Performance 1978; Univ of MD (MM) Cello Performance 1982; George Mason Univ (MA) Eng & Linguistics 1992; TESOL Cert 1991; *cr:* Montgomery Coll Music Librn 1978-84, Lang Lab Dir 1984-91, Eng as Second Lang Asst Prof 1991-; *office:* Montgomery Coll At Rockville 51 Mannakee St Rockville MD 20850*

THOMAS, EVELYN THOMPKINS, English Teacher; *b:* Amityville, NY; *m:* Nathaniel G.; *c:* Janeen, Michelle; *ed:* Hofstra Univ (BA) Eng 1974, (MS) Scndry Ed 1976; Post Grad Work 21 Credits; *cr:* Hofstra Univ NOAH Summer Prgm Eng Tchr 1976; Tchr in Upwd Bnd Prgm 1976; *ai:* Black Lit Comm; Cultural Awareness Prgms; Forensics Tournaments; Multicultural Club; AFT, ATA 1977-; St Paul's Young People's Assn 1978-, Chm; *office:* Amityville Memorial HS Merrick Rd Amityville NY 11701

THOMAS, HILMA REHARD, Fifth Grade Teacher; *b:* Coshocton Co, OH; *m:* William L.; *c:* William, Teri Thomas Gilfilen, R. Brent; *ed:* Post-Grad Hrs Ashland Coll; Elem Ed Muskingum Coll 1974; *cr:* West Lafayette Elem Schl Third-Fourth Grd Tchrs 1954-56; Coshocton City Schls Fifth Grd Tchr 1970-; *ai:* CCEA, NEA 1970-.

THOMAS, IRENE WEST, High School English Teacher; *b:* Spfld, MA; *m:* Rene P.; *c:* Karen Taylor, Robert P.; *ed:* Amer Int Coll (BA) Eng 1966; 33 Grad Hrs Eng Westfield St Coll 1983; *cr:* Phelps Elem Schl Grd 1 Tchr 1966; Clark Elem Tchr Grds 5 & 6 Tchr 1966-72; Agawam MS Grd 6 & 7 Tchr 1972-87; Agawam Jr HS Grds 8 & 9 Tchr 1987-91; Agawam HS Eng Tchr 1991-; *ai:* Eng Curr, System-wide Curr Revision; Renaissance Adv; Schl, Bus Alliance; NEA, MTA, AEA 1966-; Agawam Jr Women; Cath Women's Club; Amer Lung Assn 1995-, Comm Work; Articles Pub; *office:* Agawam HS 760 Cooper St Agawam MA 01001

THOMAS, JAMES LEE, French & Spanish Teacher; *b:* Batavia, NY; *m:* Tammy Fichter; *ed:* SUCNY at Fredonia (BA) Fr 1986; OH St Univ (MA) Fr 1988; Cert des Hautes Etudes Faculte des Lettres Avignon France; *cr:* OH St Univ Tchng Assoc 1986-88; Irondequoit HS Fr, Span Tchr 1989-, Theater Tchr 1994-; *ai:* Schl Based Planning Team; Attendance Comm; Fr Club, United Stdnts & Staff Advs; Dir of Schl Musicals; NYSFLT 1992-; AATF 1993-; FLATRA 1992-, Sec; Phi Delta Kappa 1993-; *office:* Irondequoit HS 260 Cooper Rd Rochester NY 14617*

THOMAS, JANETTE BUCKI, Health Information Tech Prof; *b:* Lackawanna, NY; *m:* Bruce Albert; *c:* Kristen, Lauren, Steven; *ed:* Alfred St Coll (AAS) Med Rec Tech 1974; Daemen Coll (BS) Med Rec Admin 1976; Alfred Univ (MPS) Comm Svcs Admin 1983; *cr:* Erie Co Med Ctr Med Rec Tech 1974-76; St James Mercy Hosp Dir, Med Records 1976-79; Alfred St Coll Dir Hlth Info Prgm 1979-; *ai:* Hlth Info Tech Club Adv; Hnrs Convocation Commencement, Orvis Awds Comm; Hlth Fair; UUP 1979-; Amer Hlth Info Mgt Assn 1976-, Panel Surveyor 1989; NYHIMA 1976-,

Chair, Ed Comm, Ed Perspectives; Roch Regnl 1976-, Chair, Awds Comm; *office:* S U N Y Coll Of Tech At Alfred Allied Health Bldg Alfred NY 14802

THOMAS, JANICE MARIE WHITE, Jr HS Christian Educator; *b:* Waycross, GA; *c:* Roosevelt, Rebecca; *ed:* South GA Coll (AS) Sociology 1970; Valdosta St Coll (BA) Sociology 1986; Manhattan Coll Spec Ed; *cr:* Waycross Pub Schls Tchr 1972-87; Yonkers Chrstn Acad Edctr 1987-90; Yonkers Pub Schl Spec Ed Tchr 1988-94; Yonkers Chrstn Acad Jr HS Tchr 1995-; *ai:* Yrbk Adv, Coord; Praise, Worship, Devotional Ldr; NABSE 1990-; Recorded Songs of Praise, Wkshps, Seminars, Retreat Facilitator Yth, Womens Ministry; Pub Newsletters; *office:* Yonkers Christian Acad 229 N Broadway Yonkers NY 10701*

THOMAS, JANICE MISCHEL, Choral Director; *b:* Sioux City, IA; *c:* Anna Mc Inerney, Katherine Mc Inerney; *ed:* Clarke Coll (BA) Music 1972; Univ of Western Ontario (MMUS) Piano Perf 1981; 30 Grad Credits Choral Conducting Univ of ME at Orono; *cr:* WA Elem Schl 5th-6th Grd Music Tchr 1972-75; St Mary's Schl K-8th Grd Music Tchr 1976-77; Greeley HS 7th-12th Grd Choral Music Tchr 1981-; Portland Comm Chorus Accompanist 1994-; *ai:* Dir HS Madrigal Singers, Jr HS Select Choir; MENC, ACDA 1985-; MEA 1981-; ME Dist II Music, Treas 1990-94; Peaks Island Childrens Choir 1995-; TA; Article Pub 1995; Guest Conductor Dist Music Festivals 1993, 1994, 1996; *office:* Greely HS 303 Main St Cumberland Center ME 04021*

THOMAS, JAY J., Latin Tchr & Frgn Lang Chprsn; *b:* New Castle, PA; *m:* Cathleen A. Lapa; *c:* Katherine, Adam; *ed:* Duquesne Univ (BA) Classics & Philosophy 1973; St Marys Univ (MA) Theology 1979; Duquesne Univ (MED) Ed 1983; *cr:* Marquette Univ Tchng Asst 1979-80; North Allegheny Schl Tchr 1981-; North Allegheny Foreign Lang chair Chprsn 1987-; *ai:* After-Schl Foreign Lang Coord; ACTFL 1987-; Univ or Pittsburgh Tchr excl Awd; *office:* North Allegheny H S 10375 Perry Hwy Wexford PA 15090

THOMAS, JEFFERY JOSEPH, Mathematics Teacher; *b:* Wilkes-Barre, PA; *m:* Jennifer Lynn Haney; *ed:* Kings Coll (BA) Math 1992; *cr:* Middletown HS Math Tchr 1993-; *ai:* Bsbl, Bsktbl, Ftbl Asst Coach; NEA, AEA 1993-; *office:* Middletown HS 504 S Broad St Middletown DE 19709*

THOMAS, JIMMIE ELAINE, Associate Prof of English; *b:* Arkadelphia, AR; *m:* Rex P. Stevens; *c:* Melissa, Vandiver, Thomas, Luxton; *ed:* Univ of Cntrl Arkon (BSE) Eng 1971; Univ of Cntrl AR (MSE) Eng 1974; Univ of AR (PHD) Medieval Lit 1982; Brigham Young Univ Provo UT 1971-72; St Peters Coll Oxford England 1976; *cr:* Beijing Second Frgn Lang Inst Lecturer 1984-85; Univ of AR Lecturer 1985-87; AR St Univ Asst Prof 1987-88; Western New England Coll Assoc Prof 1988-; *ai:* Stageless Players Spon; Pgm for Arts & Scis Coord; Intnl Congress of Medieval Stud 1993-; Numerous Articles Pub; *office:* Western New England Coll 1215 Wilbraham Rd Springfield MA 01119*

THOMAS, JINU DANIEL, Seventh Grade English Teacher; *b:* New Delhi, India; *ed:* St Johns Univ (BA) Eng 1992, (MA) Eng 1993; *cr:* Chrstn HS Eng Tchr 1993-95; Copiague Jr High 7th Grd Eng Tchr 1995-; *ai:* St Johns Pres Silver Medal 1992; St Johns Grad Assistantship 1993.

THOMAS, JOHN JOSEPH, Mathematics Teacher; *b:* Easton, PA; *m:* Josephine Scalzo; *c:* John, Joseph; *ed:* East Stroudsburg Univ (BS) Ed 1964; Lehigh Univ (MS) Ed 1976; 8 Post Grad Hrs Math Univ of Southern IL; 9 Post Grad Hrs Math Coll of the Holy Cross; 12 Post Grad Hrs Ed Univ of Southern MS; *cr:* Shawnee Intermediate HS Asst Prin 1982-85; Penargyl Area HS Prin 1985-88; Easton Area HS Asst Prin 1988-91; Shawnee Intermediate HS Math Tchr 1991-95; Easton Area HS Tchr 1995-; *ai:* Local Schlsp for Easton Area Schl Dist Coord; NEA, PSEA, Easton Area 1991-; Ed Assn 1992-; ASCD 1976-; Northampton-Carbon Counties Fed Credit Union 1966-, Bd of Dirs; Easton Area Schoolmens Assn 1966-, Bd of Dirs, Schoolman of Yr 1982; Var E 1986-, William Brotzman Mem Awd 1991; Day Honoree 1995; Natl Sci Fnd Stipends 1966, 1969; *office:* Easton Area HS 2601 William Penn Hwy Easton PA 18045*

THOMAS, JOYCE A., Professor of English; *b:* Annapolis, MD; *ed:* Shepherd Coll (BA) Eng 1968; WV Univ (MA) Eng 1970; SUNY at Albany (PHD) Eng 1978; *cr:* WV Univ Tchng Asst 1968-70; SUNY at Albany TA, Ajunct Instr 1974-80; Albany Girls Acad Eng Tchr 1977-80; Castleton St Coll Eng Prof 1980-; *ai:* Northeast MLA 1988-; AFT 1980-; Book Author 1989; VT St Colls Fac Fellow 1988-89; Poems, Articles, Reviews Pub; *office:* Castleton State College English Dept Seminary St Castleton VT 05735

THOMAS, JUDITH ANN WAUGH, Professor of Education & Chair; *b:* New Kensington, PA; *m:* James A.; *c:* Michelle Lynn, Bradley Arthur, Brian James; *ed:* Edinboro Univ of PA (BS) Eng, Span 1962; Duquesne Univ (MED) Ed 1967; West VA Univ (EDD) Ed Curr Instr 1971;U of Puget Sound (Span); Kalamazoo Coll; NW Univ; Northwestern U Lily Fnd Grant Research in Ed 1979; Kalamazoo Coll NDEA Inst Cert Span 1963; U of Puget SOund NDEA Inst Cert Span 1965; *cr:* Highlands Schl Dist Tchr of Eng, Span, Debate 1962-66; Penn Hills HS Dist Tchr of Eng, Span, Debate 1966-67; WV U Tchng Fellow 1967-70; Penn St Univ Asst Prof of Speech 1970-71; West Liberty St Coll Assoc Prof of Speech 1971-74; Philadelphia Coll of Textiles & Sci Visiting Dean of St Affairs 1987-88; Lincoln Univ Chair, Prof of Ed, Chair of Soc Sci Division 1974-; Interim VP of Enrlmnt; Plng, Stu Life; *ai:* PA Govenor's Commission of African Am Affairs; Chair Ed Subcommittee; Past Pres Chester Cty Ed Fnd; Pres PA BACK Conf on Highed Ed; Honors Bd James Madison Univ Phil Fndtn & Chester Co Hist Soc Bd Mem; Amer Assn of U Professors, Pres; Phi Delta Kappa 1977-, Pres; Kappa Delta Pi 1993-; PA Bl Conf on Highed Ed 1980-, Pres, Mary Baltimore Awd; Chester Co Ed Fnd 1984-, Pres, Leadership Plague; Delta Sigma Theta 1963-, Rotary Club; Jack & Jill Inc VP; Continental Soc Inc, Mem & Chair of Ed Com; Drifters Inc VP; Danforth Fellow for Outstanding Tchng; Lindbach Distinguished Tchr Awd; Distinguished Fac Awd; Zeta Phi Zeta Distinguished Fac Awd; Articles Pub; *office:* Lincoln Univ Education Dept Lincoln Univ PA 19352*

THOMAS, KAREN LYNN, 7th Grade Language Arts Tchr; *b:* Elyria, OH; *m:* Mac Arthur; *c:* Shea; *ed:* Bowling Green St Univ (BA) Elem 1-8 1975; Baldwin Wallace (MA) Supvr, Admin 1979; *cr:* Elyria City Schls Sub Tchr 1975-77; Keystone MS Lang Arts Tchr 1977-; *ai:* Spelling Bee Coord; NEA, Keystone Ed Assn 1980-; Outstdng Tchr Awd Twice; *office:* Keystone MS 301 Liberty St Lagrange OH 44050

THOMAS, KATHLEEN ECK, Biology & Earth Science Tchr; *b:* Riverside, NJ; *m:* Robert G.; *c:* Marcia, Bridget, Kevin; *ed:* Cabrini Coll (BS) Bio 1966; *cr:* Palmyra HS Tchr, Adv, Coach 1966-; *ai:* Interact Club Adv; NHS Fac Cncl; Grad Awds Comm; NEA 1966-; NJESTA 1986-; PEA 1966-, Mbrshp Chair, 5 Yr Svc Awd; NASSP, Chair; Rotary, Paul Harris Fellow; PTA 1980-, Historian; BSA 1994-, Asst Ldr; Gov's Excl Tchng, Spec Person Awds; *office:* Palmyra HS 5th St & Delaware Ave Palmyra NJ 08065*

THOMAS, KATHLEEN L., French Teacher; *b:* Ellwood City, PA; *m:* Robert F.; *c:* Michael, David, James; *ed:* IN Univ of PA (BSEd) Fr & Ed 1973; Attnd OH Univ at Chillicothe & Univ of Dayton; *cr:* Waverly HS Fr Tchr 1988-89; Ottoville HS Tchr & Foreign Lang Chair 1989-; *ai:* NHS; OH Foreign Lang Assn 1988-; NEA, OEA 1989-; *office:* Ottoville Local Schl E 3rd St PO Box 248 Ottoville OH 45876*

THOMAS, KATHLEEN SUSAN, Assistant Principal; *b:* New Castle, PA; *ed:* Youngstown St Univ (BS) Elem Ed 1987, (MS) Ed Admin 1992; Post-Grad Stud Elem Prin Cert; *cr:* Animal Charity of OH Ed Dir 1984-92; Jefferson Elem Schl 6th Grd Tchr 1987-90; Sheridan Elem Schl 6th Grd Tchr 1990-93; Harding Primary Learning Ctr Asst Prin 1993-; *ai:* OAESA 1993-; *office:* Harding Primary Learning Ctr 1903 Cordova St Youngstown OH 44504*

THOMAS, KENNETH CHANNING, Reading Teacher; *b:* Elmer, NJ; *ed:* Stockton St Coll (BA) His 1978; Glassboro Coll Tchr Cert 1985; *cr:* Morris Goodwin Schl Resource Ctr Instr 1985-; *ai:* Stu Cncl Adv; PTO Sec; Lang Arts Curr Comm; NEA, NJEA 1986-, Local VP; NJRA 1990-; Red Cross VIP Blood Donor 1977-, 2 Gallon Pin; St John Bosc Church 1988-, Eucharistic Minister; Greenwich Twp Tchr of Yr 1988-89; *office:* Morris Goodwin Schl PO Box 360 Greenwich NJ 08323*

THOMAS, LAURENCE M., Professor; *b:* Baltimore, MD; *ed:* Univ of MD (BA) Philosophy 1971; Univ of Pittsburgh (PHD) Philosophy 1976; *cr:* Univ of NC at Chapel Hill Assoc Prof 1980-86; Oberlin Coll Prof 1986-89; Syracuse Univ Prof 1989-; *ai:* Amer Philosophical Assn 1975-; Soc for Pol & Legal Philosophy 1980-; Natl Hum Ctr Flwshp 1982-83; Stanford Hum Flwshp 1987-88; Andrew Mellon Flwshp Harvard Univ; *office:* Syracuse Univ Dept of Pol Sci Eggers Hall Syracuse NY 13210*

THOMAS, LORETHA LANGHAM, Business Teacher; *b:* Mobile, AL; *m:* Troy Calvin Jr.; *c:* Elihu-Malik; *ed:* Faulkner St Jr Coll (AS) Sec Sci 1975; AL St Univ (BS) Bus Ed 1980; Oswego St Univ (MS) Voc Ed 1988; *cr:* Albert P Brewer Dev Ct Sec & Relief Supvr 1980-81; Nottingham HS Bus Tchr 1981-83; Fowler HS Bus Tchr 1983-84; Thomas H Corcoran HS Bus Tchr 1984-; *ai:* Future Bus Ldrs of Amer; Syracuse Yth Roundtable; Future Bus Ldrs of Amer Tchrs Awd; *home:* 2410 Redmond Street Mobile AL 36617

THOMAS, LULU L., Language Arts & Reading Tchr; *b:* Honolulu, HI; *ed:* Millersville Univ (BSEd) Elem Ed 1985, (MSEd) Elem Ed 1993; Currently Working toward and have 6 Credit Hrs Temple Univ Toward Prin Cert Prgm; *cr:* Schl Dist of City of NY Elem Tchr, Co-Coord of Stu Cncl, Act 1987-; *ai:* Coord E. F. SMith Awds Assembly; NEA, PSEA 1988-; York City Ed Assn 1988-, Rep; *office:* Edgar Fahs Smith MS 701 Texas Ave York PA 17404

THOMAS, LYNDA D'ELIA, First Grade Teacher; *b:* Atlantic City, NJ; *w:* Kenneth W. (dec); *c:* Elaine, Kathleen; *ed:* Glassboro St Coll (BA) Kndgtn, Primary Ed 1974; Endorsement Early Chldhd 1976; Rel Ed Cert; *cr:* St Peter Schl 1st Grd Tchr 1979-; *ai:* NCEA 1980-; RC of Southern NJ, NJSTA 1994-; USABDA 1995-; FTA 1984-; *office:* St Peter Schl Chestnut & Decatur Aves Pleasantville NJ 08232*

THOMAS, LYNETTE HARRIS, Reading Specialist; *b:* Mt Vernon, NY; *c:* Joel, Aaron; *ed:* Bowie St Univ (BS) Elem Ed 1978; Coll of New Rochelle (MS) Rdng 1980; *cr:* Longfellow Elem Schl 3rd Grd Tchr 1980-91; Nelson Mandela HS Rdng Specialist 1991-; *ai:* AIM Founder & Coord; Rdng Mentorship Coord; Mandela SPTO Adv; Kappa Delta Pi 1976-; Alpha Kappa Mu 1978-; Alpha Kappa Alpha 1993-; Outstdng Young Women of Amer 1979; Natl Cncl of Negro Women Outstdng Tchr Awd 1993.*

THOMAS, MARK PHILLIP, Senior High Band & Chorus Dir; *b:* Sellersville, PA; *m:* Eileen Tracy Brown; *ed:* West Chester Univ (BS) Music Ed 1984; Kutztown Univ (MS) Music Production, Telecommunications 1989; Choral, Orchestral Conducting Eastman Schl of Music, Univ of Rochester; *cr:* Minersville Area Schl Dist Sr HS, Elem Band, Choral Dir 1985-86; Bucks Cty Comm Coll Performing Arts Prof 1989-92; Schuylkill Cty Comm Chorus, Music Dir, Conductor 1986-; Southern Columbia Area Schl Dist Sr HS Band, Chorus Dir 1992-; *ai:* Mark P. Thomas Ensemble Music Dir, Conductor; Southern Columbia Sr HS Marching Band Dir, Girls Bsktbl Coach; MENC 1980-; PA Music Edctrs Assn 1985-; Amer Choral Dir Assn 1987-; Chorus Amer 1991-; Kappa Kappa Psi 1983-, Treas; Heidelberg Germany Music Fesival Awd of Hnr 1991; Commonwealth of PA House of Rep Citation 1993-94; PA St Legislature Acknowledgement Awd 1993-95; Bd of Schuylkill Cty Commissioners Proclamation 1991-93; *home:* 130 Market St Bloomsburg PA 17815

THOMAS, MARY LYNNE C., Mathematics Teacher; *b:* Frederick, MD; *c:* Seth Gideon; *ed:* Hood Coll (BA) Math 1969; Western MD Coll (MED) Math 1979; Data Processing; Cmptr Programming; Spec Ed; *cr:* Governor Thomas Johnson HS Math Tchr 1968-75, 1980-84; Linganore HS Math Tchr 1984-; *ai:* FCTA 1968-, Rep; MSTA, NEA 1968-; FCAR, MAR, NAR 1992-; *office:* Linganore HS 12013 Old Annapolis Rd Frederick MD 21701*

THOMAS, MARY JOYCE PAPROSKI, English Teacher; *b:* Springfield, MO; *m:* H. Gordon II; *c:* Jonathan, Nathan, Anna; *ed:* Evangel Coll (BA) Eng 1972; Austin Peay St U Rdng Specialist 24 Credit Hrs; US Army Civilian Prsnl Cert; *cr:* Rothschild Jr High Tchr 1973-74; Big Bend Comm Coll Tchr 1976-79; Bellevue Chrstn Acad Tchr 1984-88; Zweibrucken Germany Child Care Ctr Asst Dir 1991; Calvary Acad Tchr 1992-; *ai:* Stu Cncl Adv; Ath Trainer; *office:* Calvary Chrstn Acad 1103 E Cty Line Lakewood NJ 08701

THOMAS, PATRICIA ANN, Health Teacher; *b:* Cassville, NY; *ed:* Herkimer Cty Comm Coll (AS) PE 1975; SUNY at Cortland (BS) PE 1977, (MS) Hlth Ed 1983; *cr:* Sauquoit Vly Cntrl Schl PE Tchr 1979-85; Adirondack Cntrl Schl Hlth Ed Tchr 1985-; *ai:* Vllybl Coach; SADD Adv; Modified Soccer & Sftbl Coach; NYSUT 1979-; *office:* Adirondack Central Schl 110 Ford St Boonville NY 13309

THOMAS, PAULA N., Mass Media & Asst Professor; *b:* Parkersburg, WV; *ed:* Marshall Univ (BA) Broadcasting 1987, (MA) Comm 1989; *cr:* Cabell Cty Schls Production Consultant 1986-87; Marshall Univ Tchng Asst 1987-89; Washington St Comm Coll Prgm Coord, Asst Prof 1989-; *ai:* Mass Media Club Adv; Broadcast Ed Assn 1989-, Chair 2 Yr Coll Division; SALT 1994-; NAPTE 1996; *office:* Washington State Comm Coll 710 Colegate Dr Marietta OH 45750*

THOMAS, PHILOMENIA JONES, Mathematics Teacher; *b:* Washington, DC; *m:* Fred Jr.; *c:* Larry L. Jones, Ronnica T. Brown, Fred III; *ed:* Univ of MD at College Park (BS) Bus Ed 1976; Trinity Coll 21 Post Grad Hrs; *cr:* Suitland HS Bus Ed Tchr 1977-81, Math Tchr 1988-91; Eleanor Roosevelt High Bus Ed Tchr 1981-88; Cntrl HS Math Tchr 1991-; *ai:* Church Announcer; Chrstn Ed Dept Co-Dir; FBLA & Modeling Club Spon; NEA MD 1977-; PGCEA & MSTA 1977-; ASCD & NCTM 1990-; P E Williams Acad Ctr PTA 1987-, Sec; DC Campfire Girls Assn Area Dir; *office:* Central HS 200 Cabin Branch Rd Capitol Heights MD 20743*

THOMAS, RAY A., Math & Computer Science Tchr; *b:* Paden City, WV; *m:* Linda Ann Allen; *c:* Brian, Angie, John; *ed:* Marshall Univ (BA) Math 1969; Attnd Kent St Univ, Ashland Coll, Akron Univ, Asuza Pacific Univ, Bowling Green St Univ; *cr:* Cardington-Lincoln HS Tchr & Coach 1969-71; Massillon Tuslaw HS Tchr & Coach 1971-73; Marion Elgin HS Tchr & Coach 1973-91; Olentaugy HS Tchr & Coach 1991-; *ai:* Asst Ftbl Coach, Defensive Coord; Head Girls Bsktbl Coach; NEA 1969-; OEA 1969-; Olentangy Tchrs Assn 1991-; Prospect Lions Club 1986-; *office:* Olentangy HS 675 Lewis Center Rd Lewis Center OH 43035

THOMAS, RICHARD J., Sixth Grade Teacher; *b:* Queens, NY; *m:* Sandra L.; *c:* Renee Marie, Rhea Lynn & Sondra Christiana; *ed:* Pt Park Coll (BA) Early Chlhd Ed 1968; Adelphi Univ (MA) Elem Ed 1972; 20 Credit Hrs Spcl Ed; 6 Credit Hrs Spcl Ed Hofstra Univ; 3 Credit Hrs Northern AZ Univ; *cr:* Connetquot Cntrl Schl Dist Kndgtn Tchr 1968-75, 4th Grd Tchr 1976-77, 6th Grd Tchr 1977-; Connetquot Tchrs Assn Building 1972-95; *ai:* Sci Fair Coord 1983-, Judge 1988-; NYSUT 1968-, Bu Rep; Brookhaven Natl Lab Sci Fair Comm 1990-, 1990 Tchr of th NASA Project Seeds 1990-91; *office:* Connetquot Cntrl Schl Distr Islip First St Ronkonkoma NY 11779

THOMAS, RICHARD N., Fifth Grade Teacher; *b:* Coraopolis, PA; *m* Clancy; *c:* Robyn; *ed:* Edinboro St (BS) Elem 1966; Master Equiva PA Dept Ed; *cr:* Warren Cty Schls 5th & 6th Grd Tchr 1966-67; I Elem Schl 5th Grd Tchr 1967-; *ai:* Intramurals; Montour Tchrs Exch Montoul Ed Assn 1967-, Treas; PA St Ed Assn, NEA 1966-; Coraopol FD 1973-, Capt; OH Valley Firemans Assn 1978-, Sec & Treas 198 Outstanding Service 1987; River Valley Firemans Assn 1978-, Sec & 1980-87; St Joseph Parish Cncl 1986-90; Co Chprsn Coraopolis Cent 1986; Coraopolis Civil Service Bd; *home:* 1216 Ridge Ave Coraopo 15108

THOMAS, ROBERT SWAN, Social Studies Teacher; *b:* Washington *ed:* Univ of MD at College Park (BA) Pol Sci 1989, (BS) His Ed 199 Van Grack Axelson & Williamowsky Attorneys Intern, Law Clerk Galland Harashch Morse & Garfinkle PC Paralegal 1990-91; Sherwo Soc Stud Tchr 1994-; *ai:* Acad, Mock Trial Spon; NEA, Montgomer Ed Assn 1994-; *office:* Sherwood HS 300 Olney Sandy Spring Rd Spring MD 20860

THOMAS, SHERRY LEE, Business Teacher; *b:* Oil City, PA; *ed:* In Univ of PA (BS) Bus Ed 1974; 12 Addl Grad Credits; 12 Addl Grad C Clarion Univ of PA; *cr:* Venango Chrstn HS Bus Tchr 1974-93; Cra Area Jr-Sr HS Bus Tchr 1993-; *ai:* Cranberry Ed Assoc 1993-; 1993-; *office:* Cranberry Area Jr-Sr HS 1 Education Dr Seneca PA 1

THOMAS, STEWART P., Biology & Hum Physiology Tch Philadelphia, PA; *m:* Kathy Reilly; *c:* Jennifer Chamick, Ray Chamick; *ed:* Wilkes Coll (BA) Bio 1972; Wilkes Univ (MS) Ed 199 Grad Credits Boston Univ, FIT, Carlow Coll, Univ of AK SE, UT Uni North Pocono Schl Dist Sci Instr 24 Yrs; Maywood Coll Anatomy Spring 1995; *ai:* Scenery & Lighting Designer for HS Theater Product NEA 1972-; BSA 1961-68, Dist Chm, Dist Awd of Merit, 1987-, Cncl Bd; *office:* North Pocono HS 701 Church St Moscow PA 18444*

THOMAS, TAMARA JANE, Special Educator; *b:* Framingham, M Francis G. Jr.; *c:* Hannah, Jordan; *ed:* Fitchburg St Coll (BS) Spec Ed Currently Enrolled Masters in Spec Ed Prgm Multicultural Ed; *cr:* MS Spec Edctr 1987-; *ai:* Issues Group Adv; Spec Ed Team Ldr; *o* Memorial MS 615 Rollstone St Fitchburg MA 01420

THOMAS, THOMAS JAMES,JR., Program Counselor; *b:* Bridg CT; *m:* Anne Aimetti; *c:* Joshua; *ed:* East Stroudsburg Univ (BS) S Ed, His 1979, (BS) Elem Ed 1979; Wilkes Univ (MS) His Ed 198 Unionville-Chadds Ford HS His Tchr 1980-82; Wilkes Univ Up Bound Prgm Res Dir 1981, His Dept Lecturer 1986-88, Upward B Prgm Cnslr 1982-; *ai:* Phi Delta Kappa 1986-; Natl Cncl for His Ed 1 PA Assn of Educl Opportunity Prgms 1983-; Inspirational Tchr Awd Outstanding Young Men of Amer 1989; Who's Who Among Huma Profs 1988; Prgm Selected as Natl Career Ed Model by NCEOA Publications; *office:* Wilkes University Upward Bound Prgm Wilkes PA 18766

THOMAS, VENITA RUTH, 6th Grade Teacher; *b:* Washington, D Ashley Magee, Justin Magee; *ed:* CA St Univ (BS) Elem, Spec Ed Bowie St Univ (MA) Rdng Specialist Ed 1996; Working on MA Spe *cr:* Arch of Washington Cath Schls 3, 6-12 Grd Tchr; Prince George's Pub Schls 1988-; *ai:* Poverty Grant Tutor; Kappa Delta Epsilon 1974- Kappa Delta Pi 1975-; CEC 1972-, VP CSC Campus; *office:* Glass Elem Schl 1011 Marcy Ave Oxon Hill MD 20745*

THOMAS, WILLIAM BENJAMIN, High School Art Teache Pittsburgh, PA; *m:* Dar C.; *ed:* Edinboro Univ (BS) Art Ed 1977; Pittsburgh Film Maker, Univ of Pittsburgh, Edinboro St, Slippery Roc South Park HS Art Tchr 1981-; *ai:* Ski Club; PSEA & NEA 1981-, Paintings in Juried Shows; *office:* South Park HS 2178 Ridge Rd Li PA 15129

THOMAS, WILLIAM D., Music Teacher; *b:* New Brighton, PA; *m:* Monroe; *c:* Beth Horton, W. David, Janet; *ed:* IN Univ of PA (BSME) 1964; Penn St Univ (MED) Mus Ed 1967; *cr:* Peters Twp Schl Dist Choral Mus Tchr 1964-68; Cleveland Hghts City Schl Dist Dir o Hghts Singers 1968-; *ai:* AFT 1964-; MENC 1964-; OMEA 1964- Delta Kappa 1967-; ALCM 1967-; *office:* Cleveland Heights HS 1 Cedar Rd Cleveland Heights OH 44118

THOMAS, WILLIAM J., Eighth Grade Social Stud Tchr; *b:* Elmira, *m:* Vivian Luden; *c:* David M., Sara M.; *ed:* Mansfield Univ (BS) So Geog 1969; Elmira Coll (MS) Ed 1974; *cr:* Northside-Blodgett MS Stud Tchr 1969-; *ai:* Mansfield Un Stu Tchr Assessment Comm; Ea Var Bsbl Head Coach 1985-, Summer Bsbl Camp Dir 1994-; Man Univ Summer Bsbl Camp Staff 1985-;Outcome Based Ed Comm CTA, NYSUT, AFL-CIO 1969-; NBSA 1969-, Soc Chm; Elks Club # 1982-; NRA 1979-; USA Bsbl Coaches 1995-; Amer Lung Assn 1 Neighborhood Chm; Elmira Umpires Chptr Coaching Awd Star-Gazette Twin Tiers Coach of Yr 1995; *office:* Northside Blodget 143 Princeton Ave Corning NY 14830

THOMAS, WILLIAM JOSEPH, High Schl Mathematics Teache Orange, NJ; *m:* Lisa Allen; *c:* William II, Sydney, Jordan; *ed:* Jersey St Coll (BA) Math, Chem; Rutgers Univ at Newark 15 Credits Ap Math; Attnd Saint Peters Coll; NJIT Engrng 1994; *cr:* Ciba-C Pharmeceutical Lab Tech 3 Yrs; Newark Bd of Ed Math Tchr 1 Rutgers Univ Adj Prof of Math 1994-; *ai:* Stu Govt, Brotherhood Bsktbl Coach; Mentor One to One; Attendance Comm; Tutor; NC NJEA 1993-; NAME 1995-; Howard Hughes Flwshp 1995, Bridges Flwshp 1994-95 Rutgers Univ; *office:* University HS 55 Clinton Pl Ne NJ 07108*

THOMAS, WILLIAM RICHARD, Music Teacher; *b:* Pittsburgh, P Diane Spencer; *ed:* Morehead St Univ (BM) Music Performance 198 St Univ (MM) Music Performance 1983; *cr:* Cordova Elem Schl M Tchr 1984-86; Easton HS Music Tchr 1987-; *ai:* Dir Concert C Chamber Singers, Music Theater; SGA Spon; NEA 1984-; MENC 1 MSMTA 1994-, Pres Easter Region; Christ Episcopal Church, Org 1985-; Talbot Cty Arts Cncl Arts Edctr of Yr 1994; *home:* 305 Railroa Saint Michaels MD 21663

THOMAS-HOLDER, SUSAN A., Physics & Chemistry Teache Philadelphia, PA; *w:* Oscar E. (dec); *c:* Duane E. Thomas; *ed:* Che Univ (BS) Scndry Ed Sci 1969; Univ of DE (MS) Chem Ed 1970; Te Univ (MA) African Amer Stud 1990, (PHD) African Amer Stud 1994 Shaw Jr HS Sci Tchr 1968; Howard HS Chem, Physics Tchr 197 Delcastle Tech HS Chem, Physics Tchr, Dept Chair 1980-; *ai:* Umoja of Passage Prgm; NHS Co-Spon; AFT 1970-, Bldg Rep; DTS 1980 Matthew's Episcopal Church 1969-, Vestry Man; NSF Flwshp; NC Dist, DE St, USA Top 4 Tchr of Yr 1985; *office:* Delcastle Tech HS Newport Rd Wilmington DE 19804

THOMBS, TODD WESLEY, Eighth Grade Mathematics Tch Cleveland, OH; *ed:* Mount Union Coll (BS) Math 1991; OH Math & Project Discovery; *cr:* J R Williams Jr HS 8th & 9th Grd Math 1991-95; Chagrin Falls MS 8th Grd Math Tchr 1995-; *ai:* Var Ftbl & T 8th Grd Class Adv; Scorekeeper for Bsktbl Teams; NCTM 1995-; OAT

Leroy Comm Chapel 1993-; Sunday Schl, Mission Trip Ldr; *office:* n Falls MS 77 E Washington St Chagrin Falls OH 44022

IPKINS, LORETTA MARIE, Elementary Teacher; *b:* Chicago, IL; gie E. Jr.; *c:* Katrina, Algie III, Kevin; *ed:* Youngstown St Univ Elem Ed 1970, (MS) Spec Ed 1972; 45 Addl Credit Hrs; *cr:* stown City Schls Elem Tchr 1970-; *ai:* NEA, YEA, OEA 1971-; Mary Haddow Elem Schl 2800 Oak St Ext Youngstown OH 44505

IPSEN, JOHN, Physics Teacher; *b:* Brooklyn, NY; *m:* Mary; *ed:* s Inst (MS) Mechanical Engr 1963; Cooper Union (BME) nical Engr 1961; Attnd PA St Univ; *cr:* US Rubber Research Engr; d Research Lab Engr 1970-73; Penn St Univ Math Instr 1972-; Penn HS Sci Tchr 1973-; *ai:* Intnl Soc Biomechanics 1990-; PSEA 1973-; 973-; Lead Tchr PSC Supercomputing: An Innovative Tool for Tchrs 93; GTE Gift Fellow 1991-92; *office:* Penns Valley Jr Sr HS RD 2 6 Spring Mills PA 16875*

IPSON, AMY JANE (HERMAN), Chemistry Teacher; *b:* York, PA; rey Paul; *c:* Sarah; *ed:* Elizabethtown coll (BS) chem 1991; Working ds Masters Degree in Tchng, Curr PA St Univ; *cr:* Hempfield HS Tchr 1991-; *ai:* Yrbk Adv; Fac Cncl; Mentor Tchr; NEA 1991-; Pub; Nom for Chem Tchr of Yr; summer Rsrch Ldr for HS, Coll ; *office:* Hempfield HS 200 Stanley Ave Landisville PA 17538*

IPSON, ANNA FULLER, Teacher of Handicapped; *b:* Parkers g, PA; *m:* C. Robert; *c:* Gayle Ann, Roberta Lynne; *ed:* Clarion St Coll (BS) Ed, El Ed, Spec Ed 1958; Youngstown St Univ (MS) Ed, 86; Kent St Univ, Westminster Coll at New Wilmington Post Grad *cr:* Northem Butler Schl Dist Spec Ed Tchr 1958-61; Austintown Schl Dist Spec Ed Tchr 1961-91; Merry Moppet Tchr of 0-18 Month hildren 1994-95; OH Central Schl System Spec Ed Tchr, Tchr of opmentally Handicapped, Coord 1995-; *ai:* Dev Spec Ed Prgms for erated Individuals; OH Ed Assn 1961-; NEA 1958-; Correctional Ed 995-; Martha Holden Jennings Scholar.*

IPSON, ANNE, Educational Technology Teacher; *b:* Brockton, MA; drew E.; *c:* Stephanie A., Elizabeth C., Adam R.; *ed:* Bridgewater St (BA) Bio 1972, (MAT) Physics 1984; Attnd FL St Univ at asse,Cambridge Coll; *cr:* North Jr HS Sci Tchr 1972-94, Educl Tech *ai:* PALMS Specialist; Prof Dev Provider; Brockton After Schl Instr; NSTA, MASS, SEMASS, MTA, BEA, NEA, PCEA 1972-; Church of Christ 1975-; *office:* North Jr HS 108 Oak St Brockton 2401

IPSON, CATHERINE PERRY, Math Teacher; *b:* New Brunswick, John B.; *c:* Janelle, Kathleen, Caryn; *ed:* Douglass Coll (BA) Math el 1981; Trinity Coll (MS) Schl Admin 1996; *cr:* St Vincent Pallotti ath Tchr, Dept Chprsn 1983-88; Holy Family Educl Ctr 8th Grd Tchr 90; Seneca Vly HS Math Tchr 1990-; *ai:* MCEA, MSTA 1990-; Seneca Valley HS 12700 Middlebrook Rd Germantown MD 20874*

IPSON, CHRISTY N., Administrative Vice Principal; *b:* Millville, *l:* Glassboro St Coll (BA) Hlth & PE 1978, (MA) Hlth & PE 1981, Schl Admin 1993; Nova Southeastern Doctoral Pgm Educl Ldrshp; llville Sr HS Hlth, PE, Driver Ed Tchr & Admin Vice-Prin 1978-; *ai:* r Act Coord; Field Hockey, Track & Field, Bsktbl, Swimming, Tennis Sftbl Former Coach; NAASP & NJSPA 1993-; NEA; Red Cross Spcl Olympics 1991-; Amer Career Soc 1993-; *office:* Millville Sr 0 Wade Blvd Millville NJ 08332

MPSON, CLIFTON C., Math Department Chairman; *b:* Johnstown, Janet Steward; *c:* Scott, Gary, Jeff, Mike; *ed:* Gannon Univ (BA) 1965; Univ of Buffalo (MS) Math Ed 1971; Attnd SUNY at Fredonia nestown Comm Coll; *cr:* Jamestown Comm Coll Part-Time Instr 87; Southwestern HS Math Tchr 1965- & Dept Chm 1985-; *ai:* Vllybl Coach; NEA & NYEA 1965-; Southwestern Tchrs Assn 1965-, Pres ief Negotiator; Chautauqua Cty Ath Assn 1975-85, Sec & Treas; western Ftbl Parents Booster 1981-, Pres 1991; Natl Sci Fndtn ient; *office:* Southwestern Central H S 600 Hunt Rd Jamestown NY

MPSON, DOLORES BAK, Business Teacher; *b:* Troy, NY; *m:* rick E.; *c:* Greg, Diana Rye; *ed:* Russell Sage Coll at Troy (BS) Bus Johns Hopkins Univ at Baltimore (MED) Ed 1976; 16 Addl Hrs; *cr:* port HS Bus Tchr 1959-60; Towson HS Bus Tchr 1960-71, Adult Ed; een HS Bus Tchr 1971-; *ai:* FBLA Spon 1972-; Waiver Comm; rd Co Tchrs Assn, MD St Tchrs Assn 1971-; *office:* Aberdeen H S 251 ise Rd Aberdeen MD 21001

MPSON, EDWIN G., Assoc Prof of Bus, Office Tech; *b:* nsburg, NY; *m:* Debra; *c:* Jonathan, Jeffrey, James; *ed:* North Cnty n Coll (AS) Bus Admin 1971; Univ at Albany (BS) Bus Admin 1973, Bus Ed, Advanced Classroom 1977; Post Grad Robert Morris Coll, FL Univ, NY Univ, Amer Univ; *cr:* Henderson Cntrl HS Bus Tchr 74; Copenhagen Cntrl HS Bus Tchr 1974-83; Univ at Albany Adj Prof 83; Jefferson Comm Coll Assoc Prof of Bus 1983-; *ai:* Club Adv, Chaperone, Lib, Petitions Comm; Acad Advisement Task Force; NYS Chrs 1972-; NYS Office Tech Edctrs 1983-; NYC Bus Ed; Theodore evelt Assn 1988-; North Side Improvement League 1986-; Jefferson istorical Soc 1990-; Clarence Seeber Fitness Awd 1995-; Article Pub; ip Awds; *office:* Jefferson Comm Coll Outer Coffeen Street town NY 13601

MPSON, ELAINE CARTER, Retired Elementary Principal; *b:* ndaiqua, NY; *m:* Jay F.; *c:* Laurie, Carrie, Craig, Julie, Catherine; *ed:* iv of Geneseo (BA) Gen Ed, Speech, Dramatic Art 1956; Addl 33 Hrs Ed 1972; *cr:* Gates Schl 2-3 Grd Tchr 1956-58; Chili Dist Schl 2-3 Chr 1956-58; Penfield Cntrl Dist Schl Kndgtn Tchr 1958-61, K-6 Grd Chr 1965-78; New Covenant Chrstn Schl Gr 5, Kndgtn Primary Supvr, Prin 1978-89; *ai:* Care & Concern Chprsn; Bethel Tchr, Prayer ; Young Audiences of Rochester 1989-, Prgm Mem; Penfield United Church 1962-, Chaired & Served on Comms; Asbury Storehouse ; Started Presch Prgm for New Covenant; *home:* 230 Commodore Rochester NY 14625

MPSON, ERNEST FRANCIS,JR., Reading Specialist; *b:* urgh, PA; *m:* Barbara Lynn Rice; *c:* Jill S., Elizabeth B.; *ed:* Indiana of PA (BS) Eng Ed 1971, (MED) Eng 1973; Shippensburg Univ) Rdng 1976; Rdng Specialist Cert; Millersville Univ Rdng Suprv Penn St York Campus Addl Grad Credits; *cr:* York Suburban Schl Dist 1972-; *ai:* Newspaper Adv;Eng as a Second Lang Coord; York rban Ed Assn 1972-, Pres, Sec, Membership; PSEA & NEA, Chair, Rep; Phi Kappa Psi 1970-, Adv; *office:* York Suburban MS 455 ale Dr York PA 17402

MPSON, EUGENIA GAY, Art Teacher; *b:* Uniontown, PA; *ed:* oro Univ (BS) Art Ed 1973; 38 Addl Credits Art, Ed; *cr:* ellsville Area Schl Dist Art, 7th, 9th Grd Advanced Art Tchr 23 Yrs; chl Newspaper Spon 1991-; PDE In-Svc Credit Course Tchr; Art Dept 1973-; Mentor, Cooperating Tchr Seton Hill Coll; NEA, PSEA , Pub Relations Dir 1988-; CAEA 1973-, Pub Relations Dir 1988-, Rep 1990-92; NAEA 1973-, Outstanding PA Mid Art Educator of Yr Westmoreland Coll Art Natls, Westmoreland Arts & Heritage val 1992; Seton Hill Coll Art Educators Show 1987, 1989, 1991, 1994; of Pittsburgh at Johnstown One Person Show 1985; Illustrated, Wrote Assisted 4-6 Art for Young Child Curr Guide; *office:* Connellsville Jr HS E Locust St Extension Connellsville PA 15425*

THOMPSON, EVELYN BOYD, Second Grade Instructor; *b:* Yellow Creek Twp, OH; *m:* Ronald K.; *c:* Elizabeth Thompson-Davis, George, Megan, Ira; *ed:* Univ of Steubenville (BS) Elem Ed 1972; Univ of Dayton (MS) Rdng 1985; *cr:* Southern Local Schls First, Second Grd Instr 1969-; *ai:* SLTA, OEA, NEA 1969-; Delta Kappa Gamma; 4-H; *office:* Southern Local Primary Schl 38825 State Route 39 Salineville OH 43945*

THOMPSON, FRANCIS A., Retired Science Teacher; *b:* Bloomingdale, NY; *m:* Catherine Fettig; *c:* Joseph; *ed:* Union Coll (MS) Geology, Chem 1965; *cr:* North Syracuse Cntrl Schl 7th Grd Adv Placement 1958-59; Hoosic Vly Cntr Schl Earth Sci, Chem 1959-94; *ai:* Bldg Mngmt Team; NYSUT; AFT; NEA; NSF Grant 1960-64.*

THOMPSON, GILBERT ROSS, Math Teacher & Coach; *b:* Bethesda, MD; *m:* Angela Lorenzo; *c:* Ross, Emma; *ed:* Univ of MD (BS) Ed 1971; 85 Credit Hrs Post Grad Stud; *cr:* Pyle Jr HS Tchr 1971; Western Jr HS Tchr, Coach 1972-89; Walt Whitman HS Coach 1982-88; Quince Orchard HS Math Tchr, Coach 1989-; *ai:* Var Boys Vlybl Coach; Natl Fed Interscholastic Coaches Assn 1982-; Amer Vlybl Coaches Assn 1988-; Nine Coach of Yr Awds; *office:* Quince Orchard HS 15800 Quince Orchard Rd Gaithersburg MD 20878

THOMPSON, HENRY B.,JR., 5th & 6th Grade Teacher; *b:* Wilkinsburg, PA; *m:* Bella D. Mangaoang; *ed:* CA St Coll (BS) Elem Ed 1969; WV Univ (MA) Elem Ed 1976; Attnd LaVerne Coll, OH Univ, Univ of Akron; *cr:* Hancock Co Schls 4th Grd Lang Arts Tchr, Ath Dir 1969-70; Lorain Schls 6th Grd Tchr 1970-78; Turtle Creek Schls Remedial Math Tchr 1978-80; St Peter Schl Title 14 Logical Thinking Tchr 1980-81; Woodland Hills Schl Remedial Math Tchr 1981-83; Churchill Acad Elem Sci Tchr 1983-85; Cheswick Chrstn Acad Head Tchr, 5th-6th Grd Tchr 1985-; *ai:* HS, Jr HS Ftbl, Jr HS Track, HS Girls Bsktbl, JV Boys Bsktbl, HS Boys Flag Ftbl, Elem IM Flag Fbtl Boys, Girls, Elem IM Bsktbl, Elem Co-Ed Vlybl Coach; Prins Comm; Logical Thinking Games Coach; Summer Dance Festival Announcer; Spon of Sci, His Newsletter; Field Trips; Editor of Tomorrow Ecology; Flwshp of Chrstn Anglers Soc; Monroeville Assembly of God; Natl Family Opinion Pollster; Lorain City Schls Tchr of Yr Nominee; Tomorrow Ecology Newsletter 3rd Place Nationally Royal Crown Cola Environment Contest; Producer, Writer, Dir comm Access Cable TV Shows; Honors with Fishin UNFS, Animalingo Shows; *office:* Cheswick Christian Acad 1407 Pittsburgh St Cheswick PA 15024

THOMPSON, JEAN (CAVANAGH), English Teacher; *b:* Attleboro, MA; *m:* William B.; *ed:* Bridgewater St Coll (BA) Eng 1973; Lesley Coll (MED) Curr Dev Integrating The Arts 1994; *cr:* North Attleboro Jr HS Eng Tchr 1973-; *ai:* Yrbk, Writing Club Adv; Schl Improvement Cncl; AFT 1985-; NCTE 1994-; *office:* North Attleboro Jr HS 45 S Washington St North Attleboro MA 02760

THOMPSON, JOAN HULSE, Assoc Prof of Political Sci; *b:* Washington, DC; *m:* Robert R.; *c:* Jonathan, Katharine; *ed:* Gettysburg Coll (BA) Pol Sci 1971; Johns Hopkins Univ (MA) Pol Sci 1972, (PHD) Pol Sci 1978; *cr:* US Office of Ed Prgm Asst UNESCO 1972-73; Union Coll Visting Asst Prof 1978-79; Luther Coll Asst Prof 1979-86; Beaver Coll Assoc Prof 1986-; *ai:* Pre Law Adv; Amer Pol Sci Assn 1979-; PA Pol Sci Assn 1986-, Bd 1987-88; Amer Assn of Univ Women 1982-, Bd & Pub Policy Chair, Outstanding Woman NEMCO Branch 1994; AAUW Fellow 1983-; APSA Congressional Fellow 1985-86; Chapter in Women in Politics Outsiders or Insiders 1996; Entry in Womens Interest Groups 1995; *office:* Beaver Coll 450 S Easton Rd Glenside PA 19038

THOMPSON, JOHN R., Lead Teacher; *ed:* Univ of Cincinnati (BA) His 1972, (MA) Medieval His 1973; Dartmouth Coll Cmptr Learning Information Processing; *cr:* Heinold Jr HS Tchr 1973-83; Western Hills HS Tchr 1983-86; Walnut Hills Coll Prep Acad Lead, Ancient, Medieval, European His, AP, Philosophy Tchr 1986-; *ai:* Soc Stud Curr; AFT, CFT 1975-, Exec Cncl; NCSS 1990-; Natnl Cncl His Ed 1996-; West Chester Soccer Club 1987-, Coach; Jennigs Scholor St Awd.*

THOMPSON, JOHN ROBERT, Mathematics Department Chair; *b:* New Castle, PA; *m:* Elizabeth; *c:* Carolyn, Philip; *ed:* Allegheny Coll (BS) Math 1962; Duke Univ (MAT) Ed 1963; Rutgers Univ (MA) Math 1967; *cr:* George Washington HS Math Tchr 1962-64; Ardsley HS Math Tchr 1964-66; Gilman Schl Math Tchr 1967-; *ai:* Cross Cntry Head Coach; Track Asst Coach; Math Contests Spon; NCTM 1983-; Cathedral of Incarnation 1980-, Registrar; Russell Chair Winner 1992; Corcoran Awd 1994; *office:* Gilman Schl 5407 Roland Ave Baltimore MD 21210

THOMPSON, JON STEPHEN, Social Studies Teacher; *b:* Gloversville, NY; *m:* Sharron Lee Pellegrino; *c:* Sean Keven, Shane Courtney, Joshua Colin; *ed:* St Univ at Plattsburgh (BS) Scndry Soc Sci 1970; 30 Addl Hrs Ed; *cr:* Fonda Fultonville Cntrl Schl 7-8, 9th-10th Grd Scndry Soc Stud Tchr 1970-; *ai:* Seventh Grd & Yrbk Adv; Fonda Fultonville Tchrs Assn 1970-, Treas 10 Yrs; NY St United Tchrs, Amer Fed of Tchrs 1970-; Barbara Gray Achievement Awd by Bd of Ed 1991; *office:* Fonda Fultonville Central Schl Cemetery St Fonda NY 12068*

THOMPSON, JUDY A., 6th Grade Teacher; *b:* Bucyrus, OH; *m:* Allan Starr; *c:* Duane, Allyson Thiele, Melinda; *ed:* OH St Univ (BS) Elem Ed 1962; SUNY at Brockport Soc Stud, Rdng 30 Hrs; *cr:* North Robinson 1st Grd Tchr 1960-62; Albion MS 5th Grd Tchr 1973-83, 6th Grd Tchr 1983-; *ai:* NYSUT 1973-; Bldg Rep; Albion Tchrs Assn 1973-; Albion BPW 1988-; United Meth Church Dist Bd of Trustees; West Barre UMC 1972-, PPR Chm, Sunday Schl Tchr, Choir, Admin Bd, Garrett Club; Bus & Prof Women's Assn; Prof Woman of Yr 1991; Barre Councilwoman 1980-88; *office:* Albion MS 254 East Ave Albion NY 14411

THOMPSON, JULIA A., Professor of Physics; *b:* Little Rock, AR; *m:* David E. Kraus Jr; *c:* Diane E., Vincent S. Szewczyk, Lawrence L. Lynch; *ed:* Cornell Coll (BA) Math, Physics 1964; Yale Univ (MS) Physics 1966, (PhD) Physics (Elem Particle) 1969; *cr:* Brookhaven Natl Lab Research Assoc 1969-71; Univ of UT Res Assoc, Assoc Instr 1971-72; Univ of Pittsburgh Asst Prof 1972-78, Assoc Prof 1978-86, Prof 1986-, NSF REV Dir 1992-; *ai:* Research Experiences for Undergrad in Physics Dir; APS 1969-, Status of Women in Physics Comm; Unitarian Church 1973-, Bd Mem; Woodrow Wilson Fellow 1964-65; Mortar Bd; Phi Beta Kapp Natl Acad of Sci Exchange to USSR 1989-90; Pub Articles; 1 Ed Book; Conf Talks; *office:* Univ Of Pittsburgh Dept of Physics, Astronomy Pittsburgh PA 15260*

THOMPSON, KAROL MARGERY, Instructor Emeritus; *b:* Ft Myers, FL; *ed:* FL St Univ (BS) Art Ed 1960; Amer Univ (MA) Fine Art 1965; Penn St Univ (PHD) Art Ed & Phil 1979; *cr:* Terry Parker HS Art Tchr 1960-62; Suitland HS Art Tchr & Dept Chair 1962-87; Penn St Univ Art Ed Grad Instr 1970-71; Catonsville Comm Coll Evening Instr 1975; Suitland Ctr for The Arts Visual & Performing Arts Magnet Instr & Dept Chair 1987-92; *ai:* NEA 1992-; Prince Geo Retired Tchrs 1992-; MD Art Ed Assoc, St Outstdng Art Edctr 1984; Sierra Club; ASPCA; Amnesty Intnl; Chesapeake Bay Fndtn; Teach Drawing Classes; Have Woodworking Shop Making Furniture; Paint; Write Short Stories & Work in My Small Comm; Chaired Visual Art Dept 25 Yrs; Helped Design & Open Cty Wide Magnet in the Visual & Performing Arts; WA Post Agnes Meyer Outstdng Tchr of the Yr 1988; St of MD Governors Citation 1992; Cited & Commended in the Congressional Record US House of Reps 1992; Proclamation of Achvmt by Prince Geo Co MD Cty Exec Farris Glendening 1992; Cert of Merit Bd of Ed 1989; *office:* Suitland Ctr for the Arts 5200 Silver Hill Rd Forestville MD 20747

THOMPSON, KELLY LORRAINE, Mathematics Teacher; *b:* Oneonta, NY; *ed:* Rochester Inst of Tech (BS) Bus Admin, Fin 1990; SUNY Oneonta (BA) Scndry Ed, Math 1992; Working Toward MA SUNY at Binghamton; *cr:* DE, Chenango Cty Schls Sub Tchr 1992-94; Norwich City Schls Math Tchr 1994-; *ai:* JV Sftbl, Asst Var Girls Bsktbl Coach; NEA 1992-; *office:* Norwich HS Midland Dr Norwich NY 13815

THOMPSON, LESLIE ROBERTS, Eighth Grade Teacher; *b:* Altoona, PA; *m:* Dennis M.; *c:* Suzanne, Mark; *ed:* St Francis Coll (BS) Elem Ed 1974; Permanent Cert; *cr:* Belletonte MS Lang Arts Tchr 1974-75; Holy Name Schl 8th Grd Tchr 1983-; *ai:* Yrbk Adv; NCEA 1983-; *home:* 414 Ashbrook Cir Ebensburg PA 15931

THOMPSON, LINDA DUNSTON, High School Principal; *b:* Orange, NJ; *m:* Alfred Jr.; *c:* Tamika, Altwan, Ayana; *ed:* Denison Univ (BA) Sociology 1973; Montclair St Univ (MA) Guid, Cnslng 1980; 45 Post Hrs Supervision, Ed; *cr:* YWCA Yth Dir, Day Group Dir 1973-80; Univ Hosp Soc Worker 1978-81; Orange MS Tchr, Guid Cnslr, VP 1981-89; Roselle Bd of Ed Dir of Guid 1989-94, HS Prin 1994-; *ai:* St Matthew Bowling Team, Sr Choir; Roselle Admin Assn 1989-; NJP&SA, NAACP, NABSE 1985-; Essex Cty Girl Scouts 1993-, Bd; Orange Juvenile Conf 1974-, Chprsn, 20 Yrs Svc; Heywood Ave PTA 1992-; Delta Sigma Theta 1993-; Montclair St EOF Bd 1994-; *office:* Abraham Clark HS 122 E 6th Ave Roselle NJ 07203*

THOMPSON, LUCY DAWSON, Language Arts Teacher; *b:* Detroit, MI; *m:* Charles S.; *c:* Stephen W.; *ed:* Bowling Green St Univ (BSEd) Eng & Speech 1972; Wrights St Univ (MED) Curr & Supervision 1978; Univ of Dayton (MED) Guidance 1993; Attnd Antioch Univ; *cr:* Urbana Jr HS 7th & 8th Grd Lang Arts Tchr 1973-, Guidance Counseling 1993-; *ai:* Past Dept Chair; Urbana City Schls Merit Awd 1991, 1992, 1994; *office:* Urbana Jr HS 500 Washington Ave Urbana OH 43078

THOMPSON, LYNN P., 6th Grade Mathematics Teacher; *b:* Dayton, OH; *m:* Robert M.; *c:* Jennifer, Emily; *ed:* Wilmington Coll (BA) Elem Ed & Eng 1965; Urbana Univ Elem Ed 1963; Addl Work Wright St Univ, Miami Univ & Ashland Univ; *cr:* Felicity-Franklin Schl 5th-6th Grd Tchr 1965-69; Oakwood City Schl 6th Grd Tchr 1970-71; Springboro Comm Schl 6th Grd Tchr 1971-; *ai:* 6th Grd Team Ldr; Jr High Chrldng Adv; OEA & NEA 1965-, St MAT Team; CEA 1971-, Pres 3 Times; OMSA 1988-; OCTM 1986-; PTO, Rep; Presbyn Church, Session-Elder; Elem Jr High Stud Comm, Sec; All Amer Drill Team Bd, Pageant & Camp Dir; Math Curr Comms; Eisenhower Grant Math; *office:* Springboro Jr HS 705 S Main St Springboro OH 45066*

THOMPSON, MARGARET, Physics & Chemistry Teacher; *b:* Boston, MA; *c:* Mark, Ann Thompson Buckley; *ed:* Emmanuel Coll (BA) Chem 1952; Boston Coll (MED) Sci Tchng 1989; 37 Credit Hrs Beyond Masters Degree; *cr:* Boston Pub Schl HS Tchr 1970-; *ai:* In-Schl Sci Fair Spon; AFT 1970-; NEA 1970-; Chem Curr Guide for HS Pub & Used by St Dept of Ed.*

THOMPSON, MARGARET A. (FRANKS), Music Teacher; *b:* Wilkes-Barre, PA; *m:* Charles L. Jr.; *c:* Kathryn; *ed:* Wilkes Univ (BS) Music Ed 1969; Marywood Coll (MA) Music 1981; 60 Post Grad Credit Hrs; *cr:* Hazleton Area Schl Dist Music Tchr, Choral Dir 1969-; *ai:* Renaissance Prgm Exec, Area Schl Dist Multi-Cultural Comm; Stu Cncl Adv; Stu Assistance Prgm; NEA, PSEA 1969-; NASAA 1994-; West Hazleton Trinity Luth 1994-, VP Congregational Cncl; Luth Welfare Svc 1990-, Aux Mem; Helping Hands 1985-, Vol; Vol Home Care 1995; Conyngham Vly Civic Org Vol; *office:* West Hazleton Jr HS 325 North St West Hazleton PA 18201

THOMPSON, MARIA REGINA,IHM, Eighth Grade Teacher; *b:* Philadelphia, PA; *ed:* Immaculata Coll (AB) Theology, Bio, Elem, Scndry Ed 1988; *cr:* SS Clement-Irenaeus Schl Seventh Grd Tchr 1988-89, Eighth Grd Tchr 1989-93; St John Bosco Schl Eighth Grd Tchr 1993-; *ai:* Stu Cncl Moderator; Rel Coord; NCEA 1988-; *home:* 189 E County Line Rd Hatboro PA 19040

THOMPSON, MARIAN SHARP, 6th Grade Teacher; *b:* Zanesville, OH; *m:* Terry William; *ed:* OH St Univ (BS) Elem Ed 1973; *cr:* Maysville Local Schl Dist 6th Grd Tchr 1973-; *ai:* 6th Grd Club Adv; Dist Spelling Bee Comm; Percheron Horse Assn of Amer 1989-, 2 World Championships 1996; Amer Quarter Horse Assn 1991, World Qualifier; Martha Holdren Jennings Scholar; Tchr of the Week 1994; *home:* 270 Kopchak Rd Zanesville OH 43701

THOMPSON, MARK ANDREW, K-6th Grd PE Teacher; *b:* Cincinnati, OH; *m:* Melissa Anna Birkofer; *c:* Robert Scott, Kara Nicole; *ed:* Univ of Cincinnati (BS) PE 1985; 10 Grad Hrs Educl Admin; *cr:* Westwood Elem Schl PE Tchr 1985-; *ai:* Elder HS Var Bsbl Coach; 6th Grd Boys Bsktbl Coach; Instrl Bsktbl League Coord; IMs Coord; Tchr in Charge; Discipline Comm; Sports Medicine Comm Advy Bd; Say Soccer Coach; Southwest OH Bsbl Coaches Assn 1986-, VP, Pres; OHSBCA 1990-; AAHPERD 1987-; CFT 1985-; Phi Epsilon Kappa 1988-; Greater Cincinnati Jaycees Edctr of Yr; GCL Coach of Yr; PTA Outstdng Edctr Finalist; *office:* Westwood Elem Schl 2981 Montana Ave Cincinnati OH 45211*

THOMPSON, MARY, Eng Lit & Composition Teacher; *b:* Buffalo, NY; *ed:* Cath Univ (BA) Eng 1952; St Bonaventure (MA) Eng 1960; Univ of Notre Dame (MA) Theology 1978; Mc Master Univ (PHD) Biblical Stud 1985; *cr:* Mt St Mary Eng Tchr 4 Times; Daemen Coll Rel Stud Tchr 1982-84; Canisius Coll Rel Stud Tchr 1984-95; Trocaire Coll Cath Biblical Schl Bible Tchr 1994-; *ai:* Mid Sts Evaluation Comm; Cath Biblical Assn 1995-; Soc of Biblical Lit 1984-; Books: The Role of Disbelief in Mark; Mary of Magdala: Apostle and Leader Adult Education Classes; Many Articles & Pub Speaking Engagements; *office:* Mt St Mary Acad 3756 Delaware Ave Kenmore NY 14217

THOMPSON, NANCY L., Adjunct Instructor in Art; *b:* Corinth, NY; *c:* Maurice D.; *ed:* St Univ of NY at New Paltz (BS) Art Ed 1968; 6 Grad Credits Painting; *cr:* Ockawamic Cntrl Schl Elem Art Tchr 1969-71; Essex Cty ARC Daily Living Skills Tchr 1986-89; North Cntry CC Adj Art Inst 1993-; *ai:* Variety Show Stage Design, Performance, People Asst; Ticonderoga Assembly of God Church 1983-, Sunday Schl; Girls Scouts, Cub Scouts 1980's-; Various Art Exhibits; *office:* North Country Community Coll Montcalm St Ticonderoga NY 12883*

THOMPSON, NANCY LEE, First Grade Teacher; *b:* New Castle, PA; *m:* Dennis A.; *c:* Melissa, David; *ed:* Edinboro (BA) Elem Ed 1972; *cr:* Mercer Elem Schl Tchr 1972-; *ai:* NEA, PSEA, MEA 1972-; Bethany U P Church 1974-, Elder, Lab I Instr, Worship Team; *office:* Mercer Elem Schl 301 Lamor Rd Mercer PA 16137

THOMPSON, NANCY MARIE, Psychology Teacher; *b:* Sewickley, PA; *m:* James C.; *ed:* Waynesburg Coll (BA) Soc Sci 1974; Geneva Coll Scndry Ed Eng Degree; *cr:* Ambridge Area Schl Dist Psych, Sociology, Amer Cultures Tchr 1975-; *ai:* Former Class, Chrldng Spon; Schl Act Chaperone; NEA, PSEA, AAEA 1975-; Bus & Prof Women 1983-86, Schlsp Chprsn; *office:* Ambridge Area HS 909 Duss Ave Ambridge PA 15003

THOMPSON, PATRICIA, Fifth Grade Teacher; *b:* Nashville, NC; *ed:* Fayetteville St Univ (BS) Elem Ed 1961; Coll of New Rochelle (MS) Ed, Rdng 1972; 60 Addl Credits; Attnd East Carolina Univ, UNC at Chapel Hill; *cr:* South Nash Elem Schl First Grd Tchr 1961-68; W. L. Greene Elem Schl Second Grd Tchr 1968-69; Longfellow Elem Schl Fourth-Sixth Grd Tchr 1969-; *ai:* Grd Chprsn; AFT, NYSUT 1969-, Mbrshp Sec; PTA

Jenkins Awd; Grant Establish Schl Store Math Class; *home:* 45 S 13th Ave Mount Vernon NY 10550

THOMPSON, PATRICIA TERRY, Fifth Grade Teacher; *b:* New York, NY; *ed:* NY Univ (BS) Elem Ed 1972; City Coll of NY (MS) Elem Ed 1976; Fordham Univ Credits in Admin; *cr:* CES 55 Tchr 1972-74; CES 70 Tchr 1974-75; PS 109-JHS 82 Rdng Tchr 1975-76; PS 122 Tchr 1976-; *ai:* UFT 1972-; *office:* PS 122 Marble Hill 260 W Kingsbridge Rd Bronx NY 10463*

THOMPSON, PAUL, HS Social Studies Teacher; *b:* Los Angeles, CA; *ed:* Oral Roberts Univ (BA) Soc Stud Ed 1987; Montclair St Univ (MA) Amer His 1992; *cr:* East Ramapo Cntrl Schl Dist Jr High Soc Stud Tchr 1987-90; Nyack Union Free Schl Dist HS Soc Stud Tchr 1990-; *ai:* AFT 1990-; NCSS, NY St Cncl for Soc Stud 1988-; Rockland Cncl for Soc Stud 1989-, Sec; *office:* Nyack HS 360 Christian Herald Rd Upper Nyack NY 10960*

THOMPSON, PHILLIP J., Associate Professor; *b:* Logwood Hanover, Jamaica W. I.; *c:* Mark Anthony; *ed:* West Indies Coll (BTH) Theology 1970; Andrews Univ (MDIV) Divinity 1973; Howard Univ (MSW) Soc Work 1976; Univ of MD (PHD) Soc Welfare 1986; George Washington Unvi Multicultural, Cultural Diversity Cert 1992; *cr:* Columbia Union Coll Instr, Asst Prof, Prof 1977-; Hadley Meml Hosp Family Hlth Dir 1989-92; Childrens Natl Med Ctr Soc Work 1987-; DC Govt Supervisory Soc Work 1994-95; Hillcrest Childrens Ctr Clinical Supvr 1995-; *ai:* Intnl Acad of Prof, Behavioral Medicine 1982-; MD Neighborhood Networks 1979-; Sligo Comm Hlth Ctr 1987-, Bd Mem.*

THOMPSON, RANDY JAROLD, 7th-8th Grade Teacher; *b:* Cambridge, OH; *m:* Cheryl Dymidowski; *c:* Joshua, Miranda; *ed:* Bethany Coll (BS) Math 1974; OH Univ & West Liberty St Coll Grad Hrs; *cr:* Bethesda Elem 7th-8th Grd Math & Sci Tchr 1990-; *ai:* Ftbl Coach 1989-; Bsktbl Coach 1990-; 8th Grd Class Adv 1990-; Math Counts Coach 1991-; Sci Fair Dir 1992-; Women in Sci Adv; 5th-6th Grd Flag Ftbl Dir; Head Track Coach; NEA 1990-; OEA 1990-; NCTM 1990-; Flushing Chrstn Church 1980-, Deacon; Union Local Booster Club 1990-; *office:* Bethesda Elem Schl PO Box 98 Bethesda OH 43719

THOMPSON, RENNY MILLEN, High School English Teacher; *b:* Greensburg, PA; *c:* Brandon; *ed:* Grove City Coll (BA) Commnctn Arts 1974; Duquesne Univ (MS) Ed & Rdng Specialist 1979; Forest Univ 18 Credit Hrs; *cr:* Norwin Schl Dist Jr High Rdng Tchr 4 Yrs, K-12th Grd Rdng Specialist 10 Yrs, HS Eng Tchr 4 Yrs; *ai:* Knight Krier Newspaper Adv; NEA 1977-; *home:* 33 Meadow Dr Greensburg PA 15601

THOMPSON, ROBERT LUTHER, History Mentor; *b:* Delaware, OH; *m:* Betty Sander; *c:* Robert j., Sandra, Susan, Steven, Laurie; *ed:* North AL Univ (BA) His & Ger 1954; Duke Univ (MA) His 1958, (EDD) Higher Ed 1968; *cr:* Duke Univ Financial Aid Dir 1958-66; Duke Univ Medical Schl Exec & Sec Admission Comm 1966-69, Assoc Dir Analytical Stud 1969-72; Assn Amer Med Coll Dir Stu Svcs 1972-75; Assn Amer Colls Osteo Med Dir Ed Ser 1975-77; Univ of Med Dent of NJ Asst & Assoc Dean 1977-91; Thomas Edison St Coll Mentor in His 1992-; *ai:* Amer Assn Hist Med 1980-; Med Hist Soc NJ 1980-, VP & Pres; Section on Med Hist 1985-; Coll of Phy of Phil; Coll of Physicians of Philadelphia Flwshp; Numerous Articles Pub; *home:* 9 Beechtree Ln Plainsboro NJ 08536

THOMPSON, ROBERT W., Principal; *b:* Blytheville, AR; *ed:* Westfield St Coll (BS) Ed 1975, (MS) Educl Admin 1986; *cr:* Powder Mill MS Hlth & PE Tchr 1976-77; Granville Village Schl His Tchr 1980-90, Prin 1990-; *ai:* MA Elem Schl Prin 1990-; NAESP 1990-; *office:* Granville Village Schl 409 Main Rd Granville MA 01034

THOMPSON, ROGER P., 7th Grade Teacher; *b:* Caribou, ME; *m:* Beatrice Ann Caldwell; *c:* Shannon Caldwell; *ed:* Univ of ME (BS) Eng 1969; Tchng at Rdng, Bldg Portfohos, Cmptr Courses, Let & Right Brian; *cr:* Sincocli Schl 4th Grd Tchr 1969-72; Hilltop Elem Schl 5th Grd Tchr 1973-80; Intermediate Schl 5th Grd Tchr 1981-82; Caribou MS 7th, 8th Grd Tchr 1983-; Summer Migrant Tchr 1-8 Grd Coord 1993-95; *ai:* Talent Show; Open House Chm; Summer Span Migrant Schl Age Coord; Comm Project Fund Raisers with Class; Caribou Tchrs Assn 1969-; ME Tchr Assn 1969-; NEA 1969-; CAribou Cares About Kids Parade; Church Chm of Bd of Dirs; Chrstn Ed Comm; *home:* RR 4 Box 7160 Caribou ME 04736

THOMPSON, SHIRLEY D., Sci Chprsn & Chemistry Tchr; *b:* Fort Eustis, VA; *m:* Bruce C.; *c:* Kimberly, Brianne; *ed:* Clarion Univ (BS) Chem 1974; SUNY at New Paltz (MS) Ed 1990; Univ of NH 60 Hrs Organic Chem; Ed Admin; *cr:* Middletown HS Chem Tchr 1985-; *ai:* Sci Club Adv; Scholastic Bowl Adv; Amer Chem Soc; Sci Tchrs of NYS; NSTA; *office:* Middletown HS Gardner Ave Ext Middletown NY 10940

THOMPSON, STEPHANIE LYNN, Computer Technology Teacher; *b:* Florence, AL; *ed:* Boro Of Manhattan Comm (AA) Lbrl Arts 1990; 30 Credits Occupational Ed, Spec Ed, Ed; *cr:* Aspex Inc Cmptr Technician 1983-89, Purchasing Mgr 1986-89; Modulation Scis Inc Electronics Technician, Purchasing Agent 1989-91; Queens Voc & Tech HS Cmptr Tech Tchr 1992-; *ai:* Cmptr Lab Tutoring; Programming, Cmptr Maintenance, Repair Vol; Cmptr Technician; NYSUT, UFT, AFT 1992-; All Saints' R. C. Church 1989-; Article Pub; *office:* Queens Voc & Tech HS 37-02 47th Ave Long Island City NY 11101*

THOMPSON, SUSAN I., Elementary Principal; *b:* Catlettsburg, KY; *m:* Tommy G.; *c:* Emme; *ed:* BluefieldSt Coll (BS) Elem Ed 1987; OH Univ (MED) Educl Ldrshp 1994; Post-Grad Principalship Cert; *cr:* Morgantown Day Schl 2nd Grd Tchr 1987-88; Homer-Union Elem Schl 5th-8th Grd Tchr 1988-95; Morgan Local Schls Elem Prin 1995-; *ai:* NAESA, OSESA, NCTM 1995-; OCTM 1992-; OCTELA 1993-; *office:* Morgan Local Schls 78 E Main St Mc Connelsville OH 43756

THOMPSON, TERRY ALLEN, Biology & Earth Science Tchr; *b:* Coatesville, PA; *m:* Leanne McComsey; *ed:* Westchester Univ (BSEd) Bio 1982, (MA) Virology 1989; 15 Addl Credit Hrs; *cr:* Downington Jr HS Bio, Earth Sci Tchr 1983-; *ai:* 7th & 8th Grd Asst Bsbl Coach 1984-86; DAEA 1983-, Rep Cncl 1989-; PSEA, NEA 1983-; Presentation of Research Findings on Respiratory Syncytial Virus Amer Society Microbiology Assn; *office:* Downingtown Jr H S 335 Manor Ave Downingtown PA 19335*

THOMPSON, TIMOTHY JOHN, Science & Mathematics Tchr; *b:* England; *m:* Donna Jean Radcliffe; *c:* Logan, Austin, Donald, Allison; *ed:* Monroe Comm Coll (AS) 1976; UT St Univ (BS) Plant Sci 1978; *cr:* Marietta Chrstn Schl Sci Tchr 1981; Zanesville Chrstn Schl, Sci & Math Tchr 1981-; *ai:* Sr Class Adv; Honor Soc Selection Comm; Debate Team Adv; General Knowledge Team Adv; *office:* Zanesville Christian Schl 2400 Chandlersville Rd Zanesville OH 43701

THOMPSON, VALERIE M., Elementary School Teacher; *b:* Belize City, Cntrl America; *m:* Johnny L.; *c:* Deborah, Angela; *ed:* St Joseph Coll (BA) Continuing Ed 1961; Accredited Status 18 Diocese of Brooklyn 1962; CE 13 Tchng Arithmetic Grds 1-6; CE 15 Psych of the Elem Schl Child; CE 16 Tchng Art Elem Schl; 40 Hrs Drug Use & Abuse Prevention; *cr:* Fourteen Holy Martyr's Elem Grds 5-8 Tchr 1965-76; Our Lady of Peace Tchr Grds 6-8 Tchr 1977-88; Cath Learning Ctr Math & Rdng Summer Tchr 1980-84; St Jerome Elem Grd 7 Tchr; *ai:* Stu Drug Use & Abuse Prevention Prgm Cnslr; After Schl Stu Homework Assignments Tutor; Facilitator, Mentor 1976-; CBS Block Assn 1990-, Sec; Rdng is Fundamental 1992-, Mentor; Cath Sci Cncl 1980-; Cath Ed Div of Rel Ed Silver Achvmt Awd; Intnl Wood Fnd Applied Sci-Sci Tchr of Yr; City Cncl Citation Exemplary Svc Comm 1995; *home:* 4622 Clarendon Rd Brooklyn NY 11203

THOMPSON, VICKY SOUTHCOTT, 8th-12th Grade French Teacher; *b:* Milwaukee, WI; *m:* Timothy M.; *c:* Jessica, Jennifer; *ed:* Miami Univ at Oxford (AS) Botany 1972; Univ of WI at Stevens Point (BA) Fr 1988; Aurora Univ (MAEd) 1995; *cr:* John Meier MS 8th Grd Fr Tchr 1989-92; Cardington Lincoln HS 8-12 Grd Fr Tchr 1992-; *ai:* Fr Club Adv; OH Ed Assn 1992-; NEA 1989-; Church Yth Group 1992-; *home:* 778 Lincrest Dr Westerville OH 43081*

THOMPSON, WILLIAM, Instrumental Band Director; *b:* Flemington, NJ; *m:* Kate Gillen; *ed:* Rutgers Univ (BA) Music Ed 1986; *cr:* Franklin Twp Schls Instrumental Band Dir 1986-94; Branchburg Cntrl Schl Instrumental Band Dir 1994-; *ai:* Franklin & Somerville HS Percussion Instr, Arranger; Percussive Arts Soc 1990-, Mem-at-Large; NJ Music Edctrs Assn 1986-, Percussion Coord Region II; Somerville Schl of Music, Owner; Governors Tchr of Yr Awd 1986; Cadets Marching Band Cooperative Best Percussion 1991-95; *home:* 855 N Branch Rd Bridgewater NJ 08807*

THOMPSON-CAGER, CHEZIA BRENDA, Professor of Literature & Lang; *b:* St Louis, MO; *c:* Chezia Jr.; *ed:* WA Univ (BA) Eng, Black Stud 1973, (MA) Curr Design 1975; Carnegie-Mellon (DA) Eng Lit, Lang 1984; Attnd Univ of Nigeria at Lagos-Ife, Univ of the West Indies at Mona Jamaica, Haitian-Amer Inst Port au Prince Haiti, Aspen Inst for Hum; *cr:* WA Univ Black Stud Prgm Tchng Asst 1972-74; St Louis Comm Coll Eng, African Amer Stud Dept Instr, Asst Prof 1974-70; Clarion St Univ Eng Dept Asst Prof 1980-82; Univ of MD Asst Prof 1982-86; Smith Coll Theatre Dept, African Amer Stud Dept Tchr 1986-89; Bowie St Univ Visiting Eng Instr 1989-90; Park Hghts Dev Corp Sr Dev Consultant 1990-93; Baltimore Comm Coll Visiting Eng Instr 1993-94; Baltimore City Pub Schls Curr Consultant 1993-; MD Inst Coll of Art Lit, Lang, Performance Art Prof 1994-; *ai:* AFT, NCTE l975-; MLA, MAWA, ATHEA l986-; BTN l992-; St LOuis Comm Coll Forest Park, Treas; Girl Scouts of Amer 1956-69; WA Univ 1972-73, Stu Trustee; MD Art Place 1993-, Bd of Dirs; Ctr Stage, Theatre for a New Generation Bd of Dirs; Acad Schlsps; Wye Exec Seminar, Aspen Inst for Hum; Experiment in Intnl Living; Black Stud Prgm Flwshp; Publications: Jumpin Rope on the Axis, The Presence of Things Unseen: Giant Talk; Poems, Articles Pub; *office:* MD Inst Coll Of Art 1300 W Mount Royal Ave Baltimore MD 21217

THOMS, FRANK R., Middle School History Teacher; *b:* Brooklyn, NY; *m:* Kathleen Cammavata; *c:* Steven, Holly Thoms Casey; *ed:* Williams Coll (BA) His 1960; Wesleyan Univ (MAT) His, Tchng 1962; Grad Stud Ed Univ of CT 1969-70; *cr:* Hanover Jr-Sr HS Soc Stud Tchr 1962-69; Queen's Dyhe Cty Primary Schl Asst Master 1970-71; Frances C. Richmond Schl MS Tchr 1971-87; Bancroft Schl His Tchr, Interdisciplinary Team Ldr 1991-; *ai:* Adv; Coach of Soccer, Sftbl; Cntrl MA Cncl for Soc Stud 1995-; AFS Exchange Tchr to Former Soviet Union 1986-87; Severl Articles Pub; *office:* Bancroft Schl 110 Shore Dr Worcester MA 01605*

THOMSON, ALEXANDER L., Agri-Sci & Tech Dept Dir; *b:* Waterbury, CT; *m:* Janet Leonard; *ed:* Univ of Ct (BS) Ag Engrng 1977; 30 Addl Credits Ed, Ag, Voc Ed; Tchr Cert 1978; *cr:* Nonnewaug HS Ag Sci, Tech Tchr 1980-, Dir Ag Sci Dept 1985-; *ai:* Stu Recruitment; Budget Preparation; Schedule Dev; Co-ordination of Summer Visits; CT Vo-Ag Tchrs Assn 1977-, 15 Yr Awd; Natl Vo-Ag Tchrs Assn 1977-; CEA, NEA 1980-; CT FFA Fnd, Pres 1989-; Two Cylinder Club 1990-; Secure Grants for Capital Eq[illegible]ment for Ag Ctr; *office:* Nonnewaug HS Clark Regnional Ag Dept 5 M[illegible]town Rd Woodbury CT 06798

THOMSON, HARRIET MARCIA SHENK, HS Mathematics Teacher; *b:* Queens, NY; *m:* Jeffrey Craig; *ed:* York Coll CUNY (BS) Math 1977; Montclair St Univ (MA) Math 1979; Tchr of Math Cert 1979; Stu Personnel Svcs Cert 1989; *cr:* Ridge HS Math Tchr 1979-84; Hanover Park HS Math Tchr 1984-85; Dover HS Math Tchr 1985-; *ai:* NCTM; NEA; NJEA; AMTNJ; Governors Tchr Recognition Prgm Cert of Recognition 1990-91; Cert of Appreciation 1991; Cert of Accomplishment 1992; *home:* 73 Brookwood Rd Stanhope NJ 07874*

THOMSON, PETER S., Mathematics Teacher; *b:* Glen Ridge, NJ; *m:* Carol Pettebone; *c:* Heather, Kacie, Jessica, Karen; *ed:* Lafayette Coll (BS) Math 1972; *cr:* Union Cath HS Math, Sci Tchr 1972-76; The Pingry Schl Math Tchr 1976-; *ai:* JV Bsbl, Bsktbl Coach; Acad Judicial Bd; AMTNJ 1995-; *office:* The Pingry Schl Martinsville Rd Martinsville NJ 08836

THOM-WOODSON, AMANDA, Dance Director; *b:* Edinburgh, Scotland; *m:* J. Neal; *c:* Hannah Kathryn; *ed:* Bedford Coll (BED) Dance 1983; OH St Univ (MFA) Dance 1989; *cr:* Abbotsford HS Performing Arts Coord 1984-86; OH St Univ Dance Lecturer 1986-89; Goucher Coll Assoc Prof of Dance 1989-; Carver Ctr Dance Dir 1994-; *ai:* AAUP 1990-; DNB 1989-, Comm Mem; Grad Fellowship OH St Univ; *office:* Carver Ctr For Arts & Tech 938 York Rd Baltimore MD 21204

THORNBER, NORA S., Assistant Prof of Math Dept; *b:* Palo Alto, CA; *m:* Karvel; *c:* Karen, Carol; *ed:* Univ of CA at Riverside (AB) Math, Physics 1962; CA Inst of Tech (PHD) Physics, Applied Math 1967; *cr:* Newark Coll of Engrng Asst Prof 1969-71; Raritan Vly Comm Coll Asst Prof 1987-; *ai:* MAA; AAPT; APS; Sigma Xi; AAUW; *office:* Raritan Valley Comm Coll PO Box 3300 Somerville NJ 08876

THORNBER, SHARON LOUISE, English Teacher & Dept Chprsn; *b:* Oswego, NY; *ed:* Murray St Univ (BS) PE & Eng 1974, (MA) PE & Eng 1978; *cr:* Fulton Schl System Sub Tchr 1976-81; Sackets Harbor Cntrl Eng Dept Chprsn & Tchr 1981-; *ai:* Girls Jr Var Soccer Coach; NEA 1981-; Amer Legion Aux 1994; *office:* Sackets Harbor Central Schl PO Box 290 Sackets Harbor NY 13685

THORNBERRY, VICKI LYNN, 9th-10th Grd English Teacher; *b:* Bevinsville, KY; *m:* Lloyd W.; *c:* Lloyd Wayne; *ed:* Xavier Univ (MA) Eng 1985; Attnd Mayerson Acad; *cr:* Campbell Cty HS 9-11 Grds Eng Tchr 1971-79; Cincinnati Pub Schls 9-12 Grds Eng Tchr 1980-; *ai:* St Proficiency Tests Tutor, Stu Mentor; AFT, Cincinnati Fed of Tchrs 1980-; Cincinnati Fed of Tchrs Super Tchr Awd 1985; Project Bus Awd of Merit; *office:* Withrow HS 2488 Madison Rd Cincinnati OH 45208*

THORNE, RUTHELLYN MURPHY, 3rd-4th Grade Teacher; *b:* Montclair, NJ; *m:* Christopher G.; *c:* Matthew Murphy, Melissa S. LaFiura, Peter Murphy; *ed:* NY St Univ at Oneonta (BS) Ed 1964; Univ of Manchester England Grad Stud British Primary Ed 1968; Adirondack Comm Coll Cert Drafting Tech 1984; *cr:* N Warren CS Kndgtn & 4th-6th Grd Tchr 1964-66; Glens Falls City Schls 2nd Grd Tchr 1966-67; Lake George Elem Schl 1st-6th Grd Tchr 1968-83; N Amer Phillips Lighting Machine Shop Draftsman, Blue Print Reader & Spare Parts Crib 1983-84; Lake George CS 1st-6th Grd Tchr 1984-; *ai:* Cmptr & Family Improvement Comms; AFT, NYSUT, NYSRA 1964-; Iroquoa Ridge Council 1968-; NYSAS 1993-, Charter Mem; Archaeology Soc Comm Wrkshp 1994-; *office:* Lake George Elem Schl 69 Sun Valley Dr Lake George NY 12845

THORNHILL, ANN TROUPE, Spanish Teacher; *b:* Claremore, OK; *c:* David; *ed:* Central St Univ at Wilberforce OH (BS) Span 1968; *cr:* Montclair HS Span Tchr 1968-; *ai:* Awds Comm 1978-; Minority Achvmt Comm 1993; Span Club Adv 1983-94; Twirlers Adv 1970; NEA, Montclair Ed Assn 1968-; NJ Foreign Lang Tchrs; *office:* Montclair HS 100 Chestnut St Montclair NJ 07042

THORNHILL, KATHY ANN, English Teacher & Dept Chprsn; *b:* Hagerstown, MD; *ed:* Western MD Coll (BA) Eng 1974, (MLA) Liberal Arts 1981; Attnd Towson St Univ 6 Post Grad Hrs, Hood Coll 3 Post Grad Hrs; *cr:* S Hagerstown HS Eng Tchr 1974-; *ai:* Drama Coach; Washington Cty Tchr Assn, MD St Tchr Assn & NEA 1974-, NCTE; Delta Gamma 1990-; Potomac Playmakers 1981-; MD Writing [illegible] Tchr-Consultant; Performed in 6-Part Internationally Distribute[illegible] Series on Tchr Effectiveness; *office:* South Hagerstown HS [illegible] Potomac St Hagerstown MD 21740

THORNTON, ALVIN, Professor; *b:* Roanoke, AL; *m:* Annette; *c:* Detavia; *ed:* Morehouse Coll (BA) Pol Sci 1971; Howard Univ (Ph[illegible] Sci 1978; *cr:* Morgan St Univ Asst Prof 1974-80; Legislative A[illegible] House of Rep 1980-82; Howard Univ Prof 1982-1995; *ai:* Prince G[illegible] Cty MD, Bd of Ed Mem; NCOBPS 1978-, Exec Comm, Fannie Lou Awd; NAACP 1972-; Fullbright Schlsp, W Africa; Ford Fnd Fellow; Howard Univ 2400 6th St NW Washington DC 20059

THORNTON, JAMES MICHAEL, Eighth Grade Science Teac[illegible] Dayton, OH; *m:* Marietta L.; *c:* Tiffanie Green, Britany, Aja Ree[illegible] Cntrl St Univ (BS) Chem 1976; Univ of Dayton (MS) Educl Admin[illegible] Aims Trng; Sepup Trng; Learning, Tchng Styles; *cr:* Calgon Corp[illegible] Chemist 1975-78; Monsanto Corp Chemical Tech 1980-83; [illegible] Polymer Rsrch Polymer Chemist, Asst Super 1983-86; Kiser MS Sc[illegible] 1990-; *ai:* Sci Club Adv; Fac Cncl Pres; Spending Comm Co-Chai[illegible] Writing, Textbook Review Comms; Phi Delta Kappa 1995-; DEA, NEA 1990-; NSTA, SECO 1994-; Environmental Cncl of OH Buckeye Assesment; Team for Sci 1993-95, West Region Coord; Kiser Middle School 1401 Leo St Dayton OH 45404*

THORNTON, JO B., Social Studies Teacher; *b:* Montclair, NJ; *m:* L.; *c:* Sarah, Hannah; *ed:* Smith Coll (BA) Amer Stud 1966; 48 Ad[illegible] at Univ of MA, Syracuse, Union, North Adams St & Columb[illegible] Whitehall Cntrl Schl Soc Stud Tchr 1966-67; Hoosick Falls Cntrl Sc[illegible] Stud Tchr 1967-; *ai:* NHS Adv; NYSUT, AFT; United Fund; Ad[illegible] Placement Fac Consultant; Golub Corp 4 Time Most Influential Tc[illegible]

THORNTON, LOUISE M., Mathematics Teacher; *b:* Woonsocket, [illegible] Stephen G.; *c:* Joseph; *ed:* RI Coll (BA) Scndry Ed, Math 1974, [illegible] Phys Sci & Chem 1979; *cr:* Woodsocket Jr High Phys Sci 19[illegible] Woodsocket Sr High Chem Tchr 1974 Half Yr, Math Tchr 1975 RIMTA, NCTM 1994-; 1991 St Awd; Presdential Awd for Excl in M[illegible] Sci Tchng; *office:* Woonsocket HS 777 Cass Ave Woonsocket RI 02[illegible]

THORNTON, MICHAEL FRANCIS, Dean of Students; *b:* Wilkes-[illegible] PA; *m:* Josephine T. Dait; *ed:* Wilkes Univ (BA) Sociology, His 198[illegible] Stroudsburg Tchng Cert, Soc Stud; Temple Univ Educl Ldrshp Grad Attending Wilkes Univ; *cr:* Stroudsburg HS Soc Stud Tchr, Asst 1988-92; Elk Lake HS Soc Stud Tchr, Dean of Stdnts 1992-; *ai:* Girls Track Coach Asst; Sr HS Stu Cncl Adv; Prom Steering Adv; Prin Adv Soc, ELEA Schlsp Comm; NEA, PSEA 1988-; ASCD 1995-; *offic[illegible]* Lake HS PO Box 100 Dimock PA 18816*

THORNTON, NANCY BLAKELY, Hlth & Physical Education T[illegible] Warwick, RI; *m:* David John; *ed:* Ithaca Coll (BS) PE 1974; Over 3[illegible] Hrs at St Univ of NY at Brockport in Hlth Sci 1979; *cr:* Churchvill[illegible] CS Hlth & PE Tchr 1974-81; Spencerport Cntrl Schl Hlth Tchr 19[illegible] Churchville-Chili MS PE & Hlth Tchr 1991-95; *ai:* Jr Var Girls So[illegible] Sftbl Coach; Modified Girls Vlybl Coach; *office:* Churchville Ch[illegible] 139 Fairbanks Rd Churchville NY 14428

THORNTON, THOMAS E., English Teacher; *b:* St Cloud, M[illegible] Kathleen Max; *c:* Michael, Ian Christopher, Kyra; *ed:* St Univ [illegible] Oneonta (BA) Eng 1970; SUNY at Albany (MA) Eng Ed 1974; 30 Ad[illegible] Eng; *cr:* Columbia HS Tchr 1974-; *ai:* Lit, Art Magazine Adv; N[illegible] AFT 1974-; Poems Pub Eng Journal; *office:* Columbia HS Couse C[illegible] East Greenbush NY 12061*

THORPE, BETTY RAWLES, Health Educator; *b:* Orange, NJ; *m:* [illegible] Alan Sr.; *c:* Wayne Jr., Glenn, Elizabeth Pierson; *ed:* Jersey City S[illegible] (BA) Schl Nrs & Hlth Ed; East Stroudsburg Univ (MS) Hlth Ed Orange Memrl Hosp RN; Post Grad SAC Credits NJ Cert; CHES; *c[illegible]* Lakeland Schl Nrs & Hlth Ed Tchr 1976-78; Welkind Neurologica[illegible] Dir of Nrsng 1978-80; The Matheny Schl Team Ldr & Hlth Ed 1980-83; Bedminster Twp Schl Hlth Ed Tchr & SAC 1983-; *ai:* Com[illegible] Conflict Mediator & Yrbk Adv; Peer Ldr; Bedminster Ed Assn Treas; NJEA 1983-; NOOD 1989-; BSA 1974-, Merit Badge Cnslr; Bedminster Twp Elem Schl 234 Somerville Rd Bedminster NJ 0792[illegible]

THORPE, LINDA DARNELL, Fourth Grade Teacher; *b:* New Have[illegible] *c:* Marshall; *ed:* Southern CT (BS) Ed 1973; Univ of CT (MS) Ed 197[illegible] Martin L. King Schl Tchr 1973-; *ai:* Staff-Parent Mngmt Team; New [illegible] Pub Grants for Excl 1990, 1992; *home:* 269 Greene St New Have[illegible] 06511

THORPE, PHILLIP ARTHUR, Instrumental Music Teache[illegible] Rochester, NY; *m:* Elizabeth Ann Monn; *c:* Alexandrea Elizabeth, G[illegible] Phillip; *ed:* Mansfield Univ (BMEd) Music Ed 1984; 24 Grad Credi[illegible] *cr:* East Jr High Band Dir 1985; 3rd ID Band Army Bandsman Sgt 19[illegible] Tidioute Schl K-12th Grd Vocal & Instrumental Music Dir 1988-89; Warren MS 5th-8th Grd Instrumental Music Dir 1989; Waynesbor[illegible] MS 7th-8th Grd Instrumental Music Dir 1990-; *ai:* Waynesbo[illegible] Marching Band Asst Dir; PSEA 1990-; NEA 1990-; Army Commen[illegible] Medal; *office:* Waynesboro Area MS 702 E 2nd St Waynesboro PA [illegible]

THORPE, RICHARD KEVIN, Amer, World His & Soc Teach[illegible] Marion, OH; *m:* Marianne Roberts; *c:* Douglas, Leanne; *ed:* OH S[illegible] (BS) Ed 1970; Bowling Green St Univ 14 Sem Hrs; Ashland Univ 1[illegible] Hrs; *cr:* Col Crawford Schls Soc Stud Tchr 1970-; *ai:* Dept Chm; S[illegible] Comm; Asst Ftbl Coach 17 Yrs; Asst Bsktbl Coach 9 Yrs; OEA, CCEA 1970-; Martha Holden Jennings Fnd Jennings Scholar 199[illegible] *office:* Colonel Crawford HS St Rt 602 North Robinson OH 44856

THORSEN, CARL F., Social Studies Teacher; *b:* Teaneck, N[illegible] Kathleen Cooper; *ed:* Univ of Scranton (BA) Elem Ed 1976; Penn St Elem Ed 1995; Stu Assistance Prgm Team 32 Trng Hrs; Fascili[illegible] Groups for Adolescents Grp Facilitator 32 Trng Hrs; *cr:* Delaware V[illegible] 6th Grd Tchr 1976-77, 8th Grd Soc Stud Tchr 1977-81, 6th Grd 1981-82, 8th Grd Soc Stud Tchr 1982-; *ai:* Golf Club Coach, Adv; Cncl; Portfolio Comm; NEA, PSEA 1977-; PCEA 1977-, Exec Bd [illegible] *office:* Delaware Vly MS Rt 6 & 209 Milford PA 18337

THORSON, PAUL KENNETH, Professor of Composition; *b:* O[illegible] NE; *m:* Gail Lynn Nelson; *c:* Jonathan, Martin, Nathaniel; *ed:* Wa[illegible] Coll (BS) Music Performance 1970; Seminary Inst Cert Biblical 1973; Western Conservative (MCM) Church Music 1982; W[illegible] Seminary Dr of Ministries Stud; *cr:* Campus Crusade Soloist 1970-8[illegible] Chrstn Univ Fac Prof 1983-88; Belmont Univ Fac Prof 1989-91; Tr[illegible] Zazarene Coll Fac Adv Prof 1989-94; Christ Presbyn Acad Bible Dep[illegible] 1989-94; *ai:* Wrestling Coach; ASCAP 1975-; Freelance Writer; [illegible] 1184 Brookside Dr Franklin TN 37069

THREN, JOANNE MARIE, 5th Grade Teacher; *b:* Reading, PA Kutztown Univ (BS) Elem Ed 1965-, (MS) Elem Ed 1968; 6 Post Courses; *cr:* Riverside Elem Schl 5th Grd Tchr 1965-75; 12th & M[illegible] Elem Schl 5th Grd Tchr 1975-; *ai:* Arts Cncl Rep; Play, C[illegible] Accompanist; REA 1965-, Rep; NEA, PSEA 1965-; Church Organi[illegible] Yrs.

THREN, VICKI L. (KING), Phys Ed Teacher & Dept Chprs[illegible] Sellersville, PA; *m:* Gregory Michael; *c:* Nicole, Alyssa; *ed:* Stroudsburg Univ (BS) Hlth, PE, Ath Coaching 1979; West Chester (MED) Hlth, PE 1984; 31 Addl Credits; *cr:* Upper Perkiomen HS Hlt[illegible] Tchr 1979-; *ai:* Reach Out Against Drugs Adv; Assistance Core [illegible] h Grd Hockey Coach; Wellness, Fitness Dept Chprsn; Water Safety, iarding Instr; NEA, PSEA 1979-; Upper Perk Educ Assn, Treas; Amer 'ross Instr; VOICE; Upper Perk Child Care Ctr, Exec Comm; Amer Assn Instr; *office:* Upper Perkiomen HS 2 Walt Rd Pennsburg PA

)CKMORTON, DENNIS A., Teacher & Director; *b:* Atlantic City, : Karen L. Confroy; *c:* Tara, Kevin; *ed:* Glassboro St Coll (BA) Elem i68; Glassboro St Coll (MA) Educl Admin 1978; 15 Credit Hrs Adult :hl Pub Relations, Schl Law; *cr:* Egg Harbor Twp Schls Tchr 1968-, dult Ed 1988-; *ai:* Safety Patrol Adv NJ St Police 28 Yrs; Public Schl Comm; Lang Arts Curr Comm; NEA, NJ Ed Assn 1968-; Egg Harbor d Assn 1968-, VP; Articles Pub; *office:* Egg Harbor Twp Pub Schls gh School Dr Egg Harbor Tp NJ 08234

)NE, ROBIN M., Spanish Teacher; *b:* Brooklyn, NY; *ed:* Univ of IL)ana (BA) 1976; Univ of MI (MA) Hispanic Lit 1978; Addl Stud iam, St John's Univ, LIU, Southampton Coll; *cr:* Univ of MI Tchng 1976-78; Univ of Richmond VA Span Instr 1978-81; NY City Bd of an Tchr 1985-89; Herricks HS Span Tchr 1989-; *ai:* NHS Selection ı; AATSP 1976-; LILT, NYSAFLT 1989-; Phi Beta Kappa; Sigma Pi; Phi Kappa Phi; Magna Cum Laude; Renaissance Stud NEH p 1992; Project Pluma NEH Flwshp 1994; *office:* Herricks Sr HS 100 :r Rock Rd New Hyde Park NY 11040*

.IN, EDWARD ROGER, Band Director; *b:* Waterbury, CT; *m:* ; *c:* Roger III, Melissa; *ed:* Hartt Coll of Music (BA) Music Ed 1967; of Bridgeport (MS) Sci Ed 1988; Univ of CT 33 Credit Music Lit Post Grad Work; *cr:* Ctr Schl Band Dir 1967-68; Bacon Acad Band, s Dir 1968-85; Fairfield HS Band Dir 1985-; *ai:* Tri-M Music Hnr dv; Marching Band Dir; CT Music Ed Assn 1976-, Pres; Phi Beta Mu ; Phi Mu Alpha 1965-; NBA; MENC, Eastern Div Exec Bd; US :s 1968-72; Clinician, Guest Conductor CMEA, MENC, ASBDA, Accompanist; *office:* Fairfield HS 755 Melville Ave Fairfield CT

.IN, KATHLEEN NORTON, 3rd Grd Tchr of Gifted; *b:* Highland MI; *m:* Carl V.; *c:* Andrew; *ed:* Univ of MI (BS) Elem Ed 1972; 15 Credits in Gifted & Talented Ed; *cr:* Little Egg Harbor Schl Dist Tchr ; *ai:* Shrub Club Adv; Staff Chorus & Annual Third Grd Musical Dir; of Staff Roundtable; NEA 1974-, Bldg Rep; Delta Kappa Gamma Local & St Music Chair; Brant Beach Yacht Club 1984-, Commodore Rear & Vice Commodore; Manahawkin Bapt Church 1974-, Soloist, Mem, Youth Choir Dir & Kings Kids; Intnrl Order of the Blue Gavel; of the Long Beach Island Yacht Racing Assn; Southern Regnl HS Parents Org; Interim Choir Dir of Manahawkin Baptist Chruch; Grant ist Shrub Club Efforts; *office:* Little Egg Hrbr Twp Schl Dist N Green tle Egg Harbor NJ 08087

MA, KATHY KNAUB, Home Economics Teacher; *b:* Carlisle, PA; muel D.; *c:* Sara, Benjamin Philip, Jacob; *ed:* Messiah Coll (BS) Ec 1973; 24 Hrs for PA Cert; *cr:* Dover HS Home Ec Tchr 1973-78; ern HS Home Ec Tchr 1990-; *ai:* Teen Issues Activity; NEA 1990-; : Northern York Cty HS 655 S Baltimore St Dillsburg PA 17019

MM, MICHAEL JAMES, Guidance Counselor; *b:* Teaneck, NJ; *ed:* rs Univ (BA) His 1991; Fordham Univ (MS) Cnslng, Prsnl Svcs 1996; ramus Cath Girls HS Soc Stud Tchr 1991-95, Guid Cnslr 1994-; *ai:* Trial; Stu Cncl; Advy Comm; ACA, ASCA 1995-; Phi Delta Theta , Historian, Alumni Sec, Order of Omega; Outstdng Contribution NJ ssn Mentor Prgm; *home:* 364 Summit St Norwood NJ 07648

RANSKY, GEORGE J., 8th Grd American History Tchr; *b:* urgh, PA; *m:* Sally Simon; *c:* Jennifer; *ed:* CA St Coll (BS) Sec Ed, tud 1967; Seton Hill Coll (BA) Elem Ed 1992; Grad Stud PA St at Mc ort, Pitt Univ at Pgh, Seton Hill Coll at Greensburg; *cr:* South heny Schl Dist Tchr 1967-; *ai:* Radio Club; NEA 1967-; South heny Ed Assn 1967-, Grievance Comm; PA St Boro Assn 1974-, / Comm; St Mayor's Assn 1983-, Mayor of Yr 1995; Westmoreland Boro Assn 1974-, Pres; *office:* South Allegheny Schl Dist 2743 ington Blvd Mc Keesport PA 15133*

RANSKY, SALLY SIMON, Speech & English Teacher; *b:* Mt ant, PA; *m:* George Joseph; *c:* Jennifer; *ed:* CA St Coll (BS) Ed 1969; 30 Credits; *cr:* Elizabeth Forward Sr HS Tchr 27 Yr; *ai:* West ton Historical Soc 1966-, VP 4 Hrs; West Newton Womens Club , Pres 2 Yrs; West Newton Planning Commission 1986-, CH 1 Yr; g Officer 10 Yr; Western PA Historical Soc; Bariatric Consultant; : Elizabeth Forward Schl Dist 1000 Weigles Hill Rd Elizabeth PA

RBER, BERT HENRY, History Teacher; *b:* Houston, TX; *m:* Jane rth Fisher; *c:* Christopher, Alison, Karin; *ed:* Princeton Univ (BA) 962; Yale Univ (MA) His 1966, (MPhil) His 1966, (PHD) His 1973; getown Univ Lang, Linguistics 1963-64; Ludwig Maximilian Univ at ch 1960-61; *cr:* US Dept of St Frgn Svc 1962-63; Yale Univ Lecturer 69; Loomis Chaffee Schl His Tchr 1973-; *ai:* Org of Amer Historians ; Endowed Instructorship Third World, Global Stud; *home:* 223 ado Ave Windsor CT 06095

RBER, JAMES ALLEN, Professor of Political Science; *b:* Albany, *n:* Claudia J. Hartley; *c:* Mark, Kathryn H. Thurber-Smith; *ed:* Univ (BS) Pol Sci 1966; IN Univ Pol Sci (MA) 1970, (PhD) 1973; *cr:* WA niv Asst Prof 1970-74; Amer Univ Prof 1974-; *ai:* Ctr for ressional & Pres Stud Dir; Amer Pol Sci Assn 1967-; Midwest Pol Sci 1968-; Capitol Area Pol Sci Assn 1974-, Pres; Pub Books 1991, 1995; : American Univ Dept of Government 4400 Massachusetts Ave NW ington DC 20016

RSTON, DONNA, 4th Grade Teacher; *b:* New Orleans, LA; *c:* Arthur oy, Sonja Thurston Djossou, Michael Jr.; *ed:* Jersey City St Coll (BA) Ed 1979, (MA) Admin & Supervision 1989; *cr:* P S #34 Title I Basic Tchr 1979-81; P S #12 Tchr 1981-; Home Instruction Tchr 1987-89; Early Waring Prgm Head Tchr 1991; *ai:* Girls Bsktbl, Track Coach; Improvement Design; JCEA, NEA 1979-, Dir 1995-; MIC 1992-, Pub ions Asst; NAACP 1972-; Phi Delta Kappa 1982-; GRASP 1996; PS Parent Cncl 1984-; NAACP 1970-; Tchr Perfect Attendance Awd; Tchr gnition.

RSTON, MARY JANE MURTAUGH, Sixth Grade Teacher; *b:* port, NY; *m:* John M. II; *c:* Kathleen S., Bryan N.; *ed:* St Univ Coll ffalo (MS) Elem Ed 1976; *cr:* Medina Cntrl Schl Dist Elem Tchr -; *ai:* Decorating Chm for Kenan Showhouse Revisited 1996-, Comm MTA, NYSUT 1971-; Lockport Jr Svc League 1986-, VP Life ining; Lockport Coll Womens Club 1989-; *office:* Clifford Wise MS Gwinn St Medina NY 14103

RTELL, CRAIG MARTIN, US History Teacher; *b:* Grand Rapids, *n:* Margo Harris; *c:* Leila; *ed:* Univ of MI (BA) Eng 1973; Columbia Tchrs Coll (MA) Tchng of His 1983; Columbia Univ (MA) His 1984, il) His 1986; PHD Prgm Dissertation in Progress; *cr:* Bard Coll ing Instr 1986; Monroe-Woodbury HS US His Tchr 1987; James I. ill HS US His Tchr 1988-1995; Ardsley HS, US His Tchr 1995-; *ai:* UT 1988-, VP & Pres 1991-92; Org of Amer Historians 1986-; iern His Assn 1990-; Pres Fellow Columbia Univ 1984-86; Meyer e US His Masters Essay Awd Columbia His Dept 1985; Archie K. s Fellowship; NC Soc 1992; *office:* Ardsley HS 300 Farm Rd Ardsley 0502

TIBBETTS, PAUL E., Professor of Philosophy; *b:* Worcester, MA; *m:* Roberta Shylo; *c:* Elizabeth Lloyd, Sarah, Lee; *ed:* Purdue Univ (PHD) Philosophy 1973; Univ of IL (PHD) Sociology 1986; *cr:* Univ of Dayton Prof of Philosophy 1969-; *ai:* Brain Behavioral Sciences 1993-; Civil Air Patrol 1986-, Chief Check Pilot; Numerous Articles Published in Referred Journals; *office:* Univ Of Dayton 300 College Park Ave Dayton OH 45469

TIBBITTS, ELIZABETH ANN-WIRKUS, English & French Teacher; *b:* Brecksvillew, OH; *m:* Jack R.; *c:* Kathleen Dolan, Mark & Matthew; *ed:* Kent St Univ (BA) Eng & Fr 1958; 42 Credit Hrs Supervision; *cr:* Brecksville HS Eng Tchr 1959-60; Valley Forge HS Eng Tchr 1968-; *ai:* Sports Spirit Group Ldr; Sr Class Adv; Schl Fund Raisers Comm; NEA 1968-; OEA 1968-; NEOEA 1968-; PEA 1968-; Cleveland Cncl Tchrs Comm; Writing, Implementing & Tchng Interdisciplinary Team Curr 1972-82; Writing, Implementing & Tchng Prep Corr 1992-; Tchng Gen Motors YES Pgm 2995-; *office:* Valley Forge HS 9999 Independence Blvd Parma OH 44130*

TIBERIO, RONALD SETH, Mathematics Instructor; *b:* Leominster, MA; *m:* Sheila White; *c:* Stephanie, Ronald Jr.; *ed:* UMASS at Amherst (BS) Math 1968; Framingham St Coll (MED) Math Ed 1975; Worcester Polytechnic Inst (MM) Math 1992; 32 Hrs Boston Univ 1977-80; Ldrshp Prgm Discrete Math Rutgers Univ 1992; *cr:* Hopkinton HS Math Instr 1970-71; Natick HS Math Instr 1971-72; Wellesley HS Math Instr 1972-; *ai:* Steering Comm 10 Yr Evaluation 1986-87; K-12 Curr Review Math 1994-; NHS 1973-77; NCTM 1995-; AMS 1990-; MAA 1967-; BPOE Lodge 1986-; VFW 1976-, Sr Vice Cmndr, OD; Crockett Awd Excl in Tchng; Redfield Tchr of Yr; Visiting Scholar Worcester Polytechnic Inst; Articles Pub; *office:* Wellesley HS 50 Rice St Wellesley Hills MA 02181

TIBERIO, WILLIAM S., Instrumental Music Teacher; *b:* Rochester, NY; *m:* Debra R. Wemple; *c:* Sara, Benjamin, Geordan; *ed:* Ithaca Coll (BS) Music Ed 1984; SUNY at Fredonia (MS) Music Ed 1989; *cr:* Auburn HS Music Tchr 1984-88; Fairport HS Music Tchr 1988-; *ai:* Symphonic Band Dir; 2 Jazz Ensembles; Musicals Pit Orch Conductor; Studio Jazz Orch Conductor; NYSSMA, AFT 1984-; IAJE 1985-; Commencement Speaker 1993; Univ of Rochester Scndry Schl Tchng Excl Awd 1994; NYS All Cty, Area All St Bands Guest Conductor; Eastman Schl of Music HS Summer Jazz Band Dir; *office:* Fairport HS 1358 Ayrault Rd Fairport NY 14450*

TICE, LYNDIA ANN, English Teacher; *b:* San Diego, CA; *c:* Kevin; *ed:* San Diego St Univ (BA) Eng 1971; Stony Brook Univ (MA) Liberal Arts 1982; Addl 160 Credit Hrs; *cr:* Lansdowne HS Eng Tchr 1972-76; Patchoque-Medford HS Eng Tchr 1977-; *ai:* NEA, AFT 1971-; NYSUT 1978-; *office:* Patchogue-Medford HS Buffalo Ave Medford NY 11763

TICH, MARY LOU P., Latin & Classics Teacher; *b:* Cincinnati, OH; *m:* John G.; *ed:* Univ of Cincinnati (BA) Philosophy 1960; Bryn Mawr Coll (MA) Ancient Greek 1962; 65 Grad Credit Hrs Villanova Univ; *cr:* Great Vly HS Eng & Latin Tchr 1963-84; Covington Latin Schl Latin Tchr 1985-86; Southern OH Coll Art His & Eng Tchr 1986-87; Conestoga HS Latin Tchr 1987-91; St Ursula Acad Latin Tchr 1991-; *ai:* Classics Club Spon; Amer Classical League 1963-; OH Classical Conf 1991-; Classical Assoc of Midwest & South 1993-; St Xavier Choir 1984-; Schlsps to Univ of Cincinnati & Bryn Mawr Coll; Articles Pub; Hildesheim Trophy for Excl in Latin Pgm in OH 1995; *office:* St Ursula Acad HS 1339 E Mcmillan St Cincinnati OH 45206

TICHIO, ANNA, Guidance Counselor; *b:* New York, NY; *m:* Daniel Joseph; *c:* Daniel, Christopher, Robert; *ed:* St Johns Univ (BA) Eng; Montclair St Univ (MA) Cnslng; 6 Credit Hrs St Peters Coll; 18 Credit Hrs Montclair St Univ; 3 Credit Hrs William Paterson; *cr:* Katherine Gibbs Dir of Admission 1988-92; Acad of St Aloysius Guid Cnslr 1992-93; Paramus Cath HS Guid Cnslr 1993-; *ai:* Peer Minister Testing Coord for Goades; Career Day Coord; Coll Night Coord; Governors Schl Coord; Hudson Guid Assn 1 Yr, Dir 2 Yrs, Acting Dir 1 Yr; *office:* Paramus Cath HS 425 Paramus Rd Paramus NJ 07652

TICKEL, NANCY BOYD, Fourth Grade Teacher; *b:* Deposit, NY; *m:* David Cleve; *c:* David Leland, Ruth Anne; *ed:* Miami Univ (BS) Ed 1958; Attnd Trenton, Widener Univ, Marywood Coll, Bloomsburg Univ; *cr:* Sherman Elem Schl 1st Grd Tchr 1958-60; Fitch Elem Schl 1st Grd Tchr 1960-61; Edgewood Elem Schl 4th Grd Tchr 1 Yr, 3rd Grd Tchr 1977-; *ai:* NEA; PSEA; Bucks Cty Comm Interracial Harmony 1980-, VP, Sec, Comm Svc Awd 1995; Amer Assn Univ Women 1968-, Pres, VP, Sec; Beta Sigma Phi 1961-, Pres, VP, Sec; Bucks Co Peace Ctr 1987-, Steerling Comm; United Chrstn Church 1969-, Deacon, Ed, Outreach; Outstdng Young Women of Amer 1971; *office:* Edgewood Elem Schl 135 Yardley Ave PO Box 338 Yardley PA 19054

TIDD, MICHAEL ALAN,FSC, Former Rel & Soc Studies Tchr; *b:* Philadelphia, PA; *ed:* Univ of PA (BA) European His 1991; La Salle Univ (MA) Theology 1995; Boston Coll Cath Schl Ldrshp Prgm, Scndry Schl Admin 1995; *cr:* West Cath HS Rel, Soc Stud Tchr 1991-92; Central Cath HS Rel, Soc Stud Tchr 1992-95; Christian Brothers Novitiste Sabbatical, Divinity Stu 1995-; *ai:* Debate Coach, World Affairs Cncl Magazine Drive Moderaton 1992-94; Stu Cncl, IM, Magazine Dr World Affairs Cncl 1994-95.

TIEDEMANN, JOHN E., Chprsn & Prof Mech Engr Tech; *b:* Brooklyn, NY; *m:* Susan Jean; *c:* Michael, Melinda Johnson, Carolyn Hartley, Cheryl Larosa; *ed:* SUNY at Farmingdale (AAS) Mechanical Engrng Tech 1960; CA Polytechnic Univ (BS) Mechanical Engrng 1963; Univ of Cincinnati (MS) Mechanical Engrng 1971; *cr:* Gen Electric Heat Transfer Engr 1963-67; Grumman Aerospace Thermodynamics Engr 1967-70; SUNY at FarmingdaleChprsn & Prof 1970-; *ai:* Stu Manufacturing Club Adv; ASHRAE 1978-, Schlsp Chair; IFMA, ASSE 1994-, SME 1992-; Marriage Encounter 1970-, Team Couple; Engaged Encounter 1993-, Team Couple; Register Prof Engr NYS 1978-; *office:* S U N Y Coll Of Tech At Frmgdl 1250 Rte 110 Farmingdale NY 11735

TIEMANN, MARYLI KENOE, English & Fine Arts Teacher; *b:* Lapeer, MI; *m:* David H.; *c:* Joseph; *ed:* Univ of MI (BA) Speech & Eng Ed 1968; Post Grad Stud Univ of ME Ed, Amer Univ Eng, Naropa Inst Psych; *cr:* Barrington HS Eng Tchr 1968-69; Parkman Elem K-5th Grd Tchr 1972-73; Morse High Eng Tchr 1973-76, Eng & Fine Arts Tchr 1979-; Wayland HS Eng Tchr 1976-; *ai:* Gifted & Talented Prgm, Real Performances; Re-Cert Rep; 1-Act Play, Schl Variety Show Dir; NEA 1973-, Local BTA Pres 1982-84; Friends of Longfellow 1993-, Publicity Chair; League of Women Voters 1989-, VP 1989-91; Unitarian Universalist 1992-; Church Choir, Sunday Schl Tchr; NEH Grant with Folger; AMES Distinguished Tchr Awd 1986; Shakespeare Lib 1984.*

TIERNAN, TERRY A., 12th Grade English Teacher; *b:* Massena, NY; *m:* Vivian C. Angelo; *c:* Meghan Elieen, Kathleen Elizabeth; *ed:* SUNY at Potsdam (BA) Eng Ed, Philosophy 1974; Middlebury Coll (MA) Eng 1988; Attnd: Oxford Univ, Yeats Intnl Schl, Winterim Stud Tour; *cr:* Norwood-Norfolk Cntrl Schl 12 Grd Eng Tchr 1988-; Potsdam Coll Adjunct Instr 1991-; *ai:* Area Schls Consultant 1989-; NY ST Ed Dept Elem Scndry, Continuing Ed Bureau Consultant 1985-87; St Lawrence Univ Upward Bound 1980; NY St Eng Cncl Tchr of Excl 1993; Reynolds Aluminum Co Tchng Excl Grant 1991; Schlsps: Raymond A. Waldron 1988, Full Tuition 1985-88, Yeats Intnl Summer Schl 1974, Potsdam Coll Alumni Assn Winterim British Stud 1973, NY St Regents 1970; Bread Loaf at Middlebury Presidential Scholar 1985; Selected for: AT&T's Intnl Long Distance Learning Network 1987, BLSE's Rural Telecommunications Network 1985-, Bread Loaf's Tchrs-as-Researcher Grants 1985-86; Natl Endowment for Hum Fellowship 1984; *office:* Norwood Norfolk Central Schl PO Box 194 Norwood NY 13668

TIERNEY, JAMES H.,SR., US Air Force JROTC Instr; *b:* Jersey City, NJ; *m:* Joan Rhodes; *c:* James H. Jr., Shawn J., Jennette M., Justin I.; *ed:* Air Univ (BA) Aerospace Sci 1988; Attnd Univ of MD, Trenton St, Ocean Coll in Bus; *cr:* US Air Force 1959-81; Deep Creek HS Tchr 1981-82; Brick Twp HS Tchr 1982-; *ai:* Core Team; Color Guard; Drill Team; Hnr Soc; AFJROTC 1981-, Instr of Yr; NJEA 1982-; NEA 1982-, Tchr of Yr; Air Force Assn 1981-, Pres, Scott Awd; VFW 1981-, Bd Mem, VFW Medal; Elks 1982-; Worked on Various Town Comms 1981-; *office:* Brick Twp HS 2001 Lanes Mill Rd Brick NJ 08724

TIERNEY, MARTIN J., English Teacher; *b:* Cincinnati, OH; *ed:* OH Univ (BSEd) Eng 1972; Xavier Univ (MED) Eng 1974; *cr:* Berry MS Eng Tchr 1972-; *ai:* IM Prg Dir; Chprsn, Admin, Staff Liaison; Mentor; Lebanon Tchrs Assn 1972-, Bldg Rep; OH Ed Assn, NEA 1972-; Perfect Attendance 2 Yrs; *office:* Berry MS 23 Oakwood Ave Lebanon OH 45036

TIERNEY, SIMONEE AKSTIN, 5th Grd Teacher & Coordinator; *b:* E Vandergrift, PA; *m:* Charles H.; *c:* Jennifer H. Stewart; *ed:* SUNY at New Paltz (MS) Elem Ed 1965; Attnd L I UN; *cr:* North Belmore 3rd Grd Tchr 1957-58; Skokie IL 3rd Grd Tchr 1958-60; Goshen Cntrl 2nd-5th Grd Tchr 1960-; *ai:* NYSUT 1957-; GTA 1960-; NEA 1957-; Warwick Historic Soc; Law Day USA Liberty Bell Awd 1989; *office:* Goshen Cntrl Intermediate Schl Mc Nally St Goshen NY 10924*

TIERNEY-BUCHANAN, PATRICIA, Reading & Study Skills Teacher; *b:* Bridgeport, CT; *m:* Donald Bruce Buchanan; *c:* Mary Elizabeth, Kathryn Louise; *ed:* St Mary's Dominican Coll (BA) Psych 1972; Univ of Bridgeport (MS) K-12 Rdng, Lang Arts Consultant 1980; Sacred Heart Univ Tchr Cert PreK-8 1976; Harvard Univ Inst on Thinking Critical & Creative 1989; Harvard Grad Schl of Ed Cert; *cr:* Our Lady of Good Cncl 4th Grd Tchr 1972-73; Bristol Myers Co Rates, Audits Dept, Transportation Dept Mgr; Our Lady of the Assumption 2, 5 Grd Tchr 1977-82; Darien HS Rdng Consultant 1982-; *ai:* Rdng, Writing, Staff Dev Comms; Departmental Cncl; IRA, NEA 1984-; CT Assn of Child with Learning Disabilities; NCTE; Natl Assn of Underwater Instrs, Open Water I Scuba Diver; *office:* Darien HS 80 High School Ln Darien CT 06820

TIERNO, ANGELA M., First Grade Teacher; *b:* Binghamton, NY; *ed:* SUNY at Cortland (BA) Ed 1969, (MS) Ed 1973; *cr:* Theodore Roosevelt Binghamton City Schls 1st Grd Tchr 1969-; *ai:* Odyssey of the Mind Coach 1992-; Bing Area Rdng Cncl 1985-; NEAYC 1990-; Bing Teachers Union, NEA 1969-; Binghamton City Schl Dist Tchr of Yr 1996; Presenter of NYS Rdng Conf; Mentor Prgm Bing Schls; *office:* Theodore Roosevelt Elem Schl 9 Ogden St Binghamton NY 13901

TIETJEN, RUSSELL, Physical Education Teacher; *b:* Hollis, NY; *m:* Claire Hansen; *c:* Jessica, Melanie; *ed:* Hudson Valley Comm Coll (AA) Liberal Arts 1974; Slippery Rock Univ (BS) Hlth, PE 1976; Adelphi Univ (MA) Hlth Ed 1981; Univ of TX at Houston Eart, General Sci Cert 1984; *cr:* Locust Valley Schls PE 1976-80; Westbury Friends Schls PE 1980-82; Channelview ISD Hlth Ed, Eart Sci 1982-84; Northport Schls PE, Hlth Ed 1984-; *ai:* Asst Var Bsbl, MS Bsktbl, MS Ftbl Coach; Spec Act Coord; NYSAHPERD 1994-; UTN 1984-; St Anthonys 1995-, CYO Bsktbl Coach; Long Island Baymen 1996-, Summer Bsbl Coach; Jr Var Bsbl Coach of Yr 1986, 1988; *office:* Northport-East Northport Schls 110 Elwood Rd Northport NY 11768

TIFFANY, DIANE ROBERTA, English Teacher; *b:* Windber, PA; *ed:* Shippensburg St Col (BS) Eng 1968; IN Univ of PA (MED) Eng 1975; *cr:* Shanksville-Stonycreek HS Eng Tchr 1968-; *ai:* Sr Class, Newspaper Cty Highlights Adv; NHS Fac Comm; NEA, PSEA NCTE 1968-; Who's Who in Amer Ed 1989-90; *office:* Shanksville Stonycreek Schl Box 128 Main St Shanksville PA 15560

TIFFANY, FREDERICK GLENN, Economics Professor; *b:* Kalamazoo, MI; *ed:* Kenyon Coll (BA) Ec 1977; Univ of PA (MS) Ec 1987, (PHD) Ec 1988; *cr:* Ursinus Coll Lecturer of Ec 1983-84; Bryn Mawr Coll Instr of Ec 1984-85; Wittenberg Univ Instr of Ec 1987-89, Asst Prof Ec 1989-; *ai:* Amer Econ Assn 1982-; Midwest Econ Assn 1989-; *office:* Wittenberg Univ PO Box 720 Springfield OH 45501

TIGHE, PAULINE MARTHA, 5th Grade Teacher; *b:* Woodbury, NJ; *m:* Rudolph L.; *c:* Christine, Rudolph John; *ed:* Glassboro St Coll (BA) Elem Ed 1975; *cr:* St Michael's Cath Schl K-1-2 Grd Tchr 1975-79; Logan Twp Schl 5 Grd Tchr 1979-; *ai:* Mentor Prgm for New Tchrs; Math, Geog Club; Stud Skills, Lang, Math, Soc St Comms; LTTA 1979-, Sec 1987-1990; Paulsboro Planning Bd, Sec 1972-74; Gibbstown PTA 1979-80; Logan Twp Home, Schl League 1979-; *office:* Logan Township Elem Schl 110 School Ln Swedesboro NJ 08085

TIKALSKY, PAUL J., Civil & Envrnmntl Engrng Tchr; *b:* Denmark, WI; *ed:* Univ of WI (BS) Civil & Environmental Engrng 1983; Univ of TX (MS) Civil Engrng 1986, (PHD) Civil Engrng 1989; *cr:* Robert E. Lee & Assoc Staff Engr 1983-84; Carrasquillo & Assoc Staff Engr 1986-89; Santa Clara Univ Asst Prof 1989-95; Penn St Univ Assoc Prof 1995-; *ai:* ASCE 1980-; ACI 1984-, Chair Comm 232 & E701 Fellow; ASTM 1990-, Comm C-09; Habitat for Humanity 1992-, Bd of Dir, VP; Christmas in April 1990-, Bd of Dir; Sierra Club 1990-, Life Mem; Author of More Than 20 Publications; Ford & GE Fellowships; *office:* The Pennsylvania St Univ 212 Sackett Bldg University Park PA 16802

TILDEN, GARY M., Social Studies Teacher; *b:* Haverhill, MA; *m:* Patricia A. Philip; *c:* Tonya Lee; *ed:* Salem St Coll (BS) His, Geog 1969, (MA) His, Modern 1972; *cr:* Exeter Area Jr HS Soc Stud, Sci Tchr 1969-; *ai:* NEA, NHNEA 1969-; NH Astronomnical Soc 1992-; Speaker 26th Northeast Regnl Conf 1995; The Atomic Bomb Should it Have Been Dropped Boston Fellow Japan 1994; *office:* Exeter Area Jr HS 38 Linden St Exeter NH 03833

TILE, MICHAEL DAVID, Oral Comm & English Teacher; *b:* Du Bois, PA; *m:* Sally Jane Seaman; *c:* Christopher, Breanna; *ed:* Slippery Rock St (BA), (BS) Speech Comm 1969; 30 Hrs Univ of MD; 60 Hrs MCPS in Svc; *cr:* Montgomery Cty Pub Schls Oral Comm, Eng Tchr 1969-; *ai:* Forcensics Team Coach 1969-; WJFK Radio Spon 1975-; Montgomery Cty Forensic League Pres 1985-; MD Speech Coach of Yr 1971, 1980; Montgomery Cty Forensic League Team Champion Coach 1977-79, 1982, 1985-87, 1989-; *home:* 17700 Ridge Rd Rockville MD 20853*

TILGHMAN, KATHY QUINN, Stu Advisor, Stu Relation; *b:* Lyon, NY; *c:* Herman Jr., Rafael; *ed:* DE St Coll (BS) Hlth, PE, Sci 1972; Wilmington Coll (MS) Human Resources; Human Relations Trng; Conflict Resolution Trng; Staff Dev; Multicul Ed Trng; *cr:* Dickinson HS Tchr 16 Yrs; Red Clay Dist HS Stu Relation Specialist 4 Yrs; Cat CAlloway Schl of Arts Acting Dean 1 Yr; Alex I DuPont HS Admin Team; *ai:* Reach Team, At Risk Prgm Coord; Conflict Resolution, Multiculture Dist Comms; Youth Coalition, Chrldr Adv; Fed of Tchrs 10 Yrs; BSA, Den Mother, Recognition; Supts Recognition Awd; Tutor Prgm Coord; Hlth Curr Task Force; Effective Tchr Presentor.*

TILLAR, ELIZABETH KENNEDY, Asst Prof of Religious Studies; *b:* Roanoke Rapids, NC; *ed:* Univ of NM (BA) Eng 1979, (MS) Eng 1983; Colgate Rochester Divinity Schl (MA) Theology 1988; Fordham Univ Candidate PHD in Theology 30 Credit Hrs Doctoral Work; *cr:* Rochester Inst of Tech Adj Instr 1984-88; Long Island Univ Adj Asst Prof 1990-93; Mount St Mary Coll Asst Prof 1993-; *ai:* Curr Comm 1993-; Sub Comm Fnds Curr Review Chair 1994-; Amer Acad of Rel 1994-; NY St Union of

Tchrs 1990-; Natl Endowment Hum Grant 1993; Pew Charitable Trusts Fac Dev Grant 1993-; Article Pub 1992; Paper Presented Amer Acad of Rel Regnl Conf 1996; *office:* Mount Saint Mary Coll 330 Powell Ave Newburgh NY 12550

TILLE, MARY ANN, English & Speech Teacher; *b:* Defiance, OH; *m:* Carrol; *c:* David, Susan; *ed:* Bowling Green St Univ (BS) Eng, Speech 1964, (MS) Rdng 1993; *cr:* Cntrl Local Schls Tchr 1964-69; Ayersville Local Schl Tchr 1969-71; Northeastern Local Schl Tchr 1980-84; Ayersville Local Schls Tchr 1985-; *ai:* Tech Comm; NEA, OEA, NCTE 1964-; Ed 2000 1993-; Tchr of Yr 1991; Article Pub; Chptr in Book; *office:* Ayersville HS 28046 Watson Rd Defiance OH 43512

TILLERY, JUANITA TYNES, Diversified Occupations Coord; *b:* Newport News, VA; *m:* James; *ed:* Norfolk St Univ (AB) Eng 1968; Addl 63 Hrs Ed, Curr, Supervision, Cooperative Learning, Diversified Occupation Courses; *cr:* Huntington HS Eng Tchr 1968-71; Lansdowne MS Eng Tchr 1971-84; Deer Park Jr HS Cooperative Ed Coord 1984-87; Randallstown HS Diversified Occupations Coord 1987-; *ai:* Girls Debutante Club, Class of 95 Spon; Stu Svc Learning Coord; TABCO, MSTA 1971-; NEA 1968-; MACE, MVA 1984-, Pres of MACE; Alpha Kappa Alpha 1966-, Pres, Sec; *office:* Randallstown Sr HS 4000 Offutt Rd Randallstown MD 21133*

TILLI, SUSAN, French & Spanish Teacher; *b:* Northampton, PA; *ed:* Moravion (BA) Fr, Span 1969; Lehigh (MAEd) Ed, Fr 1973; 9 Credits Guid Cnslng; *cr:* Freedom HS Span, Fr Tchr 1969-72; East Hills Schl Span Tchr 1972-76; Libert HS Span, Fr Tchr 1976-; *ai:* NEA, BEA, PSEA 1969-; *home:* 3946 Birch Dr Bethlehem PA 18017*

TILLIS, BEVERLY BARNETT, Third Grade Teacher; *b:* Huntington, WV; *m:* Larry Edwin; *c:* Trisha N., Julianne E.; *ed:* Marshall Univ (AB) Early Chldhd Ed 1974, (MA) Elem Ed 1978; *cr:* Chesapeake East Elem 5th Grd Math Tchr 1974-77; Chesapeake Elem Tchr 1978-; *ai:* Pub Relations; Chesapeake Ed Assn 1974-, Sec-Treas2 Yrs; Kappa Delta Pi 1 Yr; OH Ed Assn; Chesapeake Local Tchrs Assn; Chesapeake Schls Participant in First TESA 1986-87; *office:* Chesapeake Elem Schl Old Rt 52 Chesapeake OH 45619*

TILLMAN, ERNESTINE PORTER, Science Teacher & Dean; *b:* Perry, OK; *m:* Naaman L. Sr.; *c:* Naaman Jr., Julian, Larry, Rachell Yeager; *ed:* Langston Univ (BA) Sociology, Sci 1954; Temple Univ (MED) Sci Ed 1971; 30 Credits City Coll NY, Queens Coll, Columbia Univ, Adelphi Univ; *cr:* Sulzberger Jr HS Tchr, Grd Chm 1962-74; Astoria IS 126Q Tchr, Dean, Acting AP 1974-; *ai:* Arista Spon; Glee Club; United Fed of Tchrs 1974-; Yth Org 1985-, Prgrm Dir, Cert for Svc; Bd Mem 1990-, Diamond Awd; Comm Org 1987-, Participation Awd; Tchr of Yr NYC Comm Schl Dist 30; Chrstn Ldrshp Awd The Black Bus & Prof Womens Club; *home:* 391 Windsor Rd Englewood NJ 07631*

TILLMAN, SUSAN SVERD, Alternative Educator; *b:* New York, NY; *m:* Morton; *c:* Jonathan C., Pamela I.; *ed:* Adelphi Univ (BA) Bio, Chem 1959; NY Univ (MA) Sci Ed 1962; Adelphi Univ Physics; *cr:* Elmont HS Bio Tchr 1959-64, Sub Sci Tchr 1974-78; Long Island Rsrch Inst Office of Mental Hlth Researcher 1979-80; Alternative Schl Tchr 1981-; *ai:* Long Island Sci Fair Adv, Evaluator; NEA; NY Sci Tchrs Assn; PTA, Advy Bd; Rsrch Paper Pub; *office:* Alternative Schl C/O H. F. Carey HS 230 Poppy Ave Franklin Square NY 11010

TILLOTSON, LUCIA E., Biology Instructor; *b:* Buenos Aires, Argentina; *m:* Daniel C.; *ed:* IN Univ (BS) Medical Tech 1970; Rutgers Univ (MS) Microbiology & Molecular Genetics 1986, (PHD) Microbiology & Molecular Genetics 1989-; *cr:* Raritan Valley Hosp Medical Technologist 1972-78; CABM at Rutgers Post-Doctoral Fellow 1989-91; Middlesex Cty Coll Instr 1992-; *ai:* NSF Grant for Math & Sci Tchrs Participant; Acad Adv; Hispanic Soc; Intnl Stdnts Acad Stans Mentor; Amer Soc for Microbiology; Amer Assn for Advancement of Sci; Amer Bio Tchrs; Local Church, Youth Act, Pianist; Natl Cancer Inst Research Awd 1986-89; Theobald Smith Soc Awd 1986; Scientific Papers Pub in Journal of Virology 1992; Contributing Author in Molecular Bio of Staphylococci 1990; *office:* Middlesex County Coll 155 Mill Road Edison NJ 08837*

TILNEY, JOANNE M., Fourth Grd Tchr & Asst Prin; *b:* Detroit, MI; *ed:* Miami Univ (BS) Elem Ed 1979, (MED) Lang Arts 1992; *cr:* Immanuel Luth Schl 3rd-4th Grd Tchr 1979-90, 4th Grd Tchr 1990-, Asst Prin 1994-; *ai:* Luth Ed Assn 1979-; *office:* Immanuel Lutheran Schl 1285 Main St Hamilton OH 45013

TIMA, DIANNE LUTHER, Lang Arts Tchr & Dept Coord; *b:* Pittsbugh, PA; *m:* Michael A. Sr.; *c:* Michael A. Jr., Mark A., Meghan A.; *ed:* Duquesne Univ (BS) Eng, Scndry Ed 1971 (MS) Ed, Schl Psych 1993; Stu Assistance Prgm 1993; *cr:* St Pius X Schl Jr HS Lang Arts, Art Tchr 1966-69; Resurrection Schl Jr HS Lang Arts, Art Tchr 1969-70; St Sebastian Schl Jr HS Lang Arts, Art Tchr 1970-71; Resurrection Schl Jr HS Lang Arts, Art Tchr 1971-74, 1986-; *ai:* Forensic Judge; NCTE 1991-, WPCTE 1990-; Scorer PA Dept of Ed Writing Assessment; Allegheny Intermediate Unit Presenter Wkshp on Coop Learning, Writing Process; *office:* Resurrection Schl 1100 Creedmore Ave Pittsburgh PA 15226*

TIMBARIO, PHYLLIS DATO, 8th Grade Teacher; *b:* Pittsburgh, PA; *m:* John W.; *c:* Nathan, Laura; *ed:* Univ of Pittsburgh (BS) Elem Ed 1975, (MED) Elem Rdng 1981; Cmptr Tech; *cr:* St Luke Schl 7th Grd Tchr 1975-79; ACLD Resource Rdng Tchr 1984-89; Chartiers Vly Schl Rdng Specialist 1979-82; Holy Child Schl 8th Grd Tchr 1983-; *ai:* Vocal Coach Class Play; 8th Yr Spon Jr Great Books Court; Fac Rep; Chorus Dir; WPCTE 1991-; NCEA 1983-; Char-Val Singers 1986-, Pres; St Margaret Pre Cana 1987-; Stage 62 1994-; BSA 1989-, Treas; *home:* 70 School St Pittsburgh PA 15220*

TIMCHAK, ROBERT M., Dir of Religious Formation; *b:* Wilkes-Barre, PA; *ed:* Univ of Scranton (BS) Lbrl Stud 1987; Seton Hall Univ (MDiv) Theology 1992; *cr:* St Mary's Church Asst Pastor 1992-94; Seton Cath HS DRF, Rel Tchr 1994-; *ai:* IM Bsktbl Coach; CLC Moderator; Big Brothers, Big Sisters; Liturgical Comm; NCEA 1994-; K of C 1985-; *office:* Seton Catholic HS 37 William St Pittston PA 18640

TIMKO, DONNA ZELEHOSKI, English Teacher; *b:* Plainfield, NJ; *m:* Steven; *c:* Lindsay, Hunter; *ed:* Seton Hall Univ (BS) Eng Ed, Comm 1972, (MA) Eng 1979; *cr:* South Plainfield MS Eng Tchr 1972-80; AT&T, Johnson & Johnson of Timko Assoc Pres, Sale Rep, Prof Writer, Trainer 1980-92; South Plainfield HS Eng Tchr 1992-; *ai:* Woods Rd Schl Yrbk Chprsn; Girls Track Coach; Past Twirling Adv; NEA, NJEA, SPEA 1972-; Woods Rd Home Schl 1986-, VP; *office:* South Plainfield HS 200 Lake St South Plainfield NJ 07080

TIMLIN, JAMES T., Chemistry Teacher; *b:* Pittston, PA; *m:* Kay Zaladonis; *c:* Terri, Susan Leigh; *ed:* Univ of Scranton (BS) Chem & Ed 1973; Attnd Penn St Univ & East Stroudsburg St Coll; *cr:* Pittston Area Schl Dist Chem Tchr 1973-; *ai:* Bsktbl Coach; PAFT 1973-, Chm Cope Comm; Luzerne Cty Sci Tchrs 1973-, on Bd; AOH 1985-, Pres, Man of the Yr; RR & G Club 1973-, Pres; St Marys Holy Name Soc 1965-, Pres; PA Sci & Humanities Symposium; *office:* Pittston Area HS 5 Stout St Pittston PA 18640

TIMMEL, CYNTHIA EVELYN, Home Economics Teacher; *b:* Buffalo, NY; *m:* Bill; *c:* William, Timothy, Matthew; *ed:* SUC at Buffalo (BS) Home Ec 1977; SUC at Buffalo (MS) Home Ec 1980; Inservice Trng at Cornell Univ; *cr:* Ticonderoga HS Home Ec, Hlth Tchr 1977-78; Cooperative Extension 4-H Agent 1978-80; Mt Mercy Acad Home Ec Tchr 1980-83; Business Mgr, Educator 1983-91; Holland HS Home Ec Tchr 1991-; *ai:* SASS Stu Asst Team; Teen Cnslr; Workgroup Facilitator; Dance, Prom Chaperone; Dist AIDS Comm Co-Chair; Phi Upsilon Omicron 1977-; NEA 1991-; HETA; AHEA; 4-H Club Head Ldr 1992-; *office:* Holland HS 103 Canada St Holland NY 14080*

TIMMERMAN, GREGORY WILLIAM, HS Social Studies Teacher; *b:* Alexandria Bay, NY; *m:* Joan Mary Nicholson; *c:* Geoffrey; *ed:* St Univ of NY at Potsdam (BA) His & Ed 1976, (MSEd) Rdng 1981; St Lawrence Univ (SDA) Ed Admin 1987; NYS Cert; MS St Univ 12 Grad Credit Hrs; *cr:* Heuvelton Cntrl Schl Tchr 1977-78, 1981-; Thousand Islands Bridge Authority Tourism Interest Mgr 1978-81; *ai:* NHS & Sr Class Adv; Adult Ed Coord; Adj Fac; Bsktbl Score Keeper; Amer Red Cross Blood Dr Spon; AFT 1981-; NYSUT 1981-; Heuvelton Tchrs Assoc 1981-, Treas; St Lawrence Vly Cncl for Soc Stud 1981-; Heuvelton Presbyn Church 1978-, Church Yth Group & Nominating Comms, Trustee; BSA 1988-, Asst Scoutmaster, Merit Badge Cnslr & Troop Advancement Chm, Scouters Awd; *home:* 5 Todd Rd Heuvelton NY 13654

TIMMINS, PETER RIEHM, Former Bible Teacher; *b:* Cleveland, OH; *m:* Karen Marie Nestor; *c:* Sarah, Jenny; *ed:* Bryan Coll (BS) Bus Admin 1978; 102 Credits Pastoral & Bible Stud Bible Bapt Schl of Theology; *cr:* West Chester Chrstn HS Bible Tchr 1 1/2 Yrs; *ai:* Var Boys Bkstbl Coach; *home:* 1266 Upton Cir West Chester PA 19380

TIMMINS, THEODORE, High School Guidance Counselor; *b:* Brooklyn, NY; *m:* Arlene Edebohls; *c:* Michael, Robert; *ed:* St Francis Coll (BA) His 1968; Long Island Univ (MS) Guid, Cnslng 1971; Post Grad Work Pace Univ, NYU, Brooklyn Coll, The New Schl Scuola Lorenzo De Medici Florence Italy; *cr:* IS 293 6th-8th Grd Tchr 1968-74; JHS 142 8th Grd Spec Ed Tchr 1974-75; Franklin Roosevelt HS Guid Cnslr 1975-; *ai:* AFT, UFT 1968-; NBCC 1988-; NYC Cnslrs Assn 1981-; *office:* Franklin Delano Roosevelt HS 5800 20th Ave Brooklyn NY 11204

TIMMONS, MARGARET SIMS, Third Grade Teacher of GATE; *b:* Columbia, SC; *m:* Simeon Kenneth; *c:* Kenneth D., Simeon M., Brian D.; *ed:* Kean Coll at Union (BA) Early Chldhd Ed 1964, (MA) Early Chldhd Ed 1988; Nova Southeastern Univ at Ft Lauderdale 52 Addl Credits Child & Yth Stud1993-; *cr:* Paterson Bd of Ed Tchr 1964-; *ai:* After Schl Parent-Tchr-Child Partnership 1987-95; After Schl Enrichment Prgm 1994-95; Dist Sci Curr Comm 1991; Dist Arithmetic Curr Comm 1991-92; Dist Rdng, Lang Arts Comm 1993-95; Dist Biling Assessment Comm; ASCD 1988-; Paterson Ed Assn, NJ Ed Assn, NEA 1978-; Kappa Delta Phi 1986-; Delta Sigma Theta 1961-; Aenon Bapt Church Usher Bd 1990-, VP, Schlsp Comm 1990-; Vauxhall Civic Assn 1989-, Sec; Jeanette Shell Schlsp Comm 1993-, Sec; Vauxhall & Brookside African-Amer Yth Lit Club 1992-, Adv, Mentor; Vauxhall Ed Dev Advy Bd 1994-; Tchr or Yr 1984; After Schl Parent-Tchr-Child Partnership Grants 1987-95; ABC Day Care Ctr African-Amer Awd 1991; *home:* 19 Arcadia Pl Vauxhall NJ 07088*

TIMPANELLI, LUCINDA A., Foreign Languages Dept Chair; *b:* Bridgeport, CT; *m:* Anthony; *ed:* Univ Bridgeport (BA) Span 1973; Fairfield Univ (MA) Biling, ESL 1978, (CAS) Supervision, Admin 1985; *cr:* Trumbull HS Span Tchr 23 Yrs, Dept Chair 12 Yrs; Univ of New Haven Instr Interns, Stdnts entering Tchng Profession 3 Yrs; St of CT Assessor, Beginning Tchrs 8 Yrs; *ai:* Adv Stu Cncl; Tchr Evaluation Comms; Mentor, Cooperating Tchr; AATSP; CASCD; ASCD; *office:* Trumbull HS 72 Strobel Rd Trumbull CT 06611*

TINI, KATHLEEN A., Industrial Engrng Tech Instr; *b:* Chester, PA; *w:* Albert (dec); *c:* Daun DePetris-Doyle, Nikole De Petris; *ed:* DTCC (AAS) Industrial Engineering 1978; Neuman Coll (BS) Industrial Mngmt 1982; Wilmington Coll (MS) Human Resource Mngmt 1989; *cr:* Lic Real Estate 1976-78, Prof Skater 1966-78; General Motors Ind Engr 1978-82; DTCC Fac Ind Engr 1982-; *ai:* Adopt An Angel Inc Pres Founder Est 1984; IET Club Adv; Deans Advy Comm; Inst of Ind Engrs 1976-, Former Pres, VP, Bd of Dirs; DE Coll Prsnl Assn 1983-; NAFE 1993-; Fairway Falls Civic Assn 1986-; Outstanding IET Alumnus 1980; Outstanding Alumnus 1987; Jefferson Awds 1995; *office:* Delaware Tech & Comm Coll 400 Stanton-Christiana Rd Newark DE 19713

TINLIN, SHELLEY RAE, Spanish Teacher; *b:* Canton, OH; *m:* Douglas Allen II; *ed:* Kent St Univ (BSEd) Span & Eng 1990; *cr:* Crestview Local Schls Span Tchr 1990-; *ai:* Span Club Adv; NEA 1990-; First Friends Church 1990-; *office:* Crestview Local Schl Dist 44100 Crestview Rd Columbiana OH 44408*

TINNELLY, PAMELA JEANNE, Third Grade Teacher; *b:* Queens, NY; *m:* Robert Alan; *ed:* St John's Univ (BS) Elem Ed 1973; Hofstia Univ (MS) Elem Ed 1976; 24 Credit Hrs Various In-Svc & Courses Offered by Nassau BOCES; *cr:* New Hyde Park Rd Schl Fourth Grd Tchr 1973-79, Second Grd Tchr 1979-81, Fifth Grd Tchr 1981-86, Third Grd Tchr 1986-; *ai:* Bldg Level Team; Personnel Selection, Curr Comms; New Hyde Park Garden City Park Tchrs Assoc 1973-, Bldg Rep, Treas; NYSUT, AFT 1973-; St Joseph's Church 1980-, Eucharistic Minister; New Hyde Park Rd Schl PTA 1973-, Tchr Rep; *office:* New Hyde Park Road Elem Schl New Hyde Park Rd New Hyde Park NY 11040*

TINNER, JOHN JOSEPH, History Department Chairman; *b:* Kingston, PA; *m:* Barbara C. Kalinowski; *c:* John, Joyce, Jeff; *ed:* Mansfield Univ (BS) His & Soc Stud 1966; Penn St (MS) His 1983; Univ of Scranton (MS) Scndry Admin 1991; Attnd Bloomsburg Univ 12 Credit Hrs & Lehigh Univ 6 Credit Hrs; *cr:* Tunkhannock Schl Dist His Dept Chm, Advanced Placement US His, Anthropology, US His & European His Tchr 1966-; *ai:* Historians Club Adv; European Tour Adv; Staff Dev Comm; Discipline Comm; Communications Comm; Tunkhannock Ed Assn 1966-, Prof Rights & Responsibilities Chm; PA St Ed Assn 1966-, St Ethics Comm; NEA 1966-; Dallas Planning Comm 1980-88; Back Mountain Bsbl 1973-88, VP, Svc Awd; Back Mountain Soccer Club 1973-88, Pres; Numerous Conf Presentations; Morale Article Pub; Collaborated on HS His Textbook; *office:* Tunkhannock Area HS 120 W Tioga St Tunkhannock PA 18657

TINQUIST, DENISE HARRINGTON, English Teacher; *b:* Montclair, NJ; *m:* Alan H.; *c:* Leigh, Rachel, Connor; *ed:* Montclair St Coll (BA) Eng 1976; *cr:* Roxbury HS Eng Tchr 1976-; *ai:* NEA; NJEA; REA; NCTE; *office:* Roxbury HS 1 Bryant Dr Succasunna NJ 07960

TINSLEY, LOIS D. (MITCHELL), 3rd Grade Teacher; *b:* New York City, NY; *m:* Thomas E.; *c:* Jayson, Benjamin; *ed:* Hampton Inst (BS) Elem Ed 1976; *cr:* Longwood Cntrl Schl Dist Tchr 1976-; *ai:* Long Island Black Edctrs Assoc; *office:* Longwood Schl Dist 105 Ridge Rd Ridge NY 11961

TINTI, ANTONIA MARIE, Tchr of the Talented & Gifted; *b:* Erie, PA; *ed:* Villa Maria Coll (BSED) Elem Ed 1966; Edinboro St Univ (MED) Elem Ed 1968; 18 Grad Hrs Cert Talented, Gifted; Cert Spec Ed 50 Addl Credit Hrs; *cr:* Millcreek Schl Dist Elem Tchr 1966-70, 1974-78; Dept of Defense Overseas Schls Elem Tchr 1970-74, Tchr Talented, Gifted 1978-; *ai:* Advy Comm; Curr Chprsn for Specialists; Chprsn Enrichment Comm; Overseas Fed Tchrs 1995-; Ed Assn Schl Dist Tchr of Yr 1977; 11 Exceptional Perf Awds, 9 Sustained Superior Monetary Awds, Dept of Defense Overseas Schls; *home:* PSC Box 2 Box 5167 APO AE 09012*

TIPPETT, BRYAN KEITH, Professor of Biology; *b:* Pittsburgh, PA; *ed:* Gannon Univ (BS) Bio 1979; Duquesne Univ (MS) Bio 1982; Cert to Train in Total Quality Mgmt; Univ of Sarasota Ed Ldrshp Course; *cr:* Allegheny General Hospital Lab Tech 1982-90; Comm Coll of Allegheny Cty Prof of Bio 1990-; *ai:* TQM Trainer & Facilitator; Chair Coll Cmptr Tech Planning Comm; Stu Club Adv; Church Ec, Ed Comm Chair; Church Misician; Chair Church Cmptr Tech Comm; AFT 1990-; PA Black Conf on High 1996-; Comm Coll African-Amer Caucus 1990-; Second Bapt C 1984-, Trustee; Established 1st Sci Learning Ctr Grant Funded by Fnd; *office:* Comm Coll Algny Co Algny Cmps 808 Ridge Ave Pitts PA 15212

TIPPIN, LISA IRENE, Lang Arts & Soc Stud Tchr; *b:* Toledo, O Michael Samuel; *c:* Kaitlin Irene, Melissa Ann; *ed:* Bowling Green S (BA) Elem Ed 1983; Univ of Toledo (MS) MS Ed 1989; Addl Cred From Drake Univ & Univ of AK Southeast; *cr:* Maumee City Schls I Grd Sub Tchr 1983-84, Tutor of Vision-Hearing Impaired & Ho Bound 1984-85; Saint Marys Schl 5th-6th Grd Tchr 1985-86; Mon Exempted Village Schls 5th Grd Lang Arts & Soc Stud Tchr 198 5th-6th Grd Internet & E-Mail Trainer; Soc Stud & Schoolnet Plus Comms; OH Assn Soc Stud Tchrs 1995-; Montpelier Ed Assn 1986- Rep; OEA, NEA 1986-; Montpelier PTO 1995-; *office:* Superio 10-034 St Rt 576 Montpelier OH 43543

TIPPIN, SUSAN PALMER, Third Grade Teacher; *b:* Philadelphia, P Ross S. Jr.; *c:* R. Scott; *ed:* Wheelock Coll (BS) Ed; Temple Univ (Rdng 1971; 30 Plus Credits Lang Arts; *cr:* Abington Schl Dist Tchr & Specialist 1970-; *ai:* NEA 1970-; *office:* Glenside Weldon Elem Sc Easton Rd Glenside PA 19038

TIPPLE, ANN BEATTY, Science Teacher; *b:* Troy, NY; *m:* Davi SUNY at Albany (BS) Sec Sci, Physics 1972; 48 Post Grad Credits; Prgm; *cr:* Red Hook Cntrl Schl MS Sci Tchr 1972-; *ai:* Hyde Reformed Church 1976-, Tchr, Yth Ldr, Treas; *office:* Linden Avenu 65 W Market St Red Hook NY 12571

TIRONE, LAWRENCE D., Science Teacher; *b:* Staten Island, N Mary Ellen Noone; *c:* Kevin, James; *ed:* Providence Coll (BA) Bio-C Ed 1974; Richmond Coll at City Univ (MA) Ed, Sci 1979; *cr:* St Pete Tchr 1974-78; James Madison HS Sci AP Chem, Regents Chem 1978-; *ai:* Mentoring Comm 1984-, Chm 1989-90; UFT 1978-; Ou Tchr 1987; *office:* James Madison HS 3787 Bedford Ave Brookly 11229

TISA, KEN, Fine Arts Dept Teacher; *b:* Philadelphia, PA; *ed:* Pra (BFA) Painting 1968; Yale Schl of Art & Arch (MFA) Painting 197 MD Inst Coll of Art Tchr 1990-; Parson's Schl of Design Tchr 199 Ind Curator of Art Exhibitions; Collections Shown Around World; *ho* Greene St New York NY 10013*

TISA, SHERYL SMITH, Fourth Grade Teacher; *b:* Rochester, N Stephen R.; *c:* Stephen, Travis; *ed:* St Univ Coll at Brockport (B 1965; 40 Plus Credit Hrs Post Grad Stud; *cr:* Penfield Schl Dist 2n Tchr 1965-69; English Village Schl 3rd Grd Tchr 1972-78; Lakeshore Schl Tchr of Gifted Ed 1978-81, 4th Grd Tchr 1981-93; Pine Brook Schl 4th Grd Tchr 1993-95; Buckman Heights Elem 4th Grd Tchr *ai:* Bldg Resource Comm; Delta Kappa Gamma-Alpha Xi 1994-, Sec; 1972-; Owasco Watershed Assn 1987-; Core Team of Pine Brook *office:* Buckman Hghts Elem Schl 550 Buckman Rd Rochester NY 14

TISCHLER, BARBARA L., History Professor; *b:* Minneapolis, M Steven; *c:* Ben, Daniel; *ed:* Douglass Coll (BA) Music 1971; Manh Schl of Music (MM) Performance 1973; Columbia U (PHD) His 198 Barnard Coll Asst Prof 1985-89; Tchrs Coll Lecturer 1991-; Colum Lecturer 1991-; *ai:* West Side Little League Coach; Amer His Assn Org Amer Historians 1982-; Sannick Soc 1984-; Author of an Amer 1986; Ed of Sights on the Sixties 1992; *office:* Columbia Univ Lewisohn Hall New York NY 10027*

TISCI, MARILYN ANN (STRATTON), Sixth Grade Mathematics *b:* Salem, OH; *m:* Kenneth J.; *c:* Jason Musselman, Cheri MUss Welsh; *ed:* Malone Coll (BS) Elem Ed 1966; Univ of Akron (MS) Ed Addl 32 Post Grad Credits Ed; *cr:* Summit Elem Schl Tchr 196 Worley Elem Schl Tchr 1978-93; Lehman MS Tchr 1993-; *ai:* Sixt Comm Team Ldr; Adult Ed Instr; CPEA, OEA, NEA 1966-; Impact II Ameritech Fdn; *home:* 3302 Cherrywood St Norton OH 44203

TISHKEVICH, FRANCES MARY, Professor of Mathematic Worcester, MA; *c:* Joseph Gorgol-Tishkevich, David Gorgol-Tishke *ed:* Plymouth St Coll (BS) Math Ed 1975; Norwich Univ (MA) Gift 1989; *cr:* Manchester West HS Math Tchr 1975-81; New Hampshire Math Prof 1989-; NH Tech Coll Job Trng Instr Math 1991-92; Notre Coll Math Prof 1992-; *ai:* Swift Water Girl Scout Cncl Women in Presenter; Amer Mensa 1987-, Gifted Children's Coord; Gifted Child Coord of Yr 1990; East Soccer League 1994-, Coach; Kids Coll 199 Bd of Dirs; Odyssey of Mind 1988-, Regnl Problem Coord, Judge; Little League 1989-, Team Mother; Handbook Pub; *office:* Notre Coll 2321 Elm St Manchester NH 03104

TISO, MARY M. (PETRECCO), English Teacher; *b:* Philadelphia *m:* Victor G.; *c:* Jennifer Stewart, Victoria Kobol; *ed:* Bucks Cty C Coll (AA) Lbrl Arts-Magna Cum Laude-Phi Theta Kappa; Trenton S (BA) Eng-Summa Cum Laude 1990, (MA) Eng Lit-Magna Cum L 1996; *cr:* Pennsbury Schl Dist Tchrs Asst 1975-88; Council Rock HS Tchr 1990-93; Newtown Jr HS Eng Tchr 1993-; *ai:* Scndry Instrl Su Team; Child Study Team; Good News PR Comm; NEA, PSEA 1 CREA 1990-, Pol Action Co-Chair; St John Evangelist Schl Bd 7 Yrs, Bishop Conwell HS Parent Assn, Ofcr 3 Yrs; Article, Short Story, P Pub; *office:* Newtown Jr HS 116 Richboro Rd Newtown PA 18940

TITE, JOHN GREGORY, Math Dpt Chr & Calculus Inst Southbridge, MA; *ed:* Univ of MA (BS) Math 1963; Worcest St (MED) Ed 1966; Clarkson Coll of Tech (MS) Math 1971; NSF Summe Grants Rutgers Univ, MI St Univ, Univ of San Francisco; Cmptr Ass Math Project Grant Univ of MA: Graphing Calculator Pre-Calculsus Worcester Polytechnic Inst; *cr:* Grafton Pub Schls Math Instr 196 In-Svc Instr of Metrics 1974-76, Math Dept Chprsn, Calculus Instr 1 Anna Maria Coll Adj Prof of Calculus 1986-88; *ai:* NHS Selection C NCTM 1965-; Assn Tchrs of Math in MA 1965-, NCTM Rep 197 Neighborhood Assn Math Dept Heads 1968-, Bd of Dirs 1976-79; Gr Tchrs Assn; MA Tchrs Assn; NEA; MA ASCD, Speaker Mass Competency 1978; MA Tchrs Assn, Speaker Mass Math Competency Assn Tchrs Math New England, Speaker Mass Math Competency Western MA Math Fairs, Judge Regnl Math Fairs 1974-80; One of Math Edctrs Chosen to Serve on Math Task Force 1976-80; N Conventions Films, Filmstrips Chprsn 1973, 1979; Sales of N Material schm 1976; Assn Tchrs Math in New England Conve Exhibits Chprsn 1970, 1979; *office:* Grafton Meml Sr HS 24 Provid Rd Grafton MA 01519

TITE, SARA J., 9th-12th Grade Math Teacher; *b:* Pottsville, PA Edward R. III; *ed:* Kutztown Univ (BS) Scndry Math Ed 1989; 24 C at Allentown Coll of St Francis de Sales Towards (MEd) in Cmptr E Jim Thorpe Area Math, Cmptr & Tchr of Gifted 1991-; *ai:* KMO MAA 1989-, Charter Mem; NEA 1989-; *office:* Jim Thorpe Area HS Center St Jim Thorpe PA 18229

TITKEMEIER, PATRICIA R., 9th Grade English Teacher; *b:* Bo Green, OH; *m:* Larry L.; *c:* Kelly R., Kimberly K., Andrew L. Muskingum Coll (BA) Eng, Ed 1972; BGSU 7 Grad Hrs; *cr:* Otsego I Schl Dist 8th Grd Lang Arts Tchr 1973-75; Eastwood Local Schl Dis Grd Eng Tchr 1989-; *ai:* Parent Adv Comm; Pub Relations; OH Ed Eastwood Ed Assn 1990-; *office:* Eastwood H S 4900 Sugar Ridg Pemberville OH 43450

OW, PETER G., High School Math & Sci Teacher; *b:* Abington, PA; orter White; *c:* Meade, Arden, Daniel; *ed:* Syracuse Univ (BS) ical Engr 1969; Mansfield Univ Tchng Cert 1987; *cr:* Chrstn ing Ctr Math, Sci Instr 1987-; *ai:* Asst Admin; Prof Engr PA 1976-, 993-; *office:* Christian Learning Ctr 109 Ellicott St Corning NY 14830

S, BETTY J., Mathematics Teacher; *b:* Lucinda, PA; *w:* Irvin (dec); win, Kevin, Brian; *ed:* Youngstown St Univ (BS) Ed, Math 1991; 6 ster Hrs Ed Walsh Univ; *cr:* John F. Kennedy HS Math Tchr 1992-; nnual Fund Dr Comm; NCTM 1991-; OCTM, NCEA 1992-; Phi a Phi, Kappa Delta Pi, Golden Key 1990-; *office:* John F Kennedy HS Central Parkway Ave SE Warren OH 44484

S, DONNA PANCKERI, English Teacher; *b:* Hazelton, PA; *m:* James; *c:* Nathaniel, Colin, Alaina; *ed:* Bloomsburg Univ (BS) y Ed 1980; Scranton Univ (MA) Eng 1985; *cr:* MMI Prep Schl Eng 1980-; *ai:* Handicrafts Club, NHS Adv; Induction Comm Mentorship Co-Chprsn; NASSP 1987-, Adv; Church Cncl 1986-, Sec; Promoted ept Chair 1992; *office:* MMI Prep Schl 154 Centre St Freeland PA *

S, ROBERT CHARLES, Geology Professor; *b:* Paterson, NJ; *ed:* rs Univ (BS) Ag 1968; Boston Univ (PHD) Geology 1974; *cr:* nam Coll Instr 1973-74; Hartwick Coll Prof 1974-; *ai:* GSA 1974-; ill Cty Conservation Dev 1992-; Articles Journal Paleontology; s Purple Mountain Press; Columnist Catskill Life Magazine; *office:* ick Coll Oneonta NY 13820

O, CHERYL, Computer Teacher & Coordinator; *b:* Brooklyn, NY; *c:* Casey; *ed:* Fordham (MS) Rdng 1995; *cr:* Kingsborough Comm Coll ct Tchr 1980-90; Bishop Kearney HS Tchr 1990-92; St Joseph HS r Tchr, Coord 1992-; *ai:* Cmptr Club; Lit Magazine; *office:* St Joseph Willoughby St Brooklyn NY 11201

C, CAROL M., Eng, Spch, Creative Write Tchr; *b:* Cleveland, OH; seph R.; *c:* Victoria, Sarah; *ed:* M A John Carroll Univ (MA) Eng 60 Semester Hrs Drake Univ, Univ of AK, Ashland Univ, Notre Dame Cleveland St; *cr:* Shore Jr HS Eng Tchr 1968-78; Euclid HS Eng Tchr ; *ai:* NEA, OEA 1968-; Amer Assn of Poets Poetry Contest rable Mention; Pub Lib of Poetry.*

CZ, JOYCE (KOLODZIEJ), Retired Mathematics Teacher; *b:* ngton, NJ; *m:* Raymond; *ed:* William Paterson Coll (BA) Jr HS Ed, Math 1965; *cr:* Clifton Schl System 7th-8th Grd Math Tchr; topher Columbus MS Tchr 1965-94; *ai:* Math Dept Helping Tchr; Dist Testing Math Articulation; Cmptr Math Curr Revision, Team ach Comms; Affirmative Action; T & E Goals; Conducted Career ion Prgm; CTA, NJEA, NEA 1965-94; NJREA, NEA-R 1994-; SHANDS 1965-94, Treas 1976-89; CCMSFO 1965-94, Nominating n, Treas, VP; Deborah; AARP 1994-.

TCH, NANCY P., Culinary Arts Teacher; *b:* Nanticoke, PA; *m:* ael; *ed:* Luzerne Cty Comm (AS) Hotel, Rest Mngmt 1977; Temple (BS) Voc Ed 1995; Tchr Ldrshp; Co-Operative Ed; *cr:* Luzerne Cty n Part-time Non-credit Instr 4 Yrs; Temple U Part-time Ldrshp 3 Yrs; es Barre Area Vo-Tech Tchr Asst 11 Yrs; Hazleton Area Schl Dist Tchr ; *ai:* VICA, Clubs Advy Cncl Adv; Lead Tchr; Staff Dev; NEA, PSEA ; ASCD 1995-; VICA 1988-; AVA 1994-; ABWA 1989-91; Craft Advy n 1994-; North Cntrl Tchr Ldrshp Ctr Governing Bd 1995-; Project RN; IU Inservice Cncl; Outstdng Voc-Ed Grad 1995; *office:* Hazleton Career Ctr 1451 W 23rd St Hazleton PA 18201*

L, GREGORY C., Former Alt Spec Ed Prgm Tchr; *b:* Manhattan, NY; san; *c:* Michael, Gregory, Brian; *ed:* VA Tech (BA) Ed 1975; William son (MS) Schl Admin 1984; *cr:* Bergen Cty Spec Svcs Schl Dist Spec chr 1975-85; River Dell Reg Schl Dist Spec Ed Tchr 1985-90; ensack HS Spec Ed Tchr 1990-95; *ai:* Head Ftbl, Asst Sftbl, Weight Coach; NEA, NJEA 1975-; NJ Ftbl Coaches Assn 1980-; Bergen Cty Coaches Assn 1990-, Pres 1994; Hack Ath Alumni Assn, Hack Troast 1990-; Wychoff Bsbl Assn 1988-; Ftbl Coach of Yr 1985, 1987; Coach 1993-94; Article Pub; *home:* 393 Butternut Ave Wyckoff NJ 07481

E, MARGARET K. ZEHRINGER, German Teacher & Dept Head; rtland, IN; *m:* Michael L.; *c:* Abbey, Chelsea, Ethan; *ed:* Bowling n St Univ (BS) Ger 1981; Wright St (MED) Ed Tchr Ldr 1988; *cr:* a Sr HS Ger Tchr 1981-, Dept Head 1994-; *ai:* Adv Jr Class 13 Yrs, Club 15 Yrs; OFLA 1994-; OEA, NEA, WOEA 1981-; Chrstn Mothers -; Mentor Chair WSU-Celina Partnership; *office:* Celina Sr HS 715 E e St Celina OH 45822

ER, SANDRA MOLLEN, HS Social Studies Teacher; *b:* Toledo, OH; ichard C.; *c:* Matthew; *ed:* Univ of Toledo (BED) Soc Stud 1972, O) Admin, Supervision 1978; *cr:* Whitmer HS Soc Stud Tchr 1974-; all of Fame Comm; OH Citizen Bee Adv; NEA, OEA 1974-; OCSS, SS Charter Prgm Chm; Tchr Assoc of WA Local Schls 1974-, Comms, Outstdng Tchr Awd; NHS Torch Awd; *office:* Whitmer HS 5601 Clegg oledo OH 43613

EY, JEAN, High School Science Teacher; *b:* Passaic, NJ; *m:* James *d:* William Paterson Coll (BA) Bio 1977, (MA) Bio 1984; *cr:* Clifton f Ed Sci Tchr 1977-; *ai:* NEA, NJEA 1977-; New Jersey Sci Tchrs c.

IA, JOSEPH ANTHONY, Special Ed Tchr & Athletic Mgr; *b:* ing, NY; *m:* Elisa Marie Tornatore; *c:* Christine, Matthew; *ed:* ery Rock St Coll (BS) Spec Ed 1980; Mansfield Univ (MS) Spec Ed ; *cr:* West Canada Valley Jr-Sr High Spec Ed Tchr 1980-81; Watkins MS Spec Ed Tchr 1981-86; Corning East HS Spec Ed Tchr 1986-; *ai:* acrosse Coach; Bldg Leadership Team; Comm on Spec Ed Rep, Mid vltn Team; Corning Tchrs Assn 1986-; US Lacrosse Coaches Assn -, 100 Club; *office:* Corning E HS 201 Cantigny St Corning NY 0*

IAS, ANN GREENAWALT, 5th Grade Teacher; *b:* Reading, PA; *m:* les; *c:* Gregory; *ed:* Kutztown Univ (BS) Elem Ed 1963; East idsburg Univ (MED) Reading Specialist 1990; *cr:* Parsippany Troy Twp Schls 2nd & 4th Grd Elem Tchr 1963-66, 3rd-5th Grd Tchr -80; The Childrens Place Trng, Dev & Store Mgr 1981-87; Randolph Schls 5th Grd Tchr 1987-; *ai:* NEA 1963-80 & 1987-; IRA 1995; A 1963-80 & 1987-; REA 1987-; *office:* Shongum Elem Schl 9 Arrow andolph NJ 07869

IAS, CHARLES JOHN, Band Director; *b:* Reading, PA; *m:* Ann nawalt; *c:* Gregory; *ed:* Lebanon Vly Coll (BS) Music Ed 1961; Attnd of MI Music Ed, Univ of Bridgeport, St Peters Coll & Jersey City St ; *cr:* Hanover Park HS Band Dir 1962-74; Randolph HS Band Dir -; *ai:* Wind, Jazz & Woodwind Ensembles; Symphonic Band; Musical Mid Sts Music Chair; NEA 1962-; NJEA 1962-; MENC 1962-; EA 1962-; IAJE 1962-; NJSMA 1962-; NJABA 1974-; Guest ductor: All-Sussex Cty, NJ Area, NJ Regn & NJ Jr HS Regn Bands; cian: NJ MEA & NJEA Conventions; Merit Tchr; Adjudicator & ician CAWS Wkshps; *office:* Randolph HS Millbrook Ave Randolph 7869

IAS, DAVID ALLAN, Director of Bands; *b:* Temple, PA; *m:* Nancy ; *c:* Douglas, Shari Tobias Duffin; *ed:* Lebanon Vly Coll (BS) Music 959; Tchrs Coll Columbia Univ (MA) Music Ed 1962; Prof Diploma, ialist Music Ed 1963; Performance Percussion Julliard Schl of Music ; 15 Credits Supvrs Cert Rowan St Coll 1989; *cr:* Northern Lebanon r HS Band Dir 1959-61; Tchrs Coll Columbia Univ Tchng Flwshp Conducting Percussion 1961-63; Atlantic City HS Band Dir, Music Tchr 1963-64; Oakcrest HS Dir of Bands, Marching, Concert, Jazz 1964-; *ai:* Dir Marching, Concert, Pep, Jazz Bands, Drama Productions; Drama Mentor; Steering Comm; Tchr Rep Bd Ed Meetings; NEA, NJEA, MENC 1965-; Natl Band Assn 1968-; Kappa Delta Phi 1963-; Tournament of Bands 1974-; Oakcrest, Absegami Tchrs Assn 1964-; St Marching Festivals 1980-, Band Host; Amer Fed Musicians 1950-; Cadets Marching Band Cooperative 1989-, Band Host; Eastern Marching Band Assn 1980-; Elks, Knights of Columbus 7 Yrs, Outstdng Musical Contributions; Suncoaster, Chamber Commerce 1974-, Honorary; KY Colonel 1981-, Honorary; Life Guard AC 1976-, Honorary; Proclamation, Resolutions 25 Yrs Ldrshp, Dedication, Svc Presented by Governor Thomas Kean, Congressman William Hughes, Speaker of House Chuck Hardwick, Assembly Dolores Cooper, Atlantic Cty Exec Richard Squires, Hamilton Twp Mayor John J. Percy III; NAFEC Judge; Miss Amer Band Selection Comm 1975-; Outstdng Educator Awd, NJ Governors Awd 1995; Tchr of Yr 1996; *office:* Oakcrest HS 1824 Vienna Ave Mays Landing NJ 08330*

TOBIAS, DAVID ALLEN, Social Studies Teacher; *b:* Lima, OH; *m:* Lila L. Coble; *c:* Jonathan, Joseph; *ed:* Defiance Coll (BS) Comprehensive Soc Stud 1970; Wright St Univ Masters Ed 1994; *cr:* Continental Local Schl Tchr 1972-; *ai:* Golf & Bsktbl Coach; Sr Class Adv; CEA 1972-; OEA 1972-; NEA 1972-; Lions Club 1980-; *home:* 305 W Rice St Continental OH 45831

TOBIN, DOUGLAS WILLIAM, Latin & Greek Teacher; *b:* New York, NY; *ed:* St Peters Coll (BA) Classics 1972; Fordham Univ (MA) Classics 1977; *cr:* Spartanburg Day Schl Latin & Greek Tchr 1972-74; Fordham Preparatory Schl Latin & Greek Tchr 1974-85; Pelham Meml HS Latin & Greek Tchr 1985-86; Trinity Schl Latin & Greek Tchr 1986-; Hunter Coll Adjunct Roman Civilization 1987-89; Hunter Coll Adj Class Etymology 1994-; *ai:* Jazz Club, Jazz Band Saxophone Player & Fac Dev Comm 1987-; Tabla Player; Headmasters Citation for Outstanding Tchng 1977 & 1981; Citation for Outstanding HS Tchng from Tufts Univ 1992; Recipient of Trinity Yrbk Dedication 1991; *home:* 635 E 14th St New York NY 10009

TOBIN, LINDA L., Math Tchr & Stu Asst Pgm Coord; *b:* McKeesport, PA; *m:* Guy G.; *c:* Nicholas; *ed:* California Univ of PA (ME) Math 1974; Scndry Math 1972; Stu Assistance Prgm; Instruction Support Trng; Schl Renewal; *cr:* Clairton Schl Dist Mid HS Math Tchr 22 Yrs; *ai:* Stu Assistance Prgm Coord; NEA 1975-; *office:* Clairton Education Ctr 501 Waddell Ave Clairton PA 15025

TOBIN, MAURINE MOTTER, English Teacher; *b:* San Antonio, TX; *m:* Robert W.; *c:* Miller, Richard, Elizabeth, Robert, Karen; *ed:* Univ of TX Austin (BA) His 1960; Boston Univ (MED) Eng Ed 1979; Texas Tech Univ; Boston Coll; St Georges Coll; *cr:* The Canterbury Schl His & Eng Tchr 1967-72; Winchester HS Eng Tchr 1976-82; Lubbock HS Eng Tchr 1982-87; Watertown HS Eng Tchr 1987-88; Brookline HS Eng Tchr 1988-; *ai:* Eng Dept Curr Comm; NEA, BEA 1976-; Christ Church 1987-; *office:* Brookline HS 115 Greenough St Brookline MA 02146

TOBIN, PATRICIA ANNE GENDRON, Elementary School Principal; *b:* Lowell, MA; *m:* Kevin Patrick; *c:* Daniel A., Patricia M., Kristina E.; *ed:* Univ of MA at Lowell (BA) Math, Elem Ed 1975; Fitchburg St Coll (MS) Elem Ed 1982; 30 Credit Hrs Educl Admin, Cmptr Stud, Curr Dev; *cr:* F. J. Dutile Schl Elem Schl Grd 5 Tchr 1975-93; Billerica Meml HS Girls Cross Cntry Var Head Coach 1985-92, Boys, Girls Track Asst Coach 1985-92; F. J. Dutile Schl Elem Schl Prin 1993-; *ai:* Billerica Pub Schls Assessment Comm Co-Chm; Site Cncl Co-Chair; MESPA; NESPA; ASCD; Friends of Lowell High 1995-; Reilly Elem PTO 1986-; Sullivan MS PTO 1992-; Greater Lowell Rd Runners 1983-; Horace Mann, Portfolio Assessment Prgm Grants; Curr Frameworks Stud Group; MA Ag in Classroom; Northern Middlesex Skating Assoc; *office:* Frederick J. Dutile Schl 10 Biagiotti Way North Billerica MA 01862*

TOBIN, SUSAN BAVERLEIN, Art Teacher; *b:* Buffalo, NY; *m:* John V.; *ed:* Buffalo St Coll (BS) Art Ed 1978, (MS) Art Ed 1981; *cr:* East Aurora Union Free Schl Dist Art Tchr 1978-84; Hamburg Cntrl Schl Dist Art Tchr 1983-; *ai:* Stu Cncl Adv; Crisis Intervention Team; Fine Arts Festival Organizer; NY St Art Tchrs Assn 1978-, Treas 1985-90; Buffalo Fine Arts Acad 1978-; Re-Writing NYS Syllabus Studio Art 1987; *office:* Hamburg Jr HS 360 Division St Hamburg NY 14075

TOCCAFONDI, BARBARA L., Instructor in French; *b:* Jamestown, NY; *m:* Rolando; *c:* David, Lisa; *ed:* Allegheny Coll (BA) Fr 1965; Middlebury Coll (MA) Fr 1967; Grad Work in Ed & Fr at Univ of DE; *cr:* Newark Schl Dist Fr Tchr 1967-71; Cavavel Acad Fr Tchr 1975-88; Univ of DE Fr Instr 1988-; *ai:* Stud Abroad Prgms in France Dir or Co-Dir; Acad Adv; Course Coord; Pi Delta Phi; AATF; *office:* Univ Of DE 326 Smith Hall Newark DE 19716

TOCCI, MARLENE PERSCHEID, Child Development Teacher; *b:* Paterson, NJ; *m:* N. Michael; *c:* Margaux; *ed:* Green Mountain Coll (AA) Retailing 1969; Monclair St Univ (BA) Family & Consumer Scis 1971; Parsons Schl of Design Cert Interior Design 1987; Jersey City St 16 Credit Hrs; *cr:* Parsippany HS Family & Consumer Scis Tchr 1971-; *ai:* Curr Comm; NEA 1972-; PTHEA 1972-; *office:* Parsippany HS 309 Baldwin Rd Parsippany NJ 07054

TOCHEFF, JANET POOLE, High School Social Stud Tchr; *b:* Hamilton, OH; *c:* Kyle, Kimberly, Clay; *ed:* Mt Vernon Nazarene Coll (AA) 1972; Olivet Nazarene Univ (BS) Psych, Soc Welfare 1974; Wright St Univ (BS) Scndry Ed 1976; Schl Cnslng, Assertive Discipline; *cr:* Upper Vly JVS HS Govt Tchr 1978-81; Centerburg HS His Tchr 1989-94; Cardington HS Soc Stud Tchr 1994-96; *ai:* Stu Cncl, Sr Class, His Club Adv; NEA 1995-; Church of the Nazarene 1962-; Tchr of Yr 1995-; Knox Cty Star Tchr Awd 1994; *home:* 893 S Division St Mount Vernon OH 43050

TOCHELLI, PHILIP AUGUST,JR., Scndry Ed & Math Teacher; *b:* Peckville, PA; *m:* Mary Ann Mroczka; *c:* Philip, Jason; *ed:* Univ of Scranton (BS) Sec Ed, Math 1973, (MS) Sec Ed, Math 1975; *cr:* Lakeland Schl Dist Scndry Math Tchr 1973-; *ai:* Cross Cntry, Boys Track, Field Head Coach; PA St Ed Assn 1973-; Lakeland Ed Assn 1973-, VP, Pres, Sec; *office:* Lakeland Schl Dist RD 1 Jermyn PA 18433

TOCHTERMAN, MARK STEPHEN, Physics & Biology Teacher; *b:* Brooklyn, NY; *m:* Merle W.; *ed:* Brooklyn Coll (BA) Bio 1971; Univ of Pittsburgh (MPH) Environmental Hlth 1973; Addl 30 Credit Hrs Physics, Ed; *cr:* Franklin K. Lane HS Physics, Bio Tchr 1978-; *ai:* AFT 1978-; NSTA 1988-; US Pub Hlth Svc Traineeship; *office:* Franklin K. Lane HS 999 Jamaica Ave Brooklyn NY 11208*

TOCZYLOWSKI, MARY BREEN, Kindergarten Teacher; *b:* Philadelphia, PA; *m:* Francis; *c:* Theresa, Thomas, James, Gregory; *ed:* LaSalle Univ (BA) Fr Ed 1974; 15 Credit Hrs; *cr:* St Bartholomew Schl Kndgtn Tchr 1991-94; Our Lady of Ransom Kndgtn Tchr 1994-; *office:* Our Lady Of Ransom Schl 6740 Roosevelt Blvd Philadelphia PA 19149

TODARO, JOSEPH N., Professor; *b:* New York, NY; *m:* Marlene Mare; *c:* Giannella; *ed:* Pace Univ (BA) Eng, Ed 1974; Univ of MA (MED) Ed 1984; New York Univ (MA) Studio Art 1990; Working Toward Doc; *cr:* Bronx Comm Coll Prof 1987-; *ai:* MLA 1992-; CUNY Creative Incentive Awd.

TODD, ANN M. KNOLL, Business Teacher; *b:* Sandusky, OH; *m:* James Curtis; *c:* Seth David, Kristen Renee, Nolan Ryan; *ed:* Findlay Coll (BA) Comprehensive Bus Ed 1987; Ashland Univ 11 Hrs Grad Courses; *cr:* New London HS Bus Tchr 1988-; *ai:* Yrbk & Soph Class Adv; Tech Comm; OEA & NEA 1988-, Local Rep; New London Ed Assn 1985-, Treas; Inducted to Delta Kappa Gamma 1995; Grants: Roth Corp & New London Acad Booster Club; *office:* New London HS 17 Park Ave New London OH 44851

TODD, EDWARD H., HS Chemistry Teacher; *b:* York, ME; *m:* Judith; *c:* Lindsay; *ed:* Univ of ME (BS) Bio 1965; Univ of NH (MS) Chem 1970; *cr:* Stephen's HS Bio, Chem Tchr 1966-69; Randolph HS Chem Tchr 1969-; *ai:* NEA, MTA 1969-; NSTA 1980-; *office:* Randolph Jr Sr HS Memorial Dr Randolph MA 02368

TODD, LINDA STOHR, Third Grade Teacher; *b:* Niagara Falls, NY; *c:* Amy Todd Fowler, Beth Todd Snyder, Abby, Thomas; *ed:* Clarion Univ (BS) Elem Ed 1966; Univ of Buffalo (MS) Ed 1972; 38 Addl Credit Hrs; Enrolled Gannon Univ Masters Curr & Instruction; *cr:* Coudersport Elem Schl Grd 2 Tchr 1966-72; Seneca Highlands IU9 Tchr Presch & Handicapped 1981-85; Coudersport Elem Schl Grd 3-4 Tchr 1985-; *ai:* Sci, Outcomes Based Ed Comms; Wrtng Comm; NEA, PSEA 1966-; CAEA 1966-, Legislative Chm; PTSA 1978-; *office:* Coudersport Area Elem Schl 802 Vine St Coudersport PA 16915

TODD, THOMAS ALEXANDER, English Teacher; *b:* Lowell, MA; *ed:* Bates Coll (BA) Eng, Speech 1967; NY Univ (MA) Eng 1968; *cr:* The Rhodes Schl Eng Dept Chprsn, Eng Tchr 1974-87; The Lenox Schl Eng, Soc Stud Tchr 1987-91; St Hildas Schl Eng Tchr 1991-93; St Hughs Schl Eng Tchr 1991-93; Bronx HS of Sci Eng Tchr 1993-; *ai:* Rhodes Schl Yrbk Adv 1974-87, Lit Magazine Adv, Theatre Club Spon; St Hilda's, St Hugh's, The Lenox Schl Lit Magazine Adv; *home:* 72 Park Ter W Apt E87 New York NY 10034*

TODOROFF, DONNA J., Second Grade Teacher; *b:* Wheeling, WV; *m:* Michael A.; *c:* Steven, Marissa; *ed:* OH Univ (BS) Elem Ed 1981; Univ of Dayton (MS) Child, Yth Dev 1987; *cr:* Buckeye Cntrl Jr HS 7th, 8th Grd Lang Arts Tchr 1983-85; Buckeye West Elem Schl Third Grd Tchr 1985-94, Second Grd Tchr 1994-; *ai:* NEA, OEA, BLCTA 1982-; Mini-Grant Awd Jefferson Cty Bd of Ed 1995; *office:* Buckeye West Elem Schl Bridge St Adena OH 43901

TOEDTMANN, LORE SUSAN, German Teacher; *b:* Hackensack, NJ; *ed:* Montclair St Coll (BA) Ger & Eng 1980; Elem Schl Cert William Paterson Coll; *cr:* Marshall Hill Schl Supplementary Ed Tchr 1981-; Westbrook Schl Supplementary Ed Tchr 1981-82; High Point Regnl HS Ger Tchr 1982-; *ai:* Adv to Stdnts Tchng Ger in Elem Schl; NEA 1981-; Governor Tchr Awd 1994; *office:* High Point Reg HS 299 Pidgeon Hill Rd Sussex NJ 07461

TOEVS, ELAINE F., 1st Grade Teacher; *b:* Providence, RI; *m:* Norman E.; *c:* Eric J., Ryan C., Erin B.; *ed:* Mt Saint Joseph Coll (BA) Elem Ed 1971; 36 Post-Grad Credit Hrs at URI, RIC & CCRI; *cr:* Saint Kevin Schl 2nd Grd Tchr 1971-72, 1st Grd Tchr 1972-75, Kndgtn Tchr 1981-82, 1st Grd Tchr 1982-; *ai:* Diocese of Providence Self-Stud Bd; NCEA 1971-; ADK Sorority of Tchrs 1995; Saint Kevins Womens Club 1971-, Treas; *home:* 14 Michael Dr Warwick RI 02889

TOEWS, BETTE, Ger & Eng as Second Lang Tchr; *b:* Lancaster, PA; *m:* Lorrie Dellinger; *c:* Graham, Aubrie, Garth; *ed:* Lebanon Vly Coll (BA) Ger 1978; PA St Univ (MA) Ger 1993; *cr:* Solanco HS Ger Tchr 1978-79; Penn St Univ Tchng Asst 1979-80; Hempfield HS Ger Tchr 1980-81; Lebanon HS Ger Tchr 1981-94; Lebanon MS ESL Tchr 1994-; *ai:* After Schl Ger Prgm Cornwall Elem; AATG 1981-, VP 1992-; Pub Articles; *office:* Lebanon MS 350 N 8th St Lebanon PA 17046

TOFANI, MARYANN JOY, Science & Biology Teacher; *b:* Sharon, PA; *m:* Gino; *c:* Matthew; *ed:* Clarion Univ of PA (BS) Bio 1989; Scndry Ed Cert at Slippery Rock Univ of PA 1990; 24 Credit Hrs for Permanent Tchr Cert From the Midwestern Intermediate Unit IV; *cr:* Reynolds Jr & Sr HS Sci & Bio Tchr 1990-; *ai:* Jr Class & Prom Adv; Dist Cncl; In-Svc Instr; Reynolds Ed Assn 1990-, Sec; NEA & PSEA 1990-; NSTA 1994-; *office:* Reynolds HS 531 Reynolds Rd Greenville PA 16125*

TOHILL, MARY DIETSCH, English Composition Instructor; *b:* Clinton, IL; *m:* H. Arden Jr.; *c:* Adam J., Patrick A.; *ed:* Eastern IL Univ (BSEd) Eng 1973; IL St Univ (MA) Eng 1979; Cert Tchng of Composition Univ of Akron 1996; *cr:* Cornell HS Eng, Span, Speech Tchr 1973-79; Wapella HS Eng Tchr 1979-81; Univ of Akron-Wayne Coll Part-time Eng Composition Tchr 1982-; Kent St Univ Part-time Eng Comp Tchr 1994-; *ai:* NCTE 1973-; CCC 1992-; *office:* Univ Of Akron-Wayne Coll 1901 Smucker Rd Orrville OH 44667

TOIA, KATHLEEN INEZ, Kindergarten Teacher; *b:* Lorain, OH; *m:* Robert Earl Jr.; *ed:* Univ of Dayton (BS) Ed 1970; Addl Credit Hrs Sinclair Comm Coll; Post-Grad Credit Hrs Univ of Dayton, Wright St Univ, Miami Univ at OH; *cr:* Menlo Park Elem Schl Kndgtn Tchr 1970-71; Shenandoah Elem Schl Kndgtn Tchr 1971-78, Developmental 1st Grd Tchr 1978-83, Kndgtn Tchr 1983-89; Lamendola Elem Schl Kndgtn Tchr 1989-; *ai:* Comp Coord; Math & Sci Curr Comms Huber Hghts Schls; Occupational Work Adjustment Mentor St of OH Dept of Ed; NAEYC 1985-; OAEYC 1985-; DAYC 1985-; Shenandoah Elem Schl Tchr of Yr 1972; Univ of Dayton Martha Holden Jennings Scholar 1977-78; Math Grant Co-Recipient 1991-92 Dayton Montgomery Cty Ed Fund; Math & Sci Project Gemma Grant Recipient 1992-93 Dayton Montgomery Cty Ed Fund; TV WDTN Class Act 1993, 199; *office:* Lamendola Elem Schl 5363 Tilbury Rd Huber Heights OH 45424*

TOKARSKI, FELECIA HOODAK, 9th-11th Grd English Teacher; *b:* Elmira, NY; *m:* Ted W.; *c:* Thomas, Jennifer, Jill; *ed:* Elmira Coll (BA) Elem Ed, Scndry Eng 1986, (MS) Elem Ed, Scndry Eng 1991; 27 Addl Hrs; *cr:* Elmira Free Acad Eng Tchr 1986-; *ai:* Co-Adv Lit Magazine; Quiz Crew Adv; NYSET, ETA 1987-; *office:* Elmira Free Acad 933 Hoffman St Elmira NY 14905

TOKARSKI, LORRAINE (JARUSINSKY), Tchr of Gifted & Talented; *b:* Bridgeport, CT; *w:* John (dec); *c:* Joseph, Mark, Justin; *ed:* Southern Ct St Univ (BSEd) Intermediate Upper Elem 1963; Fairfield Univ (MA) Scndry Fr 1976; Southern CT St Univ 6th Yr Admin 1984, 15 Addl Credit Hrs; *cr:* Edison Schl Grd 2 Tchr 1963; Bearvoir Elem Schl Grd 5 Tchr 1963-64; Bunnell HS Grd 10 Fr Tchr 1966-67; Boota Hill Schl 5-6 Grd Tchr 1970-83; Shelton HS Project Reap 4-6 Grd GATE Tchr 1984-95; *ai:* Tchr of Yr Comm; Phi Delta Kappa 1984-; NEA 1971-; Amer Assn of Univ Women 1985-, Recording Sec 1993; Friends of Lib 1980-, Bd Mem; Intelligence Conversion Conf Presenter 1995; Amer Bronds Awd 1995; Celebration Excl Awd 1992, 1994; IDEA Grants 1990, 1992-95; Tchr of Yr 1995; *office:* Shelton HS Project REAP 120 Meadow St Shelton CT 06484*

TOKASZ, MARIE D. SCHLEINING, Music Teacher & Orchestra Dir; *b:* Lackawanna, NY; *m:* William S.; *c:* Joseph; *ed:* Potsdam Coll Crane Schl of Music (BM) Music Ed 1983; St Univ of NY at Buffalo (MM) Music Ed 1993; *cr:* Fourteen Holy Helpers Schl Pre K-8 Grd Music Tchr 1983-88; Nativity of Our Lord Schl K-8 Grd Music Tchr 1988-90; Iroquois Cntrl Schls 4-5, 9-12 Grd Music Tchr, Orch Dir 1990-91; Lancaster Cntrl Schls 7-12 Grd Music Tchr, Orch Dir 1991-; *ai:* String Quartet Adv; Aurora MS 7th-8th Grd Orch Dir; ECMEA 1988-, Jr HS Orch Chm 1993, 1995; NYSSMA 1988-; ASTA 1991-; AFT 1990-; Our Lady of Grace Church 1995-, Folk Group Dir; Campfire Girls & Boys 1968-, 10 Yr Adult Mem; Religious Edctr of Yr Awd Diocese of Buffalo 1991; *office:* Lancaster Cntrl HS 1 Forton Ave Lancaster NY 14086

TOKUNAGA, YASUKO, Chairperson of Dance Division; *b:* Salt Lake City, UT; *ed:* The Juilliard Schl (BFA) Dance 1970; *cr:* Tokunaga Dance Co Co-Founder & Co-Artistic Dir 1974-89; The Boston Conservatory Instr 1985-89, Chprsn of Dance Division 1989-; *ai:* Boston Conservatory Dance

Theater & Boston Dance Theater Artistic Dir; Tokunaga Dance Co-Adv; Dance Umbrella 1989-; Amer Dance Guild; NASD; Japan Soc of Boston; Tchr of the Month Attitude April 1983; Meritorious Svc Awd at Licoln Univ 1983 & SC St Coll 1984; Nara & Okayama Municipalities in Japan 1984; Pro Arts Pub Svc in the Arts Awd 1993; Dance Magazine Articles Pub 1994 & 1995; *office:* The Boston Conservatory 8 Fenway Boston MA 02215

TOLAND, HEATHER E.S., Program Director; *b:* Danville, PA; *m:* John M.; *ed:* SUNY at Delhi (AAS) Vet Tech 1977; Thomas Edison St Coll (BSAT) Vet Tech 1994; Beaver Coll (MA) Envrmntl Ed; 24 Continuing Ed Credits; Animal Asstd Therapy Ed Cert Harcum Coll; *cr:* SUNY at Delhi Tchng Asst 1979-80; Univ of PA Schl of Dentistry Research Asst 1980-81; Harcum Coll Lab Instr 1982-, Asst Prog Dir Vet Tech 1982-, Prgm Dir Equine Stud Prgm 1993-94; *ai:* Org Animal Tech Stdnts, Equine Club Adv; Coord & Facilitate CE Seminars for Grad Techs PA, NJ, NY, DE, MD area Harcum Coll; NAVTA, AALAS 1984-; AVTE 1982-; VTTC 1994-; Pub Vet Tech Journal 1990, 1995; *office:* Harcum Coll Montgomery Ave Bryn Mawr PA 19129

TOLBERT, EFFIE ANN FOOTMAN, Fifth Grade Teacher; *b:* Tallahassee, FL; *c:* Rhonda, Tess Y.; *ed:* Univ of DC (BA) Elem Ed 1974; Attnd Trinity Coll, Cath Univ Grad Stud; *cr:* Fletcher Ed Ctr 2nd Grd Tchr 1979-80, 4th Grd Tchr 1982-83; Wilkinson Primary Schl Kndgtn Tchr 1980-82; Martin L King Elem 4th Grd Tchr 1983-84; Thomas Elem Pre-Kndgtn Tchr 1984-85; Winston Ed Ctr 5th Grd Tchr 1985-; *ai:* 5th & 6th Grd Tchrs Team Ldr 1986 & 1995; Parent Involvement Chprsn 1990-91; WA Tchrs Union 1983-; Work with AIDS Children; Work with Alcoholic & Substance Abuse Teenagers.*

TOLCHIN, GAIL LYNN, 8th Grade Reading Teacher; *b:* New York City, NY; *m:* J. Robert; *c:* Scott, Marc, Glenn; *ed:* NYU (BS) Elem Ed 1964; Coll of New Rochelle (MS) Rdng 1979; Manhattanville Coll Spec Ed Cert 1981; *cr:* Ramapo II Pub Schl 1st Grd Tchr 1964-67; Eastchester Pub Schls Rdng Tchr 1981-83; White Plains MS Rdng Tchr 1983-; *ai:* Stu Govt Adv; Chprsn Discipline Comm; Adv Advisee Comm; NYSTA, AFT 1981-; NRA 1983-; Harrison Day Care Ctr 1985-, Bd of Dirs; *office:* White Plains MS 128 Grandview Ave White Plains NY 10605

TOLEP, MARCIA L., Teacher in REACH; *b:* Brooklyn, NY; *m:* Stephen; *c:* Andrew, Scott; *ed:* Brooklyn (BA) Ed, Eng 1970, (MS) Ed, Rdng 1972; 30 Addl Credits Curr, Educl Testing; *cr:* NYC 3-5 Grd Tchr 1970-75, Math Enrichment Tchr 1976-79; Fair Lawn Supplemental Tchr 1980-84, Grd 5 Tchr 1985-86; *ai:* Sponsored Fifth Grd Stdnts Publishing Contest; Coached Fifth Grd Team Word Master's Challenge; NJAGC 1986-; NJEA 1980-; Dev MS Enrichment Prgm Photograph Cover Prof Dev Brochures; A+ Kids Grant; *office:* Warren Point Elem Schl 30-07 Broadway Fair Lawn NJ 07410

TOLER, CHARLES ROBERT, Mathematics Teacher; *b:* Hopewell, VA; *m:* Bertie Osborn; *c:* Elizabeth Oldham, John William; *ed:* East TN St Univ (BS) Eng 1957; Univ of NC at Chapel Hill (MAT) 1966; Univ of VA at Charlottesville 12 Sem Hrs; *cr:* Norfolk Acad Math Tchr 1962-65; Wilmington Friends Schl Math Tchr 1967-89; DE Tech, Comm Coll Math Tchr 1989-93; Towle Inst Math Tchr 1994-; *ai:* Math Consultant Reader; CEEB AP Exam AB Level; *home:* 511 Eskridge Dr Wilmington DE 19809

TOLERTON, TY DANIEL, 5th Grade Teacher; *b:* Tucson, AZ; *m:* Jana Sue; *c:* Ryan, Cory; *ed:* Towson St Univ (BA) Elem Ed 1975; Western MD Coll (MA) Ed, Admin & Supv 1985; Westminister Coll Elem Ed; Western MD Regnl Assessment Ctr Future Admin 1990; *cr:* Greenbrier Elem Schl 4th, 5th Grd Tchr 1975-89; Salem St Elem Schl 5th Grd Tchr 1989-90; Western Heights MS Head Tchr 1989-90; Boonsboro Elem Schl 5th Grd Tchr 1990-; *ai:* CAC 1990-92, PTA 1975-, Schl Improvment Team 1985-88, 1993-95, Report Card 1980-81 Comms; Prin Designate 1977-82, 1985-89; Supervisory Tchr of Field Eperience & Stu Tchng Stdnts of Shepherd Coll 1977-95; Fac Advy 1983-84, Discipline 1983-84, Career Ladder 1986-89, Schl Visitation 1988-89, At-Risk 1985-86 Comms; Stu Cncl 1975-77, Safety Patrol 1977-82 Advs; 4th Grd Team Ldr 1976-78, 5th Grd Team Ldr 1985-88, 1992-95; Supvr Spirit Week 1975-89; MS, Elem Schl Transition Comm 1;8WCTA 1975-89, Schl Rep 2 Yrs; MSTA 1975-89; NEA 1975-89; Maugansville Bsbl Yth Org 1990-, Bd Pres 1993; Yth Leagues Soccer, Swimming, Bsktbl Coaching; Elks 1988-; Jaycees 1984-; *office:* Boonsboro Elem Schl 5 Campus Ave Boonsboro MD 21713*

TOLIVER, KAY FRANCIS, Teacher of Challenger Program; *b:* New York, NY; *ed:* Hunter Coll (BA) His 1967, (MS) Ed 1971; Long Island Univ Fame Prgm Math; City Coll of NY Post Grad Math; *cr:* East Harlem Tech Schl Tchr 1967-; *ai:* Math Tchrs Mentor; Wrkshp Speaker, Ldr; UFT 1967-; Benjamin Banneker Assn 1991-, Cert of Merit; NCTM; Black Engrs Assn, 1995-, Spec Ed Awd; Math Assn 1992-; ASCD 1993-; Disney Amer Outstdng Math Tchr, NY Presidential Awd Scndry Math 1992; MS Tchr of Yr Reliance Awd, Documentary Spec PBA 1993; *office:* East Harlem Tech Schl 131 E 104th St New York NY 10029

TOLLE, STUART A., 8th Grade Science Teacher; *b:* Columbus, OH; *ed:* Bowling Green St Univ (BA) Lbrl Arts 1987; Kent St Univ (BA) 1994; *cr:* Erwine MS 8th Grd Sci Tchr 1994-; *ai:* Var Ftbl Coach; Club Adv-Sci Olympiad; NSTA 1995-; NFL Alumni Assn 1988-; *office:* Erwine MS 1135 Portage Lakes Dr Akron OH 44319*

TOLLEY, JANICE BASLER, 4th Grade Teacher; *b:* Trenton, NJ; *ed:* Trenton St Coll (BS) Early Chldhd 1971; 32 Grad Credits; *cr:* East Windsor Regnl Schl Dist Elem Tchr, Sci Content Specialist 25 Yrs; *ai:* NJ Young Astronauts Co-Founder, Exec Bd Mem; East Windsor Comm Relations Comm; East Windsor Ed Assn Past Pres; NSTA 1980-; NJEA, NEA 1971-; East Windsor Ed Assn 1971-, Pres 1989-94; Air Force Assn 1987-, Instr Excl Awd; Civil Air Patrol 1991-, Capt, Aerospace Educator; NJEA 1992-, Consultant; Aerospace Educators Assn 1991-; Presidential Awd for Sci St Finalist 1995; Distinguished Svc to Ed, Excl in Tchng, Air Force Assn Instr Excl Awds; grants for Inovative Ideas; NEWEST Honors Tchrs Awd; *office:* Grace Norton Rogers Schl 386 Stockton St Hightstown NJ 08520

TOLLEY, LINDA ANN, Spanish Teacher; *b:* Taunton, MA; *m:* Earl A.; *c:* Lauren; *ed:* Univ of ME (BS) Art Ed 1975; Univ of MA at Dartmouth K-6 Elem Ed Cert 1990; Europa House Stu Exch Ind Stud 3 Credits 1974; Cemanahuac Inst at Cuernavaca Mexico 6 Credits; *cr:* Bristol-Newfound Meml HS Art Dir 1977-78; Seekonk North Schl Alternative Sub Itinerant Tchr 1991-92; Coyle Cassidy HS Sub Span Tchr 1992; Bishop Stang HS Span Tchr 1992-; *ai:* After Schl Flex Prgm; St Mary's Schl Curr Dev; Spts Lit Course for Stan Stdnts; Jr Class Santa Breakfast 1995-; MAFLA 1992-; MA Whole Lang Steering Comm 1991; ASDF 1992-; Luther Schl PTO 1988-89, VP, Pres; Rdng Writing Ctr 1990-92, Conversation ESL Tutor; Christ Church 1990-91, Sunday Schl, Rel Tchr; Mary Louise Walsh Frgn Lang Stud Schlsp Univ of MA at Dartmouth 1993; Excl Appreciation Cert; Innovation for Portfolio Assessment.*

TOLLIVER, ANN E., Sixth Grade Teacher; *b:* Ashland, OH; *m:* Ty; *c:* Adam; *ed:* Wittenberg Univ (BA) Elem Ed 1989; Minor in Eng; Working Towards Masters Degree Wright St Univ; *cr:* Berry Jr HS Eighth Grd Eng Tchr 1989-95; Berry MS Sixth Grd Lang Arts Tchr 1995-; *ai:* Power of the Pen Writing Team Adv Berry; Dist Tech Comm; Proficiency Intervention Coord; NEA, Lebanon Ed Assn 1989-; Trinity Luth Church; Schl Net Plus Grant; *office:* Lebanon City Schls 25 Oakwood Dr Lebanon OH 45036

TOLLO, RICHARD PAUL, Assistant Professor of Geology; *b:* Quincy, MA; *m:* Stacie J. Kreitman-Tollo; *c:* Spencer; *ed:* Tufts Univ (BA) Geology 1972; Univ of NH (MS) Geology 1976; Univ of MA (PHD) Geology 1983; *cr:* Hingham Pub Schls 8th Grd Sci Tchr 1972-74; George Washington Univ Asst Prof 1984-; *ai:* Undergrad Stud Assoc Dean; Geological Soc of Amer 1980-; NSF Rsrch Grant; Numerous Articles Pub; *office:* George Washington Univ 2029 G St NW Washington DC 20006*

TOLOMEO, JOHNNA ANNETTE, Health Teacher; *b:* Teaneck, NJ; *ed:* Montclair St Coll (BS) PE, Hlth Tchr 1992; Pursuing Cnslng Masters at Montclair St Univ; *cr:* Caldwell HS PE, Hlth Tchr 1992-93;Lazar MS PE, Hlth Tchr 1993-94; Montville Twp-Lazar MS Hlth Tchr 1993-; *ai:* Var Sftbl Coach; Founder of Montville Sisters in Sftbl Prgm; Conflict Resolution Trainer; NEA 1992-; MTEA 1993-; AAPHERD 1991-; *office:* Montville Twp HS-Lazar MS 123 Changebridge Rd Montville NJ 07045*

TOLPA, CHRIS ANN, English Teacher; *b:* Holyoke, MA; *ed:* Univ of MA (BA) Eng & Ed 1990; Springfield Coll MS Admin will Complete 1997; *cr:* West Springfield HS Eng Tchr 1993-; *ai:* Class of 1996 Adv; TQE Comm Relations Comm; Pub Relations Rep; Chicopee Womens Sftbl 1986-, Mgr & Player Bd of Dirs 1994-; Chicopee Womans Vllybl 1988-, Coach & Player; *office:* West Springfield HS 425 Piper Rd West Springfield MA 01089*

TOLSTEDT, LOWELL C., Dean of Division Fine Arts; *b:* Burke, SD; *m:* Janet; *c:* Stephanie, Brad; *ed:* St Univ of SD (BFA) Art 1961; Univ of IA (MA) Painting & Drawing 1967; *cr:* Pitman Pub Schls HS Art Tchr 1962-64; Columbus Coll of Art & Design Dean Division of Fine Arts 1967-; *ai:* Natl Endowment of the Arts Fellowship Grant 1983, OH Arts Cncl Fellowship 1983, 1988, 1994; Museum Collections: Art Inst of Chicago, MN Museum of Art, Columbus Museum of Art, Natl Museum of Amer Art, Smithsonion Inst, AR Art Ctr; *office:* Columbus Coll Of Art & Design 107 N 9th St Columbus OH 43215

TOM, JOHN, Chemistry Teacher; *b:* New York, NY; *ed:* SUNY at Stony Brook (BS) Engr Chem, Bus Admin 1985; Empire St Coll of SUNY (MA) Culture, Policy Stud; Regents Coll Univ of NY Examinations; NYSUT Effective Tchng Prgm; *cr:* Brooklyn Tech HS Chem Tchr 1990-; *ai:* AP Chem Coord; Chem Squad Adv; AFT, NYSUT, UFT 1990-; Brooklyn Tech HS Alumni Assn 1996-, Life Mem; City Gardens Club NYC Schlrsp Audubon Ecology Wkshp 1992; Metlife Fellow IMPACT II Tchr Policy Inst 1995-; *office:* Brooklyn Tech HS 29 Fort Greene Pl Brooklyn NY 11217*

TOMA, DEBORAH VERONICA, First Grade Teacher; *b:* Quincy, MA; *ed:* Bridgewater St Coll (BS) Elem Ed 1972; *cr:* Monatiquot Schl 3rd Grd Tchr 1973-80; Montiquot Schl 2nd Grd Tchr 1980-81; Lakeside Schl 1st Grd Tchr 1981-; *ai:* NEA, MTA, NCTA 1973-; IRA 1995-; Parish Pastoral Cncl 1993-; *office:* Lakeside Elem Schl Lakeside Dr Braintree MA 02184

TOMAINO, DAVID ALLEN, 7th-8th Grd Soc Stud Teacher; *b:* Warren, OH; *m:* Susan L. Hambrick; *c:* David Charles, Nicholas Andrew, Alexander Lee; *ed:* Youngstown St Univ (BS) Elem Ed 1986; Working Toward Ath Admin Kent St Univ; *cr:* Jackson Milton Schl Coach, SBH Aide 1980-85, Tchr, Coach 1985-; *ai:* Jr HS Ftbl, HS Wrestling Coach; Builders Club; Stu Cncl; NEA 1986-, Pres; AFT 1995-; *office:* Jackson Milton Jr HS 10748 Mahoning Ave North Jackson OH 44451*

TOMAK, DANIEL E., Sixth Grade Teacher; *b:* Johnstown, PA; *m:* Dianne Vuckovich; *c:* Daniel L., Damian; *ed:* WV (BS) Elem Ed 1970; *cr:* Roxbury Elem 6th Grd Tchr 1970-76; Garfield Jr HS 6th Grd Tchr 1976-80; Chandler Elem 6th Grd Tchr 1980-81; Johnstown MS 6th Grd Tchr 1981-; *ai:* PSEA, NEA 1970-; *office:* Johnstown MS 280 Decker Ave Johnstown PA 15906

TOMANN, KIMBERLY, Choir Director; *b:* Grand Rapids, MI; *c:* Alexander, Julia; *ed:* Orange Cty Comm Coll (AS) Music, Lbrl Arts 1981; SUNY at Buffalo (BFA) Music Ed 1984; Western CT St Univ (MS) Music Ed 1991; *cr:* Middletown HS Choir Dir 1985-94; Vly Cntrl HS Choir Dir 1994-; *ai:* Schl Musical Dir; NYSSMA, MENC, OCMEA 1985-; ACDA 1991-; NYSSMA Certfd Adjudicator 1991-; Choir Selected to Perform Disney World Orlando 1993; *office:* Valley Central HS 1175 Rt 17k Montgomery NY 12549*

TOMASELLO, CHRISTINE DIANNE, 8th Grade English Teacher; *b:* Sharon, PA; *m:* Bruce M.; *ed:* Westminster Coll (BA) Eng, His 1987; Westminster Coll (MS) Scndry Ed 1993; Completed Classes Intermiate Unit IV; *cr:* Grove City MS Eng Tchr 1989-; *ai:* Stu Asst Team; Planning, Dance Comms, His Day Spon; Theme Week Coord; NEA, PSEA 1989-; ACA Alumni Cncl, Recording Sec; *office:* Grove City MS 130 E Main St Grove City PA 16127

TOMASELLO, LEONARD A., Principal; *b:* Greenwich, CT; *m:* Irene Bernasici; *c:* Jennifer Cafarelli, Marabeth Pereira, Leonard Jr.; *ed:* Central CT St Coll (BS) Elem Ed 1965; Univ of Hartford (MS) Elem Ed 1968; Nova Univ (EDD) Early Chldhd Ed 1975; *cr:* Wethersfield Pub Schls Tchr 1965-68; Hartford Pub Schls Tchr 1968-71; Univ Schl of Nova Univ Dir 1971-80; New Canaan Pub Schls Acting Supt 1992-93; West Schl-New Canaan Pub Schls Prin 1980-; *ai:* Consultant; NCEA, CEA 1971-; ASCD 1980-; NCTE 1982-; NCTM 1986-; Ridgefield Emmaus 1990-, Cncl Pres; Author Discover The Deck, Just for Openers, Nuts & Bolts; *office:* West Elem Schl 769 Ponus Ridge Rd New Canaan CT 06840*

TOMASELLO, MARCY BRADWELL, Business Education Teacher; *b:* Philadelphia, PA; *m:* Lee; *c:* Natalie, Norman Lee; *ed:* Bloomsburg St Univ (BS) Bus Ed, Acctng 1968; Glassboro St Univ Voc Co-Op Cert 1986; *cr:* Edgewood Sr HS Tchr, Dept Chprsn 1968-, CBE Coord 1989-; *ai:* FBLA, Stu Newspaper Adv; Pub Relations Liaison; Stu of Month, Schlsp Comms; NBEA 1968-; NJBEA 1968-, Co-Ed Observer 2 Yrs; SJBEA 1986-, Prgm Dir 2 Yrs; NJCBECA 1991-; NJ Governor's Tchr Recognition Awds 1988, 1994; *office:* Edgewood Reg Sr HS 250 Coopers Folly Rd Atco NJ 08004

TOMASETTI, ANNETTE DELLA CAVA, English Teacher; *b:* New York, NY; *m:* Michael L.; *ed:* Coll of Mt St Vincent (BA) Eng 1962; Herbert H. Lehman Coll (MA) Eng 1975; 30 Addl Grad Credit Hrs Writing, Eng; *cr:* Truman HS Eng Tchr 1978-82; IS #181 MS Eng Tchr 1982-90; Bronx HS of Sci Eng Tchr 1990-; *ai:* Newspaper Adv; Schl Base Mngmt Comm; NYC Cncl Tchr of Eng; *office:* Bronx HS Of Science 75 Bronx Science Blvd Bronx NY 10468

TOMASIAK, JOANNE C., 9th-12th Grd English Teacher; *b:* Warren, OH; *c:* Sarah Ann; *cr:* Chalker HS Tchr; *ai:* OH Ed Assn 1975-; NEA; *office:* Southington-Chalker HS 3346 St Rt 305 Southington OH 44470

TOMASO, PATRICE LISA, High School Art Teacher; *b:* Forest Hills, NY; *m:* Robert Vincent; *ed:* SUNY at New Paltz (BS) Art Ed 1979, (MS) Painting 1986; *cr:* Chatham MS 5-8th Grd Art Tchr 1980-89; Chatham HS 9-12th Grd Art Tchr 1989-; Chatham Art Dept Coord 1989-91; Chatham HS Class Adv for Class of 1993, 1991-93; *home:* PO Box 187 Claverack NY 12513*

TOMAYKO, CAROLE ANNE, Eng & Creative Writing Tchr; *b:* Detroit, MI; *m:* Donald D.; *c:* Mary, Collette, David; *ed:* Univ of MI (BA) En Lit 1967; Tchr Cert Hood Coll 1984; Masters Equivalency Montgomery Cty Schl System 1986; *cr:* Montgomery Cty Schl System Composition Asst 1981-85, Eng Tchr 1985-; *ai:* Spon of Montgomery Blair's Lit Magazine; NEA; MCEA 1985-; NCTE 1995-; Montgomery Cty Gifted & Talented Scndy Tchr of Yr 1992-93; Most Outstanding Tchr Univ of Chicago 1992; *home:* 1631 Belvedere Blvd Silver Spring MD 20902

TOMAYKO, YVONNE, Art Teacher; *b:* Sewickley, PA; *ed:* Edinboro Univ of PA (BS) Art Ed 1972; Du Quesne Univ at Pittsburgh Guidance Master's Prgm 1974; Univ of Pittsburgh Credit Hrs Schl of Gen Stud, Art His, Foreign Lang, Greek Lit 1975; *cr:* New Brighton Schl Dist 1-12 Tchr 1972, 9-12 Grd Art Tchr 1973-; *ai:* Schl Backdrops; Perm Murals; Comm Sponsored Activities Art Work; Awds, Certs Letterin Shows; PA Art Ed Assn; PSEA 1972-; The Carnegie 1988-; *office* Brighton Sr HS 3200 43rd St New Brighton PA 15066

TOMCZAK, TIMOTHY PETER, Assistant Professor of Psych; *b:* PA; *m:* Lynnlee Kohler; *c:* Theodore, Marissa; *ed:* Mercyhurst Coll Psych 1985; SUNY at Geneseo (MA) Psych 1989; *cr:* Genesee Comm Instr, Asst Prof Psych 1987-; St Univ of NY at Geneseo Adj Lecturer 1990-; *ai:* Chair Mid Sts Self-Stud Task Force on Stu Svcs, Steering, Tech Advy Comm; Div Amer Psych Assn 1989-; Cncl Undergrad Tc Psych 1995-; Chancellor's Awd Excl in Tchng 1994-; *office:* Ge Comm Coll 1 College Rd Batavia NY 14020*

TOMEDI, JAMES FRANCIS, Language Arts Teacher; *b:* Mount C PA; *m:* Debra A.; *c:* Sara Maria, Mary Elizabeth, James Aaron, J Benjamin; *ed:* Bloomsburg Univ (BA) Psych 1983; Wilkes Univ (MS Ed 1986; *cr:* WY Seminary Coll Prep Schl Eng Tchr, Stud Skills 1986-88; Pocono Mountain Schl Dist Lang Arts Tchr 1988-; *ai:* Promising Young Writers Awds Adv; Russell C. Hughes Monro Spelling Bee Coord; Scholastic Writing Awds; PA Poetry Soc; R Essay & Advertisement Contest; Yearly Class Poetry Book; PSEA, 1988-; WY Seminary Post Grad Activities Coord 1987-88; WY Sem Bd of Stu Appeals 1987-88; Two Ind Research Stud Presented at E Psychological Assn Meetings 1984-85; *office:* Pocono Mountain Sch School Rd Swiftwater PA 18370

TOMEO, CLAIRE A., 8th Grade Teacher & Advisor; *b:* Jersey Cit *m:* Benjamin G.; *c:* David, Aline Tomeo Dymkowski, Robert; *ed:* Cal Coll (BA) Eng Lit, Fr 1956; Fordham Univ 25 Hrs Fr; *cr:* Wm L. Dick HS Fr, Eng Tchr 1956-64; Our Lady of Lake L Arts, Lit Tchr; *ai:* N Hnr Soc; Grad; Grd 8 Act; Yrbk; NCEA 1981-; NASSP Archdiocesan Tchr of Yr 1994; *office:* Our Lady Of The Lake Lakeside & Montrose Aves Verona NJ 07044

TOMEO, VINCENT J., Social Studies Teacher; *b:* Flushing, N Sylvia; *ed:* Queens Coll (BA) His 1975, (MA) His Ed 1978; NYU Mu Stud 1980; Columbia Univ Doctoral Candidate Scndry Ed 1984; *cr* Cty Clerk's Archives Educl Design Curator 1977-80; Francis Lewis H Stud Tchr 1985-; NY City Bd of Ed Human Relations Instr 198 Fordham Univ Adj Fac Instr Human Relations 1991-92; *ai:* Estab Five Schlsp Funds; Victims Hurricane Andrew 1992, Children of So 1993 Fund Drive; Asian, Korean Culture Club Adv 1987-; Kappa De 1977-, Hnr Cert; Phi Alpha Theta 1974-, Hnr Mem, Hnr Cert; Landn Schlsp 1975-, Scholar, Schlsp; Washington Crossing 1990-, Hist Reenactment; NY City Bd of Ed 1991-, Tchr of Yr, Hnr Roll Nom; N Conservancy 1990-; Queens Museum Local His Honorarium; Amer F Flwshp Studying Ramayana; CUNY Flwshp Japan Focus Project Culture Soc Korea Flwshp Stud Yonsei Univ; NY Historical Soc Constitution Flwshp; *office:* Francis Lewis HS 5820 Utopia Pky Flu NY 11365

TOMESCO, LORI ANN, First Grade Teacher; *b:* Teaneck, NJ; *m:* F T.; *ed:* Felician Coll (BA) Ed 1985; William Paterson Coll (MA) Ed *cr:* Euclid Elem Schl 3rd Grd Tchr 1986-89, 1st Grd Tchr 1989-93; Li Elem Schl 1st Grd Tchr 1993-; *ai:* Cheerleading Vol Coach; NJEA, Natl & Local 1986-; *home:* 52 Parker Ave Hawthorne NJ 07506*

TOMKO, THEODORE MICHAEL, 9th Grd Sci & Adult Ed Teach Youngstown, OH; *m:* Susan Jayne Armstrong; *c:* Sommer, Brandon, *ed:* Youngstown St Univ (AB) Bio-Cum Laude 1981, (BSE) Ed 1983; OH Univ at Ironton; 4 Hrs Univ of Cincinnati; *cr:* PIME Seminary Sci Chair 1983-90; Notre Dame HS Sci Tchr 1992-94; Portsmouth H Adult Edctr 1994-; *ai:* Grant Writing, Course of Stud Comms; OEA, 1994-; OCEAA 1983-94; Fulbright Grad Recommendation; *home:* Ridgeway Ave Ashland KY 41101

TOMLINSON, BRUCE LLOYD, Assoc Prof Dev, Bio & Dept Cl Toronto, Canada; *m:* Donna Elaine; *ed:* Univ of Waterloo (BS) Bio (MSC) Dev Bio 1977, (PHD) Dev Bio 1983; *cr:* OH St Univ Post Do Flwshp 1983-85, Rsrch Assoc 1985-88; SUNY Coll of Fredonia Asso 1988-; *ai:* AAAS, Dev Bio 1984-; Sigma Xi 1989-; Cottrell Rsrch Grant; *office:* S U N Y Coll At Fredonia Dept Biology Fredonia NY

TOMLINSON, LOUISE, English Teacher; *b:* Greenwich, CT; *m:* I Charles; *c:* Matthew, Andrew; *ed:* Brown Univ (BA) Amer Lit-Cum L 1960; Attnd CANE; *cr:* Andover West Jr High Eng & Soc Stud 1973-82; Andover HS Eng Tchr 1982-; *ai:* Newspaper Club Adv; 1973-; *home:* 148 Salem St Andover MA 01810

TOMLINSON, MICHAEL STEVEN, High School Spanish Teach Washington, DC; *ed:* Penn St Univ (BS) Scndry Ed & Span 1991; Univ of Salamanca Spain; *cr:* Delmar Area Schl Dist Span Tchr 2 Yr Span Club Dir; Action Team Restructuring Comm; Frgn Travel C NEA, PSEA 1993-; *office:* Huntingdon Area HS 2400 Cassady Huntingdon PA 16652*

TOMLINSON, RONDA KAYE, Second Grade Teacher; *b:* Harris PA; *m:* Curt Steven; *c:* Nathan R., Megan E.; *ed:* Millersville Univ Elem Ed 1984, (MS) Elem Ed 1989; *cr:* Penn Manor Schl Sub 1985-86; Lancaster City Schl Sub Tchr 1985-86; Le Tort Elem Schl Grd Tchr 1986-90; Conestoga Elem Schl Second Grd Tchr 1991-; *ai:* PMEA 1986-; *office:* Penn Manor Schl Dist PO Box 1001 Millersvil 17551

TOMPKINS, CHRISTY LYNN, Drama Teacher & Choral Dir; *b:* Pleasant, NJ; *m:* Douglas R.; *c:* Justin Douglas, Ryan Peter; Susquehanna Univ (BMEd) Music, Vocal 1983; *cr:* Veterans Mem Music, Drama Tchr 1984-93; Brick Twp HS Music, Drama Tchr 1993 Dover Twp Savoyards Drama Dir 1987-89; Brick Meml HS Dram 1985-88; *office:* Brick Township HS 346 Chambersbridge Rd Bric 08723

TOMPKINS, WILLIAM LEWIS,JR., PE Teacher & Coach; *b:* Boot Harbor, ME; *m:* Louise Marchand; *c:* Keith, Laura; *ed:* Springfield (BS) PE, Hlth 1973; *cr:* Walpole HS PE Tchr & Coach 1973-; *ai:* Hea Bsbl Coach 1979-; Head Amer Legion Bsbl Coach 1983-; Head Girl Soccer Coach 1981-; IAABO Bsktbl Ofc 1973-; NEA & MA Tchrs 1973-; NRA 1969-; Natl Soccer Coaches Assn 1984-; Mechical Trng A 1990-, CPR, First Aid Instr 1990-; Enlass Girls Soccer Assn Coach 1986; Boston Globe Coach of Yr 1989 Bsbl & Girls Soccer 1994; *o* Walpole HS 275 Common St Walpole MA 02081*

TOMS, SUSAN BARTON, Gifted Support Teacher; *b:* Waynesboro *m:* Michael J.; *c:* Rebecca, Karey; *ed:* Shippensburg St Coll (BS) Ele & Psych 1976; Shippensburg Univ (MS) Gifted & Elem Ed 197 Credits Beyond Masters Degree; *cr:* Tuscarora Schl Dist Elem 1978-93, Gifted Support Tchr 1993-; *ai:* Odyssey of the Mind Dist C NEA 1978-; PSEA 1978-; Tuscarora Ed Assn 1978-; PA Assn for Gifte 1993-; Waynesboro Coll Club 1995-; *office:* Tuscarora Schl Dist 1 Seminary St Mercersburg PA 17236

TOMSCHECK, JACQUELINE A., Third Grade Teacher; *b:* Bridge CT; *ed:* Fairfield Univ (MS) Ed 1965; Southern CT Univ 7th Yr Rdng *cr:* Middlebrook Schl 6th Grd Tchr 1961-62; Daniels Farm Schl 6th Tchr 1962-63; Middlebrook Schl 6th Grd Tchr 1963-64; Nicholas Sch Grd Tchr 1964-72; Center, Tashua Rdng Consultant 1973-81; Jane Schl 3rd, 5th Grd Tchr, Consultant 1981-; *ai:* TEA 1961-, Pres, VP, T

EA, NEA 1961-; St James Church 1959-, CCD Work, Soc Concerns , Lectera; *office:* Jane Ryan Elem Schl 190 Park Ln Trumbull CT

RELLI, PATRICIA ANN GUZZIE, Home Economics Teacher; *b:* roi, PA; *w:* Gerald D. (dec); *c:* John, Jeff; *ed:* Glenville St Coll) Home Ec 1968; CA St Coll 24 Credits; *cr:* Monongahela HS Home ar 1968-72; Belle Vernon Area HS Home Ec Tchr 1980-; *ai:* Home b Adv; Stu Asst Prgm Comm; NEA, BVAEA 1980-; St Anne Church Chrstn Mothers 1978-, Sec 2 Terms.

, MAUREEN A., Third Grade Teacher; *b:* Bronx, NY; *m:* James; *ed:* ood (BS) 1955; *cr:* Sacred Heart Tchr 1 Yr; *ai:* Lioness; *office:* La Academy 309 1st Ave Jessup PA 18434

R, JANET LARKIN, Special Education Teacher; *b:* Newton, MA; nald; *c:* Nicole, Lauren; *ed:* Univ of MA at Amherst (BA) Ed 1977; Coll (MED) Spec Ed 1981; *cr:* Dept of Yth Svcs Spec Ed Clinician, 981-84; Bureau of Institutional Schls Educl Liaison 1985; Attleboro hsl Spec Ed Tchr 1986-; *ai:* NEA, MTA 1986-; Girl Scouts 1993-, ducl Investors of Attleboro 1992-, Sec; *office:* Attleboro HS Rathbun d Dr Attleboro MA 02703

R, JUDITH ANNE CARTER, Social Studies Teacher; *b:* rstown, NY; *m:* James Allen; *c:* Jason, Jennifer, Jamie; *ed:* SUC at m (BA) Elem Ed 1967; SUC at Fredonia (MS) Ed & Soc Stud; Attnd ase Univ, Cornell Univ, SUC at Geneseo, RIT, PA St Univ, ST 's Univ; *cr:* Richfield Springs Cntrl Schl Head Start Tchr 1967; ola Cntrl Schl 5th Grd Tchr 1967-68; Salamanca City Schls 5th Grd HS Soc Stud Tchr 1968-; Seneca Nation of Indians Adult Ed Admin 1975-78; *ai:* NHS, Close Up Club Adv; JV Soccer Coach; NEA, A 1967-; Beta Epsilon Sec; NYS Soc Stud Cncl 1971-, augus-Allegany Ctys Soc Stud Cncl; Genetaska 1969-, Pres, VP, Sec, First Congregational UCC, United Meth Church 1969, Bd of Trustee Bd of Deacons Chm; Yrbk Dedication 1995; *office:* Salamanca HS quois Dr Salamanca NY 14779*

Y, BRENDA KAY, 9th-12th Grd Eng & Speech Tchr; *b:* Norwalk, Billy Gene; *c:* Drake; *ed:* Bowling Green St Univ (BS) Eng, Speech 1971; Attnd BGSU, Ashland Univ Continuing Ed Classes; *cr:* eville Local Schls 7th, 8th Grd Lang Arts Tchr 1972-73; Monroeville eph's Schl 7th, 8th Lang Arts Tchr 1973-76; Western Reserve Schls th Eng, Speech Tchr 1976-; *ai:* Schlsp Comm for Tchrs Assn; NEA, 1971-; WRTA 1976-; St Peter Luth Women 1983-; St Paul's PTO *home:* 1035 State Route 18 Norwalk OH 44857

Y, ROBERT LOUIS, Principal; *b:* New Kensington, PA; *m:* Mary Newhouse; *c:* Andrea, Alexander, Michael; *ed:* Edinboro Univ of S) Elem Ed 1975; Bowling Green St Univ (MS) Schl Admin 1981; 12 rad Credits Bowling Green & Ashland Univ; *cr:* Sandusky City Schls d Tchr 1975-91, Elem Schl Prin 1992-; *ai:* Vol of Amer 1995-, Bd *home:* 114 46th St Sandusky OH 44870

KIN, ELIZABETH THERESA, Music Teacher; *b:* New York, NY; *c:* as R. K.; *ed:* Univ of NH (BM) Music & Ed 1986; Continuing Ed 10 s; MA Pgm 14 Credits; *cr:* Musical Theater Insts Actress, Singer & r 1980-93; Sports & Pol Events & Weddings Freelance Vocalist Private Voice Instr 1986-; Summer Musical Cmedy Wkshp Dir 95; Candia Moore Elem Music Tchr 1990-; St John The Bapt Church 1994-95; St Kathryns Church Music Dir 1995-; *ai:* Chorus, Band & Dir; Grad & Schl Events Music Provider; Curr Comm; Staff Chorus EH 1988-; MENC 1990-; PTO 1990-; St John the Bapt Church 1970-, t; St Kathryns Church 1995-, Music Dir; Provide Music for: Candia ome Days, JFK Coll Skating Shows & Mayoral Inaugurations; Key y of Boston & Manchester; Musical Compositions Commercially ble; Sang Natl Anthem for Boston Red Sox; Prof Singer Since Age z Swing Groups Perform all over Seacoast Area, Boston & Europe; Henry W Moore Schl 12 Deerfield Rd Candia NH 03034

ETICH, SUSAN RHODES, Spanish Teacher; *b:* Danville, PA; *m:* c: Zachary, Nicholas; *ed:* Elizabethtown Coll (BA) Span 1969; ebury Coll (MA) Span 1970; *cr:* Shikellamy HS Span Tchr 1970-; *ai:* Club Adv; Natl Span Hnr Soc Adv; NEA 1970-; AAISP 1972-, Chptr 91-93, Chptr Pres 1993-95; PSMLA 1994-; Delta Kappa Gamma Soc 1995-; NEH Grant 1986; Commonwealth Partnership Fellow 1988; Shikellamy HS 6th & Walnut Sts Sunbury PA 17801*

HEY, MATTHEW JOSEPH, 6th Grade Teacher; *b:* Hoboken, NJ; *m:* Devito; *ed:* Seton Hall (BA) His 1963; *cr:* David E. Rue Schl 6th chr 3 Yrs; Cntrl Schl 6th Grd Tchr 1 Yr; Memorial Schl 6th Grd Tchr s; *ai:* NJEA, NEA 1963-; *office:* Memorial Schl Morningside Ave Beach NJ 07735

HEY, SUSAN ALICE, Physical Education Teacher; *b:* Weymouth, *ed:* Univ of ME (BS) Hlth, PE, Recreation, Dance 1972; Attnd ewater St Coll, Boston St Coll; *cr:* Weymouth Park Dept Playground 9 Yr, Playgrounds Supvr 9 Yrs, Supvr of Handicapped Prgms 2 Yrs, Commissioner 8 Yrs; Braintree Pub Schls PE Tchr 21 Yrs; *ai:* Coach Upvr; PTO Tchr Rep; Schl Cncl Tchr Rep; Schl Act; CMT; MTA, BEA 1972-; MAHPERD 1972-; EDA 1978-, Pub Relations, VP ation; New England Park & Rec 1983-; Weymouth Par Commission 91, Commissioner Chm 3 Yrs, 1st Woman Elected, 1st Woman Chm; outh Meml CMT 1983-91; Numerous Golden Apple Tchr Awds; a Mc Auliffe Awd; MAHPERD, NELMS Assns Conventions ner; *home:* 119 Pleasantview Ave Weymouth MA 02188*

KER, DORINDA M., Mathematics Teacher; *b:* Trenton, NJ; *m:* John; ontclair St Coll (BA) Math Ed 1967; *ai:* Odyssey of Mind Judge; , NEA, ETEA, MCEA 1967-; *office:* John P Stevens HS Grove Ave n NJ 08820

LE, AUDREY MEDLEY, 4th Grade Teacher; *b:* New Haven, CT; *m:* rd F.; *c:* Edward Jr., Peggy Ciacchero, Brian; *ed:* NHSTC (BS) Early d 1958, (MS) Elem 1980; Many Prof Courses; *cr:* West Haven Pub Sub Tchr 1960-74; St Lawrence Schl Tchr 1975-; *ai:* Coord, tator Rainbows for All God's Children; Rcng Coord; NEASC Steering n; NCEA 1975-; Knights of Lithuania 1984-, Sec, 4th Degree Awd.

LE, MARIETTA, Third Grade Teacher; *b:* Pittston, PA; *m:* Michael Erin E.; *ed:* Coll Misericordia (BS) Elem Ed 1967; Masters velency Elem Ed; 54 Grad Credit Hrs PA St; *cr:* Lake Lehman Elem Third Grd Tchr 1967-; *ai:* NEA, PSEA, LLEA 1967-; Coll of icordia Tchr of Yr 1984.

LE, MICHAEL PATRICK, America Cultures Teacher; *b:* Pittston, *m:* Marietta Resio; *c:* Erin Elizabeth; *ed:* Scranton Univ (BS) logy 1966; Masters Equivelency 54 Addl Credit Hrs Soc Stud PA St; ake Lehman Schl Dist Home, Schl Visitor 1966-93, Amer Cultures 1993-; *ai:* NEA, BSEA 1966-; LLEA 1966-, Pres; *home:* 1339 Chase aavertown PA 18708

MBS, JEAN CARTER, Home Economics Teacher; *b:* Charleston, *ed:* Marshall Univ (BA) Home Ec 1958; Wilmington Coll (MED) Ed Admin Cert; 30 Addl Grad Hrs Shepherd Coll, Univ of DE, ington Coll; *cr:* KY Power Co Head Home Ec 1958-61; Martinsburg Eng Tchr 1962-64; Brandywine HS Home Ec, Eng Tchr 1964-; *ai:* BEA 1965-; *office:* Brandywine HS 1400 Foulk Rd Wilmington DE 3

TOOMEY, JOANN MARY, Fifth Grade Teacher; *b:* Brooklyn, NY; *m:* Dennis; *c:* Michelle, Sean; *ed:* St John's Univ (BS) Elem Ed 1968; Queen Coll (MS) Elem Ed 1972; *cr:* James H. Boyd Schl Tchr 26 Yrs; *ai:* Rel Tchr 8 Yrs; Elwood Tchrs Alliance; St Elizabeth Ann Seton Tchr of Rel; *office:* James H Boyd Intermediate Sch 286 Cuba Hill Rd Huntington NY 11743

TOOMEY, MICHAEL PATRICK, American Studies Teacher; *b:* Long Isl City, NY; *m:* Linda A. Reisig; *c:* Erin, Ryan; *ed:* St Univ at Buffalo (BS) Ed 1967, (MS) Ed 1977; Addl 12 Credit Hrs Grad Level Stud; Amer Univ 30 Credit Hrs Grad Level Stud; *cr:* M & T Bank Mgmt Trainee 1967; US Navy Naval Security Group Admin 1967-71; West Seneca Cntrl Schls Scndry Soc Stud Tchr & Dept Chm 1971-; *ai:* Yorkers Club Adv; West Seneca Tchrs Assn 1971-, VOTE-COPE Coord, Union Rep; AFT, NY St United Tchrs 1971-; Saint Pauls Evangelical Luth Church, Deacon; Ed Articles Pub in Buffalo News & West Seneca Tchrs Assn Newspaper The Viewpoint; East MS Shared Decision Making Team Former Co-Chair; *office:* East MS 1445 Center Rd West Seneca NY 14224

TOOMEY, SUSAN MENDOLIA, Guidance Counselor; *b:* Buffalo, NY; *m:* Gary M.; *c:* Jennifer A., John C.; *ed:* SUNY at Buffalo (BA) Psych 1978, (MA) Psych 1986; Addl Grad Hrs; Minor in Theatre; *cr:* South Buffalo Comm Dev Cnslr 1978-93; RSDP Productions Actress, Fin Adv 1979-; Mt Mercy Acad Guid, Dir of St Svcs 1993-; *ai:* Drama Club Dir; Musical Dir, Producer; Chrldng Coach; WNYCA, WNYCCA, NCEA 1993-; NYSCA 1995-; Hamburg Little Theatre 1979-, VP, Best Actress Awd; West Seneca Historical 1990-, Bd Trustee, 3 1st Pl Display Awds; Girl Scouts 1962-, Ldr, 1st Class; Theatre Assn of NYS 1985-, Dist Rep; *office:* Mount Mercy Acad 88 Red Jacket Pky Buffalo NY 14220

TOOMEY-CARROLL, MAUREEN A., Science Teacher; *b:* Fall River, MA; *m:* James F. Carroll; *ed:* Bridgewater St Coll (BS) Ed, Sci 1968; 32 Grad Credits R. I. Coll, Bridgewater St Coll, Boston St Coll, Univ of MA at Dartmouth, CO St; *cr:* Somerset South MS 5-6 Grds Sci Tchr 1970-81; Somerset North MS 7-8 Grds Sci Tchr 1981-89; Somerset Jr HS 7-8 Grds Sci Tchr 1989-95, 7 Grd Sci Tchr 1995-; *ai:* Tchr, Stu Handbook Comm; NEA, MA Tchrs Assn, Somerset Tchrs Assn 1968-; German Shepherd Dog Club of R. I. Past Mem Bd of Dir; League of Women Voters Past Mem Bd of Dir; Natl Sci Fnd Grants Boston St Coll, Bridgewater St Coll, Univ of MA at Dartmouth; *office:* Somerset Jr HS 1141 Brayton Ave Somerset MA 02726

TOONKEL, MANNY JOSEPH, Health Teacher & Coach; *b:* NY, NY; *ed:* Lehman Coll (BA) Ed 1975; NY Univ (MA) PE, Tchrs 1991; Attnd Ulpan Hebrew Schl at Nahariya Israel; *cr:* Brooklyn Friends Schl Tchr, Bsktbl, Soccer Coach, Ath Dir 1980-90; Laguardia HS Tchr, Bsktbl, Bsbl Coach 1992-95; US Environmental Stud Bsktbl Coach 1994-95; Martin Luther King Schl Tchr 1995-; *ai:* Bsktbl Coach; AAPEHRD 1990-; Data Based PE Prgm for Manhattan Occupational Ctr Grant; Lifetime Svc Awd; Amer Camping Assn; Prof Bsktbl Player; *home:* 80 N Moore St Apt 37A New York NY 10013*

TOOTHMAN, GEORGIA KRNICH, English Teacher; *b:* Steubenville, OH; *c:* Ted, Amy, Meribeth; *ed:* Marietta Coll (BA) Eng 1962; Franciscan Univ 9 Hrs; *cr:* Steubenville HS Eng Tchr 1962-65; Indian Creek Schls Eng Tchr 1989-93; Mingo MS 1994; Indian Creek HS 1995-; *ai:* Reserve, Var Chrldr Adv; Odyssey of Mind; Cnslr Performing Arts; NEA, OEA, ICEA 1989-; *home:* RR 1 Box 513 Bloomingdale OH 43910

TOPAZIO, CELESTE, High School Art Teacher; *b:* Providence, RI; *m:* Lawrence DeMarco; *ed:* Hofstra Univ (BS) Art Ed 1968-72; C.W. Post (MA) Fine Arts 1979; SUNY at Stonybrook (MA) Liberal Stud, Hum 1985; Hofstra Univ Sunday Lecture Series, Continuing Ed Liberal Art Stud; C.W. Post Graphic Illustration Cert Prgm; *cr:* Babylon Schl Dist Elem Art Tchr 1972-86; Project N Seek Weekend & Summer Prgm Art Tchr 1989-92; Islip Schls Summer Enrichment Prgm 2 Yrs; Babylon Schl Dist Jr-Sr HS Art Tchr 1986-; *ai:* Natl Art Honor Soc & Theater Arts Set, Scenery Division Adv; Schlsp Awds Comm; Babylon Schls Friends of the Arts Founding Participant; Interdisciplinary Stud Trips Co-Adv; NAEA 1990-; Babylon Tchrs Assn 1980-, Bldg Rep; Pub Illustration Work; Vol Work Arts & Crafts Babylon Presbyn Church Outreach Prgm, Graphic Design Babylon Youth Project; Panel Speaker St John's Univ 1 Yr; Scout Groups; Adv to 2 Congressional Art Awd Winners; Babylon Tchrs Recognition Awds 22 Yrs Svc; *office:* Babylon Jr Sr HS 50 Railroad Ave Babylon NY 11702

TOPE, LANA FELLER, Third Grade Teacher; *b:* Orrville, OH; *m:* Stephen Alan; *c:* Megan, Ethan; *ed:* OH Northern Univ (BA) Elem Ed 1983; 18 Hrs Kent St Univ; *cr:* New Phila City Schls Third Grd Tchr 1986-; *ai:* Cooperating Tchr for Three Kent St Stdnts; Guest Speaker Kent St Univ; *office:* Central Elem Schl 145 Ray Ave NW New Philadelphia OH 44663*

TOPELY, CHARLES JOHN, English Teacher; *b:* Philadelphia, PA; *m:* Kelly McCormick; *c:* Casey O'Neill, Michael, Jake; *cr:* Olney HS Sub Tchr 1981-93; *ai:* Class of 1996 Spon; AFT 1981-; *office:* George Washington HS Bustleton Ave & Verree Rd Philadelphia PA 19116

TOPITZER, MARY JANE LYNCH, Retired English Teacher; *b:* New Haven, CT; *m:* Neil Patrick; *c:* Paul F., John E., Katherine M. Erwin, David L., Maria S.; *ed:* Albertus Magnus Coll (BA) Eng 1954; Southern CT St Univ (MS) Ed 1979; *cr:* St Marys HS Eng Tchr 1954-57; M J Whalen Jr HS Eng Tchr 1974-78; Hamden HS Eng Tchr 1978-95; *ai:* NEA, HEA 1980-95; 1986 & 1995 Hamden Rotary 1 of Top 10 Tchrs Chosen by Top 10 Stdnts; 1991 Cited by Awd Recipient of Annual Super Leadership Awd as Most Inspiring Tchr.*

TOPOLESKI, JANICE MARIE, Second Grade Teacher; *b:* Jersey City, NJ; *c:* Dennis, Jay; *ed:* Jersey City St Coll (BA) Spec Ed 1968; Rutgers Univ (MED) Sci Ed 1993; 9 Credit Hrs Supervision Cert; *cr:* Hollie M. Davis Schl Spec Ed Tchr 1968-70; Clifton Ave Grd Schl 3rd Grd Tchr 1970-72; Bayville Schl Tchr of Gifted & Talented, 3rd Grd 1972-83; Clara B. Worth Schl Tchr of Gifted & Talented, 3rd, 6th Grds 1983-; *ai:* Garden Club; Past Rocketry Club, Young Astronauts, OM Coach; Kappa Delta Pi 1994-; NEA, NJEA 1968-; NJ Governors Tchr Recognition Prgm 1986; JCP&L Energy Grant 1994; *office:* Clara B Worth Elem Schl 57 Central Pky Bayville NJ 08721

TOPOLOSKY, KATHLEEN MC CANN, Sixth Grade Teacher; *b:* Braddock, PA; *m:* Paul R.; *c:* Lynn Marie, Kristin Ann, Mark Douglas; *ed:* Indiana U of PA (BS) Elem Ed 1964; Penn St (MS) Elem Ed 1967; *cr:* Penn Hills Schl Dist First Grd Tchr 1964-71; Gateway Schl Dist Sub Tchr 1972-75, 1982-89; St Edward Schl Sixth Grd Tchr 1989-; *ai:* 4-6 Grd Kids Against Crime Adult, Tchr Adv; Norwin Elks Auxillary; Grant for Schl from Hills Dept Store for Drug Prevention Acts Through Kids Against Crime; *office:* St Edward Schl 89 6th Street Ext Herminie PA 15637

TOPOLSKI, CAROL C., Junior High School Teacher; *b:* Toledo, OH; *m:* Thomas; *c:* Richard, Amy, Mary Beth, Alan; *ed:* Siena Heights Coll (BA) Elem Ed 1995; Univ of Toledo Elem Ed Music 1958; 14.5 Credit Hrs Post Grad Stud; *cr:* Organist, Choirmaster Meml Luth Church 22 Yrs; St Adalbert Schl Tchr 9 Yrs; *ai:* Amer Guild Of Organists Search Comm; Band Booster Parent; Fac Adv Stu Theatre Group; Mu Phi Epsilon 1958-, Sec, Pres, Past Pres; Toledo Area Cncl & Intnl Rdng Assn 1987-; Stu Tchr of Yr 1986; Who's Who in Amer Coll and Univ; Schl Rep math Ldrshp Cncl; *home:* 208 North Ln Blissfield MI 49228

TOPP, ROBERT, Assoc Prof & Dir Clin Rsrch; *b:* Toledo, OH; *m:* Anne Noe Oliver; *c:* Natalie, Lauren; *ed:* Toledo Univ (BSN) Nrsng 1982; Univ of Cincinnati (MSN) Nrsng 1984; OH St Univ (PHD) Hlth Ed; Post Doctoral Flwshp Univ of PA Geriatric Med; *office:* Med Coll of OH 3355 Glendale Ave Toledo OH 43614

TOPPER, ROBERT QUINN, Asst Professor of Chemistry; *b:* Greeley, CO; *m:* Gayle Gruskin; *ed:* FL St Univ (BS) Physics & Chem 1986; Yale Univ (MSM) Phil & Chem 1989, (PHD) Phys Chem 1990; *cr:* Univ of MN Post Doctoral Rsrch Assoc 1990-92; Univ of RI Post Doctoral Rsrch Assoc 1992-93; Cooper Union Asst Prof 1993-; *ai:* Cooper Union Engineering Fac Sec; Cong Brai Jacob Newsletter Ed; Amer Chem Soc 1987-; Amer Phys Soc 1987-; Cncl on Undergraduate Rsrch 1993-; Outstdng Svc Awd; Argonne Comm of Tchrs & DEP; Argonne Natl Lab 1993; Numerous Articles Pub; *office:* Cooper Union Schl of Engrng 51 Astor Pl New York NY 10003*

TOPPMAN, EVELYN LEA, Retired Lang Arts Teacher; *b:* Montclair, NJ; *m:* Robert M.; *c:* Lawrence, Russell; *ed:* Douglass Coll (BA) Eng 1950; 39 Credit Hrs in Ed Trenton St Coll; *cr:* Hainesport Twp Elem Schl Kndgtn Tchr 1965-69, 6-8 Grd Lang Arts Tchr 1969-94; *ai:* Comm to Coordinate Lang Arts Curr 7th-12th Grd; Schls Lit Magazine Coord; Spelling Bee, Elocution Prgm Dir; Liason Between 8th Grd & HS; HEA, BCEA 1965-; NJEA, NEA 1965-, Lifetime Mbrshp; HEA 1965-, Pres 1968-72, 1984-86; United Campaign of Burlington Cty, Responsible for Collection of Funds from Hainesport Staff; Child Placement Review Bd 1994-, Vol; Hainesport Tchr of Yr 1985; Douglass Coll Promote Vol Svc Comm 1992; Mt Holly Ctr Nrsng Home Act Vol.

TORBIC, CAROL A., 4th Grade Teacher; *b:* Rochester, PA; *ed:* CA Univ of PA (BSED) 1972; Geo Mason Univ (MED) 1978; *cr:* Cty Pub Schls 4th-6th Grd Tchr 1972; Prince George's 4th Grd Tchr 1993-; *ai:* AFT 1972-; *office:* Rose Valley Elem Schl 9800 Jacqueline Dr Ft Washington MD 20744

TORCELLO, MARY JO, Biology Teacher; *b:* Meriden, CT; *c:* Tara R., Zachary J.; *ed:* Albertus Magnus (BA) Bio 1968; Cntrl CT St Univ (5th Yr) Bio 1978; *cr:* Hillhouse HS Bio Tchr 1968-69; Lincoln MS Life Sci Tchr 1970-71; Middletown HS Bio Tchr 1971-; *ai:* NHS Adv; AFT 1972-, Bldg Rep; *office:* Middletown HS Hunting Hill Ave Middletown CT 06457*

TORCHIA, JOHN F., 6th Grade Teacher; *b:* Pittsburgh, PA; *m:* Mary Louise Laux; *c:* James A., Thomas L., Jill L.; *ed:* Clarion Univ (BA) Elem Ed 1973; Penn St Univ MS Equivalency Elem Ed 1976; *cr:* Carlynton Schl Dist Elem Schl Tchr 1973-; *ai:* PIAA Wrestling Ofcl 17 Yrs; AFT 1973-, Bldg Rep, Pres, VP; *office:* Carnegie Elem Schl Franklin Ave Carnegie PA 15106

TORCHIA, THOMAS ANTHONY, Mathematics Teacher; *b:* Pittsburgh, PA; *m:* Susan; *c:* Kristy, Joseph, Thomas; *ed:* Duquesne Univ (BS) Scndry Math 1973; Univ of Pittsburgh (MEd) Scndry Math 1976; Attnd Penn St & Kent St Univ; *cr:* Southview HS Math Tchr 1973-74; Churchill Jr HS Math Tchr 1974-75; Shaler Area Schls Math Tchr 1975-77; Hampton HS Math Tchr 1977-89; Hampton MS Math Tchr 1989-; *ai:* Jr HS Wrestling Coach; 9th Grd Ftbl Asst Coach; Math Counts Supvr; Math Chm; PSEA 1988-; NCTM 1990-; Duquesne Univ Grad Asst 1980; *office:* Hampton MS 4589 School Rd Allison Park PA 15101*

TORI, IRENE M., Math Chairperson & Teacher; *b:* Philadelphia, PA; *m:* Carl A.; *c:* Angela Raub, Michael; *ed:* Chestnut Hill Coll (BS) Math 1977; Penn St Univ 1981-82; St Joseph's Univ Post Grad Credits 1977-79, Working on MED Math; *cr:* Archbishop Ryan HS Math Tchr 1977-83, 1987-94, Math Chair, Tchr 1994-; *ai:* NCTM 1983-; ATMOPAV 1994-; Assn of Cath Tchrs 1977-, Exec Sec; Parish Choir 1990-; Exec Comm 1994-; J. W. Hallahan Cath Girls HS Alumnae; *office:* Archbishop Ryan HS 11201 Academy Rd Philadelphia PA 19154

TORMEY, RICHARD JOHN,JR., Eighth Grade Science Teacher; *b:* Jersey City, NJ; *m:* Cheryl Lynn Watkins; *c:* Brett; *ed:* Jersey City St Coll (BA) Elem Ed 1974; Seton Hall Univ (MA) Gen Prof Ed 1994; *cr:* Beer St Schl 8th Grd Sci Tchr 1974-76; Reading-Fleming MS 8th Grd Sci Tchr 1976-; *ai:* Sci, Tech Club Adv; YMCA Girls Summer Bsktbl Clinic Head Coach 15 Yrs; FREA, NJEA, NEA 1974-, Fac Rep; NJSSTA 1985-; Kappa Delta Pi 1993-, Pres; Aerospace Ed Ambassador; US Space Fnd Sci, Tech Aerospace Ed Presenter; Soviet Union Delegation Ldr 1990-91; *home:* 64 Old York Rd Ringoes NJ 08551

TORMEY-MILLER, JILL D., First Grade Teacher; *b:* Summit, NJ; *m:* Arthur V. Miller III; *c:* Ashley; *ed:* Kean Coll (BA) Elem Ed 1976, (MA) Rdng Specialist 1981; Post Grad Stud Admin, Supervision; Continuing Ed Credits; *cr:* Silver Bay Rdng Specialist 1977-80, 6th Grd Tchr 1980-93, 1st Grd Tchr 1994-; Ocean Cty Coll Adj Fac 1991-; *ai:* Chrldng Coach; Yrbk; Schl Fair; Spelling Bee, 6th Grd Play Comms; NEA, NJ Educl Assn, IRA, Toms River Ed Assn 1977-; Howell Food Pantry 1991-; Grad Thesis Pub; Who's Who Among Stdnts in Amers Colls, Univs 1976; *office:* Silver Bay Elem Schl Silver Bay Rd Toms River NJ 08753

TORNEY, PEGGY CAIN, Asst Principal & 8th Grd Tchr; *b:* Bronx, NY; *m:* Patrick; *c:* Patrick, Peggy Ann; *ed:* Dominican Coll (BA) Spec Ed 1971; Coll of New Rochelle (MA) Ed, Permenent Sp Ed 1975; *cr:* NY Inst for the Blind Sp Ed Tchr 1971-75; Our Lady of Solace 8th Grd Tchr 1982-; *ai:* Stu Cncl Adv; Moderator for Sports Prgm; Pres Altar Rosary Soc; Sec Parish Cncl; Var Chrldng Coach; Chprsn Rev Stephen Kelley Schlsp Fund; FCT 1982-.

TORNIKOSKI, KATHLEEN VERA, English Teacher; *b:* Fitchburg, MA; *m:* Erkki Jakko; *c:* Mika, Aliisa; *ed:* Fitchburg St Coll (BS) Ed, Eng 1969, (MAT) Tchng Eng 1973; 30 Addl Credits 1983; Univ of Hartford 2 Credits Advanced Placement Eng 1991; *cr:* North Middlesex Regnl Eng Tchr 1969-; Kathleen's Doll Romance Founder 1987-; *ai:* Amnesty Intnl, Lit Magazine Adv; Acad Decathlon Coach; MA Tchrs Assn, NEA 1969-; NCTE; Phi Delta Kappa 1993-; Schl Cncl 1994-; Whole Lang Grant Commonwealth of MA Ctr Tchng, Learning 1991; *home:* 229 Rollstone St Fitchburg MA 01420

TORNROSE, RUSSELL T., Eng & Theatre Arts Teacher; *b:* New York, NY; *m:* Marianne Elizabeth Horne; *c:* Shane Young; *ed:* Princeton Univ (AB) Lit & Religion 1965; Boston Univ (MED) Ed 1978; *cr:* Karachi Amer Schl Tchr & Coach 1965-67; Emerson Schl Tchr 1967-68; Weston MS Prin 1970-77; Wayland MS Tchr 1978-84; Brooks Schl Prin 1984-89; Wayland HS Tchr 1989-90; Telstar HS Eng, Theatre Arts & Speech Tchr 1989-; *ai:* Track Coach; Drama & Rota Adv; MEA, NEA, ASCD; *office:* Telstar Regional HS 284 Walkers Mills Rd Bethel ME 04217

TORONTO, ANTHONY PHILIP, Physical Education Teacher; *b:* Passaic, NJ; *m:* Margaret M.; *c:* Philip; *ed:* Glassboro St Coll (BA) Hlth & PE 1971; SUNY at New Paltz (MS) Admin & Supervision 1991; *cr:* North Rockland CSD PE Tchr 1972-; North Garnerville Elem Schl PE Tchr 1972-84; Haverstraw MS PE Tchr 1984-; *ai:* Var Sftbl Coach 1986-; NRTA, NYSUT, AFT 1972-; *office:* Haverstraw MS 16 Grant St Haverstraw NY 10927

TORQUATO, BARBARA TERLECKI, Special Education Teacher; *b:* Brooklyn, NY; *m:* Philip; *c:* Andrea; *ed:* St Joseph's Coll (BA) Early Chldhd & Elem Ed 1968; Fordham Univ (MS) Educl Psych, Testing & Guid 1969; 24 Credits Cert Staff Dev & Admin Coll of New Rochelle; 30 Credits Cert Spec Ed Long Island Univ; *cr:* PS 132 Elem, Early Chldhd Tchr 1969-77; Lake Hills Nursery Schl Dir 1979-88; Murphy Jr HS Spec Ed Tchr 1988-91; Albert G. Prodell MS Spec Ed Tchr 1991-; *ai:* Rep Spec Ed Parent Group; Stud Buddy Group Moderator; NYSUT 1969-; ASCD 1992-; Fordham Univ Assistantship; Tchr of Yr Village CSD 1991-93; Nom Tchr of Yr 1989; *office:* Albert G. Prodell MS Randall Rd Shoreham NY 11786*

TORRE, MARIANNE BUBERL, German & Mathematics Teacher; *b:* Pollikeu, Germany; *w:* Vincent (dec); *c:* Kathryn, Stephan; *ed:* Johann W. Goeth Univ (BA) Ger, Math 1966; Rutgers 33 Credits Ger; *cr:* Middlesex HS Ger Tchr 1968-74; Chathan HS Ger, Math Tchr 1984-88; Westfield HS Ger, Math Tchr 1988-; *ai:* Ger Club Adv; AATG, F L Tchrs of NJ 1984-; *home:* 8 Old Farm Rd Chatham NJ 07928

TORRE, NANCY ANN, 6th-8th Grade Math Teacher; *b:* Hoboken, NJ; *m:* Thomas; *c:* Thomas Jr.; *ed:* Jersey City St Coll (BA) General Elem Ed 1968; *cr:* Lyndhurst Bd of Ed Self-Contained 4th Grd Tchr 1969-82, Self-Contained 3rd Grd Tchr 1982-88, 4th-6th Grd Math Tchr 1988-93; Jefferson Schl 6th-8th Grd Math Tchr 1993-; *ai:* NEA, NJEA 1969-; AMTNJ 1993-; Ed & Hlth Ctrs of Amer 1988-, Bd Mem; Gov Florio's Tchr Recognition Awd; *office:* Jefferson Schl Lake Ave Lyndhurst NJ 07071

TORRELLI, ROBERT ANTHONY, 8th Grade Math Teacher; *b:* Cleveland, OH; *m:* Christina DiMatteo; *c:* Anthony; *ed:* Cleveland St Univ (BS) Physics, Math 1990, (MS) Curr, Instr 1995; Assertive Discipline; *cr:* Case Western Reserve Univ Math Instr 1992-; Roxboro MS Math Instr 1990-; *ai:* Ftbl Head Coach; Book Room Coord; Math Dept Chprsn; AFT 1990-.

TORRENCE, DAVID MICHAEL, Science Teacher; *b:* Toledo, OH; *m:* Juanita Allen; *c:* Jenner, Jesse; *ed:* Univ of ID (BS) Fish & Wildlife Mgmt 1976; Bowling Green St Univ 9 Credit Hrs; *cr:* Self Employed Const Trades Owner 1977-85; Self Employed Solar Energy Bus Owner; Central Cath HS Sci Tchr 1986-; *ai:* Environmental & Hispanic Culture Clubs Spon; Discipline Comm; Track Team Vol Asst Coach.

TORRENCE, WILLIAM T.,JR., Theology Teacher; *b:* Philadelphia, PA; *m:* Marie Mc Gowan; *c:* Michele Maenner, Christine, Melissa; *ed:* St Joseph's Univ (BS) Eng 1970; 30 Grad Hrs in Theology St Charles Seminary Grad Div; Sacred Congregation for the Clergy Diploma; *cr:* West Cath Boys HS Theology, Eng Tchr 1970-81; Cardinal O'Hara HS Theology, Eng Tchr 1981-; *ai:* NHS Adv; ACT 1970-; *office:* Cardinal Ohara HS 1701 S Sproul Springfield PA 19064

TORRES, LILLIAN, High School Math Teacher; *b:* Villaba, PR; *ed:* Trenton St Coll (BA) Math, Scndry Ed 1993; *cr:* Plainfield HS Math Tchr 1993-; *ai:* Shades of Beauty Club Adv; Math Spring Offensive Comm; PEA, NJEA, AMTNJ NEA 1993-; NCTM 1992-; *office:* Plainfield HS 950 Park Ave Plainfield NJ 07060

TORRES, MAGGIE MARRERO, Bilingual Teacher; *b:* Puerto Rico ; *m:* Octavio; *c:* Magdalis Jo Octavio Jr.; *ed:* St Josephs Coll (BA) Child Stud 1980; CW Post Coll (MS) Biling Ed 1983; *cr:* River Ave Schl Tchr 1980-81; PS60-GL 3rd-5th Biling Tchr Grd 3rd-5th 1981-; *ai:* AFT 1981-; *office:* PS 60 George L Gallego 888 Rev James A Polite Ave Bronx NY 10459*

TORRES, OLGA CASTELLANOS, Spanish Teacher; *b:* Oriente, Cuba; *m:* Pablo F.; *c:* Pablo F., Raul A., Olga Torres Murphy, Cecilia Torres Roos; *ed:* Univ of Havana (MS) Botany 1950, (MS) Zoology 1951, (PHD) Bio 1958; 3 Credits Each Genetics, Flora, Pre His, Eng Composition, Writing; *cr:* Havana Inst Bio Tchr 1953-58; St Gabriel HS Span Tchr 1964-67; Scarsdale Alternative HS Span Tchr 1979-86; Ursuline Schl Jr Sr HS Span Tchr 1980-; *ai:* Span Circle Club Adv; Philosophy Comm; Tchrs Expectations Stdnts Achvmt; NY St Assn of Frgn Lang Tchrs, Amer Assn of Tchrs of Span & Portuguese 1980-; Italian Inst 1982-; Sutton Manor Assn 1962-; Mother's Club of New Rochelle 1976-; Parent's Assn 1981-83, Co-Pres; Rite of Chrstn Initiation of Adults 1994-; *office:* Ursuline Jr Sr HS 1354 North Ave New Rochelle NY 10804

TORRES, OSCAR,JR., Spanish Teacher; *b:* Orocovis, PR; *m:* Amy P.; *c:* Nicholas O.; *ed:* Temple Univ (BS) Scndry Ed, Span 1989, (MED) Scndry Frgn Lang Ed 1994; *cr:* St Hugh Schl Elem Tchr 7th Grd 1989-93; Nazareth Acad Span Tchr 1993-94; The Lawrenceville Schl Master of Span 1994-; *ai:* Financial Aide, Diversity Comms; Lawrenceville Schl Housemaster; Hamill Comm Svc, Latinos Unidos Stu Org, Span Club Moderators; Asst Housemaster Hamill House; Central Jersey Penn Frgn Lang, Acad Alliance 1996; Yth Task Force 1989-, PA Coord, Rep; Cath Yth Org 1989-, Hispanic Yth Ministry; Temple Univ Grad Tchr Awd; Cigna Schlsp for Excl; Speaker at World Yth Day Conf 1993; *office:* The Lawrenceville Schl Main St Lawrenceville NJ 08648

TORRES, SHELBY C., English Teacher; *b:* Clark, NC; *ed:* NY City Comm Coll (AA) Libl Arts 1971; Herbert H Lehman Coll (BA) Eng & Ed 1972; Rutgers Univ (MS) Soc & Philosophical Fndtns 1981; Writing a Multicultural Curr 1 Credit at Kean Coll; Attndng NY Tech Inst; *cr:* JHS 118 Bronx NY Eng Tchr 1973; Rahway Intermediate Schl Eng Tchr 1974-79; Rahway Sr HS Eng Tchr 16 Yrs; *ai:* Mem of HS & Intermediate Schl Transistion Team; Worked on Comm to Initiate 1st Multicultural Festival; Tutor Stdnts with Spcl Needs; Rutgers Univ Alumni Soc; NJ Ed Assn 1974-; St Lukes Episcopal Church 1982-, Adult Ed & vestory; Certified Stdnts I Sent Contributions for the Homeless-Elijahs Promise; Arranged for Visit of Russian Tchr & Stdnts to Our Dist; Host Japanese Tchr Kenji Yamamoto; Wrote & Copywrited Multicultural Curr for the Dist; *office:* Rahway HS 1012 Madison Ave Rahway NJ 07065

TORRO, PATRICIA LEWIS, Fifth Grade Teacher; *b:* New Haven, CT; *m:* Paul; *c:* Zachary; *ed:* Cntrl CT St Univ (BS) Comm 1987; Southern CT St Univ (MA) Rdng 1992; Cntrl Ct St Univ Tchng Cert 1988; Southern CT St Admin, Supervision Cert 1993; *cr:* Savin Rock Comm Schl 4th Grd Tchr 1988-89, 5th Grd Tchr 1989-; *ai:* Stu Asst Team; AFT 1988-, Asst Steward; *office:* Savin Rock Cmty Elem Sch 50 Park St West Haven CT 06516

TORTORA, ANNE HALLORAN, Director of Music; *b:* Brooklyn, NY; *m:* Michael; *c:* Jeffrey, Daniel; *ed:* Univ of CT (BA) Music, (BS) Ed 1990; 8 Credits Grad Stud; *cr:* Norwich Pub Schls Vocal & Gen Music Tchr 1990-91; Griswold HS Vocal & Gen Music Tchr 1991-94; New London HS Dir of Music 1994-; *ai:* Marching & Jazz Band Dir; NEA & CT Ed Assn 1990-; Music Edctrs Natl Conf 1990-; CT Music Edctrs Assn 1990-, Stu Affairs Commission Sec; New England Music Festival Assn 1991-, Dean of Women; BSA 1984-, Adult Ldr; Montville Yth Soccer Club 1993-, Coach; Pub in Teaching Music; *office:* New London HS 490 Jefferson Ave New London CT 06320*

TORTORELLI, JOSEPH ANTHONY, English Teacher; *b:* Philadelphia, PA; *m:* Rose Rodia; *ed:* La Salle Univ (BA) Eng & Ed 1978; Temple Univ (MS) General Ed 1982; *cr:* Acad Park HS Eng Tchr 1978-86; Lenape HS Eng Tchr 1986-; *ai:* NEA 1978-; Lenape HS Tchr of Yr 1988; PA Writing Project Fellow; Penn-Lit Inst Fellow; *office:* Lenape HS 235 Hartford Rd Medford NJ 08055

TORTOSA, MANUEL RAMON, ESOL Teacher; *b:* New York, NY; *ed:* Pace Coll (BA) Eng 1965; NY Univ (MA) Eng 1966; Georgetown Univ Applied Linguistics; Ed Credits at Cath Univ; *cr:* US Information Agency Frgn Svc Ofcr 1966-74; Montgomery Cty Pub Schls ESOL Tchr 1974-; *ai:* NEA 1974-; WATESOL 1994-; *office:* Walt Whitman HS 7100 Whittier Blvd Bethesda MD 20817

TOSCANO, RALPH A., English Teacher; *b:* Danbury, CT; *m:* Noreen McWilliams; *c:* Susan Barovich, Michael, Elizabeth Van Bezooijen, Ann; *ed:* Danbury St Coll (BS) Elem Ed 4th-8th Grd & Eng 7th-12th Grd 1961; Western CT St Coll (MS) Ed 1969; *cr:* Danbury Elem & Jr HS 5th-6th Grd Tchr & 7th-9th Grd Eng Tchr 1961-85; Danbury Adult Basic Ed Evening Prgm Eng as a Second Lang Tchr 1962-82; Amer Inst of Banking Adult Evening Effective Eng Tchr 1975-78; Danbury HS Bus Eng & Amer Lit Tchr 1985-; *ai:* Intnl Club Co-Adv; Selection Comm NHS; K-12th Grd System-Wide Rdng & Writing Curr & 9th-12th Grd Eng Curr Revision Comms; NEA 1965-; CT Ed Assn & Danbury Ed Assn 1961-; St Marguerite Bourgeous Church 1988-; Union Carbide Outstanding Tchr 1990; Univ of CT Alumni Assn Awd for Excl in HS Tchng 1992.*

TOSTI, RONALD MICHAEL, Science Teacher; *b:* Milford, MA; *m:* Lorraine Woodman; *c:* Cory; *ed:* Worcester St Coll (BS) Sci Ed 1963; AZ St Univ (MNS) Earth Sci 1969; 30 Addl Credit Hrs; 4 Credit Hrs Univ of NV at Las Vegas; 3 Credit Hrs Columbia Univ; 3 Credit Hrs Univ of Hartford; *cr:* Holliston HS Sci Tchr 1963-67; AZ St Univ Planetarium Dir 1967-70; Holliston HS Sci Tchr 1970-; *ai:* Environmental Club Adv; Globe Prgm, Greenhouse Project & Courtyard Restoration Project, Recycling Prgm Lead Tchrs; AFT; Blackstone Vly Regnl Voc HS, Adv Comm; NSF Grant: Environmental Stud UNLV 1972, Earth Sci AZ St Univ 1966-68, Bio Boston Univ 1964-65; Natl Assn Geology Tchr Plate Tectonics Stud Columbia Univ 1971; Holliston Ed Fnd Grant 1995-96; Finalist Tchr of Yr Awd 1992, 1993; *home:* 144 Old Westboro Rd North Grafton MA 01536

TOSUN, ZEKE, Spanish Teacher; *b:* Cyprus Island ; *m:* Leyla Bahar; *c:* Sevil, Meral, Tamara; *ed:* Bloomfield Coll (BA) Span 1967; *cr:* Clinton Pl Jr HS Span Tchr 1967-81; East Side HS Span Tchr 1982-; *ai:* Var Girls Soccer, Bsktbl Coach; Var Boys Bsbl Coach; Inducted into Bloomfield Colls Hall of Fame for Soccer; *home:* 2515 Doris Ave Union NJ 07083

TOTH, JOHN PAUL, Fourth Grade Teacher; *b:* Allentown, PA; *m:* Linda A. Talotta; *c:* Jessica, Michael; *ed:* Kutztown Univ (BS) Elem Ed 1971; Grad Stud PA St & Wilkes Coll; *cr:* Whitehall-Coplay Schl Dist Fourth Grd Tchr 25 Yrs; *ai:* PSEA, NEA 1971-; *home:* 4966 Abbey Rd Coplay PA 18037

TOTH, M. JANE, Science Tchr & Dept Chprsn; *b:* Cleveland, OH; *ed:* OH Dominican Coll (BA) Bio 1961; Washington Univ (MAEd) Sci Ed 1966; Doctoral Stud Curr & Instr Emphasis in Environmental Ed at Kent St Univ; *cr:* Kilakala Scndry Schl Sci Tchr 1966-69; St Rita Schl Sci Tchr 1970-71; Maple Hghts HS Sci Tchr 1971-; Cleveland St Univ Adjunct Instr 1980; Maple Hghts HS Sci Dept Head 1991-; *ai:* NSTA 1966-; NEA, OEA, MHTTa 1971-; NEOEA 1971-, Chm Env Concerns Comm; Environmental Ed Grant From US Office of Ed 1976-77 Schl Yr; *home:* 4330 Tamalga Dr South Euclid OH 44121*

TOTH, TWILA S., English Teacher & Dept Chair; *b:* Clarksburg, WV; *m:* Gabriel J.; *c:* Todd, Scott; *ed:* Bob Jones Univ (BS) Eng, Speech & Scndry Ed 1961; Attnd Kent St Univ, Univ of Akron & Ashland Coll; *cr:* Wadsworth City Schls 9th Grd Eng & Speech Tchr 9 Yrs, 9th & 11th Grd Eng Tchr 24 Yrs; *ai:* NEA, NEOEA & WEA 1961-; NCTE 1985-; Kiwanis 1989-, VP, Pres; Chamber of Commerce, Citizen of Yr Awd 1992; Barberton Lib Bd 1982-84; Wadsworth HS Tchr of Yr 1973 & 1989; Dept Chprsn 1975-; *office:* Wadsworth HS 625 Broad St Wadsworth OH 44281

TOTILO, CAROL, Social Studies Teacher; *b:* Brooklyn, NY; *ed:* Mercy Coll (BS) Eng Lit 1987; Iona Coll (MS) Eng Lit 1994; *cr:* St Augustine Schl Rdng Tchr 1987-94, Soc Stud Tchr 1994-; *ai:* Stu Cncl Adv; NCSS 1994-; NCTE 1987-; *office:* St Augustine Schl 301 Eagle Park Ossining NY 10562

TOTIN, DAVID WILLIAM, Fourth Grade Teacher; *b:* Pittsburgh, PA; *m:* Donna Alice Goettmann; *c:* Jennifer A., Lorrie R.; *ed:* Slippery Rock Univ (BS) Elem Ed K-8 1971; Westminister Coll (MA) Elem Schl Admin 1973; 40 Addl Credits; *cr:* North Allegheny Schl Dist Elem Tchr 1971-; *ai:* Jr Red Cross Club, Stu & Nursing Home Pen Pal Prgm, 4th Grd Sci Fair, Two Read-Ins Per Yr Spon; AFT 1971-, VP 1 Yr; Allegheny Center Alliance Church 1976-, Govt Bd 1988-93, Chrstn Ed 1985-, Bd of Elders 1991-; Outstanding Educator 1986 PA Div Amer Assn of Univ Women; Amer Red Cross Svc Awd 1993, 1994; Special Ed Parent Support Grp Awd 1994; *office:* Espe Elem Schl 8711 Old Perry Hwy Pittsburgh PA 15237

TOTMAN, KATHLEEN SHEERIN, English Teacher; *b:* Brooklyn, NY; *m:* Joseph; *c:* Mary, Christopher, Elizabeth; *ed:* Coll of Mt St Vincent (BA) Eng 1968; Boston Coll Grad Schl (MA) Eng 1970; Inservice Courses Boces & Westbury Schls; *cr:* Weymouth Pub Schls Eng Tchr 1970-77; Westbury Schl Dist Eng Tchr 1987-; *ai:* Chrldng Adv; Writers Club; Broadcasting Club; Home Tutoring Pgm; NCTE; Long Island Lang Arts Cncl; Rockville Centre Soccer Club 1984-, Vol Parent; Lead Tchr in Mentor Tchng Pgm 1992-94.

TOTMAN, LISA FARREL, Third Grade Teacher; *b:* New Haven, CT; *m:* David Thomas; *c:* Serena, Rachel; *ed:* Smith Coll (BA) Ec 1964; SCSU (MS) Early Chldhd Ed; Cambridge Coll (MS) Math, Elem Ed 1995; Univ of New Haven Bus Courses Acctg; *cr:* Foote Schl Third Grd Tchr 1966-69, Asst Spec Ed, V, IV Grd, MAG Tchr, Lib 1970-78, Third Grd Tchr 1978-; *ai:* 4-6 Grd Afterschool Cooking Class; Math Dept Co-Chair; CAIS Prof Dev Comm; NCTM; Eli Whitney Museum Bd 1996; NH Preservation Trust 1970's-; *office:* Foote Schl 50 Loomis Pl New Haven CT 06511

TOTTEN, JILL NOELLA, Computer Bus Application Tchr; *b:* Columbus, OH; *m:* Roger W.; *c:* Victoria; *ed:* OH St Univ (BS) Prof Ed 1986; DOS; EXCEL; ACCESS; Bus Concepts; Lotus 1-2-3; *cr:* Scarlet Oaks CDC Jr Exec Sec 1986-87; Laurel Oaks CDC Jr Banking & Acctng 1987-88; D. Russel Lee Career Ctr Adult Secretarial Procedures & Data Processing 1988-92; Fairfield HS Admin 1992-93; Lakota HS Computerized Bus Applications Tchr 1993-; *ai:* Bus Prof of Amer, Chptr Adv Region 17; Adv of BPA; OBTA, OVA, AVA 1986-; OEA, NEA 1988-; Hosted Russian Tchr in Schl Exch 1995.*

TOTTEN, LEO MARK, Physical Education Dept Chair; *b:* Gettysburg, PA; *m:* Patricia J.; *c:* Kristen, Kari; *ed:* West Chester St Coll (BS) Hlth, PE 1973; Western MD Coll (MS) PE 1987; Cert Admin, Supervision 1993; *cr:* Francis Scott Key HS Hlt, PE Tchr 1977-79; Westmister HS Hlth, PE Tchr 1979-82; East MS PE 1982-85; Francis Scott Key HS PE Dept Chair 1985-; *ai:* Var, Weightlifting Club Adv; NHS Comm; Var Vlybl Coach; Strenght Coach All Sports; 4 Period Day Advy Comm; NEA 1975-; MAPHERD 1975-, VP Ath; Natl Strength Conditioning Assoc 1984-; US Weightlifting Fed 1984-, Bd of Dir; Vlybl Coach of yr 1995; Carroll Cty Outstdng Tchr 1992; Head Coach US Olympic Festival Weightlifting 1994-95; USA Team Ldr Weightlifting 1995 Pan Am Games, 1996 Olympic Games; Articles Pub; *home:* 654 Georgetown Rd Littlestown PA 17340

TOTTY, JUDITH PASQUA, Scndry English & Theatre Tchr; *b:* North Charleroi, PA; *c:* Leigh Ann; *ed:* CA Univ of PA (BS) Ed, Eng 1970-; Eng; Theatre Univ of Pgh; *cr:* Upper St Clair Schl Dist Permanent Sub Tchr 1970-71; West Jefferson Hills Schl Dist Eng Tchr 1971-77; Washington Schl Dist HS Eng, Theatre Tchr 1988-; *ai:* Drama, WHS News Coaches; Future Tchr of Amer Spons; PSEA 1990-; KDKA Thansk to Tchr Nom; *office:* Washington HS 201 Allison Ave Washington PA 15301*

TOUB, ELEANOR GOMAN, Kindergarten Teacher; *b:* Phila, PA; *m:* Charles Jerrold; *c:* Steven, Michael; *ed:* Temple Univ (BS) Ed, Scndry Ed Eng, His 1959; (BS) Elem Ed K-12 1978; (MS) Ed 1978; *cr:* Lower Merion Schl Dist Elem Grd 5 Tchr 1956, 7-8 Grd Scndry Tchr 1958-63; Philadelphia Schl Dist Elem K-1 Grd Tchr 1972-; *ai:* Primary Assembly Ldr; Safety Patrol Spon; Stage Crew Adv; AFT, Phila Fed of Tchrs 1968-, Bldg Rep 1972-88, Del AFT Convention 1984; Schl Dist Facilitator; Ldrshp Team Creighton Schl 1991; Semi-Finalist Thanks to Tchrs Awd 1990; *home:* 833 Grand Blvd Warrington PA 18976

TOUCHETTE, LINDA, English Teacher; *b:* Plattsburgh, NY; *m:* Christopher J. Delello; *ed:* Le Moyne Coll (BA) Eng, Comm 1983; Univ of Hartford (MED) Ed 1991; *cr:* Sothebys I R Ed 1985-87; Artec Distributing Mrktg 1987-89; Morse Schl of Bus Eng Tchr 1990-92; Suffield HS Eng Tchr 1992-; *ai:* Stu Cncl Adv; Schlsp Comm; NEA, CEA 1992-; CCTE, NETE 1991-; *office:* Suffield HS 350 Mountain Rd Suffie 06078

TOUCHETTE, MARTIN JOHN, History Teacher; *b:* Holyoke, M Julie Yarrows; *ed:* Univ of MA at Amherst (BS) Recreation 1988, Ed 1994; Greenfield Comm Coll Outdoor Ldrshp Prgm; *cr:* MA Au Soc Naturalist 1990-91; Mt Tom Reservation Museum Curator 19 Look Meml Park Supvr 1992-94; Cathedral HS His Tchr 1994-; *ai:* Adv; Soc Stud Curr Dev Comm; NCSS 1994-; *office:* Cathedral H Surrey Rd Springfield MA 01118

TOUCHSTONE, DONNA ALBRECHT, Guidance Counsel Vineland, NJ; *c:* Allen, Aubree; *ed:* Univ of South FL (BA) Elem Ed Univ of GA (MED) Stu Prsnl 1980; *cr:* Hillsborough Cty Schls 1977-78, Guid Cnslr 1981-86; Hillsborough Comm Coll Parenting 1989; Vineland Pub Schls Guid Cnslr 1992-; *ai:* NEA 1992-; NJEA VEA 1992-; Project Follow Through Comm Svc Awd.

TOUGHMANIAN, MARGUERITE, French & Spanish Teacher; *b:* France; *ed:* Montclair St Coll (BA) Fr & Span 1972; Addl 32 Credi Saint John the Bapt Fr & Span Tchr 1973-78; Saint Mary Span 1978-79; Queen of Peace HS Fr & Span Tchr 1985-; *ai:* Fr Club A Foreign LEA 1985-; Alliance Francaise; NCEA 1985-; *office:* Que Peace HS 191 Rutherford Pl North Arlington NJ 07031

TOUHEY, JULIE ANN MAZELLA, English Teacher; *b:* Staten NY; *m:* Gerard M.; *ed:* Seton Hall Univ (BA) Eng & Jrnlsm 1992, Eng 1994; *cr:* Seton Hall Univ Tchrs Asst 1992-94; Huntington Le Ctr SAT, Eng Tchr 1992-94; Moore Cath HS 7ath Tchr 1993-94; Farrell HS Eng Tchr 1994-; *ai:* Grammar Turorial Prgm; Super Chaperone; Poetry Pub; *home:* 90 Wentworth Rd Bedminster NJ 07

TOUMA, STEPHEN M., English Teacher; *b:* West Caldwell, NJ; *m:* Clare Mc Cabe; *ed:* Seton Hall Univ (BA) Eng 1987; Rutgers Univ Brunswick (MA) Eng 1989; Seton Hall Unvi Schl of Law (JD) Law *cr:* Cty Coll of Morris Eng Instr 1989-92; Queen of Peace HS Eng 1989-; *ai:* Educl Overseas Trips Coord; Natl Endowment for Hum Su Seminar Flwshp 1993; Creative Tchng Proposal Awd 1994; *office:* Of Peace HS 191 Rutherford Pl North Arlington NJ 07031

TOURRE, MARC LOUIS, Music Teacher; *b:* Pittsburgh, PA; *m:* L.; *c:* Thea M., Heather G., Christopher M.; *ed:* St Vincent Coll (Music Ed 1975; IN Univ of PA (MA) Voice Performance 1978; Att Univ at Bloomington, CA Univ of PA, Chataqua Inst; *cr:* Greater L Schl Dist Music Tchr 1975-; *ai:* Fine Arts Chm; Fac Advy Comm; Dev Ldr; NEA 1975-; PMEA & MENC 1975-; ACDA 1993-; Madiso Church 1978-, Choir Dir & Fin Chprsn; Sound & Light Comm Article Pub 1980; Song Pub 1981; *office:* Greater Latrobe Sr HS C Club Rd Latrobe PA 15650

TOUZEAU, JEANNE MARIE, French Teacher; *b:* Rochester, N Christopher, Stephan; *ed:* U of MD (BA) Ed 1988; Master's Equiva Addl 30 Hrs; *cr:* Thomson CSF Eng Tchr 1973-81; Good Counsel Tchr 1988-89; Sligo MS Fr Tchr 1989-; *ai:* Intnl Travel Spon; NEA Two NEH Grants Bringing Culture into Foreign Lang Classroom; Sligo MS 1401 Dennis Ave Silver Spring MD 20902

TOWLE, DENNIS G., English Teacher; *b:* Augusta, ME; *m:* Joan F *c:* Gary, Shawn; *ed:* UM at Farmington (BA) Eng 1963; Extensive Activity 1984; Course Work in Tchng Models, Re-Cert, Co-ope Learning, Spec Ed, Psych, Various Law Offerings; *cr:* Hodgkins Schl Arts Tchr 1963-77; Cony HS Eng Tchr 1977-; *ai:* NEA 1963-, R 1984-; MEA 1963-, RA Rep 1980-; MEA Bd of Dir 3 Terms, Benefits 2 Terms; AEA 1986-93, Pres; Bargaining Team, Chief Negotiator 19 BPOE96Y Elks 1965-, Trustees 9 Yrs, Chm 7 Yrs; Capitol Area Recr Assn, 1978-83, Pres; Augusta East Little League 1972-, Pres; St Commission 2 Terms, Chm 1983-84; Cntrl Miami Soccer Ofcls 1965-84, Pres 1978-80; IAABO 1965-85; *office:* Cony HS Cony St Au ME 04330

TOWLE, KEVIN ARTHUR, Hlth, PE Tchr & Stu Ath Coord; *b:* Li ME; *m:* Kim Marie Murphy; *c:* Jenifer Jean, Jeremy Amasa, Joshua *ed:* Univ of ME at Presque Isle (BS) Hlth, PE, Recreation 197 Jonesport-Beals HS Ath Dir, PE Tchr 1979-84; Woodland HS Hlth, PE 1984-; *ai:* Stu Act, Ath Coord; Stu Assistance, Crisis Intervention T NEA 1979-; MEA 1979-, Local Pres; DBAU 1984-, Interperater, DAC Coach of Yr 1989-90; *home:* 1 Evergreen St Woodland ME 04

TOWLE, MICHAEL THOMAS, World Geography Teacher; *b:* Por ME; *m:* Sheryle Lane; *c:* Sherri-Lynn, Lori-Ann; *ed:* Univ of Souther (BS) Soc Sci 1970; 30 Hrs Prof Growth Courses; *cr:* Mahoney MS 7t World Geog Tcher 1970-, 8th Grd US His Tchr, Cross Cty, Ind Outdoor Track, Bsktbl Coach 1970-; USM Mens Cross Cty Coach; *ai:* Cross-Country, Spring Track, Var Asst HS Bsktbl, Head Indoor Track, Head Track Coach; Chess Club Adv; NEA, ME Tchrs Assn, NC Portland Tchrs Assn 1970-; Lions Club, Congregational Church Choi Track Club, ME Spec Olympics Bd of Dirs Former Mem; Citizens A Substance Abuse Comm; Involvement in ME Spec Olympics Svc USM Husky Hall of Fame Inductee 1995; Outstdng S Portland Tchr Awd; *home:* 229 Cottage Rd South Portland ME 04106*

TOWNE, SHELDON ELLIS, Prof of Natural Resource Mgm Plymouth, NH; *m:* Rebecca Jean Pederson; *c:* Abigail Carol, Christ Lucas, Joshua Frank, Michelle Lee; *ed:* Plymouth St Coll Environmental Bio, (MED) Environmental Sci 1992; Western NM U Credits Toward Bachelors 1971-74; *cr:* Water Supply & Pollution C Field Tech, Lab Asst 1974-81; Winnipesoutree River Basin Fa Operator & Chemist 1981-85; NH Tech Coll Prof of Natural Res Mgmt 1985-; *ai:* Schl to Work, Waterworks Cert Advy & Waste Operations Ed Comms; NH Water Pollution Control Assn Whitefield Regnl Airport Comm 1995-; Alfred E Pelequin Awd; *offi* H Technical Coll 2020 Riverside Dr Berlin NH 03570

TOWNS, WILLIAM, Technology Teacher; *b:* Utica, NY; *m:* Mary Hughes; *c:* Todd; *ed:* St Univ Coll at Oswego (BS) Industrial Arts Ed 30 Hrs Grad Work; *cr:* Whitney Point HS Tech Tchr & Occupation Dept Chair 1970-; *ai:* NYS Tech Ed Assn 1970-; Whitney Point HS of Yr 1992; *office:* Whitney Point HS Keibel Rd Whitney Point NY

TOWNSEND, CAROL A., Lecturer in Design Department; *b:* Monti NY; *m:* Thomas C. Cist; *ed:* Nazareth Coll of Rochester (BS) Art 196 Univ (MFA) Ceramics 1973; Addl Credit Hrs State Univ Coll at Broc East TN St Univ; *cr:* OH Univ Lecturer 1973-74; Daemen Coll Ass Prof 1974-88; Niagara Cty Comm Coll Fine Arts Instr 1989-95; State Coll Design Dept Lecturer 1994-; *ai:* Empire St Crafts Alliance 198 of Dir 1994-; Buffalo Soc of Artists 1989-, Pres 1992; Natl Educl C Ceramic Arts 1996-; Buffalo Diocesan Ligurgical Commission Consultant 1980-; Ron Concilla Awd 1994; Fac Rsrch Grant OH 1974; Distngd Fac Awd Daemen Coll 1979; Fac Rsrch Awd Daeme 1985, 1988; Colby Awd Outstdng Woman Artist Buffalo Seminary Mastercraftsman Awd Kenan Ctr 1989; Contribution, Achvmt Aw Senate NCCC 1992; *home:* 307 Roycroft Blvd Snyder Square NY 14

TOWNSEND, DUANE A.,JR., Third Grade Teacher; *b:* North Tonaw NY; *m:* Christine N. Nicholson; *c:* Kevin, Amanda; *ed:* Villa Mari (AAS) Early Chldhd Ed 1971; Rosary Hill Coll (BS) Ed 1973; Ni Univ (MS) Ed 1976; Coll of St Rose Post Grad; *cr:* Niagara Whea Cntrl Schl Dist K-6th Grd Tchr 1973-; *ai:* Niagara Wheatfield Tchrs

, Bldg Rep; Dist Tchr of the Yr Nom; *office:* Errick Road Elem Schl Errick Rd North Tonawanda NY 14120

NSEND, JOHN C., Industrial Education Teacher; *b:* Philadelphia, : Ann Bennett; *c:* Gabrielle; *ed:* Trenton St Coll (BA) Indstrl Arts Ed *ai:* Schl Photographer; NJEA, NEA 1979-; ITEA 1989-; Burlington chr of Yr 1983; Earl Murphy Outstdng Edctr Admin Awd NJ Voc ns & Supvrs Assn 1995; *office:* Cherokee HS 120 Willow Bend Rd on NJ 08053

NSEND, MICHAEL L., Photography Teacher; *b:* Buffalo, NY; *m:* a Adair Hube; *c:* Kecia Boncek, Katie Boncek, Kyle; *ed:* Niagara a Coll (AA) Art 1972; SUC at Buffalo (BSED) Art Ed 1974, (MSED) d 1979; *cr:* Niagara Falls Pub Schls Art Tchr 1975-76; Lewiston Cntrl Schls General Art, Photography Tchr 1976-; Niagara Univ graphy Cont Ed 1981-89; Asst Admn Dir New York State Summer of Art 1993-94; *ai:* Girls Var Gymnastics Coach 1981-93; Boys Var s Head Coach 1989-93; NY St United Tchrs 1976-, Bldg Rep; NY St chrs Assn 1976-; Media Arts Tchr Assn 1990-, Pres; Photo Imaging sn 1992-; *office:* Lewiston-Porter Sr HS 4061 Creek Rd Youngstown 4174*

NSEND, MURIEL (BURBANK), Art Teacher; *b:* Providence, RI; ward A.; *c:* Peter, Lauren Townsend Skeldon; *ed:* RI Schl of Design) Illustration 1961, (MS) Art Ed 1962; RI Coll 3 Credits Spec Ed; Decorative Arts RISP Museum Course 1 Credit; *cr:* Cranson HS West chr 1962-68, 1988-; Cranston Extended Ed Adult Ed Summer Prgm 93; RI Coll Tchr 1975-95; Cranston HS East Art Tchr 1976-83; Park Jr HS Art Tchr 1984-; *ai:* After Schl Specialized Trng, 3D, 2D cts, Wheel Throwing & Sculpture; RIAEA, NEA 1962-; NAEA 1995-, n Museum of Art, RISD Museum of Art; Potterville Vol Fire Dept , Firefighter, Comm Ofcr; Church Deaconate; Schl Arts Magazine e Pub; *office:* Cranston HS West 80 Metropolitan Ave Cranston RI)*

NSEND, TRACI VERNON, Science Teacher; *b:* Cleveland, OH; *m:* ayne; *c:* Danielle; *ed:* Miami Univ (BS) Scndry Ed 1988; *cr:* ersburg HS Sci Tchr 1989-; *ai:* NEA 1989-; MCEA 1989-; Alpha a Alpha 1990-; Natl Inst of Hlth Howard Hughes Flwshp; *home:*) Woodboro Ter Sterling VA 20165

NSLEY, GERLINDE MUELLER, German Teacher; *b:* Linz, ia; *c:* Christina, Eric; *ed:* Wright St Univ (BSEd) Ger 1972, (MA) : 1991; *cr:* Page Manor Theatre Mgr 1970-72; Anthony Supply Co Purchasing Mgr 1972-75; West Carrollton Schls Ger Tchr 1975-79, Rdng Tchr 1984-; *ai:* Ger Club Adv; Jr Cncl on World Affairs Adv; Cncl; NEA 1975-; AATG 1995-; OFLA 1984-; Dayton Sister City 1988-, Chprsn; Taken Stdnts to Augsburg Germany 1988, 1990, 1992; : West Carrollton Sr HS 5833 Student St West Carrollton OH 45449

, TAMARA RASTATTER, High School Math Teacher; *b:* Erie, PA; N Univ of PA (BS) Marketing 1989; Edinboro Univ of PA (BS) Scndry 1992; Working on Masters in Math; *cr:* King George HS Math Tchr 93; Fairview HS Math Tchr 1993-; *ai:* Class Adv; Ski Bus Chaperone; 1992-; *home:* 5430 West Rd Mc Kean PA 16426

ZI, ANNE FRANCES PASCUCCI, 2nd Grade Teacher; *b:* delphia, PA; *m:* Attilio; *c:* Audra, Alicia; *ed:* Cabrini Coll (BS) Elem 67; West Chester Univ 25 Grad Credits; *cr:* Chester Upland Schl Dist 1967-73; Brensalen Schl Dist Sub Tchr 1980-82; St Ephrem Schl Math Coord 1984-; *ai:* Math Coord Primary Grds; NCEA 1984-; Cath hters of Am Fin Trustee; *office:* St Ephrem Schl 5340 Hulmeville Rd alem PA 19020

BOSH, CAROLYN CELLA, High School Art Teacher; *b:* delphia, PA; *m:* Nicholas; *c:* Ryan, Marissa; *ed:* Trenton Jr Coll (AA) Arts 1967; Montclair St (BA) Fine Arts 1970; Univ of the Arts Cmptr nics Course; Rowan Coll Grad Course; Fine Arts Studio Courses; *cr:* ford Twp HS Art Tchr 1970-; *ai:* SADD Tchr Rep; Stu Awds & gnition Comm; Project 180 Tchr; NJEA, NEA, AENJ 1970-; Camden Coll Bd of Trustees 1974-, Treas, Asst Treas, Sec, Honorary Degree, c of Letters; *office:* Deptford Twnshp HS 575 S Fox Run Rd Deptford 3096*

BUCCO, MARY A., Fifth Grade Teacher; *b:* Stoneham, MA; *ed:* n St Coll (BA) Elem Ed 1967; *cr:* C W Holmes Schl 3rd, 5th, & 6th Tchr 1967-; *ai:* MTA, NEA 1967-; *office:* C W Holmes Schl 257 ntain Ave Malden MA 02148*

CANNA, SUZANNA ESTVANIC, Sixth Grade Teacher; *b:* neburg, PA; *m:* Clyde Tracanna; *c:* Nathan, Justin; *ed:* California Univ A (BS) Elem Ed 1973; *cr:* Jefferson-Morgan Elem Schl Primary, mediate Classroom Tchr 1976-; *ai:* Math Comm; Sixth Grd Team Ldr; A 1979-; NCTM, PCTM 1993-; Geometry, Art Unit on Tessellations Exch with Omiya Schl in Japan; *home:* PO Box 137 Rices Landing PA 7

CE, THOMAS E.,JR., 7th-8th Grade Science Teacher; *b:* Columbus, *m:* Sarah H.; *c:* Amy; *ed:* Capital Univ (BA) Scndry Ed, PE, Gen Sci ; Capital Univ Post Grad 6 Semester Hrs; OH St Univ Post Grad 8 ter Hrs; *cr:* Whitehall City Schls Sub Tchr 1988-90; Westerville City s Sub Tchr 1989-90; Hilliard City Schls 7th-8th Grd Sci Tchr 1991-; th Grd Ftbl Head Coach; Hilliard HS Var Boys, Girls Swim Team Head ch; NEA, OH Ed Assn, Hilliard Ed Assn 1990-; *office:* Hilliard age MS 5670 Scioto Darby Rd Hilliard OH 43026

CEY, BYRON, History Teacher; *b:* Kearny, NJ; *ed:* Jersey City St (BA) His, Scndry Ed 1990; Psych; St Peters Coll at Jersey City Prof *cr:* New Providence HS His Tchr 1991-; *ai:* Track Coach; Model ed Nations, Youth & Govt, Amnesty Intnl, Environmental Awareness , Citizens Bee, Natl Soc Stud Olympiad Adv; Phi Alpha Theta, Delta pa Pi 1988-; NEA 1991-; Camp Fatima of NJ 1987-; Natl Endowment Grant, Visiting Scholar Syracuse Univ 1995; *office:* New Providence 35 Pioneer Dr New Providence NJ 07974

ACEY, DIANE PEYTON, Social Studies Teacher; *b:* Yonkers, NY; *m:* nis; *c:* Alanna, Brianna; *ed:* SUNY at New Paltz (BS) Scndry Soc Ed); NYIT (MS) Learning Tech 1990; LIU, Coll of New Rochelle 30 Hrs; North Rockland HS Tchr 1972-; *ai:* Tech Comm Chprsn 3 Yrs; Schl rovement Planning Team Cncl 2 Yrs; Ninth Grd Interdisciplinary Team s; NYSUT, NY Cncl Soc Stud, Rockland Cty Cncl Soc Stud, NCSS -; League of Women Voters, PTSA 1980-; Started Sr Elective Linking , Tech; *office:* North Rockland HS 106 Hammond Rd Thiells NY 84

ACEY, ROBERT MICHAEL, Social Studies Teacher; *b:* Bethesda, *m:* Minta Diana Norman; *ed:* Western MD Coll MA Equivalent lance 1981; 39 Hrs General Soc Stud Courses; *cr:* E. W. Broome Jr HS Stud Tchr 1968-77; J. Belt Jr HS Soc Stud Tchr 1978-82; Montgomery r HS Soc Stud Tchr 1983-; *ai:* SGA, Frosh Class Spon; Sftbl, Track ch; Montgomery Cty Ed Assn 1968-, Schl Rep; MSTA, NEA 1968-; *e:* Montgomery Blair Sr HS 313 Wayne Ave Silver Spring MD 20910

ACHL, MARY LORETTA, French & Spanish Teacher; *b:* Toledo, OH; David J.; *c:* Daniel, Dena Henry, Joseph; *ed:* Bowlington Green St Univ) Fr 1970, (MA) Fr & Span 1971; 4 Credit hrs; *cr:* Phylo HS Span & Tchr 1980-81; Fairview HS Fr & Span Tchr 1983-; *ai:* Frgn Lang Soc ; OEA 1983-; TACLS 1983-, Union Rep; NEA 1983-; *office:* Fairview 06289 US 127th Sherwood OH 43556

TRACHTENBERG, CRAIG L., Science Teacher; *b:* Brooklyn, NY; *m:* Suzanne Wood; *c:* Nicole; *ed:* SUNY at Brockport (BS) Ed 1983; Adelphi Univ (MA) Ed 1990; *cr:* Webutuck Cntrl Schl Sci Tchr 1990-; *ai:* Class Adv 1991-; Peer Tutorship ldr; Jr Var Bsbl Coach; NSTA 1991-; *office:* Webutuck HS Box N Haight St Amenia NY 12501*

TRACY, JAMES, History Instructor; *b:* Boston, MA; *ed:* Stanford Univ (MA) His 1988, (PHD) His 1993; *cr:* Yale Univ Visiting Fellow 1994-95; Hotchkiss Schl His Instr 1993-; *ai:* Amer Historical Assn; *office:* The Hotchkiss Schl Lakeville CT 06039

TRACY, LINDA ELLIFF, Third Grade Teacher; *b:* Elizabeth, NJ; *c:* Jonthan, Jarod; *ed:* Newark St Coll (BA) Elem Ed 1971; Addl 40 Post Grad Credits; *cr:* Mount View Schl Dist Tchr 1971-; *ai:* NEA, PSEA 1971-; MVEA 1971-, Bldg Rep; Delta Kappa Gamma 1981-, 2nd VP; Harford Historical Soc 1975-, Sec; *office:* Mountain View Elem Schl RR 1 Box 339a Kingsley PA 18826*

TRACY, PATRICIA STREICH, Health Teacher; *b:* Titusville, PA; *m:* Timothy E.; *c:* Kimberly K., Todd W.; *ed:* Slippery Rock St Coll (BS) Hlth & PE 1972; SUNY At Buffalo (MED) PE 1975; *cr:* Lewiston Porter Cntrl Schl HS PE Tchr 1972-78; Millcreek Twp Schl Dist Hlth Tchr 1988-; *ai:* Stu Cncl; Stu Asst Prgm; PSEA, NEA 1988-; Crop Bd 1993-; Footsteps Bd 1995-; Employee of the Month 1990; Yrbk Dedication 1995; *office:* Mc Dowell Intermediate HS 3320 Caughey Rd Erie PA 16506*

TRACY, R. LEE,JR., Health & Phys Ed Instructor; *b:* Suffern, NY; *m:* Dale A.; *c:* Shawn, Kelly; *ed:* Springfield Coll (BS) PE 1968; Montclair St Univ (MS) Hlth Ed 1975; 34 Credits Supervision Cert 1978; *cr:* Midland Pk HS Hlth, PE, Dr Ed Instr 1968-, Ath Dir 1984-86; *ai:* AIDS Awareness Club Adv; Vlybl, Indoor Track, Sftbl Asst Coach; Advy Bd World AIDS Day of Learning NJ Yth; NEA, BCEA, NJEA, MPEA 1968-; Midland Pk Love Fund 1984-, Advy Bd; Midland Pk Bsbl 1983-, Equipment Mgr, Coach; Midland Pk Fire Dept 1972-87; *office:* Midland Park HS 250 Prospect St Midland Park NJ 07432

TRACY, SANDY ARN, 7th & 8th Grd Sci & Rdng Tchr; *b:* Brown Cty, OH; *m:* Don L.; *c:* Brian, Seth, Chris, Andrea; *ed:* Southern St Comm Comm (AS) Ed 1988; Wright St Univ (BA) Ed, Rdng 1990; Univ of Dayton (MS) Supervision 1992; Lee Canter High Performing Tchr; *cr:* Eastern Local Schls Tchr 1990-; *ai:* Sci Fair Dir; Cincinnati Section of Amer Chemical Soc, Brown Cty Office of Ed Educl Grants.

TRADER, LONNIE KAY DAHM, Biology Teacher; *b:* New Kensington, PA; *m:* Carl L.; *ed:* Edinboro St Univ (BS) Scndry Ed, Bio 1971; 35 Addl Post Grad Hrs Univ of Pittsburgh, Carlow Coll, Duquesne Univ, Univ of PA, CA St Univ; *cr:* South Park Scl Dist Bio Tchr 1971-; *ai:* Core Team; Acad Bowl Teams Coach; Hlth Fair Comm; SPEA 1971-, Bldg Rep; PSEA, NEA 1971-; PSTA 1985-, NSTA 1980-; Tri Comm Ambulance Svc 1981-; IUP Cooperative Learning NSF Grant; Conoco Coal Rsrch Grant; HS, Grd Schl Cooperative Learning Project; HS, Hosp Mentoring Prgm; *office:* South Park HS 2178 Ridge Rd Library PA 15129*

TRAHAN, EMERY ANTHONY, Finance Professor; *b:* Plattsburgh, NY; *m:* Rosanne Mary Collins; *c:* Jules Matthew, Brian Joseph Emery; *ed:* SUNY at Plattsburgh (BS) Accounting 1979; SUNY at Albany (MA) Financial Ec 1987, (PhD) Financial Ec 1988; *cr:* Peat, Marwick, Mitchell & Co Sr Accountant 1979-81; Ceramaseal Inc Controller 1981-83; SUNY at Albany Lecturer 1983-88; Northeastern Univ Finance Prof 1988-; *ai:* Salem & Swampscott Youth Hockey Assn Head Coach; Swampscott Cub Scouts Den Ldr; Financial Mgmt Assn, Amer Finance Assn 1987-; Eastern Finance Assn 1990-; Author of 2 Pub Books & 19 Pub Scholarly Articles; Joseph G. Riesman Research Prof 1993-95; 40 Prof Presentations; *office:* Northeastern Univ 413 Hayden Hall Boston MA 02115

TRAHAN, EMILE ROGER, English Teacher; *b:* Southbridge, MA; *m:* Lauria J. Saulnier; *c:* Therese, Michelle, Denise, David; *ed:* Assumption Coll (BA) Eng 1960; Boston Coll (MA) Eng 1969; 20 Credits Harvard Univ; 6 Credits Clark Univ; 6 Credits Worcester St Coll; *cr:* Assumption Prep Schl Eng Tchr, Dept Head 1960-70; Westborough HS Eng Tchr, Dept Head 1970-; *ai:* Prof Dev Tchr; Westborough Tchrs Assn, MA Tchrs Assn 1970-; System Wide Trainer in Dimensions of Learning; Facilitator for Peer Partnership; *office:* Westborough HS 90 W Main St Westborough MA 01581*

TRAHAN, THERESE P., English Teacher; *b:* Worcester, MA; *ed:* Saint Anselm Coll (BA) Eng 1983; *cr:* Pembroke Acad Eng 1983-86; Pinkerton Acad Eng 1986-; *ai:* Asst Var Girls Bsktbl Coach; NHATE 1986-; NCTE 1985-; *office:* Pinkerton Acad 5A Pinkerton St Derry NH 03038

TRAINER, LINDA SCOTT, Mathematics Teacher; *b:* Fredericton NB, Canada; *m:* Jon S.; *c:* Lauren E., Jonathan S.; *ed:* Bob Jones Univ (BS) Math Ed 1986, (MS) Pupil Prsnl Svcs 1987; *cr:* Northside Chrstn Schl Math Tchr 1987-89; Southside HS Math Tchr 1989-92; Northside Chrstn Schl Math Tchr 1992-; *ai:* Sr Class Adv; *office:* Northside Christian Schl 2655 Schrock Rd Westerville OH 43081

TRAINI, JACKIE SUE, 8th Grade Science Teacher; *b:* Columbus, OH; *w:* Jim (dec); *c:* Tom, Joanna; *ed:* OH St Univ (BS) Elem Ed 1970, (MA) Educl Admin 1990; *cr:* J. C. Sommer Elem Schl 1st-2nd Grd Tchr 1970-74; E. Franklin-Monterey Schl L. D. Tutor 1984-86; Finland MS 8th Grd Sci Tchr 1986-; *ai:* Tchr Ldr, Mentor; Yrbk Adv; Comm Reviewing Tech Prep HS Prgm; NEA, OEA, SWEA 1970-, Local Rep 1970-71, 1996; Welcom Wagon 1979-82, VP, Treas; PTA 1979-82, Treas; *office:* Finland MS 1825 Finland Ave Columbus OH 43223

TRAINOR, HELEN A., Kindergarten Teacher; *b:* Lowell, MA; *ed:* St Bonaventure (BS) Ed 1970, (MS) Admin 1974; Attnd Univ of VT, Univ of Buffalo; *cr:* Allegany Elem Kkdgtn Tchr 7 Yrs; Limestone Union Free Schl Rdng Specialist 19 Yrs; St Johns Schl 1st Grd Tchr 2 Yrs; St Patricks Schl 1st Grd Tchr 2 Yrs; St Marys Schl 1st & 3rd Grd Tchr 2 Yrs; *ai:* Exec Comm for Allegany & Limestone Tchrs Assn; AFT & NYSUT 1970-88, Vp of Local NYSUT; NEA 1988-; S Tier Rdng Assn 1970-80, Pres & VP, Pres, Pres Pin; Intl Rdng 1970-84; Phi Delta Kappa 1981-94, VP, Oficers Pin, 1981-94, Pgm Chprsn; Tchr of Yr Awd 1973; Appreciation Awd from Intnl Rdng Assoc 1974; Panel Mem at Intnl Rdng Conference Anaheim Co; Comm Mem for St Bonaventure Masters Pgm; Administered Rdng Comps St Bonaventure Univ; *office:* Allegany Elem Schl Maple Ave Allegany NY 14706

TRALLI, ROSEMARY HARABURDA, Resource Teacher; *b:* Manchester, CT; *m:* Thomas Joseph; *c:* Justin, Melissa; *ed:* Southern CT St Univ (BS) Spec Ed 1975; Cntrl CT St Univ (MS) Cnslng 1984; Univ of CT Pursuing 6th Yr Cert Schl Admin; *cr:* East Windsor HS Spec Ed Tchr 1977-86; Wethersfield HS Resource Tchr 1986-; *ai:* BEST Prgm Cooperating, Mentor Tchr; AFT 1986-; EMSPAC 1996; Tchr of Yr 1993-94; Distgnd Edctr Awd, Tchr of Yr Wethersfield Learning Disabilities Assn 1990; Strategies Intervention Model Trainer Univ of KS 1989-; *office:* Wethersfield HS 411 Wolcott Hill Rd Wethersfield CT 06109

TRAMA, ANTHONY GERARD, Social Studies Teacher & Coach; *b:* Rochester, NY; *c:* Alison, Rena; *ed:* St John Fisher Coll (BA) Pol Sci 1977; Nazareth Coll Ed 1995; *cr:* Mercy HS Soc Stud Tchr 1989-91; Greece HS Soc Stud Tchr 1991-92; Mc Quaid Soc Stud Tchr 1992-; *ai:* Cross Cntry Running, Outdoor Track Coach; Assembly, Sr Class Moderator; Articles Pub; Greater Rochester Track Club 1980-85; Alternative Track Club 1990-; Articles Pub; *office:* Mcquaid Jesuit HS 1800 Clinton Ave S Rochester NY 14618

TRAMMELL, RICHARD LOUIS, Assoc Professor of Philosophy; *b:* Shelbyville, KY; *m:* Catherine Louise Muder; *c:* John Kent, Julia Kate McGill, Mark E.; *ed:* Berea Coll (BA) Philosophy 1964; Union Theological Seminary (BD) Philosophy of Religion 1967; Columbia Univ (PHD) Philosophy of Religion 1971; *cr:* Morehead St Univ Instr in Philosophy 1967-; Grove City Coll Assoc Prof of Philosophy 1971-; *ai:* Numerous Articles Pub; *office:* Grove City Coll 101 Campus Dr Grove City PA 16127

TRAMPLER, NANCY PETERS, 5th Grade Math & Science Tchr; *b:* Wilmington, OH; *m:* Mark Steven; *c:* Tiffany Michelle, Joshua Mark, Cody Weston, Aubrey Megan; *ed:* Wilimington Coll (BS) Elem Ed 1978; Miami Univ (MA) Supervision 1985; Clinton Massie Elem Schl Kndgtn 1979-81, 4th Grd Tchr 1981-85, 5th Grd Tchr 1985-; *cr:* Clinton Massie Elem Schl Kndgtn Tchr 1979-81, 4th Grd Tchr 1981-85, 5th Grd Tchr 1985-.

TRANO, JENNIFER MARLENE, English & Social Studies Tchr; *b:* Calcutta, India; *m:* Michael; *ed:* St Marys Coll Twickenham (BA) Jr Course 1961; Trafalgar Jr Schl Tchr 1971-74; Westfields Primary Schl Dept Head Art, Tchr 1974-77; Campion Schl Tchr ESOL 1977-78; British Yeoward Schl Dept Head Jr, Art, Tchr 1978-80; Fwight Schl 7th Grd Geog, 8th GrdAncient His, 9th Grd Modern European His Tchr 1980-83; Village Comm Schl 6th Grd Soc Stud, Eng, Art, Math, Adv, Tchr, 7th Grd Soc Stud, Eng, Math Adv, Tchr, 8th Grd Eng Tchr 1983-; *cr:* Trafalgar Jr Schl Tchr 1971-74; Westfields Primary Schl Dept Head Art, Tchr 1974-77; Campion Schl Tchr ESOL 1977-78; British Yeoward Schl Dept Head Jr Dept, Art, Tchr 1978-80; Dwight Schl 7th Grd Geog, 8th Grd Ancient His, 9th Grd Modern European His Tchr 1980-83; Village Comm Schl 6th Grd Soc Stud, Eng, Art, Math Adv, Tchr, 7th Grd Soc Stud, Eng, Math Adv, Tchr, 8th Grd Eng Tchr 1983-; *ai:* ATIS 1983-, Fac Rep; Wkshps ATIS, PS Dev Soc Stud Curr; *office:* Village Comm Schl 272 W 10th St New York NY 10014*

TRANO, MICHAEL ANTHONY, English Teacher; *b:* New York, NY; *m:* Jennifer; *ed:* Hunter Coll (BA) Eng Lit 1971; Working Toward Masters; *cr:* Dwight Schl MS & HS Eng Tchr 1980-87; Lycee Francaise MS & HS Eng Tchr 1987-88; York Prep MS & HS Eng Tchr 1988-89; Berkeley Carroll MS & HS Eng Tchr 1989-; *ai:* HS Adv; Fac Comm Chprsn; *office:* Berkeley Carroll Schl 181 Lincoln Pl Brooklyn NY 11217*

TRANQUILLA, RONALD E., English Professor & Chair; *b:* Latrobe, PA; *m:* Penny Seaton; *c:* Ryan; *ed:* Allegheny Coll (BA) Eng 1963; Univ of Pittsburgh (PHD) Eng 1973; *cr:* St Vincent Coll 1964-; *ai:* Interdisciplinary Writing Project, Tchng Dev Project, Lib Comm Chair; Stu Lit Magazine Moderator; ACSUS 1987-; MLA 1964-; Redstone Presbyn Hunger-Action Enabler 1983-; CASE Prof of Yr Prgm Natl Bronze Medalist 1989; Canadian Embassy Fac Enrichment Prgm Grant 1985; Poetry & Short Fictions Pub; *office:* Saint Vincent Coll 300 Fraser Purchase Rd Latrobe PA 15650*

TRANQUILLO, VALARIE ANN, Seventh Grade Teacher; *b:* Altoona, PA; *m:* Victor; *c:* Victor, Vinnie; *ed:* St Francis Coll (BS) Elem Ed 1983; IN Univ of PA (MED) Rdng 1989; *cr:* Penn Cambria MS Tchr 1983-; *ai:* Rdng Competition Adv; PSEA 1983-; *office:* Penn Cambria MS 401 Division St Gallitzin PA 16641

TRANSUE, SUSAN B., Science Educator; *b:* Allentown, PA; *c:* Shea; *ed:* Penn St Univ (BS) Hlth, PE 1985; Lock Haven Univ General Sci 1987; East Stroudsburg Univ 27 Post Grad Hrs Toward Masters; *cr:* Northampton Area Schls Sci Educator 1987-; *ai:* NEA, NSTA, PSTA 1987-; Moore Twp Lioness 1988-; Trout Unlimited 1990-; *office:* Northampton Jr HS 1617 Laubach Ave Northampton PA 18067

TRANTO, PEARL (PSAROS), Guidance Counselor; *b:* Steubenville, OH; *m:* Nicholas J.; *c:* Maria N.; *ed:* West Liberty St Coll (BA) Ed; Univ of Dayton (MS) Admin, Cnslr Ed 1976; Ed OH St Univ; *cr:* Stanton HS Eng Tchr 1970-90, OWA Coord 1990-93; WV Northern Comm Coll Part-time Instr 1973; Stanton Jr HS Guid Cnslr 1993-; *ai:* Drug Awareness Cncl; NEA, OEA, Edison Local EA 1970-; All Saints Greek Orthodox Church; Daughters of Penelope; *home:* 181 Joseph Blvd Weirton WV 26062

TRAPP, FRANCES MARTIN, Fifth Grade Teacher; *b:* Lawrenceburg, TN; *m:* Charles Jack; *c:* Dennis, Denise Langston; *ed:* Wright St Univ (BS) Elem Ed 1975; Univ of Dayton (MS) Interdisciplinary Stud 1979; *cr:* Fairlawn Schl Tchr 1975-; *ai:* NEA 1975-; Tchr Grant Project "Hands on Experience" in Sci; *office:* Fairlawn Elem Schl 18800 Johnston Rd Sidney OH 45365

TRAPP, MICHELE STAATS, Remedial Ed & Stud Skills Tchr; *b:* Staten Island, NY; *m:* Thomas J.; *c:* Shawn, Mark; *ed:* Glassboro St Coll (BA) Elem Ed 1976, (BS) Speech Pathology 1976; 12 Credit Hrs Speech Pathology Paterson Coll; *cr:* Ridgefield Schls Kndgtn, Speech Tchr 1977; North Bergen HS Remediation Ed, Speech Tchr 1977-87; Perceptograph Equine Photographer, Handicapped 1987-; Goshen HS Remediation Ed, Stud Skills Tchr 1991-; *ai:* NBFT 1977-87, Exec VP; Heritage Riding for the Handicapped 1993-, Sec, Bd of Dirs, Vol; Hudson Highlands Photo Assn 1988-, Pres, VP, Dupcak; Step by Step Stud Skills Guide; Dev of Lang Dev Series; Photographic Excl Awds; *office:* Goshen H S Scotchtown Ave Goshen NY 10924*

TRASKEN, JOSEF M., Physics Teacher; *b:* Philadelphia, PA; *m:* Michelle Levin; *c:* Caryn; *ed:* Temple Univ (BS) Ed 1980, (MS) Ed 1983; Addl 21 Credit Hrs Beyond Masters; *cr:* Darby-Colwyn HS Physics Tchr 1980-81; Phoenixville Area HS Physics Tchr 1981-85; Benjamin Franklin HS Phys Sci Tchr 1985-88; M L King HS Phys Sci Tchr 1988-91; Northeast HS Physics Tchr 1991-; *ai:* Hlth Care & Medical SLC Mem; AFT 1985-; NEA, AAPT, NSTA 1980-85; *office:* Northeast HS Cottman & Algon Aves Philadelphia PA 19111

TRAUGER, DAVID LAMAR, Sixth Grade Teacher; *b:* Doylestown, PA; *m:* Frieda E. Wolf; *c:* Christian, Heidi Tison, Matthew; *ed:* Millersville Univ (BS) Elem Ed 1969; PA Cert 24 Hrs; *cr:* Pennridge Schl Dist Elem Tchr 1969-; *ai:* Curr Comms; NEA, PSEA, PEA 1969-, Longevity Awd; Bedminster Township 1982-88, Supvr, Sec Treas; *office:* Bedminster Elem Schl 2914 Fretz Valley Rd Bedminster PA 18910

TRAUM, CAROL FRANCESCHI, 7th-8th Grd Math Teacher; *b:* Vineland, NJ; *m:* Theodore J.; *c:* Justin, Teddi Ann, Kerstin; *ed:* Backs Cty Comm Coll (AA) Math 1985; Gwynedd-Mercy Coll (BS) Math 1989; *cr:* Hatboro-Horsham Schl Dist Sub Tchr 1989-90; Centennial Schl Dist Sub Tchr 1989-90; Cncl Rock Schl Dist Sub Tchr 1989-90; St Bede The Venerable Schl 7th-8th Grd Math Tchr 1990-; *ai:* Math Counts Coach; Math Assn of Amer 1989-; NCTM 1989-; NCEA 1990-; *home:* 35 Sophia Dr Churchville PA 18966

TRAUPMAN-CARR, CAROL A., Asst Prof of Music; *b:* Allentown, PA; *m:* David F. Carr; *ed:* Moravian Coll (BM) Music, Soc Sci 1986; Cornell Univ (MA) Musicology 1989, (PHD) Musicology 1995; *cr:* Cornell Univ Grad Tchng Asst 1986-90; Ithaca City Schl Dist Vocal Music Tcht 1990-92; Moravian Coll Adj Instr of Music 1992-94, Asst Prof of Music 1994-; *ai:* Hnrs, Strategic Planning Comms; AAUW 1994-; Amer Musicological Soc 1986-; Coll Music Soc 1991-; Gamma Pi Chptr Delta Omicron, Chptr Adv; St Ann's RC Church 1992-, Choir Dir; Allentown Arts Acad 1995-, Bd Mem; *office:* Moravian Coll 1200 Main St Bethlehem PA 18018

TRAVAGLIO, E. GAY, Elementary Education Teacher; *b:* Butler, PA; *m:* David L.; *c:* Tracy; *ed:* Slippery Rock St Coll (BS) Elem Ed 1975; Grad Courses Including Stud in Europe, HI & Assortment of Grad Level Courses; *cr:* Dassa McKinney Elem 6th Grd Tchr 1975-84, Kdngtn Tchr 1984-90, 3rd Grd Tchr 1990-; *ai:* Cmptr Comm; Prof Dev Comm Chprsn;

Inclusion & Strategic Planning Comms; MEA 1975-, Sec; Gift of Time Recipient; Assisted in Developing a Nature Trail & Outdoor Amphitheater; *office:* Dassa Mckinney Elem Schl 391 Hooker Rd West Sunbury PA 16061*

TRAVEN, BARBARA ANN (TOUBY), Spanish Teacher; *b:* Mansfield, OH; *m:* Dale C.; *c:* Amber; *ed:* Ohio St Univ (BS) Ed 1968; Continous Hrs in Lang Ed; 4 Courses in Ec; *cr:* Gahanna & Westerville Span Tchr 1968-69; Mansfield City Schls Span Tchr 1969-71; Ontario Schls Span Tchr 1971-74; Willard City Schls 1977-78; Shelby City Schls Span Tchr 1980-; *ai:* Intnl Club Adv; Lang Alliance of Tchrs; OH Frgn Lang Tchrs Assn 1968-, NEA; OEA; SEA; Episcopal Cursillo; *office:* Shelby HS 109 W Smiley Ave Shelby OH 44875

TRAVEN, DALE C., 8th Grade Science Teacher; *b:* Cleveland, OH; *m:* Barbara A. Touby; *c:* Amber N.; *ed:* OH St (BS) Biological Sci 1968; Heidelberg Coll (MA) Clinical Counseling, 16 Sem Hrs in Clinical Course Work; 12 Quarter Hrs Cleveland St; 10 Post Grad Hrs Ashland Univ; 34 Post Grad Hrs Heidelberg Coll; *cr:* Cleveland Schls 7-8 Grd Sci Tchr 1968-69; Willard City Schls 8th Grd Sci Tchr 1969-; Wrkng PT Cnslr at Samaritan House, Mansfield, OH; *ai:* Boys & Girls 7-8 Grd Head Track Coach 23 Yrs; WEA, OEA, NEA 23 Yrs; Amer Counseling Assoc; Amer Psychologist Assoc; Natl Episloral Cursillo Comm 1984-87, Chm 3 Yrs Subcommittee; *office:* Willard City Schls 955 S Main St Willard OH 44890

TRAVER, HEIDI HACKNAUER, Biology Teacher; *b:* Rochester, NY; *m:* Dennis; *ed:* St Univ of NY at Albany (BS) Bio 1990; Montclair St Univ (MAT) Tchng 1993; *cr:* Parsippany Hills HS Sci Tchr 1992-; *ai:* PALS Adv; NEA, NJEA, NJSTA 1992-; *office:* Parsippany Hills HS 20 Rita Dr Parsippany NJ 07054

TRAVER, SHARON RIDEOUT, Fourth Grade Teacher; *b:* Toledo, OH; *m:* Craig L.; *c:* Jodi L., Jaci R.; *ed:* Bowling Green St Univ (BS) Elem Ed 1980; Univ of Toledo (MA) Elem Ed 1995; *cr:* Genoa Area Local Schls 3rd & 4th Grd Tchr 1968-71; Woodmore Local Schls 2nd, 4th & 5th Grd Tchr 1984-; *ai:* Woodmore Ed Assn Exec Comm; Elem Quiz Team Coach; NEA 1984-; OEA 1984-; WEA 1984-, Sec & Bldg Rep; Delta Kappa Gamma 1995-; St Johns United Church of Christ 1970-, Elder & Consistory Sec; *home:* 607 Water St Woodville OH 43469

TRAVER, SHARON RUTH, English Teacher; *b:* Clifton Park, NY; *m:* Barry; *c:* John Calvin; *ed:* St Univ NY at Albany (BA) Eng 1965; Temple Univ (MED) Ed 1984, (EDD) Ed 1989; Westminster Theological Ctr; PA St; *cr:* Riverview Collegiate Eng Tchr 1965-66; Pyne Poynt Jr HS Eng Tchr 1966-68; Upper Dublin HS Eng Dept Chm 1973-81, Eng Tchr 1968-; *ai:* Cmptr & Coffeehouse Clubs; Phi Delta Kappa 1983-; NEA, PSEA, UDEA 1977-; NCTE 1981-; MENSA 1981-; Intertel 1991-; Nationally Honored by Scholastic Magazines 1991; *office:* Upper Dublin HS 800 Lock Alsh Ave Fort Washington PA 19034

TRAVERS, JANET BARRETT, English Teacher; *b:* Washington, DC; *m:* William Leitch; *c:* Heather, William; *ed:* James Madison Univ (BA) Eng 1972; Attnd Univ of MD, Bowie St Univ; *cr:* Calvert HS Eng Tchr 1972-74; Northern HS Eng Tchr 1974-79; Calvert HS Eng Tchr 1991-92; Northern HS Eng Tchr 1992-; *ai:* SADD Spon; Substance Abuse Prevention Network; NEA, CEA 1972-; *office:* Northern HS 2950 Chaneyville Rd Owings MD 20736*

TRAVERS, LINDA A., Middle School Teacher; *b:* Passaic, NJ; *m:* Jack R.; *c:* Bryan L., Jacqueline M.; *ed:* Seton Hall Univ (BS) Bus Ed 1970; *cr:* Sawyer Schl of Bus Tchr 1970; East Orange Cath HS Tchr, Dept Chm, Distributive Ed Coord 1970-73; St Philip The Apostle Schl MS Tchr 1985-; *ai:* Mid Sts Accredidation Comm; Broadway Club Adv; Adv, Advisee Prgm; 1st Yr Math Tchr Mentor; NJSTA 1993-; NCEA 1985-; *home:* 17 E 1st St Clifton NJ 07011

TRAVERS, MARIE P., Mathematics Teacher; *b:* Fall River, MA; *m:* Joseph E.; *c:* Kara Pitocchelli, Jill Pitocchelli; *ed:* Univ of RI (BA) Scndry Eng 1971; Attnd Roger Williams Coll & Bristol Comm Coll in Scndry Math 1984; *cr:* Portsmouth MS Eng Tchr 1971-82, Math Tchr 1983-90; Portsmouth HS Math Tchr 1990-; *ai:* NEA, RI Ed Assn 1971-.

TRAVIS, HAROLD L., Eng Tchr & Cross Cntry Coach; *b:* Pittsburgh, PA; *m:* Ann Burtner; *c:* Matthew, Laura, Harold; *ed:* Shippensburg Univ (BS) Ed & Eng 1968; Shippensburg Univ & Univ of Pittsburgh (MS) Ed & Counseling 1973; Grad Stud in Speech Pathology; *cr:* Carlisle HS Eng Tchr 1968-; *ai:* Cross Cntry Coach 28 Yrs; Carlisle 1000 Mile Club 28 Yrs; HS That Work Comm; CAEA, PSEA, NEA 1968-; Coaching to 15 League Chamionships, 18 Yrs Team Qualified for PA St Championships; *office:* Carlisle Sr HS 623 W Penn St Carlisle PA 17013

TRAVIS, SHARON A., Guidance Counselor & Math Tchr; *b:* Steubenville, OH; *m:* John W.; *ed:* Mills Coll (BS) Ed 1970; Univ of Dayton (MS) Cnslng 1975, (MS) Admin 1991; *cr:* Steubenville City Schls Math Tchr 1970-, Guidance Cnslr 1985-; *ai:* Peer Tutoring Admin; Math Counts Coach; Beta Club Spon; Dist Curr Comm Mem; NEA, OEA & SEA 1970-; NCTM 1989-; OSCA 1985-; OCTM; Delta Kappa Gamma 1980-, Corresponding Sec.

TRAVITZ, ROYAL C., 6th Grade Classroom Teacher; *b:* Pottsville, PA; *m:* Sandra Hershey; *c:* Mike, Denise Dorwart; *ed:* Millersville Univ (BS) Ed 1965; Temple Univ (MS) Ed 1970; *cr:* Manheim Twp Schl Dist Mid 4th & 6th Grd Tchr 1966-89; Manheim Cntrl Schls 6th Grd Tchr 1989-; *ai:* NEA 1965-, Bldg Rep; PSEA 1965-; PSEAR 1995-; *office:* Manheim Central School Dist Adele Ave Manheim PA 17545

TRAYNOR, LUCILLE BURNS, Mathematics Chairperson; *b:* Phila, PA; *w:* Gerard Sr. (dec); *c:* Gerard, Joann Cleland; *ed:* Lasalle Univ (BA) Math, Cmptr Sci 1983; Beaver Coll (MED) Math 1990; *cr:* Bishop Mc Devitt HS Math, Cmptr Tchr 1983-, Math Chprsn 1986-; Comm Coll of Phila Advanced Coll Experience Prgm 1986-; LaSalle Univ Instr Math in the Evening Division 1990-; *ai:* Cmptr Club; MC2 Math Curr, Archdiocesan Evaluating Comms; Admin AHSME; NCTM, PCTM, ATMPOV 1986-; Connelly Grant for Cmptr Lab; GTE Gift Fellow 1995-96; *office:* Bishop Mc Devitt HS 125 Royal Ave Wyncote PA 19095

TRBOVICH, DONNA SERGI, Reading Teacher; *b:* Canton, OH; *m:* William P.; *c:* Matthew; *ed:* KSU (BA) Ed, Elem 1966, (MS) Supvr of Ed 1969; *cr:* Head Start 1966-67; Dueber Schl 3rd-4th Grd Tchr 1966-77; Belle Stone 3rd-6th Grd Tchr 1978-95, Rdng Specialist 1995-; *ai:* Child Abuse Prevention, Rdng Curr Comm; Kappa Delta Pi 1965-; *office:* Belle Stone Elem Schl 2100 Rowland Ave NE Canton OH 44714

TREACY, KATHLEEN MARIE, Mathematics Teacher; *b:* New York City, NY; *ed:* St Univ of NY at Albany (BA) Sociology 1982; Fairleigh Dickinson Univ (MAT) Ed 1992; *cr:* Fort Lee Schl Dist Math Tchr 1990-; *ai:* Curr Cncl; Fort Lee Tchrs Assn, NJEA 1990-; NCTM, AMTNJ 1991-; NJ Governors Tchr Recognition Awd 1993-94; *office:* Fort Lee HS 3000 Lemoine Ave Fort Lee NJ 07024

TREACY-RUBIN, SUSAN E., Third Grade Teacher; *b:* Cornwall, NY; *m:* Michael L.; *ed:* Elmira Coll (BS) Elem Ed 1975; SUNY Coll at New Paltz (MS) Elem Ed 1987; In-Svc Credit Newburhg Enlarged City Schl Dist 90 Credits; *cr:* Fostertown ETC Magnet Schl Second Grd Tchr 1985-88, Kndgtn Tchr 1988-93, Third Grd Tchr 1993-; *ai:* Support Group Adv; NYSUT 1985-; NY St Tchrs Retirement System 1982-; *office:* Fostertown ETC Magnet Schl 216 Fostertown Rd Newburgh NY 12550

TREADWELL, JULIA E., Dean of Students; *b:* Bangor, ME; *ed:* Univ of ME (BS) Ed 1984, (MS) Ed 1993; *cr:* ME Cntrl Inst PE Tchr 1984-88, PE Dept Head & Tchr 1988-90, Asst Dean Residental Life & Ath Dir 1990-93, Residential Life & Dean of Stud 1993-94, Dean of Stud 1994-; *ai:* Bsktbl Coach 1984-; MPA 1993-; NASSP 1993-; NAIS 1993-; *office:* Maine Central Inst 125 S Main St Pittsfield ME 04967

TREADWELL, SUSAN N., French Teacher; *b:* Binghamton, NY; *m:* Jerry G.; *ed:* SUC at Geneseo (BS) Scndry Ed, Span 1971; SUC at Cortland (MS) Fr 1983; Russian Permanent Cert; Lit Fr Cert in Translation; Cert Pratique De Francais, Commercial Et Economique De La Chambre De Commerce Et Dindustrie De Paris; *cr:* Seton Cath Cntrl HS Span, Fr Tchr 1971-80; Marathon Cntrl HS Span, Fr, Russian Tchr 1980-; *ai:* Jr HS Field Hockey Coach; Art & Frgn Lang Club Adv; Stu of Month Selection Comm Chprsn; NEA, NY, AATF, AATSP, NYSAFLT, Maranthon Tchrs Assn 1980-; Translation Pub; *office:* Marathon Cntrl Schl PO Box 399 Marathon NY 13803

TREANOR, MARK ANDREW, Special Education Teacher; *b:* Medford, MA; *m:* Janice; *c:* Alyssa, Kayla; *ed:* Univ of MA (BA) Ed 1976; St Rose (MS) Spcl Ed 1982; Attnd SUNY at Albany; *cr:* St Catherines Ctr Dir of Residence, Asst Dir of Schl & Tchr 1976-85; Niskayuna HS Tchr & Coach 1985-; *ai:* Var Ftbl & Bsktbl Coach; AFT; *office:* Niskayuna HS 1626 Balltown Rd Niskayuna NY 12309

TREBILCOCK, CAROLINE M., High School English Teacher; *b:* Lewiston, ME; *m:* Edward S.; *c:* Scott, Ted, Tobin, Benjamin; *ed:* Univ of ME at Gorham (MA) Eng Ed 1970; St Josephs Coll (BA) Fr & Soc Stud 1965; *cr:* Oxford Hills Schl Dist Fr & Eng Tchr 1965-68, Eng Tchr 1974-; *ai:* Class Adv; Tech Prep Comm; Mstr Tchr Cert; NEA & SAD Tchrs Assn 1976-; *office:* Oxford Hills HS Main St South Paris ME 04281*

TREDEAU, LOUIS, Guidance Counselor & Eng Tchr; *b:* Milford, MA; *m:* Wendy Burns; *c:* James, Lauren; *ed:* Univ of MA at Amherst (BA) Eng 1974; Worcester St Coll (MED) Guid, Ed 1986; *cr:* Marian HS Cnslr, Tchr 1976-; *ai:* Newspaper Adv; NACST; Boston Archdiocese Tchrs Assn; NAET; MA Schl Cnslrs Assn; Milford Sftbl Assn 1993-, Coach; Milford Jr Jeague 1980-, Coach; *office:* Marian HS 273 Union Ave Framingham MA 01701

TREESE, DEBORAH, First Grade Teacher; *b:* Altoona, PA; *ed:* PA St Univ (BS) Elem, Kndgtn Ed 1972, (MEd) Early Chldhd 1975; *cr:* Hollidaysburg Area Schl Dist First Grd Tchr 1972-; *ai:* PSEA, NEA 1972-; *office:* Frankstown Elem Schl RR 3 Box 592 Hollidaysburg PA 16648

TREESE, WILLIAM SHERRATT, English Teacher & Dept Chm; *b:* Pittsburgh, PA; *m:* Judith Kesten; *c:* William S. Jr.; *ed:* Tufts Univ (AB) Eng 1960; Univ of PA (MA) Eng Lit 1962; Princeton Univ Bio Undergrad; *cr:* Du Pont Walston Grain Trader 1967-75; Gulf Oil Corp Strategic Planning Dir 1976-84; Brewster Acad Eng Tchr 1985-88; Worcester Acad Eng Dept Chm 1988-; *ai:* Var Wrestling, JV Bsbl Head Coach; Acad Comm; NCTE 1988-; Andrew O'Connel Tchr Excl Awd; *office:* Worcester Acad 81 Providence St Worcester MA 01604*

TREGGOR, JOSEF PHILIP, Marine Biology Instructor; *b:* Hartford, CT; *m:* Kumi Sato; *c:* Alyssa Bordonaro, Kristyn Churchill; *ed:* Univ of Hartford (BM) Music Ed 1967; CT St Univ (MS) Bio 1983; Working Toward PHD in Marine Bio at Columbia Pacific Univ; Marine Biological Lab Research Assoc at Woods Hole; Ctr for Coastal Stud at Provincetown Research Assoc; Univ of CT Curr & Instruction of Sci; *cr:* Newington HS Marine Bio Instr & Music Dir 1967-; Newington Schls Prgm for the Gifted & Talented in Marine Bio Dir 1980-; Northeastern Univ Schl for Field Stud Sr Fac-Humpback Whale Ecology 1986-88; *ai:* Natl Undersea Research Ctr Aquanaut Prgm; Musical Production Dir; Ars Musica Chamber Ensemble Dir; Clinton Harbor Research Station Dir; CT Ed Assn 1967-; CT Music Educators Assn 1969-, All St Chm, Regnl Chm; North Amer Marine Mammal Assn 1988-; Newington Conservation Commission, Chm 1977-80; Sea Grant Univ CT DEP Outstanding Educator 1994; CT St Tchr of Yr Finalist 1993; Newington Tchr of Yr 1993; Marine Biological Lab Summer Fellowship 1983; Dept of Environmental Protection Research Grants 1990, 1991 & 1993; *office:* Newington HS 605 Willard Ave Newington CT 06111*

TREGLIA, MARIA ORNELLA, Adj Lecturer of ESL; *b:* Formia, Italy; *ed:* Hunter Coll (BA) Eng & Romance Langs 1983, (MA) Eng & Amer Lit 1990; Univ of Perugia Laurea Eng Lit 1995; *cr:* Hunter Coll Grad Asst 1988-89; Oxford Schl of Langs Eng Instr 1990-91; Borough of Manhattan Comm Coll Adj Lecturer 1992-; NY City Tech Coll Adj Lecturer 1993-; *ai:* Tchng Ctr Pgm Comm; NYS TESOL 1995-; Soccorso Amico 1991-, Fund Raiser, Pres 1 Yr; Children Intnl Spon 1992-; Presented a Wkshp at CUNY ESL Cncl 21st Annual Conf; 2nd Prize Winner of Poetry Coll Contest; Poetry Pub; *office:* Borough Of Manhattan Comm Coll 199 Chambers St New York NY 10007*

TREGNAN, NANCY L., Health & Physical Ed Chrprsn; *b:* Philadelphia, PA; *ed:* West Chester St (BS) Hlth, PE 1962, (MED) Hlth, PE 1965; Temple Univ Admin Cert 1972; 60 Addl Credit Hrs Temple, Penn St, FSU, Univ of AK, St Joseph Univ; *cr:* Philadelphia HS for Girls Hlth, PE Tchr 1962-, Dean of Stdnts 1979-92, Dept Chprsn, Ath Dir 1994-; *ai:* Stu Ath Assn & Cnslng Spon; HIV-AIDS Peer Group Club Adv; AFT 1964-, Exec Bd, Sr HS Rep; *office:* Philadelphia HS For Girls 1400 W Olney Ave Philadelphia PA 19141*

TREHERNE, BRENDA O'NEILL, Social Studies Teacher; *b:* Drexel Hill, PA; *m:* David R.; *c:* Mitchell D., Addison C., Ashlyn E.; *ed:* Millersville Univ of PA (BA) Sec Ed, Soc St 1984; Wilmington Coll (MS) Human Resources Mgmt 1990; 15 Addl Inservice Credit Hrs DE Dept Pub Instruction; *cr:* Seaford Sr HS Soc St Tchr 1984-; *ai:* NEA 1984-; *office:* Seaford HS 399 N Market St Ext Seaford DE 19973

TREICHEL, CLARE MARIE, Guidance Director; *b:* Washington, DC; *ed:* St Bonaventure Univ (BA) Psych 1976; Bowie St Univ (MED) Guid & Cnslng 1981; *cr:* Holy Family Schl 3rd Grd Tchr 1977-80; St Mary of Assumption 3rd Grd Tchr 1981-83; La Reine HS Guid Dir, Psych Tchr 1983-92; Prince George's Comm Coll Cnslr 1989-; Bishop Mc Namara Schl Guid Dir, AP Psych Tchr 1992-; *ai:* It's Acad Moderator; Black Pursuits Quiz Team; Filipino Amer Cultural Awareness Club; Amer Psych Assn, Am Cnslng Assn 1985-; Am Schl Coun Assn 1986-; Natl Cath Ed Assn 1977-; Private Schls Guid Assn 1983-, Co-Pres; *office:* Bishop Mc Namara HS 6800 Marlboro Pike Forestville MD 20747

TREIS, ALINA MILDRED, English College Instructor; *b:* Zanzibar, East Africa; *m:* Terry A.; *c:* Richard, Tania; *ed:* Univ of Bombay India (BA) Lit 1964; Coll of St Rose (BA) Sec Ed Eng 1972; SUNY at Albany (MA) Adv Clsrm Eng 1982; *cr:* Schoharie Vo Tech Tenured 9-12 Grd Eng Tchr 1987-90; Schoharie Cntrl Schl 9 Grd Tchr, Drama Adv 1990-91; Schenectady Job Trng GED Tchr 1991-; SUNY at Cobleshill Eng Instr 1991-; Schenectady Cty Comm Coll Eng Instr, GED Tchr 1991-; *ai:* Drama Club Adv; Literacy Vol of Am; Comm Svc & GED Craig St Stdnts; NYSUT 1987-; UUP 1991-TR; Poem in Poetic Voices of Amer 1994; *office:* Schenectady County Comm Coll 78 Washington Ave Schenectady NY 12305*

TREISBACH, JEAN ELIZABETH, Mathematics Tchr & Dept Chprsn; *b:* W Reading, PA; *m:* Gordon E. Jr.; *ed:* College Misericordia (BS) Math 1973; Millersville Univ (MED) Math 1976; Attnd Immaculata Coll; Calculator, Cmptr Pre-Calculus, Enhanced Calculus Insts; *cr:* York Cath HS Math Tchr 1973-79, Dept Chprsn 1977-79; Villa Maria Acad Math Tchr 1979-, Dept Chprsn 1992-; *ai:* Jr, Sr Prom Moderator; Eucharistic Minister; NCTM 1978-; PCTM, ATMOPAV 1979-; NCEA 1973-; Univ of Richmond Stdnts Educl Preparation Contributions Recognition Cert; *office* Maria Acad Green Tree Malvern PA 19355

TRELEASE, LAURIE A., Mathematics Teacher; *b:* Liberty, N Thomas J. Jr.; *c:* Eric, Andrew; *ed:* St Univ Coll at Oneonta (BA) M Math Ed 1976; 40 Addl Credit Hrs in Math, Math Ed & Cmptr S Liberty CS Math Tchr 1977; Charlotte Valley Cntrl Schl Math Tchr *office:* Charlotte Valley Central Schl Rt 23 Davenport NY 13750

TREMAGLIO, ROBERT C., Social Studies Dist Chairman; *b:* Wat CT; *m:* Catherine W.; *c:* Patrick, Andrew, John-Thomas; *ed:* Fairfiel (BA) His, Ed 1973; Manhattanville Coll (MAT) GATE 1978; Do Schl of Bus & Pub Mngmt Univ of Bridgeport 1986; Law & Admi of CT Southwestern Univ; *cr:* Greenwich Cath Dist Tchr 19 Stamford Cath Dist Tchr 1974-78; Newtown Schl SWAS Co-Coord Chm, Grds 7-12 Tchr 1978-92; Amity Schls Dist Chm, Tchr, Admin *ai:* Staff Dev, Dist Chprsn Comms; BOWA Comm Co-Chm; Former Soccer Coach; CEA; NASS; Wakeman Boys, Girls Club Pres; Fa Historic Soc Past Bd of Dirs; Fairfield Univ Advy Cncl Bd; Yth Spor Prgms; *office:* Amity Regnl Schls 190 Luke Hill Rd Bethany CT 06

TREMBA, ROGER LEE, Physics Teacher; *b:* Parker, PA; *m:* Jo Gardner; *c:* Richard, Renae Barger; *ed:* IN Univ of PA (BA) Chem & Physics 1967; Carnegie Mellon Univ (MA) Natural Sci 1968; *ai:* Team Coach; NEA 1968-; PSEA 1968-; *office:* Butler Area Sr HS 16 Castle Rd Butler PA 16001

TREMBLAY, BARBARA STANFORD, Principal; *b:* Keene, N Anthony M.; *c:* Andrew G., Adam S., Suraiya; *ed:* Colby Coll (B 1968; Keene St Coll (MED) Ed Admin 1988; Attnd Sorbonne, Cedar Coll, Harvard Grad Schl of Ed Prin Ctr, Kutztown Univ of PA; *cr:* Fr Pierce Coll & Various Schl Dists Fr & Ger Tchr 1970-84; Keene S Dir of Adult Learner Svcs 1984-86; Keene Schl Dist Dir of Com 1986-90; Keene HS Asst Prin 1990-94; Franklin Schl Prin 1994-; *a* Mentor Tchr Pgm Adv 1992-; NHASP 1990-; NASSP 1990-; NH Pa in Ed 1994-, Bd of Dirs; NAESP 1994-; Cedarcrest Inc 1990-, Dir; E Ed Awds Pgm 1995-, Bd; Prospect Hill Home Inc 1996, Incorporat Asst Prin of Yr 1995; *office:* Benjamin Franklin Elem Schl 217 Wash St Keene NH 03431*

TREMBLAY, LOUIS JOSEPH, MS Mathematics Teacher; *b:* Leb NH; *m:* Marian V. Taylor; *c:* Lou Ann Koustoubardis, Eric; *ed:* Ply St Coll (BS) Chem 1968, (MS) Educl Admin 1974; Grad Stud Nova Post-Grad Stud Univ of VT, Castleton St Coll, Johnson St Coll, St A Coll; *cr:* Lebanon HS Chem Tchr 1967-70; Dartmouth Coll Project Regnl Dir 1970-73; Lebanon Jr High Title I Coord 1973-74; Woodsto Vice Prin 1974-80; Woodstock MS Math Tchr 1980-; *ai:* Team Ldr; 1967-; NCTM, VCTM 1980-; Lebanon Jaycees 1973-, Leadership Knights of Columbus 1963-, Grand Knight; *office:* Woodstock Unic Rt 4 Woodstock VT 05091*

TRENCH, ALBERTA CONTE, Foreign Lang & French Teacher; *b.* Haven, CT; *ed:* Albertus Magnus (BA) Fr 1971; Assumption (MA 1973; CAS Fairfield Admin; 30 Credit Hrs Span; *cr:* Amity Regnl Tchr 1972-, Dist DDT Chair Frgn Lang Tchr 1982-92, Dist Dept Chai Lang Tchr 1992-; *ai:* Trip to France Coord; AATF 1972-, Exec Bd; C of Lang Tchrs 1975-, Fall Conf 1994-, Chair; NEA, CEA, AEA Amity Tchr of Yr 1986; Gold Pen Recipient 1993; *office:* Amity Ohman Ave Orange CT 06477*

TRENDLER, ELAINE BABBONI, English Teacher; *b:* Vineland, N William A.; *ed:* Rider Coll (BA) Eng 1968; Masters Equivalenc Benjamin Franklin Jr HS Eng Tchr 1969-71, 1973-78; Neil A Armstr HS Eng Tchr 1971-73; Delhaas HS Eng Tchr 1978-81; Frank Roosevelt Jr HS Eng Tchr 1981-; *ai:* Yrbk Adv; NEA, PSEA & 1969-75; AFT Local 3700 1975-87; NEA, PSEA & BTEA 1987-; *o* Franklin D Roosevelt Jr HS 1001 Rodgers Rd Bristol PA 19007

TRENDLER, WILLIAM A., Art & Photography Teacher; *b:* Philade PA; *m:* Elaine M.; *ed:* Kutztown St Univ (BS) Art 1966; *cr:* Benja Franklin Jr HS Art Tchr 1969-78; Emerson Elem Schl Art Tchr 197 Maple Shade Elem Schl Art Tchr 1978-87; Harry S Truma Photography Tchr 1987-; *ai:* Schl & Yrbk Photographer; NEA, PS BTEA 1969-75; AFT Local 3700 1975-87, Treas; NEA, PSEA & E 1987-; *office:* Truman Sr HS 3001 Green Ln Levittown PA 19057

TRENT, EDWARD, Earth Science Teacher; *b:* New Brunswick, N Irene F.; *c:* Victoria, Andrea; *ed:* Rutgers Univ (BA) Biological Sci Trenton St (MA) Scndry Ed 1971; 32 Hrs Admn, Supv Rutgers Uni Avenel Jr HS Tchr 1967-80; Woodbridge HS Tchr 1980-; *ai:* Coach, WTEA; MCEA; NEA; NJSTA; NJESTA; Ecolab Excl Ed; *o* Woodbridge HS Kelly St Woodbridge NJ 07095

TRENT, TONY LEON, American History Teacher; *b:* Topeka, K Nancy Elizabeth wise; *c:* Kyle; *ed:* Bowling Green St Univ (BS) S Ed 1977; Wright St Univ (MS) Principalship 1979; *cr:* Weisenborn M Stud Tchr 1977-; *ai:* Soc Stud Dept Chprsn; Dist Blood Bank Coord; Wrestling, Bsbl, Cross Cntry Coach; NEA, OEA 1977-; HHEA 1977-, Rep; Southwest OH Wrestling Ofcls Assn 1987-, VP; *office:* Weise MS 6061 Old Troy Pike Huber Heights OH 45424

TRENT-FRASER, JAN ANN, Reading Consultant; *b:* New Haven, C Ann Iuraduri, John Jacobsen; *ed:* SCSC (BS) Eng Lit, (MS) Consultant; Fairfield Univ Ad Cert Admin, Supervision; Mentor Tchr *cr:* Jefferson Elem Schl Rdng Consultant 1970-73; Coleytown MS Consultant, Dept Chair 1974-75; Redding Elem Schl Rdng Consu 1975-85; Weston MS Rdng Consultant 1986-; Four Town Summer Prin 1993-95; *ai:* Adv, Advisee Prgm; Tech Comm; NEA; IRA; N United Church of Christ, Outreach Ministry; St Enrichment Grant; *o* Weston MS 135 School Rd Weston CT 06883

TRENTHAM, EDWINA ANN, Associate Professor of English Hamilton, Bermuda; *c:* Benjamin Burland; *ed:* Wesleyan Univ (BA) 1980; Univ of MA at Amherst (MFA) Poetry 1983; *cr:* Middlesex C Coll Adjunct Instr 1983-84; Univ of Hartford Adjunct Instr 1984-86 Coll Visiting Instr 1986-89; Asnuntuck Comm Tech Coll Asst Prof 1 Wesleyan Univ Grad Lib Stud Visiting Instr 1989-95; *ai:* Poetry Club Instructional Excl Comm Co-Chair; CT Comm Coll Merit Recogn Tchng Awd 1990; Phoenix New Writers Series Awd 1991; Fellow at Y 1989; 40 Poems Pub in Magazines; *office:* Asnuntuck Comm Tech Col Elm St Enfield CT 06082

TREONZE, RICHARD, Physical Education Teacher; *b:* Bayonne, N. Karen Pede; *c:* Lynette, Richard M.; *ed:* St Mary of the Plains (BA) Hlth 1973; *cr:* Bayonne HS PE Tchr 1974-; *ai:* Head Boys, Girls T Coach 1974-; Class Adv 1981-82, 1991-95; NEA, NJEA, BTA 1 Hudson Cty Track Coaches Assn 1976-, VP, Boys Coach of Yr 198 Girls Coach of Yr 1991; Spec Olympics Vol Humanitarian Awd 198 *office:* Bayonne HS 29th St & Ave A Bayonne NJ 07002

TREPKO, JO-ANN G., Seventh & Eighth Grade Teacher; *b:* Jersey NJ; *ed:* Jersey City St Coll (BA) Elem Ed 1974; *cr:* St Joseph Schl 1986-88; St Vincent De Paul Schl Tchr 1988-; *ai:* Forensics Adv 1992 Drama Club Adv 1988-; Stu Cncl Adv 1989-90; NCEA 1986-; *offic* Vincent De Paul Schl 80 W 47th St Bayonne NJ 07002

TREROTOLA, LEONARD MICHAEL, Music Department Chai Statan Island, NY; *m:* Linda Nancy D'Antuono; *c:* Victoria, La Francesca; *ed:* Wagner Coll (BA) Music, Performance 1978; Broc Conservatory of Music (MA) Music, Performance 1983; College of S

(MS) Supervison, Admin 1988; *cr:* New Dorp HS Tchr 1978-90; NY Adjunct Tchr of Guitar 1990; New Dorp HS Chm of Music 1990-94, of Music, Art, Tech, Human Svcs 1995-; *ai:* Clarinet, Guitar, hone, Percussion, Jazz Ensembles; Sound Crew Dir; UFT 1978-; A, SAG 1988-89; Staten Island Childrens Orchestra 1995-, Mem, Bd ; Natl TV, Radio Commercials for KY Fried Chicken; Recordings Chubby Checker & Paul Schaefer; Musician, Vocalist, Arranger for assions; Brooklyn, Staten Island Tchr of Yr 1994; Recorded a CD HS Guitar Ensemble; Arranger, Musician for Tiny Tim; Curr Design ourses in Guitar, Recording Tech; Musician, Singer for many 1950s 0s Recording Acts; *home:* 69 Stratford Dr Manalapan NJ 07726*

SCH, GLORIA A., Science Teacher; *b:* Jobstown, NJ; *ed:* Rowan BA) Ed 1982; Sci Process Skills Villanova Univ 1987; Marine Ed Stud MA Maritime Acad 1988; Natl Geographic Kids Network ton Plasma Physics Lab 1992; *cr:* Young Learners Pvt Day Schl n Tchr 1982-84; Northern Burlington Jr HS Sci Tchr 1985-86; ampton MS Sci Tchr 1986-; NJ Dept Environmental Protection ltant 1988-; *ai:* Sci Coord; Sci Curr Comm Chair; NEA, NJEA 1986-; atl Sci Tchrs Assn 1987-; Kappa Delta Pi 1982-; Women's Hlth ork 1991-, Lay Advy Comm; Meml Hosp; Tchr of Yr 1992; *office:* mpton MS 1 Student Dr Mount Holly NJ 08060*

SHAM, PATRICIA ANN, Kindergarten Teacher; *b:* New York City, : Lawrence; *c:* Kevin, Daniel; *ed:* St Univ Coll at Oneonta (BS) Elem 969; SUNY at Stony Brook (MS) Liberal Stud 1975; *cr:* Green Ave Kndgtn Tchr 1969-70; Cherry Ave Elem 1st Grd Tchr 1976-79, 2nd 'chr 1980-90, Kndgtn Tchr 1970-76, 1990-; *ai:* STA Bld Rep; NYSTA ; *office:* Cherry Ave Elem Schl 155 Cherry Ave West Sayville NY

SKA, MEREDITH I., English Instructor; *b:* Boston, MA; *m:* Michael ; *c:* Aerie, Ashley; *ed:* Northeastern Univ (BA) Eng 1968; Plattsburg of (MS) Eng Equivalency 1975; *cr:* Middletown HS 11th Grd Eng Instr 69; Lake Placid HS 11th & 12th Grd Eng Instr 1969-79; Saranac Lake HS 12th Grd Eng & Advanced Placement Tchr 1980-; *ai:* Sr Class 0 Yrs; *office:* Saranac Lake Cntrl HS 99 La Pan Hwy Saranac Lake 2983

TTEL, JOSEPH FRANCIS, Instrumental Music Teacher; *b:* urgh, PA; *m:* Susan Alling; *c:* Marisa, Ian; *ed:* Clarion Univ of PA Music Ed 1973; Univ of MD (MA) Scndry Ed 1980; 30 Credit Hrs Level Tchr Trng Classes Montgomery Cty Pub Schls; *cr:* N Bethesda Gen Music Tchr 1973-75; Edward Broome Jr HS Instrumental Music 1975-78; Edward Broome MS Instrumental Music Tchr 1978-81; John ker Intermediate Instrumental Music Tchr 1981-88; Thomas Wootton nstrumental Music Tchr 1988-; *ai:* Marching Band Flag Squad Spon; pline Comm; NEA, MSTA, MCEA, MENC 1973-; *office:* Thomas S ton HS 2100 Wootton Pky Rockville MD 20850*

OVAC, SHERRY D., Choir Director; *b:* Lewistown, PA; *ed:* field Univ (BM) Music Ed 1983; Eastman Schl of Music Conducting *cr:* Belleville Mennonite Schl Elem Gen Music Tchr 1985 Mifflin chl Dist Elem & MS Gen Music Tchr 1986-87; Indian Valley HS Sr Choral Music Tchr 1988-; *ai:* Asst Marching Band Dir; Dir of uary & Handball Choirs; Lewiston Presbyterian Church Active Comm st & Accompanist; Private Piano & Voice Instr; PSEA & NEA 1985-; lusic Ed Assn & Music Ed Natl Conf 1984-; Amer Choral Dirs Assn -; Chrch Organist; Feature Soloist Susquehana Valley Chorale; *office:* n Valley HS 700 Cedar St Lewistown PA 17044

ANT, RICHARD PAUL, Secondary Science Teacher; *b:* Brooklyn, *m:* Wendy Lynn Busch; *c:* Jessica Holm, Nicole Susan; *ed:* SUNY at eskill (AAS) Fisheries & Wildlife 1974; SUNY at Cornell (BS) mology 1976; SUC at Cortland (MS) Scndry Sci 1989; 30 Post Grad Stu Tchng Wells Coll; *cr:* Boyce Thompson Inst for Plant Research arch Asst II 1977-85; Port Byron HS Scndry Sci Tchr 1985-; *ai:* Honor & Schlsps Selection Comms; Ski Club Adv; Class of 1993 Adv; PB s Assn 1985-, Exec Comm 1991-; NYSUT 1985-, Del to Rep Assembly -; *office:* Port Byron HS Maple Ave Port Byron NY 13140

BE, IVAN MATHEWS, Professor of History; *b:* Albany, OH; *m:* ana Lynn Tripp; *ed:* OH Univ (BSEd) His & Govt 1962, (MA) His ; Univ of Toledo (PHD) Amer His 1976; Addl Hrs at Univ of Dayton owie St Coll; Attnd NEH Summer Inst at IA St; *cr:* Vinton Cty HS Tchr -67; Meigs Cty HS Tchr 1967-70; Univ of Toledo T A 1970-75; Univ o Grande His Fac 1976-; *ai:* Phi Alpha Theta Co-Adv 1982-; Org of r Historians 1976-; OH Acad of His 1975-; Natl Assn of Scholars ; Appalachian Stud Assn 1986-; Free & Accepted Masons 1962-, er 1966-67; York & Scottish Rite Masons 1963-, KYCH Awd 1992; e 1965-; Grange 1962-; Berea Coll Appalachian Stud Fellowships & 1985; Author of Mountaineer Jamboree-Cntry Music in WV 1984, Stonemans-An Appalachian Family & Music that Shaped Their Lives 3; Co-Author Definitive Cntry 1995; Many Articles & Reviews; right-Hays Seminar in Egypt; Phelps-Stokes Seminar in West Africa; Summer Seminars at CA, NC, MI & MS; *office:* Univ Of Rio Grande Grande OH 45674

BE, MARY AIKEN, Interdisciplinary Curr Coord; *b:* Oneida, NY; *m:* n C.; *c:* David M., Christine Casella, Kathryn Cardogno, Barbara ; *ed:* Cornell Univ (BA) Amer Stud, Eng 1953; Framingham St Coll D) Elem Ed 1969; *cr:* Margaret Zeh Schl 6 Grd Tchr 1969-71; hborough MS 6-8 Grd Eng Tchr 1971-91, 7 Grd Team Ldr, Tchr -92, 5-8 Grd Curr Coord Interdisciplinary, 8 Grd Lang Arts Tchr 2-; *ai:* Dist Lang Arts Curr Frameworks Comm; Portfolio Assessment hp Team; NCTE 1973-; ASCD 1992-; NEA, MA Tchrs Assn, Tchrs 1969-; Anna M. Seaver Awd 1983; *office:* Northborough MS 145 coln St Northborough MA 01532

CARICO, DONALD THOMAS, Professor of Sociology; *b:* New , NY; *m:* Nina Jude; *c:* Marina Yita, Dominique; *ed:* Fordham (BS) Ec); New Schl for Soc Rsrch (MA) Sociology 1972, (PHD) Sociology 0; *cr:* Bronx Comm Coll Instr 1974-76; Jersey City St Coll Instr 5-77; Queensborough CC Prof 1977-; *ai:* AAUP; ASA; AIHA; Book: Italians of Greenwich Village; Book Chapters, Journal Articles, Book iews, Prof Papers Pub; *office:* Queensborough Comm Coll 22205 56th Bayside NY 11364*

CK, CAROLYN KELLY, Art Teacher; *b:* Hamilton, NY; *m:* Richard; dam, Richard II; *ed:* Potsdam Coll (BA) Art 1977, (MS) Ed 1984; Addl Credit Hrs at St Lawrence Univ for Cert in Art K-12; *cr:* Lowville Acad Tchr 1977-79, Art Tchr 1979-; *ai:* Art Dept Chprsn; Art Club Adv; AFT 9-; NYSUT; *home:* 7652 Easton St Lowville NY 13367

DICO, ANTHONY JAMES, Former Teachers Coach; *b:* Warren, PA; Univ of AR (BS) Kinesiology Ed 1994; *cr:* Warren Cty Schl Dist Sub r 1994-95, HS Ftbl Coach 1994-95; *home:* 513 4th Ave Warren PA 65

FORE, ROBERT EDWARD, Biology Teacher; *b:* Miami, FL; *ed:* rl CT St Univ (BS) Bio 1978; Southern CT Univ (MS) Bio 1982; field Univ 15 Hrs Bio; *cr:* Brien Mc Mahon HS Bio, Earth Sci Tchr 8-; *ai:* Head Ftbl, Indoor & Outdoor Track Coach; NFT 1983-; Many icles Pub; Underwater Photographs Pub; *office:* Brien McMahon HS Highland Ave Norwalk CT 06854*

MBLE, ELEANOR SEELEY, 11th-12th Grade English Tchr; *b:* Bryn wr, PA; *m:* John N.; *c:* Tyghe, June; *ed:* CT Coll (BA) Eng 1976; Lehigh Univ (MA) Scndry Ed 1989; Simmons Coll Post-Baccalaureate Dip Comm 1977; Certfd Jrnlsm Ed 1993; *cr:* Northwestern Lehigh HS Eng Tchr 1988-89; Easton Area HS Eng Tchr 1989-; *ai:* HS Newspaper Adv; JEA 1994-; NCTE; PSEA 1989-; PSPA 1990-, Keystone 1995; Wesley UMC 1986-, Staff-Parish Chair; PTA-BASD 1988-; Grad Assistantship Lehigh Univ Coll of Ed 1985-87; Lehigh Vly Bus Ed Partnership 1995-; *office:* Easton Area HS 2601 William Penn Hwy Easton PA 18045*

TRIMBLE, GERALD, Chem Tchr & Sci Dept Chprsn; *b:* New Castle, PA; *m:* Marilyn Kimmel; *c:* Alan; *ed:* Slippery Rock Univ (BS) Chem 1968, (MS) Guidance, Ed 1972; *cr:* Wilmington Area Schl System Chem, Physics Tchr 1968-75; Shenango Area Schl System Chem Tchr 1976-; *ai:* NEA, PSEA 1968-; Wilmington Area Tchrs Assn 1968-75, Pres, Tchr of Yr 1973; Shenango Area Tchr Assn 1976-; *office:* Shenango Area Schl System 2550 Ellwood Rd New Castle PA 16101

TRIMBLE, RICHARD M., Social Studies Teacher; *b:* Philadelphia, PA; *m:* Jean L. Huebner; *c:* Abigail, Carolyn Jill, Andrew; *ed:* Univ of Bridgeport (BS) His, Ed 1971; Seton Hall Univ (MA) European His 1978; Brookdale Comm Coll (AS) Criminal Justice 1986; Rutgers (EDS) 1995; *cr:* Manasquan HS Tchr 1971-; Wm. Patterson Coll Adjunct Prof, His 1986-88; Brookdale Comm Coll Adjunct Prof, His 1988-; *ai:* Bsbl 19 Yrs, Ftbl 15 Yrs, Hockey 11 Yrs, Weight Trng 20 Yrs Coach; Club Adv His, Ecology; Fac Comms; NJ Cncl for Soc Stud 1989-; Manasquan Hockey Club 1971-, Pres, Founder; Squan Soccer Club 1988-, Bd; Summer Spec Police Officer 1978-86, Spring Lake NJ; Spring Lake Recreation 1986-91; Manasquan Brielle Little Lg 1980-87; Occar Hockey Schl 1992-; Author Book In The Classroom: Suggestions & Ideas Beginning Tchrs Univ Press of America 1991; Tchr of Yr 1984, 1986, 1991; First Dist Recipient NJ Outstanding Sec Schl Tchrs Awd; Finalist Princeton Univ Outstanding Sec Schl Teach Awd 1990; NJ St Tchr of Yr for Amer His 1995; Monmouth Cty Tchr of Yr 1996; *home:* 76 Wyckoff Ave Manasquan NJ 08736*

TRIMMER, CATHY SUE (MILLER), Sixth Grade Teacher; *b:* Columbus, OH; *m:* Daniel Eugene; *c:* Devon Marie; *ed:* Capital Univ (BA) Elem Ed 1977; Univ of Dayton (MS) Guid, Cnslng 1983; Attnd OH St Univ, OH Univ; *cr:* CArroll Elem Schl Sixth Grd Tchr 1977-80; Medill Elem Schl Fourth Grd Tchr 1980-82; Sanderson Elem Schl Fourth Grd Tchr 1982-92; Sanderson Elem Schl Sixth Grd Tchr 1992-; *ai:* Statistician 2nd-3rd Grd Girls Bsktbl; Sci Fair Judge for 8th Grd; NEA, OEA 1977-; LEA 1980; Alpha Nu Chptr, Alpha Delta St, Delta Kappa Gamma 1991-; Mable Olsen-Bell Awd for Cooperating Tchrs; Jennings Scholar; USAF Recruiting Svc Cert of Appreciation; Outstdng Tchr 1979; *home:* 3132 Reyn-Baltimore Rd Baltimore OH 43105

TRIMMER, MARY JANE, Fourth Grade Teacher; *b:* Morristown, NJ; *ed:* Rowen Coll (BA) Elem Ed 1962; Montclair St Univ (MA) Environmental Ed, Stud 1975; Pace Univ, Trenton St Coll, Univ of ME, Monmouth Coll, NJ St Schl of Conservation 74 Addl Grad Credits; *cr:* Valley Schl 3rd Grd Tchr 1962-65; 3 Bridges Schl 2nd, 4th Grd Tchr 1965-; *ai:* Safety Patrol; Standards Comm; Merck Ldr Tchr; NJEA, NEA 1962-; NSTA 1995-; Stonybrock-Millstone Watershed Assn 1985-; South Branch Watershed Assn 1993-, River Monitor; Project WET 1995-, Facilitator; LDS Church, Numerous Offices; Sci Excl Rudolph Awd 1995; *office:* Three Bridges Elem Schl Main St Three Bridges NJ 08887

TRIMNAL, WANDA LEE, English & Journalism Teacher; *b:* Baltimore, MD; *ed:* Frostburg St (BA) Eng, Fr 1972; Johns Hopkins Univ (MLA) Lbrl Arts 1977; *cr:* Arundel HS Eng Tchr 1972-, Newspaper Adv 1985-; *ai:* NEA, MSTA 1972-; Tchrs Assn Anne Arundel Cty 1972-; MD Schl Press Assn 1985-, Bd of Dir Mem; NSPA, CSPA, Quill & Scroll 1985-; Jrnlsm Ed Assn 1992-; Arundel Singers 1982-88, 1996, Pres 1985-88; Tchr of Month 1994; Judge CSPA Newspaper Contest; Advised Schl Newspaper 1991; *office:* Arundel Sr HS 1001 Annapolis Rd Gambrills MD 21054

TRINKLE, THERESE KAIVEN, Fifth Grade Teacher; *b:* Brooklyn, NY; *m:* Alfred; *c:* Rosemary; *ed:* Brentwood Coll (BS) Elem Ed 1965; Queens Coll (MS) Elem Ed 1973; *cr:* Acad of St Joseph 5 Grd Tchr 1969-72; St Angela Hall Acad 8 Grd Tchr 1972-75; Somers Cntrl Schls 5 Grd Tchr 1975-; *ai:* NYS United Tchrs, AFT, NCTE 1975-; *office:* Somers Central Schls Rt 202 Somers NY 10589

TRIOLO, AUDREY P., Math Teacher; *b:* Teaneck, NJ; *m:* Robert; *c:* Matthew, Michael; *ed:* Fairleigh Dickinson Univ (BA) Ed 1968; Post Grd Work Univ of MD at College Park, Univ of MD at Baltimore Cty; *cr:* Annapolis Jr HS Math Tchr 1968-75; Severna Park HS Math Tchr 1977-78; Chesapeake HS Math Tchr 1978-84; Severna Park HS Math Tchr 1985-86; Chesapeake HS Math Tchr 1986-; *ai:* NHS; NEA, MSTA, TAAAC 1968-; NCTM 1988-; Comm Assn 1973-, Sec; *office:* Chesapeake HS 4798 Mountain Rd Pasadena MD 21122

TRIOLO, JAMES JACK, Sixth Grade Teacher; *b:* Springfield, MA; *m:* Linda Susan Eliff; *ed:* Amer Intnl Coll (BS) Elem Ed 1971; Trenton St Coll (MED) Dev Rdng 1980; Supervisory & Prin Cert 1981; 45 Grad Credits from Rutgers & Seton Hall Univ; *cr:* Eli Whitney Schl 5th & 6th Grd Tchr 1972-74; Readington MS Prin Intern 1988-91, 7th Grd SS Tchr 1989-91, SS & Rdng Tchr 1974-89, 6th Grd Tchr 1992-; *ai:* Long Term Planning Comm Co-Chair; NEA, NJEA & REA 1974-, REA Chief Negotiator 1982-90; NMSA & NJAMLE 1993-; NJCSS 1993-; NJGA 1995-; Natl Conf of World His Assn Participant 1992; NJ Comm for the Hum Rediscovering the Encounter: The World of 1492 Participant 1992; NJAMLE Conf Wkshp Co-Presenter 1995; NJGA Conf Wkshp Presenter 1995; NJAMLE Conf Wkshp Presenter 1996; *office:* Readington MS PO Box 2 Readington NJ 08870

TRIPATHY, SUKANT K., Provost & Prof of Chemistry; *b:* Bihar, India; *m:* Susan Thomson; *c:* Sheila, Aneil; *ed:* IIT Kharagpur (BS) Physics 1972, (MS) Physics 1974; Case Western Reserve Univ (PHD) Micromolecular Sci 1981; *cr:* GTE Labs Inc Tech Staff 1981-83, Rsrch Mgr 1983-86; Univ of MA Assot Prof 1986-87, Chem Prof 1987-, Provost, Vice Chancellor Acad Affairs 1994-; *ai:* MA Tchrs Assn 1986-; Amer Chemical Soc 1981-, Carl S. Marvel Creative Polyner Chem Awd; APS; SPIE; MRS; SPE; Sigma Xi; AAAS; Numerous Articles Pub; 20 Patents; Numerous Grants, Awds; *office:* Univ Of MA At Lowell 1 University Ave Lowell MA 01854*

TRIPP, DEANNA ALICE, Second Grade Teacher; *b:* Morrisville, VT; *ed:* Johnson St Coll (BS) Elem Ed 1962; Boston Univ (MA) Elem Ed 1969; Univ of VT, St Michael's Coll, London Univ Addl Credits; *cr:* Barre City Schl First Grd Tchr 1962-65; Johnson Elem Schl First Grd Tchr 1965-79; Morristown Elem Schl Third Grd Tchr 1979-82, Second Grd Tchr 1982-; *ai:* Tech Comm; Morristown Ed Assn 1979-; VT NEA 1962-; Delta Kappa Gamma 1983-; Coral Chptr #16 Order of Eastern Star 1961-; Puffer United Meth Church 1953-; *office:* Morristown Elem Schl RR 15A Morrisville VT 05661

TRIPP, DONALD RAY, Bible Teacher & Dept Chrmn; *b:* Windsor, NC; *m:* Eolin Ann Akers; *c:* Brian, Elisabeth, David; *ed:* Columbia Union Coll (BA) His & Rel 1964; MD Univ (MA) Soc Stud Ed 1976; *cr:* Shenandoah Vly Acad Soc Stud Tchr 1973-79; Fresno Adventist Acad Bible & Soc Stud Tchr 1979-82; Vienna Jr Acad Prin & Upper Grd Tchr 1983-89; Takoma Acad Bible Tchr 1990-; *ai:* Dept Chair; Mission Trip Spon; Curr Comm.

TRIPP, GEORGE D., Guidance Counselor; *b:* Niagara Falls, NY; *m:* Cheryl A. Roszmann; *c:* Renee Tripp Anderson, Steven; *ed:* SUNY Brockport (MS) Scndry Ed 1965, Ed & Counseling 1972; Attnd Niagara Univ for Counseling; *cr:* Wilson Cntrl Soc Stud Tchr 1965-70; Newfane Jr High 7-9th Grd Cnslr 1970-73; West Seneca E Jr 6-8th Grd Cnslr 1973-74; Lyndonville HS 9-12th Grd Cnslr 1974-89; Newfane Sr High 11-12th Grd Cnslr 1989-; *ai:* Peer Leadership Adv; Ath Supervision Chprsn; Newfane Tchrs Assn 1989-; AFT & NYSUT 1965-; *office:* Newfane Sr HS 1 Panther Dr Newfane NY 14108*

TRIPP, LYNDA HENDRICKS, English Dept Chairman & Tchr; *b:* Amarillo, TX; *m:* Jack; *ed:* Northeast LA Univ (BA) Eng 1963, (MA) Eng 1967; Bridgewater St Coll 60 Addl Hrs; *cr:* Ouachita Parish HS Eng Tchr 1963-66; Riser MS Eng, His Tchr 1966-68; Taunton HS Eng Tchr 1968-, Eng Dept Chm 1992-; *ai:* NEA 1963-; MA Tchrs Assn 1968-; Taunton Ed Assn 1968-, Pres, Chair of Negotiating Coun; NCTE, MA Cncl Tchrs of Eng 1992-; Delta Kappa Gamma 1976-, Sec; *office:* Taunton HS 50 Williams St Taunton MA 02780

TROBERG, BEVERLY JO ANN, Substitute Teacher; *b:* Philipsburg, PA; *m:* Lars O.; *ed:* Univ of DE (BS) Sci 1948; Penna St Univ (MED) Elem Ed 1954; In-Svc Prgms Metric System Inst Packets for Classroom; Rdng Instruction; Proper Use Kits Games; Cmptr Use in Classroom; Mngmt U of Pitt Bradford; Recreation Leadership Techniques Penn St; *cr:* St Georges Schl 7th-8th Grd Eng, Sci Tchr 1948-49; Alfred I. DuPont Elem 3rd Grd Tchr 1949-50; Milford Del Elem 3rd-4th Grd Tchr 1950-53; Lancaster Pub Schls 3rd Grd Tchr 1953-54; St Marys HS 1st-12th Grd Gym, Hlth Tchr 1954-55; Emporium Pub Schl 1st, 3rd-4th Grd Tchr 1955-64; St Marys Elem Schls 3rd-4th Grd Tchr 1964-86; *ai:* Traveling; Dancing; Gardening; Vol St Mary's Regnl Med Cntr; Book Clb; Bridge; Water Aerobics; DE St Ed Assoc 1948-53, St Rep St Convention; PA St Ed Assoc 1954-; NEA 1949-; St Marys Tchr Ed Assoc Founding Mem; PA Assn Schl Retiree 1986-, Pub Relations Chair; Am Assoc of Univ Women Treas, VP, Outstanding Women of Yr Elk Co Branch; Comm Nurses Assoc Bd Mem; St Marys Reg Med Ctr Hosp Aux Prgm Chair; AARP 1985-; Tchr of Yr Highland Rdng Cncl; *home:* 645 Sherry Rd Saint Marys PA 15857*

TROCCHIA, ROBERT CLIFTON, Music Supervisor; *b:* Rockbridge, OH; *m:* Carol Barker McLain; *c:* Lisa Troccia Hathaway; Vincent, Ann Taiganides; *ed:* OH Univ (BSED) Music 1960; Attnd Western Carolina Univ & Westminster Choir Coll; *cr:* Lancaster Chorale Artistic Dir 1987-; OH Univ at Lancaster Choral Conductor 1980-; Fairfield Union Schls Dir Music & Choral Conductor 1987-; *ai:* MENC 1960-; OMEA 1960-; ACDA 1970-; *home:* 417 Purvis Ave Bremen OH 43107

TROCCHIO, JOSETTE T., French, Latin & His Teacher; *b:* Egypt; *m:* Dennis; *c:* Rachel, Sarah; *ed:* Rockford Coll (BA) Fr & His 1970; Duquesne Univ (MA) European His 1972; Attnd Tufts Univ, Harvard Univ, CO Coll; *cr:* Duquesne Univ Grad TA His; Foxhollow Schl Fr, His & Eng Tchr 1973-75; Winslow Jr HS Eng Tchr 1976-78; Grafton HS Frgn Lang Tchr 1978-79; Bellingham HS Frgn Lang Tchr 1979-; *ai:* NHS Adv; Frgn Lang Club; Comm to Elect VP; Spon Trips to Europe & Exch Pgm; NEA 1978-; BTA 1978-; AAPT 1978-; Amer Classical Inst 1978-; Horace Mann Grant; MIT, Tufts & Simmons Most Influential HS Tchr; Most Likely to Be Remembered Tchr; *office:* Bellingham Memorial Jr Sr HS Blackstone St Bellingham MA 02019

TROCCOLO, JOAN MUNLEY, Sixth Grade Teacher; *b:* Meriden, CT; *m:* Louis Anthony; *c:* Robert Anthony; *ed:* Central Ct St Univ (BS) Elem Ed 1971; Post Grad Stud St Joseph's Coll, Central Ct St Univ; *cr:* Robert Earley MS 7th-8th Grd Tchr 1971-79; Moran MS 6th Grd Tchr 1979-80; Moses Y. Beach Elem Schl 3rd Grd Tchr 1980-95; Dag Hammarskjold MS 6th Grd Tchr 1995-; *ai:* Club Adv; WEA, CEA, NEA 1971-, WEA Bldg Rep Svc Awd; Delta Kappa Gamma 1979-, Treas, Schlsp Co-Chair; Ladies Guild of Church of Resurrection 1994-; Best Prgm of CT, Mentor, Co-operating Tchr; Area Evaluator for Town of Wlfd; *home:* 3 Anna Dr Wallingford CT 06492*

TROEST, DONNA MARIE, Fourth Grade Teacher; *b:* Fitchburg, MA; *c:* Kimberly, Toby; *ed:* Fitchburg St Coll (BAEd) Elem Ed 1981; Substance Abuse, Portfolios & Inclusion; *cr:* YMCA Presch Tchr 1981-82; Sacred Heart 2nd & 4th Grd & 5th-6th Grd Soc Stud Tchr 1982-, Vice-Prin 1994-; *ai:* Pat Brody Cat Shelter Vol; Tutoring; After Schl Pgm; NCEA 1993-.

TROFATTER, SUSAN G., English Teacher; *b:* New Haven, CT; *ed:* Elizabethtown Coll (BA) Eng 1972; Post-Grad Stud at Southern Ct St Univ, Marywood Coll, Millersville Univ, PA St Univ; *cr:* Eastern York Schl Dist Eng Tchr 1981-; *ai:* Future Tchrs of Amer Club Adv; Yth Ed Assn; E York Ed Assn 1981-, Rep, Treas; PA St Ed Assn, NEA 1981-; NCTE; PA Cncl of Tchrs of Eng; US Holocaust Meml Museum 1994-, Charter Mem; AmFar 1986-; St Francis Acad 1985-; *office:* Eastern York HS PO Box 2002 Wrightsville PA 17368*

TROHA, RICHARD JOSEPH, Industrial Arts Teacher; *b:* Clevand, OH; *m:* Denise Ann Gulas; *ed:* OH St Univ (BS) Industrial Arts Ed 1971; Cleveland St MS in Cmptr Sci; *cr:* Lake Cath HS Tchr, Dept Chm 1971-; *ai:* Sr Class Adv; Homecoming, Grad Moderator; CHALTA 1980-; Drawings & Renditions to City Bldg Code Book; Construction of Emergency Spine Bds for Fire Dept; *office:* Lake Catholic HS 6733 Reynolds Rd Mentor OH 44060

TROHA, ROBERT ANTHONY, Architectural Drafting Instr; *b:* Kenvil, NJ; *m:* Shirley Margaret Barnish; *c:* Teresa, Nancy, Robert Jr.; *ed:* Kean Coll (BA) Indstrl Ed 1969, (MA) Behavioral Sci 1974; *cr:* Dover HS Architectural Drafting Tchr 1964-; *home:* 39 Ferro Monte Ave # 141 Kenvil NJ 07847

TROIANELLO, VINA MARIE, Teacher; *b:* Methuen, MA; *ed:* Merrimack Coll (BA) His, Tchng 1973; Boston St Coll (MA) Tchng in Scndry Schl 1975; Univ of MA 3 Hrs; Fitchburg St Coll 3 Hrs; *cr:* St Margaret Schl Tchr 1974-78; St Mary Immaculate Conception Schl Tchr 1978-; Lawrence Pub Schls Adult Learning Ctr ESL Tchr 1984-95; St Mary Immaculate Conception Schl Vice Prin 1989-90; New Balance Shoe Factory ESL Consultant 1992-94; Northern Essex Comm Coll ESL Tchr 1993; Salem St Coll ESL Instr 1994; Hunington Learning Ctr MA Tchr 1995; New Balance Shoe Factory ESL Consultant 1996; *ai:* Soc Stud, Schlsp Coord, ESL Curr Coord 1995-; Cath Schl Week Comm 1995-; Grad Act Dir 1995-; ESL Testing Assessor 1995-; AM Prgm Co-Dir 1995-; Natl Cath Tchrs Assn; Natl Assn for Curr Dev; MTA; *office:* St Marys Imaculate Cncptn Schl 300 Haverhill St Lawrence MA 01841

TROIANO, DONNA MARIE, ESL Tchr & Biling Dept Chprsn; *b:* Camden, NJ; *c:* Alexander; *ed:* Wesley Coll (AA) Eng 1980; Glassboro Coll (BA) Eng 1982; Attnd Washington Coll Eng; Grad Stud ESL Cert, Linguistics; *cr:* Lehigh Press Editorial Supvr 1982-83; Bayada Nurses Staff Supvr 1983-85; Glassboro St Coll Writing Instr 1985-88; Camden Schls ESL Tchr 1987-; *ai:* Biling, ESL, Frgn Lang Chprsn; Multicultural Comm Chprsn; Hispanic Heritage Dance Troupe, Multicultural Celebrations Adv; TESOL 1988-; NEA, NJEA, CCEA, CEA 1987-; Wash Coll Alumni 1989-; *office:* East Camden MS 3064 Stevens St Camden NJ 08105*

TROIL, LINDA INNES, 5th Grade Teacher; *b:* Philadelphia, PA; *m:* Carmen; *c:* Jamie Lyn; *ed:* Millersville Univ (BS) Elem 1969, (MEd) Elem 1972; Rdng Specialist Cert; 26 Post Masters Degree Credits; *cr:* Penn Delco Schl Dist Intermediate Tchr 1969-70; Eastern Lebanon Cty Schl Dist Rdng Specialist Tchr 1976, 4th-5th Grd Tchr 1970-; *ai:* Environmental Ed Camp Comm & Staff; Coach for Odyssey of the Mind Tm; Peer Mediator Coord; Dist Staff Dev Comm; ELCEA 1970-, Sec; PSEA & NEA 1969-; Central Park United Meth Church 1979-, Chair of Worship Comm & Lay Reader; Adult Ed Commission; Rdng Food Ministry; Adv to Chruch Yth Grp; Nurture Comm; Presenter at St Rdng Convention; Delta Kappa Gamma; *office:* Fort Zeller Elem Schl RD 1 Richland PA 17087

TROILO, ANTHONY R., 5th Grade Teacher; *b:* Vandergrift, PA; *m:* Karen; *ed:* Edinboro St Coll (BS) Elem Ed 1974; *cr:* Kisk Area Schl Dist 5th Grd Tchr 22 Yrs; *ai:* St Gertrude Bsktbl Team Coach CYO; PSEA, NEA, Kisk Area Ed Assn 1974-; *home:* 226 Emerson St Vandergrift PA 15690

TROLLER, FRED, Professor of Design; *b:* Zurich, Switzerland; *m:* Beatrice Stocklin; *c:* Simon, Meret Piderman; *ed:* Kunstgewerbeschule Zurich (BFA) Graphic Design 1950; *cr:* Geigy Chemical Corp Design Dir 1961-66; Troller Assoc Ind Designer 1966-91; Alfred Univ Prof of Design & Chair Div of Design 1991-; *ai:* Strategic Planning & Art on Campus Comm; AIGA 1962-; AGI 1967-; *home:* 12 Harbor Ln Rye NY 10580

TROMBETTI, VINCE MICHAEL, Science Dept Chair & Teacher; *b:* Steubenville, OH; *m:* Nora Ann Wunderle; *c:* Katie; *ed:* OH St Univ (BSEd) PE 1983, (MAEd) Educl Admin 1991; *cr:* Columbus South HS Bio, Life Sci Tchr 1984; Groveport Madison HS Bio, Gen Sci Tchr 1984-91; Worthington Kilbourne HS Bio, Earth Sci Tchr 1991-; *ai:* Defensive Coord Var Ftbl, OHSAA Wrestling Ofcl; NSTA 1991-; NEA, OEA, WEA 1984-91; PTO Tchr of Yr 1993-94; *office:* Worthington Kilbourne HS 1499 Hard Rd Columbus OH 43235

TROMBLEY, LARRY LEE, HS Soc Stud Tchr & Bsbl Coach; *b:* Northfield, VT; *m:* Susan Muir; *c:* Lee, Justine; *ed:* Assumption Coll (BA) His 1972; Univ of VT (MED) Ed 1991; Bridgewater St Coll 15 Credit Hrs Elem Ed 1973-77; *cr:* Brockton Child Dev Ctr Tchr 1973-76; Children Place Tchr 1977-78; Missisquoi Vly Union HS Tchr, Coach 1978-89; Bellows Free Acad Tchr, Coach 1989-; *ai:* Var Boys Bsbl Coach; Archaeology Club Adv; Comm Svc Coord; NEA, VEA 1978-; Jaycee Tchr of Yr Awd 1980-81; Grant Comm Svc Prgm; Schlsp, Article Publication His of MUU Project; Swanton Historical Soc Text; *office:* Bellows Free Acad HS 71 S Main St Saint Albans VT 05478

TROMBLEY, VIRGINIA HASKIN, High School Science Teacher; *b:* Austin, TX; *m:* Larry James; *c:* Laura, Matthew; *ed:* Plattsburgh St Univ Coll (BSMT) Med Tech 1982, (MST) HS Bio 1991; *cr:* Au Sable Vly HS Sci Tchr 1991-; Clinton Comm Coll Adj Bio Instr 1992-93, 1995-; *ai:* Stu Discipline Comm; Bldg Planning Comm; ASCP 1977-; ASPT 1994-; NYSUT, AFT 1991-; Broad St PTO 1985-, VP, Pres; Plattsburgh CSO 1995-; Girl Scouts 1986-; NY Sci, Tech & Soc Project Resource Agent; Texaco-CPB-Natl Tchr Trng Inst Awd; WCFE Video-in-the-Classroom Awd; *office:* AuSable Valley HS 1490 Rt 9N Clintonville NY 12924

TROSKOSKY, MARIE CAROL, Secondary English Teacher; *b:* Jamaica, NY; *m:* Paul; *c:* Aaron; *ed:* Hartwick Coll (BA) Eng, Ed 1968; Coll of St Rose (MA) Eng 1972; 21 Grad Hrs for Diagnostic, Remedial Rdng; *cr:* Schalmont Cntrl Schl Scndry Eng 1968-72; Little Valley Cntrl Schl Scndry Eng 1972-; *ai:* Theatre Club, Newspaper, 8th Grd Adv; NCTE 1968-; Bradford Creative & Performing Arts, Lit Judge-Patron; *office:* Little Valley Central Schl 207 Rock City St Little Valley NY 14755

TROSSMAN, PATRICIA BURKS, Associate Professor; *b:* Brooklyn, NY; *m:* Herbert D.; *ed:* Univ of WI Madison (BS) Occupational Therapy 1964; Columbia Univ Tchrs Coll (MA) Applied Physiology 1978, (MED) Applied Physiology 1989, (EDD) Applied Physiology 1992; *cr:* Kings Cty Hosp Staff, Sr, Asst Supvr OT 1965-72; Gouverneur Hosp Supvr Occupational Therapy Dept 1972-76; SUNY Hlth Sci Ctr at Brooklyn Instr, Asst Prof, Assoc Prof, Chair Occupational Therapy 1976-, Assoc Dean Fac Dept 1994-; *ai:* Admissions, Acad Standing Comm Chair; Prgm Dev Comm; Amer Occupational Therapy Assn 1965-, Steering Comm Prof Prgm, Dirs Cncl, Fellow of the AOTA; Amer Soc Hand Therapists 1982-; Metropolitan NY Dist NYSOTA 1965-, Bd, Rsrch Comm Co-Chair, Svc; Amer Littoral Soc 1970-; NY City Audubon 1985-, Conservation, Prgm Comms, Svc; Grants Amer Occupational Therapy Fnd, Dept Hlth, Human Svcs; Articles Pub; SUNY Chancellors Awd Excl in Tchng 1993; *office:* SUNY Hlth Sci Ctr at Brooklyn Occupational Therpay Program 450 Clarkson Ave Box 81 Brooklyn NY 11203

TROTMAN, JOEANNA C., Business Tech Tchr & Coord; *b:* Glenridge, NJ; *m:* Roscoe E.; *c:* Keshia M.; *ed:* Montclair St Univ (BA) Bus Admin 1981; Jersey City St (MA) Urban Ed 1988, (MA) Counseling 1996; *cr:* NJ St Dept of Ed Spec Prgm Coord 6 Yrs; Clifford Scott HS Tchr & Coord 13 Yrs; *ai:* DECA-Mrktg Tech Club Adv; Girls Track Asst Coach; Schl Based Mgmt Comm; NEA 15 Yrs; NBA 10 Yrs; Alpha Kappa Alpha 1983-, Bd Mem; Fellowship Policy Decision Making Inst; *office:* Clifford J Scott H S 129 Renshaw Ave East Orange NJ 07017*

TROTMAN, SARITA WALKER, 6th Grade Teacher; *b:* New York City, NY; *m:* Robert; *c:* Melissa, Ericka; *ed:* Long Island Univ (BS) Ed 1965; 60 Credit Hrs; *cr:* PS 39 5th Grd Tchr 1965; PS 212 4th-5th Grd Tchhr 1966-69; Howard T Herber MS 5th-6th Grd Tchr 1969-; *ai:* More Effective Schls; Union Rep Malverne Tchrs union; Fac Advy Comm; Chrldng Coach; Frost Vly Outdoor Ed; MTA 1969-; NYSTA 1969-; Delta Kappa Gamma 1986-; NY St Eng Tchr of Yr; Malverne Schls Tchr of Yr; *home:* 510 Whitestar Ave West Hempstead NY 11552

TROTT, LINWOOD ROGER, 7th-12th Grade Bible Teacher; *b:* Milford, CT; *m:* Ann Paxton; *c:* Rachel, Jesse, Abigail, Grace; *ed:* Lancaster Bible Coll (BS) Bible 1982; Word of Life Inst Cert Bible; Liberty Bapt Seminary 30 Hrs Toward MA Rel; *cr:* Harrisburg Chrstn Schl Bible Tchr 1982-83; Faith Chrstn Schl Bible Tchr 1983-; *ai:* 8th Grd Advy; IM Floor Hockey Spon; ACSI 1988-; *office:* Faith Christian Schl 122 Dante St Roseto PA 18013

TROTTER, GARY J., Physics Teacher; *b:* Passaic, NJ; *ed:* Fairleigh Dickinson Univ (BA) Sci Ed 1978; Univ of Cntrl FL (MED) Sci Ed 1994; *cr:* Rutherford HS Sci & Physics Tchr 1978-89; South Lake HS Physics & Chem Tchr 1989-95; Leonia HS Physics Tchr 1995-; *ai:* Ski Club Adv; NEA 1978-; AAPT 1978-; Los Alamos Natl Lab Dept of Energy Tchr Rsrch Pgm 1993; South Lake HS Tchr of Yr 1993; Univ of FL Tchr Rsrch Update Experience 1994; *office:* Leonia HS 100 Christie Heights Rd Leonia NJ 07605

TROTTER, ROSA SNOW, Kindergarten Teacher; *b:* Hemingway, SC; *m:* Webster D. Jr.; *c:* Shylla, Chenile, Shynaya, Chelaye; *ed:* St Augustine's (BA) Early Chldhd Ed 1974; Wilmington Coll (MS) Ed 1994; Attnd Univ of PA, DE St Univ; Wilmington Coll; *cr:* Cools Spring SchlEarly Chldhd Tchr 1974-75; Mary C. I. Williams Schl Kndgtn Tchr 1975-78; Brandywood Schl Math & Rdng Tchr Title I 1978-80; Old Mill Lane Schl 1st Grd Tchr 1980-81; Mc Cullough Schl Kndgtn Tchr 1981-83; Carrie Downie Schl Kndgtn Tchr 1983-; *ai:* Schlsp Comm St of DE Churches of God in Christ Pres; Delta Sigma Theta; Rdng Comm; Mentor for Intercity Yth; NEA 1974-; Belvedere Fire Co Ladies Aux 1988-, Chm of Pub Relations; Belvedere Civic Assn 1980-; Outstdng Tchr Awd 1985; *home:* 212 Kiamensi Rd Wilmington DE 19804*

TROTZ, DONALD WILLIAM, English Teacher; *b:* Johnstown, PA; *m:* Janice K. Kasonovich; *ed:* Valley Forge Chrstn Coll (BS) Theology, Comm 1984; Univ of Pittsburgh at Johnstown (BA) Eng 1993; *cr:* Greater Johnstown HS Eng Tchr 1 Yr; *ai:* Theatrical Dept; Drama Club Adv.

TROUNSTINE, JEAN R., Humanities Professor; *b:* Cincinnati, OH; *m:* Robert Wald; *ed:* Beloit Coll (BA) Theat4re Arts, Eng 1969; Brandeis Univ (MFA) Theatre Arts 1973; *cr:* Middlesex Comm Coll Hum Prof 1989-; Mt Wachusett Comm Coll Adjunct Framingham Womens Prison 1990-; Boston Univ Adjunct Framingtham Womens Prison 1995-; *ai:* Matter of Fact Improvisational Theatre Troupe; Direct Plays at Framingham Womens Prison; NEA, CCCC, MCCDA, ICEA; MA Fnd for Hum Grants 3 Yrs; Women Who Care Awd; Publications in The Book Group Book, Boston Cruise Magazine, Catalyst Magazine, NADIE Journal; *office:* Middlesex Comm Coll 33 Kearney Sq Lowell MA 01852

TROUP, MARY LEE THOMAS, 5th Grade Teacher; *b:* Williamsport, PA; *m:* LaMar E.; *c:* Todd, Marla Troup Connaham, Deanna Troupe Harvey; *ed:* Lycoming Coll (BA) Biological Sci, Span, Sec Ed 1958; Wilkes Univ (MS) Ed 1989; 6 Credits Univ of Madrid Spain 1961; 33 Credit Hrs Penn St; *cr:* Montgomery Area SD Hlth, PE Tchr 1959-60; Newport SD Span, Eng Tchr 1960-61; Warrior Run SD Span, Eng, Bio Tchr 1961-63; West Beaver Elem Schl Tchr 1969-; *ai:* MWEA 1970-, Schlsp Ch; NEA, PSEA 1955-; St Paul's UCC 1969-, Cncl Pres 6 Yrs, UCW Pres 2 Yrs, VP; Snyder Co 4-H 1972-, Ldr; Beaver Springs Womens Home & Comm; Taught PLS Grad Courses Wilkes Univ 1991-93, LaSalle Coll 1993.*

TROUT, GARY JOEL, Speech, Drama Tchr & Cnslr; *b:* Parkersburg, WV; *ed:* Marietta Coll (BA) Speech & Drama 1967; Hunter Coll (MA) Theatre 1975; *cr:* Bureau of Speech Improvement Creative Dramatics Tchr 1967-71; Washington Irving HS Speech & Drama Tchr 1972-80; Brooklyn Tech HS Speech & Drama Tchr 1980-94; *ai:* Schl Play Dir 1980-84; Drama Club; Forensics Coach; UFT, Speech Tchrs Assn 1967-; Washington Irving HS Tchr of Yr 1976; *office:* Brooklyn Technical HS 29 Fort Green Pl Brooklyn NY 11217

TROUT, ROBERT JAY, Fifth Grade Teacher; *b:* Lebanon, PA; *m:* Judith Ann Margut; *c:* Robert E. Lee, Desiree Kristine; *ed:* Millersville St Coll (BS) Soc Sci 1969; Masters Equivalency; *cr:* Eastern Lebanon Cty Schl Dist Elem Tchr 1969-; *ai:* Safety Patrol Adv; Strategic Planning & Tech Comms; NEA, PSEA, ELCEA 1981-; 3 Civil War His Books-They Followed the Plume, Riding With Stuart, With Pen & Saber; DAR His Educator Awd.*

TROUTMAN, BARBARA JANE ROTHENBERGER, 2nd Grade Teacher; *b:* Buffalo, NY; *m:* Martin A.; *ed:* Univ of Buffalo (BA) Early Chldhd Ed 1965-66; Credit Hrs Univ of Buffalo, Buffalo St Coll; *cr:* Warner Robins Schl Kndgtn Tchr 1977-78; Lincoln Schl 1st Grd Tchr; Terrace Schl 2nd Grd Tchr; Cayuga Heights Schl 2nd Grd Tchr 1965-; *ai:* PTO, NYS Tchrs 1965-; *office:* Depew Pub Schls Como Park Blvd Depew NY 14043

TROUTMAN, GREGORY GENE, High School Math Teacher; *b:* Norristown, PA; *m:* Kristi D. Lederer; *ed:* Shippensburg Univ of PA (BSEd) Math, Scndry Ed 1992; Grad Stud Cnslng Psych; *cr:* Pottstown HS Math Tchr 1993-; *ai:* Stu Govt Adv; Head Soccer Coach; AFT 1993-; NCTM, PA Cncl Tchrs of Math 1989-; Kappa Sigma 1987-, VP; March of Dimes Awd, Top Schl Walk Ldr; *home:* 980 Terrace Ln Pottstown PA 19464*

TROUTMAN, JAMES BARRY, 7th Grd English & Math Teacher; *b:* Harrisburg, PA; *ed:* Shippensburg Univ (BS) Elem Ed, 1968, (MS) Elem Ed 1971; *cr:* Greenwood Elem Schl 5th & 6th Grd Tchr 1968-73; Greenwood HS 7th Grd Eng & Math Tchr 1973-; *ai:* Scndry Instructional Support Team; PA St Ed Assn, NEA, Greenwood Ed Assn 1968-; St John Luth Church 1958-, Cncl VP; *home:* RR 2 Box 421 Millerstown PA 17062

TROUTT, BOBBYE VARY, Asst Prof of Cnslng & Afr-Am; *b:* Harlan Cty, KY; *m:* George; *c:* Eve T. Powell, David, Margot; *ed:* Columbia Univ (MA) Clinical Psych 1989, (PHD) Clinical Psych 1980; NY Univ Postdoctoral Prgm Psychoanalysis, Psychotherapy, Postdoctoral Degree Clinical Psych 1990; *cr:* John Jay Coll of Criminal Justice Asst Prof 1987-; *ai:* Exec Comm Family Therapy & Psychoanalysis Project NY Univ; Advy Bd Citizens Advocates for Justice; Amer Psych Assn 1980-; *office:* John Jay Coll 445 W 59th St New York NY 10019

TROWELL, MADY ALLEN, Third Grade Teacher; *b:* Bar Harbor, ME; *c:* Tristan; *ed:* Westbrook Coll (AA) Liberal Arts 1968; Univ of ME at Orono (BS) Elem Ed 1970; Lesley Coll (MED) Creative Classrooms 1989; 27 Addl Grad Credits; *cr:* ASA Adams Elem Schl 1st Grd Tchr 2 Yrs; Sandown Cntrl Schl 2nd Grd Tchr 16 Yrs, 3rd Grd Tchr 2 Yrs; *ai:* Soc Stud & Lang Arts Curr Revision Comms; Peer Coaching Prgm; New England Accreditation Schls Steering Comm, Rep; Staff Dev Rep; AFT 1992-; St NH Rep USA Today; Natl Writing Prgm 1989; Beta Test Site Classroom for IBM Writing-to-Write Cmptr Prgm 1990; Presentor at New England Educators; *office:* Sandown Elem Schl Main St Sandown NH 03873

TROXELL, JEAN (MAXWELL), Kindergarten Teacher; *b:* Greensburg, IN; *m:* James M.; *c:* Julie Barker, Elizabeth White, Tom, Michael; *ed:* Elem Ed Miami Univ 1974; *cr:* Greenville City Schls 3rd Grd Tchr 1956-58; West Carrollton City Schl Kndgtn Tchr 1974-; *ai:* NEA; Cntrl Presbyn Church Elder, Church Choir 1966-; *office:* Harold Schnell Elem Schl 5995 Student St W Carrollton OH 45449

TROY, ROBERTA MAXINE, Professor of Biology; *b:* Philadelphia, PA; *m:* Eugene Davis; *c:* Kenneth, Kevin; *ed:* Tuskegee Inst (BS) Bio 1977, (MS) Bio Genetics 1980; Univ of FL (PHD) Biochemistry 1990; *cr:* Paine Coll Coord, Instr 1980-84; Cleveland Clinic Fnd Postdoctoral Research Fellow 1989-93; Lincoln Univ Assoc Prof 1993-; *ai:* Bio Club, Sigma Gamma Rho, Pre-Nursing Adv; Acad Standing Comm; LU-AAUP 1993-; McKnight Predoctoral Fellowship; *office:* Lincoln Univ Dept of Bio PO Box 179 Lincoln University PA 19352*

TROYAN, VIRGINIA ANDES, Social Studies Teacher; *b:* Port Jefferson, NY; *m:* Peter Jr.; *ed:* Univ of Rochester (BA) Psych 1989, (BS) Ec 1989, (MS) Ed 1990; *cr:* Westhampton Beach Schls Tchr 1991-; *ai:* Class 1991-95 Adv; AFT 1991-; NYSUT 1991-; *office:* Westhampton Beach HS Westhampton Beach Schls Westhampton Beach NY 11978

TROYER, DALE SHIELDS, Health & Phys Education Tchr; *b:* No Tonawanda, NY; *m:* Ronald Edward; *c:* Krystin, Ryan; *ed:* Niagara Cty Comm Coll (AA) Liberal Arts, Soc Sci 1970; SUNY Coll at Cortland (BS) PE 1972; 30 Grad Credit Hrs Hlth Ed; Attnd Univ of Buffalo, Niagara Univ, Oswego St Univ, Coll at Cortland; *cr:* Niagara Wheatfield Sr HS 9-12th Grd PE Tchr 1972-74; Oxford Rd Elem Schl K-3rd Grd PE Tchr 1975; Whitesboro Jr HS 8th Grd PE Tchr 1977-78; Madison Cntrl Schl K-12th Grd Hlth, PE Tchr 1979-; *ai:* Schl Crisis Team; Girls Var Swim Team Coach 1972-74, Jr Chrldng 1972-74, Var Sftbl 1979; NYS Certified Vllybl Off 1975-80; STA PEP 1992-; NY St United Tchrs 1990-; NEA 1979-; Numerous wkshps & seminars on health-related topics; *office:* Madison Central Schl Rt 20 Madison NY 13402

TROYER, RONALD EDWARD, Health & Physical Ed Teacher; *b:* Buffalo, NY; *m:* Dale Shields; *c:* Krystin, Ryan; *ed:* Niagara Comm Coll (AA) Liberal Arts 1970; St Univ of NY at Cortland (BS) PE 1972; Univ af Buffalo (MS) Hlth Ed 1976; Credit Hrs at Niagara Univ; *cr:* Camden HS Hlth & PE Tchr 1974-; *ai:* AFT 1974-; Amer Red Cross 10 Yrs Svc; Article Pub Journal of Schl Hlth; Track-Field & Cross Cntry Coach 1974-89; St Ranked Vlybl Ofcl; *office:* Camden Cntrl HS Oswego St Camden NY 13316

TRUAX, PATSY L., Fourth Grade Teacher; *b:* Woodsfield, OH; *ed:* OH Univ (BSEd) PE 1962; OH Univ Elem Ed 1993; *cr:* Cleveland Pub PE 1962-79; Caldwell Exempted 4th Grd Tchr 1979-93, Third Grd Tchr 1993-94; Fourth Grd 1995-; *ai:* Math Curr, Writing Comms; AFT 1962-, Bldg Chprsn; NEA, OEA 1980; *office:* Caldwell Exempted Village 44350 Fairground Rd Caldwell OH 43724

TRUBIC, MARY RITA, Social Stud & Lang Arts Tchr; *b:* Pittsburgh, PA; *ed:* OH Dominican Coll (BA) His & Scndry Ed 1968; Univ of Pittsburgh (MED) Ed 1973; Attnd DuQuesne Univ at Pittsburgh elem Ed Cert 1991; *cr:* Sharpsburg Cath Schls 4th Grd Tchr 1968-70; St anthony Schl 6th-8th Grd Soc Stud & Lang Arts Tchr 1970-80; St John Neumann Regnl Cath Elem Schl 6th-8th Grd Soc Stud & 8th Grd Lang arts, Rdng & S 1980-; *ai:* Stu Cncl & Former Spelling Bee Moderator; NCEA 19 MS Assn 1993-; Thanks to Tchrs Nom 1991; Golden Apple Awd Nor *office:* St John Neumann Cath Elem Sch 250 44th St Pittsburgh PA

TRUCANO, JOHN WILLIAM, 7th-8th Grade English Teac Vineland, NJ; *m:* Leslie Aleshire; *ed:* Glassboro St Coll (BA) E 1970; *cr:* Maurice River Twp Elem Schl 3rd Grd Tchr 1970, 5th G 1970-71, Head Tchr 1971-76, 6th-8th Grd Eng Tchr 1971-; *ai:* Aft Ftbl, Bsktbl, Hockey Bowling Prgms; ECHO Prgm; NEA 1970-; Club 1991-; Amer Legion 1989-; Maurice River Twp Elem Schl Tch 1987-88; *home:* 2557 Venezia Ave Vineland NJ 08360

TRUDEAU, ISABEL LOIS, Third Grade Teacher; *b:* Nanticoke, Donald C.; *ed:* Lycoming Coll (BA) Math 1966; Southern CT St Co Elem Ed 1971; 6th Yr Univ of Bridgeport Elem Ed 1975; 15 Cre Sacred Heart Univ; *cr:* Middlebrook Jr HS 7th-8th Grd Math Tchr 19 Jane Ryan Elem Schl 5th Grd Tchr 1969-82, 3rd Grd Tchr 1982-; Tech Comms; Schl Resource Tchr; Schl Choir Accompanist; NEA TEA 1967-; Delta Kappa Gamma 1975-, Chptr Pres 1979-81; Ph Kappa 1988-; ATOMIC; NCTM; CSTA; NSTA; Golden Hill Unite Church 1967-, Admin Bd Chprsn; Gen Electric Fnd Math Grant 1987; Sacred Heart Univ Math Ldrshp Prgm 1989; *office:* Jane Rya Schl 190 Park Ln Trumbull CT 06611

TRUDEL, R. I., Social Studies Teacher; *b:* Taunton, MA; *m:* Dodemont; *c:* Patrick, Chrissy Sholtes; *ed:* Western CT St Univ (B Soc Sci 1966; Fairfield Univ (MA) Soc Sci 1969, (CAGS) Supervision 1970; Univ of Bridgeport, Univ of CT Addl Credi Dnbury HS Soc Stud Tchr 1966-; *ai:* Safety, Tech Cncl; Mentor Tch 1965-; CEA, DEA 1966-; PDK 1971-, Historian; St Gregory Parish, 1963-; Amer Phitalelic Soc 1973-; Around the World Travel Grant Union Carbide Tchr of Yr 1989; *office:* Danbury HS Clapboard Ri Danbury CT 06811*

TRUE, PAMELA W., Fifth Grade Teacher; *b:* Norwich, NY; *ed:* S of NY at Cortland (BS) Elem Ed 1985; St Univ of NY at Albany (MS 1991; *cr:* Milton Terrace Elem Schl 5th Grd Tchr 1987-; *ai:* Alter in Stu Groupings Comm; BSEA, NYSUT 1987-, Bldg Rep; Amer Soc, Vol; *office:* Milton Terrace Elem Schl 100 Wood Rd Ballston S 12020

TRUE, RUTH BROWNING, Former Teacher; *b:* Norwich, CT; *m:* Anthony; *c:* Troy A., Kenneth A., Matthew A.; *ed:* Univ of Farmington (BS) Elem Ed 1966; 45 Post Grad Hrs; 15 Credit Hrs Ins Prgms; *cr:* Voluntown Elem Schl 2nd Grd Tchr 1966-67; Jay Elem S Grd, Remedial Rdng, 1st Grd Tchr 1967-93; Marnov Ed Su Consultant 1993-; *ai:* Support, Crisis Intervention Teams; Improvement Team Chprsn; Educl Advy Cncl; NEA-Retired, MRTA NEA 1966-93; MTA, Jay Tchrs Assn 1967-93; NCTM 1991-; Jay Church 1975-; Otis Credit Union 1990-, Supervisory Comm Chprsn Bd of Dirs 1991-95; Cntry Classic Car Club 1988-94; John H Fellowship 1984-85, 1991-92, 1993-94; Edcore Schl Project 19 Edcore Open Opp Grant 1990-91; ME Presidential Awd Excl in 1993.*

TRUE, STEPHEN EDWARD, Chemistry & Physics Teacher; *b:* N NY; *ed:* Univ of Buffalo (BA) Physics & Tchng of Sci 1992; 12 Cre MA in Scndry Ed in Progress; *cr:* Univ at Buffalo Tchrs Asst 19 Caledonia-Mumford CS Chem Tchr 1994-; *ai:* Chess Club; Summer Instr; AFT 1994-; NYSUT 1994-; *home:* 91 Prospect St Avon NY 1

TRUESDALE, CAROL ANN, 5th Grade Teacher; *b:* Rochester, N SUNY Geneseo (BS) Eng, Ed 1972-78; Attnd RIT, UOFR, MC Chestnut Ridge Elem Schl 1st, 4th, 5th, 6th Grd Tchr 19 Chruchville-Chili MS 6th Grd Eng, Soc Stud Tchr 1993-94; Fair Road Elem Schl 5th Grd Tchr 1994-; *ai:* Dist Rep for FRAT; Dram Grd Drama, Musical Coord; Spon Tchr for 3 Area Coll; Peer Coach; 1975-; NRA; Roch Museum, Sci Cent 1994-; ASCAP 1985-; Ge Alumni 1975-; RAMS 1986-; Pub Lyricist, Articles, Local Paper; C Rochester Cert of Merit 1984; Stu, Tchr Adv 7 Yrs; *office:* Fairbanks Elem Schl 175 Fairbanks Rd Churchville NY 14428*

TRUEX, MARCI ANN, Science Teacher; *b:* Canton, OH; *ed:* Mt V Nazarene Coll (BS) Comprehensive Sci 1994; Capital Univ 4 Hrs Univ at Lancaster 5 Hrs; *cr:* Lancaster HS Scndry Sci Tchr 1994-; *ai:* Hockey Goalie & JV Girls Bsktbl Coach; Destructuring Comm; 1994-; OEA 1994-; LEA 1994-; OHSCA 1994-.*

TRUITT, BRETT J., English Teacher; *b:* Fayetteville, NC Fayetteville St Univ (BS) Eng 1974; Adelphi Univ (MA) Eng 19 Credit Hrs; *cr:* Hemstead HS Eng Tchr 1980-; Bronx Comm Coll Eng 1995-; Empire St Coll at NY Eng Prof 1996; *ai:* Var Sftbl, Vlybl C Newspaper, Yrbk Adv; NCTE, NYSUT 1979-; NAFE 1995-; Delta S Theta 19720; Mellon Grant; *office:* Hempstead HS President Peninsula Blvd Hempstead NY 11550

TRUITT, CHERYL LYNNE, 6th Grade Science Teacher; *b:* Salis MD; *ed:* James Madison Univ (BS) Elem Ed 1981; Salisbury St Univ Elem Ed 1989; *cr:* Chesapeake Individualized Learning Ctr Tchr 19 Rosemont Elem 6th Grd Tchr 1982-84; Sub Tchr 1984-85; Frankford 4th Grd Tchr 1985-91; Selbyville MS 6th Grd Tchr 1991-; *ai.* Olympiad Asst Coach; Chrstn Edctrs Assn Intnl 1994-; Eagles Nest F Church 1993-, Yth Group Asst Ldr 1995-, Sussex Pregnancy Care Ctr Bd Sec, Bd of Dirs; Frankford Elem Tchr of Yr 1987-88; Selbyvil Tchr of Yr 1993-94; Supts Order of Excl 1993; *office:* Selbyville M Box 230 Selbyville DE 19975*

TRUITT, MARGARET LOCKERMAN, Fourth Grade Teache Salisbury, MD; *w:* Richard A. (dec); *c:* Barbara J., David I.; *ed:* Sali St Univ (BS) Elem Ed 1963; 18 Addl Credits; *cr:* Delmar HS 3rd Grd 1963-64; Delmar Elem Schl 1st Grd Tchr 1964-66; East High Elem 4th Grd Tchr 1976-; *ai:* NEA, EAEA 1976-; St Paul's United Meth Ch Choir Mem; *home:* 521 Mulberry St Elizabethtown PA 17022*

TRUITT, OSTEIN BARNES, Associate Prof of Microbiolog Chester, PA; *m:* Haywood; *c:* Jocelyne, Candace, Lauren; *ed:* Th Jefferson Univ (MS) Clinical Microbiology 1975; *cr:* Marymount Asst Prof 1976-80; Univ of MD Instr 1980-81; Barrie Montessori Sch Tchr 1987-89; Montgomery Coll Assoc Prof 1989-; *ai:* Professional Com Chair; Amer Soc of Microbiology 1989-; NIA Investment Club 1 VP; Ldrshp Dev Inst Cert.

TRUMAN, DALE W., Sixth Grade Teacher; *b:* Pittsburgh, PA; *m:* K Vaupel; *c:* Kelly; *ed:* Slippery Rock Elem Math 1972; Addl Credi Penn St; *cr:* Shaler Elem Schls Tchr 1972-; *ai:* Alg I Club; Intram Girls Bsktbl Coach; SAEA, PSEA 1972-; *office:* Shaler Area MS 700 Ave Glenshaw PA 15116

TRUMBAUER, DAVID S., Naval Science Instructor; *b:* Sellersville, *m:* Mary M. Neal; *c:* David Jr., Karen, Daniel; *ed:* Univ of MD Microbiology 1960; Naval Postgraduate Schl (MS) Phys Oceanogr 1966; MSA Prgm; Attn Bowie St Univ, Geo. Washington Univ, Cath U *cr:* US Navy Active Duty 1960-81; US Naval Acad Navigation, Ocean 1970-72; Suitland HS Naval Sci Instr 1981-93; Bowie HS Naval Sci 1993-; *ai:* Dept Chair; Acad Team Spon; PGCEA, MSTA, NEA, Ret C Assn 1981-; Amer Legion, VFW 1994-; *office:* Bowie HS 15200 Annap Rd Bowie MD 20715*

ıBORE, BARBARA DAVIS, History & Bible Teacher; *b:* Blakely, *:* Jeffrey; *c:* Deidral, Jeffrey Micah; *ed:* Troy St Univ (MS) Ed 1986; Valdosta St Univ, Columbia Union Coll; *cr:* Calhoun Cty Schl Tchr 85; Sylvandale Elem Schl Tchr 1985-91; Greater Philadelphia Jr Tchr 1992-; *ai:* 7th Grd, Puppet Ministry Spon; 10th Grd Homeroom; ledge Chm, Curr Comms; Schl Bd 1994-; Daycare Comm 1995-, n; Numerous Articles Pub; *office:* Greater Philadelphia Jr Acad 1845 ry Rd Huntingdon Valley PA 19007*

ıBORE, JUDITH ANN,IHM, Theology Teacher; *b:* Sellersville, *d:* Immaculata Coll (BA) Theo, Soc Stds 1968; St Charles Seminary Theo 1976; Cath Univ of Amer (MA) Church Admin 1976; *cr:* Good erd Schl 5 Grd Tchr 1964-67; St Aloysius Acad 6 Gr Tchr 1968-75; culata HS Theology Tchr 1977-79, 1985-91; Queen of Heaven Elem Prin 1979-82; St Maria Goretti Elem Schl Prin 1982-85; Kenndy ck Cath HS Theology Tchr 1991-; *ai:* NCEA; Outstdng Edctr culata HS 1989-90; *office:* Kennedy-Kenrick Cath HS 250 E Johnson Norristown PA 19401

ıMP, CARL WILLIAM, 6th Grade Science Teacher; *b:* ricktown, PA; *m:* Patsy Arlene Wilson; *c:* Megan, Amanda; *ed:* heny Co Comm Coll (AS) Police Sci 1972; California Univ of PA Elem Ed 1976; Pub Schl Admin 27 Grd Credit Hrs; *cr:* Waynesburg Dept Patrolman 1972-73; Cntrl Greene Schl Dist Elem Tchr 1976-; urr Cncl; Sci Dept Chprsn; Strategic Planning Comm; Waynesburg Prof Assn, PSEA, NEA 1976-; *office:* Margaret Bell Miller MS 126 coln St Waynesburg PA 15370*

ıNCALI, CONSTANCE HENCHENSKI, Departmental Lang Arts *b:* Jersey City, NJ; *m:* Joseph; *c:* Joseph; *ed:* Felician Coll (BA) Elem 973; Fairleigh Dickinson Univ Eng as Second Lang Cert 1996, 18 ts Toward Masters in Lang Acquisition; *cr:* Sacred Heart 8th Grd Arts Tchr 8 Yrs; Memorial Schl Departmental Lang Arts Tchr 11 Yrs; rbk & 8th Grd Adv; NJEA, NEA, BCEA 1985-; Ed Assn of South ensack 1985-, Pres, VP, Treas; *home:* 300 Williams Ave Hasbrouck ıts NJ 07604*

ıNICK, GAIL GORDON, Visual Arts Teacher; *b:* Sharon, PA; *m:* rt E.; *c:* Austin, Annah; *ed:* Kent St Univ (BFA) Painting, Sculpture *cr:* Kent St Univ Tech Coll Continuing Ed, Art Instr 1981-83; Artist l, Fine Arts Cncl Tech Coll Traveling, Visiting Artist Instr 1983; bull Cty Arts Excel Visual Arts, Arts Excel Instr 1993-; *ai:* Odyssey nd Coach; Regnl Scholastic Arts Show Judge; PTO 1990-; Trumbull uild 1982-, Bd of Dir 1983, Ed Dir; OH Designer Craftsmen 1983-; *:* 4509 State Route 7 Burghill OH 44404*

ıST, DEBORAH ANNE, Family & Consumer Science Tchr; *b:* more, MD; *m:* James Schleppy; *ed:* Univ of MA at Amherst (BS) Ec Ed 1975; Keene St Coll (MED) Cnslng, Consultation 1988; rol Theory; Critical Skills; *cr:* Pioneer Vly Regnl Schl Home Ec Tchr -76; Dennis-Yarmouth HS Home Ec Tchr 1976-78; LUnenburg HS Bio 1978-79; ConVal Schl Dist Hlth, Consumer Sci Tchr 1979-; *ai:* FHA Natl Adv 1989-90; Peer Outreach Adv; AAFCS 1988-; NEA 1975-, Negotiations Comm; Grants Carl Perkins Yearly 1985-, United Way Crisis Hotline; *office:* Conval HS Rt 202 N Peterborough NH 03458*

BUS-DUBIEL, TAMMY LYNN, Social & Iroquois Studies Tchr; *b:* wanda, NY; *m:* Gerald John Jr.; *ed:* Buffalo St Coll (BA) Scndry Soc Ed & Anthropology 1992; Working on Masters Scndry Soc Stud; *cr:* ca Nation of Indians Johnson O'Malley Tutor 1993-95; Gowanda Cntrl HS Iroquois Stud Tchr 1993-, Soc Stud Tchr 1995-; *ai:* 8th Grd Class Tech Comm; Whale Club Adv; NY St Council for the Soc Stud 1994-; ve Amer Educators Action Research Forum 1994; *office:* Gowanda Jr Sr HS 24 Prospect St Gowanda NY 14070

ıCINSKI, RICHARD, Math Dept Head & Teacher; *b:* New Britain, *m:* Mary M. Levy; *ed:* Cntrl CT St Univ (BS) Ed, Math 1975; 40 Grad CCSU, Boston Univ; *cr:* Bloomfield Jr HS Math Tchr 1975-85; mfield HS Math Tchr 1985-; *ai:* Boys & Girls Vlybl Coach; otiating Team Bloomfield Ed Assn; NEA 1975-; ASCD, Am VB ches Assn 1992-; *office:* Bloomfield HS Huckleberry Ln Bloomfield 6002

HOPP, CHARLES, Fifth Grade Teacher; *b:* Abington, PA; *ed:* ntown Coll of St Francis De Sales (BA) Politics 1989; *cr:* St Leo the t Schl Fifth Grd Tchr 1990-; *ai:* Commissioner of Bsbl; Soccer Coach; Comm Assn 1989-, Commissioner of Bsbl; *office:* St Leo The Great 6649 Tulip St Philadelphia PA 19135

ıEN, F., Computer Programming Teacher; *b:* Shanghai, China; *m:* ce; *c:* Laura; *ed:* Univ of CA Berkeley (BS) Chem Engr 1965; Univ of Seattle (PHD) Chem 1969; *cr:* Exxon Chem Co Sr Engr 1974-83; ny HS Tchr 1984-; *ai:* NJIT Cmptr Olympics Spon; ACS; AICHE; A; Chinese Chrstn Church 1978-, Prin Sunday Schl; *home:* 78 Elm St nia NJ 07067

ıGOUNIS, PAMELA ANN, Spanish & Japanese Teacher; *b:* Camden, *m:* John; *c:* John Jr., Christopher; *ed:* Goucher Coll (BA) Span 1982; Kenwood HS Span Tchr 1982-85; Deep Creek MS Span Tchr 1982-85; rokee HS Span Tchr 1985-; *ai:* Span Club Adv; Cheerleading Coach; A 1985-; NEA 1982-; Federal Grant Used to Train for Conducting reach Wkshps in Tchng Japanese Summer 1994; *office:* Cherokee HS ow Bend Rd Marlton NJ 08053

ıOTOS, NICHOLAS, Second Grade Teacher; *ed:* Suffolk Univ (BS) Ed 7; Univ of MA (MA) Ed 1982; *cr:* Barnes MS Eight Grade Eng Tchr 9-80; Mattahunt Elem Schl Kndgtn-1 Tchr 1980-81; Madison Park HS Tchr 1981-83; Mattahunt Elem Schl Fifth Grd Tchr 1983-91; James Elem Schl Second, Fifth Grd Tchr 1991-; *ai:* Voice of Winthrop HS St tbl Champs 1995; Spokesman Non-Profit Fnd Harry Agganis Statue rts Museum of New England; Amer Hellenic Educl Progressive Assn mpic Centennial Tribute Statue Comm 1996; AFT, BTU, MFT 1979-; er Hellenic Educl Progressive Assn 1976-; Suffolk Univ Alumni Assn 9; AHI 1995; Winthrop HS Hall of Fame Comm 1995; Author Pub Book Golden Greek; NECTA Sports Awd; Childrens Hosp Cardiac Fund Vol draiser; Hellenic Nrsng Home Vol.

ıONOS, PETER THEMIS, Mathematics Teacher; *b:* Pawtucket, RI; *ed:* vidence Coll (BA) Math, Ed, Spec Ed 1975; *cr:* Riverside Jr HS Math r 1975-76; Martin Jr HS Math Tchr 1976-82; Behavior Rsrch Inst Tchr Autistic 1982-83; Martin Jr HS Math, Cmptr Literacy Tchr 1983-90; t Prov HS Math Tchr 1990-; *ai:* Adult Ed GED Prep, Cmptr Sci, Word c; MEA, NEARI, EPEA 1975-; *office:* East Providence Sr HS 2000 vtucket Ave East Providence RI 02914*

ıOUKALAS, GEORGE CHRISTOS, Chemistry Teacher; *b:* Lowell, *m:* Joan Maurogianis; *c:* Katherine Olga, Christa Theodora; *ed:* folk Univ (BA) Psych 1970; River Coll (MA) Cnslng 1978; 33 Post d Credit Hrs; *cr:* Windham Schls Sci Tchr, Chm 1972-75; Billerica ls Sci Tchr 1975-; *ai:* Adv Billerica Team North Shore Sci League; AFT 5-; Intnl Brotherhood of Magicians 1974-; Soc of Amer Magicians, s, Closeup Magic Awd Assembly 118; *office:* Billerica Memorial HS 35 er St Billerica MA 01821

ıAZON, FE L., 8th Grade Teacher; *b:* Manila, Philippines; *m:* Ernesto; Louis Albert, Ma Aurora Trinidad; *ed:* Univ of St Thomas (BSEd)Elem 1967; Pope Pius XXII (AS) Theology 1969; Admin & Supervision 1-83; Mngmt 1983-86; *cr:* St Isabel Coll 6th Grd Tchr 1967-71; legio San Agustin Co-Curricular Coord, Tchr 1971-87; St Ann Schl 8th Grd Tchr 1988-90; John Paul II Schl 8th Grd Tchr 1990-; *ai:* Yrbk Adv; Prgm Coord; Filipino-Amer Tchrs Assn 1993-; Loyalty Awd 1981; Best Tchr 1995; Tchr Recognition Awd 1995; *office:* John Paul II Schl 555 7th St Hoboken NJ 07030

TUBAUGH, MARILYN ALBERT, Instructor of Accounting; *b:* Wheeling, WV; *m:* Albert V. Jr.; *c:* Jennifer Bruce, Jeff; *ed:* OH Univ (AA) Psych & Sociology 1974; Hocking Coll (AA) Acctng 1975; Wheeling Jesuit Coll (BA) Acctng 1983, (BS) Acctng 1983; *cr:* Belmont Tech Coll Acctng Instr 1983-91; Jefferson Comm Coll Acctng Instr 1991-; *office:* Jefferson Comm Coll 4000 Sunset Blvd Steubenville OH 43952

TUBBS, STEPHEN WALTER, HS Soc Stud Tchr & Chprsn; *b:* Waverly, NY; *m:* Julia Lamb; *ed:* SUNY at Geneseo (BS) Scndry Ed, His 1972; Elmira Coll (MS) Scndry Ed, His 1975; *cr:* Athens Area HS Soc Stud Instr 1976-80; SRU HS Soc Stud Instr 1980-89; Athens Area HS Soc Stud Instr 1989-; *ai:* Class of 1980 & 1982, NHS Adv 1988-; Waverly Hook, Ladder Fire Dept 1976-; SUNY at Brockport Natl Endowment for Hum 1986; *office:* Athens Area HS Frederick St Athens PA 18810

TUBMAN, JOANNE MORRIS, English & ESL Teacher; *b:* Mt Holly, NJ; *c:* Samantha; *ed:* Howard Univ (BA) Eng 1975; Kean Coll 30 Credit Hrs Grad Stud; *cr:* Comm Coll of Baltimore Instr 1983-87; Burlington City HS Tchr 1987-; *ai:* Right to Know Coord; NEA 1987-; NJEA 1987-; BCEA 1987-; *office:* Burlington City HS 1001 Dewey St Burlington NJ 08016

TUCCERI, ROBERT GENE, High School Math Teacher; *b:* Cambridge, MA; *m:* Lillian V. Lauzon; *c:* Robert P., Kenneth J., Laura I.; *ed:* Salem St Coll (BS) Math, Sci Ed 1972; Fitchburg St Coll (MS) Sci Ed, Math 1979; 48 Addl Hrs; *cr:* Beverly Voc HS Math, Sci Tchr 1972-73; Billerica Meml HS Math Tchr 1973-; *ai:* AFT, MFT 1973-; *office:* Billerica Memorial HS 35 River St Billerica MA 01821*

TUCCI, MARIA, English Teacher; *b:* Greensburg, PA; *ed:* Setor Hill Coll (BA) Eng 1976; Duquesne Univ (MA) Eng 1978; *cr:* Duquesne Univ Tchng Asst 1976-78; Seton Hill Coll Opportunity Prgm Eng Tchr 1980-95; Greensburg Cntrl Cath HS Eng Tchr 1978-; *ai:* Adv Acad Quiz Team; Stu Asst Prgm; NCTE 1979-; Ligonier Vly Writers Assoc 1991-; *office:* Greensburg Cntrl Catholic HS 901 Armory Dr Greensburg PA 15601

TUCCILLO, JEAN PELL, 2nd Grade Teacher; *b:* Brooklyn, NY; *m:* Francis; *ed:* Oneonta St (BA) Psych 1967; 30 Grad Hrs; *cr:* Sauquoit Vly Cntrl Schl 2nd Grd Tchr 1967-; *ai:* Dist Shared Decision Making Elem Math Comm; Bldg Shared Decision Making Team; AFT, NYSUT 1967-; Tchrs Assn 1967-, Bldg Rep, Negotiations Chprsn; *office:* Sauquoit Valley Central Schl 9449 Jennifer Ln Oneida St Sauquoit NY 13456

TUCK, LONNETTE RILEY, Social Studies Teacher; *b:* Memphis, TN; *m:* Robert E.; *c:* Marissa; *ed:* TN St Univ (BS) His, Ed 1978; TX Southern-Thurgood Marshall Schl of Law (JD) Law 1981; *cr:* US Navy Attorney 1983-85; White Plains MS Tchr 1988-; *ai:* Natl Jr Honor Soc; African-Amer His Month Comm; NYSUT 1988-; Alpha Kappa Alpha 1975-; Fisher Hill Assn 1993-; Jack & Jill of Amer 1994-; Westchester Cty Women's Advy Bd; *office:* White Plains MS 128 Grandview Ave White Plains NY 10605

TUCKER, CHARLES EDWARD, 5th Grade Teacher; *b:* Niagara Falls, NY; *m:* Linda Joyce Wyno; *c:* Linda Renee Tucker-Gueli; *ed:* Niagara Cty Comm Coll (AA) Lbrl Arts, Hum, SS 1972; D'Youville Coll (BS) Elem Ed, Eng 1989; Niagara Univ (MS) Cnslng 1992, (MS) Ed Admin 1995; *cr:* HSB Factory Mutual Engrng Nuclear Quality Assurance 1974-87; *ai:* Self-esteem Group Moderator; Redistricting Comm; Annual WA Trip Comm Chair; Phi Delta Kappa 1994-; Kiwanis Club of N Niagara Falls 1993-; Knights of Columbus 1977-; *office:* Harry F Abate Elem Schl 1625 Lockport St Niagara Falls NY 14305

TUCKER, EDWARD, Social Studies Teacher; *b:* Lewiston, ME; *m:* Delene Strout; *c:* Cindy Cormier, Edward, Bethany; *ed:* Univ of ME (BA) Pol Sci 1967; NEI Diploma Funeral Sci 1968; *cr:* Elem Street Schl Soc Stud Tchr 1968-; *ai:* Union #29 Cert Comm; Mechanic Falls Tchrs Assn, Negotiator; NEA, MEA 1967-; *office:* Elm Street Elem Schl 119 Elm St Mechanic Falls ME 04256*

TUCKER, JOYCE B., Spanish Teacher; *b:* Waterbury, CT; *m:* Lawrence D.; *c:* Elizabeth, Mary Catherine; *ed:* SCSU (BS) Span 1970; Candidate for Biling Ed Masters; Learning Styles Tchr Trainer, Trained in Chicago 1992-93 with Bernice Mc Carthy 4 Mat Excel; Talents Unlimited Natl Trainer 1996; *cr:* Guilford HS Span Tchr 1970-74, Span Tchr 1986-; *ai:* Dist Prof Dev Comm; Span Honor Soc, Jr Class Adv; Asst Dir Summer Schl Guilford Schls; Adv One Act Plays; AATSP, NEA, COLT 1986-; ASCD 1991-; Excel Inc 1992-; 4-MAT Learning Styles in Chicago 1992-93 Grant; Celebration at Excl Awd 1994; Dept of Ed Celebration of Excl Advy Cncl 1994-; *office:* Guilford HS 605 New England Rd Guilford CT 06437*

TUCKER, MICHAEL STUART, History Teacher; *b:* Elizabeth, NJ; *m:* Catherine; *ed:* Marietta Coll (BA) His 1967; Montclair St (MA) His 1973; *cr:* Bloomfield High His Tchr 1971-; *ai:* Soc Sci club & Amnesty Intnl Adv; NEA 1971-; NJEA 1971-; BEA 1971- Schl Rep; Prof Singer; Bands; Local Theater; Schl Productions; *office:* Bloomfield HS 160 Broad St Bloomfield NJ 07003

TUCKER, PAMELA J., Mathematics Teacher; *b:* Washington, DC; *ed:* Univ of DC (BS) Math 1987; 42 Grad Hrs Scndry Curr, Instruction Howard Univ; *cr:* Kelly Miller JHS Math Tchr 1987-; *ai:* Sr Class Spon; Yrbk Adv; Local Schl Restructuring Team Mem; Recruitment Team Chprsn; WA Tchrs Union 1988-; DC Pub Schls Math, Sci, Tech Framework Writer; WA Parent Group Fund Grant Recipient; Tchr of Yr Winner 1993-94; *office:* Kelly Miller Jr HS 49th & Brooks St NE Washington DC 20019*

TUCKER, SHEILA S., Earth Science Teacher; *b:* Syracuse, NY; *c:* Jason, Jonathan, Julie, Heather, Elizabeth Tucker-Schultz; *ed:* Syracuse Univ (BA) Sci, Ec; Univ of MI (MA) His; Cornell (MED) Sci; *cr:* Ithaca HS Tchr 1979-81; Tompkins CoHand Comm coll Assoc Prof 1981-, Baldwinsville Cntrl Schl Tchr 1983-; *ai:* Honor Soc Adv; NEA 1984-; Auburn Schl Bd 12 Yrs, Pres; *office:* Durgee Jr HS E Oneida St Complex Baldwinsville NY 13027*

TUCKER, STEPHEN ALFRED, Supervisor; *b:* Providence, RI; *m:* Barbara Lawrence; *c:* Stephen Jr., Benjamin; *ed:* Univ of RI (BS) Ag Tech 1964; St Univ of NJ at Rutgers (MEd) Voc Tech Ed 1974; 62 Credits Beyond Masters; *cr:* Voorhees HS Agriscience Tchr 1964-68; North Hunterdon HS Agriscience Tchr 1968-76; Allentown HS Supvr, Agriscience, Ind Tech, Voc Ed 1976-; *ai:* FFA, Agriscience Club Adv; NJ Agriscience Tchrs Assn 1964-, Pres, Treas, Outstdng Tchr; NJ Ed Assn 1964-; NJ Voc Tchrs Assn 1964-, Ag VP; Unionville Cemetery Assn 1968-, Pres; FFA Alumni 1978-, Life Mem; Montgomery Historical Soc 1985-; Montgomery Arts Assn 1995-; Honorary Garden St FFA Degree Recipient; Epsilon Pi Tau; Cooperating Tchr for Cook Coll Stu Tchrs; Thirty Yr Agriscience Tchr Svc Awd; *office:* Allentown HS 256 County Road 513 Glen Gardner NJ 08826

TUCKER, THOMAS E., Music Teacher; *b:* Belding, MI; *m:* Bianka Ludwig; *c:* Noelle, Thomas; *ed:* MI St Univ (BA) Music Ed 1967, (MM) Music Ed 1970; *cr:* Wiesbaden Jr HS Music Tchr 1969-73; Berlin HS Music Tchr 1973-76; Cntrl Vly HS Music Tchr 1976-81; Wuerzburg HS Music Tchr 1981-; *ai:* Marching Band; Show Choir; Musical Dir; NEA 1969-; OEA 1981-; *office:* Wurzburg American H S Cmr 475 APO AE 09036

TUCKER, WILLIAM J., 4th Grade Tchr; *b:* Fillmore, NY; *m:* Rebecca Wingert; *c:* William II, Nathan; *ed:* Hougton Coll (BA) His, Elem Ed 1971; Alfred Grad Schl (MS) Bio 1982; Buffalo St Coll Dr Ed Cert; *cr:* Rushford Cntrl Schl 3rd Grd Tchr 1980-81; Cuba-Rushford Cntrl Schl Kndgtn, 3-4th Grd Tchr, Dr Ed Tchr 1982-; *ai:* NEA 1985-.

TUCKMAN, LYN ANNE, Curriculum Associate; *b:* Philadelphia, PA; *m:* Mervyn; *c:* Jennifer Rackow, Ken Rackow; *ed:* Beaver Coll (BS) K-Elem Ed 1967; Temple Univ (MS) Psych of Rdng 1971; Addl 50 Grad Credit Hrs Beyond Masters; Currently in Grad Prgm for Curr Supervision; *cr:* Schl Dist of Cheltenham 3rd Grd Tchr 1967-75, Title I Tchr 1982-84, 1st & 3rd Grd Tchr 1985-88, Curr Assoc for Rdng, Lang Arts & Eng as Second Lang 1989-; *ai:* Federal Prgms Coord; Cheltenham Ed Assn 1967-, Bldg Rep; PSEA, NEA, Kappa Delta Pi 1967-; IRAI, ASCD, NCTE 1973-; Childrens Hospital of Philadelphia 1975, Auxiliary Pres, Fundraising; Amer Heart Assn 1960-, Fundraiser; Amer Red Cross 1967-, Spec VIP Donor; Cheltenham Schl Dist Fnd 2 Grants; *office:* Schl Dist of Cheltenham Twp Admin Bldg 1000 Ashbourne Rd Elkins Park PA 19027*

TUE, PHILIP JAMES, Fifth Grade Teacher; *b:* Dover, DE; *m:* Ernestine Hailey; *c:* Carol, Darryl; *ed:* Morris Brown Coll (BA) Sociology 1956; City Coll, The City Univ of NY (MS) Elem Ed 1975; NY Univ 12 Hrs Elem Ed 1967; 30 Addl Hrs Elem Ed 1975-76, 16 Hrs Elem Ed 1983; *cr:* NY City Pub Schls Tchr 1967-; *ai:* NY Jr Tennis League Site Dir 1985-; AFT, UFT 1971-; Kappa Alpha Psi 1953-; Schoolyard Tennis Prgm Tchr of Yr Awd, NY Jr Tennis League 1990; *home:* 119 Tree Ave Box 153 Central Islip NY 11722

TUERTSCHER, DANIEL P., Mathematics Teacher; *b:* Cincinnati, OH; *m:* Geraldine H. Hatley; *c:* Jennifer, Leslie, Amanda, Michael; *ed:* Univ of Cincinnati (BA) His & Math 1967, (MED) Scndry Ed 1968; 4 Yrs Post Grad Work Philosophy; 15 Semester Post Grad Math; 3 Semester Post Grad Miami Univ of Ohio Math; *cr:* Courter Tech HS Math Tchr 1967-71; Taylor HS Math Tchr 1971-; *ai:* Math Dept Chair 1973-; Three Rivers Ed Assn 1971-, Pres (3 Times); OEA & NEA 1971-; OCTM 1994; Ashland Oil Golden Apple Achvmt Awd 1993; Effective Schls Grant 1991; NSF Grant 1978; Martha Holden Jennings Schlr 1995-96; *office:* Taylor HS 30 36 Harrison Ave North Bend OH 45052*

TUFANO, HARRY J.,JR., 6th Grade Teacher; *b:* Rochester, NY; *c:* Andrew Joseph; *ed:* Monroe Comm Coll (AS) Recreation, PE 1969; SUNY at Geneseo (BA) Elem Ed N-6 1971; SUNY at Brockport Perm Cert Elem Ed N-6; *cr:* Greece Cntrl Schl Dist Elem, MS Tchr 1972-; *ai:* NEA 1972-, Bldg Rep; *office:* Apollo MS 750 Maiden Ln Rochester NY 14615*

TUFANO, NEIL JOSEPH, Spcl Ed & Resource Room Tchr; *b:* Brooklyn, NY; *m:* Patricia Ann Ardita; *c:* Christopher, Neil Jr., Frank, Philip; *ed:* Adelphi Univ (BS) PE 1966; Long Island Univ (MS) Spec Ed 1976; Univ of Bridgeport at Huntington 20 Addl Credits in Guid; *cr:* St Patricks Schls K-8 Grd PE Dir 1966-74; Woodward Mental Hlth Ctr Spec Ed Tchr, Coord 1974-76; California Ave Schl Spec Ed Resource Room Tchr 1976-; *ai:* After Schl Sports Club Spon; Bsbl Coach; Discipline, Fac Relations Comms; Uniondale Tchrs Assn 1976-; AFT, NEA 1966-; Spec Ed PTA 1974-, Cncl Del; PTA 1974-; Stdnts with Learning Disabilities 1974-; Hofstra Univ Pride Club 1992-; Brentwood Yth Assn 1970-; Islip Sports Assn 1987-; Uniondale Pub Schls Spec Ed Dept Jenkins Meml Awd 1992; *home:* 100 Atlanta St Bay Shore NY 11706

TUITE, JOHN J., Math Teacher; *ed:* Stonehill Coll (BA) Math 1965; Bridgewater St Coll (MED) Scndry Math 1971; *office:* Randolph HS 70 Memorial Pkwy Randolph MA 02368

TUITE, KATHLEEN A., Religion Teacher; *b:* Montclair, NJ; *ed:* County Coll of Morris (AAS) Applied Sci 1985; Caldwell Coll (BA) Theology 1992; Pursuing MA Pastoral Ministry & Spirituality St Michael's Coll; Grad Courses Aquinas Inst Theology; *cr:* Warner Lambert Co Admin Asst 1985-89; St Dominic Acad Rel Tchr 1992-; *ai:* Stu Cncl Moderator; NCEA, Theata Alpha Kappa 1992-; Commission on Global Issues 1991-; *office:* Saint Dominic Acad 2572 Kennedy Blvd Jersey City NJ 07304

TULIN, ELIZABETH N., English Teacher; *b:* Hartford, CT; *m:* Leonard D. Gross; *c:* Matthew Tulin-Gross, Daniel Tulin-Gross; *ed:* Univ of Toronto (BSC) Soc Sci, Eng 1971; SUNY at Albany (MSC) Ed 1973; Attending NY Univ; Fairfield Univ Spec Ed; 30 Credit Hrs Inservice Ed, Effective Tchng, Writing Prgm, NYSUT Courses, Cooperative Ed; *cr:* Fox Lane MS Soc Stud Tchr 1973-75, Eng Tchr 1975-; *ai:* Holocaust Curr, Dist Inclusion Comms; Dist Eng Standards, Benehmark Writer of Draft; Dist Educl Dev Leaves; Stu Govt Schl Adv; After Schl Writing Prgm; AFT, NYSUT, BTA 1971-, Rep; NCTE 1973-; WCTF 1976-; Temple Beth Torah 1984-, Bd Trustee; Nanuet SEPTA, PTA 1986-; Articles Pub; Writing Across Curr Dist Wkshps; *office:* Fox Lane MS Rt 172 Bedford NY 10506*

TULINO, ERNEST ANTHONY, Business Dept Chairperson; *b:* Brooklyn, NY; *m:* Jane Peat; *c:* Anthony, Jennifer LiPari, Jodi McSwegan; *ed:* Manhattan Coll (BBA) Industrial Mgmt 1966; Pace Univ (MS) Bus Ed 1973; Brooklyn Coll Ed Credits 1968; Prof Diploma in Admin & Supv 1975; Coll of Insurance License to Sell Property & Casulty Insurance 1979; Barbizon Schl of Modeling Prgm & Syllabus 1978; *cr:* NYC Bd of Ed Parks Dept Recreation Dir & Nautilus Instr 1963-74; St Stephens HS Tchr, asst Prin & Ath Dir 1966-78; Prudential Insurance Co Sales Rep 1978-79; St Peters Boys HS Tchr, Dept Chm & Coach 1979-; ECC & ASC 1987-; *ai:* Var Bsbl Coach 1984-; Bus Club Moderator 1990-; Seasonal Work Parks Dept Supvr; Former Jr Var Bsktbl & Bsbl Coach 1980-83; NBEA 1988-; NYS Bsbl Coaches Assn 1984-, Century Club, 100 Wins Awd; PSAL FOA 1980-, Ftbl Ofcl, Top Linesman Awd 1987 & 1994; St Christophers Schl Bd 1974-78, VP; Meals on Wheels, Spon; Red Cross; USA Bsbl; NY Daily News Bsbl Coach of Yr 1990; JV SI Coach of Yr 1983 Bsbl & Bsktbl; McGowan Meml Awd Brooklyn Kiwanis Bsbl 1970; Private Schls Coach of Yr Brooklyn Bsktbl 1974; *office:* Saint Peters Boys HS 200 Clinton Ave Staten Island NY 10301

TULL, DAVID A., High School Math Teacher; *b:* Lewes, DE; *m:* Susan Oney; *c:* Leigh Anne, Matthew; *ed:* Concord Coll (BS) Math 1971; *cr:* Cape Henlopen Schl Dist Tchr 1971-; *ai:* 9th Grd Math Team Coach; DSEA, NEA, DCTM 1971-; *office:* Cape Henlopen HS Kings Hwy Lewes DE 19958

TULLI, STEPHEN MICHAEL, Chemistry Instructor; *b:* Franklin, MA; *ed:* Fitchburg St Coll (BS) Chem 1991; Ed in Educl Leadership, Management, Admin Fitchburg St Coll 1995; *cr:* Fitchburg St Coll Upward Bound Ed Coord 1991-92, Upward Bound Sci, Math Instr 1991-93, 95; Fitchburg HS Chem Instr 1991-95; Mansfield HS Chemistry Instr 1995-; *ai:* Jr & SR Class Adv, Double Dutch, Environmental Club Adv; YMCA Teen Outreach Asst; Honor Soc Comm; Ice Hockey Booster Club; Latin Amer Club Co-adv; Pol Campaign, Homeless Vol; CS 2; NEA, MTA, FTA, Fitchburg Tchrs Assn 1993-95, Bldg Rep 1993-95; Phi Delta Kappa; Kappa Delta Pi; ASCD; Sigma Pi Internation 1992-, Alumni Comptroller; MA Chiefs of Police Assn 1993-; Order of Sons of Italy 1994-; Who's Who Among Amer HS Stdnts 1985-87; Warren Litsky Distinguished; Tchr's Awd Nom 1995; *office:* Mansfield HS 250 East Street Mansfield MA 02048*

TULLY, ANGELA RIPP, Eighth Grade Teacher; *b:* Rockville Centre, NY; *m:* Patrick; *c:* Margaret, James; *ed:* Ladycliff Coll (BA) Eng 1975; 24 Grad Credits, IU Colonial Northampton, Long Island Univ, Penn St Univ; *cr:* St Anne Schl 8th Grd Lang Arts, Rdng, Soc Stud & Rel Tchr 1987-; *ai:* Mid Sts Steering Comm Chprsn 1989-92; Revise Report Card Comm; Rainbows Facilitator; Visiting Team Mid Sts; NCEA 1987-; NCTE 1994-; Bethlehem

Cath HS Advy Bd 1991-; *office:* St Anne School 375 Hickory St Bethlehem PA 18017

TULLY, DEBORAH IMRI, Reading, Writing & Comm Tchr; *b:* Norwalk, CT; *m:* John Gannon; *c:* David, Katie; *ed:* Boston Coll (AA) Psych, Sociology 1974; Wheelock Coll (MS) Primary Ed 1975; Pierce Schl Tchr Aide 1975-77, K-1st Grd Tchr 1977-78; Enon Elem 2nd Grd Tchr 1978-79; Indian Valley MS 7th Grd Lang Arts Tchr 1979-; *cr:* Levy, Curr, Writing Competency Comms; *ai:* AFT 1985-; OH Federation of Tchrs 1985-, Exec Comm Mem 1994; Mad River Green Fed of Tchrs 1985-, Sec, VP, Pres; *office:* Indian Valley Schl 510 Enon-Xenia Rd Enon OH 45323

TULLY, JAMES RICHARD, English Teacher; *b:* Hermon, NY; *m:* Deborah Ann Barfoot; *c:* James R. Jr., Kimberly Kristin; *ed:* New England Coll (BA) Ed 1970; 30 Grad Hrs st SUNY at Oswego, SUNY at Oneonta; *cr:* Inverness MS Eng Tchr 1970; Altmar-Parish-Williamstown Jr Sr HS Eng Tchr 1970-73; Bainbridge-Guilford HS Eng Tchr 1974-79; East Syracuse0Minoa HS Eng Tchr 1979-; *ai:* Adv Spartan Express; Instructional Improvement Comm; NYSUT 1970-; Taft Rd Little League 1980-, VP, Div Ldr, Others, Local Titles, SEction 8 Major Div Champions; *office:* East Syracuse Minoa Schls 6400 Fremont Rd East Syracuse NY 13057

TULLY, JEANNE A., English & Literature Teacher; *b:* Hinsdale, IL; *c:* Lauren, Brendan; *ed:* Emmanuel Coll (BA) Eng 1970; 12 Credits Univ RI Lib, Infor Stud; *cr:* St Joseph Schl 3rd-6th Grd Tchr 1970-75; Sacred Heart HS 9th-12th Grd Eng Tchr, Dept Chprsn 1982-86; Dean Luce Schl Librn 1988-92; St Francis Xavier Schl 6th-8th Grd Eng, Lit Tchr 1986-88, 1992-; *ai:* Yrbk Comm; NCEA; Awds The Patriot Ledger, Boston Coll HS Tchr; Grants Commonwealth MA Bd Lib Commissioners; *office:* St Francis Xavier Schl 236 Pleasant St South Weymouth MA 02190

TULLY, JUDY KREWSON, Business Education Teacher; *b:* Wilkes-Barre, PA; *m:* Edward; *c:* Carolyn Oliver Crawford, Cindy Oliver, Erin Oliver Corbett; *ed:* Keystone Jr Coll (AA) Secretarial 1979; Wilkes Coll (BS) Bus Ed 1983; Penn St Univ 6 Credit Hrs; Univ of Scranton 6 Credit Hrs; *cr:* Mountain View Jr Sr High Bus Ed Sabbatical Sub 1985, Full Time Bus Ed 1986; Blue Ridge HS Bus Ed Sabbatical Sub 1986; *ai:* NEA 1986-; MVEA 1986-; NBEA 1995-.*

TULLY, KATHLEEN ANN, Religion Teacher; *b:* Lynbrook, NY; *ed:* Fordham Univ (BA) Philosophy 1991; *cr:* St Jean Baptiste HS Religion Tchr, Choral Dir & Drama Club Dir 1991-; *ai:* Drama Club Moderator & Dir; Choir Dir; Awded Grant From Natl Endowment of Hum for 6 Week Summer Seminar in Italy; *office:* St Jean Baptiste HS 173 E 75th St New York NY 10021

TULSEY, RICHARD LEE, Social Studies Teacher; *b:* Johnson City, NY; *m:* Sharon Murano; *c:* Michael, Suzanne; *ed:* Niagara Univ (BA) His, Ed 1963; Cortland (MS) Ed; Attnd Ithaca Coll; *cr:* US Army Ofcr 1963-65; Cath Cntrl HS Soc Stud Tchr 1966-71; Tioga Cntrl HS Soc Stud Tchr 1972-; *ai:* Ftbl, Bsktbl Coach; Track Ofcl; Stu Cncl; Class Adv; NEA 1973-; Tioga Tchr Assn 1973-, Pres, Negotiator, Bldg Rep; Appalachian Yth Org 1975-, Pres; Owego Booster Club 1980-, Pres; BPOE 1039 1980-, Chm, Trustee, Elk of Yr; Southern Track Ofcls 1985-, Pres; *office:* Tioga Cntrl HS Maple Ave Tioga Center NY 13845

TUMAVITCH, MARTHA CONON, First Grade Teacher; *m:* Paul J.; *c:* Paul A.; *ed:* Millersville St Coll (BS) Elem Ed 1974; Univ of Scranton (ME); 36 Credits Beyond Masters; *cr:* Susquehanna Comm Schl Dist Kndgtn Tchr 1975-76; Old Forge Schl Dist K-3rd Grd Tchr, Presently Tchng 1st Grd 1976-; *ai:* PSEA 1975-; *home:* 311 McClure St Old Forge PA 18518

TUMBLESON, SUE ANN, High School Art Teacher; *b:* Bentonville, OH; *ed:* Univ of Cincinnati (AA) Ed 1971; Wilmington Coll (BS) Art 1973; Miami Univ of OH (MED) Curr & Supervision 1982; 12 Credit Hrs; Cert renewal; *cr:* Blanchester Local Schls 1st-8th Grd Art Tchr 1972-81, 4th-6th Grd Art Tchr 1981-88, 9th-12th Grd Art Tchr 1988-; Wilmington Coll of OH Asst Prof of Art Ed & Adj 1982-95; *ai:* HS Bldg Ldrshp Team 1995-; Drug Policy Revision Comm; Block Scheduling; OEA OH & Natl Ed Assoc; NAEA; BEA; OAEA 1972-, Pres (2 Terms), Treas & Sec; Phi Delta Kappa 1985-, Induction Team; Tuesday Club Local Lit 1985-, Pres & Sec; Heart & Cancer Fund Club, Collector Donations; Blanchester Schls 3 Yrs; Tax Levy, Planning Comms; Exceptional Ed Awd 1992-93; Presentations at OH Art Ed Conf 3 Yrs; Natl Art Ed Convention 1 Yr; Chair Wilm Coll Stans Revision, Art Ed Revision Comms; *home:* 215 N Wright St Blanchester OH 45107

TUMIN, JUDTIH, MS Director & English Tchr; *b:* Newark, NJ; *ed:* NYU at Univ Hts (BA) Philosophy 1967; Jewish Theological Seminary (MA) Ed Admin 1984; Prof Cert for Supvrs & Prins; Bank St Coll of Ed MS Pgm; C olumbia Tchrs Coll Grad Coursework; *cr:* Children Comm Wkshp Schl K-2nd Grd Tchr 1972-73; PS 20 1st & 2nd Grd Tchr 1973-74; Hebrew Acad of Pelham Pkwy Pre-K & Kndgtn Tchr 1974-75; Solomon Schecler of Bergen Cty Kndgtn & 4th-6th Grd Tchr & Admin 1975-79; SAJ Hebrew Schl Dir 1979-83; Abraham Joshua Heschel Schl Pre-K, Kndgtn, 1st & 3rd-8th Grd Tchr, Lower & MS Dir & Dir of Gen Stud 1983-; *ai:* 8th Grd & HS Adv; Svc Club Spon; Alumni Assn Liaison; Yrbk Producer; Co-Ed MYSAIS Ten Yr Self-Evaluation; NYSAIS; ATIS; ASCD; Joseph Gruss Excl Tchr Awd; Kohl Fndtn Outstdng Tchr Awd; *office:* Abraham Joshua Heschel Schl 314 W 91st St New York NY 10024

TUMMEY, RUTH J., Biology Teacher; *b:* Fast Orange, NJ; *m:* Christopher J.; *ed:* Monmouth Univ (BS) Bio 1984, (MAT) Scndry Sci Ed 1990; 30 Addl Credits Above Masters in Various Grad Stud; *cr:* Southern Rgnl HS Bio Tchr 1988-; *ai:* NJ Sci League; Promotion Comm; Restructuring Cncl; Prins Advy Comm; NEA 1988-; NJEA 1988-; BTANJ 1989-; Sallie Mae First Year Tchr Awd; Nom for Presidential Awd for Excl in Math & Sci; Grant Winner-Classrooms Connections to the Future; *office:* Southern Regional HS Dist 75 Cedar Bridge Rd Manahawkin NJ 08050

TUNANIDAS, IRENE, Teacher of Deaf Students; *b:* Youngstown, OH; *ed:* Gallaudet Univ at WA DC (BA) Art 1970; Kent St Univ (MED) Ed, Deaf, Hard of Hearing 1972; CA St Univ at Sacramento (MS) Cnslng; Post Grad Youngstown St Univ 18 Hrs, Univ of CA at San Francisco 30 Credit Hrs; *cr:* Stambaugh Elem Schl Tchr of the Deaf 1972-77; Woodrow Wilson HS Tchr Hearing Impaired Prgm 1977-82; Paul C. Bunn Elem Schl Tchr Hearing Impaired Prgm 1982-83; Woodrow Wilson HS Tchr of the Deaf, Hard of Hearing 1985-; *ai:* Chm Hearing Impaired Prgm; Adv Teen-Tymers Club 1992; Optimist Club Oratorical Contest for Hearing Impaired Stdnts; Youngstown Ed Assn 1972-; Delta Kappa Gamma 1988-, Chm Legislative Comm; Conf of Amer Instrs of the Deaf 1975-; Tchrs of Eng, Lang Arts Conv 1992-, Pres-Elect, Recording Sec; YWCA Women of Yr 1993-, Chm Awd Comm; Daughters of Penelope 1991-; Quota Club of Youngstown 1980-, Chm Svc to Yth; Deaf Advy Comm 1979-, Sec 1979, 1981; OH Assn of the Deaf 1975-, Sec 1976-82; Outstdng Deaf Lobbyist 1989; Outstdng Tchr of Yr Conf of Amer Instrs of the Deaf 1995; YWCA Women of the Yr 1992; Article Pub 1993; *office:* Woodrow Wilson HS 2725 Gibson St Youngstown OH 44502

TUNIS, AMELIA LATORI, Curr & Instruction Supervisor; *b:* Union, NJ; *m:* Albert A.; *c:* Stephen Anthony, Paula Jeanette Hoff, Suzanne Mary Stephens; *ed:* Newark St Tchrs Coll (BS) Ed 1956; Georgian Court Coll (MA) Ed 1980; 33 Addl Post Grad Credits in Ed at Rutgers & Trenton St; Hard of Hearing Handicapped Cert 1956; Supvr Cert Ed 1991; *cr:* Brookside Elem Schl 2nd Grd Tchr 1956-58; Drum Point Rd Elem Schl 3rd-6th Grd Tchr & Slowtrack Modified 5th-6th Grd 1967-;Brick Bd of Ed Curr & Instruction Supvr 1994-; *ai:* ASCD, BTASA 1994; ADK 1987-, Rec Sec 2 yrs, Pres Elect 2 yrs, Pres 2yrs; OCRC of IRA 1977-, Sec 2 yrs; NJTESOL; NJPSA; NCTM; Phi Delta Kappa 1995-; Garden St Philharmonic Chorus 1987-90; Creative Writing & Poetry Wrkshp;CoPresented Prgm Writing Skills & DARE Prgm for Local TV Station; Ocean Cty Cncl of IRA Spec Svc Awd 1988; Governors Recognition Awd 1988; Brick Twp Tchr of the Yr 1991-92; *home:* 77 Nottingham Dr Brick NJ 08724

TUNNAT, LINDA DAVIS, English Teacher; *b:* Upland, PA; *m:* Paul M; *c:* Lauren, Ryan; *ed:* West Chesters St Coll (BS} Scndry Ed, Eng 1968; *cr:* Wm Penn HS Eng Tchr 1968-; *ai:* Prin Cabinet; NHS Comm; NJEA, Kingsway Ed Assoc 1982-Rep; *office:* Kingsway Regional HS Kings Hwy Swedesboro NJ 08085

TUOMISTO, GALE MOORE, Science Teacher; *b:* Shamokin, PA; *m:* Roy S.; *c:* Jocelin, Jenni, Erik; *ed:* Susquehanna Univ (BA) Geology & Ed 1973; Bloomsburg Univ 16 Credit Hrs towards MS in Curr Design & Instruction; Addl 12 Credit Hrs toward BA in Bio; *cr:* Beacon Bapt Acad 7th-12th Grd Sci Tchr 1979-83; Shaffer Schl Sr HS Sci Tchr 1984-85; Dept of Labor & Industry Adult Instr 1987-89; Sunbury Chrstn Acad 7th-12th Grd Sci Tchr 1990-; *ai:* Stu Cncl Adv; Sci Fair Coord; Reg 5 PA Jr Acad of Sci; DAR 1986-, Chm Jr Amer Citizens; Rsrch Grants from PA Power & Light Co 1994 & 1996; *office:* Sunbury Christian Acad RR 1 Box 226 Northumberland PA 17857*

TUPPER, EILEEN COSTELLO, 4th Grade Teacher; *b:* Boston, MA; *m:* Arthur Leonard; *c:* Wayne, Ruth Heffernan, Nancy McKinley, Stephen; *ed:* Framingham St (BS) Ed 1955; Post Grad Stud Through Travel in Asia, Europe, East Africa & Eurasia; *cr:* Saxonville Schl Framingham 1st Grd Tchr 1955-56; Marion E Zeh Schl 3rd Grd Tchr 1967-81; Peaslee Schl 4th Grd Tchr 1981-; *ai:* Tchng Frameworks Comm for Educl Reform in MA 1996; MA Tchrs Assn 1967-; Northborough Tchrs 1967-; NEA 1967-; Anna Seaver Awd for Excl 1973; *home:* 159 Stearns Rd Marlborough MA 01752

TURANO, FRANK JOSEPH, Biology Teacher; *b:* Jamaica, NY; *m:* Nancy Schmit; *c:* Charles, Frank, William, Jonathan, Alyssa; *ed:* St Johns Univ (BS) Bio, Chem 1962; Adelphi Univ (MS) Marine Bio 1968; SUNY at Stony Brook (MA) Anthropology 1993, (PHD) Historical Archaeology 1994; *cr:* Lindenhurst HS Bio Tchr 1962-68; Ward Melville HS Bio Tchr 1968-; SUNY Lecturer, Ecology, Evolution 1976-; *ai:* Hum Curr Develop Comm 1967-69; Environmental Bio Develop Comm 1972-73; Multi Disciplinary Tchng 1976-81; AFT 1962-, Treas 1965-66; NYSTA 1962-; Soc, Amer Arch 1982-; Soc Historical Archaeology 1986-; Islip Town Environmental Cncl 197-85, Chair 1982-85; Suffolk Cty Conservation Cncl 1971-78 VP; Fire Island Wilderness Cncl 1976-; Long Island Stud Cncl 1978-92, VP 1984-90; NABT Outstdng Bio Tchr 1972; Dedication to Sci Ed 1986; Man of Yr in Ed 1988; Tandy Tech Scholar 1991-92; *office:* Ward Melville HS 380 Old Town Rd Setauket NY 11733

TURANSKY, JEANNE A., Prof of Eng & Fac Developer; *b:* Buffalo, NY; *ed:* St Univ Coll at Fredonia (BA) Eng 1966; Niagara Univ (MA) Eng 1971; *cr:* Sweet Home Jr HS 7-8 Grd Eng Tchr 1966-69; St Univ Coll at Buffalo Admissions Cnslr 1972-76; Niagara Univ Office of Spec Prgms 1978-80; Erie Comm Coll Eng Prof, Tchng Res Ctr Coord 1981-; *ai:* City Acad Campus Cncl, Curr, Collegewide Cncl, Dev Learning, Lbrl Arts Planning, Long Range Planning, Mid Sts, Tchng Res Ctr Coord, Recognition, Eng Dept Budget & Reappointments, Niagara Frontier Fac Dev Network Comms; NEA 1966-; Natl Cncl for Staff, Prgm, Org Dev 1993-; NY St Tchrs 1966-; Erie Comm Coll Fac Fed 1981-; Town Tonawanda Crime Watch 1986-, VP, Recognition; Erie Cty Employees Credit Union 1984-; Kenmore East Sr HS Class Reunion 1962, 1991 Co-Chair; *office:* Erie Comm Coll 121 Ellicott St Buffalo NY 14203

TURBIN, JONATHAN EDWARD, Librarian, Eng & Cmptr Tchr; *b:* Bronx, NY; *m:* Kathryn C. Gross; *c:* Alexander Benjamin; *ed:* City Coll of NY (MS) His Ed 1978; Columbia univ (EDM) Ed 1980; Tchrs Coll (EDD) Fnds of Ed 1981; *cr:* Salauter Akiba Acad Math, Eng Tutor 1978-79; Martin Luther King Jr Schl Eng Tchr 1979; JAmes Monroe HS Eng Tchr 1980-; Manhattanville Coll Basic Skills Ctr Dir 1980-81; Queensborough Comm Coll Asst Eng Prof 1990; Hostos Comm Coll Asst Eng Prof 1992-93; *ai:* Tchr Advocacy Agency; Chess, Cmptr Club Coord; Librn; UFT, AFT 1979-; Impact II 1985-, Grant Comm Dev, Adapter Grants; NY Telephone Telecommunications, Scirda Grants; Various Publications, Articles, Lectures, Wkshps, Pannels; *office:* James Monroe HS 1300 Boynton Ave Bronx NY 10472*

TURCHETTA, BRUCE A., Health & PE Professor; *b:* Lancaster, PA; *m:* Linda Jean Ferzer; *c:* Lindsay, Anthony; *ed:* IN Univ of PA (BS) Ed 1978, (MS) Sports Sci 1980; Penn St Univ (PHD) Hlth Ed 1995; *cr:* IN Hlth Ctr Rehab & Fitness Mgr 1980-81; Racquet Time Fitness Ctr Gen Mgr 1981-87; CCAC Boyce Campus Prof 1987-; *ai:* Amer Coll Sports Medicine, AAHPERD, AFT 1987-; *office:* Comm Coll Algny Co Boyce Cmps 595 Beatty Rd Monroeville PA 15146*

TURCO, ANGELO D., Algebra I Teacher; *b:* Kittanning, PA; *m:* Angela Muto; *c:* Maria, Domenic; *ed:* IN Univ of PA (BSEd) Math 1973, (MED) Counseling 1977; *cr:* Ford City Jr Sr HS Math Tchr 1973-77; Kittanning Jr HS Math Tchr 1977-90; Armstrong Cntrl Jr HS Math Tchr 1990-92; Kittanning Area MS Math Tchr 1992-; *ai:* Sr League Bsbl Team Coach; Transition Team; Advy Comm; NEA, Armstrong Ed Assn 1973-; Latin Amer Club 1973-; Knights of Columbus 1980-; St Mary's Parish Cncl, Kittanning Little League 1990-; *office:* Kittanning Area MS 210 N Mc Kean St Kittanning PA 16201*

TURK, CHARLES K., APE TV & English Teacher; *b:* Venesello, Hungary; *m:* Ruth Anne; *c:* Frank, John, Christopher, Tara, Alisa; *ed:* Canisius Coll (BA) Eng, His, Photos 1969; 14 Hrs Rdng Skills; *cr:* Queen of Heaven Eng Tchr 1967-69; McQuaid Jesuit HS Eng Tchr 1969-; *ai:* Schl Newspaper Moderator; NHS Selection Bd; NMS 1985-, Essay Reader; APTV Exams 1990-, Reader reader; Updated Eng Dept Syllabus 1978; *home:* 21 Timberline Dr West Henrietta NY 14586

TURK, DAVID F., Prof of English & Dept Head; *b:* Auburn, NY; *m:* Vara S. Neverow; *ed:* Nyack Coll (BA) Eng 1975; NY Univ (MA) Eng, Amer Lit 1979, (PHD) Eng, Amer Lit 1989; *cr:* Nyack Coll Eng Prof 1979-; NY Univ Adj Eng Prof 1984-89; *ai:* Drama Ensemble Dir; Coll Newspaper Adv; Milton Soc 1988-; Merit Awd for Tchng 1995; Gordon Ray Schlsp for Dissertation Research NYU 1988; *office:* Nyack Coll 1 S Boulevard Nyack NY 10960

TURKETT, CAROL WOOLVER, Mathematics Teacher; *b:* Cooperstown, NY; *m:* Douglas Joseph; *c:* Matthew, Laura; *ed:* St Univ of NY at Geneseo (BS) Elem Ed & Math 1971; St Univ of NY at Brockport (MS) Elem Ed 1976; *cr:* Churchville-Chili Schls 5th Grd Tchr 1971-77, 8th Grd Math Tchr 1977-78, 5th Grd Tchr 1978-87, 7th & 8th Grd Math Tchr 1987-88, 5th Grd Tchr 1988-93, 7th & 8th Grd Math Tchr 1993-; *ai:* NEA 1971-; Aesthetic Ed Inst 1982-; AMTNYS 1987-; Union Church 1980-, Chrstn Ed Comm Chprsn, Bd of Deacons Chprsn; *office:* Churchville-Chili MS 139 Fairbanks Rd Churchville NY 14428

TURKOVICH, DONALD H., Physical Education Teacher; *b:* Rochester, PA; *m:* Margaret Pratt; *c:* Julie, Brian; *ed:* West Liberty St Coll (BA) Hlth, PE, Soc Sci 1972; Univ of Pittsburgh (MED) Hlth, PE 1977; *cr:* Hopewell Meml Jr HS His Tchr 1972-78; Hopewell Sr HS Hlth, PE Tchr 1978-; *ai:* Var Ftbl Coach, Defensive Coord; NEA, PSEA, Hopewell Ed Assn 1972-; Hopewell Bsbl League 1990-, Coach; *office:* Hopewell Sr HS Longvue Ave Aliquippa PA 15001*

TURNBULL, CAROLYN YOEST, Sixth Grade Teacher; *b:* Pitts PA; *m:* James W.; *c:* James D.; *ed:* Youngstown St Univ (BS) Elem E Laude 1968; Slippery Rock St Univ (MED) Spec Ed 1972; Post M Prgm Supvr, Admin Cert; *cr:* Sharon City Schls 3rd-4th Grd Tchr 19 Mid-Western IU 4 Spec Ed Tchr 1969-72; Slippery Rock St Univ Master Demo Tchr 1974-76; Crawford Cntrl Schl Dist 6th Grd, Le Support Tchr 1976-; *ai:* Meadville HS Ftbl Booster, Schl Improv Cncl, Class Reunion Chprsn; Baldwin-Reynolds House Museum 1976-; NEA, CCEA 1968-, Comm & Ed; PSEA 1968-, Comm & Internal Comm Awd 1986-87, 1988-90; Phi Delt Kappa 1989-, Edint Univ Chapter; Crawford Cty Historical Soc 1976-, Spec Events Stone Meth Church 1965-, Admin Bd, Worship Cncl, Womens Ou Rep; Crawford Cty Fair 1976-, Co-Chprsn Art, Photo, Handcrafts Cncl for Exceptional Children Outstanding Spec Educator Awd; Innovative Tchng Grant Awd 1995; PA Spec Ed High Tech Grant; Cra Cntrl & Allegheny Coll Tchng Grant 1995-96; St, Natl Conve Presenter; Articles on Spec Ed & Cmptr Ed; *office:* West End Eler RD 4 Box 203 Brooks Rd Meadville PA 16335*

TURNBULL, DIANE LUCAS, English Teacher; *b:* Florence, S Esmond; *ed:* City Coll (MA) Eng Lit 1976; Brooklyn Coll Towar Guid, Cnslng; Columbia Univ Conflict Resolution Cert; *cr:* Prospect HS Conflict Resolution Specialist 4 Yrs, Eng Tchr 15 Yrs; *ai:* Mediation Coord; *office:* Prospect Heights HS 883 Classon Ave Bro NY 11225

TURNBULL, KINSA, English Teacher; *b:* Princeton, NJ; *c:* Vollbrecht Jr., Helen; *ed:* Smith Coll (BA) Eng 1961; Harvard Univ Eng 1962; Temple Univ (MA) Eng 1970; *cr:* Hathaway Brown Sch Tchr 1963-64; Laurel Schl Eng Tchr 1964-65; North Plainfield H Tchr 1965-66; Moorestown HS Eng Tchr 1970-; *ai:* ACE 1993-; N NCTE 1980-; First Tchr of Yr; *office:* Moorestown HS Bridgebo Moorestown NJ 08057

TURNER, ADRIENNE BARRINGER, Earth Science Teache Roanoke, VA; *ed:* VA Tech (BS) Geology 1982; 22 Semester Hrs Cmp Univ of Southern ME; *cr:* Blacksburg MS Phys Sci Tchr 19 Blacksburg HS Earth Sci Tchr 1984-87; Bonny Eagle HS Earth Sc 1987-; *ai:* Coach Girls Cross Cntry, Indoor Track; NEA 1986-; M 1989-; AAUW 1995-; *office:* Bonny Eagle HS 700 Saco Rd Standis 04084*

TURNER, ALLEN B., Mathematics Teacher; *b:* Kingston, PA; *m:* M L. La Bonte; *c:* Allen, Aaron; *ed:* East Stroudsburg (BS) Scndry 1975; 24 Hrs Admin Credits Scranton Univ; *cr:* Benton HS Tchr 1975 Dir 1985-; *ai:* Boys Bsktbl Coach 6 Yrs, Girls 13 Yrs, Sftbl 2 Yrs; Adv; Tchr Mentor; Math Dept Chm; Ath Dir; PSEA 1975-, Treas; 1975-; Town Zoning Bd 1986-, Chm; *office:* Benton Area Schls RR 2 St Benton PA 17814

TURNER, AMELIA JOANNE, Basic Skills Math Teacher; *b:* Plain NJ; *m:* Mitchell Seth; *c:* Jaclyn S.; *ed:* Kean Coll (BA) Elem 1978, Guid 1982; *cr:* EHS Basic Skills Tchr 1979-; *office:* EHS Halsey 600 Pearl St Elizabeth NJ 07202*

TURNER, BENJAMIN CURTIS, Physics Teacher; *b:* Washington *m:* Tara Parker; *ed:* Howard Univ (BS) Physics 1990; Univ of MA (Sci Ed 1995; Attnd Klingenstein Summer Inst Tchrs Coll Columbia *cr:* NASA Goddard Space Flight Ctr Engr 1990-92; Williston Northar Schl Physics Tchr 1992-; *ai:* Girls Bsktbl Coach; Stu Cncl, Black Union Adv; *office:* The Williston Northampton Schl 19 Payson Easthampton MA 01027*

TURNER, CATHIE AZARAVICH, English Teacher; *b:* Wilkes-B PA; *m:* Robert C.; *ed:* Univ of Scranton (BS) Scndry Ed & Eng 1987; of Scranton Rdng Cert 1990; *cr:* Seton Cath HS Eng Tchr 1990-; *ai:* D Club Asst Dir & Moderator; NCTE 1990-; NCEA 1990; Eng Dept *office:* Seton Catholic HS 37 William St Pittston PA 18640

TURNER, CHRISTINE LEVALLEY, Fine Arts Dept Chair & Teach Elmira, NY; *m:* F. Gordon; *c:* Keren M., Adam B.; *ed:* Muskingum (AB) Art 1967; Syracuse Univ (MS) Art Ed 1975; SUNY At Oswego (Educl Admin 1990; *cr:* Binghamton Cntrl HS Art Tchr 1973-74; Live HS Art Tchr, Fine Arts Chair, Acting Prin 1975-77; J. C. Birdleboug Art Tchr 1978-81; Liverpool HS Art Tchr, Fine Arts Chair, Acting 1982-; *ai:* Block Scheduling, Staff Dev Comms; NYSUT, NEA 198 League 1980-; Scholastic Art Advy Bd 1977-; 2 Legislative Grant Tech; *office:* Liverpool HS 4338 Wetzel Rd Liverpool NY 13090*

TURNER, DONALD HAROLD, HS Counselor & Coach; *b:* Cincir OH; *m:* Lynnette E. Jones; *c:* Bryan; *ed:* Miami Univ (BS) Speech & Ed 1968; Xavier Univ (MED) Educl Admin Guid & Cnslng 1971; Masters Educl Admin 1972; *cr:* Wayne HS Prin 1973-74; Wekenbo High Asst Prin 1974-77; Norwood MS Prin 1977-91; Norwood HS 1991-; Cincinnati St Coll Admission Cnslr 1992-; *ai:* HS Var Reserve F Ftbl & 7th-8th Grd Jr High Boys Track Coach; NEA & OEA 1968, 1 NASSP 1974-87; Lions Club 1977-, Fund Raiser Chprsn; Hamilton Cty Assn 1978-, Pres; LaKota Optimist Club 1987-, Pres; Effective Schls C 1986; North Cntrl Assn of Ms Cert; *office:* Norwood HS 2020 Sherman Norwood OH 45212*

TURNER, DOUGLAS G., Biology & Chemistry Teacher; *b:* Roche NY; *m:* Laura Nygren; *c:* Michelle, Samantha, Justin; *ed:* SUN Oswego (BS) Ed 1979; SUNY at Oneonta (MS) Ed 1988; Cornell Ur Hrs; *cr:* Andes CS Sci Tchr 1983-85; Hancock CS Bio & Chem Tchr 1 *ai:* Class Adv; Honor Soc Advy Comm; NEA 1985-; STANYS 1985-, Presenter; CIBT 1991-; BSA 1965-, Regnl Comm; Cornell Inst of Tchrs; STANYS Conf Presenter; *office:* Hancock Central Schl 16 Rea Hancock NY 13783

TURNER, ERIC JAMES, Social Studies Teacher; *b:* Augusta, ME Adria Wells Louell; *ed:* Colby Coll (BA) Sociology, Philosophy 1992 Kents Hill Schl Tchr, Admin 1992-; *ai:* Hockey Coach; Dorm Parent *office:* Kents Hill Schl Rt 17 Kents Hill ME 04349

TURNER, FRANCES WILLIAMS, Fifth Grade Teacher; Ruckersville, VA; *c:* Tracy, Stephanie, Clyde Jr.; *ed:* Lock Haven (BS) Elem Ed 1960; 15 Credit Hrs Elem Ed; 6 Credit Hrs Gifted Ed; *c* R. Masterman Lab & Demo Schl 5 Grd Tchr 1973-; *ai:* African Amer Club; Phila Fed of Tchrs 1975-, Excl in Tchng Awd; Natl Alliance of B Schl Edctrs 1991-; Phila Soc Stud Cncl 1994-; NAACP Phila Chptr 19 Phila OIC Auxiliary 1995-; NCNW 1990- Excl Tchng Awd; Afro-Amer & Cult Mus 1981-, Outstdng Svc Awd; Distngd Achvmt Commenda 1994; Distngd Edctr Awd 1991; Cert of Merit Women in Ed 1995; Outst Svc to MS Stdnts Citation 1995; *office:* Julia R Masterman HS 17t Spring Gardens Sts Philadelphia PA 19130

TURNER, GEORGE HERBERT, English & Music Teacher; *b:* Mode CA; *m:* Johanna Smith; *c:* Christopher Joseph, Jonathan Michael, Brian Carlotta J.; *ed:* San Jose St Coll (BA) Music 1965; Pupil Prsnl S Credential; Addl 90 Semester Hrs Music, Lit; *cr:* Piedmont Jr HS M Tchr 1969-72; Sylvan USD Music Tchr 1973-78; Keyes Union Schl Eng, Music Tchr 1980-92; A T Mahan HS Eng, Music Tchr 1992-; Music Dir; Lang Arts Chm; Newspaper Adv; NEA, FEA 1992-; NEA Tchrs Assn 1969-; Amer Fed of Musicians 1981-; Schl Bell Awd Stanis Cty; Mentor Tchr 1989-92.

NER, KATHLEEN MAE, French Teacher; *b:* Worcester, MA; *ed:* rd Univ (BA) Fr Studies 1994; Middlebury Fr Schl 1992; Inst of ean Stud Nantes France 1993; *cr:* Sharon HS Fr Tchr 1994-; *ai:* Fr Adv; European Trip Coord; World Lang Stud Group Self-Stud ation Comm Mem; MA Frgn Lang Assn, MA Tchrs Assn, Sharon Assn 1994-; *home:* 316 Pollard Rd Northbridge MA 01534*

NER, LEE JAMES, Instrumental Music Teacher; *b:* Syracuse, NY; drey; *ed:* Crane Schl of Music (BM) Music Ed & Trumpet 1978; OH (MM) Applied Music & Trumpet 1980; *ai:* Onondaga Cty Music Wind Ensemble Prin Trumpet; Finger Lakes Brass Works; Syracuse Orchestra; Bear Cat Jass Band; Intnl Trumpet Guild 1976-; NYSUT ; Syracuse Musicians Assn 1980-; Amer Homebrewers Assn 1990-; Schl of Music Performers Cert 1978.

NER, MAXINE, Music Teacher; *b:* Holt, AL; *ed:* Tougaloo Coll (BA) 1965; Mississippi St Univ (MA) Music Ed; 60 In Svc Credits; *cr:* n Pub Schls Music Ed, Chorus, Eng Tchr 1965-68; Lauderdale Cty Chorus, Music Ed Tchr 1969-71; Copiague Pub Schls Music ciation Tchr 1971-; *ai:* AFT, NYSUT 1971-; SCMEA 1985-; NAACP Mbrshp; *office:* Copiague Jr HS 2650 Great Neck Rd Copiague NY

NER, RANDY LEON, Math Teacher; *b:* Parkersburg, WV; *m:* er Anne Moore; *c:* Calvin, Benjamin; *ed:* Alderson-Broaddus Coll Scndry Ed 1981; Working on MA in Schl Cnslng at Dayton Univ; *cr:* p MS Lib & Media Specialist 1981-83; Westover Jr High Math Tchr 88; Rutherford B Hayes HS Math Tchr 1989-; *ai:* Flwshp of Chrstn Huddle Coach; Chess Club Adv; JV Bsktbl Coach; NEA 1980-, nbly Rep 1995; OH Ed Assn 1989-; Delaware City Tchrs Assn 1989-, 1996-97; NCTM 1992-; Compassion Spon 1980-; 1st Bapt Church , Deacon & Adult Sunday Schl Tchr; Hospice Vol 1990-92; Aircrft rs & Pilots Assn 1990-; Ashland Oil Golden Apple Awd 1990; dng Man in Ed & Spcl Pgms at A-B Coll 1981; *home:* 102 Euclid Ave ware OH 43015*

NER, RAYMOND E., Div of Math & Sci Tech Chair; *b:* Portsmouth, : Margaret; *c:* Ebony; *ed:* Brooklyn Coll (BS) Chem 1974; Fordham (MS) Biochem 1982; Polytechnic Univ (PHD) Chem 1986; Harvard Post Doc Nutrition 1987-88; *cr:* Polytechnic Univ Rsrch Fellow 86; Roxbury Comm Coll Asst Prof 1987-89, Assoc Prof 1990-92, Prof ; *ai:* Sigma Xi 1986-; Phi Theta Kappa-Hon 1992-; Amer Chem Soc ; Amer Legion 1993-; Major US Army Reserves; Adv Biomedical Sci r Conf, Sci, Eng Acad Support; New England Bd of Ed Network

NER, ROBIN LYNN, Seventh Grade Reading Teacher; *b:* gstown, OH; *m:* Jay W.; *c:* Jason M., Justin R.; *ed:* Youngstown St (BS) Elem Ed 1988, (MS) Rdng 1992; *cr:* Mohawk HS Rdng alist Tchr Chptr 1 1988-90, Rdng Tchr 1990-, Dept Chprsn 1993-; *ai:* awk Ed Assn, PA Ed Assn, NEA 1988-; *office:* Mohawk Area Schls wk School Rd Bessemer PA 16112

NER, STEVE, Twelfth Grade English Teacher; *b:* Hamilton, OH; *m:* Ann Turner; *c:* Kelly, Kyle, Mary Elizabeth; *ed:* Bowling Green St (BS) Eng, His 1971; Miami Univ (MA) Eng 1978; *cr:* Roosevelt Jr ng Tchr 1972-80; Garfield Jr HS Eng Tchr 1981-83; Hamilton HS Eng 1984-; *ai:* Lang Arts Course of Stud, Textbook Adoption Comm for Bsbl Coach; NCTE 1992-; NEA, OEA 1993-; OHSAA 1991-; Nom shland Oil Tchr of Yr 1992; Nom for Fifth Edition of Marquis Who's in Amer Edification; *office:* Hamilton HS 1165 Eaton Ave Hamilton 5013

NER, SUSAN ZIGLER, Gen Ed Curriculum Consultant; *b:* Alliance, *m:* Donald K.; *ed:* Kent St Univ (BS) Elem Ed 1979, (MED) Curr & uction 1993; *cr:* Beaver Local MS Lang Arts Tchr 1984-93; mbiana Cty Ed Svc Ctr Curr Consultant 1993-; *ai:* Odysey of Mind taneous Coach; NEA, OEA 1980-; NMSA 1988-; ASCD 1993-; NCTE ; Beta Sigma Phi Epsilon Tau Chptr 1980-96, VP, Sec; Columbiana ty 1993-; Phi Delta Kappa 1992-; Martha Holdens Jennings Scholar ; Thanks-to-Tchrs Prgm Golden Apple 1991.

NER, TERESA A., Vocal & Music Teacher; *b:* Marion, OH; *m:* ld Allen; *ed:* OH Wesleyan Univ (BM) Vocal Music Ed 1977; OH St (MA) Early, Mid Ed 1986; Heidelburg Univ Music Camps Post Grad; River Vly Elem Schl 1st-6th Grd Music Tchr 1977-86; River Vly MS 2th Grd Vocal Music Tchr 1986-; River Vly HS 7th-12th Grd Vocal c Tchr 1986-; *ai:* Show Choir; Mens' Ensemble; Musical Vocal Dir; ccompanist; NEA, OMEA, River Vly Tchrs Assn 1977-; Marion Civic us 1971-80; Delta Kappa Gamma 1985-95; Palace Theater Shows -95, Vocal Dir; *office:* River Vly Local Schls 1267 Columbus usky Rd N Marion OH 43302

NER, THOMAS GARY, High School Art Teacher; *b:* Bridgeport, CT; ebra Soroko; *c:* Ethan; *ed:* Kutztown Univ (BS) Art Ed 1973; Parsons of Design, Indstrl Design 15 Credits; *cr:* Edinger Wyckoff Inc Interior gner 1966-69; Hamburg Area Schl Dist Art Tchr 1974-; *ai:* Art Club *office:* Hamburg Area Schl Dist Windsor St Hamburg PA 19526

NER, VALERIE L., Self-Contained Classroom Tchr; *b:* Chestertown, *m:* Charles A.; *c:* Danielle Wright; *ed:* Chesapeake Comm Coll (AA) Ed 1972; DE St Coll (BS) Elem Ed 1974; Credit Hrs Equal APC WA John's Hopkins Univ; *cr:* Rock Hall MS 6-8 Grd Tchr 13 Yrs; kingham Elem Schl Grd 4 Tchr 10 Yrs; *ai:* NEA 1974-; WCTA 1987-, Rep; *home:* 2741 Ocean Pnes Berlin MD 21811*

NWALD, BLYTH MARIE, 7th Grade Teacher; *b:* Lima, OH; *m:* nis; *c:* Michael, Emily, Elizabeth; *ed:* Bowling Green St U (BS) Mrktg ; OH St Univ (BA) Elem Ed 1988; U of Dayton (MS) Supervision ; *cr:* Delphos St John 7th Grd Tchr 1988-95; *office:* Delphos St John Schl 110 N Pierce St Delphos OH 45833

ROCZY, ROBERT JOHN, English Teacher; *b:* Cleveland, OH; *m:* e R. Wesoloski; *c:* Kathryn Lee, Kristen Ann; *ed:* OH Univ (BSEd) Eng ; John Carroll Univ (MA) Counseling 1972; *cr:* St Joseph HS Eng Tchr , 1964-83; Lake Cath HS Eng Tchr 1983-; *ai:* Forum Lit Magazine; TA, NEA, NCTE 1964-; CHALTA 1969-, Soc Chm; Upward Bound 5 St Margaret Credit Comm 3 Yrs; St Mary Magdalene 250 Club 7 Yrs; Army Artillery Officer 1962-64; Stu Voter Favorite Tchr 8 Yrs; *office:* e Catholic HS 6733 Reynolds Rd Mentor OH 44060

RPIN-PETROSINO, CAROLYN, Asst Prof of Criminal Justice; *b:* adelphia, PA; *m:* Anthony; *ed:* Howard Univ (BS) Psych 1974; Rutgers v (MSW) Admin in Criminal Justice 1975, (PHD) Criminal Justice 3; *cr:* Garden St Correction Ctr Soc Svcs Dir 1975-80; NJ St Parole Bd ring Officer 1981-93; Univ of MA at Lowell Asst Prof 1993-; *ai:* Cncl Diversity & Pluralism; Fac Senate Lab & African-Amer Archives ms; Acad of Criminal Justice Scis, Amer Soc of Criminology 1993-; Bapt Temple 1994-; Past & Current Research Project Concerning ision Making Comm Policing Hate Crimes; *office:* Univ Of MA At vell 1 University Ave Lowell MA 01854

RPYN, SUSAN ENGLE, High School Art Teacher; *b:* Batavia, NY; *m:* hael J.; *c:* Courtney; *ed:* Genesee Comm coll (AS) Lbrl Arts, Art 1978; erts Wesleyan Coll (BS) Art Ed 1988; Nazareth Coll of Rochester (MS) Ed 1994; *cr:* Gates Chili HS Sub Art Tchr 1988-89; Albion Cntrl Schl HS Art Tchr 1989-; *ai:* Soph Class Adv; Set Design Coord Schl sicals, Plays; AFT 1988-; NYSATA 1989-; United Meth Church dbell Choirs 1994-, Teen Choir Dir; *home:* 20 Erie St Albion NY 14411

TURRI, JOHN JOSEPH, Earth, Phys Sci & Bio Teacher; *b:* Hazleton, PA; *m:* Cheryl Sweet; *c:* Jason, Jaclyn, Jennifer; *ed:* PA St Univ (BS) Sec Ed & Bio 1973; Masters Equivalency 1980; 90+ Grad Credits from E Stroudsburg Univ, Bloomsburg Univ & Wilkes Univ; *cr:* H F Grebey Jr HS Bio Tchr 1973-92; Hazleton Jr HS Bio, Earth Sci & Phys Sci Tchr 1992-; *ai:* PA Jr Acad of Sci Spon; Teens Against Cancer Adv; NEA 1973-; PA St EA 1973-; Hazleton Area EA 1973-; Hazleton Univ Amer Cancer Soc 1980-, Bd of Dirs; PTA 1986-; Knights of columbus 1986; Hazleton Area Schl Dist Tchr Recognition Awd; PA PTA Honorary Life Mbrshp.

TURRI, LOUIS A., Fourth Grade Teacher; *b:* Seneca Falls, NY; *m:* Julie M.; *c:* Jennifer, Jeffery, Matthew; *ed:* SUNY at Geneseo (BS) Ed 1967; SUNY at Brockport (MS) Math 1971; *cr:* Churchville Chili Fifth Grd Tchr 1967-93, Fourth Grd Tchr 1993-; *ai:* Credit Union Sec; NEA 1967-; Vince Lombadi Ftbl 1980-; *home:* 193 Greenaway Rd Rochester NY 14610

TURRO, STEPHEN J., English Teacher; *b:* Newark, NJ; *m:* Karen Hughes; *c:* Jacqueline Lynch, Stephen J., Michael J., Edward; *ed:* Bloomfield Coll (BA) Eng, Ed 1966; William Paterson Coll (MA) Eng 1969; *cr:* Ramapo HS Eng Tchr 1966-; *ai:* Var Bsbl Coach 1971-85; Var Ftbl Coach 1973-86; Peer Ldrshp Group 1992-93; NEA, NJEA, BCEA 1966-; RIHEA 1966-, Exec, Negot Comms 1966-70; BCCA Century Club Awd; *office:* Ramapo HS George St Franklin Lakes NJ 07417

TURSHMAN, ALFRED H., Secondary Mathematics Teacher; *b:* Cortland, NY; *m:* Jane Henry; *c:* Brian, Kevin; *ed:* SUNY at Cortland (BA) Math Ed 1977; SUNY at Binghamton (MS) Math Ed 1982; *cr:* Chenango Forks MS Jr HS Math Tchr 1977-78; Chenango Vly Jr Sr HS Scndry HS Scndry Math Tchr 1978-; *ai:* Chenango Vly Tchrs Assn Pres; AFT, NYSUT 1978-; Chenango Vly TA 1978-, Pres; Hiawatha Soccer Assn 1994-, Sec; *office:* Chenango Vly Cntrl Schl 1160 Chenango St Binghamton NY 13901*

TURTON, ROBERT S.,III, Minister, Bible Tchr, Chaplain; *b:* New Brunswick, NJ; *m:* Sandra H. Bross; *c:* Robert IV, Elisabeth, Michael, Rebecca; *ed:* Zarephath Bible Seminary (BSD) Biblical Theology 1960; Alma White Coll Ed; Attnd Reformed Episcopal Philadelphia Theological Seminary; *cr:* Nondenominational Evangelical Pastor Ordained 1961; Amer Resue Workers Natl Mission Church Major 1962; *ai:* Yth Temperance Cncl Adv; Supervised Ministries Dir; Corps Cadets Overseer; ACSI 1987-; Order of St Luke the Physician 1982-, Chaplain; NJ Cncl for Alcohol, Drug Ed 1977-, Bd Mem; NJ Chrstn Conf on Legislation 1980-, Sec; Area Ministerial Assns 1965-, Sec, Treas; Intnl Union of Gospel Missions 1965-, Dist Bd; Natl Assn of Evangelicals 1965-; Grange-Patrons of Husbandry 1993-, Sec; Civil Air Patrol, USAF Aux 1966-, Chaplain; Intnl Org of Good Templars 1984-, NJ Pres; Shepherd of Bethlehem 1995-, Local Lodge Chaplain; Articles Pub; *home:* PO Box 9033 Zarephath NJ 08890

TURTURIELLO, VINCENT FRANK, Mathematics Teacher; *b:* Orange, NJ; *ed:* Montclair St Coll (BA) Math 1961, (MA) Math 1964; Addl 32 Credits Scndry Ed; *cr:* Nutley HS Math Tchr 1961-; *ai:* Boys, Girls HS Tennis Coach; NJEA, NEA, NJ Math Tchrs Assn 1961-; *office:* Nutley HS 300 Franklin Ave Nutley NJ 07110

TUTEN, APRIL BORUM, Math Teacher; *b:* Ft Knox, KY; *m:* Robert Michael; *c:* Michael Roger; *ed:* Univ of SC (BS) Math 1988, (MAT) Math Ed 1989; 3 Addl Credit Hrs in Ed; 3 Addl Credit Hrs in Math; *cr:* Dreher HS Math Tchr 1990-93; Mayfield Alternative HS Math Tchr 1993-94; Milford Mill Acad Math Tchr 1994-; *ai:* JV Chrldr Coach; NHS Co-Spon; Governor's Citation for Attending Governor's Acad of Sci & Math Tech 1995; *home:* 325 Logan Ct Abingdon MD 21009

TUTHILL, ANNETTE MASARYK, Math Teacher; *b:* Jamaica, NY; *m:* Allen; *c:* Christopher, Alyssa; *ed:* SUNY New Paltz (BS) Ed 1972, (MS) Ed 1975; *cr:* Pine Bush Cntrl Schl Dist Math Tchr 1972-80; SUNY New Paltz Asst Prof Math, Supvr Stud Tchng 1987-92; Pine Bush Cntrl Schl Dist Math Tchr 1992-; *ai:* Team Ldr; Dinner Dance Decorating Comm Chprsn; Phi Delta Kappa 1989-; Assn Math Tchrs NYS; NCTM; AFT, NYSUT 1972-; *office:* Pine Bush Cntrl Schl Dist Rt 302 Pine Bush NY 12566

TUTHILL, PAUL C., Band Director; *b:* Oceanside, NY; *m:* Cathy Kender; *ed:* Kent St Univ (BA) Music 1973; Long Island Univ (MS) Educl Admin 1981; *cr:* Green Meadows Jr HS Band Dir 1973-74; St Patricks Schl Band Dir 1974-79; Salk Jr HS Band Dir 1979-80; Washington St Schl Band Dir 1980-; *ai:* NMEA, NYSUT 1980-; AFM Local 802 1973-; Intnl Trumpet Guild 1980-; *office:* Washington Street Schl 760 Washington St Franklin Square NY 11010

TUTNAUER, KAREN, Chemistry & Mathematics Tchr; *b:* Bronx, NY; *c:* Melissa, Elizabeth, Samantha; *ed:* Temple Univ (BA) Chem 1972; NY Univ (MS) Chem 1975; Manhattanville Coll Problem Solving Math & More, Math for LD Stdnts; Long Island Univ Ed Evaluation; Polytechnic Inst of Brooklyn Polymer Chem; *cr:* Mercy Coll Chem Instr 1980-89; Marymount Coll Chem, Math Asst Prof 1984-; Archbishop Stepinac HS Chem, Math Tchr 1986-; Key Inst for Learning Strategies Tchr, SAT's, Achvmt in Math & Chem 1992-; *ai:* Mathematical Assn of Amer 1995-; Congretation Sons of Israel 1988-; Tchr of Month 1995; Asst Prof Math, Chem Marymount Coll; NYS Cert Math & Chem.

TUTTLE, CATHERINE BOCCABELLA, First Grade Teacher; *b:* Bellaire, OH; *c:* Thomas L., Tamara T. Medovic; *ed:* OH Univ (BS) Elem Ed 1970; *cr:* Bellaire City Schl System 2nd Grd Tchr 1955-56, Sub Tchr 1963-64, Kndgtn Tchr 1964-65, Sub Tchr 1965-66, Kndgtn Tchr 1966-76, 1st Grd Tchr 1976-77, 2nd Grd Tchr 1977-78; 3rd Grd Tchr 1978-79, 1st Grd Tchr 1979-; *ai:* NEA 1963-; OEA 1963-; Bellaire Ed Assn 1963-, Bldg Rep 1994; First United Meth Church 1965-; United Meth Women 1965-, Treas 1992-; Bellaire HS Alumni Assn, Trustee; Edgar Burrows Schlsp Fund, VP; Rose Hill Elem PTA, Treas 1994-; Rose Hill Elem Tchr of the Yr 1986; Bellaire City Schls Tchr of the Yr 1986; OH PTA Dist 19 Tchr of the Yr 1986; Ashland Oil Tchr Achvmt Awd Nom 1992; *home:* 4965 Atchison Rd Bellaire OH 43906

TUTTLE, DOUGLAS, Math Teacher; *b:* White Plains, NY; *m:* Abby Crockett; *c:* John; *ed:* Pace Univ (BS) Math 1977; Univ of South FL (MED) Math Ed 1982; *cr:* Eisenhower Jr HS Math Tchr 1977-82; Rye HS Math Tchr 1982-; *ai:* MS Soccer, Boys Var Bsktbl Coach; AFT 1982-; *office:* Rye HS Parsons St Rye NY 10580

TUTTLE, EVELYN DI PASTINA, Middle School English Teacher; *b:* Utica, NY; *c:* Diane Billings, Joyce, Robert; *ed:* Utica Coll of Syracuse Univ (BA) Eng, Phil 1958; Eng Potsdam St Tchrs Grad Stud 36 Credit Hrs 1960-65; *cr:* VVS HS Eng Tchr 1959-68; LA Schl Dist Rdng Tchr 1975-78; VVS MS Eng Tchr 1979-; *ai:* Team Ldr 14 Yrs; Honor Soc Adv; Drama Club; Child Stud Comm; AFT, VVS Tchrs Assn 1979-; Assn Retarded Children, Advy Bd; St Dept Mental Hlth DDSO 5 Yrs, Advy Bds; Parent Advocate for Retarded COH 7 Yrs; *office:* VVS Cntrl HS Rt 31 Verona NY 13478

TUTTLE, HOLLY CHRISTINA, High School Art Teacher; *b:* Springfield, MA; *ed:* Westfield St (BA) Art, Scndry Ed 1974; Amer Intnl Coll (MA) Scndry Ed 1980; 12 Post Grad Credits to Date; *cr:* Chestnut Jr HS Art Tchr 1974-90; Springfield Cntrl HS Art Tchr 1990-; *ai:* Catalina Pool Club Assn Pres 1992-95; Natl Art Honor Soc Adv 1990-; YMCA Mem 1978-; NEA 1974-; Natl Art Ed Assn 1980-; Springfield Art League 1985-; YMCA Bd of Corporators 1993-95, Forest Park Zoological Assn, Vol 1988-93; Town Gallery 1990-; Natl Wildlife Fed; NY Conservation Soc; Defenders of Wildlife; Greenpeace; City of Springfield Beacon Awd 1993, 95; Long Meadow Tow Gallery 1990-; NAHS Mural Painting Comm Svc 1990-; Springfield Multicultural Curr Coord 1993; SPFLD Art Curr 1992-; Outcomes & Assessments Comm 1995-; *office:* Springfield Central HS 1840 Roosevelt Ave Springfield MA 01109

TUTTLE, JONATHAN G., United States History Teacher; *b:* Utica, NY; *ed:* Providence Coll (BA) His 1989; Bridgewater St Coll (MAT) His 1994; *cr:* Wareham HS Soc Stud Tchr 1994-; *ai:* Environmental Awareness Club Adv; SSCSS 1994-; *home:* PO Box 3403 Wareham MA 02571

TUTTLE, SALLY GAGNIER, Retired Teacher; *b:* Springfield, MA; *m:* Robert J.; *c:* David, Anne, Sara, Judith, Robert; *ed:* Our L;ady of the Elms (BA) Sociology, Eng 1953; Amer Intnl Coll 3 Credit Hrs Psych; *cr:* Dept Pub Welfare Soc Worker 1953-55; Holy Cross Elem Schl Classroom Tchr 1973-95; *ai:* Homework Helpline Spon Big Cy Ford Corp Springfield MA Still Active in Area; Pioneer Vly Rdng Assn 1982-95; Providence Hosp Systems 1985-, Bd of Trustees; St Vincent Nursing Home Holyoke MA, Mbrshp; *home:* 19 Mandalay Rd Springfield MA 01118

TUTUSKA, DENNIS M., English Teacher; *b:* Buffalo, NY; *c:* Heather, Christopher; *ed:* SUNY Coll at Buffalo (BA) Eng 1968, (MS) Ed 1972; *cr:* Erie Cty Comm Coll Eng Tchr 1973-75; Frontier Cntrl Schl System Eng Tchr 1968; *ai:* Frosh Class Adv; JV Hockey Coach; Safe Schls Comm; NYSUT 1968-, St Del W NY Ldrshp Awd 1995; AFT 1968-, Natl Del; Frontier Cntrl Tchrs Assn 1968-, Pres, VP, Recording Sec, Negotiation Head Bldg Rep & Grievance Chm; Western NY Umpires 1972-92; Hamburg Municipal Hockey Assn 1984-91, VP; Buffalo AFC & CIO Labor Cncl; *office:* Frontier Central Sr HS 4432 Bay View Rd Hamburg NY 14075

TVENSTRUP, LISA M., Social Studies Teacher; *b:* Providence, RI; *m:* Scott N.; *c:* Ian; *ed:* RI Coll (BA) Soc Stud, Scndry Ed 1985; Providence Coll (MS) Spec Ed 1996; *cr:* Ponanganset HS Soc Stud Tchr 1985-; *ai:* Class Adv 1992-; NEA 1985-, Local Sec, St Del; *office:* Ponaganset HS 137 Anan Wade Rd North Scituate RI 02857

TWAREK, GREG L., Sixth Grd Sci & Math Teacher; *b:* Port Clinton, OH; *m:* Natalie Mazurik; *c:* Zachary, Melissa, Nicole; *ed:* Kemper Military Schl & Coll (AA) 1972; Bowling Green St Univ (BS) Elem Ed 1974; Post Grad Bowling Green; *cr:* Immaculate Conception Fifth-Sixth Grd Tchr 1974-75; Portage Elem Sixth Grd Tchr 1975-; *ai:* Asst Cross Cnty Coach 1994-; Asst Track Coach 1976-80, 1989-; Elem Sci Dept Head 1992-; IM Bsktbl; AFT, OFT 1975-; PCFT 1975-, VP; Marblehead Lions 1985-, Pres; Jennings Scholar 1995; Consulting Tchr 1991, 1993; *home:* 117 Lucien Dr Marblehead OH 43440

TWAROG, SUSAN CROMBIE, Fourth Grade Teacher; *b:* Springfield, MA; *m:* Theodore J.; *c:* Elizabeth, Peter, Matthew; *ed:* Cntrl CT St Coll (BS) Elem Ed 1964, (MS) Rdng Specialist 1968; 45 Credit Hrs; *cr:* East Hartford CT 2nd Grd Tchr 1964-68; Lexington MA 3rd Grd Tchr 1968-69; Dunstable MA 3rd Grd Tchr 1970; Barre MA 4th Grd Tchr 1982-; *ai:* Odyssey of Mind Coach; Sci Coord; Negotiation Comm; QRTA, MTA & NEA 1982-; Grievance Comm; Rel Instr 1979-92; East Hartford CT Outstdng Young Edctr Awd 1968.

TWISSELMANN, DIANE MEREDITH, 8th Grade Earth Science Tchr; *b:* Milford, DE; *m:* Daniel C.; *c:* Jamie, Jenna, Cory; *ed:* DE Tech & Comm Coll (AS) Human Svcs 1980; DE St Univ (BS) Sci Ed 1992; Wilmington Coll (MS) Schl Counseling 1996; *cr:* Playtex Inc Credit Rep 1981-88; Indian River Schl Dist Earth Sci Tchr 1992-; *ai:* Inservice Comm Chprsn; Chrstn Ed Assn 1993-; Kappa Delta Pi 1990-; 30 Invervice Credit Hrs; *office:* Selbyville MS Rt 17 Selbyville DE 19975*

TWITTY, GERALDINE WILLIAMS, Professor of Biology; *b:* Roanoke, VA; *w:* Donald Mason (dec); *c:* Andrea Donnette, Angela Denise Adams; *ed:* Howard Univ (BS) Zoology 1952, (MS) Zoology 1955, (PHD) Biochemical Genetics 1975; Recombinant DNA Tech; Environmental Sci; *cr:* FL A&M Univ Asst Prof 1956-60; Tuskegee Univ Asst Prof 1960-63; Hampton Univ Asst Prof 1963-67; Howard Univ Prof 1967-; *ai:* Minority Women in Sci; Environmental Roundtable; DC Coalition for Environmental Justice; AIBS 1960-, Bd; AAAS 1960-; Sigma Xi 1975-, Sec, Qualifications Comm; ASB, Bd; Outstdng Tchr Awds; EPA Office of Environmental Justice, MWIS, AAAS Outstdng Svc; *office:* Howard Univ Dept of Biology 415 College St NW Washington DC 20059*

TWOMBLY, ALICE JACOBS, AP & Honors English Teacher; *b:* New York, NY; *c:* Jonathan Dana, David Ethan; *ed:* Brandeis Univ (BA) Eng 1962; Harvard Grad Schl of Ed (MAT) Eng, Scndry Ed 1963; Columbia Univ Tchrs Coll Writing Prjt 9 Credits; Univ WI Grad Schl of Arts & Sci 12 Credits; Manhattan Coll AP Seminar Course 6 Credits; *cr:* Bigelow Jr HS Intern Tchr 1963; R. M. La Follette HS Eng, Soc Stud Tchr 1963-68; Ben Franklin Jr HS Eng Tchr 1974-78; Teaneck Gifted, Talented Prgm Dir 1978-81; Teaneck Alternative HS Coord, Dir 1981-84; Teaneck HS Eng Tchr 1984-; *ai:* Debate, Speech Coach 1984-; Restructuring Comm Mem; NJEA, NEA 1974; TTEA 1974-; NCTE, NJTE 1989-; Mayors Civil Rights Commission 1965-66, Chm, Coord; Presenter: NJ Soc Stud, Eng Cncl Multi Cultural Ed Eng Curr 1993, Jr HS Gifted Ed Model Ramopo Coll 1982; NJ Poetry Contest Winner 1983; Citation from NJ St Legislature Recognizing Achvmt with Debate Tm; Resolution Read in Front of NJ St Assembly 1994; Prin Excl Awd for Outstdng Contributions to Teaneck HS 1994; *office:* Teaneck HS 100 Elizabeth Ave Teaneck NJ 07666*

TWYMAN, ANN LYNN, Sixth Grade Teacher; *b:* Whitehall, NY; *ed:* Adirondacl Comm Coll (AA) Lbrl Arts 1988; Potsdam St Univ (BA) Elem Ed 1972; 30 Hrs Russell Sage Coll, St Univ at Plattsburg Elem Ed; *cr:* Dorothy Nolan Elem Schl 6th Grd Tchr 1973-91; Maple Avenue MS 6th Grd Tchr 1992-; *ai:* Dist Soc Stud Comm; Saratoga Springs Tchr Assn; NY St Tchrs Assn; *office:* Maple Avenue MS 515 Maple Ave Saratoga Springs NY 12866

TYLER, CAROLYN JEANETTE VANCE, Second Grade Teacher; *b:* East Meadow, NY; *m:* George A. Saunders; *c:* Tamiko A. Cropper, Marleen D. Jones, Herbert E. Jr, Anthony F.; *ed:* Nassau Comm Coll (AA) Liberal Arts 1974; SUNY at Old Westbury (BSEd) Ed 1976; Adelphi Univ (MS) Spec Ed 1981; D#25 Succeeding With Difficult Stdnts Drake Univ; Cooperative Discipline, Grad Course Coll of St Rose; GRSS 93-5 Collaboration Cooperative Efforts Helping Spec Needs Stdnts; *cr:* Elmont Tchr Aide 1964-71; Sewanhaka Dist Tchr Aide 1971-76; Yonker Day Care Tchr 1978-77; Elmont 2nd Grd Tchr 1978-; *ai:* Soccer Coach; Computer Club; Homework Ctr; Summer Schl; Enrichment Prgm; Dist Lang Arts, Ethnic, Math, Sci Comms Mem; Elmont Elem Tchr Assn 1989-, Membership Chprsn; AAUW Sewanhaka Branch 1980-, Hospitality; Awded PTA Life Membership; *home:* 93 Frederick Ave Floral Park NY 11001

TYLER, GAIL FAIN, Music Specialist; *b:* Raleigh, NC; *m:* Richard J. Jr.; *c:* Winona, Rukaiyah; *ed:* VA St Univ (BS) Pub Schl Music 1974, (MS) Music Ed 1976; George Washington Univ (MA) Ed, Human Dev 1981; *cr:* St Mary's Cty Pub Schls Instrumental Music Tchr 1976-86, Music Specialist, Instrumental, Gen & Vcal 1986-; *ai:* Schl Improvement Team; Comer Facilitator; All Cty Hnr Band, Hnr Chorus Prgm; NEA, MSTA 1976-; ASCD 1993-; NAFE 1994-; AKA 1972-; PTA 1992-, Parliamentarian; PSTA 1994-; Prince George's Cty GATE Prgm; Outstdng Personality 1979; Young Women in Amer 1978; Who's Who in Amer Ed; Creator, Guest Conductor All Cty Elem Hnr Band; 2000 Notable Amer Women 1996; Who's Who Amer Women 1996; *home:* 3335 Huntley Square Dr Apt A-2 Temple Hills MD 20748*

TYLER, JANE B., Cmptr Stud & Bus Dept Chair; *b:* New York, NY; *ed:* Fordham (BS); Hunger (MS) 1977; Iona (MA) 1990; *cr:* Msgr Scanlan Schl Tchr 1968-; *ai:* All Sr Acts; Yrbk Finances; Cmptr Club; Schl Newspaper; NBEA 1972-; NCEA 1969-; FBLA 1995-; ASCD 1992-; *office:* Monsignor Scanlan H S 915 Hutchinson River Pkwy Bronx NY 10465

TYLER, JANE M., Sixth Grade Science Teacher; *b:* Freeport, NY; *m:* Bruce D.; *c:* Rebecca J., B. David Jr.; *ed:* Newton Coll (BA) His 1965; Manhattanville Coll (MAT) His 1966; *cr:* Osborn Schl Non-Graded Elem Tchr 1966-71; Mills Pond Schl Sixth Grd Tchr 1971-76; Avery MS Grds 5 & 6 Tchr 1981-; Somers Elem Schls Primary GATE Ed Tchr 1989-91; *ai:* Somers Pub Schls Strategic Planning Comm, Outdoor Environmental Ed Design Comm, Sci Curr Comm; NEA 1966-; CT Ed Assn 1981-; Somers Ed Assn 1981-, Chair Mbrshp; NSTA 1992-; New England Sci Tchrs 1995-; Somers Village Players 1978-, Ways & Means Co-Chair; Delta Kappa Gamma 1990-94; Savings Bank of Rockville 1989-, Advy Bd; Justice of the Peace St of CT; NY & CT Permanent Cert; CT Certfd Mentor & Cooperating Tchr; Somers Tchr of Yr 1986-87; CT Tchr of Yr Runner-up 1987; MA Inst of Tech Sci & Engrng Prgm Flwshp 1995; *office:* Avery MS Ninth District Rd Somers CT 06071

TYLER, ROBERT STEPHEN, Chemistry Teacher; *b:* Pottstown, PA; *m:* Ellen Kinnealey; *ed:* Harvard Univ (BA) Bio 1984; Northeastern Univ (MS) Chem 1996; *cr:* Avon Old Farms Schl Sci Tchr 1985-88; Milton Acad Chem Tchr 1988-; *ai:* Var Swimming Coach; Amer Chem Soc 1989-; NISCA 1990-; *office:* Milton Acad 170 Centre St Milton MA 02186

TYMINSKI, CLAIRE NIXON, Clinical Instructor; *b:* Brattleboro, VT; *m:* Thomas John Jr.; *c:* Michelle M., Wynne Marie Tyminski Sarvan, Thomas John III, Monique Marie, Jonathan Sydney; *ed:* Cambridge Coll (MED) Ed 1994; Mercy Hosp Nrsng Diploma 1964; *cr:* Mercy Hosp Inservice Instr, Supvr 1974-84, Admin Coord 1984-89; Holyoke Hosp Staff Nurse Intensive Care 1990-92, Inservice Instr Dept of Ed 1992-; Springfield Tech Comm Coll Clinical Instr Medl Assisting Dept 1992-; *ai:* Gateway HS Let There Be Lights Comm; Gateway HS Booster Club Fundraiser; Medl Assisting Stu Club Adv; Mercy Hosp Alumni Assoc 1964-, MA Tchrs Assn 1992-; Cncl on Aging Adv; Amer Heart Assn CPR Instr, Trainer; Amer Red Cross CPR Instr; Advanced Cardiac Life Support Instr; *office:* Springfield Tech Comm Coll One Armory Sq Springfield MA 01105

TYMINSKI, LINDA GLINKA, Art Teacher & Dept Head; *b:* Cleveland, OH; *m:* James; *c:* Jennifer Peganott, Jim, Allyson, Michael; *ed:* Case Western Reserve Univ, Cleveland Inst of Art (BS) Art Ed 1965; 15 Addl Hrs at Mather Grad Schl for CWRU; *cr:* Richardson Elem Schl Art Tchr 1965-66; Cuyahoga Hts Elem Sch Art Tchr 1966-67; Trinity HS Art Tchr, Dept Head 1988-; *ai:* Art Partners Show; Art Club; NAEA 1988-; ASCEND 1994-; *office:* Trinity HS 12425 Granger Rd Garfield Heights OH 44125*

TYRRELL, DAWN HUDGINGS, General Music & Band Teacher; *b:* Logansport, IN; *m:* Michael A.; *c:* Kyle T. C., Catherine E.; *ed:* Ball St Univ (BA) K-12 Music Ed 1986; Grad Credits Coll of St Joseph the Provide; *cr:* Green Mtn Union HS Chorus, Music Tchr 1986-87; West Rutland Schls K-12 Grd Band, Gen Music Tchr 1987-; *ai:* Jazz Band; NEA, VMEA 1987-.

TYRRELL, NANCY HOLMES, Business Ed Dept Chprsn & Tchr; *b:* Lewiston, ME; *c:* James; *ed:* Husson Coll at Bangor (BS) Bus Ed 1963; Univ of ME (MS) Ed 1972; Cmptr Word Processing, Ed, Bus Ed Credit Hrs; *cr:* Andover HS Bus Ed Tchr 1961-62; Edward Little HS Bus Ed Tchr 1963-64; Oxford HS Bus Ed Tchr, Dept Chprsn 1965-; Oxford Hills HS Bus Ed Tchr, Dept Chprsn 1965-; *ai:* Dist Keyboarding Comm; Accreditation Steering Comm Mem Twice; Schlsp, NHS Selection Comms Past Mem; Former FBLA, NHS, Yrbk Adv; Former Sec Music Boosters; Former Adult Ed Tchr; OH, ME Tchrs Assns; Bus Ed Assn of ME, Past Region K Chprsn; Dr. Moore Schlsp Selection Comm; New England Assn Schls & Colls Commission on Pub Scndry Schls Past Visiting Team Mem; St Ed Dept Bus Ed Consultant 1983-88, Svcs; Former Citizens Schlsp Selection Comm Mem; Local FBLA Over 25 Yrs Adv Svc Recognition Plaque; *office:* Oxford Hills HS 250 Main St South Paris ME 04281

TYRRELL, SALLY BYRNE, ESL Teacher; *b:* Lynn, MA; *w:* Harold Curtis (dec); *c:* D. Scott, jenifer Whitmor; *ed:* Regis Coll (BA) Eng, Fr 1959; Salem St (MED) Dev Rdng 1962; *cr:* Saugus HS Eng Tchr 6 Yrs; Tower Schl Eng Tchr 6 Yrs; Ipswich HS Eng Tchr 2 Yrs; Marblehead HS ESL Tchr 10 Yrs; *ai:* League of Women Voters 1971-, Mbrshp Chm; 50 Articles Pub; *office:* Marblehead HS Duncan Sleigh Sq 217 Pleasant St Marblehead MA 01945

TYSIACHNEY, DARLENE NELSON, Scndry Schl Reading & Eng Tchr; *b:* Geneva, PA; *m:* Daniel; *c:* Jonathan, Joshua; *ed:* Edinboro Univ of PA (BS) Eng 1966, (MED) Eng 1968; Clarion Univ of PA ITEC 3 Credits; Moody Bible Inst Bible 3 Credits; Empire St Bapt Seminary Bible 3 Credits; Northwest Tri-Cty Intermediate Unit Cmptr 2 Credits; *cr:* Iroquois Jr Sr HS Lang Arts Dept Chm, Jr HS Eng, Rdng Tchr 1966-72; Calvary Bapt Acad Scndry Lang Arts Tchr 1972-74; Bethel Christian Schl Lang Arts Dept Chm, Scndry Schl Eng, Rdng Tchr 1985-; Guidance Counselor 1994-; *ai:* 7th Grd Class Adv; ACSI Lang Arts Coord; Speech Meets, Spelling Bee, Writing Festival Competitions; HS Cnslr; Natl Honor Society Adv; Assn of Chrstn Schls Intnl 1985-; Northwest PA Cncl Tchrs of Eng 1986-; Edinboro Bapt Church 1958-, Clerk 7 Yrs, Sunday Schl Tchr 1975-80, 1987-, Awana, Jr Church Ldr 1974-1978, Womens Missy Group Pres 1977-81; Edinboro Little League, Team Mother 1984-86; Erie Cty Y-Teen Adv of Yr 1970; Yrbk Dedication 1992; *home:* 12570 Silverthorn Rd Edinboro PA 16412

TYSON, BETH MILNER, Mathematics Teacher; *b:* Grove City, PA; *c:* Loralee; *ed:* Grove City Coll (AB) Math 1975; Alfred Univ (MS) Ed 1983; *cr:* Bryant Station HS Math Tchr 1975-77; Randolph HS Math Tchr 1977-78; Madison Schl System Math Tchr 1978-79; Wellsville HS Math Tchr 1979-; *ai:* WEA, NEANY, NEA 1979-, Pres, Treas, Negotiation Comm Chair; AMTNYS 1983-; Scio UM Church 1993-; *office:* Wellsville HS 126 W State St Wellsville NY 14895*

TYSON, JOY, Assistant Professor; *b:* Berkeley Springs, WV; *ed:* Univ of MD (BS) Nrsng 1982, (MS) Nrsng 1988; Enrolled Univ of VA Post Masters FNP; *ai:* Amer Coll Hlth 1988-; *office:* Catonsville Comm Coll 800 S Rolling Rd Catonsville MD 21228*

TYSON, LORENA E., Sci Dept Chair & Chem Tchr; *b:* Montclair, NJ; *ed:* Coll of St Elizabeth (BS) Chem 1956; Cath Univ of Amer (MS) Chem 1965; NSF Math Inst 15 Credits; Attnd Seton Hall Univ 2 Yrs; Rutgers Univ 12 Credits Chem, PHD; HJIT 3 Credits; Kean Coll of NJ 18 Credits Ed, Supvr Cert; *cr:* Acad of the Sacred Heart Math, Chem Tchr 1956-59; St Joseph HS Math, Chem, Phys Tchr 1959-62; St Peter & Paul HS Math, Chem, Phys Tchr 1962-71; Essex Cty Coll Math Adjunct 1971-78; Kean Coll Math Adjunct 1971; Montclair HS Chem, AP Honors Tchr 1971-; *ai:* Ticket Sales Mgr for Fall & Winter Sports; Phi Delta Kappa 1979-, Treas; NEA, NJEA 1971-; ECEA 1971-, Treas, Human Relations; MEA 1971-, Treas, Educator of Yr Awd; ACS Tchrs Affiliate 1971-, Exec Comm, HS Chemistry Regnl Awd; NSTA, NJSTA 1971-, HS Chemistry NNJ Awd; Montclair Vol Ambulance Unit 1991-94, Exec Comm; NSF Math Awd 2 Yrs; Princeton Univ Distinguished Scndry Schl Tchng; *office:* Montclair HS 100 Chestnut St Montclair NJ 07042

TZALLAS, MARY PAPADOPOULOS, English Teacher; *b:* New York, NY; *m:* Anastasios; *c:* Vasilis, Nicholas-Napoleon; *ed:* Reistotelion Univ of Thessaloniki (BA) Eng 1983; St John's Univ (MA) Eng 1986; *cr:* Greek Lang Inst Greek Tchr 1983-93; William Spyropoulos Schl Eng Tchr 1986-; St John's Univ Eng Prof 1986-; *ai:* Yrbk Adv; Eighth Grd Coord; AAUP 1986-.

U

UBIETA-MENDEZ, ARLENE, Spanish Teacher; *b:* New York City, NY; *m:* John Mendez; *ed:* St John's Univ (BA) Span & Fr 1982, (MA) Span Ed 1983; Addl 120 Hrs Universidad Madrid, 120 Hrs Universite Montpellier, 120 Hrs Coll Intnl Cannes; *cr:* Franklin K. Lane Span Tchr 1986-87; City-as-Schl Span Tchr & Adv 1987-88; John Bowne Span & ESL Tchr 1988-89; Stuyvesant HS Span Tchr 1991-; *ai:* Span Club Adv; Travel Abroad Prgms to Spain & Mexico Spon; Manhattan Test Ctr Coord; ACTFL 1991-; AATSP 1987-; NYSAFLT 1991-, James E. Allen Awd; Hispanic Yth Ldrshp Prgm 1992-94; Assistanship for Grad Stud Awd 1982; *office:* Stuyvesant HS 345 Chambers St New York NY 10282*

UCCIARDO, ANTHONY J., English Teacher; *b:* Kittanning, PA; *m:* Doris; *c:* James, Jill, Jeffrey; *ed:* Indiana Univ of PA (BS) Eng Ed 1969, (MA) Eng 1973; Staff Dev of Tchng Staff; *cr:* Ford City HS Tchr, Gifted Coord 1971-; *ai:* Textbook Selection Comm; PA Goals 2000 Local Comm; NEA, NCTE 1971-; *office:* Ford City HS 1100 Fourth Ave Ford City PA 16226*

UELAND, ELIZABETH PRITCHARD, English Teacher; *b:* Minneapolis, MN; *m:* Mark; *c:* Mara, Anne Ueland Bailey, Michael; *ed:* Manhattanville Coll (BA) Eng 1959; Temple Univ (MED) Eng Ed 1983; *cr:* Girard Coll Eng Tchr 1982-83; Chestnut Hill Acad 3rd Grd Tchr 1983-84; Cntry Day Schl of Sacred Heart Eng Tchr 1985-90; Merion Mercy Acad Eng Tchr 1990-; *ai:* Frosh Moderator; NCTE, Jane Austen Soc North Amer 1990-; Chestnut Hill Comm Assn, Chestnut Hill Historical Soc 1979-; *office:* Merion Mercy Acad 511 Montgomery Ave Merion Station PA 19066

UETRECHT, ANITA MALTINSKY, Family & Consumer Science Tchr; *b:* Sidney, OH; *m:* David; *c:* Natalie, Sarah, Audrey, Carmen; *ed:* OH St Univ Voc Home Ec 1975; *cr:* Waynesfield-Goshen Instr 1975-81; St Henry HS Instr 1982-; *ai:* FHA 20 Yrs; FTA; SADD; OEa, NEA 1975-; OVA; AVA; Botkins Comm Club 1993-, Bd 1993-, Sec 1993-94; Amer Field Svc 1991- Coord for Area, Chptr Pres; Rel Ed Instr 1985-, Sophomore Level Instr; Honorary Member FHA Ohio Assn, 4-H Club; *office:* Minster Local Schls 100 7th St Minster OH 45865*

UGELOW, CAROL MEISELS, Math Teacher & Advisor; *b:* Brooklyn, NY; *m:* Robert A.; *c:* Stefanie, Allison; *ed:* City Coll of NY (BS) Math Ed 1967; Queens Coll (MS) Math Ed 1972; St Johns Univ (MBA) CIMS 1983; 6 Credits NSF Yeshiva Univ; *cr:* Newtown HS Math Tchr 1967-84; Queensborough Comm Coll Adj Lecturer Math 1977-78; Ft Hamilton HS Math Tchr, Grd Adv 1984-; Kingsboro Comm Coll Adj Lecturer Math 1995-; *ai:* UFT 1967-; ATMNYC; Inst of Mngmt Sci; *office:* Fort Hamilton H S 8301 Shore Rd Brooklyn NY 11209*

UHLIK, KIM STEPHEN, Geography Instructor; *b:* Cleveland, OH; *m:* Nan Garrison; *ed:* Baldwin-Wallace Coll (BS) Earth Sci 1974; Kent St Univ (MA) Geography 1976; Currently in PHD Prgm in Higher Ed Admin; *cr:* Medina Cty Planning Agency Staff Cartographer 1976-77; Prof Enterainer 1977-88; Ember Group Inc Pres 1988-; Kent St Univ Geography, Sports & Leisure Stud Instr 1990-; Crestwood HS Girls Team Tennis Coach 1993-; Kent Roosevelt HS Boys Team Tennis Coach 1994-; *ai:* Kent Parks & Recreation Tennis League & Parkview Racquet Club Doubles Nights Dir; Davey Jr HS Tennis Club Adv; Portage Cty Open Tennis Tournament Dir; US Prof Tennis Assn 1989-, Northern OH Div Sec, Svc Awd; US Tennis Assn 1989-; Amer Amateur Racquetball Assn 1991-; Omicron Delta Kappa 1974-; US Badminton Assn, Phi Epsilon Kappa 1993-; Certified Prof 1 By the US Prof Tennis Assn; Won Grant From USTA to Start a Summer Tennis Prgm for Kent Parks & Recreation; 3 Pub Articles & 1 Submitted for Publication; Awd Presented By the Tennis Players of Portage Cty in Recognition of Leadership & Dedication; *office:* Kent St Univ 264 MACC Kent OH 44242*

UIBEL, JENNIFER MACK, Language Arts Teacher; *b:* Philadelphia, PA; *m:* Stephen; *c:* Stephanie; *ed:* Douglass Coll Rutger Univ (BA) Eng, Ed 1980; Rider Univ (MA) Educl Admin-Hnrs 1995; *cr:* Thomas E. Harrington MS Lang Arts Tchr 1980-; *ai:* NCTE 1982-; *home:* 19 Ridgemount Dr Marlton NJ 08053

UJVARI, AMY E., Teaching Fellow; *b:* Buffalo, NY; *ed:* Saint Bonaventure Univ (BA) Philosophy 1992, (MA) Eng 1994; Working Toward Doctorate in Eng at Kent St Univ; *cr:* Saint Bonaventure Univ Tchng Asst 1992-94; Kent St Univ Tchng Fellow 1994-; *ai:* MLA 1994-; Sr Mary Anthony Brown Philosophy Medal; Research Grant for Masters Thesis at Saint Bonaventure Univ; *office:* Kent St Univ Dept of English Kent OH 44242

UKAZIM, EMENIKE, Math Professor; *b:* Otampa, Abia St Nigeria; *m:* Chidi Ndubuike; *c:* Chizuruoke, Nkechi, Chiemena, Amarachi; *ed:* Juniata Coll (BS) Physics 1974; TX A&M Univ (MS) Math 1976, (PHD) Geophysics 1980; Creative Real Estate Investment Trng; *cr:* Schumberger Co Rsrch, Regnl Geophysicist 1982-86; Project Seed Natl Math Co Math Tchr 1989-91; Montgomery Cty Comm Coll Math Prof 1990-; Temple Univ Adj Math Prof 1992-; *ai:* Gospel of Jesus Christ Minister; Speaker Local, Natl, Intnl Gatherings; Chrstn Flwshp Club Adv; Amer Math Assn, AFT 1992-; Natl Water Well Assn 1991-; Mission Bd 1994-; Promise Keepers 1993-; Installed One of Deepest Solar Energy Water Well Pumps in W Africa; Numerous Internal Publications; *home:* 358 W Reliance Rd Souderton PA 18964

UKPONG, LEO U., Finance Professor; *b:* Nigeria ; *m:* Mary U.; *c:* Ime U.; *ed:* AL A&M Univ (BS) Ec 1983; ST Univ of NY (MBA) Finance 1988; Univ of PA (MS) Ec 1993; Univ of PA (PHD) Ec, Finance 1994; *cr:* IBM Corp Fin Analyst 1988-92; Morgan St Univ Asst Prof 1995-; *ai:* Natl Urban Bankers Assn; Amer Fin Assn, Fin Mngmt Assn 1992-; Amer Ec Assn 1983-; *office:* Morgan St Univ Cold Spring La-Hillen Rd Baltimore MD 21239

ULBRICH, MARY (STEINBACH), English Tchr & His Dept Chair; *b:* New York, NY; *m:* Volker R.; *c:* Ciona Suzanne, Amber Menemsh Mierisch; *ed:* Swarthmore Coll (BA) Eng 1963; Northwestern Univ (MAT) Eng Ed 1964; Univ of Monmouth (MSEd) Ed & Guid 1988; *cr:* Chicago Pub Schls Eng Tchr 1963-65; ME Twp HS Eng Tchr 1965-67; Hopewell Vly Cntrl HS K-12th Grd Curr Coord & Eng Chair 1967-70; Red Bank Regnl HS Eng & Hum Tchr 1981-90; Bancroft Schl Eng Tchr & His Chair 1991-; *ai:* Admissions Comm; Adv; Mentor; Interdisciplinary Comm Chair; Childrens Schl of Sci 1977-, Pres, Sci Chair, Bd of Dirs; Marine Bio Lab Assoc 1989-, VP, Exec Bd; Friends of Wor Lib 1990-, Pres, VP; Wor Historical Museum 1995-, Ed Comm; NEH Flwshp; Article Pub Fndtn Grant; AISNE Sr Tchng Fellow; *office:* Bancroft Schl 110 S Worcester MA 01605

ULIANO, NICHOLAS J., Spanish Instructor; *b:* Philadelphia, Penn St Univ (BS) Scndry Ed 1969; Temple Univ (MED) Frgn L 1971, (DED) Frgn Lang Ed 1984; Stud Abroad Pgrm Univ of Sala Post-Grad Stud Univ Iberoamericana; *cr:* Phoenixville Area Jr H Lang Dept Chr 1969-92; Phoenixville Area HS Span Instr 1992-; *a* Adv Class of 1995, 1999; Spring Stud Tour Coord; NEA, PSEA, AATSP, ACTFL 1969-; Phi Sigma Iota 1969-; Amer Family Inst Tchng Awd 1985; Phoenixville Jaycees Outstdng Edctr Awds 197 Outstdng Scndry Edctrs of Amer Awd 1972; Ldrs of Amer Scndry 1975; Pub Doctoral Dissertation 1984; *home:* 1602 Linden Way Prussia PA 19406

ULICH, DOROTHY BRUMM, English Teacher; *b:* Cleveland, Carl Lewis; *c:* Katherine, Constance, Carl W.; *ed:* Hiram Coll (B 1966; Univ of Akron (MAE) Eng Ed 1984; Post Grad Stud Eng I Univ of Akron; *cr:* Medina Sr HS Eng Tchr 1966-95; *ai:* Educl Test Eng Reader AP Exams; Midwest Coll Bd Fac Consultant; Delta Gamma 1987-; Kappa Delta Pi 1965-; Pi Lambda Theta 1982-; OC NCTE, NEA, OEA, Medina City Tchrs Assn Exec Bd; Hiram Coll Exec Bd 1991-95, Sec; United Church of Christ 1966-95, Deacon; Holden Jennings Scholar; Dow Chemical Excl in Ed Awd; Eng Dep 1980-86; *office:* Medina Sr HS 777 E Union St Medina OH 44256

ULIZIO, JENNIFER TAFI, High School Social Stud Tchr; Kensington, PA; *m:* Michael; *c:* Lindsey; *ed:* Clarion Univ (BS) Scr 1985; Post Grad Stud Carlow Coll, IN Wesleyan Univ; *cr:* Bamberg HS West Germany Cultures Tchr 1987-89; Leechburg HS Hi 1990-91; Lenape HS Cultures, Ec Tchr 1992-93; Burrell HS His, 1993-; *ai:* Prins Advy Comm; Drama Club Spon, Dir; NEA, PSEA BEA 1993-; Gift of Time Awd; *office:* Burrell HS 1021 Puckety Chu Lower Burrell PA 15068*

ULLERY, RONNIE ZORN, Mathematics Teacher; *b:* Dayton, Kimberly Sue; *c:* Terry, Kristy, Brent, Sean, Tommy; *ed:* Bowling (BS) Math 1977; Univ of Dayton (MS) Ed, Admin 1984; *cr:* Centerv Math Tchr 1977-; *ai:* Asst Ftbl Coach; AFCA 1985-; Unit Tchr of Y Nom OH Tchr of Yr 1994; *office:* Centerville HS 500 E Fran Centerville OH 45459

ULLMAN, CLAIRE TICKER, Mathematics Teacher; *b:* Manhatta *m:* Dennis; *c:* Josh, Alana; *ed:* CUNY at Lehman (BS) Math 1972 Math, Ed 1976; admin Grad Courses; *cr:* Peeksill HS Math Tchr 1 Mary Mt Coll Adjunct Prof 1978-87; Mercey Coll Adjunct Prof Westchester Comm Coll Adjunct Prof 1983; Somers HS Math Tchr *ai:* Frosh Stu Mentor; Attendance, Discipline, Alternative Au Comms; AFT, NYST 1985-; ORT 1981-; Phi Beta Kappa 1973-; Somers HS Rt 139 Lincolndale NY 10541*

ULLMAN, WENDY COLLIER, Adjunct Instructor of Engli Oneida, NY; *m:* Daniel S.; *c:* Katherine, Julia, Margaret; *ed:* SU Potsdam (BA) Eng 1974; Univ of ME (MA) Eng 1977; *cr:* Univ of M TA 1975-77; Bucks Cty Comm Coll Adj Instr of Eng 1989-; DE V Adj Instr of Eng 1990-93; Montgomery Cty Comm Coll Adj Instr 1993-; *ai:* 3 Articles Pub; *office:* Montgomery County Comm Co Dekalb Pike Blue Bell PA 19422

ULLO, CAROL MICHAELS, French Teacher; *b:* E Stroudsburg, John Thomas; *c:* Emily, Allison; *ed:* E stroudsburg Univ (BS) Scn 1971; Tri St Univ Eng Cert; Purdue Univ 18 Credit Hrs Scndry Adn of PA Masters Equivalency; *cr:* Fremont Comm Schls HS Eng, F 1973-77; E Stroudsburg HS Eng Tchr 1978-88; Bangor Jr Sr HS F 1982; J.S. Bunnell Jr HS Eng, Fr Tchr 1988-92; J.T. Lambert Int S Tchr 1992-; *ai:* Jr, Sr Play Dir; Sr Class Spon; Yrbk Adv; Young Hist Adv; Jr High Eng Dept Chprsn 1988-92; NEA 1985-; NCTE 19 AATF 1978-; Steben Cty Jr Historical Soc Adv; Clock Fund Resto Chm; *office:* J T Lambert Intermediate Schl 2000 Milford Rd Stroudsburg PA 18301

ULRICH, BEVERLY GISH, Third Grade Teacher; *b:* Hershey, Louis J. Jr.; *c:* Louis J. III; *ed:* Millersville St Tchrs Coll (BS) El 1958; Elizabethtown Coll 6 Credit Hrs; *cr:* Elizabethtown Area Sch Third Grd Tchr 1958-62, Sub Tchr 1962-66, Third Grd Tchr 196 Mentor Tchr; Bldg Goals Comm; Trvlng, Bkng, Bk Fair Comm, Chrc Parish Comm; Historical Soc 1980-; GFWC Elizabeth Hughes Elizabethtown Chapter 407 OES 1991-; Elizabethtown Preser Assocs Inc 1989-; Heritage House; Tchr of Yr 1985; PA Tchr of Y 1990, 1993; Amer Family Inst Awd 1990-91; Comm Svc Proj "Ac Ctzn" 1994-; PSBA Summer Wkshp 1991; "Read In' Womens Clb 1986-.

ULRICH, JAMES D., Head Track Coach; *b:* Buffalo, NY; *m:* Lind Ramsey; *c:* James R., Kathleen A. Anzalone; *ed:* IN St Univ (BS) PE (MS) PE 1973; *cr:* Lockport HS Tchr & Track Coach 1969-72; SU Fredonia Assoc Prof & Track Coach 1974-; *ai:* Head Track Coach; Div III Track Coaches Assoc Pres; SUNY Conf Champs 19 Yrs in a 65 All-Amers; *office:* S U N Y Coll At Fredonia Dods Hall Fredon 14063

ULRICH, JOHN EDWARD, CAD Drafting Teacher; *b:* Steubenville *m:* Mary Jane; *c:* Jonathan, Justin, Jordan, Julianna; *ed:* Eastern MI (BAE) Art Ed 1971; Fitchburg St Coll 9 Credits; Industrial Ed 9 CRE Fine Arts 4 Credits; *cr:* Bechtel Power Corp Designer 9 Yrs; Ray Engrs & Constructors Inc Supervising Designer 6 Yrs; Whittier Re Tech HS CAD Drafting Tchr 2 Yrs; Self Employed Owner & Consul Yrs; *ai:* Tech Prep Mentor; Rube Goldberg Competition Spon; NEA 1 Whittier Reg T A 1995-; *office:* Whittier Reg Voc Tech HS 114 Ame Line Rd Haverhill MA 01830

ULRICH, SANDRA ANNE, Speech & Language Pathologist; *b:* M Rocks, PA; *c:* Bethany, Corrie, Tom Jr., Tyler; *ed:* CA St Coll (BS) Pathology, Audiology 1972, (MED) Speech Pathology, Audiology *cr:* Intermediate Unit #1 Speech Lang Pathologist 1972-; *ai:* PA Assn, PA Speech Hearing Assn 1972-; Burgettstown Grange 1978-; Intermediate Unit #1 Schl 1 Intermediate Unit Dr Coal Center PA 15

ULRICH, WALTER KURT, Calculus, Physics & Math Tch Edinburgh, NY; *m:* Donette Mallon; *c:* Karen, Heidi; *ed:* Adiron Comm Coll (AAS) Chem 1968; Plattsburgh St UC (BS) Sci Ed Plattsburgh St Coll (MS/CAS) Schl Admin, Ed Media 1976; 24 Hrs C Sci; 16 Hrs Effective Tchng; *cr:* Corinth Central Schl Math, Sci, C Tchr 1970-82, 1985-87; Kennedy Schl Chem Tchr 1982-84; Schuyler Central Schl Math Tchr 1984-85; DODDS Math, Sci, Cmptr Tchr 1 *ai:* Sr Class, NHS, NJHS Spon; FEA 1987-, FRS, Treas; NCTM 1 NSTA 1974-, NSELA 1988-; PDK 1992-, Historian; Mensa 1976-; Ch Choral 1977-; St Level Presidential Awd Excl Tchng Math 1990, Sci 1 *office:* Incirlik American HS Psc 94 APO AE 09824*

ULSH, E. JANE MCGOEY, 5th-8th Grd Soc Stud Teacher; *b:* Potts PA; *m:* Roger; *ed:* Kutztown Univ (BS) Scndry Ed & Soc Stud 1 Permanent Cert 1988; WW II Conf Kutztown Univ 1990; *cr:* St Amb 5th-8th Grd Soc Stud & 8th Grd Homeroom Tchr 1992-; *ai:* Dance Adv; Geography Bee Coord; Talent Show & 8th Grd Class Adv; Mi Comm; Natl Geography Week Coord; NECA 1982-; Phi Alpha T 1980-; Sch Cty Ballet Co 1978-83; Dancer With Vivian's Dance St

Grad Summa Cum Laude & Received Eugene Grossman Awd; St ›se Tchr of the Yr 1987; *office:* Saint Ambrose Schl 302 Randel St ›kill Haven PA 17972

, MARK STEPHEN, Health Teacher; *b:* Harrisburg, PA; *m:* Karen Mc Causlin; *c:* Stephanie Marie, Jessica Marie, Matthew Sebastian; ›mple Univ (BS) Hlth, PE 1976; Attnd Penn St Univ, Millersville *cr:* New Cumberland MS Hlth Tchr 1977-80; Cedar Cliff HS Hlth, hr 1980-88; Red Land HS Hlth, PE Tchr 1988-; *ai:* Ski Club Adv; 1977-; *office:* Red Land HS 560 Fishing Creek Rd Lewisberry PA

AS, LORETTA GALVIN, EMT Instructor; *b:* Brooklyn, NY; *m:* r; *c:* Jennifer, David; *ed:* Brooklyn Coll (BS) Psych 1986; NY St ›gency Med Tech, Certfd Lab Instr, Certfd Instr Coord Pending; *cr:* ›nill Montessori Schl Tchr 1987-94; Cath Med Ctr EMT Instr 1991-; ›Gerritsen Beach Fire Dept; NY St Vol Ambulance & Rescue Assn , Treas; Articles Pub; *home:* 59 Eaton Ct Brooklyn NY 11229

TATTER, JACK DAVID, High School English Teacher; *b:* Jamaica, : Christine Murphy; *c:* Kate, Maureen; *ed:* Manhattan Coll (BA) Eng SUNY at Stony Brook (MA) Eng 1975; Long Island Univ (PD) Ed ›n 1991; *cr:* Udall Rd Jr HS Eng Tchr 1972-84; West Islip HS Eng Tchr ›94; Dowling Coll Ed Prof 1989-; Cold Spring Harbor HS 1994-; *ai:* ›n Acad Team, Girls Var Bsktbl 1983-88, Spec Olympics; Suffolk Cty Bsktbl Coach of Yr 1988; Long Island Acad Team Champions 1991; ›elta Kappa 1991-; AFT; Cold Spring Harbor TA; Islip Little League ›n 1987-; CYO Bsktbl Coach 1992-; Tchr of Yr 1986, 1988, 1992; 3 ›ks; *office:* Cold Spring Harbor HS 82 Turkey Ln Cold Spring NY ›*

YOUNG, History Teacher; *b:* Wilmington, DE; *m:* Julie Gunzelman; ›ma Y., Abigail D.; *ed:* Dickinson Coll (BA) Pol Sci 1985; Harvard (AM) East Asian Stud 1989; *cr:* China Pharmaceutical Univ Eng Tchr ›88; Milton Acad His Intern 1989-90; Wheeler Schl His Tchr 1990-; ›l Multicultural Journal; Dir Asian Stud Portfolio Prgm; Geraldine R. ›e Curr Planning Awd; *office:* Wheeler Schl 216 Hope St Providence ›906

ERBERG, LEE HENRY, Principal; *b:* West Allis, WI; *m:* Judy ›; *c:* Denise Underberg Golden; *ed:* Lakeland Coll (BS) Elem Ed Ashland Univ (MS) Ed Admin 1995; Akron Univ, Wright St Lib ›a Sci; *cr:* Cooper Elem 4th-5th Grd Tchr 1963-67; Waller Elem 5th ›Tchr 1967-87; Gardner Elem 5th Grd Tchr 1987-89; Clark Elem Schl ›rd Tchr 1989-91; Killbuck Elem Schl 6th Grd Tchr 1991-95, Prin ›; *ai:* Phi Delta Kappa 1993-; OH Assn Elem Schl Ad 1995; *home:* ›Allison Ave Killbuck OH 44637

ERDONK, LESLIE GALL, English Teacher; *b:* Glen Dale, WV; *m:* ›; *c:* Josh, Zack, Ryan, Chad; *ed:* WV Univ (BS) Lang Arts 1975, (MA) ›n 1986; *cr:* John Marshall HS Eng Tchr 1975-78; Greenbrier East HS ›Tchr 1978-82; St Clairsville HS Eng Tchr 1986-; *ai:* Teen Inst; NEA ›; Cub Scout Ldr 1986-, Den Ldr, Assist Pack Master; MYF 1991-, Sunday Schl Tchr 1989-, Grds 7-9; *office:* Saint Clairsville HS 102 ›lrow Ave Saint Clairsville OH 43950

ERKOFFLER, PHILIP EUGENE, Science Teacher; *b:* ›amstown, PA; *m:* Carolyn J. Hoover; *c:* Amber, Lara, Leslie; *ed:* ›msburg St Tchrs Coll (BS) Gen Sci, Soc Stud 1960; Bucknell Univ ›Scndry Ed, Bio 1968; *cr:* Williamstown Jr, Sr HS Sci Tchr 1960-65; ›ams Vly Jr, Sr HS Sci Tchr 1965-; *ai:* Advy Cncl; NHS Comm; Sci Chair; WVEA, PSEA, NEA 1960-, Treas; Lykens Minstrel Assn ›-; Williams Vly Comm Choir 1985-.

ERWOOD, CAROLE BAHNSEN, Spanish & English Teacher; *b:* ›lo, OH; *m:* Winston Dale; *c:* David, Shawna; *ed:* Heidelberg Coll (BA) 1966; Attnd Bowling Green St Univ & Univ of Toledo; *cr:* Lakota ›l Schls 5th Grd Tchr 1965-66; Lakota HS Eng Tchr 1967-68; ›sville HS Span & Eng Tchr 1970-84, 1986-; *ai:* AAUW 1966-; 1965-; Hemingway Soc 1992-; Book Printed 1980.

ER, NANCY SESLER, 4th Grade Teacher; *b:* Uniontown, PA; *m:* ›s; *c:* Brian Lucas; *ed:* Univ of MD (BS) Elem Ed 1987; MCPS (MS) 1994; *cr:* Jones Lane Elem 4th & 5th Grd Tchr 1987-90; Judith Resni ›& 6th Grd Tchr 1991-92; Cold Spring Elem Ctr for the Highly Gifted Grd Tchr 1993-94; Jones Lane Elem 4th Grd Tchr 1995; *ai:* NEA, ›EA, MCTM 1987-; NCHE 1994-; NCSS, MDCSS 1989-; MICCA ›-; *office:* Jones Lane Elem Schl 15110 Jones Ln Gaithersburg MD ›78*

ER, TOM C., Dir of Learning Skills Prgm; *b:* Pittsburgh, PA; *ed:* IN ›of PA (BS) Eng 1967; Rider Coll (MA) Ed Supervision, Admin 1976; ›A Southeastern Univ Doctoral Prgm, Child & Youth Stud, Mgmt of ›ns; *cr:* Westmont Hilltop Sr HS Eng Tchr 2 Yrs; Kildonan Schl ›ning Disability Specialist 11 Yrs; Solebury Schl Learning Disabilities ›cialist, Admin 15 Yrs; *ai:* Tennis Coach; Stained Glass Instr; Orton ›lexia Soc 1967-; CEC, LDA 1994-; Quaker Schl at Horsham Bd of Dirs ›-, Chm; Woodsorrell Summer Camp for Dyslexic Girls Dir 1974-78; ›*e:* Solebury Schl Phillips Mill Rd PO Box 429 New Hope PA 18938

CE, LYNNE VOLPE, 5th Grade Teacher; *b:* Newark, NJ; *m:* Charles ›ard; *c:* Tracy, David; *ed:* Kean Coll (BA) Elem Ed 1978; *cr:* Cntrl Schl ›l Aide 1987-88; Irwin Schl 5th Grd Tchr 1988-; *ai:* Safety Patrol Adv; A, EBEA 1987-; NJSTA 1995-; *home:* 442 Old Stage Rd East ›nswick NJ 08816*

TES, IMELDA MCDERMOTT, English Teacher; *b:* Duquesne, PA; ›Robert; *c:* Angela; *ed:* California Univ of PA (BS) Scndry Eng Ed 1970; ›Grad Work at PA St Univ; *cr:* Homestead Jr HS Rdng Tchr 1970-71; ›odlawn Mid Eng Tchr 1971-91; Steel Valley Sr HS Eng Tchr 1991-; *ai:* ›A, PSEA 1970-; SUEA 1970-, VP, Fac Rep; Mon Valley Consortium ›r Leadership; *office:* Steel Valley HS 3113 Main St Munhall PA 15120

ROE, CHRIS FRASER, English Teacher; *b:* PA; *m:* Larry James; *c:* ›k; *ed:* Marshall Univ (BA) Eng, Speech & Jrnlsm 1969; Marietta Coll ›A) Eng 1988; *cr:* Cabell Cty Schls Eng Tchr 1969-72; Kanawha Cty ›ls Sub Tchr 1973-74; Wood Cty Schls Eng Tchr 1974-77; Marietta Coll ›r & Writing Lab Dir 1988; Marietta City Schls Eng Tchr 1989-; *ai:* ›ners in Ed; Sports Related Act; Shadow Day Spon; Tech Prep Comm; ›A, MEA 1989-; *home:* 108 Keyser St Marietta OH 45750

TERNAHER, MARLENE K., Math & Algebra Teacher; *b:* Goshocton, ›*m:* Jeffrey L.; *c:* Jordan, Johnathon Crouso; *ed:* OH Univ (BED) Math ›8; Attnd Ashland Univ, Walsh Coll, Dayton Univ, OH St Newark ›nch; *cr:* Licking Vly Jr HS 7-8th Grd Math Tchr 1988-; *ai:* Stu Cncl ›/; CORE; IAT; Mem Team of Tchrs Hepling Convert Jr High to MS; ›A, OEA, LVEA, OCTM 1988-; Dow Grant Receipient; *office:* Licking ›ley Jr HS 1379 Licking Valley Rd NE Newark OH 43055*

WIN, ROBERT C., Sci & Math Gifted Prgm Teacher; *b:* Hartford, CT; Barbara B.; *c:* Laurel M.; *ed:* Univ of CT (BA) Bio, Chem 1970; Cntrl ›St Univ (MS) Bio 1977; Addl 60 Hrs Post Masters Grad Credits, Many ›Gifted Ed; *cr:* New Britain HS Bio, AP Bio Tchr 1971-81, Tchr of Gifted ›81-; *ai:* CT Assn for Gifted Ed; Nom for Local Tchr of Yr; *office:* New ›tain HS 110 Mill St New Britain CT 06051

DEGROVE, BRUCE HOWARD, 11th Grd American History Tchr; *b:* ›yertown, PA; *m:* Wallis Lynne; *c:* Chad, Brad; *ed:* West Chester Univ ›S) His, Soc Sci 1965, (MED) Geog 1968; 45 Post Grad Credits East ›oudsburg Univ, PA St Univ, Drexel Univ; *cr:* US Marine Corps Enlisted 1956-61; Glassboro HS Tchr 1965-66; Boyertown Sr HS Tchr 1966-; *ai:* PSEA, NEA 1966-; Co of Military Historians 1968-; Marine Corps League 1980-, Historian; Article Pub; Schlsp to Civil Ware Inst 1994; *home:* RR 5 Woodside Dr Boyertown PA 19512

UPDEGROVE, KATHLEEN FLACK, Third Grade Teacher; *b:* Newport, RI; *m:* Richard E. Jr.; *c:* Lauren, Andrew, Bradley; *ed:* Univ of RI (BS) Child Dev & Family Relations Elem Ed 1976; Rdng Specialist K-8; 36 Credit Hrs Ed; East Bay Collaborative Statewide Systemic Initiative Summer Ldrshp Inst Sci; KITES Trng Summer 1996; *cr:* The New Schl 6th Grd Tchr 1976-78; Batell Schl Rdng Spec 1978-79; J. F. Wilbur Schl Kndgtn Tchr, Rdng Coord, Rdng Specialist, 3rd Grd Tchr 1979-; *ai:* RI Sci, Math Ldrshp Team; Math Framework Dev for East Bay Collaborative Participate; Coord for Book It, 100 Schl Wide Act Day; NEARI 1979-; Sakonnet Rdng Cncl 1979-, Liason for Little Compton; RI Rdng Assn 1980-; St Barnabus Church 1982-, Rel Tchr; Elmhurst Parent Tchr Group; Portsmouth MS Parent Tchr Group; Little Compton Substance Abuse Prevention Task Force Grant; Self-Esteem Prgm Stu of Week; *office:* J. F. Wilbur Schl The Commons Little Compton RI 02837

UPDYKE, LORI L., French Teacher; *b:* Hornell, NY; *ed:* Nazareth Coll (BA) Fr 1983; univ of Northern IA (MA) Fr Lit 1990; Universite de Haute Bretagne Frgn Stud, Fr 1984; *cr:* Dansville Cntrl Schls Fr Tchr 1985-90; Haverling Cntrl Schls Fr Tchr 1990-; *ai:* Fr Club Adv; Girl's Track, Field Coach; NSAFLT 1985-.

UPOLE, PAULA M., French Teacher; *b:* Boston, MA; *m:* Rick R.; *c:* Crystal M. Vest, Tiffany E. Frank; *ed:* RI Coll (BA) Scndry Ed, Fr 1992, (BA) Fr 1994; 7 In-Svc Credits Frgn Lang Instruction; *cr:* RI Coll Tchng Asst 1992-93; East Providence HS Fr Tchr 1993-; *ai:* Fr Club Adv; NEA 1993-; RI Frgn Lang Assn, Kappa Delta Pi 1991-; AATF 1995-; Nelson Guertin Awd 1992; *office:* East Providence Sr HS 2000 Pawtucket Ave East Providence RI 02914*

UPPERCO, H. SHARON (SAUNDERS), 4th Grade Teacher; *b:* Wauseon, OH; *m:* Sterling Jacob; *c:* Steven Marcus, Tamara Elizabeth; *ed:* Bowling Green St Univ (BS) Ed 1967; IN Univ (MS) Ed 1970; Toledo Univ (EDS) Curr 1991; *cr:* Archbold Pub Schl 1st-2nd Grd Tchr 1966-68; Tiffin Schl 4th-5th Grd Tchr 1968-70; Prince William Co Schl 3rd Grd Tchr 1970-72; Pike Delta York Migrant Educ Jr HS Tchr 1974-75; Evergreen Schl Title I Rdng Tchr 1974-75; Evergreen Lyons Bldg Schl 2nd Grd Tchr 1977-87; Evergreen Schl Dist Gifted Ed 5th-8th Grd Tchr 1987-90; Evergreen Fulton Bldg Schl 3rd-4th Grd Tchr 1990-; *ai:* Arts Unlimited Tchr; Fulton Cty Curr Comm; Delta Kappa Gamma 1985-; Phi Delta Kappa 1987-; Christ United Meth Church; Martha Holden Jennings Scholar; *office:* Evergreen Fulton Schl 10538 County Road 4 Swanton OH 43558

UPTON, LINDA PULIDO, Chemistry Teacher; *b:* Newark, NJ; *m:* Thomas S.; *c:* Jennifer, William, Daniel, Elizabeth; *ed:* Fordham Univ (BS) Chem 1972; Seton Hall Univ (MS) Chem 1975, (PHD) Chem 1978; Montclair St Univ Tchng Cert 1993; Tchng of AP Chem 3 Grd Credits; *cr:* Schering-Plough Chemist 1972-76; Seton Hall Adj Prof 1978-84; Roxbury HS Chem Tchr 1993-; *ai:* Environment Club Adv; NEA, NJEA 1993-; Girls Scouts 1984-, Ldr; Analytical Chem Flwshp 1976; 3 Articles Pub; *office:* Roxbury HS 1 Bryant Dr Succasunna NJ 07876

URAM, JEROME F., Fifth Grade Teacher; *b:* Nanticoke, PA; *m:* Marie Wojcik; *c:* Brian, Krista; *ed:* Mansfield Univ (BS) Elem Ed 1968; Bloomsburg Univ (ME) Elem Ed 1992; 52 Credits Beyond ME; *cr:* Plumsted Twp Schl Dist 6th Grd Tchr 1 Yr; Crestwood Schl Dist 5th Grd Tchr 27 Yrs; *ai:* Act 178 Comm; PA St Assessment Comm; NEA 1969-; PSEA 1969-, Exec Bd; Wright Twp Recreation Bd 1972-, Sec; PIAA Umpire 1985-, Exec Bd; ASA Umpire 1985-; PA St Assessement Comm Mem; *office:* Rice Elem Schl Church & Stairville Rd Mountaintop PA 18707*

URBAN, PETER F., Social Studies Teacher; *b:* Hackensack, NJ; *m:* Mary Weber; *c:* Daniel; *ed:* Ramapo Coll of NJ (BA) His 1977; Montclair St Univ (MA) Soc Stud 1986; 6 Grad Hrs in Research Univ of VA; *cr:* Acad of St Aloysius Soc Stud Tchr 1977-81; Columbia HS Soc Stud Tchr 1981-83; Millburn HS Soc Stud Tchr 1983-; *ai:* Acad Quiz Bowl Team Head Coach; NEA 1981-; NCSS 1994-; Colonial Williamsburg Seminar US Constitution 1987; Monticello Stratford Hall Summer Seminar for Tchrs; *office:* Millburn HS 462 Millburn Ave Millburn NJ 07041

URBAN, SHIRLEY GENHLE, Chemistry & Physics Teacher; *b:* Pawcatuck, CT; *m:* Rudolph Joseph; *c:* Dana, Matthew, Jake; *ed:* Cntrl CT St Univ (BS) Chem Ed 1973, (MS) Chem Ed 1978; 6th Yr Degree 1985; BEST Trained 1995; *cr:* Westbrook Jr Sr HS Sci Tchr 1973-78; Woodrow Wilson HS Sci Tchr 1981-82; Guilford HS Sci Tchr 1982-; *ai:* NEA, CEA 1973-; Guilford Ed Assn 1982-, Sec, Negotiations Comm; Chester Cub Scouts, Treas; *office:* Guilford HS New England Rd Guilford CT 06437

URBANI, PAUL JOSEPH, Coordinator of Gifted Ed; *b:* Redstone Twp, PA; *m:* Mary Ann Puhalla; *c:* Theresa, Lori; *ed:* Duquesne Univ (BA) His, Soc Sci 1969; Univ of Pittsburgh (MEd) His, Soc Sci 1971; 24 Hrs Post Grad Stud; *cr:* Sto-Rox Jr HS Soc Stud Tchr 1969-88; Sto-Rox Jr Sr HS Coord Scndry Gifted Ed 1988-; *ai:* People to People Inc Traveling Delegation Ldr; Law Team Adv; Sto Rox Ed Assn 1969-, Sec; PSEA, NEA 1969-; St John of God Parish, Lector; *office:* Sto-Rox Jr Sr HS 1105 Valley St Mc Kees Rocks PA 15136

URBANOWSKI, MARTHA ANN GARABEDIAN, Spanish Professor; *b:* Whitinsville, MA; *m:* William J. Urbanowski Jr.; *ed:* Worcester St Coll (BA) Span-Summa Cum Laude 1975; Univ of CT (MA) Span 1978, (PHD) Span 1984; *cr:* Univ of CT Grad Tchng Asst Span 1975-79; Assumption Coll Lecturer, Visiting Asst Prof of Span 1984-90; Worcester St Coll Adj Prof of Span 1985; Western New England Coll Asst, Assoc Prof of Span 1990-; *ai:* Human Relations, Stu Commencement Speaker Selection Comms; Task TEam on Tchng Excl; Span Lunch Hour & Tertulia Coord; Minority Stdnts Mentor Prgm; MLA, MAFLA 1984-; AATSP 1977-; ACTFL 1985-; NEMLA 1986-; FLTWM 1990-; AAUP 1994-; AAUW 1993-; Univ of CT Alumni Assn 1994-, Life Mem; Worcester Art Museum 1988-; WGBH PBS Station 1991-; The Smithsonian Inst 1992-; Natural His Museam 1994-; Numerous Articles Pub; Tchr of Yr Awd Finalist 1994-95; Nom Danforth Flwshp; Natl Dir of Latin Americanists; Who's Who Among Stdnts in Amer Univ & Coll; Simga Delta; Kappa Delta Pi; Phi Kappa Phi; Josefina Romo-Arregui Meml Schlsp First Recipient; Univ of CT Dissertation Flwshp; Doctoral & Travel Flwshp; Summer Grants; *office:* Western New England Coll 1215 Wilbraham Rd Springfield MA 01119

URBIN, JEFFREY S., Instructor of Government; *b:* Lexington, KY; *ed:* Dutchess Comm Coll (AA) Liberal Arts 1984; SUNY at Albany (BA) Pol Sci 1986; Rockefeller Coll (MPA) Pub Admin 1990; Cert Advanced Stud Latin Amer, Carribbean Affairs 1989; *cr:* Dutchess Cty Dept of Parks Creative Consultant 1982-; Rockefeller Inst of Govt Governance 2000 Project Intern 1987-88; Dutchess Comm Coll Govt Instr 1990-; Mt St Mary Coll Instr 1995-; Orange Cnty Comm Coll Instr; *ai:* Harry S. Truman Schlsp Fnd Fac Rep; NEA 1992-; Goerge C. Marshall Fndtn Seminar in Govt Alumni; Comedy Capers Players 1990-, Dir; Urbin Entrprs Creative Cnsltnt Co Pres; Harry S. Truman Schlsp 1984; Sheridan Excl Awd His, Govt, Ec; Non-Traditional Stdnts Excl Tchng Awd; *office:* Dutchess Community College 53 Pendell Rd Poughkeepsie NY 12601

URBINE, MARY BRICE, Fifth Grade Teacher; *b:* Williamsport, PA; *m:* L. Raymond; *c:* Ann Marie, Lawrence, Angel; *ed:* Millersville Univ (BS) Elem, Span Minor 1963; Elmira Coll (MS) Ed 1974; Rdng Specialist Cert 1974; *cr:* Dwtn Schl Grd 3 Tchr 1963-64; Tioga Cty Schl Grd 2 Tchr 1967-68; Grayson Cty Schl K-2 Grd Tchr 1974-78; Twin Vly Schl Dist Grd 9-11 Rdng Specialist, Grd 7-8 Gifted Tchr 1983-90, Grd 5-6 Tchr 1991-; *ai:* PSEA; NEA; Outstdng Elem Tchrs of Amer 1975; *office:* Honey Brook Elem Ctr 1530 W Walnut Rd Honey Brook PA 19344

UREY, LINDA PHILSON, Third Grade Teacher; *b:* Grove City, PA; *m:* Daniel W. Sr.; *c:* Joel T., Jared N.; *ed:* Slippery Rock Univ (BS) Lib Sci & Elem Ed 1974; Slippery Rock Univ Post Grad Credits; *cr:* West Elem Schl Elem Librn 1975-81; Mercer Elem Schl 3rd Grd Tchr 1981-; *ai:* PSEA 1975- VP; NEA 1975-; Lake Latonka Womens Club 1995-; *office:* Mercer Elem Schl 301 Lamor Rd Mercer PA 16137

URIBE, MARIA PAZ, Dir of Formation for Nuns; *b:* Autlan, Jalisco Mexico; *ed:* Instituto De Capacitacion Magisterial (BA) His 1972; Univ of San Diego (MA) Rel Stud 1987; *home:* Juan Bernardino 650 Guadalajara Jalisco 45000 Jalisco XX

URNER-BERRY, NANCY GRAHAME, Chemistry Teacher; *b:* Elizabeth, NJ; *m:* Richard P. Jr.; *c:* Margaret; *ed:* Middlebury Coll (BA) Chem 1985; Wesleyan Univ (MALS) Sci 1996; *cr:* Westminster Schl Chem Tchr, Coach, Dean of Stdnts 1985-89, 1991-; Mac Duffie Schl Math Tchr, Field Hockey Coach 1989-91; *ai:* Dean of Stdnts; *home:* 995 Hopmeadow St Simsbury CT 06070

URNOSKI, BARBARA KEATING, Third Grade Teacher; *b:* Peckville, PA; *m:* Nicholas Jr.; *ed:* East Stroudsburg St Univ (BS) Ed 1971; Univ of Scranton (MS) Elem Ed 1973; 80 Additional Credit Hrs; Accredited Ski instr; *cr:* Abington Hghts Schl Dist Elem Tchr 1971-; *ai:* Comm Mem; Curr Dev in all Curr Areas; Stud Tchr Mentor (14 Times); PSEA 1971-, Bldg Rep; NEA 1971-; Prof Ski Instr of Amer 1980-, Level II Cert; Natl Cncl of Math Tchrs 1975-; *office:* Grove St Elem Schl 200 E Grove St Clarks Summit PA 18411*

URSILLO, ROSALIE L., Kindergarten Teacher; *b:* Brooklyn, NY; *m:* James J.; *c:* Monica, Jennifer, Justine; *ed:* Notre Dame Coll (BS) Elem Ed 1965; Inst of Children's Lit Cert 1983; Coll of New Rochelle, Fordham Univ, Coll of SI 32 Post Grad Credits 1989-92; *cr:* PS 31 R Tchr 1965-68; Ebronix Nursery Schl Tchr 1973-75; Holy Child CCD Tchr 1974-85; PS 4 Tchr 1984-; *ai:* Grds 2 & 3 Drama Tchr 1984-85; Kndgtn Grd Ldr 1990-; Schl Based Planning Team Chprsn 1994-; Rdng Tchrs Assn 1965-; Early Chldhd Assn 1984-; Cath Tchrs Assn 1994-; Nom Tchr of Yr 1990; *office:* PS 4 Maurice Wollin Schl Nedra Ln Staten Island NY 10312

URTZ, JILL, HS Mathematics Teacher; *b:* Utica, NY; *c:* Tammy Jo; *ed:* Univ of CT (BS) Elem Ed 1970, (MA) Ed 1971; 90 Addl Credit Hrs; *cr:* Winthrop Schl 5 Grd Tchr 1970-78; New London Jr HS Math Tchr 1978-86; New London HS Math Tchr 1986-, Dept Chair 1992-; *ai:* Jr Class Adv; IIP Team; Standard Comm; NEA, AFT 1970-, AFT Past Treas; Atomic 1985-; Pimms Fellow; *home:* 10 Riverbend Dr Mystic CT 06355

U-RYCKI, PAULETTE ZUMPANO, English & Social Studies Tchr; *b:* Akron, OH; *m:* Stanley J. Jr.; *c:* Charity, Mia U-Rycki Spraclen; Trini, Joseph Zumpano, Luke; *ed:* Univ of Akron (BA) Eng 1966, (MA) Spcl Ed 1973; Post Grad Stud at Univ of Findlay, Kent St Univ & Ashland Coll; *cr:* Akron Pub Schls Tchr 1985-; The Univ of Akron Multicultural Ed Instr 1990-; *ai:* Adv: Sr Mentors, Peer Mediation & Conflict Resolution, Key Club, Say Yes to Work Pepsi Challenge, On TASC; AEA 1985-; Intnl Alliance for Invitational Ed 1994-, Presenter at Conf 1994; Stow Precinct 1990-, Comm Person; Stow Democratic Club 1990-; Task Force for Quality Ed 1990-; Task Force for Multicultural Ed 1991-; Stow Civil Svc Comm 1991-; Division Tchr of the Yr; Martha Holden Jennings Scholar; Italian-Amer Achvmt Awd; Article Pub; Impact II Grant Recipient & Presenter at Conf 1991 & 1992; Ambassador Awd; *office:* Central Hower HS 123 S Forge St Akron OH 44308

USHER, LINDA L., Elem Reading Teacher & Tutor; *b:* Steubenville, OH; *c:* Christopher; *ed:* Alderson-Broaddus Coll (BA) Elem Ed 1969; Univ of Cincinnati (MED) Elem Rdng 1978; Rdng Supervision; Attention Deficit Disorder; *cr:* Hancock Co Schls 2 Grd Tchr 1969-71; Cincinnati Pub Schls K-1 Remedial, 4-6 Grd Rdng Tchr, 1-3 Grd Rdng Tutor 1971-; *ai:* Discipline Comm; Stu Store; AFT, CFT 1976-; Discipline Grant; *office:* Frederick Douglas Elem Schl 2825 Alms Pl Cincinnati OH 45206

USHER, NANCY SPEAR, English Teacher; *b:* Malden, MA; *m:* Frederic L.; *ed:* Univ of Southern ME (BS) Ed 1961; Salem St Coll (MA) Eng, Amer Lit; Boston Univ Guid, Cnslng 36 Hrs; 15 Addl Hrs; Tufts Univ Educ Law 9 Hrs; *cr:* Roosevelt Schl Grd 5 Tchr 1961-63, Grd 7 Tchr 1963-65; Lincoln Schl Grd 7 Spec Ed Tchr 1965-70; Melrose MS Grd 7 Eng Tchr 1970-; *ai:* Past Coach Frosh Girls Bskbtl 5 Yrs; Past Stu Cncl Adv 3 Yrs; NEA 1961-; Melrose Ed Assn 1961-, Exec Bd, Grievance Comm; Newspaper Articles; *home:* 28 Princeton St Danvers MA 01923

USHLER, FREDERICK C., Social Studies Teacher; *b:* Philadelphia, PA; *m:* Donna Cicciolí; *c:* Rebecca, Daniel; *ed:* Rowan Coll (BA) Soc Stud 1967; *cr:* Bridgeton Jr HS Soc Stud 1968-79; Bridgeton HS Soc Stud 1980-; *ai:* Fac Advy Comm; NEA, NJEA 1968-; BEA 1968-, Exec Comm; *office:* Bridgeton HS West Ave Bridgeton NJ 08302

USICH, NANCY CALANDRUCCIO, Second Grade Teacher; *b:* New Rochelle, NY; *m:* Louis Nicholas; *c:* Jed, Kristen, Jonathan; *ed:* Anna Maria Coll (BS) Early Chldhd Ed 1966; Cntrl CT St Univ (MA) Elem Ed 1987; *cr:* Eastbury Schl 1st Grd Tchr 1966; Roaring Brook Schl Math Resource Tchr 1981-83, 2nd Grd Tchr 1983-; *ai:* Gifts of Love Bd of Dir; Tutoring; CEA, NEA, AEA 1966-; Phi Delta Knappa 1995-; Avon Jr Women's Club Pres; Avon Historical Soc Dir; Avon Tchr of Yr 1995-; Tchr Spec Awd Project 1992; Bd of Ed Spec Awd Project 1991; Presenter Natl Assn of Bio Tchrs Conv; Mentor Tchr; *home:* 59 Highwood Dr Avon CT 06001*

USIFER, PETER J., Science Teacher; *b:* Beacon, NY; *m:* Barbara Jean Sitler; *c:* Lori Jean, Kyle Peter, Teri Ann; *ed:* Dutchess Comm Coll (AA) Lbrl Arts 1963; SUNY at Cortland (BA) Bio 1966; SUNY at New Paltz (MS) Bio 1971; *cr:* Arlington HS Sci Tchr 1966-; Dutchess Comm Coll Adj Bio Tchr 1982-; *ai:* AFT 1966-; NYSUT 1966-; Arl TA 1966-; NABT 1970-; Pleasant Vly Little League 1985-87, Coach; Vly Dale Sewer Assn 1992-; *office:* Arlington HS 263 Rt 55 Lagrangeville NY 12540

USINOWICZ, VICTOR PAUL, Seventh Grade Teacher; *b:* Paterson, NJ; *m:* Donna Larry; *c:* Eric, Emily; *ed:* Univ of CT (BS) Elem Ed 1975; William Paterson Coll (MED) Rdng 1980; Certfd High Ropes Challenge Instr; Certfd Instr Shared Inquiry to Lit Great Books Fndtn; *cr:* Pequannock Twp Pub Schls Rdng Specialist 1975-88; North Warren Regnl Schl Dist 7th Grd Tchr 1988-; *ai:* Patriot Challenge Course Pgm Spon; NEA, NJEA, WCEA 1975-; NWREA 1988-; Bloomingdale Precreation Commission 1990-, VP; *office:* North Warren Regional HS PO Box 410 Lambert Rd Blairstown NJ 07825

USTICK, PATRICIA F., English Department Chair; *b:* Elizabeth, NJ; *m:* Daniel L.; *c:* Ryan, Benjamin, Lori; *ed:* MWC of Univ of VA (BA) Eng 1970; RI Coll (MED) Cnslr Ed 1975; Univ of RI (MA) Eng 1982; Doctoral Stud; *cr:* Portsmouth HS Eng Tchr & Guid Cnslr 1974-90, Dept Chair & Eng Tchr 1990-; *ai:* New England Assn of Scndry Schls & Colls Accreditation Process Chprsn; Lang Arts Comm; NEA 1974-; Tufts Univ Distngd Edctr Awd 3 Yrs; *office:* Portsmouth HS Lincoln Ave Portsmouth RI 02871

UTER, JOHN ANTHONY, Language Arts Instructor; *b:* Kingston, PA; *m:* Carm Bucci; *c:* Christopher, Rebecca, Jennifer; *ed:* Kings Coll (BA) Eng 1968; Univ of Scranton (MA) Eng 1980; 61 Credit Hrs Various Areas of Ed Penn St, Wilkes Univ, Coll of Misericordia, Luzerne Cty Intermediate Unit

18; *cr:* Bishop OReilly HS Eng Dept Head & Eng Tchr 1968-85; Luzerne Cty Comm Coll Adjunct Fac 1976-; Northwest Area HS Eng Tchr 1985-; *ai:* Stu Cncl Adv; NEA, PSEA, & NWAEA 1985-; Knights of Columbus, 3rd Degree; Fine Arts Fiesta Poetry Awd; Poems Pub in Anthology of Poems 1982, 30th Natl Poetry Anthology of Tchrs & Librns; *home:* 38 Owen St Forty Fort PA 18704

UTLEY, BEVERLY NELSON, Computer Lab Instructor; *b:* Benton, KY; *m:* Harold Thomas; *c:* Cynthia Ann Poppe, Brian Thomas, Adam Nelson; *ed:* Murray St Univ (BS) Bus Ed 1965; Univ of TN (MS) Bus, Ed, Office Admin 1966; Supervision, Cmptr Classes; *cr:* Miami Univ Adj Instr 1973-74; Stebbins HS Instr 1974-77; Univ of Dayton Instr 1977-78; Southern OH Fabricators Admin Asst to Treas 1979-80; D. Russell Lee Career Ctr Instr 1980-; *ai:* Schl Yrbk Adv; Variety Show Spon; Partner Schls, Tech Comms; OH Bus, Industry Advy Cncl 1995-, Chair; OH Bus Tchrs Assn 1990-, Mem at Large, Treas; Delta Pi Epsilon 1989-, Historian; Encouraging Parents Inspiring Children 1995-, Founder, Pres; NEA 1989-; Mason United Meth Church 1978-, Fin Chrprsn 9 Yrs, Chair of Admin Bd 3 Yrs; Mason Schls Task Force Gifted Ed 1995-; Mason Schls Levy Comm 1990-; OH Bus & Industry Advy Cncl Produced Brochure Promoting Bus Ed in OH; Produced Brochure for EPIC-Purpose of Org Goals & Act; *office:* D Russel Lee Career Ctr 3603 Hamilton Middletown Rd Hamilton OH 45011

UTNE, PRISCILLA MILLER, Retired First Grade Teacher; *b:* Oak Park, IL; *m:* Torleif; *c:* Tor, Eve Sauter; *ed:* Univ of Chicago (PHB)1946; Cert Requirement Credits Kean Coll, Trenton St; *ai:* NEA, NJEA 1968-; *home:* 5 Mimi Ln Warren NJ 07059

UTT, LAWRENCE ALFRED, Latin & English Teacher; *b:* Morgantown, WV; *m:* Regina Marie Neuhausel; *c:* Larry, Jay, Amy; *ed:* WV Univ (BA) Latin 1969; Post Grad Univ of Dayton, Wright St Univ; *cr:* Lakota Local Schls Latin, Eng Tchr 1969-70; Fairborn City Schls Latin, Eng Tchr 1970-; *ai:* Latin Club Adv; FEA. OEA, NEA 1969-; Exec Comm; Amer Classical League; Greater Miami Vly Wrestling Assn; Fairborn Little League; Say Soccer; North Beavercreek Neighborhood Assn; Fairborn Neighborhood Bd; *home:* 2943 Kemp Rd Beavercreek OH 45431

UTTER, LINDA LEA (YARGER), Fourth Grade Teacher; *b:* Canandaigua, NY; *m:* Wesley E.; *ed:* St Univ of NY at Geneseo (BS) Elem Ed 1963; *cr:* Zoller Schl 4th Grd Tchr 1963-64; Manchester-Shortsville Cntrl Schl 3rd Grd Tchr 1965-89, 4th Grd Tchr 1990-; *ai:* Red Jacket Fac Assn, AFT 1965-; Delta Kappa Gamma Soc 1973-, Treas 19 Yrs.

UZNANSKI, LOUISE QUINN, High School Guidance Counselor; *b:* Philadelphia, PA; *m:* Richard J.; *ed:* Trenton St Coll (BS) Hlth, PE 1972; Glassboro St Coll (MA) Hlth, PE 1988, (MA) Stu Prsnl Svcs 1991; *cr:* Delsea Regnl HS Tchr, Coach 1972-89, Guid Cnslr 1989-; *ai:* Stu Recognition Prgm Chm; Glouc Cty Prof Cnslrs Assn, NJ Assn Coll Admissions Cnslrs 1989-; NEA, NJEA 1972-; *office:* Delsea Regional HS 405 Fries Mill Rd Franklinville NJ 08322

UZZI, JAMES CHRISTOPHER, Secondary Orchestra Director; *b:* Flushing, NY; *m:* Bernadette Felczak; *ed:* Suny Potsdom (BM) Music Ed 1987; Suny Stony Brook (MA) Lbrl Stud 1990; *cr:* Bellport MS Orch Dir 1987-; Bellport HS Orch Dir 1992-; *ai:* Musical Pit, Variety Show Pit Bands Dir; MENC, Bellport TA 1987-; Suffolk Cty Music Ed Assn 1987-, Chprsn; Long Island String Festival Assn 1987-; NYSSMA 1987-, Adjudicator; Guest Conductor Suffolk Cty Music Ed Assn Division II Orch 1996; *office:* Bellport HS Beaver Dam Rd Brookhaven NY 11719

V

VACCARO, CHARLES JOHN, Social Studies Teacher; *b:* Rome, NY; *m:* Karen M. Colton; *ed:* St Univ of NY at Albany (BA) Soc Stud Ed 1975, (MA) Soc Stud Ed 1980; 15 Credits Hrs Inservice Trng Cooperative Learning, Diversified Learning Strategies, Conflict Mngmt; *cr:* Shenendehowa CSD Soc Stud Tchr 1976-; *ai:* World Cultures Hnrs, European Travel Prgm Organizer, Ldr 1983-; AFT, NYSUT 1976-; Rsrch Sabbatical 1988; Tchr of Yr 1990; Excl in Ed Awd 1988-90, 1992; *office:* Shenendehowa HS 970 Route 146 Clifton Park NY 12065

VACCARO, KATHERINE ANN, Italian Teacher; *b:* Youngstown, OH; *ed:* Youngstown St Univ (BSEd) Italian & Elem Ed 1982; 20 Addl Hrs Grad Work Kent St Univ & Ashland Coll; *cr:* Girard HS Italian Tchr 1982-; *ai:* Italian Club Adv; Stu Assistance Pgm Core Team Mem; Trumbull Cty Frgn Course of Stud Comm; NEA, OEA & GEA 1982-; Sons of Italy Lodge 2539 1983-; Delta Kappa Gamma 1990-, Sec; AATI 1992-; *office:* Girard HS 31 N Ward Ave Girard OH 44420

VACCARO, SUSAN HANER, First Grade Teacher; *b:* Oceanside, NY; *m:* Robert; *c:* John, Kathryn; *ed:* Saint Johns Univ (BS) Elem Ed 1982, (MS) Rdng Specialist 1984; *cr:* Blessed Sacrament Schl 3rd Grd Tchr 1982-88, 1st Grd Tchr 1988-; *ai:* Summer Pgrm; Tchr Forum Rep; NCEA 1982-; Kappa Delta Pi 1979-82, VP 1981-82; *office:* Blessed Sacrament Schl 50 Rose Ave Valley Stream NY 11580

VACCHETTO, BERNADETTE BAUER, Math Teacher; *b:* Elmira, NY; *m:* Richard H.; *c:* Richard C., Brad A.; *ed:* LeMoyne Coll (BA) Math 1968; Colgate Univ (MA) Math 1969; *cr:* Roth JHS Math Tchr 1969-73; Webster JHS Math Tchr 1979-80; Churchville-Chili MS Math Tchr 1980-; *ai:* Mathcounts Coach 1983-; NEA & NEANY 1980-; AMTNYS 1982-; *office:* Churchville Chili MS 139 Fairbanks Rd Churchville NY 14428

VACCHIO, GEORGE FRANCIS, PE Teacher & Bsbl Coach; *b:* Brooklyn, NY; *m:* Betty; *c:* George, John, Thomas; *ed:* C. W. Post Coll (BS) Hlth, PE; *ai:* Little, Sr League Coach; *home:* 2234 7th St East Meadow NY 11554

VACHIRAPRAPUN, SURAPEE, Sixth Grade Teacher; *b:* Bangkok, Thailand; *m:* Vatchara; *c:* Penney, Paul; *ed:* Chulalongkorn Univ (BED) ESL 1970; NY Univ (MA) ESL 1978; 30 Credits Above MA; *cr:* Daroonpitaya HS Tchr 1970-74; Pub Schl 2 Manhattan Tchr 1980-; *ai:* Extended Day Pgm; Safety & Discipline Comm for Schl; AFT 1980-; UFT 1980-; *office:* Pub Schl 2 Manhattan 122 Henry St New York NY 10002

VACHRIS, DAVID ROBERT, History Teacher; *b:* Mineola, NY; *m:* Amy Beard; *c:* Madison E.; *ed:* Coll of Holy Cross (BA) His 1988; *cr:* Vermont Acad His Tchr 1989-93; Blair Acad His Tchr 1993-; *ai:* Dir Weekend Act; Sexual Harassment Comm; Head Var Boys Lacrosse, Asst Var Boys Bsktbl Coach; Class Monitor; Asst Housemaster Insley Hall; USLCA 1995-; Donald T. Brodine Meml Awd Outstanding Fac Vermont Acad 1991.*

VACIRCA, JOANNE MARIE, High School Math Teacher; *b:* Boston, MA; *ed:* Boston Coll (BA) Math 1987; *cr:* Mc Donald Corp Store Mgr 1981-88; F. L. Putnam Inv Mgmt Co Account Admin 1988-; Archdiocese of Boston Yth Minister 1992-; Ursuline Acad Math Tchr 1988-; *ai:* Yrbk Moderator; Stdnts Offer Svc Club Co-Moderator; Peer Minister; NCTM 1995-; Ofc for Yth Ministry 1994-, Advy Bd; Cath HS Ldrshp Group 1989-, Adult Adv; *office:* Ursuline Acad 65 Lowder St Dedham MA 02026*

VAETH, MARY TERESA, Fourth Grade Teacher; *b:* Garden City, NY; *m:* Jerome M.; *c:* Nancy A.; *ed:* Nassau Comm coll (AA) Elem Ed 1972; Molloy Coll (BA) Psych, Elem Ed 1975; Adelphi Univ (MS) Spec Ed, Learning Disabilities 1979; In-Svc Ed Courses 75 Credit Hrs; *cr:* Davison Ave Schl 4th Grd Tchr 1975-; *ai:* Guest Lecturer, Cooperating Tchr Molloy Coll Stu Tchr Pgm; Pub Relations Photographer Malverne Schls; Malverne Tchrs Assn 1975-, Sec, Elem Rep, Exec Bd, 10 Yr Svc Awd; NYSUT 1975-; Delta Kappa Gamma Soc Intnl 1986-; Outstanding Tchr Malverne Pub Schls 1986; Master Tchr Awd Molloy Coll 1988, 1995; *office:* Davison Avenue Schl Davison Ave Lynbrook NY 11563

VAFFIS, CAROL ANNE (FEICK), 3rd Grade Teacher; *b:* Toledo, OH; *m:* Peter James; *c:* Christopher, Shannon, Jonathon; *ed:* OH Univ (BS) Elem Ed 1969; Post Grad Hrs Toledo Univ; *cr:* Green Springs Elem 2nd Grd Tchr 1968-69; Fremont City Schls 2nd Grd Tchr 1969-71, 5th Grd Tchr 1971-79, 3rd Grd Tchr 1979-; *ai:* NEA; OEA 1968-; FEA 1969-; Ross Swim Booster Assn 1987-93, Pres 1991-93; St John's, Sunday Schl Tchr, Luther League Adv 1990-; *home:* 1625 County Road 65 Fremont OH 43420*

VAFIDES, ALEXIS, World & American History Tchr; *b:* New York, NY; *ed:* Wittenberg Univ (BA) His; Miami Univ (MAT) Soc Stud Ed 1986; *cr:* Fairfield HS Classroom Tchr 1986-; Miami Univ Visiting Instr 1991-92, 1994, 1996-; *ai:* Directions in Geography, Ec for Edctrs Summer Seminars Miami Univ; Soc Stud Dept Chprsn; OH Mock Trail Team Adv; Strategic Plan Planning Comm; NEA, OEA 1986-; Fairfield Classroom Tchrs Assn 1986-, Bldg Rep, Negotiontions Team; NCSS, OH Cncl For Soc Stud 1986-; Phi Delta Kappan 1991-; Fulbright Hays Scholar 1991; CT Gas, Electric Partners Ed Awd 1991, 1993, 1995; Ambassador Awd; Ec Ed BP Amer Awd 1990; Citizens Federal Outstdng Ed Awd 1990; Outstdng Soc Stud Edctrs Annabel Cathcart Awd 1986; *office:* Fairfield Sr HS 1111 Nilles Rd Fairfield OH 45014*

VAFLOR, EDNITA GONZAGA, Sixth Grade TAG Teacher; *b:* Iloilo City, Philippines; *m:* Gabriel D.; *c:* Eduardo Jesse, Jeffrey John; *ed:* Ottawa Univ at Ottawa (BA) Music 1960; *cr:* Cntrl Philippine Univ Tchr 1960-68; Oakland Elem Schl Tchr 1968-69; Edison MS Tchr 1969-; *ai:* Yrbk Adv; Soc Stuc & TAG Curr Comm Mem; MAGC Mem; OEA & NEA 1984-; OH Assn for Gifted Children 1991-; Marion Civic Chorus 1985-, Pres 1991-94; Marion Lecture Recital Club 1987-, Pres 1995-, VP 1993-95; Trinity Bapt Church 1976-, Choir Dir; *office:* Edison MS 871 Chatfield Rd Marion OH 43302

VAGEDES, JOSEPH CARL, Chemistry Teacher; *b:* Dayton, OH; *m:* Carolyn Gunn; *c:* Amy, Eric, Ryan; *ed:* Univ of Akron (BA) Bio & Chem 1981; Ashland Univ (MS) Ed Admin; 24 Credit Hrs; *cr:* St Thomas Aquinas Tchr 1981-; *ai:* Ecology Club Co-Chair; Mentor Tchr; Steering Comm Mem for Acredidation; Schl Liaison; NCEA 1981-; *office:* Saint Thomas Aquinas HS 2121 Reno Dr NE Louisville OH 44641

VAGT, FRANCIS REGIS, Jr High Lang Arts Teacher; *b:* Savannah, GA; *ed:* Marywood Coll (BS) Elem Ed 1961, (MS) Elem Ed 1971; St John Univ (PD) Supvr of Rdng1978; Rel Ed Cert; Prof Dev Cert Learning Disabilities; Suicide Prevention Crisis Calling Cert; *cr:* St John Schl Tchr, Primary Tchr 1968-73; St Ephrem Schl Rdng Coord Tchr 1973-84; St Peter of Alcantara Rdng Coord, Tchr 1984-95; St Sphrem Schl Jr High Lang Arts Tchr 1995-; *ai:* Acquinas Enrichment for Gifted; NCEA 1970-; Suicide Prevention Crisis Calling 1974-; Montessouri, GATE Wkshps; Early Chldhd Wkshpr Univ of PA; Diocese of Brooklyn Remedial Rdng in Classroom; *home:* 935 Bay Ridge Pkwy Brooklyn NY 11228

VAHEY, ELLEN O'HARA, 2nd Grade Teacher; *b:* Erie, PA; *m:* William John; *c:* Patrick Wm, Joseph M., William J., Elizabeth Seibert, Ellen N.; *ed:* Villa Maria Coll (BS) Elem Ed 1962; Gannon Univ (MED) Ed; Post Grad Stud Ec 3 Credit Hrs Duquesne Univ, 3 Addl Credit Hrs; Gifted Stud IN Univ; *cr:* HS Regnl Classroom Eng Tchr 1962-66; Remedial Rdng Traveled1972-75; Gifted Travel Grd 2 & MS Tchr 1976-79; Edison Elem Schl 2nd Grd Tchr 1979-; *ai:* East HS PTSA Pres; Soc Comm; Lead Tchr Erie Schl Dist; North West PA Cncl of Tchr, Bd Mem; NEA 1964-, Rep; PSEA 1964-; AAUW 1967-80, Pub Rel; Soc Barber Ctr 1985-; PTA 1964-, Chairmanships; Alumnae Assn 1964-, Bd Mem, Chairwoman; Villa Maria Gannon Fall Dinner; Grant for Intergenerational Teas; Tchr of Yr 1990; *home:* 219 Sanford Pl Erie PA 16511*

VAHEY, MARY C. (CLANCY), Bio, Chem & Anatomy Teacher; *b:* Melrose, MA; *m:* Paul K.; *c:* Paul K. Jr., Jaynemarie; *ed:* Newton Coll of the Sacred Heart (BA) Bio 1960; Univ of NC (MA) Zoology & Genetics 1967; Plymouth St Coll 6 Grad Credit Hrs in Curr 1993-94; Keene St Coll 3 Grad Credit Hrs in Applied Dev & Bio Chem 1995; *cr:* St Genevieve of the Pines Tchr, Asst Prin & Prin 1962-69; Arundel HS Bio, Math & PE Tchr 1969-70; Melrose HS Chem, Bio & Anatomy Tchr 1970-80; Alvirne HS Chem Tchr 1984-85; Pittsfield HS Bio, Chem & Anatomy Tchr 1985-; *ai:* Prins Advy Comm; Spon Stdnts & Help Them to Find Extra Pgms for Summer Advancement Gifted & Talented; Curr Comm; Class Adv; Sci Club; NEA 1969-; NHSTA 1984-, Currently VP & Pres Elect; Local Educ Pittsfield Assoc 1984-, Pres 2 Yrs & Bargaining Team 4 Yrs; Amer Cancer Soc Vol; Nom for Presidential Awd for Outstdng Tchrs; Tandy Scholar Awd; Grant for Comps in Sci Via St of NH; Nom for Outstdng Tchr of the Yr; *office:* Pittsfield Jr Sr HS 5 Oneida St Pittsfield NH 03263

VAHEY, REGINA GRANT, Teacher & Chairperson; *b:* New York City, NY; *m:* Harry M.; *ed:* Georgian Court Coll (BA) Math 1968; OH St Univ (MA) Math 1971; Trenton St Univ 12 Credit Hrs Supvr Cert Prgm; Shennadoah Coll, Conservatory of Music 6 Credit Hrs; *cr:* St James Grammar Schl Tchr 1956-59; Red Bank Cath HS Tchr 1959-66; Notre Dame HS Tchr, Math Chprsn 1966-72; Holy Cross HS Tchr, Math Chprsn 1972-; *ai:* NHS Adv; Math Tutors Moderator; Fac Cncl; Curr Comm Tech Comm; Reviw of Policy Comm; AMTNJ 1960-; NCTM 1963-, Svc Awd; NCEA, NA, ASCP 1990-; NASAA 1984-; CCD 1988-, Tchr; NSF Grants; Presidential Awd Excl Math Tchng; Brotherhood Awd Comm Svc; *office:* Holy Cross HS 5035 Rt 130 S Delran NJ 08075

VAIDEAN, SALLY WILBUR, Computer & Mathematics Teacher; *b:* Norfolk, VA; *m:* John Edward Lauer; *c:* J. E. Jr., Christopher Glenn; *ed:* Williams & Mary Coll (AA) Chem, Math 1959; Clevelans St Univ (BA) Math, Ed Minor 1978; Chemical Dependancy Trng NSF Inst OH Univ 18 Grad Hrs; Group Facilitation Trng, Ec 3 Grad Hrs UCLA; Adv Group Facilitation Trng Ec 9 Grad Hrs Lake Erie; Related Trngs Cleveland St Univ 24 Grad Hrs; Facilitator Test Taking Skills Trng; *cr:* Willoughb-Eastlake Schls Sub Tchng, Tutor 1968-78; Painsville Local Schls Math, Cmptr Tchr 1978-; Auburn Career Ctr Adult Ed, Cmptr Apps, Programming Lit Tchr 1983-; *ai:* Head Coach Acad Decathlon; Jr HS Stu Cncl, Core Team Support Group Facilitator & TAD Adv; Tech, Bldg, Hlth & Safety Comm 1993-94; VCG Comm; Staff A Team 1994-95; Girls Bsktbl Jr HS 1978-84; Painesville Twp Ed Assn 1978-, Bldg Rep, Schlsp Chair, Mentorship, Pgrm New Tchrs; OEA, NEA 1978-; NCTM 1978-85; Thomas Jefferson PTA 1966-75, VP, Pres, Ways & Means; Co-Authored Grant to Introduce PC's 1981; Instituted Cmptr Pgrm, Programming 1983-; Presenter Group V on Computerism Class 1983; NSF Participant OH Univ 1981; Tech Rooms on Network; *office:* Riverside HS Complex 625 Riverside Dr Painesville OH 44077*

VAIL, BENJAMIN P., Vice Principal & US His Tchr; *m:* She Hannah, Abigail; *ed:* Springfield Coll (BS) Phys Ed, His 1982; Univ (MED) Admin 1994; *cr:* Medomah Valley HS Soc Stud Tchr, 1984-89; Hodgdon HS Soc Stud, PE, Hlth Tchr, Coach 1990-93; G Valley HS His Tchr, Admin 1993-; *ai:* Ath Dir; NASSP 1994-; Georges Valley HS Valley St Thomaston ME 04861

VAIL, CHRIS L., HS Mathematics Teacher; *b:* Brunswick, GA; *m:* M. Flores; *c:* Cory D., Brian D.; *ed:* OH St Univ (BS) Mrktg 197 Dominican Coll Math Cert 1991; 21 Hrs Toward Masters in Ed Adm Grove City HS Tchr 1991-; *ai:* Ftbl & Bsktbl Coach; *office:* Grove C 4665 Hoover Rd Grove City OH 43123*

VAIL, DAVID S., Mathematics Teacher; *b:* Albuquerque, N Kathleen Marie Nealon; *c:* Melissa K., Matthew D.; *ed:* Wright S (BS) Scndry Ed, Math 1981; Univ of Dayton (MS) Educl Admin 198 Grad Ed Admin; *cr:* Tower Heights MS Math Tchr 1981-82; Bell Bro Math Tchr 1982-85; Patterson Cooperative HS Math Tchr 1985-87; HS Math Tchr 1987-89; Oakwood HS Math Tchr 1989-; *ai:* Asst Va Var Bsbl; OTA 1989-; OEA, NEA, OCTM 1981-; GEMMA Partic Seminar Presider; WOEA Presenter; *office:* Oakwood HS 1200 Far Ave Dayton OH 45419*

VAIL, JOSEPH THOMAS, Social Science Teacher; *b:* Little Falls *m:* Helen Penrose; *c:* Joe, Mike; *ed:* Utica Coll (BA) Soc Sci 1965; 36 Hrs; *cr:* Owen D Young Cntrl Tchr 1966-69; Ilion Cntrl Schl Tchr *ai:* Key Club & Class Adv; Bsktbl, Yth Bsbl & Soccer Coach; Poli Mem; Mohawk Regnl Tchr Ctr; BOCES 1st Comm; Regents Action Compact for Learning Facilitator; NY St United Tchrs 1966-, Del; Ilion Tchrs Assn 1969-, VP Exec Bd Pres; Cub Scouts Pgm Chair; Cncl Bd Mem; *home:* 22 Lewis St Little Falls NY 13365

VAIL, R. GARRETT,JR., English Teacher; *b:* Atlanta, GA; *m:* Lori Hopkins; *c:* Sam Sanger; *ed:* OH Wesleyan Univ (BA) Eng Manhattanville Coll (MAT) Eng 1988; Yale Univ Secure Lt Tchng 1985-86; *cr:* Greenwich HS Writing Tutor 1986-86, Eng Tchr 198 Camden-Rockport HS Eng Tchr 1987-; Univ of ME at Augusta A Instr 1988-; *ai:* ME Ed Assn 1987-; NEA 1986-; Meguntilook Tchrs 1987-, Pres & VP; ME Innovative Tchng Grant 1988; NEH Su Seminar 1994; *office:* Camden - Rockport HS Knowlton St Camde 04843*

VAILE, JONATHAN REED, English Teacher & Dev Directo Washington, DC; *ed:* George Mason Univ (MA) Lit 1991; MFA Co Completion of Advanced Placement Inst at Fordham U; *cr:* Roberts & Inc Insurance Agent 1985-88; Friedman Fuller & Hudson Inc Rsk Consultant 1988-90; St Anselms Abbey Schl Eng Tchr & Dev Dir *ai:* St Anselms Cultural Stu Org Fac Adv; IM HouseHead; St An Mrktng & Pub Relations Comm Chair; Amnesty Intl 1991-; The Write 1991-; Natl Endowment for the Hum Grant Recipient 1994; Poetry P Poet Love, Phoebe, Hudson Vly, Echoes, Black Bear Review & O *office:* St Anselm's Abbey Schl 4501 S Dakota Ave NE Washingto 20017

VAILLANCOURT, ALICE PAQUIN, Third Grade Teacher Providence, RI; *m:* J. Normand L.; *c:* Christina Kilcline, Maycee (Mercy, J. Normand II; *ed:* Salve Regina Coll (BA) Ed 1962; 12 Credit 24 Credit Hrs RI Coll; *cr:* Cath Schls First Grd Tchr 1962-69; Harris Fourth Grd Tchr 1969-83; Globe Schl First, Third Grd Tchr 1983-86 Savoie Schl Third Grd Tchr 1996; *ai:* CCD Parish Coord; AFT, NEA 1 *home:* 187 Madeleine Ave Woonsocket RI 02895

VAILLANCOURT, SANDRA F. W., 7th-12th Grade Art Teache Detroit, MI; *c:* Danielle, Jessie, Jonas, David; *ed:* Lesley Coll (Lesley Coll at Cambridge MA Curr, Instr, Integrating Arts into Curr Addl 36 Credits; *cr:* Swanton Elem Schl 3rd Grd Tchr 1975-76; Berk Elem Schl Kndgtn Tchr 1977-87; Enosburg Falls K-12 Grds Art 1987-95; Enosburg Falls HS 7-12 Grds Art Tchr 1995-; *ai:* NAEA 1 Opera House Restoration Comm; All Arts Cncl 1995-, Bd Mem, Under Their Banner; Suprv Union Helped Write Goals 200, Tech in WEB Grants; *office:* Enosburg Falls HS PO Box 417 Enosburg Fall 05450

VAJDA, CHERYL COSTANZO, Fourth Grade Teacher; *b:* Hamilton, *c:* S. Joseph, James, Elizabeth; *ed:* Miami Univ (MED) Sci 1989 Hanover Schl IGE 1975-79; Somerville Schl 3rd Grd Tchr 198 Collinsville Schl 3rd Grd Tchr 1981-82; Mc Guffey Schl 4th Grd 1982-89; Stewart Schl 4th Grd Tchr, Grd Level Chair 1989-; *ai:* Head 4th Grd Chprsn; NEA, OEA 1975-; TEA 1975-, VP, Negotiations T Nom Tchr of Yr 1990; Mentor Tchr Tchng Sci with Toys; *office:* St Schl 315 S College Ave Oxford OH 45056*

VALACHOVIC, JOHN W., Mathematics Department Chprsn Schenectady, NY; *m:* Mary Susan Bernaski; *c:* John Wm., Amy S. Mu *ed:* SUNY at Albany (BS) Math 1971; Grad Work at Elmira, SUN Albany & SUNY at Oneonta; *ai:* AFT & NYS Tchrs of Math 1971-; *of* Fonda Fultonville Central Schl Cemetery St Fonda NY 12068

VALALIK, WILLIAM A., Biology Teacher; *b:* McKeesport, PA Barbara; *c:* Stacey, Jason; *ed:* Univ of PA at CA (BS) Bio 1965; Wes (MA) Bio 1969; Attnd Indiana Univ at Bloomington, Univ of Rochest Univ of Pittsburgh; *cr:* Carlynton HS Bio Tchr 31 Yrs; *ai:* Bsktbl, Bs Track Coach; Stud Cncl Adv; Sr Class Spon; NSTA; NABT; West PA Tchrs 1986-, VP 1986; Helped Form Western PA Bio Tchrs Assn; *of* Carlynton H S 435 Kings Hwy Carnegie PA 15106*

VALANZOLA, DIANE LOUISE, Fourth Grade Teacher; *b:* Jersey NJ; *m:* Salvatore; *c:* Donna Lanza, Dena Todd; *ed:* Jersey City St Coll Elem Ed 1974; 32 Credits Guidance Univ of Bridgeport; *cr:* Corpus C Schl Eighth Grd Tchr 1976-79; St Joseph's Schl Eighth Grd Tchr 197 Prin 1981-86; Euclid Schl Fourth Grd Tchr 1987-; *ai:* Stu Govt Moder Wrote, Directed Schl Plays; Textbook, Curr Comm Chm; Master Whole Lang; NEA, NJEA, HHEA 1987-; Tchr of Yr; Prin of Archdiocese of Newark.

VALASEK, MARY JO, Art Teacher; *b:* Kittanning, PA; *m:* Joseph A David W.; *ed:* Indiana Univ of PA (BS) Art Ed 1963; Addl Credit Hrs St; *cr:* Freeport Area Schls Art Tchr 1963-68; Ford City Jr Sr HS Art 1968-; *ai:* NEA, PSEA 1963-; Delta Kappa Gamma 1970-, Past P Arrowhead Chptr Trout Unlimited 1990-; Awd Recognition, Apprecia 1996; *office:* Ford City Jr Sr HS 4th Ave & 11th St Ford City PA 162

VALDES, MARY H., Eighth Grade Bilingual Teacher; *b:* Havana, C *m:* Daniel A.; *c:* Marc, Eric; *ed:* Jersey City St Coll (BA) Span 1975 Grad Credits; Biling, ESL Cert, Elem; *cr:* Harry L. Bain Biling, ESL 1976-90; PS #5 Biling, ESL Tchr 1990-; *ai:* NJEA 1976-; *office:* P School No 5 5401 Hudson Ave West New York NJ 07093

VALDINA, DIANA LO CASTRO, Associate Prof of English Dept Columbia, SC; *m:* Jon P.; *c:* Christopher, Peter; *ed:* St Lawrence Univ (Eng 1965; Northwestern Univ (MA) eng 1966; 90 Post Grad Hrs Cr Doctoral Syracuse UNiv 1978-92; *cr:* Glenbrook South HS Eng 1966-67; Mamaroneck HS Eng Tchr 1967-68; Cayuga Comm Coll 1968-71, Asst, Assoc Prof 1988-; *ai:* Curr Comm Chm; Deans Sem Adv; Phi Theta Kappa Coord; Eng Adj; Distance Learning Adv Bd; Assn; Exec Comm Chair; Grad Awds Comm; NEA, NCTE 1988-; Phi Kappa 1965-; Cayuga Cty Arts Cncl 1978-, Pres; Schweinfirth Muse Bd of Dir; Alzheimers Assn 1993-; United Way, Bd of Dir 1992-94; Cay Advantage Prgm, Eng Adjs Coord; Natl Inst Ldrshp Dev; Ldrs Selec

a Acad Dean; *office:* Cayuga Comm Coll Franklin Street Auburn NY

DON, PABLO HERIBERTO, Swimming, Phys & Hlth Ed Tchr; *b:* NY; *m:* Laura Jean; *c:* Alexis Marie, Kelli Ann; *ed:* City Coll of NY E 1985; Queens Coll of NY (MS) Exercise Physiology 1993; 3 Writing Course Lehman Coll; 3 Credits Tchng Spec Ed Stdnts Coll Rose; *cr:* Queens Coll Grad Asst 1986-88; Grover Cleveland HS Phys, Hlth Ed Tchr 1988-89; Cardozo HS Swim, Phys, Hlth Ed Tchr 0; Bayside HS Swim, Phys, Hlth Ed Tchr 1990-; *ai:* Boys, Girls Var Girls Outdoor Track Coach; United Fed of Tchrs 1987-; NYC es Assn 1987-, Coach of Yr 1993-94; Amer Coll of Sports Medicine Team Extreme Triathlon Club 1987-, Bd Mem; Appointed Grad VP of Exercise Physiology Club 1 Yr; Boys & Girls Swim Coach's 1995; *office:* Bayside HS 208th St & 32nd Ave Bayside NY 11361*

NT, PAUL M., Chemistry Teacher; *b:* Coaldale, PA; *m:* Stacy; *ed:* wn Univ (BS) Scndry Ed 1986; Bucknell Univ (MS) Chem 1988; Co Fire Schl; *cr:* William Allen HS Chem Tchr 1988-; *ai:* NEA Quakertown Fire Co #1 1979-, Fire Fighter, VP 1988; US Jaycees nding Fire Fighter Awd; Outstanding Coll Stdnts of Amer Awd; synthesis of Steroidal Cannabinoids Via an Intramolecular; Dieis Reactions; *home:* 121 San Francisco Dr Quakertown PA 18951

NTE, CAROL PELZER, Fifth Grade Teacher; *b:* Atlantic, IA; *m:* ond G. Jr.; *ed:* Dakota Wesleyan Univ (BA) Psych, Sociology 1969; Lesley Coll, Notre Dame Coll, Boston Univ, Plymouth St Coll, NH ech Coll, Franklin-Pierce Schl; *cr:* Belmont Elem Schl 5th Grd Tchr ; *ai:* Schl Store, Geography Club Advs; Sexual Hrssmnt Curr Comm; NH NEA 1978-; SREA 1978-, Treas 1980-81, Pres 1984-85, Co-Pres 93; Belmont Elem Support Team 1986-; Tilton Democratic Party Sec; Nom NH Tchr of Yr 1991; Outstanding Educator BES 1984; Panel 1986 NH Prin Acad; Tchrs Panel 1987 Mid-Winter Prin Conf; Diversity Team Governor's Initiative for Excl in Ed 1988; *office:* ont Elem Schl Best St Belmont NH 03220*

NTE, RITA QUINTAS, Art Therapist; *b:* New York, NY; *m:* Bruce *l:* Schl of Visual Arts (BFA) Photography 1980; Pratt Inst (MPS) ve Arts Therapy 1992; Adelphi Univ (MS) Spec Ed 1995; *cr:* Dept of ctions Art Therapist 1983-84; Summit Schl Spec Ed Tchr 1982-84, herapist 1984-; *ai:* Grad Art Therapy Stu Internships Supv; NYATA ; AATA 1982-; ASCD 1994-; Dean's Awd Outstdng Acad Achvmt Ed Adelphi Univ; *office:* Summit Schl 187-30 Grand Central Pkwy ca NY 11432

NTI, BETTY ANN DE LUCCA, Second Grade Teacher; *b:* nonton, NJ; *c:* Sherri Ann, Kenneth James; *ed:* Rowan Coll of NJ General Elem 1966; Gifted & Talented Ed Grad Courses; Real Estate for NJ License; *cr:* Berlin Comm Schl Second Grd Tchr 1966, 70; Atco Elem Schl Third Grd Tchr 1971-74, Second Grd Tchr 1974-; len Levering Schlsp Fund Chprsn; NJEA, NEA 1966-; WTEA 1971-; r Camden Cty Bus & Prof Women's Club 1984-, Sec, 1st VP, Pres -94; Rainbows for God's Children 1992-, Facilitator; Church of nption 1966-, Lector 1994; Assumption Chruch RCIA Pgm 1996; NJ Tchr Recognition Awd 1990; *home:* 2315 Memorial Ct Atco NJ 08004

NTI, JOYCE G., Life Sci, Bio, & Peer Tchr; *b:* Bronx, NY; *m:* John ael; *c:* Genevieve, Serena; *ed:* SUNY at Cortland (BA) Bio 1977; Y at Albany (MS) Bio Ed 1981; Cornell Inst for Regnl Bio Mentors Tech Prep Trng Inst 1995; *cr:* Westhill HS 10th Grd Bio Tchr 1977; ham-Ashland Jewett Cntrl Schl 7th Grd Life Sci Tchr & 10th Grd Bio 1977-; *ai:* Sci Club Adv; Vinegar Factory, Mission to Planet Earth Yr Act; Co-Dir of Stream Festival; Discipline Comm; Co-Adv of Jr HS; Peer Buddy for 9th-12th Grds; STANYS 1977-; BALSA 1992-; A, NSTA 1993-; NYSTOY 1995-, Pres in 1996; Robert Leathers n Playground Comm 1988-, Planning Comm; PTSA 1991-; Grants for us Projects 1993-; NY St Tchr of Yr 1994-95; NSA Schlsp to Intnl e Camp 1995; Goals 2000 Tchr Forum 1995; Regnl Bio Mentor for ide Network; Natl Inst Tchr Seminar 1993-94; Bard Coll Estuarine arch Wkshp 1993; *office:* Windham Ashland Jewett Ctl Sch Main St 429 Windham NY 12496

ENTIN, JOAN MARIE (HESS), Senior High Mathematics Tchr; *b:* sburg, PA; *m:* Javier; *c:* Andrea, Samuel; *ed:* Shippensburg Univ d) Math Ed 1982; Millersville Univ (MS) Math Ed 1994; +30 Grad its; *cr:* Downingtown HS Math Tchr 1982-; *ai:* NEA & PSEA 1982-; M 1982-; *office:* Downingtown HS 445 Manor Ave Downingtown PA 5

ENTINE, PENELOPE LISY (KOVAL), 8th Grade English Teacher; ridgeport, MI; *m:* A. John; *ed:* Cntrl MI Univ (BA) Eng & His 1986; hamton Univ SUNY (MA) Eng 1995; Eastern Coll St Davids PA disciplinary Tchng 15 Credits 1988; *cr:* Reese HS 9th-10th Grd Eng th Grd His Tchr 1986-87; Bainbridge-Guilford Schls 8th Grd Soc Stud 1987-90; Johnson City HS 8th Grd Eng Tchr 1992-; *ai:* Color Guard Wildcat Marching Band 1992-; The Network Club Adv for Girls p 1995-; *office:* Johnson City HS 666 Reynolds Rd Johnson City NY 0*

ENTINE, RALPH BURNET, Head of Music; *b:* New York, NY; *m:* e Kirk; *c:* Christopher, Wende; *ed:* Harvard Univ (AB) Music 1966; on Theological Seminary (SMM) Sacred Music 1968; Attnd minster Choir Coll, St Andrews Univ Scotland; *cr:* Convent of Sacred t Head of Music 1968-69; St John's Episcopal Church Organist & rmaster 1976-; Choate Rosemary Hall Music Tchr & Schl Orangist -; *ai:* Festival & Chamber Chorus Dir; Chapel Music Organist & rmaster; Maiyeros & Whimawehs Adv; Paul Mellon Arts Ctr Prgm ning Comm; Amer Guild of Organists 1962-, Chapter Dean; Amer ral Dirs Assn 1985-; Assn of Anglican Musicians 1986-; Organ orical Soc 1970-; Meriden Wallingford Hospital Assn 1980-, Dir; Law orcement Assistance Fnd 1972-, Dir; Schl Tchrs Fellow St Andrews v Scotland; *office:* Choate Rosemary Hall Schl 33 Christian St lingford CT 06492

ENTINE, SUSAN AMY, Secondary Principal; *b:* Reading, PA; *ed:* ion Univ (BSEd) Eng 1972; St Bonaventure Univ (MSEd) Admin 1990; Grad Hrs Mansfield Univ Eng; 3 Hrs St Bonaventure Univ Post Admin; Northern Potter Jr Sr HS Eng Tchr 1972-93; Prin 1994-; *ai:* Class Adv; s & Musicals Co-Dir; Stu Cncl Adv; Var Bsktbl Scorekeeper; NEA, A 1973-, Pres; PASSP, NASSP 1995-, Delta Kappa Gamma 1995-; er Cty Human Svc 1995-, Initiative Bd; Senator Peterson's Advy Ed 1995-; *office:* Northern Potter Jr Sr HS RR 1 Box 400 Ulysses PA 48*

LENTINI, ALFRED JOHN, Italian Teacher; *b:* Troy, NY; *m:* Maria R. taro; *c:* Arianna; *ed:* SUNY Albany (BA) Italian 1972, (MA) Ed 1973; NY coll at Cortland (CAS) Ed Admin 1994; Universita Per Stranieri erugin Italy 1971 & 1989; nazareth Coll of Rochester 1986; Scuola per nieri dell Universita di Siena Italy 1988; *cr:* T R Proctor HS Tchr of ian 1974-75; Schreiber HS Tchr of Italian 1975-76; Mohawk Valley nmunity Coll Adj Instr of Italian 1976-79; T R Proctor Sr HS Tchr of ian 1976-; *ai:* Intnl Club Adv; Arts in Ed Collaborating Tchr; Curr m; AFT 1974-; NYSUT 1974-; NYSAFLT 1985-, Bd of Dirs 1991-92, of Newsletter 1991-, Travel & Study Grant 1989; ITACNY 1986-, Pres 7-91, VP 1991-94; AATI 1987-; PDK 1994-; Amer Italian Heritage oc 1986-; Natl Italian Amer Assn 1993-; Decentralization Bd of Cntrl Comm Arts Cncl 1994-; Commission for Soc Justice 1995-; Rotary Outstdng Edctr 1986-87; NY St Ed Dept Consultant 1987-; Multinational & Comparative Ed Schlsp to Italy 1988; On Cultural & Linguistic Generalizations NYSAFLT Bulletin 1990; Lincoln Ctr Edctrs Aesthetic Ed Scndry Schls 1996; Co-Author Books; *office:* T. R. Proctor Sr HS Hilton Ave Utica NY 13501*

VALERI, CAROLE G., First Grade Teacher; *b:* Mashpee, MA; *m:* Ernest R.; *c:* Peter, Laurianne Gilbert, Vicki; *ed:* Bridgewater St Coll (BS) Elem Ed 1956; *cr:* James F. Peebles Schl First Grd Tchr 1956-58; Otis Meml Schl First-Second Grd Tchr 1961-64; James F. Peeble Schl First-Second Grd Tchr 1964-; *ai:* NEA, MTA 1956-; Bourne Edctrs Assn 1963-, Exec Bd, Negotiating Team; Monument Beach Civic Assn 1992-, VP; Bourne Jr Womens Club 1960-62, Pres; Trustee Bourne Meml Bldg Comm 1982-, Sec; Cape Cod Educl Commission Grant; PTA Nom Tchr of Yr 1994-95; *home:* 360 Shore Rd Buzzards Bay MA 02532

VALERIANI, GINO PAUL, Science Instructor; *b:* Somerville, MA; *m:* Patricia Ann Tuttle; *c:* Delian, Peary; *ed:* Univ of MA at Amherst (BS) Astronomy 1977; Univ of ME (MS) Ed 1990; Boston Univ Astronomy Dept 20 Credits Grad Astronomy Tchng Flwshp; *cr:* Hebron Acad Sci Instr 1979-; OMNI Camp Asst Dir, Flight Pgm Coord, Transport Dir & Russian Trip Coord 1991-; *ai:* Head Coach Cross Cntry Running & Track & Field; Radio Club Adv; Satellite TVRO Usage Coord; Amer Atronomical Soc; Amer Radio Relay League; Aircraft Owners & Pilots Assn; Oxford Hills Schl Dist 1989-95, SAD 17, Bd Mem Chair; Facilities, Supt Search & Prsnl Comms; FCC Vol Examiner; FAA Safety Cnslr; Sky & Telescope Magazine with Tom Arny 1977; Amateur Radio Vol 5 Number 17 1985; Pvt Pilot Land, Sea & Instrument Ratings; Advanced Ground Instr; Extra Class Ham; Commercial Gen Radio-Telephone License; Group Ldr Tomsk, Siberia & Hebron Acad Project Harmony Exchange 1994; *office:* Hebron Acad PO Box 309 Hebron ME 04238*

VALERIO, DENISE WALKER, A P Eng & Journalism Teacher; *b:* Chateauroux, France; *m:* Gerard P.; *c:* Sarah, Nicholas; *ed:* Frostburg St Coll (BS) Eng 1978; Addl Credit Hrs Grad Schl; *cr:* Bruce HS Eng, Jrnlsm Tchr 1979-83; Hempfield HS Eng Tchr 1990-92; Blairsville HS Eng, Jrnlsm Tchr 1992-; *ai:* Adv All-Columbian; Spon Video Comm Club; NEA 1992-; Ncte 1995-; *office:* Blairsville HS 100 School Ln Blairsville PA 15717

VALERIO, LUCILIA M.C., College Lecturer; *b:* Ponta Delgada, Portugal; *ed:* Univ MA Boston (BA) Eng & Span 1981; Tufts Univ (MA) Eng 1983, (PHD) Eng 1996; 110 Credit Hrs Univ of Azores; *cr:* Tufts Univ Grad Tchng Asst 1984-88; MA Coll of Art Visiting Lecturer 1992; Clark Univ Lecturer 1989-; Univ MA Lowell Lecturer 1995-; *ai:* Rdng Club on Comparative Lit; Writing Ctr Tutor; Free Lance Translator; MLA 1986-; Portugese Continental Union 1980-; Entry for Evelyn Waugh Dictionary of Biography; Travel Grant Evora Portugal & Tras-Os-Montes Portugal; *office:* Clark Univ 950 Main St Worcester MA 01610

VALIANTE, SUSAN K., Music Teacher; *b:* Altoona, PA; *m:* Mark A.; *c:* Matthew D., Michael L., Nicole L.; *ed:* Univ of DE (BA) Music Ed 1973; Attnd Wright St Univ; *cr:* Gauger MS Vocal, Gen Music Tchr 1973-76; Pennyroyal Elem Schl Gen Music Tchr 1991-94; Franklin HS Vocal Music Tchr 1994-; *ai:* Spring Musical Dir; Muse Machine Adv; Music Course of Stud Review Comm; MENC, OMEA 1992-; NEA; MSBG Soccer Assn 1985-, Treas; Parkview UM Church 1991-, Choir Dir; *home:* 8465 White Cedar Dr Apt 832 Miamisburg OH 45342

VALICENTI, JOSEPHINE VIVONA, School Counselor; *b:* Endicott, NY; *m:* Vincent R.; *c:* Meg Reed, Joseph, Michael; *ed:* Broome Comm Coll (AA) Acad 1970; SUNY at Oneonta (BS) Eng Ed 1972; Alfred Univ (MS) Cnslng Ed 1991; Control Theory, Reality Therapy Trng; 30 Addl Grad Hrs; *cr:* Frankfort-Schuyler Schl Dist Eng Tchr 1972-79; Victor Cntrl Schls Eng Tchr 1979-85; Corning-Painted Post Schl Dist Eng Tchr 1985-93; Thomas A. Edison Jr Sr HS Cnslr 1993-; *ai:* Schl to Work Comm Facilitator; Testing Assessment Comm; NEA 1972-; Arnot Art Museum 1993-, Vol; Jr League of Elmira 1985-, Pres; *office:* Thomas A Edison Jr/Sr HS 2083 College Ave Elmira NY 14903

VALIENTE, IRVING MANUEL, Social Studies Teacher; *b:* New York, NY; *m:* Nancy Leeman; *c:* Joseph, Sean; *ed:* Coll Staten Island (BA) His, Span 1971; 16 Grad Credits His Northern MI Univ 1973; *cr:* LaSalle Acad Soc Stud Tchr 1977-; *ai:* Asst Var Bsktbl Coach; Moderator Self-Defense Club; NEA 1994-; Isshin-ryu Karate 1991-, Black Belt; Nihon Gashin Aikido 1982-84, Green Belt; Tang So Do 1995-, Green Belt; Chinese Goju-ryu 1977-, Black Belt; *office:* LaSalle Acad 44 E 2nd St New York NY 10003*

VALITZSKI, MARY CECILIA, Principal; *b:* Eatontown, NJ; *ed:* Assumption Coll for Sisters (ARA) Rel 1982; Seton Hall Univ (BA) Scndry Ed, Math, Sci 1987; NY Univ (MA) Math Ed 1993; *cr:* Villa Walsh Acad HS Math, Sci Tchr 1986-92; St Lucy Filippini Acad 8th Grd Tchr 1992-94, Vice-Prin 1994-95, Prin 1995-; *ai:* Newark Archdiocese Retreat Work; Jesus 2000; Music Ministry; NCEA 1992-; NCTM, AMTNJ 1986-; Sci, Math Wkshps for Tchrs; *office:* Saint Lucy Filippini Acad 142 Jefferson St Newark NJ 07105

VALK, RICHARD H., 12th Grade English Teacher; *b:* New York, NY; *m:* Donna Lee Martinez; *c:* Scott; *ed:* Iona Coll (MA) Eng Ed 1967, (MS) Scndry Ed, Eng 1970; Manhattan Coll (MA) Eng Lit 1974; 90 Grad Credits; *cr:* Hawthorne Jr HS Eng Tchr 1967-72; Yonkers HS Eng Tchr 1972-86; Burroughs Jr HS Eng Tchr 1986-89; Gorton HS Eng Tchr 1989-; *ai:* AFT, YFT 1967-; *office:* Charles E Gorton HS 100 Shonnard Pl Yonkers NY 10703

VALLEE, ANITA GOMEZ, Cooperative Work Coord & Tchr; *b:* Hartford, CT; *m:* Leo J. Jr.; *ed:* Cntrl CT St Univ (AS) Secretarial Sci 1971, (BS) Bus Ed 1975, (MS) Guid, Cnslng 1980; *cr:* Middletown HS Bus Ed Tchr 1975-; Middlesex Comm Tech Coll Part-time Instr 1980-; Middlesex Cty Chamber of Commerce Instr, Job Placement Dir 1987-; *ai:* Spon, Adv Girls' Entrepreneurial Exploration Prgm; CT Bus Ed Assn 1975-; CT Bus Ed Advy Bd 1991-95; NBEA 1989-; Middlesex Cty Tech Coll Exceptional Svc Awd 1987; *office:* Middletown HS Hunting Hill Ave Middletown CT 06457

VALLEJOS, ARLEENE M., 2nd Grade Teacher; *b:* Trinidad, CO; *ed:* Mount St Joseph (BA) Elem Ed 1971; Univ of Cincinnati (MED) Early Chldhd Ed 1975; *cr:* St John Bapt de la Salle 1st Grd Tchr 1968-71; St Antoninus Schl 2nd Grd Tchr 1971-; *home:* 2322 Dautel Ave Cincinnati OH 45211*

VALLI, ROBERT, PE & Health Teacher; *b:* Newark, NJ; *m:* Catherine; *c:* Gregory, Glenn, Lauren; *ed:* Montclair St Coll (BA) PE 1977, (MA) Admin of Ath & PE 1985; 15 Credits Beyond Masters; *cr:* Cresskill HS PE & Hlth Tchr 1977-; *ai:* Ftbl Head Coach; Weight Trng Supvr; NEA, NJEA 1977-; Berge Cty Coaches Assn 1977-, Pres; NJ Ftbl Coaches Assn 1987-, Pres; Coach of Yr Honors 1987, 1989, 1990, 1992; NJ Ftbl All Star Game Coach 1987, 1989, 1992; UNICOs Man of Yr 1989; *office:* Cresskill HS 1 Lincoln Dr Cresskill NJ 07626*

VALLINO, KENNETH JOHN, Art Teacher; *b:* Pittsburgh, PA; *m:* Charlene Rene; *c:* Danielle, Dylan; *ed:* Edinboro Univ of PA (BAE) Art Ed 1979; Working Toward MA at IN Univ of PA; *cr:* Kelton Elem Schl Art Tchr 1979-80; Ligonier Vly Schl Dist Art Tchr 1980-; *ai:* PSEA, NEA 1990-, Comm Rep; Trout Unlimited 1983-, Dir; Ward Fnd 1983-; Ligonier Jaycees Outstdng Young Edctr Awd 1983; PTA Outstdng Tchr Awd 1995; Ward Fnd Numerous Ribbons, Awds for Wood Carvings.

VALLOMBROSO, ANN M., HS Social Studies Teacher; *b:* New Haven, CT; *ed:* St Louis Univ (BA) European His 1967, (MA) US His 1973; Post Grad Stud at Southern CT St Univ; *cr:* St Ambrose Schl Soc Stud Tchr 1962-68; Cor Jesu Acad Soc Stud Dept Chair & Tchr 1968-75; New Milford HS Tchr 1977-; *ai:* BEST Pgm; NEA, CEA & NM Ed Assoc 1978-, Treas & Head Rep; NCSS; CT Consortium for Law & Citizenship Ed; CT Citizens Action Grp; New Milford Trust for Historic Preservation; New Milford Bd of Ed Cert of Recognition for Acad Ldrshp; New Milford Schl Dist Recognition for the Best in Tchng & Learning; New Milford Dist Tchr of the Yr 1995; *office:* New Milford HS 25 Sunny Valley Rd New Milford CT 06776

VALLONE, ANTONIO, Associate Professor of English; *b:* Rochester, NY; *m:* Jacquelyn K. Atkins; *c:* John Anthony Atkins; *ed:* Monroe Comm Coll (AS) Bus Admin 1977; SUNY at Brockport (BS) Eng, Writing 1979, (MA) Eng, Writing 1982; IN Univ (MFA) Eng, Writing 1989; PHD Coursework in Rhetoric, Composition Purdue Univ 1983-87; *cr:* SUNY Creative Writing Tchng Flwshp 1979-81; Purdue Univ Tchng Asst 1983-87, Visiting Instr 1987-89; IN Univ Creative Writing Tchng Flwshp, Visiting Instr 1987-89; DePaw Univ Visiting Instr 1987-89; PA St Univ Eng Prof 1989-; *ai:* Campus Newspaper, Lit Magazine, Acad Adv; Fac Congress Chair; Exec Steering, Univ, Campus Comms; Associated Writing Prgms, PA Coll Eng Assn 1989-; Books: The Blackbirds' Applause, Chinese Bats, Grass Saxophones, Introductory Creative Writing Study Guide; 4 Grants; Associated Writing Prgms, PA Coll Eng Assn Presentations; Poems, Prose Pub; Poetry Rdngs; Delta Mu Sigma Tchr of Yr; Tchng Awd; St, Local, Natl Writing Contests Judge; *office:* PA St Univ Du Bois Cmps College Place Du Bois PA 15801*

VALLONE, JOHN RICHARD, English Teacher; *b:* Smithtown, NY; *m:* Lisa Falkner; *c:* Rachel, Emily, Edward; *ed:* Suffolk Cty Comm (AA) Hum 1983; St Josephs Coll (BA) Eng 1985; Dowling Coll (MS) Ed 1992; *cr:* Patchogue Medford HS Eng Tchr 1985-86; Calhoun HS Eng & Soc Stud Tchr 1986-87; Miller Place HS Eng Tchr 1987-; SAT Instr; *ai:* Ftbl 1986-, Bsbl 1987- & Wrestling 1989-90 Coach; AFT & NYSUT 1985-; *office:* Miller Place HS 15 Memorial Dr Miller Place NY 11764*

VALLONE, MARIA LIBERA, Italian Teacher; *b:* Providence, RI; *ed:* Univ of RI (BA) Italian 1966; Middlebury Coll (MA) Italian 1971; Univ di Firenze (MA); *cr:* Esek Hopkins Jr High Italian Tchr 1966-70; Western Hills Jr High Eng Tchr 1971-72; Newton North HS Italian Tchr 1972-; *ai:* Italian Club Adv; Adult Comm Ed; Fulbright Regnl Selection Comm; Fulbright Assoc 1978-, Scholar; MITA 1990-; Dante Alighieri Soc 1994-; Sons of Italy 1975-; Ctr for Italian Culture 1994-; NDEA Grant 1968-; Fulbright Scholar Summer 1978; Rockefeller Fellow 1987; WB2-TV Ch 4 Thanks to Tchrs Excl Awd 1990; Fulbright Exch Tchr to Italy 1991-92; *office:* Newton North HS 360 Lowell Ave Newton MA 02160

VALORI, JOHN PAUL, Social Studies Teacher; *b:* Lancaster, PA; *ed:* Shippensburg Univ (BS) Scndry Ed 1977; Millersville Univ Credit Hrs Tchng Cert; *cr:* J. P. Mc Caskey HS Soc Stud Tchr 1979-; *ai:* Quiz Bowl Adv; Stu Asst Team; Statistician VAr Soccer, Bsbl Teams; Lancaster Ed Assn, PA St Ed Assn, NEA 1979-; Sons of Union Veterans 1988-, Jr Vice Commander; Assn of Licensed Battlefield Guides 1991-; 30th PA Co E 1988-, Sergeant; Finished 1st at Gettysburg Natl Military Park Licensed Guide Exam; *office:* J P Mc Caskey HS 445 N Reservoir St Lancaster PA 17602

VALUCK, SANDRA JEAN, Assistant Professor of Nursing; *b:* Wauseon, OH; *c:* Tiffany Leigh, Jeffrey William; *ed:* Univ of Toledo (BSN) Nrsng 1985; Med Coll of OH (MSN) Psychiatric Nrsng 1988; Diploma Nrsng 1968 at Flower Hosp Schl of Nrsng; *cr:* Emma L. Bixby Hosp RN 1968-79; Meml Hosp RN 1979-80; Owens Comm Coll Asst Prof 1988-; *ai:* Vol Schl Nurse St Johns Jesuit HS; Pub Speaking Bureau Battered Womens Shelter; Sigma Theta Tau 1987-; Phi Kappa Phi 1985-; AFT 1988-; *office:* Owens Comm Coll PO Box 10000 Oregon Rd Toledo OH 43609

VALVANO, DEE R., Retired Kindergarten Teacher; *b:* Canandaigva, NY; *m:* Vincent L.; *c:* Vincent, Thomas, Joy, Andrew; *ed:* SUNY at Geneseo (BA) Ed 1956; 30 Credit Hrs Ed; *cr:* Canandaigua City Schl Dist Kndgtn Tchr 1956-60, Sub Tchr 1960-68, Kndgtn Tchr 1968-94; *ai:* Wkshp Presenter Tchrs 4 Yr Olds; Comm Org Vol; NYSUT 1968-; Excl in Ed Awd 1992; *home:* 3431 W Lake Rd Canandaigua NY 14424

VANAGS, JOHN ROBERT, Physical Education Teacher; *b:* Cleveland, OH; *m:* Pamela Jean Vorse; *c:* Chad, Katrina, Jacob; *ed:* Kent St Univ (BA) Indstrl Arts, PE 1978, (MS) Scndry Prin 1987; *cr:* Crestwood Schls Ind Arts Tchr 1978-82, PE Tchr 1982-; *ai:* Coach Vlybl 8 Yrs; NEA 1978-; CEA 1980-, Bldg Rep; Western Reserve Wrestling Assn 1983-; Vlybl 4 PCC Champions, 3 2nd Pl; *office:* Crestwood Schls W Prospect St Mantua OH 44255

VAN ALSTYNE, RUTH BEATTIE, Fifth Grade Teacher; *b:* Pittsfield, MA; *m:* Douglas Roger; *c:* Deryck; *ed:* Russell Sage Coll (BA) & (BS) Psych, Spec Ed & Elem Ed 1987; St Univ of NY (MS) Ed, Psych & Statistics 1992; *cr:* New Lebanon Schls K-8th Grd Remedial Rdng & Math Tchr 1988-89; East Greenbush Schls 5th Grd Tchr 1989-; *ai:* After Schl Intramurals Tchr; Russell Sage Coll Womens Vlybl Coach 5 Yrs; Genet MS Ski Club Adv 1989-; Sci Curr Comm Mem 1994-; Sci Curr Writer; USVBA, Mem & Player; *office:* Genet MS Rt 4 East Greenbush NY 12061

VAN AUSDALL, DIANE SULLIVAN, Social Studies Teacher; *b:* Orange, NJ; *m:* Richard H.; *c:* Richard, Lauren; *ed:* Marietta Coll (BA) His 1964; 6th Yr Cert Cntrl CT St Univ; *cr:* Berkeley Terr Schl 7th-8th Grd Soc Stud Tchr 1964-66; Windsor HS Soc Stud Tchr 1966-; *ai:* LINK Adv; Cross-Age Mentoring Pgm; Speaker at Natl Confs; Co-Operating Tchr Mentor; Windsor Ed Assn 1966-, VP; Phi Delta Kappa 1975-; Intnl Soc for Tech in Ed 1990-; CT Cncl for Soc Stud; Windsor Town Schlsp Comm 1985-; Windsor Budget Advy Group 1990-, Tchr Rep; SNET Tech, A&E Tech, CNN & Multi-Cultural Grants; Tchr of Yr, Tech Tchr of Northeast, Milken Natl Ed, Celebration of Excl Awd; Ed for High Performance Awds; SNET Learning Ldrshp Team; Numerous Articles Pub; *office:* Windsor HS 50 Sage Park Rd Windsor CT 06095*

VAN BENTHUYSEN, RICHARD N., Science Teacher; *b:* Point Pleasant, NJ; *m:* Patricia Morrisy; *c:* Derek Andrew, Douglas Ryan, Alison Marie Cavaiola; *ed:* Seton Hall Univ (BSEd) Bio 1971; *cr:* St Rose HS Bio Tchr 1971-78; Marlboro MS Sci Tchr 1978-; *ai:* After Schl Sci Wkshp, Acad Bowl Adv; NSTA 1991-; ASCD 1996; NJ Ed Assn 1970-; NJ Governors Awd for Outstdng Tchng; Sci Activity Exch Winning Entry; Dev, Implemented Enchanced Curr for Sci Hnrs Prgm; Sci, Soc Stud Hnr Stdnts OrganizedJoin t Symposium; *home:* 31 Wesley St Monmouth Beach NJ 07750

VANBEVEREN, ABRAHAM,JR., HS Social Studies Teacher; *b:* Passaic, NJ; *m:* Susan Paluh; *c:* Abraham III, Rachel; *ed:* Paterson St (BA) Jr High Ed 1969; Jersey City (MA) Admin & Supervision 1988; 30 Credits Beyond MA; *cr:* Lodi High Tchr 1969-; *ai:* NJEA 1969-; NEA 1969-; BSA 1961-, Chm, Comm Mem, Merit Badge Cnslr; *office:* Lodi HS 99 Putnam St Lodi NJ 07644

VANBOURGONDIEN, JULIE SHANLEY, Guidance Counselor; *b:* Lockport, NY; *m:* James; *ed:* St Univ Coll at Buffalo (BA) Art 1985; Niagara Univ (MSEd) Schl Cnslng 1991; *cr:* Lockport Yth & Recreation Dept Yth Cnslr 1987-91; Starpoint Cntrl Schl Guid Cnslr 1991-; *ai:* Starpoint Stu Against Animal Abuse Adv; ASCA 1991-; *office:* Starpoint Central Schl 4363 Mapleton Rd Lockport NY 14094

VAN BRUNT, ARTHUR (PETER), Associate Professor of Bus; *b:* Orange, NJ; *m:* Priscilla Davis Scott; *c:* Kristina; *ed:* Tufts Univ (BA) Ec 1965; Univ of PA (MBA) Bus Finance 1967; Univ of WI Cert in Coop Dev 1970; *cr:* Peace Corps Venezuela Vol 1967-69; Basico Intnl VP 1970-75; Manufacturers Hanover Trust Co Asst VP 1976-80; Save the Children Dir Strategic Planning 1980-84; CARE Regnl Mgr Latin Amer 1984-90; SUNY Delhi Assoc Prof of Bus 1990-; *ai:* Intnl Comm; Coll Planning Cncl; Strategic All Steering Grp; UUP 1990-; Chapter Treas; Natl Bus Educ Assn; Tchrs of Accntng at Two Yr Coll; Habitat for Humanity of DE Cty NY 1990-, VP; Tanglewood Lake Assn 1990-, Pres; *office:* SUNY at Delhi Sanford Hall Delhi NY 13753*

VAN BUREN, BEVERLY WALL, 6th Grade Teacher; *b:* Syracuse, NY; *m:* Richard; *c:* Lisa Van Buren Biviano, Tiffany Heflin, Samantha, Joshua, Troy Heflin; *ed:* Cortland St (BS) Ed PE 1967; Russell Sage Coll (MSEd) Rdng 1992; 7 Grad Credits Passed Masters; *cr:* Ramapo Schl Dist PE Tchr 1967-72; Mahivah Schls Sub Tchr 1972-84; Cohoes Schls 4th Grd Tchr 1987-88; Shenendehowa Schls 6th Grd Tchr 1988-; *ai:* Lang Arts, Stud Skills & Reconfiguration Comms; NEA, NYSUT, STA 1988-; Phi Kappa Phi Honorary Soc; *office:* Shenendehowa Schls 970 Route 146 Clifton Park NY 12065

VANBUSKIRK, DOLORES D., Third Grade Teacher; *b:* Montour Falls, NY; *m:* Roger E.; *c:* Katrina VanBuskirk Gonsalves, Peter; *ed:* SUNY at Brockport (BA) Elem Ed 1959; *cr:* Pittsford Cntrl Schls Third Grd Tchr 31 Yrs; *ai:* Tech Comm; AFT, NYSUT 1971-; Odyssey of the Mind, Judge; PTSA Life Mbrshp; *office:* Pittsford Cntrl Schls 42 Jefferson Rd W Pittsford NY 14534

VANCE, BEATRICE ELIZABETH, Math & Science Teacher; *b:* Washington, DC; *m:* Robert Carroll; *c:* Roberta; *ed:* Univ of MD (BS) Elem Ed 1975; Post Grad Stud; *cr:* Thomas Claggett Elem 5th Grd Tchr 1975-78; Concord Elem 5th Grd Tchr 1978-84; Vly View Elem 2nd-6th Grd Tchr 1984-92; Marlton Elem 4th-5th Grd Tchr 1992-95; Owens Rd Elem 3rd Grd Tchr 1995-; *ai:* Kids for Sci Steering Comm; Awds Chprsn; NSTA 1993-; *office:* Owens Rd Elem Math-Sci Magnet 1616 Owens Rd Oxon Hill MD 20745

VANCE, DOLORES FRICANO, Spanish Teacher; *b:* Mt Pleasant, PA; *m:* William G.; *c:* Glen William; *ed:* California Univ of PA (BS) Eng & Span, Scndry Ed 1972, (MED) Rdng Specialist 1975; 15 Addl Hrs Univ of Valencia Spain; *cr:* Southmoreland HS Eng Tchr 1972-75, Rdng & Span Tchr 1976-85, Rdng Tchr & Specialist 1986-93, Span Tchr 1994-; *ai:* Span Club, Span NHS, Hum Day Spon; NEA, SEA, PSEA 1972-; *office:* Southmoreland Sr HS Southmoreland Schl Dist PO Box A Alverton PA 15612

VANCE, GERALD ALAN, Laboratory Instructor; *b:* Hornell, NY; *m:* Cynthia L. Barden; *c:* Carrie, Patrick; *ed:* Alfred St Coll (AAS) Air conditioning Engrng Tech 1974, (BT) Mechanical Engrng Tech 1994; *cr:* Alfred St Coll Tech Specialist 1977-93, Lab Instr 1993-; *ai:* Facilities Master Planning Team Ldr; ASHRAE 1995-, Stu Chapter Adv; Andove Historic Preservation Corp 1985-, Chm; St Univ Of NY Chancellors Awd for Excl in Prof Svc; Many Tech Seminars in Area of Engrng Tech; *office:* S U N Y Coll Of Tech At Alfred Met Dept Alfred NY 14802

VANCE, LINDA S., Spanish & French Teacher; *b:* Williamsport, PA; *m:* Terry W.; *c:* Nicole, Ryan; *ed:* Lock Haven Univ (BS) Fr, Sec Ed 1973; Lebanon Vly Coll (BS) Span, Sec Ed 1982; 43 Credit Hrs Ed, Frgn Lang; *cr:* Northern Potter HS Sp, Fr Tchr 1973-77; Lebanon HS Fr Tchr 1978-79; Palmyra MS Sp, Fr Tchr 1979-88; Newark HS Span, Fr Tchr 1991-; *ai:* Span Club Slappin Leather Cntry Line Dance Club, Chrldng, Fr Club, Frosh Class Adv; Frgn Travel Club; NEA, AATF 1973-; AATSP 1979-; West Branch Civic Assoc 1991-; Englewood Civic Assoc 1977-; PA Dept of Ed, Assns of Elem & Scndry Schl Prins Awd; Rep FLAIR for Del Pub Instruction; *office:* Newark HS E Delaware Ave Newark DE 19711*

VANCE, ROBERT CARROLL, Math & Science Teacher; *b:* Salisbury, MD; *m:* Beatrice Wells; *c:* Jeff, Lane, Roberta; *ed:* Salisbury St Coll (BS) Elem Ed 1966; Bowie St Coll Post Grad Stud; *cr:* Snow Hill Elem 6th Grd Tchr 1966-68; Concord Elem 6th Grd Tchr 1968-87; Owens Rd Elem 6th Grd Tchr 1987-; *office:* Owens Road Elem Schl 1616 Owens Rd Oxon Hill MD 20745

VANCE, TERESA, Art & Geography Teacher; *b:* Union City, IN; *m:* John W. Binkley; *c:* Adrian, Annen, Evan Binkley; *ed:* Wright St Univ (BS) Art Ed 1972, (MED) Art Ed 1975; 15+ Hrs Grad Stud From Univ of Cincinnati, Miami Univ, Coll of Mt St Joseph, OH St Univ; *cr:* Greenville City Schls 1st-3rd Grd Elem Art 1972-74; Wright St Univ Grad Asst in Art Ed Dept 1974-75; Wright St Univ Adj Prof Ceramics 1975-77; Bradford Ex Village Schls K-6TH Grd Elem Art 1975-81; Bright Local Schls 7th-12th Grd Art & Geog 1981-; *ai:* 9 Yrs Yrbk Adv; OEA & NEA 1983-; *office:* Whiteoak HS PO Box 297 Mowrystown OH 45155*

VANCE, THERESA ALFANO, Spanish & French Teacher; *b:* Newark, NJ; *m:* Michael Elliott; *c:* Troy Michael (dec), Nicholas Joseph; *ed:* Marymount Coll (BA) Fr, Span 1964; Seton Hall Univ (MA) Fr, Ed 1970; Univ of Paris at Sorbonne Superieur, Fr 1963; *cr:* West Orange HS Fr Tchr 1964-66; Stroudsburg HS Fr Tchr 1966-67; Dulaney HS Adult Ed Prgm Fr Tchr 1975-81; Aifs Amer Inst of Frgn Stud Tchr of Eng to Foreigners 1986; Coll of Notre Dame of MD Tchr of Fr & Eng as a Frgn Lang 1975-80; Loyola Coll Span Tchr 1977-80; Loyola HS Fr, Span Tchr 1980-; *ai:* Span Club, Chess Club Moderator; Fac Soc Comm Chprsn; NJEA, AIMS 1980-; AATSP 1983-; Baltimore Intnl Cncl for Visitors 1975-, Vol; Translating, Interpreting for Civic Insts; *office:* Loyola HS PO Box 6819 Towson MD 21285

VANCOOTEN, RONALD ANTHONY, Science & Computer Sci Teacher; *b:* Brooklyn, NY; *c:* Gloria, Cheyanne; *ed:* Brooklyn Coll (BA) Bio 1979; Long Island Univ (MS) Bio Ed 1981; 99 Addl Credits, Doctoral Candidate NY Univ; Cognate Areas; Sci, Biling, Cmptr Sci Ed; *cr:* John Jay HS Bio Tchr 1979; Wm. A. Maxwell HS Bio Tchr 1980-81; F. D. Roosevelt HS Bio Tchr 1981-83; Kingsborough Comm Coll Bio Instr, Lecturer 1983-87; Boricua Coll Adj Prof of Bio 1983-90; Intnl HS at LaGuardia Sci Tchr 1985-; *ai:* Sci Club, Latin Band Adv; Sr Mentor; AIDS Ed, Awareness, Coll Cmptr, Curr Comms; Cmptr Coord 1986-89; UFT, AFT 1979-; NYSBT, NYBT 1980-; NY Acad of Sci 1980-, Judge; NY Botanical Garden, Amer Musuem of Natural His 1980-; Aspira 1977-; PE Alliance Alumni 1981-; Doctoral Flwshp 1983; Microcomputer Applies Cert; Seminars Dev 3 Bio Courses; Articles Pub; Coord AIDS Awareness Day; Dev Over 10 Courses; *office:* International HS At Laguardia 31-10 Thomson Ave 3110 Thomson Ave Long Island City NY 11101

VANCUREN, MARY LONSWAY, 7th & 8th Grade Math Teacher; *b:* Tiffen, OH; *c:* Kristin, Karin; *ed:* Mary Manse Coll (BA) Elem Ed 1968; Heidelberg Coll 4 Credit Hrs; Mt St Joseph 4 Credit Hrs; Ashland Coll 2 Credit Hrs; *cr:* St Wendelin 6th Grd Tchr 1962-64, 1980-; St Angela Merici 7th Grd Tchr 1964-66; Maple North 5th Grd Tchr 1966-69; *ai:* MS Coord; NCTM,OCTM 1994-; Vol for Nursing Home; *office:* St Wendelin HS 533 N Countyline St Fostoria OH 44830

VAN DE CAR, NANCY SHANE, Third Grade Teacher; *b:* Rochester, PA; *m:* William H.; *c:* Jennifer, Amy, Jason; *ed:* WV Wesleyan (BA) Elem Ed 1971; Attn PA St; *cr:* Ambridge Area Schl Dist 1971-; *ai:* NEA, PSEA 1971-; AAEA 1971-, Bldg Rep; Economy PTA 1974-; Freedom Soccer Boosters 1994-, Sec; Trustee of Baden Meth Church, Sec; Beaver Cnty Prof Bus Grant for Environmental Ed; Conway Schlsp Honoree; *office:* Ambridge Area Schl Dist 3151 Conway Wallrose Rd Baden PA 15005

VAN DE CARR, THERESA JOANNE, Professor of Education; *b:* Oneonta, NY; *m:* Dirk J.; *c:* Michelle, Sara; *ed:* Geneseo St Univ (BS) Ed 1966; Boston Coll (MA) Rdng 1985; Boston Univ (EDD) Lang, Literacy 1992; *cr:* Canandaigua Pub Schls 1 Grd Tchr 1966-68; Brookline Pub Schls 1 Grd Tchr 1968-71; Lexington Pub Schls Rdng Specialist 1992; Bradford Coll Ed Prgm Dir 1993-94; Curry Coll Prof 1994; Lasell Coll Prof 1994-; *ai:* IRA; MA Rdng Assn; ASCD; MACURE; MATE; NERA; Phi Delta Kappa; Chelmsford Friends of Music; Boston Univ Doctoral Flwshps; *home:* 32 Horseshoe Rd Chelmsford MA 01824*

VANDEHEI, RICHARD PAUL, Senior Army Instructor; *b:* Green Bay, WI; *m:* Elaine A.; *c:* Marcin, Artur; *ed:* St Norbert Coll (BS) Psychology 1962; Boston Univ (MA) Psychology 1971; Amer Univ (MBA) Bus Admin 1993; Army War Coll; Ind Coll of the Armed Forces; Joint Staff Coll; *cr:* Scientific & Tech BN Commander 3 Yrs; Dept of Defense Dir of Pgms 4 Yrs, Dir Natl Military Intelligence Ctr 3 Yrs; *ai:* JROTC Drill Coach; Acad Excl Team Coach; Physical Fitness Competition Coach; Land Navigation Team Coach; TROA 1992; Friends of Tenley Lib 1992, Dir; Wilson PTA 1991; Articles Pub; *office:* Woodrow Wilson Sr HS Nebraska Chesapeake NW Washington DC 20016*

VAN DEN BERG, BARBARA C., 6th Grade Teacher; *b:* Paterson, NJ; *m:* Thomas; *c:* Nadyne; *ed:* Coll of Steubenville (BA) Ed 1972; Montclair St Univ Math 1992; Arizona St Univ Summer Courses; *cr:* Goshen Schls 5th Grd Tchr 1 Yr; OH Schl #14 6th Grd Tchr 8 Yrs; Woodrow Wilson MS 8th Grd Math Tchr 15 Yrs, 6th Grd Tchr 1 Yr; *ai:* Stu Cncl, NY Times Knowledge Bowl & Fashion Club Adv; Teaming Comm; NEA 1973-; NJEA 1973-; Organized Hawthorne Womens Vllybl League; *office:* Woodrow Wilson MS 1400 Van Houten Ave Clifton NJ 07013*

VANDENBERG, DANIEL KASE, Chemistry Teacher; *b:* Phoenix, AZ; *m:* Rebecca A. Helms; *c:* Jonathan Daniel; *ed:* Penn St Univ (BS) Scndry Chem & Bio Ed 1986; Drexel Univ (MS) Environmental Sci 1992; *cr:* Springfield HS Sci Tchr 1987-; *ai:* Frosh Boys Bsktbl Coach; NEA 1987-; NSTA 1994-; *office:* Springfield HS 49 W Leamy Ave Springfield PA 19064

VANDENBERGH, PETER, 5th Grade Elementary Teacher; *b:* New York, NY; *ed:* Hartwick Coll (BA) Psych 1969; Hofstra Univ (MS) Elem Ed 1976; *cr:* Kings Park St Hosp Psych Soc Worker 1961-67; Harbor Cntry Day Schl 4th Grd Tchr 1967-68; Mid Cntry Pub Schl Spcl Ed Tchr 1968-70; Alden Cntrl Schl 5th-6th Grd Tchr 1970-; *ai:* Var Boys & Girls Tennis Coach; Shared Decision Making Team; NYSUT 1968-; NEA 1970-; Alden Cent Tchrs Assn 1970-, Contract Negotiator; *home:* 1 Harvey Dr Lancaster NY 14086

VANDERBILT, DEBORAH LYNN, Associate Professor of English; *b:* Tokyo, Japan; *m:* William B. Soleim; *c:* Colin, Owen; *ed:* Univ of WI at Madison (MA) Eng Lit 1984, (PHD) Medieval Lit 1990; *cr:* St John Fisher Coll Assoc Eng Prof 1990-; *ai:* Eng Club & Sigma Tan Delta Local Chptr Adv; Modern Lang Assn 1990-; ISAS 1992-; Numerous Articles Pub; *office:* Saint John Fisher Coll 3690 East Ave Rochester NY 14618

VANDERCLUTE, ELAINE CULLEN, Speech & English Instructor; *b:* Rockeville Ctr, NY; *m:* Bruce E.; *c:* Jeanne, Elizabeth; *ed:* Le Moyne Coll (BA) Eng 1975; Syracuse Univ (MS) Ed 1977; Boston Univ (MBA) Gen Mgmt 1982; Wilmington Coll; *cr:* Cntrl CT St Univ Part-Time Fac 1987-89; Del Tech Comm Coll Part-Time Instr 1990-91; Wor-Wic Comm Coll Instr 1991-; *ai:* Stu Govt Assn Fac Adv; Dir of Plays; Girls Scouts of Amer 1993-, Brownie Ldr; Atlantic Gen Hosp Auxiliary 1993-, Newsletter Contributing Ed; *office:* Wor-Wic Comm Coll 32000 Campus Dr Salisbury MD 21801

VANDERGROUND, RUTH DUNN, Second Grade Teacher; *b:* Cleveland, OH; *m:* James Philip; *c:* Jason, Rebecca; *ed:* Cedarville Coll (BS) Chrstn Ed 1966, (BS) Elem Ed 1967; St John Coll (MS) Elem Ed 1970; Notre Dame 15 Hrs Learning Disabilities; *cr:* Euclid Pub Schls Second Grd Tchr 1968-70, Third Grd Tchr 1971-74; Mentor Chrstn Schl Third Grd Tchr 1984-86; Willo-Hill Chrstn Schl Second Grd Tchr 1986-; *ai:* K-6 Sci Fair, Spelling Bee Co-Chair; Fall Rdng Emphasis Week Chair; Intervention Team for Stdtns with L-D; Assn of Chrstn Schls 1986-; Right to Life 1989-; Chagin Vly Comm Church 1996; *office:* Willo-Hill Christian Schl 4200 State Route 306 Willoughby OH 44094

VANDERHOEF, AUDREY HALL, MS Science & Health Teacher; *b:* New York, NY; *m:* Scott Charles; *ed:* Hudson Vly Comm Coll (AS) Sci 1978; Russell Sage (BS) Schl, Comm Hlth Sci 1979; SUNYA at Albany (MS) Sci Ed 1994; Post Bachelors Syracuse Univ, TX Southern Univ, Univ of Houston; Siena Post Masters Woodrow Wilson Prgm; *cr:* Vernon Verona Hlth Ed Tchr 1980; Houston ISD Hlth, Sci, Child Dev Tchr 1980-87; Berlin Cntrl MS Sci, Hlth Tchr 1988-; *ai:* Chrldng Coach; Alumni Comm; Shared Decision Making; Enrichment Coord; Sr Class Grad Organizer; Ind Stud Mentor; 1st Aid Instr; Prom Promise Initator; AFT Local 1988-, Ed; Amer Red Cross 1980-, Vol Instr; BCS Alumni Assn 1975-, Bd of Dirs; Outstdng Young Edctr 2 Yrs; Tchr of Yr Nominee; Crystal Apple Awd 2 Yrs; Vol, Extracurricular Awd for Dist 2 Yrs; *office:* Berlin Central Jr Sr HS Rt 22 Cherry Plain NY 12022*

VANDERKRAATS, BARBARA-JO (FRIESE), Choral Music Teacher; *b:* Allentown, PA; *m:* Arie R.; *c:* Heather Fellman, Leigh Fellman; *ed:* West Chester Univ (BS) Music Ed 1970, (MM) Music Ed, Vocal Performance 1974; 15 Addl Credits in Music Ed, Choral Music, Show Choir Choreography; *cr:* Downes Elem Schl Music Tchr 1970-74; Avon Grove Elem Schl Music Tchr 1980-83; Avon Grove HS Choral Dir, Gen Music Tchr 1990-; *ai:* Concert, Show, Club Choirs; Golden Chorale; Madrigal Singers; Boys & Girls Barbershop, Sr, Drama Ensembles for Broadway Medleys; Vocal Coaching for Broadway Musicals; NEA, MENC 1970-; PMEA 1980-; West Grove Mothers Cncl 1975-, Pres, VP, Sec; Sigma Alpha Iota 1967-, Pres; Dist, Regnl, St, All-Eastern Choruses Spon by MENC; *office:* Avon Grove HS 237 E State Rd West Grove PA 19390*

VANDERMAY, RAY EVAN, PE Instructor & Coach; *b:* Glenridge, NJ; *m:* Patricia Watson; *c:* Ryan Scott; *ed:* Montclair St Univ (BS) PE, Hlth 1975; *cr:* Cedar Grove Schls PE Instr, Coach 21 Yrs; *ai:* Var Sftbl, Prof Hitting, Pitching Sftbl Coach; Dir Starmaker Sftbl Summer Camps; Cedar Grove Ed Assn, NJEA, NEA 1975-; Comm Church of Cedar Grove 1952-, Deacon; NJ No 1 Ranked Team, Group I St Champions, Coach of Yr Star-ledger 1978, Governor Tchr of Yr Recognition Pgrm 1991; Several Conf, Cty, St Sectional C hamps; *office:* South End Schl Harper Terr Cedar Grove NJ 07009

VANDERPOOL, ROSEMARY SCANLON, General Education Professor; *b:* Philadelphia, PA; *c:* David B.; *ed:* Peirce Jr Coll (AA) Lbrl Arts 1969; Penn St Univ (BA), (MA) Hum 1971-73; Attnd Temple Univ; *cr:* Peirce Coll Gen Ed Prof 1973-; *ai:* Phi Theta Kappa Intnl Hnr Spon; Retention Commencement; Hnrs Comms; PSEA; Tchr of the Yr 1973; Employee of the Quarter 1993; Ldrshp & Svc Awds Annually; *office:* Peirce Coll 1420 Pine St Philadelphia PA 19102

VANDERVORT, RONALD CHARLES, Science Teacher; *b:* Binghamton, NY; *ed:* Lebanon Valley Coll (BS) Bio, Physics 1976; Loma Linda Univ (MA) Bio 1985; PA St Univ Ecology 37 Hrs; Univ of Southern CA Cinematography 8 Hrs; Univ of MD Ed 3 Hrs; Columbia Union Coll Ed 3 Hrs; *cr:* J. N. Andrews Elem Schl Sci Tchr 1977-78; Sligo Adventist Schl Sci Tchr 1979-86; Takoma Acad Sci Tchr 1989-; *ai:* Biota Club; Fac Chm; NSTA 1979-; *office:* Takoma Acad 8120 Carroll Ave Takoma Park MD 20912

VANDERVORT, SHARYN L., English Teacher; *b:* Warren, OH; Univ (BS) Ed 1980; Univ of Dayton (MS) Ed 1995; *cr:* Roosevelt D Tutor 1983-84; Kennedy Jr HS Rdng Tchr 1984-85; Lincoln Jr Tchr 1985-88; Newark HS Eng Tchr 1988-; *ai:* NEA 1980-; NCTE *office:* Newark HS 314 Granville St Newark OH 43055

VANDEVELDE, SUSAN OWENS, High School Math Teac Westfield, NY; *m:* Carl; *c:* Angela, Mark; *ed:* Clarion Univ (BA Math 1973; SUNY at Fredonia (MS) Ed & Math 1993; *cr:* Westfi Math Tchr 1984-; *ai:* Key Club & Frosh Class Adv; NEA at NY & N 1988-; Westfield Tchrs Assn 1987-; YWCA; Tandy Tech Schola *office:* Westfield High School E Main St Westfield NY 14787

VANDEVENTER, JAMES B., Retired Earth Science Teach Syracuse, NY; *m:* Joan L.; *c:* Susan D. Smith, Brian, Paul; *ed:* B Green St Univ (BS) Geology 1961; Univ of Akron (MS) Geology 19 Akron Pub Schls Earth Sci Tchr 33 Yrs; Univ of Akron Geology L 5 Yrs; *ai:* Bldg Rep; Fac Cncl; City Expulsion Review Comm; S Coord; Sci Dept Chm; Chess Club; Sci Club; Akron Ed Assn 1962 Rep, Bd of Trustees; Natl Excl; St Krecker Sci Awd; Numerous A Pub.

VAN DEVENTER, JOSEPHINE MEADE, Retired Fourth Teacher; *b:* New York City, NY; *m:* Peter B. Sr.; *c:* Peter B. Jr., K M., John M., Paul M.; *ed:* Coll of Mount Saint vincent (BS) Soc Stuc NY Univ (MA) Ed 1953; Ed Credits Kean Coll; *cr:* New York City I Welfare Soc Worker 1949-52; Deerfield Schl Elem Schl Tchr 1967- Curr Comm; Supervised Stu Tchrs; NEA; NJEA; *home:* 19 Addi Short Hills NJ 07078

VAN DUSEN, KAREN HUDSON, 7th & 8th Grd Writing Teach Cambridge, NY; *m:* George H.; *c:* Benjamin Hugh, Kyle Georg Pfeiffer Coll (BA) Eng, Ed 1977; SUNY at Plattsburgh (MS) A Supervision 1988; *cr:* Okeechobee Jr HS 9th Grd Eng Tchr 19 Cambridge Cntrl Schl Jr HS Eng Tchr 1978-80; East Lee Jr HS 7th-9 Eng Tchr 1980-86; Ft Ann Cntrl Schl 7th & 9th Grd Eng Tchr 19 Warrensburg Jr Sr HS 11th Grd Eng Tchr 1990-; *ai:* HS Newspape Acad Quiz Bowl Adv; NHS Fac Council Mem; Tchr Mentor; NCT St United Tchrs, AFT 1986-; Warrensburg Tchrs Assn 1990-; Tc Writers Collaborative; Assn Retarded Citizens 1986-; Stony Creek I 1992-94; Down Syndrome Aim High 1986-; *office:* Warrensburg Jr Horicon Ave Warrensburg NY 12885

VANDUSEN, SUSAN MILDRED, Fourth Grade Teacher; *b:* Well PA; *ed:* Mansfield Univ (BS) Elem Ed 1979, (MS) Ed 1986; Specialist Cert 1983; Lockhaven Univ Driver Ed, Safety Cert 199 Northern Potter Children's Schl 2-6th Grd Tchr 1980-, Driver Ed 10-12th Grd 1991-; *ai:* PA Math Assessment Advy Comm Grd 5; 1990-; PA Assn for Safety Ed 1992-; Ladies Aux VFW Post 6753 *office:* Northern Potter Children's Sch RR 1 Box 401 Ulysses PA 16

VAN DYKE, FAY DEANE, Art Teacher; *b:* Whitinsville, MA; *m:* Robert; *c:* David James, Thomas John, Christine Ann Elliott, Kirsten Desnoyer; *ed:* Wesleyan Univ (BA) Art Ed 1976, (MLA) Lbrl Art 1979; Paier Coll of Art Engrng Graphics 12 Credit Hrs; Northw Comm Coll Cmptr Graphics 6 Credit Hrs; *cr:* Daniel Hand HS Art Tc Yrs; *ai:* Ct Avt Assn 1976-; NAEA 1978-; Tech Action Team 1990-; NAEA Washington DC Convention; Producing Cmptr Graphics Im Portfolio; *office:* Daniel Hand HS 302 Green Hill Rd Madison CT 0

VAN DYKE, WILLIAM JOHN, Foreign Language Teacher; *b:* Island, NY; *ed:* Hofstra Univ (BA) Fr & Scndry Ed 1977, (MA) Scnd 1981, (CAS) Educl Admin 1989; *cr:* Long Beach City Schl Dist 1977-, Foreign Lang Chprsn 1989-94; *ai:* MS Yrbk & Stu Org Ad Foreign Lang Honor Soc Adv; HS Stu Relations Comm Chprsn; Num Comms Mem; NYSFLT, AATF, LILT; *office:* Long Beach HS 322 La Dr W Long Beach NY 11561*

VANEEDEN, CECILIA F., French, Spanish Tchr & Chprs Lynchburg, VA; *c:* Patricia, Emily; *ed:* Mary Washington Coll (B 1967; Bloomsburg Univ (MED) Fr 1971; Bloomsburg Univ Span Cer Bethlehem Cath HS at Bethlehem Fr Tchr 1967-68; York Cath HS at Fr Tchr 1968-69; Muncy HS Fr Tchr 1969-73; Bishop Hafey H Hazelton Fr, Span Tchr 1980-; *ai:* Intnl Club; NHS; Fr Natl Honor AATF 1980-; AATSP 1985-.

VANELLIS, JOHN B.,JR., Biology Teacher; *b:* Trenton, NJ; *m:* Va Folis; *c:* Christina; *ed:* Rider Univ (BA) Bio 1969; Grad Courses Tre St Coll Rider Univ; *cr:* Jr HS #3 Trenton Sci Tchr 1969-74; Trenton HS Sci Tchr 1975-; *ai:* NSTA, NEA, NJEA, MEA, TEA; *office:* Tre Central HS 400 Chambers St Trenton NJ 08618

VAN ERK, NINA, Phys Ed & Athletics Director; *b:* Fresh Meadow, *ed:* Marymount Coll (AS) PE 1975; Ithaca Coll (BS) PE 1977; Russell (MS) Hlth Ed 1981; SUNY at New Paltz (SAS) Schl Admin 1984 Rhinebeck Cntrl Schls PE Tchr & AD 1977-95; Katonah Lewisboro Dir of PE & Ath 1995-; *ai:* NYSPHSAA Exec Comm; Dr Ed; Coac Section One 1987-, Ex Comm; Young Women in Sports Symposium 1995; *office:* Katonah Lewisboro Schls Rt 121 Katonah NY 10536

VANETTEN, CAROLYN P. (TOMB), Librarian; *b:* Ft Bragg, NC Elwin R. II; *c:* Steven; *ed:* Mansfield Univ (BS) Lib Sci 1972; 24 Post Hrs Courses for Permanent Cert; *cr:* Galeton Area Schl Librn 197 Northern Potter Schl Sub Tchr 1975-78; First Citizens Natl Bank T Data Processing, New Accounts 1978-90; Cowanesque Vly HS L 1990-; *ai:* Yrbk, Newspaper, Enrichment Adv; Stu Assistance Team; P 1991-; NEA, PSEA, Northern Tioga EA 1990-; Ulysses Lib Bd 199 Treas; Cub Scout Pack 530 1992-, Den Ldr.

VAN GEONS, LORETTA COPPOLA, Second Grade Teacher; *b:* Chester, NY; *m:* Michael R.; *c:* Robert, Michael J., Jonathan; Westchester Comm Coll (AA) Lbrl Arts 1966; Western CT St Univ (BS 1970; Cntrl CT St Univ 30 Credits Ed 1974; *cr:* Anna H. Rockwell E Schl Classroom Tchr 1971-; *ai:* Bethel Ed Assn, CT Ed Assn, NEA 19 St Paul's Luth Church 1968-; *home:* 67 Oakville Ave Waterbury CT 06

VANGERMEERSCH, RICHARD, Accounting Professor; *b:* Provide RI; *ed:* Bryant Coll (BS) Acctng 1959; Univ of RI (MS) Acctng 1964; of FL (PHD) Acctng 1970; Univ of RI Lbrl Arts Cert 1962; RI Cert Accountant 1965; Cert Mngmt Accountant 1978; *cr:* Glass, Dittle CPA's Staff Accountant 1959-60; Lawson Products Indstrl Accour 1960-62; US Gen Acctng Office Accountant, Auditor 1964-65; Univ o Instr 1965-67; Univ of ME Asst Prof 1967-71; Univ of RI Prof 1971- Beta Alpha Psi Fac VP 3 Times; Acctng Dept Chm 1981-84; Fac Se Exec Comm 1974-75; MS in Acctng Dir 3 Times; Acad of Ac Historians 1973-, Pres 1987, Chair of Trustees 1990-92, Hourglass 1988; Natl Assn Scholars 1993-, RI Chptr Treas; Narrogansett Republ Town Comm 1975-; Fin Reporting Techniques in 20 Indstrl Cos Since 1 1979; Origins of a Great Profession 1987; Alexander Hamilton Church Man of Ideas for All Seasons 1988; The His of Acctng: An I Encyclopedia 1996; *office:* Univ Of RI 316 B Ballentine Kingston 02881*

VAN GILDER, SHARIE HUSTED, Fourth Grade Teacher; *b:* Pont MI; *m:* Harold W.; *c:* Kurt Ramsey, Denise Ramsey; *ed:* Eastern MI U (BS) Elem Ed 1956, (MA) Soc Stud 1965; *cr:* Douglas Elem Schl 1st Tchr 1956-58; Woodrow Wilson Schl 1-4 Grd Tchr 1958-70; Home St Schl 2, 4 Grd Tchr 1970-; *ai:* Act #178 Comm; Warren Co Ed Assn B Rep; Wayne Ed Assn, MI Ed Assn 1956-70; Warren Co Ed Assn, PA

70-; Bus & Prof Women 1965-70; Assn of Coll Women 1985-; 0 Nathan St Warren PA 16365

UNDY, JOELLEN KLEINSCHMIDT, Business Teacher; *b:* us, OH; *m:* Richard Benson; *c:* Zac; *ed:* Findlay Coll (BA) Bus ayton Univ (MA) Guidance & Counseling 1993; *cr:* St of OH Hlth & Retardation Sec & Exec 2 Yrs; Findlay Coll Sec & Librn 3 NEA 1974-, Mem; BSA.

SE, PATRICIA PINGITORE, Math Dept Chairperson; *b:* , NJ; *m:* Robert P. Walker; *c:* Wayne, Jayne Bruinooge; *ed:* Trenton (BA) Math 1965, (MA) Math 1974; Rutgers Univ Educl Admin, Inst in Discrete Math; Cmptr Programming Trenton St Coll; *cr:* n East Steinert Schl Tchr 1965-66; Hamilton West HS Tchr 1976-; h Team Adv; Cmptr Assisted Instruction Coord; NEA, NCTM *office:* Hamilton HS West 2720 S Clinton Ave Hamilton Twp NJ

OUTEN, EDWARD B., Social Studies Teacher; *b:* Columbia, SC; ica M. P. Kean; *ed:* Montclair St Univ (BA) Soc Stud 1964, (MA) d, Ec 1966; NY St Supervision & Admin Cert; *cr:* Dumont HS Soc hr 1964-69; Tappan Zee HS Soc Stud Tchr 1969-95, Soc Stud Dept 1984-95; South Oronggtown Cntrl Schl Dist Curr Coord 1993-95; y Bd; Stu Court Sec; Ed Assn of So Oronggtown; Benefit Trust; , AFT 1969-; NJ Symphony Orch 1995-, Supporter.

OVEN, JAMES B.,JR., Art Teacher; *b:* Framingham, MA; *m:* adieu; *c:* Joseph, Amy; *ed:* Wesleyan Univ (BA) Fine Arts 1988; niv (MFA) Painting & Print Making 1993; *cr:* Kingswood-Oxford & 8th Grd Art Tchr 1988-89; King & Low Heywood Thomas Schl Grd Art Tchr 1990-91; Mater Christi Schl 3rd-8th Grd Art Tchr 4; Cicero-North Syracuse HS 10th-12th Grd Art Tchr 1994-; *ai:* ecathalon; NYSUT 1994-; *office:* Cicero-North Syracuse HS Rt 31 NY 13039

, DAVID C., Mathematics Teacher; *b:* Hartford, CT; *m:* Louise : Damion, Heather, Olan; *ed:* Univ of Hartford (BS) Personnel 1969, (MED) Urban Ed 1971; Masters Plus 75 Hrs; *cr:* Weaver HS 1968-73; Isfahan Amer Schl Math & Sci 1973-79; Parents ative Schl at Jeddah Math 1979-85; Canadian Acad at Kobe Math 985-88; Hartford Pub HS Math Tchr 1988-; *ai:* Peer Mediation; Ski Outdoor Club; AFT, NCTM 1988-; PIMMS Fellow 1995-; Civitian 9; BSA; Extensive World Travel; *office:* Hartford Public HS 55 St Hartford CT 06105

URA, WILLIAM J., US & World History Teacher; *b:* Painesville, : Sarah Lanigan; *ed:* OH St Univ (BS) Comprehensive Soc Stud Kent St Univ (MED) Curr & Instruction 1983; 48 Semester Hrs d Masters Including Stud in Spain, Mexico, London & Ireland; *cr:* Pub Schls Tchr 1978-; *ai:* Soc Stud Dept Head; NEA, OEA, PEA PTA Excl in Tchng Awd; Pub in Journal of Rdng; *office:* Valley HS 9999 Independence Blvd Parma OH 44130

IRK, MICHAEL R., Math Teacher; *b:* Beaver Falls, PA; *ed:* ry Rock Univ (BS) Math 1968; Univ of Pittsburgh Post Grad; IN Math, Sci, Natl Fnd Prgm; *cr:* Langley HS Stu Tchr 1968; western HS Math Tchr; Lackey HS MathTchr; United HS Math Tchr *ai:* Edinboro Univ Bsktbl Camp Coach 1989-90; Jr HS Dance rone; Detention Tchr; Bsktbl Coach-Mohawk & Northwestern; UEA, UPT, NEA, AQHA, NCTM, OCTM; LRP Comm Advisory Math Sci ; United Testing Comm; Exemplary Attendence Awd; Natl Sci Fnd, ept of Ed Driver Ed Wkshp Participants; North Cntrl Evaluation Dedicated Tchr, Cert of Merit, Tandy Tech Scholar, Jennings Scholrs *office:* United Local H S 8143 State Rt 9 Hanoverton OH 44423

OOLBERGEN, GERARD A., Guidance Counselor; *ed:* Iona Coll r 1963; Montclair St Univ (MA) Guid 1969; *cr:* Fair Lawn HS Guid 1969-; *office:* Fair Lawn HS Berdam Ave Fair Lawn NJ 07410

KOSKI, JAMES, 9th Grade Social Studies Tchr; *b:* Chester, PA; *m:* ra Fabeny; *c:* Brett, Jim Jr.; *ed:* West Chester Univ (BS) Geography an Planning 1968, (MED) Ed 1972; Widener Univ Comprehensive ud 1976; *cr:* Showalter Jr Hs Tchr 1968-69; Nether Providence MS 969-70; Strath Haven HS Tchr 1970-; *ai:* Bsbl Head Coach; Close Govt Club Adv; NEA, PSEA 1968-; WSEA 1969-, Schl Cncl; Natl or Geographic Ed; Delaware Gulls Bsbl Club 1995-, General Mgr; Strath Haven HS 205 S Providence Rd Wallingford PA 19086

KOUWENBERG, PATRICIA CULLEN, HS GT Program Coord & er; *b:* Tarrytown, NY; *m:* Clifford J.; *ed:* Univ of Rochester (BA) Eng 962, (MA) Eng Ed 1969; Univ of CT & Columbia Univ Gifted Ed; at Brockport NYS Educ Admin Cert; *cr:* Penfield Jr HS Eng Tchr 66; Bay Trail Jr HS Eng Tchr 1966-73; Penfield HS Eng Tchr 95, HS GT Prgm Coord & Leadership Seminar Tchr 1986-; *ai:* NHS Acad Quiz Team Coach; PCSD Instructional Cncl; AGATE 1986-; 1962-; AFT 1970-; AAUW; Title IX Grant to Dev HS Stdnts ership Course; NEA Linguistic Stud Fellowship 1966; NYS Cncl on Sum Wkshp 1995; *office:* Penfield HS High School Dr Penfield NY 5

LANDINGHAM, MARGUERITE H., Professor of Finance; *b:* ston, IL; *ed:* Univ of FL (BA) Ec-Hnrs 1968, (PHD) Fin 1972; *cr:* a Univ Asst Fin Prof 1972-75, Coll of Bus Acting Dean 1974-75; St Univ Asst Fin Prof 1975-79; Clarion Univ of PA Fin Prof 1981-, of Bus Admin Dean 1983-88; *ai:* AT&T Collegiate Investment enge Adv; Fac Spon; Presidential Commission on Sexual Harassment ; Am Fin Assn 1972-; Southern Fin Assn 1974-; Fin Mgmt Assn 1975-; rn Fin Assn 1975-; Red Cross Bd of Dir 1987-; Kiwanis 1988-; on Incubator Advy Bd 1991-; Intnl Whos Who in Ed 1986; Invited rer & Consultant Kozan Inst of Fin & Ec Republic of Tatorstan an Fed 1993; Sabbatical Awd Rsrch of the Bahamas 1995-; Article *office:* Clarion Univ Of PA Still Hall Clarion PA 16214*

LOAN, NANCI LYNN, Economics & Government Teacher; *b:* nta, NY; *m:* Richard Ranieri; *ed:* Hamilton Coll (BA) Ecs 1988; hamton Univ (MAT) Ed, His 1991; *cr:* Walton Cntrl Schl Ecs, Govt 1990-; *ai:* Stud Cncl, Sr Class, Adv; Educl Policy Comm; -Walton TA 1990-; NCSS 1988-; Wells Ridge Fire Dept 1995-; *office:* on Cntrl Schl 47-49 Stockton Ave Walton NY 13856*

METER, CARROLL L., Vocational Agriculture Teacher; *b:* dburn, KY; *m:* Carol Jeanne Keller; *c:* Christopher, Maria; *ed:* Uni vof BS) Agronomy 1966, (MS) Entomology 1969; Tchr Cert Western KY 1972; Artificial Insemination Schooling Amer Breeders Svc; *cr:* Univ Y Rsrch Technician 1965-68; US Army SP-K Stenographer, Clerk -71; Wellston City Schls Voc Ag Tchr 1972-75; Minford Local Schls Ag Tchr 1975-; *ai:* FFA Chptr Adv; Minford Ed Assn, Bldg Rep, otiations Comm; OH Ed Assn, NEA, Natl Voc Ag Tchrs, OH Voc Ag s 1972-; Natl Rifle Assn 1975-, Life Mem; DuBois Family Assn 1985-; r Legion 1990-; Huguenot His Society 1985-; KY Historical Soc -; 4 Journal Articles Pub; US Army Commendation Medal; Tchr of Yr ; *home:* PO Box 27 Minford OH 45653

METER, SUE HONEY, English & Journalism Teacher; *b:* ngstown, OH; *m:* Donald C.; *c:* Christopher, Caroline; *ed:* Bowling n (BA) Fr, Eng 1966, (MED) Cnslng Psych 1971; ABD Ed Psych Kent niv; *cr:* Sylvania HS Tchr 1966-71; Cleveland Hts HS Tchr 1971-73; nd Seminary HS Tchr 1983-; *ai:* Chrldng Coach; NEA 1990-; PEA 1983-; NCTE 1993-; *office:* Poland Seminary HS 3199 Dobbins Rd Poland OH 44514

VANNATTA, ANNA MARIE DELVECCHIO, English Teacher; *b:* Telesa, Italy; *m:* Anna Marie DelVecchio; *c:* Thomas Owen, Timothy Wayne; *ed:* Wm Paterson Coll (BA) Eng 1966, (MA) Ed 1976; Mass Comm, Television Production, Television Directing, Broadcast Jrnlsm, Process Writing 3 Credits Each; *cr:* Paterson Schl Dist Tchr 26 Yrs; *ai:* Class, NHS, Publications Advs; Future Tchrs, Sunshine Clubs; Laison, Philosophy, Curr Comms; PREP Tchr; Paterson Ed Assn, NEA, NJEA, NCTE 1965-; ACD 1980-; Kappa Delta Pi 1987-; Bloomingdale Bd of Ed 1987-, Ed, Policy Chprsn; Governor's Tchr Recognition Awd 1993; Paterson Ed Writing 1988, Geraldine Dodge Playwriting 1993, Martini Matching 1994 Fnd Grants; *office:* Rosa Parks Schl Fine, Perf Art 413 12th Ave Paterson NJ 07403*

VAN NATTA, RICHARD C., 4th & 5th Grade Math Teacher; *b:* Washington, DC; *m:* Marietta R.; *ed:* Prince Georges Comm Coll (AA) Elem Ed 1964; Salisbury St Coll (BS) Elem Ed 1966; Bowie St Coll (MA) Admin, Supervision 1972; 30 Addl Hrs Ed; *cr:* Oaklands Elem Schl Classroom Tchr 1966-74; Carole Highlands Elem Schl Classroom Tchr 1974-79; Morningside Elem Schl Classroom Tchr 1979-87; Ft Washington Forest Elem Schl Classroom Tchr 1987-89; Henry G. Ferguson Elem Schl Classroom Tchr 1989-; *ai:* Grade Level, Recycling Prgm Chprsns; Audio Vis, Math, TAG Enrichment Math Prgm Coords; NEA 1966-; AFT 1994-; Solomons Island Yacht Club, Bd of Governors; Boating Ed Instr.,; *office:* Henry G Ferguson Elem Schl 14600 Berry Rd Accokeek MD 20607

VANNESS, RAYMOND KENNETH,JR., Professor; *b:* Troy, NY; *c:* Allison, Raymond III; *ed:* Broome Comm Coll (AS) Accounting 1963; Elmira Coll (BS) Bus Admin, Acctng 1973, (MS) Mngmt, Ed 1983; Post-Grad Research Enpowerment through Knowledge, Speaking The Lang of Intnl Bus; *cr:* Binghamton Univ Lecturer 1974-76; Broome Comm Coll Lecturer 1977-82; SUNY at Albany Entrepreneur in Residence 1983-87; Broome Comm Coll Assoc Prof 1988; *ai:* Accounting, Entrepeneurship Comms; Coll Lacross Spon; Intnl Stdnts Spon; Intnl Bus Mgr Stdwng Pgm; NEA 1988-; TACTYE 1993-; Amer Entrepreneur 1980-; Amer Acctng Assn; Amer Legion 1966-, Soldiers Medal; Italian Amer Ctr 1992-; Republican Natl Comm 1980-, Pres Achvmnt; Research How the Art, Sci of Bus is Taught, Conducted in Netherlands Grant; *office:* Broome Community Coll Front St Binghamton NY 13904*

VAN NESS, RICHARD J., Professor of Management; *m:* Mary H.; *c:* Richard, Michael, Robert; *ed:* Coll of St Rose (MA) Ed & Psych 1972, (MS) Mgmt 1982; Union Grad Schl (PHD) Org Dev 1989; *cr:* Cntrl MI Univ Mgmt Consultant 1980-, Assoc Grad 1994-; Schenectady Comm Coll Prof of Mgmt 1983-; Norwich Univ Adj Prof 1995-; *ai:* NEA 1983-; Capital Region Human Resource Assn 1985-; Soc of Manufacturing Engrs 1988-; Robotics Intnl 1988-; Written Numerous Training Pgms for Various Industries; Books: Finance the Key to Development Management, Management Science for Organization Development & The Upside of Downsize; Conducted Rsrch Projects, Mgmt & Culture & Japan, NAFTA & The Impact on the Indigenous People of Mexico.

VANNEST, NANCY COLLINS, Work & Family Life Teacher; *b:* Barnesville, OH; *m:* Bruce L.; *c:* Matthew, Brian, Melissa; *ed:* OH St Univ (BS) Home Ec Ed 1977; *cr:* Union Local HS Home Ec Dept Tchr 1977-; *ai:* FHA, Buckeyes 4-H Club, FHA, HERO St Officers Adv; OM Coach; NEA, OH Ed Assn, Union Local Assn Classroom Tchrs 1977-; Eastern OH Mentors 1996; Bethesda United Meth Church, PTO 1990; Oakleigh Garden Club; Jr Bsbl League 1995; Master, Mentor Adv; *office:* Union Local HS 66859 Belmont-Morristown Rd Belmont OH 43718

VANNETT, R. MICHAEL, Ath Dir, Head Basketball Coach; *b:* Bowling Green, OH; *m:* Beth Ann Dutcher; *c:* Lindsay, Matt; *ed:* Wittenberg Univ (BA) Hlth, PE 1980; Bowling Green St Univ (MED) Ath Admin 1982; *cr:* Bowling Green St Univ Grad Asst 1980-82; Riverdale Local Schls Elem PE Tchr, Coach 1982-87; Ashland Crestview Schls HS PE, Hlth Tchr, Ath Dir, Head Bsktbl Coach 1987-90; Bowling Green City Schls Ath Dir, Head Bsktbl Coach 1990-; *ai:* OHSBCA 1982-; League & Area Coach of Yr 1991; *office:* Bowling Green Sr HS 530 W Poe Rd Bowling Green OH 43402

VANNOSTRAND, BERNICE CRAWFORD, 5th Grade Teacher; *b:* Princeton, NJ; *m:* Maitland; *c:* Virginia Sweeton, Nancy Curtis, Barbara Van Liew; *ed:* Trenton St (BS) Elem Ed 1958; 12 Credits Administer Rider Coll; *cr:* Hillsborough Twp 3rd Grd Tchr 1958-59; Montgomery Twp 3-6 Grd Tchr 1960-; *ai:* Montg Twp Ed Assn, NJEA, NEA 1960-; Governor's Tchr Recognition 1990.*

VAN NOTE, CONSTANCE ARROM, First Grade Teacher; *b:* Atlantic City, NJ; *ed:* Philadelphia Coll of Bible (BS) Sociology 1964; Rowan Coll (MA) Ed 1971; 3 Credit Hrs Ed at Monmouth Coll 1980; 3 Credit Hrs Ed at Queens Coll 1985; 42 Credit Hrs Ed at Nova Southeastern Univ 1997; *cr:* Emma C. Attales Schl Elem Tchr 1964-69; Fort Howard Elem Schl Primary Tchr 1969-70; Erlton Elem Schl Primary Tchr 1970-78; A. Russell Knight Schl Primary Tchr 1978-79; James Fenimore Cooper Schl Primary Tchr 1979-; *ai:* Pupil Assistance, Peer Mediation Comm; NEA, NJEA 1964-; ASCD 1992-; AAUW 1994-; Girl Scouts of Amer Spec Svcs Awd 1987; Governors Tchr Recognition Prgm 1988; *office:* James Fenimore Cooper Schl 1960 Greentree Rd Cherry Hill NJ 08003*

VAN PATTEN, KATHERINE GRAULICH, 3rd Grade Teacher; *b:* Buffalo, NY; *m:* William Frederick; *c:* Christopher, Corey, Scott; *ed:* SUNY at Plattsburgh (BS) Elem Ed 1981; SUNY at Cortland (MS) Curr & Instruction 1987; *cr:* West Canada Vly 2nd Grd Tchr 1982-86, 3rd Grd Tchr 1986-; *office:* West Canada Vly Elem Schl PO Box 360 Rt 28 Newport NY 13416

VAN PELT, ELSIE, Eighth Grade English Teacher; *b:* Columbiana, OH; *ed:* Eastern Mennonite Univ (BS) Ed 1964; Attnd Kent St; *cr:* Somalia Tchr 1964-73; South Range MS Tchr 1973-.

VAN PELT, WILLIAM EDWARD,II, Music Teacher; *b:* Jeanette, PA; *ed:* WV Univ (BS) Music Ed 1992; *cr:* Lawrence Elem General Music Tchr 1992-; Frontier HS Music Tchr 1992-; *ai:* Marching, Pep, Jr HS, Concert Bands; Concert, Jr HS Choirs; Music Dept Chprsn; MENC, OMEA, NEA, Frontier Local Educ Assn 1992-; OH Ed Assn 1992-; Frontier Local Ed Assm Treas 1995-; Certfd Mentor for Entry Level Tchrs 1995-; Historian Frontier Band Boosters 1995; *home:* PO Box 62 Newport OH 45768

VAN PUTTEN, JOSEPH P., Asst Professor of Fine Art; *b:* Paterson, NJ; *ed:* Wm Paterson Coll (BFA) Fine Art, Design 1987, (MA) Visual Art 1988; Pratt Inst (MFA) Sculpture 1994; *cr:* Wm Paterson Coll Adj 1988-92, Instr 1992-94, Asst Prof 1994-; *ai:* Adv Stu Art Assn; Chair Var Athletics Cncl, MFA Comm; Collaborative Stud Cncl; AFT 1992-; Amer Assn of Woodturning 1988-; Woodturning Ctr 1988-, Ed Comm; Lib Arts Cncl 1993-; Numerous Groups, One Person Exhibitions; Founding Mem Untitled #130; Alternative Exhibition Space Dir; Stone Hill Quarry Park Residency; *office:* William Paterson Coll 300 Pompton Rd Wayne NJ 07470

VANSCOY, BARBARA WAINWRIGHT, English Teacher; *b:* Berwick, PA; *c:* Wendy Ruskowski, Heidi, Mark, Todd; *ed:* Bloomsburg Univ (BSEd) Eng 1960; Addl Grad Stud LIU, Adelphi; *cr:* Hampton Bays HS Eng Tchr 1960-62; Riverhead HS Sub Tchr 1963-73, Eng Tchr 1976-96; *ai:* Attendance Comm Chm; News Brief Columnist; Mentathletes Former Adv; NHS; PGO; NYSEC, Tchr of Excl Awd; RCFA, Tchr of Yr Awd; NYSUT; Our Redeemer Luth Church 1970-, Bd of Chrstn Ed; Tchr of Excl 1989; Tchr of Yr 1994; *home:* 388 Howell Ave Riverhead NY 11901

VAN SCYOC, CINDY ANN, 6th Grade Teacher; *b:* Jackson, MI; *m:* Martin L.; *c:* Amanda R., Jared L., Andrea L.; *ed:* Spring Arbor Coll (BA) Elem Ed, Eng, His 1985; *cr:* Pleasant City Elem 5th-6th Grd Tchr 1985-86; Bartlett Elem 6th-8th Grd Lang Arts, His Tchr 1986-87; Caldwell Jr High 7th-8th Grd Lang Arts Tchr 1987-93; Caldwell Elem 6th Grd Tchr 1993-; *ai:* Lang Arts Novel Selection Comm; Writing Competency Test Grader K-8th Grd; OH Cncl of Tchrs of LA 1988-; OH Ed Assn, NEA 1986-; Cald Tchrs Assn 1987-; Schl of Inst of Childrens Lit; *office:* Caldwell Elem Schl 44350 Fairground Rd Caldwell OH 43724

VAN SICKLE, CHRISTINE LIZZA, Kindergarten Teacher; *b:* Pittsburgh, PA; *m:* Kenneth W. Jr.; *c:* Kenneth W. III; *ed:* CA Univ of PA (BS) Elem Ed 1973, (MS) Elem Ed 1976; Mgmt, Office Mgr & Commnctn Series Trng; *cr:* Springfield Elem Schl 1st Grd Tchr 1973-79, Kndgtn Tchr 1979-; *ai:* Amer Ed Week Comm; PSEA 1973-; Connellsville Area Ed Assoc 1973-; NEA 1973-; CA St Coll Grants; *office:* Springfield Elem Schl RD 1 Box 26 Normalville PA 15469

VANSICKLE, RAY L., Spanish Teacher; *b:* Uniontown, PA; *ed:* Geneva Coll at Beaver Falls (BA) Span 1991; Attnd La Universidad Catolica at Ibarra, Universidad De La Yucatan at Merida; *cr:* Beaver Falls HS Span Tchr 1990-91; Berkeley Co Pub Schls Span Tchr 1991-; *ai:* NHS, Drama Club Spon; Musical Dir; Lead Stdnts Trips; Modern Lang Assn 1991-; Amer Cncl Tchng Frgn Lang 1991-; Rotary Club 1995-; Articles Pub; *home:* 2 Steele St Brownsville PA 15417*

VANSICKLE, STEPHEN CARL, Emergency Care Instructor; *b:* Parkersburg, WV; *m:* Susan Hope Schermer; *c:* Amber Dawn, Stephen Chaz; *ed:* Hocking Coll (AEMT) Emergency Victim Care 1993; Attnd Valencia Coll at Orlando 1986, WV Univ at Parkersburg, Marshall Univ at Huntington; *cr:* Hocking Coll First Responder in Emergency Care Instr, CPR, First Aid Coord 1993-; *ai:* Outdoor Club Adv; Pace Coord; NAEMT, OPOTA 1995-, NREMT 1992-, Amer Heart Assn 1992-, IT, Coord Prgm Coord HC 1992; Amer Red Cross 1992-, IT, Hlth, Safety, Bd Mem; OH Peace Ofcr Trng 1995-, Instr; *office:* Hocking Coll 3301 Hocking Pkwy Nelsonville OH 45764

VAN TASSEL, LAURA LEAH, Band Director; *b:* Columbus, OH; *ed:* Otterbein Coll (BME) Music Ed 1985; Succeeding with Difficult Stdnts Univ of Dayton; Cooperative Learning, Questions for Life Bowling Green St Univ; *cr:* Carroll HS Asst Band Dir 1986-88; Fairport MS Band Dir 1988-; Gibsonburg HS Band Dir 1994-; *ai:* Marching Band; Pep Band; Flag Corps; NEA 1988-; Dayton Ed Assn 1988-, Staff Dev 1993-94; MENC, OMEA 1983-88, 1994-; Family Channel Tchr of Yr 1994; C-SPAN Tchr of Yr 1994; IBM, Tech, Learning Magazine St Tchr of Yr 1992; Excl in Tchng Awd Dayton 1992; *office:* Gibsonburg HS S Harrison St Gibsonburg OH 43431

VAN TOL, JERRY LEROY, English Teacher; *b:* Sioux Center, IA; *c:* Lindsay, Seth, Hannah; *ed:* Dordt Coll (BA) Eng 1977; 18 Hrs Toward MST Univ of NH; *cr:* Hull Western Chrstn HS Eng Tchr 1978-79; Whitinsville Chrstn Schl Eng Tchr 1982-; *ai:* Drama Dir; NCTE, NEATE 1982-; Tchrs, Writers 1989-; *office:* Whitinsville Chrstn HS 279 Linwood Ave Whitinsville MA 01588

VAN TRYON, PATRICIA JEAN, Life Science Teacher; *b:* West Chester, PA; *ed:* Temple Univ (BS) Scndry Ed 1991; Beaver Coll (MA) Environmental Ed 1995; *cr:* North Penn Schl Dist Life Sci Tchr 1991-; *ai:* Reorganization Comm 1992-94; Schl Newspaper Adv 1992-94; IM Sports Adv & Coach 1993 & 1996; Curr Writing Comm 1995 & 1996; NEA 1991-; NSTA 1995-; US Dept of Environmental Protection 1994-, Comm Liason; Schuylkill Ctr for Environmental Ed 1995-; NP Ed Fndtn Grant 1992; Whos Who Amer Coll Stdnts 1995; Graduated with Distinction from Beaver Coll; *office:* Pembrook MS 1201 Walnut St North Wales PA 19454*

VANUCH, JOSEPH PAUL, Vocational Special Ed Coord; *b:* Lakewood, OH; *m:* Jilleen Allender; *c:* Pat, Dave, Chris, Kate, Kyle, Dan; *ed:* Wittenberg Univ (BA) Ed 1975; Cleveland St (MS) Admin 1983; *cr:* Springfield Local Schls Spec Ed Tchr 1975-78; Clark Cty Schls Work Stud Coord 1978-80; Lakewood Schls Voc Spec Ed Coord 1980-; *ai:* Head Track Coach; LTA 1980-; *office:* Lakewood City Schls 14100 Franklin Blvd Lakewood OH 44107

VAN VESSEM, LISA ANN, Music Teacher; *b:* Niagara Falls, NY; *ed:* SUNY at Buffalo (BFA) Music Ed 1985, (MA) Music, Children's Lit 1990; *cr:* Letchworth Cntrl Schl Music Tchr 1985-; *ai:* Drama Club, Marching Band Adv; GUSMA 1985-, Sec 1994-96; JNEA 1985-; Castile Gala Club 1990-; Castile Resuce Squad 1996; *office:* Letchworth Cntrl Schl 5550 School Rd Gainesville NY 14066*

VAN VOORHIS, MAREVE ELIZABETH (HUGHES), Instructor of Human Svcs Pgm; *b:* Poughkeepsie, NY; *m:* James; *c:* Meghan, Ryan, Jimmy, Matthew; *ed:* Dutchess Comm Coll (AAS) Child Care 1974; Empire St Coll (BA) Prof Stud 1996; *cr:* St Josephs Childrens Home Child Care Worker 1973-77; Cardinal Hayes Home Child Care Worker 1977-78; Dutchess Comm Coll Field Supvr & Instr 1979-; *ai:* Sr Girl Scout & Peer Ldr; Talking to Children About AIDS Trainer; NY St Human Edctrs Assn 1991-, Pres; Child Development Cncl 1994-, Exec Comm Mem, Vice Chair & Bd; PTA 1985-; Ulster Cty Girl Scous 1993-, Co-Ldr; *office:* Dutchess Comm Coll 53 Pendell Rd Poughkeepsie NY 12601

VAN WEY, NATE J., Physics Teacher; *b:* Newark, OH; *m:* Jae Ellen Benson; *c:* Jason, Erin, Emily; *ed:* Otterbein Coll (BA) Math 1972; Univ of Akron (MA) Scndry Physics Ed 1979; Attnd Kent St Univ Cmptr Sci, WV Univ Ed, Univ of IA Space Sci; *cr:* Perry HS Physics Tchr 1972-; *ai:* Grils Track Coach; NHS Adv; NEA, OEA 1972-, Local Pres & Treas; AAPT 1972-; NSTA 1983-; SECO 1992-; Natl Radio Astronomy Observatory Investigating the Universe Wkshps 1991-93; Stark Cty Tchr of Yr 1993; NSF Tchr in Antarctica 1994; Phi Delta Kappa Tchr of Yr 1995; *office:* Perry Sr HS 3737 Harsh Ave SW Massillon OH 44646*

VANWICKLE, DAVID THOMAS, Mathematics Instructor; *b:* Upper Darby, PA; *c:* Deryck, Brynn; *ed:* Mt St Mary's Coll, Dayton Univ (BS) Math, Philo 1967; Univ of DE (MED) Math 1973; Natl Sci Fnd Fellow; *cr:* Dayton Univ Tchng Asst 1968; St Elizabeth HS Tchr 1969; Mt Pleasant HS Tchr 1970-78; Newark HS Tchr 1978-; *ai:* DSEA, NEA, NCTM 1970-; *office:* Newark HS E Delaware Ave Newark DE 19711

VAN WINKLE, PRUDENCE BRIDGES, Prog Dir of Early Chldhd Ed; *b:* Boston, MA; *m:* Peter K.; *c:* Trintje, Elizabeth; *ed:* Mills Coll (BA) His 1964; Bank Street Coll of Ed (MSEd) Educl Ldrshp 1987; Amer Montessori Soc Preprimary Cert 1975; *cr:* Palm Beach Comm Coll Tchr, Dir 1982-87; Daylight Daycare Consulting Schl Curr Dir 1988-91; Fisher Coll Prgm Dir 1991-; *ai:* Chair, Prof Dev, Curr Comm; Interim chair; Phi Theta Kappa, Vol Club Adv; Boston Assn Ed Young children 1987-, Bd, Sec; Child Care Careers Inst 1991-, Highed Ed Consortium; Parents Anonymous 1994-, Advy Childcare; *office:* Fisher Coll 118 Beacon St Boston MA 02116

VANYA, MARY KATHLEEN, Seventh & Eighth Grade Teacher; *b:* Bethlehem, PA; *ed:* Moravian Coll (BA) Eng, Elem Ed 1976; Lehigh Univ (MED) Admin, Supervision 1981; *cr:* St Anne Schl Tchr 1978; Notre Dame of Bethlehem Tchr 1977, 1978-; *ai:* His Day, Yrbk, Newspaper, Stock Market Game Advs; Math Counts, Vlybl Coaches; Soc Stud Coord; Alpha Delta Kappa 1989-, Treas; NCEA; Girl Scouts 1972-, Ldr, Cnslr, Trainer, Area Dir, Great Valley Pin, Honors Pin; Cath Youth Org 1972-, Coach,

Vlybl Coord, Bishops Awd, St Elizabeth Medal; *home:* 1831 8th St Miller Hghts Bethlehem PA 18017

VANZANDT, JAMES G., 6th Grade Teacher; *b:* Erie, PA; *m:* Judith A. Weber; *c:* Joseph D., Jennifer L.; *ed:* Edinboro St Coll (BS) Elem Ed 1967, (MED) Elem Ed, Rd Specialist 1970; *cr:* First Dist Elem Schl 6th Grd Tchr 1967-; *ai:* Instrl Support Core Team 1993-95; NEA, PSEA 1967-; Crawford Cntrl Ed Assn 1967-, Bldg Rep; Cambridge Springs Band Parents 1991-, Pres 1992-; Crawford Cty Schl Employees 1983-85, Bd Sec 1984-85; Fed Credit Union Bd of Dirs; *office:* First Dist Elem Schl 725 N Main St Meadville PA 16335*

VARANESE, PHILIP MICHAEL, Guidance Counselor; *b:* Oneida, NY; *ed:* Utica Coll (BA) Psych 1962-; SUNY at Oswego (MA) Cnslng, (CAS) Cnslng 1972; SUNY at Brockport Admin 30 Cr; *cr:* Holley CS Cnslr 1971-74; Westmoreland HS Cnslr 1974-79; San Clemente HS Cnslr 1979-87; Rome Free Acad Cnslr 1987-; *ai:* NYSUT, NYS Cnslng Assn, Natl Assn of Cnslrs 1985-; Rotary 1972-; Elks 1970-; *office:* Rome Free Acad 500 Turin St Rome NY 13440

VARELA, ANA M., Spanish Teacher; *b:* Guayaquil, Ecuador S.A.; *m:* Antonio M.; *c:* Malena, Daniel, Kristen; *ed:* St Johns Univ (MA) Span 1978; Universidad de Guayaquil Licenciate Span & Lit 1968; *cr:* Liceo Moderno Span, Lit Tchr 1981-83; Kings Park HS Span Tchr 1988-89; Preston HS Span Tchr 1989-; *ai:* Span Club, ASPIRA Club Moderator; LILT 1992-; Contenta Awd; *office:* Preston HS 2780 Schurz Ave Bronx NY 10465

VARELA, KAREN ANN (GITELES), English Teacher; *b:* Bayonne, NJ; *m:* Oreste; *ed:* Montclair St Univ (BA) Eng 1989; *cr:* Delsea Regnl HS Eng Tchr 1989-90; Florence Twp HS Eng Tchr 1990-; *ai:* Schl Detention Monitor; Discipline, Prin Liaison Comms; Mentor New Eng Tchrs; Former Class Adv; Drama Coach; NEA, NJEA 1989-; FTEA 1990-; *office:* Florence Twp Mem HS 500 E Front St Florence NJ 08518

VARELLA, HAZEL M. LUKE, Social Studies Chair; *b:* Beverly, MA; *m:* M. David; *c:* John David, James Robert; *ed:* Bridgewater St Coll (BS) Ed, His 1954, (MED) Ed, His 1956; Boston Univ (MA) His 1962; *cr:* East Bridgewater Jr Sr HS His, Eng Tchr 1954-56; Easton Schl System Soc Stud 1956-, Chair 1963-; *ai:* Mock Trial Dir, Class of 1998 Co-Adv, Co-Dir Easton Evening Schl; Curr Co-ordinating Cncl Mem; NCSS 1972-, Delta Kappa Gamma 1970-, Local Chptr Pres 1980-82; Easton Historical Soc 1967-, Pres 1969-71, 1990-94; Easton Historical Commission, Chm 1974, 1984-85; Ames Free Lib 1989-, Dir, Clerk 1990-; North Easton Savings Bank 1982-, Corporator; Contributor to Experiments in His Tchng by Harrard-Danforth Ctr; Easton Historical Materials Writer; Natl Endowment for the Hum Independent Scholar 198 4; NEH Summer Inst; AP Corrector 1989; *office:* Oliver Ames HS 100 Lothrop St North Easton MA 02356

VARELLA, MANUEL DAVID, Biology Teacher; *b:* Easton, MA; *m:* Hazel M. Luke; *c:* John David, James Robert; *ed:* Boston Univ (BS) PE 1957, (MED) Ed, Sci 1958; *cr:* Easton Schl System Tchr, Jr HS Prin 1958, 1963-74, Admin Asst to Supt 1974-78, Tchr 1978-; *ai:* Co-Adv Class 1998; Co-Dir Evening Schl; NSTA 1960-, Life Mem; Phi Delta Kappa 1958-, Life Mem, Pres 1968-70; MA Jr HS, MS Prins Assn, Pres 1973-74; AASA 1960-, Life Mem; Easton Fin Comm 1980-92; Lions, Rotary Clubs, Past Mem; Univ CT Conf on Ed 1972; Annual Summer Conf Jr HS Prins Univ of CO; Outstdng Ldrshp Awd 1974; *office:* Oliver Ames High School 100 Lothrop St North Easton MA 02356

VARGAS, BOLGEN, School Counselor; *b:* Dominican Republic ; *ed:* Sung Coll at Blackport (MSEd) Cnslng Ed 1991; *cr:* SUNY at Brockport Cnslr 1988-91; Monroe Cty Schl Yth Advocate 1986-88; Greece Cntrl Schl Dist Schl Cnslr 1991-; *ai:* Care Team; Adv Class 1995; NEA 1991-; Schl Bd 1996-,; Articles.

VARGAS, MARTHA LUCIA, Spanish Teacher; *b:* Dominican Repblc ; *ed:* Brooklyn Coll (BA) Span 1991; *cr:* Midwood HS Span Tchr 5 Yrs; *ai:* Animals Rights Club Adv; *home:* 569 72nd St Brooklyn NY 11209*

VARGO, MARK EDWARD, Secondary Math Teacher; *b:* West Mifflin, PA; *ed:* CA Univ of PA (MS) Ed, Math, Comp Sci; *cr:* South Allegheny Schl Dist Scndry Math Tchr 1993-; *ai:* Bowling Team Coach; Schl Renewal Team; Stu Tutor Prgm Advy Bd; NEA 1993-; *office:* South Allegheny Jr Sr HS 2743 Washington Blvd Mc Keesport PA 15133

VARGO-SIDNEY, LINDA, English Teacher; *b:* Washington, DC; *m:* Arthur L.; *c:* Kelly Somers, Jaime, Tracy; *ed:* Bowie St Univ (BS) Eng 1989; Western MD Coll 9 Credits; Liberty Univ 21 Credits; *cr:* Walker Mill MS 7th-8th Grd Eng, Pre-Algebra Tchr 7 Yrs; *ai:* ACE Adv; NEA, NCTE 1989-; Acad Champions of Excl MD St Advy Bd, Lead Tchr, Univ of MD at College Park & Morgan St Univ Part-time Fac; *home:* PO Box 35 Wye Mills MD 21679

VARGULICH, LUKE HORVATH, High School Math Teacher; *b:* Hammond, IN; *ed:* OH St Univ (BE) Math Ed 1986; *cr:* Youngstown South HS Math Tchr 1986-93; Youngstown Wilson HS Math Tchr 1993-; *ai:* NEA, OEA, YEA 1986-; *office:* Wilson HS 2725 Gibson St Youngstown OH 44502

VARIANO, NANCY D'UVA, Health & PE Teacher; *b:* Ossining, NY; *m:* Joseph; *c:* Lisa, Joseph; *ed:* Springfield Coll (BS) PE 1974; Lehman Coll (MS) Hlth 1979; 65 Addl Credit Hrs; *cr:* Ossining Schl System Hlth, PE Tchr 1974-81, 1986-; Ursuline Schl Hlth, PE Tchr 1981-86, Ath Dir 1985-86; *ai:* Peer Mediation Prgm Coord; Mem Antiviolence Comm; HS Dare Instr; AFT, NYSUT 1974-; *office:* Ossining HS 29 S Highland Ave Ossining NY 10562

VARJIAN, LEON D., Mathematics Teacher; *b:* Hackensack, NJ; *ed:* Montclair St Univ (BA) Math 1972; IN Univ (MAT) Math 1975; Attnd Univ WI, Univ MN, Jersey City St Coll, Fordham Univ, Montclair St Univ; *cr:* Linden HS Math Tchr 1986-88; Ramapo Coll Math Instr 1988-90; Midland Park HS Math Tchr 1988-; *ai:* Math Team Adv; NHS Selection Comm; NCTM, MAA, NJEA, NEA 1986-; Governor's Tchr Recognition Prgm Tchr of Yr 1992; *office:* Midland Park HS 250 Prospect St Midland Park NJ 07432

VARLEY, JOY A., Choir & Theatre Director; *b:* Chicago, IL; *m:* Gregory E.; *ed:* Univ of Akron OH (BMusic) Piano Performance 1978, (BS) Music Ed 1978; Lehman Coll (MAT) Music Ed 1988; *cr:* Buckeye HS Choir Dir 1979-80; Overdale MS Choir Dir 1980-82; Eastchester HS Choir & Theatre Dir 1983-87; Byram Hills HS Choir & Theatre Dir 1987-; *ai:* Theatre Dir three or More Major Productions Annually; WCSMA 1990-; ACDA 1996; *office:* Byram Hills HS 12 Tripp Ln Armonk NY 10504

VARN, RONALD CHRISTOPHER, Instrumental Music Teacher; *b:* Canton, OH; *c:* R. Michael; *ed:* Bowling Green St Univ (BM) Music K-12th 1987; *cr:* North Canton MS Band Dir 1987-; *ai:* Marching, Jazz Band; OH Music Ed Assn, OEA, NEA 1987-; *office:* North Canton MS 200 Charlotte St NW North Canton OH 44720

VARRICCHIO, KAREN A., Foreign Language Teacher; *b:* New York, NY; *ed:* SUNY at Stonybrook (BA) Hum, Italian 1987, (MA) Labor Mngmt Stud 1993; Universita Curbino Italy Italian Lang & Lit 1985-86; Univ of San Diego 9 Credits Span Lang, Lit, Culture 1991; 30 Post Grad Credits Pedgogy, Psycology, Ed; Theatre & Frgn Lang; *cr:* Connetquot Cntrl Schl Dist Frgn Lang Tchr 1988-90; East Meadow Schl Dist Frgn Lang Tchr 1990-; East Meadow HS Resident Choreographer 1990-; *ai:* Dance Wkshp Club Adv; Spring Musical Choreographer; Frgn Lang ClubFrgn Lang Week Show Dir, Coord; Long Island Lang Tchr, NY St Frgn Lang Tchr Assn 1988-; AATI 1987-; NYS Flwshp Stud Siena Italy Summer 1993; *office:* East Meadow HS 101 Carmen Ave East Meadow NY 11554*

VARRICCHIONE, JOHN ROBERT, 7th Grd Geography Teacher; *b:* New Britain, CT; *m:* Agatha Angela Garzone; *c:* Jerry, Angie, Johnny, Melanie; *ed:* Cntrl CT St Univ (BS) Elem Ed 1967, (MS) Curr & Supervision 1973; 6th Yr Ed 1991; *cr:* SouthSide Schl 6th Grd Tchr 26th Yrs; Chippens Hill MS 7th-8th Grd Lang Arts & Rdng Tchr 1 Yr; *ai:* Drama Tchr; AFT 1967-; Bristol Fed of Tchrs 1967-; Plainville Midget Ftbl League 1982-84, Asst Comm & Announcer; Hole-In-The-Wall Theater 1983-, Actor, Dir & Bd; New Britain Rep Theater 1986-, Actor; Producing Guild 1992-, Actor; *home:* 21 Liberty St New Britain CT 06052

VARSOKE, DEIDRE KAREM, 7th Grade Lang Arts Teacher; *b:* Brookline, MA; *m:* Robert A.; *ed:* Nasson Coll (BA) Eng 1970; *cr:* Breed Jr HS 9th Grd Eng Tchr; Timberlane Jr HS Lang Arts Tchr; South Range Elem Schl 5th Grd Self Contained Class Tchr; Hudson Meml Schl Lang Arts Tchr; *ai:* Intnl Literacy Learning Wkshp; Studying World Cultures; AFT.

VARVAGLIONE, KATHLEEN GRACE, Business Education Teacher; *b:* Berwick, PA; *ed:* Bloomsburg Univ (BS) Bus Ed 1993; *cr:* Parkville HS Bus Ed Tchr 1993-; *ai:* Class Spon 3 Yrs; Grad Comm Mem; MD Bus Ed Assn 1996; *office:* Parkville HS 2600 Putty Hill Ave Baltimore MD 21234

VAS, JOSE MARIA, Social Studies Teacher; *b:* Hong Kong ; *m:* Patricia Noreen Haley; *c:* Allison Victoria; *ed:* Western CT St Univ (BBA) Bus Admin 1986, (MA) His 1994; CT Cert; *cr:* Immanuel Luth Schl 6th Grd Tchr 1989-94; Kolbe Cathedral HS Soc Stud Tchr 1995-; *ai:* Soph Class Moderator; NCHE 1992-; NCSS 1995-; DBEA 1995-; *office:* Kolbe Cathedral HS 33 Calhoun Pl Bridgeport CT 06604

VASATURO, ANNETTE M., 8th Grade Teacher & Asst Prin; *b:* Derby, CT; *m:* Michael Stephen; *c:* Michelle, Stefanie, Jaclyn; *ed:* Albertus Magnus Coll (BA) Acctng 1984; Southern CT St Univ Math Scndry Schls Tchr Cert; Sacred Heart Univ Puruing MA Cath Schls Ldrshp; *cr:* St Vincent De Paul Schl 8th Grd Homeroom, 5-8 Grd Math Tchr, Rainbows Coord, Asst Prin 1990-; *ai:* Stu Cncl Adv; Rainbow Coord; Spec Events Coord; NCTM, ATOMIC 1991-; East Haven Yth 1991-, Advy Bd; New Haven Cncl of Cath Women 1989-; *office:* St Vincent De Paul Schl 35 Bishop St East Haven CT 06512

VASCO, BETTY JOAN, 8th Grade Communications Tchr; *b:* Lancaster, PA; *m:* James Edwin; *c:* Sharon Faye Noonan, Lisa Kay Minnich, Stanley Lewis, James Edwin II; *ed:* Millersville Univ (BS) Eng 1959; Attnd Temple Univ; *cr:* Swift MS Solanco Dist 8th Comm Tchr 1969-; *ai:* Spelling Bee; Awds Assembly, AV Comm; SEA, PSEA, NEA 1969-; *office:* Swift MS Solanco Dist 1866 Robert Fulton Hwy Quarryville PA 17566

VAS DIAS, RICHARD ANDRE, English & Journalism Teacher; *b:* New York City, NY; *m:* Bernadette Susan Branas; *c:* Peter Andre, Rosalynde Ann; *ed:* St Francis Coll (BA) Eng 1968; Temple Univ (MS) Ed 1980; Lehigh Univ 18 Creidt Hrs Eng, Post Grad; *cr:* Central Cambria HS Eng Tchr 1967; Southern Lehigh HS Eng, Journalism, Creative Writing, Hum Tchr 1970-; *ai:* Awd Winning Schl Newspaper Adv; The Spotlight Mem; Supt Comm Comm; PSEA, NEA 1970-, St Prof Rights, Responsibilites Commissioner, Region PR, R Chprsn; PA Schl Press Assn 1992-, Bd of Dir; Kempton Comm Fire Co 1970-; Tchng Assistantship Dept of Eng Lehigh Univ 1968-70; *home:* RR 1 Box 18 Kempton PA 19529*

VASEY, WENDY SNYDER, Eighth Grade Teacher; *b:* Sunbury, PA; *m:* Darryl T.; *ed:* Temple Univ (BS) Early Chldhd & Elem Ed 1989; 6 Credits at Beaver Coll & 6 Credits at Saint Josephs Univ Toward Masters in Math Ed; *cr:* Philadelphia Schl Dist 8th Grd Tchr 1990-; *ai:* Sci Resource Ldr; Sci Fair Chprsn; Tutor; *office:* Robert S Vaux MS 2300 W Master St Philadelphia PA 19121*

VASILE, MARY ANN ROCHELLE, First Grade Teacher; *b:* Wilkes-Barre, PA; *ed:* Coll Misericordia (BS) Elem 1968; Bloomsburg Univ (MS) Ed, Early Chldhd 1972; Post Grad Stud Penn St Univ; *cr:* Mackin Elem Schl Tchr 1968-71; HUD Supvr Housing 1972; Hoyt Elem Schl Tchr 1971-76; Sold Art Paintings 1979-81; Kistler Elem Schl Tchr 1976-94; Maffett Elem Schl Tchr 1995-; *ai:* Math Comm Mid Atlantic Sts; PSEA, NEA 1968-; WBEA 1970-; Tchrs Women's Club 1969-; Girl Scout Ldr 1970-76; Church 1976-, Religious Org; Wrote Math Book Schl Dist Curr; Chm Heart Fund Comm; *office:* Maffett Elem Schl Maffett St Wilkes Barre PA 18702

VASILIADES, MARTHA WERT, 8th Grade Science Teacher; *b:* Harrisburg, PA; *m:* Chris; *ed:* Shippensburg St Coll (BSEd) Chem 1965; Syracuse Univ (MS) Gen Sci 1971; Univ of MD Insti for Chemical Ed 1988; *cr:* Cntrl Bucks Schl Dist 8-9 Grd Sci Tchr 1965-70; Pine Grove Jr HS 8 Grd Sci Tchr 1971-; *ai:* NY St United Tchrs, AFT 1971-; Natl Sci Fnd Grant 1970-71; NY St Item Writer for NY St Regents Competency Test 1986-87; Several Articles Pub; Presenter at Natl Sci Tchr Convention 1992; *office:* Pine Grove Jr HS 6320 Fremont Rd East Syracuse NY 13057

VASS, ERNEST ALLEN, Biology Teacher; *b:* Martins Ferry, OH; *m:* Linda L.; *c:* Michael, Jennifer, Scott, Jeffrey; *ed:* OH Univ (BS) Biological Sci 1963; Univ of OK Ecology 8 Hrs; Coll of Mt St Joseph Educl Methods; Notre Dame Coll of OH Sci Ed; *cr:* Warren Consolidated HS Bio Tchr 1963-64; St Clairsville HS Bio Tchr 1964-69; Linsly Military Inst Bio Tchr, Asst Commandant 1969-78; St Clairsville HS Bio Tchr 1978-; *ai:* NEA, OEA 1963-; SEA 1963-, Past Pres; St Clairsville City Planning Commission 1992-, Pres; St Clairsville Charter Review Commission 1994-, Chair; 2 NSF Grants; Outstanding Scndry Educators of Amer Twice; Jennings Scholar; Natl Sci Fnd Excellent Sci Tchr Awd; *office:* Saint Clairsville HS 102 Woodrow Ave Saint Clairsville OH 43950*

VASSAK, REGINA BURKE, Foreign Language Teacher; *b:* Port Chester, NY; *m:* John P.; *c:* Greg, Jim, Paul; *ed:* Mount St Vincent Coll (BA) Fr 1966; Assumption Coll (MA) Fr 1968; Attnd Western CT St Univ, SUNY Purchase, Manhattanville Coll, Coll of New Rochelle, SUNY of Buffalo; *cr:* Worcester MA Pub Schls Fr Tchr 1966-67; Cushing Acad Fr Tchr 1967-68; North Salem MS Frgn Langs Tchr 1968-; North Salem HS Frgn Lang Tchr 1968-; *ai:* Intnl Club Adv; AATF 1975-; NYSUT 1968-; CAAS 1990-; North Salem Tchrs Assn 1968-; St Josephs Church; 4-H Clubs of Amer; North Salem Booster Clubs; *office:* North Salem MS, HS 230 June Rd North Salem NY 10560

VASSALLO, MARIO, Professor; *b:* St Julians, Malta; *m:* Mary Ann; *c:* Rebecca E., Danielle M.; *ed:* Univ of Malta (BA) Math, Ec 1981; SUNY at Buffalo (MS) Cmptr Sci 1986; Malta Coll of Ed Math Ed Cert 1974; Univ of Malta Cmptr Stud Diploma 1984; 9 Hrs Mngmt Sci; 24 Hrs Cmptr Sci; *cr:* Malta Ed Dept HS Math Tchr 1974-81, Jr Coll Accounts Tchr 1981-84; SUNY at Buffalo Tchng Asst, Instr 1984-86; SUNY at Fredonia Math, Cmptr Sci Prof 1986-; *ai:* Fac Cncl; Cmptr Sci Curr Comm; ACM SIGSCE 1985-; Sigma Xi 1986-; Notices of Amer Mathematical Soc Cmptr Software Reviewer; Pub Papers; *office:* S U N Y Coll At Fredonia Dept of Math & Cmptr Sci 227 Fenton Hall Fredonia NY 14063*

VASSALOTTI, WAYNE, Technology Education Dept Chm; *b:* Chester, PA; *m:* Pamela Kay Hickey; *c:* Michael Joseph, David Francis (dec); *ed:* West VA Univ (BS) Indstrl Arts Ed 1967; *cr:* Claymont HS Auto Tech Instr 1967-68; John Dickinson HS Auto Tech Instr 1968-; *ai:* Asst Ftbl Coach Claymont 1967-68, Dickinson 1968-79, St Elizabeth HS 1980-86; Head Wrestling Coach St Elizabeth HS 1982-86; NEA 1967-; DTEA 1980-93, Exec Bd 1990-93; DE Automotive Tech Tchr of Yr 1988; *offi*[...] Dickinson HS 1801 Milltown Rd Wilmington DE 19808

VASSEL, MARY J. (LYNCH), 4th Grade Teacher; *b:* Marlboro, [...] George A.; *ed:* Mt St Mary Coll at Hooksett (BA) Elem Ed 1972; P[...] Stud Framingham St Coll, Fitchburg St Coll; *cr:* Hildreth Elem [...] Grd Tchr 1972-; *ai:* MTA, NEA 1972-; Marlboro Edctrs Assn 19[...] Rep 1974-; Excl in Ed Awd Nom; *office:* Hildreth Schl 85 S[...] Marlborough MA 01752

VASSER, BEATRICE WRIGHT, Health, PE Dept Head & Ath[...] Long Branch, NJ; *m:* Theodore R. Jr.; *c:* Theodore III, Rosa[...] Vasser-Benjamin; *ed:* NC Cntrl (BS) Hlth, PE 1954; Univ of Pi[...] (MA) Cnslr Ed 1975, (PHD) Cnslr Ed 1984; PE Stud Abroad[...] Europe, Canada; All China Sports Fed Beijing, Technische Un[...] Munchen at Munich, Sveriges Riksidrottsforbund Boson at L[...] Brussels Certs of Achvmt; *cr:* Northampton HS Tchr, Coach [...] Pittsburgh Pub Schl Tchr 1961-64; The Ellis Schl Head PE, Ath Di[...] Ruth Kane & Assoc Therapist 1986-; *ai:* Coach; Club Adv; Supvr; [...] Sports Camp Dir; Stu Intern Mentor; Heads Assn; Long Range Pl[...] Chm Stu Act Comms; AAHPERD 1954-; ISGAL 1974-, Pre[...] NAIS-People of Color 1980-, Rep; ACA 1984-, Cert; Amer Re[...] 1974-, Vol; Bd of Women Space East 1989-, Comm Person; Alpha[...] Alpha 1983-, Chprsn Founders Day 1995; NAACP 1954-; African [...] Assn Inc 1967-, Pres; Pub Two Articles; Intnl Certs; Nation Certfd[...]

VASVARY, CATHERINE SCHVETZ, Science Teacher; *b:* Br[...] NY; *m:* Louis M.; *c:* Amy Louise; *ed:* Rutgers Univ (BS) Pre-Me[...] Chem 1967; Cmptr Sci 16 Credit Hrs 1977-79, Grad Schl of Ed 24[...] Hrs; Kean Coll Scndry Tchr Cert 1970; *cr:* New Brunswick Jr H[...] Tchr 1967-69; Hillsborough Twp Pub Schls 6th Grd Math & S[...] 1970-72; Franklin Twp Pub Schls 7th Grd Sci Tchr 1986-90, HS S[...] 1990-95; *ai:* Environmental Club, Raritan River Watch Adv; Natl [...] Fed Project Earth Tomorrow An Urban Challenge Adv; NEA, FTEA[...] 1986-95; NJ Governor's Tchr Recognition Awd 1988; *home:* 1595 [...] Rd Somerset NJ 08873

VASWANI, SHEILA ANN, Global Studies I Teacher; *b:* New Yo[...] *c:* Neela; *ed:* Hofstra Univ (BA) Euroasian His, Asian Stud 1971; S[...] Univ (MA) Chinese Stud 1977; 80 Post Grad, 30 Addl Underg[...] Credit Hrs; *cr:* Babylon HS Tchr 1984-; *ai:* NHS, Compass Comm[...] Ec Club; Human Relations Comm; Advy Prgm; BTA, LICSS, NCSS[...] Metropolitan Museum 1986-; Natural His; Asia Soc; Most Admire[...] Sr Survey 1989; Nom Channel 12 Tchr of Month 1993, NY St Tch[...] 1994; Who's Who Amer Women 1995-96; Who's Who Women of the[...] 1996-; Who Amer Ed 1996-; *office:* Babylon Jr Sr HS 50 RR Ave B[...] NY 11702

VATALARO, SUSAN, Principal; *b:* Somerville, MA; *ed:* Salem S[...] Elem, Early Chldhd 1971, (MED) Elem Ed 1978, (MED) Schl Admir[...] *cr:* Leonard Schl Grd 2 Tchr 1972-81; Maplewood Schl Grd [...] 1982-93, Asst Prin 1988-93; Emerson Schl Prin 1993-; *ai:* Malde[...] Schls Prof Dev Comm; NAESP, MA Elem Schl Prin Assn 1993-, [...] Malden Teachers' Federal Credit Union 1993-, Sec; *home:* 45 Loo[...] Malden MA 02148

VATAVUK, JOHN PAUL, Fifth Grade Teacher; *b:* Johnstown, [...] Janet L. Berkey; *c:* Michael J., Shelly L.; *ed:* Univ of Pittsburgh (BS[...] Ed 1971; St of PA (MA) Elem Ed; 24 Addl Grad Credits Univ of Pitts[...] *cr:* North Star Schl Dist Elem Tchr 1971-; *ai:* Stu Cncl, IM Spor[...] Advs; NEA, PSEA 1971-; North Star Ed Assn 1971-, Treas 4 Yrs; W[...] Area Schl Bd 1989-, Bd Pres 1993-, St Thomas Luth Church 1956-, [...] 1988-, Sunday Schl Supt, Church Cncl, SS Tchr; Somerset Co Dem[...] 1994-, Exec Bd; *home:* 1016 Berkey Rd Windber PA 15963

VATAVUK, MICHAEL JOHN, General Music Teacher; *b:* Windbe[...] *m:* Kimberly Ann Jones; *c:* Lisa Marie; *ed:* Indiana Univ of PA (BS) [...] Ed 1992; *cr:* Windber Area Schl Dist 6-12 Choral, 6-7 Gen Music[...] 1993-; *ai:* Chorus; Marching Band Asst Dir; Percussion Instr; Stage [...] PA Music Educators Assn, Windber Area EA, NEA 1993-; Amer [...] Musicians 1988-; St Thomas Luth Church Cncl 1993-, Sec; John[...] Symphony Orch 1988-, Percussionist; Keystone Wind Ensemble [...] Percussionist; *office:* Windber Area HS 2301 Graham Ave Windb[...] 15963

VATHIS, JAMES B., History Teacher; *b:* Philadelphia, PA; *m:* Eri[...] Varhalmi; *c:* Erika, Christina; *ed:* Shippensburg St Univ (BS) His [...] 1972, (MS) His & Ed 1974; Attnd Salisbury St Univ 9 Grad Credits, [...] of OR 6 Grad Credits, Western IL Univ 6 Grad Credits; *cr:* Stephen D[...] HS Educator 1973-; *ai:* Pol Action Club Spon; Scholastic Awds [...] Mem; Schl Improvement Comm; HNS Comm; NEA, MSTA & [...] 1973-; NCSS 1980-; Natl Endowment for Hum Semina[...] KANT-Rousseau at Univ of MN at Morris 1985, Middle East at Pri[...] 1983, 1986 & 1990, Roman Family at Marshall Univ 1989 & Vier[...] Univ of OR 1991; *office:* Stephen Decatur HS 9913 Sea Hawk Rd [...] MD 21811*

VAUGHAN, HALLIE ANNE (FREEBOURN), 4th Grade Teache[...] Erie, PA; *w:* Robert Bruce (dec); *c:* Tristram E., Trevor B.; *ed:* Sli[...] Rock Univ (BS) Elem, Spec Ed 1969; Post Grad Penn St Berks Car[...] Slippery Rock U; *cr:* Connoquenessing Vly Elem Schl 6th Grd [...] 1969-70; Neptune City Elem Schl Spec Ed Tchr 1970-71; C. E. Cole [...] Ed, Elem Tchr 1973-; *ai:* NEA, PSEA, MEA 1973-; DAR 1979-, Chap[...] AAUW 1990-; Amer Cancer Soc 1995-, Bd; PA Commission for W[...] Tchrs Competition Winner 1990, 1992; Nom PA Tchr of Yr.

VAUGHAN, JULIA ANN, Elem Reading & Math Teacher[...] Ravenswood, WV; *m:* Andrew B.; *c:* Aaron, Corey; *ed:* OH Univ (BS) [...] Ed-Cum Laude 1977; Post Grad Courses Continuing Ed; Rio Grande[...] Cert Learning Disabilities; Math, Sci Minor; *cr:* Pomeroy Elem [...] Learning Disabilities Tchr 1981-83; Salem Center Elem Schl Fourth[...] Tchr 1983-89; Pomeroy Elem Schl Second Grd Tchr 1989-90, F[...] Grade Grd Tchr 1990-94; Salem Center Elem Schl Title Rdng, Math [...] 1994-; *ai:* PTO, PTO Rutland Elem Schl; OEA, NEA, MLTA 1981-; A[...] Phi 1975-; *office:* Salem Ctr Elem Schl 28764 State Route 124 Langs[...] OH 45741

VAUGHAN, NANCY H., English Teacher; *b:* Orange, NJ; *m:* James [...] *c:* David; *ed:* Univ of MD (BA) Eng 1980; 60 Hrs Maryland Inst; *cr:* M[...] de Sales Acad Eng Tchr 1980-; *ai:* Fac Adv Lit Mag; Mid Sts Accredita[...] Comm; *office:* Mount De Sales Acad 700 Academy Rd Baltimore [...] 21228

VAUGHAN, SHEILA GAITHER, Curriculum & Instruction Coor[...] Washington, DC; *m:* Robert Allen; *c:* Amy Christine Lavsa; *ed:* Frost[...] St Univ (BA) Eng 1968; Post Grad Stud Univ of MD Scndry Rdng, Cat[...] Univ of Amer Film Stud; *cr:* Prince George's Cty 6-12 Grds Tchr 1968[...] Surrattsville HS Eng Tchr 1985-93, Eng Tchr Coord 1993-95, Cu[...] Instruction Coord 1995-; *ai:* Schl Based Implementation Team, Pre[...] Steering Comms; ADD,ADHD Steering Comm; AFT, PGCFT 1975-[...] Dir PGCFT 1989-91; NCTE, ASCD 1990-; MCTELA 1994-; Pil[...] Pacesetter Eng 1994-95; Trained as Pacesetter Instr of New Pacese[...] Eng Tchrs 1996; Outstanding Tchr Awd Parent Advy Comm 1992; *of*[...] Surrattsville HS 6101 Garden Dr Clinton MD 20735*

VAUGHAN, VIRGINIA MASON, Professor of English; *b:* Washing[...] DC; *m:* Alden T.; *ed:* Univ of MI (BA) Eng 1968, (MA) Eng 1970, (P[...] Eng 1972; *cr:* Allegheny Coll Asst Prof 1973-76; Clark Univ 1976-,

0; *ai:* Eng Dept Chair 1984-89; Higgins Schl of Hum Dir 1991-94; ir 1994-; MLA 1972-, Pres & ADE; Shakespeare Assn of Amer Worcester Chorus 1984-; O B Hardison Flwshp to Folger eare Lib 1987; Andrew Mellon Flwshp to Huntington Lib 1989; or & Author Books: Shakespeares Caliban, Othello: a Contextual

N, CAROLYN SCHRADER, Art Teacher; *b:* Indiana, PA; *m:* W.; *c:* Christopher Garland, Benjamin; *ed:* IN Univ of PA (BS) Art 3, (MED) Art Ed 1973; Continuing Ed Univ of Pittsburgh at wn, PA St Univ, Pittsburgh Art Inst, Mount Aloysius Coll; *cr:* River Schls 6th Grd Tchr 1958-60; Dept of Defense Ed Group Tchr ; Mt Brook Schls Art Tchr 1966-68; Central Cambria Schls Art 968-; *ai:* Art Club Adv; Central Cambria Ed Assn 1968-, Pres , Bldg Rep; PSEA, NEA 1968-; Alpha Delta Kappa 1974-, Pres; Artists of Johnstown 1970-, Chm Summer Show Comm; Southern nies Museum of Art 1985-; Ebensburg Presbyn Church 1974-, dult Tchr; Nom PA Tchr of Yr 1992; Drawing Selected Permanent PSERS Bldg; Curr Writing Comm Mem Southern Alleghenies n of Art; *office:* Central Cambria MS 205 W Highland Ave urg PA 15931

IN, COURTNEY COLLEEN, Physical Education Teacher; *b:* re, MD; *ed:* Salisbury St Coll (BS) K-12 PE 1985; Loyola Coll Equivalency 1990; *cr:* Sacred Heart Schl K-8 Grd PE Tchr ; Liberty HS 9-12 Grd PE Tchr 1986-; *ai:* Var Field Hockey, se Coach; St LaCrosse Comm Rep; NEA, USFHA 1985-; CCEA USWLA 1988-; BFHA 1985-; *office:* Liberty HS 5855 Bartholow esville MD 21784

IN, DARLENE FRANCES, Fifth Grade Teacher; *b:* Philadelphia, Michael A. Sr.; *c:* Beatrice A., Michael A. Jr., Michelle L.; *ed:* Coll of Philadelphia (Assoc) Gen Stud 1975; Temple Univ (BS) 1980; Masters Equivalency Beaver Coll Ed 1991; *cr:* Schl Dist of lphia Sub Tchr 1979-80; St Elizabeth Schl Tchr 1980-85; Schl Dist adelphia Tchr 1985-; *ai:* Power of Positive Stdnts Coord; Ldrshp Tchrs Awds Comm; Philadelphia Fed of Tchrs 1985-; AFT 1985-; omm 1991-, Alt Rep; Standard Task Force 2000; ET Steel Schl nce Abuse Grant; Substance Abuse Cert of Appreciation; lphia Renaissance in Sci & Math; St Elizabeth Asst Bsktbl Cert of iation.*

IN, NANCY WOLCOTT, Reading Recovery Teacher; *b:* Johnson Y; *m:* James K.; *c:* Christopher J., Stacey, Feighan; *ed:* Centenary r Women (AS) Lbrl Arts 1962; SUNY at Cortland (BS) Ed, Early 1974; Elmira Coll (MAEd) Rdng Specialist 1978; Rdng Recovery Cert 1994 NY Univ; *cr:* Johnson City Schl First Grd Tchr 1974-93, ecovery Tchr 1993-; *ai:* NEA 1974-; Delta Kappa Gamma 1978-; 1985-; IRA 1986-; *office:* Johnson City HS 666 Reynolds Rd n City NY 13790

ER, DREW JOHN, Social Studies Teacher; *b:* McKeesport, PA; *m:* Ann Hritz; *c:* Brian, Beth Ann; *ed:* CA St Coll (BSEd) ehensive Soc Stud 1973; Univ Pittsburgh (MED) Soc Stud 1990; *cr:* el Supvr 1974-84; Steel Valley Schl Dist Tchr 1986-; *ai:* Boys HS Coach; NEA, PSEA, SVEA, NSCAA, WPSCA; WPIAL Soccer of Yr 1994, 1995; *office:* Steel Valley MS 3113 Main St Munhall PA

A, PHILLIP D., Science Dept Chair & Bio Tchr; *b:* Wilmington, Kathleen Healy; *c:* Kathleen Edwards, Phillip J.; *ed:* St Josephs S) Bio 1970; Univ of DE (MED) Bio Sci 1975; Attnd Temple Univ ical Sci; *cr:* Salesianum Schl Bio Tchr, Sci Chair 1971-; *ai:* Sci Advanced Placement Bio Consultant, Bio Exam Reader; NABT St Dir, Outstdng Bio Tchr; NSTA 1971-; DABT; Tandy Awd 1996; at Fellow 1994; Access Excl Fellow 1994; Woodrow Wilson Fellow Advanced Placement Awd 1992; Presidential Commission 1986; itment to Ed Awd 1992; Westinghouse Awd 1987; *office:* Salesianum 801 N Broom St Wilmington DE 19802*

A, SUSAN, English & Remedial Wrtng Tchr; *b:* Gloversville, NY; lton-Montgomery Comm Coll (AA) Liberal Arts 1973; SUNY at urgh (BA) Scndry Ed 1975; Elmira Coll (MED) 1978; *cr:* heim-Ephratah Cntrl Schl Tchr 19 Yrs; *ai:* Boy Scout Merit Badge Oppenheim-Ephratah Tchrs Assn; NY St United Tchrs; Rainbow ce; 1982 Adv Sr Class; *office:* Oppenheim-Ephratah Cntrl Schl RD ohnsville NY 13452

UEZ, ELIZABETH RIVERA, Guidance Counselor; *b:* Bethlehem, Hector Luis; *c:* Kristin Lee, Hector Luis Jr.; *ed:* Moravian Coll (BA) 1978; Lehigh Univ (MED) Scndry Cnslng 1979; Wikes Univ 15 Hrs; *cr:* Liberty-Freedom HS Tchr 1978; Northeast MS Guid Cnslr 80; Broughal MS Guid Cnslr 1980-85; Liberty HS Guid Cnslr 1985-; tino Yth Ldrshp Club Adv; Schlsp Comm; Bethlehem Area Voc & Schl Perkins Participatory Planning Comm; PABE 1978-; NEA 1979-; 1979-; Cncl of Span Speaking Org 1980-, Mem-at-Large; *office:* y HS 1115 Linden St Bethlehem PA 18018

UEZ, MARTIN JOHN, Computer Science Teacher; *b:* Brooklyn, : Nancy Harger; *c:* Matthew, Daniel; *ed:* Vassar Coll (BA) Bio, Psych 12 Credit Hrs Ed SUNY at New Paltz 1985; 12 Credit Hrs Bio rd Ext Schl 1988-89; 8 Credit Hrs Cmptr Sci Univ of MA at Boston *cr:* US Peace Corps Vol Sci Tchr 1983-85; Poughkeepsie HS Sci Tchr 86; Mission Church HS Sci Tchr 1986-88; Arlington Cath HS Cmptr Tchr 1988-; *ai:* Cmptr Club Adv; Numerous Articles Pub; *office:* gton Catholic HS 16 Medford St Arlington MA 02174

QUEZ, PEDRO,JR., Mathematics Teacher; *b:* Meriden, CT; *m:* Amy etcher; *c:* Raquel C., Marisol A., Laura M.; *ed:* Southern CT St Univ Math Ed 1983; 45 Credits Schl Counseling Fairfield Univ; Univ of Mechanical Engrng 1977-81; *cr:* Harding HS Math Tchr 1983-90; cultural Magnet 6th-8th Grd Math Tchr 1990-; *ai:* 6th-8th Grd Math Comm; Math Meet Adv; Algebra Curr Revision; Boys Soccer, Boys l, Girls Sftbl Coach; NCTM 1990-; ATOMIC 1987-; Bridgeport n Church 1983-, Treas, Elder; PIMMS, CBIA, AT&T Governors ws; *office:* Multicultural Magnet Schl 700 Palisade Ave Bridgeport 5610

ZANA, STEPHEN S., Seventh Grade Teacher; *b:* Baltimore, MD; *ed:* on St Univ (BA) His, Ed 1969; Addl 21 Grad Hrs; *cr:* St Louis Schl Prin 1976-86, Tchr 1970-; *ai:* Schl Textbook, Accreditation & Testing ns; Natl Cncl of Tchr-Archdiocese of Baltimore; *office:* Saint Louis Rt 108 Box 155 Clarksville MD 21029

SEL, WILLIAM EDWARD, Electrical Tech & HVAC Teacher; *b:* berland, MD; *m:* Lorraine Carlton Jenkins; *c:* William, Frank; *ed:* of MD BS Scndry Ed Pending; Associated Builders & Contractors rical Apprenticeship; Construction Ed Fnd Craft Instr Trng; *cr:* rical Contractors Apprentice, Foreman 1970-78; Manufacturing, stry Electrical Journeyman, Foreman 1979-83; Southeastern Tech HS 1983-; *ai:* Advy Bd Dundalk Comm Coll Electrical Prgm; Steering m Baltimore Cty Pub Schls Apprenticeship; Fac Cncl Chm; NEA, A 1983-; TABCO 1983-, Alternate; BSA Troop 811 1989-, Comm; BAltimore Cncl 1995-Cnslng, Merit Badge; *office:* Southeastern nical HS 325 Sollers Point Rd Baltimore MD 21222

CHIOLLI, JOYCE A., Second Grade Teacher; *b:* Philadelphia, PA; W Chester Univ (BS) Elem Ed 1960; Goddard Coll (MA) Elem Ed 1975; 15 Addl Hrs Grad Level; *cr:* Sugartown Elem Schl Classroom Tchr Grds 2, 3, 4, 6 1960-; *ai:* Ele Math Curr Comm; NEA, PSEA 1960-, Sec, Grievance Chair, Negotiations Comm; *office:* Sugartown Elem Schl 611 Sugartown Rd Malvern PA 19355

VEDDER, DEBRA SCOTT, Spanish Teacher; *b:* Columbus, OH; *m:* Charles Lord; *c:* Rodger Scott; *ed:* Otterbein Coll (BA) Span Ed 1973; 12 Hrs Towards Masters Ashland Univ; *cr:* Westerville City Schls Span Tchr 1973-; *ai:* NHS Fac Comm; Church of the Master 1993-, Ed Commission, Circle 4; *office:* Westerville South HS 303 S Otterbein Ave Westerville OH 43081

VEECK, ROBERT EDWARD, Math Teacher; *b:* Rockville Ctr, NY; *m:* Catherine Frances; *c:* Carrie Degaro, Allison, Tracey; *ed:* SUNY Albany (BA) Math 1970; SUC New Paltz, SUNY Stonybrook, Columbia Univ 55 Post Grad Hrs; *cr:* Croton-Harmon Schls Math Tchr 1970-73; Levittown Schls Math Tchr 1973-74; Commack Schls Math Tchr 1974-83; Westhampton Beach Schls Math Tchr 1983-; *ai:* Ftbl 1971-75, 1977-79, 1984-95, Bsbl 1972-74, 1985-87, Sftbl 1988- Coach; AFT, NYSUT 1970-; WHB Tchrs Assn 1983-; Suffolk Cty Ftbl Coaches Assn 1974-; Suffolk Cty Stbl Coaches Assn 1988-, VP; Championship Sftbl Teams Coach 4 Times in 8 Yrs; *home:* 28 Wedgewood Ln Brookhaven NY 11719

VEET, MARY (WALTON), English Teacher; *b:* Hazleton, PA; *m:* Daniel M.; *c:* Jennifer, Jody; *ed:* Bloomsburg St Coll (BS) Eng 1970, (MED) Eng 1974; 62 Addl Credits; *cr:* Hazleton HS Eng Tchr 1970-92; Hazleton Area HS Eng Tchr 1992-; *ai:* Cheerleading Coach 1972-73; Mid States Evaluation Planning Comms; HAEA, NEA 1970-; Hazleton General Hospital Auxiliary 1976-; *office:* Hazleton Sr HS 1601 W 23rd St Hazleton PA 18201

VEGA, ADRIANA INES, Spanish Teacher; *b:* Jackson Heights, NY; *ed:* Queens Coll (BA) Span 1989, (MSE) Cnslng Ed 1995; *cr:* B. N. Cardozo HS Span Tchr 1989-, Grd Adv 1992-; *ai:* Latino Amer Club Adv; Cardozo HS Alumni Assn Pres; Nassau Cnslrs Assn 1995-; *office:* Benjamin N Cardozo HS 57-00 223rd St Bayside NY 11361

VEGA, GLADYS TORRA, Math Teacher & Dept Head; *b:* Havana, Cuba; *m:* Jose; *c:* Carlos, Luis, Jose; *ed:* Univ of PR (BA) Eng, Math 1973; Cleveland St Univ (MA) Modern Lang 1995; *cr:* Colegio Espirita Santo Math Tchr, Dept Head 1973-83; Hebrew Acad of Cleveand Math Tchr 1985-87; Incarnate Word Acad Math, Span Tchr, Math Dept Head 1987-; *ai:* Math Club Adv; Math Teams Coach; Self-Stud Steering Comm; OCTM, GCCTM 1987-; Tchr of Yr 1977; *office:* Incarnate Word Acad 6618 Pearl Rd Cleveland OH 44130

VEGLIA, DANIEL R., Math Chairperson & Teacher; *b:* Newark, NJ; *m:* Judith A. Plaviak; *c:* Marietta, Michele, Monica, Meredith; *ed:* Montclair St Coll (BA) Math Ed 1969, (MA) Math Ed 1972; Attnd Woodrow Wilson Inst at Purchase SUNY, NSF Prgm Hofstra Univ, UCISM at Columbia Univ; *cr:* Westwood HS Math Tchr 1970-72; Mahopac Jr, HS Math Tchr, Chprsn 1972-; *ai:* Var Vlybl, Bowling, Golf Coach; Regents Task Force; NYSUT, Mahopac Tchrs Assn 1972-; AMTNYS 1975-, Cty Chair; Section I Golf Coaches 1978-, Pres, Coach of Yr 1985; Section I Vlybl Coaches 1984-; Holy Name Soc 1990-; Bowling Coach of Yr 1992-93; *office:* Mahopac HS 421 Baldwin Place Rd Mahopac NY 10541

VEGLIA, MARILYN ROSE, 7th-8th Grd Soc Stud Teacher; *b:* New York City, NY; *m:* Vincent; *c:* Adrienne L., Jeffrey R., Lauren B.; *ed:* Queens Coll (BA) His 1971; Hofstra Univ (MS) Scndry Ed 1981; 30 Addl Grad Credits; *cr:* Burrs Lane J H Soc Stud Tchr 1973-82; West Hollow J H Soc Stud Tchr 1982-92; West Hollow MS Soc Stud Tchr 1992-; *ai:* Stu Govt, 8th Grd Class Advs; Half Hollow Hills Tchrs Assn, NYST 1973-; NCSS 1971-; Girl Scout Troop 2269 1992-, Asst Ldr; Dist Conf Chprsn Supts Conf Day 1992; PTA Jenkins Meml Lifetime Awd 1993; *office:* West Hollow MS 250 Old East Neck Rd Melville NY 11746*

VEIDT, CHRIS E., Health & Physical Ed Teacher; *b:* Lancaster, OH; *m:* Kelli Howard; *ed:* Wilmington Coll (BS) Hlth, PE 1987; Working on MA Univ of Dayton; *cr:* Wilmington Coll Asst Bsbl Coach 1987-91; Whiteoak HS Var Bsbl Coach, HPE Edctr 1991-; *ai:* OEA, NEA 1991-; OH St Bsbl Coaches Assn, Southeastern Dist Coaches Assn 1992-; Southeastern Dist Division IV Coach of Yr 1995; *office:* Whiteoak Jr Sr HS PO Box 297 Taylorsville Rd Mowrystown OH 45155

VEIT, WALTER CHARLES, Professor of Sociology; *b:* Palisades Park, NJ; *m:* Irene M.; *c:* Eric,, Lesley Welch, Brian; *ed:* Montclair St Coll (BA) Sociology 1957; Rutgers Univ (EDM) Admin Supv 1964; Temple Univ (EDD) Higher Ed 1975; Post Doctoral in Soc Sci 24 Hrs; *cr:* Central Reg HS Tchr 1957-581 Saddle Brook HS Tchr, Dept Head 1958-64; Morse HS Tchr, Dept Head 1964-68; Miami Dade CC Prof of SSC 1964-68; Burlington Cty Coll Prof of SOC 1968-; *ai:* NEA; PDK; Rotary 1981-; Fulbright Grant to England 1962-63; Natl Sci Fnd Study Grants 1964-65; Wrote Chapter in Text, Several Articles in Field of Critical Thinking; Presented Papers at Prof Assns in NJ, CA, FL; *office:* Burlington County Coll County Rt 530 Pemberton NJ 08068

VEITH, CALVIN J., Science Teacher; *b:* Guatemala City, Guatemala; *ed:* Grace Coll (BA) Bio & Scndry Sci Ed 1985; Rutgers Univ (MS) Environmental Sci 1993; *cr:* Lower Bucks Chrstn Acad Sci Tchr 1985-91; the Kings Chrstn Schl Sci Tchr 1991-; *ai:* Photography Club Adv; Shawnee Bapt Church 1992-; *office:* The Kings Christian HS Winston Way Cherry Hill NJ 08034

VEJDOVEC, JENNIFER A., Social Studies Teacher; *b:* Lakewood, OH; *ed:* OH St Univ (BS) Ed 1987; John Carroll Univ (MA) Rdng Ed 1992; Walsh Coll, Kent St Univ, Akron Univ Post Grad Stud 12 Hrs; *cr:* Mayfield HS Tchr 1987-; *ai:* Acad Decathlon; AP Amer Govt; NEA, OEA, NCSS 1987-; *office:* Mayfield HS 6116 Wilson Mills Rd Cleveland OH 44143

VELANNO, ELAYNE BUCCINO, Honors English Teacher; *b:* Manchester, CT; *ed:* Eastern CT St Univ (BA) 1983; Tchng Cert Eng 1985; Post Grad MS Total Credits 32+; Andover Newton Theological Schl Grad Level; Univ of CT Theatre Stud; *cr:* Hillhouse HS Hnrs Eng 12 Tchr 11 Yrs; *ai:* Commnctns Club & Drama Club Adv; SPMT; Fac Senate; Mental Hlth Team; AFT 1985-; *office:* Hillhouse HS 480 Sherman Pky New Haven CT 06511

VELARDI, DOREEN M., HS Science Teacher; *b:* Far Rockaway, NY; *m:* Joseph Charles; *ed:* Seton Hall Univ (BSEd) Ed 1989; Pursuing MA Admin, SUpervision; Prins Cert; *cr:* Garfield HS Sci Tchr 1989-; *ai:* AFT 1989-; *office:* Garfield HS 500 Palisade Ave Garfield NJ 07026

VELASCO, AMPARO, Mathematics Teacher; *b:* Canary Islands, Spain; *m:* Asterio; *c:* Monica, Victoria, David; *ed:* Jersey City St Coll (BA) Math 1970, (MA) 1974; *cr:* Montclair HS Math Tchr 1970-; *ai:* Girls Bsktbl Coach; Chrldr, Yrbk Staff Adv; NJEA, NEA, MEA, NCTM 1970-; Church, Yth Ministry, Choir; *office:* Montclair HS 100 Chestnut St Montclair NJ 07042

VELASQUEZ, GERALDINE KHANER, Professor of Art; *b:* NYC, NY; *m:* Joseph M.; *c:* Brenda, Mark; *ed:* Hunter Coll (BFA) Studio Arts 1964; Montclair St Univ (MAFA) Studio Arts 1976; Rutgers Univ (EDD) Creative Arts 1987; *cr:* LBI Fnd for Arts & Sci Curator of Exhibitions 1985-90; Georgian Court Coll Asst, Full Prof, Dir BFA Prgm 1980-; *ai:* Mentor BFA Prgm; Dir Cmptr Graphics Lab, Forum for Rsrch & Criticism in Crafts; JSPRAA 1982-; Art Dirs Club of NJ 1985-; NJ Designers Craftsmen, Juror of Exhibitions; AAUW; NJSCA, Evaluator; Guest Speaker Bd of NJ St Cncl on Arts; Article Pub; *office:* Georgian Court Coll Lakewood Ave Lakewood NJ 08701

VELEY, NINA GOULD, Mathematics Teacher; *b:* Langley Field, VA; *m:* H. Arden; *c:* Kara, Kristin, Erika; *ed:* Cornell Univ (BA) Math 1968; Harvard Univ (MAT) Math, Ed 1969; 30 Hrs Past Masters; *cr:* Lexington Pub Schls Math Tchr 1969-79; Olson Manufacturing Co Cmptr Programmer 1980-81; Acton-Boxborough Regnl HS Math Tchr 1982-; *ai:* Coach Academic Decathlon Team, 3rd in MA in Rookie Yr 1990, 2nd in St 1991, 1st Place for 1992, 1st in St 1993, 7th in Nation 1993, 4th in Nation 1994, 5th in Nation 1995; NEA 1971-; Distinguished Tchr Leadership Awd; *office:* Acton Boxborough Regional H S 96 Hayward Rd Acton MA 01720

VELEZ, AZALIA, Spanish Teacher; *b:* Rio Piedras, Puerto Rico; *m:* Arturo Guzman; *c:* Patricia Guzman, Arturo Guzman; *ed:* Lehman Coll (BA) Span & Ed 1985; Tchrs Coll at Columbia Univ (MS) Span Lit 1988; *cr:* St Cloud HS Span Tchr 1 Yr; Grace Dodge VHS Span Tchr 11 Yrs; *ai:* Aspira Club Adv; UFT 1974-; AFT 1976-; *home:* 42 Pine St Yonkers NY 10701

VELLA, DIANE-ELAINE, 6th Grade Teacher; *b:* Johnstown, PA; *m:* Nino F.; *c:* Michael Antonio, Anthony John; *ed:* Penn St Univ (BS) Ed of Exceptional Children 1978; St Francis Coll at Loretto (BS) Elem Ed 1991, (MS) Ed 1991; Ind Rsrch; ADD, ADAD; Tourettes Syndrome; *cr:* Ebensburg St Schl & Hosp Tchr 1978-80; Hollidaysburg Area Schl Dist Learning Support Tchr 1980-92, 6th Grd Tchr 1993-; *ai:* Strategic Planning; Fac Advy; Act Comms; NEA 1978-; HAEA 1992-; PSEA 1978-; *office:* Foot Of Ten Elem Schl 450 Foot Of Ten Rd Duncansville PA 16635*

VELLANTE, ANTHONY C., English Teacher; *b:* Waltham, MA; *m:* Kathleen Ann Madigan; *c:* Mark A.; *ed:* St Coll at Boston (BSED) Eng, Ed 1961, (MED) Eng,Ed 1967; 30 Addl Credits Boston Coll, Boston Univ, Anna Maria Coll, Univ MA at Boston; *cr:* Randolph Jr Sr HS 9th-12th Grd Floor Master 1976-95, Eng Dept 1961-; *ai:* Randy Acad Achvmt Prgm Chm; NEA, MTA, RTA 1961-; Norfolk Cty TA, Longevity Awd; *office:* Randolph HS 70 Memorial Pky Randolph MA 02368*

VELLONE-PAINTEN, MARYANN, Spanish Teacher; *b:* Bronx, NY; *c:* Christopher, Robert; *ed:* Iona Coll Scndry Ed, Span (BA) 1980, (MS) 1987; *cr:* Brewster HS Span, Italian Tchr 1981; Pleasantville Span Tchr 1981-82; Rye Span Tchr 1982-84; Mahopac Span, Italian Tchr 1984-87; Yorktown Span, Italian Tchr 1989-92; Lakeland Span, Italian Tchr 1992-; *ai:* AFT 1980-; *office:* Lakeland HS E Main St Shrub Oak NY 10588

VENA, DIANE (LAMAR), Social Studies & Reading Tchr; *b:* Johnstown, PA; *m:* Robert F.; *c:* Barbi, Benjamin, Bradley; *ed:* Univ of Pittsburg at Johnstown (BA) Elem Ed 1989; 24 Credits Towards Instrl II Cert & Masters Equivalency 1995; *cr:* Forest Hills MS Tchr 1990-; *ai:* Jr HS Forensics Team, Rdng Competition Coach; Drama Club Co-Dir; Jr Achvmt; NEA, PA St Ed Assn 1989-; PA Cncl for Soc Stud Project of Yr Awd 1995; Interdisciplinary Project; *office:* Forest Hills MS 1427 Frankstown Rd Sidman PA 15955

VENABLE, SUSAN GORDON, Early Childhood Professor; *b:* Fort Bragg, NC; *m:* Gene Dubois; *c:* Christopher, Andrew, Sarah, Dory; *ed:* Colby-Sawyer Coll (AA) Lbrl Arts 1963; Natl-Louis Univ (BED) Elem Ed 1965; Seton Hall Univ (MED) Rdng 1971; Early Chldhd Course Work; *cr:* Penacook Pub Schl One Grd Tchr 1965-66; Summit Pub Schl One Grd Tchr 1966-72; Hilltop Cntry Day Schl Pre-K, Kndgtn Tchr 1976-83; Andover Pre Schl Tchr, Dir 1983-89; Sparta Pub Schls Kndgtn Tchr 1989-90; Sussex Cty Comm Coll Instr, Early Chldhd Prgm Coord 1991-; *ai:* Phi Theta Kappa Adv; Curr Comm; Prof Dev Comm; NJAEYC 1979-, VP; Soc of Childrens Book Writers 1993-; NW Jersey Rdng Cncl 1992-; CESNJ 1991-; SCAKE 1989-; Sparta United Meth Church 1990-, Admin Cncl, Ed Chair; SCNJAEYC Newsletter Ed; *office:* Sussex County Comm Coll College Hill Newton NJ 07860*

VENDER, CYNTHIA MACIBORSKI, Fifth Grade Teacher; *b:* Scranton, OH; *ed:* Coll Misericordia (BS) Elem Ed 1975; 24 Credit Hrs beyond Degree; Cert of Proficiency in Cath Tchng 1988; *cr:* St Mary's Schl 5th-7th Grd Tchr 20 Yrs; *ai:* Learning Fair 1978-80, Chprsn; Eng Pgm Stud 1989-91, Chprsn; Self Stud Pgm 1989-91, Co-Chprsn; Schl Newspaper 1991-92, Chprsn; Young Writers 1991-; NCEA 1985-; St John Newman Awd; *office:* St Mary's Schl 216 Grace St Old Forge PA 18518

VENDETTI, DINA CAROL, Choir Director; *b:* Baltimore, MD; *ed:* Concordia Coll (BS) Music, Elem Ed 1985; Towson St Univ (MED) Elem Ed 1994; *cr:* St John Luth Church Tchr, Music Minister 1985-89; Baltimore Luth Tchr 1989-, Asst Prin 1993-; *ai:* Singing Group; Concert Choir; ASCD 1994-; *office:* Baltimore Luth Mid & Upper Sch 1145 Concordia Dr Baltimore MD 21286*

VENDITTI, THOMAS S., Theology Teacher; *b:* Willingboro, NJ; *m:* Margaret; *c:* Catherine; *ed:* Franciscan Univ (BA) Theology 1985; Regent Univ (MS) Theology 1988; *cr:* Father Judge HS Theology Tchr 1992-93; Roman Cath HS Theology Tchr 1993-95; *ai:* Yth Grp Dir; Svc Project Coord; Pro Life Moderator; *home:* 2116 Scovel Ave Pennsauken NJ 08110

VENEZIANO, JOAN PESCE, Mathematics Teacher; *b:* Waterbury, CT; *c:* Joan Frances; *ed:* Manhattanville Coll (BA) Math 1969; Univ of CT (MA) Math 1971; Attnd Univ of Ct, Quinnipiac Coll, Fairfield Univ; *cr:* Wolcott HS Math Tchr 1970-; *ai:* St of CT Certfd Cooperating, Mentor Tchr; Fac Adv, Total Quality Mngmt Comm; Chrldng Coach 1971-73; NCTM 1992-; NEA, CEA, Wolcott Ed Assn 1970-; *office:* Wolcott HS 457 Bound Line Rd Wolcott CT 06716

VENEZLANI, TRICIA O'NEILL, Drama & English Teacher; *b:* Prince Frederick, MD; *m:* Damian; *c:* Lauren, Scott; *ed:* Towson St Univ (BA) Eng, Drama 1975; PA St Univ (MA) Eng 1976; Attnd Bowie St Univ, Trinity Coll; *cr:* Prince George's Comm Coll Part-time Eng Instr 1978-82; Northern HS Eng, Drama Tchr 1976-; *ai:* Thespian Spon; Drama Coach; NEA 1976-; Lambda Iota Tau 1975-; Delta Kappa Gamma 1987-; Intnl Thespian Soc 1992-; Young Careerist 1983; MD Outstdng Schl of Drama Dir 1996; *office:* Northern HS 2950 Chaneyville Rd Owings MD 20736*

VENICE, JANET I., Art Teacher; *b:* New Bedford, MA; *m:* Thomas J.; *c:* Brant, Janna; *ed:* UMass at Dartmouth (BS) Textile Design, Fashion 1965; Bridgewater St Coll 27 Credit Hrs; *cr:* Freetown Lakeville Regnl Schl Art Tchr 1965-69; Meml Jr HS Art Tchr 1974-; *ai:* Schl Climate, Southeast MA Schl Alliance Steering Comm; Yrbk Co-Chair; Middleboro Ed Assn 1974-, 2nd VP; NEA 1974-; Crescent Art Assn 1983-; Former Arts Lottery; Middleboro Tennis Assn.

VENNA, NAGAGOPAL, Assoc Prof of Neurology; *b:* Masulipatam, India; *m:* Usharani Karri; *c:* Suraj, Praveen; *ed:* Gunter Med Coll (MD) Medicine 1968; Diplomat of Amer Bd of Neurology, Psychiatry 1981; MBBS Gunter Med Coll 1968; MRCP Internal Medicine 1975; *cr:* Osmania Gen Hosp Intern 1969-70; Govt Gen Hosp Physician 1970-70; Kakatiya Med Coll Tutor 1970-71; Cty Hosp House Physician 1971-72; Regnl Hosp Resident Internal Med 1972-73, Registrar Internal Medicine 1973-75; St Lawrence's Hosp Registrar Internal Medicine 1975, Registrar Neurology 1975-79; Boston Univ Schl of Medicine Clinical Fellow 1975-79; Boston City Hosp Attending Neurologist 1979-; Boston City Hosp Assoc Clinical Dir 1979-82; Mattapan Chronic Disease Hosp Neurology Consultant 1980-81; New England Deconess Hosp Courtesy Neurology Staff 1981-; Boston Univ Schl of Medicine Neurology Instr 1981-82; Boston City Hosp Neurologist 1981-91; Boston Univ Schl of Medicine Assoc Dir 1982-87; Boston City Hosp Assoc Dir Neurological Unit 1982-87, Clinical Neurology Dir 1987; Boston Univ Schl of; *ai:* Metcalf Comm Selecting Excl Tchng Awds Boston Univ; Amer Acad of

Neurology 1982-; MA Medical Soc 1981-; Amer Coll of Physicians 1986-; MA Medical Soc Amer Acad of Neurology 1983-; Boston Soc of Psychiatry, Neurology 1985-; Amer Coll of Physicians 1986-; Royal Soc of Medicine 1991-; Metcalf Awd Excl in Tchng at Boston Univ 1988; Chapters on Neurological Diseases; Articles on Clinical Neurology; *office:* Boston Univ Schl of Medicine Neuro Unit Boston City Hosp 818 Harrison Ave Boston MA 02118

VENNEMEIER, CHRISTINA MARIA, Sixth Grade Teacher; *b:* Piqua, OH; *m:* Mark Joseph; *c:* Kyle; *ed:* Univ of Cincinnati (BS) Elem Ed 1987, (MS) Educl Admin 1991; Numerous Courses Admin, Inclusion at Mayerson Acad; *cr:* Dater Jr HS Tchr 1987-92; Covedale Elem Schl Tchr 1992-; *ai:* Tchr-in-Charge of Schl; Inclusion Team; Stu Cncl Adv; Discipline Comm; Career-Day Coord; Tchr Interview Team; Cincinnati Cncl for Tchrs; ASCD 1993-; Tchr of Yr 1992; Grant Awded for Implemented Self-Esteem Prgm; *office:* Covedale Elem Schl 5130 Sidney Rd Cincinnati OH 45238

VENNER, CAROL ANN HOOPER, 6th Grade Teacher; *b:* Syracuse, NY; *m:* Robert J.; *c:* Sara; *ed:* St Rose (BS) Elem Ed 1964; Syracuse Univ (MS) Sp Ed, LD, MR 1973; Numeros Svc Credit Hrs Childrens Lit to Cmptrs; *cr:* Parochial Schls 1st-2nd Grd Tchr 1963-68; West Genesee Schl Dist 1st-5th Grd Tchr 1968-71; Tolly Schl Dist Spec Ed Tchr 1971-76; JD Schl Dist Spec Ed Tchr 1971-76; Syracuse Schl Dist LD Prgm 5th-6th Grd Tchr 1976-; *ai:* Handicap Comm Chprsn; 6th Grd Fund Raiser Chprsn 5 Yrs; Syracuse Tchrs Assn 1976-; Performing Arts Pgm; New Justice Prgm; Peer Ldrshp Prgm; Church Act 20 Yrs; Spec Ed Grants; *office:* Van Duyn Elem Schl 401 Loomis Ave Syracuse NY 13207

VENSEL, JANET L., Reading Specialist; *b:* N Washington, PA; *m:* Clarence R.; *c:* Clarence, Kathryn, Lisa; *ed:* Slippery Rock Univ (BS) Elem Ed, Scndry Eng 1973, (MS) Elem Ed 1978; 16 Post Grad Hrs Ed; *cr:* Karns City Area Schl Dist Tchr 1973-; *ai:* NHS Adv; Testing Comm; Strategic Planning-Assessment Chprsn; IST Team Mem; NEA 1973-; KSRA 1995-; Title I Grant 1996; *office:* Bruin Elem Schl School St Bruin PA 16022

VENT, MARYANNE CIARDULLO, Professor of English; *b:* Bronx, NY; *m:* Alfred; *c:* Amy, David; *ed:* Coll of New Rochelle (BA) Eng 1966; Fordham Univ (MA) Eng 1968, (PHD) Eng 1971; Attnd Columbia Tchrs Coll, CUNY Grad Ctr; *cr:* Fordham Grad Fellow 1969-71; Manhattan Coll Adj 1971-73; Queensborough Adj 1971-75; Westchester Instr & Full Prof 1973-; *ai:* Adj Instruction Coord; AFT; Fordham Tchng Flwshp 1969-71; SUNY Chancellors Awd for Excl in Tchng 1983; CUNY Mellon Flwshp 1983; Sears-Roebuck Flwshp in Coll Tchng & Acad Ldrshp 1989-90; *office:* Westchester Comm Coll 75 Grasslands Rd Valhalla NY 10595

VENT, THOMAS E., AD, Football Coach & PE Tchr; *b:* Cumberland, MD; *m:* Jo Ann Holt; *c:* Jamie Jo; *ed:* Frostburg Univ (BS) Hlth & PE 1972, (MED) Hlth & PE 1975; 60 Plus Grad Hrs WVU; *cr:* Allegany CC Tchr & Coach 1975-79; Parks & Recreation Dir 1980-82; Waynesburg PA Tchr & Coach 1983-85; Northern Garrett AD Tchr & Coach 1986-; *ai:* AD; Dist Rep AD; Ftbl Coach; Amer Legion; VFW; *office:* Northern Garrett HS 86 Pride Pkwy Accident MD 21520

VENTOLA, RONALD, Language Arts Teacher; *b:* New York City, NY; *m:* Laura Caruso; *c:* Vincent, Vanessa; *ed:* Queens Coll (BA) Ed 1974, (MS) Ed 1978; *cr:* JHS 189 Lang Arts Tchr 1979-; PS 2 Sci Tchr 1978-79; *ai:* MS Initiative Comm; Loyal Opposition Spokesperson; Room 200 Revolutionary Cell; Kappa Delta Pi 1978-; AFT, UFT 1979-; UU Church of Flushing 1967-, Bd of Trustees, Fac Chair, RE Comm, Sunday Schl Tchr; *office:* Daniel Carter Beard JHS 14480 Barclay Ave Flushing NY 11355

VENTURA, JULIANNE PYATTE, English Teacher; *b:* Battle Creek, MI; *m:* Lory Thomas; *c:* Jennifer Mary, Lisabeth Jane; *ed:* Eastern MI Univ (BA) Ed, His 1967; St Univ of NY (MS) Eng 1973; *cr:* Jamestown HS Eng Tchr 1967-70; Maple Grove HS Eng Tchr 1984-; *ai:* NHS Adv; Youth Newspaper Fac Rep; NEA, NYEA 1967-, Sec, BPFA; Sts Peter, Paul Church Choir 1994-; *office:* Maple Grove HS RD 1 Dutch Hollow Rd Bemus Point NY 14712

VENTURA, LOUIS, Biology Teacher; *b:* Brooklyn, NY; *m:* Nancy Counts; *c:* Marie, Diana, John; *ed:* Brooklyn Coll (BS) Bio 1970; Univ of RI (MS) Bio 1973; 30 Credit Hrs; *cr:* Bishop Hendrickson HS Sci Chprsn 1977-; Comm Coll of RI Sci Tchr 1985-; *ai:* Bowling Coach; NSTA; NBTA; OBTA; 443rd Civil Affairs Bn US Army Reserve 1979-, Major, Army Commendation Medal 2 Times; Outstdng Bio Tchr Awd 1981; Presidential Awd Excl in Sci Tchng 1986; *office:* Community College of RI 400 East Ave Warwick RI 02886

VENTURINI, MARIAN T., Physics Teacher; *b:* San Bernardino, CA; *m:* Glenn E.; *c:* Liona, Eric, Gregory, Nicholas; *ed:* Univ of OK (BS) Math 1980; Widener Univ (MED) Ed 1988; Indiana Univ of PA Physics Cert 1991; *cr:* George Lynn Cross Acad Math Tchr 1980-81; Mercer-Meidinger Inc Actuarial Analyst 1981-86; Interboro HS Physics, Math, Environmental Sci Tchr 1986-; *ai:* Tchr Mentor; NEA, IEA 1986-; *office:* Interboro HS 16th & Amosland Rds Prospect Park PA 19076

VERBA, RITA K. (ZANAGLIO), Learning Support Teacher; *b:* Erie, PA; *c:* Julia M., Kristen D., Danielle E., Alysha L.; *ed:* Clarion Univ (BS) Spec Ed 1978; Indiana Univ of PA (BS) Elem Ed 1982; *cr:* Southern York Cty Schl Elem Spec Ed Tchr 1978-79; United Schl Dist HS Learning Support Tchr 1987-; *ai:* SADD Adv; Stu Assistance Team; Tech Comm; PA St Ed Assn, NEA 1987-; United Ed Assn 1987-, Del; Girls Scouts of Amer 1981-, Comm Mem; *office:* United HS PO Box 168 Armagh PA 15920

VERBEKE, KAREN A., Assoc Prof of Spec Education; *b:* Clearfield, PA; *ed:* PA St Univ (BA) Elem, Kndgtn Ed 1970; Univ of MD (MED) Spec Ed 1971, (PHD) Spec Ed, Math Ed 1982; Post Grad Stud at St Univ of NY at Albany, Univ of CO, Cath Univ ofAmer; *cr:* Dade Cty Pub Schls Spec Ed Tchr 1971-72; Howard Cty Pub Schls Elem, Spec Ed, Math Tchr 1972-82; Univ of MD Fac Rsrch Assoc 1982-85; Beaver Coll Asst Prof of Ed 1985-90; Univ of MD Assoc Prof, Coord of Spec Ed 1990-; *ai:* Fac Adv Kappa Delta Pi; Co-Adv Stu CEC; MD St Advy Comm for Spec Ed; MD Advy Bd for GATE; MD Impartial Hearing Ofcr for Spec Ed; Eastern Shore Phi Delta Kappa 1990-, VP Mbrshp; MD Coalition for GATE 1991-, Conf Chair; CEC 1971-, St TED Coord; NCTM 1986-; Natl Assoc for Gifted Children 1982-; Lower Shore Learning Disabilities Assn 1991-, Sam Kirk Awd; Phi Delta Kappa Awd Outstdng Edctr of Yr; Lindback Awd for Tchr of Yr; Pres Awd for Tchr-Scholar of Yr; 6 Grants; Who's Who in the World, Amer Ed, East; Outstdng Rsrch Grant; *office:* Univ Of MD Eastern Shore Dept of Ed Princess Anne MD 21853*

VERBENA, ALBERT, Director of Bands; *b:* Natrona Hghts, PA; *m:* Stella Meidus; *c:* Dayna, Michael; *ed:* Mansfield St Un (BS) Music 1968; Penn St Un Cert Music 1973; *cr:* Kiski Area HS Band-Choral Music 1968-69; Freeport HS Band 1969-; *ai:* Marching, Symphonic, Pep, Jr High Bands; Musical Pit Orch; Wind Ensemble; NEA, PSEA, PMEA 1968-; AF of M 1962-; Church Choir 1990-, Elks 1968-; My Bands Have Performed at Washington, Toronto, Williamsburg, FL; *office:* Freeport Area HS Drawer H Freeport PA 16229*

VERCILLO, PETER PAUL, 5th Grade Teacher; *b:* Brooklyn, NY; *c:* Jonathan, Michael; *ed:* New Paltz (BA) Ed & His 1969, (MS) Ed 1972; 50 Credit Hrs; *cr:* Brentwood Pub Schl 4th-6th Grd Tchr 1969-; *ai:* Film Stud Enrichment Group Adv; AFT 1969-; NYSUT 1969-; Brentwood Tchr Assn 1969-, Chief Del; St Lukes Rel Tchr 1980-86; Northwest Schl & Twin Pine Schl PTA Tchr Rep 1969-; Produced, Dir & Wrote Numerous Schl Plays.

VERCOLEN, BETH LANNI, High School Art Teacher; *b:* Rochester, NY; *c:* Ben Fiorucci, Adam Fiorucci, Laura; *ed:* RIT (BFA) Fine Art 1973, (MST) Art Ed 1975; Addl Hrs Painting, Lbrl Stud; *cr:* East Rochester HS Art Tchr 1975-; *ai:* Art, Lit Magazine, Art club, Field Trips Adv; Delta Kappa Gamma 1990-; NY St Art Tchrs Assn; NEA; Print Club of Rochester, Pyramid Art Ctr 1992-; Meml Art Gallery 1980-; *office:* East Rochester HS 200 Woodbine Ave East Rochester NY 14445

VERDE, JAMES J., Professor of Biology; *b:* Providence, RI; *ed:* Boston Univ Schl of Ed (BS) Sci 1961, (MA) Bio 1963; 30 Addl Hrs; *ai:* NEA 1969-; Ecology Action for RI 1969-71, Pres; Dame Forum 1969-73, Pres; *office:* Community Coll Of RI 1762 Louisquisette Pike Lincoln RI 02865

VERDILE, VINCENT NARPONE, Mathematics Teacher; *b:* Philadelphia, PA; *ed:* Glassboro St Coll (BA) Bus Admin 1987; Alternate Route Prgm Tchr Cert 1989-90; Post Baccalaureate Prgm Math Rowan Coll of NY 1991-93; 6 Credits Grad Prgm Math Ed Trenton St Coll 1994-95; *cr:* Veterans MS Math Tchr 1989-95; Yorkship Family Schl Math Tchr 1995-; *ai:* Vlybl Coach; Grad Comm; NEA, NJEA, CEA 1989-; Amer Math Soc 1995-; Alpha Phi Delta 1986-, S Jersey Dist Governor; *office:* Yorkship Family Schl Collings Ave Camden NJ 08107*

VERENNA, CHARLES ANTHONY,JR., Chemistry Teacher; *b:* Allentown, PA; *m:* Karen E. Stalsitz; *ed:* Allentown Coll of St Francis Working on MED; *cr:* Pen Argyl Sr HS Chem Tchr 1990-92; Parkland HS Chem Tchr 1992-; *ai:* Supvr for PHS Electric Vehicle Team 1994-95; Mentor Tchr 1993-94; NEA 1990-; Parkland Ed Assn 1992-; Air Products & Chemicals Inc CRSD 1995; *office:* Parkland HS Box 2675 PA Rt 309 Orefield PA 18069*

VERGADOS, JAMES, Biology Teacher; *b:* Sparta, Greece; *m:* Anna M. Reppucci; *c:* Johanna; *ed:* Univ of MA at Lowell (BS) Bio 1976; 18 Post Grad Credit Hrs; *cr:* Greater Lowell Regnl Voc Tech Schl Tchr 1976-; *ai:* NEA 1976-; AHEPA 1972-, Pres; Stu Ath Awd 1975 UMass at Lowell; *home:* 50 Westview Rd Lowell MA 01851*

VERGERS, CHARLES A., Prof of Elect Engrng Tech; *b:* Hagerstown, MD; *ed:* Capital Inst of Tech (AAS) Electronics 1967, (BSET) Electronic Engrng Tech 1968; Johns Hopkins Univ (MS) Microwaves 1989; *cr:* Capitol Coll Prof 28 Yrs; *ai:* EET Advy Bd; IEEE 1967-; AMS 1976-; ASEE 1968-; Otterbien United Meth Church 1959-; Handbooks: Electrical Noise 1979, 1987; Network Synthesis 1982; Awds: Fellow Inst 1984, Heritage 1985; *office:* Capitol Coll 11301 Springfield Rd Laurel MD 20708

VERHOFF, PATRICIA, Mathematics Teacher; *b:* Lima, OH; *ed:* OH St Univ (BS) Math 1975; Attnd Bowling Green St Univ, Univ of Dayton; *cr:* Riverdale HS Math Tchr 1975-; *ai:* Math Contests; Math Cty Curr Head Tchr; Class Adv; OH Cncl of Tchrs of Math 1975-; OH St Univ C2PC Participant; *office:* Riverdale HS 20613 SR 37 RR 1 Mt Blanchard OH 45867

VERHOVEC, JODEE STRAUS, 7th & 8th Grade Science Tchr; *b:* Wheeling, WV; *m:* Julius Jr.; *c:* Karey, Amie; *ed:* OH Univ (BS) Jrnlsm 1975; Univ of Dayton (MS) Ed 1987; Attnd Muskingum Coll 1971-72, Univ Steubenville 53 Hrs Ed; Rdng Cert K-12 1988-89; *cr:* Buckeye Local Schls Classroom Tchr 1977-78 & 1983-; *ai:* 6th Grd Outdoor Ed Pgm Instr 1983-; Initiated Paper Recycling Pgm 1996; OH Sci Tchrs Assn 1995-; Smithsonians 4-H Club 1988-, Adv; Martha Holden Jennings Grant 1991; Jefferson Cty Schl Dist Grant; *home:* PO Box 321 Smithfield OH 43948

VERKEY, RODNEY E., Physical Education Teacher; *b:* Sodus, NY; *m:* Charlene; *c:* Jason, Matt, Andy; *ed:* Cortland (BA) PE 1973; Oswego Admin; *ai:* Ath Dir; Section II Bsktbl Comm; Wayne Cty Ath Assn Pres; NEA; NYS Coaches; Teashers Assn; Coach of Yr 3 Times; *office:* Lyons Jr Sr HS 10 Clyde Rd Lyons NY 14489

VERMILYA, RAY N., Retired Vocal Music Director; *b:* Columbus, OH; *m:* Linda Way; *c:* Dale N., Michelle R.; *ed:* OH St Univ (BA) Music Ed 1959, (MA) Music Ed 1964; *cr:* Three Rivers Schl Dist Vocal Music, Instrumental Tchr 1960-61; Upper Arlington Schls Vocal Music Tchr 1961-67; Shelby Schls Vocal Music Tchr 1967-93; *ai:* Adjudicator for Vocal, Choral Contests in OH; Direct Comm Chorus in Seasonal Concerts; OH Music Educators Assn 1960-, Competitions Comm 1989-90, Vocal Affairs Chm 1991-; Articles Pub: Triad, NFIMA Journal; *home:* 26 E Jefferson Ave Shelby OH 44875

VERMUTH, JEFFREY WAYNE, Fifth Grade Teacher; *b:* Philadelphia, PA; *ed:* Millersville Univ (BS) Elem Ed 1971; Marywood Coll (MED) Integrative Ed 1983; Regnl Environmental Ed Prgm; *cr:* Woodland Elem Schl Fifth Grd Tchr 1974-95; Cabrini Coll Adj Ed Prof 1993-; Audubon Elem Schl Fifth Grd Tchr 1995-; *ai:* Methacton Schl Dist 5th Grd Group Ldr, Steering Comm, Curr & Instruction Advy Cncl, Tech Comm, Internet Advy Bd; Tech Support Specialist; New Tchr Mentor; NEA 1974-, Instruction, Prof Dev Chair, Fac Rep; Audubon Home & Schl Assn 1995-; Playcrafters of Skippac 1977-, Pres, Dir, Producer; Montgomery Theater Project 1993-; All Saints Episcopal Church 1986-, Vestry, Rectors Warden; *office:* Audobon Elem Schl 2765 Egypt Rd Audubon PA 19403*

VERNARR, SUSAN BRAY, First Grade Teacher; *b:* Phillipsburg, NJ; *m:* John David; *ed:* Northampton Comm Coll (AS) Early Chldhd Ed 1978; Lockhaven Univ (BS) Early Chldhd Ed 1980; Millersville Univ (MED) Elem Ed 1982; *cr:* Northampton Comm Coll Child Dev Head Tchr 1982-85; Northampton Comm Coll Adj Prof 1983; Wilson Area Schl Dist Elem Ed Tchr 1985-; *ai:* NEA 1985-; *office:* Wilson Area Schl Dist 21 & Washington Blvd Easton PA 18042*

VERNEAU, SUZANNE, English Teacher; *b:* Chester, NY; *ed:* Hartwick Coll (BA) Eng 1991; Long Island Univ (MS) Rdng 1996; *cr:* Yorktown HS Eng Tchr 1991-; *ai:* Sr Class Adv; NCTE 1994-; *office:* Yorktown HS 2727 Crompond Rd Yorktown Heights NY 10598

VERNER, DIANA DENKMAN, Math Tchr of the Gifted; *b:* Memphis, TN; *m:* Harris; *c:* Susan Verner Harrington; *ed:* Memphis St Univ (BS)-Cum Laude Ed 1872; 15 Credit Hrs Trenton St Univ Child Psych, Gifted Ed; *cr:* Waldron Acad for Boys 3 Grd Tchr 1973-76; Pennsauken Pub Schls Remedial Math Tchr 1977-82, Math Tchr for Gifted 1982-; *ai:* Stu Cncl Spon; Odyssey of Mind Team Coach; Math Curr Comm; Kappa Delta Pi; NCTM; Assn of Math Tchrs of NJ; Pennsauken Tchrs Ed Assn, VP; Amer Assn of Women Tchrs; Goals 2000-Educate Amer Act Grant; Wkshp Ldr, Tchr Hands-on Equations Algebra Prgm; *home:* 136 Mansfield Blvd S Cherry Hill NJ 08034*

VERNIERI, SUSAN JEAN, Business Admin & Tech Teacher; *b:* Nashua, NH; *m:* Anthony John; *c:* Lauren; *ed:* Ocean Cty Coll (AA) Bus 1980; Montclair St Coll (BS) Comprehensive Bus Ed 1982; Rider Coll 3 Credits; *cr:* Howell HS Bus Admin, Tech Tchr 1983-; *ai:* NJEA, NEA, NJBEA 1983-; *office:* Howell HS Squankum-Yellowbrook Rd Farmingdale NJ 07727

VERNO, ANITA D. SANDERS, BITS Teacher; *b:* New York City, NY; *m:* Michael Patrick; *c:* Aharon BEck, Marnie Lee, Julia Elaine; *ed:* Univ of Rochester (BA) Gen Sci 1976; Fairleigh Dickinson Univ (MS) Cmptr Sci 1984; *cr:* Compu-Serv Network inc Account Rep 1976-77; United Computing Systems inc Tech Rep 19767-81; Self-employed Cmptr Consultant 1981-92; Fairleigh Dickinson Univ Adj Fac 1981-93; Bergen Comm Coll Adj Fac 1981-93; Felician Coll Adj Fac 1981-93; Passaic Comm Coll 1981-93; Don Bosco Prep HS Cmptr Tchr 1992-93; Bergen Cty Tech HS BITS Tchr 1993-; *ai:* Soph Class 1994-95, Jr Class 1995- Adv; Talent Show 1995-; NEA 1993-; Grad Tchng Fellow Fairleigh Dickinson Univ 1982-83; *office:* Bergen Co Tech HS 200 Hackensack Ave Hackensack NJ 07601*

VERNO, JOHN ANTHONY, History & Health Teacher; *b:* Pottst[...] *ed:* West Chester Univ, (BS) Criminal Justice 1979; Cert Soc St[...] Cert Police Ofcr St Police Trng Acad 1978; Grad Credits Ed; Gra[...] Sports Mngmt WV Univ; *cr:* St Pius HS Soc Stud Tchr 1979-[...] Chester Henderson HS Soc Stud Tchr 1982; Vly Forge Military A[...] Stud, Bus Tchr 1983-90; Malvern Prep Schl Soc Stud, Hlth Tchr [...] Var Head La Crosse, Asst Var Ice Hockey, Var Asst Ftbl Coach; Fa[...] Pres; Asst Ath Dir; Hlth, PE Dept Chm; Civil War His Expert; K[...] Columbus 1979-; Tau Kappa Epsilon 1977-, VP, High GPA Avg[...] Crosse Assn 1985-, Pres; Intnl Soc Sci Hnr Soc; Natl His Hnr S[...] Criminal Justice Hnr Soc; All Amer Power Lifter; MVP Semi-P[...] Times; *office:* Malvern Prep Schl For Boys Warren Ave Malvern PA[...]

VERNON, JOYCE L., English Teacher; *b:* Madison, IN; *m:* P[...] Jessica, Rebecca Bellora; *ed:* Hanover Coll (BA) Ger 1963; IN Ur[...] Scndry Ed 1970; Attnd NY St Univ at Albany, Union Coll; *cr:* U[...] Corps Tchr 1964-65; Bloominton HS Tchr 1966-70; Churchill [...] 1973-77; Scotia Glenville HS Tchr 1980-; *ai:* SGTA, NYSUT[...] *office:* Scotia Glenville HS 1 Tartan Way Scotia NY 12302

VERNON, ROBERT PAT, Architectural & Comp Instr; *b:* Pittsbu[...] *m:* Elizabeth Ritzco; *c:* Ryan, Ian; *ed:* Penn St Univ (BS) Ind Tec[...] (MS) Ins Tech 1995; *cr:* Tyrone HS Instr 1973; St Coll HS Archite[...] Comp Graphics Instr 1974-; *ai:* Tech Stu Assn Adv; Tech Assn of P[...] VP; ITEA 1986-; Wrote a Comm Trng; *office:* State College [...] Westerly Pky State College PA 16801*

VERNON, TRUDY GOODE, Hlth & Physical Education T[...] Newton, NJ; *m:* Richard W.; *c:* Douglas Daniel Olsen; *ed:* Glass[...] Coll (BA) Hlth & PE 1971; 25 Credits Toward MA in Guid; *c*[...] Landing MS Hlth & PE Tchr 1971-; *ai:* Girls Soccer Team Asst[...] Chrldng Squad Coach; Peer Group Adv; NEA 1971-; NJEA 1971-[...] 1971-; St Pauls Presbyn Church 1989-, Deacon 1991-94; *offic*[...] Landing MS 85 Little Gloucester Rd Blackwood NJ 08012

VERNON-WORTZEL, HEIDI, Professor of Manageme[...] Washington, DC; *m:* Lawrence H.; *c:* Joshua, Jennifer Stiller; *ed:* Univ (BA) Fr, His 1960; Boston Univ (MA) Bus His 1978, (PHD[...] Bus His 1980; *cr:* Northeastern Univ Asst Prof 1980-85, Ass[...] 1985-90, Mngmt Prof 1990-; *ai:* Intnl Prgms Dir; Coord Intnl Bu[...] Acad of Mngmt, Acad Intnl Bus 1980-; Eastern Acad of Mngm[...] Fellow; Lowell; Bus & Soc; Global Strategic Mngmt; Title VI [...] Grant; *office:* Northeastern Univ 313 Hayden Boston MA 02115

VERONESI, MARA M., Religions Education Teacher; *b:* Spri[...] MA; *ed:* Working Towards Masters Applied Theology; *cr:* Cathe[...] Rel Ed Tchr 1986-; *ai:* NCEA 1986-; Cropwalk 1992-, Coord.

VERREAULT, KATHRYN MARY, Coll of Mngmt Interim D[...] Amesbury, MA; *c:* Amy Lynn; *ed:* Univ of Lowell (BSBA) Acctn[...] TX A&M (MBA) Taxation 1979, (PHD) Acctng 1982; *cr:* Bentley C[...] Prof 1981-85; Univ of MA at Lowell Assoc Prof 1985-94, Interi[...] 1994-; *ai:* Amer Acct Assn 1986-92; Mt Vernon Kndgtn Bd Mem 1[...] Mt Vernon Budget Comm 1988-90; Multiple Publications & A[...] *office:* Univ Of MA At Lowell 1 University Ave Lowell MA 01854

VERRIGNI, ROCCO GERALD, Prof of Hotel Mgmt Dept; *b:* S[...] Springs, NY; *ed:* LeMoyne Coll (BS) Bus Admin 1973; SUNY at [...] (MS) Educl Psych 1989; *cr:* Schenectady Cty Comm Coll Prof o[...] Mgmt, Culinary Arts, Tourism 1981-; *ai:* Coll, Dept Comms; Stu Adv[...] 1981-; Assn of Experiential Ed 1991-; *office:* Schenectady County[...] Coll 78 Washington Ave Schenectady NY 12305

VERSTEEG, PETER J., Biology Teacher; *b:* Star Lake, NY; *m:* K[...] Varecka; *c:* Elizabeth F.; *ed:* SUNY at Geneseo (BS) Bio 1985; SU[...] Brockport (MS) Ed 1991; US Army Combined Arms & Svcs Staff S[...] Wheatland Chili Bio Tchr 1989-; *ai:* Girls Var Vllybl Coach; WC[...] Tchrs, NYSUT & AFT 1989-; NABT 1991-; NY St Challenger F[...] Dev Software Pub 1992; *office:* Wheatland Chili HS 940 No[...] Scottsville NY 14546*

VERTICCHIO, PHILLIP, History Teacher; *b:* Bronx, MY; *m:* [...] Joan; *c:* Maria, Phillip, Kenneth; *ed:* St Peters Coll (BS) His 1961; Hall Univ (MA) Asian Stud 1975; Chinese Lang Summer Inst 1968-[...] Pub Schl 16 6th Grd Tchr 1961-62; USAF Capt 1962-67; Dreyfu[...] Math Tchr 1967-75; Totten IS 34 His Tchr 1975-; *ai:* Bsktbl Coac[...] Grd Act & Grad Coord; AFT, UFT 1968-; Lib of Congress Assocs [...] Staten Island Tchrs of Soc Stud 1985-; United Act Unlimited Youth[...] NYC Outstanding Tchr Cert; *office:* IS 34 Totten 34 Academy Ave [...] Island NY 10307

VERTOLLI, AUDREY MARY, Second Grade Teacher; *b:* Vinelan[...] *ed:* Mount Saint Agnes (BA) Elem Ed 1960; 30 Grad Credits Lang[...] Guid Loyola Coll, Rowan Coll, Temple Univ; *cr:* Edmondson H[...] Elem Schl Third Grd Tchr 1960-68; Rieck Ave Elem Schl Second Gr[...] 1969-; *ai:* NEA, NJ Ed Assn, Millville Tchr Assn 1969-; Amer A[...] Univ Women 1974-; Governor's Tchr Recognition Awd 1993.

VERVERS, JUDITH ELLEN, Translator; *b:* Paterson, NJ; *ed:* [...] Univ (BA) Eng, Ger 1970; IN Univ (MA) Eng 1979; PA St Univ, [...] Bremen Fed Rep of Ger, Goethe Inst, St Michael's Coll Post Grad [...] Cecchetti Cncl of Amer Trng, Ballet Instr; *cr:* Claysburg-Kimmel H[...] Ger Scndry Tchr 1970-85; Hollidaysburg Area HS Ger Scndry [...] 1985-89; Rochester HS Eng, Ger Scndry Tchr 1989-90; Whitcomb H[...] Ger Scndry Tchr 1990-92; Essex Junction HS Eng, Ger Scndry [...] 1992-95; Engrng, Tech Ger Translator 1996; *ai:* Ger Club; Lit Mag[...] Comm Liaison; NEA, PSEA, VT NEA 1970-, Local Pres; AATG [...] Delta Kappa Gamma 1975-, Theta Chptr Pres; Amer Translators' [...] 1995-; Moretown Historical Soc 1994-; Women Centered 1995-; [...] Intnl 1984-92, Local Coord; Chowan Coll Younger Poets Competitio[...] Mention, Work Pub 1976; Cntrl PA Flood of 72 Staff Writer, Photog[...] Johnstown Flood Co-Ed 1977; Commonwealth partnership Frgn Lang[...] Flwshp 1988.*

VERVILLE, RICHARD F., Professor of Marketing; *b:* Holyoke, M[...] Wanda K.; *c:* Lisa, Mark, Nathan, Zachary, Joshua, Jonathan; *ed:* W[...] New England Coll (BBA) Mrktg 1971, (MBA) Mrktg 1980; Harvard [...] Schl Mngmt Prgm Cert; *cr:* Combustion Engrng Buyer 1964-66; Buxt[...] Mrktg Rsrch Analysis 1966-70; Gift Packaging Industries Sales [...] 1970-72; Creative Rsrch Svcs Pres 1972-80; Verville Assocs Inc [...] 1980-84; Springfield Tech Comm Coll Mrktg Prof 1984-; *ai:* Mrktg [...] Alpha Beta Gamma NHS Campus Chptr Adv; NEA 1984-; Make-A-[...] Fnd of Western, Cntrl MA 1987-, Exec Dir; Pub Numerous Articles; *o*[...] Springfield Tech Comm Coll 1 Armory Sq Springfield MA 01105

VERYZER, ROBERT W., Marketing Professor; *b:* Royal Oak, MI[...] Olivet Coll (BA) Mrktg, Mngmt 1983; MI St Univ (MBA) Mrktg [...] Univ of FL (PHD) Mrktg 1993; Post Grad Stud in Design at MI St [...] *cr:* St of MI Mrktg Asst 1985; Gen Motors Product Rsrch Asst 1986; [...] Gen Foods Asst Product Mgr 1987-89; *ai:* Formula SAE Race Car Pr[...] Adv; SAE Lightning Electric Race Car Project Adv; Beta Gamma S[...] Epsilon Delta Sigma Adv; Amer Mrktg Assn 1993-; Assn for Cons[...] Rsrch 1992-; Mrktg Sci Inst Grant; Numerous Articles Pub; *o*[...] Rensselaer Lally Schl of Mngmt Lally Management Center Troy NY 1[...]

VERZONI, ANNE THIBODEAU, Sixth Grade Teacher; *b:* Ft Kent, [...] *m:* Stephen L.; *c:* Kevin J. Flaherty, Andrew J. Flaherty; *ed:* Univ So[...] (BS) Ed Elem 1975; Addl 45 Credit Hrs Rdng, Exceptionality, [...] Effectiveness; *cr:* Manchester Elem Schl 4, 6 Grd Tchr 1975-77, 1, 4[...]

ng Specialist 1977-80, 6 Grd Tchr 1980-94; Windham MS 6 Grd 994-; *ai:* Bldg Dev Team Chprsn; Windham Educ Assoc, ME Educ 975-; Windham Ath Boosters, CADRE 1990-; Project Grad 1995-; ng Tchr Awd Young Men, Women Org; Project Enterprise Grant; s Pub; Soc Stud Curric Guide Publication 1991; *office:* Windham s Gray Rd Windham ME 04062

VI, JAMES C., Architecture & Design Teacher; *b:* Somerville, Anne; *c:* Jason, Melissa; *ed:* William Penn (BA) Industrial Arts *cr:* Manchester HS Drafting Instr 1976-79; Toms River East HS cture & Design Tchr 1980-; *ai:* Wrestling Coach & Ofcl; Track NEA, NJEA, Tech Ed Assn 1976-; TREA 1976-, Bldg Rep; Natl ng Ofcl Assn 1987-, Dist & Shore Conf Ofcl; South Jersey Tech Ed 979-; Mid States Eval Comm 1990-, Tech Ed Prgms Evaluator; Shop Tchr of Yr Stu Selected; Tchr of Yr Awd Fac Selected; nding Young Men of Amer Awd; *office:* Toms River HS East Raider oms River NJ 08753

AL, PHYLLIS CHICANO, English Interdisciplinary Tchr; *b:* elphia, PA; *m:* John Thomas; *c:* Carrie Ann; *ed:* Univ of DE (BA) 69; Montgomery Cty Pub Schls Masters Equivalency; *cr:* Pyle MS Music, Drama Tchr & Dir 1969-85; Montgomery Cty Pub Schls Curr & Test Writer 1977-84, GATE Summer Inst Tchr 1981-83; rsburg MS Eng Interdisciplinary Resource Tchr 1985-; *ai:* Rdng, g Wkshp Trnr & Presenter; MCPS Eng Curr Revision Comm; NEA MSTA 1969-; NCTE 1969-; Grants: 2 MCPS Ed Fndtn & ngton Post; NCTE Spring Conf Presenter 1983; Play Pub; nporary Drama Svc; Rdng, Writing Wkshp Curr Materials; Apple Press; MD Tchr of Yr & Disney Amer Tchrs Awd Nom; *office:* rsburg MS 2 Teachers Way Gaithersburg MD 20877

RI, FRANK, Social Studies Dept Chairman; *b:* Bronx, NY; *ed:* Iona BA) His & Pol Sci 1977; NY Univ (MA) Pol Sci 1979; Manhattan MSEd) Ed 1985; 51 Credit Hrs at St Johns Univ Doctor of Arts Prgm; esian HS Chm of Soc Stud Dept, 9th & 10th Grd Global Stud & 12th mer Govt Tchr 1983-, 12th Grd Poltical Sci Tchr & 11th Grd Amer chr; Coll of New Rochelle Adjunct Prof of Political Sociology & ogy 1996-; *ai:* Bsbl Moderator 1985-87; Summer Schl Asst Prin NHS Asst Moderator 1988-; His Club Adv 1989-; Schl Recruitment 1988-90; Big Brother Prgm 1989-93; Yrbk Moderator 1993-96; His e Club 1989-92; NCEA 1981-; Amer Pol Sci Assn 1977-80, 1987-88; Historical Soc 1994; St Johns Luniv Fellowship 1990-93; Whos Who g Stdnts in Coll 1977; Outstanding Young Men of America 1978; f Month 1986; *office:* Salesian H S 148 Main St New Rochelle NY

TEIN, HARVEY, Coordinator of Educl Svcs; *b:* Boston, MA; *m:* a Paula Arnold; *c:* Scott, Michael, Amy; *ed:* Northeastern Univ (BA) Jrnlsm 1961, (MA) Eng 1964, (CAGS) Rehabilitation Admin 1975, Higher Ed Admin 1986; Grad Work at Boston Coll; *cr:* Northeastern Eng Instr & Asst Prof 1963-69, Asst Dean of Stdnts 1969-78, Assoc of Stdnts 1978-93, Ed Svcs Coord & Eng Sr Lecturer 1993-; *ai:* Fac Comm Chair; Hillel Advy Bd; Fac Dev Prgms in Adult Ed Coord; E, NUCEA 1993-; ASJA 1989-, Charter Mem, Rep Circuit Dist 1; A 1970-; Articles Pub in Encyclopedia of Higher Ed & Intnl lopedia of Higher Ed; Doctoral Dissertation Pub; *office:* eastern Univ 360 Huntington Ave 263 Ryder Hall Boston MA 02115

ORE, DANIEL ANTHONY, Social Studies Teacher; *b:* Brooklyn, *m:* Ann Marie Kirchmer; *c:* Jessica, Corey, Daniel; *ed:* Hobart Coll His 1970; SUNY at Albany (MA) Ed 1972; Addl 60 Credit Hrs; *cr:* alem Ave Jr HS Soc Stud Tchr 1972-85; Grand Ave Jr HS Soc Stud 1986-; *ai:* Cross Cntry, Girls Bsktbl, Bsbl Coach; NYSUT 1972-, 20 c Awd; AFT 1972-; BM United Sec Tchrs 1972-, Bldg Rep, Outstdng PTA 1972-, 1977 Hon Life Mem; St Martin of Tours 1979-, Parish Cross & Shell Awd; Amityville Little League 1990-; Nassau Umpires n of Yr 1993; Bellmore-Merrick United Scndry Tchrs Outstdng Prof *office:* Grand Ave Jr HS 2301 Grand Ave Bellmore NY 11710

, JULES G., Retired Teacher; *b:* Holyoke, MA; *m:* Helene Lillis; *c:* h, Mary Cappabianca; *ed:* Assumption Coll (BA) Philosophy 1949; of MA (MA) Lang 1954; Attnd Univ of Laval, Cath Inst; *cr:* nption Prep Tchr, Asst Dean of Men 1952-53; Canterbury Schl Fr, Span 1954-94, Lang Chair 1985-93; *ai:* Translations of Fr rials; *home:* 94 Aspetuck Ave New Milford CT 06776

NO, PAUL ALANSON, Dir of Guidance; *b:* New York, NY; *m:* etta; *c:* Marc, Steven, Teresa; *ed:* Queens Coll (BA) Math 1967; City MS) Math Ed 1969; St Johns Univ (MS) & (PD) Counseling & Admin & 1978; Forham Univ (PhD) Counseling & Admin 1984; 30 Addl Grd t Ed at NY Univ 1971; *cr:* Intermediate Schl 117 Math Tchr 1967-68; well Jr HS Math Tchr 1968-71; Bayside HS Math Tchr & Tchr Cnslr -85; Newtown HS Guidance Cnslr 1985; Townsend Harris HS Coll d 1985-94; Pelham Memorial HS 1994-; *ai:* PSAT & SAT I & II Test d; Acad Awds Comm; Phi Beta Kappa 1967-; Phi Delta Kappa 1979-; Bd for Cert Cnslrs 1988-; Acad of Clinical Mental Hlth Cnslrs 1993-; Counseling Assn 1975-; Natl Bd for Certified Counselors; Natl wment for Hum Fellowship 1989 & 1993; *office:* Pelham Memorial Colonial & Corlies Aves Pelham NY 10803

K, GERALD KEITH, Sci Lrng Ctr Adj Instr & Dir; *b:* Dixon, IL; *m:* cia Anne Kenney; *c:* Roger Keith, Kathryn Ann Aleis, Christopher ; *ed:* Univ of IL (BS) Chem 1952; Univ of Rochester (PHD) Organic n 1956; *cr:* Exxon Rsrch & Engrng Co Various Inc, Lab Dir 1955-86; s Cty Comm Coll Adj Instr 1988-, Sci Learning Ctr Dir 1990-; *ai:* Soc Chem 1959-; Soc of Automotive Engrs 1962-; Amer Assn ancemnt of Sci 1969-; Amer Inst of Chemists 1986-, Fellow; Patent for Cranking Simulator; 25 Tech Pub; *office:* Bucks County Comm Coll np Road Newtown PA 18940

KERY, SHERRAN HOWER, Second Grade Teacher; *b:* Iowa City, *m:* Roger A.; *c:* William, Brian, Benjamin; *ed:* Univ of IA (BA) Elem 968; Lesley Coll (MED) Creative Arts 1992; Addl 18 Credits; *cr:* ison Elem Schl 2nd Grd Tchr 1966-68; No Rehoboth Schl 2nd Grd 1969-80, Tchng Prin 1974-78; Palmer River Schl 2nd Grd Tchr 1980-; Lang Arts Curr Task Force 1992-93; NEA 1967-; MTA 1969-; RTA -, Pres 1980-81; West Side Benevolent 1984-, Appeals Chair; *office:* ner River Schl 326 Winthrop St Rehoboth MA 02769

TOR, STEPHEN MICHAEL, Math Teacher; *b:* New London, CT; *m:* yn Linn Klopp; *ed:* Cntrl CT St Univ (BS) Math, Ed 1988, (MS) Scndry 995; 30 Addl Hrs Ed 1993; *cr:* Southington HS Math Tchr 1988-90; J. ennedy Jr HS Math Tchr 1990-94; Southington HS Math Tchr 1994-; Math Club Adv 1989-90; Math Counts Adv 1991-92; Coach Boys JV cer 1989-, Golf 1995-; NEA, CEA, SEA 1988-; *office:* Southington HS Pleasant St Southington CT 06489

TOR, SUELLEN SAMPLES, Spanish Teacher; *b:* Barberton, OH; *c:* elyn; *ed:* Kent St Univ (BS) Span & Speech 1970; Coll of Mount Saint ph (MED) Ed 1993; Attnd Univ of Cincinnati & Northern KY Univ n Ed; *cr:* Retail Mgmt 1970-80; Portsmouth Notre Dame Schl Span & ech Tchr 1981-84; Ayer Elem Schl K-6th Grd Span Tchr 1984-85; oin HS Span Tchr 1985-; *ai:* Schlsp Selection Comm; NHS Selection nm; Supt Instructional Advy Comm; NHS Adv; OEA & NEA 1993-; A 1991-; Notre Dame HS Tchr of Yr 1984; 1985 Scripps Howard Grant Project in Mexico; Turpin HS Tchr of Month 1993; Turpin HS Edctr of 1995; *home:* 6835 Le Conte Ave Cincinnati OH 45230

VIDA, SHIRLEY MOODY, Fourth Grade Teacher; *b:* Pittsburgh, PA; *m:* Paul W.; *ed:* Point Park Coll (BS) Behavioral Scis 1973; 15 Credit Hrs in Theology-Advanced Degree will be in Pastoral Ministry; *cr:* Saint Teresas Schl 2nd Grd Tchr 1962-65; Nativity Schl 2nd Grd Tchr 1966-69; Assumption Schl 2nd Grd Tchr 1970-83, 1st Grd Tchr 1984-87, 4th Grd Tchr 1988-; *ai:* Sunshine Club-Vols for Elderly Adv; Rainbows for Gods Children Divorced Grief Group Facilitator; Peer Tutoring Prgm Dir; NEA 1989-; *home:* 400 Winterset Dr Pittsburgh PA 15209

VIDMAR, GLENDA KAY (STEVENS), Fifth Grade Teacher; *b:* Steubenville, OH; *m:* Stephen; *c:* Mark Stevens; *ed:* Kent St (BS) Elem Ed 1966; 24 Grad Hrs; *cr:* Buckeye Schl 3rd Grd Tchr 1966-78; Hale Rd 1st Grd Tchr 1979-80, 3rd Grd Tchr 1980-82, 5th Grd Tchr 1982-; *ai:* Painesville Twp Elem Sci Comm; NEA 1966-; OEA 1966-; NEOTA 1966-; PTEA 1966-; *office:* Hale Rd Schl 56 Hale Rd Painesville OH 44077

VIDO, FAY WAGNER, English Teacher & Dept Chair; *b:* Hazelton, PA; *m:* Frank Jr.; *c:* Victoria Ireland, Durbin, Frank, Paul; *ed:* PA St Univ (BA) Scndry Ed 1952; Attd Univ of Rochester, Miami Univ & Univ of Cincinnati; *cr:* West Irondequoit HS Eng & Soc Stud Tchr 1956-62; Plymouth-Whitemarsh HS Eng Tchr 1962-63; Catholic Central Comm Schl Eng Tchr 1974-76; Badin HS Eng Tchr & Eng Dept Chair 1976-; *office:* Stephen T Badin Schl 451 New London Rd Hamilton OH 45013

VIECELI, SAMUEL JOHN, Physical Education Teacher; *b:* Pittsburgh, PA; *m:* Judith Ann Cooper; *c:* Cynthia; *ed:* WV Univ (BS) PE, Spec Ed, Hlth 1974; Penn St Univ (MA) Ed; *cr:* Bethel Park Schl Dist PE, HLth, Spec Ed Tchr 1976-; *ai:* Boys Var Head Soccer Coach 1977-94; Boys Asst Track Coach; Boys MS Schl Wrestling Coach; AFT 1976-; US Golf Assn; Amer Soccer League Prof 1976; ST Champions Boys Soccer, WPIAL Coach of Yr 1994; Beadling Soccer Club Hall of Fame 200 Plus Career Wins; *office:* Bethel Park Sr HS 309 Church Rd Bethel Park PA 15102

VIEHMAN, LIDIA L., Social Studies Teacher; *b:* Allentown, PA; *m:* Richard M.; *c:* Stephanie, Christopher; *ed:* Kutztown Univ (BS) Scndry Ed, Soc Stud 1973; Lehigh Univ (MED) Ed, Admin 1977; *cr:* Northeast Jr HS Soc Stud Tchr 1973-75; Broughal Jr HS Soc Tchr, Dept Chprsn 1975-80; Freedom HS Soc Stud Tchr 1981-; *ai:* Mid Sts Comm; Cooperative Tchr Kutztown Univ & Moravian Coll; NEA, PSEA, BEA 1973-, Bldg Rep, PSEA Del; Delta Kappa Gamma, Exec Bd 4 Yrs, PSEA Intnl Relations Comm Alternate 1988, Auditor; *office:* Freedom HS 3149 Chester Ave Bethlehem PA 18017*

VIETZE, STEPHEN B., Director of Music; *b:* Concord, NH; *ed:* Coll of Wooster (BME) Music Ed 1990; Post Grad Work at Univ of Dayton; *cr:* Russia Local Schls Music Dir, 5th-12th Grd Band Dir & 1st-7th Grd General Music Tchr 1990-; *ai:* Pep & Marching Bands Dir; Muse Machine Adv; Academia Co-Adv; Russia Ed Assn, OEA, NEA 1990-, VP, Pres Elect; MENC OH Music Ed Assn 1987-; Natl Band Assn 1990-; Shelby Cty Band Dir Assn 1990-, Pres, Sec-Treas; OH Valley British Brass Band 1994-; Muse Machine Advanced Tchr Trng Schlsp 1995; Grant from OH Arts Cncl for Artist-in-Residence 1995-; *office:* Russia Local Schl 110 E Main St PO Box 8 Russia OH 45363*

VIGGIANI, FRANCES ANNE, Prof of Mgmt, Orgnl Behavior; *b:* New York City, NY; *c:* Rosa Viggiani Pullman; *ed:* Univ of MA at Amherst (BA) Ec 1979; Cornell Univ (MA) Cty, Rgnl Planning 1984, (PHD) Orgnl Behavior 1991; *cr:* Cornell Univ Adj Prof 1991-93; SUNY Adj Prof 1991-93; Ithaca Coll Adj Prof 1991-93; Alfred Univ Coll of Bus Asst Prof 1993-; *ai:* Consultant Neighborhood Based Alliance Allegany Cty NY; Fac Cncl, Coll of Bus, Curr Comm; Fac Adv FBLA, Career Woman & Assoc; ASA, Acad of Mngmt 1990-; *office:* Alfred Univ Coll of Bus 26 N Main St Alfred NY 14802

VIGGIANO, CHRISTINE MC BRIDE, Spanish Teacher I-VI; *b:* Philadelphia, PA; *m:* Michael D.; *ed:* Mt St Mary's Coll (BA) Span, Sociology 1981; La Salle Univ (MA) Bilingual, Bicultural Stud in Span 1991; 6 Addl Ed Credits Eastern Coll; 3 Addl Ed Credits Temple Univ; *cr:* St Boniface Elem 6th Grd Tchr 1981-84, 8th Grd Tchr 1984-87; St Basil Acad Span I-IV Tchr 1987-; *ai:* Span Club & Jr Class Moderator; Tutor; Diocesan Scholar Comm Mem; Admis Comm Chprsn; Lang/ Visual Arts Aux Comm Mem; NCEA, MCATFL, AATSP, NATFL 1987-; Master's Thesis Cross-Cultural Study of Cuban, Mexican & Puerto Rican Teenagers; *office:* St Basil Acad 711 Fox Chase Rd Fox Chase Manor PA 19046

VIGGIANO, THERESA KLUSKA, Second Grade Teacher; *b:* Salem, MA; *m:* Michael; *c:* Elizabeth Rose; *ed:* Salem St Coll (BS) Elem Ed 1970; *cr:* Broad St Schl 5th Grd Tchr 3 Yrs, 2nd Grd Tchr 22 Yrs; *ai:* Nashua Tchrs Union 1970-; *home:* 46 Wire Rd Merrimack NH 03054

VIGLIOTTI, PATRICIA MYOR, Home Economics Teacher; *b:* Monongahela, PA; *m:* Joseph J.; *c:* Matthes J., Michael D., Mark, Michelle; *ed:* Indiana Univ of PA (BsEd) Home Ec Ed 1972; 18 Credits PA St Univ; 6 Credits California Univ of PA; *ai:* NEA, 1972-; Ringgold Ed Assoc 1972, Bldg Rep; Girl Scouts of SWPA 1991-, Troop Ldr; BSA 1993-, Comm Chm, Treas; Cub Scouts 1988-, Den Ldr, Asst Cub Master.

VIJAYASEKAR, JAYA DEVARAJAN, Fr, Span Tchr & Team Ldr; *b:* Madras, India; *m:* Manisundaram; *c:* Kavitha Devi; *ed:* Fairfield Univ (BA) Fr, Span 1979; Madras Univ (MA) Eng Lit 1981; Central CT St Univ 6th Yr Educl Admin 1995; Wesleyan Univ Pimms Inst on Tech, Internet, Worcester St Coll, FLES; *cr:* Fairfield Woods MS Fr Tchr 1983-87; Middlebrook MS Span Tchr 1987-88; Griswold MS Fr, Span Tchr, F.L. Coord 1988-; *ai:* Gifted, Talented Task Force; Prof Dev, 6th Grd Prgm Comms; Schl Newspaper; Young Educators Soc; Team Ldr; Foreign Lang Coord; NEA 1983-; CT NEA 1983-, Svc Awd, Womens Leadership Cadre; AATF 1984-; AATSP 1988-; COLT, Regnl Dir; Spec Olympics Comm Summer 1995, Lang Svcs Coord; Long Range Planning Comm Svc Awd; Tchr of Yr 1991; *office:* Albert D Griswold MS 144 Bailey Rd Rocky Hill CT 06067*

VIJUK, SANDRA L., Mathematics Teacher; *b:* Greensburg, PA; *m:* Ronald P.; *c:* Wade, Laura Jean; *ed:* PA St Univ (BS) Math & Ed 1965; Attnd Seton Hill; *cr:* Thomas Jefferson HS Math Tchr 1965-67; Duquesne HS Math Tchr 1967-68; Yough HS Math Tchr 1986-; *ai:* YEA, PSEA & NEA 1987-.

VILANDRE, DAVID A., English Teacher & Dept Chm; *b:* Worcester, MA; *m:* Mary Elizabeth Rogers; *c:* Rachel, Nathaniel; *ed:* Assumption Coll (BA) Eng 1980, (MAT) Eng 1984; Attnd Harvard Univ; *cr:* St John's HS Eng Tchr 1980-, Quinsigamond Comm Coll Eng Tchr 1991-; *ai:* Lit Magazine; Jr Class, Eng Club Moderator; NCTE 1980-; MCTE 1987, Worcester Cty Chm; Worcester Cty Young Writers' Inst 1989-, Founder, Dir; *office:* Saint Johns HS 378 Main St Shrewsbury MA 01545*

VILARDI, MARY ALICE TOOLAN, Social Studies Teacher; *b:* Carbondale, PA; *m:* Robert G.; *c:* Courtney, Robert J., Maureen; *ed:* Marywood Coll (BS) Fr Ed 1966; Univ of Scranton (MS) Sec Ed 1970; *cr:* Carbondale Area Sch Dist Fr Tchr 1966-70; St Marys 5th-6th Grd Soc Stud Tchr 1982-84; St Denis & St Columbia Sch 7th-8th Grd Soc Stud Tchr 1984-; *ai:* Golf Coach 1966-70; NCEA 1984-; Mid-Hudson Soc St Cncl 1990-; *office:* St Denis-St Columbia Schl Rt 82 Hopewell Junction NY 12533

VILD, ROSE M., Fourth Grade Teacher; *b:* Rochester, PA; *c:* Traci Mattern; *ed:* Geneva Coll (BSED) Elem Ed 1968; 36 Credit Hrs; *cr:* Lincoln Schl 3rd Grd Tchr 1967-68; Big Knob Elem Schl 3rd Grd Tchr 1968-81; Unionville Elem Schl 1st Grd Tchr 1981-83; Big Knob Elem Schl 1st Grd Tchr 1983-85, 4th Grd Tchr 1985-; *ai:* Piano Player; FAEA, PSEA, NEA 1967-; Big Knob Grange; *office:* Freedom Area Schl Dist 8th Ave Freedom PA 15042

VILLANI, KATHLEEN, Professor of Accounting; *b:* Washington Hghts, NY; *m:* Harry Whitbeck; *c:* Kristin Whitbeck, Jennifer Whitbeck, Lynnnn Whitbeck; *ed:* Nassau Comm Coll (AA) Lbrl Arts 1972; Queens Coll (BA) Acctng 1974; Hofstra Univ (MBA) Acctng 1979; CPA, Continuing Ed Courses; *cr:* NY St Dept of Hlth Bureau of Audit & Investigation Assoc Auditor 1974-78; Ernst & Young CPA's Sr Accountant 1978-79; Margaret Tietz Ctr for Nrsng Care Controller, Asst Admin 1979-84; Queensborough Comm Coll Prof 1984-; *ai:* Deputy Chair of Acctng 1990-93; AICPA 1979-; NY St Assn of Two Yr Colls 1985-; Tchrs of Acctng at Two Yr Colls 1992-; CPA NY 1979-; Nrsng Home Admin License 1984-; Books: Instructor's Manual to Accompany Polimeni/Fabozzi/Cost Accounting Concepts and Applications for Managerial Decision Making, Study Guide to Accompany Polimeni/Fabozzi/Adelberg Cost Accounting Concepts and Applciations for Managerial Decision Making; Practice Sets: Job Order Costing and Process Costing to Accomp any Polimeni/Fabozzi/Adelberg Cost Accounting Concepts and Applications for Managerial Decision Making; Wkshp Presented; Curr Dev; *office:* Queensborough Comm Coll 222-05 56th Ave Bayside NY 11364

VILLANI, MARY, Tchr, Biological Sciences Dept; *b:* New York City, NY; *ed:* Lehman Coll (BA) Biological Scis, Fr 1972, (MA) Biological Scis 1972; Fordham Univ (PD) Educl Admin, Supervision 1988; Attnd Manhattan Coll, City Coll, Schl of Medicine & Dentistry at Rochester, Harvard Univ, NY Univ Tchrs Coll, Columbia Univ; *cr:* Newtown HS Tchr, Sci Dept 1972-76; Mount Vernon HS Tchr, Sci Dept 1976-78; Walton HS Tchr, Sci Dept 1978-81; City Coll Macy Med Professions Prgm Tchr, Curr Writer, Staff Dev 1981-84; Bronx HS of Sci Tchr, Biological Scis Dept 1984-90; RF, CUNY LOGO, Moving to Learn, Connect Prgms Dir 1990-91; Adelphi Univ Stuyvesant Intnl & Math, Sci Residential Prgms On-Campus, Acad Dir, Stu Act Coord, Tchr 1988-91; NYC Bd of Ed Prof Dev Office CIMS Sci Prgm Mgr, Curr Writer, Staff Dev 1991-92; Bronx HS of Sci Tchr, Biological Scis Dept 1992-; *ai:* NYC Bd of Ed Sci Cncl 1991-92; Franklin Museum Electronic Learning Project Sci Resource Person; Hlth Careers Club Adv 1972; Inventers Club, Bio Journal Adv 1984-; Pre-Law Soc, Ad Nostram Salutem Pre Med Club, Italian Cultural Skateboard Contention Adv 1984-88; Clao Club Adv 1994-95; Epiarean Club Adv 1992-94; Chinese Stu Union Adv 1993-; Cooking Club Adv 1995-; Lincoln Douglas Debates, NY Acad of Scis Sci Fair Competitions Judge; NYC Bd of Ed Prek-12 Grd Staff Dev; SCONYC; STANYS; ASCD; NYC Bio Tchrs Assn; NABT; Make-A-Wish Fnd 1990-, Wish Granter; Impact II Dev Grant 1987; Nom Natl Sci Tchrs Awd 1988; *office:* Bronx HS Of Science 75 W 205th St Bronx NY 10468

VILLANO, CHRISTINA ZIKKOS, Spanish & English Teacher; *b:* Charleston, WV; *m:* Robert; *c:* Victoria; *ed:* Univ of Charleston(BA) Span, Eng 1978; 24 Hrs Continuing Ed, 6 Grad Hrs; *cr:* Walton HS Tchr 2 Yrs; Charleston HS Tchr 1 Yr; Bladensburg Jr HS Tchr 2 Yr; Grace Brethren Chrstn Schl Tchr 13 Yrs; *ai:* Jr Class Spon; Eng Dept Chprsn; *office:* Grace Brethren Christian Schl 6501 Surratts Rd Clinton MD 20735

VILLANO, JOSEPH ANTHONY, History Teacher; *b:* New York City, NY; *m:* Carol A.; *c:* Todd, Matthew; *ed:* Marist Coll (BA) European His, Ed 1966; SUNY at New Paltz (MS) European His, Ed 1970; 30 Post Credit Hrs Cultural Anthropology, Archaeology Hunter Coll; *cr:* Arlington Cntrl Schl Amer His, Anthropology Tchr 1968-; Dutchess Comm Coll Adj Lecturer 1981-95; Rochester Inst of Tech Adj Lecturer 1992-95; *ai:* NYS Cncl of Soc Stud, NEA 1970-; Mid-Hudson Cncl of Soc Stud 1985-; Project on Russian, Soviet His for Sec Schl Tchrs, Taft Inst in Govt at SUNY New Paltz; NYS Ed Dept for Regents Writer; Educl Testing Svc for Amer Hist AP Grader; *office:* Arlington HS-N Campus 263 State Route 55 Lagrangeville NY 12540*

VILLARD, WALTER L.,III, Anatomy & Physiology Teacher; *b:* Chicago, IL; *ed:* Lehigh Cty Comm Coll (AA) Lbrl Arts 1984; Boston Coll (BA) Psych 1991; Attnd Kutztown Univ 1984-87; *cr:* Lehigh Vly Hosp Ctr Pulmonary Lab Technician, Phlebotomist, Microbiology Lab Technician 1985-89; Mc Lean Hosp Rsrch Asst, Sleep Lab Technician 1991-92; Lehigh Vly Hosp Ctr Sleep Lab Technician 1992; Lehigh Cty Comm Coll Anatomy, Physiology Instr, Para Prof Tutor 1993-; Tutors Unlimited Prof Tutor 1995-; *ai:* Jaycees 1992-, Sec, St, Dist Dir, Best Speaking, Jaycee of the Quarter; *office:* Lehigh Carbon Comm Coll 4525 Education Park Dr Schnecksville PA 18078

VILLATICO, NANCY JANE, History & Sociology Teacher; *b:* Providence, RI; *ed:* RI Coll (AB) His, Scndry Ed 1968, (MAT) His 1974; Critic Tchr Cert; Bryant Coll 24 Hrs Law Enforcement; RI Street Law Insts; *cr:* Burrillville HS Tchr 1968-; *ai:* Adult Ed Tchr 1969-72; Girls Sftbl Coach 1970-73; Chrldrs Adv 1970-76, 1984-85; Stu Cncl Adv 1970-76; NHS Co-Chair 1974-77; Girls Bsktbl Coach 1979-81; Schlsp Trustee 1982-; RI Model Legislature Adv 1971-75; Newspaper Adv 1983-89; Class Adv 1974-77; Acad Decathlon Coach 1985-86; Hnrs Night Co-Chair 1983-86; Christmas Food Drive Coord; Vol Tutor; NEA 1968-; New England His Tchrs Assn 1987-92; Letters From Santa 1978-; Burrillville Yth Guid Drug Comm 1973-75; Burrillville Supts Comm on Child Sexual Abuse Awareness 1984-85; Burrillville Lions Club RI Heart Fund Drive Liason 1975-76; Recreation Rehabilitation Vol VA Hosp 1972-; Robert Taft Schl of Govt Flwshp; Letters of Commendation; USMC Selectee for US Army Civilian Medal for Desert Storm; Natl Edctrs Command Visit Wkshp; NASA Tchr in Space Candidate 1985; Stu Cncl Tchr of Yr 1988.

VILLELLA, KATHLEEN COPPOLA, 5th-8th Grade Teacher; *b:* Youngstown, OH; *m:* Edward F.; *c:* Samantha, nikki, Brent; *ed:* Youngstown St Univ (BS) Elem Ed 1974; *cr:* Our Lady of Loreto Schl 1-3 Grd Tchr 1974-77; St Christine Schl 5-6 Grd Tchr 1982-83; St Joseph Schl Tchr 1983-; *ai:* Rdng, Spelling Bee Chprsn; Church Lector 1980-; Eucharistic Minister 1982-; *office:* St Joseph School-Youngstown 4565 New Rd Austintown OH 44515

VILLELLA, PATRICIA MARIA, Spanish, French & Italian Tchr; *b:* Danbury, CT; *ed:* Marist Coll (BA) Fr 1980; Southern CT St Univ (MS) Biling Ed 1989, (MS) Span & Italian 1993; *cr:* Notre Dame HS Fr & Span Tchr 1981-84; Amity Regnl HS Fr & Span Tchr 1984-87; Danbury HS Fr & Span Tchr 1987-; *ai:* NHS Comm; AATSP 1981-; NEA 1984-; CEA 1987-; Alpha Delta Kappa 1992-; *office:* Danbury HS 43 Clapboard Ridge Rd Danbury CT 06811*

VILLELLA-COLE, PRISCILLA FASCIA, Fourth Grade Teacher; *b:* Newark, NJ; *m:* James Cole; *c:* Cara Villella, Danielle Villella; *ed:* Jersey City St (BA) Ed 1967; 64 Addl Credits; *cr:* Garfield Schl Fourth Grd Tchr 1967-; *ai:* Honor-Roll Citizenship, Schl Spirit Comm; Grd Level Chprsn; NJEA, KEA, Kearny PTA 1967-; Kearny HS PTA 1994-95, Exec Bd, Cultural Arts Chprsn; Kearny HS Band Parents Assn 1990-95, Pres, Exec Bd; Kearny Bd of Ed, Comm Liason 1994; Dev Career Ed Curr; Dev Comm New Report Card System; *office:* Garfield School 360 Belgrove Dr Kearny NJ 07032

VILLENEUVE, GRACE LINDA, 6th Grade Teacher; *b:* Providence, RI; *m:* Rene T.; *ed:* RI Coll (BA) Elem Ed 1969; Univ of IR (MA) Guid Cnslng 1973; Addl 30 Credit Hrs Elem Ed; *cr:* Randall Holden Schl 4-5 Grds Tchr 1969-71; Drum Rock Schl 1-6 Grds Tchr 1972-; *ai:* Co-Creator, Adv Extended Day Rdng, Book Discussion Group; Co-Creator, Presenter Girls Career Night Spon by Amer Assn Univ Women-Warwick West Bay Branch; AFT 1969-, Bldg Rep; Amer Assn Univ Women 1981-, Pres 1994-, Sec

1990-91; Warwick PTO 1969-, Tchr of Yr 1991; Busom Buddies; Breast Cancer Support Group; *home:* 71 Claflin Rd Warwick RI 02886*

VILSMEIER, BETH BEDFORD, Music Director; *b:* Philadelphia, PA; *m:* George C. III; *c:* Danielle, Paul; *ed:* Univ of the Arts (BM), (BME) Clarinet 1972; 26 Credit Hrs 1973; Villanova Univ 6 Credit Hrs; *cr:* Paul VI HS Clarinet Instr 1974-93; Immaculata Coll Clarinet Instr 1975-; Holy Ghost Prep Schl Music Dir 1991-; Northeast Cath HS Music Dir 1993-; *ai:* NCEA; AFM & Local; MENC; PMEA; *home:* 736 Longshore Ave Philadelphia PA 19111*

VINAL, CORRINE, English Teacher; *b:* Brooklyn, NY; *m:* Robert W.; *c:* Allison, Pamela; *ed:* Wagner Coll (BA) Eng 1973; St Univ NY at Albany (MA) Eng 1974; CUNY at Bernard Baruch Coll (MPA) Pub Admin 1981; Enrolled in 6th Yr Cert Prgm in Educl Admin at CUNY, Coll of Staten Island; *cr:* Port Richmond HS Eng Tchr 1989-91, 1993-; Lafayette HS Eng Tchr 1991-92; Kinsborough Comm Coll Adjunct Lecturer Of Hum 1994-; *ai:* Schl Newspaper Adv; NYS Cncl of Eng Tchrs 1994-, Tchr of Excl 1994-95; NYC Scholastic Press 1992-, Newspaper Adv 1992, Wayne Hamm Awd 1993; One of NYC Tchrs of Yr 1994-95; *office:* Port Richmond HS 45 Innis St Staten Island NY 10302

VINCE, MELVIN JAMES, Retired Teacher; *b:* Cleveland, OH; *m:* Beverly Love; *c:* James, Susan Underwood, Renee; *ed:* OH Univ (BA) Elem Ed 1961; *cr:* N Royalton MS Math, Soc Stud Tchr 1958-91; *ai:* OEA Ret Tchrs 1991-, Life Mem; Ed Assn Co-Founder 1961-, Past-Pres; Tchr of Yr; *home:* 7916 Parmenter Dr Parma OH 44129

VINCENT, RICHARD LOUIS, Tenth Grade Teacher; *b:* Holyoke, MA; *m:* Christina Faith; *c:* Pamela Macaluso, Marc; *ed:* Amer Intnl Coll (BA) Ec 1966, (MA) Ec Ed 1973; Sixth Level Tchng Cert 30 Hrs Beyond Masters Univ of CT, Univ of Hartford 1973-86; Addl 24 Hrs Amer Coll in Paris 1986-87; *cr:* Enfield HS Soc Stud Tchr 1967-88; Enrico Fermi HS Soc Stud Tchr 1988-; Enfield Adult Ed Soc Stud Tchr 1991-; *ai:* Stdnts Against Drunk Driving Adv; Adult Ed; NEA 1967-; CT Ed Assn 1967-, Local Rep; Enfield Tchrs Assn 1967-, Pres, Svc Awds; Enfield Jaycees 1971-; Close-up Fnd 1982-, Area Coord; NSF Psych Seminar in Behavioral Sci for Tchrs Grant 1980-81; Flwship Curr Units on Latin Amer 1985; Hallmark Cards Dev of Curr Slide Units Grant 1985; Sabbatical Leave Awd Cultural Stud 1986-87; fulbright Schlsp Hebrew Univ 1988; Flwship Fiv Coll Ctr for Cultural Stud 1989; *home:* 14 Davis Ave Enfield CT 06082*

VINCENT, SHIRLEY JONES, English Teacher; *b:* Newark, NJ; *m:* Reginald P.; *c:* David Lance, Sarah Christina; *ed:* Susquehanna Univ (BA) Eng 1969; St Univ of NY at Albany (MA) Advanced Classroom, Eng 1979; West Chester St Coll Post Grad Courses Cnlsr Ed 1973; Simons Rock Writing Course 1980; U of MA at Amherst Critical Thinking Skills 1983; N Adams St Univ Rsrch for Better Tchng 1994; *cr:* No Plainfield HS 9-10th Grd Eng Tchr 1969-72; Marple Newtown Jr HS 7-9th Grd Eng, Rdng Tchr 1972-74; So Glens Falls HS 11-12th Grd Eng Tchr 1975-76; Lenox Meml HS 8-9, 11-12th Grd Eng, Speech Tchr 1978-; *ai:* Jr Sr Class Adv; MS Coord; Founder PTO; Ed MS Writing, Ninth Grd Creative Writing Publications; NEA 1969-; MCTE 1979-; Lenox Historical Soc 1980-; Berkshire Cty Historical Soc 1980-; Featured on TV Prgm Chronicle; 5 Part Series on Ed TV; Prof Grant to Stud in Belize; Toyota Grant for Interdisciplinary Tchng; *office:* Lenox Meml HS 197 East St Lenox MA 01240

VINCENT, SUSAN HANIAN, Math Teacher; *b:* Weymouth, MA; *m:* Thomas B.; *ed:* Univ of MA at Amherst (BA) Elem Ed 1972; 45 Credit Hrs Bridgewater St Coll; 9 Credit Hrs Massasoit Coll; *cr:* Nash Schl 4th Grd Tchr 1972-75, 6th Grd Tchr 1975-91; East Intermediate Schl 6th Grd Tchr 1991-94; Adams Intermediate Schl 7th Grd Math Tchr 1994-; *ai:* Peer Mentor New Tchrs; Fac Coord Peer Mediation Prgm; Lead Tchr; NEA, MA Tchrs Assn, Norfolk Cty Tchrs Assn, Weymouth Tchrs Assn 1972-; *office:* Abigail Adams Intermediate Sch 89 Middle St East Weymouth MA 02189

VINCENT, THOMAS, 5th Grade Teacher; *b:* Homestead, PA; *m:* Helen G.; *ed:* CA St Univ (BA) Elem Ed 1972; Pitt Post Grad Stud; *cr:* Park Elem Schl Tchr 25 Yrs; *ai:* Safety Club; NEA 1972-; SVEA 1972-; PSEA 1972-; Schl Grants; *office:* Steel Vly Schl Dist E Oliver Dr Munhall PA 15120

VINCENZI, JOSEPH PERRY, Spanish Teacher & Admin Asst; *b:* Bridgeport, CT; *ed:* Sacred Heart Univ (BA) Sec Ed, Span 1973; Fairfield Univ (MA) TESOL 1982; Univ of Bridgeport 6th Yr Equivalent Admin, Prof Dev 1986; *cr:* Central HS Span Instr 1975-, Adult Ed Prgm TESOL Instr, Coord 1975-91; *ai:* PTSO Fac Mem-at-Large; Prof Dev Assoc; BEA, CEA, NEA 1975-; ASCD 1995-; NSDC 1992-; Mayor's Commission Persons with Disabilities, Commissioner 1990-92; Kennedy Ctr Parents, Friends 1990-; Tchr of Month 1987; Rotary Club Svc Above Self Tchr of Yr Awd 1990-91; Tchr of Yr Nom; *office:* Central Magnet HS 1 Lincoln Blvd Bridgeport CT 06606

VINCI, DORIS OPATRNY, Second Grade Teacher; *b:* Cleveland, OH; *m:* Dennis J.; *ed:* Cleveland St Univ (BA) Elem Ed 1979; Bapt Bible Coll Cert Bible 1980; *cr:* 4 Credit Hrs Baldwin Wallace Coll; 3 Credit Hrs Drake Univ; *ai:* Cedar Hill Chrstn Schl Third Grd Tchr 1980-84, Second Grd Tchr 1984-; Chrstn Ed Comm; Yrbk Coord; After Care Prgm Dir; *office:* Cedar Hill Christian Schl 12601 Cedar Rd Cleveland OH 44106*

VINCI, JULIA ANN, Lang Arts & Soc Studies Tchr; *b:* Canton, OH; *ed:* Kent St Univ (BS) Scndry Eng & His 1962;, (MS) Curr & Supv 1980; MS Rdng & Rdng Supv; Cert Elem Ed; *cr:* canton Local Schls Tchr 1962-63; Belize British Honduras Tchr 1963-67; Plain Local Schls Tchr 1967-; *ai:* Intramural Golf; NEA 1967-; OEA 1967-; ECOEA & PLTA 1967-, Bldg Rep; Martha Jennings Fndtn Scholar; Ashland Inc Tchr Achvmt Awd Candidate; *office:* Middlebranch MS 7500 Middlebranch Ave NE Canton OH 44721

VINCITORE, KATHLEEN GIACCHI, First Grade Inclusion Teacher; *b:* Syracuse, NY; *m:* Michael John; *c:* Michael, Kimberly; *ed:* SUNY at Oswego (BS) Elem Ed 1967; 42 Addl Grad Hrs also Syracuse Univ; *cr:* Craven Crawford Elem Schl First Grd Tchr 1967-72; Donlin Drive Elem Schl Kndgtn First Grd Tchr 1973-77; Donlin Drive, Soule Rd Elem Schl Resource Tchr 1977-78; Chestnut Hill Elem Schl 4-5 Milti-Age Tchr 1979-81, 2nd Grd Tchr 1981-83, 5th Grd Tchr 1983-95, First Grd Inclusive Tchr 1995-; *ai:* Union Bldg Rep; IM Bsktbl Coach; CCD Tchr; United Liverpool Fac Assn 1967-, Bldg Rep; NYSUT, AFT 1967-; Tchng Ctr Grant for 5th Grd Ec; Co-Dev Pride Comm; Co-Authored 2 Grants from NY St; *office:* Chestnut Hill Elem Schl 200 Saslon Park Dr Liverpool NY 13088

VINE, JANET DIANE, English Teacher; *b:* Albany, NY; *ed:* Syracuse Univ (BA) Eng Ed 1959; SUNY (MA) Ed 1964; 30 Addl Hrs at Murray St Univ, Hofstra, Univ of Maine at Orono, Wright St Univ, Kent St Univ; 47 Hrs Through Ken-ton Tchrs Ctr; *cr:* Herbert Hoover Jr HS Eng Tchr 1959-66; Kenmore east Sr HS Eng Tchr, Dept Chm 1970-83; *ai:* Chrldr Coach 1959-77; Various Curr Comms; AFT, NYSUT, NCTE, Phi Lambda Theta 1959-; KTA 1959-, Bldg Rep; Amer League of Amer Penwomen 1979-, Pres 1984-86, NYS St Treas 1990-94; Assoc Prof Women Writers, The Write People 1978-; Write Assocs 1981-; Amer Assoc of Univ Women 1990-; Co Authored Books; Articles in Newspapers; *office:* Kenmore East Sr HS 350 Fries Rd Tonawanda NY 14150

VINEBERG, CAROL, 6th Grade Teacher; *b:* New York, NY; *ed:* C. W. Post (BA) Elem Ed 1970, (MS) Elem Ed 1973; Addl 38 Credits; *cr:* Baldwin Schl Dist K-6 Grd Tchr; *ai:* Soc Skills Comm; Baldwin Tchrs Assn, NEA, AFT 1970-; Lifetime PTA Tchng Awd 1994; *home:* 6120 Grand Central Pkwy Forest Hills NY 11375*

VINET, GEORGE ELLSWORTH,JR., Hlth & Physical Education Coor; *b:* Staten Island, NY; *ed:* Brooklyn Coll (BSHS) Hlth Sci 1977; Hunter Coll (MSHS) Comm Hlth Ed 1979; Coll of Staten Island (ACE) Schl Admin & Supervision 1981; Univ of IL PHD 30 Hrs in Hlth & Safety Ed; *cr:* Lakeland Regnl HS Hlth Specialist 1981-85; Hyde Park Cntrl Schl Dist Hlth & PE Dir 1985-87; New York City Hlth Dept Sr Pub Hlth Specialist 1987-90; New York City Emergency Medical Svc Exec Educator 1990-91; Curtis HS Hlth & PE Coord 1991-; *ai:* HIV-AIDS Team & Peer Ldr; moderator; Prins Cabinet; AAHPERD 1974-, Mem, Outstanding NYC Hlth & Physical Educator; AASECT 1976-, Mem, Certified Sexuality Educator; Natl Commission for Credentialing in Hlth Ed Inc 1989-, Mem, Certified Hlth Ed Specialist; United Fed of Tchrs 1991-, Mem, George Meany Awd; BSA 1963-, Exploring Chair, Silver River; Amer Red Cross 1970-, Water Safety Instr & Trainer, ARC Safety Medal; AAHPERD Aquatics Cncl Certified Master Clinician in Instruction of Swimming; Lifeguard Trng; Twice Pub in Prof Ed Journals; *office:* Curtis HS 105 Hamilton Ave Staten Island NY 10301*

VINICKY, SANDRA (SZYMCZYK), Seventh Grade Teacher; *b:* Cleveland, OH; *m:* Gary S.; *ed:* Cleveland St Univ (BA) Eng 1969; Addl Hrs Cmptr Sci, Cooperative Learning, Rdng; *cr:* St Mary Schl Grd Seven Tchr 1969-70, Grd Six Tchr 1970-80, Grd Five Tchr 1980-88, Grd Seven Tchr 1988-; *ai:* Safety Patrol Adv; NCEA 1969-; *office:* Saint Mary Schl 237 4th St Elyria OH 44035

VINIK, BRUCE, Upper School Principal; *b:* Deal, NJ; *m:* Virginia Levin; *c:* Annie, Jessie; *ed:* Duke Univ (BA) Anthropology 1975, (MA) His 1977; *cr:* Georgetown Day MS Tchr 1977-80; Germantown Acad Upper Schl Tchr 1980-82; Georgetown Day MS Tchr 1982-91, Asst Prin 1988-91, Dir of Coll Cnslng 1991-95; Barrie Schl Upper Schl Prin 1995-; *ai:* NAIS; AIMS; AISGW; *office:* Barrie Schl 13500 Layhill Rd Silver Spring MD 20906

VINING, TED, Teacher; *b:* Keene, NH; *m:* Eileen; *c:* Eric, Rebecca, Benjamin; *ed:* Leslie Coll (MA) Ed 1994; 30 Addl Hrs; *cr:* Monument Mtn Fegnl HS Tchr 1967-; *ai:* Class, Yrbk Adv; MTA, NEA, TEAM 1967-; Conservation Commission 1980-.

VINOPAL, ANN M., English Teacher; *b:* Titusville, PA; *ed:* Clarion Univ of PA (BS) Ed & Eng 1989; Shippensburg Univ of PA (MS) Ed & Rdng Specialist 1994; *cr:* Dover Area Schl Dist Eng Tchr 1989-; *ai:* Eng Dept Task Force; PRIDE Stu Assistance Team; NEA 1989-; PSEA 1989-; DAEA 1989-; *office:* Dover Area HS W Canal St Dover PA 17315

VIOLA, FLORENCE SZOKOLI, 7th-8th Grd Soc Studies Tchr; *b:* Philadelphia, PA; *m:* Louis C.; *c:* Florence Ann Viola Lanzillo, Louis A., Donnamarie A., Deborah A.; *ed:* Holy Family Coll (BA) Pol Economy 1967; *cr:* Our Lady of Fatima 2nd Grd Tchr 1967-68; St Michael Archangel 2nd, 3rd, 7th, 8th Grd Tchr 1970-; *ai:* Chrldng Coach 15 Yrs; Bishop Egan HS Chrldng Coach 5 Yrs; CCD Asst 5 Yrs; Mid Sts Comm 1993-95; Visiting Team; NEA 1967-; *office:* Saint Michael Archangel Schl 66 Levittown Pky Levittown PA 19054

VIOLA-BARRETT, JENNIFER JEAN, High School Mathematics Tchr; *b:* Bedford, OH; *m:* M. B. Dailey; *c:* Patricia, Damien, Anthony; *ed:* Rock Vly Coll at Rockford (AS) Scndry Ed, Math 1984; Northern IL Univ at DeKalb (BS) Math, Scndry Ed 1986; *cr:* Hiawatha HS Math Tchr 1986-87; John Hay HS Math Tchr 1988-; Case Western Reserve LTV Steel Summer Prgm for HS Stdnts Math Tchr 1991-; *ai:* Union Conf Comm; AFT 1988-; *office:* John Hay HS 2075 Stokes Blvd Cleveland OH 44106*

VIOLANTI, ANNE MARY, Band Director; *b:* Buffalo, NY; *m:* John C. Krenitsky; *c:* Courtney, Patrick; *ed:* St Univ of NY at Buffalo (BFA) Music Ed, Performance 1985, (EDM) Educl Admin 1989; Schl Admin, Supervision Cert 1995; Schl Dist Admin Cert 1996; *cr:* Orchard Park Cntrl Schls Band Dir 1986-; *ai:* Jazz Ensemble, Marching Band Dir; Century of Excl Chm; Erie Cty Music Edctrs Assn 1982-, Bd; Western NY Women in Admin 1994-; Phi Delta Kappa 1995-; Orchard Park Cncl of Arts 1987-, Pub Relations Chm; Orchard Park Chamber of Commerce 1994-, MS Rep; *office:* Orchard Park MS 60 S Lincoln Ave Orchard Park NY 14127

VIOTTI, STEPHEN MICHAEL, Honors Math & Algebra Teacher; *b:* Chester, PA; *ed:* Temple Univ (BBA) Acctng 1978; *cr:* Holy Savior St John Fisher Hnrs Math Tchr 1988-; *ai:* Mathletes Adv; NCEA 1991-; Holy Saviour St John Cyo 1975-, Past Pres & Chief Adv, Outstdng Svc 1990; Holy Saviour-St John Fisher Schl Fin Cncl 1977-; Holy Saviour Parish Cncl 1993-; *office:* Holy Saviour-St J. Fisher Schl 122 E Ridge Rd Marcus Hook PA 19061

VIRASITH, MICHELE L., Spanish Teacher; *b:* Portland, IN; *m:* Boungnang Virasith; *ed:* Ball St Univ (BA) Span 1983, (MA) 1990; Cert in Eng 1992; *cr:* St Henry HS Part-time Span Tchr 1984-91; Coldwater Ex Vill Schls Span Tchr 1985-; *ai:* Span Club Adv; PTO Carnival Comm Chm; Foreign Lang Dept Chm; Curr Cncl; AATSP 1986, 1991-; Miami Valley F L Assn, OFLA, IN FLTA, OEA, NEA 1984-; Ft Wayne Alliance 1989-; Mercer Cty F.L. Alliance 1994-; Jay Co Arts Cncl 1984-; St Marys Sister Cities Inc 1992-; *office:* Coldwater Exempted Village Sch 310 N 2nd St Coldwater OH 45828

VIRGA, MICHAEL GANDOLFO, Spanish Teacher; *b:* New York City, NY; *m:* Kathleen Trojan; *c:* Heather, Michael; *ed:* Marist Coll (BA) Span 1973; New Paltz St Coll (MA) Ed 1982; 21 Post Master Grad Credits; Univ de Madrid 30 Credits Toward BA; *cr:* St Joseph Regnl HS Span Tchr 1973-74; Marlboro MS Span Tchr 1974-; *ai:* 7th Grd Class Adv; Pilot Pgm Team; NYSUT 1974-; *office:* Marlboro MS Rt 9W Marlboro NY 12542*

VIROSTKO, JOAN, Elementary Specialty Educator; *b:* Queens Jackson Hts, NY; *ed:* St John's Univ in Jamaica (BS) Elem Ed, (MS) Elem Ed, (PO) Curr, Tchng, (MBA) Mrktg Mngmt, (PHD) Instrl Ldrshp; Oxford Univ in England Cert Stud Intnl Ed; *cr:* Pavmanok Schl Edctr; Oxford Univ Lecturer; St John's Univ Adj Prof; Columbia Univ Tchrs Coll Adj Prof; *ai:* Sloan Kettering Hosp Blood Donor Drive; NYSUT 1980-; Kappa Delta Pi 1980-, Most Distngd Intnl Dissertation 1983; Phi Delta Kappa 1985-; St John's U Deans List; Sacred Heart Church, Lector; St Bernard's St Vincent De Paul Soc; Republican Natl Comm 1980-, Spon; PTA; St John's Univ Alumni Assn 1980-; Who's Who Amer Coll & Univ; Who's Who Amer; Who's Who World; Who's Who Distngd Ldrs; Who's Who Among Intnl Women; *office:* Pavmanok Schl 1 Seamans Neck Rd Dix Hills NY 11746*

VIRULEG, MARY KATHLEEN, Math Department Chairperson; *b:* Providence, RI; *m:* R. Andrew; *c:* Daniel, Ellen; *ed:* Salve Regina Coll (AB) Math 1965; Worcester Polytechnic Inst (MS) Physics 1980; Attnd Boston Coll, Providence Coll, Princeton Univ; *cr:* Lincoln Pub Schls Math Tchr 1967-95; *ai:* NCSM 1994-; NCTM 1984-; RIMTA 1989-; N Smithfield Lib Trustee 1985-, VP, Sec; RI Finalist Presidential Awd Excl Sci, Math Tchng; Tandy Tech Scholar; Woodrow wilson Natl Flwshp Fnd Master Tchr; *office:* Lincoln HS 135 Old River Rd Lincoln RI 02865

VISCARDO, GERTRUDE RIEKER, Accelerated Math Teacher; *b:* Buffalo, NY; *m:* William; *c:* William Jr., Christine Devenney, Gregory; *ed:* NYS Coll at Bflo (BS) Ed; *cr:* Kenmore Schls 6th Grd Tchr 1959-64; Christ the King Schl Grds 6-8 Acc Math Tchr 1980-; Williamsville Cntrl Schl Home Instr 1990-; Diocese of Buffalo Jr HS Math Coord 1992-; *ai:* Amherst Cntrl MS, HS PTA 1977-91, VP, Pres 1977-91; Amherst Yth Prgm & Bd VP, Pres 1976-89; Eggertsville Snyder Quality Life Cncl Founder, Pres 1981-91; Canisius Coll Schlsp Assn Fin Sec, Pres 1971-; St Benedicts Yth Bd, Chm Guid Healing 1983-86; Comm Rep IRB Bd Roswell Pk Meml Inst 1977-88; St Benedict's Church Eucharistic Minister; YMCA, Amherst Yth Prgm Vol of Yr 1980-81; Amherst Yth Bd Svc to Yth 1983; NYS PTA Life Mbrshp 1983; Natl PTA Life Mbrshp 1991; Amherst Cha[mber of] Commerce Svc to Yth Awd 1990; *office:* Christ The King Schl 2 [...] Dr Amherst NY 14226

VISCHER, LINDA BRECKENRIDGE, Chemistry Teac[her; *b:*] Greenville, PA; *m:* Carl V. IV; *c:* Heather Schweizer, Heidi Schwe[...]; Allegheny Coll (BS) Chem 1970; Temple Univ (MS) Sci Ed 1973; Coll Supvrs Cert in Scndry Sci; *cr:* William H Roher Chemist [...] William Tennent HS Chem Tchr 1971-78; Wissahickon HS Che[m Tchr] 1979-83; Upper Dublin HS Chem Tchr 1983-, Sci Dept Chair 19[...] NSTA, PSTA 1971-; ACS 1992-; Montgomery Cty Outstanding S[...] Amer Chemical Soc Excl in Pre-Coll Tchng; *office:* Upper Dubli[n ...] 800 Loch Alsh Ave Fort Washington PA 19034

VISCO, CHRISTOPHER, Earth Science Teacher; *b:* Amityville, [NY; *m:*] Peggy; *c:* Brianna, Travis; *ed:* SUC At Onenota (BS) Geology 1975[; ...] at Binghamton (MA) Geological Sci 1977; *cr:* Sachem HS Earth S[ci ...] 1985-; Coll of New Rochelle Adj Prof 1993-; *ai:* Geologic Rsrch; [...] *office:* Sachem HS South 51 School St Ronkonkoma NY 11779*

VISCONTI, PATRICIA E. (SMALL), Sixth Grade Teac[her; *b:*] Gouverneur, NY; *m:* Leo A.; *c:* Laura A. Carbone; *ed:* SUNY at [...] (BA) N-6 Ed & Soc Sci 1972; 30 Post Bachelor Hrs with Emphasis [...] Sci & Ec; *cr:* Harrisville Cntrl Schl 6th Grd Tchr 1972-; *ai:* 6th G[rd] Adv; Harrisville Tchrs Assn 1972-, VP; AFT 1973-; NY St Unite[d ...] 1973-; Jefferson-Lewis Tchr Ctr 1995-; E J Noble Hospital Auxilary[; ...] Friends of Lib 1990-.

VISGILIO, GAIL THELIN, High Schl English & Rdng Tchr; *b:* [...] NJ; *m:* Patrick W.; *c:* Patrick T., Van P.; *ed:* Jersey City St Coll (B[A)] Soc Stud 1963; Univ of Southern CA (MS) Scndry Ed 1967; 28 Cr[...] Rdng Brigham Young Univ, Univ of CA, Univ of RI, MI St Univ, [...] Adenauer Inst; *cr:* North Arlington HS Eng Tchr 1963-64; Dept of [...] Dep Schls Eng, Soc Stud Tchr, Rdng Specialist 1964-80; Stoning[ton ...] Soc Stud Tchr 1980-84; Dept of Def Dep Schl HS Eng, Rdng Tchr 1[...] Westerly HS Eng, Rdng Tchr 1990-; *ai:* High Schl Collaborative [...] Team; NEA, NEARI, IRA, NCTE 1993-; Tchr of Yr 1992-93; [...] Defense Dep Schls Superior Tchr Performance Awd; Exceptional [...] Performance in Rdng & Eng; Fellowship Offered Univ of HI; [...] Westerly HS 23 Ward Ave Westerly RI 02891*

VISHIO, SUSAN A., Spanish & French Teacher; *b:* Reading[, ...] Kutztown Univ (BA) Span, Fr 1975, (MS) Scndry Counseling 19[...] Credits Past Masters; *office:* Boyertown Jr HS-WEST 200 S Mad[ison ...] Boyertown PA 19512

VISHNESKY, CARMEN LORRAINE, Fr Tchr & Frgn Lang Dep[t ...]; *b:* Williamsport, PA; *m:* Norbert A.; *ed:* Bloomsburg Univ of PA ([...]) 1968; Attnd West Chester Univ, Millersville Univ, Lebanon Vly C[oll ...] Cntrl Dauphin Schl Dist Fr Tchr 1968-, Chair Frgn Lang Dept 19[...] Fr Club; Mid Sts Evaluation Chair Frgn Lang; CDEA, PSEA [...] 1968-72, 1988-; MLAPV, PASE 1993-; ACTFL, MLA, PSMLA[; ...] Capitol Strand Theatre; *office:* Central Dauphin HS 4600 Loc[...] Harrisburg PA 17109

VITAGLIANO, DAVID HAROLD, English & Journalism Teac[her; ...] Baltimore, MD; *m:* Mary Jo Julia Kachik; *ed:* Towson St Univ (BS[) ...] Comm & Psych 1976; Loyola Coll (MS) Modern Stud 1987; *cr:* A[...] HS Jrnlsm & Eng Tchr 1978-; *ai:* Newspaper & Yrbk Adv; Var Sftbl [...] Baltimore WA Corridor Chamber of Commerce Tchr of Yr 1991; [...] Atholton HS 6520 Freetown Rd Columbia MD 21044

VITALE, JAMES LEO, Guidance Dept Chairperson; *b:* Queens, [NY; ...] Lorraine (dec); *c:* Michael; *ed:* Soc Work Cert NY St 1993; Natl So[...] Cert 1981; St Johns Residence, Schl for Boys Child Care Cnslr [...] 1970-74, Child Care Dir 1974-86, Asst Admin 1986-89; Our L[ady of] Perpetual Help HS Guid Cnslr, Chrprsn Guid Dept 1990-; *cr:* [...] Moderator; *ai:* Acad of Certified Soc Workers 1975-81; NYS C[...] Workers 1993-; St Francis De Sales Parish 1967-, Ldr Song, [...] Rockaway Little League Bsbl Coach 10 Yrs.

VITALE, JANET L., Fifth Grade Teacher; *b:* Lorain, OH; *c:* J[...] Suzanne Varney; *ed:* Baldwin-Wallace Coll (BA) Elem Ed 1963 [...] Classes Akron Univ, Ashland Univ, Kent St Univ; *cr:* Warrenton Sch[l ...] 1962-63; Emerson Schl Tchr 1963-66; Bonita springs Schl Tchr 19[...] Palm Schl Tchr 1972-77; Masson Schl Tchr, Jr HS Coach 1977-; *ai:* [...] Vlybl, Soccer Coach; Classroom of the Future Mbrshp, Curr C[...] Supervised Stu Tchrs; Elem Stu Professional Exchange Prgm; Lor[ain ...] Assoc; OH Ed Assoc; NEA; IRA; AAUW; Proclamation from OH [...] for Excl in Tchng; *office:* Masson Elem Schl 1400 W 40th St Lora[in OH] 44053

VITALE, RONALD L., English Teacher; *b:* Rochester, NY; *ed:* S[t John] Fisher Coll (BA) Eng 1972; Nazareth Coll (MS) Ed 1974; 30+ Post [...] Hrs; *cr:* Rush-Henrietta Schl Dist Eng Tchr 1972-; *ai:* Pen Pal Club[; ...] Rdg & Writing Club; Performance Based Assessment Comm; MS R[...] Comm; AFT 1972-; Phi Delta Kappa 1974-; NY St Eng Cncl 1988-[; ...] MS Assn 1982-; Tchr of the Yr 1976; NYS Eng Tchr of the Yr 1976; [...] Henry Burger MS 639 Erie Station Rd West Henrietta NY 14586*

VITARTAS, PAUL, English & American His Tchr; *b:* Canton, OH; [...] Deluse Russell; *c:* Ariel, Hava, Nathan, Mary, Matthew; *ed:* OH S[t Univ] (BS) Ed 1981; 28 Grad-Ed Hrs Ashland Univ; *cr:* Lakewood HS Eng [...] 1985-86; Cardington-Lincoln HS Eng, Soc Stud Tchr 1986-89; Tri-[...] Joint Voc Schl Eng, His Tchr 1989-; *ai:* NEA, OH Ed Assn 1986-; M[...] City Cncl 1994-, Pres; US Army Reserve 1988-, Staff Sergeant; M[...] Chamber of Commerce 1995-; *home:* 475 S Prospect St Marion OH [...]

VITEK, SUSAN PERKINS, 6th Grade Teacher; *b:* Kingston, N[...] Patrick L.; *c:* Jefferson Patrick; *ed:* Upsala Coll (BS) Psych 1968; S[UNY] at Stony Brook (MA) Lbrl Stud 1972; Long Island Univ 39 Grad C[...] Hrs; Adelphi Univ 12 Grad Credit Hrs; *cr:* Norwood Elem Schl 3rd-6t[h] Tchr 1968-88; East Northport MS 6th Grd Tchr 1988-; *ai:* ENCORE [...] AFT 1968-; NYSUT 1968-; United Tchrs of Northport [...] Environmental Ctr of Setauket Smithtown 1989-, Trustee; *offi[ce:]* Northport MS 5th Ave East Northport NY 11731

VITENAS, DIANA, 9th Grade English Teacher; *b:* Metairie, LA[; ...] Carnegie-Mellon Univ (BA) Prof Writing 1985; Duquesne Univ (ME[d) ...] 1991; *cr:* Keystone Oaks HS Eng Tchr 1991; Keystone Oaks MS 8t[h ...] Eng Tchr 1991; Keystone Oaks HS Eng Tchr 1992-; *ai:* Odyssey of [...] Judge 3 Yrs; NEA, PSEA 1991-; *office:* Keystone Oaks HS 1000 K[...] Ave Pittsburgh PA 15216

VITIELLO, JO ANN DIGANGI, Principal; *b:* Brooklyn, NY; *m:* Jo[...] *ed:* St Francis Coll (BA) Elem Ed 1974; Adelphi Univ (MA) Elem Ed [...] *cr:* St Martha Schl 1, 6 Grd Tchr 1976-84; St Athanasius Schl 4[...] Tchr1984-85; St Angela Hall Acad 5 Grd Tchr 1985-86; JFK Dir Day [...] Ctr Pre-K, K 1986-87; St. Joseph's Coll Adj Prof, Early Chldhd [...] 1986-87; St Anastasia Schl Prin 1987-92; St Leo Schl Prin 1992-; *ai:* [...] Schl Comm Chrprsn; Home Schl Assn Moderator; St Leo C[...] Extraordinary Minister of Eucharist; NCEA, CSAANYS, Cath Sci [...] Elem Math Cncl 1987-; Little Neck Douglaston Comm Svc Awd 199[...] Yr Catechetical Ministry Awd Brooklyn Diocese 1995; Merit Ci[...] Queensborough Pres 1992; 4 Articles Pub 1976-84.

VITKO, DONALD ROBERT, Communication Arts Teacher; *b:* Norw[...] CT; *ed:* Elizabethtown Coll (BA) Eng 1991; PA Writing Pr[...] Westchester Univ; 6 Grad Credits Summer Inst 1994; 3 Grad Cr[...] Portfolio Assessment Course 1995; *cr:* J. P. Mc Caskey HS Comm [...]

92-; *ai:* PSEA, NEA 1992-; Red Cross Comm on Yth At Risk Issues 993-94; *office:* J P Mc Caskey HS 445 N Reservoir St Lancaster PA

DAVID ROBERT, Biology Teacher; *b:* Providence, RI; *m:* Lynda astasi; *c:* David, Tara, Jon, Ashley, Allissa, Audrianna; *ed:* RI Coll o 1975, (MA) Bio 1985; Cert Advanced Stud Prgm; *cr:* North o HS Bio Tchr 21 Yrs; Bristol Comm Coll 6 Yrs; *ai:* Sci Fair Adv ci Fair Judge Local, Regnl, St Level; Jr Sci, Hum Symposium Adv; Mentor Elem, Jr HS Stdnts, Tchrs; New England Bio Tchrs Comm Exhibitors; Region III Sci Fair Comm 1986-, Pres, Tom Cahill Awd; Sci Fair 1988-, Judging Co-Chair, Mentor Awd; MA Assn Sci Tchrs, sn Sci Supvrs 1991-; Sci Fair Tchr Mentor Awd; Excl Sci Tchng dv: Sci Fair Stdnts Earned 57 First Place Awds Regnl, St Sci Fairs, Rep MA Intnl Sci, Engineering Fair, Stu Rep US London Youth um; *office:* North Attleboro HS 570 Landry Ave North Attleboro 760*

I, WILLIAM SCOTT, Chemistry Teacher; *b:* Ft Dix, NJ; *c:* Kelsey, Alex; *ed:* PA St Univ (BS) Chem Ed 1973; California Univ MED) Environmental Ed 1982; Indiana Univ of PA (MA) Chem Princeton Univ Woodrow Wilson Inst Chem 1986; *cr:* Elizabeth HS AP Chem & Chem Instr 1973-; Comm Coll of Allegheny Cty ne Chem Instr 1988-; Westmoreland Cty Comm Coll Part-Time nstr 1988-; *ai:* Jr Class Spon; Dist APEX Comm Mem; NSTA 1984-, ar Reviewer-Search for Excl Comm; PSTA 1983-, Southwestern EA & NEA 1973-; Soc of Analytical Chemists of Pittsburgh 1986-, reach Comm, Kelvin Burns Awd for Outstanding Sci Tchng 1986; scopy Soc of Pittsburgh 1986-, HS Equipment Grants Comm; Amer al Soc 1991; Gave Presentation at "Chem Ed 1987" Kingston ; Dreyfus Master Tchr 1986; Pub Article for "Chem 13 News 1985; ation at NSTA Cnvntn 1995; Presentation at 14th BCCE; *office:* th Forward HS 1000 Weigles Hill Rd Elizabeth PA 15037*

ROBERT C., High School Tchr & Band Dir; *b:* Greenwich, CT; n Zadrauecz; *c:* Melissa; *ed:* Mercy Coll (BA) Music Ed; tanville (MS) Music Ed; *cr:* Port Chester HS Asst Band Dir 8 Yrs, ir 4 Yrs; *ai:* Hurricans & Brassmen Drum & Bugle Corp; NYSSMA CMBC 1994-; NYFB 1994-; Premier Percussion Educl Staff; *office:* ester Pub Schls Bowman Ave Port Chester NY 10573

RIO, LYNN E. (CLIFTON), First Grade Teacher; *b:* Youngstown, Michael J.; *ed:* Westminster Coll (BA) Elem Ed 1974; Youngstown v Early Chldhd 1983; *cr:* Central Elem Remedial Rdng Tchr 5; Howland Chrstn 4th Grd Tchr 1977-78; Good Apple Presch 4 & d Tchr 1980-81; Youngstown Chrstn 1st Grd Tchr 1981-; *ai:* Schl sst; Staff Soc Comm Chm; Liberty Presbyn Church 1964-, Sunday c, Jr Choir Ldr, Music & Worship Comm, Vacation Bible Schl Dir; Youngstown Christian Schl 125 Wychwood Ln Youngstown OH

LO, JANICE MARIE, High School Latin Teacher; *b:* town, OH; *ed:* Univ of TX at Arlington (BA) Classical Stud 1990; Univ (MA) Latin 1993; *cr:* Glenoak HS Latin Tchr 1993-; *ai:* Latin Plato Group Adv; Amer Classical League, OH Classical League, al Assoc of the Midwest & South 1991-; *office:* Glen Oak HS 1015 NW Canton OH 44709

LO, RAYMOND D., Band Director; *b:* Youngstown, OH; *m:* Del Garbino; *c:* Andrea, Sara, John; *ed:* Univ TX at Arlington (BM) Ed 1985; Youngstown St Univ (MS) Music Ed 1991; *cr:* East ne City Schl Dist Band Dir 1985-91; *ai:* Marching, Concert & Jazz NEA 1985-; MENC 1985-; OMEA 1985-; Warren Tribune cle A+ Tchr Awd 1994; Youngstown City Schl Dist All Star Band Conductor 1989; *office:* Liberty HS 317 Churchill Hubbard Rd stown OH 44505

NS, ROBERT EDWARD, 7th Grd Social Studies Teacher; *b:* bus, OH; *ed:* Princeton Univ (BA) Sociology 1083; *cr:* Princeton HS ad Tchr 1984-88; John Witherspoon MS Soc Stud Tchr 1988-; *ai:* S Bsbl, Ftbl, Chrldng Coach 10 Yrs; Adv Heritage Prgm; NEA, 1984-; Princeton Reg Ed Assoc 1984-, Pres 1986-88; First Bapt Outstdng Edctr 1994; PU Comm House Ldrshp Awd 1994; *office:* Witherspoon MS 217 Walnut Ln Princeton NJ 08540

NO, ANTHONY S., College Counselor; *b:* Detroit, MI; *ed:* Western iv (BA) His & Pol Sci 1965, (MA) Counseling 1967; Attnd Western v & Univ of CT; *cr:* Western MI Univ RA & Assoc Dir of Res Hall 67; Western IL Univ Dir of Res Hall 1967-69; Capital Comm Tech nslr 1969-; *ai:* Wellness Dir; TQM Comm; Coll Senate; Curr & Acad s Comm; Affirmative Action Officer; Stu Act Dir; Cnslrs Assn Chair; Natl Bd for Certified Cnslrs 1985-; Congress of CT Comm Coll 1971-; Wrote Article Persistence in Coll; Alcohol & Other Drugs Fipse; Stu Senate Awd; ETS & ACT Awds; Retraining Grant in l & Other Drugs; *office:* Capital Comm-Tech Coll 61 Woodland Hartford CT 06105

RITO, JOSEPH JOHN, Technology & Driver Ed Teacher; *b:* New City, NY; *m:* Patricia Mary Fox; *c:* Carissa, Jonathan; *ed:* SUNY at ngdale (AAS) Mechanical Engineering 1971; SUNY at Oswego (BS) rial Arts 1973, (MS) Industrial Arts 1974; SDA, Cert Advanced Stud at Brockport; *cr:* Palmyra Macedon HS Tech Tchr 1983-; *ai:* Boys rls Var Tennis Coach 1986-90; Photo Club, Yrbk Advs; Four Cty Tech Assn 1985-, Pres; Pub Broadcasting, Tech Prep Grants; *office:* ra Macedon HS 151 Hyde Pky Palmyra NY 14522

A, WILLIAM A., English Teacher; *b:* Pittsburg, PA; *m:* Teresa ne; *c:* Christopher, Mark, Marie; *ed:* Slippery Rock (BS) Eng 1964; niv of PA (MA) Eng 1970; *cr:* Warren HS Eng Tchr 1965-67; Baldwin g Tchr 1967-; *ai:* Asst Bsktbl Coach; Class Spon; AFT 1970-; Pony of Amer 1984-, Field Dir; Italian Sons & Daughters of Amer 1960-; Baldwin HS 4653 Clairton Blvd Pittsburgh PA 15236*

HOS, ZACHARY J., History Department Chairman; *b:* Sharon, PA; ary Wagner; *c:* Mary Grace Muster, Anne Wagner Zachara, Stephanie e Harris; *ed:* Bethany Coll (BA) His 1954; Univ of Pittsburgh (MLitt) 955; 30 Credits towards PHD at Columbia Univ; *cr:* Woodmere Acad & Coach 1957-61; Kiskiminetas Springs Schl Tchr & Admin 1961-; bl, Bsktbl, Bsbl, Tennis & Swimming Coach; Dev, Alumni & Stud AIS; PAISTA, VP; AHA; CASE; NEH Flwshp; *office:* Kiskiminetas gs Schl 1888 Brett Ln Saltsburg PA 15681

KE-MC GOVERN, ANN, Fifth Grade Teacher; *b:* Napoleon, OH; *m:* ence; *ed:* Eastern MI Univ (BS) Elem Ed 1971; Salem St Coll Grad Hrs Rdng; *cr:* St Anthony's Schl 2 Grd Tchr 1972-73; Sacred Heart 2 Grd Tchr 1973-79; MA Migrant Ed prgm Summer Schl Tchr 92; Sacred Heart Schl 5 Grd Tchr 1979-; *ai:* Schl Choir Dir; After Math Prgm; NCEA 1977-; PTA 1995-; *office:* Sacred Heart Schl 581 n St West Lynn MA 01905

KINS, JERE RICE, Social Studies Teacher; *b:* White Plains, NY; *c:* Christopher, Heather Lee; *ed:* Tchrs Coll at Columbia Univ (MS) y Ed 1967; Attnd Fordham Univ, Hartford Univ, Univ of CT; *cr:* and HS Soc Stud Tchr 1967-70; John Jay HS Soc Stud Tchr 1970-72; ster HS Soc Stud Tchr 1986-; *ai:* Stu Govt Adv; AFT 1967-; Amer r Soc, Fundraiser; Elmira Coll, Class Rep; Tchr of Yr 1993-94; Tchr 1986-, Amer His; *office:* Brewster HS Foggintown Rd Brewster NY

VODOKLYS, MICHAEL J., 8th Grade Lang Arts Teacher; *b:* Framingham, MA; *m:* Joan Folino; *c:* Jami, Lindsay; *ed:* Univ of MA at Amherst (BA) Eng 1972; Worcester St Coll (MED) Spec Needs 1980; *cr:* Framingham Schl Dist Tchr 1975-; *ai:* Framingham Tchrs Assn 1975-; MA Tchrs Assn 1975-; NEA 1975-; Framingham United Soccer Club 1984-; *office:* Walsh MS 301 Brook St Framingham MA 01701

VODOUNON, MAURICE A., Mathematics & Cmptr Sci Prof; *b:* Porto-Novo, Republic Benin; *m:* Andrea Gordon; *c:* Desiree, Raissa; *ed:* Univ of Niamey (BS) Math 1978; Baruch Coll (BBA) Fin 1988; Columbia Univ (MA) Math Ed 1990; Tchrs Coll (EDM) Math 1992, (EDD) Math 1994; *cr:* Ministry of Ed HS Math, Bio Instr 1978-83; Baruch Coll Asst 1984-87; UNDP United Nations Consultant & Researcher 1989; John Jay Coll Asst Prof 1990-; *ai:* Vol Under Grad Acad Adv; Exec Comm of Coll Cncl; VP, Chm Prgm of KDP; AFT, NYSUT 1990-, Mem at Large; VP KDP 1990-, VP Prgms, VP Doctor Art; Intnl Stud in Ethomathematics 1991-; CUNY Campaign 1990-, Capt., 2 Certs; Exec Bd KDP 1990-, VP, NSF Grant; Vol Speaker Summer Camp; Tenured at John Jay; United Nations Prgm in Geneva; Book Pub 1995; Article Pub 1995; *office:* John Jay Coll Criminal Justice 445 W 59th St Ofc New York NY 10019*

VOEGELE, MILTON JOE, Social Studies Teacher; *b:* Cincinnati, OH; *m:* Teresa Schinaman; *c:* Tara, Brad, Catherine; *ed:* Univ of Cincinnati (BE) Soc Stud 1971; Xavier Univ (ME); *cr:* Aiken HS Tchr 1971-; *ai:* Soc Stud Lead Tchr, Dept Head; Wyoming HS Var Bsbl Coach; *office:* Aiken HS 5641 Belmont Ave Cincinnati OH 45224

VOEGELIN, JUNE EDWARDS, Spanish Teacher; *b:* Middletown, NY; *m:* William W.; *c:* Emma, Kelley; *ed:* OCCC (AA) 1971; SUNY at New Paltz (BA) Span 1973, (MA) 1978; Fr Second Cert 1988; *cr:* Wappingers Falls Schl Dist Span Tchr 11 Yrs; Vly Cntrl Schl Dist Span Tchr 11 Yrs; *ai:* VCTA 1985-; NYSUT; *office:* Valley Cntrl Schl Dist 1175 Rt 17K East Montgomery NY 12549

VOERG, VINCENT, Writing Instructor; *b:* Kingston, NY; *m:* Diana Francello; *c:* Rachel, Ryan; *ed:* Belknap Coll (BA) Eng 1971; Middlebury Coll (MA) Eng 1976; *cr:* John A. Collman HS 9-12th Grd Tchr 1973-78; Marist Coll Adjunct Instr 1989-; Kingston HS 9-12th Grd Tchr 1978-; *ai:* Harvard Model United Nations Adv; Kingston Tchrs Assn VP; NYSUT, NEA, AFT 1978-; KTF 1978-, VP; Phi Delta Kappa 1987-, VP 1988-89; Amer Order of Hiberniars 1988-; NY St Cncl for Tchrs of Eng Tchr of Excl 1993; Article Pub; *office:* Kingston HS 403 Broadway Kingston NY 12401*

VOGEL, KEN J., Private Drum Instructor; *b:* New York, NY; *cr:* Pvt Drum Instr 20 Yrs; Westtown Schl Pvt Drum Instr 1992-; *ai:* Books: Drum Set Unlimited, Melodic Solo Encounters for Drum Set, The Creative Rock Drummer Volume I, II, Bass Busters; Articles Pub; *office:* Westtown Schl PO Box 56 Gradyville PA 19039

VOGEL, MAXINE D. (MARCUS), Mathematics Teacher; *b:* New York City, NY; *ed:* CCNY (BA) Math 1963, (MA) Math 1967; Adelphi Univ (CFP) Fin Planning 1987; Licensed Stock Broker; *cr:* Jordan L. Mott Jr HS 22 Math Tchr 1963-65; Taft HS Math Tchr 1965-69; South HS Math Tchr 1969-; *ai:* Investment Club Adv; Retirement Sys Del; Exec Cncl; AFT; Intl Bd Fin Planners 1987-; *office:* Valley Stream South HS 150 Jedwood Pl Valley Stream NY 11581

VOGEL, RICHARD MARK, Associate Professor; *b:* New York, NY; *m:* Frances Yuan; *c:* Jared, Noah, Eli; *ed:* Univ of VA (BS) Engrg Sci 1977, (MS) Environmental Sci 1979; Cornell Univ (PHD) Water Resource Systems 1984; *cr:* Tufts Univ Asst Prof 1984-91, Assoc Prof 1991-; *ai:* ASCE 1979-, Assoc Ed; AGU 1979- Ed; Walter Huber Rsrch Prize 1995; Best Rsrch Paper 1989; John R Freeman Flwshp; *office:* Tufts Univ Medford MA 02155

VOGEL, RONALD EUGENE, Earth Science Teacher; *b:* Tarentum, PA; *m:* Nancy Hill; *c:* Marnie, Jolene; *ed:* Univ of Clarion (MS) Bio, Earth Sci 1966; Attnd IN Univ of PA, PA St Univ, WI St Univ; *cr:* Burrell Sr HS Earth Sci Tchr 1966-; *ai:* Sci Club Adv; NEA, PSEA, PSTA 1966-; NAGT 1980-; West Leechburg Boro 1975-82, Councilman; West Leechburg Boro 1985-88, Mayor; West Leechburg Vol Fire Co 1974-, Chief, Fire Fighter of Yr; Lower Kiski Ambulance Svc 1990-94, Bd of Dirs; Natl Sci Tchr Grant 1971; *office:* Burrell Sr HS 1021 Puckety Church Rd Lower Burrell PA 15068

VOGEL, SUSAN GRAMSKY, Social Studies Teacher; *b:* Bethesda, MD; *c:* Evan J.; *ed:* Frostburg St Univ (BS) Scndry Ed, Geog 1971; 24 Hrs Toward MA Cnslng Psych Bowie St Univ; *cr:* Better Bus Bureau Washington DC Sr Trade Practice Consultant 1972-74; Northwestern HS Soc Stud Tchr 1974-91; Eleanor Roosevelt HS Soc Stud Tchr 1991-92; Northwestern HS Soc Stud Tchr 1992-; *ai:* Mentor Schl Violence Reduction Prgm; Co-Founder Women of Northwestern Prgm; NEA, PGCEA, MSTA 1974-; Washington Post Grants Ed Awd 1983; Curr Co-Writer & Dev Modern World Geog 1984-85; Washington Post Agnes Meyer Outstdng Tchr Pringe George's Co Pub Schls 1990; *office:* Northwestern HS 7000 Adelphi Rd Hyattsville MD 20782

VOGELSONG, NORMA MUNOZ, Spanish Teacher; *b:* Hammonton, NJ; *m:* William Michael; *c:* Erin, Colin; *ed:* Rutgers Univ (BA) Span & Ed 1978, (EDM) Ed Theory 1981; *cr:* Woodrow Wilson HS Span Tchr 1978-88; Camden Cty Coll Adj Span Tchr 1989-; Williamstown HS Span Tchr 1988-; *ai:* Forensic Tournament Act Spon; Fgn Lang Club Adv; Span Tutor; NEA 1978-88; AFT 1988-; Camden Cty Vol Probation Ofcr 1976-; *office:* Williamstown HS 532 Clayton Rd Williamstown NJ 08094*

VOGLER, BERNARD J., Chemistry Teacher & Dept Head; *b:* Ft Knox, KY; *m:* Lois Vaughn Tiffany; *c:* Lisa Jeanne, David Alan; *ed:* Washington & Jefferson Coll (BA) Chem 1964; Univ of Pittsburgh (MA) Ed 1967; Attnd California Univ of PA, Duquesne Univ, Carnegie Mellon Univ, PA St Univ & Hope Coll; *cr:* N Hills HS Chem Tchr 1964-65; Moon Area Schls Chem Tchr 1965-; *ai:* Odyssey of the Mind Coord & Coach; NEA & PSEA 1965-; Moon Ed Assn 1965-, Pres 1972-74; ACS Chem Ed Division 1966-; PAGE Assn 1980-, Pres 1985-86, VP 1984-85, Treas 1986-; Moon PTA 1970-; Spectroscopy Soc of Pittsburgh Keiven Burns Awd for Excl in Sci Tchng; Moon Schls Tchr of Yr 2 Time Nom; Attnd NSF Summer Insts at Hope Coll for Chem & Indiana Univ of PA for Cmptrs in Chem; *office:* Moon Area HS 904 Beaver Grade Rd Moon Township PA 15108*

VOGT, CAROL A., History Teacher; *b:* Hackensack, NJ; *m:* Robert C.; *c:* Alexis Megan, Justin Gregory; *ed:* Univ of Denver (BA) His 1965; City Univ of NY Hunter Coll (MA) Soc Stud Ed 1972; NY Univ (PHD) Soc Stud Ed 1974; NDGA Inst in Asia Stud 1965; *cr:* N Tonawanda Sr HS His & Soc Stud Tchr 1965-68; NY St Bureau of Soc Stud Ed Demonstration Tchr & Consultant in Soc Stud 1969; Williamsville MS Soc Stud Tchr 1970-71; NYU Rsrch Asst & Adj Soc Stud Instr 1972-74; The Fieldston Schl Hist Tchr 1977-78, the Wheatley Schl Tchr & CUN Asst 1983-; *ai:* ICU Adv; Long Island Cncl for Soc Stud 1980-; E Milliston Tchr Assn 1983-; NY St United Tchrs 1983-; Sea Cliff Landmark Soc 1976-, Treas 1979; Sea Cliff Beach Comm 1980-84; Sea Cliff Bsbl League Exec Bd 1986-88; Citizens Advy Cnc Cncl 1986-90; Sea Cliff Environmental Comm 1992-; Amherst Project 1968; E Milleston Tchr of the Yr 1991; *office:* The Wheatley Schl 11 Bacon Rd Old Westbury NY 11568

VOGT, CHRISTINE CUCORE, 7th-8th Grade Teacher; *b:* Media, PA; *m:* David; *c:* Andrew A., Morgan C.; *ed:* Widner Univ at Brandywine (AA) Juvenile Criminal Justice 1978; C. W. Post Long Island Univ (BA) Juvenile Criminal Justice 1980; West Chester Univ Working Towards MA 1996; *cr:* Our Lady Star of Sea IGE Schl 3rd-5th Grds Tchr 1981-84; St John Chrysostom Schl 5th-8th Grd Tchr 1985-89; Assumption BVM Schl 7th-8th Grd Tchr 1990-; *ai:* 1st-8th Grd Sci Fair, K-8th Grd Career Day Coord; 5th-8th Grd Sci Chprsn; NCEA 1984-; *office:* Assumption BVM Schl State Rd West Grove PA 19390

VOGT, TOM DUNCAN, English & History Teacher; *b:* Louisville, KY; *m:* Susan E. Wacha-Vogt; *c:* Ruth, Kathleen, Mary, Tom, Adam; *ed:* Yale (BA) Eng 1943, (MA) Eng, His 1952; *cr:* LaJolla Cntry Day Schl Dean of Fac, Eng, His Tchr 1968-74, 1076-78; Chadwick Schl Eng, His Tchr 1979-81; Rhodes Schl Assoc Headmaster 1981-85; Nightingale-Bamford Schl Eng, His Tchr 1985-; *ai:* ATIS; Five Levels of Incompetence 1969.

VOGTMAN, THOMAS ALLEN, SR., Mathematics Teacher; *b:* Frostburg, MD; *m:* Frances Anna Lutz; *c:* Thomas Jr., Teresa; *ed:* Frostburg St Univ (BS) Math 1972, (MED) Admin & Supervision 1978; Cmptr Sci; *cr:* Keyser HS Math Tchr 1972-76; Valley HS Math Tchr 1976-77; Bruce HS Math Tchr 1977-83; Allegany Voc Tech Ctr Cmptr & Data Processing Tchr 1983-85; Westmar HS Math & Cmptr Sci Tchr 1985-; *ai:* Cmptr Club Adv; ACTA, MSTA 1976-; NEA 1972-; NCTM 1995-; Frostburg Vol Fire Dept 1971-, Treas 2 Yrs; Troop 24 1988-, Asst Scoutmaster; Stage Left Theatre 1989-, Treas 2 Yrs; Trout Unlimited 1985-; Nature Conservancy 1993-; Selected 1 of 11 Nationally to Participate NSF Prgm for Mathematically Gifted Sponsored at Univ of IL at Champaign-Urbana; *office:* Westmar HS Rt 36 Lonaconing MD 21539*

VOGTSBERGER, DIANE M., English Teacher; *b:* Queens, NY; *m:* Thomas; *c:* Elizabeth, Kathleen; *ed:* Bowling Green St Univ (BA) Eng, Bio 1971, (MED) Guidance, Cnslng 1977; 32 Hrs Educl Studs; *cr:* Bowling Green City Schls HS Eng Tchr 1972-; *ai:* Lang Arts Comm; Dept Chprsn 1978-82; Soph Class Adv; Tchr In-Svc Ldr; NCTE, OCTELA, NEA, OEA 1972-; Montessori Bd of Trustees 1990-, VP, Sec; APHC, MAPHC 1992-; Tchr of Yr 1989; Jennings Scholar 1976; *home:* 1515 Cedar Ln Bowling Green OH 43402

VOGUIT, STEVE GEORGE, Social Studies Teacher; *b:* Reading, PA; *m:* Ellen Stewart; *c:* Tracey Pollackov, Melinda Steven; *ed:* Millersville Univ (BSEd) Soc Stud 1969, (MED) Soc Stud 1974; *cr:* Wilson Schl Dist Tchr 1969-; *ai:* Debate Coach; Jr Statesman Adv; AFT; Article Pub; Started the Wilson His Fair; PA Tchr of Yr Nom (Twice).

VOIGT, DAVID J., Social Studies Instructor; *b:* Reading, PA; *m:* Nancy Joan Douthat; *c:* Carly, Jesse, Grady; *ed:* FL Southern Coll (BS) Soc Stud, Comm 1978; Kutztown Univ (MED) Soc Stud 1985; 30 Hrs Penn St; *cr:* Kent Co HS Soc St Instr 1978-79; Schuylkill Vly HS Eng Instr 1979-80; Fleetwood HS Soc Stud Instr 1980-82; Wyomissing HS Soc Stud Instr 1982-83; Twin Vly HS Soc Stud Instr 1983-84; Tulpehocken HS Soc Stud Instr 1985-; *ai:* Var Bsbl Coach 1984; Comm Svc Club Coord; NEA 1981-; Tulpehocken Dugout Club 1995-; *home:* 400 Spohn Rd Sinking Spring PA 19608

VOIGTLANDER, WALTER ROBERT, Social Studies Teacher; *b:* Bronx, NY; *m:* Audrey Ruth Minck; *c:* Suzanne L., Ross, Scott R., Steven R.; *ed:* Montclair St Tchrs Coll (BA) Soc Stud 1958; Montclair St Coll (MA) Soc Stud 1962; 30 Addl Credit Hrs; *cr:* Orange Schl 7-8 Grd Soc Stud Tchr 1958-60; Haworth Schl 7-8 Grd Soc Stud Tchr 1960-62; Clifton HS 11-12 Grd Soc Stud Tchr 1962-; *ai:* NEA, NJEA 1958-; Clifton HS Fac Org 1962-, Pres 1980-82; Phi Delta Kappa 1974-; Vernon Twp Zoning Bd 1974-80, Vice Chm; 1989 Governor's Tchr Recognition Awd; *home:* 15 Robin Hood Ln Highland Lakes NJ 07422

VOIROL, SARAH L., Sixth Grade Teacher; *b:* Lima, OH; *m:* William L.; *c:* William Jr., Trace, Lauren Beck, Erin Jury; *ed:* Miami Univ at Oxford (BS) Elem Ed 1969, (MED) Guidance & Counseling 1970; Continuing Ed Credits; *cr:* Cleveland City Schls 1st Grd Tchr 1969-70; Dayton City Schls 3rd Grd Tchr 1970-71; Delphos City Schls Elem Tchr 1971-73; Wayne Trace Schls Elem Tchr 1973-; *ai:* First Bapt Church, Sunday Schl Tchr; Martha Jennings Holden Scholar; *office:* Grover Hill Elem Monroe St Grover Hill OH 45849

VOISINE, RONALD ARTHUR, Social Studies & Math Teacher; *b:* Waterville, ME; *m:* Cathy Ann Michuad; *c:* Angela, Jessica; *ed:* Univ of ME at Farmington (BS) His & Math 1975; Addl Courses in Cmptr, Method, His, Math & Coaching; *cr:* Lawrence HS Sub Tchr 1975-76; Vassalboro Schl Math, Soc Stud & Sci Tchr 1976-86; Lawrence HS Math & Soc Stud Tchr 1986-; *ai:* Field Hockey, Bsktbl & Sftbl Coach; NEA, ME Tchrs Assn 1976-; Vassalboro Tchrs Assn 1976-86, Pres, Negotiator; NCTM, MCSS 1976-; ME Coaches Assn, ASA 1986-; USFHA 1988-; Elks 1974-; Police Athletic League 1992-, Field Hockey, Bsktbl & Sftbl Coach; Vassalboro Schl Field Hockey, Bsktbl, Sftbl & Stu Govt Coach; *office:* Lawrence HS 9 School St Fairfield ME 04937

VOITKO, STEPHEN ANDREW, Lecturer; *b:* Point Pleasant, NJ; *m:* Nancy Bonita; *c:* Joshua; *ed:* Monmouth Univ (BFA); BFA Monmouth Univ 1986; NY Acad of Art Cert 1987; *cr:* Monmouth Univ Lecturer 1992-; Grad Schl of Figurative Art Anatomy Instr 1993; *ai:* Helen Foster Barnett Awd; AAPL Medal of Hnr; Lindsey Morris Meml Awd 1990; AAA Awd of Hnr; HVAA Gold Medal 1991; Woodmere Art Museum Best in Show 1992; Exhibited in NSS Show, Seravezza Italy 1994; *office:* Monmouth Univ Cedar Ave West Long Branch NJ 07764

VOJTKO, DEBORAH JEAN (FINNISS), Chemistry Teacher; *b:* Pittsburgh, PA; *m:* J. David; *c:* Dana Elizabeth, Courtney Marie; *ed:* IN Univ of PA (BSEd) Chem 1974; Univ of Pittsburgh (MED) Scndry Sci 1980; Duquesne Univ (MSEd) Elem & Scndry Schl Cnclng 1988; *cr:* Steel Valley Intermediate Schl Chem & Phys Sci Tchr 1975-78; Pine-Richland HS Chem Tchr 1978-; *ai:* NEA 1975-; PSEA 1975-; PA Sci Tchrs Assn; *office:* Pine-Richland HS 4300 Warrendale Rd Gibsonia PA 15044

VOJTKO, GAIL F., German & Latin Teacher; *b:* Wilkes Barre, PA; *ed:* Cabrini Coll (BA) Elem Ed 1964; Millersville Univ (MA) Ger 1975; *cr:* Saint Stephen Elem Schl 4th & 5th Grd Tchr 1965-66; Blessed Sacrament 5th Grd Tchr 1967; Lebanon Cath HS Ger & Latin Tchr 1967-; *ai:* Schl Newspaper Adv; Lit Journal Adv; Ger Club; Foreign Lang Dept Chprsn; NCEA & AATG 1967-; CSPA 1989-; Free-Lance Writer for "Harrisburg Patriot" Newspaper; *office:* Lebanon Catholic HS 1400 Chestnut St Lebanon PA 17042

VOLANTE, WILLIAM, Guidance Dir, US History Instr; *b:* Newton, MA; *ed:* Coll of the Holy Cross (BS) US His; Univ of MA at Boston (MED) Scndry Ed; Columbia Univ (MA) Guid, Stu Prsnl; *cr:* US Army Hosp Admin 33 Yrs; SS Peter & Paul HS Guid Dir, US His Instr 7 Yrs; *office:* SS Peter & Paul HS 900 High St Easton MD 21601

VOLBERT, KEVIN M., Lang Arts Teacher & Ath Dir; *b:* Lima, OH; *m:* Julie Burton; *c:* Gage, Lauren; *ed:* Bowling Green St Univ (BS) Speech, Eng 1986; *cr:* West Jefferson HS Eng Dept 1986-88; Madison-Plains HS Eng Dept 1988-91; Hilliard Heritage MS Lang Arts Dept 1991-; *ai:* Boys, Girls Bsktbl Coach; Founder SADD Chptr; Svc Club Adv; Intervention Assistance Team; Team Ldr; Assessment Team Tchr Rep; NEA, OEA, NETA 1986-; *office:* Hilliard Heritage MS 5600 Scioto Darby Rd Hilliard OH 43026*

VOLK, NANCY WROBLEWSKI, Language Arts Teacher; *b:* Philadelphia, PA; *m:* James William; *ed:* Penn St (BA) Anthropology 1966; LeHigh (MA) Elem Ed 1972; Attnd Villanova in Ed; Rdng Specialist Supervision Cert; Doctoral Stu in Rdngy, Supervision Lehigh Univ; *cr:* Camden Schl Dist Elem Tchr 1966-70; Bethlehem Area Schl Dist Elem Tchr MS 1970-76; Penn St Univ Instr 1977-78; Bethlehem Area Schl Dist

HS Tchr 1978-; *ai:* Class Adv; HS Restructuring Comm; Instrl Support Team; BEA, PSEA, NEA 1970-; BPW, AAUW, IRA 1972-; Phi Delta Kappa 1976-, Pres, Chptr Lehigh Univ; Delta Kappa Gamma 1974-, Exec Bd, Chptr Lehigh Vly; Lehigh Alumni Cncl 1972-, Pres, Schl of Ed; Rsrch Flwshp Diagnostic Classroom; Outstdng Alumni Awd 1980; Numerous Articles Pub; *office:* Freedom HS 3147 Chester Ave Bethlehem PA 18017*

VOLLER, KATHLEEN GRIGNON, Classroom Teacher; *b:* Bourne, MA; *m:* John J.; *c:* T. J., Marissa; *ed:* Plymouth St Coll (BSEd) Elem 1974; Simmons Working Towards MS Spec Ed; Bridgewater St, Framingham St Post Grad Work; *cr:* Raynham Pub Schls 4th Grd Tchr 1974-86, 1st, 5th Grd Tchr 1990-94; Bridgewater-Raynham Schls 6th Grd Tchr 1994-; *ai:* BREA, BCEA, NEA 1974-; PCEA 1994-; Raynham Pub Lib 1988-, Bd of Dirs; Friends of Raynham Lib 1988-, Founder, Co-Chprsn; RAVE 1980-, Vice Chprsn, Treas; United Way 1990-, Rookie of Yr; United Way; Who's Who in Amer; Who's Who in The East; *office:* LaLiberte Jr HS 777 Pleasant St Raynham MA 02767*

VOLLINGER, JAMES FRANCIS, Math Teacher; *b:* Northampton, MA; *m:* Faye Anne Kaltner; *c:* Casey, Matthew; *ed:* Univ of MA (BA) Ec 1975, (BA) PE 1979; *cr:* Eaglebrook Schl Math Tchr 1980-86; Northfield Mt Herman Math Tchr 1987-; *ai:* Var Soccer Coach; Yth Soccer & Bsbl Coach; *home:* 7 Bolton Rd Northfield MA 01360

VOLMERING, RONALD EUGENE, 8th Grd American History Tchr; *b:* Cincinnati, OH; *m:* Kimberly Jo Diegel; *c:* Jaimie, Derek; *ed:* Eastern KY Univ (BS His 1978; Xavier Univ (MED) Scndry Supervision 1986; *cr:* Berry Jr MS 8th Grd Tchr 1978-; *ai:* Jr High Stu Cncl Adv; District Soc Stud Comm; Jr HS Extra Curr Comm & Awds Comm; NEA, OEA, LEA 1978-; Lebanon Fraternal Order of Eagles 1986-; *office:* Berry Jr HS 23 Oakwood Ave Lebanon OH 45036*

VOLOCH, LILIAN AIZMAN, Spanish Teacher; *b:* Santiago, Chile; *m:* Marcio; *c:* Daniel; *ed:* Beit-Sefer-Le-Morot (BA) Elem Ed 1974; Purdue Univ (MA) Foreign Lang & Lit, Spanish, Amer Lit 1982; 30 Credit Above MA Purdue Univ; *cr:* Colegro Moral y Lucer 5th & 6th Grd Hebrew Tchr 1974-75; Bishop Ahr HS Span Tchr 1984-; *ai:* Amnesty Intnl Advy 1985-, Founded & Organized; Foreign Exchange Stu Pgm Adv; David Ross Awd; *office:* Bishop George Ahr HS 1 Tingley Ln Edison NJ 08820

VOLONNINO, MARIANNE, Language Arts Teacher; *b:* Paterson, NJ; *m:* Antonio; *c:* Michael, Julie Ann; *ed:* Caldwell Coll (BA) Eng 1970; *cr:* St Anthony of Padua Grd 2 Tchr 1970-79, Grd 5 Tchr 1983-85; St Philip The Apostle Grd 6-8 Lang Arts Tchr 1985-; *ai:* Broadway Club Moderator; Mid Sts Comm; Mentor New Tchrs of Lang Arts; Mentor to 8th Grd Stdnts; NCEA 1970-; *office:* St Philip The Apostle Schl 797 Valley Rd Clifton NJ 07013

VOLPE, MARGARET DOYLE, English Teacher; *b:* Mount Clemens, MI; *m:* John A.; *c:* Dominic J., Annemarie, Christina M.; *ed:* D'Youville Coll (BA) Eng 1972; SUNY at Geneseo (MS) Ed 1990; *cr:* Cathedral Schl Grd 7-8 Eng Tchr 1973-76; Project Renewal Tchr, Co-Dir 1983-87; St Mary Schl Grd 3 Tchr 1987-89; St Joseph Schl Grd 6-8 Eng Tchr 1989-; *office:* St Joseph Schl 2 Summit St Batavia NY 14020*

VOLPE, MARIA R., Professor of Sociology; *b:* Peekskill, NY; *ed:* SUNY at Plattsburgh (BA) Sociology 1970; NY Univ (MA) Sociology 1975, (PHD) Sociology 1981; *cr:* John Jay Coll of Criminal Justice CUNY Prof of Sociology, Dir, Dispute Resolution Prgm 1981-; *ai:* Soc of Profs in Dispute Resolution 1985-, Pres Elect, Distngd Svc Awd; William & Flora Hewlett Fnd Grant; NIMH Fellow NY Univ; Articles Pub; *office:* City Univ Of NY John Jay Coll 445 W 59th St Ofc New York NY 10019

VOLPE, MICHAEL VINCENT, Physics Teacher; *b:* Bad Krueznach, West Germany; *m:* Andrea Marie Hilgenhold; *ed:* IN St Univ (BS) Physics 1985; *cr:* Forest View HS Physics Tchr 1985-86; Saint Thomas Aquinas HS Physics Tchr 1986-92; Summit Cntry Day Schl Physics Tchr 1994-; *ai:* Girls Var & Reserve Vlybl Head Coach; Chess Club & SADD Adv; Physics Trip Dir; Sci Bowl & JETS Coach; Physics Olympics Dir; Sr Retreat Comm; AAPT 1986-; US Chess Fed 1995-; Pub The Physics Tchr 1994; Tandy Tech Outstanding Tchr 1992; Miami Herald Silver Knight Tchr Awd 1991; Broward Cty Golden Apple Awd 1991; Univ of Miami Cert of Excl in Tchng 1991; Univ of Chicago 1990 Outstanding Tchr Awd; USAF Honorary Admissions Liaison Officer; USAF Acad Educator Airlift, AAPT Advanced Placement Physics Tchng Seminar 1987, 1988 & 1995; AAPT Physics Cmptr Wkshp; *office:* The Summit Country Day Schl 2161 Grandin Rd Cincinnati OH 45208

VOLPE, PAMELA DAWN, Reading Teacher; *b:* New York, NY; *c:* Kimberly; *ed:* St John's Univ (BA) Eng 1971; SUNY at Stonybrook (MA) Liberal Stud 1992; Dowling Coll Grad Work Tchng, Rdng Gdes K-12; *cr:* Connetquot HS 11 Gde Tchr 1984-85; St Anne's Schl 6-8 Gde Tcr 1986-92; Out Lady of Providence 6-8 Gde Tchr 1992-; *ai:* Schl Newspaper, Yrbk Adv; 8th Grd Fundraising Comm; Pianist Schl Functions.

VOLPE, RITA RIZZELLO, Science Consultant; *b:* Jamaica, NY; *m:* Thomas A.; *c:* Michael (dec), Thomas C.; *ed:* St John's Univ (BS) Elem Ed 1966; 300 Addl Credit Hrs Sci Ed, Bereavement Counciling, Hall of Sci; Summer Inst Sci Mentors; TCF Natl Symposiums Bereavement; *cr:* St Vincent de Paul Schl Grd 6 Tchr 1966-67; Diocese of Brooklyn Sub Tchr 1983-86; Mary's Nativity Schl Sci Tchr, Coord 1986-94; Diocese of Brooklyn Regnl Sci Mentor 1992-; St Ed Dept Regnl Sci Mentor 1992-; Lakeville Schl Sci Consultant 1994-; *ai:* Sci Fair Coord; Stu Vol Svc Projects; Coord Rainbows All God's Children; Dir Schl Theater Productions; Run Schl Bus; Coach Stdnts Sci Competitions; NYS Sci Mentors Network 1992-, Regnl Mentor; Cath Sci Cncl, NCEA 1986-94; The Compassionate Friends 1987-, Group Ldr Molloy Coll; Bereavement TV Appearances; Am Chem Soc Mid Atlantic Regnl Meeting Hofstra Univ, St Joseph Coll Sci Tchng Speakers; Prof Wkshps Sci Tchrs; NYS Assn Ind Schls Symposium Presenter; *office:* Lakeville School 47-27 Jayson Ave Great Neck NY 11576

VOLPE, TECKLA ANNE, English Teacher; *b:* Camp LeJeune, NC; *ed:* Rosemont Coll (BA) Eng Lit 1967; *cr:* Pleasantville HS Eng Tchr 1974-86; Hammonton HS Eng Tchr 1986-; *ai:* NHS Adv; Soc Stud ED 2000 Comm, Foreign Lang, Lit & Lib Mem; Schl Advy Cncl; HS Mgmt Team; NJEA 1974-; HEA, Sec 1991-93; Hammonton Womens Civic Club 1988-, Treas 1990-; Dames Investment Club 1988-; *home:* 30D Rose Rita Ter Hammonton NJ 08037*

VOLPE, VICKI JOHNSON, Chem Tchr & Science Dept Chm; *b:* Millville, NJ; *m:* Joseph J. III; *ed:* Glassboro St Coll (BA) Phys Sci 1983, (MA) Scndry Ed 1990; Scndry Ed Cert Supv 1992; *cr:* Ravan Coll Adj Prof Organic Chem 1993-94; Vineland HS South Tchr 1983-, Sci Dept Chm 1992-; *ai:* Sci League Adv; Sci Olympiad, Cinema, Fair Chm; NEA, NSTA, NJSTA 1983-; PDK 1994-; NJ Governors Tchr Awd 1986; Amer Chemical Soc Sci Tchr of Yr; NJ Sci Tchrs Convention Presenter 1994-95; *office:* Vineland HS South 2880 E Chestnut Ave Vineland NJ 08360*

VOLPENHEIN, SAM ANTHONY, 8th Grade Math Teacher; *b:* Cincinnati, OH; *m:* Margaret Bunker; *c:* Samuel, Brian, Leah; *ed:* Eastern KY Univ (BS) Elem Ed 1981; 150 Hrs Grad Work Xavier Univ, Miami of OH Univ, Univ of Cincinnati; *cr:* Glen Este MS 8th Grd Math Tchr 1981-; *ai:* Head Var Boys Bsktbl Coach; Math Curr Comm West Clermont Schls; Southwest OH Coaches Assn 1985-; St Benedicts Parish Cncl 1992-, Pres, VP; *office:* Glen Este MS 4342 Glen Este Withamsville Rd Cincinnati OH 45245*

VOLPETTI, BARBARA A., Kindergarten Teacher; *b:* Kingston, PA; *m:* Nicholas; *c:* Nicholas, Nadine; *ed:* Wilkes Coll (BS) Elem Ed; Intermediate Unit Penn St; *cr:* Kingston Schl Dist 2nd Grd Tchr 1963-64; West Pittston Schl Dist 6th Grd Tchr 1969-70; Wilkes Barre Schl Dist 2nd-3rd Grd Tchr 1975-80, Kndgtn Tchr 1980-; *ai:* PSEA, NEA 1975-; WBEA 1975-, Rep 1978; Natl Math Assn 1994-; PTO 1975-, VP; Cancer Soc, Heart Assn Vol; *office:* Bear Creek Elem Schl 2000 Bear Creek Blvd Wilkes-Barre PA 18702*

VOLPICELLA, BARBARA PARILLO, Language & Literature Teacher; *b:* Bronx, NY; *c:* Ronald; *ed:* Queens Coll (BA) Fine Arts 1977; PDHP Trng; *cr:* IS 192 6th-8th Grd Tchr 1977-82; St Luke Schl 8th Grd Tchr 1988-; *ai:* RAP Groups Ldr; Sr Adv; NCEA 1988-, Tchr Assoc; *office:* St Luke Schl 16-01 150th Pl Whitestone NY 11357*

VOLPONE, RONALD ANTHONY, English Teacher; *b:* New York City, NY; *m:* Mary Kay; *ed:* Oswego St Univ (BA) Eng, Writing Arts 1990; Iona Coll (MS) Ed-Hnrs 1992; 3 Addl Credits; *cr:* Rutherford HS Scndry Eng Tchr 1992-; *ai:* Class Adv 1993-; Weight Room Supvr 1994-95; NEA, REA, NJEA 1992-; Phi Kappa Tau 1988-; *office:* Rutherford HS 56 Elliott Ter Rutherford NJ 07070

VOLRATH, ROGER L., Physics Teacher; *b:* Baltimore, MD; *ed:* Western MD Coll (BA) Physics 1968; Advanced Prof Cert; *cr:* Glenele HS Physics, Sci Tchr 1968-95; *ai:* Cross Cntry, Indoor Track, Track & Field Coach; NEA, MD St Tchrs Assn, AAPT 1968-; Howard Cty Tchrs Assn 1968-, Past Bd of Dirs; BSA 1957-, Cncl Exec Bd, Trng Chm, Eagle Scout Silver Beaver Founders Awd; MD Tchr of Yr Finalist 1991; Howard Cty Tchr of yr 1991; Baltimore Metro Coach of Yr 1992; *office:* Glenelg HS 14025 Burntwoods Rd Glenelg MD 21737*

VONA, CAROLINE LEHMANN, Mathematics Teacher; *b:* Lockport, NY; *m:* P. Andrew; *c:* Nicholas, Megan; *ed:* ST Bonaventure Univ (BS) Ed 1984; SUNY at Buffalo (MS) Math & Ed 1989; 20 Grad Credit Hrs Past Masters; *cr:* Lyndonville Cntrl Schls Math Tchr 1984-85; Newfane Cntrl Schl Math Tchr 1985-; *ai:* Soph Class Adv; Peer Ldrshp Vol; AFT 1984-; Newfane Tchrs Assn 1985-; Lockport Coll Womens Club 1987-, Bd Mem; DeSales Homeschool Assn 1995-; *office:* Newfane Sr HS 1 Panther Dr Newfane NY 14108

VON HOFE, HAROLD EDWARD, Horizons Teacher; *b:* Los Angeles, CA; *m:* Kathleen; *c:* Erin, Alaric, Morgan; *ed:* Univ of So. Calif (BA) Comp Lit, Classics, Ger 1972; Yale Univ (PHD) Comparative Lit 1981; *cr:* PNM Access Systems Poet 1976-79; US Postal Svc Letter Carrier 1979-84; PNM Bank Story-Teller 1984-86; Branford HS Tchr 1986-; *ai:* Act Coord Flwshp of Grail; Anarcho Syndicalist League 1931-, Operations Technician, Citation M. VanderLubbe; US Heraldry Assn 1951-; Ancient Free & Accepted Masonry 1992-, Jr Warden; *home:* 31 Therion Ln Branford CT 06405

VON HOLTZ, BARBARA SCHMITT, Fifth Grade Teacher; *b:* Brooklyn, NY; *m:* David; *c:* Rebecca, David Jr., Brian; *ed:* St Univ of NY at Oswego (BA) Elem Ed 1969; 30 Hrs Rdng Ed; *cr:* Cato-Meridian Schls Remedial Rdng Tchr 1970-71; St Mary's Schl Tchr 1981-; *ai:* NEA 1981-; SMS Schl Bd 1988-91, VP & Sec; *home:* 3490 County Route 6 Mexico NY 13114

VOORHEES, MARTHA CESPEDES, Spanish Teacher; *b:* Chicago, IL; *m:* Mark; *ed:* IN Univ (BS) Jr HS, MS Ed 1989; Working Toward Masters; Post-Grad Stud Purdue Univ & Montclair Univ; *cr:* A L Spohn Schl Span Tchr 1989-93; Randolph HS Span Tchr 1993-95; *ai:* Randalph HS Acad Decathlon; IN Frgn Lang Tchr Assn 1989-; Frgn Lang of NJ Edctrs, Amer Assn of Tchrs of Span & Portuguese, NEA 1993-; NJEA; REA; *office:* Randolph HS Millbrook Ave Randolph NJ 07869

VOORHEIS, DONALD MARK, Fourth Grade Teacher; *b:* Rochester, NY; *m:* Donna Jean Ainsworth; *ed:* SUNY at Brockport (MS) His 1983, (MS) Rdng 1988, (CAS) Admin 1991; Working toward EDD Univ of Rochester; *cr:* St Charles Borromeo Schl 6th Grd Tchr 1983-84; Albion Cntrl Schls 6th Grd Tchr 1984-85; Brockport Cntrl Schls 4th Grd Tchr 1985-; *ai:* Spec Events Comm; Intermediate Schl Yrbk Adv 1995-; Var Swim Team Coach 1984-; Modified Swim Team Coach 1990-; Pioneer Day Co-Chprsn 1995-; Shared Decison Mading Team; AFT, NYSCT 1984-; Western Monroe Historical Soc 1988-, Bd Mem; SUNY at Brockport Admin Flwshp; Roy Bibb Awd; Richard E. Canetuson Schlsp; Elizabeth & Frank Manno Awd; *office:* Brockport Fred Hill Intrmdt 40 Allen St Brockport NY 14420*

VOORHIS, THOMAS CHARLES, Music Teacher; *b:* Manhattan, NY; *ed:* Rowan Coll (BA) Music Ed 1985; Cntrl CT St Univ MS Music Ed; Orff Shulwerk Certified; *cr:* Bergen Cty Spec Svcs Schl Dist Music Tchr 1985-88; Ridgefield Pub Schls Music Tchr 1988-; *ai:* HS Musical, Elem Show Choir, Marching Band Asst Dir; PTA Musical Coord; NJEA 1985-; MENC 1985-, Adjudicator; AGM 1990-, Adjudicator, Sec, Amer Choral Dirs Assn; Schlsp Show 1986-, Publicity, Music Dir; Amer Sings 1990-, Annual Master of Ceremonies; Various Choral Works Pub; NJ Educators Assn Convention Speaker 1993-1995; Natl recognized clinician; Innovator of Spec Ed & Music Honored by NJ Newspaper Assn 1988; *office:* Slocum Skewes Schl Prospect Ave Ridgefield NJ 07657

VORCE, ELLIOT, HS Social Studies Teacher; *b:* Watertown, NY; *m:* Susan W.; *ed:* Hobart Coll (BA) Amer His 1969; Post Grad Stud SUNY at Oswego, SUNY at Geneseo, Elmira Coll; *cr:* Penn Yan Acad Tchr 1969-; *ai:* Stu Cncl Adv; Comm On Excl, Accountability; NEA 1976-, Local Pres, NEA Achvmt Awd; Soldiers, Sailors Hosp Bd 1992-, Trustee; Penn Yan Lions Club 1976-, Pres, Sec, Achvmt Awds; Penn Yan Vlg Historic Preservation Commission 1992-, Commissioner; Penn Yan Historical Soc 1993-, VP; Writer, Ed Schl Wide Newspaper; Contributing Photgrapher Local His Book: An Inheritance of Time; *office:* Penn Yan Acad 305 Court St Penn Yan NY 14527

VORCHHEIMER, JUDITH N., Mathematics Teacher; *ed:* NYU-WA Square Coll of Arts & Sci (BA) Math 1954; NYU WA Square Grad Schl of Arts & Sci 36 Grad Credits; *cr:* (wm H Taft HS Math Tchr 1955-61; Manhattan Hebrew HS for Girls Math Tchr 1976-82; Yeshiva Univ HS for Girls Math Chm 1982-86; Westchester Day Schl Math Tchr 1986-87; Shevach HS Math Tchr 1987-; *ai:* NCTM 1979-; Amit Women Life; Local Synagogue-Womens Division, Treas; PTA of Childrens Schls, Treas.

VORNBROCK, CHERYL L., English Teacher; *b:* Columbus, OH; *m:* Page M.; *c:* Kelley, Kristin; *ed:* Miami Univ (BS) Eng, Speech 1971; OH St Univ (MA) Hum Ed 1984; Post Grad Work Ashland Univ; *cr:* Vermilion Jr HS Eng Tchr 1972-77; Gahanna-Lincoln HS Eng Tchr 1978-84; Dublin Coffman HS Eng Tchr 1984-; *ai:* Chrldr Adv 6 Yrs; Class Adv; Various Schl, Dist Comms; NEA, OEA 1978-; DEA 1984-; NCTE 1972-94; New Hope Reformed Church 1993-, Deacon; Emerald Ball Comm 1990-95, Co-Chm 1992; Dublin Arts Cncl 1988-92; *office:* Dublin Coffman HS 6780 Coffman Rd Dublin OH 43017

VORNDRAN, DAVID N., Mathematics Teacher; *b:* Bridgeton, NJ; *m:* Janet Gorgo; *c:* Jason, Brittany, Tony; *ed:* Glassboro St Coll (BA) Ed 1985; 24 Addl Credit Hrs Stu Prsnl Svcs Rowan Coll of NJ; *cr:* Vineland HS Math Tchr 1986-; *ai:* Math Lab & Leaning Ctr; NEA, NJEA, VEA 1986-; *office:* Vineland HS 3010 E Chestnut Ave Vineland NJ 08360*

VOROBA, SUSALEA, Asst Prin for Acad Subjects; *b:* Bronx, NY; *c:* Boris, Katharine; *ed:* Queens Coll (BA) Comp Lit 1964; Adeolphi Univ (MA) Eng 1968; C. W. Post, LIU Prof Diploma Schl Admin 1982; 2 Yr Stud of Fr; Some Credit Towards PHD in Eng; *cr:* Grover Cleveland HS Eng Tchr 1965-82, Eng Tchr Asst Prin 1982-84; Queens Voc Tech HS Asst Prin Acad Subjects 1984-; *ai:* Supervise PM Schl, Schl Newspapers, Magazine, Debate Teams; NYCAAPSE 1984-, Sec, Standing Comm; AW NCTE 1966-; CTSA 1984-, Exec Bd; Won Several Grants for S Enrichment; Numerous Articles Pub; *office:* Queens Voc Tech HS Ave Long Island City NY 11101

VORON-BULTENA, SHARYN R., First Grade Teacher; *b:* Phila PA; *m:* Lance P. Bultena; *c:* Stefani Lyn; *ed:* Univ of Houston (ME Lang Arts 1985; *cr:* Houston Independent Schl Dist Grd S 1981-85; Schl Dist of Phila Grd Schl Tchr 1986-; *ai:* Extracurricu Story Time Rdng Comm; Schl Climate Comm; Tchr of Month Nom for Jaycees Outstdng Young Educator Awd 1984-85; *office:* Elem Schl 9th & Oregon St Philadelphia PA 19148*

VORONKA, ZIRKA, Associate Professor of ESL; *m:* Roman; *c:* Bilash, Nestor V.; *ed:* Rutgers Univ (BA) Span, Lang & Lit 196 Linguistics & Span 1964; Kyiv Polytechnic Inst (PHD) Honori 1991; Kean Coll 1984; *cr:* Rugers Univ Instr 1963-64; Essex 1977-80; Hudson Co Comm Coll Asst Prof 1980-86; Passak Co Co Assoc Prof 1986-; KPI Prof 1990-; *ai:* Dir of Summer Inst on Methods & Practices in TESOL Ukraine 1992-95; TESOL NJTESOL 1980-; TESOL Ukraine 1994-; Ukrainian Inst of Ame Outstdng Tchr of Yr at PCCC 1989; USIA Liaison EFL Fellow in 1994-95; Co-Author of Eng, Lang, Textbook Series Lets Start Passaic County Comm Coll College Boulevard Paterson NJ 07509

VOSBURGH, DAWN LYNN, Bus Teacher & Tech Coordinator; *b:* Creek, MD; *m:* Michael George; *ed:* Heidelberg Coll (BA) Bus Ad 1992; 6 Post Grad Hrs; *cr:* Old Fort Local Schl Bus Tchr, Tec 1994-; *ai:* Soph Class Adv; Tech Comm; NEA 1993-; Big Brot Sisters 1992-; *office:* Old Fort Local Schls 7635 N County Road Fort OH 44861

VOSHELL, SHARON P., Seventh Grade Lang Arts Tchr; *b:* Oxf *m:* Michael P.; *c:* Ryan, Eric; *ed:* Univ of DE (BS) Ed 1983; DE (MA) Ed 1990; *cr:* Cntrl MS 7th-8th Grd Spec Ed Tchr 1983-92, Consulting Tchr 1992-93, 8th Grd Lang Arts, Math Tchr 1993-95, Lang Arts Tchr 1995-; *ai:* Comm Svc Club Adv; Odessey of Mind NEA, DSEA 1983-, Pres, Grievance Chprsn; Tchr of Yr 1991; *offic* MS DE PA Ave Dover DE 19901

VOSNICK, CAROLYN LEE, Math Teacher; *b:* Washington, Donald George; *c:* Robert, Christine; *ed:* CA Univ of PA (BS) Mat 32 Addl Credits; *cr:* Canon McMillan Schl Dist Math Tchr 1 Glenwood MS Math Tchr 1968-69; Ft Cherry Schl Dist Math Tchr *ai:* Jr HS Chrldr, Soph Class Spon; Math Count Coach; PSEA, NEA 1982-; NCTM; MCWP; SNPJ 1946-; Chrstn Woman's of Guardia Church 1971-93, Pres 9 Yrs, Treas 3 Yrs, Sec 3 Yrs, VP 3 Yrs; Nor Thanks to Tchrs Excellence in Partnership; Gift of Time Awd; *of* Cherry Jr & Sr HS RD 4 Mc Donald PA 15057*

VOSS, LINDA RASMUSSEN, 8th Grd Reading & English T Marshalltown, IA; *ed:* Univ of Northern IA (BA) Eng, Ed 1974; ME at Orono (MA) Rdng, Ed 1990; *cr:* Walnut Comm Schl Eng, G 1974-75; Green Mountain Ind Schl Eng, Ger Tchr 1975-81; Realschule Stengele Fulbright Exch Tchr 1981-82; Bonn Amer H Drama Tchr 1982-83; Winslow Jr HS Eng Tchr 1983; Camden R HS Eng Tchr 1983; China Elem Schl 6th-8th Grd Eng, Rdng, Ge Tchr 1984-88; Winslow Jr HS Eng, Rdng Tchr 1988-; *ai:* Coord of W Summer Trips; NEA 1974-; ME Ed Assn 1984-; ME St Tchr of Y 1995-; NEA 1974-; ME Ed Assn 1984-; ME St Tchr of Yr Assn Holocaust, Human Rights Ctr of ME 1984-, Bd; ME Tchr of Y Recipient of Flwshp to Stud Holocaust & Jewish Resistance in Israe Grant to Edctrs 1991; ME Holocaust Edctr of Yr 1992; Kohl Intnl Awd 1994; *office:* Winslow Jr HS 10 Danielson St Winslow ME 04

VOSS, VICTOR JOSEPH, English Teacher; *b:* Doylestown, Jennifer; *ed:* Univ of Scranton (BA) Eng 1967; Univ of HI Anthropology 1968; 30 Hrs Univ of Hartford; *cr:* Torrington HS En 1968-; *ai:* HS Task Force; Ethics, Disciplinary Comms; NEA, CEA 1968-; NCTE 1980-; NDEA Univ of HI; *office:* Torrington HS Major Dr Torrington CT 06790

VOTAVA, MARI ANNE, English & Comm Arts Tchr; *b:* New Yor NY; *ed:* Queens Coll of CUNY (BA) Comm Arts & Drama 1985, (M & Ed 1988; Amer Acad of Dramatic Arts; *cr:* Intermediate Schl Tchr 1985-86; Newtown HS Eng & Comm Arts Tchr 1986-; Stu Act Stu Org Adv; *ai:* Schl Play Dir; Writing Projects Tchr; Grad & Comms; Educl Theater Assn; *office:* Newtown H S 4801 90th St El NY 11373*

VOUVOUNAS, ROSEANN J. (ANTONUCCI), Sixth Grade Teac Youngstown, OH; *c:* Michael; *ed:* Youngstown St Univ (BA) El 1969, (MS) Rdng 1973; *cr:* Warren City Schls 3rd Grd Tchr 1969- Grd Tchr 1975-; *ai:* Stu Cncl Adv; Warren Ed Assoc 1969-, Bld NEA, OEa 1969-; Lakeview Booster Club 1991-; *office:* Mc Kinley Schl 1321 Elm Rd NE Warren OH 44483*

VOVERIS, JOAN MARIE, Music Teacher & Dept Chprsn; *b:* Pa NJ; *ed:* Coll Misericordia (BM) Music Ed 1962; Univ of Scranto Scndry Ed 1967; Coll Misericordia Supervisory Cert in Music; Pos Stud Awded Scndry Schl Cert; *cr:* Turnpike Area Schls Music Chorus, Band 1-12 Grd 1962-63; Nescopeck Area Schls Music Chorus, Band 1-12 Grd 1963-69; Berwick Area Schls Music Dept Music Tchr, Choral Dir 9-12 Grd 1969-; *ai:* Womens & Mens C Swing Choir, Ninth Grd Chorus, Select Girls Chorale Ensemble, Chorus Dir; MENC, PMEA 1962-, Music Tchr 25 Yr; Berwick A Assn 1969-; NEA, PSEA 1962-; U of S Alumni Assn 1967- Misericordia Alumni Assn 1962-; Berwick Area Comm Chorus 1985 Commonwealth of PA Citation; House of Representatives 20 Yr Ded Svc & Invaluable Contributions to Music Ed 1983; *office:* Berwick 1100 Fowler Ave Berwick PA 18603

VOYLES, JAMES A., Fourth Grade Teacher; *b:* Evansville, IN; *m:* Stearns; *c:* Diana, Julie; *ed:* Miami-Dade Jr Coll (AA) Bus Admin Univ of NH (BS) Recreation & Parks Admin 1974; *cr:* Mc Clellan Fourth-Fifth Grd Tchr 1976-83; Paul Schl Fourth-Fifth Grd Tchr 198 Prof Ski Instrs of Amer 1985-, Ski Instr; NEA 1976-80, 1987- 1980-83; *home:* 554 Lovell Lake Rd Sanbornville NH 03872

VOZAB, JOHN B., English Teacher; *b:* New York, NY; *m:* P McCarthy; *c:* Chrissy; *ed:* St Francis Coll (BA) Eng 1970; Queen (MS) Eng Ed 1974; *cr:* Mater Christi HS Eng Tchr 1970-74; Web Cntrl Schl Eng Tchr 1974-; *ai:* Asst Girls Var Bsktbl Coach; NYSAT WBCA 1990-, Section I Coach of Yr; AAU Bsktbl 1988-; Web Commitment to Excl Awd; *office:* Webutuck Cntrl HS Box N Amen 12501

VRABEL, FRED A., English Teacher; *b:* Altoona, PA; *m:* Charlo Palmer; *c:* Brian F.; *ed:* St Francis Coll (BA) Eng 1974, (MEd) Ed Villanova Univ Grad Asst Theatre 1987-88; Univ of Arts at Philad Grad Seminar Samuel Beckett; *cr:* Forest Hills Jr Sr HS Eng, Dra Tchr 1975-77; Hollidaysburg Area HS Eng Tchr 1977-78; Wes Hilltop Jr HS Eng Tchr 1978-79; Portage Area HS Eng Tchr 1979 Drama, Schltc Quiz Coach; NEA, PSEA 1977-; Intnl Brotherho Magicians 1978-; FellowCncl for Basic Ed NEH Ind Research Prgm; Natl Endowment for Hum Summer Scholars Prgm 1989; Playw Commissioned Twice by Natl Parks Service; *office:* Portage Area H High St Portage PA 15946

L, KATHRYN KOHANOV, Spanish & French Teacher; *b:* ›wn, OH; *m:* Myron; *c:* Brianna; *ed:* Youngstown St Univ (BA) Fr, 89; Working on MA; *cr:* Chaney HS Fr, Span Tchr 1989-; *ai:* Fr v; Core Team; OEA, NEA, Youngstown Ed Assn 1989-; *office:* HS 731 S Hazelwood Ave Youngstown OH 44509

CH, VLADAMIER, 10th-12th Grade Biology Tchr; *b:* phia, PA; *m:* Joan Alice Walczak; *c:* Lisa Wirstrom, Stephen, Burr, Jason; *ed:* Rutgers Univ (BS) Animal Sci 1965; Glassboro A) Ed 1973; 12 Credit Hrs Post Grad in Sci Ed; *cr:* Squibb eutical Sales Veterinary Division 1967-68; Cherry Hill HS East r 1968-; *ai:* Bio Lab Aide Supervision; Bowling Coach; NEA, NJ , ECEA, Cherry Hill Ed Assn 1968-; NJ Sci Tchrs Assn 1980-; St C Church 1964-; Co-Authored Series of Bio Pamphlets for 1st Yr *office:* Cherry Hill HS East 1750 Kresson Rd Cherry Hill NJ 08003

AND, JAMES EDWARD,II, High Schl Mathematics Teacher; *b:* FL; *m:* Pamela Jane Flockencier; *c:* Lynne N. Vreeland Schnuth, . III, Ellyn E., Jeryd McCaig; *ed:* Findlay Coll (BS) HPER & Math owling Green St Univ (MED) HPER 1975; 46 Sem Hrs Post Grad uza Pacific Coll 9 Sem Hrs Post Grad Stud; *cr:* Bowling Green chls Jr HS Gen Math & 9th Grd Hlth Tchr 1970-74; ir-Kimberely Acad MS Math Tchr 1974-75; Delta HS Math, Gen Adv Alg Tchr 1975-76; Wavseon HS PE & Alg I Tchr 1976-80; y St Marys CCHS Alg I & Geom Math Tchr 1980-85; Oak Harbor I, Alg II & Math Tchr 1985-; *ai:* Freestyle Wrestling Team Dir & andusky Bay; SSWOA Schlsp Comm 1985-; OEA & NEA 1970-; 1985-; South Shore Wrestling Ofcls Assn 1980-, Pres 1987-; Lodge #495; Moose Lodge 1610; Vly of Toledo Scottish Rite; egion Post #114; OH St Wrestling Ofcl 1988-; Natl HS Wrestling nent Ofcl 1996-; Inducted into OH HS Wrestling Coaches Hall of 996; Pub MS Thesis Aquatics; *home:* 3821 S Bolsinger Rd Oak OH 43449*

'OS, JAMES S., Sociology Professor; *b:* New York, NY; *m:* Passman; *ed:* Columbia Univ (BA) Sociology 1968, (MA) gy 1971; *cr:* John Jay Coll Sociology Professor 1992-; *ai:* hor Book: Elementary Forms of Statistical Reason; *office:* City NY John Jay Coll 445 W 59th St Ofc New York NY 10019

EMA, JOHN KENNETH, Bible Teacher & Guid Cnslr; *b:* ood, NJ; *m:* Sandra Foster; *c:* Kristen, Jonathan, Matthew; *ed:* Coll (BA) Psych 1986; Calvin Theological Seminary (MA) Church ; *ai:* Chapel Comm Coord; JV Girls Bsktbl Coach; Spiritual Life *office:* Whitinsville Chrstn HS 279 Linwood Ave Whitinsville MA

AN, PATRICIA LYNN, English Teacher; *b:* Coatesville, PA; *m:* ; *c:* Jennifer, Daniel; *ed:* Kutetown Univ (BS) Comm 1975; West Univ (ME) Eng 1991; Writing Instruction Cert; *cr:* Exeter Jr HS 7, Eng Tchr 1975-; *ai:* Dept Chprsn; Enrichment Prgm Handcrafts; ating Tchr; NEA, PSEA 1975-; *office:* Exeter Jr H S 151 E 39th St g PA 19606

M, CHARLOTTE MC CORMACK, English Teacher; *b:* Jersey J; *c:* Megan Elizabeth; *ed:* Douglass Coll (BA) Eng 1975; Attnd s St Univ, Jersey City St Coll Grad Schl; *cr:* Cedar Ridge HS Eng 976-78; Henry Snyder HS Eng Tchr 1986-94; Wm L Dickinson HS *ai:* Class Adv 1990-94; NEA 1986-; Liberty Sci Ctr Jersey City Vol, Charter Mem; The Great Books Fnd 1993-, Group Ldr; *office:* L Dickinson HS 2 Palisade Ave Jersey City NJ 07306

M, PETER V., 8th Grd Earth Science Teacher; *b:* Cincinnati, OH; cy Compton; *c:* Andrew, Katherine; *ed:* Davis & Elkins Coll (BS) & Environmental Scis 1975; Tufts Univ (MEd) Ed 1982; 17 Addl m Ed Davis & Elkins Coll 1978; 6 Addl Hrs William Paterson Coll r: Morris Cty Soil Conservation Dist Ed Coord 1978-80; Medford b Schls Sub Tchr 1980-82; Ridgewood NJ Pub Schls Sci Tchr 7; West Windsor Plainsboro MS Sci Tchr 1987-; *ai:* Var Girls Sftbl Coach; NEA, NJEA 1982-; WWP Tchrs Assn1987-; NJSTA *office:* West Windsor Plainsboro MS 55 Grovers Mill Rd Plainsboro 36

EL, KATHLEEN GLANTON, Fourth Grade Teacher; *b:* Rochester, John; *c:* Sarah, Adam; *ed:* SUNY at Brockport (BS) Elem Ed; th Coll (BS) Masters in Ed; *cr:* Palmyra-Macedon CS Tchr Grds 1969-, 24 Yrs; *ai:* His Bowl Coord, Mem of Bldg Team; NYSUT Sec, Bldg Rep, VP; Girl Scout Ldr, Rel Ed Tchr; *office:* a-Macedon Central Dist 150 Hyde Pkwy Palmyra NY 14522*

LA, ROBERT JOHN, Business Ed Teacher; *b:* Pittsburgh, PA; *m:* ary Williams; *c:* Samuel, Lisa; *ed:* IN Univ of PA (BA) Bus Ed 1966; of Pittsburgh (MA) Distributive Ed 1971; *cr:* Gladstone HS Tchr 76; Reisenstein MD Tchr 1976-79; Brashear HS Tchr 1979-84; ly HS Tchr 1984-87; Oliver HS Tchr 1987-; *ai:* AFT 1970-; *office:* B. Oliver HS 2323 Brighton Rd Pittsburgh PA 15212

VICH, RUTH RAMSEY, English Teacher; *b:* Youngstown, OH; *m:* J. Jr.; *c:* Joseph R., Patrick R.; *ed:* Youngstown St Univ, (BA) Eng (MA) Eng 1983; *cr:* Hubbard HS Tchr & Dept Chair 1969-; *ai:* Eng Chair; Dist Tech Comm; Right to Read Co-Chair; NEA, OEA, A & Hubbard Ed Assn 1970- Secy & Pres; NCTE 1967-; Western e of OH Tchrs of Eng 1990-, Secy & Pres; OH Cncl of Tchrs of Eng Arts 1975-; St Patrick Chrch 1985-, Chair & Worship Ministry; LA Presenterspring Conf; Martha Holden Jennings Scholar 1993-, WROTE Conf Featuring Stephen Dunning; *office:* Hubbard HS 350 ve Hubbard OH 44425*

NOVIC, RELJA, Assistant Mathematics Prof; *b:* Becej, lavia; *m:* Tatjana Hrubik-Vulanovic; *c:* Ivan, Milan; *ed:* Univ of Novi ugoslavia (BS) Math 1980, (MS) Math 1983, (PHD) Math 1986; *cr:* of Novi Sad Asst Prof 1987-92; Oberlin Coll Visiting Asst Prof 1993; St Stark Asst Prof 1993-; *ai:* ACL 1991-; SIAM, MAA 1995-; Pub 1 3 Manuals, 54 Articles; *office:* Kent St Univ Stark Cmps 6000 Frank W Canton OH 44720

CANO, PAT,JR., Marketing, Bus Tchr & Coord; *b:* Easton, PA; *m:* a P. Alercia; *c:* Michele G.; *ed:* Churchman Bus Coll (ASB) nting & Finance 1968; Ft Lauderdale Coll (BBA) Bus Admin & nting 1970; IN Univ of PA (BSEd) Mrktg & Bus Ed 1973; Lehigh MEd) Career & Cooperative Ed 1976; Attnd Kutztown Univ in PA & e Univ at Philadelphia; *cr:* Central Chester Voc Tech Schl Mrktg 1973-75; Bethlehem Area Voc Tech Schl Mrktg Tchr & Coord 76; Northampton Area Sr High Mrktg, Bus & Cooperative Ed Tchr & 1976-; *ai:* DECA Chapter Adv; Pres PA DECA Bd of Trustees; anization & Prep Tech Comms; Natl & PA DECA 1972-, Pres PA, Bd ustees, Srv Awd; NEA & PSEA 1973-, Former Local Pres; US & la Municipal Treas Assn 1988-; PA Controllers Assn 1992-; Natl, PA ston Area Exchange Club 1983-95, Dir,; Easton Area Jaycees 1978-84, Svc Awd; St Anthonys United Way Youth Ctr 1968-, Past Pres, anding Svc Awd; Easton- Northampton Cty Columbus 1973-, Bd n, Outstanding Svc Awd; Org Inc 1992-, Elected Half Time oller Easton, PA 1992-; Columbus Day Honoree 1995; PA Jaycees St anding Educator Awd 1982; 10 Top Best Educators in St 1984-85; anding Educator from PA 1986; Who's Who in Govt 1990; Who's Who us 1993; *office:* Northampton Area Sr HS 1619 Laubach Ave ampton PA 18067*

VULPIS, ROBERT ALAN, Social Studies Teacher; *b:* Bronx, NY; *m:* Diane Driscolo; *c:* Alana Abbene, Danielle, Mariel; *ed:* Tarkio Coll (BA) His, Pol Sci 1966; Long Island Univ (MA) Scndry Ed 1970; Fordham Univ (MS) Ed Supervision 1973, (PD) Ed Admin 1975; NY Law Schl 15 Credit Hrs Law 1967; *cr:* MacArthur HS Soc Stud Tchr 3 Yrs; Salk Wisdom MS Soc Stud Tchr 16 Yrs; Division Ave HS Soc Stud Tchr 5 Yrs; Patchosue Medford Pub Schls Soc Stud Tchr 2 Yrs; Notre Dame Elem Schl Common Branch Tchr 3 yrs; *ai:* Renaissance Bldg Comm Coord; Sunshine Club; NY St EPE Prgms for Mid Cntry Cntrl Schl Dist Adult Ed Coord; Levitown United Tchrs, NY St Tchrs Assn, Membership 1972-; Levittown Assoc of Schl Admin 1981-91, Pub Relations, Cncl Rep, 10 Yr Svc Awd; PTA 1970-, Comm Chm; Nassau Cty Coaches Assn 1973-76, Membership; Summer Schl Prins Assoc 1981-91, Membership; in Svc Tchr Prep Courses for Mid Schls Dev Spon; Dev Staff Courses for Levittown Schl Dist Non Verbal Comm; Bicentennial Comm Coord; *office:* General Douglas Mac Arthur HS Old Jerusalem Rd Levittown NY 11756*

VUONO, RICHARD GERALD, Mathematics Teacher; *b:* Mononsalala, PA; *m:* Donna Furiga; *c:* Michael, John; *ed:* Penn St Univ (BS) Scndry Ed 1962; Univ of Pittsburgh (MED) Scndry Math Ed 1966; Columbia Univ Prof Diploma Math Supervision 1969; Attnd MI St Univ 1967, Univ of Pittsburgh 1967-71, CA Univ of PA 1963-64; *cr:* Owen J. Roberts Jr Sr HS Math Tchr 1962; Elizabeth Forward HS Math Tchr 1962-67; Upper St Clair HS Math Tchr & Coll Adj Fac 1967-; *ai:* AFT 1982-; USCEA 1967-; Math Cncl West PA 1978-; *office:* Upper Saint Clair HS 1825 Mclaughlin Run Rd Pittsburgh PA 15241

VYE, REBECCA WITTMEYER, English Teacher; *b:* Riverside, NJ; *m:* H. Kemp; *c:* Justine, Ethan; *ed:* Univ of DE (BA) Eng 1972; Wiedner Univ (MS) Scndry Ed 1988; Addl 30 Grad Hrs; *cr:* Stanton MS Eng Tchr 7 Yrs; John Dickinson HS Eng Tchr 6 Yrs; *ai:* NEA; NCTE; *office:* John Dickinson HS 1801 Milltown Rd Wilmington DE 19808

W

WAACK, RONALD, Guidance Director; *b:* Teaneck, NJ; *m:* Carol Byrns; *c:* Denise Palozzola, Christopher; *ed:* St Peters Coll (BS) Bus & Mrktg 1965; Montclair St Univ (MA) Stu Prsnl 1967; *cr:* Palisades Park HS Guid Dir 1967-90; Paramus Cath Guid Dir 1990-93; St John Vianney Guid Dir 1993-; *home:* 123 Howard Ter Leonia NJ 07605

WAARA, CARRIE LYNNE, Assistant Professor; *b:* Manitou Springs, CO; *m:* Kevin Scott Wong; *c:* Sarah Tai Yuan Wong; *ed:* MI St Univ (BA) Chinese Lang, Comparative Cultures 1976; Univ of MI (MA) His 1983, (PHD) His 1994; Inter-Univ Prgm in Chinese Lang Stud Taipei Taiwan 1982-84; *cr:* Univ of MI at Dearborn Adj Lecturer 1985-86; Williams Coll Visiting Lecturer 1994; Castleton St Coll Asst Prof 1992-; *ai:* Jr Class Adv; Women's Stud Fac Advy, Cultural Affiars Comms; Hum Seminar; AFT 1992-; Assn for Asian Stud 1985-; World His Assn 1994-; AAUW 1989-; Open Door Soc of MA 1993-; Natl Org of Women 1975-; Natl Abortion Rights Action League, Natl Women's Hlth Network 1977-; AAS Comm on Tchng About Asia 1985-, Bd Mem 1988-89; Frgn Lang, Area Stud Flwshps; MI Coll Flwshp; Republic of China Ministry of Ed Flwshp; Natl Merit Spec Schlsp; Castleton St Coll Fac Dev Grant; Most Outstdng New Fac Tchng Awd 1993; Articles Pub; *office:* Castleton St Coll Seminary St Castleton VT 05735*

WACHTELHAUSEN, SUSAN JOHNSON, English Teacher; *b:* Derby, CT; *m:* Thomas R.; *c:* Gregg, Tyler; *ed:* Cntrl CT St Univ (BS) Eng 1971, (MS) Rdng 1975; *cr:* Silas Deane MS Eng Tchr 1972-82; Wethersfield HS Eng Tchr 1982-; *ai:* Sr Class Adv; NHS Advy Cncl; CEA, EAW 1972-; Ceatacen Soc Intnl 1987-, Bd of Dirs; CCD Tchr 1989-; Peer Excl Awd; Jaycees Tchr of Yr; *office:* Wethersfield HS 411 Wolcott Hill Rd Wethersfield CT 06109

WACHTER, CHERYL ANN (VASKO), 8th Grd Math & 5th Grd Teacher; *b:* Sharon, PA; *m:* Richard B.; *c:* Aaron, Megan, Rebecca; *ed:* Edinboro Univ (BS) Elem Ed 1976; Slippery Rock Univ (MA) Rdng 1980; *cr:* Msgr Monti Schl 3rd Grd Tchr 1977-85, 8th Grd Math, 5th Grd Tchr 1985-; *ai:* NCEA 1977-; *office:* Msgr Geno J Monti Schl 1225 Union St Farrell PA 16121

WADACH, JOHN B., Associate Professor of Physics; *b:* New Hartford, NY; *m:* Bonnie Lehrer; *c:* Rachel, Brendon; *ed:* SUNY at Geneseo (BA) Physics 1981; Univ of ME (MS) Physics 1983; *cr:* W.S. Fleming Assoc Engrng Consultant 1983-84; Monroe CC Physics Prof 1984-; *ai:* Engrng Club, Design Team Adv; AAPT 1984-; SUNY 2 Yr Engnrg Sci Assn 1990-; Village of Lima 1987-92, Trustee; Lima Pk Commission 1992-, Commissioner; MCC Strategic Planning Grant Winner 1994-95; *office:* Monroe Community Coll 1000 E Henrietta Rd Rochester NY 14623

WADDINGTON, WILLIAM SCOTT, Technology Education Teacher; *b:* Norristown, PA; *m:* Jill Moyer; *ed:* Millersville Univ (BSEd) Industrial Arts 1986, (MED) Tech Ed 1990; *cr:* Wissahickon Schl Dist MS Elem Tchr 1988-89; North Penn Schl Dist HS Tchr 1989-95; *ai:* Boys Vllybl Coach 1993-95; TEAP 1988-, Regnl VP 1994, Pres Elect Tchr Excl; Intnl Tchr Ed Assn 1991-, Tchr Excl 1995; Articles: TEAP Journal.

WADE, BRENDA FAYE (BROWN), Secondary Mathematics Teacher; *b:* Ironton, OH; *m:* Richard L.; *c:* Amanda F., Adam R.; *ed:* OH Univ (BSEd) Scndry Ed, Math 1971, (MSEd) Ed, Cmptrs 1986; *cr:* Symmes Vly HS Math Tchr 1971-78, Math, Cmptrs Tchr 1981-; *ai:* Yrbk, Soph Class Adv; School Net, Venture Capital, Tech Prep Grant Writing Comms; Ed Assn 1971-, Treas; OH Ed Assn, NEA 1971-; OH Cncl of Tchrs of Math, NCTM1970-; Palestine Missionary Bapt Church 1967-, Pianist, Asst Treas, Sunday Schl Tchr; Palestine Church Women's Missionary Group 1976-, Pres, Sec, Treas; Outstdng Scndry Edctrs of Amer 1973; *home:* 18856 State Route 141 Willow Wood OH 45696

WADE, HEIDI MITCHELL, English Teacher; *b:* Houlton, ME; *m:* Dennis; *ed:* Univ of ME (BA) Eng 1990; Working Towards Masters in Guid; *cr:* Van Buren Scndry Schl Eng Tchr 1992-93; Houlton HS Eng Tchr 1993-; *ai:* JV Boys Soccer, 8th Grd Girls Bsktbl, Asst Var Sftbl Coach; Yrbk Adv; *office:* Houlton HS 5 Bird St Houlton ME 04730

WADE, JAMES EDWARD, HS Integrated Science Teacher; *b:* Sharon, PA; *ed:* Bowling Green St Univ (BS) Geology, Chem 1970; *cr:* Mentor Schls Earth Sci Tchr 1974-75; Joseph Badger Bio, Phys, Integrated Sci Tchr 1976-; *ai:* Girls Bsktbl; Boys Bsbl; OEA, NEA 1976-; Village Cncl 1995-, Councilman; NEO Dist Coach of Yr 1984; Giant Eagle Class Act Tchr 1995; *office:* Joseph Badger Local Schl Dist PO Box 99 8319 Main St Kinsman OH 44428

WADE, JANICE M. (MYERS), Fourth Grade Teacher; *b:* Willard, OH; *m:* Michael R.; *c:* Adam; *ed:* Ashland Coll Univ (BS) K-8th Grd Elem Ed & K-12th Grd Rdng 1975; Plus 30 Hrs Above BS; *cr:* Crestview Local Schl 1st Grd Tchr 1975-86, 4th Grd Tchr 1986-88, 4th & 5th Split Grd Tchr 1988-89, 4th Grd Tchr 1989-; *ai:* Local Soc Stud & Cty Soc Stud Comm; Local Proficiency Intervention Team; Kappa Delta Pi 1974-; OH Ed Assn 1975-; NEA 1975-; 4-H 1973-, Adv; Grange Local, St & Natl 1974-, Lady Asst Steward; OH Edison Sci & Altrusa Intnl Literacy Grants; *office:* Crestview Local Schls 1575 State Route 96 Ashland OH 44805

WADE, MARY ANN, Guidance Counselor; *b:* Richmond, VA; *m:* Frank B. Jr.; *c:* Michelle Wade-Scheuerman, Frank B. III; *ed:* Radford Univ (BA) Eng & Psych 1964; Bowie St Univ (MED) Guid & Cnslng 1990; Chesapeake Fndtn Environmental Ed; *cr:* Christ Church Schl 3rd Grd Tchr 1978-84; McDonough HS Eng & Psych Tchr 1984-90; La Plata HS Cnslr 1990-; *ai:* Renaissance; Supts Schl Rep; Prins Advy Comm; EACC 1984-; NEA 1984-; Soc for Restoration of Port Tobacco 1968-, Bd Mem; *office:* La Plata HS PO Box 790 La Plata MD 20646

WADL, CHARLES JEFFREY, Amer Govt & Economics Teacher; *b:* Cincinnati, OH; *m:* Ella Youtsler; *ed:* Univ of Cincinnati (BSEd) Scndry Ed 1988; Assoc Degree Bus Mgmt; 5 Hrs Paideia Trng at Xavier; *cr:* Withrow HS Amer & World His Tchr 1988-89; Bloom MS 8th Grd Amer His Tchr 1989-91; Roberts Paideia Acad 7th & 8th Grd Soc Stud Tchr 1991-94; Western Hills HS Advanced Placement Amer His, Ec & Govt Tchr 1994-; *ai:* Youth in City Govt Adv; Var Ftbl Asst Coach; Cincinnati Fed of Tchrs 1988-; Southwest OH Ftbl Coaches Assn 1986-; *home:* 4739 Primrose Ln Middletown OH 45044

WAGAR, CHARLES C., Mathematics Teacher; *b:* Wichita, KS; *c:* Wendy Ann, Keith Leon; *ed:* Belknap Coll (BS) Math 1970; Univ of Hartford (MS) Ed 1971; *cr:* West MS Tchr Core Intern 1970-71; Bulkeley HS Tchr of Math 1971-95; Univ of Hartford Hillyer Coll Adj Instr of Math 1987-; *ai:* AFT Local 1018 1972-; NCTM, ATOMIC 1980-; *office:* Bulkeley HS 300 Wethersfield Ave Hartford CT 06114

WAGAR, DIANE M., English Teacher; *b:* Little Falls, NY; *m:* Charles M.; *c:* Tina M. Wagar Bode, Jennifer G. Wager Smith; *ed:* SUNY at Oneonta (BA) Scndry Eng Ed 1970; Elmira Coll Permanent Cert Eng; *cr:* Stratford Cntrl Schl 8-12 Grd Eng Tchr 1971-77; Dolgeville Cntrl Schl 10-12 Grd Eng Tchr 1989-; *ai:* HS Musician Dir; Fac Adv Stu Writers Club; Jr Class, Prom Adv; HS Bldg Team; Intnl Women Writers 1995-; Active Parenting Today 1993-, Ldr; HS Bldg Team 1990-; St Johns Theatre Group 1978-, Dir; Mohawk Vly Choralairs 1989-, Conductor, Dir; St John Reformed Church 1970-, Supt, Co-Dir Marriage, Relationship Seminar; Co-Dir Parenting Seminars.

WAGELEY, WILLIAM HAROLD, 8th Grd Amer History Teacher; *b:* Fairmont, WV; *ed:* Fairmont St (BA) Soc Stud 1969; 18 Post-Grad Hrs Akron Univ; *cr:* Amos Mc Daniel Schl 5th-6th Grd Tchr 1966-69; Walker Jr HS 7th-9th Grd Tchr 1970-79; Faircrest MS 6th-8th Grd Tchr 1980-; *ai:* 8th Grd Track Coach; Mentor Tchr; Canton Local Ed Assn 1966-, Past Pres, Negotiator; OEA, NEA 1966-, Del; Jr Achvmt 1982-, Project Bus; Kiwanis 1970-78, Pres; Jennings Scholar 1994; Nom Ashland Oil Tchr of Yr; *home:* 519 Harmon St SW North Canton OH 44720*

WAGENER, JOHN ANDREAS,JR., Earth Science Teacher; *b:* Nyack, NY; *m:* Barbara Sage; *ed:* Cornell Univ (BS) Bio & Ed 1970; Elmira Coll (MS) Bio & Ed 1975; *cr:* Mynderse Acad Sci Tchr 1970-; *ai:* NY St Hunter Ed Instr; HS Steering Comm & Schl Improvement Sub-Comm Chm; NEA, NYNEA & STANYS 1970-; Pocahotas Lodge #211 F & AM 1980-, Jr Warden 2 Yrs; Seneca Upland Game 1970-, Pres 22 Yrs; Natl Rifle Assn 1970-; Natl Corvette Restorers' Soc 1995-; Emergency Medical Technician 1971; NY St Hunter, Bowhunter Ed Instr 1986; Seneca Falls Rotary Rotary Intnl Preserve Planet Earth Symposium Rep 1991; *office:* Mynderse Acad 105 Troy St Seneca Falls NY 13148*

WAGGONER, TODD CHARLES, Technology Systems Asst Prof; *b:* Mansfield, OH; *ed:* Bowling Green St Univ (BSEd) Manufacturing 1979, (MED) Career & Tech Ed 1981; Univ of Toledo (PHD) EDAS, Higher Ed 1988; Acuity's Image Anayst Machine Vision Prgm, Algor's 988 Finite Element Analysis Course, Emco Maier Tmoz Control Trng 1995; *cr:* M. J. Owens Tech Coll Mech, Engr, Tech Instr 1979-82; GA Southern Coll Indstrl Tech Asst Prof 1982-84; Univ of Toledo GA Asst Prof of Ed Lead 1984-89; Bowling Green St Univ Tech System Asst Prof 1987-; *ai:* Stu Soc of Manufacturing Engrs Adv; Epsilon Pi Tau 1990-, Honorary Tech; Phi Delta Kappa 1992-, Honorary Admin; Model A Ford Res Club 1991-; Studebaker Drivers Club 1981-; Natl Yth Sci Camper 1974-, OH Rep Alum 1974; Prof Presentations; Written Proceedings of Prof Paper Presented; *office:* Bowling Green St Univ Coll of Tech Bowling Green OH 43403

WAGNER, ANTHONY WAYNE, Mathematics Teacher; *b:* Piqua, OH; *m:* Lucinda A.; *c:* Kersten, Gretchen, Lauren; *ed:* Wright St Univ (BA) Ed 1977; Univ of Dayton (MS) Ed 1980, Specialist ED 1996; *cr:* Sidney City Schls 8th Grd Sci Tchr 1977-81 & 9th-12th Grd Math Tchr 1981-; Edison St Comm Coll Math Instr 1985-; *ai:* 9th Grd Ftbl & 7th & 8th Grd Wrestling Coach; Sr Class Adv; NEA, OEA, WOEA & OCTM 1978-; NCTM 1987-; SEA 1978-, Pres 1 Yr, Tchr of Yr Awd 1990; Tchr of Year 1991; Elks 1978-; Sidney City Schls Outstanding Citizen Awd; Local Pool Mgr 12 Yrs; *office:* Sidney H S 1215 Campbell Rd Sidney OH 45365*

WAGNER, BARBARA BURGMAIER, English & Basic Speech Teacher; *b:* Toledo, OH; *c:* Sandra Wagner DeMoscio, Mary Beth Wagner Perry; *ed:* Univ Toledo (BED) Eng 1957, (MED) Eng 1979; *cr:* Huff Jr High 7-8th Grd Eng Tchr 1 & Half Yrs; Ottawa Hills HS 7-12th Grd Eng Dept 30 & Half Yrs; Monroe Cty Comm Coll Basic Writing Tchr Half Yr; *ai:* Quiz Bowl Coach; NHS, Sr Class Spon; Eng Dept Chair; OHEA, NWOEA, NEA 1989-; Phi Alpha Theta 1956-; Phi Delta Kappa 1992-; Awds Pub Relations Assn of NW OH, MIT, Univ Chicago; 3 Copyrights Held; *office:* Ottawa Hills Jr Sr HS 2532 Evergreen Rd Toledo OH 43606*

WAGNER, BARBARA PLACE, Junior High Teacher; *b:* Lima, OH; *m:* Frederick; *c:* Ashley Nicole; *ed:* OH St (BS) Ed 1977; Comm Cert OH St; *cr:* Hilliard City Schls Sub Tchr 1988-90; Maranatha Chrstn HS Eng, Math Tchr 1990-92; Wyandot Chrstn Acad Admin, HS Tchr 1992-95; Home Schl Eighth Grd Tchr 1995-; *ai:* Morning Deejay WXML Chrstn Radio; Handbell Choir Dir; Comm Theatre; Natl Day of Prayer Yth Coord; Assn of Chrstn Schls Admins 1992-; *home:* 459 N 5th St Upper Sandusky OH 43351

WAGNER, BETH CARDELLO, Sixth Grade Teacher; *b:* Johnson City, NY; *m:* Bruce; *c:* Michael, Kylie; *ed:* Millersville Univ (BA) Elem Ed 1981; Enrolled Grad Prgm Penn St; *cr:* Mountville HS 6th Grd Tchr 1984-95; *ai:* PMEA 1984-; *office:* Mountville Elem Schl 2121 Temple Ave Lancaster PA 17603

WAGNER, CYNTHIA (ANDALORO), Fifth Grade Teacher; *b:* Canton, OH; *m:* David Paul; *ed:* Mt Union Coll (BA) Elem Ed 1986; Univ of Akron (MA) Elem Ed Admin 1992; Cert Elem Prin 1994; *cr:* T. C. Knapp Elem Schl Fourth Grd Tchr 1986-95, Fifth Grd Tchr 1995-; *ai:* Stark Cty Staff Dev Action, Perry Local Ldrshp Implementation, Rep to Admin, Tchr Levy Teams; Common Inservice Day Eval Subcommittee; Local Staff Dev Cncl; United Way Campaign Coord; NEA 1986-; Natl Batchelder Meml Scholar 1991; Canton Regnl Chamber Commerce Tchr of Yr Nom 1994; Canton Respository Spring Tchr Feature Nom 1994, Apples for Tchr Awd 1995; Canton Regnl Chamber Commerce Tchr of Yr Top Ten Semi-finalist 1996; Ashland Oil Outstdng OH Tchr Nom; *home:* 10391 Blough Ave SW Bolivar OH 44612

WAGNER, DIANE MCCORMACK, Biology Teacher; *b:* Jersey City, NJ; *m:* William; *ed:* Jersey City St Coll (BA) Bio 1978; NY Univ Cert of Respiratory Therapy 1980; 30 Post Grad Credits; *cr:* Overlook Hospital Respiratory Therapist 1982-84; Saint Anthonys HS Bio & Chem Tchr 1985; Irvington Pub Schl 7th & 8th Grd Sci Tchr 1986-88; Lodi HS Bio Tchr 1988-; *ai:* NEA 1985-; *office:* Lodi HS 99 Putnam St Lodi NJ 07644

WAGNER, EDWARD DEMMY, 6th Grade Teacher; *b:* Harrisburg, PA; *m:* Mary Jane Higgins; *c:* Joshua, Tracy; *ed:* Bloomsburg St Coll (BS) Elem Ed 1972; *cr:* Central Dauphin East Jr High Math Tchr 1973-74, Ftbl Coach 1973-79; Linglestown Jr High Math Tchr 1975-80, Ftbl Coach 1973-79; North Side Elem 6th Grd Tchr 1981-; *ai:* All 6th Grd Intramural Sports; Scenery Adv For Elem Musical.

WAGNER, FREDERICK LLOYD, Band Director; *b:* Waynesboro, PA; *m:* Beverly Tyson; *c:* Andrew; *ed:* Peabody Conservatory of Music (BMED) Trumpet, Ed 1970; Attnd Cntrl CT Univ at Hartford, Vandercook Coll at Chicago, Villanova at Philadelphia; *cr:* James Buchanan HS Dir of Bands 1986-; *ai:* Class Adv; Strategic Planning Comm; Prinipals Advy Cncl; Music Dept Chm 1987-; PA Music Edctrs Assn, Music Edctrs Natl Conf 1986-; Natl Band Assn 1990-; Mercersburg Area Comm Band 1986-, Dir; *home:* 6380 Hillcrest St Mercersburg PA 17236*

WAGNER, JACQUELYN SPAIDE, Biology I & II Teacher; *b:* Long Island, NY; *c:* Zane; *ed:* Williamsport Area Comm Coll (AA) Gen Stud 1981; Bloomsburg Univ (BS) Scndry Ed 1983; 24 Addl Hrs; *cr:* Berwick Area MS Life Sci Tchr 1984-85; Columbia Montour VoTech Schl Summer Bio Tchr 1985; Penns Vly Jr Sr HS Bio Tchr 1985-86, 1988-; Mifflinburg HS Summer Schl Bio Tchr 1986-87; *ai:* Prof Dev Comm; Stu Assistance Prgm; Fac Advy Team; PSTA, NABT 1990-; NEA 1984-; NVEA 1985-; Unitarian Universalist; *office:* Penns Valley Jr Sr HS RR 2 Box 116 Spring Mills PA 16875

WAGNER, JANET TARRANT, Chemistry Teacher & Sci Coord; *b:* Watertown, NY; *m:* Alan Ross; *c:* Stephanie, Christopher; *ed:* SUNY at Albany (BS) Bio 1966; SUNY at Oneonta (MS) Ed 1975; *cr:* Berne Cntrl Schl Physics, Gen Sci Tchr 1966-68; Knox Cntrl Schl Physics, Gen Sci Tchr 1966-68; Westerlo Cntrl Schl Physics, Gen Sci Tchr 1966-68; Schoharie Cntrl Schl 7th Grd Sci Tchr 1970-72, Chem, Gen Sci Tchr 1975-, K-12 Sci Coord 1989-; *ai:* Local Tchrs Assn Early Retirement Incentive Comm Chair; Tech Planning Comm; Chem Hygiene Ofcr; Delta Kappa Gamma 1984-, 1st VP Local Chptr; NSTA 1989-; NYS Sci Supvrs Assn; NYS Sci Tchrs Assn 1989-; Capital Area Sci Supvrs Assn 1989-; Amer Chem Soc Tchr of Yr Eastern NY St; Tchr of Yr 1990; Awd 2 Mini Grants Amer Chem Soc to Improve Jr HS Sci Stud Chem 1992, 1995; *office:* Schoharie Cntrl Schl Main St Schoharie NY 12157

WAGNER, JEAN VANALSTYNE, Assoc Prof of Life Science; *b:* Cooperstown, NY; *m:* Robert Michael; *c:* James M.; *ed:* Herkimer Cty Comm Coll (AA) Sci 1969; Univ of New England (BA) Bio 1971; Syracuse Univ (MS) Sci Ed 1981; *cr:* Faxton Hosp Lab Technologist 1971-72; St Elizabeth Hosp Lab Technologist 1972-75; Mohawk Vly Comm Coll Adj Instr 1981-86, Asst to Assoc Prof 1986-; *ai:* Coll Senate 1990-95; Senate Advy Comm; Staff Dev Comm 1992-95; Events Comm Common Hour 1996; Empire St Assn 2 Yr Coll Biologists 1988-90; NSTA 1994-95; NABT 1995-; Planned Parent Ed Comm; Comm Course Improving Habits, Effective Living 1981-95; Wkshps 1996; *office:* Mohawk Valley Comm Coll 1101 Sherman Dr Utica NY 13501

WAGNER, LENORE M., HS Music Teacher; *b:* Dellsburg, PA; *m:* Richard L.; *c:* Laura Wagner Strickland; *ed:* Westchester Univ (BS) Music Ed 1960; Western MD Coll (MLA) Lbrl Arts 1986; Addl 24 Credit Hrs at Various Insts; *cr:* Northern York Co Schls Fourth Grd Tchr 1960-61; Dover Area HS Music Tchr, Choral Dir 1961-70; Lancaster Bible Coll Adj Music Prof 1993-95; Chrstn Schl of York HS Music Tchr 1995-, Choral Dir 1976-93; *ai:* Dir Crusader Singers; PMEA, MENC 1961-; 25 Year Awd PA Music Edctrs Assn; Natl Registerd MENC; *office:* Christian Schl Of York 907 Greenbriar Rd York PA 17404

WAGNER, LINDA LONG, Social Studies Teacher; *b:* Altoona, PA; *m:* Marshall J.; *c:* Emily J., Gregory M.; *ed:* PA St Univ (BA) Sociology 1971; Attnd Gettysburg 1967-69; PA Tchrs Cert Albright Coll 1980; *cr:* Cntrl Intermediate Unit Schl Tchr of Intellectually GATE 1981-85; Osceola Mills Jr HS His Tchr 1985-87; Philipsburg-Osceola HS His, Psych Tchr 1987-; *ai:* Stu Cncl, Soc Stud Club Adv; Individual Prof Dev Comm; Philipburg-Osceola Ed Assn, PSEA, NEA 1985-; Trinity UMC Choir 1982-; PA Assn Stdnts Cncl Dist V Adv of Yr 1994; *home:* RR 3 Box 291A-1 Philipsburg PA 16866

WAGNER, LINDA MITCHELL, Intervention Counselor; *b:* Erie, PA; *m:* David J.; *c:* Eric T. McClung, Ryan D. McClung; *ed:* Alderson-Broaddus Coll (BS) Ed 1970; SD St Univ (MED) Ed, Pupil Prsnl & Guid Svcs 1974; Certfd Drug & Alcohol Prevention Specialist; *cr:* David McChesney Dental Asst 1982-84; Greater Erie Comm Action Comm Drug & Alcohol Prevention Specialist 1984-88; Northwest Tri-Cty Intermediate Unit Drug Free Schls Coord 1989-90; Harbor Creek Intervention Cnslr 1988-; *ai:* SADD Adv 1988-95; NEA 1988-; PA Ed Assn 1988-; Harbor Creek Ed Assn 1988-; Who's Who of Amer Women Nom; *office:* Harbor Creek Jr Sr HS 6375 Buffalo Rd Harborcreek PA 16421

WAGNER, MARY MASSARO, Kindergarten Teacher; *b:* Jamaica, NY; *m:* Gregory Ralph; *c:* Gregory E., Jennifer R., Guy M., Justin P.; *ed:* Mount St Mary Coll (BA) Eng, Elem Ed 1973; C. W. Post Coll (MA) Rdng 1976; 3 Credits Story Whole Lang Learning Inst 1990; *cr:* Saint Patrick Schl Second Grd Tchr 1973-79; Smithtown Schl Dist Rdng Tchr 1983-84; Saint Patrick Schl Third Grd Tchr 1985-87, First Grd Tchr 1987-93, Kndgtn Grd Tchr 1993-; *ai:* St Joseph Church Kings Park Confirmation Class Rel Ed Tchr; Breakfast Club Organizer; Pvt Tutoring; NCEA 1985-, Tchr Assoc; *office:* St Patrick Schl 284 E Main St Smithtown NY 11787*

WAGNER, NANCY H., English Teacher; *b:* Raleigh, NC; *m:* C. C. II; *c:* Morgan Anderson, C. Conaugh III; *ed:* Salem Coll (BA) Eng & Voice 1965; Wilmington Coll (MS) Human Resources Mgmt 1989; 45 Credit Hrs; Cert Admin; *cr:* Milford HS Tchr 1965-66; Dover HS Tchr 1966-70, Schl to Work Transition 1987-89, Eng Tchr 1989-; *ai:* Capital Edctrs Assn 1989-; DE St Ed Assn 1989-; Univ of DE, Parents Bd 1991-93; 31st Dist House of Rep, St Rep 1992; DE St Univ, Bd of Visitors 1995; Modern Maturity Ctr, Bd of Dirs 1995; AIP in Power Bd of Dirs 1995; Delta Kappa Gamma Honorary Ed Soc; St Team Force on Ed Requirements; *office:* Dover HS 1 Pat Lynn Dr Dover DE 19904

WAGNER, PATRICK ALAN, Physical Education Teacher; *b:* Gallipolis, OH; *m:* Barbara Ann Steinman; *c:* Scott, Sara, Jennifer, Kyle; *ed:* Bluffton (BS) Hlth, PE 1971; Miami at Oxford (MED) Ed 1975; *cr:* Spencerville K-8 Grd PE Tchr 1972-75; Sheridan 9-12 Grd PE Tchr 1975-76; Berne Union K-12 Grd PE Tchr 1976-79; Liberty-Benton K-12 Grd PE Tchr 1979-; *ai:* Head Girls Track & Cross Cntry, 7th-8th Grd Girls Bsktbl Coach; OEA; NEA; OAT CCC, Dist Rep; Pres Elect St Coaches Assoc; Church, Admin Cncl; St Coach of Yr Cross Cntry 1988, Track 1990; St Track & Cross Cntry Hall of Fame 1993; Hancock Cty Hall of Fame 1993; *office:* Liberty-Benton HS St Rt 12 W Findlay OH 45840*

WAGNER, RICHARD C., Earth & Physical Sciences Tchr; *b:* Medina, NY; *m:* Carolyn Winter; *c:* Keith; *ed:* St Univ of NY at Brockport (BS) Sci 1974; St Univ of NY at Buffalo (MS) Sci 1987; *cr:* Lockport Cntrl Schl Hlth Sci Tchr 1978-81; Royalton-Hartland Cntrl Schl Earth Sci & Phys Sci Tchr 1981-; *ai:* Little League & Soccer Coach 1988-90; Jr HS Ftbl Coach 1993; JV Ftbl Coach 1980-88; Volunteer Ftbl Coach 1994-96; NY St United Tchrs; Royal-Hart Tchrs Assn; *office:* Royalton-Hartland Cntrl Schl State St Middleport NY 14105

WAGNER, SALLY STERRETT, High School Band Director; *b:* Pittsburgh, PA; *m:* Michael David; *c:* Michael David Jr., Caroline Elaine; *ed:* Univ of DE (BMAS) Music Ed 1973; MI St Univ (MMUS) Music Ed 1980; *cr:* Dover AFB Schls Elem Vocal & General Music Tchr 1973-74; Smyrna HS Dir of Bands & Choir 1974-77; Portland MS Vocal & general Music Tchr 1979-80; Beltsville Jr HS Bands, Orch & General Music Dir 1980-81; Eleanor Roosevelt HS Band Dir 1981-; *ai:* Jazz Band & Dixieland Combo Dir; Chamber Ensembles Coach; Women Band Dir Natl Assn 1986-; Music Educators Natl Conf 1973-; MD Band Dir Assn 1981-, Exec Bd 2 Yrs; NEA 1980-; Nationally Registered Music Educator 1990; Prince Georges Cty Chamber of Commerce Outstanding Educator Awd 1986; City of Bowie Local Govt Excl in Tchng Awd 1985; *office:* Eleanor Roosevelt H S 7601 Hanover Pkwy Greenbelt MD 20770

WAGNER, SAMUEL ROBERT, Agricultural Teacher; *b:* Mifflintown, PA; *m:* Mary Eleanor Haines; *c:* Sharon, Patricia; *ed:* PA St Univ (BS) Agricultural Ed 1963, (MED) Agricultural Ed 1981; *cr:* Susquenita Schl Dist Agricultural Tchr 1963-64; West Perry Schl Dist Agricultural Tchr 1964-74; Chambersburg Schl Dist Agricultural Tchr 1974-75; West Perry Schl Dist Agricultural Tchr 1975-; *ai:* BLT Dept Head; FFA Adv; NEA, PSEA NVATA, AVA 1963-; PVATA 1963-, Pres, PA Outstdng Ag Tchr 1991; PA Lions 1966-, Pres Local Club, Zone, Regnl Chm; PA Governor's Svc Awd; Messiah Luth Church 1966-, Exec Dir; PA Lions Club Pres Awd; Lions Intnl Pres Cert of Appreciation; *office:* West Perry Schl Dist RR 1 Box 7 Elliottsburg PA 17024

WAGNER, SUSAN MARIE, English, German & ESL Tchr; *b:* Reading, PA; *ed:* Albright Coll (BA) Ger 1969; Middlebury Coll (MA) Ger 1975; Kutztown Univ 30 Credit Hrs Ed, Ger & Eng; Laubach Literacy Cncl 2 Credit Hrs Eng as Second Lang; *cr:* Mainland Regnl HS Tchr 1973-72; Pine Grove Area HS Tchr 1972-; Private Eng as Second Lang Tutor 1985-; *ai:* Quiz Bowl Coach; Assembly Comm; Theater Field Trip Organizer; NCTE 1975-; NEA 1972-; ACTFL 1993-; Berks Ballet Theater, Bd of Dirs 1987-; PSU Berks Campus, Fine Arts Comm 1992-; Shoestring Productions, Producer 1985-; Laubach Literacy Cncl Eng as Second Lang Tutor-Trainer 1981-92; Dir of Cty Best Prodctn of the Yr Play 1995; *office:* Pine Grove Area HS School St Pine Grove PA 17963*

WAGNER, TIMOTHY R., Assistant Chemistry Professor; *b:* Reedsburg, WI; *m:* Patricia E. Bergum; *c:* Sarah; *ed:* Univ of WI at River Falls (BS) Chem 1981; AZ St Univ (PHD) Solid St Chem 1986; Postdoctoral Rsrch Fellow Northwestern Univ 1988-90; *cr:* Hughes Aircraft Software Dev, Radar Systems Group 1986-90; IL Inst of Tech Visiting Asst Chem Prof 1990-92; Youngstown St Univ Asst Chem Prof 1992-; *ai:* Co-Adv Amer chem Soc Stu Affiliates; Comm Outreach Prgms; Amer Chem Soc 1983-, Local Chair 1994; OH Ed Assoc 1992-; Two NSF Instrumentation Grants; 5 Publications; *office:* Youngstown St Univ Dept of Chemistry 410 Wick Ave Youngstown OH 44555

WAGNER, VIRGINIA E. (SOLANO), Spanish Teacher; *b:* San Jose, Costa Rica; *m:* Harry Norman; *c:* Jennifer E., Jeannette E.; *ed:* Univ of Costa Rica (BS) Bio 1968; Univ of MD (BA) Modern Lang, Ling 1980; Bowie St Univ (MED) Guid, Cnslng 1995; *cr:* Mount St Joseph HS Span Tchr 1981-82; Lindale Jr HS Exploratory Lang Tchr 1982-83; Annapolis HS Span Tchr 1983-84; Old Mill Sr HS Span Tchr 1985-; *ai:* Frgn Lang Club Spon; Fac Cncl Mem; Multicultural Comm; NEA, TAAAC 1982-; MFLA 1985-; ACA 1994-; Excl in Tchng Awd Nom 1990; *home:* 261 Scotts Manor Dr Glen Burnie MD 21061

WAGNER, WILLIAM GLENN, Chemisty & Physics Teacher; *b:* Sistersville, WV; *m:* Deborah Ann Mc Culley; *c:* William, Gwendolyn; *ed:* West Liberty St (BA) Chem Ed 1972; Post Grad WV Univ, WV Comm Coll, Norte Dame of OH, OH St, OH Univ Eastern; *cr:* Martins Ferry HS Tchr 1970-; Wheeling Cntrl Cath HS Asst Track Coach 1988-91; Wheeling Jesuit Coll Adj Instr 1994; West Liberty St Coll Asst Track Coach 1995-; *ai:* NEA, Martinsferry Ed Assn 1970-; East OH Amature Wireless Assn 1992-, Pres 1993-94; Northern Panhandle Amature Radio Club; Northern Panhandle Firemen Assn 1980-, Treas 1990-; West Liberty VFD 1976-, Pres 1985-89; Natl Sci Fnd Grants 1973-90; *office:* Martins Ferry HS 810 Hanover Martins Ferry OH 43935

WAGONER, M. JOANN, Middle & High School Teacher; *b:* Baltimore, MD; *ed:* Notre Dame of MD (BA) Elem Ed 1973; Towson St Univ, Loyola Coll 30 Addl Grad Credits; *cr:* St Paul Schl 4th Grd Tchr 1970-73; St Thomas Aquinas Schl 1st-5th Grd Sci Tchr 1973-74; Notre Dame Preparatory Schl 5th-8th Grd Tchr 1974-79; St Augustine Schl 6th-8th Grd Tchr 1979-; *ai:* Stu Cncl Adv; Svc Projects Coord; NCEA 1980-; ASCD, NSTA 1990-; Parish Cncl 1989-, Sec; Schl Bd 1992-; Rep Payee 1990-, Coord; Archdiocese of Baltimore St Augustine Schl Tchr of Yr; *office:* St Augustine Schl 5990 Old Washington Rd Elkridge MD 21227

WAHL, GLENN G., 7th-12th Grade Science Teacher; *b:* Rochester, NY; *m:* Ruth Turner; *c:* Christopher; *ed:* SUNY Coll at Geneseo (BA) Geology 1975; SUNY Coll at Fredona (MS) Bio, Ed 1987; St Bonaventure, Rutgers NJ Schl of Conservation 60 Credit Hrs; *cr:* Watching Hills Reg HS 9-12 Grd Sci Tchr 1975-78; Little Vly Cntrl Schl 7-12 Grd Sci Tchr 1978-; *ai:* Stu Cncl, Jr Class Adv; Scheduling Comm; AFT, Little Vly Tchrs Assn 1978-, Pres 1994-, VP, Sec; West Vly Coalition, Cattaraugus Cty Action Group 1990-; Fulbright Tchr Exch Prgm 1988; Explorer Adv of Yr 1982, 1985; Allegheny Highland Cncl Awd Merit; NYS Ed Dept Regents Exam Review Comm 1992-; *office:* Little Valley Central Schl 207 Rock City St Little Valley NY 14755

WAHL, HEINZ WOLFGANG, Electronics Instructor; *b:* Watertown, NY; *m:* Roedic Patrice Geno; *c:* Corey Ellis, Toni Patrice; *ed:* DeVry Inst (BSEET) Electronic Engrng Tech 1988; NYS Cert Electronics Instr; *cr:* Fr Creek Marina Electronic Engr 1988-; Island Systems Owner 1994-; *ai:* VICA Chprsn; Tech Expo, Tech, VICA, PR Comms; NYSRT Assn 1993-; Clayton VFD 1990-, Firefighter; *office:* Jefferson Tech Ctr 20104 NYS Rt 3 Watertown NY 13601*

WAHL, MEGAN LYNN, 7th Grd Earth Sci Tchr & Dean; *b:* Summit, NJ; *ed:* Colby Coll (BA) Geology 1990; Schl Cnslng Wilmington Coll; 4 Credit Hrs Methods of Tchng Earth Sci Univ of DE; 3 Credit Hrs Environmental Sci Tchg Methods Ashland Nature Ctr; *cr:* Wilmington Friends Schl Sci Tchr 1990-, Sci Tchr, Dean 1994-; *ai:* 7th Grd Adv; Knitting, Camping Clubs; Field Hockey, Lacrosse Coaches; MS Steering, Worship, Earth Day Comms; NSTA 1991-; DE Sci Tchrs 1992-; Vol Big Brothers Big Sisters 1995-; Led Many Camping Trips to Chile, South Amer & Australia Been Featured in News Journal & Outside Kids Magazine; *office:* Wilmington Friends Schl 101 School Rd Wilmington DE 19803*

WAHL, RUTH TURNER, Science Teacher; *b:* Jamestown, NY; *m:* Glenn G.; *c:* Christopher; *ed:* SUNY at Geneseo (BA) Geology 1975; St Bonaventure Univ (MS) Advanced Tchr Ed 1996; *cr:* North Hunterdon HS Sci Tchr 1976-77; Randolph Cntrl Schl Math Tchr 1978-79; Ellicottville HS Sci Tchr 1979-80; Brandford Cntrl Chrstn HS Sci, Math Tchr 1982-84; Allegany Limestone Cntrl Schl Sci Tchr 1988-; *ai:* NEA 1988-; *office:* Allegany Cntrl Schl N 4th St Allegany NY 14706

WAHLBERG, BRIAN LUTHER, Camp Director; *b:* New Prague, MN; *m:* Jean Habecker; *c:* Jeffrey Brian, Scott Brian, Todd Brian; *ed:* Pillsbury Bapt Bible Coll (BS) Bible, Pastorology 1980; Calvary Bapt Theological Seminary (MDIV) 1984; *cr:* Calvary Bapt Church, Schl Yth Pastor, Bible Tchr 1982-95; Camp Calvary Camp Dir, Yth Pastor, Part-time Tchr 1995-; *ai:* Sr Adv 1984-94; Bsktbl Coach 1992-94; ACCAC 1984- Ordination 1985; *office:* Calvary Baptist Schl 1380 S Valley F Lansdale PA 19446*

WAHLENMAYER, CAROL WILLIAMS, English Teacher; *b:* NY; *m:* Gerald A.; *c:* Kimberly Apelgren, Douglas B.; *ed:* Rutger-C Permanent Cert Rdng 1980; SUNYC at Buffalo (MA) Eng 1966, (B 90 Grad Hrs; *cr:* Orchard Park Jr HS Eng, Rdng Tchr 1964-68; W Jr High Eng, Rdng Tchr 1976-85; O'youville Coll Writing Instr; Park HS Eng Tchr 1982-; *ai:* Adv Writers Club; Dir Canisius Co Writers Camp; NYSUT; NY Council Eng Tchr; Phi Delta Kappa I James Church Bd; Friends of the Hamburg-OP Lib; Western NY Project Fellow 1988; Wkshp Presenter Diocese of Buffalo; Eng Articles, Pub Short Stories, Articles, Poetry; Consultant to the Rdng, Univ of NE 1996.*

WAHLSTROM, PETER ALLAN, Industrial Technology Tea Worcester, MA; *m:* Donna Lee Wiberg; *c:* Erik, Kara; *ed:* Fitchburg (BS) Indstrl Ed 1982; *cr:* David Prouty HS Indstrl Tech Tchr I Quaboag Regnl HS Indstrl Tech Tchr 1983-; *ai:* JV Soccer, V Coach; Prof Dev Comm; Tchr Resource Team; Adult Ed Tchr; Qua Assn 1983-; MA Tchrs Assn, NEA 1982-; Tech Ed Assn of MA 19 Hockey Coach 1995-; Millbury Little League 1991-, Coach; Quaboag Reg Jr Sr HS 284 Old W Brookfield Rd Warren MA 010

WAICKMAN, DOROTHY DOERRER, English Teacher; *b:* Akr *m:* Robert; *c:* Lynn Pedulla, Michael; *ed:* Kent St Univ (BS) Ed, Bio, (MED) Rdng 1987; *cr:* Cuyahoga Falls HS Eng Tchr; Tallma Sub Tchr; Ravenna HS Eng Tchr 1984-; *ai:* North Cntrl Eva Co-Chair; Ravenna Ed Assn, HS Rep; NEA, OH Ed Assn; NCTE Ravenna HS 345 E Main St Ravenna OH 44266

WAIDELL, GEORGE, 8th Grade Social Studies Tchr; *b:* Coald *m:* Sandra Gill; *c:* George, Douglas; *ed:* Penn St (BS) Scndry E Grad Stud Penn St, Marywood Coll; *cr:* Tamaqua Area Jr HS Soc St 1970-; *ai:* Jr High Boys Bsktbl Coach 1976-; Formerly Jr Hig Coach; Formerly Stu Cncl Adv; South Ward Fire Co 1970-, Past Pr VP; *office:* Tamaqua Area Jr HS High St Tamaqua PA 18252

WAIKSNIS, EMALYN LOPIPARO, Reading Teacher; *b:* Queen, William; *c:* Bryan, Jeffrey, Corinne; *ed:* Queens Coll (BA) En Hunter Coll; *cr:* Saint Gabriel Schl 5th Grd Tchr 1969-72; Holy Sp 6th Grd Tchr 1989-90, 1st Grd Tchr 1991-92, Rdng Specialist 19 Sunshine Club Coord; NEA 1969-; *office:* Holy Spirit Schl 13 S 6th Hyde Park NY 11040

WAINER, SUSAN PLOSCOWE, Engish Teacher; *b:* Brooklyn, Arnold; *c:* Brett, Glenn; *ed:* Univ of Bridgeport (BA) Eng 1968; Univ (MS) Rdng, Scndry Ed 1972; Queens Coll (PHD) Schl Supervision 1986; Lehman Coll Writing Project; *cr:* JHS 189 Q La Tchr, Rdng, Writing Specialist, Asst Dean, Interim Acting Asst Prin *ai:* Sr Act, Yrbk, Comm Based Newsletter Adv; MS Initiative; Quee Cncl of Rdng 1980-; UFT 1968-; Schl of Intl Studs, Curr Guide, ES Contributor; *office:* JHS 189 14480 Barclay Ave Flushing NY 113

WAINWRIGHT, TERRI A., Eng & Creative Writing Instr; *b:* Bal MD; *m:* William Wainwright; *c:* Katherine, Jonathan; *ed:* John H Univ (BS) 1977, (MLA) 1987; *cr:* Bel Air HS Eng Instr, Gifted-Talented Prgm 1977-80; N Harford HS Eng Instr 1986-87; HS Eng, Creative Writing Instr 1988-; *ai:* Spon Lit Magazine; Ass Forensic Team; Coord Writing Assts Prgm; NEA, MSTA, HCEA NCTE 1988-; ASCD 1991-; Delta Kappa Gamma 1992-; *office:* Be S 100 Heighe St Bel Air MD 21014*

WAITE, DARLENE ROSE (WALTERS), VP for Academic Aff Knox, IN; *m:* Daniel; *c:* Jonathan, Nicholas; *ed:* Ball St Univ (BS) 1980; Univ of Dayton (MBA) Bus 1993; *cr:* Miami-Jacobs Coll 1991-92, Ed Dir, Enrollment Mngmt 1992-94, Operations VP 1 Acad Affairs VP, Bus Principles Instr 1994-; *ai:* ASCD 1993-; Miami-Jacobs Coll 400 E Second St Dayton OH 45402

WAITE, GREGORY MICHAEL, Technology Education Teac Zanesville, OH; *m:* Mindy Jo Haddox; *c:* Coulton; *ed:* OH Univ 1983; *cr:* Self Employed Contractor 1977-83; Zanesville City Sch Tchr 1983-84; Maysville Local Schls Tchr 1984-; *ai:* Tech Ed Club Adv; *office:* Maysville HS 2805 Pinkerton Ln Zanesville OH 4370

WAITE, JENNIFER R., Asst Prof of Alchl & Chem Stud; *b:* Cant *ed:* Cortland St (BA) Sociology 1980; St Lawrence Univ (MED) 1986; Masters in Soc Work Syracuse Univ; Credentials in Alcoho Substance Abuse Cnslng; *cr:* St Lawrence Cty Alcohol & Sub Abus Alochol Cnslr, Sr Alcohol Cnslr, Clinic Supvr 1980-90; Mater De Fac, Div Chair 1990-; *ai:* Division of Prof Stud Chprsn; Admi Comms; SEACAP, Bd of Dir; Reachart Bd of Dir; NY St C Credential Work, Arbitration Bds; *office:* Mater Dei Coll 5428 St H Ogdensburg NY 13669

WAITE, WILLIAM FOSTER, Asst Prof of Business Admin; *b:* D MI; *ed:* Bob Jones Univ (BS) Bio 1969; Clemson Univ (MS) Zoology Univ of IL at Chicago (MBA) Bus Policy 1980; 3 Credits Grad Pu Trng in Educl Outcomes Assessment; *cr:* Rush-Presbyn St Lukes M Rsrch Technician 1975-76; GD SEarle & Co Mgr, Biomedical Infor 1976-85; Ciba-Geigy Corp Scientific Info Mgr 1985-87; Sussex Cty Coll Instr, Asst Prof of Bus 1987-; *ai:* Phi Theta Kappa Co-Ad Outcomes Assessment Prgm Coord; Total Quality Ldrshp Cncl; AFT Pres of Local 4780 3 Yrs; NJ Collegiate Bus Asmin Assn 1987-; Mo Twp Bd of Hlth 1993-, Chm 1993-95; Presentations on Incorpora Bus Diversity Topics & Multiculturalism; *office:* Sussex Cty Comm College Hill Newton NJ 07860

WAJBEL, PATRICIA K., Math Teacher; *b:* Balto City, MD; *m:* Pau *c:* Paul III, Jessica; *ed:* Towson St Uinv (BS) Scndry Ed, Math 1974; Loyola Coll 60 Credit Hrs Post Grad Work; *cr:* St Michael the Arc 7-8th Grd Math Tchr 1974-76; St Clement 6-8th Grd Math Tchr 19 Ridgely MS 8th Grd Math Tchr 1982-83; Dulaney HS Math Tchr *ai:* Class of 1996 Adv; Stu Svc Learning Coord; Music Evaluation Chair, Schl & Comm Comm Mem for Mid Sts Review; Schl Bd Nomi Convention 1996-; *home:* 2901 York Manor Rd Phoenix MD 21131

WALASINSKI, ALICE DZIEWIATKA, Jr HS Language Arts Teac Toledo, OH; *m:* Leo Joseph; *c:* Kevin, Michael, Mary Ann; *ed:* Mary Coll (BA) 1st-8th 1962; *cr:* St Vincent de Paul Schl 1st Grd Tchr 19 Little Flower Schl Jr HS Tchr 1981-; *ai:* Quiz Bowl, Math Coun Mediation, Yrbk Adv; NCTE 1995-; *office:* Little Flower Schl Olimphia Rd Toledo OH 43615

WALBORN, SERENO BERNARD, English Teacher; *b:* Lebanon, Sandra Jean Sterling; *c:* Suzanne Hendershott, Stacy Storey, Sereno Millersville Univ (BSEd) Eng 1954; Paterson St Post Grad Course Writing; *cr:* US Army Clerk Typist 1954-56; Graver Tank & Mfg Co Mgr & Sales Engr 1956-63; Stanhope Elem Eng Tchr 1963-68; Suss Vo-Tech Eng Tchr 1968-71; Newton HS Eng Tchr 1971-; *ai:* Basic & Dist Writing Coord; Core Team; Stu Asst Prgm; Editor of News Ex-Coach Ftbl, Bsktbl, Bsbl & Sftbl; NEA & NJEA 1963-; Local Tch 1963-, Pres 1969-71; NCTE 1978-; Juvenile Conf Comm 1988-; St T Roman C.C. 1988-, Lector, Tchr of CCD & RCIA & Eucharistic Mi St Testing Evaluation 1992; *office:* Newton HS 44 Ryerson Ave New 07860

HALK, RICHARD KEITH, Guidance Counselor; *b:* Akron, OH; ; *c:* Lisa, Brett; *ed:* Akron (BA) Ed 1975; Youngstown (MS) Cnslng *r:* Southeast MS Soc Stud Tchr 1975-77; Southeast HS His Tchr ?, Cnslr 1982-; *ai:* 7th Grd Boys Bsktbl; 10th Grd Class Adv; OEA 1975-; *office:* Southeast HS 8423 Tallmadge Rd Ravenna OH

OTT, CARMEN LYNN, Fourth Grade Teacher; *b:* Malone, NY; *ed:* n St Univ (BA) Elem Ed 1974; Attnd Oswego St Univ, Cortland St yracuse Univ; *cr:* Woodland Elem Schl Sub Tchr 1974-76, 5th Grd 76-80; BOCES HS Equivalency ESOL Tchr 1980-90; Heman Street Grd Tchr 1981-88; Fremont Elem Schl 4 Grd Tchr 1989-; Iaondaga ional Facility HS Equiv Tchr 1992; *ai:* Lang Art Ldr; Worked on ev Projects; CII Mem; Bldg Comm Rep; Tchr Selection Comm; PTO utor; Helps Stu Tchrs; NEA; NCTE; NY St United Tchrs 1974-; al Resources 1990-; Cncl Inst Aesthetic Ed; Excl Tchng Awd ; *office:* Fremont Elementary Richmond Rd W East Syracuse NY

BURG, KATHERINE VAUGHAN, Fifth Grade Teacher; *b:* yn, NY; *w:* Harris (dec); *ed:* Morgan St Univ (BS) Elem Ed 1970; n Paterson Coll (MS) Spec Ed 1980; Supvr 1977; *cr:* Washington St h Grd Tchr 1970-71; Chancellor Ave Schl 5th Grd Tchr 1972; unt Elem Schl 5th Grd Tchr 1973-; *ai:* Mentor; NEA, BCEA 1973-; n Church 1994-, Worship Music Comm Chprsn; *office:* Fairmount chl 105 Grand Ave Hackensack NJ 07601

EN, DENISE E., Asst Dir & Upward Bound Prgm; *b:* Pittsburgh, ; Lincoln Univ (BA) Psych 1975; Duquesne Univ (MSEd) Schl 1979; *cr:* TOD Svcs Prsnl Cnslr, Svc Aide 1976-79; Lincoln Univ ir Upward Bound Prgm 1979-; *ai:* PA Assn Ed Oppty Prgm Prsnl Treas 1990-93, Outstdng Svc 1995; Mid Eastern Assn Ed Oppty ers 1980-, Comm Chair, Outstdng Svc 1995; Amer Psych Assn Delta Sigma Theta 1976-, Keeper of Records 1978; Freedom Vly Girl Cncl 1988-90, Opportunity Fund Comm; Spec Svcs Advy Bd 0, Comm Chprsn, Cert for Svc; Outstdng Young Women in Amer Henderson HS Black Stu Union Comm Honoree 1992; *office:* n Univ PO Box 179 Lincoln University PA 19352

EN, PATRICIA, US History Teacher; *b:* Upper Sandusky, OH; *ed:* Univ (BA) Comprehensive Soc Stud 1974, (MA) Ath Admin 1982; wling Green HS Tchr, Coach 1974-81; Natl Jr Coll Ath Assn Admin 982-83; Natl Collegiate Ath Assn Admin Asst 1983-85; Princeton HS Coach, Ath Admin 1985-; *ai:* Assoc Ath Dir; OEA, NEA, OCSS *office:* Princeton HS 11080 Chester Rd Cincinnati OH 45246*

MAN, CAROL LANGEMASS, Math Teacher & Program Chprsn; oklyn, NY; *m:* Neil; *c:* Lee, Randee; *ed:* Brooklyn Coll (AA) Ed (BA) Sociology 1971; Coll of Staten Island (MSE) Math Ed 1987; t Grad Credits Math, Cmptrs; *cr:* Laguardia Comm Coll GED Tchr 2; Seward Park HS Para Tchr 1978-81, Math Tchr 1981-; *ai:* AFT, 981-; ATMNYC 1985-; Curr Criting Bd of Ed Sequential Math I, Tech Coll; Book Reviewer Pre-Algebra Addison Wesley; *office:* d Park H S 350 Grand St New York NY 10002

MAN, STEPHEN RICHARD, Social Studies Teacher; *b:* Jamaica, Lenore Sue Wohlberg; *c:* Sandra, Craig; *ed:* Lebanon Vly Coll (BA) 60, Hofstra Univ (MA) Soc Sci 1971; Long Island Univ (SDA) (SAS) Ldrshp 1978; 17 Credits Art His; *cr:* Ballston Spa HS Soc Stud Tchr 52; Massapequa HS Soc Stud Tchr 1962-68; West Islip HS Soc Stud 968-91; Beach St Jr HS Soc Stud Tchr 1968-91; NY Inst of Tech Adj World His, Am Govt 1988-89; Udall Rd MS Soc Stud Tchr 1991-; *ai:* er Schl Prin 1978-88, 1991; Steering Comm for Mid Sts Accr; Dist Cncl; Climate, Discipline Comm; GO Adv; Long Island Cncl for Soc 1985-, Pres, VP; Organ His Tchrs 1994-, Exec Bd; NCSS 1992-, ng & Resolutions Comms; NYSCSS 1988-, Chair Awds Comm, MS ; PDK Dowling Coll Chptr, Historian; Sayville Lib Bd 1994-, VP; e Shalom 1966-, Trustee; Sayville Ftbl Booster Club 1986-, Pres; n Stud Fellow 1992; Natl Endowment of Hum Fellow 1993; Woodrow n Fellow 1994; *office:* Udall Road MS 900 Udall Rd West Islip NY *

DO, KIMBERLY FARRA, 7th Grade Math Teacher; *b:* Phoenix, AZ; illiam Wesley; *ed:* North Adams St Coll (BA) Ed, Math 1994; achian St Univ 98 Credit Hrs Math Scndry Ed; *cr:* Mt Anthony Union ath Tchr 1994-95, MS 7th Grd Math Tchr 1995-; *ai:* Snow Ski Club K-12 Curr Comm Mem; MS Task Force Action Team Mem; Schedule ing Comm; Team Ldr; Staff Dev Inst Mem; *office:* Mt Anthony Union ast Main St Bennington VT 05201*

DRON, DONNA CIOFFI, Spanish Teacher; *b:* Rutland, VT; *m:* n; *c:* Ryan Evan; *ed:* Trinity Coll (BA) Span 1970; Attnd Univ of cia, Univ of VT at Burlington, St Michaels Coll, Lesley Coll; *cr:* n C Hunt MS Tchr 1970-79; G F Edmunds MS Tchr 1979-84; ester MS Tchr 1984-; Colchester Schls Summer Schl Dir 1988-90; T Educ Assn 1970-; NEA 1970-; Delta Kappa Gamma 1979-; VT Frgn Assn 1990-; VT Assn Mid Level Edctrs 1990-; *home:* 37 Tallwood Ln ngton VT 05401*

DRON, JILL MURPHY, Business Teacher; *b:* Waterbury, CT; *m:* ; *c:* Collin; *ed:* Stonehill Coll (BS) Bus Mngmt 1987; Sacred Heart (MAT) Scndry Ed 1991; *cr:* Laurelton Hall Bus Tchr 1992-; *ai:* Yrbk Editorial Staff; Ski CLub Adv; Sunshine Comm; CBEA 1994-; bury Jaycees 1990-, Sec 2 Yrs, Received Project of Month Awd ; *office:* Lauralton Hall Schl 200 High St Milford CT 06460

DRON, WILLIAM ALEXANDER, Chemistry Teacher; *b:* Jersey NJ; *ed:* Jersey City St Coll (BA) Geoscience, Geology 1983; St s Coll 26 Credits Ed 1984; Metropolitan Inst of Tech Cert in SNA r Systems Network Arch 1991; *cr:* St Aloysius HS Sci Tchr 1983-84; emic HS Sci Tchr 1984-86; William Dickinson HS Sci Tchr 1986-90; al Regnl HS Sci Tchr 1990-; *ai:* Chem Sci League Adv; Tech Comm; ; NJ Ed Assn 1984-, Assn Rep, Working Conditions Comm; Acad tance Sci Instr for Amer Online E-Mail Tchr; Superior Tchr Awd -94; *office:* Central Regional HS Forest Hills Pkwy Bayville NJ 1*

ENDZIEWICZ, WALTER CYRIL, Spanish Teacher; *b:* Homestead, *n:* Cheryl Lynn Mohney; *c:* Ann Lynne; *ed:* Duquesne Univ (BSEd) 1969, (MED) Ed 1972; 15 Addl Credits Rdng Spec Cert; *cr:* West in S HS Span Tchr 1969-82; Lebanon Jr HS Dev Rdng Tchr 1982-83; Mifflin S HS Span Tchr 1983-84; West Mifflin Mid Edison Jr HS , Remedial Rdng Tchr 1984-87; West Mifflin Area HS Span Tchr -; *ai:* Cert Excl in Tchng 1992; *home:* 422 Nantucket Dr Pittsburgh 5236

FORD, DEBORAH W., HS Art & K-12 Enrichment Tchr; *b:* gstown, OH; *m:* James; *c:* Dylan, Graeme; *ed:* Edinboro St Univ (BS) d 1967; Johnson St Coll (MS) Gifted Ed 1996; Attnd Univ of VT, Univ T; *cr:* Northwestern HS Art Tchr 1967-68; St Albans Schl 8th Grd Eng 1969-72; BFA HS Eng, Art, K-12 Enrichment Tchr 1986-; *ai:* EA, FXEA 1987-; NEAE 1989-; VT Cncl on Arts 1994-; VT Cncl on d 1995-; Fairfax Fire Aux 20 Yrs, Past Officer; VT Art Assess Design 1 3 Yrs; Outstdng BFA Tchr 1989; Editing Decks Grant; Cmptr, hics Prgm; *office:* Bellows Free Acad PO Box 68 Hunt St Fairfax VT 4

WALIGORA, LORI DIANE POWELL, Third Grade Teacher; *b:* Troy, NY; *m:* Alan E.; *c:* Michael, Diana; *ed:* Oneonta St (BS) Elem Ed 1977; SUNY at Albany (MS) Rdng 1980; *cr:* Scotia Glenville 4th Grd Tchr 1977-78 & 1993-95, 2nd Grd Tchr 1979-80 & 1992-93, Kndgtn Tchr 1980-91, 3rd Grd Tchr 1995-; *ai:* Saturday Recreation Dir 1977-80; Comms: Dist Sci, Lang Arts & Math; NYSUT 1977-, Rep; Involved in Church; PTA Founders Day Awd 1986; *office:* Scotia-Glenville Schl Dist Business Blvd Scotia NY 12302

WALISZEK, JOANNE TUFTS, Fourth Grade Teacher; *b:* Lewiston, ME; *m:* Donald J.; *c:* Kristin, Matthew, Daniel; *ed:* Univ of ME at Farmington (BS) Elem Ed 1971; Univ of NH (MED) Early Chldhd Ed 1973; 3 Hrs Univ of South ME; 4 Hrs Taylor Univ; 6 Hrs Casco Bay Coll; *cr:* York Elem Schl Third Grd Tchr 1971-75; Southeastern NH Chrstn Acad Fourth Grd Tchr 1983-; *ai:* Amer Assn Chrstn Schls 1995-; York Street Bapt Church, AWANA Bible Dir, Jr Church Tchr; *home:* 144 Cider Hill Rd York ME 03909

WALK, EILEEN FIELD, Art Teacher; *b:* New York, NY; *m:* Steven M.; *c:* Hunter, Alyssa; *ed:* NY Univ (BS) Art & Ed 1966, (MA) Art & Ed 1967; 40 Credit Hrs Post Masters Art & Ed; *cr:* Herricks Schls Art Tchr 1967-73; Samuel Field YMHA Art Coord & Tchr 1976-85; Glen Cove Schls Art Tchr 1985-86; North Shore Schls Art Tchr 1986-; *ai:* Mosaic Lit Magazine Adv; Sr Experience Comm; NYSATA 1967-; LIATA 1967-; NY St Art Tchr of Achvmt 1991; Illustrator of Educl Text; Integration of Art into Currs Presenter; NYS Olmypics of Visual Arts Co-Chprsn; *office:* North Shore HS 450 Glen Cove Ave Glen Head NY 11545

WALKER, BARBARA J., Teacher of GATE; *b:* Gloversville, NY; *m:* James; *ed:* Univ of ME (BA) Eng 1974; Dartmouth Coll (MALS) Liberal Stud 1980; Middlebury Coll Breadloaf Schl of Eng (MA) Eng 1986; Post Grad Stud at Rutgers Univ, UVM, Univ of Puget Sound, Dantmouth & NYU; *cr:* Sumner HS Eng Tchr 1974-76; Steinert HS Tchr of GATE & Eng 1978-; *ai:* Pub Speaking; Debating; Mock Trial; Acad Quiz Bowls; NJEA, HTEA & NEA 1978-; Delta Kappa Gamma 1989-; NIH Ind Stud Fellowship; NEH Fellowship 1987, 1991 & 1993; *office:* Steinert H S 2900 Klockner Rd Trenton NJ 08690

WALKER, BARBARA JOHNSON, First & Second Grade Teacher; *b:* Greenfield, MA; *c:* Shawn Michael, Brent Frederick, Scott Douglas, Brad David; *ed:* Westfield St Coll (MSEd) Grd K-8 Ed 1964; Univ of MA (MAEd) Elem Ed 1985; Courses at North Adams St, Univ of MA, Fitchburg St, Keene St Coll; *cr:* Erving Schls 1 Grd Tchr 1964-68, 3 Grd Tchr 1969-70; Northfield Elem Schl 5-6 Grd Soc Stud Tchr 1972; Warwick Ctr Schl 1-2 Grd Tchr 1983-; *ai:* Curr Frameworks Stud Group; Historical Soc Prgm, Bldg Needs Comms; MTA, NEA 1994-; Delta Kappa Gamma, Alpha Upsilon St 1993-; Alpha Epsilon 1993-, Sec 1995, 2nd VP 1995-; Coach Peanuts Ball Team; Den Mother Cub Scouts; Order of Easter Star 1972-, Chaplain; Schl Cncl 1993-94, Sec; *office:* Warwick Ctr Schl 22 Orange Rd Warwick MA 01378

WALKER, CARLA RICHBURG, Business Teacher; *b:* New York, NY; *ed:* Bernard M Baruch Coll (BS) Bus Ed 1986, (MS) Bus Ed 1995; *cr:* Wood Schl Tchr 1986-89; Norman Thomas HS Tchr 1991-; Schl-to- Work Alliance Field Coord 1995.*

WALKER, CATHERINE MCANDREW, English Teacher; *b:* Carbondale, PA; *m:* Paul M.; *c:* Lori, Paul Brian, Chad, Christopher; *ed:* Wilkes Univ (ME) Elem Ed 1988; Attnd Marywood Coll, Univ of Scranton Elem Ed; Inservice Courses & Grad Cmptr Ed Courses; *cr:* Forest City Regnl Part-Time Rdng Support Tchr 1972, 1st & 2nd Grd Tchr 1973-74, 4th Grd Tchr 1974-75, 2nd Grd Tchr 1976-91, 5th & 6th Grd Tchr 1991-; *ai:* Strategic Planning Comm Assessment Comm Chair & Work with Tech Adult Cmptr Class Tchr; PSEA 1973-; Home Schl; *home:* HC 65 Box 38 Pleasant Mount PA 18453*

WALKER, CHRISTINE TATALIBA, English & Spanish Teacher; *b:* Somerset, PA; *m:* Jay V.; *c:* Linda, Jayson, Nathan; *ed:* IN Univ of PA (BS) Span & Scndry Ed 1972; Juniata Coll Masters Equivalency in Eng Ed 1990; *cr:* Huntingdon Area MS Span Tchr 1972-73; Huntingdon Area Schl Dist Sub Tchr 1977-89; Huntingdon Area HS Eng & Span Tchr 1990-; *ai:* Steering Comm Chprsn; NEA, HAEA, PSEA 1990-; Aid Assn for Luths 1981-, Local Chapter VP; *home:* 1330 Washington St Huntingdon PA 16652

WALKER, DAVID C., Mathematics Teacher; *b:* Lock Haven, PA; *m:* Kay B.; *c:* Deborah Keane, Susan Bond, Steven; *ed:* Lock Haven Univ (BSEd) Math 1963; Kent St Univ (MED) Math 1966; *cr:* Crestwood HS Math Tchr 1965-66; Kutztown Area HS Math Tchr 1966-; *ai:* Wrestling Coach 1967-75; Ath Dir 1976-82; PSEA, NEA, Kutztown Area Tchrs Assn 1966-; Lions Club; Huguenot Lodge No 377 F & AM; Tchng Assistantship Kent St Univ 1963-65; *office:* Kutztown Area HS 50 Trexler Ave Kutztown PA 19530

WALKER, DEBORAH ANNE (SPINA), Secondary Math Teacher; *b:* Syracuse, NY; *m:* Michael Joseph; *c:* Joseph M.; *ed:* Syracuse Univ (BA) Scndry Math Ed 1977, (MS) Educl Admin 1978; *cr:* Roosevelt Jr HS Math Tchr 1978; Shea MS Math Tchr 1979-; *ai:* 7th-8th Grd Math Legue Coach; St Jude Childrens Rsrch Hosp Mathathon Coord; Schl Tech, Teaming Skills Assertive Communication Comm; Syracuse Tchrs Assn, Onondaga Cty Math Tchrs Assn, NYSUT 1978-; St Margaret's Schl Bd 1993-95, Co-Treas; St Margaret's RC Church Comm Vol Worker, Eucharistic Minister; *office:* Shea MS 1607 S Geddes St Syracuse NY 13208

WALKER, DEBRA K., HS Resource Room Teacher; *b:* Bath, NY; *m:* Tom A.; *c:* Nicholas A., Adam A., Kelly L.; *ed:* SUNY at Geneseo (BS) Spcl Ed 1972; Elmira Coll Permanent Cert Spcl Ed 1976; *cr:* Savona Cntrl Schl Spcl Ed Tchr 1972-92; Campbell-Savona CS HS Resource Room Tchr 1992-; *ai:* NEA 1972-; *home:* 213 Burton St Bath NY 14810

WALKER, DENNIS PATRICK, Health & PE Teacher; *b:* Wilmington, DE; *m:* Lori Ann; *c:* Kevin, Sara; *ed:* West Chester Univ (BS) Hlth, PE 1980; 18 Credit Hrs Wilmington Coll; *cr:* El DuPont & Co Stationary, Forms 1981-84; Terry Childrens Psychiatric Ctr Tchrs Aid 1984-88; Salesianum HS Tchr 1988-; Wilmington Dept of Parks Vly Garden Park 1988-; *ai:* JV Bsktbl Head Coach 1987-; Var Bsbl Head Coach 1992-; Dept Chprsn 1994-; DAPHERD 1995-; DBCA 1992-; *office:* Salesianum HS 1801 N Broom St Wilmington DE 19802

WALKER, DOUGLAS L., Biology Teacher; *b:* Lodi, OH; *m:* Robin C.; *ed:* Baldwin Wallace Coll (BS) Bio 1967; Post Grad Stud at Univ of Akron & Kent St Univ; *cr:* Medina HS Bio Tchr 1967-; *ai:* Girls Track Head Coach; Golf Head Coach; Medina City Tchrs, NEOTA, OEA & NEA 1967-; Medina Life Support 1979-95; *office:* Medina HS 777 E Union St Medina OH 44256

WALKER, EDNA B., Mathematics Teacher; *b:* Daytona Beach, FL; *ed:* St Josephs Coll (BA) Child Stud 1975; Fordham Univ (MS) Ed 1988; *cr:* NYC Hlth & Hosps Systems Analyst 1975-83; St Angela Hall Acad Tchr 1983-93; Mount Carmel Acad Tchr 1993-; *ai:* Novice Tchrs Mentor; NCTM 1990-; Kings Cty AMA Excl in Tchng of Math Awd 1992; *office:* Mount Carmel Acad 10 Withers St Brooklyn NY 11211

WALKER, ELAINE POST, High School Math Teacher; *b:* Kearny, NJ; *m:* Ken; *c:* Jeffrey, Michelle; *ed:* Montclair St Coll (BA) Math 1973; St of PA Masters Equivalency Ed 1991; 18 Addl Grad Credits Penn St; *cr:* USDESEA Preparatory Cnslr & Tchr 1973-76; Tunkhannock Area HS Math Tchr 1985-; *ai:* NCTM 1986-; PSEA 1985-; Tunkhannock Lib Assn 1985-, Treas 1985-89, VP 1990, Pres 1991-; *office:* Tunkhannock Area HS 200 Franklin Ave Tunkhannock PA 18657

WALKER, ERICK C., English Teacher; *b:* McArthur, OH; *ed:* OH Univ (BSEd) Eng Ed 1991, (AB) Eng 1992; *cr:* Vinton Cty Bd Habilitation Spec II 1992-94; Vinton Cty HS Eng Tchr 1994-; *ai:* Newspaper, Yrbk Adv; NCTE; Golden Key; Kappa Delti Pi; Vinton Cty Ecumenical Choir Dir; St Sylvester Cath Church Organist; *office:* Vinton Cty HS 307 W High St Mc Arthur OH 45651

WALKER, FINESIA DUNOVANT, History Teacher; *b:* Danville, VA; *m:* Jeffrey L.; *c:* James Smith, Karana Smith, David Smith; *ed:* Bloomfield Coll (BA) His 1977; 3 Hrs Employability Skills Columbia Univ; *cr:* Parsippany Troy Hills Bd of Ed His Tchr 1982-85; Plainfield Adult Ctr Coord NJ Yth Corps 1985-87; East Orange Bd of Ed His Tchr, Guid 1988-91; Essex Cty Voc HS His Tchr 1991-; *ai:* Sr Adv; NJEA, NEA 1980-; Essex Cty Voc Tchrs Assn 1991-; Natl Urban League 1990-; NJ Governor's Tchr of Yr, East Orange Schl Dist Tchr of Yr 1990; *office:* Essex Cty Voc HS 300 N 13th St Newark NJ 07107*

WALKER, GAIL C., Professor of Psychology; *b:* Antlers, OK; *ed:* OK St Univ (BS) Psych 1974, (MS) Psych 1976, (PHD) Psych 1978; EMT Trng; Critical Incident Stress Debriefing; Advanced Grief Cnslng; Amer Sign Lang; Essential Russian; *cr:* Marian Coll Asst Prof 1978-80; Cook Cty Office of Spec Ed Tchr of Spec Ed 1980-81; Alfred Univ Asst Prof 1981-85, Assoc Prof 1986-90, Prof Psych 1990-; *ai:* Critical Incident Stress Debriefer; Certfd Instr Non-Violent Crisis Intervention; Instr Death-Care Allied Hlth Professions; Security Guard Instr; Assn Death Ed, Cnslng; Fnd Thanatology; Intnl Cirses Prenvention Inst; Intnl Critical Incident Stress Fnd; A. E. Crandall Hook, Ladder Co 1986-, EMT, CISD; Excl Tchng Awds 1984-85; Citizen Ambassador to USSR 1989; Intnl Directory Distngd Ldrshp 1990; Sears Fnd Excl Tchng, Campus Ldrshp Awd 1991; Ind Coll FUnd NY Tchng Excl Awd 1993, 1995; *office:* Alfred Univ Saxon Dr Alfred NY 14802

WALKER, IVA L., Social Studies Educator; *b:* Oberlin, OH; *ed:* Hiram Coll (BA) His, Pol Sci 1964; Kent St Univ (MED) Ed, Guid & Cnslng 1976; Univ of Akron Ec Ed; *cr:* James A. Garfield Schl Dist Soc Stud Edctr 1964-; *ai:* Drama; VB Scorekeeping; Track Meet Mngmt; GEA, OEA, NEA 1964-, Sec, Admin Cncl; Hiram Coll Alumni Exec Bd; Twentieth Century Club of Garrettsville 1975-, Sec; Garrettsville Comm Players 1971-; United Meth Church 1955-; Martha Holden Jennings Scholar; Ashland Achvmt Nom; James A. Garfield Hum Awd; *office:* James A. Garfield Local Schl 8233 Park Ave Garrettsville OH 44231

WALKER, JAMES C., Physics Teacher; *b:* Fountain Hill, PA; *ed:* East Stroudsburg Univ (BS) Scndry Physics Ed 1990; Specialized Trng Diploma in Photography at Northampton Comm Coll; *cr:* Southern Lehigh HS Physics Tchr 1991-; *ai:* PA Jr Acad of Sci Spon; NEA, ISEA 1991-; SEPS, AAPT, CPS 1993-; *office:* Southern Lehigh HS 5800 Main St Center Valley PA 18034

WALKER, JANET LOIS, Professor of French & Dept Chm; *b:* London, England; *ed:* Chatham Coll (BA) Fr & Philosophy 1967, (BA) Math 1993; Bryn Mawr Coll (MA) Fr 1969, (PHD) Modern Fr Lit 1974; Span Minor 1993; *cr:* Chatham Coll Fr Instr 1970-76, Asst Fr Prof 1976-81, Assoc Fr Prof 1981-92, Fr Prof 1992-; *ai:* Ind Stud in Latin, Classical Greek & Italian; Promotion & Tenure & Acad Standing Comms; ASECS 1974-; AATG 1990-; Greater Pittsburgh Literacy Cncl, Tutor, Excl Awd; Phi Beta Kappa; NDEA Title IV Fr Flwshp; Irene Heinz Given Professorship; Buhl Professorship in Hum; *office:* Chatham Coll Woodland Road Pittsburgh PA 15232

WALKER, JOHN CHALMERS, Adjunct Prof of Music; *b:* Johnstown, PA; *ed:* Amer Conservatory of Music (BMus) Organ 1963, (MMus) Organ 1995; Stanford Univ (DMA) Performance Practices 1972; Fellow of Amer Guild of Organists 1968; *cr:* San Jose St Univ Lecturer in Music 1975-79; Riverside Church Dir of Music & Organist 1979-92; Manhattan Schl of Music Chair & Dept of Organ 1980-92; Shadyside Presbyn Church Dir of Music & organist 1992-; Westminster Coll Adj Prof of Music 1993-; *ai:* Amer Guild of Organists 1962-, Natl Treas & Dean NYC & San Jose Chapters; Alumnae Awd for Prof Achvmt 1984; Numerous Articles Pub; *office:* Westminster Coll New Wilmington PA 16142

WALKER, JOHN H., Principal; *b:* Brooklyn, NY; *ed:* Seton Hall (BS) Psy & Ed 1963, (MA) Admin 1969; *cr:* Washington Schl 6th Grd Tchr 1964; Yantacaw Schl Prin 1973-; *ai:* Dist Staff Dev, Resrch Clb Adv; PSA 1973-; PDK 1975-, Sec, Treas; Red Cross Exec Comm 1967-; Bloomfield Coll EOF Advy BD 1975, Chprsn; Tchr of Yr Awd 1967-68; Martin Luther King Awd 1974; Jaycees Awd 1977; Red Cross Awd 1979; Rotary Awd 1996; *office:* Yantacaw Schl 20 Yantacaw Pl Nutley NJ 07110

WALKER, JOSEPH A., Mathematics Teacher; *b:* Carbondale, PA; *m:* Jean Mumma; *c:* Jason Henry, Joseph M., Matt Henry, Chris, Jeanine; *ed:* Shippensburg Univ (BA) Math 1968, (MEd) Math 1970; Super Math 1993; *cr:* Cumberland Valley HS Math Tchr 1968-; *ai:* Var Girls Bsktbl Head Coach; *office:* Cumberland Valley HS 6746 Carlisle Pike Mechanicsburg PA 17055

WALKER, KAREN ELIZABETH, Asst Professor of Biology; *b:* Cincinnati, OH; *c:* Alison; *ed:* Univ of NC Chapel Hill (BS) Nursing 1981; Temple Univ Schl of Medicine (PHD) Physiology 1991; Medical Coll of PA Dept of Physiology, Biochemistry 2 Yrs Postdoctoral Fellowship 1991-93; *cr:* Coll Misericordia Asst Prof 1994-; *ai:* Biological Soc Adv; Amer Physiol Soc, AAUP 1996; NSF Young Scholars Prgm Grant 2 Yrs; Article Pub 1993; *office:* Coll Misericordia 301 Lake St Dallas PA 18612

WALKER, KAY HARNER, Fourth Grade Teacher; *b:* Hagerstown, MD; *m:* Kenneth Wayne; *c:* Kelly, Kasey, Korey; *ed:* Salisbury St Coll (BS) Elem Ed 1971; MS Equivalency in Elem Ed Univ of DE, Shepherd Coll, MD St Dept of Ed; Hood Coll, Western MD Coll 1982; *cr:* Cascade Elem Schl First Grd Tchr 1971-74; Silver Lake Elem Schl Fifth Grd Tchr 1975-76; Conococheague Elem Schl First, Third, Fourth Grd Tchr 1976-; *ai:* Soc Stud Liason; WA Cty Tchrs Assn, NEA 1976-; *office:* Conococheague Elem Schl 12408 Learning Ln Hagerstown MD 21740

WALKER, KENNETH THOMAS, Soccer Coach; *b:* Newark, NJ; *m:* Elaine Post; *c:* Jeffrey, Michelle; *ed:* US Military Acad (BS) Engrng 1972; Univ of Scranton (MBA) Fin 1983; *cr:* US Army Ofcr 1972-79; Procter & Gamble Mgr 1979-; *ai:* Girls & Boys Soccer Coach; Amer Soc of Safety Engrs 1991-; *office:* Tunkhannock Area HS 120 W Tioga St Tunkhannock PA 18657

WALKER, LARRY ERNEST, Science Teacher; *b:* Bethlehem, PA; *m:* Joanne E. Geisler; *c:* Scott, Kimberly, Debra, Brian; *ed:* Kutztown St Coll (BA) Bio 1964; Temple Univ (MS) Ed 1968; *cr:* Raub MS Sci, Bio Tchr 1964-; *ai:* Sci, Ski, Fly Fishing Clubs; NEA 1988-; Allentown Tchrs Credit Union 1983-, Investment Comm; Allentown Schoolmans 1965-; Allentown Tchr of Yr 1992; *office:* Raub MS St Clous & Walnut Sts Allentown PA 18104

WALKER, LARRY ROBERT, Instrumental Music Teacher; *b:* Lima, OH; *m:* Cheryl Lehman; *ed:* Bowling Green St Univ (BM) Music Ed 1970; Grad Work; Amer Sign Lang OH Hi-Point Joint Voc Schl; *cr:* Bellefontaine City Schls Tchr 1970-; *ai:* Chancel Choir Singer; NEA, OH Ed Assn, Bellefontaine Ed Assn, OH Music Ed Assn 1970-; West Cntrl Comm Band 1991-, Bd Mem; Logan Cty Comm Concerts Assn 1980-, Bd Mem; Church, Handbell Choir Dir; *home:* 3121 Road 32 S Bellefontaine OH 43311

WALKER, LUCY DORIS, Dance Teacher; *b:* Ridgeway, NC; *c:* Lucretia; *ed:* Fairleigh Dickinson Univ (BA) Eng Ed 1975; Montclair St Univ (MA) Theatre Arts 1977; *cr:* Teaneck Schl System Eng, Drama, Dance Tchr 1979-; *ai:* Dance Ensemble Co Adv, Coach; NEA, Teneck Township Ed Assn 1979-; Produced, Pub Play.

WALKER, MARGARET M., His, Spanish & English Teacher; *b:* Meadowbrook, PA; *m:* Scott P. Vallette; *ed:* Acad of New Church Coll (AA) His & Soc Sci 1988; Univ of PA (BA) His 1990; Villanova Univ Law Schl (JD) Law 1993; *cr:* Acad of New Church His, Span & Eng Tchr 1993-; *ai:* Asst Dormitory Dir; *office:* Acad Of The New Church PO Box 707 Bryn Athyn PA 19009

WALKER, MARILYN THELMA (BAILEY), Fourth Grade Teacher; *b:* New York City, NY; *m:* Elbert Allen; *c:* Allene L. Walker-Simmons, Adam Brett; *ed:* The City Univ of NY (BA) Soc Sci 1962, (MS) Educ, Elem Ed 1973; 49 Addl Credits in Aesthetics & Easthetic Ed Webster Coll, CUNY, Tchrs Coll Columbia Univ; Lehman Coll; City Univ; *cr:* New York City Bd of Ed 3rd Grd Tchr 1966-69, 4th Grd Tchr 1969-; *ai:* NYC United Fed of Tchrs, AFT, NYS United Trs 1966-; Truman HS Ftbl Parents Assn 1979-81, Founder, Pres, Assn's President's 1980; St Joseph's Episcopal Church 1971-, Clerk, Jr Warden, Sr Church Warden; Lincoln Cty Inst of Arts 1992-, Advy Bd; Tchr of Yr 1977 & 1992; Schl Bd Comm Schl Dist Eleven's Discretionary Awd Excl in Tchng Outstanding Achvmt 1990; Talented & Gifted Renzulli Method Presenter, Instr to Tchrs Across the Five Boros Chosen to Rep NYC State-Wide at Concord Hotel 1990; *office:* P S 78 Anne Hutchinson Schl 1400 Needham Ave Bronx NY 10469*

WALKER, MARVIN LEON, History Teacher; *b:* Passaic, NJ; *ed:* Bergen Comm Coll (AS) Bus Admin 1987; Hampton Univ (BS) Mrktg 1990; Montclair St Univ (MA) Soc Sci, His 1993; *cr:* Passaic Comm Coll His, African Amer Stud Tchr 1992-93; Passaic HS His Tchr 1992-; *ai:* Adv African Amer Stud Club; NEA 1992-; NJ His Task Force 1995-; *home:* 108 Sherman St Passaic NJ 07055*

WALKER, MICHAEL J., Asst Professor of English; *b:* Oakland, CA; *m:* Kathy A. Luckey; *c:* Liana, Justin, Jeff; *ed:* CA St Univ at Haywood (BA) Eng 1976, (MA) Eng 1984; Univ of OR (PHD) Eng 1990; *cr:* Raymond Walters Coll Eng Fac 1990-; *ai:* Frosh Eng Coord; Hrns Eng; Exit Exam Dir; PAMLA 1991-; NCTE 1991-; MLA 1992-; Stud in Short Fiction; *office:* Raymond Walters Coll 9555 Plainfield Rd Cincinnati OH 45236

WALKER, PAULINE SULLIVAN, Sixth Grd World History Tchr; *b:* Cambridge, MA; *c:* Noralee A., David M.; *ed:* Univ of MA (BSEd) K-8 Ed 1958; 45 Credit Hrs Post Grad Stud; *cr:* Sarah Bradlee Fulton Elem Schl Third Grd Tchr 1958-69; George Davenport Elem Schl 3-6th Grd Tchr 1971-80; Brooks Hobbs MS 4-6th Grd Tchr 1980-; *ai:* Sixth Grd Adv; World His Curr Comm; Activity Sponsorship; Medford Tchrs 1985-, Curr Chair; MA Tchrs, NEA 1958-; Medford Cath Women's Club 1987-, Publicity Exec Bd; Medford HS Band & Orch Parents Assn 1981-, VP, Treas, Publicity, Achvmt; Pub Svc; Educl Grants; Medford Citizen Newspaper Tchr of Yr 1994-95; Curr Comms; *office:* Brooks Hobbs MS 25 Auburn St Medford MA 02155*

WALKER, PHIL KARL, Math Teacher & Coach; *b:* Palembang Sumatra, Indonesia; *ed:* Wheaton Coll (BS) Math 1989; *cr:* Mercer Chrstn Acad Math, Bible, PE Tchr, Soccer, Bsktbl, Sftbl Coach 1989-95; *ai:* Dir Elem Soccer Prgm; *home:* 31 W Afton Ave # 1 Yardley PA 19067

WALKER, ROBERT B., Studio Art Teacher; *b:* Plainfield, NJ; *ed:* William Paterson Coll (BA) Art Ed 1970; Penn St Univ (MFA) Sculpture 1972; Rutgers Univ (EDS) Creative Arts Ed 1980; Tchrs Coll Columbia Univ 40 Credits Arts in Ed; *cr:* Newgrange Schl Art, Ind Art Tchr 1981-82; Summit HS Studio Art Tchr 1982-; *ai:* Curr Dev HS, K-12 Dist Level; Union Cty Ed Assn, NJ Ed Assn, NEA, NAEA 1982-; Art Edctrs of NJ 1980-; Natl Sculpture Fnd 1976-; Office of Emergency Mngmt 1989-, Municipal Coord; NJ St First Aid Cncl 1966-, Life Mem; Prof Assn of Diving Instrs 1975-; *office:* Summit HS 125 Kent Place Blvd Summit NJ 07901*

WALKER, ROBERT JAMES, Chemistry Teacher; *b:* Lewistown, PA; *m:* Anita Gay Peters; *c:* Matthew, Michael; *ed:* Lock Haven Univ (BS) Hlth, PE 1981; Shippensburg Univ (BS) Chem 1987; 15 Addl Credit Hrs Scndry Schl Admin; *cr:* Chambersburg Area MS 8th Grd Sci Tchr 1987-89; Faust Jr HS 9th Grd Sci Tchr 1989-90; Chambersburg Area Sr HS Chem Tchr 1990-; *ai:* Head Cross Cntry, Asst Track & Field Coaches 1985-; Amer Chem Soc 1990-; St John's United Church of Christ 1984-, Chrstn Ed Chprsn; PA St Ath Assn Cross Cntry Coach of Yr 1990; *office:* Chambersburg Area Sr HS 511 S 6th St Chambersburg PA 17201*

WALKER, SELENA WILSON, 6th Grade Math Teacher; *b:* Orange, VA; *ed:* Passaic Cty Comm Coll (AA) Lbrl Arts 1974; Wm Paterson Coll of NJ (BA) Early Chldhd Ed 1976; *cr:* US Postal Svc Mail Clerk 1968-70; Diocese of Paterson Neighborhood House Yth Cnslr 1970-74; W T Giants Dept Store Cashier & Sales Asst 1974-76; Paterson Pub Schls Tchr 1977-; *ai:* Passaic Cty Probation Dept Vol Cnslr 1984-; Teen Hlth Fair & African-Amer Expo Coord; Mentor; CORE Team Org Chprsn; NJEA 1977-; George Washington Carver Alumni Assn 1995-; Wm Paterson Coll Alumni Assoc; Tchr of Yr & Governors Recognition Awd 1987; *office:* Martin Luther King Jr Schl 20th Ave & E 28th St Paterson NJ 07513

WALKER, SHIRLEY CINTORINO, Business Education Teacher; *b:* Derby, CT; *m:* William; *c:* Scott, Brian; *ed:* Cntrl CT St Univ (BS) Bus Ed 1969, (MS) Bus Ed, Acctng 1987; 30 Addl Credits; Cooperative Work Ed Coord Cert; *cr:* Derby HS Bus Ed Instr 1969-73; Pomperaug HS Region 15 Bus Ed, CWE Instr 1981-; *ai:* Tech, Restructuring, Distance Learning, Tech Prep, Schl to Work Comms; NEA, CEA, PEA, CBEA 1981-; ASCD 1994-; PTO Boosters 1990-; Local BSA, Chprsn; CCD Rel Ed Instr Vol 14 Yrs; *office:* Region 15 Pomperaug HS 234 Judd Rd Southbury CT 06488

WALKER, STEVEN A., HS Science Teacher; *b:* New Bedford, MA; *m:* Carolann Paulino; *c:* Jaryd, Justyn; *ed:* Bridgewater St Coll (BA) PE 1988; Univ of MA at Dartmouth (BA) Sci 1992; Fitchburg St Coll Masters Prgm Occupational Ed; *cr:* GNB Voc Tech Tchr, Coach 1988-; *ai:* Ftbl, Track Coach 1988-; Employee Benefit, Prof Dev Comms; Co-partner in Aqua Lab; Adult Edctr in Aqua Culture; MA Voc Assn 1996; GNB Voc Tech Alumni Assn 1993-; Cath Church Lifetime Mem; *office:* Gr New Bedford Reg Voc Tech HS 1121 Ashley Blvd New Bedford MA 02745*

WALKER, SUZANNE ROSS, High School Mathematics Tchr; *b:* Johnston, RI; *m:* Paul Joseph; *ed:* Providence Coll (BA) Math, Math Educ 1982, (MED) Counseling, Guidance 1992; 36 Addl Hrs Bus Admin & Cmptr Sci; Rhode Island Coll, Comm Coll of RI, Univ of RI Credits in Math, Cmptrs, Sci, Bus; *cr:* Bay View Acad HS Math Tchr 1983-85; Hall Inst Tech Adult Math Tchr 1983-90; La Salle Acad HS Math, Cmptr Tchr 1985-87; Woonsocket Jr HS Math & Cmptr Tchr 1987-90; Woonsocket HS Math & Cmptr Tchr 1990-; *ai:* Technological Improvement Comm; Liasion for RI Coll Sonja Kovalevsky Day for Women in Math; AFT, Woonsocket Tchrs Guild 1987-; RI Math Tchrs Assn 1983-, NCTM 1994-; RI Coll Math Fellowship Tchng Asst 1983; Univ RI Math Fellowship 1983; *office:* Woonsocket HS 777 Cass Ave Woonsocket RI 02895

WALKER, THOMAS RAY, English Instr & Newspaper Adv; *b:* Canton, OH; *m:* Julie Ford; *c:* Nathan, Rachel, Tyler, Dylan; *ed:* Malone Coll (BA) Eng 1974; Masters Work Eng at Akron Univ; *cr:* Minerva Local Schl Eng Instr 1974-; *ai:* Track, Cross Cntry Coach; Newspaper Adv; MLEA, OEA, NEA 1974-; Church Bsktbl Coach; Sr HS Sunday Schl Tchr; Victory Bapt Church Deacon; *home:* 412 East St Minerva OH 44657*

WALKINS, VIRGINIA BURNS, 6th Grade Teacher; *b:* Denver, CO; *m:* David; *c:* Bart, Amy, Amanda; *ed:* Bridgewater St Coll (BS) Elem 1973, (MS) Elem 1977; 24 Credit Hrs; *cr:* Freeman-Centennial Schl 6 Grd Tchr 1973-; *ai:* Site Based Mngmt Team; Curr Dev Comms; NEA; MTA; NCTA; *office:* Freeman-Centenial Elem Schl 70 Boardman St Norfolk MA 02056

WALL, ANNE MARIA, Secondary Biology Teacher; *b:* Los Angeles, CA; *m:* Donald R.; *ed:* Univ of Scranton (BS) Bio 1985; 28 Addl Credits; *cr:* Wyoming Area HS Daily, Permanent Sub Tchr 1986-92; Dallas HS Permanent Sub Tchr 1992-93; Wyoming Seminary Sci Enrichment Tchr 1992-95; Wyoming Area HS Scndry Bio Tchr 1993-; *ai:* Var Girl's Sftbl Team Coach; Soph Class Adv; Sci Olympiad Team Asst Coach; NHS Co-Adv; NEA 1992-; NSTA, Luzerne Cty Tchrs Assn 1993-; *office:* Wyoming Area HS 20 Memorial St Exeter PA 18643

WALL, KAREN D., History & Lang Synthesis Tchr; *b:* Bayonne, NJ; *ed:* Montclair Univ (BA) His 1970; Post Grad Credits in His; *cr:* Charles H. Brewer Schl 7th Grd Soc Stud & Eng Tchr 1970-84; Carl H. Kumpf MS 8th Grd His & Lang Synthesis Tchr 1984-; *ai:* Soc Stud Comm 1970-84; Yrbk Adv 1973-85; Schl Pub Relations; Calligraphy Club; Tennis, Badminton IM Coach; NEA, NJEA, NCTE, NCSS, Clark Ed Assn 1970-; *office:* Carl H Kumpf M S Mildred Terr Clark NJ 07066

WALL, KATHLEEN ANN, Anatomy & Physiology Professor; *b:* Valparaiso, FL; *ed:* Univ of FL (BS) Poultry Sci 1970; Clemson Univ (MS) Poultry Sci 1973, (PHD) Animal Physiology & Zoology 1975; *cr:* Clemson Univ Visiting Asst Prof of Zoology 1975-77; Univ of ME Postdoctoral Fellow of Anatomy 1977-79, Animal & Veterinary Sci Instr 1979-80; Husson Coll Fac, Arts & Scis Chair & Asst to Pres 1981-; *ai:* Promotion & Tenure Comm; Admissions Comm; Undergraduate Judicial Bd of Appeals; Fac Org VP; Amer Cncl on Ed Leadership Dev Finalist; Tchr of Yr 1986 & 1993; Honorary Mem of Graduating Class 1989; *office:* Husson Coll 1 College Cir Bangor ME 04401*

WALL, SHARON BARBER, English Teacher & Dept Chair; *b:* Troy, NY; *m:* John M.; *c:* Katherine; *ed:* Russell Sage Coll (BA) Eng, Scndry Ed 1978; SUNY at Albany (MA) Eng Lit 1983; *cr:* Ichabod Crane HS Eng Tchr 1978-, Eng Dept Chair 1991-; *ai:* NHS Adv; AFT, NYSUT 1978-; *office:* Ichabod Crane HS Rt 9 Valatie NY 12184

WALLACE, AUDREY SCHROECK, Kindergarten Teacher; *b:* Chicago, IL; *m:* Robert; *c:* Robert Francis, Amy Lynn, Melissa Ann, Michael Clayton; *ed:* Fairleigh Dickinson Univ (BA) Elem Ed 1974; *cr:* Tuckerton Elem Schl Tchr 1977-; *ai:* Comm Involvement, Spirit, Schl Newsletter, Liaison, Soc Comms; Coord Christmas Toy Drive; NJEA 1977-; TEA 1977-, Pres, VP; NJAKE 1990-; PTA 1977-; *office:* Tuckerton Elem Schl PO Box 217 Marine St Tuckerton NJ 08087*

WALLACE, DEE ANN, Prof of Education; *b:* Monongahela, PA; *ed:* CA U (BS) Elem Ed 1961; WV U (MA) Rdng 1965; Penn St U (DED) Rdng Lang Arts 1981; *cr:* West Jefferson Hills Schl Dist 2nd Grd Tchr 1961-62; West Mars Hilltop Sch Dist 2nd-3rd & 5th Grd Tchr 1962-69; St Francis Coll Prof 1969-; *ai:* IRA 1961-; Keystone Rdng Assoc 1961-; Internesim Ctr 1985-, Vol; Open Door Crisis 1988-, Bd Pres 1995-; *office:* Saint Francis Coll Raymond Hall III Loretto PA 15940

WALLACE, DON L., Math Teacher; *b:* Akron, OH; *m:* Christina Y. Joyner; *c:* Ryan Lynn, Thomas Cory; *ed:* Hiram Coll (BA) Math 1972; Attnd Kent St Univ, Univ of Akron; *cr:* Springfield HS Math Dept Tchr 1972-; *ai:* Former Coach Var Ftbl Asst 10 Yrs, Var Bsbl Head 7 Yrs, Intramurals 10 Yrs, Lettermans Club 7 Yrs; SLACT, NEA, OEA, OCTM 1972-; PTSA Tchr of Yr 1988; Ashland Oil Tchng Awd 1991; *office:* Springfield HS 2966 Sanitarium Rd Akron OH 44312

WALLACE, ELEANORE GAWLAK, Retired 2nd Grade Teacher; *b:* Canton, OH; *m:* Eugene L.; *c:* Donna L. Wallace Eibel, Dean L.; *ed:* Kent St Univ (BS) Elem Ed 1969; 25 Semester Hrs Psych, Math, Rdng Akron Univ; *cr:* Fairmount Schl 3rd Grd Tchr 1966-74; Mason Schl 2nd Grd Tchr 1974-76; Allen Schl 2nd Grd Tchr 1976-77; Worley Elem Schl 2nd-3rd Grd Tchr 1977-95; *ai:* Kappa Delta Pi 1972-; Delta Kappa Gamma 1979-; Coll Club Canton 1874-; Lake Cable Woman's Club 1986-; Symphony League Canton 1995-; *home:* 5349 Peninsula Dr NW Canton OH 44718

WALLACE, JAMES EDWARD, Math Dept Head & Teacher; *b:* Huntington, WV; *m:* Mary Ann Soltis; *c:* Michael, David, Steven; *ed:* Cleveland St Univ (BA) Math 1988; MS Cert Baldwin Wallace Coll 1994; Post Grad Stud Cleveland St Univ; *cr:* Cleveland Pub Schls Tchr 1989-; *ai:* Head Girls Bsktbl Coach, 2 Time City Champs; Asst Soccer, Track Coach; Math Club Adv; NCTM, OCTM, GCCTM 1989-; Tchr of Yr 1992-93; Tchr of Month 1992; *office:* Alexander Hamilton MS 3465 E 130th St Cleveland OH 44120*

WALLACE, JAMES MICHAEL, Assistant Professor of English; *b:* Wilkes-Barre, PA; *ed:* Wilkes Coll (BA) Eng 1980; Lehigh Univ (MA) Eng 1986, (PHD) Eng 1989; *cr:* Lehigh Univ Tchng Fellow 1981-87; Kings Coll Asst Prof 1988-; *ai:* The Crown Newspaper Adv; Bd of Stu Media Chprsn; Jr Class Adv; Writing Ctr Dir; Modern Lang Assn 1995-; NCTE 1994-; Delta Epsilon Sigma 1991-; Sigma Tau Delta 1985-; All Coll Awd 1993; Journal Publications; Produced a Video; Presented Papers; *office:* Kings Coll 133 N River St Wilkes-Barre PA 18711

WALLACE, KATHERINE HEANEY, Second Grade Teacher; *b:* Greenport, NY; *m:* Robert J.; *c:* Gregory S., Jacquelyn M., Nicole M.; *ed:* Southampton Coll (MS) Elem Ed 1987; *cr:* Greenport Schls Sub Tchr 1977-86, 3rd Grd Tchr 1986-91, 2nd Grd Tchr 1991-; Oysterponds Schl Sub Tchr 1977-86; *ai:* Costume Coord Plays; NYSUT, AFT 1986-; Greenport Tchrs Assn 1986-, Sunshine Comm; Girl Scouts 1962-, Ldr 20 Yrs; St Agnes Church, Choir Dir 1980-, Organist 1965-; BSA 1985-, Finance Comm; *office:* Greenport H S 720 Front St Greenport NY 11944

WALLACE, KAY I., Math Teacher; *b:* Decatur, IL; *m:* Robert J.; *c:* Bobby J., Beth A.; *ed:* Eastern IL Univ (BS) Math Ed 1973; OH St Univ (MA) Math Ed 1978; 50 Addl Sem Hrs Math, Ed, Tech; *cr:* Northside Jr HS Math Tchr 1973-74; Whitehall HS Math Tchr 1974-78; Pickerington HS Math Tchr 1978-; *ai:* Venture Capital Core Comm; Schedule Restructuring, Venture Capital Comms; NCTM, NSTA, OCTM 1993-; NEA, OEA 1973-; GTE Integrating Math & Sci Gift 1993; OH Edctr Talent Pool 1995; Presenter NCTM, T3, SECO Confs 1996; Pilot CMS Inst 1994; *office:* Pickerington HS 300 Opportunity Way Pickerington OH 43147*

WALLACE, KEVIN ALEXANDER, Science Teacher; *b:* Cheverly, MD; *ed:* Western MD Coll (BA) Bio 1991; *cr:* Allegany HS Chem, Sci Tchr 1993-; *ai:* Class Co-Adv; Stu Assistance Team; Chem-a-thon Asst Coach; MD Assn Sci Tchrs, NSTA, NEA 1994-; *office:* Allegany HS 616 Sedgwick St Cumberland MD 21502

WALLACE, LARRY, 5th Grade Teacher; *b:* Syracuse, NY; *ed:* SUNY at Albany (BA) His 1971; 30 Grad Hrs Syracuse Univ; Permanently Certfd Elem Ed, His Grd 7-12 1976; *cr:* Fayetteville Elem Schl 5th Grd Tchr 1971-75; Wellwood MS 6th Grd Tchr 1975-86, 5th Grd Tchr 1986-; *ai:* Coaching Bsktbl, Bsbl; Spec Olympics; AFT, NYSUT, FMTA 1971-; *office:* Wellwood MS F-M Road Rt 257 Fayetteville NY 13066*

WALLACE, LUCY ANN PARKER, Kindergarten Teacher; *b:* Prince Frederick, MD; *m:* Alvin Esteph; *c:* Marion, Ossino, Wallace; *ed:* Bowie St Coll (BS) Elem Ed 1967, (ADC) Early Chldhd Ed 1985; *ai:* Just Say No & Comp Skills Club; Mentor for Stdnts & Tchrs; MSTA 1968-; NEA 1968-; CEA 1968-; Church High Blood Pressure Specialist 1981-, Asst; The Delta Kappa Gamma Soc 1983-, Chm World Flwshp; Comm Free Tutoring 1994-; Sanctuary Choir 1995-; Sr Ministries Spiritual Growth 1995-; Calvert Elem Schl 1450 Dares Beach Rd Prince Frederick MD 20

WALLACE, MARY HUDAK, Teacher; *b:* Farmington, WV; *m:* K.; *c:* Robert, John; *ed:* WVU (BS) PE 1960; Attnd Utica Coll; *cr:* Schl PE, 3rd Grd Tchr 26 Yrs; *ai:* NYSTA; NEA; *office:* Poland Schl PO Box 8 Poland NY 13431

WALLACE, MARYANNE C., Social Studies Teacher; *b:* New Yo NY; *m:* John A.; *c:* Anne Christine, Maureen; *ed:* Seton Hall Un Scndry Ed, Soc Stud 1968; *cr:* Pequannock Twp HS His Tchr 1 Passaic Valley Regnl HS Homebound Inst 1976-80; Mount Olive Stud 1980-87, 1991-; Mount Olive HS US His Tchr 1987-91; *ai:* Ch 8th Grd Trip 8 Yrs; Staff Dev Comm; Attnd Jr Statesman Natl Con Washington DC 1990; NEA 1968-; NJEA 1968-69, 1980-; Ho Foreign Exchange Stdnts 1986-; US His I Stdnts Participated Paterson Coll Thomas Jefferson Day Lecture Essay Contest Won 2 Olive HS Tchr of Yr Awrd 1993-94; *office:* Mount Olive MS Su Budd Lake NJ 07828*

WALLACE, REBECCA LARKIN, 7th-8th Grade Reading Tea Houlton, ME; *m:* Dennis James; *c:* Ryan Tyler, Matthew James; *e* of Southern ME (BS) His, Eng 1975; Univ of ME at Orono (MS) 1980; *cr:* Pittsburg Schl System Tchr 1975-76; SAD #34 Etna-D Schl Tchr 1977-88; Union #34 Glenburn Schl Tchr 1988-; *ai:* Cr Coach; MS Play, Civic Oration, Spelling Bee Dir; 8th Grd Clas Glenburn Recertification Comm Chprsn; NEA 1977-; GTA 198 First Congregational Church Yth Ldr; *office:* Glenburn MS 991 Hud Glenburn ME 04401

WALLACE, RODNEY E., Math Dept Chairperson; *b:* Washingt *m:* Leslie M.; *c:* Ryan, Lindsay; *ed:* Univ of MD (BS) Math 1970, Math 1976; 30 Hrs PHD Prgm; *cr:* Wheaton HS Math Tchr 1970- Hebron HS Math Tchr 1976-77; Hammond HS Math Dept Chprsn *ai:* NCTM 1969-; Loyola Univ honorary Doctorate 1988.

WALLACE, ROGER LAWRENCE, Sixth Grade Teacher; *b:* Spri MA; *m:* Jacqueline Davis; *c:* Mareatha Mae Bowern, Adrienne; *ed* Univ (BA), (BS) His, Ec 1973; Univ of MA (MED) Curr Dev 1978; Park Comm Schl 4th Grd Tchr 1973-74; Fort River Elem Schl 6th G 1974-; *ai:* Schl Improvement Cncl; Traveling Storyteller; 4-5th Gr Bsktbl Coach; 4-5th Grd Sftbl Team Coach; APEA & NEA 1974- Meeting 1984-; Coll Church, Elder Lay Pastor; Tchr of Merit 19 Just Schoolwork New Directions in Written Expression; Co-Author Units of Stud Ancient Egypt; World Regions, Contemporary Issues

WALLACE, TERRY LEE, Sixth Grade Teacher; *b:* Philadelphia, Rutgers Univ at Camden (BA) Hist1975; Elem Tchr Cert 1975; *cr:* Garden St Sch & Sacred Heart Schl 4th Grd Tchr 1975-80; Charles 6th Grd Tchr 1980-; *ai:* Unit Ldr 6th Grd Tchrs; Stu Base Mngmt; Comm for Stdnts at Risk; Report Card, Tchr Evaluation Revision C Writing, Newspaper, Chess, French Club Adv; Telecomnctn Com Stud & Sci Txtbk Comm; NEA, NJEA 1975-; West Jersey Rdn 1990-; Asbury United Meth Church 1966-, Sunday Schl Tchr, Minitries Cncl Mem, Admin Bd, Inspirational Choir; Girl Scouts o 1961-, Troop Ldr, Cookie, Calendar Chm; Alpha Kappa Alpha 197 Schl Cncl & Chldrns Cncl; Governor's Tchr Recognition Prgm 199 Person, Valuable Svc Awds; Palmyra Bd of Ed Cert of Excl Dedication Tchng; Outstanding YoungWomen of Amer; As bury Meth Church Appreciation Banquet Honoree 1984; Girl Scouts; C Cty Cncl; First Yr Tchr Mentor; *home:* 6543 Harvey Ave Pennsau 08109*

WALLER, CAROL CRAIN, Business Education Teacher; *b:* May KY; *m:* David Lee; *c:* Michael; *ed:* Marshall Univ at Huntington (A Ed Comprehension 1972; Attnd OH St Univ Classes to Meet Voc B Stan; Wright St Univ Cur Construction Class, Morehead St Univ Gr in Cnslng, OH Univ Grad Stud in Cnslng; *cr:* Natl Mine Svc Co Division Controller 1969; Marshall Univ Admissions Office Sec 19 South Point HS Bus Tchr 1973; Collins Career Ctr Voc Bus Tchr 19 Dawson-Bryant HS Bus Tchr 1984-; *ai:* Chrstn Yth Group Adv; Bus Working with Bus Ldrs in Area to Update Curr Changes; NEA; Assn; Dawson-Bryant Ed Assn; OH Bus Tchrs Assn; Zoar Bapt C Zoar Bapt Church Choir; Southeastern OH Rep to OH Bus Tchr *office:* Dawson-Bryant HS 1 Hornet Ln Ironton OH 45638*

WALLER, JERRY, Computer & AP Accounting Tchr; *b:* Passaic, Susan Potusky; *ed:* Montclair St Univ (BA) Bus Ed, Acctng 1969, Bus Ed 1973; Cmptrs in the Curr, LOGO, Word Processing for IBM 6 Credits; NJ Insurance Exam; H&R Block Tax Preparation Course, Perfect for Windows 7 CPE Credits; *cr:* Clifton NJ Scndry Schls Permanent Contracted Sub 1969-70; Columbus Jr HS Intro t Typewriting Tchr 1970-85; Clifton HS Cmptr Software, AP Acctn 1985-; *ai:* Dist Cmptr Curr Comms 1988-92, 1995-; Cmptr So Applications Course Curr Comm Chprsn; Coll Level Acctng A Comm Chprsn; Fac Grading Comm 1991-93; Mid Sts Philosophy, Comm 1995-; Clifton Tchrs Assn, NJ Ed Assn, Passaic Cty Ed As Bus Ed Assn, Montclair St Univ Alumni Assn 1969-; Columbus Jr H Org 1970-85, Pres, Treas; Fac Org, Parent Tchr Stu Assn 1985-; Au Unpublished Manuscript; Dev Curr for Cmptr Software Aplications Level Acctng Courses; Researched, Prepared Coll Level Acctng Portfolio; Numerous Articles Pub; Presented Cmptr Software Applic Course Packet to NASSP; NJ HS Bus Tchrs have Visited, Observe Classes; Guest Speaker Montclair St Univ Grad Schl Course, 17th A Wkshp for Bus Dept Supvrs, Delta Pi Epsilon Bus Grad Schl Frat Presenter Round-Table Discussion NJBEA Conf; NJ Tchr Provi Prgm Mentor Tchr; Mitchell Kapor Letter of Congratulations; M Evaluation Comm Commendation 1985-86; Clifton Bd of Ed Commendation; Governor's Tchr Recognition Awd; Cable Televi Golden Apple Tchr of Yr Awd; Nom Princeton Tchr Recognition *office:* Clifton HS 333 Colfax Ave Clifton NJ 07013

WALLER, MIKE, Physical Science Teacher; *b:* Alliance, OH; *m:* M Annette Baker; *c:* Kiley Baker, Trevor; *ed:* Univ of Akron (BA) Bi Gen Sci 1989; 4 Hrs Steps Prgm; *cr:* Edison MS 8th Grd Sci Tchr 19 Springfield Jr HS PE Sci Tchr 1993-; *ai:* JV Boys' Bsktbl, Jr H Coach; Jefferson Cty Curr Comm; Jr HS Advy Comm; NEA 1990-; Springfield Jr HS Rd 1 Bergholz OH 43908*

WALLER, SUSAN NEALY, English Teacher; *b:* Upland, PA; *m:* Joh Grace Coll (BA) Eng 1985; Hunter Coll of CUNY (MA) Eng 1990; 18 Hrs at Widener Univ; *cr:* Delaware Cty Comm Coll Instr 19 Northeastern Chrstn Jr Coll Asst Prof 1989-93; Chrstn Acad Tchr *ai:* NHS Adv; Lang Arts Curr Comms; Northeastern Chrstn Jr Coll T Yr 1993; *office:* Christian Acad 704 S Old Middletown Rd Media PA

WALLESHAUSER, BARBARA MARY BERGLER, Math Depar Chairman; *b:* Buffalo, NY; *m:* James J.; *c:* Dr. Mary B. Wallesh Porter; James B.; *ed:* D'Youville Coll (BA) Math 1964; Canisius Coll Ed 1976; 30 Addl Credit Hrs St Univ of NY at Buffalo; *cr:* Clarence Tchr 1972-; *ai:* Schlsp Comm; Technology Comm; K-12 Math Curr C AFT 1972-, Rep 1987-89; NCTM, NY St Math Tchrs Assn 1980-; T Mem; Alpha Delta Kappa 1977-, VP 1989-; Nativity Church, Soup Ki Comm 1990-; *office:* Clarence Cntrl Sr HS 9625 Main St Clarenc 14031*

WALLIN, DANIEL J., Math Teacher; *b:* Pennsauken, NJ; *m:* Lou *c:* Jon, Jason, Mike, Matt, Jordan; *ed:* Bapt Bible Coll (BRE) Rel r Univ (MA) Math 1983; *cr:* OK Bible Acad Math Tchr 1979-81; Acad Math Tchr 1981-83; *ai:* Soccer, Bsktbl, Bsbl Coach; Math Adv; *office:* E T Richardson MS 20 W Woodland Ave Springfield 54

ING, ELIZABETH ERICKSON, Second Grade Teacher; *b:* us, NJ; *w:* Jack (dec); *ed:* Kean Coll (BA) Early Chldhd 1962; h Dickinson Univ (MA) Hum Dev 1981; 30 More Credit Hrs 1991; port Cntrl Schl Kndgtn & 1st Grd Tchr 1961-93, 2nd Grd Tchr ai: After Schl Rdng Tutor; K-3rd Grd Needs Comm; Hall of Fame Sec; Orton Dyslexic Soc; NEA & NJEA; Rdng Reform; Chrstn Sci e Mem, Clerk, Treas, Sunday Schl Tchr, Reader & Comms; Garden Ctr Vol; Tchr of Yr 1986-87; Governors Recognition Awd 1986-87; HS Hall of Fame 1991; Co-Author for 2 Tchrs Manuals Phonics ught A & B Workbooks; *home:* 53 Washington St Keyport NJ

S, JENNIFER LYNN, Math Teacher; *b:* Fort Knox, KY; *m:* Eric ison; *c:* Andrew; *ed:* Univ of Akron (BA) Scndry Ed 1991, (MA) Ed 1996; *cr:* Akron Pub Schls Tchr 1991-; *ai:* People Accepting s Everywhere; Catalina Club; Stu Action Comm; JV Softbl, Speech, Coach; Greater Akron Math Edctrs Soc, NCTM 1991-; *office:* ne HS 333 Rampart Ave Akron OH 44313

S, KATHLEEN STEVENS, Physical Education Teacher; *b:* ına, NY; *m:* Carl Walter; *c:* Kent, Thomas, Katie; *ed:* Orange Cty Coll (AAS) PE 1967; St Univ at Brockport (BS) PE 1969; 33 Grad Duanesburg Cntrl Schl PE Tchr 1969-; *ai:* Girls Var Soccer Coach; burg Sports Booster Club; Summer Soccer Camp Adv; NHS Comm Sr Project Comm; NYSUT 1969-; Duanesburg Tchrs Assn 1969-, Pres; Berne Fire Auxiliary 1980-; Local Yth Commission 1985-, ffice: Duanesburg Cntrl Schl School Dr Delanson NY 12053

S, ROBERT THOMAS, Mathematics Teacher; *b:* Port Clinton, Katherine Jean Meachen; *c:* Carrie, Jennifer; *ed:* Univ of Toledo Ed Soc Stud, Math 1973; Bowling Green St Univ (ME) Guid, 1982; *cr:* Monroeville Pub Schls Math, His Tchr 1973-79; Port Pub Schls Math Tchr 1979-; *ai:* Consulting Tchr; NEA 1973-79; 979-; St John Luth Church 1951-; *office:* Port Clinton HS 821 on St Port Clinton OH 43452

S, STACY LYNN, World History Teacher; *b:* Wilmington, DE; *ed:* f DE (BA) His & Ed 1993; Working Towards MS Amer His; *cr:* num Schl World His Tchr 1993-; *ai:* Yrbk Adv; Democratic Party Comm Mem 6th Dist; Phi Alpha Theta; Outstdng Stu Tchr 1993; f DE Educl Alumni Schlsp; Diamond St Bell of PA Schlsp; *office:* num Schl 1801 N Broom St Wilmington DE 19802

OTH, SCOTT RICHARD, High School Art Teacher; *b:* own, NY; *m:* Catherine Ann Granger; *c:* Saran Ann, Mary Catherine; sdam Coll (BA) Fine Art 1982; Syracuse Univ (MFA) Synaesthetics; rence Univ Cert Art Ed 1982; *cr:* Gen Brown HS Art Tchr 1983-84; rne-Earlville HS Art Tchr 1984-; *ai:* Boy's Modified Soccer, y of the Mind Coach; Art Club Adv; Dist Tech Planning Comm; Ice Referee; NAEA 1991-; NY St Art Tchrs Assn 1990-; Grants Tech Comm of Southern Tier 1992-95, Catskill Regnl Tchr Ctr Schl e 1990-91, Math Sci Awd 1989; Demonstrator, Speaker NYSC&TE Regnl Conf 1990-95, Techs in Ed Day 1993, New Movements 1994, cape Chenango 1995, Open Market 1990, Multi Media on 1989, Media NYSC&TE Conf 1987; Cmptr Graphics, Animation Tchr 0; Intnl Magazine's Cmptr Video Artist; Art Shows Tamed, Untamed Gallery, Paper & Print Chenango Co Cncl of Arts 1989, Reality & Foreman Gallery 1988, Cooperstown Natl Juried Art Exhibition 8; *office:* Sherburne-Earlville Cntrl Schl 15 Utica Rd Sherburne NY

H, ANN MARIE, 8th Grd Soc Stud & Lit Teacher; *b:* Kingston, PA; eph V.; *c:* Kelly Ann; *ed:* Univ of Scranton (BA) Eng 1977; 27 Towards Masters Eng Lit; Religious Ed Inst at Scranton Diocese dits; *cr:* WY Area HS 9th Grd Eng, Perm Sub Tchr, Tutor 1978-89; y's Assumption Schl 8th Grd Tchr 1990-; *ai:* Forensics Club Coach; derator Stu Cncl; St Mary's Advy Bd Mem; St Mary's HSO Exec Bd, P of HSO; Marians Cncl #8598 1994-, Sec; *office:* St Mary's ption Schl 41 Carroll St Pittston PA 18640

H, ARDIS, 6th Grade Language Arts Tchr; *b:* DuBois, PA; *m:* Tom *c:* Christopher; *ed:* Edinboro Univ (BA) Elem Ed 1975; Rdng list 1984; *ai:* Curr, Budget Comms; Stu Cncl Adv; Lead Tchr Prgm; IRA, Erie Cncl Past Mem; *office:* James S Wilson MS 901 W 54th PA 16509

H, BARBARA A., Former Kindergarten Teacher; *b:* Kingston, PA; rman F.; *c:* Michael J.; *ed:* Bloomsburg Univ (BA) Elem Ed 1960; r Coll (MS) Elem Ed 1990; Writer's Courses; *cr:* Upper Perkiomen st 2nd Grd Tchr 1960-61; Wyoming Vly West Schl 2nd Grd Tchr 55; Perkiomen Sch Dst K, 2nd-4th Grd Tchr 1965-70, 1980-96; *ai:* PSEA; PVEA; Nutrition Tchr of Yr 1985; *home:* 1625 Old Plains Rd ourg PA 18073*

SH, DARYL EDWARD, English & Philosophy Teacher; *b:* Ft Knox, *d:* Williams Coll (BA) Eng 1987; Studied at Bread Loaf Schl of Eng ddlebury; 3 Credits Each at Millersville Univ, Penn St at Harrisburg; ncaster Cty Day Schl Eng, Philosophy Tchr 1988-; *ai:* Head MS Boys r Coach; MS Newspaper Club; Early Assistance Support Team Mem; ssions Comm; MS Club Coord; Hershey Sumphony 1988-95, 2nd Fr Natl Endowment of Hum Seminar for Schl Tchrs Intellectuals & unism Emory Univ at Atlanta 1993; Grants for Prof Dev for Stud at Loaf; *office:* Lancaster Country Day Schl 725 Hamilton Rd ster PA 17603

SH, DIANE, Science Teacher; *b:* Brooklyn, NY; *m:* Francis; *ed:* St Univ (BA) Bio & Ed 1970, (MS) Bio 1972; *cr:* Regis HS Sci Tchr *ai:* Sci Dept Chprsn; Regis Drama Soc Costumes; NSTA 1970-; 1970-; NSF Grad Traineeship; Columbia Univ Summer Rsrch Pgm p; *office:* Regis HS 55 E 84th St New York NY 10028

SH, DOUGLAS TIMOTHY, English Teacher; *b:* Springfield, MA; thy; *c:* Tara, Ben, Patrick; *ed:* Westfield St Coll (BA) Eng 1976; *cr:* am Jr High Eng Dept Coord 1988-; *ai:* MTA 1979-; NEA 1979-; Agawam Jr HS 1305 Springfield St Feeding Hills MA 01030

SH, EILEEN ELIZABETH, Theatre Teacher; *b:* Jersey City, NJ; *c:* ine Long, Ned Long, David Long; *ed:* Rowan St Coll (BA) Speech & er 1971; *cr:* Elizabeth HS Eng, Pub Speaking & Theater Tchr 1971-; neater Arts Soc; Fall & Spring Musicals Dir; *office:* Elizabeth HS son Arts House 600 Pearl St Elizabeth NJ 07201

SH, F. GEORGE,III, Modified Curriculum Dept Chm; *b:* New York, Carolyn Grace Sesny; *c:* Daryl, Kevin; *ed:* Hofstra Univ (BA) His Adelphi Univ (MA) Scndry Ed; 90 Addl Credit Hrs Ed Admin; a Univ Cert Adv Stud Ed Admin; *cr:* Sachem Schls Tchr 1966-68; Modified Lead Tchr 1968-73; CurrPrgm Dept Chm 1973-; *ai:* Schl or Ed Club Adv; Guest Instr Frost Vly Field Trip Prgm; Fac Adv of Seneca Competitive Color Guard; SCTA, NYSUT 1966-; Orton 975-; Natl Assn Core Curr 1982-; The Phantom Regiment CG 1970-, Dir, Life Mem; Natl Judges Assn 1973-, Chief Judge, E Bd Mem; 1966-, High Adventure, Trng Chm Wood Badge; Dev Specialized Schl Oriented Stdnts Who Experienced Acad Difficulties Prgm Pub tl Assn of Core Curr; *home:* 65 Bellhaven Rd Brookhaven NY 11719*

WALSH, JAMES MATTHEW, Theater Teacher & Director; *b:* Pittsburgh, PA; *ed:* Duquesne Univ (BS) Ed 1990; Univ of MD (MED) Admin 1995; *cr:* Milton M Somers Lang Arts Tchr 1990-92; Westlake HS Theater Tchr & Dir 1992-; *ai:* Intnl Thespian Soc Spon; Morning News TV Show & Theater Co-Dir; Voice of the Wolverines Play-by-Play Announcer; Performance Grant in Ed Charles Cty Arts Alliance; Milton M Somers Schl PTA Outstdng Svc Awd; Westlake HS Schl Newspaper Super Tchr Awd; *office:* Westlake HS 3300 Middletown Rd Waldorf MD 20603

WALSH, JAMES MICHAEL, English Coordinator; *b:* Newark, NJ; *m:* Lois Bricklin-Walsh; *c:* Gabriel, Erica; *ed:* Seton Hall Univ (BA) Eng 1968; NY Univ (MA) Educl Theater 1974; Drew Univ PHD Prgm 19th C Stud; Seton Hall Univ Admin, Supervision; Stanford Univ Theater His; *cr:* Verona HS Eng Tchr, Drama Dir 1974-80; Vernon Twp HS Eng Tchr 1980-, Drama Dir 1981-96, Eng Coord 1992-; *ai:* Area Coord; Dist Tech, Dist Standardized Testing Comms; NEA, NJEA 1974-; VTEA 1980-, Grievance Rep; NJ Tchr Scholar 1990; Dodge Fnd Grant 1992; NEH, CBE Fellow 1988; *office:* Vernon Township HS Box 800 Rt 565 Vernon NJ 07462*

WALSH, JAMES RICHARD, Social Studies Teacher; *b:* Malden, MA; *m:* Jane Brochu; *c:* Kerrie, Kailey; *ed:* Univ of ME (BS) PE & Soc Stud 1973, (MED) Ed 1978; 4 Courses Toward CAS; *cr:* Sanford HS Tchr & Coach 1973-77; Helen Dunn Schl Tchr 1977-78; Dow Ln & Vine St Schls Tchr 1978-79; Husson Coll Coach; Old Town MS Tchr & Coach 1979-83; Old Town HS Tchr 1983-; *ai:* Ftbl Head Coach 10 Yrs; NEA, MTA 1973-; OTEA 1979-, VP of Union Negotiating Team; IAABO 1985-; ECAC 1994-; Sanford HS Ftbl Asst Coach & Jr Var Bsbl Coach 4 Yrs; Bangor HS Ftbl Asst Coach 2 Yrs; Husson Coll Bsbl Head Coach 4 Yrs; Old Town MS Jr HS Ftbl Coach 4 Yrs; *home:* 250 Husson Ave # 1E Bangor ME 04401

WALSH, JENNIFER J. (SMITH), High School English Teacher; *b:* Trenton, NJ; *m:* Kevin M.; *ed:* Mercer Cty Comm Coll (AAS) Paralegal Stud 1988; Rutgers Univ (BA) Eng Lit 1991; Trenton St Coll (MAT) Scndry Ed, Eng 1994; *cr:* Trenton St Coll Grad Asst 1992-94; Cliffside Park HS Eng Tchr 1994-; *ai:* Class of 1988 Adv 1994-; NJEA, NEA, NCTE 1994-; *office:* Cliffside Park HS Palisade & Riverview Aves Cliffside Park NJ 07010

WALSH, JOANNE ELIZABETH, English Teacher; *b:* Rochester, NY; *ed:* Coll of Mt St Vincent (BA) Eng 1963; Marquette Univ (MA) Eng 1965; Post Grad Stud at Univ of PA, NY Univ; *cr:* Cleveland St Univ Eng Instr 1966-68; Villanova Univ Eng Instr 1969-74; Darby-Colwyn Sr HS Eng Tchr 1974-78; Haverford Coll Eng Instr 1984-87; Temple Univ Eng Instr 1987-90; Malvern Prep Schl Eng Tchr 1990-; *ai:* Acad Competition, Newspaper, Yrbk Moderator; NCTE 1995-; Natl Endowment for the Hum for Ind Stud in the Hum Grant; *office:* Malvern Prep Schl 418 S Warren Ave Malvern PA 19355

WALSH, JOHN, Secondary English Teacher; *b:* Pittsburgh, PA; *m:* Beth Newport; *c:* Sean, Ryan; *ed:* Univ of Pittsburgh (BA) Ed 1971; *cr:* Canevin Hs Eng, AP Eng Tchr 1971-78; Peters Twp Schl Eng, Writing Tchr 1978-; *ai:* AFT 1984-; NEA 1979-83, Exec Bd; Pittsburgh Sftbl Umpires Assn 1975-, 2 Terms Pres, Exec Bd 17 Yrs; *office:* Peters Twp HS 264 E Mcmurray Rd Mc Murray PA 15317

WALSH, JOSEPH G.,JR., English Teacher; *b:* Neptune, NJ; *m:* Marie Ellen Tighe; *c:* Joseph, Caitlin; *ed:* Monmouth Univ (MAT) Ed 1982; Georgian Court Coll Methodology Classes ESI 9 Credits, Substance Awareness Coord 6 Credits; Kean Coll Cmptr Sci 6 Credits; *cr:* Asbury Park Adult Learning Ctr ESL Tchr 1979-81; Asbury Park Adult Night Schl ESL Tchr 1979-94; Manasghan HS Span Tchr 1981-82; Lakewood HS ESL, Eng Tchr 1982-; *ai:* Frgn Stu Club Adv; NJTESOL 1986-; NJEA, NEA, Lakewood Ed Assn, Ocean Cty Ed Assn 1980-; Belmar First Aid Squad 1974-, Pres; Monmouth Cty Assn of F A Squads 1980-, Pres, Vol Svc Awd; NJ St First Aid Cncl 1979-, VP; Amer Red Cross 1976-, Instr, Vol Svc Awd; BSA, Outstdng Svc Awd; Tchr of Month; *office:* Lakewood HS 855 Somerset Ave Lakewood NJ 08701

WALSH, MICHAEL ANTHONY, High School Science Teacher; *b:* Burlington, IA; *m:* Grace Ann Winkler; *c:* Randall, Michelle, Megan; *ed:* Southeast IA Comm Coll (AA) Gen Stud 1961; Western IL Univ at Macomb (BSEd) Bio 1964; Univ of MO at Columbia (MA) Botany 1967; Univ of WI at Madison (PHD) Botany 1972; UT St Univ at Logan SAS Curr Dev Cert 1981; *cr:* WI St Univ Instr 1967-68; Univ of Pittsburgh Asst Prof 1972-76; UT St Univ Asst Prof 1977-81; Horseheads Cntrl Schl Dist Sci Tchr & Supvr 1985-87, 1991-; Williamsville Cntrl Schl Dist Sci Supvr 1987-88; Canisteo Cntrl Schl Dist HS Prin 1988-91; *ai:* Site Based Comm; Amer Assn for Advancement of Sci; Amer Inst Biological Sci; Botanical Soc of Amer; NYSUT 1986-; AAUP Former Mem; Rotary 1988-91; Whos Who in the West 1982-83; Numerous Articles & Text Pub; Adv to Doctoral & Masters Recipients; The Phloem Translocator Founder & Ed; *home:* 6793 Chappel Rd Addison NY 14801

WALSH, MICHAEL FRANCIS, Retired PE Teacher & Asst Prin; *b:* Lebanon, NH; *c:* Karen Moore, Kevin, Sean; *ed:* Plymouth St Univ (BE) PE 1960, (ME) Ed 1976; *cr:* Berlin HS PE Tchr 1960-65; Plymouth HS PE, Gen Sci Tchr 1965-71; Berlin HS PE Tchr 1971-76; Berlin MS Asst Prin 1976-93; *ai:* Coach Ftbl, Bsbl, Bsktbl, Girls Bsktbl; Plymouth Coach Ftbl, Bsktbl, Bsbl; Underliner; NEA 1960-76; NAASP 1976-93; NAASP Ret 1993-; Berlin Ed Assn 1960-65, 1971-76; Plymouth Ed Assn 1965-71; North Cncl Prin Assn 1976-93; NH Prin Assn 1976-93; Ftbl Articles Coaching Clinic 1968, 1971; *home:* 37 Bemis St Berlin NH 03570

WALSH, MILTON JAMES, Aerospace Science Instructor; *b:* Brockton, MA; *m:* Donna Marie Brida; *c:* Deborah M. Tucker, Margaret A. Francover, Cynthia L. Haidaichuk, Shannon L. Coco; *ed:* Univ of NE at Omaha (BGS) Bus, Mngmt 1970; *cr:* USAF Military Prsnl Dir 1955-86; North Quincy HS Aerospace Sci Instr 1986-; *ai:* TROA 1986-; AFTROTC Outstdng Instr Awd 1988-91, 1993-94; *office:* North Quincy HS 316 Hancock St Quincy MA 02171

WALSH, MIRIAM, Principal; *b:* Malden, MA; *ed:* Notre Dame of Wilton (BS) Elem Ed 1971; MA at Fordham (MA) Admin, Supervision 1978; *cr:* St Rita Schl Tchr 1960-75; St John Schl Prin 1975-76; St Leo Schl Prin 1976-79; Holy Name Schl Prin 1979-80; Schl Sisters of Notre Dame Admin 1980-86; Imm Con Tchr 1986-87; St Gregory Prin 1987-92; Immaculate Conception Prin 1992-; *ai:* NCEA 1960-; *office:* Immaculate Conception Schl 306 Highland Ave Malden MA 02148

WALSH, NANCY, Resource & Consultant Tchr; *b:* Buffalo, NY; *ed:* Madaille Coll at Buffalo (BS) Ed 1970; St Univ Coll at Buffalo (MS) Ed 1975; NY St Certs Nursery, Kndgtn 1st-6th Grd 1976, 7th-12th Grd Eng 1976, Rdng Tchr 1981, Spec Ed 1984; *cr:* Conners Childrens Ctr Remedial Rdng Specialist 1976-83; St Ambrose Schl Remedial Rdng Tchr 1984-85; Buffalo Traditional Schl Resource, Consultant Tchr 1985-86; City Honors Schl Resource, Consultant Tchr 1986-; *ai:* After Schl Prgm Adv, Tchr; NEA 1985-; *home:* 938 E Eagle St Buffalo NY 14210

WALSH, NANCY SHERMAN, Kindergarten Teacher; *b:* Lowell, MA; *m:* John G.; *c:* Joel G., Steven J., Lincy A.; *ed:* Univ of MA at Lowell (BA) Eng 1972; Archdiocese of Boston Rel Cert 1994; *cr:* Regis Coll Fin Aid Ofcr & Asst Dir 1972-78; Lowell Pub Schls Jr High Sub Tchr 1978-81; St Louis Jr HS Eng Composition & Lit Tchr 1988 -94; St Louis Elem Schl Kndgtn Tchr 1994-; *ai:* Rainbows for All Gods Children Coord & Facilitator 1990-93; Chrstn Doctrine Tchr 1994-95; NCEA 1988-; St Louis Alliance of Parents & Tchrs 1989-; Parents of Lowell HS Show Choir 1994-; *office:* Saint Louis Elem Schl 77 Boisvert St Lowell MA 01850

WALSH, PATRICIA A., Religious Education Director; *b:* Troy, NY; *ed:* Coll of St Rose (BS) Elem Ed 1961, (MS) Ed 1965; North Adams St Coll 9 Credits Admin; *cr:* Albany Diocese Cath Schls Tchr 1965-67; Syracuse Diocese Cath Schls Tchr 1967-70; Albany Diocese Cath Schls Tchr 1970-91; St Joseph's Parish Rel Ed Dir 1991-; *ai:* Pyramid Life Ctr 1993-, Bd Mem; Immaculate Conception 1994-, Schl Bd Mem; Greater Capital Region Tchrs Ctr Grants 1985-86; *office:* Saint Joseph's Parish 45 Mac Arthur Dr Scotia NY 12302

WALSH, PATRICIA A., Second Grade Teacher; *b:* Philadelphia, PA; *ed:* Nazareth Coll (BS) Elem Ed 1967; *cr:* H Ashton Marsh Schl Elem Ed Tchr 1967-; *ai:* NEA, NJEA 1967-, AEA 1967-, Pres, VP Negotiation Team; City of Absecon Planning Bd 1991-; Governors Tchng Recognition Awd for Exceptional Tchng Ability 1987-88; *office:* H Ashton Marsh Schl Webb Rd Absecon NJ 08201

WALSH, PATRICK CHARLES, Guidance Counselor; *b:* Windber, PA; *m:* Ellen Marie Holsopple; *c:* Shane P. Travisch, Seth M. Conland, Evan P.; *ed:* Slippery Rock Univ (BS) Hlth & PE 1973, (MED) Guid & Cnslng 1978; Alliance Theological Seminary (MSP) Theological Stud 1989; *cr:* Oakland Schl Tchr & Bsktbl Coach 1973-74; Davis & Elkins Coll Instr 1974-75; Slippery Rock U Admissions Cnslr & Coach 1976-78; Shanksville Stony Creek Guid Cnslr 1979-; *ai:* PZAA Bsktbl Ofcl; Cross Cntry Running; Somerset Cty Cnslrs 1979-, Pres, VP & Sec; PA Schl Cnslrs Assoc 1980-; *home:* RR 1 Box 181 Friedens PA 15541*

WALSH, PATRICK KENNETH, Social Studies Teacher; *b:* Cleveland, OH; *m:* Kathleen M.; *c:* John, Shannon, Kevin, Ryan; *ed:* John Carroll Univ (BA) His 1968, (MA) His 1970; Univ of Akron PHD Prgm His 1972-76; Cleveland St Univ 1980; *cr:* Wickliffe HS Tchr 1969-73; Dyke Coll Tchr 1973-75; Cleveland Cath HS Tchr 1975-76; Westlake HS Tchr 1976-; *ai:* Westlake Tchrs Assn 1976-, Pres, VP, Chief Negotiator, Grievance Ofcr; Inst for Soviet, East European Stud JCU, Freedom Fnd Vly Forge, Fnd for Ec Ed, Irvington NY Grants; *office:* Westlake HS 27830 Hilliard Blvd Westlake OH 44145*

WALSH, THOMAS DAVID, Composition Adjunct Faculty; *b:* Long Beach, CA; *ed:* Northern AZ Univ (MA) TESL 1988; Univ of Northern CO (MA) Eng 1994, (MA) Educl Leadership 1994; Defense Lang Inst; Basic Russian Course; *cr:* Saint Anselm Coll Composition Adjunct Fac 1994-; New Hampshire Tech Coll Composition Adjunct Fac 1995-; *office:* Saint Anselm Coll 100 St Anselm Dr #1709 Manchester NH 03102

WALSHAK, ALMA IPPOLITO, French & Spanish Teacher; *b:* Tarrytown, NY; *m:* Louis; *c:* Andrew, Elizabeth; *ed:* Tchrs Coll, Columbia Univ (MA) Fr 1965; NDEA Lev 2 Fr Summer Session 1965; NEH Fr, Princeton Univ 1986; 30 Credit Hrs 1992; *cr:* Montgomery HS Fr, Span Tchr 1984-86; North Brunswick Twp HS Fr, Span Tchr 1986-; *ai:* Adv Fr Club; Spon Fr Honor Soc; Acad Affairs Comm NBTHS; FLENJ, AATF 1986-; *office:* North Brunswick Township HS Raider Rd & Rt 130 S North Brunswick NJ 08902

WALSLEBEN, LYNORE HEINZELMANN, Bio & Environmental Sci Tchr; *b:* Bryn Mawr, PA; *m:* Paul J.; *c:* Matthew K.; *ed:* Lebanon Vly Coll (BS) Bio 1977; Westchester Univ (MS)Bio 1980; *cr:* Downingtown Sr HS Bio Tchr 1977-84, Bio, Env Tchr 1989-; *ai:* IMPACT Club; Stu Forum Adv; One-to-One Rep Help Stdnts; HS Intensive Scheduling, Dist Mentoring Comms; Welcome Inc Club; DAEA, PSEA, NEA 1977-; BSA; *office:* Downingtown Sr HS 445 Manor Ave Downingtown PA 19335*

WALSTRUM, WENDY SUE, Third Grade Teacher; *b:* Havre de Grace, MD; *ed:* Frostburg St Univ (BS) Elem Ed 1970; Loyola Coll (MS) Elem Ed 1992; *cr:* Wee Care Day Care & Nursery Tchr, Dir 1980-86; Prospect Mill Elem Schl Third Grd Tchr 1986-; *ai:* Grd Level Chprsn; Soc Stud Comm; *office:* Prospect Mill Elem Schl 101 Prospect Mill Rd Bel Air MD 21015

WALTER, CHERYL BRABENDER, Choral Director; *b:* McKeesport, PA; *m:* Charles William; *c:* Karl, Nancy; *ed:* Carlow Coll (BA) Music Ed 1972; 46 Credits Masters Equivalency at Duquesne Univ, Penn St, Univ of Pittsburgh; *cr:* Wilkinsburg Schl Dist Elem Music Tchr 1972-77; Norwin Jr HS East Chorus & General Music Tchr 1987-91; Norwin HS Chorus Dir 1991-; *ai:* Chorus Show Choir; L T Harmony Girls Barbershop; Spring Musical Music Dir & Producer; MENC, PMEA 1971-; PSEA 1972-; PTA 1982-, Cncl Pres 1988-89, Honorary Life Mem; First Presbyn Church 1986-, Youth & Teen Choirs Dir; Apple Hill Theater Summer Theater Wkshp Tchr; *office:* Norwin Sr HS 251 Mcmahon Dr North Huntingdon PA 15642*

WALTER, CORA VAN ORD, Science Teacher; *b:* Farmington Twp, PA; *m:* Frank M.; *c:* Paula Kay, Karen Jacobs, Craig; *ed:* Lock Haven St Univ (BS) Hlth & PE 1965; Mansfield Univ (MED) Sci 1992; Attnd Binghamton Univ, Univ of MD, George Washington Univ; *cr:* Union-Endicott Cntrl Schl Tchr 1966-68; Dept of Defense Pacific Tchr 1969-71; Dept of Defense Atlantic Tchr 1978-81; Broome Cty Cath Sch Tchr & Sci Coord; *ai:* Drug Quiz Show Adv; IMs; Cath Edctrs Assn 1986-; NSTA 1993-; Sci Tchrs of NY 1993-; Phi Delta Kappa 1995-; NY St Electric & Gas Mini Grant; Daughters of Charity Tech Grant; *office:* Broome Cty Cath Schls 143 Main St Johnson City NY 13790

WALTER, CYNTHIA BENSON, English Teacher; *b:* West Palm Beach, FL; *m:* George Mark; *c:* Kate Duffy; *ed:* Tufts Univ (BA) Eng 1975; Masters Equivalency Johns Hopkins Univ; *cr:* Montgomery Cty Pub Schls Eng Tchr 1975-80; Hartford Cty Pub Schls Eng Tchr 1988-; *ai:* NHS Adv; Girls Jr Var Bsktbl Coach; NCTE 1990-; PTA 1986-; Co-Wrote Curr; Taught Women Perspective Course Bel Air HS; Cooperative Learning Mentor for Cty; *office:* Bel Air HS 100 Hieghe St Bel Air MD 21014

WALTER, DALE ALLEN, Government & Psychology Tchr; *b:* Garfield Heights, OH; *w:* Cynthia Hanzak (dec); *c:* Kristen; *ed:* Kent St Univ (BS) Soc Stud 1973, (MA) Soc Stud 1985; Attnd Ashland Univ, Cleveland St Univ; Walsh Univ; *cr:* Maple Heights HS Tchr, Adv 1974-; *ai:* Stud Cncl, NHS, Ath Renovation, Class Adv; Strategic Plan Comm; Girls Bsktbl Coach; NEA, 1974-; OH Assn Stud Cncl 1982-, Outstanding Adv for St; Amer Psychological Assn 1992-; Maple Heights Historical Soc 1990-; Animal Protective League 1989-; Grant St of OH Geography Research; Kudzieu Grant Improve Govt Ed; Tchr of Yr 1986; Nom St Tchr of Yr 1986, 1987; Maple Hts Ctzn of Yr 1995; *office:* Maple Heights HS 5500 Clement Maple Heights OH 44137*

WALTER, DENNIS H., Band Director; *b:* Buffalo, NY; *m:* Judith Erny; *c:* Natalie, Dennis Joseph; *ed:* SUNY at Fredonia (BM) Music ed 1975; Post Grad Work at New England Conservatory, Berklee Schl of Music, Robert Ceely at Boston Electronic Experiment Project; Pvt Percussion with Michael Bookspan, Philadelphia Orch, Jazz Improvization with Tony DeNicola, Trenton St Coll; *cr:* Pulsifer Schl of Music Percussion, Guitar Tchr 1975-81; Stoneham Pub Schl Dir of Bands 1975-81; No Burlington Co Regnl Jr Sr HS BandDir 1985-; *ai:* Asst Marching, Lab, Jr Sr High Stage Band Dir; Musical Dir for Musical Productions; MENC 1978-; Tchr of Yr 1990-91; *office:* Northern Burlington Reg HS 160 Georgetown Rd E Columbus NJ 08022

WALTER, DONNA KEITH, Fifth Grade Teacher; *b:* Cleveland, OH; *m:* Edward John Sr.; *c:* Dennis Megraw, Edw J. Jr., Patricia; *ed:* St John Coll of Cleveland (BS) Elem Ed 1967, (MS) Elem Ed 1973; 12 Semester Hrs Post Grad Work Kent St Univ, Coll of Mount St Joseph, Drake Univ, Humboldt St Univ; *cr:* St Columbkille Schl 5th Grd Tchr 1960-62; St Michael Schl 5th Grd Tchr 1963-64; Mill Schl 4-5th Grd Tchr 1964-65; Parma City Schls 4-5-6th Grd Tchr 1967-; *ai:* Curr Connection Comm

1992-; Right to Read Comm 1993-; NEA, NEOTA, OEA 1967-; Nom Ashland Oil Inc Tchr Achvmt Awd 1993; Nom Parma Tchr of Yr; *office:* Pleasantview Elem Schl 7700 Malibu Dr Cleveland OH 44130

WALTER, JOSEPH RAYMOND, Spanish Teacher; *b:* Buffalo, NY; *m:* Kathleen M. O'Brien; *c:* Joseph D., Ryan J., Christopher M.; *ed:* St Univ on NY at Buffalo (BA) Span 1982, (MA) Span 1985; *cr:* SUNY at Buffalo Tchng Asst 1983-84; Clarence Cntrl Schl Span Tchr 1985-86; Starpoint Cntrl Schl Span Tchr 1986-; *ai:* Class Adv 1986-89, 1990-92, 1994; JV Sftbl Coach 1991-; Effective Schls Comm 1991-94; Var Club Adv 1993-; NYSUT, Starpoint TA 1986-; *office:* Starpoint Central H S 4363 Mapleton Rd Lockport NY 14094

WALTER, KEVIN JOSEPH, History Teacher; *b:* Jamaica, NJ; *m:* Kathleen Mc Dermott; *ed:* Univ of VA (BA) His 1990, (MT) Tchng 1990; *cr:* Salem HS His Tchr 1991; Demarest HS His Tchr 1991-; *ai:* Soccer, Winter & Spring Track Coach; NEA 1991-; *office:* Nrthn Vly Reg-Demarest HS 150 Knickerbocker Rd Demarest NJ 07627

WALTER, SHARON GARTHWAITE, Fifth Grade Teacher; *b:* North Tonawanda, NY; *m:* Gary Edward; *c:* Allison Walter Seymour, John E. Hastings, Andrew E. Walter, Shane D. Hastings; *ed:* Buffalo St Univ of NY (BS) Elem Ed 1961; *cr:* Starpoint Cntrl First Grd Tchr 1961-63; North Collins Cntrl First-Second Grd Tchr 1963-70; Lake Shore Cntrl Fifth-Sixth Grd Tchr 1970-; *ai:* NEA 1961-; Lake Shore Teach Assn 1970-, NYSTA 1961-; Phi Delta Kappa 1988-; *office:* Lake Shore Cntrl Schls 100 High St Angola NY 14006*

WALTER, TANYA LYNN, Vocal Music Teacher; *b:* Johnstown, PA; *m:* Steve; *c:* Jaime, Rachel; *ed:* Lakeland Comm Coll (AA) Music Ed 1981; Lake Erie Coll (BS) Music Ed 1983; Case Western Reserve Univ Music Ed Towards Masters; *cr:* Mentor Exempted Schl Vocal Music 1 Yr; Chardon Local Schls Sub Tchr 2 Yrs; Painesville City Schls Vocal Music Tchr 7 Yrs; *ai:* Drama, Harveyaires Show Choir, Hobart MS Swing Choir Dirs; NEA, OMEA, OMSA 1988-; Who's Who in Amer Univ Coll 1983; Outstdng First, Second Yr Theory Stu Lakeland Comm Coll 1978-79, 1979-80; Recipient INA Forbes Schlsp 1981-82; Recorded Two Gospel Albums; *office:* Thomas W. Harvey HS 167 W Washington St Painesville OH 44077*

WALTERS, BERNARD, English Teacher; *b:* Pittsburgh, PA; *m:* Ellen Sitkoff; *c:* Lori Michele Rubin, Jeffrey Michael; *ed:* Univ of Pittsburgh (BA) Eng, Ger & Scndry Ed 1964; Temple Univ (MEd) Eng & Scndry Ed 1967; 30 Grad Cr Eng at Columbia Univ 1964-65; 12 Grad Cr at Gratz Coll 1990-92; *cr:* Marple Newtown HS Eng Tchr 1965-68; Plymouth Whitemarsh HS Eng Tchr 1968-; *ai:* Colonial Schl Dist Curr Writer 1970-; NEA & PSEA 1965-; CEA 1968-; Natl Endowment for Hum Fellow 1987; *office:* Plymouth Whitemarsh HS Germantown Pike Plymouth Meeting PA 19462*

WALTERS, CAROLYN MARIA, High School Math Teacher; *b:* White Plains, NY; *ed:* Yeshiva Univ (MS) Math Ed 1974; Attnd Hofstra Univ, Colgate Univ, Rutgers Univ, Pace Univ; *cr:* Mt Vernon HS Math Tchr 1970-; *ai:* Fac Club Pres; Acad Team Coach; Sr Awds Comm, Convocation Comm Chair; Word Comm; Westchester Cty Comm Urban Yth; NCTM 1987-; AFT 1970-; NSF Grants; Outstdng Svc Employeees, Jennings Meml PTSA Awds; *office:* Mt Vernon HS 100 California Rd Mount Vernon NY 10552

WALTERS, CHERYL ANN, Mathematics Instructor; *b:* Petersburg, VA; *c:* Charles, Christine; *ed:* Univ of Pittsburgh (BS) Math, Psych 1975, (MED) Scndry Math Ed 1989; 18 Hrs Cmptr Sci; *cr:* Somerset Cty Voc Schl Math Tchr, Dept Head 1986-; Westmoreland Cty Comm Coll Math Instr 1990-; *ai:* Stu Motivation Comm; NEA, PSEA 1986-, Local Pres; *office:* Westmoreland County Comm Coll College Station Youngwood PA 15697*

WALTERS, CHRISTINE ELIZABETH RYAN, Lang Arts Tchr of Gifted; *b:* Warren, OH; *m:* Jerry A.; *ed:* Youngstown St Univ (BS) Ed & Eng 1991; 11 Quarter Hrs Grad Schl; *cr:* Niles City Schls Eng & Lang Arts Tchr 1991-; *ai:* Drama Club Asst Dir 5 Yrs; NEDEA 1992-; NEA 1992-; OEA 1992-; Nom Ashland Awd; *office:* Edison Jr HS 36 W Church St Niles OH 44446

WALTERS, CYNTHIA ANN, Assoc Athletic Dir for Women; *b:* Roaring Spring, PA; *ed:* Lock Haven St Coll (BS) Hlth & PE 1962; Univ of Pittsburgh (MED) PE 1963; *cr:* Sarah Heinz House Recreation Dir 1963-64; North Allegheny HS PE Tchr, Coach 1964-66; Grove City Coll Women's Ath Dir, Aquatic Dir, Women's PE Dir, Intramural Dir, Tchr 1966-; *ai:* Intramurals; Water Show; Parents' Weekend; Cheerleaders; AAHPER, Red Cross WSI-WSIT 1966-; Pres Ath Conf 1985-, Bd Mem; Red Cross 1963-, Cty Bd, 30 Yr Svc Awd; Florence Mac Kenzie Awd 1985; Virginia Napoli Davis Meml Awd 1983; *office:* Grove City College 100 Campus Dr Grove City PA 16127

WALTERS, ERIC A., Science Dept Chm & Teacher; *b:* Malden, MA; *ed:* Univ of Lowell (BS) Meterology 1986; St Univ of NY at Albany (MS) Atmosphere Sci 1988; 6 Credits Brooklyn Coll; 3 Credits Manhattan Coll 1993; 3 Credits Coll of Staten Island; *cr:* SUNY at Albany Tchng Asst 1987-88; The Francis Schl Sci Tchr 1988-90; St John Villa Acad Chem, Env Issues & Physics Tchr 1990-, Sci Dept Chm 1992-; *ai:* Museum of NY City Ed Advy Comm Mem; Racquetball Fac Adv; Eco-Rama; Sci Hnr Soc; Sci-By-Mail Scientist & Mentor; Liberty Sci Ctr; NSTA 1987-; Staten Isl Sci Tchrs Assn 1990-; AAPT 1994-; Amer Chemical Soc 1995-; Sci-Mat Flwshp Cncl for Basic Ed 1992; Manhattan Coll Centennial Awd 1992; Pres Environmental Yth Awd 1992; NSTA & OHAUS Awd for Innovations in Sci Tchng 1993; Whos Who in Amer Ed 1995; *office:* St John Villa Acad-Richmond 26 Landis Ave Staten Island NY 10305*

WALTERS, JEFFREY FRANK, Global Studies Teacher; *b:* Syracuse, NY; *m:* Danielle Wagar; *ed:* SUNY at Potsdam (BA) His 1990; Attnd Liverpool of Higher Ed; SUNY at Albany; *cr:* New Hartford Cntrl Schl Global Stud, AP European His Tchr 1991-; *ai:* Yrbk Adv; Dist Crisis Team; Comm Ed Cmptr Tchr; New Hartford Yth Coalition 1994-; *office:* New Hartford Cntrl Schl 33 Oxford Rd New Hartford NY 13413*

WALTERS, LAURA PLESLUSKA, Learning Support, Spec Ed Tchr; *b:* Pittsburgh, PA; *m:* Richard; *c:* Allison, Noelle, Amy; *ed:* Duquesne Univ (BS) Music Ed 1963; Extended Cert Spec Ed 1986; Over 50 Credits Post Grad Stud; *cr:* Avonworth Schl Dist Sub Tchr; Holy Family Inst Resource Tchr 1980-88; Montour Schl Dist Learning Support Tchr 1988-; *ai:* PSEA, MEA 1988-, Bldg Rep; *office:* David Williams MS Porters Hollow Rd Coraopolis PA 15108

WALTERS, LAURA TRAVERS, First Grade Teacher; *b:* Cambridge, MD; *m:* Doug; *c:* Bradley, Brianne; *ed:* Chesapeake Coll (AA) Soc Scis 1982; Salisbury St Univ (BA) Elem Ed 1985, (MS) Early Chldhd 1992; *cr:* Warwick Elem Schl Pre-Kndgtn Tchr 1985; Hurlock Elem Schl Pre-K, K Tchr 1985-94; Maple Elem Schl First Grd Tchr 1994-; *ai:* Dorchester Emergency Med Svcs 1996; St Pauls Meth Church 1995-, Bd; *office:* Maple Elem Schl 5225 Egypt Rd Cambridge MD 21613*

WALTERS, MEG, Assistant Head & English Tchr; *b:* Philadelphia, PA; *ed:* Rosemont Coll Eng 1975; Villanova Univ Eng, Theater 1981; Doctoral Stud Temple Univ; *cr:* St Aloysius Acad 6th Grd Tchr 1975-77; Rosemont Schl of Holy Child Asst Head 1977-; Rosemont Coll Prof Eng, Theater 1981-; *ai:* Founded Schl Newspaper, HS Prep Course; Theater Act Vol; ISTA, NCTE 1978-; PAPAS 1982-; Vietnainese 1976-84, Vol Tutor; Rosemont Manor Nrsng Home 1985-, Vol; Produced, Wrote Play; Dir Rosemont Coll 1977-; Pub Articles, Poems; *office:* Rosemont Schl Of Holy Child 1344 Montgomery Ave Rosemont PA 19010

WALTERS, NANCY TAUNTON, Former Teacher; *b:* Tallassee, AL; *m:* Mitch; *ed:* Fitchburg St Coll (BS) Ed 1976; Natl Louis Univ (MED) Ed 1990; Attnd Alexander City Comm Coll; UC Berkeley Extension Approaches to Tchngs of Writing; MS Acad Univ of South FL, Boston Univ Rdng, Writing Child's LIt, Mod Mths; *cr:* Ft Rucker Elem Schl 4th, 6th Grd Tchr 1980-85; Sportfield Elem Schl 3rd, 6th Grd Tchr 1985-89; Hanau Amer MS 7th-8th Grd Tchr 1989-93; *ai:* Family Support Group; AEA, NEA, OEA Former Mem; OWC; *home:* Unit 20194 Box 109 Hhc 4th Bde 1st Ap APO AE 09165*

WALTERS, PAULA LAURENS, ESL Teacher; *b:* Middletown, OH; *m:* Ronald; *ed:* Georgetown Coll (BA) Eng 1973; Wright St Univ (MAEd) Intnl Childrens Lit, Linguistics 1991; Post Grad Stud Rdng Recovery Tchr; *cr:* Owensboro City Schls Eng Tchr 1973-75; Beavercreek Schls Eng, Rdng Recovery, ESL Tchr 1975-; *ai:* TESOL 1995-; OH ESL Tchr of Yr 1995-; *office:* Main Elem Schl 2940 Dayton-Xenia Rd Beavercreek OH 45385*

WALTERS, ROGER L., Building Trades Teacher; *ed:* Univ of Toledo (BS) Voc Ed; *office:* Sentinel Vocational Schl 793 E Township Road 201 Tiffin OH 44883

WALTERS, VICKI JORDAN, 4th Grade Teacher; *b:* Sayre, PA; *m:* Mark S.; *c:* Matthew S.; *ed:* Mansfield (BS) Elem 1973; Elmira Coll (MS) Elem; *cr:* Audrielle Lynch, Gladys Burnham, Harlan Rowe MS, Main Elem 4-6 Grd Tchr 22 1/2 Yrs; *ai:* Calendar Comm; PSEA, AAEA 1973-; *home:* RR 2 Box 349B Sayre PA 18840

WALTHER, DANIEL B., Science Teacher; *b:* Cleveland, OH; *m:* Deanna Martin; *ed:* Kent St Univ (BSEd) Bio 1991; *ai:* Stu Cncl; Ski Club; NABT; NSTA; United Church of Christ; Lorain Cty Metro Parks; *office:* Lorain Catholic HS 760 Tower Blvd Lorain OH 44052

WALTON, DAVID J., Professor of Economics; *b:* Watertown, NY; *m:* H. Karen Mc Donald; *c:* David, Peter; *ed:* St Lawrence Univ (BA) Sociology 1961; Syracuse Univ (MBA) Bus 1967, (PHD) Bus 1972; *cr:* Jefferson Comm Coll Prof 1966-; *office:* Jefferson Comm Coll Outer Coffeen Street Watertown NY 13601

WALTON, KEVIN DEANE, American History Teacher; *b:* Wooster, OH; *ed:* Coll of Wooster (BA) His, Art 1978; *cr:* Dalton HS World His Tchr 1980-81; Dalton Intermediate Schl Amer His Tchr 1981-; *ai:* NEA 1982-; Dept Chm; *office:* Dalton Intermediate Schl 151 W Main St Dalton OH 44618

WALTON, KURT GEORGE, Athletic Director; *b:* Albany, NY; *m:* Beth Jones; *c:* Rachel, Adam; *ed:* Hobart Coll (BA) His 1983; Albany St Univ (MA) Scndry Ed 1985; Jersey City St Coll Supvr Cert; *cr:* Duvbo Idrotbklub Player, Coach Bsktbl 1985-86; Wallkill Valley Regnl HS Tchr, Bsktbl Coach 1986-94; Kittatinny Regnl HS Ath Dir 1994-; *ai:* PE Supvr; Bsktbl Head Coach; NEA 1986-94; PSA 1994-; *office:* Kittatinny Regnl HS 77 Halsey Rd Newton NJ 07860

WALTON, MARY FRANCES, Science Teacher; *b:* Washington, DC; *c:* Shaundra-Elizabeth Francoise, Kathleena-Dominique Francesca; *ed:* Wilberforce Univ (BS) Bio, Pre-Med 1973; Howard Univ (MED) GATE Ed 1986; Bowie St Univ 15 Hrs Guid, Cnslng; Trinity Coll 15 Hrs Admin, Supervision; *cr:* J. Hayden Johnson JHS Environmental, Bio, Life Sci Instr 23 Yrs; *ai:* Young Astronauts; Sci Fair Coord; Sci Dept Chprsn; NSTA 1984-; Ebenezer AME Church Vacation Bible Schl 1995-, 6 Yr Old Instr; GTE 2 Yr Awd; Sci Math Integrating Learning Experiences; Grad Stud Flwshp Howard Univ; *home:* 2913 Henson Bridge Ter Fort MD 20744*

WALTON, ROBERT CHARLES, Bible Department Chrmn; *b:* Philadelphia, PA; *m:* Christine Craig; *c:* David, Susan; *ed:* Muhlenberg Coll (BS) Physics 1972; Westminster Theological Seminary M Div Theology 1975; *cr:* Lower Bucks Chrstn Acad Bible, Math & Sci Tchr 1975-77; Burlington Cty Chrstn Schl Bible, Math, Sci & Eng Tchr 1977-79; The Christian Acad Bible Chm & Math, Sci & His Tchr 1979-; *ai:* Drama Dir; Acad Quiz Team Adv; Ed Comm Chm; Faith Reformed Bapt Church 1980-, Elder; Pub Church His Chronological & Background Charts 1986; *office:* The Christian Acad 704 S Old Middletown Rd Media PA 19063

WALTON, THOMAS GAY, Health & Related Fitness Tchr; *b:* Philadelphia, PA; *m:* Deborah Joan Lee; *c:* Alison, Sarah; *ed:* Hawthorne Col (BA) Eng, Psych 1971; Attnd Northeastern Univ PE; River Coll 15 Hrs Cnslng; *cr:* Rundlett Jr HS Eng 1971-72; NH St Hosp PE 1972-73; Concord HS Jrnlsm Tchr 1973-79; Rundlett Jr HS Hlth, Related Fitness Tchr 1979-; *ai:* IM Strength Trng Dir; Nordic Ski Coach; Bldg Ldrshp Team; NEA, CEA 1971-; NHAHPERD 1975-; Concord Outright Inc 1995-, Facilitator Coord; NH Family Planning Cncl Bd Mem; Women's Hlth Family Planning Advy Comm; Smoke Free NH Alliance; Boston Maraton Qualifier 1996; US Canoe Assn Natl Canoe Tandem Triathlon Champion 1992-93, 1995; Knowledge is Power Awd by Planned Parenthood of Northern New England 1994; Appearances in Concord Monitor Series; *home:* 413 Broad Cove Rd Contoocook NH 03229*

WALTON, VIRGINIA A., Fr, Latin Tchr & Dept Head; *b:* Pittsburgh, PA; *m:* Stanley F.; *ed:* Penn St (BA) Gen Arts & Scis 1968; U of Pittsburgh (MAT) Sec Ed 1969; Loyola Coll (MBA) Fin 1982; Attnd Univ of Strasbourg 1967, Univ of Rouen 1969; *cr:* Aberdeen HS Fr Tchr 1970-90; Frick IS Acad Tchr 1990-91; Westmar HS Tchr 1991-; *ai:* Fr Club; Phi Delta Kappa 1995-; *home:* 61 Summit Pl Frostburg MD 21532

WALTON, YVONNE LELIA, Health & Physical Ed Teacher; *b:* Philadelphia, PA; *w:* Henry M. (dec); *c:* Derek Bostic, Felicia; *ed:* Morgan St Coll (BS) Hlth, PE; Glassboro St Coll (MA) Hlth, PE; Univ of PA Cert in Real Estate 1982-84; Temple Univ Admin of Hlth, PE; *ai:* Coach Badminton City Championship 1990, 1989-; AFT 1969-; Hearts of Joy Choir 1994-; R. E. Refereal Svc 1992-; *office:* South Philadelphia HS Broad & Snyder Ave Philadelphia PA 19148

WALTOS, ROSEMARY A., Kindergarten Teacher; *b:* Auburn, NY; *c:* Mark, Jeffrey; *ed:* Nazareth Coll (BA) His, Eng 1961; SUNY at Cortland (MS) Elem Ed 1964; *cr:* Seymour St Schl 2nd Grd Tchr 1961-64; A. A. Gates Elem Schl 2nd Grd Tchr 1964-67; Northminster Nursery Schl Tchr 1973-74; A. A. Gates Elem Schl Kndgtn Tchr 1974-; *ai:* Kndgtn Team Ldr; FOSPA Coord; Schl Climate, Report Card Update Comms; AFT, NEA, PBTA 1974-; St Rose Church 1973-; Home Bureau 1978-; *office:* A. A. Gates Elem Schl Maple St Port Byron NY 13140

WALTY, MARGARET, English Teacher; *b:* Indianapolis, IN; *ed:* Marywood (BA) Theater Arts 1967; Temple Univ (MED) Psych Educl Processes 1978; 30 Post Grad Stud; 50 Inservice Hrs T Dev Courses; *cr:* Morris Hills Regnl HS Eng, Speech Tchr, Dir of Theater 1967-69; Infant of Prague Gifted of 3-5 Grd Tchr 1969-70; Riverside Elem Schl Gifted of 4-6 Grd Tchr 1970-71; Central Bucks HS West Gifted Speech, Eng, Theater Tchr, Theater Dir 1971-; *ai:* CES Coord; Grad by Exhibition Mentor; Prof Dev Liaison; Dist Directions Comm; NEA; PSEA 1970-, Delegate to House 4 Yrs; NCTE; ASCD; Opera Intl, Stage Dir; Future Problems Evaluator for PA, NJ; Rome Opera Festival; Opera Theater Concert Performances Dir, Major Performer; *office:* Central Bucks-West HS 375 W Court St Doylestown PA 18901*

WALZER, MICHAELENE ANN (BAKER), Sixth Grade Teacher; *b:* Lewisburg, PA; *m:* David A.; *c:* Sara E.; *ed:* IN Univ of PA (BSE) Elem Ed 1973; Ashland Univ (MSE) Curr, Instruction 1992; *cr:* S. S. Cyril & Methodius 6th, 7th Grd Tchr 1974-76; Langston MS 6th Grd Tchr 1976-; *ai:* Yrbk, Candle of Knowledge Honors Prgm, Carnival Adv; Delta Kappa Gamma 1992-; NEA, OEA 1976-; Martha Holden Jennings Scholar; Plain Dealer Crystal Apple Nom; *office:* Langston MS 150 N Pleasant OH 44074

WAMBOLD, JUDITH Z., French Teacher & Dept Chprsn; *b:* Selle PA; *m:* Stanley B.; *c:* Matthew; *ed:* Millersville Univ (BS) Ed, F West Chester Univ (MED) Fr 1977, (MED) Cnslr Ed 1986; *cr:* Spri Sr HS Tchr, Dept Chair 1972-; *ai:* Fr Club Adv; Montgomery Co AATF 1972-;PSMLA 1986-; ACTFL 1976-; *office:* Spring-Ford Sr S Lewis Rd Royersford PA 19468

WAMBOLD, SUZANNE, Associate Professor; *b:* Toledo, OH; *m:* G.; *c:* Kelli, Katie; *ed:* Owens Tech Coll (AAS) Nursing 1977; Toledo (BEd) Ed & Allied Hlth 1985, (MEd) Higher Ed 1991; H Exercise Sci Grad Stud; *cr:* Riverside Hospital Staff Nurse 1976-81 Outpatient Cardiac Rehab 1981-85; Flower Hospital Cardiovascul Mgr 1985-89; Univ of Toledo Assoc Prof, Cardiovascular Prgm Dir *ai:* ACLS Instr; Human Subjects Review Comm; Cardiov Credential Internship for CCT Exam Chair; AAUP 1994-; ASE RDCS Awd; Fac Senate 1995-, Senator.

WAMPLER, NAN SEARLES, English Dept Chr & Tchr; *b:* Col OH; *m:* M. Keith; *c:* Jay; *ed:* Otterbein Coll (BA) Eng 1969; OH (MA) Educl Hum 1983; 56 Addl Hrs OH St; *cr:* Worthington HS E 1969-90; Worthington Kilbourne HS Eng Tchr 1990-; *ai:* Acad B Eng Dept Chair; NEA, OEA & WEA 1969-; OCTELLA 1995-; NC

WANAMAKER, JAMES ROBERT, Science Teacher; *b:* Porcupir SK, Canada; *m:* Jennifer Thiele; *ed:* Capital Univ (BA) Chem Ed Addl Hrs Univ of Buffalo; 12 Addl Undergrad Hrs Bowling Green 1992; *cr:* Sweet Home Cntrl Schls Sub Tchr 1992-93; Tonawan Schls Sub Tchr 1992-93; Mt St Mary Acad Chem Tchr 19 Lewiston-Porter HS Sci Tchr 1994-; *ai:* Key Club Adv; NYSUT NSTA, STANYS 1995-; St Martin Choir 1992-; St Martin Luther 1992-, Adv; *office:* Lewiston Porter Sr HS 4061 Creek Rd Youngsto 14174

WANAMAKER, JENNIFER THIELE, Math Teacher; *b:* N Tona NY; *m:* James R.; *ed:* 24 Hrs Toward MS Math Ed; *cr:* Lewistown HS Math Tchr 1992-; *ai:* NCTM 1992; Church Yth Group Adv; St Luth Church, Choir, Cr Chairwoman; Named by Stdnts as One of Fiv Influential & Helpful Tchrs 1995; *office:* Lewiston Porter Sr H Creek Rd Youngstown NY 14174

WANCEVICH, JOHN HUGH, Eng, Speech Arts & Drama T Columbus, OH; *m:* Silvia Fleites; *c:* Patricia; *ed:* Monmouth Uni General Ed 1967, (BA) Speech & Drama Ed 1970; Montclair St Uni Speech & Theatre (The Conc) 1992; Tchng Certs in Eng & Span Peter's Coll 1973-76; Speech Arts & Dramatics 1990; *cr:* KEarny Tchr 1973-; *ai:* Creating a Course about the Hist of Intol in the US 1973-, Former Assn Rep; NJ Ed Assn 1973-, Kearny Ed Assn 197 Poems Pub; *office:* Kearny HS 336 Devon St Kearny NJ 07032

WANDALL, SHARON SUE (YOST), 6th Grade Challenge Teac Wooster, OH; *m:* Earl L.; *c:* Jeremy; *ed:* Ashland Univ (BA) Elem E Rdng Validation 1979; Gifted Cert; 12 Credit Hrs; *cr:* Cloverleaf Schls 5th Grd Tchr 1979-81, 6th Grd Gifted Challenge Pgm 1981-; Coord; Spelling Bee Adv; Eisenhower Sci Comm; Challenge Netwo Rep; Westfield PTA 1979-; OAGC 1994-; Medina Cty Bd of Ed Excl 1989; Recipient of Several Grants; Cty Level Sci & Gifte Comms; Martha Holden Jennings Grant Co-Recipient 1989; Le Magazines Prof Ldrshp Awd Honorable Mention 1990; *office:* W Elem Schl 9055 S Leroy Rd PO Box 5003 Westfield Center OH 44

WANDEL, GARY LEWIS, Mathematics Teacher; *b:* Connellsvil *m:* Patrice M. Cupp; *c:* Thomas, Carrie, Zachary; *ed:* Univ Pittsburg Math 1972; Penn St Univ Grad Credits; *cr:* Shaler Area Schls Mat 1972-73; Connellsville Area Schls Math Tchr 1973-; *ai:* Asst Ma Band Instr; CAEA, PSEA, NEA 1972-; BPO Elks 1974-, Exalted 1978; Cub Scout Ldr 1984-; Boy Scout Asst Scoutmaster 1985-, O the Arrow 1988; First Bapt Church 1981-, Trustee, Sunday Schl Tch SS Supt, Woodbadge 1992; Jaycees Outstanding Young Educator 1 Vincent Coll Outstanding Educator Awd 1991; Tandy Outst Educator Awd Nom 1991; PA Tchr of Yr Nom 1991; St Vincer Outstdng Ed Award 1995; *office:* Connellsville Area Sr H S Fal Connellsville PA 15425*

WANG, LINDA C., Mathematics Instructor; *b:* Taiwan, Republic *m:* Yung-Terng; *c:* Jade P., Raemin; *ed:* Univ of CA at Berkeley (BA 1974, (MA) Math, Stat 1976; Brookdale Comm Coll (AAS) Cm 1987; *cr:* Dept of Ag Cmptr Programmer 1976-79; Ranney Schl 9- Math Tchr 1989-92; Brookdale Comm Coll Math Instr 1992-; *ai:* Asi Club Adv; Intnl Adv Comm; Amer Math Assn of Two Yr Coll 1992- Assn of Two Yr Coll NJ 1992-, Amer Statistical Assn 1995-; Mayor Task Force Comm Yth Group 1992-, Co-Chair; *office:* Brookdale Coll 765 Newman Springs Rd Lincroft NJ 07738

WANG, XINGWU, Assoc Prof Electrical Engrng; *b:* Hangzhou, Chi Changjiang Xu; *c:* Changcheng John; *ed:* Harbin Naval Engrng Ins Electrical Engrng 1978; Hangzhou Univ (MS) Physics 1981; St Univ at Buffalo (PHD) Physics 1987; Post Doctoral Fellow Electrical 1987-88; *cr:* USAF Wright Lab Visiting Electrical Engr 1994; FL S Visiting Assoc Prof 1994; Alfred Univ Asst Prof of Electrical Eng 19 Assoc Prof of Electrical Engr 1993-; *ai:* Task Force, R-R-A 1995-; 1988-; Amer Phys Soc 1984-; Amer Ceramic Soc 1988-; Rsrch Gra US Patents; Pub Articles; *office:* Alfred Univ Saxon Dr Alfred NY 1

WANGERIN, PAULA BAPTISTA, Spanish Teacher; *b:* Ca Venezuela; *m:* Roger; *c:* Diana; *ed:* Adelphi Univ (BA) Span, Latin Stud 1970; Hofstra Univ (MA) Eng, Span Lit 1974; ESL C. W. Pos 1986; 21 Credits Ind Stud Lit; *cr:* Elmont Meml HS Span Tchr 19 Rockeville Cntre Span Tchr 1971-72; Turtle Hook Jr HS Span 1972-79; Uniondale HS Span, TESOL Tchr 1979-; *ai:* Span Club; M Cooperating Tchr; Uniondale Tchrs Assn 1992-; AFT 1970-; B Meadowlane Estates 1985-91, VP; Doctoral Tchng Flwshp 1970; T Month 1994; Flwshp Multicultural Ldrshp Prmg 1991; *office:* Unic HS 933 Goodrich St Uniondale NY 11553*

WANKO, JUSTINE DWORZANSKI, Dev Child & Parenting Ed T Bayonne, NJ; *m:* Michael A.; *c:* Jason; *ed:* Jersey City St Coll (BA Ed, Schl Nrsng 1975; Bayonne Hosp Schl of Nrsng RN 1971; Cer Edctr, Schl Nurse, Elem Schl Tchr; *cr:* Bayonne Hosp Post-Su Primary Care Nurse 1971-74, Asst Head Nurse 1974-77; Exxon Co Indstrl Relief Nurse 1977-80; Bayonne Bd of Ed Schl Nurse 198 Bayonne HS Tchr 1994-; *ai:* Adv Project Grad; Bayonne Tchrs A NJEA 1994-; Part of Very First Resuscitation Team at Bayonne Valedictorian in Nrsng Schl, Highest Average in 2 Decades; Bayonne HS 669 Ave A Bayonne NJ 07002

WANN, DONALD CARLTON, Physical Ed & Health Teache Baltimore, MD; *m:* Carole Vivian Dorsch; *c:* Steven, David, Tim; *ed:* of MD (BS) PE 1966; Towson St Coll Master Equivalence in Ed 19 Credit Hrs Beyond; *cr:* Parkville MS PE 1966-67; Parkville HS PE & Tchr 1966-; *ai:* JV Soccer; Var Boys Indoor & Outdoor Track; Site Mgmt Team; NEA 1966-; MSTA 1966-; TABCO 1966-; Parkville Ja 1974-79; Baltimore Sunpapers All-Metro Indoor Track; Coach of t 1995; Boys & Girls Indoor Track Team 3A East Regional Champion 1996; *home:* 9107 Covered Bridge Rd Baltimore MD 21234

:MACHER, CHRISTOPHER JON, Chemistry & Physics , *b:* Verona, NJ; *m:* Kimberly Ruth; *c:* Aleksasha; *ed:* Lebanon Vly 5) Chem 1978; Montclair St (MA) Envirenmental Sci 1992; Addl its; *cr:* S. B. Penick Chemist 1978-79; MG-Scientific Gas Products 1979-81; Scientific Gas Products Chemist 1981-83; US Peace chr 1983-85; Spring Lake Ranch Cnslr 1987-88; Manchester Regnl Tchr 1989-; *ai:* Adv Physics, Chem I, II, Sci League, Physics :s Teams; Instructional Cncl; Hnr Soc Selections Comm; Table Coach; NEA, NJEA 1989-; NJAPT 1994-; *office:* Manchester l HS 70 Church St Haledon NJ 07508

:R, ANN-LOUISE FOCHT, English Teacher; *b:* West Lawn, PA; ard J.; *c:* Sharon Hockman, Lois Aldrich, William, Stephen; *ed:* n Univ (BS) Ed 1972, (MA) Eng 1984; +30 MA; *cr:* Wilson HS h Grd Coll Prep Eng Tchr 1972-76, 11th Grd Coll Prep Eng Tchr 3rd AP 1976-91, 11th Grd Coll Prep Eng Tchr 1992-; *ai:* AFT 1989, :xec Bd; Distngd Tchr of Hnrs Stdnts 1991; Penn St Univ Scholars me: 325 Vinemont Rd Reinholds PA 17569

:R, PAUL MICHAEL, Elem Physical Education Tchr; *b:* Reading, Christine Leah ONeal; *ed:* Messiah Coll (BS) Elem Ed 1994; *cr:* rethren Chrstn Schl 2nd Grd Tchr 1994-95, Var Bsbl Coach 1994-, : Tchr 1995-; *ai:* Field Day Coord; *office:* Grace Brethren Christian)1 Surratts Rd Clinton MD 20735

:R, DIANE L., Physical Education Teacher; *b:* Middletown, NY; l CT St (BS) PE 1973; Orange Cty Comm Coll PE, Recreation attnd East Stroudsburg St Coll; *cr:* Enlarged City Schl Dist of own PE Tchr 1973-; *ai:* Girls Var Soc; NSCAA 1992-; *office:* Twin MS 112 Grand Ave Middletown NY 10940

:R, NORMAN, Instrumental Music Teacher; *b:* Poughkeepsie, Norman III; *ed:* Eastman Schl of Music (BM) Ed 1968s; SUNY at ı; Buffalo St Univ; SUNY at Oswebo; Coll of ST Rose; West St Univ; UNC at Raleigh; *ai:* Onondage Civic Symphony, ga Music Edctrs Wing Ensemble 1st BAssoon; Euphonium, Bass ne Skaneateles Brass; MENC, NYSSMA 1964-; TUBA; N Amer and Assoc 1981-; *office:* Baldwinsville Cntrl Schls E Oneida St ısville NY 13027

, BEVERLY A., Secondary Mathematics Teacher; *b:* Buffalo, NY; hael W.; *c:* Jeffrey, Kimberly, Timothy; *ed:* Buffalo St Coll (BS) Math Ed 1968, (MS) Scndry Ed 1970; *cr:* Frontier Sr High Math 985-; *ai:* AFT 1979-; AMTNYS 1992-; Phi Delta Kappa 1994-; Frontier Central HS 4432 Bay View Rd Hamburg NY 14075

, BJ, Poetry Instructor; *b:* Union, NJ; *ed:* Stockton Coll (BA) Lit yracuse Univ (MA) Creative Writing 1991; *cr:* NJ St Cncl on the riters in the Schls Prgm 1991-; Arts HS Poetry Instr 1994-; *ai:* Pub Not Rose Petals-17 Love Poems with No Despair; Landing in Soft Hands 1994 Pub by North Atlantic Books; NJ St Cncl on Arts of St Poetry Fellowship 1994-95; *office:* Middlesex County Arts Somerset St New Brunswick NJ 08901

CHERYL S., Fourth Grade Teacher; *b:* Fremont, OH; *m:* Thomas :: Kristen; *ed:* Bowling Green St Univ (BS) Elem Ed 1976; 25 Post rs at MSJ, Heilderburg & Drake Univ; *cr:* Field Elem 4th Grd Tchr ai: Lang Arts Writing Comm Mem; NEA, OEA 1977-.

CORY REED, English Teacher; *b:* Cleveland, OH; *ed:* Bowling St Univ (BS) Comm 1985; OH St Univ 5 Hrs Theatre Dept; *cr:* e Yth Ctr Eng Tchr 1986-88; Highland HS Eng Tchr 1989-; *ai:* Dir; Yrbk Adv; NEA, OEA 1985-; Mt Vernon Players 1990-, Actor, okie of Yr 1986; Employee of Month 1987; *office:* Highland HS Rts 229 & 314 Sparta OH 43350*

, CRYSTAL D., Soc Stud Dept Head & Govt Tchr; *b:* Fort Fairfield, Erica Watson; *ed:* Univ of ME (BS) His, Pol Sci-Graduated With tion 1973; *cr:* Crosby Jr HS Tchr 1973-80; Lewiston HS Soc Stud ead, Tchr 1980-; *ai:* Mock Trial Team Coach; Cert, Safe & Drug chl, Common Ground Grant Comms; St Task Force on Dispensing tion; Lewiston Ed Assn 1973-, Pres, Geneva Kirk Awd; ME Ed Assn Govt Relations Comm; NEA 1973-, Rep Assembly Del; Boosters United Meth Church 1980-; Lewiston Aspiration Partnership 5, Steering Comm; Delta Kappa Gamma Soc Intnl 1976-, Local eneva Kirk, Golden Apple, Prof Image, Russell Galt, Amer Legion Pub in NEA Today; *office:* Lewiston HS 156 East Ave Lewiston ME

, DANIEL J., Social Studies Teacher; *b:* Jersey City, NJ; *ed:* s Univ (BA) His, Pol Sci 1989; Univ of MA at Amherst (MA) His *cr:* Bayonne HS Soc Stud Tchr 1992-; *ai:* Yrbk Adv; NJEA 1992-; :l for Soc Stud 1994-; Bayonne His Soc 1998-; Irelands 32 1992-; Dodge Summer Fellow; NJ Cncl For Hum Seminar Participant; bia Scholastic Press 2nd Place Awd for 1996 Garnet & White HS

, DARLENE R., Spanish & Math Teacher; *b:* Bangor, ME; *m:* nt; *c:* Susan, Nancy; *cr:* Belfast Chrstn Acad Ace Monitor, Span 983-90; Temple Acad HS Span Tchr, Jr High Math Tchr 1991-; *ai:* lub, Soph Class, Jr Class, Sr Class Advs; *office:* Temple Acad 60 W Rd Waterville ME 04901

, DAVID LEIGH, Third Grade Teacher; *b:* Bangor, ME; *m:* nce Van Sant; *c:* Margaret, Daniel, Anna; *ed:* Univ of MA at Boston sych 1975; New England Coll 24 Addl Hrs; Antioch of New England Hrs; Keene St 6 Addl Hrs; UNH 3 Addl Hrs; *cr:* Hollis MS 6th Grd 976-79; Hollis Elem Schl 6th Grd Tchr 1979-94, 3rd Grd Tchr 1994-; ff Dev, Sci Curr, Restructuring Comms; Pupil Prsnl Chair; Math Curr NEA 1976-; Hollis Ed Assn 1976-, Bldg Rep 1995-; Prof Ski Instrs er 1994-; BSA 1993-, Comm Mem Liason; Church Yth Group 5, Adv; Church Deacon 1984-94; *office:* Hollis Elem Schl 36 Silver Rd Hollis NH 03049

, DENISE LOGOZZO, Spanish Teacher; *b:* Canton, OH; *m:* el A.; *ed:* Kent St Univ (BA) Span 1990; Eng Cert, Grad Stud Walsh *cr:* United HS Span, Eng Tchr 1992-; *ai:* Span Club, Frosh Chrldng, ne, Majorette Adv; Asst Var Track Coach; Newspaper Past Adv; Prins ng Comm; NEA, OEA 1992-; Carroll Cty Historical Soc 1988-; 2252 Southeast Blvd Salem OH 44460

), ELIZABETH LOWE, 3rd Grade Teacher; *b:* Cincinnati, OH; *m:* el R.; *c:* Zachary, Kaitlyn; *ed:* Univ of Cincinnati (BA) Elem Ed *cr:* Springmyer Elem Tchr 1984-; *office:* Charles W Springmyer Sch 4179 Ebenezer Rd Cincinnati OH 45248

), GILDA P. HUNTINGTON, Science Teacher & Yrbk Adv; *b:* , NY; *m:* Matthew James; *c:* Adam N.; *ed:* Alfred St Coll (AAS) Med 976; SUC at Potsdam (BA) Bio 1978; Attnd SUC at Oneonta; *cr:* m Industries Plating Chemist 1978-81; Local Schls Sub Tchr 32; Valley Hghts Chrstn Acad Sci & Hlth Tchr & Yrbk Adv 1982-85 0-; *ai:* 9th & 10th Grd Adv; Former 4-H Ldr; Judge for Sci Fair; NYS of Chrstn Schls; Calvary Bapt Church 1982-, Soloist; United Citizens ailford 1978-, Pres; United Citizens of NY 1979-, Sec; Yrbk ation 1985; *office:* Valley Heights Christian Acad 75 Calvary Dr ch NY 13815

), JAY A., Honors Eng Prof & Dept Chair; *b:* Shelbyville, IN; *m:* een A. Frosch; *ed:* Butler Univ (BA) Eng 1965; IN Cntrl Univ (MA) 970; Ball St Univ (PHD) Eng 1977; Kent St Univ Sabbatical Stud Comm Theory 1985; *cr:* Warren Cntrl HS Eng Tchr, Debate Coach 1966-75; Ball St Univ Doctoral Fellow, Instr 1975-78; Thiel Coll Eng Prof 1978-; *ai:* Forensics Dir; Mid Sts Task Force on Enrollment Chair; Act 101 Advy Bd; Western Hum Coord; Honors Prgm Comm Chair; MLA, NEMLA, CEA, PCEA, NCTE, CCCC, NCHC, AFA, NFA, Bryon Soc, ACR, NAASR; Mid East Honor Assn, Pres; ACLU; Sharon Lifelong Learning Cncl; Book The Critical Reputation of Byrons Don Juan in Britain; 8 Articles; 20 Conf Papers, 6 Wkshps; Lily Endowment Schlsp; Luth Higher Ed Sabbatical Grant; *office:* Thiel Coll 75 College Ave Greenville PA 16125

WARD, JEFFREY PHILLIP, SS, PE Teacher & Asst Prin; *b:* Newport, VT; *m:* Cheryl Trottier; *c:* Tara, Megan; *ed:* Johnson St Coll (BS) Elem K-6, Spec Ed & PE K-12 1977; Addl 21 Credits; UVM 22 Credits; *cr:* Montgomery Elem Schl Tchr, Asst Prin 1977-; *ai:* Soccer 5th-8th Grd, 5th-6th Grd Bsktbl, 7th-8th Grd Sftbl Coach; St Jude's Bike-a-Thon, Jump Rope for Heart, 5th-8th Grd Field Trips Coord; Model Schl Team; NEA 1989-; NCUHS Bd 1990-; Outstdng VT Tchr Awd 1993; *office:* Montgomery Elem Schl 9 Montgomery VT 05471

WARD, JOHN THOMAS, Art Teacher; *b:* Massena, NY; *m:* Jane Squires; *c:* Liam Robert; *ed:* Niagara Univ (BS) Pre-Law, Criminal Justice 1980; SUNY at Plattsburg (MA) Art Ed 1989; Syracuse Univ (MA) Illustration 1992; St Lawrence Univ NYS Tchr Cert; SUNY at Potsdam Fine Arts Grad Credit; *cr:* ALCOA Security, Fire Fighter 1983-85; Saranac Lake HS Art Tchr 1986-; North Cntry Comm Coll Art Tchr 1994-95; *ai:* Weightroom Coach; Hnr Soc Comm; Graphic Artist Guild 1991-; NYSUT 1996, Pres; Local NYSUT 1995-, VP; Massena Jaycees 1984-85; Saranac Lake Young Arts Assn 1995-; Saranac Lake Village Winters Carnival Chamberlan 1989-; Illustrated for Publishers; Work Displayed; Portraits; Art Work Featured; *office:* Saranac Lake HS La Pan Hwy Saranac Lake NY 12983*

WARD, KAREN ANN, Business Teacher; *b:* Orange, NJ; *c:* Desare T.; *ed:* Mont St Coll (BA) St Coll (BA) Bus Ed 1975; Essex Cty Coll Pre-Bus 1972; Seton Hall Univ Child Psych 1995-; 25 Credit Hrs Mont St Coll; *cr:* Essex Cty Coll Adj Bus EducTchr 1995-; Abraham Clark HSBus Ed Tchr 1976-; *ai:* FBLA Adv 1992-94; Diversity 2000 Adv 1995-; Yrbk Adv 1985-90; NJEA, NJBEA 1976-.

WARD, KENNETH F., Fifth Grade Teacher; *b:* Newark, NJ; *m:* Theresa Lorenzo; *c:* Kenneth Jr., Kellianne; *ed:* Monmouth Coll (BS) Elem Ed 1972, (MS) Admin, Supervision 1980; *cr:* Marlboro Elem Schl Tchr 23 Yrs; *ai:* NEA, NJEA, MTTA 1973; *office:* Marlboro Elem Schl 100 School Rd W Marlboro NJ 07746

WARD, KENNETH VANDIVER, Chemistry Teacher; *b:* Westernport, MD; *m:* Laura Virginia Tibbetts; *c:* Kenneth V. Jr., Molly B.; *ed:* Potomac St Coll (AA) Bio 1950; WV Univ (BA) Chem & Bio 1950; attnd Univ of Pittsburgh, Frostburgh St Coll; *cr:* Parke-Davis Salesman 1958-61; Ft Ashby HS Tchr 1961-64; Southern HS Tchr & Vice-Prin 1964-67; Bruce HS Tchr 1967-90; Westmar HS Tchr 1990-; *ai:* NEA 1961-; MSTA 1967-; ACTA 1967-; *home:* 80 Maple Ave Keyser WV 26726

WARD, LEO J., Adjunct Psychology Instructor; *b:* Paterson, NJ; *m:* Eileen Mead; *c:* Dan, Mark, Kim; *ed:* Cath Univ of Amer at Washington (BA) Philosophy 1971; Ball St Univ at Muncie (MA) Counseling & Psych 1974; Our Lady of the Lake Univ at San Antonio (MSW) Soc Work 1977; Cert in Leadership & Communication at Plattsburgh St Univ 1982; *cr:* Chapman Coll Psych Adjunct Fac 1975-76; Clinton Comm Coll Soc Work Adjunct Fac 1982-83; Boston Univ Placement Supvr & Counseling 1984-86; USAF Acad FT, Psych & Sociology Fac 1986-90; Clinton Comm Coll Psych Adjunct Fac 1991-; *ai:* Psych Club Asst Adv; Natl Assn of Soc Workers 1977-; NAADAC 1986-; Cntrl NY Psych Assn 1992-; Amer Assn Counseling & Dev 1987-; Lic Clinical Soc Worker NY 1995-; Lic Counselor CO 1990-; Natl Cert Counselor 1987-; Natl Cert Alcohol Counselor 1990-; Bd Cert Clinical Soc Work 1988-; Air Force Meriterious Medals 5 Times; Air Force Commendation Medals 3 Times; Whos Who Among Human Svc Profs 1987-88; Jr Officer of The Yr 1980 & 1984; *office:* Clinton Comm Coll Bluff Point Rd Plattsburgh NY 12901*

WARD, LINDA M., General & Vocal Music Teacher; *b:* Muncy, PA; *m:* David J.; *c:* Scott Mc Donald, Kristen Mc Donald; *ed:* West Chester St Univ (BS) Music Ed 1967; 12 Hrs Post Grad; *cr:* Watsontown Elem Schl K-6 Grd Music Tchr 1967-70; Duboistown Elem Schl K-6 Grd Music Tchr 1975-84; Messiah Nursery Schl Tchr 1984-85; South Williamsport Jr-Sr HS 7-12 Grd Gen, Vocal Tchr 1984-; *ai:* Schl Vocal Jazz Ensemble; Musical Theater Dir; MENC, PMEA 1984-; ACDA 1996; Messiah Luth Church 1978-; Audubon Soc, Northcent PA Conservancy 1991-; Civic Chorus; *office:* South Williamsport Jr/Sr HS 700 Percy St South Williamsport PA 17701*

WARD, LISA, English Teacher & Dept Chprsn; *b:* Mineola, NY; *ed:* SUNY at Stony Brook (BA) Eng 1980, (MS) Technological Systems Mngmt 1988; Post-Grad Stud in Educl Admin & Supervision St John's Univ, Shakespearean Stud Univ of London 1978-79; *cr:* H. Frank Carey HS Eng Tchr 1981-83; CT General Insurance Co Sr Benefit Analyst 1983-85; St Catharine Acad Eng Tchr, Chprsn 1985-; *ai:* Moderator Adopt-A-Station Prgm, NHS, Raven Lit Magazine; Pres Fac Assn; Dir SAT Prgm; Coord Cmptr Sci 1988-90; Evaluation, Blue Ribbon Comms; Bronx Bd of Realtor's Essay Contest Dir; Police Commissioner Essay Contest; NCTE 1987-; NCEA 1985-; ASCD 1988-; Amer Creativity Assn 1993-; *office:* Saint Catharine Acad 2250 Williamsbridge Rd Bronx NY 10469

WARD, MARCIA BALMUT, Sub Abuse Prevention Coord; *b:* Springfield, OH; *m:* Gregory Dow; *c:* Katherine, Vincent, Anthony; *ed:* Wittenberg Univ (BS) Bio HPED Ed 1968; Univ of Dayton Working on MS Ed; *cr:* Georgesville Schl for Emotionally Disturbed K-6th Grd Tchr 1968-69; Miami E Local Schls Jr High Sci Tchr 1969-74; Graham Local Schls HS Bio & Substance Abuse Tchr 1974-; Champaign Cty Schls Teen Pregnancy Prevention; Gifted Tchr & Title I Coord 1994-; OH Dept Transportation Curr Writer; *ai:* DARE Cncl; CHAPTER; Champaigne Cty Teenage Sexuality & Pregnancy Prevention Adv; 4-H ldr 15 Yrs; Intl Schl to Schl Experience 1982-87, Bd 1977-87; St Paris Antique Study Club 1980-, Pres; Champaign Cty Heart Dr 1981-, Chm; St Paris Lib 1990-, Bd of Trustee, Grant Writer, Pres; German Import 1994-, Owner; Westville U Meth Church, Choir & Sunday Schl Tchr, Flame Awd; Pride & OH Parents for Drug Free Yth Schlshp; Martha Holden Jennings Grant Title I; Childrens Intl Summer Village USA Del; KTA Grant 1981; Article Pub; Who's Who in Amer Women in the Midwest; *home:* 156 Eris Rd Urbana OH 43078*

WARD, MARY KATHRYN, English Teacher; *b:* Lockport, NY; *ed:* SUC at Geneseo (BS) Scndry Eng Ed 1964; SUC at Buffalo (MS) Scndry Eng Ed 1969; SUC at Brockport (MS) Counseling 1983; *cr:* Canandaigua Acad Eng Tchr 1964-65; Niagara Wheatfield HS Eng Tchr 1965-70; Wheatland Chili HS Eng Tchr 1970-; *ai:* NCTE 1964-; UFT, NYSUT, WCFT 1970-, Schlsp Chprsn; *office:* Wheatland Chili HS 940 North Rd Scottsville NY 14546

WARD, MATTHEW, Mathematics Teacher; *b:* Ogdensburg, NY; *m:* Lynnette Ann Horn; *c:* Lindsay Ann, Eric Matthew; *ed:* SUNY at Brockport (BS) Math 1989; *cr:* Merrimack Vly MS Math Tchr 1989-91; Tobey Schl Job Trng Tchr 1992-95 Summers; John Stark Regnl HS Math Tchr 1991-; *ai:* JV Bsktbl Coach; NEA; NCTM; ATMNE; Yth League T-Ball Coach; Paul Douglas Natl Tchrs Schlsp; *office:* John Stark Regional HS N Stark Hwy Weare NH 03281

WARD, NANCY HANNA, English 2nd Language Teacher; *b:* San Diego, CA; *m:* Robert D.; *c:* Leah Eve, Tai Hanna; *ed:* San Diego St (BA) Span 1978; Salisbury St (MEd) Guid 1990; 74 Addl Credits; Biling, ESL Credential San Diego St Univ 1979; Math Cert Univ of DE; *cr:* Sweetwater Schl Dist Biling, Math Tchr 1981-83; Indian River Schl Dist Span, Math Tchr 1983-91, Migrant Ed Tchr 1991-94, Eng 2nd Lang Tchr 1994-; *ai:* NEA 1983-; Del Lim Eng Prof 1991-; PTO 1990-; Beta Sigma Phi 1985-, Sec, Treas; DE St Math Study 1985-86; *office:* Sussex Central HS 301 W Market St Georgetown DE 19947

WARD, PATRICIA ANN, Literature & Soc Studies Tchr; *b:* Springvale, ME; *m:* Peter; *c:* Timothy, Shannon, Sean; *ed:* Gorham St Tchrs Coll (BA) Ed 1964; Fairfield Univ (MA) 1976; *cr:* Fairfield Pub Schls 5th Grd Tchr 5 Yrs; Our Lady of Assumption Schl Jr HS Tchr 18 Yrs; *ai:* NEA 1978-; *office:* Our Lady of Assumption Schl 605 Stratford Rd Fairfield CT 06432

WARD, PATRICIA LYNNE, 4th Grade Teacher; *b:* Wooster, OH; *ed:* Warren Wilson Coll (AA) Ed 1966; Berea Coll (BS) Ed 1968; Towson St Univ (MED) Ed 1977; *cr:* Hillsdale Elem Schl 4th Grd Tchr 1968-; *ai:* GATE, Fac Advy, Cmptr Comms; Grd Level Chprsn; *home:* 815 Martin Rd Havre De Grace MD 21078

WARD, PATRICIA M., English & Humanities Teacher; *b:* Boston, MA; *ed:* Emmanuel Coll (BA) Eng 1964; Univ of VA (MA) Eng 1965; Attnd Boston Coll, Univ of Redlands; *cr:* Randolph Jr Sr HS Tchr, Eng Chm 1966-; *ai:* Acad Tutor, Coach; NCTE; Randolph Tchrs Assn; MA Cncl of Tchrs of Eng; Golden Apple Awd; *office:* Randolph Jr Sr HS 70 Memorial Pky Randolph MA 02368

WARD, RONALD F., Science Teacher; *b:* Cincinnati, OH; *c:* Ian, Joshua, Sarah; *ed:* Univ of Cincinnati (BS) Earth Sci 1978; 6 Addl Hrs Earth Sci Purdue Univ; Environmental Ed, Project Discovery Miami Univ; *cr:* Peoples MS Tchr, Coach 1978-; *ai:* Bsktbl Coach; Ath Dir; MZSE Coord; NSTA 1992-; ASCD 1991-; DAV 1974-; Learning Links Grant 1995; Tchr of Yr 1993; *office:* Peoples MS 3030 Erie Ave Cincinnati OH 45208*

WARD, ROSEMARY, English Teacher; *b:* Philadelphia, PA; *c:* John, Anthony; *ed:* LaSalle Univ (BA) Eng 1984; Beaver Coll 24 Credit Hrs; PWP 20 Hrs; *cr:* Archdiocese of Philadelphia Tchr 1986-; *ai:* SAP Team Chair; FCC & Press Coord; NEA 1987-; *office:* Roman Catholic HS 301 N Broad St Philadelphia PA 19111*

WARD, SHAWN MICHAEL, Math Teacher; *b:* Portsmouth, VA; *m:* Becky; *c:* Michael, Derek, Kelly; *ed:* Bob Jones Univ (BA) Bible 1988, (MA) Bible 1989; *cr:* Hilton Night Auditor 1987-89; Faith Bapt Church, Acad Tchr, Tth Pastor 1989-; *ai:* Girls, Boys Soccer, Boys Var Bsktbl Coach; *office:* Faith Baptist Acad 7312 Van Buren Rd Baldwinsville NY 13027

WARD, SHERRILL REIGLE, Soc Stud Tchr & Dept Chprsn; *b:* Ithaca, NY; *m:* William Jeffery; *ed:* Ithaca Coll (BS) Soc Stud 1983; SUNY at Cortland (MS) Ed 1987; *cr:* Newark Valley HS Soc Stud Tchr 1983-, Soc Stud Dept Chair 1992-; *ai:* Sr Class Adv; Resource Dev Team; NYSUT 1983-; *office:* Newark Valley HS 68 Wilson Creek Rd Newark Valley NY 13811

WARD, STUART GROEL, English Teacher; *b:* New York, NY; *m:* Linda Johnson; *ed:* Colgate Univ (BA) Eng 1985; Bread Loaf Schl of Eng Middlebury Coll (MA) 1995; *cr:* Avon Old Farms Schl Eng Tchr 1986-89; Montclair Kimberley Acad Eng Tchr 1991-; *ai:* Adv; *home:* 22 Saint Lukes Pl Apt 44 Montclair NJ 07042

WARD, SUSAN MILLER, Eng & Creative Writing Teacher; *b:* Chester, PA; *m:* David B.; *c:* Jason B., Evan C.; *ed:* Salisbury St Coll (BA) Eng & Scndry Ed 1976; Salisbury St Univ (MED) Ed 1985; *cr:* Wicomico HS 10th Grd Eng, 11th Grd Gifted & Talented Eng & 12th Grd Eng, Creative Writing, Speech Commnctn & Drama Tchr 1976-; *ai:* HS Lit Magazine Adv; Stu Behavior Mgmt Team Mem; Fac Advy Comm Elected Rep; WCEA 1976-; Wicomico Cty HS Tchr of Yr 1991; *office:* Wicomico HS 201 Long Ave Salisbury MD 21801

WARD, THOMAS JOHN, 9th-10th Grade English Teacher; *b:* Coaldale, PA; *m:* Ruth Ann Steele; *c:* Lauren, Emily; *ed:* PA St Univ (AA) Mass Comm 1981; Bloomsburg Univ (BS) Scndry Ed & Comm 1984; Grad Work at Wilkes Univ, Kutztown Univ & Penn St Univ; *cr:* Nativity BVM HS Eng Tchr 1986-; *ai:* Stage Crew & Peer Listener Moderator; Stu Asst Team; NCTE & NCEA 1986-; *office:* Nativity BVM HS 1 Lawtons Hill Pottsville PA 17901

WARD, W. JEFFERY, PE Teacher & Coach; *b:* Springfield, MA; *m:* Sherrill L. Reigle; *ed:* SUNY at Cortland (BS) PE & Bio 1973; Permanent Cert in PE, Gen Sci & Bio fron NY St; *cr:* Tioga Cty Boys Club PE & Hlth Dir 1973-74; Newark Valley Tchr, Ath Dir, Coach, Adv 1974-; *ai:* Tennis & Wrestling Coach; Var Club Adv; Jr Class Adv; PE Dept Chm; Exec Comm of Interscholastic Ath Conf; Various Other Comm in Schl Dist; NYSUT & AFT 1974-; NYSHPERD 1982-; Owego Meth Church 1980-, Trustee Comm & Admin Comm; Var Ftbl Coach 18 Yrs; Girls Track Coach 14 Yrs; Boys Track Coach 15 Yrs; 4 Pub Articles; Ath Dir 12 Yrs; Southern Zone of NY Ath Dir of the Yr 1991; Teams Won 5 Ftbl Championships; 5 Girls Track & 6 Boys Track Championships; Various Comm within our League (IAC) & Section IV of NYS from 1979-; *office:* Newark Valley HS 68 Wilson Ck Rd Newark Valley NY 13811

WARD, WENDY L., Mathematics Teacher; *b:* Catskill, NY; *ed:* SUC at Cortland (BS) Ed 1979; SUNY at Albany (MS) Ed 1986; *cr:* Greenville Jr Sr HS Math Tchr 1980-; *ai:* Coaching Girls Soccer, Girls Bsktbl; Grade Level Ldr; Continental Math League Co-Adv; NCTM 1993-; NYSUT-AFT 1980-; Club Soccer Coach 1992-; Church Benevolence Comm 1992-; *office:* Greenville Jr/Sr HS Rt 81 Greenville NY 12083

WARDE, DIANE ROSE, Spanish Teacher; *b:* Perth Amboy, NJ; *m:* Alan M.; *c:* Michael A., Christopher J.; *ed:* Niagara Univ (BA) Span Ed 1975; St Univ of NY at Albany (MA) Ed 1979; *cr:* Mack's Svc Ctrs Inc Office Mgr 1971-79; Shenendehowa Cntrl Schls Sub Tchr 1975-76; Manufacturers Hanover Trust Co Asst Branch Mgr 1979-82; Doane Stuart Schl 7-12 Grd Span Tchr 1988-; *ai:* Span Club, Sr Class, DS Chptr Amnesty Intnl Adv; Trips Abroad Chaperone; Amer Assn Tchrs of Span & Portuguese 1990-; Delta Epsilon Sigma 1975-; St Helen's Church 1982-, Eucharist Minister, Rel Ed Tchr; NEH Grant 1992; *office:* Doane Stuart Schl 799 S Pearl St Albany NY 12202

WARDE, ROBERT M., Math, German & History Teacher; *b:* Brooklyn, NY; *m:* Janet P. Powers; *c:* Andrew, Peter, Elizabeth, Sarah, Anna; *ed:* Lafayette Coll (BA) Math & Ger 1976; Dartmouth Coll (MA) Rel 1986; Pensacola Chrstn Coll (MA) Bible 1989; *cr:* Raymond HS 7th-12th Grd Math Tchr & Coach 1977-78; Kearsange Regnl MS 7th Grd Math Tchr & Coach 1978-84; Henniker HS 7th-12th Grd Math Tchr & Coach 1984-87; Trinity Chrstn Schl Tchr, Coach, Disciplinarian & Scndry Supvr 1987-; *ai:* Boys Bsktbl, IM Vllybl, Sftbl & Hnr Soc Coach; AACS 1987-; NHACS 1987-; Trinity Bapt Church 1983-, Deacon, Sunday Schl Supt, Sunday Schl Tchr & Choir Mem; White House Presidential Scholar Most Influential Tchr; Yrbk Dedication; *office:* Trinity Christian Schl 80 Clinton St Concord NH 03301*

WARDEINER, MARK RICHARD, 6th Grade Teacher; *b:* Euclid, OH; *m:* Nada B.; *c:* Danielle, Alan; *ed:* Cleveland St (BA) Elem Ed 1988, (MS) Curr, Instr 1992; Addl 45 Credit Hrs; *cr:* Lake Elem Schl 5th Grd Tchr 1988-90; Rice Elem Schl 4th Grd Tchr 1990-92; Garfield Elem Schl 6th Grd Tchr 1992-; *ai:* Var Asst Soccer Coach Mentor; Cmptr Coord; System Wide Tech Comm; Mentor Tchrs Assn 1988-; Outstdng Edctr Awd from Meml Jr HS Stu Cncl; *home:* 5960 Silver Ct Mentor OH 44060

WARDELL, PATRICK JOSEPH, Professor of Social Work; *b:* Erie, PA; *c:* Patrick J. II; *ed:* Gannon Univ (BS) Sociology 1963; SUNY at Buffalo (MSW) Soc Work 1967; PA St Univ (PHD) Soc Welfare, Adm Justice Planning 1983; *cr:* PA St Univ Asst Prof 1972-73; Gannon Univ Asst Prof 1973-74; PA St Univ Instr, Asst Prof 1974-88; Lock Haven Univ Assoc Prof 1988-93, Prof 1993-; *ai:* Field Work Coord; Soc Work Club Adv; Natl Assn Soc Workers 1967-, PA Chptr Pres, Del, West Cntrl Div Soc Wk of Yr; Cncl Soc Work Ed; Book Reviews; 3 Articles; *office:* Lock Haven Univ 106 Thomas Field House Annex Lock Haven PA 17745

WARDROP, JAMES RICHMOND, Photography Teacher; *b:* Pittsburgh, PA; *ed:* Brooks Inst (BA) Photography 1972; Kodak Mrktg Ed Ctr 1974; Grad Stud 1990; *cr:* Saigon Schl of Fine Arts Photography Instr 1968-69; Sewickley YMCA Photography Instr 1982; Sewickley Acad Photography Instr 1975-; *ai:* Schl Pub Relations, Yrbk, Newspaper, Ath Photography; Sports Pub Relations; Photographic Soc of Amer; Soc of Photo Edctrs; *office:* Sewickley Acad 315 Academy Ave Sewickley PA 15143

WARE, RUTH PORTER, Eighth Grade Teacher; *b:* Newark, OH; *m:* Wendell Ross; *c:* Todd; *ed:* OH St Univ (BA) Elem Ed 1972; *cr:* Hopewell Elem Schl Fifth Grd Tchr 1963-65, Kndgtn Tchr 1965-66; Hopewell Jr HS 7th Grd Math Tchr 1968-74; West Muskingum MS 8th Grd Math, Lang Arts Tchr 1974-95; *ai:* Math Counts Coach; Team Ldr; RPDC Dist Comm; Sites Coord; West M Tchrs Assn 1963-, Past Pres; OEA, NEA 1963-; Delta Kappa Gamma 1986-, St Trust Bd; NCTM, OCTM 1980-; MCCTM 1980-, Past Pres; Bethesda Hosp Guild 1991-; Alumni Vol Band 1986-; Bldg Tchr of Yr; Dist Tchr of Yr; Jennings Scholar; Outstdng Math Tchr of OCTM; *office:* West Muskingum MS 100 Kimes Rd Zanesville OH 43701

WARE, SHERRI COX, Jr HS His & Sci Teacher; *b:* Steubenville, OH; *m:* Rod; *c:* Shannon; *ed:* Bethany Coll (BA) PE & His 1972; Univ of Steubenville (BA) 1st-8th Elem Ed 1988; 22 Hrs Toward Masters; *cr:* Jefferson Cty Christian Schl Jr HS His & Sci Tchr 1984-; *ai:* Bsktbl Coach; Math Olympics, Geography Bee, Bible Club & Prayer Room Adv; Stu Cncl Adv; Jefferson Cty Historical Soc 1988-; *office:* Jefferson Cty Christian Schl 2501 Commercial St Mingo Junction OH 43938*

WARG, ASTRIDA K., German Teacher; *b:* Mannheim, Germany; *m:* Dennis E.; *c:* Kristoffer, Erik D.; *ed:* Lycoming Coll (BA) Ger Scndry Ed 1967; Trenton St Univ (MED) Guid, Cnslng 1973; *cr:* Bensalem HS Ger Tchr 1967-73, Guid Cnslr 1974-75; Council Rock HS Ger Tchr 1989-; *ai:* Chrldng Adv 1967-69; Ger Club, Chess Tournament Adv; NEA 1989-; PSEA 1967-; CREA, AATH 1989-; Ger Soc 1989-; Achvmt Cert of AATG; *office:* Council Rock HS 62 Swamp Rd Newtown PA 18940

WARG, MARGARET BOYLE, French Teacher; *b:* Hazeleton, PA; *m:* Charles R.; *ed:* Marywood Coll (AB) Fr 1965, (MS) Eng 1970; Bloomsburg Univ (MEd) Fr 1975; Supervisory Cert in Foreign Lang; 45 Addl Credits from Univ of Scranton, Coll Misericordia, & Penn St Univ; *cr:* Hazleton HS Tchr & Dept Chair 1965-92; Hazleton Area HS Tchr & Dept Chair 1992-; *ai:* Societe Honoraire De Franchia Adv; Stu Trip to France Tchr & Cnslr; NEA, PSEA, & HAEA 1965; PA St Modern Lang Assn 1975; Amer Assn of Tchrs of Fr 1970; Outstanding Young Ed; Hazleton Area Jaycees; PEARL Awd; Hazleton YM YWCA; Honors Outstanding Prof Women; *office:* Hazleton Area HS 1601 W 23rd St Hazleton PA 18201

WARGO, EUGENE M., Physics Teacher; *b:* Pittsburgh, PA; *m:* Sandra Hitt; *c:* Robert, Debra; *ed:* California Univ of PA (BSEd) Physics 1967; Univ of WI (MS) Physics 1972; Univ of Pittsburgh 60 Plus Credit Hrs; *cr:* Bethel Park HS Physics Tchr 29 Yrs; Part-Time Coll Physics Tchr 15 Yrs; *ai:* Sci Club Adv; AFT 1968-; NSTA 1975-; Univ of Pittsburgh Visiting Scholars Prgm; *office:* Bethel Park Sr HS 309 Church Rd Bethel Park PA 15102*

WARGO, ROBERT JOSEPH, Social Studies Teacher; *b:* Mt Carmel, PA; *m:* Joan A. Williams; *c:* Laura, Keith, Michael, Natalie; *ed:* IN Univ of PA (BSEd) Soc Stud 1974; Trenton St (MED) Soc Stud 1980; Attnd Villanova Univ Cmptr Literacy, East Stroudsburg Cooperating Ed Motivation, Wilkes Coll Tchng Through Learning Changes; *cr:* Delhaas HS Soc Stud Tchr 1974; Bensalem Sr HS Soc Stud Tchr 1974-; *ai:* Asst Ftbl Coach; Mentor for Soc Stud Tchrs; NEA, PSEA, BTEA 1974-; Visited Schls in Former Soviet Union & Lectured on Soviet Culture, Ed; *office:* Bensalem Twp Sr HS 4319 Hulmeville Rd Bensalem PA 19020

WARING, RICHARD DANA, Technology Education Teacher; *b:* Hartford, CT; *m:* Joan M.; *c:* Wayne E., Sharon M., Kevin L.; *ed:* Univ of NM (BS) Indstrl Arts Ed 1969; Cntrl CT St Univ (MS) Schl Cnslng 1989; Transitional Wkshps; *cr:* Portland HS Indstrl Arts Tchr 1969-81; Porter & Chester Inst Drafting, Design Tchr 1983-85; Putnam HS Cooperative Work Ed 1985-86; Manchester HS Indstrl Arts Tchr 1986-87; Montville HS Tech Ed Tchr 1987-; *ai:* NEASC Evaluation, Schl to Career Dev, Stu Recognition Comms; TSA Adv; US First Robotics Competition Co-Adv; ITEA 1965-; CTEA, NEA 1969-; *office:* Montville HS Old Colchester Rd Oakdale CT 06370

WARMAN, DONALD EDWARD, Jr High Math Teacher; *b:* Cleveland, OH; *ed:* Univ of Dayton (MS) Guid 1983; Cuyahoga Comm Coll Assoc Acctng 1973; Cleveland St Univ Bachelors Elem Ed 1977; *cr:* Ottawa Elem Schl Jr High Math Tchr 1977-; *ai:* 8th Grd Boys Bsktbl; 7th & 8th Grd Girls & Boys Track; NEA 1977-; OEA 1977-; Ottawa-Glandorf Assoc 1977-; Comm Policing 1994-, Advy Bd; *office:* Ottawa Elem Schl 751 E 4th St Ottawa OH 45875

WARMAN, LINDA K., English Dept Chair & AP Instr; *b:* Indiana, PA; *ed:* Moravian Coll (BA) Eng 1964; PA St Univ, Kutztown Univ, Lehigh Univ M Equiv Comprehensive Eng 1969; 3 Grad Credits Religious Lit of the West PA St Univ; *cr:* Easton Area HS Eng Instr 1964-, Eng Dept Chair 1989-; *ai:* Night Schl Instr; Chair Steering, Negotiations, Implementation Comms; NEA, PSEA 1964-; EAEA 1964-, Past Rep; Bach Choir of Bethlehem 1970-75; Homeowners Assn 1980-, Treas; Outstanding Scndry Educators of Amer 1975; PA St Univ Awd for Distinguished Tchng Scndry Honors Stdnts 1987; Contributor to Book; *office:* Easton Area HS 2601 William Penn Hwy Easton PA 18045*

WARNASCH, SUZANNE WEILL, Eng as a Second Language Tchr; *b:* Bronx, NY; *m:* Albert E. Jr.; *c:* Jill S. Mozier, Christopher A., Jennifer J.; *ed:* Wm Paterson Coll (BA) Eng, His 1964; Working on MAED Human Svcs Ldrshp; Wm Paterson Coll ESL Cert Grad Prgm 1987; Multicultural Ldrshp Inst Rutgers Univ; Foxfire Approach Tchng, Learning Goddard Coll; *cr:* Manchester Regnl HS Eng, SS Tchr 1964-65; Netcong Elem Schl 6-8 Grd Eng Tchr 1966-67; Roxbury Pub Schls K-6 Eng Second Lang Tchr 1984-; *ai:* Adult Ed ESL Mt Olive Pub Schls 1980-; Equity, Human Dignity, Affirmative Action Comm; NJ Tchrs Eng Second, Other Lang 1985-; Amer Assn Univ Women 1994-; NEA, NJEA 1984-; NJ Governor's Tchr Recognition Prgm Awd 1987.

WARNECKE, ROSE MARY KUZMA, Music Education Teacher; *b:* Tiffin, OH; *m:* David J.; *c:* Meghan, Jessica; *ed:* Findlay Coll (BS) Music Ed 1978; 6 Semester Hrs Drake Univ; *cr:* Delphos St John Schl 5th-12th Grd Instrumental Dir 1978-87; Jennings Local Schls K-12th Grd Musci Ed Tchr 1993-; *ai:* Marching, Concert, Pep Bands; HS, Jr HS Choir; HS, 6th Grd Musical Dir; OMFA, MENC 1978-; OEA, NEA, FJEA 1993-, Bldg Rep; Asst Girl Scout Ldr 1994-; St John's Folk Choir 1988-93; St Joseph's Folk Choir 1990-93; St Joseph's HS Choir 1991-94; Soccer Coach 1995-; 1st-2dn Grd Girls Sftbl Coach 1994-95; Putnam Cty Grd Schl Choir Dir 1996; Guest Alumni Dir Findlay Coll Symphonic Band 1980; *office:* Jenning Local Schls Water St PO Box 98 Fort Jennings OH 45844

WARNER, ANDREA SUSAN, High School English Teacher; *b:* Winthrop, MA; *ed:* Salem St Coll (BA) Eng 1967; 30 Hrs Post Grad SUNY System; 90 Hrs Inservice Sponsored Wayne Cntrl Schl Dist; *cr:* Salem HS Eng Tchr 1967-69; Wayne Cntrl Schl Eng Tchr 1970-; *ai:* Tutoring; NEA 1970-, Bldg Rep, VP, Grievance Chprsn, Consitutional Comm; *office:* Wayne Central H S Rt 350 Ontario Center NY 14520

WARNER, D. P., Art Professor; *b:* New Haven, CT; *m:* Carrie Nardie; *c:* Gaia, Cead, Pippa, Iska, Finn Nardie; *ed:* Roanoke Coll (BA) Fine Arts 1976; Univ of AZ (MFA) Painting 1989; Attnd VA Commonwealth Univ, Univ of VA, AZ St Univ; *cr:* Univ of AZ Adj Lecturer 1989; Univ of MT Asst Prof 1989-90; Edinboro Univ of PA Asst Prof 1990-; *ai:* Adv Stu Art League; Planning Comm, Tenure, Evaluation, Curr Comms; Organizer Annual NY City Art, Stu Tour; Fnds Art, Theory, Ed, Assoc Arts Pittsburgh 1993-; Coll Art Assn 1989-; 3 Solo Exhibitions, 6 Juried Exhibitions, 1 Invitational Exhibition, 10 Group Exhibitions; *office:* Edinboro Univ Of PA Edenboro S C PA 16444*

WARNER, DAVID RICHARD, AP Amer His & Psych Teacher; *b:* Pittsburgh, PA; *m:* Barbara Palyo; *c:* Jeffrey M., Janice L., Timothy S.; *ed:* IN Univ of Pa (BA) Ed 1969; 4 Addl Credit Hrs; 30 Credit Hrs Duquesne Univ; *cr:* Brentwood HS Tchr, Coach 1970-; *ai:* Stu Assistance Prgm; Boys, Girls Cross-Cntry, Girls Bsktbl, Girls Sftbl Coach; Brentwood Ed 1970-, Pres; PSEA, NEA 1970-; Brentwood Ath Boosters 1970-; Brentwood Historical Soc Man of Yr; Western PA Sports Hall of Fame; Selected Class AA Girls Coach of Yr Twice; *office:* Brentwood HS 3601 Brownsville Rd Pittsburgh PA 15227

WARNER, MARK MOSHER, Acting Dean & Assoc Professor; *b:* Ithaca, NY; *m:* Susan; *c:* Mark, Amy; *ed:* Monmouth Coll (BA) Ec 1966; Cornell Univ (BS) Hotel Admin 1969; St Univ of NY (MA) Human Resources 1977; Univ of AL (DPA) Pub Admin 1991; *cr:* USAF Pilot, Tchr, Various Staff 1969-89; Univ of New Haven Prof 1989-; *ai:* Eta Sigma Delta; Univ Culinary Club; Numerous Univ Comm; CHRIE, Pi Signa Alpha 1989-; Cornell Soc of Hotel Men 1969-; BSA, Scoutmaster, Dist Awd of Merit; Spec Olympics; Air Univ Review; *office:* Univ Of New Haven 300 Orange Ave West Haven CT 06516*

WARNER, MICHELLE BUTLER, English Dept Chairman, Teacher; *b:* Columbus, OH; *m:* Robert E.; *c:* Megan, Rob; *ed:* PA St Univ (BA) Scndry Ed, Eng 1969; Attnd AZ St Univ, W Maryland Univ Masters Equivalency in Ed, Eng 1974; *cr:* William Penn Sr HS Eng Tchr 1969-75; York College of PA Eng Tchr 1977-82; York Cath HS Eng Tchr 1982-; *ai:* Schl Newspaper, Mock Trial Adv; Eng Dept Chair; Stu Assistance Team Mem; WCTE 1982-; *office:* York Catholic HS 601 E Springettsbury Ave York PA 17403

WARNER, MICHELLE LOUISE, Family & Consumer Sci Teacher; *b:* Barberton, OH; *m:* Jeffrey Scott; *ed:* Univ of Akron (BA) Home Ec, Family Ecology 1991; Credit Hrs, CEU's in Ed, Work & Family Life; *cr:* City of Akron Clerk Typist II 1983-88; Univ of Akron Account Clerk 1988-91; Springfield Local Schls Tchr 1992-; *ai:* Club Adv; Choir Mem; Sunday Schl Tchr; GRADS Advy Comm; NEA 1992-; OVA, AVA 1993-; SLACT 1992-, Bldg Rep; Arlington Church of Nazarene 1993-, Bd Mem; *office:* Springfield HS 2966 Sanitarium Rd Akron OH 44312

WARNER, PATRICIA ANN, English Teacher; *b:* Wooster, OH; *ed:* Coll of Wooster (BA) Eng 1972, (MAT) Eng 1973; *cr:* Orrville HS Eng Tchr 1974-; Wayne Coll Eng Instr 1988-91; *ai:* Jrnlsm Club; NEA 1974-; NCTE, OCTELA 1977-; IRA 1992-; Jennings Scholar 1994-95; Orrville City Schls Tchr of Yr, Orrville HS Tchr of Yr 1987-88; *office:* Orrville HS 841 N Ella St Orrville OH 44667*

WARNER, PEGGY MILLS, Music Teacher; *b:* Hillsboro, OH; *c:* Ernest L. III; *ed:* Conservatory of Music (BMEd) Music Ed 1969; Univ of Cincinnati (MEd) Elem Ed 1971; Addl 15 Hrs; *cr:* Cincinnati Pub Schls Music Tchr 1969-71; Georgetown Exempted Village Schls Music Tchr 1971-79; Batavia Local Schls Music Tchr 1979-; *ai:* NEA, OEA, SWOEA, BPEA 1969-; OH Child Conservation 1979-, St Mbrshp Chair, Rose Awd; League Clermont Cty Cncl of Arts 1993-; Mercy Hosp Vol 1996; Mt Olive Bapt Church 1979-, Several; Evangelical Free Church; Produced Children's, Jr, HS Musicals 27 Yrs; Pvt Piano, Vocal Tchr 33 Yrs; *office:* Batavia Elem Schl 215 Broadway St Batavia OH 45103

WARNER, RICHARD CHARLES, Assoc Prof of Bus; *b:* Tonawanda, NY; *m:* Laura Louise Wallace; *c:* Jennifer Jill, Katie Lynn; *ed:* Erie Comm Coll (AAS) Respiratory Care 1976; Ottawa Univ at KS (BA) Hlth Admin 1983; Univ of Scranton (MS) Human Resource Adm 1987; Nova Southeastern Univ Doctorin Higher Ed Admin 1996; *cr:* USAF Medic 1965-69; Degraff Mem Hosp Staff Respiratory Therapist 1969-76; Children's Hosp Evening Supvr 1976-77; Quakertown Comm Hosp Asst Dept Dir 1977-83; Lehigh Carbon Comm Coll Assoc Prof 1983-; *ai:* Resp Care Club Founder, Adv; Jen's House Inc Bd Mem; Am Assoc of Resp Care, Natl Bd for Resp Care 1976-; Easter Dist Resp Care 1983-, Ed Comm Chair; PA SEA 1983-, Treas; Allentown Lib Bd 1993-; Salisbury Schl Bd 1988-, Treas; Who's Who in Jr Colls 1976; *office:* Lehigh Carbon Comm Coll 4525 Education Park Dr Schnecksville PA 18078

WARNER, RODNEY K., Science Teacher; *b:* Canton, OH; *m:* Sharon Kay Matz; *c:* Mariah, Lacy; *ed:* Mount Union Coll (BS) Bio 1973; Attnd OH Univ, Akron Univ; *cr:* Stanton HS Bio Tchr 1973-85; United Local Schls Sci Tchr 1986-; *ai:* Var Boys & Girls Cross Cntry & Jr High Boys Track Coach 7th-8th Grd Ftbl; 7th-8th Grd Bsbl; 9th Grd Boys Bsbl; Boys & Girls Var Track; NEA 1973-; OEA 1973-; *office:* United Local HS St Rt 9 Hanoverton OH 44423

WARNER, ROLAND JOHN,OFM, Pastoral Associate; *b:* Baltimore, MD; *ed:* Essex Comm Coll (AA) 1974; Univ of Baltimore (BS) Bus Admin 1976; 15 Credits Towson St Univ; 33 Credits St Hyacinth Coll & Seminary; 12 Credits Coll of Notre Dame; 4 Credits Catonsville Comm Coll; 3 Credits Univ of MD at Baltimore Cty; *cr:* Archbishop Curley HS Math, Bus Instr 1982-89; Holy Cross Hosp Chaplain Intern 1989-90; St Stanislaus Parish Pastoral Assoc 1991-92; Mt De Sales Acad Math Instr 1992-95; *ai:* NCEA 1982-; Archdiocesan Comm for Curr Ldrshp 1993-; Knights of Columbus 1988-; Deans List Univ of Baltimore 1974-75; *home:* 700 S Ann St Baltimore MD 21231*

WARNER, SARA F., Mathematics Teacher; *b:* Hillsboro, OH; *m:* R. Richard; *c:* Richard, Bret; *ed:* Wright St Univ (BS) Elem Ed 1976, (MED) Ed 1984; Addl 42 Quarter Hrs Beyond Masters; *cr:* Tipp City Schls 7-8th Grd Tchr 1976-; *ai:* Math Curr & Competency Comm; West Regnl Tchr Trng Ctr 1993-94, Project Joint, Planning & Coordinating Comms; Tipp City Schls Tchr of Yr 1993; *office:* L T Ball Jr HS 575 N Hyatt Tipp City OH 45371*

WARNER, SHERMAN AMMON, Math Teacher; *b:* Elmira, NY; *m:* Helena Botto; *c:* Brett, Alicia; *ed:* Mansfied Univ (BS) Math 1973; Elmira Coll (MS) Math 1989; *cr:* Williamson HS Math Tchr 1984-89; Cowanesque HS Math Tchr 1989-93; Corning Comm Coll Adj Fac 1990-94; Wellsboro HS Math Tchr 1993-; Mansfied Univ Adj Fac 1995-; *ai:* Asst Womens Track Coach; PSEA 1984-; Wellsboro Ed Assn 1993-; *office:* Wellsboro Area HS 67 Nichols St Wellsboro PA 16901

WARNER, STEPHEN DOUGLAS, English Professor; *b:* Far Rockaway, NY; *m:* Linda Seifried; *c:* Christopher, Michael, Sarah; *ed:* Dickinson Coll (BA) Eng 1962; IN Univ (MA) Amer Lit 1969, (PHD) Amer Lit 1971; Russian Lang Army Lang Schl; *cr:* IN Univ Instr 1968-70; SUNY Coll at Fredonia Eng Prof 1970-; *ai:* Intercultural, Phi Kappa Sigma Adv; Blue & White Club; UUP, AFT 1975-; Barker Lib 1994-, Bd; Van Buren Po Pres; Intnl Torch Outstndng Mem 1992; Newton St Irregulars 1975 Cncl on Ed Flwshp 1977-78; Fulbright Sr Lectureship Romania 1 East Berlin 1990; *office:* S U N Y Coll At Fredonia Central Ave F NY 14063*

WARNICK, SUSAN FARRELL, Kindergarten Teacher; *b:* Oran *m:* Clay; *c:* Wm. Clay, John F., Laurel W. Degnan, Elizabeth W. C Caldwell Coll (BS) Elem Ed 1975; Kean Coll (MA) Early Chldh Tchr of Handicapped 1992; *cr:* Our Lady of Sorrows 2nd Grd Tch Redwood Schl Kndgtn Tchr 16 Yrs; *ai:* NEA 1980-; *office:* Redwo 75 Redwood Ave West Orange NJ 07052

WARNOCK, JUDITH E., Allied Hlth Technologies Instr; *b:* Mil WI; *c:* Bryan C., Jennifer M. Hackney; *ed:* Indian River Comm Co Elem Music Ed 1971; Dret (AA) Med Assisting 1988; Wright St Credit Hrs Voc Ed; *cr:* Walter E. Stebbins Schl Allied Hlth Te 1992-; *ai:* VICA Adv; Sr Class Adv; Acad Standards, Career Ed Sinclair Comm Coll Tech Prep Advy Bd 1995-; NEA, OEA, A 1992-; AAMA, OSMA 1990-; Med Assisting Natl Cert 1990, 1995; Walter E Stebbins HS 1900 Harshman Rd Riverside OH 45424*

WARNOCK, LINDA DETOMMASO, Spanish Teacher; *b:* S Wey MA; *m:* Richard D.; *c:* Kyla, Damon; *ed:* Bridgewater St Coll (BA) Frgn Lang 1973; 9 Credits Heidelberg Coll at Tiffin 1977; *ai:* Jr Cl 1985-; Frgn Travl Schl Trip Coord 1977-; NEA, Boston Archd Tchrs Assn 1974-; MAFLA 1979-; *office:* Cardinal Spellman HS 73 St Brockton MA 02402

WARNSLEY, JOHNNYE VANBUREN, History Teacher; *b:* Cant *m:* Joseph H. Sr.; *c:* Jerelyn, Joseph; *ed:* Jackson St Univ (BS) Soc 1970; Univ of Toledo (ME) Scndry Ed 1985; Addl 12 Hrs in Cu Bowling Green St Univ Rdng Specialist Cert; *cr:* Toledo Pub Sc Tchr 1970-71; Jesup W. Scott HS Tchr 1972-; *ai:* Asst Ath Dir; NH Scott High Staff Dev Comm; Toledo Fed of Tchrs 1972-, Bldg NAACT 1975-, Ed Comm; Natl Alliance of Black Schl Educators TABSE Tchrs Assn 1990-, Pres, Outstanding Tchr; Art Tatum Soc Bd Mem; Rosa Morgan Ctr 1989-, Bd Mem, Outstanding Tchr; N Ashland Oil Inc Golden Apple Tchrs Achvmt Awd Coalition of Qua Outstanding Tchr Awd as Pres of TABSE, Sponsored Educl C Educators; OH St Bd Cert of Recognition for Leadership, Svc to Natl Alliance of Black Schl Edctrs Outstanding Edctr Aw.*

WARONSKY, FRANK T.,JR., Art Teacher; *b:* Pittsburgh, PA; *m* Papalia; *c:* Frank III, Clint; *ed:* Edinboro Univ (BSEd) Art Ed 1964; Univ (MSEd) Art Ed 1971; Attnd Carnegie Mellon Univ, U Pittsburgh; *cr:* Penn Hills Schl Dist Art Dept Chm 32 Yrs; *ai:* A Spon; NEA, PSEA, PHEA 1964-, Local Art Dir; Tchr Art Ed Asse Comm; Mid St Evaluation Team; Former Track & Golf Coach; *offic* Hills Schl Dist 12200 Garland Dr Pittsburgh PA 15235

WARREN, BARBARA BETH, Mathematics Teacher; *b:* Jersey C *m:* John Bryant Phillips; *ed:* Fairleigh Dickinson Univ (BA) Mat (MAT) Ed 1994; Supvrs Cert William Patterson Coll; *cr:* Eastside H Tchr 1989-; *ai:* NHS, Motorol Shadowing, Math Club Spon; Schl P Comm; Odyssey of Mind Coach; NEA, NJEA 1989-; Bergen Cty 1984-; Bus Mgr; Vista Assn 1990-, Treas; Presidential Awds Excl Math Tchng Nom 1996; Distngd Tchr Awd Nom; *office:* Eastside Park Ave Paterson NJ 07501*

WARREN, CYNTHIA DOUGLAS, Social Studies Teacher; *b:* El City, NC; *m:* Roy C. Jr.; *c:* Chrishanna, Iyesha; *ed:* Elizabeth City Sociology 1974; Trinity Coll 15 Credit Hrs Sch & Comm; Catholic Credit Hrs Ed; 15 Addl Credit; *ai:* Stu Govt, Class of 1986, Class & Cheerleading Spons; Vlybl Coach; Mentor of New Tchrs; NEA Soc Stud Cncl 1993-; Womens Aglaw Fellowship 1983-, Pres; Exe Tchr of Soc Stud for Charles Cty 1993; *home:* 4023 Posey Ct Wald 20602

WARREN, DAVID F., Math Teacher & Dept Chair; *b:* Bedford, Brenda L.; *c:* Kimberly E., Michelle L., Courtney H.; *ed:* SU Oneonta (BS) Math Ed 1974; Elmira Coll (MS) Ed 1980; SU Cortland CAS Ed Admin 27 Hrs; *cr:* Bradford Cntrl Schl Tchr, Dep 1976-80; Watkins Glen Cntrl Schl Tchr, Dept Chair 1980-; *ai:* Bsbl NCTM 1976-; NYSUT 1980-; Phoebe Hearst PTA Tchr of Yr 199 NY St Tchr of Yr 1994; *office:* Watkins Glen HS 12th St Watkins G 14891

WARREN, JACK, Fifth Grade Teacher; *cr:* Hartland Schl 5th Gr 1976-; *office:* Hartland Elem Schl Fairgrounds Rd Hartland VT 050

WARREN, JANET NENTWICK, 6th Grade Science Teacher; Liverpool, OH; *m:* Thomas M.; *c:* Abigail F.; *ed:* Kent St Univ (BA Ed Minor Art Ed 1989; Schl Cnslr Masters Prgm 1995; *cr:* St Joseph Schl 6th Grd Tchr, 7th-8th Grd Sci Tchr 1989-; *ai:* Sci Fair Dir; 1989-; *home:* 309 Lake St Kent OH 44240*

WARREN, JAYNE, First Grade Teacher; *b:* Chambersburg, P Shippensburg St Coll (BS) Elem Ed 1974, (MA) Elem Ed 1978; 6 Credits Beyond Masters; *cr:* Orrstown Elem Schl 2nd Grd Tchr 19 Nancy Grayson Elem Schl 1st Grd Tchr 1980-94, Librn 1994-95, Tchr 1995-; *ai:* 1st Grd Level Chprsn 1995-; NEA 1974-; 1st Grd Chprsn 1987-94; *home:* 9549 Muddy Run Rd Orrstown PA 17244

WARREN, KENNETH E., High School Mathematics Tchr; *b:* Plai NJ; *m:* Linda Stockdale; *c:* Matthew, Gary; *ed:* Montclair St Col Math 1968; Monmouth Coll (MS) Math 1975; Attnd Jersey City S Kean Coll 30 Hrs Cmptr Programming; *cr:* Brick Twp HS Math 1968-71; Thorne Jr HS Math Tchr 1971-76; Middletown HS North Tchr 1976-; *ai:* Ski Club Adv; NJEA, NEA 1968-; BSA Scoutmaster, Awd of Merit; Local Dist Whytecombe Grant; *home* Cedar St Point Pleasant NJ 08742

WARREN, MAREDIA D. LEWIS, Vocal Music Director; *b:* Hen TX; *m:* Charles A.; *c:* John, Maredia Dionne; *ed:* Howard U Washington (BME) Music Ed 1965; Columbia Univ Tchrs Coll Music, Music Ed 1967; Columbia Univ at NY City (EDD) Music, Ed 1989; Kodaly Musical Trng Inst 18 Credit Hrs; Univ of Ha Kordaly Cert; *cr:* Howard Univ Instr Part-time 1964-65; Herb Lehman Coll Stud Tchrs Supvr, Music Instr 1973-79; Fairleigh Dic Univ Stud Tchrs Supvr, Music Instr 1975-79; Teaneck Pub Schls Music Dir 1979-; Teaneck HS Vocal Music Dir 1979-; Montclair S Mus Ed Visiting Specialist 1984-92; *ai:* Schl Musical Vocal Mus Gospel Choir Adv, Spon; Honor Choir Participants in Cty, Regio Divisional Chorus Vocal Music Adv; NEA; Music Educators Assn; Kodaly Educators Org, Natl Bd 1987-89; Music Educators Natl NJ Choral Dirs Assn; NAACP; Alpha Kappa Alpha 1976-; Teanec Centenniel Comm 1995-; Westminster Choir Coll 1990-92, Adv Princeton Univ Prize Distinguished Scndry Tchng 1993; Prins Citation, Natl Assn Negro Bus, Prof Women's Club IncEd Awd Bergen Passaic Howard Un iv Alumni Charter Day Outstanding Com Awd 1989; Cndctr NJ All St Chorus 1994; *office:* Teaneck H Elizabeth Ave Teaneck NJ 07666*

WARREN, MARYGRACE CRISPO, Retired Teacher; *b:* Watervlie *m:* William; *c:* Pamela; *ed:* Coll of St Rose (MA) Span 1952; Oneonta St Univ, SUNY at Plattsburg; *cr:* Our Lady of Mt Carmel Grd Tchr 1962-67; St Anastasia Schl 6-8th Eng, Soc Stud Tchr 19 trl HS Eng, Compostion, Lit Tchr 1977-80; Cohoes Cath Schl Third ır 1986-95; *ai:* NYEA; *home:* 2 Verdi Blvd Latham NY 12110

EN, PETER DANA, Humanities Tchr & Dept Chair; *b:* Los s, CA; *m:* Terri Rea Jones; *c:* Lisa, Amy, Benjamin; *ed:* Univ of CA eley (BA) African Stud 1975; Univ of London (MA) African Stud urr Stud at Johns Hopkins Univ Schl of Continuing Ed; *cr:* Changes His & Eng Tchr 1978-79; Saint Anns Schl Lower & MS Tchr ; Brinmawr Schl Mid & Upper His Tchr 1981-86; the Park Schl MS chr & Dept Chair 1987-; *ai:* Upper Schl Film Soc; 8th Grd Adv; NCCC 1989-; Articles in Cross Currents, Baltimore Family ne & Baltimore City Paper; *office:* Park Schl Of Baltimore Old d Brooklandville MD 21022

EN, SUSAN WALRAND, Fifth Grade Teacher; *b:* Mount Holly, Richard M.; *c:* Michael, Gregory; *ed:* Elizabethtown Coll (BA) d 1975; 24 Credits Post Grad Stud Toward Masters Degree at n Court Coll; *cr:* Forked River Schl 2nd-5th Grd Tchr 1977-92; Harbor Schl 5th Grd Tchr 1993-; *ai:* NJEA, NEA 1977-; Forked chl Tchr of Yr 1986; *office:* Lanoka Harbor Elem Schl Manchester noka Harbor NJ 08734*

ENFELTZ, DAVID JOHN,JR., Math Teacher & Dept Chair; *b:* town, MD; *m:* Jodie Ann Taylor; *c:* David III, Michael; *ed:* gton Univ & Lee Univ (BA) Math 1984; Shippensburg Univ 15 Hrs; Western MD Coll 12 Credit Hrs; *cr:* North Hagerstown HS chr 1984-, Dept Chair 1994-; *ai:* Asst Bsbl & Ftbl Coach; Head Bsbl Ray Kroc Tchr Achvmt Awd; Bsbl Coach of the Yr 1994; Coach of 1994; *office:* North Hagerstown HS 1200 Pennsylvania Ave own MD 21742

NER, RUTH ANN, 7th-12th Grade Teacher; *b:* Coudersport, PA; ghton Coll (BA) Math 1977; 3 Hrs TE Temple; 1 Hr Mansfield; 3 n St; *cr:* Pleasant View Chrstn Acad 3-12 Grd Tchr 1977-78; Valley Acad Tchr 1978-; *ai:* C&MA Alliance Church 1977-, Chrstn Ed Deaconness; *home:* RR 1 Box 470 Harrison Valley PA 16927

CHAWSKI, PAUL, Professor of Humanities; *b:* La Paz, Bolivia; *m:* Blowers; *c:* Heidi, Daniel, Justinn; *ed:* Long Island Univ (BA) Ger 1962; Glassboro St Coll (MS) His 1968; 30 Credits SUNY at *cr:* Atlantic City HS Span Tchr 1962-68; Atlantic Comm Coll Span Instr 1964-68; Fulton-Montgomery Comm Coll Eng, Span & Ger 68-; *ai:* Stu Life Comm; AAVD; FACE 1968-; NEA 1968-; ACTFLT NCTE 1975-; Jewish Comm Ctr 1968-; Fulton Cty Jr Soccer ; Excl in Tchng Nom; Numerous Articles; *office:* Fulton mery Comm Coll 2805 St Hwy 67 Johnstown NY 12095

HAWSKY, HERSHEY, Professor & Acting Chair; *b:* Montreal, ; *m:* Goldie Kaplansky; *c:* Bryna Warshawsky Lomax, Aurum, Paul; George Williams Coll (BSC) Bio 1959; McGill Univ (MSC) y 1961, (PHD) Anatomy 1966; *cr:* McGill Univ Lecturer 1963-66, of 1967-70, Assoc Prof 1970-77, Prof 1977-, Acting Chair 1995-; er Assn of Anatomists 1966-; Intnl Assn of Dental Research 1966-, h in Oral Bio Awd; Medical Research Cncl of Canada Grants Since eo Yaffe Awd Tchng in Fac of Sci McGill 1988; Dr Odont Honoris Royal Dental Coll Denmark 1991; Pub Over 90 Papers; *office:* Mc iv Dept Of Anatomy 3640 Univ St Montreal PQ H3A 2L6 Canada

HAWSKY, NANCY TIGHE, Social Studies Teacher; *b:* lphia, PA; *m:* Larry; *c:* James Brown, Edward Brown, Nancy *ed:* West Chester Univ (BS) Ed 1977; Grad Work Millerville Univ; d Coll, Franklin & Marshall Travel Stud; *cr:* Norristown HS Sub Yr; Downingtown Sr HS Tchr 17 Yrs; *ai:* UN Club; Law Day Essay ; NEA 1979-; Five Points Neighborhood Assn 1993-; Extensive Europe; *office:* Downingtown Sr HS 445 Manor Ave Downingtown 35

HOWER, RUTH M., Guidance Counselor; *b:* Brooklyn, NY; *m:* ; *ed:* Long Island Univ (MS) Counseling 1989; *cr:* Midwood HS Fr 965-76; August Martin HS Fr Tchr 1976-82; Erasmus Hall HS Fr Guidance Cnlsr 1983-; *ai:* AFT, UFT 1965-; Phi Beta Kappa; orough Comm Coll Comm Svc Awd 1991; *office:* Erasmus Hall HS tbush Ave Brooklyn NY 11226

ELLA, ELLEN HART, Diversified Health Instructor; *b:* ille, NY; *m:* Robert; *c:* Kathleen, Andrew; *ed:* Jamestown Comm Assoc); St Francis Schl of Nrsng LPN; SUNY at Utica 16 Credits r: Overlook Hosp Staff RN, Relief Charge Nurse 1981-88; Oneida osp Staff, Relief Charge Nurse 1988-94; Inservice Infection Control Ross 1994-95; ScndryEdctr Boces 1995-; *ai:* Girl Scout Cookie Mgr; rd Classroom Mother; *home:* 354 Leonard St Oneida NY 13421

O, JOHN, Teacher of the Gifted; *b:* Beaver Falls, PA; *m:* Mary Jo tney; *c:* Michael, David; *ed:* IN Univ of PA (BS) Bus Ed 1968, Counseling 1974; 40 Credits Univ of Pittsburgh; Univ of PA; Morris Coll; Duquesne Univ; *cr:* Montour HS Bus Ed Tchr 1968-92, f the Gifted 1992-; *ai:* NEA, PSEA 1968-; PA Assn for Gifted Ed Midway Vol Fire Dept 1978-, Sec; Rails to Trails Conservancy, ır Trail Cncl 1991-; *office:* Montour HS 90 Clever Rd Mc Kees PA 15136

BURN, BRIAN, Professor of Chemistry; *b:* Watertown, NY; *m:* S. Stickles; *c:* Elizabeth, Christopher; *ed:* St Univ of NY at Oneonta hem 1970; St Univ of NY at Buffalo (MA) Chem 1973; *cr:* St Univ at Canton Chem Instr 1973-75, Asst Prof of Chem 1976-78, Assoc Chem 1978-85, Prof of Chem & Environmental Sci 1985-; Clarkson rganic Chem Instr Summer Sessions 1994-; *ai:* Sci & Hlth Care Prof Acad Adv; Instructional Tech, Chem Hygiene & Phys Therapy Asst search Comms Mem; UUP 1975-; NY St Dept of Environmental vation-Steward for Grasse River; Ducks Unlimited 1980-, CoChm s 1988-90; 2 Journal Articles in Inorganic Chem; Participant in ous Natural Sci Fnd; Short Courses & Summer Prgms for Coll Profs; S U N Y Coll Of Tech At Canton Canton NY 13617

BURN, RICHARD WILBUR, Mathematics Teacher; *b:* Freeport, Ana Iris Delgado Perez; *c:* Juan Reyes, Janette Ivone Reyes; *ed:* of IL (BS) Tchng of Math 1969, (MS) Math 1970; *cr:* Univ of IL Asst 1969-70; Antilles Cons Schl System Math Tchr 1972-; *ai:* NHS Sr Class Spon; NEA, OEA 1978-; ACEA 1978-, Pres 1 Yr; NCTM MAA 1988-; APMM 1994-; ACEA 1978-, Treas 5 Yrs, VP 1 Yr, 3 Yr; Phi Beta Kappa Univ of IL 1969; *office:* Roosevelt Roads S PSC 1008 Box 3035 FPO AA 34051

BURN, WILLIAM HENRY, Mathematics Teacher; *b:* Brockton, d: Bridgewater St Coll (BA) Math 1970; 21 Credit Hrs Bridgewater ; *cr:* Rockland HS 9-12th Grd Math Tchr 1970-; *ai:* Natl Honor Soc ormer Soph Class Adv, Track Coach, Pres of Fac Cncl, Chm ofAcad Schl Cncl Mem; Rockland Ed, MA Tchrs, NEA 1970-; South Shore s Tchr Assoc; *office:* Rockland HS 52 Goddard Ave Rockland MA

INGTON, COURTNEY WILLIS, Mathematics Teacher; *b:* ngham, England; *m:* Charles Paul; *c:* Christina, Sonia, Angela; *ed:* lair St (BA) Math 1988; 10 Credits Towards Masters at Kean Coll; ount Hebron Schl Math Tchr 1988-, Math Subject Matter Ldr 5; *ai:* Drill Team Instr; NJEA, MEA, NCTM, AMTNJ, ASCD 1988-; Ministry 1990-, 1st Lady-Pastors Wife; Chrstn Soldiers 1988-, Instr, 1st Place in Several Competitions; *office:* Mount Hebron MS 173 Bellevue Ave Upper Montclair NJ 07043*

WASHINGTON, J. CHARLES, Assoc Professor of English; *ed:* Bradley Univ (BA) Ger 1961; Howard Univ (MA) Ger 1970; Cath Univ of Am (DrA) Eng 1981; *cr:* Univ of DC Instr 1970-78; FL Intnl Univ Lecturer 1981-84; Howard Univ Lecturer 1979-86; Bowie St Univ Assoc Prof 1987-; *ai:* Torch Co-Ed; Rdng Cr Discussion Group; Stdnt Poets Mentor; Mid Atlantic Writers Assn 1988-; NCTE 1994-; Numerous Articles Pub; *office:* Bowie St Univ Jericho Park Road Bowie MD 20715

WASHINGTON, MARGIE GOODWIN, Family & Consumer Sci Teacher; *b:* Philadelphia, PA; *m:* Lawrence; *c:* Meaghan Francis, Morgan Shelby; *ed:* Cheyney St Coll (BS) Ed 1981; Univ of the Arts (MS) Cmptr Sci 1995; *cr:* Stoddart-Fleisher MS Home Ec Tchr 1984-85; Wagner MS Home Ec Tchr 1986-87; Sulzberger MS Home Ec Tchr 1988-89; Turner MS Home Ec Tchr 1990-92; *ai:* Sr Class, Chef's Club, Yrbk Spon; Newsletter Ed; Amer Jewish Comm Tchr Coord; AFT 1982-; Family & Consumer Sci Assn 1993-; Concerned Tchrs of Home Ec 1994-, Org; Philadelphia Fed of Tchrs 1982-, Del; Anti Violence Mini Grant 1994; Mid Linc Nutrition Grant 1994-95; *office:* Stoddard-Fleisher Middle Schl 528 N 13th St Philadelphia PA 19123*

WASHINGTON, ROCHELLE ELOIS, 5th Grade Teacher; *b:* Philadelphia, PA; *c:* Cheree; *ed:* Cheyney St Univ (BS) Elem Ed 1974; Attnd St Joseph Univ, Beaver Coll; *ai:* Mentor Prgm 1991; PFT 1975-, Union Rep 1973-74; AFT 1975-; Order of Eastern Stars 1979-; Delta Sigma Theta 1973-; Comm Person Democratic Party 1992-; Miss Courtesy 1972; *office:* Tanner Duckrey Elem Schl 1501 W Diamond St Philadelphia PA 19121*

WASILCHAK, ANN CAVAGNARD, Health & Phys Ed Teacher; *b:* Jessup, PA; *m:* Gerald J.; *c:* Jeffrey, Heidi, Scot; *ed:* East Stroudsburg (BS) Hlth, PE 1956; Attnd Marywood Coll; *cr:* Jessup HS Tchr 1956-67; Vly View Tchr; *ai:* Spirit Club; Health Fair; Vlybl Tournament; Jump Rope-A-Thon; VVEA 1976-; PSEA 1956-; *office:* Valley View MS 1 Columbus Dr Archbald PA 18403

WASILCHUK, STEPHEN G., MS Mathematics Teacher; *b:* New York, NY; *m:* Judith Ann Ferguson; *c:* Elizabeth, Ann, John; *ed:* Franklin Coll (MA) Math 1972; Hofstra Univ (MA) Math, Ed 1978; *cr:* Roslyn Pub Schls Math Tchr 1972-; *ai:* AFT 1972-; NCTM; *office:* Roslyn MS Locust Ln Roslyn Heights NY 11577*

WASILENKO, BRUCE JOSEPH, Earth Science & Chemistry Tchr; *b:* Cortland, NY; *m:* Lorianne Clare; *c:* john, Joby, Leela; *ed:* Tompkins Cortland Comm Coll (AAS) Sci Lab Tech 1979; St Univ Coll at Cortland (BS) Geology, Chem 1982, (MSEd) Earth Sci, Chem, Scndry Sci 1986; *cr:* Agway Research Ctr Lab Tech 1978-79; Smith Corona Corp Design Drafter 1979-83; South Jefferson HS Earth Sci, Chem Tchr 1986-; *ai:* Whiz Quiz Team Coach; Tandy Sci 1994-95, HS 1994-95 Outstanding Tchr Awds; Empire St Sci Tchr Fellowship 1984; Deans List 1975; *office:* South Jefferson HS Rt 11 Adams NY 13605

WASIUK, KATHLEEN PAGE, Director of Academic Resources; *b:* Princeton, NJ; *m:* Joseph S.; *c:* Virginia H.; *ed:* Univ of AZ (BFA) Art His 1970; Dartmouth Coll (MALS) Womens His 1988; *cr:* Tilton Schl Fac 1975-87; Northfield Mt Hermon Chair, His Tchr 1988-95; Dir of Acad Resources 1995-; *ai:* Salaries & Benefits Comm; Fac Exec Comm; Elephant Rock Assn 1970-, Pres; NH Bus & Prof Women, Outstanding Young Career Woman 1973; United Church of Christ, Deacon; *office:* Northfield Mt Hermon Schl E Main St Northfield MA 01360

WASKIE, ANTHONY J., Language Teacher & Curr Coord; *b:* Bloomsburg, PA; *m:* Darlene E. Greenly; *c:* Anthony III, Denise, Elizabeth, Nicholas; *ed:* Bloomsburg Univ (BS) Ger & Russian 1968; NY Univ (MA) Ger 1971, (PHD) Germanic Philology 1978; Attnd Universitat Marburg Germany, Charles Univ Prague & Universitat Salzburg Austria; *cr:* Holy Family Coll Part-Time Tchr 1 Yr; Chestnut Hill Coll Part-Time Tchr 2 Yrs; Pennsbury Schl Dist Curr Supvr & Tchr 27 Yrs; *ai:* Foreign Lang Club Adv; Curr Cncl; Strategic Planning Comm; ACTFL 1980-; PSMLA 1970-; GPCIE 1989-, Chair; Northeast Conf Advy Cncl; GAR Civil War Museum 1984-, Bd of Dirs; SUVCW 1984-, Commander; DE Valley Civil War Round Table 1992-, Man of Yr Awd 1994; Bucks Cty Civil War Round Table 1990-, Founder; Numerous Articles Pub on Topics Relating to Amer Civil War; *office:* Pennsbury Schl Dist 705 Hood Blvd Fairless Hills PA 19030*

WASOWSKI, JAMES ANDREW, History Teacher; *b:* South Bend, IN; *m:* Isabel Kulick; *c:* Matthew, Antoinette; *ed:* IN Univ (BS) Ed 1969; Cleveland St Univ (MA) His 1976; 12 Hum Hrs Univ of CA at Santa Cruz 1977; *cr:* Cleveland Pub Schls His Tchr 1969-; *ai:* Boys Bsktbl Coach; Historical Drama Club; Schl Ath Comm; AFT 1969-; Greater Cleveland Cncl of Soc Stud 1969-; Greater Cleveland Bsktbl Coaches Assn 1986-; Wrote for Ctr for Learning & Have Pub 7 Books that Serve as Soc Stud Curr Supplements; OH Master Tchr Awd 1977; In Tchr Exch Pgm 1994; Grants to Write Oral His Curr; *office:* Cleveland John Marshall HS 3952 W 140th St Cleveland OH 44111*

WASS, RUSSELL DAVID, Accounting Professor; *b:* Leominster, MA; *ed:* Bentley Coll (BS) Math & Acctng 1985; MIT Sloan Schl (SM) Mgmt 1989; *cr:* Merrimack Coll Asst Prof of Acctng & Fin 1993-95; *ai:* Acctng & Fin Soc Adv; Income Tax Assistance Prgms Vol; MA Soc CPAs & Inst of Mgmt Accountants 1993-; US CPA Exam Bronze Medal Awd 1985; MA CPA Exam Gold Medal Awd 1985; *home:* 84 Arlington St Leominster MA 01453

WASSER, DAVID A., High School Mathematics Tchr; *b:* Doylestown, PA; *m:* M. Ruth; *c:* Morgan Rose; *ed:* The Kings Coll (BA) Math 1989; Beaver Coll (MEd) Scndry Math Ed 1992; Pennridge-Centennial-Upper Bucks Voc Tech Sub Math Tchr 1988-90; Upper Bucks Voc Tech Schl 10th-12th Grd Math Instr 1990-; *cr:* Strategic Planning Comm; Mentor Tchr; Post Grad Tutoring & HS Tutoring; *ai:* PSEA, NEA 1990-; *home:* 4724 Old Easton Rd Doylestown PA 18901

WASSER, RONALD E., Music Teacher; *b:* Sellersville, PA; *m:* Diane Wright; *ed:* OH Wesleyan Univ (BM) Music Ed 1982; Grad Hrs West Chester St Univ & Bowling Green St Univ; *cr:* Lenape Jr HS Instrumental & Gen Music Tchr 1983-84; Otsego Local Schls Instrumental Music Tchr 1984-87; Berwick Area Sr HS Band Dir, Instr of Instrumental Music & Music Theory 1987-; *ai:* Jazz Ensembles Dir; Music Curr Revision Comm; MENC 1982-; NEA 1983-; IAJE; Good Sheperd Luth Church 1988-, Church Cncl; *office:* Berwick Area Sr HS 1100 Fowler Ave Berwick PA 18603

WASSERMAN, CAROL, Asst Prof of Modern Languages; *b:* Brooklyn, NY; *m:* Marvin; *ed:* NY Univ Schl of Ed (BS) Span, Fr Ed 1967; NY Univ Grad Arts, Sci (MA) Span 1969, (PHD) Span 1981; Stud Madrid Spain Fr, Bus Chamber De Commerce, Industrie De Paris 1965-66; *cr:* NY Univ Asst Prof of Span 1967-69; Hunter Coll Adj Lectuner1969-76; Johnson Coll Adj Asst Prof 1976-93; BMCC Adj Lect, Asst Prof 1976-93, Asst Prof 1993-; *ai:* Dept P&B, Cncl at Large Instrl, Hnrs, Mid Sts Sub Comms; Dept Self Stud; AATSP; Assn Intnl De Hisponistas; Assn Europea De prof De Espunol; Co-author 6 HS Textbooks; Pub Articles; *office:* Borough Of Manhattan Comm Coll 199 Chambers St #N540 New York NY 10007

WASSERMAN, MOE, Electrical Engrng Assoc Prof; *b:* Hampton, VA; *m:* Josephine Supcoff; *c:* David, Michael, Deborah Morosohk; *ed:* Univ of VA (BS) Chem 1946, (MS) Chem 1947; Univ of MI (PHD) Chem 1955; *cr:* General Electric Co Dev Chemist 1947-49; GTE Corp Prin Mem of Tech Staff 1955-86; Boston Univ Assoc Prof 1986-; *ai:* Inst of Electrical & Electronic Engrs 1961-; Temple Beth Am 1972-, Pres; GTE Corp Leslie Warner Tech Achvmnt Awd 1984; Outstanding Engrng Prof of Yr 1992.

WASSERMAN, NADIA L., French Teacher; *b:* Alexandria, Egypt; *m:* Joseph; *c:* Jamie; *ed:* Univ of MD (BA) Ed 1967, (MA) Fr 1971; 26 Addl Credit Hrs Span; *cr:* Hyallsville Jr HS Fr Tchr 1968-71; Parkdale HS Fr Tchr 1971-72; Oxon Hill MS Exploratory Tchr 1979-81; Northwestern HS Span Tchr 1981-89; High Point HS Fr, Span Tchr, Track Coach 1990-; *ai:* Cross Cty, Outdoor Track Coach; Stu Paren Mngmt Team; NEA, MSTA, AAFT, GWATFL 1980-; Howard Co Stud 1981-, Pres, VP, Comm Chair, Numeros Awds, Comm Awds; *office:* High Point HS 3601 Powder Mill Rd Beltsville MD 20705

WASSERMAN, SUSAN HARRIS, 5th Grade Teacher; *b:* New York, NY; *c:* Sheryl E.; *ed:* Adelphi Univ (BS) Elem Ed 1963, (MA) Elem Ed 1965; Attnd Hofstra Univ; Natl Geographic Soc Summer Geog Inst 1989; London Schl of Ec 1962; *cr:* Dist 30 VS 4th-6th Grd ESL, Frgn Lang 1963-95; *ai:* NY Geographic Alliance Dir Summer Geog Inst 1992, 1995, Staff SGI 1990-95; NYS Cncl for SS 1987-, Chair El Comm, Outstdng Tchr of Yr 1996; MCGE 1989-; PTA, AFT, VSTA, NYSUT 1963-; LICSS 1990-; Fulbright Hayes Flwshp 1992; The Data Connection 1985; *office:* Shaw Ave Schl USFD 30 99 Shaw Ave Valley Stream NY 11582*

WASSERMAN, WENDY ELLEN (BROWN), LRC Teacher; *b:* Brooklyn, NY; *m:* Howard M.; *c:* Jason, Marc, Hopi; *ed:* William Paterson Coll (BA) Early Chldhd Ed 1968; Temple Univ (MED) Psych of Rdng 1970; Rowan Coll 15 Hrs; Univ of AZ 15 Hrs; *cr:* Bradley Beach Grammar Schl Rdng Specialist 1970-71; Tanque Verde Schl Tchr of the Handicapped 1971-74; Oakcrest HS Rdng Specialist 1981-86; Eag Harbor Twn HS LRC Tchr, Rdng Spec 1986-; *ai:* Holocaust Comm; Tchr Mentor Prgm; Intnl Rdng Assoc 1981-; Phi Delta Kappa 1995-; *home:* 219 Dogwood Ave Egg Harbor Tp NJ 08234

WASSI, MARY CRAMER, 3rd Grade Teacher; *b:* Cold Spring, NY; *m:* Joseph S.; *ed:* Mt St Mary Coll (BA) Soc Stud 1972; St Univ at New Paltz (MA) Elem Ed 1975; *office:* Sargent Schl 445 Wolcott Ave Beacon NY 12508

WASSMER, AGNES,OP, Retired Mentor; *b:* Brooklyn, NY; *ed:* Molloy Coll (BA) Soc Stud 7-12 1971; *cr:* St Luke's Tchr 4th Grd 1947-49; St Agnes Tchr 7th Grd 1949-53; OLPH Tchr 8th Grd 1953-56; St Leonard's Jr HS Tchr 1956-59; St Boniface Tchr 8th Grd 1959-67; St Martin of Tours Jr HS Tchr 1967-94; *ai:* Edctrs Mentor; Tutor; NCEA, Long Island Cncl Soc Stud, NY Cncl SS 1967-; Amityville PS Election Bd, Natl Election Bd Babylon Twp 1994-, Supvr; *home:* 41 Union Ave Amityville NY 11701

WASSON, KAREN JO STALMA, 1st Grade Teacher; *b:* New Castle, PA; *m:* Dennis G.; *c:* Megan, Annalee, Jillian; *ed:* Youngstown St Univ (BS) Ed 1974; Post Grad Stud Youngstown St Univ, Kent St Univ & Ashland Univ; *cr:* Noble Cty Schls Spcl Ed Tchr 1974-75; South Range Schls Spcl Ed, 1st & 2nd Grd Tchr 1975-86; Springfield Local Schls Spcl Ed 1990-91; Salem City Schls Spcl Ed & 1st Grd Tchr 1991-; *ai:* Capital Venture, Family Sci & Math Comms; OEA & NEA 1974-; *office:* Reilly Elem Schl 491 Reilly Ave Salem OH 44460

WASYLYSHYN, YVONNE BROERE, Kindergarten Teacher; *b:* Rochester, NY; *w:* Charles Broere (dec); *c:* Mark Broere, Christopher Broere, Leslie Indence; *ed:* SUNY at Binghamton (BS) Lbrl Arts 1961; Univ of CO at Boulder (MS) Elem Ed 1979; Hofstra Univ Post Grad Stud Rdng; Stoneybrook Univ Post Grad Stud Ed; *cr:* Brentwood Schls 2nd Grd Tchr 1963-65; Mid Cntry Schl Dist #11 Unity Dr 4th Grd Tchr 1966-69; Mid Cntry Schl Dist #11 Stagecoach Elem 4th Grd Tchr 1969-82, 2nd Grd Tchr 1982-93, Kndgtn Tchr 1993-; *ai:* PTA Cultural Arts Chprsn; Stagecoach Garden Club Pres; Whole Lang NCTE 1989-; IRA 1992-; NAEYC 1994-; Jenkins Awd Stagecoach Elem 1990; *office:* Stagecoach Road Elem Schl 205 Dare Rd Selden NY 11784*

WASZMER, JACK, Biology Teacher & Coach; *b:* Freeport, NY; *m:* Deborah E. Hamilton; *c:* David, Karyn, Brianne; *ed:* Dowling Coll (BA) Bio, Math 1976, (MA) Sci, Ed 1986; SUNY at Stony Brook MALS Natural Sci; *cr:* William Floyd Schls Sci Tchr 1976-78; Sachem Schls Sci Tchr 1979-81; 3-Village Schls Sci Tchr 1981-; *ai:* Boys Var Bsktbl, Girls JV Soccer, Jr HS Boys Bsbl Coach; Horticulture, Teen Ctr Adv; Field Trip Adv, Coord; PTSO Rep; STANYS, NYSUT 1981-; Sierra Club 1985-; Nature Conservancy 1989-; Influential Tchr Recognition Awd Westinghouse Sci Competition Semi-finalist 1995; *office:* Paul J Gelinas Jr H S 25 Mud Rd Setauket NY 11733

WASZMER, PAULA SPATAFORE, Mathematics Teacher; *b:* New York, NY; *m:* Michael J.; *c:* Matthew, Michael, Sarah, Alison; *ed:* St Univ Coll at New Paltz (BA) Math 4 Yrs; Long Island Univ CW Post Coll (MA) Spcl Ed 3 Yrs; 18 Post Grad Credit Hrs; *cr:* Hillcrest Schl 7th-8th Grd Tchr 1 Yr; St Josephs Schl 8th Grd Math Tchr 2 Yrs; HH Well MS Math Tchr 10 Yrs; *ai:* NCTM 1989-; *office:* Henry H Wells MS RR 312 Brewster NY 10509*

WATERHOUSE, JOAN L., English Teacher; *b:* Beverly, MA; *m:* George; *ed:* Salem St Coll (BA) Eng 1970; Credit Hrs Eng, Cmptr; *cr:* Cntrl Grammar Schl Eng Tchr 1970-71; Milton L. Fuller Schl Eng Tchr 1971-73; Ralph B. O'Maley Schl Eng Tchr 1973-86; Gloucester HS Eng Tchr 1986-; *ai:* Class Adv 1989, 1994; Handbook, Follow Up Comms; Fac Adv Cncl; MTA, NEA, NCTE, MCTE 1970-; Sawyer Free Lib 1991-, Dir; Lyceum comm 1995-, Bd Mem; Site Based Mngmt 1995-, Bd; Alumni Schlsp Fund 1995-, Bd; Cape Ann Savings Bank 1990-, Corporator; *office:* Gloucester HS 32 Leslie O Johnson Rd Gloucester MA 01930

WATERHOUSE, JOHN ALMON, Head Teacher; *b:* Hartford, CT; *ed:* Kenne St Coll (BEd) Soc Sci 1965; Cntrl CT St Coll (MS) Soc Sci 1971; Wesleyan Univ (CAS) Soc Sci 1983; Southern CT St (CAS) Admin 1992; *cr:* Glastonbury Pub Schls His, Soc Sci Tchr 1966-; *ai:* Co-Adv Intnl Relations Club; Glastonbury Ed Assn, CT Ed Assn, NEA 1966-; Calvin Coolidge Meml Fnd 1967-, Trustee; CT FFA Fnd 1988-, Trustee; Assn for Stud of CT His 1985-; Book Calvin Coolidge Meets Charles Edward Garman; Co-Authur Coolidge County Cookbook; Tchrs Awds Natl Soc Daughters, Colonial Wars 1978, Nat Soc Daughter of Founders, Patriots of Amer 1979, CT St DAR Tchr Am His 1986, Cntrl CT St U Alumni Asso Outstdng Tchr 1989, Celebration of Excl 1988; *office:* Glastonbury HS 330 Hubbard St Glastonbury CT 06033*

WATERHOUSE, JOHN DAVID, English Teacher; *b:* Plattsburgh, NY; *m:* Angela Beth Coopy; *ed:* Plattsburgh St Univ (BS) Scndry Eng Ed 1986, (MS) Admin, Supervision 1992; *cr:* Ausable Vly Cntrl Schl Eng Tchr 1987-; *ai:* Grad Adv; NY St United Tchrs 1987-; *office:* Ausable Vly Cntrl Schl Rt 9 N Clintonville NY 12924

WATERS, LINDY KAY, 5th Grade Teacher; *b:* Cincinnati, OH; *m:* Larry; *c:* Eddie; *ed:* Miami Univ (BS) Elem Ed 1973, (MED) Media 1993; *cr:* John Foster Dulles Elem Schl 5th Grd Tchr 1976-; *ai:* Curr Comm; OHEA, OEA, NEA, PTA 1976-; Grad Asst 1992-93; *office:* John Foster Dulles Elem Schl 6481 Bridgetown Rd Cincinnati OH 45248

WATERS, ROLF ALBERT, History Teacher; *b:* Neurbrooke, West Germany; *m:* Yvonne Mc Intosh; *c:* Erica K., Camron R.; *ed:* Canton Tech (AS) Independent Stud 1983; Brockport St (BS) His, Ed 1985; St Lawrence Univ (MEd) Ed 1992; *cr:* St Lawrence Univ Summer Upward Bound Tchr 1986-87; Potsdam HS His Tchr 1987-; *ai:* Boys JV Soccer, Var Bsktbl, Girls Var Sftbl Coach; Prof Advancement Comm; NYS 1989-; St Lawrence

Co, AFT 1987-; *office:* Potsdam Central HS 29 Leroy St Potsdam NY 13676*

WATKINS, ALLEN RICHARD, Technology Education Teacher; *b:* Northport, NY; *m:* Cheryl Ilene Berlin; *c:* Stephanie A., Matthew R., Chase A., Samuel R.; *ed:* SUNY at Oswego (BS) Indstrl Arts 1976; SUNY at Stony Brook (MS) Applied Scis 1982; *cr:* East Northport Jr HS Tech Ed Tchr 1976-77; Earl L. Vandermeulen HS Tech Ed Tchr 1977-; *ai:* Var Soccer, Sftbl Coach; Cmptr Club Adv; Tech Comm; Suffolk Cty Sftbl Coach Assn 1980-, Treas, Outstdng Svc Awd 1993; Suffolk Cty Soccer Coaches Assn 1978-, Coach of Yr Awds, 1979, 1981, 1983, 1985; Suffolk Cty Macintosh Users Group 1994-; Royal Fnd Grant 1995-; Columbia Univ Yrbk Awd 1987; Jostons Golden Galleon Yrbk Awd 1986; Multimedia Presenter at Apple Cmptr Sympsoium 1989; *office:* Earl L Vandermeulen HS Old Post Rd Port Jefferson Sta NY 11777*

WATKINS, CELINE SAXE, Math Teacher; *b:* Sayre, PA; *c:* Allison Watkins Long, Linda Watkins McCord, J. Arnold Watkins; *ed:* Catholic Univ of America (BA) Physics 1960; Elmira Coll (MEd) Ed 1975; Addl 40 Credit Hrs; *cr:* Natl Bureau of Standards Physicist 1960-66; Waverly HS Math Tchr 1981-; *ai:* Waverly Tchrs Assn 1981-, Treas 2 Yrs, Sec 4 Yrs; NEA NY, NEA 1981-; *office:* Waverly Jr-Sr H S 1 Frederick St Waverly NY 14892

WATKINS, CHARLES PETE, Sixth Grade Mathematics Tchr; *b:* Carmel, NY; *m:* Corinne Watson; *c:* Janlyn, Terence; *ed:* SUNY at New Paltz (BA) Elem Ed 1968; 30 Hrs Grad Stud; *cr:* Highland Cntrl Schls 6th Grd Tchr 1968-95; *ai:* Girls Var Soccer & Sftbl Coach; AFT 1968-; HTA 1968-, Past Treas; *office:* Highland Cntrl Schl Dist 71 Main St Highland NY 12528

WATKINS, KATHLEEN A. R., Acting Science Dept Chprsn; *b:* Middlesboro, KY; *m:* Timothy Christian; *ed:* IN Univ (BS) Bio 1983; Attnd Univ of MD, Purdue Univ; *cr:* David Starr Jordan HS Sci Tchr 1985-86; Woodlawn MS Sci Tchr 1992-93; Southeastern Tech HS Sci Tchr 1993-; *ai:* New Tchr Mentor; Attendance Comm Chm; Open House Comm; ACT Team; NEA, NAST 1993-; Honorable Order KY Colonels 1993-; Navy Relief Soc 1000 Hr Pin; Outstanding Young Women of Amer 1991; *office:* Southeastern Technical HS 325 Sollers Point Rd Baltimore MD 21222*

WATKINS, MARILYN ORZELEK, Social Science Teacher; *b:* Johnson City, NY; *m:* Mark Edward; *c:* Matthew Elias, Claire Aimee; *ed:* SUNY at Binghamton (BA) Amer His 1966; Coll of St Rose (MA) Intnl Relations 1990; *cr:* Rensselaer Cty Dept of Soc Svcs Soc Worker 1967-71; Cundello & Ryan Lobbyist Asst 1980-81; Acad of the Holy Names Soc Stud Tchr 1989-; *ai:* SADD Moderator; Soph Class Coord; Publicity Chprsn Schl Musical; NCEA 1989-; Albany Cty Stop DWI Grant 1989-; *office:* Acad Of The Holy Names 1075 New Scotland Rd Albany NY 12208

WATKINS, MILDRED LOUISE, Mathematics Teacher; *b:* Mt Savage, MD; *ed:* Frostburg St Univ (BS) Ed 1960; Univ of NH (MST) Math Ed 1978; Frostburg St Univ Post Grad Stud 1980-84; *cr:* Severna Park HS Tchr 1960; Ft Hill HS Tchr, Dept Chair 1961-; *ai:* Schl Improvement, Spectra Math Comms Chm; MSTA, NEA, NCTM, MCTM 1960-; Mt Savage United Meth Church 1956-, Admin Cncl Chprsn, Financial Sec; NSTDP 1986-; Western MD Coll Distinguished HS Educator 1992; Mc Donald-Ray C. Kroc Tchr Awd 1993, 1995; *office:* Fort Hill HS 500 Greenway Ave Cumberland MD 21502

WATKINS, WILLIAM JOHN, Professor of Humanities; *b:* Coaldale, PA; *m:* Sandra Prano; *c:* Tara, Wade, Chad; *ed:* Rutgers Univ (BS) Eng Ed 1964; Rutgers Grad Schl of Ed (MED) Eng Ed 1965; *cr:* DE Vly Coll Hum Instr 1965-68; Asbury Park HS Eng Tchr 1968-69; Brookdale Comm Coll Hum Prof 1969-; *ai:* NEA 1965-; NJEA 1968-; Educl Software Awd 1988; Nashaminy HS Ftbl Hall of Fame 1989; SFWA Nebula Awd Nom 1993; IBM League for Innovation In the Comm Coll Computition for Excl; Numerous Articles Pub; *office:* Brookdale Comm Coll Newman Springs Road Lincroft NJ 07738

WATMAN, LUISE CAROLINE, Science Teacher; *b:* Rochester, NY; *m:* Michael; *ed:* UNH (BS) Pre Med 1968, (MAT) Sci 1971; 454 Credit Hrs; *cr:* Somersworth HS Sci, Hlth, PE Dept Chair 1981-95, Sci Tchr 1970-; *ai:* FAc Cncl; Stu of Month; NEA 1996; NHSTA 1971-; NSTA 1980-; *office:* Somersworth HS 11 Memorial Dr Somersworth NH 03878

WATRO, MARSHA ALEKSA, 7th Grade History Teacher; *b:* Paterson, NJ; *m:* John P.; *c:* Ami L.; *ed:* Trenton St Coll (BA) His 1971; 20 Addl Credits; *cr:* Ewing Schls 7th Grd His Tchr 25 Yrs; *ai:* Cmptr Club Adv; NJEA, NEA 1970-; Ewing Women's Club 1971-, VP, Pres; Ewing Twp Multicultural Divirsity, Chprsn 1994-; Awds: Cty Film Maker 1973, A+ for Kids Tchr 1990, Governor's Tchr Recognition 1991; Who's Who in Amer 1992; Who's Who in Amer Ed 1993; Who's Who in Amer Women 1993; Golden Apple Tchr Awd 1992; *home:* 117 Ingleside Ave Pennington NJ 08534

WATSON, AMY (STEWART), Sixth Grade Teacher; *b:* Brookville, PA; *m:* Glenn; *c:* Alana, Zane; *ed:* Clarion Univ (BS) Ed 1986; Gannon Univ (ME) Ed 1994; Post Grad Credits Sci Ed; *cr:* Day Care Svcs Inc Tchr 1986-87; Brookville Area Schl Dist Sixth Grd Tchr 1987-; *ai:* Elem Yrbk, Newspaper; Sixth Grd Talent Show; Cmptr Comm; K-12 Tech Comm Sec; Lead Tchr; NEA, PSEA, BAEA 1987-, Bldg Rep; Oakwood Church Session 1985-92, Clerk; *office:* Hickory Grove Elem Schl Jenks St Ext Brookville PA 15825*

WATSON, ANDREW COMPTON, Former English Teacher; *b:* Cleveland, OH; *ed:* Harvard Univ (AB) His, Lit 1988; Spec Stu at Harvard Univ Eng Dept 1990-91, 1995-; *cr:* Loomis Chaffee Schl Eng Tchr, Dir of Theater, Dorm Fac 1988-90, 1992-95; *ai:* Theater; Comm Svc; Debate Team; Dorm Fac; GLSTN 1992-.

WATSON, ANN LOUISE, English Teacher; *b:* Hanover, PA; *m:* James W. II; *c:* Peyton Mackenzie; *ed:* York Coll of PA (BA) Comm 1975; Western MD Coll MLA Liberal Arts 1983; *cr:* New Oxford SR High 9-12th Grd Eng & Elective Speech, Writing, Jrnlsm Tchr 1977-; *ai:* Drama Dir; Stu Assistance Team; Fine Arts Week Coord; Fellow Lit Inst Franklin, Marshall Coll; PA Tchr of Yr Finalist 1989; Outstanding Educator, Guest Lecturer Shippensburg Univ 1989; *office:* New Oxford HS 130 Berlin Rd New Oxford PA 17331

WATSON, BARBARA REICH, Social Studies Teacher; *b:* Liberty, NY; *ed:* SUNY at Albany (BA) His 1965; Post Grad Stud SUNY at New Paltz, Ithaca Coll, Univ of CO, Bridgeport Univ; *cr:* Wappingers Cntrl Schl Soc Stud Tchr 1965-; *ai:* Stu Govt, Yrbk, Drama Club Adv; AFT, NYSUT, Wappingers Congress of Tchr 1970-; NY St Historical Soc 1988-; *office:* Wappingers Jr HS 90 Remsen Ave Wappingers Falls NY 12590

WATSON, BRENT DUANE, Fifth Grade Teacher; *b:* Brooklyn, NY; *c:* Adrienne, Corey; *ed:* St Augustine Coll (BS) Ed 1980; City Coll of NY (MS) Ed; *ai:* PE Dir; UFT 1982-; AFT 1983-; Kappa Alpha Psi 1977-, Life Mem; Salvation Army-Bedford Temple; *office:* Benjamin Banneker Schl PS 256 114 Kosciusko St Brooklyn NY 11216

WATSON, C. KAY TAYLOR, English Teacher; *b:* Louisville, KY; *m:* John J. Jr.; *ed:* Eastern KY Univ (BA) Eng 1970; Xavier Univ (MED) Comm Art 1977; OH Writing Project 1990-; Advanced OH Writing Project 1991, 1992; *cr:* Dayton HS Eng Tchr 1970-76; Lakota HS Eng Tchr 1976-; *ai:* WLHS; NEA 1970-; OEA, SWOEA 1976-; Who's Who in Entertainment 1992; *office:* Lakota HS 5050 Tylersville Rd West Chester OH 45069*

WATSON, DIANA MICHAELS, Director of Theater; *b:* Waterville, ME; *c:* Katherine; *ed:* Boston Univ (BA) Eng Lang & Lit 1971; Univ of CT (MFA) Theater Directing 1979; Attnd Omega Inst, Interface, Webser Univ Theater Conservatory, & Westfield St Coll; *cr:* Southwick HS Eng & Drama Tchr 1972-76; Univ of CT at Storrs Lecturer 1976-79; WA Univ in St Louis Asst Prof of Theater 1979-86; Worcester Acad Dir of Theater 1986-; *ai:* Drama Assn Dir; Comm for Soc Action Adv; O Connell Awd for Excl in Tchng 1989; Coll of Arts & Scis Awd for Outstanding Tchr of Yr 1986; *office:* Worcester Acad 81 Providence St Worcester MA 01604

WATSON, DONALD LLOYD, 7th Grade Life Science Teacher; *b:* Washington, PA; *m:* Mary Lou; *c:* David, Kelly; *ed:* Ca St Coll of Pa (BS) Earth Sci 1970; Masters Degree in Scndry Ed; *cr:* West Mifflin Area Schl Dist Tchr 1970-; *ai:* Head of Sci Dept; Spon Horticulture Club; HS Band Drum Line Coord; AFT 1974-; West Mifflin Parents Band Boosters 1992-, VP; *office:* West Mifflin Area Schl Dist 371 Camp Hollow Rd West Mifflin PA 15122

WATSON, DONNA DRESCHER, High School English Teacher; *b:* Troy, NY; *m:* Edward; *ed:* St Univ of NY at Albany (BA) Eng, Span 1991, (MA) Eng Ed 1993; Stud Abroad Spain, Portugal, France Summer 1991; *cr:* Acad of the Holy Names Span Tchr 1992-93; Watervliet Jr Sr HS Eng Tchr 1993-; Watervliet City Schl Dist Adult Ed Span Tchr 1994-; *ai:* Jr Var & Var Ftbl & Basktbl Cheerleading Coach; NCTE, ACTFL 1991-; *office:* Watervliet Jr Sr HS Wiswall Ave Watervliet NY 12189

WATSON, EILEEN MURNIN, Special Education Teacher; *b:* Baltimore, MD; *m:* Richard Lee; *c:* Meghan, Caitlin; *ed:* Towson St Coll (BS) Elem Ed 1974; Johns Hopkins Univ (MS) Ed, Communicative Disorders 1981; Inservice Spec Ed; Cmptr; *cr:* St Clare Schl 2-3 Grd Tchr 1975-84; St Elizabeth of Hungary Schl 2-8 Grd Tchr 1984-94; Edgewood MS 6-8 Grd Spec Ed Tchr 1994-; *ai:* NEA, MSTA, HCEA 1995-; Watersedge Recreation Cncl 1990-, Sftbl Chprsn; JHU Alumni Assn 1981-; Defenders Day Vol 1993-; Title II Grant Environmental Sci, Tech, Soc Loyola Coll 1991; Consultant Grantback Prgm Chptr I Baltimore City Schls 1989; *office:* Edgewood MS 2311 Willoughby Beach Rd Edgewood MD 21040*

WATSON, GEORGETTA ANN, Third Grade Teacher; *b:* Clymer, PA; *c:* Hugh M., Marie T.; *ed:* Mt Aloysius Jr Coll (AA) Elem Ed 1959; IN Univ of PA (BA) Elem Ed 1961; Grad Stud at Cleveland St Univ, Baldwin Wallace Univ & Walsh Coll; *cr:* Charles Orr Elem Schl 1st Grd Tchr 1961-63; Iowa Maple Elem Schl 1st Grd Tchr 1963-65; Cleve Rdng Improvement Dept Rdng Consultant & Diagnostician 1965-81; Wm C Bryant Elem Schl 3rd Grd Tchr 1981-; *ai:* On TASC & Union Conf Comms; Schl Safety & Rdng Enrichment Club Adv; Stu of the Month & Perfect Attendance Act; AFT 1961-; Cleveland TV 8 Tchr of Week Awd; *office:* William C Bryant Primary Sch 3121 Oak Park Ave Cleveland OH 44109

WATSON, JUDITH, Sixth Grade Teacher; *b:* Utica, NY; *ed:* Utica Coll of Syracuse Univ (BA) Eng 1964; 30 Grad Hrs; *cr:* Bellamy Elem Schl 2nd Grd Tchr 1964-65; Kernan Schl 2nd Grd Tchr 1965-67; Smith Rd Elem Schl 1st, 4th-5th Grd Tchr 1967-81; Gillette Rd MS 6th Grd Tchr 1981-; *ai:* Judge Cntrl NY Sci Olympiad 1992-; NSEA, NYSUT, AFT 1967-; Co-Produced ZAP; *office:* Gillette Road MS 6150 S Bay Rd Cicero NY 13039

WATSON, KATHY ANN, Spanish Teacher; *b:* Zanesville, OH; *m:* Mark Andrew; *c:* Kaleigh Nicole; *ed:* OH St Univ (BS) Span, Eng 1979; *cr:* Zanesville HS Span Tchr 1979-81; White Oak Jr HS Span Tchr 1981-83; Zanesville City Schls Span Tchr 1983-85; Zanesville HS Span Tchr 1985-; *ai:* NEA, OEA, ZEA 1985-; Trinity Luth Church 1981-; Outstdng Tchr Daybreak Rotary Club; *home:* 2815 Dresden Rd Zanesville OH 43701

WATSON, LINDA ANN, Business Education Dept Chprsn; *b:* Cheverly, MD; *m:* Douglas A.; *c:* Devin, Dustin; *ed:* Univ Of MD (BS) Bus Ed 1978, (BS) Cmptr Prgmng 1988; 45 Plus Credits Cmptr Prgmng 1988; *cr:* Walker Mill Jr HS Tchr 1978-1980; Eleanor Roosevelt HS Tchr 1980-; *ai:* Dept Chprsn; Instructional Counsel; Schl-Based Mgmt; Budget, Cmptr Comms; Tech Prep; St Approved Prgms; PGCEA 1978-; NEA, NBEA, MBEA, EBEA 1978-; MICCA 1990-; BSA 1985-, Merit Badge Cnslr; HSA 1985-; Outstanding Tchrs Award 1980; *office:* Eleanor Roosevelt HS 7601 Hanover Pky Greenbelt MD 20770

WATSON, LINDA LOUISE, Communication Arts Teacher; *b:* Pittsburgh, PA; *m:* James Rocky; *c:* James Jeffrey, Matthew Kyle; *ed:* PA St Univ at St Coll (BS) Comm Arts, Scndry Eng 1970; PA St Extension 24 Credits 1976; *cr:* Downington Jr HS 9th Grd Comm Arts Tchr 1970-76; Reynolds Jr HS 7th-9th Grd Comm Arts Tchr 1986-; *ai:* NHS Comm; RIF, Spelling Bee Chprsn; NEA, PSEA 1987-; NCTE; *home:* 84 Garden City Dr Lancaster PA 17602

WATSON, MARK S., Instrumental Music Teacher; *b:* Lancaster, PA; *m:* Sharon Kashner; *c:* Matthew, Christopher; *ed:* Levanon Valley Coll (BS) Music Ed 1980; West Chester Univ Master Music Ed 1988; *cr:* Schl Dist of Lancaster Instrumental Music Tchr 1981-; *ai:* Concert, Jazz Band Dir; NEA, PSEA, LEA, MENC, PMEA; Jaycees Outstanding Young Educator 1983; Natl Deans List 1988; *office:* Wheatland Jr HS 919 Hamilton Park Dr Lancaster PA 17603

WATSON, MARY ANN DIEVENDORF, Choral Music Teacher; *b:* Amsterdam, NY; *m:* Stanley C.; *c:* Thomas A. Bickerstaff Jr., David A Bickerstaff; *ed:* Chatham Coll (BA) Music 1970; Rowan Coll Tchng Cert; Hartt Coll of Music Grad Work 20 Credits; *cr:* Edgewood HS ChoralMusic Tchr 1987; Glassboro HS Choral Music Tchr 1987-; *ai:* Spring Musical; Equity ASETS Trng; Schl Profile Comm; NEA, NJMEA, MENC 1987-; Choristers Guild 1986-; Trinity Presbyn Church 1986-, Music Asst Dir; Minna Kaufmann-Ruud Scholar Chatham Coll; Outstdng Tchr Awd 1993; *office:* Glassboro HS Bowe Blvd Glassboro NJ 08028*

WATSON, MICHELLE LAFOUNTAINE, Reading Teacher; *b:* Dover, OH; *m:* Kelly L.; *c:* Christopher, Matthew; *ed:* OH St Univ (BS) Elem Ed 1982; Ashland Coll, Walsh Coll, Akron Univ Credit Hrs; *cr:* Bolivar Elem Schl Second Grd Tchr 1983-85; Tusc Vly Jr HS Rdng Tchr 1985-; *ai:* OCTELA 1995-; IRA 1993-; TVTA 1990-; Selected as Trainer OH Model Lang Arts Curr; *office:* Tuscarawas Vly Schl 2637 Tusc Valley Rd NE Zoarville OH 44656

WATSON, PAMPALENA C., Life & Earth Science Teacher; *b:* York, PA; *c:* Dawnee Watson-Bouie; *ed:* Cheyney Univ (BS) Elem Ed 1973; Spec Ed Minor 1984; *cr:* Bureau of Ed of NY Remedial Rdng Tchr 1974; Andrew Hamilton Schl Life Sci, Earth Sci Tchr 1986-; Schl Dist of Phila Summer Schl Tchr 1987-90; *ai:* Urban Systemic Initiative Team Children Achieving; Cobbs Creeks Comm Environmental Ed Coord; Schl Coord Phil, Camden Informal Sci, Phila Regnl Introduction Minorities Engrng; PFT 1986-; PAESTRA 1994-; NSTA 1990-; Mentoring, Coord of Adopt-a-Schl Prgm 1990-; Outcome Based Ed Grant, PARTNERS Grant 1993-95; Black Employment Prgm Advy Cncl of Environmental Protection Agency 1996; *office:* Andrew Hamilton Elem Schl 57th & Spruce Sts Philadelphia PA 19139

WATSON, RICHARD L., Fifth Grade Teacher; *b:* Southampton, NY; *m:* Susan Abetz; *c:* Kelly Ann, Christopher Jay; *ed:* Eastern CT St Coll (BS) Elem Ed, Math 1979; Cntrl Ct St Univ (MS) Admin, Supervision 1988; 6th Yr Educl Ldrshp 1996; *cr:* Myrtle H. Stevens Elem Schl 5th, 6th Grd Tchr 1979-; *ai:* Unit Ldr 5th Grd; Rock Hill HS Boys Var Bsktbl Coach; Rocky Hill Thrs Assn, CT Ed Assn, NEA 1979-; Manchester Soccer Club 1994-, Coach; St James Church 1990-, Parishoner; Tchr of Yr 1986; *office:* Myrtle H Stevens Elem Schl 322 Orchard St Rocky Hill CT 06067

WATSON, ROBERT E., Mathematics Teacher; *b:* Old Forge, PA; *m:* Nancy L. Hurchick; *c:* Robert Jr.; *ed:* Uinv of Scranton (BS) Scndry Ed 1966; Grad Schl 30+ Credits; *cr:* Tioga Cntrl HS Math, Sci & S Tchr 1966-68; Johnson City HS Math Tchr 1968-; *ai:* NYSTA 1966 1966-; JCTA 1968-; *office:* Johnson City HS 666 Reynolds Rd J City NY 13790

WATSON, SAMUEL P., Instrumental Music Teacher; *b:* Willia PA; *m:* Barbara Grey; *c:* Sean P., Kari E.; *ed:* Mansfield St Coll (BS Ed 1968; Grad Schl PA St Univ; *cr:* Kane Cntl Schl Instrumenta Tchr 1969-70; Haverling Cntrl Schl Instrumental Music Tchr 1970 Elem Bands; NYSUT, AFT, NYSSMA.

WATSON, SHIRLEY BROCKMAN, Social Studies Teacher; *b:* OH; *m:* Leroy N; *c:* Stephen Zwiesler, Eric Zwiesler, Amy Sommer Likens, Rebecca Zwiesler, Patricia Whisler; *ed:* Wright St Uni Comprehensive Soc Stud 1986; *cr:* Valley View HS Govt Tchr 19 Lady of Mercy Schl Soc Stud Tchr 1990-; *ai:* Stu Cncl Adv; Cub Sc Yrs Den Leader, Tiger Coord, Den Leader Coach; Dayton Pub Sch Ed Cncl 1974 Chprsn & Sec; *office:* Our Lady Of Mercy Schl 54 Ave Dayton OH 45405

WATSON, SUSAN SCOTT, French Teacher; *b:* Newark, OH; *m:* Rollin; *c:* Jason; *ed:* Miami Univ 1963 BS Ed; Newark HS Frenc 1963-70, 1987-; *cr:* Fr Club Adv; Textbook Selection Comm; *ai:* Garden Club, Monday Talks 1983-; Unity Club 1982-, Prgm Chm Nom Ashland Tchr of Yr 1993; Article Pub Writing across the Curr Univ; Ashland Tchr Yr 1995; *home:* 11271 Hazel Dell Rd NE New 43055

WATSON, WILLIAM WORDEN, Science Teacher; *b:* Buffalo, Dorothy Myers; *c:* Jay, Guy, Dorothy, William; *ed:* Baldwin-Walla (BA) His 1965; SUNY at Buffalo (MA) Geology 1970; Attnd Univ St Univ Coll at Buffalo, Alfred Univ; *cr:* Millard Fillmore Coll G Instr 1966-67; SUNY at Buffalo Geology Instr 1967-68; West Senec Schls Earth Sci Tchr 1968-69; Buffalo Pub Schls Sci Tchr 1970-; *ai* Club, Astronomy Club, Math Club, Lab Club, Sci Olympiad Ad Seneca Tchrs Assn 1968-69; NEA, Buffalo Tchrs Fed 1970-, Pre Del, Alternate Retirement Convention; City of Tonawanda Pub 1983-, Bd of Ed; Holy Cross Head Start 1993-, Bd of Dirs; Ornithological Soc 1985-; Fed of NY St Bird Clubs 1987-, John Ellic Amer Assn of Lunar & Planetary Observers; NSF Grant 1978; Pub A *home:* 771 Fletcher St Tonawanda NY 14150

WATSON, WILMA MOODY, Retired Physical Ed Teacher; *b:* KY; *m:* James Darrell; *ed:* Cumberland Coll (BS) Hlth, PE Ed 1993 Miami Univ; *cr:* Wayne Local Schls Hlth, PE Tchr 1963-93; *ai:* S Adv 4 Yrs; Track Coach 1 Yr; Class Spon; Waynesville Ed Assn Cc Yrs; Chrldr Coach 20 Yrs; Tax Levy Comm Chm; Waynesville E 1964, Several Offices Held; NEA 1964-; Natl Assn of PE Tchrs Delta Kappa Gamma 1986-; Lioness Club 1986-, Sec, Treas; Prof W Club Chamber of Commerce 1990-; Awd of Excl in Tchng 1988; *hon* Robindale Dr Waynesville OH 45068

WATT, CHRISTINE A. DUDENHAVER, Third Grade Teac Meadville, PA; *m:* F. Gordon; *c:* Shannon Lynn Shuffstall, Matt Shuffstall; *ed:* Edinboro St Coll (BS) Elem Early Chldhd 1974, (MS Early Chldhd 1977; 30 Addl Credits; *cr:* Summit Elem Schl 2nd Gr I Math Tchr 1974-76; Graham Elem Schl 3rd Grd Tchr 1977-84 Schafer Elem Schl 3rd Grd Tchr 1984-; *ai:* Stu Assistance, Instrl S Teams; Mentor Tchr Thiel Coll Stdnts; NEA, PSEA 1974-; Conne Assn 1974-, Pub Relations Comm; Summit Vol Fire Dept; PTO; HS Boosters; *home:* RR 8 Box 348 Meadville PA 16335

WATT, VIVIAN PEROTTI, AP Lang & Composition Tchr; Pleasant, PA; *m:* Joseph; *c:* Aimee Williams, Ryan; *ed:* Slippery Roc (BS) Eng 1965; Penn St Univ; Pitt Univ; Carlow; *cr:* Glassport Sc Eng Tchr 1965-66; South Allegheny Ur HS Eng Tchr 1966-67; Nor AP Lang, Comp Tchr 1967-; *ai:* Mentor Tchr; NEA, PSEA 1965-; EA 1967-, Sec, NEA Del; Westmoreland Ed Cncl 1988-, NEA W Caucus; Caring Prgm for Children 1991-, Vol; Norwin Tchrs C. U. Supervisory Bd; Sons of Italy; Participation in Beautification Comm Awd; *home:* 1224 10th St Irwin PA 15642*

WATTERS, MELISSA, Second Grade Teacher; *b:* Phillipsburg, James; *c:* Jake, Jamie, Ben; *ed:* Rider Coll (BA) Elem Ed, Early 1980; *cr:* Willow Grove Elem Schl Third Grd Tchr 1980-81, First Gr 1982-84, Basic Skills Tchr 1985-89, Second Grd Tchr 1990-; *ai:* 1980-; Rockport Presbyn Church 1979-, Sunday Schl Tchr, Ladie Pres 1985-, Elder 1988-, Bell Ringer 1985; Governors Tchr Reco Prgm 1993-94; *office:* Willow Grove Elem Schl 601 Willow Gr Hackettstown NJ 07840

WATTERS, SALLY B., 7th Grd Social Studies Teacher; *b:* Wo MA; *m:* James E.; *c:* Rebecca, Amanda; *ed:* St Lawrence Univ (A 1967; Clark Univ (MA) His 1969; *cr:* Walpole HS Soc Stud Tchr 19 Johnson MS Soc Stud Tchr 1986-; *ai:* Yrbk Adv; Natl Geog Bee NEA, MTA, WTA 1970-; NELMS 1995-; Southboro Open Land Fnd Bd of Trustees; John F. Kennedy Presidential Lib Outstndng Tch 1990; *office:* Johnson MS 111 Robbins Rd Walpole MA 02081*

WATTLES, GEORGE V., 5th Grade Teacher & Coach; *b:* Bryn Ma *m:* Cristina C.; *c:* Evan, Emily, Schyler; *ed:* Springfield Coll (B Stud, Ed 1978; *cr:* Montgomery Schl 5th Grd Tchr, Coach 19 Shipley Schl 4th Grd Tchr, Coach 1982-85; Episcopal Acad 5th Gr Coach 1985-; *ai:* Stu Adv; Lacrosse Coach; Indep Schls Tchrs Assn Schl Adv; Penn Del Lacrosse Ofcls 1979-, Pres, Bd Mem Intercollegiate Lacrosse Ofcls Assn 1980-; *office:* Episcopal Acad Latches Ln Merion Station PA 19066

WATTS, BEVERLY E., Computer Lab Teacher; *b:* Schenectady, N Rowan Coll (BA) Elem Ed 1973; *cr:* Deerfield Twp Schl Third Gr 1973-94, Cmptr Lab Tchr 1994-; *ai:* Tech Comm Chm; CCEA Courier Ed; NJEA 1973-, Editorial Comm 1994-95; NEA 1973-, De 1991-94; Governor's Recognition Awd 1991; Tchr of Yr Awd 1990.

WATTS, BONNIE YACOUONE, Seventh Grd English Teach Youngstown, OH; *m:* Jeffrey L.; *c:* Kristine, Jeffrey; *ed:* Youngst Univ (BSEd) Scndry Ed, Bio 1985; UT St (BS) Spec Ed; *cr:* Reed S Tutor 1985-87; Byzantine Cath Cntrl Schl Jr HS Eng Tchr 1988-; Byzantine Catholic Ctl Schl 5512 Youngstown-Poland Youngstow 44514

WATTS, CHRISTINA JAMES, Education Instructor; *b:* Charlott *m:* Mc Coy C.; *c:* Joshua, Coya; *ed:* Appalachian St Univ (BS) Eng Univ of MD at College Park (MFD) Admin, Supervision 1991; Mary's Cty Bd of Ed Elem Tchr 1979-91, Asst Prin 1991-95, Resource Tchr 1995-; St Mary's Coll of MD Ed Instr 1991-; *ai:* NCTM 1990-; Children's Assn of St Mary's 1994-; *office:* Saint Mary Of MD St Marys Cy MD 20686

WATTS, JOHN MARVIN, English Department Professor; *b:* La MO; *m:* Linda Sue Lloyd; *c:* Natasha M. A., Ian F. T., Eliot W. L.; *ed* of KS (BA) Geology, Eng 1960; Univ of GA (MA) Eng 1961; *cr:* U GA Instr 1961-63; Univ of MD Far East Div Lecturer 1963-65; Univ European Div Lecturer 1965-67; Bunka Gakuin Assoc Prof 19 Montgomery Coll Prof 1971-; *ai:* Phi Theta Kappa Mems Adv; PE 1964-; Project Historic Amer 1994-; Natl Trust for His Preservation Bluemont Lib Fnd 1986-, Founding Dir, Lib of Amer Grant; Toget Lou Down 1967-, VP; Keep Lou Down Beautiful 1988-; Pie Environmental Cncl 1985-; PHP Inst Kyoto 1969-; Guest Lecturer

Jniv, Taiwan Natl Univ; Articles Pub; Appoonted to VA ›rtation Comm; Wrote & Designed Booklet; Spec Merit Awd 1994; 9227 Foggy Bottom Rd Bluemont VA 22012

S, KAREN ALEXIA, Physics & Chemistry Teacher; *b:* Essequibo, ; *c:* Glenn Herbert, Michael Herbert; *ed:* St John's Univ (BS) Chem 12 Grad Credits in Chem; 18 Grad Credits in Ed; *cr:* Sanders m Tobacco Accounts Exec 1986-93; Grover Cleveland HS Physics, Tchr 1993-; *ai:* UFT 1993-; *office:* Grover Cleveland HS 2127 St Ridgewood NY 11385*

S, MARCIA RAE, Former Riffed Spanish Teacher; *b:* Ellwood ; *m:* David G.; *c:* Erik, Lisa; *ed:* CA Univ of PA (BS) Span 1974; dit Hrs WVU; 9 Credit Hrs Kent St; *cr:* Hancock Cty Schl Span Tchr); Weir HS Span Tchr 1991-95; *ai:* Span Club Spon; WVEA 1988-; outs 1982-, Ldr, Dir, Outstdng Ldr; Church 1990-, Deacon, Elder; for Tchr of Yr 1995; *home:* 199 Hill Rd Georgetown PA 15043

S, RHONDA CATHERINE, First Grade Teacher; *b:* Nashua, NH; ier Coll (BA) Elem Ed 1976; 24 Credit Hrs Many Non-Rated Hrs e, Ecology Studies; *cr:* Florence Rideout Elem Schl First Grd Tchr Kingsbury Hill Camp Riding Instr 1978; NH 4-H Livestock Camp Instr 1979-80; NH 4-H Livestock Camp Dir 1981-93; 4-H Lancers Camp Vol Instr 1994-; *ai:* Odyssey of Mind Coach; Staff Dev, Gifted, ment Comm; Schl Gymnastics Prgm Asst; Pupil Placement Team; e, Curr Comm; Delta Kappa Gamma 1988-, Music Comm; Beta St Historian; Mensa 1988-; NH Assn for Gifted; 4-H Ldr 1973- 20 d; Hillsboro Cty 4-H Equestrian Cncl 1980-, Pres, Sec 14 Yrs; o Cty 4-H, Svc Awd; NH 4-H Horse Advy Comm 1972-, Chm 2 Yrs, Yrs; NH 4-H Curr Comm 1975-80, Sec; Intnl Side-Saddle Org 1980- omm, 2 Time US Champion; Presidential Inaugural Prade Units 989, 1993, Unit Ldr 1993; 8 Articles Pub; *office:* Florence Rideout chl PO Box 430 Wilton NH 03086*

H, JOHN C., Computer Teacher & Programmer; *b:* New York City, Susan; *c:* Ingela, Sara, John R.; *ed:* Caltech (BS) Bio 1971; St Univ S) Sci Ed 1978; Union Coll (MS) Cmptr Sci 1984; *cr:* Chester HS r 1 Yr; NY Military Acad Sci Tchr 3 Yrs; Mt St Mary HS Sci Tchr Marlbobo HS Sci, Cmptrs Tchr 15 Yrs; *ai:* Chess Club, Team; T; AFT; USCF; Cmptr Curr Design Grant; Nationally Pub Children's , Sci Articles; Designed Cmptr Software Ed.

ANGELA LABRUZZO, Mathematics Teacher; *b:* New York, NY; lip Joseph Jr.; *c:* Philip J. III, Kristen Angela Rubush, Jeannine ; *ed:* St Johns Univ (BA) Math 1967; Lehman Coll (MA) Math 1975; l Credit Hrs Anna Maria Coll; 9 Addl Credit Hrs Yeshiva Univ; *cr:* Whitman JHS Math Tchr 1967-68; Pt Chester JHS Math Tchr 0; Norwalk HS Math Tchr 1981-90; Ponus Ridge MS Math Tchr 2; Norwalk HS Math Tchr 1992-; *ai:* Class Adv 1992-; Cheerleading 1994-; AFT 1967-; Norwalk Fed of Tchrs 1983-.

FREDENE, Math Teacher; *b:* Brooklyn, NY; *ed:* Brooklyn Coll d 1972, (MS) Math 1974; Long Island Univ (MS) Math 1976; *cr:*) 4th-5th Grd Tchr 1972-76; Mahalia Jackson Intermediate Schl Tchr 1976-91; Robert H. Goddard Jr HS Math Tchr 1991-; *ai:* After ummer Schl Remedial Prgms; UFT 1972-; Natl Assn of Math Tchrs Local House of Worship Swimming Coach.*

ILENE L., Learning Specialist; *b:* New York, NY; *m:* Gary; *c:* Dara, *ed:* SUNY at Albany (BA) Tchng Scndry Math 1972; Columbia Univ Tchng Emot Dist 1973; 30 Credits; *cr:* NYC Bd of Ed Tchr of MR 7; Whitingham Schl Chptr I Tchr 1978-80; Halifax Schl Spcl Ed 983-94; Wilmington MHS Learning Specialist 1994-; *ai:* CEC NRC 1993-; ASCD 1994-; NEA; Pub Stud on Inclusion 1993; *office:* ngton Mid HS Box 397 Wilmington VT 05363*

IAN, LAURIE GOLAN, Mathematics Teacher; *b:* Boston, MA; *m:* *d:* Springfield Coll (BS) Math Ed 1980; In Process of Taking s for Masters Degree; *cr:* Wilmington North Intermediate Schl Math 980-81; Salem HS Math Tchr 1981-84; Saugus HS Math Tchr 1984-; ss Adv; NEA 1980-; MTA 1981-; SEA 1984-; NCTM 1995-; Square all Advy Bd 1994-; *office:* Saugus HS Pierce Dr Saugus MA 01906

IAN, RANDI JOY, Associate Prof of Business; *b:* Philadelphia, PA; chard; *c:* Nicole; *ed:* George Washington Univ (BS) Accounting Georgetown Univ Law Ctr (JD) Law 1988; *cr:* Melrod, Redman & n Attorney 1988-93; George Washington Univ Adjunct Instr 3; Law Office of Randi J Waxman Attorney-Prin 1993-; Columbia Coll Assoc Prof 1993-; *ai:* Alpha Sigma Beta Bus Club Fac Spon; y Cncl & Acad Discipline Comms; Amer Inst of Certified Pub ntants 1985-; Amer Bar Assn, Bar Assn of DC 1988-; Bar Assn of 989-; Childrens Cancer Fnd 1992-, Advy Bd, Various Awds; VE of Washington Metropolitan Area 1992-, Bd of Dirs; Certified ccountant MD 1985; *office:* Columbia Union Coll 7600 Flower Ave a Park MD 20912

IE, CAROLYN SETARO, 7th & 8th Grd Spanish Teacher; *b:* New , CT; *m:* Jeffrey N.; *c:* Christopher, Rebecca; *ed:* Southern CT St BS) Span 1970, (MS) Spec Ed 1974; Cert in Spec Ed 1992; *cr:* Dodd Span Tchr 1970-71; Cheshire HS Span Tchr 1971-76; High Plains Schl Spec Ed Tchr 1979-80; Hamden MS Span Tchr 1992-; *ai:* gie, Scheduling, Flex Time, Cmptr Comms; Helping Us Grow gh Svc & Smiles Coord; Off-Team Rep; Colt, HEA 1992-; *office:* en MS 550 Newhall St Hamden CT 06517

E, DEBRA ANN CATANZARO, 8th Grade Study Skills Teacher; ey City, NJ; *m:* Stephen Michael; *c:* Stephen Michael II; *ed:* Rutgers BA) Eng 1976; Univ Coll K-12 Tchr Cert 1978; Cmptr Credits ssex Cty Coll 1982; *cr:* S Stanislaus Gram Schl Tchr 1980-83; JFK l Rdng, Writing Tchr 1986-87; Colonia MS Dev Lang Tchr 1987-90; S Eng Tchr 1990-91; Colonia HS Eng Tchr 1990-91; Avenel MS ning, Stud Skills Tchr 1991-; *ai:* 6-8 Grd Arts, Crafts Club Adv 4; 6-8 Grd Girls Bsktbl 1994-95; NEA 1986-, Tchr; *office:* Avenel oodbine Ave Avenel NJ 07001

IE, JULIA ANN (YOHO), Band & Choral Director; *b:* Wheeling, *n:* Derek Carl; *ed:* WV Univ (BM) Ed 1992; *cr:* Harford Cty Schls d Gen Music Tchr 1992; Monongalia Cty Schls 1-6 Grd Gen Music 993; Martins Ferry Cty Schls 5-7 Grd Gen Music, 8 Grd Choral , 9-12 Instrumental, Choral Tchr 1993-; *ai:* Jazz Band; Percussion ble; MENC, OMEA, NEA 1993-; Pleasant Hill UMC Choir 1995-, irst Chrstn Church Jr Choir 1995-, Dir; *office:* Martins Ferry HS 614 er St Martins Ferry OH 43935

LO, SUSAN T., Music Teacher; *b:* Westfield, MA; *ed:* Westfield St BA) Music 1973; Smith Coll (AM) Music 1976; Univ of CT (CAGS) 1982; *cr:* Van Sickle Jr HS Music Tchr 1976-81; Kosciuszko Jr HS Tchr 1981-82; HS of Commerce Music Tchr 1982-; *ai:* MMEA PP of A 1988-; *office:* HS Of Commerce 415 State St Springfield 105*

WIN, JEANNE WHITNEY, 6th Grade Science Teacher; *b:* use, NY; *m:* John L.; *c:* Heather, Garrett, Aaron; *ed:* Oswego St Univ Ed 1973, (MS) Ed 1978; *ai:* 6th Grd Stu Cncl, Kids for Saving Earth Cmptr Tech Comm; Camden Tchrs Assn 1976-, Sec; NYSUT 1976-; Camden Cntrl Schl 51 Third St Camden NY 13316

OOCK, STEPHEN W., AP Amer Govt & World His Tchr; *b:* St , OH; *ed:* Bowling Green Univ (BS) His, Pol Sci, Eng 1970; Wright v (MED) Soc Sci Classroom Tchng 1974; *cr:* Sidney HS Tchr 1970-; *ai:* Sr Class, Mock Trial Team Advs; Sidney Ed Assn, Pres 1976; OH Ed Assn 1970-; NEA 1970-; Old Trails Uniserve Cncl, Chm 1976-79; Shelby Cty Democratic Cntrl Comm 1994-; Distinguished Tchng Awd 1993; *home:* 1218 Taft St Sidney OH 45365*

WEAKLAND, BONNIE LOU, Kindergarten Teacher; *b:* Spangler, PA; *ed:* Clarion St Coll (BS) Elem, Early Childhd 1975; PA St Univ 3 Credit Hrs; IUS 2 Credit Hrs; Indiana Univ of PA 18 Credit Hrs; Villanova Univ 2 Credit Hrs; Shippenburg Univ 1 Credit Hr; *cr:* Cambria Co Head Start Itinerant Specialized Tchr 1975-77, Cambria Hts Kndgtn Tchr 1977-79, First Grd Tchr 1979-89, Kndgtn Tchr 1989-; *ai:* Work with HS Foreign Travel Club, MS Yrbk Staff in Hosting Breakfast with Santa, Easter Bunny Events 5 Yrs; Help MS Acts; CHEA, PSEA, NEA 1978-; CH PTO 1982-; *office:* Cambria Heights Schl Dist Box 480 Beaver St Hastings PA 16646*

WEARSCH, RICHARD MICHAEL, Biology Teacher; *b:* Lorain, OH; *m:* Rebecca M.; *c:* Daniel; *ed:* Lorain Comm Coll (AA) Gen Ed 1977; Malone Coll (BA) Bio 1980; Addl Post Grad Work Ashland Univ; *cr:* Buckeye Vly Local Schls Jr HS Sci & Hlth 1980-81; Monroeville HS Bio 1981-; *ai:* Asst Sci Fair Adv; Firelands Challenge Acad Adv; 7th Grd Class Adv; NEA, OEA 1981-; *office:* Monroeville HS 101 West St Monroeville OH 44847

WEATHERALL, CAROL ANNE, Mathematics Teacher; *b:* Jersey City, NJ; *ed:* Fairfield Univ (BS) Math 1987; St Peter's Coll (MA) Ed Supervision, Admin 1992; *cr:* St Anthony HS Math Dept Chair 1988-92; St Dominic Acad Math Tchr 1992-93; Pt Pleasant Beach HS Math Tchr 1993-; *ai:* Peer Cnslrs, Peer Mediator Adv; Spring Track Asst Coach; NCTM, NEA 1993-; *home:* 53B Osborn Ave Manasquan NJ 08736

WEATHERHOLT, ROSE MARIE (HRYHORCHOK), Former Sci Tchr; *b:* Orange, TX; *m:* Maurice Ray; *c:* Janie, Kelli, Bradley; *ed:* Lamar Univ (BS) Scndry Ed 1987; Sam Houston St Univ (MED) Scndry Ed 1991; *cr:* Huntsville Jr HS Sci Tchr 1988-90; Cntrl MS Sci Tchr 1990-93; Bridge City Jr HS Sci Tchr 1993-94; *ai:* Parenting; Parent, Tchrs Guild 1994-; TX Career Ladder Level III; Tchr of Month; *home:* 2010 Colony Dr Aliquippa PA 15001

WEATHERLY, JON ALLEN, Professor of Biblical Studies; *b:* Indianapolis, IN; *m:* Tamra Lynn Davis; *c:* Cale Daniel, Allison Joy; *ed:* Cincinnati Bible Coll (BA) Bible & Christian Ministry 1981; Cincinnati Bible Seminary (MA) New Testament 1982; Trinity Evangelical Devinity Schl (MDiv) Ministry 1984; Univ of Aberdeen Scotland (PhD) New Testament Exegesis 1991; *cr:* Cincinnati Bible Coll & Seminary Instr of Lang & New Testament 1982-83; Southside Christian Church Assoc Minister 1984-87; Cincinatti Bible Coll & Seminary Prof of Biblical Stud 1990-; *ai:* Division Chair; Biblical Stud; Soc of Biblical Lit 1994-; Evangelical Theological Soc 1994-; White Oak Christian Church 1990-, Deacon, Missions Chair; Local Schl Decision Making Comm Fairview German Lang Schl 1995-; Articles Tyndale Bulletin, Evangelical Quarterly, Criswell Theological Review, Journal for Study New Testament, Dir of Jesus & Gospels Book; Jewish Responsibility for Death of Jesus in Luke-Acts 2 Books Forthcoming; *office:* Cincinnati Bible Coll & Sem 2700 Glenway Ave Cincinnati OH 45204*

WEAVER, ALICIA RUTH, 7th Grade Science Teacher; *b:* Bay Shore, NY; *ed:* Houghton Coll (BA) General Sci, Elem Ed-Magna Cum Laude 1985; SUNY at Oswego (MS) Scndry Ed, Bio 1990; *cr:* Mexico MS 7th Grd Sci Tchr 1985-; *ai:* Adv: Yrbk 1987-95, Mentor Club 1991-; Dist Mid Level Sci Mentor 1992-; AFT, NYSUT 1985-; STANYS, NSTA 1986-89; Baldwinsville Assembly of God 1987-95, Sunday Schl Supt 1990-93, Children's Church Coord 1990-92, Youth Ldr 1993-94; Oswego Cty Tchr Ctr Mini-Grant Recipient 1988; NY St Senate Achvmt Awd for NY St Empire St Challenger Fellowship 1986-87; 5 Stu Tchrs Master Tchr 1988-; Sci Curr Consultant Lib Skills Wkshp 1986; *office:* Mexico MS Fravor Rd Mexico NY 13114

WEAVER, EARL D., Asst Prof of Musical Theatre; *b:* Maywood, CA; *ed:* East L A Comm Coll (AA) Jrnlsm 1977; Univ of Redlands (BA) Theatre, Dance 1979; Univ of CA at Irvine (MFA) Drama, Musical Theatre 1990; Pacific Arts Mngmt Inst; *cr:* The Desert Sun Schl Instr 1979-81; Plastow Prgms Schl Instr 1981-83; Elliott-Pope Prep Schl Instr 1983-85; Point Park Coll Asst Prof 1992-; *ai:* Fac Adv Theatre Dept Annual AIDS Benefit Concert; Coord Stu Svcs, Advising, Theatre Arts; Stu Publications Bd, Stu Dev Comm Fac Rep; Theatre Arts Dept Curr Comm; Actors Equity Assn 1992-, Deputy; Point Park Fac Assn 1995-; Point Park Fac Dev Resource Assn; Travel Grant to Lead Wkshp at Amer Coll Theatre Festival 1996; Wkshp Ldr PA Thespian Festival; *office:* Point Park Coll 201 Wood St Pittsburgh PA 15222

WEAVER, EMILY I. (LINK), German Teacher; *b:* Tamaqua, PA; *m:* Richard W. Jr.; *ed:* Kutztown Univ (BS) Scndry Ed, Ger, Sci, Chem 1985; Marywood Coll (MS) Scndry Guid 1991; *cr:* Cntrl Columbia HS Ger Tchr 1986-, Guid Cnslr 1993; *ai:* Chrldng, Ger Club, Ger NHS Adv; JV Ftbl, Bsktbl; Stu Assistance Team; Track Asst; AATG, NEA, PSEA 1986-; *office:* Cntrl Columbia HS 4777 Old Berwick Rd Bloomsburg PA 17815

WEAVER, JAMES F., Science Teacher; *b:* Grantsville, WV; *m:* Takayo Nakashima; *c:* Jamie; *ed:* Glenville St Coll (AB) Bio Ed 1974; WV Univ (MA) Ed Admin 1984; Post Grad Stud Univ of MD, San Diego St, Boston Univ, CO St; *cr:* Calhoun Cty HS 1974-87; Kadena HS Bio Tchr 1988-89; Kadena MS Sci Tchr 1990-; *ai:* Jr Sci, Hum Spon; Symposium Pacific Region; NEA 1974-; Overseas Ed Assn, PSTA 1988-; Pacific Area Diving Instrs 1988-; Articles Pub; Meritorious Tchr of MS Sci 1993-95.

WEAVER, JAMES WILBUR, English Teacher; *b:* Lancaster, PA; *c:* Jennifer L. Hitz, Lawrence Anthony; *ed:* Millersville Univ (BA) Eng 1971; 27 Post Grad Credits Eng, Hlth, Sports Psych, Coaching Techniques; *cr:* Upland Schl Dist Eng Tchr 1971-72; Northern Luth HS Eng Tchr; *ai:* Cross Cntry, Head Track & Field Boys, Girls Grds 7-12 Coach; Attendance Dean Frosh Class; NCEA; PSEA; Sky Jumpers Natl Pole Vault Clinics, Summer Coach; Boot Scooters Cntry Western Dance, Tchr; *office:* Northern Lebanon HS RR 22 Fredericksburg PA 17026

WEAVER, JANE HOWSON, Biology Teacher; *b:* Bryn Mawr, PA; *m:* Robert Sheridan; *ed:* Dickinson Coll (BA) Soc Stud 1972; West Chester Univ (MA) Bio 1981; 30 Addl Credit Hrs from Beaver Coll, PA St Univ; *cr:* Great Vly HS Bio Tchr 1973-74; NOrristown Area HS Bio Tchr 1974-; *ai:* Acad Decathlon Team, Class of 1996 Spon; NEA, PSEA, EANA 1974-; Montgomery Cty Sci Tchrs Assoc 1975-; NABT1982-; *office:* Norristown Area HS 1900 Eagle Dr Norristown PA 19403

WEAVER, JOHN EDWARD, English Teacher; *b:* Buffalo, NY; *m:* Sandra Ann Giglia; *c:* Nicholas, Kathleen; John; *ed:* Buffalo St Coll (BSEd) Elem Ed 1985; (ME) Scndry Eng Ed; *cr:* Bishop Timon Schl Substitute Eng Tchr 1986; St Bonaventure Schl 7th & 8th Grd Eng Tchr 1986-90; Holland Cntrl HS Eng Tchr 1990-; *ai:* Var Track & Girls Bsktbl Coach; Schl Improvement Team; Prevention is Primary; Recreational League Bsktbl; IM Bsktbl Supvr; CORE Team Mem; NEA 1990-; *office:* Holland Central H S Canada St Holland NY 14080

WEAVER, JOSEPH HENRYH, Professor of History; *b:* Martinsburg, WV; *m:* Carolyn Boswell; *c:* Julie W. Murray, Joseph L.; *ed:* West VA Univ (BA) His 1962, (MA) His 1968; Addl Grad Stud; *cr:* West VA Univ Tchng Asst 1968-71; Allegany Comm Coll Assoc Prof, Asst Prof, Prof 1971-; *ai:* Chess Club Adv; Appalachian Stud Assn 1989-; NEA 1985-; Western MD Station Cntr Bd 1994-, Chair, Curaturial Comm; Pub 3 Books on Local His; Historian for Two Traveling Photo Exhibits, Last One won Awd of Merit; Historian for Historic Calendar; Presented Papers at Confs; *office:* Allegany Comm Coll 12401 Willowbrook Rd SE Cumberland MD 21502

WEAVER, KENNETH RAY, Mathematics Teacher; *b:* Albuquerque, NM; *m:* Judith A.; *c:* Brian, Beth, Daniel; *ed:* Marietta Coll (BS) Math 1975; Northwestern Univ (MAT) Ed 1976; *cr:* Von Steuben HS Math Tchr 1975-76; Learwood Jr HS Math Tchr 1976-79; Avon Lake HS Math Tchr 1979-; *ai:* Head Wrestling, Frosh Ftbl Coaches; OEA, NEA 1976-; ALEA 1976-, Treas; Cty Wrestling Coach of Yr 5 Times; *home:* 3625 Stoney Ridge Rd Avon OH 44011

WEAVER, KURT CHARLES, Science Teacher; *b:* Easton, PA; *m:* Linda Carol Repsher; *c:* Brad, Tricia; *ed:* Rutgers Coll (BA) Bio, Sci 1973; East Stroudsburg Univ (MS) Bio 1993; 15 Hrs Scndry Schl Admin; *cr:* Easton Area HS Chem, Physics Tchr 1973-74; Self Employed Contractor, Owner 1974-90; Notre Dame HS Wrestling Coach 1982-91; Belvidere HS Sci Tchr 1991-; *ai:* 9th Grd Class Adv; Cmptr & Tech Comm; Head Girls Soccer, Wrestling Coaches; PA Edctrs Assn 1973-76; NJEA, NEA 1991-; *office:* Belvidere HS Oxford St Belvidere NJ 07823*

WEAVER, LYLE M., Health Teacher & Coach; *b:* Watertown, NY; *m:* Nancy Rogers; *c:* Michael P., Mindy L.; *ed:* SUNY at Brockport (BS) PE 1973; Permanet Cert Hlth; *cr:* Lyme Cntrl Schl PE Tchr, Coach, Attendance Ofcr 1975-80; Sackets Harbor Cntrl Schl Hlth, PE Tchr, Coach 1981-; *ai:* Girls Var Soccer, Bsktbl, Sftbl Coach; Class Adv; Career Curr Comm; NEA 1975-; NYSUT 1981-; Vol Fireman 1979-; *office:* Sackets Harbor Central Schl Broad St Sackets Harbor NY 13686*

WEAVER, MARY K., English Teacher; *b:* Cleveland, OH; *m:* Derrick; *c:* Colleen, Andrea; *ed:* Concordia Univ (BA) Eng 1978; *cr:* Lutheran HS West Eng Tchr 1978-79; St John Luth Schl Presch Tchr 1986-90; Maple Hts HS Eng Tchr 1990-; *ai:* Class of 1998 Adv; NEA 1990-; *office:* Maple Heights HS 5500 Clement Ave Maple Heights OH 44137

WEAVER, MARY LOU (BURT), K-8th Grade Art Teacher; *b:* Detroit, MI; *ed:* Univ of Dallas (BA) Art 1968; Post Grad Stud St univ of NY at Geneseo, Eastern ME Voc-Tech Inst, Univ of ME at Orono, Portland Museum of Art, Univ of ME at Machias, Univ of ME at Augusta; *cr:* Alfred-Almond Cent Schl Scndry Art Tchr 1969-71; ME Kiln Works Artist & Craftsman 1971-88; Ella Lewis Schl K-8th Grd Art Tchr 1989-91; Winter Harbor Grm Schl Art Tchr 1989-; Gouldsboro Grammar Schl Art Tchr 1991-; Portland Museum Of Art Summer Tchr 1992-93; *ai:* Chap II Innovation Ed Coord; Dist Arts Curr Comm; Schoodic Peninsula Partnership Grant Tchr Rep; ME Art Edctrs Assoc 1990-; Puppeteers of Amer 1993-; Gouldsboro Rec Comm 1978-84, Chm, Sears Comm Betterment Awd; Winter Harbor Rec Comm 1995-, Chm; New England Rural Ldr Flwshp; Shore Stewards Trust Grant Writer & Coord; Art Reach Flwshp 2 Summers; Artwork Featured in The Downeast Guide to MEs Outstdng Craftspeople 1988; *home:* HC 60 Box 23C Winter Harbor ME 04693*

WEAVER, MURIEL MC KIBBEN, Instrumental Music Teacher; *b:* Dayton, OH; *m:* Fredrick Daniel; *c:* Meva, Kelly, Christopher, Melissa; *ed:* Miami Univ (BA) Music Ed 1965; Coll of Mount Saint Joseph (MED) Ed 1987; Addl 30 Credit Hrs; *cr:* Dayton Symphony Orch Violinist 1962-76; Columbus Symphony Orch Violinist 1962-76; Pvt String Tchr 1965-; Trotwood Schls Music Tchr 1965-73; Madison Schls Music Tchr 1965-73; Walnut St UM Church Music Dir 1980-; Chillicothe City Schls Music Tchr 1983-; *ai:* String Ensemble HS, MS Coach; NEA, MENC, OSTA 1983-; ASTA 1992-, St Secy; AGEHR 1976-; Agape Handbell Choir 1976-, Dir; Church Circle 1976-88, Chm; Mothers Club 1978-83, Chr; Chillicothe Comm Theater, Comm Oratorios Violinists; *home:* 27 Courtland Dr Chillicothe OH 45601*

WEAVER, PATRICK FRANCIS, Mathematics Teacher; *ed:* Frostburg St Coll (BS) Elem Ed 1975, (MS) Elem Ed 1981; *cr:* Ft Ashby Primary Schl 5-6 Grd Math, Sci Tchr 1975; Ft Ashby MS 6-8 Grd Math, 6 Grd Sci Tchr 1976-87; Braddock MS 8 Grd Math Tchr 1987-93; Cresaptown Elem Schl 4th Grd Tchr 1994; Washington MS 7-8 Grd Math Tchr 1995; Braddock MS 8 Grd Math Tchr 1996; *ai:* Math Counts Coach; 6th Grd MD Math League Coach; NEA, MSTA, ACTA 1987-; MCTM, NCTM 1990-, Finalist Tchr of Yr 1993; St Michael Church 1982-, Sunday Schl Tchr; Math Teams; Sci Fairs; Elected to Bobcat Hall of Fame 1983; Outstdng Young Men of Amer 1987; Finalist for MS Math Tchr of Yr 1993; Coached 3 Undefeated HS Tennis Teams 1988-89, 1993; *office:* Braddock MS 909 Holland St Cumberland MD 21502

WEAVER, RAY EDWARD, English Teacher; *b:* Lancaster, PA; *m:* Marilyn Elizabeth Hollinger; *c:* Benjamin Nicholas, Angelica Elizabeth, Gabrielle Faye; *ed:* Millersville St Coll (BS) Eng Ed 1976; Millersville Univ (MS) Eng Ed 1982; *cr:* East Juniata Jr & Sr HS 7th-12th Grd Eng Tchr 1976-; *ai:* Head Softball Coach 16 Yrs; Asst Soccer Coach 6 Yrs; Asst Hockey Coach; Sr Musical Dir 3 Yrs; Jr Class Play Dir 3 Yrs; Bunkertown Church of the Brethren 1979-, Bd Chair, Deacon Dist Bd; *office:* East Juniata Jr Sr HS PO Box 60 Cocolamus PA 17014

WEAVER, RAYMOND E. F., Math Professor; *b:* Johnstown, PA; *m:* Lois Lieb; *c:* Elaine, Russell, Matthew, Alex; *ed:* College of the Holy Cross (BS) Physics 1967; Carnegie-Mellon Univ (MS) Physics 1969; 30 Addl Credits; *cr:* CMU Physics Instr 1968-69, Rsrch Scientist 1969-72; CCAC Math, Physics Prof 1972-; Steel Structures Painting Cncl Asst Dir of Rsrch 1972-; *ai:* Hockey Team Coach 1972-77; Monroeville Yth Soccer Coach 1980-95; Acad Comms; AFT 1972-, VP; PSMATYC 1984-; Co-Authored Numerous Articles; *office:* Comm Coll of Allegheny Cty Boyce Campus 595 Beatty Rd Monroeville PA 15146

WEAVER, SANDRA JEAN, Fifth Grade Teacher; *b:* Washington, PA; *ed:* Columbia Bible Coll (BA) Bible 1966, (MA) Bible 1972; 15 Credit Hrs PA St Univ; 8 Credit Hrs Widener Univ; Eastern Coll 6 Credit Hrs; *cr:* Columbia Bible Coll Media, Circulation Librn 1964-74; Chrstn Acad Fifth Grd Tchr 1974-; *ai:* Ed Comm 1992-93; ASCI 1984-; Green Ridge Comm Church 1980-, Sunday Schl Tchr; *office:* The Christian Acad Chandler & Lister St Brookhaven PA 19015

WEAVER, WENDY JANE, Third Grade Teacher; *b:* Bremerton, WA; *ed:* Western MD Coll (BA) Eng, Ed 1985; 30 Grad Credit Hrs; *cr:* Freedom Elem Schl 3rd-4th Grd Tchr 1986-; *ai:* NEA 1987-; Nom Carroll Cty Tchr of Yr 1993; Carroll Cty Bd of Ed Wax Museum Awd.

WEAVER-COLEMAN, KAREN, Composition, Lit & Rdng Prof; *b:* Allentown, PA; *ed:* Kutztown Univ (BSEd) Eng, Pub Speaking 1963; Lehigh Univ (MA) Eng 1965; Cedar Crest Coll (BA) Art 1990; IN Univ Bloomington PHD In Progress; *cr:* William Arlen HS Tchr 1963-1965; Parkland HS Tchr 1966-67; Lebanon Vly Coll Instr 1967-69; Harrisburg Area Comm Coll Instr 1969-71; Lehigh Cty Comm Coll Instr 1971-73; Cedar Crest Coll Dir Acad Support Ctr 1973-90; Reading Area Comm Coll Prof 1990-; *ai:* Drama, Debate Club; Schl Newspaper; Yrbk Curr, Long-Range Planning, Competency Based Ed, Lib Comm; Natl Assn Dev Edctrs 1973-; PA Assn Dev Edctrs 1973-, Pres, Treas; IRA 1990-; Lib Bd Potstown, Sec; Town Watch 1980-, Organizer; Valley Ferge Historical Soc 1995-, Bd; Montgomery Cty Women's Task Force 1988-, Outstdng Woman 1993; Amer Assn of Univ Women 1980-, Pres, VP; Fulbright Schlsp; NEH Inst Tchrs, Writing; NEH Inst Cmptrs, Lang; Written Articles; Organized Natl, St Dev Edctrs Confs; *office:* Reading Area Comm Coll PO Box 1706 Reading PA 19603*

WEAVER-FLYNN, VICKI LYNN, English Teacher & Dept Chair; *b:* Barberton, OH; *m:* Eamon Anthony; *c:* Sarah Verena; *ed:* Kent St Univ

(BS) Eng 1973; Lyndon St Coll (MED) Rdng 1994; *cr:* Barberton HS Eng Tchr 1976-79; Tele-Communications Inc Office Mgr 1980-87; East Concord Schl Rdng Tchr 1988-89; White Mountain Schl Eng Tchr, Learning Assistance Prgm Dir 1989-; *ai:* NHS Adv; Acad Affairs Comm; CEC 1993-; NASAA 1994-; Linda Mc Goldrick Flwshp 1991; *office:* White Mountain Schl W Farm Rd Littleton NH 03561*

WEBB, HAROLD THOMAS,JR., Moderate Special Needs Teacher; *b:* Oakdale, LA; *m:* Lesley A.; *c:* Lauren, Bryan; *ed:* Coll of DuPage (AA) Comp Sci 1977; Northwest MO St Univ (BS) Theater & Speech 1979; Westfield St (MS) Spcl Needs 1991; *cr:* US Army Pharmacy Technician E-5 1969-74; North Aurora Ctr Spcl Ed Tchr 1974-78; Anar Chemical Sales 1980-86; Holyoke High Moderate Spcl Needs Tchr 1986-; *ai:* Frosh Ftbl & Girls JV Sftbl Head Coach; Holyoke Tchrs 1986-; CEC 1990-; *office:* Holyoke HS 500 Beech St Holyoke MA 01040

WEBB, JEFFREY LYNN, Fifth Grade Teacher; *b:* Washington, DC; *m:* Sandy; *ed:* Prince Georges Comm Coll (AA) Ed 1968; Salisbury St Coll (BS) Elem Ed 1971, (MED) Elem Ed 1982; Attnd Towson St Univ 3 Post Grad Hrs, Washington Coll 3 Post Grad Hrs, Univ of MD 30 Post Grad Hrs; *cr:* Crapo Elem Schl 5th Grd Tchr 1971-72; Warwick Elem Schl Remedial Math & Rdng Tchr 1975-76; Hurlock Intermediate Schl 4th Grd Tchr 1976-81; Hurlock Elem Schl 4th & 5th Grd Tchr 1981-83; Vienna Elem Schl 4th & 5th Grd Tchr 1983-; *ai:* Schl Improvement Team; Just Say No to Drugs Club Adult Supvr; MSPAP Sci Content Adv; US Dept of Ed Safe & Drug Free Schl Awd 1995; Salisbury Univ Adjunct Tchr of Sci Methods 1994; St of MD Conservation Ed Tchr of Yr 1993; 1991 Governors Awd for Excl for Comm Svc to Reduce Drug Use; Just Say No Intnl Natl Club Ldr Awd 1990; *office:* Vienna Elem Schl 4905 Ocean Gateway Vienna MD 21869

WEBB, JOHN BADGLEY, Foreign Lang Dept Chairperson; *b:* Cooperstown, NY; *ed:* SUNY at Albany (BA) Fr 1968; Middleburg Coll (MA) Fr 1972; NY Univ (EDD) Biling Ed 1986; *cr:* East Ramapo Cntrl Schls Foreign Lang Dept Chprsn 1968-86; Hunter Coll of CUNY HS Foreign Lang Dept Chprsn, Adjunct Assoc Prof 1986-; *ai:* Outdoors Club Adv; Cultural Pluralism Comm Chprsn; Honors, Awds, Outreach Comms; NY St Foreign Lang Tchrs Assn 1968-, Pres; Amer Foreign Lang Tchrs Cncl 1985-; Dodge Fnd Chinese Stud Grant; Biling Title VII Fellowship for Doctorate; Natl Stdnts Stans Task Force K-12 Foreign Langs; Chevalier dons L'Ordre des Palmes Academiques; Author Numerous Articles; *office:* Hunter College HS 71 E 94th St New York NY 10128

WEBB, JUDITH GAUTREAUX, Earth Science Teacher & Chair; *b:* New Orleans, LA; *m:* Gerald F.; *c:* Randall, Kimberly; *ed:* Southeastern LA U (BA) Soc Stud, Bio 1968; Western CT St U (MS) Environmental Stud 1976; Cooperative Learning; Portfolio Assessment; *cr:* Andrew Jackson HS Earth Sci, Bio Tchr 1969-70; La Grange Jr HS 7th, 9th Grd Sci 1970-74; Wappingers Jr HS Earth Sci Tchr 1983-85; Dover Jr, Sr HS Earth Sci Tchr 1985-; *ai:* Sci Dept Chprsn; Dist Safety Comm; AFT, UFT, NYS Sci Tchr Assn 1985-; NSF Grant 1971.

WEBB, NATALIE BOARD, Spanish Teacher; *b:* Cincinnati, OH; *c:* Scott Neill, Jon Neill, Jay Neill; *ed:* Hanover Coll (BA) Eng, Span 1957; Xavier Univ;(MED) Cnslng 1987; Post-Grad Stud Univ of Cincinnati, Miami Univ, Univ of Dayton; *cr:* Anderson HS Tchr 1957-60; Plant HS Tchr 1980-81; Glen Este HS Tchr 1978-80, 1982-; *ai:* Frgn Lang Club Adv; NCEA, OEA, NEA, OFLA 1980-; *office:* Glen Este HS 4342 Glen Este-Withamsville Rd Cincinnati OH 45245

WEBB, ROBERT GEORGE,JR., Technical Drafting Teacher; *b:* Phila, PA; *m:* Dolores; *c:* Mark, Christian; *ed:* Glassboro St Coll (BA) Indstrl Arts, Voc, Tech 1971; 15 Credit Hrs Schl Law Grad Credits; *cr:* Howell HS Machine Shop Tchr 1971-73, Auto Mechanics Tchr 1971-73; Millville Sr HS Indstrl Drafting Tchr 1973-83, CAD Tchr 1983-, Auto Mech Tchr, Alt Schl 1991-; *ai:* Industry Adv Cumberland Cty Coll; NEA, NJEA 1971-; NJSB 1991-; Upper Pittsgrove BOE 1991-; One of Original Founders of Cities Schls of Excl; 6 Yr Svc Local Scl Bd; Prior Owner Import Motorcar Svc; Owner of Digital Drafting & Design; *office:* Millville Sr HS 200 Wade Blvd Millville NJ 08332

WEBB, ROBERT OKEY, English Teacher; *b:* Wallace, WV; *m:* Betty Jo Griffin; *c:* Robert Mark, Pamela Ann Webb Potter; *ed:* Fairmont St Coll (BS) Speech, Dramatics 1956; Youngstown St Univ (MS) Admin 1972; 21 Semester Hrs; *cr:* Marion Harding HS Speech, Drama Coach 1956-74; Baker MS Eng, Soc St Tchr 1974-91; Marion Tech Coll Comm 1975-91; Pleasant HS Eng Tchr, Drama Coach 1992-; *ai:* All-Schl Musical Dir 3 Yrs; Soph Class, Scholastic Challenge Adv; MEA, OEA, NEA 1956-; Marion Little Theatre 1959-, Best Supporting Act; *office:* Pleasant HS 1101 Owens Rd W Marion OH 43302

WEBB, SHEILA VAN PELT, English Teacher; *b:* York, PA; *w:* P. Billy (dec); *c:* Herbert, Jill Hunte, Jane Rosenberg; *ed:* Millersville Univ (BS) Comp Eng, Rdng 1966; Shippensburg Univ (MEd) Eng, Lit 1971; Attnd Penn St, Western MD, York Coll; *cr:* Dallastown Area Eng, Rdng Tchr 1965-66; Dover Area Eng, Jrnlsm Tchr, Public Speaking 1966-; *ai:* Drama Club; Schl Newspaper, Class, Girls Ath Assoc, Cheerleading Adv; Gifted Seminar Tchr; DAEA. PSEA, NEA 1966-; PTOs 1963-77, Treas; Sunday Schl Tchr 1960-; Var Church Comms; Newspaper in Classroom Publication; Pro Mem Alpha-Beta Chapter, ADK; *office:* Dover H S W Canal St Dover PA 17315*

WEBB, SUSAN CLEMSON, History & Psychology Tchr; *b:* Frederick, MD; *m:* Danny R.; *c:* Chase; *ed:* Mt St Mary's Coll (BS) Scndry Ed, Soc Stud 1988; 12 Credit Hrs IN Univ of PA Guid, Cnslng; 3 Credit Hrs Univ Pitt at Johnstown Cmptr; 6 Credit Hrs Beaver Coll Psych, Ed; 9 Credit Hrs Shippensburg Univ Guid, Cnslng; *cr:* New Market MS Soc Stud Tchr 1988-89; Somerset Area HS Soc Stud Tchr 1989-90; Chestnut Ridge HS Voc Cnslr 1990; Bedford HS Soc Stud Tchr 1991-; *ai:* NHS Adv; BAEA, PSEA, NEA 1990-, Bldg Rep; *office:* Bedford HS 330 E John St Bedford PA 15522*

WEBB, TAMARA BOUREIER, 7th-8th Grd Language Arts Tchr; *b:* Malone, NY; *m:* Charles; *c:* Melissa, Michael; *ed:* Daemen Coll (BA) Eng 1988; Attnd Ursinus Coll, Univ of NY at Brockport; *cr:* Sacred Heart Schl Lang Arts Tchr 1987-; *ai:* Forensics Coach, Judge; Staff Curr Comm, Ed Bravado; NCEA 1987-; *office:* Area Cath Schl of Sacred Heart Lewis Rd Royersford PA 19468*

WEBBER, JOHN S., 6th Grd Social Studies Teacher; *b:* Montclair, NJ; *m:* Barbara J. Shaker; *c:* John S. III, Kurt A.; *ed:* Kings Coll (BA) Ec 1965; Western CT St Univ (MS) Elem Ed 1972; 30 Credits Dev Rdng; *cr:* Park Avenue Elem Schl 6th Grd Tchr 1968-88; Shelter Rock Elem Schl 5th, 6th Grd Tchr 1988-92; Rogers Park MS 6th Grd Soc Stud Tchr 1992-; *ai:* Danbury HS Asst Soccer Coach; CEA, NEA 1969-; *office:* Rogers Park MS 21 Memorial Dr Danbury CT 06810

WEBBER, NATHAN, Social Studies Teacher; *b:* Ephrata, PA; *m:* Andrea Lynne; *ed:* Elizabethtown Coll (BS) Bus 1987; Liberty Univ (MA) Cnslng; Rider Univ Ed 1992; Post Grad Deg from Massmutten Military Acad 1983; Liberty Univ Working Towards Masters in Cnslng; *cr:* Mc Corriston HS Tchr, Cnslr, Coach 1993-; *ai:* Boys Var Bsktbl, Track Coach; Natl Assn of Eagle Scouts 1981-; Mercer Cty Prof Cnslr Assn 1994-; Article Pub; High Achvmt Awd; *office:* Mc Corristin Cath HS 175 Leonard Ave Trenton NJ 08610

WEBBER, PAULA K., 9th Grade English Teacher; *b:* E Liverpool, OH; *m:* Charles N.; *c:* Michele Lee, C. Michael; *ed:* Kent St Univ (BA) Eng 1984; 23 Semester Hrs Grad Courses Coll of Mount St Joseph & Kent St Univ; *cr:* Springfield HS 8th-11th Grd Eng Tchr 1984-88; Edison MS 8th Grd Eng Tchr 1988-93; Springfield Jr HS 9th Grd Eng Tchr 1993-; *ai:* Lang Arts Course of Stud & Dist Spelling Bee Comms; CBE Writing Scoring Team; Bldg Advy Comm; Curr Improvement Comm; NEA, OEA & ELEA 1984-; Phi Beta Kappa 1984-; Edison Local Tchr of the Yr 1991; *office:* Springfield Jr HS RD 1 Bergholz OH 43908*

WEBBER, ROBERT BRUCE, Mathematics Instructor; *b:* Greenville, PA; *m:* Sandra Marie Perry; *c:* Robert J; *ed:* Edinboro Univ (BSEd) Math 1974; Youngstown St Univ (MSEd) Scndry Admin 1980; *cr:* Mathews HS Math Tchr 1975-; *ai:* NEA 1975-; Mathews Ed Assn 1975-, Building Rep 1987-; NCTM; Edinboro Univ Alum Assn 1975-; YSU Alum Assn; Head Track Coach 1975-83; Head Class Adv 1977-81; Bowling Club Adv 1977-81; Var Club Adv 1976-80; Who's Who Amer Ed 1991; *office:* Mathews H S 4429 Warren-Sharon Rd Vienna OH 44473

WEBBER, RUTH, Fourth Grade Teacher; *b:* Lowell, MA; *ed:* Boston Univ (BA) Eng 1969; Northeastern (MED) Rdng & Lang 1972; Eng Ed London Univ; *cr:* Tyngsborough Pub Schls Tchr 1969-85, Rdng Supvr 1985-90, Tchr 1990-; *ai:* Accreditation Steering, Rdng Comms; Tchrs Assn Tyngsborough 1970-, Sec; MTA, NEA 1970-; Merrimack Vly Rdng Cncl 1975-, Pres; MRA, IRA 1975-; Greater Lowell Pastoral Cnslng Ctr 1990-, Sec, Bd of Dirs; Outstdng Elem Tchr 1972; *office:* Norris Road Elem Schl 50 Norris Rd Tyngsboro MA 01879

WEBBER, SANDRA MARIE (PERRY), English Teacher; *b:* Youngstown, OH; *m:* Robert Bruce; *c:* Robert J.; *ed:* Youngstown St Univ (BS) Eng 1973, (MS) Guidance & Counseling 1978; *cr:* Mathews HS Eng Tchr 1973-; *ai:* NEA, OEA & Mathews Ed Assn 1973-; NCTE 1975-; Delta Kappa Gamma 1984-, Newsletter Publisher 1987-; OH Cncl Tchrs of Eng 1990-; Youngstown Panhellenic Assn 1975-, Pres 1985-86; Jr Womens Club of Girard 1983-, Pres 1993-94; Phi Mu Sorority Alumni Pres 1984-85; Jennings Scholar Awd 1978; Dev & Granted Rdng & Writing Lab Grant 1978; YWCA Woman of Yr in Ed Nom 1988; *office:* Mathews HS 4429 Warren-Sharon Rd Vienna OH 44473

WEBBER, SHARON COYLE, English Teacher; *b:* Albany, NY; *c:* Christopher, Timothy; *ed:* Coll of St Rose (BA) Eng 1974; SUNY at Brockport (MA) Lbrl Arts 1991; Daemen Coll Tchr Cert Pgm; *cr:* Batavia MS 8th Grd Eng Tchr 1986-89; Clarence MS 8th Grd Eng Tchr 1989-; *ai:* Spring Musical Dir; Holiday Food Dr Adv; NYSTR System 1986-, Dist Rep; NYSUT 1986-; Clarence Tchrs Assn 1989-, Bldg Rep; NCTE 1993-; NYS MS Assn 1994-; Clarence Yth Ctr 1988-, Bd of Dir; *office:* Clarence MS 10150 Greiner Rd Clarence NY 14031

WEBER, ALAN J., 5th Grade Teacher; *ed:* CCNY (BA) Ed 1964; Brooklyn Coll (MSE) Ed 1969; *cr:* PS 158 Brooklyn Schl 6 Grd Tchr 1963-66; PS 345 Brooklyn Schl Sci Tchr, Asst Prin 1966-69; PS 23 Staten Island Schl 5 Grd Tchr 1969-; *ai:* Phi Delta Kappa 1988-; UFT 1963-; *office:* PS 23 The Richmondtown Schl 30 Natick St Staten Island NY 10306

WEBER, CHARLES RICHARD, Dean of Freshmen & Ath Dir; *b:* Prince Frederick, MD; *m:* Kay Williams; *c:* Eli, Mattie; *ed:* Roanoke Coll (BBA) Bus Admin 1980; Old Dominion Univ (MS) Scndry Admin Ldrshp 1993; *cr:* Woodlawn Intermediate Math Tchr 1980-84; Calvert HS Math, Cmptr Tchr 1984-89; Old Dominion Univ Asst Bsktbl Coach 1989-91; Northern HS Tchr, Dean, Ath Dir 1991-; *ai:* Ath Dir; Boys Bsktbl Coach; Var Club; Schl Improvement; Boosters Club; NASSP 1995-; SMAC Bd of Control 1984-, VP; MSADA 1988-; Optimist Club 1987-; Coach of Yr, 1983, 1987-89, 1995; *office:* Northern HS 2950 Chaneyville Rd Owings MD 20736

WEBER, DENISE DUSZA, AP European History Teacher; *b:* Johnstown, PA; *m:* Thomas W.; *c:* Heidi, Gretchen, Michael; *ed:* IN Univ of PA (BS) His 1968, (MA) His 1969; *cr:* Indiana Area Jr High Old World His Tchr 1969-83; Indiana Area Sr High AP European & US His Tchr 1983-; *ai:* Dist Co-Coord Natl His Day Contest; IAEA, PSEA & NEA 1969-; PA Historical Assn 1986-, Exec Cncl 1990-96; Historical & Genealogical Soc of IN Co 1982-, Sec 1984-88; C&E Rails to Trails Cncl 1992-; "Delanos Doman" Pub; Fulbright Hays Group Stud in Ed in Hungary 1993; *office:* Indiana Area Sr HS 450 N Fifth St Indiana PA 15701

WEBER, EDWARD EARL, Chemistry & General Sci Tchr; *b:* Pittsburgh, PA; *ed:* IN Univ of PA (BS) Chem 1972; Tchrs Cert 1976; Addl 33 Credit Hrs Grad Stud Clarion Univ of PA; *cr:* Yough Schl Dist Chem Tchr 1987; Redbank Valley Schl Dist Chem, Gen Sci Tchr 1987-; *ai:* Acad Competition Spon; Co-Sr Adv; RUEA, PSEA, NEA 1987-; PSTA 1990-; *office:* Redbank Valley Schl Dist 910 Broad St New Bethlehem PA 16242

WEBER, FREDERICK HENRY, Assoc Prof & Bus Admin; *b:* Schenectady, NY; *m:* Sandra Jean Hadley; *c:* Shylah Jean, Colton Michael, Michaela Hadley; *ed:* Hudson Vly Comm Coll (AAS) Transportation & Dist Mgmt 1975; Niagara Univ (BS) Transportation, Travel & Tour 1977; SUNY at Albany (MS) Educl Admin 1985; *cr:* Wilson Freight Co Inc Rate & Billing Clerk & OS&D Agent 1977-80; Smiths Transfer Inc Dispatcher 1981; Hudson Vly Comm Coll Instr 1981-; *ai:* Hunting Club & Course Selection Stu Adv; Grant: HVCC Ctr for Effective Tchng Summer Support Recipient 1994; *office:* Hudson Valley Comm Coll 80 Vandenburgh Ave Troy NY 12180

WEBER, HADDIE FREY, Elementary Music Teacher; *b:* Washington, PA; *ed:* Duquesne Univ (BME) Music 1963, (BSME) Ed; Attnd Duquesne Univ, Univ of Pittsburgh; *cr:* McGuffey Schl Dist Music Supvr 1963-64; Munhall Schl Dist Music Tchr, Choral Gen 1964-68; West Mifflin Schl Dist Music Tchr, Choral Gen 1968-; *ai:* Music Curr Writing; Music Textbook Selection; WMAFT; MENC; PMEA; Delta Kappa Chamma 1984-, Recording Sec, 1st VP, Pres; Garden Club Munhall 1975-; Vira Heinz Grant; Newspaper Articles Pub; *office:* West Mifflin Area Schl Dist 2000 Clairton Rd West Mifflin PA 15122*

WEBER, JEANETTE GRECO, School Social Worker; *b:* Brooklyn, NY; *m:* Charles R.; *c:* Michael, Matthew; *ed:* St Johns Univ (BS) Bus Admin 1968, (MS) Counseling, Human Svc 1972; Adelphi Univ (MSW) Soc Work 1986; Inst Trng 3 Yrs NY Schl for Psychoanalytic Psychotherapy; *cr:* H. Frank Cary HS Schl Soc Worker 10 Yrs, Guidance Cnslr 5 Yrs; Valley Stream HS Bus Tchr, Cnslr 5 Yrs; St Michaels HS Bus Tchr 5 Yrs; *ai:* Parent Network, Peer Mediation, Bereavement Group Prgms; Parenting Wkshps; NEA 1979-; NASW 1986-; Soc of Clinical SW 1986-.

WEBER, JUDY S., First Grade Teacher; *b:* Warrington Twp, PA; *m:* Wayne Sr.; *c:* Michael Lee Brenneman, James Brian Brenneman Wayne C. Jr.; *ed:* Shippensburg Univ (BA) Elem Ed 1968, (MA) Rdng 1970; *ai:* Sunday Schl Tchr; NEA 1968-.

WEBER, KATHLEEN FEARON, Sixth Grade Teacher; *b:* Dover, OH; *m:* Robert; *c:* Dana, Bob; *ed:* Kent St Univ (BA) Ed 1971; Akron Univ (MS) Ed 1988; 5 Credit Hrs Ashland Univ; *cr:* New Phila South Elem 1st Grd Tchr 1984-91, 5th Grd Tchr 1991-94; Welty MS 6th Grd Tchr 1994-; *ai:* NEA 1984-; OEA 1984-; *office:* Welty MS 315 4th St NW New Philadelphia OH 44663

WEBER, KEITH ALLEN, Social Studies Teacher; *b:* Kenton, OH; *m:* Sheryl Joan; *c:* Nathan, Natalie; *ed:* OH St Univ (BS) Ed 1979; Coll of Mt St Joseph (MA) Ed 1987; Cooperative Learning OH Univ; *cr:* Cambridge City Schls Soc Stud Tchr 1979-; *ai:* Cambridge Cooperative Cncl Steering Comm; North Cntrl Comm; Stu of the Month Comm; NEA, OEA 1980-, Rep Assembly Del; Cambridge Ed Assn 1980-, Past Pres; OH Cncl for the Soc Stud 1983-, Tchr of the Yr 1985; East Muskingum Planning Commission 1996; *office:* Cambridge HS 1201 Clairmont Ave Can OH 43725

WEBER, KIMBERLY COCHRAN, Voc Commercial Art Teac Parma, OH; *m:* Timothy Patrick; *c:* Jack; *ed:* Art Inst of Ft Lauderda Ad Design 1984; 24 Semester Hrs Kent St Univ; Voc Commercial A OH Tchng Cert; *cr:* Kaufman Container Co Graphic Designer 1 Parma City Schl Dist Voc Commercial Art Tchr 1992-; *ai:* NEA, Pa Assn 1992-; *office:* Valley Forge HS 9999 Independence Blvd Par 44130*

WEBER, LAUREN J., English Teacher; *b:* New Hartford, NY; *m:* S Clayton; *c:* Maxwell A., Britton L.; *ed:* Syracuse Univ (BA) En (MS) Eng Ed 1986; *cr:* Delaware Acad Eng Tchr 1980-81; West Tchr 1982-92; Auburn HS Eng Tchr 1992-; *ai:* Team Tchr; Ski Cl Writing Task Force, Yrbk Adv; Whole Lang Conf Presenter; *office:* HS Lake Ave Auburn NY 13021

WEBER, MARIA B. (DIGIOVANNI), English & Remedial Rdng Irvington, NJ; *m:* Donald E. Jr.; *c:* Alyssa Lynn, Brielle Sarah; *ed:* 2 Credits Rdng, Cnslng; *cr:* Great Mills HS Writing, Math Tchr; *ai* Writing Test Coord St Functionals Mentor; Schl Improvement Tean NEA 1977-; *office:* Great Mills HS Great Mills Rd Great Mills MD

WEBER, MATTHEW KARL, Religion Teacher; *b:* Noblesville, Susan Torgerson; *c:* Mitchell; *ed:* Bethle Coll (BA) Eng Lit 1981; MN (MA) Eng Lit 1985; Northern Theological Seminary (MDiv) Th 1987; *cr:* New Hope Bapt Church Assoc Pastor 1986-88; Inn Evangelism Missionary 1988-89; Montgomery Bapt Church Yth 1989-91; Woodland Hills Bapt Church Pastor 1991-94; Cincinna Chrstn Acad Tchr 1994-; *ai:* Chapel Coord; Impact Group; Habi Humanity 1989-; Elgin Inter-racial Clergy 1988-; *office:* Cincinna Chrstn Acad 11525 Snider Rd Cincinnati OH 45249

WEBER, PATRICIA ANN (LOHR), Secondary Art Teacher; *b:* Gl WV; *m:* Barry E.; *c:* Jodi Ann Shell, Stacie Leigh; *ed:* West Liberty (BA) Art, Speech 1964; Western MD Coll (MA) Ed 1988; *cr:* Firs Elem Schl Eng Tchr 1964-67; Moundsville Jr HS Art Tchr 19 Moundsville HS Art Tchr 1969-71; Moundsville Jr HS Art Tchr 19 Nashua Jr HS Art Tchr 1973-83; Edgewood MS Art Tchr 1983-; *a* Improvement Team; Schl Based Instrl Decision-Making Team; A Chair; Art Curr Comm; AFT, NEA 1983-; *home:* 1226 Saint Francis Air MD 21014*

WEBER, PATRICIA G., English Teacher; *b:* New Kensington, Michael; *c:* Lisa, Heidi; *ed:* Edinboro (BS) Eng, Math 1960, (ME 1964; *cr:* Hopewell HS Eng Tchr 1960-61; Beatty Jr HS Mat 1961-65; Shaler HS Eng Tchr 1973-; *ai:* Stratford Shakespeare F Trip; Hugh O'Brien Ldrshp Contest; NEA, PSEA 1960-; NCTE SAEA, WCTE 1973-; Natl Endownment For Hum Flwshp; *office:* Area Sr HS 381 Wible Run Rd Pittsburgh PA 15209

WEBER, PEGGY RAMSEY, Choral Director & Dept He Cincinnati, OH; *m:* Larry Howard; *c:* Alisa Margaret; *ed:* Miam (BSME) in Ed 1973; Grad Stud OH Univ; *cr:* Reading Comm Schls Coach, Music Tchr & Choir Dir 1973-77; Coll Hill Presbyn Churc Minister of Music 1977-80; Pvt Studio Voice & Piano Tchr 1968-85; City HS Choral Dir & Dept Head 1986-; *ai:* Show Choir; Schl Mu NEA, OEA & Music Edctrs Assoc 1973-; Amer Choral Dirs 1985-, Region Chair; OH Hnrs Choral 1985-, Pres, Asst Dir; *office:* Grov HS 4665 Hoover Rd Grove City OH 43123*

WEBER, SANDIE MELNIKOFF, First Grade Teacher; *b:* Scrant *m:* Henry William Jr.; *c:* Henry III; *ed:* Bloomsburg Univ (BS) E 1972; Trenton St Coll (MED) Elem, Early Chldhd Ed 1978; Addl 30 Hrs; *cr:* Churchville Elem Schl Third Grd Tchr 1972-80, First Gr 1982-; *ai:* Dist Curr Cncl; Grd Level Chm; Guest Author Comm; Assn of Univ Women 1979-, VP 1981-82; Delegation Ldr of Pe People Stu Ambassador Prgm; *office:* Churchville Elem Schl 100 N Churchville PA 18966

WEBER, SUSAN ELISABETH, German & English Teacher; *b:* Ja NY; *m:* Friedhelm Karl; *c:* Katherine, Paul James; *ed:* LIU CW Po (BA) Ger Ed 1975; SUNY at Stonybrook (MA) Eng Lit 1982; LIU C Coll Rdng MS 24 Credits; *cr:* Trans World Airlines Flight Att 1975-90; Garden City HS Ger, Eng Tchr 1990-; *ai:* Adv Ger Lang H 1992-, Ger Lang Lit Magazine 1991-; AATG 1991-; Delta Epsil Comm Svc Awd 1994-95; Governor Clinton Awd; Mason's; Ou Comm Svc Awd 1995; *office:* Garden City Sr HS 170 Rockawa Garden City NY 11530

WEBER, SUSAN G., Kindergarten Teacher; *b:* Salem, OH; *ed:* (AA) Early Chldhd Ed 1980, (BS) Elem Ed 1981; Attending Kent S Chldhd Ed; *cr:* Canton Comm Jewish Ctr Tchrs Aid 1978-80; Malor Child Dev Ctr Tchrs Aid 1980-81; Crestview Schl Dist Kndgtn Tchr *ai:* Building Improvement Team, Lang Arts Curr Comms; PTO Boosters; NEA, OEA, Crestview Tchrs Assn 1981-; Lisbon Trinity Church 1977-, Coord of Church Growth, Outreach; Columbiana Cty Ctr 1992-, Early Chldhd Bd; Northeast OH Friends Church Ex Outstanding Young Amer Women 1991; Instr Magazine Pub Original Mailbox Magazine Kndgtn Tchr Ambassador 1994-95; *office:* Cre Elem Schl 3407 Middleton Rd Columbiana OH 44408*

WEBER, WALLBURGA MANK, Chemistry Teacher & NHS A New York City, NY; *m:* Oscar Walter; *c:* Laura; *ed:* Gettysburg Col Chem 1963; NY Univ (MA) Sci Ed 1966; 30 Grad Credits Penn St *cr:* Brooklyn Friends Schl Sci, Bio Gen Sci Tchr 1964-66; Lawrence Sci, Math Tchr 1966-67; Reading Area Comm Coll Adj Chem 1976-78; WIlson HS Chem Tchr Part-time 1976-78; Conrad Weis Chem Tchr 1978-; *ai:* Adv NHS, Asst Jr Class, Asst Prom; Cmptr, St Plan Comms; Stu Assistance Prgm; NEA; PSEA; Amer Chem Atonement Luth Church 1970-; *office:* Conrad Weiser Jr/Sr HS 347 Ave Robesonia PA 19551*

WEBSTER, CYNTHIA BUEHLER, Language Arts Teacher; *b:* W OH; *m:* James R.; *c:* Robb, Erin; *ed:* Ashland Univ (BS) Ed 1973; U Akron Masters in Rdng 1981, 15 Credit Hrs After Masters; *cr:* North Schl 5th-6th Grd Tchr 1973-; *ai:* Safety Patrol Supvr; Outdoor E NEA, OEA 1973-; Heartland 1994-, Character Dev Comm; Martha H Jennings Scholar; *office:* North Elem Schl 605 Mineral Springs St O OH 44667

WEBSTER, ELAINE GERBER, History Teacher; *b:* Jersy City, Peter B.; *c:* Amy Elizabeth, Peter B. Jr., Timothy James; *ed:* Cornel (BA) Amer Stud 1963, (BS), (MED) Ed 1965; Univ of Southern ME Gifted Ed, 18 Hrs His, Art His; *cr:* Watkins Glenn HS His, Eng 1964-65; South Portland HS His Tchr 1965-67; Yarmouth HS GAT Tchr 1979-; *ai:* Swimming, Tennis, Track Teams Coach; Schl News NHS Adv; NEA 1979-86; MTA 1979-90; Arts & Humanties Book 1992-; AAA Northern New England, Bd Mem, Sec; Lib Bd 19 YMCA Bd 1984-88; YWCA Bd 1988-92; *office:* Yarmouth H S W Yarmouth ME 04096*

WEBSTER, FORREST GRAYDON, Government & History Teach Baltimore, MD; *m:* Elizabeth Clara Timney; *c:* Tracy, Patricia, Bri Frosburg St Univ (BS) His 1971; Loyola Univ of MD (APC) Soc Scis 42 Credit Hrs in Ed; Working on Admin & Supervision Masters Prg Atholton HS His, Govt Tchr 25 Yrs; *ai:* Indoor, Outdoor Track Coach Improvement Team Chm; 10th Grd Stdnts St Mandated Proficienc

NEA, MSTA, HCEA 1972-; St Track Ofcls Assn 1986-; Natl :al Soc 1988-; Natl Capital Historical Soc 1989-; Chamber of rce Tchr of Yr Awd; Sr Class, Black Stu Union Most Favored Tchr; Yr Nom Howard Cty; *office:* Atholton HS 6520 Freetown Rd ia MD 21044*

ER, JOAN PALUMBO, Mathematics Teacher; *b:* Norwalk, CT; d A.; *c:* Christian T.; *ed:* Southern CT St Coll (BS) Elem Ed 1-8 airfield Univ (MS) Educl Media 1985; 54 Credits Grad & Inservice Ed; *cr:* Fox Run Elem Schl 5th Grd Tchr 1974; West Rocks MS 6-8 ath Tchr 1974-; *ai:* NFT Union Rep; Yoga Instr; Modified Grd AFT, NFT 1974-, Steward; *office:* West Rocks MS 81 W Rocks Rd k CT 06851

ER, LAURA JOYCE, Associate Professor; *b:* Cooperstown, NY; Thompson, Jeffrey Thompson, James Thompson, Jared Thompson; kimer Cty Comm (AS) Bio 1971; Syracuse Univ (BS) Bio Ed 1973; at Oneonta (MS) Bio Ed 1977; *cr:* Herkimer Cty Comm Coll Assoc 77-; *office:* Herkimer County Comm Coll Reservoir Road Herkimer 50

ER, LEWIS KENNETH, Secondary Education Teacher; *b:* lphia, PA; *m:* Eula R.; *c:* Joi; *ed:* Cheyney Univ (BS) Soc Sci 1975; in Educl Seminars & Skillful Tchng; *cr:* Philadelphia Schl System rm Sub Tchr 1975-77; Milton Hershey Schl Scndry Ed Tchr 1977-; d Boys Bsktbl Coach; 9th Grd Team Apex Ldr; Fac Observer; Boy's Track Jump Coach; Permanent Sr Class Adv; PCSS 1988-; *office:* Hershey Schl 300 Hotel Rd Hershey PA 17103

ER, RONALD SANFORD,III, Language Arts Teacher; *b:* NY; *m:* Carol M. Fritz; *c:* Adam S., Drew E., Abigail B.; *ed:* West Univ (BA) Eng Lit 1969; Univ of DE (MA) Eng Lit 1983; gton Coll (EDD) Ldrshp & Innovation 1996; *cr:* Mt Pleasant Sr HS th Grd Eng 1969-78; Erick HS 9th-12th Grd Eng 1978-84; Cape en HS 10th-12th Grd Eng 1984-89; Milton MS 8th Grd Eng 1989-; or Soc; Dist Tech Comm; NEA, OSEA & CHEA 1969-; Phi Delta 993-; ASCD 1994-; Christa McAuliffe Awd.

ER, THOMAS JONES, Band Director; *b:* Wilmington, DE; *m:* Hunt; *ed:* Trenton St Coll (BA) Music Ed 1971, (MA) Music 1972; r Univ (MED) Ed Admin 1993; *cr:* Penns Grove HS Band Dir); Pennsauken HS Band Dir 1976-; *ai:* Marching Band; Winter NEA, NJEA, Pennsauken Ed Assn 1976-; MENC 1971-; *home:* 5 Carneys Point NJ 08069

ER, WILLARD L., Biology Teacher; *b:* Youngstown, OH; *m:* Blake; *c:* David, Paula; *ed:* Youngstown Univ (BSEd) Bio 1966; Univ (MS) Bio 1972; Post Grad Credit Hrs Penn St Univ, IN Univ Duquesne Univ; *cr:* Beaver Area HS Bio Tchr 1966-; Comm Coll er Cty Bio Instr 1993-; *ai:* SATs Supvr & Stu Cncl Spon; NEA SEA 1966-; Beaver Area Ed Assn 1966-, Past Pres; NSF Grad Stud *office:* Beaver Area Middle-HS Gypsy Glen Rd Beaver PA 15009

TENHISER, BRUCE A., Mathematics Teacher; *b:* Johnstown, PA; v of Pittsburgh at Johnstown (BS) Electrical Engrng Tech 1986, cndry Math Ed 1993; Gordon-Conwell Theological Seminary 9 1988-91; *cr:* Coalition for Chrstn Outreach Yth, Campus Ministry ; Riverside Chrstn Acad Tchr 1993-94; St Francis Coll Div I Tennis Coach 1993-94; Westmont HS Math Tchr 1994-; *ai:* Jr, Sr Vlybl Coach; PSEA 1994-; Greater Johnstown Tennis Assn 1991-, 93-94; *office:* Westmont Hilltop HS 200 Fair Oaks Dr Johnstown 05*

TER, EILEEN TOFFEL, Principal; *b:* Jersey City, NJ; *m:* Jeffrey Brian J., Jill M.; *ed:* Jersey City St Coll (BA) Math, Ed 1968, (MA) 971; 6 Post Grad Credits; *cr:* Bayonne HS Tchr 1968-72; Solomon er Acad Tchr 1979-, Prin 1993-; *ai:* 8th Grd Adv; NJEA, NC Cncl Math, NJCTM, NCTM 1968-; Solomon Schechter Day Schl Prins 993-; Amer Cancer Soc 1974-, VP Fundraising; Howell Twp Cncl ce Abuse 1985-; Who's Who Among Stdnts Amer Univ & Coll; Delta Pi; *office:* Solomon Schechter Acad 395 Kent Rd Howell NJ

ERLY, GARY L., Industrial & Technology Tchr; *b:* Sligo, PA; *c:* Mike, Kelly; *ed:* California Univ of PA (BS) Industry, Tech 1973; rion Area Schls Indstrl Tech Inst 1973-; CAD Drafting 1983-; *ai:* ays Tech Dir; Stu Assistance Prgm; Clarion Area Ed Assn, PSEA, 973-; *office:* Clarion Area H S 219 Liberty St Clarion PA 16214

PATRICIA HACHTEN, Biology Teacher; *b:* Marion, OH; *m:* J.; *c:* Adam; *ed:* OH Wesleyan Univ (BS) Bio 1970; Temple Univ) Sci Ed 1982; *cr:* Amer Schl Bio Tchr 1970-72; Rdng City ative Schl Bio, Math Tchr 1972-74; Gov Mifflin HS Bio Tchr); Ephrata HS Bio Tchr 1979-; *ai:* Sci Fair Club; Lancaster Cty Sci rng Fair, Sci Fair Dirs; NSTA, PSTA, NEA, PSEA 1979-; East :o Twp Planning Commission 1994-, Commissioner; Book Pub ng Successful Sci Fair Projects 1996; *office:* Ephrata Sr HS 803 vd Ephrata PA 17522*

, SYLVIA YEARICK, German Teacher; *b:* Altoona, PA; *m:* R.; *c:* David H., Douglas L., Kathryn M.; *ed:* OH St Univ (BS) Eng Goethe Inst Schwabisch Hall Germany; 6 Grad Credit Hrs Eng Ed; Credit Hrs Corrective Rdng; *cr:* Columbus Pub Schls Home Instr , Sub Tchr 1979-82; Tree of Life Chrstn Schls Ger Tchr 1982-; *ai:* ıb Adv; Ldr European Stud Tours; Pi Lambda Theta 1970-; Articles *ffice:* Tree of Life Chrstn Schls 935 Northridge Rd Columbus OH

ES, DOROTHY, 4th Grade Teacher; *b:* Atlantic City, NJ; *w:* e G. (dec); *c:* Brian, Kevin, Armenta, Donelle; *ed:* Montclair St Eng 1955; Tchrs Coll Columbia 17 Credits; *cr:* PS 151Q Tchr 1; PS256K Tchr 1981-; *ai:* Stu Govt Adv; Dist Stu Cncl Ldrshp UFT 1977-.

ES, LOUISE SCRIVEN, 11th Grade Cosmetology Teacher; *b:* yn, NY; *m:* Keith; *c:* Brandon; *ed:* Attending City Univ of NY Ed; Wilfred Acad of Hair NY St License Granted 1977; *cr:* ne Valmy Intl Skin Care Schl Tchr 1984-86; Sarah J. Hale HS tology Tchr 1986-; *ai:* City of NY Human Resource Admin Family, Svc Vol; HS Fashion Show Coord, Adv; Off Broadway ıp-Artist; NY Reg Transplant Prgm Inc Donor; AFL CIO 1986-, FT; Sigma Pi Epsilon 1985-, Esthetician Alpha Chptr; Bd of ner St of NY 1987-; *home:* 160 Parkside Ave Brooklyn NY 11226*

S, ANNE MACLEOD, Coll Guid Dir & Eng Tchr; *b:* Princeton, NJ; nes O.; *c:* Jedediah; *ed:* Lawrence Univ (BA) Eng, SLavic 1977; va Univ (MA) Eng 1988; *cr:* Elhart Lake-Glenbeulah HS Eng Tchr); Perkiomen Schl Eng Tchr 1979-88; Oldfields Schl Dri Coll Guid, hr 1988-; *ai:* Jr Class Adv; Dorm Parent; NACAC, PCACAC 1988-; 1988-, Presidential Cnslrs Group; MENSA 1984-; AP Rdr for Coll ontinuing Ed Seminary LDr Goncher Coll; Article Pub; *office:* ds Schl Box 697 Glencoe MD 21152

S, ANNE MARIE DE PROSPO, Science Teacher; *b:* Brooklyn, Gary Alan; *ed:* Lafayette Coll (BA) Chem 1983; Colgate Univ Natural Sci 1991; Kutztown Univ, Univ of ME at Orono, SUNY at ta 3 Credit Hrs Each; *cr:* Perkiomen Schl Sci Tchr 1983-86; rne-Earlville HS Sci Tchr 1987-; *ai:* Stu Cncl Adv; Bldg Advy Colgate Univ Sci Affiliates; AAPT 1990-93; St Mary's Church Cncl 4; Chenango Cty Environmental Cncl Awd 1990; Spectrochimica Acta Article Pub 1984; *office:* Sherburne-Earlville HS School St Sherburne NY 13460

WEEKS, JOSHUA N., 9th Grd Human Dev & PE Teacher; *b:* Pittsfield, MA; *m:* Darlene Polcaro; *ed:* Univ of MA (BS) PE 1982, (MS) PE 1991; *cr:* Pittsfield YMCA Phys, Aquatic Dir 1983-87; Pittsfield Pub Schls Elem PE Tchr 1987-91; Adult Learning Ctr Gen Ed Tchr 1991-92; Pittsfield HS Human Dev, PE Tchr 1992-; *ai:* Class of 1996 Co-Adv; Boys Track & Field Coach 1988-; Boys & Girls Swimming Head Coach 1987-; AFT 1987-; Pittsfield YMCA 1995-, Bd of Dir; Amer Red Cross 1980-, Safety Svcs Vol, Instr Trainer 1994-; Pittsfield Schls PE Outstdng Tchr Awd 1988; Berkshire Cty League Outstdng Swimming Coach, Boys Outstdng Track & Field 1995; *office:* Pittsfield HS 300 East St Pittsfield MA 01201*

WEEKS, KARL ALLEN, Social Studies & History Tchr; *b:* Chester, PA; *m:* Linda Ulmer; *c:* Katherine P. Mason; *ed:* Franklin & Marshall (AB) His 1972; Temple Univ (MED) Ed 1983; *cr:* Indiana Univ of PA Robt Taft Govt Fellowship; Millersville UNiv 6 Credits; Marywood Coll 4 Credits; *ai:* Lancaster Cath HS Soc Stud, His Tchr 1972-; Cheerleading, Debate Coach; Ski Club Moderator; Youth Day Govt Coord; NCSS: PA Geographical Soc; Lancaster Cty Historical Soc; Neff Elem PTO Bd, Pres; Manheim Twp MS PTO Bd, Pres; *office:* Lancaster Catholic HS 650 Juliet Ave Lancaster PA 17601

WEEKS, PHILIP, History Professor; *b:* Elyria, OH; *m:* Jeanette Darvas; *c:* Michael; *ed:* Kent St (BA) His 1971, (MA) His 1977; Case Western Reserve (PHD) Amer Stud 1989; Trinity Evangelical Divinity Schl Post Grad Work; *cr:* Kent St Univ Prof 1986-; *ai:* Org of Amer Historians; Books: Farewell My Nation, Land of Liberty, the American Indian Experience & Subjugatim & dishonor; *office:* Kent St Univ 6000 Frank Ave NW North Canton OH 44720

WEEMAN, MARGARET ANN CRILL, Second Grade Teacher; *b:* Wooster, OH; *m:* James Lee; *c:* Molly, Timothy, Sara; *ed:* Kent St Univ (BS) Elem Ed 1977; Cmptr Sci Cert; *cr:* Orrville City Schls 2nd Grd Tchr 1977-; *ai:* OSHA, Rdng Curr Comms; OEA; NEA; Wayne Cty Rdng Cncl 1977-; Trinity Meth; Stephen's Minister, Heartland-ECC Steering Comm 1994-; Tchr of Yr 1984-85; *office:* Oak Street Schl 209 W Oak St Orrville OH 44667

WEFERS, MARYLOU L., Fifth & Sixth Grade Teacher; *b:* Lawrence, MA; *ed:* Univ of NH (BA) His 1969; *cr:* St Thomas Aquinas Schl Tchr 1969-71; St Patrick Convent Schl Tchr 1971-74, 1976-80; St Christopher Schl Tchr 1981-; *ai:* Stu Cnslr Adv; NCEA 1981-; PTA 1995-; *office:* St Christopher Schl 20 Cushing Ave Nashua NH 03060

WEGENER, MARILYN MUSSMAN, Teacher; *b:* Cincinnati, OH; *m:* John G.; *ed:* Mt St Joseph (BA) Elem Ed 1964; Attnd Univ of Dayton, Xavier Univ; *cr:* Holy Family Schl 1st-2nd Grd Tchr; St Patrick 5th-6th Grd Tchr; St Michael 5th Grd Lang Arts Tchr; St Albert 5th Grd Soc Stud & Rdng Tchr; St Mary 5th Grd Lang Arts Tchr; *ai:* Drama & Pgm Coord; Intnl Schl to Schl Exch; Tech Planning Comm; NEA; Historical SW Soc, Intepreter, 1993-, Pres; Cincinnati Art Museum; Grant to Produce Musical Pgm for the Cultural Exch Pgm; ECASE Grants; *office:* St Mary Schl 2845 Erie Ave Cincinnati OH 45208

WEGMAN, JENNIFER LYNN, Systems Furniture Company Mgr; *b:* Cincinnati, OH; *ed:* Miami Univ (BA) Sociology 1993; Working Toward Scndry Ed Tchng Cert Miami Univ; *cr:* Mother of Mercy HS Soccer Coach 1992-95; Wegman Co Asst Supver 1993-94, Mgr 1995-; Space Design Intnl Mrkgt Asst 1994-95; *ai:* Habitat for Humanity 1994-, Vol; Vol Svcs Appreciation Awd; Poems Pub; *home:* 2725 Falconbridge Dr Cincinnati OH 45238*

WEHMANN, CLAUDIA TREDWAY, English Teacher; *b:* Cincinnati, OH; *m:* Thomas Lee; *c:* Dan Robinson; *ed:* Univ of Cincinnati (BS) Elem Ed 1974; Xavier Univ (MS) Ed, Scndry Eng 1980; Attnd Miami Univ; *cr:* Mt Healthy North Jr HS 7th-8th Grd Eng, Math Tchr 1974-89; Mt Healthy HS 9-12th Grd Eng Tchr 1989-; *ai:* Jr Hnr Soc, Frosh Class Spon; Jr Yrbk Adv; NCTE 1989-; Two Articles Pub; Portfolio Grant EECAP, Raymond Walters Branch of Univ of Cincinnati; OH Writing Project 3 Yrs; *office:* Mount Healthy HS 2046 Adams Rd Cincinnati OH 45231

WEHR, M. SCOTT, Sixth Grade Teacher; *b:* Sellersville, PA; *m:* Paula J.; *ed:* Kutztown SC (BS) Elem Ed 1970, (MED) Elem Ed 1975; Addl 30 Credits; *cr:* Upper Perkiomen MS Sixth Grd Tchr 1970-; *ai:* Strategic Planning, Distngd Svc Recognition Comms; Soc Stud Curr Review; NEA, PSEA, UPEA 1970-; *office:* Upper Perkiomen MS 510 Jefferson St East Greenville PA 18041

WEHRLE, JOHN GEORGE, History Teacher; *b:* Altoona, PA; *m:* Nancy Milne; *c:* John (dec), Matthew; *ed:* St Vincent Coll (BA) His 1968; Georgetown Univ (MA) His 1972; Addl Hrs Univ of MD Pre Civil War Southern US; *cr:* Montgomery Cty Pub Schls Tchr 1968-; *ai:* Stu Govt Assn, Amnesty Intnl Adv; NEA 1968-; Laytonsville Civic Assn 1977-, Pres 3 Yrs; Redland Hunt Pony Club 1990-, Dist Commisioner 1995; NEH Grant 1989; *office:* Thomas S Wootton HS 2100 Wootton Pkwy Rockville MD 20850*

WEHRUM, ADELE DILONARDO, Spanish Teacher; *b:* Isernia, Italy; *m:* Wendell L.; *c:* Alexander, Eric; *ed:* Univ of Cincinnati (BA) Ed, Span 1975, (BS) Ed, Span 1975; Univ Xavier (MED) Rdng Specialist 1978; Miami Univ Post Grad Work 1985; Univ of Salamanca Spain Lit 1973; *cr:* Sr Francis HS Span, Rdng Tchr 1975-78; Felicity-Franklin HS & Elem Schl Span, Rdng Tchr 1978-85; Felicity Franklin HS Span Tchr 1985-; *ai:* NHS Spon 1991-; HS Mentor 1987-; Sigma Delta Pi, Pres 2 Yrs; Church Bd 1990-.

WEIDENBAUGH, THERESA GENTILI, Sixth & Seventh Grd Eng Tchr; *b:* Pottstown, PA; *m:* Jay; *ed:* Kutetown Univ (BA) Ed 1985; West Chester (MS) Ed 1990; Attnd Villanova Admin; *cr:* Springford Elem Tchr 1985-93, Eng Tchr 1993-; *ai:* Staff Dev Comm; NEA 1986; *office:* Spring Ford MS 700 Washington St Royersford PA 19468

WEIDLER, STANLEY GUY, 7th Grd Social Studies Teacher; *b:* Lancaster, PA; *m:* Gwendolyn Lois Reckard; *c:* Christopher, Tyler, Camilla; *ed:* Shuippensburg St Univ (BA) Soc Stud Scndry 1976, (MS) Geoenvironmental Stud 1980; *cr:* Conewago Vly Schl Dist Soc Stud Tchr & World Geog Prof 1976-; Harrisburg Area Comm Coll World Geog Prof 1991-; *ai:* PCSS 1989-; MOCSS 1991-, VP & Pres; *office:* Conewago Valley Schl Dist 130 Berlin Rd New Oxford PA 17350

WEIDMAN, GAIL A., Spanish Teacher; *b:* Dansville, NY; *ed:* SUNY at Potsdam (BA) Span 1971; SUNY at Geneseo Grad Credit Hrs; *cr:* St Josephs Ursuline Acad Span Tchr 1973-76; Dansville Cntrl Schl Sub Tchr 1976-77; Hornell HS Span Tchr 1977-; *ai:* NHS Co-Adv; SALT Lang Fair Co-Chm; NYSAFLT 1973-; Hornell Edctrs Assoc 1977-, Sec; NEA 1977-; Steuben-Allegany Lang Tchrs 1990-; NASAA 1996; Presbyn Church of Dansville 1963-, Elder; Delta Kappa Gamma Soc 1987-; *office:* Hornell HS 14 Allen St Hornell NY 14843*

WEIDMAN, RUTH HAINLINE, Retired First Grade Teacher; *b:* Celina, OH; *c:* Kent, Kathy E. Theisen; *ed:* OH Northern Univ (AA) Elem Ed 1952; Wright St Univ (BS) Elem Ed 1974; *cr:* Celina East Elem Schl Fourth Grd Tchr 1952-54, Third Grd Tchr 1954-55, LD Tutor 1971-74, First Grd Tchr 1974-95; *ai:* Various Comms; Celina Ed Assn; OEA; NEA; Univ Women's Club 1974-; Alpha Delta Omega 1954-, All Offices; Order of Eastern Star 1954-; Mercer Co Ret Tchrs Assn, OH Ret Tchrs Assn 1995-; St Paul's Meth Church 1949-, Ministries Cncl.

WEIDNER, JAMES H., Educator & Publisher; *b:* Carlisle, PA; *m:* Regina; *c:* David, Jeffrey, Timothy; *ed:* Univ of PA (BS) Eng, Sci 1962; Attnd Princeton Univ, Glassboro SC, Burlington Co Coll; *cr:* W. B. Saunders Co Schl Med Ed 1964-67; No Burlington Co Regnl HS Eng Dept Chm 1967-82; Burl Co Coll Sr Adj Inst 1979-82; Univ of NC Lecturer 1983; Northern Burlington Regnl HS Educator 1982-; Tycooly Publishing USA; *ai:* Newspaper Adv; BCEA; NJEA; NEA; AMWA; COSMEP; Boro of Merchantville, Bd of Hlth, Sec; Author of 5 Books Eng Grammar; Pub 100.

WEIERBACH, JUDITH HOUSEWORTH, Jr & Sr English Teacher; *b:* Phillipsburg, NJ; *m:* Harry Tilden; *c:* Sharon L., Aaron H.; *ed:* Muhlenberg Coll (AB) Eng 1967; Lehigh Univ (MED) Scndry Eng Ed 1973; 30 Post-Grad Credits; *cr:* Pennridge HS Scndry Eng Tchr 1967-; *ai:* Stu Assistance Team; NEA, PSEA 1967-; *office:* Pennridge HS 1228 N 5th St Perkasie PA 18944

WEIG, WALTER FRANK,JR., High School Mathematics Tchr; *b:* Bloomfield, NJ; *m:* Kathleen; *ed:* Montclair St (BA) Math & Accounting 1966, (MA) Pure & Applied Math 1970; *cr:* West Essex HS Math Tchr 1966-; *ai:* Attendance Appeals Comm; West Essex Ed Assn, NJ Ed Assn, NEA; Set Up & Did All Programming for Schls Cmptr 18 Yrs; *office:* West Essex Sr HS W Greenbrook Rd North Caldwell NJ 07006

WEIGAND, BERNARDINE S., 1st Grade Teacher; *b:* Perth Amboy, NJ; *m:* William J.; *c:* Kim W. Casola, Kristie W. Morris, Karrie L. Weigand; *ed:* Trenton St Coll (BA) Ed 1960; Fairleigh Dickinson Univ (MA) Ed 1978; 48 Addl Hrs; *cr:* Red Bank Pub Schls Kdgn Tchr 1960-61; Lincroft Elem Schl 1 Grd Tchr 1968-; *ai:* MTEA, NEA, NJEA 1968-; Phi Delta Kappa 1986-; *home:* 6 Deercrest Dr Holmdel NJ 07733

WEIGEL, WILLIAM M., Social Studies Teacher; *b:* Columbia, PA; *m:* Nancy Friedrichs; *c:* Biff, Kylie; *ed:* Millersville Univ of PA (BS) Scndry Ed, Soc Sci 1972, (MS) Sco Sci 1977; Addl Credit Hrs Ed; *cr:* Franklinville Cntrl Schl Soc Stud Tchr, Global Stud, AP European His 1973-, Wrestling Coach 1973-83, 1986, Girls Track, Field Coach 1976-, Cross Cntry Coach 1978-; *ai:* Boys, Girls Cross Cntry, Girls Track, Big 30 Track Team Coach; Org Schl Project Fair 1993-95; Org 2 Trips with Aths to Holland, Denmark, Sweden 1989-95; NYSUT, AFT 1973-; Franklinville Tchrs Org 1973-, Tchr of Yr; Southern Tier Wrestling Officials Assn 1983-, Pres; Allegany CAttaraugus Cty Soc Stud Org 1993-95; Jaycee 1973-91, Jaycee of Month 2 Times; PTO 1993-; Acad Sports Boosters 1991-; Silver Streaks AC 1981-, Pres, Various Gold, Silver, Bronze Medals in NY St Empire St Games; Summer Kids Track Prgm 1990-95, Org; Christmas Spirit Prgm Helder for Needy 1993-95; World Veterans T & F Championships in Buffalo NY 1995; Competed Boston Marathon 1984; ABC's Coaching AWd From Western NY HS Sport Nwspr; Grad Speaker 1995-; *office:* Franklinville Cntrl Schl 31 N Main St Franklinville NY 14737*

WEIK, BETTY L., 3rd Grade Teacher; *b:* Newmanstown, PA; *w:* Ralph L. (dec); *c:* Julie Kreiser, Lora Keppley, Robert; *ed:* Millersville Univ (BS) Elem 1955; *cr:* Reading Schl Dist 2nd Grd Tchr 1955-56; Eastern Lebanon Cty Schl Dist 3rd Grd Tchr 1963-; *ai:* Bike-A-Thon ELCO Chprsn 10 Yrs; NEA 1960-; PSEA; ELCEA; Millcreek Luth Church 1946-, Sunday Schl Tchr.

WEIKAL, JAMES E., Senior High English Teacher; *b:* Sharon, PA; *m:* Mary Beth Carnes; *c:* Shane, Adam, Zachary; *ed:* Clarion Univ (BS) Eng 1967; Westminster Coll (MED) 1973; *cr:* Reynolds HS Eng Tchr 1967-; *ai:* Voice of Democracy; NEA, PSEA, REA 1967-; First Assmbly of God & Bill Rudge Ministries; Writer & Speaker; *office:* Reynolds HS 531 Reynolds Rd Greenville PA 16125

WEIKEL, WILLIAM EUGENE, Mathematics & Accounting Tchr; *b:* Portland, ME; *m:* Carol A. Lindvall; *c:* William, Peter, Mathew, Donald; *ed:* Gorham St Coll (BS) Math & Ed 1966; Bryand Coll 51 Credit Hrs; Cambridge Coll 24 Credit Hrs; Bridgewater St Coll 6 Hrs; KS St Univ 3 Credits; *cr:* US Army Combate Surveilance Specialist 1976-1981; Town of Scarboro Police Officer 1981-1986; Town of Walpole Tchr 1986-; *ai:* Walpole Tchrs Assn Negotiator; BSA Trng Adv; Past Coach Fresh Ftbl, Bsktbl, Track 14 Yrs; Walpole Tchrs 1966-, Negotiator, Vp, Pres; MA Tchrs Assn 1966-, Convention Rep; Natl Tchrs Assn; BSA 1975-, Asst Scout Master, Scout Master, Dist Commissioner, Trng Chm, trainer, Silver Beaver Awd, Dist Awd of Merit, Wood Badge 4 Beads; With Others in Dept Wrote and Pub 8th Grd Math Book; Tchr of Month; *office:* Walpole HS 257 Common St Walpole MA 02081

WEIKERT, BARBARA SWIGART, Fifth Grade Teacher; *b:* Montgomery Cty, OH; *m:* Richard; *c:* Gerald Lee; *ed:* Miami Univ (BS) Elem Ed 1967; Wright St (MS) Elem Ed 1971; 45 Hrs in Various Subjects; *cr:* Dayton Power & Light Sec 1952-1966; Northmont City Schls 5th & 6th Grd Tchr 1967-; *ai:* Tchng Sr Citizens Comptr Classes; NEA 1967-; OEA 1967-, Del St 1975-; WOEA 1967-; NDEA 1967-, Bldg Rep; Wrkd at Election for St Senators & Representatives; Grant for Networking of Comps; *office:* O R Edgington Elem Schl 515 N Main St Englewood OH 45322

WEIL, JULIEN B., High School Mathematics Tchr; *b:* Camp Zama, Japan; *m:* Deborah Ann Derkach; *c:* Susan, Katherine; *ed:* Emory Univ (BA) Chem 1977, (BS) Bio 1977; Attnd Columbus Coll; Natl Sci Fnd; *cr:* Royal Crown Cola Co Packaging Rsrch Mgr 1978-89; Bible Bapt Church Asst Pastor 1989-92; Columbia Chrstn Acad Prin 1989-92; Tabernacle Bapt Church Pastor 1992-; Tioga Cty Chrstn Acad HS Math Tchr 1993-; *ai:* Pastors Advy Bd; *office:* Tioga Cty Christian Acad PO Box 103 Middlebury Center PA 16935

WEILBRENNER, PAM KIRK, Readiness Teacher; *b:* Manchester, NH; *m:* Ronald R.; *c:* Heather, Zachary; *ed:* Univ of NH (BA) Elem Ed 1976; *cr:* Beech St schl Title I Rdng Tchr 1976-77; Beech St Schl Readiness Tchr 1977-88; Smyth Rd Schl Readiness Tchr 1988-; *ai:* Literacy Comm Chprsn 1992-93, 1995-; NEA, NHEA 1977-; *office:* Smyth Road Schl 245 Bruce Rd Manchester NH 03104

WEIMANN, PETER J., English & Psychology Instr; *ed:* Cntrl CT St (BS) Eng Ed 1969; Univ CT (MS) Eng ED 1977; Attnd Shakespeare Inst Univ of Bridgeport; *cr:* TMHS Eng, Psych Instr 1969-; *ai:* Jr Class Major, Amer Govt WA DC Trip Adv; TEA, CEA, NEA 1969-, Negotiations Chm.

WEIMER, PETER, Chemistry & Physics Teacher; *b:* Dayton, OH; *m:* Janet Snyder; *c:* Rachel, Jonathan; *ed:* Univ of Dayton (BS) Bio, Chem 1972, (BA) Scndry Ed 1974; Wright St Univ (MS) Sci Ed 1986; *cr:* Dunbar HS Sci Tchr, Sci Chair 1975-; *ai:* Sci Bowl, Soccer Coach; Sci Dept Chprsn; NEA 1975-; Amer Chemical Soc 1989-; Sci Ed Cncl of OH 1993-; *office:* Paul Laurence Dunbar HS 2222 Richley Ave Dayton OH 45408

WEIMER, STEWART G., Mathematics Teacher; *b:* Tarentum, PA; *m:* Filippa Massard; *c:* Teresa, Gregory, Mark; *ed:* Westminster Coll (BS) Math 1966; Univ of MI (MS) Math 1967; Univ of Pittsburgh (BS) Cmptr Sci 1986; Post Grad Stud in Cmptr Sci Univ of OR, Univ of MO; *cr:* Seneca Vly Sr HS Math Tchr 1967-; *ai:* SVEA, PSEA, NEA 1970-; *office:* Seneca Vly Sr HS 126 Seneca Schl Rd Harmony PA 16037*

WEINBERG, BARBARA SLOMAN, Social Studies Teacher; *b:* NYC, NY; *m:* Lewis; *c:* Erika, Melanie; *ed:* Lehamn Coll (BA) His 1969, (MA) Scndry Ed Soc Stud 1993; *cr:* MS 118 Tchr 1996; *ai:* AFT; UFT; *office:* William W. Niles MS 118 577 E 179th St Bronx NY 10457

WEINBERG, ELLIOT GEORGE, Social Studies Teacher; *b:* Boston, MA; *m:* Sheila M. Cohen; *c:* Lisa, Dawna Weinberg-Law, Todd; *ed:* Suffolk Univ (BA) His, Soc Stud Ed 1963; Northeastern Univ (MA) His, Soc Stud 1966; RI Coll Curr Extension; *cr:* MSAD #11 HS His, Soc Stud Tchr

1966-69; Danvers Jr HS His Tchr 1969-90; Mt Hope HS His, Soc Stud Tchr 1970-; *ai:* NHS; Fac Advy Cncl; 1986 Acreditation Comm Supervision, Admin Chprsn; RISSA 1970-; BWEA 1970-, Bldg Rep; Tchr of Yr 1993; *office:* Mt Hope HS 199 Chestnut St Bristol RI 02809

WEINBERG, FRANCINE ARROW, English Teacher; *b:* Brooklyn, NY; *m:* Lawrence Jerome; *c:* Paul, Joel; *ed:* Brooklyn Coll (BA) Ed 1961; City Coll NY (MS) Ed 1964; 30 Post-Grad Hrs Eng; *cr:* Jr HS 22X Eng Tchr 1961-65; NY City Comm Coll Adjunct Lecturer Eng 1969-76; Jr HS 226Q Eng Tchr 1976-81; Martin Van Buren HS Eng Tchr 1981-983; Benjamin N. Cardozo HS Eng Tchr & Grd Adv 1983-; *ai:* UFT 1961-; NY City Tchrs Eng 1983-; Feingold Assn 1974-; Phi Sigma Sigma 1957-, Bursar 1960; Help of Retarded Childeren Children Assn 1988-; *office:* Benjamin N. Cardozo HS 57-00 223rd St Bayside NY 11364

WEINBERG, HELEN NOSEL, Fourth Grade Teacher; *b:* Brooklyn, NY; *m:* Warren; *c:* Shari, Lawrence; *ed:* Brooklyn Coll (BA) Ed 1957; *cr:* PS 272 1st Grd Tchr 1957-59; PS 279 1st Grd Tchr 1959-60; Paumanok Elem Schl 5th Grd Tchr 1969-70; Vanderbilt Elem Schl 1st, 4th-6th Grd Tchr 1970-; *ai:* Newspaper Adv 1993-94; Staff Dev Comm 1994-95; NYSUT, Half Hollow Hills Tchrs Assn 1969-; Hadassah, Life Mem; Phi Beta Kappa; Jenkins Meml PTA Awd; *office:* Vanderbilt Elem Schl 350 Deer Park Rd Huntingtn Sta NY 11746*

WEINBERG, KAREN MINKIN, Art Department Chairman; *b:* Canton, OH; *c:* Robert Jason; *ed:* Kent St Univ (BA) Art Ed, Studio Art 1971; Youngstown St Univ (MS) Scndry Ed 1988; Doctoral Level Work; Cleveland St Univ Post Grad Work in Ed; Supervisory Cert; *cr:* Aurora OH Schls Elem Art Specialist 1970-76; Kirksville Coll Osteop Med Research Librn 1976-78; Betty Rinderle Schl Art Specialist 1978-79; Austintown Fitch HS Art Dept Chair, Art Specialist 1980-; Youngstown St Univ Limited Svc Fac 1991-; *ai:* Art Club Adv; Curr Cncl Comm; Scholastic Art Regnl Advy Bd; NEA, OEA, AEA 1980-; OAEA 1970-; Phi Delta Kappa 1990-; Delta Kappa Gamma 1995-; Jr League of Yo 1980-, Publications Chair; Aurora Schl System Tchr of Yr 1975-76; *office:* Austintown Fitch HS 4560 Falcon Dr Austintown OH 44515*

WEINBERG, MARSHA HENDERSON, English Teacher; *b:* Indianapolis, IN; *c:* Matthew; *ed:* Hanover Coll (BA) Eng, Theology 1979; IN Univ (MAT) Eng 1984; *cr:* Edgewood HS Eng Tchr 1982-84; John T. Baker MS Eng Tchr 1984-; *ai:* MD Stu Assistance Prgm 1992-; Lit Club Spon 1995-; Peer Mediation Trainer 1993-94; NEA, MCEA 1984-; Damascus Comm Action Team 1993-94; Stu Ldrs Club 1993-94, Spon; Portfolio Assessment Pilot Work Group; *office:* John Baker MS 25400 Oak Dr Damascus MD 20872

WEINBERG, PAULA, ESL Teacher; *b:* Olten, Switzerland; *m:* Donald; *c:* Claude-Alain, Marc-Bernard, Raymond Francois, Pierre-Michel, Robert Daniel; *ed:* Adelphi Univ (BA) Ed 1979; L. I. Univ C. W. Post Ctr (MA) Eng as Second Lang 1980; Permanent Cert in Ger, Fr, Span & ESL; *cr:* Levittown Jr HS ESL Tchr 1981; Bellmore-Merrick HS Dist ESL Tchr 1982-86; Hicksville Sr HS ESL Tchr 1987-; *ai:* NEA, AFT, HCT 1986-; NYSTESOL 1981-; *office:* Hicksville Sr HS Division Ave Hicksville NY 11801

WEINBERGER, LINDA WELSH, Kindergarten Teacher; *b:* Youngstown, OH; *m:* Donald Karl; *c:* Leah, Matthew; *ed:* West Liberty Coll (BA) Ed 1968; Attnd Hood Coll, Western MD Coll; *cr:* Colliers Elem Tchr 1967-68; Monocacy Elem Tchr 1968-82; Title I Montgomery Co Tchr Specialist 1979-81; Beverly Farms Elem Tchr 1983-; MCPS Math Cntnt Connections Tchr Trainer, Math Miles Smnr Trainer; *ai:* Early Chldhd Screening Coord; Grd Level, Orientation Chprsn; Cmptr Rep; NEA 1967-; MSTA 1968-; MCEA 1968-, Rep; Temple Beth Ami 1989-; North Potomac Citizens Assn; PTA Quince Orchard HS; *home:* 12532 Triple Crown Rd North Potomac MD 20878

WEINER, CHRISTIANA M., Math Teacher; *b:* Flint, MI; *m:* David Scott; *c:* Elizabeth, Emily, Erica, Esther; *ed:* MI St Univ (BS) Math Ed 1985; *cr:* Waverly HS Math Tchr 1985-87; Yeshiva Greater Washington Math Tchr 1987-, Dept Chprsn 1994-; *home:* 18508 Owl Run Way Germantown MD 20874

WEINER, ELEANOR R., United States History Teacher; *b:* Brooklyn, NY; *m:* Jerome; *c:* Steven, David, Joshua; *ed:* Fairleigh Dickenson Univ (B)S SOc Stud 1962; *cr:* Fair Lawn HS Tchr 1981-; *ai:* Stu Act Asst Coord; Natl Honor Fac Senate; Vice Prin Advsy Comm; Mid Sts Evaluation; NEA 1981-; Outstdng Soc Stud Edctr NJ Cncl for Soc Stud 1989, Voice of Democracy Awd 1990; Comm Servc Awd 1994; Dist Nominee 1991; *office:* Fair Lawn HS Berdan Ave Fair Lawn NJ 07410*

WEINER, FRED, Counseling Professor; *b:* Brooklyn, NY; *m:* Johanna Grebler; *c:* Jessica L., Monica D.; *ed:* Hunter Coll (BA) His 1956; NY Univ (MA) Stu Prsnl Svcs 1961; Addl Post Grad 20 Credits Cnslng Rutgers Univ, 21 Credits Ed Trenton St Coll, 9 Credits His Brooklyn Coll; *cr:* NYC Pub Schls Tchr 1958-62; Pennsville Jr HS Cnslr 1962-66; Gateway Regnl HS Guid Cnslr 1966-67; Electronics Trng Ctr Admissions Cnslr 1967-70; Mercer Cty Coll Cnslr 1970-; *ai:* Different Voice Adv; HIV, Aids Task Force; Stu Conduct, Discipline Comm; Coll Senate; NEA, NJEA 1958-; MCEA 1970-; NJCCC 1970-, Cnslr of Yr 1994; Stu Govt Assn Club Adv, Fac Mem of Yr 1979; Hyacinth AIDS Fdn Telephone Comm; MCCC Fdn Grant; *office:* MCCC Schl 1200 Old Trenton Rd Trenton NJ 08690

WEINER, HARRY S., English Teacher; *b:* Brooklyn, NY; *m:* Julie; *c:* Jillian; *ed:* SUNY at Albany (BA) Eng 1973, (MS) Rdng 1976; 30 Hrs Post Grad Credits; *cr:* Shenendehowa HS Eng Tchr 1973-; *ai:* Sr Sing Adv; NYSUT AFT 1973-.

WEINER, JERRY, 11th-12th Grd Physics Teacher; *b:* Philadelphia, PA; *m:* Sandy Lipschitz; *c:* Morgan, Samantha; *ed:* Cheyney St (BS) Sci Ed 1971; Temple Univ (MBA) Ec 1986, (MS) Sci Ed 1991; Enrolled EDD Prgm Sci Ed; *cr:* Montgomery Cty Comm Coll Part-time Ec Tchr; Bensalem HS Physics Tchr 1986-; *ai:* Sci Olympiad Team, Penna Jr Acad of Sci Spon, Adv; Coach Chess Team; AAPT, PSTA 1989-; NARST 1996-; *office:* Bensalem HS 4319 Hulmeville Rd Bensalem PA 19020*

WEINER, MADELINE JOY, Social Studies Teacher; *b:* Brooklyn, NY; *c:* Samantha; *ed:* LIU (BA) His 1968, (MA) Ed 1971; *cr:* Brooklyn Tech HS Tchr 1968-; *ai:* UFT Consultation, Curr Dev Comms; UFT 1968-; *office:* Brooklyn Technical HS 29 Fort Greene Pl Brooklyn NY 11217

WEINER, RUTH SHATZ, English Teacher; *b:* Brookline, MA; *m:* Kenneth Roy; *c:* Daniel, Brett; *ed:* Boston Univ (BS) Ed 1969; Lesley Coll (ME) Ed 1995; *cr:* North Jr HS Eng Tchr 1969-72; Kennedy Jr HS Eng Tchr 1978-81; Stoughton HS Eng Tchr 1981-; *ai:* Schl Newspaper Adv; NEA 1978-; Stoughton Tchrs Assn 1981-, Bldg Rep; Stories Pub; MA Acad for Tchrs 1992-93; MA Ldrshp Acad 1994; *office:* Stoughton HS 232 Pearl St Stoughton MA 02072*

WEINERT, JOANNE RUTH, Kindergarten Teacher; *b:* Lakewood, OH; *m:* Raymond; *c:* Jennifer, Melissa; *ed:* Concordia at Ann Arbor (AA) Eng Lit 1967; Concordia at NE (BS) Tchng 1969; Cleveland St Univ (MA) Early Chldhd 1993; 30 Hrs Post Grad Credit Hrs; *cr:* Hosanna Tabor Schl 2nd Grd Tchr 1969-71; King's Acad Pre-First Grd Tchr 1980-84; North Ridgeville City Schls Kndgtn Tchr 1984-85; Avon Lake City Schls Kndgtn Tchr 1985-; *ai:* Kndgtn Grd Level Chprsn 1987-92, 1995-; Elem Schl Tchr of Yr 1989-90; Avon Lake Cty Schl Dist Math Sci Grant; OH Edison Sci Grant; *office:* Erieview Elem Schl 32630 Electric Blvd Avon Lake OH 44012*

WEINERT, ROBERT JOSEPH, Social Studies Teacher; *b:* Philadelphia, PA; *m:* Marie Elena Langan; *c:* Robert F., Jessica M.; *ed:* St Joseph's Univ (BS) Scndry Ed 1973; Villanova Univ (MA) Scndry Ed 1986; 6 Credit Hrs Holy Family Coll; *cr:* Father Judge HS Soc Stud Tchr 1973-78; Archbishop Ryan HS Soc Stud Tchr 1978-87; Cherokee HS Soc Stud Tchr 1987-; *ai:* Boys Jr Var Soccer Coach; World Affairs Cncl Adv; Kappa Delta Pi 1986-; Phi Delta Kappa 1993-; NEA 1987-; NJ Soc Stud Cncl 1987-; S Jersey Coaches Assn 1988-; Amer Legion Post 754 1974-; Tchr of Yr 1987; *office:* Cherokee HS Willow Bend Rd Marlton NJ 08053*

WEINFELD, LINDA RUTTER, Spanish Tchr & Adjunct Instr; *b:* Bronx, NY; *m:* Edward; *c:* Fern S., Seth M.; *ed:* New York Univ (BS) Ed, Span 1966, (MA) Ed, Span 1967; C. W. Post Coll at Long Island Tchng Cert Ed, Nursery Elem Ed 1989; *ai:* Per Diem Sub NYC Schls Span Tchr 1966-67; Benjamin N. Cardozo HS Span Tchr 1967-71; Martin Van Buren HS Span Tchr 1971-72; Maternity & Child Care Leave with Per Diem Tchng Assignments 1972-85; Hicksville HS Span Tchr 1985-; Natl Span Honor Soc Adv; Stdnts Participate in Natl Span Examination; Spon Competition; Pi Lambda Theta 1965-; NY St Assn of For Lang Tchrs, Amer Assn of Tchrs of Span & Port, Long Island Lang Tchrs, NEA 1985-; UFT 1967-72; Winner of Natl Span Exam, Long Island Lang Tchrs Poster Cmptn, NY ST Assn of Frgn Lang Tchrs Poster Cmptn, Hofstra Univ Poetry Cmptn, Long Island Lang Tchrs Original Poetry Cmptn.

WEINHOLTZ, JOANNE RICKARD, Culture Teacher; *b:* Niagara Falls, NY; *m:* Mark; *c:* Alexandra; *ed:* Rochester Inst of Tech (AS) Retailing 1978, (BA) Bus Admin 1981; St Univ of Buffalo (MS) Native Amer Stud 1987; 108 Addl Credit Hrs; 18 Credit Hrs Niagara Univ; *cr:* Manufacturers, Traders Trust Bank Bus Dev Rep 1985-87; Tuscarora Indian Schl Fourth Grd Tchr 1991-93, Sixth Tchr 1988-91, Culture Tchr 1996; *ai:* Dancing Group; Indian Defense League Amer; Tchr of Yr 1991; *office:* Tuscarora Indian Schl 2015 Mount Hope Rd Lewiston NY 14092

WEINKAUF, DAVID, Assistant Professor; *ed:* Ithaca Coll (BS) Television, Radio 1963; Boston Univ (MS) Film 1965; Attnd Bloomsburg Univ 1991, Bowling Green Univ 1981, Univ of Southern CA 1972; *cr:* Cornell Univ WHCU-AM-FM Producer, Dir, Announcer, Dir of Traffic 1960-63; Boston Univ TV Production Grad Asst 1963-65; WBZ-TV Engr 1964-65; Univ of SD Speech Instr 1965-66; KUSD-FM-TV Producer, Dir Radio, TV Productions 1965-66; WOR-TV Engr 1966-68; Edinboro Univ of PA Asst Prof of Film, Animation, Photography 1966-; *ai:* Ad Hoc Comm Classroom Cmptr Use, Dept Brochure 1993-, Interdisciplinary Film Minor 1992-; Tech, Values Comm 1991-; Cmptr Use Comm Chprsn 1988-; Art Dept Applied, Media Arts Area Chprsn 1988-90; Dept Photo Hiring Comm 1988; Art Dept 2D Area Chprsn 1985-88; Dept Evaluation, Tenure Comm 1987; Dept Curr Dev Comm, Dept Photo Hiring Comm Chprsn 1984-85; APSCUF Fine Arts Rep 1983-84; Univ Facilities Use Comm 1983; Coll Media Task Force 1981-82; Coll Terminal Degree Equivalency Com; Soc for Animation Stud, Founding Mem; Amer Fed of Film Socs; AFT; Assn of PA St Coll, Univ Facs; Intnl Brotherhood of Electricl Workers; Intnl Alliance of Theatrical Stage Employees, Moving Picture Operators; Natl Assn Educl Broadcasters; PA Film, Video Cncl; Univ Film Assn; PA Cncl on Arts 1993-, Media Arts Panelist; WQLN Comm Advy Bd 1991-; Edinboro Theater Co 1983-, Sound Designer, Actor; Area Schl, Svc Clubs Speaker 1973-; Radio Flwshp Awds, PA Radio Theater, PA Cncl on Arts 1991, Juror; Conneautville Homecoming 1990, Parade Marshall; Bucks Cty Film Festival 1990, Juror; Pittsburgh Filmmakers Emerging Artsts Series 1989, Juror, Visiting Filmmaker 1988; Spring Twp Planning Commission 1986-88; Capital Children's Museum, Arts Guild Visiting Fi;mNumerous Appearances, Film Screenings, Shows, Wkshps, Books, Articles, Filmography, Media Projects & Assns, Grants, Hnrs, Confs.

WEINLANDT, DREW RUSSELL, English Professor; *b:* New York, NY; *ed:* Brown Univ (BA) Eng 1966; NY Univ (MA) Amer Lit 1967; Fairfield Univ (CAS) Admin & Suprv 1975; Post Grad Stud at Hunter Coll, St Johns Univ; *cr:* Garden City HS Eng Tchr 1970-; Nassau Comm Coll Eng Prof 1971-; *ai:* Yrbk Adv; NEA; NCTE; *office:* Nassau Comm Coll Stewart Ave Garden City NY 11530

WEINRAUB, DAWN STUART, Russian & French Teacher; *b:* New London, CT; *c:* Claire, David; *ed:* Duke Univ (BA) Russian 1962; Columbia Univ (MA) Russian Lit 1965; Middlebury Coll Fr Grad Class; ACTR Russian Inst for Profs of Russian at Bryn Mawr Coll 1981; *cr:* SUNY at Potsdam Librn of Music in Crane Schl of Music 1965-71; Emma Willard Schl Instr in Russian & Fr 1974-; Russell Sage Coll Adj Instr in Russian 1989-; *ai:* Coord of Assembly Pgm; Violinist in Emma Willard Schl Orch; Emma Willard Chptr of Amnesty Intnl Adv; Acad Adv to 6 Stdnts; ATSEEL 1974-; NYSAFLT 1980-; SLAVA 1981-, Regnl VP for East on Natl Drama; ACTR 1985-; Troy Friends of Chamber Music Bd 1978-, VP for Mbrshp; Natl Cncl for Basic Ed Fellow Ind Stud in Hum Grant 1993.

WEINSTEIN, ALAN JAMES, Teacher & Leader; *b:* Boston, MA; *m:* Julie Levinson; *c:* Elena, Molly; *ed:* Dartmouth Coll (BA) Bio 1975; Harvard Univ (EDM) Cnslng 1981, (EDM) Admin & Policy 1990, (EDD) Admin & Policy 1995; *cr:* Cambridge Rindge & Latin Sci Tchr 1976-94, Tchr Ldr 1995-; *ai:* ASCD 1994-; *office:* Cambridge Rindge & Latin Schl 459 Broadway Cambridge MA 02138

WEINSTEIN, DAVID HOWARD, History & Sociology Teacher; *b:* Brooklyn, NY; *m:* Amy Itkin; *ed:* Univ of MI (BA) Pol Sci 1986; Harvard Grad Schl of Ed (EDM) Tchng Curr & Learning Environment 1989; *cr:* Young Judaea Educl Dir 1986-87; Dwight Morrow HS His Tchr 1989-93; Columbia HS His Tchr 1993-; *ai:* Sr Class Adv; NEA 1989-; Natl Comm for Soc Stud 1990-; ASCD 1991-; Dodge Tech Flwshp; Natl Endowment for the Hum; Summer Seminar Flwshp; *office:* Columbia HS 17 Parker Ave Maplewood NJ 07040*

WEINSTEIN, LINDA S., Fourth Grade Teacher; *b:* Cambridge, MA; *m:* Donald; *c:* Michael, Steven; *ed:* Univ of MA at Amherst (BA) Elem Ed 1966; Villanova Univ (MA) Elem Guid, Cnslng 1974; 18 Continuing Ed Units; *cr:* Tredyffrin-Easttown Schl Dist Grds 3-4 Tchr 1967-69; West Chester Schls Grd 4 Tchr 1969-71; Chapter I Remedial Math Tchr 1976-84; Merion Schl Grd 4 Tchr 1984-; *ai:* Tech, Strategic Planning for Comm Svc Comm; Soc Stud Rep; Mentor Tchr; Cooperating Tchr for Univ of PA; NEA, PSEA 1969-; LMEA 1984-; Ardwood Civic Assn 1971-; *office:* Merion Elem Schl 549 S Bowman Ave Merion Station PA 19066

WEINSTEIN, LYNN, Drama Teacher; *b:* Queens, NY; *ed:* NY Univ Tisch Schl of Arts (BFA) Grad Acting 1971-74; London Acad of Music, Dramatic Arts Acting Grad Prgm 1975; *ai:* Head of Drama CLub; Dir of all Schl Plays, Musicals; *office:* William C Bryant HS 4810 31st Ave Long Island City NY 11103

WEINSTOCK, LENORE, Cluster Teacher; *b:* Bronx, NY; *m:* Melvin; *ed:* Brooklyn Coll (BA) Elem Ed, Eng 1958, (MS) Elem Ed 1962; Pace Univ (MS) Ed Admin 1982; 50 Addl Credits; *cr:* PS 113 Brooklyn Tchr 1958-68; PS 194 Brooklyn Tchr 1968-; Brooklyn Coll Adj GATE Edctr 1982-88; *ai:* UFT 1990-, Pension Consultant; AFT 1960-, Chptr Chprsn, Trachtenberg Awd; *office:* PS 194 Raoul Wallenberg Schl 3117 Avenue W Brooklyn NY 11229*

WEINTRAUB, ELAINE CAWLEY, Social Studies Teacher; *b:* Ireland; *m:* Joel; *c:* Roisin, Aislinn; *ed:* Manchester Univ (BA) Combined Hum 1972; Lesley Coll (BSC) Soc Stud Ed 1989; Cambridge Coll (MA) Ind His Stud 1990; Presented & Pub Rsrch at Univ of Ma, Westfield St Coll, Queens Univ, Belfast, Ireland, Mystic Seaport Museum, African Meeting House; *cr:* Oak Bluffs Elem Literacy, Cultural Tchr 1986-91; Sant Bani Alternative Schl Soc Stud Tchr 1991-92; Martha's Vineyard Regnl Stud Tchr 1992-; *ai:* Stdnt Meditation Groups Admin; New Engl Tchrs Assn 1990-; Amer Conf on Irish Stud 1989-; NAACP 198 Historian, Tchr of Yr 1992; Paul Cuffe Fellow Rsrch Flwshp 1993 New England Journal of His, African Meeting House Journal, V Gazette, Cape Cod Times, Amer Irish Stud Journal; Cape Cod Edct Cultural Cncl Grants.*

WEINTRAUB, HENRY, Soc Stud Tchr & Dept Chprsn; *b:* Me Australia; *c:* Dan, Marci; *ed:* Cumberland Cty Coll (AA) E Glassboro St Coll (BA) Elem Ed 1975; Wm Patterson Coll Po Courses in Urban Ed; Rowan St Coll Post Grad Courses for Soc S for Grds 9-12; *cr:* Dane Barse Schl 6th Grd Tchr 1975-77; Wm M Schl 6th Grd Tchr 1977-80; Anthony Rossi Schl 6th Grd, 7th-8th Stud & In-Schl Suspension Pgm Tchr 1980-; *ai:* Safety Patrol Adv Trial Team Coach; Mini-Model Congress Team Coach; Tag Ftbl Annual Talent Show Dir; Morning Announcement Club Adv; Ge Coord; NEA & NJEA 1975-, Comm Mem; CCCEA 1975-; VEA 19 NJCSS 1985-; Beth Israel Mens Club 1980-, Pres; PTA 1980-, Pre Club 1985-; Outstdng Tchr of the Yr 1986; Safety Patrol Adv of Gives Wkshps to Edctrs on Tchng Holocaust Ed in 7th & 8th Grd Anthony Rossi Intermediate Sch 2572 Palermo Ave Vineland NJ 0

WEIR, MERLENE J., Fifth Grade Teacher; *b:* Grand Rapids, Robert James; *c:* James Andrew, Robert Joseph, Christina Eile Olivet Coll (BA) Elem Ed 1962; Addl Credit Hrs At Univ of MD, Ca of Washington DC, Trinity Coll; *cr:* Comstock Park Elem Schls Tchr 1963-66; Primary Acad Schls 3rd Grd Tchr 1967-69; Langl Schl PGPS Title One Aide 1975-80; Langley Park Elem 1st-5th G 1980-82; Dodge Park Elem 1st & 2nd Grd Tchr 1983-85; Langl Elem 5th Grd Tchr 1985-; *ai:* Outreach Comm Chprsn; NEA, F Langley Park Coalition; Handbell Choir Mem 1994-; Math Articl Prince Georgian of Yr; *office:* Langley Pk-Mccormick Elem Sch 82 Ave Hyattsville MD 20783*

WEIRICH, DANIEL RAY, Mathematics Teacher; *b:* Port Clinton, Lisa Ann Sampson; *c:* Grant Henry; *ed:* Working on MS Supervision Univ of Toledo; *cr:* Lakota Local Schl Math Tchr 1 Benton-Carroll-Salem Schl Math Tchr 1990-91; Woodmore Loc Math Tchr 1991-; *ai:* Var Ftbl Asst Coach; JV Boys Bsktbl Coach; C of Tchrs of Math 1989-; *office:* Woodmore Local HS 633 Fre Elmore OH 43416

WEIRICH, ROBERT J., English Supervisor; *b:* Reading, PA; *m:* E. Goodwin; *c:* Scott; *ed:* Slippery Rock St Coll (BS) Eng Ed 1969; Univ (MS) Eng Ed 1977; Lehigh Univ (SI) Supervision 1994; 36 Ad Hrs; *cr:* Wilson HS Eng Instr 1969-93, Eng Supvr 1993-; *ai:* Spelli Ftbl & Bsktbl Announcer; Holistic Scoring Coord; NEA 1969- 1969-, Chief Negotiator; Spartace Soc 1984-; Friends of the Lib Godfrey Daniels 1991-; Wilson Schlrshp Fndtn 1994-, Dir of Pu NEA Flwshp; PA Writing Assessment; PA Tchr Ed Pgm Spcl Reco Author of 5 Local Books; *office:* Wilson Sr HS 2601 Grandview Bl Lawn PA 19609

WEIRICH, SUE METZGER, Spanish Teacher; *b:* Toldeo, OH; *m* William; *c:* Kevin, Travis, Brian; *ed:* Bowling Green St Univ (BS Gen 1975; Post Grad Univ of San Diego in Guadalajara, Ashlan Drake Univ; *cr:* Mayfield HS Span, Ger Tchr 1975-81; Lexington H Tchr 1990-; *ai:* Span Club, North Cntrl Evaluation, NHS Selection C Lexington Tchrs Assoc, OH Ed Assoc, NEA, OH Frgn Lang Assoc Mentor Tchr; Martha Holden Jennings Scholar; Presenter at OH Frg Assoc Conf 1995; *office:* Lexington HS 103 Clever Ln Lexingt 44904

WEISBERG, MARK H., English Tchr & Admin Assistant; *b:* Br NY; *m:* Corinne Selinger; *c:* Benjamin, Arielle; *ed:* St Univ of Binghamton (BA) Eng Lit 1974; Hofstra Univ (MS) Scndry Ed 197 Island Univ C W Post Campus Prof Diploma Educl Admin 36 Credit *cr:* Aviation HS Spec Ed Eng Tchr 1988-89; Martin Van Buren H ESL, Soc Stud Tchr, Testing Coord, Admin Asst 1989-; *ai* Reorganization; AFT 1988-; Phi Delta Kapa 1995-, Recording Se Island Univ Chptr; NY TESOL 1992-; PTA PS 221 Queens 1989 Prin Selection Comm; *office:* Martin Van Buren HS 230-17 Hillsi Queens Village NY 11427

WEISBERG, PATRICIA ANNE, 4th Grade Teacher; *b:* Suffern, Richard S.; *c:* Danamarie, Matthew, Lauren; *ed:* St Thomas Aquin Elem Ed 1975; SUNY at New Paltz (MS) Ed 1980; Archdiocesan C Formation Prgm; *cr:* North Rockland Schl Dist Sub Tchr 1975 Peter's Schl Tchr 1976-80; Our Lady of Mt Carmel Schl Tchr 19 Drama Club Co-Dir; Bsktbl Prgm; NYS Accreditation Steering *office:* Our Lady-Mt Carmel Schl 205 Wawayanda Ave Middleto 10940

WEISE, BILLIE DEE MC ILROY, Retired Spanish Teach Pittsburgh, PA; *m:* Karl E. Jr.; *c:* Wm K., Heidi Lee Weise Todd; *ed* St (BA) Lbrl Arts, Span 1963; *cr:* Baldwin HS Span Tchr 1963- Tchr 1976-85; Bethel Park HS Span Tchr 1986-94; *ai:* Newcomer AFT 1986-; Delta Gamma Alumnae 1964-, Cable Awd; John Mc Presbyn Church, Elder, Trustee; PTA Room Mother 1973-80.

WEISENSEE, TINA, Chemistry Teacher; *b:* Bethesda, MD; *m:* M J.; *ed:* WV Univ (BS) Sec Ed 1992; *cr:* Reizenstein MS Sci Tch Butler Sr HS Chem Tchr 1993-; *ai:* Stu Cncl Adv; NEA 1993-; PSEA *office:* Butler Area Sr HS 165 New Castle Rd Butler PA 16001

WEISHAAR, CAROL, English Tchr & Lang Arts Chair; *b:* Gett PA; *c:* Aric Weishaar Hertzler; *ed:* Shippensburg Univ (BA) Fr 1974 Eng 1979, (MED) Rdng Specialist 1982; *cr:* Shippensburg Univ Gr 1975-77; Lower Dauphin HS Eng, Fr, Rdng Tchr 1977-90; Carlis Rdng Specialist 1990-91; West Perry HS Eng Tchr, Dept Chair 19 Ger Exch Coord; Debate Coach; Dist Wide Curr Alignment Project, Earth Sci Corps, Adv; Stu Assistance Team; Instrl Support Team Ldrshp Team; SADD Club, Amnesty Intnl Adv; NEA, PSEA 1980-; 1987-; NOW 1982-, Cty Pres; Outstdng Tchr of Yr Awd 1981; Artic *office:* West Perry HS Rd 1 Box 7 Elliottsburg PA 17024*

WEISHAAR, EMMA FORMWALT, Mathematics Tchr & Chair *b:* Taneytown, MD; *m:* Kenneth Marquet; *c:* Kendall, Kathy; *ed:* W MD Coll (BA) Math 1965, (MED) Ed 1971; Addl Courses in Sp Tchng Strategies & Graphing Calculators; *cr:* Francis Scott Key HS Tchr 1965-70; Carroll Cty Home Tchng Tchr 1970-78; Carroll Com Instr 1978-84; North Carroll HS Math Tchr 1984-; *ai:* NHS Adv; M of Tchrs of Math 1988-; *office:* North Carroll HS 3801 Hampstead M Rd Hampstead MD 21074

WEISHOLTZ, ANNE BERCHENKO, English Teacher; *b:* New NY; *m:* Steven; *c:* Daniel, Elizabeth; *ed:* Brown Univ (BA) Eng Hunter Coll of City Univ of NY (MA) Eng 1981; *cr:* Springfield H Tchr 1974-78; Marymount Manhattan Coll Adjunct Instr 1980-81; Cty Comm Coll Adjunct Instr 1983-85; William Paterson Coll A Instr 1985-90; The Frisch Schl Eng Tchr 1990-; *ai:* Schl Newspape NCTE 1990-; *office:* The Frisch Schl E243 Frisch Ct Paramus NJ 0

WEISMAN, EDWARD L., Fifth Grade Teacher; *b:* Bristol, CT; *ed* of Rochester (BA) Psych 1967; Univ of Hartford (MA) Ed 1971; *cr:* Side Schl 5th Grd Tchr 28 Yrs; *ai:* Run Natl Geographic Soc ɔhy Bee; NEA 1968-90, Treas; AFT 1990-; *office:* South Side Elem Tuttle Rd Bristol CT 06010

, BERNARD J., Professor of History; *b:* Jerusalem, Israel; *m:* Nero; *ed:* Univ of IL (BS) His Ed 1958; (univ of Chicago (MA) 0; Univ of IL (PhD) His 1967; *cr:* Duquesne Univ His Prof 1966-; ɔk Pub Univ of IL Press 1982; *office:* Duquesne Univ Dept of Pittsburgh PA 15282

, BRUCE J., HS Social Studies Teacher; *b:* Middletown, CT; *m:* ıssman; *c:* Sasha; *ed:* Boston Univ (BS) Human Relations 1969; 36 redits Ed, His Univ of Hartford, Wesleyan Univ 1977-79; *cr:* field HS Soc Stud Tchr 1978-81; Rham HS Soc Stud Tchr 1981-; , Soccer Coach; Newspaper Adv; Peer Cnslng, Yth Svcs; Ind Stud Stud; Ind Stud Cncl; ASCD 1990-; CT Historical Soc 1984-; NEA CT Cncl for Soc Stud 1982-; Better Chance Prgm 1977-, Treas; Conf presenter 1994; Pub Svc Awd CT Historical Soc; Presented al Works Rotary Intnl; *home:* 59 Grove Way Clinton CT 06413

, CAROL Z., 6th Grade Teacher; *b:* Brooklyn, NY; *m:* Alan; *c:* oshua; *ed:* OH St Univ (BS) Ed, Art 1968; Long Island Univ (MS) 1974; 30 Credits Above Masters; *cr:* Warrensville Heights Jr HS Tchr 1968-69; PS 195 4th Grd Tchr 1969-70; Robert Gorchs Day c Studs Tchr 1982-84; PS 183 6th Grd Tchr & Gifted Prgm 1984-; kesperson with Childrens Groups for Latchkey Kids; Arts & Crafts : Tchr; AFT, NEA & UFT 1984-; Pres of Latchkey Kids Club, Inc; ntator on Childrens News Pgrm; Led Class to Win Awds 1st Place iwide Smoke-Out Contest for Cancer Assn & 1st Place NYC ed Contest House Sense; *office:* P S 183 245 Beach 79th St Far ay NY 11693

, EDWARD PAUL, French Teacher; *b:* Philadelphia, PA; *m:* Jerri; Michael; *ed:* Villanova Univ (MA) Fr 1977; Penn St Univ (BA) Fr 973; St Josephs Univ Tchng Cert in Fr & His; Assoc Degree from Strasbourg France 1971; *cr:* Haverford HS Fr Tchr 1978-93; ical Yeshiva of Phila Fr Tchr 1982-93; *ai:* Stu Senate & Class of pon; Ldr of Fr Exch & Quebec Travel Prgm; MCA 1985-; eller Fellowship 1990; Natl Endowment for the Hum Grants 1985, 991; Tchr of Yr 1987; *office:* Haverford Sr HS 200 Mill Rd wn PA 19083*

, EILEEN CATHERINE, Social Studies Teacher; *b:* Jersey City, Trenton St Coll (BA) His Ed 1983; Inservice Courses Credit s Masters Degree in Cmptr Applications, Assertive Discipline & pplications; *cr:* Frank H Morrell HS Soc Stud Tchr 1984-; *ai:* Local dg Rep; Former Stu Cncl Adv & Swimming Coach; NEA, NJEA & 1984-; *office:* Frank H Morrell HS 1253 Clinton Ave Irvington NJ

, ELAINE IRIS, Science Department Head; *b:* New York, NY; *c:* E., Elyssa P., Stephanie B.; *ed:* CCNY (BS) Bio 1962; Iona Coll o 1978; 15 Grad Credits Hunter Coll; Woodrow Wilson Summer ioethics, Biotech; *cr:* Riverdale Jr HS Sci Tchr 1963-66; Riverdale chl Bio Tchr 1978-, Head Sci Dept 1991-, Hlth Coord 1991-; *ai:* nvironmental Comm; Curr, Standards, Fac Grants Comms; EA 1980-, Exec Bd; NSTA, NBTA 1990-; Natl Audubon Soc 1978-; e Conservation Soc 1980-; Nature Conservancy 1990-; *office:* le Country Schl 5250 Fieldston Rd Bronx NY 10471

, ELIZABETH TUCHFELD, French & German Teacher; *b:* y; *m:* Paul; *c:* Elliot, Cherie; *ed:* Queens Coll City Univ of NY (BA) , (MA) Fr 1971; Ger Cert 1994; *cr:* Newtown HS Fr Tchr 1967-71; od HS Fr Tchr 1972-73; Ocean Twp HS Fr Tchr 1977-, Ger Tchr *ai:* Fr, Ger Clubs Adv; Help & Homework Ctr Facilitator; NEA, 1982-; Sisterhood Temple Beth Torah 1973-, Family Living Chprsn; a Pi 1967-; *office:* Ocean Township HS 550 W Park Ave Oakhurst 55

, GERALD FRANCIS,JR., Physics Teacher; *b:* Pottsville, PA; *m:* Ann Lengel; *c:* Matthew, Nicole, Caitlin; *ed:* Kutztown Univ (BS) 5; Wilkes Univ (MS) Ed 1991; *cr:* Tri-Vly Schl Dist Sci Tchr 5; St Clair Schl Dist Physics, Chem Tchr 1986-87; Hamburg Area st Physics Tchr 1988-; *ai:* Physics Club, Rdng Berks Sci, Engrng ci Olympiad Adv; NEA, PSEA 1985-; HAEA 1988-; ASCD 1994-; Run Dist 1995-, Mbrshp Chair; BSA 1995-, Day Camp Prgm Dir Mtn Cncl; Named Distngd Tchr of Hnr Stdnts PA St Univ, Recipient g Edctr Awd Phila Coll Textiles, Sci 1994; *office:* Hamburg Area Jr Windsor St Hamburg PA 19526

, JOAN, Math & Cmptr Sci Tchr, Chprsn; *b:* NYC, NY; *m:* Robert; m, Michael, Tamara; *ed:* Rutgers Univ (MS) Math 1972; PHD ate Math, Ed NY Univ; *cr:* Queens Coll of CUNY Instr 1972-82; Schl Math Chprsn 1982-; *ai:* Sr Math Team Coach; Peer Tutoring MathAdv; Math Assn Of Amer, Phi Delta Kappa 1972-; NCTM *office:* Garden Schl 3316 79th St Jackson Heights NY 11372

, MARTIN J., Physics & Sci Research Teacher; *b:* Philadelphia, Doreen Solomon; *c:* Devon N.; *ed:* Glassboro St Coll (BA) Scndry 7; Univ of PA (MS) Sci Ed 1972; *cr:* Woodrow Wilson HS Modern en Sci Tchr 1967-, Environmental Sci Tchr 1969-75, Intro Rsrch 988-, Hnrs, Modern Physics Tchr 1989-; *ai:* Acad Knowledge Bowl Local, Regnl Sci Fair Competitions Lead Tchr; NEA, NJEA, CEA NSTA 1990-; NAPT 1994-; Phi Delta Kappa 1984-; Cherry Hill Relations Cncl 1993-, Cherry Hill Mayor's Appreciation Cert 5; Cherry Hill Rent Review Bd 1994-; BSA 1985-, Asst Scoutmaster 2; Princeton Univ Distngd Scndry Tchng Awd 1993; *office:* ow Wilson HS 3100 Federal St Camden NJ 08105

, MYRNA, 4th Grade Teacher; *b:* Brooklyn, NY; *m:* Stan; *c:* Stacey n, Lisa; *ed:* Brooklyn Coll (BA) Ed 1964; Stony Brook Univ (MA) uing Ed; 75 Addl Credits; *cr:* PS 256 Brooklyn Schl 3rd Grd Tchr 7; Frank P. Long Schl Enrichment, Gifted 4th-5th Grd Tchr 1981-91, l Tchr 1991-; *ai:* Math Comm; AFT 1980-; Numerous Articles Pub; g Long Island Olympics of the Mind Competition.*

, NANCY ANNE WALTERS, First Grade Teacher; *b:* Jersey City, John Landi (dec); *c:* James B.; *ed:* Glassboro St Coll (BA) Kndgtn y, Elem Ed 1965; *cr:* Berkley Street Schl Kndgtn Tchr 1965-68; Ft Army Post Schl Kndgtn Tchr 1968-69; New Bridge Schl 5th Grd 971-72; Oradell Pub Schl K-1st, 5th Grd Tchr 1972-81; Lavallette hl First Grd Tchr 1981-; *ai:* Many Comms; NEA, NJEA 1965-68, OCEA 1981-; LEA 1981-, Treas, Sec; Governors Tchr of Yr Awd *office:* Lavallette Elem Schl 105 Brooklyn Ave Lavallette NJ 08735

, PAMELA JUNE, Math & Science Teacher; *b:* New York, NY; *m:* n; *c:* Wm, Jason, Cynthia, Graig; *ed:* Albright Coll (BA) Eng 1970; Ignatius Loyola 3rd Grd Tchr 1970-73; Canaan Chrstn Acad Wng, Sci Tchr 1987-; *ai:* Honor Soc; *office:* Canaan Christian Acad Rt 2 8 Lake Ariel PA 18436

, RAYMOND T., Social Studies Teacher; *b:* Cleveland, OH; *m:* e Jill Slater; *c:* Adrienne; *ed:* OH St Univ (BS) Scndry Soc Stud n Laude 1975; Ed Grad Classes Univ of MI; *cr:* Alexander Hamilton -9 Grd Soc Stud Tchr 1975-80; Soc Security Admin Svc Supvr 6; US West Contract Coord 1986-88; All Net Comm Customer Svc 989-90; Sacred Heart Schl 2, 5-8 Grd Soc Stud Tchr 1990-; *ai:* Peer g Spon; Schl Bldg Comm Fac Adv; Schl Safety Patrol, Jr Achvmt pon; Schl Discipline Fac Adv; NDEA 1990-; AFGE Local 3239, VP; Sacred Heart Schl 824 6th St Toledo OH 43605*

WEISS, REGGIE, Business Ed Teacher & Coach; *b:* Harrisburg, PA; *m:* Gloria A.; *c:* Stephen N.; *ed:* Shippensburg Univ (BS) Bus & Acctng 1965, (MS) Bus & Acctng 1972; *cr:* Steelton Highspire HS Tchr & Coach 1965-69; Wilson HS Tchr & Coach 1969-; *ai:* Boys Var Bsktbl; Girls Var Tennis; AFT & WFT; *home:* 401 Harvard Blvd Reading PA 19609*

WEISS, SANDRA MARANO, Clinical Lab Sci Asst Prof; *b:* Philadelphia, PA; *m:* Donald John; *c:* Melissa Ann, Thomas Joseph; *ed:* Drexel Univ (BS) Clinical Lab Sci 1969; West Chester Univ (MA) Bio 1977; Working Toward EDD at Widener Univ; *cr:* Presbyterian Hosp Supvr Hematology & Coagulation 1969-75; Neumann Coll Asst Prof 1975-; *ai:* Moderator Clinical Lab Sci Club; Choreagrapher for Neumann Musicals & Plays Core Comm; Curr Comm; MT ASCP 1969-; ASCLS 1980-; AABB 1990-; Kappa Delta Pi; Chadds Ford Prof Womens 1990-, Fnd Chair, Schlsp Chair; Med Tech Awd 1969; *office:* Neumann Coll Convent Rd Aston PA 19014*

WEISS, STEVEN DOUGLAS, Science Teacher; *b:* Easton, PA; *ed:* Moravian Coll (BS) Bio 1989; Post Grad Work East Stroudsburg Univ; *cr:* Northwestern Lehigh Schl Tchr 1990-; *ai:* Drama Dir; Class, Greenhouse Club, Whalewatchers Club Adv; PSEA, NEA, NWLEA, NSTA, NABT 1990-; Beta Beta Beta 1987-; NHS Honorary Mem; *office:* Northwestern Lehigh HS 6493 Route 309 New Tripoli PA 18045

WEITKAMP, JAN LEIPHART, First Grade Teacher; *b:* York Cty, PA; *m:* Ted H.; *c:* Carla C., Seth; *ed:* York Coll of PA (AA) General Ed & Psych 1962; Millersville Univ (BS) Elem Ed 1964, (MA) Elem Ed & Rdng Specialist 1970; 45 Credit Hrs Beyond Masters from Dallastown Area Schl Dist; *cr:* Dallastown Area Schl Dist 1st Grd Tchr 1964-; *ai:* Owner of C&S Gifts & Furnitures 12 Yrs; *home:* 5 Meadow St Jacobus PA 17407*

WEITMAN, JOAN K., Learning Disabilities Teacher; *b:* New York City, NY; *m:* Nathan; *c:* Joshua, David, Rebecca, Adam; *ed:* Queens Coll (BA(Elem Ed 1953; Hunter Coll (MA) Ed Deaf 1956; 60 Credits Curr St Johns Univ; 7 Credits Spec Ed C. W. Post; *cr:* New York City Pub Schls Elem Tchr 1953-57; Commack UFSD SPec Ed Tchr 1980-; *ai:* Comm on Spec Ed; *office:* Commack HS Scholar Ln Commack NY 11725

WEITMANN, ROSEANN VITERETTI, 6th Grade Teacher; *b:* Yonkers, NY; *m:* Herb; *c:* Daria; *ed:* Coll of New Rochelle (BS) Ed 1969, (MS) Rdng 1974; 30 Credit Hrs Yonkers Tchrs Ctr, Westchester Comm Coll; *ai:* Tchr Interest Comm; Schl Improvement Plan; AFT, Yonkers Fed of Tchrs 1969-; MDA 1977-, Vol, Outstdng Svc Recognition; AIDS Walkathon; Jerry Lewis Spelling Bee; Street Theater Prgm 1988-; Learning to Read Through Arts; Tchr of Yr PS #5 1983; Kathleen Mc Grath Tchr of Yr PS #27; PTA Tchr Flwshp Awd Hawthorne Schl; Jenkins Awd 1990, PS #5 1983; *home:* 69 Heathcote Rd Yonkers NY 10710

WEITZ, ROBERTA ROSHKIND, Kindergarten Teacher; *b:* Brooklyn, NY; *m:* Mark J.; *c:* Dawn, Craig; *ed:* Brooklyn Coll (BA) Ed 1967; Grad Courses SUNY at Binghamton, Cortland St Tchrs Coll, Wright St Univ; *cr:* Vestal Hills Elem Schl 1st Grd Tchr 1967-71; Clayton Elem Schl Kdg Tchr 1981-83; Northmoor Elem Schl Kdg Tchr 1983-; *ai:* Lang Arts Curr, Math Curr, Stu Act Comm; NEA, OEA, NDEA 1981-; Alliance for Ed Grant; 3 Northmont Fnd Grants; Tchr of Yr 1988; *office:* Northmoor Elem Schl 4421 Old Salem Rd Englewood OH 45322

WEITZE, TEENA COWAN, Biology Teacher; *b:* Charlotte, NC; *m:* Charles E.; *c:* Scott A., Brian C.; *ed:* Univ of WI (BS) Zoology 1970; Fitchburg St (MED) Sci Ed 1973; 55 Addl Hrs; *cr:* Sioux Valley Hosp Anatomy, Physiology, Microbio Nursing Stu Instr 1971-72; Gardner HS 1973-; Biotech Wkshp, Acad Eisenhower Coord 1992-95; *ai:* Schl Cncl; NSTA; NABT; NEA; MTA; GEA, Rep; MWCC Fnd; *office:* Gardner HS 200 Catherine St Gardner MA 01440*

WEITZEL, RONALD L., Social Studies Chairman; *b:* Monroe, MI; *m:* Malin Jennings; *c:* Derek, Jamie; *ed:* Univ of CA at Davis (BA) His 1965, (MA) His 1967; Attnd Wellington New Zealand Tchrs Coll 1974; *cr:* Victoria Univ New Zealand Jr Lecturer 1973; New Zealand Pub Schls Elem Tchr 1975-77; Congressional Research Service Lib Tech 1977-83; House Page Schl Soc Stud Chm 1983-; *ai:* Film, Theater Clubs; Princeton, Page Model Congress; Univ of MD Fellowship 1970-73; New Zealand Journal of His Article 1973; *office:* House of Reps Page Schl Library of Congress Rm 311-LJ Washington DC 20546

WELAGE, LARRY A., Social Studies Teacher; *b:* Cincinnati, OH; *c:* Erin; *ed:* Univ of Cincinnati (AA); Northern KY Univ (BA) Soc Stud 1983; Xavier Univ (MA) Admin 1990; *cr:* Beech Acres Tchr 1983-84; Clermont Northeastern Tchr 1984-; *ai:* Girls Bsktbl, Jr HS Ftbl Coach; NHS Adv; NEA 1985-; *office:* Clermont Northeastern HS 5327 Hutchinson Rd Batavia OH 45103*

WELCH, BARBARA, English Professor; *b:* Boston, MA; *m:* Joseph R.; *c:* Breena Welch-Holmes, George N., Joseph R. Jr.; *ed:* Regis (BA) Eng 1960; Assumpton (MA) Developmental Psych 1978; Cambridge (MED) Human Resources Mgmt 1986; Univ of MA at Boston (MA) Eng 1991; *cr:* South Shore Mental Hlth Clinical Soc Work 1975-86; Central NE Coll Eng Prof 1986-88; Quincy Coll Eng Prof 1988-; *ai:* Steering, Accreditation Curr, Camps Prgms Comm; NCTE, MA Cncl Tchrs Eng, NE Writing Ctr Assn, Bristol Comm Writing Conf; Best Tchrs of Yr 1994; *office:* Quincy Coll 34 Coddington St Quincy MA 02169

WELCH, CHARLENE GENES, Biology Teacher; *b:* Homestead, PA; *c:* William R.; *ed:* Slippery Rock St Coll (BA) Natural Sci, Bio 1970; Duquesne Univ Cert Ed 1973; *cr:* South Park Schls Sci, Bio Tchr 1971-72; Garrett Co Schls Sci, Bio Tchr 1973-77; W Mifflin Area Schls Sci, Bio Tchr 1979-89; Serra Cath HS Bio Tchr 1990-91; Duquesne City Schls Bio Tchr 1991-92; W Mifflin Area Schls Sci, Bio Tchr 1992-; *ai:* Stu Cncl Adv; FHA Co-Spon; AFT 1979-; *office:* West Mifflin Area Schls 91 Commonwealth Ave West Mifflin PA 15122*

WELCH, DEBORAH, Asst Prof of History; *b:* Charlotte, NC; *m:* Peter Lawrence; *ed:* Agnes Scott Coll (BA) His 1978; Wake Forest Univ (MA) His 1980; Univ of WY (PHD) His 1985; *cr:* Amer Historical Assn Dir of His Tchng Alliance 1985-88; Elon Coll Asst Prof 1988-92; SUNY at Fredonia Asst Prof 1992-; *office:* S U N Y Coll At Fredonia Thompson Hall Fredonia NY 14063

WELCH, DEBRA WILKINS, English Instructor; *b:* Ligonier, PA; *m:* Delmar W.; *ed:* Clarion Univ (BS) Scndry Ed, Eng 1975; 9 Credit Hrs Penn St Univ; 6 Credit Hrs Wilkes Coll; 9 Credit Hrs Millersville Univ; *cr:* Greensburg Cntrl Cath HS Eng Tchr 1980-; *ai:* Acad Quiz Team Coach 2 Yrs; GCTA 1982-, former VP; NACST 1982-; NCTE 1990; Ligonier Valley Writers 1990-; Cert of Hnr, Saint Vincent Coll Grt Tchr; Rcgntn Pgm Excl in Tchng; Photos & Art Pub Dec 1994, Apr 1995; *office:* Greensburg Cntrl Catholic HS 901 Armory Dr Greensburg PA 15601

WELCH, DONALD FREDERICK, Speech, English & Drama Tchr; *b:* Warren, OH; *m:* Susan Mary Cowles; *c:* Nathan Frederick; *ed:* Lorain Cty (AA) Speech, Drama 1971; Univ of Akron (BS) Scndry Ed 1973, (MS) Tech Ed 1980; Ashland Univ, Kent St Univ Staff Dev; *cr:* American Broadcasting Co Tech Asst 1972; Revere Local Schls HS Spch, Drama, Eng Tchr 1973-; Univ of Akron Instr Mass Media 1977-78; *ai:* Chair North Cntrl, Steering, Black Scheduling, Staff Dev Comm; Frgn Educl, Travel Ldr; Revere REA, OEA, NEA 1973-; Norton Lions Club 1991-, Pres; Norton Parks Bd 1994-, VP; Strategic Planning Comm 1994-, Chm; OH Restaurant Assn 1985-, Comm; Kent St Univ Academically Talented Tchr Ed Prgm; Natl Schl Excl Awd OH Dept of Ed; Curr Grant; *office:* Revere HS 3420 Everett Rd Richfield OH 44286*

WELCH, KAREN S., 6th Grade Teacher; *b:* Lockport, NY; *m:* James B.; *c:* Scott T., Michael J.; *ed:* SUNY Buffalo St (BS) Ed 1961; 60 Grad Hrs; Tchng Cert NY St; *cr:* Starpoint Cntrl 4th Grd Tchr 1961-65; Newfane Cntrl 3rd Grd Tchr 1965-67; Wilson Cntrl 4th-6th Grd Tchr 1968-69, Tchr 1970-; *ai:* Co-Chair Discipline Comm TM; NYSUT AFL-CIO 1968-; Wilson PTA 1968-; Wilson Tchrs Assn 1970-, Bldg Rep; Mothers Club, Elder; Ghostic Guild; Womens Aglow; Local Fire Co, Vol; Taught the Discipline Policy to our Stu Body in Conjunction with My Colleagues K-6th Grd; Presented at Dist Staff Dev Sessions Discipline Ideas Used of TM; Worked on Fac Meeting Demonstrations & Videos to Present our Discipline Comm Ideas to Colleagues.

WELCH, KATHY ANN, Fifth Grade Teacher; *b:* Syracuse, NY; *ed:* St Univ of NY at Potsdam (BA) Elem Ed 1969; Attnd St Univ at Cortland, St Univ at Geneseo, St Univ at Oswego; *cr:* Thornton Ave Elem 3rd-5th Grd Classroom Tchr 1969-77; Seward 3rd-5th Grd Classroom Tchr 1977-; *ai:* Seward Site-Based Team; Seward Acivity Days & Seward Tech Comms; Odyssey of the Mind Judge; Auburn Tchrs Assn 1969-; NYSUT; AFT; *office:* W H Seward School Metcalf Dr Auburn NY 13021*

WELCH, LARRY DEAN, Math Teacher; *b:* Dennison, OH; *m:* Rebecca Ann Cantor; *c:* Jennifer Lynn, Steven Andrew; *ed:* Kent St Univ (BS) Bio 1979; OH Univ (MS) Math 1989; *cr:* Tri-Valley HS Math Tchr 1979-; *ai:* Coach Ftbl 1979-98, Bsbl 1983-84, Golf 1988-; Tri-Valley Ed Assn 1979-, Pres 1995-; NCTM 1979-; Muskingum Area Chapter Tchr of Math, OCTM 1987-; *home:* 2545 Tarkman Dr Nashport OH 43830*

WELCH, LARRY JAMES, Biology Teacher; *b:* Lancaster, OH; *m:* Janet Evans; *c:* Rebecca, Matthew, Andrew; *ed:* Defiance Coll (BS) Comprehensive Sci 1966; Univ of Toledo (MS) Admin 1985; *cr:* Elmwood HS Sci Tchr, Asst Bsktbl, Track Coach 1966-69; Maumee HS Sci Tchr, Asst Track Coach 1969-; *ai:* NEA, OEA 1966-; MEA, OHS, CCC 1969-; OH HS Ath Assn Track, Field Ofcls 1981-; Delta Lib Bd 1971-88, VP; Cub Scouts 1980-82, 1984-86, Comm Chm; Meth Church Bd of Trustees 1972-76, VP; Izaak Walton League of Amer 1984-, VP; Outstdng Tchr 1992-93; *office:* Maumee HS 1147 Saco St Maumee OH 43537

WELCH, MARIE M., Physical Education Teacher; *b:* Perth Amboy, NJ; *m:* Daniel; *c:* Scott, Maria; *ed:* Montclair St Univ (BA) Hlth, PE 1970; Grad Credits PA St Univ; *cr:* Matawan Schl Dist ELem PE Tchr 1970-72; Keystone Cntrl Schl Dist Elem Hlth, PE Tchr 1972-; *ai:* Elem IM, Reward Coord; Wellness Comm; NEA 1970-; PSEA, ACCE 1973-; PSAHPERD; Avis Elem PTO Exec Bd 1992-, Mbrshp Chair; Arts in Ed Grant; *office:* Keystone Central Sch Dist 95 W 4th St Lock Haven PA 17745

WELCH, MARY NEWELL, English Tchr & Dept Chprsn; *b:* Wilmington, DE; *m:* James E.; *c:* Jim, Sean, Megan Welch-Copeland; *ed:* Immaculata Coll (BA) Eng 1961; Ed Wilmington Coll 1992; Grad Stud Ed Univ of DE; *cr:* Bayard Jr HS Eng Tchr 1964; Ursuline Acad Eng Tchr 1965; PS DuPont HS Eng, Soc Stud Tchr 1977; Howard HS of Tech Eng Tchr 1977-; *ai:* Steering, Quest Quality IV Sr Project, Southern Regnl Ed Bd Comms; 9th Grd Team; DE St Ed Assn 1974-; NCTE 1975-; Ursuline Alumnae Assn 1957-, Pres; Immaculata Coll Alumnae Assn 1961-; Pastoral Care Ctr 1991-, Vol Drug, Alcohol Cnslr; 1988 HS Tech Tchr of Yr, Cty Vo Tech Schl Dist Tchr of Yr; Presenter Southern Regnl Educl Bd Natl Conf 1992; Nom DE Lang Arts Tchr of Yr 1995; *office:* Howard HS of Tech 401 E 12th St Wilmington DE 19801

WELCH, PATRICIA D. (CURTIN), Third Grade Teacher; *b:* New York, NY; *c:* Michael, Matthew; *ed:* Queens Coll (BA) Anthropology, Sociology 1960; SUNY at Stony Brook (MA) Ed 1975; 30 Addl Hrs; *cr:* Soc Security Admin Claims Rep 1960-62; Sub Tchng 1963-65; St Lawrence Schl 5 Grd Tchr 1965-67; Holy Angels Reg Schl 3 Grd Tchr 1968-; *ai:* Lit Prgm 1980-85; Summer Remedial & Enrichment Tutoring 1988-92; Amer Assn of Univ Women 1988-, VP, Mbrshp; Democratic Party Org 1988-; *office:* Holy Angels Regnl Schl Division St Patchogue NY 11772

WELCH, PATRICK LEWIS, College Art Teacher; *b:* Ft Wayne, IN; *c:* C. Zachary; *ed:* St Francis Coll at Ft Wayne (BA) Art 1968; Columbus Coll of Art & Design (BFA) Advertising Design 1995, (BFA) Fine Arts 1995; Attnd Cleveland Inst of Art 1965-66, 36 Credit Hrs Painting; 120 Credit Hrs & 4 Yr Diploma Advertising Design; *cr:* Merrill Publishing Co Art Dir Coll Div 1972-88; Welch Studio Freelance Architectural Illustrator 1988-91; Columbus Coll of Art & Design Tchr Fndtn Stud 1991-; *ai:* Structural Drawing Stud Tutor & Adv; Paintings & Drawings Exhibited; *office:* Columbus Coll Of Art & Design 107 N 9th St Columbus OH 43215

WELCH, RICHARD JAMES, Amer His Tchr & Dept Chprsn; *b:* Middletown, NY; *m:* Dorothy Falk; *ed:* Marshall Univ at Huntington (BA) Bus Ed & Soc Stud 1981; Lehman Coll at Bronx (MS) Bus Ed 1987; *cr:* St Catharine Acad Bus Ed Tchr 1982-89, Soc Stud Tchr 1990-, Dept Chprsn Soc Stud 1991-; *ai:* Moderator NHS; NCSS 1991-; NYCSS 1993-; *office:* St Catharine Acad 2250 Williamsbridge Rd Bronx NY 10469*

WELCOME, ANGELA ANZALONE, English Teacher; *b:* Bronx, NY; *m:* Allen J.; *c:* Kristen Welcome-Furci, Brian; *ed:* SUNY at Albany (BA) Eng & Span 1966; SUNY at Stonybrook Eng Ed 1974; *cr:* Van Corlaer Eng Tchr 66-69; Connetquot Hs Eng Tchr 1976-; *ai:* HS Newspaper, Yrbk, Frosh Class & Young Writers Conf at Breadloaf Adv; Dist Newspaper Ed; AFT, NEA 1966-; Long Island Scolastic Press Assn, Columbia Scholastic Press Asson 1976-; PTA Tchr Liaison 1994-, Tchr Rep; Dow Fellowship for Jrnlsm Seminar at Columbia; NY St Tchr of Excl NY St Eng Cncl; Monthly Articles Pub; *office:* Connetquot HS 7th St Bohemia NY 11716*

WELCOME, CLAUDE, Weight Training Supervisor; *b:* Gouverneur, NY; *m:* Karen; *c:* Kerri, Amy; *ed:* Keystone Jr Coll (AA) Ed 1971; Marietta Coll (BA) PE 1974; Post Grad Credit East Stroudsburg Univ, Millersville Univ, Penn St Univ, Marywood Coll; Olympic Trng Ctr Stud; *cr:* St Mary's of Mt Carmel PE, Hlth Tchr 1975-81; Mercy Hosp Security, Safety Supvr 1979-; Scranton Cntrl Schl Head Coach Wrestling 1981-83; Abington Heights Weight Trng Supvr 1983-; *ai:* Powerlifting Club Coach; Natl Strength & Conditioning Assn 1984-; *home:* 118 Vosburg Ln Clarks Summit PA 18411

WELCOME, MARYANN D'AMICO, History Dept Chair & Teacher; *b:* New Britain, CT; *m:* James Thomas; *c:* James A., Melissa, Jared, Michele, Jeanne; *ed:* Cntrl CT St Univ (BS) His & Soc Stud 1971, (MS) Rdng Consultant 1983; 6th Yr Admin & Supvervision 1996; BEST Prgm 32 Hrs; *cr:* Gilbert Schl His Tchr & Dept Chair 1983-; *ai:* Stdnts Working To Educate & Eliminate Prejudice Adv; Prof Dev, Admin & Democratic Town Comms; NEA, CEA 1986-; ASCD 1994-; NASS, NCSS, APA 1989-; Selectman Bd 1995-; Winsted Fire Police 1989-, Treas; Charter Pension Comm Alternative; *office:* Gilbert Schl 200 Williams Ave Winsted CT 06098*

WELDON, DIANE M., Social Studies Teacher; *b:* Brooklyn, NY; *m:* Walter; *c:* Christine, Richard; *ed:* Western CT Univ (BS) Scndry Ed 1971; Mt St Mary Coll (MS) Ed 1986; 9 Post Grad Credit Hrs; *cr:* Bishop Dunn Elem Tchr 1982-85; Beacon HS Soc Stud Tchr 1985-92; Carmel HS Soc Stud Tchr 1992-; *ai:* Site-base Comm; NYSUT, AFT 1992-; BSCSS 1988-; *office:* Carmel HS 30 Fair St Carmel NY 10512

WELFEL, LINDA CONTURSI, Mathematics Teacher; *b:* Newark, NJ; *m:* James; *c:* Scott, Kristen; *ed:* Montclair St (BA) Math Ed 1973, (MA) Math Ed 1977; *cr:* Acad of St Aloysius Math Tchr 1973-75; Bridgewater-Raritan Regnl Schl Math Tchr 1975-81; Prudential Ins Co Cmptr Programmer 1981-86; West Essex Jr HS Math Tchr 1991-; *ai:* Math Counts Coach; NJEA, NEA 1973-81, 1991-; NCTC 1873-83, 1991-; *office:* West Essex Jr HS W Greenbrook Rd North Caldwell NJ 07006*

WELLEK, EUGENE LOUIS, Secondary Social Studies Tchr; *b:* Latrobe, PA; *m:* Luciana Rosa; *c:* Anna Lisa Wellek-Ageio, Rocco Anthony; *ed:* St Vincent Coll (BA) His, Ed 1977; St Bonaventure Univ (ME) Ed 1995; Attnd Gannon Univ; *cr:* St Pius X Grd Schl 4-8 Grd Soc Stud Tchr 1977-79; West End Cath MS 6-8 Grd Soc Stud Tchr 1979-80; Bishop Mc Cort HS 9-12 Grd Soc Stud Tchr 1980-89; Warren Area HS 9-12 Grd Soc Stud Tchr 1989-; *ai:* Coached Grd Schl, HS, Coll Ftbl 21 Yrs; Head Coach Scholastic Level Coach 11 Yrs; NEA, WCEA 1989-; *office:* Warren Area HS 345 E 5th Ave Warren PA 16365*

WELLER, BETTY J., High School Business Teacher; *b:* Butler, OH; *m:* Carmon; *c:* Tracie, Jeff, Judd; *ed:* OH St Univ (BS) Bus 1974; Addl Hrs Bus; *cr:* Cardington-Lincoln HS Bus Tchr 1975-76; Fredericktown HS Bus Tchr 1976-; *ai:* NHS, Sr Class Adv; FEA 1975-, Schlsp Comm, Sec, Bldg Rep, Comm Chm, Soc Chm; OBTA 1974-; NCOBTA 1976-85; OEA, NEA 1975-; OH Twp Assn 1986-, Twp Clerk; OH Farm Bureau 1968-, Cncl Sec; Grange 1968-, Sec; Selected by Cty to Serve as Mentor; Tchr Who Influenced Them Most Awd; *home:* 19084 Lucerne Rd Fredericktown OH 43019

WELLER, TRACIE JO, Science Teacher; *b:* Mansfield, OH; *ed:* OH St Univ (BA) Comp Sci 1980; *cr:* Northman Local Schls Sci Tchr, Coach, Adv 1980-84; East Knox Local Schls Sci Tchr, Coach, Adv 1984-85; Fredericktown Local Schls Sci Tchr, Coach, Adv 1985-; *ai:* Coach Frosh Girls Vlybl; Frosh Class Adv; SECO; NPTA; NEA; FEA; Meritorious Performance; Ed Excl; Most Inspirational Tchr; *office:* Fredericktown HS 117 Columbus Rd Fredericktown OH 43019*

WELLES, LYNN KOCH, Instructional Support Teacher; *b:* Quakertown, PA; *m:* Lincoln Jr.; *c:* Loren; *ed:* Bloomsburg Univ (BS) Elem Ed 1975; 24 Credits Permanent Cert PA; *cr:* New Albany Elem Schl 2nd Grd Tchr 1976-77; Laceyville Elem Schl Kndgtn & 2nd Grd Tchr 1977-79; Wyalusing Elem Schl 2nd Grd Tchr 1979-93, Instructional Support Tchr 1993-; *ai:* WAE, PSEA & NEA 1975-.

WELLINGTON, JONNAKOTY, AP Calculus Teacher; *b:* Secunderabad, India; *m:* Sumani; *c:* Helen Dharry, Frank; *ed:* Madras Univ (BA) Pure Math 1937, (BED) Math & Sci 1941; Osmania Univ (MED) Math 1956; UW WI (MS) Statistics 1963; Credits from: Penn St, Temple, Georgetown Univ; *cr:* St Georges Grammar Schl Math Tchr, Dept Chair & Vice Prin 1937-50; Hyderabad Pub Schl Asst Prin & Prin 1950-62; Corby Grammar Schl HS Math Tchr 1958-59; Amer Intnl Schl at New Delhi Math Tchr, Dept Chair & Pres Fac Assn 1965-70; Woodrow Wilson Sr HS 11th-12th Grd Math Tchr 1970-83; Holy Ghost Prep Schl Math Tchr, Dept Chair & AP Calculus Tchr 1983-; *ai:* Math Soc, Contests & Exhibits Founder & Adv; NEA 1970-; MMA 1972-; Phi Delta Kappa 1972-; Recipient of 2 Fulbright Awds; Fr Flwshp.

WELLS, ALBERTA SUSAN, English Teacher; *b:* Passaic, NJ; *ed:* Livingston Coll & Rutgers Univ (BA) Eng 1973; Rutgers Univ (MA) Hum 1992; Montclair St Univ 12 Credit Hrs; Leonardo Tchr Inst 3 Credit Hrs; ACE Tchr Inst 3 Credit Hrs; *cr:* East Side HS Eng Tchr 1973-79; Memrl HS Eng Tchr 1979-88; Columbia HS Eng Tchr 1988-90; Parsippany HS & Parsippany Hills HS Eng Tchr 1990-; *ai:* Previous Forensics Debate & Speech Coach, Newspaper, Class & Club Adv; Renaissance Comm; Asst African Amer Club Adv; NEA & NJEA; NJCTE; NAACP; The Urbun League; Alpha Kappa Alpha Inc; NJ Governors Tchr Awd.*

WELLS, BEVERLY J., HS Choral Director; *b:* Vineland, NJ; *m:* Allen; *c:* Georgia, Leslie; *ed:* Western MD Coll (BA) Music Ed 1977, (MA) Music Ed 1987; Post Grad Stud Towson St Univ, The Peabody Conservatory Music Ed; *cr:* Sykesville MS Vocal Music Dir 1977-78; Western MD Coll Choir Dir 1986-90; Westminster West MS Vocal Music Tchr 1978-92; Westminster HS Choral Dir 1992-; *ai:* Select Choir; Pub Relations, Grad, Model, Schedule Restructuring Comms; NEA, Carroll Co Tchrs Assn, MSTA, 1977-; MD Music Ed Assn 1992-; *home:* 555 Old Westminster Pk Westminster MD 21157*

WELLS, BONNIE BITNER, English Teacher; *b:* Buffalo, NY; *m:* William A. Jr.; *c:* Michael Lombardo, Thomas Lombardo, Laura Lombardo Schie; *ed:* Buffalo St Tchrs Coll (BS) Elem Ed 1962; Grant Work Kent St OH Cmptr Tech in Classroom; 30 Hrs Post Grad; NY K-12 Tchng Cert; *cr:* Akron Elem Schl 3rd-4th Grd Tchr 1962-64; William Ramsly Schl 3rd Grd Tchr 1964-65; Kenmore Schl System Sub Tchr 1972-77; Cathedral Chrstn Schl Tchr1988-90; Ch rstn Cntrl Acad 6th-9th Grd Eng Tchr 1979-; *ai:* Gift Gathring Comm Chair Schl Auction; Conduct MS Drama Class; NCTE 1991-; Tech Grant Kent St Univ; *office:* Christian Central Acad 39 Academy St Williamsville NY 14221*

WELLS, DENNIS GEOFFREY, Biology Teacher & Athletic Dir; *b:* Cincinnati, OH; *m:* Sharon L. Anstaett; *c:* Deanna M., Darik Scott; *ed:* Cumberland Coll (BS) Hlth, PE & Bio 1972; Xavier Univ (MED) Admin 1985; Attnd Univ of Cincinnati, Univ of Dayton, Wright St; *cr:* Hamilton Taft HS Bio Tchr 1972-79; Batavia HS Bio Tchr 1980-; *ai:* Wrestling, Bsbl & Soccer Coach; Cheerleading & Class Adv; Chess Coach; OEA; NEA; Batavia Prof Ed Assn 1981-, VP; *office:* Batavia HS 800 Bauer Ave Batavia OH 45103

WELLS, DOUGLAS RAY, Elementary School Principal; *b:* Allentown, PA; *m:* Elizabeth Ann Fittrer; *c:* Matthew Douglas, Amber Elizabeth, Britani Hope; *ed:* Moravian Coll (BA) Elem Ed & Eng 1976; Lehigh Univ (MEd) Admin & Supervision 1979; Lehigh Univ Elem Prin Cert; *cr:* William A. Shoemaker Elem Schl 4th Grd Tchr 1976-79, Head Tchr & 6th Grd Tchr 1979-89, Asst Prin 1989-92, Prin 1992-; *ai:* Lang Arts Project Team Mem; E Penn Schl Dist Act 93 Elem Level Admin Rep; Integrated Learning Systems Comm Mem, Peer Coaching Ldr; E Penn Schl Dist Tech Comm Mem, Gifted Task Force Mem; Inclusionary Task Force Mem, Continuous Progress Math Coord; NAESP 1989-; NEA, PSEA & EPEA 1976-89; Outstanding Tchr of the Yr Awd 1985; *office:* William A. Shoemaker Elem Schl 4068 N Fairview St Macungie PA 18062

WELLS, JENNIFER, English & ESL Teacher; *b:* Kingston Jamica, West Indies; *c:* Cedrick Hyde Jr.; *ed:* Long Island Univ (BA) Eng, Performing Arts 1987; Exed Tchr Trng Coll Diploma in Ed Lang Arts, PE 1981; 12 Credit Hrs Long Island Univ Eng, Lit & Tchng Writing; *cr:* Mona Scndry Schl Intern 1980-81; Long Island Univ Tchng Fellow 1987-90; Walton HS Eng Tchr 1988-94, ESL Tchr 1994-; Martha Neilson Schl ESL Tchr, Adult Ed 1995-; *ai:* AFT 1988-; Amer Forum for Global Ed 1993-; Tchng Flwshp; *office:* Walton HS 196th St & Reservoir Ave Bronx NY 10468*

WELLS, LISA A. H., Spanish Teacher; *b:* Glens Falls, NY; *m:* Michael; *c:* Phoebe E.; *ed:* Potsdam Coll (BA) Span 1988; Plattsburgh St Coll (MA) Educl Stud 1994; *cr:* St Regis Falls Cntrl Schl Span Tchr 1988-91; Corinth Cntrl Schl Span Tchr 1991-; *ai:* Frgn Lang Club Adv; NYSAFLT, AATSP 1992-; *office:* Corinth Cntrl Schl 105 Oak St Corinth NY 12822

WELLS, LLOYD ARNOLD, Social Studies Teacher; *b:* Middlebourne, WV; *m:* Anna Lee Townsend; *c:* Michelle L., Jason B.; *ed:* Glenville St Coll (BA) Soc Stud Comp 1971; Univ of Dayton (MS) Admin 1979; *cr:* Iuka Elem Tchr 1971-72; Steubenville HS Tchr 1972-73; Grant Jr High Tchr 1973-82; Harding MS Tchr 1982-; *ai:* Natl His Day Adv; Respecteen Speak for Yourself Coord; Curr Comm; NEA 1972-; Univ of Steubenville Ed Advy Cncl; *office:* Harding MS 1928 Sunset Blvd Steubenville OH 43952

WELLS, M. EMILY, Social Science Educator; *b:* Valparaiso, IN; *ed:* Univ of MD at Baltimore Cty (BA) His 1981; Attnd Salisbury St Univ, Western MD Coll & Loyola Coll; *cr:* Dorchester Cty Educator 1984-91; Worcester Cty Educator 1991-; *ai:* Legal Intern; SIT Chm; Mock Trial & Frosh Class Adv; NEA 1985-; MD St Tchrs Assn 1985-, PAC Steering Comm; Worcester Cty Tchrs Assn 1991-, Pres; Worcester Cty Dem; Central Comm; Ocean City Dem Club 1995-, VP; Pocomoke HS Tchr of Yr 1995; MD Comm Svc Day Awd 1990; Dorchester Cty Citizenship Guide 1990; Whos Who Among Young Amer Profs 1988; Outstanding Young Women of Amer 1986; Presidential Classroom for Young Amers Instr 1989-; *office:* Pocomoke HS 1817 Old Virginia Rd Pocomoke City MD 21851*

WELLS, MARIELLE METTHE, Elem French Immersion Teacher; *b:* Sudbury Ontario, CN; *c:* Jennifer, Kimberly, Jeffrey; *ed:* Fr 2nd Lang Specialist; Spcl Ed Specialist; E'Cole Normale de Sudbury Laurentian Univ Brevet D'enseignement 1970; *cr:* Essex Cty Separate Schl Bd 4th Grd Tchr 1970-72; Metro Toronto Separate Schl Bd 4th & 5th Grd Tchr 1972-73; Halton Separate Schl Bd Elem Grds Tchr 1981-; Sheridan Coll Part Time Fr Tchr 1978-79; *ai:* Stu Cncl Coord; Sr Citizens & Stu Charity Org; Fr Cafe Coord; Fr Winter Carnival Org; AEFO 1970-73; OECTA 1981-; *home:* 1101 Montrose Abbey Dr Oakville ON L671A2 Canada CN *

WELLS, NAN E., Social Studies Teacher; *b:* Bluffton, OH; *m:* Rich D.; *c:* Jennifer; *ed:* Bowling Green St Univ (BA) Ed 1973; Miami Univ Ed 1985; *cr:* Riverdale Local Schls 5th Grd Tchr 1974-75; Mt Healthy Schls 4th-6th Grd Tchr 1975-; *ai:* Core Team; Venture Capital Grant; NEA 1974-; OEA 1974-; MHTA 1975-, Sec; Spcl Ed Awd 1994; *office:* Rex Ralph Elementary School 1310 Adams Rd Cincinnati OH 45231

WELLS, PHYLLIS COCCIA, Teacher of the Gifted; *b:* New Castle, DE; *m:* William Milton; *c:* David Vincent, James Justin, Tyler Anthony; *ed:* Immaculate Coll of DC (AA) Home Ec 1958; Univ of DE (BS) Ed 1961; West Chester Univ (MS) Ed 1981; 30 Credit Hrs from Different Colls; *cr:* De La Warr Schl Dist Elem Schl Tchr 1960-1979; Line Mt Schl Dist Tchr of Gifted MS 1980-89; Colonial Schl Dist Tchr of Gifted MS 1996; *ai:* Schl Newspaper Adv; Soc Comm; DSEA; NEA; DE Talented & Gifted; Smyrna Historical Soc; Tchr of Yr 1992-93; DSEA Stu Brass Bell Awd 1993-94; Olympics of the Mind Coach 1st Place Regnl, St Finals, 5th Place World; *office:* George Read MS 314 E Basin Rd New Castle DE 19720*

WELLS, RUSSELL FREDERICK, Associate Professor; *b:* Brooklyn, NY; *c:* Dayna Bradley, Leslie O'Malley; *ed:* Lafayette Coll (BA) His 1959; Springfield Coll (MS) PE 1962; UND at Chapel Hill (mACT) Zoology 1966; Purdue Univ (PHD) Bio Ed 1970; Adjunct Prof of PE at San Diego St Univ 1978-79, 1993-94; Visiting Assoc Research Physiologist Univ of CA at San Diego 1978-79; Visiting Fellow, Fac of Sci at Australian Natl Univ 1986-87; Visiting Physiologist at Australian Inst of Sport 1986-87; *cr:* Charlotte Cntry Day Schl Tchr, Coach 1962-65; Montclair St Coll Asst Bio Prof 1966-68; Purdue Univ Asst Bio Sci Prof 1970-71; St Lawrence Univ Asst Bio Prof 1971-74, Assoc Prof 1974-, Assoc Dean 1980-82; *ai:* Fac Cncl 1983-86, 1987-91, Sec 1983-86, Vice Chair 1988-91; Bd of Fac Advs to Greeks 1984-86, 1987-93, 1994-, Chair 1984-86, 1987-93, 1995-; Fac Life Comm 1991-93, 1994-; Phi Kappa Sigma Fac Adv 1972-; Bio Dept Chprsn 1992; Omicron Delta Kappa Fac Adv 1987-93, 1994-; Amer Coll of Sports Medicine 1978-; AAHPERD 1989-; AAUP 1994-; Canton Unitarian Universalist Church 1981-, Church Cncl Pres 1988-91, Trustee 1992-93; Natl Sci Fnd Acad Yr Inst 1965-66; Mellon Fnd Grant 1978-79; Dana Fellow at St Lawrence Univ 1980-81; Omicron Delta Kappa 1984-; Fac of Yr Awd 1984; *office:* Saint Lawrence Univ Bio Dept Canton NY 13617

WELLS, SUZANNE DILAURA, Art Teacher; *b:* Albion, NY; *m:* Robert L; *c:* Christopher J., Jennifer M.; *ed:* SUNY at Buffalo (BS) Art Ed 1971; 30 Grad Hrs; Attnd SUNY at Brockport & Univ of Siena in Italy; Experimental Intnl Living; *cr:* Albion Cntrl Schl Art Tchr 1971-; *ai:* Art Club Adv; Art Comm for Jazz Band Dinner Dance Decorations; Albion Tchrs Assn; NY St Art Tchrs Assn; St Josephs Church, Choir & Soloist; Exhibited Art Work at Genesee Comm Coll & Batavia Soc of Artists; *office:* Albion HS 302 East Ave Albion NY 14411

WELSEK, CAROL ANN, 7th-8th Grd Sci & Math Tchr; *b:* Port Chester, NY; *m:* William; *c:* William, Karen; *ed:* SUNY at New Paltz (BA) Chem 1966; *cr:* Kingston City Schl Sci Tchr 1966-67; St Christopher's Schl 7th-8th Grd Tchr 1981-82; Kingston Cath Schl 7th-8th Grd Math, Sci Tchr 1982-; *ai:* Adv Stu Cncl, Ambassador Club; NCEA 1982-; *office:* Kingston Catholic Schl 159 Broadway Kingston NY 12401

WELSH, ELIZABETH KAY, Math Teacher; *b:* Laurel, MD; *c:* Jamie, Todd, Tim, Joel Whitehead, Ivan Spence; *ed:* Western MS Coll (BA) Math Ed 1969; Updating Stud in Ed Trinity Coll, Univ of MD, Western MD Coll; *cr:* P. G. Cty Pub Schls Math Tchr 1969-81; St Vincent Pallotti HS Math Tchr, Dept Chair 1981-90; Natl Cathedral Schl Math Tchr, Chapel Planner 1990-94; P. G. Cty Pub Schls Math Tchr 1994-; *ai:* Open Door, Patience Policy for All Creative, Responsible Single Parenting of 2 Teenage Boys; NCTM 1972-; MSTA, PGCEA, NEA, ASCD 1995-; St Philip's Episcopal Church Vestry; Belfast Summer Children's Prgm 1982-; Tchr of Yr Pallotti HS 1989; *home:* 412 Montgomery St Laurel MD 20707

WELSH, ROSEMARY CORRADO, English & Theater Teacher; *b:* Jersey City, NJ; *m:* G. Richard Jr.; *c:* Natalie Jessica Blumberg, Tamara Clair; *ed:* Allentown Coll of St Francis de Sales (BA) Theatre 1990; Acting & Theatre NY City; West Chester Univ Eng Grad Pgm; *cr:* Bethany Church Drama Dir 1981-87; Methacton HS Drama Dir 1992-93, Eng Tchr 1994-; *ai:* MCCWF Ed Comm Co-Chair; Mose Lit Arts Magazine & Womens Performance Group Adv; Peer Mediation; NEA 1991-; Natl Cathedral 1993-; Sierra Club 1995-; Bethany Church 1984-, Drama Dir; Montgomery Cty Commission for Women & Families 1995-, Ed Comm Co-Chair; ACCESS Awd for Schlsp 1990; PA Womens Hall of Fame 1996; Irene Ryan Acting Nom; Pen Lit Fellow in Lit; *office:* Methacton HS 1001 Kriebel Mill Rd Norristown PA 19403*

WELSH, SHARON STEINER, Mathematics Teacher; *b:* Pittsburgh, PA; *m:* Shawn T.; *ed:* Masters Equivalency Univ of Pittsburgh & Slippery Rock Univ; *cr:* Hopewell HS Math Tchr 1986-; *ai:* Class Spon 7 Yrs; Ski Club 8 Yrs; NCTM 1994-; Deacon Bd of Riverdale Presbyn Church 1996-; *office:* Hopewell HS 1215 Longvue Ave Aliquippa PA 15001

WELTERS, LYNN B., Dance Chairperson; *b:* Washington, DC; *c:* Lisa Welters Johnson, Raigan Ginnyfer; *ed:* DC Tchrs Coll Elem Ed 1967-70; Art Cert Western MI Univ Russian Balet 1989-92; Natl Ballet Fredrick Franklin Dir; Jones-Haywood Capital Ballet Doris Jones Dir; Dance Theatre of Harlem Karel Shook; Amer Ballet Theatre Jurgen Schneider; Alvin Ailey Amer Dance Schl Denise Jefferson; Ballet Arts in Carneige Hall; *cr:* Lynn B WElters Schl of Ballet Owner, Dir 1968-74; Jones-Haywood Schl of Ballet Ballet & Pointe & Choreography Tchr 1979-88; Duke Ellington Schl of Arts Dance Chprsn, Ballet, Pointe Tchr, Dance His, Dance Orientation, Choreography, TADPOLE Dance Prgm Founder, Ellington Dance Ensemble 1977-; *ai:* Ellington Summer Dance Extensions Co-Dir; Introduction to Arts Tchr; Ellington Dance Ensembler Founder & Dir; Intnl Blacks in Dance 1993-; Natl Dance Assn, Tchr of Yr 1989; Prix de Lausanne Ballet Competition 1992; Xian China Fifth Ancient Culture & Art Festival 1995; Eight Week Dance Exchange Moscow Russia 1994; Intnl Dance Festival Amsterdam Holland 1996; Article Pub in Dance Magazine; *office:* Duke Ellington Schl of Arts 3500 R Street NW Washington DC 20007*

WEMETTE, ANGELA TOWLE, French Teacher; *b:* Malone, NY; *m:* Charles Jr.; *c:* Valerie, Luke; *ed:* Potsam St Univ (BA) Fr 1975; 30 Credit Hrs Grad Stud in Ed; 1 Yr Stud at Institut de Touraine; *cr:* St Joseph's Acad Fr Tchr 1975-76; Franklin Acad Fr Tchr 1976-; *ai:* Class of 1998 Ac NYSUT 1976-; Notre Dame Parish Cncl 1994-; Taken Stdnts to F Switzerland; *office:* Franklin Acad State St Malone NY 12953

WEMPLE, JONATHAN BARENT, English Teacher; *b:* Washing *ed:* Univ of MD (BA) Scndry Ed & Eng 1993; 6 Hrs Towards Scndry Ed Eng; *cr:* Oxon Hill HS Eng Tchr 1993-; *ai:* JV Wrestling NEA 1993-; PGCEA 1993-; *office:* Oxon Hill HS 6701 Leyte Dr O MD 20745

WENCK, ROMONA NELLIS, K-12th Grade Phys Ed Teac Cortland, NY; *m:* Gerald William; *c:* Jonathan William, Josiah Da Cortland St Univ (BAEd) PE 1977, (MS) PE 1982; Coll of Saint R Ed Admin 1994; *cr:* Laurens Cntrl Schl Tchr, Admin 1977-; *c* Colorguard Dir; Yth Soccer Area Coord 1990-; *office:* Laurens Cen Main St Laurens NY 13796*

WENDEL, PATRICIA R., Practical Nursing Teacher; *b:* Brookl *w:* Henry W. Jr. (dec); *c:* Michael, Dorothy, Deborah Marino, Timo Nassau Comm Coll (AS) Registered Nurse 1981; St Univ of NY (E Stud 1990; Adelphi Univ (MA) Hlth Stud 1995; NY St Cert Hlth Ed St Cert Practical Nursing Edctr; NY St Registered Prof Nurse Francis Hosp Staff Nurse 1981-88; Intnl Schl Malaysia Hlt 1989-91; Nassau Tech HS Practical Nurse Tchr 1993-; *ai:* Voc Inds of Amer Adv; BSA Chprsn; Image Comm; Safety Comm; NABCO Local Rep; AFT 1993-; BSA 1985-, Merit Badge Cnslr; United C Palsy Auxiliary 1993- Vol; Petaling Jaye Spastic Ctr M Occupational Adv; *office:* Nassau Tech HS 1196 Prospect Ave W NY 11590*

WENDELER, ELVA VIRGINIA, Second Grade Teacher; *b:* Upper PA; *ed:* Eastern Coll (BA) Amer Stud, Elem Ed 1969; Post Grad St St Univ, Millersville St Univ; *cr:* Boothwyn Elem Schl Second G 1969-95; *ai:* NEA, PA St Ed Assn 1969-; Chichester Ed Assn 1969 Red Cross Blood Driver Chprsn, PACE Chprsn; Outstdng Elem Tch 1972; *office:* Boothwyn Elem Schl PO Box 2100 Marcus Hook PA

WENDELL, DOLORES G., Science Teacher; *b:* Vineland, NJ; *m* A.; *c:* Daniel, Dianna; *ed:* LA Salle Univ (BA) Bio 1977; Villano (MS) Med Lib Sci 1984; *cr:* St Maria Goretti HSBio, Phys S 1979-81; Wyeth Pharmaceuticals Biological, Med Data 1981-84; Planning Assn Ed Asst 1985-88; Wnslow HS Bio, Chem Tc hr 19 Staff Dev Comm; Renaissance Prgm Work Team Mem Acquiring S Knowledge; ME Sci Tchrs Assn 1988-; *office:* Winslow HS 14 D St Winslow ME 04901

WENDELL, MERYL TARLOW, English Tchr & Rdng Speci Philadelphia, PA; *c:* Brandon, Carrie, Leslie; *ed:* Univ of CT (BA) 1969; Lehigh Univ (MED) Rdng Specialist 1981; Villanova Univ Credits; 15 Grad Credits, Keswick Univ at Norwich England 6 Un Credits; *cr:* Elkins Park Jr HS Eng Tchr 1969-71; Belvidere HS E 1971-73; Wilson Area HS Eng, Rdng Tchr 1977-; *ai:* Stu Cncl, S Archery Club, Awd Wining Schl Yrbk & Newspaper Jrnlsm Adv; C 1980, 1884, 1991; NEA, PSEA, Wilson Area Educ Assn 1977-; C Assn Rdng Edctrs 1981-; Tchr of Yr; First Spec Prin Dedication to 1988; Article Pub LA Rdng Tchr; *office:* Wilson Area HS 424 Wa Easton PA 18042

WENDRICH, BARBARA ANNE, Second Grade Teacher; *b:* Pass *ed:* Univ of MD (BS) Elem Ed 1971; Masters Equivalency 60 Po Hrs; *cr:* Wheaton Woods Elem Tchr 1972-; *ai:* Schl Sci Liasion; C Talented Comm; Univ of MD CITE Prgm Coach; NEA, MD St Tch 1972-; Montgomery Cty Ed Assn 1972-, Bldg Rep; *office:* Wheaton Elem Schl 4510 Faroe Pl Rockville MD 20853

WENDROFF, VARDA WASSERMAN, French & German Teache Aviv, Israel; *m:* Arnold; *c:* Jason, Lauren; *ed:* Montclair St Coll 1970; Jersey City St Coll (MA) ESL 1986; Stu Svcs, ESL Tchng, Prin Certs; *cr:* Bayonne HS Tchr 1980-; *ai:* Fr CLub, Ger Club, Trav Adv; AAFT, AATG 1980-; Jewish Comm Ctr 1979-, Pres; Tch Finalist; Governor's Tchrs Awd; *home:* 4 Elna Ct Bayonne NJ 070

WENGENROTH, LOUIS F.,IV, Mathematics & Physics Teac Goshen, NY; *ed:* Orange Cty Comm Coll (AA) Lbrl Arts 1969; S Plattsburgh (BA) Scndry Ed, Math 1971; City Coll of NY (MA) Scn Math 1990; East Carolina Univ 30 Grad Credits in Math 1976-81; *c* Hatteras 9-12 Grd Math, Physics Tchr 1972-76; East Carolina Un Grad Fellow 1976-68; Edenton-Chowan 9-12 Grd Math, Physi 1978-81; Orange Cty Comm Coll Algebra Tchr 1981-83; Burke Ca Grd Math, Calculus, Physics Tchr 1984-; *ai:* tutor; NYS Math Tchr Natl Cath Schl Tchrs Assn; Middletown Art Group; Tutored Math D Spec Admitted Stdnts, ECU Ftbl Team; Pub Solution to Problems f Math Tchrs; City Coll of NY Taught Grad Math Classes; *office:* Bur HS Fletcher St Goshen NY 10924

WENGER, CAROLYN M., Business Department Teach Shipshewana, IN; *m:* Clarence R.; *c:* Tracy, Todd; *ed:* Manchest (BS) Bus, PE 1957; Elizabethtown Coll Permanent Cert 1961; Courses 6 Hrs; *cr:* Noble Co HS Bus Tchr 1957-59; Pequea Valley Tchr 1959-63; Columbia HS Bus Tchr 1982-85; Solanco HS Bu 1985-; *ai:* Futur Bus Ldrs of America Adv 10 Yrs; NEA, PSEA, SEA *office:* Solanco H S 585 Solanco Rd Quarryville PA 17566

WENGER, ERIC P., Math, Science & Computer Tchr; *b:* Norristo *m:* Natalie R. Henwood; *c:* Erica, Shannon; *ed:* Villanova Univ (Gen Sci 1980; Math; Cmptrs Youngstown St Univ; *cr:* Tredyffin E SD Gen Sci Tchr 1980-81; Woodlynde Schl Math Tchr 1981-86; City SD Sci, Math, Cmptr Tchr 1986-; *ai:* Dist, Bldg Ldrshp Cncl; Cty Hlth Care Consortium; Tchrs Assoc Treas; Math Dept Ch Swimming Coach; K-12 Math Comm; NEA, PSEA, PCTM 1986- Cancer Soc 1988-, Bd; Elem PTO 1994-; PA Cncl Tchrs of Math Meetings Presenter; Steering Comm of Mercer Co Hlth Care Cons *office:* Sharon City Schl Dist 215 Forker Blvd Sharon PA 16146*

WENGERTER, JOHN MICHAEL, Physical Education Teac Jersey City, NJ; *m:* Ramona Ann Mc Carthy; *c:* Kelly Leigh, Case Jamie Lynn, Laurie Beth; *ed:* Coll of Santa Fe (BA) PE K-12 1973; City Coll 15 Addl Hrs; *cr:* Memorial HS Tchr 1975-; *ai:* Class of 19 Girls, Boys Vlybl Coach; NEA, WNYEA 1976-; USVBA 1988-, 20 Team Acad Awd; Sokol USA 1964-, Dist Dir; Emerson Boys & Gir 1991-, Bd; Hudson Cty Vlybl Coaches Assoc 1984-, VP, Coach of Y NJ Scholastic Coaches Assoc 1994-; *office:* Memorial HS 5501 Pa West New York NJ 07093*

WENGRYN, LINDA S., 5th Grade Teacher; *b:* Pittsburgh, PA; *m:* F *c:* Jason, Scott, Timothy; *ed:* Penn St (BA) Elem Ed 1967; U Pittsburgh (MBA) Elem Ed 1970; Rdng Cert; *cr:* Pittsburgh City Elem Tchr 1967-71; South Park Schls Rdng Specialist 1983-90, 5 Tchr 1990-; *ai:* NEA, PSEA 1983-; *office:* South Park MS 2500 S Rd Library PA 15129

WENK, THERESA ANN, Earth Science Teacher; *b:* Oceanside, N St Univ of NY at Stony Brook (BA) Sociology 1992; Grad Classes Saint Rose & Long Island Univ; *cr:* Assn for Children with Re Mental Dev Cnslr 1992-93; Lafayette HS Sci & Hlth Careers Tchr Prof Performing Arts Schl Sci Tchr 1996; *ai:* NSTA 1996; N 1994-95; *office:* Prof Performing Arts Schl 328 W 48th St New Yo 10036*

KER, BERNARD JOHN,JR., High School English Teacher; *b:* nore, MD; *m:* Velvet E. Abato-Wenker; *c:* Shannon, Emily; *ed:* Johns ins Univ (BA) Lbrl Arts, Eng 1971; Towson St Univ M Ed; Morgan iv M Writing, Rhetoric; *cr:* Mergenthaler Voc Tech HS Eng Tchr 81; Eastern HS Eng Tchr 1982-84; Baltimore City Coll Eng Tchr Overlea HS Eng Tchr 1987-88; Parkville HS Eng Tchr 1988-; *ai:* Lit Magazine, Amnesty Intnl, Poetry Club Adv; Soccer Coach; disciplinary Team; Baltimore Tchrs Union 1971-81; Tchrs Assn nore Cty 1987-; Woodhome PTA 1992-; Book Pub Common ledge; Ed, Pub Poetry Journal; *office:* Parkville HS 2600 Putty Hill altimore MD 21234

NER, DOUGLAS KEITH, English Teacher; *b:* Oil City, PA; *m:* eline Mook; *c:* Brett, Autumn; *ed:* Asbury Coll (BA) Eng 1971; ninster (MS) Eng & Ed 1977; 17 Credit Hrs from Clarion Univ, Univ in Huntsville, & Boston Univ; *cr:* Oil City Schl Dist Eng Tchr 1973-; bk Adv; Young Astronaut Club Adv; *office:* Oil City MS 69 Spring St ity PA 16301

NER, GEORGE L., Senior High English Teacher; *b:* Wilkes Barre, *n:* Ruth Ann Taylor; *c:* Karen Lee Freeman, John Joseph; *ed:* PA ary Coll (BA) Eng 1964; Masters Equivalency; *cr:* ngford-Swarthmore Schl Dist Tchr & Coach 1964-71; Garnet Vly Dist Tchr & Coach 1971-; *ai:* Cross Cntry & Track Coach; Stu Cncl NEA, PSEA & GVEA 1964-; *office:* Garnet Valley Sr HS 552 bridge Rd Glen Mills PA 19342

NERSTROM, JENNIFER SUSAN (GAISER), Vocal Music tor; *b:* East Lansing, MI; *m:* Joel; *ed:* Kent St Univ (BA) Musci Ed (MA) Music Ed 1996; *cr:* Highland Local Schls Vocal Music Dir 89; Barberton HS Vocal Music Dir 1989-; *ai:* Head of Music Dept; al Dir; Drama Coach; MENC, OMEA 1985-; NEA 1987-; *office:* rton HS 489 W Hopocan Ave Barberton OH 44203*

SELL, GEORGIA, Mathematics Teacher; *b:* Indiana, PA; *m:* John; rk, Greg; *ed:* Indiana Univ of PA (BS) Math 1963; Loyola Coll of MD Supervision 1991; Attnd Loyola & Harford Comm Coll; *cr:* Havre de HS Tchr 1964-68; Havre de Grace MS Tchr 1976-85; Havre de Grace chr 1985-; *ai:* Schl Improvement; Mid Sts Chair; NCTM, NEA, M; Delta Kappa Gamma; Friends of Lib; Lioness; Presidential Awd Finalist Twice; Honorary Doctorate from Loyola Univ of MD; *office:* de Grace HS 700 Congress Ave Havre De Grace MD 21078

TLING, ERIC PAUL, Social Studies Teacher; *b:* Lebanon, PA; *m:* Kanoff; *c:* Gabrielle, Luke; *ed:* Westchester Univ (BS) Acctng 1985; Cert Penn St at Harrisburg; *cr:* Tulpehocken HS Soc Stud Tchr ; *ai:* Head Boys, Girls Soccer Coach; NEA 1995-; *office:* hocken HS 430 New Schaefferstown Rd Bernville PA 19506

TWORTH, SHARYN A., 6th Grade Teacher; *b:* Northampton, MA; estfield St (BS) Ed K-3 1968; Cambridge Coll (MS) Bus 1987; *cr:* Elem Schl Tchr Grds K,1,3 1968-, 6th Grd Tchr; *ai:* Stamp Club min Franklin Grd 5; Cmptr Class Grd 3; NEA, MTA 1968-; Cncl 1990-, Chair 1 Yr; Selectmen 1995-; *office:* Ware MS 4 Church St MA 01082

TWORTH, STEPHEN MICHAEL, English Teacher; *b:* Houlton, *ed:* Univ of NH (BA) Eng 1973; *cr:* Portsmouth HS Eng Tchr 1973-; i Fiction Club Adv; NEA, NHEA, Assn of Portsmouth Tchrs 1973-; Dedication 1995; *office:* Portsmouth HS Andrew Jarvis Dr nouth NH 03801

TZ, BARBARA JEAN, Elem Supvr & 1st Grade Teacher; *b:* ver, PA; *ed:* Shippensburg St Univ (BS) Elem Ed 1972, (MEd) Elem 76; *cr:* Littlestown Area Schl Dist Title I Rdng Instr, Tutor 1973-74; Freedom Chrstn Schls Elem Supvr, Tchr 1974-; *ai:* Lib, Cmptr Lab ; *office:* New Freedom Christian Schl 222 N Constitution Ave PO 19 New Freedom PA 17349

TZEL, CONNIE RUSSO, 7th & 8th Grd Math & Sci Tchr; *b:* Easton, Donald C.; *c:* Cheryl Trudon, Michelle Lipko, Jill Dussault, David; oll of St Joseph (BA) Early Chldhd, Elem Ed 1975; Univ of CT (MS) Ldrshp 1992; *cr:* St Joseph Schl 1st, 4th & 8th Grd Tchr 1975-85; St s Schl 7th & 8th Grd Tchr 1986-86; Cathedral of St Joseph Schl 4th, 8th Grd Tchr 1986-; *ai:* Chrldng Coach; Sci Fair Moderator; 8th Grd Adv; Math & Rel Coord; NCEA 1976-; Vernon Girls Sftbl Assn, Bd ; Church Comms; eucharistic Minister; Rel Ed Tchr; *home:* 129 Hany rnon Rockville CT 06066*

TZEL, LYNN N., Mathematics Teacher; *b:* Reading, PA; *ed:* ght Coll (BS) Math 1981; Kutztown Univ (MED) Scndry Math Ed Post Grad Stud Penn St Univ; Emergency Medical Field Certs; *cr:* kill Vly MS Math Tchr 1981-82; Stroudsburg MS Math Tchr 1983-; AP Team; Bldg EMT; NEA, PSEA, NCTM 1983-; PA Math sment Advy Comm; Cntrl Pocono Ambulance 1991-, Lieutenant 3rd Top Runner; Monroe Co Advanced Life Support 1994-; *office:* dsburg MS Chipperfield Dr Stroudsburg PA 18360

TZEL, RICHARD WILLIAM, Director of Religious Ed; *b:* non, PA; *m:* Shirley Ann Daub; *c:* Gregory, Matthew, Andrew; *ed:* non Vly Coll (BS) Elem Ed 1967; IL Inst of Tech (MS) Sociology Attnd Cath Univ of America 2 Yrs, Univ of CT 2 Yrs, St Univ of NY eonta, Western MI Univ, Univ of MD, Univ of Southern IL & oethtown Coll; Diocese of Harrisburg Deacon Formation Inst (MS alency) Theology 1978; *cr:* St Marys Elem Schl 5th-6th Grd Tchr 67; Cornwall-Lebanon Schl Dist 6th Grd Tchr 1967-68; Lebanon HS Dir of Soc Stud & Tchr 1968-78, Dir of Rel Ed 1978-; *ai:* Stu Asst -8th Grd Planning Teams; NHS Selection, Mid Sts Evaluation & ual Life Comms; Mission Club Moderator; NCEA 1968-; BSA 1950-; nts of Columbus 1962-; Lebanon Ind Fire Co 1980-, Chaplain; on Cty Eagle Scout Soc 1988-, Chm; NSF Grants 1968-70; Full NSF p for Acad Yr 1971-72; *office:* Lebanon Catholic Jr Sr High 1400 nut St Lebanon PA 17042

TZEL, ROSEMARY KOURY, Fourth Grade Teacher; *b:* Pottstown, *n:* George R.; *c:* Lindsey, Laura; *ed:* Kutztown Univ (BS) Elem Ed (MED) Elem Ed 1978; *cr:* Rupert Elem Schl 1st-3rd Grd Tchr 81; Lincoln Elem Schl K-4th Grd Tchr 1981-; *ai:* Liaison Comm; incipals Night; Family Ed Fair; Textbook Adoption; Sub Folder; ng System Revision Comm; Vol Tutoring; PSEA 1973-80; FPT, AFT , Recording Sec; Kutztown Alumni Assn 1973-; Jr Svc League 1979-, ding Sec; Elks Doe Club 1993-; PTA 1973-, Parliamentarian; Amer er Soc Coordinate Daffodil Days Annually at Schl & Collect in hborhood Annually; Schl Dist Pub Relations Video; Seminars & sher Courses TEAM, TESA & PET Madeleine Hunter- Rdng in Elem & Discipline with Love & Logic; AIMS Houghton-Miflin Math nars; *office:* Lincoln Elem Schl 8th & York Sts Pottstown PA 19464*

ZEL, JAMES S., MS Social Studies Teacher; *b:* Glendive, MT; *m:* a Machado; *c:* Maria C., James J.; *ed:* Mt Angel Seminary (BA) sophy 1964; Maryknoll Seminary (MA) Theology 1968; Manhattan MA) Ed, as Rdng Specialist 1973; *cr:* Rochambeau Schl Adult Ed 1968-80; Pocantico Hills Cntrl Schl 5 & 6 Grds MS Soc Stud Tchr ; Boces S. Westchester Schl Adult Ed Instr, Eng Lang Learning Tchr ; *ai:* Soc Stud Comms; Pocantico Hills Tchrs Assn 1968-, VP, Pres 75; NYSUT; AFT; Westchester Cncl for Soc Stud 1975-; Beaver Conf Bd Trustee; St Patrick's Peace & Justice Comm; Empty Hand Zendo, Bd Mem; *office:* Pocantico Hills Central Schl 599 Bedford Rd N Tarrytown NY 10591

WENZELL, MARY ESTHER, Third Grade Teacher; *b:* Corpus Christi, TX; *ed:* TX A&M Univ (BS) Elem Ed 1995; 3 Hrs Psych Southwest TX Univ; 12 Hrs Rdng Corpus Christi A&M Univ; *cr:* T. H. Johnson Elem Schl Third Grd Tchr 1985-89; Cunningham Elem Schl Second, Third Grd Split Tchr 1989-90; Lakenheath Elem Schl Third Grd Tchr 1990-; *ai:* Lang Arts, Early Chldhd, Art, Soc Stud Comms; Soc Comm Chprsn; Book Club Adv; NEA 1991-; *home:* 2913 Terrace Way Altus OK 73521

WERBITSKY, SARAHJANE TAYLOR, Science Teacher; *b:* Rockville Center, NY; *m:* Darrin; *c:* Amy; *ed:* Plattsburg St (BS) Med Tech, Invitro Cell Bio 1984; Aldelphi Univ (MS) Ed 1989; *cr:* Analytab Production Tech Instrument Specialist & Scientist 1984-89; Floral Park Meml HS Sci Tchr 1989-; *ai:* NEA & SFT 1989-; *office:* Floral Park Memorial HS 210 Locust St Floral Park NY 11001

WERDEN, BEATRICE GOLDSCHMIDT, Physics & Chemistry Teacher; *b:* New York, NY; *m:* Ken; *c:* Andrew, Liz, Richard; *ed:* City Coll of NY (BS) Chem 1962; Columbia Univ (MA) Chem 1963, (MPhil) Chem 1973; Tchrs Coll 45 Addl Credits Scndry & Conn Ed; *cr:* Manhattan Comm Coll Instr 1973-77; Marymount Coll Instr 1978-82; Fieldston Schl Chem Tchr 1982-84; Bronx HS of Sci Chem & Physics Tchr 1984-; *ai:* STANYS 1993-, SAR Chem; NEA; Chem Club of NY; NY St Chem Mentor; *office:* Bronx HS Of Science 75 W 205th St Bronx NY 10468*

WERE, MARGARET CARSWELL, Vocal Music Director; *b:* Glens Falls, NY; *m:* Theodore H. Jr.; *c:* Jarod C., Brianna M.; *ed:* Coll of St Rose (BS) Music, Ed 1982, (MS) Ed, Music 1991; *cr:* St James Inst K-8th Grd Gen Music Tchr 1982-85; Estee MS Vocal, Instrumental Music Tchr 1986-91; Gloversville HS Vocal Music Dir 1991-; *ai:* Choir Club; Festivals Adv; Theater Musical Dir; NYSSMA, MENC, AFT, NYSUT 1986-; ACDA 1996; K-12 Music Dept Chrpsn; *home:* 469 Military Rd Edinburg NY 12134*

WERGER, BRIDGET SUSAN, Second Grade Teacher; *b:* Allison Park, PA; *m:* Clyde Andrew; *c:* Katrina, Christopher; *ed:* Edinboro St Univ (BS) Art Ed 1974; Cert Univ of Pittsburgh Elem Ed 1984; *cr:* Hampton Schl MS Art Tchr 1976-84, Fifth Grd Tchr 1984-85, Second Grd Tchr 1985-; Allegheny Intermediate Unit Cmptr Instr 1993-95; *ai:* Tech, Early Chldhd Comm; NEA 1976-, Pres, VP; Hampton Alliance Grants 1994-95; *office:* Wyland Elem Schl 2284 Wyland Ave Allison Park PA 15101

WERLEY, LESLIE A., Third Grade Teacher; *b:* Reading, PA; *m:* Jane Korb; *c:* Courtney, Lindsay; *ed:* Bloomsburg St Coll (BS) Elem Ed, Math 1972; PA Dept of Ed MA Equiv Elem Ed 1976; TESA Trained; *cr:* Hamburg Area Schl Dist 4th Grd Tchr 1972-82, 3rd Grd Tchr 1982-; *ai:* HAEA, PSEA, NEA 1972-, Bldg Rep, VP, Pres; BSA, Comm Chm; Twp Recreation Bd; Cub Pack 184, Comm Mem; *office:* Hamburg Elem Schl Hamburg Area Schl Dist 680 E State St Hamburg PA 19526

WERMERS, PATRICIA LYNN, Computer Science Professor; *b:* Mpls, MN; *ed:* Merrimack Coll (BA) Bio 1978, (BS) Math 1979; Univ of MA at Lowell (MS) Math 1987; *cr:* Westford HS Math Tchr 1983-84; Bedford HS Math Tchr 1981-83; North Eastern Univ Math Lecturer 1988-; North Shore Comm Coll Cmptr Sci Prof 1984-; *ai:* Cmptr Comm; ACM 1987-; AAUW 1995-; NEA 1980-; *office:* North Shore Comm Coll 1 Ferncroft Rd Danvers MA 01923*

WERNER, B. LEE, Mathematics Teacher; *b:* East Brunswick, NJ; *m:* Donald J. Sheluga; *ed:* Syracuse Univ (BA) Math Ed, Psych 1977, (MS) Cnslng, Psych 1982; Working Towards MS Educl Admin Rider Univ; *cr:* Westmoreland HS Math Tchr 1977-78; Tully Cntrl Schl Math Tchr, Dept Chprsn 1978-90; West Windsor Plainsboro HS Math Tchr 1990-; *ai:* 9th Grd Math Team Adv; PAC Comm; Mentor Tchr; AMTNJ 1990-; NCTM 1980-; MCSM 1994-; ASCD 1995-; Pi Lambda Theta; Governor's Tchr Awd 1993; *office:* West Windsor Plainsboro HS 346 Clarksville Rd Princeton Junction NJ 08550

WERNER, BLAINE JAY, HS Social Studies Teacher; *b:* Canton, OH; *m:* Vicki Sue; *c:* Brett, Krista; *ed:* Kent St Univ (AA) Gen Stud 1979, (BS) Ed Soc Stud 1980; Post Grad Stud Univ of Akron; Ed Curr Ashland Univ; *cr:* Fairless HS Soc Stud, Eng Tchr 1982-; *ai:* Wrestling, Ftbl Coach; Schlsp Comm Amer Legion Post; NEA, OEA, FEA 1982-, Bldg Rep, Negotiator; OH Cncl Soc Stud 1982-; East Cntrl Cncl Soc Stud 1991-, Past Pres; Amer Legion 1992-, Schlsp Comm; Fidelity Lodge #712 F&AM 1987-, Past Master, Grand Master's Awd 1994; Christ United Meth Church 1983-, Admin Ed Chm; BSA 1989-, Asst Dist Chm; Jennings Grant Recipient; Stark Cty Bar Assn Tchr of Yr 1991; Kent St Univ Stark Campus His Stu of Yr 1979-80; *office:* Fairless HS 11885 Navarre Rd SW Navarre OH 44662

WERNER, DARLENE MILLER, Kindergarten Teacher; *b:* Elyria, OH; *m:* Terry L.; *c:* Allison E.; *ed:* Miami Univ (BS) Elem Ed 1967; Kent St Univ (MED) Spec Ed 1975; Addl 40 Hrs Kent St Univ, Ashland Coll, Univ of Akron, Laverne Coll, Bowling Green St Univ; *cr:* Garfield Elem Schl Kndgtn, 2-6 Grd Tchr 1967-94; Lowell Elem Schl Grd One Tchr 1994-95; Meister Rd Schl Kndgtn Tchr 1995-; *ai:* Lorain Ed Assn Exec Comm Soc Chm; Lorain Schl Employees Credit Union Exec Bd; Lorain Ed Assn 1967-, Soc Chm; OH Cncl Intl Rdng Assn; NEA 1967-; OH Ed Assn 1967-, Daniel T. Gardner Chptr; Martha Holden Jennings Scholar; Positive Edctr of Month 1996; *home:* 4348 Tomahawk Lane Vermilion OH 44089

WERNER, KATHLEEN, Instructor; *b:* Rochester, PA; *m:* Robert E. Millward; *ed:* Penn St Univ (BA) Scndry Ed & His 1969, (MA) Amer His 1971; IN Univ of PA 15 Credits Doctoral Pgm Rhetorics & Linguistics; *cr:* Comm Coll of Beaver Co Instr Hum Dept 1971-82; IN Univ of PA Instr Eng Dept 1988-; *ai:* Frosh Eng Comm; Punxsutawney Fac Comm; Univ Residence Hall Judicial Bd; PSEA 1971-82; ABSCUF 1988-; NCTE 1990-; PCEA 1992-; Book with Dr E Zebrowski: Publishing Without Perishing Some Advice for Positive Textbook Authors, Teaching English in the Two-Year College 1984; Books: Writing Clear Sentences 1986, Models for Clear Writing 1994, Writing Clear Essays 1996, Writing Clear Paragraphs 1996; Rsrch Stud & Trainers Manual: Reducing Chronic Absenteeism 1984; Selected by NASSP to Dev Commnctn Skills Manual: From The Desk Of 1990; Scriptwriter for Trng Films IUP Tchr Assessment Ctr; Article Pub 1992; *home:* RR 3 Box 207B Indiana PA 15701*

WERNER, MADELEINE, 4th Grade Teacher; *b:* Bronx, NY; *ed:* Alfonso Coll (AA) Lbrl Arts 1970; Seton Hall Univ (BS) Nursery-6th Grd Elem Ed 1975, (MM) Spec Ed 1984; Manhattan Coll 6 Credits Admin, Supervision; *cr:* St James Schl 4th Grd, 2nd Grd Tchr 1974-78; St Dominic Schl 5th Grd, 2nd Grd Tchr 1978-86, 4th Grd Tchr 1995-; St John Villa Schl 3rd Grd Tchr 1986-87; St Roch Schl 3rd Grd Tchr 1987-95; *ai:* NCEA 1980-; *office:* St Dominic Schl 1684 White Plains Rd Bronx NY 10462

WERNER, ROBERT, English Dept Chairman & Tchr; *b:* Latrobe, PA; *m:* Linda Frichtel; *ed:* St Vincent Coll (BA) Eng 1958; Latin Minor Citadel; Media Specialist Seton Hill Coll; 90 Addl Hrs; Masters Equivalency IN Univ of PA 1975; Attnd Duquesene Univ, Univ of Pittsburgh, Penn St; *cr:* Charliers Vly HS Eng Latin Tchr 1958-62; Derry Area HS Tchr, Eng Dept Chm 1962-; *ai:* Stu Tchr Instr, Ldr; Curr, Strategic Planning Comms; Mentor for New Tchrs; NEA 1958-; DAEA 1962-, Pres, VP; WPCTE 1985-; NCTE 1964-; Church, Cncl VP, Comms; Kangweon Natl Chuncheon Korea Tchr & Tutor Eng Ed; Natl Defense Ed to Stud at Univ of Pacific, Univ of IA, IN Univ of PA; NCTE Conf Awd; Derry Area Schl Bd Outstdng Tchr.

WERNER, THEODORE J.,II, Principal; *b:* Altoona, PA; *m:* Sonia Y. Yankovitch; *c:* Heidi Alexia; *ed:* Penn St (BS) Ed, Spec Ed 1970; Niagara Univ (MS) Ed 1981; NC St Engrng Ed 1964; Admin; *cr:* Niagara Falls Cntrl Office 1981-83; Niagara Falls HS VP 83-86; Emmet Belknap VP 1986-94; Lockport HS Vice Prin 1994-95; John E. Pound Elem Prin 1995-; *ai:* NAESP 1986-; United Way; NY St PTA Distngd Svc Awd; PTA Life Mbrshp Awd; *office:* John E. Pound Elem Schl 51 High St Lockport NY 14094*

WERT, TIMOTHY DALE, Physics Teacher; *b:* Lock Haven, PA; *m:* Amy C. Moyer; *c:* Sarah F., Elizabeth M., Thomas W., Kathryn M.; *ed:* Lock Haven Univ (BA) Ed, Math & Physics 1985; 15 Credit Hrs Penn St Univ; *cr:* Red Lion Schl Dist Physics & Phys Sci Tchr 1985-89; York Tech Inst Electronics Instr 1992-93; Cntrl York Schl Dist Physics Tchr 1993-; *ai:* Physics Club & Sci Olympiad Adv; Sci Fair Coord; NEA 1993-; PSEA 1993-; CYEA 1993-; *office:* Central York HS 775 Marion Rd York PA 17404

WERTIS, SANDRA KARAUS, Math Teacher; *b:* Rockville Centre, NY; *m:* Richard Lawrence; *c:* Alexandra; *ed:* Molloy Coll (BA) Latin & Math; St John's Univ (MA) Latin; Columbia Univ (PHD) Greek & Latin; *cr:* Garden City Sr HS Math Tchr; *ai:* Math Tutors; Math Curr, Placement Comms; AFT; Vergiliay Soc; Classical Assn of Empire St; Natl Endowment for Arts Flwshp; Amer Schl of Classical Stud at Athens 2 Flwshps; Article Pub; *office:* Garden City Sr HS Merillon Ave Garden City NY 11530*

WERTZ, DAVID EMORY, 4th Grade Teacher; *b:* Bedford, PA; *m:* Sharon Kaye Sciranko; *ed:* Clarion Univ (BA) Elem Ed 1976; *cr:* Cumberland Vly Elem Schl Tchr 1976-; *ai:* IM Ath Dir; NEA, PSEA, BAEA 1976-; Bedford Jaycees 1994-; Bedford Elks 1982-; Bedford Moose 1978-; *office:* Cumberland Valley Elem Schl RR 3 Box 138 Bedford PA 15522

WERTZ, JAMES THOMAS, Mathematics Teacher; *b:* Canton, OH; *m:* Susan R.Baer; *ed:* Malone Coll (BA) Math 1986; *cr:* Glen Oak HS Math Tutor 1986-87; Jackson HS Math Tchr 1987-; *ai:* Jr Var Bsktbl; Asst Var Bsbl; Young Life; *office:* Jackson Local HS 7600 Fulton Dr NW Massillon OH 44646*

WERTZ, KATHRYN REICHERT, High School Mathematics Tchr; *b:* Wooster, OH; *m:* Raymond Scott; *ed:* Lenoir-Rhyne Coll (BA) Math 1972; Ashland Univ (MA) Comp Ed 1995; IFSMACE at Kent St 1989-90; *cr:* Northwestern Local Schls Tchr & Coach 1972-, Math Dept chprsn 1994-; *ai:* Sr Class Adv; Fall Ath Fac Mgr; Var Girls Track; OEA & NEA 1972-; NCTM 1980-; OCTM 1985-; *office:* Northwestern HS 7473 N Elyria Rd West Salem OH 44287

WERTZ, SHARON SCIRANKO, English Teacher; *b:* Bedford, PA; *m:* David E.; *ed:* Slippery Rock Univ (BS) Elem 1973; Frostburg St Univ (MS) Rdng 1980; *cr:* Kettering Elem Schl 1st Grd Tchr 1973-75; Laurel Elem Schl 2nd-3rd Open Space Tchr 1975-76; Cumberland Vly Elem Schl Rdng Specialist 1976-89; Bedford MS Eng Tchr 1989-; *ai:* Ski Club Adv; Adv-Advisee Club Ldr; NEA 1973-; PSEA 1976-; BAEA 1976-, Treas; Women of the Moose 1988-; *office:* Bedford MS 440 E Watson St Bedford PA 15522

WESCHE, KEVIN JAMES, Technology Education Instr; *b:* Bridgeport, CT; *m:* Christine Ann Scribe; *c:* Andrea, Brandon, Alana; *ed:* Cntrl CT St Univ (BS) Tech Ed 1981; Cert Drivers Ed 1981; 33 Credit Hrs Educl Ldrshp; 30 Credit Hrs 7-12th Grd Math; 30 Credit Hrs Mngmt; *cr:* Orchard Jr HS Tech Ed 1981-82; Naugatuck HS Tech Ed 1982-; *ai:* Boys Var Bsktbl Head Coach; Class of 1997 Adv; Naugatuck Tchrs League, CT Ed Assn, NEA 1984-; CT Tech Ed Assn 1985-; Oxford Soccer League, Boys Minor League 1995-, Coach; Girls Sftbl 1995-, Asst Coach; BEST Prgm for Tchrs Mentor; Here's Looking at You 2000 Self-Esteem Prgm; Yrbk Dedication 1992; Coach of the Yr 1990; Sportsmanship Awd for Coaching 1995-; *office:* Naugatuck HS 543 Rubber Ave Naugatuck CT 06770*

WESEL, BARBARA J., English Composition Instructor; *b:* Greenville, CA; *c:* Stephanie, Jennifer; *ed:* Bowling Green St Univ (BS) Ed 1983; Addl Hrs Marietta Coll; *cr:* Eastern Local Schls Spec Ed Tchr 1983-85; WA St Comm Coll Eng Composition Instr 1992-; *ai:* Fac Vlybl Team; OH River Sternwheel Festival 1988-, Bd Mem, Comm Chair; *office:* Washington State Comm Coll 710 Colegate Dr Marietta OH 45750

WESNESKI, OLGA FRANKOS, Sixth Grade Teacher; *b:* New York City, NY; *m:* Anthony C.; *c:* Anthony C. II; *ed:* SVC at Plattsburgh (BS) Elem Ed 1962, (MS) Elem Ed 1970; SVC at Ithaca 3 Hrs Grad; SVC at New Paltz 3 Hrs Grad; Newburgh Bd of Ed 20 In-Svc Cr Hrs; *cr:* Vails Gate Elem Schl Third Grd Tchr 1962-65, Sixth Trd Tchr 1965-70; Temple Hill Acad Sixth Grd Tchr 1970-83, Fifth Grd Tchr 1984-85, Sixth Grd Tchr 1985-; *ai:* Sewing Club; Magnet Schl Comm; THA Tchr Liaison to Greece; NEA, AFT, NYSTA 1962-; Newburgh Tchrs Assn 1963-, Del; SUC at Plattsburgh 1962-, Alumni; Temple Hill Theater Players 1972-b; Magnet Grant Comm; Newburgh Tchrs Bright Ideas Awd.

WESOLOWSKI, JACK ALAN, Social Studies Teacher; *b:* Buffalo, NY; *m:* Deborah Mc Evoy; *c:* Keith, Kelly; *ed:* Univ of NY at Buffalo (BA) His 1969, (MA) Ed 1971; Post Grad 60 Credit Hrs in Ed; *cr:* Maryvale Union Free Schl HS Sub Tchr 1969-71; John F Kennedy HS HS Sub Tchr 1969-71; Williamsville North HS Tchr 1972-75; Williamsville East HS Tchr 1976-80; Wlliamsville North HS Tchr 1981-; *ai:* Supervise Weight Training Room; Vol Buffalo Psychiatric Ctr; Williamsburg Soc St Cncl 1985-; Williamsville Tchrs Assn 1972-, Svc Awd 25 Yrs; NYS United Tchrs, Amer Fed of Tchrs 1972-; Pendleton Historic Soc 1980-, Adv; Chicago Outstdng, Inspiring HS Tchr Awd 1987; Williamsville 25 Yr Svc Awc; *office:* Williamsville North HS 1595 Hopkins Rd Williamsville NY 14221

WESOLOWSKI, WANDA ELEANOR, Prof & Radiologic Tech Chprsn; *b:* Philadelphia, PA; *ed:* Hahnemann Med Univ (AS) Radiologic Tech 1974; LaSalle Univ (BA) His 1980; Beaver Coll (MED) Hlth Ed 1983; Addl Hrs Continued Ed Courses; *cr:* Albert Einstein Med Ctr Staff Radiographer 1958-64, Angiography Supvr 1974-74; Comm Coll of Philadelphia Prof 1974-; *ai:* Stu Mentor; Consultant; ARRT 1958-; ASRT 1958-, Fellow Awd; Alpha Eta 1976-; Copernicus Soc 1980-; Alumni Spec Achvmt Awd Thomas Jefferson Univ 1981; NEMA Awd Amer Soc of Radiologic Tech 1973; *office:* Comm Coll Of Philadelphia 1700 Spring Garden St Philadelphia PA 19130*

WESSEL, SHARON STEWART, Home Economics Teacher; *b:* Neptune, NJ; *m:* Paul A.; *c:* Stewart A., Heather A.; *ed:* Montclair St Univ (BA) Home Ec 1968; *cr:* Holmdel Inter Schl Home Ec Tchr 1968-70; C. T. Barkalow Schl Home Ec Tchr 1979-; *ai:* Chrldng Coach; Yrbk Adv; NEA 1968-; MCEA 1979-; FTEA 1979-, Bld Rep; United Church of Christ 1976-, Chrstn Ed, Worship, Growth, Cncl; *home:* 48 Bucks Mill Rd Colts Neck NJ 07722

WESSELS, JOYCE RITA LAVOY, Visual Education Teacher; *b:* Bad Axe, MI; *m:* Frank Jude; *c:* Angela, Frank; *ed:* Xavier Univ (BA) Fine Art 1973; Attnd IN Univ, OH St Univ, OH Dominican Coll; *cr:* Our Lady of Perpetual Help Schl Visual Ed, K-8 Grd Tchr 1988-95; St Michael Schl Visual Ed, 1-8 Grd Tchr 1991-; *ai:* Artists in Schls Comm 1991-; Report Card Comm 1996; Curr Dev Comm 1993-95; Organized Stu, Rel Stu Art Show 1991-; NCEA 1988-; Worthington Art League 1984-87; Who's Who Among Stdnts Amer Coll Univ 1973; *office:* Our Lady Of Perpetual Hlp Schl 3752 Broadway Grove City OH 43123*

WEST, ANN GARLAND, English Dept Chairman; *b:* Kingston, NH; *m:* Richard A.; *ed:* Univ of NH (BA) Govt, Eng 1956; Grad Work Univ NH,

Assumption Coll, Howard Schl Ed, Rivier Coll; *cr:* Berlin HS Eng Tchr 1956-58; Nashua Jr HS Eng Tchr 1958-59; Pinkerton Acad Eng Dept Chm 1959-; *ai:* Drama Club Adv; Play Dir; Fac Awds Comm Chm; Ldrshp Team; NCTE 1970-, Liaison Ofcr; NEATE 1970-, Pres, Charles Swain; NHATE 1965-, Pres, Thomas Awd; Delta Kappa Gamma 1970-, Pres; Educl Dir Granite Girls St 1959-; Govt Staff Girls Nation 1995; NH Tchr of Yr Finalist; Sci Awd NHATE; Svc Awd Dept NH Amer Legion Auxiliary; *home:* 843 Gould Hill Rd Contoocook NH 03229

WEST, CAROL VAIANA, Applied Comm & Speech Teacher; *b:* New York, NY; *c:* J. Christopher; *ed:* Mansfield Univ (BS) Ed, Speech 1970; Bloomsburg Univ M Equiv Eng 1976; 45 Addl Credits 1990-; *cr:* Shamokin HS Eng, Speech Tchr 1970-72; Tunkhannock HS Eng, Speech, Schl to Work Tchr 1973-; Luzerene Cty CC Night Class Speech Instr 1992-; *ai:* Yth App Pgrm Rep; PSEA, NEA, TAEA 1970-; *home:* PO Box 584 Tunkhannock PA 18657*

WEST, CONSTANCE SCOLES, Gifted Education Teacher; *b:* Columbus, OH; *m:* Paul A.; *c:* Megan, Craig; *ed:* Miami Univ (BSEd) Elem Ed 1972, (MEd) Classroom Tchng 1976; *cr:* Forest Hills Schls Intermediate, Gifted Ed Tchr 1972-; *ai:* Martha Holden Jenings Scholar; Educator of Yr Maddux Schl; *office:* Wilson Elem Schl 2465 Little Dry Run Rd Cincinnati OH 45244*

WEST, DANIEL E., Physical Education Teacher; *b:* Watertown, NY; *m:* Cindy Scott; *c:* Cory, Melissa, Benjamin; *ed:* Ithaca Coll (BS) PE 1973; 30 Credit Hrs; *cr:* Franklin Acad HS Tchr, Coach 1973-; *ai:* Var Swim Coach 1973-90; Var Ftbl Coach 1979-95; NEA, AFT 1973-; NY St Coaches Assn; Won Several Section X Championships Coaching Swimming, Section X Champtionship Ftbl 1983; *home:* 2 Smith Ave Malone NY 12953

WEST, DARREN A., US History Teacher; *b:* Mars Hill, ME; *m:* Carol A.; *c:* Lauren; *ed:* Univ of ME (BS) His, Eng 1990; Working Toward Post-Grad Degree His; *cr:* Houlton HS Classroom Tchr 1990-; *ai:* Soc Stud Dept Chair 1994-; Restructuring Comm; Class Adv; NCSS 1995-; Extra Mile Awd 1991; *office:* Houlton HS 5 Bird St Houlton ME 04730

WEST, DENNIS JAMES, Social Studies & Reading Tchr; *b:* Mount Gilead, OH; *m:* Gail Rena Zwick; *c:* Alexander, Branson, Camden; *ed:* MT St Univ (BS) Scndry Ed Soc Stud 1985; Rndg Cert; *cr:* J. F. K. MS Geography & PE 1985-86; Mt Gilead High His & Rdng Tchr 1986-; *ai:* Boys & Girls Var Cross Cntry & Asst Track Coach; Var Ath Club Adv; His; OEA & Mt Gilead Tchrs Assn 1986-; First Bapt Church 1991-, Trustee; OH Track & Cross Cntry Coaches 1986-, Coach of Yr 1991-92; Cntrl Dist Cross Cntry Coaches 1990, Cntrl Dist Coach of Yr 1993; Perfect Attendance 6 Yrs; *office:* Mount Gilead HS 333 Park Ave Mount Gilead OH 43338

WEST, DOROTHY H., Social Studies Teacher; *b:* New Castle, PA; *m:* John C.; *c:* Barbara Plummer, John C. Jr.; *ed:* Youngstown St (BS) Bus 1962; Univ of Pittsburgh 12 Grad Hrs; Westminster 3 Grad Hrs; Slippery Rock 18 Credit Hrs; *cr:* Youngstown Schl Tchr 3 Yrs; Carlywton Tchr 2 Yrs; Butler Tchr 25 Yrs; *ai:* NEA 1972-; PSEA; BEA; AAUW 1970-; *office:* Butler Area Sr HS 167 New Castle Rd Butler PA 16001

WEST, EILEEN O'BRIEN, Sixth Grade Teacher; *b:* York, PA; *m:* Lawrence E.; *c:* Jacob L., Kate E.; *ed:* Millersville Univ (BS) Elem Ed 1972; Mansfield Univ (MS) Ed 1990; *cr:* Dallastown Area Schl Dist 4th Grd Tchr 1972-74; Wellsboro Area Schl Dist K-6 Sub Tchr 1974-83, 6th Grd Tchr 1983-; *ai:* Mentor Tchr; Amer Edctrs Assn; First Bapt Church 1975-, Deaconess, Bd of Chrstn Ed; *office:* Rock L Butler MS 9 Nichols St Wellsboro PA 16901

WEST, EVE ADELMAN, ASL & Eng Interpretation Prof; *b:* Philadelphia, PA; *m:* Dennis; *c:* Alana, Gabriella; *ed:* Temple Univ (BA) Speech, Hearing Sci 1971; Western MD Coll (MED) Deaf Ed 1975; West Chester Univ (MA) TESOL 1996; *cr:* Comm Coll of Philadelphia Coord & Asst Prof Interpreter Ed 1975-; *ai:* Amer Sign Lang Club Adv; Fac Tchng Ctr Vol; Acad Curr Sub-Comm; Registry of Interpreters for the Deaf 1976-; Greater Phila RID 1975-, Sec, Pres; Conf of Interpreter Trainers 1979-; Natl TESOL Assn 1996; Deaf Hearing Comm Ctr 1973-, Bd of Dirs, Chair, Referral Svc Oversight Comm; Articles Pub; *office:* Comm Coll Of Philadelphia 1700 Spring Garden St Philadelphia PA 19130

WEST, HARLAN R., Science Teacher; *b:* Coaldale, PA; *m:* Susan T.; *ed:* PA St Univ (BS) Sec Ed, Bio, Gen Sci 1973; Ed St Cert 24 Hrs; *cr:* Pottsville Area Schl Dist Sci Tchr 1973-; *ai:* NEA, PA Ed Assn 1973-; Pottsville Educ Assn 1973-, VP, Pres, Negotiations, Crisis Comm; Schuylkill Cty Penn St Alumni Assn 1973-, Bd of Dirs; Norwegian Twp Zoning, Planning Commission 1986-, Chm, Vice Chm; *office:* D H H Lengel MS 1541 Laurel Blvd Pottsville PA 17901

WEST, HERBERT LEE,JR., Social Studies Teacher; *b:* Warrenton, NC; *m:* Mary Bentley; *c:* Marcus, Tamekah; *ed:* NC Cntrl Univ (BA) Geography & Sociology 1969; Univ of MN (MA) Soc Sci 1971, (PHD) Soc Sci 1974; Post Grad Univ of NC at Chapel Hill; *cr:* Univ of MD Balt Cty Asst Prof 1974-80; Howard Univ Asst Prof 1980-85; Howard Cty Bd of Ed Educator 1985-; Univ of MD-Balto Cty Adj Prof; *ai:* Mentor; BSAP Advising; Curr Comm; NEA, MSTA 1985-; Assoc Stud African-Amer Life & His 1978-; BSAP 1987-, Parent Advisory; Bd Mem Tri Agency African-Amer Youth Initiative; Gamma Theta Upsilon Society in Geography; Commission on Geogrpahy & Afro-Amer Fellowship; Ford Fnd Doctoral Fewllowship; Who's Who in Black America; *office:* Wilde Lake H S 5460 Trumpeter Rd Columbia MD 21044*

WEST, MARY ELIZABETH, High School Guidance Counselor; *b:* Washington Ct Hous, OH; *ed:* Rio Grande Coll (BS) Eng 1988; OH Univ (MED) Cnslng 1990; 16 Credit Hrs Educl Admin Wright St Univ EDS; *cr:* Springfield South HS Eng Tchr 1990-92; Wilmington HS Guid Cnslr 1992-94; Little Miami HS Guid Cnslr 1994-; *ai:* Frosh Cheer Coach; Care Team Adv; Prin Advy Team; Amer Cnslng Assn, Amer Schl Cnslng Assn, Natl Certfd Couns 1989-; NEA 1994-; OH Bd of Regents Scholar; Who's Who Among Amer Coll & Univ; Acad All- Amer, Scholastic All-Amer; Wilmington HS Rooker of Yr 1992-93; *home:* 3147 Snow Hill Rd SW Wshngtn Ct Hs OH 43160*

WEST, MICHAEL EDWIN, Phys Tchr & Outdoor Pgm Coord; *b:* Pittsburgh, PA; *ed:* CO Coll (BA) Physics 1993; *cr:* Cape Cod Adad Physics Tchr 1993-; *ai:* Outdoor Pgms Coord; X-C Ski Coach; Phi Beta Kappa; *home:* 61 Davis Dr Guilford CT 06437

WEST, ROBERT D., Associate Professor; *b:* Cleveland, OH; *m:* Nancy Joyce; *c:* Laurent, Douglas, Kimberly; *ed:* Kent St Univ (BA) Jrnlsm 1950, (BS) Eng 1950; Western Reserve Univ (MA) Eng 1956; *cr:* WERE Radio News Reporter, Operations 1950-62; WDBN Radio Station Mgr 1963-66; Wyse Advertising Traffic Mgr 1967-71; WERE Radio Pgm Dir 1972-75; Kent St Univ Asst, Assoc Prof 1975-; *ai:* Universalist Church of Westfield Ctr Minister; Minorities, Peer Evaluation Comms; OH Educl Broadcasting Network Commission Awd; 8 Regnl Emmy Nominations & 1 1st Pl; Most Outstanding Classroom Tchr 3 Times; *office:* Kent St Univ Journalism & Mass Comm Kent OH 44242

WEST, SABRINA LAVELLA, Business Teacher; *b:* Lewes, DE; *ed:* DE St Univ (BS) Bus Ed 1990, (M) Curr & Instruction 1996; *cr:* Caesar Rodney-DE Adolescent Pgm Inst Bus Tchr 1990-91; DE St Univ Bus Tchr 1990-95; Indian River HS Bus Tchr 1991-; *ai:* Gospel Choir, Bandfront, Drill Team & Stu Cncl Adv; NEA 1991-; IREA 1991-; IREA-MAC 1991-, Co-Chprsn 1994-; DSEA 1991-; *home:* RR 1 Box 136 Selbyville DE 19975*

WEST, SUSAN R., First Grade Teacher; *b:* Herkimer, NY; *ed:* Herkimer Cty Comm Coll (AA) Gen Hum 1977; SUNY at Oneonta (BS) Elem Ed 1979, (MS) Elem Ed 1983; *cr:* Mohawk Valley Schls Sub 1979-84; Annunciation Regnl 3rd-4th Grd Tchr 1984-87; Herkimer Cntrl 1st Grd Tchr 1987-; *ai:* Lit Club Adv; Morning Pgm Comm; Schl Improvement Team; Curr Cncl Sec; Mohawk Regnl Tchr Cntr Chm & Bldg Ambassador; AFT 1987-; Whole Lang Umbrella 1989-; TAWL Group 1989-; Parent Tchr Group 1987-, Pres; Mohawk Regnl Mini Grants Awded; *office:* Herkimer Cntrl Schl 301 Gros Blvd Herkimer NY 13350*

WEST, WALTER SCOTT, Science Teacher; *b:* Washington, DC; *ed:* Univ of WI (BS) Geog 1975, (MS) Ed, Guid Cnslng 1977; *cr:* West Wind Music Publishing House Composer, Instrumentalist 1979-; Creative Music Conservatory Composer, Instrumentalist 1979-; Our Saviour Luth HS Sci Tchr 1988-; Nippon Budo Sogo Dojo Inc Martial Arts Instr 1994-; *ai:* Geologic Map Pub; Music Album; *office:* Our Saviour Luth Schl 1734 Williamsbridge Rd Bronx NY 10461

WESTBAY, THERESA DATZ, Asst Professor of Biology; *b:* Rochester, NY; *m:* Joseph; *c:* Katherine; *ed:* Univ of Rochestrer (MS) Microbiology, Immunology 1990, (PHD) Microbiology, Immunology 1994; *cr:* St John Fisher Coll Asst Prof of Bio 1994-; *ai:* Chair of Admissions Comm; Adv Nrsng Stndts Journal Club; NIH Predoctoral Trng Grant; Articles Pub; *office:* Saint John Fisher Coll 3690 East Ave Rochester NY 14618

WESTBERRY, BONNIE LEE (BILLINGS), Accounting Teacher; *b:* Johnstown, PA; *m:* William Steven Jr.; *c:* Steve II, Jeremy, Seth; *ed:* Toccoa Falls Coll (BS) Music Ed, Vocal, Choral 1982; Attnd Shippensburg Univ in PA; *cr:* Shalom Chrstn Acad Math, Acctng, Elem Music Tchr 1984-91; Whitetail Ski Resort Admin Asst in Human Resources 1992-93; Shalom Chrstn Acad Acctng, Bus, Gen Math, Bible, Hlth Tchr 1993-; *ai:* Ski Club, Chapel Comm Adv; Teens in Missionary Svc 1993-, Co-Dir; Antrin Brethren in Christ Church 1990-, Sr HS Sunday Schl Tchr, Yth Advisor; Who's Who Among Colls & Univs 1972-73; Natl Deans List 1981-82; Grad Cum Laude 1982; *office:* Shalom Christian Acad 126 Social Island Rd Chambersburg PA 17201

WESTBERRY, DOUGLAS BRUCE, Music Teacher & Choral Dir; *b:* Miami, FL; *m:* Janice Willis; *ed:* FL Intnl Univ (BS) Music Ed 1974; Loyola Coll (MED) Ed Mgmt, Supervision 1987; Prins Cert 1987; Tchng Stdnts with Spec Needs, Dimensions of Learning in Music Ed, Wordperfect; *cr:* Silver Bluff Elem Gen Music Tchr, Chorus Dir 1974-78; Aberdeen MS Gen Music Tchr, Choral Dir 1978-80; North Harford MS Gen Music Tchr, 6-8 Grd Choral Dir 1980-; *ai:* GATE Comm 1984-93; Girls Chorus 1992-95; Vocal Ensemble 1992-95; MS Music Curr Wkshps; Music Dept Chprsn 1984-92; NEA, MSTA, HCEA 1978-; Huxford Soc 1986-; Sons of Conf Veterans 1991-; Telephone Pioneers Partner 1994-; Superior Rated Choruses 1983-95; Blue Ribbon Schl of Excl MD, Natl; Periodicals 1985-87; *home:* 435 Crisfield Dr Abingdon MD 21009*

WESTBROOK, JACK ROGERS, Mathematics Teacher; *b:* Sayre, PA; *m:* Cynthia Zentz; *c:* Molly; *ed:* St Univ of NY at Geneseo (BA) Math 1989, (MS) Scndry Ed 1995; St Univ of NY at Brockport 3 Credit Hrs; *cr:* Several Schl Dists Sub Tchr 1989, 1991 & 1992; Harpursville Cntrl Schl Math Tchr 1990-91; Hilton Cntrl Schl Math Tchr 1992-; *ai:* Bsktbl Asst Coach; NYSUT 1990-; *office:* Hilton Cntrl Schl 400 East Ave Hilton NY 14468

WESTCOTT, CLOE STINEBISER, Second Grade Teacher; *b:* South Fork, PA; *ed:* Univ of Miami (BED) Elem Ed 1952; Attnd Indiana Univ of PA; *cr:* Dept of Navy Sec 1942-44; US Navy Yeoman 1st Class 1944-48; Forest Hills Schls 1952-; *ai:* Humanitarian Club Adv; NEA; PSEA; FHEA; *office:* Forest Hills Elem Schl 547 Locust St PO Box 156 Sidman PA 15955

WESTCOTT, JAN HARRIS, Third Grade Teacher; *b:* Edinboro, PA; *m:* William D.; *c:* Laurie, John, Scott; *ed:* Clarion Univ (BS) Elem Ed 1957; Temple Univ (MED) Elem Ed 1961; 24 Addl Hrs; *cr:* Warren Schl Dist Elem Tchr1957-58; Pennsbury Schls Elem Tchr 1958-61; Souderton Schl Dist Elem Tchr 1975-; *ai:* Souderton Area Ed Assn; NEA, PSEA 1957-; AAUW Lansdale Branch 1964-, Sec; Hatfield Women's Civic Club 1964-, Sec, Treas; Hilltown Civic Assn 1970-; Who's Who in Amer Colls & Univs; *office:* Franconia Elem Schl 366 Harleysville Pike Souderton PA 18964

WESTCOTT, SUSAN GAIL, Fifth Grade Teacher; *b:* Watertown, WI; *ed:* Concordia Univ (BA) Elem Ed 1974; *cr:* Faith Luth Schl Fourth Grd Tchr 1974-76; Concord Luth Schl Fourth Grd Tchr 1976-82; Messiah Luth Schl Fifth Grd Tchr 1982-; *ai:* Dir Timbrel Choir, Lord's Choir, Chapel; Steering Comm ELEA Accreditation; Choristers Guild 1988-, Chptr Pres; Northeast OH Synod 1992-, Cncl Mem; Cncl of ELCA; *office:* Messiah Lutheran Elem Schl 4401 W 215th St Fairview Park OH 44126

WESTERMANN, ANN L., High School French Teacher; *b:* Cincinnati, OH; *ed:* Univ of Cincinnati (BS) Scndry Ed Fr 1991; Bachelor of Music Harp Performance 1977; Inst De Tours France Summer 1990; *cr:* Prof Harpist 1977-; Norwood City Schls HS Fr Tchr 1991-; *ai:* Foreign Lang Org Adv; NHS Social Comm 1994-; North Central Evaltn Comm, Atten Chprsn 1995; NEA & Kappa Delta Pi 1991-; Alliance Francase 1990-, Travel Schlsp; Amer Harp Soc 1977-, Treas; *office:* Norwood HS 2020 Sherman Ave Norwood OH 45212

WESTGATE, VICTOR R., History Teacher; *b:* Sidney, NY; *m:* Lisa B. Cowley; *c:* Christopher, Samantha; *ed:* SUC at Geneseo (BA) His 1974; SUNY at Stony Brook (MS) Ed 1979; 15 Post Grad Hrs LI Univ 1990; 6 Post Grad Hrs Dowling Coll 1991; 60 Post Grad Credits SCOPE; *cr:* The Leeway Schl Tchr for Child with Learning Disabilities 1975-77; Eastern Military Acad His Tchr 1977-78; Southold UFSD His Tchr 1978-; *ai:* Yrbk Adv; Jr Class Adv Coord; Hnr Soc & Stu Schlsp comms; AFT 1978-, Treas Local Union; PTA 1978-, Pres 1990-94; Stony Brook Univ William Robertson Coe Flwshp; *office:* Southold Unified Schl Dist Oaklawn Ave Southold NY 11971*

WESTHOFF, COLETTE GIRARD, French Teacher; *b:* Aix-Les-Bains, France; *m:* Eugene P.; *ed:* SUNY at Stony Brook (ABD) Fr & Span; *cr:* Southold HS Fr Tchr 1977-78; Dowling Coll Fr Instr 1981-84; Centereach HS Fr & Span Tchr 1985-86; Bellport HS Fr Tchr 1985-; *ai:* Fr Club; Fr Hnr Soc; AATF; LILT; NYS; AP Fr Guide for the Lang Course; *office:* Bellport HS Beaver Dam Rd Brookhaven NY 11719*

WESTLEY, SHARON LOUISE, US History Teacher; *b:* Reading, PA; *ed:* Albright Coll (BA) Amer His 1975; 48 Post-Grad Credits at Wilkes Coll, Gratz Coll, Carlow Coll, Marywood Coll, Penn St; *cr:* Historical Soc of Berks Co Curator of Ed 1975-77; Antietam Schl Dist 8th Grd Amer His Tchr 1978-80; Exeter Twp Schl Dist 9th Grd Amer His Tchr 1980-; *ai:* Broadway Style Musicals Stage Mgr Jr-Sr HS; NEA, PSEA 1978-; ETEA 1980-; Rdng Civic Opera Soc 1976-, Former Mem Bd of Dirs; Genesius Theatre 1987-; Rdng Comm Players 1988-; Rdng Madrichor Ensemble 1979-; *office:* Exeter Twp Jr HS 151 E 39th St Reading PA 19606

WESTON, JAMES K., Chemistry & Physics Teacher; *b:* Baltimore, MD; *m:* Pamela J. Seng; *c:* Jennifer; *ed:* Johns Hopkins Univ (BA) Lbrl Arts 1968, (MS) Ed of Gifted 1981; 30 Addl Credits; *cr:* Rock Glen Jr HS Sci Tchr 1968-78; Johns Hopkins Univ Lab Asst, Physics Lab 1973-75; Baltimore Polytechnic Inst Physics, Chem Tchr 1979-; *office:* Baltimore Poly Tech Inst 403 1400 W Cold Spring Ln Baltimore MD 21209

WESTON, JANE A., Biology Instructor; *b:* Oxford, England; *m:* Alan; *c:* Robert, Jamie; *ed:* Chatham Coll (BS) Bio 1971; Univ of Kent England (PHD) Bio 1974; *cr:* Erie Comm Coll Part-Time Instr 1983-91; Sacred Heart Acad Bio Tchr 1991-93; Genesee Comm Coll Instr 1993-; *ai:* NEA 1993-; Univ of Warwick Coventry England Post-Doctoral Fellows Bio 1975; *office:* Genesee Comm Coll 1 College Rd Batavia NY 14(

WESTON, LORIE ANN, Developmentally Handicapped; *b:* Philade PA; *ed:* OH St Univ (BS) Spec Ed 1992; *cr:* Urbana City Schls HS DH 1992-; *ai:* Acad Aid Tutor; Intervention Asst Team; Prom, FHA Hor Adv; NEA 1992-; Cert of Merit 1994; *office:* Urbana HS 500 Washi Ave Urbana OH 43078

WESTON, RAYMOND, 8th Grade US History Teacher; *b:* Middle CT; *c:* Christina, Greg; *ed:* Southern CT St Univ (BA) Psych 1973, Scndry Ed 1980; *cr:* Shelton HS Soc Stud Tchr 1977-91; Sh Intermediate Schl US His Tchr 1991-; *office:* Shelton Intermediate S Perry Hill Rd Shelton CT 06484

WESTPHAL, MARK L., Biology & Science Teacher; *b:* Jersey Cit *m:* Rebecca Claire; *c:* Vincent, Christa, Ritchie; *ed:* FDU Teaneck Mrktg 1977; Kean Coll of NJ (PB) Bio Ed 1987; *cr:* West Essex Reg Bio Tchr 1987-91; Parsippany HS Bio & Sci Tchr 1992-; *ai:* Boys & Head Indoor & Outdoor Track & Head Coach.*

WETCHER, NEIL STEVEN, Math Teacher & Department Ch Brooklyn, NY; *m:* Judith Asen; *c:* Debra, Caryn; *ed:* Brooklyn Coll Math 1967; Lehigh Univ (MS) Math 1969; *cr:* Liberty HS Math 1968-; *ai:* NEA & PSEA 1968-; NGTM 1991-; *office:* Liberty HS Linden St Bethlehem PA 18018

WETHERBEE, LAURIE A., Biology Teacher; *b:* Worcester, MA Rensselaer Polytech Inst (BS) Interdisciplinary Sci 1986; Brown (MAT) Bio Ed 1990; *cr:* Rensselaer Polytech Inst Coll Admissions 1986-88; Chatham HS Bio Tchr 1990-; *ai:* Girls Var Bsktbl Coach; C in Hlth Field Planning Comm; NEA 1990-; *office:* Chatham H Woodbridge Ave Chatham NY 12037

WETHERHOLD, RENEE CRUCKENMILLER, 6th Grade Teach Bethlehem, PA; *m:* Donald E.; *c:* Kristina Pearson Bachman, V Albright, Douglas Lobach; *ed:* Wittenberg Univ (BSEd) Elem Ed Kutztown Univ Grad Classes; Muhlenberg Coll, Moravian Coll, Aller Coll Masters Equiv, Math Cert k-12th Grds; Working on Maste Computer Ed; *cr:* South Elem 1st Grd Tchr 1968-70; Yokohama In Japan K-3rd Grd Tchr 1971-73; Allentown Schl Dist K-1st, 5-6th, 8t Tchr 1974-; Muhlenberg Coll Part Time Tchr 1995-; *ai:* Lead Tech Staff Dev, Homework Ctr Coord; Budget Chm of Schl Cncl Coordir Comm; Computer Club Adv; AEA, PSEA, NEA 1974-; Lehigh Valle Ed Collegial Network, NSTOY Chapter of PA 1995-; BSA 1993-, Cub Coord; Emmaus Chorale 1991-; Allentown Comm Concert 1994-, Bd Mem; Sigma Kappa Alumnae Chapter 1976-, Pres 19 PSEA 2nnovative Tchng Grant Awd 1993; PA Tchr of Yr Finalist Rider Poole Grant 4 Time Winner; *home:* 1134 Little Lehigh Dr S Em PA 18049*

WETHERILL, ELIZABETH PHILLIPS, English & Reading Teach Kenton, OH; *m:* Robert Scott; *c:* Scott Christopher, Matthew R Benjamin Joseph; *ed:* OH St Univ (BA) Eng 1981; Attnd OH Northern Tchng Cert Eng Ed 1983, Dayton Univ 20 Credit Hrs Rdng Cert K Grd & 3 Credit Hrs Cmptr Skills; *cr:* Riverdale Jr HS 7th Grd Rdng, Grd Eng Tchr 1983-; *ai:* Riverdale Ed Assn 1983-, Bldg Rep 2 Newsletter & PR Chprsn 2 Yrs, Negotiations Team 1 Yr; Precious Mo OCCL 1990-, Sec 2 Yrs; Martha Holden Jennings Schlr 1994-95; As Tchng Awd Nom 1996; *office:* Riverdale Jr HS 105 W Franklin Wh OH 43359

WETMORE, CYNTHIA LORRAINE, Physical Education Teach Lowville, NY; *ed:* Herkimer Cty Comm Coll (AS) PE 1980; Univ (BS) PE, Hlth 1982; Southern IL Univ (MS) PE 1985; *cr:* Southern IL G A Field Hockey Coach 1983-85; North Syracuse Cntrl Schls PE Head Field Hockey, Lacrosse Coach 1986-; *ai:* Head Field Hc Lacrosse Coach Resposible Dev Prgms, Overseeing Lower Level Pr Aths Receiving Ath Schlsps; NYSUT, AFT 1986-; United Meth C 1973-; NYS Pub HS Ath Assoc Dir I Girls Lacrosse Champions; Rec to Coach Field Hockey Internationally at World Yth Games London Org of Women Unsung Heroin Awd for Dev, Promoting Girls S Responsible for Starting, Dev Girls Lacrosse Prgm; *office:* Cicero-Syracuse HS Cicero NY 13039

WETMORE, THOMAS L., Special Educator; *b:* Easton, PA; *m:* Marcotte; *c:* Ada, Jenevra; *ed:* Keene ST Coll (BS) Spec Ed Plymouth ST Coll (MED) Guidance & Counseling 1987; *cr:* Sprin HS Spec Ed Tchr 1978-81; Hanover St Elem Schl Spec Ed Tchr 1981- Prin 1991-; *ai:* Spec Needs Ski Club Founder, Coord; SAU 32-Staf Comm Chprsn; NH Regnl Coord Educating Children for Parenting; 1978-; LEA 1981-; Regnl Coord Pool Expansion Plan; PEP St NH Certifying Tchrs in Spec Ed; Semi Finalist 1991 NH Tchr of Yr Awd SAU 32 Commendations for Excl in Ed 1993, 1994; *office:* Hanover Schl 193 Hanover St Lebanon NH 03766

WETZEL, CHRISTINA JENNIFER, Physical Science Teacher; *b:* York, NY; *ed:* Montclair St Univ (MS) Environmental Ed 199 Chatham HS Phys Sci Tchr 1993-; *ai:* Sci League & Peer Awareness Adv; Site Cncl Mem; NJSTA 1993-; NSTA 1994-; *office:* Chatham H Lafayette Ave Chatham NJ 07928

WETZEL, CINDY L., English Teacher; *b:* Butler, PA; *m:* James; *c:* Jeff; *ed:* Clarion Univ (BS) Eng 1971; Elem Ed Cert; *cr:* Moniteau Dist Eng Tchr 1988-; *home:* 138 Pal Mar Dr Butler PA 16001

WETZEL, DEBORAH ALEX, Spanish Teacher; *b:* Brooklyn, N Ashley E., Kelly M., Lauren F.; *ed:* Coll of Notre Dame (BA) Langs 6 Credit Hrs at Johns Hopkins Schl of Continuing Ed; MS Ec 199 Mount de Sales Acad Span Tchr 1992-; *ai:* Adv & Organized Govt Stu Adv to 15 Stdnts; Adv to YMCA Yth & Govt Pgm; MFLA 1 Patapsco Vly Republican Club 1992-, Pres 1996-; Johns Hopkins S Continuing Stud Ec Ed Grant Pgm 1992-94; *office:* Mount De Sales 700 Academy Rd Baltimore MD 21228

WETZEL, ROBERT CHARLES, Physics Teacher; *b:* Passaic, N Carolyn A. Corless; *ed:* Montclair St Univ (BA) Physics, Sci 1973; N of Tech (MS) Physics 1976; AT&T Bell Labs Hlth Safety, Cmpt Lasers, Electron Optics Courses; *cr:* Passaic Vly HS Physics Tchr 197 West Orange HS Physics Tchr 1976-81; AT&T Bell Labs Rsrch Sci 1981-94; Montville HS Physics Instr 1995-; *ai:* HELP Club, Ski Clu League Adv; Drama Club; NEA, NJEA 1973-; NSTA 1994-; K Raiders VHF Club 1966-, Pres; Amer Radio Relay League 1966-; A Co-Author Pub Papers; 1 Patent; *office:* Montville HS 100 Horsene Montville NJ 07045

WETZEL, SALLY, Spanish Teacher; *b:* Sewickley, PA; *ed:* Clarion (BS) Span 1969; Millersville Univ (MA) Span 1976; Penn St Univ S Prin Cert 1992; *cr:* Curwensville Area Schl Dist Span & Eng Tchr 1 Saint Marys Area Schl Dist Sabbatical Internship 1991-92; Coope Learning Instr 1991-; Performance Based Ed & Strategic Plan Facil 1992-; Millersville Univ PA Governors Schl for Excl in Tchng Instr 1 *ai:* Span Club-Field Trips to Cultural Events & Span Speaking Coun NEA 1969-; PA St Ed Assn 1969-, PACE-Cntrl Region, Instructional Dev; Curwensville Area Ed Assn 1969-, Pres, Chief Negotiator; Pe Chapter Phi Delta Kappan 1991-; ASCD; PA Assn for Supervision & Dev 1985-; Strategic Planning Core Team 1993-94, Consultant; Pa Standards & Practices Commission Appointed by Governor of PA 1 ultant for Various Schl Dists-Performance Based Ed & Assessment; : Curwensville Area HS 650 Beach St Curwensville PA 16833

ZLER, JOHN LEWIS, Guidance Cnslr & Ftbl Coach; b: Bellefonte, : Mary Ann Hendershot; c: Jeff, B. J.; ed: Lock Haven Univ (BS) Soc 972; Penn St Univ (MED) Counseling 1983; cr: Bellefonte Area HS tud Tchr 1973-86, Cnslr 1986-; ai: Ftbl Head Coach; Girls Sftbl Asst h; Bellefonte Elks No 1094; Bellefonte F&AM No 268; office: fonte Area HS 830 E Bishop St Bellefonte PA 16823*

LER, DEBORAH, Home Economics Teacher; b: New York City, NY; ison, Michael, Adam; ed: Queens Coll (BA) Early Chldhd Ed 1970, Early Chldhd Ed 1971; Adelphi Coll (MA) Comm Hlth Ed 1981; Addl Grad Credits & In-Service Credits; cr: NYC Pub Schls Elem 1970-73; Division Ave HS Home Ec Tchr 1988-91; Levittown Meml enter Childcare Tchr 1993-94; Salk Mid Schl Home Ec & Hlth Tchr -95; MacArthur HS & Division Ave HS Home Ec 1995-; ai: NYSUT -; Article-Woman Week Magazine; Game-Western Publishing; home: adwick Rd Great Neck NY 11023

LER, JOEL ALAN, HS Mathematics Teacher; b: Liberty, NY; m: Ward; c: Jessica, Rachael, Sarah Neunzig; ed: St Univ of NY at nta (BA) Math 1973; St Univ of NY at Albany (MA) Math Ed 1977; YS Dept of Correctional Svcs Chptr I & Title I Math Tchr 1978-88; son Cntrl Schl Dist HS Math Tchr 1973-; ai: Quiz Team, Knowledge er Open, Chess Club & Math Club Adv; Enrichment Comm; Jeffeson Assn 1973-; NEA 1975-; AMTNYS 1978-; office: Jefferson Central Rt 10 Main St Jefferson NY 12093

LER, RICHARD, Language Arts Teacher; b: Bronx, NY; m: anne; c: Jason, Sarah; ed: S. I. Comm Coll (AA) Lbrl Arts 1974; nond Coll (BA) Eng 1976; Kean Coll (MA) Supervision 1981; 50 t Hrs Coll of S. I., South Hampton Univ, Fordham Univ, St John's cr: Rocco Laurie Intermediate Schl Tchr 1977-; ai: Back to Schl , Fac Conf Planning Comm; UFT, S. I. Rdng Assoc, NYSTE 1978-; elta Kappa 1994-; Westerleigh Inprovement 1984-, Dir; Rocco Laurie Fund 1978-, Dir; BSA 1993-, Asst Scoutmaster; NYC Parks Vol 1988-, of Apprec; office: Rocco Laurie Intermediate Schl 33 Ferndale Ave n Island NY 10314

LER, ROBIN GOLD, 5th Grade Teacher; b: New York City, NY; m: l; c: Melani; ed: Fairleigh Dickinson Univ (BA) Elem Ed-Magna Cum e 1975; 46 Post Grad Credits; cr: Dumont Schl Dist 1st, 2nd, 4th, 5th fted-Talented Tchr 1975-81; The Moriah Schl 4th & 6th Grd Tchr -86; Roosevelt Elem Schl 5th Grd Tchr 1986-; ai: Presenter of Math i Staff Dev Wkshps; Instrl Cncl; Math & Sci Comms; Art & Lit zine Ed; SETI Pilot Pgm & Open Court Publishers Consultants; 1975-; REEA; AMTNJ; MAPS; Buehler Challenger & Sci Ctr, Advy ergen Cty HS of Jewish Stud, Bd of Trustees; Recipient of the NJ nors Recognition Awd 1992; office: Roosevelt Elem Schl 711 Summit River Edge NJ 07661*

ANT, LEE E., Adjunct Instructor Bus Admin; b: Altoona, PA; m: otte Clapper; c: Matthew, Thomas; ed: Shippensburg Univ (BS) Math 972; St Mary's Univ (MS) Systems Mngmt 1978; 26 Hrs Doctoral Stud Southeastern Univ; 6 Hrs Masters Level MBA Courses St Francis 3 Hrs Masters Level MED Courses Univ of Tx at San Antonio; 15 Hrs ers MED CoursesShippensburg Univ; cr: Northern York City Schl Math Tchr 1972-74; USAF Captain 1974-81; R. R. Donnelley Supvr -91; Mount Aloysius Coll Adj Prof 1992-; ai: Co-Adv Bus Admin SHRM, ASTD 1994-; office: Mount Aloysius College 7373 Admiral Hwy Cresson PA 16630

HE, JILL ELAINE, Fourth Grade Teacher; b: Bloomsburg, PA; ed: rville Coll (BA) Elem Ed 1994; cr: Seaford Chrstn Acad Fourth Grd Ath Coach 1994-; ai: Past Var Boys Head Soccer Coach; Jr Var Girls Coach; Yrbk, Piano Tchr, Span Tutor Co-Adv.

MOUTH, LORRAINE M. TURNER, Special Education Teacher; b: n, MA; m: Scott A.; c: Melissa, Matthew, Sydney, Kelsey; ed: Univ (BS) Spec Ed 1985; Univ of Southern ME Lang Courses; cr: Sanford gh Resource Room Tchr 1986-87; Sweetser Childrens Home B D Tchr -89; NRI Mental Hlth Ctr Spec Ed Tchr 1991-; ai: Mansfield HS Head Coach; home: 62 Robinson Ave North Attleboro MA 02763*

LEN, ELIZABETH WALSH, Art Teacher; b: Brooklyn, NY; m: el; c: Kathryn; ed: St Univ Coll at Oneonta (BS) Elem Ed & Art entrate 1977; cr: St Pauls Elem Schl 5th Grd Tchr 2 Yrs; McCorristin HS Art Tchr 9 Yrs; ai: Art Dept Chprsn; Art Club Moderator; Set gn & Stage Crew; Art Edctrs of NJ 1995-; office: McCorristin Cath HS eonard Ave Trenton NJ 08610

LEN, LINDA RUSSO, Fifth Grade Teacher; b: Bridgeton, NJ; m: ent J.; ed: Glassboro St Coll (BA) Elem Ed 1979; K-12 Rdng Cert; cr: r Deerfield Twnshp Schls 5th Grd Tchr 1979-; ai: Cmptr Comms; wner Antique Bus 1981; NEA, NJEA 1979-; Red Amer Cross 1975-, r Safety Instr; office: Elizabeth F Moore Elem Schl 1373 Highway 77 eton NJ 08302*

LEN, MARY LOUISE, History Teacher; b: Dorchester, MA; ed: n Coll (BA) His 1962; St Coll at Boston (MED) Ed 1966; 45 Addl ts; cr: St Catherine's Schl Soc Stud Tchr 1956-61; Boston Pub Schls tud Tchr 1962-63; Braintree Pub Schls Soc Stud Tchr 1963-; ai: 8 Washington DC Trip, Jr Achvmt Prgm, Tax-Related Ed Coord; Lawyer, Partnership Prgm Coord; Achvmt Awd Evening Coordinate; NEA, BEA, NCTA 1963-; NELMS 1986-; St Ambrose Pastoral Cncl 1994-; nbrose Parish 1980-, Lay Minister; Tchr of Yr Awd 1991; office: South 32 Peach St Braintree MA 02184

LEY, DONNA M., School Nurse; b: Lewes, DE; m: Wayne C.; c: erly Whaley Parker, Michele Whaley Oney, Larry A.; ed: Temple (RN) Nursing 1965; Wilmington Coll (BS) Psych 1981; 30 Addl t Hrs Beyond Bachelors; cr: Wilmington Medical Ctr Intensive Care 1965-66; Kent General Hospital Staff Nurse 1966-67; Nanticoke orial Hospital Intensive Care Head Nurse, Emergency Room Nurse -92; Laurel Schl Dist Schl Nurse 1982-; ai: Established Shelter for eless; Sussex Cty Interagency Cncl; Nurse for all Ath Events; dance Comm; DE Schl Nurse Assn 1982-, Sec; Natl Schl Nurse Assn -; Laurel Ed Assn, DE St Ed Assn 1982-; PTSA VP; Laurel Little ue 1970-90; Laurel Pop Warner 1976-; Laurel Youth Sports 1994-; St ps Episcopal Church 1970-; Established Peer Counseling Group; D, BAAD Spon; Started Summer Recreation Prgm; DCCASA Mem; : Laurel Intermediate Schl 801 S Central Ave Laurel DE 19956

LEY, SHARON WHEATLEY, 3rd Grade Teacher; b: Cambridge, m: Vincent Lee; c: Wendy L., Melanie A.; ed: Shepherd Coll (BA) Ed 1966; cr: West Seaford Elem 3rd Grd Tchr 1966-67; Cntrl Elem rd Tchr 1967-71; North Laurel Elem 3rd Grd Tchr 1974-; ai: NEA -; DSEA 1974-; Centenary United Meth Church 1974-, Pres UMW; : North Laurel Elem Schl 300 Wilson St Laurel DE 19956

LEY, WILLIAM RICE,II, Soc Stud Dept Chprsn & Teacher; b: hiana, KY; m: Alexandra Vuich; c: Caitlin E., Adam R.; ed: Clarion of PA (BS) Scndry Ed 1990; cr: Hermitage MS His Tchr 1992-93; ory HS His Tchr 1993-; ai: Stu Cncl, Jr Class Adv; NEA, PSEA 1992-; 264 Spencer Ave Sharon PA 16146

LLEY, CHRISTOPHER, High School Latin Teacher; b: Buffalo, d: Boston Univ (BA) Latin 1980; Univ of MI (MA) Classics 1984; ew-Forest Schl Latin Tchr 1991-; ai: Photography Club Spon; ACL 1990-; CAAS 1990-; NEH Summer Flwshp; ACL Schlsp; office: Kew-Forest Schl 119-17 Union Tpke Forest Hills NY 11375

WHALLEY, DAVID A., Science Department Chair; *b:* Salem, MA; *m:* Susan Langfur; *c:* Brian, Elizabeth; *ed:* Salem St Coll (BSEd) Math & Sci 1974; Fitchburg St Coll (MED) Sci Ed 1976; Northeastern Univ (CAGS) Admin 1980; *cr:* Shawsheen Tech HS Sci Tchr & Dept Head 1974-; *ai:* NSTA 1975-; MTA 1974-; Soka Gakkai Intnl 1982-; Investigating the Universe 1991; NASA Hubble Space Telescope Educl Conf 1993; *office:* Shawsheen Tech HS 100 Cook St Billerica MA 01821*

WHANGER, DENNIS WYATT, French Teacher & SERC Coord; *b:* Steubenville, OH; *ed:* Franciscan Univ at Steubenville (BA) Fr-Cum Laude 1976; Univ of Dayton (MSEd) Interdisciplinary Stud 1990; 6 Post Grad Semester Hrs Carlow Coll at Pittsburgh; 3 Post Grad Semester Hrs Walsh Univ at Canton; *cr:* Coll Eng & AP Eng Tchr; Theatre & Drama Tchr; Western Reserve HS Fr Tchr & SERC Coord 1977-; *ai:* Fr Club & Soph Class Adv; NEA; OH Frgn Lang Assn; Amer Translators Assn Former Mem; St Marys Hot Meal Pgm 1987 & 1989, Faithful & Valuable Svc Awd Cath Charities; Alphi Chi Hnr Soc Natl Coll Awd 1976; Franciscan Univ Dept of Frgn Langs Awd 1976; Jennings Scholar Awd 1988-89; Poetry Pub; *office:* Western Reserve HS 3841 US Rt 20 E Collins OH 44826

WHARTON, KYM, English & Publications Tchr; *b:* Dayton, OH; *m:* Rick; *c:* Nate, Amanda; *ed:* Eastern KYN Univ (BA) Span, Eng 1979; Wright St Univ (MED) Ed 1994; 2 Credit Hrs Univ of Dayton; *cr:* Madison HS Span, Eng Tchr 1979-91; Dixie HS Span, Eng Tchr 1991-; *ai:* Stu Cncl; Yrbk; NLEA 1991-; New Lebanon United Meth Church; Runner-Up Tchr of Yr 1995; *office:* Dixie HS 200 S Fuls Rd New Lebanon OH 45345

WHATLEY, RONALD GENE, Special Education Teacher; *b:* Wichita, KS; *m:* Pamela Sherwood; *c:* Joel Lofton, Jill Ayn; *ed:* Edmond OK (BS) Hlth, PE, Recreation 1965; Cntrl St Univ (MS) Admin, Ed 1968; Long Island Univ (MS) Ed 1983; 15 Credit Hrs Post-Grad Stud; *cr:* Western Oaks Jr HS Hlth, PE Instr 1965-70; Ossining HS Driver Ed Tchr 1970-81; Roosevelt Ed Ctr Spec Ed Emotionally Disturbed 1981-; *ai:* Child Study Team Section I Indoor Track Comm; Boys, Girls Cross Cntry, Indoor Track Coach; Boys Spring Track Coach; Westchester Track, Field Coaches Assn 1970-; AFT, Tchrs Assn 1970-; NY St Union of Tchrs 1970-; United Meth Church 1976-, Trustee 1991-; Coach of Yr 1988-89; *office:* Ossining Pub Schls 190 Croton Ave Ossining NY 10562

WHEATLEY, ANN MERCER, Chapter One Teacher; *b:* Brookline, MA; *c:* Kristen, Jan; *ed:* Johnson St Coll (BS) Elem Ed 1985; 15 Grad Credits from UVM, Trinity, St Michaels; *cr:* South Royalton Schl 5th-6th Grd, Chapter 1 Tchr 1986-; *ai:* Instructional Support Team; Standards Bd Mem; Literacy Comm; NEA 1986-; *office:* South Royalton Schl S Windsor St South Royalton VT 05068

WHEATLEY, ELAINE LIPPY, French Teacher; *b:* Baltimore, MD; *m:* Craig Alan; *c:* Tyler, Travis; *ed:* Western MD Coll, Univ of Paris (BA) Fr 1983; Master Equiv; *cr:* Worcester Cntry Schl Fr, Latin Tchr 1984-85; Marley MS Fr Tchr 1986-; *ai:* Fr Club Spon; Chprsn Fac Cncl; Schl Improvement Team; Comm & Human Relations Comm; Dept M; NEA, TAAC 1994-; Faith Bapt Church 1985-; *office:* Marley MS 7730 Baltimore Annapolis Blvd Glen Burnie MD 21060

WHEATON, GAIL L., Kindergarten Tchr & Admin Asst; *b:* Bath, NY; *ed:* Marina Regina Coll (AS) Child Care 1973; SUNY at Brockport (BS) N-6 Elem Ed 1975, (MS) Elem Ed 1979; *cr:* Nazareth Hall Elem Tchr 1975-; *ai:* Fundraiser, Testing Coord; Admin Asst; Mid Sts Accredidation Participant; Recruiter; NCEA 1982-; Diocese of Rochester Early Chldhd 1975-; *office:* Nazareth Hall Schl 180 Raines Park Rochester NY 14613

WHEATON, MARK G., Instrumental Music Teacher; *b:* Bronxville, NY; *m:* Darla Dick; *ed:* Ithaca Coll (BM) Music 1972; Eastman Schl of Music (MM) Music 1977; St Univ of NY at Brockport CAS Educl Admin 1980 & SAS Educl Admin 1981; *cr:* Churchville-Chili Cntrl Schl Dist Instrumental Music Tchr 1972-; *ai:* NEA, MENC & NYSSMA 1972-; NYSBDA 1982-, MCSMA 1972-, Pres 1977-79; IAABO 1982-; Eastman Schl of Music PHD Prgm Stu Grad Awd 1977; *office:* Churchville-Chili Sr HS 15786 Buffalo Rd Churchville NY 14428

WHEELER, ELLEN DOUGLASS, Eighth Grade English Teacher; *b:* Malone, NY; *m:* Brian D.; *c:* Daniel, Ashley; *ed:* Green Mountain Coll (AA) PE, Eng 1972; Univ of VT (BS) PE, Eng 1974; Syracuse Univ (MS) PE, Eng 1979; Post Grad Studies Cert Elem Ed; *cr:* Jamesville-Dewitt Cntrl PE Tchr 1975-77; Marluis Pebble Hill Schl Eng, PE Tchr 1977-82; Canastota Cntrl Schl Eng Tchr 1982-; *ai:* Model Schls Prgm; Eng Cncl Rep; Child Stud Team; NCTE 1990-; NYSUT, AFT 1982-; Amer Cancer Soc Annual Campaign; Amer Heart Assn Annual Campaign; Diabetes Campaign; Mothers Against Drunk Drvng; *office:* Canastota Jr-Sr HS Roberts St Canastota NY 13032

WHEELER, GEORGE RAYMOND, 5th Grade Teacher; *b:* Westfield, MA; *m:* Judith N. Beebe; *c:* Heidi A. Emery, Douglas N.; *ed:* Westfield St Coll (BS) Ed 1964, (MS) Elem Prin, Supervision 1968; 30 Addl Hrs; *cr:* Franklin Ave Elem Schl 4th Grd Tchr 1964-82; Smith Ave Elem Schl 6th Grd Tchr 1982-92; Highland Elem Schl 6th Grd Tchr 1992-95, 5th Grd Tchr 1995-; *ai:* Mass Frameworks Math Comm; WFLD Tchr Assn 1964-, Fac Rep; NEA 1974-; MA Tchrs Assn 1964-; NCTM 1995-; Church Exec Bd, Chm; Town Moderator 1991-93; Masons 1970-, Pres, Treas; Chester Fnd 1990-, Treas; *office:* Highland Elem Schl 34 Western Ave Westfield MA 01085*

WHEELER, HERBERT ELLIS, Cmptr Office Tech, Mngmt Instr; *b:* Newbury, VT; *m:* Virginia Eastman; *c:* Stephanie Wheeler Cassidy, Steven; *ed:* Plymouth St Coll (BED) Bus 1960; 19 Addl Hrs; *cr:* Hartford HS Bus Instr 1960-71; Lebanon Coll Evening Div Instr, Bus Dept Chm 1960-85; Hartford HS Dept Chm 1965-75; Voc Schl Dept Chm 1965-75; Hartford Area Career, Tech Ctr Sec, Clerical 1971-86, Cmptr Office Tech, Mngmt 1986-; *ai:* FBLA; Collaborative Comm; VT Bus Tchrs Assn 1960-, Pres, VP; HTA 1960-, Pres; Newburg Alumni Assn 1955-, Pres; Hartford Outstdng Edctr; Three Best Voc Prgms VT Selected Twice; Highest Schlsp Natl Bus Exam US First Place Awd; *home:* 6 Templeton Ave White Riv Jct VT 05001*

WHEELER, JAMES IDE, US History Teacher; *b:* Leominster, MA; *m:* Roslyn A. Nelson; *c:* Jacob, Holly; *ed:* Harvard Coll (AB) Psych 1968; Tufts Univ (MED) Elem Ed 1974; Fitchburg St Coll (MED) Tchng of His 1978; *cr:* Harvard Elem Schl 1st Grd Tchr 1974-77; The Bromfield Schl 5th-8th Grd Soc Stud Tchr 1977-85, Dept Chm 1980-84; Lawrence Schl US His, World Geog Tchr 1985-; *ai:* Mock Trial Coach 1995-; Article Pub; *office:* Lawrence Schl Lakeview Ave Falmouth MA 02540

WHEELER, JANICE BUBERNACK, Science Teacher; *b:* Mt Carmel, PA; *m:* James D.; *c:* James D., Paul R.; *ed:* Bloomsburg St Univ (BS) Ed, Bio 1969; PA St Univ (MED) Rdng, Ed 1973; TMI The Nuclear Option; *cr:* Central Dauphin SD 4th Grd Tchr 1969-71; St Joseph Schl MS Sci Tchr 1971-; *ai:* Sci Fair, Text Book, Materials Coord; NCEA 1971-; PA Sci Tchrs Assn 1986-; GFWC Mechanicsburg 1986-, Past Pres; Cntrl PA Sci Ctr 1986-, Sec, Bd Mem; *home:* 99 Brindle Rd Mechanicsburg PA 17055*

WHEELER, JOE LAWRENCE, English Department Chair; *b:* St Helen, CA; *m:* Connie Palmer; *c:* Greg, Michelle Wheeler Culmore; *ed:* Pacific Union Coll (BA) His 1959, (MAT) His 1963; Sacramento St Univ (MA) Eng 1968; Vanderbilt Univ (PHD) Eng 1975; *cr:* Oakwood Coll Eng Assoc Prof, Eng Chair 1968-70; Southwestern Adventist Coll Prof of Eng, Eng Chair 1970-79, Adult Degree Prgm, Dir of Cultural Affairs Dist 1979-84; Columbia Union Coll Prof of Eng, Part Time Chair 1986-; *ai:* Fac Dev Comms; NCTE; Zane Grey's West 1983-, Founder, Exec Dir 1983-; Chamber of Commerce Svc Awd; Presidential Honor; Purple Sage Awd; Sr Fellow Ctr The New West; Pub Bks & Audio Tapes; Western His for New TNT Documentary 1996; *home:* 186 Severn Way Arnold MD 21012

WHEELER, KAREN PERKIO, Kindergarten Teacher; *b:* Conneaut, OH; *m:* Mark; *c:* Toni Annette, Taylor Jayne; *ed:* Univ of WI at Madison (BS) Elem Ed 1984; Addl 7 Grad Credit Hrs; *cr:* Chestnut Elem Schl 6th Grd Tchr 1986-87; Lakeview Elem Schl 5th Grd Tchr 1987-89; West Main Elem Schl Kndgtn Tchr 1989-; *ai:* Coord of West Mains Involvement With the Born Free Fnd; Stu Cncl Adv; NEA 1986-; Miss Conneaut Schlsp Pageant 1986-, Bd of Dir; Born Free Fnd 1991-; Jennings Fnd Grant 1995, 1993; USA Today's Make A Difference Day Animal Protective League Coord Project; *office:* West Main Elem Schl 836 Main St Conneaut OH 44030

WHEELER, KARRIE LYNN, English Teacher; *b:* Westerly, RI; *ed:* Univ of ME at Farmington (BS) Ed 1989; *cr:* Madawaska HS Eng Tchr 1988-89; Lawrence HS Eng Tchr 1989-; *ai:* Stu Asst Team Co-Chair 1991-; Var Ftbl Cheering Coach 1994-; Var Bsktbl Cheering Coach 1995; Stu Cncl Adv 1989-91; Class Adv 1991, 1995; Color Guard Instr 1991-93; Outward Bound Participant 1991; MTA 1989-; Integration, Mainstreaming ME Guest Speaker; Cooperative Consultation Augusta ITV ME Guest Panelist; *office:* Lawrence HS School St Fairfield ME 04937*

WHEELER, KATHLEEN GARVEY, School Social Worker; *b:* Springfield, MA; *m:* Frederick C.; *c:* Jason, Daniel, Timothy, Joshua; *ed:* Holyoke Comm Coll (AS) Early Chldhd Ed 1977; Univ of Southern ME (BSW)-Summa Cum Laude 1995; Working Toward MSW Soc Work Boston Univ Schl of Soc Work; *cr:* Portland Hosp Yth Mentoring Prgm Soc Worker 1994-; Portland HS Soc Worker 1996-; *ai:* Group Ldr; Mentoring Prgm; NASW 1994-; Phi Kappa Phi; St Marys Parish Comm 1987-, Pastoral Cncl, Jr High Yth Ministry; Child Welfare Grant; *home:* PO Box 731 Ogunquit ME 03907

WHEELER, SHARON CLARK, Fifth Grade Teacher; *b:* Columbus, OH; *m:* James Wilson; *c:* James Clark, Laura Lynn; *ed:* OH St Univ (BS) Elem Ed 1965; Ashland Univ (MS) Rdng Supervision 1985; Addl Hrs OH St, Ashland Univ Cmptr Tech, Sci; 2 Week Class Bronx Zoo 1990; *cr:* Mark Twain Elem Schl 5th Grd Tchr 1980-88; Cntrl Coll Magnet Schl 5th Grd Tchr 1989-; *ai:* Sci Comm; Venture; NEA; WEA 1980-, Fac Rep, Outstdng Tchr Nom; Phi Delta Kappa 1989-; PTA 1971-, Outstndng St Edctr; Cntrl Coll Church 1970-, Chrstn Ed Comm; Jennings Grant; Pub Articles Natl Gardening Publication; Jennings Scholar; Supt A+ Awd 1987, 1994; *office:* Cntrl Coll Elem Schl 825 S Sunbury Rd Westerville OH 43081*

WHEELER, WILLIAM ROBERT, AP & Honors Biology Teacher; *b:* Elizabeth, NJ; *m:* Joan Marie Brandt; *c:* William T., Christopher D.; *ed:* Bethel Coll (BS) Bio 1972; 27 Credit Hrs Scndry Ed Seton Hall Univ; *cr:* Mac Farland Jr HS Tchr 1972-79; Jackson Meml HS Tchr 1979-; *ai:* Area 25 NJ Sci League Coord; Sci League Team Adv; Stdnts Environmentaly Active Adv; NEA 1972-; Jackkson Ed Assn 1979-; NJ Sci Tchr 1972-; NJ Div Fish, Game & Wildlife 1970-, Vol Edctr; *office:* Jackson Memorial HS 101 Don Connor Blvd Jackson NJ 08527*

WHEELOCK, CYNTHIA, English Teacher; *b:* Rochester, NH; *ed:* Univ of NH (BA) Eng & Psych 1976; *cr:* Nute HS Eng Tchr, Drama Coach 1976-79; Exeter Area HS Tchr Drama Coach 1979-83; Salem HS Eng Tchr 1983-84; Epping HS Eng Tchr 1984-; *office:* Epping Middle Sr HS 21 Prospect St Epping NH 03042

WHEELOCK, MARJORIE MC NAMARA, Religion Teacher; *b:* Greenfield, MA; *m:* Geoffrey D.; *c:* Rebecca, Kimberly; *ed:* N Adams St Coll (BS) Elem Ed 1974; Elmira Coll (MS) Ed 1981; *cr:* Holy Trinity Schl 2nd Grd Tchr 1974-77; Immaculate Conception Schl Kndgtn Tchr 1977-83, Pre-K, MS Tchr 1987-; *ai:* NCEA.

WHELDEN, VIRGINIA GOSTANIAN, English Instructor; *b:* Cambridge, MA; *m:* John M.; *ed:* Northeastern Univ at Boston (BS) Ed 1979, (MA) Eng, Writing, Linguistics 1983; Cmptr Literacy, Dos Systems; Amer Sign Lang Course I, II Cert; *cr:* Northeastern Univ Eng Instr 1981-84; Voorheesville HS 10-12 Grd Eng Tchr 1985-89; Hudson Vly Comm Coll Eng Instr 1990-; *ai:* NYSUT 1985-; NCTE 1979-; Excl in Tchng Awd 1995; Baccalaureate Speaker Voorheesville HS 1988-89; *office:* Hudson Valley Comm Coll 80 Vandenburgh Ave Troy NY 12180

WHETHERHOLT, DEBORAH BRUCK, Language Arts Teacher; *b:* Columbus, OH; *m:* Gary L.; *c:* Megan, Samantha, Joshua; *ed:* OH Univ (BA) Eng 1975; Addl 45 Quarter Hrs, 150 Total Hrs; *cr:* Fairfield Union HS Eng Dept Chprsn 1987-89, Lang Arts Tchr 1976-; Fairfield Union Js HS Eng Dept Chprsn 1987-89, Lang Arts Tchr 1976-; *ai:* Head Adv Frosh Class; NEA, OEA 1976-; Fairfield Union Ed Assn 1977-; Jennings Scholar 1991-92; *office:* Fairfield Union HS 6401 Cincinnati Zanesville Rd Lancaster OH 43130

WHETSTINE, THOMAS ROBERT, Social Studies Teacher; *b:* Morristown, NJ; *m:* Theresa Ann Sullivan; *ed:* Seton Hall Univ (BS) Scndry Ed, Soc Stud, Archaeology 1988, (MA) Gen Prof Ed 1990; *cr:* Franklin Schl Soc Stud Tchr 8 Yrs; *ai:* Jr HS Report Card, Soc Stud Curr Comms; Kappa Delta Pi, NJ Ed Assn 1988-; NJ Geographic Alliance 1994-, Tchr Coord; VFW 1970-, Life Mem; Disabled Amer Veterans 1975-, Life Mem; Grad NJ Geographic Alliance Summer Inst 1994, Natl Geographics Individual Ldrshp Inst 1995; NJ Geog Awareness Week Coord 1995; *office:* Franklin Schl 100 Davis Ave Kearny NJ 07032

WHETSTONE, BARBARA SUE, Second Grade Teacher; *b:* Celina, OH; *m:* Richard A.; *c:* Kimberly S. Whetsone Parks, Mark A.; *ed:* Wright St Univ (BS) Ed 1981, (MA) Curr, Supervision 1986; *cr:* Vly Forge Elem Schl Educl Aide 1973-80, Kndgtn Tchr 1981-89, Second Grd Tchr 1989-; *ai:* Phi Delta Kappa 1990-; Kappa Delta Pi 1980-; NEA, OEA 1985-; Vandalia Lioness Charter Bd of Dir; Altrusa Club of Vandalia-Huber Heights 1994-, VP; Ladies Nine Hole Golf League; Ladies Eighteen Hole Golf League; One of Top Ten Tchrs in Montgomery Cty to Receive Excl in Tchg Awd 1987-88 Schl Yr; Martha Holden Jennings Scholar 1986-87; Candidate for OH Tchr of Yr 1988; *home:* 145 S Dixie Dr Vandalia OH 45377

WHETSTONE, EMILEE ANNE, Spanish & French Teacher; *b:* Middletown, OH; *w:* David E. (dec); *c:* Charlotte M., Stephanie J.; *ed:* Northern AZ Univ (BA) Fr, Span-Summa Cum Laude 1974, (MAEd) Scndry Ed-Summa Cum Laude 1975; Intnl Study at Sorbonne, Exchange Stu Santiago Chile; Addl 45 Hrs Scndry Admin Toward Doctorate; *cr:* Riverdale HS Fr, Span Tchr, Dept Chair 1979-; *ai:* Foreign Lang Club; Adv Newspaper, Jr, SR; NEA, OEA, REA 1979-, Pres, Local Svc Awd; OH FL Assn 1979-; OH Northern FL Alliance 1989-, Steering Com; 4-H 1990-, Ldr; Church Chair 1980-; *office:* Riverdale HS 20613 State Route 37 Mt Blanchard OH 45867

WHETSTONE, JONI LEE, Vocal Music Instructor; *b:* Cumberland, MD; *c:* Leanna; *ed:* IN Univ of Pennsylvania (MA) Music 1982; Lee Coll BME; *cr:* Everett Chrstn Acad Vocal, Instrumental Music Inst 1977-78, 1980-83; Everett Area HS 7-12 Grd Vocal Music Instr 1983-; Penn St Altoona Campus Part-time Instr 1986-; *ai:* TRIBE Select Vocal Ensemble; Grad Proj, NHS Selection Comms; NEA; PSEA; MENC; PMEA.

WHICHELLO, CAROL DIANE, Social Studies Teacher; *b:* Newton, NJ; *ed:* Salem Coll (BAEd) Scndry Ed 1967; Trenton St Coll (MED) Soc Stud, Pol Sci, Sociology 1978; Georgian Court Coll 3 Credit Hrs; Penn St 1 Credit Hr; *cr:* Clifton T. Barkalow MS Soc Stud Tchr 1967-; *ai:* Acad Team Adv; NEA, NJEA; FTEA 1967-, Exec Bd, Legislative Chprsn; Mid Sts

Cncl Soc Stud Awd Tchr of Yr 1989; Taft Seminar Freedom Fnd, Judicial Seminar; *office:* Clifton T Barkalow MS 498 Stillwells Corner Rd Freehold NJ 07728*

WHIDDEN, ELSIE S., High School English Teacher; *b:* Gardiner, ME; *c:* Robert A. III, Emily Elizabeth; *ed:* Univ of ME at Orono (BA) Eng, Fr 1968; *cr:* Cape Elizabeth HS Eng Tchr 1968-76; Brunswick Times Record Journalist 1978-80; Deering HS Eng Tchr 1981-; *ai:* Yrbk Adv 1981-87 Named One of Top Yrbks Taylor Publishing 1987; Newspaper Adv Ramblings Awd Winning Newspaper; Schl Improvement Mngmt Team; Eng Curr Coll; Comm Svc Project Adv; 5 Coord & Mentor Tchr UME Grad Tchng Prgm Former Bd Mem; Brecia Creative Wrtng Mag Adv; NEA, MTA 1981-; Deering TA 1981-, Bldg Rep; League of Women Voters Former Mem; Comprehensive Planning Comm Pownal; Former Republican Town Chm Pownal; Jr Great Books Ldr; Pownal Sci Historical Soc; Recipient of Yrbk Dedication by Stdnts 1986: UME Recipient Univ Excl in Tchng Awd 1991; Recognized AYW Rand Writing Fnd Excl Writing Instr Stud Nomination 1989; Presenter ME Writing Inst 1982-84; Named By Dean-Carleton Coll Inspiring Tchr Stud Nomination; *office:* Deering HS Stevens Ave Portland ME 04101*

WHIELDON, THOMAS JOHN, Elementary Physical Ed Teacher; *b:* Buffalo, NY; *m:* Kathleen; *c:* Jack, Claire; *ed:* Ithaca Coll (MS) PE 1974; Math Cert 7th-12th 24 Hrs; *cr:* Potters Road Elem PE 1974-83, 1985-86; Allendale Elem PE 1986-87; Northwood Elem PE 1987-89; West Seneca East HS PE, Adapted PE 1989-95; Potters Road Elem PE 1995-; *ai:* Var Girls Cross Cntry & Track; NYSUT 1974-; *office:* Potters Road Elementary 675 Potters Rd West Seneca NY 14224

WHIFFEN, MARY BORDEN, English Teacher; *b:* Liberty, NY; *m:* John; *c:* Christopher, Abigail; *ed:* Hartwick Coll (BS) Eng Ed 1969; Iona (MSE) Eng Ed 1974; Post Grad Stud Syracuse Univ, SUNY at New Paltz; *cr:* Ramapo Sr HS Eng Tchr 1969-82; Guest Prgm Eng Tchr 1982-88; Pomona Jr HS Eng Tchr 1988-91; Spring Vly Sr HS Eng Tchr 1991-; *ai:* Newspaper Adv; Fac Rep Stu Fac Cncl; NYEA 1976-; NYSEC 1993-; Highland Falls-Ft Montgomery Bd of Ed 1992-, VP 1993-; Ed of Excl Awd NY St Eng Cncl 1994; Adj Instr Syracuse Univ Project Advanced Eng; *office:* Spring Valley Sr HS 361 Route 59 Spring Valley NY 10977*

WHILDIN, ANNEMARIE LINKERT, Assoc Prof of Early Chldhd Ed; *b:* Cleveland, OH; *m:* Jim; *c:* Chris Briggs, Emily; *ed:* Oberlin Coll (AB) Govt 1964; Univ of Rochester (MA) Ed 1966; IN Univ (MS) Ed 1976; Attnd Syracuse Univ; *cr:* West HS Soc Stud Tchr 1965-68; Northampton Comm Coll Assoc Prof Early Chldhd Ed 1976-; *ai:* AFT 1965-68, 1976-; NAEYC 1976-; Local Day Care Ctr Bds; *office:* Northampton Comm Coll 3835 Green Pond Rd Bethlehem PA 18017

WHIPPLE, LORI JO, 5th Grade Teacher; *b:* WAchington, OH; *m:* Roy E. Jr.; *c:* Clay Tyler, Caylee Anne, Carly Mae; *ed:* Otterbein Coll (BA) Elem Ed 1984; Classes Ashland Univ, OH St Univ; *cr:* Gahanna Lincoln HS Reserve, Var Chrldng Adv 1985-88; Lincoln Elem Schl 5th Grd Tchr 1983-; *ai:* Grd Level Chprsn; Tchr Mentor; Math, Venture Capital Grant CORE Teams; Assessment Chprsn; Vision Awd 1994; Outstdng Tchr Ed Awd 1990; Ashland Oil Nom 1994; *office:* Lincoln Elem Schl 515 Havens Corners Rd Gahanna OH 43230

WHIPPLE, RUTH B. (ERB), Retired Teacher; *b:* Nashua, NH; *c:* Karen E. E. Fitzpatrick; *ed:* Univ of NH (BS) Home Ec Tchr Prep 1948; Tufts Univ (MA) Ed 1958; Eliot-Pearson Schl Grad Cert; 30 Hrs Post Grad Work RI Coll 1959-79; *cr:* Univ of NH Nursery Schl Tchr 1948-58; RI Coll, Henry Barnard Schl Early Chldhd Asst Prof 1985-87; Self-Employed Tutor 1987-; *ai:* ACII RI Branch 1965-, Advy Role; NEA 1980-; Providence Beneficent House Bd of Governors 1982-, Asst Sec; Conducted Sci, Math, Lit, Multi-Age Grouping Wkshps; Articles Pub; Designed a Mixed Age Curr at British Infant Schls in England & Wales; *home:* 11 Hawthorne St N Providence RI 02904*

WHIRL, ROBERT J., Mathematics Teacher; *b:* West Reading, PA; *m:* Patricia A. Blankowitsch; *ed:* Kutztown St Coll (BS) Math 1967, (MED) Math 1969, (MED) Scndry Guid & Cnslng 1972; NSF Lafayette Math & Comp Lafayette Coll & Allentown Coll; Lehigh Univ Gifted Ed Stud; *cr:* Daniel Boone HS Math Tchr 1967-70; Penn St Univ Adj Prof 1969-70; Freedom HS Math Tchr 1970-73, 1979-, Guid Cnslr 1973-79; Lehigh Univ HS for Gifted Stdnts Tchr 1987; *ai:* Class Adv; Band Announcer; Restructuring Comms; NEA, PSEA & BEA 1970-; NSF Grants; Spcl Olympics St Summer Games Comm; USOC Gymnastics & USA Gymnastics Scorer; Pub Article Math Tchr Magazine; *office:* Freedom HS 3149 Chester Ave Bethlehem PA 18017

WHISNER, ANN ELIZABETH, High School Physical Ed Tchr; *b:* Hagerstown, MD; *ed:* Frostburg St Univ (BS) Recreation 1985; 34 Grad Hrs towards Master's; Attnd East Stroudsburg Univ, Towson St Univ for Tchr's Cert in PE Grds K-12; *cr:* South Hagerstown HS PE Tchr 1992-96; *ai:* Girls Var Bsktbl Coach; PE Advy Cncl; NEA; WCTA 1992-; MAHPERD; Grad Asst at East Stroudsburg Univ; *office:* South Hagerstown HS 1101 S Potomac St Hagerstown MD 21740

WHISNER, MARK ANDREW, Health & Phys Education Instr; *b:* Clarion, PA; *m:* Deborah J. Murphy; *c:* Briana, Garret; *ed:* IN Univ of PA (BS) Hlth & PE 1980; 36 Credit Hrs Cnslr Ed; *cr:* Brockville HS Hlth & PE Tchr 1980-81; Cochranton HS Hlth & PE Tchr 1981; Keystone HS Hlth & PE Instr 1981-; *ai:* Ftbl & Track Vol Coach; Stu Assistance Pgm; Drug-Free Schls Advy Cncl; NEA 1981-; PSEA 1981-; KEA 1981-, Exec Comm.

WHITAKER, C. MARTHA HACKETT, English Teacher; *b:* Providence, RI; *m:* Lee R.; *ed:* Regis Coll (BA) Eng 1970; RI Coll (MAT) Eng 1976; Providence Coll Cmptr Prgms; *cr:* North Providence HS Eng Tchr 1970-; Brown Univ Master Tchr, Ed Consultant 1983-88; RI Coll Adj Fac 1983-; Univ of RI Adj Fac 1995-; *ai:* Acad Improvement Comm 1996; AFT 1970-; NCTE 1985-; RICTE 1974-; *office:* North Providence HS 1828 Mineral Spring Ave North Providence RI 02904*

WHITAKER, CYRIL W., Latin & Theology Teacher; *b:* Cincinnati, OH; *ed:* Xavier Univ (AB) Classics & Philosophy 1978, (AM) Classics & Philosophy 1986; *cr:* All Saints Schl 7th,8th Grd Tchr 1978-81; Lima Cntrl Cath HS Latin,Eng Tchr 1981-82; All Saints Schl 7th,8th Tchr 1982-92; Archbishop Moeller HS Latin,Spanish,Theol Tchr 1992-96; *ai:* Asst Snr Play Costumer; Latin Club; LIFE; *office:* Moeller HS 9001 Montgomery Rd Cincinnati OH 45242

WHITAKER, TERESA RENE, Fourth Grade Teacher; *b:* Brooklyn, NY; *ed:* Brooklyn Coll-CUNY (BA) Elem Ed 1984, (MS) Rdng Tchr 1988; 6 Addl Grad Credits; *cr:* I S 291 Roland Hayes Eighth Grd Eng Tchr 1984-86; P S 299 Thomas Warren Field Elem Schl Fourth Grd Tchr 1986-; *ai:* UFT, AFT 1984-; Cert of Appreciation Comm Schl Bd 1985; Gift of Time Tribute Amer Family Inst 1994; *office:* Thomas Warren Field Elem Schl 88 Woodbine St Brooklyn NY 11221*

WHITBOURNE, SUSAN KRAUSS, Professor of Psychology; *b:* Buffalo, NY; *m:* Richard Desmond O'Brien; *c:* Stacey Beth, Jennifer Louise O'Brien; *ed:* St Univ of NY at Buffalo (BA) Psych 1970; Columbia Univ (PHD) Psych-Dev 1974; Post-Doctoral Trng Clinical Psych 1986-88; *cr:* St Univ of NY Coll at Geneseo Asst Prof 1973-75; Univ of Rochester Asst to Assoc Prof 1975-84; Univ of MA at Amherst Assoc to Full Prof 1984-; *ai:* Adv Psi Chi Univ of MA Chptr; Hnrs Coord Psych Dept; Assist in Recruitment of Hnrs Stdnts, Stu Ath for Admissions Univ of MA; Amer Psychological Assn 1975-, Pres Div 20, Fellow Div 2, G. Stanley Hall Lecturer, Nom Distngd Tchng Awd; Outstdng Coll Tchr Awd Univ of MA, Coll of Soc & Beh Sci; Pub Books: The Aging Individual 1996, Abnormal Psychology 1994; Pub Journal Articles, Book Chptrs Psych; *office:* Univ Of MA At Amherst Psychology Dept Amherst MA 01003

WHITCHER, JOEL MICHAEL, Sixth Grade Soc Studies Tchr; *b:* Olean, NY; *m:* Amy Brown; *c:* Erica Amy, Zachary Michael; *ed:* Alfred Univ (BA) Elem Ed 1987; St Bonaventure (MS) Elem Ed 1991; *cr:* Bolivar Cntrl Schl Elem Tchr 1987-94; Bolivar-Richburg Cntrl Schl Elem Tchr 1994-; *ai:* Head Var Ftbl, Track; NEA 1987-; Lions Club 1989-, Bd Mem; Coached Two Big 30 All Star Ftbl Games; *office:* Bolivar-Richburg Central Sch 100 School St Bolivar NY 14715*

WHITCOMB, CORNELIUS JAMES, Owner; *b:* Belfast, ME; *c:* Jennifer, Sarah King; *ed:* Thomas Coll (BS) Bus Ed, Math Minor 1970; 24 Addl Hrs; *cr:* Skowhegan Area HS Classroom Tchr 1970-71; Waterville HS Classroom Tchr 1971; Cony HS Classroom Tchr 1971-95; Kennebec Vly Voc Tech Inst Classroom Tchr 1972-75; Univ of ME Classroom Tchr 1973-74; Whitcomb Electric Owner; *ai:* Past Class Adv; Augusta Drug Abuse Prevention Team 10 Yrs; Cony HS Talent Show Exec Comm 5 Yrs; Augusta Tchrs Assn 1971-, VP, Sec, Treas, Rep; ME Tchrs Assn 1971-, Augusta Area Rep; NEA 1971-; Bus Ed Assn of ME; Recognized by ME Army Natl Guard, Governor's Office for Drug Prevention Prgms Work.

WHITCOMB, THOMAS W., Chemistry Teacher; *b:* Portage, PA; *m:* Kathleen Johnson; *c:* Maria, Diane, Michelle; *ed:* Indiana Univ of PA (BS) Chem 1982; Cert of Ed 1983; *cr:* Bishop McCort HS Physics Tchr 1983-84; Portage Area HS 7th Grd Sci Tchr 1984; United HS Chem Tchr 1984-; *ai:* Chess Club & Wrestling Helpers AM Co-Adv; Sci Steering Comm; HS Wrestling Coach; NEA 1984-; *office:* United HS PO Box 168 Armagh PA 15920

WHITCOMBE, DAVID R., Science Teacher; *b:* Batavia, NY; *m:* Pamela Allein; *c:* Richard, Jeffery, Ryan; *ed:* Hartwick Coll (BS) 1967; SUNY Brockport (MS) Zoology 1975; SUL Brockport Cornell Univ 1995; *cr:* Oakfield-Alabama Cntrl HS Sci Tchr 1968-81; US Dept Interior-Fish & Wildlife Sci Dir Environmental ed & Yth Conservation Corps 1974-77; Batavia HS Bio, Chem & Environmental Sci Tchr 1981-; St Univ Coll at Brockport Adj Instr & Field Natural His Tchr 1991-94; Genese Comm Coll at Batavia Adj Instr & DDE Summer Sci Tchr 1990-; Sci & Engrng Tech Intl Biological Consultant 1991-; *ai:* 1998 Class Adv; Batone Tchrs Assn, AFT & NYSUT 1968-; NEA 1968-; NABT 1975-; Genesee Cty Fish & Game Protective Assn 1970-; Bergen Swamp Preservation Soc 1975-, Pres; Publications NY St Conservationist 1988 & Genesee Cntry 1994; NY Regnl Bio Mentor 1992-; *office:* Batavia HS 260 State St Batavia NY 14020

WHITE, ANGELA R., Chair of Sci Dept & HS Tchr; *b:* Leicester, England; *m:* Richard J.; *c:* Helen, Jon, Natasha, Ross; *ed:* Northeast London Polytechnic (BS) Applied Bio 1976; Southern CT St Univ (MSc) Environmental Sci 1992; *cr:* Glaxo Research Scientist 1965-77; Ragozzino & Sons Microbiologist 1986-87; Cheshire Acad Sci Dept Chair 1987-; *ai:* Sr Class & Prom Adv; Weight Lifting & Aerobics After Schl Prgm; Fac Mentor; Curr 2000 Comm; NSTA 1987-; Doug Morton Fac Excl Awd; *office:* Cheshire Acad 10 Main St Cheshire CT 06410

WHITE, ARTHUR A., Professor of Philosophy; *b:* Richmond, VA; *m:* Mary L.; *c:* Christopher; *ed:* Univ of VA (MA) Philosophy 1972, (PHD) Philosophy 1974; *cr:* Univ of VA Asst Prof 1972-74; Univ of KY Asst Prof 1974-75; Thiel Coll Asst, Assoc, Full Prof 1976-; *ai:* Stu Govt Adv; AAUP, APA 1976-; NEH Flwshp 1984; Danforth Fellow; Numerous Articles Pub; *office:* Thiel Coll 75 College Ave Greenville PA 16125*

WHITE, BARBARA HIGGINS, Language Arts & Reading Tchr; *b:* Elkhart, IN; *m:* Barry A.; *c:* Nathan, Seth; *ed:* OH Wesleyan Univ (BA) Eng 1971; Univ of Southern ME (MSEd) Literacy Ed 1993; *cr:* North Canton Jr HS Eng Tchr 1971-74; Brunswick HS Eng Tchr 1974-86; Augusta Schl Literacy Specialist 1992-93; Sugg MS Eng, Rdng Tchr 1993-; *ai:* Goals 2000 Grant Writing Comm, Planning Team; ME Tchrs Summit on Learning Results Rep; Stu Pubications Adv; Tchr Evaluation Comm; Natl Rdng Assn; NCTE; ME Cncl of Eng, Lang Arts Tchrs; *home:* Eben Hill Rd Yarmouth ME 04096

WHITE, BENNY JOE, Sixth Grade Teacher; *b:* Coudersport, PA; *m:* Ronda K. Mc Caslin; *c:* Eric J., Jared A.; *ed:* Marshfield Univ (BS) Elem Math 1988, (MS) Ed 1991; *cr:* Northern Potter Childrens Schl Sixth Grd Tchr 1988-; *ai:* Var Track Boys Head Coach 1989-; Prin Advy Comm 1994-; Jr HS Soccer Coach 1989-90; PSEA, NEA 1988-; *office:* Northern Potter Childrens Schl Box 401 Ulysses PA 16948*

WHITE, BEVERLY SPANGLER, 3rd Grade Teacher; *b:* Philadelphia, PA; *w:* Duane T. (dec); *c:* Margo L., Lauren L.; *ed:* Lynchburg Coll (BA) ELem Ed 1970; Penn St at Chestnut Hill (MS) Elem Ed 1988; *cr:* Colonial Schl Dist Tchr 1970-; *ai:* Girl Scout of Amer; NEA; Lioness Club 1980-84; Nom for Tchr of Yr; *office:* Ridge Park Elem Schl 200 Karrs Ln Conshohocken PA 19428

WHITE, BRIAN N., World History & Geography Tchr; *b:* Portsmouth, OH; *ed:* Capital Univ (BS) Comprehensive Soc Stud 1990; Grad Hrs at Ashland Univ; *cr:* DeSales HS Tchr 1990-; *ai:* Asst Var Ftbl Coach; Head JV Sftbl & Wrestling Coach; CDEA 1990-; *home:* 4869 Northtowne Blvd Columbus OH 43229*

WHITE, CAROL OWEN, Seventh Grade Teacher; *b:* Delaware, OH; *m:* John W.; *c:* Sara Elizabeth; *ed:* OH Wesleyan Univ (BA) Geog Ed 1970; Miami Univ (MA) Geog Ed 1971; Post Grad Stud Ashland Univ, Univ of UT, OH St Univ; *cr:* Eber Baker MS Sci Tchr 1971-; *ai:* Marion City Schls Chm Sci Day, Sci Curr, Strategic Planning Comms; NEA, OEA, MEA 1971-; Phi Delta Kappa 1981-; Kappa Delta Gamma 1984-, Sec; Marion Musicians Assn 1985-, Rep; Marion Garden Club 1992-, VP; Marion YMCA 1981-, Bd Dirs; OH Kreger, OH Acker, Marion City Schls Tchr of Yr Awds; *office:* Eber Baker MS 400 Pennsylvania Ave Marion OH 43302*

WHITE, CHERYL MARTIN, Math Teacher; *b:* Woodbury, NJ; *m:* Joseph; *c:* Joseph, Christopher; *ed:* Western MD Coll (BA) Math 1976; *cr:* Delta Regnl HS Math Tchr 1976-77; Sacred Heart HS Math Tchr 1980-85; Cumberland Regnl HS Math Tchr 1985-; *ai:* Soph Class Adv; CREA 1985-, Schl Rep; NJEA, NEA 1985-.

WHITE, CHRISTOPHER J., Earth Sci Tchr & Adult Ed Adm; *b:* Philadelphia, PA; *m:* Susan Blume; *c:* Stephen R., Heather K.; *ed:* Middlebury Coll (AB) Geology 1963; Syracuse Univ (MS) Sci Ed 1966; Univ of Rochester (CAS) Ed 1978; 200 Addl Hrs Millersville St Coll, Boston Univ, SUNY at Oswego, Univ of Rochester; *cr:* Phoenix Cntrl Schls Sci Tchr 1966-68; NYS Ed Dept Consultant 1966-71, 1992; Wheatland Chili Cntrl Schl Sci Tchr, Admin 1968-; *ai:* Sr Class, Stu Cncl, Ski Club Advs; NYSUT, AFT, NEA 1966-; Lions Club of Scottsv 1979-; US Army Reserve 1963-, LTC; Presented Paper to AAAS 1978; *home:* 15 Cavalier Rd W Scottsville NY 14546

WHITE, CONNIE AIKEN, Tenth Grade Biology Teacher; *b:* New Castle, PA; *m:* Ronald; *c:* Ronald, Ryan; *ed:* Carlow Coll (BS) Bio 1982; Slippery Rock Univ (BS) Scndry Ed, Chem 1992; *cr:* Kennedy Chrstn HS Chem, Human Anatomy Tchr 1993-94; Wilmington Area Schl Bio Tchr 1994-; *ai:* PSEA, NEA 1992-; NSTA, PA Bio Tchr 1995-; Order of Eastern Star 1980-; Assoc of Children & Adults with Learning Disabilities 1993-; Daughters of Amer Revolution 1995-; *office:* Wilmington Area MS 350 Wood St New Wilmington PA 16142

WHITE, DENNIS A., Vice Principal; *b:* Washington, DC; *m:* Cher *c:* Matthew R., Lauren K.; *ed:* Univ of MD at Coll Park (BS) Elem Ed Bowie St (MEd) Admin & Supervision; 30 Hrs in Post Grad Course Laurel Elem Classroom Tchr 1971-79; James H. Harrison Elem Class Tchr 1979-80; Wm Wirt Mid Classroom Tchr 1980-85; Kenmon Elem Math Tchr 1985-86; Ft Washington Forest Sci Math Coord 1986-91 Hill Mid Vice Prin 1991; *ai:* Natl Eagle Scout Assn 1965-; BPOE 1995-; *office:* Oxon Hill MS 9570 Fort Foote Rd Fort MD 20744

WHITE, DOLORES LEVY, Reading Specialist; *b:* Lexington, K Eugene M.; *c:* Hilary M. Steinroeder, Jennifer L.; *ed:* NY Univ (MS) Ed 1963; Coll of New Rochelle (MA) Rdng 1979; 60 Credits above Ma Degree Monmouth Coll, Coll of New Rochelle, Southampton Coll, Island Univ, St Univ of NY at New Paltz; *cr:* Garneiville Elem Sch Grd Tchr 1963-66; Coll of New Rochelle Adj Tchng Asst 1979; Rockland HS Rdng Specialist 1979-; *ai:* 1998 Class Adv; AFT, NY North Rockland Tchrs Assn 1979-; North Rockland Cntrl Schl Summer Grant.*

WHITE, DORIS OLIVER, First Grade Teacher; *b:* Bassett, VA Wilbert G.; *c:* Reginald A. Sr.; *ed:* St Paul's Coll (BS) Elem Ed 1955; Southern LA St Univ, Bowie St Univ; *cr:* Henry Cty Schl 1st Grd T Yrs; Terrebonne Parish Schl 1st Grd Tchr 10 Yrs; Prince George's Cty 1st Grd Tchr 11 Yrs; *ai:* NEA 1955-; Local Women Org 1985-, Outstdng Edctr 1992.

WHITE, ESTELLA M., Academic Advisor; *b:* Bartley, WV; *ed:* NC Univ (BS) Bus Ed 1964; Temple Univ (MS) Ed 1975; Nova Uni Credits; Univ of DE at Newark 9 Credits; MI St Univ 6 Credits; *cr:* of Charlotte Legal Sec 1964-66; Redding & Wms Law Firm Lega 1966-69; Howard HS Bus Ed Tchr 1969-73; DE Tech & Comm C Wilmington Bus Admin Instr & Acad Adv 1973-; *ai:* SGA, Clubs & C Groups Parliamentary Procedure Presenter; NEA 1969-; DSEA 1 Exec Bd Mem; Natl Assn Univ Women 1974-, VP, Women of Yr Awd NAUW-Wilmington Branch, Parliamentarian; NC Cntrl Univ A Assn-Wilmington, VP, DE Chapter Treas & Parliamentarian; P Settlement Assn 1968-, Advy Comm; Delta Sigma Theta Corresponding Sec; PDK Inc 1978-, Supreme Tamias; Ezion Mount C United Meth Church, Pres, Exec Bd Mem, Miss Zion Mount C Queen; Cert from UD-Most Likely to Succeed in a Multiculture W *office:* DE Tech & Comm Coll Wilmington Campus 333 Shipl Wilmington DE 19801*

WHITE, HELEN CATHERINE, Eng Teacher & Rdng Specialis Wilmington, DE; *ed:* Univ of DE (Assoc) Secretarial Stud 1968, (BA) Ed 1971, (MED) Rdng Specialist 1973; *cr:* Talley Jr HS Eng Tchr 2 Fugett MS Rdng Specialist 1 Yr; Thomas Jefferson Jr HS Rdng Speci Eng Tchr 1 Yr; Stetson MS Rdng Specialist, Eng Tchr 18 Yrs; *ai:* Lang Dept Chair; Yrbk Adv; PAC Tchr Rep; 7th Grd Team Ldr; NEA, WC 1984-; IRA 1995-; NCTE 1993-; *office:* Stetson MS 1060 Wilmington West Chester PA 19382*

WHITE, JANE GIEGENGACK, Lang Dept Chair & Latin Tchr; *b:* York City, NY; *m:* Robert J.; *c:* Elizabeth, David, Nancy; *ed:* Coll Of Rochelle (BA) Classics 1963; Yale Univ (MA) Classic 1964, (PHD) Cl 1969; *cr:* Dickinson Coll Instr 1966-68; Hunter Coll Lecturer, Adj Prof 1969-86; Trinity Schl Latin Tchr 1986-89; Dwight Englewood Chm 1989-; *ai:* Costumes for Plays; Intnl Current Events Club; Vergilian Soc 1989-; CALICO, ASCD 1995-; Book Written; Dwight-Englewood Schl 315 E Palisade Ave Englewood NJ 07631

WHITE, JANET GLEASON, Reading & Lang Arts Teacher; *b:* Fuk Japan; *m:* Robert L. Jr.; *ed:* Frostburg St Univ (BA) Psych 1971; Bow Univ (MA) Spec Ed 1977; *cr:* Bel Alton MS Spec Ed Tchr 197 Piccawaxen MS Spec Ed Tchr, Spec Ed Dept Head 1976-87; Benj Stoddert MS Spec Ed Tchr, Spec Ed Dept Head 1987-; *ai:* Spec Olyn Writing Resource Guide Comm; MSPAP, Morale Comms; NEA; MD of Tchrs of Eng Lang Arts 1994-; Delta Kappa Gamma 1995-; Alph Delta 1969-; *office:* Benjamin Stoddert MS 2040 Saint Thomas Dr Wa MD 20602

WHITE, JEFFREY ALAN, Gymnastics Teacher; *b:* Rochester, NY Catherine Marie Krajnyak; *c:* Sean Robert, Casey Alan, Colin Jeffrey USA Gymnastics Org Safety Cert; Kent St Univ Architecture 197 Ithaca Coll PE 1974-76; *cr:* Ithaca Gymnastics Ctr Asst Dir 197 J-Cats Gymnastics Instr 1976-79; Southern Tier Gymnastics Ins Co-Owner 1979-; *ai:* Spcl Olympics Gymnastics Spon by My Gym C USA Gymnanstics 1974-; Natl Gymnastics Judges Assoc 1990-, J Nationally Related Awd; NY St Mens Gymnastics Coach of the Yr Mens & Womens Gymnastics Competitor Coach for Meets in Fran Natl Competitions; *office:* Southern Tier Gymnastics Acad 2901 Way Endwell NY 13762

WHITE, JERRY, Science Teacher & Dept Chair; *b:* Curtice, OH Beverly A. Dillion; *c:* Stephanie A.; *ed:* Wittenberg Univ (BS) Ge 1976-77; Grad Hrs Environmental Stud, Geology Wright St Univ, Un Akron; Cmptr Ed Univ Dayton; *cr:* Springfield City Schls Subs 1976-77; Tecumseh Local Schls Tchr 1977-, Sci Dept Chair 1982-; O Butterfly Acres Orchards; *ai:* Building Level Intervention Team, Ste Comm; Cty Sci Curr; March for Parks 1992-93; Life Group for Ar Welfare League Fundraiser; NEA, OEA 1977-; SECO; New Carlisle Water Quality Bd 1990-; Calssic Cty Bd Ed 1993-93; Grants From M Holden Jennings Fnd 1986, Clark Cty Bd Ed 1991-93; *office:* Tecums S 9830 W National Rd New Carlisle OH 45344

WHITE, JOHN IVAN, Eighth Grade Science Teacher; *b:* Bucyrus, *m:* Catherine Yvette Offmiss; *c:* Christin CD, Joshua JD; *ed:* OH St (BS) Ed 1984; K-12 Indstrl Tech; 7-12 Gen Sci; Addl 10 Hrs Grad *cr:* USAF & OH Air Natl Guard Commander 1976-; Chrstn Books Mgr, Salesman 1982-89; Lexington Jr HS SLD Tutor 1989-90; Ontari Sci, Ind Tech Tchr 1990-; *ai:* Ftbl, Track, Cross Cntry Coach; New Mentor; Sci Dept Co-Chair; Educl Action Team; Prin Advy Comm Restructuring Team; Sci Day Dir, Judge; AFT 1990-; Natl Guard As US, OH Natl Guard Assn 1985-; Berean Bapt 1991-, Tchr, Choir; Airlift Gp OH Air Natl Guard 1980-, Ofcr; AF Comm Medal; Natl De Medal; Air Force OUtstdng Unit Awd; Mohican Sci Day Most Superi HS, Highest Percent of Superiors; *home:* 950 S Lexington Springmi Mansfield OH 44903

WHITE, JOSEPH O., Principal; *b:* Bridgeton, NJ; *m:* Deloris M. G *c:* Angela Y., Brian J.; *ed:* Glassboro St Coll (BA) Scndry Sci Ed 1 William Paterson Coll (MA) Biological Sci 1975, (MEd) Educl Ad Supervision 1977; Rutgers Univ (EDS) Sci Ed 1994; *cr:* Delsea Regr Sci Tchr 1967-68; South Jr HS Sci Tchr 1968-85; North Jr HS Sci Chprsn 1985-87; Bloomfield MS Team Ldr 1987-88; Teaneck HS A Prin 1988-95; Thomas Jefferson MS Prin 1995-; *ai:* NASSP, NJ Bergen Cty Prin, Supvr Assn 1988-; Bergen Cty Urban League 1 Amer Legion 1988-; Shiloh AME Zion Church 1976-; Outstdng Selectee Bloomfield MS; NJ St Governor's Tchr Recognition 1987-88; Presidential Sci, Math Tchng Excl Awds Bloomfield's Sci 1984; Features in Newspaper 1983; *office:* Thomas Jefferson MS Teaneck Rd Teaneck NJ 07666

WHITE, JOYCE M., Fourth Grade Teacher; *b:* Kingston, Jamaica Desmond A.; *c:* Garfield O., David A.; *ed:* Pace Univ (BPS) Ed N-6 Lehman Coll (MS) Elem Ed 1991; *cr:* Jamaica Civil Svc Clerical Of I & 2 1960-67; Western Union Tel Co Sr Clerk, Telegraph Oper 196

Bd of Ed Tchr 1985-; *ai:* Neighborhood Yth Prgm Dir; AFT 1986-; x Bapt Church 1967-, Bd Mem, Yth Tchr & Group Dir; Dereimer er Comm Org 1991-, Bd Mem; *office:* CES 132nd Elem Schl 1245 ington Ave Bronx NY 10456

TE, KAREN LEE, Fifth Grade Teacher; *b:* Chester, PA; *ed:* Indiana of PA (BA) Elem Ed 1970; Penn St Univ (MS) Elem Ed 1985; *cr:* side Elem Schl Kndgtn Tchr 3 Yrs, Transitional First Grd Tchr 3 Yrs, rd Tchr 3 Yrs, 4th, 5th Grd Tchr 14 Yrs; Pennell Elem Schl 5th Grd 3 Yrs; *ai:* Pennell Pals, Friends; PDEA 1970-, Bldg Rep; PSEA, NEA -; Girl Scouts 1956-, Ldr; Pioneer Girls 1980-, Pal; *office:* Pennell Schl Richard's Rd Aston PA 19014*

TE, KARYN ADELIA, Guidance Counselor; *b:* Salisbury, MD; *c:* i Patrice; *ed:* Salisbury St Univ (BS) Elem Ed 1984; Loyola Coll of MS) Guidance, Counseling 1990; *cr:* Fruitland Intermediate Schl 6th Soc Stud Tchr 1984-85; Delmar Elem Schl 3rd Grd Tchr 1984-85; er Green Elem Schl 4th Grd Tchr 1985-90; Stevens Forest, Jeffers Hill Schl Guidance Cnslr 1990-93; Owen Brown MS Guidance Cnslr -; *ai:* Crisis Intervention Cluster Team; BSAP, Human Relations ms; Stu Support Team Co-Facilitator; Peer Mediator Facilitator; NEA -; MMSA, MD St Tchrs Assn, Howard Cty Cnslrs Assn 1993-; NMSA -; St James Meth Church, Life Mem; Sister Cr 1995-, Pres; NAACP -; *office:* Owen Brown MS 6700 Cradlerock Way Columbia MD 5*

TE, KERRY ALLEN, American History Teacher; *b:* York, PA; *m:* a Weir; *ed:* York Coll of PA (BA) Soc Stud 1972; Millersville Univ) Soc Stud 1990; 30 Credits Beyond MA; *cr:* Eastern York HS Amer Tchr 1974-; *ai:* Bow Hunting, Archery Club Adv; NEA, PSEA, Eastern Ed Assn 1974-; Rocky Mountain Elk Fdn 1991-; PA Bow Hunters Soc -; Fairmount U M Church 1955-, Sunday Schl Tchr; Co Ed Rsrch ctry York Dispatch Index 1973; *office:* Eastern York HS PO Box 2002 Creek Rd Wrightsville PA 17368

TE, KIRKE J., Social Studies Teacher; *b:* Oswego, NY; *m:* Calleen *c:* Kara; *ed:* Syracuse Univ (BA) His 1968; Univ of Rochester (MA) 977; Post Grad Stud SUNY at Oswego & SUNY at Brockport; *cr:* ster HS Scndry Soc Stud Tchr 1968-; *ai:* AFT 1968-; NYSUT 1968-; ster Tchrs Assn 1968-, Sr Bldg Rep; St Margaret Mary Church 1972-, h Cncl Vice Chprsn; Outstdng Edctr Cornell Univ Presidential lars (Twice); *office:* Webster HS 875 Ridge Rd Webster NY 14580

TE, LADYLEASE GOODRIDGE, Prof & Coord of Acctng Dept; *b:* ma City, Panama; *c:* Tamica; *ed:* Trenton St Coll (BA) Bus Ed 1961; mbia Univ (MA) Bus Ed 1969; Doctoral Stu in Higher Ed at NY Univ; ssex Cty Coll Prof & Coord 27 Yrs; Jersey City St Coll Adj Prof 10 Rutgers the St Univ Adj Prof 2 Yrs; Panama Canal Co Accountant 2 *ai:* NEA 1969-; NJEA 1969-; YWCA of Essex & W Hudson, Bd of & Asst Treas; Pub Learning Guide for Acctng; Mayoral Svc Awd for rs; *office:* Essex County Coll 303 University Ave Newark NJ 07102*

TE, LOLITA LOOMIS, High School Art Teacher; *b:* Cortland, NY; arold M.; *c:* Gregory Clark Hotaling, Bradley Alan Hotaling; *ed:* awk Vly Tech Inst (AAS) Advert, Design, Production 1962; SUNY at and (BA) Visual Arts 1972; 34 Addl Hrs Elem Ed; *cr:* Cincinnatus Schl HS Art Tchr 1972-; *ai:* Art Club Adv; Site-Based, Scheduling ms; Art Dept Chm; Drama Productions Stage Design; NEA, NYEA -; NAEA, NYSATA 1980-; Bronze Statue Created by Art Stdnts; : RR 1 Box 389 Marathon NY 13803*

TE, LOREN F., Sixth Grade Teacher; *b:* Spangler, PA; *ed:* Edinboro (BS) Elem Ed 1974, (MS) Elem Guid 1978; *cr:* Gen Mc Lane SD Tchr -; *ai:* NEA, PSEA, GMEA 1974-; Edinboro Triathlon, GMEA Vol; ort Tchr 1986; *office:* James W. Parker MS 11781 Edinboro Rd boro PA 16412

TE, MARGARET KEENE, Fourth Grade Teacher; *b:* Watertown, n: Leroy F.; *ed:* SUNY Cortland (BA) Elem Ed 1967; SUNY Potsdam Elem Ed 1970; *cr:* St Rd Elem Schl 3rd Grd Tchr 1967-70; Owego Schl 2nd-4th, 6th Grd Tchr 1971-; *ai:* 4th Grd Chprsn; Elem Steering, icultural Dist Comm; NYSUT, AFT 1967-; Delta Kappa Gamma 986-; Tchrs Recognition Awd 1988; *office:* Owego Elem Schl George vego NY 13827

TE, MARILYN JOHNSON, Senior Guidance Counselor; *b:* Akron, *c:* Kemuel, Kolaiah; *ed:* Univ of Akron (BA) Elem Ed 1971, (MS) ıg 1978; 18 Addl Hrs; *cr:* Robinson Elem Schl 2nd Grd Tchr 1971-78; on Elem Schl 1st Grd Tchr 1978-87; Perkins MS Cnslr 1987-92; tel HS Sr Guid Cnslr 1992-; *ai:* Yrbk, Peer Mediation, 3.0 Club, Key Adv; Stu Relationship; AEA 1971-; OCEA 1992-; Jack & Jill of Amer -, Treas, Sec; Alpha Kappa Alpha.*

TE, MARTHA BURTON, 5th Grade Teacher; *b:* Henderson, NC; *ed:* orie Webster Jr Coll (AA) Kndgtn Ed 1962; Amer Univ (BA) Elem Ed ; Master's Equivency Addl 30 Credit Hrs; *cr:* Gaithersburg Elem Schl Grd Tchr 1964-66; Mill Creek Towne Elem Schl 2-5 Grd Tchr 1966-; dyssey of Mind Coach, Problem Captain; Gifted & Talented Comm ; Tchng Pilot Prgm Highly Gifted Rdng Prgm; Math Olympiad, ling Bee, Thinking Cap Cmptr Contest Spon; MO Co Ed Assn, MD St s Assn, NEA 1964-; Friendship Star Quilters 1990-, Treas; Nom Agnes r Outstanding Tchr Awd; *office:* Mill Creek Towne Elem Schl 17700 Mill Dr Derwood MD 20855*

TE, MARTHA PAGE, English Teacher; *b:* Lewiston, ME; *c:* dler W, Jennifer P.; *ed:* Rollins Coll (BA) Ger, Fr 1964; Univ of ME) Ed 1990; *cr:* Univ of AL Grad Schl Asst To Dean 1964-68; Lake t Merrill Hills Schl Tchr Asst 1972-74; Hampden Acad Lib Asst -84; Dexter Regnl HS Fr, Eng Tchr 1985-; *ai:* Golf Coach, Grad sp Comm; NEA 1985; Cntrl ME Medical Ctr 1980-, Corporator; ston-Auburn Sports Hall of Fame 1988-, Inductee; ME Golf Hall of 1992-, Inductee; ME Sports Hall of Fame 1980-, Inductee; WMSGA -, Handicapper; *home:* 18 George St Hampden ME 04444

TE, MARY A., High School Math Teacher; *b:* Kingston, PA; *m:* mas J.; *c:* Barbara White-Sax; *ed:* Penn St Univ (BA) Math & Eng , (MS) Scndry Math 1959; *cr:* Long Branch HS Math Tchr 1959-61; mouth Regnl HS Math Tchr 1963-70; Brookdale Comm Coll Math 1976-78; Long Branch HS Math Tchr 1980-; *ai:* Adult Math Anxiety se Tchr at Brookdale Comm Coll; NEA, NJEA 1959-; St Michaels ch Comm 1995-; *office:* Long Branch HS Westwood Ave Long Branch 7740*

TE, MARY E., Prof of Hlth Information Mgmt; *b:* Bluefield, WV; *m:* s; *c:* Brian, Brent; *ed:* Wright St Univ (MA) Ed 1983; OH St Univ (BS) ed Hlth 1973; *cr:* Good Samaritan Hospital Medical Records Dir -80; Wright St Univ Hlth Information Dir 1980-85; Sinclair Comm Hlth Information Mgmt Prof 1985-; *ai:* Boy Scout Merit Badge Cnslr; r Hlth Info Mgmt Assoc 1972-, Item Writing Comm 1995; Miami y Hlth Info Assoc 1973-, Pres, Distinguished Mem 1995; Terrific en in Giving 1990-; Prof Presentations on Natl, St & Local Level for s in Hlth Information Mgmt; *office:* Sinclair Comm Coll 444 W 3rd ayton OH 45402

TE, MARY ELIZABETH, Music Dept Teacher & Chair; *b:* Queens, *ed:* Coll Misericordia (BMus) Music Ed 1971; NY Univ (MA) Music apy 1973; *cr:* St Andrew Avilino Elem Music Tchr 1973-89; Luth HS atics Pgm Dir 1987-; Sacred Heart Acad Music Dept Chprsn 1989-; *ai:* Dir of Musical Theater; Var Swim Team Coach; Folk Group; NCEA 1973-; Nassau Music Edctrs Assn 1989-; Music Edctrs Natl Conf 1989-; Fllwshp from Diocese of Brooklyn-Office of the Handicapped 1992; *office:* Sacred Heart Acad 47 Cathedral Ave Hempstead NY 11550

WHITE, MARY BENITA HAGEMAN, Math Teacher; *b:* Covington, KY; *m:* Robert J. Jr.; *c:* Jenn, Laura, Karen; *ed:* Coll of Mt St Joseph (BA) Elem Ed 1975; Eastern MI Un (MA) Rdng 1987; 6 Post Grad Hrs at Xavier Univ; 3 Post Grad Hrs at Miami Univ; 2 Post Grad Hrs at IN Univ; *cr:* Ft Rucker Primary Schl 1st Grd Sub, Tchr 1976-79; St Anthony Schl 1st Grd, Sub Tchr 1979-81; Oak Hills Schl Sub Tchr 1986-87; Coll of Mt St Joseph Adj Instr 1992-94; St Dominic Schl Math, 6th Grd Tchr 1987-; *ai:* 7th-8th Grd Acad Team Fac Coach, Adv; Math Counts Team Fac Coach, Adv; Parish Choir, Cantor, Eucharistic Minister; St Dominic Festival Seton HS 1986-, Booth Chprsn; Mom, Dads Assn 1992-, Treas; Nominee for Ashland Individual Achvmt Awd; *office:* Saint Dominic Schl 371 Pedretti Rd Cincinnati OH 45238

WHITE, MICHAEL FRANCIS, 6th Grade Teacher; *b:* Philadelphia, PA; *m:* Mary Jane Merz; *c:* Christopher, Theresa, Matthew; *ed:* Millersville Univ (BA) Ed 1961; Trenton St (MA) Ed 1969; Temple Univ Admin Elem Prin; *cr:* Neshaminy Schl Dist Tchr 1964-67; Cheltenham Schl Dist Tchr 1967-71; Colonial Schl Dist Elem Prin 1971-73; North Penn Schl Dist Tchr, Prin 1973-; *ai:* Bsktbl Coach; Floral Design Club Spon; North Penn EA, PAEA, NEA 1965-; Montgomery Cty Prins Assn 1972-82, Pres; North Penn Cancer Soc 1975-77, Bd of Dirs; *office:* A M Kulp Elem Schl Hatfield Valley Rd Hatfield PA 19440

WHITE, MICHAEL R., Math Teacher & Stu Cncl Adv; *b:* Sellersville, PA; *m:* Lucille M. Stracka; *c:* Kristin, Gary; *ed:* Millersville St (BS) Scndry Ed & Math 1975; Lehigh Univ (MED) Admin & Supervision 1981; Attnd Kutztown St & Wilkes Coll; *cr:* N Penn Schl Dist Tchr 1975-76, Up With People Promotion & Scheduling 1977-78; Pennridge Schl Dist Tchr 1978-; *ai:* Stu Cncl Adv; PA Stu Cncl Dist Assn; AP Calculus Dir & Reader, AP Calculus Coll Bd Consultant; PSEA & NEA 1978-; NCTM 1988-; MAA & PCTM 1989-; Pennridge Jaycees Young Educator of Yr Awd; St Fin Pres Awds for Excl in Sci and Math Tchng; PA Assoc of Stu Cncls Dist Adv of Yr; *office:* Pennridge H S 1228 N 5th St Perkasie PA 18944

WHITE, MOURINE ELLIOTT, Physical Ed & Health Teacher; *b:* Besoco, WV; *m:* Robert Marcus; *c:* M. Elliott, Holly Lee; *ed:* Towson St Univ (BS) PE 1971; Attnd Towson St Univ, Loloya, Bowie St, Notre Dame; *cr:* Kenwood HS Tchr 1971-; Dulaney HS Tchr 1996; *ai:* Sftbl Coach; META, NEA, Balto CO Coaches Assn 1971-; *office:* Dulaney HS 255 Padonia Rd Timonium MD 21093

WHITE, NANCY GUHL, Spanish Teacher; *b:* Lackawana, NY; *m:* Stephen; *c:* Christopher, Nathan, Nicholas; *ed:* SUNY at Fredonia (BA) Span Scndry Ed 1973; Attnd Univ of Madriel Spain, St Univ of NY at Buffalo, Edinboro St Coll; *cr:* Springville Griffith Inst Span I-IV 1973-; Clymer Cntrl Schl Span Tchr & Librn 1973-76; Cassadaga Vly Cntrl 9th-12th Grd Span Tchr 1973-; *ai:* Span Club Adv 1973-; Yrbk Adv 1973-76 & 1977-79; NYSUT 1973-; NYSFLT 1973-; Delta Kappa Gamma Intnl 1980-, Past Nominations Chprsn; Ladies Auxilary of WFFC 1981-95, Treas, Publicity; ELCA 1994-, Treas; NHS Tchr of Yr 1977; *office:* Springville-Griffith Inst 290 N Buffalo St Springville NY 14141*

WHITE, NAOMI CORTS, Science Teacher; *b:* Buffalo, IN; *m:* George Jefferson; *c:* Deborah White McEniry, Diane White Musolf; *ed:* GA St Univ Elem Ed (BS) 1975, (MEd) 1977; Kean Coll Sci, Prin, Supverision Cert; *cr:* Hooper Alexander Elem Schl Sci Tchr 1976-77; Our Lady of Victory Sci Tchr 1978-79; Manalapan-Englishtown MS Sci Tchr 1979-; *ai:* St Sci Fair Spon; NEA, NJ Sci Tchrs Assn, NSTA 1979-; East Brunswick Bapt Church 1977-, Bible Stud Dir, Organist; Governors Outstanding Tchr, Commissioner of Ed Awds 1986; Wkshp at Natl Sci Tchrs Convention; Booklet Taking Moans & Groans Out of Sci Fairs; Presidential Awd Nom 1988; *office:* Manalapan-Englishtown MS 155 Millhurst Rd Englishtown NJ 07726*

WHITE, NOEL JEAN DUNKER, Secondary Soc Studies Teacher; *b:* Linthicon, MD; *m:* Tramel A.; *c:* Eric Beaudin; *ed:* Lenoie Rhyne (BA) Ec His 1966; George Washington (MA) Admin Supervision 1972; *cr:* Arundel Sr HS Tchr 1966-70; A A Bd of Ed Specialist in Stu Affairs 1971-76; Chesapeake Sr HS Tchr 1977-; *ai:* SGA; Cty Wide Stu Govt Adv; MD St Ldrshp; TACC 1966-; MSTA 1966-; NEA 1966-.

WHITE, PATRICIA, English Teacher; *b:* Buenos, Argentina; *c:* Peter; *ed:* Tulane Univ (BA) Eng 1968, (MA) Ger 1977; Drew Univ (MA) Eng 1980; *cr:* MLHS Tchr 1968-; *ai:* Sr Class Adv; NEA, NTEA, MLEA 1968-; Lib Vol 1984-; Woodrow Wilson, Natl Endowment for Hum Scholars; *office:* Mountain Lakes HS Powerville Rd Mountain Lake NJ 07046

WHITE, PATRICIA ANN, Social Studies & Religion Tchr; *b:* Boston, MA; *ed:* St Thomas Aquinas Coll (BS) Ed 1970; Level II Advanced Rel Ed, Conflict Mediation Certs; Admin Grad Courses Manhattan Coll; *cr:* St Rose of Lima Spec Ed Tchr 1970-71; Aquinas HS PE Tchr 1971-72; SS Cyril & Methodius Schl Soc Stud, Rel Tchr 1975-; *ai:* Soc Stud Chprsm; Soc Stud Fair, Cath Schls Week, Grad Dinner Dance Comms; Yrbk Adv; Grad Coord; NCEA 1975-; *office:* Saint Syril & Methodius Schl 105 Half Hollow Rd Deer Park NY 11729

WHITE, PATRICIA FOGARTY, Biology Teacher; *b:* Pittsburgh, PA; *m:* Christopher F.; *c:* Sarah, Maggie; *ed:* PA St Univ (BS) Microbiology 1979; Duquesne Univ (MS) Scndry Ed 1986; *cr:* Mercy Hosp Lab Technician 1980-84; Allegheny Gen Hosp Lab Technician 1984-85; Mt Alvernia HS Tchr 1985-87; Pine-Richland HS Tchr 1987-; *ai:* Frosh Class Adv; NEA, PSEA, PREA, PSTA 1987-; *office:* Pine-Richland HS 4300 Warrendale Rd Gibsonia PA 15044

WHITE, PAUL F., Criminal Justice Director; *b:* Boston, MA; *m:* Rita McCann; *c:* Dan, Nancy, Ryan, Jennifer; *ed:* Boston Coll (BS) Ger Lit 1966; FL St Univ (MS) Criminology 1971; Northeastern Univ (MPA) Admin 1977; Doctoral Work in Sociology; Attnd Simmons Coll, Harvard Law Schl Ctr, MT St Univ, TX Tech, Boston Univ; *cr:* US Peace Corps Vol 1966-68; MA Dept of Yth Svcs Comm Rep 1968-72; Boston Yth Commission Exec Dir 1972-74; Westfield St Coll Asst Prof 1974-76; Quincy Coll Dir of Criminal Justice Stud 1977-; *ai:* CJ Club Adv; Org & Govt Comm; Acad Policies Scheduling Sub Comm; Little League & Soccer Coach 1984; Bsktbl Coach 1985; US Chess Club 1987; NEA, MTA, QEA & ASPA 1976-, CJ Sub Comm Chair; Quincy Coll Tchr of Yr Awd 1991, 1994 & SGA Awd; *office:* Quincy Coll 34 Coddington St Quincy MA 02169

WHITE, RAE MYLES, English Teacher & Dept Chprsn; *b:* Stirling, Scotland; *ed:* IL St Univ (BA) Eng 1967; Eastern IL Univ (MS) Eng 1972; Addl Hrs Eng Ed; *cr:* Mattoon HS Eng Tchr 1970-80; Dept of Defense Dependents Schls Eng Tchr, Dept Chair 1980-84; Magruder HS Eng Tchr 1984-89; Ridgeview Intermediate Schl Eng Tchr 1990-92; Gaithersburgh HS Eng Tchr, Dept Chair 1992-; *ai:* Global Access Tech Comm; Resource Tchrs; Liaison Comm; NEA 1967-; MCEA 1985-, Bd of Dir; MSTA 1985-, St Mbrshp Chair; Upcounty Citizens Advy Bd; Gaithersburg Presbyn Church; *office:* Gaithersburg HS 314 S Frederick Ave Gaithersburg MD 20877

WHITE, REGINALD RICHARD, 7th Grd Social Studies Teacher; *b:* Syracuse, NY; *m:* Sandra Jean Alsid; *c:* Andrew, Shannon, Mitchell; *ed:* SUNY at Cortland (BS) Elem, Early Sec 1985, (MS) Ed, Curr Dev 1993; *cr:* Roxboro Road MS Soc Stud Tchr 1985-; *ai:* Dist Steering Comm; Commissioner Regulation Comm; North Syracuse Ed Assn 1985-, VP; NYSUT, AFT 1985-; *office:* Roxboro Road MS 300 Bernard St Syracuse NY 13211*

WHITE, RICHARD ALBERT,SR., Asst Prof of Human Services; *b:* Baltimore, MD; *m:* Emma Valmorida Postrero; *c:* Richard A. Jr., Rhonda V. White-Yakoub, Roxanne A.; *ed:* Comm Coll of Baltimore (AA) Human Svcs 1985; Morgan St Univ (BSW) Soc Work 1987; OH St Univ (MSW) Soc Work 1988; *cr:* Baltimore City Dept of Soc Svcs Soc Worker 1988-90; Morgan St Univ Adjunct Fac 1988-; MD Dept of Hlth & Mental Hygiene AIDS Prevention Specialist 1990-92; Baltimore City Comm Coll Human Svcs Asst Prof 1992-; *ai:* Allied Human Svcs Club Fac Adv; Food, Clothing & Toy Drives for Needy Coord; Select Coll Comms; Great Blacks Wax Museum 1993-, Bd of Trustees; *office:* Baltimore City Comm Coll 2901 Liberty Heights Ave Baltimore MD 21215

WHITE, RICHARD B., Physical Education Teacher; *b:* Rochester, NY; *m:* Sharon Lee; *c:* Darci Lee, Jared James; *ed:* Orange Cty Comm Coll (AS) Hlth, PE 1972; Southern CT St (BS) Hlth, PE 1974; Grad Marion Cntrl; Addl 30 Hrs; *cr:* Marion Cntrl Schl PE Tchr 21 Yrs; *ai:* Boys Var Soccer Coach; Natl Soccer Coaches, NEA, NYSUTA 1975-; Marion Soccer Club 1984-, Bd of Dirs; Natl Rifle Assn 1975-; NY St Class C Soccer Champions 1988-89; 4 Time Coach of Yr; *office:* Marion Cntrl Schl 3863 N Main Marion NY 14505

WHITE, ROBERTA WEINHAUER, Spanish & Latin Teacher; *b:* New York, NY; *m:* Robert David; *ed:* Fordham Univ (BA) Eng 1972; Rutgers Univ (MED) Eng 1976; Span 18 Credit Hrs; Latin 25 Credit Hrs; *cr:* Florence Crittenton Home Tutor 1976-78; Mattanawcook Acad Tchr 1983-; *ai:* Latin & Span Club Adv; Kappa Delta Pi 1977-; *office:* Mattanawcook Acad 15 Reed Dr Lincoln ME 04457*

WHITE, RONALD I., Guidance Counselor; *b:* Corinth, NY; *m:* Roxanne Gardner; *c:* Katherine, Erin, Andrew; *ed:* St Lawrence Univ (BA) His 1973; SUNY at Plattsburgh (MS) Cnslng 1984, (CAS) Cnslng 1985; *cr:* Hague Cntrl Schl 7-12 Grd Eng Tchr 1974-76; Corinth Cntrl Schl 7-8 Grd Eng Tchr 1976-84, 7-12 Grd Cnslr 1984-; *ai:* Girls Bsktbl Coach; Shared Decision Making Team; Adirondack Cnslng Assn 1984-, VP, Sec, Pres; Corinth Little League 1988-, Bd of Dirs, Coach; *office:* Corinth Cntrl Schl 105 Oak St Corinth NY 12822

WHITE, ROSEANN, Assoc Dept Chair of Legal Stud; *b:* Boston, MA; *c:* Joshua W. Port, Matthew W. Port; *ed:* Emanuel Coll (BA) Soc; BC Schl of Management (MBA) 1989; Boston Coll Law (JD) 1989; BC Grad Schl Arts & Sci Sociology Dept 9 Credit Hrs; *cr:* Wiggin & Nourie Lawyer 1989-91; Newbury Coll Part-time Instr 1991-92, Dept Chair 1992-95, Assoc Dept Chair 1995-; *ai:* NH Bar Assn, Amer Bar Assn 1989-; MA Bar Assn 1990-; AAHE 1992-; FLPSE Grant 1993-94; *office:* Newbury Coll 129 Fisher Ave Brookline MA 02146

WHITE, RUTH MANN, Third Grade Teacher; *b:* Bethesda, OH; *m:* Starling Arthur; *c:* Jerry Arthur, Jeffrey David; *ed:* OH Univ at Athens (BA) K-8 Elem Ed 1965; K-8 Grd Elem Ed Akron Univ 18 Hrs 1983, Kent St 4 Hrs 1990, Ashland Univ 7 Hrs 1993, OH St 5 Hrs 1995; *cr:* Lincoln Schl 2nd Grd Tchr 1961-68; Preston Schl 3rd Grd Tchr 1970-78; Newbery Schl 4th, 6th Grd Tchr 1978-80; Bode Schl 5th Grd Tchr 1980-81; Lincoln Schl 3rd Grd Tchr 1982-; *ai:* Kappa Kappa Iota; Goals 2000; Fac Adv; Textbook Comm; Make It Take It Family Math; SWEEP in Sci; Family Hlth, Sci Night; Cub Scout Ldr; Church Fin Sec; NEA, OEA 1962-; Cuy Falls Ed Assn 1962-, Bldg Rep, Alternative Bldg Rep; *office:* Lincoln Elem Schl 3131 W Bailey Rd Cuyahoga Falls OH 44224*

WHITE, SANDRA HRYWNAK, Third Grade Teacher; *b:* Scranton, PA; *m:* David Michael; *ed:* East Stroudsburg St Coll (BS) Elem Ed 1970; Masters Equivalency 36 Credit Hrs; 53 Addl Hrs; *cr:* Henry Drinker Elem Schl Third Grd Tchr 1970-94, Head Bldg Tchr 1982-94; Moscoe Elem Ctr Third Grd Tchr 1994-; *ai:* Tcnr Induction Prgm Mentor; PSEA, NEA 1970-; PTA 1973-, Life Mem1994-; Foxfire Condominium Assn 1987-, Soc, Budget Comms; *office:* Moscow Elem Schl 851 Church St Moscow PA 18444

WHITE, SHARON VANORDEN, Media Specialist; *b:* Paterson, NJ; *m:* Richard J.; *c:* Danielle; *ed:* William Paterson Coll (BA) Art Ed 1971, (MA) Media Specialist 1989; *cr:* Butter HS Art Tchr 1971-89; Richard Butler Schl Media Specialist 1989-; *ai:* Stage Crew Adv; NEA 1971-; NJEA 1971-, Del Assembly; Butler Ed Assn 1971-, Pres, VP, Sec; Educl Media Assn 1989-; VFW Ladies Aux 1988-; *office:* Richard Butler Schl Pearl Pl Butler NJ 07405

WHITE, SONYA RENEE, String Teacher; *b:* Islip, NY; *ed:* Boston Univ (BMus) Music Performance 1988, (MMus) Viola Performance 1990; Post Grad Stud Boston Conservatory; *cr:* Greater Boston Yth Symphony Orch Tchr, Coach 1986-; Tanglewood Music Ctr Fellow 1988; Boston Classical Orch Viola 1990-92; Portland Symphony Orch Viola 1990-; *ai:* Music Dir, Conductor String Ensemble; Adv, Coach Chamber Ensemble; AFT, BTU 1992-; Amer Fdn Musicians 1987-; Project STEP 1994-, Bd Mem; *office:* Boston Latin Schl 78 Avenue Louis Pasteur Boston MA 02115*

WHITE, STEPHANIE A., Resource Teacher; *b:* Providence, RI; *m:* David A.; *ed:* RI Coll (BS) Spcl Ed & Ed 1976; Providence Coll (MED) Ed & Spcl Ed 1982; *cr:* Sanders Schl Self-Contained Spcl Ed 1976-79; RI St Insts Summer Tchr for Severly Handicapped 1976-82; Cranston HS East Resource Tchr 1979-; *ai:* Spcl Ed Club & Project Respect Adv; AFT 1976-.

WHITE, THOMAS MICHAEL, Technology Teacher; *b:* Binghamton, NY; *m:* Donna Caverly; *c:* Michael Author, Kathleen; *ed:* SUC at Oswego (BS) Industrial Ed 1976; SUNY At Albany 30 Credit Hrs; *cr:* Niskayuna Cntrl Industrial Arts Tchr 1976-81; HUCC Adj Prof Carpentry Apprentice 1986-90; Shenendehowa Cntrl Tech Tchr 1988-; Bast-Hatfield Construction Dir of Employee Trng 1994-; *ai:* Stage Crew Adv; Tech & Drama Club; Shared Decision Making Facilitator; Peer Mediation; Strategic Planning; NYSUT 1976-, Bldg Rep; KT Nursery Schl 1987-, Chm of Bd Trustees; PTA & PTK 1989-, Play Ground Vol Coord; Carpentry Apprentiship; Yrbk Dedication; Articles Pub; *office:* Shenendehowa Cntrl Schl 1 Fairchild Sq Clifton Park NY 12065

WHITE, THOMAS MICHAEL, HS Social Studies Teacher; *b:* Keene, NH; *ed:* Norwich Univ (BA) Summa Cum Laude His 1985; Keene St Coll (MAT) His 1994; Research Historian for Film Project About Amer Women Who Served in World War I to Finish Masters; *cr:* Keene HS Soc Stud Tchr 1985-; *ai:* Stu Cncl Adv 1985-; KHS Soviet Tour 1986-87, 1989; Alpha Chi, Natl Honor Schlsp Soc 1985-; The Simon Wresenthal Soc 1991-; The US Holocaust Mem Museum 1993-; Western Front Assn 1992-; Tchr of Yr, Yrbk Dedication 1989; Initated & Established AP European His Course; Initated Established Sociology & Holocaust Course; Stu Cncl Honor Cncl Awd Best Stu Cncls 1993; Selected for Arthur & Rochelle Belfer Natl Conf fo Edctrs At US Holocaust Memorial Museum in Washington DC 1993; *home:* 86 Colonial Dr Keene NH 03431

WHITE, W. QUINN, 6th Grade Teacher; *b:* Indianapolis, IN; *m:* Julie Bagley; *c:* Haley; *ed:* Taylor Univ (BS) Elem Ed 1988; OH St Univ (MA) Childrens Lit 1996; *cr:* Crooked Creek Elem Schl 4-5th Grd Tchr 1988-89; Grover Hill Elem 6th Grd Tchr 1989-91; Franklin Elem 6th Grd Tchr 1991-; *ai:* HS Boys Track, Jr High Girls Cross Cntry Coach; Schl Newspaper, Video News, Safety Patrol Adv; AFT 1991-; IRA 1995-; Mayors Campaign Comm; Cancer Soc Vol; Red Ribbon Vol; Youth Group Cncl Mem; Book Reviews, Artwork, Articles; Martha Holden Jennings Scholar, Master Tchr Nom, Grant Recipient; Tech Grant Recipient; Sally

Mae Nom; Whos Who Young Professionals; *office:* Franklin Elem Schl 305 Frothingham Van Wert OH 45891

WHITE, WILLIAM J., Senior Social Studies Teacher; *b:* Elmira, NY; *m:* Bonnie Dotey White; *c:* Irene, William P.; *ed:* Mansfield Univ (BS) Soc Stud Ed 1965; East Stroudsburg Univ (MS) Soc Stud 1972; *cr:* Sayre Soc Stud 1965-67; Stroudsburg Jr HS 8th Grd Soc Stud 1967-74; Stroudsburg MS 8th Grd Soc Stud 1974-91;Stroudsburg HS Sr Soc 1991-; *ai:* 8th Grd Boys Bsktbl Coach; 5-6 Grd Bsktbl Coord; Greater Pocono Bsktbl Tournament Dir; SAEA 1967-, Exec Bd 15 Yrs; PSEA, NEA 1965-; *home:* RR 1 Box 1091A Stroudsburg PA 18360*

WHITEBREAD, GAIL K., HS Mathematics Teacher; *b:* Kingston, PA; *m:* Donald L.; *c:* Dawn L., Denise L.; *ed:* Lycoming Coll (BA) Math 1965; 60 Plus Grad Credits from Bloomsburg Univ, Penn St Univ & Bucknell Univ; *cr:* Northwest Area HS Math Tchr 1965-67; Council Rock HS Math Tchr 1967-69 & 1978-; *ai:* SADD & BABES Adv 1998-94; NEA, PSEA & CREA 1965-78; NCTM 1983-; Alliance to Build Comm 1992-; NSF Grant 1966; Finalist Ed Yr-Bucks Cty Comm on Drugs & Alcoholism; *home:* 6 Cloverly Dr Richboro PA 18954*

WHITED, DARLENE MAY (SIMMONS), First Grade Teacher; *b:* Celina, OH; *m:* Thomas H.; *c:* Greg J.; *ed:* Wright St Univ (BS) Elem Ed 1970, (MS) Elem Ed 1979; Numerous Credit Hrs Beyond MS; *cr:* Coldwater Exempted Village Schl First Grd Tchr 1970-71; Celina City Schls Fifth Grd Tchr 1972-73, First Grd Tchr 1973-; *ai:* Rdng, Math Comm; NEA, OEA, WOEA 1970-; CEA 1972-, Bldg Rep; *office:* Celina West Elem Schl 1225 W Logan St Celina OH 45822*

WHITED, LINDA LEE (DAVIS), English Teacher; *b:* Akron, OH; *m:* Eugene H.; *c:* Wendy, Jefferson; *ed:* Univ of Akron (BS) Scndry Ed 1986, (MS) Elem Admin 1995; *cr:* Springfield HS Bus Tchr 1987-92, Eng Tchr 1992-; *ai:* Springfield Local Assn Classroom Tchrs Bldg Rep; Advy Comm; Project Understanding Adv; NEA, OEA, SLACT 1987-; NCTE 1995-; Pi Lambda Theta, Kappa Delta Pi 1985-; PTSA 1993-, Outstdng Edctr Awd 1995; Univ of Akron Outstdng Stu Tchr, Outstdng Bus Edctr 1986; Who's Who in Amer Ed 1996; *office:* Springfield HS 2996 Sanitarium Rd Akron OH 44312

WHITEFORD, EILEEN M., 7th-12th Grd Home Ec Teacher; *b:* Schenectady, NY; *c:* Collin; *ed:* Plattsburgh St Univ (BS) Home Ec Ed 1981; The Univ of Albany (MS) Ed Theory & Planning 1989; Castleton St Coll Educl Admin; *cr:* Saratoga Springs City Schl 7th-8th Grd Home Ec Tchr 1982-83; Mt Markham Cntrl Schl 7th-8th Grd Home Ec Tchr 1983-86; Greenwich HS 7th-12th Grd Home Ec Tchr 1986-; *ai:* FHA & Jr Class Adv; HETA; *office:* Greenwich Central Schl 10 Gray Ave Greenwich NY 12834

WHITEHEAD, CARL A., Retired Fifth Grade Teacher; *b:* Sayre, PA; *m:* Jacqueline Elvidge; *c:* Dale R., Ned C., John A., Stephanie Gathany, Laura Coats; *ed:* Mansfield Univ (BS) Elem Ed 1962; Post Grad Stud Penn St, Elmira Coll; *cr:* Northeast Bradford Dist 6th Grd Tchr 1962-68; Wyalusing Area Dist 5th Grd Tchr 1968-95; *ai:* PSEA, NEA 1962-; Wyalusing Area Ed Assn 1968-, Bldg Rep, Various Comms; Northeast Bradford Stu Loan Fund 1978-, Dir; HOPS Ambulance Assn 1982-, EMT Vol; Dille Parish UCC 1962-, Head Trustee; *home:* PO Box 123 Le Raysville PA 18829

WHITEHEAD, CAROLYN TAFT, Eng Tchr & Stu Org Advisor; *b:* Jamestown, NY; *ed:* Fredonia St Univ (BA) Eng 1964; Attnd Buffalo St Univ, Univ of CO, St Bonaventure; *cr:* Jamestown HS Eng Tchr 1965-; *ai:* Class, Amer Field Svc, Stu Org, NHS Adv; NEA; Chautauqua Chamber Singers 1981-; *office:* Jamestown HS 350 E 2nd St Jamestown NY 14701*

WHITEHEAD, JEANETTE ODEM, Secondary Guidance Counselor; *b:* Sharon, PA; *m:* Donald; *ed:* Penn St Univ (AS) Bus Admin 1984; Gannon Univ (BA) Soc Work 1985; Slippery Rock Univ (MA) Cnslng Svcs 1987; Cert Scndry Guid; *cr:* Penn St Univ Asst to Dir of Stu Affairs 1988-93; Hermitage Schl Dist Cnslr 1993-; *ai:* Girls Bsktbl Asst Coach; Matron Jr Ushers Comm Missionary Bapt Church; Mercer Cty Drug & Alcohol Comm, Bd Mem; Shenanego Vly Urban League Bd Mem.*

WHITEHEAD, LE ROY GUILBERT,JR., Vice Principal; *b:* Oak Ridge, NJ; *m:* Cheryl Stoltzfus; *c:* Megan, Sarah; *ed:* Lebanon Vly Coll (BS) Music Ed 1987; Rider Univ (MA) Educl Admin 1995; *cr:* Stonybrook Elem Schl Vocal Music Tchr 1987-89; Marlboro MS Vocal Music Tchr 1989-90; Matawan Regnl HS Vocal Music, Choir Dir 1990-; Rumson-Fair Haven Regnl HS Asst Prin 1996-; *ai:* Spring Musical Producer, Dir; Chamber Choir, Vocal Music Dir; Girls Choir; Barbershop, All-Shore, All-State Chorus; Pupil Assistance, Schl Climate, Harassment Gender, Equity, Tchr Recognition Comms; NHS Fac Advy Cncl ui; NASSP 1995-, ASCD 1993-; MENC 1987-; Amer Choral Dir Assn 1993-; Phi Mu Alpha 1984-; All-Shore Chorus Pres, Conductor 1993; Music Adjudication; Various Musical Compositions; *office:* Rumson-Fairhaven Regnl HS 74 Ridge Rd Rumson NJ 07760

WHITEHILL, LESLIE, Health Educator; *b:* Williamsport, PA; *c:* Rachel P. Skinner, Elijah B. Skinner; *ed:* PA St Univ (BS) Hlth, PE 1979; Purdue Univ (MS) Hlth Sci 1980; *cr:* PA St Univ Hlth Edctr, Instr 1980-81; James Madison Univ Hlth Edctr, Instr 1981-85; Williamsport Hosp & Med Ctr Comm Ed Specialist 1985-87; Williamsport HS Hlth Edctr 1987-; *ai:* HIV-AIDS Peer Edctr Adv, Trainer; PSEA 1987-; Eta Sigma Gamma 1978-; AASECT 1980-; AAHPERD 1979-; Florence Crittenton 1990-, Pres; AIDS Resource Alliance 1986-, Bd Mem; Preventing Teen Pregnancy 1987-, Bd Mem; Numerous Articles Pub; *office:* Williamsport HS 2990 W 4th St Williamsport PA 17701*

WHITEHOUSE, ELIZABETH KING, English Teacher; *b:* Bronxville, NY; *ed:* Colgate Univ (BA) Eng Lit 1988; Trinity Coll (MAT) Scndry Eng 1995; *cr:* Magruder HS Tchrs Aide 1992-95, Eng Tchr 1995-; *ai:* Yrbk Adv; *office:* Magruder HS 5939 Muncaster Mill Rd Derwood MD 20855

WHITEHOUSE, RAYMOND CHARLES, Biology Teacher; *b:* Boston, MA; *m:* Gail; *c:* John, Kathryn; *ed:* Univ of MA (BS) Bio 1967, (MSEd) Sci Ed 1973; Attnd Boston Univ; *cr:* Cntrl MS Sci Tchr 1967-88; Quincy HS Bio Tchr 1988-; *ai:* Yrbk Supvr; Head Coach Vlby; Jr Olympic Traveling Team; NSTA, QEA, MTA, NEA, Natl Geographic Soc; NRA; VSVBA; Text Pub Curr Guide to Warm Pullution Act 1969; *office:* Quincy HS 52 Coddington St Quincy MA 02169*

WHITEHURST, JAMES PATRICK, Social Studies Dept Chair; *b:* Havre De Grace, MD; *m:* Karen Elizabeth Mc Manus; *c:* J. Jeffrey; *ed:* Millersville Univ of PA (BS) Scndry Ed Soc Stud 1980; Towson St Univ of MD (MD) Lbrl Stud 1990; *cr:* Edgewood HS Earth Sci Tchr 1980-87; Bel Air HS Soc Stud Tchr 1988-; *ai:* SADD Adv; Stu Page Prgm Coord; Schl Cncl; Kid's Vote USA Coord; Selective Svc Registrar; Law Day Coord; Learning & Mentoring Prgm; Curr Comm; NEA, MSTA, HCEA 1980-; BSA 1992-, Den Ldr, Pack Comm Pack 238; Foresthill Recreation League 1992-, Soccer & Bsbl Coach; Harford Cty Tchr of Yr 1995-; Finalist MD Tchr of Yr 1995-; Statewide Winner Thanks to Tchrs Awds 1990; *office:* Bel Sr HS 100 Hieghe St Bel Air MD 21014*

WHITELEY DISTLER, CAROLYN DE SALES, Guidance Counselor; *b:* Easton, MD; *m:* James A.; *c:* Mary Allyn, Caitlyn, James; *ed:* Wilson Coll (BA) Psych, Ed 1977; Salisbury St (MED) Ed 1980; Bowie St (MED) Guid & Cnslng 1992; *cr:* Talbot Co Pub Schls Child Care Tchr 1977-83, First Grd Tchr 1983-86, Fourth Grd Tchr 1986-89, Elem Guid Cnslr 1989-; *ai:* Stdnts Helping Others & Understanding Themselves Adv 1993-95; Voc Indstrl Clubs Amer Adv 1977-82; Cmptr Club Adv 1986-89; NEA 1978-; SS Peter & Paul Church 1956-; Maritime Festival Chprsn Vol 1993-; A Caring Edctr Awd 1995; Drug Free Schls Recognition Grant; Talbot Partnership Drug Awareness Grant 1995; 2 Governor's Citation St of MD Drug Prevention 1991-92.

WHITEMAN, CAROL SZMURLO, Biology & Physical Sci Tchr; *b:* Wilkes-Barre, PA; *m:* John David; *c:* Eileen Lisa, Sharon Ann; *ed:* Immaculata Coll (BA) Bio 1967; Univ of DE Post Grad Stud 10 Credit Hrs; Chestnut Hill Coll PA Tchr Cert 22 Credit Hrs; *cr:* E. I. Dupont de Nemours & Co Patent Analyst 1967-72, Environmental Information Scientist 1972-75; Archbishop Ryan HS Environmental Sci, Eng Tchr 1991-92; Lasdale Cath HS Bio, Phys Sci Tchr 1992-93; Archbishop John Carroll HS Bio, Phys Sci Tchr 1993-; *ai:* Natl Amer Bio Tchrs 1992-; Natl Cath Edctrs Assn 1991; DE Cty Sci Tchrs Assn 1995-; NSTA 1993-; *office:* Archbishop John Carroll HS 211 Matson Ford Dr Radnor PA 19087

WHITEMAN, FERN VARGO, 5th Grade Teacher; *b:* Suffern, NY; *m:* Robert F.; *c:* Robert F. Jr., Heather L.; *ed:* SUC at Fredonia (BA) Elem Ed, Soc Stud 1972; Permanent Cert 1977; SUNY at Oneonta Post Grad Stud; *cr:* Cherry Vly CS Schl K-1, 5-6 Grd Tchr 1972-88; Cherry Vly Springfield Schl 4-5 Grd Tchr 1988-; *ai:* Girls Bsktbl JV Coach; Marching Band Color Guard; Sci, Hlth Curr; Handbook Coach; Taught Mini-Courses Law, Local His, Primary Documents; Hlth, Wellness Comm; NYSUT 1972-; St Magisgrates Assn 1974-; Otsego Co Magistrates Assn 1974-, Past VP, Pres; CV Meml Lib Trustee; Village Justice 1984-88; Acting Village Justice 1988-; Town Justice 1984-; 4-H 1988-91, Ldr; Girl Scouts 1972-74, Asst Ldr 1972-74; JC Soccer 1982-85, Coach, Asst Coach 1984-88; Little League 1984-88; Museum 1990-, Vol; Deputy Clerk Village of Cherry Vly 1993-94; CVS Booster Club; SEPA Grant Educl Prgm MIB Hosp; Soc St Grant Ed Prgm through NYS Hist Assn; *home:* PO Box 536 Cherry Valley NY 13320

WHITFIELD, STEPHEN VENARD,SR., PE & Health Teacher; *b:* Washington, DC; *m:* Brenda Kaye Smith; *c:* Stephen, Brandon, Marquita Shackleford; *ed:* Hampton Univ (BS) PE 1981; Attnd Trinity Coll; *cr:* Hamilton Jr HS PE Tchr 1987-89; Howard D Woodson Sr High PE Tchr 1989-95; Thurgood Marshall-Ft Lincoln PE Tchr & Ath Dir 1996; *ai:* Ftbl Defensive Line City Champs 1993-95; Girls Sftbl City Champs 1993-95; Boys & Girls Bsktbl Coach 1996; Boys Bsbl; Girls Sftbl; Alpha Phi Alpha 1978-, Brother, Mbrshp Awd; Whos Who Amongst Best Tchrs Candidate 1992, 2 Plaques Awded; My Child My Love for Life, A Guide to Better Understanding Your Child and Teenagers in Their Earlier Years & Skate Like Me, Fall of 1996; *home:* 9119 Grandhaven Ave Upper Marlboro MD 20772

WHITFORD, PATRICIA ANNE, Spanish Teacher; *b:* Wakefield, RI; *m:* Gilbert; *c:* John, Robert, Melissa; *ed:* Univ of RI (BA) Span, Ed; Eastern CT St Univ (MBS) Ed, Human Relations; 15 Addl Credit Hrs; *cr:* Warwick V. M. HS Span & Italian Tchr; St Bernard's HS Span Tchr; Griswold HS Span Tchr; *ai:* Jr Adv; Sr Adv Co-Moderator; Span, Intnl Club; NEA, GEA 1985-; COLT 1978-; Cub Scout Ldr, Den Mother; Webelos Ldr, Den Mother; Sprague, Franklin Sr, Little League, Sec; BEST Prgm; *office:* Griswold Jr-Sr HS Slater Ave Jewett City CT 06351*

WHITING, GREGORY ROBERT, Pastor; *b:* Des Moines, IA; *m:* Teresa Ann Campagna; *ed:* Bapt Bible Coll (BS) Bible 1989; Bapt Bible Seminary (MDiv) Bible, Pastoral 1992; *cr:* Bapt HS Bible, PE Tchr, Coach 1992-94; Faith Flwshp Bapt Pastor 1994-; *ai:* Ordained to Ministry 1994; *home:* 39 Linron Dr Danbury CT 06810

WHITING, JANET SUBERS, US His & Philosophy Teacher; *b:* Upper Darby, PA; *w:* Robert D. Sr. (dec); *c:* Robert D. Jr., Anne M.; *ed:* West Chester Univ (BS) Ed 1963; Widener Legal Ctr Paralegal 1994; Univ of DE Pol Sci; Villanova Pol Sci; *cr:* Forwood Jr HS Tchr 1964-72; Talley Jr HS Tchr 1972-82; Brandywine HS Tchr 1982-; *ai:* Stdnts in Govt Adv; NEA, DEA, BEA 1963-; Washington Seminar.*

WHITING, KATHLEEN M., Elementary French Teacher; *b:* Seneca Falls, NY; *ed:* Nazareth Coll (BA) Fr 1968, (MS) Gen Ed 1978; Brockport Coll Span Credit Hrs 1990-92; Monroe Comm Coll 6 Span Credit Hrs 1992-93; *cr:* John Marshall HS Fr Tchr 1969-70, 1973-75, 1984-85; St Charles Borromeo 6th Grd Tchr 1983-84; Schl #35 Elem Fr Tchr 1986-; *ai:* Schl-Based Planning Team; Fr Club Adv; Peer Mediation Coach; RTA 1983-; *office:* Pinnacle Schl #35 194 Field St Rochester NY 14620

WHITLEY, RICHARD A., Secondary English Teacher; *b:* Tarboro, NC; *m:* Karen Lee Kleckner; *c:* Michael, Wendy Monzo, Jessica Manion, Rachel, Rebecca; *ed:* Kutztown St Univ (BA) Eng 1963; Rider Coll (MA) Admin, Supervision 1977; *cr:* Avon Grove Schl Dist Eng Tchr 1963-68; Pennsbury Schl Dist Eng Tchr, Coord 1968-; *ai:* Rdng, Eng, Lang, Arts Advy Cncl; PSEA 1963-; PEA 1968-; NCTE 1991-; MPCS 1994-, VP; *office:* Pennsbury Schl Dist Yardley Ave Fallsington PA 19067*

WHITLEY, WILLIAM THURMON, Professor of Mathematics; *b:* DeLand, FL; *m:* Wilma Yates; *c:* Andrew; *ed:* Stetson Univ (BS) Math 1963; Univ of NC (MS) Math 1966; VA Polytechnic Inst & St Univ (PHD) Math 1969; *cr:* VA Polytech Inst Instr 1969-70; Marshal Univ Asst Prof, Assoc Prof 1970-79; Univ of New Haven Assoc Prof, Prof 1979-; *ai:* FAc Adv Delta Sigma Alpha; Acad Stan, Enrollment Mngmt Comms; Honors Pgm Comm; AAUP; Amer Math Soc 1967-; Math Assn of Amer 1968-, Chair Northwestern Section 1984-85; First United Meth Church West Haven CT 1983-, Church Treas, Cncl on Ministries Chair, Co-Lay Ldr; Eight Articles Pub Scholarly Journals, Two Univ of New Haven Publications, Eight Presented Prof Meetings & Symposia; *office:* Univ of New Haven 300 Orange Ave West Haven CT 06516

WHITLOW, DOREATHEA SIMS, Cooperative Voc Ed Tchr, Coord; *b:* Halifax, VA; *m:* Kenneth Levi; *c:* Byron G. Raney; *ed:* Elizabeth City St Univ (BA) Bus Ed 1965; 45 Credit Hrs Univ of MD; *cr:* Kennard HS Tchr 1965-66; Cortez Peters Bus Coll Tchr 1966-70; Benjamin Tasker Jr HS Tchr 1972-79; Benjamin Stoddard Jr HS Tchr 1979-82; High Point HS Tchr, Coord 1982-; *ai:* Mentor; Mid Sts Evaluation Schl Facilities Comm; NEA 1970-, Meritorious Svc; PGCEA 1970-, NBEA 1995-; MBEA 1992-; ECSU Alumni, Natl Cncl of Negro Women 1995-; NAACP 1990-; *office:* High Point HS 3601 Powder Mill Rd Beltsville MD 20705

WHITMAN, BARBARA CARR, Tchr of Eng Gifted & Talented; *b:* Narrows, VA; *m:* N. Lyon; *c:* Cathy, Heather; *ed:* Longwood Coll (BA) Eng 1969; Johns Hopkins (MED) Ed 1974; *cr:* Franklin Jr High Eng Tchr 1969-76; Franklin High Eng Tchr 1976-; Baltimore Cty Gifted & Talented Resource Tchr 1994-; *ai:* NCTE Writing Contest St Chm; Stu Support Team; Hospitality Comm; Multi-Cultural Comm; Franklin Centennial Celebration Comm; TABCO 1969-; MSTA 1969-; NEA 1969-; All Saints Episcopal Church 1984-, Vestry; Historic Glyndon 1986-, Pres; Glyndon Comm Assn 1986-, Sec; Chamber of Commerce Awd HS Tchr of the Yr 1994; *office:* Franklin HS 12000 Reisterstown Rd Reisterstown MD 21136

WHITMAN, KENT B., 6th Grade Teacher; *b:* Fremont, OH; *c:* Nathan, Tony; *ed:* Bowling Green (BS) Ed 1976; Toledo (ME) Counseling 1986; *cr:* Oak Harbor Jr HS Tchr 1977-; *ai:* Var Sftbl, Jr HS Cross Cntry Coach; NEA 1976-; St Paul Church 1976-, Treas; *home:* 543 N Church St Oak Harbor OH 43449

WHITMAN, MARY LOU MC ILROY, Fifth Grade Teacher; *b:* Huntingdon, PA; *m:* Terry L.; *c:* Matthew, Joseph; *ed:* Lock HAven Univ (BA) Elem, Spec Ed 1972; *cr:* Bellefonte Schl Dist Tchr 14 Yrs; *ai:* Math, Sci Comms; NEA, PSEA 1987-; MArion-WAlker PTO 1988-; *office:* Marion-Walker Elem Schl 100 Schl Dr Bellefonte PA 16823

WHITMAN, ROBERT L., English Composition Professor; *b:* Newton, MA; *ed:* Boudoin Coll (BA) His & Ec 1984; Harvard Univ (MEd) Curr & Assessment 1989; *cr:* Lesley Coll Lit Rsrch Asst 1989-90; Learning V Inc Ed Software Dev 1990-91; Tech Ed Rsrch Ctr Rsrch assoc 1991 MBCC Asst Prof 1993-; *ai:* New England Assessment Network; 1991-; MCCC 1991-; NEH Self Study 1995; *office:* MA Bay Comm 50 Oakland St Wellesley MA 02181*

WHITMAN HOFF, JOAN, Assoc Prof of Philosophy; *b:* Providence *m:* Stephen B.; *c:* Emily, Madeline, Charles, Alexandra; *ed:* R Williams Coll (AA) Liberal Arts 1973, (BA) Philosophy 1974; Univ c (MA) Philosophy 1977; The Amer Univ (PHD) Philosophy 1982; PA-S Summer Acad for the Advancement of Higher Ed 1994; MA Lynn Y Resource Bureau Cert in Mediation 1988; Univ of Nairobi Cert in Afr Stud 1973; *cr:* San Antonio Coll Instr of Philosophy 1980-84; Northern Univ Asst Prof of Philosophy 1984-86; Bentley Coll Asst Pro Philosophy 1986-90; Lock Haven Univ Assoc Prof of Philosophy 19 *ai:* Womens Coalition Co-Adv; Fac Prof Dev Comm; Accessability Co Honors Comm & Chair; Amer Philosophical Assn 1975-; Cana Philosophical Assn 1994-; Intnl Dev Ethics Assn 1988-; Loch H Hospital Ethics Comm 1995-; Loch Haven Hospital Ethics Subcommittee Chair 1995-; Loch Haven Cath Schl 1994-, Vol; PA Sc Tchng Scholars 1994-; NEH Summer Seminar for Coll Tchrs 1983 & 1 Canadian Embassy Grants 1989, 1990 & 1995; Over 11 Articles Pu Current Book Contracts; Over 65 Presentations Nationally Internationally; *office:* Lock Haven Univ Lock Haven PA 17745*

WHITMER, MARIE CARNESALE, Substitute Teacher; *b:* Brock PA; *m:* John E.; *c:* Lisa Brochelli, Mark, Leslie Huey, Merle, Eliza Bartoe; *ed:* Slippery Rock Univ (BS) Hlth & PE 1950; PA St Coll 6 C Hrs Permanent Cert 1953; *cr:* Brockway Area HS Hlth & PE Tchr 1950 East Brady HS Hlth & PE Tchr 1951-56 & 60-63; *ai:* Past: Chrldng Majorettes, Schl Plays, Spring Concerts, Prom Adv, Gym Shows; *h* 1258 Kittanning Pike Chicora PA 16025

WHITMORE, JOSEPH ARMSTRONG,JR., PE & Head Ath Traine Warrenton, VA; *m:* Lois Bowman; *c:* David Michael, Dona Jo Whitr Mc Donough; *ed:* Bridgewater Coll (BA) PE 1961; Attnd Springfield Elizabeth Coll; *cr:* Turner Ashby HS Hlth, PE, Sci Tchr, Coached 196 Agawam elem Schls PE Tchr 1967-68; Elizabethtown Coll PE T Coaching, Head Ath Trainer 1968-; *ai:* Amer Alliance for Hlth, Recreation, Dance 1970-; Natl Soccer Coaches Assn of Amer 1973-; Ath Trainers Assn 1971-; PA, Eastern Ath Trainers Assn 1972 Eas 1977 PA; John F. Steinman Fnd Awd for Tchng Excl 1976; Joh Steinman Awd for Excl Tchng 1982; *office:* Elizabethtown Coll 1 Alph Elizabethtown PA 17022

WHITMURE, SUSAN M. RISHER, High School English Teache Massillon, OH; *m:* Robert W. II; *ed:* Kent St Univ (BA) Scndry Ed & 1994; *cr:* Claymont High Eng Tchr 1 Yr; *ai:* Yrbk, Jr Class, Prom & D Team Adv; Oasis XV Comm Mem; NCTE; 1994-; OH Cncl Tchrs of Lang Arts 1995-; OCTELA; NCTE; Presenter at OH Cncl of Eng T Conf; *office:* Claymont HS 215 E 6th St Uhrichsville OH 44683

WHITNEY, ANN M., Social Studies Teacher; *b:* Elmira, NY; *m:* Mic T.; *c:* Megan A., Robert J., David M.; *ed:* Elmira Coll (BA) Amer 1990, (MS) Ed 1995; *cr:* Horseheads HS Soc Stud Tchr 1991-; *ai:* Challenge Team Coach; Horseheads Tchrs Assn 1992-; NYSUT 1 NYS Soc of Soc Stud Tchrs 1994-; *office:* Horseheads HS 401 Fletch Horseheads NY 14845

WHITNEY, BERNADETTE, 7th & 8th Grd Lang Arts Tchr Somerville, MA; *ed:* Notre Dame Coll (BA) Ed 1981; Grad Work R Coll; Grad Courses Notre Dame Inst VA Theology; *cr:* Rochester Fourth-Sixth Grd Tchr 1981-88; St Theresa Fifth Grd Tchr 1988-8 Catherine CCD Coord 1989-90; Sacred Heart Jr High Lang Arts 1990-; *ai:* Asst Coach Girls Sftbl Team; Stu Cncl Supvr; Spiritual D Camp Bern; Chrldng Adv; Yth Comm; Drama Coach; Sisters of Our of Lourdes 1985-; *office:* Sacred Heart Schl 289 Lafayette Rd Hamptor 03842

WHITNEY, CAROL ELIZABETH, Mathematics Teacher; *b:* Win VT; *ed:* Gordon Coll (BA) Math 1980; Univ of VT (MAEd) Cu Instruction 1987; 12 Credit Hrs Beyond Masters; *cr:* S Royalton Schl Tchr 1982-; *ai:* Acad, Soph Class & NHS Adv; Asst Dir of Drama.

WHITNEY, CHARLES DANA, Science Teacher; *b:* New Haven, C Nancy Reed; *c:* Beth; *ed:* Univ of SC (BS) Bio 1977; U of ME Tchr *cr:* US Navy Hosp Corpsman & Lab Tech 1969-73; Hosps & Physic Offices Consultant & Med Tech 1974-90; Summer Memrl HS Sci 1990-; *ai:* Track Team Head Coach; Outing Club Ldr; Adult Ed Ins Ornithology, Bio & Chem; NEA 1990-; NSTA 1990-; MSTA 1990-; Audubon Soc 1972-; HCMSC 1994-, Charter Mem; *home:* RR 5 Box 3 Ellsworth ME 04605*

WHITNEY, CYNTHIA BAKER, Fifth Grade Teacher; *b:* Columbus, *m:* James Jay; *c:* Candice Byrley, Matthew; *ed:* OH St Univ at Colun (BS) Summa Cum Laude Elem Ed 1987; Post Grad Stud 10 Hrs Otter Coll at Westerville; *cr:* Christ the King Chrstn Schl MS, HS Tchr 1989 Mc Vay Elem Schl 5th Grd Tchr 1990-; *ai:* Stu Cncl Co-Adv; Stu- Assistance Team; WEA Back to Schl Comm; NEA; WEA; Nom Ash Tchg Awd 2 Times; *office:* Mc Vay Elem Schl 270 S Hempstead Westerville OH 43081

WHITNEY, MATTHEW CHARLES, Business & Mathematics Teac *b:* Springfield, MA; *ed:* Western New England Coll (BSBA) Acctng 1 36 Cred Hrs Math Westfield St Coll; *cr:* Springfield Pub Schls HS Math Tchr 1985-; *ai:* NCTM 1995-; *office:* HS Of Commerce 415 Sta Springfield MA 01105

WHITNEY, SANDRA M., Speech Pathologist; *b:* Ilion, NY; *m:* Dre Piaschyk; *ed:* SUNY at Fredonia (BS) Music Ed 1968; Syracuse Univ (Speech Pathology 1995; 30 Grad Hrs in Music, Gen Ed; *cr:* Pub S Vocal, Gen Music Tchr 1968-92; Delaware-Chenango-Madison-Otseg of Cooperative Ed Svcs Speech Pathologist 1995-; *ai:* ASHA 19 NYSSLHA 1994-; Music Ed, Tchr of Speech & Hearing Handicap Permanent Cert; Syracuse Univ Rsrch Traineeship; VA Hosp in Syra Speech Dept Traineeship; Completion of Master's Thesis; *home:* HC Box 112 Plymouth NY 13832

WHITNEY, STARR, English Teacher; *b:* Gary, IN; *m:* Starr Giese Suzanne; *ed:* Purdue Univ (BA) Eng, Span 1967; West Chester Univ (Eng Lit 1972; *cr:* Haverford HS Tchr 1969-; *ai:* Schl Wide An Speaking Contest; MTEA 1969-, Exec Cncl; PSEA, NEA 1969-; Reader 6th Year Appointment; *office:* Haverford HS 210 Mill Havertown PA 19083*

WHITNEY, STEWART BOWMAN, Professor & Chair of Sociology Buffalo, NY; *m:* Joan Noel Conti; *c:* Scott Boyd, Edythe-Louise B Elizabeth Constance, Stewart Bowman; *ed:* Univ of Buffalo (Sociology 1961; SUNY at Buffalo (MA) Sociology 1965; (PHD) Socio 1972; Family Therapy CFLE; Sex Therapy Clinical Supervision FAA Rutgers Univ Post Grad Alcohol Stud Ctr; *cr:* SUNY at Buffalo Stud 1962-65; Ithaca Coll Asst Prof 1965-69; SUNY at Buffalo Asst 1969-70; Antioch Coll Asst Prof 1970-72; Niagara Univ Prof, Chair 19 *ai:* Space Settlement Stud Project Dir; Black Family Stud Adv; B Family Ctr Vice Chair; Amer Sociological Assn; Amer Pub Hlth A Eastern Sociological Soc; Natl Cncl Family Relations; Challenger Robert Heinlein Expeditions; Natl Space Soc; Inner City Acad; Partne s; US Children's Bureau, Natl Acad of Sci, Univ Grants; Books; : Niagara University Lewiston Rd Niagara Univ NY 14109

TNEY, TIMOTHY LEROY, Spanish & German Teacher; *b:* ninster, MD; *ed:* Western MD Coll (BA) Span & Ger 1989; Post Grad *cr:* Westminster High Span & Ger Tchr 1989-; *ai:* Future Edctr of Adv, Amer Edctr Week, Fac Schlshp Comm Chair; NEA 1989-; 3 1995; *office:* Westminster HS 1225 Washington Rd Westminster MD 7

TTEMORE, JANET BRADY, Second Grade Teacher; *b:* lessex, England; *m:* Norman Kimm; *c:* Norman Mick; *ed:* SUNY at seo (BA) Elem & Early Chldhd Ed 1968; SUNY at New Paltz (MS) Ed 1972; *cr:* Hallsville Elem Schl Kndgtn Tchr 1968-69; LaGrange Schl 1st-2nd Grd Tchr 1972-79; Beekman Elem 2nd Grd Tchr 1979-; rts in Ed Comm; NYSUT 1972-; *office:* Beekman Elementary Schl Ridge Rd Poughquag NY 12570*

TTEMORE, MAUREEN AUSTIN, Fifth Grade Teacher; *b:* Fall , MA; *m:* Ronald R.; *ed:* Bridgewater St (BS) Elem Ed 1972; RI Coll) Elem Ed 1987; *cr:* Swansea Pub Schls Tchr 1972-; *ai:* Schl Cncl; 'urr Comm; NEA 1972-; RI Women's Ctr 1992-, Vol; *office:* E. A. n Schl Gardners Neck Rd Swansea MA 02777

TTEN, FRANCIS,III, Health & Psychology Teacher; *b:* Winchester, *m:* Susan A. Mann; *c:* Francis IV; *ed:* Boston Coll (BA) His Ed 1978; n Univ (MED) Hlth & PE 1983; Credit Hrs in Admin; In Svc Credit *cr:* Natick Sr HS 10th-12th Grd Soc Stud Tchr 1978-79; Hopedale HS 7th-12th Grd Tchr 1979-90, K-12th Grd Hlth Tchr 1983-, K-6th E Tchr 1990-92, Curr Coord 1992-; *ai:* Ath Dir; Var Soccer Coach 91; Var Sftbl Coach 1979-; Class of 1983 & 1989 Adv; MHSSCA ., Pres; NEA, NTA & HTA 1979-; MADA & NADA 1993-; PERD; Smoking Cessation 1995-, Instr; SADD Adv 1985-, Peer r Adv 1985-; Yrbk Dedication 1983 & 1989; Hlth Protection & rnors Alliance Against Drugs Grants; *office:* Hopedale Jr Sr HS 25 St Hopedale MA 01747*

TTINGTON, LORRAINE WHITE, Co-Chprsn Foreign Lang Dept; ainfield, NJ; *m:* Dale Martin; *c:* Douglas Alan, Stephen Todd; *ed:* St of NY at Albany (BA) Eng 1965; Nazareth Coll (MS) Ed 1987; 30 Grad Hrs St Univ of NY at Brockport, Saint John Fischer Coll in Eng & Ed; *cr:* Henry V Burger Jr HS Eng & Latin Tchr 1965-72; us Schls Eng, Latin & Lib Sub Tchr 1984-88; Penfield HS Foreign Dept Co-Chprsn & Latin & Eng Tchr 1988- Bay Trail Mid Schl Latin 1995-; *ai:* Cmptr Comm; Parkng Comm; K-12 Dist Ldrshp Comm; JT 1988-; ACL, NYSAFLT & CAES; ULTIMA; Henrietta Jaycees anding Young Educator Awd 1972; Webster Cntrl Schl Dist Bd of Ed nguished Svc Awd 1988; *home:* 77 Alberta Dr Penfield NY 14526

TWELL, DORIS, Third Grade Teacher; *b:* Lockport, NY; *ed:* SUC at lo (BS) Elem Ed 1962, (MA) Elem Ed 1972; Post Grad Courses SUC iffalo, Univ of Buffalo; *cr:* Williamsvile Schl Elem Tchr 1962-; *ai:* ren's Theater Group Dir; AFT, Williamsville Tchrs Assn 1962-; e Ringers 1989-; *office:* Williamsville Cntrl Schls 415 Lawrence Bell illiamsville NY 14051

RTON, BARBARA YOUNG, 6th-7th Grade English Teacher; *b:* delphia, PA; *m:* W. Riley; *c:* Kelly, Tanya, Page Whorton Barnes; *ed:* of MD (BA) Eng, His 1964; Coll of Notre Dame (MA) Lbrl Stud Gender Stud Seminar 3 Yrs; Black His Awareness; Gender, Sexual in Schls; *cr:* Glenwood MS 6th Grd Lang Arts Tchr 1986-93; Owen n MS 7th Grd Eng Tchr 1993-95; Clarksville MS 6th-7th Grd Eng 1995-; *ai:* Mentor Tchr Stu Tchrs; Cross-Curr Coord Asian Stud, His, Latino Stud; NCTE; Article, Anecdote Pub; *home:* 3014 hstone Rd Ellicott City MD 21042*

'SONG, MYRA (DIBERT), Algebra Teacher; *b:* Bedford, PA; *c:* M.; *ed:* Shippensburg St Univ (BSEd) Math 1980; 13 Addl Post Baccl ts; 12 Addl Masters Credits; *cr:* Cntrl Dauphin Schl Dist 8th Grd Tchr 1981; Forest Hills Sr HS Math Instr 1982-; *ai:* NHS Fac Cncl; ss, Prom Adv; NEA 1981-; Pavia Twp Auditor 1994-; *home:* RR 1 36B Imler PA 16655

'TE, WILLIAM F., Criminal Justice Instructor; *b:* Rochester, NY; *m:* l P.; *c:* Justin, Joshua; *ed:* Rochester Inst of Tech (BS) Criminal e 1980; SUNY at Brockport (MS) Educl Admin 1994; Cert in ntry, Pub, Pvt Security, Admin; *cr:* NYS Division for Yth Carpentry 1982-90; Eastern Monroe Career Ctr Criminal Justice Instr 1990-; *ai:* ndstrl Club of Amer Adv; Awds Night Comm; AFT 1982-; Newark League 1989-, Past Pres, Bd Mem; Alex Eligh Comm Ctr 1989-, Vol; Staff Achvmt Awd 1995; *office:* Eastern Monroe Career Ctr 41 nor Rd Fairport NY 14450

RD, HERB, Social Studies Teacher; *b:* Augsburg, Germany; *m:* ie; *c:* Zachary, Nicole; *ed:* OH St Univ (BS) Scndry Ed 1980; Univ ayton (MA) Guid Cnslng 1987; *cr:* Southwest-Licking Local Schls 1980-; *ai:* Drug Free Schls Coord; Peer Ldrshp Coord; Peer Mediation ; NEA 1980-; Watkins Memrl Tchr of the Yr 1987 & 1993; Grant for Dev Northeast Regnl Ctr for Drug Free Schls & Comms 1989; Dow ical Excl in Ed Awd 1994; Ashland Oil Tchr Achvmt Awd 1994; : Watkins Memorial HS 8868 Watkins Rd Pataskala OH 43062

LE, MARY C., 6th Grd Reading & English Tchr; *b:* Philadelphia, PA; lanor Jr Coll (AS) Legal Secretarial Sci 1973; Holy Family Coll (BA) Ed 1982; *cr:* St Timothy Schl 5th Grd Eng, Rdng Tchr 1975-76, 4th Eng, Rdng Tchr 1976-77; 5th Grd Eng, Rdng Tchr 1977-82; 6th Grd Rdng Tchr 1982-; *ai:* Ath Bd; Spirit Day Coord; Marketing, rated Lang Arts Comm; *office:* St Timothy Schl 3033 Levick St delphia PA 19149

AL, JANICE MARLENE SNIDER, Third Grade Teacher; *b:* Lima, : Stephanie N., Geoff A.; *ed:* OH St Univ (BS) Ed 1976; 150 Semester Project Discovery Math Inst 1993; *cr:* Botkins Local Schl Kndgtn 1977-80; Waynesfield-Goshen 4th Grd Tchr 1983-85, 3rd Grd Tchr -; *ai:* 4-H Schl Prgm Adv; Right to Read Week Co-Chair; IRA; United Church, 6th-12th Grd Youth Ldr; Botkins Band Spons, Sec 1994-95; : Waynesfield-Goshen Sch PO Box 370 Waynesfield OH 45896

HELNS, JEROME B., Assoc Prof of Philsphy & Eng; *b:* Newark, NJ; ne B. Ludlam; *c:* Andrew, John Henry, Kathryn, George; *ed:* Rutgers (BA) His, Eng 1959; Columbia Univ (MA) Philosophy 1990; Attnd of Vienna 1962; Potsdam Univ 1982, Pursuing a Doctorial Degree in ious Stud; *cr:* Xerox Corp Ed Educl Publications 1964-66; Mount ony HS 9-12th Grd Tchr 1972-78; Copenhagen HS 9-12th Grd AP 1978-85; Jefferson Comm Coll Asst Prof of Philosophy & Eng 1985-; C Senate Pres; Analytical Stud Group; NEA 1986-; Amer Phil Assoc; of Denmark Planning Bd 1986-, Chm; Grace Church 1990-, Vester; anding Fac Mem 1992; US Philosophy Delegation to Peoples Rep of a 1993; Articles Pub; Presenter International Symposium Ethics 1996; : Jefferson Community College Outer Coffeen St Watertown NY 1*

HTOWSKI, MARY C., English Teacher; *b:* Albany, NY; *m:* Richard John, Lynn Monshower, Eric; *ed:* Univ of ALbany (BA) Latin 1963, Eng 1965; Grad Credits Tchng Writing, Cooperative Learning; *cr:* endehowa HS Eng Tchr 1979-; *ai:* World Lit-Cult European Trip erone; Various Schl, Dept Comms; Curr Wkshps; NYSUT, AFT 1979-; E 1985-; Church Comm 1994-; *office:* Shenendehowa HS 970 Route Clifton Park NY 12065

WICK, JOHN R., Career Counselor; *b:* Hartford, CT; *m:* Susan; *c:* Emily, Jessica; *ed:* Coll of Wooster (BA) Philosophy 1970; Univ of Hartford (MS) Cnslng 1977; *cr:* Mattatuck Comm Coll Career Cnslr 1977-93; Naugatuck Vly Comm Tech Coll Career Cnslr 1993-; *ai:* Coll Choral Soc Adv; Chorus; CCUCA 1992-, Sec, Meritorious Svc Awd; *office:* Naugatock Valley Comm Coll 750 Chase Pky Waterbury CT 06708

WICKERSHAM, TILNEY, Social Studies Teacher; *b:* Greenwich, CT; *m:* Keith R. Mestrich; *c:* Nora; *ed:* Yale Univ (BA) His 1988; 15 Hrs of Grad Level Stud Ed Trinity Coll; *cr:* Cntr for Population Options Prgm Asst 1988-89; Alice Deal Jr HS Soc Stud Tchr 1989-; *ai:* Schl Newspaper Spon; WA Tchrs Union, AFT 1990-; NCSS 1996-; DC Geographic Alliance 1994-, Steering Comm; *office:* Alice Deal Jr HS Nebraska Ave & Ft Dr NW Washington DC 20012*

WICKERT, GABRIELE MARIA, Dean of Studies & German Prof; *b:* Langenneufnach, Germany; *c:* Eve; *ed:* Univ of Rochester (BA) Eng Lit 1968; SUNY at Albany (MA) Ger Lit 1971; U of MA at Amherst (PHD) Ger Lit 1980; *cr:* Manhattanville Coll Ger Prof, Intnl Stud 1976-95, Dean of Stud 1995-; *ai:* Lang Lab 1980-83, Westchester Consortium Intnl Stud 1990-92 Dirs; AATG 1978-; IREX Grant East Berlin 1984, Praque 1992; Fulbright Grant West Berlin 1987-88; *office:* Manhattanville Coll 2900 Purchase St Purchase NY 10577

WICKLUND, BONNIE-LOU, Adjunct Mathematics Professor; *b:* Gardner, MA; *c:* Ashley, Christian; *ed:* Mt Wacgusett Comm Coll (AA) Gen Stud 1970; Fitchburg St Coll (BS) Physics 1973, (MED) Sci Ed 1982; Critical, Creative Thinking Inst UMASS at Boston; Post Grad Math Stud UMASS at Lowell; Trng Inst-TRIO Prgm Prsnl Marquette Univ; *cr:* Middlesex Comm Col Math Prof 5 Yrs; Quinsigamond Comm Col Math Prof 6 Yrs; Mt Wachusett Comm Col Dev Math Specialist, Math Prof 17 Yrs; *ai:* Fac Adv, Tutor, Coll Fac, Adj Fac, LAANE Conf 1989-94, Conf Chair 1990-91, AMATYC Natl Conf 1993 Comms; Text Reviewer Houghton Mifflin Co; Conf Presentor; LAANE 1984-, Conf Chair; NADE, NEMATYC 1989-; AMATYC 1992-; Commonwealth of Mass Pride Inperformance Awd 1989; Fnd Fac Grant 1990; *office:* Quinsigamond Comm Coll 670 W Boylston St Worcester MA 01606

WIDDIS, MARY ELIZABETH, French Teacher; *b:* Troy, NY; *m:* James E. Jr.; *c:* Steven J.; *ed:* Skidmore Coll (BA) Fr 1982; NY St Univ at Albany (MA) Fr 1995; *cr:* Saratoga Cntrl Cath HS Fr Tchr 1988-89; Fonda-Fultonville Cntrl Schl Fr Tchr 1989-; *ai:* MS Frgn Lang Comm Chrprsn; NY St United Tchrs, NY St Assn of Foreing Lang Tchrs 1989-; Capital Org of Lang Tchrs; Adirondack Mountain Club 1986-, Former Club Treas; Wings Falls Quilt Guild, Burnt Hills Oratorio Soc; *office:* Fonda-Fultonville Central Schl 112 Old Johnstown Rd Fonda NY 12068*

WIDEN, BRUCE GREGORY, Social Studies Teacher; *b:* Jamestown, NY; *m:* Eileen Elizabeth Quinn; *c:* Curtis, Bradley, Gregory; *ed:* St Univ at Fredonia (BA) Ed 1962, (MA) Ed 1968; Supervision, Admin 1977; *cr:* Jamestown City Schls 6th Grd Tchr 1962-; *ai:* 7th-8th Grd Ski Club Adv; Shared Decision Making, Discipline Comms; NYSTA, NEA, JTA 1962-; *office:* G. A. Persell MS 375 Baker St Jamestown NY 14701*

WIDMANN, WAYNE BRUCE, 8th Grd Language Arts Teacher; *b:* Newark, NJ; *m:* Cheryl L. Johnson; *c:* Bonney; *ed:* Montclair St Univ (BA) Eng 1973; Kean Coll (MA) Hum & Ed 1976; Tchng Cert; Post Grad Stud Supvr, Prin Certs Kean Coll 1978; *cr:* Long Vly MS Grds 6-12 Lang Arts Tchr 1973-83, Grds 7-8 Lang Arts Tchr 1983-; *ai:* 8th Grd Team Ldr, Class Adv; NEA, NJEA 1973-; WA Twp EA 1983-, Fac Rep 1985-89, Chm 1988-; Church Organist & Choir Dir 1972-; *office:* Long Valley MS 51 W Mill Rd Long Valley NJ 07853

WIDMER, WALTER H., 10th Grade Biology Teacher; *b:* Jersey City, NJ; *m:* Rosemarie; *c:* Leslie Woodworth, Susan; *ed:* St Univ NY Delhi (AAS) Ag 1954; Fairleigh Dickinson (BS) Bio, Chem 1960, (MS) Ed Sci 1970; *ai:* Bio, Chess, Renaissance Clubs; NEA 1960-; NYNEA 1965-; Nature Conservation; *office:* Ramapo Sr HS 400 Viola Rd Spring Valley NY 10977

WIDMEYER, FREDERICK PAUL, 10th-12th Grade Math Teacher; *b:* Cincinnati, OH; *m:* Vickie C. Welborn; *c:* Alexander, Lauren; *ed:* Univ of Cincinnati (BSEd) Math 1975, (MAT) Math 1976; 15 Grad Hrs; *cr:* Regina HS Tchr 1976-77; Roger Bacon HS Math Tchr 1977-; Mt St Joseph Coll Tchr 1989-93; Raymond Walters Coll Tchr 1990-92; *ai:* Var & Reserve Golf Team; Chess Club; Greater Cincinnati Math Tchrs 1981-; OH Tchrs of Math 1991-; Cincinnati Gas & Electric & WLWT Awd of Inspiration for Exel in Tchng 1995; NSF Discovery Tchr 1996; *office:* Roger Bacon HS 4320 Vine St Cincinnati OH 45217

WIDOM, DAVID, Teacher; *b:* Brooklyn, NY; *m:* Carol Ramos; *c:* Amanda, Brian; *ed:* CCNY (BA) Chem 1969; *cr:* Erasmus Hall HS Tchr 1981-94; Midwood HS Tchr 1994-; *ai:* New Action Coalition-UFT 1985-.

WIDRICK, KYLE W., Math Tchr & Guidance Cnslr; *b:* Lowville, NY; *m:* Tammy J. Roes; *c:* Brittany M., Jordan B., Kurt J.; *ed:* Elizabethtown Coll (BS) Math 1989; *cr:* Jefferson Comm Coll Math Instr 1991-95; Faith Fellowship Chrstn Schl 1993-; *home:* 12373 Co Rt 66 Adams Center NY 13606

WIDRICK, LYNN S., English Teacher; *b:* Utica, NY; *m:* Barry K.; *ed:* SUNY at Geneseo (BA) Eng 1972; Syracuse Univ (MS) Rdng Ed 1975; *cr:* Whitesboro HS Eng Tchr 1972-; *ai:* Comms; Bldng Decision-Making Team; Union Bd of Dir; Mentor Tchr; Supervising Tchr; AFT & NYSUT 1972-; W Tchrs Assn 1972-, Bldg Rep; NCTE 1972-; *office:* Whitesboro HS 6000 Rt 291 Marcy NY 13403

WIDULSKI, WILLIAM F., Math & Comp Sci Asst Professor; *b:* New Rochelle, NY; *ed:* SUNY at Purchase (BA) Math 1987; NY Univ (MS) Math 1989; Working on MS in Cmptr Sci Polytechnic Univ; Cmptr Sci Cert SUNY at Purchase 1987; *cr:* Westchester Comm Coll Asst Prof 1990-; *ai:* Fac Senate 1991-; Fac Prsnl Policies Comm 1993-; Linear Algebra Ind Stud Tchr 1992; BASIC Programming 1994; Assisted Math Modeling Team; MAA 1989-; ASA 1991-92; NYSMATYC 1995-; Articles Pub; *office:* Westchester Comm Coll 75 Grasslands Rd Valhalla NY 10595*

WIEAND, WILLIAM GEORGE, Social Studies Teacher; *b:* Parris Island, SC; *m:* Betsy Halberstadt; *c:* Bruce, Valerie Ramzi, Adrienne Danforth, Theresa, Jennifer Follin, William Jr.; *ed:* Santa Clara Univ (BS) Eng 1953; Georgetown Univ (BS) Frgn Svc 1954; George Washington Univ (MA) Intnl Affairs 1972; US Army Command & Gen Staff Coll; *cr:* Bullis Schl Soc Stud Tchr 1987-; *ai:* Stu Newspaper Adv; JV Boys Tennis Coach; Fac Rep Bd of Trustees; *home:* 4519 Nebraska Ave NW Washington DC 20016*

WIEBOLDT, ROBERT WILLIAM, Social Studies Teacher; *b:* East Stroudsburg, PA; *m:* Carol Spencer; *c:* Thomas, Cheryl Burns, Chris Day, Jeffrey; *ed:* East Stroudsburg Univ (BA) Soc Stud 1968; East Stroudsburg (MS) Admin & Scndry Ed 1990; *cr:* Pleasant Vly Tchr 1968-70; North Warren Regnl Tchr 1970-; *ai:* Soccer & Golf Coach; NEA 1968-.

WIECOREK, KATHLEEN HURLEY, Instructional Support Coord; *b:* Rochester, NY; *c:* Kimberly, Wakeisha; *ed:* Nazareth Coll (BA) Sociology 1971, (MA) Ed 1973; Brockport Coll (MA) Admin 1989; *cr:* Rochester City Schls 5th Grd Tchr 1982-89, Enrichment Tchr 1984-89, Basic Skills Tchr 1989-90, 5th Grd Tchr 1990-93, Instrl Support Ldr 1993-95; *ai:* Schl Based Mngmt; Educl Rsrch & Dissemiation Ldr; Phi Delta Kappa 1989-; Tchr of Yr 1992; Fed Grant; Schl to Work Grant; *office:* Schl #19 465 Seward St Rochester NY 14608*

WIECZOREK, CORRINE BUSH, Business Education Teacher; *b:* Olean, NY; *m:* Russell; *c:* Jason, Nicole, Ashley; *ed:* Mercyhurst Coll (BA) Bus Ed 1976; 36 Credits Univ of KY, Wilkes Coll, Duquesne Univ, Clarion Univ, Gannon Univ, Univ of Fredonia, Coll of Saint Rose; *cr:* Sherman Cntrl Bus Tchr 1976-78; Iroquois HS Bus Tchr 1981-83; Mercyhurst Prep Bus Tchr 1986-88; Erie Cntrl HS Bus Tchr 1988-; *ai:* CORE SAP Team; Asst to Bus Club; FBLA; Chrldr Adv; Class Adv 1992-; PSEA, NEA 1988-; PTA Millcreek Schls; *office:* Erie Cntrl HS 3325 Cherry St Erie PA 16508

WIEDERHOLD, L. JEFF, Math Teacher; *b:* Cincinnati, OH; *m:* Mary Kim Wolfer; *c:* Katie, Anna, Chas, Tim; *ed:* Wilmington Coll (BS) Ed, Math, His 1983; Wright St Univ (MS) Educl Leadership 1992; *cr:* Wilmington HS Math Tchr, Coach 1984-; Chatfield Coll Instr 1992-; *ai:* Wrestling Coach; Intervention Co-Coord; Math Dept Co-Chair; OH Ed Assn, Wilmington Ed Assn 1983-; NCTM 1993; SAY Soccer Bd; SAY Soccer Coach 1990-; Soc Action Dir 1990-, Chprsn; Church Youth Adv 1984-; Schl Bus Partnership Awd; Clinton Co Tchr of Yr 1995; *office:* Wilmington HS 300 Richardson Pl Wilmington OH 45177*

WIEDL, EVELYN J., 5th & 6th Grd Math & Sci Tchr; *b:* Bethlehem, PA; *m:* John S.; *c:* Michael, Thomas, Richard; *ed:* Moravian Coll (BS) Elem Ed 1968; 20 Credit Hrs Creative Bulletin Bds, Child Abuse, Cmptrs, Schls Without Failure; Math Conn Through Eisenhower Grant; *cr:* Quakertown Schl Dist Transitional Tchr 1968-69; Brunswick Schl Dist First Grd Tchr 1969-70; St John Capistrano Fifth Grd Tchr 1980-81; Sacred Heart Schl Sixth, Third, Second Grd Tchr 1982-; *ai:* Grades 4-8 Arts & Crafts Activity Dir; ADLTA 1988-, Fac Rep; Sacred Heart Schl Fac Rep, ADLTA Fac Rep 1995-96; *office:* Sacred Heart Schl 1814 2nd St Bethlehem PA 18017

WIEDMAN, COLLEEN O'NEIL, Physical Education Teacher; *b:* Olean, NY; *m:* William; *c:* Abigail; *ed:* SUNY at Cortland (BA) PE 1984; St Bonaventure (MS) Remedial Rdng 1991; *cr:* Salamanca HS PE Tchr, Coach 1984-89; Prospect Elem Schl PE Tchr, HS Coach 1989-; *ai:* Girls Var Bsktbl, Western NY Empire St Girls Bsktbl Coach; NEA 1984-; NY St Coach of Yr 1988; *office:* Prospect Elem Schl 300 Prospect Ave Salamanca NY 14779

WIEHE, JAMES MICHAEL, History Teacher; *b:* Harrisburg, PA; *m:* Deborah L.; *c:* Kerry M., Kristin M.; *ed:* IN St Univ (BS) His, Hlth & Safety 1969; Attnd PA St Univ, East Stroudsburg Univ, Wilks Coll, Carlow Coll; *cr:* David Breaeley HS Tchr 1970-71; Harrisburg Schls Tchr 1971-72; St of PA Drug, Alcohol Supvr 1973-76; Conrail Conductor 1976-79; Susquenita HS Tchr 1979-; *ai:* Var Bsbl Coach 1982-87; Mentor Tchr; Stu Tutor; NEA 1979-; Duncannon Girls Sftbl Assn; Duncannon Teener Bsbl; *office:* Susquenita HS 1765 School House Rd Duncannon PA 17020*

WIENAND, ROBERT ALLEN, Chemistry Teacher; *b:* Pittsburgh, PA; *m:* Amy L.; *ed:* Grove City Coll (BS) Chem 1974; Grad Credits at Edinboro Univ & Univ of Pittsburgh; *cr:* Northwestern HS Chem Tchr 1974-77; N Allegheny HS Chem Tchr 1977-; *ai:* Supervise Intramural Weight Trng; AFT 1977-; Amer Chem Soc Ed Group 1985-; Past Mem of Sci Advy Bd for Up Magazine; *office:* North Allegheny H S 10375 Perry Hwy Wexford PA 15090

WIENER, GARY ALAN, English Dept Coord & Teacher; *b:* Brooklyn, NY; *m:* Iris Schifren; *c:* Jacob, Michael, Mollie; *ed:* SUNY Buffalo (BA) Eng 1976; SUNY Binghamton (MA) Eng 1978; Univ of Rochester (PhD) Eng 1986; SAS, SDA Earned SUNY Brockport; *cr:* Cincinnati Pub Schls Tchr 1978-80; Brighton MS Tchr 1984-85; Brighton HS Tchr 1986-90, Dept Coord, Tchr 1990-; *ai:* Galaxy Magazine Adv; Silver Crown Awd Columbia Press Assn 1991; NCTE 1986-; NEA 1978-; ASCD 1993-; Outstanding Tchr Cincinnati Pub Schls 1978; Univ of Rochester Univ Fellow, Rush Rhees Fellow 1980-82; Commended in NY St Assembly for Work with Galaxy 1991; *office:* Brighton H S 1150 Winter Rd S Rochester NY 14618

WIENER, HARVEY, Science Teacher; *b:* New York, NY; *m:* Monica Goldschmidt; *c:* Michael, Amy; *ed:* SUNY at Albany (BS) Chem 1969; Adelphi Univ (MA) Scndry Sci Ed 1974; Hofstra Univ (CAS) Ed Admin 1981; 45 Credit Hrs Chem Inservice Ed; *cr:* Grand Avenue Jr HS Sci Tchr 1969-89; Kennedy HS Chem Tchr 1986-89; Mepham HS Chem Tchr 1988-; *ai:* STANYS 1978-, Treas, Nassau Section, Svc Awd 1995; NSTA 1980-; ACS, Div Chem Ed 1990-, Nichols Awd 1995; Chem Club of NY 1992-, Mbrshp Co-chr; PTA 1969-, Hon Life Mem 1985; Temple Judea 1979-, Pres 1992-94, Man of Yr 1987; Outstdng Tchr RITEC Awd 1990; UTIE Awd, WNET 1991; Manhattan Coll Centennial Awd 1992; DDE Chem Centennial Awd Instr 1991-95; NY St Chem Mentor 1992-; *office:* Mepham HS 2401 Camp Ave North Bellmore NY 11710*

WIENER, LISA GOLDEN, Fifth Grade Teacher; *b:* Philadelphia, PA; *m:* Jack Jay; *c:* Cayla Fay, Stephanie Alyse; *cr:* Harker-Wylie Schl Basic Skills Tchr 1979-84; Emmons School 5th Grade Tchr 1984-90; Newcomb Schl 5th Grd Tchr 1990-; *ai:* NEA, NJEA, BCEA 1979-; *office:* Newcomb Schl Pemberton Ft Dix Rd Pemberton NJ 08068*

WIENER, SANDRA M., Computer & Math Teacher; *b:* Hartford, CT; *ed:* Univ of CT (BA) Math 1961; Fairfield Univ (MA) Math Ed 1964, (CAS) Cmptr Ed 1968; 6 Credit Hrs Cmptr Ed Trinity Coll; *cr:* Stamford HS Math Tchr 1961-64; Dept of Defense Sci, PE Tchr 1964-65; Stamford HS Cmptr, Math Tchr 1965-; *ai:* HS Restructuring, Staff Dev, School-to-Career, Dist, Schl Tech Comm; SEA, CEA, NEA 1961-; Trumbull Emergency Med Svc 1978-, Ambulance Driver; Flwshp Cmptr Ed Trinity Coll.

WIENS, DAVID F., Chemistry Teacher & Dept Chm; *b:* Buffalo, NY; *m:* Anne Quigley; *c:* Matthew, Elizabeth, Joseph; *ed:* St Univ of NY at Fredonia (BS) Scndry Ed & Chem 1970, (MS) Ed & Chem 1978; 15 Addl Credit Hrs; *cr:* Gowanda Cntrl Schls Chem Tchr 1970-, Dept Chm 1993-; *ai:* Bldg Improvement Team; Sci Dept Chm; AFT 1970-; NYSUT 1970-, Contract Negotiating Team, Ldrshp Awd; Gowanda Area Jaycees 1977-, Pres, Outstdng Pres in NYS; Gowanda Little League Bsbl 1985-, Mgr; St Josephs Parent Assn 1990-, Pres & VP; St Josephs Church Parish Cncl 1990-, Pres & VP; Nom by Gowanda Cntr Schl Dist; *office:* Gowanda Cntrl Schl Prospect St Gowanda NY 14070

WIEPRECHT, CHARLES THOMAS,JR., Music Tchr & Rdng Dept Coord; *b:* Baltimore, MD; *m:* Sandra J. Edmondson; *c:* Charles T. III, William M.; *ed:* Towson St Univ (BS) Music Ed-Cum Laude 1977, (MED) Music Ed 1988; 3 Credit Hrs Drake Univ; *cr:* Baltimore City Pub Schls Music Tchr 1977-82; St Joseph Schl Music Tchr 1984-85; Bishop John Neumann Schl Music Tchr 1984-90; St Pius X Schl Music Dept Chm, Rdng Dept Coord 1985-; *ai:* Chorus, Drama Dir; Safety Patrol Moderator; MENC, Md Music Edctrs Assn, Kappa Delta Pi 1977-; Elem Schl Tchrs Assn 1984-; *office:* St Pius X Schl 6432 York Rd Baltimore MD 21212

WIERMAN, KEVIN CARL, 7th & 8th Grade History Tchr; *b:* Lima, OH; *m:* Janet Louise Williams; *c:* Kara C., Benjamin M.; *ed:* The Defiance Coll (BS) Elem Ed 1978; Dayton Univ (MA) Educl Admin 1987; *cr:* Elida Local Schls 5th Grd Tchr 1978-79, 3rd Grd Tchr 1979-80; Bath Local Schls 5th Grd Tchr 1980-81, 7th, 8th Grd Eng Tchr 1981-94, 7th, 8th Grd His Tchr 1994-; *ai:* Head Var Bsbl Coach; MS Grant Writing Comm; Bath Ed Assn, OEA, NEA 1980-90, 1992-; Ryan Young Meml Schlsp Bd 1990-, Pres; Grace Bapt Church 1982-, Deacon, Trustee, Sunday Schl Tchr, Choir Mem, Soloist, Quartet Mem, Co-Dir Summer Sports Camp; *office:* Bath Local Schls 2850 Bible Rd Lima OH 45801

WIERZBICKI, JUDITH DUANE, 6th Grade Math Teacher; *b:* Jersey City, NJ; *m:* Frank; *c:* Diane Kennedy, Michael, Dennis; *ed:* Jersey City St

Coll (BA) Scndry Ed, Math, Sci 1962; *cr:* St Andrew Schl 6-8th Grd Sci Tchr 1980-93, 6-8th Grd Math Tchr 1994-; *ai:* NCEA 1980-; Outstdng Edctr Newark Archdiocese 1995; *home:* 63 W 7th St Bayonne NJ 07002

WIERZBICKI, PAMELA MORRIS, High School Physical Ed Tchr; *b:* Coronado, CA; *m:* Michael; *c:* Aimee; *ed:* Cortland (BS) PE 1973; Nazareth Coll (MS) Ed 1986; Brockport 30 Post Grad Hrs; *cr:* Durand Eastman Elem Schl PE Tchr 1973-74; Eastridge HS PE Tchr 1974-77; Minerva Deland Schl 9-10 Grd PE Tchr 1977-83; Fairport HS PE Tchr 1983-; *ai:* Class Adv; Core-Wellness Comm; Red Ribbon; Modified Gymnastics, Modifield Hockey Coach; NYSUT, NYSAHPERD- Cent Western Zone 1973-; Fairport Edctrs Assn 1977-; PTSA 1985-, Exec Bd; Pub Conditioning Prgm; *office:* Fairport HS 1358 Ayrault Rd Fairport NY 14450

WIESEL, MARY HELEN, English Teacher; *b:* Baltimore, MD; *ed:* Chestnut Hill Coll (BA) Eng 1968; *cr:* DE Pub Schl Dist Eng Tchr 1969-70; Holy Spirit Schl Eng Tchr 1970-74; Padua Acad Eng Tchr 1974-; *ai:* Moderator of Youth Leadership Contests, Schl Club Related To Young People who Visit & Work With Nursing Home Residents; SL Club in Which Stdnts Have Pub Poetry in Local Newspapers; Modrtr of Acad Comp Club, Creative Wrtng Club, & Shakespeare Club; *office:* Padua Acad 905 N Broom St Wilmington DE 19806

WIESSNER, JOHN, English Teacher; *b:* Hammonton, NJ; *m:* Joanne Catherine Battaglia; *c:* Joseph, John Thomas, Stephen; *ed:* Glassboro St Coll (BA) Tchr, Jr HS 1965, (BA) ED 1970; Addl 30 Credit Hrs; *cr:* Hammonton Elem Schl Tchr 1965-68; Hammonton HS Eng, Soc Stud Tchr 1969-76; Hammonton MS Eng Tchr 1977-; *ai:* Schl, Region, Cty Spelling Bee Coord; Consultant Schl Think Day Team; NEA, NJEA 1965-; Hammonton Ed Assn 1965-, VP 1966-71; Hammonton Lions Club 1976-, Pres 1982-83, Lion of Yr Local Club 1980; Given Wkshps Ctny, St Levels Video Writing Lessons Dev Higher Level Thinking Skills; Project Silly Sounding Rhymes Primary Schl Stdnts Pub Ideal Schl Supply Co Chicago 1976; *office:* Hammonton MS Central Ave Hammonton NJ 08037*

WIEST, KAREN MACHTLEY, English, Hum & Gifted Tchr; *b:* Johnstown, PA; *m:* William Harvey; *c:* Joel, Rachel, David, Tobias, Elisabeth, Chad; *ed:* Clarion Univ (BS) Eng 1968; Bucknell Univ MS Ed 1994; Attnd Lebanon Valley Coll, Kent St Univ, Shippensburg Univ; *cr:* Loysville Youth Dev Ctr Tchr 1968-69; Shaker Hghts Schls Tchr 1969-71; Line Mountain HS Tchr 1971-73, Tchr of Eng, Hum & GATE 1986-; *ai:* Odyssey of the Mind Coord; Prom Adv; Stu Assistance Team; Habitat for Humanity Coord; PAGE 1979-; *office:* Line Mountain HS RD 1 Herndon PA 17830*

WIETHORN, ROBERT NELSON,SM, Cmptr Sci Dept Chprsn & Tchr; *b:* Cincinnati, OH; *ed:* Univ of Dayton (BS) Chem 1964; Purdue Univ (MS) Chem 1972; Edu Admin 24 Hrs Grad 1973-74; Cmptr Sci 24 Undergrad, 21 Grad Hrs 1988; *cr:* North Cath HS Tchr 1964-65; Chaminade HS Tchr 1965-73; Chaminade-Julienne HS Tchr, Admin 1973-79; Marianists of OH Vocation Dir 1979-86; Chaminade-Julienne HS Tchr 1988-; *ai:* Coach Jets, Sci Bowl Teams; Moderator Engrng Tech Club; NCEA 1988-; OSTE 1991-; Marianist Urban Stdnts Prgm 1992-; Outstdng Tchr Miami Vly Cath Ed Cncl 1994; *office:* Chaminade-Julienne HS 505 S Ludlow St Dayton OH 45402

WIETRY, LINDA LOUISE, Fifth Grade Teacher; *b:* Rahway, NJ; *ed:* Shippensburg St Coll (BS) Elem Ed 1972, (MED) Elem Ed 1975; 27 Addl Grad Credit Hrs Wilkes Univ, Wilson Coll, Allentown Coll of St Francis de Sales, PA St Univ at Mont Alto, Millersville Univ; *cr:* Fairview Elem Schl 5th-6th Grd Tchr 1972-; Lincoln Intermediate Unit Migrant Child Dev Prgm Summer Schl 1st Grd Tchr 1989-92; *ai:* NEA, PSEA, WAEA 1972-; *office:* Fairview Elem Schl 220 Fairview Ave Waynesboro PA 17268

WIFORD, MELANIE JANE, Biological Science Teacher; *b:* Sidney, OH; *ed:* Urbana Univ (BS) Comprehensive Scis 1981; Wright St Univ (MED) Ed 1990; Project Discovery Resource Tchr Inst Miami Univ; Project Discovery Summer Inst; Tchr Expectation, Stu Achvmt Univ of Dayton; *cr:* Covington Exempted Village Schls Scndry Biological Scis 1986-89; Fairlawn Local Schls Scndry Biological Scis 1993-; *ai:* Sr HS Stu Cncl Adv; Strategic Planning Comm Schl System Stu Dev; Amer Inst Biological Scis, ASCD 1995-; NEA, OEA, FEA 1994-; Project Discovery Resource Tchr Inst; *office:* Fairlawn HS 18800 Johnston Rd Sidney OH 45365

WIGFALL, DOROTHY BROWN, Reading & Language Arts Tchr; *b:* Shelby, NC; *c:* Nicole K.; *ed:* Morris Coll (BA) Elem Ed 1965; Montclair St Coll (MA) Prsnl Svcs 1976; Elizabeth City St Coll 9 Credits; Friendship Jr Coll at Rock Hill 30 Credits; Fairleigh Dickinson Univ at Teaneck 12 Credits; Prot Dev Harold Wilson Schl at Newark Cert; *cr:* Burnet St Schl Tchr 29 Yrs; *ai:* Stu Patrol, Stu Cncl Adv; Mentor for New Tchrs, Adv One to One; newark Pub Schl Clean-Up & Beautification Schl Site Coord; NEA, PTA 1966-; Block Assn 1986-; Mc Govern Campaign Worker 1968; Morris Coll Alum Org 1967-; St of NJ Governor's Awd; Outstdng Tchng Awd; Parent Involvement Corp Cert of Merit; Prins Awd for Excl in Tchng; Black United Fund of NJ Cert; Stdnts Essays Pub in Book for Children; *home:* 339 N Grove St East Orange NJ 07017

WIGFIELD, STEPHANIE HANNAN, Special Ed & 4th Grd Teacher; *b:* Wheeling, WV; *m:* Joseph C.; *c:* Joseph, Colleen; *ed:* West Liberty St (BS) Ed 1973; Coll of Mt St Joseph (MS) Ed 1985; Working on Gifted Cert at Ashland Univ; *cr:* Stark Cty Head Start 1970-71, 1972-75; Sandy Valley Local Schls Tchr 1976-; *ai:* Seeds Sci Leadership, Spec Ed Comms; Cheerleading Adv; Phi Delta Kappa 1994-.

WIGGINS, BLONEVA FLOWERS, Kindergarten Teacher; *b:* Miami, FL; *m:* George J.; *c:* Jerome, Andre; *ed:* FL Meml Coll (BS) Elem Ed 1972; *cr:* Clairton Ed Ctr Tchr 1972-; *ai:* NEA 1972-; *home:* 530 B Dr West Mifflin PA 15122

WIGGINS, CHARLES, US Government & History Tchr; *b:* Boston, MA; *m:* Bev Golorsky; *c:* John Samual, Christy; *ed:* Colby Coll (BA) His 1962; Columbia Univ (MA) His Ed 1967; *cr:* Santa Famiglia Univ His Prof 1964; Wilton HS African Stud Tchr 1968-70; B. Mc Mahon Anthropology, His, Govt Tchr 1990-; *ai:* Mock Trial Team, Schls Govt, Model United Nations Club Adv; AFT 1978-, Steward; CT Cncl for Soc Stud 1985-, Yankee Forum Ed, Bd of Dirs 1986-90, Ct Original for Outstdng Writing in SS; Cornell's Outstdng Edctr Awd 1992; Article Author; Who's Who in Amer 1995; Who's Who in Amer Ed 1994-95; Fulbright Schlsp Ghana 1969; NDEA Grant Univ of Bridgeport 1968; *office:* Brien McMahon HS 300 Highland Ave Norwalk CT 06854

WIGGINS, JANE L. (PRICE), Principal; *b:* St Clairsville, OH; *m:* Douglas A.; *c:* Shannon, Lindsay; *ed:* Morehead St Univ (AA) Univ Stud 1977; Univ of Dayton (BS) Bus Ed 1987, (MS) Supervision 1994; Prins Cert; *cr:* Carroll HS Bus Tchr, Dept Chair 1987-95; Resurrection Cath Schl Prin 1996; Sinclair Comm Coll Part-time Instr; *ai:* Stu Cncl; Jr Achvmt; OH Bus Tchrs; ASCD; NCEA; Phi Delta Kappa; Ascension PTO, Sec, VP, Pres; Girl Scouts, Cookie Mgr; *office:* Resurrection Cath Schl 138 Gramont Ave Dayton OH 45417

WIGGINS, KARLA RIDLEY, Mathematics Teacher; *b:* Jersey City, NJ; *m:* Horace; *ed:* Montclair St Univ (BA) Sociology, Ed K-12 1975, (MA) Cnslng; Jersey City St Coll Cert Elem Ed K-8 1976; *cr:* Jersey City Schl Dist Math Specialist, Chptr 1, Grd 1, Magnet Schl Tchr 1975-87; Miller Street Schl 8th Grd Tchr 1988-89; South Orange MS 7th Grd Math Tchr 1989-; *ai:* Asst Dir All Schl Musical; Drama Club Dir; Edctrs African Descent 1995-; NCTM 1994-; NEA, NJEA 1975-; *office:* South Orange MS 70 N Ridgewood Rd South Orange NJ 07079*

WIGGINS, MARY JEAN (ALGAR), Fourth Grade Teacher; *b:* Pittston, PA; *m:* David Wiggins; *c:* Eric, Amy, David James; *ed:* Mansfield St Coll (BS) Elem Ed 1971; Grad Courses St Univ of NY-Bing, St Univ of NY-Cortland; *cr:* Vestal-Tioga Hills Elem Schl 6th Grd Tchr 1971-79, 4th Grd Tchr 1979-; *ai:* NEA, Tchrs Assn 1971-; Little League 1987, Bd of Dir, Pres Ladies Auxiliary; PTA 1971-, Tchr Rep on Bd; PTA Honoree Dist Schlsp; *office:* Tioga Hills Elem Schl # 48 40 Glann Rd Apalachin NY 13732

WIGGINS, RAYMOND F., Music Teacher; *b:* Philadelphia, PA; *m:* Marcella; *c:* Debbie, Mark, Sharon; *ed:* Temple Univ (BS) Music 1958; Trenton Coll (MA) Music 1961; 30 Addl Hrs Supvrs; *cr:* Swedesboro Schls K-12th Grd Music Tchr 5 Yrs; Kingsway Reg HS 7th-12th Grd Music Tchr 2 Yrs; Pennsauken HS 9th-12th Grd Music Tchr 31 Yrs; *ai:* Jazz Band Dir 1985-, Won St Championship 6 Times; NJ Ed Assn 1958-; Intnl Assn Jazz Edctrs 1976-, NJ Pres, Jazz Educator of Yr 1995; Prof Musician Jazz, Commercial Sax, Flute; Guest Conductor Cty Symphonic Band; Guest Dir Region III NJ St Jazz Band; *office:* Pennsauken HS 800 Hylton Rd Pennsauken NJ 08110

WIGGINTON, MARY LOU FURGIONE, Religion Teacher; *b:* Hammonton, NJ; *m:* Donald; *c:* M. Deborah Suipizio, Dena Hannum, John R. Lassiter, Donald, Joseph, Robert, James, Charles; *ed:* Glassboro St Coll (BA) Elem Ed 1977; 12 Credits Theology at LaSalle Univ; *cr:* St Joseph Elem Schl 6th Grd Tchr 1966-67; St Gregory Elem Schl 2nd Grd Tchr 1970-80, Religion Ed Coord 1975-80; St Jude Elem Schl 1st-6th Grd Tchr 1982-84; Paul VI HS 9-12th Grd Tchr 1985-; *ai:* Hospitality Club Coord; Mrktg Comm Mem; SCTO Union 1985-; NCEA; *office:* Paul VI HS Hopkins Rd Haddonfield NJ 08033

WIGHTMAN, MELANIE MUMMA, English Teacher; *b:* Mc Keesport, PA; *m:* Michael E.; *c:* Geoffrey J., Teegan E.; *ed:* Miami Univ (BSEd) Eng 1974; Bowling Green St Univ Rdng Cert; Harvard Grad Schl Ed Inst in Rdng, Writing, Civic Ed; Oberling Tchrs Acad; *cr:* Lakewood HS Eng Tchr 1976-, Eng Dept Chair 1985-94; *ai:* United Church of Christ 1987-, Church Schl Tchr, Mbrshp Chm; Lead Tchr Urban Initiatives Prgm; Eng Advy Bd Scholastic Publishers 1990; Critical Reader Adventures in English Literature 1996; *office:* Lakewood HS 14100 Franklin Blvd Lakewood OH 44107*

WILBEKIN, THERESA MACK, English Teacher; *b:* New York, NY; *m:* Earl; *c:* Michael, Mark, Matthew; *ed:* Iona at New ROchelle (BS) Hum 1987, (MST) Eng, Scndry Ed 1994, (MSEd) Admin 1996; *cr:* Archdiocese of NY 2-8 Grd Tchr 1983-94; St Catharine Acad Tchr 1994-; *ai:* Moderator A World of Difference; NCEA 1984-; Natl Women's Fed for World Peace 1995-, US Del.

WILBER, DAVID B., High School English Teacher; *b:* Huron, OH; *m:* Judith Lee Maurer; *c:* Janet Emma, Sarah Elizabeth; *ed:* Coll of wooster (BA) Hlth, PE 1973; Attending Ashland Univ Curr, Instruction; *cr:* Sandusky HS Eng Tchr 1974-; *ai:* Former Boy's Bsktbl Coach; Acad Team Adv; NEA 1980-; Church 1956-, Trustee, Staff-Parish Relations Comm, Yth Club Tchr; *office:* Sandusky HS 2107 Hayes Ave Sandusky OH 44870

WILBER, SHARON LOUISE, High School English Teacher; *b:* Geneva, NY; *ed:* SUC at Geneseo (BA) Scndry Eng 1978; SUC at Oswego (MS) Scndry Ed 1985; Post Grad Hrs at Syracuse Univ & Univ of NH; *cr:* North Rose Wolcott HS Eng Tchr 1978-; *ai:* Stu Cncl Adv 1979-; Prins Advy Comm; NEA & North Rose Wolcott Tchrs Assn 1978-; Univ of Rochesters Awd for Excl in Scndry Tchng 1990.

WILBERDING, DONNA MARIE, Spanish Teacher; *b:* Jersey City, NJ; *m:* Larry; *c:* Christopher, Lisa Samancy, Stephanie; *ed:* Marian Coll (BA) Scndry Ed 1968; Attnd Univ of Dayton 1992, Edison Comm Coll 1991-92, Wright St univ 1978-79; *cr:* Christ the King Elem Schl 6th Grd Tchr 1968-69; Ft Recovery HS Span, Eng Tchr 1969-70; Bradford HS Span Tchr 1978; Newton HS Span, Eng, CreativeWriting Tchr 19 79-; *ai:* Class Adv Stu Act Cncl; Span Club Adv; Trip Coord to Europe; OH Frgn Lang Assn 1993-, 1 Grant, 3 Proposals; W OH Cncl Tchr Lang Arts 1988-89, Accepted for Conv Presentations; NEA, OEA, WOEA 1979-; Evergreen Marriage Enrichment Prgm 1996; Ldr; Church 1978-, Lay Distrightor, Yth Adv, Lector; 12 Articles Pub; 1 Book Self-Pub on Tchng Jrney.*

WILBUR, DORA LYNNE, Third Grade Teacher; *b:* Bellevue, OH; *ed:* Olivet Nazarene Univ (BS) Elem Ed 1985; *cr:* Reddick Schl Dist Primary Chapter 1 Tchr 1985-86; Herscher Schl Dist Rdng Tchr 1986-89; Margaretta Schl Dist Jr Hs Soc Stud Tchr 1989-90; Milan Elem Schl Primary Rdng & Sci Tchr 1990-; *ai:* Var Vlybl Coach; Ldr Multiple Intelligence Comm, Venture Capital Grant; NEA 1989-; Division 3 Vlbyl Coach Achvmt Awd 1993 & Coach of Yr 1993, 1994; *office:* Milan Elem Schl 140 Main St S Milan OH 44846

WILBUR, DOUGLAS C., Chemistry & Physics Teacher; *b:* Oneida, NY; *m:* Constance Lamb; *c:* Kimberly Wilbur Ravenelle, Brian D.; *ed:* Univ of Buffalo (BA) Chem 1969; Rensselaer PolyTechnic Inst (MS) Natural Sci 1973; Attnd Clemson Univ, Syracuse Univ, Oswego Coll; *cr:* Mohawk Valley Comm Coll Chem Instr 1980-85; SYracuse Univ Adjunct Instr Chem 1982-; Utica Coll Adjunct Instr Chem 1988-; Canastota Cntrl Schls Chem Physics Tchr 1968-; *ai:* NHS Adv; Sci Tchrs Assn NYS; Canastota Tchrs Assn 1968-, VP, Pres; AFT; ACS; NSTA; VVS Bd of Ed 1979-84, VP 1983-84; Dollars for Scholars Bd of Dir 1987-90; Oneida Tchrs Credit Union Bd of Dir 1989-; Woodrow Wilson Dreyfus Fellowship Princeton 1986; Inspirational HS Tchng Awd Clarkson Univ 1990; Canastota HS Yrbk Dedication 1972, 1977, 1988; Utica Coll continuing Ed Distinguished Tchng Awd 1993; *home:* 370 E Seneca St Sherrill NY 13461

WILBUR, GEORGE EVERETT, Latin & World Cultures Teacher; *b:* Clarendon, PA; *m:* Evadene Smith; *c:* George Gregory, Geoffrey Daniel; *ed:* PA St Univ (BA) Latin & Eng 1955, (MED) Medieval His & Admin 1968; Juniata Coll Summer Schl; Shippensburg St Univ Summers for Multiple Cert; E Stroudsburg St Coll Post Grad Stud; *cr:* Saltille HS Latin, His & Eng Tchr 1955-62; Southern Huntingdon HS 9th-10th Grd Eng Tchr 1962-63; Tyrone Area HS latin, His, Eng & Dr Ed Tchr 1963-; *ai:* NHS Adv; Latin Club; Head Frgn Lang Dept; NEA 1955-; PSEA 1955-; Phi Delta Kappa 1967-; Tchr of the Yr for Jr & Sr High 1965, 1972; Employee of the Month 1985; Yrbk Dedicator 1987; Gift of Time Tribute from Amer Family Inst 1994; Renaissance Tchr of the Yr 1995; *office:* Tyrone Area Jr Sr HS Clay Avenue Ext Tyrone PA 16686*

WILCOX, DIANNE GROSSER, Substitute Teacher; *b:* Rochester, NY; *m:* Roy S.; *ed:* Empire St Coll (BS) Educl Stud 1982; *cr:* St Boniface Schl Grd 4 Tchr 1966-68; St Mary's Schl Grd 5-8 Tchr 1968-94; Bloomfield Cntrl Schl Dist Sub Tchr 1995-; Midlakes Cntrl Schl Dist Sub Tchr 1995-; Canandaigua Cntrl Schl Dist Sub Tchr 1995-; *ai:* Arts & Crafts Show Vendor; *home:* 1384 Cty Rd #8 Shortsville NY 14548

WILCOX, EILEEN JOAN (ERNST), Business & History Teacher; *b:* Spencerville, OH; *m:* James A.; *c:* Jerolyn S.; *ed:* Mary Manse Coll (BA) Ed 1963; Univ of Detroit (MA) Bus 1970; Intensive Office Ed & Comprehensive Bus Ed Cert; 24 Post Grad Credit Hrs; *cr:* Toledo Diocese Schl System Jr High Tchr 1953-63; Notre Dame Acad HS Tchr 1963-64; St Wendelins HS Tchr 1964-65; Cntrl Cath HS Tchr 1965-69; Ft Jennings HS Tchr 1969-; *ai:* Yrbk Adv 1969-94; Sr Adv 1978-94; Ft Jennings Ed Assn 1969-, Sec & Treas 2 Terms; OEA, NEA & NWOEA 1969-; Uniserv 1969-; Insurance Tchr of Yr Awd 1991; *office:* Ft Jennings HS PO Box 98 Jennings OH 45844*

WILCOX, EMMA ELIZABETH, Eng Instructor & Dept Coor Indiana, PA; *m:* Michel P.; *c:* Christina Bowser, Patrick Bowser, Cla *ed:* IN Univ of PA (BS) Eng 1966; 19 Grad Hrs Speech Pathology Edir Univ; *cr:* Rocky Grove HS Eng Fac 1966-67; Cochranton Area Jr S Eng Fac 1977-; *ai:* Co-Adv Schl Lit Magazine; NEA, PSEA, CCEA, N 1978-; Unitarian Universalist Church 1982-; Outstdng Instr Awd Ame Banking 1989, 1990; *office:* Cochranton Jr Sr H S 2nd St Box Cochranton PA 16314*

WILCOX, GERARD E., Heavy Equip & Hydraulics Tchr; *b:* Bath *m:* Amy W. Smith; *c:* Gregory R. Smith-Wilcox; *ed:* Penn St Coll of (AS) Repair & Operation of Heavy Equipment 1979; SUNY at Os (BS) Voc, Tech Ed 1987; *cr:* WE-MO-CO Voc, Tech Ctr Monroe #2 BC Heavy Equipment, Hydraulics Instr 1987-; *ai:* VICA Club Adv; Ex Accountability Comm; Pub Speaking Competition Chprsn; NEA 1 NY St Voc Tchrs Assn, Past Legislative Co-Chair; Bristol Historica 1991-; *office:* We-Mo-Co Vocational Tech Ctr 3589 Big Ridg Spencerport NY 14559

WILCOX, MARIA BERRIZBEITIA, Spanish Teacher; *b:* Hartford *m:* John L.; *ed:* Empire St Coll (BA) Span Lang & Lit 1992; St Univ o at Buffalo Foreign Lang Ed 1993; 42 Grad Credits Toward Maste Foreign Lang Ed- Span; *cr:* Ingram Software Dir of Mrktg 1986-87; King & White Advertising VP 1987-90; East Aurora HS Span 1993-94; Frontier Cntrl HS Span Tchr 1993-; *ai:* Intnl Club Co-Adv; Cncl on Tchng Foreign Langs, NY St Assn of Foreign Lang Tchrs, We NY Foreign Lang Educators Cncl 1993-; AATSP 1995-; Crystal Prism for Outstanding Contributions to the Prof Communicators of Westerr Awded Schlsp to NYSAFLT Annual Meeting; Vol of Yr Awd for Multiple Sclerosis Soc; *office:* Frontier HS S-4432 Bayview Rd Ham NY 14075

WILCOX, SALLY ROOT, Fifth Grade Teacher; *b:* Rochester, NY Paul Edward; *c:* Brenda, Christopher; *ed:* RIT (AAS) Bus, Retailing SUNY at Brockport (BS) Elem Ed 1989; *cr:* Greece Schl System Sub 1990; Brockport Schl System Sub Tchr 1990; St John The Evangelist Fifth Grd Tchr 1990-; *ai:* Peace & Justice Coord; Proud of Me Spon Kappa Delta Pi 1988-; Professionally Highlighted in Article Pu Rochester Newspaper; *office:* St John Evangelist Schl 65 Marth Spencerport NY 14559

WILCOX, SEAN A., 9th Grade English Teacher; *b:* Columbus, OH Lynette; *c:* Taylor, Kennedy; *ed:* Otterbein Coll (BA) Eng & Ed 1989; Grad 12 Hrs OH St Univ; *cr:* South Western City Schls Sub Tchr 198 Galloway Westland At-Risk Tutor 1991-92; Learning Disabled 1992-93; 9-11th Grd Eng Tchr 1993-; *ai:* Strength Coach 1991-; Head Coach 1995-; Tech Prep Team Tchng 1994-; NEA 1993-; OH Coaches 1991-; Westland Boosters 1993-; 9th Grd Eng Curr Guidelines fo Innovative Night Schl for HS Drop-Outs; *office:* Galloway Westlan 146 Galloway Rd Galloway OH 43119

WILD, GEORGE F., Math Teacher; *b:* Hackensack, NJ; *c:* Christo Scott; *ed:* William Patterson Coll (BA Jr HS Ed 1969, (MA) Math Ed *cr:* Fieldstone MS Tchr & Tech Curr Facilatator 1969-; *ai:* Comp Field Trip & AVA Coord; Vision 2000 Chprsn; Pasack Vly Articulation Comm; NEA 1969-; Bergen Cty Ed Assn 1969-; Mon Tchrs Assn 1969-; Immaculate Conception Church 1974-, CCD Tch Governor Tchr Recognition Awd 1993; TKR-Cable in the Classroom 1995; Mahwah Sports Boosters 1980-90; *office:* Fieldstone MS 47 S Valley Rd Montvale NJ 07645*

WILDE, JOAN CAROL, Assistant Principal; *b:* Plainfield, NJ; *m:* H W.; *c:* Russell, Stephen; *ed:* Rutgers Univ-Douglas Coll (BA) Eng 1967; Seton Hall Univ (MA) Admin, Supervision 1973; 30 Cr Learning Disabilities, Exceptional Children; *cr:* South Plainfield HS Tchr 19967-76; Manasquan Pub Schls Curr Consultant 1976-78; Cra HS Eng Tchr 1979-92, Asst Prin, Supvr Spec Ed 1995-; *ai:* Newspaper, Lit Magazine, Peer Dev Prgm Adv; Pupil Assistance, HS Relations Comm; Dist Enrollment Comm Chair; Prof Dev Comm; Cncl; Field Trip Comm; NASSP, NJ PSA, CASA 1992-; CEC 1 Cranford Human Relations Comm, Teen Ctr Adult Advy Bd 1992-; Centennial Comm 1994-; *office:* Cranford HS 201 W End Pl Cranfor 07016

WILDEMAN, KATHRYN ANN (RADKE), English Teacher; *b:* Be Harbor, MI; *ed:* Western MI Univ (BA) Eng 1957; Univ of MI Grad H Cert; *cr:* Watervliet High Eng Tchr 1957-59; Lincoln Park High Eng 1959-62; Bloomfield Hills High Eng Tchr 1962-73; Lake Forest High Tchr & Sub Tchr 1974-77; Mount St Mary Acad Eng Tchr 1980-; *a* Class Moderator; Discipline Bd; Curr Comm; Directress Advy NCEA 1980-; NCTE; NJ Assn of Ind Schls 1980-; *office:* Mount Mary Acad 1645 US Rt 22 W Watchung NJ 07060*

WILDERMAN, MARION EBERMAN, Second & Third Grade Tea *b:* New York, NY; *m:* Michael Paul; *c:* Kefira, Noah; *ed:* City Coll of (BA) His 1965; Bowie St Coll (MED) Scndry Ed 1992; *cr:* WLP Board Schl 4-6th Grd Tchr 1966-69; Live Oak Schl 4-6th Grd Tchr 197 Hebrew Day Inst 5th Grd Tchr, Secular Stud Prin 1981-87; Kettering Schl 4th Grd Tchr 1987-94; Kingsford Elem Magnet Schl 2nd-3rd Grd 1994-; *ai:* Supvr Debate Team; Staff Dev Comm; NEA 1987-; N 1991-; PGCEA 1987-; Facilitator Equity 2000 Summer Math Inst 1994 Comm & Acad Stud Curr Writer Soc Stud; *home:* 1606 Timberlin Silver Spring MD 20904

WILDERMUTH, ANN KYLE, Mathematics Teacher; *b:* Xenia, OH Dale; *c:* Brian, Jeffrey, Jill; *ed:* Miami Univ (BS) Ed & Math 1975; W St Univ (MS) Curr & Supervision 1981; Attnd OH St Univ, Univ of Day Earlham Coll & Wright St Univ; *cr:* Benjamin Logan HS Math Tchr 1 *ai:* NHS Adv; Math Dept Chprsn; Referee for Articles Submitted to Journal; NCTM, OCTM & NEA 1975-; Farm Bureau Cncl 1983-; Jenn Scholar; OCTM Cntrl Dist Outstanding Math Classroom T Bellefontaine Rotary Club Excl in Tchng Awd; *office:* Benjamin Loga 6609 St Rt 47 E Bellefontaine OH 43311

WILDERMUTH, LARRY GUY, Social Science Teacher; *b:* Reading, *m:* Margaret R.; *c:* Jenel, Erika; *ed:* Albright Coll (BA) His 1969; Grad Lehigh Univ; *cr:* Oley Valley HS Tchr 26 Yrs; *ai:* Wrestling Co NEA, PSEA 1969-; Wrestling Coaches Assn, Local to Natl; *office:* Valley HS Main St Oley PA 19547*

WILDER-WOKOUN, CONSTANCE, HS English Teacher; *b:* New City, NY; *m:* E. Robert Wokoun; *c:* Elizabeth Wokoun Richard Constance Ann Wokoun; *ed:* Fordham Univ (BS) Comm Arts 1954 Credits Trenton St NJ Cert Deans List; 3 Credits Rutgers; *cr:* St Ant HS Eng Tchr 4 Yrs; East & West Windsor Schl Perm Elem Sub 5 Yrs; N Dame HS Eng Tchr 1 Yr; Mc Corristin Cath HS Eng, Creative Writing, Speak Tchr 19 Yrs; *ai:* Talisman Schl Lit Magazine; Mock Trial Co NCTE 1 Yr; NCEA 19 Yrs; Hamilton Twp Arts Commission 10 Chairwoman; NJ Theatre Guild Inc 1 Yr, Dir of Plays; Fiction Acce Natl Cncl Eng Tchrs Journal; *office:* Mc Corristin Cath HS 175 Leo Ave Trenton NJ 08610*

WILDONGER, DAVID MARTIN, Physical Education Teacher Allentown, PA; *m:* Beverly Marie Ambrogio; *c:* Spencer; *ed:* Stroudsburg Univ (BS) Hlth, PE 1975; Marywood Coll Ed Master's

Penn St Extension at Fogelsville Sports Awareness; Univ of DE s Med; Penn St Univ Hershey Med Ctr Sports Med; *cr:* William Allen llth, PE Tchr 1977-; *ai:* Head Var Ftbl Coach; Touchdown Club; gth Adv; Facilitator Goals & Objectives Steering Comm; PSEA, AEA 1977-; PA Ftbl Coaches Assn 1994-; East Penn League Ftbl hes Assn 1995-; Jewish Comm Ctr 1989-; First Presbyn Church 1973-; : William Allen HS 126 N 17th St Allentown PA 18104*

ES, LISA J., HS Art Teacher & Dept Chprsn; *b:* Cambridge, England; ffrey D.; *c:* Ervin, Scott, Trisha; *ed:* Coll of Wooster (BA) Fine Arts ; Kent St Univ; *cr:* Wooster HS Art Tchr 1976-; *ai:* Art Dept Chprsn; lub Adv; NEA, OEA 1979-; OAEA 1990-; Silver Trowel Garden Club -, Pres, Record Secy; *office:* Wooster HS 515 Oldman Rd Wooster OH 1

EY, HELEN ROLLEY, Eighth Grade Math Teacher; *b:* Cheriton, VA; hnson Hayes Jr.; *c:* Tiffany, Johnson 3rd; *ed:* Jersey City St Coll (BA) 1970; Jersey City St Coll 6 Credit Hrs in Rdng; *cr:* Vernon L. Davey S 7th-8th Grd Math Tchr 1970-77; Elmwood Ave Schl 7th-8th Grd Tchr 1978-80; Myrtle Ave Schl 7th Grd Math Tchr 1983-86; Hubbard th Grd Math Tchr 1986-; *ai:* MS Team Ldr 1990-; Stu Cncl Adv; NEA -; PEA 1986-; Church Schl, Supt; Mid Schl 1974-77, Chprsn; Tchr of 994; *office:* Hubbard MS 661 W 8th St Plainfield NJ 07060

EY, JOHNETTA DENISE, Chemistry & Biology Teacher; *b:* nwood, MS; *ed:* MS Vly St Univ (BS) Chem 1984; Ashland Univ D) Curr, Instruction 1996; *cr:* James Ford Rhodes HS Bio Tchr -88; South HS Chem, Bio Tchr 1988-; *ai:* Coach Girls Tennis, Track; Track Throwing Coach; Pre-Med Club Adv; Sci Tutor; NEA 1987-; 1988-; NSIA 1994-; Delta Sigma Theta 1982-, Pres, Treas, Chair Comm, Ldrshp, Merit Scholar; *office:* Columbus South HS 1160 Ann olumbus OH 43206*

GOREN, RICHARD ALLEN, History Teacher; *b:* Boston, MA; *m:* lie A. Jenkin; *c:* Robb, Michele; *ed:* Univ of MA (BA) His 1961; eyan Univ (MAT) Ed 1963; Harvard Univ (AS) Ed 1968; Univ of MA) Ed 1973; *cr:* Levington HS Tchr 1963-71; North Brookfield HS Prin -77; Plymouth Area HS Prin 1976-77; Whitman Hanson HS Prin -79; Spaulding HS Prin 1979-88, Tchr 1988-; *ai:* Close Up Adv; In & Curr Comm Chair; NEA 1963-; Barre Ed Assn, Pres; Barre City Cncl -, Mem; Barre City Democratic Comm 1992-, Chm; *home:* 7 Sunrise Barre VT 05641*

GUS, WILLIAM DAVID, Senior Army & JROTC Instr; *b:* adelphia, PA; *ed:* Norwich Univ (BA) Bus Admin 1967; Webster Univ Mngmt 1986; Command & Gen Staff Coll Grad 1978; *cr:* Career US Ofcr Ret at Rank of LtCol 1967-91; Dickinson Col Prof of Military 986-91; Pine Grove Area HS Sr Army JROTC Instr 1991-; *ai:* Drill , Color Guard, Raider Challenge Tam, JROTC Act Adv; *office:* Pine e Area HS School St Pine Grove PA 17963

HELM, CATHERINE SIMPKINS, 8th Grade English & Rdng Tchr; ew York City, NY; *m:* Lawrence; *c:* Michael Kyle, Melanie Kyle; *ed:* Akron (BS) Ed 1975, (MS) Ed Admin 1980; Post Grad Crs at U of and, Drake Univ, Coll of Mt St Joseph, U of Akron; *cr:* Highland Local s Tchr 1976-; *ai:* Drama & Writing Clubs; Newspaper, Yrbk, ESL & Soc Adv; HEA 1976-, Pres, VP & Treas; OEA & NEA 1976-; OCTELA -; Now 1982-; AAUW 1985-; Medina Co Mental Hlth Assn; Boy ts Adv Bd; Lib Selection Bd; Jennings Scholar 1983-84; Highland of Yr 1985; *office:* Highland Local Schls 3940 Ridge Rd Medina OH 6*

HELM, CHARLES WILLIAM, Mathematics Department Chm; *b:* eling, WV; *m:* Carole Ann Thalman; *ed:* W Liberty St Coll (BA) Ed ; WV Univ (MA) Ed 1962; *cr:* Cameron HS Math Tchr & Coach -65; Wheeling HS Math Tchr 1966-67; Wheeling Coll Math Tchr -73; St Clairsville HS Math Dept Chm 1973-; *ai:* Sr Class Adv; Coach; 1959-; Ftbl Ofcl 1966-; OH St Univ Honor Roll of Outstanding HS s; *home:* 148 Courtland Ave Wheeling WV 26003

HELM, JEFFREY H., Biology Teacher; *b:* Sharon, PA; *m:* Sharon; aurie, Rebecca, Jennifer; *ed:* Clarion Univ (BS) Bio; Slippery Rock (MA) Bio; *cr:* SVJH Tchr 1969-; *ai:* Ftbl, Wrestling; NEA; PSEA; e: Seneca Valley Jr HS RD #1 Harmony PA 16037*

HELM, LESLIE ANN, Family & Consumer Science Tchr; *b:* Oxford, *ed:* Miami Univ (BA) Family, Consumer Sci 1989; *cr:* Aiken HS act Home Ec Tchr 1989-90; Garfield Jr HS 7-8 Grd Home Ec Tchr -92; Harrison HS Family, Consumer Sci Tchr 1992-; *ai:* Soph Class, HERO Adv; Core Team; PTA Rep; NEA 1989-90; FHA Alumni -, VP; Amer Bus Women's Assn 1986-, VP, Treas; Tchr of Yr 1994-95; e: Wm Henry Harrison HS 9860 West Rd Harrison OH 45030

HELM, LINDA SCALZO, Teacher of Gifted & Talented; *b:* ewood, NJ; *m:* Matthew; *c:* Kristin; *ed:* Jersey City Coll (BS) Gen Ed ; Montclair St Univ (MS) Rdng & Supervisory 1984; Prins Cert; *cr:* aucus Pub Schls 3rd-6th Grd Tchr 22 Yrs; Hudson Cty Gifted & nted Assn G&T Tchr 4 Yrs; *ai:* Safety Patrol Coord; *office:* Clarendon uber St Schls 685 5th St Secaucus NJ 07094

HELM, MARK ANDREW, Elementary Physical Educator; *b:* timore, MD; *m:* Jacquelyn Lee Hickey; *c:* Andrew J.; *ed:* Univ of MD ollege Park (BS) Kinesiological Sci 1986; Cert K-12th Grd Ed 1988; St Dept of Ed Stan Prof Cert 1989; Advanced Prof Cert 1994; *cr:* treville Elem Phys Edctr Tchr 1988-; *ai:* Cross Cntry Coach; Wings to cess Fac; Jump Rope for Heart Coord; NEA 1989-; MSTA 1989-; HFERD; Annapolis Striders 1989-; Amer Heart Assoc 1993-, rtwalk Adv; Tchr of Yr Nomination 1992; MSTA Run for Statehouse mpion 1992 & 1993; Governors Preventive Initiative Gold Medal 1994 995; Tchr of Yr 1994; Mid-Shores Cross Cntry Coach of Yr 1995; e: Centreville Elem Schl 300 Homewood Ave Centreville MD 21617

HELM, PETER WILLIAM, His & Cultural Geog Professor; *b:* iance, OH; *m:* Julie Ann; *c:* Rachel, Zachary, Samuel; *ed:* Bowling en St Univ (BSEd) His, Ger 1973, (MS) His 1983; Attnd Justus-Liebig v West Germany 1971-72; *cr:* Four Cty JVS Soc Stud Instr 1973-80; ST Comm Coll Gen Stud Instr 1985-, Retraining Coord 1985-; *ai:* m Orgs Slide Presentations & Atifact Displays; OH His Soc 1986-; umee Valley His Soc 1986-; NW OH Rural Conservation Comm 1989-; Thesis; *office:* Northwest State Comm Coll 22-600 Sr 34 Archbold OH 02

LHELM, RICHARD KIRKHOFF, Choral Music Teacher; *b:* Reading, *c:* Christopher A., Kiera L.; *ed:* PA St Univ (BS) Music Ed 1970; West ester Univ (MM) Music 1976; *cr:* Upper Dublin Schl Dist Elem rumental Music Tchr 1970-82, HS, MS Elem Tchr 1982-89, HS Choral sic Tchr 1990-; *ai:* Music Dir HS Musical; Dir of Madrigal, Jazz, Men's, men's Choirs; Upper Dublin Ed Assn 1970-, Tchng Excl; MENC, NEA, A 1970-; Amer Choral Dir Assn 1982-; Ambler Symphony Comm Orch nductor 1980-90; *office:* Upper Dublin HS 800 Loch Alsh Ave Fort shington PA 19034*

LHJELM, CHRIS, Band Director; *b:* Long Branch, NJ; *m:* Roberta; *c:* l, Hannah; *ed:* New England Conservatory of Music (BM) Music 1968; nton St Coll (MM) Ed 1979; Grad Work Columbia Univ, Temple Univ, st Chester St Coll, VA Commonwealth Univ; *cr:* Ridgewood HS Band 1979-82; Rye HS Band Dir 1982-84; Pascock Hills HS Band Dir 1984-; ntchair St Univ Bank Dir 1994-; *ai:* Marching, Jazz Bands; NEA, NC 1979-; AFT 1994-; Ridgewood Concert Band 1983-, Music Dir; Leonard Bernstein Fellow Tanglewood Rotary Intnl Paul Harris Awd; Pub Articles; Guest Conductor Region, All-State Band Act; *office:* Pascack Hills HS Grand Ave Montvale NJ 07645

WILHOUR, DONALD EUGENE, Mathematics Department Chair; *b:* Jacksonville, FL; *m:* Linda Gayle Lizambri; *c:* Scott David, Tricia Lynn; *ed:* Indiana Univ of PA (BS) Math Ed 1975; Shippensburg Univ (MS) Instructional Comm 1979; *cr:* Selinsgrove HS Math Tchr 1976-86, Math Dept Chm & Tchr 1987-; *ai:* Susquehanna Univ Math Coord & Part Time Math Ed Instr; Math Stu Tchng Prgm Coord; Var Boys Track Coach 17 Yrs; Key Club Adv; Cl ass Adv 4 Yrs; 8th Grd Ftbl Coach 9 Yrs; Started Girls Track Prgm 1976; Var Boys Track Coach 28 Yrs; PSEA; NEA; Dist 4 Track Championships 1979 & 1982-88 & 1991-95; Susquehanna Valley Track League Champions 1978-81 & 1983-95; 16 Yr Ind Study of the Worlds Conifers, Dwarf Conifers & Japanese Maples; Teams Regnl Competition Winners 1993; Regnl PA Math League Winners 1990-95; *office:* Selinsgrove Area H S N Broad St Selinsgrove PA 17870*

WILIAMS, SARAH JEAN, English Teacher; *b:* Tuscaloosa, AL; *m:* Ronnie George; *c:* Tavis, Steven, Tevis; *ed:* Bloomfield Coll (BA) Eng 1973; William Paterson Coll 24 Addl Credits; *cr:* Calvary Bapt Church Supervising Tchr 1975-78; Paterson Pub Schl #2 Supvr Alternate Schl 1978-79; Paterson Pub Schl Eng 9-12th Grd Instr 1979-; *ai:* Chrldr Coach; Band Complement, Frosh Class Adv; Chprsn Black His Month Comm; NEA 1984-; Seminary Bapt Church 1991-, Deaconess, Sunday Schl Tchr, Yth Dir, Prgm Coord; Perfect Attendance 2 Yrs; Passaic Cty Sheriff Dept Club #628 Received Edctrs Awd from Mayor Pascrell, Sheriff Dept, Congressman, Cnclman.

WILK, ADELINE JONES, Adjunct Professor of Math Dept; *b:* Johnstown, PA; *m:* Arthur L.; *c:* Alyson J., Gregory T., Jonathan C., Douglas M.; *ed:* Indiana Univ of PA (BS) Math 1956; *cr:* Cochran Jr HS Math Tchr 1956-57; Longmeadow HS Math Tchr 1958-59; East Longmeadow HS Math Tchr 1962-86; Springfield Tech Comm Coll Adj Prof 1986-; *ai:* Sr Class Adv 1964-86; Steering Comm Evaluation; Visiting Evaluation Team; CORE Prgm for Coll Prep Sophs; ELTA, NEA, MTA 1970-86; MTA, NEA 1994-.

WILK, AGNES MARY, French Teacher; *b:* Youngstown, OH; *ed:* SUC at Oswego (BA) Scndry Ed Fr 1969; *cr:* Oswego Cath HS Fr Tchr 1969-70; P. V. Moore HS Fr Tchr 1970-; *ai:* Shared Decision Making Site Level Team; NYSUT, AFT 1970-, Union Local Bldg Rep; Zoning Bd 1988-, Pres; *office:* Paul V Moore HS Caughdenoy Rd County Rt 12 Central Square NY 13036

WILK, ANN ROUSSEAU, Math Teacher; *b:* Lowell, MA; *m:* Edward; *c:* Jonathan, Kendrick; *ed:* Merrimack Coll (BA) Math 1972; U MA at Lowell (MMT) Math 1977; *cr:* Lowell Pub Schls Math Tchr 1972-; *ai:* UTL, MFT, NEA 1972-.

WILK, FRANCES CORNELY, HS Math Teacher; *b:* Somerville, NJ; *m:* John C.; *c:* Seth, Theresa, Andrea, Lara; *ed:* Trenton St Coll (BA) Math Ed 1974; Peer Mediator Facilitator Course Somerset Cty Police Assn 1995; *cr:* Hamilton HS Math Tchr 1978-79; Hillsborough Twp Schl Sub Tchr 1990-93; Immaculata HS Math Tchr 1993-; *ai:* Cty 4-H 1986-93, Prep Ldr; *office:* Immaculata HS Mountain Ave Somerville NJ 08876

WILK, LEON J., English Teacher; *b:* Phoenixville, PA; *m:* Patricia H.; *c:* Karen L. D'Onsogna; Krista L.; *ed:* Millersville (BSEd) Eng, Soc Stud 1962; Attnd Temple Univ; *cr:* Lower Merion Schl Dist Eng Tchr 1962-; Lower Merion Ed Assn Chief Negotiator 1991-; *ai:* Staff Dev, Instruction, Curr Cncl; Strategic Planning Comm; NEA, PA St Ed Assn 1962-; Lower Merion Ed Assn 1962-, VP, Chief negotiator; *office:* Lower Merion Schl Dist 245 E Montgomery Ave Ardmore PA 19003*

WILK, PATRICIA SAVAGE, High School Mathematics Tchr; *b:* Elizabeth, NJ; *m:* George; *c:* Kathryn, Christopher; *ed:* Douglass Coll, Rutgers Univ (BA) Math 1984; Kean Coll (MA) Supervision 1987, (MA) MATH, Cmptrs 1989; 30 Addl Credits Math, Cmptrs; *cr:* Lafayette MS Math Tchr 1984-85; David Brearley HS Math Tchr 1985-90; Linden HS Math Tchr 1990-; *ai:* NJEA 1990-; NCTM 1984-; *office:* Linden HS 121 W Saint Georges Ave Linden NJ 07036

WILK, THERESA ANN, Business Education Dept Chair; *b:* Kingston, PA; *ed:* Coll Misericordia (BS) Secretarial Sci 1966; Marywood Coll (MS) Bus Ed 1976; 12 Addl Hrs Post-Grad Stud Scndry Ed, Cmptr Sci; *cr:* Lake-Lehman HS Bus Tchr 1966-67, Bus Ed Dept Chair 1968-; *ai:* Yrbk Adv 1966-76; FBLA Adv 1975-85; Citizens Advy Comm Chprsn 1980-86; NEA, PSEA 1966-; *office:* Lake-Lehman HS Market St Lehman PA 18627

WILKERSON, JESSIE MORRIS, Retired English Teacher; *b:* Newark, NJ; *w:* Kenneth C. (dec); *ed:* Upsala Coll (BS) Ed 1950; *ai:* Natl Jr Hnr Soc, Schl Newspaper, Yrbk, Stu Cncl Adv; East Orange Curr Cncl, Eng Textbook Comm; SAGE Prgm Coord, Originator; Phi Delta Kappa, Sec; Phi Delta Kappa; Phi Delta Kappa Schlsp Comm Chprsn; NCTE; City of Orange Amer Revolution Bicentennial Celebration Chprsn 1974-78; East Orange Status of Women Comm; Vernon L. Davey Jr HS Renaming Comm; Church of Epiphany, First Female Sr Warden; Churchof Epiphany Schlsp Comm, Vestry Mem, Altar Guild; Soc Justice Comm Diocese of Newark Chprsn; Recognition, Appreciation Outstdng Ldrshp as Chprsn Bicentennial 1977; Directory of Distngd Amers, Extraordinary Svc as Tchr of Eng 1980; Tchr of Yr 1985; Recognition of Faithful Svc First Female Sr Warden Church of Epiphany 1989; Exceptional Commitment to Vernon L. Davey Jr HS 1987-88; Recognized by NJ St Gen Assembly for Influence on Stdnts of Eng 1991; Awd of Excl from VLO PTO Org 1992; Resolution from Mayor, City Cncl for Self-Esteem, Valuable Life Skills Instilled in Stdnts 1993; Recognition of Outstdng Svc as Chprsn, Mem Souvenir Journal for 90th Anniversary Church of the Epiphany.

WILKERSON, KATHRYN H., Business Ed Tchr & Dept Chprsn; *b:* Martinsville, VA; *m:* Randy S.; *c:* Amanda; *ed:* Carson-Newman Coll (BS) Bus Admin, Ed 1973; George Washington Univ (MA) Supervision, Human Relations 1982; *cr:* Thomas Stone HS Bus Ed Instr 1973-74; La Plata HS Bus Ed Instr 1974-, Dept Chprsn 1990-; Charles Cty Comm Coll Part-time Instr 1980-82; Wilkerson's Landscaping Svc Inc VP 1986-; *ai:* FBLA; NEA, EACC 1973-; MBEA 1994-; Charles Cty Chamber of Commerce 1995-; *office:* La Plata HS PO Box 790 Radio Station Rd La Plata MD 20646

WILKEY, ROBERT W., Fifth Grade Teacher; *b:* Lancaster, PA; *ed:* West Chester Univ (BS) Elem Ed 1971, (MED) Elem Ed 1976; Univ of PA Rdng Specialist Cert 1983; Operation Chem; 120 Addl Credits; *cr:* Green Tree Schl Fifth Grd Tchr 1971-79, Tchr of Academically Talented 1977-81; Charlestown Schl Tchr of Academically Talented 1981-87, Fifth Grd Tchr 1987-; *ai:* Outdoor Ed Prgm Coord; NEA, PSEA, GVEA, Chester Co Rdng Assn, DE Vly Rdng Assn 1971-; Coll Settlement 1971-, Corp Bd; Great Vly Nature Ctr, Chester Co Historical Soc 1971-; Presidential Awd for Outstdng Achvmt in Environmental Ed; PDE Writing Project; Operation Chem; Snag in the River Awd; *office:* Charlestown Elem Schl Charlestown Rd Devault PA 19432*

WILKIE, GRACE A., Mathematics Teacher; *b:* Brooklyn, NY; *m:* Peter L.; *ed:* SUNY at Oneonta (BS) Math Ed 1971; Western CT (MS) Ed 1976; Long Island Univ (MS) Soc Stud 1987; Attnd SUNY at New Paltz, Coll of New Rochelle, Coll of Saint Rose, Columbia Univ, Princeton Rutgers Univ; *cr:* Blue Mountain MS Math Tchr 1971-84; Hendrick Hudson HS Math Tchr 1984-; *ai:* Mentor; Tutor; Union Budget, Sunshine Dinner Comms; Union Bldg Rep; NY St Assn of math Supvrs, Pres Elect; Assn of math Tchrs of NYS, Sr HS Rep, Prgm Chprsn, Turnkey to Speaker; Ten Cty Math Ed Assn, Bd of Dir; NCTM; NYSUT; AFT; MAA; ASCD; Lions Club 1993-; Desmond-Fish Lib 1995-, Bd Trustee; HHEA, Mbrshp Chprsn 1993, Benefit Trust Fund Chprsn 1986; NYS to Washington for INTASC Project Rep; Mid Sts Assn of Colls, Schls Awd for Outstdng Svc; Wrote Instrl Materials; *office:* Hendrick Hudson HS 2 Albany Post Rd Montrose NY 10548*

WILKINS, BETH BISHOP, Sixth Grade Science Teacher; *b:* Emlenton, PA; *m:* Donald S.; *c:* Michael Zinchini, Molly Mc Lendon, Jenny Terwilliger; *ed:* Clarion Univ (BS) Elem Ed 1961, (MS) Sci Ed 1987; 40 Addl Credits; *cr:* Allegheny-Clarion Vly Schl Dist Elem Tchr 25 Yrs; *ai:* Just Say No Club Spon; Kappa Delta Pi 1986-; PA Sci Tchrs Assn 1970-; Am Cancer Dr, Chm; Clarioun U Regnl Cmptr Resource Ctr, Bd Mem 1986-90; PA Tchr of Yr Honoree Top 10 Finalist; Thanks to Tchrs Honoree 1990; Sci, Children Magazine Article 1987; *home:* PO Box 257 Emlenton PA 16373

WILKINS, DAVID BENJAMIN, Former Teacher; *b:* Washington, DC; *ed:* Anne Arundel (AA) EDP, Cmptrs 1983; Univ of MD (BS) IFSM, Math, Cmptrs 1986; Tchng Cert; *cr:* Univ of MD Cmptr Operator 1983-85; Anne Arundel Pub Schls Sub Tchr 1986-90; Mechina HS Math Tchr 1990; Mt de Sales Acad Math, Cmptrs Tchr 1991-95; *ai:* Tutor; Vol; Courageous Achvmt Awd.

WILKINS, MARSHA R., Kindergarten Teacher; *b:* New York, NY; *m:* Lawrence; *c:* Ronald, Michael; *ed:* SUNY at Cortland (BA) Elem Ed 1967; CUNY at Hunter (MS) Elem Ed 1973; 30 Addl Credits Post Grad; *cr:* PS 113 Queens 3rd Grd Tchr, Kndgtn Tchr 1977-; *ai:* Parent in Charge of HS Debate Team; AFT 1977-; VFT 1967-; Cardozo HS P-A 1992-; Reaching Out Comm 1994-95; *office:* PS 113 Queens 87-21 79th Ave Glendale NY 11385

WILKINS, PATRICIA SHORT, Biology & Chemistry Teacher; *b:* Kingston, NY; *m:* William Chester; *c:* Ryan, Brittany, Aaron; *ed:* SUNY at Potsdam (BA) Bio, Chem, Scndry Ed 1977; 36 Grad Credits in Bio & Ed; *cr:* Meyers Corners Schl 7th Grd Sci Tchr 1974; All Saints Episcopal Schl 10th-11th Grd Bio Tchr 1979-81; Wyndcroft Schl 6th-8th Grd Sci Tchr 1983-85; Boyertown HS Bio, Chem Tchr 1993-; *ai:* NHS Comm; Home Schl Network Exec Bd; PSEA, NEA 1993-; NSTA, MCTA 1994-; *office:* Boyertown Area Sr HS Monroe & 4th Boyertown PA 19512

WILKINS, REBECCA KING, Vocal Music Tchr & Dept Chair; *b:* Oneida, TN; *m:* Charles Phillip; *c:* Nicholas; *ed:* Eastern KY St Univ (BS) Music Ed 1966; OH St Univ (MA) Vocal Music 1969; 16 Hrs in Music Ed, Theatre & Supervision; *cr:* Westville United Meth Church Choir Dir, Minister of Music 1966-68; Graham Local Schls Vocal Music Tchr 1966-68; Bolich Jr HS Vocal Music Tchr 1969-80; Cuyahoga Falls HS Vocal Music Tchr 1980-; *ai:* Melodymen & Melodettes Chamber Ensemble, Show, Choir, Spring Musical, Choir Prgms, Competitions, Festivals Involving 6 Choirs; MENC, OMEA, 25 Yr Awd; NEA; OEA; CFEA; ACDA; OCDA; NEOTA; Kappa Delta Pi; Stow 1st United Meth Church 1978-; Bolich Jr HS Tchr of Yr 1978; Tchr of Month 1989; Sallie Mae Tchr Tribute Awd 1989; Newsweek Mentor Tchr Awd 1989; Rita Dove Awd Creativity in Work with Stdnts 1993; Woman of Hr, Women's His Project 1993; PTA Tchr of Yr 1994; *office:* Cuyahoga Falls HS 2300 4th St Cuyahoga Falls OH 44221*

WILKINS, VICTORIA A., Mathematics Teacher; *b:* Victoria, TX; *m:* Edward Jr.; *c:* Frances, Edward III; *ed:* Worcester St (BA) Math 1978; 33 Post Grad Credits; *cr:* Marlboro HS Math Tchr 2 Yrs; Quaboag Regnl HS Math Tchr 15 Yrs; *ai:* Jr Class; Stu & Tchr Assistance Teams; Discipline Comm; MTA; AS Curr; Girl Scouts of Amer 1990-, Ldr; Saint Josephs Church 1981-, Lector; Nominate & Design Awd; Articles in Paper Regarding Projects; *office:* Quaboag Reg Jr Sr HS 284 Old W Brookfield Rd Warren MA 01535*

WILKINSON, EILEEN FRANCES, Amer His Teacher & Dept Chair; *b:* Philadelphia, PA; *ed:* Comm Coll of Philadelphia (AGS) Gen Stud 1980; Chestnut Hill Coll (BA) His 1985; Villa Nova Univ (MA) Ed 1991; 3 Hrs Natl Achives Univ of VA 1994; 3 Hrs Natl His Day Univ of MD 1993; 4 Hrs Geog Alliance Univ of DE 1993; *cr:* St Bartholomew Elem Tchr 1983-86; Holy Name Jr HS Tchr 1986-91; St Mark's HS Amer His Tchr 1991-; Wilmington Coll Adj Instr 1995-; *ai:* Model UN Moderator; Mock Trial Coach; DE HS Mock Trial St Coord; NCSS 1993-; MSCSS 1993-, DE St Rep; DCSS 1993-, Treas, Pres Awd 1996; NCEA 1983-; Phi Theta Kappa 1980-; De Law Related Ed Project, Bd Mem 1992-94; *office:* St Mark's HS Pike Creek Rd Wilmington DE 19808

WILKINSON, GARY F., Health & Physical Ed Tchr; *b:* North Olmsted, OH; *m:* Carolyn G. Smith; *c:* Sandi L., Amy K.; *ed:* Heidelberg Coll (BA) Hlth, PE 1965; Cntrl St Univ 3 Credit Hrs; Wright St Univ 15 Credit Hrs; Miami Univ 12 Credit Hrs; *cr:* Fairborn City Schls Hlth & PE, Driver Ed Tchr 1966-; *ai:* Coach Jr High Ftbl, Track, High Schl Bsktbl; Tennis Ath Trainer; NEA, OEA, WOEA, FTA, Hlth & PE 1966-; Dr Ed 1968-; Jaycees 1968-70; *office:* Fairborna HS 900 E Dayton-Yellow Springs Rd Fairborn OH 45324

WILKINSON, JAMES W., English Teacher; *b:* Coudersport, PA; *m:* Peggy Erway; *c:* Scott, Christopher; *ed:* Lock Haven Univ (BS) Eng 1972; 46 Credits Speech Comm at Penn St Univ Grad Schl; *cr:* Wilkinson-Dunn Co Real Estate Broker 1975-79; Sears Authorized Merchant Owner 1980-92; *ai:* Boys Golf Coach; Var Club Adv; Intensive Scheduling Curr Comm; NEA, PEA 1993-; Rotary Intnl Honorary Mem, Former Pres; *office:* Coudersport Area Jr Sr HS 698 Dwight St Coudersport PA 16915

WILKINSON, MAUREEN C., Psychology Teacher; *b:* Philadelphia, PA; *ed:* Temple Univ (BA) Speech & Hearing Sci 1976; Saint Charles Seminary 15 Grad Credits Sacred Scripture; *cr:* Nazareth Acad Tchr & Forensics Coach 1982-; Holy Family Coll Adult Ed Tchr 1991-93; *ai:* Forensics Moderator & Coach; Schl Nwspr Moderator 1994-; Rosary Club Moderator 1994-; Mem Fac Admin Comm 1994-; NCEA 1985-; HS APA Tchr Affiliate Prgm 1993-; Natl Assoc of Deaf 1982-; Veterans of Foreign Wars Awd 1994, 1996.*

WILL, JOHN W., Chemistry & Physics Teacher; *b:* Batavia, NY; *m:* Patricia Hunter; *c:* Michael, Anna; *ed:* St Univ Coll at Oneonta (BS) Chem 1968; Attnd Univ of Rochester, Rochester Inst of Tech, Univ of WI, SUC at Geneseo; *cr:* Pembroke HS Chem, Physics Tchr 1968-; Geneseo Comm Coll Eisenhower Prgm Dir 1990-; *ai:* NHS; Ski Club; Acad Team; Sci Dept Chm; STANYS; AFT; Alexander Sports Boosters; *office:* Pembroke HS Rts 5 & 77 Corfu NY 14036*

WILL, ROBERT I., 12th Grd Psychology Teacher; *b:* Pittsburgh, PA; *m:* Gail Stewart; *c:* Andrew, Julie; *ed:* Slippery Rock Univ (BA) Pol Sci 1969; Duquesne Univ (MED) Scndry Ed 1972; Prins Cert Scndry 1975; 30 Addl Hrs; *cr:* Pittsburgh Pub Schls Soc Stud Tchr 1969-79; North Allegheny Schl Dist Soc Stud Tchr 1979-; *ai:* Sr Class Adv; AFT 1969-; Amer Psychological Assn 1990-; PIAA 1985-, PA Interscholastic Ath Assn; VOW 1982-; Thanks to Tchrs Awd 1990; United Mental Hlth Honored at Western PA Convention for Service with Stdnts at Mental Hospital 1991; Power of Partnerships Conf Univ of Pittsburgh Presentor 1991; Nom Rdrs Digest "Heroes of Ed" Awd 1993; Nom Thomas Wolfe Outstanding Ed Awd 1994; "Gift of Time" Awd 1994; Wolfe Aw Hon 1995; PA Welfare Sec Vol Aw 1995; *office:* North Allegheny H S 10375 Perry Hwy Wexford PA 15090

WILLARD, MARIE M., Social Studies Teacher; *b:* Sharon, CT; *m:* George F.; *c:* Robert, John; *ed:* SUNY Coll at Buffalo (BS) Scndry Ed

1973, (MS) Scndry Ed 1976; Post Grad Stud; *cr:* West Seneca East Sr Soc Stud Tchr 1973-; *ai:* NYSUT 1973-; WSTU 1973-; *office:* West Seneca East Sr HS 4760 Seneca St West Seneca NY 14224

WILLEFORD, CONSTANCE E. IRWIN, Assoc Prof & Music Therapy Dir; *b:* Knoxville, TN; *m:* Michael J.; *c:* Steven Michael, Kimberly Willeford Mc Mahon; *ed:* Georgetown Coll (BA) Music 1960; FL St Univ (MM) Music Therapy 1972; Working Towards MS Degree in Cnslng Psych St Bonaventure Univ; Post Grad Work at Univ of Miami; *cr:* St of FL Pub Schl Music Tchr 1960-68; Parsons St Hops, Trng Ctr Music Therapy Dir 1970-73; Univ of Miami Music Therapy Dir 1973-76; SUNY Coll Assoc Prof, Music Therapy Dir 1976-; *ai:* Church Organist; Choir Dir; Music Therapy Club Adv; Exec Asst to Coll Pres 4 Yrs; Clinical Placement Coord; Natl Assn Music Therapy 1970-, Cncl Coord; Mid-Atlantic Region NAMT 1976-, Pres, Svc Awd; Pvt Practice Grief Cnslng 1994-; Articles Pub; *office:* S U N Y Coll At Fredonia Schl of Music Fredonia NY 14063

WILLENBROCK, MARSHA F., First Grade Teacher; *b:* Salem, NJ; *m:* Jack H.; *c:* Peter, Phil, Gretchen; *ed:* Glassboro St Coll (BA) Primary Ed 1962, (MS) Rdng Ed 1968; *cr:* Cntrl Park Elem Schl 1st Grd Tchr 1962-68; Radio Park Schl 1st-2nd Grd Tchr 1976-; *ai:* IRA 1990-; Phi Delta Kappa 1989-; NEA 1976-; St Paul United Meth Church 1969-, Ldrshp, Comm, Chairs.

WILLETS, JOAN MARIE, Mathematics Teacher; *b:* Ticonderoga, NY; *m:* Richard G.; *c:* Katherine, Abigail; *ed:* Marymount Coll (BA) Math 1973; Univ of Lowell (MMT) Math 1976; *cr:* Haverhill HS Math Tchr 1973-; *ai:* NEA, MTA, HEA 1973-; NCTM 1990-.

WILLETT, CAROL JEAN, 3rd Grade Teacher; *b:* Detroit, MI; *c:* Kurt; *ed:* Wayne St Univ (BA) Ed 1956; Remaining Thesis Towards MS in Ed 1952-56; Ed Courses OH St Univ 1959-60; Tchng Exch Blenheim Infant Schl 1974; *cr:* Coffey Schl Kndgtn Tchr 1 Yr; K-9 Grd Sub Tchr 1 Yr; Nursery Tchr 1 Yr; Berwich Schl 1st Grd Tchr 2 Yrs; *ai:* Orginated, Directing, Tchng Discovery Summer Enrichment Prgm; NJAIS Tchr Rep, Grd Level Wkshps; Head Lower Schl Report Card, Reding Series Comms; AFT, NEA; NJAIS, NAIS 1969-; *office:* Rumson Country Day Schl 35 Bellevue Ave Rumson NJ 07760*

WILLETT, FRANCIS MERRILL,III, Social Studies Teacher; *b:* Brooklyn, NY; *m:* Susan Hussong; *c:* Francis, Terrance, Jenniebeth, Catherine; *ed:* Niagara Univ (BA) Soc Stud 1972; Attnd Glassboro St Coll at Rowan; *cr:* Slaybaugh Schl Soc St Tchr 1972-76; Davenport Schl Soc St Tchr 1976-79; Slaybaugh Schl Soc St Tchr 1979-83; Egg Harbor Gwp HS Soc St Tchr 1983-; *ai:* Ftbl 1984-, Bsktbl 1974-76 Asst Coach; NEA, NJEA 1972-; Egg Harbor Twp EA 1972-, Exec Comm; Mainland Regnl HS Bd of Ed 1976-; *office:* Egg Harbor Twp HS 24 High School Dr Egg Harbor Townshi NJ 08234

WILLETT, JACK TINSLEY, 5th Grade Teacher; *b:* Alliance, OH; *m:* Ann Kellers; *c:* Esther Dawn, Hannah Ruth; *ed:* Vincennes Univ (AS) Recreation 1977; Youngstown St Univ (BS) Elem, Spec Ed 1982; *cr:* Death Vly Elem 3-6 Grd Spec Ed, 4-6 Grd Combined Elem Tchr 1982-85; Dakar Acad 4-6 Grd Tchr 1985-89; Tecopa Francis Elem K-3 Grd Combined Tchr 1989-90; Bethel Chrstn Schl 6th Grd Tchr, 4-7 Grd Soc Stud Tchr 1990-92; Plantation Hill Chrstn Acad K-12 Tchr, Prin 1992-95; Santiago Chrstn Schl 5th Grd Tchr 1995-; *ai:* Soccer; Girls Flag Ftbl; Elem Drama; Curr Evaluation Comm; St Paul's United Meth Church 1992-; *office:* Santiago Christian Schl Santiago De Les Caballeros #62 Dominican Republic XX

WILLETTE, WAYNE A., Alternative Education Tchr; *b:* Patten, ME; *c:* Tracy A., Kyle R.; *ed:* Univ of ME (BS) Ed 1966, (MS) Ed; *cr:* Etma Schl Sys Tchr 1966-68; Dixmont Schl Sys Tchr 1966-68; Warsaw Jr HS Tchr 1968-72, Prin 1972-74; Fifth St Jr HS Alternative Ed Tchr 1974-84; Bangor HS Alternative Ed Tchr 1984-; *ai:* Class of 1989, Key Club, Class of 1994 Adv; BEA 1974-, Bldg Rep; MEA 1966-; NEA 1966-; Schl Comm SAD #63 1978-80, Local Rep; ME Dist Yth 1970-, Dir; *office:* Bangor HS 885 Broadway Bangor ME 04401*

WILLEY, WILBUR W., Retired English Teacher; *b:* Littleton, NH; *ed:* Plymouth St Coll (BED) Eng 1948; Univ of ME at Orono (MA) Guid 1954; 6 Hrs Boston Univ; Attnd Univ of VT, Lyndon St Coll; *cr:* Tifton-Northfield HS Scndry Eng Tchr 1948-54; Attleboro HS Scndry Eng Tchr 1954-57; Hull HS Eng Dept Head 1957-76; Littleton HS Sub Tchr 1976-96; *ai:* NEA 1949-, Life; Littleton Zoning Bd 3 Yrs; Littleton Historical Soc 1976-, Historian; Glenwood Cemetery Assn 1986-, Bd Dirs; 3 Books, Numerous Articles, Weekly Column Pub; *home:* 842 Foster Hill Rd Littleton NH 03561

WILLHELM, DEBORAH A., Counselor; *b:* Dayton, OH; *ed:* Ashland Univ (BS) PE K-12, Hlth 7-12 1974; Univ of Akron (MS) Admin, Super 1983; Cert Cnslng 1990; Cmptr Ed; Spec Ed, Title I Supervision; *cr:* Ontario Local Schls PE K-5th Grd, 3rd Grd Tchr, Intermin Prin, Cnslr, Pupil Svcs; *ai:* Comm Family Drug & Alcohol Abuse, Consumer Ed Advy Bd; Intervention Assistance, Crisis Intervention Teams; Fed of Tchrs 1974-; St Park Vol 1992-, 60 Plus Hrs Svc; Odyssey of Mind Judge; Helped Organize Fund Raiser to Asst Staff Mem; *office:* Ontario-Stengel Elem Schl 416 Shelby-Ontario Rd Mansfield OH 44906

WILLIAMS, ANN JOHN, Dir of Surgical Tech & Instr; *b:* Salamanca, NY; *m:* Robert J.; *ed:* SUNY at Buffalo (BS) Nrsng 1976; D'Youville Coll (MS) Nrsng 1991; Buffalo Gen Hosp Schl of Nrsng RN Diploma 1955; *cr:* Buffalo Gen Hosp Staff, Head Nurse, Inservice Edctr 1958-75; Trocaire Coll Dir of Surgical Tech 1977-87, Instr of Perioperative Nrsng, Dir of Grants Svcs 1985-93, Asst Prof, Dir of Surgical Tech, Instr of Perioperative Nrsng 1993-; *ai:* Acad Adv, Cncl; Evaluation of Instruction Comm Chprsn; Assn of Operating Room Nurses Inc 1959-, Pres 4 Times, Every Office Except Treas Locally; AORN of Western NY 1959-; Sigma Theta Tau, Intnl Nursing Hnr Soc; Amer Cancer Soc Patient Ed Comm 1990-; *office:* Trocaire Coll 360 Choate Ave Buffalo NY 14220

WILLIAMS, ANNEMARIE HAUBER, History Teacher; *b:* Schorndorf, Germany; *m:* Evan J.; *c:* Niccole Anne Young; *ed:* Univ of SC (BA) His Ed 1968; SUNY at New Paltz (MA) His 1974; Attnd Univ of London Schl of Ec 1969, Potsdam Coll 1985, Manhattan Ville Coll 1983, Allgheny Coll 1987; *cr:* Monticello HS 9th-10th Grd His Tchr 1968-70; Yorktown HS 9th-10th Grd His Tchr 1970-71; Hendrick Hudson HS 9th-10th Grd His & 12th Grd AP European His Tchr 1971-; *ai:* Coached Male Var Tennis 1971-73; Textbook Rater; Cmptr, Wise Comms; Tchrs Adv To & For Stu Tchng Taxe Stdnts to Metro Museum of Art; AFT 1968-; ASCD 1993-; NYS Cncl for SS 1985-; NCSS 1985-; Sunday Schl Tchr; Study Grant 1969; Outstdng Tchr Awd 1988; *home:* 7 Lord Rd #365 Rock Hill NY 12775*

WILLIAMS, ANN MARIE KUPLINSKI, 7th Grd Social Studies Teacher; *b:* Taylor, PA; *w:* David C. (dec); *c:* Kristen, Lisa; *ed:* Marywood Coll (BA) Comprehensive Soc Sci 1970; Univ of Scranton (MA) His 1981; 30 Grad Credits Beyond Masters Degree; *cr:* Pittston Area Schl Dist Soc Stud Tchr 26 Yrs; *ai:* Ticket Seller Ftbl, Girls-Boys Bsktbl, Wrestling; Young Lawyers Club Moderator; Instrl Support Team; AFT 1970-; *office:* Pittston Area Schl Dist 5 Stout St Yatesville Pittston PA 18640

WILLIAMS, BARBARA LEE, Social Studies Teacher; *b:* Clearfield, PA; *ed:* West Liberty St Coll (AB) Soc Stud 1974; *cr:* Moshannon Vly Jr-Sr HS Soc Stud, Music Tchr 1974-77; Clearfield Area HS Soc Stud Tchr 1977-; *ai:* Band Front Adv; NEA, PSEA 1974-; CEA 1977-; *office:* Clearfield Area HS PO Box 710 Clearfield PA 16830

WILLIAMS, BERNICE COHEN, 10th Grade Biology Teacher; *b:* Riverside, NJ; *m:* Roy V.; *c:* Vicki Lyn, Williams Polansky, Wendy Lee; *ed:* Burlington Co Coll (AAS) Bio 1978; Trenton St Coll (BS) Bio 1981; Temple Univ Intern Pgm 11 Credit Hrs; *cr:* Camden City Schls Earth Sci & Bio Tchr 1988-; *ai:* NEA 1988-; EMT for Palmyra Ambulance Assn 1983-, Bd of Trustees; Reach to Recovery Amer Cancer Soc 1990-; *office:* Woodrow Wilson HS 3100 Federal St Camden NJ 08105

WILLIAMS, BONNIE B., Dir of Developmental Education; *b:* New Orleans, LA; *c:* Charlotte, James, Anne; *ed:* Tulane Univ (BA) Eng, Span 1964; Univ of Cincinnati (MED) Ed 1970; ABD All But Dissertation Curr, 1995 EdD Curr & Instr; *cr:* Mairemont Schls Eng Tchr 1964-72; Southern OH Coll Resource Ctr, Eng, & Rdng Tchr 1980-86; UC Clemont Coll Acad Dir, Eng Tchr 1986-; *ai:* Spon Women's Ctr; OEA, AAIA 1965-, NCTE, AAWA 1970-; IRA, NADE 1975-, OADE; NCTE; Clemont Cty Lit Cncl 1986-, Sec; ClermontCty Lit Task Force 1986-; Stu Literacy Corps Grant from Dept of Ed; JOBS Grant; *office:* Univ of Cincinnati Clermont 4200 College Dr Batavia OH 45103

WILLIAMS, C. ROGER, Mathematics & Cmptr Sci Tchr; *b:* Piketon, OH; *m:* Conchida; *c:* Patrick Bryan; *ed:* Morehead St Univ (BS) Math 1968; Xavier Univ (MED) Math 1973; Post Grad Work OH Univ, XAvier Univ; *cr:* Piketon HS Math, Cmptr Sci Tchr 1968-; Shawnee St Univ Part-time Math Tchr 1980-; *ai:* OEA, NEA, OH Cncl Math Tchrs 1968-; *home:* 6105 Laurel Ridge Rd Piketon OH 45661

WILLIAMS, CAROL MARGRETANNE, Second Grade Teacher; *b:* Washington, DC; *ed:* NC Cntrl Univ (BA) Elem Ed 1988; 15 Credit Hrs Spec Ed, Sci Gen, Biblical Stud; *cr:* Eastern MS Sub Tchr 1988; Charles R. Drew Elem Schl Classroom Tchr 1988-; *ai:* Asst Chrldr Coach, Spon; Choir, Glee Club; Washington Tchrs Union 1988-, Bldg Rep; Cornerstone Assembly Abundant Life Ctr 1981-; *home:* 534 E Indian Spring Dr Silver Spring MD 20901*

WILLIAMS, CAROLYN A., HS English Teacher; *b:* PA; *ed:* Millersville Univ (BS) Eng 1992; 6 Hrs Univ of DE Eng; *cr:* SAlesianum Schl Eng Tchr 1992-; *ai:* Soph Class, Toys for Tots Moderator; Jump Rope Heart Coord; PSEA 1992-; *office:* Salesianum Schl 1801 N Broom St Wilmington DE 19802

WILLIAMS, CELESTE CARR, Science Dept Chair; *b:* Wilmington, NC; *m:* Leroy F. Jr.; *c:* Orson F., Jarvis D.; *ed:* Elizabeth City St Univ (BS) Bio 1964; Univ of MD Earth Sci; Towson St Math; Western MD Coll Earth Sci; Grad Courses Drug Awareness, Sickle Cell, Humna Growth, Dev, Educl Gift Stu Statistics Methods, Sco Con Concepts, Spec Problems in Ed, Field Ecology, Current Trends in Sci Ed, Educl Psych-Energy, Resrct Conservation; *cr:* Henry Garnett HS Bio Tchr; John Hanson Jr HS Earth Sci Tchr; GArlene HS Sci, Math Tchr; Friendly HS Sci Dept Chair; *ai:* Sci Fair Coord 1988-; Lead Tchr Partnership for Minority Stu Achvmt in Sci, Math; Spon Sr Class 1994, Black His Quiz Pursuit Contest 1988-91; Project Sucess Prgm; Prince Geo Co Edctr Assn 1988-, Bd Dirs; NEA 19765-, Del; NSTA 1991-, Steering Comm, Sci Conventions; MD St Tchrs Assn 1990-94, Chair; Prince Geo Co Woman Commission Wkshp, Chair 1990; PGE-Evaluation Team 1990-91; Elizabeth City Univ 1989, Bd Dirs; MD St Tchrs 1987-94; Human Rights in Ed; Awds Elizabeth City St Univ Pres, Outstdng Young Women of Amer 1978, Outstdng Sci Tchr 1991, PTSA Dedicated Sci Fair 1987-88, Svc Awd for Stu Prgms 1982-88, NAFEO 1992; *office:* Friendly HS 10000 Allentown Rd Fort Washington MD 20744*

WILLIAMS, CHARLENE DAVIS, Sixth Grade Teacher; *b:* Washington, DC; *ed:* Bowie St Univ (BA) Elem Ed 1971, (MS) Guid Cnslng 1977; Spec Ed Stud; *cr:* Margaret Edmondston Elem Schl; Laurel Elem Schl; Hyattsville Elem Schl Grd Level Chprsn 1992-93; *ai:* Gospel Singer; NEA 1971-; Tchrs Assn; *home:* 1223 Eye St NE Washington DC 20002

WILLIAMS, CHRISTOPHER R., Adjunct Assist Prof; *b:* London, England; *ed:* Univ of MA at Amherst (BA) Soc Thought & Pol Economy 1986; Univ of MI at Ann Arbor (JD) Law 1992; Oxford Univ; Trinity Coll Yr Abroad 1985; *cr:* Clark Atlanta Univ Rsrch Analyst & Instr 1990-92; Medgar Evers Coll Adjunct Asst Prof 1993-; *ai:* Yth Minister 1993-; New York Cty Lawyers Assn 1993-; Scholary Achvmnt Awd Soc Thought & Pol Economy 1985-86; Commonwealth Scholar Univ of MA 1986 & The Golden Key Natl Hnr Soc 1986; Grad Magna Com Laude BA; *office:* Medgar Evers Coll 1650 Bedford Ave Brooklyn NY 11225*

WILLIAMS, DANIEL KENNETH, Elementary Counselor; *b:* Rochester Mills, PA; *m:* Elaine Henry; *c:* Lauren Elaine, Kristen Marie; *ed:* IN Univ of PA (BS) Elem Ed 1974; Slippery Rock Univ of PA (MED) Elem Guidance & Cnslng 1980, (MA) Cnslng Svcs & Psych; STAR Suicide Prevention Trng at Western Psychiatric Inst; Valentine Discipline Trng; Instructional Support Trng; *cr:* Keystone Schl Dist 5th Grd Tchr 1974-80, Elem Cnslr 1980-; *ai:* Bsktbl Coach Elem Presently & Jr Var 1975-82; Americorps Comm Ctr; Headstart & Evenstart Family Svcs; Amer Cnslng Assn 1992-; Amer Schl Cnslrs Assn 1992-; PA Schl Cnslrs Assn 1980-, Unit Rep; Clarion Cty Cnslrs Assn 1994-, Pres; PSEA 1974-; Knox United Meth Church Choir 1980-; Grants for Violence Prevention Materials & Schl to Work Prgm; *office:* Keystone Elem Schl RR 2 Box 3d Knox PA 16232*

WILLIAMS, DAVE, Junior High Science Teacher; *b:* Crestline, OH; *m:* Cheryl; *ed:* OH St Univ (BS) Bio Ed 1966; *cr:* Barnes Manufacturing Co Production Control Clerk 1958-62; Burpee Seed Co Asst to Plant Breeder 1962-64; Dublin Local Schls Tchr 1966-72; Perry Local Schls Tchr 1972-; *ai:* Schl Greenhouse Mgr; NEA & OEA 1966-; Perry Ed Assn 1972-; Prof Plant Growers Assn 1981-; Lions Club 1975-; Lima Mens Garden Club 1974-, Past Pres; Extension Advy Comm 1984-, Chm; Started & Operate My Own Greenhouse Bus; *office:* Perry Local Schls 2770 E Breese Rd Cridersville OH 45806

WILLIAMS, DAVID LEROY, Technology Teacher; *b:* Sidney, NY; *m:* Kathryn Downin; *c:* Melissa, Todd; *ed:* SUNY at Oswego (BS) Industrial Arts 1971, (MS) Industrial Arts 1974; 14 Credit Hrs Beyond Masters; *cr:* Hancock Cntrl Schl Industrial Arts Tchr 1971-72; Norwich City Schls Industrial Arts & Tech Ed Tchr 1972-; *ai:* Tech Stu Assn & Video Club Adv; Channel 4 Advy, Workforce Preparation Steering & Dist Tech Planning Comms; NEA & NEANY 1972-; NYS Tech Edctrs Assoc 1979-; Three Rners Tech Tchrs Assoc 1988-, Pres 1993-94, Sec 1995-; East Guilford Presbyn Church 1964-, Ruling Elder; NY St Electric & Gas Energy Grant 1985; *office:* Norwich HS Midland Dr Norwich NY 13815

WILLIAMS, DAVID MICHAEL, History Teacher; *b:* Plainfield, NJ; *ed:* Fairfield Univ (BA) His 1990; Univ of Notre Dame (MA) His 1992; Attnd Grad Inst in Lbrl Ed St John's Coll at Annapolis, Inst on Comparative Pol, Ec Systems Georgetown Univ; *cr:* Union HS His Tchr 1992-; *ai:* Great Books Discussion Club Adv; His Curr Comm; Natl Cncl His Ed 1995-; Intercollegiate Stud Inst 1990-; Fairfield Dean's List, Phelan Awd; Notre Dame Tuition Schlsp; Phi Alpha Theta; *office:* Union H S N 3rd St Union NJ 07083*

WILLIAMS, DAVID RONALD, Spanish, French & ESOL Tchr; *b:* Baltimore, MD; *ed:* Morgan St Univ (BA) Scndry Ed Mod Langs 1974; Loyola Coll & Towson St Univ (MA) Supervision & Admin 1980; Loyola Coll & Towson St Univ +60 Supervision & Admin 1980; Univ of San Marcos at Lima Peru Post Grad 1974; *cr:* Loch Raven Sr High Modern Langs Tchr 1974-79; Pikesville MS Modern Langs Tchr & Team Ldr 1980-88; Dumbarton MS Modern Langs & ESOL Chm & Coord 1988-94, Modern Langs Instr 1996; *ai:* World Vision Club & Stdnts Understanding Nations Adv; Natl Jr Hnr Soc Asst; NEA & MSTA 1974-; MFLA 1992-; Associated Black Charities 1988-; Fulbright Alumni Assn 1988-; Fulb[illegible] Scholar 1974; NEA Inst Fellow 1984 & 1992; Fulbright Summer Fellow 1991; Chamber of Commerce Tchr of Yr 1991; *office:* Dumba[illegible] MS 300 Dumbarton Rd Baltimore MD 21212

WILLIAMS, DEBRA JONES, Physical Ed & Health Teacher; *b:* Nor[illegible] VA; *m:* Thaddeus H.; *c:* Taylor Danielle, Taryn Dominique; *ed:* Ham[illegible] Inst (BS) PE, Hlth 1977, (MS) Scndry Ed, Hlth 1984; *cr:* D[illegible] Intermediate Schl Hlth Tchr 1977-81; Hampton Inst PE Tchr 1983; B[illegible] St Coll PE Tchr 1984-85; Charles Caroll MD Sci Tchr 1985-86; Seneca[illegible] HS PE Tchr 1986-; *ai:* Pom Pon Coach, Spon 1992-; Trach Coach 19[illegible] NEA 1978-; MSTA 1986-; AAHPERD 1977-; Delta Sigma Theta 19[illegible] *office:* Seneca Valley HS 12700 Middlebrook Rd Germantown MD 20[illegible]

WILLIAMS, DIANE DETULLIO, 8th Grade Social Science Tch[illegible] Vineland, NJ; *m:* Robert L.; *c:* Heather; *ed:* Glassboro St Coll (BA) Sc[illegible] Soc Stud 1972; Elem Cert 1973; *cr:* Durand Elem 6th Grd Tchr 1978[illegible] Johnstone Elem 6th Grd Tchr 1979-81; Reber Elem 6th Grd Tchr of G[illegible] & Talented 1981-83; Rossi Intermediate Schl 7th-8th Grd Sci & Soc[illegible] Tchr 1983-; *ai:* Mini Model Congress & Odyssey of the Mind Adv; Ca[illegible] Day, Discipline & Soc Stud Comms; NJEA 1980-; NEA 1980-; NJ[illegible] 1995-; Delta Kappa Gamma 1986-90, Intnl Soc for Womens Ed[illegible] Cumberland Cty Coll Bd 1990-, Sec, Treas; Amer Heart Assn Vol; *of*[illegible] Anthony Rossi Intermediate Sch 2572 Palermo Ave Vineland NJ 0836[illegible]

WILLIAMS, DIANNE, Merchandising Teacher; *b:* New York, NY; Bernard M. Baruch Coll (BS) Bus Ed 1987, (MS) Bus Ed 1992, (MS[illegible] Admin & Supervision 1995; *cr:* Fashion Industries HS Tchr 6 Yrs; *ai:* Tchrs Assn, ASCD 1992-; NBEA 1990-; Alumni Assn 1987-; *office:* H[illegible] Fashion Industries 225 W 24th St New York NY 10011

WILLIAMS, DONALD CLYDE, Government Professor; *b:* Colum[illegible] OH; *m:* Audrey Wong; *c:* Leah, Benjamin; *ed:* Miami Univ (BA) His & Sci 1984; Univ of FL (MA) Pol Sci 1988, (PHD) Pol Sci 1991; Grad African Stud 1991; *cr:* Western New England Coll Asst Prof 1991-; *ai:* Sci Assn Adv; African Stud Assn 1987-; Amer Pol Sci Assn 1988-; Kappa Phi 1988-; Pi Sigma Alpha 1992-; Numerous Articles Pub; B[illegible] Chptr in Governance in Africa; *office:* Western New England Coll [illegible] Wilbraham Rd Springfield MA 01119

WILLIAMS, DONALD G.,II, Math Teacher & Dept Chair; *b:* Buf[illegible] NY; *c:* Brett R., Eric S., Melissa E.; *ed:* St Univ Coll at Buffalo (BS) M[illegible] Ed 1967; SUNY Coll at Buffalo (MS) Math Ed 1973; *cr:* Niagara Falls Math Tchr 1967-70; West Seneca West Sr High Math Tchr 1970-90; Comm Coll Part-Time Math Instr 1978-; West Seneca West MS Math [illegible] 1990-; *ai:* Dept Chprsn; Budget & Schedule Comms; AFT & NY[illegible] 1967-; WSTA 1970-; Lodge of the Ancient Landmarks F&AM 19[illegible] Chaplain; *office:* West Seneca West MS 395 Center Rd West Seneca 14224

WILLIAMS, DONALD G., Retired Social Studies Teacher; *b:* Priced[illegible] PA; *m:* Marilyn Milsom; *ed:* CA Univ of PA (BA) Soc Stud 1958; Rostraver Jr HS Soc Stud Tchr 1958-65; Belle Vernon Area Schl Dist Stud Tchr 1965-93; *ai:* Coached Ftbl 28 Yrs, Bsktbl 6 Yrs, Vlybl 2 Track & Field 2 Yrs; NEA, PSEA 1958-88; AFT 1988-93; BVA[illegible] 1965-93; REA 1958-65; Univ of Pittsburgh 1982-, Golden Panther of[illegible] 1986; *home:* RR 4 Box 145A Belle Vernon PA 15012

WILLIAMS, DOROTHY AYERS, 7th & 8th Grd Mathematics Tchr[illegible] Ewing, VA; *m:* John Wayne; *c:* Andrew Wayne, John Edward; *ed:* B[illegible] Coll Math, Sci; Lincoln Meml Univ (BS) Math, Sci 1965; Miami U[illegible] (MED) Guid, Cnslng 1971; 30 Addtl Credit Hrs Various Courses Uni[illegible] Dayton, Wright St Univ, Miami Univ; *cr:* Franklin City Schls HS Ch[illegible] Physics Tchr 1965-67; Mound Lab Rsrch Physicist 1967-68; Mason [illegible] Schls HS Math Tchr 1968; Valley View Local Schls Sci, Math Mid [illegible] Tchr 1969-; *ai:* Math Counts Coach; Math-a-Thon Spon; Dist, Cty [illegible] Comm; Alliance for Ed Tchr Cncl; VV Tchrs Assn 1969-, Sec, Pres; N[illegible] OEA 1965-; OCTM 1970-; Carlisle Bd of Ed 4 Yrs Pres, VP Tracks to E[illegible] 1987; Ploited Calculator Materials That Were Later Pub; Nom OH M[illegible] Tchr of Yr; Nom for Presidential Awd; *home:* 130 Vernon Pl Carlisle 45005*

WILLIAMS, DOUG EUGENE, Business Tchr & Athletic Dir; *b:* De[illegible] OH; *m:* Vicki Homiev; *c:* Tori; *ed:* Bowling Green St Univ (BA) Ac[illegible] 1974; *cr:* Continental HS Tchr 1977-; *ai:* Ath Dir; Head Bsktbl Coa[illegible] NEA, OEA, LEA 1977-.

WILLIAMS, DOUGLAS JAMES, PE Teacher; *b:* Pitts, PA; *m:* Susan Katie, Quinn, Rachael, Johannah; *ed:* Towson St (BA) PE 1981; *ai:* [illegible] Head Coach.

WILLIAMS, EDWARD EMANUEL, Prof of Mgmt & Orgl Studies Brooklyn, NY; *m:* Gail R. Ricketts; *c:* Charles, Kathryn R.; *ed:* Linc[illegible] Univ (AB) Philosophy, His 1955; Andover Newton Theological (BD) [illegible] Testament Stud 1958; Drexel Inst of Tech (MBA) Organ Behav, Plan[illegible] Change 1969; Drexel Univ (PHD) Org Dev 1975; Tavistock Inst Hur[illegible] Relations London England; Applied Soc Psych Inst Copenhagen [illegible] Dropsie Coll Hebrew & Cognate Lang Phila PA; *cr:* Widner Univ Adj [illegible] Prsnl Mngmt 1980-81; Cheyney Univ of PA Dept Chr of Bus; *ai:* Fulbr[illegible] Assoc 1989-; West Chester NAACP 1980-, Pres, Comm Svc; Chester [illegible] OIC 1985-, Bd Pres, Comm Svc; 1993 Nissan Flwshp; 1987 Fulbr[illegible] Rsrch, Lectorship Aarhus DK; *office:* Cheyney Univ Of PA Busin[illegible] Administration Box 407 Cheyney PA 19319

WILLIAMS, ELAINE LOUISE, English Teacher & Coordinator; Zanesville, OH; *m:* Charles Douglas; *c:* Matthew D., Mitchell R.; *ed:* U[illegible] of MD (BA) Eng, Ed 1972; Geo Washington Univ (MA) Human D[illegible] Remedial Rdng 1979; *cr:* Thos Johnson MS Eng Tchr 1972-73; Du Val Eng, Coord Tchr 1973-; *ai:* Adv Gabriel Du Val Chptr NHS; NEA 19[illegible] *office:* Du Val Sr HS 9880 Good Luck Rd Lanham MD 20706*

WILLIAMS, ELLA MARILYN M., Mathematics Teacher; *b:* Ralei[illegible] NC; *ed:* NC Cntrl Univ (MED) Ed 1973; Post Grad Stud Cath Univ, U[illegible] of DC; *cr:* NC Greensboro City Schls Jr HS Math Tchr 1972-76; Univ Dist of Columbia Math Specialist; DC Pub Schls Sr HS Math Tchr 19[illegible] *ai:* SADD Spon; NCTM, DCCTM 1984-; Phi Delta Kappa 1995-; D[illegible] Sigma Theta 1970-; *home:* 3715B Alabama Ave SE Washington DC 200[illegible]

WILLIAMS, ELLWOOD ELIJAH, Speech & Theatre Arts Prof; Jacksonville, NC; *ed:* TN A&I St Univ (BA) Speech, Drama 1965, (M[illegible] Speech, Drama 1966; Addl 3 Credits Columbia Univ 1985; *cr:* Linc[illegible] Univ Eng, Drama Tchr 1966-68; Trng Resources for Yths Eng T[illegible] 1968-69; Manhattan Comm Coll Eng, Speech, Drama Tchr 1969-; Departmental Prsnl, Budget Comm 1993-; Drama Club Adv; Acting Co[illegible] 1993-94; Created Annual Playwriting, Rdng Seminar 1988; Prsnl Revi[illegible] Comm 1993-95; AFT, NEA 1969-; Univ Fac Senate 1995-; Frank Silv[illegible] Writers Wksp 1980-; Amer Comm Theatre 1975-, Playwright [illegible] Residence; Actors Equity Assn 1972-; Screen Actor's Guild 1973-; Wh[illegible] Who in The East 24th Marquis Ed 1993-94; Wrote Plays, Produced; Play[illegible] Prin Role in Broadway Tony Awd Winning Musical 1972-73; *home:* 176 87th St New York NY 10024*

WILLIAMS, ETHEL BRACE, Retired Elem Teacher; *b:* Hunlock Cre[illegible] PA; *m:* William; *c:* Todd, Alison Wian, Lisa Homan, William T.; *cr:* Dall[illegible] Area Schl Dist 5th Grd Tchr 1955-57; Selinsgrove Area Schl 5th Grd T[illegible] 1957-58; Bald Eagle Area Schl Sub Tchr 1977-82; Clarence Schl 6th C[illegible] Tchr 1982-95, 6th Grd Head Tchr 1991-95; *ai:* Unionville-Union T[illegible] 1971-, Sec 1987-; *home:* General Delivery Fleming PA 16835

LLIAMS, EVERETT PENDLETON,JR., Choral Music Teacher; *b:* ma, WA; *ed:* Oberlin Conservatory (BM) Piano 1974, (MMT) Music 1974; Grad Stud Tchrs Coll, Univ of SC at Columbia, CA St Univ, tminster Choir Coll; *cr:* Allen Univ Music Dept Chair, Choir Dir 5-78; C. A. Johnson HS Choral Tchr 1978-79; Muir Fundamental Schl ral, Gen Music Tchr 1979-81; Bethesda Chevey Chase Hs Dept Chair, ral Tchr 1984-; *ai:* Dir Montgomery Cty Yth Chorus; Accompanist DC s Choir; Organist, Choir Dir Shiloh Bapt Church; Dir 19th St Bapt rch Male Chorus; NEA, MENC 1981-; ACDA 1985-; Natl Tchng ow 1975-76; Composed Opera; Montgomery Cty Area I Tchr of Yr; nder, Dir E. P. Williams Ensemble; *office:* Bethesda-Chevy Chase HS E West Hwy Bethesda MD 20814

LLIAMS, GARY DENNIS, Chemistry Teacher; *b:* Palmerton, PA; *m:* inia Wittmeyer; *c:* Leah A., Amy E.; *ed:* Kutztown Univ (BS) Scndry 1973; East Stroudsburg Univ (MED) Gen Sci 1978; *cr:* Dieruff HS m Tchr 1973-77; Northwestern Lehigh HS Chem Tchr 1977-; *ai:* Head k Coach; Asst Ftbl Coach Moravian Coll; Asst Bsktbl Coach; NEA 3-; Co-Authored Rsrch Paper 1978; *office:* Northwestern Lehigh HS 3 Route 309 New Tripoli PA 18066*

LLIAMS, GARY ROBERT, Psychology Instructor; *b:* Johnson City, *c:* Matthew, Jeremy; *ed:* Corning Comm Coll (AA) Lib Arts 1967; NY at Oswego (BA) Psych 1969; Binghamton Univ (MASS) Soc Sci 6; Grad Coursework Syracuse Univ; *cr:* Vestal Sr HS Psych Instr 1969-; TOPSS, APA HS Tchr Affiliate 1994-; NEA, Vestal Tchrs Assn 1969-; Instr Psych Syracuse Univ; *office:* Vestal Sr HS 205 Woodlawn Dr tal NY 13850

LLIAMS, HOWARD GEORGE, Band Director; *b:* Canton, OH; *m:* icia Kay Hill; *c:* Marcus, Nathan; *ed:* Bowling Green St Univ (BM) sic Ed 1972, (MM) Woodwind Specialist 1979; Musical Instrument air, GATE Ed, Carrer Ed Courses, Complete Band Dir9 Sem Hrs; *cr:* odmore Local Schls Band Dir 1972-; *ai:* Marching, Pep Bands; Pit h; Sr of Month Nominating Comm; Dist Festival Band Mem Selection m; MENC 1972-; KKY 1968-; NBA 1982-; NEA 1972-; United Karate n 1995-; USGA 1988-; Boy Scouts 1993-, Merit Badge Cnslr; Concert d under my Direction has 16 Superior Ratings; *office:* Woodmore Local ls 633 Fremont St Elmore OH 43416*

LLIAMS, IYABO OGUNNAIKE, Chemistry Teacher; *b:* Dgun State, eria; *m:* Adeyinka; *c:* Foluso, Segun; *ed:* Univ of IFE (BS) Chem 1976; v of WI at Madison (MS) Curr, Instruction 1981; *cr:* Univ of IFE Asst turer 1985-86; Souderton HS Chem Tchr 1995-; *ai:* Mem Acoya a up of Parents Helping Yth Pastors at Church; NSTA 1995-; *office:* derton Area HS 41 N School Ln Souderton PA 18964

LLIAMS, JAMES,JR., Multi Level Voc Dev Teacher; *b:* Eutaw, AL; *c:* ill, Angela, Jacqueline; *ed:* Stillman Coll (BA) Psych & Ed 1961; vie St Univ (MED) Ed & Guid 1971; Attnd Howard Univ, George shington & Stout St Univ 1975; DC Tchr; *cr:* DC Dept Voc Rehab Voc lrs 1962; Orme Elem Schl Spcl Ed Tchr 1970; Kent Jr HS Pupil Svc lr 1974; Potomac HS Multi Level Tchr 1996; *ai:* Amer Red Cross Instr; CEA 1970-, Fac Rep, Svc Awd; NEA 1970-; Voc Ed Assn 1970-, Svc d; Ardmore Ardwick Civic Assn, Past Pres & Mem; Natl Evaluation m for Colls.

LLIAMS, JAMES DALE,SR., World History Teacher; *b:* Frostberg, ; *c:* James D. Jr., Kimberly S. Truly; *ed:* Frostburg St Univ (BS) Scndry 1962; *cr:* Allegany HS Soc Stud, Drivers Ed Tchr 1962-81; Valley HS rld His Tchr 1981-84; Westmar HS World His Tchr 1984-; *ai:* endance Adv; Allegany Cty Tchrs Assn 1962-; MSTA; NEA; Elks 2-; Moose 1993-; Frostburg Fire Dept 1960-, Fireman of Yr; *office:* stmar HS Rt 36 Lonaconing MD 21539

LLIAMS, JAMES F., Freshman World History Teacher; *b:* ladelphia, PA; *ed:* Allentown Coll (BA) His 1985; *cr:* Kennedy Inst PE r 1965-75; Father Judge HS Asst Ath Dir 1975-80; Allentown Coll Asst Dir 1980-84; Northeast Cath Schl Soc Stud Tchr 1985-; *ai:* Var Bsktbl ach; PA Cncl of Soc Stud Tchr 1986-; City, News, Cath League Coach Yr 1994; *office:* Northeast Catholic Boys HS 1840 E Torresdale Ave ladelphia PA 19124

LLIAMS, JAMES G., Professor of Religion; *b:* Tulsa, OK; *m:* rgaret Yvonne Idol; *c:* Katherine, Michael, Shanah; *ed:* Tulsa Univ (BA) 1959; Southern Meth Univ (BD) Theology 1962; Hebrew Union Coll (PHD) Hewbrew Bible 1966; Attnd Univ of Chicago 1962-63; nderbilt Univ Grad Schl on Judaism June 1969; Univ of Strasbourg eological Fac 1974-75; *cr:* Syracuse Univ Asst, Assoc & Full Prof 1966-; Colloquium on Violence & Rel 1990-, Exec Sec; Soc of Biblical Lit 56-, Lit Criticism Chair 1983-89; Amer Acad of Rel 1966-; St Therese h Church 1994-, Lector, RCIA Instruction; Schroeppel His Soc 1985-, air Bd of Trustees 1991-94; Bible, Violence & Sacred 1991, 1995; Those o Ponder Proverbs 1981; NEH Grant for Experimental Course 1979; *ice:* Syracuse Univ 206 Steele Hall Syracuse NY 13244*

LLIAMS, JAMES R., Fifth Grade Teacher; *b:* Lykens, PA; *m:* Deborah Walter; *c:* James C., Hallie E.; *ed:* Bloomsburg Univ (BS) Elem Ed 1975; Credit Hrs; Masters Equivalency Elem Ed 1986; Space Camp for Tchrs; STA Summer Ldrshp Prgm 1995; *cr:* Second Street Schl Fifth Grd Tchr 75-; *ai:* Sci, Fac Advy Comms; Tech Integration Teams; Eighth Grd Ftbl ach 1992-93; Video Review Team; NEA, PSEA 1975-; SEA 1975-, Bldg p; *office:* Second St Elem Schl Second & Orange St Northumberland PA 357

LLIAMS, JAMES STODDART, Sixth Grade Teacher; *b:* Pittsburgh, ; *ed:* CA Univ (BA) Elem 1974; PA St 30 Credit Hrs; *cr:* Freedom Area hl 1, 5-6, 8 Grd Tchr 1976-; *ai:* PSEA, NEA 1976-.

LLIAMS, JANEL POWELL, Special Education Teacher; *b:* New unswick, NJ; *m:* Lorenzo; *ed:* Norfolk St Univ (BA) Spec Ed 1990; tending Kean Coll for Masters in Admin Prin or Supvr; *cr:* Highland rk HS Spec Ed Tchr 1992-; *ai:* Bsktbl 1992, Soccer 1993-94 & Sftbl 95- Coach; Black Pearls Club Adv 1992; Tchr Mentor 1994-1995; *office:* ghland Park HS 102 N 5th Ave Highland Park NJ 08904*

ILLIAMS, JANET BEAN, Reading Specialist; *b:* Syracuse, NY; *ed:* JNY at Oswego (BS) Elem Ed 1963; Syracuse Univ (MS) Rdng Ed 1967; st Grad Stud in Ed; *cr:* Marcellus CSD Elem Tchr 1963-65; West ndequoit CSD Elem Tchr 1965-68; West Genesee CSD Rdng Specialist 68-; *ai:* Shared Decision Making Team; Prof Dev Comm; AFT; IRA; elta Kappa Gamma Ed Soc; WG Tchrs Assn; *office:* West Genesee Cntrl hl Dist Sanderson Dr Camillus NY 13031

ILLIAMS, JOHN CHARLES, History Teacher & Dept Chm; *b:* unton, MA; *ed:* Univ of MA (BA) His 1960, (MAT) His, Ed 1962; arvard Univ (CAS) Learning, Environment 1972; *cr:* Pioneer Regnl High s Tchr 1960-62; Havermill HS His Tchr 1962-67; Waston HS His Chair 67-; *ai:* Winston Tchrs 1960-; Organ of Amer Historians 1978-; Amer storical Assn 1985-; *office:* Weston HS 444 Wellesley St Weston MA 193*

LLIAMS, JOSEPH HENRY, 5th Grade Teacher; *b:* New York, NY; *m:* eronica Smith; *ed:* Hunter Coll (BA) Elem Ed & Psych 1985, (MA) Gen 1991; 30 Post Grad Credit; *cr:* PS 83 6th Grd Tchr 1986-88; Daniel ebster Schl 5th Grd Tchr 1988-; *ai:* Asst Bsktbl Coach Afterschl Pgm oord; Readers Digest Tall Trees Comm; Prin Cabinet; NYSUT 1986-, chr; *office:* Daniel Webster Magnet Schl 95 Glenmore Dr New Rochelle Y 10801

WILLIAMS, KARLA B., German & French Teacher; *b:* New York City, NY; *m:* Thomas E.; *c:* Evan; *ed:* Rutgers Coll (BA) Art His, Ger 1977; Columbia Univ (MA) Art His 1978; Fairleigh Dickinson Univ (MAT) Ger, Fr 1981; 15 Addl Credits; *cr:* Pascack Vly HS Ger Tchr 1981; Pascack Hills HS Ger, Fr Tchr 1981-; *ai:* Ger Club Adv; Stu Trips to Europe Coord, Guide; NJEA, NEA 1981-; Phi Beta Kappa; Delta Phi Alpha; Zertifikat Deutsch Goethe Inst; NJ Governor's Tchr Recognition Awd 1995; NJ Network for Educl Renewal Grant 1996; *office:* Pascack Hills HS Grand Ave Montvale NJ 07645

WILLIAMS, KATHRYN ANN, Health & Physical Ed Teacher; *b:* Camden, NJ; *ed:* Glassboro St Coll (BA) Hlth, Pe, Driver Ed 1985; Addl 9 Hrs Grad Prgm Master's Hlth Ed West Chester Univ; *cr:* Oaklyn Pub Schl Hlth, PE Tchr 1986-88; Delsea Regnl HS Hlth, PE Tchr 1988-; *ai:* Weight Trng, Natural Helpers Trainer, Teens as Tchrs, Systematic Trng for Effective Parenting Adv; Staff Dev Comm; NEA, NJEA 1986-; NJAHPERD 1993-, VP Hlth, Citation; Writing Team NJ Core Course Proficiencies; Writing Team Core Course Proficiencies Resource Guide; Trng Team Core Course Proficiencies; NJ Comprehensive Hlth Ed Curr Writing Chprsn; *office:* Delsea Regional HS Blackwoodtown Rd Franklinville NJ 08322*

WILLIAMS, KATHY J., Business Education Teacher; *b:* Erie, PA; *ed:* IN Univ of PA (BS) Bus Ed 1977; Various Cmptr Courses; Wilkes Coll Master's Equivalent Ed 1991; *cr:* Erie Schl Adult Ed Bus Tchr 1977-; Erie MS Bus Tchr, Career Specialist 1977-; Erie HS Bus Tchr 1977-; PA St Behrend Coll Stud Skills Instr 1989-92; Erie Cty Tech Schl Bus Tchr 1987-90; *ai:* Sr Class, Jobs for PA Grads Adv; Chprsn Stu Asst Prgm; Erie Ed Assn 1977-, Union Rep; PA St Ed Assn, NEA 1977-; Alpha Kappa Alpha 1977-; Performance Recognition VA Hosp; Cert of Achvmt; Spec Commendation Awd; Cert of Outstdng Svc; *office:* East HS 1151 Atkins St Erie PA 16503

WILLIAMS, KENNETH ALAN, German Teacher; *b:* Mc Keesport, PA; *m:* Cathy Barchony-Williams; *ed:* IN Univ of PA (BS) Scndry Ger Ed 1992; 17 Credit Hrs Univ Gesamthoch Schule Duisburg 1989-90; 6 Credit Hrs Grad Level Duquesne Univ; *cr:* Fox Chapel Area HS Ger Tchr 1992-; *ai:* SADD, Maximizing Adolescent Potentials Ldrshp Spon; MS Wrestling Coach; NEA 1992-; North Humtingdon Rescue 8 Ambulance 1986-, First Captain 1995-, First Lieutenant 1993-94, Meritorious Svc 1991-; Irwin VFD 1995-, Paramedic; *office:* Fox Chapel Area High School 611 Field Club Rd Pittsburgh PA 15238

WILLIAMS, LAURETTA, English Specialist; *b:* Dayton, OH; *c:* Quentin, Rochelle; *ed:* Univ of Dayton (BS) Speech 1974; Howard Univ (MED) Curr & Supervision 1979; *cr:* Suitland HS Eng Tchr 1984-90; Cntrl HS Eng Tchr 1990-93; Forestville HS Eng Specialist & Tchr 1993-; *ai:* Drama Club; NEA 1974-; PGCEA 1981-; MSTA 1981-; ASCD 1989-; Excl in Ed 1992; *office:* Forestville HS 7001 Beltz Dr Forestville MD 20747*

WILLIAMS, LAWRENCE ALAN, Former English Teacher; *b:* Titusville, PA; *m:* Sharon Leigh Rosman; *c:* Taunya Christian OConner Sprake, Chad Israel; *ed:* Westminster Coll (BA) Art 1978; PA Cert Art Ed 1982; Masters Degree Prgm 5 Courses; *cr:* Chrstn Life Acad 7-12 Grd Eng Tchr 1989-95; *ai:* Chapel Coord; Jesus Airlift 1990-95, Missions Bd Mem; *home:* 1488 Pulaski Mercer Rd Mercer PA 16137

WILLIAMS, LEAH ANN (RIEG), High School Biology Teacher; *b:* Pittsburgh, PA; *m:* Michael P.; *c:* Madeline; *ed:* Grove City Coll (BS) Pre Med, Bio 1986; Slippery Rock Univ (MS) Tchng Cert 1987; 36 Credits in Sci, Cmptrs; *cr:* Moniteau HS Sub Tchr 1986-87; Butler Area Schl Dist Bio Tchr 1987-; *ai:* Head Var Cross Cntry, Asst Var Girls Track Coach; Stu Asst Prgm; Sci Club, PA Jr Acad of Sci Adv; NABT 1993-; Western PA Bio Tchrs 1994-; Jaycees 1990-; Tornado Grant 1994-95; *office:* Butler Area Schl Dist 167 Newcastle Rd Butler PA 16001

WILLIAMS, LORETTA KEAN, English Teacher; *b:* Rockwell Ctr, NY; *m:* David M.; *c:* Kevin, Timothy, Jenna; *ed:* Caldwell Coll (BA) Eng 1982; Attnd Emmanual Coll, Harvard Univ, Seton Hall Univ; *cr:* Nashoha Reg HS Eng Tchr 1984-; Westboro HS Eng Tchr 1988-89; *ai:* NHS Adv 1993-95; Accreditation Steering Comm 1993-95; NEA 1984-; Habitat for Humanity 1994-; Horace Mann & Carnegie Grant; Natl Endowment for the Hum.

WILLIAMS, LYDIA HARRY, Fourth & Fifth Grade Teacher; *b:* Trinidad, West Indies; *m:* David; *c:* Tristan, Jonathan; *ed:* SUNY-Coll at Old Westburg (BS) Elem Ed 1985; Long Island Univ (MS) Educl Tech 1993; 3 Credits Tchng Exceptional Stdnts; *cr:* Five Block Day Care Ctr Asst Tchr 1978; Crown Heights Svc Ctr Asst Tchr 1979; David Grayson Chrstn Acad Sub Tchr 1986; PS 206 4th Grd Tchr 1985-86, 3rd-6th Grd Tchr 1986-; *ai:* After Schl Rdng Prgm Tutor 1989-; Children in Rdng; Bd of Ed Breakfast, Lunch Prgm; Feed Poor, Homeless During Thanksgiving Seasons; *office:* PS 109 Century 215 E 99th St New York NY 10029

WILLIAMS, MARK C., History Teacher; *b:* Albany, NY; *m:* Anne McCormick; *c:* Adam, Amy, Lonnie, Benjamin, Taegan; *ed:* Yale (BA) His 1970; Univ of CT (MA) His & Ed 1975; *cr:* L P Wilson JHS His Tchr 1971-75; Loomis Chaffee His Tchr 1975-; *ai:* Swimming Coach; NCSS 1976-; CT Soc for Geneologists 1977-; CT Coord Comm for Promotion of His 1992-; Salmon Brook Historical Soc 1974-, Bd Mem; Connecticut Case Studies Pub 1990; A Tempest in a Small Town Pub 1996; *office:* Loomis Chaffee Schl Batchelder Rd Windsor CT 06095

WILLIAMS, MARY RUTH GOETZ, Business Education Teacher; *b:* Williamsport, PA; *m:* Scott L.; *c:* Amy E., Emily A.; *ed:* Shippensburg Univ (BS) Secretarial, Date Processing 1976; PA St Univ (MED) Curr & Instruction 1984; *cr:* Bucktail Area HS Bus Ed Tchr 1976-; *ai:* FBLA Adv; PSEA, NBEA 1976-; Penn St Alumni Assn 1984-; Immaculate Conception Liturgy Cncl 1994-, Sec; PA Assn for Educl Comm & Tech Extra Mile Awd; *office:* Bucktail Area Jr Sr HS 1300 Bucktail Ave Renovo PA 17764

WILLIAMS, MARYLOU LAZZARO, English Teacher & Admin; *b:* Philadelphia, PA; *m:* Peter J.; *c:* Kathleen; *ed:* La Salle Univ (BA) Eng, Ed 1979, (BA) Psych 1979; Temple Univ (MED) Psy of Rdng 1982; Addl 18 Credit Hrs Toward EDD; *cr:* Stella Maris Tchr 1979-80; St Leonard's Acad Eng Tchr 1980-81; Bishop Eustace Prep Eng Tchr 1981-; Bishop Eustace Pres Admin 1995-; *ai:* Sr Class, Spirit Club Moderators; Talent Showcase, Career Day Coord; 40th Anniversary Comm; Field Day Comm; *office:* Bishop Eustace Prep Schl 5552 Rt 70 Pennsauken NJ 08109

WILLIAMS, MATTIE LOUISE (HARRIS), Dir of Pre-Nursing Prgm; *b:* Spartanburg, SC; *m:* Noah; *c:* Sharon Williams-Benton, Pamela; *ed:* Univ of Bridgeport (BSN) Nursing 1983, (MS) Counseling 1990; Columbia Hosp Schl of Nursing Diploma 1959; *cr:* Veterans Admin Hospital & Medical Ctr Staff Nurse 1964-69; Yale New Haven Hospital Registered Nurse & Asst Head 1970-90; Quinnipiac Coll Clinical Nurse Instr 1983-90; Capital Comm Tech Coll Dir Pre-Nursing Prgm 1990-; *ai:* Pre-Nursing Club & Acad Adv; Recruitment & Retention; Fundraising for Pre-Nursing Prgm; Nursing Stdnts Schlsp; YWCA Adult Ed Advy Bd Mem; Sigma Theta Tau 1980-, Mem; Natl Black Nurses Assn 1975-, Mem; *office:* Capital Comm-Tech Coll 61 Woodland Street Hartford CT 06105

WILLIAMS, MICHAEL J., English Teacher & Supervisor; *b:* Orange, NJ; *m:* Elizabeth Grace; *c:* David; *ed:* BA IA Coll (BA) Eng 1966; IA Coll (MS) Eng Ed 1971; Admin & Supvry Credits From Fairfield, Fordham, Manhattan & Jersey City; *cr:* Blessed Sacrement HS Guid Dir, Tchr 1966-73; St Cecilias Grd Schl Prin 1973-75; Orange HS Athl Dir, Tchr 1975-84; Morristown Beard Prep Schl Tchr 1984-85; Montville Twp HS Tchr & Supvr 1985-; *ai:* Natl Hnr Soc Review & Head Lang Arts Comms; PSA 1991-; Our Lady of Mercy Choir Whippany 1985-; Presidential Commission Honored Tchr; Numerous Articles Pub; Numerous Screenplays; *home:* 2 White Birch Dr Morris Plains NJ 07950*

WILLIAMS, MICHAEL L., Adaptive Physical Ed Teacher; *b:* Bronx, NY; *ed:* York Coll (BS) PE 1993; Post Grad Stud Adelphi Univ; *cr:* Louis Pasteur MS Adaptive PE Instr 3 Yrs; *ai:* Asst Bskt Coach; Afternoon Mentor Small World Ctr Pilgrim Psych Ctr; UFT 1993-; *office:* Louis Pasteur MS 51 60 Marathon Pkwy Little Neck NY 11362

WILLIAMS, MICHAEL PARRISH, High School History Teacher; *b:* Tampa, FL; *m:* Leah Ann Rieg; *c:* Madeline; *ed:* Slippery Rock Univ (BS) His & Tchng 1985; Indiana Univ of PA (BS) Safety & Drivers Ed 1992; 9 Credits Toward Masters; *cr:* Conway Jr HS His Tchr 1986-87; Edgewater Sr HS His Tchr 1987-89; Allegheny-Clarion Valley HS His Tchr 1993-; *ai:* Var Boys Bsktbl Head Coach; Var Club Spon; Var Track Asst Coach; Jaycees 1992-94; *home:* 761 Sarsi Trl Mercer PA 16137

WILLIAMS, MONIQUE ROCHELLE, Electronics Instructor; *b:* Harrisburg, PA; *ed:* Cheyney Univ (BS) Indstrl Arts, Electronics 1987; 3 Credit Hrs Mathematical Statistics at Temple Univ; Adult Continuing Ed at Cheyney Univ Grad Prgm 1997; *cr:* PA Dept of Transportation Asst Electronics Svc, Tech 1987-88; Amplifonics Electronics Tech 1988-89; Berean Inst Electronics Chprsn 1989-94, Electronics Instr 1994-; *ai:* Planning, Action Comm Chair Pub Contacts; Cheyney Univ Alumni Assn; Natl Assn for Indstrl Tech 1993-; Grad Assistanceship Cheyney Univ; *home:* 417 Herr St Harrisburg PA 17102

WILLIAMS, MYRON DAVID, Academic Dean & Chrstn Ed Prof; *b:* Lebanon, IN; *m:* B. Sue Wolfe; *c:* Noel D., Sara R.; *ed:* KY Chrstn Coll (BA) Comm & Bible 1969; Lincoln Chrstn Seminary (NRE) Chrstn Ed 1982; MI St Univ (PHD) Ed 1989; Post Grad Stud MI St Univ, Cincinnati Bible Seminary; *cr:* NY Chrstn Inst Practical Ministries Instr 1978-81; Great Lakes Chrstn Coll Chrstn Ed Prof 1981-91; Cincinnati Bible Coll & Seminary Chrstn Ed Prof, Acad Dean 1991-; *ai:* ASCD 1986-; Prof Assn of Chrstn Edctrs 1996; First Church of Christ 1991-, Chm of Elders; Phi Kappa Phi 1986; Delta Epsilon Chi 1991; *office:* Cincinnati Bible Coll & Sem 2700 Glenway Ave Cincinnati OH 45204

WILLIAMS, NANCY WELCH, Drivers & Physical Ed Tchr; *b:* Long Branch, NJ; *ed:* Trenton St Coll (BA) Hlth, PE 1970; 18 Post-Grad Hrs; *cr:* Shore Regnl HS Tchr, Field Hockey Coach 1970-, Bsktbl Coach 1972-84, Sftbl Coach 1979-95; *ai:* USFHA 1970-, Rep; Democratice Comm Women 1985-; *home:* 41 Wall St West Long Branch NJ 07764

WILLIAMS, NICHOLAS M., Vocal Music Teacher; *b:* Batavia, NY; *ed:* Crane Schl of Music (BM) Music Ed 1977; Eastman Schl of Music (MM) Music Ed 1981; Westminister Choir Coll; *cr:* West Ave Elem Schl Vocal Music Tchr 1977-88; Hilton HS Vocal Music Tchr 1988-; *ai:* Rochettes TAP Corp; Dir of HS Musical, Stage Crew; MENC 1978-; ACDA 1988-; *office:* Hilton HS 400 East Ave Hilton NY 14468

WILLIAMS, NOEL DESMOND, English Teacher; *b:* Guyana, South America; *m:* Ruth Iola Brookes; *c:* Kwesi Alejandro, Coltrane Ayinde; *ed:* Univ of the West Indies (BA) Eng Lit 1970, (MA) Eng Lit 1974; 30 Grad Credits Ed; *cr:* Adlai Stevenson HS Eng Tchr 1984-92; Andrew Jackson HS Eng Tchr 1992-94; John Adams HS Eng Tchr 1994-; *ai:* AFT, UFT 1984-; Case de las Americas 1976 Awd for Best Work of Fiction Ikael Toras; *office:* John Adams HS Rockaway Blvd & 102nd St Ozone Park NY 11417

WILLIAMS, OLIVER SPENCER,III, Eighth Grade Science Teacher; *b:* Rushville, NY; *m:* Lynn; *c:* Stacey Williams Hughes, Oliver S. IV, Jennifer L.; *ed:* Cornell Univ (BS) Sci Ed 1972; Grad Stud SUNY at Brockport, Univ of Rochester, St John Fisher Coll; *cr:* Brighton Cntrl Schls 7-8th Grd Sci Tchr 1972-; *ai:* Dist Mid Level Sci Mentor 1993-; Dist Chrpsn K-12 Sci Curr Stud 1995-; BTA, NYEA, NEA 1974-; Middlesex Ambulance Corp 1974-, Pres, Bd of Dir; Middlesex Heritage Group 1979-, Pres, Bd of Dir; Cty Republicn Comm, Town Chprsn 1986-; *office:* Brighton Cntrl Schls 2035 Monore Ave Rochester NY 14618

WILLIAMS, OLIVIA LEE, Mathematics & Futures Teacher; *b:* Baltimore, MD; *m:* Revelle M. Sr.; *c:* Revelle Jr., Janel, Travis; *ed:* Morgan St Univ (BS) Math 1973; Coppin St Univ (MS) Spec Ed; *cr:* Patterson HS Tchr 1973-; *ai:* 9th Grd Success Acad Team Ldr; Prof Dev Comm; SIT Mem; Dale Carnegie Awd.

WILLIAMS, PAMELA KAISER, 1st Grade Teacher; *b:* Cincinnati, OH; *m:* Jerry Pate; *c:* J. Pate, Laurie D.; *ed:* Wilmington Coll (BA) Ed 1968; Miami Univ (MSE) Ed 1969; Attnd Univ of Cincinnati, Miami Univ, Univ of Dayton; *cr:* Milford Exempted Village Schl Dist Tchr 26 Yrs; *ai:* NEA; MEA; HHS 1988-, Pub Relation; KCC, SLC 1979-; Young Republican Club 198-, Soc Dir; Cincinnati gas, Electric Outstdng Tchr Awd; Schl Dist Distngd Svc Awd; Articles Pub; *home:* 8497 Wetherfield Ln Cincinnati OH 45236*

WILLIAMS, PATRICIA ANN (KINNEY), Accounting Professor; *b:* Newark, NJ; *m:* Charles L.; *c:* Jennifer Barrett, Stephanie Barrett; *ed:* Montclair St Univ (BA) Fr 1963; Middlebury Coll (MA) Fr 1965; Southern Meth Univ (MBA) Acctng 1981; Boston Univ (DBA) Acctng 1992; Stanford Univ Doctoral Work Fr; *cr:* Pacific HS Fr Tchr 1965-67; Brookline HS Fr Tchr 1970-72; San Francisco St Acctng Instr 1986-87; Boston Univ Acctng Instr 1988-92; Fordham Univ Acctng Asst Prof 1992-; *ai:* Frosh Adv; Grad Curr Comm; Amer Acctng Assn 1988-; Intnl Section 1992-; Fin Acctng Section 1992-; Articles Pub; *office:* Fordham Univ 113 W 60th St 6th Floor New York NY 10023

WILLIAMS, PATRICIA DAVIS, Third Grade Teacher; *b:* Manhattan, NY; *m:* R. Michael; *c:* Kevin, Kelly, James; *ed:* St Univ of Oneonta (BA) ED, Psych-With Hnrs 1973; Stony Brook Univ (MA) Ed 1976; Cert Outdoor Sci Ed; *cr:* Mt Sinai Elem Schl 2nd Grd Tchr 1973-75, Pilot Prgm Combined 2nd-3rd Grd Tchr 1975-77, 2nd Grd Tchr 1980-83, 3rd Grd Tchr 1985-; *ai:* Supts Conf Day Orgainzer; Sunshine Comm; Adv Asst Ski Club 1984-91, Lit Magazine 1985; Tchr of GATE Writing Prgm; Mt Sinai Tchrs Assn, NYSUT, MSPTO, SWRPTO 1973-; ST Marks Church 1983-90, Pre Cana Ldr; *office:* Mt Sinai Elem Schl North Country Rd Mount Sinai NY 11766*

WILLIAMS, QUENTIN DARRELL, Science Teacher; *b:* Toledo, OH; *m:* Sharon A. Benson; *c:* Taylor; *ed:* Cntrl St Univ (BS) Bio 1974; Toledo Univ (BS) Comprehensive Sci Ed 1985; Eastern MI Univ Post Grad Stud in Physiology; *cr:* A. H. Robins Research Asst 1977-82; Toledo Pub Schls Tchr 1982-85; Columbus Pub Schls Tchr 1985-; *ai:* Ftbl, Boys Track Coach; Upward Bound Supvr; Young Scholars Adv; Tri-Beta 1973-; NEA, OEA 1983-; Black Educators of Columbus 1985-; Upward Bound 1985-, Tchr; Young Scholars 1987-, Tchr; NAACP 1980-; Research Apprenticeship Prgm; Pub Articles; Grants Established for Research in Research Apprenticeship Prgm; *office:* Briggs HS 2555 Briggs Rd Columbus OH 43223*

WILLIAMS, RANDOLPH ANDREW, Professor & Chairman; *b:* New York, NY; *m:* Julie Broglin; *c:* Keryatta, Justin; *ed:* NY Univ (BS) Art Ed 1970; Sir George Williams (MA) Art Ed 1972; *cr:* Metropolitan Museum of Art Museum Edctr 1972-; Manhattanville Coll Prof of Art 1988-; *ai:* Numerous Solo, Group Exhibitions; AAUP 1994-; Natl Endowment Art Flwshp Amer Acad in Rome 1982; NY St Cncl Art Visual Arts Svcs, NY Fnd Arts Sculpture Flwshp 1987; Fac Excl Awd Manhattanville Coll 1995; *office:* Manhattanville Coll 2900 Purchase St Purchase NY 10577*

WILLIAMS, RAY STANLEY, Retired Instrmntl Music Tchr; *b:* Greenport, NY; *m:* Karen S. Nielsen; *c:* Kristina, Erik; *ed:* Juilliard Schl of Music (BS) String Bass 1966; Southampton (BA) 1975; Attnd Hofstra Univ; George Mason Univ, Berkley Schl of Music 45 Credits; Vanderbilt Univ, Regis Coll 45 Credits; *cr:* Free Lance Bassist Performer 1966-68; Greenport HS Sub Music Tchr 1968; Lindenhurst Pub Schls Instrumental Tchr 1968-94; East Sulfolk Schl of Music Instr 1976-92; *ai:* Pvt Tutoring; Wood & Clay Sculpting, Pen & Ink; Atlantic Wind Symphony 1995-; ASCAP 1971-; Local 802 1964-; SCMEA, NYSSMA 1968-; LI String Fest Assn, All-St 1968-, Judge; Cert of Accomedation for Meritorious Svc 1988; Bower Schl You Bring Music to Our Lives 1984; Lindenhurst Newspaper Articles; Pub Work 1971; Composed Classical & Jazz Pieces; Article of Commendation Lindenhurst.

WILLIAMS, REDA EZELL, Third Grade Teacher; *b:* Bronx, NY; *m:* Frederick J.; *c:* Jay Frederick, Barri Reda; *ed:* St Univ NY at Plattsburgh (BS) Elem Ed 1961; Adelphi Univ (MS) Rdng 1968; Attnd Coll of St Rose at Albany, Bank Street Schl NY; *cr:* Fulton Schl 3rd-4th Grd Elem Tchr 1961-68; Adelphi Univ Rdng Lab Instr 1964-68; *ai:* Word Melville Site Based Mngmt Team 1994-95; Sit Based Mngmt Team 1995-; Three Village Multicultural Comm; Three Village Tchrs Assn 1968-; Hempstead Tchrs Assn 1961-68; Three Village Safe Homes 1993-, Spec Tchr Awd; The Word of Melville Music, Ath Boosters 1993-; *office:* William Sidney Mount Elem Sch 50 Dean Ln Stony Brook NY 11790*

WILLIAMS, RICHARD F., Social Studies Teacher; *b:* Utica, NY; *ed:* The Hiram Scott Coll (BA) Elem Ed 1971; Attnd Colgate Univ, SUNY at Cortland; *cr:* Stratford Cntrl Schl 1st,3rd-4th, 6th Grd Tchr 1971-85; Dolgeville Cntrl Schl Elem Sci, Elem Soc Stud 1985-; *ai:* NYSUT, AFT 1971-; Dolgeville TA 1985-, VP; St David's Soc of Utica 1990-; *office:* Dolgeville Central Schl Slawson St Ext Dolgeville NY 13329*

WILLIAMS, RICHARD WALLACE, Physics Teacher; *b:* Waltham, MA; *m:* Sharon Baker; *c:* Allen, Richard Jr., Robert, Stefanie Bounassi; *ed:* Ithaca Coll (BA) PHT 1959; Montclair St Univ (MA) Sci 1973; 16 Hrs Bus Admin Cornell Univ; 8 Hrs Physics NJ Inst of Tech; *cr:* Northern High Rec High Physics Tchr 1972-76; Lyndhurst HS Physics Tchr 1992-; *ai:* Asst Wrestling Coach; Sci Club Adv; AAPT, NEA, NJEA 1972-; Natl Assn of Sci Tchrs 1992-; Tchng Eng to Foreign Born 1996-, Tchr; NSF Grant Harvard Project Physics NJIT 1973, Princeton Earth Physics Project 1994, Assessments Sci Tchng Rutgers Univ 1996; *office:* Lyndhurst HS Weart Ave Lyndhurst NJ 07071

WILLIAMS, RITA PEER, French & English Teacher; *b:* New York, NY; *m:* Phillip M.; *c:* Marc, Ian; *ed:* CT Coll (BA) Eng 1966; John Hopkins Univ (MAT) Ed 1968; Attnd Univ of Northern IA, Columbia Univ, OH Univ Grad Stud; *cr:* Bedford Jr HS Eng Tchr 1968-69; University City HS Amer Stud Tchr 1969-71; Eastern HS Fr & Eng Tchr 1977-; *ai:* Jr Class Adv; NEA & ELTA 1977-; 4 Trips to France for Stdnts; *home:* 18521 Bucks Lake Rd Guysville OH 45735

WILLIAMS, ROBERT B. R., English & Social Studies Tchr; *b:* Sandusky, OH; *m:* Sandra Hall; *c:* Robyn Moore, Holly Brown, Megan, Tracy, Alex; *ed:* OH Wesleyan Univ (BA) Soc Stud 1961; OH Univ (MED) Scndry Ed, Soc Stud 1968; Attnd Tulane Univ, Univ of Cincinnati; *cr:* Forest Hills Schl Dist 7th Grd Tchr 1964-67, 1968-; *ai:* Turpin HS Diving Coach; IM Dir; Asst AD; Anderson HS Swim Coach; Forest Hills Tchrs Assn 1964-, Bldg Rep, St, Natl Convention Del, Soc Chm; Mt Lookout Civic Club 1972-, Dir; Southwest OH Swim Ofcls Assn 1974-92; Cinti Rail Road Club 1993-; Amer Legion 1974-, Trustee; OPEIU Usher's Local 1968-, VP; Seabee Amer Veterans 1980-; BPOE; F & AM; *office:* Anderson HS 7560 Forest Rd Cincinnati OH 45255

WILLIAMS, ROBERT MICHAEL, 5th Grade Teacher; *b:* Long Branch, NJ; *m:* Carol Ann Newbauer; *c:* Christopher, Ryan; *ed:* Murray St Univ (BS) Soc Stud 1968; *cr:* Asbury Park HS Soc Stud Tchr 1968-69; Howell Twp Pub Schls 5th-6th Grd Tchr 1969-; *ai:* 5th-6th Grd Bsktbl Team Coach; NEA 1968-; NJEA 1968-; HTEA 1969-; *office:* Edith Griebling Elem Schl 130 Havens Bridge Rd Farmingdale NJ 07727

WILLIAMS, RUSSELL DAVID, Mathematics Teacher; *b:* Woodbury, NJ; *ed:* Glassboro St Coll (BA) Elem Ed 1974, (BA) Art Ed 1980; Rowan Coll Math Ed 12 Hrs Post Grad; *cr:* Haddon Twp Jr-Sr HS Math Tchr 1974-; *ai:* Girls Var Track & Field Coach; HTEA, NJEA, NEA 1974-, Negotiations Team; Midget Soccer 1993-, Coach; Little League Bsbl 1995-, Auxiliary Coach & Umpire; *office:* Haddon Township HS Memorial Ave Westmont NJ 08108

WILLIAMS, SANDRA M. (SWELLER), HS Physics & Earth Sci Teacher; *b:* Newton, NJ; *m:* Martin R.; *ed:* Drew Univ (BA) Physics, Math 1992; SUNY at Stony Brook (MA) Physics 1994; *cr:* Drew Univ, Physics Dept Instrl Lab Asst 1988-92; SUNY at Stony Brook Physics Dept Grad Rsrch Asst 1993-94; South Shore Chrstn Schl HS Sci Tchr 1994-; *ai:* AAPT 1992-; Phi Beta Kappa; Sigma Pi Sigma; US Dept of Ed Flwshp for Grad Stud; Ciba-Geigy Pharmaceuticals Div Annual Sci Awd 1992; Drew Univ Prize in Physics for Outstdng Ind Rsrch Project; *home:* 20 Woodhull Ln Holtsville NY 11742

WILLIAMS, SCOTT ALAN, Chemistry Teacher; *b:* Philipsburg, PA; *m:* Diane Marie Biddle; *c:* Matthew, Timothy; *ed:* Lock Haven St Coll (BS) Chem 1971; Indiana Univ of PA (MED) Chem 1973; 24 Credit Hrs PA St Univ; 3 Credit Hrs Juniata Coll; 3 Credit Hrs Manhattan Coll; *cr:* Bellefonte Area HS Sci Tchr 1973-; *ai:* Amer Chemical Soc, NEA, PSEA, BAEA 1973-; *office:* Bellefonte Area HS 830 E Bishop St Bellefonte PA 16823

WILLIAMS, STEPHANIE MARIE, Family & Consumer Sci Tchr; *b:* Washington, PA; *m:* James M. Lindenberger Jr.; *c:* Elyssa, Ashley, Marah; *ed:* IN Univ (BS) Home Ec & Early Child 1978; Edinboro Univ (MA) Elem Ed 1981; PA Dept of Ed St Insvc Trng; Stu Assistance Pgm Trained; *cr:* Iroquois HS Home Ec Tchr 1978-79; McDowell HS Family & Consumer Sci Tchr, Dept Co-Chair & Teen Parent Pgm Coord 1979-; *ai:* Family & Consumer Scis Co-Chair & Advy Cncl Co-Chair; Teen Parent Pgm Coord; Train the Trainer Coord; MTSD Curr Cncl; MTSD Curr Design & McDowell HS Budget Comms; MEA, NEA & PSEA 1979-; PAFCS & AAFCS 1992-, NWPA Past Pres, 1996 PA F&CS Tchr of the Yr; Vo-Tech Adv Bd 1989-; Presenter: PA Dept of Ed Consumer & Homemaking Ed Pgm Improvement Grant 1994-95; PDE Teen Parent Coords Insvc 1995; Conf on Integrated Learning 1995; HE Update IN U of PA Conf 1994; Articles Pub; Several Rsrch Projects with Colls; *office:* Mc Dowell Sr HS 3580 W 38th St Erie PA 16506*

WILLIAMS, STEPHEN ELLIOT, Professor of Special Education; *b:* Boston, MA; *c:* Erika, Aaron; *ed:* Univ of Montreal (BA) Eng 1972; Bridgewater St Coll (MED) Educl Assessment 1980; Clark Univ (PHD) Learning Theory & Spec Ed 1990; *cr:* Paula Dever Schl Tchr of Spec Ed & Dir of Spec Ed Prgm 1979-81; Self-Employed Prof Prgm Design Specialist 1981-88; D'Youville Coll Prof of Spec Ed & Learning Theory; *ai:* NARH, NALD 1995-; PSICHI 1994-; Amer Psychological Assn; Western NY Assn for Learning Disabilities, Latch Key Tutoring Prgm Coord; Childrens Hospital, Transitional Planning Comm; Scholar & Educator 1995-, Managing Ed; Doctoral Fellowship Clark Univ & D'Youville Coll; Various Natl & St Prgm Grants; Articles on Mental Retardation & Distance Learning; Invited Chapter Author for Coll Text on Learning Disabilities & Cmptr Tech.

WILLIAMS, TERRI DENISE, 7th Grade Teacher; *b:* Philadelphia, PA; *ed:* Xavier Univ of LA (BA) Elem Ed 1993; *cr:* Holy Ghost Schl 8th, 4th Grd Tchr 1986-89; St Charles Borromeo Schl 7th Grd Tchr 1989-; *ai:* Pep Squad; After Schl Prgm; Schl Mid Sts Self-Stud Comm Chair; Prgm Mngmt Comm NBSC; NCEA 1986-; Natl Black Sisters Conf 1984-, Exec Sec 1995-; Natl Black Cath Congress 1995-, Bd Mem, Exec Bd Del at Large; Office of Black Ministry 1996, Advy Bd.

WILLIAMS, THOMAS C., Industrial Arts Teacher; *b:* Pottsville, PA; *m:* Allene A. Francavage; *c:* Alicia; *ed:* Millersville St Univ (BS) Industrial Arts 1975; Penn St Univ 24 Grad Hrs; *cr:* Pine Grove Area Schl Dist Industrial Arts Tchr 1975-; *ai:* Prin Advy Cncl; NEA 1975-; PSEA 1975-; Echo Vly Grace Brethren Church 1978-, Elder; Pine Grove Tchr of Yr 1988; *home:* 20 Middlecreek Rd Tremont PA 17981

WILLIAMS, VAN OLIVER, Spcl Ed Intervention Specialst; *b:* Akron, OH; *m:* Regina Renee Gresham; *c:* Brandon; *ed:* Hiram Coll (BA) Elem Ed, Spec Ed LD, BD 1976; 14 Hrs Curr & Instruction Kent St; 18 Addl Hrs Ashland Univ; *cr:* Portage Cty Juvenile Ct Tchr 1976; East Cleveland Bd of Ed Tchr 1976-, Ftbl Coach 1977-84; *ai:* Cleveland Hts HS Defensive Coord; Shaw HS Head Swim Coach, Pool Mgr; Elem IM Bsktbl Coach; Greuten Cleveland Ftbl Coach 1982-; NISCA, ASCA, NE Swim Coach of Yr; Swim ECEA 1976-, VP, Negotiator; NEA 1976-; OEA 1976-, Rep, Chair Mem; Swim for Diabetes 1986-94, Vol; Shoes for Kids, Vol; East Cleveland Long Range Planning Comm 1993-94; TV-8 Tchr of Yr 1994; Campaigners to Win 1995; Articles Pub; Wrote Grant; Assisted in New Venture Capitol Grant.*

WILLIAMS, VERONICA ELIZABETH, Science Teacher; *b:* Washington, DC; *ed:* Wilberforce Univ (BS) Bio 1973; *cr:* Hart Jr HS Math, Sci Tchr 1973-76; Winston Educl Ctr Sci Tchr 1976-79; Eliot Jr HS Sci Tchr 1979-; *ai:* Ski Club Adv; AFT 1973-; NSTA; DCSEA; Hospitality Comm 1967-, Bd Dirs; Federal Credit Union, Credit Comm; *office:* Eliot Jr HS 1830 Constitution Ave NE Washington DC 20002

WILLIAMS, VICKY BLATTENBERGER, Science Teacher; *b:* Bedford, PA; *m:* Norman L.; *c:* Tyler, Tanner; *ed:* IN Univ of PA (BS) Environmental Hlth 1983; Univ of Pittsburgh (BS) Scndry Ed, Bio, Gen Sci 1990; *cr:* Bedford HS Environmental Sci Tchr 1991-95, Applied Bio, Chem Tchr 1995-; *ai:* NHS Comm; Ski Club; NEA, PSEA, Bedford Ed Assn 1991-; *office:* Bedford HS 330 E John St Bedford PA 15522*

WILLIAMS, WENDY BARRICK, High School Math Teacher; *b:* Alliance, OH; *m:* David F.; *c:* Erin, Julie, Drew; *ed:* Bowling Green St Univ (BS) Ed 1973; Malone Coll (MS) Curr, Instruction 1991; Grad Hrs Kent St Univ, Akron Univ; *cr:* Marlington HS EMR Tchr, Work Stud Coord 1974-80, LD Tutor, Migrant Tchr 1980-83; Easton Canton HS Math Tchr 1983-84; Marlington HS Math Tchr 1984-; *ai:* SADD Adv 1985-; GCCTM, Phi Delta Kappa 1992-; OCTM 1990-; NCTM 1989-; HS Tchr of Yr 1987; Alliance Area Chamber of Commerce Tchr of Month 1992; *office:* Marlington HS 10450 Moulin Ave Alliance OH 44601

WILLIAMS, WILLIAM H. A., Professor & Advisor; *b:* Philadelphia, PA; *m:* Leslie Ann; *c:* William III, Lavinia; *ed:* Lafayette Coll (BA) His 1959; John Hopkins Univ (MA) His 1962, (PHD) His 1971; IN Univ (MLS) Lib & Info Sci 1985; *cr:* Natl Univ Lecgurer 1966-72; Justus-Liebig Univ Visiting Prof 1972-74; AZ St Univ Visiting Prof 1975-78; Org Amer Historians Project Dir 1985-87; Union Inst Prof, Adv 1987-; *ai:* Amer Conf Irish Stud 1987-; Irish Amer Cultural Inst 1987-, Four Masters Awd; Org Amer Historians 1985-; Cincinnati Folk Life 1987-, Bd Mem; Phi Beta Kappa; Eddy Flwshp; John Edward Noble Ldrshp Grant; Woodrow Wilson Fellow; Martin Vincent Fellow; Four Masters Awd; Books: H. L. Mencken 1977, Twas Only An Irishman's Dream: Image of Irish and Ireland in Am Popular Songs 1996; *office:* Union Inst 440 E Mcmillan St Cincinnati OH 45206*

WILLIAMS-GIULIANI, JOAN M., Prof of Jrnlsm & Communication; *b:* Pittsburgh, PA; *m:* Brian L.; *c:* Serena M. Williams; *ed:* OH Univ (BFA) Telecommunications & Speech 1963; Univ of Pittsburgh (MA) Pol Rhetoric 1970; 57 Addl Credit Hrs Rhetoric, Communication Theory, Educl Tech 1973-81; *cr:* Harrisburg Area Comm Coll TV Studio Coord, Asst Assoc Prof Commum 1970-79; Univ of Pittsburgh Rhetoric Tchng Fellow 1976-77; Slippery Rock Univ Asst Comm Prof 1979-80; Cannon Univ Assoc Comm Prof 1980-81; Point Park Coll Jrnlsm, Comm Prof, Studio Operations Mgr 1981-; *ai:* Travel Comm Chair; TV Internship Undergraduate, Grd Stdnts Coord; FAc Adv; Coll Stdnts Broadcasting PPC TV; Studio Operations Mgr; Exec Producer Pub Affairs TV Programming; Point Park Coll Rep Educl Tech Comm; Pittsburgh Cncl Higher Ed; Amer Women in R-TV Inc 1970-, Fac Liaison CSB Pgh Chptr; Pittsburgh R-TV Club 1980-90; R-TV News Dir Assn 1980-; AD Fac Comm Information Tech; CCD Classes1980-, Grd Vol, Tchr; World Affairs Cncl; World Federalist Assn; Peace Links Western PA; NDEA Fellow; Tchng Fellow Univ of Pittsburgh; TV Producer News, Pub Affairs Programming; Outstdng Svc Awd Harrisburg Area Comm Coll; Sers Roebuck Fnd Tchng Excl, Campus Ldrshp Awd Point Park Coll; Psych Huma Comm Book Ed; *office:* Point Park Coll 201 Wood St Pittsburgh PA 15222*

WILLIAMS-JACKSON, BRENDA L., Assistant Principal; *b:* Rockaway Beach, NY; *ed:* Brooklyn Coll (BA) Elem, Spec Ed 1982, (MA) Spec Ed, Learning Disabilities; Advanced Cert Admin & Supervision 1991; *cr:* PS 215Q Asst Prin 1991-; PS 223Q, J 180Q, J226 Mentor, Tchr 1990-91; PS 183Q Librn, Grd 6, Spec Ed Tchr 1982-90; *ai:* Coord Big Sister Little Sister Prgm PS 183Q; Assn of Asst Prins 1992-; New Hope Missionary Bapt Church, Yth Ldr; Allen AME Church; Wrote, Received Parent Involvement Grant 1993; Co-Wrote & Received Lib Power Grant De Witt Wallace 1994; *office:* PS 215Q 535 Briar Pl Far Rockaway NY 11691

WILLIAMS-KENNEDY, CHERRI DAWN, Mathematics Teacher; *b:* Frederick, MD; *m:* Richard Andrew Kennedy; *c:* Connor; *ed:* Juniata Coll (BS) Math Ed 1990; Western MD Coll (MS) Spec ed 1995; Cooperative Learning Trng; Heterogeneous Grouping Trng; Dimensions of Learning Trng; *cr:* Heather Ridge Schl Math, Cmptr Tchr 1990-93; Frederick HS Math Tchr 1993-; *ai:* Algebra Ldr; NEA, NCTM 1990-; Speaker at MCTM Regnl Conf, NCTM Natl Conf; *office:* Frederick HS 650 Carroll Pky Frederick MD 21701

WILLIAMS-LORD, MARY MARCIA, 5th Grd Tchr & Enrichmnt Coord; *b:* Woburn, MA; *m:* Gregory William; *c:* Briana Mae; *ed:* Salem St Coll (BS) Elem Ed 1973; 9 Credit Hrs; *cr:* Glover Schl 4th & 5th Grd Tchr & TAG Pgm 1973-92; Marblehead MS 5th Grd Tchr & Enrichment Coord 1992-; *ai:* Project STAR Coord; Lang Arts Task Force; MEA, MTA & NEA 1973-; Girl Scout Ldr 1991-, Treas & Cookie Fundraiser Coord; Childrens Comm, Chr; 3 Grants for STAR Pgm; MA Tchr of the Yr Nom (3 Times); Readers Digest Amer Heroes in Ed Awd Nom.*

WILLIAMSON, KATHLEEN HINES, Vocational Teacher; *b:* Stratford, CT; *m:* John; *c:* Megin, Nicole; *ed:* VT Coll of Norwich Univ (ADN) Nursing 1983; Wilmington Coll (BSN) Nursing 1991; *cr:* Howard HS of Tech Voc Instr Nurse Technician Prgm 1990-; *ai:* Stu Govt Assn Adv; Amer Nurses Assn 1990, DE Nurses Assn; ASCD; *office:* Howard HS of Tech 401 E 12th St Wilmington DE 19801

WILLIAMSON, KENT, 6th-8th Grd Social Stud Tchr; *b:* Erie, PA; *m:* Andrea Lucarotti; *c:* Remy, Alexa; *ed:* Mercyhurst Coll (BA) Elem Ed 1977; Gannon Coll (MS) Environmental Ed 1996; *cr:* Jefferson Elem Schl 4th-5th Grd Sci Tchr 1977-78; Glenwood Elem Schl 2nd Grd Tchr 1978-79; Wilson Jr HS Bio Tchr 1979-81; Wayne MS 7th Rdng Tchr 1981-82; Gridley MS 7th Grd His Tchr 1982-83; Emerson 3rd Grd Tchr 1983-87; Harding Schl 6th-8th Grd Tch 1987-; *ai:* Boys & Girls Intramurals; Boys Elem Bsktbl; HS Bsbl & Bsktbl; NEA & PSEA 1977-; *home:* 8870 Valley Rd Girard PA 16417*

WILLIAMSON, MICHAEL MASON, English Teacher; *b:* London, england; *m:* Martha; *c:* Benjamin J., Timothy M. R.; *ed:* Camb England (BA) Eng 1970, PGCE Ed 1973, (MA) Eng 1978; Royal Sc Arts TEFL Diploma Eng 1983; *cr:* Frontistirion Kyriazopoulos Eng 1980-85; Sekokah Men Masai Eng Tchr 1985-90; Medomak Vall HS Tchr 1990-92; Boothbay Regl HS Eng Tchr 1992-; *ai:* Chess Club; Sr C Adv; Stu Assistance Team; Soccer Coach; *office:* Boothbay Region Townsend Rd Boothbay Harbor ME 04538

WILLIAMS-YOUNG, DIANE L., Accounting & Computer Teache Wilmington, DE; *m:* Eugene R. Young Sr.; *c:* Eugene R. Jr., E. Zakiya DE St Univ (BS) Bus Ed 1971; Wilmington Coll (MS) Ed 1992; *cr:* Du HS Tchr 1974-75; Wilmington Skill Ctr Tchr 1975-76; Glasgow HS 1980-81; Conrad MS Bus Ed Tchr 1980-90; *ai:* DE Bus Ed Assn; NE Alpha Kappa Alpha.

WILLIG, ROGER P., Mathematics Professor; *b:* Chicago, IL Elizabeth Deuber; *ed:* CA St Politechnic Coll (BS) Math 1965, (MA) M Ed 1966; Grad Courses Math UCLA, Temple Univ, West Chester U Villanova Univ, Penn St Univ; *cr:* Vly Forge Military Jr Coll Math 1966-71; Montgomery Cty Comm Coll Math Instr 1971-; *ai:* Written Bank Elem Algebra Book; Created Video Course Elem Statistics; *off* Montgomery County Comm Coll 340 Dekalb Pike Blue Bell PA 1942

WILLIKENS, INGRID NORMAN, Social Studies Teacher; *b:* New Y City, NY; *m:* Donald; *c:* Kaia, Donn, Ian; *ed:* Univ of NH (BA) Govt 1 30 Addl Hrs City Coll of NY, St John's Univ, Notre Dame Coll; *cr:* Va Schl Tchr 1967-70; Parker Varney Schl Tchr 1970-76; Weston Schl 1977-; *ai:* NEA, NHEA 1967-; MEA 1967-, Rep.

WILLMAN, STEPHEN MARK, Physical Education Teacher; *b:* Ma OH; *m:* Martha R.; *c:* Ashlee, Erica; *ed:* Owens Tech Coll (AA) Recrea 1978; Findlay Coll (BA) Hlth, Phys Educ 1980; Bowling Green St Addl 38 Grad Hrs; *cr:* Old Ft HS Phys Ed, Dr Educ Tchr 3 Yrs; Gailior Occupational Work Adjustment Tchr 2 Yrs; Liberty Benton HS Earth Dr Ed, Phys Educ 10 Yrs; *ai:* Golf, Boys Var Bsktbl Coach; OH HS Bs Coaches Assn 1978-; OH HS Golf Coaches Assn 1987-94; NEA 1980 Bsktbl Coach of Yr Blanchard Valley Conf 1991, 1994, 1995, 1996; Dist 6 Coach of Yr 1983; Dist 8 Coach of Yr 1991, 1994, 1995; Northw OH Bsktbl Coach of Yr 1995; Northwest OH Dist Golf Coach of Yr 1 *office:* Liberty Benton HS 9050 SR 12 W Findlay OH 45840

WILLIS, BARBARA HOTTEL, Senior Ballet Teacher; *b:* Boston, *m:* Richard Montgomery; *c:* Richard, Benjamin, Charles; *ed:* Denison U (BA) Eng 1961; *cr:* Carter Schl of Dance Sr Ballet & Classical Ballet 1976-; *ai:* Cecchetti Cncl of Amer E Coast Comm 1987-, Licentiate VI; *office:* Carter Schl Of Dance 17 Cypress Creek Rd Severna Park 21146

WILLIS, CRAIG C., Social Studies Teacher; *b:* Salem, MA; *m:* Patri *c:* Jessica, Audrey; *ed:* Gordon Coll (BA) His 1984; Franklin Pi (Assocs) Acctng 1991; Ed Masters UNH; Defense Lang Inst Cert Russ 1986; *cr:* US Army Military Intelligence 1985-89; Raymond HS Soc S Tchr 1991-; *ai:* Drama Club, Raymond Action Corps Comm Svc Dir Class Co-Adv; Chprsn; Grading Comm; Tchr of Yr Raymond High Body Nom 1991-1995; *office:* Raymond HS 45 Harriman Hill Rd Raym NH 03077*

WILLIS, ELEANOR REICHSTETTER, Computer Literacy Teacher Providence, RI; *m:* Herbert; *c:* Stephen, Linda Kunzmann, David, Jeff Peasley; *ed:* RI Coll (BA) Elem Ed 1964; 45 Credit Hrs Math, Cmptr Soc Stud; *cr:* Cranston Elem Schl 3-4th Grd Tchr 1964-68; Coventry E Schl K-6th Grd Sub Tchr 1973-75, 1975-78; Hopkinston Elem Schl 5- Grd Tchr 1975-77, 1978-80, 1982-89; Chariho Regnl MS Cmptr Lit T 1989-; *ai:* Tech Comm; Cmptr Tutor; ARTESSY Comm; House Ldr Unified Arts; NEA 1975-, RIEMA 1992-; RILMS 1993-; NEA, Char 1975-, Bldg Rep 1982-84; RI Croans, Ileitis 1989-; Senate, House of Awds for Sr Citizens; Single Parent of Yr 1978; *office:* Chariho MS 4 Switch Rd Wood River Junctio RI 02894*

WILLIS, GLADYS JANUARY, Prof of English & Dept Chair; *b:* Jacks MS; *m:* Andrew H. Jr.; *c:* Juliet Christina, Michael; *ed:* Jackson St C (BA) Eng 1965; MI St Univ (MA) Eng 1968; Princeton Univ (PHD) 1973; Ind Stud Bryn Mawr Coll 1965-66; M Div Candidate L Theological Seminary 1996; *cr:* Cheyney St Coll Eng Instr 1967-68; Ri Coll Eng Instr 1968-70; Manhattan Comm Coll Asst Eng Prof 1973- Lincoln Univ Eng Prof 1977-; *ai:* Hum Division Chair; Tolson Soc A NCTE 1989-; AAVP 1992-; First Redemption Evangelist Church, A Pastor 1992-; Philadelphia Chrstn Acad, Bd VP 1977-; Outstdng You Women of Amer 1978; Intnl Biography 1978; Who's Who Among Bl Amers 1980; Who's Who in Amer Ed 1990; Awded Lindback Fnd A Dstngd Tchng 1984; *office:* Lincoln Univ Lincoln University PA 1935

WILLIS, JEAN MARIE, 5th & 6th Grade Teacher; *b:* Westfield, MA; The Cath Univ of Amer (BA) Rel & Rel Stud 1981; RI Coll (MED) El Ed 1990; *cr:* Dominican Acad 4th Grd Tchr & Asst Prin 1984-89; Stanislaus Schl Remedial Tchr 1989-90, 7th & 8th Grd Tchr 1990-93, & 6th Grd Tchr 1993-; *ai:* Soc Stu Fair; *office:* St Stanislaus Schl Rockland St Fall River MA 02724

WILLIS, KAREN AMANDA, Music Teacher; *b:* Philadelphia, PA; Susquehanna Univ (BS) Music Ed K-12 1975; Master's Equiv Plus Peabody Inst, Temple Univ, Towson St Univ, Goucher Coll, Loyola C Western MD Univ; *cr:* Kingston NY Consolidated Schls Elem Music T 1075-76; Baltimore Cty Pub Schls Elem Music Tchr 1976-; *ai:* Music Cu Writing Comm Summer Wkshps; Elem Music Festivals; NEA 1975-; M St Tchrs Assn, Baltimore Co Tchrs Assn 1976-; *office:* Padonia Elem S 9834 Greenside Dr Cockeysville Hunt MD 21030*

WILLIS, KAREN REYNOLDS, English & Journalism Teacher; Carmichaels, PA; *m:* Thomas L.; *c:* Kevin L., Mark R.; *ed:* Waynesbu Coll (BA) Eng 1971; *cr:* Jefferson-Morgan HS Eng, Jrnlsm Tchr 1989-; Newspaper Spon; Natl Jr Honor Soc; Delta Kappa Gamma; NCTE; Fi Chrstn Church 1970-, Fin Sec, Yth Ldr; Herald Standard Tchr of Yr 199 *office:* Jefferson-Morgan Jr Sr HS Box 158 Greene St Jefferson PA 153

WILLIS, MILDRED KASHIMA, Fifth Grade Teacher; *b:* Paia Maui, H *m:* Donald R.; *c:* Kent M.; *ed:* Univ of HI (BED) Elem Ed 1965; Cntrl St Coll (MS) Rdng 1971; 5th Yr Elem Ed Univ of HI 1966; 15 Post Gr Hrs Univ of CT Elem Ed 1972-75; *cr:* Hale Kulas Elem Schl 1st-2nd G Tchr 1965-67; Flanders Elem Schl 2nd-5th Grd Tchr 1967-; *ai:* Cmp Lang Arts, Prof Dev Comms; Safety Adv; Cooperating Tchr Trng C Stdnts; NEA 1965-; CEA 1967-; SEA 1967-, VP Negotiations; Ment Tchr; Articles Pub; *home:* 14 Maryland Dr Middlefield CT 06455

WILLIS, RICHARD CRAIG, Biology Teacher; *b:* Harrisburg, PA; Lebanon Valley Coll (BS) Bio 1984; 9 Credit Hrs WV Univ Dental Sc 1984; *cr:* Palmyra HS Bio Tchr 1986-; *ai:* Stu Ind Research Project Supv PAEA, PSEA, NEA 1986-; Summa Cum Laude Lebanon Valley Co *office:* Palmyra HS 1125 Park Dr Palmyra PA 17078

WILLMAN, DANA M. (MILLER), Band Director; *b:* Willard, OH; Christopher J.; *c:* Austin Lee, Marissa Kay; *ed:* Heidelberg Coll (B Music Ed 1989; Credit Hrs Received Univ of Akron; *cr:* Seneca East Lo Schls Choral Dir, Gen Music Tchr 1989-90; Seneca East Local Schls Ba Dir 1990-; *ai:* Heidelberg Coll Brass Band 1993-, Solo Concert; NE

, OMEA, MENC 1989-; *office:* Seneca East Local Schls 109 Seneca tica OH 44807*

LMANN, JEFFREY SCOTT, Mathematics Professor; *b:* Boston, *c:* Wiley, Emma, Katherine; *ed:* Tufts Univ (BS) Math 1972; Univ of MED) Math Ed 1991; *cr:* Naragaugus HS Math Tchr 1983-84; ME ime Acad Math Prof 1984-87; Univ of ME Dev Math Prof 1987-90; Maritime Acad Math Prof 1991-; *ai:* Fac Welfare Comm Chair; Amer Research Assn, mathematical Assn of Amer 1991-; Bay Schl Bldg n 1993-; *office:* Maine Maritime Acad Castine ME 04421

LMARTH, JACQUELIN LOUISE TILLACK, First Grade Teacher; dgeway, PA; *m:* John Henry; *ed:* Edinboro Univ (BS) Elem, Spec Ed ; Spec Ed 1977; Gannon Univ, Edinboro Univ, Slippery Rock Univ, rsburg Univ, Duquesne Univ, Shippensburg Univ, Wilkes Coll 49 it Hrs; *cr:* Giddings Elem Schl Spec Ed Tchr 1972-73; Conneaut Lake Schl Spec Ed Tchr 1974-82; Conneaut Lake HS Spec Ed Tchr -82; Conneaut Vly Elem Schl Kndgtn Tchr 1982-83, Learning Support 1982-84, Spec Ed Tchr 1983-84; Conneaut Vly HS Spec Ed, Learning ort Tchr 1983-84; Conneaut Vly Elem Schl First Grd Tchr 1984-; *ai:* s Advising Tchrs, Instrl Support Teams; NEA, PA St Ed Assn, eaut Educ Assn 1974-; Delta Kappa Gamma 1980-, Pres, First, nd VP, Recording, Corresponding Sec, Comm Chm, St Comms; Luth ch 1952-, Cncl, Evangelism Chm; *office:* Conneaut Valley Elem Schl Box 197 Conneautville PA 16406*

LMORE, CHARLES CHRISTIAN, Librarian & Media Specialist; ewark, OH; *m:* Sandra Phillips; *c:* Andy; *ed:* OH St Univ (BS) Eng, ch & Theatre 1974, (MA) Eng Ed 1982; Course Work to Obtain Gifted alented Cert; Course Work to Obtain Media Specialist Cert; *cr:* mbus City Schls 7th Grd Eng Tchr 1974-75; Westerville City Schls 2th Grd Eng Tchr 1975-93, Media Specialist & Librn 1993-; *ai:* Dist Cncl Tchr Rep; Gifted & Talented Stdnts Acad Adv; HS Report uction Team Co-Adv; Stu Discussion Group Facilatator; WEA, OEA EA 1975-, Fac Rep; Westerville City Cable Commission 1994-, Schl Rep & Vice- Chm; Received Supts A+ Awd 1995; Have Presented erous Wkshps Both in Schl Dist & at Ed Confs; *office:* Westerville h HS 950 County Line Rd Westerville OH 43081

LOUGHBY, C. STEPHEN, Third Grade Teacher; *b:* Dundalk, MD; aura Lee Golden; *ed:* Essex Comm Coll (AA) Music Performance ; Towson St Univ (BS) Elem Ed 1983; Loyola Coll (MED) Rdng cialist 1990; *cr:* White Marsh Elem Schl Fifth Grd Tchr 1983-84, th Grd Tchr 1984-90; Easton Elem Schl Fifth Grd Tchr 1990-92, Fifth Rdng Resource Tchr 1992-93, Third Grd Rdng Tchr 1993-95, Third Tchr 1995-; *ai:* Newspaper Adv; Sit Team; IRA 1989-; NEA 1983-; *e:* 725 Elwood Ave Easton MD 21601

LOUGHBY, EARL ORR, Business Education Instructor; *b:* Mt ling, OH; *m:* Nancy L. Heberle; *c:* Scott A., Mark A., Todd M.; *ed:* is St Univ (BS) Mrktng 1960; York Coll of PA Type II Permanent Tchng 1994; ShippensburgUniv Cmptr Literacy; *cr:* Cntrl Penn Bus Instr 5-86; York Cath HS Instr 1986-; *ai:* Coaching; NCEA 1977-; *office:* Catholic HS 601 E Springettsbury Ave York PA 17403

LOUGHBY, LYNNE EVE, Equine Science Instructor; *b:* kensack, NJ; *ed:* Bucks Cty Comm Coll (AS) Cmptr Sci 1983; Temple (BS) Bus Admin & Accounting 1987; Working Towards Masters in nt at La Salle Univ; *cr:* B R Willoughby & Assocs Bar Code Systems grammer 1986-88; The Curiosity Shoppe Equestrian Prgm Dir 1988-90; Valley Coll Equine Sci Fac 1990-; *ai:* Vaulting & Drill Teams Coach; ne Sci Org Adv; AAUP 1993-; Assn for Horsemanship, Safety & Ed 3-, Advanced Eng Riding Cert; Amer Horse Show Assn 1986-; US ssage Fed 1986-, Bronze Medal Performance Awd; Amer Riding Instr Dressage & Combined Trng 1989, 1994; *office:* Delaware Valley Coll E Butler Ave Doylestown PA 18901

LLS, MELISSA WRIGHT, Elementary Multi-Age Teacher; *b:* ford, DE; *m:* Franklin Knight III; *c:* Jeremy Brian, Joshua Louis, Jordan Jenna Coale; *ed:* Millersville Univ (BS) Elem Ed 1975; Widener Univ ED) Gifted Ed 1987; Early Chldhd Cert 12 Cr Hrs 1992; *cr:* West Seford m Schl Grd 1 Tchr 1982-88; Seaford Kndgtn Tchr 1989-92; West ford Elem Schl Multiage Tchr 1993-; *ai:* NEA, DE SEA 1982-; Seaf c Assn 1982-, Sec 1 Yr; Seaford Lioness Club 1986-, 1st VP, 2nd VP, Chm Comms, Mbrshp, Attendance, Lioness of Yr; Nom Tchr of Yr; ner DE Agenda for Schl Improvement; *home:* 622 Penn Ave Seaford 19973

LLS, ODETTE RENEE, Math Specialist; *b:* Georgetown, Guyana SA; Baruch Coll CUNY (BS) Elem Ed 1979; Queens Coll CUNY (MS) ng Ed 1986; Queens Coll CUNY (PD) Supervision, Admin 1993; *cr:* en Chrstn Schl Elem Tchr 1982-87; Bayview Avenue Schl 3rd Grd Tchr 7-88; Bayview Avenue Schl 4th Grd Tchr 1988-95; Bayview Avenue l Math Specialist 1995-; *ai:* Dist Planning Cncl Mem; Freeport Tchrs n Del; NYS United Tchrs, AFL-CIO 1987-; Bethel Gospel Tabernacle 6-, Sunday Schl Supt, 1971-86 Sunday Schl Tchr; NY St Congress of ents & Tchrs Honorary Lifetime Mem 1993-; Nassau Cty Exec Tchr of 1993; Queens Coll Schl of Admin, Supervision Awds for Superior alsp, Outstanding Svc 1993; *office:* Bayview Avenue Schl 325 W rrick Rd Freeport NY 11520*

LLS, STEVEN R., English Dept Chair & Teacher; *b:* Rochester, NY; Susan Barnes; *ed:* Syracuse Univ (BA) Eng, Ed 1971; PA St West ester Univ (MS) Ed, Psych 1991; *cr:* Colonial Schl Dist Tchr 1971-, ot Chair 1995-; Freelance Writer, Author 1985-; *ai:* Schl Newspaper v; NEA 1976-; ASCD 1992-; NCTE 1984-; Whitemarsh Women's Club cl Ed Awd 1988-89; Writers to Watch for the 90's 1994; Articles Pub 85-; Book: Mind-Boggling Astronomy 1995; *office:* mouth-Whitemarsh HS Germantown Pike Plymouth Meet PA 19462

ILLSON, C. WESLEY, Math Teacher; *b:* Lowell, MA; *m:* Linda Kay nningham; *c:* Kevin Wesley, Shane Eric; *ed:* Millersville Univ (BS) em Ed 1966; Towson Univ (BS) Math 1985; Masters Equivalency; *cr:* ndsor Manor Elem 3rd Grd Tchr 1966; Mazie Gable Elem 5th Grd Tchr 57-70; Red Lion Jr HS 8th Grd Math Tchr 1971-; *ai:* Sports Card Club; ramural Bsktbl; RLAEA 1966-, Negotiator, Bldg Rep; PSEA, NEA 66-; St Pauls Chapel United Meth Church 1966-; Windsor TWP creation Bd 1975-85; 1st Capital Compact Grant; *office:* Red Lion Area HS 200 Country Club Rd Red Lion PA 17356

ILLSON, DAVID EUGENE, Mathematics Teacher; *b:* Bedford Hts, I; *m:* Deborah A. Good; *c:* Jordan, Lindsay; *ed:* Heidelberg Coll (BS) ath 1986; Cleveland St Univ (MEd) Math Ed 1995; Project Discovery 95; Quantitative Lit; *cr:* Olmsted Falls Math Tchr 1986-; *ai:* Comp ord; Bsktbl Coach; NCTM, OCTM & GCCTM 1986-; NEA, OEA & EA 1986-, Treas; OBCA & GCBCA 1986-; Presidential Awd in Tchng ath Nom; *office:* Olmsted Falls MS 26184 Bagley Rd Olmsted Falls OH 138*

ILLSON, FREDERIC AUSTIN, Spanish Teacher; *b:* Indianapolis, IN; Jane Forcellina; *ed:* Fairfield Univ (BS) Ec 1986; Univ of Bridgeport IS) Ed 1990; 12 Credits Math; Pvt Pilot Cert 1982, US Coast Guard Aux sic Sailing, Seamanship, Coastal Navigation; *cr:* Brien Mc Mahon HS tern 1989-90; Nathan Hale MS Span Tchr 1990-91; Wheeler HS Span hr 1991-; *ai:* Jr Class Adv; Wise Prgm Srs Coord; NEA 1990-; North onington Ed Assn 1991-; Svc Appreciation for Coordinating Wise Prgm; *fice:* Wheeler Jr Sr HS Rt 2 PO Box 6001 North Stonington CT 06359*

WILSHERE, JANE BARAN, English Teacher; *b:* New York, NY; *c:* Allison M.; *ed:* St Univ Coll at Plattsburgh NY (BA) Scndry Eng 1969; 30 Credit Hrs; *cr:* Ausable Vly Cntrl Schl 7th-9th Grd Eng Tchr 1969-70; Queensbury Schl 7th-8th Grd Eng Tchr 1970-; *ai:* Queensbury Supt Advy Cncl 1979-82; MS Advy Cncl Sec 1989-90; NYSUT & AFT 1970-; Queensbury Faculty Assoc 1970-, Recording Sec 1971-74; N Cty Arts Cntr Bd of Dirs, Past Mem; Hyde Museum Vol Cncl, Past Mem; Aerobic Dance Instr-YMCA-Vol 1975-79; NYSUT Bd of Curr Guides 1977; Cancer Soc Major in 1980 Ward 3 Pledge Dr; NYS Writing Conf Presenter 1981; NYS Ed Dept 5th Grd Writing Test Consultant 1982-84; TESA Trainer; *office:* Queensbury School 455 Aviation Rd Glens Falls NY 12804

WILSON, ALICE MC ATEER, Math Teacher; *b:* Staten Island, NY; *m:* Van Ray; *c:* Clorinda; *ed:* Wells Coll (BA) Math 1969; Richmond Coll (MS) Scndry Math Ed 1971; 30 Addl Hrs; *cr:* Tottenville HS Math Tchr 1970-; *ai:* UFT 1971-; Phi Beta Kappa 1969-; Wells Coll Alumnae Cncl 1992-; *office:* Tottenville HS 100 Luten Ave Staten Island NY 10312

WILSON, ANDREW JOSEPH, 8th Grade Mathematics Teacher; *b:* Brooklin, NY; *m:* Vivian; *ed:* SUNY at Stony Brook (BS) Math 1990; Brooklin Coll (MA) Math 1996; *cr:* West Hempstead MS Math Tchr 1990-; *ai:* Head MS Ftbl,JV Vlybl Coach; NCTM 1990-; Paul Douglas Tchr Schlsp.

WILSON, AUDRA EWONCE, Math Teacher; *b:* Kennedy Twp, PA; *m:* James D.; *ed:* Grove City Coll (BA) Math 1991; *cr:* Montour Math Tchr 1993-; *ai:* Math Team; Strategic Planning Comm; Staff Dev; Ken Mawr UP Church 1969-, Organist; *office:* Montour HS Clever Rd Mc Kees Rocks PA 15136*

WILSON, AUDREY, Media Specialist; *b:* Manhattan, NY; *c:* James, Leticia Wilson Jarrette; *ed:* Herbert H Lehman Coll (BA) PE 1978; Pratt Inst of Tech (MS) Media Specialist 1983; 12 Post-Grad Credit Hrs Spcl Ed; *cr:* Harlem Savings Bank Teller 1977-78; NY Pub Lib Young Adult Librn 1979-84; NY City Bd of Ed PE Tchr & Media Specialist 1984-; *ai:* Bsktbl, Vllybl, Swimming & Tennis Coach; Multicultural Club, Dance Club & Storytelling Club Adv; Chorus; Hispanic Pgms, African-Amer & Multi-Cultural Coord; AFT 1985-; Pratt Inst Media Specialist Flwshp; *office:* NY City Bd of Ed 240 E 109th St New York NY 10029*

WILSON, BARNEY JOE, Associate Professor; *b:* Baltimore, MD; *m:* Felecia Ann Porter; *c:* Shannon, Erin; *ed:* Carnegie Mellon Univ (BS) Electrical Engrng, Ec, Math 1980, (MS) Indstrl Admin 1982; 6 Courses Cmptr Information Systems; *cr:* Coppin St Coll Assoc Prof 1987-93; Essex Comm Coll Adj Prof 1995; Catonsville Comm Coll Adj Prof 1992-; Univ of Baltimore Assoc Prof 1994-; *ai:* Ran for Congress 7th Dist 1996; Exec Dir Small Bus Dev Ctrs; Bd Dirs MD Homebased Bus Assn; Chamber Commerce Small Bus Comm; MD Bus Resource Ctr 1995-, Advy Bd; MD Rites of Passage 1992-, Advy Bd; Awds Initiating Entrepreneurship, Job Creation Cntrl MD, Serving Mc Nair Schlsps Mentor, Mentoring MD New Directions Prgm, Baltimore Rites of Passage Prgm; *home:* PO Box 671 Reisterstown MD 21136

WILSON, BONNIE A., Math Tchr & Department Chair; *b:* Cincinnati, OH; *m:* David K.; *ed:* AZ St Univ (BA) Chem 1968; Xavier Univ (MED) Scndry Admin 1971; OH Univ Bio NSF Grant; *cr:* OLPH Tchr 1964-68; Rdng HS Tchr 1968-70; Latham Local Tchr 1970-71; Rdng Jr Sr HS Tchr 1971-; *ai:* Drill Team, Cheerleading, Pep Club, NHS, Head Class, Devilette Spon; NEA, OEA, SWOEA 1968-; REA 1968-, Treas, Outstanding Treas 1993-; OCTM, VCTM 1984-; GCCTM; Sweet Adelines 1985-, Treas, Sec, Sweet Adeline of Yr 1988-89; *office:* Reading Jr/Sr HS 810 E Columbia Ave Cincinnati OH 45215

WILSON, BRADLEY LEROY, Health & Physical Ed Teacher; *b:* Andrhus AFB, MD; *m:* Molly; *c:* Lindsay; *ed:* Towson St Univ (BS) Hlth, PE 1987; Hlth Cert in Process; *cr:* Marley, Ferndale Elem Schl PE Tchr 1988-; Traceys, Deale Elem Schl PE Tchr 1988-89; Severn Elem Schl PE Tchr 1989-93; North Cty HS PE, Hlth Tchr 1993-; *ai:* Var Ftbl Asst Defensive Coord; Boys Bsktbl, JV Sftbl Head Coaches; *office:* North Cty HS 10 1st Ave E Glen Burnie MD 21061

WILSON, BRIAN SCOTT, History Department Chair; *b:* Oxnard, CA; *m:* Deborah Jane; *c:* Scott, Ashley; *ed:* Coll of William & Mary (AB) Religion 1986; Univ of VA Ed Grad Stud; *cr:* Chrstn Ctr Schl Scndry Dir 1988-91; Montrose Chrstn Schl His Dept Chair 1991-; *ai:* Girls Var Bsktbl & Softbl Coach; Instructional Cncl; WBCA 1991-; *office:* Montrose Christian Schl 5100 Randolph Rd Rockville MD 20852

WILSON, BRUCE M., Eng & Comparative Lit Prof; *b:* Washington, DC; *m:* Teresa Iannitelli; *c:* Peter M., Crispin A.; *ed:* Bates Coll (BA) Eng 1970; Univ of VA (PHD) Eng 1977; Stud Italian Lang & Civilization at Centro Di Cultura Per Stranieri in Florence Italy 1969; Stud Japanese Lang & Noh Theatre at Sophia Univ in Tokyo Japan 1970; Stud Chinese Lang at John Hopkins Schl of Advanced Intnl Studs 1984; *cr:* St Marys College of MD Prof of Eng 1976-; *ai:* Fudan-St Marys Exch Pgm Dir; Asian Studs Assn 1992-; Amer Lit Translators Assn 1992-; Phi Beta Kappa 1970-; Dela Brooke Pony Club 1989-, Dist Commissioner; NEH Summer Seminar in Chinese Lit at Stanford Univ 1980; Fulbright Lectureship in China 1984-85; NEH Inst in Asian Lit at Columbia Univ 1987-89; Pub 100 Tang Poems 1988; Head Division of Arts & Letters at St Marys Coll of MD Since 1992; Articles & Reviews in Asian & Comparative Lit; *office:* Saint Marys Coll Of MD St Marys Cy MD 20686

WILSON, CAROL CONNELLY, Dev Handicap Specialist; *b:* Martins Ferry, OH; *m:* Robert H.; *c:* Timothy, Paul; *ed:* OH Univ (BS) Ed 1969; Steubenville Coll Spec Ed; *cr:* Hazel Atlas Glass Sec 1954-55; Bldg Trades Welfare Asst Mgr 1955-62; Citizens Savings Bank Head Bookkeeper 1962-68; Martins Ferry Schls Instr 1969-70; Bridgeport Schl Instr 1970-; *ai:* Yrbk Adv; Bridgeport Ed Assn 1970-, Pres 1994-; Natl Trl Cncl 1994-; *home:* 17 S 11th St Martins Ferry OH 43935

WILSON, CATHLEEN M., English Teacher; *b:* Trenton, NJ; *m:* Harry E.; *c:* Meghan, Jonathan; *ed:* Montclair St Coll (BA) Eng 1970; U of RI (MA) Eng 1972; *cr:* U of RI Tchng Asst, Eng Tchr 1970-72; Middlesex Cty Coll Adj Eng Instr 1974-75; Ocean Cty Coll Adj Eng Instr 1977-79; Freehold Regnl HS Dist Eng Tchr 1973-; *ai:* Adv Lit Magazine; NJEA 1973-; Tchr of Yr 1994; *office:* Marlboro HS Rt 79 Marlboro NJ 07745

WILSON, CHRISTINE ANN MAZUREK, Professor of Biology; *b:* Kitchener, Canada; *m:* George Harlan; *c:* James, Ben, Nathan; *ed:* Univ of Waterloo (BA) Hnrs Sci, Biol 1977; Univ of Waterloo (MS) Sci 1980; Attnd St Andrew's Rsrch Station New Brunswick 1977; ALgonquin Rsrch Station Ontario 1976; *cr:* Univ of Waterloo Tchng Asst 1977-78; Thiel Coll Adj Instr 1988-92; PA St Univ Adj Instr 1989-92; Comm Coll Allegheny Cty Bio Instr 1992-; *ai:* Acad Planning Comm; Boyce Sci Club Adv; Co-Dir Human Anatomy Physiology Soc Regnl Conf 1996; Human Anatomy, Physiology Soc 1992-; Sigma Xi 1991-, Rsrch Supvr; AFT 1992-; BSA 1988-, Comm Mem; Audubon Bartramian 1992-, Osprey Vol; Carnegie Sci Ctr 1992-; Mini Grant Recipient 1994, 1996; 2 Artcles Pub 1983; 1 Article Pub 1982; *office:* Comm Coll Algny Co Boyce Cmps 595 Beatty Rd Monroeville PA 15146

WILSON, CHRISTY BARTHOLOMEW, Eng, Speech & Drama Teacher; *b:* Syracuse, NY; *m:* Ray G.; *c:* Peter James; *ed:* St Lawrence Univ (BA) Eng 1972; SUNY Potsdam 30 Grad Hrs; *cr:* Lisbon Cntrl Schl 11th-12th Grd Eng Tchr 1972; Hermon DeKalb Cntrl Schl 7th-8th Grd Eng Tchr 1972-76, 11th-12th Grd Eng Tchr 1976-; *ai:* AFT 1972-; NCTE 1985-; *home:* 53 E Main St Canton NY 13617

WILSON, CONSTANCE TERESSA, Third Grade Teacher; *b:* Danville, VA; *ed:* Richmond Coll at St Island (BA) Psych 1971; Tchrs Coll Columbia U at NYC (MA) Rdng Ed 1974; Manhattan Coll at Bronx (MS) Spec Ed 1989; *cr:* PS 26 Brooklyn Second Grd Tchr 1971-75; PS 121 Bronx First Grd Tchr 1975-76; PS 7 Bronx First-Third Grd Tchr 1976-, After Schl Ctr Tchr 1983-89; Inst of Cognitive Dev Manhattan Coll Learning Disabled After Schl Tchr 1987-88; PS 7 Bronx Learning Disabled After Schl Tchr 1991; *ai:* UFT, NYSUT, AFT 1971-; Kappa Delta Pi 1987-; NYC Tchrs License Early Chldhd 1971; NYS Tchrs Cert Nursery, Kndgtn, Grd 1-6 1977, Spec Ed 1991; *office:* PS 7 The Kingsbridge Schl 3201 Kingsbridge Ave Bronx NY 10463*

WILSON, DAVID G., English Teacher; *b:* Boston, MA; *m:* Maura Dolan; *c:* Matthew, Brian; *ed:* Norwich Univ (BA) Eng 1971; Bridgewater St (MAT) Eng 1978; 30 Addl Credit Hrs Univ of MA at Boston; *cr:* East Jr HS Eng Tchr 1972-79; Braintree HS Eng Tchr 1979-83; South MS Eng Tchr 1983-89; East MS Eng Tchr 1989-; *ai:* NEA, MTA, BEA 1974-; NCTE 1975-; Boston Writing Project Tchr Fellowship 1991, Advance Lit Inst Fellowship 1992, Tchr of Tchrs Grant 1993; MA Alliance MS Tchr Grant 1993, 1996; *office:* East MS 305 River St Braintree MA 02184

WILSON, DAVID W., History Teacher; *b:* New Milford, NJ; *m:* Christina Holstrom; *c:* Kimberly, Andrew; *ed:* Cook Coll, Rutgers Univ (BS) Environmental, Bus Ec 1984; *cr:* New Milford HS Tchr 1985-; *ai:* Var Girls Bsktbl, Tennis Coach; Yrbk Bus Adv; Acad Decathlon Lecturer; Sr Class Adv; NEA 1985-; NCSS 1990-; Governors Tchr Recognition Prgm; New Milford HS Tchr of Yr 1990; *office:* New Milford H S 1 Snyder Cir New Milford NJ 07646

WILSON, DAWN E., Vocal & General Music Teacher; *b:* Akron, OH; *m:* LaMont; *c:* Candace, Allyson; *ed:* Case Western Reserve Univ (BS) Music Ed & Music Therapy 1981; Univ of Akron (MS) Scndry Schl Admin Ed 1995; *cr:* Akron Pub Schls Vocal & Gen Music Tchr 1981-; *ai:* Schoolwide Grant Comm Chprsn; Drama Club Adv; Music Edctrs Natl Comm 1980-; Phi Delta Kappa 1989-; ASCD 1995-; Alpha Kappa Alpha 1980-; Bldg Tchr of Yr 1994; *office:* Riedinger MS 77 W Thornton St Akron OH 44311

WILSON, DEAN MARLON, Elementary Music Specialist; *b:* Warren, PA; *m:* Mary Ann Raiser; *c:* Christopher, Eric; *ed:* Mt Union Coll (BME) Music Ed 1975; Youngstown St Univ (MM) Music Ed 1981; 19 Post Grad Hrs; *cr:* Boardman Schls Elem Music Specialist 1975-; *ai:* After Schl Childrens Chorus; OH Ed Assn 1975-; Boardman Ed Assn 1975-; Arts Edctr of the Yr 1995; A Child At Heart Recording Artist; *office:* Robinwood Lane Elem Schl 835 Indianola Rd Youngstown OH 44512*

WILSON, DELORES HARRIS, Lang Arts & Soc Stud Teacher; *b:* Kershaw, SC; *w:* Edward Clarence (dec); *c:* Edward Corey, Keith Lamar; *ed:* Barber-Scotia Coll (BS) Elem Ed, Soc Stud 1971; George Washington Univ (MS) Elem Ed, Human Dev 1982; *cr:* St Mary's Cty Bd of Ed 2-5 Grd Tchr 1971-; *ai:* First Missionary Bapt Church; Usher Ministry; Worked with Chrstn Ed MInistry; Taught Vacation Bible Schl; Directed Christmas & Arican Amer His Plays, Prgms; Worked with Yths; NEA, PTA 1971-; MD Cncl Soc Stud 1995-; Southern MD Chain Links 1991-, Svcs to Yth; NCAAP 1976-; Cert for Directing Plays, Prgms; Nom by So MD Chain for Women's His Intermediate Grd Chm; Intermediate Soc Stud Chm; *office:* Park Hall Elem Schl 380 Leonardtown Point Lookout Rd Park Hall MD 20667

WILSON, DIANE F., Economics & Psychology Teacher; *b:* Meshoppen, PA; *m:* David G.; *c:* Jeremy, Nathan; *ed:* Mansfield Univ (BS) Scndry Ed & Soc Stud 1971; 26 Credits Beyond BS; *cr:* Wyalusing Area HS Ec & Psych Tchr 1972-; *ai:* Commencement & Stu of Month Comms; NEA, PSEA & WAEA 1972-; United Meth Church 1964-; *office:* Wyalusing Valley HS RR 2 Box 7 Wyalusing PA 18853*

WILSON, DIANNE ANDERSON, Academic Support Coordinator; *b:* Newport, VT; *m:* John F.; *c:* Sarah, Anna; *ed:* Univ of VT (BA) Eng 1966; Columbia Univ (MAT) Eng 1968; Univ of MA at Lowell (MED) Rdng 1991; *cr:* HS of Fashion Industries Eng Tchr 1968-70; Shaw Prep Schl Dir, Tchr GED Prgm 1971-73; St Sebastians Schl Coord, Acad Support 1991-92; Acton-Boxborough HS Coord, Acad Support 1994-; *ai:* Adv, Peer Tutoring Prgm; NEA 1994-; MRA, IRA 1988-; Pi Lambda Theta; St Andrews Soc 1994-; Title IV Flwshp; *office:* Acton Boxborough Reg HS 96 Hayward Rd Acton MA 01720

WILSON, DOLORES MARGARET, English & TAG Teacher; *b:* New York City, NY; *c:* Claire Wilson Bolton, Jennifer; *ed:* Marymount at Manhattan (BA) Eng; St Johns Univ (MA) Amer Lit; New Schl for Soc Research Certified Graphologist; *cr:* New Hyde Park Meml HS Eng, TAG Tchr 28 Yrs; *ai:* TAG Mentor; Professionalism Comm Tchr Rep; NEA 1978-; NCTE; NHS; PTSA Awd; 5 Plays Produced; Poetry Pub; *office:* New Hyde Park Memorial JR HS 500 Leonard Blvd New Hyde Park NY 11040

WILSON, DONALD GLEN, Math Dept Chair & Teacher; *b:* Bethlehem, PA; *m:* Miriam Moon; *c:* Lisa, Kimberly Rowe; *ed:* PA St Univ (BS) PE, Math 1961; Univ of CT (MA) Admin 1965; Reed Coll (MALS) Math 1969; 30 Credit Hrs Univ of Bridgeport; *cr:* Ponus Ridge Jr HS Tchr 1961-64; Brien Mc Mahon HS Tchr 1964-; *ai:* Ski Club Adv 32 Yrs; Boys Tennis Coach 20 Yrs; HS Soccer Ofcl 32 Yrs; NFT 1972-; Rowayton Civic Assn 1992-, Yth Dir; Rewayton Tennis Assn 1971-, Pres; Pimms Fellow; NSF Grant to San Diego St Coll & Reed Coll; *office:* Brien McMahon HS 300 Highland Ave Norwalk CT 06854*

WILSON, DONNA JEAN, Special Educator; *b:* Providence, RI; *m:* Peter; *c:* Alissa, Meghan; *ed:* Keene St Coll (BA) Spec Ed 1977; Providence Coll (MED) Spec Ed, Rdng 1982; *cr:* Riverside Jr HS Resource Tchr 1977-80; Austin T. Levy Schl Spec Edctr 1980-82; Rutland HS Resource Tchr 1982-; *ai:* NEA 1977-, Treas; 4-H 1994-, Ldr; *office:* Rutland HS 22 Stratton Rd Rutland VT 05701

WILSON, DORIS EDWARDS, Social Studies Teacher; *b:* Gloucester, VA; *m:* John Sr.; *c:* Linda, Sharifa, Gayle, John Jr.; *ed:* Adelphi Univ (BA) Soc Sci, Ed 1991; *cr:* Bd of Ed Paraprofessionl 1989-93; Sarah J. Hale HS Tchr 1993-95; John Jay HS Tchr; *ai:* Gospel Chorus Adv; Project Achieve Comm; Magna Cum Laude from Adelphi; *office:* John Jay HS 237 7th Ave Brooklyn NY 11216

WILSON, DOROTHY JEAN, English & Literature Teacher; *b:* Tupelo, MS; *m:* Thomas D.; *c:* Miesha L.; *ed:* Jackson St Univ (BA) Amer Lit 1966; Baldwin Wallace (MA) Ed 1993; MS Cert; Cleveland St Univ Rdng Cert; *cr:* South HS Dept Head 1968-78; Aviation HS Eng Dept Head 1979-80; Whitney Young Jr HS Amer Lit Tchr 1983-88; Garret Morgan Schl of Sci Amer Lit Tchr 1988-; Jane Adams HS Adult Ed Tchr 1989-; *ai:* Sr Class Spon; Drama Dir 1985-; Career Cnslr 1985-87; Creative Writing Club Adv 1989; NHS Adv 1990-95; Educl Comm 1985; Natl Tchrs Assn 1971-; NAACP 1969-; Martha Holden Jennings Fnd Awd; TRW Excl in Tchng Awd; OH Acad for Schl Improvement Strategies Grant; *home:* 28840 Chagrin Blvd Apt 209 Beachwood OH 44122

WILSON, DWIGHT LAMONT, Executive Director; *b:* Middletown, OH; *m:* Carol Shepard; *c:* Kai, Rai, Tai, Mignon, Mai, Diana; *ed:* Bowdoin Coll (BA) His, Sociology 1973; Bangor Theological Seminary (MDIV) Theology, Cnslng 1973; *cr:* Friends Gen Conf Exec Dir 1977-82; Oakwood Friends Schl Dean 1982-89; Moorestown Friends Schl Asst Prin 1989-92; NJ SEEDS Exec Dir 1992-; *ai:* Samaritan Hospice 1990-; Haverford Coll Corp 1980-; Burlington Cty YMCA Bd 1993-; Burlington Cty Explores

Scout Bd 1994-; Honorary Degree Human Reconstruction from Wilmington Coll; Leonardo de Vinci Scholar NEH 1990; Publications.*

WILSON, ELEANOR KELLY, Mathematics Teacher; *b:* Wilmington, DE; *m:* David Lee; *c:* David K.; *ed:* Immaculata Coll (AB) Math 1964; *cr:* George Read Jr High Math Tchr 1964-66; Brandywine HS Math Tchr 1974-76; St Marks High Math Tchr 1976-; *ai:* DCTM, NCEA; *office:* St Mark's HS Pike Creek Rd Wilmington DE 19808

WILSON, EZZARD SYLVESTER, Science Teacher; *b:* Sandy Point, West Indies; *m:* Linda N. Stevens; *c:* Sakeina, Maubaki; *ed:* ID St Univ (BS) Bio, PE 1980; NJ Inst of Tech (MS) Env Sci 1993; 73 Addl Credit Hrs Bus & Ed Rutgers, Mt Clair St, Kean Coll, Essex Comm Coll; *cr:* Verchilds & Sandy Point HS Tchr 1973-82; British Vergin Islands HS Tchr 1982-84; PS 136 Tchr 1985-86; East Orange HS Tchr 1986-90; Irvington HS Tchr 1991-; *ai:* HSPT Tutoring; Multicultural Club Adv; EIP Comm; Track Coach; Ath Dir; NEA 1986-; IEA 1991-; Curr Comm 1995-; *office:* Irvington HS 1150 Springfield Ave Irvington NJ 07111*

WILSON, GERALD WILLIAM, 6th Grade Teacher; *b:* Columbus, OH; *m:* Carol Anne Surko; *c:* Jason, Todd, Michelle; *ed:* OH St Univ (BS) Elem Ed 1974; 78 Addl Grad Hrs Educl Admin & Guidance; *cr:* Whitehal City Schls 1st Grd Tchr 1974; Westerville City Schl 5th-6th Grd Tchr 1974-78; Worthington City Schl 5th-6th Grd Tchr 1978-; *ai:* Career Ed, Bldg Concerns Comm; Odessey of Mind, Soccer, Bsktbl, Vlybl Club Coach; Dart League Adv; Camp OH Coord; Pupil Prsnl Team; PTO Fac, Mini Grant Rep; NEA, OEA 1974-; Westerville Ed Assn 1974-78; Worthington Ed Assn 1978-, Fac Rep 1979, 1984, 1985, 1990, 1992, Negotiatioan Team 1985; *home:* 100 Electric Ave Westerville OH 43081*

WILSON, HEATHER ELLEN, Health Teacher; *b:* Providence, RI; *ed:* SUNY Coll at Cortland (BSE) Hlth Ed 1985, (MSE) Hlth Ed 1990; Advanced Emergency Med Tech Critical Care; Lions Quest Skills for Adolscence Trng; Amer Red Cross CPR, Stan First Aid Instr; *cr:* Marcellus Cntrl Schl Dist Driver Ed Tchr 1985-86; Gouverneur Cntrl Schl Dist Hlth Tchr 1986-; *ai:* Class Adv; AIDS Advy Cncl; Tech, Fac Advy Comms; NYSUT 1975-; NYSAHPERD 1983-, Past Hlth Section Pres; Gouverneur Vol Rescue Squad 1994-, Crew Chief; *office:* Gouverneur Cntrl Schl Dist 133 E Barney St Gouverneur NY 13642

WILSON, JANE HUGHEY, First Grade Teacher; *b:* Pittsburgh, PA; *m:* Edward Wright; *c:* Carolyn Quinn, Edward, Barbara, Deborah Deck; *ed:* Mansfield Univ (BS) Elem Ed 1977, (MS) Elem Ed 1987; *cr:* Southern Tioga Schl Kndgtn-2nd, 4th Grd Tchr 1980-; *ai:* Recreation; NEA, PSEA 1980-; *office:* Southern Tioga Schl 1 Dorsett Dr Mansfield PA 16933

WILSON, JANICE FISCUS, ESOL & Resource Teacher; *b:* New Kensington, PA; *m:* James M.; *c:* Roberta M. Williams, Megan W. Yeager; *ed:* Lake Erie Coll for Women (BA) Span, Eng 1961; Amer Univ (MA) Span 1974; Middlebury Grad Schl Abroad 1961-62; Univ of Madrid 1961-62; Middlebury Coll Schl of Lang Grad Stud 1960; Lake Erie Coll for Women Abroad 1960; Middlebury Schl of Lang 1960-61; *cr:* DC Elem Schls Frgn Lang Tchr Tchr 1963; Stone Ridge Cntry Day Schl of Sacred Heart HS Span Tchr 1973-76; Richard Montgomery HS ESOL Summer Schl Tchr 1974; Montgomery Cty Pub Schls Eng, Span Tchr Home Instruction 1976-77; Wheaton HS Span Tchr 1976-77, Adults ESOL Tchr 1979; Montgomery Cty Pub Schls ESOL Tchr 1977-80, Human Relations Seminar Tchrs Instr Summer 1980; Blair HS Night Schl Adult ESOL Tchr Summer 1980, ESOL Tchr Summer 1981; Northwood HS Soc Stud ESOL Tchr 1980-82, Writing Vol Book ESOL Vols, Lit Curr Dev Summer 1982; Walt Whitman HS ESOL Tchr 1983-86; WATESOL Convention Presenter, Instr ESOL Tchrs Summer 1984; Richard Montgomery HS ESOL Resource Tchr 1986-89; Walt Whitman HS ESOL Resource Tchr 1989-; *ai:* FOES Club Spon; ESOL Dept Chprsn; Ldrshp Team; NEA, MSTA 1976-; Montgomery Cty Pub Schls Advanced Cert Span, Eng, ESOL 1986; MCEA 1987-; Amer Lang Inst 1974-; Outstdng ESOL Tchr of Yr 1993-94; *office:* Walt Whitman HS 7100 Whittier Blvd Bethesda MD 20817*

WILSON, JEAN NEUTZ, Chemistry Teacher; *b:* Saint Paul, MN; *m:* Floyd Scott; *c:* Amy Christine; *ed:* Lawrence Univ (BA) Math 1968; Canisius Coll (MS) Scndry Ed 1987; 24 Grad Credits at Univ of MN; Working Toward Medical Technologist Cert; *cr:* Minneapolis Pub Schls Math Tchr 1969-72; Edina Pub Schls Math & Sci Tchr 1974-75; Buffalo General Hospital Medical Technologist 1979-86; Buffalo Sacred Heart Acad Math Tchr 1986-90; Orchard Park HS Chem Tchr 1990-; *ai:* Schl Musical Costume Coord; AFT, NYSUT 1990-; *office:* Orchard Park HS 4040 Baker Rd Orchard Park NY 14127

WILSON, JEFFREY DEAN, Agricultural Education Instr; *b:* Kenton, OH; *m:* Lori Gamble; *c:* Brian, Allison; *ed:* OH St Univ (BS) Ag Ed 1975; Credits Ed; *cr:* Arlington HS Ag Edctr 1975-; *ai:* FFA Chptr Adv 21 Yrs; Tech, Intervention Comms; OFT, AFT 1985-, Pres; OVA, AVA, OVATA, NVATA 1975-; Walnut Grove Church 1965-; Meml Pk Bd 1988-; Advy Comm OH St Univ at Lima; *office:* Arlington HS S Main St Arlington OH 45814

WILSON, LAROYAL, Social Studies Teacher; *b:* Mt Pleasant, PA; *m:* Bonnie Tomlinson; *c:* Marcella Biller, Patricia Wilson; *ed:* Westminster Coll (BA) His 1970; Attnd Penn St Univ; *cr:* John F. Kennedy HS Soc Stud Tchr 1970-74; Wendover Jr HS Soc Stud Tchr 1974-90; Hempfield Area HS Soc Stud Tchr 1990-; *ai:* Track, Ftbl Coach; NEA 1970-; PSEA, PIAA 1974-; Recreation Bd 1980-, VP; 2nd Bapt Church 1954-, Treas; Mt Pleasant Girls Sftbl League 1983-, Commissioner; Mt Pleasant Experience Dir 1982-; John F. Kennedy HS Tchr of Yr 1974; Amer Family Inst Tchr Awd 1986; Thanks to Tchr Awd 1991; *office:* Hempfield Area Sr HS Rd 6 Box 77 Greensburg PA 15601

WILSON, LARRY E., Associate Prof of Chemistry; *b:* Auglaize Cty, OH; *m:* Julia M. Henry; *c:* Steven, Katherine Petersen; *ed:* OH St Univ (BS) Chem 1957, (PHD) Analytical Chem 1963; *cr:* Dow Chem Co Rsrch 1963-1969; OH Univ at Lancaster Prof 1969-; *ai:* Amer Chem Soc 1958-; Kiwanis 1973-, Bd of Dirs; Textbooks Pub; *office:* OH Univ 1570 Granville Pike Lancaster OH 43130

WILSON, LUCIA FRONCZAK, French & Spanish Teacher; *b:* Buffalo, NY; *m:* Lyman Girard; *c:* Travis, Shannon; *ed:* St Univ Coll at Buffalo (BS) Scndry Ed, Fr 1977; St Univ of NY at Buffalo (MS) Scndry Ed Foreign Lang 1979; *cr:* Keshequa Cntrl Schl Span, Fr Tchr 1978; St Univ of NY at Buffalo Grad Asst, Instr 1979; North Tonawanda HS Span, Fr Tchr 1979-; *ai:* Stu Travel Organizer; Shared Decision Making Comm; Sr Class Activities, NHS Activities Asst; Mentor Tchr; NHS, Foreign Lang Honor Soc Adv; Dept Coord; AFT, North Tonawanda United Tchrs 1979-; NYSAFLT, WNYFLEC 1977-; St Matthew Luth Sunday Schl Tchrs 1993-; Vacation Bible Schl Tchr 1983-; Comm to Review 1995-; Curr for St Matthew Luth Schl; Pub in Foreign Lang Annuals 1979; Presenter at Northeast Conf 1978, St & Local Conf 1978-95; Grant Awarded to Improve Foreign Lang Speaking Curr 1995; *office:* North Tonawanda Sr HS 405 Meadow Dr North Tonawanda NY 14120*

WILSON, MARGARET CLARK, Spanish Teacher; *b:* Tuxedo, NY; *m:* Gerard R.; *c:* Christopher, Mary, Anne; *ed:* SUNY at Albany (BA) Span 1970; Iona Coll (MSEd) Span, Ed 1975; *cr:* J.A. Farley MS Span Tchr 1972-83; North Rockland HS Span Tchr 1970-72, 1983-; *ai:* Class of 1999, Stu Against Animal Violations & Exploitations Adv; NYSAFLT 1970-, Bd of Dir & Historian; PETA, Natl Wildlife Fed, Wilderness Soc, Nature Conservancy & World Wildlife Fed 1983-; Amer Indian Relief Cncl 1984-; *office:* North Rockland HS Hammond Rd Thiells NY 10984*

WILSON, MARIANNE NIEHOLD, Music Teacher; *b:* Jersey City, NJ; *m:* David; *c:* Robert, David; *ed:* Jersey City St Coll (BA) Music Performance, Ed 1981, (MA) Music His 1983; *cr:* Woodbridge Twp Schl Dist Music Tchr 1982-; *ai:* Concert Choir; Sr Play Voc Dir; Iselin MS String Orch; NJEA, WTEA 1982-; St Joseph's Church 1995-, Choir; *office:* John F Kennedy Memorial HS Washington Ave Iselin NJ 08830

WILSON, MARILYN BUCKLEY, 6th Grade Teacher; *b:* Plattsburgh, NY; *c:* Erin Michelle Helm, Nathan; *ed:* SUNY at Plattsburgh (BS) Elem Ed 1968, (MS) Elem Ed 1973; 15 In-Svc Credit Hrs; *cr:* Peru Cntrl Schl Grd 3 Tchr 1968-79; Grd 4 Tchr 1979-91, Grd 6 Tchr 1991-; *ai:* Play Cast, Chorus; Yrbk Adv 1994-; Natl His Day Contest Adv; NEA 1976-, Rep, VP; NEA, Natl Del 1991-, St Del 1985-; Peru Assn of Tchrs, Negotiating Team 1991-, VP 1994-; Peru Theater Club 1992, 1995; St Augustine's Liturgy Group 1993-; St Augustine's Church, Lector; Article Pub; Grants Written & Attained; *home:* PO Box 226 Peru NY 12972

WILSON, MARK CHRISTOPHER, Ninth Grade Teacher; *b:* Southbridge, MA; *ed:* Wesleyan Univ (BA) Pol Sci 1984; Tufts Univ (MAT) His 1990; *cr:* Tantasqua Tchr 1984-; *ai:* Stu Advy Coord; George F Mozley Prize for Promotion of Intnl Affairs; *office:* Tantasqua Regnl HS 319 Brookfield Rd Fiskdale MA 01518*

WILSON, MARVIN RUSSELL, Prof of Biblical & Thlgcl Stud; *b:* Stoneham, MA; *m:* Pauline Berfield; *c:* Tassa Rose; *ed:* Wheaton (BA) His 1957; Gordon Conwell Theological Seminary (MDIV) Theological Stud 1960; Brandeis Univ (MA) Mediterranean Stud 1961, (PHD) Mediterranean Stud19 63; *cr:* Barrington Coll Prof of Old Testament 1963-71; Gordon Coll Prof of Biblical, Theological Stud 1971-; *ai:* Fac Senate; Soc of Biblical Lit 1966-; Evangelical Theological Soc 1959-; Inst for Biblical Rsrch 1987-; Author Coptic Future Tenses, Our Father Abraham, Jewish Roots of the Christian Faith; Co-Editor Evangelicals and Jews in Conversation, Evangelicals and Jews in an Age of Pluralism, A Time to Speak, The Evangelical Jewish Encounter; *office:* Gordon Coll 255 Grapevine Rd Wenham MA 01984

WILSON, MARY K. (ROHMAN), Gifted Program Teacher; *b:* Dayton, OH; *m:* Eugene B.; *c:* Marie T. Evans, Kathleen M. Larimer; *ed:* Miami Univ (BS) Elem Ed 1964; Wright St Univ (MS) Gifted Ed 1982; 15 Addl Hrs Including Counseling of Gifted, Media, Math, Sci; *cr:* Southeastern Schls 2nd Grd Tchr 1961-62; Beavercreek Schls 1st & 2nd Grd Tchr 1962-64, 1959-61; St Marys Schl Panama Canal Zone 1st, 4th Grd Tchr 1978-79; Beavercreek Schls 2nd Grd Tchr, Tchr of Gifted 1982-83; Sugarcreek Schls 5th-6th Grd Tchr, Tchr of Gifted 1983-; *ai:* Staff Dev Comm; Intervention Assistance Team; Talents Unlimited Certified Trainer; NEA, OEA; Sugarcreek Ed Assn 1983-, Treas, Outstanding Treas; Phi Delta Kappa 1982-; Tchng Asst Fellowship; Kappa Delta Pi Honorary; Martha Holden Jennings Schlsp; *office:* Sugarcreek Local Schls 60 E South St Bellbrook OH 45305*

WILSON, MARY VAUGHN, Math, Science & Religion Tchr; *b:* Cambridge, MA; *m:* Robert D.; *c:* Richard, Katy, Paul, Suzanne; *ed:* Boston St Coll (BS) Elem Ed 1965; Stud in Religion; *cr:* City of Boston Grd 6 Tchr 1965-66, 7th-8th Grd Math Tchr 1966-67; Sacred Heart Schl Grd 6 Tchr 1985-; *ai:* Archdiocese of Boston Schl Acculation & Visiting Team 1993, 1994, 1995; NCEA 1986-; St Ann's CYO 1990-, Adult Adv; *office:* Sacred Heart Schl 340 Hancock St Quincy MA 02171

WILSON, RICHARD EDWARD, 7th & 8th Grd Soc Studies Tchr; *b:* Brunswick, ME; *m:* Cheryl A. Sleeper; *ed:* Univ of ME at Farmington (BS) Scndry Ed Soc Sci 1988; 21 Addl Grad Credits Environmental & Ag His; *cr:* SAD #50 7 & 8 Grd Soc Stud Tchr 1988-91; Brunswick Jr HS 7 & 8 Grd Soc Stud Tchr 1991-; *ai:* Jr High Girls Bsktbl, Var Girls Soccer Asst Coach; Jr Var Girls, Intramurial Indoor Soccer Coach; Academically Talented Stu Comm; Stu Tchr Adv Bowdoin Coll Stdnts; ME Cncl for Soc Stud 1989-; ME Geography Alliance 1991-, Tchr Consultant; NCSS 1991-; Brunswick Topsham Land Trust 1994-, Bd of Dir; Accepted from ME into Natl Geographic Socs 1993 Summer Geography Inst; Tchr, Consultant, Presenter ME Geographic Alliance; Brunswick Ag His Articles Pub Local Paper; Dedicated in Yrbk 1990; *home:* 171 Brackett Rd Brunswick ME 04011*

WILSON, RICHARD LEE, Language Arts Teacher; *b:* Zanesville, OH; *c:* Adam (DEC), Brian (DEC), Craig (DEC); *ed:* OH Univ (BS) Eng 1974, (MED) Educl Admin 1994; Prin Cert MS & HS 1994-95; *cr:* Roosevelt MS Lang Arts Tchr 1974-; *ai:* Act Mgr; NEA, OEA, EOTA, ZEA 1974-, Bldg Rep; Big Brothers, Big Sisters 1993-; Lions Club 1991-; Jennings Scholar 1979; *home:* PO Box 2397 Zanesville OH 43702

WILSON, RITA MARIE (NOLAN), Third Grade Teacher; *b:* Celina, OH; *m:* Thomas L.; *c:* Starla Marie Ross, Stephanie Irene Shutt; *ed:* Wright St Univ (BA) Ed 1971; *cr:* Spencerville Elem Schl 2nd-3rd Grd Tchr 1967-71; Elida Elem Schl Kndgtn, 3rd Grd Tchr 1978-; *ai:* NEA 1967-71, 1978-; *office:* Elida Elem Schl 300 Pioneer Rd Elida OH 45807

WILSON, ROBERT B., Social Studies Teacher; *b:* Framingham, MA; *m:* Elaine Grehoski; *c:* Christina, Cody Michael; *ed:* Boston Univ (AB) His 1965, (ME) Scndry Ed 1966; PHD Coursework Completed; *cr:* Holliston Pub Schls Tchr 1966-; *ai:* Coach Mock Trial Team; Amnesty Intnl Adv; MA Tchrs Assn 1966-74; AFT 1974-; MA Fed of Tchrs; MS Project His Adv; Outstdng Tchr of Yr 1993; MS Curr Coord; *office:* Holliston HS 370 Hollis St Holliston MA 01746*

WILSON, ROBERT J., English Teacher; *b:* Niskayuna, NY; *ed:* Iona (BA)Eng, Rel Stud 1974; Fordham (MS) Rel Ed 1978; NYU (MA) Eng 1984; CUNY Grad Ctr PHD Cand Eng; *cr:* Sacred Heart Schl Fifth Grd Tchr 1974-75; Bergen Cath HS Eng Tchr 1975-78; Sacred Heart HS Eng Tchr 1978-83; Suffern HS Eng Tchr 1983-; *ai:* Adv Ginter Club, Talen Show; Selection, Climate, SEED Comms; AFT 1983-; MLA 1985-; Dictionary Soc North Amer 1986-, Life Mem; Intnl Linguistic Assn 1986-; NCTE 1988-; Yonkers Historical Soc 1991-, Trustee; NAACP 1986-, Life Mem; Articles, Letters Pub; Papers Read Confs; Grant NEH Summer Session 1987; Harvard Univ Schl of Ed Grant 1993 Civil Responsibility, Multiculturalism; *home:* 56 Bon Aire Cir # D-9 Suffern NY 10901*

WILSON, ROBERT WESLEY, Mathematics & Physics Teacher; *b:* Windber, PA; *m:* Sandra Theresa Rzeszut; *c:* Juleen, Jonetta, Eric, Brian; *ed:* OH Univ (AS) Comp Sci & Bus 1984; Marshall Univ (BA) Math & Physics 1988; *office:* Pennview Christian Acad PO Box 970 Penns Creek PA 17862

WILSON, RODGE FLOYD, Science Teacher; *b:* Tiffin, OH; *m:* Cherri Ann Sinnes; *c:* Hannah Leigh, Eva Christine, Evan Joseph Edward; *ed:* Otterbein Coll (BS) Math, Bio 1989; Stud in Amer Sign Lang, Cooperative Ed in Math Classroom; *cr:* Western Reserve HS Math & Sci Tchr 1989-; *ai:* Stu Cncl Adv; WR Tchrs Assn, OEA, SECO, NEA, NCTM 1989-; *office:* Western Reserve HS 3841 US Rte 20 E Collins OH 44826

WILSON, SCOTT WILLIAM, History Teacher; *b:* Euclid, OH; *ed:* Baldwin-Wallace Coll (BA) Psych & His 1981; Cleveland St Univ (MA) Ed Admin 1992; Prin Cert; Stud in Assertive Discipline, Tchr Expectations & Stu Achvmt Trng; *cr:* Euclid City Schls Tchr & Coach 1986-; *ai:* Cross Cntry, Bsktbl & Track Coach; Euclid Tchr Assn 1986-; Chagrin Vly Assembly 1988-; *office:* Central Middle Schl 20701 Euclid Ave Euclid OH 44117

WILSON, SHARON M., Spanish & English Teacher; *b:* Lewistown, PA; *m:* Daniel P.; *c:* Amanda; *ed:* (BS) Span 1972; Post Grad Work PA St Univ, Shippewnsburg Univ; *cr:* Chief Logan HS Span Tchr 1982-87; Indian Vly HS Span, Eng Tchr 1987-; *ai:* Sr Project Comm; Span Club; Former Adv 10 Yrs; NEA, PSEA, AMCE 1982-; White Mem United Chur Christ 1961-, Choir, SS Tchr,BB Tchr, Deaconess; Who's Who A Stdnts in Amer Colls, Univs; *office:* Indian Valley HS 700 Ced Lewistown PA 17044

WILSON, STEVEN LYNN, Soc Studies & English Teacher; *b:* Alt PA; *m:* Janie Kaye Jackson; *c:* Janee, Lindsey, Kaylin; *ed:* Pur Master Cathechists Degree Altoona-Johnstown Diocese; *cr:* St Joh Evangelist Schl Tchr 1978-; *ai:* Instrl Bsktbl Coach; Vllybl C Celebrate Diversity Coord; Eucharistic Minister; NCEA 1978-; Outs Tchr Awd Altoona-Johnstown Diocese 1990-91; *office:* St John Evan Schl 311 Lotz Ave Lakemont Altoona PA 16602

WILSON, TERESA SCHMITT, French Teacher; *b:* Washington, D William G.; *c:* William Justin; *ed:* Univ of MD (BA) Fr 1972; Univ o (MED) Frgn Lang Ed 1974; 30 Post-Grad Stud; *cr:* Nicholas Orem J Frgn Lang Tchr 1975-80; Governor Thomas Johnson HS Fr Tchr 1982 Fr Club Adv; It's Academic Team Coach; ACTFL 1987-; NFLA 1980-, NEA 1975-; AATF 1992-; Alliance Francaise 1988-; NEH Flwshp Post Tchng Grant; *office:* Governor Thomas Johnson HS 1501 N Mar Frederick MD 21701*

WILSON, THOMAS H., Professor of Mathematics; *b:* Dayton, OH Wittenberg Univ (BA) Math 1969; Northwestern Univ (MAT) Ed Stanford Univ (MA) Math Ed 1975; *cr:* Glenbard East HS Math 1969-74; Miami Valley Schl Math Tchr 1975-81; NCR Corp Curr Analyst 1981-85; Sinclair Comm Coll Math Prof 1985-; *ai:* Intr Comm; Coord Stdnts Leadership Dev Prgm; AMATYC 1988-; Allianc Ed 1988-, Wright Correction Acad Adv; Westminster Presbyn Ch 1981-, Elder; AFS 1977-, Chm Schlsp Comm; Participant Leade Dayton 1992-93; *office:* Sinclair Community College 444 W 3rd St Da OH 45402

WILSON, THOMAS LEE, Sr High School Guidance Cnslr; *b:* Ca OH; *c:* Seth, Drew; *ed:* Kent St Univ (BS) Ed 1968, (MED) Guid & C 1972; OH St (PHD) Curr & Instruction 1980; *cr:* McKinley HS 1966-71; Timken Voc HS Tchr 1972-75; McKinley Sr HS Tchr 197 Tchr & Guid Cnslr 1980-83; Timken Sr HS Guid Cnslr 1977-78; *ai:* Y Yth Bsktbl Coach; Study Group with Fellow Cnslr; Supt Reorganiz Comm; CPEA 1969-, Canton Prof Ed Bldg Rep; NEA; Fac Adv Comm Rep; OEA; Lib Comm Rep 1980-83; North Canton YMCA 1989-, Yth & Bsktbl Coach; NHS; Military Coord; Sci Dept Chm; Commence Speaker 1979 & 1980; Cronshaw Jr HS Commencement Speaker 1 Outstdng Dissertation Nom; Sci Tchr of Yr Nom; North Cntl Chm *office:* Mc Kinley Sr HS 2323 17th St NW Canton OH 44708

WILSON, TINA MICHELE, 5th Grade Teacher; *b:* Syracuse, NY; SUNY at Alfred (AAS) Med Assisting; Potsdam Univ (BA) N-6 Ed, 7-9 Ext 1989; St Lawrence Univ (MS) Ed 1993, (MS) Pub Schl Admin *cr:* Potsdam Cntrl Schl 6th Grd Sci Tchr 1989-91, 5th Grd Tchr 1991- Potsdan Bd of Ed Facilitaor; Mentor Intern New Tchr Prgm Coord; MS Assn 1992-; Big Brother-Big Sister Prgm 1988-, Big Sister; Abroad 1989; Reynold's Excl in Ed 1992; *office:* Potsdam MS O Lawrence Ave Potsdam NY 13676*

WILSON, VIOLA WASHINGTON, Instructional Resource Teache Columbia, SC; *m:* Ulysses L.; *c:* Theresa Durham, Marjorie Tur Alfreda Thomas; *ed:* Barger Scotio Coll (BA) Elem Ed 1956; IN Univ Ed Psych 1967; Charles Cty Comm Coll Field Ecology 1976 6 Hrs; of MD ConsumerEd 1976 3 Hrs; Western MD Coll Project Teach & P 1986 6 Hrs; Cath Univ Increasing Effective Writing 1986 6 Hrs; Hopkins Elem Schl Rdng Tchr 1969-71; DUD Elem Ed Tchr 1971 Foulois Jr HS Soc Stud Tchr 1975-78; Yale Univ Orientation in Co Process 1985-; Flintstone Elem Schl Instrl Resource Tchr 1978-; *ai:* Chprsn 9 Yrs; PTA Liason; Math & Sci Inservice for Tchrs & Parents; Cncl Adv; Organized Schl Black His; Natl Tchrs Assn 1974-; NEA To 1975-; Iota Gamma Chptr AKA 1987-; NAACP 1971-; Pace Set Charities 1975-, Sec; Sunday Club 1975-; Christa MC Auliffe Outst Tchr Awd 1993; Berkshire Elem Schl Outstdnt Tchr.

WILSON, VIRGINIA P., Health & Physical Ed Teacher; *b:* New Brigh PA; *ed:* IN Univ of PA (BS) Hlth & PE 1986; West Chester Univ of (MS) Ed 1991; *cr:* Manheim Twp HS Hlth & PE Tchr 1986-; *ai:* Head Sftbl, Frosh Girls Bsktbl Coach; Manheim Twp Ed Assn, PA St Ed A NEA 1986-; *office:* Manheim Twp HS Box 5134 School Rd Lancaster 17601

WILSON JONES, MOLLIE, Instrumental Director; *b:* Bethesda, MD Gary Valentine; *ed:* PA St Univ (BS) Music Ed 1974; Post Grad S Humanistic Ed Marywood Coll; *cr:* Pennridge Sch Dist Orchestra 1974-75; Delaware Vly Schl Dist Instrumental Dir 1975-; *ai:* NEA 19 AFM 1980-, Bd of Trustees; The Episcopal Diocese of NY Prope Support Comm 1992-; Matamoras Planning Commission 1990-, Chp Episcopal Church 1990-, Eucharistic Minister; *office:* Delaware Valley HC 77 Box 379c Milford PA 18337

WILSON MASHAW, NANCY, Kindergarten Teacher; *b:* Ogdensb NY; *m:* Mark T.; *c:* Zachary, April; *ed:* Pittsburg St Univ (BS) Elem 1988; SUNY at Potsdam (MS) Rdng K-12 1989; *cr:* Heuvelton Cntrl S 6th Grd Tchr 1989-91, Kndgtn Tchr 1991-; *ai:* Encore Drama Club A *office:* Heuvelton Central Schl Washington St Heuvelton NY 13654*

WILT, ROSEANNE (HAMER), Art Education Teacher; *b:* Pittsbur PA; *m:* John Edward; *c:* Ashley Lynn, Carleigh Ann; *ed:* Edinboro U (BS) Art Ed 1977; Grad Courses Masters Equivalency 1995; *cr:* Keyst Cntrl Schl Dist K-12th Grd Art Tchr 1980-; *ai:* Yrbk, Sr & Jr HS Art Cl 9th & 10th Grd Adv; NAEA, PAEA; PSEA 1980-; Clinton Cty Arts C VP; *office:* Bald Eagle Nittany HS 200 Ben Ave Mill Hall PA 17751

WILTSHIRE, BERNADETTE, Mathematics Dept Chprsn & Tchr; Pompton Plains, NJ; *ed:* Montclair St Coll (BA) Math 1977; *cr:* St Cecil HS Math Tchr 1977-78; DePaul HS Math Tchr & Chprsn 1978-; *ai:* N Adv; Jr Var & Var Ftbl & Bsktbl Cheering Moderator; NCTM; Diocese Paterson Tchr of Yr Awd 1987; Dawn DeStefano Honoraruim Awd 19 *office:* DePaul Diocesan HS 1512 Alps Rd Wayne NJ 07470

WILUSZ, EDWARD JOSEPH, CAD & Drafting Teacher; *b:* Manches NH; *c:* Jennifer, Timothy; *ed:* NH Voc-Tech Coll (AS) Electro-Mech, T 1970-; Keene St (BS) Industrial, Comp Ed 1974; *cr:* Donovan Eng Draftsman 1968-70; Sanders Assocs Designer 1970-73; Salem HS T 1974-; *ai:* US First Robotics Competition Adv; Salem Educl Assn; NEA 1985-; *office:* Salem HS 44 Geremonty Dr Salem NH 03079

WILUSZ, KAY MARIE, Art Teacher; *b:* Toledo, OH; *m:* W. Tho Bryan; *c:* Kazzien, Zefiryn; *ed:* Bowling Green St Univ (BFA) Art, Cra 1976, (MA) Art Ceramics 1978; 15 Addl Hrs; Overseas Stud Parso Ceramic Prgm Japan; *cr:* Paulding Exempted Village Schls Kndgtn-8th Art Tchr 1976-78; Lincolnview HS 7th-12th Grd Art Tchr 1979-; Wassenberg Art Ctr Ed Comm; Art Act; OH Art Ed Assn 1979-, Regnl Northwest OH Outstdng Art Tchr; OH Ed Assn 1979-; Wassenberg Art 1980-, Comms, Designer Gala Invitations, Prgms; Linna Artspace 198 Art Exhibits; Medici Art Commission; *office:* Lincolnview Jr Sr HS 15 Middle Point Rd Van Wert OH 45891

WIMER, MARTIN B., English Teacher; *b:* Grove City, PA; *m:* Chri Clinger; *c:* Barrett, Benjamin, Hannah; *ed:* Slippery Rock Univ (BS) E Writing 1984; *cr:* Hollidaysburg Jr HS Eng Tchr 1987-; *ai:* Sr HS Bo

:, Sr HS Boys, Girls Cross Cntry Coach; NEA, PSEA, HAEA 1987-; : 34 Scenic Dr Hollidaysburg PA 16648

ER, SHARON ANN, Fifth Grade Teacher; *b:* Havre de Grace, MD; irk D.; *c:* Kristen, Kimberly, Allison; *ed:* Harford Comm Coll (AA) Stud 1976; Towson St Univ (BS) Elem Ed 1978; Loyola Coll 15 Grad it Hrs; *cr:* Halls Cross Rds Elem 5th Grd Tchr 1978-80; Deerfield 4th Grd Tchr 1980-81; Norrisville Elem 5th Grd Tchr 1981-; *ai:* ILA, SBIDM & SOC Comms; Grd Level Chprsn; Cncl of Ministry 1994-, Minister; Candidate for Harford Cty Tchr of Yr 1988; *office:* sville Elem Schl 5302 Norrisville Rd White Hall MD 21161

CEK, PATRICIA DENAULT, HPE Teacher; *b:* Scronton, PA; *m:* ard J.; *c:* Matthew, Amy; *ed:* Penn St (ME) HPE 1980; LIU 18 Hrs; 'restwood HS HPE Tchr 1972-; *ai:* IMs; *office:* Crestwood HS 281 S ntain Blvd Mountain Top PA 18707

CHELL, BARBARA KEERY, 5th Grade Teacher; *b:* Lisburn, N nd; *m:* Alastair F.; *c:* Keith, Rodney; *ed:* SUNY New PLatz (BS) Ed 1972, (MS) Ed K-6 1977; Alcohol, Chem Dependency; Whole Lang; Ed Stdnts Classroom, Math, Effective Tchng Strategies; Cmptr rvice; *cr:* Vly Cntrl Schl Dist 3rd Grd Tchr 1972-73, 2nd Grd Tchr -82, 5th Grd Tchr 1982-; *ai:* AFT, NYSUT 1972-; VCTA 1972-, len Rep; *office:* Walden Elem Schl 75 Orchard St Walden NY 12586*

ICHELL, ELAINE (FOLEY), Band & Elem Instrumental Tchr; *b:* igton, MA; *m:* Scott W.; *c:* Justin; *ed:* Univ of Lowell (BA) Music Ed ; Attnd Boston Coll; *cr:* Hudson Pub Schl Jr Band, Music Tchr 1984; ua Pub Schl HS Band, Music Tchr 1984-87; Billerica Pub Schl HS l, Music Tchr 1988-; *ai:* HS Marching Band; Elem Band; Billerica Fed s 1989-; MENC 1995-; EMBA 1988-; EMBA Champions Div II 1991, , 1994; Citrus Bowl Music Festival Champions 1995; *office:* Billerica orial HS 35 River St Billerica MA 01821

IDISH, ROBERTA M. (REINERT), Mathematics Teacher; *b:* stown, PA; *m:* George; *c:* Todd M., Craig A.; *ed:* Mansfield St Univ Scndry Ed & Math 1973; 24 Credit Hrs Kutztown Univ, 32 Credit Hrs ntown Coll, 6 Credit Hrs Penn St, 9 Credit Hrs East Stroudsburg St ard Masters in Ed; *cr:* Boyertown Area HS Math Tchr 1974-; *ai:* Math n Adv; Math Dept Ldr; NEA, PSEA, BAEA 1974-; NCTM, PCTM ?-; Soroptimists of Upper Perkiomen Valley 1987-90, Past Pres; Upper iomen Valley Little League 1985-95, Asst Coach; Cub Scouts of Amer '-91, Den Ldr, Den Ldr Coach, Cubmaster; BSA 1991-, Troop Treas, it Badge Cnslr; *office:* Boyertown Area Sr HS 500 E 4th St Boyertown 9512

IDLEY, KAREN C., Spanish Teacher; *b:* Newport, RI; *m:* Daniel C.; ephanie, Daniel; *ed:* Salve Regina Univ (BA) Span & Scndry Ed 1972; ddl Hrs Univ of RI; *cr:* South Kingstown HS Span Tchr 1974-95; *ai:*)D, Class Adv; NEA 1974-, NEA-RI 1974-, Sec 2 Yrs, Bldg Rep; 'SP; *home:* 37 Sherman St Newport RI 02840

NDSOR, CHARLENE, English Teacher; *b:* Toledo, OH; *m:* John J.; *c:* stopher, Laura, Ashleigh; *ed:* Univ of Toledo (BE) Scndry Ed 1974,) Scndry Ed 1983; Comm Cert 1988; 34 Addl Credit Hrs in Cnslng; *cr:* rgreen Jr HS Rdng Tchr 1974-77; Evergreen HS Eng, Speech, Jrnlsm r 1977-79; Whitmer HS 9th-12th Grd Eng Comp, Jrnlsm, Yrbk, temp Lit Tchr 1980-; Washington Jr HS Comm Tchr 1985-86; *ai:* Act rd; NEA, OEA 1974-; TAWLS Teach Assn 1980-, Honored Tchr 1984; of Yr 1987; Honored as Influential Tchr by Valedictorian 1990; nor, Co-Author Two Curr Guides; Comms for Producing Levels 7-12 pe & Sequences; *home:* 2824 Scott Ct Genoa OH 43430

NDSOR, KATHY L., Mathematics Teacher; *b:* Chester, PA; *m:* Frank s; *c:* Matthew, Daniel; *ed:* West Chester St (BA) Math 1970; Glassboro MA) Math Ed 1976; *cr:* Washington Twp HS Math Tchr 1970-; *ai:* Math gue Coord; Stu Tchr Supvr; NJEA, WTEA, GCEA 1970-; AMTNJ 5-; Cub Scout 1989-, Den Ldr, Comm Chair; Wash Twp Tchr of Yr 3; Golden Apple Awd Cable Television Network 1994; *office:* shington Twp HS 529 Hurffville-Cross Keys Rd Sewell NJ 08080

NDT, THOMAS J., Professor of English; *b:* Syracuse, NY; *m:* hleen Maginnis; *c:* Jonathan, Rebecca; *ed:* Onondaga Comm Coll (AA) n 1970; Syracuse Univ (AB) Eng 1972; SUNY at Binghamton (MAT) 1974; SUNY at Albany 60 Addl Credits for DA; *cr:* Cayuga Comm l Instr 1974-75; Onondaga Comm Coll Instr 1974-75; Canton Coll of h Prof 1975-95; *ai:* Ski Team Coach; PTK, Outing Club, Weight Trng b Adv; Lit Magazine Ed; Acad Stans, Judicial Bd, Fac Affairs Comms; T, UUP 1975-, Legislative Rep; NCTE 1980-; BSA 1984-, Aquatics r; Girl Scouts of Amer 1990-, Asst Ldr; Lib Bd 1982-88, Pres; Schl Bd 8-93, VP; Articles, Poetry Pub; *office:* S U N Y Coll Of Tech At Canton nton Coll Canton NY 13617*

NE, CATHY A., Home Economist; *b:* Columbus, OH; *ed:* Otterbein l (BA) Home Ec Ed 1974; OH St Univ Vocational Degree Home Ec Ed '4; Muskingum Coll Rdng Cert 1989; *cr:* Circleville Cty Schls Home Tchr 1974-78; Crooksville HS Home Ed, Rdng Tchr 1979-; *ai:* Rdng ervention Instr; Perry Cty Extension Advy Bd 1988-, AIDS Taskforce 3-; St Nicholas Womens Guild 1979-; Consumer Educator of Yr 1986; Univ World Wise Schls Grant; Martha Holden Jennings Scholar; *office:* ooksville HS Schools 4075 Ceramic Way Crooksville OH 43731

NEBRENNER, WIRT SHRIVER,JR., English Teacher; *b:* Hanover, ; *m:* Joan Comly Scarlett; *c:* Anne, Wirt III, Jonathan; *ed:* Yale Univ 3) His 1958; Harvard Law Schl (LLB) 1961; *cr:* Mercersburg Acad Eng r 1965-, Asst Headmaster 1969-76, Dir of Coll Cnslng 1982-88; *ai:* ercersburg News & Marshall Literary Soc Adv; Dormitory Dean; genstein Chair in British Lit; F&M Coll & Univ of Chicago Outstdng ndry Schl Eng Tchr; *office:* The Mercersburg Acad 300 E Seminary St ercersburg PA 17236

INER, JANE M., Prof of Art, Art History & Hum; *b:* Minneapolis, MN; Univ of AZ (BFA) Studio Art 1969, (MFA) Intaglio Printmaking 1971; nd Merrimack Coll, Bennington Coll, Cath Univ, Peabody Conservatory Music, John Hopkins Univ; *cr:* Univ of SC Asst Prof of Art & Art His 76-79; Howard Comm Coll Prof of Art, Art His & Hum 1979-; *ai:* neral Ed Comm; Coll Art Assn; Chamber Music Amer; Resource & slng Ctr of Whitman-Walker 10 Yrs Peer-Rap Ldr; Natl Endowment for m 1977 & 1991; Fulbright Scholar 1983; Natl Endowment for Arts 1974 1975; *office:* Howard Comm Coll 10901 Little Patuxent Pkwy Columbia D 21044

INER, SUSAN HOPE, 6th Grade Science Teacher; *b:* Poughkeepsie, ; *m:* Gerald A.; *c:* Jennifer B., Kimberly S. Weiss; *ed:* SUNY at New ltz (BS) Ed 1964; OH St Univ (MA) Ed 1979; 45 Hrs Beyond MA; *cr:* rewsbury Schls 1st Grd Tchr 1963-64, 6th Grd Sci & Math Tchr 1964-68; olumbus Schl Learning Disabilities Tchr 1974-77; Bexley Schls 6th Grd i Tchr 1977-; *ai:* Schl Theme Comm; Fun Run Chprsn; Project scovery; Project Water; BEA 1977-; OEA 1977-; NEA 1977-; Ort 1972-; adassah 1972-; Temple Sisterhood; Bexley Schls Outstdng Tchr Awd 93; BP Spon 1st Place Ec Awd; *office:* Cassingham Elem 250 S ssingham Rd Bexley OH 43209

INEY, W. FRED H., Science Dept Chairman & Tchr; *b:* Johnstown, PA; Marilynn F.; *ed:* Washington & Jefferson Coll (BA) Bio 1958; Univ of A at Amherst (MA) Zoology 1961; Post Grad Stud Brown Univ, Taft chl, Univ of MA at Dartmouth; *cr:* Univ of MA Tchng Assoc 1958-60; innechug Regnl HS Bio, Phys Tchr 1960-63; Bristol Comm Coll Bio Instr 988-94; Dartmouth HS Sci Dept Chm 1973-, Bio, AP Bio Tchr 1963-; *ai:* Sci Ldrshp Team; Sci Fair Adv, Judge; Curr Comm; Cooperating Tch; Tcher Trng Prgm; NEA; MTA; MA Assn Sci Supv 1988-; Sigma Xi 1960-; Town Meeting Mem 1985-; Preservation Soc New Port Cty 1993-; Fairhaven Historical Soc 1993-, Improvement Assn 1992-; St Josephs Church 1975-, Music Minister, Cantor; Presenter NAST Conf, MA Assn Sci Supvs Conf; *office:* Dartmouth HS 366 Slocum Rd North Dartmouth MA 02747

WINFIELD, CLIFTON ELWOOD, Social Studies Teacher; *b:* Newark, NJ; *ed:* Wyoming (BA) Amer Problems 1979; *ai:* Peer Ldr Coord, Track Coach; NEA 1984-; Big Brothers of Amer; *office:* Elizabeth HS 600 Pearl St Elizabeth NJ 07202*

WING, DEBBIE, Assistant Librarian; *b:* Long Beach, CA; *m:* Michael; *c:* Daniel, Emma; *ed:* Wellesley Coll (BA) Music 1975; Columbia Tchrs Coll (MA) Elem Ed 1978; *cr:* Riverdale Cntry Schl 5th-6th Grd Tchr 1978-88, Dir of Day Care Ctr 1989-, Asst Librn 1996-; Riv Presbyn Church Nursery Schl Asst Tchr 1995; *ai:* Past: Fac Interest Comm, Advy Comm on Fac Employment, Fac Grants Comm, Steering Comm for NYAIS Evaluation, Sci Curr Comm Advy Comm, Curr & Stans Comm, Admissions Interviewer, Swimming Instr After Schl Pgm, Tutoring, Theatre Productions Asst; Current: Dir & Co-Founder of On-Campus Day Care Fac; Riverdale Presbyn Church Nursery Schl 1993-, Bd Treas; RCS Master Tchr Merit Awd; Fac Grant; *office:* Riverdale Country Schl 5250 Fieldston Rd Bronx NY 10471

WING, JUDITH PATTERSON, Art Teacher; *b:* Saranac Lake, NY; *m:* Stuart Michael; *c:* Molly Catherine; *ed:* Northern IL Univ (BSEd) Art Ed & Spec Ed 1980; Wright St Univ (MA) Art Therapy 1984; 8 Credit Hrs Toward Learning Disabilities Cert; *cr:* Thornton Cntrl Schl Art & Spec Ed Tchr 1 Yr; Ashland Schl System Art & Spec Ed Tchr 2 Yrs; Spaulding Youth Ctr Art Therapist & Spec Ed Coord 2 Yrs; Nashua Brookside Hospital Art Therapist 2 Yrs; Wilton-Lyndeborough Cooperative Jr-Sr HS Art Tchr 7 Yrs; *ai:* Class of 2000 Co-Adv; Authentic Assessment Comm; Negotiations Team Mem; Amer Art Therapy Assn 1984-; NEA 1995-; Wilton-Lyndeborough Cooperative Jr-Sr HS Tchr of Yr 1993; *office:* Wilton-Lyndeboro Jr Sr HS 57 School Rd PO Box 255 Wilton NH 03086

WINGATE, JAMES L., Social Studies Teacher; *b:* Troy, NY; *c:* Michelle E., Michael J.; *ed:* SUNY at Albany (BA) His 1966, (MA) Soc Stud 1967; Attnd Univ of MA at Amherst, Univ of OK, Western MI Univ, Syracuse Univ, UT St Univ, Southern IL Univ, Penn St Univ, SUNY at Brockport, SUNY at Potsdam; *cr:* Guilderland HS Soc Stud Tchr 1967-; Syracuse Univ Adj Prof of Sociology 1974-; Guilderland HS Dir of Enrichment 1989-94; *ai:* SADD, Class of 2000 Co-Adv; Tchr-Admin Liaison Comm; Capital Dist Cncl for Soc Stud 1975-; NCSS 1980-; Phi Delta Kappa 1982-; St Vincent's Order of Acolytes 1979-; Awds: Distngd Svc to Ed of Tchrs Awd SUNY at Albany 1984; Outstdng Accomplishment, Svc Guilderland Bd Of Ed 1981, Outstdng SE Edctr of Amer 1975; Flwshps, Grants: NEH Inst War in Pacific 1995, US Dept of Energy, Univ of OK Energy, Pub Policy, Environment 1993-94, NY St Cncl for Hum Inst Quincentary 1992, NEH Flwshp Univ of Cincinnati 1991, Freedom Fnd Flwshp 1990, Taft Flwshp 1989, NSF Juv Del Grant W MI Univ, NSF Demography Grant UT St Univ 1971, COMPUTER BYTES 1994; *home:* 2603 Turner Ave Schenectady NY 12306

WINGER, JOANNE B., Third Grade Teacher; *b:* Harrisburg, PA; *ed:* Messiah Coll (BA) Sacred Music 1965; Millersville (MA) Elem 1968; Inservice Courses All Areas; *cr:* West Shore Schl Tchr 1965-68; Harrisburg Schl Tchr 1968-; *ai:* HEA, PSEA, NEA 1965-; *office:* Marshall Elem Schl 301 Hale Ave Harrisburg PA 17104*

WINGER, TERRI SUE, Music Classroom Teacher; *b:* Grove City, PA; *ed:* Mount Union Coll (BMEd) Music Ed 1977; Youngstown St Univ (MM) Trumpet Performance 1979; ITEC Micro Cmptrs Ed; *cr:* Franklin Area Schl Dist Marching, Pep Band Dir 1982-87; Grove City Coll Adj Prof in Trumpet, Horn, Methods 1982-88; Allegheny Coll Adj Prof in Trumpet 1983-88; Westminster Coll Adj Prof in Trumpet, Methods Course 1988-89; Oil city Schl Dist Band, Classroom Music Dir 1988-; *ai:* Stage, Pep Band Adv; Instrumental Dir Schl Musicals; NEA, PSEA, 1988-, OCAEA 1988-, Treas 1993; PA Music Edctrs Assn, Dist 3 Sec, Treas; Music Edctrs Nat'l Conf; Fanklin Silver Cornet Band 1968-, Bd Dirs, Sec, Asst Dir, 25 Yr Silver Awd; Venango Chamber Orch 1993-; Kennerdell Summer Arts Festival 1989-, Pres; *office:* Oil City Area Schl Dist Grandview Rd Oil City PA 16301

WINGERD, KATHY L., Biology Teacher; *b:* Hagerstown, MD; *ed:* York Hosp Schl of Nrsng (RN) Nrsng 1976; Millersville Univ (BS) Sec Ed, Bio 1981; Masters Equivalency Cert PA 1995; *cr:* York Hosp Registered Nurse 1976-; Wm Penn Sr HS Bio Tchr 1982; Spring Grove Area Sr HS Bio Tchr 1982-; *ai:* Strategic Planning Comm; Stu Assistance Prgm Team; PA St Educl Assn, NEA, Spring Grove Ed Assn 1982-; NABT 1986-; Mt Zion UCC Church Cncl 1993-, Pres 1996, VP 1995; *office:* Spring Grove Area Sr HS Hanover & Jackson Sts Spring Grove PA 17362

WINGERT, ANNA LOUISE (WILLIAMS), Health Occupations Instructor; *b:* Reading, PA; *m:* L. Michael; *c:* Michael Stephen, David Bryan; *ed:* Reading Hosp Schl of Nrsng (RN) Nrsng 1959; Temple Univ Voc I Ed 1990; Continuing Ed Courses Kutztown Univ, Penn St Univ, Reading Area Comm Coll; *cr:* Reading Hosp, Med Ctr Staff Nurse 1960-75; Amer Red Cross Asst Dir Hlth, Safety 1975-78; Dept of Hlth Pub Hlth Nurse 1978-82; Berks Career, Tech Ctr Hlth Occupation Instr 1987-; *ai:* Hlth Occupations Stdnts of Amer Adv; Medic First Aid In-Service Instr; Prof Dev Comm; PA St Ed Assn, NEA 1987-; BSA 1954-, Merit Badge Cnslr, Den Ldr Coach; Amer Red Cross 1954-, Vol, Instr Outstdng Vol of Yr 1983; NHS; *home:* 19 Magnolia Ln Temple PA 19560

WINGERTSAHN-SAVAGE, SUSAN MARY, Chemistry Teacher; *b:* Pittsburgh, PA; *m:* Russell E. Savage Jr.; *c:* Megan, Jake; *ed:* WV Univ (BS) Chem 1983; Xaiver Univ (ME) Educl Admin 1995; *cr:* Chemical Rsrch & Dev Ctr APG Chemist 1983-85; US Army Environmental Hygiene Agency Chemist 1985-87; Indian Hill HS Chem Tchr 1995-; *ai:* Head Boys & Girls Cross Cntry, Track & Field Coach; NTA 1995-; NEA 1995-; OEA 1995-; *office:* Indian Hill HS 6845 Drake Rd Cincinnati OH 45243

WINIARSKI, BENEDICT, Mathematics Teacher; *b:* Holyoke, MA; *m:* Georgena Young; *c:* Peter, Susan Allen, Michael, Paul, Sarah, Mark, Katherine; *ed:* Univ of MA (BA) Math 1964; Wesleyan Univ (MALS) Math 1971; Attnd Cntrl CT St Univ, Fairfield Univ, Westfield St Coll Cmptr Stud, St Thomas Seminary Theology; *cr:* Pulaski HS Math Tchr 1964-69; Simsbury HS Math Tchr 1969-; *ai:* Ath Fac Mgr 1971-73; 1997 Class Adv 3 Yrs; Bsktbl Scorekeeper 1973-; NEA 1964-, Life Mem; CEA 1964-, SEA 1969-, Past Negotiator & Grievance Chair; Sacred Heart Roman Cath Church Hartford Archdiocese Ordained Deacon 1980-; Walker Prison Vol 1992-; *home:* 67 Chestnut Dr West Suffield CT 06093

WINK, EMILY M. (BOHNET), Librarian; *b:* Binghamton, NY; *m:* James T.; *c:* Timothy J. Kibbey, Sandra L. Kibbey Folta; *ed:* St Univ of NY at Albany (BS) Eng Ed 1976, (MLS) Schls Lib; Schenectady Cty Comm Coll; Many Inservice Courses for Discipline & Cmptr Tech at Shenendehowa; *cr:* Broadalbin Cntrl Schl Librn 1978-80; Shenendehowa Cntrl Schl Librn 1980-; *ai:* Tech & Dist Software Comms; Buddy Prgm; Lib Club; Eastern NY Schl Lib Media Assn 1978-; Big Sisters-Big Brothers 1986-87; Former Stu Cncl Adv 6 Yrs; Former Mem of Districtwide Equipment Comm 2 Yrs; PTA Lifetime Membership Awd; *office:* Tesago Elem Schl 970 Route 146 Clifton Park NY 12065

WINKEL, PATRICIA MURPHY, English Teacher; *b:* Pottstown, PA; *m:* Francis J.; *c:* Thomas C., Peter F.; *ed:* Cabrini Coll (BA) Eng 1964; MA Equivalency; *cr:* Owen J. Roberts 4th Grd Tchr 1964-65; Norristown Schls Title I Rdng Tchr 1966-70, Substitute Tchr 1971-79; Norristown HS Eng Tchr 1979-; *ai:* Spon YES; NAHS Stu Service Org; NEA, PSEA, EANA 1979-; Dow Jones Newspaper Fund Fellowship; Art Goes to Schl Commendation; Gift of Time Tribute; *office:* Norristown Area H S 1900 Eagle Dr Norristown PA 19403*

WINKELBAUER, MARY TOELKE, Language Arts & Lit Teacher; *b:* Valparaiso, IN; *m:* Dennis; *c:* Kristy A., Kelly E.; *ed:* Valparaiso Univ (BS) Eng Ed 1976; *cr:* Baltimore Luth HS Eng Tchr 1976-77; Highland HS Eng Tchr 1978-81; St Mark Luth Schl Eng & Rel Tchr 1988-; *ai:* natl Luth Schls Week & Spelling Bee Chm; Advy Bd Mem; OTRS 1979-; LEA 1989-; Medina Cty Joint Voc Schl 1985-, Advy Bd; *home:* 8035 Chippewa Rd Lodi OH 44254

WINKLE, JAMES P., 7th-8th Grd Eng & Rdng Teacher; *b:* New York, NY; *ed:* (BA); *cr:* Good Shepherd 7th & 8th Grd Tchr 10 Yrs; *ai:* Moderator of Good Shephard Swim Club.

WINKLER, JAMES EDWARD, Family Life & Sex Ed Tchr; *b:* Wadsworth, OH; *m:* Jan Ellen Richards; *c:* Jillian; *ed:* Wittenberg Univ (BS) Hlth & PE 1975; Wright St Univ (MA) Schl Cnslng 1986; Post-Grd Hrs in Cnslng; *cr:* Urbana HS Schl Tchr, Cnslr 1975-; *ai:* Boys Soccer Head Coach; Pee Mediation Adv; Sub Abuse Prgm Coord; Steering Comm Tchr In-Svc; West Cntrl Wrestling Ofcl Assn 1995-; Greater Dayton Wrestling Coach's Assn 1975-, Coach of Yr 1992; OH HS Soccer Coach's Assn 1989-; Amer Red Cross 1980-; CPR Instr Lifeguard; Urbana City Schl Cert of Merit 1991; *office:* Urbana HS 500 Washington Ave Urbana OH 43078

WINKLER, JANET L., Spanish Teacher; *b:* Cleveland, OH; *m:* Alan L.; *c:* Dale A., Steven R.; *ed:* Oberlin Coll (AB) Span 1964; Lake Erie Coll (MSEd) Span 1990; Attnd Universidad Complutense at Madrid Spain 1991; *cr:* West Geauga HS Span Tchr 1975-86; Brush HS Span Tchr 1986-89; John Carroll Univ Span Tchr 1989-90; Notre Dame Cathedral Latin Schl Span Tchr 1990-; Lake Erie Coll Span Tchr 1995-; *ai:* Span Club Adv; Acad Challenge Team Co-Moderator; NDEA 1990-; OFLTA; NOTA 1992-; *office:* Notre Dame Cathedrl Latin Schl 13000 Auburn Rd Chardon OH 44024

WINKLER, LINDA A., Bio & Anthropology Assoc Prof; *b:* Columbus, OH; *c:* Marisa, Richard; *ed:* Univ of Pittsburgh (MA) Anthropology 1983, (PHD) Anthropology 1987; Grad Stud Schl of Pub Hlth Univ of Pittsburgh; *cr:* Univ of Pittsburgh Instr 1983-87, Asst Prof 1987-95, Assoc Prof 1995-; *ai:* Fac Senate Rep; Women Together in Renewal Club Adv; Phys Theraphy Asst Prgm Advy Comm; Amer Assn of Phys Anthropology Sts 1981-; Dental Anthropology Assn 1987-, Bd Comm Mem; Sigma Xi the Scientific Rsrch Soc 1983-; Ft Franklin Archaeological Project 1984-; NWPA Synod Comm 1991-; Grants: NSF, LS Bleakey Fnd, Mellon Flwshp; Articles Pub; Edited Volumes; *office:* Univ Of Pittsburgh At Titusvle PO Box 287 Titusville PA 16354

WINKLER, STEVEN ROBERT, Spanish & English Teacher; *b:* Chesterland, OH; *ed:* Univ of Akron (BS) Ed 1992; Post-Grad LaUniversidad Complutense de Madrid, LaUniversidad de Costa Rica; *cr:* Lake Erie Coll Span Instr; Regina HS Span, Eng Tchr 1992-; *ai:* Tech Dir Drama Club; Tech Adv Jrnlsm; Cmptr Consultant; NDEA, OMLTA 1992-; *office:* Regina HS 1857 S Green Rd South Euclid OH 44121

WINN, DENNIS MICHAEL, Assistant Principal; *b:* New Bedford, MA; *m:* Judity V. Augustyn; *c:* Patrick, Victoria, Meredith; *ed:* Univ of MA at Dartmouth (BS) Bus Mngmt 1974; RI Coll (MAT) His 1981; Providence Coll (MED) Elem Admin 1991; Blake Cmptr Programming Inst Cert; *cr:* New Bedford Pub Schls Elem Tchr 1975-90, Cmptr Tchr 1981-, Advanced Learning Tchr 1991-93, Asst Prin 1993-; *ai:* NBEA 1975-, Fac Rep; MTA; NEA; St Vincent de Paul 1978-, Sec; Project SHARE 1995-, Coord; *office:* Hayden-Mc Fadden Elem Schl 361 Cedar Grove St New Bedford MA 02746

WINN, LAURA L., French Teacher; *b:* Prichard, AL; *m:* Ulysses R.; *c:* Ulysses Matthew; *ed:* Knoxville Coll (BS) Fr 1966; Univ of Pittsburgh (MED) Ed 1982; Curr, Supervision Cert 30 Credits; *cr:* Langley HS Fr Tchr 1969-; *ai:* ACTFL 1990-; AFT 1971-; Langley Tchng Acad Outstdng Tchr Awd 1994; *office:* Langley HS 2940 Sheraden Blvd Pittsburgh PA 15204

WINN, PATRICIA BAKER, 9th Grade Earth Science Tchr; *b:* Rolette, ND; *m:* David Brooke; *ed:* St Lawrence Univ (BS) Bio 1984; SUNY at Brockport (MS) Scndry Sci Ed 1989; 72 Credit Hrs; *cr:* Fairport HS Bio & Chem Tchr 1984-88; Martha Brown Jr HS Life & Earth Sci Tchr 1988-89; Minerva Deland Schl Earth Sci Tchr 1989-, Dept Ld Tchr 1994-; Johanna Perrin MS 8th Grd IPS 1992-93; *ai:* Class Adv; Core Team; Bsktbl, Track Coach; CWS STANYS 1985-; St Lukes Episcopal Church 1986-; *office:* Fairport Central Schls 140 Hulbert Rd Fairport NY 14450*

WINNICKI, CHERIE KLINE, Mathematics Teacher; *b:* Grand Rapids, MI; *m:* Robert T.; *c:* Robert S., Anastasia; *ed:* Wayne St Univ (BA) Math 1969, (MED) Math 1972; Working on PHD Math Ed; 21 Credit Hrs Syracuse Univ; *cr:* Liverpool HS 9th & 10th Grd Math Tchr 1969-72; 9th & 10th Grd Math Tchr 1973-74; Zogg MS 6th Grd Math Tchr 1972-73; Driver MS 7th & 8th Grd Math Tchr 1985-88; Eagle Hill MS 7th Grd Math Tchr 1989-94; Marcellus HS 9th-12th Grd Math Tchr & Dept Chprsn 1994-; *ai:* SADD, Stu Govt & Stu Newspaper Adv; Annual Math Contest & Math Club Coord; Compact for Learning Dist Comm; Math Curr Team; Dept Chprsn; NYSUT 1988-; MFA 1988-, VP 1995 & 1996; OCTMA 1988-; MTRC 3 1993-; SUPER 1994-; NSF Funded MTRC 3 Participant; Onondaga Comm Coll Conf Presenter 1994 & 1995; NCTM Conf Presenter 1995; *office:* Marcellus Sr HS 1 Mustang Hl Marcellus NY 13108*

WINN-RITZENBERG, MARK OLIN, English Second Lang Teacher; *b:* New Orleans, LA; *m:* Katherine M.; *c:* Leah, Noah; *ed:* Antioch Coll (BA) Ec 1979; 18 Grad Credit Hrs Georgetown Univ; 15 Credit Hrs Univ of DC; 15 Grad Credit Hrs Trinity Coll; *cr:* Delgado Comm Coll ESL Tchr 1981-83; Alice Deal Jr HS ESL Tchr 1983-; *ai:* Recycling Club Spon; Chess Team Coach; United Way, United Black Fund Keyperson; Machar Congregation for Humanistic Judaism 1993-, Bd Mem; Bicycle Recycle 1995-, Charity Founder; Tchr to Tchr Grant; *office:* Alice Deal Jr HS Ft Dr & Nebraska Ave NW Washington DC 20016

WINOGRAD, HELENE, Art Teacher; *b:* Brooklyn, NY; *m:* Ivan; *c:* Craig, Jaime Manenti; *ed:* Brooklyn Coll (BA) Art Ed 1964; Adelphi Univ (MA) Art Ed 1972; 60 Addl Hrs; *cr:* Glendale Jr HS Art Tchr 1964-66; Mc Arthur HS Art Tchr 1971-72; Cntrl Islip Sr HS Art Tchr 1972-; *ai:* Jr Class Adv; NYSATA 1980-; AFT, CITA 1972-; Cntrl Islip Historical Soc Comm Svc Awd 1995; Jr Class Dedication Ring Ceremony 1995; *office:* Cntrl Islip Pub Schl 85 Wheeler Rd Central Islip NY 11722

WINSHIP, MICHELLE MARIE, Third Grade Teacher; *b:* Salamanaca, NY; *ed:* St John Fisher Coll (BA) Psych 1991; Nazarath Coll (MS) Spec Ed 1996; *cr:* Rochester City Schl #6 Kndgtn Tchr 1994-95; Chester E. Dewey Schl #14 3rd Grd Tchr 1995-; *ai:* Disciplinary Advy Bd; Parent Involvement Comm; Schl Based Planning Team; NAEYC, AFT, ANYSEED 1994.*

WINSLOW, DOUGLAS LEE, World Cultures Teacher; *b:* Lock Haven, PA; *m:* Cathy Harvey; *c:* Matthew Mc Dermit, Andrew Mc Dermit, Erin Mc Dermit; *ed:* Lock Haven Univ (BS) Soc Sci 1977; 24 Addl Credit Hrs Lbrl Arts Prgm; 12 Addl Credit Hrs Penn St Univ Scndry Guid; *cr:* Lock Haven

HS US His Tchr 1985-88; Bald Eagle-Nittany HS World Cultures Tchr 1988-; *ai:* Soc Stud Dept Bldg Prgm Ldr; Sick Leave Bank Bd of Dir Chm; Assn of Clinton Cty Edtrs Bldg Rep; Phi Delta Kappa 1992-; NEA PSEA 1985-, Bldg Rep; Howard Area Lions Club 1980-, Fin Sec; Clinton Cty Arts Cncl 1990-, Sec; *office:* Bald Eagle-Nittany HS 200 Ben Ave Mill Hall PA 17751*

WINSPER, W. DAVID, Prof of Eng & Dept Chprsn; *b:* New Bedford, MA; *m:* Debra Gay Pinucci; *ed:* Vassar Coll (BA) Eng 1975; Univ of MA at Amherst (MA) Eng 1979; Attnd Northeastern Univ; *cr:* Springfield Tech Comm Coll Eng Prof 1979-, Eng Dept Chair 1986-; Amer Intnl Coll Eng Prof 1981-82; *ai:* Hnrs Pgm Stu Adv; Acad Affairs Comm Mem; Title 3 Advy Team; Advising Steering Comm; NEA 1979-; MA Tchrs Assn 1979-; NCTE 1981-; Book: Learning Through Writing: A Campus Sourcebook 1987; Adj Fac Trng Project STCC Fndtn Grant 1993; *office:* Springfield Tech Comm Coll 1 Armory Sq Springfield MA 01101*

WINSTON, MARIA T., French, German Tchr & Dept Hd; *b:* Budapest, Hungary; *m:* Alan; *c:* Molly; *ed:* Elmira Coll (BA) Modern Lang 1971, (MS) Ed 1973; Attnd Cornell Univ, Western WA Univ, Coll of New Paltz; *cr:* Elmira City Schls Tchr, Dept Head 1971-; *ai:* Lang Club; NYSFLT, AATG 1975-; CASA Bd 1991-, Sec, Vol of Yr; *office:* Southside HS 777 S Main St Elmira NY 14904*

WINSTON, PATRICK HENRY, Art Professor; *b:* Portland, ME; *m:* Karen Mc Keone; *ed:* Univ of Miami (BFA) Painting, Sculpture 1973; Temple Univ (MED) Art Ed 1985; Schl of Visual Arts (MFA) Painting 1989; Attnd St Martin's Schl of Art; *cr:* Antonelli Inst of Art Prof 1984-86; Drexel Unvi Art Prof 1993-95; Montgomery Cty Coll Art Prof 1989-; *ai:* Selected Prof Exhibitions Museum of Fine Arts, Allentown Art Museum, St Museum of PA, NJ Ctr of Contemporary Arts, Chrysler Art Museum, San Fran Art Inst, Acad of Arts, Michner Art Museum, Visual Arts Gallery, Woodmere Art Museum, DeCordova Museum, Hoyt Inst Fine Arts; *office:* Montgomery County Comm Coll 340 Dekalb Pike Blue Bell PA 19422*

WINTER, ANNE KELLY, First Grade Teacher; *b:* Pittsfield, MA; *m:* John Martin; *c:* Jennifer, Alison; *ed:* Coll of Our Lady of the Elms (BA) Sociology 1964; Working Toward Masters Coll of New Rochelle; *cr:* Dawes Schl Grd 1 Tchr 1964-67; North Street Schl Grd 1 Tchr 1967-69; Sts John & Paul Schl Grd 1 Tchr 1983-; *ai:* 1st Grd Rdng Olympiad; Cultural Act Spon; Fed of Cath Tchrs 1983-, Schl Rep; NCEA 1983-; Natl Heart Assn, CPR Awd; Pub Big Book Written by 1st Graders; Co-Facilitated Math Their Way Wkshp; Wright Group Whole Lang Prgm, Childe Abuse Wkshp, Getting Started Writing in the Early Yrs, Dev Math Processes Attendee; *office:* Sts John & Paul Schl 280 Weaver St Larchmont NY 10538*

WINTERBERG, JAMES JOSEPH, 6th Grade Teacher; *b:* Cumberland, MD; *m:* Sandra Kay Snyder; *c:* Shawn, Guy; *ed:* Frostburg Univ (BS) Elem Ed 1967, (MA) Admin & Supervision 1972; *cr:* Frederick Cty Elem 6th Grd Tchr 1967-68; Allegany Cty Elem 5th & 6th Grd Tchr 1968-84; Allegany Cty MS 6th Grd Tchr 1985-; *ai:* Audio Visual Chair; Lib Cty Comm; All Cty Tchr Assn 1968-, Schl Rep; MD St Tchrs Assn 1968-; NEA 1973-; Red Cross Blood Bank 1967-, Multi Gal Donor; MD Hunter Safety Inst 1975-, Sr Instr; BSA 1991-, Advy Bd; Chesapeake Bay Fndtn Grants; *office:* Braddock MS 909 Holland St Cumberland MD 21502

WINTERBOTTOM, MICHELE E., Science Teacher; *b:* Phila, PA; *m:* Harry Thomas; *c:* Elizabeth, Lynne, Allyson; *ed:* Eastern Coll (BS) Bio, Scndry Ed 1976; *cr:* Cedar Grove Chrstn Acad Sci Tchr 1976-94; Cedar Grove Chrstn HS Sci Tchr 1994-; *ai:* Pep Squad, Mentor Spon; Brigantine Bible Church 1989-; *office:* Cedar Grove Christian HS 413 E Tabor Rd Philadelphia PA 19120

WINTERS, BARBARA KEEPING, English Teacher; *b:* Newburgh, NY; *m:* David; *c:* Shawn, Erin; *ed:* SUNY at New Paltz (BA) Eng, Speech 1969; 30 Grad Credits Eng, Ed NY St Permanent Life Cert 1972; *cr:* Wallkill HS Eng, Speech Tchr 1969-85; Ulster Cty Comm Coll Eng Instr, Part-time Adj Fac 1980-85; Marlboro HS Eng Tchr 1985-; *ai:* Modena Rescue Squad 1973-, Asst Commander 1 Yr; BSA Den Mother 2 Yrs; Wallkill Little League Bd of Dirs 1985-88; *office:* Marlboro HS 50 Cross Rd Marlboro NY 12542

WINTERS, BILL, Social Studies Teacher; *b:* Brooklyn, NY; *m:* Joyce Morgan; *c:* Asa, Meredith; *ed:* Waynesburg Coll (BS) His, Ed 1972; 18 Hrs Spec Ed; Stu Asst, Crisis Intervention Trng; 4 Mat Trng; *cr:* Wbg HS Soc Stu, Dean, Coach 18 Yrs; Wbg Coll Ed Dept Instr 1996; *ai:* Lettermans Club Spon; Dean; Stu Asst Team; Former 4 MAT Trainer; NEA 1978-; *office:* Waynesburg Central HS RR 2 Box 39A Waynesburg PA 15370

WINTERS, DOLORES LEIS, Choral Director; *b:* Spencerville, OH; *m:* Thomas Bernarr; *ed:* OH St Univ (BS) Music 1970; Grad Hrs Univ of Cincinnati, Univ of MI, Univ of IN; *cr:* Marysville Exempted Schl Dist Music Edctr 1968-; *ai:* Swingers Unlimited Dir; Amer Choral Dirs, MENC, NEA, OEA, MEA 1968-; OMEA 1968-, Dist XI Pres; Delta Kappa Gamma 1972-; Chamber of Commerce Good Citizenship Awd; Tchr of Yr 2 Times; *home:* 20267 State Route 347 Raymond OH 43067

WINTERS, ELIZABETH, Italian Teacher; *b:* Jersey City, NJ; *m:* Thomas Joseph; *c:* Thomas Michael; *ed:* Rutgers Univ (MAT) Italian, (MED) Biling & Bicultural Ed; Attnd Gonzaga-in-Florence Italy, L Universita Per Stranieri; *cr:* Antwerp Intnl Schl Elem Tchr 1979; East Brusnwick Schls ESL Tchr 1984-90, Italian Tchr 1991-; *ai:* NJEA 1986-; TESOL 1986-90; *office:* Churchill Jr HS Rues Ln Univ & Norton Rd East Brunswick NJ 08816

WINTERS, LORI ANN (ENGLE), Choral Dir & Music Dept Chprsn; *b:* Baltimore, MD; *m:* Herman Harrison; *c:* Ann Elizabeth (dec), Nathan Harrison, Andrew William; *ed:* Frostburg St Univ (BS) Music Ed, Piano Performance 1982; Working Towards Masters in Music Prgm Shenandoah Univ; Villanova Univ 6 Credit Hrs in Music; Liberty Univ 15 Credit Hrs in Cnslng; 12 Credit Hrs in Music, Spec Ed; *cr:* Braddock Jr HS Gen Music Tchr 1983-84; Vly HS Choral Dir 1984-86; Barton Elem Gen Music Tchr 1989-93; Cresaptown Elem Schl Gen Music Tchr 1989-93; Westernpo rt Elem Schl Gen Music Tchr 1989-93; Westmar HS Choral Dir 1994-; *ai:* Show, Sr Choir Dir; Drama Club, Soph Class Adv; Schl Newsletter; Schl Improvement Team Subcommittee; Assoc Cnslr; NEA 1983-; MMEA 1978-85, 1995-, Chaperon 1996, MD All-State Jr Chorus; ACTA 1983-; MENC 1978-85, 1995-; Eckhart United Meth Church, Pianist, Choir; Tchr of Yr Westernport Elem Schl 1992-93; Nom Cty Tchr of Yr 1992-93; Original Music Composer, Arranger; *home:* PO Box 384 20411 Pond Circle Rd Midlothian MD 21543*

WINTERS, RAE-ANN, Fourth Grade Teacher; *b:* Pittsfield, MA; *ed:* Berkshire Comm Coll (AA) Lbrl Arts 1967; Westfield St Coll (BS) Elem Ed 1969; North Adams St Coll (MED) Elem Ed 1976; 51 Addl Credits; *cr:* Center Schl 4th Grd Tchr; Craneville Schl 4th Grd Tchr; *ai:* NEA, MTA 1969-; CBTA 1969-, Sec 4 Yrs, Exec Bd 10 Yrs; Berkshire Cty Women's Bowling Assn 1970-, Pres, VP, Sec, Treas; *office:* Craneville Elem Schl 71 Park Ave Dalton MA 01226

WINTERS, RAPHAELA ELLEN, English Teacher; *b:* Queens, NY; *ed:* St Johns Univ (BA) Sociology Speech 1982; Adelphi Univ (MA) Speech & Theatre 1984; Queens Coll 70 Credits Post Grad Work; *cr:* JHS 237 Eng Tchr 1990-92; John Adams HS Eng Tchr 1993-; *ai:* Lit Fair & Story Telling Contest Coord; Drama Coach; AFT 1989-; *office:* John Adams HS 101-01 Rockaway Blvd Ozone Park NY 11417

WINTERS, THOMAS JOSEPH, Guidance Counselor; *b:* New Brunswick, NJ; *m:* Elizabeth Venutolo; *c:* Thomas Michael; *ed:* Seton Hall Univ (BS) Soc Stud Ed 1971; Montclair St Coll (MA) Stu Prsnl Svc 1976; 4 Credit Hrs Ed Harvard Univ 1985; *cr:* Essex Cath HS Eng Tchr 1972-73; St Peter's HS Eng, Soc Stud Tchr, Guid Intern 1973-76; Morris Knolls HS Soc Stud Tchr, Guid Cnslr 1976-78; Antwerp Intnl Schl Guid Cnslr, Tchr 1978-79; Wall HS Guid Cnslr 1980-; *ai:* Girls Cross Cntry, Indoor, Spring Track Coach; NEA, NJEA, WTEA, Monmouth Cty Guid Assn 1980-; Shore Track Coaches Assn 1982-; USA Track, Field Yth Comm 1989-; NJ Governors Excl Tchg Awd 1988; *home:* 39 Avenue F Jamesburg NJ 08831

WINTERS, VALERIE A., Third Grade Teacher; *b:* Lancaster, PA; *m:* Ronald C.; *ed:* Millersville St Coll (BS) Elem Ed 1963; Credit Hrs; Post Grad Credits; *cr:* Manheim Cntrl Schl Dist Elem Tchr 1963-; *ai:* Mentor; Co-Operating Tchr for Stu Tchrs; MCEA 1963-, Rep Cncl; PSEA; NEA; Manheim Women's Club; *office:* Stiegel Elem Schl 3 S Hazel St Manheim PA 17545

WINTERS, WENDY RUSSELL, Sociology Professor; *b:* Norwalk, CT; *m:* Irving J.; *c:* Allison Glasgow, Roger Glasgow; *ed:* Cntrl CT St Coll (BS) Elem Ed 1952; Columbia Univ Schl of Soc Work (MS) Psychiatric Soc Work 1954; Yale Univ (PHD) Sociology 1975; Harvard Univ Inst Educl Mgmt; *cr:* Yale Child Stu Ctr Rsrch Assoc Chief Soc Workers 1968-75; Univ of CT Schl of Soc Work Assoc Prof & Asst Dean Acad Affairs 1975-78; Smith Coll Dean of Coll 1979-85; Howard Univ Dean of Coll of Lib Arts & Prof Sociology 1994-; *ai:* Black Womens Agenda Bd of Dirs; Undergraduate Sociology Adv; NASW 1954-; ASA 1975-; AERA 1995-; Alpha Kappa Alpha 1984-; Annapolis Yth Svcs Links Inc 1995-, Advy Bd; The Practice of Soc Work in Schls An Ecological Pespective C F Easton; African Amer Mothers & Urban Schls; The Power of Participation; St of MD Governors Citation 1996; *office:* Howard Univ PO Box 987 Washington DC 20059*

WINTERSTEIN, ALECIA M., 8th Grd Language Arts Teacher; *b:* Red Bud, IL; *m:* Charles A.; *c:* Thomas J.; *ed:* Concordia Univ (BA) Elem Ed 1987; Drake Univ 3 Sem Hrs; *cr:* Salem Luth Schl Seventh, Eighth Grd Tchr 1987-91; Trinity Luth Schl Eighth Grd Lang Arts Tchr 1991-; *ai:* Vlybl, Power of Pen Writing Team Coach; Yrbk Comm; LEA 1984-; Article Pub; *office:* Trinity Lutheran Schl 4560 Glendale Ave Toledo OH 43614

WINTERSTEIN, CHRISTINE ANN (PIERSON), Sixth Grade Teacher; *b:* Endicott, NY; *m:* Joseph H.; *c:* Patti Jo, Julie Ann; *ed:* SUNY at Cortland (BA) N-6th Elem Ed 1968; SUNY at Binghamton 35 Post Grad Hrs; BOCES & In-Svc Trng 30 Hrs; *cr:* Willow Point Elem Schl 1st & 4th Grd Tchr 1968-78; Vestal Hills Elem Schl 2nd & 6th Grd Tchr 1979-93; Vestal MS 6th Grd Tchr 1993-; *ai:* Whole Lang Steering Comm Co-Chair 1993-94; Bldg Planning Team 1993-95; Tchng Trainer; Vestal Tchrs Assn Collaborative Negotiator; NEA NY & V Tchrs Assn 1968-; BARC 1980-95; Delta Kappa Gamma Soc Intl Beta Rho Chapte of Pi St Org 1995; ASCD 1994-; AMTNYS 1995-; NCTM 1994-; Port Dickinson Comm Assn 1977-, Woman of Yr; *office:* Vestal MS 600 S Benita Blvd Vestal NY 13850*

WINTJE, MARTIN, French, Span Tchr & Dept Chair; *b:* Hudson, NY; *m:* Kim Craig; *ed:* SUNY at Oswego (BA) Ed & Fr 1972; Attnd univ of NH, Middlebury Coll & Sorboune in Paris; *cr:* Spaulding Jr HS Fr Tchr 1977-82; Spaulding HS Fr & Span Tchr 1982-, Dept Chm 1991-; *ai:* Schlsp Comm; Mentor Tchr Prgm; AFT 1977-; *office:* Spaulding H S N Wakefield St Rochester NH 03867*

WINTON, DEBRA L., Reading Specialist; *b:* Sellersville, PA; *m:* Gary J.; *c:* Michael, Chris, Rodd, Melissa, Jonathan; *ed:* Muhlenberg Coll (AB) Psych, Elem Ed 1977; Lehigh Univ (MED) Rdng 1984; *cr:* Pennridge Schl Dist Elem Tchr 1977-92, Rdng Specialist 1992-; *ai:* PSEA, NEA 1977-; IRA 1994-; Bucks Cty Rdng Assn 1994-, Bd; *office:* Sellersville Elem Schl 122 W Ridge Ave Sellersville PA 18960

WIONS, DIANE BERG, Music Teacher; *b:* Bronx, NY; *m:* Joseph; *c:* Danny, Julie; *ed:* Douglass Coll (BA) Music Ed 1973; Trenton St (MA) Music Ed 1976; *cr:* Woodrow Wilson Jr HS Music Tchr 1973-80; Edison Schl System Elem Music Tchr 1982-88; John Adams MS Music Tchr 1988-; *ai:* Various Choral Groups; Bel Canto; Girls, Boys Ensemble; MENC 1973-; ACDA 1991-; Governor's Tchr Recognition Awd 1993; NJ MS, Jr HS Hnrs Choir Conductor 1994; Choirs Performed at MENC Convention 1996; Conducted Wkshps for MENC, ACDA & Various Colls; *office:* John Adams MS New Dover Rd Edison NJ 08820*

WIPFLER, WILLIAM MICHAEL, 5th Grade Teacher; *b:* New Rochelle, NY; *m:* Kathy Jane Martin; *c:* Holly L., Lesley A. Reiman, Katie E.; *ed:* Mansfield St Univ (BA) Elem Ed 1967; Elmira Coll (MS) Ed 1971; *cr:* Vestal Schl Dist 5th Grd Tchr 1967-68; Horseheads Schl Dist 5th Grd Tchr 1968-; *ai:* Audio-Visual Coord; Var Sports Supvr; Boys, Girls Var and JV Track & Field Event Coord; Math, Sci Soc Sci Comms; NYSUT, NEA 1967-; Elks Club 1984-, Youth Comm, Elk of Month; Town Planning Bd 1990-; *home:* 162 Dunn Rd Horseheads NY 14845

WIRE, COLLEEN FRANCES HOGAN, Science Teacher; *b:* Baltimore, MD; *m:* Frederick C.; *c:* Ashley E., Jessica S.; *ed:* Southern Coll (BS) Elem Ed 1978; Andrews Univ (MA) Ed 1985; Columbia Union Coll 1991 1 Hr; Univ MD Coll Park 6 Hrs 1981-82; *cr:* Murphy Schl 5-8th Tchr 1978-79; Beltsville Adventist Schl 4th, 7-8th Grd Tchr 1979-85; John Nevins Andrews Schl 7-8th Math, Sci Tchr 1985-87; Beltsville Adventist Schl 7-8th Math, Sci Tchr 1987-91; Francis S. Key MS Sci 7th Grd Tchr 1991-; *ai:* Adventurer Club Instr; Tchng Mentoring; Network Seminar Tchr, Coord; NEA, MSTA 1991-; Zapara Excl Tchng Awd 1991; Numerous Articles Pub; *home:* 14408 Basingstoke Ln Silver Spring MD 20905*

WIRT, STEVEN JAMES, Physics Teacher; *b:* Rochester, NY; *m:* Kathleen; *ed:* SUNY Oswego (BS) Physics Scndry Ed 1990; SUNY Potsdam (MS) Instrl Design 1991; *cr:* Ithaca HS Physics Tchr 1991-; *ai:* Site Based Decision Making Comm; NEA 1991-; NSTA 1989-; Toshiba Grant; *office:* Ithaca HS 1401 N Cayuga St Ithaca NY 14850*

WIRTH, DONALD EDWARD, President; *b:* Los Angeles, CA; *m:* Lynn Ada; *c:* Shawn, Robin, Misty; *ed:* CA St Univ (BS) Mngmt 1969; Natl Coll of Martial Arts at Los Angeles (MA), (PHD) Mngmt (PHD) Mngmt 1996; Attnd Army Command, Gen Staff Coll; *cr:* US Army Chief Exec Ofcr 1969-93; Natl Miltary Martial Arts Pres 1992-; Ocean Cty Coll Prgm Coord 1996; *ai:* Assn of US Army 1969-; World Black Belt Bureau 1992-, Master Instr; United Knpo Jujitu Assn 1995-, 8th Degree Black Belt; World Kempo Alliance, Pres; Airborne Commando Elite, Pres; Law Enforcement Self Defense League, Pres; Whiting Bible Church 1977-, Sunday Schl Supt; Manchester United Soccer Club 1978-, Co-Founder; Navy Sea Cadet 1994-, Sr Army Adv; Lakehurst Police Dept Cert of Appreciation; Army Awds: 3 Meiterious Svc Medals, 4 Army Commendation Medals, 2 Army Achvmt, Medals; *home:* 1700 Trenton Ave Whiting NJ 08759

WIRZBURGER-SEYMOUR, RITA ANN (BRINE), Third Grade Teacher; *b:* Whitman, MA; *c:* Paul Jr., Mark, John, Matthew; *ed:* Tufts Univ (BS) Elem Ed 1962; Tchng Cert Presch, Primary Perry Normal Schl 1956; 4 Post Grad Credits Univ of MA; 3 Post Grad Credits Framingham St; 3 Credits Lesley Coll; *cr:* Henry T. Wing Schl Grd 1 Tchr 1956-57; Regal Park Elem Schl Grd 1-2 Tchr 1957-59; Park Ave Elem Schl Grd 2 Tchr 1961-62; Roosevelt Schl Grd 4 Tchr 1968-88, Head Tchr, Acting Prin 1973; Greem Meadow Elem Schl Grd 3 Tchr 1988-; *ai:* Lang Arts, Hlth Comms; Stu Tchng Coach; NEA, Maynard Tchrs Assn 1968-; Pub Svc Lectures.*

WISBY, QUENTIN RAY, Mathematics Teacher; *b:* Cincinnati, Oh Sharon Kay Napier; *c:* Jennifer, Jacqueline, Melissa; *ed:* Morehe Univ (BA) Scndry Ed 1972; Univ of Dayton (MS) Ed Admin 1985; 30 Grad Credit Hrs Ed Admin, Ec; *cr:* Western Brown Local Schls Math 1972-; *ai:* Supts Acad Comm; Math Tutor; Cincinnati Gas, Electric A Inspiration Excl in Tchng 1992; Brown Cty Grant for Math, Sci *home:* 30 Heritage Hill Dr Georgetown OH 45121*

WISCOUNT, BRENDA ATKINS, Second Grade Teacher; *b:* Leba PA; *m:* Robert Charles; *c:* Joseph F., Beth Ann Wolff, Robert M. Millersville Univ (BS) Elem Ed 1966, (MS) Elem Ed 1975; Moody Inst Chrstn Ed 1962-63; Rdng Supvrs; *cr:* Northern Lebanon SD 4th Tchr 1966-67; Pine Grove Area SD Elem Tchr 1967-75, Rdng S 1976-80, Elem Tchr 1980-; *ai:* Schuylkill Co Rdng Assn; PSEA, 1966-; Local Lib Bd 1980-, Pres 5 Yrs; *home:* 114 Spring St Tremo 17981*

WISE, JEANNE HARVEY, Second Grade Teacher; *b:* Wellsboro, PA Richard; *c:* Joy, Melissa, Katherine; *ed:* Mansfield Univ (BS) Eler 1978, (MED) Elem Ed 1993; *cr:* Mansfield Area Nursery Schl Tchr 1978-84; Wellsboro Area Schl Dist Tchr of Gifted Grds 1-8 1987-92; Gill Elem Schl 2nd Grd Tchr 1992-; *ai:* Elem Math Curr Cncl Odyssey of Mind Coach 1998-95; NEA, PSEA 1987-; WAEA 1992-, Rep; *office:* Don Gill Elem Schl 10 Sherman St Wellsboro PA 16901*

WISE, JUDITH KUHNS, 8th Grade Math Teacher; *b:* New Bethle PA; *m:* Ronald C.; *c:* Todd, Brian; *ed:* Clarion Univ of PA (BS) Bio, 1965; Baldwin Wallace Coll (MA) Supervision 1992; Attnd Penn St U Ashland Univ, Drake Univ; *cr:* Greensburg Elem HS Bio Tchr 1965 Bald Eagle HS Math Tchr 1967-69; Brunswick CitySchl Math Tchr 19 *ai:* Math Counts Adv; Curr, Planning Commission; Presider OC Convention; NCTM Convention Accepted Stu Projects Display; N OEA 1979-; NCTM, OCTM, GCCTM 1985-; United Meth Church 19 Baldwin Wallace Fac Women's Club 1973-, Pres; MS Tchr of Yr 1 *home:* 324 Crossbrook Dr Berea OH 44017*

WISE, MARTHA ANN (ZUZICH), 5th-8th Grade Hlth & PE Tch Braddock, PA; *m:* William Charles Jr.; *c:* Brigette Scala, Chad; Slippery Rock St Coll (BS) Hlth, PE, Geography 1965, (MS) PE 1970 PA Joint Schl Dist Hlth, PE Tchr 1965-66; New Castle Area PE 1966-74; Villa Maria PE Tchr 1983-84; Commodore Perry Elem Hlt Tchr 1985-86; Wilmington Area Schl Dist Elem Hlth, PE Tchr 1988- Specials Team Ldr; Wilmington Area Ed Assn, PSEA, NEA 1988-; AAHPERD 1967.

WISE, SARAH E. KANE, Sixth Grade Teacher; *b:* Athens, OH; *m:* E.; *c:* Jeremy W., Joshua K., Jamison J.; *ed:* OH Univ (BA) Elem Ed 1 (MS) Ed 1994; 15 Credit Hrs Curr Dev Lang Arts; *cr:* West Elem Schl S Grd Tchr 1989-; *ai:* Dir Stu Conflict Mngmt; Co-Coord Resident Out Ed; Lancaster City Schls Tchr, Mentor Prgm; NEA, OEA 1989-; *off* West Elem Schl 625 Garfield Ave Lancaster OH 43130*

WISE, SHIRLEY TIMMONS, Principal; *b:* Baltimore, MD; *m:* W R.; *c:* Stephen, Scott; *ed:* Mt St Agnes Coll (BA) Elem Ed 1967; Lo Coll (MED) Ed Mgmt & Supvr 1992; Western MD Coll 9 Credits Sp *cr:* Immaculate Heart of Mary Schl 1st & 6th Grd Teacher 1965 Frederick Cty Bd of Ed Home Visitor 1977-80; St John Schl 4th, 6th, & 8th Grd Tchr 1981-93; St Martins Schl 1993-; *ai:* Parish Cncl M NCEA 1981-; ASCD 1993-; BSA 1979-86, Comm Chair; St Peters Pa Cncl 1983-85, Sec; Whos Who Among Amer Exec; *office:* St Marti Tours Elem Schl 115 S Frederick Ave Gaithersburg MD 20877

WISE, THOMAS SCOTT, Vocal Music Teacher; *b:* York, PA; *m:* Mel Marie Good; *c:* Megan Jan; *ed:* West Chester Univ (BS) Music Ed 19 (MS) Music Ed 1992; 45 Credits Beyond Masters; *cr:* Red Lion Area 9-12 Vocal Music 1986-; *ai:* Marching Band; Vocal Coach for Music Show Choir; Womens Ensemble; Barbaershop Quartet; Mixed Choru Tchng Festival Music to Stdnts in P M; PA Music Educators Assn, M Educators Natl Conf, PA St Educators Assn 1986-; Amer Choral Direc Assn; *office:* Red Lion Area Sr HS 200 Horace Mann Ave Red Lion 17356

WISE, WILLIAM CHARLES, Guidance Counselor; *b:* New Castle, *m:* Marti Zuzich; *c:* Brigette Scala, Chad; *ed:* Slippery Rock Univ (BS) 1966, (MS) Guidance 1969; *cr:* Riverside Jr Sr HS Tchr 1966-68; N Castle HS Tchr & Cnslr 1968-94; Commodore Perry Schl Cnslr 1984- Grove City MS Cnslr 1987-; *ai:* Adopt-A-Grandparent Club Spon; Assistance Team Mem; PSEA, NEA 1966-; PA Schl Cnslrs; *office:* Gr City MS 130 E Main St Grove City PA 16127

WISE-GLADWELL, LUCY L., French Teacher; *b:* Fairmont, WV; Jerry M.; *ed:* Fairmont St Coll (BA) Fr 1977; Post Grad Stud WV Univ Linguistics, Ed, Psych; Summer Stud Overseas WVU Cannes France; Liberty HS Fr Tchr 1984-87; Amer Cancer Soc Dir of Trng 1988-89; Milton Wright HS Fr Tchr 1991-; *ai:* Acad Team Coach; Fr Club Sp AATF 1978-; *office:* C Milton Wright HS 1301 N Fountain Green Rd Air MD 21015

WISEMAN, DOUGLAS CARL, Assoc Dean of Acad Aff & Prof; Nashua, NH; *c:* Mark, Lori Wiseman Stoffel, Kathleen; *ed:* Plymo Tchrs Coll (BED) PE, Sci 1961; IN Univ (MS) PE, Hlth 1962, (PED) Research 1970; *cr:* Portage HS Instr 1963-64; Northeastern Univ Asst P 1969-71; Plymouth St Coll Instr, Asst Prof 1964-69, Prof, Chair, As Dean 1971-; *ai:* Adv Kappa Delta Pi; Head Coach Cross Cn Gymnastics, Soccer, Tennis, Wrestling; Acad Standards, Curr, Disciplin Appeals, General Ed, Grad Cncl, Human Subjects Research, Self-S Accreditation Steering Comms; Phi Kappa Phi Pres; AAHPERD 1960-, of Governors, Honor Awd; CEC 1985-; EDA, AAHPERD 1960-, Pr Honor Awd; NH Spec Olympics 1968-, Bd of Dirs; Ashland Police D 1990-, Investigator; NH Bd of Examiners 1980-, Bd Mem; Tchr Cert; for Exceptional Children 1994; Distinguished Tchr 1993; ED AAHPERD Scho9lar 1991; Outstanding Coll Tchr Awd 1981; Yrbk D 1994; Sports Hall of Fame 1995; *office:* Plymouth State College Spea 208D Plymouth NH 03264*

WISEMAN, EARLEEN HUMBERTSON, Spanish Teacher; Cumberland, MD; *m:* John B.; *c:* Emily Streib, Jennifer Streib; Frostburg St Univ (BA) Eng, Span 1964; Attnd OH Univ & Towson Un *cr:* James M. Bennett Sr HS Eng & Span Tchr 1964-68; Parkersburg C HS Span Tchr 1973-81; Bruce HS Span & Drama Tchr 1981-87; Allega HS Span Tchr 1987-; *ai:* Amer Field Svc; Chrch Organist; NEA; MD Tchrs Assn; Allegany Cty Tchrs Assn; MD For Lang Assn 1982-; AAU 1971-, Pres, Local VP, WV St Sec, WV Name Grant; Grant UMBC F Lang Inst; For Lang Dept Chair 1974-86; *office:* Allegany HS 6 Sedgwick St Cumberland MD 21502

WISER, STEPHEN, Youth Counselor; *b:* Clarksville, GA; *m:* Martha A Moody; *c:* Conrad, Elizabeth Ann, Dorien; *ed:* St Univ of NY at Oneor (BA) Ed 1973; St Univ of NY at New Paltz (MS) Ed 1974; *cr:* Woodcre MS Tchr 1978-81; Darvell MS Headmaster 1981-87; New Meadow R Schl Prin 1987-91, Yth Cnslr 1991-; *ai:* Nature, Ag Club Adv; Bsbl Coac Boys Club; 4-H Act Dir; *office:* New Meadow Run Schl PO Box 240 Rt Farmington PA 15437

WISKER, LISA SPANZIANI, Fifth Grade Elementary Teacher; Pittsburgh, PA; *c:* Kristy Lynn, Jenna Marie; *ed:* IN Univ (BS) Elem E PS Permanent Cert; Masters Credits; *cr:* Benjamin Franklin Elem Sc Fifth Grd Tchr 1972-76; Eisenhower Elem Schl Fourth Grd Tchr 1976-7

rs Twp MS Sixth Grd Rdng Tchr 1991-92; St LOuise de Marillac Schl t Grd Tchr 1992-93, Fifth Grd Tchr 1993-; *ai:* Spelling Bee Monitor, ch; IRA; NEA; NCEA; Tri-Comm South EMS Bd 1976-83, Chm; South Elem PTA 1985-90, Pres, Exec Bd Mem; Heart Assn 1977-86, Trainer; Audio Visual Instruction; Svc Awds Heart Assn, Tri-Comm South S; Nom Thanks to Tchrs Campaign; Pittsburgh Diocesan Golden Apple l Nom; *office:* St Louise De Marillac Schl 310 Mcmurray Rd Pittsburgh 15241*

SLA, SHARON ROTHSTEIN, Social Studies Teacher; *b:* Brooklyn, *m:* Gerard A.; *c:* Susan, Ira; *ed:* SUNY at Albany (BA) Soc Stud 1972; stra Univ (MA) Scndry Ed, Soc Stud 1975; *cr:* Mepham HS Soc Stud r 1973-84; Grand Ave Jr HS Soc Stud Tchr 1984-85; Kennedy HS Soc l Tchr 1984-85; Mepham HS Soc Stud Tchr 1986-87; Calhoun HS Soc l Tchr 1987-; *ai:* It's Acad Club Adv; Calhoun Staff Assn Co-Pres; SS, NCSS 1973-; NYSUT 1973-, 15 Yr Svc Awd; Girl Scouts of Nassau 1991-95, Ldr, Svc Team; Grant through ESL Lexicons in US His, Govt; *ce:* S H Calhoun HS 1786 State St Merrick NY 11566

SMAR, DONALD E., Mathematics Teacher; *b:* Kane, PA; *m:* Julie A. es; *c:* Anna; *ed:* Univ of Pittsburgh at Bradford (AS) Cmptr gramming 1982; Univ of Pittsburgh (BS) Math 1985; Edinboro (TC) Ed 7; *cr:* Kane HS Math Tchr 1987-; *ai:* Class Adv; Scndry Instrl, Schl ety Comms; KATA, PSEA, NEA 1987-.*

SNER, ELLEN SMITH, Cosmetology Instructor; *b:* Fulton, NY; *m:* eodore C.; *c:* Theodore II, Lisa, Sara; *ed:* Attnd Oswego St; Tchng Cert Personal Svc Occupations Univ of St of NY; *cr:* Seaway Tech Ctr smetology Instr 1987-89; Northwest Tech Ctr Cosmetology Instr 1989-; Northwest Tech Newspaper Ed; Northwest Tech Booster Club Sec; SUT 1987-; *home:* 6738 County Route 27 Canton NY 13617

SNESKI, J. JERROLD, Social Studies Teacher; *b:* Middletown, CT; Carmen Gloria Santiago; *c:* Siobhan, Eamonn, Roisin; *ed:* St Michael's A) His 1966; Marquette Univ (MA) His 1968; Attnd Schl of Irish Stud, iv Coll at Dublin, Wesleyan Univ, Univ of Hartford, Cntrl CT St Univ; Maloney HS Soc Stud Tchr 1969-; *ai:* Upward Bound Club, Crescent b Adv; Ftbl Announcer; AFT 1969-; Little League Coach 1987-; Yth ccer Coach 1992-; Wesleyan Univ Upward Bound Prgm Man of Yr 1973, 32, 1994; Miller HS Hometown Hero 1992; *office:* Francis T Maloney 121 Gravel St Meriden CT 06050

ISNIEWSKI, CHARLOTTE CASTRONOVO, English Teacher; *b:* ooklyn, NY; *m:* Lawrence Joseph; *c:* Michael; *ed:* St Joseph's Coll (BA) g 1973; 30 Credits Western CT St Coll; *cr:* Brooklyn Diocese Schl stem Eng Tchr 1973-83; Broadview Eng Tchr 1984-; *ai:* Eng Curr, Eng sesment Comms; Natl Eng Assn 1984-; New England Assn Tchrs of Eng 94-; CEA, NEA 1985-; *office:* Broadview MS Hospital Ave Danbury CT 310

ISNIEWSKI, JEANINE GABRIELLA, English Teacher; *b:* Staten and, NY; *ed:* Univ at ALbany (BA) Eng 1983, (MA) Eng Ed 1986; Studs r for Tchng, Learning Lit; *cr:* Troy HS 9-10, 12 Grd Eng Tchr 1986-91; yle MS 8 Grd Eng Tchr 1991-; *ai:* NYSUT, AFT 1986-; Dist, Tchr Ctr ants; Article Pub 1990; Mentor Tchr Univ at Albany Tchr Preparation gm; *office:* Doyle MS 1976 Burdett Ave Troy NY 12180*

ISNIEWSKI, MARK EDWARD, Science Teacher; *b:* Lakewood, OH; Debbie Williamson; *ed:* Kent St Univ (BS) Ed 1973; Coll of Mount int Joseph on the Ohio (MA) Ed 1987; 87 Addl Semester Hrs Sci, Ed; rtfd Scuba Instr 1982 YMCA, NAUI, PADI; *cr:* Lakewood HS Earth Sci, ysics Tchr 1974-; *ai:* Stu Bible Stud Club Adv; Lakewood Tchrs Assn 74-; Third Intnl Creationism Conf Speaker 1994; Article Pubyj; *office:* kewood HS 14100 Franklin Blvd Lakewood OH 44107

ISNIEWSKI, MARK STEPHEN, Language Arts Teacher; *b:* Reading, .; *m:* Carol Ritner; *c:* Kathryn, Christiana; *ed:* PA St Univ (BS) Sec Ed g 1973; Kutztown St Univ (MED) Sec Ed Eng 1981; *cr:* Schuylkill aven HS Lang Arts Tchr 1974; Wilson HS Lang Arts Tchr, Dir of Pub 74-; Reading Area Comm Coll Adj Instr 1978-82; *ai:* Morning nnouncement Team; News Magazine; AFT 1987-; Ordained Deacon 92-, Polish Natl Cath Church; *office:* Wilson HS 2601 Grandview Blvd est Lawn PA 19609

ISNIEWSKI, MICHELE A., Physical Education Teacher; *b:* ttsburgh, PA; *c:* Melissa, Grant; *ed:* Slippery Rock Univ (BS) Hlth, PE 73; Attnd Penn St Univ; *cr:* West Allegheny Schl Dist K-6th Grd PE Tchr 73-78; St Colmans Schl K-8th Grd PE Tchr 1988-94; St Bernadettes Schl -8th Grd Tchr 1992-95; Gateway Schl Dist K-6th Grd PE Tchr 1995-; *ai:* wimm Team Boosters Pres; Monroeville Marine Fitness Challenge o-Coord; Monroeville Vlybl Tournaments Supvr; Bel-Aire Municipal ol Mgr; PSAHPERD; USPE 1995-; Amer Red Cross 1973-, Vol Hrs; unicipality of Monroeville 100 Hrs Awd; CPR First Aid, Water Safety str; Certfd Pool & Spa Operator; *office:* Gateway Schl Dist 2609 Mosside vd Monroeville PA 15146*

VISSENBACH, DONNA ELAINE, Jr Sr High Mathematics Teacher; *b:* lbany, NY; *m:* David Wayne; *c:* Brandon; *ed:* SUNY at Potsdam (BA) ath Ed 1987; SUNY at Albany (MS) Math Ed 1991; Inservice Credit pplied Math Tech Prep Madeline Hunter Course; *cr:* Niskayuna HS ummer 10th Grd Geometry 1987; Schoharie Cntrl Schl Jr Sr HS Math chr 1987-; Cobleskill Coll Summer 7th-10th Grd Gen Math Tchr 1991; : Tutor; AFT 1987-; Schoharie Tchrs Union 1987-, Bldg Rep 1993; eukemia, Cancer Soc 1994-; Coll Challenger Schlsp; Tech Prep Prgm rant; Helped Write Pre-Course I Curr; *office:* Schoharie Central Schl lain St Schoharie NY 12157

VISSER, DENISE L., Health & Physical Ed Tchr; *b:* Reading, PA; *ed:* ast Stroudsburg Univ (BS) Hlth & PE 1978; Wilkes Univ (MS) Ed 1989; *:* Pottstown Schl Dist Long Term Sub Tchr 1979-82; Tunkhannock Area chl Dist Tchr 1982-; *ai:* Bsktbl, Soccer & Field Hockey Coach; NEA, SEA 1982-; Tunkhannock Area Ed Assn 1982-, VP; Phi Epsilon Kappa 978-; PA St Coaches Assn 1994-; Keystone St Games 1988-, Coach, layer; Coach of Yr Awd 3 Times; *office:* Tuckhannock Area Schl Dist hiladelphia Ave Tunkhannock PA 18657

VISSER, ROBERT CLAYTON, 9th-12th Grd Science Instr; *b:* olumbus, OH; *m:* Renee Kananen; *c:* Tyler; *ed:* Miami Univ (BS) Bio Ed 986; *cr:* Lakota HS Sci Instr 1987; Seymour Comm Schls 1987-; Wayne ocal 1990-; *ai:* Var, Jr HS & Kids Wrestling Coach; SECO 1990-; NEA 995-; *office:* Wayne Local Schl 735 Dayton Rd Waynesville OH 45068*

VISSERT, JOAN KENNEDY, Asst Prof of Ornamental Hort; *b:* Olean, Y; *m:* Walter W. Jr.; *c:* Kelsey Marie, Kellen Ann; *ed:* Alfred St Coll AAS) Floriculture Merchandising 1979; SUNY Coll of Tech AT tica-Rome (BS) Voc-Tech Ed 1981; Alfred Univ (MSEd) Ed 1986; Addl redit Hrs Ed, Spec Ed; *cr:* SUNY Alfred Asst Prof 1981-, Ag, Hort Dept chr 1996-; *ai:* Horticulutre Club, Flower & Garden Show Coord; Niagara ntnl Assn FTD 1981-, Bd Dirs; United Univ Professions 1981-, Treas 988-90; Cornell Cooperative Extension 1994-, Bd Dirs; Mrktg Comm; UNY Chancellor's Awd Excl Tchng 1986; Alfred St Coll Alumni Assoc chr of Yr Schl of Ag 1986; *office:* SUNY at Alfred Agiculture Bldg Alfred Y 14802

VISSINGER, ELIZABETH M., Business Instructor; *b:* Spangler, PA; *m:* . Larry; *c:* Derrick, Trevor; *ed:* IN Univ of PA (BS) Bus Ed 1973; hippensburg Univ (MED) Bus Ed 1976; Attn Penn St, Amer Univ; *cr:* Conrad Weiser SD Bus Instr 1973-75, Rdng SD Bus Instr 1976-78, Bus Instr 1978-; *ai:* PA Bus Ed Assn; *office:* Conrad Weiser Jr Sr HS 347 E Penn Ave Robesonia PA 19551

WITHAM, DEAN, Fifth Grade Teacher; *b:* Burlington, VT; *ed:* Univ of VT (BSC Ed 1981, (MED) Ed 1986; CAS in Ed Admin; *cr:* Pine Plains Cntrl Schl Dist 5th Grd Tchr 1985; Wallkill Cntrl Schl Dist 5th Grd Tchr 1986-; *ai:* Dist Elem Sci Coord 1988-; Olster Cty Rdng Cncl 1987-, VP, Literacy Awd 1993; Intnl Rdng Assn 1988-; Gardiner Fire & Rescue 1994-, Emergency Med Tech 1996; Habitat for Hum 1995-; Whole Lang Philosophy Presenter & Tchr Trainer for Many Dists; *office:* Ostrander Elem Schl Viola Ave Wallkill NY 12589*

WITHAM, MARIE E., English Teacher; *b:* Providence, RI; *m:* Thomas A.; *c:* Jessica R., Amanda M.; *ed:* Univ of RI (BA) Eng Ed 1971; 36 Credits Scndry Ed, Eng; *cr:* East Greenwich HS Eng Tchr 1971-; *ai:* Class Adv 1976, 1993; NEA, EGEA RI 1971-; *office:* East Greenwich HS 300 Avenger Dr East Greenwich RI 02818

WITHEE, PAUL J., Mathematics Teacher; *b:* Ft Belvoir, VA; *m:* LeAnn Buzzell; *c:* Joshua, Courtney; *ed:* William Penn Coll (BA) PE 1991; 15 Credit Hrs Toward Masters in PE at Univ of ME at Orono; *cr:* B E Moore Schl Math Tchr 1982; Sanford HS Math Tchr 1982-90; Foxcroft Acad Math Tchr 1990-; *ai:* Sr Class Adv; Ftbl & Bsbl Head Coach; Accreditation Comm; NEA 1996; NCTM 1995-; *office:* Foxcroft Acad 147 W Main St Dover Foxcroft ME 04426*

WITHEROW, CATHERINE SASLAWSKY, English Teacher; *b:* Bayshore, NY; *m:* Stephen Michael; *c:* Jennifer, Eric, Alan, Scott; *ed:* SUNY at Geneseo (BA) Eng & Speech Ed 1971; Elmira Coll (MS) Eng 1978; *cr:* R L Thomas HS Eng Tchr 1971-72; Canaseraga C Schl Eng Tchr 1977-79; Andover Central Schl Eng Tchr 1981-; *ai:* NYSEC 1985-; NCTE, NEA & NYEA 1981-; Andover Tchrs Assn 1981-, Pres 1991-94; *office:* Andover Central Schl Elm St Andover NY 14806

WITHEROW, WENDY LEE (BLOOM), Swimming Instructor; *b:* Rome, GA; *m:* Craig Michael; *c:* Megan Marie; *ed:* Lock Haven Univ Hlth, PE 1987; IN Univ of PA Aquatics Schl Summer Credits; *cr:* Treasure Lake Lifeguard 1984-87; YMCA Swimming Instr, Lifeguard 1986-87; Curwensville Area HS Swimming Instr 1987-; *ai:* Lifeguard Club Adv; Bsktbl Referee; PIAA, NEA 1987-; Church, Sanctuary Worker; Red Cross, Vol; *office:* Curwensville Area HS 650 Beech St Curwensville PA 16833

WITHERSPOON, ROGER, VP of Student Development; *b:* Lenoir, NC; *m:* Barbara Caviness; *c:* Rodney, Nicole; *ed:* NCA&T Univ (BS) Soc 1960; Adelphi Univ (MSW) Comm Org 1967; Univ of MA (EDD) Soc Psy 1983; Harvard Educl Ldrshp Cert; *cr:* Lehman Coll Assoc Prof 1975-90; John Jay Coll Prof 1990; *ai:* Stu Act; NASPA 1987-; Assoc Blk Soc Wk 1980-; Establishment of Branch Campus in PR; Intnl Conf on Criminal Justice in Russia, Ireland; Dev of Relations Between Korean's, African Amers.*

WITIAK, DONNA M., Mathematics Tchr & Dept Chprsn; *b:* Scranton, PA; *m:* Daniel N.; *c:* Thomas; *ed:* Bloomsburg Univ (BS) Math Ed 1974; Univ of Scranton (MS) Math Ed 1980; Credit Hrs at PA St Univ, Wilkes Univ; *cr:* Bishop Hannan HS Math Tchr 1975-, Dept Chprsn 1985-; Univ of Scranton Instr 1988-; *ai:* TEAM Moderator; NHS Adv; NCTM 1974-; PCTM 1990-; NCEA 1990-; NPCTM 1993-; *office:* Bishop Hannan HS 330 Wyoming Ave Scranton PA 18503

WITKOWSKI, BARBARA B., Coordinator of Gifted; *b:* Kittanning, PA; *m:* Phillip H.; *c:* Zachary, Brock; *ed:* IN Univ of PA (BS) Bus Ed 1978; 24 Addl Credits at Clarion Univ of PA; 4 Addl Credits at Wilkes Univ; Several Non-Credit Cmptr Classes at Clarion Univ of PA; *cr:* Keystone Jr-Sr HS Bus Ed Tchr 1978-92; Clarion Cty Voc-Tech Schl Chief Examiner for GED Testing 1992-94; Keystone Schl Dist Gifted Coord 1993-; *ai:* Delta Kappa Gamma 1994-, World Fellowship Chair-Elect; NEA 1978-; PA St Ed Assn 1978-; Keystone Ed Assn 1978-, Grievance Comm; *office:* Keystone School Dist RR 2 Box 3D Knox PA 16232

WITMAN, JEFFREY PAUL, Instructor; *b:* Lancaster, PA; *m:* Kathryn Wing; *c:* Martha; *ed:* Elizabethtown Coll (BS) Soc Sci 1973; Univ of OR (MS) Therapeutic Recreation 1977; Boston Univ (EDD) Spec Ed 1989; Project Adventure Inc Basic & Advanced Trng; *cr:* Univ of NH Project Mgr 1978-83; Hampstead Hospital Dir of OT & TR 1983-91; Kent St Univ Asst Prof 1991-93; Philhaven Activity Therapist 1993-; *ai:* Wrestling Ofcl; NTRS 1977-, Bd of Dirs; Donegal Presbyn Church, Deacon; Author & Co-Author of Books, Articles & Assessment Tools; *home:* 1349 Harrisburg Ave Mount Joy PA 17552

WITT, DONALD, Band Director; *b:* Connellsville, PA; *m:* Lynda Spotts; *c:* Jeffrey, Eric; *ed:* IN Univ of PA (BS) Music Ed 1972; Attnd CA Univ of PA & Penn St Univ Post Grad Credits; *cr:* Connellsville Area Schl Dist Band Dir 1973-80, 1985-95; Henco Fundraising Sales Rep 1980-83; Parker & Hunter Inc Stock Broker 1983-85; *ai:* Jazz Band & Band Act Dir; PMEA 1985-; CAEA 1985-; Disciples of Christ Chrstn Church 1977-, Sunday Schl Supt, Congregation Chprsn & Diaconate Mem; B P O Elks, Esquire; *office:* Connellsville Jr HS West 215 Falls Ave Connellsville PA 15425

WITT, JUDITH M., Mathematics Teacher; *b:* Queens, NY; *ed:* Queens Coll (BA) Math, (MSEd) Math 1995; Working on Admin-Supervision Cert; *cr:* Grove Cleveland HS Math Tchr 1993-; *ai:* Tutoring; Math Team Adv 1993; NCTM 1993-; *office:* Grover Cleveland HS 2127 Himrod St Ridgewood NY 11385

WITTE, BILL THOMAS, Assoc Prof of Cmptr Applctns; *b:* Washington, DC; *m:* Mary Jo Porada; *c:* John; *ed:* Univ of MD (BS) Math, Educ 1980; Johns Hopkins (MS) Tech Educ 1988; *cr:* Archbishop Carroll HS Math Tchr 1980-88; Tracor Applied Sci Cmptr Analyst 1988-92; Montgomery Coll Assoc Prof 1992-; *ai:* Advising Cadre; Advsing, Email Course Comm; Continuing Ed Tchr; Discipline Bd; Capital PC Users Group 1995-; East Coast Ath Conf 1985-, NCAA Ftbl Ofcl; Washington Dist Ftbl Ofcls 1980-, Fed Ftbl Ofcl; *office:* Montgomery Coll At Germantown 20200 Observation Dr Germantown MD 20876

WITTE, PHYLLIS F., English Teacher; *b:* New York, NY; *ed:* Empire St Coll (BA) Eng Lit & Creative Writing 1978; Brooklyn Coll (MFA) Creative Writing 1994; *cr:* New Dorp HS Eng Tchr 1986-89; Brooklyn Tech HS Eng Tchr & House Admin 1989-; *ai:* SADD; *office:* Brooklyn Tech HS 29 Fort Greene Pl Brooklyn NY 11217

WITTENBERG, BARBARA SOUTHER, Ldrshp Trainer & Reading Tchr; *b:* Norwalk, CT; *c:* Evan; *ed:* Smith Coll (BA) Art His 1964; NY Univ (MA) Learning Disabilities & Rdng 1976; 45 Credit Hrs Above MA; Master Tchr Trng; *cr:* The Childrens Meeting Presch Founder & Dir 1971-74; NY Univ Rdng Inst Tchr & Librn 1974-76; Passaic HS Tchr & Peer Pgm Coord 1976-; Princeton Ctr for Ldrshp Trng Master Tchr Trainer 1986-; *ai:* Diversity 2000 Group Adv; Parent Trainer; Supts Ldrshp Core; NEA & NJEA 1976-; IRA 1976-; Peer Pgm Best Practice St of NJ 1994-95; *office:* Passaic HS 170 Paulison Ave Passaic NJ 07055

WITTKOP, VICKIE L., Senior English Teacher; *b:* Wooster, OH; *m:* David A.; *c:* Christopher, Bethany; *ed:* Muskingum Coll (BS) Eng, Soc Stud 1963; Attnd Ashland Univ, Univ of Dayton, Akron Univ; *cr:* Bedford City Schls Eng, Soc Stud Tchr; Fairview Park Schls World His, AP; New Philadelphia Eng Tchr, Sr Advanced 1979-; *ai:* Stu, Soph Class Adv; Acad Challenge Coach; NEA 1963; AAUW 1992-, VP; NCTE 1980; Broadway Meth Church Intnl Rdng Assn 1972-; Martha Holden Jennings Schlsp; Quaker Fdn Grant; *office:* New Philadelphia HS 343 Ray Ave NW New Philadelphia OH 44663

WITTMAN, JENNIFER R., High School English Teacher; *b:* Smithtown, NY; *ed:* SUNY Geneseo (BA) Eng, Scndry Ed 1992; Dowling Coll (MS) Rdng 1996; *cr:* Sayville HS Eng Tchr 1992-; *ai:* Coach 7th, 8th Grd Coed Cross Cntry 1992-, Spring Track 1992-, JV Sftbl 1995-, Var Girls Bsktbl Asst 1992-95; NCTE 1992-; IRA, AUA 1996; Mid East Suffolk Tchr Ctr Grant; Alpha Upsilon Alpha; *office:* Sayville HS 20 Brook St W Sayville NY 11796

WITTMANN, KATHY ANN, Math & German Teacher; *b:* Youngstown, OH; *ed:* Youngstown St Univ (BSEd) Scndry Ed Math & Ger 1984, (MSEd) Educl Admin 1990; *cr:* Ravenna HS Math Tchr 1984-85; Austintown Fitch HS Math Tchr 1985-87, Math & Ger Tchr 1987-; *ai:* Ger Club Adv; Strategic Plan & Standardized Testing Comm; NEA, OH EA & Austintown EA 1985-; Delta Kappa Gamma Soc Beta Pi Chptr 1990-, Recording Sec; *office:* Fitch HS 4560 Falcon Dr Austintown OH 44515

WITTNER, PETER S., Health & Physical Ed Teacher; *b:* New York, NY; *m:* Susan Mattivi; *ed:* Herbert Lehman Coll CUNY (BA) PE 1979; SUNY at Cortland (MS) Ed 1981; Pace Univ (MS) Educl Admin 1992; *cr:* Paul Hoffman JHS 45 Tchr 1981-82; The Mc Burney Schl Tchr 1982-86; Hunter Coll HS Tchr 1986-; *ai:* Boys Cross Cntry, Bsktbl, Tennis Coach; Time Intensive Activity, Hnrs & Awds Comms; Co-Authored Project Super Heart Manual for Tchng Cardiovascular Fitness to Elem Schl Children; *home:* 34 Lenape Dr Montville NJ 07045

WITWER, MARK TURIN, High School Science Dept Chair; *b:* Chicago, IL; *m:* Andrea Ruth Strock; *c:* David Bruce; *ed:* Grace Coll (BA) Eng 1977; Villanova Univ (MSSS) Scndry Schl Sci, Bio 1993; 63 Credit Hrs Grace Theological Seminary 1977-79; 18 Ed Credits George Washington Univ, Univ of MD 1981-84; 13 Sci Credits Prince Georges Comm Coll 1980-82; *cr:* Grace Brethren Chrstn Schl Tchr, Sci Dept Chair 1979-85; DE Cty Chrstn Schl Tchr, HS Sci Dept Chair 1985-; *ai:* Natl Sci Tchrs Assoc; Soc for Stud of Amphibians, Reptiles,Herpetologists League; Chicago Herpetological Soc 1990-; Amer Fed of Herpetoculturists 1991-; Amer Soc of Ichthyologists & Herpetologists; Vol Herpetological Field Work in Chester Cty; Herpetological Pub & Edu Prgms; *office:* Delaware County Christian Schl 462 Malin Rd Newtown Square PA 19073

WITZMANN, PAMELA JO, Physical Education Teacher; *b:* Upper Sandusky, OH; *m:* Bernhard; *ed:* Kent St Univ (BS) Hlth & PE 1979; Western MI Univ (MA) Spcl PE 1986; Univ of Dayton (MA) Ed Admin 1994; *cr:* New Lebanon Schls Hlth & PE Tchr 6 Yrs; Centerville City Schls PE & Adapted PE Tchr 11 Yrs; *ai:* PE Dept Head; Girls Vllybl Coach 15 Yrs; Boys Vllybl Coach 6 Yrs; Tournament Mgr 2 Yrs; Operations Comm 2 Yrs; OHSAA Sportsmanship Ethics & Integrity Comm 4 Yrs; OHPERD 1981-, Pres & VP; OHSVCA, Dist Ofcr & St Rep; AVCA; Excl in Tchng Nom & Semi Finalist 1990 & 1992; St Boys Vllybl Coach of Yr 1994; *office:* Centerville City Schls 500 E Franklin St Centerville OH 45459*

WNEK, ANDREW PAUL, Science Teacher; *b:* Latrobe, PA; *m:* Deborah Fletcher; *c:* Drew, Patrick; *ed:* Kent St Univ (BA) Bio, Chem 1973; Univ of Pittsburgh (PHD) Biochemistry 1982; Post Doctoral Stud Schl of Medicine Univ of Pittsburgh; *cr:* Greater Latrobe Jr HS Sci Tchr 1990-91; Penn-Trafford HS Sci Tchr 1991-92; Greater Latrobe Jr HS Sci Tchr 1992-; *ai:* Fac Advy Comm; Ninth Grd Ftbl, Seventh, Eighth Grd Track Coach; NEA, PSEA 1989-; ASM 1982-; Post Doctoral Fellowship; Eleven Peer-Review Articles Pub in Biochemical & Microbiological Journals; St Vincent Coll Bridges Prgm Grant Recipient; *office:* Greater Latrobe Jr HS 131 Country Club Rd Latrobe PA 15650

WNEK, GARY EDMUND, Chemistry Professor; *b:* Amsterdam, NY; *m:* Maria T. Dufresne; *c:* Janice, Christine; *ed:* Worcester Polytech Inst (BS) Chemical Engrng 1977; U MA at Amherst (PHD) Polymer Sci & Engrng 1980; *cr:* MIT Asst Prof Materials Sci & Eng 1980-85, Assoc Materials Sci & Eng 1985-87; RPI Assoc Prof Chem 1987-92, RPI Chem Prof 1992-; *ai:* Polymer Sci & Engrng Pgm Dir; Amer Chem Soc 1978-; Am Assoc for Advancement of Sci 1980-; Govt & Industrial Grants; 90 Publications; Eastern NY Intellectual Property Law Assn Inventor of the Yr Awd; *office:* Rensselaer Polytechnic Inst 110 8th St Troy NY 12180*

WNEK, THOMAS J., English Teacher; *b:* Buffalo, NY; *m:* Mary D. Hartley; *ed:* Buffalo St Coll (BS) Scndry Eng Ed 1973; Fairleigh Dickenson Univ (MA) Eng 1976; 42 Addl Credit Hrs Post Grad Stud; *cr:* Williamsville South HS Eng Tchr 1973-; Buffalo St Coll Adjunct Prof Eng Ed 1993-94; *ai:* AFT, NYSUT,Williamsville Tchrs Assn 1973-; NCTE 1980-; *office:* Williamsville South HS 5950 Main St Williamsville NY 14221*

WNUK, RUTH SHARKUS, Spanish Teacher; *b:* Kingston, PA; *m:* Andrew Peter; *c:* Andrew Charles; *ed:* Wilkes Coll (BA) Span 1972; Masters Equivalency 24 Addl Hrs Loyola Coll, WA Coll; *cr:* North Caroline HS Span Tchr 1973-77; St Marys Assumption Schl Elem Tchr 1979-93; WY Valley West HS Span Tchr 1993-; *ai:* Jr Class Adv; PSEA, NEA 1993-; St Marys Church, Rel Instr; *office:* Wyoming Valley West Schl 150 Wadham St Plymouth PA 18651*

WOCKLEY, MARILYN HAHNEFELD, Spanish Tchr & Dean of Women; *b:* Baltimore, MD; *m:* Raymond C.; *c:* Bryan, Melissa; *ed:* Western MD Coll (BA) Fr & Ed 1965; Grad Stud at Univ of DE & Salisbury St Univ; *cr:* Middle River Jr HS Fr & Span Tchr 1965-66; Rising Sun HS Span Tchr 1966-68; Charles Carroll Jr HS Fr & Span Tchr 1970-72; Lord Baltimore Jr HS Span Tchr 1974-75; Shafer Schl Span Tchr 1982-83; Bishop McNamara HS Fr & Span Tchr & Dean 1983-; *ai:* Foreign Lang Dept Chair; NHS Adv; Stu Fac Advy Cncl; Sociedad Honorar Hispanica Spon; Tchr Svc Corps Mentor; NCEA 1983-; GWATFL 1990-; ACTFL 1996; AATSP 1995-; Mount Airy Homemakers 1977-, Pres, VP, Dist Dir; Bishop McNamara HS Caritas Awd for Fac Svc 1992; *office:* Bishop Mc Namara HS 6800 Marlboro Pike Forestville MD 20747

WODZANOWSKI, KENNETH JOHN, Religion Teacher; *b:* Jersey City, NJ; *ed:* Rutgers Univ (BS) Mrktg 1991; Attnd Livingston Coll & Schl of Bus; *cr:* Casa Oscar Romero Eng Tchr 1990; Marist HS Rel & Lang Arts Tchr 1991-; *ai:* Yrbk Moderator; Retreat Coord; Asst Drama Club & Choir Dir; Fac Senate; Campus Ministry Asst; Esopus Vols 1986-; Natl Convocation of Chrstns & Jews 1991-, Fac Adv, Recognition of Svc; Herff Jones Publishing Silver Awd for Pub of Yrbk 1994; *office:* Marist HS 1241 Kennedy Blvd Bayonne NJ 07305*

WOEHR, EUGENE WALTER, Social Studies Teacher; *b:* Philadelphia, PA; *m:* Beatrice M. Borden; *c:* Robert, Angela; *ed:* Temple Univ (BS) Sec Ed Soc Stud 1972, (MS) Soc Stud Ed 1976, (MBA) Acctng & Finance 1986; 12 Credit Hrs Jewish His Gratz Coll; 24 Credit Hrs Supervisory Ed Cert; *cr:* Overbrook HS Soc Stud Tchr 1973-83; S A Douglas HS Soc Stud Tchr 1983-92; A Lincoln HS Soc Stud Tchr 1992-; *ai:* Bldg Comm; NHS Nominating Bd; AFT 1973-; Torresdale Boys Club 1984-; Safeguard Scientifics Ctr for Ec Ed 1993-; *office:* Abraham Lincoln HS Rowland & Ryan Aves Philadelphia PA 19136

WOGE, GASPERINA MOROCCO, Spanish Teacher; *b:* Sharon, PA; *c:* James Anthony; *ed:* Youngstown St Univ (BA) Span 1977, (BA) Italian 1979; PA St Univ 12 Credit Hrs; Duquesne Univ 9 Credit Hrs; Commonwealth of PA Masters Equivalency; *cr:* Sharon City Schl Dist Span Tchr 1984-; PA St Univ Shenango Campus Italian Instr 1985-, Span Instr 1991-93; *ai:* Span Club 1984-; Italian Club 1995-; For Lang Dept Chair 1995; NEA, PA St Ed Assn, Sharon Tchrs Assn 1984-; Amer Assn of Tchrs of Italian 1980-; PA St Modern Lang Assn 1993-; *office:* Sharon Sr HS 1129 E State St Sharon PA 16146

WOHL, MATTHEW DEFOREST, Social Studies Teacher; *b:* New York, NY; *m:* Tessa; *ed:* Johns Hopkins Univ (BA) Art His 1986; Boston Univ (MAT) His 1993; Middlebury Coll Completed Summer Prgm in Intensive Italian 1983; *cr:* Chicopee HS Soc Stud Tchr 1993-; *ai:* Alternative Schl Oversight Comm, Curr Frameworks Stud Group Chair; Ed Reform Task Force; ASCD, NCSS 1995; Sallie Mae First Yr Tchr of Yr Nom 1994; Honorable Mention 21st Century Tchr of Yr 1995; *office:* Chicopee HS 650 Front St Chicopee MA 01013

WOJCIECHOWSKI, DIANE HODGSON, High School Orchestra Teacher; *b:* Wilkes-Barre, PA; *m:* David S.; *c:* David John, Mark Jason; *ed:* Marywood Coll (BM) Music Ed 1968; 33 Grad Credits Ed; *cr:* WY Vly West Schl String Tchr 1968-74; Gate of Heaven Schl Vocal, Instrumental Music Tchr 1983-91; WY Vly West Schl Orch Tchr 1992-; *ai:* Orch, Music Dir All Schl Musical; PSEA, PMEA 1992-; *office:* Wyoming Valley West HS Maple Ave Kingston PA 18704

WOJDON, FRANCINE LUTZ, Fifth Grade Teacher; *b:* Camden, NJ; *m:* Richard A.; *c:* Tracey, Kenneth; *ed:* Glassboro St (BA) Elem Ed 1968; *cr:* H. B. Wilson Elem Schl Fourth Grd Tchr 1968-69; M. L. King Sixth Grd Tchr 1969-73; Mark Newbie Elem Schl Fifth Grd Tchr 1979-; *ai:* Safety Patrol Adv 1985-; Cmptr Tech Comm; PTA Fac Liason; Negotiations; CEA, CCEA, NEA, NJEA 1979-; Tchr of Yr 1988.*

WOJTKOWSKI, ROBERT S., Social Studies Dept Chm & Tchr; *b:* Rochester, PA; *ed:* IN Univ (BS) Soc Sci 1970; Slippery Rock Univ (MED) Scndry Ed 1976; *cr:* Hopewell Jr HS His Tchr 1970-86; Hopewell HS Soc Stud Dept Chm, Psych Tchr 1986-; *ai:* NEA, PSEA 1970-; NCSS 1976-; *office:* Hopewell Sr HS 1215 Longvue Ave Aliquippa PA 15001

WOJTUKIEWICZ, CARLA J., Kindergarten Teacher; *b:* Gardner, MA; *m:* Robert J.; *c:* Nicholas; *ed:* Fitchburg St Coll (BS) Elem Ed 1974; Working Towards MS Creative Arts Lesley Coll 1996; *cr:* Elm St Schl 4th-5th Grd Tchr 1975-80; Schl St Schl Kndgtn Tchr 1980-81; Gardner HS Kndgtn 1981-; *ai:* MTA, NEA, GEA 1975-; Whole Lang Tchrs Assn 1990-; Hosp Aid Assn 1990-; Grant for Inservice Course on Whole Lang; *office:* Gardner HS 200 Catherine St Gardner MA 01440

WOLANSKI, ANTHONY S., Math Teacher; *b:* Zerniki Wroclawski, Poland; *m:* Carol M. Angelini; *c:* Nicole L., Dina; *ed:* Univ of DE (BA) Math, Russian 1964; *cr:* US Army Ofcr 1969-72; Salesianum Schl Math Tchr 1972-; *ai:* Soccer, Tennis Coach; DE Tchrs of Math 1974-; DHSSCA 1975-, Soccer Coach of Yr 1982; NSCAA 1980-; DSSAA Soccer Comm 1985-; DE Soccer St Champs 1983, 1989, 1993; DE Cmptr St Fair Winner 1982; *office:* Salesianum Schl 1801 N Broom St Wilmington DE 19802

WOLBERT, KRISTINE BATTO, Coordinator of Gifted Ed; *b:* Rochester, PA; *m:* John; *c:* Lauren; *ed:* Geneva Coll (BA) Eng 1971; PA St Permanent Cert, Prgm Spec; *cr:* Quigley HS Eng Tchr 1971-72; Rochester MS Eng Tchr 1972-77, Fourth Grd Tchr 1977-87, Coord of Gifted Ed 1987-; *ai:* Acad Games Coach; Mock Trial Spon; Beaver Cty Acad Games League 1990-; Beaver Cty Tchrs of Gifted 1990-, Sec; Beaver Cty Enrichment Consortium 1993-; PAGE 1988-; Beaver Area Heritage 1993-; *office:* Rochester Area Schl District 540 Reno St Rochester PA 15074

WOLBERT, STEPHANIE ANN, Math, Sci & Soc Stud Teacher; *b:* McKeesport, PA; *m:* Dean A.; *c:* Kalyn Ann, Ian Patrick; *ed:* Clarion Univ (BSEd) Elem 1987; Univ of DE Will Complete MS of Instruction in 1997; B +30 Credit Hrs; *cr:* St Agnes Elem Schl 5th-6th Grd Math & Sci Tchr 1987-88; DE Adolescent Pgm Ctr Dir 1988-90; John Bassett Moore MS 6th Grd Math & Sci Tchr 1990-93, 7th Grd Life Sci Tchr 1993-94; North Elem 6th Grd Math & Sci Tchr 1994-; *ai:* HS Boys & Girls Cross Cntry, HS Girls Track & MS Girls Asst Bsktbl Coach; NEA, DSEA & SEA 1990-; Read-Aloud DE 1990-, Bd Mem 1990-91; DuPont Sci Tchr 1992; Article Pub; *office:* Smyrna North Elem Schl 365 N Main St Smyrna DE 19977*

WOLCOTT, CONNIE MEREDITH, MSPAP Teacher Specialist; *b:* Easton, MD; *m:* David Edwin; *ed:* Chesapeake Coll (AA) Gen Stud 1975; Briarcliff Coll (BA) His 1977; Working Towards Ed MS Salisbury St Univ; *cr:* Denton Elem Schl 4th Grd Tchr 1987-94, MSPAP Tchr Specialist 1994-; *ai:* 4th Grd Newspaper Group, Cmptr Club Adv; Schl Improvement Team; Stu Assistance Comm; Mid Shore Rdng Cncl 1988-, Newspaper Chm 1995-; NEA 1987-; NSTA, NCTM, IRA 1995-; Septem Homemakers Club 1985-, Sec; Chesapeake Bay Trust Newspaper Publishing Grant; Caroline Cty PTA Tchr of Yr 1994; Attnd MD Historical Soc Summer Inst, Geog Summer Mini-course 1995; Local, St, Natl Confs Presentations; *office:* Denton Elem Schl 303 Sharp Rd Denton MD 21629

WO LEE, CHUN, Mathematics Teacher; *b:* Canton, China; *m:* Peter Lem You; *c:* Regan Lee You, Travis Lee You, Courtney Lee You; *ed:* Queens Coll (BA) Math 1972; Teachers Coll Columbia Univ (MA) Math, Ed 1974; *cr:* Sarah J. Hale HS Math Tchr 1974-93; Ft Hamilton HS Math Tchr 1993-; *office:* Ft Hamilton HS 83 01 Shore Rd Brooklyn NY 11209

WOLF, ANN ELIZABETH, Chemistry Teacher; *b:* Herkimer, NY; *ed:* Franklin Coll (MA) Chem 1974; Bridgewater St Coll (MAT) Chem 1989; 30 Addl Credits Past MA, MAT; *cr:* Notre Dame HS Chem Tchr 1976-77; Amer Schl Kuwait Head Sci Dept & Chem Tchr 1977-81; Amer Cultural Assn of Turino Italy Chem & Math Tchr 1981-83; Plymouth Schls Chem Instr 1983-; *ai:* Stud Cncl Adv; PCEA 1983-, PR&R Mem; MTA, NEACT 1983-; Coalition for Buzzards Bay 1992-; Amer Nuclear Soc Ed 1990-, Ed Chair; *office:* Plymouth South HS 490 Long Pond Rd Plymouth MA 02360

WOLF, DONNA NAVARRA, French Teacher; *b:* Albion, NY; *m:* William; *c:* Bryan, Karyn; *ed:* SUC at Oswego (BA) Fr 1970; SUC at Brockport & SUC at Geneseo Post Grad Stud; *cr:* Spencerport Central Fr Tchr 1974-; *ai:* Fr Club Adv; AFT & NYS United Tchrs 1974-; *home:* 141 Creekwood Dr Rochester NY 14626

WOLF, ELAINE, K-12th Grd Lang Arts Chprsn; *b:* New York City, NY; *m:* Ira K.; *c:* Judy, Adam Fruitman; *ed:* NY Univ (BA) Sociology-Summa Cum 1970, (MA) Spec Ed 1971; Long Island Univ (PD) Schl Dist Admin 1992; Hofstra Univ Rdng Cert 1988; *cr:* NY Assn for Blind Spec Ed Tchr 1971-72; Manhattan Ch Treatment Ctr Spec Ed Tchr 1972-73; Rosewood Park Elem Schl Spec Ed Tchr 1973-76; Island Trees HS Rdng Specialist 1988-93; Island Trees Lang Arts Chprsn 1993-; *ai:* Schl Improvement Team; Extracurricular Eligibility, Stu of Month & Summer Rdng Comms; Dist Bk Selection Comm; Dist Assessment Comm; Dist Summer Pgm Comm; IRA & NY St Rdng Assn 1988-; Nassau Rdng Cncl 1988-, Young Authors Contest Chprsn 1990 & Judge 1988-90; NCTE 1993-; ASCD 1993-; Phi Beta Kappa 1970; Trng Fellowship 1970-71; NYU Founders Day Awd 1970; Great Neck Tchrs Assn Awd 1966; Designed & Implemented New Courses at Island Trees HS 1988-93; Implemented Elem Lang Arts Prgm 1993-; *office:* Island Trees Public Schls 100 Owl Pl Levittown NY 11756

WOLF, ELISE R., English & History Teacher; *b:* Virginia Beach, VA; *m:* Asher; *c:* Hadassah, Leah, Shlomo; *ed:* Touro Coll (BA) Eng, Ed 1989; Johns Hopkins Univ (MA) Educl Admin 1991; 30 Addl Credits His UMBC; *cr:* Sara Schnirer HS Regento His, Earth Sci Tchr 1988-89; Bais Yaakov Schl for Girls 1989-; *ai:* Rdng Enrichment Prgm, Multi Media His Exhibition Club Adv.

WOLF, HELEN, Religion Teacher; *b:* Brooklyn, NY; *ed:* Pace Univ (BA) Sociology, Anthropology 1989; *cr:* St Pius IV R. C. Schl 6th-8th Grd Rel, Soc Stud Tchr 1986-95; Bishop Loughlin Mem HS Rel Tchr 1995-; *ai:* LaSallian Yth Adv; Lay Fac Assn 1261 1995-; Schola Cantorum Diocesan Choir 1994-; St Matthias Choir 1978-; Amer Humanics Yth Agency Admin Cert 1989; Advanced Catechism Cert 1990; Multinational, Comparative Eds Prgm Schlsp 1990; Seminar South Africa, Apartheid; *office:* Bishop Loughlin Mem HS 357 Clermont Ave Brooklyn NY 11238*

WOLF, JANET KATHERINE, Teacher of Gifted Students; *b:* Cleveland, OH; *m:* Robert J.; *c:* Robyn Corum, Wendy Loughlin, Sara; *ed:* Bowling Green St Univ (BS) Ed 1962; Widener Univ (MS) Gifted Ed 1992; Rdng Credits at Rowan Coll; *cr:* Maple Schl Kndgtn Tchr 1962-63; Poplar Hills 1st Grd Tchr 1963-64; Tabernacle Schl 6th Grd Tchr 1979; Indian Mills Meml 1st Grd, Lit & Rdng Tchr 1980-83, Tchr of 3rd-8th Grd Gifted Stdnts 1984-; *ai:* Acad Challenge Team Coach; NEA, NJEA, NAGC 1984-; NJAGC 1985-; Garden St Horse & Carriage Assn 1993-, Soc Chm; Brandywine Valley Driving Club 1993-; *office:* Indian Mills Memorial Schl 295 Indian Mills Rd Shamong Twp NJ 08088

WOLF, JEAN LEHMAN, Jr HS Bible, Math & PE Tchr; *b:* Fort Wayne, IN; *m:* Robert L.; *c:* Matthew, Melanie Williams, Stephen; *ed:* Taylor Univ (BS) PE 1970; Univ of Toledo (MEd) Ed 1972; *cr:* Emmanuel Baptist Jr HS Tchr 1971-74; Hope Town Christian Schl Residence Sup, Bible Tchr 1975-79; Emmanuel Baptist Jr HS Teachr 1979-; *ai:* AACS; ACSI; Sunshine Ministries 1980-; Pub Book; ACSI Convocation Trips to Russia; *office:* Emmanuel Baptist Chrstn Schl 4207 W Laskey Rd Toledo OH 43623

WOLF, LOIS WEISER, Political Science Professor; *b:* Newark, NJ; *w:* Arno (dec); *ed:* Rutgers Univ (BA) His-Highest Hnrs 1953, (MA) Pol Sci 1960; 60 Hrs The New Schl; 18 Hrs L'Institute des Etades Politique Paris; 18 Credit Hrs Ed Cert Seton Hall Univ; *cr:* Woodbridge Pub Schls 5th Grd Tchr 1954-55; West Orange Pub Schl 9th Grd His Tchr 1955-64; Wm Paterson Coll Prof Pol Sci 1964-; *ai:* Fac Senate; Governance Cncl; Senate Parliamentarian; Lbrl Arts, Prof Comms; Pol Sci Internships Dir; AFT Exec Comm Charter Legislative Rep; NJICTL 1989-; Focus Group; WO Animal Welfare League 1985-; Fulbright Hayes Scholar Paris; Phi Beta Kappa; Pi Sigma Alpha; 3 Merit Awds; 1990 Stdnts First Awd; 5 Terms Chair Fac Senate; Univ of MI FIPSE Grant Participant; Map, Globe Skills Text 3 Ed; *home:* 18 Crystal Ave West Orange NJ 07052

WOLF, MICHAEL ALLEN, Music Dept Chair & Band Dir; *b:* Lancaster, PA; *ed:* Millersville Univ (BA) Music His, Theory 1993, (BSE) Music 1993; Addl Grad Stud at Eastman Schl of Music, Univ of Rochester; *cr:* Eastern York SD Bands Dir, Dept Chair 1993-; *ai:* Marching Band Dir; Musicals, Plays Producer; Music Edctrs Natl Conf 1989-; Internal Assn of Jazz Edctrs 1993-; NEA; PSEA; *office:* Eastern York Schl Dist PO Box 2002 Cool Creek Rd Wrightsville PA 17368

WOLF, REGIS JOSEPH, Physical Science Teacher; *b:* Braddock, PA; *m:* Elizabeth A.; *c:* Darren, Carrie Catone; *ed:* CA Univ of PA (BS) Elem Ed 1968; Univ of Pittsburgh (MED) Ed 1972; *cr:* Steel Valley Schl Dist Sci Tchr 1968-; *ai:* Stu Asst Team; SVEA 1968-; PSEA 1968-; NEA 1968-; Vol Fire Dept 1965-, Treas; *office:* Steel Valley Schl Dist 3113 Main St Munhall PA 15120

WOLF, STEVEN ANTHONY, Vice Principal; *b:* Syracuse, NY; *c:* Stephanie; *ed:* LeMoyne Coll (BA) Bio 1983; SUNY at Oswego (MS) Ed 1990; SUNY at Cortland (CAS) Ed Admin 1995; *cr:* Huntington Schl Sci Tchr 1984-94; Grant MS Spec Assignment Tchr 1994-95; Dr. Weeks Elem Schl Vice Prin 1995-; *ai:* Supts Issues Analysis Team; Chair Pupil Svcs Team; Reducing Violence in Schls, Frameworks & Assessment Steering Comms; Regnl Assessment Stud Group; ASCD 1994-; Phi Delta Kappa 1994-, Corresponding Sec; NAESP, Schl Admin Assn of NYS 1995-; Bristol Myers Comm Advy Cncl 1994-, Bd Mem; Northeast Comm Ctr Prgm Bd 1995-, Bd of Dirs; Star Schls Mini-Grant; *office:* Dr. Weeks Elem Schl 710 Hawley Ave Syracuse NY 13203

WOLF, WANDA GANG, School Counselor; *b:* Albany, GA; *m:* Thomas; *c:* Sarah, Samantha; *ed:* Case Western Reserve Univ (BA) Psych 1975, (MA) Psych 1975; Temple Univ (MED) Couns Psych 1978; *cr:* CORA Svcs Cnslr, Asst Prgm Coord 1978-; *ai:* Costume Design Jenkintown Music Theater 6 Yrs; Jenkintown Ed Found 1992-95, Bd of Dirs; We Can Say No 1995-; Prgm Bd Mem; Margaret Glenn Estey Awd 1989, Svc to Girls; *office:* CORA Services 733 Susquehanna Rd Philadelphia PA 19111

WOLFE, ANTOINETTE KLIMKOWSKI, 4th Grade Teacher; *b:* New York City, NY; *m:* Charles E. Jr.; *ed:* NY Univ at Oneonta (BA) Ed 1969; St Univ at Stonybrook (MA) Ed 1973; Towson Univ Specialization in Tchng Gifted 1988; 30 Credit Hrs OH St Univ; *cr:* Chippewa Elem Schl Tchr; Ramstein Elem Schl Tchr of Gifted 1979-83; Grace Schl Tchr 1984-89; St Peters Schl Tchr 1984-89; Columbus City Schls Tchr 1989-; *ai:* Video Club Adv 1970-; Taught Saturday Morning Arts Prgm; NEA 1969-; OEA 1989-; Article Pub; IMPACT II Grant St of OH 1995; Instrl Fair Presenter 1996; *office:* Georgian Heights Elem Schl 784 Georgian Dr Columbus OH 43228*

WOLFE, DANIEL EDWARD, Chemistry Physics Teacher; *b:* Bloomsburg, PA; *m:* Sharon Ann; *c:* DeAnn, DeDra; *ed:* Bloomsburg Univ (BA) Ed & Chem 1966; Univ of Scranton (MS) Chem 1973; Attnd Woodrow Wilson Inst, Gettysburg Coll & Gatlin Gabel Schl; *cr:* Pennsburg Schl Dist Jr HS Sci Tchr 1966-67; Susquehanna Comm Chem & Physics Tchr 1967-; *ai:* Sr Class, NHS Adv; Sci Math Dept Chprsn; Curr cncl; NEA 1966-; PSEA 1966-; NSTA 1991-; PSTA & AAPT 1992-; Meth Church 1992-, Sunday Schl Supt; Rural Tchr of Yr Honorable Mention 1995; Telecomms Awd; Cross Cntry Journal & Sci Scope; *home:* 422 Grand St Susquehanna PA 18847*

WOLFE, ELIZABETH SIMMONS, High School Art Teacher; *b:* Bluffton, OH; *m:* Lewis S.; *c:* Jerrod S., Jonathon S.; *ed:* Bowling Green St Univ (BSEd) Art Ed 1975; Addl Hrs OH Univ, OH St Univ; *cr:* Tri Vly Local Schls 4 Elems & Jr HS Art Tchr 1975-76; Tri Vly HS Art Tchr 1976-; *ai:* Muskingum Cty Art Course of Stud Comm; T-VEA 1975-, Bldg Rep, Assn Sec, Dist Rep to OEA Rep Assembly; OEA, NEA 1975-; OAEA 1980-; Dresden Village Assn 1988-; Hebron Elem Schl PTO 1989-, Rcdng Sec 1991-93, 1995-; BGSU Alumni Assn 1975-; *office:* Tri-Valley HS 36 E Muskingum Ave Dresden OH 43821

WOLFE, ENID IONE, Guidance Counselor; *b:* Norwalk, OH; *c:* Darren J., Shannon, Ty; *ed:* Bowling Green St Univ (BS) Elem Ed 1975; Univ of Akron (MS) K-12 Guid, Cnslng 1990; *cr:* Western Reserve Local Schls 1st Grd Tchr 1975-94, K-8 Grd Guid Cnslr 1994-; *ai:* NEA 1975-, Rep; Tchrs Assn Western Reserve 1975-, Treas; OH Schl Cnslr Assn 1990-; League of Women Voters 1995-; Wakeman Lib Bd 1963-, BSA 1967-78, Den Mother; Bath United Church of Christ 1996; *office:* Western Reserve Local Schls 28 River St Wakeman OH 44889*

WOLFE, GARY L., High School Math Teacher; *b:* Defiance, OH; *m:* Candace L. Dock; *c:* Nickolus, Gregory, Brian; *ed:* Adrian Coll (BA) Math, Ed 1975; Univ of Dayton (MA) Supervision, Admin 1982; Attnd Bowling Green St U, Drake Univ, Wright St Univ; *cr:* Mohawk HS Math Tchr 1975-77; Upper Scroto Vly HS Math Tchr 1977-84; Lima Bath HS Math Tchr 1984-; *ai:* NCTM, OCTM, NEA, OEA 1975-; Bath Sports Club 1987-, VP; *office:* Lima Bath HS 2850 Bible Rd Lima OH 45801*

WOLFE, GLORIA JEAN (PARKS), Fifth Grade Teacher; *b:* Zanesville, OH; *m:* Vernon Keith; *c:* Scott C., Amy B.; *ed:* Oh Univ (BS) Elem Ed 1970; Attnd OH Univ, Ashland Univ, Muskingum Coll, Univ of Charleston; *cr:* Grant Elem Schl 3rd Grd Tchr 1967-71; Garfield & Madison Elem Schls LD Tchr 1973-81; Gen Rufas Putnam Comm Schl 5th Grd Tchr 1981-; *ai:* Prin Advy Comm; Peer Mediation Facilitator; Plan Monthly Behavior Awds; Responsible for New Playground Equipment for Schl; NEA 1967-; Zanesville Ed Assn 1967-; Oh Ed Assn-1967-; Soccer Boosters 1986-90; Chrldng Boosters 1991-95, Treas 1993-94; Muskingum Coll Classroom of the Future Project; Martha Holden Jennings Scholar; Co for Tchr Evaluation Model; Hnrd by Spcl Ed Tchr Group for Work Inclusion; CFTEM Unit on Self-Esteem & Goal Setting; *office:* Gen Rufus Putnam Comm Schl 920 Moxahala Ave Zanesville OH 43701*

WOLFE, JEFFREY LEE, Chemistry Teacher; *b:* Reading, PA; Melissa F. Favinger; *c:* Austin John; *ed:* East Stroudsburg Univ (BS) C 1980; Lehigh Univ (MED) Ed 1991; *cr:* Fleetwood HS Chem 1986-87; Muhlenberg HS Chem Tchr 1987-88; OLey HS Chem 1988-89; Hamburg Area HS Chem Tchr 1989-; *ai:* Co-Coach Sci Olym Team; Rep Cncl; NEA 1986-; Tiger Optimist Club 1995-; Fleetw Orioles 1981-; *office:* Hamburg Area HS Windsor St Hamburg PA 195

WOLFE, KEITH SAMUEL, Choral Dir & Music Dept Chm; *b:* Kensington, PA; *m:* Patricia Lynn Negley; *ed:* IN Univ of PA (BS) M Ed 1991, (MED) Prof Growth 1996; *cr:* North Allegheny Schls Music 1991-92; New Kensington Arnold Schl Dist Choral Dir 1993-; *ai:* S Choir, Asst Marching Band Dir; Track Coach; MENC 1988-; PMEA 19 ACDA 1989-; Alle-Kiski Concert Assn 1992-, Bd of Dirs; Grace M Church 1992-, Prof Singer, Bell Choir Dir; *office:* Valley HS 703 Steven Blvd New Kensington PA 15068

WOLFE, KELLY, 7th Grade Mathematics Teacher; *b:* Logan, OH; Sheila; *ed:* OH Wesleyan Univ (BA) Math, Ed 1991; *cr:* Logan Hock Schls Math Tchr 1992-; *ai:* Var Bsbl, Ftbl Asst Coach; MS Math D Chprsn; NEA 1992-; *office:* Logan Hocking MS 1 Middleschool Dr Lo OH 43138

WOLFE, KRISTIE (BECK), English Teacher; *b:* Pittsburgh, PA; Thomas J. Jr.; *c:* Alexander, Andrew, Madison; *ed:* Univ of Pittsburgh (Scndry Ed Eng 1992; IN Univ of PA Educl Psych Pgm MED; *cr:* Bis Guilfoyle HS Jr Eng Tchr 1992-93, HS Eng Tchr 1994-; Hollidaysb Cath Schl Lang Arts Tchr 1993-94; *ai:* Altoona Johnstown Cath Schl Tc Assn 1994-; NCEA 1994-; *office:* Bishop Guilfoyle HS 2400 Pleas Valley Blvd Altoona PA 16602

WOLFE, NORMAN WILLIAM, Instrumental Music Teacher; Morrisville, VT; *m:* Nancy Sturtevant; *c:* Nicholas; *ed:* Johnson St C (BA) Music Ed 1973; *cr:* Hartford Schl Dist Music Tchr 1973-; *ai:* A Coach Girls Soccer; Coach Boys LaCrosse Club; MENC 1963-; I 1995-; NEMFA 1989-; Hartford Town Band 1994-, Dir; Regnl Bd Symphony Orch 1995-, Trustee; Schl Dist Outstdng Tchr Awd 1988; *offi* Hartford MS, HS Highland Ave White River Juncti VT 05001

WOLFE, PAMELA KLINE, Soc Stud Dept Chair & Teacher; Richmond, VA; *m:* Robert E.; *c:* Matthew, Hannah; *ed:* Univ of MD (M European His 1983; Univ of Strasbourg 2nd Yr Degree Fr 1978; P Pending; AP US Govt, US His, European His Confs; *cr:* Univ of MD Tchr 1979-80, His Tchr 1980-85; Yeshiva of Greater Washington Fr, Tchr 1981-, Soc Stud Dept Chm 1988-; *ai:* Debate Club, Citizen Coach; Discipline Code, Curr Dev Comms; Geography Bee, Natl Pe Essay Contest Advs; Neighborhood Watch 1993-, Dist Organizer; Geo C. Marshall Fellow; Natl Peace Essay Contest Judge; *office:* Yeshiva Greater Washington 1910 University Blvd W Silver Spring MD 20902

WOLFE, RENEE L., English Teacher; *b:* Hamilton, OH; *ed:* Miami U of OH (BA) Theatre 1977; Wright St Univ (MEd) 1987; *cr:* Prof Thea Costumer, Dresser 1976-84; Brookville HS Eng Tchr 1989-; *ai:* Spee Debate Coach; Past Theatre Dir; NEA, OEA 1987-; NFL 1990-; *offi* Brookville HS 106 Hill St Brookville OH 45309

WOLFE, SUSETTE (BROWN), Fifth Grade Teacher; *b:* Richland, PA; John Guy; *c:* Alexander, Andrew; *ed:* Bloomsburg Univ (BA) Elem 1984; Millersville Univ (MED) Elem Ed 1989; 24 Past (MS); *cr:* Colum Schls Remedial Math Tchr 1987-88; Conrad Weiser 5th Grd Tchr 198 *ai:* Cooperating Tchr for Kutztown & Alvernia Univs; Pride Comm; PSE NEA & CWEA 1988-; Brown Family Reunion 1994-, Treas; *office:* Con Weiser School Dist 347 E Penn Ave Robesonia PA 19551

WOLFE, TERRI JEAN, Math Tchr & Var Chrldng Coach; *b:* Wilmingt OH; *ed:* Wilmington Coll of OH (BS) Ed, Math, Music 1984; Worki Toward MA Guid Cnslng Univ of Dayton of OH, Wright St Univ of O *cr:* Hillsboro City Schl Math Tchr, Coach 1984-; *ai:* Var, Reserve Chrldr Natl Competition Chrldng Coach; St Certified Judge Venture Capi Grant, Stu & Tchr Recognition Comms; NEA, OEA, NEA, NCTM 198 Mt Olive Church of Christ 1974-, Tchr, Pianist; Nom Ashland Oil Tchr Yr; Several Nationally Ranked Chrldng Squads Coach; *home:* 10091 M River Rd New Vienna OH 45159*

WOLFF, FRED S., Elementary Curriculum Coord; *b:* Youngstown, O *m:* Jean Corson; *ed:* OH Univ (BSC) Comm 1973; Univ of NH (ME Scndry Ed 1982; Boston Univ (EDD) Curr & Tchng 1991; *cr:* Hudson Sc Dist HS Eng Tchr 1975-77, Coord of Gifted & Talented 1978-80; Der Schl Dist Coord of Gifted Ed 1980-94; Amer Inst Schl Portgual HS E Tchr 1984-85; Londonderry Schl Dist Elem Curr Coord 1994-; *ai:* PD 1989-; ASCD 1993-, St Bd of Dirs; NCTE 1990-; Distinguished Tchr A from Presidental Scholar Commission; *office:* Londonderry Schl Dist 2 Mammoth Rd Londonderry NH 03053*

WOLFF, LAWRENCE ALAN, Psychology Teacher; *b:* Bronx, NY; Stacey Robyn Ehrlich; *ed:* Univ of MA (BS) Psych 1983; Montclair Univ (MAT) Math 1986; Rutgers Univ (EDM) Counseling Psych 1992; S Personnel Svcs Cert 1996; *cr:* Teaneck HS Math, Cmptr Tchr 1985-8 Psych Tchr 1989-; *ai:* Yrbk Co-Adv; Asst Boys, Girls Vlybl Coach; Int Excursion Chaperone; Teaneck Twp Tchrs Assn, NJEA, NEA 1986-; Cncl for Soc Stud 1990-; Teaneck Schl Employees Fed Credit Union 1986 Supervisory Comm; Amer Red Cross 1979-92, Water Safety, Life Gua Instr, 10 Yr Svc Awd; *office:* Teaneck HS 100 Elizabeth Ave Teaneck 07666

WOLFF, MARY T., Biology Teacher; *b:* New Brunswick, NJ; *m:* Carl *c:* Alexander, Geoffrey; *ed:* Seton Hall Univ (BS) Bio 1971; Long Islan Univ 20 Credits Toward Masters in Tech Ed; *cr:* Carter Wallace Inc Pharmacologist 1968-71; Blau-Kaptain Assoc Exec Recruiter Pharmaceuticals Tchr 1984-87; Freehold Twp Bd of Ed MS Sci Tc 1987-93; Highland Park Bd of Ed Bio Tchr 1994-; *ai:* Environmental Clu Adv; NSTA 1987-; Spotswood Bd of Ed 1982-92, Pres & VP; Merck Rutgers MS Sci Ldrshp Participant; Minority HS Stu Rsrch Apprenticeshi Tchr & Coord; *office:* Highland Park HS S 5th Ave Highland Park NJ 0890

WOLFF, THOMAS LEE, Asst Principal & Athletic Dir; *b:* Tiffin, OH; Laura Caylor; *c:* Mike, Heather; *ed:* Otterbein Coll (BA) His 1978; Akro Univ (MS) Scndry Admin 1985; Tiffin Columbian HS Coll Prep Cours 1974; *cr:* Hopewell-Loudon HS Govt & Amer His Tchr 1978-8 Northwestern HS Amer & World His Tchr 1983-86; Madison Jr High & H Amer His & Govt Tchr 1986-95; Madison Jr High Asst Prin & Ath D 1995-; *ai:* Var Ftbl Coach; Class Adv; Jr High Bsktbl Coach; Weigh Lifting Coach; NEA 1978-; Ashland Coll Ashbrook Scholar 1993; *hom* 785 Woodcrest Dr Mansfield OH 44905*

WOLFF, WARD L., Adjunct Professor; *b:* Rochester, NY; *m:* An Grentzinger; *c:* Penny, Scott; *ed:* SUNY at Oswego (BS) Industrial Arts E 1962; SUNY at Brockport (MS) Cnslr Ed 1974; Post Masters 30 Credit Hr Cnslr Ed; *cr:* Coral Gables Sr HS Indstrl Arts Tchr 1962-64; Hilton H Industrial Arts Tchr 1964-68; Holley Jr HS Cnslr 1968-71; Brockport H Cnslr 1971-; SUNY at Brockport Adjunct Prof 1980-; *ai:* Cnslng Inter Supvr; Advanced Placement Test Coord; Stu Asst Team Mem; AFT 1964- United Univ Prof 1980-; Monroe Cty Cnslrs 1971-; Aircraft Owners & Pilots Assn 1964-; Antique Auto Club of Amer 1962-; Plymouth Owner

& Genesee Valley Antique Car Soc 1992-; Presenter on Learning bled Theory; Spec Ed Advy Cncl Mem; Wemoco Voc Schl Advy Cncl ; SUNY at Brockport Cnslr Ed Advy Cncl Mem; *home:* 380 Lawton Hilton NY 14468*

LFGANG, GREG ROBERT, English Teacher; *b:* York, PA; *ed:* East idsburg Univ (BS) Comm 1985; Post Grad Work at Penn St Univ, son St Univ, Wilkes Univ, Allentown Coll, Carlow Coll; *cr:* York City Dist Lang Arts Tchr, Eng Dept Chprsn 1985-; *ai:* Dir of Debate, natics; SAT Supvr; Curr Advy Comm; Strategic Planning Action Team; ., PSEA 1991-; YCEA 1991-, Chair of Communications Comm; OPEN -; Covenant Church 1968-, Vice Chair Elders; Tchr Flwshp for Dow s Newspaper Dirs 1991; *office:* William Penn Sr HS 101 W College York PA 17403

LFGANG, SUSAN MAHER, Sixth Grade Teacher; *b:* Salem, OH; *m:* e; *c:* Kasey, Ryan, Max; *ed:* Youngstown St (BS) Ed 1984; 30 Addl *cr:* Immaculate Heart of Mary Fourth Grd Tchr 1985-86; Parma City s Fourth Grd Tchr 1986-88; Salem City Schls Sixth Grd tchr 1988-; *e:* South East Elem Schl 2200 Merle Rd Salem OH 44460

LFIELD, DALE, Art Instructor; *b:* Kingston, NY; *m:* Mark R. Boyer; SUNY at Oswego (BA) Studio Art, Museum Stud 1979; SUNY at New z (MA) Ceramics 1993; Bennington Coll Fresco Painting 1994; *cr:* an Marsh Visual Merchandising Mgr 1984-85; Eddie Bauer Dist play Coord 1986-87; Lord & Taylor Visual Merchandising Dir 1987-88; eora HS Art Instr 1990-; *ai:* Mural Project; Ind Stud; Woodstock Artists n 1989-, Bd of Dirs 1993; Reullen Sculpture Awd 1993; Woman's lio Wkshp 1995-; Various Area Galleries Art Exhibitions; Group, ed, Solo Art Shows.*

LFORD, BRENT MASON, Biology & Anatomy Teacher; *b:* Oil City, *m:* Marsha Fredlund; *c:* Brenda Wolford Lorenzo; *ed:* Edinboro Univ) Bio 1965; Fredonia St Univ (MS) Ed 1972; *cr:* Forestville HS Bio, Sci Tchr 1965-67; Dunkirk HS Bio, Chem, Anatomy Tchr 1968-; *ai:* Club Adv; Dunkirk Tchrs Assn 1968-, Exec Comm; Assn for Sup, Curr 1994-; Anson Co No 3 Fire Co 1970-, VP, Trustee; Fraternal Order of ose 1985-; Natl Musicians Union 1962-; NSF Grant to Millersville St ; Established St Accredited Anatomy Course; *home:* 11 Lafayette Ave kirk NY 14048

LFSKILL, HEIDI A., Music Department Head & Tchr; *b:* Lebanon, *ed:* Messiah Coll (BS) Music Ed 1982; West Chester Univ (MM) Music 1996; *cr:* Plumstead Chrstn Schl Instrumental Music Tchr 1982-, Music t Head 1986-; *ai:* Music Edctrs Natl Conf 1986-; PA Music Edctrs n 1986-; *office:* Plumstead Christian Schl 5765 Old Easton Rd nsteadville PA 18949*

LFSON, JOSH, Accounting Professor; *b:* Mineola, NY; *m:* Zena; *c:* per; *ed:* Univ of Buffalo (BS) Mgmt 1978; Hofstra Univ (MBA) Acctng 0; *cr:* Person & Wolinsky CPA Review Courses Lecturer 1985-; BMCC outy Chprsn 1989-94, Acctng Prof 1984-; *ai:* Acctng Club Adv; Hnrs nm Co-Chair; TACTYC 1984-, BOD 1988-90; Certfd Pub Accountant of NY; BMCC Acctng Club Outsdng Svc Awd; *office:* Borough Of nhattan Comm Coll 199 Chambers St New York NY 10007

LK, MORRIS, Art Teacher; *b:* Baltimore, MD; *ed:* MD Inst of Art A) Art Ed 1974; Morgan St Univ (MS) Urban Ed 1977; *cr:* thwestern Sr HS Art Tchr 1974-; *ai:* Art Logic Problems 9th-12th ls-Currently Used in Baltimore City Pub Schls; Studio 6001 Artists operative Founder 1990; *office:* Northwestern Sr HS 401 6900 Park ghts Ave Baltimore MD 21215

LL, BERNARD D., Elementary Teacher; *b:* Danville, PA; *c:* Lauren, deleine; *ed:* Bloomsburg Univ (BS) Elem Ed, Early Chldhd 1973, (MS) m Ed, Span, Eng 1975; *cr:* St Joseph Schl Prin, Asst Prin, 2nd-3rd, -8th Grd Tchr 7 Yrs; Diehl Schl 3rd, 5th Grd Tchr 11 Yrs; Mahoning oper 4th Grd Tchr 5 Yrs; *ai:* Danville Ed Assn, PA St Ed Assn 1979-; EA 1972-.*

LLAM, DENNIS RUSSELL, Band Director; *b:* Warren, OH; *m:* borah Frances Shields; *c:* Jennifer Lynn Pittser, Julie Ann; *ed:* Otterbein ll (BME) Instrumental Music 1969; *cr:* Ashland Crestview HS Band Dir 59-71; Westland HS Band Dir 1971-75; Washington City Schls Band Dir 75-; *ai:* Asst Golf Coach; OMEA 1969-, Dist Pres 25 Yr Awd; Phi Beta 1984-; ASBDA 1989-; MENC & OEA; Fayette Comm Band, nductor; Fayette Comm Concert Assn, Bd of Dir; *home:* 1360 Brakefield Wshngtn Ct Hs OH 43160

LLASTON, DIANE, American History Teacher; *b:* Harrisburg, PA; James Edward Jr.; *c:* Andrew; *ed:* Bloomsburg Univ (BS) Ed 1986; llersville Univ (MA) Amer His 1995; Supervisory Cert Soc Stud 1996; Penn Manor HS Amer His Tchr 1986-87; Elizabethtown Area HS Amer s Tchr 1987-; *ai:* Class, Citizen Bee Adv; PSEA, EAEA 1987-; *office:* izabethtown Area HS 600 E High St Elizabethtown PA 17022*

OLLMAN, BARBARA JEAN (CHASE), Secondary English Teacher; Plainfield, NJ; *m:* Michael Steven; *c:* Rebecca Susan; *ed:* Rutgers iv-Douglass Coll (BA) Eng 1977; *cr:* Hubbard MS Eng Tchr 1977-87; ainfield HS Eng Tchr 1987-; *ai:* Yrbk; Flag Squad Adv; PEA, UCEA, EA & NEA 1977-, MS Exec Ofcr; Motherhood 1986-; *office:* Plainfield 950 Park Ave Plainfield NJ 07060

OLNY, HOWARD A., History Teacher; *b:* Rahway, NJ; *m:* Suzanne; *c:* nnifer, Matthew; *ed:* Mulhenberg Coll (BA) His 1968; Attnd Monmouth iv; *cr:* Howell Twp Tchr 1968-; *ai:* Track Coach; Stu Cncl Adv; Career Coord; NEA, NJEA 1968-; HTEA 1968-, Treas; Green Peace 1976-; indstar 1978-; *office:* Howell Twp MS 13 Squankum Yellowbrook Rd owell NJ 07731

OLOSKI, JOHN J.,JR., Music Teacher & Orchestra Dir; *b:* ilkes-Barre, PA; *m:* Cheryl A. Polak; *c:* John, Jason; *ed:* Wilkes Coll (BS) usic Ed 1981; Scranton Univ (MS) Schl Admin 1986; Attnd Scranton niv, Wilkes Univ; *cr:* Wilkes-Barre Area Schl Dist Music Tchr, Orch Dir 81-; *ai:* Sr Class Adv; All Area Orch, HS Orch Dir; PMEA, MENC, NEA, ocal 140 Music Union 1981-; Knights of Columbus 1983-; Holy Name c 1981-, Pres; St Joseph's CCD Prgm Coord, Tchr; Church Lector; Holy ame Soc Pres Awd; Who's Who Among America's Finest Men; Host MSA All St Music Festival 1993; PMEA Regnl Orch Festival Host 1985; MEA Dist Orch Festiv al Host 1981; *office:* GAR Meml HS 250 S Grant Wilkes Barre PA 18702

OLOSON, JOAN ESSICK, Sixth Grade Teacher; *b:* Burlington, VT; *c:* lake K., Wendy A.; *ed:* Mary Washington Coll of Univ of VA (BA) Psych, lem Ed 1959; Elmira Coll (MS) Ed 1972; 24 Addl Credit Hrs; *cr:* Geo. ashington Elem Schl 1st Grd Tchr 1959-60; Genesee Hills Elem Schl 1st rd Tchr 1960-62; Gardner Rd Elem Schl 6th Grd Tchr 1965-; *ai:* Stipend omm; AFT, NY St United Tchrs 1965-; Horseheads Tchrs Assn 1965-, dg Rep; Amer Assn of Univ Women 1990-, Co-Prgm Chm; *office:* ardner Road Elem Schl 541 Gardner Rd Horseheads NY 14845

OLPERT, DEBRA ANN (BETZ), Algebra & Geometry Teacher; *b:* anton, OH; *m:* David Scott; *c:* Andy, Melissa; *ed:* Mount Union Coll (BS) lath 1973; Attnd Coll of Mount St Joseph, Kent St Univ, Walsh Coll; *cr:* ackson HS Math & PE Tchr 1973-74; Louisville Jr HS Math Tchr 1974-; ouisville HS Math Tchr 1991-; *ai:* NEA 1974-; OEA 1974-; LEA 1974-; lliance Cntry Club 1973-; Marlington Ath Booster Club 1991-; Canton hamber of Commerce Tchr of Yr Finalist 1985; *home:* 14517 Cenfield St E Alliance OH 44601

WOLSON, KAREN SUSAN, Assoc Prof of Biological Sci; *b:* New York, NY; *w:* Morton (dec); *c:* Scott, Robin Robertson; *ed:* St Univ of NY (AAS) Dental Hygiene 1962; NYU (BS) Ed & Sci 1965; Montclaire Univ (MA) Hlth Ed 1975; Continuing Ed 300 Credit Hrs 1986-; Lynn Univ Geriatric Medicine Cert 22 Credit Hrs 1990, Internship 250 Credit Hrs; *cr:* Bergen Comm Coll Assoc Prof Dental Hygeine Dept 1973-; *ai:* Advisement; Senate Coll Wide Comms; NJEA 1972-; NJDHA 1975-; Womans Club 1980-; Comm Outreach 1985-; *office:* Bergen Comm Coll 400 Paramus Rd Paramus NJ 07652

WOLSTONCROFT, HOWARD STEVEN, US History & Amer Govt Tchr; *b:* Mc Keese Rocks, PA; *m:* Lorrie Russo; *ed:* IN Univ of PA (BSEd) Comprehensive Soc Sci 1970; Duquesne Univ of Pittsburgh (MS) Admin 1975; *cr:* Churchill HS Psych, Sociology, 20th Century Amer, World Cultures, Ec Tchr 1970-88; Woodland Hills East Jr HS US His, Amer Govt, Civics Tchr 1988-; *ai:* Asst & Head Wrestling, Asst Ftbl, Defensive Coord Coach; NEA, PSEA, WHEA 1970-; Lib Power 1995-; Old Folks Home Vol; Animal Soc Mem; *home:* 212 Thunderwood Dr Bethel Park PA 15102*

WOLTERS, JEANETTE MARIE, Social Studies Teacher; *b:* New York City, NY; *ed:* St Josephs Coll (BA) His 1992; SUNY at Stony Brook MA Lbrl Arts Pending; *cr:* Lindenhurst HS Soc Stud Tchr 1992-; *ai:* Class of 1997 & Yrbk Adv; Phi Alpha Theta 1990-; *office:* Lindenhurst HS 300 Charles St Lindenhurst NY 11757

WOLVEN, BARRY D., Physical Education Teacher; *b:* Saugerties, NY; *m:* Sara; *c:* Scott, William; *ed:* Rutgers Univ (BS) PE 1964; SUNY at Cortland (MS) PE 1972; *cr:* Catskill Central Schl Soc Stud Tchr 1966-67, PE Tchr 1967-; *ai:* JV Bsbl Coach; Catskill Tchrs Assn 1966-; NYSUT 1966-.

WONDER, JAMIE LYNN, French Teacher; *b:* New Orleans, LA; *ed:* Muhlenberg Coll (BA) Fr 1989; Millersville Univ (MA) Fr 1996; Kutztown Univ Tchrs Cert Ed 1990; Centres d'Etudes Francaises, Univ of Northern IA Fr Prgm; *cr:* Wilson Central Jr HS Fr Tchr 1991-95; Wilson Sr HS Fr Tchr 1995-; *ai:* Fr Club Adv; AWFT 1991-; AAFT 1991-; Jean Paul Levy Schlrshp Millersville Univ; *office:* Wilson Sr HS 2601 Grandview Blvd West Lawn PA 19609*

WONDRAK, GERALD A., Vocal Music Teacher; *b:* Cleveland, OH; *m:* Judith Ann Brinker; *c:* Alice; *ed:* Bowling Green St Univ (BME) Music 1967; IN Univ (MM) Music & Composition 1970; Attnd Berklee Schl of Music 1 Yr; *cr:* Allen Elem Schl Tchr 1967-70; Lakewood HS Vocal Music Tchr 1970-94, 1995-; *ai:* Lakewood Road Show Jazz Choir Dir; NEA, OEA, IAJE, OMEA 1970-; Lakewood HS Tchr of Yr 1994; *home:* 8475 Lakeview Rd West Yellowstone MT 59758

WONG, BELLA T., Science Teacher; *b:* Boston, MA; *m:* Steven Brand; *ed:* Harvard Univ (BA) Bio 1982; Univ of CA Law Schl at Davis (JD) Law 1987; Harvard Schl of Ed (EDM) Ed 1991; Post Grad Stud in Molecular Bio Stanford Univ 1982-84; *cr:* LeBoeuf Lamb Leiby & Macrae Attorney 1987-90; Lincoln-Sudbury Regnl HS Sci Tchr 1991-; *ai:* Club Adv to Asian Cultures Club; Tchrs Assn Pres; Amer Bar Assn; CA Bar Assn; MA Bar Assn; MA Tchrs Assn; *office:* Lincoln-Sudbury Regnl HS 390 Lincoln Rd Sudbury MA 01776

WONG, ELLIOTT, Social Studies Teacher; *b:* New York, NY; *ed:* NY Univ (BA) Pol Sci 1986-; Westminster Theological Seminary (MA) Rel 1989; Brooklyn Coll (MA) Pol Sci 1995; *cr:* Bayard Rustin HS for Hum Eng Tchr 1989-90; Brooklyn Tech HS Soc Stud Tchr 1986-87, 1990-; *ai:* Soc Sci Research Inst; Fantasy Roleplay Club; AFT, NYSUT, UFT, Phi Beta Kappa 1986-; *office:* Brooklyn Technical HS 29 Ft Greene Pl Brooklyn NY 11217

WONG-HO, IVY YAU-WAH, Music Teacher; *b:* Hong Kong, BCC; *m:* Lee Wing Ho; *c:* Timothy Christian Ho; *ed:* Univ of Pacific (BM) Piano, Choral Conducting 1974; Trinity Coll of Music (LTCM) Piano 1975; Univ of MA (MM) Piano, Conducting, Music Ed 1977; Attnd Royal Schls of Music; *cr:* Muriel Snowden Intnl Schl Frgn Lang Tchr 1986-88; Harreit Baldwin Schl Biling Ed 1988-90; William Howard Taft Schl Biling Ed 1990-93; Boston Latin Schl Music Tchr 1993-; *ai:* Concert Choir Dir; Music Adv to Asian Stu Club; BTU 1978-; AFT, MABE 1981-; Boston Chinese Evalelical Church 1983-, Pianist, Organist; Lead Tchr 1995; Golden Apple Awd 1993; *office:* Boston Latin Schl 78 Avenue Louis Pasteur Boston MA 02115*

WONNELL, JANE NICHOLS, 2nd Grade Teacher; *b:* Port Clinton, OH; *m:* Daniel William; *c:* Daniel Gerald, Stephie Maureen; *ed:* Otterbein Coll (BSEd) Elem Ed 1977; Coll of Mt ST Joseph (MS) Tchng Proficiency 1989; Working on Masters +30 Credit Hrs; *cr:* Westerville City Schls Elem Classroom Tchr 1978-; *ai:* Soc Comm for Tchrs; Bldg Rep for Planet Westerville Playground; OEA 1978-; NEA 1978-; WEA 1978-; AHASA 1985-; Windsor Bay Civic Assoc 1989-; *office:* Annehurst Elem Schl 925 W Main St Westerville OH 43081

WOOD, ALLAN HICKS, Social Studies Teacher; *b:* Rochester, NY; *m:* Catherine Ann Knight; *c:* Peter; *ed:* St Univ of NY at Geneseo (BS) Ed 1971; 36 Grad Hrs St Univ of NY at Oswego, Ithaca Coll; *cr:* Cato Meridian Cntrl Schl 4th Grd tchr 1971-76, 8th Grd Soc Stud Tchr 1976-; *ai:* Yorker Club Adv; AFT 1971-; NYSUT 1975-; Cato Meridian Tchrs Assn 1971-, Bldg Rep; Cato Rotary Club 1978-,Yth Exch Ofcr, Paul Harris Fellow; Civic Heritage 1983-; MS Tchr of Yr 1978-79; HS Tchr of Yr 1991; *office:* Cato-Meridian MS PO Box 100 Cato NY 13033

WOOD, BILL LYN, English & Social Studies Tchr; *b:* Reform, MS; *m:* Mehtap Gozen; *c:* Jessica; *ed:* MS St Univ (MS) Admin 1986; WI St Univ (MS) Ed 1994; 30 Addl Hrs; *cr:* Gulfport Jr HS Eng Tchr 1969-71; Bitburg HS Eng, Soc Stud Tchr 1971-74; Ankara HS Eng, Speech, Drama, Sociology, Geog Tchr 1974-77; Bahrain HS Eng, Speech, Drama, Sociology, Geog Tchr 1977-78; Incirlik HS Eng, Speech, Drama, Sociology, Geog Tchr 1978-83; Izmir HS Eng, Speech, Drama, Sociology, Geog Tchr 1983-; *ai:* Stu Govt Assn, Jr Class Spon; Dept of Defense Ldrshp Acad Dir; Izmir Fed of Tchrs 1983-, Sec; Schl Advy Comm 1995-, Vice Chm; Black Heritage Comm 1995-, Chm; Tchr of Yr Awd 1980, 1984, 1995; *office:* Izmir American HS Psc 88 APO AE 09821*

WOOD, CASEY HOWARD, HS Social Studies Teacher; *b:* Bloomington, IN; *m:* Michelle Gaffner; *ed:* Cedarville Coll (BS) Soc Stud Comp, His 1993; Univ of Cincinnati Masters Prgm Curr & Instruction; *cr:* Southeastern HS Soc Stud Tchr 1993-; *ai:* Girls Var Track, Asst Var Boys Bsktbl Coach; Frosh Class, Stu Cncl Adv; Improving Instruction Comm; Natl Assn Stu Activity Advy 1995-; ASCD 1993-95; Grace Bapt Church 1987-, Sr High Youth Spon, Sunday Schl Tchr; *home:* 46 Regency Dr Cedarville OH 45314

WOOD, CATHERINE S., Mathematics Teacher; *b:* Chester, PA; *m:* Stephen L.; *c:* Stephen W., Patrick G.; *ed:* Immaculata Coll (BA) Math 1965; Masters Equivalency; *cr:* St Francis Indian Schl Math Tchr 1965-72; Pulaski Jr HS Math Tchr 1972-74; Chester HS Math Tchr 1974-92; CHS Acad Math Tchr 1992-; *ai:* NEA, PSEA, CUEA 1972-; Nativity BVM Home, Schl Assn 1984-, Treas 1991-93; Natl Sci Fnd, Chester Ed Fnd Apple Grants; *office:* Chester HS Acad 501 W 9th St Chester PA 19013

WOOD, DEBORAH BOROVSKY, MS Guidance Counselor; *b:* Burlington, VT; *m:* Duane A.; *c:* Kathryn, Kelsey; *ed:* St Rose (MS) Schl Cnslng 1988; Attnd Plattsburg St Coll; *cr:* Draper MS 6th-8th Grd Guid Cnslr 1988-; *ai:* Natl Jr Hnr Soc Co-Adv 1992-94; Newspaper Adv 1995; *office:* Draper MS 2070 Curry Rd Schenectady NY 12303

WOOD, DEBRA ANN, Physical Education Teacher; *b:* Ogdensburgh, NY; *ed:* SUNY at Brockport (BS) K-12 PE 1981, (MS) Elem Ed 1990; *cr:* Albion Cntrl Schl PE Tchr 1983-; *ai:* Var Girls Bsktbl; Jr High Girls Vllybl; NY St Tchrs Assn 1983-; AFT 1983-; USGA 1995-; *office:* Albion Cntrl Schl 254 East Ave Albion NY 14411

WOOD, DOROTHY C., Seventh Grade English Teacher; *b:* Hazleton, PA; *m:* Edward W.; *ed:* Wilkes Univ (MS) Ed 1993; *cr:* Harmon Jr HS Scndry Eng Tchr 1990-92; Hazleton Jr HS Scndry Eng Tchr 1992-; *office:* Hazleton Jr HS 700 N Wyoming St Hazleton PA 18201

WOOD, ELAINE M. (ROGOZINSKI), Business Teacher; *b:* Olean, NY; *m:* Daniel B.; *ed:* Jamestown Comm Coll (AS) Bus Admin 1972; SUNY at Albany (BS) Bus Ed 1974, (MS) Bus Ed 1978; *cr:* Campbell Cntrl Schl Bus Tchr 1974-92; Campbell Savona Cntrl Bus Tchr 1992-; *office:* Campbell Savona Central Schl Main St Campbell NY 14821

WOOD, FRANCIS JOSEPH, Chem & Earth Science Teacher; *b:* Watertown, NY; *m:* Karen Brower; *c:* Peter B., Briana L.; *ed:* Mohawk Vly Comm (AS) Math & Sci 1970; SUNY at Oswego (BS) Chem 1972, (MS) Chem 1977; 24 Stud Hrs Beyond MS; *cr:* Gen Brown High Chem & Earth Sci Tchr 1972-; *office:* General Brown HS Cemetary Rd Dexter NY 13634

WOOD, HAROLD MAURICE,III, Mathematics Teacher; *b:* Hornell, NY; *m:* Susan; *c:* Lindsay, Logan; *ed:* Alfred Univ (BS) Math 1992, (MS) Math 1996; *cr:* Airport Ctr Schl Math Tchr 1993-; *ai:* Var Bsbl Coach; Extended Learning Comm; Ath Cncl; NEA 1993-; *office:* Arkport Central Schl 35 East Ave Arkport NY 14807

WOOD, HERBERT THOMAS, Math Teacher; *b:* Alexandria, VA; *m:* Kathleen O'Connor; *c:* Kevin, Amy, Christopher, Elizabeth, Timothy, Michael, Margaret, Joanna; *ed:* Univ of WI (PHD) Phys Chem 1965; Cath Univ of Amer (BChE) Chem Engrng 1981; *cr:* Cath Univ of Amer Asst Prof 1966-72; Dist of Columbia Govt Pub Hlth Engr 1972-86; St Anselms Abbey Schl Tchr 1987-; *ai:* Engrng Team Coach; BSA 1972-, Scoutmaster; Article Pub; *office:* Saint Anselms Abbey Schl 4501 S Dakota Ave NE Washington DC 20017

WOOD, KATHERINE WATSON, Associate Prof of Human Svcs; *b:* Hyattsville, MD; *m:* Ronald A.; *c:* Melissa Wood Aleman, Caroline Elizabeth; *ed:* Western MD Coll (BA) Psych 1968; Hood Coll (MA) Human Sci 1976; The Catholic Univ of Amer (MSW) Clinical Work With Families 1993; Attnd Towson St Univ, Univ of MO at St Louis; *cr:* Frederick Comm Coll Adjunct Fac 1976-80; Counseling Svcs Inc Family Cnslr 1976-81; Frederick Comm Coll Psych Prof, Fac 1981-; *ai:* Coll Senate; Fac Assn Chair; Pres Cabinet; Mid States Assn Steering Comm for Coll Self Study; AAMFT 1980-; NASW 1991-; Amer Assn for Counseling & Dev; Mental Hlth Assn 1977-, Pres, VP; Frederick Womens Fair, Chair, AAUW 2nd Pl Ed; *office:* Frederick Comm Coll 7932 Opossumtown Pike Frederick MD 21702

WOOD, KEVIN RICHARD, Fourth Grade Teacher; *b:* Norwalk, OH; *m:* Susan K. Runner; *c:* Andrea, Jennifer; *ed:* Bowling Green St Univ (BS) Elem Ed 1974; *cr:* St Joseph Elem Schl Fourth Grd Tchr 1974-; *ai:* Altar Server Coord; Tech Dept Head; Math Ldrshp, Tech Trainers Cncls; NDEA; NCEA; *office:* St Joseph Elem Schl 79 Chapel St Monroeville OH 44847

WOOD, LEONARD A., Social Studies Teacher; *b:* New York City, NY; *ed:* C. W. Post Coll (BA) His-Cum Laude 1968; 30 Addl Post Grad Credit Hrs; *cr:* Candlewood Jr HS Soc Stud Tchr 1969-91; Half Hollow Hills HS West Soc Stud Tchr 1991-93; Half Hollow Hills HS East Soc Stud Tchr 1991-; *ai:* NYSUT 1969-; Long Island Cncl for Soc Stud 1985-; *office:* Half Hollow Hills HS East 50 Vanderbilt Pkwy Dix Hills NY 11746

WOOD, MARY LOU DONOVAN, High School English Teacher; *b:* Cincinnati, OH; *m:* Paul W.; *c:* Paul W. Jr., Suzanne M. Bruckner, Douglas L., Rebecca C.; *ed:* Coll of Mt St Joseph on the Ohio (BA) Eng 1959; Ed at St Bonaventure Univ; Eng at St Xavier Univ; *cr:* Seton HS Eng, Jrnlsm Tchr 1959-62; Olean HS Substitute 1971-79; Portville Cntrl HS Eng Tchr 1979-; *ai:* Natl Honor Soc Bd; Stdnts At Risk Comm; NMA Speech Comp Coach; Sports, Dance Chaperone; Class, Environmental & AFS Adv; NCTE, Phi Delta Kappa 1983-; Exch Prgm LEPA Erstein France 1991; Tchr of Eng to 15-21 Yr Old Fr Speaking Stdnts; *home:* 102 Virginia St Olean NY 14760*

WOOD, PAMELA M., Science Teacher; *b:* Atlanta, GA; *ed:* Stonehill Coll (BS) Bio 1973; Bridgewater St Coll (MAT) Bio 1982; Attnd Eastern CT St Coll 12 Credit Hrs 1986, Boston Univ 1993; *cr:* Mansfield HS Sci Tchr 1973-; *ai:* NHS Adv; NSBT 1975-; MA Assn Sci Tchrs 1986-, Cty Dir 1990-92; MA Assn Bio Tchr 1995-; *office:* Mansfield HS 250 East St Mansfield MA 02048

WOOD, PRISCILLA ANN BERNIER, Sixth Grade Teacher; *b:* Westbrook, MA; *m:* James O.; *c:* Brian James, Denise Marie, Keith Alan; *ed:* Univ of S ME (BS) Ed 1985; *cr:* Waterboro Elem Schl Grd 6 Tchr 1985-; *ai:* Yrbk; Cert Steering Comm Sec; Massabesie Ed Assn 1985-, Pres; ME Ed Assn, NEA 1985-; Buxton Jaycee Women 1977-83, Sec, St Dir; ME Jaycee Women 1977-83 St Historian; *home:* RR 3 Box 418 Gorham ME 04038

WOOD, RALPH BERNARD, Asst Professor of Mathematics; *b:* Greenville, MI; *m:* Cecily Cummings; *c:* Abigail, Joshua; *ed:* Case Inst of Tech (BS) Math 1962; Johns Hopkins U (MAT) Math 1963; 90 Credits Accumulated at Rutgers U, U of MD, Loyola Coll of MD, Hope Coll; *cr:* Baltimore Cty Pub Schls Math Tchr, Asst Prin, Prin 1963-92; U MD Balk Cty Support Office, Math 1992; Towson St U Adj Prof Math 1992; Carroll Comm Coll Asst ProfMath 1993-; *ai:* Coll Governance System; Math Curr, Information Ed, MD St Comm; Phi Theta Kappa; Math Assn of Amer 1994-; MD Math Assn of Two-Yr Coll, Assn of Fac Improvement of Comm Coll Tchng 1993-; Southern Poverty Law Carter 1993-; Natl Preservation Trust 1992-; Smithsonian Assn 1980-; *office:* Carroll Community College 1601 Washington Rd Westminster MD 21157

WOOD, ROBERT JOHN, Social Studies Teacher; *b:* Bellefonte, PA; *c:* Hannah; *ed:* Shippensburg Univ (BED) Soc Stud 1972; Kutztown Univ (MED) Soc Stud 1977; Attnd Penn St Univ, Scranton Univ, Villanova Univ, DE Vly Coll; *cr:* Easton Area Schl Dist Tchr 1973; Souderton Area Schl Dist Tchr 1973-; *ai:* Bdktbl Coach 1973-87; Track Coach 1980-84; Souderton Area Ed Assn 1973-, Pres; PA St Ed Assn, NEA 1973-; *office:* Souderton Area Sr HS 41 N School Ln Souderton PA 18964

WOOD, ROBERT RUSSELL, Eighth Grade Science Teacher; *b:* Martins Ferry, OH; *m:* Judy Ann Talasis; *c:* Eric, Robert, Alyssa; *ed:* OH Univ (BS) 1-8 Ed 1971; Univ of Dayton (MS) Jr HS, MS Ed 1979; *cr:* Martins Ferry City Schls; *ai:* NEA; OEA; MF Tchr Assn; *office:* Martins Ferry Jr HS 56731 Colerain Pike Martins Ferry OH 43935

WOOD, ROBIN BENENSOHN-ROSEFSKY, Theatre Department Head; *b:* Binghamton, NY; *m:* Jeremy Scott; *c:* Alexis, Jonas, Augusta; *ed:* Univ of PA (BA) Eng 1966; Yale Univ (MFA) Theatre & Directing 1969; Northeastern Univ Interpreting Amer Sign Lang Pgm, Cert Degree Deaf Stud 1993; Attnd Gmindet Univ; *cr:* The Cambridge Schl Theatre & Fac 1970-; Lesley Coll Adj Tchr 1994-; *ai:* Intnl Stu Fac; Early Intervention Pgm; Drug Ed Comm; AATE; ATA; NETIC; MSAD; NAD; Mortar Bd; DEAF Inc Vol 1990-; Galtham Comm Inc 1992-; Book: Why Day Care in High School; *office:* Cambridge Schl of Weston Georgian Rd Weston MA 02193

WOOD, RON EDWARD, English Teacher; *m:* Karin Marie; *c:* Ryan Michael; *ed:* Cleveland St (BA) Eng, Ed 1987; 12 Hrs Sport, Hlth Ed; *cr:*

Shore Jr HS Eng Tchr 1988-; *ai:* Ftbl, Girls Bsktbl 9th Grd Coach; Boys Jr Var Tennis Coach; NEA 1988-; USTA 1986-, Tennis Tchng Prof; *office:* Mentor Shore Jr HS 5670 Hopkins Rd Mentor OH 44060*

WOOD, SANDRA LEE, Third Grade Teacher; *b:* Pontiac, MI; *ed:* Monticello Coll (AAS) Lbrl Arts 1970; St Bonaventure Univ (BS) Elem Ed 1972, (MS) Ed 1978; *cr:* Scio Cntrl Schl Third Grd Tchr 1972-76, Fifth Grd Tchr 1976-78, Third Grd Tchr 1978-; *ai:* NEA 1972-; Scio Tchrs Assn 1972-, Sec 1980-82; Allegany Cty Tchrs Assn 1985-87, VP, Pres, Golden Apple; Scio Cntrl PTSA 1995-; *home:* 21 Coats St Wellsville NY 14895

WOOD, THOMAS EDWARDS, High School Mathematics Tchr; *b:* Milford, CT; *m:* Bridget O'Brien; *c:* Shannon, Conor; *ed:* St Univ Coll at Buffalo (BS) Math 1991; 12 Credit Hrs Cmptrs in Ed; *cr:* Buffalo Pub Schls Math Tchr 1991-93; Cleveland Hill Schls Math Tchr 1993-; *ai:* Girls Sftbl, Boys Bsbl Coach; NCTM 1990-.

WOOD, WILLIAM ALEXANDER, Coord of Civil Engrng Tech; *b:* Syracuse, NY; *m:* Mary Lynn; *c:* Alexander N., Nathan R., Steven P.; *ed:* Cornell Univ (BS) Civil Engrng 1974, (MCE) Civil Engrng 1976; Univ of Pittsburgh (MBA) Gen Mngmt 1983; *cr:* GAI Consultants Project Engr Civil 1976-81; ACRES Intnl Project Mgr Structures 1981-83; L. Robert Kimball & Assoc Mgr Structural Engrng 1983-88; Youngstown St Univ Asst Prof CET Coord 1988-; *ai:* Acad Senate Exec Comm 1993-; Cub Pack Comm Chm 1988-; Stu Retention Comm 1994-95; Lib Comm 1988-92; NEA, OEA 1988-; Amer Soc of Civil Engrs 1974-, Stu Chptr Pres; Natl Soc of Prof Engrs 1979-; Mc Cnadless Ath Assn 1988-, Bsbl Mgr; John Mc Millan Engrng Flwshp Cornell Univ; *office:* Youngstown St Univ 410 Wick Ave Youngstown OH 44555

WOOD, WILLIAM KENNETH, Instructional Support Teacher; *b:* Pittsburgh, PA; *m:* Nancy Marie; *c:* Paula, Jennifer; *ed:* Clarion Univ (BS) Elem Ed 1970; Duquesne Univ (MS) Elem Ed 1973, (MS) Admin, Supervision 1991; 6 Credits Allegheny Intermediate Courses; *cr:* Carnegie Elem Schl 4th Grd Tchr 1970-93, Instrl Support Tchr 1993-95, Elem Prin 1995, Instrl Support Tchr 1995-; *ai:* Elem IM Supvr; Strategic Plan Comm; Rdng Comm Chprsn; Instrl Support Team; AFT 1970-, Negotiating Team 1970-74; *office:* Carnegie Elem Schl Franklin Ave Carnegie PA 15106

WOOD, WILLIAM RANDALL, Health & PE Teacher; *b:* Mt Pleasant, PA; *c:* Heather Lynn Graniero, Karri Leanne; *ed:* SUNY at Brockport(BS) Hlth, PE 1968, (MS) PE 1992; 30 Hr Cert 1975; Cooper Inst for Aerobic Stu Personal Fitness Specialist 1991; *cr:* Churchville Chili Cent S Elem PE Tchr 1968-89, MS PE Tchr 1989-90; Sr HS Hlth, PE Tchr 1990-; *ai:* Girls Var Cross Cntry, Winter Track, Outdoor Track; NEA, NYEA 1968-; NYSAHPERD 1975-, Cntrl Western Zone Comm; AAHPERD 1989-; Red Cross 1968-, Instr, 28 Yr Svc Awd; SUNY Brockport Hall of Fame 1987; Catrl West Zone NYSAHPERD Tchr of Yr Nom 1990; Secion V Coach of Yr Class AA Track 1994; Monroe Cty Div III Track Coach of Yr 1993-94; *office:* Churchville-Chili Sr HS 5786 Buffalo Rd Churchville NY 14428*

WOODARD, DONALD L., Social Studies Teacher; *b:* Syracuse, NY; *m:* Mary; *c:* Sarah, Kate, Stella, William; *ed:* Hobart (BA) His 1966; 42 Post-Grad Hrs; *cr:* Greece Cntrl Schl Dist Tchr 1972-; *ai:* Earth Action Environment; Greece Tchrs Assn 1970-, Pres; NEA 1972-; NEA NY 1972-; SODAG Schl Bd, Trustee 1983-95; *office:* Greece Arcadia HS 120 Island Cottage Rd Rochester NY 14615

WOODARD, KATHLEEN THOMPSON, Business Teacher; *b:* Westerly, RI; *m:* Roger A. Jr.; *c:* Roger, Susan; *ed:* Husson Coll (BS) Bus Tchr Ed 1978; Masters Pgm at Johnson & Wales Univ; 27 Credit Hrs; *cr:* Upper Kennebeck Vly Memrl HS Bus Tchr 1978-79; Ocean St Bus Inst Bus Tchr 1981-84; Coventry HS Bus Tchr 1984-; *ai:* RIBEA 1981-; AFT 1984-; CTA 1984-; *office:* Coventry HS 40 Reservoir Rd Coventry RI 02816*

WOODBURN, MORROW, 6th Grade English Teacher; *b:* Pittsburgh, PA; *ed:* Edinboro Univ of PA (BS) Elem 1967; *cr:* West View Elem Schl 6th Grd Eng Tchr 29 Yrs; *ai:* 9th Grd Girls, Boys Bsktbl Coach; Safety Patrol Spon; NEA 1967-.

WOODBURY, STEPHEN W., Lang Arts & Soc Stud Tchr; *b:* Lynn, MA; *m:* Patricia Conroy; *ed:* Salem St Coll (BS) 1969, (MED) 1975; 45 Addl Credit Hrs; *cr:* Timony MS 8th Grd Eng Tchr 1969-75; Tenney MS 8th Grd Eng, Soc Stud Tchr 1975-; *ai:* Peer Mediation Coach; Staff Support Team; MTA 1969-; IAABO 1975-, Bsktbl Ofcl; *office:* Tenney MS 75 Pleasant St Methuen MA 01844

WOODEN, ADRIENNE HEARST, 8th Grade Teacher; *b:* Philadelphia, PA; *m:* Richard K.; *c:* Bryan, Jason; *ed:* Cheyney Univ (BS) Elem Ed 1969; Temple Univ (MS) Ed Rdng 1972; Drexel Univ Cmptr Tech in the Classroom; Schl Dist of Philadelphia Peer Mediation Trng; *cr:* Hopkinson Elem Schl Tchr 1972-79; Sharswood Elem Schl Tchr 1979-91; Pepper MS Tchr, Asst Dir of Small Learning Comm 1991-; *ai:* Yrbk Spon; Stu Cncl Ldr; Re-Org Tech Comms; After Schl Tutor; Mentor Tchr; Schl Ambassador, Prof Cons Presenter; AFT 1972-; PFT 1972-, Bldg Rep; Jack & Jill of Amer 1991-, Recording Sec; Church Ed & Schlsp Comm 1985-, Pres, Treas; Alpha Kappa Alpha 1966-; Ldrshp Awd 1995; Paths Prisom Chprsn Grant Comm Svc Awd; Prin Cabinet Recognition of Svc Awd; City of Philadelphia, Senate of Commonwealth Women in Ed Citation; *office:* Pepper MS 84th & Lyons Ave Philadelphia PA 19153

WOODGEARD, LINDA VAN REETH, Speech Teacher; *b:* Alliance, NE; *m:* Timothy Lee; *c:* Lori Sue Fulk, Wendy Lynn, Timarie LeeAnn Gentry; *ed:* OH Univ (BSC) Speech & Theater 1970; Attnd Wright St Univ; *cr:* Colonel White HS For the Arts Speech Tchr 1970-; *ai:* Speech Coach; Conflict Mgmt Team; Programatic Change Process Writing Team; DEA, OEA & NEA 1970-; Bethel Meth Church 1960-; Plainview Open Bible 1988-; *office:* Colonel White H S For The Arts 501 Niagara Ave Dayton OH 45405*

WOODGER, BETTY LOIS, Assistant to the President; *b:* Allentown, PA; *ed:* Christ Hosp Schl of Nrsng (RN) Nrsng 1969; Jersey City St Coll (BA) Hlth Ed, Schl Nrsng 1970, (MA) Admin, Supervision Hlth Svcs 1977; *cr:* Christ Hosp Schl of Nrsng Clinical, Theory Nrsng Instr 1970-91; Christ Hosp Asst to Pres 1991-; *ai:* Christ Hosp Schl of Nrsng Alumni Assn 1969-, Pres; Christ Hosp Auxiliary 1991-, VP; Abercrombie Guild 1988-.

WOODHOUSE, CAROL B., Latin Teacher; *b:* Syracuse, NY; *m:* Robert J.; *c:* Christine, Jessica; *ed:* Syracuse Univ (BA) Latin 1964; Univ of WA (MA) Latin 1967; 6 Credit Hrs Amer Acad in Rome, 6 Credit Hrs Tufts Univ Summer Inst; *cr:* Naples Cntrl Schl Latin Tchr 1964-66; Fairport Cntrl Schl Latin Tchr 1968-72; Bridgewater-Raritan Latin Tchr 1977-81; Bishop Connolly Latin Tchr 1983-88; Silver Lake Regnl 1988-; *ai:* Latin Club Adv; Amer Classical League 1964-; Classical Assn of New England 1981-, MA Rep; Classical Assn of MA 1983-, MA to Cane; Rockerfeller Flwshp 1991; *office:* Silver Lake Reg HS-Kingston 132 Pembroke St Kingston MA 02364

WOODING, JOHN CHARLES, Associate Professor of Pol Sci; *b:* Northampton, England; *m:* Joan Parker; *ed:* London Schl of Ec (BSc) Intnl Relations 1975; Brandeis Univ (PHD) Pol Sci 1990; Attnd Cornell Univ; *cr:* Univ of MA at Lowell Educator 1988-90, Assoc Prof 1990-95; *ai:* Fac Adv; Stu Govt; Cncl on Diversity Chair; MA Tchrs Assn 1990-; Amer Pol Sci Assn 1985-; *office:* Univ Of MA At Lowell 1 University Ave Lowell MA 01854

WOODMAN, RICHARD DENNIS, Honors & AP Biology Tchr; *b:* Bay Village, OH; *ed:* OH St Univ (BA) Ed, Biological Sci 1978, (MA) Exercise Physiology; *cr:* Memorial Jr HS Life Sci Tchr 1978-85; Mentor HS Bio Tchr 1984-; *ai:* Head Var Vlybl Coach; MTA Schlsp Comm Chm; NHS Selection Comm; Acad Decathalon Coach; Sci Olympiad Adv; NEA, OEA, MTA 1978-; Excl in Tchng Awd 1994; Coach of Year; *office:* Mentor HS 6477 Center St Mentor OH 44060

WOODMAN LAQUERRE, CLAIRE ROSINA, High School Biology Teacher; *b:* Woonsocket, RI; *m:* John; *ed:* RI Coll (BA) Bio 1986, (MAT) Bio 1995; *cr:* Woonsocket Cath Regnl Schl Sci Tchr 1986-87; Woonsocket Jr HS Sci Tchr 1987-88; Woonsocket Sr HS Bio Tchr 1988-; *ai:* RISTA 1995-; *home:* PO Box 150 Glendale RI 02826

WOODRING, DEAN, English Teacher; *b:* Ann Arbor, MI; *ed:* Univ of MI (BA) Comparative Lit 1990; Miami Univ Oxford (MAT) Eng 1995; Cert Eastern MI Univ Scndry Eng Ed 1992; 6 Credit Hrs Bread Loaf Schl of Eng M Lit; OH Writing Project Summer Inst; *cr:* Indian Hill HS 9-12 Grd Eng Tchr 1992-94; Miami Univ Tchr Scholar 1994-95; Indian Hill MS 7-8 Grd Eng Tchr 1995-; *ai:* Newspaper, Yrbk Adv; Tech Curr Comm; NCTE 1991-; Tchr Rsrch Network 1993-; Cincinnati Nature Ctr Vol; Cincinnati Pub Radio 1992-; Bread Loaf Schl of Eng Tchr Rsrch Grant; OH Writing Project Tchr Scholar Flwshp; OWP Fall Conf Presenter; NCTE Natl Convention Presenter; *office:* Indian Hill Schls 6845 Drake Rd Cincinnati OH 45243

WOODRING, DEANE CARSON, Social Studies Teacher; *b:* Waynesboro, PA; *m:* Carole Ann; *c:* Deborah Martin, Brian; *ed:* Shepherd Coll (BA) Soc Stud, His 1969; Mt St Mary's 9 hrs; Shippensburg Univ 6 Hrs; Univ of MD 6 Hrs; *cr:* North Hagerstown HS Soc Stud Tchr 1969-71; Boonsboro HS Soc Stud, Psych, His, Govt Tchr 1971-; *ai:* Soc Stud Dept Chm; MCSS 1995-; E. Russell Hicks, Louis Tuckerman Awd 1988; Ray A. Kroc Tchr Achvmt Awd 1992; *office:* Boonsboro HS 10 Campus Ave Boonsboro MD 21713

WOODRUFF, DIANE GIFFORD, Scndry Social Studies Teacher; *b:* Utica, NY; *m:* Norman Charles; *c:* Brendan, Corbin; *ed:* Oneota St (BS) Scndry Ed Soc Stud 1972; 30 Grad Hrs Scndry Ed Soc Stud; *cr:* Herkimer Cntrl Schl Tchr Scndry Soc Stud 1972-89; Richfield Springs Cntrl Schl Scndry Soc Stud Tchr 1991-; *ai:* NYSUT 1972-; *office:* Richfield Springs Ctl Schl Main St Box 631 Richfield Springs NY 13439

WOODRUFF, JUDY MARIE, Computer Science Instructor; *b:* Portsmouth, OH; *m:* Philip Raymond; *c:* Philip Thomas, Robert Theodore; *ed:* Bowling Green St (BS) Bus, Cmptr Mrktg 1968, (MS) Guid, Cnslng 1978; Working Towards Cnslng MA Heidelberg Coll; Quest, Group Facilitator Licenses; *cr:* Terra Tech Coll Cmptr Sci Tchr 5 Yrs; Tiffin Univ Bus Tchr 10 Yrs; Columbian HS Cmptr, Bus Tchr 28 Yrs; *ai:* SADD, Key, Cmptr Clubs, DECA Adv; Tech Advy Cncl; Tech Action Comm; OMEA, OEA, TEA, NEA, OBTA 1968-; Kiwanis 1990-; Core Team Comm Chprsn; Venture Capital Motivation Comm; VFW Tchr of Yr; *home:* 30 Harvest Ln Box 56 Tiffin OH 44883*

WOODRUFF, MARY BRENNAN, 5th Grade Teacher; *b:* Medina, NY; *m:* Paul; *c:* Christopher, Jeffery; *ed:* SUNY at Brockport (BS) Elem Ed 1968; SUYNY at Buffalo (MS) Interdisciplinary Sci 1987; Perm Cert Elem Ed 1975; Classroom Mgmt & Cooperative Learning; *cr:* Middleport Elem 3rd Grd Tchr 1968-76, 5th Grd Tchr 1979-; *ai:* Schl Store Adv; Curr Dev Comm; RHTA Prof Cncl Chprsn; NYSUT 1968-; AFT & CIO 1968-; RHTA Assoc for Supervision & Curr Dev 1968-, Sec, VP & Bldg Rep; Orelans Cty Cncl on the Arts 1992-, Bd Mem; Delta Kappa Gamma 1993-; Lake Plain Players, Co-Dir; Curr Dev Handbook Guide; 5th Grd Spelling Pgm; Whos Who in Amer Ed; Project DEEP Elem Ec; *office:* Royalton-Hartland Jr Sr HS State St Middleport NY 14105

WOODRUFF, THOMAS H., Social Studies Teacher; *b:* Batavia, NY; *m:* Susan Mac Pherson; *c:* Bryan K.; *ed:* Hobart Coll (BA) His 1972; St Univ of NY at Brockport (MS) Ed 1986, (SDA) Ed Admin 1986; *cr:* Olean City Schl Dist 7th-9th Grd Soc Stud Tchr 1972-75; Morrisville-Eaton Schl Dist 7th-12th Grd Soc Stud Tchr 1975-81; Oakfield-Alabama Cntrl Schl 11th-12th Grd Soc Stud Tchr 1981-; *ai:* St Univ of NY at Brockport Ftbl Asst Coach & Offensive Coord; NYSUT 1972-; NY St Soc Stud Assn 1985-; UUP 1988-; *office:* Oakfield-Alabama Central Schl 7001 Lewiston Rd Oakfield NY 14125

WOODS, CHRISTOPHER BEAUMONT, Guidance Cnslr & Track Coach; *b:* Fitchburg, MA; *m:* Anne-Marie; *c:* Haley Anne; *ed:* Univ of ME at Orono (BA) His, Pol Sci 1980; Fitchburg St Coll (MS) Cnslng 1985; 30 Addl Grad Credits; *cr:* Fitchburg Pub Schls Attendance, Transportation Officer 1986-89; B. F. Brown MS Guid Cnslr 1989-91; Fitchburg Pub Schls Parent Coord 1991-92; Fitchburg HS Guid Cnslr 1992-; *ai:* Coach X-Cnty 1989-, Indoor & Outdoor Track 1983-; MTA, FTA 1991-; USAT&F Ofcls 1994-; CMT, FOA 1981-; Reipas Ath Club 1987-, Track & Field Dir.

WOODS, DARRELL SCOTT, Physics Tchr & Teen Inst Adv; *b:* Canton, OH; *m:* Jacalyn A. Weibl; *c:* Zachary, Joshua; *ed:* Walsh Coll (BA) Bio 1983; Univ of Akron (MS) Bio 1985; Addl 25 Hrs; OK St Univ 3 Post Grad Hrs; *cr:* St Thomas Aquinas HS Sci Tchr 1983-92; Jackson HS Sci, Math Tchr 1992-; *ai:* NSTA; OH Cncl Tchrs of Math; OH Ed Assn; NEA; BSA 1979-, Asst Scoutmaster, Eagle Scout; NEWMAST 1995; *office:* Jackson HS 7600 Fulton Dr NW Massillon OH 44646

WOODS, DENNIS THEODORE, Health & Physical Ed Tchr; *b:* Cleveland, OH; *c:* Scott, Brian, Dennis Jr.; *ed:* Miami Univ (BS) PE, Hlth & Recreation 1964; Kent St Univ (MED) Ed 1970; *cr:* Glenville HS Tchr 1964-; *ai:* Bsbl Head Coach; Hlth & PE Dept Chprsn; Cleveland Pub Schls Sr Bsbl & Sftbl All Star Game Chprsn; Hall of Fame Chprsn; Natl HS Bsbl Coaches 1990-, Charter Mem; FCA 1988-; OH HS Bsbl Coaches 1966-, Cleveland Pub Schls Rep; Forest Hills Area Cncl 1994-; Marantha Bible Coll 1993-, Trustee; Greater Cleveland Bsbl Coaches Assn 1969-, Exec Bd Past Pres; Glenville HS Hall of Fame; South HS Hall of Fame; Greater Cleveland Coach of Yr 1973; *office:* Glenville HS 650 E 113th St Cleveland OH 44108

WOODS, DOUGLAS ELLIOT, English Teacher; *b:* New Kensington, PA; *m:* Aimee Haser; *c:* Alexis, Alison; *ed:* Indiana Univ of PA (BS) Ed 1972, (MA) Lit 1976; *cr:* Butler Intermediate HS Eng Tchr 1972-; Westmoreland Cty Comm Coll Writing & Lit Instr 1976-; PA Governors Schl for Arts Fiction Instr 1985-, Asst Pgm Dir 1995-96; *ai:* Asst Dir & Chair Creative Writing PA Governors Schl for Arts; *home:* 519 Oaklake Rd New Kensington PA 15068

WOODS, EVELYN HARGROVE, Teacher; *b:* Manson, NC; *m:* Herbert M.; *c:* Christopher, Kelly; *ed:* Livingstone Coll (BS) Bus ED 1960; Long Island Univ, Brooklyn Coll, Foordham Univ (MS) Elem Ed 1978; Long Island Univ, Brooklyn Coll, St Johns 30 Credits addl 1991; *cr:* Greer Schl Exec Dir Sec 5 yrs; Pacific HS, Aux Schl Part-time Rdng Tchr 7 yrs; Summer Schl Dist 13 Part-time Rdng Tchr 5 yrs; P S 256 Benjamin Banneker Tchr 28 yrs; *ai:* NEA 1978-; Delta Sigma Theta 1959-; Livingstone Coll Alumni, Ms. Alumni 1994-95; Brooklyn Queens Assn Chptr; Excl Tchng Plaque, Excl Lib Sci Awd P S 256; Tchng High Intensity Rdng Plaque; *home:* 3306 Avenue D Brooklyn NY 11203*

WOODS, MARY LOU DIOGUARDI, Second Grade Teacher; *b:* Meriden, CT; *m:* Christopher; *ed:* Cntrl CT St Univ (BSEd) Early Chldhd Elem Ed 1987; Working Towards MSEd Elem Ed; Concentration in Music Ed; *cr:* Pulaski Elem Schl 5 Grd Tchr 1988-94, Sci Resource Tchr 1991-, 2 Grd Tchr 1994-; *ai:* Holy Angels Church Liturgical Music Dir; Stu Cncl Adv; Family Sci Facilitator; Mentor, Cooperating Tchr; Nature Stud, Prof Dev Comms; Meriden Fed of Tchrs 1988-; Alpha Delta Kappa 1994-; Charity Club of Meriden 1989-, Sec; Schl was Awded Nature Stud Grant Written by Me; *office:* Pulaski Elem Schl 100 Clearview Ave Meride[n] 06450*

WOODS, SALLY TAYLOR, Art Teacher; *b:* Stamford, NY; *m:* Wi[...] V.; *c:* David; *ed:* SUCO (BS) Elem Ed, Rdng 1970; SUC Oneonta (MS[...]) 1976; SUCO Perm Art 1972; Cobleskill AAS Childcare 1964; *cr:* Win[...] Ashland 1st Grd Tchr 1 Yr; Cairo Schl 1st Grd Tchr 6 Yrs; Scotland[...] Art Tchr 2 Yrs; Schenevus Cntrl Schl Art Tchr 22 Yrs; *ai:* Odyss[...] Mind coach 15 Yrs; Class Adv 10 Yrs; UCCC Arts 1972-, Bd Mem; Ctr Rep 1972-, Bd Mem 1992-94; NYSUT 1972-, Sec, Treas, Negotiations; Natl Art Tchrs Assn 1976-; PTO 1974-; Booster[...] Oneonta 1987-; Schlsp Comm 1990-; NIE Daily Star Newspaper 1[...] Tchr of Yr 1993-94; Inst Tchng Eng Second Lang 6 Yrs; Adult Ed 15 *office:* Schenevus Central Schl PO Box 8 100 Main Schenevus NY 12[...]

WOODS, SHARON NEEDLES, English Teacher; *b:* Hamilton, O[H] Tammy Collins, Tanya, Toni; *ed:* Miami Univ (BSEd) Eng; Attnd W[...] St Univ, Univ of Dayton & OH Univ; *cr:* Stebbins HS Eng Tchr 196[...] Beavercreek HS Eng Tchr 1968-; *ai:* Boys & Girls Jr Var Tennis &[...] Cheerleading Coach; Asst SADD, Philosophy Club & Bsktbl Buddies[...] NEA; OEA; WOEA & BEA; *office:* Beavercreek H S 2660 Dayton-X[...] Rd Beavercreek OH 45434*

WOODS, SUSAN DOLORES, Kindergarten Teacher & Coach; *b:* Lake, NY; *ed:* Oswego St Coll (BS) Elem Ed, Ath Trng & Coaching 1[...] Potsdam St Coll (MS) Instrl Tech & Media 1992; 9 Credit Hrs Toward[...] Masters Degree; *cr:* Garden Gate Elem Day Care Dir 1986-87; Sy[...] Learning Ctr Tchr & Dir 1987-88; Clifton-Fine Cntrl Kndgtn Tchr &[...] Musical Dir 1988-; *ai:* Var Girls Soccer Coach; Co-Chprsn Tech Co[...] Var Girls & Boys Track; Asst Dir for Musical; NYSTA 1988-; *home.* Box 66 Newton Falls NY 13666

WOODS, TONY, Earth Science Teacher; *b:* Chillicothe, OH; *m:* Chr[...] L. Kennedy; *ed:* Univ of TN (BS) Forestry Resource Mngmt 1976; Univ (BA) Sec Ed Bus 1988; 18 Addl Hrs Univ of Dayton; *cr:* Fore[...] 1977-85; HS Tchr 1987-; *ai:* Ftbl, Wrestling, Bsbl Coach; NEA, C[...] OEA 1988-; Elks 1995-; Amer Legion Post 757 1986-; Navy Petty O[...] Club 1992-; *office:* Chillicothe HS 381 Yoctangee Pky Chillicothe 45601

WOODS, VIRGINIA PYNN, Second Grade Teacher; *b:* Brooklyn, NY Ronald T. dec; *c:* Diane Lauren Woods Mastrodomenico; *ed:* Brooklyn [...] (BA) Ed 1962; Hofstra Univ (MS) Ed, Rdng 1981; *cr:* PS119 Brook[...] Elem Ed Tchr 1962-66; East Meadow Pub Schls Tchr Grd 1 & 2 1982- East Meadow United Meth Church 1967-, Chprsn Ed, Trustee, Ad Cncl, Lay Ldr; *office:* East Meadow Public Schls 500 May Ln East Mea[...] NY 11554

WOODSON, AMANDA, Associate Professor of Dance; *b:* Edinbu[...] Scotland; *m:* Neal; *c:* Hannah Kathryn; *ed:* Bedford Coll of HE (B[...]) Dance 1984; OH St Univ (MFA) Dance 1989; *cr:* Abbortsford Performing Arts Coord 1984-86; OH St Univ Dance Lecturer 1988- Goucher Coll Assoc Prof of Dance 1989-; *ai:* Dance Notation Bur 1989-; AAUP 1990-; Soc of Dance His 1996; Amer Coll Scholars Da[...] Festival Assn 1989-, Bd Mem; Grad Fellowship OH St Univ; 20 M[...] Choreographic Works Presented; Dance Reconstruction; *office:* Gouc[...] Coll Dulaney Valley Rd Baltimore MD 21204

WOODWARD, DEBORAH JEAN, Second Grade Teacher; *b:* Corn[...] NY; *m:* Paul; *c:* Jennifer; *ed:* Mansfield Univ (BS) Elem Ed 1971; Oswayo Valley Tchr 1971-; *ai:* Mentor; Mem ISI; Mem Pub Relati[...] Comm; PSEA, NEA 25 Yrs; OVTA 25 Yrs, Past Pres.

WOODWARD, DOROTHY, 5th Grd Sci & Reading Teacher; Johnstown, PA; *c:* Anna, William, Jeffrey; *ed:* Penn St Capital Cam[...] (BA) Elem Ed 1973; Grad Pgm 1975; *cr:* Lyall J Fink Elem 4th Grd T[...] 1973-89; Alice Demey Elem 5th Grd Rdng & Sci Tchr 1989-; Aero-Space Edctr; MAEA, PSEA & NEA 1973-; PSTA 1991-; You[...] Astronauts 1987-, Chptr Ldr; Challenger Ctr 1987-; ABWA 199[...] Recording Sec; Planetary Soc 1995-.

WOODWARD, LYNNE HESS, German Teacher; *b:* New York, NY; William; *c:* Amanda, Jeffrey; *ed:* Chatham Coll (BA) Ger 1972; Univ Pgh (MED) Ed, Curr, Supervision 1976; *cr:* Pgh Bd of Ed Ger T[...] 1971-79, 1990-; *ai:* Outdoor Club Adv; Hiking, Juggling Club; Pra[...] Team Ldr; Act Dir; PMLA; ACFLA; Chrstn Edctrs Network; Highla[...] Park Comm Club; Curr Design Team Pgh Bd of Ed; New Amer Sc[...] Support Team; *office:* Langley HS 2940 Sheraden Blvd Pittsburgh 15204

WOODWARD, MARTHA C., Instructor of English; *b:* Marietta, GA; David R.; *c:* Catherine; *ed:* Univ of GA (BA) Eng 1964, (MA) Eng 19[...] *cr:* Univ of WI Instr 1964-65; Univ of OH Instr 1970-72; Marshall U[...] Instr 1974-90; Univ of OH Instr 1989-; Marshall Univ Asst Dir Soc Yea[...] Scholars 1990-92, Exec Dir John Hall Ctr Aca Excl 1992-; *ai:* Yea[...] Steering Hnrs Cncl, Assessment, Schlsp, Campus Ministry, SCOR[...] Steering Comms; Grievance Evaluator; Lib Assoc; WV Hum Cncl 199[...] Pres; LWV 1965-; H'tgn Jr League 1972-; *office:* Ohio Univ Southe[...] Campus 1804 Liberty Ave Ironton OH 45638

WOODWARD, PETER MICHAEL, English Teacher & Coach; Rockland, MA; *m:* Stephany; *c:* Christopher, Elizabeth; *ed:* Univ of N[...] Hampshire (BA) Eng 1973; Attnd Sussex Univ at England, Bridgewater Coll; *cr:* Rockland Jr HS Eng Tchr 1973-77; Rockland HS Eng Tchr 197[...] *ai:* Jr Var Girls Soccer, Var Girls Track Coach; Jr Class, Art & lit Magazi[...] Adv; REA, MTA, NEA 1973-; 2 Promising Practice Grants; *offic[e]* Rockland HS MacKinlay Way Rockland MA 02370*

WOODY, MICHAEL E., Government Teacher; *b:* Manchester, KY; Sheila Rae Brandenburg; *c:* Michael Clark; *ed:* Wright St Univ (BS) S[...] Stu Comprehensive 1971; Post Grad Stud Wright St Univ & Univ of Dayt[...] 36 Hrs Credits; *cr:* Bellbrook HS Govt Tchr 1971-; *ai:* Soc Stu De[...] Chprsn; Golf Coach; Im Bsktbl Dir; NEA 1972-; OH Ed Assn 197[...] Sugarcreek 1972-; Robert A Taft Inst of Govt Participant; *office:* Bellbro[...] HS 3491 Upper Bellbrook Rd Bellbrook OH 45305

WOOLDRIDGE, GAYE J., English Teacher; *b:* Berkeley Springs, W[...] *m:* Robert J.; *c:* Kelli Collins, Jeff; *ed:* Shepherd Coll (BA) Eng 196[...] Shippensburg Univ (MED) Eng 1969; *cr:* McConnellsburg HS Eng Tc[...] 1968-; *ai:* PSEA; NEA; *office:* Mc Connellsburg Jr Sr HS Cherry St [...] Connellsburg PA 17233

WOOLEY, ALLAN, Dept Classical Lang Chair; *b:* Rumford, ME; Helena Cunningham; *ed:* Bowdoin Coll (BA) Classics 1954; Pinceton Un[...] (PHD) Classics 1962; Universitat Hamburg Classics 1960; Assembly La[...] Programming Hesser Coll; *cr:* Duke Univ Asst Prof 1962-67; Gould Ac[...] Inst, Chair Dept 1967-68; Phillips Exeter Inst, Chair Dept 1968-; *ai* Classical Assn NE 1968-, Pres, Exec Sec; Amer Philological Assn 1962[...] Amer Classical League 1988-; NEH Inst Tchr; CANE Summer Inst Tch[...]

WOOLF, DAVID WILSON, Assoc Prof of Art; *b:* Portsmouth, VA; Vanessa Adrienne Alegra Lauren; *ed:* Mount Union Coll (BA) Fine A[...] 1967; CA St Univ at Fullerton (MA) Painting 1974; Schl of Visual Arts [...] NYC 1968; *cr:* CCAA South Campus Assoc Prof of Art 1973-; *offic[e]* CCAC-South Campus 1750 Clairton Rd West Mifflin PA 15122

WOOLLEY, JUDITH ANN, 8th Grd Language Arts Teacher; *b:* Howa[...] Beach, NY; *m:* Kenneth; *c:* Garrett, Jennifer Woolley Jackson; *ed:* Trento[...] St (BA) Scndry Eng 1965; Marywood (MS) Cnslng 1986; *cr:* Park Jr Hig[...] 7th-9th Grd Eng Tchr 1965-68; Terrill Jr High 7th-9th Grd Eng Tc[...]

76; Newton HS Eng & Spcl Ed Tchr 1978-80; Pike Cty Dev Ctr Asst 982-84; Port Jervis Mid Schl 8th Grd Eng Tchr 1984-; *ai:* Peer Ldrshp Communicator with Media & NY Educl Task Force; NEA 1965-76; 1984-; *office:* Port Jervis MS E Main St Port Jervis NY 12771*

LLEY, MARY LOU, Biology Teacher; *b:* Neptune, NJ; *ed:* gian Court Coll (BS) Bio 1970, (MA) 1981; Addl 42 Credits; *cr:* Brick HS Bio Tchr 1979-; *ai:* NEA, NIEA, BTEA, NJSTA 1979-; *office:* Twp HS 346 Chambersbridge Rd Brick NJ 08723*

LSCHLAGER, KATHLEEN PICCIANO, Instrumental Music ier; *b:* Syracuse, NY; *m:* Peter J.; *c:* Lillia, Adriana; *ed:* Ithaca Coll Music 1985; Potsdam Coll (MM) Music 1991; *cr:* Whitesboro Schls umental Music Tchr 1985-86; Beaver River Cntrl Schl Instrumental c Tchr 1986-; *ai:* MENC, NY St Schl Music Assn 1982-; Natl Flute 1989-; Sigma Alpha Iota 1985-; NY ST Band Dirs Assn 1986-.

MER, MURIEL FAYE, Fourth Grade Teacher; *b:* Altoona, PA; *m:* s Allen Jr.; *c:* Rebecca Harshaw, James III, Katharine Ozio; *ed:* Saint is Coll (BS) Elem Ed 1982; 24 Post Grad Credits; PA Permanent Cert ; *cr:* St Joseph Schl Tchr 1982-85; Hollidaysburg Area HS Rdng Tchr -88; Mc Nelis Schl Sci Tchr 1988-; *ai:* NCEA 1982-; PA Sci Tchrs 1994-; Easter Seals Soc; Smithsonian Assoc.

OSTER, PAUL D., Orchestra Director; *b:* Brooklyn, NY; *m:* Catherine a; *c:* Jennifer Freudenberg, Megan Wooster; *ed:* Manhattan Schl of c (BM) Cello 1968; Antioch Putney Grad Schl (MA) Ed 1969; *cr:* VT ym Cellist 1967-68; Springfield Sym Asst Prin Cellist 1967-69; estral Soc of Westchester Prin Cellist 1970-80; Ridgefield Sym Solo st 1971-; *ai:* AFT 1970-; MENC 1985-; AFM 1965-; *office:* Carmel 0 Fair St Carmel NY 10512

OTEN, TERRY SIMS, Special Education Teacher; *b:* Snow Hill, NC; nthony Jerome; *ed:* East Carolina Univ (BS) Spec Ed 1988; *cr:* Lenoir Pub Schls Spec Ed Tchr 1988-95; Winton Woods City Schls Spec Ed 1995-; *ai:* Bsktbl, Sftbl Head Coach; NCCA 1992-; Order of Eastern 1993-, Assoc Conductress; NAACP 1993-; Elem Math Tchr of Yr ; *home:* 47 Chapel Hill Dr Fairfield OH 45014

OTON, JOAN BELMAN, Mathematics Teacher; *b:* Baltimore, MD; obert Paul; *c:* Robert, Steven, Michael, Susanne; *ed:* Glassboro St Coll Ed-Magna Cum Laude 1959; Addl Hrs in Math; *cr:* Glassboro Pub Tchr 1959-60; Clearview Regnl HS Tchr 1960-61; Washington Twp Tchr 1973-75; Clayton Pub Schl HS Math Tchr 1986-; *ai:* Math Dept l, Chprsn; Phi Dela Kappa 1988-, Sec; NCTM 1989-; Assn Math Tchrs 988-; NEA, CEA 1986-; Nom Governor's Tchr Recognition Awd, a Delta Phi; *home:* 400 Ronald Ave Glassboro NJ 08028*

OTTON, SUZANNE DAWSON THOMAS, English Teacher & Dept ; *b:* Darby, PA; *m:* Glenn T.; *c:* Scott, Kurt, Matthew; *ed:* Gettysburg (BA) Eng 1972; Middlebury Coll (MA) Eng 1983, (MLITT) Theatre ; *cr:* Southwestern HS Eng Tchr 1972-85; Mercersburg Acad Eng Tchr -; *ai:* Dorm Dean; Dept Head; Theatre Dir; NCTE 1975-; ASCD -; *office:* Mercersburg Acad 300 E Seminary St Mercersburg PA 17236

RBIS, DEBORAH GEPHART, Spanish & English Teacher; *b:* innati, OH; *m:* Adrian; *c:* Melissa, Edward; *ed:* Univ of Rochester Span 1974; Univ Iberoamericana (MA) Span Lit, Linguistics 1979; d Wright St Univ, Xavier Univ, OH Acad; *cr:* Franklin Jr HS Span Tchr 5-76; Interlingua de Mexico Eng Tchr 1976-80; Universidad Nacional lexico Eng Tchr 1982-83; Middletown HS Span, Eng Tchr 1986-; *ai:* Club, Span NHS Adv; NHS Selection, Honor Roll Recognition m; Bldg Ldrshp Team; NEA, OEA, Middletown Tchrs Assn, AATSP -; AAUW 1986-, VP; MiddFest Conversations Comm; Middletown ien Tchrs Club; Honorable Mention Golden Apple Achiever Awd 1994; dletown City Schls Champion Awd 1993; *office:* Middletown HS 601 reiel Blvd Middletown OH 45042

RCESTER, MARIE, English Teacher; *b:* Boston, MA; *m:* Edward; *c:* berly, Jennifer, Elizabeth, Kristin; *ed:* Bridgewater St (BSEd) Eng, Fr , (MED) Rdng 1975; *cr:* Stamford Pub Schls Eng, Fr Tchr; Peekskill Eng Tchr; Weymouth HS Eng Tchr; *ai:* Yrbk, Lit Magazine Adv; ; MTA; WTA, Pub Relations; *office:* Weymouth HS 1051 Commercial Veymouth MA 02189

RKMAN, AMARYLIS JARRELL, Chemistry Teacher; *b:* Edwight, ; *m:* William R.; *c:* Shannon, Russell; *ed:* Evangel Coll (BS) Bio Ed 3; WV Coll Grad Stud (MA) Scndry Sci Ed 1977; *cr:* George hington HS Chem Tchr 1964-66; Keyser HS Chem Tchr 1981-85; he Biomedical Labs Sales Rep 1985-88; Allegany HS Chem Tchr 8-; *ai:* Chem Team Coach; NEA; MD Assn Sci Tchrs; Alleghany Cty rs Assn; Ray A. Kroc Tchr Achvmt Awd; Oak Ridge Natl Lab Hnrs d; MD Governor's Acad Math & Sci; *office:* Allegany HS 616 gwick St Cumberland MD 21502

RKMAN, CARLOTTA PETERSON, Guidance Counselor; *b:* esville, OH; *m:* James Edward Jr.; *c:* Royce; *ed:* OH Univ (BS) Ed ; OH St Univ (MA) Ed 1977; Grad Courses at OH Univ, Muskingum ; *cr:* North Kingstown Pub Schls Primary Spec Ed Tchr DH 1971-74; umbus OH Pub Schls DH Jr HS Spec Ed Tchr 1976-77; Zanesville OH / Schls DH Jr HS Spec Ed Tchr 1980-84, HS Guid Cnslr 1984-; *ai:* Svc rning Stu Vols Adv; NEA, OH Ed Assn, Zanesville Ed Assn 1980-; OH l Cnslrs Assn 1984-; YWCA 1992-, Sec 1992-95, Pres 1996; Wings of e Tabernacle 1989-, VP 1991-; YWCA Tribute to Women of Achvmt d 1993; *office:* Zanesville HS 1701 Blue Ave Zanesville OH 43701

RK-NARDONE, JUDY SWAN, 2nd Grade Teacher; *b:* Connellsville, *m:* Evan Nardone; *c:* Kimberly L. Work, Kathryn Work Enos; *ed:* erbein Coll (BS) Early Chldhd, Elem Ed 1961; Grad Hrs California v 1962-63, WV Univ 1965-67; *cr:* Columbus OH Schl Dist Kndgtn Tchr 1-62; Connellsville Area Schls Kndgtn Tchr 1963-70, 2nd Grd Tchr 5-; *ai:* PA St Ed Assn 1963-; Connellsville Area Ed Assn 1963-, Bldg 1991-92; DAR 1986-; Beta sigma Phi 1986-, Treas; Order of Eastern r 1963-; *home:* 610 Eliza St Connellsville PA 15425

RLEY, BARBARA LYNN (WEBER), Spanish Teacher; *b:* Summit, *m:* John H.; *c:* Joe, Jen; *ed:* Allegheny Coll (BA) Fr 1976, (MAE) Ed 8; Span Tchr Cert 1982-83; *cr:* Cleveland Pub Schls Fr Tchr 1976-78; enville Schl Dist Fr, Span Tchr 19810; *ai:* Span Club Adv; AATSP 1-; PA Modern Lang Assn Activity Awd 1993; *home:* RR 2 Conneaut e PA 16316

RLEY, GRACE CASALE, Physical Education & Hlth Tchr; *b:* wark, NJ; *m:* Edward Wayne; *c:* Debbie Worley Malba; *ed:* Montclair St v (BA) PE, Hlth, Sci 1959; 17 Post Grad Hrs; *cr:* Parsippany HS PE, h, Dr Ed Tchr 1959-64; Belleville HS PE, Hlth, Driver Ed Tchr 1964-; U Bsktbl, Vlybl Coach 1982-85; *ai:* Hlth Curr Dev Comm; Chprsn PE r Dept; Mid Sts Curr Dev; Vlybl Coach 20 Yrs; Vlybl Ofcl Northern NJ ptr; Colorguard, Chrldng Adv; Rec VB Prgm Coed-Women Dir; nnastic Coach; NEA, NJEA, JOHPER, BEA 1959-; Essex Cty Coaches, Vlybl Coaches, NJSIAA, NNJ Chptr Ofcls, NNJIL Coaches Org 1979-; leville Ath Cncl, Hall of Fame Awd; Belleville Hall of Fame 1985-, Hall Fame Awd; Exec Bd NJ AAU 1980-, Bd Mem; Recreation Dept 1980-, l; Ath Dept Mgr, Security 1980-; Belleville Var Club 1960-; All-Sport l; Mgr Wrestling Tournament; Natl AAU VB Prgm; Natl Inst for mens Sports Rep NJ Represting Gymnastics 1960; 1st Place Awd NNJIL ssaic-Essex Division Vlybl 1986-88; Sportsmanship Awd 1980, 1996; *ice:* Belleville HS 100 Passaic Ave Belleville NJ 07109*

WORMALD, RANDY JOHN, Mathematics & Computer Teacher; *b:* Lawrence, MA; *ed:* Univ of ME at Farmington (BS) Scndry Ed Math, Comp 1988; Univ of WY (MST) Math Ed 1996; Grad Credits Univ of Virgin Islands Educl Tech; *cr:* Londonderry Jr HS Math Tchr 1988-89; All Saints Cathedral Schl Cmptr Tchr 1990; Londonderry Jr HS Math Tchr 1990-91; Andover Elem MS Math Cmptr Tchr 1991-93; Univ of NH Math Edctr 1993-94; Andover Elem MS Math, Cmptr Tchr 1995-; *ai:* Bsbl, Bsktbl, Sftbl, Floor Hockey Coach; Seventh Grd Class Adv; Advy Comm; NCTM 1990-; ATMNE 1991-; ISTE 1995-; NSF Model Masters Degree Prgm Univ of WY 1994-95; Univ NH Math Tchng Flwshp 1993-94; Pilot Classroom Christa Mc Auliffe Fellow 1992-93; *home:* PO Box 41 Andover NH 03216

WORMLEY, TERESA RENEE SUOZZI, Spanish Teacher; *b:* Batavia, NY; *m:* Geoffrey Gerard; *c:* Amanda Marie, Brittany Renee; *ed:* Genesee Comm Coll (AS) 1986; SUNY Oswego (BS) 1988; SUNY Brockport (MS) Lbrl Sci 1988; *cr:* Churchville-Chili MS Span Tchr 8 Yrs; Attica MS Span & Fr Tchr 1 Yr; *ai:* Stu Cncl Co-Adv; Span Club Adv; NEA; *office:* Churchville Chile MS 139 Fairbanks Rd Churchville NY 14428

WORONIK, STANLEY RICAHRD, 7th-8th Grade Science Teacher; *b:* Norwich, CT; *m:* Jeanne Smart; *ed:* Eastern CT Univ (BA) Intermediate Ed 1976, (MS) Sci Ed; *cr:* CM McGee MS 8th Grd Sci Tchr 1976-77; Voluntown Elem Schl 7th-8th Grd Sci Tchr 1977-; *ai:* Ski Club; Prof Dev; Stu Cncl Adv; Evaluation Comm; Sci Curr Review; NEA 1976-; CEA 1976-; YEA 1977-, Pres, Negotations Chair; CT Acad for Ed in Math & Sci Grant; *home:* 123 Scott Hill Rd Colchester CT 06415

WORONOWICH, NANCY ARPAIA, Elementary Education Teacher; *b:* Brooklyn, NY; *m:* John; *c:* Lauren, John; *ed:* St Univ at Oneonta (BA) Elem Ed; Hofstra Univ (MA) Elem Ed; *cr:* John F. Kennedy Schl 5th Grd Tchr 1969-86; Tooker Ave Schl 4th, 5th Grd GATE Class 1986-92, 4th Grd Tchr 1992-; *ai:* GATE Comm; AFT; West Babylon Tchrs Assn 1969-; NY St United Tchrs; Grants Western Suffolk Tchrs Ctr 1990, 1995; Articles Pub Games & Great Ideas 1995; Bd of Ed Cert of Recognition 1992; *home:* 16 Pimlico Dr Commack NY 11725

WORRELL, DOREEN OSTROWSKI, Home Economics Teacher; *b:* Hudson, NY; *m:* William J.; *ed:* SUNY at Plattsburgh (BS) Home Ec 1978; Coll of St Rose (MS) Educl Psych 1983; *cr:* Rhinebeck HS Home Ec Tchr 1978-; *ai:* NHS Adv; Costume Designer for Schl Musical; Bldg Level Planning Team; AFT, NYSUT, NYSHETA, Rhinebeck Tchrs Assn 1978-; Cornell Feline Hlth Ctr 1991-; *home:* PO Box 131 Rhinebeck NY 12572

WORRELL, FRANK, Education Professor; *b:* Port-of-Spain, West Indies; *ed:* Univ of Western Ontario (BA) Psych 1985, (MA) Psych 1987; Univ of CA at Berkeley (PHD) Educl Psych 1994; Pupil Personnel Svcs Credential; Schl Psych Cert; *cr:* DEC HS Prin 1987-88; U C Berkeley Instr 1989-; Penn St Asst Prof 1994-; *ai:* AERA 1988-; APA 1991-; ABP 1995-; Grad Schl of Ed UC Berkely Outstdng Dissertation Awd 1995; *office:* The Pennsylvania St Univ 227 Cedar Bldg University Park PA 16802

WORTH, JANE CURLEY, First Grade Teacher; *b:* Boston, MA; *m:* Jack; *c:* Gretchen A., Heidi J., Michael J., Heather J.; *ed:* Boston Coll (BS) Soc Sci 1955; St Univ Coll of Fredonia (MS) Elem Ed 1985; Attnd Univ of IA, Nazareth Coll at Rochester, Marywood Coll at Pennsylvania, New York Univ, St Univ of NY at Buffalo, Canisius Coll at Buffalo, St UNiv Coll at Buffalo; *cr:* Prospect Elem 2nd Grd Tchr 1955-57; Danvers Elem 2nd Grd Tchr 1957-58; Grant Wood Elem 1st Grd Tchr 1970-72; Barker Rd Elem 2nd Grd Tchr 1973-74; West Bradford Elem 1st Grd Tchr 1974-76; Ellicott Elem 1st Grd Tchr 1976-; *ai:* Bldg Wellness Team; Dist Wellness Policy, Bldg Staff Dev Comms; Bldg Whole Lang Support Group; Employee Asst Team; Orchard Park Tchrs Assn 1976-, Tchr of Yr 1982; Life Transitions Ctr 1983-, Vol, Outstanding Svc to Bereaved Adele Meyer 1990; *home:* 230 Highland Ave Orchard Park NY 14127

WORTH, PAUL EDWARD, Science, Math & Phys Ed Tchr; *b:* Stoneham, MA; *m:* Claudia Joan Ripley; *c:* Caitlin, Shannon; *ed:* Springfield Coll (BS) PE 1975; *cr:* Immaculate Conception Schl PE Tchr 1975-77; Assumption Schl PE Tchr 1977-79; Self Employed Auto Dealer, Contractor 1979-94; North Shore Tech Sci, Math, PE Tchr 1994-; *ai:* Head Ftbl Coach; Head Alpine Ski Coach; Jr Class Adv; Bldg Expansion Comm; Admissions Comm; Pres Ski League; AAHPER, MVA, MTA 1995-; USSA, USSCA 1988-; Kiwanis Middleton 1995-; Coach of Yr 1992-93; *office:* North Shore Technical HS 30 Logbridge Rd Middleton MA 01949*

WORTHINGTON, DEBORAH ECKHARDT, English & Journalism Teacher; *b:* Anderson, IN; *c:* Drew, A. Eric, Jason; *ed:* Purdue Univ (BA) Eng 1971; Montclair St Univ (MA) Rdng 1991; Centenary Coll Lic Spec Ed 1986; *cr:* Harrison HS Eng Tchr 1973-74; Bloomington HS Eng Tchr 1978-79; Roxbury HS Eng Tchr 1986-88; Dover HS Spec Ed Eng, Jrnlsm Tchr 1988-; *ai:* Yrbk; Class ADv; HSPT Review Classes; Mentor Made in Dover; Disabilities Comm; NEA 1986-; Yrbk 1st Place Spec Merit 1994, 1995; *office:* Dover HS 100 Grace St Dover NJ 07801*

WORTHINGTON, MARK, Mathematics Teacher; *b:* Columbus, OH; *m:* Cindy Lee Haney; *ed:* Morehead St Univ (BA) Math 1988, (MS) Guid, Cnslng 1994; *cr:* Holy Family Elem Schl Cmptr Tchr 1989-; St Joseph Cntrl Cath HS Math Tchr 1991-; *ai:* Math Counts; Math-a-thon; Governor's Cup; Cmptr Graphing Competition; NCEA 1991-; *office:* St Joseph Cntrl Cath HS 912 S 6th St Ironton OH 45638

WORTMAN, CLAUDIA G., Biology Teacher & Dept Chmn; *b:* Lincoln, NE; *m:* David C.; *c:* Dana, Andrew; *ed:* Univ of NE (BS) Bio Ed 1970; Univ of Guam (MS) Marine Bio 1976; VA Wesleyan 21 Hrs Church Music; Loyola Univ 6 Hrs Geology; St Marys Coll 3 Hrs Bio; *cr:* New London Jr High Sci Tchr 1973-74; Amer Coll of Paramedical Arts & Sci Tchr 1977-78; Univ of MD Instr 1978-80, 1983-85; Great Mills HS Sci Tchr, Dept Chair 1990-; *ai:* Sci Dept Chair; Envirothon Spon; Sci Fair Coord; CEAI 1995-; *office:* Great Mills High School Great Mills Rd Great Mills MD 20634

WOTRING, TIMOTHY J., Social Studies Teacher; *b:* Rising Sun, PA; *m:* Linda; *c:* Jonathan, Sherry, Susan; *ed:* Kutztown Univ (BS) Scndry Ed 1973; Grad Courses at Lehigh Univ & Penn St Univ; *cr:* Parkland Schl Dist Tchr 1973-; *ai:* PSEA; N Whitehall Twp Historical Commission 1992-, chm; Upper Lehigh Historical Soc Pres; Private Bus Auction Gallery Antiquities; *office:* Parkland Schl Dist 2219 N Cedar Crest Blvd Allentown PA 18104

WOY, ALAN BRUCE, Prof of Clarinet & Conducting; *b:* Chicago, IL; *m:* Roxanne Brockriede; *c:* Katherine; *ed:* IL Wesleyan Univ (BMUS) Performance, Clarinet 1967; Univ of CO (MMUS) Performance, Clarinet 1969, (DMUSA) Performance, Clarinet 1979; *cr:* Crane Schl of Music Prof 1971-; *ai:* Natl New Music Solo Competition Chm; Chamber Orch Prin Clarinet; Woodwind Quintet 1971-; NY St Schl Music Assn; Intnl Clarinet Assn; Coll Music Sox; *office:* S U N Y Coll At Potsdam Crane School of Music Pieerepont Ave Potsdam NY 13676

WOZNAK, JOHN FRANCIS, Assoc Prof of English; *b:* Johnstown, PA; *ed:* Saint Francis Coll (BA) Eng, Comparative Lits 1977; IN Univ of PA (MA) Eng Lit 1979, (PHD) Eng Lit 1988; *cr:* IN Univ of PA Tchng Asst 1977-80; Mount Aloysius Jr Coll Adjunct Instr 1983; Saint Francis Coll Assoc Prof of Eng 1982-; *ai:* Creative Writing Contest Judge; Eng Club Adv; Grad Stud, Salary & Benefits, Jr Eng Exam, Various Departmental & Campus Search, Schlsp Comms; ACT101 Advy Bd; Fac Senate; Eng Adv; MLA, NCTE 1992-; Delta Epsilon Sigma, Phi Sigma Iota 1977-; Numerous Parish & Diocesan Orgs 1980-, Pastoral Musician, Chair, Presenter, Etc; Departmental Awds in Eng, Span, Comparative Lits 1977; Grad Assistantship Awds 1977-80; Awd for Excl in Tchng 1989; Tenured 1993; Promoted 1988 & 1993; Prof Articles Pub; Distngd Fac Awrd 1994; *office:* St Francis College PO Box 600 Loretto PA 15940

WOZNIAK, GEORGE NELSON, Director of Bands; *b:* Erie, PA; *m:* Sherry Lynn Mitchell; *c:* Ian Mitchell; *ed:* IN Univ of PA (BS) Music Ed 1989; Univ of Akron (MA) Trumpet Performance 1992; *cr:* Kiski Area HS Dir of Bands 1993-; *ai:* Conduct Symphonic, 9th Grd Concert Band, Cavalier Brass Choir, Jazz Ensemble B; Assoc Conductor of Wind Ensemble; Phi Mu Alpha Sinfonia 1985-; MENC, PMEA 1993-; 2 Time Bands of Amer Eastern Regnl Grand Champion; Class AA Natl Champion with Cavalier Marching Band within First 3 Yrs; Superior Ratings with Symphonic Band 3 Out of 3 Yrs; *office:* Kiski Area HS 200 Poplar St Vandergrift PA 15690

WOZNIAK, NINALEIGH STRATTON, 7th-8th Grd Special Ed Teacher; *b:* Wilkes Barre, PA; *m:* Thomas R. Jr.; *ed:* Bloomsburg Coll (BS) Spec Ed 1982; Wilkes Univ (MS) Ed 1989; Attnd Scranton Univ, PA St Univ, East Stroudsburg St, Chapman Univ; *cr:* LIU 18 Spec Ed Tchr 2 Yrs; LIU 12 EMR Tchr 3 Yrs; Wyoming Valley West Learning Support Tchr 9 Yrs; *ai:* Girls Swimming Head Coach 1986-; NEA 1980's-; ASCD; Swimming: 9 All Amers, 3 Jr Natl Qualifiers, Finalists, 8 Dist Titles, 6 Consecutive PIAA League Championships, Top 7 Ranking St, Natl Level, Natl HS All Amer (2); *office:* Wyoming Valley West MS Chester St Kingston PA 18704

WOZNIAK, SANDRA STROUD, Environmental Ed Tchr; *b:* Dover, NJ; *m:* Edward J.; *c:* Jonathan, Matthew; *ed:* Douglass Coll (BA) Bio Sci & Ed 1977; Rutgers Univ (MST) 1986; 24 Post Grad Credits Tech in Ed; *cr:* Mt Olive MS 7th Grd Gen Sci 1977-79, 8th Grd Life Sci 1979-94, Environmental Ed 1994-95; *ai:* MOMS Sci Olympiad Team Coach; Revise the Evaluation System Comm; NJ Sci Tchrs Assoc 1977-, Industrial Liason Chair; NJEA & NEA 1977-; Ed Assoc of Mt Olive 1977-, Mbrshp Chair & Pres; BSA 1994-, Advancement Chair; Dodge Grant Recipient; Awds: Amer Express Geog, Morris Cty Recycling, Tchr of the Yr & Rudolph for Sci Excl; *office:* Chester Stephens Mt Olive MS 99 Sunset Rd Budd Lake NJ 07828*

WOZNIUK, VLADMIR, Assoc Professor of Government; *b:* Munich, Germany; *ed:* CT (BA) Russian 1975; Yale (MA) Rel 1982; VA (PHD) Frgn Affairs 1984; *ai:* AAUP; Books: From Crisis to Crisis; Soviet-Polish Relations; Understanding Soviet Foreign Policy 1990; *office:* Western New England Coll 1215 Wilbraham Rd Springfield MA 01119

WRAY, DENNIS CLARK, Third Grade Teacher; *b:* Natrona Heights, PA; *m:* Janet Ann Burd; *c:* Tyler, Travis, Tara; *ed:* Slippery Rock Univ (BS) Elem Ed 1972; Penn St Univ Masters Equivalency Elem Ed 1994; Attnd Univ of Pittsburgh, Portland St Univ; *cr:* 3rd Ward Elem 4th Grd Tchr 1973-75, 5th Grd Tchr 1975-84; Grandview Elem 5th Grd Tchr 1984-89, 4th Grd Tchr 1989-94, 3rd Grd Tchr 1994-; *ai:* Stu Cncl Spon; Caring Prgm Coord; NEA, HEA 1973-; Natrona Heights Little League 1977-, Sr Division VP, Coach; Natrona Heights Presbyn Church, Deacon, Elder, Weekday Nursery Schl; Sylvan Park Pool 1995-, Prsnl Comm; Highlands Area Soccer Club 1995-, Coach; *office:* Grandview Elem Schl 9th at Ross Sts Tarentum PA 15084

WRAY, GILBERT ANDREW, Research Professor; *b:* Montreal PQ, Canada; *m:* Nicole Flynn; *c:* Jon; *ed:* Univ of Montreal (BS) Mechanical Eng 1963; Stevens Inst of Tech (MME) Mechanical 1967, (ENG) Civil 1990; *cr:* Loyola Coll Lab Instr 1963-64; Stevens Inst of Tech Rsrch Eng, Div Mgr 1965-89, Lecturer, Adjunct Prof 1989-92, Res Prof 1992-; MDIC Ing Pres 1980-; *ai:* SAE Stu Fac Adv; Stu Act Comm; Stevens Rep Bd of Dirs Transportation Rsrch Consortium FHA Dist II; SAE 1969-, Mem; ASTM 1970-, Mem; Amer Acad Forensic Sci 1982-, Mem; NY Acad of Sci 1982-, Mem; Loyola Gold Medal; *office:* Stevens Inst of Tech Castle Point On The Hudson Hoboken NJ 07030*

WREN, MARY PLUMMER, Math Teacher; *b:* New York City, NY; *m:* James Clay Jr.; *c:* Michael Voorhees, Stephen Andrew; *ed:* Paterson St (BA) Elem Ed 1966, (MA) Math Ed 1969; Addl Courses at Jersey City St, Keane St, Dominican Coll; *cr:* St Anastasia 4th, 7th Grd Tchr 1966-67; Grant Schl 5th Grd Tchr 1967-69; Holdrum MS 7th-8th Grd Tchr 1969-; *ai:* Math Curr Revision, Regnl Math Articulation Comms; NEA, NJEA, BCEA, RVEA 1967-; NCTM 1991-; PTA 1969-; Montvale Ath League; NJ Governors Awd for Excl in Ed 1991-92; *office:* Holdrum MS 393 River Vale Rd River Vale NJ 07675

WRIGHT, ANITA D., 9th & 11th Grd English Tchr; *b:* Pittsfield, ME; *m:* David; *c:* Brandon, Taylor; *ed:* Colby Coll (BA) Eng 1987; Attnd Antioch Coll; *cr:* MCI Eng Tchr 1987-88; Mt View HS Eng Tchr 1989-; *ai:* Class of 1997 Adv; Various Comms; Critical Skills Ldrshp Team; ME Tchrs Assn, NEA 1989-; Presented at Alternative Assessment Wksph; Participated in PBS Network TV Show On Initiatives in Ed.*

WRIGHT, BENJAMIN FRANKLIN, Physical Education Teacher; *b:* St Louis, MO; *ed:* Univ of MD (BS) PE 1972; Bowie St Coll (BS) Scndry Ed 1982; +30 Credit Hrs Beyond BS; *cr:* Andrew Jackson Jr PE Tchr 1972-76; Eleanor Roosevelt Sr PE Tchr 1976-84; Thomas Johnson Sr PE Tchr 1985-; *ai:* Head Ftbl Coach; Asst Track Coach; NEA 1972; Natl Strength Coaches Assn 1984; *office:* Governor Thomas Johnson HS 1501 N Market St Frederick MD 21701

WRIGHT, BRYAN R., Science Teacher; *b:* Presque Isle, ME; *m:* Debra E.; *c:* Melissa Anne, Emerson Myles; *ed:* Univ of ME at Presque Isle (BS) Bio 1976; 36 Credits in Various Sci Disciplines, Ed & Cmptr Tech; *cr:* Schl Admin Dist #33 Sci & Math Tchr 1976-77; Easton Schl System Sci Tchr 1977-; *ai:* HS Admin Asst; Sr Class Adv; Vlybl Coach; NEA 1976-; Easton Tchrs Assn 1977-, Negotiations; *home:* 36 Maple St Presque Isle ME 04769

WRIGHT, CARL, Social Studies Teacher; *b:* Goshen, NY; *m:* Carolyn Shaffer; *c:* Ginger, Scott, Amy, Kevin; *ed:* St Univ of NY at Oneonta (BS) Soc Stud 1963; SUNY Grad Schl of Pub Affairs at Albany (MA) Pol Sci 1965; *cr:* Tappan Zee HS Soc Stud Tchr 1964-66; South Orangetown Jr HS Soc Stud Tchr 1966-70; Rockland Comm Coll Adj Fac 1967-90; Tapan Zee HS Soc Stud Tchr 1970-; *ai:* Ed Assn of South Orangetown 1964-, Pres 1971-73; AFT, NEA 1964-; Village of Sloatsburg, Mayor 1975-81, 1985-89; Sloatsburg Fire Dept 1964-, Sec, Active-Life Mem; Sloatsburg Police Dept 1970-75, Sergeant; Congressional West Point Acad Review Bd 1977-; NY St PTA Jenkins Meml Awd; Bugbee Fnd Schshp; Author Prof Articles, Comm Bulletins, Pamphlets, Pub Svc Newsletters; Assistantship Grad Schl of Pub Affairs 1963-64; *office:* Tappan Zee HS Dutch Hill Rd Orangeburg NY 10962*

WRIGHT, CATHERINE R., History Teacher; *b:* Brooklyn, NY; *ed:* Lehman Coll (BA) His 1992; Working Towards MS in His Brooklyn Coll; *cr:* Andrew Jackson HS His Tchr 1992-94; Canarsie HS His Tchr 1994-; *office:* Canarsie HS 1600 Rockaway Pky Brooklyn NY 11236

WRIGHT, CHARLES EDWARD, Art Teacher; *b:* Washington, DC; *m:* Mildred Cantrell; *ed:* Park Coll (BA) Art 1955; Yale Univ (BFA) Painting, Sculpture 1959, (MFA) Painting 1961; Attnd NY Univ Educl Cert, Film Production; *cr:* Northern Vly RHS Demarest Art Tchr; *ai:* Art Club Adv; Natl Soc Painters 1983-, Casein, Acrylic; NJEA, NEA 1964-; Soloway Awd 1984; Finch Coll Museum; Stu of Josef Albers 1954-60; Sculptural Asst to Seymour Lipton 1964-68.

WRIGHT, CHRISTINA TARBUTTON, Mathematics Teacher; *b:* Chestertown, MD; *m:* Allan Kennedy; *c:* Gail Elizabeth, Kirk Allan; *ed:* WA Coll (BA) Math 1961, (MA) Psych 1984; 9 Addl Hrs; *cr:* Kent Schl Inc Math Tchr 1980-; *ai:* NCTM 1985-; The Compleat Bookseller 1994-,

Co-Owner, Co-Mgr; 1990 Grant Geometry Inst; *office:* Kent Schl Inc PO Box 507 Chestertown MD 21620

WRIGHT, COLLEEN ANDREA, Secondary Ed Science Teacher; *b:* Jamaica, West Indies; *ed:* Hofstra Univ (BA) Bio 1988; Queens Coll (MS) Ed 1995; *cr:* Uniondale HS Bio, Chem Tchr 1989-; *ai:* Chrldr, Sci Olympiad Club Adv; AFT 1989-; *office:* Uniondale HS 933 Goodrich St Uniondale NY 11553

WRIGHT, CONNIE SPRAGUE, 3rd & 4th Grade Teacher; *b:* Watertown, NY; *c:* Trisha Davis, Julie, Steven; *ed:* Jefferson Comm Coll (AA) Lbrl Arts Sci 1989; Empire St Coll SUNY (BS) Tchng, Music Performance 1996; Grace Downs Schl Airline, Secretarial Grad 1965; *cr:* The Turquoise House Pre Schl Owner, Operator, Tchr 1982-84; HT Wiley Schl 4-6 Grd Asst Tchr1984-86; Faith Flwshp Pre K-8 Grd Tchr 1986-; EF Educl Fnd Prgm Coord, Summer Frgn Exchange Prgm 1991-94; *ai:* Yrbk Adv; Ensemble Dir; Drama, Mime Coaches; Women Aglow Flwshp 1975-, Pres; Recorded 2 Albums, Songwriter; *home:* 441 S Hamilton St Watertown NY 13601

WRIGHT, DANA MARIE, Business Teacher; *b:* Dayton, OH; *m:* Gregory Lee; *c:* Morgan Leigh; *ed:* OH St Univ (BA) Bus Ed 1988; Addl Hrs Field of Instrl Design, Tech; *cr:* St James the Less Schl Cmptr Tchr 1988-90; St Paul Schl Cmptr Tchr 1988-90; Jonathan Alder HS Bus Tchr 1990-; *ai:* FBLA Adv; Dist Tech Comm; *office:* Jonathan Alder HS 6440 Kilbury Huber Rd Plain City OH 43064

WRIGHT, DAVID BRIAN, Physics Teacher; *b:* Denville, NJ; *m:* Lori Ambrose; *c:* Jessica; *ed:* Rowan Coll of NJ (BA) Phys Sci 1985; *cr:* WA Twp HS Chem Tchr 1985-92, Physics Tchr 1987-; *ai:* Asst Sci League Adv; NEA, Gloucester Cty Ed Assoc, WA Twp Ed Assoc, NJEA 1985-; NSTA 1986-; Tiny Tim Fund Inc 1991-, Lt of Fundraising; *office:* Washington Township HS 529 Hurffville Crosskeys Rd Sewell NJ 08080

WRIGHT, DOLLIE CLAIBORNE, Vocal Music Teacher; *b:* Richmond, VA; *ed:* VA St Univ (BS) Vocal Music Ed 1967; West Chester St Univ Masters Equivalency Cert; Attnd James Madison Univ & Salisbury St Univ; *cr:* Fauquier Cty Bd of Ed Vocal Music Tchr 1967-68; Wicomico Cty Bd of Ed Vocal Music Tchr & Fine Arts Dept Chm 1969-; Univ of MD Eastern Shore Dir Gospel Choir 1987-89; *ai:* Schl Improvement Team Co-Chm; Music Curr Comm Scndry Vocal Rep; Discipline Comm; Schl Crisis Team; Admin Comm; NEA, MD St Tchrs Assn & Wicomico Cty Ed Assn 1969-; Music Educators Natl Conf 1964-; Amer Choral Dir Assn; Eastern Shore Choral Dir Assn; Delta Sigma Theta 1965-; NAACP 1972-; Nom Outstanding Bus & Prof Woman 1984; Outstanding Tchr of Yr 1984-85; Chms Choice Faculty Mem of Yr 1988; Nom for Induction to Natl Tchrs Hall of Fame; Leadership Awd Commission for Women 1993; Nom for Outstnding Tchr of Yr 1994, 1995, 1996; *office:* Parkside HS 1015 Beaglin Park Dr Salisbury MD 21801*

WRIGHT, GAY BECKNER, Fifth Grade Teacher; *b:* Harrisburg, PA; *m:* Edward M.; *c:* Elizabeth, Perry, Bo, Jennifer; *ed:* Lock Haven univ (BS) Elem Ed 1970; 40 Grad Hrs; *cr:* Sullivan Ave Elem Schl 5th Grd Tchr 1970-72; Midlakes Intermediate Schl 5-6th Grd Tchr 1972-; *ai:* PCSFA VP; Dist Shared Decision Making, Dist Ed, Prof Improvement Comms; Mentor Intern Prgm; Conflict Resolution; Cooperative Discipline, OBE Trainer; NYSUT, PCSFA 1970-; Ontario Cty Day Care Bd 1993-; United Meth Church; *home:* 164 White Springs Rd Geneva NY 14456

WRIGHT, GERRY LINWOOD, Vocal Music Director; *b:* Lewiston, ME; *m:* Sharon L.; *c:* Steven (dec), Jennifer; *ed:* Thoms Coll (BS) Bus Ed 1969; Univ of ME at Orono (BS) Music Ed 1983; *cr:* Messalonskee Schl Dist Vocal Music Dir 1970-; *ai:* Chamber Choir; Amer Choral DA, MENC 1975-; Natl Assn Jazz Ed 1980-; Masons, 1963-; Elks 1977-; *office:* Messalonskee HS 62 Oak St Oakland ME 04963

WRIGHT, HENRY S., French Teacher; *b:* Bronx, NY; *ed:* Iona Coll (BA) His 1959; Seton Hall Univ (MA) European His 1968; Certiticut de La Langue francaiye Sorbonne Paris; *cr:* Canadian Schls Tchr 1959-65; Blessed Sacremant HS Tchr 1965-66; Essex Cath HS Tchr, Dean, Chair 1966-69; Cardinal Farley Mil Acd Tchr, Chair 1969-71; Bishop hendricken HS Tchr, Dean, Chair 1971-74; Msgr Farrell HS Tchr, Chair 1974-; *ai:* Golf, Bowling Coaches; Bowling IMs Dir; AATF, NYSAFLT 1965-; NACY 1970-; *office:* Msgr Farrell HS 2900 Amboy Rd Staten Island NY 10306

WRIGHT, HERMAN W., Cnslr & Cooperative Ed Instr; *b:* Charleston, SC; *c:* Jennifer, Lugenia; *ed:* City Coll at CUNY (BA) Psych 1972, (MS) Educl Psych 1977; *cr:* Bd of Higher Ed Asst Dir Spec Prgms 1973-89; York Coll Cnslr, Instr 1989-; *ai:* Stu Programming & Ldrshp Dev Ctr Asst Dir; Indian Pakistan & Bandledash, Alpah Omega, Muslin Club, Apiva Fac Liaison York Coll Alumni Adv; CUNY VA, York Coll Events Comm; *office:* City Univ Of NY York Coll 92-20 Guy R. Brewer Blvd Jamaica NY 11451

WRIGHT, JOAN SIMPSON, 6th Grade Teacher; *b:* Freeport, NY; *m:* Randal F.; *c:* William, Timothy; *ed:* SUNY at Oneonta (BS) Elem Ed 1975; CW Post Coll (MS) Spcl Ed 1978; 30 Credit Hrs Post Grad Work Cert Renewal; *cr:* Freeport Pub Schls K-6th Grd Sub Tchr 1975-79; Rutland City 5th-6th Grd Tchr 1979-81; Neshobe Elem 6th Grd Tchr 1981-; *ai:* NEA & VEA 1979-; *office:* Neshobe Elem Schl Rd 3 Brandon VT 05733

WRIGHT, K. SIOBHAN, Assistant Professor of English; *b:* Buffalo, NY; *m:* Daryl W. Gonder; *c:* Maeve; *ed:* St Univ of NY (AB) Eng 1985; PA St Univ (MFA) Creative Writing 1989; *cr:* PA St Univ Tchng Asst, Lecturer 1985-90; Carroll Comm Coll Asst Prof 1990-; *ai:* Co-Chair Information Lit Across the Curr Prgm; Ctr for Tchng Excl Comm; Assoc Writing Prgms 1989-; Wrote Play Produced in Baltimore 1993; Short Story Pub 1990; *office:* Carroll Community College 1601 Washington Rd Westminster MD 21157

WRIGHT, KATHLEEN O'BRIEN, Second Grade Teacher; *b:* Hartford, CT; *m:* John Jay Jr.; *c:* Jessica, John III, Stephanie; *ed:* Castleton St (BS) Elem Ed 1971, (MA) Lang Arts 1993; 30 Credit Hrs; Attnd NERA Conf 1995; *cr:* South Windsor Schl 1st Grd Tchr Half Yr; Fisher Schl 1st Grd Rdng Tchr 3 Yrs; Sunderlund Schl Kndgtn, T, 3 Grd Tchr 7 Yrs; Dorset Schl 3, 2, 1 Grd Tchr 6 Yrs; *ai:* NEA, VEA; Local Mbrshps DTA 1990-, VP, Pres; Delta Kappa Gamma 1986-, Sec; Drug Free Schls 1993-; Arlington Nrsng Assn 1994-; Past Cub Scout Ldr; Catechism Tchr; Tchr of Yr UVM 1992; *office:* Dorset Elem Schl Box 290 Morse Hill Rd Dorset VT 05251*

WRIGHT, LENNA MORRIS, Retired Elem & HS Teacher; *b:* Mussoorie, India; *m:* Maurice E.; *c:* Rembrandt, Bernard, Adele Swain, Dawn Stilphen, Norman; *ed:* Andrews Univ (BA) Elem Fr 1959; Univ of MI (MA) Elem Ed 1963; *cr:* Brookside Acad 1-8 Grd, 2 Gr Fr Tchr 1940-41; Union Springs Acad 1, 2 Grd Fr Tchr 1944-48; Holly SDA Church Schl 4-6 Grd Tchr 1956-64; Holland SDA Schl 1-4 Grd Tchr 1964; Edenville SDA Church 1-4, 7-8 Grd Tchr 1971-76; The Wright Schl 1-9 Grd Tchr 1976-84; Lapeer Church Schl 1-2, 7-8 Grd Tchr 1976-78; *ai:* Tutor; Storyteller; Recorder Playing; SDA Tchr Org; Parkview Hosp 1986-, Aux, Vol, 100 Hrs Svc; Taught in Nepal 1986; *home:* 24 Peary Dr Brunswick ME 04011

WRIGHT, LUEVINA, Cnslr & Freshman Seminar Instr; *b:* Cincinnati, OH; *c:* Lance, Michael; *ed:* Kean Coll (BA) Soc Work 1975; Trenton St (MED) Ed 1979; Rutgers Univ (MSW) Soc Work 1991; Addl Hrs Conflict Mediation, Eating Disorders, Alcohol Ed; *cr:* Raritan Vly Comm Coll Cnslr, Tchr 1979-; *ai:* BSU Adv 3 Yrs; Acad Stans, Fac Review Comms; Mentor; NASW; NJCCC; AFT; Bound Brook Adult Schl Dedicated Svc Awd; NJCCC Schlsp; Natly Cert Cnslr; *office:* Raritan Valley Comm Coll PO Box 3300 Somerville NJ 08876*

WRIGHT, MARCIA KORNBLUM, Fifth Grade Teacher; *b:* New York City, NY; *m:* R. Timothy; *c:* Michael Supon, Stefan Supon; *ed:* Syracuse Univ (AB) Eng, Ed 1968; Univ of Bridgeport (MA) Eng, Ed 1971; 6th Yr Rdng Consultant, Admin, Supervision 1974; Sacred Heart Univ Elem Cert K-8; Fairfield Univ Credit Hrs; Columbia Univ CEUE; *cr:* Bridgeport Schl Eng Tchr 1971-73; Stamford Schl Title I Rdng Tchr 1973-74; Penfield Schl Rdng Resource Tchr 1974-76; Westport Schl 1-8th Grd Tchr 1976-; *ai:* WEA, CEA 1976-; IRA; NCTC; Womens Club Temple Beth El; Co-Authored Articles; Celebration of Excl Awd; *office:* Bedford MS 170 Riverside Ave Westport CT 06880

WRIGHT, MARTHA ELIZABETH, Second Grade Teacher; *b:* Washington, DC; *ed:* DC Tchrs Coll (BA) Elem Ed 1970; Univ of MD (MA) Supervision, Admin 1972; 40 InSvc Credit Hrs; 36 Hrs Towards MA Biblical Stud; *cr:* Carderock Springs Schl Tchr 24 Yrs; *ai:* Intnl, Safety Comm; Grd Level Chair; Montgomery Cty ed Assn 1973-, Co-Chair; MD St Tchrs Ass, NEA 1973-; Sunday Schl Supt; Who's Who in Colls, Univs 1972.

WRIGHT, MARY ANN KONECHECK, 7th-8th Grd Math, Algebra Tchr; *b:* Charleroi, PA; *c:* Nisha Lynne; *ed:* CA Univ of PA (BS) Scndry Math 1989; Allegheny Intermediate Unit 24 Credit Hrs; *cr:* Steel Vly Schl Dist Math, Algebra Tchr 1990-; *ai:* SVEA, PSEA, NEA 1990-; *office:* Steel Vly HS MS E Oliver Rd Munhall PA 15120

WRIGHT, MARY SUE WILLIAMS, Business Teacher; *b:* Troy, NY; *m:* Leland George; *c:* Gregory, Gail, Cynthia Kocelski, Steven, Robert; *ed:* SUNY at Albany (BS) Bus Ed 1952; Attnd SUC at Oswego, Coll of St Rose, Univ of MO; *cr:* Philadelphia HS Bus Tchr 3 Yrs; Canastota HS Bus Tchr 24 Yrs; *ai:* NYSUT, CTA 1976-; ASCD 1986-; *office:* Canastota Jr Sr HS 101 Roberts St Canastota NY 13032

WRIGHT, NANCY ARNOLD, Third Grade Teacher; *b:* Dayton, OH; *m:* Gary L.; *c:* Kyle D.; *ed:* Otterbein Coll (BS) Ed 1969; 26 Quarter Hrs Univ of Dayton 1977-78; 26 Quarter Hrs Wright St Univ 1992; *cr:* Moraine Meadows 3rd Grd Tchr 1969-71; J. E. Prass El Schl 5th Grd Tchr 1971-72; Moraine Meadows 5th Grd Tchr 1972-75, 5th-6th Grd Tchr 1975-76, 2nd Grd Tchr 1978-93, 3rd Grd Tchr 1993-; *ai:* Comm Ed Cncl Bd; Spelling Bee, United Way Coord; NEA, OEA, KEA 1972-; Germantown Historical Soc 1978-; Good Shepherd UM Church, Chancel Choir 1975, Bd of Trustees 1996; *office:* Moraine Meadows Elem Schl 2600 Holman St Dayton OH 45439*

WRIGHT, NANCY MAZIS, 11th Grade English Teacher; *b:* Camden, NJ; *m:* Gayle N.; *ed:* Post Grad 15 Hrs Fine Arts Amer Univ, 6 Hrs Eng Penn St, 9 Hrs Ed Montclair; *cr:* Bernards HS Eng Tchr 3 Yrs; Chief Logan HS Eng Tchr 3 Yrs; Keystone HS Eng Tchr 1 Yr; Blair HS Eng Tchr 4 Yrs; Bethesda Chevy Chase HS Eng, Drama Tchr 12 Yrs; Churchill HS Eng Tchr; *ai:* Summer Rdng Prgm Comm; PTSA Rep; NEA 1966-; WA Post Contest Winner Trip to Spain 1992; Flwshp Univ of MD Summer 1992.

WRIGHT, PAMELA POWELL, Physical Education Teacher; *b:* Baltimore, MD; *m:* Dennis F.; *c:* Precious, Jewel; *ed:* Morgan St Univ (BS) K-12 PE 1981; Master Equivalent +36 Credit Hrs; *cr:* Woodlawn MS & Sr HS Tchr 6 Yrs; Lansdowne MS Tchr 1 Yr; Lansdowne Sr HS Tchr 1 Yr; Milford Mill Acad Tchr 6 Yrs; *ai:* Bsktbl, Vlybl, Tennis Head Womens Coach; NEA.

WRIGHT, PETER J., High School Math Teacher; *b:* St Johnsbury, VT; *m:* Sandra J.; *c:* PJ; *ed:* Bryant Coll (BS) Bus Admin 1988; Univ of VT Working Towards MED; *cr:* St Johnsbury Acad Tchr 1988-; *ai:* Alumni Cncl; Head Dorm Proctor; Var Bsbl Coach; Jr Var Bsktbl Coach; NCTM 1993-; Natl HS Bsbl Coaches Assn 1989-; *office:* St Johnsbury Acad 7 Main St Saint Johnsbury VT 05819

WRIGHT, ROBERT LYNDON, World Cultures Teacher; *b:* Euclid, OH; *m:* Patricia Dougherty; *c:* Adele, Carly; *ed:* Kent St Univ (BS) Scndry Ed & Soc Stud 1983; Malone Coll (MA) Curr & Instruction 1995; Masters Degree Practicum; *cr:* Scottsdale Chrstn Acad Tchr & Coach 1984-85; Bucyrus HS Tchr & Coach 1985-88; East Palestine HS World Cultures & Amer His Tchr 1988-; *ai:* 8th Grd Girls Bsktbl Coach; Memorial Bapt Church 1988-, Adult Sunday Schl Tchr; *office:* East Palestine HS 360 W Grant St East Palestine OH 44413*

WRIGHT, RONA TEMPLE, Social Studies Teacher; *b:* New York, NY; *c:* Atiba Jaja; *ed:* St Johns Univ (BA) Pol Sci 1973; Fordham Univ (MAT) His, Scndry Ed 1974; Attnd Brooklyn Coll Masters Educl Admin; *cr:* Tenton Jr HS #2 Tchr 1982-86; Bayside HS Tchr 1986-; *ai:* African-Amer Club Fac Adv; UFT 1986-, Dept Rep; *office:* Bayside HS 3224 Corporal Kennedy St Bayside NY 11361*

WRIGHT, SANDRA E., 4th Grade Teacher; *b:* Utica, NY; *ed:* St Joseph Coll at Maryland (BA) Ed 1969; SUNY at Cortland (MS) Ed 1984; Youngstown St Univ 18 Credit Hrs; *cr:* St Charles Schl 5th, 7th, 8th Grd Tchr 1963-69; St Joseph Schl at Youngstown 3rd & 5th Grd Tchr 1969-75; St Peter's Schl 4th Grd Tchr 1977-80; Our Lady of Lourdes 6th Grd Tchr 1980-85; Our Lady of Bed-Stuy Holy Rosary 6th Grd Tchr 1985-90; Utica City Schls 4th Grd Tchr 1990-; *ai:* 7th & 8th Grd Boys Bsktbl Coach 1988-90; Folk Group Dir Lourdes Schl 1980-85; AFT, NYSUT 1990-; IRA 1 Yr; Hope House, Hospitality House Soup Kitchen 1992-, Bd of Dirs; Agape House Day Care 1986-, Summer Prgm Coord; Thea Bowman House 1996, Pres of Bd of Dirs; Lourdes Refugee Resettlement Prgm 1983-85, Co-Chprsn; Wilming United Neighbors 1977-80,Bd Mem 1978-80; Pax Christi Utica & USA; *office:* Watson Williams HS 107 Elmwood Pl Utica NY 13501*

WRIGHT, SANDRA J., Health Education Teacher; *b:* St Johnsbury, VT; *m:* Peter J.; *c:* P.J.; *ed:* Lyndon St Coll (BA) Psych 1982; Univ of VT (MED) Curr & Instruction 1993; *cr:* St Johnsbury Acad Hlth Ed Tchr 1984-; *ai:* Support Group Ldr; *home:* RR 3 Box 262A Saint Johnsbury VT 05819

WRIGHT, SANDRA LOUISE, Chemistry Teacher; *b:* Baltimore, MD; *c:* Brian; *ed:* Morgan St Univ (BS) Bio 1975, (MS) Sci 1975; 10 Credits Johns Hopkins Tchr Cmptr Prgm; 9 Credits UMBC Governors Acad, Martin Marietta Rsrch Project; *cr:* YCC Instr 1980-90; Baltimore City Pub Schls Tchr 1971-; Morgan St Univ Instr 1983-; UMBC Summer Prgm Dept Head 1995-; *ai:* Track & Field, Cross Cntry Coach 1988-; Stdnts Helping Other People Club 1995-; UMBC Summer Prgm for Medicine Intnl Baccalaureate Comm Class Adv; MAST 1988-; NSTA 1990-; NAACP 1975-; Morgan St Alum 1991-; Douglass HS Alum 1990-; Martin Marietta Grad Fellows, Acad of Sci, Math Prgms; Guide Drugs HS 9-12 1990; Eenergy Guide 1980; *office:* Baltimore City Coll HS 3220 The Alameda Baltimore MD 21218*

WRIGHT, SANDRA LEE SCHEID, Kindergarten Teacher; *b:* Elyria, OH; *ed:* Ashland Univ (BS) Elem Ed 1970; 32 Credit Hrs Akron Univ, Kent Univ, LaVerne Coll; *cr:* Grafton Elem Schl Kndgtn Tchr 1970-; *ai:* NEA, OEA 1970-; *home:* 17600 State Route 511 Wellington OH 44090

WRIGHT, STACY RAE, Span, Practical Computing Tchr; *b:* Meadville, PA; *ed:* Slippery Rock Univ (BS) Span 1992; Edinboro Univ (MA) Cnslng, Human Dev 1996; Attnd St Bonaventure Univ, Univ of Seville in Spain; *cr:* Warren Cty Schl Dist Span Cmptr Tchr 1992-; *ai:* Girls Var Bsktbl, Jr HS Bsktbl, Asst Sftbl Coach; Span Club Adv; PSEA, NEA 1992-.

WRIGHT, SUSAN WEISMANTEL, Eighth Grade Teacher; *b:* Springville, NY; *m:* Jeffrey; *c:* Stephen, Matthew; *ed:* Kent St (BS) Elem Ed 1972; Post Grad 8 Hrs; *cr:* Nordonia Hills 5th Grd Tchr 1972-78; Notre Dame Elem 7th Grd Tchr 1980-84; St Helen Schl 8th Grd Tchr 1985-; *ai:* Stu Cncl Chm; Numerous Comms; ABC Day Care 1980-85, Bd of After Prom Kenston 1995-; Stewardship Holy Angels 1995-; *offic* Helen Schl 12060 Kinsman Rd Newbury OH 44065*

WRIGHT, TERRI LASSOND, Third Grade Teacher; *b:* Medina, O David; *c:* Abigail, Zachary; *ed:* Bowling Green St Univ (BA) Ed 198 Credit Hrs Akron Univ; *cr:* C. R. Towslee Elem Third Grd Tchr 1984 Brunswick HS Tennis Coach 1985-89; Just Say No Club Adv 1986-8 Advy Comm 1990-92; NEA 1984-; BEA 1984-, Bldg Rep; Schl Dist Tchr of Yr 1989; *office:* C R Towslee Elem Schl 3555 Center Rd Bruns OH 44212

WRIGHT, THOMAS R., Social Studies Teacher; *b:* Poughkeepsie *m:* Judith Male; *ed:* SUNY at Plattsburgh (BA) Sociology 1983; W CT St Univ (MA) Amer His 1993; STET, Reality Therapy, Coope Learning, Madeline Hunter In-Service Courses; *cr:* Dover Jr Sr H Stud Tchr 1988-; *ai:* MS Planning Team; Founding Mem Seventh Tchng Team; Asst Modified Ftbl Coach; Created Spec Course Civil AFT 1988-; 7th Grd Team Tchrs Honored for Tchr-Adv Prgm; *o* Dover Jr Sr HS Rt 22 Dover Plains NY 12522

WRIGHT, TRUDY FEIL, AP English Teacher; *b:* Long Beach, N Gene; *c:* Lori Radabaugh, Lisa Hipple; *ed:* Trenton St Coll (BA) Eng Attnd Univ of Akron, Ashland Univ, OH St Univ, OH Weslyan Northridge Local Schls HS Eng Tchr 1985-; Henry Hudson Regnl Grd Lang Arts Tchr 1994-95; Norton Local Schls 7-8th Grd Lang Arts 1995-; *ai:* OGA, NEA, COTA, NREA, NCTE 1985-; OCTELLA 1 NOTE 1995-, Bd Mem; Family Counseling Svc 1990-, Vol; Dow, Babcock Fnd Grant 1994; *office:* Northridge HS 6066 Johnstown Uti Johnstown OH 43031*

WRIGHT, WENDY LYON, Third Grade Teacher; *b:* Mahopac, N Kevin; *c:* Adam, Ashley; *ed:* Gordon Coll (BS) Elem Ed 1981; Wester St Univ (MS) Rdng 1989; *cr:* Ambassador Chrstn Acad 2nd-3rd Grd 1980-81; Mahopac Cntrl Schl Sub Tchr 1981; Hudson Valley Chrstn 3rd-4th Grd Tchr 1981-89; Faith Chrstn Acad 3rd Grd Tchr 1995- Drama, Speech, Sports Adv; Assn of Chrstn Schls Intnl; Faith Assemb God 1989-, Ldrshp; Vacation Bible Schl 1977-, Dir; Womens Minis 1993-, Treas; Sunday Schl 1979-, Tchr; *home:* 8 Ricky Ln Poughke NY 12601

WRIGHT, WILBUR L., English Teacher; *b:* Valparaiso, IN; *ed:* SUN Plattsburg (BA) Eng 1966; SUNY at Albany (MA) Eng 1972; Attnd Lir Coll & Oxford Univ ASA; *cr:* Lisha Kill Schl Eng Dept Subject C 1970-83; Colonie Cntrl HS Bldg Planning Team 1988-92; Colonie Cnt SCTA Bldg Pres 1993; *ai:* Theatre Arts Tech Dir & Production Coord St United Tchrs 1969-; NEA; NCTE; CYR Drama Awd; *office:* S Co Cntrl HS 1 Raider Blvd Albany NY 12205

WRIGHT, WILLIAM F., Fifth Grade Teacher; *b:* Clifton Springs, N Linda Susan Barone; *c:* Matthew J.; *ed:* Fredonia St Univ Coll (BS) Ed 1983, (MS) Curr Instruction Ed 1988; *cr:* Silver Creek Cntrl Sch Grd Tchr 1983-; *ai:* Various Schl Comms; SCCS Tchrs Assn 1 NYSUT 1983-; First United Presbyn Church 1994-; Buderkin Awd Outstdng Stu Tchng 1983.

WRIGHT PETERS, DENISE, English Teacher; *b:* Louisville, KY Carl D.; *c:* Dora; *ed:* Univ of Louisville (BA) Eng 1977, (MA) Eng 1 *cr:* Univ of Louisville PTL, GTA, Eng Tchr 1977-82; Our Lady of M Acad Eng Tchr 1983-85; Holy Cross HS Eng Tchr 1986-; *ai:* NACST, 1986-; Tchrs Guide for Book Pub by Ctr for Learnig; *office:* Holy C HS 5035 Route 130 Delran NJ 08075

WROBEL, ANNA MIRIAM, Social Studies Teacher; *b:* Brooklyn, N Corinna, Barak; *ed:* Queens Coll CUNY (BA) His 1982; Columbia (MA) Amer His 1984; Tchrs Coll & NYC Bd of Ed Cert Con Negotiation & Mediation; MPhil, ABD Amer His 1986; *cr:* Columbia Assistantship 1983-84, Flwshp 1984-85 & 1985-86; Cleveland HS Stu Adv & Conflict Resolution 1987-; *ai:* Stu Affairs Coord; Extra-Curricular Dept; Fund-Raising; Dances; Prom; Grad; Stu Govt T Sports; Poetry Wkshp; Lit Magazine; AFT 1987-; UFT 1987-; Tch Writers 1995-; Hadassah 1975-, Newsletter; AKIM 1990-, Assis Events; Natl His Hnr Soc; PBS & Greenpeace; 2 Full Flwshps f Columbia Univ; Poetry Performance NY City; Natl Conf of Chrstns & Human Relations Awd; *office:* Grover Cleveland HS 2127 Himro Ridgewood NY 11385*

WROE, PATRICIA PETTIGREW, 6th Grade Teacher; *b:* Detroit, M Peter, Polly Wroe Knowles, Michael; *ed:* Miami Univ (BA) Lbrl Arts 1 Western CT St Univ (MS) Ed 1973; Attnd Escuela Conversa Costa Ri Fairfield Univ; *cr:* Hurlbutt Elem Tchr 1971-85; Weston MS Tchr 19 *ai:* NEA 1971-; CEA 1971-; Weston Tchrs Assn 1971-, Treas.

WRONKA, ALEXIUS MICHAEL, Vocal Music, Music Theory Tch Passaic, NJ; *m:* Suzan Collins; *c:* Alexius, Anthony, Matthew, Thadd *ed:* Manhattan Schl of Music (BM) Piano Performance 1978; A Cortland St, SUNY at Oneonta; *cr:* Blaic Acad Adj Music Fac 1983 Music in the City Piano Tchr 1990-93; Utica City Schl Dist Sub M Tchr 1991-92; Donovan Jr HS Music Tchr 1992-93; T. R. Proctor Sr Vocal Music, Music Theory Tchr 1993-; *ai:* Mentor Act-so Prgm; Gospel Choir, Rock Band for Stdnts; Mid Sts Adv Bd; NYSUT, AFT 19 *office:* Thomas R. Proctor Sr HS Hilton Ave Utica NY 13501

WRONSKI, STEPHEN JOHN, Fifth Grade Teacher; *b:* New Haven, *m:* Sharon Greco; *c:* Jonathan, Jennifer; *ed:* Southern CT St Univ (1st-8th Grd Ed 1973, (MS) Rdng 1978; 6th Yr Admin Supervision 19 Attnd Yale Univ Russian Stud, Fairfield Univ Career Ed, CT Stenogra Inst Court Reporting; *cr:* Mill Road 5th & 6th Grd Tchr 1973 Clintonville 6th Grd Tchr 1981-86; Green Acres 6th Grd Tchr 1986 Montowese 5th Grd Tchr 1991-; *ai:* Schl Pub Relations; Created & Charge of Yearly Schl Wide Americanism Essay Cont for 5th grd; N Haven Ed Assn 1973-, Bldg Rep; CT Ed Assn 1973-; NEA 1973-; A Legion 1993-, Pub Relations; Veterans of Foreign Wars 1995-; US Radio Operator Overseas Vietnam War 1962-66; *home:* 39 Twin Oak F Rd Wallingford CT 06492*

WRUCK, LINDA A., English Teacher; *b:* Providence, RI; *m:* Keith; Alex; *ed:* RI Island Coll (BA) Eng 1969, (MA) Scndry Eng-Summa C Laude 1975; *cr:* Mt Hope High Eng Tchr 1969-; *ai:* Former Lit Magaz Schl Newspaper & 2 Classes Co-Adv & Adv to Stu Cncl; NEA 196 BWEA 1969-, Bldg Rep, Grievance Comm & Negotiating Team; Read Poetry in Pub (Twice); *office:* Mount Hope HS 199 Chestnut St Bristol 02809

WRYE, MARION, English Teacher; *b:* Wallington, Surrey, England; Univ of RI (MA) Eng 1981; *cr:* Univ of RI Tchng Asst, Eng 1975-77; S of Medical Secretarial Sciences Eng Tchr 1979-81; Dean Jr Coll Eng T 1983-84; Bay View Eng Tchr 1986-; *ai:* Adv to ZOE Bay View's Magazine; Grammaricks A book of Limericks on Grammar, Curre Under Consideration by Houston-Mifflin; Pub Various Poems; *office:* S Mary Acad Bay View 3070 Pawtucket Ave Riverside RI 02915

WRYST, MARY LOUISE, English Teacher; *b:* Moundsville, WV; John Allen; *ed:* OH Univ (BS) Ed 1987, (BA) Eng 1987; 20 Quarter Towards Masters in Scndry Admin; *cr:* Amer Schl Fnd Eng Tchr 1989- Athens HS Eng Tchr 1991-; *ai:* N Cntrl Steering Comm, Bldg Level; Re Prof Dev Ctr- Western Consortium; NEA 1991-; OEA 1991-; Phi De Kappa 1993-; Marth Holden Jennings Scholar 1994-95; *office:* Athens 1 High School Rd The Plains OH 45780*

ZESINSKI, MARY (MACIEJEWSKI), Practical Nursing Teacher; *b:* alo, NY; *m:* Paul J.; *c:* Andrew, Laura; *ed:* ST Univ of NY at Buffalo N) Nrsng 1977; Ed Course Work for Tchng Cert 18 Credits; *cr:* rans Admin Med Ctr Orthopedics Staff Nurse 1977-80; Sister's of ity Hosp Cardiac Care Staff Nurse 1980-84; Hemophilia Ctr of WNY e Clinician, Wellness Coord 1985-91; Erie I. Boces Adult Ed Schl ical Nursing Instr 1991-94; Erie I. Boces-Potter Road Ctr Secndry , Practical Nrsng Tchr 1994-; *ai:* Stu of Month, Safety Comm Mem; st with Voc Indstrl Clubs of Amer Store 1 Day Per Week; NYSUT -; Cheektowagna Cntrl PTA 1986-; Article Pub in Collaboration with Staff on Cancer Treatments in Hempophilic Patients Fed Grant-Prgm d-Wellness, Retreats for Hemophilia Ctr; *office:* Potter Rd Occ Ctr 1 Boces 705 Potter Rd West Seneca NY 14224

ULICH, RITA F., Mathematics Tchr & Dept Chair; *b:* Brooklyn, NY; dward B.; *c:* Edward Paul, Christina; *ed:* St Josephs Coll (BA) Math ; Fordham Univ (MS) Math 1972; Stevens Inst Tech Comp; SUNY at kport Tech; *cr:* Newton HS Math Tchr 1967-72; Salesian Jr Seminary n Tchr 1980-86; John S Burke Math Tchr 1986-; *ai:* Sr Class & onwide Ins Prom Promise Adv; NCTM 1980-; NEA 1980-; ATMNYS -; *office:* John S Burke Catholic HS Fletcher St Goshen NY 10924

, CLARA C., Professor; *b:* Shanghai, China; *m:* Tak-Sek Chan; *c:* ia Chan Liao, Iris Chan; *ed:* Natl Taiwan Univ (BS) Chem 1959; Univ A (MS) Phys Chem 1961; Carnegie-Mellon Univ (PHD) Phys Chem ; *cr:* LaGuardia Comm Coll Asst Prof 1986-90, Assoc Prof 1990-93, 1993-; *ai:* Human Subject Comm; Steering Comm Third World Fac, f Assn; Coord Barnard-LaGuardia Intercollegiate Partnership; Amer mical Soc 1968-; Natl Insts Hlth Bridges to the Future Prgm 1993-95, 5- Grant Awds; Can J. Chem 1993; J. Thermochim Acta 1990; *office:* uardia Comm Coll 31-10 Thomson Ave Long Island City NY 11101

, DAVID, Bilingual Teacher; *b:* Shanghai, China; *m:* Pei Ping Jung; *c:* or, Xin; *ed:* Beijing Univ of Sci, Tech (BA) Mettalurgy 1956; didate of Doctor Phys Chem of Metallurgical Process Moscow Inst of , Steel 1963; 12 Credits CUNY; 9 Credits NY Univ; 3 Credits Adelphi ; 3 Credits Fordham Univ; 6 Credits New Rochell Coll; *cr:* Shanghai of Metullurgy Head Rsrch Group 1963-74; Chinese Acad of Sci uty Dir Semiconductor Lab 1974-80, 1982-86; Daisburg Univ Flwshp xander von Humboldt Fnd 1980-82; *ai:* Book: Metal-Semiconductor rface: The Theory, Test and Technology of Ohmic Contact Pub 1989; cles Pub; *home:* 10547 63rd Ave Forest Hills NY 11375

, LORETTA, ESL Teacher; *b:* New York, NY; *ed:* City Coll of NY) His 1959; Columbia Univ (MA) Chinese His 1974; Hunter Coll City of NY (MA) Eng as Second Lang 1991; *cr:* PS 69Q Third Grd Tchr 5-86; PS 148Q Fourth Grd Tchr 1986-88; Jacqueline Kennedy Onassis Eng, Soc Stud Tchr 1994-95; George Washington HS Eng as Second g Tchr 1995-; *ai:* Curr Comm; United Fed of Tchrs 1970-; Lions Clubs 1984-, Region Chm, Past Dist Governors Ldrshp Awd 1992, Dist Zone ; NY Cosmopolitan Lions Club 1987-, Charter Pres, 100 Percent Pres ; *office:* George Washington HS 549 Audubon Ave New York NY 40

, WEI-HSIUNG, English Professor; *b:* Nanch'ang, China; *m:* Anna C., C.; *ed:* Soochow Univ (BA) Eng 1961; UCLA (MA) Eng Lang, Lit 5; Univ of MD at College Park (PHD) Eng Lang, Lit 1989; UCLA Grad Tchng Eng as Second Lang 1963; *cr:* UCLA Rsrch Asst & Translator 4-66; Arundel Cty Bd of Educ Teacher 1966-68; The Evening Capital lishers Librn 1970; Univ of MD Lecturer 1975; US Dept of Educ Grant iewer 1987-; *ai:* Catalog Editing, Eng Dept Curr, Univ & Dept Rank & ure, MA in Eng Prgm Dev Comms; CEA-MAG Coll Eng Assn 1987-, of Mid Atlantic Group; Modern Lang Assn 1986-; Asian Amer Stud -; Amer Lit Assn; Soc for Stud of Narrative Lit; Soc of Multi-Ethnic of US; Asian-Pacific Amer Advy Cncl; Guest Lecturer at Ctr for Scndry s Tchrs & Texts 1992; Fourth Annual Comm Svc Luncheon Guest aker Amer As sn of Univ Women 1991; Cond of Amer Assn of Univ nen Panalist 1990; Taiwan Friendship Comm Prince Georges Cty 7-; Schsp Comm Elearnor Roosevelt HS 1982-84; rpreter-Translator for Pastor Timothy Ang of Chinese United Meth rch 1976-79; Friends of Soochow Univ Bd of Dir 1978-80; *office:* vie St Univ Jericho Park Road Bowie MD 20715*

ESCHER, KIM (WOODHALL), English Teacher; *b:* Cleveland, OH; Richard D.; *c:* Christian, Diane; *ed:* Akron Univ (BA) Ed, Eng, Earth 1992; *cr:* Barberton HS Eng Tchr 1994-; *office:* Barberton HS 489 W oocan Ave Barberton OH 44203

NDER, NANCY E., Hlth & Phys Education Instr; *b:* Lyons, NY; *ed:* uga Cty CC (AA) Lbrl Arts Hum 1975; SUNY at Brockport (BS) PE 7, (MS) Hlth 1994; *cr:* Border City Schl PE Tchr 1977-79; Our Lady of rcy PE Tchr 1979-82, PE & Hlth Dept Chair 1985-; Allendale-Columbia & Hlth Tchr 1982-85; *ai:* SADD Moderator; Var Vllybl Coach; Red ss Blood Dr & Am Cancer Soc Smoke-Out Coord; Excl in Scndry Schl ng Awd 1988 & 1996; Honored By Duquesne Univ of Excl in Tchng & nmittment 1995; *office:* Our Lady Of Mercy HS 1437 Blossom Rd hester NY 14610

NDER, WILLIAM LLOYD, Principal; *b:* Philadelphia, PA; *m:* Kathy en Myers; *c:* Andrew, David, Sarah; *ed:* Penn St Univ (MED) Educl min 1993; Doctorate Prgm Ed Admn 60 Credits; *cr:* Lock Haven HS strl Arts Tchr 1966-93, Asst Prin 1993-94; Sugar Vly Schl Prin 1994-; NASSP, PASSP, Pi Lambda Theta, PSBA 1993-; ASCD 1995-; Mill l Rotary Club 1995-; Masons 1988-; Who's Who Among Am Bus Ldrs 6; *office:* Sugar Valley Schl RR 2 Box 10 Loganton PA 17747

RSTER, JEFFREY D., Music Teacher; *b:* Regensburg, Germany; *ed:* NY New Paltz (BS) Music 1981; Mount Mt Mary Coll (MS) Spec Ed 1; Attnd Western CT St Univ, Long Island Univ, Manhattanville Coll, stman Schl of Music; *cr:* Fostertown Elem Schl Music Tchr 1987-90; rth Jr HS Band Dir 1990-; *ai:* HS Marching Band; Jr HS Jazz Ensemble; NC, NYSSMA 1987-; IAJE 1995-; NYSBDA 1992-; Church Choir 0-, Dir; NJH Symphonic Band & Jazz Ensemble Gold Rated formance at NYSSMA Festival.

URSTNER, LAURA LEE, English Teacher; *b:* Buffalo, NY; *m:* Thomas *ed:* St Univ Coll at Buffalo (BS) Scndry Eng 1965, (MS) Ed 1970; *cr:* st Seneca West Sr HS Eng Tchr 1965-; *ai:* Bldg Congruence & Quantum d Comms; AFT 1965-; West Seneca Tchrs Assn 1965-, Bldg Rep; NCTE 0-; NYUST 1965-; Presenter at MN High Success Consortium ctioners Paradise & NY St Ed Whole Lang Conf; *office:* West Seneca st Sr HS 3330 Seneca St West Seneca NY 14224*

URTH, HENRY B., Sixth Grade Teacher; *b:* Spokane, WA; *m:* Kathy L. bone; *ed:* OH St Univ (BS) Elem Ed 1976; Univ of Dayton (MSEd) unseling 1992; Preceptorship CCDC III Drug & Alcohol Cnslr; *cr:* aham Jr HS Tchr 7th Grd Learning Disabled 1977; Graham South Elem Grd Tchr 1977-87, 6th Grd Tchr 1987-; Shelbo Co Addiction Cnslr 2-1994; Riverview Mental Hlth 1994-; *ai:* Head Tchr; NEA, OEA 6-; Graham E A 1977-, Rep; OH Schl Cnslrs 1992-; Temprance Lodge AM 1978-, PM; Houston Comm 1992-; *office:* Graham South Elem Schl 5 Jackson St Paris Rd Saint Paris OH 43072

URZEL, BELQUIS, Second Grade Teacher; *b:* Habana, Cuba; *m:* lson; *ed:* Mercy Coll (BS) Sci in Ed 1976; Long Island Univ (MS) ingual, urban Ed 1979; William Paterson Coll 30 Credits Eng as Second ng 1986; Attnd Escuela de Educacion Fisica at Madrid 1970; *cr:* Escuela Educacion Fisica Tchr 1956; Instito Pedagogico Enrique Jose PE Tchr 1959-68; Escuela Normal de Maestro Tchr 1961; Escuela La Merced PE Tchr 1970-74; PS Roberto Clemente Kndgtn Tchr 1980-88; PS #2 2nd Grd Tchr 1989-; *ai:* Mentor Tchr; Parent's Trng for New Immigrants; NEA 1980-; St of NJ Governor's Tchr Recognition Prgm 1988.*

WURZEL, NELSON, Science Teacher; *b:* New York City, NY; *m:* Belquis; *ed:* City Coll of NY (BS) Bio 1966; Grad; Hunter Coll Undergraduate; Belfer Grad Schl; *cr:* Ericsson Jr HS Sci Tchr 1966-; *ai:* Handball Coach; United Federation of Tchrs, AFT 1966-; Natl Sci Fnd Grant; *home:* 2 Horizon Rd Fort Lee NJ 07024

WURZELBACHER, LYNN RAKER, French Teacher; *b:* Philadelphia, PA; *m:* Thomas; *c:* Michael, Alan; *ed:* Univ of Dayton (MS) Ed & Interdisciplinary Stud 1993-; OH Univ (BSEd) in Ed 1972; *cr:* Franklin City Schls Fr & Eng Tchr 1972-80; Springboro HS Fr & Eng Tchr 1984-; *ai:* Muse Machine & Lang Club Spon; NEA & OH Foreign Lang Tchrs Assn 1972-; Warren Cty Project Excl Winner 1993; *office:* Springboro HS 1605 S Main St Springboro OH 45066*

WYATT, PAUL A., Dir of Academic Advisement; *b:* Brooklyn, NY; *m:* Gennie Beaumont; *c:* Christopher; *ed:* Brooklyn Coll CUNY (BA) Elem Ed 1980; John Jay Col of Criminal Justice (MPA) Pub Admin 1985; *cr:* PS 396K Paraprofessional 1977-80; Eastern Airlines Inc Flight Attendent 1980-82; John Jay Coll Admissions Cnslr 1982-83, Asst Dir of Admissions 1983-92, Dir, Acad Advisement 1992-; Adjucnt Lec of Pub Admin 1988-; *ai:* Stu Club Fac Adv; CUNY Connections Customer Svc Trainer; Sexual Harassment Panel Mem; NACAC 1982-, NACADA 1992-; NYCRRC 1977-; *office:* John Jay Coll Criminal Justice 899 Tenth Ave New York NY 10019

WYATT, QUENTIN, Teacher; *b:* Baltimore, MD; *m:* Mary Alice; *c:* Meredith, Lindsay, Gabrielle; *ed:* Coppin St Coll (BS) Ed 1970; Loyola Coll (MS) Ed 1978; Coppin St Coll Masters Eq Corrections; Univ Baltimore Master Eqiv Pol Sci; Stud Correctional Admin, Supervision, Pol Sci; *cr:* Woodlawn Jr HS Tchr 7 Yrs; Woodlawn MS Team Ldr, Tchr 7 Yrs; Milford Mill Schl Tchr 12 Yrs; *ai:* Multicultural Ed Ctr Adv, Kappa Lapa Psi Kappa Yth League Dir; Ed Jazz Sweets Historic Journal; ASHLA, Tchr Awd for Excl, Meritorious Awd; NEA; MSTA; Lochearn Comm Club 1980-, Bd Mem; Baltimore Urban League 1970-74, Bd Mem; Natl Historical Soc Tchr Scholor; Natl Jaycees Awd; Baltimore's Best Awd; *office:* Milford Mill Acad 3800 Washington Ave Baltimore MD 21207*

WYER, EILEEN, Soc Studies & Psychology Tchr; *b:* New Brunswick, NJ; *ed:* Trenton St Coll (BS) Criminal Justice, (MAT) Ed; *cr:* Jackson Meml HS Soc Stud, Psych Tchr 1994-; *ai:* Girld Field Hockey, Sftbl; Women's His Month Comm Chprsn; USI, Intensive Scheduling Evaluation Comms; Prom, Formal Chaperone; NEA, Jackson Ed Assn 1994-; Amer Psych Assn 1995-; Spec Olympics Vol 1990-; *office:* Jackson Memorial HS 101 Don Connor Blvd Jackson NJ 08527

WYETH, FRANCES KENNEDY, 6th-8th Grade English Teacher; *b:* Springfield, IL; *m:* Robert K.; *c:* Erika, Josh; *ed:* IL St Univ (BA) Eng 1969, (BA) Soc Stud 1969; Canisius Coll (MS) Eng in Ed 1979; Springfield Jr Coll 2 Yrs Lbrl Arts Degree 1967; *cr:* Queen of Heaven 4th Grd Tchr 1969-70; West Seneca East Jr HS 8th grd Eng Tchr 1970-71; West Seneca West Sr HS 10th-12 Grd Eng Tchr 1972-84; Queen of Heaven Grd 6 Eng, Soc Stud Tchr 1988-94, Grd 6-8 Eng Tchr 1994-; *ai:* Yrbk, Spelling Bee, Quiz Bowl Moderator; NEA, NYSTA, West Seneca Tchrs Assn 1970-84; DETA 1994-; *office:* Queen Of Heaven Schl 839 Mill Rd West Seneca NY 14224

WYLEGALA, AMY PATRICE, ESL Teacher & Grade Advisor; *b:* Buffalo, NY; *ed:* SUNY at New Paltz (BS) Visual Arts 1984; Tchrs Coll at Columbia Univ (MA) TESOL 1991; *cr:* US Peace Corps Vol Dominican Republic 1985-87; Lower East Side Prep HS ESL, Family Group Tchr, Grd Adv 1991-; *ai:* Empire St Challenger Flwshp 1989-91; *home:* 163 W 79th St Apt 1R New York NY 10024

WYLLIE, ROBERT B., Photography & Graphic Art Tchr; *b:* Ft Wayne, IN; *m:* Jeanna M. Parmelee; *c:* Kip, Patrick; *ed:* SUNY at New Paltz (BS) Art Ed 1984; 30 Credit Hrs MALS Prgm Wesleyan Univ; *cr:* Offset Press Operator 1975-85; Free Lance Photographer 1975-85; East Hampton HS Tech & Art Tchr 1985-; *ai:* Yrbk Adv; Ski Club Adv; Tchr Assoc Negotiating Chair; NEA, CEA, EHEA 1985-, Neg Chair; CTEA 1987-; PIEA 1993-; Kodak Pro Passport 1992-; Montville Amer Little League 1990-, VP; Hiantic Bay Yacht Club 1954-, House Chm; Various Photography Exhibits; Numerous Newspaper Articles; *office:* East Hampton HS N Maple St East Hampton CT 06424

WYMER, ELIZABETH FESSEMYER, 9th-12th Grade Teacher; *b:* Akron, OH; *m:* Larry J.; *c:* David, Angela, Sarah; *ed:* Univ of Cincinnati (BS) Ed 1972; Xavier Univ (MS) Montessori Ed 1989; Attnd Miami Univ of OH, Coll of MT St Joseph, Univ of OR; *cr:* Oak Hills Local Schls Tchr 1973-75; Cincinnati Pub Schls Learning Disabilities 1979-86; North Avondale Montessori Schl 9th-12th Grd Class Tchr 1987-; *ai:* Tech & Assessment Comm; Local Schl Advy Cncl; Rdng Improvement Planning; AFT 1979-; CFT 1979-; Sci Ed Cncl of OH 1990-; North Amer Montessori Tchr Assn; Amer Field Svc 1993-; Jennings Scholar; CGE Awd of Inspiration; Greater Cincinnati Fndtn Grant (Twice); Numerous Articles Pub; *office:* North Avondale Montessori 615 Clinton Springs Ave Cincinnati OH 45229

WYNER, SYBIL, Social Studies Teacher; *b:* Chattanooga, TN; *ed:* Rutgers Univ (BA) Soc Stud 1971; Seton Hall Univ (MA) Soc Stud 1984; Temple Univ Continuing Ed Soc Stud 1979; Bowie St Tchrs Coll Educl Courses; Loyola Univ Tchng Cert; *cr:* United Home of Jerusalem Exec Dir Amer Office 1962-79; Elmora Hebrew Schl Tchr 1963-79; *ai:* NJ Jr Exec Women's Club Adv; Performing Arts Team; Elmora Hebrew Schl Prin; Multi-Cultural Comms; NEA 1986-; Natl Historical Soc; Elmora Hebrew Ctr 1962-, Bd, Tchng & Writing Awds; Short Stories Pub; Noval Written; Numerous Childrens, Adults Plays Written, Produced, Directed; Write Curr Guides US His I, II, World His Soc Stud Dept; *home:* 500 Jersey Ave Elizabeth NJ 07202*

WYNGAARDE, JEANNE EVANS, Biology & Earth Sci Teacher; *b:* Buffalo, NY; *w:* Richard (dec); *c:* Erin, Brenna, Pierce; *ed:* St Univ of NY at Buffalo (BS) Scndry Sci Ed 1962, (MS) Multi-Disciplinary Ed 1984; 30 Credit Hrs Beyond Masters; *cr:* North Jr HS 7th-8th Grd Gen Sci Tchr 1963-68; Grand Island HS Earth Sci Tchr 1968-70; Pub Schl #80 7th-8th Grd Gen Sci Tchr 1970-78; Buffalo Traditional Schl Bio, Earth Sci Tchr 1978-; *ai:* Buffalo Tchrs Fed 1970-, Exec Comm, Sick Leave Bank Trustee, Bldg Comm; NEA, NY 1976-; NEA 1968-; *office:* Buffalo Traditional Schl 450 Masten Ave Buffalo NY 14209

WYNKOOP, ROBERT THOMAS,JR., Sr Instr of Architectural Tech; *b:* Bronx, NY; *m:* Sally Homovich; *ed:* Pratt Inst (BFA) Indstrl Design 1953; US Maritime Ofcrs Candidate Schl Grad Degree Ship Comm Ofcr 1944; Attnd Inst of Design & Construction; *cr:* SLS Designers Staff Architect 1960-67; Beeston & Patterson Staff Architect 1968-72; DeLoitte, Haskins & Sells Admin Architectural svcs 1973-86; Federal Express Architect, Consultant 1987-91; Inst of Design & Construction Sr Instr 1991-; *ai:* Emeritus NY Soc of Architects 1968-, Bd of Dirs, Distngd Svc Awd 1974; Emeritus Amer Inst of Arch NY 1985-; Knights of Columbus, Castilian Cncl Grand Knight; 2 A1A, Interiors Magazine Project of Yr Awds 1984-85; *office:* Inst Of Design & Construction 141 Willoughby St Brooklyn NY 11201

WYNN, JEAN BORIS, Anthropology & Psychology Prof; *b:* Detroit, MI; *m:* Charles M. Sr.; *c:* Charles M. Jr., Joseph J., Michelle B., Andrew M.; *ed:* Univ of Detroit at Mercy (BSN) Nrsng 1962; Univ of MI (MA) Ed, Psych 1966; Univ of CT (PHD) Anthropology 1991; Post Grad Course in His-Taking & Phys Assessment Wayne St Univ at Detroit 1979; CT & MI Registered Nurse; MI Certfd Soc Worker; *cr:* Detroit Metropolitan YMCA Camp Nissokone Camp Nurse 1974-75; Med Examination Svc Med Examiner 1974-75; Substance Abuse Treatment & Rehabilitation Ctr Psychiatric Clinician, Trainer 1975-79; Oakland Comm Coll Med Asst Prgm Part-time Instr 1976; Manchester Comm Coll Women's Ctr Dir, Individual & Group Cnslng 1980-81; ANA Cert Reader, Evaluator 1981-83, Examination Item Writer 1980-82; Trinity Coll Visiting Lecturer 1985-86; Univ of CT Tchng Asst 1986; Windham Hospice, Comm Hlth On-Call Nurse 1988-89; Windham Heights Child Dev Project Consultant, Coord 1988-89; Greater Hartford Comm Coll Adj Fac 1981-90; Manchester Comm Tech Coll Adj Fac 1982-93, Soc Scis Instr 1993-; *ai:* Curr, Fulbright Comms; Adults in Transition, Psi Beta Adv; H. Porter Schl Sci Fair Judge; Amer Anthropological Assn; Soc for Med Anthropology; Amer Educl Rsrch Assn; Archeological Inst of Amer, Hartford Soc; St Columba Church 1980-, Parish Cncl, Fin Conn; Assn for Women in Sci; Doctoral Dissertation Flwshp 1989-90; Univ of CT Pre-Doctoral Flwshp 1986-88; CT Rsrch Fnd Flwshp 1987; US Fed Govt Crippled & Impaired Flwshp 1965-66; Tri-Cty League of Nurses Schlsp 1962; Mercy Coll of Detroit Hnr Schlsp 1958-59; *office:* Manchester Comm Tech Coll 60 Bidwell St Manchester CT 06045*

WYNN, RONALD, HS Social Studies Teacher; *b:* Queens, NY; *m:* Marianna Farrauto; *c:* Joshua, Gregory; *ed:* City Coll of NY (BA) Pol Sci, His 1972, (MS) Ed, Pol Sci 1976; *cr:* Evander Childs HS Tchr Soc Stud 1972-73; Olinville Jr HS Tchr Soc Stud 1973-76; St Basil Acad Tchr Soc Stud 1976-84; Mt St Mary's Coll Adj Instr His, Pol Sci 1990-; FL Union Free Schl Dist Tchr Soc Stud 1984-; *ai:* Adv Orange Cty Yth in Govt 1989-; Bsktbl Coach; FL Tchrs Assn 1984; Wappinger Little League 1993-, Coach; *office:* Florida Union Free Sch Dist 53 N Main St Florida NY 10921

WYNNE, JUNE FRANKLIN, French Teacher; *b:* Marshall, NC; *m:* James Jerome; *c:* Joseph, Jeff, Jeannine; *ed:* Western Carolina Univ (BS) Fr & Eng 1962; Appalachian Univ (MED) Fr & Ed 1970; Mansfield Univ Cert Soc Stud 1989; Univ of Poitiers Diploma; Tchng of Frgn Lang in Elem Schl at Univ of NC; Pre-Courses to Prepare For PHD Penn St Currently Lang Pre-Requisites; *cr:* High Point Cntrl HS Fr & Eng Tchr 1962-64; Lee H Edwards HS Fr & Eng Tchr 1964-66; Canton Area HS Fr & Eng Tchr 1966-69, 1988-; Mansfield Univ Fr Tchr 1985-86; *ai:* NHS Adv; NEA, PSEA & CAEA 1966-70, 1984-; AATF 1962-70, 1985-, St Chptr Sec NC; ACTFL 1962-70, 1995-; Phi Delta Kappa 1987-, Local Sec; Delta Kappa Gamma 1990-, Schlsp Chm Local; *office:* Canton Area Jr Sr HS 139 E Main St Canton PA 17724*

WYNNE, ROBERT W., Retired Teacher; *b:* Newark, NJ; *m:* Ann Forgione; *c:* Kristin, Karin, Lauren; *ed:* Montclair St (BA) Hlth, PE 1963; Seton Hall Univ (MA) Schl Admin 1969; Addl Courses Schl Admin Cert Elem Schl Tchr; *cr:* Kearny HS Pe, Hlth Tchr 1963-74; Franklin Schl Dir Summer Schl 1969-73, Vice Prin 1976-80; Roosevelt Schl Prin 1980-93; Kearny Schl Dist Asst Supt 1993-95; *ai:* Kearny HS Bsbl Coach 1968-74, Bsktbl Coach 1965-71; NJ HS Bsbl Coach of Yr 1973; NEA, NJEA 1963-; Natl Ashl Schl Adm 1976-; Prin, Supvr Assn 1980-; Kearny PTA 1963-, Life Mem; Cedar Grove Bd of Ed 1975-78, VP; *home:* 103 Harper Ter Cedar Grove NJ 07009

WYSE, JUDY, Mathematics Teacher; *b:* Wauseon, OH; *m:* Sanford; *c:* Anna, S. Joseph, Katrina, Desmond, Nathan; *ed:* Hesston Coll (AA) Liberal Arts 1967; Eastern Mennonite (BA) Math 1969; Univ of Toledo (ME) Educl Tech 1992; *office:* Stryker Local Schls Box 624 Stryker OH 43557

WYSKIEL, LOUISA JAMISON, Middle School Mathematics Tchr; *b:* Baltimore, MD; *c:* Matthew Walter, Richard Jamison; *ed:* Univ of PA (BA) Art His 1965; Attnd Johns Hopkins Univ 21 Hrs, Univ of NE 9 Hrs, Towson St Univ 9 Hrs, Notre Dame Coll 12 Hrs; *cr:* Saint Pauls Schl for Girls Sci Tchr 1965-66; Intnl Coll of Beirut Sci Tchr 1967-69; Saudi Arabias Parent Cooperative Schl Math Tchr 1973-77; Roland Park Cntry Schl MS Math Tchr 1978-; *ai:* MS Admissions; 7th Grd Adv; Math Tutor; NCTM 1993-; MCTM 1991-; Woodrow Wilson Participant 1990 & 1995; Assn of Ind MD Schl Math Coord 1989-91; AIMS Master Math Tchr 1994; *office:* Roland Park Country Schl 5204 Roland Ave Baltimore MD 21210

WYSOCK, JOSEPH JAMES, High School English Teacher; *b:* Lancaster, PA; *m:* Valerie Lynn Brown; *c:* Christina, Joseph, Justin; *ed:* Millersville Univ (BA) Eng, Scndry Ed 1985; St of PA Masters Equivalency; *cr:* Caeser Rodney HS Eng Tchr 1985-90; Hempfield HS Eng Tchr 1990-; *ai:* Asst HS Ftbl, HS Strength, Powerlifting Coach; CD Club Adv; Hempfield Ed Assn 1990-; *office:* Hempfield HS Stanley Ave Landisville PA 17538

WYSOCKI, LINDA ANN DIMARZO, Vocal & Instrmntl Music Tchr; *b:* West Orange, NJ; *c:* Jason, Bryan; *ed:* William Paterson Coll (BS) Music Ed 1976; Montclair St Coll 30 Credits Music Ed; *cr:* Kittatinny Regnl HS Instrumental Music Tchr 1976-81; Long Vly MS Inst, Vocal Music Tchr 1981-; *ai:* 7th Grd Band, Choral, Ensemble, Select Chorus Dir; Jr Region Chours; Area, Jr Region Band; Modern Dance Adv; Bsktbl Coach; NEA 1976-; NJMEA 1976, Treas Reg I; NJAB 1976-, Pres, VP, Jr HS Mgr; WTEA 1981-; LV Presb Church 1995-; Childrens Choir, Chorus Dir; North Jersey Jr HS Area Band Conductor 1980, 1987; *office:* Long Valley MS 51 W Mill Rd Long Valley NJ 07853

WYSOLMERSKI, THERESA B., Professor of Biology; *b:* West Rutland, VT; *ed:* The Coll of Saint Rose (BA) Bio 1953; Univ of Notre Dame (MS) Bio 1961; Rutgers Univ (PHD) Zoology 1973; IN Univ Medical Schl Anatomy 1965; *cr:* Saint John the Evangelist Acad Scndry Bio & Chem Tchr 1955-59; The Coll of Saint Rose Bio Tchr 1959-; *ai:* Sigma Xi 1973-, Pres 1994-95; Delta Epsilon Sigma 1975-, Delta Kappa Gamma Intnl Ed Honor Soc 1980-; coll of Saint Rose Alumni Assoc 1959-, Fac Rep, Admissions Comm 1994-; NSF Research Grant Fac Dev at Dartmouth; coll of Saint Rose Thomas Manion Distinguished Fac Awd; Coll of Saint Rose Distinguished Achvmt Awd 1990; *office:* Coll Of Saint Rose 432 Western Ave Albany NY 12203

WYZYKOWSKI, CARMELA, 8th Grade Teacher; *b:* Phila, PA; *ed:* Marywood Coll (BA) Elem Ed 1963, (MS) Ed, Eng 1971; 24 Credit Hrs Theology; *cr:* St Mary's 5th Grd Tchr 1955-58; Our Lady of Perpetual Help 6th Grd Tchr 1958-60; St Boniface 8th Grd Tchr 1960-63; St Margaret Mary's 8th Grd Tchr 1963-67; St Ann's Acad 8th Grd Tchr 1967-71; St Michael's Prin 1971-77; Our Help of Chrstns 8th Grd Tchr 1977-80; Our Lady of Lourdes 9-12 Grd Eng Tchr 1980-88; Our Lady Help of Chrstns 8th Grd Tchr 1988-; *ai:* Schl Decorating; Lit Magazine; Schl Patrol; Tutoring; NJET 1980-88; NSTA 1988-; NMTA 1994-; NCEA Annual Mbrshp; NJHS 1971-77; Vol Svc Action Aids org 1995-; Columbia Press Silver Medalist Natl 1 Yr, 1st Place Winner 4 Yrs, Honorable Mention 2 Yrs; *office:* Our Ldy Help Of Christian Schl 2420 E Allegheny Ave Philadelphia PA 19134*

WYZYKOWSKI, NANCY, English Teacher; *b:* Buffalo, NY; *ed:* St Univ of NY at Buffalo (BS) Scndry Eng Ed 1966, (MS) Scndry Eng Ed 1969; 18 Hrs Beyond Masters; *cr:* Lakeshore Cntrl Eng Tchr 1966-68; Frontier Cntrl Eng Tchr 1968-; *ai:* AFT, NEA, FTC, ETA 1966-; USET, AHSA, SPHA Horse Orgs; SPCA; *office:* Frontier Central HS S-4432 Bay View Rd Hamburg NY 14075

Y

YABLON, SHELLY BETH, English Teacher; *b:* Forest Hills, NY; *ed:* Syracuse Univ (BS) Drama, Eng 1989; Hofstra Univ (MS) Sec Ed, Eng 1990; *cr:* Parkdale HS 10, 10 Tag, 11 Grd Tchr 1990-91; Northwestern Drama, 11 Tag, 11, 12 Grd Tchr 1991-94; Highpoint 9, 10, 11, Advanced Rdng Tchr 1994-; *ai:* Drama, Fashion, Crafts Clubs; Class Spon; Staff Dev Comm; Vlybl Coach; SGA Adv; ATLAS Philosophy & Goals Rep; *office:* High Point HS 3601 Powder Mill Rd Beltsville MD 20705*

YACINA, GEORGE, Technical Writing Teacher; *b:* Hazleton, PA; *m:* Susan Hunt; *c:* Tanya, Joh; *ed:* Bloomsburg St Coll (BS) Eng 1967; Univ of Scranton (MS) Admin 1978; Attnd Penn St, East Stroudsburg, UN of Northern CO & Wilkes Univ; *cr:* West Hazleton HS Eng Tchr 1967-92; Hazelton Area HS Tech Writing Tchr 1992-; *ai:* Wrestling, Track & X-Cntry coach; Sr Class Adv; A-V Dir; Act 178, SLC & Evaluation Comm; NEA, HAEA & PSEA 1967-; Planning Commission Kline Twp 1992-; *office:* Hazleton Area HS 1601 W 23rd St Hazleton PA 18201

YACK, MARGUERITE DETTLINGER, Third Grade Teacher; *b:* Jersey City, NJ; *m:* Gustave Andrew; *c:* Gretchen, Marybeth Yack Wollmuth, Marguerite E.; *ed:* Jersey City St Coll (BA) Ed 1961; Seton Hall Univ (MA) Ed 1964; Univ of VA (MA) Spec Ed 1977; 51 Addl Credit Hrs Spec Ed, Admin & Supervision; *cr:* Our Lady of Victories Elem Schl 4th Grd Tchr 1955-57; St Michaels HS PE Tchr 1957-58; Jersey City St Coll Lab Schl Demonstration Tchr 1964-67; Mont Co MD Pub Schl Tchr of Multiple Handicapped 1968-69, 5th, 6th Grd Tchr 1969-71, Diagnostic-Prescriptive Tchr 1978-81, Resource Tchr for Learning Disabled 1981-87, 3rd Grd Tchr 1987-, Staff Dev, New Tchr Mentor 1990-93; *ai:* HS Girls Bsktbl Coach; Soc Comm Chm; Mentor Disadvantaged Children; Discipline, GATE Comms; NEA, NJEA 1962-; MCEA 1967-; So Others May Eat 1985-, Co-Dir Parish Food Prgm; Montgomery Soccer Inc 1983-, Commissioner; Girl Scouts 1976-, Ldr; Bluebirds, Ldr; Grant for Tchng of Blind; First Place Awd Natl Garden & Flower Show for 5th Grd Class; *home:* 7419 Oak Ln Chevy Chase MD 20815*

YACKINOUS, FRANK ROBERT, 9th-12th Grd Math Teacher; *b:* Newark, NJ; *m:* Virginia McEnroe; *c:* Jean Marie Mardaga, Paul A.; *ed:* Rutgers Univ (BA) Math 1964; Grad Work at Kean Coll & Jersey City St Coll 140 Credits; *cr:* Woodbridge Twp Schl System Ave L Jr High 17 Yrs; Woodbridge HS 15 Yrs; *ai:* NHS Adv; Bsbl Asst Coach; NEA 1982-; Knights of Columbus 1994-, Inside Guard; Woodbridge HS Tchr of Yr 1988; *office:* Woodbridge HS Kelly St Woodbridge NJ 07095*

YACOBOZZI, BARBARA LENDICK, French & English Teacher; *b:* Ellwood City, PA; *c:* Heather, Brooke; *ed:* Edinboro Univ (BS) Eng, Fr 1963; 12 Credit Hrs Gannon Univ; 6 Credit Hrs Edinboro Univ; *cr:* Brecksville HS Tchr 1963-64; Northwestern HS Tchr 1964-65; Mc Dowell HS Tchr 1965-69; Mc Dowell Intermediate HS Tchr 1976; GED Instr 1986-95; *ai:* NEA, PSTA, NCTE, NCTL 1976-; Articles Pub; Poetry Anthology; *office:* Mc Dowell Intermediate HS 3320 Caughey Rd Erie PA 16506

YACOVINO, ANNE FRANCES, 7th & 8th Grade Teacher; *b:* Philadelphia, PA; *ed:* Immaculata Coll (BA) Elem Ed, Eng 1974; Villanova Univ (MA) Elem Schl Admin 1986; Boston Coll Inst of Rel Ed & Pastoral Ministry; *cr:* St Michael 5th Grd Tchr 1981-82; St Barnabas 4th Grd Tchr 1983-85; SS Philip & James Lang Arts, Rel Tchr 1985-86; Our Lady Help of Chrstns Lang Arts, Soc Stud Tchr 1986-91; Immaculate Conception Schl ILA, 7th-8th Grd Soc Stud Tchr 1991-; *ai:* Acad Octathlon Team Coach; Forensics Team Co-Moderator; Integrated Lang Arts Curr Co-Coord; NCEA 1970-; Kappa Delta Pi 1986-; ASCD 1995-; Connelly Fnd Schlsp; *office:* Immaculate Conception Schl 606 West Ave Jenkintown PA 19046

YADLOSKY, RICHARD D., Social Studies Teacher; *b:* Waymart, PA; *m:* Nancy Knolles; *c:* Justin, Nathan; *ed:* Mansfield Univ (BS) Soc Stud 1966; PA St Univ (ME) Ed 1974; 7 Addl Credit Hrs; *cr:* Wyalusing HS Soc Stud Instr 30 Yrs; *ai:* Yrbk Adv 24 Yrs; Ski Club Adv 6 Yrs; NEA, PA St Ed Assn 1966-; Wyalusing Ed Assn 1966-, Pres 1978-79; Lions Club 1975-, Sec 5 Yrs; *home:* RR 1 Box 165 Sugar Run PA 18846

YAGER, SHARON ELIZABETH, Fourth Grade Teacher; *b:* Herkimer, NY; *m:* George F.; *c:* Elizabeth, Robert; *ed:* SUNY at Oswego (BS) Elem Ed 1967; Syracuse Univ (MS) Elem Ed 1970; *cr:* Deerfield Elem Schl Tchr 1968; Clark Mills Elem Schl Sixth Grd Tchr 1968-72; DeForest Hill Elem Schl 4th Grd Tchr 1985-; *ai:* Lang Arts Comm; Shared Decision Making; NEA; NYSUT; Westmoreland Tchrs Assn 1985-; Questers 1991-, Sec; Establishment Homespun Day for 4th Grd Stdnts; PTA Co-Pres Bringing Parents as Partners to Schl Rdng Partners.

YAGER, TARA FLANGER, 4th-5th Grd Multi-Age Teacher; *b:* Manhattan, NY; *m:* James D.; *c:* Brandon, Haley; *ed:* SUC at Oneonta (BS) Elem Ed 1987; SUNY at Albany (MS) Rdng 1991; *cr:* Mayfield Elem Schl 5th Grd Tchr 1987-94, 4th Grd Tchr 1994-95, 4-5 Multi Age Tchr 1995-; *ai:* Elem SADD Adv; Var Girls Soccer, Sftbl Coach; *office:* Mayfield Elem Schl N Main St Mayfield NY 12117

YAGODZINSKI, JOHN CHARLES, 7th Grd Math Teacher; *b:* Northampton, MA; *m:* Christine Zerneri; *c:* Michael, Travis; *ed:* Univ of MA (BS) Math 1971; Westfield St Coll (MED) Admin 1977; NELMS; *cr:* JFK MS 7th-9th Grd Math Tchr 1971-73; Hawley Jr High 7th & 8th Grd Math Tchr 1973-80; JFK MS 7th Grd Math Tchr & Team Ldr 1980-; *ai:* Former Track & Soccer Coach; Former Mem MS Task Force Comm; NEA & MTA; Northampton Tchrs Assn; Hatfield Recreation Comm Coach; Smith Acad Ath Awds Comm; IAABO Bsktbl Referee; PVSA Soccer Referee; MASSPIROG; Most Influential Tchr Awd Northfield Mt Hermon Schl; *office:* John F Kennedy MS 100 Bridge Rd Northampton MA 01060

YAHN, EDWIN L., Art Instructor; *b:* Grove City, PA; *ed:* Westminster (BA) Art 1988; *cr:* Yth Dev Ctr Art Instr 1988-89; Aliquippa Schl Dist Art Instr 1989-92; Neshannock Twp Schl Dist Art Instr 1993-; *ai:* Natl Art Honor Soc, Natl Jr Art Honor Soc, Griffins Peer Ldrshp Group Spon; Stu Access Team Mem; Curr Action Team; NEA 1988-; Neshannock Tchrs Ed Assn 1993-; PA Art Ed Assn, Natl Art Ed Assn 1989-; Grant from Arts in Spec Ed Project of PA; Inclusion Wrshps Local, St Presenter; Video Teleconference Panelist; *office:* Neshannock Twp Schl Dist 301 Mitchell Rd New Castle PA 16105

YAHNER, WILLIAM A., Associate Professor of English; *b:* Spangler, PA; *c:* William T., Meghann; *ed:* Edinboro Univ (BSEd) Eng 1971, (MA) British Lit 1976; IN Univ (PHD) Rhetoric, Linguistics 1990; *cr:* Union City HS Scndry Eng Tchr 1971-89; CA Univ Assoc Prof, Dir Writing Ctr 1989-; *ai:* Eng Assn of PA St Univ 1989-, Pres; NCTE; AFT; NEH Flwshp 1985; Articles Pub; *office:* California Univ Of PA 250 University Ave California PA 15419

YAKOPCIC, MICHELE TERESE, Special Education Teacher; *b:* Syracuse, NY; *m:* Kenneth D.; *c:* Wesley, Loren; *ed:* Salem Coll (BS) Spec Ed, Elem Ed 1975; 6 Credit Hrs Rowan Coll, 6 Credit Hrs St Peters Coll; *cr:* Ripley Schl Dist Spec Ed Tchr 1975-76; Linwood Schl Dist Spec Ed Tchr 1978-; *ai:* Upper Twp Recreation Coach Soccer, Bsktbl, Chrldng; Brownie Ldr; Four Dist Inservice Comm; Linwood Ed Assn 1978-, VP, Treas; NJ Ed Assn 1978-, St Comm Mem; NEA 1978-, Natl Comm Mem; Cntry Shore Womens Club 1987-, 1st VP, 2nd VP, Trustee Mbrshp Awd; Exceptional Children Comm 1995-, Comm; Habitat for Hum 1994-; Linwood Ed Assn 1980-, Pres; Governor's Tchr Recognition Prgm; Cert of Commendation Geog Awareness; Tchr of Yr Nom; Cert of Recognition; *office:* Seaview Ave Schl Walbash Ave Linwood NJ 08221*

YAMAMOTO, PAMELA MCDONOUGH, English & ESL Teacher; *b:* NYC, NY; *ed:* Hunter Coll (MA) Eng & Hnrs 1991; Hunter Coll CUNY (MA) Eng 1996; *ai:* Lit Tutoring Pgm Lunch Time & Presch; VFT 1992-; *office:* Washington Irving HS 40 Irving Pl New York NY 10003

YAMBOR, ELAINE MARGARET, Mathematics Teacher; *b:* Cleveland, OH; *ed:* Cleveland St Univ (BA) Math 1974, (MA) Guid, Cnslng 1984; Univ of NC at Greensboro (MS) Sport Psych 1989; Grad Hrs in Math; *cr:* North Olmsted HS Tchr 1974-; *ai:* Class Adv; Ldrshp, Block Schedule Comms; Sftbl Coach; NEA, OEA, NOEA,NCTM 1974-; *office:* North Olmsted HS 5755 Burns Rd North Olmsted OH 44070*

YAMULLA, JUDITH SIPPLE, Secondary English Teacher; *b:* Hazleton, PA; *m:* Joseph A.; *c:* Katie; *ed:* Bloomsburg Univ (BS) Comprehensive Eng 1970, (MED) Ed 1972; 60 Addl Credits Penn St Highacres & Scranton Univ; *cr:* D. A. Harman Jr HS Eng Tchr 1971-72; Hazleton HS Eng Tchr 1972-92; Hazleton Area HS Eng Tchr 1992-; *ai:* NEA, PSEA, HAEA 1972-; Drums Lioness Club 1980-, Past Pres, VP, Bd of Dirs, Charter Mem, Nuremburg Comm Plyrs 1995-; *office:* Hazelton Area HS 1601 W 23rd St Hazleton PA 18201

YANACHIK, BETTI ANN (DEDO), Librarian; *b:* Greensburg, PA; *m:* Richard J.; *ed:* Alderson Broaddus Col (BA) Sec Ed Soc St 1971; Shippensburg Univ (MSLS) Lib Sci 1973; 6 Credits Comp Penn St Univ; *cr:* Yough Schl Dist Librn 1973-; *ai:* Lib Assts Club & Young Creative Writers Club Spon; NEA 1973-; PSEA 1973-; YEA 1973-, Past Treas & Pres; WCASL 1974-, Treas; PSLA; *office:* Yough Senior HS 97 Lober Rd Herminie PA 15637

YANG, KAREN M., High School Mathematics Tchr; *ed:* St Univ of NY at Fredonia (BS) Math & Physics 1978; PA St Univ (MED) Math & Ed 1980; *office:* Framingham HS 115 A Street Framingham MA 01701

YANG, KATHLEEN, AP Biology & Chemistry Teacher; *b:* Shanghai, China; *m:* Denis C.; *c:* Randall, Ruth; *ed:* Harvard Univ (BA) Chem 1956; Columbia T C (MA) Tchng Sdnry Schl Chem 1961; 7 Credits Columbia Univ; 7 Credits Purchase SUNY; 3 Credits Coll of New Rochelle; 3 Credits Univ of Bridgeport; 1 Credit Hunter Coll; 3 Credits Woodrow Wilson Inst; *cr:* Master Schl Sci Tchr 1965-88; Loyola Schl Sci Tchr 1988-; *ai:* ACHEMY 1991-; Articles Pub; *office:* Loyola Schl 980 Park Ave New York NY 10028

YANITY, LYNNE PATTERSON, Elementary Teacher; *b:* Indiana, PA; *m:* Frederick A.; *c:* Melissa; *ed:* Indiana Univ of PA (BS) Elem Ed 1968; (MED) Elem Ed 1969; *cr:* Westmont Hilltop Schl Dist Elem Tchr 1968-; *ai:* Past Track Coach; PSEA, NEA, WHEA 1968-; Oakland United Meth Church 1969-, Tchr, Comm Chprsn; *office:* Westmont Hilltop MS 827 Diamond Blvd Johnstown PA 15905*

YANKO, ROBERT NICHOLAS, Social Studies Teacher; *b:* Akron, OH; *m:* Mary; *c:* Kristin, Beth, Nathan; *ed:* Unif of Akron (MA) His 1978; 36 Addl Hrs Past Masters; *cr:* Hudson HS Soc Stud Tchr 1971-; *ai:* Golf Coach; NEA, OEA, HEA 1971-; 1978 Fulbright Schlsp, Tchr Exchange England; 1990 NEH Fellowship Russian Revolution Rollins Coll; 1995 NEH Fellowship, Industrial Revolution Univ MA at Dartmouth; 1991 Inducted in OH Golf Coaches Hall of Fame; *office:* Hudson HS 2500 Hudson Aurora Rd Hudson OH 44236

YANKOWSKI, LINDA JEAN PILVER, Science Teacher; *b:* Manchester, CT; *m:* Michael Peter Wayne; *ed:* Loma Linda Univ (BS) Bio 1984; Univ of CT (MA) Scndry Sci Ed 1985; 6th Yr Educl Admin 1991; Coll of Desert Nrsng; Univ of Hartford Cmptrs; Manchester Comm Tech Coll Gen Stud, Cmptrs; Manchester Meml Hosp Schl of Radiology Cert 1975; *cr:* Manchester Meml Hosp X-Ray, CAT Scanning Technician 1976-79; Harry B. Hoffman MD Inc VP 1979-85; Coll of Desert Math, Sci Tutor 1980-81; Manchester Pub Schls Sub Tchr 1984-86; Rham HS Sci Tchr, Schl to Career Tech Prep Coord, Interim Asst Prin 1986-; Vernon Pub Schls Adult Evening Ed Instr 1991-94; Manchester Comm Tech Coll Adj Fac Sci Dept 1991-; *ai:* Stu Stud Team; Schl Concerns; Ninth Grd Planning; Ind Learner E CT Region D Steering Comm; Regnl Prgm Review, Planning Comm; MCTC HS to Coll Transition Comm; Consortium, Mrktng Comm; Schl to Career Comm; Scheduling Curr, Schl Philosophy; Educl Quality, Diversity; Sci Task Force; NEASC Steering, Curr, Attendance, Displine Comm; ASCD; NASCO; NSBT; ARRT; AAAS; NECEL; Desert Hosp Auxiliary Vol; ADK; Carnation Schlsp; Fulbright Heys Schlsp Eligibility; Perkins Grant Allied Hlth Prgm; St of CT Awd Educating High Performance; Red Cross Awd Blood Drive; Pub Booklet; Critical Thinking Lesson Plans; *office:* Rham HS 67 Rham Rd Hebron CT 06248*

YANNO, JACK ANTHONY, 11th-12th Grade Soc Stud Tchr; *b:* Manhatten, NY; *m:* Ursula Frankel Yanno; *c:* Anthony, Scott; *ed:* Univ of Buffalo (BA) His; SUNY at Buffalo (Edm) Ed 1970; Certified in Guidance, Supervision & Admin; *cr:* Maryvale HS Soc Stud Tchr 1966-; *ai:* Chm Schl Improvement Team; Adv Var Club; Var Bsbl Coach; NEA, MTA & MPTO 1966-; NYSAT 1967-; NYSCSS 1966-; NYSUT; Outstanding Tchr 1978, 1984 & 1991; Nom NY St Tchr of the Yr; *office:* Maryvale HS 1050 Maryvale Dr Cheektowaga NY 14225*

YANNO, THOMAS A., Guidance Director; *b:* Little Falls, NY; *m:* Joan; *c:* Andi, Meg; *ed:* Cortland St (BA) Eng Ed 1968, (CAS) Ed Admin 1986; Colgate Univ (MA) Cnslng Psych 1973; Attnd Boston Univ, Syracuse Univ; *cr:* East Syracuse-Minoa Scndry Eng Tchr 1968-72, Guid Cnslr 1973-85, Guid Dir 1985-; *ai:* Dirs of Guid Svcs Treas; Coaching & Officiating Ftbl & Lacrosse; Instrl Improvement Comm; NYSUT 1968-85; Onondaga Cty Dirs of Guid Svcs 1986-, Pres & Treas; NACAC 1990-; NYS Assoc Certfd Ftbl Ofcls 1980-, Pres, VP & Mbrshp Chm, Spcl Merit Awd; Morrisville Tech Advy Bd 1994-, Del; SUNY Advy Bd 1995-, Del; Onondaga Cty Coll Fair Chm; NACAC Natl Coll Fair Co-Chair 1996; *office:* East Syracuse-Minoa HS 6400 Fremont Rd East Syracuse NY 13057*

YANNONE, DENISE LINDA, Elem Special Ed Teacher; *b:* New York City, NY; *ed:* Hofstra Univ (BA) Psych, Elem Ed 1973, (MS) Spec Ed 1974; 40 Addl Credits; *cr:* Hicksville Schl Dist Learning Disabilities Specialist, Resource Room 1974-79, Elem Spec Ed Classroom Tchr 1979-92, MS Spec Ed 1992-, Elem Spec Ed Tchr 1995-; Coll of New Rochelle for Spec Ed Tchr; *ai:* Spec Ed Comm Hicksville Schl Dist; NEA 1974-; CEC 1995-; Bus & Prof Women Nassau Cty 1982-, VP, Young Career Woman 1982; Author's Guild; Soc of Childrens Book Writers; Over 100 Articles, Stories, Poems Pub; *office:* Old Country Road Schl Rhodes Ln Hicksville NY 11801

YANNOTTI, ANGELA LAUREN, Fifth Grade Teacher; *b:* Hackensack, NJ; *cr:* St Joseph Schl 5-8 Grd Tchr 1972-; *ai:* NCEA 1972-; Tchr Recognition Awd Outstdng Cath Schl Edctr 1993.

YANNUZZI, PAUL MICHAEL, Sci Dept Chprsn & Bio Tchr; *b:* Baltimore, MD; *m:* Ellen M. Fraim; *c:* Jason, Joel, Jared, Jonathan; *ed:* Univ of MD at Coll Park (BS) Sci & Ed 1971; Loyola Coll Master Equivalency in Admin Supvr; *cr:* Severna Park Jr HS Sci Tchr 1971-74; Severn River Jr HS Sci Tchr 1975; Old Mill Sr HS Sci Tchr 1976-82; Severna Park Sr HS Sci Tchr 1983-90; Arundel Sr HS Sci Dept Chair 1991-; *ai:* Var Girls Soccer & Var Sftbl Coach; TAAAC 1971-; MSTA 1971-; NEA 1971-; Sftbl Coach of Yr 1987; Soccer Coach of Yr 1[...] *office:* Arundel Sr HS 1001 Annapolis Rd Gambrills MD 21054

YANTZ, MICHAEL JAMES, Jr High Special Education Tch[...] Sandusky, OH; *m:* Dana Sue Turnwald; *c:* Katie Ann, Lindsey Ni[...] Kelsey Renee; *ed:* Bowling Green St Univ (BS) Bus Ed 1987; Ash[...] Univ (MED) Curr & Instruction 1995; *cr:* Margaretta HS Jr High Sp[...] Tchr 1988-; *ai:* Phi Delta Kappa 1996; *office:* Margaretta HS 209 Lo[...] St Castalia OH 44824

YANUSHEFSKY, ALBERT, Electrical Occupations Teacher; *b:* Danv[...] PA; *m:* Cindy; *c:* Stephen, Albert; *ed:* Steven St Univ Electrical 1[...] Penn St Voc Ed; Univ of Pittsburgh Voc II 1980; *cr:* Lancaster Ele[...] Electrician 1969-72; Reading Crane & Hoist Electrical Troublesho[...] 1972-73; Heiser Electric Supt 1973-75; Tonolli Corp Supt Elec Dept 1[...] Western Area Voc Tech Electrical Instr 1975-; *ai:* VICA Adv; PSEA 1[...] Sec, VP; Proficiency in Electrical Trade Awd; Helped Write OSHA Sa[...] Guides for Electrical Safety; Instr for Adults & Union Apprentices.

YANUSKIEWICZ, BONNIE KAPLAN, English Instructor; *b:* Ashl[...] PA; *m:* Michael Matthew; *c:* Alyse, Rachyl; *ed:* Penn St Univ (BS) Sc[...] Eng 1973, Masters Equiv St Cert; Attnd Marywood, Penn St, Villanova[...] 29; *cr:* North Schuylkill Jr Sr HS Eng Instr 1973-; *ai:* Stu Asst Prgm; Group Facilitator; Pub Relations; Peer Mediators Adv; NEA 1973-; [...] Auxiliary 1973-; Hadassah, Sisterhood 1989-; BNai Brith Auxiliary 1[...] Correspondence Sec; *office:* North Schuylkill Jr Sr HS RR 2 Bo[...] Ashland PA 17921

YANUSKIEWICZ, MICHAEL MATTHEW, Third Grade Teacher[...] Danville, PA; *m:* Bonnie Kaplan; *c:* Alyse, Rachyl; *ed:* Bloomsburg [...] (BS) Elem Ed 1972; Attnd Penn St, Western MI, Marywood; West On[...] for Grad Credits; St Cert ME Elem Ed 1995; *cr:* North Schuykill Schl [...] Elem Tchr 1972-; *ai:* Sftbl League; Negotiating Comm; Elem Schl [...] Biddy Bsktbl Coach; Lead Tchr; NSEA, PSEA 1972-; Elks 1978-[...] Mary's Church Groups 1976-; St Jos Church Groups 1979-; Boys [...] Bsktbl Coach of Yr 1976-78; *office:* North Schuykill Elem Schl Oa[...] Center Sts Frackville PA 17931

YARBOROUGH, DAVEY S., Instrumental Music Teacher; [...] Washington, DC; *m:* Esther W.; *c:* Davie C.; *ed:* Federal City Coll ([...] Music 1976; UDC (BMEd) Music 1978; Howard Univ (MM) Music 1[...] Trinity Coll 8 Credit Hrs; Pvt Stud; *cr:* Wilson HS Tchr 1978-80; [...] Woodson Band Dir 1981-82; U.D.C. Assoc Prof 1982-84; Duke Elling[...] Schl Jazz Stud Dir, Saxophone Instr 1986-; *ai:* Jazz Ensembles [...] Saxophone Chamber Group Dir; Lecturer, Clinician Ellington Youth [...] Festivals; IAJE 1986-, Outstdng Performance; DC Fed of Musicians 19[...] MENC; DC Arts Ed Fnd 1995-; Natl Endowment for Arts Flwshp 1[...] Cafritz Flwshp 1990; DC Commission Grantee 1994-; Three Recor[...] Projects 1990-; *office:* Duke Ellington Schl of Arts 3500 Reservoir Rd [...] Washington DC 20007

YARBOROUGH, PHYLLIS (KEYS-DAVIS), Tchr of the Giftec[...] Talented; *b:* Montclair, NJ; *m:* Quincy; *c:* Daniel, Sean, Tamara; *ed:* C[...] CT St (BS) Elem Ed 1968; Kean Coll (MA) Curr, Instruction 19[...] Rutgers, NJ St Univ Workings Towards MLS Degree; *cr:* Meriden S[...] Tchr 1968-69; Montclair Schl Tchr 1969-70; Plainfield Schl Tchr, L[...] 1978-; *ai:* LINCC Team; NEA, Plainfield Tchrs Assn 1978-; Delta Sig[...] Theta Inc 1967-; PTA 1968-; Governor's Tchr Recognition 1989-[...] Westry G. Horne Excl in Ed Awd 1989; Kappa Delta Pi 1986; *off*[...] Cedarbrook Elem Schl 1049 Central Ave Plainfield NJ 07060*

YARMUS, REUBEN L., Foreign Language Dept Head; *b:* New York, [...] *m:* Michele Bercou; *c:* Leah, Dina; *ed:* NY Univ (BA) Fr 1973, (MA)[...] 1974; Temple Univ (MED) Scndry Ed 1980, (EDD) Scndry Ed 1982; U[...] of PA Supervisory, Prin Cert Prgm 1984; *cr:* ITT Subsidiary France En[...] Foreign Lang Tchr 1973-74; RCA Educl Svcs ESL, Span, Fr Tchr 1975-[...] Schl Dist of Philadelphia Sr HS Lang Tchr 1977-87, Sr HS Dept H[...] 1987-; *ai:* Magnet Schl Asst Grant, Schl Wide Evnts Coord; IndoPak [...] Org Spon; NHS, Foreign Lang Hon Soc Co-Spon; AFT 1977-; AATF; A[...] Assn of Tchrs of Span, Portuguese; Modern Lang Assn of Philadelphi[...] Vicinity, Exec Bd; HS Renewal Project Dir; Colloquium Series [...] Philadelphia Alliance Tchng Hums; Fulbright Tchr Exchange G[...] Recipient; Doctoral Examinations Passed with Distinction Aut[...] Handbook Foreign Lang Tchrs; *office:* Northeast High School Cottman [...] Algon Aves Philadelphia PA 19111*

YARNALL, LOIS GROFF, Social Studies Teacher; *b:* Hagerstown, M[...] *m:* Robert; *c:* Brandon; *ed:* Usinus Coll (BA) His 1987; E Stroudsburg U[...] (MEd) Ed 1996; *cr:* E Stroudsburg HS Scndry Soc Stud 1988-; *ai:* F[...] Hockey Coach; Stu Govt Adv; NEA 1989-; *office:* E Stroudsburg HS[...] Courtland East Stroudsburg PA 18301

YARNALL, WENDY COLTMAN, Special Education Teacher; [...] Philadelphia, PA; *m:* S. Wayne; *c:* Jillian, Andrew; *ed:* Univ of PA ([...] Elem Ed 1973; PA St Univ (ME) Spe Ed for Emotionally Disturbed 19[...] *cr:* Wallingford-Swarthmore Schl Dist Spec Ed Tchr 1975-; *ai:* SA[...] Adv; WSEA, PSEA 1975-; *office:* Strath Haven HS 200 N Providence [...] Wallingford PA 19086

YARNELL, REBECCA GRAU, Reading Specialist; *b:* Pittsburgh, PA; [...] John Eric; *c:* Michael L., Daniel L.; *ed:* Clarion Univ of PA (BS) Elem [...] 1987; Med Rdg 1993; *cr:* Hasson Hghts Elem Schl 3rd Grd Tchr 1987-[...] Oil City Schl Dist TELS Tchr 1989-90; Hasson Hghts Elem Schl 1st [...] Tchr 1990-91; Smedley St Elem Schl Rdng Specialist 1995-; *ai:* NE[...] PSEA, OCEA 1987-; Oil City Women's Club 1993-, Pres, Past VP & S[...] Oil City Boat Club 1993-; Venango Cty Newcomer's 1994-, Bd; Grant fr[...] Venango Ed 2000 1995; *office:* Smedley Street Elem Schl 310 Smedley[...] Oil City PA 16301

YAROSH, JOHN KEITH, Gen & Accelerated Chem Tchr; *b:* Canonsbu[...] PA; *c:* John K. Jr., Khristine Ann; *ed:* Lycoming Coll (BA) Math, Scn[...] Ed 1975; Univ of Pittsburgh Chem Cert; Duquesne Univ Ed Post-G[...] Stud; *cr:* Cannon Mc Millan HS Math Tchr 1975-76; Chartiers-Hous[...] HS Math, Chem Tchr 1976-80; West Allegheny HS Math Tchr 1980-[...] Seton La Salle HS Chem, Earth Sci Tchr 1981-92; Elizabeth Forward [...] Chem, Phys Sci Tchr 1992-; *ai:* Asst Var Ftbl Coach 19 Yrs; Boys H[...] Track, Field Coach 8 Yrs; Ski Club Moderator 14 Yrs; Mentor Tchr 1 [...] NEA, PSEA 1992-; ACS Educl Subgroup 1982-; Russian Brotherhood [...] 1971-; *office:* Elizabeth Forward Sr HS 1000 Weigles Hill Rd Elizabeth [...] 15037*

YAROSZ, BARBARA EMR, Chemistry Teacher; *b:* Hackensack, NJ; [...] Stanley E.; *ed:* Montclair St Univ (BA) Scndry Sci Ed 1968; Kean Coll[...] NJ (MA) Earth Sci Ed 1989; 21 Credits Oceanography; 12 credits Writi[...] & Comm; 12 credits Supervision & Admin; *cr:* Saddle Brook HS Sci T[...] 1968-; *ai:* Girls Cross Cntry Coach 9 Yrs; NJIT Chem Olympics Coa[...] Environmental & Ski club Adv; Globe Lead Tchr; NEA 1964-; SB[...] Saddle Brook 1964-, Sec; NJESTA 1985-, Pres; *office:* Saddle Brook [...] 355 Mayhill St Saddle Brook NJ 07663

YASIN, JON ABDULLAH, Professor of English; *b:* Birmingham, AL; [...] Sarah Terry; *ed:* CA St Univ at Hayward (BA) Soc, Anthro 19[...] Northeastern Univ (MED) Ed, Applied Ling 1973; Boston Coll (CAGS) [...] 1977; Harvard Univ (MPA) Lang Pol 1980; IN Univ of PA (PHD) E[...] 1983; Columbia Univ (EDD) Applied Linguistics 1996; *cr:* US Pea[...] Corps Vol 1967-69; Clara Muhammad Schl Dir 1971-75; Roxbury Com[...] Coll Assoc Prof 1973-81; United Arab Emirates Univ Linguistics Lectu[...] 1981-88; Bergen Comm Coll Assoc Prof 1988-; *ai:* Muslim Stdnts Assn F[...]

African AMer His Month Comm; African Amer Latino Males Mentor; an Amer Conf on Lang Organizer; NEA, NJEA 1988-, St Comm; r Assn of Applied Ling 1989-; Black Ling Circle 1990-, Convenor; a Delta Pi 1990-; Islamic Ed Fnd 1994-; Alpha Phi Alpha 1965-; 6 pus, 4 TV Prgms; Article Pub; Co-Authored African Legacy: A ural Heritage Through Art; *office:* Bergen Comm Coll 400 Paramus Rd nus NJ 07652*

ES, BERNICE-MARIE, Social Studies Teacher; *b:* Jersey City, NJ; airleigh Dickinson Univ (BA) Fine Arts, Amer His 1973; CA St Univ Hum 1976; Union Inst (PHD) Amer His 1993; Lehigh Univ Admin; ers Univ Eagleton Inst of Politics; RVCC Archaeoastronomy, oastronomy; *cr:* Warren Cty Comm Coll Asst Prof Hum 1984-85; ipsburg Cath HS Soc Scis Tchr 1985; Franklin Twp Schl Soc Stud Tchr -; *ai:* Soc Stud Curr Revision Comm; Eighth Grd, Law Adventure 8 Mock Trial St Competition, Geography Bee, Starlab Adv; NJ ernor's Tchr Recognition Selection Comm; NEA, NJEA 1973-; ertown Ed Assn 1986-; North Hunterdon Articulation, Soc Stud Pres -89; Phi Alpha Theta 1992-; Fairleigh Dickinson Alum 1973-; CA St Alum 1976-; Assn for Preservation of Civil War Sites, Stuart-Mosby orical Soc 1991-; Eagleton Inst of Politics Tchr Assoc, Contribution or; NJ Governor's Tchr Recognition1992; Numerous Articles Pub; s: Thomas Jefferson at Home Monticello, Jeb Stuart Speaks An view with Lee's Cavalryman; *office:* Franklin Twp Schl PO Box 368 ertown NJ 08868*

ES, CARA CHAMBERLAIN, Third Grade Teacher; *b:* Washington, *c:* Cherryll Yates-Turner, James Jr, Claudia; *ed:* 3 Credits Howard ; 3 Credits Cath Archdioces; *cr:* In the Home Day Care Provider -60; HD Cooke Elem Vol Sub Tchr & Aide 1953-60; Holy Comforter Ciprum Schl Chair, 3rd & 4th Grd Tchr 1965; St Francis de Sales Schl 3rd Tchr 1965-; *ai:* Help Plan & Coord All Rel Holiday Act & Pgms; d Black His Month Pgms & Act; Assist in Supervision of Lunch & ground Act; Providence Hosp 1976-, Vol; Basilica 1986-, Vol Cert of eciation; Lions Club 1992-, Vol, Cert of Appreciation; *office:* St cis De Sales Schl 2019 Rhode Island Ave NE Washington DC 20018

ES, CAROLYN HERRINGTON, English Teacher; *b:* Meridian, MS; llie P.; *c:* Lynn, Lisa, Brian, Alison, Lori; *ed:* Univ Southern MS (BS) 1957; Lesley Coll (MS) Cmptrs in Ed 1996; *cr:* Univ Southern MS Eng Tchr 1958-60; Savannah HS Eng Dept Tchr 1961-65; Wazata Schl Sub Tchr 1983-85; Nashua Sr HS Eng Dept Tchr 1985-; *ai:* 2000 Stu iciencies, Stans; Curr Cncl; Curr Task Force; SNTAS Initiative; TE, NCTE, NEA 1985-; AFT 1990-, Newsletter Ed; Dist Mentor Tchr; erating Tchr for Stu Tchrs; *office:* Nashua Sr HS 36 Riverside Dr ua NH 03062*

ES, EDWARD C., Math Dept Chairman & Teacher; *b:* OH; *m:* Sheila Brammer; *c:* Krysta, Kirsti, Kirk; *ed:* Rio Grande Coll (BS) Math ; Univ of Dayton (MS) Ed Admin 1995; *cr:* Bradford Exempted HS Tchr 1989-91; Greenfield HS Math Tchr 1991-92; Adena HS Math Chm & Tchr 1992-94, 1995-; Madison Plains HS Math Tchr 1994-95; Var Ftbl & Var Bsktbl Asst Coach; Madison Plains Bsbl Head Coach -95; *office:* Adena HS 167 W High St Frankfort OH 45628

ES, SANDRIA L. (BROWN), Secondary Health Teacher; *b:* idence, RI; *c:* Sondria Michele, Shonda Marie; *ed:* Comm Coll of RI Lbrl Arts 1981; RI Coll (BS) Hlth, Sci 1984; *cr:* Cancer Soc Outreach ker 1978-81; Providence Schl Dept Tchr 1984-; *ai:* African, Amer , Tchr Acad Adv; RI Schl Hlth Assn 1986-; Sojournal House 1984-94, of Dir; Labor Inst 1994, Union Cnslr; HOPE N England 1994-; phone Cnslr Cancer Information Svc; Air Natl Guard Cert of eciation; *office:* Mt Pleasant HS 434 Mount Pleasant Ave Providence 2908

SINKO, MARY ANN, Sixth Grade Teacher; *b:* Dickson City, PA; *ed:* of Bridgeport (BS) Elem Ed 1965; Southern CT St Coll (MS) ology 1969; LaSalle Univ (PHD) Educl Sociology 1993; Southern CT niv 6th Yr Admin, Supervision 1986; 99 Addl Hrs; *cr:* Bridgeport Bd d 3rd Grd Tchr 1965-67; Easter Seal Rehab Ctr Tchr of Preschool ring Imparied & Physically Handicapped 1969-70; Park Cty Hospital Medical Soc Work 1970-74; Lord Chamberlain Nursing Fac Dir Med Work Admissions1976-77; Bd of Ed 6th Grd Tchr 1977-; *ai:* nebound Tchr for Medically Incapacitated Stdnts; Adj Prof LaSalle ; NEA, CT Ed Assn, Bridgeport Ed Assn 1977-; Visiting Nurse Assn ical Record Review Comm 1973-76; Vol amer Diabetes Assn 1993; ed Bridgeport Pub Ed Grants for 3 Proposals Totalling $2700; Cert standing Prof Commitment; Dev St Certified Prgm Physically dicapped Youngster; Thesis Commendation; *office:* Maplewood School Linwood Ave Bridgeport CT 06606*

SKO, JEROME WILLIAM, Science Teacher & Dept Chprsn; *b:* ticoke, PA; *m:* Grace Marie Samo; *c:* Jerome J., Melissa Ann; *ed:* gs Coll (BS) Bio 1963; Wilkes Univ (MS) Ed 1976; 48 Credit Hrs ond Masters; *cr:* Pemberton Boro Sci Tchr 1963-65; New Egypt Sci r 1965-72; Crestwood HS Sci Tchr 1972-; *ai:* Sci Dept Chprsn; PSEA, A, Luzerne Cty Sci Tchr Assn 1972-; NEA 1963-; Wright Twp reation Bd 1980-86, Chm, Bd Mem; HS Cross Cntry Team Head Coach 7-80; Track & Field Asst Head Coach 1977-80; Crestwood Schl Dist reciation Awd 1990; *office:* Crestwood HS 281 S Mountain Blvd untain Top PA 18707

ZKANIC, STEVEN JOSEPH, 6th Grade Teacher; *b:* Olean, NY; *c:* rtney, Katie; *ed:* St Bonaventure U (BS) PE 1976, (BS) Elem Ed 1983,) Rdng 1986; *cr:* Cuba-Rushford CS 6th Grd Tchr 1983-; *ai:* Bldg el Team; Spelling Bee & Saturday Boys Bsktbl Dir; Var Bsbl Coach; Scheduling Team; NEA 1983-; *home:* 839 Garden Ave Olean NY 14760

UN, HARRIET PENDERGAST, Second Grade Teacher; *b:* Troy, NY; Clifton R.; *c:* David, Jeffrey, Laura, Meredith; *ed:* Coll of St Rose (BS) n Ed 1962; Arch of NY Level II Cert as Cath Schl Catechist 1991; *cr:* rlook Presch Tchr & Prin 1978-82; Kingston Cath 6th Grd Tchr 1984; osephs 3rd Grd Tchr 1984-86, 2nd Grd Tchr 1986-; *ai:* W Hurley PTA, 1982-83; *office:* St Joseph Schl 235 Wall St Kingston NY 12401

VELAK, WILLIAM MICHAEL, American History Instructor; *b:* laire, OH; *m:* Alexandria Suzanne Zink; *c:* William J., Rachel D.; *ed:* St Univ (BA) His, Rel 1968; OH Univ (MS) His, Scndry Ed 1972; nin Cert Scndry 1973; *cr:* St Clairsville HS His Instr 1970-73, Assoc 1973-82, Prin 1982-85, His Instr 1985-; *ai:* Jr Class Adv; NHS Mbrshp m; Natl Cncl His Ed 1990-; NEA 1986; Grad Flwshp Stud of His Ed Univ; *office:* Saint Clairsville HS 102 Woodrow Ave Saint Clairsville 43950*

V, AMY SEABURG, Seventh Grade English Teacher; *b:* Batavia, NY; Todd R.; *c:* Bret, Chelsea; *ed:* St Univ of NY at Cortland (BS) Elem, ly Sec Eng Ed 1982; Binghamton Univ (MS) Scndry Eng Ed 1988; *cr:* quehanna Vly Jr HS 8th Grd Eng Tchr 1982-83; Jennie F. Snapp MS 7th Eng Tchr 1983-; *ai:* Dist Planning, Bldg Planning Team; Risk Prgm Comm Co-Chm; AFT, NYSUT, Endicott Tchrs Assn 1983-; Our Lady Sorows Church, Rel Ed Tchr; Glwnwood Schl Comm Assn 1993-; PTA ole Awd 1991; *office:* Jennie F Snapp MS 101 S Loder Ave Endicott NY 60

WIN, ROBERT ARTHUR, Math Professor; *b:* New Britain, CT; *m:* en Ferrarese; *c:* Camille Paradis, Lenore Vinelli, Robert A. Jr., rguerite, Kathryn Veronesi, Pamela Fitts, Peter V., Alexander; *ed:* Cntrl St Univ (BS) Math 1959; Bowling Green St Univ (MA) Math 1961; Univ of CT (PHD); *cr:* Hamden-New Haven Coop Ed Ctr Ind Stud Project Coord 1967-69; Curr Rsrch & Dev Unit Math Coord 1971-73; CT St Dept of Ed Consultant 1973-75; Springfield Tech Comm Coll Math Prof 1975-; *ai:* Dev Math Comm; MAA 1961-, Prgm Chair NE Section; AMATYC 1978-, Del; NEMATYC 1976-, Pres, VP; NCTM 1958-, Book, Manuscript Reviewer; NEA 1980-; Books : Math Games and Puzzles, Math Puzzles and Diversions, Arthmetic for Col. Students, Introductory Algebra, Intermediate Algebra, Discremathematical Structures; *office:* Springfield Tech Comm Coll 1 Armory Sq Springfield MA 01101

YEAGER, ROBERT LEE, 8th Grd Crrnt Wrld Prblms Tchr; *b:* Bloomsburg, PA; *m:* Mary Pantalone; *c:* Deidre, Matt; *ed:* Bloomsburg Univ (BS) His & Govt 1967; 27 Credit Masters; 12 Hrs Supvr Works; *cr:* Berwick Jr HS Tchr 1967-73; Berwick MS Tchr 1978-; *ai:* TV Station Adv; MS Soccer Coach; Var Ftbl Announcer; Homework Club Adv; Bsktbl Games Timer; NEA 1967-; BAEA 1967-; *office:* Berwick Area MS 1100 Evergreen Dr Berwick PA 18603

YEAGER, RONALD ALFRED, English Teacher; *b:* Wapwallopen, PA; *ed:* Bloomsburg Univ (BS) Eng 1964, (MA) Eng 1968; Addl 60 Credit Hrs Doctorate Equivalency; *cr:* Palmerton Area HS Eng Tchr 1964-; *ai:* Debate, Oratorical Clubs; PAEA 1964-, Pres, Bldng Rep, Chief Neg; NEA, PSEA 1964-; Basic Ed Fellowship Awd; *office:* Palmerton HS Fireline Rd Palmerton PA 18071

YEARING, JEFFREY LEE, PE Teacher & Coach; *b:* Teaneck, NJ; *m:* Barbara Jean Spencer; *c:* Tadd Jeffrey, Nancy Christine; *ed:* Springfield Coll (BS) PE, Hlth-Cum Laude 1970; OH St Univ (MA) PE 1971; Memphis St Univ 60 Credits 1966-68; William Paterson Coll 6 Credits 1975-76; Salem St Coll 3 Credits 1986; *cr:* Millburn Pub Schls PE Tchr, Coach 1971-73; Ridgewood Pub Schls PE Tchr, Coach 1973-; Pool Mgr Graydon Pool Ridgewood NJ, Ridgewood Parks & Rec Commision 1980-; *ai:* Head Women's Var Soccer, Asst Var Men's Bsbl Coach; Bsktbl Official IAABO Bd #33; NJ Girls Soccer Coaches Assn 1988-, Exec Comm, Reg I Coach of Yr 1991; Bergen Cty Women's Coaches Assn 1985-, Soccer Tournament Dir, Coach of Yr 1993; Bergen Cty Coaches Assn 1973-; NEA, NJEA 1971-; Ridgewood Bsbl Assn 1973-, Schlsp Comm; Ridgewood Soccer Assn 1980-, Exec Comm; Jersey United Soccer Club, European Select Team Prgm U-19 Head Coach 1993-; NJ Hearld News All Area Coach of Yr 1989; Pub Project Adventure Curr Model, HS Cowtails & Cobras II; *office:* Ridgewood HS 627 E Ridgewood Ave Ridgewood NJ 07451

YEARWOOD, INEZ LUCINA (WALTERS), Ret Communication Arts Teacher; *b:* Charlestown-Nevis, British Leeward; *w:* Thomas (dec); *c:* Faith Gregg; *ed:* Hunter Coll (BA) Eng Lang Arts 1979; Lane Coll Eng 1957-58; Tchrs Coll Eng 1946-50; *cr:* St Kitts Elem Tchr 13 Yrs; NYC Parochial Schl Elem Tchr 10 Yrs; IS 158 Schl Comm Arts, Main Stream, GATES, TAG Tchr 17 Yrs; *ai:* Coach TAG 7th-8th Graders; Tutor Eng Lang Arts Hunter Coll, Conversational Span Parochial Schl NYC; Tchr of Yr 1985; Honoray Degree Phi Beta Kappa NY Univ; Cert Bus Eng Monroe Bus Schl, Henry George Schl of Soc Sci.

YEATER, KATHLEEN WECKER, Dir of Orch & String Instr; *b:* York, PA; *m:* Robert A.; *c:* Amy L. Diehl, Jennifer L. Diehl; *ed:* IN Univ of PA (BS) Mus Ed 1969; Penn St Univ 24 Credit Hrs; Vandercook Coll Mucis 3 Credit Hrs; Univ of the Arts 6 credits; Carlow Coll 3 Credits; *cr:* Southern York Cty Schl Dist Dir of Orch & String Instr 1974-; *ai:* Susquehannock String Quartet; NEA, PSEA & MENC Amer Fed of Musicians 1974-; PMEA 1974-, Citation of Excel Dist 7 1986; Natl Schl Orch Assn 1980-, St Pres; Amer String Tchrs Assn 1980-; York Youth Symphony Bd 1985-; York Symphony Orch 1974-, 1st Violin Section; St Matthew Sunday Schl Orch, Dir; Salem String Quartet, 1st Violinist; Dir York Jr Symphony Orch; Southcentral PA Joint Cncl Schl Improvement Outstanding Tchr Awd 1989 Guest Dir Co Orch Festvls in PA & MD; *home:* 3965 Eldine Ave York PA 17404

YEATMAN, DOROTHY ANN, 10th-12th Grade English Tchr; *b:* Salisbury, MD; *ed:* Salisbury St (BA) Eng, Speech & Drama 1972; MA Equivalent; *cr:* Parkside HS Tchr 12 Yrs; *ai:* WCEA Bldg Rep; MSTA, NEA, WCEA 1972-; MCTELA 1990-; Wicomico Co Women's Commission 1 Yr; Christ United Meth Church Lay Ldr, Historian; *office:* Parkside HS 1015 Beaglin Park Dr Salisbury MD 21801*

YEAZELL, JAMES GERARD, Instrumental Music Director; *b:* Huntsville, AL; *m:* Jodi Shingledecker; *c:* James II, Jennifer, Justin; *ed:* Univ of Dayton (BS) Music Ed 1975, (MS) Schl Admin 1986; *cr:* Cedar Cliff Schls Instrumental Dir 1976-78; Miami East Schls Instrumental Dir 1984-87; Northwestern Schls Instrumental Dir 1987-; *ai:* Marching, Pep, Jazz Band; After-Prom Adv; Renaissance Comm; Vlybl Referee; OMEA 1975-; North Amer Brass Band 1991-; NEA 1987-, Pres 1990-91; Knights of Columbus 1983-; St Bernards Parish Cncl 1991-93; Clark Cty Bd of Ed Ed Excl Recognition Awd; Ashland Oil Tchng Excl Awd Nom; Clark Cty Mentor Tchrs Prog; *home:* 2108 Simon Ct Springfield OH 45503

YECKLEY, LINDA BENDER, Business Education Teacher; *b:* York, PA; *m:* Earl R.; *c:* Joseph, Laura; *ed:* York College of PA (BS) Bus Ed 1976; Master Equivalency in Ed Plus 15 Credits; *cr:* York Division Borg-Warner Sec 1970-74; Baltimore Cty Schls Bus Ed Tchr 1976-77; Southern Schl Dist Bus Ed Tchr Permenant Sub 1977-78; York Cath HS Bus Ed Tchr 1979-87; Red Lion Area Sr HS Bus Ed Tchr 1987-; *ai:* Cheerleading Coach; FBLA; Schl Store; Mentor Prgm Dept Ldr; PSEA, PBEA, NBEA; Local Fire Co, Fund Raisers; *office:* Red Lion Area Sr HS 200 Horace Mann Ave Red Lion PA 17356*

YEE, MARY WING, Second Grade Teacher; *b:* Chicago, IL; *m:* Cy G.; *c:* Cherise, Cybill, Carlton; *ed:* Univ of IL (BA) Elem Ed 1971; Queens Coll (MS) Elem Ed 1988; Post Grad Stud 30 Credits; *cr:* Chicago Pub Schls Elem Ed Tchr 1972-73; PS 42 Man Schl 2nd Grd Tchr 1985-; *ai:* HS Adult Ed ESL; Summer Schl LEP Stdnts; AFT, NCTM 1972-; UFT 1985-; *office:* PS 42 Manhattan 71 Hester St New York NY 10002

YEHL, RONDA KRAMER, Language Arts Teacher; *b:* Olean, NY; *m:* Dan A.; *c:* Michael; *ed:* St Univ of NY at Buffalo (BA) Eng 1968; St Bonaventure Univ 30 Hrs; Genesco St Coll 60 Hrs Spec Ed; *cr:* Rush Henrietta Central Schls Eng Tchr Jr High 1968-71; Rehab Center Pre-Schl Tchr 1972-81; Salamanca City Central Dist Eng Tchr HS, MS 1987-; *ai:* NEA, NCTE 1987-; St Johns Luth Church 1979-, Head Elder; *office:* Salamanca Middle School 50 Iroquois Dr Salamanca NY 14779

YELAGOTES, ZAFERULA VALUDES, Fourth Grade Teacher; *b:* Lancaster, PA; *m:* George J.; *c:* Melissa Vulopas, Dana Keares, Elizabeth; *ed:* Millersville Univ (BS) Ed 1962, (MS) Ed 1970; *cr:* Thomas Mifflin Schl 4th Grd Tchr 1962-64; James Hamilton Schl 3-4 Grd Head Tchr 1964-65; Garrettford Schl 4th Grd Tchr 1965-68; James Hamilton Schl 5-6 Grd Head Tchr 1968-69; George Washington Schl 4th-6th Grd Tchr 1979-85; George Ross Schl 5th Grd Tchr 1985-76; James Hamilton Schl 4th-6th Grd Tchr 1987-; *ai:* NEA, PSEA, LEA 1962-; Lititz Woman's Club 1976-, Sec; Millersville Campus Club 1968-, Pres; Daughter's of Penelope 1975-, Pres, Treas.

YELDER, JOYCE DYSON, Fifth Grade Teacher; *b:* Newport News, VA; *c:* Monique S., Eunice N.; *ed:* Cntrl St Univ (BS) Elem Ed 1969; Post Grad Stud, Inservice Credit Hrs Towards Master's Equivalency Temple Univ, St Joseph Univ, Beaver Coll; *cr:* Frederick Douglass Second Grd Tchr 1970-71; George Clymer Third Grd Tchr 1971-75; S. Solis-Cohen Schl Fifth Grd Tchr 1975-; *ai:* Stu Cncl Spon; PFT, AFT 1975-; Cntrl St Alumni Phila Chptr 1995-; *office:* S. Solis-Cohen Elem Schl Tyson And Horrocks St Philadelphia PA 19149

YELICH, MICHAEL JOSEPH, Guidance Counselor; *b:* Buffalo, NY; *m:* Janine Pirk; *ed:* SUNY at Albany (BA) Psych 1983; SUNY at Buffalo (EDM) Schl Counseling 1987; *cr:* Genesee-Wyoming Boces Crisis Cnslr 1987-88; West Seneca Schls Guidance Cnslr 1988-; *ai:* Ftbl & Lacrosse Coach; Weight Lifting Intramurals; Ski Club Adv; *office:* West Seneca East Sr HS 4760 Seneca St West Seneca NY 14224*

YELLAND, EDITH MAY, Fifth Grade Teacher; *b:* Stapleton, NY; *ed:* Massau Comm Coll (AA) Eng 1962; St Univ at Oswego (BS) Elem Ed 1965; Hofstra Univ (MA) Elem Ed 1970; *cr:* Clear Stream Ave Schl Fourth Grd Tchr 1965-73, Fifth Grd Tchr 1973-74, 1990-, Sixth Grd Tchr 1974-90; *ai:* Kappa Delta Pi 1965-; NY St United Tchrs; Vly Stream Tchrs Assn 1965-, Bldg Vice Chm, Sec, Sunshine, Rep to VS Cncl; PTA 1965-, Cncl Sec Del, Honorary LIfe Mbrshp 1973-; *office:* Clearstream Avenue Elem Schl 30 Clearstream Ave Valley Stream NY 11582

YENCHIK, CAROL ANN HRABCSAK, Second Grade Teacher; *b:* Muse, PA; *c:* Susan C., Mark A.; *ed:* Carlow Coll (BS) Elem 1960; IN Univ of PA St Cert, Continuing Ed Credits; ARIN Intermediate Univ Continuing Ed Credits; *cr:* Third Ward Schl 4th Grd Tchr 1960-62, 1963-64; Canon-Mc Millan Elem Schl Sub Tchr 1967-69; Burrell Elem Schl 3rd, 2nd Grd Tchr 1970-71; Third Ward 3rd, 2nd Grd Tchr 1971-94; Blairsville Elem Schl 3rd, 2nd Grd Tchr 1994-; *ai:* Lang Arts Curr, Portfolio Comms; Class Plays; PTA Projects; NEA, PSEA, BSEA 1960-64, 1970-; PTA 1960-64, 1970-, Treas; Elks Ladies Auxiliary 1965-; Italian Ladies Soc 1975-; Cath Daughters of Amer 1960-; Carlow Coll Alumni, Phonathan; Mentor for New Tchrs; Nom PA Tchr of Yr 1990-91; Cooperating Tchr for IN U of PA Stu Tchr & Jr Block Prgms; *office:* Blairsville Elem Schl 106 School Ln Blairsville PA 15717

YENICK MOIR, JEAN-MARIE, Choral Director; *b:* Southampton, NY; *m:* David George Moir; *c:* Hayley; *ed:* Hofstra Univ (BS) Music Ed 1984; Stonybrook Univ (MA) Music, Theatre Ed 1990; *cr:* Tremont-Barton Ave Elem Schl Music Tchr 1984-85; Centereach HS Choral Dir 1985-; *ai:* Theatre Arts Club Adv; Intnl Thespian Soc Troupe Spon; Musical Production Dir, Vocal Dir; NYSUT 1984-; MCTA 1985-.

YERGER, RONALD LEE, Sci & Environmental Ed Teacher; *b:* Reading, PA; *m:* Michelle G. Burns; *c:* Paul M., Rachel L., Rebekah L.; *ed:* Penn St Univ (BS) Ag Ed 1981; Cert Masters Equivalency; *cr:* Southern Tioga Schl Dist Ag Tchr 1981-84; Lower Dauphin Schl Dist Ag, Sci, Environmental Ed Tchr; *ai:* Ecology Club Adv; Envirothon Coach; NEA, PSEA 1981-; PA Alliance for Environmental Ed 1990-; Outstdng Environmental Edctr Dauphin Cty; Co-Author Environmental Ed Resource Directory; *office:* Lower Dauphin Sr HS 201 S Hanover St Hummelstown PA 17036

YETTER, CAROLE SHORT, Business Tech Tchr & Dpt Chair; *b:* Louisa, KY; *m:* Edson James; *c:* Stephanie Rudloff, Stacy Ernst, Scott Edson; *ed:* Morehead St Univ (BA) Bus Ed & Music 1962; OH St Univ (MA) Bus Ed 1986; Attnd Purdue Univ, Muskingum Coll, Univ of Akron, Walsh Coll, Columbus St; *cr:* Lebanon Schl Dist Music Tchr 1962; Logan Elm HS Bus Ed Tchr 1963-66; Marysville HS Bus Ed Tchr 1972-73; Muskingum Area Tech Coll Adj Instr 1973-81; Zanesville HS Bus Tech Tchr 1979-; *ai:* ZHS Parent Connection Newsletter Ed; Tech-Prep Curr & Venture Capital Grant Comm; NEA 1979-; OH Bus Tchrs Assn 1979-; OH Ed Assn 1979-; Zanesville Ed Assn 1979-; Delta Pi Epsilon 1988-, Corresponding Sec; Cntrl OH Bus Tchrs Assn; St John Luth Church 1966-, Luth Church Women Pres & Treas; Phi Delta Kappa Outstdng Edctr 1986; Muskingum Tech Coll Outstdng Scndry Tchr Recognition; *office:* Zanesville HS 1701 Blue Ave Zanesville OH 43701

YETTO, LYNETTE M., Teacher of the Gifted & Eng; *b:* Kane, PA; *ed:* PA St Univ (BA) Theatre Arts 1977; Clarion St Univ (BS) Eng Tchr Cer 1978; *cr:* Morrisville Schl Dist Scndry Eng Tchr 1978-86, Tchr of Gifted 1986-95; Central Bucks Mid Level Eng Tchr 1995-; *ai:* Drama Club Adv; Scholars' Bowl Coach; Verbal SAT Review Instr; Parental Newsletter Comm Chair; NEA, PSEA, Morrisville Ed Assn 1978-95; ASCD 1993-; Central Bucks Ed Assn 1995-; Bucks Cty Theatre Co 1982-; Outstanding Tchr of Yr: Schl Dist 1989-90, PA Acad Prof Tchng 1990-; Who's Who of Amer Women; *office:* Central Bucks Schl Dist 16 Weldon Dr. Doylestown PA 19067

YEWCIC, JOHN PAUL, Health & Physical Ed Teacher; *b:* Johnstown, PA; *m:* Stephanie J. Devine; *c:* Ashley, Alicia, Christopher; *ed:* Indiana Univ of PA (BS) Hlth, PE 1986; 12 Credits Towards Master of Sport Sci US Sports Acad; *cr:* Bishop Carroll HS Tchr 1988-; *ai:* Golf Coach, Stu Assistance Prgm Coord; NCEA 1988-; Make-A-Wish Fnd 1992-; Hilltop AYSO 1995-, Coach Admin; PIAA Bsktbl Offcls Steel City Chptr 1985-, Bd of Control 1994-95.

YEZILSKI, SUZANNE LUNDSTEN, Social Studies Teacher; *b:* Ridgway, PA; *m:* Michael; *c:* Tracy Y. Cournier, Michael C.; *ed:* Indiana Univ of PA (BS) Music Ed 1970; *cr:* Linwood MS 4-8 Grd Vocal Music Tchr 1970-71; Pinewood Presch Instr of 4 Yr Olds 1980-85; Calvary Acad Vocal Music, Soc Stud Tchr 1985-; *ai:* Ldrshp Convention Adv; Drama Dir; Calvary Lighthouse Church 1981-, Choir Dir 1991-94; *office:* Calvary Acad 1133 E County Line Rd Lakewood NJ 08701

YI, XIAOXIONG, Asst Prof of Political Sci; *b:* Beijing, China; *ed:* Bejing Normal Univ (BA) World, Chinese His 1982; PA St Univ (MA) Companion Politics, Asian Stud 1985; Amer Univ (PHD) Intnl Relations, US, Frgn Poliyc, East, Southeast Asian Stud 1993; *cr:* Dickinson Coll Instr 1988-89; Marietta Coll Asst Prof China Prgm 1989-; OH St Univ Ctr Intnl Stud Rsrch Assoc 1994-; *ai:* Assn for Asian Stud 1989-; Intnl Stud Assn 1992-; Amer Enterprise Inst Assoc, Amer Pol Sci Assn 1990-; Articles Pub; *office:* Marietta Coll Dept of His-Pol Sci & Religion 215 5th St Marietta OH 45750*

YILEK, RUTH S., Third Grade Teacher; *b:* Elmira, NY; *m:* John A.; *c:* John W., Theresa Yilek Swartz, Joseph A.; *ed:* Mansfield Univ of PA (BS) Elem Ed 1962; Attnd PSU, Clarion, Edinboro, Millersoille, East Stroasburg & Gannon; *cr:* Northern Tioga Schl Dist Classroom Tchr 1962-65; Keystone Cntrl One Room Schl Tchr 1966-67; Northern Tioga Schl Dist Tchr 1967-68; Galeton Area Schl Dist 3rd Grd Tchr 1968-; *ai:* Vlybl & Bsktbl Ticket Taker; Abbott Twp Auditor; NEA, PSEA, GEA; Germania Fire Co Auxiliary, VP; Galeton Chapter Bus & Prof Women; *home:* RR 1 Box 72 Galeton PA 16922

YOAKAM, RONALD ALLEN, Social Studies Teacher; *b:* Cleveland, OH; *m:* Jan M. Wildes; *c:* Shane, Corey; *cr:* Crestview MS Jr HS Soc Stud Tchr 23 Yrs; *ai:* Intramural Dir; 8th Grd Vllybl & 5th & 6th Grd Bsktbl Coach; OH Ed Assn 1973-, Exec Comm; *office:* Crestview MS 3062 Fairfield School Rd Columbiana OH 44408

YOCUM, MARY ANN P., Algebra II & Geometry Teacher; *b:* Ashland, PA; *c:* Leigh Ann; *ed:* Alvernia Coll (BA) Scndry Math 1974; Attnd Villanova Univ, Bloomsburg Univ, Millersville Univ; *cr:* Holy Name HS 9th-12th Grd Tchr 1969-72; Phoenixville, Shamokin & Sunbury Cath Elem Schls 5th-8th Grd Tchr 1972-76; Southern Columbia HS 9th-12th Grd Tchr 1977-; *ai:* Jr HS Stu Cncl Adv; PSEA 1977-; 4-H, Adv, Ldr; *office:* Southern Columbia Schl Dist RR 2 Box 372a Catawissa PA 17820*

YOCUM, TINA M., Anatomy, PE & Tchr of Gifted; *b:* Buffalo, NY; *ed:* East Stroudsburg Univ (BS) Hlth & PE 1978; Western MA Coll (MS) Curr Instruction 1990; *cr:* Line Mountain SD Hlth, Anatomy & Physiology, PE, Psychology, & Gifted Tchr 1980-; *ai:* Peer Helper & Ski Club Adv; Fac Senate & Curr Cncl Mem; Stu Assistance Team, Drug & Alcohol Dist & OM Coord; Line Mountain Ed Assn 1980-, VP; PA St Ed Assn, Natl Ed

Assn & AAHPER 1980-; *office:* Line Mountain HS RR 01 Box 1660 Herndon PA 17830

YODER, ALVIN L., Bible Teacher; *b:* Goshen, IN; *m:* Ruth Ann Weber; *c:* Nathan, Sheldon, Michael; *ed:* Rosedale Bible Inst (diploma) Bible 1971; Cedarville Coll (BA) Bible Comprehensive 1984; Ashland Theological Seminary Working on MS; *cr:* Rosedale Bible Inst Fac & Tchr 1972-, Acad Dean 1983-93; Shiloh Mennonite Church Pastor 1980-; *ai:* Tchng in Kenya 1 Month 1988; *office:* Rosedale Bible Inst 2270 Rosedale Rd Irwin OH 43029

YODER, KARA MARIA (MENOSKY), Sixth Grade Teacher; *b:* Youngstown, OH; *m:* Timothy; *c:* Joshua, Craig, Tyler; *ed:* Kent St Univ (BS) Elem Ed, Spec Ed 1977; *cr:* East Cleveland Schls Second Grd Tchr 1977; Cardinal Schls Fifth Grd Tchr 1977-79; Cleveland Diocese St Joan of Arc 7, 8 Grd Sci, His Tchr 1980-86; Berkshire Schls Sixth Grd Tchr 1988-; *ai:* NEA, BEA 1988-; Conservation Edctr of Yr 1993.*

YODER, RICHARD D., Social Studies Teacher; *b:* Sellersville, PA; *m:* Sylvia K. Hollenbach; *c:* Susan E. Flacx, Elizabeth M. Hale; *ed:* Kutztown Univ (MAEd) 1973; 30 Addl Credits; *cr:* Pennridge HS Soc Stud Tchr 1967-; *ai:* Sftbl Coach; East Penn Interpretor Sftbl Umpire; NEA, PSEA, PEA 1967-; Church, Sunday Schl Tchr, Supt, Deacon, Awana Ldr, Planning Comm 3 Yrs.

YODER, RODNEY LYN, High School Science Teacher; *b:* Bellefontaine, OH; *m:* Billie Jo Kennedy; *c:* Sonya Kay; *ed:* Otterbein Coll (BS) His, Scndry Ed 1988; Columbus Paraprofessional Inst Cert Cmptr Programming 1982; Addl 13 Hrs Wright St Univ; *cr:* OH St Hwy Patrol Dispatcher 1979-81; Wallick Companies Cmptr Programmer 1982-85; Otterbein Coll Intramural Dir 1986-88; Riverside HS Sci Tchr 1988-; *ai:* Var, Reserve Golf, Var Girls Sftbl Coach; Ftbl Announcer; HS Stu Cncl, Morning TV Announcement Adv; Caught Being Good Awds Prgm Coord; South Union Mennonite Church 1959-, Sunday Schl, Bible Schl Tchr; Logan Cty Grant Learning Sci by Cmptr, Constructing Human Model Anatomy, Learning Sci with Toys; Excl in Tchng Top 10 Finalist Rotary Intnl 1993-; *office:* Riverside HS 200 W Moore St Box 190 De Graff OH 43318*

YODERS, BARBARA STERI, Business Data Processing Tchr; *b:* New Kensington, PA; *m:* E. Blair; *c:* Scott, Jeffrey; *ed:* IN Univ of PA (BS) Bus Ed 1968; Univ of Pittsburgh (MED) Bus Ed 1971; *cr:* Burrell HS Bus Tchr 1968-72; Western AVTS Bus Data Processing Tchr 1972-; *ai:* VICA Club Adv; NEA, PSEA 1968-; WAVTEA 1972-, Sec, Treas; Lib Bd 1990-; BPW 1980-, Sec, Treas; Delta Pi Epsilon; *office:* Western Area Voc Tech Sch 688 Western Ave Canonsburg PA 15317

YOHEY, MICHAEL TODD, Chemistry Teacher; *b:* Celina, OH; *m:* Catherine E. Holtman; *c:* Emma, Ellen, Erin; *ed:* Wright St Univ (BS) Ed 1988; Univ of Dayton (MS) Ed Admin 1995; *cr:* Fairlawn HS Chem Tchr 1988-89; Ansonia HS Chem Tchr 1989-91; Van Wert HS Chem Tchr; *ai:* Fac & Renaissance Cncls; Mentor; AFT 1992-; ASCD 1994-; *office:* Van Wert HS 205 W Crawford St Van Wert OH 45891*

YOKEL, ELLEN MORSE, 9th Grd Global Studies Tchr; *b:* Washington, DC; *m:* Donald D.; *c:* Bonnie L., Jennette M., Grant M.; *ed:* Univ of FL (BS) His & Pol Sci 1969, (MED) Black Stud 1970; *cr:* Franklin HS Soc Stud Tchr 1971, 1976-80; Wilson Jr HS Soc Stud Tchr 1971-75; Thomas MS 9th Grd Soc Stud Tchr 1987-; *ai:* AFT 1970-; Webster Tchrs Assn 1986-; RACSS 1986-; *office:* Thomas MS 800 Five Mile Line Rd Webster NY 14580

YOMMER, BONNIE JANE, Sixth Grade Math Teacher; *b:* Meyersdale, PA; *m:* Ken; *c:* Brandi, Kristin, Keena; *ed:* Frostburg St Univ (BS) Elem Ed 1984, (MA) Curr, Instr 1995; *cr:* Southern MS Sixth Grd Math Tchr 1986-; *ai:* NEA 1986-; Cornerstone Assembly of God Church 1992-, Yth Ldr; *home:* 343 Old Salisbury Rd Grantsville MD 21536

YONISKI, THOMAS JOSEPH,III, 8th Grade Social Studies Tchr; *b:* Fairfax, VA; *m:* Sharon Ann Evans; *c:* Kaitlyn; *ed:* Bloomsburg Univ (BS) Comprehensive Soc Stud 1988; 24 Grad Credits; *cr:* Lake-Lehman Middle Level Bldg Soc Stud Tchr 1988-; *ai:* Asst Ftbl Coach, Strength, Conditioning Specialist at Dallas HS, IM Coord; PSEA 1988-; PIAA Coaches Assn; *home:* 49 Tamanini Dr Wyoming PA 18644*

YONKA, JOYCE BAUM, English Teacher; *b:* Cincinnati, OH; *m:* Walter Wm.; *c:* Aaron David, Bryan Nicholas; *ed:* IN Univ (BS) Ed, Eng 1966; Univ of Cincinnati (MED) Ed, Guid 1969; Post Grad Stud; *cr:* Cincinnati Pub Schls Eng Tchr 1966-71, 1978-; Schl for Creative & Performing Arts Lead Tchr, Dept Chair 1900-; *ai:* Sr Class, Grad Spon; Curr, Scheduling, Dist Curr Comms; CFT, AFT 1971-; NCTE, Delta Kappa Gamma 1990-; Temple Sholom Sisterhood 1970-; Lakeshore Womens Club 1976-; *office:* Schl Creative & Performing Art 1310 Sycamore St Cincinnati OH 45210

YONKER, MARTHA MILLER, Communication Arts Teacher; *b:* Lafayette, IN; *m:* Robert Harold; *c:* Bethany Lauren; *ed:* Purdue Univ (BA) Elem Ed, Hum 1975, (MA) Ed 1978; Post Grad Counseling, Comm Stud Penn St at York; *cr:* Dayton Elem Schl Third Grd Tchr 1975-83; Klondike Elem Schl Fifth Grd Tchr 1983-84; Spring Grove Intermediate Sixth Grd Tchr 1985-; *ai:* Team Ldr; Fac Cncl Rep; Beginning Tchr Mentor; Stu Tchrs Supvr; NEA 1975-; First Presbyn Church 1985-, Adult Ed; Deacon; Boston Marathon 1992; Lead Tchr Grant Rcpnt; *office:* Spring Grove Intermediatr Schl RR #4 Box 4621A RothsChurch Rd Spring Grove PA 17362*

YONOSIK, SHERYL TUCCI, Home Economics Teacher; *b:* Clevland, OH; *m:* Robert L.; *c:* Brian R., Kristen L., Lynsey M.; *ed:* Bowling Green St Univ (BSEd) Home Ec 1969; Addl 44 Qtr Hrs Cleveland St Univ; *cr:* Perry HS Home Ec Tchr 1969-70; Mentor Meml Jr HS Home Ec Tchr 1970-72; Lumen Cordium HS Home Ec Tchr 1983-87; Villa Angela Acad Home Ec Tchr 1987-90; Villa Angela St Joseph HS Home Ec Tchr 1990-; *ai:* SADD Fac Adv; Respect, Discipline, MJS Selection Comms; NCEA 1990-; Parish Vol 15 Yrs, Pres, Ed Comm, Parish Cncl, Confirmation Team; *office:* Villa Angela St Joseph HS 18491 Lake Shore Blvd Cleveland OH 44119

YOOST, BARBARA LYNN, Nursing Professor; *b:* Warren, OH; *m:* Charles D.; *c:* Timothy R., Stephen M.; *ed:* Kent St Univ (BSN) Nursing 1977, (MSN) Nursing Ed 1994; *cr:* Akron General Medical Ctr Intensive Care Staff Nurse 1977-84; Kent St Univ Nursing Instr 1979-84; Western Reserve Care System Per Diem Nurse 1986-92; North Cntrl Tech Coll Assoc Prof of Nursing 1993-; *ai:* East OH Conf United Meth Women; First United Meth Church Camping Coord; Kent St Univ Schl of Nsg Alumni 1977-, Pres, Bd of Dirs; Sigma Theta Tau 1992-; OH Organ of Assoc Degree Nursing 1994-; Linnea Henderson Acad Awd; *office:* North Central Tech Coll 2441 Kenwood Cr Mansfield OH 44906*

YORGEY, BARBARA J., Second Grade Teacher; *b:* Pottstown, PA; *ed:* Kutztown Univ (BA) Elem Ed 1966, (MS) Ed 1969; 17 Addl Credit Hrs; *cr:* Boyertown Schl Dist 5th Grd Tchr 1966-78, 2nd Grd Tchr 1978-; *ai:* PSEA, NEA, BAEA 1966-; Hope Comm Church 1995-, Childrens Ministries Dir; *home:* 180 Popodickon Dr Boyertown PA 19512

YORK, JENNIFER S., 5th Grade Teacher; *b:* Presque Isle, ME; *m:* Thomas R. III; *c:* Logan, Ethan, Wilder; *ed:* Univ of ME at Presque Isle (BS) Elem Ed 1985; Environment & Whole Lang Courses Credit Hrs; *cr:* Zippel Elem Schl 5th Grd Tchr 1985-; *ai:* Var Cheering Coach; 5th Grd Ldrshp Team Piloting MEs Math & Sci Curr Framework; Tchng Project Exlore GT Pgm; ME Tchrs Assn 1985-; NEA 1985-; Delta Kappa Gamma 1988-, Sec, 1st VP & Pres 1996; Beta Sigma Phi 1986-; Vol Dirs Assn 1996; Presidential Awd for Excl in Sci & Math Tchng Nom 1996; MSAD #1 Writing Grants (Twice); *office:* Eva Hoyt Zippel Elem Schl 42 Fort St Presque Isle ME 04769*

YORK, MARGARET CHAGARULY, Chemistry Teacher; *b:* New Bedford, MA; *m:* Michael; *c:* Alethea; *ed:* Salve Regnl Univ (BA) Bio, Chem 1980; Univ of MA at Dartmouth Tchr Cert Prgm 1986; *cr:* Westport MS Sci, Math, Rdng Tchr 1987-89; New Bedford HS Bio, Chem Tchr 1990-; *ai:* Global Awareness Club Adv; New Bedford Edctrs Asso, MA Tchr Assn 1990-; *office:* New Bedford HS 230 Hathaway Blvd New Bedford MA 02740

YORK, ROSEMARY E., Frgn Lang Dept Chprsn & Tchr; *b:* Springfield, MA; *ed:* Plymouth Tchrs Coll (BE) His 1953; Attnd NDEA Inst 1957, Universidad de Saltillo 1971, UNH Russian 1973-75; *cr:* Hancock Acad Grds 9-12 Eng Tchr 1953-54; Conant HS Grds 9-12 Eng Tchr 1954-57; Portsmouth HS Grds 1-5 Span Tchr 1957-; *ai:* Prin Advy Comm; Portsmouth Fl Comm Chm; ACTFL; NHATFL Pres; MAFLA; FLAME; ADK, ADRNH 1977-, NH St Pres, Intnl By-Laws Comm; *office:* Portsmouth HS 50 Andrew Jarvis Dr Portsmouth NH 03801

YORK, TERRY E., Third Grade Teacher; *b:* Lexington, KY; *c:* Zachary, Alex; *ed:* Wright St Univ (BS) Elem Ed & Spec Ed 1975; Addl 25 Grad Hrs; *cr:* Tecumseh Local Schls Tchr of Spec Ed 1975-80, 2nd Grd Tchr 1975-80, 3rd Grd Tchr 1993-; *ai:* Tecumseh Ed Assn 1975-, Bldg Rep; Tchr in Excl Awd Presented by HS Valedictorian 1994; *office:* Medway Elem Schl 116 Middle St Medway OH 45341

YORKS, KATHY (FLEISHER), Science Teacher; *b:* Lock Haven, PA; *m:* Charles L. II; *c:* Grahm Dion, Justin Stoner, Meredith Stoner; *ed:* Lock Haven Univ (BSEd) Bio & General Sci 1981; PA St Univ (MED) Curr & Instruction 1995; Continuing Post Grad Work in Sci Supervisory Cert; *cr:* Bishop Neumann HS Tchr 1981-82; Lock Haven HS Tchr 1982-; *ai:* Scndry Sci Dist Prgm Ldr; ASCD 1993-; NSTA, NSELA 1994-; PSTA 1989-; PA St Univ Tchr-in-Residence 1995-; *office:* Lock Haven HS W Church St Lock Haven PA 17745

YOST, CAROL SPIES, Social Studies Teacher; *b:* Boston, MA; *m:* James A.; *c:* Brett, Lauren, Kyle; *ed:* Smith Coll (BA) Amer Stud 1963; Univ of Rochester (MAT) His 1964; *cr:* Rush Henrietta HS Tchr 1964-65; Pittsford HS Tchr 1965-68; Brighton HS Tchr 1978-; *ai:* Model United Nations Club; NEA 1978-; Rochester Area Cncl of Soc Stud 1990-; Multinational & Comparative Educl Schlsp 1994; *office:* Brighton HS 1150 Winton Rd S Rochester NY 14618

YOST, JASON LYNN, Music Director; *b:* Columbus, OH; *m:* Jennifer Lynn Joyner; *c:* Lauren Elizabeth; *ed:* Bowling Green St Univ (BM) Music Ed, (MM) Music Ed 1996; *cr:* St John's Jesuit HS Asst Dir of Music 1992-95, Dir of Music 1995-; *ai:* Musical Theatre, Pit Orchestra Dir; OMEA, MENG 1992-; ATMI 1995-; Pi Kappa Lambda 1992-; Produced Professional Recording; *home:* 5956 Walnut Cir Apt 3 Toledo OH 43615

YOST, JILL LEMON, Art Teacher; *b:* Toledo, OH; *m:* Richard A.; *c:* Rick, Alan, Drew; *ed:* Capital Univ (BFA) Art Ed K-12 1977; Ashland Univ (MED) Supervisioin 1990; Attnd Andrews Univ; *cr:* Licking Vly Schls Elem Art Tchr 1977-78; Southwest Licking Schls MS Art Tchr 1978-; *ai:* Mentor Tchr; Intervention Assistance Team; OH Art Ed Assn 1984-; NEA 1980-; Dow Excl in Ed Awd 1994; Bldg Mentor 1987-90, 1993-; *office:* Watkins MS 8808 Watkins Rd SW Pataskala OH 43062

YOST, MICHAEL JOSEPH, Seventh Grade Science Teacher; *b:* Fountain Hill, PA; *c:* Jennifer Lynn, Allyson Marie, Michael Joseph II; *ed:* Univ of PA (BA) Bio 1977 & (MS) Ed 1978; Temple Univ Grad Courses; DE Cty Intermediate Unit Courses; *cr:* Drexel Hill Jr HS 9th Grd Chem 1979-80; Drexel Hill MS 6th- 7th Grd Sci 1980-; *ai:* Head Ftbl Coach Unlimited Ftbl Team; Co-Director Intramural Ath; Bowling, Ping-Pong, Vlybl Activity Adv; Clubs Coord 1983-88; Team Ldr 1996-; Mentor 1995-; NSTA 1992-, Mem; UDEA, PSEA, NEA Union Mem 1979-; Messiah Lutheran Church Youth Dir 1990-, Sunday Schl Tchr, Vlybl Coach & Youth Ldr; American Heart Assn Vol 1988-,Neighborhood Fund Dr Coord; Newtown Sq Petticoat League Sftbl Team 1987-, Coach; Broomall Little League Coach; 1989 Toyota Coach of the Year Awd Ftbl; Nom for PA Sci Tchr of Yr 1991-92, Upper Derby Schl Dist; DE Cty Intermediate Unit Sci Dept Evaluation Team, Radnor Schl Dist; Impact Awd Winner for "You Are Spec Unit" 1989; *office:* Drexel Hill MS State Rd & Penn Ave Drexel Hill PA 19026*

YOST, SHIRLEY SCHUYLER, French Teacher; *b:* Lewisburg, PA; *m:* Robert J.; *c:* Christopher, Aimee; *ed:* Bloomsburg Univ (BS) Scndry Fr 1968, (BS) Elem Ed 1974; Univ of Northern IA 8 Credit Hrs Fr Angers France; In Svc Skills for Adolescence, Basic Cmptr, SAP Trng; *cr:* Mt Carmel Schl Dist Fr Tchr 1968-69; Benton Area Schl Dist Fr Tchr 1970-95; *ai:* Stu Assistance Team Coord; Frgn Lang Club Adv; Dist Long Range Steering Curr Comm; NEA 1968-; PSEA 1968-, Sec; *home:* RR 1 Box 336 Turbotville PA 17772*

YOTS, THOMAS JOSEPH, Chemistry Teacher; *b:* Utica, NY; *m:* Louise E.; *c:* Jason, Benjamin; *ed:* Niagara Univ (BS) Chem 1967, (MS) Chem 1969; 33 Credit Hrs Beyond MS; *cr:* Lewiston Porter Cntrl Schl Chem Tchr 1969-; *ai:* Yrbk Adv; AFT & NYSUT 1969-, Del; Lewiston Porter United Tchrs 1969-, Pres; Center City Dev Corp 1985-, Pres 1990; Amer Chem Soc Western NY Tchr of the Yr; Niagara Univ Tchr of the Yr; *office:* Lewiston Porter Cntrl Schl 4061 Creek Rd Youngstown NY 14174*

YOUMANS, BARBARA JEAN, Assistant Nurse Instructor; *b:* Cape Vincent, NY; *ed:* HGS (RN) Nursing 1958; SUNY at Plattsburgh (BSEd) Schl Nursing 1961; VA at Albany (CRNA) Anethesia; SUNY at Cortland (MSHE) Hlth Ed; *cr:* HGS-CGH General Duty Nursing 8 Yrs; Medical Coll of VA Anesthesia Tchng 1 Yr; St Joseph Hospital Schl Nurse Ed 2 Yrs; Oswego Cty Boces Nurse Asst Instr 6 Yrs; *ai:* Supt Day, Shared Decision Making Comms; RNNYSNA 1959-; CRNA-AANA 1976-, Nominating Comm; NYSTA 1990-; ARC, Bloodmobile; PUMC, Chair 6 Yrs; OSC, Ski Trip; Acrobic, Worked On Ski Show; *office:* Oswego County Boces Rt 64 Mexico NY 13114

YOUMELL, PAULA MARIE, Health Education Teacher; *b:* Massena, NY; *ed:* SUNY at Canton (AAS) Nrsng 1985; SUNY at Cortland (BS) Hlth Ed 1990; Syracuse Univ (MS) PE 1992; Post Grad Stud in Natural Healing, Nutrition; *cr:* Syracuse Univ PE Grad Tchr, Rsrch Asst 1991-92; Henninger HS Parenting Ed 1993, Hlth Ed 1993-; *ai:* Teen AIDS Task Force; AIDS Comm Resources; AFT, NY St United Tchrs 1993-; NY St Nurses Assn 1985-; North Amer Vegetarian, Nutrition Ed Soc, Lifelong Wellness 1995-; Adirondack Mountain Club 1993-; Grad Assistantship, Schlsp at Syracuse Univ 1991-92; *home:* PO Box 1043 Elbridge NY 13060

YOUNG, ALBERT L., Physical Science Teacher; *b:* Camden, NJ; *m:* Catherine Rich; *c:* Alan; *ed:* Temple Univ at Philadelphia (BS) Bus Admn 1969; Drexel Univ at Philadelphia (MS) Hydrology, Env Mngmt 1972; 9 Credit Hrs in Cmptr Ed; *cr:* Carusi Schl Phys Sci Tchr 1971-80; Cherry Hill East HS Phys Sci Tchr 1980-; *ai:* Adopt-A-Grandparent Club Adv; Sci, Math, Tech Comm; Cherry Hill Acad Bd of Dirs; NSTA 1986-; ASCD 1987-; *office:* Cherry Hill HS East Kresson Rd Cherry Hill NJ 08003*

YOUNG, AMY JO, English Teacher; *b:* Piqua, OH; *m:* John A.; *ed:* Bowling Green St Univ (BS) Scndry Eng Ed 1990; Addl Hrs OH Univ at Zanesville Interpersonal Comm, OH Univ, Muskingum Coll; *cr:* Houston HS 7 & 12 Grds Eng Tchr 1990-91; Philo HS 10-12 Grds Eng Tchr 1991-; *ai:* Poem Pub; Article Pub; Early Eng Composition Assessment Prgm Grant, Portfolio Assessment at OH Univ; *office:* Philo HS 200 Broad St Philo OH 43771*

YOUNG, ANNE BENNIGHOFF, Third Grade Teacher; *b:* New Tri PA; *m:* R. Jay II; *c:* Nathan, Jennifer; *ed:* Mansfield Univ (BS) Hom 1966; Shippensburg Univ (MED) Elem Ed; *cr:* Northern Cty Schl Dis Grd Tchr 1966-68; 3rd Grd Tchr 1977; *ai:* Envirothon Coach; Schl Production Comm; NYEA 1966-, Dist Outstdng Tchr 1986; PSEA 19 NEA 1966-; Woman's Club of Dillsburg 1970-94, Most Active Woman Awd 1978; PCAA 1991-; Mansfield Univ Alumni Bd 1991- 1995 & 1996; Pioneering Partners Awd 1995; Classroom Close-Up T for PSEA 1996.

YOUNG, BETH ANN GRIESINGER, Physical Education Teache Hamilton, OH; *m:* Gary Lee; *c:* Richie, Scott; *ed:* Miami Univ (BA 1978; Attnd Wright St at Dayton, Univ of Dayton; *cr:* Harrison Elem PE Tchr 1978-79; Lincoln Elem Schl PE Tchr 1979-81; Cleveland Schl PE Tchr 1981-88; Wilson Jr HS PE Tchr 1988-; *ai:* Ath DIr; 9th Adv; OEA, NEA 1992-; YMCA 1984-, Bd of Trustees; Camp Cam Gard, Bd of Trustees; *office:* Wilson Jr HS 1200 Eaton Ave Hamilton 45013

YOUNG, BRENDA MCGAVISK, Secondary Mathematics Teache Erie, PA; *m:* Jeffrey; *c:* Brandon, Tiffany; *ed:* Univ of Pittsburgh Applied Math 1990; Gannon Univ 30 Credit Hrs; St Bonaventure U Credit Hrs; *cr:* North Tier Summer Schl Math Tchr 1990-; Smethport HS Math Tchr 1991-; *ai:* Bandfront Adv; Sr Project Comm; Mat Challenge Organizer; PSEA 1991-; NEA 1991-; NCTM 1991-; Smeth Fire Dept 1990-; Smethport Fire Police 1995-; Memrl Recreation 1995-, Bd Mem; *office:* Smethport Area Jr Sr HS 412 S Mechani Smethport PA 16749

YOUNG, BRUCE ALAN, Mathematics Teacher; *b:* Allentown, PA Kelley J. Oswald; *c:* Lisa, Lara; *ed:* Clarion St Coll (BS) Elem Ed & 1979; 36 Post Grad Hrs Toward Masters in Math & General Ed Jefferson Elem Schl 5th Grd Tchr 1980-82; South Mountain MS 6th & Grd Math Tchr 1982-; *ai:* Girls Bsktbl Head Coach; Intramural Sp Allentown Schl Dist Math Curr Revision Comm; NEA, AEA, PSEA 19 Zions Evangelical Luth Church 1988-, Cncl; Rider Pool Grant Stdn Consumers Unit; Coached 4 Boys & 3 Girls League Championship South Mountain MS; *office:* South Mountain MS S Churck & W E Allentown PA 18103*

YOUNG, BRUCE E., Mathematics & Science Teacher; *b:* Kingston, *m:* Kathryn A. Medvecky; *c:* Austin, Amy; *ed:* East Stroudsburg Univ Hlth & PE 1975; Bloomsburg Univ (MBA) Bus Admin 1983; Gen Tchng Cert 1991; *cr:* Hazleton YMCA Pgm Dir 1975-76; Penn St Un Hazleton Ath & Recreation Coord 1976-90; Immanuel Chrstn Schl 1990-; *ai:* Sports Club Adv; Track & Field Coach; Christ Refor Episcopal Church 1983-, Sr Warden; *home:* RR 3 Box 754 Drums PA 1

YOUNG, BRYAN ALAN, Band Director & Music Teacher; *b:* Brock MA; *m:* Beth Anne Vasil; *c:* Jeremy, Benjamin; *ed:* Boston Conserva (BM) Classical Performance 1986; Berklee Coll of Music (BMEd) M Ed 1988; Univ of CT MM Music Ed; *cr:* Norwood After Schl Music 1986-87; Newton After Schl Music, Drama, Supvr, Tchr 1988 Fairhaven Pub Schls Band Dir, MS Tchr 1993-; *ai:* Jazz Band Freelance Performer Woodwind Specialty; MMEA, MENC 1986; *of* Hastings MS 30 School St Fairhaven MA 02719

YOUNG, CATHY (DIETZ), 4th Grade Teacher; *b:* Lock Haven, PA Wayne D.; *c:* Megan; *ed:* East Stroudsburg (BS) Elem Ed 1979, Equivalency 1992; *cr:* Lamar Twp Elem TELLS Tutor 1979-86; Wood Elem TELLS Tutor 1979-86; Woolrich Elem Permanent Sub 1984 Dickey Elem Permanent Sub 1984-86; Beech Creek Elem Permanent 1984-86; Renovo Elem Kndgtn, 4th-5th Grd Tchr 1986-; *ai:* Instrl Sup Team, Core Team; Lang Arts Comm; Writing Assessment Comm; Su Schl Tchr; NEA, PSEA, ACCE 1986-; *home:* 15 E Allison St Lock H PA 17745*

YOUNG, CINDY MC KAY, English Teacher; *b:* Barbers Point, HI Richard W.; *ed:* Wesleyan Coll (BA) Eng, Scndry Ed 1991; *cr:* Cntrl Eng Tchr 1991-93; Chopticon HS Eng Tchr 1993-; *ai:* Eng Dept Ch Drama Club Co-Spon; Thespian Soc Co-Spon; Schl Improvement T NEA, MSTA 1993-; *office:* Chopticon HS Rt 242 Morganza MD 2066

YOUNG, CLARIBEL (MELE), History Professor; *b:* North Brookf NY; *w:* Leo Henry Jr. (dec); *c:* Marilyn, Frances Scott, Harold, James; Georgian Court Coll (BA) His 1975; Rutgers Univ (MA) British His 1 (PHD) Anglo, Amer His 1989; *cr:* Georgian Court Coll Lecturer 1976 Instr 1978-79, Asst Prof 1980-89, Assoc Prof 1990-93, Prof 1994-; *ai:* Alpha Theta Intnl His Honor Soc, Clionaes His Club Adv; Fac Conc Comm; Handbook Sub-Comm Chair; AAUP 1990-, Local Pres 1993 Point Pleasant Historical Soc 1985-; Pt Pleasant Beach HS Alum 19 Hall of Fame; NJ Stud Acad Alliance 1989-, Task Force on Ed Ch Publications 1977, 1987, 1989; *office:* Georgian Court Coll Lakewood Lakewood NJ 08701

YOUNG, DAVID ROBIN, Third Grade Teacher; *b:* Newton, MA; Denise Maikis; *c:* Jason, Suzanne; *ed:* Tufts Univ (BS) Civil Eng 19 Boston St Coll (MED) Elem 1973; *cr:* Hastings Elem Schl 4th Grd 1973-76, 3rd Grd Tchr 1976-; *ai:* JV Sftbl 1974-78, Bsktbl 1976-78 & Bsktbl Coach 1978-88; Hands-On Sci Comm Chm 1987-90; Westb Tchrs Assn 1973-; MA Tchrs Assn 1973-; NEA 1973-; Amateur Coa Assn 1985-; Natick Soccer Club 1988-; Northboro-Westboro Chambe Commerce Excl in Ed Awd 1991; *home:* 18 Euclid Ave Natick MA 01

YOUNG, DIANA SERIO, Second Grade Teacher; *b:* Columbus, OH Philip Don; *c:* Mike, Scott; *ed:* Kent St Univ (BS) Elem Ed 1969; Uni Dayton (MS) Interdisciplinary 1983; *cr:* Longcoy Elem Schl LD 1969-70; Cookson Elem Schl 1st-3rd Grd Tchr 1973-; *ai:* Sci Curr Co TCEA 1980-; OEA; NEA; First United Church of Christ 1973-; M Holden Jennings Fnd Scholor 1980-81; *office:* Cookson Elem Schl Mystic Ln Troy OH 45373

YOUNG, DOUGLAS JOHN, 7th & 8th Grade Math Teacher; Rochester, NY; *m:* Darcy; *c:* Douglas Jr., Carley; *ed:* SUNY at Gene (BA) Scndry Ed & Math 1982, (MS) Ed & Math 1989; *cr:* Marcus Whit HS 9th-12th Grd Math Tchr 1982-83; York Cntrl Schl 8th & 12th Grd 1983-86; Livonia Jr-Sr High Jr High Math Tchr 1986-; *ai:* Jr High M Comp & Wrestling Coach; Former Coach Var Wrestling 2 Lea Championships; AFT 1986-; Assoc Math Tchrs of NYS 1987-.

YOUNG, ELIZABETH ARNONE, Spanish Teacher; *b:* Buffalo, NY Bradley C.; *c:* Pierce Vincent; *ed:* St Univ Coll at Buffalo (BS) Frgn L Stud & Scndry Ed 1988, (MA) Multi Disciplinary Stud 1990; Span S Cert at Universidad De Espana in Spain; *cr:* Edward Town MS 7th & Grd Span Tchr 1988-; *ai:* ETMS Hnr Soc Adv; Sigma Delta Pi Span N 1987-, Local Pres; NYSUT 1988-; WNYFLEC 1988-; NYSFLT 19 Intnl Inst 1986-, Vol; Mussomeli Soc Comm 1995-, Archivist; *off* Edward Town MS 2292 Saunders Settlement Rd Sanborn NY 14132

YOUNG, F. MICHAEL, Engineering Professor; *b:* Augusta, ME; Wendy Billings; *c:* Joshua, Kira, Meaghan, Erin, Seth; *ed:* ME Marit Acad (BS) Marine Engrng 1977; *cr:* Amer Export Lines 3rd Engr 1977- Global Marine Drilling Co Chief Engr 1978-91; ME Maritime Acad Eng Prof 1991-; *ai:* Marine Engrng Operations Prgm Coord; Trng S Conversion Comm; Class of 1997 Adv; Ocean Inst Marine Diesel P Coord; Dedham Schl Comm 1992-, Chair; Holden Recreation Lea 1991-, Bsktbl Coach; *office:* Maine Maritime Acad Castine ME 04421

NG, FRANK J., Teacher & Coach; *b:* Clemson, SC; *ed:* Federal City (AA) Comm Ed, (BS) PE, (MA) Adult Ed; 80 Addl Hrs; *cr:* Univ of 972-75; Eastern Sr HS Tchr, Coach 1975-78; Anacostia Sr HS Tchr, h 1978-81; P.R. Harris Schl Tchr, Coach 1981-84; Frank W. Ballou Sr Tchr, Coach 1984-; *ai:* Head Ftbl Coach; Sr Class Spon; WA Tchrs n, AFT 1972-; DC Coaches Assn 1972-, Coach of Yr 1995; Kappa a Psi 1969-; Advy Neighborhood Commissioner 1993-; *office:* Frank allou Sr HS 3401 4th St SE Washington DC 20032*

NG, JANICE BESECKER, High School German Teacher; *b:* E idsburg, PA; *m:* Robert; *c:* Emily; *ed:* Millersville Univ (BS) Ger ; East Stroudsburg Univ (MS) Scndry Ed 1985; Attnd Middlebury Wilkes Univ; *cr:* Stroudsburg HS Ger Tchr 1977-80; Pleasant Vly HS Tchr 1980-; *ai:* Intnl Club Adv; ADvy Comm Fac; Pleasant Vly Ed 1980-, Fac Rep; PA St Ed Assn 1977-; AATG 1980-; Monroe Cty Arts 1994-; Article Pub 1992; *home:* RR 3 Box 2245 Effort PA 18330

NG, JOANNE MARIE, Kindergarten Teacher; *b:* Canton, OH; *ed:* St Univ (BA) Elem Ed 1978; 30 Addl Hrs Kent St Univ, Akron Univ; auder Elem Schl K & 1st Grd Tchr 1978-; *ai:* Soc Comm Chm 10 Yrs; a Delta Pi, NEA, JMEA 1978-; Pet Therapy Local Nursing Homes; Cty Humane Soc; Jennings Scholar; *office:* Sauder Elem Schl 7503 brook Rd NW Massillon OH 44646*

JNG, JOSEPH, Assistant Principal; *b:* Myrtle Beach, SC; *m:* Linder ; *c:* Joseph A.; *ed:* Brooklyn Coll (BA) Pol Sci & S S 1974; Fordham (MS) Supv Admin 1978; 9 Credits Post Grad Stud Child Dev; *cr:* tive Thinkers Supvr, Dir 1977-82; ENY NAACP Day Care Ctr Acting 1983-84; PS 202 Elem Schl Tchr 1984-85; JHS 263 7th Grd SS Tchr, n, Asst Prin 1985-; *ai:* SS Dept, Math & Rdng, Multicultural Curr Act, RI Soc Supvr; Organize Comm Based Prgms; NYCPD 1994-, Cert of reciation; Yth Advy Cncl 1991-, Tchr of Yr; Comm Schl Bd 1994-, Cert ppreciation; Malcom X Comm 1993 Awd; *home:* 360 Dumont Ave Apt Brooklyn NY 11212*

JNG, JULIA R. PATAKI, Med Lab Tech Pgm Dir & Instr; *b:* sonville, NC; *ed:* Gannon Univ (BS) Med Tech 1982; *cr:* Preston Meml Med Technologist-Generalist 1982-83; St Frances Med Ctr Med nologist-Generalist 1983-86, Med Technologist-Immunopathology -89; PA St Univ Instr, MLT Prog Dir 1989-; *ai:* Lenape Vo-Tech MLT y Bd; ASCP 1982-; *office:* PA St Univ N Kensington Cmps 3550 7th et Rd New Kensington PA 15068*

NG, KIRK J., Instrumental Music Director; *b:* Hartford, CT; *ed:* of ME at Orono (BS) Music Ed 1993; Post-Grad Stud Providence MO Western St at St Joseph; *cr:* Cumberland HS Dir Inst Music -; *ai:* Concert, Symphonic Bands; Small Ensembles; Tech Comm; RINEA 1993-; MENC 1988-, Outstdng Commitment to Music Ed ; SPEBSQSA 1987-; Knights of Columbus 1986-; Barbershopper of 995; Chorus Performance at Intnl Festivals; Vocal Quartet Performs all US, Canada, Europe Giving Wkshps; *office:* Cumberland HS 2600 don Rd Cumberland RI 02864*

JNG, LAURA ANNE, 8th Grade English Teacher; *b:* Bellefonte, PA; PA St Univ (BA) Jrnlsm 1983, (MED) Curr, Inst 1989; *cr:* Upper Adams Dist Drama Coach 1988-95, 8th Grd Eng Tchr 1988-; *ai:* Strategic ning Steering Comm; Spelling Bee Coord; Video Club Adv; NEA, A 1988-; VAEA 1988-, Pres 1995-; NCTE 1987-; *office:* Upper Adams N Main St Biglerville PA 17307*

JNG, LAURETTA DORSEY, Voice & Diction Teacher; *b:* xandria, VA; *c:* Rehya Danielle, Heather Rachelle, Andrea Garielle; *ed:* body Inst of Johns Hopkins (BA) Voice & Music Ed 1963; Juilliard Schl) Voice & Opera Theatre; *cr:* Duke Ellington Schl Tchr 1975-85; liate Artists Artist in Residence 1978-81; MD Bible Coll & Seminary 1987-; Baltimore Schl for the Arts Tchr 1987-; *ai:* Direct Intnl Chrstn ir, Frontline Asst Dir To Opera North; Phi Mu Epsilon 1960-; Balt ts for Girls 1994-, Adv; Seventh Productions 1995-, Bd Mem; Won l & Natl Competitions; Metropolitan Opera Auditions Winner; Work in er-City Act for Greater Grace World Outreach; *office:* Baltimore Schl The Arts 712 Cathedral St Baltimore MD 21201

JNG, LEROY JAMES,JR., Adjunct Professor; *b:* Baltimore, MD; *ed:* v of MD (BS) Psych 1968; George Washington Univ (MA) Ed & Dev 4; Howard Univ Coll of Med 1970-71; John Hopkins Univ Fellow 4-85; Columbia Univ Tchrs Coll Doctoral Candidate; *cr:* nestead-Montebello Ctr of Antioch Univ Adj Prof 1973-80; ourner-Douglass Coll Adj Prof 1980-; *ai:* Admissions Comm Chair; e: Sojourner-Douglass Coll 500 North Caroline Street Baltimore MD 05*

JNG, LORI MILLER, Spanish & Latin Teacher; *b:* Springfield, OH; Robert C.; *ed:* Miami Univ at Oxford (BSE) Latin 1976; *ai:* Frgn Lang t Chprsn; NEA; OEA; Northwestern Tchrs Assoc; Kappa Delta 1973-; e: Northwestern HS 5650 Troy Rd Springfield OH 45502

JNG, LOUIS ALONZO, Mathematics Teacher; *b:* Bryn Mawr, PA; *m:* y Elizabeth Grimard; *c:* Jason, Joe, Luke; *ed:* Dartmouth (BA) Psych 0; Monterey Inst of Intnl Stud (MAT) Ed 1983; Attnd Univ of VT; *cr:* Telephone of PA Mgr 1970-74; Robert Louis Stevenson Schl Tchr, n Dir & Coach 1974-83; Chonte Rosemary Hall Tchr, Dean & Coach 3-91; Woodstock Union HS Tchr & Coach 1991-; *ai:* NHS Adv; Lacrose d Coach; 8th Grd Bsktbl Coach; NCTM 1974-; MAA & Lacrosse Fnd 3-; Pentangle, Bd Mem 1993-; Ftbl Coach of Yr Runner Up 1976; rosse Coach of Ys 1993; VT St Fnlst for Presdntl Tchr Awd for Math, 1995; Woodstock Tchr of Yr 1994; *office:* Woodstock Union HS Rt 4 odstock VT 05091*

JNG, LYNN SUSAN, Jr HS Eng Tchr & HS Librarian; *b:* Cleveland, ; *m:* Robert J.; *c:* Lonny; *ed:* Kent St Univ (BS) Eng 1973; Ed Media; ptr Lit 4 Hrs; Tchng Writing 3 Hrs; Clssrm Methods 9 Hrs; *cr:* Old Fort Librn, Eng Tchr 1973-; *ai:* Asst Play Dir; Treas Tchrs Union; Yrbk Adv; ver of Pen Adv; Acad Awd Comm; OEA, NEA 1973-, Pres 1980, Treas 1-82; Volunteered 12 Yrs Nursery Schl Summer Prgm for Lang Delayed ldren Betty Jane Rehabilitation Center; 4 Successful Schl Levies; Vol ohol, Drug Addiction & Mental Hlth Services; *office:* Old Fort H S nty Rd 50 Old Fort OH 44861

JNG, MARILYN S., Science Teacher & Dept Chm; *b:* New York City, *m:* Everett C.; *c:* Joshua; *ed:* Temple Univ (BA) His 1967; MA aivalency in Ed 1986; Grad Work in Sci at Chestnut Hill Coll, St Josephs v, Beaver Coll, Temple; *cr:* Dewey-Mann Elem Tchr 1967-68; Reynolds n Schl Tchr 1968-72; John Story Jenks Elem Schl Sci Tchr 1974-; *ai:* Fair & PA Jr Acad of Sci Spon; Environmental Ed Coord; Tchr Assoc v of PA Field Ecology Prgm; Sci Resource Ldr; PAESTA 1986-, ecutive Sec 1986-94, VP 1991, Pres 1992; PSST 1988-, Executive Bd; TA; PSTA; ATMOPAV; PFT; ACS Vol; Nom Presidential Awd for Excl 2; Nom PA Tchr of Yr 1993; Semi-Finalist Philadelphia Tchr of Yr 1; Awd Established M. Young Sci Awd J. S. Jenks 1990-92; 2 Prism ants 1987-88; 2 Articles Pub Cmptr Learning Month 1988-89; Nom denbaum Improvement of Ed Tchr Awd 1992; *office:* John Story Jenks l Germantown & Southampton Aves Philadelphia PA 19118*

JNG, MARISA TIGUE, Vocal & Instrmntl Music Tchr; *b:* Kingston, ; *c:* Micaela Ann; *ed:* Ulster Cty Comm Coll (Assocs) Lbrl Arts 1984; Hartt Schl Univ of Hartford (BMus) Music Ed 1987; Western CT St v (MS) Music Ed 1989; Bard Coll Flute Master Class; *cr:* Wappingers s Cntrl Schls Elem & Jr High Band 1987-89; Saugerties Cntrl Schl Dist JH Vocal & HS Instrumental Tchr 1989-; *ai:* Band Mem Participating in Day Without Art AIDS Awareness; Caroling at Sr Citizen Residence; Playing for Spcl Olympics Games; Ulster Cty Music Ed Assn VP & Pub Relations Chprsn; NYSSMA & MENC; NFA; Woodstock Chamber Orch 1995-, Bd of Dirs; Hudson Vly Philharmonic 1995-; Educl Advy Comm; *office:* Saugerties Jr Sr HS Washington Ave Ext Saugerties NY 12477

YOUNG, MARLA RUSSICK, First Grade Teacher; *b:* Easton, PA; *m:* Ralph H.; *ed:* Glassboro St Coll (BA) Elem Ed 1976; Lehigh Univ (MA) Elem Ed 1983; *cr:* Oxford Cntrl Schl 1st-3rd Grd Tchr 1976-; *ai:* Ski, Fitness, Heritage & Cultural Club Adv; NJEA 1976-; NEA 1976-; OEA 1976-; *office:* Oxford Central Elem Schl Kent St Oxford NJ 07863

YOUNG, MARY CEBASEK, Third Grade Teacher; *b:* Conneaut, OH; *m:* Rodney L.; *c:* Gary, Michelle, Molly; *ed:* Edinboro St Univ (BA) Elem Ed 1970; Grad Hrs; *cr:* Southeast Schl 3rd Grd Tchr 5 Yrs; Lakeview Schl 4th-5th Grd Tchr 18 Yrs; Chestnut Elem Schl 3rd Grd Tchr 2 Yrs; *ai:* Hnr, Merit Roll; Pupil Evaluation, Cty Soc Stud Curr Dev Comms; CEA, NEA, NEOTA 1970-; Conneaut Music Boosters 1980-, Comm Mem; *office:* Chestnut Elem Schl 755 Chestnut St Conneaut OH 44030

YOUNG, MELODY GYLES, Spanish Teacher; *b:* Dayton, OH; *c:* Walter A. III, Benjamin R., Merrill L.; *ed:* Wake Forest Univ (BA) Fr, Span 1966; Post Grad Stud, Cert Prgms Univ of VA, Univ of DE, Univ of CT, Johns Jopkins; *cr:* Tach Jovett Jr HS Span, Fr, Latin Tchr 4 Yrs; George Read MS Span, Fr Tchr 1 Yr; Magnet Schl for Gifted Tchr 2 Yrs; Gunning Bedford MS Span, Gifted, Fr Tchr 14 Yrs; Wm Penn HS Span, Gifted, Fr Tchr 9 Yrs; *ai:* Co-Chair Dist GATE Comm; Stud Hall Coord; NEA 1966-; DSEA 1970-; NAGC, CEC-TAG 1974-, Pres, St Assoc for Gifted; PDK 1985-; Goo's Advy Cncl Exceptional Citizens 1974-, Treas, Prsnl Comm Chir, 20 Yr Cert; GATE Speaker; *office:* William Penn HS Basin Rd New Castle DE 19720

YOUNG, MOVIAS EISENHOWER, Third Grade Teacher; *b:* Mill Hall, PA; *m:* James Joseph; *c:* Lacrenda, Beth Young Cartagena; *ed:* Lock Haven Univ (BA) Elem 1973; 33 Addl Credits; *cr:* Liberty Curtin Elem Schl First Grd Tchr 1973-78; Dickey Elem Schl First Grd Tchr 1978-93; Liberty Curtin Elem Schl Third Grd Tchr 1993-; *ai:* Young Authors Day, Soc Stud Comms; Fitness Unlimited; PSEA 1975-, Rep; NEA 1990-; Womens Assn of Clinton Cntry Club 1992-; *office:* Liberty Curtin Elem Keystone Cntrl Blanchard PA 16826*

YOUNG, NANCY SOUTHARD, French & World History Teacher; *b:* Chicago, IL; *m:* Joseph B.; *c:* Jeffrey, Amy; *ed:* Kalamazoo Coll (BA) Fr 1967; Western MI Univ (MA) Fr 1971; 12 Hrs Toward Masters Plus 30; *cr:* Bound Brook HS Fr & World His Tchr 1972-; *ai:* Fr Club Adv; Peer Mediation; NEA 1967-; NJEA, BBEA 1972-; United Family & Childrens Soc 1984-94, Trustee; *office:* Bound Brook HS 111 W Union Ave Bound Brook NJ 08805

YOUNG, NOEL CHRISTIAN, Instrumental Music Teacher; *b:* New Britain, CT; *m:* Patricia Louise Bell; *c:* Christian; *ed:* William Paterson Coll (BA) Music Ed 1969; 20 Addl Credit Hrs of Post Grad Work; *cr:* Ramsey Pub Schls Instrumental Music Tchr 1969-; Marching Band Dir 1985-; Ensembles Dir 1992-; *ai:* NEA, NJEA, BCEA & RTA 1969-; Metro Amer Adjudicators 1975-, Assn Chief Judge, Svc Awd; Eastern Marching Band Assn 1980-, Coord, Dirs Awd; Amer Fed of Musicians 1967-; North Jersey Schl of Music Assn 1970-, Tryout Chm, Mgr of Region Bands, Instrumental Div Co-Chair; Clinican at NJMEA Convention 1984; Clinician at NJEA Convention 1991; IN & OH St Band Championships Adjudicator 1984-85; Winterguard Intnl Adjudicator 1982-85; All North Jersey Jr HS Band Conductor 1975; *home:* 31 Horton Ave Hawthorne NJ 07506

YOUNG, PATRICIA LEE, Guidance Counselor; *b:* Providence, RI; *m:* Peter A.; *c:* Christopher Lawrence, Jason Ellis; *ed:* Bryant Coll (BS, BED) Bus Admin, Bus Ed 1962; Unif of RI (M) Counseling 1977; *cr:* East Greenwich Frenchtown Schl Elem Cnslr 1977-82; Dept of Deffense Dependents Schl Alconbury AFB England Guidance Cnslr 1989-90 East Greenwich HS Guidance Cnslr 1982-; *ai:* Adv Quill & Scroll Natl Honor Soc, Interact Rotarian Svc Club; RI Counselors Assn 1980-, Sec; Natl Assn of Coll Admissions Counselors 1985-, Mem Sec; The Coll Bd 1985-, Rep Coll Admissions Del; Not Pub Book Aimed to Stdnts Abroad; *office:* East Greenwich HS 300 Avenger Dr East Greenwich RI 02818*

YOUNG, PATRICIA MORGAN, First Grade Teacher; *b:* Oak Hill, OH; *m:* Loren H.; *c:* Jeff, Lorna Music, John; *ed:* Rio Grande Univ (BS) Elem Ed 1972; Attnd OH Univ, Shawnee St Coll, Drake Univ; *cr:* Beaver Elem First Grd Tchr 1968-; *ai:* Sci Comm; Grand Comm; Cmptr Sysop; NEA, OEA 1968-; Electa 1975-; Grace U M Church 1969-, Sunday Schl Tchr; *home:* 274 State St Jackson OH 45640*

YOUNG, PATTY ANN LEVASSEUR, Spanish & French Teacher; *b:* Fort Kent, ME; *m:* Mark; *ed:* Univ of ME at Orono (BA) Intnl Affairs in Fr & Ed 1990; *cr:* Gardiner Area HS Span & Fr Tchr 1991-; *ai:* Yrbk Co-adv; *office:* Gardiner Area HS W Hill Rd Gardiner ME 04345

YOUNG, PHYLLIS ARLENE, Physical Education Teacher; *b:* Richmond, VA; *c:* Sydney, Marvin; *ed:* Winston Salem St Univ (BS) Hlth, PE 1982; 21 Hrs Spec Ed DE St Univ; *cr:* Alexander Hamilton HS PE, Coach 1986; Christiana HS PE, Coach 1991-; *ai:* Sr Class Adv; Co-Adv SPAACE Club; Girls Bsktbl Asst Coach, Frosh Sftbl; Schl Cncl Mem 1991-92; NEA 1991-; DAHPERD 1992-; DE Women's Alliance for Sports & Fitness 1996; NAACP 1982-87, 1994-.

YOUNG, RAYMOND ALBERT, World History & Geography Tchr; *b:* Fremont, OH; *m:* Diane Krakowski; *c:* Margolyn, Carrie Ann; *ed:* Miami Univ (BSEd) Soc Stud 1966; Akron Univ (BS) Admin 1979; 15 Addl Hrs; *cr:* Lima Cntrl Cath HS Soc Stud Instr 1966-67; VISTA Soc Worker 1967-68; Columbus Grove HS Soc Stud Tchr 1968-71; Marlington HS Soc Stud Tchr 1971-; *ai:* Fr Boys Bsktbl Coach; Marlington Ed Assn 1975-, Pres 1988-90; Elks 1986-; Knights of Columbus 1990-; *office:* Marlington HS 10450 Moulin Ave NE Alliance OH 44601*

YOUNG, RAYMOND ARTHUR, Language Arts Teacher; *b:* Lancaster, OH; *m:* Lois M. Wickline; *c:* Joshua, Jason, Jamie, Julie; *ed:* OH Univ (AA) Ed 1974, (BS) Ed 1976; Attnd Bowling Green St Univ; *cr:* OH Youth Commission Tchr 1976-78; Toledo Chrstn Acad Tchr, Prin 1978-81; Gibsonburg HS Tchr 1983-; *ai:* Stu Cncl Adv; Vlybl Coach; OEA, NEA, OCTELA; *office:* Gibsonburg Jr/Sr HS S Harrison St Gibsonburg OH 43431

YOUNG, RAYMOND L., Mathematics Teacher; *b:* Rockland, ME; *m:* Julianne Boothby; *c:* Shayne; *ed:* Univ of ME at Gorham (BS) Math Ed 1970; Bowie St Coll Scndry Ed; *cr:* William Wirt MS Math Tchr 1972-83; High Point HS Math Tchr 1983-; *ai:* NEA, MSTA, PGCEA 1973-; Provinces Civic Assn 1981-85, Good Neighbor Awd; Ridgewood Comm Assn 1985-, Bd of Dir; *office:* High Point HS 3601 Powder Mill Rd Beltsville MD 20705*

YOUNG, RONALD G., 7th & 8th Grade Teacher; *b:* New Kensington, PA; *m:* Dianne L. Manniko; *c:* Bethany, Chip; *ed:* Edinbro Univ (MED) Ed 1977; 23 Post Grad Hrs; *cr:* Lakeview Elem Schl Grd 5 Tchr 1970; Chestnut Elem Schl Grd 6 Tchr 1971-75; Southeast Elem Schl Grd 4 Tchr 1976-78; Monroe Elem Schl Grd 5 Tchr 1979-81; Rowe MS Grd 7 & 8 Tchr 1982-; *ai:* HS Bsbl Var, MS Bsktbl, Vlybl Coach; NEA 1970-; *home:* 611 Furnace Rd Conneaut OH 44030

YOUNG, RONALD ULRICH, American Government Teacher; *b:* Kenton, OH; *ed:* OH St Univ (BS) His, Pol Sci 1965, (MA) Pol Sci, Ed 1966; 45 Addl Hrs; 40 Hrs Wright St Univ; 6 Hrs Univ of Dayton; *cr:* Mad River Local Schl Dist Amer Govt, Hnrs Pol Sci Tchr 1966-, Soc Stud Dept Chm 1979-, Adv, Stu Senate 1967-; *ai:* Soc of Acad Excl Adv 1973-; Grad Adv 1972-; Admin Advy Cncl 1970-90; Elected Chm of Cncl 1970-90; Steering Comm Chm for North Cntrl Evaluation 1981, 1988, 1995; NEA 1966-, Bldg Rep 5 Yrs; OH Ed Assn, Mad River Ed Assn 1966-; United Meth Church 1955-; Montgomery Cty Bd of Elections Deputy Registrar; OH St Univ Alumni Assn 1970-; Boosters Club 1966-, Several Fund Raising Chairmanships; Tchr of Yr 1985; Recipient of Excl in Tchr Awd 1988; OH St Alumni Assn Career Tchr Awd 1991; Bd of Ed Recognition Awd for Stu Senate Sponsorship 1991; Outstdng Scndry Edctrs of Amer 1973-74; Soc Stud Cncl Awd; Elected to Dayton-Montgomery Cty Acad Excl in Ed 1989; Elected by Acad of Excl to Serve on Selection Panel for Excl in Tchng Awds 1991-93; Serve on Excl in Tchng Awds Panel 1991-; Pub Article; Featured in Article; Serve on Kettering Fnd Rsrch Project 1991; All OH Stu Cncl Adv Awd 9 Yrs; St Judge of St of OH to Amer Legion St Oratorical Cntest 1995-; *office:* Walter E Stebbins HS 1900 Harshman Rd Dayton OH 45424

YOUNG, SANDRA M., Second Grade Teacher; *b:* Bryn Mawr, PA; *ed:* West Chester Univ (BS) Elem Ed 1968; Masters Equivalency + 60 Credits; *cr:* Valley Forge Elem Schl Primary & Mid Team Tchr 1968-73; Schweinfurt Amer Schl 3rd Grd Tchr 1973-75; Goose Bay Schl 1st Grd Tchr 1975-76; W Bradford Elem Schl 2nd Grd Tchr 1980-; *ai:* Lacrosse Coach 1969-73; TEEA-NEA 1968-73, Rep 2 Yrs; OEA-NEA 1973-76; DAEA-NEA 1980-, Rep 2 Yrs, Sec 2 Yrs; *office:* West Bradford Elem Schl 1475 Broad Run Rd Downingtown PA 19335

YOUNG, SCOTT A., Math Dept Chairperson, Teacher; *b:* Dennison, OH; *ed:* West Liberty St Coll (BA) Math 1986; Miami Univ at Oxford (MAT) Math 1990; Working on Prin Cert at Akron Univ; *cr:* indian Valley Math Tchr 1986-; *ai:* Head Boys Track; Var Ftbl, Var Wrestling Asst; Prin Advy Comm; Acad Standards for Ath; OCTN, NCTM, NEA 1986-; OTCCCA 1987-; *office:* Indian Valley HS PO Box 130 Gnadenhutten OH 44629

YOUNG, SHERRY, Professor of Law; *b:* Columbus, OH; *ed:* MI St Univ (BA) Soc Sci 1981; Harvard Law Schl (JD) 1984; *cr:* Porter Wright Morris & Arthur Attorney 1984-87; OH Northern Univ Prof 1987-; *ai:* Moot Court Adv, Legal Assn of Women; Acad Retention Prgm; American Bar Assn; OH St Bar Assn; Amer Inns of Court Wm Howard Taft Inn 1992-, Pres; ONU Street Law 1988-, Dir; *office:* OH Northern Univ 525 S Main St Ada OH 45810

YOUNG, SHONA S., Mathematics Teacher; *b:* Newark, NJ; *m:* Bernard; *c:* Benjamin, Judith Maisel; *ed:* Douglass Coll (BA) Math, Physics 1957; NSF Grant Ldrshp Prgm Rutgers Univ; 4 Woodrow Wilson Natl Fnd Flwshps; 6 Credit Hrs GATE Prgm Kean Coll; Attnd William Paterson Coll; *cr:* Fanwood HS Math Tchr 1957-58; Mc Manus Jr HS Math Tchr 1958-62; Hillside Ave Jr HS Math Tchr 1976-79; Orange Ave Jr HS Math Tchr 1976-79; Jewish Educl Ctr Math Tchr, Chr 1979-; *ai:* Assisted Stud Prgm Supvr; NCTM 1991-;; AMTNJ 1981-; NJ Math Coalition 1992-; Project Home 1992-; Hadassah, B'nai Brith 1968-; Tchng Eng to Immigrants 1992-93; NCTM, AMTNJ Math Confs Presenter; *office:* Jewish Educational Ctr 330 Elmora Ave Elizabeth NJ 07208

YOUNG, STEPHANIE G., Biology Teacher; *b:* New Brighton, PA; *ed:* Grove City Coll (BS) Bio, Scndry Ed 1993; Intermediate Unit Credit Hrs; *cr:* New Castle HS Bio Tchr 1994-; *ai:* Youth Alive Bible Club Spon; AFT 1994-; *office:* New Castle Sr HS 300 Lincoln Ave New Castle PA 16101

YOUNG, SUSAN FLEMING, Fourth Grade Teacher; *b:* Clearfield, PA; *m:* Robert E.; *c:* Ashley Laura; *ed:* PA St Univ (BS) Elem Ed 1971; *cr:* Clearfield Area Schl Dist Fourth Grd Tchr 1971-; *ai:* Prof Dev, In-Service Cncls; Lead Tchr Ctr Advy Bd; SAAD Adv; PSEA 1971-; PASCD 1989-; PSDC 1990-; *office:* Centre Elem Schl RD 4 Country Club Hills Clearfield PA 16830

YOUNG, SWAZETTE DICKASON, Social Studies Teacher; *b:* Washington, DC; *c:* William; *ed:* DC Tchrs Coll (BA) Spec Ed 1969; Federal City Coll (MA) Comm Psych 1975; Univ of Baltimore (JD) Law 1988; Beaver Coll Credit Hrs; *cr:* Detroit Pub Schls Tchr 1969-70; PG Cty Pub Schls Tchr 1970-; PG Comm Coll Adjunct Prof 1990-; *ai:* Mock Trial Spon & Coach; NCSS 1976-; ASCD 1993-; APA Assoc 1991-; Natl Sci Fnd Summer Inst for Tchrs of Psych 1992 & 1993; ETS Advanced Placement Psych Reader Reviewer-Psych & You; *home:* 513 Springloch Rd Silver Spring MD 20904*

YOUNG, VALERIE SECOR, English Teacher & Dept Chair; *b:* Roselle, NJ; *m:* James P.; *c:* Lawrence, Douglas; *ed:* Fairleigh Dickinson (BA) His, Eng 1960; Rutgers Univ (MED) 1968; Columbia Univ 12 Cr Hrs; Seton Hall Univ 6 Cr Hrs; Univ of DE 4 Cr Hrs; *cr:* Fairleigh Dickinson Univ Fellow, Tchr 1960-61; Maxson Jr HS Tchr 1961-63; Lakewood HS Tchr 1963-66; St Elizabeth HS Tchr, Dept Chair 1985-; *ai:* Lit Magazine, Sr Class Moderator; NEA 1961-; NCTE 1986-; DATE 1987-; AAUW, League of Women Voters 1982-; Kappa Delta Pi 1970; *office:* St Elizabeth HS 1500 Cedar St Wilmington DE 19805

YOUNG, WANDA KOCHERSPERGER, HS Sci Teacher & Dept Chair; *b:* Union City, IN; *m:* Larry K.; *c:* Joel S., Alissa C.; *ed:* Miami Univ (AB) Zoology 1969; Univ of Dayton (MS) Schl Cnslng 1983; 20 Semester Hrs; *cr:* Franklin-Monroe HS 8th-12th Sci Tchr 1970-78; Mississinawa Vly HS 10th-12th Grd Sci Tchr 1979-; *ai:* NHS, Envirothon Team & Sci Club Adv; Acad Team Coach; NEA, OEA & WOEA 1970-; MVCTA 1979-, Schlsp Chm, Tchr of Yr; SECO 1980-; BSA 1989-, Troop Comm; West Dist OH Acad of Sci Outstdng Sci Tchr 1974; Martha Holden Jennings Scholar 1974-75; Admins Awd 1975; *office:* Mississinawa Valley HS 1469 State Road 47 E Union City OH 45390

YOUNG, WILLIAM F., Band Dir & Music Theory Tchr; *b:* East Liverpool, OH; *m:* Molly Marie Wilds; *ed:* Youngstown St Univ (BA) Music Ed 1992; Course Work Towards Masters in Music Ed Kent St Univ; *cr:* Brown Local Schls Band Dir 1992-; *ai:* Marching, Jazz, Pep Bands; NEA, Malvern Ed Assn, OH Music Ed Assn 1992-; BSA 1984-, Camp Bus Mgr; Church Camp Bd Trustee 1993-; *office:* Malvern HS 401 W Main St Malvern OH 44644*

YOUNGE, DENISE, Kindergarten Teacher; *b:* Cameron, TX; *ed:* Dickinson Coll (BA) Eng Lit 1975; *cr:* Calvary Chrstn Schl Kndgtn Tchr 1975-81; All St Insurance Co Claims Rep 1981-85; Dawn Treader Chrstn Schl Kndgtn Tchr 1985-; *ai:* PTA Chaplain, Liaison; Read-A-Thon Prgm Coord; *home:* 65 Philip Pl Irvington NJ 07111

YOUNGER, ROBERT GEORGE, Biology & Health Teacher; *b:* Baltimore, MD; *m:* Ina Menicon; *c:* Ruth E. Cleveland, Christiana; *ed:* Towson St (BS) Ed & Bio 1966; Morgan St (MS) Ed & Sci 1973; Attnd UMBC, Western MD Coll, SUNY at Stonybrook; *cr:* Harlem Park Jr High Sci Tchr 1966-76; North Western Sr High Sci Tchr 1976-; Comm Coll of Baltimore Part-Time Instr & Lab Instr 1976-82; Ner Israel HS Part-Time Bio Tchr 1977-78; *ai:* Baltimore Tchrs Union 1869-79, VP Jr High, Sec & Treas; Fed of MD Tchrs 1974-79, Sec & Treas; Congregation Rosh Pina 1984-, Shamash & Home Group Ldr; NECO 1975-85; *office:* Northwestern Sr HS 401 6900 Park Heights Ave Baltimore MD 21215

YOUNGSTER, CAROL A., English Teacher & Adj Eng Prof; *b:* Kearny, NJ; *m:* Robert B.; *ed:* Montclair SU (BA) Eng 1973; Northeastern U (MA) Eng 1988; 9 Addl Credits; *cr:* Pt Pleasant HS Eng Tchr 1982-; *ai:* Writing Coord; NEA, NCTE 1982-; Northeastern Writing Advy Bd 1989-; ECA

Beach 1982-, Pres; *office:* Pt Pleasant HS Laura Herbert Dr Po Pleasant Bch NJ 08742

YOUNKER, ADAM B., Business Law Professor; *b:* Hazleton, PA; *m:* Sandra Zmiejko; *c:* Michelle Simmons, Gregory, Rachel Mihok, Melinda Kunkel; *ed:* Kings Coll (BS) Bus Admin 1964; Scranton Univ (MBA) Bus 1969; Addl 28 Hrs; *cr:* Bethlem Steel Corp Analyst, Sales Dept 1964-70; Broome Comm Coll Prof Bus Dept 1970-; *ai:* Departmental Standing Co Chm; Prof Evaluation Co-Chm of Comm; Entrepreneuship Comm Co-Chm; General Steering Group Rep Cncl; Moral Reasoning Sub-Comm; Extra Curr Sub-Comm of General Ed Steering Group; AFT, NEW 1970-; NE Acad of Legal Stud in Bus 1977, Natl Bus Law Assoc 1977-; Southern Tier Bee Assoc 1986-, 4th Team Bd of Dir; German club 1991-; *office:* Broome Community College PO Box 1017 Binghamton NY 13902*

YOUNKER, NANCY BIVENS, Fifth Grade Teacher; *b:* Chambersburg, PA; *m:* Carl T.; *c:* Susan Younker, Carri Lynne; *ed:* Shippensburg Univ (BS) Elem Ed 1969, (MS) Elem Ed 1974; 30 Hrs After MA in General Elem Ed; *cr:* McConnellsburg Elem Elem Tchr 1969-; *ai:* Supt Advy Comm; PSEA & NEA 1969-; ASDC 1991-; Beta Sigma Phi 1972-, Pres, Exec Office & Sec; Fulton Cty Med Ctr 1993-, Dir; Hancock Presbyn Church 1988-, Clerk & Elder; *office:* McConnellsburg Elem Schl 151 E Cherry St Mc Connellsburg PA 17233

YOUNKINS, JAMES E., Mathematics Teacher & Chm; *b:* Freeport, PA; *m:* Debra J. Pile; *ed:* Clarion St Coll (BS) Math 1970; Post Grad Courses George Washington univ; *cr:* U S Navy TD-3 1970-74; Chopticon HS Math Tchr 1974-; *ai:* NHS & Math Competition Co-Spon; Golf Coach; Hall of Fame Selection Comm; NEA, MSTA & EASMC 1974-; Hollywood Optimist Club 1985-, Bd of Dirs, Educator of Yr 1988; *office:* Chopticon HS Rt 242 Morganza MD 20660

YOUNT, CLAIR L., Social Studies Teacher; *b:* DuBois, PA; *m:* Gale; *c:* Jeffrey; *ed:* Edinboro Univ (BS) Comprehensive Soc Stud 1969; Post Grad 30 Credit Hrs Bowling Green Univ Soc Stud, Ath Mgr; *cr:* Lakota HS Soc Stud Tchr 1969-; *ai:* Head Golf Coach; Voter, Selective Svc; Soc Stud Chair; Action Team Chair; Stu of Month Comm; NEA, Ohio EA 1969-; EA 1969-, Mbrshp Chair, Friends of ED; Phi Sigma Kappa 1968-, Historian; Presbyn Bd 1988-; Lakota Levy Cntrl Comm 1991-; Coach of Yr in Wrestling; Pinewood Derby Excl Awd; Spec Svc Awd; Cty Ed Dedicated Tchr Awd; Friends of Ed Awd; *office:* Lakota HS 5186 County Road 13 Kansas OH 44841*

YOUNT, GALE E., English Teacher; *b:* Pittsburgh, PA; *m:* Clair L.; *c:* Jeffrey J.; *ed:* Bowling Green St Univ (BS) Elem Ed 1982; 30 Hrs Post Grad Credits from Coll of Mount Saint Joseph, BGSU, Univ of Findlay, Ashland Univ, Drake Univ; Scndry Cert 1990; *cr:* Bettsville Bd of Ed 4th-6th Grd Eng & Rdng Tchr 1985-86; New Riegel HS 7th-10th & 12th Grd Eng Tchr 1988-; *ai:* Jr Class Adv; Golf Coach; Tech Comm; Conflict Mgmt Team; New HS Tchrs Mentor Tchr; NREA, OCTELA 1988-; NEA 1985-; First Presbyn Church 1989-, Deacon, Pres of Deacons; Meml Bell Choir 1989-; Tiffin Panhellenic 1985-, Pres 1 Yr, Sec & Treas 2 Yrs; Fostoria Comm Band 1995-; Pub The Write Stuff Style Manual for Stdnts at New Riegel 1989; *office:* New Riegel HS 44 N Perry St New Riegel OH 44853*

YOURISH, KENNETH PAUL, Social Studies Teacher; *b:* Latrobe, PA; *ed:* Grove City Coll (BA) Pol Sci 1971; IN Univ of PA (MED) His 1987; *cr:* Seneca Vly HS Tchr, Coach 1971-74; Greensburg Cntrl Cath HS Tchr, Coach, Ath Dir 1974-89; Derry Area HS Tchr, Coach 1989-; *ai:* PSEA, NEA 1989-; Westmoreland Cty Spec olympic Advy Bd 1989-; *home:* 4 Meadow Dr Latrobe PA 15650

YOUSE, RUTH E., 9th-12th Grade German Teacher; *b:* Reading, PA; *m:* Jay L.; *ed:* Albright Coll (BA) Ger & Span 1962; Middlebury Coll (MA) Ger 1967; *cr:* Kutztown Area Schl Dist Ger & Span Tchr 1962-; *ai:* PSEA 1962-; NEA 1962-; Church Organist & Choir Dir; *office:* Kutztown Area Schl Dist Trexler Ave Kutztown PA 19530

YOUSSEF, NADINE SHALABY, Math Teacher; *b:* Cairo, Egypt; *m:* John; *c:* Sandra J.; *ed:* Ainshams Univ (BA) Physics, Math 1965-70, (MS) Math 1971, (MA) Admin 1995; Jersey City St Coll Tchr Ed 1977, Rdng Process & Product Content; 6 Credits Hudson Comm Coll 1990; 6 Credits Stevens Inst of Tech 1991; 3 Credit Hrs Schl Law, Problems in Admin at St Peter Coll, working toward masters in Admin; *cr:* Ainshams Univ Adjunct Math 1969-70; Lycee Francais Sci & Math Tchr 1970-71; Diamondche Co Accounts Payable & Receivable 1971-79; St Mary 3rd & 5th Grd Tchr 1979-86; Holy Family Acad Math Summer Schl 1987-88; Marist HS Fr & MathTchr 1986-95; Long Branch HS Math Tchr 1995-; *ai:* Tutor Huntington Learning Center 1991-; Moderator Lang & Fr Honor Society Clubs; Organizing Trips to Europe & Egypt 1988-; ASCD 1988-; Awded Summer Cert of Achvmt Stevens Inst of Tech; Nom Outstanding Math Tchr for Tandy Tech Scholars Awd; *office:* Long Branch HS 391 Westwood Ave Long Branch NJ 07740

YOVICH, JAMES ELI, 5th Grd Math, Sci & Rdng Tchr; *b:* Union City, PA; *m:* Suzann L. Shield; *ed:* Edinboro Univ of PA (BS) Elem Ed 1976, (MEd) Schl Admin 1981; *cr:* Corry Area Schl Dist Tchr 1976-; *ai:* Var HS Bsbl & Elem Bsktbl Coach; Math, Cmptr, Liason, Sterring & Act 178 Comms; Mentor Tchr Prgm; PSEA & NEA 1976-; CAEA 1976-, Treas & VP; AMTONP 1991-; Sugar Grove Lib Bd 1985-, Treas; Sugar Grove Gas Pipeline Assn 1977-, Pres; *office:* Conelway Schl 18700 Conelway Rd Corry PA 16407*

YOVICH, SUZANN SHIELD, Second Grade Teacher; *b:* Warren, PA; *m:* James E.; *ed:* Murray St Univ (BS) Elem Ed 1971; Masters Equivalency; Child & Adult CPR, Hlth & First Aid Certs; *cr:* Russell Elem Schl 4th Grd Tchr 1971-76, 2nd Grd Tchr 1976-78, 3rd Grd Tchr 1978-79, 2nd Grd Tchr 1979-; *ai:* Started 2nd Grd Penpals Ftbl Booster Prog with Local HS Ftbl Team; Mentor Tchr; Jamestown Comm Coll Teen & Kids Coll Bd; Eisenhower HS Educl Fund Bd; Started Performing Puppet Grp With Church Youth; Warren Cty Ed Assn, PA St Ed Assn & NEA 1971-; Delta Delta Kappa Gamma 1985-, Sec 1988-90; Spec Olympics Vol; Sugar Grove Rdng Club 1979-, VP 4 Yrs; Adopt-a-Hwy Prgm Vol; Church, Worship Chprsn, Parsonage Club Sec; Credit Union Bd of Dirs; Russell PTA 1971-; Warren Concert Series Bd of Dirs; Runner-Up for 1st Annual Albert Loranger Outstanding Tchr Awd for Warren Cty; Albert Loranger Outstanding Tchr Awd 1992; Time Warner Cable Cert of Achievement; Natl Tchr Awds Honorable Mention 1993-94; *office:* Russell Elem Schl RD 1A Box 1032 Russell PA 16345*

YOWELL, TIMOTHY O., Instrumental Music Teacher; *b:* Detroit, MI; *m:* Laurel Ann Whitaker; *c:* Bethany; *ed:* Kent St Univ (BA) Music Ed 1970; Attnd Bowling Green Univ, OH St Univ, Mt St Joseph, Akron Univ, Cleveland St; *cr:* Mentor Pub Schls Elem Band Dir 1970-, HS Band Dir 1974-85, Jr HS BAnd Dir 1985-; *ai:* OH Music Ed Adjudicator; Pep, Jazz Band; Summer Band Prgm Dir; Jazz Improvisation Tchr; Private Tutor; Team 1000 Mem; Clothe-a-Child Concert Coord; Lake Cty Music Ed Assn 1970-; Intnl Assn Jazz Ed 1974-; OH Music Ed Assn 1970-, Mem of Spec Ed, Music Comm; Music Ed Natl, MTH 1970-; MTA, Mt Carmel 1975-, Music Dir; Yth for Christ 1990-, Adv; St Andrew Episcopal 1982-, Music Minister; Excl in Tchng Awd; Tchr of Yr; Tchng Music Spec Ed Classes; Perform Local Churches; Cited for Excl Jazz Ed IAJE Magazine; Music Groups Performed at Natl Level; *office:* Mentor Memorial Jr HS 8979 Mentor Ave Mentor OH 44060*

YU, ALBERT P., Chemistry Professor; *b:* Shanghai, China; *m:* Beverly Chen; *c:* Irene, David; *ed:* Natl Taiwan Univ (BA) Chem 1959; Natl Tsing Hua Univ (MS) Nuclear Sci 1961; Rice Univ (PHD) Chem 1967; *cr:* Amoco Corp Rsrch Scientist 1967-77; Union Chemical Laboratories VP, Dir 1978-85; Chinese Petroleum Co VP 1985-87; PPG Industries Pres Taiwan Chlorine Operations 1987-91; Massachusetts Bay Comm Coll Assoc Prof 1992-; *ai:* Energy Comm, Chinese Bible Church of Greater Boston Young Profs Adv; Amer Chemical Soc 1970-; Chinese Engineering Soc 1979-, Pres Local Chptr, Outstdng Mgr; Rotary Club 1984-, Local Chptr Sec; 2 Issued Patents; *office:* MA Bay Comm Coll 50 Oakland St Wellesley MA 02181

YUHAS, SHERRI LEE-LEHMER, Varsity Cheerleading Coach; *b:* Newton, NJ; *m:* Robert Michael; *c:* LaKyn Brielle; *ed:* Sussex Cty Comm Coll (AA) Lbrl Arts 1993; East Stroudsburg Univ, Ed; *cr:* YWCA Head Tchr 1990-92; Sparta Parks, Recreation Arts, Crafts Dir 1992-94; Bright Horizons Child Care Infant Tchr 1994-95; Newton HS Var Chrldng Coach, Sub Tchr 1993-; *ai:* Head Var Ftbl, Bsktbl Chrldng Coach; UCA Safety Clinics 1992-, Cert 1993-95; WCA 1992-; Shawnee Presbyn Choir 1995-; NJAL Coach of Yr 1991; Universal Chrldng Assn Ldrshp Awd 1993-94, Camp Championships 1993-95; *office:* Newton HS 44 Ryerson Ave Newton NJ 07860*

YUNINGER, DIANNE M., English Teacher; *b:* Lancaster, PA; *m:* Harold R.; *c:* David H., Todd A., Jenny E.; *ed:* Millersville Univ (BS) Eng Ed 1967, (MED) GATE 1988; Post Master's Credits Desktop Publishing; PA Assessment West Chester Univ; GATE Univ of CT; Rdng Specialist 1986; *cr:* Solanco HS Eng Tchr 1967-69; Garden Spot HS Eng Tchr 1983-84; Pequea Vly HS Eng Tchr 1984-, Coord of GATE 1988-; *ai:* Newspaper, Yrbk Adv; Co-Chair HS Restructuring, Dist Strategic Planning, Dist Assessment Comms; New Tchr Mentor; Peer Coach; NEA, PSEA, PVEA, NCTE 1984-; Phi Delta Kappa 1992-; Leacock Pres Church 1961-, Elder, Clerk of Session; *home:* 12 Ocola Dr Paradise PA 17562

YUN JEONG, MARK, Mathematics Teacher; *b:* Seoul, South Korea; *ed:* Bowdoin Coll (AB) Math & Ec 1992; Emergency Med Technician; *cr:* Park City Ski Patrol Ski Patrolman 1992-93; Brewster Acad Math Tchr 1993-94; Middlesex Schl Math Tchr 1994-; *ai:* JV Girls Squash & Var Boys Tennis Coach; Diversity Comm; Concord Prison Vol 1996, GED Tutor; Natl Ski Patrol Aware 1993; *office:* Middlesex Schl 1400 Lowell Rd Concord MA 01742

YURATOVICH, AMALIA MARIE, English & Spanish Teacher; *b:* Brownsville, PA; *m:* Thomas A.; *c:* Thomas S., James P.; *ed:* CA Univ of PA (BS) Scndry Span 1970, (BS) Scndry Eng 1988; Univ of Saltillo Mexico 9 Credit Hrs; *cr:* Brownsville Cath Schl Span, Eng Tchr 1980-85; Bethlehem-Center Schl Dist Span, Eng Tchr 1992-; *ai:* Drama Club Spon 1992-94; NEA, PSEA 1992-; NCTE 1988-; *home:* 349 Ridge Rd Brownsville PA 15417

YURFICK, JOYCE SZEDNY, Instruction Support Teacher; *b:* Sewickley, PA; *m:* Joseph G.; *c:* Pamala Yurfick Learn, Rachel Yurfick Bergandy; *ed:* Youngstown St Univ (BS) Ed 1969; Duquesne Univ MS Elem Admin Presently Completing; Natl Curr Stud Inst of ASCD Textbook Adoption Cert; PA Dept of Ed Cert for Instrl Support Trng; *cr:* St Veronica Cath Schl Elem Tchr 1966-67; Baden Economy Schl Dist Elem Tchr 1967-68; Ambridge Area Schl Dist Elem Tchr 1968-, IST 1993-; Shift Enterprises Merchandising Asst Mgr 1991; YMCA Pre-School Asst Dir; *ai:* Class Alumni Reunions Chprsn; Safety Comm Founders; Ambridge Area Site Base Organizer; Meml Day Coord; IST Tutoring Pgm; BEEA 1966-, House of Rep; PSEA 1966-, ADEA Rep Del; AAEA 1967-, Pres, VP, Pres Awd; NEA 1968-, Dist Rep Del; PTO & PTA 1968-, VP & Soc Chprsn; ASCD; Big Brothers & Big Sisters; Duquesne Univ Guest Speaker & Presentation of IST Pgm; CA Univ of PA Coordinated IST Presentation Overview; Wendys Cert of Achvmt; Rdng Series Article Pub; Amer Family Inst at Vly Forge Gift of Time Tribute Awd; Recognition of Achvmt for Developing & Coordinating Curr; Fox 53 Television Stud, Class & Tchrs Featured Ridge Rd Schl 1993; *office:* Anthony Wayne Elem Schl 2001 Lenz Ave Ambridge PA 15003*

YURKEWICZ, WILLIAM, Physics Teacher; *b:* Amsterdam, NY; *m:* Diane Valerio; *c:* Susan, Michael; *ed:* Union Coll (BS) Physics 1964; SUNY at Albany (MS) Curr & Instruction 1972, (Ed D) Ed & Cognitive Dev 1988; Specialist Cert in Curr & Instruction from SUNY at Albany 1987; *cr:* South Glens Falls Sr HS Physics & Psych Tchr 1964-; Skidmore Coll Lecturer in Physics 1978-; Consultant in Physics 1988-; Sci Dept Chprsn; *ai:* Restructuring Comm; AAPT 1985-; Sci Tchrs Assn of NY St 1964-; NSTA 1985-; NY St United Tchrs 1964-; South Glens Falls Faculty Assn 1964-, Bldg Rep 1977-; Book Pub A Guide Book for Tchng Physics 1985; Sci Tchrs Assn of NY Awd: Excl in Sci Tchng 1986; Outstanding Doctoral Dissertation Pres Awd SUNY at Albany 1988; *office:* South Glens Falls Sr HS Merritt Rd South Glens Falls NY 12803

YURKY, CHRISTINE BEWLEY, Social Studies Teacher; *b:* Erie, PA; *m:* Michael J.; *c:* Matthew, Elizabeth, Jennifer, Patrick; *ed:* Indiana Univ of PA(BSED) Scndry Soc Sci Ed 1987; Grad Stud; *cr:* IN Area Schl Dist Sub Tchr 1987-92; Homer-Ctr Schl Dist Jr HS Soc Stud Tchr 1992-; *ai:* Yth, Govt Adv; Spon Jr HS Natl Honor Soc, Class 2000; START Comm; SAAC; HEROES Comm; NEA, PSEA, HCEA 1992-; PTA 1993-, Treas 2 Yrs; Alpha Xi Delta 1984-, Chptr Adv 6 yrs, IUP Outstdng Adv Awd; BSA 1993-, Den Ldr, Treas; *office:* Homer Ctr Jr Sr HS 20 Wildcat Ln Homer City PA 15748

YUSCHAK, GLORIA, School Counselor; *b:* Charleroi, PA; *ed:* CA Univ of PA (BS) Fr, Sec Ed 1966; Univ of Pittsburgh (MED) Fr, Ed 1969; WV Univ (MA) Cnslr Ed 1981; *cr:* Charleroi Jr Sr HS Fr Tchr 1966-67; Belle Vernon Area HS Fr Tchr 1967-89, Cnslr 1989-; *ai:* NEA, PSEA 1968-; Belle Vernon Area Ed Assn 1968-, Pres 1988-91, 1994-; Westmoreland Cty Cnslrs Assn 1989-; PA St Cnslrs Assn 1994-; PA St Ed Assn Svc Awd; *office:* Belle Vernon Area HS Rd #2 Crest Ave Belle Vernon PA 15012

YUSEM, DEBBI ELLEN, Special Education Teacher; *b:* Havertown, PA; *ed:* The George Washington Univ (BA) Spec Ed 1988; St Joseph's Univ (MS) Rdng Specialist 1992; *cr:* Lynnewood Elem Schl Primary Learning Support, Spec Ed Tchr 1988-; *ai:* Publicity Comm 1993-; Rdng Incentive Comm 1993-95; Haverford HS Ath Advy Cncl 1994-95, Chrldng Coach 1989-; PSEA, NEA 1989-; Haverford HS Alumni Grant 1994; *office:* Lynnewood Elem Schl 1400 Lawrence Rd Havertown PA 19083*

YUSIM, MARAT, Drama Teacher; *b:* Kiev, USSR; *m:* Heather Alice Golden; *ed:* Kiev St Conservation of the Performing Arts (BA) His 1965, (PHD) Stage Directing, Producing 1974; Moscow Art Theatre, Theatre on Taganka Residency Stage Directing; *cr:* USSR Theatres & Schls Dir, Actor, Tchr 1965-76; Sonia Moore Studio of NY Drama Tchr 1977-78; Hollywood Actor 1979; Moscow Dirs Theatre of NY Artistic Dir, Producer 1980-84; La Guardia HS of the Arts Drama Tchr 1982-; *ai:* Spring Drama Festival Dir; Films, TV Productions Actor; UFT, NYSUT 1982-; NY Screen Actors Guild of Amer 1979-; Ukrainian Drama Competition 1st Prize Best Stage Directing 1975; White House Commission Presidential Scholars Distngd Tchr 1990; Natl Fnd for Advancement in Arts Distngd Tchr in Arts 1992; *office:* La Guardia HS of the Arts 100 Amsterdam Ave New York NY 10023*

YUSPA, ELEANOR HECHT, HS Photography Teacher; *b:* Baltimore, MD; *m:* Stuart H.; *c:* Catharine M., Margaret E.; *ed:* Towson St Univ (BA) Art 1965; Univ of MD (MED) Art Ed 1969; *cr:* Montgomery Cty Pub Schls HS Photography Tchr 1985-.

YUX, JUDITH ANN, Tchr of Learning Disabilities; *b:* Dayton, OH; *ed:* Univ of Dayton (BS) Home Ec 1971, (MS) Educl Ldrshp 1991; LD & BD Cert at Wright St Univ 1987; *cr:* Aguinas Coll Home Ec Tchr 197 Beavertown Elem LD Tutor 1975-87; Fairmont HS LD Tchr 1987-; *ai* Against Deadly Decisions Adv; Peer Mentor; Post Polio Support G Facilitator; VFW Womens Auxillary 1980-, Soloist; Amer Le Auxillary 1980-; *office:* Kettering Fairmont HS 3301 Shroyer Rd Kett OH 45429

Z

ZABIELSKI, JOSEPH STEVEN, Acting Principal; *b:* Westfield, MA Jane Eleanor Frawley; *c:* Joseph, Edward; *ed:* Westfield St (BA) Soc & His 1968, (MA) Admin 1994; 15 Credits Univ of MA; 6 Credits Bo Univ; 12 Credits Westfield St; *cr:* Agawan HS Soc Stud Tchr 196 Prin, Asst Prin & Deputy Prin 1995-; *ai:* Stu Govt Adv; Acad of Exch Partnership & Time & Learning Comms; Ski & Tennis Team Co Summer Inst Team; NEA 1968-; MTA 1968-; MSSPA 1995-; Agaw Lions 1990-, Exec Bd, Speech Contest Chm; Westfield Little Le 1991-, Coach & Umpire; Westfield Youth Soccer 1991-, Coach; Phi Kappa; Young Edctr of Yr; *office:* Agawam HS 760 Cooper St Agawam 01001

ZACCAGNA, MARJORIE CENSULLO, English Teacher; Weehawken, NJ; *m:* Richard G. Sr.; *c:* Richard Jr., Matthew; *ed:* Misericordia (BA) Eng 1965; NY Univ (MA) Theater Arts 1968; Bilin Cert Jersey City St; *cr:* Emerson HS Tchr 1965-; *ai:* Fac Cncl; SAT Co NEA, UCEA 1965-; NCTE 1970-; *office:* Emerson HS 318 18th St U City NJ 07087*

ZACCARI, JUDITH MC FARLAND, Fourth Grade Teacher; *b:* Be Falls, PA; *m:* Michael J. Jr.; *ed:* Edinboro Univ (BS) Elem Ed 1 Slippery Univ (MS) Math 1974; *cr:* Hopewell Elem Schl Grd 4 Tchr 19 *ai:* Act 178; Staff Dev Comm; TESA Trainer; Grd 4 Dept Chm 25 Strategic Planning Action Team; New Tchr Induction Comm Mentor T NEA, PSEA, HEA 1968-; PTA 1968-; Natl Humane Sco; Beaver City Soc; Environmental Def League; *home:* 2308 Woodbine Rd Aliquipp 15001

ZACHARKO, DAVID M., Spanish & French Teacher; *b:* Baltimore, *ed:* Towson St Univ (BA) Span, Fr 1977; 40 Addl Credit Hrs; *cr:* Dun HS Span, Fr Tchr 1977-81; Holabird Jr HS Span, Fr Tchr 1981 Parkville HS Span, Fr Tchr 1983-85; Hereford HS Span, Fr Tchr 1985- Grad, Schl Fund-Raising Comms Co-Chm; Acad Team Coach; AA 1994-; NEA, MSTA, TABCO 1977-; *office:* Hereford HS 17301 York Parkton MD 21120

ZACHARY, CLARIE DEAL, High School Theatre Tchr & Dir Brunswick, GA; *m:* Samuel J.; *ed:* Mercer Univ (BA) Theatre, Psych 1 Furman Univ (MA) Eng, Ed 1985; Univ of NC at Greensboro (M Directing 1990; *cr:* Northern HS Theatre Tchr, Dir 1985-89; Univ of at Greensboro Lecturer, Head of Comm Ed 1990-91; Mc Auley HS The Tchr, Dir 1992-; *ai:* Dir Plays, Musical; Drama Club Adv; Educl The Assn 1995-, Bd Mem.

ZACHARY, NICHOLAS, Math Teacher; *b:* New York, NY; *m:* Carole Carroll; *c:* Michael, Nicole; *ed:* Northeastern Univ (BA) Sociology 1 Harvard Univ (MAT) Scndry Ed 1972; *cr:* Picnic Point HS Math T 1973-74; Nature's Classroom Math, Environmental Ed Tchr 1974 Wooster Schl Math, Sci Tchr 1977-84; Bellows Falls Union HS Math T 1984-; *ai:* Math Team Coach; NEA 1984-, Negotiator; *office:* Bellows F Union HS Rt 5 S Bellows Falls VT 05101

ZACHER, MARY ELLEN MORGAN, First Grade Teacher; *b:* Cort NY; *m:* William F.; *c:* Catherine A., Christine M.; *ed:* St Univ of N Cortland (BS) Elem Ed 1965; Attnd Brockport St, Geneseo St; *cr:* Gr Cntrl Schls Third Grd Tchr 1965-68; Friendship Cntrl Schl First, Th Kndgtn Tchr 1968-; *ai:* Timer for All Bsktbl Games; Chm St Mathathon; NEA 1965-; NYSUT 1965-, Sec; Amer Legion Auxillary 1168 1968-, Pres; Sacred Heart Parish Cncl 1989-, Sec; *office:* Friend Central Schl 46 W Main St Friendship NY 14739*

ZACHER, WILLIAM FREDERICK, Associate Professor; *b:* Hinsd NY; *m:* Mary Ellen Morgan; *c:* Catherine, Christine; *ed:* SUNY at Al (AOS) Electrical & Electronics 1973; SUNY at Oswego 9 Credit SUNY at Utica & Rome 11 Credit Hrs; Fredonia St Coll 3 Credit Hrs; A Inst for Prof Ed 2 CEUs; *cr:* Guernsey Products Electronic Comm 1962 Friendship Cntrl Schl Electronics Technician AV-ETV 1966 Cattaraugus BOCES Electronics Technician 1972-81; Friendship Vid Cable TV Maintenance 1970-81; SUNY Assoc Prof 1977-; *ai:* Schl Dev & Review Comm Chair; Dept Course Consolidation Comm; Elect & Electronics Curr Coord 1994-; UUP 1970-; Instrument Soc of A 1985-90, 1995-; Amer Legion 1972-, Bd of Dirs 1991-94 & Schlsp Co 1972; US Navy 1962-66; Participated in ITCA Project for El Salva 1985; Dept Chair 1985-94; *office:* SUNY Coll Of Technology S Brook Ave Wellsville NY 14895

ZACHMANN, KENNETH DWIGHT, Science Department Head; *b:* C Ridge, NJ; *m:* Dorothy Ann Rorabaugh; *c:* Amanda, Nathan; *ed:* Uni MD (BS) Zoology 1972, (MS) Biochemistry 1976; 20 Credit Hrs; *cr:* N Carroll High Chem Tchr 1976-77; Hammond High Dept Head 1977-; Var Girls Soccer & SAC Club Soccer Coach; Class 96 Spon; S Improvement Team; NEA 1977-; NSTA 1992-; *office:* Hammond HS 8 Guilford Rd Columbia MD 21046*

ZACHRY, SHIRLEY MC CLANAHAN, ESOL Teacher; *b:* Memp TN; *m:* John; *c:* Margaret Elizabeth, Wm. Drew; *ed:* Southwester Memphis (BA) Ger 1969; Attnd GA St Univ, Univ of MD at Baltimore *cr:* Avondale HS Eng, Ger Tchr 1969-72; Clarksdale HS German T 1969-72; J. B. Brown MS Eng, Ger Tchr 1972-74; Girls Prep Schl L Tchr 1981-82; Prince George's Co Pub Schls ESOL Tchr 1983-; *ai:* Pri George's Co Ed Assn 1983-; Landover Chrstn Church 1982-, Chrstn Dept Chair, Elder; *office:* William Wirt MS 62nd Ave & Tuckerma Riverdale MD 20737*

ZACK, DANIEL F., Social Studies Teacher; *b:* Uniontown, PA; Marjorie A. Doman; *c:* Brittney Anne; *ed:* California Univ of PA (BA) 1972; PA St Univ 1967-71; 17 Hrs Towards Masters 1975; *cr:* Lafayett HS 7th & 8th Grd Soc Stud Tchr 1972-77; A J McMullen Jr HS 7th & Grd Soc Stud Tchr 1977-81; Uniontown HS 10th & 12th Grd Soc Stud T 1981-89; A J McMullen MS 7th-8th Grd Soc Stud Tchr 1989-.

ZAEDER, J. PHILIP, Instructor in English; *b:* Erie, PA; *m:* Sylvia Thayer; *c:* John P., Alison L., S.; *ed:* Yale Univ (BA) Eng 1958, (MD Theology 1962; Univ of NH Grad Stud in Eng; *cr:* Taft Schl Chaplain,

1960-69; Yale Univ Assoc Univ Chaplain 1969-77; Phillips Acad stant Chaplain, Eng Tchr 1977-95, Dean of Fac 1995-; *ai:* Jazz t; Stone-Wall Builder NH Farm Museum Demonstrations 1987-95; ıt Hall at Yale 1954-, Bd Chm 1969-89; United Presbyn Church ; Oxfam Amer 1979-, Schl Organizer; Mailliard Tchng Awd 1968; el Harvey Taylor Fnd Awd 1983; *office:* Phillips Acad S. Main St ver MA 01810

'UTS, GERALD, Director of Bands; *ed:* Crane Schl of Music (BM) 75; Univ of Northern CO (MM) Performance 1976; Post Grad Stud niv; *cr:* Freelance Performer Trombonist 1973-; Skidmore Coll ore Jazz Inst Dir 1981-; Bennington Coll Brass Instruments Instr 95; Averill Park Cntrl Schls Bands Dir 1992-; *ai:* AFofM 1973-; ITA ; NYSSMA 1992-; *office:* Averill Park HS 146 Gettle Rd Averill Park 2018

ARINS, JURIS, Professor & Dept Chairman; *b:* Riga, Latvia; *m:* Varnum; *c:* Marija, Sofija; *ed:* Tufts Univ (BSME) Mech Engng MIT (Mat Eng) Materials Sci 1983; *cr:* US Peace Corp fghanistan 1970-73; STCC Prof 1975-; *ai:* Tchr in Boston Latvian ASEE; *office:* Springfield Tech Comm Coll 1 Armory Sq Springfield 1105

ATTA, ROSANNE MANDARA, Social Studies Teacher; *b:* Paterson, : George; *c:* Elizabeth, George V., Rebecca; *ed:* Montclair St Univ Soc Stud 1973, (MA) Amer His 1976; Attnd Woodrow Wilson Inst; ssaic Evening HS His Tchr 1974-78; Paterson News Ed Dir 1974-78; orne HS His Tchr 1987-89; Lincoln MS 6-8 Grd Soc Stud Tchr ; *ai:* Ecology Club Adv; Affirmative Action Comm, Ofcr; GATE ı; HTA, NJEA, NEA 1987-; Second Reformed Church 1982-, Elder, n, VBS Dir; Governor's Recognition Awd Tchr of Yr 1992; *office:* ln MS Hawthorne Ave Hawthorne NJ 07506

ER, BETTY, English Teacher; *b:* Akron, OH; *ed:* Univ of Akron (BA) 966; Univ of Cincinnati (MA) Comm 1975; *cr:* Spicer Demonstration Tchr 1966-68; Roswell Kent Jr HS Tchr 1968-74; Central-Hower HS 1975-, Eng Dept Chprsn 1993-95; *ai:* Originated 9th Graders Sr oring Prgm; Future Edctrs of Amer Adv; Akron Ed Assn 1966-; Univ ron Comm Ambassador to Italy; Tchr of Yr 1995; Akron Pub Schls on Tchr of Yr 1995; *office:* Central Hower HS 123 S Forge St Akron 4308

KA, WILLIAM JOSEPH, Professor of Economics; *b:* Boston, MA; vian Karsa; *c:* Tina Michel, Carrie; *ed:* Boston Coll (BA) Ec 1950; n Univ (MA) Ec 1951; Univ of PA (MA) Ec 1966; PHD Candidate in yn Mawr Coll 1966-72 ABD; *cr:* USAF Manpower Mgmt Analyst 55; Wm Filenes Sons Asst Buyer 1955-59; Widener Univ Prof of Ec ; *ai:* Alpha Chi Honor Soc Adv; Rank, Tenure & Promotion Comm; Ecs Laureate Comm; Honors Cncl; Civil Svc Commission, Chm Home & Schl Assn, Pres 1975 & 1976; Sales & Mrktg Execs of ban Philadelphia, 1974 & 1975, Pres; Atlantic Ec Soc 1973-, Area ; Alpha Chi Region VI 1973-, Pres 1988-90 & 1994-, VP 1992-94; 5 Recipient Widener Univ Schl of Mgmt Distinguished Prof Awd; Idea Contest Winner; Ec & Mgmt Consulting; Numerous Articles & Reviews Pub; *office:* Widener Univ 1 University Pl Chester PA *

NER, KIMBERLY ANN (PRYOR), Seventh Grade Teacher; *b:* , OH; *m:* Kenneth; *c:* Matthew, Adam; *ed:* OH St Univ (BS) Ed 1983; Mary's Schl Kndgtn Tchr 1985, 6th Grd Tchr 1986-89, 7th Grd Tchr ; *ai:* Yrbk Adv; Schls Ath Bd Mem; *office:* Saint Marys Schl 75 S sky St Tiffin OH 44883

ORA, WENDY STRAW, Special Education Collaborator; *b:* Lykens, : Kenneth R.; *c:* Joseph, James, Jade; *ed:* Mansfield Univ (BS) Spec 74; Penn St Univ (BS) Rdng 1980; Marywood Coll (MS) Spec Ed *cr:* Intermediate Unit 11 Tchr of Mentally Disabled 1974-78; Juniata Dist Rdng Tchr 1978-80; WY Conf Childrens Home Tchr of onally Disturbed 1985-87; Johnson City Schl Dist Tchr of Learning led 1987-; *ai:* NEA, NYEA 1987-; Girl Scouts of Amer 1991-, Ldr; 1985-, Merit Badge Cnslr; Grange 1985-; Church 1980-; *office:* on City HS 666 Reynolds Rd Johnson City NY 13790

ORAN, JOHN MICHAEL, English Teacher; *b:* Johnstown, PA; *m:* la Langietti; *c:* Danielle Maria, Michol Anna, Jesse David; *ed:* n St Coll (BS) Eng 1970, (MA) Eng 1980; Attnd Indiana Univ of PA st MA Credits Amer Lit; *cr:* Clarion-Limestone HS Eng Tchr 1970-; Clarion-Limestone Area HS RD 1 Strattanville PA 16258

URANIC, DEBRA LOUISE, Business Education Teacher; *b:* be, PA; *ed:* IN Univ of PA (BS) Bus Ed 1991, (MED) Bus Ed 1994; edar Crest HS Bus Tchr 1992; Hempfield Area HS Bus Tchr 1993; Area HS Bus Tchr 1993-; *ai:* Soph Class, Interact Adv; Coach Girls HS JV, MS Head; PSEA 1993-; Alpha PI Omega 1994-; *office:* Derry HS Rd 1 Box 169 Derry PA 15627

URANIC, MARY LOUISE KORZAK, Business Education Teacher; trobe, PA; *m:* Robert S.; *c:* Debra, Michael; *ed:* Shippensburg Univ Ed 1963; Attnd Indiana Univ of PA 23 Grad Credits & Saint Vincent 3 Credits; *cr:* Greater Labrobe Sr HS Bus Ed Tchr 1963-68 & 1977-; etterman's Club Adv; PBEA & NEA; *office:* Greater Latrobe Sr HS try Club Rd Latrobe PA 15650

, LATIFAH, Global Studies & Science Tchr; *b:* Brooklyn, NY; *ed:* Coll (BA) Sociology & Intnl Stud 1989; Hunter Coll (MA) Ed 1996; TV Researcher 1987; Dept of Employment Field Supvr 1988; Berlitz as Second Lang Tchr 1990-91; Cncl on Intnl Ed Exch Admin Asst -91; Bridge Schl Tchr 1991-; *ai:* 9th Grd Grad Coord; Conflict ution Trainer; After Schl Rdng Prgm; Accelerated Schl Curr Dev n; *home:* 135 6th Ave Brooklyn NY 11217*

AC, ELISE TANNER, Second Grade Teacher; *b:* Chestertown, MD; ichael Peter; *c:* Michael Peter, Ashley-Anne; *ed:* Cheseapeake Coll 1973; Univ of MD (BA) Elem Ed 1975; Attnd Loyola Coll; *cr:* eville Elem Schl 2nd Grd Tchr 1977-82; Kent Island Elem Schl 2nd, 3rd Tchr 1982-89; Bayside Elem Schl 3rd Grd Tchr 1989-94; Kent d Elem Schl 2nd Grd Tchr 1995-; *ai:* NEA, Q A Co Tchrs Assn 1976-; R MAC; 4-H 1960-; *home:* 113 Main Brace Dr Queenstown MD 8*

, EDWARD LEE, HS Technology Teacher; *b:* Syracuse, NY; *m:* ara A. Schade; *c:* Maria, Jennifer; *ed:* SUNY at Oswego (BS) Ind Arts 78, (MS) Ind Arts Ed 1984; Addl 5 Hrs; *cr:* Pine Buch HS Indstrl Arts 1979-85; Vly Cntrl HS Indstrl Arts Tchr 1985-86; Westmoreland Cntrl Tech Tchr 1986-93; Sauquoit Vly HS Tech Tchr 1993-; *ai:* Nysten Tchr Mentor; Holland Patent Elem Bldg Ldrshp Team Facilitator; and Patent Dist Tech Planning Comm; Curr Dev Team for Modern ıfacturing Inst; Mohawk Vly Tech Ed Assn 1986-, Pres; SVTA 1993-; TEA 1986-; Oneida Cty STOP-DWI 1996, Traffic Safety Advy Cncl ; NEWMAST Hnrs Tchr Awd 1992; NASA Seeds Experiment; *office:* uoit Valley Cntrl Schl 2601 Oneida St Sauquoit NY 13456*

, MADALENA MANCUSO, Bio, Anatomy & Physiology Tchr; *b:* , NY; *m:* John Allen; *c:* John-Peter, Christina, Joseph; *ed:* William son Coll (BS) Bio 1995; *cr:* Hackensack HS Sci Tchr 1995-; *ai:* Jr & lass Adv; NJTA 1995-; *office:* Hackensack HS First & Beech St ensack NJ 07601

ANYCH, ANDREW, 8th Grade Science Teacher; *b:* Linden, NJ; *m:* Sakowski; *c:* Laura; *ed:* Seton Hall Univ (BS) Sci, PE 1958, (MA) Admin 1960; Princeton Univ Chaos Theory, Physics; *cr:* Winfield Tchr 1958-59; woodridge Tchr 1959-60; Fair Haven Tchr 1960-; *ai:* Past Ftbl, Bsbl Coach; Bsktbl Coach; NEA, NJEA 1960-; FHEA 1960-, Pres; NJST 1970-; *office:* Knollwood Schl 224 Hance Rd Fair Haven NJ 07704

ZAKAR, GAIL MARIE, Physical Education Teacher; *b:* Brooklyn, NY; *m:* Richard; *c:* Dustin, Danielle; *ed:* Stony Brook Univ (MA) Liberal Arts 1976; Masters Plus 60 Credit Hrs; *cr:* Erasmus Hall HS PE Tchr 1972-73; Deer Park HS PE Tchr 1973-77; Longwood Jr HS PE Tchr 1984-; *ai:* NYS-AHPERD 1980-; AFT 1972-; Longwood Youth Soccer Assn, Former Coach; *office:* Longwood Jr HS 198 Longwood Rd Middle Island NY 11953

ZAKRZEWSKI, FRANK JOSEPH, Social Studies Teacher; *b:* Rutland, VT; *m:* Mary Lou Gallagher; *c:* Karen, Kristen; *ed:* Castleton St Coll (BS) His 1963; St Michaels Coll Post Grad Stud Guid; *cr:* St Mary's HS Soc Stud Tchr 1963-66; Cntrl Cath HS Soc Stud Tchr 1966-69; Bellows Free Acad Soc Stud Tchr 1969-; *ai:* NEA, VEA, BFAEA 1969-.*

ZAKUTINSKY, JONATHAN DAVID, Judaic Studies Teacher; *b:* New Haven, CT; *m:* Shulamith; *c:* Ahuvah, Sara, Rachel, Chaim, Tehila; *ed:* Adelphi Univ (BA) Psych 1981, (MA) Educl Admin 1985; Yeshiva Torah Vadaath (PHD) Jewish Philosophy 1985; *cr:* Hillel Yeshiva HS Judaic Stud Tchr 12 Yrs; *ai:* Bus, Ec Clubs Adv; Dir of Stu Act; *home:* 1051 E 29th St Brooklyn NY 11210

ZALECKY, ROBYN HOUSE, Business Technology Teacher; *b:* Euclid, OH; *m:* Richard Allen; *c:* Erika, Richard III; *ed:* Cleveland St Univ (BBA) Bus Ed 1982, (MS) Cmptr Uses in Ed 1990; Adventures in Bus OSU; Lake-Geauga Chemical Dependency Ashland; Internet & Telecommunications Ashland; Producing, Designing Newsletters; ECCO Multimedia; Quality Ed; Classroom Network Implementation; *cr:* Wickliffe HS Bus Tchr 1982-; *ai:* Schlsp Club, Pep Club Adv; Positive Action, Pepsi Challenge Work Ethic Comms; Career Day Coord; Network System Operator; OBTA, NBEA, CABTA, WEA 1982-; ISTE 1990-; YMCA 1993-; Cleveland Area Bus Tchrs Distngd Svc Awd; IBM's Outstdng Edctr; Outstdng Tchr; *home:* 6510 Durham Ct Mentor OH 44060*

ZALEDONIS, MARY ANN DARU, 6th Grade Teacher; *b:* Wilkes-Barre, PA; *m:* Ronald A.; *ed:* Miser, Cordia Coll (BS) Elem Ed 1967; Bloonsburg Univ (ME) Elem Ed 1971; Attnd Wilkes Univ, Carlow Coll; *cr:* Jamesburg Elem Schl 3rd Grd Tchr 1967-68; Wilkes-Barre Area Schl Dist 1st, 4th-6th Grd Tchr 1968-; *ai:* IPD Instrl Prof Develop; NEA, PSEA, WBAEA 1968-; Heights Murray PTA 1968-, Pres; Wilkes-Barre Area Womens Club 1975-, Treas; CCD Tchr, Lector, Coord 1990-; Lionness Club 1993-; *office:* Heights Elem Sch-Murray Complx 1 S Sherman St Wilkes Barre PA 18702

ZALESKI, DAVID GEORGE, Lead Physical Ed Teacher; *b:* Orange, NJ; *m:* Bernadette H. Ziobro; *c:* Christopher, Gregory, Kevin; *ed:* Montclair St Univ (BA) PE & Hlth 1973; 36 Credit Hrs in Admin, Hlth & PE; *cr:* Parsippany Schls Elem PE Tchr 1973-82; Parsippany HS PE, Hlth & Lead Tchr 1990-; *ai:* Head Girls Sftbl & Asst Soccer Coach; Dist Assessment Comm; East Hanover Vol Yth Coach; NEA & NJEA 1973-; NJ St Coaches Assn 1995-; E Hanover Bsktbl Assc 1989-, Treas; E Hanover Soccer Assn 1989-, Dir of Coaching & IM; East Hanover Strategic Planning Comm 1993-; Morris Cty Coach of the Yr 1985; NJ St Sftbl Coach of the Yr 1986; Dist Mini Grant on Wellness; *office:* Parsippany HS 309 Baldwin Rd Parsippany NJ 07054*

ZALETA, LEX, Secondary English Teacher; *b:* Wilkes-Barre, PA; *m:* Marsha Ann Kranisky; *c:* Amy Lynn, Aaron Alexander, Andrew Dylan; *ed:* Wilkes Coll (BA) Eng 1969, (MS) Eng Ed 1974; *cr:* Wilkes-Barre Twp Jr Sr HS Eng Tchr 1969-72; James M. Coughlin HS Eng Tchr 1972-78; Wilkes-Barre Twp Jr HS Eng Tchr 1978-91; G. A. R. Meml Jr Sr HS ATP, Hum, Eng Tchr 1991-; *ai:* Mentor Prgm; Goals 2000 Integrated Curr Project; NEA, PSEA, WBAEA 1969-; Intnl Brotherhood of Magicians 1972-; Assn for Rsrch & Enlightenment 1978-; Articles; Awd Short Stories; Magic Books: A Demonstrator's Dream, Parts 1-3, Getting Down to Business Vols 1, 2; *home:* 2415 Ransom Rd Clarks Summit PA 18411*

ZALEWSKI, PATRICIA HABERER, Soc Studies Tchr & Dept Chprsn; *b:* Sterling, IL; *m:* Stephen P.; *c:* Aaron, Jennifer, Paul; *ed:* IL St Uiv (BS) Soc Stud Ed 1971; Syracuse Univ (MS) Rdng Ed 1979; *cr:* Liverpool HS Soc Stud Tchr 1974-; *ai:* Soc Stud Dept Chair; AFT, NYSUT, United Liverpool Fac Assn 1974-; Cntrl NY Cncl for Soc Stud, NYS Cncl for SS, NCSS 1976-; Cornell Coop Extension Human Dev Comm 1994-; Articles Co-Author 1989, 1991, 1996; Cntrl NY Cncl for Soc Stud Tchr of Yr 1994; *office:* Liverpool HS 4338 Wetzel Rd Liverpool NY 13090

ZALEWSKI, STEVEN PAUL, HS Mathematics Teacher; *b:* Syracuse, NY; *m:* Patricia Haberer; *c:* Aaron, Jennifer, Paul; *ed:* SUNY at Fredonia (BS) Math 1968; 24 Grad Hrs SUNY at Oswego; 18 Grad Hrs St Coll at Bridgewater; *cr:* Liverpool HS Math Tchr 1968-72; Scituate HS Math Tchr 1972-76; Liverpool HS Math Tchr 1976-; *ai:* AFT, NYSUT 1968-; United Liverpool Fac Assn 1968-, Pres; NCTM 1992-; Holy Cross Church 1946-, Parish Comm Chprsn; Solvay Bd of Ed 1993-, Asst Clerk; Solvay Boy Scout Troop 72 1993-, Chm; AFT Ed & Labor Consultant to Poland 1990-91, 1994; *office:* Liverpool HS 4338 Wetzel Rd Liverpool NY 13090

ZALINSKI, BARBARA KAY (SNELL), Math & Computer Teacher; *b:* Cleveland, OH; *m:* Dennis; *c:* Matt, Melissa; *ed:* Bowling Green St Univ (BSEd) Math 1971; Cmptr Sci Minor 1990; Post Grad Ed Courses 6 Sem Hrs 1995; *cr:* Fremont HS Math Tchr 1971-78; Wood Cty Schls Sub Tchr 1985-86; Owens Tech Coll Math Instr 1986-90; Findlay HS Math Tchr 1990-; *ai:* NCTM, OCTM 1991-; NEA, OEA, FEA 1990-; Church CCD Tchr 1989-90; Gifted Prgm Statistics Text Tech Adv.

ZALKA, PATRICIA ANN, Fourth Grade Teacher; *b:* Youngstown, OH; *ed:* Youngstown St Univ (BS) Elem Ed 1976, (MS) Ed, El Principalship 1986; Early Chldhd Cert; Rdng K-12 Cert; Gen Sci 7-12 Cert; Project Discovery; *cr:* Holy Name Schl 4th Grd, Kdg, 1st-2nd Grd Tchr 1976-86; Rayen HS 12th Grd Rdng Tchr 1987-89; Bennett Elem Schl 6th Grd, 4th Grd Tchr 1989-; *ai:* All City Sci Fair Comm Mem, Judge; Sci Curr, Course Stud Comm; Sci Fair Coord; NEA, YEA 1987-; OEA, NEOEA 1987-, Del; Mentor Tchr; Project Discovery Tchr; *office:* Bennett Elem Schl 767 Mabel Ave Youngstown OH 44502*

ZALONIS, JOHN JOSEPH, Biology Teacher; *b:* Frackville, PA; *m:* Charlotte H. Rhoades; *c:* Jason, Brett; *ed:* Bloomsburg Univ (BS) Bio & Scndry Ed 1967, (MED) Bio & Scndry Ed 1972; Attnd Bucknell Univ 6 Credit Hrs & Lycoming Coll 1 Credit Hr; *cr:* S Williamsport HS Tchr 1967-70; Montgomery HS Tchr 1970-; *ai:* S Williamsport HS Head Ftbl Coach; Lead Tchr; PSEA & NEA 1967-; MAEA 1967-, Pres 2 Yrs; PSEA Task Force on Educl Excl; Developed Competency Tests for Bio for Graduating Coll Srs in Ed; Articles & 1 Book Pub; *office:* Montgomery Area H S Penn St Montgomery PA 17752

ZALUSKI, DEBORAH (KURTZ), Spanish Teacher; *b:* Mercer, PA; *m:* Dennis M.; *c:* Matthew Milan; *ed:* Westminster Coll (BA) Span 1985, (MED) Guid Cnslng 1987; Attnd Youngstown St Univ Cnslng; *cr:* Champion HS Span, Eng, Publications Tchr 1987; Howland HS Span Tchr 1987-88; Mercer HS Span Tchr 1988-89; Midwestern IU IV Sex Equity Coord 1989-90; Mercer HS Span Tchr 1990-; *ai:* Span Club Adv; NEA 1988-; PSMLA 1985-; Life Skills Mini Grant Prgm; Who's Who Among Amer Women; Thanks to Tchrs 1996; *home:* 4884-3 Westchester Dr Austintown OH 44515*

ZAMAGIAS, CONSTANTINE JAMES, Social Studies Teacher; *b:* Johnstown, PA; *m:* Kathleen Shertzer; *c:* Stephen, Elizabeth; *ed:* Carnegie Mellon (BA) His, Ger 1979; Frostburg St (MEd) Ed 1987; *cr:* Bishop Walsh Schl Soc Stud Tchr 1979-; *ai:* Mock Trial Team; Intramurals; nCSS 1983-; St Patricks Church 1979-, Lector, Eucharistic Minister; Dapper Dan Club 1980-, Little League Mgr, 1984 Mgr of Yr; MD St Mock Trial Champions 1990; *office:* Bishop Walsh Schl 700 Bishop Walsh Rd Cumberland MD 21502

ZAMARELLI, JOHN ANDREW, High School Choral Teacher; *b:* Salem, OH; *m:* Jennifer K. III; *c:* Morgan, Parker; *ed:* Mt Uion Coll (BME) Music Ed 1987; Youngstwon St Univ (MME) Music Ed 1993; *cr:* Columbia HS Band Dir 3 Yrs, Choir Dir 3 Yrs; Marlinginton MS Choral Dir 3 Yrs; West Branch HS Choral Dir 3 Yrs; *ai:* Salem Comm Theatre; Kent St Comm Choir; Salem Italian Club; St Paul Parish Cncl; St Paul Cath Church Music Dir; Carnation Players Guild Salem Playground Comm; Youngstown Playhouse; OMEA, MENC; *home:* PO Box 1113 Salem OH 44460

ZAMFIRESCU, CHRISTINA M. D., Computer Science Professor; *b:* Bucharest ; *m:* Romania; *c:* J. D., Gil; *ed:* Bucharest Univ at Romania (BS, MS) Math, OR 1971; RWTH Tech Univ Aechen Germany (PHD) Applied Math, Cmptr Sci 1978; *cr:* Tech Univ Aechen, Dortmund Univ Rsrch Scientist 1972-77; Western MI Univ Guest Fac 1977-78; Hunter Coll Assoc, Asst Prof 1978-; CUNY Grad Schl Engrng, Cmptr Sci Doctoral Fac 1981-; *ai:* Rsrch Journals Reviewer; Intnl Meetings US, Abroad Orgnl Bd; PHD Prgm Exec Comm; NY Acad Sci, Ed Adv Comm, Operations Rsrch Soc of Amer 1979-; ACM 1978-; DMV, AMS, AWM 1977-; Math Olympic Club 1992-, Organizer; Rsrch Journal Network Editorial Bd; 10 Grant Awds; 20 Papers Pub; Who's Who in Amer Women; Invited Talks at Univs, Confs in 10 Countries; Visiting Prof at Univs in USA, Europe; *office:* City Univ Of NY Hunter Coll 695 Park Ave New York NY 10021

ZAMPERETTI, DONALD JAMES, Prof of Business Admin; *b:* Oneida, NY; *m:* Nancy O.; *c:* Brien, Kiernan; *ed:* Mohawk Valley Comm Coll (AAS) Bus Admin 1966; Saint John Fisher Coll (BA) Bus Admin 1972; St Univ of NY at Albany (MS) Bus Ed 1977; *cr:* Eastridge HS Bus Tchr 1972; Canandaigua Acad Bus Tchr 1972-79; Finger Lakes Comm Coll Bus Admin Prof 1979-; *ai:* Tchng Fac Bargaining Cncl Chair; Grievance Comm Mem; Travel & Tourism 1990-, Resarch Asst; Soc of Travel & Tourism Educators 1985-; Ontario Cty Tourism Bureau, Bd Mem; *office:* Finger Lakes Comm Coll 4355 Lake Shore Dr Canandaigua NY 14424*

ZAMPERINI, RICHARD LOUIS, Band Director; *b:* Kittanning, PA; *ed:* IN Univ of PA (BS) Music Ed 1985; Aaron Copland Schl of Music at Queens Coll (MS) Music Ed 1991; *cr:* Monesson HS Band Dir 1988-89; Wisdom Lane MS Band Dir 1989-91; Herricks HS Band Dir 1991-92; Southmoreland HS Band Dir 1992-; *ai:* DCE, DCM & PFCJ Judge; Drum Corps & Marching Bands Arranger, Instr & Consultant; NEA 1992-; *office:* Southmoreland HS Rt 981 Box A Alverton PA 15612

ZAMPERLIN, FRANK U., Asst Principal; *b:* Mt Kisco, NY; *ed:* Manhattan Coll (BA) Ed 1985, (MS) Admin, Supervision 1992; *cr:* Good Shephard Schl 6th Grd Soc Stud Tchr 1985-86; Immac Conception Schl 6-8th Grd Soc Stud Tchr 1986-92, Vice Prin 1992-94; Marlboro MS Asst Prin 1994-; *ai:* ASCD, CSAANYS 1992-; NCSS 1986-; SAANYS, NASSP, ASCD, Kappa Delta Pi, Middle States Assoc of Coll & Schls; *home:* 275 Hudson St Apt 3 Cornwall Hdsn NY 12520*

ZANDT, DOROTHY ANN D., Fourth Grade Teacher; *b:* Brooklyn, NY; *m:* Charles F.; *ed:* St Univ at Oneonta (BS) Home Ec Ed 1958, (MS) Elem Ed 1966; *cr:* Deposit Cntrl Schl 7-12 Grd Home Ec Tchr 1958-63; Windsor Cntrl Schl 1-4 Grd Tchr 1963-; *ai:* Curr, Cultural Enrichment Comms; WTA 1963-; *office:* Floyd L. Bell Elem Schl 15 Golden St Kirkwood NY 13795*

ZANDY, PATRICIA WORLEY, Elementary Principal; *b:* Gloversville, NY; *m:* David J.; *c:* Kyle, Matthew, Aaron; *ed:* SUNY at Oswego (BS) Ed 1959; Binghamton Univ (MS) Ed 1976; SUNY at Cortland CAS Admin; Attnd Siena Coll, Elmira Coll, SUNY at Brockport, Johnson St Coll; *cr:* Mohannesen CSD 1st Grd Tchr 1963-64; Union-Edicott CSD 1st Grd Tchr 1964-66, Sub, Remedial Rdng, Spec Ed Tchr 1966-73; Owego- Apalachin CSD Kndgtn, 2nd Grd Tchr 1973-91, Elem Prin 1991-; *ai:* Nature Cnslr; New Voice Group; NASSP,SAANYS 1991-; Phi Delta Kappa 1994-; Delta Kappa Gamma Beta Rho 1976-, Recording, Corr Sec; Bus-Prof Women 1991-, Recording Sec, Yth Ldrshp; Owego Kiwanis 1991-; St Anthony 1964-; Who's Who in Amer Colls, Univs; Tchr, Admin Outstdng Performance Recognition; PTA Lifetime Svc, Pres Awds; NYS Tchr of Yr Nom; *office:* Owego Elem Schl George St Owego NY 13827

ZANELLA, KATIE, German Teacher; *b:* Pittsburgh, PA; *m:* Scott; *c:* Julie; *ed:* Univ of Pittsburgh (BA) Ger 1990, (BS) Psych 1990, (MAT) Frgn Lang hEd 1991; 15 Addl Credit Hrs; *cr:* Allerdice HS Permanent Ger Sub 1991; West Allegheny HS Ger Tchr 1991-; *ai:* SADD Spon; Took 17 to Germany Last Yr; NEA 1991-; West Allegheny Ed Assn 1991-, Fac Rep; *office:* West Allegheny HS 205 W Allegheny Rd Imperial PA 15126*

ZANGHI, DOUGLAS C., Chemistry & Biology Tchr; *b:* Dunkirk, NY; *m:* Mary Jo Caccamise; *c:* Mallory Kay; *ed:* St Univ Coll at Fredonia (BS) Bio & Chem 1973; St Univ Coll at Brockport, St Univ Coll at Buffalo & Coll of Saint Rose NY St Scndry Ed Tchng Cert 1975; Various Grad Courses 51 Hrs of Credit; *cr:* Lederle Labs Research Scientist of Neuro-Pharmacology 1973-75; Pine Valley Cntrl Schl Chem & Bio Tchr 1975-; *ai:* Involved with Ftbl, Bsktbl, Sftbl & Track; Girls Bsktbl Team Ath Trainer; Dist Compact for Learning Comm; Pine Valley Tchrs Assn 1975-, VP, Grievance Comm, Neg Comm; AFT & NYSUT 1975-; Pine Valley Tchrs Assn Tchr of Yr; Amer Chem Soc Western NY-Northwestern PA Tchr Awd; Pub in Pharmacological Research Comm Vol 6 No 3 1974; NY St Grant to Upgrade Lab Fac at Pine Valley Cntrl Schl; *office:* Pine Valley Central School Rt 83 South Dayton NY 14138

ZANGHI, JUDITH CECCACCI, Fifth Grade Teacher; *b:* Scranton, PA; *m:* Michael M.; *c:* Michael, Matthew; *ed:* Marywood Coll (BS) Elem Ed 1972, (MS) Elem Cnslng 1975; Whole Lang Seminar; Cmptr Wkshp, Eisenhower Grant Prgm; PA Ed Dept Inservice; *cr:* Mc Nichols Plaza Schl 4th Grd Tchr 1987-89; George Bancroft Elem Schl 5th Grd Tchr 1989-; *ai:* Ski Club Adv; Math Book Review Comm; AFT, SFT 1973-; Women Tchrs 1973-, Secd; Marywood Alumni Advy Bd 1994-; *office:* George Bancroft Elem Schl 34 1002 Albright Ave Scranton PA 18508*

ZANK-REHWALDT, CAROL H., English Teacher; *b:* Long Island, NY; *m:* Bradley Rehwaldt; *c:* Dylan Rehwaldt; *ed:* IN Univ (BA) Eng 1977; Natl Louis Univ (MED) Curr & Instruction 1993; *cr:* Silver Lake Jr-Sr HS Eng Tchr 1979-80; Saints Peter & Paul Schl Eng & Soc Stud Tchr 1980-81; Kelly Child Dev Ctr Germany Ed Specialist 1982-83; Stuttgart Amer HS Germany Eng Tchr 1983; Stuttgart Amer HS Germany Eng Tchr 1983; Patch Amer HS Eng Tchr 1983-; *ai:* Eng Dept Chair; NHS Spon; AFT 1983-; Sustained Superior Performance Awd; *home:* Unit 30401 Box 2813 APO AE 09131

ZANONE, PATRICIA, 2nd-3rd Grade Science Teacher; *b:* Denville, NJ; *ed:* Rider Univ (BA) Elem Ed 1985; *cr:* Columbian Schl Elem Classroom Tchr 1985-; *ai:* Essex Cty Ed Assn; NJ ED Assn; NEA; Chrstn Public Ed Advocates Tchr Who Made Difference Awd 1989; *office:* Columbian Elem Schl 410 N Grove St East Orange NJ 07017

ZANTAY, DOUGLAS WILLIAM, Band Director; *b:* Rockville Ctr, NY; *m:* Karen Scott; *c:* Chelsea, Dakota, Jazz; *ed:* Manhattan Schl of Music (BM) Music 1978, (MM) Performance 1980, (MME) Ed 1984; Fordham Univ (PD) Admin 1994; *cr:* Simons Rock of Band Univ Music Tchr 1978-80; Byram Hills Schl Dist Band Dir 1984-85; Hastings-on-Hudson

Dist Band Dir 1985-88; Eastchester UFSD Band Dir 1988-; *ai:* HS Jazz Band Dir; Eastchester Yth Cncl Theater Prgm Musical Dir; Music Dir 1990-93; AFT, WCSMA, NYSSMA 1984; AFM 1974-; Red Cross 1970-, Water Safety Instr; On Jazz CD Bolero Studio Recording Work for TV Jingles; Toured with Broadway Natl Co; *office:* Eastchester Schls 580 White Plains Rd Eastchester NY 10707

ZAPATA-MORALES, WILLIAM, Spanish Teacher; *b:* San Antonio, Venezuela; *m:* Elaine Rotz; *c:* Mikhail Zapata-Rotz, Lech Zapata-Rotz; *ed:* Natl Univ of Tachira (BS) Argronomy Engrng 1982; OK St Univ (MS) Agricultural Ec 1986; Shippensburg Univ Instrl level I Cert 1990, Level II Cert 1995, MS Scndry Schl Cnslng 1996; *cr:* Natl Univ of Tachira Chem Lab Instr 1978-82, Forage Crops Instr 1979-82; Jesus Lossada Coll Ec Instr 1986-87; Milton Hershey Schl Span Tchr 1991-; *ai:* SALVD Club Adv; AATSP 1991-; PSCA 1994-; ACA 1995-; NEA 1995-; *office:* Milton Hershey Schl 300 Hotel Rd Hershey PA 17033

ZAPPA, PAUL JOSEPH, Music Teacher; *b:* Cincinnati, OH; *m:* Marjorie Meiners; *c:* John, P. Joseph; *ed:* Univ of Cin Coll of Music (BM) Composition 1967; Univ of KY (MM) Composition 1970; Attnd Univ of Cincinnati; *cr:* Holy Cross Church, Schl Music Dir 1967-71; Blessed Sacrament Church, Schl Music Dir 1972-74; Center Civic Opera Artistic Dir 1976-83; St Xavier HS Music Dir 1984-; *ai:* Jazz, Marching Band Dir; MENC 1984-; NCBA 1986-; ACDA 1995-; Cincinnati Musicians Assn Loc #1 1975-; Pleasant Ridge Neighborhood Assn 1995-; Articles Pub; Artist in Residence 1981-82; Judge for KY St Orch Contests Two Yrs; *home:* 5927 Pandora Ave Cincinnati OH 45213

ZAPPALA, JOHN, Science Teacher; *b:* Bronx, NY; *m:* Teresa; *c:* Krystin, Kerri, Jon Erik; *ed:* SUNY at New Paltz (BS) Chem 1960; Syracuse (MS) Phys Sci 1965; 60 Addl Credit Hrs Environmental Sci; *cr:* New Paltz Schl Grad Asst Tchr 1960; Syracuse Schl Grad Asst Tchr 1965; Mamaroneck Bd of Ed Sci Tchr 1960-; *ai:* Boys Var Soccer & Girls Modified Soccer Coach; Negotiating Comm; Environmental Prgms Dir; AFT, NYSTA, NEA, NYSSTA, SEANYS 1960-; MTA 1960-, VP 1966; Long Island Sound Stud 1985-, CAC; Long Island Sound Task Force 1989-93, Bd of Dir; Sound Waters 1990-91, Bd of Dir; Long Island Sound Amer 1990-91; NSF-SEA Grant; Westinghouse Sci Talent Mentor; *home:* 10 Braxmar Dr N Harrison NY 10528*

ZARBA, JOSEPH ANGELO, Photography Teacher; *b:* Jersey City, NJ; *c:* Zachary Troi, Sacha Michel; *ed:* Trenton St (BA) Psych 1970; NY Univ (MA) Physically Handicapped 1979; 30 Credit Hrs in Sci Brooklyn Coll 1984; Photography Courses Hunter Coll 1993; *cr:* Avard Learning Ctr MS Spec Ed Tchr 1972-74; PS 157 Manhattan Schl Elem Spec Ed Tchr 1974-75; PS 56 Brooklyn Schl Elem Spec Ed Tchr 1977-85; MS 51 Brooklyn Schl Photography Tchr 1986-; *ai:* Yrbk Adv; Photography Club Adv; NCAA Bsbl Official; Summer Camp Photography; SFT 1971-; UFT Local 2 1971-, Del to Del Assembly 1978-81; Brooklyn Camera Club 1995-; Media Arts Tchr Assn 1994-; Photo Instr Tchrs Assn 1994-; *office:* MS 51 William Alexander 350 5th Ave Brooklyn NY 11215

ZAREMSKI, SHARON L., 2nd Grade Teacher; *b:* PA; *m:* Paul E.; *c:* Tara, Tyler; *ed:* Slippery Rock St (BS) Spec, Elem Ed 1981; *cr:* Diocese of Pittsburgh Elem Tchr 1982-87; Pittsburgh Schl Remedial Math Specialist 1987-90; Mt Oliver IU Schl Remedial Math Specialist 1987-90; Wesley Highland Svcs Schl Spec Ed Tchr 1990-93; Penn Hills Schl Elem Tchr 1993-; *ai:* Var Chrldng Coach; NEA 1993-; Founder of Bethel Park Chrldng Schlsp Fund; Nom for Thanks to Tchrs Awd; *home:* 2857 W Munroe St Bethel Park PA 15102*

ZARETSKY-CROLL, RUTH GAIL, First Grade Teacher; *b:* New Haven, CT; *m:* Elliott R.; *c:* Jessica Anne, Jonathan M., Seth R., Jeremy S.; *ed:* Southern CT St Univ (BS) Early Chldhd Ed 1973, (MS) Early Chldhd Ed 1978; 6th Yr Classroom Tchr Specialist 1995; *cr:* M. L. Keefe Elem Schl 4th Grd Tchr 1973-74; West Woods ELem Schl 1st-3rd Grd Tchr 1974-; *ai:* NEA, HEA, CEA 1973-; Henry Barnard Awd for Excl in Ed; *office:* West Woods Elem Schl 350 W Todd St Hamden CT 06518*

ZARING, VICKY LYNN, Resource Room Teacher; *b:* Ft Lee, VA; *ed:* Fitchburg St Coll (BS) Spcl Need & Elem Ed 1981; 12 Credit Hrs Towards Masters; *cr:* Stow Pub Schls Resource Room Aide 1981-83, Tutor 1983-85; East Brookfield & Spencer Schls Resource Room Tchr 1985-; *ai:* Memrl Schl Cncl Mem; PTO Co-Chprsn 1985-95; Girls Jr High Bsktbl Coach 1985-94; Girls HS Summer League Coach; NEA 1986-; MTA 1986-; EB Recreation Comm 1986-, Summer Recreation Dir, Sftbl Coach; Organized Fundraisers for East Brookfield Schls; Helped to Organize East Brookfields 4th of July Celebration; *office:* Memorial Elem Schl Connie Mack Dr East Brookfield MA 01515

ZARRELLA, JULIE-ANNE, Foreign Language Teacher; *b:* Warwick, RI; *m:* Mark Joseph; *c:* Anthony Joseph; *ed:* Providence Coll (BA) Italian, Hum 1986; 21 Grad Credits Providence Coll, RI Coll Admin, Guid, Langs; *cr:* Toll Gate HS Italian Tchr 1990-91; Johnston Sr HS Italian, Span Tchr 1991-; *ai:* Model Legislature Adv 1993-94; Grad. Supts Scheduling Comms; Steering, Awds Comms 1992-94; RI Tchrs of Italian, RI Frgn Lang Assn, AFT 1990-; DAE 1986-; *office:* Johnston Sr HS 345 Cherry Hill Rd Johnston RI 02919*

ZARRELLA, MARK JOSEPH, Physical Education Teacher; *b:* Providence, RI; *m:* Julie-Anne; *c:* Anthony; *ed:* Univ of RI (BS) PE & Hlth 1986; 18 Credits Providence Coll; *ai:* Track & Wrestling Coach; Stu Mediation Coord; RI AAPHERD 1986-; NWCA 1996, RI Rep; RIWCA 1989-; Natl Guard 1986-, Captain Commander, Numerous Awds; Exercise Guide for Adults 1985; Television Prgm Ask A Doctor 1985; Cardiac Rehabilitation Coord & Adult Fitness Coord 1983-86; Former Ftbl Coach; *office:* Johnston Sr HS 345 Cherry Hill Rd Johnston RI 02919*

ZARRELLO, LOUIS, Mathematics Teacher; *b:* Newark, NJ; *m:* Gail Glaudel; *c:* Joseph, Joanne; *ed:* Montclair St Coll (BA) Math 1960, (MA) Admin 1971; *cr:* Springfield HS Math Tchr 1960-63; Long Valley MS Math Tchr 1968-; *ai:* WTEA 1968-; NJEA 1968-; NEA 1968-; *office:* Long Valley MS 51 W Mill Rd Long Valley NJ 07853

ZARROW, ALAN S., Teacher & Athletic Director; *b:* Brooklyn, NY; *ed:* Brooklyn Coll CUNY (BS) PE 1976; Ithaca Coll (MS) PE 1978; Adv Cert Admin, Supervision Brooklyn Coll CUNT 1988; *cr:* Erasmus Hall HS Tchr 1978-; *ai:* Schl Ath Dir; Var Vlybl Coach 1980-; Var Sftbl Coach 1982-86; Golf Coach 1988, 1995; AAHPSRD 1978-; NYSAHPERD 1978-, Pres NYC Zone, Treas Hlth Sect; IAABO 1979-; NYC Bd of Ofcls; Pub Referee Magazine, Horse & Horseman; *office:* Erasmus Hall HS 911 Flatbush Ave Brooklyn NY 11226

ZARZYCKI, KAREN, 4th Grade Teacher; *b:* Springfield, MA; *ed:* Southern CT St Univ (BS) Spec Ed 1975, (MS) Spec Ed 1984; *cr:* Winchendon MS Spec Ed Tchr 1975-77; Plainville Schls Spec Ed Tchr 1977-91, 6th Grd Tchr 1991-93; Toffolon Schl 4th Grd Tchr 1993-; *ai:* PTO Tchr Rep 1985-; Mentor Tchr 1979-; Robert Houston Cooperating Tchr Awd 1986; Dev Videotape for Insvc Trng Wkshp 1985; *office:* Louis Toffolon Elem Schl 145 Northwest Dr Plainville CT 06062

ZASA, RICHARD J., English Department Head; *b:* Akron, OH; *m:* Shelli Blank; *c:* Jason, Julie; *ed:* OH St Univ (BS) Eng, His 1965; 90 Addl Hrs Eng Lit; *cr:* Parma Sr HS Eng Tchr 1965-76; Vly Forge HS Eng Tchr 1976-84; Parma Sr HS Eng Dept Head 1985-; *ai:* Annual Play Writing Competition, Performance, Fiction Writing Contests 1985-, Underclass Achvmt Awds Spon; Yrbk Adv 1977-85; PEA, OEA, NEOEA, NEA 1965-; *office:* Parma Sr HS 6285 W 54th St Parma OH 44129*

ZATKO, FRANK, Physics Professor; *b:* Cleveland, OH; *m:* Mary Beth Hayes; *c:* Kathryn; *ed:* Xavier Univ (BS) Bio 1976; Case Western Rsrch Univ Schl Medicine (PHD) Physiology, Bio Physics 1989; Test Engrng Aptitude Math, Sci Adv 1995; Swimming Coach; *ai:* Test Engrng Aptitude Math, Sci Adv 1995; Swimming Coach; AAPT 1991-; ASCA 1988-, Level 3; HISCA 1988-; Amer Heart Assn Rsrch Fellow; Pub Journal; *office:* Hathaway Brown Schl 19600 N Park Blvd Shaker Heights OH 44122

ZATORSKY, NANCY SHACKELFORD, First Grade Teacher; *b:* Norton, VA; *m:* Bernard B.; *c:* B. Jason, Jessica; *ed:* Univ of Pittsburgh (BS) Elem Ed 1974; 30 Post Grad Credit Past MS; *cr:* Northern Cambria 1st Grd Tchr 1982-; *ai:* PSEA 1981-; NEA 1981-; Friend of Barnesboro 1993-; Pub Lib; *office:* Northern Cambria Schl Dist 601 Joseph St Barnesboro PA 15714

ZAUN, BARBARA KLUEBER, French Teacher; *b:* Pittsburgh, PA; *m:* Hartmut U.; *ed:* Clarion Univ (BS) Eng & Fr 1973; Univ of Pittsburgh (MED) Curr & Supervision 1981; 12 Credit Hrs in Prof Translation; *cr:* Southern Huntingdon Schls Eng & Fr Tchr 1974-76; Avonworth Schl Dist Eng & Fr Tchr 1976-77; North Allegheny Schl Dist Fr Tchr 1977-; Allegheny Intermediate Unit ESL Tchr 1978-80, ESL Supvr 1980-92; Univ of Pittsburgh ESL Instr & Curr Coord 1980-94; *ai:* Fr Club Adv; Total Quality Comm; AFT 1977-; AATF 1983-; TESOL 1994-; PSMLA 1995-; N Hills Jr Womens Club 1985-, Treas, Vol of Yr Awd 1994; *office:* North Allegheny H S 10375 Perry Hwy Wexford PA 15090*

ZAVACKY, PATRICIA A., First Grade Teacher; *b:* Somerville, NJ; *m:* Jack D.; *c:* Maureen Smolenyak, Jennifer; *ed:* St of PA Masters Equivalency; *cr:* Washington Twp Schl Tchr 1968-70; Pen Argyl Area Schl Tchr 1982-; *ai:* NEA, PSEA 1982-; PAAEA 1982-, Bldg Rep; *office:* Pen Argyl Area Schl Dist 1620 Teels Rd Pen Argyl PA 18072

ZAVISKAS, JENNY, Fifth Grade Teacher; *b:* Hartford, CT; *ed:* Eastern CT St Univ (BS) Elem Ed 1974; 15 Addl Hrs; *cr:* ME Schl Admin Dist #60 2nd Grd Tchr 1976-86, 5th Grd Tchr 1987-; *ai:* Math Curr Dev Team; Girls Exploring Math, Sci Adv; NEA, ME Ed Assn 1976-; NCTM 1989-; PTA 1977-, VP 1991-92; Xi Alpha Omega 1991-, Pres 1994-95, Woman of Yr 1994.

ZAWACKI, RICHARD G., HS Social Studies Teacher; *b:* Summit, NJ; *ed:* Bloomfield Coll (BA) Pol Sci 1971; Montclair St Univ Post Grad Work Towards MA; *cr:* Don Bosco Prep HS Soc Stud Tchr 1971-; *ai:* Soccer Head Coach 19 Yrs; Tennis Head Coach 21 Yrs; Bowling Head Coach 10 Yrs; *office:* Don Bosco Prep HS N Franklin Tpke Ramsey NJ 07446*

ZAWATSKY, JOHN JOSEPH, Physical Education Teacher; *b:* Hazelton, PA; *m:* Marie Adams; *c:* John, Sharon, Joseph; *ed:* East Stroudsburg Univ (BS) Hlth & PE 1957; Addl 30 Hrs; *cr:* Hancock Cntrl Math Tchr 1961-62; Saint Josephats Cath Schl Hlth & PE 1962-65; *ai:* Bsbl Coach; Athletic Dir; NEA.

ZAWIERUCHA, CHRISTINA F. M., High School English Teacher; *b:* Buffalo, NY; *ed:* St Univ Coll at Buffalo (BS) Ed, Eng 1975, (MS) Ed 1980; Jagiellonian Univ Post Grad Work in Polish Lang, Culture, His; Beijing Coll of Foreign Lang China Chinese Lang & Culture Classes; *cr:* Beijing Univ Beijing Coll of Foreign Lang Foreign Lang Expert to Chinese Tchr of Eng 1988; Orchard Park MS 8th Grd Eng Tchr 1975-82; Orchard Park HS 9-12th Grd Eng Tchr 1982-; *ai:* Sr Mentor for Novice Tchrs; NHS Selection Comm Mem; Whole Lang Circle Mem; Initial Adv & Coord of "Windscript"; Eng as Second Lang Tutor, Instr; AFT 1975-; Phi Delta Kappa 1986-; NCTE 1975-; Sovereign Military Order of St John Knights of Malta 1983-; Chopin Singing Society 1975-; Nom 4 Times for Orchard Park Tchr of Yr; Won Fulbright Schlsp for Study in India 1995; *office:* Orchard Park H S 4040 Baker Rd Orchard Park NY 14127*

ZAYAC, GENE, Chemistry Teacher; *b:* Cleveland, OH; *m:* Rita L. Rysh; *c:* Kyle C., Ryan M.; *ed:* OH St Univ (BS) Chem, Math 1968; Attnd Akron Univ, Cleveland St Univ, Kent St Univ, Seton Hill Coll; *cr:* Valley Forge HS Chem Tchr 1968-; *ai:* Parma Ed Assn, OEA, NEA 1968-; Parma Amateur Ath Assn 1975-, Treas, Outstanding Contribution Sftbl 1988; Jennings Scholar 1984-85; Westinghouse Sci Talent Search Tchrs Honor Group 1975; Denison Univ Outstanding Tchr Awd 1992; NSF Summer Inst Grant 1972; *home:* 11228 Gordon Dr Parma OH 44130

ZAZA, JOSEPH F., Senior Advisor; *b:* Brooklyn, NY; *m:* Clara DeRosa; *ed:* Brooklyn Coll (BA) His, Film 1986, (MA) His 1990, (MA) Ed 1994; *cr:* Edward R. Murrow HS Sr Adv, Soc Stud Tchr, Unity Cncl 1986-; *ai:* Peer Negotiation, Mediator; AFT 1986-; *office:* Edward R. Murrow HS 1600 Avenue L Brooklyn NY 11230*

ZBIB, IMAD JIM, Production Mgmt Professor; *b:* Beirut, Lebanon; *m:* Nancy Mokdad-Zbib; *ed:* Univ of Lebanon (BS) Acctng 1982, (BA) Mngmt 1983; Univ of North TX (MS) Acctng 1986, (PHD) Operations Mngmt 1990; *cr:* Univ of North TX Instr of Mngmt 1987-90; East TX St Univ Asst Prof of Mngmt 1988-89; Cntrl MO St Univ Asst Prof of Operations Mngmt 1990-93; Romapo Coll of NJ Asst Prof of Operations Mngmt 1993-; *ai:* Amer Production & Inventory Control Soc, Delta Sigma Pi Fac Advs; Chair & Mem Several Fac Comms; APICS, ARC 1987-; AGB, DSI 1990-; Excl Tchng Awd Cntrl MO St Univ 1992, 1993; Numerous Articles Pub; *office:* Ramapo Coll Of NJ 505 Ramapo Valley Rd Mahwah NJ 07430

ZBOZNY, FRANK T., Professor of English; *b:* Pittsburg, PA; *m:* Louise Muffett; *c:* Samuel, Michael, Jennifer; *ed:* Duquesne Univ (MA) Eng Lit 1964; Univ of Pgh (PHD) Medieval Eng Lang & Lit 1970; *cr:* Univ Pgh at Greensburg Instr 1964-65; Duquesne Univ Asst Assoc Prof 1966-; *ai:* Natl Assn of Scholars 1991-; *office:* Duquesne Univ Pittsburgh PA 15282

ZDANOWICZ, VIRGINIA M. (BERTI), French Teacher; *b:* Wilkes Barre, PA; *m:* Vincent P.; *c:* Gina, Jill; *ed:* Coll MIsericordia (BA) Eng, Fr 1972; Univ of Scranton (MS) Scndry Schl Guidance 1977; Undergrad Univ of Dijon Dijon France Summer 1970; 3 Credits Wilkes Univ; 3 Credits Millersville Univ Summer Schl fo Fr; *cr:* Wilkes Barre Area Fr, Eng Tchr 1972-; *ai:* Fr Club Adv; SAP; NEA, PSEA, WBAEA 1972-; PTSO of Coughlin HS 1991-92; Adult Mem PA Woods Girl Scout Cncl 1988-; *office:* Coughlin H S 80 N Washington St Wilkes Barre PA 18701

ZDILLA, LARRY, Guid Counselor & Ftbl Coach; *b:* Monessen, PA; *c:* Michael, Dan; *ed:* CA Univ of PA (BS) Ed 1971; Millersville Univ of PA (MA) Ed 1975, (MA) Guid & Cnslng 1983; *cr:* Governor Mifflin Elem Tchr 1971-78; Solanco HS Tchr & Cnslr 1979-92; Marlboro HS Cnslr 1993-; *ai:* Head Ftbl Coach; Lancasaster-Lebanon Coach of Yr 1983, 1990 & 1991; Shore Conf Monmouth Cty Cntrl; Jersey Coach of Yr 1995; *office:* Marlboro HS 95 N Main St Marlboro NJ 07746

ZDROIK, SUSAN THORNTON, English Teacher; *b:* Willard, OH; *m:* Paul; *c:* Adam, Lauren, Scott; *ed:* OH Univ (BSEd) Eng 1974; 3 Credit Hrs Creative Writing Class Ashland Univ; *cr:* Willard HS Eng Tchr 1979-; *ai:* Sr Class Adv; Goals 2000 Comm; NEA, OEA 1978-; WEA 1978-, Exec Comm 1992; OCTELLA, NCTE 1985-; *office:* Willard HS 123 W Whisler Dr Willard OH 44890

ZEEDYK, LARRY JOSEPH, Computer & Business Ed Teacher; *b:* Mark Center, OH; *m:* Brenda L. Conkey; *c:* Spencer, Derek, Brian; *ed:* Campbell Coll (BBA) Bus 1973; Boston Univ (EdM) Ed 1977; Attnd Defiance Coll, Bowling green St & Memphis St Univs & Univ of Toledo; *cr:* US Army Inf Ctr Leadership Instr 1969-71; FCJUC Bus Tchr 1980-81; Hicksville HS Bus Ed & Cmptr Tchr 1982-; *ai:* Jr High Bsktbl Coach 1982-87; Soph Class Adv 1982-; Yearround Schl Comm; Bsktbl Ofcl 1988-; Phi Delta Kappa 1984-; HEA 1992-; Officers of the 1st Div 1967-; OH Trustees Assn 1982-, Pres & VP; Hicksville Hosp 1982-, Pres, 2 Million Dollar Expantion; *office:* Hicksville HS Smith & Main St Hicksville OH 43526

ZEEH, ANN, Assistant Professor of Biology; *b:* Kingston, NY; *m:* C. Sandwick; *ed:* Clarkson Univ (BS) Bio 1983; St Univ of NY at A (PHD) Molecular Bio 1989; *cr:* Skidmore Coll Visiting Asst Prof 19 St Univ of NY at Fredonia Asst Prof 1991-92; The Coll of St Rose Prof 1993-; *ai:* Acad Grievance, Undergraduate Acad, Prof Dev, Review, Affirmative Action Comms; Sci Olympiad Coord; Mentor H Rsrch Prgm; Sigma Xi 1983-, Grant-In-Aid Rsrch 1983; Ame Microbiology 1985-; AAAS 1989-; NSF Rsrch Undergraduate Insts 1993-; Articles Pub; *office:* Coll Of Saint Rose 432 Western Ave A NY 12203

ZEGAR, JANET MORICZ, Choral & Dance Teacher; *b:* Ft Wayn *m:* Stephen; *c:* Alexandra; *ed:* Duquesne Univ (BS) Music Ed 1978; Park Coll (BA) Dance 1982; Robert Morris Coll (MBA) Arts Mgmt *cr:* Mt Lebanon Elem Music Tchr 1979-80; Plum Jr High Choral & Music Tchr 1980-82; Plum Sr High Choral & Dance Tchr 1982 Chamber Choir Dir; Dance Ensemble Spon; PMEA 1978-; NEA ACDA 1984-; Duquesne Univ Tamburitzans; *office:* Plum Sr H Elicker Rd Pittsburgh PA 15239

ZEGARELLI, JOY E., Kindergarten Teacher; *b:* Yonkers, NY Herbert H. Lehman Coll of the City Univ of NY (BA) Anthropolo Elem Ed 1969; Coll of New Rochelle (MS) Rdng 1975; 60 Credit Hrs Ed; *cr:* School Thirteen 1st Grd Tchr 1969-95, Kndgtn Tchr 1995-; *a* of the Month Pgm Coord; Schl Thirteen Schl Comm; Columbia Chldhd Intervention Pgm; Columbia Univ Family Lit Pgm; Elem Sch 1989; Career Day Comm 1990; AFT 1969-; NYSUT 1969-; Gui Garibaldi Lodge 1988-, Recording Sec for 2 Yrs; St Johns Hosp 1990- *home:* 3 Consulate Dr Tuckahoe NY 10707

ZEGESTOWSKY, JANE HABINA, Mathematics Instructo Philadelphia, PA; *m:* Stephen; *c:* Gwen, Gregory, Joseph; *ed:* Holy F Coll (BA) Math 1974; West Chester Univ (MED) Ed 1977; *cr:* Gra Math Tchr 1975-81; Lower Moreland HS TELLS Instr 1988-91; G Opportunity Ctr Ed Specialist 1988-91; Manor Jr Coll Math Coord 1991-; Abington Schl Dist Homebound Instr 1995-; *ai:* Phi Theta Adv; NHS; Retention, Coord Self-Stu Steering, EX Cordae Comms; NCTM 1991-; PSMATYC 1993-; Mc Kinley ES PTO 1981-, Treas Pres; St Hilary Pastoral Cncl 1995-, Sec; St Hilary Rel Ed Fac Coord; Nom Outstdng Young Woman in Amer 1987; Wrote Text C *office:* Manor Jr Coll 700 Fox Chase Rd Jenkintown PA 19046*

ZEH, EVELYN FISCHER, Retired Third Grade Teacher; *b:* Orang *m:* William; *c:* David; *ed:* Kean Coll (BS) Elem Ed 1958; *cr:* Washi Schl Second Grd Tchr 1958-70, Third Grd Tchr 1971-90; *ai:* Math C NEA, NJEA, UCEA, UTEA 1958-.

ZEHNLE, BRUCE E., Spanish Teacher; *b:* Philadelphia, PA; *ed:* L Univ (BA) Span & Latin Ed 1966; Univ of IA (MA) Span 1968; Supv & Work Toward Doctorate at Seton Hall Univ; *cr:* Union Cath HS Tchr 1968-; *ai:* Span Honor Soc; Soph Class Adv; Stock Market Club; Club; Span Team Coach; AATSP 1968-; NJAATSP 1968-, Pres; F 1970-; Sociedad Honoraria Hispanica 1968-, St Dir; Span Honor Soc of Yr Three Times; Motivational Wkshps Local, St & Natl Levels; S Articles & Tchr Tips Pub; Outstanding Foreign Lang Tchr in NJ; *o* Union Catholic Reg HS 1600 Martine Ave Scotch Plains NJ 07076*

ZEHR, DAVID, Associate Professor of Psych; *b:* Pittsburgh, P Elizabeth; *c:* David, Jonathan, Laurel; *ed:* Penn St Univ (BA) Psych Univ of Datyon (MA) Psych 1979; Kent St Univ (PHD) Psych 198 Univ of Dayton Instr 1982-83; Beloit Coll Asst Prof 1983-85; Plymo Coll Assoc Prof 1985-; *ai:* Psi Chi Fac Adv; Amer Psych Soc Midwestern Psych Assn 1979-; *office:* Univ Of NH Plymouth St Plymouth NH 03264

ZEIGLER, CAROL ELAINE (MOVER), English Teache Chambersburg, PA; *m:* Donald Earl; *c:* Robyn Beth Strickler, Mindy Mover; *ed:* Shippensburg Univ (BA) Eng & Elem 1959; Ma Equivalency; *cr:* Hanover Schl Dist 3rd Grd Tchr 1959; Shaull Ele Grd Tchr 1959-60; Middlesex Elem 3rd-6th Grd Tchr 1960-72; MS 6th Grd Tchr 1972-84; Cumberland Vly HS 9th Grd Tchr 1984-; *ai:* 1959-; PSEA 1959-; CVEA 1959-; ADK 1970-; Carlisle Civic Club; Sigma Phi 1960-, Pres; *office:* Cumberland Valley HS 6746 Carlisle Mechanicsburg PA 17055

ZEIGLER, PAMELA SOHM, Biology Teacher; *b:* Cleveland, O Rodney; *c:* Chelsea, Brooke, Molly; *ed:* Kent St Univ (BS) Ed, Bio *cr:* Kenston HS Bio Tchr 1990-92, 1994-; *ai:* Envirothon Team C Greenhouse Adv; Mentor; NEA 1991-; *office:* Kenston HS 17425 S Rd Chagrin Falls OH 44023

ZEINER, DIANE ELIZABETH, English & Journalism Teache Fitchburg, MA; *m:* Ronald A.; *c:* Kerrianne; *ed:* Fitchburg St Coll (B 1970; 36 Credit Hrs; *cr:* Memrl Jr HS Eng Tchr 1970-82; Fitchburg H & Jrnlsm Tchr 1981-; *ai:* Sr Class Adv; FHS Schl Cncl; Handbook C Prof Dev Cncl Block Scheduling Comm; ASCD; Phi Delta Kappa; N NEATE; NEA 1970-; MA Tchrs Assoc 1970-, Bd of Dir; Fitchburg Assoc 1970-, Pres, PR&R Chair; Natl Cncl of Girl Scouts 1955-, Ldr; Democratic Town Comm; Westminster PTO 1983-85, Pres; *o* Fitchburg HS 98 Academy St Fitchburg MA 01420*

ZEISLOFT, RUTH BOVAIRD, AP & Hnrs Eng Tchr; *b:* Philade PA; *m:* O. Samuel; *c:* Eric, Marc, Brian; *ed:* Univ of PA (BA) Amer 1959; Temple Univ (MED) Scndry Ed 1962; 21 Grad Credits B Masters in The Natl Writing Project, Coe Fnd Amer Lit & Performance Learning Systems Courses; *cr:* Darby-Colwyn Schl Seventh Grd Core Tchr 1959-62; Upper Merion Schl Dist Scndry Eng 1962-71; Millcreek Schl Dist 11th Grd A Pand Creative Writing 1986-; *ai:* Model UN Spon; Adult Ed; PTSA Exec Bd; NHS Co- Writers Club; Schl Restructuring Comm; Fac Liaison; Erie Area Fun Arts Steering Comm; EFG Curr Collaborative; Tchr of Young W Wkshp 1995; MEA, PSEA, NEA 1986-; PTA, PTSA 1974-, Pres & NWPCTE, NCTE 1987-, Treas; NW PA Lead Tchr 1989-; Northwe Tchr Ldrshp Ctr Bd of Governor Mem; Shenandoah Mea Homeowner's Assn 1971-, Treas 1981-; Millcreek Schl Dist Employ Month 1992; Fellow NW PA Writing Project; NCTE Writing Achvmt Judge 1993, 95; Received HS Yrbk Dedication 1995; NWPCTE Valuable Mem Awd 1994; *office:* Mc Dowell HS 3580 W 38th St Er 16506*

ZEITZHEIM, ERIC, History Teacher; *b:* Lakewood, OH; *m:* Malooly; *ed:* John Carroll Univ (BA) His 1989; Univ of Toledo Scndry Ed 1992; *cr:* Benton-Carroll-Salem Schls His Tchr 199 Sandusky Co Schl SBH Tchr 1991-92; Port Clinton City Schls His 1993-; *ai:* HS Ftbl Coach; *office:* Port Clinton HS 821 Jefferson St Clinton OH 43452*

ZELAZNY, MICHELE ANN, High School French Teacher; *b:* Cleve OH; *m:* Ted; *c:* Zachary, Zoe Ann; *ed:* Miami Univ of OH (BA) Fr, 1970; Middlebury Grad Schl of Fr in France (MA) Fr Lang & Lit Attnd Inst of Amer Univs Aix-en-Provence France, Univ de Paris Fr Akron Univ; *cr:* North Olmsted Schls Fr Tchr 1970-71; Ecole D'E Commerciales Paris France Eng Tchr 1971-72; Cuyahgoga Hghts Frgn Lang Tchr, Dept Coord 1972-; *ai:* Fr Club Adv; Discipline, Restructuring, Staff Dev Comms; Cuyahoga Heights Assn of Tchrs S Comm Chm; Cuyahoga Hghts Assn of Tchrs 1972-, Negotiating Team Ed Assn, NEA 1972-, Schlsp Comm Chm; OH Frgn Lang Assn, 1972-; PSR 1994-, Kndgtn Tchr; Highland Pride Comm 1990-; Local

990-; Martha Holden Jennings Scholar; *office:* Cuyahoga Heights Pub 4820 E 71st St Cleveland OH 44125

ENKY, SUSAN SMITH, Biology Teacher; *b:* Clearfield, PA; *m:* h M.; *ed:* IN Univ of PA (BS) Bio 1981; Ed Cert; Univ of Rochester t Hrs; *cr:* Glen Area Jr HS Bio, Sci Instr 1983-84, Biol Instr 1985-; cad Comm; Girls Bsktbl Asst Coach 6 Yrs; Clearfield Ed Assn 1985-; Bd; PSEA, NEA 1985-; St Francis Rosary & Altar Soc 1995; SPLA raising; *office:* Clearfield Area HS PO Box 910 Clearfield PA 16830

., MICHAEL LEE, Second Grade Teacher; *b:* Ephrata, PA; *m:* Anne e Huber; *c:* Elizabeth, Catherine, Allison; *ed:* Millersville Univ (BS) 73, (MA) Ed 1977; 36 Credits Beyond Masters; *cr:* Schaeffer Elem 2nd & 4th Grd Tchr 1973-86; Brecht Elem Schl 2nd Grd Tchr 90; Nitrauer Elem Schl 2nd Grd & Head Tchr 1990-94; Bucher Elem 2nd Grd & Multi-Yr Primary Tchr 1994-; *ai:* Var Sftbl Asst Coach; ra Club Instr; Consultant for Growing Healthy; Hlth Curr; Elem Sci Early Chldhd & Tech Comms; Manheim Twp Ed Assn, PA St Ed Assn, 1973-; *office:* Bucher Elem Schl 450 Candlewyck Ave Lancaster PA *

LER, TERRENCE LEE, World History & Geography Tchr; *b:* gfield, OH; *ed:* Urbana Univ (BS) Comprehensive Soc Stud 1974; *cr:* Branch Jr High OH His & World Geography Tchr 1975-80; *ai:* Var Bsktbl & Asst Girls Track Coach; NEA 1975-; *home:* 2253 Medway sle Medway OH 45341

LNER, JACK KARL, Eighth Grd Social Studies Tchr; *b:* Montclair, : Mary Jane Meyer; *c:* Jason R.; *ed:* Paterson St Coll (BA) S S 1968; am Patterson Coll (MA) S S 1974, (MA) Urban Ed 1977; Prins rvision 1979; *cr:* Wayne Hill HS S S Tchr 1968; Schuyler-Colfax Schl Tchr 1970-; *ai:* Fencing Ofcl 1972-; Fencing Coach 1971-72; NEA, 1968-; Am Legion 1980-, Adjutant; Who's Who in Am Colls & Univs *office:* Schayle-Colfax MS 15090 Hamburg Turnpike Wayne NJ)

LNER-ZEGLEN, HILDEGARD, Spanish & German Teacher; *b:* ig, West Germany; *m:* Mark Zeglen; *c:* Michelle, Matthew, Angela; H St Univ (BA) Span 1976, (BS) Frgn Lang Ed, Span, Ger 1992; son Univ Private Voice Lessons; *cr:* OSU Private Tutor for Ger Stu Granville HS Private Tutor for Span Stu 1985; Heath City Schls Sub 1986-87; Heath Schl Sub Tchr 1988-89, 1992-93; Newark Schl Sub 1988-89, 1992-93; Granville Schl Sub Tchr 1988-89, 1992-93; Joint chl Adult Ed Tchr 1991-93; Liberty Union Thurston HS Tchr 1992-; amen Choir; Woodworkers Assn; Friends of Daves Arborathim; OEA, 1992-; OFLA 1994; Phi Lambda Theta 1992-93; Miss Lieder Kranz OH St Univ Dean's List, Hnr Stu, Worked as Psych Lab Asst; Summa astic Awd.*

ONIS, JOAN MILLETT, 3rd & 4th Grade Teacher; *b:* Nashua, NH; ber; *ed:* Univ of NH (BA) Elem Ed 1965; Addl Credit Hrs; *cr:* Broad hl 3rd Grd Tchr 1965-66; Oyster River Schl Dist 3rd-5th Grd Tchr ; *ai:* NEA 1965-; NHEA 1965-; *office:* Moharimet Elem Schl 11 Lee adbury NH 03820

A, SUSAN GUYETTE, Bio, Chem & Gen Sci Teacher; *b:* Ravenna, n: Roger Luke; *ed:* Kent St Univ (BS) Sci of Ed Bio 1990, Sci of Ed 1993; Case Western Reserve 2 Grad Hrs Physics; Univ of Akron 3 Hrs Biochem; *cr:* Crestwood HS Sub 1990-91; Aurora HS Sub 91; Hudson HS 91; Sci Tchr 1991-; *ai:* High Schl Gymnastics Coach ; NEA, OEA 1991-; Hudson Ed Assn 1991-, bldg Rep 1995-96 Schl ffice: Hudson HS 2500 Hudson Aurora Rd Hudson OH 44236

AN, JAMES A., Mathematics Teacher; *b:* Mt Pleasant, PA; *ed:* oro Univ of PA (BS) Math Ed 1970; Attnd Univ of VA & George ington Univ; *cr:* Benjamin Stoddert Jr High Tchr & Dept Chair 77; Potomac Sr High Math Tchr 1977-; *ai:* AFT 1974-; *home:* 5309 n Pl Alexandria VA 22315*

KE, DONNA LYNN, Mathematics Teacher; *b:* Baltimore, MD; *ed:* on St Univ (BS) Math Ed 1980; 30 Credit Hrs Math, Ed 1989; *cr:* apeake Sr HS Math Tchr 1980-; *ai:* Acad Ath Adv; Asst Coach Tennis ; NEA, TAAAC 1980-; MCTM 1984-; NC Schl of Sci & Math Lead Prgm; *office:* Chesapeake Sr HS 4798 Mountain Rd Pasadena MD 2*

MEL, EDWIN LEON, History Teacher; *b:* New York, NY; *c:* David, ; *ed:* City Univ of NY (MA) His 1966; New York Univ (MA) His 9 Credit Hrs Columbia Univ; *cr:* White Plains HS His Tchr 1961-95; chester Comm Coll Adj Prof 1966-95; Highlands JHS Chprsn & Soc Tchr 1966-70; *ai:* Var Track & Field Coach; White Plains TA 1961-; 1961-; West Track & Field Coaches Assn 1979-; Columbia Univ A 1966; *office:* White Plains HS 550 North St White Plains NY 10605

YAN, STEPHEN MICHAEL, Professor of Mathematics; *b:* Grand , ND; *ed:* Univ of DE (BA) Math 1970; Univ Of MD (MA) Math 1974,) Math 1978; 30 Credit Hrs Towards MEd in Counseling, nological Svcs; *cr:* Penn St Univ Math Prof 1982-; *ai:* Promotion, re, Fac Affairs Comm Chm; Amer Mathmatical Soc 1982-; NSF wship 1970; 13 Articles Pub Prof Journals; *office:* PA St Univ Mont Cmps Mont Alto PA 17237

ZICKI, JOHN EDWARD, Wrestling Coach; *b:* Bloomfield, NJ; *m:* ; *c:* John, Katherine, Margaret, James; *cr:* Ironworkers Local #11 eyman 1977-93; Twp of Parsippany Knoll CC Arborist 1993-; *ai:* Wrestling Coach; *office:* Morris Catholic HS Morris Ave Denville NJ 4

MSEK, CAROL PINTER, Second Grade Teacher; *b:* Cleveland, OH; oger; *c:* Karen S. Holzwarth, Daniel S.; *ed:* Miami Univ (BS) Elem 959; Kent St Univ (MED) Cnslng 1990; 16 Addl Hrs in Cnslng; *cr:* dale Elem First-Second Grd Tchr 1959-65; Wilcox Elem Second Grd 1975-95; Bissell Elem Second Grd Tchr 1995-; *ai:* NEA, OEA 1959-; 1975-, Rep; Martha Holden Jennings Scholar 1990-91; Chi Sigma *office:* Bissell Elem Schl 1811 Glendale Dr Twinsburg OH 44087

O, CARL ARTHUR, Assoc Professor of Philosophy; *b:* Colchester, n: Mary Egan Archambault; *c:* Jason, Giles; *ed:* St Michaels Coll (BA) osophy 1967; Marquette Univ (MA) Philosophy 1970, (PHD) osophy 1976; *cr:* St Michaels Coll Philosophy Prof 1970-; *ai:* sing; Cnslng; Title IV Flwshp Marquette Univ; Numerous Articles & y Pub; *office:* Saint Michaels Coll Winooski Park Colchester VT 9*

O, CARL LOUIS, 7th Grade Math Teacher; *ed:* WV Univ (BS) Math 1974; Attnd Penn St; *ai:* PIAA Wrestling Ofcl 1974-.

T, SALLY INEZ, Second Grade Teacher; *b:* Yamacraw, KY; *c:* mond t., Deborah A., Robert J.; *ed:* Wright St Univ (BA) Ed 1970, (MS) 972; 30 Credit Hrs Ed; *cr:* O R Edgington Elem 2nd Grd Tchr 1970-; NDEA 1970-; OEA 1970-; *home:* 331 W Nottingham Rd Dayton OH 5

TNER, ALTON RAY, Principal; *b:* Hamburg, PA; *m:* Debbie J.; *c:* Jean, Ben Joel, Heather; *ed:* Hampton (BA) Music; Lexinton (MED) Univ of MA (AWT); Christian Cncslng Ed Fndtn (CCEF); *cr:* Gateway n Schl Prin; *ai:* Mid Atlantic Schl Assn 1988; Chrstn Law Assn; Amer Testing Inst; MACSA; PAACE; ACSI; U.S. Jaycees 1968-, Treas, m Awd; Civil Svc Comm; Emergency Mgmt Coord; Dept of Ed, Adv; Pres; Natl Ethic Comm; Kutztown Bus Assn, Pres; Franconia Mennonite Ed Cncl; *office:* Lighthouse Christian Acad 195 Forgedale Rd Fleetwood PA 19522

ZENTNER, JEFFERY J., Instrumental Music & Band Dir; *b:* Watertown, NY; *m:* Melody Elkhardt; *c:* Morgan, Jessica; *ed:* SUNY at Fredonia (BM) Music Ed 1974; Ithaca Coll (MM) Trumpet Performance 1976; *cr:* Gilbertsville CS 4-12 Grd Band, Inst Music Dir 1976-82; Belleville Henderson CS 4-6 Grd Inst Music Dir 1982-89; Watertown HS 9-12 Grd Band, Inst Music Dir 1989-; *ai:* MYSSMA, MENC 1978-; *office:* Watertown HS 1335 Washington St Watertown NY 13601

ZENTZ, MELISSA O., Spanish Teacher; *b:* Philadelphia, PA; *m:* Gerry; *ed:* Univ of MD 33 Grad Hrs; *cr:* Suitland Sr HS; *ai:* Span Honor Soc; Span Club; Amer Cncl of Tchrs of Span & Portuguese 1981-; *office:* Suitland Sr HS 5200 Silver Hill Rd Forestville MD 20747

ZENTZ, RICHARD CHARLES, Social Studies Teacher; *b:* Scranton, PA; *m:* Bonnie Wisenauer; *c:* Tyler, Daniel; *ed:* Loyola Coll (MA) Modern Stud 1986; Bucknell Univ (BA) Ec 1973; Towson St Univ Tchr Cert; *cr:* Hokebird Jr HS Soc Stud Tchr 1977-84; Dundalk HS Soc Stud Tchr 1984-92; Abington Heights MS Soc Stud Tchr 1992-93; Chesapeake HS Soc Stud Tchr 1993-; *ai:* Ath Dir; Head Ftbl Coach; NEA, MSTA, TABCO 1977-; MSFCA 1985-; *office:* Chesapeake HS 1801 Turkey Point Rd Baltimore MD 21221

ZENTZ, ROBERT L., Adj Professor of Science Ed; *b:* Gloversville, NY; *m:* Judith Miller; *c:* Karin Yettru, Gary Robert; *ed:* SUNY Brockport (BS) Chem 1961; Union Coll (MS) Sci Ed 1968; 45 Credits Past Masters; Attnd Franklin & Marshall, Univ of CO, SUNY Albany, Siena; *cr:* Coll of St Rose Sci Ed Prof 1 Yr; Schamont HS Sci Chair, HS Chem Tchr 30 Yrs; *ai:* Soccer Coach 29 Yrs; NYSUT, AFT, NYSSTA 1961-; NYSSA 1965-; Lake Hill Soccer Club 1977-, Founder, Pres; Tchr of Yr 1993; Section II Soccer Coach of Yr 1984; *home:* 364 Goode St Burnt Hills NY 12027

ZERBE, ERIC S., Health & Physical Ed Teacher; *b:* Pine Grove, PA; *m:* Susan Mc Henry; *c:* Eric M., Drew J.; *ed:* E Stroudsburg Univ (BS) Hlth, PE 1968, (ME) Hlth, PE Ed 1974; *cr:* Tamaqua Jr HS Hlth, PE Tchr 28 Yrs; *ai:* BASS Club Adv; Tchr Mentor & Co-op Tchr for Stu Tchrs; Var HS Wrestling Coach 17 Yrs; NEA 1968-; Bass Anglers Sportsman Soc 1985-; Schuylkil Cty Ofcls Wrestling Hall of Fame; Wresting Hall of Fame.

ZERBE, SUSAN MCHENRY, Health & Phys Education Tchr; *b:* Darby, PA; *m:* Eric S.; *c:* Eric M., Drew J.; *ed:* East Stroudsburg Univ (BS) Hlth & PE 1968; 30 Post Grad Credits in Ed & Spec Ed at Penn St; *cr:* Tamaqua Area Schl Dist Elem PE Tchr 1970-89, Jr HS Hlth & PE Tchr 1989-; *ai:* Tamaqua Ed Assn 1968-, Negotiations Comm, Pub Relations Comm; PA Ed Assn, NEA 1968-; Schuylkill Cty Gift of Time Awd 1992; Former Girls Var Vlybl Coach; *office:* Tamaqua Area Jr HS High St Tamaqua PA 18252*

ZERBY, CLAIR W., Agriculture Teacher; *b:* Centre Hall, PA; *m:* Carol A. Kroeck; *c:* Brian, Susan, Judy; *ed:* PennSt Univ (BSC) Animal Sci 1960, (MED) Ag Ed 1977; *cr:* Warwick HS Ag Tchr 1965-69; Mansfield HS Ag Tchr 1969-70; Cowanesque Vly HS Ag Tchr 1970-; *ai:* FFA Adv; NHS Adv; Voc Ed Dept; Local, St, Edctrs 1965-, Local Outstdng Ed; St, Natl Ag Tchrs 1965-, Rep VP St; Cty Fair Bd 1970-, Pres, Sheep Ch; Jr Livestock Sale Comm 1980-, Outstdng Svc; Cty, St Sheep, Wool Grds 1970-, Sec Local, Pres St; Knoxville Meth Church 1970-, Ch at Several Comm; Honorary St, Natl FFA Degrees; Conservation Educator of Yr; *home:* RR 1 Box 980 Knoxville PA 16928*

ZEREBNICK, MICHELE, Associate Professor; *b:* Wilkinsburg, PA; *ed:* Univ of Pittsburgh at Greensburg (BA) Admin of Justice 1978; Univ of Pittsburg (MA) Admin of Justice 1982, (MA) Sociology 1985, (ABD) Sociology 1985; *cr:* Care for Yth Inc Cnslr 1978-80; Univ of Pittsburgh Part-time Instr 1985-88; Comm Coll of Allegheny Cty Assoc Prof 1987-; *ai:* Criminal Justice Club Adv; AFT 1987-; ACA 1988-; AFP 1988-92; FOP Lodge #39 1995-; Outstdng Young Women of Amer 1984; Apple for Tchr Awd Univ of Pittsburgh 1986; Who's Who in Amer Law Enforcement 1989; *home:* 7303 Ringertown Rd Export PA 15632

ZEREMENKO, STEPHANIE PANKAS, Spanish Teacher; *b:* Canonsburg, PA; *m:* James Joseph; *c:* Alexa Marie; *ed:* Univ of Pgh (BS) Elem Ed 1979; Cert Span 1983; Addl 30 Credit Hrs Fr; 30 Credit Hrs Elem Ed; *cr:* Chartiers Houston Sub Tchr 1979-83, Span Tchr 1983-, Soc Stud Tchr, Frgn Lang Dept Chm 1995-; *ai:* Cheerleading 1979-89, Stu Gov 1984- Spon; Foreign Lang Club 1984-; CHFT 1984-, Sec 1989; Church Choir 1970-, Dir 15 Yrs.

ZERR, CINDY SHOLLENBERGER, Spcl Ed Learning Support Tchr; *b:* Reading, PA; *m:* Dwight D.; *c:* Melissa, Laura; *ed:* Kutztown St Coll (BED) Spec Ed, Elem Ed Tchr 1973; Lehigh Univ (MED) Spec Tchr 1976; 30 Addl Credits; *cr:* Schuykill Cty IU #29 Spec Ed Tchr 1973-80; St Luke's Church Nursery Schl Non-Profit Nursery Schl Tchr 1983-86; Hamburg St Theater & Video Pvt Bus Owner 1981-86; Berks Cty IU #14 Spec Ed Tchr 1986-91; Hamburg Area Schl Dist Spec Ed Tchr 1991-; *ai:* Vol Coord Hawle Vol Corps; Fac Advy Bd; Parish Ed Comm; NEA 1973-; Sunday Schl Tchr; *home:* 409 Hill Dr Hamburg PA 19526

ZERVOULIS, DONNA HURLEY, High School English Teacher; *b:* Jersey City, NJ; *m:* Peter M.; *c:* Meghann, Molly; *ed:* St Peters Coll (BA) Eng 1975; Boston Coll 24 Grad Schl Credits Eng, Fordham Univ 3 Grad Credits Eng, New Schl of Jrnlsm 3 Credits 1977; *cr:* Boston Coll Remedial Rdng Tchr 1975-77; Robinson Schl 7th-8th Grd Eng Tchr 1979-84; Bayonne High Eng Tchr 1987-88, 1989-; *ai:* Class of 1999 Adv; Excl Comm Chprsn; Broadway Scholar Prgm Coord; BTA, NJEA 1978-; NCTE 1995-; Bayonne Symphony 1995-, Bd of Dirs, Pub Relations Dir; Bayonne Bridgemen Alumni Assn 1974-, Sec, Pub Relations Dir; Vroom Schl Parent Assn 1988-, Mem; Adopt-a-Schl Theatre Grant 1989-95; St Dept Rdng Wkshps 1994; Governors HSPT Comm 1982; *office:* Bayonne HS 29th St & Ave A Bayonne NJ 07002

ZETARSKI, ROBIN ANN, Math & Programming Instr; *b:* Hartford, CT; *ed:* Boston Coll (BA) Math 1992; Boston Univ Post Grad Courses; *cr:* Lexington High Math & Comp Sci 1992-; *ai:* Tech & Ethics Comm; Facilitators for Change; MTA 1992-; NEA 1992-; *office:* Lexington HS 251 Waltham St Lexington MA 02173

ZETTY, NINA, Math & Cmptr Programming Tchr; *b:* Brownsville, PA; *m:* John K.; *c:* Tiffany N., John P.; *ed:* CA Univ of PA (BS) Scndry Ed, Math 1988, (MED) Sec Ed, Math, Cmptr Sci 1989; WV Univ (EDD) Curr, Instr, Cmptr Ed 1992; Credit Hrs Toward Cert as Scndry Prin; *cr:* Jefferson-Morgan HS Math, Cmptr Programming Tchr 1989-; CA Univ of PA Upward Bound Prgm Math Instr 1994-; *ai:* Cmptr Coord; NHS; Acad League; NEA, PSEA 1989-; PA Cncl Tchrs of Math; NCTM; ASCD; Delta Kappa Gamma; BSA Troop 630 1988-, Treas; All Star Edctr 1993-94; Nom for Presidential Awd for Sci, Math Tchng 1994; *home:* 548 Pearl St Brownsville PA 15417*

ZEZULKA, CHARLES, MS Developmental Reading Tchr; *b:* Norwich, CT; *m:* Marie Haddad; *c:* Amy, Lori, Tami; *ed:* Eastern CT St Univ (BS) Ed 1965; Univ of CT (MA) Ed 1969; Admitted to PHD Pgm 1971 30 Credits; CT Fellow, Ed Policy Flwshp Pgm Inst for Educl Ldrshp Washington DC 1990-91; *cr:* N Stonington Pub Schls 5th-6th Grd Tchr 1966-70; S B Butler Schl Elem Tchr 1970-89; CT Coll Cooperating Tchr 1973-; CT St Dept of Ed Assessor, Mentor & Trainer 1988-; Cutler MS Developmental Rdng Tchr 1989-; *ai:* Young Edctr Soc Adv; CT Tchr Of the Yr Selection Comm; Editorial Bd Ctr for Tchng Resources Mazer Corp; Lecturer & Speaker on Ed Topics; NEA 1970-; CT Ed Assn 1970-, Salutes Awd 1993; Groton Ed Assn 1970-, Bd of Dirs & Treas GEA & PAC, 1989 Groton Tchr of the Yr; Groton Pub Lib 1977-, Bd of Trustees; Town of Groton 1983-, Town Cnslr 6 Times; Town of Groton 1995-, Justice of the Peace; Groton Ed Fndtn Inc 1995-, Founding Mem; CT Tchr of the Yr 1990; Producer of Video Reflections on Tchng 1990; Milken Family Fndtn Natl Edctr Awd 1992; Highlighted in Book How Award Winning Teachers are Shaping Our Childrens Future 1992; *office:* Carl C Cutler MS 160 Fishtown Rd Mystic CT 06355*

ZHANG, ENDE, Associate Professor; *b:* Xianyang Shaanxi, China; *m:* Fang Chen; *c:* Forbes, Eric; *ed:* Xian Jiaotongo Univ (BS) Math 1982; Univ of WI at Madison (MA) Applied Math 1988, (MS) Comp Sci 1992, (PHD) Bio Math 1992; *cr:* Xian Jiaotongo Univ Lecturer 1982-86; Univ of WI at Madison Tchng Asst & Instr 1986-92; WA St Comm Coll Assoc Prof 1992-; *ai:* Campus Qigong Club Adv; IYXQA Coordinating Comm; WSCC Enrollment Comm; AMS 1986-; IYXQA 1992-, Coord; *office:* Washington State Comm Coll 710 Colegate Dr Marietta OH 45750*

ZICARI, DORIS JUNE MCKINSEY, Third Grade Teacher; *b:* Hagerstown, MD; *m:* Richard; *c:* Zev Richard, Steven McKinsey; *ed:* Albion Coll (BA) Liberal Arts & Ed 1957; Univ of MI (MA) Ed 1965; Whole Lang Stud; *cr:* Southfield Schls Elem Tchr 1957-65; Penfield Cntrl Schls Elem Tchr 1965-; *ai:* Club Adv for Young Adult Group for Spec Adults; AFT; Penfield Ed Assn 1965-; AAUW 1994-; Alpha Xi Alpha 1956-; Many Inservice Hrs in Dist; *home:* 99 Sagamore Dr Rochester NY 14617*

ZICCARDI, JOSEPHINE, English Teacher & Chairperson; *b:* Bronx, NY; *m:* Alfonso; *c:* Christina, Danielle; *ed:* Hunter Coll (MS) Eng 1972; *cr:* Wm. W. Niles Schl Eng Tchr 1972-76; J.F.K. HS Eng Chprsn 1987-; *ai:* NHS Adv; NCTE, NYSEC 1986-; WCEE 1990-; Ed Schl of Excl Awd; Great Books Facilitator; Rdng Lab Dir; Coll Internship Prgm; *office:* John F Kennedy Cath HS 54 Route 138 Somers NY 10589

ZICHITTELLA, GAIL EBERHARDT, Chemistry Teacher; *b:* Buffalo, NY; *m:* Robert J.; *c:* Anne, Lauren; *ed:* SUC at Brockport (BS) Bio & Chem 1971; SUNY at Buffalo (MS) Natural Sci 1983; 30 Grad Hrs; *cr:* Depew Union Free Schls Sci Tchr 1985-86; Cheektowaga Cntrl HS Chem Tchr 1986-; *ai:* Class of 1999 Adv; Responsibility Trainer; Recognition Stu Comm; STANYS 1986-; Amer Chemical Soc 1992-; Sci Supv WNY 1995 -; *office:* Cheektowaga Central H S 3600 Union Rd Cheektowaga NY 14225*

ZICKER, PAUL STEVEN, History Teacher; *b:* Westwood, NJ; *m:* Carol Johnson; *c:* Ashleigh, Stephen; *ed:* Montclair St Coll (BA) His 1987; PUrsuing (MA) in Admin, Supervision, Mngmt; *ai:* NEA 1987-; *office:* Howell HS Squankum-Yellowbrook Rd Farmingdale NJ 07727*

ZICKES, JANE M., Science Tchr & Dept Chairman; *b:* Cleveland, OH; *ed:* Notre Dame Coll (AB) Hlth & PE, Bio, Gen Sci 1960; John Carroll Univ (MA) Sci Ed 1968; Ed-Cmptr Literacy 4 Hrs 1984; *cr:* Benjamin Franklin Jr HS Sci Tchr 1960-61; St Augustine Acad Bio, Hlth & PE Tchr, Bio, Envir, Sci & Cont Sci Dept Chm 1961-; *ai:* AAHPERD 1966-; NABT 1965-; NCEA 1980-; CRCST, CWPERA, NWE 1980-, Advy Bd 1992-; APL 1991-; USTA 1984-; *office:* St Augustine Acad 14808 Lake Ave Lakewood OH 44107

ZIDONIS, PEG MCGINTY, English Tchr & Newspaper Adv; *b:* Cleveland, OH; *m:* Frank J.; *c:* Frank, Bill, Anne Straub, Kathryn; *ed:* Coll of Mount Saint Joseph (BA) Eng 1956; OH St (MA) Ed 1980; Attnd Northern IL & Marquette; *cr:* Cleveland Pub Schls Eng Tchr 1956-59; Bexley City Schls Eng Tchr 1975-; *ai:* Newspaper Adv; Lit Magazine Adv 4 Yrs; Eng Dept Chair 1989-; Great Lakes Interscholastic Press, Jrnlsm Assn of OH Schls, NOSPA 1975-, Bd; Wall Street Journal Fellow 1959 & 1989; Jrnlsm Tchr of Yr; Bexley Educator of Yr 1995; *home:* 1724 Churchview Ln Columbus OH 43220

ZIEGENFUS, THEODORE T., Associate Professor of Biology; *b:* Latrobe, PA; *c:* Susan A., Theodore F., Karl A.; *ed:* St Vincent Coll (AB) Bio 1964; WV Univ (MA) Bio-Botany 1966, (PHD) Botany-Genetics 1970; Post Doctoral Stud 1979-80; North TX St Univ & Wilmington Med Ctr Med Genetics; *cr:* WV Univ Grad Tchng Asst 1964-67, Instr 1967-70; Penn St Univ Asst Prof 1970-77, Assoc Prof 1977-; *ai:* Plan for the Future, Promotion, Tenure & Admissions Ofcr Search Comms; Discipline Bd Chm; NABT 1970-; PA Acad of Sci 1970-, Exhibits Chair; ASHG 1979-; BSA 1952-, Distngd Commissions Dist Awd of Merit Silver Beaver; NSF Grants; 25th Publications; In House Lab Manual & Genetics Book.*

ZIEGENFUSS, RANDY MICHAEL, Music Teacher; *b:* Bethlehem, PA; *ed:* Moravian Coll (BMUS) Music 1987; Attnd Westminster Choir Coll; *cr:* East Penn Schl Dist Music Tchr 1987-, Dept Chair 1993-; *ai:* Concert, Chime Choir; Les Chanteves; Women's Ensemble; Spring Musicial; Tri-M Music Hnr Soc; MENC, NEA 1987-; ACDA 1995-; *office:* Eyer Jr HS 5616 Buckeye Rd Macungie PA 18062

ZIEGER, JUDITH GAY, First Grade Teacher; *b:* Dover, NJ; *ed:* Paterson St Coll (BA) Early Chldhd Ed 1969; 20 Credit Hrs; *cr:* C E Lawrence Elem 1st Grd Tchr 27 Yrs; *ai:* NEA 1969-; NJEA 1969-; SCEA 1969-; SWEA 1969-, Recording Sec; *office:* Clifton E Lawrence Primary Sch 31 Ryan Rd Sussex NJ 07461

ZIEGLER, DANA ROBERT, 4th Grade Teacher, Coordinator; *b:* Franklin, NJ; *m:* Peggy H.; *c:* Dana James, Jason J., Kevin C., Renee J.; *ed:* Tusculum Coll (BA) Elem Ed 1970; *cr:* Vernon Twp Schl Dist 4th Grd Tchr 1970-71, 1st Grd Tchr 1972, 5th Grd Tchr 1972-74, 3rd Grd Tchr 1974-84, 4th Grd Tchr 1984-; *ai:* UTHS Musicals Assoc Dir, Choreographer; Grd Level Coord; NEA, NJEA 1970-; SCEA 1970-, Treas; VTEA 1970-, Treas; Intnl Thespian Soc 1992-; Governor's Tchr Recognition Prgm; Tchr Scholar in Residence; *office:* Rolling Hills Primary Schl Sammis Rd Vernon NJ 07461

ZIEGLER, JAMES ROBERT, English Teacher; *b:* New Brighton, PA; *ed:* Geneva Coll (BA) Eng 1993; 15 Credit Hrs Westminster Coll Eng; *cr:* Freedom Area HS Eng Tchr 1993-; *ai:* Asst Band, Play Dir; NEA, PSEA, FAEA 1993-;NCTE 1990-; Natl Conf of Governor's Schls 1995-; PA Governor's Schl for Arts 1991-, Admin Asst; PIAA Bsktbl Ofcl 1992-; *office:* Freedom Area HS 1190 Bulldog Dr Freedom PA 15042

ZIELINSKI, EDWARD J., Science Education Professor; *b:* Ft Bragg, NC; *m:* Helen E.; *c:* Zachary, Ashley; *ed:* Univ of TX (BSEd) Ed 1976, (MED) Sci Ed 1981, (PHD) Sci Ed 1986; Microcomputer Interface in Sci Classrooms; Project WILD, Learning Tree, WET, Facillitator; Use of World Wide Web in Tchng Sci; *cr:* Austin Pub Schls Sci Tchr 1976-1981; Austin Comm Coll Asst Prof 1981-86; Clarion Univ of PA Prof 1987-; *ai:* Chair Bio Curr, Acad Stans; Dir NSF St Initiative for Biotechnology Ed, Inner City Minority Sci Enhancement; PA Sci Tchrs Assn, Past Pres, Mem Horizons, Awards, Constitution, Bylaws Comms; PSTA 1986-, Pres; NSTA 1980-, MS Review, NCATE Comms; NARST 1980-; Phi Delta Kappa 1982-; Red Cross 1986-, Exec Bd; NSF Statewide Initiative for Biotechnology Ed; Dir Saturday, Summer Sci Prgms for Elem Stdnts; Articles Pub; *office:* Clarion Univ Peirce Science Ctr Clarion PA 16214

ZIELINSKI, PAUL, Science Teacher; *b:* Toledo, OH; *m:* Marianne Elizabeth Morrin; *c:* Carolyn, Laura; *ed:* Univ of Toledo (BS) Bio, Chem 1981, (BED) Scndry Sci 1984, (MED) Admin, Supervision 1989; 6 Credit Hrs Internet Network Comms; 5 Credit Hrs Medical Genetics; 3 Credit Hrs Water Quality Testing Techs; *cr:* Whitmer Sr HS Sci Tchr 1984-; *ai:* Maumee Bay Watershed Project Water Quality Testing Coord; Steering, Cmptr Comms; NABT, SECO 1986-; OEA 1984-, Bldg Rep; NEA 1984-;

Presidential Environmental Youth Svcs Awd; *office:* Whitmer HS 5601 Clegg Dr Toledo OH 43613

ZIELINSKI, STEPHEN FRANCIS, High School Math Teacher; *b:* Buffalo, NY; *m:* Mary Brady; *c:* Steve, Mike, James, Linda, Peter; *ed:* Univ of Buffalo (BA) Math 1963; Canisius Coll (MS) Ed 1965; *cr:* Maryvale Jr HS Math Tchr 1964-70; Maryvale Sr HS Math Tchr 1971-; *ai:* Var Bowling Coach 30 Yrs; 9th Grd Babl Coach 5 Yrs; Southline Ath Assn 1974-, Pres, Boys Bsbl Commissioner, Yth Bd Awd; Erie Cty Interscholastic Cncl 1968-, Bowling Chm, 25 Yr Svc Awd; *office:* Maryvale HS 1050 Maryvale Dr Cheektowaga NY 14225

ZIEMER, RICHARD CARL, Professor of Liberal Arts; *b:* Gresham, OR; *m:* Adelle W. Yeakel; *c:* Elleda Claire; *ed:* Bob Jones Univ (MA) (BA) Rel, Eng, Fr 1961, (PHD) Ancient Lang 1966; Temple Univ (MED) Eng Ed 1973; Dropsie Coll Ugaritic, Ancient Semitic Lexicography 8 Hrs 1965-66; Univ of PA Hebrew Poetry, Akkadian 9 Hrs 1967-68; *cr:* DE Vly Coll Prof 1966-; Eden Mennonite Church Sr Pastor 1985-92; Flatland Mennonite Church Sr Pastor 1970-77; *ai:* Bob Jones Univ Alumni Assn 1970-, Life Mem, Club Adv; AAUP 1970-73, 1995-; Amer Oriental Soc 1964-, Life Mem; Rolls-Royce Owners Club 1986-; Titanic Intnl 1990-; Evangelical Theol Soc 1968-; Grad, Post Grad Flwshps, Schlsps; *office:* Delaware Valley Coll 700 E Butler Ave Doylestown PA 18901

ZIEMIAN, CAROL ANN, English & Journalism Tchr; *b:* Springfield, MA; *m:* Robert P.; *c:* Robert, Jessica; *ed:* Westfield St Coll (BA) Eng 1966; Northeastern Univ (MA) Writing 1992; Trinity Coll CT 6 Hrs Eng Lit; Boston UNiv 9 Hrs Jrnlsm; Univ of MA 6 Hrs Psych; *cr:* Chicopee Comprehensive HS Eng Tchr 1966-69; Antilles Consolidated;HEW Naval Air Base in PR Eng Tchr 1969-72; Dedham HS Eng Tchr 1972-; *ai:* HS Newspaper Adv; Ed, Chief of Newspaper Sent to Taxpayers Spotlighting K-12 Classroom; League of Women Voters 1972-, Pres; LWV Voter Svc Comm Chm; Yankee Pen Bd; JEA; NCTE; NSPA; Founded K-12 Newspaper Sent to Comm, Celebrates Whats Going on Pub Schl System MA; Inservice Grant Cmptr Project; Horace Mann Grant to Fund Training of 12 K-12 Tchrs Write, Take Photos for K-12 Newspaper; Dedham Ed Assn Grant-Tri-Dept for Photography Project; *office:* Dedham HS 140 Whiting Ave Dedham MA 02026*

ZIEMIANSKI, MICHELE M., 2nd Grade Teacher; *b:* Youngstown, OH; *m:* Thomas G.; *c:* Christine Black, Sharon Coates, Patricia Gstell, Kathryn; *ed:* Youngstown Univ (BA) Elem Ed 1964; *ai:* Multi-Cultural Comm; Comm Rep PTA; Wildlife Comm; Math, Rdng, Sci & Soc Stud.

ZILAI, JAMES W., History Teacher; *b:* Hoboken, NJ; *m:* Maria S. Dudok; *c:* Debra Normann, Kristina Vehling; *ed:* Wagner Coll (BA) His 1967; *cr:* Woodbridge JHS 8th Grd His Tchr 1968-80; Woodbridge MS 7th Grd Geog Tchr 1981-90; Avenel MS 8th Grd His Tchr 1991-; *ai:* Soc Stud Dept Head; IM Sports Dir; Site Mgmt Comm; NEA 1968-; NJEA 1968-; *office:* Avenel MS Woodbine Ave Avenel NJ 07001

ZILLA, RICK KENNETH, Technology Teacher; *b:* Ford City, PA; *ed:* CA Univ of PA (BS) Tech Ed 1993; Working Towards MS Tech Ed; *cr:* Greenville HS Tech Ed 1993-; *ai:* Jr Var Ftbl Coach; NEA, PSEA, Intnl Tech Ed Assn 1993-; Tech Ed Assn of PA 1993-, Region 2-W VP; 1995 Gift of Time Tribute Spon by Amer Family Inst; *office:* Greenville HS 9 Donation Rd Greenville PA 16125

ZIMBOUSKI, HARRIET, Sixth Grd Soc Studies Teacher; *ed:* Ladycliff Coll (BA) Eng Lit 1964; Cen Ct St Coll (MS) Elem Ed 1970; *cr:* Bristol Pub Schls Permanent Sub Tchr 1964-65; Edgewood Elem Schl 4th-6th Grd Tchr 1965-93; Chippens Hill MS 6th Grd Soc Stud Tchr 1993-; *ai:* NEA 1964-74; AFT 1974-; *office:* Chippens Hill MS Peacedale Ave Bristol CT 06010

ZIMKUS, JOHN JOSEPH, Soc Studies & Amer His Tchr; *b:* Stamford, CT; *m:* Patricia Dugan; *c:* Charles; *ed:* Miami Univ (BS) Soc Stud & Speech 1971; Wright St Univ (MAEd) Soc Stud Scndry Classroom 1978; *cr:* Lucille Berry MS 7th Grd OH Stud Tchr 1972-95, 7th Grd Amer His Tchr 1995-; *ai:* Fac Mgr of Ath 1992-; K-12th Soc Stud Comm 1993-; NEA 1972-; OH Ed Assn 1972-; Lebanon Ed Assn 1972-; Warren Cty Historical Soc 1975-, Historian; Excl in Tchng Fndtn Awd Progress Cncl of Warren Cty Inc 1990; Contributing Author Ohio History Resource Guide for Teachers 1991; Co-Author Get to Know OH, OH Studies Module 1994 for Pub Expenditure Cncl; *office:* Berry Jr HS 23 Oakwood Ave Lebanon OH 45036

ZIMMER, LAWRENCE ALTON,JR., Sociology Professor; *b:* Bath, NY; *m:* Gale Alice Nevidjon; *ed:* Corning Comm Coll (AA) Liberal Arts 1967; Alfred Univ (BA) His 1971; SUNY Albany (MA) Sociology, Ed 1973; Curr Dev & Design, GrantS Marship, Ed Leardership Training; *cr:* NY St Ed Dept Coord of Vol Svc, Lib for the Blind 1985-95; Empire St Coll Sociology, Adj 1990-; Schenectady Cty Comm Coll Sociology Prof, Adjunct 1990-95; Finger Lakes DDSO 1995-; *ai:* Writing Plans for Disbilities into Fall Spectrum of Coll Courses, Prgms; Prof Employees Assn, vol Admin Assn 1985-95; Pub in Journal of Assn of Vol Admins, Bookmark; *office:* Empire State University 2 Union Ave Saratoga Springs NY 12866*

ZIMMER, NADINE (DENLINGER), Computer & Business Teacher; *b:* Greenville, OH; *m:* Kent; *c:* Stacy, Tara; *ed:* Wright St Univ (BS) Ed 1988; Univ of Dayton Disk Operating Systems 1990; Soita of Miami Univ Computing Seminar 1990; Wright St Univ Novell NetWare Courses 1995; *cr:* Gem Savings Assn Proof Clerk, Branch Auditor 1967-70, Acctng Clerk, Acct Systems Consultant 1970-77, Systems Analyst, Programmer 1977-80, Project Control Analyst 1980-83; Covington Exempted Vly Schl Cmptr, Bus Tchr 1988-; *ai:* Newspaper Adv 1991-; Curr Cncl; Tech Comm; NEA 1988-; Arcanum Swim Club Team Stingray Inc, Treas 1992-95, Pres 1996; Church of Brethern 1985-, Bd Mem; Arcanum-Butler Schl Dist, Advy Cncl; Tandy Tech Scholars Outstdng Tchr Awd 1991-92; *office:* Covington HS 807 Chestnut St Covington OH 45318

ZIMMER, WILLIAM F., English Teacher; *b:* Oceanside, NY; *ed:* Nassau Comm Coll (AA) Lbrl Arts 1989; SUNY at New Paltz (BA) Eng Ed 1991, (MS) Ed; *cr:* Pine Bush HS Eng Tchr 1992-; *ai:* Lit Magazine Adv; Yrbk Co-Adv; NCTE 1992-; *office:* Pine Bush HS Rt 302 Pine Bush NY 12566

ZIMMERMAN, BARBARA REITMEYER, Kindergarten Teacher; *b:* Oneida, PA; *m:* Harold; *c:* Mary Zimmerman Thomsen, Paul Joseph; *ed:* Bloomsburg Univ (BS) Elem Ed K-8 1955; *cr:* Emerson Schl Fifth Grd Tchr 1955-63; Cedarbrook Schl Kndgtn Tchr 1970-; *ai:* Assembly, Discipline, Kndgtn, Inservice Planning, Dist-Wide Comms; NEA, NJEA, PEA, Union Cty Ed Assoc 1955-; St Joseph Rosary Soc 1959-63, VP; Fish Organization for Needy 1986-; Christmas Wish Tree for Needy; St Bernard's Cncl; Bellcore Tchr Inst; Tchr of Yr; *office:* Cedarbrook Schl 1049 Central Ave Plainfield NJ 07062*

ZIMMERMAN, CLIFF BLAKE, Earth Science Regents Teacher; *b:* Bronx, NY; *m:* Stacy Ina Kahn; *c:* Joel, Alex; *ed:* Queens Coll (BS) Environmental Sci & Geology 1984;, (MS) Scndry Sci Ed 1991; 12 Credith Hrs Learning Disabilities Scndry Ed; 12 Credit Hrs Environmental Geology of NYC Waters; *cr:* Alfred E. Smith HS Earth Sci Regents Tchr 1987-; Shaarei Torah of Rockland Earth Sci Regents Tchr 1992-; Ramapo Coll Geology Adj 1993-95; Mercy Coll Geology Adj 1995-; *ai:* Ind Sci Stud Supvr Graduating Stdnts; Exec Comm Sci Schl Awareness; NSTA 1988-, Honorable Mbrshp; AFT, UFT 1986-; NYSTA 1987-; Tchr of Yr NYC Bronx 1988; Rsrch Contributor Coll Text Geohazards; *office:* Alfred E Smith HS 333 E 151st St Bronx NY 10451*

ZIMMERMAN, DAVID MATTHEW, Music Instructor; *b:* Williamsport, PA; *m:* Susan C. Cole; *ed:* Mansfield Univ (BS) Music Ed 1974, (MS) Music Ed 1981; 15 Addl Grad Credit Hrs; *cr:* Bishop Neumann HS Music Instr 1974-78; Prof Musician Vocalist & Keyboards 1979-85; Sayre Area Schl Dist Music Instr 1986-; *ai:* Marching Band Arranger & Drill Instr; Jazz Band & Musical Production Pit Dir; Asst Bsktbl & Asst Track Coach; NHS Adv; PMEA & MENC 1986-; PSEA & NEA 1986-, Local Assn VP; Phi Mu Alpha Sinfonia 1971-; Organized Red Cross Blood Mobile 1987-91; Sayre Recreation Staff 1987-; Soloist for Little League World Series Natl Anthem 1981; Performed at Natl Jazz Edctrs Assn Conv 1984; Guest Conductor at Music Festivals; *office:* Sayre Area Schl Dist 331 W Lockhart St Sayre PA 18840*

ZIMMERMAN, GEORGE ALBERT, Math Teacher & Dept Chair; *b:* Elmhurst, IL; *m:* Kathy Vete; *c:* Jeffrey, Scott; *ed:* Edinboro St Coll (BS) Ed 1975; Univ of Pittsburgh (MED) Math 1978; *cr:* West Mifflin North HS Math Tchr 1975-; *ai:* Textbook Comm Chm, Math Dept Chair; Part-time Instr CCAC; AFT 1975-; *office:* West Mifflin Area Schl Dist 91 Commonwealth Ave West Mifflin PA 15122

ZIMMERMAN, JANE M., Third Grade Teacher; *b:* Somerset, PA; *ed:* Madison Coll (BMEd) Music 1954; Penn St Univ (MED) Music Ed 1959; Credit Hrs Elem Ed Cert; Numerous Cmptr Classes; *cr:* Stanley Schl Band Dir 1954-59; Donegal Elem Schl Music, Kdg Tchr 1959-73, Kdg Tchr 1973-85, Third Grd Tchr 1985-; *ai:* NEA 1952; PSEA 1959-; *home:* 333 Patriot St Somerset PA 15501

ZIMMERMAN, JOHN WILLIAM, Sixth Grade Teacher; *b:* Mishawaka, IN; *m:* Connie Marie; *c:* Jame Douglas, Tonya Lynn; *ed:* Shippensburg St Univ (BS) Elem Ed 1969, (MS) Elem Ed 1973; *cr:* Tuscarora Schl Dist Fifth Grd Tchr 1969-71; West Shore Schl Dist Sixth Grd Tchr 1971-; *ai:* Sci Chm; PSEA 1969-; West Shore Ed Assn 1971-; Tuscarora Ed Assn 1969-71 Negotiation Comm; *office:* West Shore Schl Dist 507 Fishing Creek Rd PO Box 803 New Cumberland PA 17070

ZIMMERMAN, KAREN ANCARANA, Business Teacher; *b:* Mc Keesport, PA; *c:* Rick; *ed:* Univ of IN (BA) Bus Ed 1965; Bloomsburg Univ (MS) Bus Ed 1968; Addl 30 Credit Hrs; *cr:* Williamsport Area HS Bus Tchr 1965-; *ai:* Williamsport Ed 1965-, Ed Newsletter, Exec Bd; NEA 1965-; *office:* Williamsport Area HS 2990 W 4th St Williamsport PA 17701*

ZIMMERMAN, KAREN BERG, Business Teacher; *b:* Blossburg, PA; *m:* Shawn P.; *c:* Zachary, Toby; *ed:* Bloomsburg Univ (BS) Bus Ed 1982, (MS) Bus Ed 1993; *cr:* St Marys Jr Sr HS Bus Tchr 1983-88; Jersey Shore Jr Sr HS Bus Tchr 1989-; *ai:* Girls Bsktbl; FBLA: Tech Comm; Schl to Work Comm; Stu Assistance Prgm; PSEA Bldg Rep; PSEA 1982-; Outstdng Female Tchr; 2 Merit Awds; FBLA Svc Awd; *office:* Jersey Shore Jr Sr HS 601 Thompson St Jersey Shore PA 17740*

ZIMMERMAN, KENT L., Professor of Communication Art; *b:* Plymouth, IN; *m:* Julianne; *c:* Emily, Andrew; *ed:* Manchester Coll (BA) Speech & Ger 1974; OH Univ (MA) Interpersonal Comm 1977; Wright St Univ Post-Masters; Venkateswara Univ Cert; Attnd Phillps Univ; *cr:* Manchester Coll Speech Instr 1978-82; Sinclair Comm Coll Comm Arts Asst Prof 1982-86, Comm Arts Assoc Prof 1986-91, Comm Arts Prof 1991-; *ai:* Tchng Effectiveness Project Coord 1993-; Fac Resource Desk Coord 1995-; Author-in-Residence 1996; Natl Inst for Staff & Orgnl Dev Master Tchr 1993; Sinclair Comm Coll Endowed Distngd Tchng Awd 1993; OH Assn of Two-Yr Colls Tchr of Yr 1995; *office:* Sinclair Comm Coll 444 W 3rd St Dayton OH 45402

ZIMMERMAN, LAURA HENRY, English Teacher; *b:* Charlottesville, VA; *m:* Clayton Shaeffer; *c:* Allan, Adam; *ed:* Wittenberg Univ (BA) Eng 1970; Kutztown Univ (MA) Eng 1994; PA St At Harrisburgf Rdng Specialist; Attnd Advanced Placement Eng Inst, Carnegie-Mellon Univ; *cr:* Annville-Cleona HS Eng Tchr 1970; Luth Soc Svcs Eng as Second Lang In-Home Tutor 1978-80; Eastern Lebanon Cty HS Eng Tchr 1980-; *ai:* Stu Support Team; Stu Assistance Prgm; Delta Kappa Gamma 1993-; NEA 1980-; Fellow PA Lit Project at West Chester Univ; *office:* Eastern Lebanon Cty HS 180 ELCO Dr Myerstown PA 17067*

ZIMMERMAN, LORRAINE, Retired Teacher; *b:* New York, NY; *m:* George; *c:* Barbie Bier, Rina Traub; *ed:* Brooklyn Coll (BA) 1970; Richmond Coll (MS) 1971; Sixth Yr Prof Degree Admin 1976; *cr:* PS 14 4-6 Grds Tchr 1970-79; CSD #31 Math Tchr Trainer 1979-82; PS 42 GATE Tchr 1982-95; *ai:* AFT; IRA.

ZIMMERMAN, MARK J., 8th Grade Amer History Teacher; *b:* Akron, OH; *m:* Jone Faye Spirek; *ed:* Ashland Coll (BS) Elem Ed 1969; Attnd Bowling Green St Univ, Kent St Univ, Oh St Univ, Ashland Univ; *cr:* Marysville City Schls 6th Grd Tchr 1969-70; Shelby City Schls 5th-6th Grd Tchr 1970-78; Shelby Jr High 1978-; *ai:* Soc Stud Curr Chm; Tech & SEA Exec Comm; NEA 1969-; OEA 1969-, Convention Del; SEA 1970-, Bldg Rep; Shelby Kiwanis 1991, Pres; *office:* Shelby Mid Schl 16 Park Ave Shelby OH 44875

ZIMMERMAN, NICOLINA LAMANNA, Regents & Gen Earth Sci Tchr; *b:* Pentone Catanzaro, Italy; *m:* Richard L.; *c:* D. Shayne, Daniele N., Tinamarie; *ed:* Lehman Coll (BA) Geology 1976; City Coll (MA) Environmental Sci 1984; *cr:* Dewitt Clinton HS Regents Earth Sci Tchr 1975-76; Castle Hill MS 127 Regents Earth Sci Tchr 1978-, Gen Sci Tchr 1978-, ESL Sci Tchr 1989-95; *ai:* Lab Specialist 1986-; Sci Fair Project Coord 1988-; Intnl Stud Mini Schl Core Ldr 1993-95; AFT 1978-; NSTA 1982-; BSA 1985-93, Den, Troop Ldr; Borough Sci Fair Judging & Svc Awds NY Acad of Scis 1993, Amer Inst of Sci & Tech 1986-87, 1995; *office:* Castle Hill MS 127 1560 Purdy St Bronx NY 10462*

ZIMMERMAN, RICHARD THOMAS, Fifth Grade Teacher; *b:* Danville, PA; *m:* Janet Wirtz; *c:* Thomas, Todd, Beth; *ed:* Bloomsburg Univ (BS) (MS) Elem Ed 1968, 1973; 50 Credit Hrs Sci, Cmptrs, Environmental Ed; *cr:* North Schuylkill Schl Dist 6th Grd Tchr 1968-69; Crestwood Schl Dist 4-6th Grd & Head Tchr 1969-; Lazerne Intermediate Unit Grad Courses Instr 1993-; *ai:* Crestwood Schl Dist Elem Environmental Ed Coord, Tchr; Asst Var Girls Bsktbl Coach; Crestwood Ed Assn 1968-, Bldg Rep, Rep Cncl; PSEA, NEA 1968-; Amer Legion 1993-; PA Alliance for Environmental Ed 1991-, Presenter & Conf Comm; Northeast PA Ec Dev Cncl Environmental Awd 1992; Mountaintop Distinguished Svc Awd 1993; Crestwood Bd of Ed Tchr Recognition Awd 1992; Article Pub; *office:* Fairview Elem Schl 117 Spruce St Mountain Top PA 18707*

ZIMMERMAN, ROBERT EARL,II, High Schl Mathematics Teacher; *b:* Landstuhl, W Germany; *m:* Lisa M. Lombardi; *ed:* Erie Comm Coll (AS) Engrng Sci 1989; SUNY Coll at Buffalo (BS) Math Sec Ed 1992; Western CT St Univ MS Ed Curr 1996; *cr:* Mahopac CSS HS Math Tchr 1992-; *ai:* JV Bsbl & Modified Wrestling Coach; MTA 1992-; NCTM 1996; *office:* Mahopac HS Baldwin Place Rd Mahopac NY 10541

ZIMMERMAN, SANDRA TURNER, Integrated Language Arts Tchr; *b:* Bryn Mawr, PA; *m:* George K.; *c:* Jessica, Geoffrey; *ed:* Rosemont Coll (BA) Eng Lit 1992; *cr:* General Electric Admin 1966-73; Pius X Tchr 1992-; *ai:* Integrated Lang Arts Coord; NCEA 1992-, Tchr Assoc; Delta Epsilon Sigma; Optimist Club Awd; *office:* St Pius X Schl 204 Lawrence Rd Broomall PA 19008

ZIMMERMAN, STEVEN R., Mathematics Teacher; *b:* Chicago, IL; *m:* Mary Catherine Rich; *c:* Amy Catherine Casenheiser; Sara Maureen; *ed:* Univ of Akron (BA) Math 1969, (MA) Scndry Admin 1976; Addl 15 Credit Hrs; *cr:* Washington HS Math & His Tchr 1969-74; Stow-Munroe Falls HS Math Tchr 1974-; *ai:* NEA 1969-; Math Achvmt & Career Ed Grants; *office:* Stow-Munroe Falls HS 3227 Graham Rd Stow OH 44224*

ZIMMERMAN, THOMAS WARREN, High School English Teach[illegible]; Lebanon, PA; *m:* Jane L.; *c:* David R.; *ed:* Harrisburg Area Comm (AS) Eng 1970; Penn St (BH) Ed, Scndry 1972; Masters Equiv Pl[illegible] Credit Hrs; *cr:* M. S. Hershey Jr HS Eng Tchr 1972-85; Hershey H[illegible] Tchr 1985-; *ai:* Past HS Newspaper Adv; 9th, 10th Grd Play Scholarship Play Dir; NIE, Dist Discipline Comms; Spring Track Hersey Ed Assn Pres; Stu Assistance Team; NEA, PSEA 1972-; He[illegible] Ed Assn 1972-, VP, Pres; PASAP 1992-; Newspaper in Ed 1987-; [illegible] Hershey HS Homestead Rd Hershey PA 17033*

ZIMMERMAN-APTEKAR, RONNI ILENE, High School En[illegible] Teacher; *b:* Far Rockaway, NY; *m:* Sheldon I. Aptekar; *ed:* Hunter (BA) Eng 1970; Brooklyn Coll (MA) Eng 1975; 12 Credit Hrs Eng Kingsborough Comm Coll 17 Credit Hrs Theatre Arts, Eng 1988-8[illegible] JHS 180 Q Eng Tchr 1970-76; JHS 226 Q Eng Tchr 1976-79; Lotos Exec Asst 1979-81; Harcourt Braa Pub Writer 1979-81; Frankl[illegible] Roosevelt HS Eng, Drama Tchr 1983-; Kingsborough Comm Dramaturg, Lit Adv 1989-95; *ai:* Cooperating Tchr of New Tchrs; [illegible] 1984-; ECTC, IWWG 1990-; AFT, UFT 1970-; Tchng Drama in Class Stu Tchr Wkshps; Stu Poetry Sponsorship Awd 1979; *office:* F D Roo[illegible] HS 5800 20th Ave Brooklyn NY 11204*

ZINGER, PATRICIA MISCIMARRA, Second Grd, Instrl Tchr Le[illegible] *b:* Pittsburgh, PA; *m:* Samuel Lee; *c:* Rachel, Justin; *ed:* Grove City (BA) Sociology 1973; Univ of Pittsburgh (MAT) Ed 1974; 3 Hrs C[illegible] Coll; 3 Hrs Univ of OR; *cr:* Pgh Pub Schls Tchr 1974-; *ai:* New Induction Cncl, ITL Advy Bd, Parent Comm Cncl, Parent Fac Assn [illegible] Red Cross Club Former Spon; Ed, Rsrch & Dissemination Instr; [illegible] Kappa Gamma 1979-, Recording Sec, Benefit Chprsn; Carlynton Stra[illegible] Planning Comm 1995-; Carlynton Band Parent Org 1995-, Comm Ch[illegible] St Elizabeth Ann Seton 1989-92, CCD Tchr; Mini Grant Winner; [illegible] Beechwood Elem Schl 810 Rockland Ave Pittsburgh PA 15216*

ZINGERMANN, KAREN, Health & Physical Ed Teacher; *b:* Scra[illegible] PA; *ed:* East Stroudsburg Univ (BS) Hlth & PE 1974; West Chester (MED) Hlth & PE 1981; 50 Credits Beyond Masters; *cr:* Melmark Spec Ed & PE Tchr 1978-80; North Pocono HS Hlth & PE Tchr 1985[illegible] Outdoor Adventure Club Adv; Vlybl Coach; Stu Assistance T[illegible] AAHPERD, PSAHPERD 1980-; PSEA 1985-; PA Vlybl Coaches 1993-; Soo Bahk Do 1992-, Black Belt; *office:* North Pocono HS Church St Moscow PA 18444*

ZINGRAF, LORRAINE A., Third Grade Teacher; *b:* Bronx, NY; *ed.* of Saint Rose (BS) Elem Ed 1961; 45 Hrs LI Univ at Southampton Kellum St Elem Schl 4th-5th Grd Tchr 1961-82; William Rall Elem 3rd Grd Tchr 1982-; *ai:* PTA Schlsp Awd Chm; NYSTU 1961-; Tchrs Lindenhurst 1961-, Awds Comm; Lindenhurst PTA 1961-, Correspo[illegible] Sec, Sec, Cultural Arts Comm Chm; Lindenhurst Band Parents Assn 1[illegible] Past Sec, Corresponding Sec 1984-86; Kellum St Schl PTA Svc *office:* William Rall Elem Schl 761 N Wellwood Ave Lindenhurs[illegible] 11757

ZINK, ROBERT DONALD, Retired History Teacher; *b:* Jersey City *m:* Marie Hilda Pedersen; *c:* Robert, Charles, Linda, Suzanne Osnato St Peter's Coll (BS) His 1961; Monclair St Univ (MA) Soc Stud 196[illegible] North Bergen HS Tchr 1961-92; *ai:* AFT 1964-, Pres, Ldrshp; [illegible] Bergen Twp 1971-75, Commissioner.*

ZINKE, NANCY C. (SNYDER), Spanish Teacher; *b:* Philadelphia *m:* Robert A.; *c:* Martha Ellen Smith, Virginia; *ed:* Houghton Coll Elem Ed, Span 1970; Temple Univ (MED) Frgn Lang Ed 197[illegible] Parochial Schls Elem, Multidisc, Span Tchr 1970-90; Private Schls [illegible] Multidisc, Span Tchr 1970-90; Lower Bucks Chrstn Acad Span 1990-91; Kings Chrstn HS Span Tchr 1992-95; Phila Coll of Bible Instr 1992-; Bensalem Bapt Schl Span Tchr 1995-; *ai:* Presented Sem[illegible] Innovative Methods Mid Atlantic Chrstn Schl Assn Conver[illegible] Montgomery Cty Frgn Lang Tchrs Assn; *office:* Philadelphia Coll of [illegible] 200 Manor Ave Langhorne PA 19047*

ZION, VILMA, Eighth Grade Science Tchr; *b:* Philadelphia, PA; *m:* Robert, Marci Feller, Terri; *ed:* Temple Univ (BS) Ed 1962; M Equ[illegible] 1985; 6 Credit Hrs Marywood Coll; 12 Credit Hrs Antioch Coll; [illegible] Prgm 1989; Making Desegration Work 1993; Cmptr Opera[illegible] Programming 1983; *cr:* Phila Schl System Long Term Sub Tchr 197[illegible] Carnell Elem Schl 6thGrd Tchr 1985-90, 8th Grd Sci, Eng Tchr 1990 Eighth Grd Co-Chm; Grad, Schl Climate, Discipline Comm, Sch[illegible] Comm Chm; Yrbk Spon; Schl Sci Coord; PFT, AFT 1978-; NCTM 1[illegible] NCTE 1980-; B'nai B'rith Edctrs 1986-; Beth Chain 1972-, Hebrew Bd; Senatorial Schlsp; Meritorious Performance Awd.

ZIPOLI, JOSEPH A., Mathematics Instructor; *b:* Waterbury, CT; Wesleyan Univ Math 1989; Univ of TX at Austin Math 1993; Un[illegible] Hartford Tech; *cr:* Wesleyan Univ Tchng Asst 1985-93; Univ of TX T[illegible] Asst 1985-93; Integrated Indstrl Systems Mill SLUG 1993-94; Brev[illegible] Acad Math Instr 1994-95; Wheeler Schl Math Instr 1995-; *ai:* Cross C[illegible] Track Head Coach; Gear Heads Charter Mem; Soc Improve Compe[illegible] Pres; INOA 1991-; W. H. Auden Soc 1987-; Hasdam Land Trust 1[illegible] Ofcr; RI Classical Guitar Soc 1996; Ford Fnd Rsrch Fellow 1985; Outstdng Coll Stdnts of North Amer 1986; Beinecke Scholar 1989; [illegible] Wheeler Schl 216 Hope St Providence RI 02906

ZIPPER, ELAINE RHODA, Music & Theater Teacher; *b:* Brooklyn, *m:* Steve; *c:* Saul, Melissa; *ed:* Syracuse Univ (BA) Music 1952; Broo[illegible] Coll (MA) Ed, Music 1975; 58 Addl Credits; *cr:* PS 244 3rd Grd 1965-66, Music Tchr 1970-81, 3rd Grd Tchr 1982-85, Music Tchr 198[illegible] PS 114 Part-time Music, Theater Tchr 1991-; *ai:* Synagogue Sister[illegible] Pres 11 Yrs; Comm Theater Theatrical Group Dir; Drama & Music Schl & Comm Affairs Music Dir; AFT, NEA, UFT 1970-; HS Tru[illegible] Democratic Club 1984-; Cncl of Jewish Orgs 1990-; Educl TV M[illegible] Prgm; *home:* 1569 E 29th St Brooklyn NY 11229*

ZIPPER, SHELLEY G., English Teacher; *b:* Baltimore, MD; *ed:* [illegible] Univ (BA) Sociology 1976; NY Univ (MA) Creative Writing 1985, ([illegible] Eng Lit 1989; ABD Eng Lit 1989; Coppin St Coll Masters Equivalen[illegible] Spec Ed 30 Credits 1978; Participation in Writing Projecet 1991- Carroll Park Sr HS Eng, Spec Ed Tchr 1976-83; Joseph C. Briscoe S[illegible] Soc Stud, Spec Ed Tchr 1984-89; Hunter & Brooklyn Coll [illegible] Composition Tchr 1984-89; Humanities HS Eng, Eng as a Second [illegible] Tchr 1989-; John Jay HS Eng Tchr 1989-; *ai:* Carroll Park Sr HS, Balt[illegible] HS Class Adv 1979-83; NY Writing Project Co-Ldr 1995-; Amer So[illegible] Project 1994-; Writing Tchrs Consortium 1991-; NYU Tchng Assistan[illegible] Awd1984-87; Schlsp to Breadloaf Writers Conf 1982; Selected to A[illegible] Natl Conf for New Stans Project 1994; New Stans Project Tchr Selected Co-Ldr 1994; NYC Writing Project Selected Asst; Selecte[illegible] Attend Seminar for AP Eng 1995; *office:* John Jay HS 237 7th Brooklyn NY 11215*

ZIRAFI, ROBERT ANTHONY, HS Honors History Tchr; *b:* Youngst[illegible] OH; *ed:* Youngstown St Univ (AB) Fr 1969, (MSEd) Scndry Admin [illegible] Advanced His Stud; Grand Lycee d'Antibes France Advanced Fr Stu[illegible] Hubbard HS Fr Tchr 1969-95, US His Tchr 1986-, Honors US His 1995-; *ai:* Soc Stud Dept Chm; Hubbard Ed Assn 1969-, Pres; NE[illegible] NEA 1974-; OH A Plus Tchr Trumbull Cty 1995; Hubbard Chrst[illegible] Action Tchr of Yr Awd 1994-95; *office:* Hubbard HS 350 Hall Ave Hub[illegible] OH 44425

NG, PAUL ELDER, Health Education Teacher; b: New York, NY; ed: Y at Oreonta (BA) Psych 1986; Hofstra Univ (MS) Hlth Ed 1992; vice Courses Inclusion Ed, Mac Intosh Applications, On Becoming an Tchr; cr: Levittown Division HS Permanent Sub Tchr 1991-92; Great South MS & HS Hlth Ed, PE Tchr 1992-93; Great Neck North HS Ed Tchr 1993-; ai: Var Girl's Soccer Coach; Var Girls Vlybl Coach Neck South MS; Assist with Peer AIDS Edctrs, Drug Free Schls; NYSFPHE, NYSUT 1992-; office: Great Neck North HS 35 Polo Rd Neck NY 11023

KE, BARBARA L., Biology Teacher; b: Cleveland, OH; ed: win-Wallace Coll (BS) Biological Sci 1973; Purdue Univ (MS) gical Sci 1975; Ashland Univ Marine Sci 1991; Project Discovery, ical Sci Summer Inst SE Regn 1994-1995; cr: Heath HS Bio Tchr -77; Maysville Local Schls Bio Tchr 1977-; ai: Var Girls Track Coach; Cheerleading Coach; NEA, OEA, MEA 1990-, Building Rep; NSTA, A, SECO, OATCCC, EDTCCCA 1975-; Maysville Ath Boosters; sville Cheerleading Boosters; Purdue Univ Grad Tchng Assistantship, Century Sci Inst 1994-1995; office: Maysville HS 2805 Pinkerton Rd sville OH 43701

KLE, BARBARA JEAN, Science Teacher; b: Piqua, OH; ed: bein Coll (BA) His, Govt 1966; Gen Sci, MS Ed, His, Govt, Chem on g Cert; cr: Shiloh MS 7th Grd Soc Stud, Lang Tchr 1966-70, 7th Grd Math Tchr 1970-74, 7th Grd Sci, Hlth Tchr 1975-85, 8th Grd Sci Tchr -90, 8th Grd Sci & 7th Grd Soc Stud Tchr 1990-94, 8th Grd Sci Tchr -95, 7th-8th Grd Sci Tchr 1996; ai: Eisenhower Sci Team; PEA 1970-, Bldg Rep, Negotiations Comm, Grievance Comm Chprsn; OEA 1966-; 1970-; Sci Ed Cncl of OH 1995-; Fletcher United Meth Church 1956-; : Shiloh MS 26 Mechanics St Shiloh OH 44878

KA, JOHN LOUIS, Social Studies Teacher; b: Painesville, OH; m: Ann; c: Samantha; ed: Univ of OR (BS) Bus Admin 1985; Kent St (BS) Ed 1990; cr: Stanbery Freshman Schl Soc Stud Tchr 1991-; ai: Cross Cntry Coach; Track Asst Coach.

AROSA, CELESTINE JESSIE, English & Drama Teacher; ed: nouth Coll (BA) Ed & Eng 1992; cr: Wall HS Eng & Drama Tchr -; ai: Spring Musical Dir; Kappa Delta Pi 1990-, Asst VP & Chptr Pres -92; NEA 1992-; NJEA 1992-; MCEA 1992-; Received Phi Delta a Most Promising Edctr Awd 1992; office: Wall HS 18th Ave & New ord Rd Wall NJ 07719

), ANDREA J. (GUZZO), 4th-5th Grade Teacher; b: New ington, PA; m: Anthony F.; c: Rececca, Anthony, Jon; ed: Slippery Univ (BS) Elem, Spec Ed 1971; Penn St at New Kensington Grad its Psych, Curr Dev; cr: Westmoreland Intermediate Schl Unit #7 Spec Tchr 1971-74; New Kensington Arnold Schls Sub Spec Ed Tchr -88; St Andrews Epsicopal Nursery Schl Presch Tchr 1980-86; ese of Greensburg 4th Grd Tchr, 5th Grd Rdng Tchr 1988-; ai: Annual emia Soc Spon; Spell-a-thon 4th, 5th, 6th Grd; ARC Svc Prgm Spon; Rehabilitation; Wellness Curr Dev Comm; NCEA 1988-; Parents ymous 1995-, Facilitator; Parish Lector 1991-; Church Choir 1995-; nize Annual Angel Tree Prgm 1989-; office: Saint Gertrude Schl 315 klin Ave Vandergrift PA 15690*

), ANTHONY J., Assistant Professor of Physics; b: Johnstown, PA; atricia Voytko; c: Regina; ed: Univ of MA (BS) Physics, Math 1989; deis (MA) Physics 1991; cr: Dutchess Comm Coll 1991-; ai: AAPT -; Poughkeepsie Little League 1995-, T-Ball Coach; NSF Grant Dev, ement Integrated Calculus-Physics Sequence at DCC 1993-; office: hess Comm Coll Pendell Road Poughkeepsie NY 12601

T, THOMAS JOSEPH, English & History Instructor; b: Dayton, OH; ennifer Marie Orlesh; ed: OH Univ (BSEd) Eng Ed 1984; Univ of WY Amer Stud 1988; Bowling Green St Univ (PHD) Amer Stud 1992; cr: of WY Tchng Asst 1986-88, Lecturer, Eng Dept 1988-89; Bowling n St Univ Fellow 1989-92; Univ of MD Overseas Division Instr 1992-; Cafe & Film Soc, Mountain Bike Club Spon; Sierra Club 1992-; Svc Flwshp 1991-92; office: Univ of MD Mannheim Campus Unit 0 New York APO AE 09183

TO, RICHARD JOSEPH, Physics Teacher; b: Lisbon, OH; m: Pamela l Irons; c: Angela Marie, Elena Michele Zitto-MacDonald; ed: OH St (BS) Sci Ed 1968, (MA) Phys Sci Ed 1978; Attnd Worcester echnic Inst, Coll of Holy Cross, VA Military Inst, Youngstown St Univ of RI, Univ of MD, Ashland Univ; cr: Kenton Jr HS Phys Sci 1968-70; Kenton Sr HS Physics Tchr 1970-76; Boardman HS Physics 1976-; Youngstown St Univ Physics Tchr 1980-; ai: Sci Club; gstown Area Physics Alliance, Physics Olmpics Coord; NEA, OEA, 1968-, Past Local Pres; AAPT 1972-, Past St Pres; OH Acad of Sci, A 1968-; Phi Delta Kappa 1986-; Columbiana Pub Lib Bd of Trust -, Pres 1993-95; Youngstown Ctr Mul Sci Soc 1976-, Trustee, Pres; s Club 1969-77, Sec; Rotary Club 1978-82 Sec; Lab Notes, ographs Pub; 5 Natl Sci Fnd Grants; AAPT Physics Tchng Resource nt 1986-; Whos Who in Med West 22nd-24th Editions; Whos Who in r Ed 3rd-5th Editions; office: Boardman HS 7777 Glenwood Ave dman OH 44512*

IC, DONNA MARIE, Mathematics Teacher; b: Pittsburgh, PA; ed: uesne Univ (BA) Ed 1979; cr: North Hills Jr High Tchr 1979-; ai: a Kappa Gamma 1993-; NCTM 1994-; office: North Hills Sr HS 53 uester Rd Pittsburgh PA 15229

CESKI, WALTER T., Physical Education Instructor; b: Elizabeth, NJ; Marietta Lerda; c: Corrine, Holly, Jenny, Cassie; ed: Seton Hall Univ Ed) Hlth & PE 1969; cr: Branchburg Township Bd of Ed PE Instr 1969-; AFT 1976-; office: Old York Elem Schl 580 Old York Rd Somerville 8876

'GRODSKI, THOMAS BERNARD, 5th Grade Teacher; b: Perth oy, NJ; m: Margaret Cattani; c: Ben, Jeff, Michael, David, Scott; ed: ton St Coll (BA) Elem Ed 1970, (MS) Elem Ed 1976; cr: S. E. Shull 5th Grd Tchr 1971-; ai: Homework Club Adv; AFT 1971-, Tchr of Yr; mbrose Liturgy Comm 1986-, Child Choir Dir; Governors Awd 1989; of Yr 1993; office: Samuel E Shull MS 380 Hall Ave Perth Amboy NJ 51

AIDEN, STEPHEN MICHAEL, History Teacher; b: Jersey City, NJ; udith Ellen Ward; ed: Western KY Univ (BS) His & Bus 1971; Rutgers (MED) Labor Stud 1979; cr: Raritan HS Tchr 1972-; ai: Girls Bsktbl d coach, Boys Soccer Asst Coach & Girls Sftbl Asst Coach; office: tan HS 419 Middle Rd Hazlet NJ 07730

BENICA, LINDSAY, Foreign Language Chair; b: Elgin, IL; m: Milan; itza, Nick; ed: Northwestern Univ (BA) Ger 1965; Oberlin Coll (MAT) 1968; Univ Dist Columbia (MA) Cnslng 1992; Spcl Ed Admin; cr: a Pub Schls Ger Tchr 1968-69; New Hyde Park PS Ger Tchr 1969-72; oll Cty PS Spcl Ed Tchr 1978-79; D C Pub Schls Spcl Ed & Chair of ign Lang 1980-; ai: Chess Team Spon; AATG 1969-; Tchrs of Frgn g 1969-; Cncl Exceptional Children 1974-94; N Assn Sci Tchrs)-90; Amer Cnslng Assn 1985-; ASCD 1988-95; Eastern Orthodox ch 1967-, Dir of Music; Pres Awd Excl in Tchng Sci 1985; office: lidge Sr HS 5th at Tuckerman NW Washington DC 20011*

)DA, PHILIP J., PE Tchr & Cross Cntry Coach; b: New York City, m: Kathleen Haywood; c: Hilda, Marie, Charles; ed: Niagara Univ Ed 1973, (MS) Ed 1975; cr: NYC Bd of Ed Tchr & Coach 18 Yrs; ai: Cross Cntry, Indoor- Outdoor Track & Field Coach; Footlocker Cross Cntry NE Regnl Dir 1991-; UFT 1975-; NY Road Runners Club 1977-, Vol; NYC Coaches Assn 1985-; Empire St Games NYC Scholastic Coach; office: South Shore HS 6565 Flatlands Ave Brooklyn NY 11236

ZODY, SHIRLEY KLENK, Tchr of Learning Disabilities; b: Cedar City, UT; m: Marion Paul; c: STeven, Scott, Mark; ed: Ashland Univ (BS) Ed, PE, Hlth, Eng 1959; 18 Addl Hrs; Akron Univ 5 Qtr Hrs; Univ of Cntrl AR 3 Hrs; cr: Triway Local Schls Eng, Girls PE 7-12 Grd Tchr 1961-63, K-12 Grd Sub Tchr 1965-81, 1982-85, 9-12 Grd Hlth, PE Tchr 1981-82, 7-8 Grd L D Tutor 1985-95, 7-8 Grd L D Tchr 1995-; ai: Core Team; NEA, OEA 1986-; Triway Local Classroom Tchrs Assoc 1986-, Bldg Rep; Shreve Lioness Club 1979-, Sec, Treas, Pres; Ashalnd Univ Alumni 1986-89; Asland Univ Hall of Fame 1989-, Comm, Chm 1992-95; Triway Ath Booster Club 1978-, Sec 1980-86; Dist Svc Awd Ashland Univ Alumni Assoc 1990; home: 4120 Columbus Rd Wooster OH 44691

ZOESCH, JANICE ORFORD, Music Teacher; b: Utica, NY; m: John Richard Jr.; c: John III, Bryan; ed: SUC Potsdam Crane Schl of Music (BS) Music Ed 1969; 3 Hrs at Eastman Schl of Music; 9 Hrs at Nazareth Coll; 6 Hrs at Potsdam Saratoga Inst; 6 Hrs at Brockport Coll; cr: Fairport Schl Dist Music Edctr 1969-82; Honeoye Falls-Lima Schl Music Edctr 1989-; ai: Select Chorus; HS Musical Vocal Dir; NYSSMA 1966-; NYSUT 1989-; office: Honeoye Falls-Lima MS 83 East St Honeoye Falls NY 14472

ZOFKIE, MICHAEL JOSEPH, Social Studies & History Tchr; b: Portsmouth, VA; ed: Wright St Univ (BS) Ed Soc Stud His 1980; Addl Grad Courses; cr: Wilmington HS Soc Stud His Tchr 1980-84; Trotwood-Madison HS Soc Stud His Tchr 1984-; ai: Var Girls Bsktbl Coach 1988-92; Honor Roll Comm 1989; Stu of Month Comm 1991-; Mentor New Tchr Mentorship Prgm 1992; Girls Sftbl Coach 1988-91, Boys Asst Bsbl Coach 1987, Boys Asst Bsktbl Coach 1984-1988; N Cntrl Evltn Comm Co-Chr 1995-; NEA 1981-; home: 956 Tristan Ct W Carrollton OH 45449*

ZOLA, JOAN W., French Teacher; b: Philadelphia, PA; m: Joseph; c: Jr, Ginger; ed: Coker Coll (BA) 1967; Univ of Paris at Sorbonne (MA) Fr Lit 1972; Attnd NY Univ, Univ de Grenoble, Mc Gill Univ in Canada; cr: DuPont Co Sec 1973-77; Beneficial Corp Asst 1983-85; MT Olive Adult Schl Tchr 1980-85; Mt Olive MS Tchr 1985-; ai: Peer Tutor Spon; Liaison Comm Rep; Calendar Comm; Chaperone for Washington DC Trip, Environmental Ed Trip; EAMO, AATF, NJEA, NEA 1985-; Long Vly Raider Assn 1990-, Sec; Newcomer Club 1980-; Recipient of Dodge Grant 1989; Participant Stu Exch Prmg in France; office: Mount Olive MS Sunset Rd Budd Lake NJ 07828

ZOLA, JUDITH ANN, Music Teacher; b: Wilkes-Barre, PA; ed: Wilkes Coll (BS) Music Ed 1975; Univ of Scranton (MS) Music Ed 1985; Stu Assistance Team Trng 1991; 27 Post Grad Credits Penn St, Wilkes, Carlow, Gratz; cr: St Leo's Schl Music Tchr 1975-78; Hanover Area Schl Sub Tchr 1979-80, Music Tchr 1980-, Dept Chprsn 1984-; ai: 9th-12th Grd Sr Chorus; Key Club; Stu Assistance Prgm; Act 178 Continuing Educ, Fac; MENC, PMEA, NEA, PSEA 1980-; HAEA 1980-, VP, Sec; office: Hanover Area Jr Sr HS 1600 Sans Souci Pky Wilkes Barre PA 18702

ZOLLARS, KATHERINE DURINZI, Retired Lang Arts Teacher; b: Slovan, PA; w: J. William (dec); c: Rebecca R. Kreider, David M.; ed: CA St Univ (BAEd) Eng, Speech Correction 1949; PA St Univ of Pgh Steubenville Coll (MA) Elem Ed 1968; cr: Penowa Coal Co Sec 1949-51; Union HS Lang Arts Tchr 1951-58; Burg Elem Schl 4th Grd Classroom Tchr 1968-81; Burg Area Jr-Sr HS Grds 7 & 8 Lang Arts 1981-92; ai: Judge for Stdnt Contests; Cath Dghtrs Ed Comm Head; Art Cont & Spllng Bee Condctr; PSEA, NEA 1951; BAFA 1967-, Corres Sec 8 Yrs; Burg Comm Lib Bd 1952-85, Sec 20 Yrs.

ZOLLI, MARY YATES, Kindergarten Teacher; b: Providence, RI; m: John R. Sr.; c: Jay, Lora, Michael; ed: RI Coll Early Chldhd 1972, (Masters) Early Chldhd 1976; Post Grad Stud in Presch Handicapped; cr: John Horton Schl Kndgtn Tchr 1972-73; Sanders Schl 1st-2nd Grd Tchr 1973-74; Wm R Dutemple Schl Kndgtn Tchr 1974-79, 1982-; Chester Barrows Schl Kndgtn Tchr 1979-80; Garden City Schl Kndgtn Tchr 1980-81; Staduim Schl & Daniel D Waterman Schl Kndgtn Tchr 1981-82; ai: Cast & Cap Mem; Schl Advy Comm; AFT 1976-; CLCF Yth Hockey 1988-, Team Mother 1989-95, Head Team Mother 1994-95; office: Wm R. Dutemple Schl 32 Garden St Cranston RI 02910

ZOLLNER, MICHELLE LOIS, Health Teacher; b: Cumberland, MD; m: James Douglas Bartholomew; c: Michael J. Bartholomew; ed: Shepherd Coll (BA) Home Ec Ed 1981; Univ of MD (MED) Human Growth, Dev 1984; Coll Credit Hrs in Hlth Ed, Eng; Quest Lifeskills for Adolescence Certfd Instr; cr: Braddock Jr HS Long Term Sub, Home Ec Tchr 1981; Southern MS Home Ec Tchr 1981-84, Hlth, Family Life Tchr 1984-; ai: Svc Learning Co-Coord; NEA, MSTA, GCTA 1981-, Bldg Rep; St Marks Luth Church 1981-, Cncl; Deep Creek St Park, Hike Ldr 1994-; Governor's Citation for Work in Drug Prevention 1991; Garrett Cty Hlth Star Awd for Work in Promoting Healthy Lifestyles; Self-Esteem in Women, Sexuality Ed Pub Speaking; office: Southern MS 605 Harvey Winters Dr Oakland MD 21550

ZOLLNER, PATRICIA FEDISHEN, Gifted Program Coordinator; b: Pittsburgh, PA; m: Ronald W.; c: David Michael, Elizabeth Anne; ed: St Francis (BS) Elem, Scndry Ed 1975; Attnd Univ of Pittsburgh, Univ of PA; cr: Gray Elem Schl Tchr; Forrest Hills MS Team Ldr; Turtle Creek HS Gifted Prgm Coord; Rankin Intermediate Schl Tchr; Ben Fairless Intermediate Tchr; Woodland Hilsl West Jr HS Gifted Prgm Coord; ai: Mon Vly Consortium Lib Power Initiative; Gifted Prgm Task Force; PSEA; NEA; office: Woodland Hills West Jr HS 7600 Evans St Pittsburgh PA 15218

ZOLOCK, SARAH RUGH, Mathematics Teacher; b: Greensburg, PA; m: Stephen; c: Ruth, John, Mary; ed: IN Univ of PA (BS) Ed 1964; WV Univ (MA) Math 1971; Attnd St Vincent Coll Summer Inst; cr: Greensburg Salem Sr HS Math Tchr 1964-; ai: NHS; GSEA; PSEA; NEA; office: Greensburg Salem Sr HS 65 Mennel Dr Greensburg PA 15601

ZOLTAN, CHRISTINE PERRETTA, HS Counselor; b: Oneida, NY; m: Stephen G.; c: Michelle; ed: SUNY At Cortland (BS) Early Scndry Ed 1982; SUNY Coll at Oneonta (MS) Schl Cnslng 1985; Post Grad Cnslng Courses at Western CT Univ 18 Credits; Coll of New Rochelle 11 Credits; cr: Central Square Jr HS Soc Stud Tchr 1982-83; Haverstraw MS Schl Cnslr 1985-86; Pawling Jr Sr HS Schl Cnslr 1986-; ai: Peer Ldrshp Coordinating Mem; Peer Mediation Coordinating Mem; NEA 1986-; Dutchess Cty Cnslrs Assn 1986-; Pawling PTA 1986-; office: Pawling Jr Sr HS Reservoir Rd Pawling NY 12564

ZOLYNIAK, TIMOTHY A., Band Director; b: Maple Hghts, OH; ed: Univ of Akron (BA) Music 1981, (BS) Scndry Ed 1983; 2 Post Grad Hrs Ashland Univ; 19 Post Grad Hrs Walsh Univ; cr: Barberton City Schls Sub Tchr 1984-85; Brecksville Schls Sub Tchr 1984-895; Akron Pub Schl Sub Tchr 1985-87, Band Dir Grds 5-12 1987-; ai: Bldg Ldrshp Team Chprsn 1991-; Music Dept Chair Assembly Coord; HS Flag Line Adv; Coord Parent Tchr Report Card Distribution Night; AEA 1987-; Kappa Kappa Psi 1979-; City-wide Elem May Festival Co-chair 1992-93; Bldg Tchr of Yr Nom; office: Goodyear MS 49 N Martha Ave Akron OH 44305*

ZONA, ANDREA, Math Teacher; b: Rochester, NY; m: Richard Lang; ed: SUNY Geneseo (BA) Math 1988; cr: Leonardtown HS Math Tchr 1989-; ai: Organize Sr Trip; office: Leonardtown HS Rt 5 Box 49-3 Leonardtown MD 20650*

ZONA, LOUIS A., Prof of Art His & Museology; b: New Castle, PA; ed: Youngstown St Univ (BS) Art Ed 1966; Univ of Pittsburg (MS) Art Ed 1969; Carnegie Mellon Univ (DA) Museology 1973; Attnd Wagner Coll & Westminster Coll Addl Stu; cr: Sharon & New Castle Art Tchr 1966-70; Westminister Coll Adjunct Prof 1976-80; Youngstown St Univ Prof of Art His & Museology 1970-; The Butler Inst of Amer Art Ex Dir 1981-; ai: Hoyt Inst 1995-, Bd of Dirs; OH Arts Cncl, Reviewer, Panel Mem; Youngstown Area Arts Cncl, Trustee, Adv; Intermuseum Conservation Assn Bd; Governors Awd for Arts in OH Arts Admin 1990; YSO Alumni Assn Spec Recognition for Prof Contributions 1981; YSO Distinguished Prof Awd 1978; Jaycees Outstanding Young Educator Awd 1970.

ZONCA, CONSTANCE M., 5th Grade Teacher; b: Monongahela, PA; c: Suzanne Richardson, Jill Marie; ed: California Univ of PA (BS) Elem Ed 1964, (MS) Elem Ed 1972; cr: Ringgold-Carroll Schl 2nd Grd Tchr 1964-66; Village Acad Tutor 1979-80; St Thomas More Schl Grds 6-8th Soc St Tchr 1981-85; Gastonville Schl 5th Grd Tchr 1986-; ai: Dev, Pub 5th Grd Newspaper; NEA, PSEA, REA 1986-; office: Gastonville Elem Schl 3685 Finleyville-Elrama Rd Finleyville PA 15332*

ZORNOW, KIMBERLY LYNN, Mathematics Teacher; b: Brooklyn, NY; ed: Pace Univ (BS) Math 1989; Univ of Akron (MS) Scndry Ed 1992; cr: Troy HS Summer Schl Math Tchr 1992; Bethlehem HS Math Tchr 1993-; ai: Girl's Var Bsktbl Coach; NEA 1992-; office: Bethlehem Central HS 700 Delaware Ave Delmar NY 12054

ZOSCHG, NANCY CLARK, 4th Grade Teacher; b: Danville, PA; m: Matthew A. Jr.; c: Eric, Ryan, Megan; ed: Mansfield Univ (BS) Home Ec 1968; St Bonaventure Univ Cert Elem Ed 1982; cr: Cameron Cty Schl Dist Kndgtn Tchr 1968-72, Home Ec Tchr, 4th Grd Tchr 1984-; ai: Bandfront Adv 14 Yrs; Strategic Planning, Site Mngmt, Textbook, Wellness, Report Card, Math, Fac, Advy Bd, Read Comms; PSEA; NEA; CCEA; Friends of the Cameron Cty Pub Lib 1993-; Emporium Garden Club; Co-Recipient Several Acad Excl Grants Awd Local Dist; Set Up Local Wkshps; Co-Write Elem Handbook; Elem Tchr of Yr 1990; New Tchrs Mentor; office: Cameron Cty Schl Dist 601 Woodland Ave Emporium PA 15834

ZOSKY, DEBORAH ANN, History Teacher & Dept Head; b: Allentown, PA; m: Philip M.; c: Michael, Jessica, Joshua; ed: East Stroudsburg Univ (BS) Scndry Ed, Soc Stud 1975; Kutztown Univ (MEd) Rdng 1987; cr: Growing Childrens Presch Dir & Tchr 1982-84; Brandywine Hghts MS Rdng Specialist 1985-87; Parkland HS His Tchr 1987-; ai: Stu Cncl Adv; South Parkland Assn Soccer Coach; NEA 1987-; Outstanding Tchr Awd 1994; office: Parkland HS 2675 Rt 309 Orefield PA 18069

ZOVINKA, EDWARD PAUL, Chemistry Professor; b: New York City, NY; m: Rose Ann Clark; ed: Roanoke Coll (BS) Chem 1987; Univ of CA at David (PHD) 1992; Postdoctoral Rsrch NC St 1993-94; cr: St Francis Coll Asst Prof of Chem 1994-; ai: Chem Club Adv; Amer Chem Soc 1986-; Cncl on Undergrad Rsrch 1994-; office: Saint Francis Coll Loretto PA 15940

ZSCHACK, ROBERT, Biology Teacher; b: Passaic, NJ; m: MarleneJaorsky; c: Paul, Mark, Peter, Thomas, Matthew; ed: Montclair St Coll (BA) Biological Scis 1958, (MA) Admin & Supervision 1964; Eastern Schl Physicians Aides X-Ray Technician 1953, Summer Inst Grant 1965, Natl Sci Fnd; Addl Credit Hrs 6-Wilkes Coll, 32-Montclair St Coll, 6-Clifton HS In Svc; cr: St Franics Hospital X-Ray Technician 1953-54; Clifton HS Dept Supvr 1963-64; Wilkes Coll Lab Instr Summer 1966; Clifton HS Bio Tchr 1958-; ai: Bio Acad Coach NJ Sci League; NEA, NJ Ed Assn 1958-; NSTA 1981-; NJ Sci Tchrs Assn 1986; NABT 1989-, St Rep 1990-91; NJ Bio Tchrs Assn 1989-; Smithsonian Inst 1992-; Polland Collectors Soc, Perillo Collectors Club 1988-; Miniature Sculpture Assn 1991-; YMCA Greater Bergen Cty, Youth Svc Awd 1986, Svc to Youth Awd 1987; Intnl Collectible Exposition, Outstanding Achvmt Awd 1992; Tchr of Month 1959, Theobald Smith Soc; Alumni Achvmt Awd 1963, Eastern Schl Physician's Aides; Outstanding Young Educator 1965, Clifton Jaycees; Wilkes Coll Summer Inst Lab Instr, Natl Sci Fnd; Man of Yr 1978, Clifton Ftbl Booster Club; Educator of Distinction 1984, Clifton Tchrs Assn; Governors Tchr Recognition Awd 1990, NJ St Dept of Ed; office: Clifton HS 333 Colfax Ave Clifton NJ 07013*

ZUBECK, M. TERESA, 6th Grade Teacher; b: E St Louis, IL; m: Robert E.; c: Andrea Lawlor, Matthew, Robin; ed: IL St Univ (BSEd) Math & Bus Ed 1952; Wright St Univ (MSEd) Curr & Supervision 1972; Attnd Cntrl St Univ, Univ of Dayton, Miami Univ; cr: Clinton HS Bus Ed Tchr 1952-54; Bloomington 3rd Grd Tchr 1955-58; WPAFB Adult Ed Tchr 1960-63; Ferguson Jr HS 7th Grd Tchr 1966; Vly Elem Kndgtn, 5th-6th Grd Tchr 1967-; ai: BEA Rep; Spelling & Soc Comms; Olympiad of the Mind Coach; NEA, OEA & BEA 1966-, Rep; Woodhaven Pool 1958-, Bd Mem 4 Terms; Beavercreek YMCA 1986-, Bd Mem, Friend of the Yr Awd; home: 813 Timberwood Dr Beavercreek OH 45430*

ZUBLER, JAMES MICHAEL, HS Special Education Teacher; b: Buffalo, NY; c: Joshua James; ed: Buffalo St Coll (BS) Exceptional, Elem Ed 1987, (MS) Learning, Behavioral Disorders 1996; cr: Gowanda Cntrl Schls Spec Ed Tchr Jr Sr HS 1990-94; East Aurora Union Free Schls Sr HS Spec Ed Tchr 1994-; ai: Asst Cross Cntry Coach; JV Girls Track Coach; Sr Class, Peer Mediation Adv; NYSUT 1990-; East Aurora Yth Ct 1996, Adv; office: East Aurora Union Free Schls 1003 Center St East Aurora NY 14052*

ZUBRICK, JAMES W., Chemistry Professor; b: New Haven, CT; ed: Univ of CT (BA) Chem 1975; SUNY at Buffalo (MA) Chem 1978; Rensselaer Polytechnic Inst PHD Rsrch Pending; cr: Mohawk Vly CC Instr 1978-79; Rensselaer Polytechnic Inst Lab Demonstrator 1980-84; Hudson Vly CC Asst Prof 1985-; ai: Undergraduate Lab Data Ctr Dir; Textbook Authors Assn 1984-; Amer Chemical Soc 1970-; The Organic Chem Lab Survival Manual Pub 3rd Edition 1992; office: Hudson Valley Comm Coll Dept of Chem 80 Vandenburgh Ave Troy NY 12180*

ZUBYK, ALAN WAYNE, Health Teacher; b: Warren, OH; m: Melissa Petruska; ed: Youngstown St 29 Quarter Hrs; cr: Niles-Edison Hlth Tchr 1985-; ai: Ftbl Coach Yr 1984-90; office: Edison Jr HS 36 W Church St Niles OH 44446

ZUCAL, DANIELE PIERRETTE, High School French Teacher; b: Nancy, France; m: Thomas W.; c: Christine Monroe, Erik Dawson; ed: Walsh Univ (AA) Bus Mngmt 1982, (BA) Ed, Fr 1988; Ashland Univ (MA) Curr Instruction 1995; 12 Sem Hrs Mngmt by Objectives, Perceptive Ldrshp; cr: Louisville HS Fr Tchr 1989-92; Walsh Univ Fr Lit, Civilization Adjunct Fac 1990-94; Perry HS Fr Tchr 1993-; ai: Fr Club Adv; Ski Club Asst Adv; Fr natl Exam Coach; NEA 1989-; TOFLA 1994-; NEOLA 1990-; Parlons Francais 1989-, Co-Founder, Pres 2 Terms, Treas; Comm House 1985-, Facilitator; Honored Edctr by top Graduating Sr 1995; office: Perry HS 3737 Harsh Ave SW Massillon OH 44646*

ZUCARO, MICHAEL A., Adj Lecturer in Eng & ESL; b: Brooklyn, NY; m: Elisa Giuliano; c: Gregory, Eric; ed: Fordham Univ Coll (BA) Eng 1966; Columbia Univ Grad Facs (MA) Contemp Amer & Brit Lit 1967; All Credits Toward PHD 1967-70; cr: Hunter Coll CUNY Adj Lecturer in Eng 1967-69; City Coll of San Francisco Instr of Eng 1977-78; NY Univ Adj Asst Prof ESL 1983-89; Borough of Manhattan Comm Coll Adj Lecturer ESL 1985-; Baruch Coll CUNY Adj Lecturer Eng 1981-; ai: Prof Staff Congress 1981-; NYSTESOL 1987-; NY St Regents Tchng Flwshp 1966; Phi Beta Kappa 1967; Opening Doors; Idioms in English Pub 1992; office: Borough Of Manhattan Comm Coll 199 Chambers St New York NY 10007

ZUCCALA, BRUNO DOMENICK, Third Grade Teacher; *b:* Butler, PA; *ed:* Slippery Rock Univ (BA) Elem Ed 1979; Westminster Coll (MS) Admin, Sup 1992; Reading Specialist 1988 at Slippery Rock Univ; *cr:* Butler Cath Schl Classroom Tchr 1979-81; Moniteau Schls Classroom Tchr, Asst to Prin 1981-89; Seneca Vly Schls Classroom Tchr, Asst to Prin 1989-; *ai:* Stu Cncl; Schl Store; Musical Dir; Literacy Comm; Long Range Planning; PTO; Math, Homework Tutor; PSEA, NEA 1981-; Cath Charities 1986-89, Pres; Diocese of Pitts Schl Bd 1984-87; Exec Bd 1980-, Sec; Bands of Amer 1990-, Adjudicator; Gift of Time Recipient 1991; Outstdng Young Man of Amer 1988-89; Honorary Cavalier Drum & Bugle Corps 1992; Deans List Stu 1978-79; *office:* Seneca Vly Schl Dist 124 Seneca School Rd Harmony PA 16037*

ZUCCARO, CAROL BESSETTE, High School English Teacher; *b:* St Johnsbury, VT; *m:* Edward R.; *c:* James, Gina; *ed:* Lyndon St Coll (BS) Eng & Scndry Ed 1990; 12 Credit Hrs Bread Loaf Schl of Eng & Middlebury Coll Eng; *cr:* St Johnsbury Acad Eng Tchr 1990-; *ai:* Tech & Lit Comms; Former Tennis Coach; BLRTN 1994-; Article in Bread Loaf Rural Tchr Network Newsletter; *office:* St Johnsbury Acad 7 Main St Saint Johnsbury VT 05819

ZUCKER, MORDECHAI, Judaic Studies Teacher; *b:* New York, NY; *m:* Rhoda Naomi Spector; *c:* Shaindel Gobiof, Yisroel Tzui, Yocheved, Menachem Aharon, Yosef Leib, Deena, Ellisheva, Shneur Nuta, Malka Raizel, Yehudis, Yaakov Nachman; *ed:* Beth Medrash Govoha Rabbi Aaron Kotler Inst for Advanced Tchng (MS) Advanced Rabbinices 1978; Rel Ed; *cr:* Bais Kaila Girls HS Judaic Law Tchr 1981-82; Hebrew Acad of Washington Judaic Tchr 1982-; *ai:* Lunchroom Supvr; Northwest Citizen Patrol 1982-; *office:* Hebrew Acad Of Washington 2010 Linden Ln Silver Spring MD 20910*

ZUCKER, ROBERT W., Mathematics Teacher; *b:* New York, NY; *m:* Jayne P. Guneau; *c:* Patricia, Kathleen, Robert M.; *ed:* C W Post Coll (BS) Math 1966, (MA) Math 1968; Iona Coll (MBA) Mgmt Sci 1978; *cr:* Monticello HS Math Tchr 1978-79; Harriman Coll Bus Divison Head 1978-81; Iona Coll Adjunct Prof 1978-86; Monroe Woodbury HS Math Tchr 1979-; *ai:* Spring, Winter Track, Cross Cntry Coach; Interact, Sr Class Adv; Tchrs Assn Hlth Comm; Tchrs Union Del; MWTA 1979-, Del; AFT 1966-; Jaycees 1972-, Past Pres; Rotary 1985-, Youth Dir; Woodbury Ramble 1986-, Schlsp Comm; Grad Assistantship C W Post Coll; Pres Math Honor Soc C W Post; *office:* Monroe-Woodbury HS Dunderberg Rd Central Valley NY 10917*

ZUCKERMAN, PHYLLIS RITA, Third Grade Teacher; *b:* Jersey City, NJ; *ed:* Jersey City St Coll (BA) Elem Ed, Music 1973, (MA) Rdng, Rdng Specialist 1980; Work Early Chldhd; *cr:* Our Lady of Mt Carmel Third Grd Tchr 1973-; *ai:* Teach Private Piano; Accompanied Schl Prgms; Worked Schl Newspaper; Phi Delta Kappa 1984-; Bayonne JCC; Thesis Pub; *office:* Our Lady Of Mount Carmel Schl 95 Broadway Jersey City NJ 07306

ZUKAS, RHONA GORSKY REISS, Director of Education; *b:* Philadelphia, PA; *m:* Stasys K.; *c:* Daniel Reiss; *ed:* Univ of PA (BS) Occupational Therapy 1966; Univ of FL (MOT) Occupational Therapy 1975; Univ of North TX Higher Ed PHD Candidate; *cr:* Univ of IL at Chicago Asst Prof 1975-77; Rehabilitation Inst of Chicago Dir of Occupational Therapy Ed 1977-85; TX Womans Univ Assoc Prof & Asst Dean 1986-95; Amer Occupational Therapy Assoc Dir of Ed 1995-; *ai:* Managed Care & Satisfaction Teams; Amer Occ Therapy Assoc 1966-, Fellow; World Fed of Occupational Therapy 1966-; Higher Ed Group of WA DC 1995-; Cumberland Coll of Hlth Scis Visitng Fellow; Fuchu Inst of Rehabilitation Visiting Instr; Numerous Articles Pub; *office:* Amer Occupational Therapy Assn 4720 Montgomery Ln Box 31220 Bethesda MD 20824*

ZUKOWSKI, NANCY (SHUPP), English Teacher; *b:* Utica, NY; *m:* Anthony Jr.; *ed:* SUNY at Oswego (BA) Eng 1966; 32 Grad Hrs; *cr:* New Hartford Sr HS Eng Tchr 1966-, Asst Dept Chair 1985-; *ai:* Lang Arts Curr Review Facilitator; NHS Adv; NCTE; New Hartford PTSA; MLA; Delta Kappa Gamma 1972-, Sec, Scholar Chair, Prof Growth & Sci Chair.*

ZULAUF, SANDER, English Professor; *b:* Paterson, NH; *m:* Madeline; *c:* Scott, Mary Beth Russell, Michael; *ed:* Gettysburg Coll (BA) Eng 1968; IN Univ (MA) Eng 1973; NJ Eng Tchng Cert; 30 Credit Hrs William Paterson Coll; *cr:* Martin Luther King Jr. HS 8th Grd Tchr 1968-69; Hanover Park RHS Eng, Hum Tchr 1969-71; Cty Coll of Morris Eng Prof 1973-; *ai:* Journal of NJ Poets Ed; Dodge Fnd 1988-, Poet; Assoc Writing Prgms, Mem; Acad of Amer Poets 1987-, Voting Mem; Thoreau, Kenneth Burkg Soc; Poetry Soc Amer; Book Ed, Producer, Dir; *office:* County Coll Of Morris 214 Center Grove Rd Randolph NJ 07869*

ZULLO, LUCY FIORENZA, Italian Teacher; *b:* Cervinara Avellino, Italy; *ed:* Herbert H. Lehman Coll (BA) Italian 1976; Hunter Coll (MA) Italian 1981; *cr:* Our Lady of Refuge Schl 7th Grd Rdng, Lang Arts, Religion Tchr 1979-85; St Catharine Acad HS Italian Tchr 1985-; *ai:* Italian Club Moderator; AAIT; Iona Univ Lang Cntst; Clumbus Alliance Schlrshp; Fordham Univ Itln Poetry Cntst; Amer Assn of Italian Tchrs 1990-; NCEA 1988-; FIAME 1994-; *office:* St Catharine Acad 2250 Williamsbridge Rd Bronx NY 10469

ZUMBIEL, BARBARA REHM, Guidance Counselor; *b:* Wooster, OH; *m:* Gary A.; *c:* Orry Andrew; *ed:* OH St Univ (BS) Food Tech 1977; Xavier Univ (MED) Ed, Guid 1982; *cr:* Hughes HS Voc Food Processing Tchr 1977-84; Bloom MS Math Tchr 1984-86; Withrow HS Math Tchr 1986-88, Guid Cnslr 1988-; *ai:* CFT, OFT, AFT 1977-; OH Cnslng Assn 1989-; Hopeful Luth Church 1985-, Yth Dir; Cub Scouts 1992-, Den Ldr; Intnl 4-H Yth Exchange 1979-; *office:* Withrow HS 2488 Madison Rd Cincinnati OH 45208

ZUMMO, JOAN E., Assistant Prof of Biology; *b:* Albion, NY; *m:* Joseph F.; *c:* Ellen Hamlin, Catherine, Francis, Marc; *ed:* Coll of New Rochelle (BA) Bio 1963; SUNY at Brockport (MS) Bio 1985; *cr:* Univ of Rochester Rsrch Technician 1963-65, 1973-75; Cameron Meml Hosp Clinical Technician 1965-66; Monroe Com Coll Lecturer, Bio Tchr 1985-86; Genesee Com Coll Asst Prof Bio 1987-; *ai:* AAUW 1996; NABT 1992-, Chr Nominating Com 2 Yr Section; ESATYCB 1988-; *office:* Genesee Comm Coll 1 College Rd Batavia NY 14020

ZUNIGA, CHARLOTTE DASZEWSKI, Chemistry & Earth Science Tchr; *b:* Brooklyn, NY; *m:* Frank; *ed:* Long Island Univ (MT) ASCP; C. W. Post Coll (BS) Med Bio 1972; St John's Univ (MS) Pharmaceutical Sciences 1995; AZ St Univ 30 Credits Scndry Ed, Scndry Ed Tchr Trng; *cr:* St John's Prep HS Sci Tchr 7 Yrs; Covenant House Under 21 Case Worker 1 Yr; St Luke's Hosp Med Technologist 8 Yrs; Gallup Indian Med Ctr Ed Coord for Med Tech Prgm 5 Yrs; *ai:* Forensic Club 1991-93; Sci Tchr Assoc of NY St 1989-; Acad Achvmt Awd St John's Univ; *office:* Saint Johns Preparatory HS 21-21 Crescent St Astoria NY 11105*

ZUPANCIC, ANTHONY J., Assoc Prof of Eng, Comm, Thtre; *b:* Cleveland, OH; *m:* Jane VanBergen; *c:* Tony, Grace; *ed:* Cleveland St Univ (BA) Eng 1970; Univ of North TX (MA) Speech, Drama 1973; Kent St Univ (ABD) Theater 1988; Post-Grad Stud Theater NY Univ 1975; Grad Stud Theater Univ of TX at El Paso 1971; *cr:* Bizerko Improv Theatre Ensemble Dir, Cast Mem 1973-78; East Tech HS Eng, Speech, Drama Tchr 1973-77; Kent St Univ Comm, Theater Instr 1977-81; Notre Dame Coll of OH Assoc Prof Eng, Comm, Theatre 1981-; Coll Bd, Ed Testing Svc Consultant 1987-; *ai:* Rho Omega Cast of Alpha Psi Omega Adv; Forensic Competitions Coach; Fac, Coll Comms; Lead Instr Basic Speech; Speech Comm Assn 1977-; Soc Prof Journalists 1987-; NCTE 1981-; Northeast OH Commission Higher Ed 1983-, Instrl Tech Comm; Cleveland Hghts Cable TV Commission 1994-, Commissioner; Shalheuet Intnl Folk Ensemble 1993-, Adv Bd;Eng Speaking Union Shakespeare Comp 1989-, Judge; Distngd Fac Awd 1994; OH Hum Scholar 1991-; OH Magazine Star Prof 1992; Outstdng Tchr Awd 1981; Slovenian Stud Awd 1979; *office:* Notre Dame Coll of OH 4545 College Rd Cleveland OH 44121*

ZUPANCIC, KEITH RONALD, English Teacher; *b:* Cleveland, OH; *ed:* Univ of Akron (BA) Eng 1988; John Carrell Univ (MEd) Ed 1991; *cr:* Valley Forge HS Eng Tchr 1991-; *ai:* Head Var Soccer, Asst Boys Track Coach; NEA 1991-; *office:* Valley Forge HS 9999 Independence Blvd Parma OH 44130*

ZUPKE, LORI HAYES, Mathematics Teacher; *b:* Akron, OH; *m:* Robert J.; *c:* Amelia, Robert; *ed:* Univ of Akron (BA) Ed, Math 1980; (MA) Scndry Schl Cnslng 1983; Intnl Baccalaureate Trng; Core Plus Math Project Trng, Field Test Tchr; *cr:* Roswell Kent Jr HS Math Tchr 1980-82; Buchtel HS Math Tchr 1982-90; Firestone HS Math Tchr 1993-; *ai:* Former Chrldr Adv; Girls Bsktbl Coach; Intnl Bacc Planning Comm; Core Plus Math Trnr; NCTM 1983-; Jr Bd Hospital Vol 1991-92; SEPF Grant 1995- to Aid in Integrating Math & Sci with Tech FLOW Firestone Lab Opening to World; *office:* Akron Harvey Firestone HS 333 Rampart Ave Akron OH 44313*

ZUPKO, DEBORAH A., English Teacher; *b:* Ft Monmouth, NJ; *m:* Joseph M.; *c:* Kimberly, Joseph Jr.; *ed:* Seton Hill Univ (BA) Eng, Writing 1985; 9 Credit Hrs Georgian Court Coll Instrl Tech; *cr:* Bay Head Elem Schl Eng Tchr 1987-; *ai:* BHTEA 1989-, Pres 1993-; *office:* Bay Head Elem Schl 145 Grove St Point Pleasant Bea NJ 08742

ZUREK, MELANIE ALEXANDRA, English & Language Arts Tchr; *b:* New Hartford, NY; *ed:* SUNY at Cobieskill (AAS) Animal Behavior 1990; Utica Coll of Syracuse Univ (BA) Eng 1993; SUNY at Cortland (MS) Rdng K-12 1996; *cr:* Vernon-Verona-Sherrill HS Eng & Lang Arts Tchr 1993-; *ai:* Schl Newspaper; Schl Art & Lit Magazine; Ski Club; FOCUS; SIP; OBE; VVS Tchrs Assn 1993-; NYSUT 1993-; Comm 4-H Club 1980-, Horseback Riding Instr; Animal Behaviorists Org 1990-, Outstdng Behaviorist 1992; Article Pub; *office:* VVS Cntrl HS Rt 31 Verona NY 13478

ZURENDA, DEBORAH KAY, Biology Teacher; *b:* Lancaster, PA; *ed:* Millersville Univ (BS) Bio, Scndry Ed 1986; Attnd DE St Coll, Penn St Univ, Amer Wilderness Leadership Schl, Univ of CT, Natl Wilderness Leadership Schl, FL Inst of Tech, Univ of OR; *cr:* Caesar Rodney HS Bio Tchr 1986-88; East Stroudsburg Area HS Bio Tchr 1988-89; New Oxford HS Bio Tchr 1989-; *ai:* JV Field Hockey, Girls Track & Field Coach; Environmental Club Adv; PA Alliance for Env Ed 1989-; Appalachian Trail Conf 1990-; Sierra Club 1992-; PA Game Commission Wild Action, Gettysburg-Hanover Chamber of Commerce Grants; Shippensburg Univ Outstanding Educator, Hanover Area Jaycees Outstanding Young Educator Awds; *office:* New Oxford HS 130 Berlin Rd New Oxford PA 17350*

ZURKEY, WILLIAM GAVIN, Vocal Music Director; *b:* Youngstown, OH; *m:* Sandra Snyder; *c:* Adam William, Megan Nicole; *ed:* Bowling Green St Univ (BA) Music Ed 1977; Cleveland St Univ (MM) Music 1986; Kent St Univ Music Ed Doctoral Stud 15 Semester Hrs; *cr:* DeVilbiss HS Vocal Music Dir 1977-79; Vermilion HS Vocal Music Dir 1979-87; Avon Lake HS Vocal Music Dir 1987-; *ai:* Chamber Ensemble Local, Regnl Performances Dir; Avon Lake City Schls Head Eighth Grd Ftbl Coach 1980-; OH Music Ed Assn 1977-, Comm Chm; Amer Choral Dir Assn 1978-; OH Choral Dir Assn 1978-, NE Regnl Chair; Amer Guild of Organists; Pi Kappa Lambda 1985-; Bay United Meth Church 1979-, Organist; Equal Housing Bd 1983-85, Rep; OMEA Convention Performance 1995; Guest Conductor: OH Music Ed Assn Dist I Hnrs Choir 1996, Ashland Univ 1989, 1993, 1995; All-St OH Regnl Choir Dir; *office:* Avon Lake HS 175 Avon Belden Rd Avon Lake OH 44012

ZURN, VICKIE C., Fourth Grade Teacher; *b:* Albany, GA; *m:* H. Jeffrey; *c:* Robin, Caryn; *ed:* Mansfield St Coll (BS) Elem 1973; Masters Equivalency from Univ of Seranton; *cr:* Elk Lake Schl Dist Kndgtn & 1st Grd Tchr 1973-75, Kndgtn Tchr Summer 1974, 4th Grd Tchr 1975-81, 3rd Grd Tchr 1981-82, 4th Grd Tchr 1983-88, Permanent Sub Tchr 1989, 4th Grd Tchr 1989-; *ai:* Fall Musicals Costume Dir; PSEA, NEA 1973-; Girl Scouts, Ldr, Jr Troop & Camp Cnslr; Hallstead Presbyn Church, Youth Bell Choir, Worship Comm, Choir; Peals of Joy Bell Choir 1991-; Note-a-Bells Choir 1990-; *home:* RR 1 Box 80A Great Bend PA 18821*

ZUROVCHAK, PAUL J., Retired Business Ed Teacher; *b:* Cleveland, OH; *m:* Barbara Collins; *c:* Janet Zurovchak Grothaus, Judy Lesko, James, Joseph, John, Jerry, Jill Neely, Kim Collins, Chelsey Collins; *ed:* Indiana Univ of PA (BS) Bus Ed 1959; Duquesne Univ (MED) Ed 1966; *cr:* Youngsville HS Bus Ed Tchr 1959-60; US Army Ofcr Quartermaster Corpse 1960-62; West Allegheny Schl Dist Bus Ed Tchr 1962-67; Titusville Area Schls Bus Ed Tchr 1967-93; *ai:* Adult Ed; Asst Bsbl, Little League Bsbl Coach; Chrldng, Bus Club, Sportsmen Club Adv; Summer Recreation Supvr; Titusville Ed Assn 1967-, Treas, Pres; Penn Ed Assn, NEA, Penn Bus Ed Assn 1959-; St Titus Schl Bd 1970-82, Treas; Big Brothers Big Sisters 1994-; Titusville Recreation Comm 1970-83; Titusville HS Tchr of Yr 1970-1971; *home:* 1561 Leslie Rd Meadville PA 16335

ZUSKIN, RONALD EDWARD, Clinical Instructor; *b:* Newport News, VA; *c:* Kirsten, Lauren; *ed:* Towson St Univ (BA) Psych 1972; UMAB-SSW (MSW) Clinical 1982; *cr:* Pvt Practice Psychotherapy 1982-; Springfield Hosp Ctr Soc Worker 1985-86; Baltimore Cty Child Advocacy Ctr Soc Work Supvr 1986-91; Baltimore Cty DSS CPS Supvr 1991-92; UMAB Schl of Soc Work Clinical Instr 1992-; *ai:* NASW 1982-; Amer Prof Soc on Abuse of Children MD Chptr 1994-, Pres; Amer Humane Assn; Cntrl MD Sexual Abuse Treatment Task Force; Assn for Advancement of Soc Work with Groups; NCCAN Trng Grant in Substance Abuse & Child Maltreatment Prin Investigator; *office:* Univ Of MD At Baltimore School of Social Work 525 W Redwood St Baltimore MD 21201

ZUSMAN, LINDA WATERS, Spanish Teacher; *b:* Brooklyn, NY; *m:* Jerry B.; *c:* Faye Alisha, Brian Geoffrey; *ed:* SUNY at Albany (BA) Fr, Span 1971; Univ of Rochester (MED) Curr Dev, Elem F L 1976; Addl Hrs Curr Dev; *cr:* Patchoque Medford Schls Fr Tchr 1971-72; Brockport HS Fr, Span, Latin, Ger Tchr 1974-76; Niskoyuna Schls Span Tchr 1987-88; Shenedehowa Cntrl Schls Span, Fr Tchr 1988-; *ai:* Frgn Lang Club; F. L. Curr, M&S Planning Comms; NYSAFLT 1976-, Treas, 3 Distngd Svc Awds; COLT 1992-, Exec Bd, Newslettr Ed; NYSUT 1987-, Local Comm Chairs; Univ of Albany 1980-, Alumni Cncl, Class Cnslr, Distngd Svc; NYSPTA 1978-, Capital Dist Based Newsletter Ed, Asst Dir, Honorary Life Mbrshp, Reflections Chair; Hudson Vly G S Cncl 1983-, Bd of Dir, Thanks Badge Outstdng Ldr, Hnr Pin, Outstdng Ldr, Vol; Hadassah 1985-, Life Mem; 5 Excl Ed Awds; Article Pub 1995; Svc Awd; Gov Clinton Cncl BSA; NYS FL Framework Exemplars; *office:* Shenendehowa Cntrl Schls Rt 156 Clifton Park NY 12065*

ZWALD, JAMES M., Spanish Teacher; *b:* Emporium, PA; *ed:* St Bonaventure Univ (BA) Span & Ed 1967, (MSEd) Scndry Admin 1970; Attnd SUNY at Geneseo; *cr:* Allegany Limestone CS Span Tchr 1968-, Interim Prin 1985; St Bonaventure Univ Adj Prof 1982-94; *ai:* Yrbk, Grad & Sr Class Adv; Chaperone Abroad; NEA & NEA NY 1968-, Negotiator; NYSAFLT 1968-, Regnl Planner; Allegany TA 1968-, Pres, Negotiator & Grievance Chair; Credit Union 1968-, Dir & Former Treas; CCD Tchr 1969-80, Buffalo Dioceses Tchr of Yr; K of C 1975-; Pub Dissertation on Ed of Blind & Visually Impared Stdnts; *home:* 100 Sherwood Dr Allegany NY 14706*

ZWEBEN, MINNETTE NEEDLE, Visual Arts Teacher; *b:* Newark *c:* Paul, Sandra Zweben-Lebowitz; *ed:* Montclair St Univ (BA) Fine Ed 1961; Seton Hall Univ (MA) Scndry Ed 1964; 36 Addl Hrs Educl, Arts Stud; *cr:* South Jr HS Art Tchr 1961-64; Bloomfield HS Art 1972-; *ai:* Art Club Adv, Renaissance Comm; BEA, NJEA, NEA, E 1972-; Oakeside-Blfd Cultural Ctr 1994-; Lecture & Exhibit Art Locally; *office:* Bloomfield HS 160 Broad St Bloomfield NJ 07003*

ZWEIZIG, TIMOTHY JOHN, 4th Grade Teacher; *b:* Pottsville, PA Kutztown Univ (BS) Elem Ed & Math 1992; 9 Credits in Post Grad S Admin Lehigh Univ; *cr:* Hamburg Area SD Elem Tchr 1993- Schvylkill Haven Area Var Boys Bsktbl Coach 1986-91; Girls Var B Coach 1994-95; Kutztown Area Boys Var Bsktbl Coach 1995-; S Month Adv; NEA 1993-; PSEA 1993-; HAEA 1993-, Asst Rep; Schv Haven Lions Club Comm Svc Altruism Awd; *office:* Hamburg Elem Windsor St 680 E State St Hamburg PA 19526

ZWICK, MICHAEL A., Associate Prof of Mathematics; *b:* Roch NY; *m:* Beverly M. Stoler; *c:* David, Joshua; *ed:* Monroe Comm (AAS) Math 1971; St Univ of NY at Geneseo (BS) Math & Scndr 1973; Syracuse Univ (MS) Math 1975; *cr:* Wellwood MS 7th-8th Grd Tchr 1975-77; Fayetteville Manlius HS 9th-12th Grd Math Tchr 197 Monroe Comm Coll Math Prof 1982-; *ai:* Adjunct Coord; Pres Cncl; 1975-; *office:* Monroe Comm Coll 1000 E Henrietta Rd Rochester 14623*

ZWIEBACH, SALLY BEVER, English Teacher; *b:* Kearny, N Burton; *c:* Michael, Peter; *ed:* Mount Holyoke Coll (BA) Eng Teachers Coll, Columbia Univ (MA) Scndry Eng Tchng 1962; Colu Univ Grad Schl of the Arts (MFA) Directing 1982; Addl 75 Credit Hr Charles Evans Hughes HS Eng Tchr 1962-65; Queens Coll Instr 196 Glen Cove HS Eng Tchr 1975-; *ai:* Past Drama Club Dir 1976-84; H Soc Spon 1988-90; Lit Journal adv 1993-; Fac Cncl Facilitator 199 Diversity, Dist Wide Shared Decision Making, Staffing Comms; Theatre Day Chm; NY St Eng Cncl 1985-, Tchr of Excl Awd 1986; N Theatre Ed Assn 1983-, Bd of Dir 1990-92; Long Island Theatre Ed 1986-, Pres 1993-94, Bd Mem; Glen Cove Tchrs Assn 1975-, Bldg Theatre II of Glen Cove 1972-; League of Women Voters 1970-; A 1995-; PTA Honoree 1992; *office:* Glen Cove HS 150 Dosoris Ln Cove NY 11542*

ZWIEBEL, JEFFREY SCOTT, High School Band Director; *b:* Potts PA; *ed:* Wilkes Univ (BA) Music Ed 1990; Gettysburg Coll Music Ed Pine Grove Area HS Band Dir 1990-; *ai:* Marching, Concert & Jazz Dir; PASIC, AF of M 1986-; MENC, PMEA 1988-; NBDA; Schuy Symphony Orchestra 1985-; Third Brigade Band 1985-, Bd of Dirs; *o* Pine Grove Area HS School St Pine Grove PA 17963

ZWIERCHOWSKI, WALTER, High School Religion Teacher Bayonne, NJ; *ed:* Saint Peter's Coll (BA) Theology 1979; Saint Mich Coll (MA) Rel Stud, Ed1995; *cr:* Mount Assumption Rel Tchr 198 Seton Cath Cntrl Rel Tchr 1991-92; *ai:* Bookstore Mgr; *office:* B Connolly HS 373 Elsbree St Fall River MA 02720

ZWINGELBERG, WILLIAM C., Prof of Art & Dept Chair; *b:* Fland SD; *m:* Tamara A. Yule; *c:* Shanando Blood, Shane, Shala Teets; *ed:* S Univ (BA) Art 1969; WV Univ (MA) Painting 1970; Univ of MD (Aesthetics 1978; *cr:* Catonsville Comm Coll Prof of Art, Dept Chair 1 *office:* Catonsville Comm Coll 800 S Rolling Rd Catonsville MD 212

ZWIRN, GAIL SANDRA, Adjunct Instructor Eng Dept; *b:* Newark *m:* Albert; *c:* Daniel; *ed:* Rutgers Univ (BA) Eng 1968; Univ of Pitts (MA) Eng 1973, (PHD) Eng 1981; *cr:* Robert Morris Coll Adj Fac 1981-90; La Roche Coll Adj Fac Eng 1991-; Point Park Coll Adj Fac 1995-; CCAC Allegheny Campus Adj Fac Eng 1991-.

ZWOBODA, JOSEPHINE, Second Grade Teacher; *b:* Catskill, NY Thomas C.; *c:* Thomas J. Kralovich Jr., Stephen L. Kralovich; Columbia-Greene Comm Coll (AA) Lbrl Arts 1973; SUNY Coll at Paltz (BS) N-6 Elem Ed 1975, (MS) Ed 1979; *cr:* Windham Ashland Je Cntrl Schl 1st-3rd Grd Elem Tchr 1975-; *ai:* K-6 Morning Prgm, Recycling, Mission to Plant Earth Comms; Sub Tchr Comm, Chprsn; NEA 1975-; WAJ Tchrs Assn 1975-, Sec; Fortnightly Club 1968-, 1974-75, VP 1973-74; *office:* Windham Ashland Jewett Ctl Sch Ma Windham NY 12496

ZWYNER, GRACE ELEANOR, Mathematics Teacher; *b:* Danbury *ed:* Marymount Coll at Tarrytown (BA) Math 1964; Fairfield Univ Math, Ed 1970; *cr:* Watertown HS Math Tchr 1964-; *ai:* WEA, CEA, 1964-; *office:* Watertown HS 324 French St Watertown CT 06795

ZYLAK, RICHARD E.,JR., Physics & Astronomy Teacher; *b:* Lat PA; *m:* Cynthia A. Petruso; *c:* Jordan, Jennifer; *ed:* Edinboro St Univ Ed, Math, Physics 1976, (MS) Ed, Earth Sci 1981, (BS) Geology 1982 Meadvillw Sr HS Physics, Astronomy Tchr 1976-; *ai:* Acad Chall Team Coach; NEA, PA St Ed Assn 1994-, Local Pres; AAPT 1 Astronomical Soc of Pacific 1990-; Jaycees Outstdng Young Edctrs 1993; *office:* Meadville Sr HS North St Ext Meadville PA 16335

ZYZNAR, LUCILLE KRAYNAK, Elementary Teacher; *b:* Youngst OH; *m:* Chester; *c:* Joyce kelly, Judith, J. Gary; *ed:* Youngstown St (BA) Elem Ed 1967; Diocese of Youngstown Ursiline Mother House (Rel; 9 Post Grad Hrs; *cr:* St Dominic Schl 3rd-8th Grd Tchr 31 Yrs Curr Fair for 5th-8th Grd Coord 8 Yrs; Judge for Sci Fair; Lake-To- Assn 1980-; Cath Collegiate Assn 1980-; NCEA 1970-; Mahoning Vly Intnl Rdng Assn St Dominic Church rosary Altar Soc 1980-, VP, Recognition for Inspiring Stu in Superior Achvmnt in Sci 1991-93, 1 Women Precinct Comm; Camp Fire Ldr; *home:* 215 Bradford Dr Can OH 44406

GEOGRAPHIC OCCUPATION INDEX

Teachers honored in all volumes are included in this index. Teachers' names and current positions are listed by their business city and state.

.ABAMA

EVILLE
ess, Martha Chapman
th Grade English Teacher
ford, Miriam
tory Teacher
Willadean Martin
h Grade Teacher
ck, Sarah Murphy
ond Grade Teacher
ter, Ginger Reeves
rd Grade Teacher
MSVILLE
, Wanda Jean
h Teacher & Department Head
land, William Thomas
ld Geog & AL His Teacher
, Kimberly Battles
lish Teacher
rd, Kenneth Allen
logy Teacher
es, Janet O'Dell
lish Teacher & Dept Chprsn
es, Micheal Stephen
d Director
on, Mary Kimbrough
oral Music & English Teacher
Vera M.
iness Education Teacher
nore, Edward Alan
letic Dir, Eng & His Tchr
r, Regina Trent
Biology, Health & PE Tchr
on, Josephine West
erican History Teacher
ISON
ns, Dorothy Jones
thematics Teacher
BASTER
n, Judy Pirkle
nch Teacher
berry, William Edwin
erican History & AP Teacher
t, Betty Hicks
lish Teacher
Cynthia Smitherman
rth Grade Teacher
Ann-Claire Elizabeth
loratory Teacher
, Nancy Johnson
Grade English Teacher
cock, J. Addison
h, Physics & Chemistry Tchr
tt, Margaret Golden
h School Principal
r, Laurie Ann
h School History Teacher
, Deborah Adams
ence Teacher
den, Thomas Kevin
d Director
npson, Deborah Gallagher
glish Teacher
, Patricia Taylor
, Theatre & Speech Teacher
ERTVILLE
ks, Barbara Henry
glish Teacher
ks, Jerry
ssroom Teacher
Lynda Archer
Grd Social Studies Teacher
er, Linda Thrasher
h Grade Reading Teacher
, Connie Duckett
ond Grade Teacher
on, Jane Campbell
rarian & Media Specialist
ll, Maryetta Van Devender
h Grade Teacher
X CITY
r, Vicki Cooper
tory & Speech Teacher
op, Misty Smith
glish Teacher
, James Theodore
thematics Teacher

Cooper, John Burton
Band Director
Dexter, David Lee
Driver Education Teacher
Elliott, John C.
Psychology Teacher
Gowan, Walter Earl
Social Studies Teacher
Harrell, Karen Sasser
Journalism, Span & Eng Teacher
Moncrief, Teresa Guy
Mathematics Teacher
Pike, Laura Lee
English Teacher
Sherrer, Pamela Smith
Senior English Teacher
Silver, Tracy Jeanne (Zaglin)
Mathematics Teacher
Vickers, Kimberly Deaneen
English & Literature Teacher
ALEXANDER CITY
Burns, Teresa Hayes
Mathematics Teacher
Eiland, Karen Walton
First Grade Teacher
Giangrosso, Peter Lawrence
Dir of Ath & Wellness, Coach
Jones, Jeanette H.
English Instructor
Kornman, Paul T., III
Math Professor
Meadows, Jan
Biology Instructor
Moseley, Marvin York
Biology Instructor
Nicholson, K. W.
Mathematics & Physics Instr
Nunnery, Hattie P.
Instr of Bus & Office Admin
Price, Nancy C.
Instructor & Coach
Roberts, Elinor Warr
English Instructor
Roberts, Walter McMahan
Band Director
Teel, Samuel Albert
Social Studies Tchr & Chprsn
Wilder, Jeanne
First Grade Teacher
Wynne, John Maurice
English Professor
ALEXANDRIA
Heath, Alex Wayne
History Teacher
ALPINE
Curlee, Johnny Frank
Instr of Computer Electronics
ALTOONA
Brannon, Teresa Parker
First Grade Teacher
Moxley, Glenda Vaughn
4th Grade Teacher
ANDALUSIA
Bozeman, Cathy Brannon
Fourth Grade Teacher
Bush, Kathryn Prestwood
Fourth Grade Teacher
Clifton, Judy Martin
First Grade Teacher
Durr, Eva Byrd
Voc Business Education Teacher
Ennis, Jenelle Godwin
5th-6th Grd Lang Arts Teacher
Hutcherson, Emma Bradley
Teacher
Lee, MaryAnn Hildreth
English & Social Studies Tchr
Peters, Jennifer Sasser
First Grade Teacher
Powell, Lynda Bulger
Social Studies & English Tchr
Rich, Lonnie Keven
Art Program Chairman & Instr
Sasser, Donald Wayne
7th Grd World History Teacher
ANNISTON
Barker, Donya Snider
5th Grd Rdng & Lang Arts Tchr

Boatwright, J. Barry
Biology & Chemistry Teacher
Burgess, Lynne Elliott
Business Teacher
Burleson, Connie Tanner
Fine Arts Chr & Choral Dir
Campbell, Everette Ringer
Third Grade Teacher
Conley, Eula A.
Biology & Anatomy Teacher
Green, William Lee
Social Studies Teacher
Hardy, Brenda S.
History Teacher
Haynes, Nancy C.
Home Economics Teacher
Hester, Karen Lynn
Latin & Language Arts Teacher
Hill, Malia Ann
7th Grade Social Studies Tchr
Howell, Laura Clark
Retired Advncd Biology Teacher
Kilbourne, Luanne V.
English Professor
Mallicoat, Sandy Housch
Sixth Grade Math Teacher
Moore, Janet Cain
Psychometrist & Choral Dir
Mullins, Allecia Mc Clain
Third Grade Teacher
Norton, Kim Gayton
Eighth Grade English Teacher
Smith, Patricia Adams
Retired History Teacher
Thagard, Jeanie
English Teacher & Dept Chair
Thagard, Redge Pearson
Guidance Dir & His Dept Chm
Weiser, Kathy Ward
Teacher of Gifted & Enrichment
Wergin, Donna Mange
Biology Teacher
Whitley, Carolyn Wade
6th Grd Math & Soc Stud Tchr
Wingo, Sandra Harris
Mathematics Teacher
Yarbrough, Owen Eugene
Science Teacher & Coach
ARAB
Bagwell, Velinda Hawkins
Teacher
Clem, Theresa Jayne
Physical Education Teacher
Cornelius, Donna Netherton
Media Specialist
Ingram, Suzanne Hill
Math Teacher
Ledbetter, Darriel Spencer
HS & Jr Coll Eng Teacher
Weaver, Carol Bunch
English Teacher
Willis, Susan Black
Principal
ARDMORE
Blizzard, Lelia Bourdin
Vocational Home Economics Tchr
Dale, Pam Woodfin
Kindergarten Teacher
Edge, Amy K.
Science Teacher
Hastings, Pamela Barron
English Teacher
Linderman, Gary Patrick
Math Teacher
Smith, Lisa Jan
English Teacher
ARITON
Bynum, Paula D.
Media Specialist
Carroll, Sandy Holt
4th-6th Grade Science Teacher
Johnston, Tammy U.
Math Teacher
Snell, Joe Frank
Agribusiness Teacher
ARLEY
Allison, Sonja Diane Newsome
Home Economics Teacher

Smothers, Micah Joe
Social Studies & PE Teacher
Smothers, Sherry Morgan
English Teacher
Waldrop, Amy Susette
Science Teacher
Youngblood, Terry
Voc Agribusiness Ed Instr
ASHFORD
Bratcher, Pamela C.
Biology & Science Teacher
Buie, Darryl P.
Bus & Office Education Teacher
Mc Daniel, Michael Jay
Government & Economics Teacher
Miller, Cristie Parmer
Mathematics Teacher
Mixon, Teresa Smith
8th Grade English Teacher
Padget, Chris Philip
Physical Science Teacher
Parker, Antionette Boykin
Eighth Grade Science Teacher
Robinson, Cynthia P.
High School Science Teacher
Sellers, Laura Green
English & Spanish Teacher
Shelley, JoAnne Whitehurst
English Teacher
Venegas, Lydia Alicia Zavala
Spanish & Science Teacher
ASHLAND
Bennett, Jerry David
Agri-Business Teacher
Bonner, Sheryl House
Social Science English Teacher
Horn, Danny L.
Health, PE Teacher & Coach
ASHVILLE
Chance, Sandra Morris
English Teacher
Gleason, Memory Hammond
Physical Ed Tchr & Coach
Hill, Tommy E.
Agribusiness Teacher
Smith, Jackie Burger
Business Education Instructor
Yarbrough, Fitzgerald, II
Biology Department Chrmn
ATHENS
Biggs, Carolyn Roberts
Mathematics Adjunct Instructor
Chandler, Ronald Gregory
Social Studies Teacher
Crow, Carolyn Clark
Enrchmnt Spec & Gifted Ed Tchr
Durm, Mark Wendell
Professor of Psychology
Eddy, Karen Maplesden
Math Tchr & Stu Council Spon
Gilbert, Betsy Strain
Second Grade Teacher
Gray, Frances DeArmond
Second Grade Teacher
Gulbro, Robert Dale
Associate Prof of Management
Haggenmaker, Laura Pankey
High School Math Teacher
Harris, Ruth Gordon
World & American History Tchr
Hemingway, Linda Krotec
Accounting Professor
Hicks, Harold J.
Senior Army Instructor
Hill, Carla Rhodes
Language Arts Teacher
Jackson, William Marvin
6th Grade Teacher
Johnston, Mildred Schrinsher
Former Kindergarten Teacher
Jones, Joe Michael
Gifted Education Specialist
Landtroop, James T.
Social Studies Teacher
Mc Kinney, Beth Holland
Math Teacher
Mierzejewski, Alfred Carl
Modern European His Asst Prof

Miner, James Robert
Math Department Chairman
Patty, Steve Lawrence
English Teacher
Roach, V. Sue
2nd Grade Homeroom Teacher
Robinson, Dianne
Fourth Grade Teacher
Searcy, Barbara Sexton
Assistant Professor of English
Shown, Elizabeth W.
American History & French Tchr
Thompson, Delores Ann (Hogan)
English & History Teacher
Warnock, Tom
Adjunct Instructor of Hum
Wheeler, Martha Peters
Math Teacher
White, Susan Marie
Kindergarten Teacher
Wiser, Kathryn Riggs
Mathematics & Science Teacher
Witt, Cindy Abercrombie
3rd Grade Teacher
ATMORE
Dean, Betty Dannelly
Retired Social Studies Teacher
Fantroy, Maxcine Eboni
Physical Science Teacher
Floyd, John
Social Studies Teacher
Green, Marcia Klopfenstein
1st Grade Teacher
Laurie, Jennifer Baggett
Mathematics Teacher
Marvin, Fannie Denise
Third Grade Teacher
Powe, Nancy J.
English Teacher
Quimby, Stan A.
Assistant Principal
Stabler, Mason Wesley
Mathematics Teacher
Stephens, Ann Moore
Math Teacher
ATTALLA
Adair, Charles, Jr.
Geography & History Teacher
Crumpler, Arthur James
Social Studies & Science Tchr
Foster, Larry J.
Physical Education Teacher
Gibson, Charles Wayne
JROTC Instructor
Gorecki, Irene J.
Third Grade Teacher
Landis, Judy
Asst Dir & Voc Guid Teacher
Limbaugh, Constance Fris
Third Grade Teacher
Mason, Nancy Winningham
5th Grade Language Arts Tchr
Mc Connell, Cynthia Silvey
Health Care Sci & Tech Teacher
Mitchell, Nancy Ellis
5th Grade Teacher & Asst Prin
Morgan, Pamela Smith
Amer Govt & Economics Teacher
Nabors, Janice Kilgore
7th Grd Language Arts Teacher
Petty, Gail Garrard
Kindergarten Teacher
Posey, Donna Turner
Social Studies Teacher
Samples, Brenda Darlene
Science Teacher
Sisson, Elaine Miller
Science Dept Chairman & Tchr
Stewart, Jane Martin
Counselor
Talley, James David
Welding Instructor
Treece, Cathy Sauls
Third Grade Teacher
AUBURN
Brawner, Jenny Roane
Math Teacher
Butler, Daniel D.
Associate Prof of Marketing

AUBURN (cont)
Byrd, Carol Tucker
English Teacher
Cannon, Effie Ogden
English Dept Chair & AP Coord
Crittenden, Robert G.
Biology Teacher
Fowler, June Gandy
7th Grade English Teacher
Gallahan, Carla Ann Allison
Band Director
Giles, Harriet Watkins
Asst Prof of Family Child Dev
Horne, Anne Griffin
Kindergarten Teacher
Housel, Susan Mc Intosh
Third Grade Teacher
Logan, Betsy Noll
Art Teacher & Yearbook Advisor
Payne, Rosolyn Jane
Fourth Grade Teacher
Pennisi, John Michael
English Teacher
Pickens, William Ware
High School Mathematics Tchr
St John, Margaret C.
10th Grade English Teacher
Scott, Princie Ingram
English Speech & Drama Teacher
Story, Carol Meadows
Library Media Specialist
Todd, Peggy Smith
French Teacher
Troy, Judy R.
English Professor
Weaver, David Bruce
Agronomy Professor
White, Carmel Parker
Former Visiting Asst Professor
Wilkinson, Susan Williamson
Second Grade Teacher
AUTAUGAVILLE
Bryant, Alvin H.
Social Studies Teacher
Morris, Cassandra Rose
Business Education Teacher
BAKER HILL
Williams, Annie L.
5th Grade Teacher
BANKS
Forbish, Kathleen Wright
Math & History Teacher
BAY MINETTE
Brown, Barbara Faye
8th Grade Science Teacher
Bulman, Wanda Davidson
12th Grd English Teacher
Corona, Barry Joseph
Chemistry Instructor
Edward, Franklin Delmor
Mathematics Instructor
Floyd, Deborah Gabel
Mathematics Instructor
Howard, Sheila Kucera
Ninth Grade English Teacher
Jackson, Barbara Howard
English Teacher
Langham, Jamie Whiteside
Mathematics Instructor
Partin, Lucia Ford
English Teacher
Peavy, Diann Ryan
Dental Assisting Instructor
Primm, Fred Daniel, Jr.
History Teacher
Riemer, Joseph Charles
Band Director
Settle, Carolyn Sutton
History Professor
Simon, Janice Crowder
3rd Grade Teacher
Thomas, Robert Lewis
History Professor
BAYOU LA BATRE
Donald, William Oscar, III
Social Studies Teacher & Coach
Joosten, Laurence Stewart
Chemistry & Physics Teacher
BEAR CREEK
Forsythe, Sandra Frederick
Business Teacher
Rushing, Charlotte Mae
History Teacher
BEATRICE
Cunningham, Lena Mae
Family & Consumer Science Tchr
Egolf, John LeRoy, Jr.
Mathematics & Physics Teacher
Lamar, E. Claudette
Secondary English Teacher
Mayes, Rosie Marie
Kindergarten Teacher
White, Willie James, Jr.
Soc Studies & Government Tchr
BERRY
Cannon, Georgia Frances
Social Science Teacher
Clements, Robin Patton
Kindergarten Teacher
Manning, Karen Oswalt
Fifth Grade Teacher
Smallwood, Lydia Johnston
Math & Computer Science Tchr
BESSEMER
Anderson, Mary Audrey
Second Grade Teacher
Ashcraft, Laura Green
AP US & American History Tchr
Colley, Anita Lynn
English & Drama Teacher
Dennis, Joe M.
Teacher
Lee, Sandra Oliver
10th Grade English Teacher
Mc Kenzie, Rebecca Meaut
Second Grade Teacher
Mc Kinney, Donna Reed
5th-6th Grade Tchr & Dance Dir
Miller, Kathryn Gilham
Fifth Grade Teacher
Moore, Harrianne
Fourth Grade Teacher
Phillips, Joy Borntreger
Kindergarten & Spanish Teacher
Phillips, Louis E., Jr.
History, Health & Bible Tchr
BIRMINGHAM
Anderson, Gloria Webb
Counselor
Ashley, Kecia Monique
English Teacher
Bailey, Mary Kraus
History & Psychology Teacher
Baker, Sue Ellen
Mathematics Teacher
Baskin, Anna Maria (Phelps)
Home Economics Teacher
Basselin, Mary Elizabeth
Mathematics Teacher
Bearden, Mary Beth Palmer
Math Teacher
Bedner, Loretta Fitzgerald
HS Theology Teacher
Beers, Geri Wood
Assistant Professor of Nursing
Belcher, Tyrone Haynes, Jr.
Science Teacher & Coach
Bennett, Madeline Cissy
AP Biology Teacher
Benscoter, Brian Keith
Asst HS Prin & Bible Teacher
Bickford, Martha Mc Laurine
5th Grade Teacher
Blackstone, Debbie
Pre-Business Advisor
Blackwell, Sandra Hill
Band Director
Bohin, Rebecca Crowder
Music Teacher
Boyd, Dawn Day
Science Teacher
Boyett, Colleen Treadaway
Third Grade Teacher
Brown, Anna Margaret Loftin
First Grade Teacher
Brown, John Andrew
Adj Prof of History & Religion
Brown, Rosie Ward
Mathematics Teacher
Burden, Cedric Jerome
English Instructor
Calloway, Olivia Wheeler
Language Arts & Reading Tchr
Camp, Patricia Elliott
Nursing Professor
Canevaro, James Antonio
History Teacher
Carter, Joe L.
US History Teacher
Cazes, Josephine DiStefano
Asst Principal & Biology Tchr
Chandler, Ann Wilkinson
6th-8th Grade English Teacher
Chew, E. Bryon
Professor of Management
Cilimberg, Michael Craig
Program Director & Instructor
Cleveland, Edwin Pittman
9th-12th Grade Choral Teacher
Clifton, Guin Robinson
Eng, Soc Stud & Rel Tchr
Coffey, Judith Tuck
Spanish & English Teacher
Cole, Charles DuBose
Professor of Law
Cole, Dewey Cecil, Jr.
World & US History Teacher
Coleman, Charlotte Lee
Asst Professor of Spanish
Colston, Patricia Baggett
Third Grade Teacher
Cooper, Elaine Davis
Fifth Grade Teacher
Cost, Frances Dianne
Chemistry Teacher
Coutler, Skip
Speech & Drama Teacher
Cox, Jacqueline LaVergne
7th Grade Language Arts Tchr
Crawford, Donald Mitchell
Band Director
Crawford, Mary (Poynter)
HS Mathematics Teacher
Cusic, Anne Moreland
Instructor of Biology
Davis, Colin
Assistant Professor of History
Davis, Martha W.
Guidance Counselor
Davis, Thelma Moore
Science Teacher
Derieux, Judy K.
Teacher of Gifted
Diehl, Mary Mason
Fourth Grade Teacher
Douthard, Patricia Davis
Third Grade Teacher
Dryden, Susan Meredith
Tenth Grade English Teacher
Dukes, Marilee
Eng Tchr & Dir of Forensics
Eady, Charles Edward
Fine Arts Dept Chm & Band Dir
Eaton, James W.
Teacher
Echols, Gregory Alan
PE Teacher
Eddleman, Myrtress G.
Eng & Frgn Langs Dept Chair
Evans, Jill Elysa
Associate Professor of Law
Feggins, Eulalia Howell
Kindergarten Teacher
Ferguson, Daniel
Teacher & Coach
Flores, W. Maria
Spanish Teacher
Flowers, Sandi Staggs
English Teacher
Floyd, Michael Dennis
Associate Professor of Law
Foster, Autherine Lucy
Social Studies Teacher
Foster, Jerrie Abrams
Language Arts Teacher
Franey, Deanna Stewart
Counselor & Soc Stud Tchr
Furnas, Howard Earl, III
Spanish Teacher
Gadilhe, Mary Siegwart
US History Teacher
Gann, Marjorie Hillhouse
8th Grade US History Teacher
Gardner, Yolande Beasley
Business Education Teacher
Garland, Ann Stewart
6th Grade Teacher
Gathers, George Enoch, II
English Teacher
Gaul, Ian Lewis, Jr.
8th Grade Social Science Tchr
Genetski, Marion B.
Exceptional Education Teacher
Gilchrist, Kayla Faith
English Teacher
Giles, Johnnie M.
Fourth Grade Teacher
Gotlieb, Joanna Schimmel
Fifth Grade Teacher
Guess, Aundrea Kay
Professor of Accounting
Gurosky, Linda Davis
Asst Prin for Curr & Instr
Guthrie, Angela Barnes
5th Grade Language Arts Tchr
Hagen, Susan K.
Professor of English
Hall, Christine
11th-12th Grade English Instr
Hallman, Mary Jackson
Spanish Teacher
Hamby, Greta Lois Martin
1st Grade Teacher
Hames, Carl Martin
Headmaster
Hand, Judith Hayes
Dir of Adult Stud & Adj Prof
Handley, Kathy Owens
Second Grade Teacher
Hardy, Carolyn Moses
Second Grade Teacher
Hare, Carrie Ann Hogan
3rd Grade Teacher
Harris, Annie Kathryn
Social Science Teacher
Harris, Mallie Stewart
Third Grade Teacher
Haynes-Pearson, Lorena
Life Science & Bio Teacher
Hill, Janice Hunter
Sixth Grd Math & Science Tchr
Hitt, Teresa Davis
Computer Science Instructor
Hogan, Sylvia Ann
Sixth Grade Teacher
Hollaway, Mary Evelyn
Eng Dept Chair & AP Tchr
Holloway, Betty Hendon
Second Grade Teacher
Housh, Sarah Whitman
Fifth Grade Teacher
Houston, Ronale Dwyane
Social Science Teacher
Hughey, Rheta Fuller
Home Economics Teacher & Coord
Hutchinson, Gretchen Hudson
History, Geog, US History Tchr
Hutto, Rebecca C.
Retired Kindergarten Teacher
Inghram, Debra (Howard)
Horticulture Instructor
James, Debra Haigler
Fifth Grade Teacher
James, Helen E.
First Grade Teacher
James, Mary John Courtney
Second Grade Teacher
Jeane, Karen Lilley
English Teacher
Jemerson, Pamela Jean
Science Teacher
Johnson, Alicia Michelle
Speech & Drama Teacher
Johnson, Vicki Davis
Social Studies Teacher
Jones, Dennis Ray
Journalism Professor
Jones, Kathryn Brazil
3rd Grade Teacher
Jones, Shawanda Harris
Science Teacher
Keith, Susan Whatley
Physical Education Teacher
Kelly, Lillie Brown
Senior High Science Teacher
Kendrick, Wayne Meredith
Sports Medicine Teacher
Kernea, Frances Marr
2nd Grade Teacher
Killingsworth, Roger Wade
Geometry, Chem & Bible Tchr
Kirkpatrick, Katherine Glass
Asst Professor
Lankford, William R.
Teacher & Coach
Lawley, Deborah Cottle
Fifth Grade Teacher
Lewis, Joan S.
Reading Teacher
Litsey, Alan Wade
Assistant Professor of Theatre
Lovoy, Sue Lockett
United States History Teacher
Lugemwa, Vincy Lwanga
Mathematics & Chemistry Tchr
Mahon, Jane Davis
AP Chem Tchr & Dept Co-Chrmn
Mallory, Kesha Nicole
Business Education Teacher
Mansfield, Lu Ann Elaine
Mathematics Teacher
Marino, Maria S.
Mathematics Teacher
Marsh, Randall Conway
English Department Chairman
Marshall, Charles Douglas
Adjunct Instructor
Mathews, Jay L.
Eng Tchr, Ftbl & Golf Coach
Mc Combs, Lynn
Fifth Grade Teacher
McElroy, Jeannine Abbott
Third Grade Teacher
Mc Kenzie, Gail Orr
Biology Instructor
McWaters, Caswell Hanley, Jr.
Chemistry Teacher
Mc Whirter, Kay Howell
Business Education Teacher
Mc Whorter, Grace Agee
Natural Sci Dept Prof & Chprsn
Medenica, Deborah Wood
Choir & Drama Teacher
Michela, Victoria Lynn
Instructor of Psychology
Milam, Betty Bramlett
Fourth Grade Teacher
Miller, Prentess Clay
Math, Sci & Soc Studies Tchr
Mitchell, Donna Hall
Special Education Tchr & Coach
Morgan, Alene Maney
2nd Grade Teacher
Morgan, Eugenia Landreth
Chemistry & Physics Teacher
Morris, Betty Francis
First Grade Teacher
Neill, Polly Lorren
Kindergarten Teacher
Neville, Nancy Jean
Mathematics Teacher
Norton, Thomas Mark, Jr.
Psychology & Government Tchr
O'Bannon, Dorene
Rdng, Lit & Lang Arts Teacher
Olowokere, David O.
Structural Engrng Prof
Owens, Thelma Jean
First Grade Teacher
Parker, Deborah Harris
Mathematics Teacher
Parker, Todd Levan
Dean of Students
Peacock, Richard Augustus
Adjunct Professor
Perkins, Charlotte P.
Title I Reading Teacher
Pickett, Annette Michael
Rdng, Eng & Soc Stud Teacher
Pierce, Kacy Jones
History & Economics Teacher
Pompey, Cora Hendricks
Fifth Grade Teacher
Popovich, Mira
Dance Dept Dir & Professor
Price, Charlotte Landreth
English Teacher
Prichard, Sherry Joann Mc Cain
Kindergarten Teacher
Quick, Joan Hagood
Vocational Counselor
Rainer, Linda Hassett
College Prep English Teacher
Ramsey, Kelvin Gerard
Social Stud & World His Tchr
Richardson, Wayne
Assistant Principal
Richey, Robert Alan
Teacher
Riddle, William Hal
Driver Education Tchr & Coach
Rinke-Hammer, Iris Beata
German & Russian Teacher
Ripp, Susan Elizabeth
Art Teacher
Robinson, Vivian Lowe
Business Education Teacher
Rogers, Kathy Cote
German Teacher
Rowe, Jan A.
Associate Professor
Rowser, Caroline Jones
Fourth Grade Teacher
Runquist, Jeanette
Professor of Biology
Ruocco, Carmine F.
Prog Coord of Bldg Sci Techs
Sample, Norma Whitson
Second Grade Teacher
Schatz, Clark T.
Economics & Statistics Instr
Sciacca, Fran C.
High School Bible Teacher
Scivley, Suzanne Hughes
Computer Science Teacher
Scott, Lanier
English Teacher
Self, Kellye Sluder
Mod World His & Prac Law Tchr
Sharman, James Edward
Professor of Exercise Science
Shaw, Elizabeth Nappier
English & Journalism Teacher
Shoemaker, Donna J. (Stanfill)
English Teacher
Sims, Barbara Serio
Latin Teacher
Sims, Jessie Ruth
Science Teacher
Singh, Sanjay K.
Management Professor
Slone, Lloyd G.
Professor of Art
Smallwood, Carolyn Cosby
Algebra & Pre-Calculus Teacher
Smith, Bernice Johnson
Fifth Grade Teacher
Smith, June Greene
Retired Elementary Teacher
Snoe, Joseph Anthony
Professor of Law
Spruill, Bessie Hunter
Music Instructor & Choir Dir
Staggs, Helen Jones
10th Grade English Teacher
Standifer, Carol Mathews
Special Education Director
Stewart, Jo Adkins
Mathematics Teacher
Stewart, Mary Austin
6th Grd Social Studies Teacher
Stewart, Thomas Wesley, Jr.
Band Director
Storey, Melinda Cox
Teacher of Gifted
Strickland, Henry Carey, III
Law Professor
Stricklin, Sandra Lyn
Mathematics Teacher
Stuckey, Gloria Wells
5th Grade Teacher
Swanson, Lauren Wendy
Government & Economics Teacher
Swartz, Billie Rhea Stringfield
Retired First Grade Teacher
Sykes, Gwendolyn Pouncy
Kindergarten Teacher
Thomas, Carol Teague
French Teacher
Thomas, William Holcombe
History Teacher
Tillman, Anita Rainwater
8th Grade Math Teacher
Tolbert, Vanessa Lorraine (Davis)
4th Grade Teacher
Towns, Tammy O'Neal
Dance Teacher
Vann, Juanita Inman
Chemistry Teacher
Waldrep, B. Dwain
Associate Professor
West, Alice S.
English Teacher
Whetstone, Bobby D.
Education Professor
White, Sarah Frances
Guidance Counselor
Whiteside, Sarah Ward
Latin Teacher
Williams, Claudia Jackson
English Department Chair
Wilson, Eugene Reynolds
Math Instr & Resource Ctr Dir
Wiygul, James Mayfield
Assoc Headmaster & Eng Tchr
Wright, Dorothy L.
Assistant Principal
Youngblood, Kathy Cruce
3rd Grade Teacher
BLOUNTSVILLE
Alexander, Betty Thomas
Business & Computer Teacher
Black, Ginger Waldrop
English Teacher
Dunn, Thomas Lee
Bio, Anatomy & Physiology Tchr
Huffstutler, Sharon K.
Teacher of Gifted Education
Kretzschmar, Wilda Jenkins
Social Studies Dept Chm & Tchr
Minshew, Kathryn Cole
Kindergarten Teacher
Nichols, Anne Jenkins
First Grade Teacher
Pinyan, Diane Miller
History Teacher
Sivley, Jackie Thrasher
Family & Consumer Science Tchr

Z
s, Patricia Beam
glish Teacher
nt, Julia Rice
st Grade Teacher
an, Jerry Wayne
ence Teacher
lan, Stella Jacobs
glish & Reading Teacher
ens, Linda Nix
Grade History Teacher
ey, Mary Lynne
th Grade Teacher
burn, Wanda Gray
m LD & MR Resource Teacher
Alpine, Johnny W., Jr.
an of Student Services
n, Christopher Wayne
ibusiness Teacher
, Susan Cox
h Grade Teacher
ge, JoAnn L.
r of Psychology, Sociology
ht, Page Hubbard
dergarten Teacher
NTLEY
e, Samuel O.
ired JROTC Instr
MEN
, Buddy
glish & Spanish Teacher
WTON
, Betty Knox
iness Education Instructor
er, Sharron Taylor
rd Grade Teacher
, Marion Laurence
ence Teacher & Coach
m, Johnny
d Director
Nancy Barron
rd Grade Teacher
s, William N.
ncipal
gan, Rosemary Casey
ence Division Chair
Elaine C.
h Teacher
hree, Cecelia Morris
m, Physics & Bio Teacher
n, Robin Ingram
ool Counselor
aas, Wyvonia Thompson
ial Studies Teacher
ams, Bonnie Lee (Lawler)
lish & Drama Teacher
DGEPORT
y, Rebecca Smith
& Earth Science Teacher
LLIANT
s, Jack, Jr.
tory Teacher & Asst Prin
er, Wanda Benton
dance Counselor
man, George Allen
ncipal
OKWOOD
hill, Carol McDonald
lish Teacher
ell, Annette Walker
nish Teacher
Kristie Griffith
rld History & AP Teacher
on, Jacqueline Hope
iness Teacher
, David
lish Teacher
NDIDGE
s, Nellie Sue
lish Teacher
y, Mary Kellie Duke
nish & English Teacher
, Mary J.
ors English Teacher
ANT
on, Glenn
tory Teacher
LER
, Arilla
rth Grade Teacher
n, Julia Duncan
& 8th Grd Reading Teacher
man, Elaine Roberts
iness Education Teacher
an, Melynda Dozier
lish & Journalism Teacher
y, Joan Thompson
, Survey of Literature Tchr
ride, Betty Singley
8th Grd Math & Sci Teacher
es, Ruby L.
e I Reading Teacher
n, Ruby Lee (Needham)
Grade Teacher
UM
ey, Elaine Wheeler
ence Teacher
ERA
lin, Lamont Wyatt
ired HS Science Teacher
ster, Mancel Ray
ibusiness Education Teacher
n, Bill
cher
n, Martha Owens
hematics Teacher
DEN
ston, Willie Joe
Bus & Horticulture Instr

Smith, Charles S.
Mathematics Teacher
Thomas, Alphenie Boykin
Retired 2nd Grade Tchr
CAMP HILL
Frayer, Robert William
Tactical Officer, JROTC Instr
CARROLLTON
Barnett, William Randall
Counselor
Smith, Jane Hannah
English Teacher
Sutton, Candace Brown
Counselor
CATHERINE
Robison, Rodger Dale
Social Studies Teacher
CEDAR BLUFF
Allen, Melinda J.
English & Drama Teacher
CENTRE
Graves, Betty Waite
Math Teacher
Green, Carol Susan
10th Grade English Teacher
Maddox, Janice Mac Donald
Health & Physical Ed Teacher
Russell, Tony F.
Eighth Grade Amer History Tchr
Shumaker, Anne Williamson
Biology Teacher
Wester, Albert Neal
Math Teacher
CENTREVILLE
Capps, Jackie Paris
Teacher of the Gifted
Hughey, Barbara Pearson
English Teacher
Smitherman, Betty Jo Hayes
Business Education Teacher
CHATOM
Deese, Cynthia Reynolds
English & Literature Teacher
Jacobs, Deborah R.
Junior High Teacher
Roberson, James H.
Band Director
Sheffield, Terry Mark
Vocational Teacher
CHELSEA
Bailey, Gail H.
Geometry Teacher
LaFrance, Lynne B.
Seventh Grade Teacher
Lawley, R. Dane
Director of Bands
Newton, Max Douglas
Visual Arts Teacher
Prentice, Holly
Choral Director
Richardson, Linda D'Amico
Spanish Teacher
CHEROKEE
Carter, Betty Deloria
Sci, Soc Studies & Rdng Tchr
Glasgow, Rexford Gates
Physical Education Teacher
Malone, Deborah Harrison
Sixth Grade Teacher
Thompson, Judy Muse
Mathematics & History Teacher
Windsor, Debra Hays
First Grade Teacher
CHILDERSBURG
Adams, Mary Charles Young
Guidance Counselor
Andrews, Bebe Yancey
8th Grd American History Tchr
Glover, Melanie Myrick
Fifth Grade Teacher
Lacey, Suzanne
Assistant Principal
Orsini, Diane Quenelle
English & History Teacher
Ricks, Robert Stephen
Seventh Grade Science Teacher
Snow, Debra M.
Science Teacher
Taylor, Deborah Carter
Math Teacher
CITRONELLE
Dunn, Harold Lewis, Jr.
English & History Teacher
Jones, Kathy Brown
5th Grade Teacher
Kubina, Beverly Powell
Math Teacher & Dept Chprsn
Kubina, Gary
Math Dept Chair
CLAYTON
Bonam, Vincent Staley
Band Director
Culpepper, Sue Dunn
1st Grade Teacher
CLEVELAND
Alldredge, Dianne Allison
Cosmetology Instructor
Holt, Gwenda Mc Cay
4th Grade Teacher
Johnson, Linda Tolbert
Kindergarten Teacher
Stephenson, Helen Griffin
Counselor
Woods, Larry Morris
Computer Science Teacher
COFFEEVILLE
Donald, Karen Bumpers
Kindergarten Teacher
Hodge, Emily Counselman
Biology Teacher

COKER
Overton, June Caines
Sixth Grade Teacher
COLLINSVILLE
Miller, Sandra Kearley
First Grade Teacher
Thrash, M. Neal
Advanced World His & PE Tchr
Townson, Patsy J.
Spanish Teacher
Willingham, Brenda Upchurch
5th & 6th Grade Science Tchr
COLUMBIA
Daniels, Sandra Carol
Mathematics Teacher
COLUMBIANA
Hill, Carol Hathcock
Home Economics Teacher
Major, Linda D.
Director of Success Program
Rasco, Darlene Hicks
Business Education Teacher
Reid, William Alan
Physics & Advanced Math Tchr
CORDOVA
Bobo, Glenn Allen
Science Teacher
Hitchcock, Edna Jean
First Grade Teacher
Mc Rae, Shirley Ann
Biology Teacher
Watkins, Anthony Irvin
Principal
COTTONDALE
Elkins, Sue V.
School Sec, Registrar & Cnslr
Hess, Roberta
Spanish & Lang Arts Teacher
Robertson, Ranette H.
Business Education Teacher
COTTONWOOD
Peoples, Isaac Leon
Band Director & Latin Teacher
Peoples, Marian Roberts
Science Teacher
Snell, Sharon Marie
Computer Lab Tchr
CRAGFORD
Harris, Josie Evans
English Teacher
Hendon, Susan Denney
Mathematics Teacher
Lee, Susan Willis
Science Teacher
Morgan, Richard Lynn
Physical Education Teacher
CUBA
Jones, Gracie Isaac
Fifth Grade Teacher
CULLMAN
Apel, Marie Uzzell
5th Grade Teacher
Boyd, Jimmy Lance
Mathematics Teacher
Brown, Jean Mc Kelvey
Chemistry Teacher
Brown, Rosemary Turner
Physical Education Teacher
Burks, Kathy White
English Teacher
Calvert, William A.
American History & PE Tchr
Cline, Carol Jane
Math, Physics & Spanish Tchr
Collins, Jackie Moore
Cntrl Office Admin
Cox, Martha Sue
English Teacher
Crawford, Leila S.
Retired Fourth Grade Teacher
Guthery, Virginia Ann Mc Donald
Math Dept Chair & Instructor
Heatherly, Charlotte Jasper
Healthcare Technology Teacher
Henke, Doris Schafer
Fourth Grade Teacher
Ivey, Mona Higdon
Fourth Grade Teacher
Michael, Gail T.
Jr & Sr Counselor
Murphree, Karen Johnson
English Teacher
Oldacre, Michael Dane
Mathematics Teacher
Sachs, JoAnn Taylor
Senior English Teacher
Skinner, Cathy Turner
Mathematics Instructor
Taylor, Garry Lance
Band Director
Watts, Oscar O., Jr.
7th & 8th Grd Science Teacher
DADEVILLE
Poeppelmeier, Frances Lowery
Retired Instructor
DALEVILLE
Burch, Sylvia Ann
English & British Lit Teacher
Kofford, Colleen Daley
Mathematics Teacher
Shimunek, Donna Johnson
Fourth Grade Teacher
Swindall, Charles Perry
Athletic Dir & His Instructor
DANVILLE
Brakke, Suzanne Fuqua
K-4th Grade PE Teacher
Coker, Howard Edward, Jr.
History & English Teacher

DAPHNE
Ansell, Samuel Tilden, III
History Teacher
Burt, Jean Adam
English Teacher
Dailey, Rita Davidson
Computer & Yearbook Teacher
Menas, Crystal Mosley
Marine Bio, Envrnmntl Sci Tchr
Tidwell, Kelton Gordon
Science Teacher
DAUPHIN ISLAND
Stapleton, Stella Taylor
Retired Elementary Teacher
DE ARMANVILLE
Bowman, Shirley Stewart
English & Science Teacher
DEATSVILLE
Billings, Cathy Farmer
Math Teacher
Stinson, James Terry
Fifth Grade Teacher
Wilson, Ferrann
Mathematics Teacher
Wood, Mary Prater
7th Grd English & Reading Tchr
DECATUR
Ackley, Alice Loughlin
English Teacher
Allen, Paul Wayne
Technology Education Teacher
Ashford, Gayla Brown
Bus Admin Instr & Dept Chair
Barrett, Sandra Duran
Fourth Grade Teacher
Barthold, Frank Edwin
Retired 1st Grade Teacher
Bishop, Susan Hand
Science & PE Teacher
Burke, Waymon E.
History & Political Sci Prof
Busby, Earlene Ferrell
Health Teacher
Cagle, William Lee
Health & Physical Ed Teacher
Cantrell, Jimmy E.
Music & Recording Tech Teacher
Cheatham, Elizabeth Cuentas
Cmptr Office Info Instructor
Chenault, Carol Deming
Sociology Instr & Dept Chair
Cox, Randall L.
Div of Natural Sci Chm
Davis, Marian Bloodworth
United States History Tchr
de Quesada, Margarita Valls
Instructor of Guitar
Duke, James Floyd
Science Instructor
Felts, Dell Gotthelf
History & Political Sci Instr
Gaertner, Karen Avadale
Math Tchr & Tech Prep Coord
Gibbs, Mary S.
Retired Teacher
Goree, Joan Anita
Music & Lecturer Teacher
Hunter, Tommy Wayne
Teacher
Johnson, Dorothy Jeanette Barden
Psych Instr, Soc Sci Div Chprn
Jones, Danna Benefield
6th Grade Language Teacher
Jones, Lynne Turney
Fifth Grade Teacher
Julich, Nancy Conner
Adjunct English Instructor
King, J. Crawford, Jr.
History Instructor
Langille, Douglas Bruce
Adjunct Instructor
Lee, Preston Ervin, Sr.
Psychology Professor
Leonard, Richard Carlton
Professor
Moss, Francess Pamela
Music Instructor
Mothershed, Alana J.
Business Education Teacher
Pahman, Jane Baker
Counselor
Parmley, Wayne
Physics Instructor
Patty, Janet Varnon
English Teacher
Pitts, Sharon Ruth
Retired Fifth Grade Teacher
Provin, Laurie Shepherd
Soc Studies, Math & Rdng Tchr
Ratcliffe, Carl James
Counselor
Rickard, Michael L.
Science Teacher
Ryan, Carole Smitherman
Fourth Grade Teacher
Sandlin, Cheryl Albright
Third Grade Teacher
Sparkman, Rebecca Ann
American History Teacher
Spears, JoAnne Cowan
English & Business Teacher
Stephenson, Donna Gunter
English Teacher
Stroh, Jeanne Ellen
English Teacher
Stueck, Patricia Dietscher
Dental Assisting Instructor
Suran, Robert E.
Adjunct Instructor of History

Tanner, Alice Hinshaw
Instr & Lang Arts Div Chprsn
Tepper, Winnie Barnes
Elementary Education Director
Tew, J. Lewis
History Instructor
Thayer, Gordon Marshall
Evening Campus Counselor
Trine, Merilyn Neild
Retired 3rd & 6th Grade Tchr
Tucker, Joye Posey
Spanish Teacher
Tyler, G. Elliott
Math, Eng Tchr & Div Chprsn
Vaughn, Kathryn Lansing
Fine & Graphic Arts Adj Prof
Watkins, Edwena Foster
Fourth Grade Teacher
Whitson, Marilyn Murphree
1st Grade Teacher
DEMOPOLIS
Calloway, Sue Shumate
Second Grade Teacher
Mason, Lucinda Kerby
Marketing Education Teacher
Stritzinger, Jane Ellen (Lewis)
English Teacher
DIXONS MILLS
Conner, John Wesley, Jr.
Band Director & History Tchr
Hinson, Jane Ray
Math Teacher & Dept Head
Lockett, Lucille Dixon
Second Grade Teacher
DORA
Berryhill, Donnie S. (Billie R.)
Guidance Counselor
Goff, Amy L.
Cmptr, Eng & Math Remed Tchr
Gurley, Melba Kirkpatrick
Biology Teacher
Jones, Marchettia Shurbitt
Business Education Teacher
Potts, Joe V.
Assistant Principal
Sides, Judith Hunter
11th Grade English Teacher
Silvey, Tony Lee
Band Director
Smith, Rebecca Kilgore
Sr HS Mathematics Teacher
York, Sara Kate
Librarian & Science Teacher
DOTHAN
Andrews, Sara N.
Soc Stud Tchr & Dept Chprsn
Bae, Ronald Phillip
Assoc Prof of Criminal Justice
Barron, James David
Health, Math Teacher & Coach
Bass, Carolyn M.
Guidance Counselor
Bilbeisi, Khamis Mohamad
Accounting Professor
Blankenship, Dinah Bass
Eleventh Grade English Teacher
Chambers, Charlotte Ann
Second Grade Teacher
Colbert, Laura Lea
HS English Teacher
Davis, Allyson Marbut
Biology & Anatomy Teacher
Devane, Martina W.
Algebra Teacher
Downing, Belinda Hornsby
Nursing Chair & Instructor
Ellis, Stanley Jay
Sr HS Learning Center Supvr
Etheridge, Linda Fay
Kindergarten Teacher
Fell, Elizabeth Paul
Curr & Instruction Dept Chair
Foster, John J.
11th Grd AP Amer His Teacher
Gilbert, Adair Whatley
Associate Professor
Hagler, Kaye R.
English Teacher
Hendrickson, Kimberly Long
Seventh Grade English Teacher
Hooks, Ruth Messick
AP English Teacher
Humphrey, Carla Snyder
Sixth Grade Teacher
Hutchinson, Robert Earl
English Instructor
Jernigan, Sonja Mitchell
Mathematics Teacher
Jones, Carol Carr
Business Instructor
King, Laura Green
Special Education Teacher
Little, Linda Delp
English Teacher
Locke, Sarah Robinson
Language Arts Teacher
Lovrich, Billie Ann Reeves
Government & Economics Teacher
Lumpkin, Cynthia Rolen
Education Associate Professor
Mc Arthur, Priscilla G.
History Professor
Mc Cready, James Wylie
HS Physics & Math Teacher
McNeill, Celeste Waid
English Teacher
Mc Williams, Dianne English
English Instructor
Middleton, Mary Elizabeth
First Grade Teacher

DOTHAN (cont)
Miley, Lynn Dale
French Teacher
Minder, Cecilia Burkett
Business Administration Instr
Murdock, Phyllis Richards
Business Administration Instr
Norman, Martha Byrd
High School Teacher
Pelham, Joseph Kenneth
Math Teacher
Pierce, Charles M.
Chemistry Teacher
Sirmon, B. Charles
Drama Teacher
Snell, William David
Social Studies Teacher
Solomon, Jean Nordan
Tchr of Multiple Disabilities
Sowell, Alice Harris
Mathematics Teacher
Stanford-Bowers, Denise Evelyn
High School English Teacher
Stern, Julianne Mitchell
Mathematics Instructor
Stewart, Dawn Kelly
Sci Dept Head & Phys Sci Tchr
Still, Beverly Bryan
8th Grade English Teacher
Upton, Doris F.
Spanish Teacher
Waters, John Ralph
Electronics Prof & Dept Chm
White, Johnny E.
World History Teacher & Coach
Wilson, Marthie Mc Leod
Business Teacher
Wilson, Sharon Jernegan
Healthcare Sci & Tech Teacher
Woodham, Georgia Ramey
Fourth Grade Teacher
DOUBLE SPRINGS
Little, Annette Batchelor
English Teacher
Rice, Sandra Adkins
Sixth Grade Teacher
Tuggle, Lynn G.
Math Teacher
DOUGLAS
Mitchell, Rex Harris
Jr High Social Studies Tchr
Smith, Arnold Lowell
Government & Economics Teacher
Thacker, Alan Layne
7th-8th Grade Math Teacher
DUNCANVILLE
Mc Brayer, Carol Mullenix
Fifth Grade Teacher
EAST BREWTON
Fountain, Gayle Cargill
Assistant Principal
Luker, Lisa Young
Middle School English Teacher
ECLECTIC
Barton, Amelia Lockwood
Science Teacher
Crutchfield, Ann Ragan
Spanish & Social Studies Tchr
Southerland, Kathy W.
7th-8th Grd Soc Stud Teacher
Venable, Renae
8th Grd Reading & English Tchr
ELBA
Grider, Mary Spinks
First Grade Teacher
King, Sue G.
Math & Science Teacher
Padgett, Sylvia J.
Eleventh Grade English Tchr
Rhoades, Jimmie W.
English Teacher
Tucker, Judith Bell
English Teacher
Weeks, Brian Keith
Science Teacher
ELBERTA
Schreiber, Robert Duane
6th Grd Soc Stud & Math Tchr
Williams, Sandy Barfield
Middle School English Teacher
ELKMONT
Brown, Glenda M.
Sixth Grade Teacher
Roach, Carla Haynes
Algebra & Life Science Teacher
ELMORE
Aiken, Johnny William
Athletic Director
Monroe, Earle S.
Business Education Teacher
ENTERPRISE
Adkison, Charla Spears
Biology Instructor
Armstrong, Rebecca Brown
English Instructor
Arnold, Michael Stone
Special Need Coordinator
Bracewell, Debbie G.
English Teacher
Ford, Charlton Kane
Band Director
Garth, Calvin Earl
JTPA Teacher
Gilder, Jean Bryson
Retired Sixth Grade Teacher
Grondin, Linda Hooks
Spanish Teacher
Harris, Amalie Sue (Elsea)
English Teacher
Kyser, Tracy Patrick
Social Studies Teacher
Lawrence, Dianne Kline
Mathematics Teacher
Lewis, Robert C.
Chemistry Teacher
Oden, Jack Porter
Professor
Sickler, Margaret Wilson
Sixth Grade Teacher
Smith, Cindy Alexander
Instr of Spanish, French & Eng
Smith, Scott Randall
Eng & Speech Division Chair
Snodgrass, Johnny Lee
Army JROTC Instructor
Torres, Marco, Jr.
Earth Science Teacher
Waters, Charles Alan
Agribusiness Teacher
Weeks, Edward Wayne
Principal
EUFAULA
Abercrombie, Deborah Dykes
Accounting Instructor
Bush, Billie Dollar
Mathematics Teacher
Klages, Timothy John
Marketing Tchr & DECA Advisor
Smiley, Robert Benjamin
Science Teacher
Whitfield, Morris Lane
Mathematics Teacher
Williams, Claudia Futrell
Engineering Graphics Instr
EUTAW
Bryant, Rita Doris
Business Education Teacher
Colbert, Bettye Walton
English Teacher
Gaines, Madie P.
7th Grade Math Teacher
Love, Toni Teresa
Cosmetology Teacher
EVA
Hudson, Rhonda Ann
Science Teacher
EVERGREEN
Gibson, Margaret T.
Physical Science & Bio Teacher
Harris, Hannah Stanton
5th Grade Teacher
Jones, Amanda Ballard
Mathematics Teacher
EXCEL
Baas, Susan Mc Cain
6th Grade Teacher
Etheridge, Pamela Lisenby
Mathematics Teacher
Mixon, Carol Day
Second Grade Teacher
FAIRFIELD
Ballard, Helen Washington
Biology Teacher
Powell, Lee Brannon
World, US His, Govt & Ec Tchr
VonLintel, Monique Randall
English Teacher
FAIRHOPE
Bishop, Karon Rushing
Marine Science Teacher
Hudson, Suzanne
Jrnlsm Tchr & Guidance Cnslr
Jones, Marjorie Kenny
Business Teacher
Marshall, Cynthia Ingersoll
High School Guidance Counselor
O'Connor-Page, Sandra Diane
Instructor of Art Education
Pharez, Emily Spaulding
Physical Education Teacher
Rogers, Luegenia Dorothy
Voc Family & Consumer Sci Adv
Threadgill, Ollie Rix, Jr.
AP Social Studies Teacher
Turner, Pamela Pitman
English Teacher
FAYETTE
Acker, Linda Webster
Chair Div of Bus & Cmptr Sci
Bagwell, Emily Jane
Senior High English Teacher
Barnes, Judith Wilson
Developmental Studies Instr
Box, Sheila McCaleb
Math Teacher
Brown, Marthanne Burgess
English Instructor
Cargile, Ned Collins, Jr.
Bus & Cmptr Applications Instr
Dahlke, Fred Milton
Dept Chair, Truck Driver Trng
Gilreath, June Cannon
US History Teacher
Gunganus, Pat M.
Cosmetology Teacher
Hammond, James Roland
History Instructor
Hamner, Anne Maples
Business Education Teacher
Harkins, June Calton
Fifth Grade Teacher
Harris, Lamar
PE Teacher & Athletic Director
Hogue, Belinda Tidwell
Practical Nursing Instructor
Jacobs, Reba Ingram
Language Teacher
Jones, Dani Small
Music Instructor
Lawhon, Nannette Guyton
English & History Teacher
Mc Collum, Janice Ruth
Instructor & Cheerleader Spon
Morrow, Joyce Steele
Science Dept Chairman & Tchr
Murphy, Claudia Loyette
Asst Prof of English & Speech
Palmer, Ruth W.
Eng Instr & Liberal Arts Chair
Short, Sandy R.
Business Education Instructor
Sizemore, Douglas R.
Biology Instructor
Smith, B. Karen
English Instructor
Swinney, Kenneth Robert
Instr of Physics & Engrng
Taylor, Gregory Rusk
Biology Instructor
Thompson, L. Paul
Biological Science Instr
Wilhite, William C.
Welding Instructor
Williams, Shirley Davis
Second Grade Teacher
Wright, Kathy Davis
Guidance Counselor
FLOMATON
Drew, Beth VanPelt
6th & 7th Grade Math Teacher
Rogers, Brenda Godwin
English Instr & Jrnlsm Tchr
FLORENCE
Basinger, Deborah Swords
Jr High Band Director
Bruce, Joyce Davis
First Grade Teacher
Bullard, Carl Edward
Teacher & Coach
Butler, Lynne Burris
Assistant Professor of English
Champion, James Edward
Director of Bands
Couch, Jim Forrest
Asst Professor of Economics
Crafton, Coleene George
Teacher of Learning Disability
Crosslin, Phillip James
Physics Teacher
Daly, Paulette Blankenship
4th Grade Teacher
Darby, Betty Norton
Fifth Grade Teacher
Darby, Rebecca Patterson
Mathematics Teacher
Davis, Cynthia Smith
Sixth Grade Teacher
Day, Gary Alfred
His, Geog & Acctng Teacher
Ellis, Sandra Matlock
Science Teacher
Glasscock, Lorraine Glock
Associate Prof of Accounting
Gonce, Mary Nell
Former Chemistry Teacher
Halfman, Susan Kupec
Principal
Hall, Harold Gene
Driver Education Teacher
Hall, Laura Harrison
Business Education Teacher
Harrison, Carol Matthews
Math & Computer Science Tchr
Hodges, Suzie Brewer
English Teacher
Hughs, Richard A.
Advanced Math & Sci Teacher
Keckley, Linda Karraker
Kndgtn Teacher
Ledbetter, Lynda H.
Eng & Creative Writing Teacher
Mc Clanahan, Nancy Mc Clendon
First Grade Teacher
McCombs, Charles Andrew
Band Director
Mc Inish, Betty (Mc Kee)
Third Grade Teacher
Mc Kenzie, Sherry Deems
French Teacher
Miller, Freddie Hogue
History & English Teacher
Montgomery, Darlene Richardson
Eng & Creative Writing Tchr
Neal, Patricia Phillips
Social Studies Teacher & Chair
Patrick, Ricky N.
Alternative School Teacher
Romine, Kimberly Todd
Fourth Grade Teacher
Shady, Ronald L.
Associate Professor of Art
Stanley, Susan Hester
Fifth Grade Teacher
Swinea, Rebecca King
Biology Teacher
Tatum, Joyce Beck
Physical Education Teacher
Thomas, Donald James
Biology Teacher
Thomas, Mechelle Wilson
Kindergarten Teacher
Townsend, William Thurston
Economics & Government Teacher
Walker, Katherine Gray
Latin Teacher
Wallace, Linda Davis
Second Grade Teacher
White, Brenda Lynch
7th Grade English Teacher
Wynne, Barbara Minor
Elementary Principal
Yancey, Donna Needham
Marketing Professor
FOLEY
Baker, Mary Louise (Mills)
Choral Music Teacher
Bohannon, Linda C.
World History Teacher
Brown, Tracie Larchell
English Teacher
Congleton, Sue Carson
Sixth Grade Teacher
Crowe, Donna Lee White
Project Jubilee Teacher
Henson, Pamela Taylor
Biology Teacher
Lindsley, Jane Marler
English & Oral Comm Teacher
Lundberg, Deborah LaVaughn
Algebra Teacher
Meads, Wilma Barnes
Retired Teacher
Owen, Cheryl C.
9th Grade English Teacher
Pence, Ronald Kaylor, Jr.
Band Director
Wenzel, Beverly McKey
Tenth Grade English Teacher
FORT PAYNE
Blackwelder, R. Jane
Third Grade Teacher
Cole, Barbara Smith
Business Education Teacher
Cunningham, James B., Jr.
Principal
Fischer, Amy Allen
Media Specialist
Groat, Cherry Williamson
US History Teacher
Hollingsworth, Herbert
JROTC Instructor
Playford, Wilma Fischer
First Grade Teacher
Sterling, Sally Bishop
Fourth Grade Teacher
FORT RUCKER
Partridge, Yolanda Romano
Sixth Grd Rdng & Soc Stud Tchr
FRUITDALE
Ballard, Emily Howard
Secondary Math & Science Tchr
Davidson, Pamela F.
Scndry Bus, Eng & Cmptr Tchr
Ferguson, Sara Florence
School Counselor
James, Otis Maxwell, Jr.
Asst Prin & English Teacher
FULTONDALE
White, Karen D.
Third Grade Teacher
FYFFE
Forester, Carolyn Gilliland
English & History Teacher
GADSDEN
Biggio, Carolyn Whitley
Special Education Teacher
Bray, Virginia Smith
Third Grade Teacher
Burford, Vicki Estes
First Grade Teacher
Bush, Dawn Ledbetter
Fourth Grade Teacher
Casey, Peggy K.
Family & Consumer Science Tchr
Christopher, Patricia Griffith
History Teacher & Dept Chrmn
Collins, Joyce Kilgore
Second Grade Teacher
Dowdy, Christopher Jay
Social Science & Speech Instr
Dunston, Carolyn June
Retired Third Grade Teacher
Gardner, Bobbie Byrant
Sixth Grd Math & Reading Tchr
Gardner, Nancy Yarbrough
Strings Teacher
Gargus, Jane Nolen
Kindergarten Teacher
Garrison, Michelle H.
Spanish & English Teacher
Goodson, Patsy Cornutt
Counselor
Herb, Jane Hartsook
Second Grade Teacher
Higgins, Peggy Nabors
High School Math Teacher
Hill, Jackie Hubbard
Third Grade Teacher
Hill, Sammye
Media Specialist
Hodges, Leslie Pitchford
English & History Teacher
Horsley, Avril Wilbanks
5th Grade Teacher
Johnson, Sandra Siniard
English & Science Teacher
Judd, Sandra Adcock
Spanish & French Teacher
King, Ann T.
11th Grade English Teacher
Lancaster, Lanny Earl
English Dept Chair
Lowery, Ginger
Health & Driver Education Tchr
Marshall, Mira Lynn
Science Teacher
Morgan, Jean Wilson
Sophomore English Teacher
Nevin, Carolyn Schledt
Science Teacher
Owens, Patricia Bagley
High School Science Teacher
Pass, Lynn Thompson
Resource Teacher
Raines, Pamela Farrar
Third Grade Teacher
Ratliff, Nancy Noojin
Second Grade Teacher
Reeves, Frances Griffith
Fourth Grade Teacher
Roberts, Peggy Christopher
Business Teacher
Ross, Paula Jane
English Instructor
Rowe, Peter Warrick
World History Teacher
Sherrill, Kathy Smith
First Grade Teacher
Skipper, Jane R.
Mathematics Tchr & Dept Head
Smith, Joy McCullers
Math Teacher
Stone, Ann C.
Cooperative Education Coord
Turnbach, Lucy Hoffman
Mathematics Teacher
Wadsworth, Elizabeth Mc Corkle
Retired First Grade Teacher
Wadsworth, James Lee, Jr.
Math Teacher
Walker, Dorothy Jeanne
8th Grade Mathematics Teacher
Whitfield, Jane Hodges
Fifth Grade Teacher
Williams, David L.
Preschool Co-Owner
Wilson, Pamela Miller
Kindergarten Teacher
Wren, Charles Lester
Math & Computer Teacher
Yates, Louie Felton
English & Drama Teacher
York, Linda Smith
Former History Teacher
GARDENDALE
Bourgeois, Georgia Robertson
12th Grade English Tchr
Burkett, Tynette Murphy
Family & Consumer Science Tchr
Duncan, Rhonda J.
K-6th Grd Teacher of Gifted
Grimes, Mary Tuck
English Teacher
Hardy, Marilyn Holt
Fourth Grade Teacher
Holmes, Theresa A. Whitt
Second Grade Teacher
Jarvis, Susan Wiggins
6th Grd Language Arts Teacher
Kimbrough, Robert L.
History Teacher
O'Laire, Mary Walt
Child Care Teacher
Smith, Tracey W.
English Teacher
GAYLESVILLE
McWhorter, Paul Kerr, III
Counselor & Asst Prin
Welsh, Michael Lee
Math Tchr & Bsktbl Coach
GEORGIANA
Farmer, Marie Salter
Special Education Teacher
Gruenewald, Brenda Bush
6th Grade Teacher
GERALDINE
Doty, Michael L.
Math & Science Teacher
Norrell, Charles Wayne
5th Grd Science & Reading Tchr
GILBERTOWN
Jayne, Richard D.
Biological Sciences Instructor
GLENCOE
Findley, Wayne
History Teacher
Weems, George Wesley
8th Grade Science Teacher
GOODSPRINGS
Best, Sherry June
English & Computer Teacher
Harrison, Linda Tidwell
Mathematics Teacher
Johnson, David Henry
Science Teacher
Sides, Sandra Riley
Science Teacher
Willingham, Dennis Ray
Soc Studies Dept Chair & Tchr
GOODWATER
Whetstone, Barbara Lois
Fifth Grade Teacher
GORDO
Bester, Loretta J.
History & Social Studies Tchr
Burns, Anthony P.
History Teacher
Todd, David Wayne
7th Grade Math Teacher
GOSHEN
Sasser, Jean M.
Second Grade Teacher
Scarbrough, Dawn Andress
Kndgtn & First Transition Tchr
Shipman, Rebecca Rushing
Sixth Grade Teacher

DY
an, Thomas D., Jr.
tory Teacher
ND BAY
Robin Gene
ibusiness Tchr & FFA Adv
on, Molly Hafner
rth Grade Teacher
NT
, Elizabeth E.
ily & Consumer Science Tchr
es, Kristie Sanders
logy & Physical Ed Teacher
Carol L.
dance Counselor
ll, Bruce
tory Teacher
n, Mary Ayers
ond Grade Teacher
ield, Keith Greggory
Math Tchr & Bsbl Coach
ore, Natasha Borden
ral Director
YSVILLE
Portia Grimes
e I Computer Lab Tchr
ENSBORO
d, Robert Wallace
English Teacher
s, Bernice Hinton
hematics Teacher
Starwanthia Eppes
ily & Consumer Sci Teacher
on, Jean Woods
ence Teacher
ley, Natalie C. H.
ory Teacher
ENVILLE
y, Jim B.
dmaster & Coach
n, Ruby Whetstone
lish Teacher
r, Susan McFerrin
hematics Teacher
on, Linda Womack
dergarten Teacher
, Starla Kelley
hematics Teacher
n, Judy Carol
sical Education Teacher
e, Linda Talley
Grade Biology Teacher
, John Wesley, Jr.
strl Cooperative Trng Tchr
er, Patricia K.
iness Education Teacher
, Suzie Lindstrom
lish Teacher
ngs, Virginia Montgomery
ior English Teacher
ams, Jo Hayes
ics, US & World His Tchr
ams, Randy
logy Teacher
VE HILL
, Dorothy
ily & Consumer Science Tchr
s, Donna Skipper
ory Teacher
, Lois Neese
nish Teacher
ntyre, Brenda Kelley
dance Counselor
Velniece Thomas
dergarten Teacher
Paula Jones
h Tchr & Asst Headmaster
Sharon Cataldo
keting Education Teacher
N
s, Randal Lewis
ial Science Teacher
er, Joy Atkinson
nselor
ell, Susan Partin
nish Teacher
, Donald Arthur
lish Teacher
TERSVILLE
son, Lettie Dekle
hematics Teacher
e, John R.
Stud Tchr & Dept Chprsn
er, Sarah K.
dergarten Teacher
nt, Pamela Leach
tory, Government & Ec Tchr
anan, Patricia Kennamer
hematics Tchr & Dept Chprsn
y, Jim M.
ld History Teacher
e, Pamela Ann (Martin)
English Teacher & Dept Head
as, Jane S.
ence Teacher
r, Freda Chandler
iness Education Teacher
ace, Jeannie
nmunity Education Coord
LEY
er, James Alan
logy & Human Anatomy Tchr
, Claudia Hanson
Grd Elementary Instructor
ard, Mickey Roland
& 8th Grd Soc Stud Tchr
KLEBURG
in, Ronnie J.
ver Education Teacher

Mordecai, Angie Kaye
Band Director
Poe, Johnnie Mann
Business Ed Teacher
HALEYVILLE
Alls, Selena Burleson
First Grade Teacher
Bradbury, Martha Manasco
Third Grade Teacher
Hogan, Diane Parrish
8th Grd American History Tchr
Lyons, Annita Cleghorn
English Teacher
Masters, Beverly Gillilan
6th Grade Teacher
Nix, Elizabeth Knight
Science Teacher
Reed, Sandra Caldwell
2nd Grade Reading Teacher
White, Willodean Laurence (Fell)
Retired 2nd Grd & Jr Coll Tchr
HAMILTON
Brumley, Kelley M.
Electronics Instructor
Burrow, Susan Little
Nursing Instructor
Ellis, Sarah Elliott
Sixth Grd Integrated Sci Tchr
Howard, Sandra Malone
Algebra Teacher
Rich, Charlotte A.
English Teacher
Trimm, Kathy Marie
Special Education Teacher
HANCEVILLE
Burks, Sylvia Nelson
Third Grade Teacher
Courington, Leigh Ann
History Instructor
Johnson, Melanie
English Professor
Rasplicka, Barbara Herrin
Guidance Counselor
Swann, William Thomas
Biology Dept Head & Teacher
HANOVER
Keel, Deawood Carlton
Physical Science & Bio Teacher
HARTFORD
Galloway, Norma Showers
Business Education Teacher
HARTSELLE
Black, Peggy Riddle
English Teacher
Brown, H. Ray
Math Teacher
Brown, Janice Ford
Third Grade Teacher
Daniel, Gloria Bond
Elementary School Counselor
Loney, Martha Mooney
Kindergarten & Journalism Tchr
Morrow, Mary Dayton
English Teacher
Pressley, Garry Don
Driver Education & Math Tchr
Rushen, Donna Bennich
English Teacher
Slaten, Monta Laurie
English & Math Teacher
Teague, Sylvia Ann
Algebra & Pre-Calculus Teacher
Waddle, James Michael
Admin & Advanced Math Teacher
Watson, Jan J.
Second Grade Teacher
Williams, LePage Ward
Science Teacher
HARVEST
Cochran, Betty J.
7th-8th Grade Teacher
HAYDEN
Baldwin, Gary Edward
Social Studies Teacher
Mallory, Clothiel B.
Third Grade Teacher
Reid, Larry Walter
Math Teacher
White, Rachel Martin
Fifth Grade Teacher
HAYNEVILLE
Gadson, Willa Mae Davis
AP Amer His & Geography Tchr
HAZEL GREEN
Birchfield, Leigh Morrow
Science Teacher
Burton, Stephanie Burwell
2nd Grade Teacher
Daniel, Donna Conn
Teacher
Davis, Robbie Foutch
Fourth Grade Teacher
Fisher, Kim Wilcher
8th Grd Math & Algebra I Tchr
Fuller, Sue Nance
Psychology Teacher
Giles, Donald Clay
Algebra Teacher
Gustine, Mary Morton
Sixth Grade Reading Teacher
Siegler, Pamela J.
Science & Choir Teacher
HEADLAND
Dunn, Marjorie Ann (Brown)
Science Teacher
Faulk, Brenda Lynn
Bio, Phys Sci & Chem Teacher
Griggs, Durwood Winston, Jr.
Math Teacher & Dept Chair

Peters, TaJauna Burgess
8th Grade Science Teacher
Plumley, Daniel C.
NJROTC Instructor
Williams, Steve Edward
Principal
HEFLIN
Cobb, Ann
Tenth Grade English Teacher
HIGDON
Buttram, Shirley Kilgore
English Teacher
Page, Rebecca Johnson
Media Specialist
HIGHLAND HOME
Cowles, Marlene Morrison
English Teacher
Gunter, Gwen Young
Library Media Specialist
Sexton, Linda Hughes
Sixth Grade Classroom Teacher
HOLLY POND
Allbright, Karen
Counselor
Bryan, Carolyn Ellard
English Teacher
Patterson, Joyce Fortner
Sixth Grade Teacher
Rice, Jerry Wayne
Physical Education Teacher
Robertson, Bettye Grace
Sixth Grade Teacher
HOLLYWOOD
Walls, Brenda Foster
4th Grade Teacher
HOLT
Cates, Gail W.
English II Teacher
Gordon, Wesley Ray
Mathematics Teacher
Hagler, Darrell E.
Mathematics Teacher
Moore, Nisa S.
Home Economics Teacher
Welker, Leslie Glenn
Instrumental Music Teacher
Williams, Julia Jones
Counselor
HOLY TRINITY
Epps, Clidean Howard
Teacher
HOMEWOOD
Corley, Lillian Scoggins
Spanish & ESL Teacher
Crawford, Lovie D.
Technology Teacher
Dye, Jackie Britain
English Department Chair, Tchr
Fly, Deborah W.
3rd Grade Teacher
Gilchrist, Melanie Smith
2nd Grade Teacher
Harrison, Donna G.
Biology I & Physics Teacher
Holbrooks, Darren Wade
His Tchr & Percussion Instr
Inman, Martha Starnes
Family & Consumer Sci Teacher
Johnson, Donna Clements
Fifth Grade Teacher
Lay, Kimberly Ivie
Biology & Physics Teacher
Marshall, Susan High
Fourth Grade Teacher
Martin, Leigh Ann
First Grade Teacher
Mays, Susan Noel
Chemistry & Algebra Teacher
Mc Guffey, Lynn Lawrence
AP English Teacher
Morgan, Kitty
Mathematics Teacher
Mouchette, Jennifer McWilliams
Eleventh Grade English Tchr
O'Barr, Charlotte Austin
English Teacher
Pressley, Elizabeth Grainger
Calculus & Pre-Calculus Tchr
Reed, Jean B.
Second Grade Teacher
Smith, Deborah Lynn
Social Studies Teacher
Sperando, Catherine Caruso
Mathematics Teacher
Stith, Cheryl Diane
Instructional Support Speclst
Toranto, Melanie Jeffers
American History Teacher
Whitson, Becky Kirkpatrick
English Teacher
HOOVER
Gannon, Marianne Folsom
Fifth Grade Teacher
HOPE HULL
Moncrief, Deborah Green
Mathematics Teacher
HUEYTOWN
Howard, Ludelia Lee
School Counselor
Winn, Carla Lindsey
Sixth Grade Science Teacher
HUNTSVILLE
Adhami, Reza
Professor
Allen, Ann Baugh
Instructor of English
Allston, Zeola B. Germany
Retired Social Studies Teacher
Anderson, John Landon
Health Teacher

Arndt, Jean Humphrey
Senior English Teacher
Atkinson, Doyle Ray
Business Education Teacher
Bailey, Suzanne Roach
Social Studies Dept Chair
Barnes, Sherman L.
Band Director
Beikmann, Micky Marohn
Retired English Teacher
Benn, Bernard Wilfred
Professor of English
Bible, Terry Mike
Assistant Principal
Bidwell, Linda Mays
English Tchr & Stu Cncl Adv
Blackburn, Darla Powell
Mathematics Teacher
Blake, John Archibald
Mathematics Professor
Bluck, Daniel Hugh
US Govt & Politics Teacher
Brown, William E.
Biology Teacher
Burton, Keith Augustus
Religion Professor
Carter, Cynthia Oliver
7th-8th Grade English Teacher
Chalk, Laura Mc Dade
English Teacher
Coker, Patricia Clark
Fifth Grade Teacher
Cook, Janice Bell
Preschool Director
Crocker, Glenn W.
Tech & Industrial Arts Tchr
Crouch, Jan Bailey
Kndgtn Teacher & Day Care Dir
Dean, Richard Calvin
Magnet Pre-Engineering Teacher
Dorsey, Paula Celeste
English Teacher
Drake, Felecia Lyons
Family & Consumer Science Tchr
Dunn, Kayra Creel
Eng Tchr, Dept Head & Team Ldr
Edmondson, Bonita Kathrine
Special Education Teacher
Edwards, Debi Sue
K-8th Grade Math Specialist
Estes, Martha
Assistant Professor
Festa, Gerald Russell
Math & Computer Teacher
Frieder, Joane Wagner
Secondary Magnet Tchr & Chprsn
Glenn, Kimberly White
English Teacher
Gonzales, Kay Sanford
Math Teacher
Gorham, Bryan Keith
Science Teacher
Greenlee, Lizzie Forbes
At-Risk Teacher
Hamner, Bonnie C.
Science Teacher
Harpe, Michael Anthony
Assistant Pastor
Hasse, Larry
Professor of History
Haygood, Nan
PE & Health Teacher & Coach
Hicks, Gregory Lamont
Social Studies Teacher
Horn, Linda A.
Middle School English Teacher
Hulman, Bradley Joseph
Social Studies Teacher
Johnson, Adriel Duland, Sr.
Assoc Prof of Biological Sci
Johnson, Regina Nichols
English Teacher
Jones, Carol King
Middle School Mathematics Tchr
Jones, Lymon E.
Fifth Grade Teacher
Kalange, June B.
Science Teacher
King, Connie Foster
3rd Grade Teacher
Kirkpatrick, Teresa Yielding
Art Teacher
Lanier, J. Roy, Jr.
AP Calculus Teacher
Lee, Richard Wayne
Sociology Professor
Leo, Toni Renee
Health & Dance Education Tchr
Lorder, James Lawrence, Jr.
Math Teacher & Chairperson
Lull, Gay Miller
American History Teacher
Main, Dorothy Phillips
Teacher of GATE
Malone, Robert Earl
Physical Education Teacher
Mc Elroy, Ellen Crawford
Assistant Professor
Mc Kenzie, Roland Loyd
Chair & Prof Dept of Education
Miller, Ola Pearl (Boothe)
Preschool Teacher
Mitcham, Patricia Hamilton
English & Social Studies Tchr
Mitchell, Thomas Steven
Band Director
Mobley, Jennifer Lynn
Biology Teacher
Moon, Virgil Carthel, III
US History & Debate Teacher

Moore, Betty Jackson
English Teacher
Moriarity, Debra Margaret
Assoc Prof of Biological Sci
Mucci, Dana McCormick
Spanish Teacher
Murphy, Jeffry Wright
World & AP European His Tchr
Nau, Joyce Madara
Mathematics Teacher
O'Dell, Elizabeth Welty
English Teacher
Owen, Sherry Hodges
Music Teacher
Parker, Thomas Randall, Jr.
Middle School At Risk Teacher
Pollard, Prudence LaBeach
VP of Admin & Bus Asst Prof
Prefling, Audra L.
Counselor
Reed, Maggie Scruggs
Voc Bus Ed Tchr & Coord
Rice, Elaine Tibbs
Special Education Teacher
Richards, Philip Gordon
Computer Science Professor
Rushton, Joseph N.
8th Grade Social Studies Tchr
Scarborough, Marcia Miller
HS Eng Tchr & Magazine Adv
Senn, Nina Swartz
German Teacher
Smith, Kay Hightower
Fifth Grade Teacher
Smith, Meryal Campbell
Chemistry Teacher
Smith, Vicki Pierce
7th Grade Math Teacher
Speck, Ann Prather
4th Grade Teacher
Stevens, Barbara Williams
8th Grd Social Studies Teacher
Swan, Ruth Maddox
Media Librarian
Thomas, Mary Frances
Teacher of Gifted & Talented
Trammell, Robert C., III
Bio, Chem Tchr & Sci Dept Chm
Warren, Barbara Moseley
Early Childhood Professor
Westbrook, Jerry D.
Engineering Management Dir
White, Dorinda Curtis
Fourth Grade Teacher
Wilksman, Karen S.
English Teacher
Williamson, Mary Talley
First Grade Teacher
Woods, Mary Betsy (Ross)
Third Grade Teacher
Zurline, Ronald David
Business Ed Chprsn & Teacher
IDER
Haynes, Hazel McCurdy
Guidance Counselor
Meeks, Sherry Moore
Mathematics Teacher
JACKSON
Chancey, Daniel Beryl
English Teacher
Odom, Gennett Hytower
Physical Ed & Health Teacher
Pugh, Judith Reid
Math Teacher & Dept Chairman
Tarleton, Lenette Hitt
Eighth Grade Teacher
Wilson, Margaret Kay
English Teacher
JACKSONS GAP
Meacham, Kristi Adams
Former French Teacher
JACKSONVILLE
Brown, Gary Lee
Retired HS History Teacher
Craven, Becky Angel
Fifth Grade Teacher
Day, Kenneth William Harvey
Marketing Professor
Duncan, Klaus Wilhelm
German Teacher
Evans, Janet Vickie
Biology Teacher
Gossett, Jeffrey David
Band & Chorus Director
Houston, Melanie Harrison
Language Arts Teacher
Hulsey, Jerri Odell
English Teacher
Hunter, Sandra Ruth
Physical Education Teacher
Johns, Eddie Clay
Technical Drafting Teacher
Mc Alister, Rex Eugene
Sixth Grade Teacher
McArthur, Betty Howell
Fourth Grade Teacher
McCormick, Micheal Brooks
Professor of Management
Mc Ginnis, Carol Ligon
Second Grade Teacher
Padgett, Sharon
Math, Sci Tchr & Dept Chair
Seay, Sharon Smith
Asst Professor of Accounting
Whaley, John Richard
Agribusiness Teacher
Wright, Rita Fields
Science Teacher

JASPER
Blackwood, Suzy
Teacher of the Gifted Ed
Dutton, John Mark
Welding Instructor
Elkins, Charlotte Mc Collum
3rd Grade Teacher
Key, Elaine Meeks
Third Grade Teacher
Kitchens, Teresa Holley
Mathematics Teacher
Larson, Duane Allen
Physics & Mathematics Teacher
Manasco, Bobbie N.
Fifth Grade Teacher
Ortega, George Luis
Bus, Econ & Acctng Instructor
Sartain, Kerry L.
Science Department Chairman
Smitherman, Sheila Key
Third Grade Teacher
Steelmon, Kenneth Martin
Science Teacher
Steelmon, Sue Smith
Mathematics Teacher
Winsett, Susan D.
English & Writing Instructor
JEMISON
Gray, Robin Argo
Learning Disabilities Teacher
KILLEN
Bracey, Carolyn G.
Mathematics Teacher
Buchanan, Terry Irons
Sixth Grade Teacher
Burns, Brenda Johnson
English & Journalism Teacher
Cox, Joan Shelton
Third Grade Teacher
McDonald, Ronnie Ray
Graphic Communications Instr
Miles, Myra Elizabeth
Physical Education Teacher
Parker, Sally K.
Title I Reading Teacher
Perry, Connie Ashley
Head Mathematics Dept
Putman, S. Annette
Third Grade Teacher
Shelton, Janis Elaine
Sixth Grade Teacher
KINSTON
Rowe, Curtiss Alan
High School Spanish Teacher
LAFAYETTE
Bledsoe, Nora Brock
6th Grade Reading Teacher
Halsey, Jo Ann
English Teacher
Perry, Barbara Coker
4th-8th Grade History Teacher
LANETT
Heard, Jamie Lee
Assistant Principal
Lindley, Suzanne Mouton
Spanish Teacher
Looser, Vickie Beard
Social Studies Teacher
Pigg, Edward Kenneth
Mathematics Teacher & Coach
LEEDS
Garrett, Charlene Elizabeth
Math Teacher
Johnson, Susan Dalton
Business Education Teacher
Partridge, James David
Mathematics Teacher
Sanders, Tim
Athletic Director & Coach
Tate, Harriett Martin
Jr High Technology Teacher
LEESBURG
Engledow, Janet Bowman
Elementary Counselor
Grimes, Penny Whorton
English Teacher
Hendon, Carolyn Wolcott
Science Teacher
Lawson, Wendell E.
His, Drivers Ed & Health Tchr
LEIGHTON
Brisendine, Doreen Hart
Phys Sci, Chem & Physics Tchr
Cobb, Betty Lanford
Kindergarten Teacher
Goss, Donna Richardson
7th Grd Eng & Cmptr Ed Teacher
Hogans, Ada King
Business Education Teacher
Jackson, Jorja Sanders
Mathematics Teacher
Mc Cormack, Evelyn Russ
Art Teacher
Russell, Ronna Whitehead
Spanish Teacher
Shaw, Martha Liner
Fifth Grade Teacher
Shirley, Jim G.
Physical Education Teacher
LEROY
Jenkins, Creola Landrum
Business Education Teacher
Wilson, Sandra J.
4th Grade Teacher
LESTER
Bass, Sandra Jackson
First Grade Teacher
Clemons, R. Ray
Drivers Ed, PE Tchr & Coach

Evans, Margie Meller
English Teacher
Harrison, Barbara J.
4th-6th Grade Math Teacher
Kennemer, Mary Ann
Business Education Teacher
Looney, Tammy Barlow
English Teacher
Nave, Michael Lynn
Football Head Coach & Teacher
Reece, Martha Brackeen
First Grade Teacher
LETOHATCHEE
Vilardi, Virginia Ann Penson
Biology & Chemistry Teacher
Walton, Gracie Jones
History Department Chairperson
LEXINGTON
Tidwell, Amy Watkins
English Teacher
White, Joel Wade
Mathematics Teacher
LINCOLN
Murrell, Thomas Alan
Mathematics Teacher & Dept Chm
LINDEN
Andrews, Shirley M.
English Teacher
LINEVILLE
East, Ginger Dawkins
First Grade Teacher
LIPSCOMB
Upton, Jeffie McPherson
Sixth Grade Teacher
LIVINGSTON
Akpom, Uchenna Nwabufo
Associate Professor of Ec
Bizzell, Bessie Jean
English Teacher
Campbell, Tommie Lee
Kindergarten Teacher
Cook, Charlie Thomas, Jr.
Assistant Professor of Mgmt
Coxwell, Joe Thomas
Chem, Physics & Bio Prof
Crooks, Betty Jean
Social Studies Teacher
DeMay, Patricia
Professor
Floyd, Robert T.
Prof of PE & Athletic Trng
Khan, Niaz Ahmed
Associate Prof of Journalism
Lenning, William N.
Assistant Prof of Technology
Marson, Alvin B., Jr.
Professor of Education
Massey, Julia England
Mathematics Assoc Professor
Mitchell, Alfred J.
Educ Supvr & Testing Coord
Outlaw, Kathleen Fincannon
Senior Biology Teacher
Pagliero, Mary
Asst Prof of Romance Lang
Said, Hassan A.
Associate Professor of Finance
Schellhammer, Richard Charles
Assistant Professor of History
Square, Mary Jo
History Dept Chm, Civics Instr
Taylor, Joe
English Professor
Underwood, Roy Madison
Lang, Lit Prof & Dept Chair
Williams, Mary Beeks
Business Education Teacher
LOACHAPOKA
Tate, Jerome
AD, PE & Health Teacher
LOUISVILLE
Abercrombie, Scarlette Greene
Principal
Baxley, William Duane
Agribusiness Instructor
Beaty, Kimberly Rainer
HS History Teacher
Carpenter, Barbara Ella
Business Education Teacher
Green, Judy Boswell
English Instructor
James, Patricia Hall
Second Grade Teacher
Meadows, Vickie C.
Jr HS Science Teacher
LUVERNE
Franks, L. Earl
Band Director
Penn, Janet A.
Art & Special Education Tchr
Watson, Sue McDougald
Retired Counselor
MADISON
Bruer, Sally Sigler
Assistant Principal
Clough, Lesa Hebert
French & Spanish Teacher
Creighton, Lorann Myrick
Lead Counselor
Finley, Christie Hindman
American Government Teacher
Fudge, Henry Lee
7th Grade Science Teacher
Jones, Regina Christine
Former History Teacher
Mc Kinney, Brigitte Kay (Wren)
7th Grade Teacher
Murphy, Randall Dee
Assistant Principal

Pickens, Melanie Turnure
Chemistry Teacher
Shelton, Charlotte Jean
Sixth Grade Teacher
Sterling, Rose Solomon
French Teacher
Sullivan, Brenda Beasley
Chemistry Teacher
Sullivan, Gina Carol
Computer Science Teacher
Turner, Barbara Hereford
Biology Teacher
Weyler, Geraldine Thielmeier
Physics & Math Teacher
MAPLESVILLE
Green, Teresa Ellison
Business & English Teacher
Smith, Mary Marjorie
First Grade Teacher
Walker, Gail Mc Lean
Business Ed & English Teacher
Ward, Deborah K.
Secondary Mathematics Teacher
MARBURY
Popwell, James Maury
Teacher & Soc Stud Dept Chm
MARION
Cleveland, Willie Mae
Fourth Grade Teacher
Jones, Corey Lee
Physical Sci & Math Teacher
Kastenmayer, Walter William
Chemistry Instructor
Tipton, Denice Granger
Campus Ministries Director
Vetzel, Michelle Massey
English Teacher
MC CALLA
Dutton, Sue Butler
Fifth Grade Teacher
Holland, Betty Martin
Teacher of the Gifted
Hunt, Kathy
Second Grade Teacher
Stalls, Shelton James
Science Teacher
Swaffield, Thomas
Agribusiness & Forestry Tchr
Walden, Amy Joyce
World & US History Teacher
Wilkinson Brasher, Marian Ruth
Third Grade Teacher
Wright, Marcia G.
Vocational Counselor
MC INTOSH
Thomas, Fred
Biology & Physical Sci Tchr
MC KENZIE
Lowe, Cindy Taylor
Physical Education & Math Tchr
MIDFIELD
Hooks, Glen Alan
English Teacher
Rust, Debra Ann
Tchr of Mntly Hndcpd & Gifted
MIDLAND CITY
Corridori, Desa Elaine
Spanish Teacher
Wood, Waynolin
Drama, Art & Social Stud Tchr
MILLBROOK
Crosby, Vivian Louise
Fifth Grade Teacher
Davis, Robin Hooper
Eng & Creative Writing Tchr
Deneve, Joan C.
Jr High English Tchr
Gantt, Dale Sanford
Spanish Teacher
Hicks, Harvey Wayne
HS Army JROTC Instructor
Mc Griff, Teresa Dunn
1st Grade Teacher
Ponds, Karen Lynn
Math & English Teacher
MILLERVILLE
Beverly, Marion Lee
Sixth Grade Teacher
MILLPORT
Bean, Barbara Jo
English Teacher
Mc Gee, Willnetta (Marie)
Kindergarten Teacher
Robertson, Nancy Duncan
6th Grade Teacher
MOBILE
Addy, Judith Thomason
Math & English Teacher
Agapos, A. M.
Prof of Economics & Finance
Akkoc, Can C.
Mathematics Instructor
Ashley, Terry
Economics Professor
Baer, Charles A.
Guidance Counselor
Baker, Melissa Hayes
Physical Ed Teacher & Coach
Bedsole, Mary Delaney
Math Department Chairperson
Belasco, Ruth E.
Associate Prof of Fine Arts
Berry, Donald K.
Assoc Professor of Religion
Black, Waynetta Grant
Guidance Department Head
Bosler, Joanne Lacek
Lower School Director
Britt, Kristy McKenzie
Spanish Teacher

Bryant, Johnnita Washam
Principal
Burchfield, Patricia Crosby
Adv Placement Math Teacher
Burtnett, Deborah Groce
World & European History Tchr
Caine, Maureen Ann
Third Grade Teacher
Capers, Nathaniel
JROTC Instructor
Carey, Steven Dale
Professor of Biology
Chard, Johnny Lester
Administrator & Youth Pastor
Clapsadl, Michael Ray
Naval Science Instructor
Coleman, Vernon Anthony, Sr.
Adjunct Professor
Creps, Lisa P.
Jr High English Teacher
Crittenden, Dorothy Overton
Fifth Grade Teacher
Crocker, Lillian Hughes
US History Teacher
Cunningham, Trudy A.
Science Teacher
Curtin, Patti Glenn
Second Grade Teacher
Curtis, Terry Wayne
Head Football Coach & Ath Dir
Donaldson, Maureen Shields
Biology Instructor
Donalson, Malcolm Drew
Assistant Prof of the Classics
Doody, Edmund Gordon, Jr.
Dean & Social Studies Teacher
Dubose, Leevones Gillespie
Science Teacher
Elmore, Rebecca Mc Cart
Elementary Schl Guidance Cnslr
Evans, Elizabeth Sue
Science Teacher
Floyd, Marilyn Friday
Physical Ed Teacher & Coach
Fox, Rebecca Ware
Music Professor
Gibson, Judith Ellen
Librarian
Giddens, Sandra Montalban
Business Education Teacher
Golson, Marcia Parden
Counselor
Gonzales, Mary Hampton
Teacher
Goodman, Jeffrey A.
English Professor
Greene, John H., III
HS Science Teacher
Griffin, Charlotte Irving-Lyons
English Teacher
Griffin, Judith Spence
Principal
Griffis, Wanda Tomlinson
Chemistry Teacher
Hafizi, Lisa Griffith
Kindergarten Teacher
Hannon, Roxanne Denise
English Instructor
Hardin, Pier Peterson
9th-10th Grade English Teacher
Harmless, J. William, SJ
Asst Prof of Dept of Theology
Heisler, Jennifer Lee
Language Arts Teacher
Hoffman, Deborah E.
English Teacher
Hollister, Laurene Susan
Fifth Grade Teacher
Hughes, Kathy Albritton
Choral Director
Johnson, Shirley A.
Mathematics Teacher
Jones, Beverly Phillips
8th Grade Math Teacher
Jones, Christa Schapitz
German & French Teacher
July, Douglas Lorenzo
Band Director
Kearley, Carmen Elizabeth
PACE Language Arts Teacher
Keller, Linda Buckhout
Lang Arts & Soc Stud Tchr
Kemp, Cynthia DeVane
Chemistry & Physics Teacher
Kendall, Anthony Brent
History Teacher
Kenyon, Donna Gray
8th Grade English Teacher
Kouadio, Kay I.
Assoc Prof of Chemistry
Kruithof, Nancy Mae
Jr HS Science & English Tchr
Laurendine, Barbara Jones
Adjunct Professor of Music
Lemmermann, Paula Evans
Mathematics Instructor
Lubel, Marilyn Levenson
Associate Tennis Coach
Lyle, Meridy Anne
5th Grade Teacher
Martin, Monique C.
Latin & French Teacher
McCloud, Gail Davis
Third Grade Teacher
McCracken, Marcella Roberts
Kindergarten Teacher
McElhaney, Lynne Meyer
Advanced Science Teacher
McGee, Laura Buckler
Latin Tchr & Frgn Lang Chm

Mc Neil, Diana Glover
Reading Instructor
Megginson, Jayne Margaret
Lecturer of Communication Arts
Michael, Susie Ward
Chemistry Teacher
Middleton, Betty Flowers
Fifth Grade Teacher
Mills, Kerrie Elizabeth
Band Director
Mires, Janice DeLuca
Psychology & Amer History Tchr
Mitchell, Joseph Christopher
Natural Sci & Math Div Chair
Morris, Larry
World History Teacher
Mosley, Darlene Lavender
Teacher of Learning Disability
Nelson, Marilyn Smith
5th Grade Teacher
Nicholson, Howard Lee
History Professor
O'Keefe, Catherine Ann
Therapeutic Recreation Instr
Pace, Marilyn Buck
12th Grade English Teacher
Palmer, Joseph Richard
Social Studies Teacher
Parker, Bettie Mc Daniel
Health Teacher & Coach
Petty, John Thomas
Chemistry Instructor
Phillips, Sara Dulaney
Honors Chemistry Instructor
Pike, Tony Lee
Band Director
Reed, Keflyn Xavier
Instructor of English
Reilly, Kathleen Dolan
Religion Teacher
Richardson, Alberta N.
English Teacher
Robinson, Frances Tucker
English Instructor
Rouse, Kelly Elizabeth
Research Assistant
Santoli, Susan P.
Secondary Social Studies Tchr
Sauer, David Kennedy
Professor of English
Shackleford, Diana B.
Counselor & Recruiter
Shah, Arvind Kantilal
Professor of Statistics
Sharma, Sarla R.
Biology Teacher
Shelton, Edward Talley
English Teacher
Snyder, Elizabeth Beach
Teacher of the Gifted
Stearns, Sonya Simmons
Choir Director
Stevens, Diane Billingsley
2nd Grade Teacher
Strode, Jan Bishop
Fifth Grade Teacher
Stutts, Ruth Deloris
Professor of Biology
Sudeiha, Lisa Mc Clure
Advanced Biology Teacher
Thompson, William H.
Funeral Service Education Dir
Turk, Margaret T.
Fourth Grade Teacher
Walker, Billy Warren
Teacher & Elem Prin
Walker, Sarah Green
Fourth Grade Teacher
Ward, Sylvia Jane
Occupational Child Care Instr
Washington, Lilly Patterson
Retired Elementary Teacher
Wattuhewa, Garvin
Physics Professor
Weaver, Mack Conley, III
History Teacher
Weldy, Teresa Gay
Management Professor
Wheeler, Donald Dean
Physics & Engineering Instr
Wheeler, Ethel M.
Gifted & Talented Elem Tchr
White, Benton Ray
History Professor
White, Herbert
Mathematics Teacher
Whitley, Sarah Jane
Physical Education Teacher
Williams, JoAnne Bailey
Mathematics Teacher
Williams, Vincentine Piazza
Private Piano Instructor
Yoder, James Allen
Associate Professor of Finance
MONROEVILLE
Goolsby, Julia Lee
Second Grade Teacher
Joiner, Linda Dees
Algebra & Geometry Teacher
Lord, Rodney Lane
English Teacher
Mayhand, Louise Preyer
Family & Consumer Sci Teacher
Stacey, Paula Vick
English Teacher & Counselor
MONTEVALLO
Al-Lami, Fadhil A.
Anatomy Professor
Basinger, Dana King
Adjunct Instructor of English

NTEVALLO (cont)
ele, Barbara Mayweather
tired English Teacher
d, Malcolm Ross
ofessor of Biology
ing, John William
soc Professor of Psychology
oler, Leland Kent
f of Cnslng, Ldrshp & Fnds
ugh, Cheri Smith
unselor Educator
y, Milton Joseph
of Emeritus of Eng Dept
n, Judy E.
st Director of Athletics
ldin, Deborah Annette
tr & Dir of Orchesis Dance
er, Scott Kendall
sociate Professor of Art
y, Jacqueline Freeman
sistant Professor
amer, Elizabeth Shaw
shman Writing Instructor
ips, Philip Richard
ysical Education Instructor
oson, Mary Lovenah
st Prof of Ed of Deaf
key, Janice Ralya
st Prof & Dir of Forensics
s, Ruth Smith
tory Instructor
NTGOMERY
ns, Marlyne Ellis
f of Business Education
worth, Amanda Denise
alth & 8th Grd Science Tchr
erson-Free, F. Corine
no Instructor
ony, Doris Cooper
ctical Nurse Educator
ield, Nadene Houser
st Prof of Chemistry
ngton, Veverly Baird
idance Counselor
, Phyllis Patterson
nguage Arts Teacher
arski, Linda
vanced Biology Teacher
er, Zenobia Patricia
rd Grade Teacher
y, Christine Elliott
Grd Social Studies Teacher
ea, David Lee
Teacher & Coach
ler, Chris Alan
strumental Music Teacher
hat, Linda Joyce
nguage Arts & Religion Tchr
now, Kathy Norris
ndergarten Teacher
chard, Nancy S.
eech & Language Pathologist
ins, Jeanne Elinor Karison
st Prof of Early Childhd Ed
lin, Tina Gaffey
emistry & Physics Teacher
l, Alicia Allison
thematics & Cmptr Ed Instr
er, Jerry E.
glish Teacher
ks, Frank Erik
slr & Instr of Orientation
eshaw, Jane Satterwhite
th Grade Language Arts Tchr
son, Theresa Hill
sistant History Professor
son, Pamela Bozeman
nguage Arts Teacher
g, Moon K.
ecial Education Professor
pell, Leila Rivers
th Grade English Teacher
tham, Augustine Hendrix
urth Grade Teacher
tham, Carl Wade
lical Studies Professor
ns, Roberta Reese
siness Education Teacher
eland, Sheila Joy
th Grade Teacher
tree, Sue Howard
sistant Professor
esh, Iraj
of of Cmptr Sci & Physics
in, E. K.
rm Dir Hnrs Pgm, Assoc Prof
hields, Vivian Watts
sociate Professor
on, Mary Simon
th Grade Teacher
er, Suzilee Y.
glish Teacher & Coordinator
est, Jacquelyn Hodges
vanced Placement Eng Instr
ards, Stanley David, Sr.
cial Studies Teacher
, Marvin L., III
cial Studies Teacher
ridge, Karen Jones
th Grade English Teacher
s, Robert Charles
stngd Rsrch Prof of English
en, Beverly J.
culus Instructor
er, Randy Paul
tist & Teacher
er, Judy
rketing Ed Coop Tchr
ous, Madie E.
st Prof of Speech

Gilchrist, Mary John Amason
Accounting Teacher
Gordon, Sabrina Hildreth
6th Grade Reading Teacher
Gunter, Jim
Art Teacher
Han, Meesoon
Mathematics Instructor
Harper, Cynthia Danner
Laboratory Chemistry Teacher
Harrell, Thomas Leon
Math Teacher
Herndon, Cristy Steele
US History Teacher
Hicks, Dixie Crawford
Assistant Prof of History
Hooper, Judy McKissick
Physical Education Teacher
Jackson, Kathy Dunn
Prof of Eng & Hum Dept Chair
Jenkins, Lovell Jerome
Geometry Teacher
Jones, Virginia Marie
Humanities Professor
Keith, Lesa Lynn Griffith
Psychology Teacher
Kim, Ki Hang
Distngd Professor of Math
Lambert, Stephen H.
Youth Minister
Lawrence, Jerry
Creative Writing Instructor
Lewis, Brenda J. Early
Instructor
Lewis, Dan
US History Teacher
Markham, Annie Pearl
English Instructor
Maryland, Wallace Jr.
Math & Science Dept Chair
McKiearnan, Cheryl L.
English Department Chairman
McNear, Velma May
Fourth Grade Teacher
Mc Neese, Carolyn Nelson
Third Grade Teacher
Mc Neil, William Edward
Assoc Professor of Psychology
Mitchell, Claudia Thomas
Physical Sci & Cmptr Ed Tchr
Moore, Nathan
Dept Chair & Professor of Eng
Mowrer, Tony A.
Assistant Professor of Music
Nelson, Kristy L.
10th Grade English Teacher
Nix, Deborah D.
Kindergarten Teacher
Norton, Laurie Greer
English Teacher
Oliviere, James
Professor of Biology
Pigg, Carol (Williams)
Mathematics Teacher
Pirnie, Sandy Key
Counselor
Pritchard, Denise Ballard
Home Economics Teacher
Shanks, Bonnie Miller
Social Studies Teacher
Sides, Levi Jackson
History Teacher
Smith, Dorothy Waver
7th Grade English Teacher
Smith, Lynne Mills
6th Grade Teacher
Smith, Rhonda Kennedy
Fifth Grade Teacher
Sorrells, Carol Hunt
Business Teacher
Speights, Julia Long
Mathematics Teacher
Sr., Bernard Frye
Math Teacher
Stafford, Michael Bruce
Teacher
Stewart, William Craig
Former History & Ec Teacher
Studdard, Michelle Blake
World History Teacher
Summerlin, Kellie F.
Chemistry & Physics Teacher
Surles, Marcia Ann
Physical Ed Dept Chairperson
Taylor, Karen V.
Asst Prof of Criminal Justice
Truett, Gayle Calhoun
Principal & Owner
Turk, Dorothy Pace
Asst Professor of Mathematics
Tyus, Sarah Farnham
Science Dept Chm & Teacher
Vainrib, Peggy Gregory
Counselor
Waldrip, Nana E.
Theatre Dept Head & Instructor
Weiss, Joyce Lacey
University Reading Professor
White, Evelyn Montgomery
Math & Science Dept Chair
White, John Edward
Sixth Grade Teacher
Williams, Charles Eddy
Director of Bands
Wright, Cathy Hess
Dance Instructor & Dept Head
Wynn, Rhea Enloe
English Teacher
York, Susan Ryals
First Grade Teacher

MOODY
Bishop, Roger Quenton
Amer History & Driver Ed Tchr
Crowe, Linda T.
Government & Economics Teacher
Cryar, Erlene Mae
7th Grd Social Studies Teacher
Duncan, Marie White
English & Literature Teacher
Johnson, Phillip
Mathematics Tchr & Asst Coach
Mc Gee, Deborah Stringer
Elementary Teacher
Voelzke, Joyce Burttram
English & German Teacher
MORRIS
Capps, Cheryl Jolly
Assistant Principal
Davis, Donna Self
6th Grade Teacher
Hillis, Kathye McCook
Physical Education Teacher
Holmes, Brenda Head
Business Education Teacher
Murray, Kathy Reno
4th Grade Teacher
Recke, Rebecca Evelyn (Bobo)
Health & PE Teacher
Snider, Jane Carr
Kindergarten Teacher
MOULTON
Clay, James C.
Counselor
Klopfenstein, Miriam Hemmer
Math, Sci, Soc Studies Teacher
MOUNDVILLE
Gvillo, Rejeana Langford
English & French Teacher
Hardy, Minnie Thomas
English Teacher
MOUNT HOPE
Wiginton, Barry Lynn
General Science Teacher
MOUNT VERNON
Smith, Cynthia Harrod
Fourth Grade Teacher
Thomas, Janice Robinson
Asst Principal
MUNFORD
Miller, Rebecca Thomas
Kindergarten Teacher
White, Betty Canada
Sixth Grade Teacher
MUSCLE SHOALS
Freeze, Judy Yeager
Assistant Principal
Gardiner, Elizabeth Underwood
Div Chair of Hum & Fine Arts
Hardy, Charles David
Carpentry Teacher
Howard, Thomas Gene
Physics Instructor
Jones, Jeremy Joseph
Advanced Placement His Tchr
Jones, Michael Thomas
Adj Instr of Criminal Justice
Mc Cully, Sue Propst
Retired Third Grade Teacher
Ownby, Terry Scott
Choral Associate Band Director
Stone, Ruth Jones
Psychology Professor
Waide, Linda Owen
Project Counselor & Coord
Weeks, James Thomas
Health Teacher & Coach
Wheeles, Glada Juanita
Math & Algebra Teacher
NAUVOO
Cain, Nancy West
First Grade Teacher
NEW BROCKTON
Moncrief, Andrew Warren
English Teacher
Strong, Sara Warr
3rd Grd Tchr
NEW HOPE
Smith, Shirley J.
K-8th Grd Counselor
NEW MARKET
Cardwell, Jon Michael
English Teacher
Johnson, John Daniel
JROTC Instr
Maness, Barbara Towry
Administrative Assistant
Nash, Johnny V.
Band Director
Rombokas, Judy Massengale
Kindergarten Teacher
NEWBERN
Bell, Mary Kate (Paige)
Second Grade Teacher
Cotney, Gaye Willoughby
Mathematics Teacher
NEWTON
Bonn, Jacqueline Marie
Fifth Grade Teacher
Smollen, Patsy Smith
Senior English Teacher
Tew, Andrea Mallory
Science Teacher
NORMAL
Banks, Bonnie Mc Quitter
Assistant Prof of Accounting
Blake, Jean A.
Professor of Mathematics
Dike, Augustine Nlemchi
Asst Prof of Business Admin

Elike, Uchenna
Assoc Prof of Ec & Finance
Gilmore, Rufus, III
Assistant Prof of Accounting
Sterling, Leroy
Asst Prof of Eng & Frgn Lang
Wyckoff, Shelley Ann
Social Work Prof & Dept Dir
NORTHPORT
Ball, Robin Sullivan
English Teacher
Bredeson, Cheryl Ann (Fritze)
Fourth Grade Teacher
Brinyark, Rhonda Bloodsworth
English Teacher
Clark, Tracy Strickland
Science Teacher
Coleman, Patrick Erin
Physics & Astronomy Teacher
Cook, Annette Galyean
Math Teacher & Dept Head
Gosa, Dianne Washington
Sixth Grade Teacher
Hall, Charles Leslie
Art Dept Head & Instructor
Harmon, Jacqueline White
Fifth Grade Teacher
Lambert, Gwen Andrea
Chemistry & Physics Teacher
Mabry, Janis Kay
Chemistry Teacher
Marable, Sharon Bagwell
Counselor
McCracken, Gary Evan
Math Teacher
Moffett, Gladys Beatrice
7th-12th Grade Science Teacher
Pate, Sharon Broadus
Second Grade Teacher
Prewitt, Teresa C.
American History Teacher
Rich, Peggy Poe
Mathematics Teacher
Skelton, Gloyce Thrasher
Language Arts Teacher
Smithson, Robbie H.
Science Teacher
Thagard, Jenny Snow
Teacher of the Gifted
Tunnell, Gail
World History Teacher
Urban, Lowell Scott
9th Grade History Teacher
Wicker, Mark
Librarian
Williams, Amanda Foster
Calculus & Geometry Teacher
Wilson, Belinda Bridges
English Teacher
Wilson, Elizabeth Snyder
Eng & African Amer Lit Teacher
Yager, Steven R.
Computer Science Teacher
NOTASULGA
Edwards, Virginia Mitchell
English & Journalism Teacher
Langford, Lisa Griggs
Mathematics Teacher
Sanders, Paula Belcher
Science & Technology Teacher
Wilcox, John P.
Social Studies Teacher
ODENVILLE
Haynes, Kimberly Bradley
Special Education Teacher
Mashburn, Alice Starrett
Sixth Grade Teacher
Nobles, Connie Patterson
Sixth Grade Teacher
Whitten, Gail McGeoch
Fifth Grade Teacher
OHATCHEE
Finley, Freda L.
English Teacher
Minter, Barbara Zinn
American History Teacher
Sprayberry, Ann Dryden
English Teacher
Studdard, Angela Hurst
Secondary Mathematics Teacher
Whiten, Kina Lynne
History, Science & PE Teacher
ONEONTA
Dickie, Glenda Woodard
Fifth & Sixth Grade Teacher
Golden, James Adrain, Jr.
Jr High Social Studies Tchr
Standridge, Sharon Melinda
7th-12th Grd PE Teacher
Stapler, Alice Mann
English & Spanish Teacher
Williams, Mildred Weaver
Chemistry & Physics Teacher
OPELIKA
Baker, Jamie E.
Choral Director
Barnes, Richard Harrison, Jr.
High School Technology Teacher
Brown, Marilyn Hill
English Teacher
Carson, Steven P.
Social Studies Teacher
Clark, Anthony Howard
History & Science Teacher
Coulter, Dian Watson
Math Teacher
Devers, Margaret Anne
Ninth Grade English Teacher
Lishak, Lisa Anne
Education Math Teacher

Martin, James Daniel, III
Band Director
Miller, Sharon Colburn
5th-8th Grd Mathematics Tchr
Morgan, Donna Carroll
English Teacher
Patterson, Dorothy Gentry
Second Grade Teacher
Price, Nancy Harris
5th Grade Teacher
Smith, Janet Morris
French & Latin Teacher
Thomas, Muriel Marsha
Kindergarten Teacher
Thornton, Mary Pinkard
5th Grade Teacher
Whatley, Mary Celia (Jones)
Mathematics Teacher
OPP
Bundrick, Linda Larigan
8th Grd Sci Tchr & Dept Chm
Faulk, Janet Crews
Mathematics Teacher
Graves, Cheryl Adams
Language Arts Teacher
Mills, Edith Slaughter
Spclst of Learning Disablities
Smith, Deborah Kilcrease
Third Grade Teacher
Sumblin, Pamila P.
Child Care Teacher
Waldorff, Judy Berry
Junior High School Teacher
ORRVILLE
Bruce, Elizabeth Lorraine
Eng Creative Writing Teacher
Swift, Elijah Raford, Jr.
Math Teacher
OXFORD
Barker, William Frederick
Band Director
Britt, Bunti Musick
English Teacher
Britt, George Timothy
World & AP Euro His Tchr
Humphries, Cristy Chase
4th Grade Teacher
Hutto, Sherri Murdock
Spanish Teacher
Keat, Judith Spidle
Learning Disabilities Teacher
Mc Call, Susan Ford
Choral Director
O'Kelley, Anita Banks
Fourth Grade Teacher
Parris, Glennis Timmons
Family & Consumer Sci Teacher
Phillips, Anita O'Neal
Mathematics Teacher
Robertson, Lisa Pillitary
Biology Teacher
Tinney, Peggy Jean
Biology Teacher
Young, Beth Thompson
Kindergarten Teacher & Dir
OZARK
Buis, Pauline Reid-feijoo
English Teacher
Cook, Louise Brown
11th Grd US History Teacher
Evans, Debra D. Teal
4th Grade Teacher
Harrison, Howard Albert
5th Grade Teacher
Hicks, Barbara Yarbrough
English Teacher
Jackson, Amy Judah
Math Teacher
Kelley, Burnie R.
Health Care Sci & Tech Teacher
Lewis, Beverly Harrison
8th Grade Math & Soc Stud Tchr
Taylor, Margaret Neal
Business Education Teacher
Teel, Darylene Yvette
English Teacher
Thompson, Martha Dan
Seventh Grd Language Arts Tchr
PANOLA
Means, Mary Eloise
Science Teacher
Russ-Jackson, Drucilla
Librarian
PARRISH
Langley, Diane
Library Media Specialist
PELHAM
Bishop, Janet Jackson
Foreign Lang Dept Chair & Tchr
Crenshaw, Eleanor RUth Robison
Mathematics Teacher
Essman, Lisa Louise
English Teacher
Gilmore, Burdine J.
Chemistry Teacher
Green, Leslee Burbic
Mathematics Teacher
Hicks, Conchita Hernandez
High School Spanish Teacher
Hogan, Jennifer Johnson
Physical Science Teacher
Martin, Linda McDonald
English Teacher & Dept Head
McAdam, Paul E., Jr.
English Instructor
Moore, Mamie E. White
Advanced English Teacher
Nall, Kim L.
Secondary Art Teacher

PELHAM (cont)
Noble, Ralph F., Jr.
Mathematics Teacher & Coach
Payne, Mirian Cunningham
Fourth Grade Teacher
Walls, Faye Drummond
Secondary American His Tchr
PELL CITY
Bennett, Dorothy Simpson
Spanish Teacher
Hardin, Mary Schuessler
Mathematics Teacher
Huntress, Thomas Edward
English Teacher
Lawley, Deanna Nolen
AP Eng Teacher & Dept Chrmn
Pepple, Michael L.
High School Science Teacher
Raughton, Linda Green
English & French Teacher
Reaves, Alicia Golden
Biology Teacher
Wood, Gayle Blalock
8th Grade Algebra Teacher
PHENIX CITY
Ashburn, Richard William
8th Grd Amer His Teacher
Baker, Eloise Taylor
Kindergarten Teacher
Blevins, Joseph Patrick
Assistant Principal
Boutwell, Debra Shawn
Mathematics Teacher
Carlisle, Minnie T.
Business Education Instructor
Cook, Earl Wayne
Mathematics Teacher
Crawford, Loy O'Neal
Director of Bands
Cunningham, Robert William
Professor & Coordinator
Elder, Margariete Hamilton Tucker
Elem Teacher
Florence, Jaspconia G.
Science Teacher
Garrett, Shirley Ann
Sixth Grade Teacher
Hicks, Jerry Wayne
Microbiology Instructor
Lockwood, Susan Keller
English Professor
Lofton, Lenore
Secondary Mathematics Teacher
McQueen, Walter Glynn
Math & Science Dept Chair
Porche, Amy Susan
English Instructor
Rogers, Marilyn Strickland
Mathematics Teacher
Sanks, Alva Gradham
English Instructor
Shores, Lisa Moore
Sci Tchr & Var Cheer Coach
Smith, Anne Anthony
English Instructor
Smith, Neva Morris
Science Teacher
Tarver, Yvonne Smith
Teacher
Thomas, Molee Mc Kinnon
Chemistry Professor
Trussell, Carolyn Sims
Fifth Grade Teacher
Walden, Jane Robison
Biology Teacher
Young, Susan E.
Bus Comp Applications Instr
PHIL CAMPBELL
Alls, Joe Mark
Biology Instructor
Hutcheson, Kaye Trapp
English & Science Teacher
PIEDMONT
Johnson, Elizabeth Hollis
English & Drama Teacher
Whaley, Missia Boozer
History Teacher
Wheeler, Donald Everett
Band Director
Wilson, James Wright
Business Education Teacher
PIKE ROAD
Frost, Jacqueline Scott
Science Teacher
Giles, Florence Cook
8th Grd Social Studies Teacher
Mixson, Tanya Leigh
9th Grade Teacher
Sikes, Ceil Etheridge
8th & 9th Grd Soc Stud Teacher
PINE HILL
Bosby, Gloria Hudson
Kindergarten Teacher
PINSON
Bandy, John Allen
Fifth Grade Teacher
Copham, Elaine Rhodes
Vocational Teacher
Dutton, Miles, Jr.
Teacher & Coach
Evans, Laneta Fullenwiley
7th Grade Math Teacher
Flanagan, Peggie Nixon
8th Grade English Teacher
King, Chris Allen
World & AP US His Tchr
Morrison, Gertrude M.
Teacher
Tracy, Sandi Glenn
Seventh Grade English Teacher
PISGAH
Frasier, Nancy K.
Social Studies & History Tchr
Griffith, Dwight David
7th & 8th Grade Anatomy Tchr
Hancock, Carter Dale
Administrator
Jones, Margaret Benson
Title 1 Teacher
Wheeler, Joe Edsel
Science Teacher
Wilbanks, Wanda Smith
Fourth Grade Teacher
PLEASANT GROVE
Byram, Wayne Alan
Anatomy & Physiology Teacher
Youngblood, Janet Thomas
Chemistry & Physics Teacher
PRATTVILLE
Davis, Susanne Barley
7th Grade Science Teacher
Gaut, Shirley Taylor
Second Grade Teacher
Hunter, Arlene Davis
Mathematics Teacher
Jordan, Karen Karrh
4th Grade Teacher
Phillips, Beatrice Landrum
Secondary Mathematics Teacher
Reed, Charles S.
English, Span & Jrnlsm Instr
QUINTON
Fox, Jane Caradine
Retired Fourth Grade Teacher
Rollins, Linda Bookout
Math Teacher
RAINSVILLE
Douglas, Brenda Vaughn
Spanish Teacher
Gorham, Cheryl Lee
History & Political Sci Instr
Millican, Gregory David
Mathematics Instructor
Richards, Donna Broyles
Mathematics Teacher
Stevenson, Paul Lee
Art Instructor
Vance, John B.
Mathematics Instructor
Veazey, Charles Frederick
Instructor in Biology
Willmon, Susan Tumlin
Sixth Grade Teacher
RANBURNE
Young, Bart E.
Jr High Math Teacher
RED BAY
Cleveland, Johnny Steven
Phys, Comp Sci & Phtgrphy Tchr
West, Frances Roberts
English Teacher
RED LEVEL
Maddox, Dawn Raley
Special Education Teacher
REFORM
Ashmore, Patsy Ann Boyett
Family & Consumer Science Tchr
Duncan, Clarice Kelley
Kindergarten Teacher
Hankins, Susan Pate
American Lit & English Teacher
Noland, Linda Wilson
English Teacher & Dept Chair
ROANOKE
Henson, Philip Gerald
Science & Reading Teacher
Marcum, Chuck Ray
Classroom Teacher & Coach
Mc Kinney, Joyce Harry
11th Grade English Teacher
Phillips, Sarha Ellen Barron
Home Economics Teacher
Willingham, Dennis Edward
Spanish & History Teacher
ROBERTSDALE
Baggett, Joy Dyess
6th & 7th Grd Mathematics Tchr
Bryant, Theresa Juanita
Adminstrative Assistant
Carden, Suzanne Sawyer
9th Grade English Teacher
Curtis, Benjamin Harrison, III
Elementary School Counselor
Goulart, Paul Arthur
Electronics Technology Teacher
Mitchell, Shella VanEtten
Art & Literature Teacher
Reeves, Johanna Allenbach
Eng, AP US His & Pysch Tchr
ROCKFORD
Burt, Stephanie L.
Tenth Grade Biology Teacher
Graham, Robert Lee
Mathematics Teacher
Wood, Shelley Wall
Adv Bio, Chem & Physics Tchr
ROGERSVILLE
Cagle, Brenda Joyce
First Grade Teacher
Creel, Mary-jane Yokley
Biology & Physiology Teacher
Ezell, Kathy Whitehead
Math Teacher
Sims, Jane Tucker
Fourth Grade Teacher
Smith, James Michael
Sixth Grade Classroom Teacher
Tanner, Pamela Thornton
Library Media Specialist
Webster, Cherie Bullard
9th-10th Grade English Teacher
RUSSELLVILLE
Hall, Susan Bradford
English Teacher
Holland, AnnaKay Franklin
Business Education Teacher
Mansell, Gretchen Williams
Mathematics Teacher
Mayfield, Rex
Agriscience Teacher
Pace, Barry D.
Biology I & II Teacher
Todd, Billy Joe
Agribusiness Teacher
Towsend, Karen Sue Moore
English History & Russian Tchr
SAINT ELMO
Turner, Robin Schnell
Sixth Grade Teacher
SALEM
Turner, Milton Wesley
Assistant Principal
SAMSON
Smith, Billie June
Fourth Grade Teacher
SARALAND
Davis, Karen Weaver
8th Grade Science Teacher
Robichaux, Marsha Louise
4th Grade Teacher
Ward, Mollye Long
English Teacher
SARDIS
Taylor, Christine Pollard
Eng, Lit, Sci & Soc Stud Tchr
SATSUMA
Greene, Jeanette Averett
English Teacher
Mayo, Sandra Sims
Math Teacher & Dept Chairman
Ulmer, Julian Hardy
JROTC Teacher
SCOTTSBORO
Burroughs, Betty Tucker
Economics & Amer Govt Tchr
Campbell, Carole H.
Second Grade Teacher
Crafton, Sherry Parrish
K-1 Developmental Kndgtn Tchr
Esslinger, Betty Sisk
English Teacher & Chrldr Coach
Esslinger, John R.
Sci, Jr Coll & Anatomy Tchr
Gibby, Stan W.
Mathematics Teacher
Hamilton, Alvie W.
History Teacher
Keller, Debra Richardson
Sixth Grade Teacher
Patrick, Sandra Farmer
5th Grade Self-Contained Tchr
Roden, Sandra Washburn
1st Grade Teacher
Russell, Becky Gaffin
Tenth Grade English Teacher
Thomas, Larry Gale
JROTC Instructor
SEALE
Cumberlander, Mario
Physical Sci Teacher & Coach
Dowdell, J. W. W.
Math Instructor
Evans, Freddie James
Hlth & Physical Education Tchr
Green, Glynda Kay Whitlock
Fifth & Sixth Grade Teacher
Jones, Monika Herring
Drama Teacher
Vendl, Angel Genene
Business Instructor
SECTION
Culpepper, Ann Nevels
Fourth Grade Teacher
Culver, Lana Stiefel
Social Science Teacher
Linville, Janet Coffey
Fourth Grade Teacher
Pickett, Sue Hancock
Language Arts Teacher
SELMA
Chesnut, Veronica Smith
Instruction Director
Dunaway, Carolyn Walker
Counselor
Hale, Barbara Fretwell
Eighth Grade Social Stud Tchr
Irvin, Dorothy Roscoe
Kindergarten Teacher
Knudsen, Marshall Schavland
French & English Teacher
Mc Daniel, Tracy Trolinger
Algebra Teacher
Mc Donald, Bruce Edward, I
Band Director
Redd, Patricia Moore
Principal
Smith, Karl Dee
Chemistry & Physics Coll Instr
Smitherman, Lynda Cooper
English & Speech Teacher
Snyder, Lee Mason
Dir of Computer Suite & Instr
Williamson, Fred Artorious, Jr.
Math Instructor
Williamson, Kitty Rambo
Mathematics Teacher
SEMMES
Bray, Barbara Smith
Fifth Grade Teacher
Durant, Sandra Rose
Elementary School Counselor
Hillman, Sandra Trammell
5th Grade Teacher
Jordan, Scott Michael
8th Grade Algebra Teacher
Pruett, Debra Porter
Sixth Grade Teacher
Richards, Elaine Dyess
Eighth Grade Lang Arts Teacher
SHEFFIELD
Bobo, Jack Powell, Jr.
Science Teacher
Sharp, Thomas H.
Technology Education Teacher
SILAS
Jimerson-Kelley, Tracie Donette
Social Science Teacher
Leddon, Leo Levy, Jr.
Band Director
SIPSEY
Chatman, Gloria A.
Fifth & Sixth Grade Teacher
Richardson, Laura Williams
History Teacher
Roberts, Brenda Gail
Kindergarten Teacher
SLOCOMB
Davis, James Pasco
Fifth Grade Lang Arts Tchr
Jones, Deborah Smith
Mathematics Teacher
SMITHS
Barrow, Aubrey Harold
Agribusiness Teacher
Beverly, Richard Donald
AL His, Geog & World His Tchr
Harris, Evelan Godwin
Mathematics Teacher
Johnson, Bonita Morgan
Business Education Teacher
Ledbetter, Karen Evans
English Teacher
Long, Brenda Dasinger
Home Economics Teacher
Lowther, Jean Walker
English Teacher
Rainge, Ronella Williams
Fifth Grade Teacher
Wilson, Brenda Davis
Kindergarten Teacher
SOMERVILLE
Allen, Ricky Keith
Health Teacher & Bsktbl Coach
Couey, Gary Wayne
Zoology Teacher
Hinton, Susan Frazier
Third Grade Teacher
Holmes, Mary Ellen
Family & Consumer Science Tchr
Jester, Susan Zimmerle
Math Teacher
Linderman, Johnnia Johnson
Science Teacher
Self, Jeffrey Brian
Psychology & History Teacher
SOUTHSIDE
Howell, Sonja P.
Sixth Grade Teacher
Rampey, Diana Johnson
Retired English Teacher
SPANISH FORT
Piontkowski, Brenda White
Fourth Grade Teacher
SPRING GARDEN
Formby, Marion Hope
Family & Consumer Sci Tchr
SPRINGVILLE
Boone, Gayle Jones
Reading & Math Resource Tchr
Hunter, Janice Jones
Second Grade Teacher
Smith, Jeff Hughes
Science & Drivers Ed Teacher
STEELE
Gleason, Philip Ellisot
Science, Geography & PE Tchr
STEVENSON
Butler, Donna R.
Spanish Teacher
Griggs, Victor Layne
Science Teacher
Hughes, Kathy Ann
Assistant Principal
Patrick, Teresa Tidmore
4th Grade Teacher
SULLIGENT
Baker, Dana Veal
Chemistry & Physics Teacher
Bozeman, Marcia Brown
Science Teacher
Dean, Rita V.
Sixth Grade Teacher
Northam, Arlene Holley
Second Grade Teacher
Pennington, Kitty Crawford
Business Teacher
Ward, Kathleen S.
English Teacher
SUMITON
Brown, James Kelvin
Auto Body Instructor
Gillham, Bradley I.
Science Teacher
Gravitt, Kris Ann
Mathematics Teacher
Griffith, James Edward
Applied Tech Division Chair
Gudger, Dorothy Denning
Business & Office Admin Instr
Jay, Donald Gerry
Diesel Technology Instructor
Key, Spring Smith
Kindergarten Teacher
Murray, Morris, Jr.
Instructor
Ridgeway, Connie Sisk
English Teacher
Sargent, Marc Stephen
Youth Leader
Willis, Rita Mc Gough
Nursing Instructor
SWEET WATER
Atkins, Brenda Stone
English Teacher
Conner, Anne Rembert
Kindergarten Teacher
Davis, Sherri Pridgen
Mathematics Teacher
Holladay, Deborah Irby
English Teacher
O'Bryant, Ruby Wright
Business Education Teacher
Robison, Carol Kirkham
Second Grade Teacher
Worthy, Willie Mae
Chemistry & Algebra Teacher
SYCAMORE
Mann, LeeAnn Gambrel
First Grade Teacher
SYLACAUGA
Aarhus, Betty H.
Kindergarten Teacher
Cantrell, Mandi Meacham
Former Kindergarten Teacher
Cleveland, Priscilla Adams
High School Librarian
Clifton, Ginger George
Third Grade Teacher
Culp, Danny Ray
Fourth Grade Teacher
Ellison, Kimberli Haynes
First Grade Teacher
Gaines, Glenda Crumpler
PE & Social Studies Teacher
Green, Debra G.
Teacher of the Gifted
Loftis, Don Allen
7th Grade Soc Stud Teacher
Mc Adam, Linda Rourke
English Teacher
Mc Donough, Sandra Morris
English Teacher
Roberts, Pamela English
Fourth Grade Teacher
Smithwick, Glenda H.
English Teacher
Wilkinson, Anthony Blaine
History & Science Teacher
Willett, Jane Lindsey
Physical Education Teacher
Williams, Janice E.
Mathematics Teacher
TALLADEGA
Cravens, Jane Dyer
Teacher of Gifted
Davis, Mildred Vincent
Science Teacher
Floyd, M. Carter, Jr.
Physical Education Teacher
Hurst, Linda Ford
Mathematics Instructor
Hutto, Lesley Paige
Physical Education Teacher
Joyner, Gloria Bishop
Fifth Grade Teacher
Kearley, Teresa Lynn
Fifth Grade Teacher
Locklin, John Marshall, Jr.
Science Dept Chairman
Morris, Ann S.
Third Grade Teacher
Morris, Eula Thomas
First Grade Teacher
Mullinax, Jeanne Taylor
Retired Fifth Grade Teacher
Ponder, Charles Hubert
Geometry Teacher
Quartey, Kojo Anim
Dean & Prof of Admin & Bus
Scott, Ola Roberson
High School Math Teacher
Sizemore, Phillip L.
History Department Chairperson
Smith, Rebecca Cline
First Grade Teacher
White, Walter Belt
Social Studies & English Tchr
TALLASSEE
Stewart, Keith Allen
Business Education Teacher
TANNER
Brown, Karen Storey
Fourth Grade Teacher
TARRANT
Cook, Judy Shaw
Teacher of Gifted Education
THEODORE
Galloway, Debbie Christ
Healthcare Tech Tchr & Coord
Harrison, Gloria Gentry
High School Supervisor
Jackson, Brenda Clark
Honors English Teacher
Parris, Patricia C.
HS Social Studies Teacher
Riley, Kerra Virginia
English Teacher of Gifted
Waggener, Frances Craig
Business Education Teacher

ODORE (cont)
›n, Margaret Lee
th Grade Guidance Counselor
MASVILLE
ıs, Bettye M. (Miller)
erican His Tchr & Dept Head
ard, Carolyn Andrews
Dept Chprsn & Jrnlsm Tchr
, Jean Chunn
iness Education Teacher
, Leah Newton
ence Teacher
air, Gay C.
, Anatomy & Physiology Tchr
kins, George J., IV
ibusiness Education Teacher
EY
her, Virginia Carol
h Grade Teacher
n, Mary C.
ond Grade Teacher
gieser, Joan Bruner Crysel
Grade English Teacher
Susan Crawford
ne Economics Teacher
n, Hedy Smith
ıth Grade Science Teacher
e, Melvin
sical Science Teacher
eri, Laura Gay
shman English Teacher
en, Les V.
t & Ecomomics Instructor
N CREEK
enter, Aaron Royal
History & Geography Teacher
ness, Marion Junior
ibusiness Teacher
pree, Gus Horton
ence Teacher
EY
s, Brenda Gray
iness Teacher & Counselor
n, Mattie J.
ence & Foreign Lang Tchr
on, Donna Kay
ory Teacher
n, Camille Scott
ligh English Teacher
ITY
n-Hayden, Agness
h Grade Teacher
land, Michelle Houston
ence Teacher & Dept Chair
gin, Donna (Wilson)
hematics Teacher
uart, Mary J.
ondary English Teacher
s, Kimberly Pierce
hematics Teacher
van, Susann James
6th Grd Guidance Counselor
, Paula Aolani
iness Education Teacher
Y
s, Linda Stricklin
h Teacher
es, Cindy Russell
dergarten Teacher
, Shirley Roundtree
ily & Consumer Sci Teacher
nan, Barbara Hawkins
ond Grade Teacher
SSVILLE
n, Katie D.
logy Teacher
e, Nancy Bryant
ence Teacher
, Beth Burroughs
h Grade Teacher
s, Anita Tortorici
enth Grade Mathematics Tchr
ett, Linda Colbert
iness Education Teacher
Karen Sparks
ior Mathematics Teacher
nan, Kirby Fulford
Grade English Teacher
erson, Helen Steele
lish Teacher
ng, Simona L.
& Speech Commnctn Teacher
es, Mary Virignia
oral Director
ko, Amanda Rabb
oral Teacher
n, Helen Reed
Grade English Teacher
ell, Cheryl Perry
ence Teacher
, Kristi Jones
ometry Teacher
CALOOSA
ns, Hilda J.
glish Teacher
way, Beth Cleino
atomy & Physiology Teacher
n, Laurel Litty
glish Teacher
oll, David Eugene
unselor
rn, Charlene Luckie
nebound Teacher
s, Tina Trammell
ondary Mathematics Teacher
r, Althea Harris
dent Services Coordinator
n, Kelley Andress
vernment & Economics Teacher

Haskins, Denise Headrick
English Teacher
Hickman, Stephanie Golden
English & Humanities Teacher
Hyche, Ida Harris
Sociology Teacher
Jarrell, Randall Eugene
Psychology Teacher & Asst Dean
Lindly, Jay K.
Civil Engrng Assoc Professor
Mann, Kathryn Scott
University Band Director
Matthews, John Surele
Seventh Grade Science Teacher
Mc Daniel, Hugh Don
Soc Stud Dept Chair & Teacher
Miller, Ruby Gibbs
Math Dept Chair & Instructor
Myers, Carol Culpepper
Biology Teacher
Nadine, Claudia
French Professor
Newell, Susan Goins
Speech, Drama & Jrnlsm Teacher
Noble, Glee Gillies
Spanish & French Teacher
Poole, Mary Upton
Director
Scheiring, Tammi Renea
Sci & Computer Sci Tchr
Sears, Elizabeth Cobb
English Department Chairman
Sides, Helen Evans (Clements)
Business Education Coordinator
Southern, James Terry
AP Eng IV & III Teacher
Sutton, Kathy Ballard
Band Director
Taylor, James Luther
Assoc Professor of Marketing
Thompson, Mary Jo
Learning Disabilities Teacher
Truhett, David Burnell
History Teacher
Winkler, Charles Wendell
Former Bible Dept Chairman
Young, Clinton William
Physical Education Teacher
TUSCUMBIA
Bracy, Wayne Stephen, Sr.
Teacher & Coach
Hovater, Sharon Mc Williams
Third Grade Teacher
Killen, Jana Leigh
Math & PE Teacher
Mills, Lori Rickman
Healthcare Sci & Tech Teacher
Moore, Jennifer Milner
9th Grade English Teacher
Mullen, Robert G.
Teacher
Oenton, James Ivan
Physical Education Teacher
Perkins, Katie Malone
Second Grade Teacher
Snipes, Terri Chittom
Math Dept Head
Ussery, Linda Deerman
Math Teacher
Vest, Shirley Mc Clure
Second Grade Teacher
White, Joyce Mc Carty
Vocational Business Ed Teacher
TUSKEGEE
Torbert, Thomas E.
Teacher & Coach
TUSKEGEE INST
Biggers, Charles, Sr.
Hlth & Physical Education Tchr
Davis, Cheryl Gardner
Medical Tech Asst Professor
Davis, Clarence
Mathematics Instructor
Dykes, Christiane
Alabama His & World Geog Tchr
Flowers, Chipman Loyd
Senior Army Instructor
Gorham, Sammy Lee
Vet Pathology Assoc Prof
Hargrove, S. Keith
Asst Prof of Mechanical Engrng
Hayes, Stephen L.
Music Instructor
Hooks, Mary Helen
Counselor
Mahfuz, Hassan
Associate Professor
Moore, Ferlisa Beatrice
English Teacher
Patrick, Jennie R.
3M Eminent Scholar
Pearson, Marye Billups
Kindergarten Teacher
Place, Ralphenia Diggs
Asst Dean & Professor
Rackley, Barbara Green
Asst Professor of Chemistry
Roberts, Darryl Lamont
Chair & Associate Professor
Sullen, Janet Thomas
Eng Teacher & Dept Chairperson
Tippett, Fredrick Earl
Assoc Prof of Vtrnry Pathology
Walker, Bertha Yarbrough
Math Teacher & Dept Chprsn
Washington, Ernest
Retired Teacher
Wheeler, Edward Lorenzo
Prof of Religion & Society

UNION GROVE
Ballew, Imalene White
Retired Chem & Math Teacher
Franks, Shannon Renee Ayers
Jr High Mathematics Teacher
UNION SPRINGS
Campbell, Inella Smith
9th Grade Social Studies Tchr
Johnson, Judy Brown
Fourth Grade Teacher
UNIONTOWN
Collins, Mildred
Biology & Chemistry Teacher
URIAH
Gandy Baggett, Vicki
English Teacher
VALLEY
Allen, Deborah Cornelia
English Teacher
Bledsoe, Denise Clanton
4th Grade Teacher
Del Signore, Kay S.
Teacher
Howard, Harmon Ricky
Science Teacher
Hunt, Caralise Weeks
Nursing Instructor
Justice, Sue Dukes
Kindergarten Teacher
Kearley, Jane
Sixth Grade Lang Arts Teacher
Kimberly, Nancy Railey
Second Grade Teacher
Owen, Sherry W.
10th-12th Grade English Tchr
Pike, Donna Aaron
Consumer Science Teacher
VALLEY HEAD
Bell, Charles Ollie
Retired Teacher & Principal
VERNON
Boyette, Brenda Hardy
English Teacher
Cook, Katrina Baccus
English Teacher
Robinson, Vicki Sumrall
Counselor
VINA
Mills, Mary Bishop
HS Home Economics Teacher
VINCENT
Bullock, Michelle Roberts
Science Teacher
Culver, Naamon Leo
Sixth Grd Math & Science Tchr
Mc Kissick, Samuel James
Social Studies Teacher
VINEMONT
Walling, Rodger Dewayne
Special Education Teacher
Wiegand, Melba G.
5th & 6th Grd Reading Teacher
WADLEY
Bryan, Suzanne Carter
Mathematics Instructor
Champion, Lucy Barrow
Instr of Psych Hum Dev & Ethcs
Howell, Randall George
Biology Instructor
Jordan, Joseph W.
Physical Education Instructor
Radford, Ron R.
Athletic Director & Teacher
Roberts, Jean H.
Business Department Chair
Sanders, Ron A.
Physics Professor
Seaman, Rebecca Marie
His, Geog & Leadership Instr
Stone, Karen Aaron
Social Science Instructor
Walker, James Ray
English Instructor
Wilhite, Judy Stallings
Mathematics Instructor
Williams, Olga Mykkanen
Dir of Displaced Homemaker
WALNUT GROVE
Clifton, Brent
Science Teacher
Standridge, Karron Melissa
PE Teacher & Coach
WARRIOR
Bradford, Joseph E.
History Teacher
Garnett, Laura Mc Crary
5th & 6th Grd Lang Arts Tchr
Prantl, Elizabeth Ann
Third Grade Teacher
Wingard, Aimee Baggett
First Grade Teacher
WEAVER
King, Lynette Johnson
Math Department Head
Nunn, Tony
Science Teacher & Coach
Shipp, Frances Ruth
Biology & Physiology Teacher
WEOGUFKA
Mc Ewen, Lisa Dobson
Fifth Grade Teacher
WEST BLOCTON
Williamson, Joan Brewer
English Teacher
WETUMPKA
Guthrie, Miriam Long
English & Psychology Teacher
Jarzyniecki, Linda Maria
Mathematics Teacher

Kerr, Jean Carol
English Teacher
Lodge, Louella M.
Retired Choral & Instrmnt Dir
McDuffie, Christopher G.
Chemistry & Physics Instructor
Pruitt, Linda Keith
PE Teacher & Coach
Williams, Billie Turner
Spanish & German Teacher
WILMER
Bradley, Janet Hynde
2nd Grade Classroom Teacher
Evans, Joanne Butler
Fifth Grade Teacher
WINFIELD
Alexander, Mary Hollis
Second Grade Teacher
Carothers, Rebecca Markham
Fourth Grade Teacher
Hughes, Dorothy Sizemore
Third Grade Teacher
Markham, LaJuana Pate
5th Grade Teacher
Roden, Robin Janice
Counselor & Registrar
Webster, Sandra Tice
PE & Cheerleader Coach
Weeks, Deborah Davis
Business Education Teacher
WOODLAND
Fincher, Robert Herman
Govt, Economics & History Tchr
Perrigin, Barbara Wallace
English Teacher
Wallace, Nancy Blackburn
4th Grade Teacher
WOODVILLE
Hodges, Marion Nelson
Kindergarten Teacher
Nichols, Gillie Gilmore
Sixth Grade Teacher
Reynolds, Wendell Ray
Secondary Social Science Tchr
YORK
Armstrong, Bobby Ray
Spanish Teacher
Bailey, Travis
Agribusiness Teacher
Bonner, Rita Baty
Math Teacher
Cobb, Allison Vick
English & Speech Teacher

ALASKA

ANCHOR POINT
Chesser, Betha Warren
Kindergarten Teacher
VanHooser, Gary Ernest
Fifth Grade Teacher
ANCHORAGE
Allen-Jones, Vara D.
Asst Professor of Counseling
Araji, Sharon Kropp
Professor of Sociology
Augdahl, Jo Ann Marie
5th Grade Teacher
Avila-Lederhos, Karen Joyce
5th-6th Grade Teacher
Baker, Kathleen Daugherty
Anatomy & Biology Teacher
Bassett, Antoinette Marie
Eng Instr of Composition
Bersch, Gretchen T.
Adult & Dev Education Prof
Bowden, Edward Austin, Sr.
6th Grade Teacher
Breeden, Phyllis L. Hess
First Grade Teacher
Brewer, Edward L.
5th-6th Grade Teacher
Browner, Mary Louise
Eighth Grade Soc Studies Tchr
Bruce, Lauren K.
Assoc Prof of Speech Commnctn
Bryner, Scott Morris
English Teacher
Chambers, Reggie I.
HS Mathematics Teacher
Christian, Charles Z.
8th Grade Math Teacher
Congdon, Joann Newton
Adjunct Lecturer of English
Creek, Larry Stephen
Jr Reserve Ofcr Trng Corp Tchr
Curtis, Nancy C.
Coord & Lang Arts & Latin Tchr
Davies, Garry
Assistant Professor of Biology
Davies, M. Hilary
Associate Prof of Math Science
Davis, Donald I., Jr.
Assistant Professor
DeLapp, Tina Davis
Prof & Assoc Dean of Nrsng
De Line, James E.
8th Grd Social Studies Teacher
Derrera, Susan Alexander
English Teacher
Dietrich, Regina Kaye
English Teacher
Dudley, Janie Louise
Choral Music Director
East, Mary Jane
Fourth Grade Teacher
Edgecombe, David P.
Theatre Professor

Egenolf, John Jacob
Associate Professor
Erikson, Christine
Design Professor
Fickey, Brenda Hutcheson
English Professor
Flournoy, Ruth Schumacher
Mathematics Professor
Forster, Suzanne Marie
Visiting Assistant Professor
Fujimura, Marie E.
Elementary Teacher
Gaal, Zoltan, Jr.
Science Teacher & Dept Chair
Giessel, Richard Smith
Math, Sci Teacher & Dept Chair
Goentzel, Marilyn Michalsen
Fourth Grade Teacher
Goodwin, John Thomas
Naval Science Instructor
Hanson, Christine L.
Assoc Prof of Anthropology
Harville, Barbara Ann
Asst Prof of Speech Comm
Hiatt, Patricia Louise Hubert
2nd Grade Teacher
Hill, Robin B.
5th Grade Teacher
Holmberg, Eric George
Associate Prof of Chemistry
Hoover, Jacqueline S.
Social Studies Instructor
Jackson, Linda A.
Photography Teacher
Josey, Leo Alexander, Jr.
Sixth Grade Teacher
Kelley, Laura W.
Professor of Human Service
Kemper, Steve Paul
Chemistry Teacher
Kerns, Kevin James
Music Teacher
Kile, Lynn F., II
Technology & Engr Courses Tchr
Kiley, Deborah Baranek
Assistant Professor of Nursing
Kincade, Darrel Harry
Music Teacher
Kinney, Nancy Jean Walker
Primary Multi-Age Teacher
Koshiyama, Lynn Keiko
Assoc Prof of Accounting
Kreuzenstein, Peggy DeWees
5th Grade Teacher
Kuhner, Arlene E.
Assoc Dean for Acad Prgm
Lampman, Claudia Beth
Asst Professor of Psychology
Lee, Linda Laine
Math & Dev Ed Asst Professor
Linton, Patricia W.
English Professor
Mastroyanis, Sotirios George
Assoc Professor of Education
Matsui, Dorothy Nobuko
5th Grade Teacher
Mc Common, Roger C., Jr.
6th Grade Teacher
Mc Connel, Patrick Vance
Retired 6th Grade Teacher
Mc Cormick, Kenneth Dean
5th Grade Teacher
Mc Coy, Rod
Third Grade Teacher
Muniz, Carolyn Baldwin
Middle School Teacher
Napier, Barbara Miller
Mathematics & Bible Teacher
Nishimura, Caroline Murata
Kindergarten Teacher
Omstead, Debra Lynne
English Tchr & Newspaper Spon
Otter, Michael Reed
Principal
Pajot, Michael E.
Professor of Sociology
Peterson, Darrell Alan
Social Studies Teacher
Petrunic, Maureen (Jaskier)
6th Grade Teacher
Prusak, Patti Jo
Retired Teacher
Purrington, Cecil Nolan
Sixth Grade Teacher
Quimby, Thomas Bartlett (Bart)
Civil Engineering Professor
Reider, Barbara Powell
Accounting Professor
Remus, Emil H.
Prof of Auto & Diesel Tech
Rizzo, Lawrence Arthur
5th-6th Grade Teacher
Rosich, Rosellen Margaret
Psychology Professor
Rubin, Jeri
Assoc Prof of Bus Admin
Sabato, Michael Joseph
Science Teacher
Sant, Christian Chad
Social Studies & Drama Teacher
Schultz, Carolyn Dehoff
Math Teacher
Sellens, Sharon Gail
Bus Partnership Class Teacher
Smith, Lee Ronalie
1st Grade Teacher
Smith, Timothy Charles
Piano Professor
Snow, W. Sterling
Chemistry & Biology Teacher

ANCHORAGE (cont)
Spencer, Rosemarie Holzer
German Teacher
Strid-Chadwick, Karen S.
Associate Professor
Stutzer, Laurel Cuddy
Biology & St Govt Teacher
Thompson, Donald M.
High School Vocation Teacher
Thompson, Lisa Cook
Fifth Grade Teacher
Toole, Wendy
HS Social Studies Teacher
Turnbull, James W.
Eighth Grade Teacher
Ventgen, Pam K.
Medical Assisting Pgm Instr
Waite, Brian
Biology & Chemistry Teacher
Widdicombe, Richard Toby
English Professor
Williams, Roberta Schnipper
Language Arts Teacher
Young, Timothy Jay
English Teacher
Zackery, Cleveland
US History Teacher
Zartmann, Andrew Duane
ESL History & Math Teacher
ANDERSON
Bailey, Norma Poffenberger
Retired Elementary Teacher
Hughes, Sylvia V. (Bahr)
Middle School Generalist
BARROW
Murphy, J. Irene (Bush)
Mathematics Teacher
BETHEL
Gross, Duane Charles
Fifth Grade Teacher
Guffin, Ronald Wreede
Math Teacher
Pollak, Richard Craig
High School Instructor
BIG LAKE
Cash, Kenneth Earl
Mathematics Teacher
Parks, Sarah J.
Home Economics Teacher
CANTWELL
Whittemore, Susan Catherine
K-12th Grade Teacher
CHEVAK
Pingayak, John F.
Biling, Bicultural Coord, Tchr
CHIGNIK
Dunton, Robert Randall
Principal
CORDOVA
Bendzak, Trudy Bodey
Second Grade Teacher
Fulton, Alvin B.
Special Education Teacher
Poor, Sandra Doris
4th Grade Teacher
Shellhorn, Richard
Mathematics Teacher
Trani, Roger Duane
Science Teacher
DELTA JCT
Beito, Howard D.
PE & Health Teacher
Cavanaugh, Brenda Mann
5th Grade Teacher
Cooper, Gary L.
Science Teacher
Dunham, William Franklin
English & History Teacher
Milligan, Ronald
Physical Education Teacher
Morris, Jack R.
Industrial Arts Teacher
Taylor, Robert William
Science Teacher
Taylor, Suzanne Marie Jessen
Art & Journalism Teacher
Ueeck, Debra Lee Hawley
Substitute Teacher
Vander Zwaag, Kathleen DeVries
Speech, Lang Arts & Cmptr Tchr
EAGLE RIVER
Brauneis, Paul C.
Mathematics Instructor
Dennis, Winnettia Faucette
3rd Grade Teacher
Dill, William L.
NJROTC Instructor
Edwards, Carl Stephen
8th Grade Science Teacher
Fullmer, Kevin Boyd
Social Studies Teacher
Gardner, Rhonda M.
English Teacher
Kenney, Joseph E.
Science & Spanish Teacher
Kirk, Kelly D.
Social Studies Teacher
Podvin, Patrick L.
Chemistry Tchr & Sci Dpt Chair
Reekie, Raymond John
Physical Education Instructor
Schroeder, Jon Roland
Language Arts Teacher
Stennette, Anne-Katherine Courtney (Stolpe)
English Teacher
Zimmerman, Lon
Biology Instructor

EIELSON AFB
Hawkins, William Evan
History Teacher
Hilgemann, Carol Lee
High School Art Teacher
ELMENDORF AFB
Bennett-Jackson, Francine E.
English Teacher
Caudle, Trina Colette
Mathematics Teacher
Moser, Robert P.
Chemistry Teacher
Wilson, Joseph Franklin
Biology Teacher
Wright, Glenn Alan
Asst Prin & Stu Svc Adv
FAIRBANKS
Betters, John Henry
Social Studies Teacher
Collins, Jeffry P.
US History & Eng Teacher
Copus, Gary D.
Professor of Justice
DeLeon, Theodore William
PE Dept Chair & Instructor
Ducharme, JoAnn K.
Dir Rural Student Services
Duncan, Rodney Gene
English Teacher
Elam, Naomi Jane
7th Grade Math Teacher
Ford, David A.
Science & English Teacher
Harris, James Charles, Jr.
5th Grade Teacher
Hazel, Kelly Lee
Asst Professor of Psychology
Helmer, Myra Jane Field
3rd Grade Teacher
Hilyard, Joyce Beeson
First Grade Teacher
Hotzfield, John Edward
Principal & Teacher
Kind, William F.
Science Teacher
Knight, Charles Winsett
Associate Prof of Agronomy
Kuehn, Kelsy Lenore
Athletic Trainer
Laursen, Gary
Assoc Prof of Bio & Wildlife
Lynch, Donald Francis
Professor of Geography
Maginnis, Tara Michele
Costume Designer & Asst Prof
Mayer, Patrica
Junior High English Teacher
Mc Kinny, Betty Jean
K-12th Grd Tchr of G & T
Merritt, Carol Joan
Drama, Debate & Compositn Tchr
Nagaoka, Hirofumi
Japanese Language Instructor
Page, Barbara E.
Chemistry Teacher
Pitney, Randall W.
Adjunct Professor & Coach
Puckett, James Paul
Math & Science Teacher
Rudig, Stephanie Scott (Marks)
Gifted & Talented Teacher
Spencer, Susan Lange
Third Grade Teacher
Stone, Theresa Saunders
Music Teacher & Lecturer
Wenstrom, Woody
Mathematics Tchr & Dept Chair
Whitehead, John Simms
History Professor
Wilbanks, Rebecca Anne
Social Studies Teacher
Woodward, Kesler Edward
Art Professor & Dept Chm
HAINES
Maple, Sarah Steil
Second Grade Teacher
HOMER
Beachy, Kathy S. (Klein)
English Teacher
Clayton, Shirley Martine Burdick
Retired Elementary Teacher
Eller, Stan John
Bio & Advanced Sci Teacher
Hagen, Patricia Ann
Sixth Grd & Jr High Sci Tchr
Kirby, Gary E.
6th Grade Teacher
Minogue, Troy Alan
Secondary Math Teacher
Neace, Hal Merwin
8th Grd Earth Science Teacher
Noreen, Raylene Elletha (Moore)
Business & Accounting Prof
Olson, Tashawna L.
Guidance Counselor
JUNEAU
Cecil, Donald Matthews
Associate Professor of English
d'Armand, John Berger
Professor of Music
Hall, Jennings Andy, Jr.
Missionary, Pastor & Teacher
Love, Lesley Clarke
Eighth Grade Teacher
Manning, Thomas William
Art Tchr & Fine Arts Dept Chr
Mathews, Elizabeth A.
Visiting Asst Prof of Bio
Morse, Leslie Scott
History Teacher

Parmelee, Janice M.
Asst Prof of Elem Ed
Zimmerman, Marilyn Sue Sherlock
English Teacher
KALSKAG
Steer, Mark A.
Special Education Teacher
KALTAG
Grammer, Eugenia Alexandrine
Resource Teacher
KASILOF
Chavka, Charles
4th-6th Grade Multiage Teacher
KENAI
Beeson, James A.
Business Teacher
Henderson, Renee Corrine
Music Teacher
Olson, Judy Lynn (Torson)
5th Grade Teacher & Chprsn
Radtke, William H.
Language Arts & Math Teacher
Standefer, Marilyn Jayne
English & Vocational Ed Instr
KETCHIKAN
Barnes, Evvalynn Jean
Special Education Teacher
Bloom, Carolyn A. (Williams)
English Teacher
Fitzgerald, Nicholas Murray
Mathematics Teacher
Marcus, Richard Louis
7th Grade Literature Teacher
Shen, Frieda Tong
Former Math Instructor
Skidmore, Lee M.
Second Grade Teacher
KODIAK
Bane, Gilbert W.
Professor
Linscheid, Eric Kendall
9th Grade Earth Science Tchr
Tollefson, Kaia-Joan Amanda
Principal
Williams, Milo M.
Middle School Teacher
KOTZEBUE
Winter, Wolfgang Kurt
Assistant Principal
KOYUK
Anasogak, Jennifer Counts
Teacher
NINILCHIK
Hilbrink, Joel T.
Vocational Ed & Spanish Tchr
Leman, Dan
Head Coach
Sandoval, Elaine Estes
Science & Health Teacher
NOME
Fuerstenau, Charles Mark
Third Grade Teacher
NORTH POLE
Alonzo, James S.
Aerospace Science Instructor
Dart, John Robert
Natural Resources Tech Tchr
Grabow, Patricia Jean
English & Reading Teacher
Mc Fetridge, Robyn B.
Kindergarten Teacher
Vanasse, Debra Lehmann
Language Arts Teacher
PALMER
Bronson, Judith (Wubben)
Philosophy & English Professor
Brown, Frederic Ray
Reading Specialist
Caswell, Dawn E.
Adjunct Instructor of Math
Christy, Kathryn Elizabeth (Yakley)
1st Grade Teacher
Forstner, Emily Abbott
6th Grd Social Studies Teacher
Hensel, Gloria Pohle
Office Mgmt Tech Instructor
Hoffman, Daniel Louis
Social Studies Teacher
Joehnk, Dewayne Edward
Tchr of Extended Learning Pgm
Jouppi, Scott Lee
8th Grd Soc Stud & Alg Teacher
Nielsen, John Dexter
Bilingual Teacher
Okeson, Alvin S.
Student Advisor
Okeson, Mark V.
English Teacher
Pagaran, Amanda Ruth
8th Grade English Teacher
Pelto, David John Fredrik
Secondary Drama, English Instr
Smith, Joanne Horner
Cheerleader Coach
Strabel, Edward W.
Senior Army Instructor
Tyson, Jeff J.
Physical Education Teacher
Van-Loon, Weston Owen
Professor of Bus Admin
Yaros, Ann Marie
Adjunct Instructor
Zalesky, Lennie Joseph
Russian Teacher
PETERSBURG
Eddy, Jack E., Jr.
Life Science Teacher
Riemer, Sally Fullerton
3rd Grade Teacher

POINT HOPE
Williams, William Eugene
Math & Computer Teacher
SAINT MICHAEL
Erickson, Jeffrey Donald
Secondary Generalist
SAND POINT
DeVault, Tyran James
Math & Science Teacher
SEWARD
Boerger, Charles Frederick
HS History & PE Teacher
Marshall, Daniel L.
Lang Arts & Photography Tchr
Tapsfield, Marvin Dale
Sixth Grade Teacher
SHISHMAREF
Stasenko, Richard Edward
7th-8th Grade Teacher
SITKA
Girardot, Cheryl L.
Mathematics Teacher
Guhl, Marilyn Gibson
First Grade Teacher
Hammons, Gayle L.
English Teacher
Marcello, Joseph Anthony
Chemistry Professor
SKAGWAY
Trozzo, Gary A.
Ed Tech Coordinator
SOLDOTNA
Andrews, John Alden
Leadership Teacher
Boyle, David B.
8th Grade Lang Arts Teacher
Brown, Don Neal
8th Grade Science Teacher
Crawford, Lorraine Sampson
AP US History & Govt Teacher
DeVenney, Jean Elizabeth
Assoc Prof of Counseling
DeVito, Judith Irene
Retired Kindergarten Teacher
Edwards, Beverly Lynn (Kuhlman)
Fifth Grade Teacher
Emery, Blair B.
Kenai Peninsula Extnsn Coord
Freeburg, Gary L.
Associate Professor of Art
Graber, Elizabeth
Prof of Composition
Kiffmeyer, Teresa Adamson
5th Grade Teacher
Petersen, Lance W.
Humanities Assistant Professor
Stanley, Carla (Treese)
Art Teacher & Dept Head
STERLING
McMichael, Sheryl Burlingame
Teacher
TANANA
Henning, Suzanne Lyn
Fifth & Sixth Grade Teacher
THORNE BAY
Hall, Sheryl Lynn
Kindergarten Prgm Coordinator
TOK
Young, Sally
English & Government Teacher
TUNUNAK
Bond, Ward Charles
High School Teacher
UNALAKLEET
Boedeker, Mary Louise
Primary Teacher
VALDEZ
Cunningham, Corinne M.
Secondary English Teacher
Garrison, Larry G.
Reading Specialist
Kubina, Dona Ann
Library Media Specialist
Mackey, Kim
Mathematics Teacher
Neslund, Kenneth A.
Science Teacher
Oster, Carla J.
Office Mgmt Tech Asst Prof
Thurston, Sean Vern
Math Chairperson
Wegner, Rhonda (Remsen)
Art & Health Teacher
WASILLA
Churchill, Linda G.
Science Teacher
Hanel, Kerstin
4th Grade Teacher
Luthi, Brenda S.
Fourth Grade Teacher
Mitchell, Alveta Virginia
Music Teacher
Parker, Bill R.
AP Bio & Hlth Occupations Tchr
Scharf, George William
Elementary Science Teacher

AMERICAN SAMOA

PAGO PAGO
Helsham, Irene Tafao
Program Coordinator & Instr
Jones, Glendell Asbury
Prof of History & Religion
Liufau, Laau Siisii
Mathematics Instructor
Meredith Malala, Regina Antoinette
Fine Arts Professor

Sinavaiana, Caroline Gabbard
Literature Professor
Stephens, Harold A.
Middle School Lang Arts Tchr
Sutherland, James Richard
Spcl Asst to Dean of Stu Svcs

ARIZONA

AJO
Byrnes, John F.
Business Teacher
Grissom, Dixie Pearce
English Teacher
Mc Bride, Orlando Watson
Industrial Arts & Voc Teacher
APACHE JUNCTION
Bodine, Wanda Galloway
Fifth Grade Teacher
Davis, Sherrie Dean
Language Arts Teacher
Greb, Steven P.
Police Sergeant
McMinn, Dawne Michelle
Bio, General & Basic Sci Tchr
Ross, Rickie Elaine Johnson
Home Economics & Choir Teacher
Stephenson, Patricia Jo
Fifth Grade Teacher
ASH FORK
Brown, Debbie S.
Science Teacher
AVONDALE
Ahrens, Darrell John
Aerospace Science Instructor
Buchholtz, Cheryl K.
Resource Teacher of Gifted
Carlson-Spellman, Marilyn Joyce
Staff Development Expert
Cavazos-Gavin, Yolanda Esperanza
Spanish Teacher
Eccles, Thomas Jeffrey
History Teacher
Fisko, Sarah Rose
English Teacher
Holston, Julie Margaret
English & Theater Teacher
Jackson, Marcia Denise
Teacher of Mentally Retarded
Jaeger, Kenneth John
Band Dir & Fine Arts Dept Chrm
Lumm, Cathy Spencer
US His Tchr & Soc Stud Chm
Mertins, Laura Waugh
7th Grade Literature Teacher
Olson, Jody Lynn
HS English Teacher
Paulino, Chris Handell
English & Sociology Teacher
Pederson, Matt W.
Biology Teacher
Smith, David Walter
Bio & Earth Science Teacher
Vaughn, Stephanie A.
English Teacher
Warner, Roger K.
American History & Art Teacher
Yamamoto, Kimberly Ann (Quintana)
English Teacher
Zielinski, Steven John
7th Grade Life Science Teacher
BAGDAD
Mathis, Janet Ann (Brokaw)
Jr HS Science Teacher
Winchester, Richard A.
Sci Teacher & Admin Asst
BENSON
Roseman, Ronny Michael
Diversified Coop Ed Coord
Saunders, Michelle Gangi
First Grade Teacher
BOWIE
Goettl, Shelley Anne
School Counselor
Lewis, Ira David
7th-12th Grd Soc Stud Teacher
BUCKEYE
Boehler, Brenda Jean
Social Studies Teacher
Grosbach, Gloria Jean Norris
2nd Grade Teacher
Grosbach, James Douglas
English Teacher
Napier, Robin Lyn
English Teacher
Sanders, B. Mark
Biology Teacher
Shibe Jones, Dianne Kay
Secondary English Teacher
BULLHEAD CITY
Ayres, Neal O.
Chemistry & AP Biology Tchr
Beatty, Robert H., Jr.
Spanish Teacher
Beck, Russell Dee
CIS Faculty
Kops, David Raymond
Soc Stud, Psych & Geo Teacher
Larson, Linda Selby
Dir of Curriculum, Instruction
Nestrick, Cheri (Royer)
Business Education Teacher
Prather, Dirk Bradford
Business Teacher
Prather, Kathy Lake
Business Education Instructor
Presler, Barbara Jill
High School English Teacher

LHEAD CITY (cont)
oni, Christopher Bruce
sical Education Teacher
y, Jean
h Grade Teacher
Thomas James
Skills Teacher
P VERDE
ter-Marx, John
logy Teacher
tyre, John Thomas
Teacher
ett, Dennis W.
Teacher
A GRANDE
son, William Thomas
hematics Tchr & Consultant
ey, Carol Seaman
lish Teacher & Yrbk Advisor
Ben L.
ational Director
zal, Connie Kay (Schroetlin)
hematics Teacher
n, Susan Kapveiler
ior English Teacher
, Connie J.
hematics Teacher
ers, Patricia Glover
g Dept Chair & English Tchr
wall, Richard William
rumental Music Director
er, Lois Elizabeth
elerated Sr English Teacher
en, Barbara Leonard
lish Teacher
r, Diane Joan
h School Math Teacher
HION
ek, George L.
rumental Music Director
E CREEK
Patricia M.
nselor
ht, Jocelyn Danielson
Lang Dept Chprsn & Tchr
er, Nancy
cipal
NDLER
son, Scott L.
hematics Teacher
Susan Denise
n of Students
er, Rod Philip
cipal
usett, Beverly Smith
red 4th Grade Teacher
am, Jeanne M.
h Instr & Aimes Pgm Dir
el, Camille (Romley)
ociate Superintendent
ey, Julie Goodman
hematics Teacher
h, N. Dennis
Stud, AP His & Ec Tchr
ano, Lynn
ology Teacher
nings, David Willard
t Grade Teacher
nte, Sally Gerchick
Grade Teacher
ney, Laurie Hoffman
Stud Tchr & Dept Chprsn
er, Michael Bryce
n of Students
mann, Richard C.
& TV Production Teacher
, Sharon Odette Keil
lish Instructor
, Dawn Elizabeth
tory Teacher
tly, Gary
unct Professor
, Monica Nadarzynski
mer Teacher
Richard G.
th Grade Teacher
vig, Kevin
ior High PE Teacher
son, Carolyn J. Hanson
dry Orchestra Tchr & Coord
on, Michael Austin
logy & Chemistry Teacher
on, Richard Anthony
vernment & Economics Teacher
on, Sharon Daiss
mentary School Principal
, Ginny Sailor
& 4th Grade Teacher
w, Peggy Jean (Buswell)
mer 6th Grd & Soc Stud Tchr
s, Denise M.
ence Teacher
la, Elaine Dionne
9th Grd Sci & Bio Teacher
r, Marilyn Joan
lish & ESL Instructor
ly, Robyn Dorn
dergarten Teacher
on, Roger Lee
Grade Math Teacher
nson, Denny Ralph
rld History & Geography Tchr
Janice Marie
Grade English Teacher
eiber, James Brian
thematics Teacher
on, William F.
4th Grade Tchr of Gifted
pe, Daniel Glenn
th Grade Teacher

Tinsley, Dawn Marie
Fifth Grade Teacher
Wood, Janet Emery
High School English Teacher
Ybarra, Stephen Andrew
Head Teacher
CHINLE
Francis, Jennifer Lynn
Social Studies Teacher
Hodson, William David
Math Teacher & Curr Specialist
Norvill, Ruth Begaye
Second Grade Teacher
Reents, Carol Snyder
English & Teacher of Gifted
Smith, Sandra Kay
Teacher of Gifted & Math
CHINO VALLEY
Bentley, Larry D.
Social Studies Teacher
Nottelman, Heidi Noelle
Science Teacher
Petaisto, Heikki Olavi
Mathematics Dept Head & Tchr
Ward, Karin Anderson
Span Tchr & Cmptr Technologist
CLIFTON
Mesa, Gilbert Rivera
Jr High Teacher
CONCHO
Detweiler, Keith Paul
6th Grade Teacher
Pannell, Richard Adolphus
4th Grade Teacher
COOLIDGE
Bond, Julie Ann
Professor of Business
Fowler, Beverly Ann
Quest & Social Studies Teacher
Freyermuth, Georgianna Kim
Director of Choral Studies
Schnoor, Chuck Alan
History Teacher
Shelton, Tresban Sherrill
Sixth Grade Tchr of the Gifted
Wickham, Jacqueline Marie
Secondary Mathematics Teacher
COTTONWOOD
Blauert, Virginia H.
4th Grade Teacher
Cunningham, Robert D.
Science Teacher & Dept Head
Pottorff, Debra Hubiak
Former Elementary Teacher
DENNEHOTSO
Lennon, Gloria Paynter
Second Grade Teacher
DEWEY
Lester, Rebecca Ann
Vocal Music Teacher
Schmidt, Debra Wooten
HS Mathematics Teacher
DOUGLAS
Carlson, Craig E.
Counselor
Galindo, Karen Marie
Administrative Assistant
Galliher, Mildred Joanna
Biology Instructor
Meeker, M. David
Music Professor
Shelden, MaryLee Moat
Dev Ed Coord
Tice, Brenda Marshall
Eng Tchr, Drama Dir & Coach
Watkins, George B.
History, Civics Tchr & Coach
DUNCAN
Harlan, Elizabeth E.
Secondary English Teacher
Patrick, Lee Ann
English Teacher
Scranton, Lance
English Teacher
EL MIRAGE
Corrigan, Wendy Cotton
High School Math Teacher
Hilts, Lynn Ann (Ellos)
7th Grade Mathematics Teacher
Poland, Susan B.
Physics Instructor
ELFRIDA
King, Calvin James
Teacher & Coach
ELGIN
Petersen, Douglas Mark
Elementary Principal
ELOY
Jaquez, Marcos
Spanish & Social Stud Teacher
Snurpus, Robert Carson
Fourth Grade Teacher
Sturgell, Barbara Marie (Thies)
8th Grd Lang Arts & Rdng Tchr
Vargo, Lori Artler
Biology Teacher
FLAGSTAFF
Bensusan, Guy
Assoc Professor
Blazquez, Louis Anthony
Math Teacher
Burke, Joseph Jeffery
8th Grade US History Teacher
Campbell, Barbara Frances
Teacher
Carreiro, A. Keith
Educl Foundations Asst Prof
Cotten, Jodi
High School Math Teacher

Cox, Sylvia F.
English Teacher
Dereshiwsky, Mary Irene
Assistant Professor
Gerhart, Karen Margaret
Asst Prof of Asian Humanities
Hannon, Patrick Roy
Exercise Science Professor
Heck, Candice Parson
Third Grade Teacher
Leachman, Lori L.
Economics Professor
Mahmoudi, Kooros M.
Professor of Sociology
Mihesuah, Devon A.
Assoc Prof of Amer Indian His
Morrissey, Steven Charles
Spanish Instructor
Nelson, Paula Guntzel
3rd Grade Teacher
Perry, Elizabeth Fife
Third Grade Teacher
Piper, Sandra Howe
6th Grade Teacher
Raines, Peggy Ann
Assistant Prof of Scndry Ed
Randall, Russell Richard
Special Education Teacher
Sheeley, Thomas F.
Senior Lecturer of Music
Turner, David Michael
6th Grade Teacher
Veteto-Conrad, Marilya Jae
Assistant Professor of German
Williams, Fannie Colley
Seventh Grade English Teacher
Wolf, Deborah Anne
Mathematics Teacher
FORT DEFIANCE
Bryant, Jepp M.
HS Spanish & French Teacher
Cansino, Carlos Espinosa
Spanish Teacher
Chee, Leonard
Social Studies Teacher
Grant, M. Esther Quintana
Alternative Education Tchr
Haynie, Barbara Jane (Tibbs)
Music Teacher
Haynie, Larry Neil
Computer Teacher
Kaulaity, Marlinda White
English Teacher
Steffen, Mary Marie
English Teacher
Williams, Sharyl Haven
Physical Education Teacher
FORT HUACHUCA
Howdeshell, Daniel Thomas
Band Dir & General Music Tchr
FORT MOHAVE
Crow, Whitney I.
Fourth Grade Teacher
FORT THOMAS
Layman, Doris Detwiler
Home Ec, Rdng & Lit Teacher
Luttrall, Dorothy Lorraine Parker
1st & 2nd Grd Teacher
Romero, David Torrio
6th Grade Teacher
FOUNTAIN HILL
David, Kathy Jackson
Art Teacher
Finley, Esta
Transitional First Grd Teacher
Oester, Dawn Embretson
English Teacher
Robinson, Cynthia Lynne
Librarian
Warren, Elizabeth Pence
Choral Director
Winter, Kay A.
Mathematics Dept Chair
GADSDEN
Anglerau, Estelle Matilda
Physical Education Teacher
Camarena, Edilia G.
Junior High ESL Teacher
GANADO
Cansler, Kerry D.
Senior Language Arts Teacher
Erickson, Robert Christ
Reading & Mathematics Teacher
Javadi, Peyman Fani
Language Arts Teacher
Keyonnie, Marie M.
HS Math Teacher
Marshall, Verna Eva
4th Grade Teacher
Povatah, Eldon D.
Jr High School Teacher
Stone, Mary Ann
11th Grd Language Arts Tchr
Woestehoff, Mark E.
Band Director
Yazzie, Merlin Andrew, Sr.
Art Teacher
GILA BEND
Nodlinski, Marsha Louise
US, AZ History & Law Teacher
GILBERT
Areghini, Lavona Beth
Fourth Grade Teacher
Ashley, David
Amer Hist Tchr & Stu Cncl Adv
Bafus, Jody (Brookshier)
Counselor
Bell, Jo Ann
English Teacher

Bell, Patricia J.
11th-12th Grd English Tchr
Bitter, William J.
Orchestra Director
Bracken, James Patrick
World History & Sociology Tchr
Chapman, Jeri Iaquinto
High School Math Teacher
Chomokos, Angela Eve
Mathematics Teacher
Corn, Jeff
Physical Education Teacher
Daley, Douglas Paul
Agriculture Teacher
Davis, David Reed
Honors Chem Instructor
Dillon, Kimberly Elaine
6th Grade Teacher
Duty, Pamela Denise
Assistant Principal
Engle, Marilyn J.
English Second Lang Teacher
Fox, Monty Lee
Indstrl Tech Tchr & Coach
Frontczak, Thomas Anton
Business Teacher
Fults, Jodi Lee
Mathematics Teacher
Gonzalez, Suzanne Marie (Clark)
Eighth Grade Math Teacher
Gordon, Ann Marie
5th Grade Teacher
Hackett, Christine Fisher
Reading Teacher & Specialist
Hamm, David Wesley
Elem Cmptr Resource Specialist
Johnson, Kenneth H.
Agriculture Education Teacher
Jones, Gerlene
Marketing Teacher
Kemmer, Marlin Bruce
Honors English Instructor
Lasch, Lisa M.
Biology Teacher
Lomeli, David Gene
English Teacher
Madril, Lisa Ray
HS Physical Education Teacher
Paes, Bradley Ronald
Sixth Grade Teacher
Perkins, Bruce Wayne
Social Studies Teacher
Phillips, Susan Cannon
Foreign Language Dept Chair
Powell, Dennis Earl
English & Journalism Teacher
Roso, Linna Marie
Dance & Aerobic Teacher
Seacat, Bertella F.
Retired Elementary Teacher
Smock, Judith Campbell
Spanish Teacher
Stone, Dan R.
Mathematics Teacher
Thompson, Barbara Anne
Art & Science Teacher
Uzumeckis, Eduard
Photo Imaging Instructor
Wahlheim, Peter Thomas
Physical Education Teacher
Wheeler, Matthew G.
Mathematics & Science Teacher
Zubeck, Tammy Lynn
Mathematics Teacher
GLENDALE
Anders, William Hal
ROTC Teacher
Apperson, Bonnie
Principal
Atwood, Margaret O'Donnell
Language Arts Teacher
Balthazor, Roberta I.
3rd Grade Teacher
Bates, Bradley Floyd
Coordinator of ESL Services
Baumhover, Cynthia Anne
Global Studies & SOAR Tchr
Bendeson, Bart Gary
English Teacher
Bjorna, Bruce
Band & Chorus Teacher
Black, Patricia Ashley
Vocal & General Music Teacher
Booth, John Anthony
Math Tchr, Dept Chm & Coord
Buck, Patricia Anne
Sixth Grade Teacher
Callahan, Chrlotte Olinger
World History Teacher
Clegg, Irene M.
Language Arts Teacher
Colliat, Marcia D.
French Teacher
Colombo, Sharon Ann (Hallberg)
Physical Education Teacher
Contrata, Robert John
History Teacher
Conzelman, Karen Ann
Professor of Biology
Cooper, Elizabeth Haines
Biology Instructor
Cusick, Nan Elizabeth
Math Dept Chprsn & Tchr
Davenport, Alena Clark
Mathematics Teacher & Dept Chm
Devlin, David Stuart
Biology Teacher
Diaz-Lefebvre, Rene
Professor of Psychology

Ditto, Ruth Ann Murray
8th Grd Science Resource Tchr
Dumitrache, Christina Marie
7th Grd Language Arts Teacher
Eubanks, Debbie Ann
Health Teacher
Eyer, Lorraine Nelson
HS Guidance Counselor
Eyres, Beth K.
Language Arts Teacher
Farris, Marilyn
High School Counselor
Feliz, Edward Frederick, Jr.
Language Arts Instructor
Fischer, David M.
7th Grade Teacher
Flaaen, Jeanne L.
Language Arts Teacher
Flaata, Ann Marie
Language Arts Teacher
Fonseca, Arnie
Strength Fitness Instructor
Frederick, Lorri Ann (Weinberg)
Fifth Grade Teacher
Galligan, Gayle Krebel
Teacher of Gifted & Talented
Gourley, Diane
Music Teacher
Griggs, John W.
Chair of Foreign Languages
Ham, Timothy Alan
Principal
Hannum, Jimmie Jane Reece
SAGE Teacher
Hillis, Richard K.
Studio Arts Professor
Israel, Barbara Anne
7th Grade Teacher
Jagernauth, Saroj
Biology Teacher
Jenkins, Carol Anne
Professor of Sociology
Johnson, Harold Ralph
History Teacher
Joice, Beth Lusk
English Teacher
Jones, Vicki Lee Dahl
Spanish Tchr & Chrldng Coach
Kafouros, Linda Kay
Physical Education Teacher
Kimble, Melanna S.
Spanish Teacher
King, Lorraine C.
US History Teacher
Kleissle, Karyn J.
Biology & Accelerated Sci Tchr
Korpan, Dennis Michael
Math Teacher
Lahman, John R.
Guidance Counselor
Landua, Barbara Kern
Art Teacher
Lawrence, Barbara Frasher
Professor
Lewis, Nancy Pickering
French & Gifted Hum Tchr
Love, Carol Burns
First Grade Teacher
Magee, Donna Jo Reed
First Grade Teacher
Martin, Christine
Mathematics Teacher
Mather, Peter W.
Reading Instructor
Mayberry, Chrissy Kenny
7th Grade Mathematics Teacher
Miller, Joseph D.
Biology Teacher
Moraga, Marta Combel
Professor of English & Spanish
Oesterle, Michael Stephen
Mathematics Teacher
Osbon, Michael Alan
Technology Instructor
Ostrander, Jane Elizabeth
Curriculum Specialist
Ouimette, Renee Lynn
Biology Teacher
Passiatore, Roseann Alonzo
English Teacher
Pfeiff, Joe L.
Journalism & English Teacher
Prado-Ortiz, Sue
Physical Education Teacher
Pruitt, Jody Michelle
Frosh Physical Education Tchr
Pyle, Susanne R.
Mathematics Teacher
Radford, John A.
7th Grade Science Teacher
Ransberger, Marilynn Sue
4th Grade Teacher
Richardson, David Paul
Science Teacher
Rivera, Frank Anthony
Mathematics Instructor
Rivers, Donna Montondo
8th Grade Teacher
Rodriguez, Jane L.
Fifth Grade Teacher
Ross, Barbara Marie
Teacher of the Gifted
Rowe, Jack
English Teacher
Saverno, Cassio Anthony
Teacher & Dept Coordinator
Schneider, Norbert Robert
Social Studies Teacher
Schultz, Christopher John
Math Teacher & Coach

GLENDALE (cont)
Seymour, Margaret A.
English Teacher
Shields, Lonnie Howard
7th Grd Sci & Reading Teacher
Shine, Barbara West
8th Grade Social Studies Tchr
Smith, Lynda Ponce
Spanish Teacher
Smith, Robert William
Honors Chemistry Teacher
Snyder, David Michael
7th Grd History & English Tchr
Talley, Wiley Keith
Biology Teacher
VanDyke, Diane Offer
Mathematics & Leadership Tchr
Van Marche, Deborah
Psychology Professor
Vargas, Cindy Wilder
Spanish Teacher
Waldman, Nan Ridberg
4th Grade Teacher
Weeks, Carol Marie
Eighth Grade Science Teacher
Weintraub, Ann Sidell
Math Teacher
White, Anita Fay
Assistant Principal
Wilimas, JoAnne Kokesch
Consultant & Mtvtnl Speaker
Yonkovich, Mike
World His & Geography Teacher
Zanin, Patrea Sarconi
Calculus Teacher
GLOBE
Alexander, Glenda (Blanco)
Speech & Drama Teacher
Cullen, Steven B.
9th-12th Grade Teacher
Garnett, David
Language Arts Instructor
Yauney, Howard Stephen
Science Teacher
Zeigler, Kenneth William
Chemistry & Physics Instructor
GRAND CANYON
Dodson, Richard Lee
Athletic Director
GREEN VALLEY
Fuer, Jean Davis
8th Grade Teacher
HEREFORD
Miller, David Eugene
Mathematics Teacher
Toresdahl, James Allan
4th Grade Teacher
HOLBROOK
Halvorson, Don Llewellyn
Geology Professor
Kenny, Patrick Henry
Social Studies Dept Chair
Kolakowsky, Nancy Caryl
Math Instructor
Richins, Barry Lane
English Professor & Dept Chair
Schicketanz, Dale E.
Photography Instructor
KAIBITO
John, Lily Chee
Elementary Teacher
KAYENTA
Black, Christine Rose
Business Education Teacher
Forbes-Lucas, Carolyn Beth Adelle
Science Teacher
LaRue, Anne Robinson
Science Teacher
Lehr, Michele Seme
8th Grade Math & Science Tchr
Loschert, Jay Maxwell
World History & Geography Tchr
Rathbun, Velva Joyce
Cnslr
Shewmaker, Joyce A.
Chemistry Teacher
Washburn, Mary L.
Tchr of the Gifted & Talented
KEARNY
Smith, Michael Dennis
Art Educator
KINGMAN
Buckelew, Dorothy J.
Math Teacher
Curran, Kevin Michael
Title 1 Instructor
Hackleu, Sharon Lyn
6th Grade Teacher
Henderson, Shirley
Physical Education Teacher
Jamieson, Alice Carol
Mathematics Teacher
Mc Evers, Richard Arthur
Cmptr Information Systems Fac
Mc Gregor, M. Joy
Registered Nurse Instructor
Reinker, Jill Wolery
Home Economics Teacher
Shults, David Howard
English & Journalism Instr
Thwing, Catherine Gail
English Professor
West, Dave
English Teacher
Yamka, Jim H.
Special Ed & PE Teacher
KYKOTSMOVI VILLAGE
Austgen, Linda M.
Teacher of Gifted & Talented

LAKE HAVASU CITY
Allinson, Stacy Goff
English Teacher
Bishop, Carleine S.
4th Grade Teacher
Cleveringa, Any Jo (Henle)
English & French Teacher
Dalman, Shawn M.
English Teacher
Goodwin, Jan DeGroot
Second Grade Teacher
Mares, Donna L.
Physical Education Teacher
Noble, Larry Dennis
Senior Guidance Counselor
Olsen, Larry Michael
Math Teacher
Painter, Lisa Marie
English & Social Studies Tchr
Reynolds, Raymond Floyd
Science Teacher
Snyder, Margie Lee
Kindergarten Teacher
Tierney, Susan Elizabeth
Lang Arts & Soc Stud Teacher
Wade, Conrad Lee
5th Grade Teacher
Wilson, Leonard Raymond
Soc Studies & Literature Tchr
LAKESIDE
Mundy, Archie B.
Principal
Thompson, Stanley J.
Spanish Teacher & Coach
LAVEEN
Bright, Doris Ann
Second Grade Teacher
LITCHFIELD PARK
Fields, Patricia Hunter
4th Grade Teacher
Herzog, Barbara Christine
Mathematics Instructor
Lock, Jo Ellyn (Bidner)
Fifth Grade Teacher
Nelson, Billie Barbara (Homan)
Second Grade Teacher
MARANA
Russell, Ned
Fifth Grade Classroom Tchr
MESA
Abraham, George
5th Grade Teacher
Anderson, Jeffery Winston
Social Studies Teacher
Andrade, Tiffany (Blanton)
Mathematics Teacher
Basilo, Gary Ronald
5th Grade Teacher
Bennett, Faith C.
Physical Education Teacher
Betts, Robert Davis, II
7th Grade CORE Teacher
Bickel, Meredith Ann
Chorus Director
Bioletto, Janet Craig
Business Teacher
Bjornholt, Ruby Haugen
Junior High Science Teacher
Blomquist, Penny Jane (McLeod)
6th Grade Teacher
Bratspir, Leonard Jerome
Social Studies Teacher
Brittin, Sonya Missal
Orchestra Teacher
Brown, David Curtis
History Teacher
Cartwright, Jacque L.
Sixth Grade Teacher
Castillo, Ron
Teacher
Chanley, Isabel Encinas
3rd Grade LEP Teacher
Christie, Patricia Susan
Jr High English Teacher
Clarke, Loyal Emory, Jr.
Art Teacher
Clemens, Jaime Reedy Olson
Chorus & Spanish Teacher
Coffman, Walt
6th Grade Teacher
Cole, Ronald Edgar
Mathematics Teacher
Colgate-Lindberg, Catharine Pamella
English Teacher
Cottam, Carolyn Mullen
Second Grade Teacher
Davis, Ethel Victoria
English Teacher
Decker, Ross Charles
Mathematics Teacher
De La Torre, George D.
Economics Teacher
Dittmar, Wendy Ann
1st Grade Teacher
Dray, Lynn A.
9th Grd Sci Tchr & Dept Chair
Dunbar, Susie Shaw
Social Studies Teacher
Dunn, Daniel A.
Mathematics Professor
Durrant, Martin H.
Spanish Teacher & Dept Chair
Dutson, Lyn Lyn
Theatre Teacher
Eby, Deborah York
Owner
Ellis, Nancy Lyn
PE Tchr & Study Skills Spclst
Emrick, Keith Eric
Astronomy & Earth Science Tchr

Falk, Jane Carroll
Amer His Literature Teacher
Finical, Jamie Berends
Math Teacher
Fitzgerald, Dolores Jane (Payton)
English Teacher & AP Coord
Frankel, Carole
Mathematics Teacher
Glenn, Wendy Jean
English Teacher
Gold-Foreman, Sherri
Social Studies Chairperson
Good, Lynnette Parks
English Teacher & Dept Chair
Gustafson, Paula L.
Fifth Grade Teacher
Halligan, Lois B.
Bus Dept Chair & COE Coord
Hanna, Thomas Michael
5th Grade Teacher
Hatch, Amy Strawn
Social Studies Teacher & Coach
Hernandez-Hall, Maria Eugenia E.
Spanish Instructor
Holt, Penny Robinett
Mathematics Teacher
Idarraga, Lucia Hurtado
Spanish Teacher
Irby, Thelma Starnes
Adj Professor of Psychology
Isaacs, Beth Ellen
French Teacher
Jacobson, Martha Wolf
English Teacher
Johnson, Josephine R.
5th Grade Teacher
Kasl, Janette Black
United States History Teacher
Kerley, Steve E.
Math Teacher
Livingston, Lori Pew
1st Grade Teacher
Malcolm, Richard Ward
Director of Research & Dev
Martinez, Joseph Anthony
English Teacher
Mc Clure, D. Lance
Sixth Grade Teacher
McCoy, Terrilyn Tovrea
Fourth Grade Teacher
Mc Donnell, Margot Gamash
English Teacher
McDonnell, Rhonda Renee
English Teacher
Mc Williams, Scott J.
Mathematics Teacher
Merlene, Robert Francis
Counseling Department Chairman
Mills, Lorraine
3rd Grade Teacher
Miracle, Joseph Michael
First Grade Teacher
Mohr, Paul Burgette, Jr.
Principal
Morris, Carol Yvonne
5th Grade Teacher
Morton, John Roger
3rd-4th Grade Teacher
Moyer, Deborah J. (Swart)
Theatre Teacher
Neil, Stephen Andrew
Third Grade Teacher
Nelson, Cheryl Cleveland
English Teacher
Palmer, Patricia Ann Breuer
English Teacher
Payne, John Thomas
Mathematics Instructor
Pew, Terry Ann
Third Grade Teacher
Pipes, Elizabeth Janet
Phys Ed Tchr & Teen Counselor
Preisser, Gayla Marie
Psychology Professor
Ramnes, Gerri Ann
Biology Teacher
Rand, Elaine Grace
Sixth Grade Teacher
Raupp, Raymond H.
Soc Stud Tchr & Tennis Coach
Reed, Peter Fulton
Science Teacher
Richardson, Danene Moore
Music Teacher
Risolo, Faith A.
English Teacher
Roederer, Arthur Wayne
String Specialist
Roper, Patricia Dee
Science Teacher
Roth, Cathie Lucille (Mc Shane)
Spanish Teacher
Sampedro, Yvette Y.
High School English Teacher
Schedler, Robert Otto
Social Studies Dept Chprsn
Snow, Pamela Ornelas
Life Management Dept Chair
Steiner, Michael Dean
World History & Geography Tchr
Steinert, Laura Marie
English Tchr
Stewart, Sheila Raye Brown
Family & Consumer Science Tchr
Szafranski, Michael John
Special Education Teacher
Tanner, Ronald David
Math Teacher
Tellef, David Mark
Mathematics Teacher

Tellef, Kathryn B.
Jr HS Choir Director
Temme, Walter Frederick
Orchestra Director
Thurston, Diane Lynn
Sixth Grade Teacher
Tramel, Peggy Lou
Guidance Counselor
Trapnell, Frederick Edward
Counselor
Turley, Gay Lyn
PE Teacher & Coach
Verch, Marlene Sundal
Third Grade Teacher
Viator, Elizabeth A. (Byrnes)
English Teacher
Watters, Maureen
Instructor
Wepfer, Timothy A.
8th Grade Civics Teacher
Weser, John Thomas
Professor of Biology
White, Blaik J.
Lang Lrng Disabilities Tchr
Wiley, Linda Lewis
Sixth Grade Teacher
Wilson, Steven Harley
Theatre & World His Instr
Wolf, Margie Romero
Dance Teacher
Wolfe, Michael Leon
Jr HS Physical Education Tchr
Wolfson, Steve
Biology Instructor
Zarchy, Sue
Head Counselor
MIAMI
Brown, Larry Dean
Commercial Art Instructor
Shannon, Raymond L.
HS Math Teacher
Versaevel, Doug
Math Teacher
MOHAVE VALLEY
Hogue, Geoffrey Douglas
Ceramics & Jewelry Teacher
Mayes, Gail L.
Bio, Anatomy & Physiology Tchr
Noll, Aaron M.
Spanish Teacher
Rosenberger, Tony Dale
English Teacher
Wilcox, Dorn E.
Business Education Teacher
MORENCI
Armbrust, Deborah Grady
Fifth Grade Teacher
Hawkins, Julia Estes
Third Grade Teacher
Washington, John S.
Biology & French Teacher
NOGALES
Becker, Judith Ann
English & ESL Teacher
Jennings, Don Ellwood, Jr.
7th Grade Phys Sci Teacher
Mathis, Barbara Blakely
English Teacher
Myrick, Deuane M.
Science Teacher
Piercy, Susan Kay
English Teacher
Scott, Kathy
English Teacher
ORACLE
Aicher, Moria Ann
PE Teacher & Counselor
PAGE
Buck, Richard K.
Counselor
Schwarz, Jean Marie
7th Grade Social Studies Tchr
Woodard, Sharon Lee
Music Teacher
PARADISE VALLEY
Allison, Rebecca Powelson
English Teacher & Chair
Bradt, Peter F.
Social Studies Teacher
Hatch, Barbara J.
Social Studies Teacher
Hendrickson, Robert J., Sr.
Student Activities Director
Martin, William David
History Department Chairman
PARKER
Fellows, Graham Boyd
Mathematics Teacher
Putz-Artrup, Cynthia Jane
First Grade Teacher
Uden, Sue Anne
Reading Teacher
PATAGONIA
Maiers, Martha Lee
Math Teacher
PAYSON
Frewin, Kyle James
Math Teacher
Ledbetter, Debra Mullins
English & Reading Teacher
Sandoval, Roy Alan
Curriculum Director
Stevens, Wendell L.
Agricultural Ed Teacher
PEORIA
Batty, Brian E.
English Teacher
Burbridge, Kenneth L.
8th Grd Eng, Govt & His Tchr

Burruel, Gus, Jr.
Physical Education Teacher
Deignan, Nanette Ruth
Dance Teacher
Domke, Lynne Handkins
Third Grade Teacher
Eaton, Kim Moody
Psychology Teacher
Faust, Gwen L.
Gen & Vocal Music Tchr
Feller, R. Michael
7th-8th Grade Teacher
Fraley, Waunita Lewis
Math Teacher
George, Casey Edward
8th Grade Teacher
Harlacher, Loretta Fisher
5th Grade Teacher
Hurd Porter, Marilyn Highfill
Language Arts Teacher
Jaeger, Dana Ann (Thomas)
Fourth Grade Teacher
Mc Anally, Margaret Akers
Sixth Grade Teacher
Nielsen, Gloria
Teacher & Journalism Advisor
Penny, David Richard
4th Grade Teacher
Penzone, Jeffrey Scott
US Government History Teacher
Price, Gregory Dean
Adjunct Psychology Professor
Rine, Robert Mark
Science Chairperson & Teacher
Sapp, John Wayne
4th Grade Teacher
Stillman, Randy Dean
Social Studies Teacher
Tiwald, Catherine Gail
Hlth Occupation Ed Tchr & RN
Watkins, William Cecil
School Counselor
Weller, Pam M.
Teacher & Department Head
Wisdom, Cheryl L.
Seventh Grade Teacher
Youngblood, Marian Benton
Math Teacher & Guidance Cnslr
PHOENIX
Adams, Sherry Edmunds
English Professor
Adamson, Thomas Harry
Math Dept Chair & Instructor
Ahrens, Renate A. Guenther
Fourth Grade Teacher
Alexander, Marilyn Tench
7th Grade Language Arts Tchr
Anderson, Nancy L.
Business Teacher & Dept Chprsn
Anderson-Smith, Daphne Oppre
Math Teacher
Antonioli, Frank Charles
English Teacher
Armstrong, Monica Renee-Tumbull
Third Grade Teacher
Aroneo, Regina Marie
English Teacher
Ashegbeyeri, Sonny John
Research & Statistician
Awtrey, Jess W., Jr.
Manuf Metals & Trans Auto Tchr
Baker, Dianne Christine
Sixth Grade Teacher
Baker, Robin Edward
History Professor
Baker, Sandra L.
High School Math Teacher
Baniszewski, Richard M.
Assistant Principal
Barrett, Darrell Gene
English Teacher
Barron, D. M. Delayne
Professor of Elementary Ed
Battle, Anna Ruth
Teacher & Coach
Baugh, James A.
Math Teacher
Bell, Charles Claude
Mathematics & Bible Teacher
Benedict, Deborah Anklam
English Teacher
Bissey, JoAnn C.
Counselor & Department Chair
Bloom, Shelley Diane (Stiles)
First Grade Teacher
Bornscheuer, Kenneth Paul
High School Math Teacher
Bowman, Richard G.
6th Grade Teacher
Boyd, Chris M.
Kindergarten Teacher
Boyer, Marcia Cohen
English Teacher
Brahs, Suellen Kuric
English Teacher & Dept Chair
Brewer, Beverly Kay
Fifth Grade Teacher
Brittain, Tom William
Science & Algebra Teacher
Bromley, Phyllis Jean
Special Education Dept Chprsn
Brouch, Virginia M.
Associate Faculty
Brown, Jay Alan
Bands Director
Bruce, Ann Woodson
American History Teacher
Bruce, Beth Chubbs
Fifth Grade Teacher

ENIX (cont)
ler, Marilyn Hasz
glish Teacher
ring, Al
rth Grade Teacher
amy, Sherry Lee
sic Ed Tchr & Choir Dir
er, Judith Weideman
-8th Grade Music Teacher
n, Samuel James
HS Mathematics Teacher
r, Susan Lyn
glish Teacher
e, Barbara Lee
r of Art & Phtgrphy Dept
Bridget Quinn
h School Band Director
eron, Allan Bruce
mputer Science Teacher
pbell, Wallace Gray
-Operative Education Advisor
son, Veronica Baird
ject Director
, David George
onomics Teacher
e, Barbara Kay
Choral Music Dir
ser, Danny Carlton
th & Computer Science Tchr
k, Claudia Eileen
cial Studies & English Tchr
pton, Kala Jane
) Resource Teacher
ver, Daniel Alan
erature Studies Teacher
ett, Linda Kathleen
glish Teacher
oran, Sara Price
st Grade Teacher
oron, Diane Jordan
tired Teacher
ello, Jennifer Curtis
ology Teacher
o, Suzanne Shourd
cond Grade Teacher
vs, Sharon
e Arts Teacher
iano, Marilyn Jean
mmunication Instructor
ningham, Bonnie Levy
urth Grade Teacher
s, Richard Wallace
m Physical Education Tchr
ney, Darrell Eric
st Principal of Activities
gostino, Diane Marie
cial Studies Teacher
mour, Nancy Lynn
ird Grade Teacher
s, Lew D.
rospace Program Manager
kins, Beth Eakins
st Prof & Math Dept Chrmn
con, Robert W.H.
athematics Teacher
roff, Barbara Tanner
athematics Teacher
Marzo, Mary Patton
glish Teacher
ohue, Stephen Thomas
ofessor of Psychology
nning, Loreto M.
rstn Formation Director
skovich, Valerie Ann
acher of the Gifted
oonson, Julie Graham
u Asst Program Facilitator
ridge, Thomas James
/ Production Teacher
er, Colleen Mohan
High Social Studies Tchr
oian, Deborah Williams
sst Professor of Mathematics
e, Gregory M.
air of Comm & Theatre Arts
alante, Delia
anish Instructor
ns, Rhonda Loats
ecial Needs Consulting Tchr
endaal, Jan Lee
r of Dental Asst Pgm & Prof
nann, Paul Emanuel
ble & Theology Prof
child, Patricia Wiegand
h Grade Teacher
nes, Mindy Lynn
nglish, Biology & Dance Tchr
nglass, Neil I.
ience Teacher
guson, Nancy Joyce
xth Grade Teacher
d, Barbara Elaine Tatham
Grade Teacher
d, Earl Lyle
en & Elem Ed Dept Chairs
bres, Jon Lea
ounseling Faculty
gerald, Eugenia Smith
athematics Professor
cier, Helene Frances
th Grade Honors English Tchr
d, Bonnie Lou
h Grade Teacher
manek, Mary Ann Greiman
etired Elementary Teacher
rest, Robert Steven
omputer Science Teacher
sman, Linda Jennings
h Grade Teacher

Foster, Virginia Ramos
Chair of Foreign Lang Dept
Frament, Kenneth Albert
Professor
Frederick, Betz R.
Assoc Prof of Math Education
Fritsch, Linda Holmes
Kindergarten Teacher
Gaines, Charles W.
Dean Coll of Chrstn Stud
Gallaher, Suzanne Cook
8th Grade Language Arts Instr
Garcia, Irene Alvarez
Business Teacher
Garcia, Richard Gastelum
HS Physical Education Teacher
Garman, Howard
Jr High Sci, Tech & Bible Tchr
Giannopoulos, James William
Middle School Teacher
Gilsenan, Christine Mary
Primary Grade Music Teacher
Goertzen, Todd John
PE & Health Teacher
Golden, Andrea R.
Reading Teacher
Golden, Michael Joe
Technology Teacher
Goldstein, Stuart P.
Speech Communication Teacher
Gonzalez, Teodora Acosta
7th & 8th Grd Soc Studies Tchr
Gorman, Kathy Green
Dance Teacher
Granger, Kathleen Marie
8th Grade Math Teacher
Granger, Mark Ryan
Mathematics Teacher
Gregory, Peggy Doyle
Journalism & English Teacher
Grieder, Debra Jean
Math Teacher
Griego, Karen S.
American & World His Tchr
Griswold, Jeffery Ross
Biology Teacher & Coordinator
Gross, Joe E.
Retired Jr HS Librarian
Grundler, Frank William
Environmental Science Teacher
Guthrie, Glenda Evans
Staff Development Specialist
Gutierrez, Elizabeth Fishbaugh
Math Teacher
Haas, Susan Marie
Math Teacher
Hallock, Lori Susan
PE Teacher & Coach
Hannsberry, Marlene
English Teacher
Hansen, Tracey Stites
Sociology, His & Geog Teacher
Harper, Paul Ellsworth
Assistant Prof of Physics
Hartman, Barbara Bool
Art Teacher
Hassel, Michael C.
7th Grade Literature Teacher
Hazelrigg, Charlotte F.
Curr Specialist & Eng Teacher
Helms, Tom M.
Language Arts Dept Chair
Henderson, Karen S.
Language Arts Chair
Henderson, Louise Regina
Jr High Lang Arts & Rdng Tchr
Hendrix, Adelaide Marie Brown
7th-8th Grd Tchr & Principal
Henry, Lavern Rhymes
8th Grade Math Teacher
Hermann, Vivian Miller
High School Spanish Teacher
Hernandez, Steffannie Weaver
English Teacher
Hetherington, Thomas F.
Physics & Chemistry Teacher
Higgins, Patrick Calvin
Spanish & French Teacher
Hogans, William Raymond
Senior Pastor
Hoganson, James Conrad
5th Grade Elementary Teacher
Holbert, Eunice Allem
English Teacher
Holguin, Lilia Duran
Ret Biling 1st & 2nd Grd Tchr
Holloway, Katie Bryant
10th Grade English Teacher
Holsten, Linda Kay Gamble
Second Grade Teacher
Hopper, Michael Bruce
ROTC Instructor
Horvath, Alexandra
6th Grade Teacher
Hovda, Eugene Lee
Jr & Sr High Teacher
Huard, Donald Vincent
Professor of Psychology
Hubbard, Kelly Anne
Fifth Grade English Teacher
Huber, Jackie L.
High School Math Teacher
Hughes, J. Edmund
Music Professor
Hughes, Robert Edward
5th Grade Teacher
Hunter, Joe B., Jr.
Biology Teacher
Huntington, Maggie
Mathematics Teacher

Hurley, Carol H.
Business Teacher & Dept Coord
Imes, Charles Kevin
Science Teacher
Ingoglia, Evelyn E.
Special Education Teacher
Iriart, Jean Paul
Social Studies Teacher
Jacobson, Helen
German & Russian Teacher
Johnson, Chandra
Third Grade Teacher
Johnson, James Michael
Physical Education Teacher
Johnson, Lora Burson
7th & 8th Grade PE Tchr
Johnson, Margaret Alix
8th Grd Math & Lang Arts Tchr
Johnson, Nancy Ellen
Jr High Teacher
Johnson, Norm
8th Grade Amer Govt Teacher
Jonas, Kathryn Lee (Jones)
English & Journalism Teacher
Jonas, Patricia Lynne (Gallagher)
6th Grade Teacher
Jones, Joanna R.
Assistant Professor
Jordan, Thomas Todd
Bio, Anatomy & Physlgy Instr
Kahler, Kim Kathleen
Physical Education Teacher
Kamradt, Janna Kay
4th Grade Educator
Kanefield, Marilyn Tureen
Kindergarten Teacher
Kayler, Keith William
Industrial Education Instr
Keller, Terry William
Science Department Chairperson
Keough, Douglas Paul
Math Teacher
Kiper, Bruce Clifford
Counselor
Klem, Lois Anne
Reading Specialist
Knoblock, Linda Phillips
Instructor of Commnctn & Hum
Knocke, Kay Woodward
Gifted K-6th Grade Teacher
Kohlhaus-McGill, Pamela Thurman
Social Studies Teacher
Kubala, Mary Anne
Second Grade Teacher
Kumlin, Howard Maurice
Eighth Grade Science Teacher
Laidig, Rebeca S.
Health Occupations Ed Tchr
Lambeth, Marilyn Louise
Family & Consumer Sci Teacher
Lawlor, LeeAnn Aguilar
Assistant Principal
Lawson, Brigit Lane
French Teacher
LeBlanc, Roger Ernest
Scndry Sci Tchr & Coach
Lemon, Barbara Randall
Sixth Grade Teacher
Lemon, Elinor Mae
Fourth Grade Teacher
Lewandowski, Lois Schulz
Home Educator
Lichte, Sherry A. (Simpson)
High School Counselor
Lindebak, Sydney DeShurley
Assistant Principal
Linderman, William Earl
Sixth Grade Teacher
Long, Matthew Kirk
Counselor
Loughrin, Patricia Stieber
Assessment Specialist
Mace, Barbara Jean (Plotts)
Honors Teacher
Maitzen, Dolores A.
Occupational Home Ec Teacher
Mandel, Philip Neil
Creative Writing & Lit Teacher
Maps, Carolynn Pearsall
Special Education Teacher
Marek, Susan
Biology Instructor
Mariahazy, Judith Eva Maria
Photography Teacher
Mass, Ella M. (Brisby)
Health, PE Tchr & Dept Chair
Matte, Nancy LaRue Lightfoot
English Instructor
Maul, Ronald James
Naval Science Instructor
Mc Courtney, Michael Allen
Mathematics Teacher
Mc Cutcheon, Peg Marshall
Coopertive Office Ed Coord
Mc Garter, Charlene Cornelia
8th Grd Reading & Lang Tchr
Mc Gowan, Joelene Love
Teacher
McIntyre, Pat Edwina
Counselor & Instructor
Meibohm-Langille, Carla
Drawing & Painting Instructor
Mena, Victor Manuel
High School Spanish Teacher
Menaugh, Karen Ackermann
7th-8th Grd Pgm Facilitator
Milam, Ann L.
Third Grade Teacher
Miller, Thomasina Spires
Retired 9th-12th Grd Rdng Tchr

Mireles, Jesse Duran
Drafting & CAD Instructor
Mitten, Martha Czepowski
English Teacher
Moline, Leeta Erdman
Latin & English Teacher
Montoya, Jay J.
Physical Education Teacher
Moody, Sheryl Louise
English Teacher
Mooney, Brenda Kano
Fifth Grade Teacher
Moore, David Gerard
English as a Second Lang Tchr
Moore, David Gus
Assistant Principal
Moore, Mary Ellen
Science Teacher
Moore, Sandra Kay
Fourth Grade Teacher
Morgan, Diane W.
English Teacher
Mostofo, Jim R.
Eighth Grade Mathematics Tchr
Mudd, Sandra Williams
Sixth Grade Teacher
Muscato, Linda Marie
Elementary Teacher of Gifted
Naughton, Elizabeth M.
English Teacher
Nelson, Carolyn
7th Grade US History Educator
Noot, Rhonda Lee
Third Grade Teacher
O'Brien, Elizabeth A.
Residential Faculty
Oliveri, Nancy L.
7th Grade Science Teacher
Olson, Keith Ward
Music Specialist
Palacio, Darla Joy
First Grade Teacher
Pallissard, Julie Barger
Fr Intnl Baccalaureate Tchr
Palsma, Mary Jacobson
Mathematics Teacher
Paredes, Maria Luisa
For Lang Dept Chprsn & Tchr
Patterson, William Arthur Abel
Math, Science & History Tchr
Pearson, Harriett Howard
3rd Grd Teacher
Peck, Shirley Ann
American History Teacher
Perez, David Alvin, Sr.
Director of Cadet Programs
Perkins, William F.
World History Teacher
Peterson, Vesta Louise Payne
3rd-6th Grd Teacher of Gifted
Pharr, Kimberly Kay (Rhoden)
Health, PE Teacher & Coach
Phelps, Elaine Peiffer
French Teacher & Dept Chair
Pirrone, Catherine Lynne
Mathematics Teacher & Mentor
Pitts-Miller, Peggy J.
6th Grade Teacher
Pitzer, Diane Miller
Business Education Teacher
Pollack, Todd H.
English Teacher
Price, Christine Alane
English Teacher
Price, William Gregg
ESL Teacher
Rader, William James
Social Studies Educator
Ranney, Scott E.
Prin, Algebra & Geometry Tchr
Rao, Robert Anthony
Physical Education Teacher
Raydl, Christine A.
8th Grade Science Teacher
Reed, Pamela Wiggins
Instructor of Art History
Reed, Timothy A.
Assoc Prof of Youth Ministry
Reichenberger, Marcella Ann
English Teacher
Reichert, Elizabeth Ann (Norton)
Biology Teacher
Relf, Vanessa
School Principal
Ricketts, Roger Dale
8th Grade Math Teacher
Ringhiser, Sheila Goldsberry
Chemistry & Physics Teacher
Rios, Joseph Andrew
Elementary PE Specialist
Rister, Gene A.
Professor of Humanities
Roberts, David Paul
Soc Studies Tchr & Dept Chair
Robinson, Sue
Third Grade Teacher
Rose, Robert Martin
6th Grade Teacher
Rosenthal, Susan Elaine
AP US History Teacher
Rosevear, Esta G.
Theatre Arts Teacher
Roski, Suzanne Monique
English & Drama Teacher
Roth, Richard Wayne, Jr.
Ethics & Family Rltnshps Instr
Rowan, Mary Geraldine
Music Teacher
Rowe, Edward
Professor of Sociology

Rowley, Robert James, II
Electronics Engr Tech Sr Prof
St Clair, Kimberly Jo (Rudge)
High School English Teacher
Saltmarsh, Joy Rector
Former Co-Administrator
Sanchez, David
Emergency Medical Tech Instr
Saylor, Lisa M.
Spanish Teacher
Schinzel, Mary Tynes
English Teacher
Schroeder, Kenneth Arthur
Teacher of Severely Disabled
Schuman, Loren Dennis
Honors Teacher
Schwartz, Nadine Susan
English Teacher
Scofield, Jeffrey Robert
English as Second Lang Tchr
Semmens, John
Economics Professor
Seymour, Cheryl Ann
Fifth Grade Teacher
Shackelford, Osborn Lanell
HPE Educator & Dept Chprsn
Shahan, Gary B.
Social Studies Dept Chair
Sharif, Al'Abiddin Umar
Social & Behavioral Sci Tchr
Sharp, Bruce William
Mathematics Teacher
Shaw, Floria Acklin
Reading Instructor
Sinclair, Todd Michael
Biology Teacher
Slamka, Annabeth Reich
Seventh Grade Reading Teacher
Slavin, Susan Wheeler
ESL Facilitator & Teacher
Smith, Teryl Coleen
Magnet Biology Educator
Smithers, David Michael
Business Teacher
Snyder, Jan David
Biology Teacher
Speer, John C.
Social Studies Teacher
Stoffers, Joyce Hedger
School Guidance Counselor
Stump, Rebecca Williams
1st Grade Teacher
Tennyson, Paul Richard
Med Arts & Biology Instructor
Thogersen, Calvin E.
School Counselor
Thomas, Paula Frances
Second Grade Teacher
Throp, George Lawrence
Mathematics Teacher
Trang, Myron Lee
Professor of Ed
Traw, K. Ann
Fifth Grade Teacher
Treloar, Robert Reno
Dir of Trng HAZMAT Tech
Tucker, Ronald James
Sixth Grade Teacher
Ubrig, Patricia Carol (Caudle)
Music Teacher
Vander Ploeg, Sue
Dean of Students & Ath Dir
Vedock, Marlene Becker
6th Grade Teacher
Vega, Rebecca Ituarte
Reading & Bilingual Teacher
Visco, Carol L. (Giordan)
Third Grade Teacher
Vogt, Andrew Allen
Music Dept Chm & Band Dir
Wadsworth, Monica Melzer
Health Unit Coord & Instructor
Waldo, Adelene W.
Education Therapist
Walker, James Vincent
Attendance Dean & Math Teacher
Washburn, Joseph Lynch
Choir & Guitar Teacher
Weathers, Joyce Angelus (Thompson)
Second Grade Teacher
Weldon, Kimberly June
Professor of Biology
Welty, Michael O.
Chemistry Teacher
Werner, Leo C.
Performing Arts Chm & Band Dir
Werner, Mari L.
English Teacher
Westenberg, Camilla A. H.
English Professor
Whalen, Patrice Marie
Biology Teacher
Whitaker, Covey Lynette
Social Studies Teacher
Willard, Roger Lee
Electronics Technology Prof
Williams, Kime J.
Kindergarten Teacher
Williams, Mark Warren, Sr.
7th Grade Science Teacher
Williams, Rosalind
Sixth Grade Teacher
Wilson, Lori Marie
Sixth Grade Teacher
Wing, David Allan
Professor of Chemistry
Wingfield, Joanne DiCapua
Fourth Grade Teacher
Wood, Patricia Carol (Butler)
8th Grade Science Teacher

PHOENIX (cont)
Yuskis, Nancy Faulkner
Fifth Grade Teacher
Zembruski, Sarah Gustafson
8th Grade Math Teacher
PICACHO
Thompson, James Edward
Language Arts & Reading Tchr
PIMA
Bryce, Phyllis McEuen
First Grade Teacher
PINON
Kiyaani, Lee James
Social Studies Teacher & Coach
PRESCOTT
Beltram, Jody Christian
History Teacher
Bradstreet, Kelli Jo (Alexander)
English Teacher
DaLessio, Ron J.
Social Studies Teacher
Davidson, Georgia Main
Social Studies Teacher
Davis, Deanna Leigh
Fifth Grade Teacher
Dodson, Dawn L.
8th Grade Mathematics Teacher
Ferencak, Andrew John
Assoc Prof Aviation Bus Admin
Frazer, Minnie Ann
Former Teacher
Golden, Barry
Instructor of Biology
Hanson, Ronald Wayne
Science Teacher
Harvey, Debbie Coleman
Director of Development
Hazlehurst, Phylils Swim
4th Grade Teacher
Herring, Pamela Flagle
Professor
Jenkins, John H.
Professor of Mathematics
Kellerman, Dorothy White
Retired Kindergarten Teacher
King, William Arthur
Vocational Education Teacher
LaBelle, Vicki L.
Second Grade Teacher
Larson, James Alan
Professor of Business
Littleton, James Isaac
Physics Teacher
Martinez, Nancy Marie
6th Grd Lang Arts & Math Tchr
Mc Intire, Diane Rebecca
4th Grade Teacher
Mc Intyre, Stephen Scott
Asst Prof of Aerospace Engrng
McMaster, David Kent
Assoc Prof of Aerospace Engrng
Nordbrock, Anita C.
Assoc Prof of Hum & Soc Sci
Nordstrom, Brian Hoyt
Physical Science Professor
Polay, Michael Jed
Aeronautical Sci Assoc Prof
Stimple, Carol Ann Rush
Kindergarten Teacher
Tucker, Cynthia Sue
Sixth Grade Teacher
Walker, Winnetta Dorrean
Social Studies Teacher
QUARTZSITE
Mc Clenning, Steven Lewis
History & Language Arts Tchr
QUEEN CREEK
Gilbert, Linda W.
8th Grade English Teacher
Lechner, Marisol
English Teacher
Robinson, Amy Lynn
Language Arts & Lit Teacher
QUEEN VALLEY
Morgan, Jerold Gibson
Retired Teacher
RED VALLEY
Begay, Betty R.
Teacher of Gifted & Talented
RIMROCK
Clifford, James Alan
Fifth Grade Teacher
Layman, Carl LeRoy
Fourth Grade Teacher
ROCK POINT
Pfeiffer, Tamarah
English Instructor
ROLL
Jorajuria, Elsie Jean Avza
1st Grade Teacher
SAFFORD
Carrier, Rodney Charles
English Teacher
Culver, Allison Leigh Stiles
6th Grade Teacher
Hernandez, Karla Cline
Seventh Grade Teacher
SAHUARITA
Payette, Marlyce J.
ESL Resource Teacher
Polsgrove, Jac
Journalism & Photography Tchr
SAINT DAVID
Crawford, Kathleen Battaglia
HS Counselor & Resource Tchr
Judd, Bary Wade
Art & Commercial Art Teacher
SAINT MICHAELS
Greenstone, Charlotte Anderson
First Grade Teacher
Hazelton, Michael
K-5th Grd Chapter I Math Tchr
SALOME
Scully, Laurie Lyn
Biology & Earth Science Tchr
SAN CARLOS
Crane, Diana G.
High School Math Teacher
Haven, Glenn Claude
PE & Health Teacher
SAN LUIS
King, Joe Lindsay
Science & Math Teacher
SAN MANUEL
Beneitone, Helen Frances
Retired Teacher
Brooks, Linda Gayle
English Teacher
Johnson, G. Kathleen Moore
6th Grade Teacher
Mansager, Jeffery Drew
Fifth Grade Teacher
SAN SIMON
Gray, Carolyn Orr
Art & English Teacher
SANDERS
Blakeslee, Richard Collins
English Teacher & Dept Chair
Kattnig, Maria Rachel Sjolander
Science Teacher
SCOTTSDALE
Albertsen, Kenneth Alan
Mathematics & Physics Teacher
Barber, Steven A.
8th Grade Earth Science Tchr
Biltz, Lynn Elaine
Math Teacher
Bond, Thomas Marlow
Foreign Language Chair
Brandt, Christopher C.
Instr of Chem & Sci Chprsn
Buckles, Barbara J.
Guidance Counselor
Button, C. Leon
Accounting Professor
Camp, Arlene Martha
Chemistry Teacher
Carrick, Deborah V.
Theater Director
Case, Donald E.
Eng & Acad Decathlon Teacher
Chadwick, Kirby Broughton
Spanish Professor
Chesser, Kathryn Elizabeth
Strings Teacher
Chong, Paul Kaleimomi
PE & Health Instructor
Coats, Edwin Wayne
Mathematics Teacher
Cohen, Beatrice (Hecht)
Mathematics Teacher
Dillon, William Patrick
AP Physics & Mathematics Tchr
Durocher, Judith S.
Choral Music Teacher
Ely, Karl Edward
4th Grade Teacher
Engilman, Brent
Science Teacher
Erickson, Carol G.
Principal
Georgoulis, Leslie Sullivan
6th Grade Teacher
Gregory, Katie Lynn
High School Special Ed Teacher
Guardiola, Salvador Alejandro
Industrial Arts Teacher
Hall, Diana Kersey
Counseling Svcs Chairperson
Harris, Annie Byron
Biology Teacher
Hatch, John S., Jr.
Academic Advsr & English Tchr
Haver, Irmgard Henriette
PE Tchr & Dean of Students
Holbrook, Gary R.
Chemistry & Physics Teacher
Homuth, William H.
English Teacher
Hori, Robin
Sci Chair, Chem & Physics Tchr
Huber, Doris Hader
Sixth Grade Teacher
Hull-Ottino, Barbara A.
Fr, Span Tchr & Dept Chprsn
Jacobs, Scott Andrew
HS English & Soc Stud Tchr
Jenson, Carolyn K.
Latin & English Teacher
Kastelic, Robert L.
Research & Development Dir
Keller, Tawana A.
English Teacher
Kumar, Dilip Christopher
Economics Professor
LeVan, Garrett J.
Retired High School Math Tchr
Loveland, Harold Alfred
Science Teacher
Lynch, Wanda Folgert
English Teacher & Peer Evalutr
Mack, Jean Alspach
Second Grade Teacher
Martin, Karen Radigan
Spanish Teacher
Marusich, Mark Christopher
Band Director
McLinn, Kathleen M.
Social Studies Educator
Medeiros, Barbara J.
Spanish Teacher
Meredith, Steven E.
Director of Vocal Music
Milewski, Isabella S.
Spanish Teacher
Miller, Robert W.
Professor of Chemistry
Montieth, Wayne William
Technology & Woods Teacher
Murphy, Rosemary Anne Daley
7th Grd Eng & Honors Eng Tchr
Nimsky-Taylor, Cheryal Baranowski
Instr of Grphc Design, Art His
Patraz, Allen G.
Government & Sociology Teacher
Perl, Linda Suzanne Newman
Social Studies Teacher
Perry, Joyce Fitzwilliam
Social Studies Teacher
Perry, Robert Joseph
Social Science Teacher
Provo, Charles F.
Retired Teacher
Rumney, Rose Kinser
Educl Television Specialist
Samfilippo, Elena
HS Mathematics Teacher
Sawyer, Douglas James
Chemistry Professor
Shaffer, Gary Morris
Anthropology & Archlgy Prof
Simpson, Ruth Wehner
6th Grade Teacher
Smith, Ronald Lee
Chemistry Instructor
Soltero, Raymond Richard
Spanish Teacher
Speciale, Sharon Aylward
Student Advisor
Talarico, Julius B.
Science Teacher
Thompson, Lois Drinkwater
Math Teacher
Thude, Margaret Ann
French, Span Tchr & Dept Chair
Whitmer, David Alan
Spanish Teacher
Williams, Larry L.
Hotel & Restaurant Mgmt Instr
Williamson, Tom E.
US History & Govt Teacher
Wise, Candice Lee
5th Grade Teacher
Woolsey, Anne-Marie (Cehula)
High School Math Teacher
Woolsey, Roger Kent
HS Math & Computer Teacher
Zaccardo, Patricia Eileen
Adjunct Instructor of English
Zarrelli, Judith Rogers
MS Mathematics Teacher
SEDONA
Barrow, Leonard Dale
Athletic Director
SELIGMAN
Paulsen, Sylvia Manriquez
Spanish & Math Teacher
SELLS
Damon, Mariana Simmons
English Teacher
SHOW LOW
Bunch, Eddie Aulton
Business Teacher
Crane, Jeffrey Pratt
His, Eng, Lit & Sci Teacher
Fox, Joan Fisher
6th Grade Teacher
Jackson, Barbara Diehl
4th & 6th Grd Tchr of Gifted
Permar, Al B.
Social Studies Teacher
Permar, Susan Kline
8th Grade Math Teacher
Wasson, Roberta Stephens
English Teacher
SIERRA VISTA
Askew, Thomas Milton
Administrator
Bowden, Michael Todd
Fourth Grade Teacher
Bredel, Linda Graciano
German Teacher
Briles, Marjorie K.
Fifth Grade Teacher
Bustamante, Lydia A.
Retired Teacher
Clark, Renee J.
Drama & English Teacher
Del Vecchio, Karen A.
Drama Dept Coach & Teacher
Greene, Charles Frank
Marketing Education Coord
Gunther, Marguerite Patricia
Fifth Grade Teacher
Hebl, Karen L.
Chemistry & Earth Science Tchr
Henson, William Richard, Jr.
High School JROTC Teacher
Hicks, William Robert
American History Teacher
Jones, Kenley Ellison
Business Instructor
Klein, Jan Marie
Fifth Grade Teacher
Licence, Terry Mc Kean
Retired Teacher
Paul, Socorro Ocano
Counselor
Phillips, Judy Eastin
Third Grade Teacher
Plumb, Paul Daniel
4th Grade Teacher
Roka, Gloria
High School English Instructor
Rothery, Terry Davison
Business Teacher
Runkle, Karl D.
Counselor
Sims, Deanna Webb
English Instructor & Acad Adv
Stickley, David Charles
English & Speech Teacher
Stuart, Kara
English Teacher
Swasey, Barbara Claire Holmes
High School Biology Teacher
Tribe, Virginia Arnold
Reading Teacher
SNOWFLAKE
Beddow, Aleathe Christensen
7th-8th Grade Art Teacher
Crowther, Evelyn N.
Business Education Teacher
Fontes, Robert G.
Sixth Grade Teacher
Kartchner, Richard M.
6th Grade Teacher
Treadway, Margaret Doreen
Special Education Tchr & Cnslr
Weir, Michael Stewart
Computer Teacher
SOMERTON
Bullington, Celia Amaya
5th Grade Teacher
SPRINGERVILLE
Haws, Willis Carl
Biology, Chem & Phys Sci Tchr
Rawlins, Janet Freshwater
Spanish Teacher
Ray, Edith Mc Cuistion
Fourth Grade Teacher
Robb, Maria Dolores
Fifth Grade Teacher
STANFIELD
Farmer, Glenda Culberson
Sixth Grade Math Teacher
SUN CITY
Hobbs, Gordeena Mc Clusky
Retired Teacher
TEEC NOS POS
Brossy, Peter H.
Social Studies Teacher
TEMPE
Adams, David Timothy
English Department Chairman
Arenz, Dorothy A.
HS Social Studies Teacher
Barkdoll, Ivan
Honors Pre Calculus Teacher
Barnard, Annette Williamson-Heinrich
7th & 8th Grade Teacher
Bayley, Bill Gerhardt
Science Teacher
Boles, Julie Gulledge
HS Admin & Activities Director
Browning, Zetta Satterwhite
Special Ed & Physical Ed Tchr
Canku, Clifford Solon
Professor
Capps, Casey William
Physics Teacher
Carlin, Michael A.
Math Teacher
Clement, John A.
Bands Director
Conner, Richard Clay
Linguistics Teaching Assistant
Creighton-Harank, Andrew John
Kindergarten Teacher
Deever, Janet Williams
Spanish Teacher
DeMarco, Bette Jayne
Third Grade Teacher
DiCesare, Margery Eckhart
Journalism & English Teacher
Dunn, Linda
Math Teacher
Edington, Darl Earl
8th Grade Math Teacher
Ellingson, Christine Louise
Family & Consumer Science Tchr
Flanagan, Maryeileen
English & Science Teacher
Fountain, James D.
Dir of Theater & Forensics
Garcia, Norma Carrera
Spanish Teacher
Ginn, Lisa Tillery
Chemistry Teacher
Girard, Vanessa P.
English Teacher & Yearbook Adv
Glazier, Karen LaVerne
Science Teacher
Golonka, Gene, Jr.
Fourth Grade Teacher
Greenwald, Marison Flys
Spanish Teacher
Haas, Kimberly Ann
Fifth Grade Teacher
Harrison, Jill Roush
Spanish Tchr & Dept Chrpsn
Hayhurst, Ronald Lee
Retired Govt, Ec & His Tchr
Haynes, Franklin Wesley
Social Studies Teacher
Hebert, Greg Alan
Choral Music Teacher
Hoffland, Derek Michael
Mathematics Teacher
Hopwood, Brian Keith
Graduate Teaching Assistant
Hoyte, Pearllena Nelson
Elem & Middle School Teacher
Hukill, Mary Riddle (Hallsted)
Substitute Teacher
Humphrey, Robert Joseph, Jr.
Jr High Science Teacher
Jones, Bernard G.
World History & Geography Tchr
Kinney, Cheri Diane
Chemistry & Honors Chem Tchr
Kortman, Sharon Molenaar
Instr of Clssrm Organization
Krause, Jon Daniel
Administrator & History Tchr
Lang, Scott Mc K
Director of Bands
Lentz, Matthew John
World History & Geography Tchr
Matwick, Betty Duarte
PE & Dance Educator
Mc Burney, Timothy Russ
Business Teacher & Ftbl Coach
Miller, Joann M.
Retired Third Grade Teacher
O'Brien, Susan R.
8th Grd Language Arts Teacher
Olsen, Brad
Biology Teacher
Parker, Jane Cave
English Teacher
Saunders, Karen Estelle (Sorgatzt)
Photography Teacher
Scheer, Jeri Lyn
Health Education Teacher
Schrenk, Alana Kay
Math Teacher
Shafer, Constance Kreicher
Spanish Teacher
Stech, Diane J.
8th Grd Honors Science Teacher
Taysom, Wayne H.
Retired 4th & 5th Grd Tchr
Tinker, Deborah Snyder Gentry
Photography Teacher
Walker, Luan Chandler
German Teacher
Wehrman, James William
Physical Education Teacher
White, Katherine Varian
HS Science Teacher
Whitehead, Sharon Suzanne
Math Teacher
Williams, Wayne O.
Physics Teacher
Zinke, Franklin C.
Chemistry Teacher
THATCHER
Cleland, Debbie Welling
First Grade Teacher
Crockett, Michael Keith
English Instructor
Flamm, Joyce
English Instructor
Lunt, David Garth
Dir Chrl Act Tchr & Dept Chair
McBride, Phil Blake
Chemistry Instructor
Nunley, Ida Hamblin
Reading & English Instructor
Shamey, Edward Michael
American Government Teacher
Simmons, Marie Seegmiller
Language & Dramatics Arts Tchr
Smith, Kenneth L.
Counselor
Weber, William Spencer, Jr.
Mathematics Instructor
TOLLESON
Hays, Alice Dawn
English Teacher
Martiny, David R.
Math Teacher
Meyer, Kim Cazier
Science Teacher
Quezada, Ramiro Arevalo, Jr.
World History & Geography Tchr
Wiener, Allison Harris
English Teacher
TONALEA
Dayzie, Lena Manygoats
Lang, Home Ec & Hlth Tchr
TONOPAH
Mc Arthur, Joy Lou
Retired Elementary Teacher
TSAILE
Ami, Carlon Glenn
Physics & Geology Instructor
Clark, Ferlin
Dir of Elementary Teacher Ed
Dawn, Carol Whitewater
Psychology Instructor
Matlock, Marcialea Scott
Instr of Speech, Lit & Tchr Ed
TUBA CITY
Lafaele, Susan Peery
Language Arts Teacher
TUCSON
Abrams, Diane Strzelewicz
Orchestra Dir & Teacher
Adamson, Alice Leeth
Mathematics Professor
Andujo, Emily
Hlth Related Professions Instr
Aquiline, Carin M.
Eng as Second Lang Teacher

SON (cont)
a, Cynthia Pascual
lical & Surgical Nrsng Tchr
nta, Barbara Crowley
hematics Faculty
trong, Neill Ford
nish Teacher
n, Ada Redd
h Grade Teacher
rt-Matz, Theresa Mary
ond Language English Tchr
r, Patricia WaHerscheid
-5th Grade Combination Tchr
tte, Kathleen M.
-5th Grd Multi-Age Teacher
, Robert Paul
chology Professor
s, Shirley Jane
emistry Instructor
nam, Christine Nelson
nish Teacher
op, Alice English
sical Education Teacher
op, Frances Arlene
th Grd Math & Reading Tchr
cher, Susan L. (Anderson)
sic & Chorus Teacher
ne, Virginia Ann
thematics Teacher
s, James N.
American Govt Tchr
and, Nancy Kathryn
glish & Drama Teacher
er, Consolacion Ruiz
ence Teacher
e, David Kendall
fessor of Justice Studies
s, William Kane
turer & Research Associate
m, David Lawrence
sics & Chemistry Teacher
ell, Douglas W.
thematics Dept Chairperson
llo, Elma B.
anish Instructor
ne, Neil Daniel
ctronics Instructor
dler, Megan
ence Teacher & Dept Head
seman, Marcia T.
nce Teacher
stie, Nancy G.
tructor of Psychology
, David Lee
& World History Teacher
ney, Huntley Guelich
glish Teacher
na, Carl
High PE Instructor
d, Julie Larson
th Grade Teacher
, Evelyn Smith
strict Wide Orchestra Tchr
pen, Ann M.
Grade Teacher
vell, Jeanette Williams
th Grade Teacher
vley, Barbara Treumann
n Dir, Dental Assisting Ed
vley, Dennis Marshall
ementary Classroom Tchr
le, Norma Peden
ading, Writing & Jrnlsm Tchr
nga, Bernadette Marie Theresa
High Drama Teacher
ante, Elizabeth Bartholomeaux
nerican History Instructor
ey, John Peter
spitality Ed Prgm Instructor
dson, Arnold C.
iting & Literature Prof
feld, Mic Aspinwall
glish & Writing Teacher
asse, Danny Frank
th Grade Teacher
Rosa, August Ignatius
rospace Science Instructor
bin, Maureen Foley
venth Grade Reading Teacher
ovan, Liane Cunningham
athematics Teacher
n, Jeanine Beevers
unselor
Martha Montiel
ird Grade Teacher
ards, Mary Gerrard
ll Prep Chem & Science Tchr
ns, Nancy
gh School Counselor
Paula
usic Prof & Keyboard Chm
io, Phyllis Balkovitz
ath Teacher
nandez, Rene Perez
cial Studies Teacher
gerald, James Philip, Jr.
glish Teacher
ak, Linda Esther
n Grade Teacher
ger, Joyce Ann
ental Studies Dept Chair
st, Ruth Ellen
nguage Arts Teacher
nco, Sandra Maciell
anish Teacher & Dept Chm
nks, James Alan
ourth Grade Teacher
itzsch, Harold W.
t Instr & Visual Art Coord

Gail-Gordon, Sunny Cramer
Counselor
Galbraith, Lynn
Univ Prof of Art Education
Gallego, Margaret Higuera
Third Grade Teacher
Galvan, Manuel
High School English Teacher
Gardiner, Ken Nasmith
Communications Graphics Tchr
Gentner, Rebecca Dianne
English Teacher
Gerdes, Albert LeRoy
Bldg Constrctn & Drafting Tchr
Gianninoto, Thomas James
Biology & Anatomy Teacher
Gomez, Tony
Journalism & Photo Teacher
Grebenok, Sherry Whitican
HS Mathematics Teacher
Guerra, Anna O'Bannon
Nrsng Fac-Mtrnl Newborn Chair
Hall, Darleen Honea
2nd Grade Teacher
Hansen, John Gregory, Jr.
Clinical Assistant
Harkins, Anita Lucille
English Tchr & Newspaper Adv
Harlos, Paul William
Cnslr & Human Dev Ed Instr
Hatten, Maureen Kelley
Tchr of Emotionally Disabled
Heinemann, Andrew Todd
Math Teacher & Coach
Heintz, James Michael
English Teacher
Hensen, Shandelle Marie
Visiting Asst Prof of Math
Hervert, Margaret Ann
Third Grade Teacher
Hicks, Geraldine Gradillas
English Teacher
Holle, Tim G.
Physical Ed Tchr & Coach
Holman, Sharron Kathryn (Haas)
HS Spanish Teacher
Hooker, Sharon Kay
Specialist of the GATE
Houston, Patricia Roth
Spanish Instructor, Dept Chair
Huxley, Angie Werner
Anatomy & Physiology Professor
Ijams, Kenith Wertman
World Geography & History Tchr
Jagodowski, Theresa Mary
Primary Resource Teacher
Jones, Jennifer (Hill)
French & English Teacher
Kaus, Christopher Michael
Math Teacher
Kenney, Anne Marie
Geog, Eng & Tchr of Gifted
King, Julia A.
Coord of Academic Advising
Konecky, Vicky Ruiz
Social Studies Tchr of Gifted
Kornmuller, David Francisco
7th Grade Science Teacher
Kotofskie, James William
English & Humanities Teacher
Kral, Kenneth E.
Mathematics Department Head
Kwapich, Ronald H.
High School Math Teacher
Lauria, Sue
English & Humanities Teacher
Lester, Judi
Gifted English & Algebra Tchr
Liebert, James W.
Astronomy Professor
Litin, Brad
Chemistry Teacher
Lloyd, Deborah (Panepinto)
Counselor & Adjunct Faculty
Lorimer, Brian Barry
Assistant Principal
Lucas, Jerelene Franklin
Retired Guidance Counselor
Lynn, Nancy Kaufmann
Guidance Counselor
Madden, Jennie Latare
Journalism Teacher
Mahon, Nancy Ellen
Teacher of Gifted
Maldonado, Rene Jesus
English Teacher
Mansouri, W. Darlene
8th Grade Mathematics Teacher
Marietti, Brenda Joyce Cockerham
Economics & Marketing Teacher
Martinez, Karen Fimbres
Fourth Grade Teacher
Mc Claughry, Eva B.
Kindergarten Teacher
Mc Crory, Teresa Louise
Studio Art & AP Art His Tchr
Mc Glamery, Marjorie G.
Second Grade Teacher
Mc Murry, Celia
Counselor
Melton, Philip D.
Art Professor
Miller, Pamela Lee B.
6th Grade Math & Science Tchr
Modica, Robert I., IV
Humanities Professor
Moffitt, Judith Lynn
Math Teacher
Moore, Jennifer Hicks
Second Grade Teacher

Moore, John Ray
Sixth Grade Teacher
Moreno, Julio
Fine Arts Teacher
Mott, Roxie Dolland
Business Teacher & COE Coord
Nelson, Kathryn M.
Senior College Counselor
Nelson, Maggie Nelson
Spanish Teacher
Niefeld, Kristin (Levin)
Mathematics Teacher
Northrop, Dwayne E.
Social Science Teacher
Nuckolls, Linda Wiles
Vocal Music Director
Oden, Sheryl Lea
Dance & Choreography Teacher
Ogden, Kimberly Louise
Asst Prof of Chemical Engrng
Oliver, Leah Holbrook
Athletic Trainer
Oropeza, Marcie Corrao
Specialist of Learning Dsbld
Orosco, Dodie
Marine Biology Teacher
O'Sullivan, Margaret J.
4th Grade Teacher
Parks, Cathryn Mary
English Teacher & Yearbook Adv
Parra, Kathleen Ann
High School Spanish Teacher
Paulos, Kiki Diane
Mathematics Teacher
Perry, Gayle Lynn
4th & 5th Grade Teacher
Phillips, Delbert Darwal
Russian Language Coordinator
Pina, Mario M.
Physical Education Teacher
Pitucco, Anthony P.
Physics Teacher
Pluta, Paula Eunice
Health Educator
Porter, Julie Tracey
World History Teacher
Priest, Quinton Gwynne
History Teacher
Proctor, Carol Shanafelt
8th Grade Math & GATE Teacher
Rees, Jay C.
Assistant Director of Bands
Riddle, Brenda
Art Teacher & Yearbook Advisor
Rinehart, Steven Michael
Language Arts Teacher
Rod, Polly Beauneir
Latin Teacher
Rodriguez, Irma Jean
Dept Chair Office Ed Teacher
Romeo, George Antonio
HS American History Teacher
Roth, William Barry
Chemistry Teacher
Rusciolelli, Jeff C.
Retired US & Wrld His Teacher
Rustici, Joseph Paul
Economics Teacher
St Germaine, Christina Sundlof
Eng & Lang Arts Teacher
Sandoval-Taylor, Patricia Anne
Curr Specialist Biling Ed
Schlumberger, Ann Lewis
Writing Instructor
Schottel, Anna Eileen
Science Teacher
Schrager, Chris
5th Grade Teacher
Schueneman, Christine Graham
MS Teacher & Coach
Schwartz, S. Daniel
Professor of Sociology
Schwarz, Susan Irene
Drama Teacher
Scurran, Jeffrey Alan
PE Teacher & Coach
Sechrest, Annette
Language Arts Teacher
Sechrist, Michael
Teacher
Shackelford, Margot Therese
Social Studies & Spanish Tchr
Shaffer, Mark Sidney
Driver Education Teacher
Shoberg, Nancy M.
Guidance Counselor
Sicilian, Bob
Human Biology Teacher
Slack, Donald Carl
Prof of Ag & Bio Engrng Dept
Sorensen, Kent Dale
Drama Teacher
Sosnicki, Sandra Mac Rury
Kindergarten Teacher
Stallings, Camille
Hosptlty Mgmt & Tourism Instr
Stanton, Charles A.
Religion Teacher & Coach
Steele, Thomas Richard
Special Education Tchr & Coach
Stuewe, Mary T.
Seventh Grade Teacher
Swaim, Donna Elliott
Humanities Professor
Thomas, Jeffrey J.
Classroom Teacher
Thomas-Chaney, Margaret Roxanne
Drama & World History Tchr
Tifft, William Grant
Professor of Astronomy

Todd, James S.
Senior Lecturer & Fac Fellow
Trujillo, Crystal Gussett
Math Teacher & Cheer Coach
Valentine, Randy L.
Life Science Teacher
Vallentine, Roxann Elizabeth
7th Grade Mathematics Teacher
Velo, Kathleen L.
Photography Instructor
Vermillion, Greg J.
K-3rd Grade Resource Teacher
Verthein, Barbara Bays
Biology Tchr & Sci Dept Chprsn
Walk-Hopkins, Christine Marie
Sr Eng Tchr & Lang Dept Chair
Wallace, Carolyn Haatainen
Co-Artistic Director
Walters, Julie
Physical Education Specialist
Weber, Christine Lynne (Harmon)
6th Grd Lang Arts & Rdng Tchr
Wesselmann, Paula Jo
4th Grade Teacher
Whaley, Craig T.
History, Government & Ec Tchr
White, Constance Ruth Haschets
Dean of Studnts & Acad Affairs
White, Teri Riley
School Administration Asst
Williams, Susan Kelley
English Teacher
Wolpa, Brenda Ann
AP & General Chemistry Teacher
Yarick, Gayle V.
Dept Chair, Bio & Chem Tchr
Young, Randy Alan
Third-Sixth Grade Teacher

TUMACACORI
Beaty, James Lee
Retired History & English Tchr

WELLTON
Sivertson, Chad Kenneth
HS Mathematics Teacher
Woodhouse, Blanca Hernandez
First Grade Teacher

WHITERIVER
Lucas, Georgia Abbitt
Lang Arts & Jrnlsm Tchr
Petermann, Ruth E.
3rd & 4th Grade Teacher
Thompson, Blue Judy
Third Grade Teacher

WICKENBURG
Hill, John Matthew
Biology Teacher
Mc Goldrick, Thomas
HS English Teacher

WICKENBURG WEST
Kenrick, Joseph H.
HS Counselor
Rigo, Maureen Ann
Head Teacher

WILLCOX
Owen, Janet C.
Home Economics Teacher

WINDOW ROCK
Egnatuk, MaryAnn
5th Grade Teacher

WINKELMAN
Celaya, Tracey Jo
Business Teacher & Dept Chair
Martinez, Lydia Lopez
Second Grade Teacher

WINSLOW
Fish, Janet M.
Mathematics Teacher
Oliva, Jeanne M.
English Tchr & Newspaper Adv
Smithson, Sarah R.
Head Counselor

YUMA
Armbruster, James H.
Agricultural & Education Instr
Atherton, Kimberly Dawn Owens
Dance Teacher
Auza, Shirley Jean
High School Counselor
Barger, Dennis John
HS Social Studies Teacher
Baumgarner, DeeDee (Ellens)
PE & Aerobics Instructor
Beckman, Jackie Parker
English Teacher
Carlos, Bennie F.
Business Education Teacher
Curtis, Jerrell Mark
ESL & Spanish Teacher
Davis, Denise D.
Biology Teacher
Doering, Laurie Jean
Staff Development Teacher
Dolezal, Nancy Elnore
High School Counselor
Donaldson, Barbara Smith
High School Counselor
Dubiel, Janet M.
Sixth Grade Teacher
Dudley, Marsha Lynn
7th-8th Grade English Teacher
Dyson, Judy Autrey
5th Grade Teacher
Eltrich, Tom E.
HS Drafting & Design Teacher
Ericson, Lynnea C.
Driver Ed & Health Teacher
Ericson, Mark William
Math Teacher
Foerstner, Debbie Anderson
High School Business Teacher

Geis, Margaret Camille
Schlsp, Fin Aid & Tstng Coord
Giss, Gerald Dana
Professor of Theatre
Gomez, Salvador Gomez
6th Grade ESL Teacher
Green, Dorothy
Retired 5th Grade Teacher
Green, Kari Lane
Science Teacher
Haugen, Cheryl Lynn
ESL Teacher
Holland, Mary Ann (Rushin)
Substitute Teacher
Holmes, Michael
Director of Operations
Hoyt, Kathryn Brewer
Retired Teacher
Huyck, Elizabeth Pier
Jr High Physical Ed Tchr
Kongable, Donna Hulley
Grant Facilitator & Writer
Leggett, Karmen Kay
English Teacher
Lofstrom, Dottie M.
Prof of Environmental Tech
Long, Krista M.
Freshman English Teacher
Mc Niel, Karen Green
English Teacher & Stu Cncl Adv
Moody, James Harry
Science Teacher & Coordinator
Murphy, Laura L.
ESL Teacher
Owens, Theodore Deorsea
Coop & OJT Teacher
Pothast, Sheilah-Margaret Theresa
World His & Honors Geog Tchr
Prehoda, Mariejose Cartau
French & ESL Teacher
Psolka, Sheila Wirkus
Staff Development Coordinator
Qualls, Robert Gene
English Teacher
Rendon-Coke, Graciela
Chem & Earth Science Teacher
Reynolds, Jason Wade
English Teacher
Roberts, Gail
Business Teacher
Robinson, Laura Ann
5th Grade Teacher
Rourke, Charles A.
Social Stud Tchr & Dept Chair
Schneider, Tesa Mae
Math Teacher
Sheppard, Colin Max
Mathematics Professor
Siderman, Michele Lynn
Social Studies Teacher
Simmons, Trace J.
Social Studies Teacher
Sivertson, Connie C. Kessler
Math Dept Chprsn & Teacher
Smith, Ann Elizabeth
Earth Sci Teacher
Starkey, Pamela R.
7th & 8th Grade Teacher
Steen, Ranae L. Feyereisn
Staff Development Teacher
Sullivan, Alan P.
8th Grd Social Studies Teacher
Taylor, Michael John
Science Teacher
Wayman, Sherri Sue
Kindergarten Teacher
Westphal, Michael Gerhard
English Department Chairperson
Wooten, Jeffrey Wayne
Math & Cmptr Programming Tchr

ARKANSAS

ALMA
Allain, Jill Witherspoon
Third Grade Teacher
Blanton, Marcella Harrell
Computer Teacher
Davis, Jeremiah Bernard
Retired Lit & Comm Teacher
Gately, Nancy Jane
Kindergarten Teacher
Godwin, Carolyn Ann
Sixth Grade Mathematics Tchr
Graham, Gayle Beth
7th Grade Social Studies Tchr
Hartman, David Alan
Oral Commnctns & Debate Tchr
Love, Scherron Meyer
Science Teacher
Lumpkin, M. Claire
Fifth Grade Reading Teacher
McKuin, Lisa Gaye
Physical Science Teacher
Sweeney, Melissa Jane
Mathematics Teacher
Valentine, Hilda Askins
Title I Supvr & Rdng Lab Tchr
Wilkins, Donna Mounce
4th Grade Teacher
Witherspoon, Paul Brooks
Health Teacher & Coach

ALPENA
Adams, Chris
Vocational Agriculture Teacher
Atchley, Clyde Ray
High School English Teacher

ALPENA (cont)
Finney, Wilma Taylor
Soc Studies Tchr & Dept Chair
Hussey, Joyce Stone
Vocational Business Teacher
Massengale, Wanda L.
3rd & 4th Grade Teacher
Williams, Ronald Lynn
Science Teacher
ALTHEIMER
King, Delores Burkett
Vocational Business Teacher
AMITY
Massey, Janet Marie (Lacefield)
Home Economics Teacher
ARKADELPHIA
Baker, Verna Webb
Dietetic Prgm Asst Prof & Dir
Fuller, Charles Lee
Associate Professor of Music
Good, Glenn E.
Associate Professor of Physics
Halbrook, William Stephen
Band Director
Hamilton, Craig Vernon
Dir of Band & Music Chair
Hamilton, Robert Lewis
Assistant Professor of Physics
Hardee, John R.
Chemistry Professor
Holsclaw, Dennis Scott
Asst Professor of Theatre Arts
Jenkins, Gregory Wayne
Retired Spanish & French Tchr
Jolley, Freddie Johnson
Assoc Prof of Admin Svcs
Jones, Jane Zullo
Mathematics Teacher
Knight, Tim
Bio Dept Chair, Assoc Prof Bio
McCommas, Betty Jo (Rasberry)
Betty Burton Peck Prof of Eng
Morgan, Carol Wasson
College Instructor
Phillips, Eric Stephen
Asst Prof of Theatre Arts
Smith, Jeffrey Mickey
Assistant Football Coach
Sommer, Maralyn Teresa
Assoc Prof of Music & Chair
Stallings, George Ann
Asst Prof of Voc Education
Thomson, David T.
Professor of English
Turner, Nancy J.
Speech Pathology Professor
Viser, William Coke
Assoc Professor of Religion
ARKANSAS CITY
Gasaway, Gwyned Kaye
Kindergarten Teacher
Hooks, Leslie Alvis
High School Principal
Johnson, Terry W.
7th-12th Grd Math & Art Tchr
ARMOREL
Booth, Rhonda Sain
Title I Reading & Math Teacher
ASHDOWN
Bertrand, Beverly Smith
Retired Fifth Grade Teacher
Cauthron, Mary Murphy Coulter
World History Teacher
Crews, Joe Mack
Ag Tech & Life Science Tchr
Lansdell, Mary Louise
Fourth Grade Teacher
Miller, Kay Smith
Second Grade Teacher
ATKINS
Cheek, Alta Luna
Retired English Teacher
Ciesla, Barbara Ann
High School Math Teacher
Clement, William Kerr
Music Supervisor & Band Dir
Gates, Loretta J.
Biology Teacher
Glasgow, Edward Scott
English Teacher
AUGUSTA
Brown, Linda Taggart
7th & 8th Grade Math Teacher
Collier, Garland Ray
6th Grd Self-Contained Teacher
Hall, Lou
Secondary Counselor
Turner, Connie Pridmore
English Teacher
BALD KNOB
Wallace, Judy Bates
Principal
BARLING
Burright, G. Doug
Retired Principal
Faries, Sharon Rogers
Third Grade Teacher
Isaacs, Karol Diane
Principal
Mc Cormick, Mary Rozanne
Sixth Grade Teacher
Russell, Judy Ann (rodgers)
1st Grd Reading Recovery Tchr
Smithson, Roger D.
6th Grade Teacher
BARTON
Apple, Dinah Bridges
Sixth Grade Teacher
Givens, William E.
History Teacher & Coach

BATESVILLE
Bone, Dana
Business Education Teacher
Davis, Janet Brown
Bus Ed Tchr & Stu Cncl Adv
Denison, Fred Vaughn, Jr.
Algebra Tchr & Softball Coach
Engles, Judy Taylor
Science Teacher
Fulcher, John L.
Asst Elementary Principal
Pace, Michelle J.
5th Grade Teacher
Tebbetts, Terrell Louis
Professor of English
Walls, Douglas Ray
Teacher & Coach
West, Kathy Emerson
Math Teacher
Wilson, Martha R.
Spanish & German Teacher
Wright, Mitch W.
Art Teacher
BAUXITE
Bradshaw, Buddy H.
American History Teacher
Davidson, Linda D.
GATE Coordinator & Teacher
Gillis, Judy Milner
Sixth Grade Teacher
Gray, Paula
English Teacher
Wiles, Mike
Social Studies Teacher
BAY
Lowery, Marsha Tillman
Eng & Oral Commnctn Teacher
BEARDEN
Carter, Reece Stephan
7th-8th Grade Science Teacher
Graham, Brenda Childers
Third Grade Teacher
Stoker, Iva Lou
Elem & Middle School Counselor
BEE BRANCH
Sutterfield, Tracy Ragsdale
Business Teacher
BEEBE
Bains, Satinder
Chemistry Assistant Professor
Couch, Ruth Lazelle
Vice Chancellor of Acad Affair
Cox, Mickey Bryant
Band Director
Cunningham, Brenda Ray
Language Arts Teacher
Darnell, James D.
Associate Professor
Davis, Teddy L.
Asst Prof of Social Sciences
Fowlkes, Vickie Ann
5th Grd English Teacher
Leach, Wilene (Wittnebert)
Asst Professor of Mathematics
Methvin, Jennifer Miller
Asst Professor of English
Raber, Jack Richard
Assistant Professor of Ec
Redd, Johnny Lloyd
Assistant Professor of English
Reilly, Thomas James, Jr.
Assistant Professor of History
Riley, Sandra Kaye
Sociology & Psych Instructor
Sandlin, Donald H.
Physical Sci Tchr & Asst Prin
Tiner, Dianne R.
Psychology Professor
Ward, Donald
Social Studies Teacher
White, Pamela Mc Callie
Mathematics Teacher
Wisdom, Ron F.
Algebra I Teacher
Woods, Lugene Ann
Asst Prof of Med Lab Tech
BENTON
Bean, Judith Anna
Science Dept Chair & Teacher
Brown, Michelle Turbyfill
Classroom Teacher
Carson, Noelene J.
Second Grade Teacher
Clay, Patti Derfler
Sixth Grade Teacher
Emmons, Lynda Darlene
Soc Studies & Jrnlsm Teacher
Gattin, Donna Floyd
Math Teacher
Heard, Janice Saffold
Fourth Grade Teacher
Hillman, Richard
Advanced Biology Teacher
Loyd, William Howard
Jr High Band Director
BENTONVILLE
Baggs, Rhonda Gayle
8th & 9th Grd Math Teacher
Gale, Gary Dennis
Band Director
Harper, Lorraine Barbara
10th-12th Grade Art Educator
Hicks, Terry D.
Choral Director
Johnson, Carolyn Dennis
Home Economics Teacher
Karstetter, Beverly Smedley
Biology Teacher
Koelling, Anna Mason
Competitive Speech, Drama Tchr

Marion, Bob G.
Accounting Instructor
Murry, Kathy Mackenzie
Math Teacher & Department Head
Neighbors, Mike E.
HS Biology Teacher & Coach
Owensby, Douglas Leon
9th-12th Grd Bio Chem Teacher
Redfield, Sarah Fields
English Teacher
Sij, James Matthew
Math Teacher
Simpson, Cheryl Payne
7th Grade Life Science Teacher
Southern, Holly L.
English Teacher
Yates, Claude Ervin
Seventh Grade Science Teacher
BERGMAN
Campbell, Vicki Jo
6th Grade Teacher
Fisk, Jim R.
Jr HS Social Studies Teacher
Martin, Deborah Jehnke
Voc Business Education Teacher
Moser, Myrna Purdom
Lang Arts Chair & Eng Tchr
Sharp, Teresia M.
Social Studies Teacher
Troutt, Twana
4th Grade Teacher
BERRYVILLE
Dobbs, Judy Collard
Senior High Eng & Jrnlsm Tchr
Gibson, Derlyne S.
English Teacher
Hagemann, Robbie Ward
Kindergarten Teacher
Roberts, Donald Lee
Superintendent
BIGELOW
Jones, Karen Jean
Chemistry Tchr & Scndry Cnslr
BISMARCK
Copeland, Michael Eugene
Director of Bands
Spradlin, Rebecca Tims
Art Teacher
BLEVINS
Cunningham, Byron Duane
Third Grade Teacher
Steely, Ruth Faulkner
English Teacher
Thurman, Teddy Lynn
Second Grade Teacher
BLYTHEVILLE
Austin, Sharon Edwards
Gifted & Talented English Tchr
Baker, Vicki Lynn
Senior English Teacher
Copeland, Timothy Wayne
Administrator
Flock, Patsy Gann
Sixth Grade Teacher
Harris, Charlie Jean
First Grade Teacher
Herrman, Theodore Arthur
Band Director
Hofmann, Donald Joseph, Jr.
Choir Director
Hubbard, Martha Richardson
Eighth & Ninth Grd Eng Tchr
Johnson, Tobey G.
Physical Sci & Tech Prep Tchr
Keller, Susan Mitchell
Kindergarten Teacher
Kortan, Marvin E.
Mathematics Dept Chairman
Michot, Stephen Scott
Instructor of His & Pol Sci
Ryan, Lynn
Secondary English Teacher
Sanders, Blanche Henderson
English Teacher
Sawyer, Brenda Colleen (Noggle)
Guidance Counselor
Smith, Gregory A.
French Teacher
Smith, Judy Yarbrough
First Grade Teacher
Wright, Larry Gayle
Civics & Journalism Teacher
Young, Gracie Carey
Third Grade Teacher
BOONEVILLE
Farris, Donna Greene
Kindergarten Teacher
Hall, Carolyn Benton
Fourth Grade Teacher
Harris, Rosemary Massey
Coord of the Gifted & Talented
Hosman, Kelly Jean
French Teacher
Miller, Carl Lee
Retired Social Studies Teacher
Rippy, Kenneth Wayne
Contemporary Amer His Tchr
Thomas, Roberta A.
Third Grade Teacher
BRADLEY
Moore, Robert Allen
History & Geography Teacher
BRANCH
Flanagan, Lana Price
Kindergarten Teacher
BRINKLEY
Conyears, Gloria Jackson
Asst High School Principal
Hubble, Judy Ann
Honors Physical Sciences Tchr

Mills, Michael S.
English Teacher
Osborne, Paul R.
High School Science Teacher
BROCKWELL
Dills, Steve Alan
Elem PE Tchr & Coach
Elliott, Sandra Marlene
Business Teacher
Mc Curley, Carolyn Blevins
English & Speech Teacher
BROOKLAND
Johnson, JoAnn French
Biology Teacher
Lenderman, Homer
Agriculture Teacher
Montgomery, Diane E.
Teacher of Gifted & Talented
Roland, Sherry A. (Bece)
Sr HS English Teacher
Stark, Mavis Carole (Johnson)
Kindergarten Teacher
Sturkie, Danny
Sixth Grade Teacher
BRYANT
Antonetti, Susan Byler
High School Band Director
Barnett, Rayanne (Perlingiero)
Spanish Teacher
Dalrymple, Verma Lois
Retired Elementary Teacher
Galbraith, Richard
Mathematics Tchr & Dept Chair
Hubbard, Ron Dale
Technology Teacher
Knight, Terry Lynn
Sixth Grd Social Studies Tchr
Walker, Joan Barker
Fourth Grade Teacher
Westbrook, Danny Ray
Head Cross Country Coach
CABOT
Burks, Rosemary Bird
Speech Pathologist
Crumpton, Stacy Booker
7th Grade English Teacher
Davis, Lynn Canterbury
English Teacher
Donham, Charlie A.
Principal
Ferguson, Paula Ann
French & English Teacher
Garrett, Marsha R.
English Teacher
Gilbert, Deborah F.
Sixth Grade Teacher
Hawkins, Henry Lee
Health Instr & Football Coach
Hirsch, B. J. Brooks
Algebra Teacher
Holmes, Barbara J. (Hill)
Fifth Grade Teacher
Jones, R. Carole
English Teacher
Jordan, Jerry C.
Health Instructor & Coach
Leach, Richard Valette
French & German Teacher
Magdaleno, Peggy Elizabeth Gibbs
Eighth Grade Mathematics Tchr
Melder, Lee
Physical Sci Tchr & Ftbl Coach
Morgan Balgavy, Jane
Forensics & Debate Director
Nash, Donna Jenkins
Seventh Grade Geography Tchr
Nichols, Jon Gilbert
Spanish Teacher
Norris, Glenda Morgan
English Teacher
O'Bryan, Sandy Barnett
English Teacher & Dept Chair
Paul, Diana Redd
Biology & Earth Sci Teacher
Robert, Sandy
High School English Teacher
Rogers, Sharon Duvall
English Teacher
Rogers, Tanna L.
Science Teacher
Speck, Lorna White
Teacher of Gifted & Talented
White, Barbara Lynn
Third Grade Teacher
Yielding, Melanee Kay (Beard)
Sixth Grade Reading Teacher
CALICO ROCK
Beebe, Danny Lee
5th Grade Teacher
Green, Mark Dennis
Jr High English Teacher
Hamby, Joni Cantrell
PE & Health Teacher & Coach
Jenkins, Janie Ducker
Sixth Grade Teacher
Scribner, Annette Cooper
Business Teacher
Shelton, John Franklin
Social Studies Teacher
Thornton, Betty Carolyn
Spanish, History & Eng Tchr
CAMDEN
Barnes, Charles Ray
Assistant Principal
Bever, Mary D.
Secondary Mathematics Teacher
Camp, Beverly Hudgens
English Teacher
Campbell, Earlena Blasdel
3rd Grade Teacher

Hale, Sharon Gilbert
G-T Coordinator
Kirtley, June S.
Advanced English II Teacher
Kirtley, Kenneth L.
Building Trades Instructor
Moore, Linda Wright
Third Grade Classroom Teacher
O'Dell, Betsy Avant
Fourth Grade Teacher
Oglesbee, Lori Ann
Publications Adv & Jrnlsm Tchr
Reddin, Connie Purifoy
Reading Recovery Teacher
Shofner, Karen Kay
English Teacher & Coach
Sindle, Patricia Lynn
Counselor
Taylor, Lorraine Word
4th Grade Teacher
Tolley, Betty Ruby
Foreign Language Teacher
Torrence, Andrea RayShund
English Teacher
Tucker, Ricky A.
Physical Ed Instr & Coach
White, Shirley Williams
Special Education Teacher
Wilson, Carmen Elkins
Fifth Grade Teacher
CARAWAY
Faulkner, Judy Vassar
Kindergarten Teacher
Higginbotham, Terri Eggers
Science Teacher
CARLISLE
Kittler, William H.
8th-9th Grade Science Teacher
Treadway, George Edward
Retired Mathematics Teacher
CARTHAGE
Bradley, Anne Wylie
Retired English Teacher
Claye, Charlene M.
French & Art Instructor
Dean, Ted L.
Business Educator
CAVE CITY
Groves, Carolyn Rae
Kindergarten Teacher
James, Marilyn Elaine
Kindergarten Teacher
Potts, Andrea Tugwell
High School English Teacher
CEDARVILLE
Butler, Paula Kay Shumard
Substitute Teacher
Hightower, Carol Ann O'Roark
Mathematics Teacher
Merrill, Sandra Gritts
Special Ed Resource Tchr
Pendergrass, Linda Jo (Williams)
Gifted & Talented Coordinator
CENTER RIDGE
Allinder, Sally Mc Gee
Jr & Sr High Art & Sci Teacher
Bryant, Bruce W.
English Teacher
Mahan, Sandra Williams
Math & Amer History Teacher
Palmer, Melissa Cox
Kindergarten Teacher
CHARLESTON
Brown, Susan E.
High School Counselor
Edwards, Gloria Aileene
Science Teacher
Efurd, Karren Peacock
Elementary Counselor
Ewing, James Gwen
5th & 6th Comp Literacy Tchr
Gordey, Gregory Lee
Band Choir Director
Stubblefield, Jeff Allen
High School Principal
Wells, Helen Rice
Retired Elem Teacher
CHARLOTTE
Boehm, Kimberly Crosby
English, Spanish & Speech Tchr
Rutledge, Iola (Staggs)
Business Education Teacher
CHEROKEE VILLAGE
Reed, Lois Rhine
Retired 1st Grade Teacher
CHERRY VALLEY
Schweighart, Fred W.
Agriculture Education Teacher
CLARENDON
Boston, Rhonda L.
2nd Grade Teacher
Woodell, Anna Marie Hardin
High School Counselor
CLARKSVILLE
Caldwell, Ronald Dale
Mathematics Teacher
Eakin, William R.
Humanities & Philosophy Prof
Farrell, Nancy S.
Asst Professor of Art
Jeffries, Douglas Lynn
Assistant Professor of Biology
Usery, Gwen Francis
English Teacher
Weathers, Anita Jane
2nd Grade Teacher
Wofford, Robert Lee
SBI Dir, Bus & Ec Assoc Prof

NTON
, Dolores Rachel (Littau)
h Dept Chair & Teacher
Carol Perry
oir Dir & Music Specialist
, Melissa Kaye
: Bus, Eng & Speech Teacher
L HILL
son, Debra R.
2 Music & Choir Teacher
LEGE STATION
e, Elizabeth Jones
ird Grade Teacher
WAY
bery, David Allen
an of Students & Music Instr
man, Cynthia Burnett
rld History & Economics Tchr
ler, Melvin Edwin
sociate Professor
rell, Mary Beth Brown
siness Dept Chairperson
ner, Ruth Ann
gebra I Teacher
oard, Judy Carole
Prof & Sci Dept Head
ver, Linda Sue
gebra I & Geometry Teacher
in, Sarah Fant
ird Grade Teacher
ling, Kimberly Huett
cial Studies Teacher
na, Joan Carter
sociate Professor of Music
gis, Linda A. (Crain)
g Tchr & Drug Prevention Ed
, Judith Owen
structor
ney, Nancy Fesler
Instructor
gston, R. David
oir Director
ett, Teresa Pinter
ird Grade Teacher
on, Sandra Potter
Grade Teacher
hell, Ronald V.
sociate Professor
re, Herff Leo, Jr.
sociate Professor of Mngmt
by, Elizabeth Hunter
ecial Education Teacher
er, Mary V.
glish & Speech Teacher
ny, Nancy Jo
Mathematics Teacher
nlee, Travis
ciology Professor
p, Sharon B.
ench Teacher & Dept Chair
neo, R. Randy
griculture Instr & FFA Adv
ley, Henry Thomas
glish Teacher
key, Terry Gwynn
Grade Math Teacher
r, P. Kathryn
mily Life Skills Teacher
mas, Jesse
ligion Department Chairman
mpson, Louise Black
Grade Teacher
ker, Dorothy Hawkins
etired Teacher
ker, Thomas Matthew
ofessor of Biology
te, Beth Lancaster
ych & Sociology Teacher
RNING
ns, Ronnie
em Physical Education Tchr
ley, Nadi Williams
athematics Teacher
ley, Tara Taylor
ath Teacher
th, Lou Little
story Teacher
deman, Mary Garrett
econd Grade Teacher
son, Lana Hale
nglish Teacher
TTER
therage, Mary Lea (Cranfill)
h & 6th Grd Reading Teacher
OSSETT
xander, Marcia Hollis
iology Teacher
gerald, Saundra E. Perritt
athematics Teacher
odwin, Linda Teague
lementary Principal
sley, Cynthia Jordan
ine Arts Teacher
ite, Rickey Lynn
h & 9th Grade Dean of Stdnts
ite, Ruth N.
enth Grade English Teacher
RDANELLE
llins, Anna Schwegler
ocial Studies Dept Chair
vrock, Eddie Newton
lth Tchr & Head Bsktbl Coach
Curdy, Brenda J.
lgebra & Geometry Teacher
llips, Page Burris
merican History Teacher
QUEEN
le, Cindy Coulter
lementary Principal

Janes, Dale Floyd
Adjunct Safety Professor
Ridlon, Linda Prescott
Special Education Teacher
Wright, Michael Louis
Mathematics Instructor
DE VALLS BLUFF
Holloway, Ramona Carlock
Math Teacher
DE WITT
Bullock, Joan Sallee
English I Teacher
Cover, Linda Place
English & Speech Teacher
Fuller, Beverly A.
Senior Eng & Jounalism Tchr
Inman, Melissa Cockrum
Journalism & World His Instr
Lepine, Joyce Currie
Fourth Grade Teacher
Prange, Naomi Jean Partridge
Med Professions Ed Instructor
DECATUR
Stone-Wright, Irene
Sci Tchr
Treat, Randy R.
Agriculture Education Instr
DELAPLAINE
Stephen, Glenna Clarida
High School Math Teacher
DELIGHT
Deaton, Jeanette Stough
Gifted, Talented & Eng Tchr
Fricks, David S.
Athletic Director & Coach
Kelley, Steve Donald
Social Studies & Spanish Tchr
Kemp, David Wayne
High School Math Teacher
Lee, Billy Ray, Jr.
Vocational Agriculture Teacher
Moorman, Cynthia Marie
English & History Teacher
Osburn, Kimra Griffith
English Teacher
DELL
Caffey, Kay Mapes
High School French Teacher
DERMOTT
Gray, Annette Burchfield
English Teacher
Hamblen, Judy Marie
Language Arts Teacher
DIERKS
Bevill, Marlene Winn
Media Specialist
Bradshaw, Carma Flemens
Fourth Grade Teacher
DODDRIDGE
Peek, Wanda Durham
Third Grade Teacher
DOVER
Christie, Randy David
Science Teacher
Cox, Sheryl C.
Math Teacher
Griffith, Barbara Ford
Sixth Grade Teacher
Karnes, John David
Sci Tchr & Ftbl Head Coach
Pittman, Catherine A.
Sixth Grade Math Teacher
Shatwell, Teresa Harris
Coord of Gifted & Talented Pgm
DUMAS
Brown, Sandra Bennett
Kindergarten Teacher
Burke, Patricia McMahan
Health, PE Teacher & Coach
Hocking, Sharron Lee
Fifth Grade Teacher
Holt, Lorrie Teeter
Bus Tchr & Gymnastics Coach
Jones, Larell Tanner
English Teacher
Porter, Carolyn Kelley
Secondary Social Studies Tchr
Walt, Linda Atkinson
Fourth Grade Mathematics Tchr
EAST CAMDEN
Cook, James Otto
Assistant Professor
Crumpler, Bill
Associate Professor of English
Hargis, Leigh A.
Asst Professor of Electronics
Sutton, Pamela Casey
Assoc Prof of English & Speech
EL DORADO
Badgley, Vicki L.
Instr of Computers & Business
Beasley, Dawn Launius
First Grade Teacher
Choate, Judith Ann
Mathematics Teacher
Edney, Deborah McGehee
Radiologic Tech Pgm Dir
Estill, Donna Rae
English & French Instructor
Helm, Virginia D.
Math Teacher
Johnson, Ben Franklin, III
History Instructor
Johnson, James Charles
Health, PE Teacher & Coach
Johnson, Michael Fitzgerald
Mathematics Instructor
Jones, Karen Curtis
Mathematics Teacher

Nolan, Terri Thompson
9th Grd Social Studies Teacher
Oswalt, Diana L.
Principal
Owen, Betty Frances
Practical Nurse Program Chm
Patterson, Sharon DeWoody
3rd Grade Teacher
Ritz, William James
Athletic Dir & Math Teacher
Rumph, Susan Bettis
Peer Leadership Teacher
Ryan, Janet Norton
Chemistry & Study Skills Instr
Sanders, Karen Keeth
Former 3rd Grd Tchr
Schultz, Becki Cox
English Teacher
Sims, Robert Stanley
Life Science Tchr & Ftbl Coach
Strickland, Judy Evans
English Teacher
Tatom, Melba Reed
LPN Instructor
Tinnin, Mabel Moore
English I Teacher
Tomlinson, Randle
Instructor & Division Chair
ELKINS
Walter, Mark Lyman
Science Teacher
EMERSON
Reeves, Sandra Davis
Second Grade Teacher
ENGLAND
Chaney, Kelly Smith
Science Instructor
Holmes, Harolyn S.
English & Journalism Teacher
EUDORA
Dunbar, Alberta Ross
English & Speech Instructor
Mc Keown, Jo Anne
Science Teacher
White, Delores Ann
Kindergarten Teacher
EVERTON
King, Rebecca
Home Economics Teacher
Urioste, Sharon Malone
HS English & Journalism Tchr
FAIRFIELD BAY
Weis, Lois Hilgendorf
Retired 2nd Grade Teacher
FARMINGTON
Bailey, Sandra Caughman
Title I Reading Teacher
Banks, Emma L.
Counselor
Eckart, DeMerle Emery
Fifth Grade Teacher
Holland, Kaylynn Ross
Bio, Phys Sci & Life Sci Tchr
McCuistion, Tonya Irene
Social Studies Chairman
Smith, Suzanne Leigh
11th Grade English Teacher
Steele, Shelley F.
AP French & English Teacher
FAYETTEVILLE
Byers, Brenda J.
Psychology Instructor
Casto, Debbie Lynn
8th Grade Science Teacher
Childers, Blake Brasel
Speech & Language Pathologist
Clark, S. Lewis, Jr.
Band Director
Cochran, Allan Chester
Prof & Vice Chm of Math Sci
Dillon, Carl Robert
Asst Professor of Ag Economics
Eldinghoff, Sylvan
Assoc Prof of Interior Design
Francis, Ken W.
Principal
Glorfeld, Kristy Dianne
Asst Prof of Cmptr Info Systms
Hassell, Mary Hampton
Teacher
Herman, David Harrison
Ancient & Medieval Civil Tchr
Hollis, Timothy David
Speech & Oral Comm Tchr
Ivey, D. Mack
Microbiology Professor
Johnson, Paula Jeannette (Lisle)
High School Math Teacher
Kral, Timothy Alan
Associate Prof of Microbiology
Lee, Paula Brooks
Physical Science Teacher
Levine, Daniel Blank
Classics Professor
Montgomery, Lyna Lee
Eng Prof & Undergrad Stud Dir
Munson, Gretchen Marie
Cultural Studies Teacher
Nies, Christi Roberts
Jr High English Teacher
Perry, Larry Gail
Math Teacher
Redfern, Betsy Smith
Seventh Grade English Teacher
Reeves, Carol Anne
Associate Professor of Mgmt
Reeves, Diana Gochenour
English Teacher
Smith, Betty J.
Social Studies Teacher

Spencer, George B.
Chemistry Instructor
Stockdell, Richard P.
Journalism Professor
Suter, Tracy A.
Marketing Instructor
Taulman, James F.
Laboratory Instructor
Thoma, Joe John
History Teacher
Tucker, William Frederick
Islamic History Assoc Prof
Weidemann, Rozanne J.
5th & 6th Grade Multi Age Tchr
Wiebe, Albert J.
Fifth Grade Teacher
Williams, Nudie Eugene
Associate Professor of History
Wolfe, Judy Elene
English & Art Teacher
Woods, Randall B.
History Professor
FLIPPIN
Blasdel, Cheryl J.
Art Teacher
Ply, Marilyn Johnson
Life & Earth Science Teacher
FORDYCE
Byrd, Bethel ReJoyce
Home Economics Teacher
Penny, Vicki Taylor
Band Director
Ponder, Auburn Cooley
9th & 10th Grade English Tchr
Totty, Edith Fleming
6th & 8th Grd Soc Stud Tchr
FORREST CITY
Bridgforth, Beth J.
Social Science Instructor
Brown, Claudia Hughes
Guidance Counselor
Guarr, Stephen Fredrick
English Teacher
Johnson, Stan Vernet
Industrial Arts Teacher
Lindsey, Nancy Elizabeth
Drama Teacher
Mc Connon, Lorena Anna
High School English Teacher
Miller, Karen Mc Daniel
Math Teacher
Petty, Veneta LaFluer
History & Civics Teacher
Phillians, Daniel
Choral Director
Shaw, Frank L., III
8th Grade Teacher
Smothers, Carol Odom
English Teacher
FORT SMITH
Besancon, Charles Frank
Physics Teacher
Besancon, Susan Branch
Mathematics Teacher
Bradley, Mitzi Noble
5th Grade Teacher
Bricker, Bret Norman
Biology & Life Science Teacher
Bricker, Carol Jean
Biology Teacher
Buchanan, Thomas M.
Professor of Biology
Bugeja, Linda C. Webb
Science Teacher
Burns, Linda Crovella
Business Education Teacher
Caselman, Bruce D.
Mathematics Professor
Clark, Patricia Molthan
Combination 1st & 2nd Grd Tchr
Clark, Susan Glasson
Instr of Legal Environment, Ec
Dye, Marcia Leah
Career Guidance Specialist
Edwards, Gayla Mc Bride
Teacher
Faught, Barbara J.
Business Instructor
Fisher, Waldo Gearld
Civics Teacher
Flatte, Jodee Jones
English Teacher
Gilkey, Betty Mitchell
Sixth Grade Teacher
Greer, Cynthia Lou
English Teacher
Griffis, Edward Brent
8th Grade Science Teacher
Haines, Susan Mouk
English Teacher
Haupert, Elizabeth Wolferman
Math Instructor & Dept Chair
Hogue, Wesley
Math Teacher
Kennedy, Virginia Lynn
Spanish Teacher
Kilgore, Bob Neil
Band Director
King, Patricia H.
Retired Elementary Teacher
Lawrence, Sara K.
Chemistry Teacher
Loux, Larry D.
Advanced Placement US His Tchr
Mainus, Nolan
Furniture Manufacturing Tchr
Mankin, Merrill G.
Health Teacher & Coach
Manley, William Gordon
Band Director

Martin, Johnny Ray
JROTC Instructor
Martin, Rick
Science Teacher
Mc Mullin, Jan Williams
Health & Study Skills Teacher
Mc Spadden, Malinda Thompson
Director
Mc Swain, Mary Huntley
High School Latin Teacher
Miller, Faye Jacob
ESL Teacher
Mullens, Carrie Sills
Surgical Tech Prgm Dir
Neely, Patricia Ann
5th Grade Teacher
Nelson, Lynda Prather
Coord of Chemistry & Instr
Nguyen, Mai Le
ESL Coordinator
Parks, Brenda Green
Speech & Drama Teacher
Pinkston, Sarah L.
5th Grade Elementary Teacher
Reed, Jeanie (Weldon)
English Teacher
Richard, Ronald Charles
Accounting Instructor
Rogers, Kathryn Hug
Mathematics Teacher
Rush, Linda Lee Stewart
Physics Teacher
Sargent, Jane
Coach & PE Teacher
Sayers, Anne B.
Fifth Grade Teacher
Schultz, Pamela B.
Director of Choral Activities
Shuffield, Sherron Sipes
English Instr & Honors Coord
Smith, Rickey Lynn
PE Teacher & Coach
Steele, Jennifer Wamock
Director of Bands
Taylor, C. Joyce
Fifth & Sixth Grade Teacher
Thellman, John A.
Orchestra Instructor
Thomas, Ron R.
Visual Arts Instructor
Timmons, Rebecca Jo
Business & Computer Instructor
Turner, Susan Yvette
Journalism Teacher
Turpin, W. Winston, Jr.
Choral Director
Walker, Duane
Band Director
Watlington, Pamela Robertson
6th Grade Teacher
Watts, Lonnie Lee, Jr.
Soc & Behavioral Sci Chair
Weakley, Denise Jean (Veroni)
HS Soph & Jr English Teacher
Weigand, Larry Hugh
Mathematics Instructor
West, Blanche Jolly
Third Grade Teacher
Wewers, Mary Ruth
Fourth Grade Teacher
Young, Catherine Owen
Jr HS Health & PE Teacher
FOUKE
Clark, Aneta Janet
Retired 5th-6th Grade Teacher
Cockman, Cara DeAnn
Voc Business Education Teacher
FOUNTAIN HILL
Harris, Sherry Mc Cain
Business Education Teacher
Sparks, Claudie Cruce
Social Studies Teacher
FOX
Thomas, Pamela Risner
Fifth Grade Teacher
GENTRY
Burton, Stephen Winfred
Fifth Grade Teacher
Cole, Samuel Eugene
Retired Teacher
Goodlett-Davis, Judieth Lee
8th Grade Math Teacher
Hill, Betty Mundy
Language Arts & Math Tchr
Holm, Jan Schilling
Math Teacher
Jackson, Jennifer Jill
High School Resource Teacher
Shelby, David Wesley
Social Studies Teacher
Wilson, Joni Denise
Business Teacher
GLENWOOD
Bolding, Tonja Geurin
Voc Home Economics Teacher
Driggers, Frankye Jo Towry
5th & 6th Grade Teacher
Leslie, Brenda Owens
Algebra & Geometry Teacher
Prince, Susan Nichols
Spanish Teacher
Smothers, Penny Jones
Second Grade Teacher
GOSNELL
Crigger, Kerri Keen
Sixth Grade Teacher
Mauney, Mona Kim
7th-8th Grd Science Teacher
Needham, Kwajalein Green
Resource Teacher

GOSNELL (cont)
Smith, Jana Lee
PE & Life Science Teacher
GOULD
Lang, Earnestine Hendricks
6th Grd Tchr & Principal
GRAVETTE
Almond, Harry D.
Vocational Business Ed Tchr
Hall, Gordon Thomas
High School Science Teacher
Mc Garrah, Darla G.
HS Counselor
Savage, Patricia Ford
7th Grade Math Teacher
Vick, Ben
Speech & Drama Teacher
GREEN FOREST
Christenberry, Tammy Stephens
English Teacher
King, Paddy J.
4th Grade Teacher
Masters, Michael Wayne
American Literature Teacher
Weidrick, Nancy Yost
Sixth Grade Teacher
GREENBRIER
Baker, Susan Fraser
Home Economics Instructor
Newland, Karen Ann
Kindergarten Teacher
Pearce, Kathy Purtfoy
Fifth Grade Teacher
Robinette, Cindy King
Chemistry & Biology Teacher
Spurrier, Virginia Garrett
Business Teacher
Young, Susan (Frets)
Eng, Speech & Drama Teacher
GREENLAND
Beckmann, Joneva Wiladine (Lovell)
Mathematics Instructor
Brawner, Linda Houser
Science Teacher
Brown, M. Rosanne
Jr & Sr HS Drama Teacher
Silkwood, Gloria Mc Kamie
English Teacher
White, Lynne Chotard
Spanish Teacher
GREENWOOD
Clements, Leslie Newman
Computer Technology Instructor
Cullen, Judy Hosier
9th Grade Media & 8th Grd Tchr
Efurd, Carolyn Graham
Fourth Grade Teacher
Fox, Carl C.
Geometry Teacher
Hill, Montgomery Kemp
Director of Bands
Jones, Mary Alice Gann
Fifth Grade Teacher
Loyd, Jay Alan
Math Teacher & Coach
Mc Donald, Allen C.
Advanced Biological Stud Tchr
Peacock, Martina Prock
Health, PE Chprsn & Tchr
GREERS FERRY
Anderson, Adrienne Lea
Life Science Teacher
Hutto, Debbie Stone
Eng, Jrnlsm, Hlth & PE Tchr
Rickert, Frederick Joseph
Math & Physics Teacher
GURDON
Beck, Mary Schoonover
Mathematics Teacher
GUY
Ward, Sullen Glover
Voc Family & Consumer Sci Tchr
HACKETT
Boyd, Cathy Dees
Counselor
Brennan, Jacquelyn
English IV & Spanish Teacher
Farris, Nancy Guthrie
Advanced Placement Eng Instr
Linker, Cindy S.
English Teacher
Pelham, Gail Naomi
Fifth Grade Teacher
HAMBURG
Myers, Arthur Glenn
Coach & Teacher
Streeter, Tammy Kinnaird
Eighth Grd Earth Science Tchr
HAMPTON
Bethea, Regina Thomason
Mathematics Teacher
Bethea, Virgil Floyd
Mathematics Teacher
Gill, Sheila Ann
English & Journalism Instr
Harton, Kim Dorrough
1st Grade Teacher
Hicks, Lora Hill
5th & 6th Grade Lang Arts Tchr
Jeffers, Evelyn Byrd
Gifted & Talented Teacher
HARDY
Sellars, Carol Elizabeth
English Teacher
Strobbe, Deanna King
5th Grade Math Teacher
HARRISBURG
Faulkner, Vicki Shaver
Sixth Grade Teacher
Murphy, Kathy Walls
Third Grade Teacher
Williams, Kathryn Hall
Fourth Grade Teacher
Williams, M. Jo Wimpy
Retired Teacher
HARRISON
Beard, Dianne Tipton
Spanish Teacher
Fish, Helen Vancuren
Chemistry Teacher
Penquite, Judith Lucero
Fifth Grade Teacher
Terrill, Marty Chadwick
Director of Honors
HATFIELD
Christensen, Riley E.
Science Teacher
Denton, Larry Dill
Social Studies Teacher
HATTIEVILLE
Benson, Brenda Denise
Kindergarten Teacher
HAZEN
Carlyle, Debbie Lynn
History Teacher
Gammill, Durinda Gordon
English & Speech Teacher
HEBER SPRINGS
Courtney, Kathleen Jo Anne
Health & Physical Ed Teacher
Lee, Jean Ann Fielder
Algebra I & Math Teacher
HELENA
Fielder, Frederick
Printing Instructor
Harper, Carolyn Carpenter
Community College Instructor
Lynn, Georgia Dilley
Computer Technology Instructor
Simes, Edelma Glover
Division of Arts & Sci Chm
HERMITAGE
Dorrough, Rebecca
History & Science Teacher
Greenwood, Joe Don
Agriculture Education Instr
Wardlaw, Carla Harrod
Sixth Grade Teacher
HOLLY GROVE
Johnson, Fannie M.
Vocational Business Instructor
Latham, Carlee
Computer Lab Teacher
HOPE
Alexander, Judy Wilson
2nd Grade Teacher
Banister, Janet Newell
8th Grd Language Teacher
Easterling, Jeri Mc Elhannon
Reading & Language Arts Tchr
Freeman, Thomas Bruce
Social Science Instructor
Mc Adams, Donald Willard
Bus Dept Chm & Acctng Instr
Oliver, Ann Anderson
Mathematics Professor
Pennington, Patricia King
Nursing Instructor
Purtle, J. Carroll
High School Principal
Radelmiller, Thomas B.
Business Education Instructor
Seel, Aaron Douglas
Head of Percussion Studies
Tullis, Regina Smith
Fifth Grade Teacher
Woodruff, Donna Whitmarsh
Gifted & Talented Coordinator
HORATIO
Hudgeons, Cynthia Lee
Social Studies Teacher
HOT SPRINGS
Bates, Zandra Gayle
Second Grade Teacher
Bush, Michael Wayne
Associate Naval Science Instr
Caldwell, Sharon Ann Stephens
Kindergarten Teacher
Compton, Kay Vandiver
Jr-Sr English Teacher
Driggers, Jo Nell
Mathematics Teacher
Freeman, Melissa Meredith (Austin)
Music Teacher
Holt, Julie Ann
Fifth Grade Teacher
Hunter, Carolyn Frances
Chemistry Instructor
Hutchison, Donna McAnulty
Humanities Instructor
Lambert, Dana Maureen
Dir of Chemistry & Biology
Longinotti, Patricia Lee
Third Grade Teacher
Lyublinskaya, Irina
Director & AP Physics Teacher
Martin, David P.
Chemistry Teacher
Meggers, Gregory D.
US History History & Coach
Nichols, Melanie Walker
Mathematics Director
Penney, Betsy Alice
English Teacher
Schman, Marie Trapp
Mathematics Teacher
Segrest, Gary Walker
Athletic Director
Simmons, David Lyle
Geog & Social Studies Chair
Smalley, Patricia Barnes
Second Grade Teacher
Stanley, Peggy Grayson
GATE Coord & Science Teacher
Tripp, Debbie Arndt
Math Teacher
Walker, Suzanne Schweer
9th-12th Grd Business Teacher
Wilborn, Jay W.
MLT-AD Program Director
HOT SPRINGS NATIONAL PARK
Capaci, Cynthia Diane
Upper Elementary Teacher
HOXIE
Foley, Mary Ann Gardner
Fifth Grade Teacher
Jones, Lana F.
Facilitator of GATE
Mace, Bonard Vincent, Jr.
Jr HS Mathematics Teacher
Mullen, Geraldine Moser
Math Teacher
Pierce, Scotty Shane
Physical Science Teacher
Truxler, Dennis Charles
Social Studies Teacher
HUGHES
Allen, Betty Rea
Math Teacher & Dept Chair
Culver, Ann Frances
2nd Grade Teacher
Jones, Jack G.
Asst Principal
HUMPHREY
Coleman, Leona
Sixth Grade Teacher
Crossland, Lillie A.
K-12th Grade Counselor
Starks, Burnestine Wilson
Social Studies Teacher
HUNTSVILLE
Holmesley, Joey B.
Mathematics Instructor
Shinn, Harry F.
Math & Computer Science Tchr
Terry, James Westzel
Fifth Grade Teacher
HUTTIG
Mc Adams, Kathy Elkins
Sixth Grade Teacher
IMBODEN
Johnson, David H.
Director of Music
JACKSONVILLE
Coleman, Sarah Jane
English & Yearbook Teacher
Dismuke, N. Karen
Band Director
Ferrell, Nola Jahna
Sixth Grade Teacher
Geiger, Robert Dean
Mathematics Teacher
Ghegan, Ann Douciere
Retired Elementary Teacher
Matthews, Barbara Ann (Schnarr)
Second Grade Classroom Teacher
McCune, Glenda L.
HS Art Teacher
McPherson, Joy Jones
Sixth Grade Teacher
Saliba, Sara J.
Speech & Theatre Tchr
Shea, Donna Anne (Hamilton)
Fourth Grade Teacher
Smith, Jeannie Linaker
Kindergarten Teacher
Wells, Peggy Huffman
Third Grade Teacher
JASPER
Moore, Paula Renee
Spanish Instructor & Counselor
Rutledge, Margie Lea
Library Media Specialist
JESSIEVILLE
Bennett, Jan Hornsby
Kindergarten Teacher
Bremer, Janis Knipmeyer
English Teacher
Levine, Paula F.
English Dept Chairperson
Rolfe, Beth Ann Goggin
Art Teacher
Travers, Cheryl (Dunn)
Counselor
JONESBORO
Burgess, Fran Munford
Business Teacher
Carlisle, Pam G.
6th Grade Teacher
Clampit, Brenda Joyce
Computer Lab Teacher
Cline, Jackie S.
Mathematics Teacher
Dellinger, Thomas Willard
Math Teacher
De Ment, Vickie Ann
Civics Teacher
DeVazier, James Albert, Jr.
Astronomy & Bio Tchr & Coach
Duncan, Carol Harrington
Second Grade Teacher
Ewing, Danny Lynn
Social Studies Teacher
Ewing, Sherry Bryant
Mathematics Teacher
George, Norma Jean
Third Grade Teacher
Glenn, Joyce (Cockrell)
Family & Consumer Sci Teacher
Gossett, Parthy
Retired English Teacher
Griffin, Richard Owen
Social Studies Teacher
Johns Spence, Elizabeth Debbie
5th Grd Self Contained Teacher
Leath, Vera (Wallis)
Business Education Teacher
Morris, Gary E.
Choral Activities Director
Neely, Stephanie Broadaway
Mathematics Teacher
Ramsey, Mack Yates
Math Teacher
Rollins, William Stephen
Band Director
Ryals, Jane Ingraham
Third Grade Teacher
Spencer, Debbie West
6th Grade Science Teacher
JUDSONIA
Layrock, Susan Miller
Second Grade Teacher
Lowery, James Wilson
Retired HS Mathematics Tchr
Williams, Becky Ann
Third Grade Teacher
JUNCTION CITY
Endel, Elizabeth Emerson
English Teacher
Kennedy, Bette Smith
Secondary Science Teacher
Lowe, Ellen Rogers
Guidance Counselor
Thomas, Cheryl Rene Saunders
Fifth Grade Teacher
KENSETT
Morris, Howard
Principal
KINGSLAND
Burnside, Anne Owens
History, Eng & Govt Teacher
Cox, Freda Granderson
Sixth Grade Teacher
Davis, Charlotte Marie
English & Art Teacher
Grice, Linnie Smith
Kindergarten Teacher
KINGSTON
Jackson, Nona Steele
First Grade Teacher
KIRBY
Arivett, Betty Zane
Social Studies Teacher
Golden, Carla Ann Manning
Mathematics Teacher
Johnson, Rhydonia Quintella (Cogburn)
English, Science & Jrnlsm Tchr
Pedron, James Russell
Biology & Spanish Teacher
Walker, Evelyn Eller
First Grade Teacher
York, Roger Glenn
Social Studies Teacher
LAKE CITY
Conner, Terry Lee
HS Mathematics Teacher
Heidelberg, Edna Murray
English & Speech Teacher
Pack, Paula Hubble
4th-6th Grade Math Teacher
LAKE VILLAGE
Cochran, Courtney Dawson
Eighth Grade English Teacher
LAMAR
Funderburg, Ronnie
Jr High Science Teacher
Johnson, Ralph D.
Music Teacher
Kondrick, Linda Bushdiecker
Math & Science Teacher
Ritchie, Diana Katherine
Third Grade Teacher
Thompson, Christel Hue (Bishop)
English Teacher
LAVACA
DuVall, Beth Dixon
Science Teacher
Sidwell, Elizabeth Watson
Coord of Gifted & Talented
Spencer, Nick
Dean of Students
Springwater, Gary Don
Voc Agriculture Instructor
LEACHVILLE
Metheny, Brenda J.
Sixth Grade Teacher
Swindle, Phillip Mack
Jr HS Counselor & Math Tchr
LEAD HILL
Center, Sandra Lynne
Secondary Science Teacher
Melton, Joyce Johnson
Fam & Consumer Science Tchr
LESLIE
Massey, Afton Randall
English Teacher
Milat, Terry
Kindergarten Teacher
Morris, Robin Lars
Music Director
Morrison, Emma Passmore
Sixth Grade Teacher
Treat, Harlie Russell
Counselor & Soc Studies Tchr
LEWISVILLE
Adair, Melissa Jane
Communication & Math Tchr
Bullock, Tessie LaRose
HS Science Teacher
Hudgins, Richard Alan
Basketball & Track Coach
LINCOLN
Simmons, Sarah Pitts
Business Technology Teacher
Williams, Johnny Cavaness
Social Studies & Spcl Ed Tchr
LITTLE ROCK
Adamson, Elizabeth Hughes
Deaf Ed Undergrad Prgm Coord
Allen, Mary Gwyn (Hansen)
Dept of Psychology Lecturer
Anderson, Phillis Nicols
Journalism Teacher
Ax, Edi R.
Tchr of GATE & Soc Studies
Bailey, Patricia Ann
English Teacher
Baldwin, Marion Elaine
Interim Director
Baltosser, William Henry
Associate Professor of Biology
Bednarz, Terri D.
Social Studies & Theology Tchr
Berry, Darrell Warren
Commercial Art Instructor
Binns, Judith Kay
Business Education Instructor
Bischof, Sherry Rothchild
7th-8th Grade English Teacher
Black, Frances Colvert
Home Economics Teacher
Boswell, Jo Lashlee
Supvr & Lang Arts Teacher
Boultinghouse, Sandy G.
Chemistry Teacher & Coach
Bowlus, Barbara M.
German Tchr & Intnl Stud Coord
Boyd, Louise Dreher
Administrator
Brack, Robert L.
Choral Music Director
Brant, Dennis Randolph
Physics Teacher
Briscoe, David Lloyd
Assistant Prof of Sociology
Cagley, Susan Anne
Social Studies Teacher
Christensen, Rose Marie
Bio, Physiology Tchr & Coach
Cleveland, Lancene
2nd & 3rd Grade Teacher
Coffin, TIna Bruning
Instructor of Mathematics
Coleman, George M.
Amer His Tchr & Soc Stud Chm
Colford, Susan Edrington
Sixth Grade Teacher
Cook, Lisa Renee
Biology Teacher
Crisp, Huey
Instructor of Writing
Croswell, Darrel William
Asst Prof of Biomed
Driskill, Gerald William
Associate Professor
Edwards, Thresia Hall
Fifth Grade Teacher
English, Art J.
Dept Pol Sci Prof & Chprsn
English, James Jaudon
Science & Biology Teacher
Feldman, Nicki Friess
High School Mathematics Instr
Ferguson, Colleen Olita
7th Grade Teacher of GATE
Fleck, Lana Boldt
Math Instructor
Flinn, Juliana Barbara
Professor of Anthropology
Francis, Bettye Harrison
Physical Science Teacher
Gale, Fredric G.
Rhetoric Associate Professor
Gates, Kathy Herrington
Algebra II Teacher
Gault, Katherine Tolleson
Fourth Grade Teacher of GATE
Gottuk, Alice Johanna
English & Language Arts Tchr
Griffin, Kathy Gene
Counselor & Athletic Coach
Hadley, Carrie D.
Civics, Gifted & Talented Tchr
Henle, Becky Langdon
English Teacher
Henslee, Tish
Prof of Early Childhood Ed
Henson, Anita Murdaugh
Mathematics Teacher
Hodges, Howard Lawrence
Professor of Chemistry
Hodges, Mary Izell
Rhetoric & Writing Dept Instr
Holland, Allison Denman
Rsrch Writing Tchr & Assoc Dir
Hoover, Amy Stone
6th Grade Teacher
Jackson, Shirley Famer
Ninth Grade English Teacher
Jeffries, Jennifer N.
First Grade Teacher
Johnson, Ivria, Jr.
7th Grade Science Teacher
Jones, Dorothy Ford
Exceptional Children Teacher
Jones, Juanita B.
English Teacher

'LE ROCK (cont)
nsen, Rebecca Steele
rd Grade Teacher
eman, Beverly Bell
cialist of Gftd & Tlntd
e, Michael
f of Rhetoric & Writing
e, Nettie Williams
Grade Teacher
s, Johanna Miller
ociate Professor of History
s, Lisa Carol
th Grade Teacher
z-Heavin, Carol S.
h School Choral Director
on, Shanda Yvette (Young)
rketing Coordinator
son, Nona Whittaker
cher of Gifted
hall, Peggy Taylor
nish Teacher
ey, Sally Wheeler
-6th Grade Teacher
es, Lisa Michelle
e Science, Pre-Algebra Tchr
Cheryl Puskarich
soc Prof & Forensic Coord
Kinnon, Gail Martin
Eng & Regular Eng Teacher
urray, Victor C.
ial Studies Teacher
er, James William
tory Professor
len, Lou Ehel
ndergarten Teacher
ngia, Hirak Chandra
f of Elect & Dept Chair
, Melanie Kennon
Instr of Early Chldhd Ed
, Daryl Hartman
itical Science Professor
ett, John Delbert
fessor of Biology
ler, Maury C.
ired Teacher
ertson, Martha Lynn
urth Grade Teacher
nson, Kristie Carson
nch Teacher
, Debra L.
glish Teacher
erford Crawford, Pamela J.
trl Cmptr Specialist
brough, Karen Ann (Usrey)
Grade Teacher
midt, Frederick Lee
Teacher
nton, Margaret E.
ofessor of Political Science
ls, Byron Scott
rld History Teacher
ely, Todd
ath Tchr & Head Ftbl Coach
ner, Kirby S.
ology & Biology Teacher
h, Darrell Jay
nd Director
h, Marcia Mayer
llege Writing Instructor
h, Patricia Truman
ucational Therapist
h, Phyllis Ann (Weaver)
cational Bus Tchr & Chprsn
n, Nicholas John
nguistics Professor
ffer, Linda Kay (Bonifield)
st Prof of Intrepretation
essle, Steven Gregory
cial Studies Teacher
-Watson, Myra
rector & Assistant Professor
xton, Paul D.
structor
eatt, Christopher
glish Teacher
ich, William J.
cial Science Teacher
nell, B. Travis
ychology Professor
ner, Victor K.
Rsrv Ofcrs Trng Corp Instr
ton, Georgia Clarissa
nth Grade English Teacher
rick, Michael Robert
ssociate Professor of Art
iteside, Carrie Helen
ommunications Teacher
der, R. Lee
S Math Teacher
liams, Joann S.
xth Grade Teacher
liamson, LouAnne
th Grade English Teacher
son, Janet Kay
riminal Justice Professor
ener, Karen Laranace
ne Arts Dept Chairman
fford, Hallethia J.
ssistant to the Dean
CKESBURG
es, Judy Lynn (Needham)
nglish & Journalism Teacher
th, Sue Ann-May
rst Grade Teacher
NOKE
ee, Rebecca Lee
pecial Reading Teacher
yd, Dale Edward
lgebra & Geometry Teacher

Clark, Jerri Lynne
1st Grade Teacher
Harrell, S. Derek
Civics & World Geography Tchr
Hobson, Elise Wedgeworth
Business Education Teacher
Nisbett, Mary Louise
English Teacher
LOWELL
Shultz, Douglas Brent
Fifth Grade Teacher
LUXORA
Mills, Gloria Ann
Fifth Grade Teacher
MABELVALE
Matlock, Nancy Salter
Gifted & Talented Specialist
MAGAZINE
Leslie, Shirley Dockery
Home Economics Teacher
MAGNOLIA
Joyner, Rosanne Sovine
Assoc Professor of Education
King, Ethel Wilcher
Counselor
Starnes, Harry Gene
Social Studies Teacher
White, Pam
Algebra Teacher
MALVERN
Bane, Michael
Chemistry Teacher
Brown, Paula Jean
Business Education Teacher
Bryant, Susan Hughes
Gifted & Talented Coordinator
Campos, Jean Ann Harp
English & US History Teacher
Conzel, Marsha Elizabeth
Sixth Grade Teacher
Coston, Marcille Keith
Media Specialist
Cowling, Bobby Wayne
Science Department Chairman
Edwards, Ruby Shockey
Retired Teacher
Glover, Patricia Ann
Coach & Phys Education Tchr
Henderson, Angela Gail
Fourth Grade Teacher
LaBeff-Sulton, Mary Jane Mountcastle
Fourth Grade Teacher
Middleton, John L.
Assistant Principal
Minyard, Rebecca Jenkins
Choral Dir & English Teacher
Morrison, Bobby W.
Mathematics Teacher
Scott, Stacey L.
History Teacher & Coach
Smith, Bob J.
Business Instructor
Williams, Cynthia Cagle
Counselor
MANSFIELD
Burgett, Kenneth Charles
Math Teacher
Frye, Bill
Athletic Director & Coach
MARIANNA
Atkinson, Kimberly Ann
Science Teacher
Clemons, Teresa Ann
Librarian
Gist, Jessamine D.
HS English Teacher
Gruby, Carolyn Croft
English Teacher
Kern, Regina Pender
6th Grade Teacher
Patterson, Jo Troxell
Mathematics Teacher
MARION
Cloud, Jane Schreiner
High School Math Teacher
Edrington, Jean Wilbourn
English Teacher
Scaife, John Bluff
Eighth Grade Math Teacher
MARMADUKE
Blackshare, Leland E.
HS Social Studies Teacher
Lange, Judy Lynne
5th Grade Teacher
Richey, Vicky Nelson
Coord of Gifted & Talented
Smith, Kellee Hensley
Third Grade Teacher
MARSHALL
Dearing, Kenda Sanders
Science Teacher
Mainord, Thomas Darrell
History & Soc Studies Teacher
Mays, Sharon Elizabeth
First Grade Teacher
Novak, Linda Carnley
Fourth Grade Teacher
MARVELL
Hudgins, Robert Leon
Scndry Math & Physics Teacher
MAUMELLE
Anderson, Rita Hale
Spanish Teacher
Daniel, Jeffrey Blake
Soc Sci Dept Head & Tchr
Haustein, JoAnn Rankin
Mathematics Instructor
Quattlebaum, Russell L.
Academic Dean

Sullivan, Karen
Business Ed & Computer Tchr
Tate, Karen Crank
Secondary Social Studies Tchr
Wilson, Gary Paul
Chorus Director
MAYFLOWER
Whited, Devonna Hawkins
Band & Choir Director
MC CRORY
Crow, Lauri Nunley
5th & 6th Grade English Tchr
Ferguson, Diane
7th-8th Grade Math Teacher
Rand, Joyce Reynolds
Vocational Business Ed Tchr
Wherry, Betty J.
Second Grade Teacher
MC GEHEE
Barrett, Diane Ford
English Teacher
Biggs, Carolyn S.
HOTS Lab Instructor
Birch, Nelwyn OBanion
Computer Technology Teacher
Crisp, Maxine Click
English Teacher
Dailey, Deborah Chesser
Physics Teacher
Fortenberry, Caprice Thompson
Vocational Home Ec Teacher
Glover, Vicki Wright
Eleventh Grade English Teacher
Hardin, Barbara Lynn
5th Grade Teacher
Mc Daniel, Billy Wayne
Sixth Grade Teacher
Moore, Anna Elizabeth
Biology & Physiology Teacher
Newton, George Alton
World History & Geography Tchr
MC NEIL
Lewis, Anita
Social Studies Teacher
MC RAE
Bowden, Camellia Jean Whitkanack
English & Math Teacher
Payne, Catherine Deanene
Soc Studies Tchr & GATE Coord
MELBOURNE
Branscum, Deborah Mangis
Sixth Grade Teacher
Hall, Linda Rich
Science Department Chair
Miller, Treva Tomlinson
First Grade Teacher
Smith, Kitty Stuckey
Nursing Instructor
MENA
Furr, M. Ann
English Instr & Hum Dept Chm
Goodner, Patricia Diane (Belcher)
Business Education Teacher
Head, Melba Doris Lewis
Fifth Grade Teacher
Hendrix, Annita Kay
Social Science Teacher
Johnson, Sheila Austin
Art Teacher
Smallwood, Kathy Ann (Jones)
Second Grade Teacher
Whorton, Randall Dennis
Driver's Ed Teacher
MINERAL SPRINGS
Turner, Maudies Owens
Fourth Grade Teacher
MONETTE
Cothren, Fran Hubble
English Teacher
Dunigan, Henry Edgar
Science Teacher
Smith, Linda Grisham
Second Grade Teacher
Stewart, Nancy Howell
HS Mathematics Instructor
MONTICELLO
Abbott, Patricia Greenwood
English Teacher
Akin, Barbara Jean
Business Teacher
Binns, Michael, Sr.
7th-12th Grd Choral Director
Gilliam, Barbara Holland
Health Teacher
Holthoff, Leonda Duncan
English Teacher
Matheny, Emma Jean
English Department Chair
Sawyer, Linda Ellen
Enrichment Tchr, G & T Coord
Schwab, Gloria Rawls
HS Special Education Teacher
Thurman, Elizabeth P.
English Teacher
Walker, Pat Murry
Retired Jr HS Counselor
MORRILTON
Bunch, Brian Kelly
Math & Drivers Education Tchr
Carter, Paula Broyles
English Teacher
Corley, Douglas Keith
8th Grade Math Teacher & Coach
Hill, Patti S.
Health, PE & Spec Ed Teacher
Huett, Pamela Darter
HS English & Journalism Tchr
Johnson, Tommy C.
Civics & Economics Teacher

Martin, Sharon Mc Elroy
Mathematics Teacher
Merideth, Joni McKee
Life Science Teacher
Rainey, Patricia L.
Counselor
White, Nina Jane
Hlth & Physical Education Tchr
MOUNT HOLLY
Calvert, Paula Jones
Science Teacher
Moore, Gammye
Agriculture Education Tchr
MOUNT IDA
Martin, Phyllis Y.
Guidance Counselor
MOUNT JUDEA
Gregory, Shelvon Lee
Science Teacher
MOUNT PLEASANT
Adkisson, Sally Davis
Eng, Span Tchr & Cnslr
MOUNTAIN HOME
Flanagin, Randy Scott
Teacher & Sci Dept Chairman
Griffith, Carolyn Nelson
First Grade Teacher
Lucas, Anne Stephens
English Teacher
Monger, Sondra Jean
Seventh Grade Math Teacher
Osmon, Janet Stogsdill
7th Grade Geography Teacher
Preis, Christy Davis
Mathematics Instructor
Preis, Kelvin
Junior High Counselor
Quick, Tammy House
Speech Teacher
Ramsey, Patsy Hawthorn
American Government Teacher
Sutherland, Suzanne Kay (Schmoker)
Instr of Dev Stud & Ed Course
Teems, Deborah Kay
Biology Teacher
Vaughan, Karyn S.
Facilitator of Gifted-Talented
Wegerer, Carol Ann
Math Teacher & Dept Chprsn
Wilber, Karen Blevins
Elementary Principal
MOUNTAIN VIEW
May, John R.
Math Teacher
Phillips, Jacqueline Blasingame
Vocal Music Teacher
Purdom, Robbie Cruse
Library Media Specialist
Stigall, Cynthia Faye
English & World His Tchr
Voyles, Mary Kay
10th-12th Grade English Tchr
MOUNTAINBURG
Bassham, Joyce L.
2nd Grade Teacher
Brown, Joyce Hamilton
Kindergarten Teacher
MULBERRY
Dunn, Michael Kevin, Sr.
Spelling & PE Tchr
King, Katie Johnson
K-12th Schl Cnslr & Test Coord
Primm, Sandra Bearden
Reading & Math Teacher
Smith, Vicky C.
English & French Teacher
Wright, Donna Kay (Stephens)
Second Grade Teacher
MURFREESBORO
Brymer, Rhonda Gailette (Cogburn)
Art & English Teacher
NASHVILLE
Davis, MayeGnell Fugitt
English & Language Arts Tchr
Elliott, Tammy Lee
Voc Family & Consumer Sci Tchr
Hughes, Karan Bowline
English Tchr & Dept Chprsn
May, Mary L.
Elementary Counselor
Oliver, Bonnie C. Reese
Coordinator of Gifted Programs
Talley, Nona Eley
Chemistry Teacher
NEWARK
Campbell, Kathy Ann (Phillips)
Science Teacher
Davis, Danny Dewayne
High School Math Teacher
Ward, Vaughn
5th-6th Grade Science Teacher
NEWPORT
Beard, Judy Engelhardt
Journalism & Speech Teacher
Dabbs, Connie Wolfe
Elementary Music Teacher
Evins, Cynthia Goings
Learning Disabilities Teacher
Knowles, Rita Venable
2nd Grade Teacher
Moore, Randy Byron
Teacher & Coach
Pruitt, Sharon Diane
HS Bio, Chem & Astronomy Tchr
Sampson, Lynda Pearle
English Teacher
Tapp, Beverly Warbington
English & Speech Teacher

NORPHLET
Ashbrooks, LaDonna Kaye
English Teacher
NORTH LITTLE ROCK
Allen, Dinah Manor
Gifted Facilitator
Amis, Paul F.
Electronics Teacher
Bivings, Barbara Reynolds
Science Teacher
Buchan, Michael Lynn
Geometry & Pre-Cal Teacher
Bunn, Gary
Mathematics Teacher
Burris, Kathy Ann
9th Grd Sci Tchr & Ath Trainer
Carroll, Joan Ogburn
Home Economics Teacher
Clark, Ramona Denise-Eddington
Chair of Ed & Instructor
Cohen, Perry Irwin
Technology Teacher
Davis, Monica Denise
Science Teacher
Derden, Curt
Band Director
Douglass, Mauri Thomas
Resource Teacher of GATE
Ewing, Michele Louise
Assoc Prof of Psych & Cnslng
Fulton, Elizabeth H.
Science Teacher & Dept Chair
Goodson, Judith Woodward
Geography Teacher
Humphrey, James Otis
Health & Athletic Teacher
Johnson, Mary Henderson
Retired Elem Teacher
Kirspel, Nellie Sue
Fifth Grade Teacher
Kite, Kathi J.
Science Teacher
Mayes, Jan Williams
Business Teacher
Mc Kenzie, Teri Lee
English Teacher
Nagel, Hamiyet
High School Biology Teacher
Noland, Mike
Speech & Drama Teacher
Ritchie, Suzanne E.
English Teacher
Robbins, Jon
Chemistry Teacher
Smith, Sheryll C.
Elementary Principal
Story, Arclista Tegtmeyer
Fifth Grade Teacher
Tiller, Lisa A.
Speech Teacher & Debate Coach
Watts, Beverly Hooks
7th-8th Grd Sci & Math Tchr
Wenger, Peggy Patterson
Home School Teacher & Artist
Whisnant, Karla Boeckmann
Mathematics Teacher
Whittington, Ted Clayton
Social Studies Teacher
OAK GROVE
Morgan, Jean Lavone
Retired Elementary Teacher
OARK
James, Anita Marie
Business Teacher
Schmocker, Oliver Edward
Counselor & Math Teacher Coord
Strubel, Cathy Lynn
HS Teacher
ODEN
Barnes, Linda R.
Math & Chemistry Teacher
Ledbetter, Brenda DeRamus
Spcl Ed, Eng & Jrnslm Tchr
OMAHA
Brand, Jacquelyn Denise
English, Speech & Drama Tchr
Bryant, Sue Edwards
First Grade Teacher
Dirst, Bill
English & Journalism Teacher
Macri, Donna M.
Science & Math Teacher
OSCEOLA
Johnson, Norma Ann Lambert
Chemistry & Astronomy Teacher
Nachlinger, O. Throys
Math Professor
Williams, Martha Thomas
Fourth Grade Teacher
PANGBURN
Harris, Mary (Fox)
Kindergarten Teacher
Poole, Ruth (Barger)
English & Speech Teacher
PARAGOULD
Adams, Armentia
Intermediate School Counselor
Adams, Jeanean H.
Fifth Grade Teacher
Bland, Sandra Kay
French Teacher
Boling, Denise D.
PE & Health Teacher
Brittingham, James G.
Assistant Principal
Fagala, Mary Jane Luttrell
English & Speech Teacher
Garrett, Betty A.
Algebra Teacher

PARAGOULD (cont)
Hagen, Doris Slatton
English & Journalism Teacher
Hodges, Michael Duane
Fifth Grade Teacher
Hurst, Linda Simpson
4th Grade Teacher
Mealer, Sheila (Clayton)
Fifth Grade Science Teacher
Richards, Sylvia Pelt
Coordinator of Gifted Ed
Smith, Dana Catherine
9th Grade Civics Teacher
Smith, Donna Dale
Choral Music Teacher
Watson, Rick J.
Athletic Dir & History Teacher
Webb, Kimberly Ann
Jr High Math Teacher
Wells, Linda J.
Language Arts Instructor
Wright, Lori Ann
English Teacher
PARIS
Green, Sandra Fry
Math & Science Teacher
Hogue, Gary Wayne
Middle School Counselor
Hutson, S. Bryan
Algebra II Teacher
Siebenmorgen, Dennis C.
Agriculture Education Teacher
Varnell, Curtis J.
Teacher
PARKIN
Wallace, Lidia Di Giusto
English & Italian Teacher
Withers, Lillian Webster
English Teacher
PARON
French, Mary Jo
Counselor
PEA RIDGE
Dickey, David Clinton, Jr.
Music Educator & Band Director
Mc Clain, Tracy Alan
Language Arts Teacher
PEARCY
Black, Linda Gardner
Eng Teacher & Dept Chair
Davis, Claudia
Second Grade Teacher
Gardner, Linda Diane
6th Grade Teacher
Lynch, Kevin Glen
Seventh Grade English Teacher
Matthews, Sandra Kay
Gifted & Talented Facilitator
Rosenbaum, Sharon White
Lang Arts & Soc Stud Teacher
Westerman, Donald Wayne
Agricultural Education Instr
PERRYVILLE
Chitwood, Bobbie J.
Social Studies Teacher
Harless, Evelyn Mc Laury
Social Studies Teacher
McCallister, Carolyn Garison
Secondary English Teacher
Smith, Charles
High School Counselor
Smith, Patsy Rankin
Life Skills Instructor
PIGGOTT
Evans, Terry Wayne
Art Teacher
Morris, Pam Pollard
7th & 8th Grade Eng Teacher
Routszong, Sandra Byrd
K-12th Grd Music Teacher
Self, Danny Mack
Mathematics Teacher
PINE BLUFF
Berry, Benjamin F.
Chemistry & Physics Teacher
Branch, Paula Scott
Mathematics Teacher
Brooks, Cynthia Rogers
Instructor of Computer Science
Burleigh, Joseph Gaynor
Entomology Professor
Collins, Lois Brooks
English Teacher
Fitzpatrick, Shelton
Professor of Biology
Gorman, Dell W.
English & Writing Teacher
Houston, Marion Hart
Former English Teacher
James, Tammy Gardner
Psych, Soc & Amer His Tchr
Jones, Judie Bihm
Drama & English Teacher
Jones, Patricia A. (Daniels)
9th Grade Civics Teacher
Joyce, Bobbie Tiner
8th Grd American History Tchr
Lott, Carl William, Jr.
Band Director
Meadows, Patricia Williams
English Instructor
Mebane, Carolyn Morrison
7th & 8th Grd His & Geog Tchr
Mitchell, William Harrison
Social Studies Teacher
Mobley, Sandra Lee
Math & Science Teacher
Parrish, Judy Turner
Former 6th Grd Soc Stud Tchr

Pierce, Iris Langley
Advanced Biology & Chem Tchr
Porter, Lenora M.
Third Grade Teacher
Ross, Evelyn B.
Retired Teacher
Rushing, Annette
Junior High Choral Director
Sewald, Carl Martin
Choral Director
Smith, Terry
English Teacher
Stanfield, Jo Ellen
Communication Specialist
Straw, Marvin LeRoy
Senior Army Instructor
Townsend, Joan Mc Bryde
Biology Tchr & Sci Dept Chair
Upshaw, Douglas E.
Science Teacher
Vaughn, Shannon Floyd
Mathematics Instructor
Williams, Lynda Deal
English Teacher
Work, Linda Hopper
Gifted & Talented US His Tchr
Young, Caryl Joy
English Teacher
PLAINVIEW
Pierce, Michael Brent
Vocational Business Teacher
Rhoades, Charlotte Jones
English & French Teacher
Shields, Madelyn Ruth
Social Studies Teacher
PLEASANT PLAINS
Burleson, Kathy Ann
Bus Ed & World His Teacher
Roberson, Mary Ann Wilson
Math & Science Teacher
Wells, Karen Hutson
Lib Media Spclst & Eng Tchr
POCAHONTAS
Dulaney, John Robert
Director of Bands
Dunn, Howard L.
Band Director
POYEN
Emerson, Dennis Paul
Science Dept Chprsn & Coach
McDermott, Patsy Cogburn
Fourth Grade Teacher
Wheat, Elaine Ashford
Art, Gifted & Talented Teacher
PRAIRIE GROVE
Gray, Tracy Smith
Earth, Phys & Bio Sci Teacher
Horton, Stan E.
Social Studies Teacher
PRESCOTT
Fincher, Wanda Whitney
Alternative Teacher
Horton, Janice M.
Sixth Grade Math Teacher
Lockwood, Gina Rena
Speech & Drama Teacher
Yowell, Sara D.
7th Grade Science Teacher
QUITMAN
Ball, Michael Wayne
Amer & World History Teacher
RAVENDEN SPRINGS
Goetz, Cheryl Armstrong
English & Oral Comm Teacher
Toney, Nancy L. (Baker)
Business Education Teacher
RECTOR
Fowler, Johnny Joe
Agriculture Teacher
Matheney, Belinda Beckley
Social Studies Teacher
Simmons, Rebecca Ann
Geography & German Teacher
Smith, J. Frank
High School Science Tchr
REDFIELD
Rhodes, Judy Carole
English & Physical Ed Teacher
RISON
Post, Rhonda Hoover
English Teacher
Stewart, Jeffrey Wayne
Coach & Teacher
Thompson, Norma
Second Grade Teacher
ROGERS
Aldridge, Wendy E. Newman
Coach, PE & General Sci Tchr
Baldridge, Jane Lee
Eighth Grade Amer History Tchr
Barnes, Mary Jo (Nelson)
Secondary English Teacher
Brown, Marty Elvin
Chem & Principles of Tech Tchr
Dake, Sukey Millspaugh
First Grade Teacher
Fike, Amy Smith
Social Studies Teacher
Kolman, Diana Rhinehart
Journalism & English Teacher
Kwarcinski, Paul C.
English Teacher
Langenegger, Frankie Hughes
Language Arts Teacher
Long, Steven
Chemistry Teacher
Norwood, Bruce Wilson
Vice Principal
Patton, Brenda Layne
Gifted & Talented Facilitator

Reagan, Betty Lynn
Retired Teacher
Ross, Robert Allen
Zoology Teacher
Smith, Michael P.
Art Teacher
Weeks, Rhonda Lynn
Advanced English Teacher
Welty, Koenia Palmer
Choral Director
Williams, Thomas Lee
Math Instructor & Coach
Winton, James Edward, Jr.
Physical Education Teacher
ROHWER
Pearce, Carline Johnson
Sr HS Studies Teacher
Sibley, Robert Bryan
Art Teacher
ROSE BUD
Bolin, Angela Gayler
2nd Grade Teacher
Hayes, Glenda Sue
English & Bus Tchr
Holder, Steven E.
Band, Choir & Music Instructor
Reilly, Patrick John
Mathematics & Art Teacher
Spradley, Pamela Claire
Art & Spanish Teacher
ROSSTON
DiCicco, Jamie Smith
9th & 10th Grade English Teach
Hastings, James Coye
Life Science & Biology Teacher
RUSSELLVILLE
Akers, Jennifer Cathcart
Speech, Drama & Eng Teacher
Bailey, Gayla Rye
Civics Teacher
Chenowith, Laura Garner
Jr HS Mathematics Teacher
Daniels, Lee Ann
Advanced Biology I Teacher
Dunbar, Euvon Johnston
5th Grade Teacher
Edmonson, Fredia Abernathy
Second Grade Teacher
Futterer, Karen L.
Associate Professor of Music
Gibson, Lisa Gist
4th Grade Teacher
Goff, Connie Lynn
7th Grade Lang Arts Teacher
Hawkins, Beth Mikles
Mathematics Teacher
Herrick, Nita Marie (Clark)
Associate Professor of Music
Hubbard, Kimberly Vernon
Senior English Teacher
Lemley, Charles Ray
History Teacher
Pickens, Mary Lou
Retired Math Teacher
Williams, Cindy Marie
Phys Ed, Hlth Tchr & Coach
SAINT JOE
Barkley, Barbara Martin
Music & English Teacher
Gilley, Susan Adams
Business & Computer Instructor
SAINT PAUL
Graham, Debra
HS Math Teacher
Webster, Nancy S.
6th Grade Teacher
SALEM
Ragan, Vicki Warren
5th-6th Grd Language Arts Tchr
SCOTLAND
Biggs, Micheal Wayne
Math & Health Teacher
SCRANTON
Gray, Melba Harvell
GATE Coordinator & Teacher
SEARCY
Akridge, Scott Houston
Social Studies Teacher
Allen, David Lee
Assoc Professor of Accounting
Bennett, Rebecca Reaves
Chemistry & AP Biology Teacher
Berryman, Sandra N.
Nursing Instructor
Cleek, Phillip Edward
English Teacher
Coleman, Bobbie R.
Junior English Teacher
Duke, Deborah Ganus
Asst Professor of Mathematics
Edwards, Terry Lynn
Director of Academic Affairs
England, Donald
Distinguished Prof of Chem
Escalante, Perry L.
Social Studies Teacher & Coach
Fortner, John David
Associate Professor of Bible
Ganus, Clifton L., III
Professor of Music
Gowan, Kay S.
Asst Prof Comm & Dir Stu Pub
Hobby, Kenneth Lester
Professor of Psychology
Howard, Thomas M.
Professor of Political Science
Koch, Tim Luke
HS Social Studies Teacher
Lee, June Jordan
American History Teacher

Mayes, Robert Wayne
Calculus, Physics & Chem Tchr
McSpadden, Bill R.
English & Speech Teacher
Morgan, Jan Chesshir
Chair of Elementary & Spec Ed
Mueller, Deborah Louise
Associate Professor
Oliver, George H.
Assoc Professor of Management
Powers, Emmett E.
Spanish Teacher
Reely, Robert H., Jr.
Professor of Management
Rumfield, Katie Jane
Spanish Teacher
Shedd, Danny Michael
Math Instructor
Shedd, Eloise T.
Secondary English Teacher
Shultz, Cathleen M.
Nursing Professor & Dean
Smith, Claude William
Band Director
Wagner, Susan Preston
Coord & Instructor of Nursing
Watson, Betty Ann
Professor of Elementary Ed
Wilson, Edmond Woodrow, Jr.
Professor
Wilson, Elizabeth Kennemer
Dept of Family & Consumer Sci
SHERIDAN
Bailey, Dean Edward
Physical Science Teacher
Cannon, Jaynie Smith
English Tchr & Journalism Adv
Henley, Michael D.
Computer Science Teacher
Parham, Mindy (Miller)
Social Studies Teacher
Rash, Tommie Mackey
Fifth Grade Teacher
Reynolds, Patsy Robinette
Home Economics Teacher
Roark, Mary Crosby
Fourth Grade Teacher
Seals, Larry Dennis
JROTC Instructor
Vailes, Linda R.
Math Teacher & Dept Chair
Wilson, Roy Lynn
8th Grade US & AR His Teacher
SHERWOOD
Armstrong, Florene Fort
Civics & Amer His Teacher
Eudy, Russell D.
High School Coach & Principal
Evans, Tomi M.
History Teacher
Gray, Jean Ann
Oral Communciation Teacher
Myers, Catherine Calhoun
Math Teacher
Pool, M. Beth (Pierce)
Art Teacher
Revis, Rebecca Manfredini
Soc Studies & Civics Teacher
Watson, Janis Rowe
Secondary Bible Teacher
SHIRLEY
Carlo, Jacqueline Joyce
Music Director
SILOAM SPRINGS
Barber, J. Robert
Retired Choral Conductor
Keesee, Barbara Gale
Fifth Grade Teacher
Killgore, Marian Frias
HS English & PE Teacher
Matchell, Constance Nystrom
Math Instructor & Coordinator
Matchell, Steven Gordon
Biology & Chemistry Teacher
Murphy, Donna Magness
Mathematics Teacher
Thompson, Bob Lee
Social Studies Teacher
SMACKOVER
Glover, Peggy Ellen
Gifted & Talented Coordinator
SPARKMAN
Crawford, Kathryn Bizzell
Kindergarten Teacher
Frazier, Joel Allan
Jr High Math Tchr & Coach
Holloway, Belinda Louise Lea
5th-6th Grd Rdng & Eng Tchr
SPRINGDALE
Alexander, Dean
Social Studies Teacher
Barclay, Debbie Sue
7th Grade English Teacher
Crownover, Carol Jeanette Dotson
Business Education Instructor
Dovell, Susan Charlesworth
Fourth Grade Teacher
Dykes, Jimmy Joseph
Athletic Director
Joenks, Peter John
Physical Science Teacher
Lawrence, Delanie Dianne
Second Grade Teacher
Lyall, Dana Beth
Mathematics Teacher
Mabry, Aleta White
Assistant Principal
McGinnis, David E.
Health Teacher

Noland, Janice Peters
Amer History & English Teacher
Overton, Judith B.
Biology Instructor
Russell, Emily Jean
Sixth Grade Reading Teacher
Shelton, Beverly Moore
US His & Kybrdng Teacher
Tisdale, Kay Campbell
4th Grade Teacher
Williams, Connie Summers
High School Counselor
Williamson, Kelley Mc Haney
Business Instructor
Wilson, Karen Melinda
HS Mathematics Teacher
Wright, Mitchell Wayne
Agriculture Teacher
Wright, Sandy Scranton
Girls Bskbl Coach & Bio Tchr
Yandell, Bobby J.
Fifth Grade Teacher
Young, Carol R.
Media Specialist
STAMPS
Gasaway, Sheryl Lynn
Business Teacher
Matarazzo, Patrick Phillip
Director of Bands
Smith, Glenda Gail
Math Teacher
STAR CITY
Foster, Joyce M.
Mathematics Teacher
Knight, Lealand Edward
Social Studies Teacher
Raley, Gloria M.
Keyboarding Teacher
Robinson, Hope H.
Asst Principal
Weatherford, Martha G.
English Teacher
STATE UNIV
Agnew, David Maxedon
Asst Prof of Agricultural Ed
Ball, Jerry L.
English Associate Professor
Bradley, MaryJane
Education Professor
Burkart, Julia M.
Assoc Professor of Social Work
Calloway, Catherine E.
Associate Professor of English
Draganjac, Mark Edward
Professor of Chemistry
England, David Emory
Associate Professor of Pol Sci
Greenwalt, Bert
Agricultural Economist
Harp, George Lemaul
Prof of Environmental Biology
Harp, Phoebe Ann (Pigg)
Instr of Biological Sciences
Hartwig, Charles Walter
Assoc Prof of Political Sci
Hinck, Lawrence Wilson
Professor of Microbiology
Johnson, Stephen Michael
Asst Prof of Comptr Info
Joiner, Charles M.
Program Dir of Social Work
Knuckles, Barbara Lawrence
Instructor of College Success
Logan, Laddie B.
Associate Prof of Marketing
Marini, Irmo Don
Program Coord & Asst Professor
Nonis, Sarath Alban
Marketing Professor
O'Neal, Thomas John
Director of Bands
Rogers, Jennifer Engles
Radio & Television Instructor
Sustich, Andrew Thomas
Physics Professor
STRAWBERRY
Powell, Dana Runyan
English Teacher
STUTTGART
Orlicek, Phyllis Riley
12th Grade English Teacher
SULPHUR ROCK
Summers, Paula Marie
Secondary Math Teacher
TAYLOR
Duke, Carol Ann
Counselor
TEXARKANA
Armstrong, Brenda Hesterly
Second Grade Teacher
Burdine, Denny Michael
Amer & World History Teacher
Fulmer, Joyce Leavelle
Adv Math & Algebra Teacher
Harrison, Donna Mssey
6th Grade Language Arts Tchr
Hill, Diana Carole (Johnson)
Language Arts Teacher
Liles, Andrea Bentley
Special Ed & Resource Eng Tchr
Meidell, Frank Arnold
1st-8th Grade Teacher
Spears, Melinda Rivers
Mathematics Instructor
Staggs, Sandra Russell
4th-5th Grade Teacher
Tirrito, Margaret Fleming
5th-6th Grade Science Teacher
Webb, Frederick Eugene, Sr.
Math, Soc Studies & Sci Tchr

ARKANA (cont)
ehead, Luke
Chemistry & Biology Tchr
BO
, Sarah Baldwin
st Grade Teacher
h, Susan E.
thematics Teacher
MANN
rd, DeAnna Evans
enth Grade Math Teacher
and, Donnie Gene
riculture Education Instr
am, Devra Marie
cher of Gifted & Talented
joy, Thyla Elaine (Case)
urth Grade Teacher
, Jane Moore
Teacher
IRE
ander, Kimberly Lovelis
cational Business Ed Teacher
aster, Scott Wayne
sketball Coach
mock, Sherry Jean
th Teacher
LEY SPRINGS
don, Lavina L.
glish Teacher
n, Wesley E.
th Grade Teacher
ess, William Wyatt
glish & Speech Teacher
BUREN
, Janet Powell
Grade Science Teacher
her, Jeffrey Lewis
Grade Civics Teacher
well, Sarah Ann
Grd Physical Science Tchr
wford, Gregory Dean
her His & Civics Teacher
can, Mary Elizabeth
World History Teacher
David Wayne
ology & Chemistry Teacher
ry, Leslie Ann
ology & Chemistry Teacher
at, Deborah Medlock
urth Grade Teacher
ore, Mary Mayhew
condary Mathematics Teacher
, Linda Robinson
ath Teacher & Coordinator
ders, Timothy Lynn
story Teacher & Coach
is, Susan Ellen
athematics Teacher
shell, Darrell T.
ath Teacher
iver, Lynn Fulton
-8th Grade English Teacher
mons, Angie F.
siness Teacher
ivan, Peggy S.
Grade Elementary Teacher
ipseed, Mary Jane Mc Kenzie
cial Studies Instr & Chprsn
mark, Terri L.
counting Teacher
kins, Tom F.
ssistant Principal
, Martga Heslet
h Grade Science Teacher
eeler, Donna Suzanne
fth Grade Teacher
itmire, Gail Alexander
xth Grade Teacher
ONIA
gs, David D.
oach & Asst Principal
then, Melba Moseley
S Math Teacher
, James Stephen
and & Choir Director
ck, Eva Fidella
ome Economics Teacher
lor, Martha Quattlebaum
nglish Teacher
LA
lie, Stephanie Conners
structor of Elem Education
LDO
licott, Jill Harper
usiness Teacher
LDRON
ker-Capron, Brooke
irector of Choral Activities
esser, Elsie Louthan
ourth Grade Teacher
ddard, Ronald Lee
hemistry & Ecology Teacher
mmer, Glenda (VanDeWiele)
ormer 4th Grade Teacher
LNUT RIDGE
se, Dale Robert
rt Instructor
ers, Bonnie Wyatt
rench Teacher
rce, M. Linda
lementary Educator
ARREN
nold, Barbara Kolb
ounselor
laway, JoEllen Lowry
indergarten Teacher
rner, Sharon Anne
h Grade Social Studies Tchr
anes, Donna Wheeler
areer Orientation Tchr, Cnslr

Richardson, Beverly Morgan
Kindergarten Teacher
Shull, Beth
Journalism Teacher
Smalling, Jan (Wulfekuhler)
Second Grade Teacher
Smith, Ramona Mc Clain
English Teacher
White, Deborah Bradshaw
English Teacher
WEINER
Greeno, Wilma West-Bell
Third Grade Teacher
WEST FORK
Walters, Joey C.
Business Teacher & Coach
WEST HELENA
Gregory, Judy P.
Social Studies Teacher
Smith, Mary P.
Mathematics Teacher & Coord
WEST MEMPHIS
Bruce, Arlee Iris
English Teacher
Edwards, Earl, Sr.
Fifth Grade Teacher
Hall, Ann Wilson
English Teacher
Hicks, Mildora Curne
2nd Grade Teacher
James, Sylvia Vickers
Math Teacher
Latimore, Michael Edward
English Teacher
Lewis, Barbara Brown
English & Language Arts Tchr
Neal, Liz Redditt
French Teacher
Quarrels, Palmer Marie
Asst Principal
WHEATLEY
Williams, Shirley Sherrer
English Teacher
WHITE HALL
Peyton, Lillian Cawthon
Sixth Grade Teacher
WICKES
Alexander, Donna Terry (Loyd)
Keyboarding & Eng I, II Tchr
WILBURN
Lafleur, Carolyn Lang
First Grade Teacher
WILSON
Bennett, Sally Eudy
Gft, Tal Pgm Supvr & Tech Dir
Brewer, Karen Dean
High School Mathematics Tchr
Ford, Stephen Steele, Sr.
Biology Teacher
Mason, Sherry Barnes
8th Grade Math Teacher
WINSLOW
Arrington, Jeff Daniel
Business Teacher & Coach
Boen, Leigh Perkins
Kindergarten Teacher
WYNNE
Ross, Georgia H.
English Teacher
Tarbutton, Barbara Brandenburg
Spanish Teacher
YELLVILLE
Sharp, Julia Thomas
Band Director

CALIFORNIA

ACAMPO
Sturman, Misty Hayes
Coach
ACTON
Adelman, Elaine Malkin
GATE Coord & Mentor Tchr
Hunter, Susan Ann
Sixth Grade Teacher
Merritt, Nancy Anne
English & US History Tchr
Notti, Maria Venezio
Eighth Grade English Teacher
Rowland, Lawrence Lloyd
Sixth Grade Teacher
ADELANTO
Ethridge, Laura Kurth
6th Grade Teacher
AGOURA
Cano, Nan
English Department Chair
Forman, Judy A.
English Teacher
Futterman, Jody H.
Spanish Teacher
Haffamier, Suzanne Yamaguchi
English Teacher
Heller, Karen
Spanish Teacher
Lundquist, Kristine Kay
Bus Ed Dept Chair
Mosley, John E.
Music Teacher
Myer, L. DiAnn
Fr Tchr & Frgn Lang Dept Chm
AGOURA HILLS
Hill, Patrick Lewis
Social Science Tchr & Chprsn
ALAMEDA
Aksionczyk, Leon Michael
Mathematics Teacher

Budd, Deborah Floyd
HS Physical Education Teacher
Chacon, Carol Ann
High School English Teacher
Dauber, Philip M.
Physics & Astronomy Teacher
Dutra, Cynthia Copeland
5th Grade Teacher
Fleming, Shayne Bowden
High School Math Teacher
Harsch, Jean Mulks
Counselor, Teacher & Director
Hooke, Michael P.
Religion & Social Studies Tchr
Jefferson, Carrie Lowery
English Professor
Kubicek, Didi Dempster
Math & Choral Teacher
Micheli, Christine
English Teacher
Moorhead, Robert William
Drama & English Teacher
Norris, Elizabeth Pelaez
Spanish & English Teacher
Olsen, Teri M.
Spanish Tchr & Dept Chair
Orear, Linda Wilkinson
Principal
Pachece, George Pacheco
Automotive Technology Teacher
Rebensdorf, Alan
Math Teacher
Richards, James Edward
Science Teacher
Rivard, Earl Jon, Jr.
Spanish & ESL Teacher
Sigmon, Joy Konno
Math Teacher
Thomas, Julie Anne
Language Arts Tchr & VP
Valterza, Vicki Gimble
Third & Fourth Grade Teacher
Williamson, Patricia Elaine
Science Teacher
Yarbrough, Linda (Dagdigian)
Science Teacher
ALAMO
Keen, Dorothy Clark
Teacher
ALBANY
Davis, Robin Schluter
7th-8th Grade Teacher
Donohue, Donna
French Teacher
Gamba, Thomas J.
Core & Drama Teacher
Lilienthal, Thomas M.
Instrumental Music Director
Martin, Kim
US History, Govt & Ec Teacher
Shaughnessy, Daniel Richard
PE Teacher & Athletic Director
Zulpo, Sonia
5th Grade Teacher
ALHAMBRA
Azeltine, Tony
Choir Director
Barnheiser, Mary Anne Spiller
Dean of Stud, Eng & Math Tchr
Brock, Judy LaNille
English Teacher
Carr, Susan Gayle
Biology & AP Biology Teacher
Emmert, Gary Franklin
7th-8th Grade Science Teacher
Fabian, Bena L.
Health Teacher
Flagan, Aulikki Pekkala
Science Teacher
Gleason, Therese Patricia
2nd Grade Teacher
Hoffman, James Brandt
7th-8th Grade History Teacher
Huntwork, Michael David Gregory
ESL & French Teacher
Liu, Ann Lew
Itinerant Teacher for Deaf
Malucky, Maralyn Ludwig
Librarian & Computer Teacher
Manchester, Gabriella Elizabeth
English Dept Chair
Mc Elhaney, Douglas John
Spanish Teacher
Meyer, Linda Karyn
Teacher & Athletic Director
Nasitka, Dennis L.
English & Drama Teacher
Nielsen, David Edward
US History Teacher & Coach
Reis, Patrick Raymond
Applied Communications Tchr
Sutton, Shelia Deniece
Lit & Creative Writing Teacher
Trikoris, Demetreos J.
Math Teacher
White, Wesley Sheldon
Secondary Math Teacher
Young, Peter Y. S.
8th Grade Teacher
ALPINE
Benjamin, Henry
Teacher
ALTA
Mc Vey, Thomas John
Scottish Bagpipe Teacher
ALTA LOMA
Burke, Donald Ray
Science Teacher
Clift, James Harvey
Science Teacher

FitzSimmons, Caren M.
Eng Dept Chprsn & ELD Coord
Kruse, Debbie
8th Grade Teacher
Lawrie, Patricia Schallert
Comm, Speech & Lang Specialist
Murphy, Dianne
Tech & Applied Studies Teacher
Prish, Linda Putnam
Third Grade Teacher
Reed Arigan, Paul
French Instructor
Rose, Eva Katherine
Assoc Prof in Speech Comm
Sahagun, Sara Guild
HS Mathematics Teacher
Scheidler, Karen M.
6th Grade Teacher
Shetley, Richard John
US History Teacher
Temple, Mary Ann Mourterot
Second Grade Teacher
Thielen, Debbie
Business Education Teacher
Thomas, Steve Andrew
Principal
Vasquez, Juan Alejo
Spanish Teacher
Willborn, Kim Queen
Biology Teacher
Zollinger, Richard Scott
Spanish Teacher
ALTADENA
Averill, Wendy
Fourth Grade Teacher
Klages, Marjorie Bakker
4th Grade Teacher
Stewart, Rayne Street
Third Grade Teacher
ALTAVILLE
Aufdenspring, Deborah Trask
Social Studies & English Tchr
Markoe, Janet Carol
English & French Teacher
Pappe-Reynoso, Amber
English Teacher & Counselor
Smith, Susan Gangwer
High School Spanish Teacher
ALTURAS
Bitter Carstens, Beverly Ann
Fourth Grade Teacher
Kaderabek, Michaelette Mc Climon
8th Grd Math & Soc Stud Tchr
Montague, Harold C.
Spanish Teacher
Siegel, Karen Lavonne
Music Director
Wood, Shaun Kevin
Physical Education Teacher
AMBOY
Bartel, Mary Tilden
K-8th Grade Teacher
ANAHEIM
Anderson, Wynn William
6th Grade Teacher
Ansari, Farhad
Mentor Teacher
Beardsley, Dana Lynn
Humanities Teacher
Behrens, Linda Patrice
First Grade Teacher
Benson, Robert S.
Chemistry Teacher
Braithwaite, John A.
Teacher
Carroll, Rose Freese
Chem Teacher & Sci Dept Chair
Cavner, Gayle Lorraine
Art Teacher
Chiodo, Suzanne Miller
6th Grade Teacher
Chylinski, Paul T.
US His, Psych Tchr & Act Adv
Davis, Lori Perkins
Resource Teacher
Dinnen, Evelyn Marie
English Teacher
Donner, Karen Anne
French & ESL Tchr
Elder, Meg Lynn (johnson)
Dance Teacher
Enenbach, Nancy Tanner
Health Science Teacher
Ernest, Ed William
Industrial Technology Instr
Esping, Alden E.
Health Dept Chair
Ewen, Mary Ellen Cummings
Journalism & Lang Arts Tchr
Ewing, Peggy Lindley
Kindergarten Teacher
Findley, Elaine (Bachlor)
Principal
Franquero, Diane Louise
Second Grade Teacher
Fraser, Fiona Bodie Smith
Co-Director & Eng Dept Chair
Gonzales, Phyllis Kowalski
English Teacher
Haack, Verna Lee
Seventh Grade Teacher
Heymers, Williams Reese
Mathematics Teacher
Hobbs, Janna Wassweiler
1st Grade Teacher
Hugo, Emil S.
Math Teacher
Jawor, John Stanley
Physics Teacher

Kakihara, Paddy Lum
6th Grade Teacher
Kimberly, Douglas
World History Teacher
Kindsfather, Susan Simmons
6th Grade Teacher
Lappin, David D.
Social Studies & English Tchr
Lum, Suzanne Leimomi
Spanish Tchr & Guidance Cnslr
Ly, Mindy
High School Mathematics Tchr
Mann, Sharon Lorraine
Fourth Grade Teacher
Mc Carthy, Kristie Agarth
Sixth Grade Teacher
Miller, Sheryl Sharp
Sixth Grade Teacher
Mitchell, Harold George
Health, Biology & Science Tchr
Myers, Vicki Katherine
8th Grade US History Teacher
Nance, Craig Higgins
Mathematics Teacher
Nichols, Pete
8th Grd US History Teacher
Pendleton, William Byron
English Teacher & Coach
Peterson, Norbert John
Physics Instr & Engng Coord
Pilgreen, Peggy Palmer
Second Grade Teacher
Polley, Karen Thornton
Sixth Grade Teacher
Pribonic, Andrea Ellen
4th Grade Teacher
Rich, Carolyn Hersman Lovein
6th Grade Teacher
Rishel, Robert John
English Teacher
Rivera, Betty Vizas
History Teacher
Rodgers, Thomas Rex
Math Teacher & Coach
Schima-Pedersen, Elisabeth C.
French, German & ELD Tchr
Seely, Diane Kay
Ger Tchr & Frgn Lang Dpt Chair
Sinatra, Christine Diane
English Teacher
Smet, Gregory Scott
Sixth Grade Teacher
Smith, Patrice Toohey
Kindergarten Teacher
Smith, Thomas James
Science Chair & Algebra Tchr
Taylor, Diane Zwicker
Physical Education Teacher
Turner, F. Robin
English Teacher
Villarreal, Yolanda
Spanish Teacher
Williams, Gregg Thomas
HS English Teacher
Wilmoth, Scott Wesley
Biology Teacher
Wise, Diana Marie
Chemistry Teacher
Wright, Allison Alden
ESL Teacher
ANDERSON
Copus, Rick Charles
Asst Prin & Soc Sci Teacher
Fisher-Comfort, Lisa Marie
High School Math Teacher
Ford, David Alan
3rd Grade Teacher
Keelan, Rosemary Romero
9th-12th Grade Spanish Teacher
Mc Carty, Thomas Merrill
Science Teacher
McGraw, Marjorie Watts
Counselor
Romero Keelen, Rosemary
Spanish Teacher
Springhorn, Mary J.
Home Economics Teacher
ANGWIN
McVay, John Kenneth
Assoc Prof of Biblical Stud
Narducci, Kenneth Anthony
Professor of Music
Richards, Dorothy Scott
High School English Instr
Ross, Dottie Ann
5th & 6th Grade Teacher
Trivett, Terrence L.
Professor of Biology
ANTELOPE
Culbert, Susan Marie
6th Grade Teacher
ANTIOCH
Beck, James
Technology Teacher
Burkholtz, Maryann Korch
Drama Teacher
Carademos, Katherine M.
Third & Fourth Grade Teacher
Chaddock, Donna Edie
Freshman English Teacher
Clinch, Theresa Claire
9th Grade English Teacher
DeBacco, Brenda Lynn
Stu Act Dir & PE Teacher
Edwards, Sheri Stanley
Economics & Government Teacher
Fly, Patti DellAntico
Second Grade Teacher
Gengler, Paul
Vice Principal

ANTIOCH (cont)
Goulding, Jeffrey Scott
Physical Ed Teacher & Coach
Griffin, Spencer Dee
5th Grade Teacher
Hurd, Lisa Kidder
Kindergarten Teacher
Kidder, Pam Hawkins
6th Grade Teacher
Klenk, Nancy Ann
French Teacher
Lawrence, Buck Nathan
PE Teacher & Track Coach
Long, Dolores Marie
Vice Principal
Mc Intyre, Edward James
Language Arts Teacher
Molina, Debra Ann
Science Teacher
Nunes, Donna K.
Computers & Into to Bus Tchr
Pulis, David Francis
History & Government Teacher
Robertson, Ron Thomas
Spanish Teacher & Dept Chair
Thomas, Katherine Ross
ESL, French & English Teacher
Thompson, Andrew Robert
English Teacher
Thorsen, Rhonda Williams
Third Grade Classroom Teacher
Tullis, Susan Duckworth
Eng & Decision Making Tchr
VanDerHaeghen, Steven Noel
8th-9th Grade History Teacher
Zinn, Rachel
Principal

ANZA
Alderson, Dale R.
Physical Education Teacher
Boam, Kay
Math & Science Teacher
Richards, Sandra
English Teacher

APPLE VALLEY
Arnt, Lance E.
English Teacher
Arredondo, Raymond
Teacher & Athletic Director
Bahney, Cindy L.
Language Arts Teacher
Bateman, Amy Beth
9th Grd Drama & English Tchr
Bennett, Leslie Winston
English Teacher
Cataneso, James J.
Social Studies Teacher
Corbett, Kathleen Krusinski
8th Grd Language Arts Teacher
Corbin, Lucille M.
English Teacher
Flinn, Janice
Assistant Administrator
Friday, Larry T.
Math & Science Teacher
Garrett, Paul Mark
Fifth Grade Teacher
Jimison, Rick A.
English & Reading Teacher
Lewis, Joel Michael
Spcl Education Teacher
McHugh, Joseph Thomas
4th Grade Teacher
Moore, Carol Marlene
Mathematics Teacher
Morgan, Vicki Lynn (Strang)
2nd-3rd Grd Combination Tchr
Murphy, Kim
English Teacher
Nygaard, Robert S.
Retired Band Director
Pulice, Frank A.
Teacher & Coach
Reed, Julie Austin
4th Grade Teacher
Sundberg, Maureen R.
Math Teacher
Tishner, Keri Lynn (Geverink)
Art Teacher
Wilkins, Sheri Brooks
Resource Specialist
Wyzlic, Gerald W.
Chem Tchr & Sci Dept Chm

APTOS
Barram, Ted
Mathematics Teacher
Bautista, Agustin Nasario
Community Liaison
Dorfman, Mark Richard
Teacher, Ath Dir & Coach
Foltz, Stephen R.
Eng & Creative Writing Teacher
Larson, Gayle
AP US History Teacher
Moscatel, Carolyn Pontuso
7th Grd Language Arts Teacher
Schwartz, David Lee
Geology & Oceanography Instr
Zieler, H. P.
Basic Math Instructor

ARCADIA
Chiu, Jenny Fwee-Yin
Chemistry Teacher
Cummings, Christina Waltz
Spanish Teacher
Dunn, Carol Isabel
Retired French Teacher
Gollhardt, Karen Rank
Sixth Grade Teacher
Hom, Larry G.
5th Grade Teacher
Huntzinger, Penney Maria
English & Journalism Teacher
Laidlaw, Jack O.
Art & Film Teacher
Loomis, Greg John
7th & 9th Grd Literature Tchr
Lucas, Diane Brazier
Curr Specialist & Music Tchr
Maxwell, Susan Fellows
Spanish Teacher
Onderdonk, Richard Pierce
US History Teacher
Peritore, Fred Anthony
US History, Speech & Govt Tchr
Ritter, Cynthia Barton
6th Grade Teacher
Sarrail, Teresa M.
Fifth Grade Teacher
Shultz, Donald Lee
English Teacher
Silverstein, Sanford Edwin
English Teacher
Sitarz, Kathryn Berry
Junior High Teacher
Sutro, Edmund J.
Social Studies Teacher
Topalian, Melanie S.
Fifth Grade Teacher
Tuttle, Georgette Susanne (Nicassio)
Fine Arts Teacher & Dept Chm
Walker, Donna Lobdell
Mathematics Teacher
Yu, Sharyn Doy
Math Teacher
Zeuli, Merilyn Anne
Seventh Grade Humanities Tchr

ARCATA
Angles, Julie Ann
English Teacher
Armin-Hoiland, Louis
Bio Teacher, Math & Sci Chair
Byrne, Chris ALan
School Psychologist
Cavanagh, Pamela Ford
English Teacher
Curry, Jane W.
Sixth Grade Teacher
Hildebrand, Greg Marcus
Physical Science Teacher
Lovato, Susan Stoob
Mathematics Teacher
Shaddix, Michael Scott
7th Grd Lang Arts Teacher
Stewart, Shelley Christine
English Teacher

ARMONA
Dove, Cynthia Taylor
Sixth Grade Teacher
Knecht, Vickie Sharon
Home Economics & Span Teacher

ARNOLD
Gallo, Deborah Jean
Fourth Grade Teacher

ARROYO GRANDE
Anderson, Robin Renee
Teacher
Bamford, Dan R.
Sixth Grade Teacher
Birlew, Rachael A.
First Grade Teacher
Byars, Jeff W.
Business Teacher & Coach
Edmondson, George Robert
English Teacher
Ertman, Christine Marie
Social Studies Teacher
Goss, Kathleen Bonfiglio
High School Math Teacher
Heaton, Susan L.
Special Education Teacher
House, Rod
Amer Govt & World His Teacher
Keetch, Linda Gamber
English Teacher
Kraker, Gretchen Marie
English Teacher
Kwid, Thomas Anthony
6th Grade Teacher
Menchaca, Santos
Sixth Grade Teacher
Wade, Laura Ann
High School English Teacher
Willems, Stanley Alvin
Math, Science & Bible Teacher

ARTESIA
Becker, Sherry Lynn
6th Grade GATE Teacher
Bender, Paul F.
Chemistry Teacher
Bodger, Cheryl L.
Second Grade Teacher
Bohannon, David G.
AP US History Teacher
Charmack, JoAnne L.
US Govt, Politics & His Tchr
Crissman, William Heber
World Geography & History Tchr
Dardenelle, Allen G.
Science Teacher
DeBie, Harold Courtney
His, Drivers Ed Tchr & Ath Dir
Goodrich, Theora Barnes
Activities Director
Kaemingk, Kelly Renee
7th Grade Mathematics Teacher
King, Patricia Brown
5th Grade GATE Teacher
Koemingl, Kevin Dale
Principal
Lau, Diane McLaughlin
Mathematics Department Chair
Mato, Vicki Yumi
Fifth Grade Teacher
Mazur, Larry Edward
4th Grade Teacher
Mc Gill, Anne Shapiro
Fourth Grade Teacher
Oyama, Eilene T.
Japanese Teacher
Smits, Mert Sinkey
English Instr & Dept Head
Stallard, Earl Lee
7th-8th Grd Math Teacher
Tanaka, Kristine Uragami
Mathematics Teacher
Terhorst, Lynda
English Teacher
Turek, Philip A.
Physics Teacher
Williams, Julietta Curry
Third Grade Teacher
Wirt, Lynn Henderson
Schl Improvement Coord

ARVIN
Irby, Candice Shutte
English & Journalism Teacher

ATASCADERO
Cappellano, Paul Anthony
Substitute Teacher & Coach
Delmartini, Sandra Mc Cartney
English Teacher
DeRose, Salvatore Michele
Physical Ed Instructor & Coach
Dery, B. Robin M.
Spanish Teacher
Desist, Cathie Carr
Sixth Grade Teacher
Lorimer, Katherine Frances (White)
Music Teacher
Martin, James W.
Computer Technology Teacher
Michalojko, Martha Mary
English Teacher
Tanimoto, Jerry H.
Teacher & Activities Director

ATHERTON
Barrette, Cheryl Ann
1st Grade Teacher
Brodkey, Jerry Joseph
Math & Social Studies Teacher
Buxton, Tanya Bauriedel
Science Teacher
Cook, Janice Beuttell
French Teacher & Academic Adv
Enenstein, Robert L.
Math & Computer Science Tchr
Fox, Susan
History Teacher
Leeper, Mark
Industrial Arts Dept Chair
Morris, Kristen Miner
French Teacher
Newman, Kevin Thomas
History Teacher
Ogren, Stanley Vernon
Biology Teacher & Dept Chair
Petersen, Allen H.
Mathematics Teacher
Thompson, Kenneth John
Math Dept Chair

ATWATER
Campbell, Suzanne Louise
3rd & 4th Grade Teacher
Johnson-Russell, Jane Margaret
Spanish Teacher
Sullivan, John Thomas
Mathematics Teacher
Verrinder, Gary Edwin
Sixth Grade Teacher

AUBERRY
Van Horbecke, Bill
Fifth Grade Teacher

AUBURN
Chandler, Doris A. Harrington
MS Teacher & Admin Assistant
Crosby, Ellen Mc Coy
CARE Program Coordinator
Haverberg, Sylvia Harnes
English, Lit & His Teacher
Hicks, Lisl Von Storch
Third Grade Teacher
Metrock, Beth Kay (Nelson)
English Teacher
Paris, Shirley Frances
Eng, Lit & History Teacher
Pitzer, Stacey Alison
Kindergarten Teacher
Prero, Michael Dwayne
Seventh Grade GATE Core Tchr
Robinson, Jennifer Michele
French & Spanish Teacher
Sigismond, Florence
Retired 6th Grade GATE Teacher
Thomasson, Melody Marie
Fourth & Fifth Grade Teacher
Wessels, Stephanie (Maurias)
7th Grade CORE Teacher

AVENAL
Tuck, Glenn A.
History Teacher

AVERY
Fessenden, Price Allen
Science Teacher
Solomon, Georgia Triscik
Coordinator of Home Schl Acad

AZUSA
Bonner, Cheryl L.
5th Grade Teacher
Cathey, Rodney Randolph
School of Music Instructor
Gahring, Sandra Steward
PE Teacher, Ath Dir & Trainer
Gyler, Diana Pavlac
Assistant Professor of English
Keedy, Judy Ann
Physical Education Teacher
Mc Cormick, Lawrence Ray
Communication Professor
Murray, Charles Robert
Mathematics Teacher
Scott, Steve
High School ESL Teacher

BAKER
O'Byrnes, Fred J.
Social Studies Teacher

BAKERSFIELD
Anderson, Cliffton
Science Teacher
Austin, Alan K.
Counselor
Bautista, Melanie Landis
Fifth Grade Teacher
Berdahl, Kelly
Instrumental Music Director
Borel, Michele Matlock
Jr HS Language Arts Teacher
Brewer, David John
History, Government Instructor
Brown, Ron
English Teacher
Cherry, Wayne
Math Teacher
Chrisco, Cathi Tilton
Eighth Grade US History Tchr
Collins, Bettie Jo Ozanich
English Teacher
Conley, Elaine Higgins
English Teacher
Dalke, Irvin Wendell
Math Teacher & Dept Chairman
Daniel, William Michael
Chemistry Professor
Dauwalder, Timothy Jay
Biology Teacher
Davis, Essie Robbins
Title I & IASA Coordinator
Dilbeck, Ginger Carol Bozarth
Lang Arts & Soc Studies Tchr
DiMundo-Grabski, Carol D.
Administrator & Prgm Coord
Dixon, Ethel Mae Sherman
Community Counselor
Dow, Ed A.
6th Grade Teacher
Dunham, Doris Hopwood
General Mathematics Teacher
Eales, James Lee
Social Studies Teacher
Frindell, Elizabeth A.
English & Forensics Teacher
Gabbitas, Donald S.
Government Teacher
Giese, Richard Eugene
Science Instructor
Green, Timothy Blake
Adult Schl Math, Ind Stud Tchr
Grimes, Russell Dorsey, III
Math & Opportunity Instructor
Handy, Susan Laverty
Counselor & Nursing Instructor
Hanley, David Brady
Bio, Life Sci & Mentor Teacher
Harriger, Kevin H.
GATE Social Science Teacher
Hartnett, Timothy John
PE Teacher & Coach
Heiller, Clarendon Swift
Professor of Math & Philosophy
Heiser, Patti S.
School Counselor
Henry, Walter LaMarr
Sixth Grade Teacher
Holland, Craig
Government & History Teacher
Hulbert, Shaun Philip
English Teacher
Jachetti, Cynthia Gilbert
English & Literature Teacher
Jensen, Steven W.
Teacher of the Deaf
Keeler, David N.
Sixth Grade Teacher
Keller, Janie Cumberford
5th Grd Math Focus Coordinator
Laskowski, Suzanne Maria Wingfield
First Grade Teacher
Letlow, Joan Lindsay
Curriculum Specialist
MacLean, Lea Edwards
English & Graphic Arts Tchr
Main, William Roy
6th Grd Core Tchr, Drama Coach
Maloney, Harry Anthony
English Teacher
Marsh, Dell-Louise (Fobes)
French & Spanish Teacher
Mata, Ricardo
English as Second Lang Tchr
Maurer, Germaine Allison
Sixth Grade Teacher
Mc Junkin, Dirk Patrick
Phys Ed Tchr & Dept Chair
Mc Knelly, Terry Richard
Technology Teacher
McQuerrey, Lawrence Michael
HS Choral Music Teacher
Mensing, Amy Elaine (Arnold)
Sixth Grade Teacher
Minyard, James Patrick
Spanish Teacher
Moore, Jan (Turner)
5th Grade Teacher & Vice Prin
Munn, Jeannie Lagera
English Teacher
Murillo, Hector Joseph
English & Speech Comm Tchr
Napier, Anthony John
Social Studies Teacher
Neal, Bruce Robert
5th Grade Classroom Tchr
Nix, Margery Jones (Leonard)
Biology Teacher
Parviainen, William John, III
Am Govt, Ec & World Hist Tchr
Peoples, Maureen Annette
English Teacher
Perrone, Kathy
Fifth Grade Teacher
Phillips, Debra J.
Third Grade Teacher
Picking, Dorothy Whisler
4th Grade Teacher
Randell, Gary George
3rd Grade Teacher
Ravotti-Danka, Celeste
3rd Grade Teacher
Rayford, Ruthann Doyel
8th Grd Language Arts Teacher
Rozell, Elizabeth Morris
Associate Professor of Math
Ryall, Mary Sylvia
Fourth & Fifth Grade Teacher
Sausedo, Rob William
Soc Stud Tchr & Bsktbl Coach
Schmalhorst, Valerie Woods
Social Studies Dept Chair
Silva, Dolores L.
Second Grade Teacher
Sipe-Russell, Nina Riddle
Sixth Grade Tchr & Choir Dir
Snelling, Patricia West
Teacher
Stamper, Ray Dean
7th Grade Social Studies Tchr
Steele, Gayle A.
Sixth Grade Teacher
Stein, Linda Marie
Visiting Assistant Professor
Stephens, Robert R.
Fifth Grade Teacher
Swisher, Joel Ray
World History Teacher
Taglieri, Fabio
ROTC Instructor
Tanner, Grace Arvidson
Kindergarten Teacher
Taylor, Diana Mederos
Fourth Grade Teacher
Turner, Verna-Lea
English Teacher
Wall, Charles C.
Management Professor
Young, Andrew
Science Teacher
Zeimet, Robert M.
Physics Teacher
Zent, Linda J. Alexander
Third Grade Teacher
Ziegler, Annette Marie-Siem
Science Teacher

BALDWIN PARK
Arvidson, Mark
Mathematics Instructor
Colletta, James Daniel
History & Social Studies Tchr
Cozen, Dennis H.
Mathematics Teacher
Harri, Vickie F.
Science Teacher
Harris, Melissa A.
3rd & 4th Grade Teacher
Itagaki, Shirl M.
Math Teacher
Jioras, Shawni Christine
4th Grade Elementary Teacher
Kalantarian, Dan
Instrumental Music Director
Kruckeberg, James Karlton
Physics Teacher
Lancaster, Jerilyn Elaine
Multi-Age Teacher
Mc Cafferty, Sean Francis
Sixth Grade Teacher
Messick, Ralph G.
Retired Teacher
Messina, Suzanne Patrice
High School Business Teacher
Sterling, Terry Warshaw
Drill Team & Physical Ed Tchr
Tomei, Rodney Katsumi
Mathematics Teacher

BANNING
Bederio, Martha Steele
5th Grade Teacher
Figueroa, Cheryl Thompson
MS Electives Teacher
Hendricks, Christy Jo
Secondary English Teacher
Hunt, Nancy Sue
4th Grade Teacher
Partain, Larry W.
5th Grade Teacher
Rice, Elsa J.
6th Grade Language Arts Tchr

STOW
Rhonda Sue
iness Teacher
Linda Cathleen
Grade Algebra Teacher
Mary Ung
Grade Teacher
Sue Lindsey
ld His & Soc Stud Teacher
ch, Morrie Allan
sical Education Teacher
sen, Maria Clark
h School English Teacher
Patricia Stevens
lish Teacher
, Patricia Louise-Schatz
lish & Speech Teacher
npson, Lesley Crystine
ial Science Instructor
ey, Carolyn
n Instrumental Music Tchr
UMONT
rds, Ron Frederic
Industrial Technology Tchr
e, Laurie A.
ence Teacher
eman, Earl L.
Dept Chair & Mentor Tchr
L
, JoAnn
Grd Self-Contained Tchr
antes, Evangelina Rios
ngual Teacher
., David R.
cher
, Beverly A.
vernment & Economics Teacher
ette, Felicitas Maria
L & Span Teacher
y, Herbert James, Sr.
ence Teacher
nillo, Robert Marshall
mentary Bilingual Teacher
inez, Raul
-8th Grade Bilingual Tchr
er, Mark Richard
unselor
no, Kizen
glish Teacher
agyi, Kristin Barmore
glish Teacher
sco, Salvador Antonio
cial Studies & English Tchr
L GARDENS
Gloria LeGrant
-2nd Grade Teacher
aksin, John V.
bstitute Teacher
ers, Betty Jean (Conlin)
g Jrnlsm Tchr, Newspaper Adv
enberg, Arthur Lee
dustrial Drawing Teacher
h, Stanley M.
History & Humanities Tchr
as, Natalia M.
ience Teacher
LA VISTA
more, Elsbeth Pieper
alth & PE Teacher
LFLOWER
tista, Michael Norman
soc Pastor
, Jon
emistry Teacher
is, Samuel C.
anish Tchr & Assoc Dir
, Florence Ruth
cond Grade Teacher
stma, Pamela Joan
d Grade Teacher
ares, Robert Joseph
hemistry & Biology Teacher
Kinley, Colleen Kennedy
ath Teacher
aker, Paul David
h Grade Teacher
zo, Peter William
S History Teacher
ler, Betty S.
usic Teacher
ee, Michael Scott
S Mathematics Teacher
ith, Teri Hellman
nglish & Social Studies Tchr
ite, James W.
ibrary Media Teacher
ett, Penny Zens
h Grade Teacher
LMONT
nilton, Laurel Louise
ighth Grade Teacher
nson, Melvyn L.
ath Teacher
vas, Glenn Lee
ccounting, EC & PE Teacher
rta, David Joseph
uropean World History Tchr
hn, Lucy Peters
eligious Studies Chair
der, Lisa Swann
athematics Teacher
queira, Barbara Coughlan
1th Grade Religious Stud Tchr
uchiyama, Robert Todd
ath Teacher
igler Mano, Rebecca Maile
nglish Teacher
N LOMOND
ok, John M.
ourth Grade Teacher

Templeman, Richard Allison
Retired History Teacher
BENICIA
Altman, Kristopher Raymond
Social Science Teacher
Anderson, Wanda Mick
Fifth Grade Teacher
Borges, Amy Parker
Kndgtn Teacher
Ferrucci, Diane B.
8th Grd English & History Tchr
Garrett, James M.
Social Science Teacher
Houser, Douglas Gene
Chemistry & Physics Teacher
Macheel, Roxanna Ralphs
Band Director
Muth, Rami L.
8th Grade His & Eng Teacher
Switzer, Alan James
Math Department Chairman
Turner, Walt
Teacher & Health Dept Chair
Washicko, Marilyn K.
English Teacher
BERKELEY
Ball, Jack Howard
PE Teacher
Berezin, Joan Ellen
History Instructor
Enriquez, Laura J.
Asst Professor of Sociology
Fox, Roberta Kathleen
Eighth Grade Teacher
Geritz, Kathleen Ann
Film History Lecturer
Glenchur, Kristin Anne
English Teacher
Kirkpatrick, Patricia Ann
Writing & English Instructor
Martin, Joyce Ann
6th Grd & Art Teacher
Mc Knight, Robert L.
African Amer Stud Dept Chprsn
Menard, Gary Eugene
Former Math & Computer Teacher
Miller, Craig Lee
Advanced Biology Teacher
Murphy-Stickney, Judith Lisa
English Dept Chprsn & Lit Tchr
Nyanda, Christine Akelo D.
Kiswahili Club Advisor
Panasenko, Alexander
Science Instructor
Peterson, Lois Ann
Biology Teacher
Polos, Iris Stephanie
Art Teacher
Price, Paul Buford
Dean of Physical Sciences
Rapson, Jeff
English Teacher
Revsen, Brenda Judith
Kindergarten Teacher
Ryken, Amy E.
Schl & Industry Coord
Sims, Annis Jean (Miles)
World & American History Tchr
Wada, Ada Yoneko
Math Teacher
Webb, Mary H.
Instructor of Creative Writing
BEVERLY HILLS
Beatty, Roberta A.
English Teacher
Fitch, Thomas G.
Mathematics Teacher
Hiatt, William Allen
English Teacher
Irmas, Todd Ethan
Spanish Teacher & Coach
Mead, Diane Winslow
Eng as Second Language Tchr
Merritt, Kay Wren
English Teacher
Shwartz, Michelle Siteman
6th Grade Teacher
Sprouse, Richard William
Amer His & Political Sci Tchr
Stern, Irene Greenberg
Assistant Principal
Thorpe, Gary Stephen
Chemistry Instructor
BIG BEAR LAKE
Bradley, Joseph Charles
Physics Teacher
Meyers, Paul Brian
Counselor
BIGGS
Hansen, Marla D.
Lang Arts & Soc Stud Tchr
Orrell, Carolyn L.
MS Teacher
Smith, Janet Jennie Danz
First Grade Teacher
BISHOP
Burgoyne, Jody
1st Grade Teacher
Gibson, Laura M.
English Teacher
Rowbottom, James W.
Mathematics Teacher
Scott, Carol Hobson
Frgn Lang Dept Chair & Fr Tchr
BLOOMINGTON
Craw, Robert L.
Mathematics Teacher
Cunningham, Delores Dee
Kindergarten Teacher

Dreiberg, Denver Chris
High School Business Teacher
Folkens, Scott L.
Social Studies Teacher
Molner, Vic
Principal
Sandoval, David Chavira
Assistant Principal
Teel, Marta Pastor
World Languages Dept Chair
Tran, Hanh My
High School English Teacher
BLYTHE
Bacus, Connie Heater
2nd Grade Teacher
Holt, Raymond Bernard
Auto Technology Instructor
Koester, Fred H.
Instr of Mathematics & Chem
Lish, Terrance J.
Professor of English & Speech
Maly, Lonn David
Principal & Teacher
Michel, Diane Louise
Psychology Instructor
Nesmith, Morris Ralston
Choral-Instrumental Music Tchr
Ponder, William Hendricks, III
Professor of CIS Bus Dept
Scott, Kenneth M.
High School Counselor
Siddall, Denise Eveline
Seventh Grade Soc Stud Teacher
BOONVILLE
Taussig, Karen Michele
Science Teacher
Tomlin, James Robert
Vice Principal
BORREGO SPRINGS
Darwin, Janet Slater
HS English Teacher & Counselor
Riolo, Linda Button
K-1st Grade Teacher
BOULDER CREEK
Billings, Judith Diane
Sixth Grade Teacher
BRAWLEY
Archer, MaryAnn Geranen
Mathematics Teacher
Cress, Deborah O.
Spanish Teacher
Eager, Darryl C.
Mathematics Teacher
Gauna, Emma S.
6th Grade Bilingual Teacher
Stauf, Edward Daniel, Jr.
Agriculture Teacher
BREA
Davis, Mary Lee Bastiaans
Physics Teacher
Hiskey, Steve
English & Phys Education Tchr
Hufferd, Dorcas A.
English & Journalism Teacher
Kennan, Lynn E.
AP AM Govt & Comp Pol Tchr
Lee, Toriann Valerie
English as Second Lang Teacher
Schultz, Carrie Christine Concialdi
Science Teacher
Sink, Jeffrey Carter
AP US History Teacher
VanGeloof, Kimber Lee
English Teacher
Walter, Lucille M.
Fifth Grade Teacher
Whitton, Lee Mc Lanahan
Fourth Grade Teacher
BRENTWOOD
Black, Jerry D.
Counselor
Blackburn, Paul
Sixth Grade Math & Sci Tchr
Borunda, Rose Mary
Counselor
Campbell, Eunice Nealeigh
High School English Teacher
Curtis, Chad Wesley
Second Grade Teacher
Dodson, John A.
Social Studies Teacher
Ghilarducci, Linda Rosa
Physical Education Teacher
Groseclose, Wanda Westman
Art & Language Arts Teacher
Jefferson, Annette Arredondo
Teacher
Lyles, Karen Ellen
Administrator & Teacher
Maedke, Deborah Lea
Spanish Teacher
Malkin, Judy Laurie
English Teacher
Nash, Jo Anne Stickrad
Math Dept Chair
Pedrotti, Hillary Fairbairn
English Teacher
Pirtle, Reta A.
Business Education Teacher
Plato, James B.
Computer Science Teacher
Rios, Juan Francisco
High School Spanish Teacher
Stillwell, Valorie Sinclair
Math Teacher
Watanabe, Karyn Foster
English Teacher
BUENA PARK
Anderson, Juanita Sue
Third Grade Teacher

Campbell, Theresa Marie Chiado
Consumer Science Dept Chairman
Elliott, Marilyn A.
Sixth Grade Teacher
Emerson, Judith Stanford
Sixth Grade Teacher
Jason, John Edward
6th Grade Teacher
Porras, Sandra Cabot
Physical Education Teacher
Shoulders, Lucy Moon
English Teacher
Sterling, Douglas Charles
History Teacher
Tillman, JeAnne Skidmore
English Teacher
Utter, Dorothiy Wilder
Combination Teacher
BURBANK
Alvarado-Sheikhi, Darlene
7th Grade Spanish Teacher
Bunch, Ted Duane
History Teacher
Cadny, Fitzmichael
Spanish & French Instructor
Campbell, Steve
Cluster Coord & Eng Teacher
DiSabatino, Peter A.
Assoc Prof of Architecture
Dungereaux, Rosa Ponce
Foreign Lang Chprsn & Teacher
Everhart, Michael George
MS Physical Education Teacher
Faust, Cynthia Bell
Third Grade Teacher
Hacker, Janette Marie
World & US History Teacher
Harjani, Arjan
Health Careers Prog Dir & Tchr
Johnson, Larry G.
Fifth Grade Teacher
Kitchel, June
Business Education Instructor
Koontz-Black, Julie Kaestle
Classroom Teacher
Marshall, Thomas Simon
AP US History Teacher
Nicolay, Lisa Campbell
Music Teacher
Rago, Mary J. (Kolegreff)
Choral Director
Reyes, Juan-Carlos
Span Tchr & Frgn Lang Dept Chm
Roberts, Jill Louise
Lead Kindergarten Teacher
Sucgang, Paul Santos
Biology Teacher
Tada, Ken
Social Studies Teacher
Turk, William C.
Sr Lecturer of Human Resources
Urioste, Emilio Javier, Jr.
Foreign Lang Tchr & Dept Chair
Webb-McHorney, Suzanne
Language Arts Teacher
Weiss, Barbara Miller
6th & 7th Grd Science Teacher
Wyatt, Carolyn LaVonne
Dance Teacher
Yates, Karen
Special Education Teacher
BURLINGAME
Cerny, Mark James
Judo Teacher
Csota, Carol Ann (Mangini)
Social Science Teacher
Firpo, Frank B.
History Teacher
Mammon, Judith Diane
Spanish Teacher
Nelson, Kevin Ross
Social Studies Teacher
Newton, Carla Hennings
Future Problem Solving Coach
O'Connor, Norma Wregg
Retired ESL Instrl Aide
Oshita, Steven K.
Science Teacher
Saito, Walter Jiro
Math Teacher
Welch, Kevin F.
Counselor
Wolff, Karen Lloyd
Vice Principal
BURNEY
Diezsi, Cynthia Primeau
Teacher
CALABASAS
Kayastha, Satish Lal
Math Teacher
Scissors, Michelle Aisenberg
Frgn Lang Dept Chm & Span Tchr
Wade, Cindy Jones
Spanish & History Teacher
Walker, Larry A.
Chemistry Teacher
Willson, Joan C.
Social Science Teacher
CALEXICO
Belcher, Herlinda
History Teacher
Castro, Ruben
8th Grade Math Teacher
Cota, Yolanda Duarte
Spanish & AVID Teacher
Ferrell, Luman Grover, Jr.
Biology Instructor
Gaytan, Julio Camacho
Spanish Teacher

Lacaze, Linda Fugate
Math Teacher
Larsson, Harold John
Astronomy, Chem & Math Tchr
Marlowe, Jay Patrich
English & Literature Teacher
Martinez, Mario
Chem Tchr & Sci Dept Chprsn
Moreno, Juan Manuel
5th Grade Teacher
Pond, Dennis Samuel
Music Teacher
Rubio, Sergio A.
US History, Govt & Ec Instr
Schelske, Joanne Belinda
10th & 11th Grade English Tchr
Thompson, Arelys Adriana
Eng Dept Head & Drama Tchr
Yturralde, Fred Ismael
Sixth Grade Teacher
Zamarripa, Frances Gracia
First Grade Bilingual Teacher
CALIENTE
Miller, Diane Vogel
Sixth Grade Teacher
CALIMESA
Dennis, Winston Robert, III
Vocal Music Director
CALIPATRIA
Schoonover, Lynda
English Teacher
CALISTOGA
Dill, Donna Funke
Fifth & Sixth Grade Teacher
Sary, Phil W.
Science, Math & Bio Teacher
CAMARILLO
Asher, Kathy Lynn (Mulloy)
5th Grade Teacher
Bjork, Marilyn Fournier
Performing Arts Teacher
Brannock, Mary Malde
English Teacher
Covert, Billie Frances
Assistant Principal
Fuerst-Dallape, Kimberley Ann
7th & 8th Grd Eng & His Tchr
Hansen, David Bruce
8th Grd Art & Photography Tchr
Hood, Milton Herbert
Latin, Sci & Mathematics Tchr
Koch, Holly Joan
6th & 7th Grd Lang Arts Tchr
Loll, Elizabeth Theriault
Fourth Grade Teacher
Potter, Herbert Thomas, Jr.
Counselor
Resnik, Heidi Joy
English Teacher
Rundlett, Nathan S.
Chemistry Teacher
Santiago, Mamerta Magdalena
9th-12th Grade Math Teacher
Swaringen, Elizabeth Anne
Jr HS Teacher
CAMBRIA
Clayton, Susan Deonne
Guidance Counselor
Di Mundo, George John
Mathematics Teacher
Leopold, Helen Hopkins
Teacher
Paul, Mary Ann
High School English Teacher
CAMINO
Cline, Carol Ann
Kindergarten Teacher
Montgomery, Adele M. (Carpenter)
Lang Arts & Soc Stud Core Tchr
CAMPBELL
Darnell-Johnston, Dana Alyce
English Teacher
Matthews, Cynthia Hurwitz
English Teacher
Okita, Charles
9th-12th Grd Eng Lang Dev Tchr
Perreira, Anthony Gregory, Jr.
Guidance Teacher
Zimmer, Susan C.
8th Grade CORE Teacher
CAMPO
Brisbois, Brian Alan
Third & Fourth Grade Teacher
CANBY
Herlin, N. Catherine
Classroom Teacher
CANOGA PARK
Agopian, Kevork H.
Science Teacher & Dept Chair
Burt, Christine Hodson
English Teacher & Dept Chprsn
Cassidenti, John P.
History Teacher
Danhof, Eric Todd
Eng Tchr & Dept Chprsn
Doyle, Thomas E.
History & Humanities Teacher
Greer, Thomas H.
History Teacher & Coach
Hagopian, Hagop
Principal
Ishakian, Hermeen Sahagian
Armenian Lang & His Teacher
Jamieson, Peter Edward
ESL Teacher & Tech Coord
Kotlerman, Jenny Brook
Math Teacher
Langton, Arthur
Physical Science Teacher

CANOGA PARK (cont)
Lischke, Janeal Irene
Fifth Grade Teacher
Momjian, Arek
Fourth Grade Teacher
Pentland, Pamela (Ness)
Third Grade Teacher
Pirkl, Janyth Fox
5th Grade Teacher
Taylor, Pamela Trotter
6th-8th Grd Mathematics Tchr
Tomita, Yoko (Kurokawa)
Fourth Grade Teacher
Young, Jeffrey Thomas
Geometry & PE Teacher
CANYON COUNTRY
Gilpin, Randall Eric
Band Director & Music Teacher
Gise, Cindy
Kindergarten Teacher
Hayes, Gregory Michael
Social Studies Teacher
Johnson, William B.
World History Teacher
King, Pamela Jean
Biology Teacher
Kraeger, Cathy Cox
Spanish Teacher
LeBarron, David Nelson
Assistant Principal
Ledbetter, Donna (La Motte)
2nd Grade Teacher
Mohr, Lawrence Vincent
Special Education Teacher
Price, Jean Miles
English Teacher
Schaeffer, Alan
Mathematics Teacher
Silsbee, Robert Craig
Eighth Grade Amer History Tchr
Thomas, Matthew Mac Dermid
Assistant Principal
Welch, Cindee Ellen
Counselor
White, Elvira A.
Sixth Grade Teacher
Zuckman, Shelley Hope
Fifth Grade Teacher
CAPO BEACH
Sylstra, Melinda Divel
Jr High His Teacher
CARLSBAD
Benowitz, Jeanne Stevens
6th Grade Teacher
Crampton, Susana Casey
Social Studies Teacher
DeCino, Paige Allison
Biology Teacher
Dixson, Thomas R.
Science Technology Teacher
Dobbs, Elizabeth L.
ESL & Creative Wrtng Tchr
Elliott, Christine Parr
English Teacher
Green, Douglas John
English Teacher
Hering, Thomas Paul
Principal & Teacher
Livingston, Christine A.
5th Grade Teacher
O'Donnell, Tanya Vone (Anderson)
Retired Teacher
Palenscar, Tom
Science Teacher
Reidy, Michael H.
Math Teacher
Riccitelli, Jeffrey Steven
Spanish Teacher
Roncaglia, Harleen Locke
Fifth Grade Teacher
CARMEL
Alan, Shelley A.
French & English Teacher
Greco, Nikki Bennetts
Language Art Tchr & Dept Head
Selby, Victor Marshall
Math Teacher
CARMEL VALLEY
Simmons, Jen
5th Grade Teacher
Smith, Phillip Lyn
Fifth Grade Teacher
CARMICHAEL
Bakken, Carolyn Holm
English Teacher & Dept Chair
Baldwin, Elaine Darby
Fifth Grade Teacher
Coleman, Marie Lima
Sixth Grade Teacher
Dunlap, Kris Kenneth
Mathematics Teacher
Luttrell, Elizabeth Jayne (Johns)
Teacher & Coach
Potter, B. Irene
K-6th Grd Substitute Teacher
Pratt, James Thomas
Social Science Teacher
Shedd, Ann Levis
Asst Prin & 4th Grd Teacher
Walsh, Kathleen Curran
Eighth Grade Tchr & Vice Prin
Waltz, Nancy Felts
Sixth Grade Teacher
Wofford, Robert Wayne
8th Grade Science Teacher
CARPINTERIA
Feaver, Ann Silva
1st & 2nd Grade Teacher
Geary, Welles
Computers & Physical Ed Tchr
Hoff, Elisabeth Chowning
English Teacher
Lindsay, Robert Bruce
Science Department Chair
Robins, Ross Porter
English Teacher
Slattery, Dennis Patrick
Interdisciplinary Coordinator
CARSON
Bergen, Daniel Michael
Special Education Teacher
Brotherton, Joseph Anthony
Math Teacher
Cappel, Mary Lou Schuler
Associate Professor
Cherin, Patricia
Writing Lab Director
Dutko, Joseph John
Physics Teacher
Ellis, Patricia L.
12th Grade AP Eng Teacher
Feuer, Lois Eisenstadt
Professor of English
Harrell, Delores Brown
6th Grade Soc Stud & Eng Tchr
Kakita, Patricia Joyce
Ldrshp Adv & Spcl Ed Teacher
Masson, Richard R.
Athletic Asst Dir & PE Tchr
Mathieu, Susan Leifer
Lecturer of Recreation Admin
Morrow, Birdie Lee
Secondary English Teacher
Nachef, Joanna Medawar
Music & Humanities Professor
Perkins, Richard Rodger
History Instructor
Peterson, Honor A.
4th Grade Teacher
Sakurai, Micheal Alan
Health & Physical Ed Teacher
Sharrar, James
German Teacher
Simmons, Patricia White
English Teacher
Toilolo, Lui Ierenimo
7th Grade Teacher
Weiner, Sydell
Professor of Theatre Arts
Zahary, Robert Gene
Assoc VP of Academic Planning
CARUTHERS
Paul, Robert A.
Bands Director
Richardson, Brian Todd
HS Bio Tchr & Athletic Dir
Spurling, Stan M.
Math & Science Teacher
CASTRO VALLEY
Arenson, Ethan A.
Mathematics Teacher
Atlas, Eileen Karp
Social Studies Dept Chair
Baldo, Peter Lawrence
Fifth Grade Teacher
Brophy, Tim Sean
Math & Physical Education Tchr
Bucklin, Terri Lynn
English Teacher
Cleveland, Patricia Davis
Fourth Grade Teacher
Costa, Judi L.
Eighth Grade English Teacher
Crater, Lyle William
5th Grade Teacher
DeGrazia, MaryAnn Jarvis
6th Grade Teacher & Team Ldr
Garcia, Katie Kinnear
English Teacher & Mentor
Hayes, Gretchen
6th Grade Teacher
Householder, Michael Bennett
English Teacher
Jones, Alma Zacur
Third Grade Teacher
Kemp, April Rolston
Science Teacher
Kutcher, Joseph Daniel
Science Teacher
Meyer, Cynthia Ann
Music Coord & Dir of Bands
Mitchell, Glenn Kevin
Mathematics Teacher
Orluck, Debra Ronayne
First Grade Teacher
Parris, Anne Witmer
English Teacher
Rutherford, LeeAnn
Lang Arts Tchr & Act Dir
Shoptaw, Shauna Lynn
English & Drama Teacher
Taylor, Kathryn Anne
HS Mathematics Teacher
Wallace, Kimberly Ann
English Teacher
CASTROVILLE
Andrews, Kelly Greelis
Dance Instructor
Beagley, Dale William
History Teacher
Forgette, Tom
High School Teacher
Grummon, Whitney Elisabeth
American Literature Teacher
Marshall-Carrillo, Elizabeth L.
HS Health Science Teacher
Parry, Dena D.
HS Physical Education Teacher
Schnelle, Cynthia Ann
Science Teacher
Uccelli, Gina Elizabeth (Miller)
Physical Education Teacher
Zwack, Julie Elizabeth
American Literature Teacher
CATHEDRAL CITY
Anzai, Rodney Katsui
AFJTROTC Department Chrmn
Bluto, Yvonne Mc Bride
Band Director
Casillas, Julie Beiser
High School French Teacher
Clark, Teresa Lynn
Counselor & Career Teacher
Fleener, Bradley Bruce
Biology Teacher
Gardner, Lucinda Louise
9th-10th Grade English Teacher
Haas, Madeleine Marie
Art Teacher
Halt, Michael Alan
History Teacher
Hull, Brenda Gene (Personett)
Math Teacher, Department Chair
Leduc, Janet Clair (Pease)
English Teacher
Olszewski, Lynn Rakow
Counselor
Remboldt, Cherry Ann
HS Guidance Counselor & Tchr
Snowden, Niki L.
7th Grd Language Arts Teacher
Stoebe, Steven B.
English Teacher
Theiss, Marlene Desy
History Teacher
CEDARVILLE
De Knikker, Marie I. Collins
Kndgtn, 4th PE & 6th Comp Tchr
Quick, Randy Kevin
5th Grade Teacher
CERES
Alvernaz, Babette Michalec
Elementary Resource Specialist
Chambers, Lee Harrison
German & Business Teacher
Cooper, Linda Reeser
Activity Director
Johnson, Robin Lynn
Physical Education Teacher
Konschak, Lori Whaley
Home Economics Teacher
Lourenco, Robin Fowler
Fifth Grade Teacher
Mc Murray, Laurie Lee
8th Grade Science Teacher
Miller, Elaine Annette
Spanish Teacher
Nichols, Leona Koehn
Publications & Lang Arts Tchr
Snell, Donna R.
Eighth Grade Science Tchr
Teves, Edilberto
Math & ESL Teacher
Wynn, Rusty Dee
Administrator
CERRITOS
Brose, Russell Alan
Mathematics, Computer Sci Tchr
Brown, Ray
English Teacher
Bryce, Mary Arreaga
Spanish Teacher
Flores, Kerry Jean Carney
Third Grade Teacher
Marcus, Ronald Kenneth
7th-8th Grade Math Teacher
Murray, Steve
Calculus & History Teacher
Rommel, Dolores Pucilauskas
Sixth Grade Teacher
Swaaley, Patricia
1st Grade Teacher
Wohlgemuth, Linda Perez
Psychology & Social Sci Tchr
CHATSWORTH
Acosta, Robert J.
Social Studies Instructor
Arnold, Noreen P.
Teacher
Ball, Susan
Secondary English Teacher
Foster, Helen C.
6th Grd Social Studies Teacher
Greenwald, David Marshall
4th Grd Teacher & Team Leader
Stone, Susie S.
Counselor
Weiler, Barbara Boldt
Kindergarten Teacher
CHESTER
Killingsworth, Gregory James
Business Teacher
Lake, Brooke A.
7th-8th Grd Eng & Yrbk Tchr
Pintel, Victor L.
Spanish & English Teacher
Rice, Don S.
English Instructor
CHICO
Barsuglia, Elizabeth Batliere
English Teacher
Bauer, David Harold
Psychology Professor
Bender, Daryl Wayne
Sixth Grade Teacher
Bertapelle, Barbara Jean (Haeussler)
Science Teacher
Carroll, Sharon Lynn
Fourth Grade Teacher
Christensen, Michael Donald
Mathematics Teacher
Clark, Herb
6th Grade Teacher
Cook, Crystal Kay
Fifth Grade Teacher
Cox, Kristine Lynn
9th & 11th Grd English Teacher
Davis, Janice Kay
6th Grade Teacher
Dillman, Bruce
Science Teacher
Flynn, Ramona Rodriguez
History & English Teacher
Fredrickson, Leslie Evan
Social Science Teacher
George, T. A.
Mathematics & Science Teacher
Hostettler, Stephen G.
English & Fine Arts Teacher
Jensen, Mary Cihak
Professor
Klassy, Michele Diane
Sixth Grade Teacher
Lampkin, Thomas E.
Physics & Chemistry Teacher
Levi, Annette E.
Ag Business Professor
Logan, Ed R.
Art Instructor
Lutz, Barbara Elliott
Fourth Grade Teacher
Marshall, Deedra Lawrence
Language Arts Teacher
Marshall, Stephanie
English & Language Arts Tchr
Matthews, Gary Edward
Fifth Grade Teacher
Mc Knight, Claudia Ann
Title I Resource Teacher
Miller, Karen Germaine
English Teacher
Murdoch, Brock Gordon
Accounting Professor
Murphy, Timothy Roy
Auto Shop Tchr & Dept Chrmn
Olberg, Karen Rohrer
Counselor
Passanisi, Dean Anthony
6th Grade Teacher
Renfro, H. Elizabeth
English & Women's Studies Prof
San Galli, Kathleen O'Hara
Fifth & Sixth Grade Teacher
Scott, Dennis Ray
Assistant Principal
Scully, Patricia Louise
High School English Teacher
Silliman, Kathryn
Assistant Professor
Smith, M. Todd
Mathematics Teacher
Snow, Thomas Wayne
Counselor & Teacher
Stephens, Anne Kinney
Science Tchr & Staff Developer
Topete-Tallerico, Janet
Spanish Teacher
Wallace, Henry N.
Agribusiness Professor
Wing, George Cessna
Sixth Grade Teacher
Wismer, Patricia Feiser
English & Photography Teacher
Young, George Alan
Span & ESL Tchr
CHINO
Alpert, Dolores
Mathematics Teacher
Capriotti, Annette-Marie
Science Teacher
Codekas, Karen Lynn (Stone)
Kindergarten Teacher
Douglass, Stephen M.
Journalism Teacher
East, Rebecca Galt
German Teacher & Yearbook Adv
Gassen, Katherine G. (Martin)
HS Agriculture Teacher
Gentry, Judy L.
Math Teacher
Gorman, Jane A.
PE Dept Chprsn & Instructor
Hall, Perry Allen
Band Director
Ishii, Georganne Mines
Cheerleading Instructor
Kolb, Christine (Potter)
Drama Teacher
Mc Clure, Stephen Douglas
Chem Tchr & Sci Dept Chairman
Reyes, Ernie Frank
Work Experience Coordinator
Shaw-Morgan, Janice Ann
Fifth Grade GATE Educator
Smouse, Frank K.
Theatre Arts Teacher
Tanner, Gay E.
English Teacher
Vander Poel, Cynthia J.
Physical Education Teacher
Vaniman, Richard R.
Psychology Teacher
Villaruicencio, Angelo Mallona
Mathematics Teacher
Villeneuve, Raymond Robert
French Tchr & Frgn Lang Chprsn
Walker, Mark Carter
GATE Teacher
Waring, Christopher Hugh
High School Mathematics Tchr
Weeks, Connie Holdgrafer
Activities Director
Williams, John Quincy
Sociology Teacher
Yaruss, Linda Lou (Barritt)
Third Grade Teacher
CHINO HILLS
Beaini, Christine Royal
6th Grade Teacher
Chandler, Jeffery Allan
Science Teacher
Deshane, Michael Howell
Physical Ed & Ceramics Teacher
Engel-Kartub, Kris S.
Mathematics Teacher
Gomez, Vince Standing Deer
Social Science Dept Chm
Haselwander, Victoria Lynn
Resource Specialist
Janis, Ellen Bevans
English Teacher
Lewandowski, Betty Gray
Economics & World His Teacher
Marchant, Kelley Elise
Drama Teacher
Merandi, Robin Knowles
Third Grade Teacher
Reynolds, Vicki Glisson
1st Grade Teacher
Robson, Diane Kane
Social Science Teacher
Sandifer, Kenneth George
Social Science Teacher
Skelton, Dennis Wayne
Art Teacher
Stevens, Laing Allen
PE & US History Teacher
CHOWCHILLA
McLaughlin, John Frederick
Industrial Arts Teacher
Stutler, Rhonda Rigby
7th & 8th Grade Teacher
CHULA VISTA
Agbede, Duro Joseph
Hlth Prof & Cross Cntry Coach
Anderson, Gloria Jean
Retired Owner & Director
Arias, Claire L. Bottini
French Teacher
Arteaga, Juan Felipe
Drama & Art Teacher
Banks, Penelope
Professor
Benkner, Thomas Drake
Sixth Grade Teacher
Biggart, Neal Wallis
Biology, AP & IB Bio Teacher
Bolles, Ronald Kent
Vocal Music Teacher
Calvet, Darla Anne De Simone
Sociology Instructor & Prof
Camara, Nick
Social Science Teacher
Chavez, Victor Manuel
Professor of History
Crescenzo, Thomas Anthony
Economics Professor
Denhoff, Sammy Taylor
Retired Third Grade Teacher
Fickett, James Daniel, Jr.
7th Grade English Teacher
Finn, Scott Allan
Counselor & Professor
Gailband, Michael Harris
US History Teacher
Gennette, Judith Jordan
Prof of Med Surgical Nursing
Henson, Charles Richard
7th Grd World Cultures Teacher
Johnson, Jerelyn (Johnson)
Journalism & English Teacher
Kelly, Patricia
ESL & Reading Instructor
Kowit, Steve M.
Dept of English Professor
LaLicata, Nicholas Joseph
European His & US Govt Tchr
Lizarraga, Steven
Biology Teacher
Loomis, Jackie Sue
English & US History Teacher
Loyer, Alana-Patris
Communication Professor
Mabrey, Eric Joseph
Instrumental Music Instructor
Madrazo, Elizabeth Dudley
Sixth Grade Teacher
Maio, Tony
US His & World Cultures Tchr
Martinez, Virginia Margaret
Philspy, AP European His Tchr
Matthews, Dewey Rhodes
Teacher
Mc Clelland, Kevin Daniel
English Teacher
Miller, David Alan
Associate Stu Body Adv & Tchr
Nagao, Norris Sadato
Professor
Planta, Elizabeth Catherine
Drama Teacher
Ricasa-Bagaporo, Arlie Natalie
Counselor
Rinner, Nancy H.
Teacher
Robinson, Elaine Followell
Kindergarten Teacher

VISTA (cont)
on, Estela Hernandez
h, Spanish & AVID Tchr
, Jane Carney
ge Educator
Gerald A.
ectural Design Prof
Carol A.
n & Social Living Teacher
Mei-Lan
ssor of Mathematics
orina V.
Counselor & Professor
Nancy S.
ce Teacher
, Jacquelyn A.
ath & Chemistry Teacher
s, Teresa Ann
biology Teacher
:, Nathan
overnment & History Tchr
ns, Warren G.
anities Teacher
jak, Marilynn S.
a & Speech Teacher
S HEIGHTS
Elaine Cavaco
ergarten Teacher
n, Helen Carole
sh Teacher & Dept Chair
Audrey Cox
n Grade Teacher
rry, Colette Dieterle
h Grade Teacher
, Constance Marie
Grade Teacher
rg, Michele Ann
rade Teacher
lt, Robert R.
Grade Teacher
Gretchen Anne
sh Teacher
OF INDUSTRY
s, Ronald Vincent
ectional Ed Instructor
EMONT
son, Douglas
ram Director
way, Charlotte (Ames)
ory, English & Rdng Tchr
LaRae Dunn
l Music Director
Bruce
Prof of Art, Hist & Hum
:, Ann Lindstaedt
guages Teacher
ell, Iris C.
ed Faculty
va, Preethi I.
c Professor
s, Damon Octavian
tor & Economics Teacher
rson, Ellin Ringler
of Eng & Amer Literature
ann, Phillip William
ish Teacher
Michael Anthony
mistry & Theatre Teacher
, Esper Hardy, Jr.
sical Education Instructor
gh, Janet Wear
e Teacher
on, Scott Alexander
12th Grd Fr & Eng Teacher
ourty-Riggs, Jenny Marie
lish Teacher
son, Sue Stanford
lish Teacher
in, Nathalie Michele
istant Professor of French
walter, Carol Jeanne
8th Grade English Teacher
ah, Dorothy Darnell
lish Teacher
, Alisa Allen
Grade Teacher
da, Robert Leonard
tory Teacher
rskey, Michael Eugene
ebra & Geometry Teacher
RKSBURG
uski, Caryl
unselor
io, Thomas
ics, Ec & Soc Stud Tchr
YTON
ch, Joni Ayres
thematics Department Chprsn
w, Hideko
th Grade Teacher
ARLAKE
Donald, Robert Bruce
Grade Math & Science Tchr
el, Alan H.
cial Science Teacher
VERDALE
ae, Ann Victoria
glish & Drama Teacher
VIS
re, John David
urth Grade Teacher
rews, Julie Lynn
Grade Academic Block Tchr
op, Eric
ghth Grade Teacher
is, Tom Howard
Grade Teacher
n, Catherine Green
Grd Academic Block Teacher

Ford, Charley Adams
Sixth Grade Teacher
Ford, Frank Anderson
US History Teacher
Franco, Shelley Ann
Head Counselor
Gregory, Dean Philip
Biology & Zoology Tchr
Gutierrez, Esther Theresa
Head Guidance Counselor
Hansen, Chris B.
Physical Education Teacher
Hayes, Laurie Anne
Anatomy & Physiology Teacher
Hitchcock, Roger Alan
Math Educator
Hurado, Raymond James
Biology Teacher
Inouye, Scott N.
Mathematics Teacher
Lanford, Mark Thornton
Choral Conductor
Lederach, Beth
English Teacher
Lundy, Michael James
Spanish & AVID Instructor
Moxley, James
Math Teacher
Nation, Thomas Walter
US History Teacher
Ohanian, Greg
Physics Teacher
Rigby, Janna Kaye
English & Drama Teacher
Serpa, Michael Vierra
Math Teacher
Simons, Jana Sharon
3rd Grade Teacher
Simpson, Martin Vincent
Chemistry Teacher
Smoot, Carole Elizabeth Hibbard
7th Grade Academic Block Tchr
Ultich, Peggy L.
Third Grade Teacher
Van Doren, Susan Schroeder
Elementary Principal
Wells, Roberta Ann
8th Grade & Mentor Teacher
Wetzel, Donna Louise
Act Dir & Leadership Teacher
Wilson, Thomas Paul
Math & PE Instructor
COACHELLA
Mc Donald, Sally Fine
First Grade Teacher
COALINGA
Mitchell, Glenn Eugene
Biological Science Teacher
Pinza, Susan Kathleen
English Teacher
Ross, Carolyn S.
Principal
Walker, Frank J.
Art Instructor & Dept Chrmn
COARSEGOLD
McCabe, Paula Alexander
8th Grade Teacher
COLFAX
Alford, Scott Michael
Private Tutor
Belcastro, Jacqueline Ann
American Government & Ec Tchr
Jessee, Gary Joseph
Science Teacher & Dept Chair
Phillips, Paul Joseph
English Teacher
COLTON
Berch, Roxanne Rene
Math Teacher
Burroughs, Daniel Mark
US History Teacher
Clark, Ronald A.
5th & 6th Grade Teacher
Cortez, Nellie Fernandez
Bilingual Teacher
Fisher, John Stephen
US History Teacher
Gerard, Robert Ernest
HS Social Science Teacher
Hauge, Kristin B.
Physical Education Instructor
Jacobs, Denise Dales
Drama & Dance Teacher
Lee, Sharyl J.
Resource Teacher
Lessard, Cheryl Neilsen
Art Teacher
Mc Intosh, John Thomas
Geology & Natural Science Tchr
Ponce-Burgos, Olivia Guadalupe
Bilingual Teacher & Mentor
Potterton, Eileen Toma
English Teacher
Rainey, David Patrick
English Teacher
Reedy, William Robert, Jr.
Instr & Career Major Coord
Richardson, Mary Beth
Language Arts Teacher
Shaw, Vivian Krawczyk
English Teacher & AVID Coord
Thurman, Alex F.
Eighth Grd Social Studies Tchr
Trevino, Joe Raymond
Science Teacher
COLUMBIA
Broaddus, Jeffrey Laurence
5th Grade Teacher

COLUSA
Giuliano, Pamela Gail
Language Arts Teacher
Shaeffer, Karla J.
HS Teacher
COMPTON
Anderson, Anunciacion Z.
Religion Teacher
Campbell, Rhogerthia Mayfield
1st Grade Teacher
Dennis, Nancy Octavia Johnson
High School Counselor
Dewart, Gilbert
Earth Science Prof
Ellis, Larry Benoris
Art Teacher
Espinosa-Parker, Norma Muriel
Spanish & ESL Professor
Hayes, Rubye Ellis
First Grade Teacher
Joiner, Robert Lee
Prof of Acctng & Dir Hmn Res
Lasley, William J.
English Teacher
Morales Izurieta, Yolanda Josefina
Spanish, French & Bus Teacher
Muhammad, Nayawiyyah U.
Principal
My, Alexander Peng
Career Vocational Counselor
Onwudiwe, Hyginus Ifeanyi
Biological Science Teacher
Sawyers, Michelle Antoinette
AP English III Teacher
Singleton, Pauline Turner
First Grade Teacher
Stagg, Shirley (Young)
English Language Arts Teacher
Starrenburg, Kathy Leonhardt
English Teacher
Stevenson, Glorious Moore
9th-12th Grade English Teacher
Washington, Velma Lee
Fifth Grade Teacher
Worthy, Rebecca Beasley
Teacher & Activities Director
CONCORD
Accatino, Steven Charles
Instrumental Music Director
Bhatt, Shirley Ritz
Mathematics Tchr & Dept Chair
Bledsoe, Dennis
History & Guitar Teacher
Bonjean-Coleman, Roxanne C.
English Teacher
Boscacci, Glen Hunter
Fifth Grade Teacher
Cockerham, Nella Sue
Biology Instructor
Conti, Scott David Patrick
Social Studies Teacher
Cullimore, Coni S.
Math Teacher & Leadership Adv
Fitzgerald, Barbara Jean
Teacher
Glennon, Kathleen
Business Ed & Economics Tchr
Griffin, Ann Woolridge
English & Social Studies Tchr
Harvey, Robert Sherman
Automotive Technology Instr
Haynes, Stephanie Whitman
English & Home Economics Tchr
Holland, Jay Davis
Mathematics Teacher
Horgan, Anna Belle
8th Grd Math & Algebra Teacher
Jay, Lesley S.
Home Economics Teacher
Johnson, Robert C.
Vice Principal
Kaiser, Carl F.
Instrumental Music Teacher
Kaplan, Arlene Stern
Independent Study Teacher
Keane, Jim Robert
Sixth Grade Teacher
Langley, Michael Douglas
History Teacher
Larsen, Gwen
Substitute Teacher
Leach, Jacqueline Cole
English & AP Amer Studies Tchr
Ligouri, Jeannine Trasvina
Kindergarten Teacher
Okey, Gary John
Soc Stud & Pub Speaking Tchr
Plath, Carolyn Sue
Vice Principal
Rich, Frederick H., II
Fourth Grade Teacher
Souza, Steve Michael
Junior High Math & Sci Teacher
Vigus, Daniel Leonard
Band Director & 3rd Grade Tchr
Zino, Roger Louis
Driver Ed Tchr & Dept Chair
COOL
Sheridan, George Groh
Middle School Teacher
Shore, Carl Ladd
5th Grade Teacher
CORCORAN
Allen, Bruce E.
Bands Dir & Music Dept Chrmn
Bennicoff, Louise A.
Elem Prin
CORNING
Brown, Betty Jane Moran
Fourth Grade Teacher

CORONA
Blanton, Tomilynn VanDalfsen
Elementary School Teacher
Bradley, Dorothy D.
Chemistry Teacher
Brandt, Dennis Jon
High School Teacher
Clark, Lynn Burdette (Sharpless)
Pre-Algebra, Rel & Art Advy
Daniels, Cass Hope
History & Drama Teacher
Demick, Christine Ryan
5th & 6th Grade Teacher
Drake, Diann Marissa
Soc Sci & Lang Arts Tchr
Evans, Audrey D.
French & Language Arts Teacher
Frost, Donald Allen
Basketball & Football Coach
Hale, Ronald Rei
6th Grade Teacher
Lance, Doreen Louise
Lang Arts & Soc Studies Tchr
Lister, Leilani Letwin
Algebra Tchr & Vice Principal
Lopez, Elaine Uribe
Fifth & Sixth Grade Teacher
Mohr, Lynn Charles
7th-8th Grd Science Instructor
Moore, Laurie Souza
Fifth Grade Teacher
Morgan, Janet Kihlken
Language Arts Teacher
Nakayama, Martha Haruyo (Yamano)
Mathematics Department Chprsn
Nieblas, Cindy Schupp
Third Grade Teacher
Pease, Harlan Frederick
Sixth Grade Teacher
Pfeiffer, Mary Pat
4th Grade Teacher
Reynen, Nancy
8th Grd Language Arts Teacher
Rhoton, Scott Everett
Kindergarten Teacher
Richens, Christine Clemente
Fifth Grade Teacher
Siddons, Beverly A. (Towle)
8th Grd Eng & US His Teacher
Spann, Toni Jean
First Grade Teacher
Sutherland, Michael Edward
Lang Arts & PE Teacher
Vitale, Julie A.
AVID Coordinator
Wallace, William Helm, Jr.
AP US His Tchr & Dept Chrmn
Warren, Mark J.
HS History & Soc Sci Teacher
CORONADO
Beatty, Karen
Math Dept Chairperson & Mentor
Heaphy, Davin M.
9th-12th Grd Soc Sci Teacher
Price, LeRoy E., Jr.
Science Teacher
CORTE MADERA
Bishop, Barry Jay
Math Teacher
COSTA MESA
Amble, Buzz
5th Grade Teacher
Bloomberg, Marilyn Corkhill
Spanish Teacher
Breece, William Howard
Anthropology Professor
Chelius, Mary Doll
2nd Grade Teacher
Crockey, Sheryl Dee
Third Grade Teacher
Faridi, Abbas M.
Professor of Physics
Gitlin, Phyllis B.
Professor of Theatre
Guillen, Alex
Comm Coll Cnslr & Assoc Prof
Hallisey, Claudette Garruba
Eighth Grade Teacher
Harmer, Ann Tonn
Assoc Prof of Biological Sci
Kane, Katherine
Science & Social Studies Tchr
Katsuki, Anna Volta
Cnslr & Career Planning Tchr
Klitzing, Mark Alan
8th Grade Teacher & Ath Dir
Moore, Arthur R. P.
Professor of Mathematics
Omaye, Patricia S.
Fifth Grade Teacher
Perez, Amelia M.
Word Processing Instructor
Schroeder, Janice E.
Teacher & Lang Arts Dept Chm
Smith, Edith Gross
Professor of Music
Smith, Susan Lee
Professor of History
Thomas, Sally (Halstead)
Mathematics Professor
Visco, Frank Joseph
Chair & Prof of Biological Sci
Wilson, John R. M.
History Professor
COTTONWOOD
Dolan, John Kevin
English Teacher
Grandell, Gregory Duane
Resource Specialist Pgm Tchr

Mitchell, Dennis Leland
8th Grade Science Teacher
Streight, Cathryn A.
Second Grade Teacher
COULTERVILLE
Henderson, Pamela Mason
4th & 5th Grade Teacher
COVELO
Carter, Colleen Elizabeth
1st & 2nd Grade Teacher
George, Sharon Mac Ewan
Social Studies, Sci & Art Tchr
Martinez, Rick
Science Teacher
COVINA
Argleben, Margaret Johnson
Art Teacher
Barber, George Lawrence
Band Dir & Accounting Teacher
Bartholomew, Dawn Annette (Bertrand)
Government & Economics Teacher
Bishop, Robert B.
History & PE Teacher
Boyd, Claudia
English Teacher
Chacon, Clive T.
RSP Teacher
Chase, Ann Yanka
Third Grade Teacher
Choo, Regina Katharyne
9th Grade English & ELD Tchr
Driscoll, Stephanie Leigh
French Instructor
Fox, Sandra Sue
Second-Third Grd GATE Teacher
Gayton, Sonia
Span & Title VII Resource Tchr
Hawks, Deborah Fields
Chemistry & Physics Teacher
Hirayama, Tetsu
Retired Teacher
Ihsen, Robert K.
Amer & European History Tchr
Jadrich, Richard J.
Music Teacher & Band Director
James, Karrie Frances
Spanish Teacher
Kasten, Georgia-Ann Leong
Mathematics Teacher
Medeiros, Michael S.
Guidance Counselor
Modica, Richard Anthony
French Teacher
Monjaraz, Teresa Marie
Fourth Grade Teacher
Owens, Donna Lee (Hunt)
Chemistry & Physics Teacher
Reineking, Tami
Math & Science Teacher
Sammelman, Glenda Terror
Counselor & At Risk Teacher
Sauvageau, Diane Kay Renier
Asst Princ Curr & Instr
Schall, Mary Martha
English Teacher
Skates, Mary Johnson
Fifth Grade Teacher
Smith, Crystal Kay
World History & Math Teacher
Strong, Steven Thomas
Math Teacher & Coordinator
Sweger, Glenda Lee
English Tchr & Dept Chprsn
Thatcher, Randall Lee
High School English Teacher
Valencia, Matt
English & Bible Teacher
Wollam, Scott Andrew
Assistant Principal
CRESCENT CITY
Anderson, Cheryl Lynn
Third Grade Teacher
Corning, Laurie J.
Fifth Grade Teacher
Johnson, Marsha E.
Teacher & Director
Mc Clung, Rosalie Marie
Humanities Teacher
McCready, Eric Gene
Math Teacher
CRESTON
Yett, Carol Youngdale
Resource Specialist
CROCKETT
Payette, Gloria Ruth
Spanish Teacher
CULVER CITY
Allison, Rose Johnson
Computer Applications Teacher
Checel, Christina Lynn
Spanish Teacher
Drake, Susan Wilson
Language Arts Tchr
Gilbert-Rolfe, Genevieve Anne
Economics & Government Tchr
Kemp, Kay B.
Substitute Teacher
Zarate, Debby Wynne
Spanish Teacher & Yrbk Adv
CUPERTINO
Arnold, Rozlynn S.
Fourth Grade Teacher
Barczi, Joanne Brogan
Choir & Orchestra Dir
Beggs, Thomas William
Adapted Physical Ed Instructor
Blaschke, James Douglas
Government & Economics Teacher
Brockbank, Carole Cooke
Fifth Grade Teacher

CUPERTINO (cont)
Burchby, Richard R.
Jr High Math Teacher
Burn, John Hamilton
Instrumental Music Teacher
Carino, Rebecca E.
Science Teacher
Cheeseman, Douglas T., Jr.
Professor of Biology
Collins, Clay Martin
English Teacher
Cress, Terry Dean
English Teacher & Tennis Coach
Dunivin, Jimmy D.
Dept of Sociology Chair
Edwards, Roger W.
Mathematics Teacher
Embrey, Caroline Mary
Teacher
Enfield, Susan Ann
English Teacher
Farber, Patricia Jarrett
Mathematics Teacher
Ferrito, Pauline A.
English Teacher
Flaming, Francee LaChapelle
French Teacher & Dept Chairman
Gabet, Lise C.
French Teacher
Heumann, Christopher A.
Science Teacher
Hooks, Sylvia
Physical Education Professor
Jensen, Gail Aparton
HS Asst Prin & Lead Teacher
Keplinger, Patricia Baratini
English Teacher
Lee, Byron Franklin
Business Teacher & Dept Chair
Lee-Wheat, Coleen P.
Physical Education Instructor
Leskinen, Anne Jenkins
Mathematics Instructor
Lewis, Carole Odale
Intervention Resource Teacher
Lilly, Karen Lee (New)
English Teacher
Lovas, John C.
English Professor
Marks, Susan Zweig
Social Science Teacher
Mc Comb, I-Heng Wang
Science & Math Teacher
Mello, W. Alan
Business Teacher
Molander, Mark Leonard
English Professor
Murayama, Mae (Sugita)
Retired 7th Grade Teacher
Murphy, Lance
Student Conduct Liaison
Patton, Marilyn Dilworth
English Department Chair
Pereira, Nelson
English & Speech Teacher
Plum, Kathryn S.
Instructor of Mathematics
Poggi, Claudine D.
ESL Instructor
Sartwell, Robert Joseph
PE Tchr, Dept Chair & Ath Dir
Schiros, Rosalind Elizabeth
Algebra & Pre-Algebra Teacher
Schuyler, Diana Mc Donald
Kindergarten Teacher
Shimazaki, Shozo
English Teacher
Signorelli, Denee Estelle
PE & CORE Teacher
Skahill, Karen Zeches
English & Social Studies Tchr
Stoll, Edwina Hinton
Prof of Speech Communication
Stringer, David Dee
Prof of Bus Admin
Ujifusa, Allannah Cardinal
Chemistry Honors Teacher
Unland, Jane E.
High School English Teacher
VanFossen, Leland C.
Biology & Marine Biology Prof
Villafana, David James
Sixth Grade Teacher
Vosovic, Larry R.
English Teacher
Wanlass, John Wesley
Instructor of Accounting
Worrall, Kim Allison
Business Teacher
Zabilski, Julie A.
Biology & Physiology Teacher
Zenk, Mary Fay
Math Resource Teacher
CYPRESS
Averill, Alison Mc Cann
Honors English III & ELD Tchr
Beard, Donald P.
Chemistry & AP Chemistry Tchr
Canova, Larry
Psychology Professor
Coley, Joyce Ann
English Teacher & Dept Chair
Cory, Shelly Smith
Performing Arts Director
Eastman, Dennis Lee
World His, Ed & Govt Teacher
Gruver, Eric Wayne
Clinical Psychologist Prof
Hansen, Sharon
First Grade Teacher
Harkey, Karl Morrill
HS Bible Teacher
Jones, Gloria J.
Bible Teacher
Lanzezio, Catherine Ware
Fr, Arbics & Career Plng Tchr
Lindner, Wendy L.
First Grade Teacher
Petrilla, Charles
7th-8th Grade Teacher
DALY CITY
Andersen, Jason A.
Third Grade Teacher
Bornholdt, Mark Edwards
HS Mathematics Teacher
Christensen, Betsi L.
Lang Arts & Soc Studies Tchr
Cunningham, Joan Marie (Hantzsche)
Sixth Grade Teacher
Dapkus, Jeanne Esposto
Kindergarten Teacher
Davis, Phil
PE Teacher
DeShazer, George McVey
Spanish Teacher
Foster, Linda Sue
Health, Home Economics Teacher
Garvey, Patricia Ann
Kindergarten Teacher
LaValle, Christopher D.
English Teacher
Ruggiero, Kathleen Mary
8th Grade Teacher & Asst Prin
Sultana-McCall, Norine Ellen
5th Grade Teacher
Wertz, Tina Chriss
5th Grade Teacher
DANA POINT
Abedi, Reza
Spanish, PE Teacher & Coach
Gunderson, John A.
Psychology & History Teacher
Morgan, Debbie
Head Academic Advisor
Rigg, Robert Edward
Drama Teacher
Rouse, Milt
High School English Teacher
Wingen, Tamarah Fulbright
High School Science Teacher
DANVILLE
Abbot, Barbara Clark
English Teacher
Budde, Sandra Thomas
French Teacher
Capuano, Gretchen Ulrich
Math & English Teacher
Etchie, Gail
Core, World His & Lit Teacher
Fredericksen, Carl L.
History, Philosophy & Rel Tchr
Glass, Cheryl Yee
Instrumental Music Director
Henze, Lynne
3rd Grade Teacher
Nordgren, Jon Eric
Instrumental Music Teacher
Tong, Roberta Fowler
Eighth Grade English Teacher
Warner, Joella
English Teacher
Williams, Paula Walker
2nd Grade Teacher
DAVIS
Floyd, Lili-Marlen Marianna
ESL & German Teacher
Flynn, Dale Bachman
English Lecturer
Hauber, Marilyn Anna
English & Speech Teacher
Holoman, Elizabeth Rock
French Teacher
Holte, Linda Mae
English Teacher
Kim, Grace Sangok (Chun)
10th-12th Grd Family Life Tchr
Meizel, Janet Elroff
Computer Science Teacher
Newman, Robert M.
5th Grade Teacher
Parker, Michele Malato
5th Grade Teacher
Rosen, Ruth E.
Professor of History
Skrago, Mark Steven
English Teacher
Stepleton, Tracy Russell
Social Studies Teacher
Surkala, Mary Pepe
First Grade Teacher
Trokanski, Pamela E.
Dance Teacher
Waterhouse, Andrew L.
Assistant Professor of Enology
DEL MAR
Dinnesen, Judith Lynn
6th Grade Teacher
Hauseur, Grace Yonemoto
Extended Studies Specialist
DELANO
Ahart, Shirley Ellen
German & English Teacher
Clark, Mary Ellen
Third Grade Teacher
Gonzalez, Saul Deleon
Assistant Principal
Heinz, Kathleen Rae
5th Grade Teacher
Layman, Thomas E.
Sixth Grade Teacher
Miller, Michael
Science Department Chair
Morrison, Arnold Wayne
Instrumental Music Teacher
Saunders, Gerald E.
PE Director & Instructor
Villa, Roberto
Seventh-Eighth Grade ESL Tchr
DENAIR
Bush, Michelle Renee
6th Grade Teacher
Doerksen, Mary McCauley
Resource Specialist
Hendrix, Barton William
Science Teacher
Thornhill, Cathy Nichols
Kindergarten Teacher
Webb, Bradford Stuart
Second Grade Teacher
DESCANSO
Ross, Charles E.
High School Teacher
DESERT HOT SPRINGS
Kauffman, William Lawrence
English Teacher
DIABLO
Spicer, Catherine D.
Retired Vice Principal
DIAMOND BAR
Brose, Jeff
Mathematics Teacher
Buccola, Christine Walton
Spanish Teacher
Chapman, Bradley Jay
Stu Staff Resource Specialist
Cleveland, Kim P.
Social Science Teacher
Conrad, Diane Ribera
Elementary School Teacher
Desmond, Dave Edward
English Teacher
Eddleman, Linda Fielder
Fifth Grade Teacher
Hewit, Dorinda Elise
Math & AP Psych Teacher
Hope, Adrienne Yates
Teacher
Iwanaga, Kerry Brent
Biology Teacher
Jex, Barbara Susan (Eastman)
Sixth Grade Teacher
Lordi, Dena Marie
High School Math Teacher
Sismondo, Charles A.
Instructional Dean
Skahill, Kari Nelson
Art Teacher
DINUBA
Coddington, Barbara Jean
Home Economics Teacher
Downing, Charlotte Sward
Counselor
Freestone, Palma
Alternative Education Teacher
McKittrick, Nancy Christopher
High School Counselor
Willems, Norman Donald
Auto Mechanics Instructor
DIXON
Banker, Nan
English Teacher
DOS PALOS
Angelone, Reno
Social Studies Teacher
Birdsong, Morris Newton
Mathematics Teacher
Nichols, Linda M.
Home Economics Teacher
DOWNEY
Bazarian, Kathy Elizabeth
Title I Teacher
Bones, Kay Marie
HS Math Teacher
Bremer, Rodney Glen
Math Teacher
Carter, Barbara Sue Filter
Third Grade Teacher
Charlebois, Mimi Nannette
English & Journalism Teacher
Clark, Steven Dean
HS Careers & Gen Math Teacher
Daniels, Josette M.
English Teacher
Drake, Kirby Paul
Secondary Mathematics Teacher
Ethridge, Suzanne Cunningham
First Grade Teacher
Gautreau, John Charles
Bible Teacher
Hille, Lorine Earhart
English Teacher
Holland, Sandra (Pollock)
Math Teacher & Dept Chprsn
Hughes, Robert John
High School Math Teacher
Jagielski, Robert Manuel
Social Studies & PE Teacher
Johnson, Jill Colette
Third-Eighth Grd Tchr
Martin, Joan Emily
Kindergarten Teacher
Miyada, Cynthia Mari
Science Teacher
Nogal, Sharon L.
Spanish Teacher
Perez, Veronica Leandra
Religion & Psychology Teacher
Rants, Jay B.
7th Grade Science Teacher
Rodgers, Tamera Louise
Special Education Teacher
Sangalang, May Cruz
HS Mathematics Teacher
Shaw, Amy Maria
Health Teacher
Skidmore, Myra J.
Home Ec & Peer Assistance Tchr
Smith, Lisa Day
SDC Primary Teacher
Stendahl, Melody M.
7th Grade Soc Stud Educator
Surfus, Kim Elizabeth
English Teacher
Tasse, Linda Jean Schneider
4th & 5th Grade Teacher
Weeks, Guy Brett
Government Teacher
Wright, Ruth Blohowiak
English Teacher
DOWNIEVILLE
Fillo, Lynn Weisheimer
Eng, Ger, Drama & His Teacher
DUARTE
Branch, Melinda S.
ESL Teacher
Douglass, Richard H.
Tchr & Frgn Lang Dept Chair
Karp, David Edward
Counselor & Tchr
DUBLIN
Dalrymple, Robert E.
Bible Teacher & Dept Chrmn
Dufresne, Kimberly
Art & Yearbook Teacher
Gutleben, Candace Anderson
French Teacher
Hesemann, Linda Hudson
English Tchr & Guidance Cnslr
Kennedy, Mary Sue S.
Teacher, Dept Chair & Mentor
King, Suzanne Dampier
Chemistry Instructor
Mara, Mary Caldwell
8th Grd History & English Tchr
Ruff, Cornelia Ruth
US & World History Teacher
Tama, Sharon Ellen
Social Studies Teacher
DUCOR
Kay, Janette Thomas
Sixth Grade Teacher
DUNLAP
Kenney, Linda Templeman
Sixth Grade Teacher
Smith, Marilyn Haycock
Fourth Grade Teacher
DURHAM
Blake, Gregory Alan
Business Education Teacher
EARLIMART
Moritz, Jean Loris
History, Language Arts Teacher
EDWARDS
Duarte, George Edward
Social Studies Teacher
Horton, Paul F.
High School Mathematics Tchr
Lewis, Debbie Lynn (Rowland)
Biology Teacher
Nally, Coralee Kimbrough
Sixth Grade Teacher
EL CAJON
Agsten, Tom H.
Fifth Grade Teacher
Andrews, Blair
8th Grd Sci Teacher & Coach
Barnes, Ronald Gary
Bible Professor
Bell, Kimberly Jeanne
PE, Health Instr & Coach
Danielson, Edward Earl
Chm of Counseling Psych Dept
Dreher, Dolores M.
Math Teacher
Emert, Charles Franklin, Jr.
Professor of Bible
Fischer, Peggy Ann
Veterinary I & II Asst Instr
Gale, Constance (Neville)
Assoc Prof of Music & English
Hackett, Barbara Ann (Stencil)
Fourth Grade Teacher
Hall, Charles Roger
Chemistry & Physics Teacher
Hiebert, Sharron Yvonne
6th Grade Teacher
Higdon, Karen D.
Chemistry Teacher
Kloor, Joan Knoernschild
Music Teacher
Mc Carthy, Timothy D.
Government & Philosophy Tchr
Moore, Nancy Ann Bray
Eighth Grd Mathematics Teacher
Nagle, Mary Lou Coxeter
Middle School Teacher
Nicolet, Katherine Marie
US & World History Teacher
Nulton, Jami Lynn
Performing Arts & Dance Tchr
Olsen, Linda Jean
7th Grade History Teacher
Ostermeyer, Maryann
English, Latin & AVID Tchr
Owens, Coy L.
PE Chair & Athletic Director
Potts, Deanna L.
Spanish Teacher
Rogers, Kirk
Social Science Teacher
Saccone, Peter Paul
5th Grade Teacher
Sako, Sheila Y.
Algebra Teacher
Saltzstein, Sally Freund
Teacher
Seaman, Bruce Edward
World History Teacher
Shannon, Don Edwin
Comparative His of Amers Prof
Stadelli, Barbara J.
Spcl Education Classroom Asst
Tomes, Elizabeth Kathleen
5th Grade Teacher
Towry, Toni
Family & Consumer Sci Instr
Whitaker, Laura Elaine
English Teacher
Zazurskey, Judy Mc Carn
Eng Tchr & Stud Acts Dir
Zazurskey, Michael Eugene
Algebra Teacher
EL CENTRO
Astone, Antonia
English & Drama Teacher
Barringer, Patrick John
English Teacher
Cordova, Julia Ann
Freshman Inquiry Teacher
Dvorak, Leo P.
Resource Teacher
Frazier, Loyal D., Jr.
History Teacher
Gienger, Stanford D.
Athletic Dir & Physics Teacher
Gruenberg, Susan Munroe
Chemistry Teacher
Jeffries, Ryan Kenneth
Math Teacher
Lomeli, Raquel
Elementary School Principal
Padilla, Jorge F.
English & Spanish Teacher
Rice, Paula J.
English Teacher
Walker, Donald O'Dell
Teacher & Counselor
EL CERRITO
Lockhart, Joyce Ann
Third Grade Teacher
O'Connor, Linda Hiscox
Math Teacher & Dept Chair
Singleton, Sheila
6th Grade Teacher
Syren, Allison Kittay
High School Science Teacher
Watson, Margo Fisher
Eighth Grade Teacher
EL DORADO HILLS
Carr, Jeff
English Teacher
Iverson, Stanley Dean
Biology Teacher
Mc Namara-Howell, Therese Anne
History Teacher
Patterson, Sue Jeffery
First Grade Teacher
EL MONTE
Buchholz, Nicki Ernenwein
High School Administrator
Burkhardt, Shirley J.
RSP Teacher
Ciardullo, Alicia Calienes
Fifth Grade Teacher
Daurio, Helen Pacheco
English Tchr & Co-Dept Chair
Delgado, Susan Allen
Principal
Echavarria, Margarita Navarro
6th Grade Teacher
Gildea, Elizabeth
English Teacher
Hanson, Denise Ann
English Teacher
Hill, Paulette Morgan
English Teacher
Houser, Thomas Lloyd
History & English Teacher
Jung, Sandra Denise
English Teacher
Levin, Ernest Lester
Bilingual & Crosscultural Tchr
Meiners, Eugene George
Math Teacher
O'Rourke, Timothy Edward
English Department Chairman
Siddiqi, Atiq Alam
Math Teacher
Thorson, Kimberlee Ann
English & Drama Teacher
Turner, Dennis Hayden
Eng as Second Language Teacher
EL SEGUNDO
Stofel, Connie Orr
Fifth Grade Teacher
Stuart, Joan Mc Bride
Retired Elementary Ed Teacher
EL SOBRANTE
Farmer, Donna Leigh (Marr)
PE Tchr & Dept Chprsn
Isaacs, Elayne P.
English & World History Tchr
Perrone, Mary Reese
ESL Teacher
Rubinoff, David Bernard
Algebra & Math Teacher

RANO
her, David T.
rd Tchr & Vice Principal
ROVE
Alana A.
sh Teacher
, Martha Elena
nd Grade Teacher
Mark David
ch, Drama, Eng & His Tchr
court, Jack
gh Science Teacher
court, Lynda Wills
ical Ed & Science Teacher
cher, Kathleen Frances
Sci Chprsn, World His Tchr
y, Kathleen C.
eacher & Department Chair
moto, Brandon Marc
ematics Teacher
, Jacquelyn Anne
ish Teacher
le, Brad Lee
ematics Teacher
er, John Louis, Jr.
c & Soc Sci Teacher
RTA
, Toni Burgess
c Teacher
rds, Robert Curtis
ed 6th-8th Grade Tchr
RYVILLE
, George Leon
& 6th Grade Teacher
, Stephen Joseph
ory & Government Teacher
n, Maryetta
er, Guid & Pub Rltns Instr
ns, Leslie Jagger
School English Teacher
RE
ngel, Karen Weitz
ish Teacher
ck, Sandra Irwin
3rd World History Teacher
ll, Carla Peden
Rdng, Speech & Drama Tchr
Alycia J.
guage Arts Tchr
vant, Jeanne Marie
Grade Science Teacher
NITAS
Andrew John
ory Teacher
d, Robert Bruce
hematics Teacher
acio, Angela Sue
nish Teacher
, Matthew Milan
ted States History Teacher
ngeli, Leslie White
ial Studies Teacher
t, Lou A. (Dickson)
ource Specialist
, Marilyn Dauchy
ependent Study Teacher
n, Douglas
ial Studies Teacher
nan-Hogue, Lynn
nch Teacher
, Sandy (Tragesser)
h School Teacher
b, Lawrence V.
ial Science Teacher
dula, Adele Fugere
glish Teacher
e, George A.
His & Applied Tech Tchr
ssapour, Lori Madoff
nish Teacher
ey, Arthur Edward, Jr.
tory & English Teacher
son, Katrina Elizabeth
ama Tchr
esteban, Rosa Alicia
anish Teacher
gand, Regina Ursula
gh School English Teacher
ams, Craig Richard
th Teacher & Lifeguard
nos, Sandra Morall
ence Educator
INO
Megerdichian, Varsenig
Dept Chm, Bio & Chem Tchr
, Muriel June
Grade Teacher
s, Glenn Jonathon
story & Journalism Teacher
abedian, Alice
st Grade Teacher
ALON
ent, John Gregory
ath, History & PE Teacher
nbella, Margaret Ehrler
siness Teacher
ONDIDO
kwell, Nancy Leigh
alth Tchr & Peer Counseling
ascet, David Ray
ience Teacher
e, Darwin John Gill
ychology & Sociology Teacher
g, Kerry O'Neill
ghth Grade English Teacher
e, Cindey Nyberg
ird Grade Teacher
ett, Robert Madison, Jr.
h Grade Teacher

George, Merrilou Kay (Shearer)
Lang Arts & Literature Tchr
Guerrero, Deborah Jean
Jr High History Teacher
Gustafson, Gary Fredric
English Teacher
Gutierrez, Paulino Rodriguez
Spanish Teacher
Haloviak, Brent Douglas
Mathematics Teacher
Hernandez, Gilbert M.
Pastor
Hill, Samye C.
6th & 8th Grd Humanities Tchr
Jones, Frank L., III
Vice Prin, Registrar & Cnslr
Lambert, Alan Leonard
Spanish Teacher
Lochridge, Arlene Mae (Chamberlain)
Retired Teacher
McChesney, Sylvia Marie
Social Science Teacher
McLeod, Stephen Allen
5th Grade GATE Teacher
Montgomery, Victoria (Milne)
Biology Teacher & AVID Coord
Moss, Douglas William
Agriculture Instructor
Pettigrew, Patti Drue
Lang Arts, Lit & Sci Teacher
Rattmann, Jane G.
Dance Teacher
Riksford, Jon Severin
Music & Band Director
Sadnick, Gary William
Photography & Yearbook Teacher
Schwarz, Bart
Teacher & Work Exprnc Coord
Silva, Catherine Jean (Marcus)
Spanish Teacher
Stout, Debra Schoch
3rd Grade Teacher
Turrentine, Christine Frances
English & Literature Teacher
Wester, Will S.
English Teacher
Wickstrom, James Carl
Sixth Grade Teacher
ESPARTO
Mullins, James L.
Mathematics Chair
ETIWANDA
Batsford, Holly Leigh
8th Grade Teacher
Christensen, Curtis Hans
HS English Teacher
Easton, Paula Wainwright
Mathematics Teacher
Elliott, Madeleine Lynn
High School Science Teacher
Hall, Eric William
English Teacher
Hester, Karl Jonathan
Physics Instructor
Whitney, Edward Leon
High School Counselor
EUREKA
Brisack, Allen Green, III
Ninth Grade Teacher
Buchner, Gary Philip
6th Grade Teacher
Crichton, Marjorie Jackson
9th-12th Grade Counselor
Feist, Eugene Paul
Math & Physics Teacher
Maisch, Patricia A.
Math Teacher
Quinby, Lucy Santino
Foreign Language Dept Chm
Shannon, Barbara Wright
Science Dept Chair
Siler, Sally Ann
Sixth Grade Teacher
Smith, Roger Lewis
Mathematics Teacher
EXETER
Standow-Hanson, Kathlyn Ann
Sci Curr Dev & Intrssn Tchr
Whitworth, Lisa G.
6th Grade Teacher
FAIR OAKS
Farney, Earl Jasper
Air Force Jr ROTC Instructor
Gillespie, James P.
6th Grade Teacher
Hand, Kim
Mathematics Teacher
Huffman, Syliva Petronaci
Math Teacher
Mireles, Lynn K.
His, Music & Frgn Lang Teacher
Moore, Edward Anthony
Band Director
Pananides, Robyn Unterthines
English Teacher
Rielli, Sharon Lynn
Spanish Teacher
Segerstrom, Joan Miller
Sixth Grade Teacher
Stewart, William Thomas
Social Science Teacher
Torre, Angie Lee
Spanish & French Teacher
Weiss, Marilee Wilson
Economics Professor
Weldon, Cameron McLeod
6th Grade Teacher
Wheeler, Christie Anne (Ford)
Business Tchr & Athletic Dir

FAIRFIELD
Anderson, Darrell L.
Retired Secondary Sci Teacher
Aronsen, Deborah Marie (Tripoli)
Sixth Grade Teacher
Berry, John Patrick
Industrial Technology Teacher
Borge, Claire (Zemi)
Social Science Teacher
Branch, Rosemary Elizabeth
Fifth Grade Teacher
Brannen, Beverly Ammerman
History & General Math Teacher
Campbell, Russell Lee
Music Educator
Carpino, Clyde Phillips
Student Activities Director
Causey, Janice Lawrence
Kindergarten Teacher
Cleaver, Joseph Patrick
Math Teacher
Colbert, Martha Selma
8th Grade Science Teacher
Dickerson, Frances Welch
English Teacher
Fawcett, Del
Math Tchr & Department Chair
Finley, Wanda Sue
Kindergarten Teacher
Gelpke, Peter Hall
HS Physics Teacher
Goodsell, Susan K.
English Teacher
Harwood, Michael G.
Sixth Grade Teacher
Heney, Timothy James
Music Specialist
Johnson, Rudolph
Bio Teacher & Psendo Admin
Kennedy, Jean H.
Ag Science Teacher
Lederer, Tom
English Teacher
Lee, Dorothy Ann
Spanish Teacher
Mack, Lorena Goodlow
Sixth Grade Teacher
Mager, Martha Mercedes
Spanish Teacher
Mary, Diane Bradley
Science Teacher
McPeek, Erin Daugherty
Math Teacher
Miller, Amy JoAnn
4th & 6th Grade Teacher
Millward, Jack Mikel
Science Teacher
Mitchell-Blacknell, Yolanda Francine
Computer Teacher & Program Mgr
Moore, Nancy Jean (Dickau)
Spanish Teacher
Mugg, Barbara Cosgrove
English & French Teacher
Pajita, Carmel Ocampo
Band Director
Robertson, Barry Gene
Language Arts Teacher
Sands, Lisa Murgo
Math Teacher
Sheeley, Alvina Riley
High School Spanish Teacher
Silva, Betty Denise (Zink)
Library Media Teacher
Souza, Michael A.
English Teacher
Stanovich, Karen
Math Teacher & Yearbook Adv
Sumner, Gary Thomas
Social Science & Ec Tchr
Tobitt, Rebecca Catharyn
7th & 8th Grd Soc Stud Tchr
Towner, Dick Lube
Business & Social Science Tchr
Wix, Donna Gallagher
Sixth Grade Teacher
FALL RIVER MILLS
Fox, Charles Robert
Fourth Grade Teacher
FALLBROOK
Bradley, Lynne Carol
Choral Director
Carpenter, Laura Silva
2nd Grade Bilingual Teacher
Kettering, R. Stephen
AP European History Teacher
Munro, Pamela S.
English Teacher
Poznanter, Linda Welch
Independent Study & Eng Tchr
Saltamachio, Alan Morgan
Biology Teacher
Sehnert, Douglas Dale
Agriculture Teacher
Stillman, Siegrid Inez
Sixth Grade Teacher
Tortorella, Wayne Stephen
Humanities & Math Teacher
FELTON
Bevernick, Mary B.
Counselor
Cannelora, Medley (Peterson)
HS English & Journalism Tchr
Cavaille, Dennis Allan
French & Math Teacher
Cavaille, Donna (Feci)
Spanish Teacher
Kallas, James Michael
Performing Arts Teacher
Nolan, Noreen Elaine
Social Studies Teacher

Steingrube, Lisa Bettar
History & Government Teacher
FILLMORE
Bereki, Debra Lynn
Science Teacher & Dept Chair
Calderon, Robert Delarosa
Head Wrestling Coach
Colvard, Stephen Randall
Principal
Elliot, Kathy McDermott
Second Grade Teacher
Riley, Mark Patrick
English Dept Chairperson
Skoe, Donald Edward
Biology Teacher
FIREBAUGH
Dedmon, Marilynne Ellen
Fifth Grade Teacher
Gravatt, Gina Lynne Diaz
Agriculture Tchr & Dept Chprsn
Magnusson, William Thomas
Industrial Technical Instr
FIVE POINTS
Perry, Susan J.
Homeroom & Soc Sci Teacher
FOLSOM
Alburn, James Leon
Mathematics Teacher
Cardwell, David Emmanuel
Phys, Earth Sci Tchr & Mentor
Doe, Stephen Clark
Science Teacher & Dept Head
Fallon, Jack D.
Retired Govt Teacher
Gaesser, Curtis L.
Band & Orchestra Director
Gibson, Ann Mc Kinley
High School English Teacher
Grundy, William J.
History & English Teacher
Hooker, Suzanne Hepp
Fifth Grd Tchr & Dept Chprsn
Lopez, Joan E.
Spanish Teacher
Moore, Kathy C.
Spanish & French Teacher
Noble, James Herron, Jr.
PE & History Teacher
Ramsey, Samantha Helene
Language Arts & History Tchr
Shackelford, Robyn Davidson
9th-10th Grade English Teacher
Wood, Sharon D. (Wager)
Intermediate Dept Chairperson
FONTANA
Archambault, Elizabeth
English Teacher
Bettger, Brian Edwin
Instrumental Music Director
Biroschak, David Michael
High School Algebra Teacher
Bradwell-Miner, Wanda
Art Teacher
Broncatello, Vincent Jim
Assistant Principal
Burris, Deborah Wilcox
Second Grade Teacher
Campbell, Patricia Marie
Biology & Life Science Teacher
Cappiello, Theresa Ann
Teacher & Basketball Coach
Dison, Janyth Holcomb
Counselor
Dison, Jerry
English Teacher
Evans, Thomas Murray
Algebra & Physics Teacher
Ewing-Chow, Nancy Diane
Peer Leader Adv & Psych Tchr
Gomes, Laurie Colton
English & Publications Teacher
Gruber, Kathleen McGinley
Kndgtn Tchr & Rdng Specialist
Harriger, Suzanne Elaine
High School Counselor
Hight, Lafayette Curtis, Sr.
8th Grade Teacher
Holliday, Kathryn Lynn
Third Grade Teacher
Jeffery, Caron Lynn (Tomlin)
Sociology Tchr
Kamper, Martin Zak
Counselor
Lauron, Elizabeth Claire
DDS Pvt Practice & Instr
Lech, Tracy DaFoe
Science Teacher
Mc Elroy, Maxine Stevenson
Social Studies Teacher
Mills, Lela Frankie Ann
Third Grade Teacher
Mumper, Diane Hagstrum
Kindergarten Teacher
Neiner, Leilani Melissa Ann
Consumer Science Teacher
Nejadpour, Jinane Annous
French Teacher
Paige, A. Tyleen Deeds
English Teacher
Patey, Alan Kent
Social Studies & Psych Teacher
Peterson, Robert Alfred
Biological Sciences Teacher
Phillips, Theodore Patrick
English Teacher
Rodriguez, Rodolfo, Jr.
Science Teacher
Starr, Rosanna Weaver
Eighth Grade Homeroom Teacher

Tennison, Claudia Leslie
Spanish Teacher
Williams, Christine Allera
English Teacher
Workman, Mary Ann Olsen
Kindergarten Teacher
Young, John Mark
AP Government Teacher
Young, Linda Christensen
Chemistry Teacher
FORESTHILL
Johnson, Sarah Macpherson
Lang Arts & US History Teacher
FORT BRAGG
Dias, Michele Coverston
Bilingual Kindergarten Teacher
Rhoades, Robert William
Art Professor
Urbani, Allen
Physical Education Teacher
FORT JONES
Lake-Thom, Robert George
Director of Social Svcs & Ed
FORT ORD
Spencer, Patricia Miriam
Kindergarten Teacher
FORTUNA
Aldinger, David Mills
Principal & 5th-10th Grd Tchr
Bowers, Sharon Chapman
Social Science I Teacher
Dwelley, Charles Douglas
Sixth Grade Teacher
Harris, Ilene H.
First Grade Teacher
Meyer, Donald K.
High School Agriculture Tchr
Ward, Josephine Olson
Retired Teacher
Willis, Allen Kent
8th Grd Tchr & Vice Principal
FOSTER CITY
Bracker, Susan Frances
Reading & Language Arts Tchr
Kast, Virginia E.
English Teacher
Marcum, Diane Hope
Principal & Kindergarten Tchr
FOUNTAIN VALLEY
Bahadoor, D. Timothy
Vice Prin & Mathematics Tchr
Barkawi, Janet G. Weymouth
Instructor & Soc Studies Coord
Buto, Dorothy Rosenberger
ELD & German Teacher
Clunk, Sharon Thompson
Combination Teacher
Dane, Alexis Bourg-Beauvais
Activities Director
Jue, Janet
Visual Arts Teacher & Coord
Mock, Gail Upton
US History Teacher
Parsek, Gerald K.
Mathematics Teacher
Richards, Anna Louise
Chem Tchr & Sci Dept Chprsn
Rolle, Robert M.
Chemistry & Physics Teacher
Skahill, Jacquelyn Bird-Riggs
English Teacher
Tuin, Lon
High School Counselor
Wampler, Gary Lee
Band Director
FOWLER
Hahn, Sandra Rae
English, Drama & Speech Tchr
Ravalin, Jo Catherine
Third Grade Teacher
FRAZIER PARK
Carter, Sandra Parsons
First Grade Teacher
Kiesner, Eileen F.
Kindergarten Teacher
FREMONT
Baker, Daniel M.
Cnslr, Instr, Assessment Coord
Bass, Michael Harland
Sixth Grade Teacher
Boegel, Dennis W.
High School Health Teacher
Caldwell, Elva Jane Lobato
Second Grade Teacher
Capelli, Gina Louise
Honors US History Teacher
Carter, Priscilla
Music Instructor
Caveglia, Jerry
US History Teacher
Cochran, Kathryn Lee
Spanish Teacher
Coleman-Knight, Jan Perry
History Teacher & Dept Chair
Conlon, Gary Michael
Physical Education Teacher
Creger, John Holmes
English Teacher
Dawson, William H.
English Department Chairman
DiJulio, Guy T.
Professor of Mathematics
Dunbar, Lois Wardlow
Sixth Grade Teacher
Edwards, Bruce W.
German & English Teacher
Evans, Neil
Retired Sci Dept Chprsn & Tchr
Fitz, Susan Helsel
Kindergarten Teacher

FREMONT (cont)
Gehrke, Linda Anne Pessagno
French Teacher & Club Advisor
George, Brian Thomas
History Instructor
Goodwin, James Richard
Professor of Biology
Griffin, Dean Ernest
Science Dept Head & Teacher
Haluza, Herman George
English Teacher
Hatland, Marion M.
Business Teacher
Holcomb, Thomas K.
Associate Professor
Holding, Betty Renee
Fifth Grade Teacher
Hottle, Maggie M.
World History & English Tchr
Hunter, M. Randolph, IV
6th Grade Teacher
Kawasaki-Hull, Kerrie E.
English Instructor
Kimble, Marlene Ann
Nursing Instr & Curr Coord
Klent, James R.
Chemistry Professor
Lamm, Adoralee Pryor
First Grade Teacher
Leenerts, Warren A.
Art & Photography Teacher
Maskatia, Shirin Arif
English Teacher
Masuda, Ronald Isao
Math Teacher
Mc Manus, James M.
Asst Professor of Music
Mitchell, Kristine Marie
Music Teacher
Moore, Cecelia Phillip
Mathematics Teacher
Nishiyama, Robert
Tchr of Gftd & High Achievers
O'Dell, Nancy Jean
Business Teacher
Orantes, Milagro Del Carmen
6th Grade Bilingual Teacher
Patton, Rick Glenn
Physics & Chemistry Teacher
Putman, Kathleen B.
Economics & American Govt Tchr
Raap, Ronald Glenn
Teacher of the Gifted Students
Ray, Madeleine Sanchez
Spanish Teacher
Richards, James Patrick
English Teacher & Drama Coach
Romero, Joseph Peter
Sixth Grade Teacher
Schneider, M. Joanna Plavcan (Payne)
Tchr of Gifted & Talented
Sexton, Ellen Kay
Third Grade Teacher
Thomson, Jeannie Elizabeth
Science Dept Chair & Teacher
Torkelson, Virginia Lee
High School Science Teacher
Webb, John Brunson
Health & Geography Teacher
Win, Soe Mvint
Mathematics Instructor
Wright, Dolores Tate
Fourth Grade GATE Teacher
FRENCH CAMP
Thompson, Donn L.
Fifth-Sixth Grade Teacher
FRESNO
Adolph, Lynn L.
HS Eng Tchr & Dept Chprsn
Akins, Yvonne Plese
English Teacher
Alexander, Betty
Eighth Grd Math & Sci Teacher
Alfano, Philip Michael
8th Grd Academic Block Instr
Bagdasarian, Mary Louise
Kindergarten & First Grd Tchr
Barker, Judy Kovacevich
Fifth Grade Teacher
Battles, Gary Michael
High School English Teacher
Berklich, David
Sixth Grade Teacher
Blankenship, Randall E.
Physical Education Teacher
Brickey, Cynthia Hansen
8th Grade Block Teacher
Cerkueira, Ronald Craig
High School Tech Ed Teacher
Christensen, Beth
Sixth Grade Teacher
Clarke, Rick A.
History Teacher
Clarke, William H.
Retired His & Eng Tchr
Cooley, Michael David
Academic Block Teacher
Cox, Tammye Lynne
Business Teacher & Dept Chprsn
Crisp, Andrea Christine
English Teacher & Dept Chair
Curtis, Carol Ann
Mathematics Instructor
Davidian, Leroy Martin
Phys Ed Teacher & Coach
Davies, Deborah Lynn
Family Daycare Owner & Providr
de Albuquerque, Claudia
Third Grade GATE Teacher
Decker, Rebecca Robinson
5th Grade Teacher
DenBesten, Wendy Leins
HS Mathematics Teacher
DiFilippo, Jonie
HS Mathematics Teacher
Ethen, Matthew Carl
Secondary Social Science Tchr
Ferguson, Marc Charles
Choral Director & French Tchr
Flettner, Sandra Jean
German & French Teacher
Godfrey, Lonnie L.
HS Math Dept Chm & Instructor
Grove, Beth Duncan
HS Mathematics Teacher
Hamilton, Daniel J.
Counselor
Harmon, Peter VanDusen
Chemistry Teacher
Harper, Lori Kay
Psychology Instructor
Hartshorn, Cheryl
7th-8th Grd Math Teacher
Harvey, Yvonne Dawson
Child Development Specialist
Hawkins, Kris Kruse
Educator
Hawkins, Theodore John
English Teacher
Haynes, Catherine Marie
English, Sociology & His Tchr
Hernandez, Janet Gieselman
US His & Lang Arts Teacher
Herzog, Helen Anita Badasci
Computer Instructor
Holford, Susan Muldown
Human Services Adjunct Faculty
Hudson, Kurt D.
High School Mathematics Tchr
Jarvis, John Harvey
Special Assignment Teacher
Johnson, Marcus Paul
Superintendent & Principal
Johnson, Willard Harold, Jr.
Fourth Grade Teacher
Johnston, H. Bruce
Professor of Biology
Jolliff, Bob Allan
English & Speech Teacher
Jones, Denise Sullivan
Science Teacher
Jones, Michael E.
High School English Teacher
Kuczler, Kathleen Elaine
2nd Grade Teacher
Leonard, William
Secondary Math Specialist
Leonardo, Diane Guerry
Vice Principal
Lindley, Christine
Chemistry Teacher
Lopez, Ana Gonzalez
Elementary & Middle Schl Tchr
Mac Donald, Mary Anne Highberg
Fr, Latin & English Teacher
Machado, Patrick John, Sr.
7th-8th Grade Phys Ed Teacher
Marshall, Joseph Emmett
Mathematics Teacher
McAllister, James Gregory
Acad Dean & Bible Instr
Mc Clure, Randall Arnold
English Instr & Athletic Dir
Mc Millan, Tani Marie Highland
US History, Eng & Mentor Tchr
Mekhitarian, Sophia Matewosian
Fourth Grade Teacher
Meyers, Earl Randolph, Jr.
Fourth Grade Teacher
Montgomery, John F., FSC
Rel Teacher & Dir of Stu Act
Navarrette, Margarita Ruiz
Spanish Teacher
Nitschke, David Charles
Athletic Director
Nitschke, Faith Faggionato
English Teacher
O'Connor, James Hugh
Music, Spanish & German Tchr
O'Leary, Roarke Patrick
Social Science & English Tchr
Olson, Jeri Gault
Mathematics Teacher
Pack, Samuel Michael
6th Grade Teacher
Page, Peggy Shea
Math & Algebra I Teacher
Parker, Judith E.
English Teacher
Perkovich, Stephen George
8th Grade Teacher
Peters, Marjorie Berke
Second Grade Teacher
Pettengill, Timothy Owen
Spanish Teacher
Quarles, Betty Wallace
Second Grade Teacher
Ricchiuti, Teri Ann
Sixth Grade Teacher
Rivas, Susan Lee Sahakian
High School Language Arts Tchr
Robertson, John Anton
7th Grade English Teacher
Robinson, Daniel M.
Assistant Principal
Rocheford, Janie Lee
8th Grade Mentor Teacher
Rohrer, Rosalie Ann
6th Grade Teacher
Rojeski, Hallie Roscoe
8th Grade Humanities Teacher
Sanchez, Janet Uota
Lead Teacher
Sanders, Susan Johnston
English Teacher
Scudder, Carl Anthony
History Teacher
Sharer, Gordon D.
Math Teacher
Sharkey, Peter Michael
Math Teacher & Bsktbl Coach
Sheets, Donald Morris
English Teacher
Silverman, Alice Perea
School Psychologist
Smith, Perry Dolph
Exploring Technology Teacher
Smith, Sophia Yvonne
US History Gate Teacher
Spencer, Jacqueline M.
Biology & Zoology Teacher
Stetsko, Dorothy Pereira
Eighth Grade Teacher
Tatum, Stephen Ira
Fifth Grade Teacher
Torres, Lori Daurine Pieper
Teacher & Frgn Lang Dept Chair
Tyler, James Rodney
JROTC Instructor
VanGalder, Nancy Sue (Wynne)
Acctng & Eng Language Teacher
Wagner, Kevin James
Student Activities Dir
Weber, Mark
Chemistry Instructor
White, David Allen
Jr High Teacher
Willett, Marilyn Mundy Grimes
US His, Coll Prep & LED Edctr
Winter, Pamela June
Mathematics Teacher
FULLERTON
Allen, H. Donald
Computer Science Teacher
Almeida, Gwendolyn Edler
English Teacher
Arabia, Carolyn A.
7th Grade Teacher
Archey, Larry Lee
Government & Economics Teacher
Aulino, Roseanne
English Teacher
Babcock, Elin R.
High School English Educator
Bock, Gregory H.
5th Grade Teacher
Cerrutti, Georgette Teresa
Advanced Journalism & Eng Tchr
Cerutti, Georgette
English Tchr & Dept Chprsn
Clark, Barbara I. (Lasunowicz)
Spanish & Journalism Teacher
Cumming, Edward Hamilton, III
Lecturer in Music
Dixon, Marcia C.
Physics Teacher
Dorman, Allan
English Teacher
Engstrom, Wayne Norman
Geography Professor
Felender, Julie A.
Psychology Instructor
Fyne, Terry Fetner
High School English Teacher
Henderson, Bruce Raymond
English Professor
Hunyadi, Nancy Walls
Home Economics Teacher
Knox, Lindsey Jon
Math Teacher
Lopez, Adela Gutierrez
Ethnic Stud Prof & Dept Coord
Marvin, John M.
Spanish Teacher
Matz, S. Irene
Business Instructor
McGinnis, Joan Sjoberg
Spanish Teacher
Mc Kellogg, Claire FitzGerald
Frosh & Soph Rel Studies Tchr
McWaid, Kim Levengood
Special Day Class Teacher
Melnyk, Susan Lynn
English & Journalism Teacher
Millikin, Carolyn Louise Brown
English Tchr & Asst Principal
Mohr, Barbara J.
3rd-4th Grade GATE Teacher
Nelson, Bill
Leadership Instructor
Nelson, Jeffrey Owen-Harold
Sci Dept Chair & Biology Tchr
Ortmayer, Ron J.
Special Ed Resource Teacher
Pautsch, Shawna L.
Act Dir & Social Stud Tchr
Phelan, Robert S.
Speech Instructor
Rabe, Alan N.
Intnl Dev Dist Ed Prof & Dir
Rafferty, Shirley Haney
English Teacher
Ringer, Sherry L.
PE, Leadership & Science Tchr
Romero, Madeleine Brady
Finance Lecturer
Schlotthauer, Jim E.
Social Studies Teacher
Scott, Randy J.
Mathematics Teacher
Simpson, Julia Ann
English Teacher
Steiner, Michael C.
Professor of American Studies
Talmo, Ronald Victor
Law Professor
Turner, Karla Bradshaw
Choral Music & Phys Ed Teacher
Wall, Brian G.
Art, Eld & Intro Cmptrs Tchr
Wiegman, Thomas Paul
English Teacher
GALT
Bills, Derek Lane
Art Teacher
Roberts, Suzanne R. (Sturch)
Economics & Business Instr
GARDEN GROVE
Abramson, Caroline Marsh
High School Science Teacher
Casas, A. J.
Spanish & Computer Teacher
Clarke, Howard Paul
Biology & Physiology Teacher
Dand, Laura
Civics, Economics & Psych Tchr
DeAngelis, Nancy
Spanish Teacher
Faura, Liliana
Spanish Teacher
Furness, Jeanine Elizabeth
Sixth Grade Teacher
Gray, Rocky Richard
Physical Education & Math Tchr
Hall, Kells
Third Grade Teacher
Hamamoto, Eric R.
Eng Teacher & Activities Dir
Inman, Ronald J.
HS Dir of Activities & Aths
Janiec, Kathleen Ann
Fourth Grade Teacher
Jones, Johnny Frank
Sixth Grade Teacher
Kelishes, Michael Allen
History Teacher
Kittleson, Chris Daniel
Business Teacher
Kowalchuk, Virginia Pegram
Fifth Grade Teacher
Kublin, Vincent Chip
Math Teacher
Lane, Virginia Kathleen
3rd Grade Teacher
Martinez, Rosalia
Spanish Teacher
Morse, Bret Wayne
HS Economics & English Teacher
Murphy, Joseph C.
Department Chair & Teacher
Pierce, Ernest, Jr.
Retired Teacher
Rauch, Allan Charles
Business Teacher
Reynozo, Paula Burns
Art Teacher
Rodriguez, Sydney Bell
ELD Sheltered Hist Tchr
Rogers, Jeannie Frances Griffith
English as a Second Lang Tchr
Settle, Judy Lenz
Resource Specialist Teacher
Smidt, Donald John
Substitute Teacher
Starnes, Lori Cardoza
English & ELD Teacher
Sundell, William Deane
Math Teacher
Taguchi, Dorothy Tayama
2nd Grade Teacher
Taylor, Kristin R.
Sixth Grade Teacher
Tinsman, Robert Linn
Sixth Grade Teacher
GARDEN VALLEY
Hendrix, Mark P.
Stu Act Dir, Eng & Jrnlsm Tchr
Holler, Harris Boyd
Computer Teacher
GARDENA
Barnes, Joy Vervene
English & Mentor Teacher
Binion, Tarltonette
Third Grade Teacher
Chavez, Norman Constantine
World History & Hnrs Eng Tchr
Classen, Linda Borodkin
Sheltered English Teacher
Duret, Joseph Thomas
Science Instructor
Horn, Caren Arnett
Kindergarten Teacher
Kai, Setsumi
Second Grade Bilingual Teacher
Kawasaki, Susan Morioka
Math Teacher
Kohara, Enid Kobayashi
5th Grade Teacher
Mena, Armando
Chem Tchr & Sci Dept Chair
Motoyasu, Ayako Meada
Biling Math Tchr & Coord
Murphy, Patricia Rosing
Fifth Grade Teacher
Ortiz, J. Victor
Social Science Teacher
Paddor, Lois Gotz
Speech, Eng Tchr & Dept Chair
Takaya, Judy Kageyama
Counselor
Wooden, Walter Emerson
High School Counselor
York, Ruth Eaton
1st Grade Teacher
GEYSERVILLE
Kennedy, Steven Ralph
Teacher
GILROY
Bravo, Robert Ronald
His Teacher & Staff Dev Coord
Carr, Michele Louise
English, History & Poetry Tchr
Chisolm, Stephanie P.
Reading Resource Teacher
Elia, Diane M.
6th Grade Teacher
Espinosa, Consuelo J.
Child Care Instructor
Gama, James M.
Social Studies Teacher
Hentschke, Curtis Charles
4th Grade GATE Teacher
Kawamoto, Nancy Yukiye
Second Grade Teacher
Marques, Carol Ann (Elia)
Core & Communications Teacher
Robb, Phillip James
Choral & Music Teacher
Roy, Rosalie Shepherd
Sixth Grade Teacher
Rubio, Pamela Sastre
5th Grade Teacher
Salewske, Claudia Kendall
English Teacher
Serigstad, Jon N.
English & Speech Teacher
GLENDALE
Bakly, Judith Hamilton
Art Teacher
Briones, Carmencita Rulloda
Religious Studies Teacher
Brogdon, Charles William
English Teacher
Brown, Mark Cameron
Bus Ed Instructor & Counselor
Busailah, Mohammad Y.
Business & Management Prof
Byrd, Larry Richard
Professor of Chemistry
Chassman, Carol Lucille
Chemistry & AP Teacher
Chesworth, Jeanne A.
Spanish & French Teacher
Coblentz, Terry
Womens Athletic Director
Coughlin, Ann K.
Spanish Teacher
Croson, Charlotte Joanne
English Teacher
Danesky, Melinda Marquez
Spanish, Health & ESL Tchr
Danielian, Hasmik Matevoss
Asst Prin for Categorical Prgm
DeLange, Glenn A.
Associate Professor of Music
Doll, Linda E.
Counselor & Teacher
Donahoo, Roger D.
Life Science Teacher
Edelman, Bart
Professor of English
Everingham, Mary Jo Ann
Word Processing Instructor
Field, Mona
Political Science Dept Chair
Fovos, Karen Marie
Art Teacher
Gross, Sandra Lee
Honors History & English Tchr
Halverson, Carl Moldt
Mathematics Teacher
Hancock, Jane S.
English & History Teacher
Johnstone, Laurie A.
5th Grade Teacher
Knighton, James
Asst Prof of Computer Science
Kohlmeier, Kris E.
Teacher & Student Body Advisor
Kolpas, Sidney J.
Mathematics Professor
Kupka, Craig L.
Music Teacher
Labinger, Kim Dodgson
Sixth Grade Teacher
Luu, Dinh Thi
EOPS Couselor
Manzano-Larsen, Linda Margaret
Child Development Professor
Matsuda, Stanley Kazuhiro
Math Teacher
Moore, Michael Wesley
5th-6th Grade Teacher
Newberry, Lawrence J.
Asst Professor of Mathematics
O'Brian, Christine Hill
Principal & Teacher
Pal, Poorna Chandra
Professor & Chair
Pelletier, Patricia Miles
Teacher Specialist
Phibbs, Mary Ellen
Science Teacher
Rabe, Patricia Ellen
Mathematics Teacher
Schaffert-Carroll, Jean
Mathematics Teacher

DALE (cont)
k, Richard Dwight, II
ier
, Nadine Antoinette
eacher & Drill Team Adv
Charles Lee, Jr.
Tchr & Dept Co-Chair
mey, Herman Ronald
ry Teacher
Kathleen Farson
sh Teacher
DORA
k, Beverly Joyce
ergarten Teacher
, Karen Reed
netry, Algebra & Cmptr Tchr
, Judith Ann
sh Teacher
n, Rosalee McIntire
sh Teacher
ansen, Marsha Lynn
ematics Teacher & Mentor
o, Eileen Mc Cormack
Grade Social Stud Teacher
h, Beverly Agler
Calculus Tchr & Dept Chair
Lisa Jeanne (Cass)
ish & Yearbook Teacher
n, Sandra J.
ish Teacher
Priscilla June
th Grade Teacher
ner, Keith O.
uctor & APL Advisor
, Greg Scott
stant Principal
Mark Allen
ish Teacher
Paula Marx
th Grade Teacher
Bonnie Lynne
ory Teacher
rt, Mary C.
red Elementary Teacher
TA
, Neal J.
School Biology Teacher
, Jan Louise (Parker)
ish Teacher & Dept Chair
i, Anita Phillips
nd Grade Teacher
, Margaret Elisabeth
ish Teacher
n, Amy Jewel
ish Teacher
Nancy L. (Green)
dergarten Teacher
William Lamont
nce Teacher
ZALES
nzar, Yolanda Zuniga Jimenez
Grd Lang Arts & Lit Tchr
, Steven Edwin
d Teacher
e, Michael J.
Tech Mentor & Math Prof
an, Edward E.
strial Ed & History Tchr
s, Marianne Margaret
sical Ed & Health Teacher
on, Porter Molone
ence Teacher
son, Nancy Vaughan
Grade Teacher
quez, Albert Lee
cipal
, Gerald T.
h Grade Teacher
NADA HILLS
drey, Dianne White
sic Chorus & Advncd ESL Tchr
w, Warren James
ounting & Marketing Tchr
Michael James
hematics Teacher
klin, Stephanie
glish Teacher
nt, Patricia L.
glish Teacher
in, Jay
ence Teacher
Michelle Margolin
th Teacher
ie, Patti Sue
ysical Education Teacher
rman, Lynne
glish Teacher
aughlin, John Henry, Jr.
gh School & Biology Teacher
re, Katherine Louise
-6th Grade Teacher
mann, Leslie Warner
anish Teacher
ips, Harvey Manuel
strl Arts Dept Chm & Tchr
vich, Robin Katherine
, French & Soc Stud Tchr
ge, Cathy McLaughlin
g as a Second Lang Tchr
bian, Haygo
ence Teacher
, Beverly Ann
glish Teacher
or, Ali Maxwell
glish & Speech Teacher
etts, Richard M.
cial Studies Teacher
Soon W.
alth Sci Tchr & Dept Chair

Zigler, Betty Anne Boyd
US History Teacher
GRAND TERRACE
Beck, Michael Joseph
Eighth Grade Science Teacher
Harris, Liese L.
Teacher & Magnet Coordinator
Massey, Patricia Diane
Retired First Grade Teacher
Penick, Linda Dianne Crimes
Principal
GRASS VALLEY
Andes, Charlean Marie-Aimo
Math & Comp Programming Tchr
Brown, Michael John
High School English Teacher
Croft, Alexander Carlile
American History & Eng Tchr
Farber, Terry Lynn
English & Psychology Teacher
Garcia, Gloria Rennow
Third Grade Teacher
Graham, Debra Cox
Eng, Speech Tchr, Debate Coach
Harter, Brian Scott
Mathematics Teacher
Haut, David Dennis
English Teacher
Hinman, Barbara Jean
GATE Teacher
Homan, Lawrence Earl
English & Social Studies Tchr
Jewett-Burdick, Lorraine
High School Journalism Teacher
Kaweski, Walter George
Band Director
Keller, Jan Ellen
Fifth Grade Teacher
Kemp, Dan G.
Agriculture Director & Teacher
King, N. Eugene
Art Teacher
LaBarge, Nancy Parsons
Kindergarten Teacher
Larsen, Gary E.
Chemistry & Physiology Teacher
Lehman, Clyde Kenneth
English Teacher
Mc Dowell, Alexandra Brown
Chemistry Teacher
Mc Lean, Patricia Tarpen
English Dept Chair & Teacher
Miller, Linda Personeni
Physical Education Teacher
Murphy, Jack Douglas
Fifth Grade Teacher
Nat, Charles James
Sixth Grade Teacher
Ostrom, Sven O.
English, World & US His Tchr
Parker, Eileen Sayles
English Teacher
Richards, James Hamilton
Sixth Grade Teacher
Rodriguez, Manuel Joseph
Student Activities Director
Smart, Michael Dean
4th Grade Teacher
Stenderup, Jane Johnson
US History Teacher
Stewart, Penny Morris
Drama & English Teacher
Underwood, Mary E. Beutler
English Teacher
Will, Barbara Elizabeth
English Teacher
Zauner, Duane Eugene
Math & Physical Education Tchr
GREENBRAE
Pamplin, Lynn Gilman
Retired First Grade Teacher
GREENFIELD
Porter, Heidi Marcia Lovett
First Grade Teacher
Salvaagno, Margaret Wilden
Title VII Resource Specialist
GREENVILLE
Gakle, Loana Constance
Principal
GRIDLEY
Garnero, Cammie
Physical Education Teacher
Haft, Carolyn Jean (Call)
Fourth Grade Teacher
Nelson, Angela Terry
Jr & Sr English Teacher
Stewart, James Andrew
Social Science Teacher
Tull, David Eugene
High School Math Teacher
Tull, Jodie Lynn
High School Counselor & Coach
Watson, Karen
Math Teacher & Dept Chair
Werner, Marianne
High School English Teacher
GROVELAND
Landeros, Martha Estela
Spanish Teacher
GUERNEVILLE
Castleberry, Loretta K.
Fourth Grade Teacher
GUSTINE
Mc Killigan, Michael Thomas, Jr.
Categorical Prgms Dir & Prin
HACIENDA HGTS
Adams, Gilbert Raymond
Music Department Chair
Asghari, Jennifer Cormack
Music & Peer Counseling Tchr

Bernard, Shelley Mc Dowell
ELD & English Teacher
Calton, Tracy W.
Social Studies & PE Teacher
Era, James Donald
German & English Teacher
Ferris, Teresa
Biology & Chemistry Teacher
Garrett, K. Shand
Social Science Teacher
Gray, Linda Lee
Third Grade Teacher
Huddle, Toby J.
Psych, Economics & Civics Tchr
Jeffords, Malcolm Leslie
Mathematics Instructor
Kraft, Richard F.
Government & Economics Teacher
Pate, Karen Susan
French & Art Instructor
Tebbs, Carol A.
English Mentor Teacher
VanRooyen, Helena
Second Grade Teacher
HALF MOON BAY
Cox, Thomas Victor
Social Studies Teacher
Olsen, Eric Jonley
Math Department Chairman
Yates, Arlette Martinsen
Retired Teacher
HAMILTON CITY
Turnbull, Rae Marie
Department Chair & Teacher
HANFORD
Billingsley, Loretta Marie
Director & Teacher
Daudistel, Gil
Geog & World History Teacher
Daudistel, Kathleen Esperanca
Visual Art Teacher
Doss, Marian Frances
7th Grade Teacher
Higham, Michael Edward
Agriculture Science Teacher
Keller, J. Terrence
Asst Prin & Soc Stud Tchr
Lopes, Tina Marie
Chemistry Teacher
May, Paula Ann
Advanced Placement Lang Tchr
Stanford, Jeanne Easley
2nd Grade Teacher
Trigueiro, James C.
PE & Drivers Training Tchr
Tunison, Mark W.
Pottery Teacher
Young, Robb C.
Business Education Teacher
HAPPY CAMP
Gabbert, Larry Ray
Industrial Arts Teacher
Saler, Jonathan Louis
Music Teacher
HARBOR CITY
Ball, Terry Alan
Social Studies Teacher
Mitchell, Jean Bracey
English Teacher & College Adv
Nevin, Denise Margaret
Business Teacher
Parnes, Barton Evan
History Teacher
Vitti, Christine M.
Middle School Teacher
Yamada, Faye Fumie
Math Teacher
HAWTHORNE
Dicus, Julianne
Counselor & Coll Counselor
Dubas, Thomas Edmund
8th Grade Math Teacher
Ellis, Linda G.
English, Govt & Economics Tchr
Faulds, Ann Marie
High School Physics Teacher
Ishibashi, Andrew Wayne
Instrumental Music Director
Klein, Susanne Lee
Eng as a Second Language Tchr
Lafferty, Edna Leith
Retired 5th Grade Teacher
Macha, Gary Pat
World History Teacher
Mertens, Edward R.
Math Teacher
Neubauer, Edward D.
Sixth Grade Teacher
Orinoco-Hart, Carmen Ala
Vice Principal
Riley, Susan Crist
Third Grade Teacher
Ringer, Tricia J.
English Teacher
Scott-Brant, Carmela
6th Grade Teacher
Shenton, Michelle Lawrence
Sixth Grade Teacher
Smith, Libby M.
Sixth Grade Teacher
Stewart, Gerald Lee
Science Instructor
Stuntdebeck, Gloria Jane
Business Instructor & Dpt Head
Takumi, Barbara Sasashima
Chemistry Tchr & Sci Dept Head
Webb, Barbara Johnston
Fourth Grade Teacher
Williams, Thomas Hardy
Fifth Grade Teacher

HAYFORK
Brainerd, Alan Bruce
Science Teacher & Principal
Roberson, Mildred D.
Social Studies Teacher
Schraeder, Wesley D.
7th & 8th Grd Math Tchr
Wagner, Joyce Katherine
Second Grade Teacher
HAYWARD
Bentley, Andree Monique Bujold
Kindergarten Teacher
Breiger, Marek
Comm Coll & High Schl Teacher
Chapman, Kelly Maroney
Mathematics Teacher
Crocker, Thomas Neal
Physical Ed Tchr & Dept Head
Dann, James John
Physics Teacher
English, Susan Charlene
English Teacher
Erker, Edgar Edward
German, Sci Teacher & Coach
Faure, William Gerard
1st Grade ELD Teacher
Fuchs, Jacob
English Professor
Gee, Janita Ruth
Science Department Chairperson
Goetschel, Charles Thomas
Chemistry Professor
Hazatone, John George
Eighth Grade Teacher
Johnson, Beverly Marie
Music Instructor
Kennedy, Barbara Ann
English & Spanish Teacher
Krisman, Christine Ann
Physical Education Teacher
Mangold, Nancy R.
Accounting Professor
Mc Carty, Kevin Robert
Theology Dept Chair
Michaud, Nancy Mitchell
Spanish Teacher
Mullen, Dorothy Allen
Telecommunication Teacher
Nichols, Patrick James
Mathematics Teacher
Pietrzak, Ted John
Marketing & Management Coord
Poynter, Anne Therese
Physical Education Teacher
Queyrel, Donald Craig
Account Executive
Rawdon, Kenneth Duane
Vocal Music Teacher
Reilly, Terence
Accounting Teacher
Robles, Juan A.
Health Sciences Professor
Schafer, Charles Richard
Chemistry Teacher
Showers, Steven James
English Teacher
Song, Sandra Chusunn
Chemistry Instructor
Stein, Robert M.
HS Eng Teacher, Baseball Coach
Villarreal, Suzanne Daly
English & Theology Teacher
Watson, Frankie Woodard
Lang Arts Consultant & Teacher
Woodside, Sandra Joan
Soc Stud & Bus Oper Specialist
HEALDSBURG
Baker, Sally Weller
High School Fine Arts Teacher
Childers, Ronald F.
Teacher & Math Dept Chair
Giampaoli, Mark Victor
Science Teacher
Sabo, Patricia Kay
Mathematics Teacher
HEBER
Galindo, Juan
6th Grade Teacher
HELENDALE
Losi, Joseph Anthony
His & Physical Education Tchr
HEMET
Arnquist, Clifford Warren
Mathematics Teacher
Baker, Hyatt Porter
Science Teacher
Barb, Jordan Chase
Math Teacher
Feely, Lynne Rittenhouse
Resource Specialist
Hofrock, James Michael
Life Science Teacher
Jordan, Michael
Teacher
Kopperud, David Matthews
English Teacher
MacMillan, Martha Smalley
Mathematics Teacher
Miller, William J.
English Teacher
Morrison, Jay
Biology Teacher
Petersen, Kathy (Kelly)
Speech, Drama & Music Teacher
Shawver, Rebecca Lee
Language Arts Teacher
Subang, F. William
Spcl Day Class & Resrc Speclst

HERCULES
Schroder, Bernice Mc Cabe
Third Grade Teacher
HERLONG
Myers, Bryan Lee
Health & Driver Education Tchr
HERMOSA BEACH
Bolger, Joan Johnson
Owner & Dir Tutorial Office
O'Brien, Kimberly White
Fourth Grade Teacher
HESPERIA
Alcorn, John F.
Math, Science & Drama Teacher
Asdel, Bradley Scott
Social Science & PE Teacher
Chansler, Kristie R.
First Grade Teacher
Durham, Laura Lillian
Mathematics Teacher
Fakatoumafi, Elaine Herman
Yrbk Adv & English Teacher
Frederick, Stan Burl
US History & Psychology Tchr
Gomez, Nica Cotroneo
Special Ed & Resource Teacher
Harper, Peggy Mary
English Teacher
Janzen, Pandora A.
8th Grade US History Teacher
Jones, Wendy Ann (Atkinson)
Math Teacher & Dept Chair
Kirk, Robert Fred
Science Tchr & Dept Chprsn
Kitchens, Bryan Ray
Government & Economics Teacher
Kramer, Shari Lynn (O'Cain)
Physical Education Teacher
Lambdin, Wanda Sue (McCourt)
8th Grd Language Arts Teacher
Laughlin, Mildred Bragunier
Bio & Anatomy Physiology Tchr
Long, William Darrell
Bible Tchr & Var Bsktbl Coach
Mac Donald, Nicole DeForrest
Biology & PE Teacher
Orum, Edwin Clay
Chemistry & Health Teacher
Pearson, Martha Elisabeth (Kelley)
Fourth Grade Teacher
Porras, Larry
Vice Principal
Price, Kenneth Guy
English Teacher
Reasby, Mary Joan
Air Force Jr ROTC Instructor
Rogers, Mary Helen
Fifth Grade Teacher
Rogers, William S.
Science & Math Teacher
Smith, Jeff Matthew
Mathematics Teacher
Stokes, Gretchen Gilbert
English Teacher
Swanson, Rebekah Pavey
5th Grade & Mentor Teacher
Tillitson, Ramona Heisig
Third Grade Teacher
Turner, Rebecca Brown
Teacher
VanderKamp, Patricia Lea
Counselor
Zubro, John Steven
8th Grd Language Arts Teacher
HICKMAN
Rossi-Swope, Karen
K-2nd Grade Teacher
HIGHLAND
Barber, Sarah Lynn
Fifth Grade Teacher
Diefendorf, Ellen Ann (Desist)
5th Grade Teacher
Newman, Linda Harrington
2nd Grade Teacher
Patterson, Richard H., Sr.
Sixth Grade Teacher
Rybak, Carol H.
First Grade Teacher
Whittemore, Charlene Ann (Schulmeyer)
6th Grade Teacher
HILMAR
Piersma, Dick Wyatt
Agriculture Instructor
HOLLISTER
Barr, Diane Rianda
Fourth Grade Teacher
Bates, Diane Nowlen
Home Economics Teacher
Caffiero, Jim Vincent
Counselor
Chen, William W.
Math Teacher & Division Chm
Contival, Nancy Anderson
5th-8th Grade Teacher
Durrell, Jane
3rd-4th Grade Teacher
Ford, Hilary
English & Social Science Tchr
Gansen, Charles L.
Metal Tech & Art Instr
Gioia, Martha
English Teacher
Logue, Randy Chris
PE Teacher & Coach
Lomanto, Krystal Kay
Science & PE Teacher
Masoni, Richard A.
Science Instr & Dept Chair
Mc Kenzie, Kate
9th-12th Grd Art Teacher

HOLLISTER (cont)
Murray, Donald Byron
Math Teacher
Petersen, Sandra Elizabeth
Eighth Grade Teacher
Quiroz, Ernesto Antonio
Social Studies Teacher
Segala, John P.
Economics Teacher
Vik, Donald Raymond
Economics & Government Teacher
Yoder, Gretchen Sue
Spanish Teacher
HOLTVILLE
Macon, Lendal Edwin
Music Director
Romero, Stella Maes
Second Grade Teacher
HOOPA
Moon, Sandra Finch
Upper Elementary Teacher
HUGHSON
Matthew, M. Dan
7th Grade Math Teacher
McCoy, Steve Bruce
Jrnlsm, Eng & Lang Arts Tchr
Nicholas, Kirk Sean
World His & Hnrs Eng Tchr
HUNTINGTON BEACH
Bates, Rebecca Hammerman
8th Grade Mathematics Teacher
Baxter, Linda Sue
Elementary Principal
Borrelli, Sheila Blyth
Middle School Physical Ed Tchr
Carroll, Stanley Mark
Fifth Grade Teacher
Collier, Mary Long
Lang Arts & Soc Stud Teacher
DeBritton, Heidi Hetzler
8th Grade Teacher
Dishno, Polly (Schwandt)
Fifth Grade Teacher
Eiswerth, Mary Marguerite
English Teacher
Ellenson, Virginia Helen
Rdng & Language Arts Teacher
Fairchild, Kenneth
English & History Teacher
Gane, James E.
Bible Teacher
Garland, William Edison
History Teacher
Geck, Rosie Dunnigan
Spanish Teacher
Gingerich, Wendy R.
Science Teacher
Haben, Susan Hovinen
First Grade Teacher
Harnett, Winifred
6th Grade Teacher
Hinds, Carreen Sue
Eighth Grade Mathematics Tchr
Kavert, Josephine Cammallarie
Math Coordinator
Kraiss, Barbara A.
Substitute Teacher
Lara, Brandee Williams
Dance & LEP English Teacher
Lester, Adorae Hansen
Kindergarten Teacher
Mc Clure, William C.
Assoc Professor of Mathematics
Mendez, Michael Frank
Biology Tchr & Sci Dept Head
Mitchell, Ann Crosbie
Kindergarten Teacher
Miyahira, Clarice A.
Third Grade Teacher
Morehouse, William H.
9th-12th Grd Photography Tchr
Morgan, Ralph Wayne
Science Teacher
Nettleton, Sue Nancy
History, Lang Arts Tchr & Chm
Perry, Patricia Lynne
Art & World History Teacher
Richards, Dorcas Wilson
4th-5th Grade Teacher
Rodriguez, Victor
Music Teacher
Santia, Zelma Jean (Davis)
Sixth Grade Teacher
Saviers, Lee A.
Science Teacher
Snetsinger, Peter Joseph
Social Science Tchr & Mentor
Speer, Bryan Michael
High School English Teacher
Stein, Konrad Mark
Physics Professor
TeGantvoort, Douglas Charles
4th Grade Classroom Teacher
Towle, Carolyne Bonnie
Kindergarten Teacher
VanTassell, Jonathan Charles
History Teacher
Ward, Linda Graham
Physical Education Teacher
Wilton, Marilyn Jeanette (Benard)
Third Grade Teacher
HUNTINGTON PARK
Antoine, Jacqueline Long
Business Education Teacher
Bell, LaRoyce Denise
5th Grade Teacher & GATE Coord
Bruno, John Michael
8th Grade Math Teacher
Mercado, Alfred James
Mathematics Teacher
Olson, Janice Lorraine
Dean of Students
Stout, Janice Marie
Fourth Grade Teacher
Taylor, Thomas T., Jr.
Science Teacher
IDYLLWILD
Barrett, Ned
Humanities Teacher
Crawford, Kara Ball
Humanities Teacher
Levinson, Judith Carol
Theatre Arts Dept Chairman
IMPERIAL
Alcorta, D. Nick
Gen Science Tchr & Bsbl Coach
Campbell, Mike John
Agriculture Instructor
Carter, Claire Jeanne
Art Teacher
Ferrell, Kathleen Allen
Second Grade Teacher
Gardner, Virginia Q.
Amer Lit & English II Teacher
Long, Marian Astrid
Substitute Teacher
McDonald, Clinton Lee
Mathematics Tchr & Dept Chair
Montes de Oca, Daisy Claudio
Spanish Teacher
Ospelt, Rita
Mathematics Teacher
Pendley, Jimmy R.
Div Chprsn of Sci, Math, Engrn
Ralls, Thomas James
7th Grade Math Teacher
Swearingen, Mike W.
US History Teacher
IMPERIAL BEACH
Czajkowski, Katrine Gram
Math, Eng, Soc Studies Teacher
Day, Patricia Lynne
Kindergarten Teacher
Fisher, P. Seth
3rd & 4th Grade Teacher
Parra, Jose Andres
Mathematics Teacher
Sanchez, Sheryl Lee
Maintenance & Motivation Cnslr
INDIO
Bowman, John Allen
History, Lit & English Teacher
Howells, John F., III
Lang Arts & Literature Teacher
Kronemeyer, Mary Kathy
Multi-Age Teacher
Mathews, Matt Price
Second Grade Teacher
Miller, Robert John
HS Language Arts Teacher
Stefan, Bonnie Barbara
Mathematics Teacher
Tiger, Erma Hays
Psychology & Amer Govt Teacher
INGLEWOOD
Brennan, Jan Lynette
Lang Arts Tchr & Eng Dept Chm
Carter, Xavier Trone
AP Govt, Civics & Ec Teacher
Cunningham, Olivet D.
Science Teacher
Dost, Nanette H.H.
Gen Sci & Religion Teacher
Ellis, Claudia Hannah
6th Grd Adv & Aerobics Instr
Francis, Mary Patricia
Junior HS History Teacher
Hawkins, Cassandra L. Crawford
Fifth Grade Teacher
Hill, Doreatha Elaine
Resource Teacher
Hughes, Wrelda Virginia
History & Spanish Teacher
Johnson, Carolyn
Third Grade Teacher
Lee, David Jung An
Science Teacher
Lewis, Ernestine Kountz
Retired Counselor
Nicolaysen, Rebecca Medrano
Third Grade Bilingual Teacher
Ra'oof, Miranda Conston
Social Science Teacher
Robinson, Deidre D.
Fourth Grade Teacher
Sambrano, Lillian Cobos
Resource Music Teacher
Schiesel-Manning, Morri S.
Drama & English Teacher
Woehler, Gloria D' Eve Ward
ESL Tchr & Dept Chair
IRVINE
Altimari-Brown, Gail
High School Teacher
Alvarez, Lisa
Professor of English
Atlee, Nancy M.
Gifted & Talented Teacher
Borst, Katherine Faith Meyer
English Professor
Brown, Jacqueline Yvonne
History Professor
Byars, Jo Salness
Math Teacher
Cacciavillani, Emilio
Teacher
Colten, Anne G.
Counselor
Donohoe, Marie Anne
Hum, Chorus Tchr & Director
Doyle, Thomas J.
Ed Prof & Dir of Grad Stud
Endsley, Celia R.
Sixth Grade Teacher
Feldt, Rainer H.
History Instructor
Fournier, Peter Planer
Instrumental Music Director
Gauld, Merrilyn Avila
Substitute Teacher
Geisler, Herbert George
Prof of Music
Guymon, Gary L.
Emeritus Prof of Civil Engrng
Holl, Mary Katherine
Education & Phys Ed Professor
Ives, Bill
Social Science Teacher
Jacobson, Norman Moron
Dept of Info & Computer Sci
Johnson, Miriam Lee
Environmental Science Teacher
Krueger, Kurt John
English Professor
Kurdziel, Barbara
Math Teacher
Lindfors, Burton Ruben
History & Government Teacher
Ludwig, Garth David
Professor of Anthropology
Martin Fritsch, Connie Frank
Kindergarten Teacher
Mercer, Joann Woodward
English Teacher
Nelson, Gretchen C.
Hum CORE Tchr & Dept Chair
Peck, Cora Linn
Social Science Teacher
Perez, Thomas
Dir of Admin Criminal Justice
Pommer, Kathleen Ellen (Richards)
Gifted Education Teacher
Prystowsky, Richard Jay
English & Humanities Professor
Raskulinecz, Susan Almy
Vocal Music Teacher
Scharlemann, Sandra F.
Assistant Professor of Ed
Shaka, Athan James
Chemistry Professor
Spar, Constance Caputo
Director of Matriculation
Taagepera, Mare
Retired Lecturer of Chem
Tanzer, Muriel Ann
Second Grade Teacher
Taylor, Linda Carrington
7th-8th Grd Span & Lang Tchr
Valletta, Robert Gerard
Economics Professor
Wada, Jeffrey Kent
HS Chemistry Teacher
Wilde, Sally Jayne
High School Ceramics Teacher
JACKSON
Arnese, Suzette Conception
Eighth Grd English & Lit Tchr
Vukovich, William Victor
US History Teacher
JAMUL
Hessel, Robyn Lee
Math, Science & PE Teacher
JANESVILLE
Stewart, John Preston
Eighth Grade Teacher
JULIAN
Gernandt, Gary Michael
Vice Principal & Counselor
Rabetoy, Lorna Weir
Sixth Grade Teacher
KELSEYVILLE
Brenton, William LeRoy
Chemistry & Science Teacher
Hagler, Candyce Lee
Tchr of Learning Handicapped
Ingalls, Deborah L.
Advanced Art, PE & Yrbk Tchr
Lawson, Kerrie J.
5th Grade Teacher
Petersen, Carl W.
Counselor
Smith, JoAnne Stewart
Third & Fourth Grade Teacher
KENSINGTON
Gillfillan, Gretchen Reuter
Retired Teacher
KENTFIELD
Pickerel, Catherine L.
Religious Studies Teacher
KERMAN
Bitter, Carol Ann (Hansen)
High School Math Teacher
Lovejoy-Miller, Margaret Quandt
Early Primary Instructor
Potstada, Leanne Martin
Agricultural Science Teacher
KING CITY
Greeno, Gary Wayne
High School Mathematics Tchr
Iwan, Joseph S.
Spanish Teacher
KINGSBURG
Deis, Mary Katherine
Eng & Creative Writing Instr
Koelewyn, Kevin Thomas
Agriculture Teacher
Pisor, William Marshall
Third Grd Tchr & Tech Coord
Torbit, Marilyn Bailey
Tech Coord & Cmptr Lab Tchr
Troisi, Barbara Jacobsen
1st Grade & Library Media Tchr
KLAMATH
Lee, Emmalie Bess
Principal
Seats, Carolyn Faye Gaylor
Kindergarten Teacher
KNIGHTSEN
Gursky, Lynn Marie
8th Grade Teacher
Racke, Shereen Thomas
Kindergarten Teacher
Zahn, Robert C.
7th Grd Self-Contained Teacher
LA CANADA FLINTRIDGE
Appels, Glen James
English Dept Chm & Teacher
Cummings, Jerome Lyons
Marriage & Religion Teacher
Mealiffe, Karen Ring
Art, Ceramics & Phtgrphy Instr
Mikrut, Eva Ilona
Math Teacher
Moran, Thomas G.
Principal
Morton, Taylor Lee
Law Instructor
Pendergast, Timothy Shaw
Theology Teacher
Rose, Elizabeth Anne
English Teacher
Sage, James Joseph
Fine Arts & Music Teacher
Smith, Edward Thomas
English Teacher & Counselor
Treacy, Annabelle Lee
Dean of Students
Valente, Ralph Patrick
Principal & Teacher
Weaver, Mary Shumway
Mathematics Teacher
Williams, Robin Willoughby
Sixth Grd Sci & Soc Sci Tchr
LA CRESCENTA
Davidson, Harold Thomas
6th Grade Teacher
Keyes, Gary Willard
Social Sci Dept Chair & Instr
Klint, Ronald V.
Mathematics Instructor
Waterman, Rosalie Isbitz
Substitute Teacher
Waters, Jennifer (Myers)
English Teacher & Dept Chair
LA HABRA
Blake, Kesten L.
Teacher & Speech Coach
Cholewa, Iris Umemoto
French & Spanish Teacher
Enriquez, Marie Pagnotta
Eighth Grd Lang Arts Tchr
Gilliam, Jacqueline Stott
First Grade Teacher
Licata, Anne Margaret
Spanish Teacher
Nash, Richel Cecilia
3rd Grade Teacher
Pergola, Michael Joseph
Band Director
Ross, Teresa Lynn
Dance Teacher
Ryal, Valoree Ann (Chilcott)
Fifth Grade Teacher
Sloniger, Mitzi
Drama & ELD Teacher
Toombs, Helen J. Rebeles
MS Bilingual Lead Teacher
Welsh, Joyce Lester
Counselor
LA JOLLA
Christensen, Richard G.
Art & Yearbook Teacher
Diamond, Patrick H.
Professor of Physics
Dressler, Julie Annette
Spanish Teacher
Erickson, Michael O'Louglin
7th Grade Teacher
Fares, Mary A. Quinn
English & Math Teacher
Groce, Barbara Ondrasik
English Teacher
Hartman, Kent
Mathematics Teacher
Hays, Judy Rasmussen
Kindergarten Teacher
Hoolko, Linda Lorenz
Math & Physical Education Tchr
Mattox, Tod Benton
English Teacher & Coach
McKenzie, Kristin Michelle
Teacher
Morgan, David W.
Mathematics Department Chair
Munzer, Harold W.
Fifth Grade Teacher
Simms, Billy W.
Physics Teacher
Smith, Jacques Cordell
Former HS Tchr
Stiles-Hall, Ayres Samuel
History & English Teacher
Stukenberg, Katherine Van Da Griff
Spanish Teacher
Wainscott, Joanne Marie Arnzen
Math Teacher & Dept Chprsn
LA MESA
Abdelnour, Mike George
Art Teacher & ASB Advisor
Anderson, Joan Marie
Resource Specialist
Babbitt, Jeffrey Michael
Math Teacher & ASB Advisor
Dunne, Aubrey
7th & 8th Grade Math Teacher
Fox, Ray S.
8th Grade English Teacher
Fromer, Leda (Romero)
Spanish Teacher
Havens, Christy Crossland
English Teacher
Hollingsworth, Edward H.
Drama Teacher
Mandell, Eileen M.
Photography Tchr & Yrbk Adv
Moorehead, Lisa LaPorte
Former Teacher
Rivera, Ruth Robinson
Teacher
Schnaubelt, Paul
8th Grade Language Arts Tchr
Torretto, Ronald Louis
World & Art History Teacher
LA MIRADA
Balius, Kirk Jeffrey
Asst Prof of Systmtc Theology
Caltabiano, Cheryl Zukerberg
Associate Professor of Nursing
Cavin, Margaret Hambrick
Assoc Prof of Commnctn
Dill, Glenn Victor
Assoc Professor of Business
Ebeling, Ruth Ellen
Assistant Professor
Gevirtzman, Bruce Jay
English & Speech Teacher
Hayward, Douglas James
Associate Prof of Anthropology
Hsieh, Howard T.
Biblical Studies Professor
Ingraffia, Brian D.
Prof Amer Lit, Critical Theory
Ingram, John Andrew
Associate Prof of Psychology
Johnson, David C.
Chemistry Instructor
Johnson, Richard Owen
Adjunct Professor
Kuld, Paul H.
Associate Professor of Biology
Lewis, Todd Vernon
Prof of Communication & Chm
Leyda, Richard James
Asst Prof of Christian Ed
Lind, Mary Ann
Associate Professor of History
Lock, William Rowland
Professor of Music
Mandarino, Candida Ann
Integrated Language Arts Tchr
Peters, C. David
Prof of Pol Sci & Dept Chair
Poelstra, Paul L.
Professor of Psychology
Richardson, Lucile Stephens
Education Prof & Dept Chair
Russell, Walter Bo, III
Biblical Stud-Theology Div Chm
Soule, Roger Gilbert
PE Professor & Chair
Stangl, Walter David
Mathematics Professor
Strauss, Gerhard Henry
Associate Professor
Wilkins, Michael James
New Testament Lang & Lit Tchr
Wilshire, Leland E.
History Professor
Woodward, Philip Lloyd
Assoc Professor of Accounting
Zuckerberg, Cheryl
Associate Professor of Nursing
LA PUENTE
Arvedson, John Peter
Sci Dept Chm & Chemistry Tchr
Barrett, Diane (Squicciarini)
Mathematics Tchr & Coll Cnslr
Beach, Christine Marie
Biology & Morality Teacher
Berry, Theresa Rae
English Teacher
Cassidy, Frank Kenneth
Physical Ed Instr & Ath Dir
Chang, Beverly Sui-Ping
Kindergarten Teacher
D'Alessandro, Ronald Thomas
9th-12th Grd Peer Cnslr Tchr
Davis, Tom Lyle
Science Teacher
DiFiori, Michael Alan
Biology Teacher
Ebiner, Frank A.
High School Science Teacher
Estrella, Rosanna Maria
Chemistry Teacher
Foltz, Teresa Behnke
Mathematics Teacher
Fujishima, Mary Morita
1st & 2nd Grade Teacher
Garcia, Alberto
High School Math Teacher
Gibson, Nancy J.
Development & Reading Teacher
Holt, Timothy J.
English Teacher
Jackowski, Cynthia Williams
ESL Teacher
Kunishima, Richard Toshio, Jr.
Physical Education Teacher

ENTE (cont)
ase, Lloyd F.
rade English Teacher
, Jay Benitez
nth & Twelfth Grade Tchr
ez, Donald Raymond
11th Grd World His Tchr
Debra Jean
uage Arts & Honors Teacher
or, Patricia Kozlowski
Ec Tchr & Dept Chrprsn
'arrie Wade
entary & Dist Mentor Tchr
, Patricia Wolters
sh Teacher
Nitza
Schl Mathematics Teacher
'ictoria Visosky
sh Teacher & Yearbook Adv
er, Aida Teresa
g Dept Guid Technician II
, Duane Edwin
8th Grd Soc Studies Tchr
Stephen Louis
l Studies Teacher
y, Ava Loudene (Batt)
Economics Teacher
, Lynn Tegtmeier
th Grd Physical Ed Tchr
Gregory Edward
ce Teacher
Larry A.
'eacher
JINTA
Jonathan Eric
sh Teacher
, Lyn Vibrock
sh Teacher
or, Dolores Casas
ish Teacher
Donald Joseph
nce Teacher
er, Karen Sue
graphy Teacher
RNE
, Shawndel Lee
ematics Teacher
, Skip
a, Video & English Teacher
Edward William
gion Teacher
Jeffrey Warren
Principal & Instructor
incoln Anthony
Ed Tchr & Ftbl Coach
Taylora (Sullivan)
nselor & Teacher
'atricia Ann
her & Consultant
, Gary Craig
& Architecture Instructor
ell, Stephen Walter
nce Teacher
en, James Denis
Lang Dept Chm & Span Tchr
Sheila Karen
ic & Drama Teacher
fer, Les Eric
nematics Teacher, Dept Head
ijn, Eva Yvonne
12th Grd Tchr & ESL Tchr
YETTE
, Peter Joseph
Art & English Teacher
, Grant W.
omotive Technology Teacher
Martha Lams
nish Teacher
aughlin, Geri Williamson
nish Teacher
asters, Roger Bruce
hp & Archtctrl Dsgn Teacher
UNA BEACH
Theodore Clark
mistry Teacher
man, Michael James
Grade Government Teacher
ensen, Deni Davidson
lish & Journalism Teacher
ath, Marilyn Faye
red Fourth Grade Teacher
ngham, John B.
red HS Science Teacher
, Albert Y.
rumental Music Teacher
nts, George Kenneth
lish Teacher
rt, Tracy Ann
glish Teacher
, J. Scott
logy & Marine Science Tchr
, Peter Morse
& Photography Teacher
UNA HILLS
, Georgia Kay
th Grade Teacher
ing, Rosemarie Nesgoda
Grd Tchr of the Gifted
n, Keith Errold
nish Teacher
, Gerard Patrick
sic Director
UNA NIGUEL
, Keith Alan
& 8th Grade Math Teacher
on, Eric C.
ysical Education Teacher
E ARROWHEAD
, Lynn M.
glish Teacher

Mc Kee, Dennis V.
Tchr of Emotionally Disturbed
Novak, Karol Hildreth
High School Counselor
Rosinski, Shirley Gene
Fifth Grade Teacher
Sanchez, Richard Daniel
Eighth Grade Soc Sci Tchr
LAKE ELSINORE
Brown, Truman L.
Bilingual Teacher
Christopher, Barbara (Solga)
Physics & Science Teacher
Cohen, Phillip F.
Science Teacher
Collins, Thomas Lowell
English Teacher
Davis, Edgar, Jr.
Aerospace Sci Instr AFJROTC
LaPorte, Mark B.
History Teacher
Little, Deanna L.
English Teacher
Mc Coubrey, Juanita Leslie Carey
Lang Arts & Soc Stud Tchr
Moore, Robin D.
English Teacher
Romo, Donna J.
Spanish & ESL Teacher
Stuck, Karl E.
Fourth Grade Teacher of GATE
Wolsey, Thomas DeVere
English & Social Studies Tchr
Wren, Anthony Christopher
HS Math & Latin Teacher
LAKE FOREST
Ford, Debby Ann
Health, PE Teacher & Mentor
Grotsky, Bernard Ira
Sixth Grade Teacher
House, Barbara Rosich
Chemistry Teacher
Johnson, David Aldis
High School Science Teacher
Nichols, Jan Allen
7th-8th Grd Science Teacher
Nitta, Larry E.
Business Education Teacher
Norton, Judith Ann
History & Literature Teacher
LAKE HUGHES
Roach, Samuel Radford
Fifth Grade Teacher
Wagner, Teresa Louise
Science, Health & PE Teacher
LAKE ISABELLA
Cassady, Diane Myrtle
Campus Supervisor
Duitsman, Jack T.
English Teacher
Wenstrand, Gerald John
Agri-Science Teacher
LAKEPORT
Svehla, Nancy Grover
Fourth Grade Teacher
LAKESIDE
Bonnel, Joan DeLasaux
Special Education Teacher
Duke, Dennis James
Geog, Career & Fmly Stud Tchr
Furrow, Don Ross
US His Tchr & Soc Sci Dept Chm
Turk, Penelope Bryant
English Teacher
Waastad, Dave
American Literature Teacher
LAKEWOOD
Alexander, Pia
English Teacher
Bronkhurst, Arthur Daniel
Social Studies Teacher
Caraco, Leon R.
Fine Art Dept Chm & Tchr
Cornejo, Cheryl A.
Technology Program Facilitator
D'Agostino, Philip Joseph
Social Department Chairperson
Duvall, Mary Ellen
English Teacher
Fedde, Pharis Franklin
Retired Guidance Administrator
Flores, Ana Isabel
Spanish, Biling & US His Tchr
Manriquez, Teresa Marrujo
Fourth Grade Teacher
Marksbury, Gary
US History Teacher
Totah, Basil Raymond
History Teacher
LANCASTER
Albrecht, Rustin R.
US His Tchr & Stu Govt Adv
Bennett, William Walter
English & US History Teacher
Betzer, Cindy Davis
Fine Art Instructor
Braden, Scott Gordon
Business & Mathematics Teacher
Brussow, Craig Alan
Eighth Grade Teacher
Carter, Betty Rogers
English Tchr & Title I Coord
Conrad, James L.
US History Teacher
Dawson, Wayne E.
Bio, Anatomy & Physiology Tchr
Donner, Richard Lawrence
Engineering Instructor
Ennis, Susan Cameron
English Teacher

Hauth, Nancy Lee
Computer Teacher
Kanner, Susan H.
Guidance Counselor
Laferriere, Lionel Michael
Religion Teacher & Dept Chair
Laird, William Alexander
History & Bible Teacher
Lalicker, Beverly Sells
Kindergarten Teacher
Lara, Gilbert J.
English Teacher
McGlothlin, Laura Ross
English Teacher & Yearbook Adv
Mc Naughton, James Emory
Psychology Teacher
Nichter, Nadine Lynn
English & Reading Teacher
Reid, Dawn Michelle
English & Drama Teacher
Scalco, Joseph
French Teacher
Shahla, George
Adjunct Assistant Professor
Spoelstra, Dean Earl
Ath Dir, US His & Bible Tchr
Steidl, Elsa Diana
Spanish Teacher
Sullivan, Catherine Hiller
7th-8th Grd Soc Stud Teacher
Tapola, Kenneth Norman
Resource Specialist
T'Sas, Eduard W.
HS Physical Education Teacher
Unnerstall, Heather Ann
Third Grade Teacher
Weiss, Sally Sparkman
Language Arts Teacher
LANDERS
Peddie, Muriel Bork
First Grade Teacher
LARKSPUR
Allen, Martha Leary
English Teacher
Brandt, Michael E.
Spiritual Teacher
Dibley, Michael W.
Phys Ed Teacher & Bsktbl Coach
Jaime, Ann
Social Studies Teacher
Koss, Roberta Kennedy
Mathematics Teacher
Lavezzo, Constantino
Social Studies Teacher
Sargent, Robert Lee
Science Teacher
LATHROP
Gratonik, Lynn Ann Antonine
Sixth Grade Teacher
LAWNDALE
Bailey, Bill
Student Activities Director
Bolton, Stephanye Marie
High School Counselor
Dolce, Jill Rene
English Teacher
Foster, Brent Larkin
US History Teacher
Jacobs, Fred Claiborne
JROTC Instructor
Kaku, Laura Uehara
Third Grade Teacher
Lynch, Denise Renee
5th & 6th Grade Teacher
LAYTONVILLE
Textor, Alice Marie
High School Spanish Teacher
LE GRAND
Higginbotham, Julia Haskett
Seventh Grade Teacher
LEE VINING
Aas, Jodelle Elaine
Fifth-Sixth Grade Teacher
LEMON GROVE
Blum, Mike
7th-8th Grade PE Teacher
Ligon, Jane Sharrow
Second Grade Teacher
LEMOORE
Allen, Stella Stewart
Kindergarten Teacher
Bowden, Harry T., Jr.
Fifth Grade Teacher
Burns, Charles Eugene
Math & Industrial Tech Teacher
Drewry, Wanda Anne (Rhea)
Eighth Grade Teacher
Garrone, Judith Ann
Art Specialist
Godinho, Margaret Short
6th Grade Teacher
Good, Karleen Wagner
8th Grd Language Arts Teacher
Hart, Sarah K.
Fifth Grade Teacher
Krend, William John
History Teacher
Langworthy, Gregory David
High School English Teacher
Newman, Larry D.
7th Grade Language Arts Tchr
Parry, Thomas Evan
Business Teacher & Coach
Pettigrew, Gloria Belezzuoli
5th Grade Teacher
Pike, Lou Ann Roe
8th Grd Social Studies Teacher
Porter, Teresa T.
English Teacher

Powell, Joan E. Edwards
Special Education Teacher
Salgado, Anna Skorstad
8th Grade Language Arts Tchr
Siegel, Catherine R.
English Dept Chm & Teacher
Sperlich, James L.
Social Studies & Reading Tchr
Taylor, Ann Elizabeth
English Language Arts Teacher
Vorhees, Mike J.
High School Teacher
Wilder, Mark David
History & Government Teacher
LENNOX
Hyman, Lethia L.
4th-5th Grade Teacher
Lang, Mary A.
Language Arts Teacher
Sopa, Adele Rose
Bilingual Special Ed Tchr
LINCOLN
Eliopulos, Elizabeth J.
Foreign Language Teacher
McCartney, Patrick John
Agriculture Teacher
O'Connell, Michael Patrick
DIS Instructor
Prychun, Myron Theodore
8th Grd Language Arts Teacher
LINDEN
Fausset, Russell Wayne
United States History Teacher
Gross, Helen Rea Pennington
First Grade Teacher
Oliver, Constance Wilson
Biology Teacher
LINDSAY
Green, Michael Roger
World & US History Teacher
LITCHFIELD
Klesper, Ray
Math Teacher & Dept Chprsn
LITTLEROCK
Briggs, Joel E.
Agriculture Tchr & Dept Chair
Viramontes, Stephanie Stafford
Math Teacher
Weyer, Teresa Ann (Donnelly)
Health, PE & Psychology Tchr
LIVE OAK
Hogan, Steven H.
High School Counselor
LIVERMORE
Alemania, Sophie Ymasa
4th Grade Teacher
Clark, Ruth Litchfield
Home Economics Teacher
Conover, Gloria Sani
Kindergarten Teacher
Daniel, Helen Anderson
English & Psychology Teacher
Danner, Donald L.
Industrial Technology Teacher
Fong, Lorraine H.
French Teacher
Fong, Nelson S.
Sci, Math Tchr & Dept Chair
Moreland, Maynard Seldon
Middle School Teacher
Poore, Patricia Keenan
Second Grade Teacher
Roberts, Daria Marengo
Elem Resource Teacher
Vest, Tom Anthony
5th Grade Teacher
LIVINGSTON
Cleckler, Rebecca
Language Arts & History Tchr
Handley, John H.
Mathematics Teacher
Lamont, John Clayton
Teacher
Nelson, John Wesley
Reading, Writing & Eng Tchr
Ritchie, Daphne F.
Eng Tchr
Rodriguez, Arleen Janet
5th Grade Teacher
Street, Acquainetta Burton
8th Grade Resource Specialist
Taylor, Ken Scott
Music Educator
Wear, Robert F.
Vice Prin, Ath & Stu Svcs Dir
LOCKEFORD
Johnson, Ammer Lafayette
Sixth Grade Teacher
LODI
Augello, John
Fourth Grade Teacher
Berbawy, Samir Hilmy
Principal
Bordner, Robert Russell, II
Biological Sciences Teacher
Braden, Anne Ganzer
Physical Educator
Conner, Joyce Aaby
English Teacher
DeBerry, Gigi Stehle
Ger & Aeronautics Tchr
Duerr, Matthew W.
7th Grade Teacher
Eustis, Mary Jo Snell
7th Grade Mentor Teacher
Hammett, Carol Lynn
Social Studies Educator
Heinrich, Ted William
Industrial Arts Dept Head

Hitchcock, Susan Yvonne
Eighth Grade Teacher
Martin, Robert LeRoy
Span, His, Govt & Hlth Tchr
Mende, Freda Ann
Second Grade Teacher
Metzger, Terry Chevalier
Sixth Grade Teacher
Muller-Kimball, Dominee S.
English & Theater Arts Teacher
Parizo, Faith Adele
World History Teacher
Peters, Regina Riley
English Teacher
Porter, Courtney Daniel
High School Biology Instructor
Rice, Connie Elaine
Kindergarten Teacher
Rohde, Kyle Kevin
Spanish Teacher
Rostomily, Charlene York
Fourth Grade Teacher
Simpfenderfer, Paula Thill
High School Math Teacher
Slabaugh, Thomas Edward, II
Director of Bands
Thompson, Julie
English Teacher
Vanden Bosch, Glenn Allen
High School Teacher
Woo, Roger Chin
Publications Adv & Eng Tchr
Wright, Victoria Jeanne (Solari)
Spanish Teacher
LOMA LINDA
Banta, Jeralyn Weber
Fourth Grade Teacher
Binkley, Philip Ralph
Director of Bands
Brandon, Antonius Desire
Marriage & Family Therapy Prof
Bruckner, Evert A.
Assoc Prof of Int Medicine
Chand, Ian Phillip
Marriage & Family Therapy Prof
Cowles, David Lyle
Assistant Professor of Biology
De Alwis-Chand, Shirani Christine
Dir of the Tchng Learning Ctr
Gober, Carla Gayle
Asst Prof & Instr of Religion
Herrmann, Marilyn Murdoch
Assoc Dean of Undergrad Prgm
Miller, Eva Goodlett
Associate Professor
Pagenkemper, Joni Jensen
Asst Professor of Nutrition
Perrio, Ralph Wesley
Dean for Student Affairs
Puerto, Sofia
Assistant Professor Of Nursing
Stewart, Sylvia D.
Assistant Professor of Nursing
LOMITA
Molina, Michael D.
Religious Ed & Worship Dir
Still, Dawn
8th Grade Teacher
LOMPOC
Abrahamsen, Glenn Martin
12th Grade Economics Teacher
Arnerich, Bill
English Instructor
Barnard, Edward Lloyd
8th Grd Soc Sci & Eng Teacher
Bean, Amy Odens
Home Economics Teacher
Bockius, Charles George
4th & 5th Grade Teacher
Brooks, Christopher Calvert
Resource Specialist & Teacher
Brooks, Mary Ellen Mahoney
English Teacher
Flinkingshelt, Raegen Beardslee
Chemistry Teacher
Hinck, Karen L.
French Teacher
Hope, Susan Roa
Home Economics & Careers Tchr
Kesler, David E.
1st Grade Teacher
Lawrence, Robert Kent
English Tchr & Aquatics Coach
Lindsay, Elizabeth Rasband
6th Grd Math & Science Teacher
Mann, Roger James
Industrial Technology Teacher
Murphy, Daniel George
Spanish Teacher
Nicastro, Suzanne Marie
English Secondary Teacher
Ofstead, Linda L.
7th & 8th Grade Teacher
Salli, Kathleen Mattson
Third Grade Teacher
Sarar, Pete
World & US History Teacher
Schwark, Suzanne Immel
HS Librarian & Media Spclst
Sipes, Maurice H.
4th Grade Teacher
Smith, Dennis Craig
Fourth Grade GATE Teacher
Smith, Gary Michael
Math Teacher
Spilman, James Bruce
AP Biology Teacher
Tate, Robert B.
10th-11th Grd Soc Studies Tchr

LOMPOC (cont)
Webster, Myron L.
History Teacher
Wuest, Gregory Norman
Vocational Ed for Spec Ed Tchr
Zambrand, Jean Marie Hood
Chapter I Reading Tutor
LONG BEACH
Allison, Robert W.
Computer Engineering Professor
Bacon, Ron
Computer Specialist
Barton, David
English Teacher
Bernstein, Susan
Third Grade Teacher
Blumenthal, Sharyn C.
Associate Professor of Film
Briggs, Karen Gail
Middle School Counselor
Browning, Robert
English & Drama Teacher
Butler, Barbara J. Riedman
English Teacher
Carlberg, David Marvin
Microbiology Professor
Cohlberg, Jeffrey A.
Biochemistry Professor
Connor, Marcia Shuck
Fourth Grade Teacher
Cretara, Domenic Julio
Professor of Art
Croke, Eileen Scollins
Asst Professor of Nursing
Dobra, Jeffrey Robert
High School English Teacher
Dublin, Stephen L.
Economics & Government Teacher
Egan, Pati
8th Grade Teacher
Finney, Robert George
Electronic Media Professor
Fleming, Nora Gaede
2nd Grade Teacher
Foss, Gina Scales
Science & Math Teacher
French, Cathy C.
History & Social Science Tchr
Green, Kenneth F.
Professor of Psychology
Hall, Horace F.
12th Grade Government Teacher
Halvorson, Scott Richard
English Teacher
Hernandez, Victoria L.
Career Management Teacher
Holland, Belinda Peters
Spanish Teacher
Hubbard, Kathy Jenny
Performing Arts Teacher
Jackson, Ruth Esther Patterson
1st Grade Teacher
Johnson, Larry Lee
Fifth Grade Teacher
Kaci, Judy Hails
Dept of Criminal Justice Prof
Kamel, Mark Takayuki
English Teacher
Kephart, Kerrill Jean (Kaiser)
AP English Teacher
Klig, Lisa S.
Professor of Biological Sci
Lax, Melvin David
Professor of Mathematics
Lopez, Marco Antonio
Chemistry Professor
Luna, Art R.
Fifth Grade Teacher
Lunniss, Catherine Mary
Language Arts Teacher
Mac Callim, Mike
Financial Aid Counselor
Madding, Carolyn Conway
Lecturer
Marshall, Suzanne Greene
Prof of Fashion Merchandising
Mc Culloch, Duncan Scott
Economics & Soc Studies Tchr
Moraga, Gonzalo
Program Coordinator
Muszynski, Betty Marcello
Regnl Occupational Pgm Tchr
Nasr, Elhami Bakr
Project Management Professor
Navlan, Paul E., Jr.
Ornmntl Horticulture Asst Prof
Nikas, Dorothy Bernardo
Fourth Grade Teacher
Niswonger, Janet Elizabeth
Sixth Grade Teacher
Oshiro, Joan Kaneshiro
4th Grade Teacher
Sarver, Christine Marie
Second Grade Teacher
Schack, Gail O'Connor
Teacher of Gifted & Talented
Schoedl, Renate Wilhelm
AP Studio Art Teacher
Shellabarger, Linda Andrade
Spanish, ESL & PE Teacher
Shere, Daniel Tobias
Creative Writing Teacher
Shuster, Terry Andrew
Professor of Biology
Spivey, Jene D.
4th Grade Teacher
Tang, Paul Chi Lung
Philosophy Professor
Tollstrup, Marie Checkal
Creative Writing Instructor
Turansky, Sharon Lynn
Performing Arts & Eng Teacher
Turner, Elizabeth Minette
SSC Lab Science Teacher
Upham, Nancy Heim
Mathematics Teacher
Victor, Kurt
Computer Science Teacher
Warken, Thomas C.
English Teacher
Weaver, Robert Harold
Electronics Teacher
Weiss, Bonnie Lauxman
Spanish Teacher
Werton, Marianne
English & Religion Teacher
LOOMIS
Earl, Kathleen Holton
Music Teacher
Ferguson, Louis Charles
First Grade Teacher
Lasley, Bob E.
Mathematics Teacher
Loring, Brett William
Spanish Teacher
Luci, Anna M.
Chem & Exploratory Sci Teacher
Perry, Karen Thompson
Eighth Grade Teacher
Rush-Martin, Karen Herreid
Health, Home Economics Teacher
Sanchez, Jack L.
English Teacher
Sanchez, Valerie Ann
English & Drama Teacher
Silveira, Susan Fleming
8th Grade CORE Teacher
LOS ALAMITOS
Allen, Ann Burke
Science Teacher
Anderson, William Maxwell
Art Teacher
Baker, Jan Pitassi
Continuation HS Tchr
Bowers, Gary Steven
History & Health Ed Teacher
Briggerman, Robert Allen
Spanish Teacher
Celestin, Mark J.
Social Studies Teacher
Dawson, Peggy Hernandez
Spanish & ELD Teacher
Flynn, Sharron Marie
English Teacher
Franzen, Lori Jean (Palmer)
English & Communications Tchr
Fullenwider, Margaret Marie
8th Grd English & History Tchr
Huff, Christine Marie
Advncd Math Tchr & Admin Asst
Kirk, Lisa Marie
English & History Teacher
Parmer, Dennis Alan
High School Counselor
Ream, Diane Curry
Tchr of Gifted, Eng & US His
Seitz, Shelley Kry
Sixth Grade Teacher
Trujillo, Judy Elsner
Honors English Teacher
Willard, Suzanne Kaelin
Mathematics Teacher
Wyneken, Margaret (Royer)
Sixth Grade Teacher
LOS ALTOS
Gikis, Bonnie Burnette
Fifth Grade Teacher
Green, Kenneth John
Biology Teacher
Losey, Steven Kent
4th-5th Grade Teacher
Moore, Laura Louise
English & Writing Teacher
Morris, Catherine
Former Teacher
Quinlan, Paula
Elem Tchr & Acting Principal
Spencer, Bertrand Harlow
Chemistry Teacher
Wada, Shoji
Art Coordinator & Teacher
Youatt, Alice
French Teacher
LOS ALTOS HILLS
Cross, Truman Bayne
Lecturer in History
Hofland, John Allen
Physics Instructor
McCarty, Lois Leone
Sociology Professor
Norton, Nile P.
Music Instructor
Thomas, Jean
Counselor
LOS ANGELES
Abaekobe, Joseph C.
Math Teacher
Abayachi, M. Ali
Mathematics Teacher
Abbott, Russell J.
Prof of Computer Science
Abrahams Spiesman, Ruth Teller
Bilingual Teacher
Acuna, Laura Chey
Asst Professor in Boradcasting
Albano, Anastacio Academia
Industrial Arts Teacher
Alexander, Althea Thomas
Teacher
Alexander, Linda
4th Grade Teacher
Ali, Clara Westbrooks
5th Grade Teacher
Altshiller, Carol Heiser
6th-12th Grd PE Teacher
Ancona, Dorothy Mace
Music Teacher
Andrews, Phyllis
Teacher
Aristov, Andrey
Science Department Chairman
Assael, Daniele
Law & Government Teacher
Astourian, Ani
French Teacher
Attig, Suzanne N.
English Teacher & Yearbook Adv
Avila, Jeffrey Manuel
Biology Teacher
Bagish, Martin Leon
Japanese Teacher
Bailey, Kenneth Richard
Mathematics Teacher
Baker, Raymon Elliott
4th Grade Teacher
Baker, Verleen
Fourth Grade Teacher
Baral, Joan Mall
Art Teacher
Barata, George James
Eng & Creative Writing Tchr
Barbara, Lucia Sutphen
English Teacher
Barner, Anita Beeks
Student Infor System Coord
Barnhouse, Michael Louis
US & World History Teacher
Batiste, Leonus Thomas, III
Fourth & Fifth Grade Teacher
Bauer, Brian Steven
ESL Teacher & Dept Chairperson
Bellon, Stephen
High School English Teacher
Bellos, David
English Teacher
Benson, John William
Social Studies Teacher
Berardi, Lou Ann Smith
English & Study Skills Teacher
Bernstein, Amie
Spanish Teacher
Bernstein, Barbara Ellen Kamm
Math Teacher
Berriman, Lloyd G., Jr.
Mathematics Dept Chair
Bickett, Jill Patricia
English Dept Chprsn & Teacher
Biles, John Alexander
Prof of Pharmaceutical Science
Bird, Tammy L.
Life Science Tchr & Dept Chair
Blake, Richard Walter
Counselor & Teacher
Bodinger-deUriarte, Cristina
Sociology Professor
Borges, Rebeca Varela
Title 1 Coordinator
Bower, Rita Linda
Resource Specialist Teacher
Brier, Peter A.
Professor of English
Bright, Brenda Nash
Teacher & Coordinator
Briscoe, Kay Glasco
Mathematics Teacher
Bulman, John Bradley
Physics Professor
Burke, Melissa A.
English Teacher
Burns, Ingrid Ulanda
7th Grade Teacher
Butler, Frances Lannin
Math & Science Teacher
Caballero, Cristina, RSM
Eighth Grade Teacher
Cahill, Eileen
English Teacher & Dean of Fac
Caldwell, Lindsay C.
Dean of Students
Calnan, Alan Lord
Professor of Law
Campbell, Melvin Dewayne
Advanced Physics Instructor
Capadocia, Sonia Estuche
Sixth Grade Teacher
Cardoso, Jeska Helene
Chemistry Teacher
Carr, Charles Matthew
Categorical Programs Advisor
Castellanos, Edward F.
Span Tchr & Foreign Lang Dept
Cazares, Roseann Millan
English Teacher
Cheney, Michael Harold
Theology Chair & Instructor
Claus, Carol Ann
Assoc Professor of Technique
Cocozza, Joseph D.
Physlgy & Ophthalmology Tchr
Condly, Steven Joseph
Physics & Acad Finance Teacher
Contarsy, Steven Alan
Science Tchr & Swim Team Coach
Cruz-Martinez, Apolonia
Spanish Teacher
Curran, Joyce Heinbaugh
Physical Education Teacher
Daggett, Merlin H.
Fifth Grade Teacher
Danielski, Lydia Ann
Language Arts & History Tchr
Danley, Celest
Third Grade Teacher
Darensbourg, Debra LeBoeuf
Middle School Art Teacher
Daum, John William
Soc Stud Teacher & Dept Chair
Davies, Aled Glyn
Acting, Voice & Speech Teacher
Davis, Carolynn Simpson
Fourth Grade Teacher
Davis, Irvin L.
Soc Stud & Spec Ed Instr
Davitt, Therese Marie
Tchr of Deaf & Hard of Hearing
Davoudian, Michael M.
Teacher
DelMonte, Ronald S.
8th Grade Science & Law Tchr
Djicich, Patricia Milinovich
Fifth Grade Teacher
Downs, Timothy Michael
Associate Professor
Dumitrescu, Domnita
Prof of Spanish Linguistics
DuPras, Jeaney Jo
Physical Education Director
Dutton, Ronald Stanley
Sco Stud Dept Chair & Teacher
Earley, Darin Craig
Math Dept Chairman & Teacher
Eiden, Susan Hunter
Drama Teacher
Ellis, Daniel Allen
ELS & English Teacher
Ellmore, Dennis B.
Associate Professor of Art
Enciso, Alfee Miguel
Eng Tchr & Jrnlsm Adv
Esquivel, James Alan
Sixth Grade Teacher
Etienne, Mildred Marie
Fifth Grade Teacher
Evans, Frances Lamarr
Special Education Teacher
Evans, Jerome Levie
12th Grade English Teacher
Fang, Hsing
Professor of Finance
Ferber, Varvara H.
5th-6th Grd Span & Biling Tchr
Fingerhut, Eugene R.
History Professor
Finley, George Louis
PE Tchr & Chprsn
Fisher, Gregory Stephen
HS Social Studies Teacher
Fletcher, Cynthia Drake
English Teacher
Flores, Z. Marie Dardarian
Kindergarten Teacher
Flowers, Beulah Olivia Mortis
Fifth Grade Teacher
Forsheit, Arleen Bandel
Science Teacher & Dept Head
Foster, Donna Loomis
Fifth Grade Teacher
Foy, Judith Gayle (Banghart)
Psychology Professor
Freed, Glenn S.
Assoc Professor of Accounting
Fuller, Michael W.
English Teacher
Gaines, Bruce Wayne
Teacher
Gill, Sonia Linette
Second Grade Teacher
Golden, Lisa Renee Green
Mentor Teacher
Goodwin, Sheila E.
English Teacher
Graves, Jack Lemorn
JROTC Teacher
Gregory, Eleanor Anne
English Teacher & Dept Co-Chm
Grijalva, Raul Thomas
Counselor
Gross, James Earl
Magnet Coordinator & Math Tchr
Guarnieri-Nunn, Elaine Marie
Social Studies & History Tchr
Haddad, Jeanette Young
High School English Teacher
Hall, Marianne Lois
AP Art Instructor
Harper, Joyce Elliott
HS Spanish Teacher
Harris, Deidre
Spanish Teacher
Harris, Linda Donald
US History Teacher
Harrison, Annette F.
English Teacher
Hashiba, Carolyn Abe
Kindergarten Teacher
Hawkins, Cassandra Crockett
English Teacher
Hayes, Sara Goldberg
Humanities & English Teacher
Hensleigh, Judy Ann
Third Grade Teacher
Herman, Douglas Paul
5th Grade Bilingual Teacher
Herman Klar, David
Science Teacher
Herrero, Anselma
Spanish Teacher
Hession, Paul Vincent
Mathematics & Science Teacher
Hicks, Eugene J.
Athletic Dir & PE Instructor
Hindinger, Rosemary Therese
English Teacher
Hokenson, Barbara Ann
Third Grade Teacher
Holland, Endesha Im
Professor
Holligan, Patrick William
Magnet Health Teacher
Holmes, Philip Duane
English Teacher
Hooks, De Vera Kathryn
Math Department Chairperson
Howard, Lenoka Jefferson
Physical Education Teacher
Hudson, Mamie Lee
Fourth Grade Teacher
Huybrechts, Jeanne Marie
Physical Science Teacher
Hyde, Jonathan Edwin
Health & Physical Ed Teacher
Inafuku, Ellen Chan
Third Grade Teacher
Ishihara, Virtue Teruo
HS Biology Teacher
Jackson, Anthony Craig
Second Grade Teacher
Jackson, Bernice Vannette
High School PE & Dance Teacher
Jackson, Lillie Scott
Assistant Principal
James, Lybroan Dennis
Math Teacher
Jenkins, Renetta Miller
Magnet Coordinator
Jimenez, Carlos M.
History Teacher
Jiminez, Gloria
Spanish Teacher
Johansen, Malana Keeler
Math, Lit & Science Teacher
Jones, Susanna Adams
Director of Upper School
Junge, Tomas
Fifth Grade Teacher
Karr, Joanne F.
Drama & English Teacher
Katz, Laurence Darryl
Sixth Grade Teacher
Kelly, George Jay
English Instructor
Kelly, Lainey
Instrl & Compliance Consultant
Kennedy, Kevin Thomas
US Government & Economics Tch
Keshishyan, Anita
Foreign Lang & Eng Teacher
Keys, Richard Taylor
Professor of Chemistry
Knudsen, Christine
HS Tchr & Rel Studies Dept Chr
Koehler, Jane Wiedlea
English Teacher
Kohon, Kenneth Warren
Advanced Mathematics Instr
Kosaka, Lynn Hatsumi
Fifth Grade Teacher
Kruse, Evaline Khayat
English Teacher
Kwong, Kwok K.
Prof of Operations Management
Kyuregyan, Akop M.
ESL Teacher
Labio, Aida Cornelio
English & ESL Teacher
Landinguin, Christopher John
Science Teacher
Lang, Jacklyn Harris
Fr Tchr & Lang Dept Chprsn
Larsen, Lanny D.
Science Teacher
Lau, Howard S.
Mathematics Teacher
Lee, Helen Owyane
Fifth Grade Teacher
Leffall, James Calvin
Math, Science & Drama Teacher
Lefkowitz, David Samuel
Asst Professor of Music Dept
Leidich, Kevin, SJ
Theology Teacher
Le Maire, Richard Arlen
Sixth Grade Teacher
Lengliz, Shedly
French & Spanish Teacher
Leon, Victoria Nishinaka
3rd-4th Grade Teacher
Lewis, Joy Lynn
Third Grade Teacher
Lilly, Karel Marie
Science Chairperson & Teacher
Lind, Robert Charles
Professor of Law
Lindner, Jerold William
English Teacher
Lipman, Heather Segal
Middle School Math Teacher
Lippa, Lisa Harwood
Biology & Physiology Teacher
Lockett, Carol W.
Math Teacher
Lomeli, Maria Luisa
Spanish Teacher
Lowenkron, Barry
Professor of Psychology
Lowenstein, Marilynn G.
French & Foreign Language Tchr
Lu, Ronald A.
Mathematics Dept Chairman

NGELES (cont)
w, John Gilbert
eacher
Dana W.
h Teacher
Erin
Teacher
, John Leslie
h Grade English Teacher
Joan
h Grade Teacher
, Arthur A.
ematics Teacher
il, Sonia Recio
rgarten Teacher
itch, Howard Steven
School Counselor
, Ted E.
tant Prof of Chemistry
Catherine Elizabeth
ssor of Anthropology
ez, Eddie
cal Ed Dept Chairperson
Patricia Carol
ciate Prof of Anthropology
, Michael James
sh Teacher
, Susan Vaneta
tre Arts Professor
Stephan Nicholas
c Professor of Diagnosis
nald, William Conroy
rer
nn, Lawrence A.
tant Prof of Geography
d, Ronald Michael
my & JROTC Instructor
Margie J. Juliette
Grade Teacher
Debra J.
School English Teacher
Raymond Richard
cs Teacher
William Joseph
ish Teacher
use, Maradel Catipon
l Studies & Art Teacher
us, Martin
itus Professor of Art
, Bereanice Bonner
ish Teacher
o, Richard A.
sh Teacher
on, Jeffrey M.
puter Programming Teacher
n, Michael Anthony
nce Department Chair
n, Jordan J.
ish Teacher & Dept Head
dian, Seranoush Susan Der
ian
Grade Teacher
, Joyce Yuen
ish Teacher
as, Anne Marie
ish Teacher
y, Bill Warren
ogy Teacher
nura, Arlene (Yamamoto)
th Grade Teacher
nura, Diane Aiko
al Studies Teacher
izian, Paul Jean
ogy Teacher
on, Joan Quigley
n Grade Teacher
ander, Barbara
al Studies Teacher
-Jenner, Leah Ann
nce Teacher & Coordinator
va, Gary K.
h Teacher
nell, Michael George
ogy Teacher
a, Alan Riki
& 8th Grade Science Tchr
Hirotsu, Meryle Hatsumi
hematics Teacher
ros, Hermilanda
t Grade Teacher
io, Claudia Patricia
nish Teacher & Dept Chprsn
Gloria Neal
lish Teacher
r, Delores Patton
Grade Teacher
al, Keith Edmond
gion Teacher
n, Dolores (Thigens)
History & Geography Teacher
Darrilyn Lemmons
d Grade Teacher
arias, Ricardo Jose
nish Teacher
eton, Ula Metsopulos
n Grade US Govt Teacher
, Raymond Y.
gion & Social Studies Tchr
d, Bharat Maharaj
ntor & Teacher
ay, Dessie Avery
lish Teacher
dler, Muriel Swindells
logy Teacher
ps, Steven Kent
nish Teacher
Gayle Altman
ernment & Economics Teacher
ll, Denise Susan
demic Counselor

Porter, Charlene Auverne
English Teacher
Pugsley, Robert
Professor of Law
Pursley, Charles Vernon
Spanish Teacher
Quarles, Gail Jackson
First-Second Grade Teacher
Ramos, Jose Armando
Spanish Teacher
Reis, Ronald Albert
Electronics Professor
Reynolds, Joseph P.
Lecturer of Comm Studies
Robinson, Moses, Jr.
12th Grade English Teacher
Roden, Martin S.
Prof of Electrical Engineering
Rombola, Heidi Mefford
Former Elem Tchr & Asst Prin
Romero, Lucille Bernadette
Biological Science Teacher
Ross, Geoffrey Allan
Philosophy Professor
Rubin, Judy S.
Library Media Teacher
Sabin, Michael
Social Studies Teacher
Sacks, Anne
Visual Arts Teacher
St John, Herb Ed
English Teacher
Sanchez, Gilbert
Fifth Grade Teacher
Schumann, Adria Folb
7th Grade World History Tchr
Schweneker, Laurell Ann
Assistant Principal
Scott, Andrea Adams
5th Grade Teacher
Senigram, Renee Michelle
Drama & English Teacher
Shakman, Loren R.
8th Grd US His & Geog Teacher
Shustek, Stefanie Anne
High School Math Teacher
Siebert, Eleanor Dantzler
Chemistry Prof & Dept Chair
Siler, Michael Joe
International Relations Prof
Simonowski, Patricia Franco
First Grade Bilingual Teacher
Skidmore, John Jacob Goldsby
US & World History Teacher
Smith, Glenda Proby
Nutrition Professor
Smolin, Barry Jay
English Teacher
Smulders, Anthony P.
Professor of Biology
Solis, Daniel Duran
Bilingual Math & Tech Teacher
Spann, Samuel Cleotho
Music Teacher
Spanswick, Ralph S.
Accounting Dept Prof & Chm
Stillwell, Raymond L.
Former Teacher
Stiven, Timothy James
History & Humanities Teacher
Stolper, Daryl
US History Teacher & Dept Chm
Stull, Robert John
Professor of Geology
Sullivan-Thompson, Donna
History, PE & Leadership Tchr
Tabrizi, Lili H.
Professor of Electrical Engrng
Takagaki, Richard Yoshio
Social Studies Teacher
Talarico, Mark W.
Principal
Thomas, Eleanore Jean (Elliott)
HS Social Studies Teacher
Thomason, Gentry Duvall
English Teacher
Thran, Gary Dean
Dir of Athletics & PE Tchr
Threadgill, Evelyn Lillian
English Teacher
Tikkanen, Wayne
Assoc Professor of Chemistry
Tinson, Marie Hines
Mathematics Teacher
Todd, Carol Warren
Math Teacher
Todd, Eric A.
Vice Principal
Toy, Helen Guerrant
ESL Teacher
Triplett, Tracy C.
English Teacher
Trujillo, Rosa Maria
English Teacher
Vaidya, Ashish
Asst Prof of Ec & Statistics
Valenzuela, Virginia Trillo
Spanish Teacher
Van Loo, Brendhen W.
Science Teacher & Coach
VanNess, Paul William
Professor of Piano
Vetrano, Peter Vincent
English Instructor & Dept Chm
Victor, Daniel David
English Teacher
Villeza, Bella B.
English Teacher
Virk, Doreen Jones
Environmental Science Teacher

Vriesman, Robert John
Mathematics Department Chair
Walling, Esther Marie
College Counselor
Wandke, Richard Dinsmore
Senior Army Instructor
Ward, Clint Lamont
Physical Science & Chem Tchr
Washington, Jeannie LaVern
Testing & Bilingual Coord
Washington, Salonie Mosley
Third Grade Teacher
Wasley, Knox Bradford
Associate Professor
Watkins, Diane L.
Biology Teacher
Watson, Catherine Kunkel
Instructor of Legal Research
Watts, Brenetta A. (Sparks)
English & Health Teacher
Watts, Linda Adelyn
Magnet Pgm, Eng & Drama Instr
Weber, Doris Jean Deroin
Professional Expert Tchr
Wenderoff, Ron J.
AP Economics Secondary Teacher
Werner, Francine
History Teacher
Wheelock, Martha E.
Amer Lit, Drama & Yrbk Tchr
White, Natalie Plachte
English Teacher
White, Todd Steven
Science Teacher
Wilhoit, Julie Ann
Womens Basketball Head Coach
Wise, Carol
Bilingual Program Coordinator
Witz, Janet LeCuyer
Retired Elem Teacher
Wong, Ricky Kin-Kwan
Associate Professor of Biology
Woolley, Susan Kaler
Fourth Grade Teacher
Yerman, Paula C.
ESL Instructor
Yokoyama, Dennis Taiji
Director of Legal Writing
Yoshizaki, Steve
Science Teacher
Yu, Albert Pak-Ngar
Physics Teacher
Zack, Ilene
Art Teacher
Zupan, Mark
Assoc Prof of Fin, Bus Ec Dept

LOS BANOS
Hatton, Susan Smith
Third Grade Teacher
Inman, Don Earl, Jr.
History Teacher
Nahas, Nicholas Victor
10th & 11th Grd Soc Sci Instr
Szuwalski, Daniel Robert
Chemistry Teacher
VanLobenSels, Patricia Jay
6th Grade Teacher

LOS FELIZ
Cleveland Brown, Odessa
English Teacher

LOS GATOS
Dahms, Lynne Carrai
Physical Education Teacher
Downs, Scott Danforth
Art Teacher & Dept Chair
Gascho, Angela Davidowski
English Teacher
Haworth, Joyce DeBenedetti
Third Grade Teacher
Hull, Martha Allshouse
Soc Stud Chair & His Teacher
Manchester, Mark John
High School Mathematics Tchr
Moore, Shana McLean
Spanish Teacher
Rachlin, Jeanne-Marie (Bourgeois)
HS Mathematics Teacher
Rudolph, Allen
History Teacher
Snelgrove, Lynda Leigh Rilea
English & Math Teacher
Strudley, Raf
VP & Technology Project Mgr
Woods, William Ronald
History, Govt & Bible Teacher
Zappacosta, Teri Ferguson
Academic Advisor

LOS MOLINOS
Farwell, Steven Ray
Algebra Teacher
Walton, Teresa P. (Bangs)
English Teacher
Way, Terry Lynn (Tipton)
Kindergarten Teacher

LOS OLIVOS
Mc Kinley, Benjamin Franklin
Math Teacher & Athletic Dir

LOST HILLS
Crawford, Donivan Chris
Computer Science Teacher

LOWER LAKE
Cox, William Walton
Biology, Phys Ed & Coach
Fiedler, Debra R.
Teacher & Principal

LOYALTON
Hendrickson, Brian Francis
Multi-Grade Classroom Teacher

LUCERNE VALLEY
Little, Jeremy F.
Life Science Teacher

LYNWOOD
Bedford, Faye Emily
Elementary Teacher
Chacon, Delia (Collins)
Theater Arts & English Teacher
Elger, Carla Ruth
Social Studies Teacher
Jones-Allen, Deborah Florazell
6th Grade Teacher
Portillo, Antonio
Art Teacher

MADERA
Baker, Louann Otto
English & Tech Writing Teacher
Belden, Laurel Ann Mastrofini
HS Business Education Teacher
Dragon, Oscar Lee
6th Grade Teacher
Eisele, John Morrison
High School English Teacher
Ferrari, Linda Hill
English Teacher
Gipson, Eric D.
Science Teacher
Gonzalez, Edward Charles
6th Grade Teacher
Gwartney, Ed Ray
Fourth Grade Teacher
Kampschmidt, Connie Marie
First Grade Teacher
Lozano, Raul
Sixth Grade Teacher
Mc Gugin, Lucretia Phillips
Middle Grades Science Teacher
Measell, Judy Romeiro
At-Risk Educator
Nixon, Teresa Rochelle (Christie)
Social Studies & PE Teacher
Pash, John Constantine
Social Science Teacher
Rabb, Kathy M.
Social Science & Business Tchr
Ryan, James Patrick
Math Instructor
Sanchez, Ismael Lalo
Physical & Earth Sci Teacher
Virden, Mitzi Louise
8th Grade Family Life Teacher
Ward, Diana Bell
Fifth Grade Teacher

MALIBU
Corbin, Damian Elizabeth
History & English Teacher
Davis, Stephen Darrel
Professor of Biology
Gibson, David E.
Professor of Philosophy
Hughes, Richard Thomas
Religion Professor
Piasentin, Joseph Keith
Professor of Fine Arts
Privitt, Robert Henry
Professor of Art
Taylor, James Lance
Political Science Professor
Warford, Stan
Professor of Computer Science

MAMMOTH LAKES
Hosking, Lisa Marie
7th Grade CORE Teacher

MANHATTAN BEACH
Adamik, Karen Smith
Language Arts Tchr & Music Dir
Cook, Michael Anthony
Latin & English Teacher, Coach
Davis, Jo Ann
Reading Teacher
Ford, Ralph D.
Science, Computer Science Tchr
Ford, Sara L.
Science & Mathematics Teacher
Gesualdi, Linda Jeanne
Math Teacher & Dept Chprsn
Henry, Jeanne Hefferman
English & Journalism Teacher
Manago-Mac Gillivray, Pamela Sylvana
High School Science Teacher
Paulsen, Marsha L.
English Teacher
Ryan, Patricia Jane
Kindergarten Teacher

MANTECA
Ellsworth, Julia Norton
English & Journalism Teacher
Gerlach, Vicki Jeannette
English Teacher
Gottard, Pamela Johnson
Resource Specialist & Teacher
Jackson, Stacey A.
HS English & AVID Teacher
Johnson, Joseph P.
Amer Govt & Economics Teacher
Lagier, Marilyn Anne
English Teacher & Dept Co-Chm
Mackey, Lenn A.
6th Grade Teacher
Mathis, Arthur J.
Life Styles Teacher & Coach
Miyamoto, Jean M.
English & Business Teacher
Norton, Nina Casareto
US History Teacher
Obrigawitch, Douglas Paul
Mathematics Teacher
Oren, William V.
English Teacher & Dept Chprsn

Rosendin, Judy Ann
Fourth Grade Tchr & Vice Prin
Sonntag, Steve Joseph
Spanish Teacher
White, Valerie K.
Fifth Grade Teacher

MARIPOSA
Ball, Sheldon Edward
Retired Vocational Ed Instr
Ellis, Richard G.
Fourth & Fifth Grade Teacher
LaNotte-Hays, Laura Lynn L.
English Teacher & Dept Chprsn
Turner, Jonathan Finley
English & Drama Teacher
Van Wagtendonk, Margene Ann
Eng Tchr, Act Dir & ASB Adv

MARTINEZ
Carroll, B. Jean Patterson
Release Teacher
DeLeon, Joe O.
Math Teacher
Doherty, Sharon Travnicek
Fourth Grade Teacher
Fisher, Anthony John
Bio, Hum Anatmy & Physlgy Tchr
Heeb, James E.
Woodworking Teacher
Kane, Loretta Sue
English Department Chair
Leal, Beverly Ann
Counselor
Ogden, Linda Chaffkin
5th Grade Teacher
Patchin, Richard Dwane
Owner & Administrator
Summerville, Lori Ann R.
Spanish Teacher
Vaughan, Pam Milligan
Social Studies Teacher

MARYSVILLE
Allison, Paul F.
Social Studies & Computer Tchr
Cunningham, Steven Lee
7th Grade Social Science Tchr
Morgan, John Glendon
5th Grade Teacher

MAXWELL
Erdman, Marilyn Jean
Spanish Teacher

MAYWOOD
King, Karen Ellen
Elementary Education Teacher

MC FARLAND
Elliott, D. Mike
Vocational Agriculture Teacher
Mata, Robert Thomas
Fifth Grade Teacher
Montalvo, Michael Quinn
7th Grd Rdng & Lang Arts Tchr
Perry-Reed, Brenda Lee
Instrumental Music Director
Sparks, Richard W.
5th Grade Teacher

MCKINLEYVILLE
Agliolo, Linda L.
Eng, Theatre Arts & Drama Tchr
Byker, James Henry
Music Teacher
Fletcher, Marylyn Brier
English Teacher
Groff, Dennis Charles
High School Art Teacher
Hannigan, Judith Shoup
Reading Specialist
Howard, Diana Rene
Business Teacher
Keldorf, Laura Carolyn
Social Science Tchr
Momber, Catherine Marie
1st Grade Teacher
Patton, Patrick Charles
Teacher & Department Chairman
Semore, Cynthia Lynn
Math & Physical Education Tchr
Sisk, Gregg Lawrence
Music Teacher
Wood, Donald
Physics & Chemistry Teacher

MENDOCINO
Rhoades, Bronwyn Ford
English Teacher

MENDOTA
Bolin, Gloria J.
English Language Dev Teacher
Rangel, Cergio
High School Bilingual Teacher

MENLO PARK
Colard, Kim Andersen
Asst Tchr, Comm Outreach Dir
Hamilton, Michael D.
Math Teacher
Hight, Patti Livingstone
Counselor
O'Connor, Michaeline Mary
Religion Teacher
Schwarz, Janet V.
Eng Teacher & Vice-Principal

MENTONE
Wedge, Eugene Paul
3rd Grade Teacher

MERCED
Barnett, Cheryl L.
Art Instructor
Bettis, C. Alan
Theatre Arts Instructor
Boykin, Susan Rosendale
English Teacher
Bushnell, Dorothy
English Instr & Coll Counselor

MERCED (cont)
Cismowski, Liane Oi
Lang Arts & Soc Stud Tchr
Clark, Matthew John
Science Instructor
Coleman, Melissa Lynne
7th Grd Social Studies Tchr
Craig, Karen Lynnette
English Teacher
Freitas, William Francis
Physics Teacher
Glassett, Dee Dee Hutchings
Instr of Anatomy & Physiology
Graham, Nancy Hage
Second Grade Bilingual Teacher
Hague, Scott Sinclair
Mathematics Teacher
Harris, Anne L.
Mathematics Instructor
Hart, Kenneth Lee
US History Instructor
Headrick, David H.
US History Instructor
Hurst, William James
Geometry & Algebra II Teacher
Johnson, Frazier Delbert
English Instructor
Johnson, Maureen McGarry
High School Teacher
Kahlert, Shirley Ann
Instructor
Ladousier, Patricia Mathews
Cnslr & Student Government Adv
Macias, Martin V.
Spanish Teacher
Maloney, Pamela Nagle
K-1st Grade Teacher
Marvulli, Patrice Ann
Kindergarten Teacher
Marvulli, Robert Daniel
American Govt & Ec Teacher
Mayfield, Ronald D.
English Teacher
Powell, Kay Dee (Lindahl)
MS Math & Science Teacher
Raglin, Ronald Alphonzo
High School Teacher
Roland, Linda Boyer
Seventh Grade GATE Teacher
Swartwood, Kevin
Biology Teacher & Athletic Dir
Taylor, Janis Lee
Teen Mentor Adv & Jrnlsm Tchr
Tilley, Lea Allison
English Teacher & Dept Chair
Wetters, Ronald C.
High School Mathematics Tchr
MERIDIAN
Jelavich, Karin R.
Supt, Principal & Teacher
MIDDLETOWN
Cara, Robin J. (Benner)
10th Grd World History Teacher
Daly, Sharon Pieper
Third Grade Teacher
Gill, Timothy Bryan
Mathematics Teacher
Pachie, Patricia Block
Agriculture Instructor
MIDWAY CITY
Leach, Randi Lynn (LeVine)
Sixth Grade Teacher
MILL VALLEY
Ascierto, Rose Marie Theresa
Spanish Teacher & Dept Chprsn
Brumbaugh, Georganne Tarasoff
Science Teacher
Carlon, Roger
Karate Teacher
Chaney, Rilla Mc Cubbins
Science Teacher
Childers, Jerry Lee
Science Teacher
Copeland, Yolanda G.
Clinical Case Manager
Irvin, George N.
Govt, Ec & US His Teacher
Kirsch, Joel Richard
High School Teacher
Themely, Nicholas Thomas
Retired Teacher
MILLBRAE
Battaglini, Lidia
Mathematics Teacher
Dowd, Jeffrey Jay
English Tchr & Bsktbl Coach
Licciardo-Musso, Lori Ann
Middle School Mentor Teacher
Saito, Kathryn Ume
Chemistry & Earth Science Tchr
Spencer-Mills, Jane E.
Japanese Language Teacher
Wainwright, James M.
Department Chair & Teacher
Welch, Jerrie Borden
English & World History Tchr
MILLVILLE
Davidson, Robin Moeschler
Instructional Aide
MILPITAS
Bielsker, L'vannah Sima
Science Teacher
Fowler, Bruce Hansen
High School Science Teacher
Franklin, Sandy
Mathematics Teacher
Gaa, Patrick Joseph
Naval Science Teacher
Gori, Dennis A.
American Government Teacher
Jordan, Cheryl Elizabeth (Davis)
AVID Coord & 8th Grade Tchr
Lawton, Cheryl
Mathematics Instructor
Tanner, Terry Noel
Science Specialist
MIRA LOMA
Boyce, Cheryl Hayman
Fr Tchr & Frgn Lang Dept Chair
Brockman, Steven Scott
High School Science Teacher
Bullard, Jennifer Martinez
First Grade Teacher
Cortez, Lauretta Wilson
Language Arts Teacher
Hines, Julie Pualani
Business Teacher, Bsktbl Coach
Mangiamelli, Ronald Thomas
Anatomy & Life Science Tchr
Obershaw-Durham, Lisa
Physical Education Teacher
Schroeder, Kathy
Business Education Teacher
Steinbrinck, Scott K.
Language Arts Instructor
MISSION HILLS
Arispe, Paulette Hershey
Math Teacher
Degnan, James Patrick, Jr.
Algebra I Teacher & Coach
Galla, Jan Sciortino
Religion & Social Studies Tchr
Korenthal, Linda T.
English Dept Chairperson
Ozella, James P.
AP Coll Prep US Hist Tchr
Wald, Marion Ellen (Stillman)
1st Grade Teacher
Walker, Mary Clare Gorman
English & Social Studies Tchr
MISSION VIEJO
Akins, Val L.
Advanced Science Teacher
Anderson, Lois Thompson
English Teacher
Bailey, Randy Rockford
5th Grade Teacher
Beidler, Paul Steven
Psych, Drama & Stagecraft Tchr
Childers, Fran
Geometry Teacher
Cunerty, William Joseph
Ftbl Head Coach & Prof of PE
Denison, Kaye Davis
Sixth Grade History Teacher
Garrity, Christine Di Leo
English Teacher & Dept Chair
Harris, Denise Shore
Pep Squad Advisor & Coach
Harris, Kathleen Cannarozzi
Visual & Performng Arts Chprsn
Isaacs, Tamera L. Ivie
8th Grd English & Drama Tchr
Keith, Dominique Lassia
French Teacher
Lynch, Jason Allan
Science Teacher
Miller, Gladys L.
Spanish Teacher
Mullin, Diane Elefson
1st Grade Teacher
Osborne, Debbie Soler
Mathematics Teacher
Sayles, Kenneth Lynn
Government & US History Tchr
Smith, William Lawrencz
Social Science Teacher
Smoral, Rosemarie Dannemiller
Former Teacher
Sponagle, James Malcolm
HS Ceramics Teacher
Wiemann, Jonathan Roy
AP Economics Teacher
MODESTO
Barney, Cheryl Ann
Spanish Teacher
Bennett, David M.
Science Teacher
Bergerson, Harold Ted
PE Department Head
Bosch, Merlys J.
Teacher
Bowers, M. Jean (Wollett)
Title I Reading Teacher
Bowles, Brad Arden
Third Grade Teacher
Brown, Leatrice Dorothy
Computer Accounting Instructor
Bryhni, Lori Anne
Fine Arts & Dance Teacher
Cardozo, Maureen DAmbrosioo
Health Educator
Castaneda, Sandra
English Instructor
Chaplin, Deborah Leann
Spanish Teacher
Clark, Dennis D.
Music Teacher
Colli, Sharon H.
Admin of Special Project
Compton, James Rodney
Science Teacher
Danielson, Julie Lenit
School Counselor
Davis, Rodger H.
7th-8th Grd Math Teacher
Decker, Patricia M.
Counselor
DeFerrari, Dee Schemmel
HS Physical Education Teacher
DeMott, Margaret Ann
English & ESL Teacher
Dinnell, Kim M.
Biology Teacher
Donohue, Tim
6th Grade Teacher
Driscoll, Jonaca Kim
German Teacher
Eisel, Daniel C.
Science Teacher & Dept Chair
Faukner, Andrew L.
Spanish Teacher
Fazal, Mumtaz Karmali
Science Teacher
Ganes, Rebecca Mink
Psychology Instructor
Gonsalves, Dan
Athletic Director
Green-Jenkins, Cheryl Ann
English Teacher
Guerrero, Jose Ignacio
Spanish Teacher
Harder, Gregory Joseph
Vocational Agriscience Teacher
Hardin, Joan Lynn
Second Grade Teacher
Harris, Daniel Joseph
Mathematics & Physics Teacher
Harrold, Merry E. (Geis)
Mathematics Tchr & Dept Chair
Hartley, Arthur William, Jr.
History Teacher
Haskett, Nancy Diane (Chisholm)
Language Arts Teacher
Hill, David Edward, Sr.
Religion Teacher
Hill, Mary E.
Second Language Pgm Teacher
Holloway, Madeline Fuentes
Bilingual Teacher
Ishihara, Tosh
4th & 5th Grade Teacher
Iverson, Daniel Dean
Sci Dept Chair & Chem Teacher
James, Susan Lynne Ames
Third Grade Teacher
Jamison, Steve Lee
5th Grade Teacher
Johnson, David Bruce
Assistant Principal
Johnson, Maryellen
Second Grade Teacher
Johnston, Cindy Russell
English Teacher
Jolly Smith, Carol Ann
2nd Grade Sheltered Teacher
Junso, Wayne E.
Mathematics Teacher
Kadani, Linda M.
Coord of Gifted & Talented Ed
Kappas, Mary
World History Teacher
Kastelic, Ian N. B.
Science & Math Teacher
Kay-Richars, Merrily Jane
First & Second Grade Teacher
Kitzmann, Marla Romanoff
7th Grade Math Science Teacher
Kiyoi, Michael N.
Business Teacher
Kline, Daris Silva
English & Journalism Teacher
Klopf, Ellen Mary (Vager)
Language Arts Teacher
Larson, Wendy A.
7th Grade World History Tchr
Lash, Brad John
ROP Marketing Instructor
Leer, Janice Rae (Davies)
Instrumental Music Instructor
Leitner, Larry D.
Mathematics Instructor
Lindberg, Kris
PE Teacher & Coach
Lindberg, Rene
Career Decision & PE Teacher
Lizar, Jennifer Roberts
High School Mathematics Tchr
Magner, Philip Stevenson
Mathematics Tchr & Dept Chprsn
Maki, Erik J.
Band Director
Mathews, Gregory Duane
Phys Ed & Health Teacher
Mc Donald, Georgianna Aileen (Johnson)
8th Grade Mathematics Teacher
Mc Kibban, Michael A.
Math Teacher
Meeuwse, Debbie Svopa
Dance Tchr, Dir, Choreographer
Neuffer, Joanne Mizutani
Band Director
Ortman, Robert George
Language Arts Teacher
Owenby, Judy Ann
Kindergarten & First Grd Tchr
Palitz, Barbara S.
English Teacher
Patterson, Andy Charles
Computer Programming Teacher
Phillips, Cheralyn Stinson
Kindergarten Teacher
Phillips, John Charles
Business Teacher
Quick, Bob
Math Teacher
Quinn, Barbara Kahn
High School Guidance Counselor
Raingruber, Robert John
Secondary Math Teacher
Rapp, Ann Hatoff
Elementary School Teacher
Remsing, May Lobello
6th Grade Teacher
Richichi, Jerome
7th-8th Grade Music Teacher
Schmidt, Kenneth Alan
History Teacher
Sessa, Deborah Vanskike
Spanish & French Teacher
Skinner, David Jay
HS US History Teacher
Stejskal, Kristina Mae
Vice Principal & Project Coord
Stephens, Gay Marie
Third Grade Teacher
Stewart, Maralyn J.
High School Counselor
Sturtevant, Dorothy J.
Dance Teacher
Taylor, Yvonne N.
Soc Sci Dept Chair & Teacher
Terry, Timothy Michael
7th-8th Grade Soc Stud Teacher
Thiessen, Steven Edward
Computer Tchr & Athletic Dir
Thomas, Clay Edward
English & Multimedia Teacher
Toepfer, Todd William
Math & Science Teacher
Vallelunga, Sebastian S.
English & Theology Teacher
Vasche, Joseph Burton, II
English Teacher
Vaughn, Alane Roubal
Lang Arts Tchr & Dept Chair
Ward, Betty Sullivan
ESL Teacher
Weber, Thomas A.
Graphic Comm & Drafting Instr
Whitford, Merlin Utah
Business Teacher
Wiinikka, Peter
Physics Instructor
Wilde, Christine Bucey
Chemistry & Physics Teacher
Williams, Gladys Evans
Kindergarten Teacher
Williams, Ken
English Teacher
Winegardner, Emily Jo
English Teacher
Yates, Bert
6th Grade Teacher
Yonan-Boxell, Diane A.
Counselor
Zambo, Janeen-Marie Harvey
10th Grade Social Sci Teacher
Zimmerman, Nancee Martin
Fourth & Fifth Grade Teacher
MOJAVE
Ketchell-Strahan, Janet Lee
Sixth Grade Teacher
White, Cynthia A.
Title I Reading Specialist
MONROVIA
Bowen, Jerry Lee, Jr.
Principal & HS Teacher
Gollihugh, Robert Gene
Second Grade Teacher
Segal, Marc Ira
English Teacher
MONTAGUE
Helweg, Sharon Weisheimer
Third Grade Teacher
Pimentel, Gilbert Dean
5th & 6th Grade Teacher
MONTARA
Rafello, Ruth Olsen
Retired Kindergarten Teacher
MONTCLAIR
Bonneville, Donald Lee
Math Teacher
Hite, Timothy Hamilton
English Teacher
Lee, Suha Adranly
AP Calculus Teacher
Leo, Kathleen A.
Math Teacher & GATE Coord
Miller, Catherine E.
Consumer Home Economics Chprsn
Petlowany, Alan John
Science Teacher
Solorzano, Carlos Alberto
Spanish Instructor
Wetzel, Cindy Painter
Social Science & Jrnlsm Tchr
MONTEBELLO
Alcala, Christa Clark
HS Mathematics Teacher
Cabrera, Carmen
Spanish Teacher
Gomez, Irene Aguilar
Spanish & Kindergarten Teacher
Hanes, Ron T.
English & Driver Ed Teacher
Honda, Stacy Keiko
Physical Education Teacher
Loya, Frank, Jr.
Language Arts Teacher
Montgomery, Cheryl Michels
Resource Specialist
Rasic, Mark Andrew
Eighth Grade Teacher
Rodriguez, Alice Perez
Spanish Teacher
Salgado, Emma Eugenia
Spanish & ESL Teacher
Sergi, Giovanna Rose
Biology Teacher
Stevens, Ellen Mitsu
ESL & History Teacher
Traeger, David James
Architecture Teacher
MONTEREY
Adams, Tracey Linden
20th Century Cultural His Tchr
Albert, Victoria W.
Drama & English Teacher
Cruzan, Wayne
Math & Oceanographic Sci Tchr
DiGirolamo, Rosina E.
English & Social Studies Tchr
Eagle, Maj-Britt Lindgren
English & French Teacher
Hart, Nicholas Andrew
Physics Teacher
Herbst, Victoria
Mathematics Teacher
Hoffman, John Chandler
English Teacher
Holt, Helen Appel
English Teacher
Kapolka, Gerard T.
English Teacher
LeSiege, Annette
Music Tchr & Music Dept Chair
Oder, Broeck Newton
History Dept Chair
Phillips, Susan Becker
Mathematics Tchr & Dept Chair
Stange, Robert Dyer
Instrumental Music Teacher
Story, William James
Retired Teacher & Admin
Sturch, Nicholas
Academic Dean
Tulloch, Allan Wiley
Naval Science Instructor
Walker, Larry E.
Coordinator & Counselor
Wethington, Joan Gay
High School Art Teacher
MONTEREY PARK
Abernethy, Carole Gates
ESL Teacher
Ho, Jennifer Linh
Physical Education Teacher
Hurley, Charles Edward
5th Grade Teacher
Jackson, John A.
7th Grd Impact Science Teacher
Kitashima, Janice Sakamoto
Second Grade Teacher
Tsang, Wing
7th & 8th Grade Teacher
MONTGOMRY CREEK
Plummer, Frank Michael
7th-8th Grade Teacher
MOORPARK
Baker, John Read
Anthropology Instructor
Burnside, Maria Marco
Second Grade Bilingual Teacher
Church, Diane Juanita (Stevens)
English Teacher
Cohen, Morley Jay
Science Department Chair
Davis, Lucy Gibson
Language Arts Tchr & Dept Chr
Fontaine, Victor Fernando
Philosophy Professor
Fulgham, Donna Walker
Eng Tchr & ELD Dept Chprsn
Gillis, Richard H.
Algebra & Computer Ed Teacher
Glass, Barbara Ellen
4th Grd Teacher & Math Mentor
McDermott, Lawrence Allen
AP Amer His & Pol Sys Tchr
Meschan, Lynn Michele
Asst Professor of Psychology
Naseri, Muthena
Professor
Robison, Patricia Reece
Resource Specialist
Romero-Mills, Susan
Sixth Grade Teacher
Sanchez, Tomas David
Professor of History
Strumpf, Michael
Prof of Eng, Rdng & Writing
Terry, Danita Redd
Associate Professor of Cnslng
West, Katherine Ann
7th & 8th Grd Lang Arts Tchr
MORAGA
Anderson, Robin
Second Grade Teacher
Clarke, Paula
Anthropology & Psych Prof
Clemmensen, Ingrid
Campus Minister
Curry, Lee Sue S.
Spanish Teacher
Danielli, Lola Lynne
Spanish Teacher
Edun, Basheer Ahmad
Math Teacher
Gray, Gail
HS Fine Arts Teacher
Hall, Lindley Lawrence
Choral Music Director
Kirkpatrick, Susan
Cmptr Applications, Psych Tchr
Nogueda, Joan A.
English Teacher
O'Brian, Bill
English Teacher

GA (cont)
, Charla Ruth
School English Teacher
solani, Paola Alessandra
ssor of Anthropology
s, Janet Hollenbach
aistry Teacher
wa, Mary Louise
Teacher
NO VALLEY
gh, Robert
Physical Science Teacher
Guillermo Rodriguez
sh Teacher
Robert, Jr.
cal Education Teacher
n, Deborah Wilson
uage Arts Teacher
ell, Amy L.
l Marketing Teacher
er, Lisa Jan
& Computer Teacher
Kathrine M.
l Science Teacher
Linda M.
sh Teacher
nbe, Steven Louis
aistry Teacher
y, Jill Diane
E Teacher
icki Lynn
urce Specialist
on, Michael L.
cal Education Teacher
onald Andrew
ner & Student Act Director
, Karl T.
& Science Teacher
, Dottie Graf
ial Education Teacher
, Nancy May
ish Teacher
vin, Royce G.
Experience Coord & Coach
John
Math Teacher & Dept Chair
es, Cristan Eveland
& At-Risk Prgm Lead Tchr
tta, Tammy Marie
nce Teacher
n, Peggy A.
Grade Math & Algebra Tchr
ns, Roberta Rosenthal
tre Tchr & Fine Arts Chair
ann, Conrad Carl
& GATE Teacher
on, Emily Marion
Teacher
, Lorraine Ogata
ish Teacher
ick, Sherry Anne
of Students
atrick, Gerda Steinbagen
Ger & Spanish Teacher
John Daniel
Skills & Spanish Teacher
Maury Vi
nematics Teacher
ey, Robert E., Jr.
nce Teacher
, Karen C.
Teacher
er, Eric Clay
al Studies Teacher
Deena Lynn
nematics Teacher
Robert A.
rict Biling Resource Tchr
n, William Gerald, Jr.
strial Technology Teacher
nez, Richard Elorriaga
Coll Prep Span Tchr
, Heike Kittlaus
Grade Teacher
arthy, Edward Barry
Grade Science Teacher
artry, Judy J.
nselor
ell, Eudora Robinson
ctor of Development Prgm
s, Gabriela
nish Teacher
Victor Gordon, III
n Grade Teacher
, David R.
n School Counselor
ia, Manuel Jose
nnology Teacher
os, William B.
ogy Teacher
ne, Roberta Lynne
orming Arts Dept Chair
er, Mark R.
ory Teacher
s, Graciela Cruz
nish Teacher
Mejs, Casimir Anthony
lt Ed & Soc Studies Tchr
rdson, David Allan
Grade Mathematics Teacher
ggio, David William
lish Teacher
vik, Vivien Kearney
lish Teacher
, Matthew, II
ence Teacher
berg, Gordon William
rth Grade Teacher
, Archibald Featherston, Jr.
h Teacher

Suntree, Lorie Susan
Floral Design Teacher
Treadwell, Kathleen Annette
English Teacher
Tulp, Steve
Math Teacher
Uithoven, Linda Susan
Mathematics Mentor Teacher
Vedo, Ruth Ann
Fourth-Fifth Grade Teacher
Vigil, Tammy Huertas
6th Grade Teacher
Wachenheim, Paul Jordan
Physical Education Teacher
Walker, Sydney E.
High School English Teacher
Westerling, Karin E.
Science & Mentor Teacher
Williams, Gitta Dixon
8th Grd Lang Arts Teacher
Williams, J. Thomas
French Teacher & Co-Dept Chair
MORGAN HILL
Bartschi, Maxine
Assistant Principal
Emerson, Kathleen Ann
Sixth Grade Teacher
Gomes, Vera Elizabeth
Agriculture & Science Teacher
Hall, Sherrie G.
French Teacher
Knofler, Jewel Ann
Sixth Grade Teacher
Lund, Richard James
High School Math Teacher
Mc Pherson, John S.
Sixth Grade Teacher
Pedersen, Bobbi Geisshirt
Fine Arts Teacher
Sacks, Valerie Jean
French Teacher
Spain, Aaron H.
English Teacher
Sparling, Brien R.
11th Grade Chemistry Teacher
Swan, Sandra Briley
Secondary Mathematics Teacher
Villegas, Carmen
PE & Dance Teacher
MORONGO VALLEY
Frantz, Karen Lee
Sixth Grade Teacher
MORRO BAY
Anderson, Larry G.
Chemistry & Computer Sci Tchr
Pauley, Kimberly Ann
Vocational Agriculture Tchr
Villa, Gary Silveira
Secondary School Teacher
MOUNT SHASTA
Helfant, Steve Mark
Eng, Drama & Leadership Tchr
Huggins, David Lee
4th Grade Teacher
Rager, Debora
Language Teacher
Ross, Carol Jean
3rd Grade Teacher
Savarese, Michael Edward
7th Grade Science & Math Tchr
White, Judith Wooten
5th Grade Teacher
Wilde, Marjorie Lynne
Fourth Grade Teacher
MOUNTAIN PASS
Del Prete, Agnes
K-3rd Grade Teacher
MOUNTAIN VIEW
Andres, Marc Takeo
English Teacher
Boudreau, Jerauld Francis
Fourth Grade Teacher
Cooper, Eleanor Jane
Retired Teacher
DeCunzo, Paul A.
Science Teacher
Devine, Dennis Thomas
United States History Teacher
Howe, Jean Mary
Religious Studies Teacher
Jones, Sharon Nemoff
5th Grade Teacher
Nakamatsu, Jon Yasuhiro
German Instructor
Whytoshek, Toni
Spanish & French Teacher
MURPHYS
Binger, Agnes Welle
2nd-3rd Grd Combination Tchr
MURRIETA
Androff, JoAnn Denise
Math Dept Chprsn & Teacher
Berry, Ted William
HS Mathematics Teacher
Blackshear, William Beryl, Jr.
Senior Marine Instructor
Boos, Bryan Lynn
Music Director
Burgess, Kiersten Weber
Secondary Mathematics Teacher
Diaz, Ed T.
Science Teacher
Dobbins, Tami M.
Substitute Teacher
Foy, Deborah Kay
Master & Secondary Teacher
Fujii, Christiane Ohara
Former Teacher
Gibson, Christine Michelle
11th Grd Eng & Amer Lit Tchr

Hatch, Sharon Wigley
Drama, French & English Tchr
Johnson, Suzanne Marsolais
French Teacher
Jones, John Paul, IV
Science Teacher
Matus, Peter Paul
9th Grade Science Teacher
Mc Carthy, Sean Robert
English Teacher
Muhlhauser, Linda Hetzler
Driver Education & PE Teacher
Oliphant, Sandra Lee
Sixth & Seventh Grade Teacher
Robertson, Karen Ann (Brassfield)
Supplemental Prgms Coordinator
Storch, Philip H.
Sixth Grade Teacher
Tokunaga, Barry Takeshi
Bio & Integrated Sci II Tchr
Tumlin, Stacy Swenck
English & AP Teacher
Walters, Mary Marentette
HS Mathematics Teacher
NAPA
Aaron, Justin P.
English Teacher
Abbott, Ernest Lee
Electronics Professor
Aceves, Salvador D.
Asst Prof of Acctng & Bus Law
Blickenstaff, James Paul
Chem & Phys Science Instructor
Bowen, June Marie
Retired Third Grade Teacher
Culbertson, Steve Roy
8th Grade US History Teacher
Dawson, Beverly Joan (Hindman)
Teacher
Dick, Carol Joan
High School English Teacher
DiGiacomo, Sally Healy
Math, Comp Tchr & Dept Chair
DiGiulio, Barbara Anne
High Risk Stdnts & Eng Teacher
Di Giulio, Vito
French & Italian Teacher
Drenon, Linda Ann
Health & Consumer Living Tchr
Eugene, Swann M.
Economics Professor
Gocke, Sharon Denise
Prof of Philosophy & Hum
Huffsmith, Jeanne Crisco
Science Teacher
Leaman, John Archiebald
Sociology & Psychology Prof
Lee, William Yun
Tae Kwon Do, Martial Arts Tchr
Meyer, Stephen H.
Dean of Students
Moore, Patricia Hill
First Grade Teacher
Niemann, Marsha Stocking
PE Teacher & Counselor
Oswald, Wilfred H.
Physics Teacher
Pearson, Michael John
Dean of Students
Perez, Gerald Juan
Coordinator & Counselor
Pollock, Sudie Carol
Tchr of Pregnant & Teen Parent
Robertson, D. Leilani Bunch
Assistant Principal
Schmitz, Gregory J.
Principal
Shurmantine, Brad L.
English Teacher
Stewart, Rhoda Iris
Professor of English
Wukas, Barbara Ann
Nursing Instructor
Yarborough, Eric Grayson
Fifth Grade Teacher
Yarborough, Marilynn Breckenridge
Fourth Grade Teacher
Zunin, Hilary Stanton
English Teacher
NATIONAL CITY
Bokesch, William M.
Mathematics Department Chprsn
Calabria, Christine (Lex)
Fourth Grade Teacher
Cuff, Linda Ann
Sixth Grade Teacher
Floyd, Marilyn Joann
Comm & PE Tchr
Follendorf, Beverly June
English Teacher
Hall, Ellen Briggs
English Teacher
Hanthorn, Russell L.
Senior Marine Instructor
Jensen, Steven John
Science Teacher
Mc Nally, Cheryl Goecke
7th-9th Grade Math Teacher
Munsterteiger, Marcy Anderson
Lang Arts & Reading Specialist
Sevilla, Francisco Javier
5th & 6th Grade Bilingual Tchr
Toler, Tracey Louise
Art Teacher
NEEDLES
Brace, Mary Hutman
Science Teacher
Howard, Mary Neilson
K-8th Grade Teacher

Long, William A.
7th Grd English Teacher
Mc Williams, Gail Arlene
6th Grade Teacher
Stahl, Teresa Sutton
PE & Home Ec Teacher
Thomas, Michael J.
Anatomy, Chemistry & Bio Tchr
NEVADA CITY
Broz, Nancy Norsworthy-White
Second Grade Teacher
Byerley, Marilyn Mc Cutcheon
Retired Grade School Teacher
Joy, Corinne
Administrator & Consultant
Kieswetter, Daria Kuzma
Kindergarten Teacher
NEW CUYAMA
Barba, Ron
Superintendent & Principal
Barnes, Russell
Eighth Grade Teacher
Des Lauriers, Pamela Ann
English Department Chairman
Des Lauriers, Richard Eugene
Soc Studs Dept Chair & Tchr
Kidd, Judith Joann
Language Arts Teacher
Reveley, Robyn Dykes
Teacher & Athletic Director
NEWARK
Barnett, Lynn Dale
Teacher
Bookout, Gary Truman
English Teacher
Conde, Terry Marie
8th Grd Physical Science Tchr
Fay, Gail Frances
Acad English Instructor
Hallford, Jeffrey Grant
English Teacher
Hinkel, Sara Margaret
5th Grade Teacher
Hoffman, Steven Richard
8th Grade Science Teacher
Knight, Kerry Evan
Teacher & Science Dept Chprsn
Sabo, Jerry L.
High School Math Teacher
Sanguinette, Nancie Sue
Student Activities Director
Schirmer, Linda
HS English Teacher
Van Ryn, Ronald Eugene
4th-5th Grade Teacher
Wright, Robert Douglas
World History Teacher
NEWBURY PARK
Dickhoff, Lynn Haines
8th Grade Teacher
Johnson, Stephen Browne
History Teacher
Jones, Marsha Sievers
Special Day Class Teacher
Mc Querrey, Dan
Sixth Grade Teacher
Miller, Robert C.
English Teacher
Reed, Amy Elias
Spanish Teacher
Snyder, Kathleen A.
Kindergarten Teacher
White, Mary Coggins
7th-8th Grade Science Teacher
Wilkes, James C.
Mathematics Instructor
NEWHALL
Bae, Paula Elizabeth (Snider)
Biology Teacher
Ford, Dennis R.
Science Teacher & Golf Coach
Frazer, Gregg Lowell
Political Studies Professor
Hamilton, Kathleen M.
High School English Teacher
Jones, Taylor Bowman
Professor of Chemistry
Kanagi, Chisato Yamamoto
5th & 6th Grade Tchr, Team Ldr
Kearney, Mary Ellen Thompson
English Teacher
Keil, Paul Richard
High School Chemistry Teacher
Lund, Dianna Louise
English Teacher
McHorney, Patricia Brown
English Teacher
Silke, Tarrylee L.
Varsity, JV & Frosh Director
Stone, George Joseph
Instrumental Music Director
NEWMAN
Beevers, Michael Joseph
Physical Education Teacher
Ghiggia, Betty Ann
Sci Tchr & Peer Mediator Adv
Magee, Sonja Christensen
Math Department Chairperson
Martin, Daniel Glenn
4th-5th Grade BiLingual Instr
Quittmeyer, Catherine Trow
English Dept Chairman
NEWPORT BEACH
Bearden, Alberta Esther
Sixth Grade Teacher
Geerlings, Nancy Holt
English Teacher
Hailey, Bob G.
Biology Teacher

Hurwitz, Gail Frances
Math Teacher & Dept Chprsn
Leach, G. William
History Teacher
Mc Guire, Michael James
Jr HS His & Soc Sci Teacher
Nelson, Lynda Mc Carty
Science & Math Teacher
Princeotto, Daniel
High School Counselor
Tomlin, James Charles
History Teacher
Topik, Martha Marcy
AP English Teacher & Chrmn
VanDyke, JoAnn Skerkoske
Former Teacher
Volding, Douglas E.
Jr & Sr High School Counselor
NICOLAUS
Simon, Gail Young
English & Drama Teacher
NILAND
Sullivan, Thelma Marie
Title I Reading Teacher
NIPOMO
Treinen, Mary Louise
2nd Grade Bilingual Teacher
NORCO
Aldrian, Melinda LaVenture
Sixth Grade Teacher
Berokoff, John William
History & Health Teacher
Berry, Nancy Young
Span, Biling & Lang Arts Tchr
Boster, Gina Maria
Agriculture Instructor
BUrkette, James Gareth
Sixth Grade Bilingual Teacher
Gatica, Elizabeth Thomas
Elementary Music Teacher
Gonzalez, Ben Samuel
World, US His, Ec & Govt Tchr
Hane, Sheryl J.
Business Teacher
Miller, Kathleen Anne (Wolfe)
6th Grade Teacher
Phelan, Mary Ann Boone
Language Arts Teacher
Yeutter, Carolyn Pessoni
Home Economics Teacher
NORTH HIGHLANDS
Alessio, Frank B.
Mechanical Drawing Teacher
Coral, Victoria Yolanda
11th Grade US History Teacher
Ditaranto, Laura Hendrix
Resource Specialist Teacher
Fender, Shirley Lee Wilson
English Department Chairman
Fowler, Karin I.
English Teacher
Janis, Tom
Sixth Grade Teacher
Oliver, John Larry
Drama & Music Teacher
Rynberk, Andrea Lively
2nd-12th Grade Teacher
Valentino, Catherine Kopinski
5th Grade Teacher
Walker, Kathleen Marie
Sixth Grade Teacher
NORTH HOLLYWOOD
Badalato, Anne A.
French Teacher
Gill, Linda Ross
Coordinator
Harper, Joseph Stafford
Performing Arts Chairman
Hilliard, Jane T.
Associate Principal
Incerpi, Kathleen Leary
Reading & Lang Arts Specialist
Jensen, William W.
English Teacher
Lager, Carl Alexander
Math Teacher
Langford, James Paul, Jr.
Physiology & Biology Teacher
Leopold, John William
Social Studies Teacher
Lewis, Alice M.
Dance, Aerobics, & Sports Tchr
Malin, Norman Harry
Plastic Technology Teacher
McHarg, Patrick Kirk
History Teacher
Mischel-Wilson, Marion
Chapter I Remedial Rdng Tchr
Rawley, Thomas Steven
History Teacher
Rose, Maie Dell C.
English Teacher
Srour, Joel
Mathematics Teacher
Strickland, Susan Strauss
Combination Teacher
Wedeen, Robbie Jane
Advisor of Bilingual Programs
Weeks, Audrey
Mathematics Teacher
NORTH SAN JUAN
Harris, Kenneth Frederick
History & Language Arts Tchr
NORTHRIDGE
Beckman, Dolores R.
Teacher & Advisor
Bethe, Don R.
Professor & Interim Chair
Calof, Naomi Meister
Third Grade Teacher

NORTHRIDGE (cont)
Cartoon, Essia
7th & 9th Grade English Tchr
Ehrman, Patricia Gallagher
Acting Assistant Principal
Fox, Lynda E.
Curriculum Coordinator
Kim, Seunghe Kang
8th Grade Math Teacher
Melcher, Frederick James
7th-9th Grade English Teacher
Moore, Terri Eaton
4th Grd & GATE Teacher
Oppenheimer, Steven Bernard
Biology Educator
Pilloud, Robert Allen
7th Grade History Teacher
VonWolffersdorff, Joy Anne
Associate Professor of Art
Williams, Noah, IV
History Teacher
Zacarias, Erica Pridonoff
Third Grade Teacher
NORWALK
Allison, Tracy Ann
Second Grade Teacher
Balmages, Mary Mungerson
Court Reporting Instructor
Bever, Howard Oakley
Counselor
Bloomfield, Edward Henry
Professor of Philosophy
Cracchiolo, Edith Eleanor
Psychobiology & Sttstcs Prof
De la Torre, Jesus A.
Bilingual Teacher
Dunroe, William D.
Psychology Professor
Edson-Perone, Lorraine
Math Professor & Dept Chair
Fobi, Charlene Davis
Professor of Nursing
Frager, Phyllis Grav
Fifth Grade Teacher
Harrison, Debra Lynn
Junior High Teacher
Keenan, Diane E.
Asst Professor of Economics
Kennedy, Ruth A.
Home Economics Teacher
Kyllingstad, Wayne E.
Tutor
Llamas-Dixon, Cecilia
Fifth Grade Teacher
Maxwell, Sharon A.
6th Grade Teacher
Munnerlyn, Ross
Lang Arts & English Teacher
Nelson, David Wendell
Professor of Music
Pribble, Mary Siegmund
Department Chair
Roberts, Lynda S.
Professor of Child Development
Ruvalcava, Vykki Caplan
Court Reporting Instructor
Stein, Gerald I.
Paralegal Professor
Swanson, John B.
Assistant Professor of English
van de Mortel, Joseph A.
Chair of Philosophy
Velazquez, Amelia
ESL & Language Arts Tchr
Wells, Douglas Irvin
Associate Professor of PE
NOVATO
Butori, Ronald Dennis
English Teacher
Derr, Joyce E. Voge James
Science Chairperson
Freeman, Daniel Thomas
Social Studies Teacher
Gates, Emily
Music Teacher
Isaacs, Eric Anthony
Junior High School Teacher
Jaeger, Patsy E.
Art & English Teacher
Jones, Kay
English & Amer History Teacher
Mc Dougall, Kathleen Zena
Teacher
Mersereau, Laurence Benjamin
Mathematics & Music Teacher
Pearlman, Richard Brian
6th Grade Teacher
Say, Christene Barbara (Almany)
Health & Phys Education Tchr
Svetcov, Carol (Lipman)
ESL, English & Lang Arts Tchr
Zechlin, Thomas L.
Mathematics Teacher
Zigas, Rita B.
MS Instrumental & Choral Tchr
NUEVO
Chandler, Cindi Burghardt
Principal
Conner, Mike
World His, Eng & German Tchr
OAKDALE
Antinetti, Pamela Laird
Principal
Hastert, Shelly Thompson
Former Teacher
Simms, JoAnn
Math Teacher & Dept Chprsn
Thomas, Judy E.
Sixth Grade Teacher

Van Cleave, Russell James
Mathematics Teacher
Wearin, Ellen Jeanne Gulian
Sixth-Eighth Grade Teacher
Wharff, Julie Looper
Kindergarten Teacher
OAKHURST
Allen, Margaret Taylor
2nd-3rd Grade Teacher
Browning, Steve Anthony
Spanish Teacher
Bullock, Joseph Hyrum, III
3rd-4th Grade Teacher
Crotti, Linda Lee
Fine Arts Mentor Tchr
Huizing, Mary Kaye Van Hook
English Dept Chair & Instr
La Belle, Nancy D.
Counselor
Larson, Scott
8th Grd Math, Sci & PE Teacher
Pope, Robert Dennis
Head Counselor
Robison, Linda L.
Business Teacher & Chair
Sebastian, Deborah Kay
Math Teacher
Sommerfield, Michael Leroy
Drafting Teacher
OAKLAND
Albert, Sheridan Brown
Mathematics Tchr & Vice Prin
Alexander, Margaret Armstead
Fifth Grade Teacher
Anderson, Mary R.
Professor of History
Arceneaux, Frederick Anthony, Sr.
Administrative Assistant Prin
Aronsen, Bridget Abbott
Former Jr HS Science Teacher
Bareilles, Jack Melvin
8th Grade Teacher
Bivens, Annie Ruth
Fifth Grade Teacher
Black, Gwendolyn Crockett
History, Govt & Ec Teacher
Brooks, Wayne
World Cultures Teacher
Brown, Kathleen Ellen (Canty)
Mathematics Teacher
Brownlee, Annyse Gayle (Eubank)
Sixth Grade Teacher
Bryan, Kurt A.
Head Football Coach
Butler, Howard Delbert
Military Science Teacher
Calderwood, John Carver
History, Govt & Economics Tchr
Campbell, Margaret M.
Assoc Prof of Hum & Rel Stud
Caruso, Nancy E.
Science Teacher
Cham, James F.
ESL & English Teacher
Chandler, Irene Scott
Computer Teacher
Clayton, Janet Elizabeth
Assistant Principal
Collier Ivey, Cherie Claire
Assistant Principal
Dugas, Denise M.
Religious Studies Dept Chm
Eimerl, Patricia Ingle
Sixth Grade Teacher
Feinstein, Gloria
French Teacher
Fong, Marydaisy W.
Math Teacher
Freeman, Welborn George
History Teacher
George, Patrick David
Head JV Football Coach
Ginsberg, Karen
Science & Math Teacher
Gorzycki, Meg
Social Studies Teacher
Graham, Mary Dorothy
Bilingual Teacher
Harrington, Hannah Karajian
Assoc Prof of Old Testament
Harris, Margaret
English Tchr & Dept Co-Chair
Hart, Thomas Joel
Asst Prof of English & ESL
Hendon, Velmateen Robinson
Social Studies Teacher
Hernandez, Harry William
Professor of Applied Theology
Ingethron, Eileen Segal
Eng & Amer Hist Tchr
Jacobs, Barbara Jeannette
Fifth Grade Teacher
Jenkins, Lillie Morris
Teacher
Jordan, Kevin D.
Science Teacher & Coach
Josiah, Claude-Elton Oscar
Mathematics Teacher
Keller, Carolyn R.
US His, Ec & Amer Govt Teacher
Larkin, Carol L.
Art Teacher
Laskey, Anne Jenkins
Kodaly Prgm Dir & Music Prof
Lee, Kathy Nakasone
Third & Fourth Grade Teacher
Ludwick, Carole Hetherton
Latin, Ancient His & Hum Tchr
Malo, John Bernard
Religion Teacher

Marquez, Mario Rene
Span, PE & Cmptr Sci Tchr
Matsuoka, Janet Hirano
4th Grade Teacher
McElwain, Lynda
Social Science Teacher
Mc Mahon, Patricia Mc Loughlin
Drama, Comm & Eng Professor
Medaglia, Rich F.
High School English Teacher
Melton, Joyce Marie
Fourth & Fifth Grade Teacher
Merzel, Jonathan Lee
Professor
Morrell, Ernest Davis
12th Grade English Teacher
Moura, Paul Joseph
US His Tchr & Dept Chprsn
Murray, Mary Ann
English Teacher & Dept Chprsn
Nedham, Shirley Martin
Instructor of English
Neely-Johnson, Sonja Christine
6th Grade & Mentor Teacher
Ng, Jacob N. K.
Professor & Cnslng Dept Chprsn
Palumbo, Roberta M.
Professor of English
Philipp, Christopher A. H.
Tech Dir, Integrated Stud Tchr
Plageman, Margaret M.
Eng, Lit & His Tchr
Quinlivan, Jo Anne V.
Assoc Prof of Biological Sci
Rivers-Taylor, Veronica Louise
Fifth Grade Teacher
Rouse, Calvin
Mathematics Teacher
Runge-Smith, Georgia Gertmenian
English & American His Teacher
Sadler, William Alan, Jr.
Professor of Sociology & Bus
Sargent, Arlene Hondl
Prof & Chairperson of Nursing
Saxton, Ruth O.
English Prof & Dean of Letters
Schaffer, Sandi
Science Teacher
Schwartz, Sondra Beth
Soph Spanish & English Teacher
Scott, Dorothy Mae
Fifth Grade Teacher
Shiguera, Bruce
Wrld Culture, US Gvt, Bio Tchr
Sinkowitz, Martin Jon
High School Science Teacher
Tam, Allen Yulun
Biling, ESL & Sci Tchr
Thompson, William Andrew
Admin of Justice Instructor
Willis, Luana
Assistant Professor of Dance
Wilson, Eboni Debra
English Teacher
Wong, Herbert
Counselor
Woo, Betty King-Lam
Music Coord & Asst Professor
Woodward, Irene
Prof of Philosophy
Wright, Margaret Carmical
6th Grade Teacher
OAKLEY
Allen, Mike
Teacher
Johnson, Marjorie Idadell
8th Grade English Teacher
Mc Carthy, Debbie Tompkins
Third Grade Teacher
Rodrigues, William G.
Instrumental Music Teacher
Smyth, Sandra Hadsell
Resource Specialist
OCCIDENTAL
McLallen, Kelly Sue
Principal & Teacher
OCEANO
Block, Dan Curt
5th & 6th Grade Teacher
De Cecco, James R.
6th Grade Teacher
Montano, Robert Allen
Elementary Educator
OCEANSIDE
Anderson, Elaine Dramis
Lang Arts & Soc Stud Tchr
Brooks, John David
English & Photography Teacher
Cunningham, Keith G.
Biological Scis Prof & Chrmn
Englehorn, Joanne Pierson
Fourth Grade Teacher
Floren, Gloria L.
Prof of Eng, Lit, Film & Hum
Foster, Sally Jane
Psychology Professor
Glover, Caroline Frazier
English Teacher
Griffin, Wendy Sue
Fourth Grade Teacher
Hayes, Karen Eiko
8th Grd Lang Arts & His Tchr
Hosaka, Linda K.
6th Grade Teacher
Huyler, Jenny Moeck
Art & English Teacher
Idica, Patrick Roy
Juvenile Comm & Court Teacher
Jackson, Valerie Teresa
Mathematics Teacher

Kinney, Cliff Ward
Health & Physical Ed Instr
Komancheck, Jan Csokmay
Mathematics Instructor
Lane, Lisa M.
History Instructor
Leonard, Arthur Judson
Banking & Finance Professor
Mc Daniel, Austin Dale
Fifth Grade Teacher
Migaiolo, Tony R.
Fifth & Sixth Grade Tchr
Newport, Mary Ann (Sharp)
Nursing Professor
Orlando, Rick A.
Social Science Teacher
Reiser, Katherine
Amer Lit & Lang Arts Teacher
Schneider, Stephen Richard
Humanities Teacher
Shaffer, Linda Lile
Associate Instructor of Health
Stevenson, Bruce R.
English Professor
Stillinger, Denise Kingsbury
Biology Instructor
Turner, Robert
Instr of Lit & Composition
White, Janet L.
Language Arts Teacher
OJAI
Coronel, Manuela H.
Spanish Teacher
Duncan, Gray Roderick
Ceramics Teacher
Farrar, Cliff Lawrence
Math Tchr & Athletic Dir
Rovin, George H.
Administrator & Math Teacher
Shippy, Janyce Peterson
Intermediate Grade Teacher
OLIVEHURST
Bryan, Vera Norton
Science Teacher
Connors, Pat
Conflict Resolution Teacher
ONTARIO
Arquieta, Joseph, Jr.
Spanish Teacher
Gass, Robin L.
English Department Chair
Giambalvo, Claire Vasilovik
Secondary Mathematics Teacher
Guilfoyle, Marge Mary
English Teacher
Gulino, Patricia Anne
Soc Stud & Art His Teacher
Haldi, Alice Miller
Elementary Principal
Harrison, Steven J.
English Teacher
Hazelton, Susan T.
Sixth Grade Teacher
Heath, Brent Edward
Soc Stud Tchr & Dept Chair
Hocking, John
English & Work Experience Tchr
Jones, Mike J.
English Teacher
Koester, Ronald Lee
Mathematics Teacher
Ness, Gayle Browning
Business & Social Studies Tchr
Noel, Linda Lorraine
Dance Teacher
O'Morrow, Shirley Stipe
4th Grade Teacher
Peters, Jacqueline Fladoos
History & English Teacher
Porras, Elidia G.
Language Dev Specialist
Puckett, Patricia Murray
GATE, AVID Coord & Tchr
Richards, Sandra Eileen
Business Education Teacher
Rush, Norm
High School English Teacher
Scarbrough, Dan
US History Teacher
Schlappi, Pamela Joy
Sixth Grade Teacher
Shannon, Virginia E.
English Tchr
Summers, Carolyn Auble
Resource Specialist
Thompson-Fonda, Wanda Cairncross
Teacher
Van Dyk, Elgene Drenth
English Teacher & Dept Head
Williams, Barbara Ann
Fifth Grade Teacher
Wilson, Carolyn Marie
Fifth Grade Teacher
Windham, Donna Gail
English Teacher
ORANGE
Adibi, Esmael
Economics Professor
Agle, Susan
Math & Computer Sci Teacher
Auer, Pamela Brandt
Ninth Grade English Teacher
Banning, Donna Walker
Art Teacher
Barnett, Robert Andrew
Bible & Psychology Teacher
Bode, James T.
Fourth Grade Teacher
Brooks, DeAnna Lynn (Pomeroy)
English & History Teacher

Burns, Bruce W.
Teacher
Carson, Virginia Gottschall
Professor of Biology
Clark, Loretta Ann D'Abaldo
Teacher of GATE
Dierker, Mary Elaine (Bathke)
Kindergarten Teacher
Esparza, Karen Ann
US History Teacher
Fisher-Wilgus, Cindy Ann
Act Dir, Pep Advisor & Coach
Gardner, Jeannette Kirchdoerfer
7th Grade CORE Eng & His Tchr
Gerhard, Nancy Lucile (Dege)
Counselor
Giannini, Suzette (Brown)
Fifth Grade Teacher
Gunther, Robert James
His & Conflict Resolution Tchr
Hansen, Matthew W.
Math Teacher
Hettick, Marilyn Heyler
Biology Teacher
Hilton, Carol Ann
Kindergarten & Art Teacher
Honda, Gary
Sixth Grade Teacher
Johnson, Norman James
English Teacher
Kester, Steve
Science Teacher
Kunau, Jim
HS Teacher & Head Ftbl Coach
Manulkin, Kathleen Kelly
Language Arts Teacher
Marquez, Emma Barela
2nd-3rd Grade Teacher
Nordyke, Darrell F.
6th Grade Teacher
Pappas, Christine Manes
High School Counselor
Pearce, Judith Ann
High School English Teacher
Pearsall, Esther Lee
Psychology Teacher & Counselor
Phelps, Ann Graber
Sixth Grade Teacher
Ramirez, Carol Shepard
Spanish Teacher
Raymond, Michele Oviatt
French & English Teacher
Rhodes, Mary Diane
Social Studies & English Tchr
Scheppmann, Barbara H.
Kndgtn & Jr High Science Tchr
Sfeir, Raymond E.
Economics Professor
Shelton, David Dale
Modern World History Teacher
Slocombe, Thomas Edwin
Management Professor
Smith, Kevin G.
Activities & Drama Director
Stehly, Michael John
Computer Teacher
Tunstall, Robyn Rae (Dishman)
Seventh Grade History Teacher
Verostek, Karen F.
English Teacher
Wallace, Nancy C.
History Teacher
Warner, Karen Marie
Spanish Teacher
Young, Joan V. Catterson
8th Grd Eng & US His Teacher
ORANGEVALE
Austin, Dan R.
English Teacher
Eaton, Yvonne Winning
Principal
Mattison, Janie H. Kruger
5th Grade Teacher
Takagishi, Christiane Reeter
Spanish Teacher
Thomas, Mary Elizabeth
1st Grade Teacher
White, Janyce M.
7th-8th Grade Math Teacher
Williams, Joanne Christine
Full Inclusion Teacher
ORCUTT
Acquistapace, Carolyn Jenkins
Business Teacher
Ferrari, Eric
Math Teacher
Garcia, Norma (Kuyper)
Span, His & Lang Arts Teacher
Gersdorf, Kathleen Fails
Speech Pathologist
Harper, Therron Louis
Spanish Teacher
Knight, Robert Lloyd
Spanish Tchr & Aquatics Coach
Lance, Joy Carol
Agriculture Teacher
Mooney, Jack A.
Sixth Grade Teacher
Noble, Sue Huchinson
6th Grade Teacher
Pedersen, Ole Sigurd
8th Grade History & PE Tchr
Pratt, Bob Allen
Speech Teacher
Provost, Matthew Alan
Math Teacher
Roy, William Eugene
Business Teacher
Sands, Betty M.
Spanish & Physical Ed Tchr

TT (cont)
ns, Earl Clinton
Grade Teacher
K
er, Nancy Ann
Principal & Teacher
DA
, Susan Barr
rade Teacher & Mentor
, Roger Alvin
cal Education Teacher
ntz, Richard Joseph
sh Teacher
y, Donnie A.
Swim Coach
Rosemary Reagan
eacher
nan, Marilyn Price
sh & History Teacher
oor, Martha G.
sh & English Teacher
r, Tracy Lynn
sh & Drama Teacher
e, Edward Robert
ematics Teacher
ND
Florence Anne (Martin)
Grade Instructor
, Eileen
cal Education Instructor
I
r, Mary Jean (Richardson)
h Grade Teacher
man, Robert Earl
nced Placement Math Tchr
artin D.
al Studies & PE Instructor
, Paula Maloney
Grade Teacher
ILLE
, Tyra Ann (Hilgers)
uctor of History
s, William Lamont
nstructor
Christopher Thomas
al Studies Teacher
ey, Neal Patrick
Teacher & Activities Dir
Gary Nielsen
essor of Biology
Carey Uyeda
c Prof of Mathematics
, James Howard
culture Instructor
Jeff R.
nistry & Physics Teacher
Willard Eugene
Arts Professor
n, Marla Bringhurst
ogy Teacher
RD
-Gawad, Myrna Lee
Grade Bilingual Teacher
ws, Susan Merrell
Sci Dept Chair
d, Louise Swindle
& Science Teacher
la, Richard Garcia
Teacher & Chairman
, George J.
hology Teacher
azia-Sanders, John J.
al Sci Chprsn & His Tchr
e, Amy Lynne
School Science Teacher
rald, Brian
Tchr, Coach & Ath Dir
da, Susan Endo
dergarten Teacher
ez-Ito, Martha
nish & ESL Teacher
ed, Jennifer Coffey
Grade Teacher
, Geraldine Yvonne
Grd Science & Mentor Tchr
Jim Robert
ness Teacher & Ath Dir
nberg, Henry Martin
lish Teacher
uist, Janet Post
lish Teacher
Barbara Jane
cher
n, Harriet Bernstein
lish & History Teacher
, Guadalupe S.
al Studies Teacher & Coach
nes, Terrie L.
h Teacher
io, Linda Perez
ding Resource Teacher
ac, Donald Raymond
nomics & English Teacher
, James Lester
h Department Chair
, Eleanor Spicer
3rd Grade Teacher
ees, Jane (Russell)
hematics Teacher
, Lori Zackula
lish Teacher
FIC GROVE
Todd W.
h School Biology Teacher
man, Mary Elizabeth
h Grade Teacher & Coach
, Thomas Howitte
hematics Teacher
nam, Edward Dale
red Classroom Teacher

Schapiro, Karen Lee (Keserich)
Foreign Language Teacher
Sloan, Madelyn Ann (Petrovich)
US History & Geography Teacher
PACIFIC PALISADES
Allen, William Henry, Jr.
Mentor & English Teacher
Dallas, Paula M.
Chemistry & Biology Teacher
Doucette, Robert Grant
Visual & Perf Arts Dept Chair
Gilbert, Rose
English Teacher
Langis, Unhae Park
Magnet English Teacher
Lasky, Brian Neal
Sci Chm, Bio & Physiology Tchr
Lissauer, John C.
History & Government Teacher
Marshall, Larry Ronald
Health Ed Dept Chm & Teacher
McCuskey, Roberta Wessell
Mathematics Coord
Millette, Ramond Victor, Jr.
Marine Science Teacher
O'Toole, Pauline Patricia
6th Grade Homeroom Teacher
Quiring, Alfred Lee
Eng Tchr & Dir of Admission
PACIFICA
Guerrero, Robert James
HS Vocational, Technology Tchr
Kong, Beverly
Science Teacher
Magee, John A.
Mathematics Teacher
Williamson, Catherine Graves
Bio Teacher & Dir of Stu Act
Zbikowski, Allison
Math & Science Teacher
PACOIMA
Canas, Myrna A.
Fourth Grade Teacher
Carrillo-Coronado, Rosa Martinez
Third Grade Bilingual Teacher
Deming, Robert B.
Fourth Grade Teacher of Gifted
Lopez-Lustgarten, Teresa
Bilingual Mathematics Teacher
PALM DESERT
Bishop, Carol Elaine
8th Grade Math Teacher
Brant, Cathleen Paul
English Professor
Colburn, Kevin J.
Fifth Grade Teacher
Cooper, Douglas Harry
Soc Stud & Drivers Ed Teacher
Engelken, James Karl
Mathematics Teacher
Ersavas, Linda Horvath
Spanish & Journalism Teacher
Kato, Monica Dolores
Spanish Teacher
Mc Cormack, Judy Marlow
Spanish & ESL Teacher
Steger, Yolande Corinne
English Teacher
Velk, Dale Bruce
Assistant Principal
PALM SPRINGS
Babcock, Elsie Marie
Resource Teacher
Decker, Linda Rae
English Chairperson & Teacher
Gardner, Doris Schumpert
Senior English Teacher
Myers, Patricia Allen
Fourth Grade Teacher
Pasqualini, Shawn David
English Teacher
Raisler, Mark
History Teacher
Turlo, Margaret Lauermann
French & Spanish Teacher
PALMDALE
Acciani, Joseph A.
History & Orchestra Teacher
Ames, Lillian Ferganchick
Fourth Grade Teacher
Beauchene, Adele Myers
Middle School Teacher
Carlsen, Tracy Lynn
Elementary Teacher
Dizmang, Gloria Ann
US History Teacher
Dvoracek, Ellen
Bio, Anatomy & Physiology Tchr
Gray, Pamela Beith
Kindergarten Teacher
Greatman, Lawrence E.
History Teacher
Holt, Cheryl Kosch
Art Teacher
Hurlburt, Martha J.
Principal
Knight, Timothy W.
English Teacher & Coach
Larson, Linda Lou
Fifth & Sixth Grade Teacher
Lomas, Randall Stephen
Math Teacher
Luckeroth-Lockhart, Patricia
Counselor Dept Chair
Root, James Allan
Work Experience Coordinator
Seargeant, Kathleen Cook
General Science Teacher
Shay, Steven Edward
Eighth Grade History Teacher

Speaks, Nancy Carol
Business Teacher
Yale, Anne
Law & Govt Academy Coordinator
PALO ALTO
Adams, David Bruce
Director of Bands & Jazz
Clarkson, Cheryl Lee
PE Tchr & Instructional Supvr
Dean, Jeannette Haysbert
8th Grade Teacher
Donnelly, Jeannette
Retired Teacher
Dunlevie, Dwight Mansfield
Retired Teacher
Feiner, Shana Lee
Math Teacher
Gaskill, Alonzo L.
Religion Professor
Ginanni, Mark Joseph
Physical Education Teacher
Haber, Marsy A.
Social Studies & Spanish Tchr
Hampton, Nancy Sweeney
Math Teacher
Hargrove, Mathelia Burroughs
Principal
Heilman, Champlin B.
English Teacher
Neal, Dianne Schou
Fourth Grade Teacher
Paugh, Kaye Petty
English Teacher & Advisor
Robinson, Patricia J.
Educational Consultant
Webster, Pamela Ball
Former Teacher
Wojcicki, Esther Hochman
Eng Instructional Supervisor
PALO CEDRO
Brown, Jerry Bob
7th Grade Teacher
Grubbs, William W.
Second Grade Teacher
PALOS VERDES ESTATES
Andrews, Terry L.
English Teacher
Byhower, Martin J.
7th Grade Life Sci Instructor
PALOS VERDES PENINSULA
Bell, Jim
Drama Teacher
Cherman, Inga Fleess
High School Counselor
Corette, Deborah W.
English Dept Chair
Dobrin, Suzanne Lahti
World History Teacher
Dorff, Nancy Lee Margaret
Owner & K-Coll Homebound Tchr
Facer, Susan Patton
Dance Teacher
Jones, Sharon Kent
US History Teacher
Maechling, Jim
Teacher & Soc Sci Dept Chair
McGehee, John Hiram, Jr.
Physics Teacher
Pawl, Carl W.
8th Grade Science & Tech Coord
Phillips, Adrienne J.
Secondary Teacher
Yamane, Kelko Kay
Math Teacher
PANORAMA CITY
Gilles, Mark Robert
Soc Stud Dept Chair & Teacher
Martin, Jacqueline Huntsman
English Lang Dev Prgm Teacher
Martinez, Adelaide Garcia
6th Grade Teacher
PARADISE
Amodia, Millie F.
Physical Education Teacher
Clark, Glenna Rae (Clover)
Second Grade Teacher
Danielson, Jack
Physical Education Teacher
Knowles, Linda S.
Fifth Grade Teacher
Marler, David Clifford
8th Grd Math & Science Teacher
Moseley, Rex K.
Teacher & Dept Chair
Najera, Yolanda
Spanish Teacher
O'Sruitean, Sitric Reamonn
Social Science Teacher
Schofield, Robert Edward
Director of Bands
Sutherland, Loren Duane
High School Science Teacher
Thompson, Sue E.
Physical Education Teacher
Vixie, David R.
Eighth Grade Teacher
Wrobel, Albert John
Fine Arts Instructor
PARAMOUNT
Cantrell, Randy
Math Instructor
Glasper-Wade, Reedy
English Teacher
Himel, Nancy
English Teacher & Yrbk Adv
Leyva, Jeff L.
Anthropology & History Tchr
Perkins, Caroll Ann
Second Grade Teacher

Polhemus, Douglas C.
High School Math Teacher
Rausch, Patricia Louise
8th Grade Teacher
Talmo, Regina Marie
Social Studies & Health Tchr
Trinh, Vinh Huong
Mathematics Teacher
PARLIER
Hernandez, Elizabeth
6th Grd Bilingual Teacher
Mechigian, Gina L.
Eighth Grade History Teacher
Rodriguez, Angelina Martinez
Sixth Grade Teacher
PASADENA
Bortz, Ave Maria DeVanon
Soc Stud Teacher & Dept Chair
Bray, Barbara Roum
Third Grade Teacher
Brown, Neville Melenon
Mathematics Teacher
Bruins, Suzanne C. H.
Mathematics Teacher
Christie, Ashley Margilyn
English Teacher
Cote, Marguerite M.
English Teacher
Daniel, Stan L.
Vice Principal
DeVore, Charles William
Mathematics Teacher
DiFiori, Russell Edward
Professor of Biology
Estrada, Christelle Martinez
Resource Teacher
Everett, Phyllis Torkells
Dean of Girls & History Tchr
Gonzalez, Judith E.
Spanish Teacher
Hajek, Alan Roy
Philosophy Professor
Haussler, Michael H.
Social Studies & English Tchr
Iida, Gary Yukio
Band Director & Music Prof
Kealey, Heather Keith
Art Teacher
Kehrmeyer, Cheryl Gollnick
10th-12th Grd English Teacher
Khalsa, Gurapreet S.
Physics & Chemistry Teacher
Koester, Edward Eugene
8th Grade Teacher
Langley, James C.
Health & Physical Ed Tchr
Leedom-Hearst, Barbara L.
Science Teacher
Lewis, Geraldine C.
Secretary
Lipschutz, Marian Shaw
Eng Tchr & Dept Chair
Maisterra, Marjo Denise
History Teacher
Miller, Brian Scott
Sci Dept Chair & Geometry Tchr
Nelson, Eric Lawrence
Science Chprsn & Biology Tchr
Norheim, Carol Johns
Professor of Communication
Nyong, Francis Etim
Political Science Professor
Pickering, Sandra Jean (Dorman)
4th Grade Teacher
Radu, Lydia
Counselor
Roche, Sherry (Moffa)
Math Teacher
Ryan, John Patrick
Algebra II Teacher
Schwartz, Marlyene Evans
English Teacher
Stellern, Gary G.
Science Teacher
Sterling, Gary Campbell
High School English Teacher
Wall, Richard Joseph
Assistant Headmaster
Whitmore, Raymond Lee
Middle School Coordinator
PASO ROBLES
Bourgault, Robert Edward
Social Science & Guid Tchr
Bradford, Mark William
Social Studies Teacher
Foust, Ginger Lee
Second Grade Teacher
Jordan, Michael Clifford
7th Grade Teacher
Lambie, John Alan
Resource Spec & Drama Teacher
Lichti, Linda Turner
Lang Arts & Soc Studies Tchr
Monteath, Douglas Thomas
HS Mathematics Instructor
Murry, Dan Newton
Resource Specialist
Plemons, Amalia Louise
Middle School Counselor
PATTERSON
Doss, Martha Neal
2nd Grade Teacher
Roberts, Frances M.
High School English Teacher
PERRIS
Campbell, Connie Miranda
Vice Prin & 7th-8th Grd Tchr
Greene, Don
Conflict Mediation Coordinator

Harvill, Doris Holve
Ed Consultant & Writer
Mays, Wilburt Leon, Jr.
Bilingual Science Teacher
Nelson, Sandra Bearman
Kindergarten Teacher
Ontiveros, Richard
Sixth Grade Teacher
Perkins, Colleen Campbell
English Teacher
Rothwell, Jammie Halberg
English Teacher
Schell, Marlene Daniels
Title I Teacher
PETALUMA
Cecchini, Kylee Jo
English Teacher
Dunlap, Linda Fahnholz
Second Grade Teacher
Gurney, Daniel M.
Kindergarten Teacher
Insull, Anne Marie Henrikson
HS English Teacher
Manhan, Julie Ann
Theology Dept Chairperson
Mc Dowell O'Brien, Bessie
Kindergarten Teacher
O'Toole, Michael William
US History & Government Tchr
Potts, Larry Kenneth
Psychology & English Teacher
RIchards, Thomas Earle
Drafting Instructor
Wadsworth, Sarah Greenfield
French & Drama Teacher
Weir, Mavis Noami
History & Mentor Teacher
Wilson, Phyllis Marilyn
Business Department Instructor
PHELAN
Adams, Daniel Martin
Chemistry Teacher
Christian, Benton M. T.
Geography, Govt & Ec Teacher
Fey, Marc A.
English Teacher
Hiller, Clifford
Composition, Lit & His Teacher
Knueven, Melissa Patton
English Teacher & Yearbook Adv
Roeber, Deborah Parker
Sr Advanced Placement Eng Tchr
Smith, Stan
Social Science Teacher
Thorne, Shelley Williams
Social Studies Teacher
Tropila, Michael J.
8th Grd PE & Dept Chair
Zuccarelli, Cheri Ames
Business Teacher
PHILLIPS RANCH
Martinez, Robin Edward
Sixth Grade Teacher
PICO RIVERA
Ayala, Lorraine Theresa (Guzman)
Primary Language Core Teacher
Cordes, Lisa Lorraine (Garcia)
Science & Drama Instr
Craft, Clifford Alen
Mathematics Teacher
Gaikar, Sheila Bhatia
5th Grade Teacher
Langston, Ernestine Armstead
7th Grade Teacher
Lawson, Lynn
Math Teacher
Mc Millen, Jodi R.
7th-8th Grade Math Teacher
Mc Mullen, Timothy Conaway
English Teacher
Moghimi-Danesh, Angela
French & Spanish Teacher
Pakradouni, Roubina
Tchr & Early Chldhd Ed Dir
Pritchett, Benny J.
Dir of Drama & Vocal Music
Rosa, Eva Cavileer
Mathematics Teacher
Royer, Jackie
Chemistry Teacher
Wakefield, Ron
Band Director
Zola, Todd Robert
Physical Education Teacher
PINE VALLEY
Covey, David William
English Teacher
Crane, Susan Thoreson
Home Economics Teacher
Gordon, Stephen L.
Principal & 6th Grade Teacher
Mc Ginnis, Cathy Fielder
Librarian
Sherbondy, Sue Wilson
Resource Specialist
Thompson, Delores T.
Kindergarten Teacher
PINOLE
Collins, Susan Quesada
Science Teacher
Fujioka, Marjorie Nagaoka
Regional Occupational Teacher
Lockard, Janet B.
Latin Teacher
Nicol, Robert Scott
Health Science Teacher
Prior, James Patrick
Math & Computer Science Tchr
Sigg, Deborah Dickey
French Teacher

PINOLE (cont)
Sredl, Rowena Schlegel
Kindergarten Teacher
PITTSBURG
Ahonen, Steven Michael
4th & 5th Grade Teacher
Baker, Laurie
ESL & Spanish Teacher
Belleci-Shipe, Patrice Marie
Assistant Principal
Buettner, Kenneth Paul
Humanities Teacher
Duke, Tanya L.
Fourth Grade Teacher
Hsieh, Durwynne
Biology Teacher
Hunter, Ena I. Nooks
Second Grade Teacher
Kaiper, Donald Dixon
Senior History Instructor
Olney, Josephine Cardinale
Fourth Grade Teacher
Orlando, Paul Jospeh
High School Sci Tchr & Coach
Pike, Scott William
Mathematics Teacher
Pineda, Linda Rose
Fifth Grade Teacher
Pon, Catherine
5th Grade Teacher
Porter, Stephen Thomas
English, Lang Arts & His Tchr
Thompson, Michael Edward
Math Teacher & Dept Chair
Traynor, Paula A.
English Teacher
Uhle, Andrea Vargo
7th Grd Lang Arts Teacher
Williams, Norma Thurston
Resource Specialist
PLACENTIA
Appleby, Joy Robinson
Mathematics Teacher
Ball, David Thomas
Teacher & Admin Intern
Christian, Teresa Lynn
Theatre Arts Teacher
Ethington, Maria Elena
Spanish Teacher
Fain, Warren Andrew
Eng & Lang Arts Instructor
Greenhill, Elizabeth Jefchak
7th Grd Language Arts Teacher
Hassan, Mahamood Mahomed
Former Acctng & Finance Prof
Jones, Gai Laing
Theatre Arts Educator
Leonard, Alan J.
English Teacher
Okazaki, Shirley
2nd Grade Teacher
Parish, Bob Ray
Assistant Principal
Perez, Christine Lee
Instructor
Shenton, Brent Jay
Chemistry Teacher
Stark, Jodeen Lynn
Language Arts Teacher
Steinwand, Dennis James
Technology Specialist
Tait, Michael Duke
Sixth Grade Teacher
Umekubo, Wendy Lynn
Secondary Math Teacher
Vernier, Linda Marie
Spanish & French Teacher
Warren, Kathryn Weishaar
Sci Dept Chprsn & Bio Teacher
Weirich, Linda Hopkins
Kindergarten Teacher
PLACERVILLE
Denega, Susan Landon Yoshida
Design Instructor
Hansen, Jennifer Dayton
English Teacher
Keeney, Judy Ann
High School Spanish Teacher
Lemos, Rebecca Ann
8th Grd Math & Algebra 1 Tchr
Mosher, Kathryn J.
Third Grade Teacher
Power, Debra Lynn
Science Teacher
Simpkin, John M.
Chemistry Instr & Ftbl Coach
Stanley, Robin Robinson
Instrl Specialist & Coord
Young, Tom
Social Science Teacher
PLANADA
Yanez, Higinio Nava
Reading Recovery Teacher
PLAYA DEL REY
Harris, Ronald James
Social Sci Dept Chm & Tchr
Roberts, Rosalie Marie
Director of Guidance
PLEASANT HILL
Almaguer, Michael Rene
Art Department Chairperson
Ballentine, Richard T.
Industrial Technology Teacher
Boyd, Marlowe
Art Mentor Teacher
Brashears, Deya Gelini
College Instr & Dept Chprsn
Brenneise, Lloyd Arden
Vice Prin, Math & Sci Tchr
Carter, Clifford R.
Chemistry & Physics Teacher
Case, Carol Newberry
Third Grade Teacher
Churchill, Peter D.
Professor of Law & Management
Gilbert, Valerie M.
English & Multimedia Teacher
Hammar, Kris
Health Science Instructor
Herbert, Richard
Social Science Teacher
Jacobs, James A.
Professor of English & Comms
Karmon, Oshri
Physics Professor
Leskiw, Larry
Mathematics Teacher
Malone, Nancy Dell
English Instructor
Martin, Daniel C.
Teacher
Mc Glibery, Colin
Professor of Architecture
McPherson, Andrew Adam
7th-10th Grade Teacher
Moore, Beatrice Auza
Science Teacher
Odegard, Marvin R.
Vocational Education Teacher
Passey, Gary G.
Science Teacher
Rawls, James Jabus
History Instructor
Rusay, Ronald J.
Department of Chemistry Chair
Sasse, Paul Michael
Astronomy Instructor
Scott, Douglas Walter
Biology & Earth Science Tchr
Wallace, Inge Lise Skov
5th & 6th Grd Tchr
Winterich, Anne Langley
English Teacher
Young, Judith Moore
Mathematics Teacher
PLEASANTON
Aguiar, Nancy Ivarson
French Teacher
Aladeen, Lary Joe
History Teacher
Alvarez, Carmen S.
Spanish Teacher
Anderson, Sheri Ann
2nd Grade Teacher
Bourg, Christine Krause
Second & Third Grade Teacher
Bradley, Carol M.
English Instructor
Buck, Marsha Sue (Meyers)
Humanities Teacher
Fisher, Judy Camfield
Head Counselor
Fuller, Clark Edward
8th Grade English Teacher
Gill, Diane M.
Social Studies Dept Chm & Tchr
Habecker, Duane Edward
Math Teacher
Hansen, Judy A.
4th Grade Teacher
Jackson, Cynthia Heinbuch
Ger & Consumer Employment Tchr
Keegan, Patricia Sullivan
Regnl Occupational Instructor
Kreutzer, Betty Schwartz
Math Teacher
Ladd, Brian Jay
Social Studies Teacher
Lutz, Lois R.
Retired 4th & 5th Grade Tchr
Morsilli, Steve A.
Varsity Swimming Coach
Moser, Sarah Young
Spanish Teacher
Nix, Joanne C.
4th & 5th Grade Teacher
Nix, John R.
Civics & History Teacher
Reinke, Deborah A.
Math Teacher
Stanley, Elizabeth Romero
Teacher & Coach
Sweeney, Matthew Joseph
Ninth Grade Math Teacher
PLYMOUTH
Christ, Jean D.
Retired Teacher
POLLOCK PINES
Gray, Jeanne Marie (Hull)
Eng, Lit, Math & Drama Teacher
POMONA
Allen, Jan LaBeur
History Teacher
Barraza, Eleanor Juanita (Sone)
5th Grade Teacher
Brookshire, Antonia Elliott
Sixth Grade Teacher
Burton, Maureen
Professor
Darrow, Mary B.
Counselor
de Luca, Peter Joseph
Associate Professor
Edge, Gennan Lynn
1st-2nd Grade Spanish Teacher
Emery, Kenneth A.
History & English Teacher
Estes, Luther Weldon
Teacher
Gancedo-Gonzalez, Maria Theresa
ESL & English Teacher
Grunden, Lee Robert
Chm & Prof of Pharmacology
Hannibal, Joe
Prof of Art & Head of Painting
Hernandez, Michael Patrick
Government & Sociology Instr
Jernigan, Jaqueline
Social Science Teacher
Lehan, James Philip
English Teacher
Lilly-Masuda, Deona Mae
Neurosciences Professor
Lindsay, Mattie Marzell
Language Arts Teacher
Mack, Gary Floyd
Math & Comp Programming Tchr
Mann, Zephyr Tate
Work Experience Coordinator
Markham, Reed B.
Professor
Matisohn, Nancy L.
Biology Teacher
Mc Carty, Teresa Esther
Language Arts Teacher
Morales, Rich
Spanish Teacher
Norman, Gloria Denice
Second Grade Teacher
Sanchez, Javier Martinez
Title I & LEP Resource Teacher
Smith, Shirley Euneece
Fourth Grade Teacher
Taylor, Jocelyn Cynthia (Menck)
General Education Professor
Wong, Jack M.
Social Studies Teacher
Wu, Hofu
Prof of Architecture
PORT HUENEME
Cajiuat, Luzviminda Jose
8th Grade Teacher
Murphy, Richard Paul
1st-8th Grade Teacher
PORTERVILLE
Benander, Kathryn Marie
English Professor
Blomgren, Kinsey Glen
Sci Dept Chm & Physics Tchr
Briscoe, Robert Lee
Spanish Teacher
Brown, Phillip Eugene
Agriculture Teacher
Burger, James M.
Math Teacher
Candelaria, Antonia G.
Primary Language Teacher
Chan, Patrick Kao-Shuang
Comp Information Systems Prof
Cloer, Carla Ann
Fifth Grade Teacher
Funderburk, Dale Christopher
Bio & Human Physiology Tchr
Hargis, Jay Jackson
History & Social Science Instr
Hearne, Al L.
Fourth Grade Teacher
Johnson, Bill Lee
Math Department Head & Tchr
Land, Carroll
US History Teacher
Mc Cusker, Patrick James
Eng & Composition Teacher
Price, Herman Henry
Math & Science Teacher
Pugh, Bob L.
English Teacher & Coach
Vieira, Alvin M., Sr.
8th Grade Science Teacher
Wise, Edward Thomas, Jr.
Professor of Language Arts
Yarbro, Katy Wood
Teacher
PORTOLA
Glynn, Monica Anne
Fifth Grade Teacher
Gress, Darold D.
Teacher
Johnston, JoAnn Gahagan
Fifth Grd Tchr & Tchr of GATE
Valle, David John
Biology Teacher
Wilson, Daniel John
Fifth Grade Teacher
PORTOLA VALLEY
Adam, Wansley S.
English Teacher
Cadile, Susan Wilson
Third Grade Teacher
POTTER VALLEY
Collins, Mary E.
Bilingual Resource Teacher
POWAY
Bailey, Elaine Allyn
Sixth Grade Teacher
Bailey, William J.
Teacher & Eng Dept Chm
Bass, Steven Frederic
8th Grd Wrtng, His & Math Tchr
Branstetter, John Wayne
Physical Education Teacher
Carter, Norma Jean
Fourth Grade Teacher
Cottrell, Martha Hill
5th Grade Teacher
Fletcher, Barbara Ann
Choral Director
Harris, Daniel Carter
High School English Teacher
Keyser, Pamela Frank
Special Education Teacher
Neff, David William
History Teacher & Ftbl Coach
Self, Dian Mahan
5th Grade Teacher
Sundberg, Colleen Karr
7th & 8th Grd Science Teacher
Templer, Mary Frances
English Teacher
Weldon, Robert Lee
Exploring Tech & Basic Ed Tchr
PRATHER
Porter, Diana Lynn
Counselor
PRINCETON
Payne, James Philip
5th Grade Teacher
QUARTZ HILL
Kemp, Michael Harry
Chem, Anatomy, Physiology Tchr
Lenaway, William E.
Math Teacher
Mc Crary, Laurel Metz
Mathematics Teacher
Remy, Michael Thomas
World History Teacher
Rocco, Lina Sportato
Spanish & ESL Teacher
Stover, Jeanne Paulette
Art Teacher
Wright, David Richard Ashley
Drama & English Teacher
QUINCY
Allen-Isenbarger, Barbara (Duran)
Counselor
Bordeaux, Carol R.
History Teacher
Cerny, Daniel David
Math Teacher & Dept Head
Colban, Stefan
Mathematics & Physics Prof
Harlan, Joseph M.
Spanish Teacher
Kent, Patricia
English Instructor
Plankey, Jeanette Diane
Chemistry & Math Instructor
Probst, John Knowles
Humanities Instructor
Valborg, Helen
Instr of Anthrplgy & Sociology
RAMONA
Anastas, Holly Christine
Spanish Teacher
Cameron, Carole Ann
AVID Coordinator & Teacher
Caravelli, Kelly Ann
6th Grade Teacher
Chapman, Edie Hultberg
English Teacher
Crossett, Janet Behn
5th & 6th Grd Montessori Tchr
Doxey, Gene
Social Science Teacher
Granquist, Elizabeth Flynn
Science Teacher
Gunnett, Judith Eunice
5th Grade GATE Teacher
Lewis, Betty J.
4th Grade Teacher
Mac Gurn, Bruce Jeffrey
Sixth Grade Teacher
Mumford, Mary Jane L.
6th Grade Teacher
Quillen, Karen Gjerset
Business Education Teacher
Ray, Debbie Lynn (Vecker)
7th & 8th Grade Teacher
Rowe, Dobbie DeStefani
PE & Psychology Teacher
Schaffer, Albert H.
Math Teacher & Coach
Sulser, Lorraine Davis
Second Grade Teacher
Swatniki, Elaine M.
English & Ceramics Teacher
RANCHO CORDOVA
Brown, Tracy Renee
Math Teacher
Burch, Sherry Denise
World Cultures & AVID Teacher
Christoff, Elizabeth Russo
First Grade Teacher
Diel, Robert Mann
Industrial Technology Teacher
Efstratis, Jeanne Jasonides
Spanish Teacher
Gordon, Cindy Rena
Math Teacher & Var Vlybl Coach
Green, Sandra Faye
Special Education Teacher
Grong, Sandra Gail
English Teacher
Miller, Keith D.
School Guidance Counselor
Rasler, Michael Lorence
Health Science Instructor
Sato, David Masashi
Sixth Grade Teacher
Sornborger-Diel, Joan Eileen
Special Education Teacher
Willeford, Dennis James
Music & Technology Teacher
RANCHO CUCAMONGA
Morrison, Robert Terrance
Bilingual Teacher
Sharp, John David
Physical Education Teacher
RANCHO PALOS VERDES
Mc Kim, Gale F.
Eighth Grade Teacher
Mitchell, Curtis Ronal
Instrumental Music Teacher
Oshiba, Helen Kawasaki
Math & Science Teacher
RANCHO SANTA FE
Isaac, Blake Grail
7th-8th Grd Math Teacher
Miano, Donna Lynn
Teacher
RANCHO SANTA MARGARITA
Andersen, Deryk Matthew
6th Grade Teacher
Fenstermaker, Mary Anne
Social Studies Teacher
Holtkamp, Steven James
Advanced Stud of Ethics Tchr
Nowlin, Jeff D.
Performing Arts Dept Chair
Perrin, Anne
Math Teacher
Schaaf, Cindy Ann
Physical Education Teacher
Smith, Carol Ann
Mathematics Teacher
Zeitler, David Andrew
Physical Science Teacher
RANCO PALOS VERDES
Battes, Jule Lorraine Teissere
English Professor
Cashion, Joan Loretta
English & Speech Assoc Prof
Culp, Mary Beth
Associate Professor
Cuseo, Joseph B.
Professor of Psychology
Desilets, Roseanne Michalek
History Professor
Given, Robert Reed
Science Professor
Guenther, Kathleen Shimko
Language Arts Teacher
Johnson, Sharon Glumm
Dir of Learning Center
Kelley, Patricia M.
Film & Photography Assoc Prof
King, Nancy Garrett
Associate Professor
Movahedi, Mohammad Reza
Math & Chemistry Instructor
Perkins, John K.
Prof & Chair of Philosophy
Pieper, Richard E.
Associate Research Professor
Shenk, Gerald Edwin
Asst Prof of History & Pol Sci
Turner, Diane Lois
Health & Fitness Instructor
Wiley-Ito, Rhonda Ann
Associate Professor of ESL
Wu, Sally Lee Graetz
Associate Professor of Psych
RED BLUFF
Buer, Julie Ross
Fifth Grade Teacher
Combes, Melanie Ann
History & Lang Arts Teacher
Fox, Kathleen Ann (Arnoldy)
Fourth Grade Teacher
Gleason, Pat
English Teacher
Palubeski, Joseph Robert
Psychology Teacher
Roa, Jose Pep
Counselor
REDDING
Aguilar, Richard Cayetano
Instructor of German & Spanish
Allio, Ericka Ann
Second Grade Teacher
Banner, Kenneth Lee
Eighth Grade Science Teacher
Beck, Stephen Carl
US History & Mathematics Tchr
Bush, David L.
Mathematics Teacher
Carlisle, Timothy Charles
English Professor
Condon, Barbara Ohlson
ESL Teacher & Program Coord
Coughran, George Andrew
Sixth Grade Teacher & Ath Dir
Cowan, Janet Fraser
Mathematics Teacher
Deaver, Jim Anthony
Title I & AVID Teacher
Decker, James Arthur
Social Studies Teacher
Drysdale, Mary Ann
4th Grade & Art Teacher
Dummer, Robin Keith
Adjunct Instr of His
Fetters, Nola M.
French, English & Spanish Tchr
Gallagher, Laurie Marie
Third Grade Teacher
Golden, Judy B.
Asst Prin & 3rd Grd Tchr
Grigsby, Brian Harrison
Science Teacher
Grubbs, Jim T.
Asst Prof of Communications
Hollahan, Gary J.
English Instructor
Holland, Nancy Tarpley
Mathematics & Science Teacher
Hull, Barbara E.
Retired Music Teacher

NG (cont)
, Martine Rudy
8th Grd Sci & Art Tchr
Charlotte R.
s, Amer Govt & Ec Teacher
erald Evans
rade Teacher
, Mary Elizabeth
n & First Grade Teacher
n, Layne
story Teacher
oo, Ronald Leon
d 5th-8th Grade Teacher
mery, Jill
rade Core Teacher
Myrna Lizarraga
ce & Spanish Teacher
baugh, Gerrine
rade Core Teacher
James Lal
sh Teacher
Eugene L.
d Math Dept Chairperson
dt, Thomas Laurence
pal, His & Eng Teacher
, Rebecca Janelle
sh Teacher
, Grace Irene Nelson
sh & Spanish Teacher
n, Traci Kara (Molhair)
ct GATE & Math Tchr
ANDS
Gilbert Douglass
Grade Teacher
, Marcia A.
History Teacher
Paul L.
Science Instructor
Brad
selor
ell, Jacqueline N.
sh Teacher
ell, Robert G.
Teacher
Rick
or & Mathematics Teacher
Harriett Iona (Clark)
sh Teacher
Nicki Patrice
terature Teacher
shank, Ray
istry Teacher
Paul N.
cs Teacher
Laura Mae
Teacher
Rafat
ciate Prof of Economics
Marie DiFrancesco
School English Teacher
d, Aaron Brent
cal Studies Teacher
Jane Beckord
sh Teacher
ock, John H.
cs, Chem Tchr & Dept Chm
Susan L.
ematics Teacher
on, Susan K.
sh Teacher
rick, Allen Ross
ssor of Mathematics
ra, Ray
nistrator
Barry Alan
gy Teacher
Paul William
umental Music Director
yre, Frederick Blix
bra, Typing & Cmptrs Tchr
za, Charles Phillip
Science Teacher
Jo (Keebler)
al Studies Teacher
Linda Lou
her
Andrew Merrill
nistry Teacher
, Stephanie S.
ical Education Teacher
, Stephen Thomas
ory & Religion Teacher
s, Rita Marie
nth Grade English Teacher
, Sandra Margaret
nan & Spanish Teacher
, Robert Joseph
Studies & ESL Tchr
elen, Timothy Mark
puter & Mathematics Teacher
Daniel Allen
nematics Teacher
Helen Hardy
nd Grade Teacher
NDO BEACH
gartner, Timothy M.
School Math Teacher
mba, Bernadette Dianne
Arts & Soc Stud Teacher
ann, Charles Arthur
red Sixth Grade Teacher
e, Mary L.
ish Teacher
ney, Carolyn Frances
al Studies & English Tchr
Mae Honda
Grade Teacher
vich, Michael
ner Teacher

Smith, Debrah Kim
High School English Teacher
Tahajian, Sallie
Literature Teacher
REDWOOD CITY
Bussey, Marlyn Rochon
Head Guidance Advisor
Clifford, Peggy McShane
8th Grade & Lang Arts Teacher
Daly, Kelly Jeanne
Science Teacher
Dempsey, Patricia Mae
Social Studies Teacher
DeWitt, Russell S.
Youth Minister
Dyer, Eunice Faye
Third-Fourth Grade Teacher
Fau, Denise Michelle
Eighth Grade English Teacher
Freedman, Jonathan Pryor
Mathematics Teacher
Frost, Anne Schwartz
Language Arts Teacher
Hooper, Diane Lynn
Math Dept Chrprsn & Teacher
Johnson, Judie M.
8th Grd Lang Arts & Lit Tchr
Kruger, Eric Arden
Lang Arts & Soc Studies Tchr
Ploeser, Virginia Seay
Vice Principal & Math Teacher
Pollock, Toby S.
8th Grade Social Studies Tchr
Stabile, Jerald Everett-Thomas
6th-8th Grades Art Teacher
Urban, Hal
Social Studies Teacher
REDWOOD VALLEY
Puterbaugh, Larry Wayne
Music & Social Studies Teacher
Wilcox, Phyllis Hill
Sixth Grade Teacher
REEDLEY
Allen, William Eugene
Math Professor
Baird, William Arthur
Career Dev Teacher & Coach
Barnes-Mileham, Lenora Lacy
Psychology Instructor
Cassidy, Mathilda Jae Klassen
Principal
Dekker, Jan
Chemistry Instructor
Festejo, Sonny
Economics & Business Law Prof
Fudge, Julie Lea
Student Advisor
Glaves, Christopher Lee
Engineering Math Instructor
Hansen, Dave
Bible Tchr & Chaplain
Heise, Clarence Buddy
Band Director
Holcroft, Nancy Elizabeth
4th Grade Teacher
Howell, Peter Sanford
Adjunct Instr Human Anatomy
Kauk, Kirby T.
Science Teacher
Knaak, Don
Teacher & Athletic Director
Krum, J. Carla
Resource Teacher
McCain, Carol Miller
Instructor of Accounting & Tax
Norwood, Mark L.
Theater Arts Coordinator
Reimer, Linda
English & Drama Teacher
Weber, Deborah Michelle
Fifth Grade Teacher
Yorizane, Ruby Chizuko
Second Grade Teacher
RESCUE
Harris, Mary Heather
3rd Grade Teacher
Peron, Ken William
Instrumental Music Teacher
RESEDA
Blumfield, Dana Lee
Physics Teacher
Braaten, Glenn Orlen
Science Teacher
Buchannan, Cheryl C.
Spanish Teacher
Crider, Kevin L.
Physical Education Teacher
Israel, Marcia Ellen
English Teacher
Kawamoto, Bryce H.
Math Tchr
Lightbourn, Melanie Laverne
English Teacher
Little, Patricia Volpe
High School Science Teacher
Mc Grath, Samuel Joseph
Math Teacher
Navarro, Elke Carol
Mathematics Teacher
Paden, William O.
Social Studies Teacher
Schwartz, Ron D.
Mathematics Teacher
Wimberley, Rosario-Perpetua Trapse
Math Teacher
Young, Ann Lee
Dance & Physical Ed Teacher
RIALTO
Applegate, Daniel Wayne
Fifth Grade Teacher

Bell, Dotsie M. St. Julian
Department of English Chairman
Bock, Sarah Whitesides
Spanish Teacher
Braggs, Sylvia Ann (Taylor)
English Dept Chairperson
Cabanas, Dante
English Teacher
Carter, Diane Pugno
High School Math Teacher
Djonne, Gary Lee
Health & Family Life Teacher
Edu, Ufokiban Molly
Physical Sci & Chem Teacher
Ennis, Leon Martin
Social Studies Teacher
Garcia, Miriam Del Rosario
Math Teacher
Gianni, Joseph Wayne
Physical Education Teacher
Gorman, John Joseph
Naval Science Instr
Harper, Jennette Hornbrook
8th Grade Mathematics Teacher
Holen, Brenda Susann
Medical Careers Teacher
Hovey, Mitchell R.
Principal
Kavigan, Roger Joseph
Social Studies Teacher
Martinez, Carolyn Cantrell
ESL Teacher
Mason, Franklin Eddy
Math Teacher
Mc Connell, Jane Elizabeth
Eighth Grade Life Science Tchr
Meyer, Kip D.
Dean of Students
Montgomery, John David
6th Grade Teacher
Neipp, Hyun Nyo Sharine
Chemistry Teacher
Payan, Sylvia Flores
Social Studies Teacher
Pesantes, Olga Antoinette
Primary Lang, Math & Sci Tchr
Pohlers, Bernadino Catherine
ESL Teacher
Radovich, Janelle L.
4th-5th Grade Teacher
Reed, Craig
Printing Occupations Instr
Roberson, Yvonne Semoria
Resource Specialist
Rogalla, Betsy Remenap
Head Counselor
Searle, Steven Allen
Mathematics Teacher
Sertic, Donna Lee
5th & 6th Grade Teacher
Smith, Kimberly Ann (Brown)
English & Social Studies Tchr
Stapler, Terry Parks
8th Grade Language Arts Tchr
Vallentine, Nicholas S.
Biology Teacher
Washington, Deborah Holmes
Preschool Teacher
RICHGROVE
Mojarra, Richard
7th & 8th Grd Teacher
RICHMOND
Ballou, Edward George
Math Teacher
Belton, Alice Porter
Computer Teacher
Carson, Francis Perry
Chemistry & Minority Lit Tchr
Felix, Teresa Lydia
PE, Health & Dance Teacher
Fields, Stephen Edward
HS Social Studies Teacher
Goble, Sally Lyn
Fourth Grade Teacher
Hawley, Diane Wright
English Teacher & Ldrshp Adv
Headington, Janet Rose
English Teacher
Otten, Melvin Henry
Soc Science & Computer Tchr
Penara, Carol M.
English Teacher
Sutton, David Arthur
Math Teacher & Assistant Prin
RIDGECREST
Austin, Simon Joseph
Instrumental Music Teacher
Bell, Ernest M., Jr.
Math, Sci Tchr & Asst Prin
Crandell, Linda Marcotte
Administrator
Dean, Dolores Honc
Secondary Math Teacher
Edwards, Cynthia Cookson
English & Drama Teacher
Howard, Christine Louise
English Teacher & Dept Head
Meyers, Christine Auld
Fine Arts Teacher
Morris, Wendy Gidget
Mathematics Teacher
Morrison, Jayne Keller
Music Teacher
RIO LINDA
Cooper, Jan
Department Head & Art Teacher
Dickau, Keith Michael
Science Teacher
Goodrich, Brian Arthur
Business & English Teacher

Morris, Michael Gerard
World History Teacher
Oertel, Richard Wayne
8th Grade Social Studies Tchr
Richardson, Gordon Lee
Science & Mathematics Teacher
Shaw, Carole R. (Pierce)
English & Drama Teacher
RIO OSO
Grosz, Quaid
8th Grd Homeroom Teacher
RIO VISTA
Christopher, Mary Williams
French & English Teacher
RIPON
Roberson, Donald Neal
HS English Teacher
Zaramskas, Margaret Jane
7th Grade Teacher
RIVERBANK
Fast, J. Timothy
Senior Counselor
Fenton, Susan Anne
English & Humanities Teacher
Hennessey, John Patrick
7th & 8th Grade Art Teacher
Roberson, Charles Bernace, Jr.
Literature & Language Teacher
RIVERDALE
Ruland, Gregory Mark
World & US History Teacher
Walker, Mary Carr
Biology Teacher
RIVERSIDE
Allbeck, Lois Elizabeth
5th & 6th Grade Teacher
Andres, Dean Jeffrey
Lang Arts Tchr & Yearbook Adv
Appleton, Ann L.
English Mentor Teacher
Bains, William H.
Industrial Technology Teacher
Bancarz, Theodore Jonathan
Economics & Religion Teacher
Benchoff, Maria Carmen
Spanish Teacher
Bobst, Richard LeRoy
Professor
Brint, Steven Gregory
Professor of Sociology
Burton, Ellen E.
Teacher
Camacho-Garcia, Ann
High School English Teacher
Decker, Meg Graham
Social Science Teacher
Dennis, William L.
8th Grd Amer His Teacher
Diamond, Rhonda Streich
2nd Grade Bilingual Teacher
Elliott, Jeri Anne
Medical Assisting Instructor
Finan, Ellen Cranston
English Teacher
Finnell-Reed, Michael Dean
History & Bible Teacher
Frost, Carolyn Zappettini
High School English Teacher
Gagnon, Becky Sue (Maag)
Phys Ed Teacher & Tennis Coach
Garrison, Adrienne Armstrong
Child Care Occupations Teacher
Giglio, Vincent Michael
World His & Philosophy Teacher
Griffin-Watson, Hilma Loleta
Assistant Principal
Haskins, Michael S.
Mathematics Teacher
Hauptman, Ira Jay
Theatre Lecturer
Hill, Scott Allen
Social Studies Teacher
Hopkins, Christiane Carreno
French Teacher
Hrubic, Rosalee DeFilippis
Mathematics Teacher
Huff, Diana Ruth
Second Grade Teacher
Hughes, Michael Orr
Span Tchr & Frgn Lang Dept Chm
Hughes, Montserrat Llaurade
Spanish Teacher
Hutcherson, Barbara Clark
French Teacher
Jackson, Mona Maria
Business Teacher
Jensen, Randy N.
US History Teacher
Ji, Chang-Ho Clyde
Educational Psychology Prof
Jimenez, Sheila Small
Algebra & Pre-Algebra Teacher
Jones, Nancy Hammerschmidt
Language Arts Teacher
Jordan, Richard B.
English Teacher
Kari, Daven Michael
Prof of Religion & Literature
Kasper, Dianne
MS Physical Education Teacher
Knauer, Helen Oreen
Fifth Grade Teacher
Kraut, Bruce I.
Fifth Grade Teacher
Krueger, Tamatha Latham
Physical Education Teacher
Laird, Jerry D.
Dean of Stdnts & Ath Dir
Levalle, Kathleen Decker
Instr of Morality & Ethics

Lewis, Nathaniel Paul
Psychology Professor
Lieux, Michele Suzanne
Science Dept Chair
Lomayesva, Dwight
Assoc Prof of History & Math
Loveless, Edna Maye (Alexander)
Professor of English
Lowden, Clara Piersma
Physical Education Assoc Prof
Mahabir, Harold Gilks
Reading Professor
Martin, Bradford
Assistant Professor of Biology
Mc Hugh, Andrew Patrick
Asst Professor of Math
Mc Laughlin, Leighton Bates, II
Journalism Professor
Mehegan, Colleen Nagle
Sixth Grade Teacher
Montano, Marianne Diehl
Mathematics Teacher
Noller, Kenneth Robert
US History Teacher
Patey, Pamela Ardelle
Prof of Information Systems
Pattanaik, Prasanta Kumar
Professor of Economics
Pounders, Dorsey Elizabeth
Social Studies & Art Teacher
Rice, Suzanne Ells
Language Arts Teacher
Robertson, Sharon Elaine
Science Teacher
Rosa, John S.
Industrial Technology Teacher
Sanford, Kenneth Ray
Mathematics Teacher
Santoyo, Michael
Science Teacher
Schimelpfening, Gretchen Marie
Biology Teacher
Schulz, Joan Elizabeth
Third Grade Teacher
Schwab, Ernest Roe
Associate Professor of Biology
Scott, Jo H.
English Teacher
Shea, Evelyn Mc Collum
5th Grade Teacher
Shuler, Laine Saunders
English Teacher
Sinclair, Patricia Ann
Sixth Grade Gate Teacher
Smyth, James F.
Third Grade Teacher
Soria-Sprinkle, Karen Sue
Teacher
Sturtevant, Kathleen O'Brien
Language Arts Teacher
Templin, Janet Priest
Fifth Grade Teacher
Thomas, Alexandra Timmons
English Teacher
Umphress, Irene Endo
3rd & 4th Grade Teacher
Veglahn, David Mark
Chairman of English Department
Vincent, Beverly Ann (Baker)
Kindergarten Teacher
Warner, Karen Elizabeth
5th Grd Teacher & Vice Prin
West, Pamela June Thomas
First Grade Teacher
West, Victor V.
Social Studies & Govt Teacher
Young, Mary Elizabeth
French Teacher
Young, Rex Thomas
Language Arts & Soc Sci Tchr
Young, Sheryl Jean
First Grade Teacher
ROCKLIN
Eskandari, Fara
Mathematics Professor
Garrison, Michael Shon
Physical Education Teacher
Matthews, Betty Joy
First Grade Teacher
RODEO
Johnson, Carol Marie
1st Grade Teacher
ROHNERT PARK
Bricker, Kimberly
Principal
Clark, JoAnn Olsen
Second Grade Teacher
Coberly Jensen, Erma Louise
Retired Teacher
Ferrick, Nancy S.
English & Public Speaking Tchr
Mantooth, Don Allen
Economics Teacher
Steffy, Dale Richard
English Teacher
Xenelis, Suzanne Loomer
High School ESL Teacher
Yonash, Donna S.
Lecturer in English
ROSAMOND
Kemble, Sharon VanCamp
English Teacher
Nickum, Susan Kay
Mathematics & Science Teacher
Simonis, Deanna Luella
English Teacher
ROSEMEAD
Arevalo, Paul S.
Business Teacher

ROSEMEAD (cont)
Barker, Marilyn M.
First Grade Teacher
Crouch, Jo Ella
6th Grd Tchr & Glee Club Dir
Cruz, Pia Jonsson
Science Teacher
Dalton, Jim
English Teacher
Denson, Philinda Stern
Mathematics Teacher
Fierro, Frances Zoidis
Teacher
Gerardo, Maria Velasquez
10th Grd Art Tchr & Yrbk Adv
Gerlach, Celia Luffman
Span, German Tchr & Dept Head
Green, Jeanine Moisi
Kindergarten Teacher
Hensley, John R.
Music Department Chair
Imperial, Rick Craig
Business Education Teacher
Iniguez, Jose Alfredo
Assistant Prin & Spanish Tchr
Knight, Anna-Maria Contreras
Resource Teacher
Martinez, Melody Butterfield
High School Math Teacher
Okeyo, Joseph Odundo
Architectural Teacher
Preston, Hilary Victoria
Math Instructor & Soph Cnslr
Pytko, Tanya
English Teacher
Reina, Nicholas Joseph
President
Rose-Lugo, Elaine Susan
Spanish Teacher
Rosenberg, Suzan Helene
2nd Grade Teacher
Scadellaro, Randall
Power & Transp Tech Dept Chair
Street, Beverly Houck
Second Grade Teacher
Van Zee, Kristi Lynn
Science & PE Teacher
Villasenor, Gerardo
Social Science Teacher
ROSEVILLE
Baker, Patti S.
Dance Teacher
Dell'Orto, Earle Brandon
HS History & Drama Teacher
Fischer, Steven Darrell
English Teacher
Givens, Tamara Jean
English Teacher
Graves, Bruce F.
Social Studies Tchr, Vice-Prin
Greene, David Paul
Independent Study Teacher
Grimes, Lonnie Michael
Physics Instructor
Kevin, Judy Ann
Mathematics Teacher
Leeper, Judith Adelle
Substitute Teacher
Lude, Joyce Edson
Family & Consumer Sci Teacher
Martinez, Deborah Fenton
Frgn Lang Coord & Span Tchr
Miller, Robert Andrew
Frgn Lang Chair & Span Tchr
Sherbert, Stephanie
English Teacher
Stenklyft, Betsy
Kindergarten Teacher
Takagishi, E. Craig
Mathematics Teacher
Wilson, Kristine Knudtzon
English & ELD Teacher
ROSS
Gottbrath, Geri
4th Grade Teacher
Procter, Margaret Flanders
Spanish Teacher
Symonds, Jeffrey Keith
English Teacher
ROWLAND HEIGHTS
Alpizar, Torry Ilona
High School Counselor
Barnett, Brooke Temple
Sixth Grade Teacher
Colletti, Nancy Jean
Fourth Grade Teacher
Donaire, Margarita Lim
Social Studies & Spanish Tchr
Doublet, Patricia Ann
Theatre Tchr & Journalism Adv
Falk, Matthew Carl
English Teacher & Yearbook Adv
Fitch, Sue Ann (Carty)
5th Grade Teacher
Girard, Arthur George
Secondary Mathematics Teacher
Gutierrez, Rosemary Escalera
High School English Teacher
Hartwig, Dorothea Ann
Sixth Grade Teacher
Phillips, Leslie Joy
Math Teacher & Dept Chprsn
Thune, Richard Gregory
English Language Dev Teacher
RUNNING SPRINGS
Dyer, Janet Anderson
Retired Physical Ed Teacher
SACRAMENTO
Albers, Marilyn B. Lambo
Kindergarten Teacher
Anderson, Christine Arlene
Principal
Anderson, Jeanne Ferguson
4th Grade Teacher
Anderson, Molly Marie (Games)
Business Teacher, Voc Ed Coord
Anshin, Judith
Instructor of Business Law
Babcock, Terri Jo
Fifth Grade Teacher
Baird, Arthur Charles
Social Studies Teacher
Barry, Edward Leo
Chemistry Teacher
Bates, Brian Franklin
Instr in English & Humanities
Beaver, Barbara Ann
Title I Resource Spclst
Blackwell, David A.
Mathematics Teacher
Boynton, Earl Willard
Chemistry & Physics Teacher
Breitenbach, Ron
Mathematics Instructor
Brida, Rita Marian
Spanish Teacher
Brooks, Barbra A.
English Teacher
Buechner, Marybeth (Helwig)
Bio & Environmental Tech Instr
Callaghan, Sandra Reid
English Teacher
Campbell, Suzanne E. (Creasey)
6th Grade Teacher
Caplinger, Paula R.
Band & Orchestra Director
Carroll, Marlene Elizabeth
3rd Grade GATE Teacher
Carter, Peggy Sachelli
English Teacher
Caston, Angelee Bennett
English Teacher
Cavallo, Carl Wayne
Automotive Instructor
Cazanis, Pauline A.
Second Grade & GATE Teacher
Chan, Carol D.
Fourth Grade Teacher
Chapman, Elaine (Jonas)
Third Grade Teacher
Clazie, Joan Louise
Language Arts Teacher
Connors, Evelyn Mc Alister
English Teacher
Conroy, Michael Joseph
US History Teacher
Cooper, Billie Miller
Professor
Cornelius, Ken
Retired Sixth Grade Teacher
Cornell, Jenice Gale
Preschool Director
DeGusta, Stephen A.
Molecular & Advanced Bio Tchr
De Luca, Rodney John, Jr.
English Teacher & Co-Dept Chm
De Ruysscher, David A.
English & Journalism Teacher
Dillingham, Martha Ann Thomas
Vice Prin
Duncan, Jill Belwood
Photography Instructor
Eason, Bob F.
Phys Ed Teacher & Dept Chair
Ebbage, Francene G.
8th Grd Language Arts Teacher
Eister, Irene Renee
6th Grade Teacher
Erickson, Cindy L.
Mathematics Chair & Instructor
Evans, Edythe Anne (Butcher)
English Teacher
Fabionar, Maria Elena Olamit
Cnslr & Re-Entry Svcs Coord
Festine, Maggie Nicolai
English Teacher
Finley, Phillip Edward
Engineering Design Tech Instr
Folan, Sheila Mary
Agriculture Instructor
Frazier, Jane Justus
Science Teacher
Freeman, Carole Jones
German Teacher
Frueh, Dorothy Carol
Band Director
Gallagher, John Patrick
Life Science & Earth Sci Tchr
Gebhardt, Charles V.
Teacher
Gibson, Frederick Earl
Phys Education Teacher & Coach
Gibson, Patrice Vandegrift
Anthropology Instructor
Gordon, Robin
Science Dept Chair & Teacher
Gray, David Arthur
Physical Ed & Hlth Teacher
Henning, Therese Poppleton
Second Grade Teacher
Henninger, Alberta Nobles
Retired Elem 6th Grade Teacher
Henson, James Ronald
Spanish & French Teacher
Hilts, Teresa Elizabeth
Social Sci & US History Tchr
Hoang, Bien-Hoa Tich
Soc Stud & Lang Dev Tchr
Holmes, Bettie Nordstrom
Head & Humanities Teacher
Horn, Kenneth George
Teacher & Dept Chair
Hotell, Michael Davin
Science Teacher
Hurley, Rebecca Ratay
Eng as Second Lang & Law Tchr
Jacobs, Joseph
Mathematics Teacher
Jemmings, Kim Flohr
Kindergarten Teacher
Jessee, Sandra Kay
Physical Education Teacher
Johnson, Kimberly Ann (Wise)
7th Grade English Teacher
Johnson, Mai-Gemu D.
MESA Director & Math Instr
Jordahl, Nancy J.
Home Economics Teacher
Jordan, Maureen
Performing Arts Dept Chair
Keen, Judi
ESL Professor
Kelley, Jack Lee
Biology Teacher
Kinunen, Eric Matthew
5th Grade Teacher
Kirkland, Vanette Price
English Teacher
Kremer, Ronald Edwin
Third Grade GATE Teacher
LaMay, Lauren Virginia
English Teacher
Lane, Julie Proctor
Reading, FACE & AVID Teacher
Lau, Kelly K.
Scndry Chem & Earth Sci Tchr
LaVecchia, Susan (Turner)
Sixth Grade Teacher
Lawlor, Michael John
Physics Professor
Lee, Terry B.
ELD Teacher
Leege, Don R.
4th Grade Teacher
Lenhart, Doreen Marie
Math Teacher & Dept Chair
Londahl, Alexandra P.
English Teacher
Lovan, Alonzo Santiago
Spanish Teacher
Luchini, Romano Massimo
High Schl Soc Sci & His Tchr
MacDonald, Joanna Margaret
Chemistry Teacher
Maffei, William Alfred
College US History Instructor
Malone, Thomas Scott
Sixth Grade Teacher
Manola, Jennifer Mathews
French Teacher
Marchand, Lisa Phares
ESL Instructor
Mazzaferro, James Joseph
Bands Director
Mc Clymonds, Alfred Dale
Vice Principal
Mendoza, Shelley J.
Physical Education Teacher
Meyer, Beverley Anne
Latin & Civics Teacher
Miner, Thomas Edward
English Instructor
Morse, James Richard
Speech, Debate Coach, His Tchr
Morton, Nileta Lerza
Foods Teacher
Myers, Lyna A.
World History Teacher
Nannini, Donald J.
Principal
Norman, Richard William
Theology Dept Chairman
Nuezel, John E.
English Teacher
Olds, Lynn G.
Vice Prinicipal
Owens, Adelaide Upson
Prep Specialist Teacher
Padley, Patricia Pepi
High School English Teacher
Paggett, Ike
Music Tchr & Director of Bands
Painter, Jody Ann
6th Grade Teacher
Patton, Marcus Hilton
English Instructor
Penso, David R.
Mathematics Teacher
Pickens, Kathryn Rainwater
Title I Curriculum Specialist
Plaskett, James Russell
Music & Choir Teacher
Poole, Jerry
8th Grade Teacher
Poppers, Laura Ann
7th Grade Language Arts Tchr
Powell, Joseph George
Humanities & English Teacher
Pugh, Linda Tietjen
1st & 2nd Grade Teacher
Quinn, John Thomas, SJ
Director of Publication
Reed, Patricia Parker
Eng Prof & Writing Ctr Coord
Regan, Debra Sue
Biology Teacher
Roachford-Gould, Louise Margaret
Title I Resource Teacher
Roemmele, Kathy Anne
AVID Director & Eng Tchr
Romani, Marcus Justin
HS Math & Physics Teacher
St John, Retter
Biology Teacher
Sarlatte, Henri Laurent
Social Science Teacher
Saunders, Edwin Mc Bride
Sixth Grade Teacher
Schumann, Rolf Richard
Math Teacher & Football Coach
Schwartz, Marjorie C.
First Grade Teacher
Scott, Susan Margaret
Professor of Biology
Shelly, William Henry, Jr.
Vocational Education Teacher
Short, Jean Ostermann
World History Teacher
Siemens, Ron T.
High School Science Teacher
Smedberg, Ronald Theodore
Organic Chemistry Instructor
Smith, Alexander Coke
Biology & Japanese Instructor
Smith, Kathleen Ellen
4th Grd Teacher of Gifted
Spencer, Robert G.
Retired 6th Grade Teacher
Stone, Edgar B.
Mathematics Teacher
Strong, Julie Porter
FACE Teacher
Stump, Linda Staehle
6th Grade Teacher
Sully, Robert John, Jr.
Aerospace Science Instr
Sun, Ting Lan
Tchr, Curr & Assessment Dir
Thomas, Jim D.
Instr of Acctng & Dept Chair
Thomas, Sue Albrecht
English Teacher
Thompson, Thomas DuWard
English & Drama HS Teacher
Thorne, Darlene Nagy
High School English Teacher
Tinnin, Freeman B.
Vice Principal
Tracy, Lynne Marie
Choir, Piano & Drama Teacher
Turner, Clint Wayne
Automotive Instructor
VanCleland, Donna
Eng as Second Lang Dept Chair
Van Patten, Charles Robert
Philosophy Instr & Hum Chair
Vendlinski, Terry Paul
Science Department Chairman
Verne, Susan Rasmussen
Teacher & Restructuring Coord
Vink, Dominique M.
US History Teacher
Vogel, Christy L.
Chemistry Instructor
Waraas, Mary Rachel Caldeira
Third Grade Teacher
Wilhelm, MaryAnn Widdifield
English Teacher
Williams, Christopher Lehua, Jr.
Choral Director & English Tchr
Wilmer, Robin Hettinger
Band Teacher
Wilson, Betty Robinson
Independent Studies Teacher
Wong, Janice Miyuki
Pre-Calculus Teacher
Wren, Lois Dougherty
Science Teacher
Wurschmidt, Lee Blakely
Mathematics Teacher
Yagen, David Soriano
HS Mathematics Teacher
Yamada, Nadine Naomi
Fifth Grade Teacher
Yannacone, Brenda Sue
Eng & Drama Tchr, AVID Coord
Zaccone, Tanya Lee
Spanish Teacher
SALIDA
Baughn, Don E.
Music Teacher
Manning, James Edward
Eighth Grade Teacher
Scott, Jack Lee
Social Studies Teacher
SALINAS
Albano, Jane
English Dept Chprsn
Allen, Charles Sumner
Teacher
Andreotti, Darlene Carol
English & GATE Teacher
Angelo, John Anthony
Language Arts Teacher
Barber, Edward Julian
Mathematics Teacher & Coach
Bates, Sharon Barber
Kindergarten Teacher
Bernhard, Nancy Lynn
Drama & English Teacher
Birkeland, Elizabeth Yee
English Teacher
Carnazzo, Jeff G.
History Teacher
Coster, Rory Wymond
English Teacher
Cude, Jesse L.
Instructor of Physics
Deaver, Donna H.
First Grade Teacher
Deckelmann, Michael R.
Math Teacher
Domelle, Margaret Lawrence
Supervisor & Teacher
Egan, Patrick Michael
English Teacher
Espinoza, Terry Eli
History Teacher
Figenshow, Elizabeth Mc Cabe
4th Grade Teacher
Garcia, Nickolas
World History Teacher
Garcia, Rudy
School Counselor
Gladwell, Michael William
Third Grade Teacher
Gomes, Jean Baccelli
Kindergarten Teacher
Hernandez, Chris M.
Foreign Language Dept Chairman
Hernandez, Nancy Bitterman
Spanish Teacher
Hileman, Corren C.
English Teacher
Jackson, Glennie G.T.
7th Grd Math Teacher
Jones-Powers, Nancy Kathryn
Director of Student Activities
Kamm, Karen Gile
Resource Specialist
Lentz, Susan Maurer
9th-12th Grd Mathematics Tchr
Lundquist, Roger Dean
5th Grd Tchr & Vice Principal
Lyon, Daryl Zapell
English Teacher
Martinez, Tim Manuel
World History Teacher
Modena, Judy R.
Fifth Grade Teacher
Noroian, Chuck
HS Physical Ed Instructor
Okumura, Jerry Tatsumi
Fifth Grade Teacher
Oliveira, Donna Hundertmark
English Teacher
Padgett, Nancy Pavley
Fourth Grade Teacher
Picardi, Dan
Asst Prin for Curr & Instr
Pratt, Merry Johnson
Physical Education Teacher
Puentes, Marilyn Davis
Vocal Music Teacher
Raptis, David Gomez
Science & Drivers Ed Teacher
Russo, Rick
Teacher
Saling, Lynda Chester
Third & Fourth Grade Teacher
Sanborn, Susan J.
Art Teacher
Shields, Gisela Thieme
Art Teacher
Sugahara, Tei Ann Dacus
7th Grd CORE & Health Teacher
Sweet, Jeff
Physics Teacher
Teodorescu, Silvia Ballara
Spanish Professor
Thomas, Mary K. Romero
Former English Teacher
Thure, Rheta V.
US History Teacher
Turner, Keith Wayne
Health Teacher
Uchiyama, Stanley E.
Agriculture Education Teacher
Uecker, Sandra Schaetzel
Visual Arts & Fashion Teacher
VonSoosten, Joe E.
Language Arts & PE Teacher
Warwick, James Joseph
Industrial Education Teacher
SAN ANDREAS
Bowe, Mark E.
Social Science Dept Chm
Larson, Cyndy
Business Teacher
SAN ANSELMO
Carlson, Sharon Mc Donald
Mathematics Teacher
Chase, Carole Adamowicz
Early Education Teacher
Dunlap, Susan Pfreundner
French & Spanish Teacher
Epke, Kristi Englehardt
Math Teacher
Fox, Susan Leslie
Environmental Sci & Bio Tchr
Moskowitz, Jackie Key
Soc Stud Tchr & Curr Coord
Sondheim, David
Science Teacher & Tech Coord
SAN BERNARDINO
Arnold, Steven W.
GATE Reading & Lang Teacher
Bartlett, James Gregory
English as a Second Lang Tchr
Bastedo, David Melville
Human Anatomy Instructor
Berman, Edward Samuel
Tchr of GATE, AP, Honors Eng
Bowman, Roylestine Jenkins
Special Ed Teacher
Brown, James Michael
Professor of English
Brown, Juanell
Science Teacher

ERNADINO (cont)
, Michelle Denise
iage Arts Teacher
David
ssor of Sociology
, Risa E.
Professor of Comm Studies
medios, Anthony Christopher
School Teacher
Foster, Linda Lee (Williams)
entary School Teacher
s, Judith Pett
sh Teacher
Vernon Harold
Studies, US His Teacher
er, Eric G.
Professor of Engineering
, Lisa Diane
rd Rdng & Lang Arts Tchr
wa, Chisa Takemasa
ese Teacher
on, Charles B., Jr.
ematics Teacher
ch, Lawrence Walter
nic Arts Instructor
n, Thomas J.
sh Teacher
David Paul
Grade World History Tchr
ner, Laura
ology Professor
y, Shelley Wilson
Grade Teacher
nn Gibbons
tant Professor of Math
Michael J.
ciate Professor of Physics
Gary Ray
ing & CAD Teacher
ws, Dolores Carlson
rer in Math Dept
gor, Linda R.
Music & English Teacher
Earlena F.
ess Education Instructor
y, Mary Howard, Sr.
Grade Teacher
, Lillie Toliver
sh Teacher
ger, Gordon L.
omy Professor
nor, Michael Wayne
School Teacher
John H.
Dept of Bio & Assoc Prof
Lisa
l Studies Teacher
nasuya
sh & ESL Teacher
Robert Charles
ora Teacher
Treadwell
ciate Professor of English
, Manuel Armando
entary School Principal
ield, Robert B.
Grade Honors English Tchr
Pryor, Pamela Enola
rican Sign Language Prof
A. Michael
S His & Amer Govt Teacher
rd, Pam D.
Grade English Teacher
Julie Christine Enfield
al Studies Teacher
, Albert Y.
Tchr, Dept Chair & Tchr
g, A. John
d Geography Teacher
Maureen A.
nistry Teacher
RUNO
Sharon Marie
her
d, Peter Ashton
School Math Teacher
er, Kurt H.
her
Betty Mae (Ng)
th Grade Teacher
, Brenda Susan
nematics Teacher
Norman O.
ish Dept Chairperson
CARLOS
on, Sally V.
Grade Teacher
wald, Joanne Elizabeth
d Grade Teacher
, Marge
Grade Teacher
, Christine F.
Grade Teacher
CLEMENTE
son, Stephanie Conley
n Grade Teacher
n, Julie Reyes
al Music Director
n, Jeffrey Lee
12th Grd Science Teacher
n, Michael Patrick
n School English Teacher
nings, Benner Thompson
ld His & Asian Studies Tchr
, Patrick Winders
lish & Psychology Teacher
ook, Larry C.
ogy Teacher
n, Joy Sellstrom
h Teacher

Neidhardt, David Christon
English Teacher & Coach
O'Rear, Robert Kent
Spanish Teacher & Athletic Dir
Riem, Michelle Johanna
Science Teacher
Smith, Bradley Shaw
Mathematics Teacher
Washington, Wendy
English Tchr & GATE Coord
SAN DIEGO
Abraham, LuEllen Nagel
English Teacher
Andrews, June Kelley
High School Teacher & Coach
Antrim, Lynell Tanya
Teacher
Arendell, Thomas Lee
8th Grade Basic Education Tchr
Arnold, Wanda Price
Third Grade Teacher
Baker, Lambert Will
Professor Emeritus
Balzer, Frank Louis
Sociology Instructor
Barbolla, Andrew Michael
AP Honors English Teacher
Barone, James Anthony
Scndry Level Spec Ed Teacher
Battilega, Jill Sanchez
Social Science Teacher
Battilega, Tony
Composition & Literature Tchr
Benfante, Vincent William
Admissions Cnslr & His Instr
Bennett, Sandra Lynn
6th Grade Teacher
Bernard, Sanford Kendall
Vice President
Bliss, Diane Colonelli
4th Grade Teacher of Gifted
Bowermaster, Janet Frahm
Law Professor
Brickley, Lori Mc Cahan
Alternative Education Teacher
Brooks, Mary Ellen Diefenbach
Associate Professor
Brothers, William A.
Prof of Biology & Dept Chrpsn
Brown, Michael Paul
United States History Teacher
Browne, Oscar Rayner
English & Language Arts Tchr
Budnick, Byron Skip
Physics Teacher
Bungard, Karen
8th Grd US His & Eng Teacher
Cassin, Lois Terpening
Mathematics Teacher
Celle, Diana Kato
3rd Grade Teacher
Chandroo, Teddy
Mathematics Teacher
Chard-Yaron, Sharon Rabinowitz
Asst Professor of Education
Chung, John Anthony
Fifth Grade Teacher
Ciaccio, Barbara Ruth
Math & Science Teacher
Clevenger, Cynthia Ann
4th-6th Grade Teacher
Clunn, Carlton Harry
Aeronautics Teacher
Cochrane, Bruce Ernest
Resource Specialist & His Tchr
Cohen, Joseph Allan
Teacher
Collier-Wade, Mary Louise
AVID & PE Instr
Conant, Kim Untiedt
6th Grade LEP Teacher
Conaway, Trudi
Lang Arts & Soc Studies Tchr
Cook, Judy Edith (Soos)
Science Resource Teacher
Cooper, Mary
Physical Education Teacher
Corr, Patrick Wayne
Math Teacher & Coach
Cravens, Russ
World Ec Government Teacher
Crawford, Charles Anthony
Counselor
Crawford, Gary Neil
HS History Teacher
Crepeau, Kathryn Loomis
English Teacher
Curtis, David
HS Math Teacher
d'Ablaing, William Frederick
High School Biology Teacher
Daniell, Janice Snowdall
High School Spanish Teacher
Dapeer, Gabriella Lou
Secondary English Teacher
Daubert, Joyce Anne
Spanish Teacher
Davis, Emma Pitner
Secondary English Teacher
Davis, Robert I.
Mathematics Tchr & Dept Chair
Davis-Winston, Janice Glee
Counselor
Dean, Robert J.
Physics Teacher
Deely, Michael Anthony
Rel Teacher & Campus Minister
Dettman, Ronald Carl
Tall Flag & Winterguard Tchr

DeYoung, Donna Jean
Math Instructor & Dept Chair
Djordjevski, Pamela Hisken
English, ESL & GATE Teacher
Dominic, Christopher Joseph
Graduate Teaching Associate
Dow, Frederick W.
Prof of International Mgmt
Doyle, Sean Jerome
Anatomy & Physiology Teacher
Duchock, Shirley Templeton
European History Teacher
Duggan, Robert Francis
Math Teacher
Emery, Jill
Seventh Grade Teacher
Filson, Linda Andre
Fifth Grade Teacher of GATE
Fleming, Daniel Arnold
7th Grd Humanities CORE Tchr
Fletcher, Diann Kern
Sixth Grade Teacher
Foster, Susan Diane
Civics & World History Teacher
Foster-King, Sandra Mae
Dance Teacher
Fousek, Alexander
Spanish Teacher
Fox, Karen Latham
Spanish Teacher
Francis, Laurie Brady
Site Resource Teacher
Freres, Kathleen Ann
Sixth Grade Teacher
Froehlich, Angela Maria
4th & 5th Grd GATE Teacher
Fulwiler, Mary Senic
AP US History Teacher
Gahan, Gregory Thomas
Spanish Teacher
Gamberale, Dawn Marie
Chemistry Teacher
Garcia, Norma Lucia
5th Grade Teacher
Geiger, Daniel Joseph
Mathematics Teacher
Giardina, James M.
Teacher & Soc Studies Dept Chm
Gibson, Carole Lee
5th Grade GATE Teacher
Gillingham, Elizabeth Riel
Mathematics Teacher
Gimber, Norma M.
Teacher & Program Coordinator
Goodwin, Linda Larsen
Fourth Grade Teacher
Grant, Beverly Ruth
English Teacher
Gray, Freddie L.
English Teacher
Gray, Nancy Jones
Vocal Music Teacher
Grimes, David Lee
Math Teacher
Gruber, Arleen Ann
English Teacher
Haas, Karen Larson
Fifth Grade Teacher
Hafner, Kathleen Sidney
Counselor
Hagan, Terry Jo (Bernard)
English Teacher
Hall, Kim Monique
Math Teacher
Hamamoto, Ron
Head Ftbl Coach & Cmptr Tchr
Harmaning, Marilyn Joy
Eng, Speech & Yearbook Teacher
Harrington, Christopher James
Eng Tchr & Asst Head
Harrison, Doina Protopopescu
Spanish & Fr Tchr & Dept Chair
Hauser, Jean Sobetzer
Fine Arts Instructor
Hayman, Nicolynn Sue
Kindergarten Teacher
Hermosillo, Manuel
Social Science Teacher
Herron, Roberta Claire
Head Counselor
Hewitt, Nancy Harper
Spanish Teacher
Hitchcock, Julie Lynne
Counselor
Hizal, Kris Jeffrey
US History & Civics Teacher
Hofmann, Norma Huhn
Fifth Grade Teacher
Holmes, Robert Burress
Retired 5th & 6th Grade Tchr
Holzman, Marie Sato
Teacher of Gifted & Talented
House, Kay Marie (Tuttle)
History & English Teacher
Howell, Leslie J.
Advanced Placement Teacher
Idos, Rosalina Vejerano
Pilipino Teacher
Ihlbrock, Thomas Eric
Advanced Placement US His Tchr
Isaacs, Gilbert Charles
English Teacher
Johnson, Susan Gannage
Public Speaking & Drama Tchr
Jones, Donald Mark
Health & Physical Ed Instr
Kear, Valerie
Honors & GATE English Teacher
Keim, Lynn S.
Sixth Grade Teacher

Kiely, Joan
Religion Teacher
Knepper, Aleen Charlette Richardson
Third Grade Teacher
Kostrukoff, Larissa
French & Spanish Teacher
Kraft, George William, Jr.
Law Professor
Labeta, John Michael
Varsity Assistant Head Coach
Lacey-Parks, Rena Elizabeth
English Teacher
Lamphiere-Tamayoshi, Monique
Amer Lit-Writing Seminar Tchr
Latimer, Carla Benson
Elementary Mentor Teacher
Lecakes, Holly
ESL & Spanish Teacher
Le Cren, Carole
English & Math Teacher
Lee, Linda Ann
English Professor
Letourneau, Mary Jo
Teacher of Gifted & Talented
Levenson, Lee H. M.
First Grade Teacher
Lightfoot, Nataha
High School Art Instructor
Locher, Paul William
Math Teacher
Long, Theodora Jawan
Mentor Teacher
Longwell, Larry L.
Fifth Grade Tchr & Asst Prin
Loozen, Paul L.
Chemistry Teacher
Lopez-Delute, Evangeline Cuerva
Pilipino & Spanish Teacher
Lunsford, Robert E.
Humanities Teacher
Lynch, William Christopher
Prof of Law & Associate Dean
MacAulay, Patricia Frances
Art Teacher & Dept Chairman
Macedo, Rita DeCassia
Spanish Teacher
Madkins, Lawrence H., Jr.
Eighth Grade Teacher
Masonbrink, Kay
Business Education Teacher
Matson, Carol Anderson
Fourth Grade Teacher
Matthews, Ardelle MarieDunlap
Sixth Grade Teacher
Matthews, Richard C.
Science & Health Chprsn
Mauricio, Colleen L.
English Teacher
McClain, Lynn Hollyfield
Counselor
Mc Claron, Duane Raynard
Resource Teacher
Mc Intyre-Lupien, Rosanna Christine
Science Teacher
Merrill, Jeanne Elizabeth
Band, Choral & Guitar Teacher
Miller, Betty J. Thornton
Second & Third Grade Teacher
Miller, Daniel Galen
English Teacher
Miller, William Barringer
Math & Science Teacher
Mobley, Michael Kevin
Sixth Grade Teacher
Molino, Michael
Math Teacher
Montgomery, Marion Horkay
8th Grade Teacher
Mora, Juan Manuel E.
Span Lit Teacher
Morgan, Dennis Eugene
Adv English & GATE His Tchr
Morgan, Ronald David
Computer Science Tchr & Coach
Morris, Rick
Fifth Grade Tchr & Trainer
Moss, Scott Howard
Sixth Grade Teacher
Mounier, Karen L.
Financial Marketing Teacher
Moura, Gualter DoRego
Mathematics Teacher
Murry, Joan B.
Assoc Dean, Professor & Adv
Napoleon, David Joseph
Math Department Chair
Naschak, Bruce Stephen
English Professor
Nelson, Daniel Craig
Music Education Professor
Newkirk, Elaine Mielnik
World & US History Teacher
Newman, C. Pat
Fifth Grade Teacher
Nold, Sharon (Saczko)
Teacher & Dept Chair
Page, Cynthia Clements
English as Second Lanuage Tchr
Parrinello, Michael John
Spanish & French Teacher
Patterson, James
Fifth Grade Teacher
Pelaez, Ileana
Spanish Teacher
Picconi, Irene Budzinsky
HS English Teacher
Pickford, Bette Marie
5th Grade Teacher
Pidgeon, Patrick Francis
Professor of Philosophy

Pisor, Jane Frances
Math Teacher
Porter, Judith Ann Domingos
5th Grd GATE & Cluster Teacher
Prewitt, Louise Jones
English & Humanities Teacher
Quinn, Teresa Bradford
Bus Ed Tchr & DECA Advisor
Quirin, Mary Jane Scaglione
Reading & ESL Teacher
Ralph, Jerome W.
World History Teacher
Rauch, Mark Victor
Biology Teacher
Reardon, Michael James
Humanities Teacher
Remillard, Bryan J.
Dean of Students
Renner, Scott A.
8th Grd Basic Education Tchr
Rion, George Paul
AP US History Teacher
Rodolff, Rebecca Cohenour
Professor & Academic Advisor
Roeder, Laurie Kim
PE Teacher & Coach
Rogness, Frances Elizabeth
Spanish Mentor Teacher
Rotsart, Ria Rebecca
Seventh Grade Teacher
Ruark, Diana Campagna-Pinto
His Teacher & Dept Chprsn
Ruz, Gabriel J.
Teacher
Sager, Timothy James
Biology & Phys Sci Teacher
Sale, Margaret Pitzinger
Biology Teacher
Saltamachio, Trudi Morgan
English Teacher
Schanberger, Joseph Anthony
Associate Professor of Math
Scherer, Lynn Anderson
Language Arts Teacher
Schlichting, Nancy Rogers
Spanish Teacher
Schmerbauch, Nancy Marie
Social Science & PE Teacher
Schwartz, Jim
English Teacher
Scott, Kristen H.
Second Grade Teacher
Scott, Michael
English Department Chairman
Shinn, Clifton Eugene, III
Sixth Grade Teacher
Shute, Duenise Louise (Sneathen)
Choral Music & US History Tchr
Slawson, Douglas James
AP US History Teacher
Slomanson, William Reed
Professor
Smalheer, Douglas Allen
Professor of History
Smith, Joan Helene (Rivell)
Fourth Grade GATE Teacher
Smith, Rosemarie Anzivino
English & Spanish Teacher
Snidecor, Gary Kurtz
Art Teacher
Snyder, Willard Shields, Jr.
Professor
Somes, Shirley Gray
Third Grade Teacher
Sommer, Linda Ann
Peer Counselor & English Tchr
Sparin, Mary E. (Cambron)
Choir & Drama Teacher
Sparks, Elizabeth Reeves
English Teacher & Dept Head
Stahlak, Pamela L.
Teacher of Gifted & Talented
Stolebarger, William Daniel
Bible, Yearbook Tchr & Ath Dir
Strovers, Andrea S.
Mathematics Teacher
Sudderth, Jennifer L.
Choir, Drama & Basic Comm Tchr
Sullivan, James
Mngmt & Ec Professor
Sullivan, Patrick Allen
Professor of Strategic Mgmt
Summer, Claire D.
Spanish Teacher
Swartz, Angela Sherry
Humanities Teacher
Swikard, Sandra
Humanities Dept Co-Chairperson
Taitano, Kristine Anne
Writers Workshop Teacher
Terry, Adele Marie
High School Pub Speaking Tchr
Thal, Donna Jean
Communicative Disorders Prof
Thomas, Dale Emery
HS English Teacher
Thomas, Kim Warren
Math & Computer Sci Teacher
Thompson, Christopher Allen
Teacher Assistant & Coach
Tobias, Hazel Sturnes
First Grade Teacher
Torns, Warren George
Director of Instrumental Music
Trevethan, Anne Lee
English & Journalism Teacher
Trotter, Philip Crawford
US & World History Teacher
Tuttle, Mark Francis
English Teacher

SAN DIEGO (cont)
Unden, John Robert
Computer Science Teacher
Underwood, Beulah Grant
Prof of Business Admin Dept
Valencia, Anthony A.
Spanish Teacher
Valentino, Mario R.
HS Advanced Mathematics Tchr
Visconti, Robin Shryock
English Teacher
Vogel, Walter Paul
College Counselor
Waisman, Marta
Spanish Teacher
Walker, Mary Grace
English Teacher
Walsh, Jeanne Gauthier
Administrator
Waynick, Deborah A.
History Instructor
Webb, Cynthia Heine
Kindergarten Teacher
Weiss, Brett Hirth-Vinik
English Teacher & AVID Coord
Wenger, Kirk Charles
Teacher
Whelan, Winifred Mednick
English Teacher
Williams, Susan Lynn
Prof of Biology & Dept Dir
Wilson, Terry L.
World History & Economics Tchr
Winters, Robert G.
Economics & Government Teacher
Wolf, Constance Jeanie
Teacher, Dept Chair & Mentor
Wood, Dina
Mathematics Teacher
Wood, Hadley H.
Professor of French
Woodfill, Brandie Ingle
5th Grade Teacher
Wright, Paul Eugene
Physics & Chemistry Teacher
Yaley, Kevin Charles
High School Teacher & Coach
Yankey, Kofi Ahwa
Economics & Math Professor
Yost, Joan Foster
English & Title I Tchr
Zeiger, Larry Elliott
Eng & Visual Prfrmng Arts Tchr
SAN DIMAS
Black, Christine Thompson
Home Economics Teacher
Coombs, Jim Le
Student Activities Director
Giangregorio, Kathleen Rea
8th Grade Teacher
Hemenover, Jeanne Bryant
English Teacher
Henry, Dora Leatrice Washington
Kindergarten Teacher
Keys, Jean C.
7th Grd His Tchr & Stu Act Dir
LaManna, Michael Bryan
Independent Study Teacher
Merica, Kay Marie Rhinehart
4th Grd & GATE Cluster Tchr
Pereda, Manfred John
English Teacher
Wallace, Mary Preston (Sandhagen)
Kindergarten & First Grd Tchr
Wiese, M. Faye
GATE Coordinator
Wolfe, Edward William, II
Instrumental Music Director
Zehe, Barbara Marie
First Grade Tchr & Vice Prin
SAN FERNANDO
Alves, Susan Moran
Elementary School Teacher
Bierling, Anne Marie (Sorensen)
Asst Prin, Coun, & Eng Instr
Bluestein, Stephen B.
Elementary School Teacher
Canale, Beryl Gregory
Instrumental Music & Fr Tchr
Huston, Lucy Solomon
Fifth Grade Teacher
Jones, Thomas Barcley, Jr.
Special Education Tchr & Coach
Kapiloff, Elizabeth Cowan
English & Humanities Teacher
Kazdoy, Jerry
English Teacher
Liebke, Julius Walter
Fifth Grade Tchr & Cmptr Coord
Mc Collum, Jean Adelle
Spanish Teacher & Dept Chprsn
Miller, Ceil Robin
Physical Ed Instructor
Petta, Laurena
7th & 8th Grd Teacher
Reiter, Edward Ronald
Sixth Grade Teacher
Rosenbloom, Herbert Gerson
Math Teacher
Salonius, Arlene Joyce
English Teacher
Snodgrass, James D.
Music Teacher
Swann, Amanda Gardiner
Drama Dept Chprsn & Eng Tchr
Werner, Susan L.
Sixth Grade Teacher
SAN FRANCISCO
Adams, Mary Elizabeth
History Instructor
Allen, Bret E.
Asst Principal & 8th Grd Tchr
Alter, Jack L., Jr.
Photography & Graphic Art Tchr
Alter, Joseph
Fine Arts & Religion Instr
Alton, Amy Elizabeth
English Teacher
Ames, Margaret Burns
5th Grade Teacher
Anthony, Valerie Moore
Director
Atienza, Araceli Reynoso
HS Social Studies Teacher
Austin, Beverly M.
Mathematics Teacher
Baccelli, Carole Ann
Coordinator of GATE Prog
Bargetto, Donna Christina
History & Literature Teacher
Barmore, Mat: Hanson
English Teacher
Bartolotti, Joanne Marie
Eighth Grade Mathematics Tchr
Batchelor, Karen Lee
ESL Instructor
Benacquista, John Joseph
Chem, Physics & Biology Tchr
Beresford, Gael
Mathematics Teacher
Bergin, Rosemary Rigney
Instructor of Nursing
Bernhardt, Roger
Professor of Law
Berston, Deborah
Second Grade Teacher
Bjorkquist, James Michael
English Teacher
Bogatsky, Ariadna Marie
Biology Instructor
Calvillo, Lucy
1st Grade Teacher
Canepa, Deborah Joan
English Teacher
Chang, Yvonne Y.
English & Computer Professor
Chiu, Betty Eng
Mathematics Teacher
Choi, Angie N.
English Teacher
Clark, Robert M., Jr.
Counselor
Clemenza, Ann Dee
Math & Science Teacher
Collins, Henry, Jr.
Admin of Justice & Fire Sci
Cortez, Doris Hamilton
ESL Instructor
Cruikshank, Margaret
Professor
da Rosa, Thais Josefina
Teacher
DeMeulenaere, Eric J.
Social Studies Teacher
DesMeules, Robert George
PE Teacher & Dept Head
Dewar, Cynthia E.
Prof of Speech Communication
Dietiker, Leslie C.
Math Tchr & Asst Dept Chair
Drummond, Judy
6th Grd Language Arts Teacher
Enderlin, Erin Phelan
Second Grade Teacher
Eng, Christine
English Teacher
Farquhar, Mary B.
German Teacher
Fong, Kevin Bruce
Physical Education Teacher
Fong-Tsukuda, Lois
Special Ed Instr & Cnslr
Frank, Jonathan James
Chemistry Teacher
Freed, Phillip Keoni
Biology Teacher & Coach
Gallegos, Matthew D.
His, Civics & Ec Teacher
Garabedian, Yeranouhi Chaghatzbanian
Dir of Armenian Stud
Garfield, Diane S.
5th Grade Teacher
Gill, Pamela R.
English Teacher
Goethals, Gregory Moen, SJ
Dir of Campus Min & Counselor
Greenhill, John L.
Technical Instuctor
Grier, Lynn
Vice Principal & 8th Grd Tchr
Groomes, Audrey E.
Head Counselor
Hagiwara, Tanako
PE Instr & Women's Ath Dir
Hansen, Carol L.
English Instructor
Hawthorne, Mark R.
Instr of Admin of Justice
Hayes, Earl
English & ESL Teacher
Heltsley, Christina
Former Teacher
Hess, Darrel Eugene
Geography Instructor
Hill, Ray Allen
Professor of Biology
Hjelle, Linda Loskutoff
Science Teacher
Hollander, Oscar
Chemistry Teacher
Holt, Daniel Victor
7th-8th Grd Soc Stud Teacher
Homan, Bonnie Muse
Business Professor
Hubbard, John H.
Commnctn Arts Acad Lead Tchr
Hunnicutt, Veronica Caresa
African Amer Stud & Eng Instr
Hyland, Bruce N.
Management Professor
Jacob, Frederick R.
German Teacher
Jacobsen, Rodger
Arts Instructor
Kalil, Jean M.
English Teacher
Kamkar, Rosemary Pozzuto
Stu Act Dir & Spec Ed Tchr
Kaneshiro, Dawn
Art Instructor
Killoran, Moira Gutman
Post Doctoral Fellow
Klein, Judy
HS Eng as a Second Lang Tchr
Kling, Fred E.
Instructor
Knecht, JoAnn
Chemistry & Biology Teacher
Kramer, Marlene Jean
Art Teacher
Krogh, Laurie Ellen
History, Govt & Acctng Teacher
Kuusisto, Sharyn Thompson
Spanish Professor
Lagumbay, Anita Koppin
English Teacher
Lai, George
Math Teacher
Lam, Carol
9th-12th Grade English Teacher
Law, Joshua Tin-Lok
Music Instructor
LeCuyer, James Macneill
English & Amer Lit Tchr
Lee, Theodore B.
Mathematics Instructor
Leung, Sau Christina Yue
Social Studies & Biling Tchr
Lew, Dora J.
Instructor
Ling, Gary A.
Mathematics Instructor
Lippi, Donald Gerard
History & Government Teacher
Lott, Lauren Harper
Biology Teacher
Lowe, James Edward
5th Grade Teacher
Lum, Alvin
Social Studies Teacher
Lum, Gregor
English Teacher
Lum, Jerry W.
Architectural Instructor
Lum, John B.
English Department Head
Lyons, Maryann L.
Literacy Specialist
Mallet, Cynthia A.
8th Grade Teacher
Mar-Beshears, Eleanor
ESL & English Teacher
Marshall, Robert A.
Managerial Accounting Teacher
Matthews, Robert Joseph
Math, Science & Lit Teacher
Mc Kleroy, Kaye
French Teacher
Meckler, Robert L.
Physiology Professor
Meggers, Sharon Pettit
Music & World Literature Tchr
Meyer, Frances E.
Math Teacher
Miller, David Anthony
Automotive Tech Instructor
Moore, Richard Lamar
Science Teacher
Morehen, Patricia E.
Math Teacher
Morel, Renee Christiane
French & Linguistic Instructor
Moriwaki, Glen T.
Art Instructor
Morris, Les R. W.
Teacher & Yearbook Adviser
Moscrip, Lynn F.
Teacher
Murphy, Kevin George
Physical Education Teacher
Nguyen, Lieu Ba
High School Teacher
Nickliss, Alexandra M.
History Professor
Ortiz, Jilma Ruth
Reading Recovery Teacher
Osipova, Georgiana Ponza
High School Spanish Teacher
Owens, E. Joyce
Behavioral Sci Teacher & Cnslr
Owyang-Lee, Sharon
Junior High School Teacher
Pacheco, Irma Josefina
5th Grade Teacher
Padua, Joseph H.
Decision Making Cnslr, Instr
Panelli, Marilyn Musante
Kindergarten Teacher
Pardini, David Eugene
English & Journalism Teacher
Patterson, Catherine Hope (Pike)
Social Studies Teacher
Peart, Judy D.
Fifth Grade Teacher
Powell, Robert L., Jr.
Army Instruction Director
Provence, Mary Ann Hurley
Math Teacher
Reinertson, Barbara Jo
6th Grade Core & Art Teacher
Richards, Hal S.
Music Teacher
Rodatos, Loys Daskarolis
PE, Modern Greek & Eng Teacher
Rohrbach, Carol Joan
Math Dept Chairperson
Rouder, Susan
Instr of Political Science
Ruzhinsky, Alexandr P.
Upper Math Tchr & Dept Chprsn
Sanazaro, Leonard Rollo
English Instructor
Schachtel, Roger Bernard
English Teacher
Schlesinger, Lester Edward
Experiential Education Tchr
Schnitzer, Robert Jay
English Teacher
Seale, James
Bilingual Social Studies Tchr
Settles, William Calvin
Music Director
Shapiro, Margaret Goodwin
Instructor of Astronomy
Slaughter, Randi
Instructor of ESL
Smith, Jane
Primary Instr of EMT
Spencer, Marc Harold
History Teacher
Steele, Jim A.
8th Grade Science Teacher
Stein, Aliyah
Psychology Prof
Stering, Edward Lee
Spanish Instructor
Stickney, Hugh S.
Construction Teacher
Stillwater, Jason
Antique Furniture Restorer
Strauhal, Walter Martin
High School Math Teacher
Strebel, John Philip
Gifted & Talented Pgm Teacher
Tagaloa, Val F.
7th Grade Teacher
Tajeldin, Sara Rankin
History Teacher
Takemoto, Kiyoko Numata
Japanese Teacher
Tam, Judy Choy
Mathematics Teacher
Tang-Quan, Ethel Beal
Speech Professor
Texson, Henry Teko
Economics Instructor
Thomas, Michael Patrick
Counseling Dept Chairperson
Tillman, Betty Banks
English Teacher
Tomczak, Tom John
ESL & Eng Teacher
Ton-Tho, Te
Science Mentor Teacher
Tray, Ken Scott
Social Studies Teacher
Tse, Janet Lee
Lang Arts & Social Stud Tchr
Valverde, Ottilie M.
Campus Ministry Dir, Math Tchr
Vanderveen, Karen Maria (Crawley)
Religious Studies Teacher
Wang, Tien Rita
Instructor
Ware, Nancy Webster
Upper School Principal
Warner, Rollin Miles, Jr.
Math & Economics Teacher
Watts, Theresa Bayze
Spanish Teacher
Won, Cynthia Jane
French & Mandarin Teacher
Wong, Wen Yee Chin
ESL, Cantonese & PE Instr
Wright, Karen Michelle
English Teacher
Yansane, Aguibou M. Y.
Professor of Political Economy
Yee, Lawrence
Math Dept Chm & Teacher
Zanetto, Janet S. (Schregardus)
Instr of English as a 2nd Lang
SAN GABRIEL
Catanese, Gloria
Kindergarten Teacher
Dare, Marilyn
Mathematics Teacher
De Los Santos, Blanca Maria
Spanish Teacher & Dept Chair
Donnelly, Michael Timothy
Cnslr & Dir of Peer Resources
Fithian, Vivian Ilene (Hurd)
Assistant Principal
Fujimoto, Carla
Physical Education Teacher
Garcia, Beatrice, RSM
Cmps Mnstr & Sr Rel Stud Tchr
Garcia, Raquel M.
Business Ed Tchr & Dept Chair
Heinrich, Paul
Math Teacher
Heinrich, Sharron Lynne
Soc Sci Dept Chm & His Tchr
Housh, David Bruce
Fifth Grade Teacher
Humbert, Tony
Life Science Teacher
Junkunc, Sandor John
5th Grade Teacher
Kanow, Larry D.
Chemistry & Physics Teacher
Morales, Sabrina
Secondary Eng & Careers Tchr
Ryan, Jerry W.
Government & Economics Teache
Slagle, Stephen H.
English Teacher & Yearbook Adv
Stai, Carol A.
Retired Elementary Schl Tchr
Torres Rangel, Evelyn
Computer Sci & Math Teacher
Zafonte, Barbara Palmer
Chemistry & Physics Teacher
SAN JACINTO
Hebenton, Lori Muschell
PE & Quest Teacher
Razavi, Shahla Rose
Assistant Professor of Math
Stange, Sherri
8th Grade Science Teacher
Turley, Robert Louis
Mgmt, Bus & PE Instructor
Whittenburg, Jeff Dee
Wood Technology Teacher
SAN JOAQUIN
Lindsey-Allen, Pam Taylor
Third Grade Teacher
SAN JOSE
Abeln, Barbara Jean
Physical Education Teacher
Adams, Marshall
Mathematics Teacher
Aguiar, Robert Anthony
Art & Yearbook Teacher
Alkire, Lee Fletcher
Music & Choral Teacher
Allen, Bruce T.
English Teacher
Alonzo, Julie Ann
English Teacher
Ancar, Keith Owen
Native Amer Educl Specialist
Anderson, Margo (Smelser)
8th Grade Teacher
Avila, Zeferina F.
Spanish Teacher
Baggett, Toni Thul
Elementary Teacher
Baird, Susan E.
Counselor
Bergantz, Megan Starr
World History Teacher
Bernstein, James D.
High School Math Teacher
Bierman, Katha Hinrichs
Math & Algebra Teacher
Bishel, Sloan Coley
Math Instructor & Dept Chprsn
Bliss, Marilyn June
Science Teacher
Blythe, William
Professor of Civil Engineering
Boac, Thelma Blantucas
Coord of Eld & Sheltered
Bohart, Jo Ann Vetrosky
ESL & Spanish Teacher
Bowden, Cynthia Ann
History & Language Arts Tchr
Briscoe, Ron T.
7th & 8th Grade Math Teacher
Brooks, Neil Barry
Mathematics Teacher
Broussard, Cathy Rodriguez
Social Studies Teacher
Brown, Barbara Gene Zahner
English Teacher & Dept Chair
Brown, Warren S.
German & History Teacher
Buchanan, Robert Bruce
Sixth Grade Teacher
Bullock, Sandra Saito
Fifth Grade Teacher
Burchard, Betty Koch
High School English Teacher
Byrd, Mildred Lynell
6th-8th Grade Choir Teacher
Byron, Denise Elizabeth
English Teacher
Cahn, Mark Edward
Sci Tchr & Co-Chair Dept Head
Campbell, Sylvia S.
Assistant Principal
Caracciolo, Caroline Perrotti
English Teacher
Cargill, Delpha Marie
HS English Tchr & Dept Head
Carlson, John Albert
5th & 6th Grd Combination Tchr
Caselli, Lorna Andreatta
Kindergarten Teacher
Cerny, Dan Benjamin
English & Reading Teacher
Certa, Diego Dino
Head Counselor
Chai, Hi-Dong
Prof of Electrical Engineering
Chambers, Yvonne Deloris Flowers
English Teacher

OSE (cont)
an, R. Gordon
Counselor
I.
Instructor
, Kathryn Long
sh Teacher
s, Jacqueline Wilkerson
l Art Teacher
ll, Michael Harold
Grade Teacher
Ronald Gary
irector & Yrbk Advisor
, Bruce William
Grade Teacher
ebecca Snyders
selor
Dolores Ann (Reda)
d Grade Teacher
, Donna R.
sh Teacher
Rosa, Alfredo
sh Teacher
ant, Kermit Daniel
Grade Teacher
nner, Karen
tor of Public Relations
ey, Christopher Gray
ology Teacher
como, Richard
ry Teacher
Debra R.
cs Teacher
nz, Joan Butteweg
Grade Teacher
Kellye
Educator
guez, Ronald Francis
School Teacher
Gene Joseph
ctor of Biology
Susan Foster
n & Photo I Teacher
Richard Oswald
of Electrical Engineering
Josephine Helene
l Arts Coordinator
Michael William
l Arts Coordinator
felder, Thomas Andrew
Teacher
Thomas Roger
ce Teacher
nk, Victoria Amick
gy Tchr & Sci Dept Chprsn
Beatrice Marie
rade Teacher
John M.
tor of Instrumental Music
e, Jack
sh & Biblical Stud Tchr
Susan Ehle
sh Teacher
Rebecca Ann
of Students
Rodrigo Martinez
endent Studies Instructor
, Susan Barbara
sh Teacher & Dept Chm
, Nancy S.
th Grade Lang Arts Tchr
, John Luis, Jr.
ry & Science Teacher
th, Sally M.
School French Teacher
ere, Heather Hendry
gn Language Dept Chair
Mary E.
ematics Teacher
, Shirley Herr
& Piano Keyboard Teacher
, Louis Roland
outer Science Teacher
y, Carol Kauffman
eacher
obles, Christine
Teacher
, Barbara Jo
th Grade Teacher
mer, Janet Leslie
sh Teacher
mer-Escobar, Janet Leslie
sh Teacher
James E.
ematics Teacher
rg, Stephen Alan
ipal & 8th Grade Teacher
r, Frederick William
Tchr & Science Dept Chm
Donna Rae
nd Grade Teacher
Evan D. H.
stant Professor
, Susan Shepherd
nce Teacher
ka, Eugene
Teacher
Linda J.
Dept Chm & Guidance Cnslr
Terry E.
ematics Teacher
ndez, Manuel Fonseca
ish Teacher
ndez, Richard Alexander
th & Drivers Ed Tchr
Kenneth Duane
tre & Fine Arts Dept Chair
an, Linda
eacher & Soc Stud Chair

Howard, Nancy Milligan
8th Grade Math Teacher
Hsu, Ping
Associate Professor
Hunter, Robert Nelson
Physical Education Teacher
Intersimone, Barbara Uebel
English Teacher
Jackson, Kenneth Bernard
Bus Law & Keyboarding Teacher
James, Elizabeth House
English Teacher
Johnson, Margaret Sjea
AP Calculus & Geometry Teacher
Johnston, Judith Unruh
High School Math Teacher
Jones, Nedra Corrinne
Social Science Teacher
Kasaitis, Patricia K.
8th Grade Language Arts Tchr
Keller, Diana Britton
Desktop Publishing & Art Tchr
Keller, Richard C.
Mathematics Teacher
Kennedy, Ruth Mitchell
Second Grade Teacher
Kerr, Cindy Lightner
Math Teacher
Kick, Paul D.
English & Journalism Teacher
Kimura, Kristine Lori
Math Teacher
Kinn, Christopher Kevin
Physical Education Teacher
Kjelstrom, Maryann Lee
3rd Grade Teacher
Klassen, Gloria Teves
Mathematics Teacher
Klick, Mark William
Math & ESL Teacher
Knight, John N., Jr.
Gifted & Social Studies Tchr
Korbel, Daniel Joseph
English & Yearbook Teacher
Labozetta, Robert Joseph
History Teacher
Lake, Corinne
Sixth Grade Teacher
Laxier, Reed B.
Fifth Grade Teacher
Lee, Francis Chuck
Science Teacher
Lewis, Alphonse Vincent
Music & English Teacher
Ligamaro, Marlene Kulzer
Fourth Grade Teacher
Llovio, Ray R.
Bible & Spanish Teacher
Lorenz, Virgil Glenn
Jr HS Teacher
Love, Matthew Torrance
Science Department Chair
Lyle, Thomas Graham
Lit, Leadership & Act Dir Tchr
Mancuso, Anthony Joseph
Teacher, Chaplain & Counselor
Mandell, Carl A.
7th & 8th Grade Science Tchr
Mangan, Kathleen Delaney
Middle School Teacher & Mentor
Mani, Padma
Mathematics Teacher
Marc, Judith Lynne (Reger)
French & English Teacher
Martinez, Nelson E.
English Teacher
Matalone, Fredric Joseph, Jr.
Independent Study Teacher
Mc Isaac, Sandra (West)
Secondary Mathematics Teacher
Mc Pherson, Annie Mijanovich
Fifth Grade Teacher
Merritt, Claire M.
Third Grade Teacher
Miller, Edna Garcia
Mathematics Teacher
Miller, Lou Dwight
Mathematics & Science Teacher
Mourtos, Nikos J.
Associate Professor
Nakano, Lynn Hanamoto
2nd Grade Teacher
Nelson, Gail (Milligan)
5th & 6th Grade Teacher
Nieman, Francis Paul
German & Spanish Teacher
Nino, Kathleen Grace
English Teacher
Novotny, Steve A.
I B Computer Studies Instr
Okada, Barbara Dillard
8th Grade Language Arts Tchr
Owczarzak, Frank E.
AP US & European His Teacher
Owczarzak, Jane Boyd
Jrnlsm & Eng Tchr
Ozemek, Haluk Sabri
Computer Engineering Dept Chm
Palmer, Joy Finley
Biology Teacher & Dept Chair
Parker, Kirk Hale
Freshman Tchr & Spirit Advisor
Pernicka, Henry John
Assoc Prof, Aerospace Engrng
Peters, Art
Social Science Teacher
Pflughaupt, Jane Ramsey
Math Teacher
Pham, Victor Bich Minh
High School Academic Counselor

Pierson, Patricia Elaine
Dance Tchr, Dept Chair & Coord
Pimentel, Robert L.
Chemistry Honors Teacher
Pollock, Steven Paul
English Teacher
Porush, Ken
Chem & Advncd Plcmt Chem Tchr
Poynter, Robert Addison
PE Teacher & Dept Head
Ramonda, Janine Anne
Kindergarten & 1st Grade Tchr
Randazzo, Patricia Aboud
Govt & Economics Teacher
Rao, Martha Carole (Blust)
Social Studies Teacher
Rasmussen, William Allen
Sophomore Honors English Tchr
Renteria, Marilyn Patricia Horton
Seventh Grd Lang Arts Tchr
Ring, Jeffrey Harrison
Physics & Chemistry Teacher
Robinson, Sandra A.
Third Grade Teacher
Rocha, Debbie Elizabeth
English & Dance Teacher
Rodericks, Bev Mandell
First Grade Teacher
Russell, Brian J.
Spanish Teacher & Coach
Samples, Dorothea Sadowski
Third Grade Teacher
Scadina-Bertoldo, Christine Anne
Dance Instr & Choreographer
Schneider, Patrick Bernard
Algebra II Teacher
Schram, Delwynne Skotland
Fourth Grade Teacher
Scoppettone, Ka-Ling Siao
Business Teacher
Scullion, Michael Charles
History & English Teacher
Serimian, Darlene Carol
Kindergarten Teacher
Severance, Amber (Metheny)
Government & Bible Teacher
Shahriari, Darioush
Former Physician & Tutor
Shannon, Pamela A.
Second Grade Teacher
Sherman, Kevin Scott
Vocational Agriculture Instr
Shores, Sheldon S.
Math Teacher
Simpson, William L.
Mathematics Teacher
Snively, Sandra G.
Teacher & Department Chair
Soli, Rosalina Maciel
Discovery Center Coordinator
Sondreal, Wayne S.
Math Teacher
Spano, Shawn Joseph
Communication Professor
Squire, Eleanor Jane
Core Teacher
Stanek, Rachel Marie
English Teacher
Stephan, Craig
English Instructor
Stride, Burt
German & Spanish Teacher
Struck, Carrie Waldschmidt
Former Teacher
Sul, David A.
Lecturer
Sumwalt, Martha Roskosz
Substitute Teacher
Swartz, Margery Maurer
Third Grade Teacher
Swenson, Joni Takuma
Instrumental Music Teacher
Thelen, Arlene Reed
Third Grade Teacher
Tomasso, Richard Vincent
Physics & Math Teacher
Tornberg, Kenneth John
Retired 8th Grd His Teacher
Tsai, Kuei-Wu
Associate Dean of Engineering
Turner, John
English Teacher
Utsumi, Gary E.
5th & 6th Grade Teacher
Uyeda, Judy Shintani
Kindergarten Teacher
Voss, Jane Williams
US & World Literature Teacher
Vukazich, Steven Martin
Asst Prof
Walker, Jim Rex
Director & Instructor
Weir, Michael Drew
Technology Teacher
White, Laura Marie
Spanish Teacher
White, Michael Eric
English Teacher
Wilkinson, Bruce K.
English Teacher
Wright, Douglas John
AP US History Teacher
Yellum, Don F.
English Teacher
Young, Richard R.
Special Education Teacher
Zisch, Rosaleen Burton
Soc Stud & Lang Arts Tchr

SAN JUAN CAPO
Bath, Robert Michael
Integrated Sci & Tech Tchr
Clark, Cheri Caudill
Jr High Science Teacher
Debalski, Thomas Earl
English Teacher & Dept Chprsn
Dougherty, Joanne Ruth
5th Grade Teacher
Easter, Donald Eugene
Mathematics & Science Teacher
Hensley, Carmen Antoinette
Elem Instrumental Music Tchr
Munoz, Jayne C.
English Teacher
Novak, Patricia Murray
English & Bible Teacher
Temple, Carol A.
4th Grade Teacher
Walker, Andrea (Schneider)
Advanced Science Teacher
Wilson, Cynthia Ann
Third Grade Teacher
SAN LEANDRO
DeRuig, Roger K.
History Teacher
Gage, Jack S.
Jr HS Geography & His Teacher
Hom, Robin S.
Assistant Superintendent
Jacobs, Nancy Duns
English & History Teacher
Lee, Lanny J.
Art Teacher
Lee-France, Jacquelyn Kristine
Lang Arts & Soc Science Tchr
Lim, Margo Tsang
Fifth Grade Teacher
Liston, Rita Juslea
2nd Grade Teacher
Louie, Stephanie Low
Fifth Grade Teacher
Mahr, Matilda
Science Teacher & Dept Chair
Mc Daniel, Mark O.
English & Yearbook Teacher
Mealing, Dean C.
US History & Phys Science Tchr
O'Callaghan, Monica Mary
English Teacher
Ramirez, Mary Lou Juras
Eighth Grade Teacher
Richmond, William O'Neal
Music Teacher
Tobin, Sean Patrick
Director of Student Activities
Vonderleid, Charles Louis
Science Teacher
SAN LORENZO
Billings, Millard F.
High School Counselor
Camezon, Mary Elizabeth
English Teacher & Dept Chair
Clinton, Carrie A.
HS Computer & Spanish Teacher
Hart, Ronald Brent
Chemistry & Physics Teacher
Hathwell, David Ronald
High School English Teacher
Hennick, Linda Parker
English & Humanities Teacher
Jorgensen, Jeffrey Moody
Science & Math Teacher
Kramm, Alice C.
Retired Teacher
Levy, Albert Lawrence
Chemistry Teacher
Marti, Andre Niklaus
Mathematics Dept Chair & Tchr
Ostrander, Kerry Ann
6th Grade Teacher
Phillips, Peggie L.
Assoc Dean of Instr Basic Sci
Ray, Suzanne Louise
Physio, Path Prof & Dept Chair
Rodrigues, James Edward
Marketing Instructor
Sarchett, Diana Roselyn
Social Sci Tchr & Dept Chair
Stearns, Roman J.
Dir of Stu Act & Span Teacher
Tucher, Philip
Math Teacher
Visperas, Romier S.
Radiologic Technologist Instr
Wells, Robin
English Teacher
West-Henisz, Marcia
French & History Teacher
Wigand, Robert
Physical & Life Science Tchr
SAN LUIS OBISPO
Allen, Richard F.
Vocational Agriculture Teacher
Anderson, David Ernest
Span, Sr Rel, Fr & Latin Tchr
Batistic, Darla Jean
Second Grade Teacher
Boaz, Steve
Math Teacher & Track Coach
Cross, William R.
Mathematics Teacher
Davis, M. LeRoy
Dept Head & Prof of Agribus
Elijah, Anaundda
Teacher of Handicapped
Francis, Mike B.
Teacher
Franklin, R. John
History Tchr & AVID Prgm Coord

Gooden, Marylou Barker
6th Grade Teacher
Kaufman, Jon Michael
Math & PE Teacher
Laney-Kobata, Colleen
Substitute Academic Teacher
Marsala, Susan Marie
Professor
Mc Neill, Carol Minton
Diving Coach & Accountant
Ruggles, Joanne Beaule
Art Professor
SAN MARCOS
Barrett, Kevin
Associate Prof of Adm Justice
Bell, Andrea G.
Professor of English
Boyajian, David Armen
Professor of Chemistry
Branch, Robert Hardin
Assoc Prof of Comm, Radio-TV
Christ, Julie Ann (Strickland)
English Teacher
Corpora, Angelo J.
Bus Ed & Paralegal Stud Prof
Dowd, Bonnie Ann
Assoc Professor of Business
Eckhart, Judith Grier
Associate Professor of Nursing
Erickson, John Robert
Assoc Prof of Frgn Langs
Esteban, Jose L.
Assistant Prof of Economics
Golden, Phyllis Ann
Spanish Teacher
Gowen, Brent D.
English Professor
Green, Richard J.
5th Grade Teacher
Greenberg, Rosario Diaz
Spanish Teacher
Ingham, Charles Andrew
Associate Professor of English
Kentner, Edward George
Adj Prof of Chemistry
Miller, Robert Thomas
Behavioral Sci Dept Chrmn
Newbrough, Michael G.
Professor of Political Science
Paes de Bairos, Deborah Rohrer
Assistant Professor of English
Pederson, Currie
Ballet Instructor
Puchi, Frank Mario
Associate Prof of Counseling
Sager, Gene Charles
Prof of Philosophy & Rel Stud
Saw, James T.
Associate Professor of Art
Scurlock, Carol A. (Tarter)
6th Grade Teacher
Spear, Steven G.
Assoc Prof of Geology & Geog
Trujillo, Alan P.
Assoc Professor of Earth Sci
Valdez, John Eduardo
Assc Prof of Chicano Lit & His
Whitehorse, David Michael
Assoc Prof, Dir Prof Programs
Zolliker, Susan Beth
English Instructor
SAN MARINO
Barbarics, Barbara Preas
English Teacher
Bush, Paula Ruth
Chem, Earth & Phys Sci Tchr
Cameron, Dougal Scott
Science Dept Chair
Chambers, Brian
Fifth Grade Teacher
Chubbuck, Cynthia Lyn
Chemistry Teacher
Corporon, Vicki Sanders
Eng, Cmptr, Arch & Music Tchr
Ford, Stephen Gualdo
Resource Specialist
Hall, Ellen Tirone
English & Social Studies Tchr
Hall, Kevin Berry
Teacher & Coach
Irie, David Kiyoshi
Social Studies Teacher
Kirk, Raymon W.
College Counselor
Koiles, Jereld N.
Technology Instructor
Koiles, Kristen Hanson
French Instructor
Lutes, Robert Charles
Spanish Teacher
Schulte, Paul James
Biology & Physics Teacher
SAN MATEO
Allen, Leslie J.
Biology Teacher
Baines, Darlene Mahelona
Business & Language Arts Tchr
Balbi, Barbara
Math & Religion Teacher
Bedford, Susan Rives
Eng, Hum Tchr & Curr Dvlpr
Bonnell, William Charles
English & Latin Teacher
Borchelt, Stephen Paul
8th Grade Teacher
Burke, Lisa Annette
Senior English Teacher
Daugherty, Ellyn A.
Biology Tchr & Sci Dept Chprsn

SAN MATEO (cont)
Del Gaudio, Christine Susanne
AP US History & Hum Tchr
Finander, Stephanie
Physics & Calculus Teacher
Francisco, Elizabeth Mangum
Eighth Grade English Teacher
Frantz, Christy L.
AP English Teacher
Friedman, Bradley Kenneth
Drama Teacher
Hall, Susan Corwin
English Teacher
Henderson, Steven Martin
History Teacher
Hession, Joseph Michael
English & Journalism Teacher
Lyons, Manota C.
Retired Elem Teacher
Mc Cabe, Ellen, OSF
English Teacher
Mc Ginley, William Michael
History & Government Teacher
Nawas, Paula Kim
HS Math Teacher
Peterson, Sandra Michele
Former Bilingual Teacher
Pleis, Wayne Francis
Chemistry Tchr & Sci Dept Chm
Ragan, W. Kevin
Spanish Teacher
Smith, James LaBorn
Social Studies Teacher
Stennet, Joan F.
Music Teacher
Stucke, Debra L.
High School Math Teacher
Sullivan, Thomas E.
English Teacher
Tribuzi, Atillio
Music Director
Usher, Lorraine M.
Science Teacher
Viotti, Beverly Jean Bilafer
Religion Teacher & Vice Prin
Vogel, Randy K.
Admissions Dir & Math Teacher
SAN PABLO
Duvall, James Grafton, III
Social Science Dept Chair
Rose, D. Candy Ferkovich
President
Smith, Suzanne de Roo
Reading & English Teacher
SAN PAULA
Coughlin, R. Glen
Tutor
SAN PEDRO
Addison, Claire K.
English & Social Studies Tchr
Armstrong, Maria J. (Guttivergi)
7th Grade Teacher
Brown, Roberta Baer
6th Grade & English Teacher
Bruhnke, Aaron John
Govt, US His & Economics Tchr
Henkel, Susan Diane
Eng Tchr & Peer Cnslng Coord
Kizu, June Wakasa
Teacher
Lucero, Stevan Arturo
5th Grade Teacher
Martin-Alveranga, Sandy
English Teacher & Ldrshp Adv
Mc Gilvray, Brenda Gail
Social Studies Dept Chprsn
Messih, Matt
English Teacher
Mitchell, Marianne
Counselor
Muller, Irene Duran
Bilingual Kindergarten Teacher
Nakakura, Kenneth
Drafting Teacher
Ryle, Sheila Havens
Mentor, Tchr & Perf Arts Chm
Sasaki, Sally Lee
Third Grd Math & Science Tchr
Spinelli, Margaret (Graziano)
Kndgtn & Schl Imprvmnt Coord
Wheeler, Sharon Gaddis
2nd Grade Teacher
Zorotovich, Nicholas Dale
Social Studies Teacher
SAN RAFAEL
Biegel, Richard Lewis
Adjunct Professor of Business
Duncan, Susan Katherine
French Teacher & Counselor
Hellman, Theodore Albert, III
US History Teacher
Kuminoff, Dale L.
Spanish Teacher
Lack, Larry L.
Science Teacher
Letsos, Nick M.
5th Grade Teacher
Mc Guinn, Louise Rolfes
Fourth Grade Teacher
Mohn, Cristina Gonzalez
Spanish Teacher
Moon, Florence R.
Elem Curr Instr, Stu Tchr Supv
Moyer, Phoebe Elinor
Theater & Dance Teacher
Peabody, Mark A.
High School Music Teacher
Peters, Michael
PE & Health Tchr & Dept Chair
Skinner, Patrick
English Teacher
Stefanski, Mark
Science Teacher
Workman, Timathea Shays
English Teacher
Zellers, Scott P.
Physical Education Teacher
SAN RAMON
Adams, Maria Isabel Gonzales
Third Grade Teacher
Bitnoff, Julie A.
Biology Teacher
Blasquez, Mary Paschal
Performing Arts & Speech Tchr
Faber, Dianne Giddens
Chemistry Teacher
Hansen, Margaret
First Grade Teacher
Knudson, Connie R.
Sixth Grade Teacher
Lewis, Edwin W.
Civics & Psychology Teacher
Mc Cullum, Marybeth
English Tchr & Stu Govt Adv
Paschal, Mary Lou Vitori
Sixth Grade Teacher
Rego, Jon J.
Spanish Teacher
Schaffer, Marlene L. (Kephart)
5th-6th Grd Acad Talent Tchr
Schneider, Lydia Merlo
English Teacher
Steinberg, Carol Hartgogian
English Teacher
SAN YSIDRO
Dunn, Maura Lynn
Third Grade Teacher
Lozada, Ray T.
Physical Education Teacher
Roberts, Josephine
English & Lit Instructor
Rodriguez, Gustavo C.
Music Teacher
Sharpe, Margo May
Art Teacher
SANGER
Brown, Jeffery A.
High School Math Teacher
Gutierrez, Sam, Jr.
Third Grade Teacher
Leal, Lydia Garcia
Sixth Grade Bilingual Teacher
Leone, Robert Wayne
Naval Science Instr
Najarian, E. Jeanne
7th-8th Grd Language Arts Tchr
Torosian, Christine Der
Third Grade Teacher
SANTA ANA
Aceves, June Magarro
ROP Invest Tchr
Anderson, R. Genevieve
Professor Emeritus
Anderson, Sheryl Leigh
Fourth Grade Teacher
Anthony, Mary Anne A.
Mathematics Professor
Antink, Suzannah Dodson
French Teacher
Aust, Diane
Teacher & Activity Director
Babayan, Diana Lee
Professor of English
Bales, Terry Wallace
Video Communications Dept Chm
Balma, Violette Ann
Choral Music Teacher
Bartholio, Mark Douglas
English Teacher
Beazell, James Waltham
Life Science Instructor
Beigbeder, Frank Richard
Accounting Professor
Beverley, Dale Alan
Math Teacher
Blackie, James Randall
Earth Science Teacher
Blankinship, Joan Pelch
Vice Prin & Jr HS Math Tchr
Bliznik, Marian Bruce
RSP & Special Ed Teacher
Burns, Judith Scott
Second Grade Teacher
Cameron, Christine
Math Teacher
Cogan, Jan Adrienne
Spanish Teacher
Corlett, Barbara Bradford
English Teacher
Davis, Deborah Diehl
Language Arts Teacher
Davis, Lenard Eugene
World His & Journalism Teacher
Davis, Susan Jane (White)
3rd-4th Grade Teacher
Doering, Robert Reid
History & Language Arts Tchr
Drake, Barry Lynn
Algebra Teacher
Eddy, Charles Christopher
Mathematics Teacher
Ellis, Gregory Scott
Vocal Music Teacher
Espinosa, Jose Manuel, Jr.
Professor of History
Fischer, Margery Carlson
Religious Studies Teacher
Fisher, Claudina Parra
AP Spanish Literature Teacher
Garner, S. Christopher
Latin & History Teacher
Gitthens, Sidney Leon, Jr.
English Teacher & Sr Class Adv
Hattendorf, Hope Ann
Mathematics Teacher
Hibben, Jean Wilcox
Speech Comm Adjunct Professor
Higgins, Jeffrey Thomas
Vice Principal
Hodges, Robert Steven, OPRA
Religious Studies Teacher
Hugh, Patricia Stoup
Vice Prin, Amer His & Eng Tchr
Hughes, Susan Byrnes
Mathematics Teacher
Kaliski, Lucy Anne
Anatomy, Physiology & Bio Tchr
Kasper, Joan Ciesielski
HS English & Journalism Tchr
Katnic, Tanya Reminiskey
English & Journalism Advisor
Kazanjy, Catherine Carey
1st Grade Teacher
Klingler, Lynne M.
Language Arts Chprsn & Teacher
Klink, Alisa Marie
English Teacher
Kutch, Marye Lizabeth
Art Instructor
La-Pham, Khoan
English & Social Studies Tchr
Laurie, Jan Renee
Drama & Dance Teacher
Leeds, Kelvin Boone
Secondary Mathematics Teacher
Lucero, Joan Hendry
Assistant Principal
Ludden, Genevieve Lee
Spanish Teacher
Mansfield, Patricia Lucas
Assoc Prof Anatomy & Psych
Marecek, LYnn Brown
Assistant Prof of Mathematics
Mazza, Sally Morrow
5th Grade Elementary Teacher
McCracken, Dulcie Ramsey
Senior Academic Counselor
Morgan, Lisa Pike
Science Teacher
Myers, Sally Jo
Fifth Grade Teacher
Napier, Rodney Scott
Physical Education Teacher
Nguyen, Lau Van
Electronics Professor
Nichols, Suzanne Cutler
6th Grade Teacher
Osle, Lizette
Spanish Teacher
Roberts, Janet Lekowski
Elementary Teacher
Rogers, Richard Michael
Dean of Students
Rollinson, Bruce Robert
US History Teacher
Sadler, Dennis
Career Counselor
Saiza, Jeanne Rice
Social Studies Teacher
Stark, Marilyn Jane (Tharp)
Science & Math Teacher
Steves, Helen Ann
Director of Campus Ministry
Stringer, Martin R.
Soc Stud Tchr & Soccer Coach
Stuckey, Elaine Bartley
English Teacher
Sullivan, Mary
Spanish Teacher
Thoma Lundberg, Patricia Louise
7th & 8th Grade History Tchr
Trivanovich, Valerie Salata
High School English Teacher
Waibel, George
Instrumental Music Director
Whitesell, Scott Bradley
Geography Teacher
Wilson, Kathy Tartol
Learning Specialist
Yamada, Ted Kiyoshi
Asst Prof & Chemistry Dept Chr
Young, Terry Martin
Physical Education Teacher
SANTA BARBARA
Bower, Travis M.
High School Math Teacher
Buckley, Sheela Beisell
Preschool Special Ed Teacher
Dawson, Rodger A.
Humanities Teacher
Dovgin, Richard Joseph
Retired English Teacher
Ellington, Jacqueline Halvorsen
Jr High English & Art Teacher
Erickson, Robert Allen
Professor of English
Grapard, Allan Georges
Japanese Religious His Prof
Hill, Roger Colin
Computer Teacher & Coordinator
Jacobson, Melanie Ann
Humanities Teacher
Kay, John Dick
Professor of Political Science
Mantyla, Susan Madith
Psychology Professor
Miller, M. Lawrence
Eng & Creative Writing Teacher
Millward, Jody
Professor of English
Nedler, Kenneth Alton
American History Teacher
Orr, Joel Yancey
Fifth Grade Teacher
Paulson, Shelise Lishman
Mathematics Teacher
Purcell, Clifden G.
Counselor & Consultant
Reinhart, Margarete Louise
Professor of Mathematics
Reuter, Diane K.
Tchr & Interdepartment Chair
Svoboda, Carri Lynn
8th Grade English Teacher
Tro, Nivaldo J.
Associate Professor of Chem
Vander Mey, Randall John
Associate Professor of English
White, C. Dana
English Teacher
Wilson, Jonathan Reford
Religion Professor
SANTA CLARA
Avila, Adrian Henry
Instr of CAO & CAM
Bell, Robert Robinson
English & Social Studies Tchr
Budisch, Joyce Vanderbeek
8th Grd Social Studies Teacher
Carroll, Mary J.
Religion, Music & Drama Tchr
Currie, David Alan
HS Phys Ed Teacher & Coach
Dawson, Catherin Cohagen
Levels 1-5 & AP French Teacher
Edwards, Dianne Murray
Mentor & SIP Facilitator
Farris, Frank A.
Associate Professor
Fedder, Steven Lee
Senior Lecturer in Chemistry
Haggerty, Elaine Hazel
French Teacher
Heideman, Elizabeth Breckenridge
2nd Grade Teacher
Holmgren, Carol Hagan
Resource Specialist
Humphrey, John Edward
Eighth Grd His & Eng Tchr
Johnston, Robert James
Kindergarten Teacher
Lau, David O. L.
Math Dept Chair
Louie, Nathan
Fifth Grade Educator
Mackie, Mary Alice
Spanish Teacher
Martin, Sonia Missirlian
English Teacher
Martin, Susan Rust
7th Grade Science Teacher
Mc Neil, Judy Rominger
4th Grade Teacher
Pine, Larry Warren
Fourth Grade Teacher
Poppema, Lois Holdwerda
English Teacher
Pringle, Lynn M.
Asst Prof of Accounting
Ross, Peter
Senior Lecturer in Mathematics
Serrette, Reynaud Louis
Engineering Professor
Shefrin, Hersh M.
Finance Professor
Shunk, Nedra Lancaster
Director of Liberal Stud Prgm
Starer, Paul A.
English Professor
Stuefloten, Jerry Telford
Science Teacher
Sutton, Vincent Robert
High School Economics Teacher
Sweet, Doug
Coord of Business Writing
Vari, Victor B.
Prof & Chair of Italian Stud
Wilson, Carol Ellen
ESL Instructor
Wise, Rosie Hudspeth
5th Grade Teacher
Zecevic, Aleksandar
Asst Prof of Electrical Engrng
SANTA CRUZ
Bolton, Lennice Lee, Jr.
Early Academic Outreach Cnslr
Burns, Dennis James
Retired Mathematics Teacher
Cox, Patricia Goodale
Math Teacher
Garza, Carol L.
Teacher
Heinrich, Milo Jay
Music Director
Hughes, Jo Ann Elizabeth
Teacher
Knapp, Larry Carl
Drafting Teacher
Landry, Elizabeth Ann
Mathematics Teacher
Martinez, George Luis
Mathematics Teacher
Mc Guire, Daniel Cean
Third-Fourth Grade Teacher
Mc Guire, Tim
Biology & Chemistry Teacher
Merotti, Donna Lee
5th-6th Grade Teacher
Moore, Susan Allison
English Teacher
Mote, Michael P.
English Teacher
Press, David B.
Fifth Grade Teacher
Shandy, Remona I.
5th Grade Teacher
Wong, Georgina
Fifth Grade Teacher
SANTA FE SPRINGS
Cabral, Irene E. Illanes
Frgn Lang Dept Ldr & Span Tchr
Garcia, Ethna Fogarty
Asst Prin & Fac Supervision
Miller, Richard
Sixth Grade Teacher
Nakashima, Richard Keith
Middle School Counselor
Tally, Susan D.
Eng Instr & GATE Coord
Workman, Kenneth Brian
Science & Physical Ed Teacher
SANTA MARGARITA
Estes, Kathleen Marie
Resource Specialist
SANTA MARIA
Brew, Maura Frances
English & Drama Teacher
Castillo, Raul Valdez
HS Teacher & Coach
Corley, Linda Lopez
Fourth Grade Bilingual Tchr
Durnin, Timothy Allen
Dean of Activities
Encinias, Manuel
Teacher
Fogarty, Cynthia (Parsons)
GATE Teacher
Galvez, Quirino James
6th Grade Teacher
Graham, Marilyn Richmond
Retired Teacher
Jeffery, Terrel Windle
Vocational Agriculture Teacher
Jones, Byron Neil
Mathematics Teacher
Lupo, Edward J.
Instructor of Criminal Justice
Malvarose, Richard Eugene
Mathematics & Science Teacher
Mc Donald, Diane A.
4th Grade Teacher
Migliore, Betty Anne (Hemdal)
Early Childhood Consultant
Ontiveros, Margaret Porter
Bilingual Kindergarten Teacher
Paulus, J. Christopher
Math Instructor
Ponce, Tony
Exploring Technology Teacher
Regan, Elizabeth Ann
Coord & Prof Early Chldhd Stud
Robinson, Judith Calkins
English Team Teacher
Sage, Edward Young
Science Instructor
Schimandle, David M.
Fifth & Sixth Grade Teacher
Sturgell, Guy Berry
Sixth Grade Teacher
Walsh, Joseph Thomas
Campus Minister, Religion Tchr
Yoshihara, Lorene Chieko
Physical Education Teacher
SANTA MONICA
Costello, Karin Bergstrom
Professor of English
Davis, Ronn L.
Professor of Fine Arts
Ellsasser, Chris Ward
Eng Dept Chair
Faucheux, Brenda S.
English as Second Lang Tchr
Fouts, Gary A.
Associate Prof of Astronomy
Fry, Jack F.
Life Science Dept Adj Prof
Gallagher, Ed
Communication Dept Chair
Hart, Sharon Klein
7th Grade Humanities Teacher
Hecht, James Douglas
Mathematics Teacher
Hipolito, Emma D.
Social Studies Teacher
Horn, Lorri
English Teacher & Jrnslm Adv
Josephs, Zina Barnard
Former Music Teacher
Joyce, Liam James
Counselor & Dean
Laichas, Thomas Michael
His Dept Chprsn & Mentor Tchr
Little, Dennis N.
Computer Teacher & Tech Coord
Merlic, Jennifer Bates
Associate Prof of Chemistry
Merz, Dianne Cox
Kindergarten Teacher
Milwe, Cindy
English Teacher
Ness, Brenda (Warren)
Professor of History
Nieman, Nancy Dale
Foreign Lang Dept Chair
Parker, Antoinette
Mathematics Teacher
Perman, Nancy Bayer
Math Teacher

MONICA (cont)
e, Michael J.
h & Latin Teacher
Marthe Tirelli
h Instructor
ori Stephanie
Teacher
David Ralph
y Professor
k, Joanne Dickinson
Grade Teacher
d, Lucia Emily
of Visual Arts
oseph Wayne
h Professor
oseph A.
s Teacher
PAULA
ian, Suzanne Jill Newman
athematics Teacher
ers, Arvid B.
pal
Melvyn Roger
School Counselor
Valerie DelRio
School English Teacher
, Jill Sweet
ome Economics Teacher
Louis Gene
mental Music Teacher
Steven
gy Teacher
Paul Alfred
ess Teacher
, Paul Edward
sh & Health Science Tchr
Teri Marvette
rgarten Teacher
, Paul Adrian
y & Soc Science Teacher
ROSA
Dorothy Alderson
d Teacher
n, Janyce Elaine
Teacher
cas, John Francis
nglish & Journalism Tchr
d, Jan Getchell
Teacher
, Susan Margaret
ng Skills Instructor
, John Ronald
a Teacher
andra Mae (Austin)
n Grade Teacher
Richard Frank
rade Teacher
i, Carla
sh Teacher
Patricia Ann
h Grade Teacher
ussell Allen
sh Teacher
Wendy Kathleen
sh Teacher
vood, Lenard Carl
graphy Teacher
Mary Beth
Medical Pathway Tchr
nn, Jeffery
nment & Pol Sci Teacher
eslie M.
ng Tchr & Dept Chair
ennifer Lee
l Director
Joanna Cedar
l History Teacher
y, Patrick Michael
Grade Teacher
Lloyd H.
sh Teacher
ey, Judy Adams
selor, Yrbk & Ldrshp Tchr
ece, Judy (Vaughn)
rade Teacher
John Anthony
ce & Language Arts Tchr
Dennis Patrick
School Art Teacher
Quentin Louis
ce & Math Teacher
Richard James
Math Tchr & Dept Chm
h, Russell Edward
gy Teacher
e, Anne Nicoletti
l History & Psych Tchr
ey, Ted Paul
ess Teacher & Dept Chair
, Rickard Ernest
ematics Department Chm
Mary Lu Brucks
h Grade Teacher
, Julie Marie
nd Grade Teacher
YNEZ
s, Mary Carolyn
ed Teacher
s, David Alan
a & Humanities Teacher
EE
son, Kristin Ann
School English Teacher
, Thomas Felix
Department Chairman
ey, Carol
h Grade Teacher
Charlene Latsha
Teacher & Dept Chprsn

Heath, Rebecca Reed Woolworth
Language Arts & US His Tchr
Mc Anally, Donald Brooks
6th Grade Teacher
Schaffer, Jane C.
Eng Dept Chairperson
SARATOGA
Anzalone, Kim RoChelle
AP US History Teacher
Bissonnette, Veva Karlene
Teacher & Forensics Director
Camp, Susan Burman
English Teacher
Colson, Kenneth M.
Anthropology Professor
Dueck, Harold John
Math Instructor & Dept Chm
Emerson, Moonyeen O'Connor
Owner & Teacher
Faulstich, Marge
Dept Chairperson & Instructor
Geredes, Theodore
Dept Chair of Engineering
Hays, Georgiana Lee
English, Speech & Debate Tchr
Krakowski-Limbach, Emily
History & Economics Teacher
Laxier, Meghan Suzanne
Speech Communication Instr
Malmuth-Onn, Ann
Director of Dance
Pierce, Heidi Gerhart
Fourth Grade Teacher
Ross, Bob H., Jr.
Sixth Grade Teacher
Viale, Deanna Lucille
First & Second Grade Teacher
Weiner, Susan Ambrus
Chemistry Instructor
Williams, Kristin Elizabeth
Eng Language Development Tchr
Zanotti, Edith E.
Foreign Lang Prof
SAUGUS
Aldrich, Fred Skip
Social Studies Teacher
Beattie, John Edward
English Teacher
Bolde, William P.
Teacher
Estes, Roberta R.
History & Economics Teacher
Fukumoto, Lorraine Noguchi
Second & Third Grade Teacher
Kelly, Mary Jane Jennings
Mentor Teacher
Stephenson, Patty Mac Kellar
French Teacher
Stroh, Kathryn Anne
Business Teacher & Coach
Yagmur, Marie Pack
US History Teacher
SAUSALITO
Nye, Sandra Casey
Consultant
SCOTIA
Barsanti, Garey Wayne
Eighth Grade Teacher
Shoop, Penny R.
Vice Prin & Lang Arts Tchr
SEAL BEACH
Gallup, Jerri J.
Media Specialist
SEASIDE
Bailey, M. Sue
Kindergarten Teacher
Foley Hickman, Linda Daseler
2nd Grade Teacher
Kipinger, Mary Kochis
Algebra, Math & Computer Tchr
Wright, Carla Diane
Third Grade Teacher
SEBASTOPOL
Bellinger, Todd Harland
8th Grd Eng & US His Teacher
Comini, Bill
Science Teacher
Cullinen, Robert E.
Choir Teacher
Gregg, Susan Marie
Fine Arts Chprsn & Acting Tchr
Grisham, Cherry Young
12th Grade English Teacher
Stansbury, Carol Ann Wilson
4th Grade Teacher
SELMA
Ault, Lee W.
Mathematics Teacher
Beatie, Judith Lynn
Special Day Class Teacher
Castle, Forest John
English Teacher
Hushek, Joseph Charles
Chemistry Teacher & Sci Chair
Smith, David James
English Teacher
Wells, Bryan David
Principal
SHAFTER
Bergen, Kelly Jay
Band & Choir Teacher
Conger, Karen E.
Math Teacher
Grayson, Lawrence Eugene, Jr.
High School Math Teacher
Guterez, Carole Lynn Bausano
Fourth Grade Teacher
Hanson, Gary L.
English & History Teacher

Hays, Barbara
Opportunity & STEP Teacher
SHASTA LAKE
Allred, David Laddie
High School Art Teacher
Ashcraft, David Carl
Math & Science Teacher
Frye, Frank L.
Social Science Teacher
Muir, Normetta Miller
English & Drama Teacher
Westphal, Anthony Scott
World His & AP Amer Govt Tchr
SHELL BEACH
Rogoff, Joanne Susan
Second Grade Teacher
Simpson, Patience Joie
Sixth Grade Teacher
SHERMAN OAKS
Allen, Lisa Beth
Director of Theatre
Bennett, Esther Bonino
Span Tchr & Foreign Lang Chair
Booth, Nancy Knowlton
English Department Chairperson
Garden, Gerald Leonard
Retired Eng & Cartooning Tchr
Rallis-Comouche, Sandra A.
Chemistry Teacher
Wilson, Robert Mc Duff
Retired 6th Grd Teacher
SHINGLE SPRINGS
Allen, Andrea L.
English Teacher
Canclini, Cindy (Petersen)
High School Mathematics Tchr
Knops, Harriet Harms
Science Teacher
Lemenager, Jon L.
Amer Govt Tchr & Soc Stud Chm
McPherson, Kathleen Ann
5th Grade Teacher
SIERRA MADRE
Ballance, Nancy Pinkham
Teacher & Vice Principal
Gary, Kyle A.
Mathematics Tchr & Dept Chair
Martin, Andrew Carl
Sixth Grade Teacher
Pelletier, Michael Jon
Economics Teacher
Pelletier, Sandra Maureen
Math Department Chair
Reffner, Linda Ann
French Tchr & Dean of Stdnts
Smith, Eric Edward
9th Grd Speech Teacher
SILVERADO
Ramos, Justin S.
Former Teacher
SIMI VALLEY
Bickford, Debra Mazalie
7th & 8th Grd Science Teacher
Boal, Lyn Kelly
Substitute Teacher & Coach
Boswell-Thomas, Robin L.
Sixth Grade Teacher
Bradbury, Darlene Jean
First Grade Teacher
Brummett, Carol Anne
Kindergarten & First Grd Tchr
Butts, Tad James
Theater Arts & Soc Sci Teacher
Conaway, Patricia H.
English Teacher
Crowley, Nicki Rae
Math Teacher & Dept Chair
Davis, Dorothy Ann
French & English Teacher
Duhm, Virginia Lynn (Ruddick)
High School English Teacher
Fedel, Ermen V.
8th & 9th Grd Science Teacher
Graham, Mary Crawford
Mathematics Teacher
Harano, Yvonne Umeda
6th Grade Teacher
Haren, Judith Gail
English Teacher
Hibbitts, Sara Sally Connick
Junior HS History Teacher
Hitz, Mary Martha
5th Grade Teacher
Johnson, Juanita K.
9th Grade History Teacher
Kelly, Mary Starr
English Teacher
Libman, Jerry
Psychology Teacher
Long, Paul Sheldon
English Teacher & Dept Chm
Lucio, Manuel Ronnie
US History Teacher
Malkin, Jim L.
English Instr & Yearbook Adv
Modell, Lynda Kay (Wellons)
Kindergarten Teacher
Mohler, June Hennix
Theater Arts & English Teacher
Murphy, Alma Marie
Vice Principal
Pringle, Geneva Schoenfelder
Third Grade Teacher
Riggs, Mary Burke
English Language Dev Teacher
Schultz, Mary Ungermann
World & Ancient His Teacher
Stevens, Faye Adell
Math Teacher

Stout, Virginia A.
English Teacher
Tamoto, Janice Eileen (Carlson)
Spanish II & III Teacher
Thompson, Robert Ray
Director of Student Activities
Wormley, LaVerne Bates
Retired Elementary Teacher
SNELLING
Addington, Vernal E.
Math Teacher
SOLANA BEACH
Carrillo, Carol Jane
Mathematics Tchr
Culley, Deborah (Dolan)
Middle School Life Sci Tchr
Denson, Robert Edgar, Jr.
History Teacher & Coach
Mc Whirter, Mary Ellen Erdo
Junior High English Teacher
Nichols, Russ
Sixth Grade Teacher
SOLVANG
Robinson, Edwin Nelson
Retired Bio Tchr & Asst Prin
SOMERSET
Walters, Kathleen
5th Grade Teacher
SONOMA
Campbell, Carol Gamas
Second Grade Aide
Knight, Dean Frederick
Science Teacher
Leone, William T.
Metal Shop Teacher
Morton, Louis
Science & Math Teacher
Romo, Richard
HS ESL Teacher
SONORA
Cavagnaro, Anne Marie
Math Instructor
Ghiorso, Ciria C.
Foreign Language Teacher
Jones, Travis
Director of Student Assistance
Kearney, John S.
Social Studies Teacher
SOUTH EL MONTE
Besocke, Kent Robert
Language Arts Teacher
Bunting, Dean Eric
Special Education Teacher
Camarillo, Rebecca Salinas
Third Grade Bilingual Teacher
Llewellyn, Patricia Louise
Eighth Grade Tchr & Vice Prin
Menendez, Oscar
2nd Grade Bilingual Teacher
Perez, Patricia
Span Tchr, Frgn Lang Dept Head
Rivera, Rebecca Apodaca
Third Grade Bilingual Teacher
Rodriguez, Janette Paula
English Teacher
SOUTH GATE
Aguilar, Jorge Alberto
Spanish Teacher
Cohen, Adelene Lang
English Teacher
Crowe, Ernestine Grant
4th Grade Teacher
Daily, John Edward
Sixth Grade Teacher
Gulugian-Taylor, Patricia J.
Secondary English Teacher
Hokanson, Ralph Edward
Social Studies Teacher
Lalonde, Kathleen Mac Donald
Pre-School Teacher
Lindly, Douglas Dean
Tchr of Learning Handicapped
Martinez, Frances Ann
High School Math Teacher
Morris, Jennifer Garnier
Sixth Grade Teacher
Walker, Carrie Hurd
Counselor
SOUTH LAKE TAHOE
Anderson, Russ LeRoy
Social Studies Teacher
Cohen, Betsy Van Sicklen
ELD & ESL Teacher
DeVore, Joyce Louise
English Teacher
Filce, Michael Paul
HS English Teacher
Harris, Alison
Eighth Grade Science Teacher
Kovac, Francis John
Athletic Director
Lannen, Pamela L.
Spanish Teacher
Martin, Linda Gauvreau
Second Grade Teacher
Morain, Heidi
American Literature Teacher
Shaw, Lynn
Kndgtn & First Grade Teacher
Treiber, Deborah A.
Secondary Social Science Tchr
Williams, Phil
Architectural Design Instr
SOUTH PASADENA
Beckham, Nancy Lietz
7th Grade Social Studies Tchr
Bernal, Paul Andrew
Secondary Teacher
Castellano, Marie Tanner
Teacher of Gifted

DeFrancisco, Carrie Mayeur
Fifth Grade Teacher
Groves, Paul Cyrus
Chemistry Teacher
Kemp, Michael Edward Dean
Physics & Chemistry Teacher
Larson, Lydia A.
Math Teacher
Mac Donald, Lori J.
English Teacher
Macomber, James
Instrumental Music Teacher
Nicholson, Skip
English Department Head
Sutherland, Carole Wong
Third Grade Teacher
SOUTH SAN FRANCISCO
Bergmans, JoAnne M.
Eighth Grd Tchr & Vice Prin
Chin, Victor M.
Math Teacher
Gantvoort, Ronald William
Assistant Principal
Johanson, Karen Denise
Kndgtn Tchr & Vice-Principal
Kadesh-Ryan, Rebecca Aronoff
ESL Teacher
Leonardos, Nickolas James
Fifth Grade Teacher
Lewis, Judith Lynn
Coord Conflict Resolution Tchr
Pangburn, Davina Lynn
Science Teacher
Selli, Kendra Lynn
English & Dance Teacher
Webb, Denise Liebert
Spanish Teacher
Wenger, Benedicte Snerding
French Teacher
Zimmer, Janet Hamilton
Honors & Coll Prep Eng Teacher
Zuardo, Louis J.
Senior Psychology Teacher
SPRECKELS
Coward, Catherine Ann
Middle School Science Teacher
Wynne, Nancy Meyers
Lang Arts & Soc Stud Teacher
SPRING VALLEY
Anthony, Roy S., Jr.
Instrumental Music Teacher
Cato, Carl Alonzo
Eighth Grade English Teacher
Ferich, Barry W.
Physical Education Teacher
Linthicum, Larry Dee
Mathematics Teacher
Yaw, Brian K.
English Department Chair, Tchr
STANDARD
Sterni, Bonnie J.
Fifth Grade Teacher
STANFORD
Klemish, Carol Kallfelz
Former Teacher
STANTON
Bisel, Karen Bachman
Research Specialist Pgm Tchr
Dixon, Shirley Hightower
Third Grade Teacher
Murillo, Deanne Todd
Sixth Grade Teacher
STEVENSON RANCH
Yannich, Alexis Manfredi
6th Grade Teacher
STIRLING CITY
Wallen, Mary Rose Pereira
4th-5th Grade Teacher
STOCKTON
Arturo, Giraldez
Associate Professor of Spanish
Bates, Gerald J.
High School Math Teacher
Benjamin, Karen Lee
Associate Prof of Psychology
Bidondo, Candice Lynn
Second Grade Teacher
Boggs, Susan Ann
GATE Lang Arts & Rdng Tchr
Bonner, Annie Kemp
Teacher
Borba, Debora Marie
6th & 7th Grade Teacher
Bowen, Jacquelyn
Fourth Grade Teacher
Cain, Janice Elaine Lewis
Sixth Grade Teacher
Cavitt, M. Pearl
First Grade Teacher
Cecchetti, Barbara Ann
Third Grade Teacher
Chandler, Elaine C.
Math Teacher
Ciccolella, Margaret Elizabeth
Professor of Sport Sciences
Coates, Laurel Ann
Science Resource Tchr
Coburn, Terence Lee
History Teacher
Cortez, Mary Lou
Jr High Science Teacher
Crumpacker, Diane Van Orden
Fifth Grade Teacher
Daniels, Loretta Sue (Riggs)
Biology & Chemistry Teacher
Davison, Pheon Rivers
Music Teacher
Dedini, Joyce Katherine
Mathematics Teacher

STOCKTON (cont)
Dell'Aringa, Yvonne Silvia Bozzini
5th Grade Teacher
Derleth, James William
Political Science Professor
Dillon, Shaye
Asst Prof of Commnctn
Dineley, Patricia A.
6th-8th Grade Teacher
Dominik, Jane Kathryn
English Instructor
Dunning, John Phillip
Head Women's Volleyball Coach
Eger, Marilyn Rae (Shaver Masoner)
AP Art Teacher
Fager, Patti Anne
4th Grade Teacher
Finney, Barrett Kevin
Sixth Grade Teacher
Fletcher, David Quentin
Engineering Professor
Fowler, Amy Mc Coun
Physical Education Teacher
Glahn, Karen Ardith
Eng Tchr & Forensics Prgm Dir
Golsan, Katherine Susan
French Professor
Gross, Paul Hans
Professor of Chemistry
Hackley, Carol Ann Hall
Public Relations Assoc Prof
Harper, Diane Frazier
Elementary Principal
Harr, Carolyn F.
Resource Specialist
Harris, Archie Cornelius
Special Day Class Assistant
Havard, Roberta Lynn Hall
High School English Teacher
Higgins, Edward Lee
Band Director
Holton, Arthur John, III
Director of Bands
Hooton, Dianne Spear
Humanities & Mathematics Tchr
Horton, Naomi Leona (Rapp)
7th Grade English Teacher
Hutchins, Daryl L.
8th Grd Lang & Literature Tchr
Johnson, Margaret Marshall
Science Teacher
Johnson, Susan Annette
Third Grade Teacher
Katz, Roger C.
Professor of Psychology
Kelley, Clark T.
Spanish Teacher
Keown, Nancie L.
Social Studies Teacher
Klo, Lynda Morgenstern
Social Science Teacher
Klunk, Brian Edward
Assoc Prof of Intnl Studies
Knickerbocker, Jo
Computer Education Instructor
Kramer, J. Curtis
Professor of Geology
LaGasca, Frank John
Social Studies Teacher
Lambdin, V. Elizabeth
Development Director
Latteri, Joseph Edward
English Language Dev Teacher
Leibner, Roberta Michalenko
English Instructor
Luntao, Ruperto Wilfredo
Fifth Grade Teacher
Lutz, Reinhart
Asst Prof of Eng & Film Stud
May, Lorna Ann
Language Development Teacher
Mayne, Heather Joy
English Professor
Merrow, James August
American Literature Teacher
Moran, Mary Saiers
ESL & Soc Studies Teacher
Neitzel, Nancy Ann (Case)
Sixth Grade Teacher
Nguyen, Thuan Van
Electrical & Cmptr Engrng Prof
Nicolas-Alvillar, Andrea
4th-6th Grade GATE Teacher
Niemi, John Robert
K-2nd Grade Teacher
Norton, Camille
Assistant Professor of English
Ota, Dwight J.
Reading Recovery Teacher
Paper, Lynne Francis
Second Grade Teacher
Pham-Peck, Uyen
High School Counselor
Porter, H. Howard
LH Tchr & Calif Yth Authority
Price, Gary M.
6th Grade Teacher
Ratto, Sharon Kay
5th Grade Teacher
Rios, Michael Joseph
Ninth Grade Teacher
Rodriquez, Olga Mercedes
Principal
Rogers, William Darrow
History Teacher
Sallee, Michelle Kathleen
Art & Yearbook Teacher
Schweigerdt, Bruce
Middle School Teacher
Simon, James Lawrence
Asst Prof & Comm Dept Chrmn
Smith-Knighton, Letha C.
Reading & English Teacher
Spaid, Marlene Brown
8th Grade English Teacher
Swingle, John C.
Choral Teacher & Dept Chair
Talbot, Steve
Sociology & Anthropology Prof
Tedards, Douglas Manning
Associate Professor of English
Thomas, Melvin Daniel
Asst Professor of Classics
Torres, Victor Sierra
Middle School Counselor
Tranel, Toni Michelle
French Teacher
Vomocil, Gordon Leslie
Fifth Grade Soc Stud Teacher
White, Lurline Yvonne
Sixth Grade Teacher
Whittock, Linda Ramirez
Elementary Teacher
Williams, Mary L.
7th Grade Teacher
Wyatt, Priscilla
Fourth Grade Teacher

STRATHMORE
Hatcher, James H.
Eighth Grade Teacher
Rodriguez, Phillip Joseph
Seventh Grade Teacher

SUISUN CITY
Adams, Lona Ray
8th Grade US History Teacher
Curiel, Dolores
Cnslr & College Survival Instr
Felker, Joe Cline
6th Grade Teacher
Harvey, Ophelia Smith
Master Advisor & Board Pres
Snider, Marilee Ann
Fourth Grade Teacher

SUN CITY
Domingo, D. June (Barger)
7th & 8th Grade Math Teacher
Flora, Ronald William
Fifth Grade Teacher
James, Midge Gillen
Principal
Kipp, Lynnette Henry
5th Grade Teacher
Stewart, Jerry L.
Fifth Grade Teacher
Villarreal, Karen (Kyhn)
4th Grade Teacher

SUN VALLEY
Brooks, Jean Tisdale
Second Grade Teacher
Carington, Homer Lathan
Middle School Teacher
Cook, Evelyn
Science Teacher
Diaz, Ricardo Alberto
Social Studies Teacher
Domke, John David
Bible & Church History Teacher
Hendricks, Joseph Monroe
Kindergarten Teacher
Ikeda, James T.
Biology Teacher
Leandro, Stan Bernardo
ESL Teacher & Counselor
Lovett, Marlene Trober
School Nurse
Modugno, Joyce Tucker
Social Studies Teacher
Morillo, Juan
Social Studies Teacher
Smith, Paulette Rodgers
Middle School Teacher
Sutherland, Linda Jo
Lead Teacher
West, Karen Ann
Teacher
Wilson, Hollie O., Jr.
Mathematics Teacher & Coach

SUNLAND
Lee, Francine Enders
Kindergarten Teacher

SUNNYVALE
Binkley, Randall Thaddeus
Science Teacher
Crutchfield, Jason Todd
Business Education Dept Chair
Geren, Nancy Ellen
Science Teacher & Dept Head
Guttadauro, Rosella Marie
8th Grade English Teacher
Jaffe, Leilani
Math, Art Tchr & Dept Chair
Kearns, Kathy Mc Carver
6th Grade Core Teacher
Kelley, Jeannette (McMurdie)
7th Grade Mathematics Teacher
Logan, Cecilia Marie (Fleo)
Health Careers Teacher
Moore, Lorraine Sylvia
5th Grade Teacher
Patten, Douglas K.
US History & Govt Teacher
Tralongo, Patricia Daniell
Lang Arts & Soc Science Tchr
Trione, Ann Marie
Science Teacher
Vettel, Cheryl Larson Stewart
Assistant Principal
Watkins, Emily
Sixth Grade Teacher
Yamada, Letty Murata
Fourth Grade Teacher

SUNOL
Dennis, Laura Ann
8th Grade Teacher

SUSANVILLE
Egan, Holly Michalik
Agriculture Teacher
McDonell, Kathy Walters
Teacher

SUTTER
Baroni, Steve M.
Science Teacher
Troxel, Bruce Kenneth
Math Teacher

SUTTER CREEK
Guthrie, Feliz
High School Spanish Teacher

SYLMAR
Bralver, Eleanor K.
High School Health Teacher
Jarvis, Harry Greger
Guidance Tchr & Dept Chairman
Rodriguez, Victor Hugo
Biology Teacher
Russell, Carol Wilcox
English & Mentor Teacher
Steinert, Deborah Anne
Magnet School Coordinator
Thomson, Robert Edward
HS Counselor & Vlybl Coach
Victoria, Edward
High School Teacher

TAFT
Brown, Kathy Buchanan
Science Teacher
Buttke, Ardith Joan
Music Teacher
Ezell, Norman G.
Special Education Teacher
Fitzsimmons, Mark A.
Commercial Printing Teacher
Le Clair, Thomas
Resource Specialist & Dept Chm
Magee, Susan Lynn (Trop)
2nd Grade Teacher
Shinn, Stephen T.
English Teacher
Simart, Harold Woodford
CAD Technology Teacher

TAHOE CITY
Curry, David Bruce
Assistant Principal
Fandl, Hal L.
Retired Math Teacher
Jackson, James M.
Math Teacher

TEHACHAPI
Hansen, Steven Williams
English Teacher & Yrbk Adv
Henderson, James Thomas
Life Science & Biology Tchr
Kerr, William R.
Algebra Teacher
Mc Lean, Bruce William
English Teacher
Montana, Tony
Criminal Justice Teacher
Neuhalfen, Marcy Reinhold
Career Advisor
Taylor, Randell Eugene
Driver Education Training Tchr
Wahlstrom, Nancy L.
English Teacher
Walker, G. Stephen
HS History & PE Teacher
Wiggins, Clifford Leon, Jr.
English Teacher

TEMECULA
Carnesecca, John Nicholas
AP US History Teacher
Heid, Delynn Susan
Language Arts Teacher & Mentor
Horton, Michael Wayne
Science Teacher
Nolen, James Russell
US History Teacher
Ralston, Bruce Kenneth
Teacher & Coach
Seeman, Lena Mae
First Grade Teacher
Skumawitz, Pamela King
Sixth Grade Teacher
Smith, Joleen Diane (Fix)
Theatre, Speech & Careers Dir
Smith, Sharon Louise
Middle School Teacher
Steadman, Betty Eagle
Lang Arts & Soc Studies Tchr
Thomas, James R.
Science Teacher
VomSteeg, Douglas R.
English Teacher

TEMPLE CITY
Byers, Matthew G.
District Choral Music Teacher
Hoague, J. Ryan
English Tchr & Journalism Adv
Rankin, Timothy Reed
Mathematics Teacher
Salazar, Raymond A.
Science Teacher
Schendel, David Warren
US History Teacher
Udell, Linda Talbert
Third Grade Teacher
Voors, Rob
Administrator
Yearick, Gary R.
District Music Teacher

TEMPLETON
Brooks, Laura Lowe
4th Grade Teacher
Hansen, Paula Schoerner
History & Social Science Tchr
Mayfield, Diane Williston
English Teacher
Platou, Alfred Glenn
8th Grade History Teacher
Smith, Dean Edward
Principal
Smyth, Paul Edward
Foreign Language Dept Chprsn

TERRA BELLA
Gorham, Clara Femat
Second Grade Bilingual Teacher
May, Robert Roy
Principal & Bilingual Coord

THERMAL
Braithwaite, Kent
Lead Teacher
Diaz, Rob Ramon
Life Science Teacher
Lux, Sia Priscella
Math Mentor & Lead Teacher
Marcinov, Sherrie Rawlings
Government & Economics Teacher
Soria, Cindy Jackson
HS English, Journalism Teacher
Williams, Philomena Chow
4th Grade Teacher

THOUSAND OAKS
Collett, Audrey Cross
Retired 1st Grade Teacher
Collins, Barbara Jane
Professor of Biology
Dietch, Tracy Beth
Spanish Teacher
Doring, Patricia Ann
Science Teacher & Dept Chprsn
Hackman, Deanna J.
5th Grade Teacher
Loritz, Jack
Counselor
Maxey, Charles Thomas
Prof of Bus & Dean Schl of Bus
McGee, Mary Lou Dombrowksi
Principal
Murphy, Daniel Patrick
Senior English Teacher
Neumayr, Catherine Elizabeth
Eighth Grade English Teacher
Reaves, Michaela Crawford
History Professor
Richards, Robert Woody
Mathematics Teacher
Sander, Vicki V.
3rd Grade Teacher
Sherman, Gerald Austin
7th Grade Science Teacher
Smith, Barbara Weber
Independent Study Teacher

THREE RIVERS
Matuskey, Gail Jean
Seventh Grade Teacher

TIPTON
Barboni, Patricia Dianne
Kindergarten Teacher
Pharis, Michael M.
8th Grade Teacher

TOLLHOUSE
Bartels, I. Sam
GATE Teacher
Ogata, Robert K.
Visual Arts Teacher

TOMALES
Campbell, Fred Michael
Music Teacher
Harr, Robert Raymond
Social Studies Teacher

TORRANCE
Alvidrez, Richard E.
Professor of Electronics Tech
Anderson, Kenneth Roy
English Teacher
Butler, Michael
Social Studies Teacher
Christensen, Michael Edward
Physical Education Instructor
Conry, Donald Leonard, II
Campus Ministry Director
Corso, Anthony Francis
HS Mathematics Teacher
Costanza, Ysabel A.
Spanish Teacher
Costigan, Colm Charles
Social Studies Teacher
Crockett, Margarette Mc Kinney
Fourth Grade Teacher
DuBon, Scheri T.
4th-5th Grade Bilingual Tchr
Egan, Richard Joseph
Rel & Philosophy Tchr
Fabbri, Maria Laura
Spanish Teacher
Fedrick, Diana Jean
Junior High Math Teacher
Floratos, George Peter
Biology Tchr & Sci Dept Chair
Fournier, Michelle Marie
High School English Teacher
Geisler, Carol Anne
Principal
Halpern, Gisela L.
Assoc Prof, Acctng & Bus Math
Kasmar, Eugene Michael, Jr.
Fifth Grade Teacher
Key, Kenneth Floyd
Academic Counselor
Kopecky, George O.
Spanish & German Teacher
Kroll, Cheryl A.
English Instructor
Krumpe, Paul Edward
Algebra Teacher
Lee, Frank William
Counselor
Lemen, Margie L. Berra
7th-8th Grade Teacher
Lynch, Patricia Elsa
English Dept Chair
Matsuda, Janet L.
Third Grade Teacher
McCampbell, Cynthia M.
Language Arts & PE Teacher
Mc Gee, Inez V. (Mc Cabe)
Journalism & English Teacher
McOsker, Kerry Meehan
Grls Dean of Discipline & Tchr
Murata, Fumie N.
Retired 4th Grade Teacher
Murphy, Diana Joy
Asst Principal & Math Teacher
Murray, Jane T.
8th Grade Lang Arts Teacher
O'Hara, Nadine Crone
Mathematics Teacher
Pang, Henry M.
Science Teacher
Peack, Brenda Jean
Fifth Grade Teacher
Pillet, Sandra Ann (Delvy)
Special Ed Resource Teacher
Poling, Sharon Wood
Fifth Grade Teacher
Pulone, Dominick
Social Studies & Amer His Tchr
Sacks, Barry Gabriel
Track & Field Coach
Schubarth, Joanne Bloechle
Third Grade Teacher
Schwartz, Richard Jay
Chemistry Teacher
Simonsen, Kevin Matthew
Religion & Computer Sci Tchr
Sirounian, Konstantin
Piano Instructor
Starkey, Michele Benson
Math Teacher, Dept Chairperson
Surina, Ronda Lynn
Math Teacher
Suzuki, Millie Ono
Fifth Grade Teacher
Warden, Sharon Mondschein
Jrnlsm Adv & English Teacher
Weinberg, Lynn
Math Teacher
Yonemura, Judy
Teacher
Young, Arthur M.
Math Teacher

TRACY
Anderson, C. Jenny Burns
Spanish Teacher
Bussey, Janice Ann
Assistant Principal
Costa, Pamela Wentworth
Vocal Music Teacher
Eddy, Nancy Ellen
English Teacher
Gold, Valeria Victoria
English Teacher
Patteson, SaraLynn Beckwith
Resource Specialist Pgm Tchr
Sordello, Teresa Isabella
Math Teacher
Spaid, Charles Thomas
Biology & Hum Physiology Tchr
Steward, Lori Anne (Overfield)
Agricultural Science Teacher
Trombino, Kathleen A. (Church)
Fifth Grade Teacher
Wallace, Lisetta Taylor
Intnl Baccalaureate Eng Tchr
Wyrick, Jodi Graham
Social Studies Teacher

TRANQUILLITY
Arnold, David R.
Teacher & GATE Coordinator
Mandel, Mark Brian
Mathematics Teacher
Morrow, Beverly Jean
Kindergarten Teacher

TRAVER
Bergmann, Walt A.
7th Grade Teacher

TRES PINOS
Johnston, Sharon Marie
7th-8th Grd Teacher & Prin

TRINIDAD
Wiley, Kathryn Mancinelli
5th-8th Grade Teacher

TRINITY CENTER
Hays, G. Scott
Teacher of the Self-Contained

TRONA
Storts, Jerry L.
Eng & Comp Tech Teacher

TRUCKEE
Hutchinson, Karen Christensen
Spanish Teacher & ESL Tchr
Lowder, Susan Gooch
Chem, Physics & Geology Tchr
Mc Kee, Merri Suzanne
Art, Drama & Chorus Teacher
Mooney, Patrick Francis
English Teacher
Pearlman, Bertica
Spanish & French Teacher

IGA
k, Roger G.
rd AP & US His Tchr
Charles H.
ce & Humanities Teacher
Frances Mc Intyre
h Teacher
RE
Tammy Garcia
ess Teacher
Jones, Halina B.
ologist & Counselor
Elaine F.
Grade Teacher
Judith Irene Lake
entary Teacher
s, Ruben, Jr.
entary Principal
a, Michelle (Richards)
dary Business Teacher
andra Lucille
ematics Teacher
, Jill Ann
sh Teacher & Dept Chprsn
borough, Sharon DuBois
rgarten Teacher
Jill Dudley
uage Arts Teacher
Linda Ton
ess Teacher
ger, Andrea Bisconer
ed Teacher
, Clarence Lee
alculus Teacher
Karen Picard
urce Specialist Pgm Tchr
n, Barbara Louise
ematics Teacher
Reed, Margaret Deane
Grade Teacher
Lynette Lisa-Anne
th Grd Social Stud Tchr
ld, Nan Claire
School Spanish Teacher
ff, Ronald B.
rnment & Economics Instr
Melany Soares
sh Teacher
y, Ruth
ed Third Grade Teacher
Randy Lee
l Studies Teacher
s, Wendy J.
rade Tchr & Vice Prin
on, Edward A., Jr.
Grade US History Teacher
, Margaret Stroben
rade Teacher
Sharon D.
School Physical Ed Tchr
ld, Melissa Hill
rade Teacher
s, Marvin L.
rade Teacher
k, Robert James
th Grd Lang Arts Teacher
Marshall Cameron
sh Teacher
Michael Peter
rd Physical Science Tchr
an, Kathleen
sh Teacher
LAKE
, Robert L.
Chairman
Candee Horton
th Grade Teacher
UMNE
nore, Laurie Ann (Rocker)
& Physical Education Tchr
ab, Mitch Albino
nglish Teacher
s, Thomas Stuart
nistrator
Robert David
ce Teacher
te, Mary Grace
ch & Spanish Teacher
Lee Eugene
ed States History Teacher
art, Dave George
e Level Coordinator
OCK
Ann Williams
School Art Teacher
n, Lisa Anne
Grade Teacher
eyer, Diann Dickson
uage Arts Teacher
Givargis George
ortunity Program Teacher
a, Darlene P.
Grade Teacher
ng, Richard A.
Instructor
an, Dolores
ergarten Bilingual Teacher
ey, Paula Rooney
Grade Teacher
on, Donna Chavez
c Teacher
en, Cynthia L.
& Language Arts Teacher
, Patricia Lynn
nd Grade Teacher
en, Marilee Kristin
ish Teacher
, Donna Jean
cipal

Pond, Bonnie L.
First Grade Teacher
Ramsey, Rhonda Mc Alister
Science Teacher
Schollenberg, Edward John
Mathematics Teacher
Sutterley, Bret Crosswick
4th Grade Teacher
Trevethan, Dana Salles
English & Language Arts Tchr
Verhasselt, Magdalena Sallge
Frgn Lang & Social Stud Tchr
TUSTIN
Boucher, Dennis S.
Art Instructor
Champion, Ellen Marie
Sixth Grade Core Teacher
Falk, Rick
Mathematics Teacher
Ground, Marvin Andy
History & Physical Ed Teacher
Jensen, Jerald Norman
Physics & Physical Sci Teacher
Klingensmith, Peg Preston
Middle School English Teacher
Kollias, Jim H.
Instrumental Music Teacher
Kraus, Susan Stilp
7th & 8th Grd English Teacher
Mazurie, Diane D. (Petti)
Title VII Coordinator
Meier, Steve G.
Science Teacher
Minor, Linda Glee (Beem)
English Teacher & Dept Chair
Nicolai, Eligia Rose
Counselor
Patton, L. Michael
Calculus Teacher
Severson, John Sigurd
Social Studies Teacher
Shirey, Thomas
Math Department Chm & Teacher
Sleeper, Enola M.
High School English Teacher
Spiak, Lori A.
Science Teacher
TWAIN HARTE
Anderson, Nancy Mc Neely
Fifth Grade Teacher
TWENTYNINE PALMS
Brunner, Evelyn Volz
Principal
Chen, Robert Leon
Private Piano Teacher
Councell, Harry W.
Retired Teacher & Principal
Fowler, Dan Gordon
Soc Science Teacher
Geddis, Robert Bates
ROP Teacher
Gentner, Michelle Renee
Mathematics Teacher
Kercheval, Patrick Stephen
Music Teacher & Dept Chair
Lejnieks, Richard
Bio Tchr & Sci Dept Chair
Rodriguez, Sylvia Elizabeth
Spanish Teacher
UKIAH
Alto, Patricia Mann
English & Speech Teacher
Barrett, Carolyn Jean
Elementary Principal
Boynton, Philip Henry
Social Science Dept Chm
Croghan, Dorothy Holloway
Business Ed & Bilingual Tchr
Drew, Jerold Selby
Cross Country Head Coach
Geronzin, Sandra
Fourth Grade Teacher
Graves, John Cyrus
Jr High Soc Studies Tchr
Heath, William Benjamin, III
English Teacher
Hunter, William A.
4th Grade Teacher
Mac Millan, Thomas Ferguson
Philosophy & English Instr
Mountainfire, Sage
Middle School Teacher
Paiva, Cynthia Louise (Cedarholm)
Math Teacher
Pettrone, Catherine A.
High School English Teacher
Rodgers, Holly L. (Stern)
AP Social Studies Teacher
Ross, Charles Earl, Sr.
Welding Instructor
Unck, Warren Thomas
Electronics & Engrng Dept Head
Wagner, Virginia E.
English Instructor
Widler, J. Tonia Goldberger
Cmptr & Information Sci Instr
Zensen, Marilynn Hanratty
Fifth Grade Elementary Teacher
UNION CITY
Anthony, Doreen Anita
Sixth Grade Core Teacher
Boylan, Ann Igarashi
Resource & Mentor Teacher
Cervantez, Julie A.
Dance Educator
Collins, Debra Anne
Tchr & Multi-Media Specialist
Cozine, Walter Dean
History Teacher

Fitzgerald, Rachel Elizabeth
Language Arts Teacher
Goldie, Cheryl
French Tchr & Leadership Adv
Griego, Gracetine Elma (Lee)
Mathematics Teacher
Griffin, Marcela
8th Grd Eng Lit & His Teacher
Hernandez, Frank
Second Grade Teacher
Iwamoto, Annette Gilbert
4th Grade Teacher
Jacobs, John A.
8th Grade Math Teacher
Johnson, Teresa Elena
Physical Education Teacher
Jones, Robert Lee
Science Teacher
Lockhart, Patsy M.
Teacher & Educl Consultant
Madrigal, Lourdes Maria
Social Science Teacher
Munoz, Eduardo Rafael
4th Grade Bilingual Teacher
Murakawa, Dawnalyn K.
History & English Teacher
Noche, Abigail Santiago
Physiology & Science Teacher
Parks, Barry
HS Mathematics Teacher
Patterson, Brad M.
Social Studies Teacher
Pizani, Scott James
Social Science Core Teacher
Radke, Robert C.
7th & 8th Grade Math Teacher
Roman, Michael Bruce
German & Mathematics Teacher
Scharf, Sharilyn A.
Social Science Teacher
Seaton, Thomas L.
English Teacher
Sherman, Joyce Ann
Math & Management Teacher
Tripepi, Patricia
Language Arts Teacher
Valle, Joe Rey
Social Science Teacher
Winding, Kami Tomberlain
English Teacher
UPLAND
Acquistapace, Kris Allen
AP Art History Instr
Barboni, Nancy Koehler
Spanish Teacher
Barnhart, Deneane Thomas
History & English Teacher
Bathauer, Daniel Ray
Sixth Grade Teacher
Bennett, Elizabeth de Lorimier
English Teacher
Carson, Carol Thomas
Fifth Grade Teacher
Chavira, Pamela Mays
Third & Fourth Grade Teacher
Dahl, Paul E.
English Teacher
Darrow, Joseph Allen
Math & Cmptr Programming Tchr
Easton, Frederick Michael
Mathematics Teacher
Fairfax, Deborah Ann
Economics & Government Teacher
Heise, Ruth Ann
High School Counselor
Henke, William E.
English Teacher
Hill, Jim
His Tchr & Soc Stud Dept Chair
Hopwood, Robert Lorne
World His & Humanities Teacher
Leiby, Richard Glenn
Chemistry Teacher
Lubarsky, Marilyn E.
Social Studies Teacher
Mailhot, Vicki Von
English Teacher
Menard, Lori Evelyn
Hlth & Physical Education Tchr
Peck, Gregory Hubart
AP Biology Instr & Sci Tchr
Robertson, Vicki Malich
Computer Teacher
Roubian, Guy
Assistant Principal
Saville, Linda Susan
Psychology & Sociology Teacher
Shapiro, Nanette Eckman
Business Ed & Mentor Teacher
Sheehy, Joseph M.
7th Grade World History Tchr
Thompson, Valerie Hamilton
English Teacher
Wavering, Michelle Lowe
Kindergarten Teacher
Wiggins, Gretchen Gandy
Math Teacher
VACAVILLE
Abel, Laura Sorvetti
English & Drama Teacher
Aquino, Sylvia Marie
Social Studies Teacher
Armosino, Ron
Physical Education Teacher
Barnhardt, Karen Kolbe
Home Economics Teacher
Beauchamp, Arthur C.
Chemistry Teacher
Bloom, Loring Ross
Fifth & Sixth Grade Teacher

Cavanaugh, Bill Richard
Environmental Sci & Hlth Tchr
Chevez, Patty Kaye
Teacher
Cueva, Mary Pilar
Second Grade Teacher
Daws, Stephen
Industrial Tech & Math Teacher
Foraker, Elizabeth Boyan
Fifth Grade Teacher
Gordon, Nancy Clausen
Fourth Grade Teacher
Haimbaugh, Margaret Louise
Preschool Teacher
Halliday, Jill Butterfield
Sixth Grade Teacher
Harris-Myers, Glenda Louise (Mitchell)
Economics Mentor Teacher
Henrickson, Mark Edward
7th Grade Mathematics Teacher
Hickerson, Deborah Shaw
Teacher & Soc Stud Dept Chair
Lepore, K. Elizabeth
Kindergarten Teacher
Long, Roseann Wristen
Spanish Teacher
Luther, Richard S.
Instrumental Music Tchr
Lyon, Gregory Alfred
Biology Teacher
McFadden, Jeri Smith
English & Journalism Teacher
Mc Ginnis, Charles Raymond
Math & Science Teacher
Millward, Ann Alice
Kindergarten Teacher
Newland, Enriqueta (Sust)
Principal
Puddy, Thalia Denise
Physical Education Teacher
Rogers, W. Dennis
Mathematics Tchr & Bible Tchr
Sisson, Margaret Lohr
Spanish Teacher
Smith, Carl D.
6th Grade Teacher
Strong, Chris Hunter
Science Teacher
Terraszas, Elizabeth Call
English Teacher
Zgraggen, Scott Matthew
Chemistry & Phys Science Tchr
VALENCIA
Ayres, Diane Frisch
English Professor
Campbell, Phyllis Madden
English Teacher & Cheer Adv
Cresap, Pamela N.
English Teacher
Crissman, David Lewis
Biology Teacher & Science Chm
Demerjian, Marlene Diane
Professor of Mathematics
Heath, Diann Y.
Instructional Assistant
Koonse, Larry
Music Faculty
McGrath, Tim M.
Business Law Instructor
Tolar, Robert A.
Professor of Mathematics
VALLEJO
Anker, Daniel
Soc Stud Chm & US His Teacher
Badilla, Carol Lee
Foreign Language Dept Chprsn
Booth, Cynthia Jo
Lang Arts, Bible & Span Tchr
Cirelli, Peter D.
Ninth Grade English Teacher
Craft, Edward Phillip
US History Teacher
DeBolt, Jimmie Baird
Middle School Science Teacher
Delgadillo, Bert Diaz
Spanish Teacher
Doehla, Donald M.
Frgn Lang Dept Chair & Fr Tchr
Elizalde, Judith Mary
Mathematics Teacher
Folkard, Mary E.
World History & English Tchr
Fredenburg, Jim
English Teacher & Track Coach
Hayson, Allen Tino
History Teacher & Track Coach
Heinzman, Marcia Estrella
Spanish Teacher
Jennings, Patrick Denis
US History Teacher
Jones, Nathaniel B.
Counselor Dept Chair
Kearney, Gus
English Teacher
Kirkley-Mc Keever, Diana
Sixth Grade Teacher
Kobak, Theresa B.
French Teacher & Dept Chr
Kraft, William Patrick
Theatre Arts & English Instr
Lichty, Esther Musuraca
4th-5th Grade Teacher
Lindley, Joanna Marie
Mathematics Teacher
Lopez, Edmundo
Span Tchr & Frgn Lang Dept Hd
Lorega, Flavia Ramona
Dir of Act, Rel & Span Tchr
Loushin, Linda Lee
Leadership & Physical Ed Tchr

Lovelace, Robert Matthew
Physics Teacher
Low, Robert
Arch & Mech Drafting Teacher
Lyles, Donald Paul
MS English & Bible Teacher
Mazaroff, Neal R.
6th Grade Teacher
Mc Capes, Roberta Joan
Retired 5th & 6th Grd Teacher
McDowell, James Smeaton
Bible Teacher
Nelson, Megan Lee
Humanities & English Teacher
Nutt, Ricky Lyn
Counselor
Petty, Howard Crosby
NJROTC Teacher
Roche, Colette M.
English Teacher
Rodgers, Nora
English & Spanish Teacher
Rodgers, Richard Donald
English Teacher & Dept Chprsn
St John, Patricia Jean
English Teacher
Santiago, Louise Colon
Campus Minister
Shang, E. K.
English & Soc Studies Teacher
Smith, Kenneth Frasier
Director of Bands
Springstead, Esther Harris
Second Grade Teacher
Steffen, Yvonne Marcelle
French & Spanish Teacher
Wilde, Max Glen
Mathematics Teacher
VALLEY CENTER
Freeman, Mary Louise
Amer History & Government Tchr
Hollingsworth, Valerie Taylor
Cmptr, Jrnlsm & Lang Arts Tchr
VAN NUYS
Anderson, Rebecca Anne
Spanish Teacher
Broslawsky, Chuck David
History Teacher
Charbonneau, Dede Mall
English as Second Lang Teacher
Delnavaz, Nader
Mathematics Teacher
DeSoto, Kathleen Brennan
Math Teacher
Diaz, Consuelo
History Teacher
Dorret, Teryne
HS Soc Stud & English Tchr
Einstein, Ahuva
Hebrew Teacher
Fisher, Nancy Leigh
English Teacher
Fullmer, Judith Magrini
Soc Stud Dept Chair & Teacher
Gika, Edward Alfred
Eng, Art His & Film Teacher
Hoyer, Pavla
Assistant Professor of Biology
Hutner, Levinia Maria
College Counselor
Jenkins, Brenda Gissing
Financial Consultant
Johnson, Lily S. Churukian
French & Spanish Teacher
Kalan, Steven Charles
AP Govt Teacher & Athletic Dir
Lane, Fred V.
Professor of Mathematics
Leibsohn, Andi Paula
English Teacher
Livingston, Jannis Lynne
College Counselor
Martindale, Valerie Sena
Physical Education Teacher
Mertens, Michael
Instrumental Music Teacher
Novinger, Barbara Lynne
Teacher
Redding, Julie Nadine
Mathematics Teacher
Richmond, Deborah Lynne
Jr HS Eng & Pub Speaking Tchr
Rodriguez, Luis Cazares
Bilingual Teacher
Ross, C. Alvin
Eng Teacher
Russell, Anita Francis
6th Grade Teacher
Shammas, Nancy S.
English Teacher
Smyth, Carolyn L.
Special Education Teacher
VANDENBERG AFB
Ludden, Douglas Allen
Seventh & Eighth Grd Math Tchr
Lynch, Gene R.
History & German Teacher
VENTURA
Bettencourt, Kara Enroth
English Teacher
Celcer, Dolores Ann
Fourth Grade Teacher
Chaney, Patricia L.
Fifth Grade Teacher
Claypool, Donelle
Teacher & Vice Principal
Curtis-Abbe, Laurel Ann
Speech, Drama & Jrnlsm Teacher
Darling, Rita Rhodes
Teacher

VENTURA (cont)
Dilworth, John B.
Jr High Math & Science Tchr
Gallaway, Sara Essa
History Professor
Garcia, Kathleen M.
Eighth Grade Teacher
Gold, Judith Lee
Kindergarten Teacher
Gray, Glenn Edward, II
World History Teacher
Grossman, Aline Yee
Spanish Teacher
Gustafson, Lorelei Smith
English & Journalism Teacher
Hughes, Jimmy Dwain
Exploring Technology Teacher
Jeans, Virgil E., Jr.
Fifth Grade Teacher
Kebayashi, Joy Mayumi
Chemistry Professor
Lawrence, Ted Patrick
English Teacher
Mack, Jon Randall
Anatomy, Algebra & PE Teacher
Magoon, Stephen W.
Math Teacher
Marra, Janet Marie (Hanna)
Spanish Teacher
Mathers, Christopher Alan
English Teacher
Munoz, Paula S.
Programs & Services Coord
Perry, Mickey Jerome
Mathematics Teacher
Rentfrow, Mary Louise
English Teacher
Ruderman, Adam Scott
Retired Teacher
Shirley, Robert John
8th Grd US History Teacher
Suel, Timothy D.
Counselor
Wilson, Ralph William
US History Teacher
VICTORVILLE
Adams, Kim J.
Adaptive Phys Ed Specialist
Basha, Claudia Ann
Instructor of English & French
Becker, Barbara L.
Business Education Instructor
Benson, Sharon Joan
Mathematics Teacher
Branstrator, Harold Henry
World History & Business Tchr
Brillant, Joseph Fernand Roland
Commandant of Cadets & Teacher
Brown, Stan Wayne
English Teacher
Bunnell, Lynn M.
Director of Educational Svcs
Cataneso, Michael Clement
History Teacher
Cave, Gerald Earl
7th-8th Grade Math Teacher
Dahl, Karen Hartle
Spanish Teacher
Dale, Robert Eugene, Jr.
5th Grade Teacher
Dalton, C. Elaine
Art Instructor
Donahue, Douglas Edward
Fifth Grade Teacher
Doyle, John L.
Paramedic Program Director
Edge, Timothy Robert
Math Teacher
Ferguson, Gregory Allan
Fifth Grade Teacher
Jahnke, Thomas Owen
AFJROTC Instructor
Kniss, David Michael
English Teacher
Lambdin, Nate Harry
Physical Ed & Health Professor
Lovelace, Jennifer J.
French & English Teacher
Mangum, George Edward
Youth Pastor & Chapel Director
McCaffrey, Carol Eisele
Mathematics Teacher
Meschter, Jayne Reynolds
5th & 6th Grd Classroom Tchr
Milhan, Patricia E.
Instructor of English
Mohon, Victoria Gilbert
Counselor
Nordbeck, Eric Scott
4th-6th Grade Teacher
Oler, Randy Lee
Math, Sci & Lang Arts Tchr
Oliver, Claude
Industrial Technology Teacher
Oliver, Jody Barr
Computer Science Teacher
Petersen, Mark A.
Sixth Grade Teacher
Phillips, Sonya D.
ELD Teacher
Preston, Lucinda Cable
Sixth Grade Teacher
Rich, Roy A.
Principal & Teacher
Riley, Dixie Lou
Eng III & IV Teacher
Robinson, Jennifer Jane
English & Speech Teacher
Root, George H.
Automotive Instructor

Shahin, Louis
Mathematics Instructor
Shibata, Kirk Michael
Math Teacher & Dept Chair
Silva, LaDonna May
High School Counselor
Smith, Sandra A.
Math Instructor
Stewart, Ted C.
Business Law & Marketing Tchr
Taylor, Kim
7th Grade Social Studies Tchr
Umstead, Burt F.
Science Teacher & Coach
Vaught, Martha White
English Teacher
Wareham, Mary Lynn Elizabeth
Instructor of Mathematics
White, William Duffy
Medical Assistant Coordinator
VISALIA
Ainley, Timothy R.
World History Teacher
Alfano, Danny Gordon
Athletic Director & Teacher
Allan, Andrew John
Science Teacher
Beck, Frank
Criminology & Sociology Prof
Bivona, Susan Lane (Williams)
First Grade Teacher
Brock, Marianne Oliver
Attorney at Law
Cano, Norma Guajardo
Library Media Teacher
Cardoza, Douglas Vincent
Secondary Science Teacher
Carless, Kathy Louse
6th Grade Elementary Teacher
Colbert, Kristine Gose Cone
Teacher Training Professor
Coletti, Reno Paul, Jr.
Amer Sign Lang Instr & Coord
Feleay, Lois Barbara
Third Grade Teacher
Goodbar, Bradley Rollin
Biology Teacher
Gragg, Cherrill A. Heath
Third Grade Teacher
Haskill, Jane Lynn
5th Grade Teacher
Howell, David Charles
Geography Professor
Huckabay, John Wayne
Trigonometry & Geometry Tchr
Jewell, Stephen O.
High School Math Teacher
Johnson, Charlene Moulster
Third Grade Teacher
Kellett, Glory Ann (Brooks)
First Grade Teacher
Kennedy, Linda Brewer
Business Instructor
Magill, Marie Bock
Spanish Teacher
Mc Clure, Darlean Mc Kinney
Business & Computer Instructor
Parry, Linda Ruth (Wilson)
Literature & English Teacher
Price, John Thomas
Industrial Arts Teacher
Purkiss, Penelope Rouch
Leadership, Girls PE Teacher
Quatraro, Dolores
Adj Instr of Speech & Commnctn
Roehl, Marlin
Eng & Advanced Placement Tchr
Rogers, Mark
Resource Specialist
Smith, Gregory Lee
Sixth Grade Teacher
Starr, Rodney Dale
Industrial Ed Tchr & Dept Chm
Stoddard, Clinton Earle
Fifth Grade Teacher
Taylor, Janice Ruth
7th Grade Eng & Reading Tchr
Tomola, Michael John
Science Teacher
Usher, Dan J.
Fifth Grade Teacher
Vincent, Mark Leroy
Activities Dir & Drafting Tchr
Watkins, Dennis DeMar
Spanish Teacher
Watte, Mary Carmichael
English & French Instructor
Wheatley, Patricia D.
4th Grade Teacher
Williams, Sara Karen Coburn
8th Grd Lang Arts Teacher
Wood, David Robert
Drama & Speech Teacher
Zimmerman, Annabelle
Kindergarten Teacher
VISTA
Barger, Cynthia Ann
Vice Principal & HS Teacher
Basmagy, Marjorie Warren
Teacher
Boehm, Sharla K.
Mathematics Teacher
Brown, David Michael
First Grade Teacher
Burnworth, Delila Jean (Fried)
English Department Chair
Cates, Judith Gail
His Tchr & Soc Stud Dept Chair
Challman, Dawn Ayles
Dean of Students

Coble, Ruth Mildred Holsinger
Retired Teacher
Colladay, Nancy M.
English & ESL Teacher
Dorsey, Marianne Margaret
Mathematics Teacher
Geisen, Judith Ann
Dean
George, Kathryn J.
Special Education Teacher
Grandi, David Alan
Choral Director
Grant, Patricia Jeanne (Moore)
Third Grade Teacher
Hidalgo, William D.
Social Studies Teacher
Hjelt, Jeanne Mc Ennerney
Math Teacher
James, Lynette Eileen
Mathematics Teacher
Johnson, Patricia Carol (Naish)
Spanish Teacher
Jorgensen, Eric E.
Math & Physical Ed Teacher
Kleinrath, Steve
Physics Teacher
Laney, Leone (Tyndale)
Language Arts & Socl Stud Tchr
Lanier, Patricia Smith
English & Speech Teacher
Linden, Rebecca Louise
English Teacher
Palmer, William Earl
Soc Stud, Art & Guitar Teacher
Porter, Darlene M.
4th Grade Teacher
Prather, Garry D.
HS Mathematics Teacher
Prather, Patricia K.
IB Coord & Tchr
Pufall, Gail Ann
Third Grade Teacher
Riehle, Steven Michael
Mathematics Teacher
Roswell, George A.
History Teacher
Sanchez, Robert Daniel
US History & Peer Cnslng Tchr
Smith, Joan Hilles
Curriculum & Assessment Tchr
Smith, Scott Andrew
Special Ed Tchr & Dept Chair
Tatum, Karen P.
Language Arts & Drama Tchr
Thurston, Valerie Teru
Assistant Principal
Turner, Jeanne Marie
Middle School Science Teacher
West, Mary Elizabeth
Career Paths Coord & Counselor
Wiebrecht, Ellen M.
World & US History Teacher
Wier, Jan Gregart
Teacher
WALNUT
Aaron, Johann K.
Math Teacher
Atchley, Stephen Jude
Adjunct Professor of Economics
Boroch, Deborah Kasten
Bio Prof & Nat Sci Asst Dean
Brandon, Lee Edward
English Professor
Cole, Barbara Hearn
Advanced Placement Bio Teacher
Conforti, John, Jr.
Professor
Cramsie, Hilde Fichman
Professor of Spanish
Diem, Andrea Grace
Professor of Philosophy
Diskin, William E.
Instructional Dean
Dorough, George Dixon, III
American Sign Language Instr
Fortner, Joel William
Cadd & Animation Professor
Frost, Linda Shaffer
Tchr & Eng Lang Dev Liaison
Fultz, Michael S.
English Language Dev Teacher
Galt, Lorry Gribble
6th Grade Teacher
Goossens, Anthony Allen
Science Teacher
Gray, Inja K.
Second Grade Teacher
Haring, Margie Mgrdichian
Third & Fourth Grade Teacher
Henkins, Kathy
English Department Chair
Hood, Robert C.
Drama Director
Jones, William David
Professor of History
Judd, Jemma Blake
English Professor
Lawson, M. Alan
Prof of Law & Bus Admin Chair
Mc Cormick, Betsy
English Professor
McMullin, Janet Neufeld
Mathematics Professor
Medina, David Jonathan
Professor of Sociology
Medina, Julian Phillip
Professor of Literature
Motz, Sandra O'Hara
Special Education Teacher

Pratt, Charles H.
Economics Teacher
Razo, Helen Lorraine
Fifth Grade Teacher
Rising, Emma Harmon
Vice Principal
Root, Richard Allen
English Teacher
Shannon, Cindy Jean
Professor of Biology
Sholars, Joan D.
Mathematics Professor
Thune, Karen Hahn
Kindergarten Teacher
Van Wagoner, Jane Ellen
Psychology & Home Ec Teacher
Woo-Sam, Sheri Kesig
Mathematics Teacher
WALNUT CREEK
Alioto, Santo Anthony
History Teacher
Barnett, Bette C.
First Grade Teacher
Buma, Hermina Klein
Second Grade Teacher
Costello, Thomas Joseph
History Teacher
DeRieux, Jack A.
Drama Teacher
Dilley, M. Robert
Soc Stud Tchr & Dept Chm
Ericksen, Nancy Minnitti
Home School Supervisory Tchr
Falk, Gary L.
Public Relations Officer
Franks, Patricia Poindexter
Math Teacher & Dept Chair
Friss, J. Richard
English Teacher
Galinat, Ralph
Jr High Teacher
Gonzenbach, Lois Feinberg
US History Teacher
Grant, Judy M.
English Teacher
Hackmeier, Mary Ellen Dodge
Resource Specialist
Haley, Sharon Kay
Math & Drafting Teacher
Huston, Matthew Alan
English Teacher
Lacey, Francie Colette
Coach
Leonard, Roger E.
Physical Education Teacher
Montgomery, Rachel Carin
Basic Algebra, Bio, & PE Tchr
Moser, Barbara Jean
8th Grade Math Teacher
Mulhair, Mona Salem
Foreign Lang Dept Chairperson
Reed, Carolyn Blake
English Teacher
Schoenfeld, Ardene Lurie
English Department Chairperson
Ten Pas, Everlyn Max
English & Speech Teacher
Wiley, Maggi Kooyoumjian
Spanish Teacher
Wood, David S.
9th-12th Grade English Teacher
WASCO
Flaming, Keith Norman
Third Grade Teacher
Grisso, Miriam Louise
Instrmtl Music Instr, Band Dir
Martens, Robert Allen
Music Teacher
Sherwyn, Art H.
Art Teacher & Dept Head
WATERFORD
Segars, Sharon Pereira
Third Grade Teacher
WATSONVILLE
Aubuchon, Michael
Ec, Govt & W Civilization Tchr
Baerg, Elizabeth Slocum
Mathematics Teacher
Baerg, Robert DeWayne
Science & Computer Sci Chm
Ballard, Sheri Lynn
Instrumental Music Teacher
Dunlap, Marsha J.
Science Dept Chair
Kachuck, Martin Sampad
Performing Arts & Eng Teacher
Kaneko, Carol Nakase
Mathematics Teacher
Lyons, Paul Michael
Sociology & Driver Ed Tchr
McCaughan, James F.
Elementary Teacher
O'Brien, Robert William
Eighth Grade Teacher
Peterson, Jayanti
Latin Teacher
Russo, Michael Thomas
Biology Teacher
Samuelson, William Allen
History & Music Teacher
Schwartz, Elizabeth Markland
Migrant Resource Teacher
Smelt, Cheryl (Schneider)
Humanities Teacher
Sorensen, Barbara (Christensen)
Mathematics Mentor Teacher
Takeuchi, Mark Ken
Retired Music Teacher
Thornhill, P. Warren
Elementary Principal

Zapfe, Janene Taylor
English & Bible Teacher
WAWONA
Horner, Michelle Phillips
Principal
WEAVERVILLE
La Fein, Racheal
English, Drama & Photo Teacher
Mc Clurg, John Robert, Jr.
7th Grade Teacher
WEED
Thompson, Eve McArdell
English Instructor & Chprsn
WEIMAR
Brownell, Steven Edward
Driver's Education Sub Tchr
Grams, Kevin D.
History Teacher
WELDON
Carroll, Ruth A.
Vice Principal
WEST COVINA
Andrade, Christopher Frank
Language Arts Teacher
Beeken, David M.
History Teacher
Breen, Kimberlee Anne
8th Grade Science Teacher
Collier, Amy Renee
Science Teacher
Duncan, Wendy Jo (Warren)
Home Economics Teacher
Ferraco, Bernadette
English Teacher
Grams, Carol C.
5th Grade GATE Teacher
Griffin, Susan Vera
Career Assessment Counselor
Kappe, Carol Ann
First Grade Teacher
Oldham, Carol Stockseth
Fifth Grade Teacher
Platt, Jeffrey John
Teacher, Coach & Athletic Dir
Raile, Frederick Newell
Retired Spanish Teacher
Rios, Ophelia Valdepena
1st Grade Teacher
Schwan, Donna Lorae (Foster)
Vocational Instructor
Shanks, Susan Hollingsworth
Spcl Projects Faciltatr & Tchr
Smith, Barbara Elaine
Lang Art Teacher & Dept Chair
Tarango, Cecilia Martinez
Science Teacher
WEST SACRAMENTO
Connolly, Judith M. Sieben
HS French Teacher
Engoron, Roy Stephen
English, Drama & Media Teacher
Hardy, Torrey Ann
Science Teacher
Higgins, Carol Lee (Ferns)
Mathematics Teacher
Shriver, Michael Dale
World His, US Govt, Ec Teacher
WESTLAKE VILLAGE
Matthews, Betty Murphy
Retired 5th-6th Grade Teacher
WESTMINSTER
Bennett, Lu Ella Hull
First Grade Teacher
Clarke, Marianne L.
Mathematics Teacher
Henderson, Alex D.
US History & Psychology Tchr
Johnson, Barbara Finn
Art & Advanced Lang Arts Tchr
Johnson, Debbie (Goldstein)
Physical Ed & Quest Teacher
Mann, Robert John
Science Teacher
Raisbeck, Thomas Wayne
Academy Chaplain & Bible Tchr
Swenson, Yolanda Olympia Contesse
Spanish Teacher
Tiedt, Rebecca Sue
Kindergarten Teacher
Whitney, Jamie Monroe
English Teacher
Wise, Robert James
Band Teacher
WESTWOOD
Church, Patricia Jean
Spanish Teacher & ASB Advisor
Kindig, Charles R.
Math Dept Chairman
WHEATLAND
Adams, Elizabeth Dale
Spanish Teacher
Bush, Robert Mc Nair
English & Acting Teacher
Davis, A. Darrel
Civics & Economics Teacher
Freitas, Diane Marie
Physical Ed Specialist & Coach
Friel, Julie Marie
Agriculture & Science Teacher
Hendran, Jennifer Dawn
English Teacher
Nightingale, Cheryl Crawford
Sixth Grade Teacher
WHITETHORN
Wilson, Cietha Wood
Primary Grade Teacher
WHITTIER
Amador, Edward
Third Grade Teacher

TIER (cont)
on, David E.
Grade Math Teacher
rson, Frederic Allan
ical Science Professor
er, Marsha M.
Grade Teacher
Kari Paige
ish Teacher
er, Nicholas Lee
d Civilizations Teacher
art, Catherine Ray
ish Teacher
ler, Glen Allen
graphy & History Teacher
mo, Joseph A.
Grd Language Arts Teacher
, Robert William
ernment & Economics Teacher
rd, Kathleen F.
Grade Teacher
, Linda Louise
ish Teacher
Lurline K.
8th Grd PE Tchr & Coach
, John Paul
t Grade Teacher
Bart N.
stant Professor
Eric James
ish & Humanities Teacher
r, Patricia Ann
her of the Gifted
Wendy Lynne (Gardner)
n Grade Teacher
Ernest Phillip
Consultant
borg, Joseph Harold
History & World Civ Teacher
onald, Wynora Sawyer
nce & Home Economics Tchr
ide, Michael J.
of Pol Sci & Foreign Stud
n, Sonia Gusiff
al Studies Teacher
ohn H.
ociate Professor
omer, Owen
ics Professor
s, Miriam Ruth
nd Grade Bilingual Teacher
, Frances Cuningham
c Prof & College Organist
ed, Elaine Marjory
nth Grade Teacher
arf, Stephen Frank
uson Prof of Economics
on, Anne Coles
nselor & Teacher
nbach, Judith Mc Cormick
Grade Bilingual Teacher
ng, Jolene
3rd Tchr & Vice Principal
z, Scott Ivan
ness & Computer Teacher
fer, Jane Ann
d Grade Teacher
, Richard Allen
hematics Teacher
nan, Vickie Eileen
hematics Teacher
hein, David Marc
ory Teacher & Dept Chprsn
Cheryl Colee
stant Prof of Biology
, Linda Ann (Baum)
d Grade Tchr & Vice Prin
r, Carol Wilde
3rd Language Arts Teacher
Keith Andrew
oc Prof, Diag Dept Chprsn
ms, Christine Marie
hematics Teacher
r, Katherine Stanovich
Grade Teacher
ITS
Douglas F.
Grade Teacher
Michel M.
ic Teacher & Dean of Stdnts
rdt, Carolyn Elizabeth
al Studies Teacher
, David R.
n Grade Core Teacher
assen, Gwen Joyce
hematics Teacher
, Linda Cardana
Psychologist & Counselor
rton, Starla Coffee
d Grade Teacher
OW CREEK
en, Margaret Alice (Jensen)
d Grade Teacher
MINGTON
d, Mikel
ish & Mentor Teacher
Maureen Bennett
her & Vice Principal
ell, Stanley Russell
Amer Govt & History Teacher
lo, Carmen
ish Professor
pine, Mary H.
mary Arts Teacher
aj, Sofia
nish Teacher
g, Robin Grebe
dergarten Teacher
ms, Willie Horace, Sr.
OTC Instructor

Yamaguchi, Doug N.
Biology Teacher
WINTERS
Dillon, Victor Thomas
Resource Specialist
Hickey, Deborah Ann (Strong)
CORE & Math Teacher
Wierman, Starla Gaylene
7th Grade CORE Teacher
Youngs, Timothy A.
Music Director
WINTON
Burke, Jack Lee
7th Grade Teacher
Denno, Adrian G.
World & US History Teacher
Plagenza, June Brenda
Fifth Grade Teacher
WOODBRIDGE
Radotic, Patricia Smith
Language Art, Rdng, Drama Tchr
WOODLAKE
Linman, Mary Lou Vold
English as Second Lang Tchr
Mc Niece, Michelle L.
Resource Specialist
Pace, Sally Stinson
Dean of Student Services
WOODLAND
Alloway, Richard M.
11th & 12th Grd His & Gov Tchr
Avalos, Frank L.
English & History Teacher
Broaddus, Alison Jones
English Teacher
Cahn, J. Peter
Student Activities Director
Callis, Claudia Anne
Lit, Grammar & Bible Teacher
Delsol, Jerry F.
Ag Sci & Mechanics Teacher
Ellison, Roberta McMills
Business Teacher
Gerhart, Gayelynn Mc Daniel
Math Teacher
Gray, Sue A.
Sixth Grade Teacher
Grose, Lori Taylor
2nd Grade Teacher
Haynam, David Robert
Science Teacher
Hudspeth, Thomas Michael
Social Science Teacher
Kowes, Susan Lynn (Pool)
5th Grade Teacher
Legrand-Bahn, Adrienne Anne
Home Economics Teacher
Lusebrink, Glen Hansen
5th & 6th Grade Teacher
Mc Reynolds, Patrick Kelly
Junior High His & Bible Tchr
Montgomery, R. Scott
Math, Music, PE Tchr & Prin
Moore, Dean
Instructor
Morelli, John Carl
Physical Ed & Math Teacher
Neese, Erik R.
Boys Program Head Coach
Ochoa, Olga
High School Counselor
Perry, Glen Joseph
Math Teacher
Reese, Barry Eugene
English & Social Science Tchr
Wimberg, Ted Douglas
Drug Prevention Educator
WOODLAND HILLS
Bizar-Morton, Carol Gene
English & Reading Teacher
Blumfield, Dara Lyn
Physics & Chem Teacher
Buncab, Flor Liban
NJROTC Instructor & Teacher
Centorino, James Rocco
Physics & Physical Sci Teacher
Clark, Lyn R.
Professor
Daruty, Kathy J.
Professor of Business Admin
Dave, Yolanda Aguilar
Spanish Teacher
Englander, Phyllis Kaplan
5th Grade Teacher
Esters, Jane Ann
HS Math Teacher
Hoffman, Abraham
History Teacher
Hovsepian, Aris
Head Coach
Hurwitz, Jeffrey Alan
Science Teacher
Katz, Edmont C.
ESL Instructor
Lee, Suzanne Jo
Math Teacher
Ludlow, Neils Foster
Mathematics Teacher
Marano, Ellen Marie
Drama Teacher
Markenson, Sharon
English Teacher
Mc Clure, Charles Lee Roy
Retired Teacher
Merrill, Dominique Louise
French Professor
Miller, Laura Wolfe
Spanish & French Teacher
Misseijer, Peter Charles
Art Teacher

Morrison, Gloria Hazuka
Mathematics Teacher
Netzer, Clytee Maddux
English Teacher
Overall, Stephen J.
English Professor
Phoenix, David D.
Professor of Special Education
Pickard, Dean
Philosophy & Humanities Prof
Sasson, Harriet W.
Spanish Teacher
Serfaty, Sheilah R. Wilson
Spanish Teacher
Siener, Geri Tani
English & Journalism Teacher
Strickland, Wendy Elizabeth
High School English Teacher
Swaim, Ruth Carolyn Arbuckle
Algebra & Geometry Teacher
Tietsort, William Vernon
High School Teacher
YERMO
Block, Michael Alan
High School Counselor
YORBA LINDA
Ashley, Kimberley Ann
Electives Lead Teacher
Bagge, Patricia Knight
Fifth Grade Teacher
Beebe, Pamela Hagen
Computer Lab & Math Teacher
Clements, Diana
Second Grade Teacher
Cole, Alice C.
Retired Special Education Tchr
Fraley, Diane Henderson
Fourth Grade Teacher
Fulton, Jeannie Trembley
Junior High School Teacher
Gebler, Donald Ray
Language Arts Department Chair
Kendall, Linda Gail
Fifth Grade Teacher
Lautrup, Diane Kay (Demaree)
6th Grade Teacher
Newman, Keiko M.
Teacher
Sawa, Tina Chase
Fifth Grade Teacher
YREKA
Barker, Helen H.
English Teacher
Caddell, Cathy (Collier)
5th Grade Teacher & Coach
Freudenburg, Mark Timothy
Math Teacher
Gliatto, Tana Shelton
Third Grade Teacher
O'Brien, Thomas Joseph
6th Grade Teacher
YUBA CITY
Barney, Wayne
Industrial Arts Teacher
Chinn, Kandace Tanabe
Fourth & Fifth Grade Teacher
D'Agostini, Daniel
8th Grd Math & Science Teacher
DeMeritt, Paul Robert
Director of Theatre Arts
McKray, Richard Allen
Physical Education Teacher
Miller, Robert Dean
10th-12th Grd PE & Bio Teacher
Monchamp, Patricia D.
4th & 5th Grade Teacher
Posner, Paulina Eduard
Eng, Soc Sci & ELD Teacher
Quijas, Jaime Aguilar
Counselor
Stout, Judith A. (Mc Anulty)
7th & 8th Grade History Tchr
YUCAIPA
Calbreath, Elizabeth Dreme
Spanish Teacher
Edwards, Debra LeLong
High School Art Teacher
Hartman, Donna Louise
Sixth Grade Teacher
Hoar, Christine Helen
Leadership Teacher
Holman, Cynthia J.
English Teacher
Kivett, David W.
Physical Education Teacher
Lockard, Steven Wayne
His, Govt Tchr & Dept Chrmn
Mitchell, Bonnie Elliott
English Tchr & Speech Coach
Peltz, Melida L.
Art Teacher & Department Chair
Poppen, Karen Nancy
Elementary Principal
Prince, Pamela Jean
Special Education Teacher
Proffitt, L. Alan
Geography Teacher
Spitler, Carole Lupo
7th Grade English Teacher
Thorpe, Lisa Dawn
Second Grade Teacher
Williams, Julia Jean
Fourth Grade Teacher
YUCCA VALLEY
Geoghegan, Abigail Lee
Third & Fourth Grade Teacher
George, Kathleen Sharon Mc Ghee
6th-12th Grade Teacher
Hartman, Larry D.
Science Teacher

Kelley, Jolie Kristine
English Teacher & Acad Coach
Kimmel, Sherry Young
Eng, Math Tchr & AVID Coord
Lotito, Lisa Ann
World His & Economics Teacher
Mattson, Frieda Baethke
Principal
May, Eneida Guerra
Retired Spanish Teacher
Mayes, Ruth Ann
Teacher, Prin & Supervisor
McMahon, Brian Douglas
3rd Grade Teacher
Merriam, Patricia J.
English Teacher
Nerud, Caroline Isler
6th Grade Teacher
Pfingsten, Marcia Kiefer
English & Latin Teacher
Stepp, Jay
Health Instructor
Walker, Michael M.
Mathematics Mentor Teacher
Zacks, Cindy Lee Falsken
Biology Teacher

COLORADO

AGUILAR
Montoya, Sherry Bevsek
Kindergarten Teacher
Ribaudo, MaryGrace Paravecchio
Fourth Grade Teacher
AKRON
Clarkson, Gregory Harold
Science & Mathematics Teacher
ALAMOSA
Armold, Anita A.
Science Teacher
Basky, Larry M.
Art Dept Head
Booth, Lorna Barr
Fourth Grade Teacher
Daley, Koos W.
Professor of English
Ford, Sally J.
Home Ec & Computer Teacher
Gillette, Sharon Marie
6th Grade Teacher & Coach
Jehlicka, Elizabeth Tufte
Fifth Grade Teacher
Kearns-Cramer, Phyllis Keesey
Professor of Education
Medina, Pressie Arguello
Retired Elem Teacher
Rust, Teri Sue
Psychology Professor
Samora, Lena C.
Professor of Psychology
Wilson, Candy Esquibel
Intern Asst Prin, 6th Grd Tchr
Ybarrondo, Brent Anthony
Assoc Professor & Chm of Bio
ANTONITO
Davis, Michelle Ann
8th Grade Teacher
Gallegos, Julia Mary
CH I Teacher
ARVADA
Bindel, Thomas Herbert
Science Teacher
Black, Mike Brian
Special Education Teacher
Brenner, Dottie Gibbons
Fourth Grade Teacher
Childers, Joann Elane
Sixth Grade Teacher
Coons, Lynne Elizabeth
PE Teacher
De Rosia, Victor Lee
World History Teacher
Difford, Kristi Marie
Elementary Principal
Ekey, Glenn W.
Teacher
Ellington, Eddie Katsumoto
Third Grade Teacher
Everding, Jo Villano
Second Grade Teacher
Franca, Lawrence John
Dean of Students
Freeman, Theone Bajorek
Language Arts & Jrnlsm Teacher
Hall, Karol Carls
Kindergarten Teacher
Hasz, Jonathan H.
Math Instr & Ath Dir
Hearrell, Gary B.
Fourth Grade Teacher
Hilpert, Alan Meyer
Fifth Grade Teacher
Horan, Elise Girard
Fifth Grade Teacher
Ishmael, Kathleen Haeffner
First Grade Teacher
Johnson, Tina
Fifth Grade Teacher
Kapushion, Blanche M.
6th Grade Teacher
Keeton, Vi Vi Van Vechten
High School English Teacher
Knight, Sandra Latimer
Retired Teacher
Law, Hope Christensen
Math & Social Studies Teacher
Lebsack, David E.
Instrumental Music Teacher

Mc Clelland, Pamela G.
4th Grade Teacher
Neely, Bonnie Keith
His, Eng Tchr & Dept Head
Pattridge, Gregory C.
Technology Teacher
Paul, Patricia Ann
English Teacher
Read, Susan Stoddard
Spanish & French Teacher
Rennels, Beth
Retired Elementary Teacher
Reynolds-Sakowski, Dana Renee
Life Science Teacher
Richmond, Kathleen Biays
English Tchr & Home Ec Aide
Roark, Claudia Beth
8th Grd Social Studies Teacher
Roberts, John Stephen
Social Studies Teacher
Rothrock, James Dodd
Science Teacher
Stocker, Linda Lee
Fourth Grade Tchr
Trebilcock, Gerald Ross
Science Teacher
Watson, Kenneth Gordon
History Teacher
Weiland, Dudley Louis
Sixth Grade Teacher
White, Allen Clark
American History Teacher
Wiebbecke, Bobbi Hansen
Fifth Grade Teacher
Zott, John David, Jr.
Physical Education Teacher
ASPEN
Burson, Kathie Martinson
French Teacher
Flynn, Michael L.
Science Teacher
AULT
Broeder, Iola
Math & Team Tchr
AURORA
Adler, Karen B.
Spanish Teacher
Alexander, Katrina M.
Title I Reading Teacher
Allingham, Patricia Diane
German Teacher
Andrews, Steven R.
Science Teacher
Arnold, Barbara Ann
Counselor
Bailey, James Elden
Sci Instr & Asst Dept Chair
Barry, Kathleen Elizabeth
English Language Arts Teacher
Becker, Penny Bunn
Art Teacher
Beel, Sarah Robin
Math Instructor
Braunlich, Kenneth Ray
Sci Dept Chprsn & Asst Admin
Brewer, Aurora G. (Magalong)
Spanish Teacher
Brown, Bruce E.
Aviation & Accounting Teacher
Brown, George L.
Biology Instructor
Buckley, Ron Dean
7th Grade Teacher
Budy, Betty Anne (Short)
GATE Resource Teacher
Burnett, Maynard O., Jr.
Physical Education Teacher
Chamberlain, LouAnne Turner
Spanish Teacher
Chilton, Doug Mitchell
History Teacher
Chin, Linda S.
Social Studies Teacher
Chopyak, Angela Veronica
English & Speech Teacher
Cichos, Alyce M.
Eng, Lit & Colorado His Dir
Claeys, Yvette Keller
Spanish, French & German Tchr
Clark, David Anthony
Assistant Professor of History
Condon, Adrienne Elizabeth (Wilcox)
Science Teacher
Condreay, Jennifer J.
Theatre Teacher
Cook, N. Marie
High School Choral Teacher
Corrigan, Russ
Language Arts Teacher
Deal, Sheri Suter
Secondary Mathematics Teacher
DeLeon, Jeanette Kay
7th Grade Language Arts Tchr
Dennis, Mardelle Vitt
Fourth Grade Teacher
Drake, Beth Susan
Science Instructor
Dunham, Kelly Stevens
Marketing Educator & Coord
Feld, Samuel F.
English Teacher
Fernald, James M.
Math Teacher
Field, June Bertorello
Business Occupations Teacher
Fleming, Barbara Stimmel
Instructor
Ford, Roberta Harman
HS Teacher & Instructional Ldr

AURORA (cont)
Fox, Kenneth Ziegler
Physics Teacher
Franklin, George B.
Chemisty & Biology Teacher
Gavato, Donald John, II
Mathematics Teacher
Giarratano, C.J. Kern
Business Teacher
Gilbert, Wayne A.
Eng Instr & Dev Specialist
Ginsberg, Maurice Norman
Social Studies Teacher
Giovanini, Sue
Social Studies Teacher
Glennon, Paul Anthony
School Counselor
Gordon, Dee E.
Accounting Teacher
Greene, Marcy I.
Second Grade Teacher
Greene, Winston Anthony
6th Grade Teacher
Gunkel, Rhonda Danzeisen
Spanish Teacher
Haar, David A.
Marketing Teacher
Halford, Sharon Lee
Public Service Dept Chair
Hansen-Vigil, Gwen
Mathematics Teacher
Hayes, Kathleen R.
English Teacher
Herman, Ruth Ester Heinberg
Biology Teacher
Hinderer, Mary Atkinson
Spanish Teacher
Hinman, Stephen H.
Director of Bands
Holloway, Patricia Wilcox
High School English Teacher
Horn, Katherine Scarlett (Zade)
English Teacher
Hostetler, John O.
Counselor
Huffman, Betty Laursen
Math Teacher
Ingle, Beverly Dawn
Lang Arts & Soc Stud Tchr
Jackel, Larry A.
Biology Teacher
Jeffery, Ida Bagsby
Special Ed Instructional Asst
Jeffords, Michelle Marie
Spanish Teacher
Johnson, Marsha F.
Mathematics Teacher
Kakac, Gayle Lesnick
Ninth Grade Geography Teacher
Killingsworth, Arthur Benjamin, II
Industrial Technology Chprsn
Killoran, Christian Gerald
Social Studies Teacher
Kleeman, Katie
9th Grade Science Teacher
Kleve, Michelle Giroux
High School English Teacher
Lanier, Andre K.
Assistant Principal
Leader-Nisttahuz, Glenda
French Teacher
Leaverton, Elizabeth Mc Donald
English Teacher
Lechuga, Joseph Michael
Science Teacher
Leggett, Celi L.
Social Studies Teacher
Lindahl, Birnna B.
Theatre Teacher & Director
Lyons, Terry J.
9th-12th Grade English Teacher
Martin, Robert J.
Technology Teacher
Martin, Ruth Ellison
3rd Grade Teacher
Martine, Joan Marie (Flinn)
Spanish Teacher
Mc Cune, Martin James
Sixth Grade Teacher
Mc Elreath, Keith Christopher
Business & Marketing Dpt Coord
McElreath, Michele Clevenger
Business & Marketing Teacher
Mc Kercher, Tod
Certified Teacher & Ath Trng
McKlem, Katherine Urban
Art Instructor
McManus, Tammi L.
Science Teacher
Merchant, Betty Lou
Science Teacher
Meyer, Kimberley May
Fifth Grade Teacher
Michaels, D.
English Instructor
Miles, Sharon
Counselor
Mills, Charles J., Sr.
Special Education Teacher
Moore, Paul Norton
3rd Grade Classroom Teacher
Moore, Robert Martin
Instr of Eng, Lit & Humanities
Morrissey, Mark Edward
Hlth, Sports & Medicine Tchr
Morse, Ronald Lee
Aerospace Science Instructor
Muldoon, Monte Joseph
History & Economics Teacher
Mylchreest, Vorrey Chapman
Foreign Language Teacher
Nisttahuz, Glenda Leader
French Teacher
Noone, Polly J.
Theatre Arts Teacher & Dir
Oborny, Gene J.
Administrator & Teacher
Olson, Thomas John
Fourth Grade Teacher
Onstott, Mark Douglas
Debate & Forensics Teacher
Osburn, Monroe
Language Arts Teacher
Ott, William L.
Math Teacher
Paricio, Cheryl Lynn (Duncan)
Science Teacher
Paricio, Mark L.
Physics & Chemistry Teacher
Patrick, Judy L.
Coord of Career Dev Ctr
Pawling, Shirley Yvonne (Coontz)
Third Grade Teacher
Peterson, Dorwin Lee
HS English, Language Arts Tchr
Poole, Tony J.
6th-8th Grd Teacher
Rasmussen, Nancy Jean
Mathematics Teacher
Rauh, Elizabeth Jo
Business Teacher
Regensberg, Linda Williams
Fourth Grade Teacher
Renes, Michael J.
Physical Education Teacher
Rogers, Michael D.
Counselor
Ross, Kerry Parker
Theatre Teacher
Rossman, Seth
Theatre Arts Teacher
Rutschow, Margaret Ann
2nd-4th Grade Teacher
Schmidt, Carol Bertelsen
8th Grade Teacher
Schmidt, Pamela Dicken
Science Teacher
Selbst, Howard Louis
Math Coordinator & Teacher
Shive, William Joseph
Social Studies Teacher
Shute, Joan Mary (Serino)
Fifth Grade Teacher
Silvers, Norma J. (McLain)
Principal
Smith, Dorothy Killebrew
Math & Science Teacher
Stephenson, Marsha J.
Eng Teacher & GATE Coord
Stewart, Rodger E.
English Teacher
Stordeur, Diana Claudia
Science Tchr & Dept Coord
Swanson, Laura Schmitt
4th & 5th Grade Teacher
Terry, Melinda Shaw
Fourth Grade Teacher
Tischner, Hans J.
German Teacher
VanderMeer, Glenda M.
Retired High School Math Tchr
Vann, Christopher L.
AFJROTC Teacher
Velando, John
6th Grade Teacher
Vockrodt, Mailys Trebncq
French Teacher
Ward, Mick Scott
Industrial Tech Tchr & Coach
Webb, Bertha Stinnett
Third Grade Teacher
Wermers, Kim Ellison
Social Studies Teacher
White, Veda Jeanne Hosman
3rd & 4th Grade Teacher
Wiggins, Lore Isa luise Haasemann
French Teacher & Dept Chair
Willsea, Charles Vincent
Principal
Yates, Daron Jonathan
Mathematics & Science Teacher
Yuan, Andrew H. M.
Media Specialist
AVON
Foster, Suzanne Marie
Speech, Drama & English Tchr
Kitzmann, Elizabeth Oliver
French & German Teacher
Phelan, Patrick William
Health, Amer Govt & Psych Tchr
AVONDALE
Anzlovar, Janet Socier
First Grade Teacher
Stapleton, Michael R.
Physical Education Teacher
BAILEY
Barth, Ruth Stewart
English & Speech Teacher
Cooksey, Mark L.
Music Supervisor & Instructor
Parsons, Mary Lou Jenkins
HS Mathematics Teacher
BASALT
Durox, Roger Dan
Mathematics Teacher
Hood, Charlotte A.
English & Physical Ed Teacher
Kennedy, Deborah A.
Title I Literacy Teacher
Olson, Karen A.
Lit, Lang & World His Tchr
Palmer, Judy Lynn
6th Grade Teacher
BAYFIELD
Cashio, Theresa Magee
Coll Prep Eng Tchr
Janus, Debbie L.
K-1st Grade Teacher
Jefferies, Barbara Wommer
5th Grade Teacher
Joswick, Pamela Brissie
Third Grade Teacher
Roastingear, Sherry Miller
4th Grade Teacher
BENNETT
Goschke, Laurie Kay
Fifth Grade Teacher
Hager, David Russell
Science Dept Chairman
Land, Dawn Marie
MS Language Arts Teacher
Rumph, Susan
High School Science Teacher
BERTHOUD
Jacobson, Diane Lynn
Kindergarten Teacher
Stephens, Maurice Robert
Vocal Music Director
BETHUNE
Williams, Donna Marie (James)
7th-12th Grd Soc Stud Teacher
BLANCA
Furukawa, Sharon L.
Math Teacher
BOULDER
Alexander, H. Scott
World & US History Teacher
Alm, James Robert
Professor of Economics
Bessett, Darren Craig
Geography Teacher
Boatman, Rosalyn Waggoner
English & Drama Teacher
Bosch, Nancy Claire
French Teacher
Briggs, MaryAnn A.
HS Health & Wellness Teacher
Burns, William Joseph
English Teacher
Burrows-Goodwill, Shivani
Kindergarten Teacher
Cessna, George James, Jr.
Bible, Science & Math Teacher
Chavez, Marianne L.
Spanish Teacher
de Lozano, Leticia Alonso
Spanish Teacher
Downing, James Paul
Science Teacher
Draper, Joan E.
Assoc Prof of Architecture
Dwyer, Jerry
Research Associate
Fisher, Douglas G.
9th & 10th Grade Homeroom Tchr
Goddard, Dale M.
Math, Cmptr Programming Tchr
Harris, Bud
Multi-Age Teacher
Horst, Kristy K. Dale
Language Arts Teacher
Horst, Thomas R.
Instrumental Music Teacher
Hudson, David John
Sixth Grade Teacher
Hult, Dennis E.
Retired Math Teacher
Hynes, James T.
Chemistry & Biochemistry Prof
Kahn, Karen Suzanne
Eng, Rdng & Greek Mythlgy Tchr
Kerlin, Gioia Marie
Spanish Teacher
Labuda, Marilyn Gregory
4th Grade Teacher
LaRue, Robert D., Jr.
World History Teacher
Malmgren, Dick James
US History Teacher & Dept Chm
Malmgren, JoAnne Wright
Mathematics Teacher
Mc Ginnis, Anthony R.
High School Teacher
Mc Lean, Polly Elise
Assoc Prof Media Stud Jrnlsm
Meade, Edward James
Architectural Design Lecturer
Mitchell, David S.
Life Science Teacher
Mulligan, Catherine Esmond
Studio Arts Tchr
Niebur, Jay Edward
Economics & World His Teacher
Ogata, Philip H.
Chemistry Teacher
Pearman, Denise Robin Schreffler
Math Tchr, Spon & Play Dir
Roberts, Marcia Erickson
Mathematics Teacher
Snowden, Chuck
Middle School PE Teacher
Strzepek, Kenneth Marc
Assoc Prof of Civil, Env Eng
White, William Bradley
7th Grade Math Teacher
Williams, Michele Lynne
Math Teacher
Yeager, Tina Alden
Psych, Sociology & His Teacher
BRIGHTON
Bacon, Melvin L.
US His & W Civilization Tchr
Blegen, Dan M.
English Teacher
Engelmann, Wendy Ann
Alternative Education Teacher
Good, Jane Elizabeth
Science Teacher
Grow, Elnore A.
Chemistry Teacher
Hamai, Donald Steven
HS Mathematics Teacher
Hoos, Letha Mae
Language Arts Teacher
Hulse, Ellen Jo Buurman
Span-Multi Cultural Stud Tchr
Iona, Steven
Science Teacher
Jansen-Hedrick, Mary Ann
7th Grd Soc Stud & Sci Tchr
Kelly, Mary Kathleen
History Teacher
Kimmel, Robert John
Science Teacher
Knuth, Bruce Garry
Art Teacher
Kreutzer, Ken
Marketing Ed Tchr & Coord
MacDonnell, Michael Brian
Dean of Students
MacDonnell, Nancy Louise
High School Counselor
Meakins, Donna Marie
Third Grade Teacher
Milyard, Marne Lynn
English Teacher
Mumby, Robert John, Jr.
Fourth Grade Teacher
Pacheco, Karen S.
English & Humanities Teacher
Ponzio, Darla D.
Bus Tchr & at Risk Prgm Coord
Quate, Stephanie J.
English Teacher
Rademacher, Dennis Walter
Coach & Mathematics Teacher
Rapp, Janice Sue
Business Education Teacher
Sandoval, Juanita E. (Martinez)
Intensive Svcs Spec Ed Tchr
Weitzel, Dennis
Math Teacher
Worth, Ted Jay
HS Instrumental Music Teacher
BROOMFIELD
Alcorn, Michael J.
HS Instrumental Music Teacher
Beach, Paula A.
Principal
Bennett, Ellen Mary
Speech Language Pathologist
Birnberg, Robert
US Society Teacher
Blakemore, E. Jane Rush
Fourth Grade Teacher
Czernicki, John Anthony
Geography Teacher
Dean, Roy Bryan
Mathematics & Computer Teacher
Dowd, Thomas Daniel
Marketing Education Teacher
Felknor, Danniel R.
Sixth Grade Mathematics Tchr
Figg, Barbara Diane
Social Studies Tchr & Dept Chm
Gill, Michael Gerard
Instrumental Music Teacher
Goff, Jane Ellen
French Teacher
Jaffe, Rebecca H.
Counselor
Little, Mark Douglas
Science Teacher
Martinez, Patricia S.
Counselor
Meerdink, Larry Kent
Choral Music Educator
Nahikian, Jean Hornkohl
4th Grade Teacher
Natale, Kim
Physics Teacher
Prey, Jason Edward
Science Teacher
Rathburn, Pamela Jane
5th-8th Grade Teacher
Roberts, Pamela Ranger
HS Spanish Teacher
Rucker, Charlene Sorensen
Multi Age Classroom Teacher
Strong, Sandra Holmes
4th Grade Teacher
BRUSH
Artery, Pauline LaVonne
8th Grd Language Arts Teacher
Bloemker, Gary Lloyd
Fifth Grade Teacher
Clift, Penny May
Retired Teacher & Supervisor
Gabriel, Don
Math & Science Teacher
Scott, Warri Joan (Neifert)
Second Grade Teacher
BUENA VISTA
Ayed, Nancy Hatcher
MS Resource Specialist
Horner, James Stetson
Music & Drama Teacher
Peppers, Sherry Lee
First Grade Teacher
Sandefur, Cecil A.
Middle School Science Teacher
Schnellinger, Thomas Herbert
Art Teacher
Young, Cecile LaRue (Williams)
6th & 8th Grade Teacher
BURLINGTON
Prochaska, Kandy Schott
Biology Teacher
Scheopner, Jessica Elizabeth O'Dono
French & English Teacher
BYERS
Greenman, Elizabeth Rose
Science Teacher
CALHAN
Breuning, Phyllis Marie (Harmon)
Third Grade Teacher
Clark, Rose Mary G.
English Teacher
Hastings, Don L.
Bio Tchr, Asst Prin & Ath Dir
Henderson, Janet Lois
Kindergarten Teacher
Henderson, Terry Dean
Math & Science Teacher
Torres, Troy Andrew
Welding Instructor
CAMPO
Cramer, Lynn D.
Mathematics Teacher
England, LeRoy D.
K-12th Grade Music Teacher
Westphal, Brandon Bryan
Social Studies Department Head
CANON CITY
Benesch, Vanette Ruzanski
English & Spanish Teacher
Bradbury, Gwen E. (Moore)
Bus Tchr & Work Program Dir
Brown, Carole Lynn
Science Teacher
Carochi, Dominic Lee
English Teacher
Kinyon, Glenda Kay
Sixth Grade Teacher
Marcy, Keith Duane
Fifth Grade Teacher
Quick, W. Ray
5th & 6th Grade Science Tchr
Riem, Mary Elizabeth
English Teacher
Roche, Ann Scott
Third Grade Teacher
Seaney, J. Duff
Science Teacher
Woods, W. Todd
Band Director
CARBONDALE
Clark, Mark
Hum Tchr & Ski Team Pgm Dir
Ogilby, Meredith Williams
Photography Teacher
Sacca, Karol A.
Speech & English Teacher
Stonington, Gordon
Math Chair & Science Teacher
Sutton, Stephen W.
English Teacher & Coll Cnslr
CASTLE ROCK
Brown, Denina Sterling
Theatre Arts Teacher
Fleet, Steven J.
History Teacher
Johnson-Cressy, Lynn
Business Tchr & Dept Chprsn
Kissler, Jodene Bartolo
Mathematics Teacher
Kissler, Kirk Douglas
Chemistry Tchr & Tech Coord
Mc Closkey, Dennis Patrick
English Teacher
Minion, Diane Marie
5th Grade Teacher
Saint Vincent, Cynthia G.
HS Lang Arts & Spec Ed Teacher
Tuccy, Carole Cantello
Staff Dev & Math Teacher
Walters, Lydia Richards
5th Grade Teacher
Wentzel, Sally Eldridge
4th Grade Teacher
CEDAREDGE
Chinn, Dan J.
Guidance Counselor
Diers, Matthew Kent
Biology & Algebra Teacher
Fairchild, Judy Martha
Third Grade Teacher
Ostrander, Kristen
English Teacher
CENTER
Haskin, Glena J.
HS Social Studies Teacher
Shriber, Suzanne Vietor
Guidance Counselor
Vasquez, Veronica Martinez
Principal
Wham, Kathy L. Moore
Math & Science Teacher
CLIFTON
Ludlam, D. Kathryn
8th Grade Science Teacher
COLORADO SPRINGS
Abeyta, Ray
6th Grade Teacher
Adamson, John W.
Mathematics Teacher
Aguilar, Cynthia Grant
Mathematics Teacher

ORADO SPRINGS (cont)
ander, Janet Campau
ructor of Drawing
ida, Michele Jo (Helms)
h Teacher
rson, Teenan Y.
us Teacher
y, Dana Scott
folio Director
, Kolette Griffin
keting Teacher & DECA Coord
y, Eddie Ray
h Grade Teacher
, Debra Barner
d Director
ica, Nancy L.
Teacher
ing, Margaret Anne
sing Instructor
, Robert Jesse
mistry Teacher
t, Mary E.
h & Spanish Teacher
s, Mary Jane
Business Education Teacher
n, William Abner
ence Teacher
y, William Brooks
Grd Social Studies Teacher
an, Gilbert Thomas
Tchr & Facilitator of Gftd
Michelle Joanne
enth Grade English Teacher
mon-Pugh, Marjorie
ial Studies Teacher
, Esther Jean Morrone
mentary Teacher
er, Rebecca L. Trowbridge
TE Prgm Coord
l, Susan Wristen
& 8th Grd Math Teacher
Leslie Pearce
lish Teacher
ng, George
logy Professor
lli, Kathleen Ann
h School English Teacher
Anne Marie
lish Teacher
ner, Andrew A.
cs & US History Teacher
, Stuart John
Grd History & English Tchr
s, David
ence Teacher
s, Lynette Houser
rth & Fifth Grade Teacher
ord, Lynn Vandenberg
al & General Music Teacher
ks, Sharon Lynn (Bagley)
graphy & Amer History Tchr
ks, Shyrlene Stewart
ond Grade Teacher
n, Patti Grills
g Specialist & Eng Tchr
ey, Cynthia Webster
y Childhood Ed Instructor
bell, Bradley M.
lish Teacher
on, Jeni J.
Grade English Teacher
enter, Dick Michael
d Director
, Judith R.
cipal
er, Dina
h Teacher
e, Lois G.
lish Teacher
dler, Kellie Currie
mentary Teacher
man, James R.
hematics Teacher
y, Ray R.
S Social Studies Teacher
tte, Caryn R.
guage Arts Teacher
els, Gerald George
hematics Instructor
, Judith Iorio
, Span Tchr, Lang Dpt Chair
oer, Dale R.
nomics Professor
elice, Michael Joe
9th Grd PE Teacher
enwick, Elaine Haas
rdinator of GATE Programs
t, Phyllis Jean
rd Grade Teacher
ets, Paul Edward
oc Prof of Computer Science
n, Karen Marshall
Grade English Teacher
ey, Howard B.
Grd Science & Math Teacher
s, Barbara Fischer
Grade Teacher
tra, Kathryn Dekker
rd Grade Teacher
ons, Gayle Lois
ond Grade Teacher
ol, Kathleen Frances
nth Grade English Teacher
, Geraldine Ruehl
lish & Reading Teacher
e, James
& Social Studies Teacher
son, Stephen Michael
istant Principal

Firestine, Barbara Froelich
First & Second Grade Teacher
Foley, Kathleen Patricia
Adj Instructor of Speech Comm
Fornander, Garold Alan
Senior Seminar Teacher
Francis, Michael Edward
Mathematics Teacher
Frech, Marsha Gourley
First Grade Teacher
Freeman, Donald Myron
Business Management Professor
Gilbert, Dana Michelle
Continuing Adult Ed Instr
Gonzales, Rudy A.
Guidance Counselor
Gordon, Bernard Gerard
Physics Teacher
Gordon, Gary Richard
Bible Teacher
Gortner, Terri Mc Lain
Third Grade Teacher
Gunnett, Merry Linda
Assistant Elementary Principal
Hamel, Ernestine Carney
Retired Teacher
Hanes, Raenelle Smith
Professor of Business Ed
Harwig, Norm L.
Fifth Grade Teacher
Hawkins, Patricia Moreau
Fourth Grade Teacher
Hays, Matthew W.
Biology & Chemistry Teacher
Heidenreich, Karen Slavin
Fifth Grade Teacher
Henderson, Bettyann Jordet
Music & Theater Teacher
Heuss, Bobbi Shoberg
Elem School Counselor
Hodges, Marty
Assoc Professor of Mathematics
Holnback, Peter Lewis
Fourth Grade Teacher
Huber, Karen Cash
High School Teacher
Iverson, Larry William
Professor of Criminal Justice
Johnson, John Edward
Biology & Hum Physiology Tchr
Kaizen, Bruce Mitchell
Teacher
Kasyon, Lisa Pearson
Science & Health Teacher
Kay, Robert A.
Physical Education Teacher
Kim, Paul Jungin
History Teacher
Knitt, Barbara Heath
Math Teacher
Kroncke, M. Holly
Teacher & Performing Art Dir
Kulbacki, Charlotte Ann
Mathematics Teacher
Kusk, Richard A.
Instrumental Music Director
Lewis, Mary Alice
Science Teacher & Dept Chprsn
LoBosco, Scott Ross
Business Education Dept Chm
Lumpkins, Fay Marguerite
Fourth Grade Teacher
Lupton, Ron E.
Art Teacher
Mahathey, Nadine Kempfer
Fourth Grade Teacher
Maisano, James Anthony
Ec & Amer His Tchr
Maisano, Sally Jo (Harpster)
Title I Reading Teacher
Markus, Sharyn K.
Language Arts Teacher
Marshall, Kevin K.
Science, Math & Health Teacher
Mascotti, Joseph Navor, III
Choir & Drama Teacher
Matthews, Christopher Carter
Science Teacher
Maykowski, Elaine Marie
Choral Music Teacher
Mc Bride, Kathleen J.
History Teacher
Mc Guire, Edward Kelly
Assoc Prof of Logistics & Mngm
McMullen, Robert W.
Biology Professor & Dept Chrmn
Mendenhall, Karen Kipp
4th Grade Teacher
Michaux, Marianne J.
Teacher
Milne, Carol Ruth
Frgn Lang Dpt Chm & Latin Tchr
Moberly, Mary Hawkinson
Retired Kindergarten Teacher
Moore, Sonia Herta
Span Tchr & FL Dept Chair
Morales, Sandra Lee
Retired Sci Tchr & Dept Head
Nelson, Martha Lynn
Guidance Counselor
Nieto, Ramon
Fifth Grade Teacher
Norton, Pam Hudick
Science Teacher
O'Neal, Patsy Dianne
5th Grade Teacher
Patterson, Richard John
Assistant Principal
Penzel, Thomas G.
American History Teacher

Pesek-Dohm, Cythia
Alternative Coop Ed Coord
Petrelli, Susan Denette
Hlth, Physical Education Tchr
Poore, Michael Alan
Athletic Director & Bus Mgr
Porter, Susan Alvey
Fifth Grd Tchr
Ramberger, Craig Allen
Performing Arts Teacher
Redding, Dorothy Joan
Retired Elementary Teacher
Reeder, Lyn Cunliffe
Fifth Grade Teacher
Renfrow, Lee Kropp
Spanish Teacher
Reynolds, Karin Riley
English & Journalism Instr
Roan, Linda Teubner
Nursing Instructor
Roberts, Josephine Ontiveros
Math & Reading Teacher
Robran, Hela B.
Theatre, ESL & English Teacher
Rogers, Robert Thomas
Science Department Chairperson
Romero, Ernest I.
Seventh Grade Teacher
Romero, Joe David
Industrial Arts Teacher
Roohr, Frances Mills
Prof of Eng & Lit
Rosburg, Jared Lynn
English Teacher & Yrbk Advisor
Rush, Roger
Music Teacher
Sansing, Michael
Mathematics & Computer Teacher
Schubert, Matthew Dale
American History Teacher
Schulzki, Anton G.
High School History Teacher
Scott, Carla Anne (Sommer)
Elementary Music Teacher
Seager, Susan Kathleen
Drama Teacher
Sebben, Aldo Anthony
HS Social Studies Teacher
Shackelford, David Lee
SIED Teacher
Shafer, Dallas E.
Professor
Shane, Kenneth Brian
Instrumental Music Director
Shattuck-Watkins, Dawn Lynne
Seventh Grade Math Teacher
Shaw, Carol Sue
Art Teacher
Shirley, M. Jane
Assistant Principal
Simons, Nelda (Osborn)
Adjunct English Instructor
Skaggs, Maria Ofelia Sanchez
Spanish Teacher
Smith, Darla
Retired English Teacher
Smith, Robert Peter
Heating Instructor
Smith, Vickie Elaine
English Tchr & Coord of Gifted
Spengler, John Christian
High School Biology Teacher
Stanton, Heather Mara
Eighth Grd Language Arts Tchr
Stave, Rita Joyce
Kindergarten Teacher
Stein, Robert Gestrich
Dean of Management
Stevens, Ted
Art & Computer Teacher
Stewart, Penelope Jane
Art Teacher
Sturdevant, Katherine Scott
His Prof & Chair of Soc Sci
Swaby, Barbara E. R.
Professor of Reading Education
Swankowski, Stephen D.
Math Teacher
Szeliga, Martin A.
Social Studies Teacher
Thomas, John T.
Library Media Specialist
Tim, Nancy Jeanne (Struble)
5th Grade Teacher
Tinucci, Catherine Joan
Math Teacher
Todd, Dana Naylor
Adj English & Music Instructor
Tuggle, George T.
Science Dept Chprsn & Teacher
Turner, Dorothy Dutton
English Teacher & Dept Chprsn
Versaw, Francis Earl
Math Teacher
Wade, Nancy Ellen (Breyer)
Business Teacher
Wahl, Andrea Lester
Instructor Interpersonal Comm
Warner, Marylin Shepherd
English Creative Writing Tchr
Webb, Sharon Marie
Fourth Grade Teacher
Weed, Patricia Ann White
French Teacher
Westbay, Nelva Gay
Title I Literacy Teacher
Wheeler, Carolyn Louise
High School Science Teacher
Whitley, Shelly Ann (Murphy)
Special Education Teacher

Whitson, Morreen J.
Second Grade Teacher
Wieting, John Gustave
Assistant Principal
Willhoit, Jane Neeham
Fourth Grade Teacher
Willshire, Mary Jane J.
Professor of Computer Science
Wood, Martha Minnis
English Teacher
Worth, Nancy Susan
High School Art Teacher
Wray, Daniel Bryan
Inclusion Facilitator
Wurtele, Sandy K.
Psychology Professor
COMMERCE CITY
Bour, Amy K.
English Teacher & Yearbook Adv
Coker, Jo G.
7th Grade Communications Tchr
Garcia, Paul C.
Science Teacher
Olivas, Cyndi Montoya
Dean of Students
CONIFER
Jacobsen, Carol Jane
Consumer & Family Stud Teacher
Mallow, Janet Louise (Holliday)
Retired Kindergarten Teacher
Roadruck, Rick
Business Instructor
CORTEZ
Anderson, Douglas T.
Mathematics & Drivers Ed Tchr
Baker, Maxine
Self Contained 6th Grade Tchr
Becker, Nancy-Lasell (Light)
Psychology & US History Tchr
Feela, David J.
AP English & Speech Teacher
Herrick, Laura Marie
Coord of the Gifted & Talented
Hollstein, Terri L.
Dir of Student Assistance Prgm
Keagy, Shirley Sue
Retired Elementary Teacher
Kirk, Dean A.
Teacher & Coach
Kraus, Georgina Chessmore
Head of Foreign Languages
Marbury, Anita Louise
Drama Teacher
Smith, Roberta Ann
French Teacher
Smith, Shelby N.
8th Grade English Teacher
COTOPAXI
Kramer, Linda Berardi
Spanish, English & Speech Tchr
Krauth, Charme Milstein
English Teacher
Krizmanich, John Peter
Social Studies Teacher
CRAIG
Cooper, James L.
Science Instructor
Kurtz, Steve
Business Instructor
Mc Avoy, Dennis E.
English Teacher & Chair
Peck, John Wesley, II
Art & English Teacher
Spicer, William K.
Vocational Agriculture Teacher
Tague, Gary Lee
Math & PE Teacher
CREEDE
Downing, Charles Verrel
Science Teacher
Goss, John Christopher
English Teacher
CRIPPLE CREEK
Crane, Samuel Philip
High School Science Teacher
Vannest, Katrina Marie
PE & Social Studies Teacher
DEL NORTE
Kernen, Shirley Jean
Consumer & Family Studies Tchr
DELTA
Ames, Robert Monroe
Language Arts & Speech Teacher
Beck, Carol Coak
3rd Grade Teacher
Cole, Urilda Mae (White)
Retired Teacher
Gibson, Caryn Webb
Business Teacher
Hansen, Dorothy Elizabeth
Retired Teacher
Ramsey, Rock
Math Teacher
Webb, Willyn Hamilton
Counselor
DENVER
Adams, Richard Lee
Assistant Professor
Adcock, Kristin Williamson
Counselor
Alaghbund, Gita
Cmptr Sci & Engrng Professor
Alexandridis, Debra Luekens
Physical Education Teacher
Allen, Don
English Teacher
Allen, Larry D.
Social Studies Teacher
Allis, Eileen Eckberg
Vocal & Piano Teacher

Antista, Kelli Lynn
Middle School Counselor
Arnold, Eric A., Jr.
Associate Professor of History
Ashley, Wes L.
High School Dean of Students
Audesirk, Gerald Joseph
Professor of Biology
Augden, Edward Andrew, Jr.
High School Geography Teacher
Bankes, Marcia G.
Elementary Teacher
Barker, Charles Thomas
Government & Economics Teacher
Beaudoin, Luc J.
Russian Professor
Belknap, Kurt Edward
Teacher & Advisor
Berg Brabec, Jean V.
Kindergarten Teacher
Bettenhausen, Kenneth Lee
Assistant Professor of Mgmt
Billmaier, Mary Elizabeth
Multi-Age Teacher
Bogard, Donna Mosbaugh
Assistant Professor of Music
Bollmann, Barbara A.
Dean of Hlth & Human Services
Boswell, Jerry Don
Finance Professor
Bowman, Craig Martin
7th Grd Eng & Lang Arts Tchr
Boyer, Connie R.
Accounting Instructor
Briel, Jan M.
High School Guidance Counselor
Brovsky, John Patrick
Language Arts Teacher
Byassee, Gerald Alvin
JROTC Instructor
Carpenter, Catherine Susanne
Instructor
Cartin, Richard Daniel
Soc Stud & Voc Ed Teacher
Champlin, Jean Hawk
Mathematics Teacher
Childs, Michael Scott
Junior High Science Teacher
Clark, Jana Meyer
Creative Writing Teacher
Clark, Thomas Arthur
Prof of Urban & Regnl Planning
Claunch, Dori Janell
Physical Ed & Health Teacher
Clinton, Patricia Ann (Garvey)
L A & Reading Teacher
Colasanti, Georgette Elizabeth
Language Arts Teacher
Cole, Kathy Milne
Third Grade Teacher
Coppola, Carol A.
Language Arts Teacher
Creber, Walter Joe
Biology Teacher
Creel, Richard Dock
Soc Stud Teacher & Dept Chair
Curry, Anita Dreiling
Third Grade Teacher
Dailey, Wendy Wikholm
Choir Teacher
Davison, Diane Dykes
French Teacher
Dawson, Sandy J.
Assoc Prof of English
Dicker, John M.
Algebra I Teacher
Dixon, Christopher Gene
Fine Arts Chairman & Teacher
Dodson, Kathryn Koning
8th Grade Algebra Teacher
Druggan, Pat
PE Instructor & Dept Chair
Dunn, Jean C.
Mathematics Teacher
Duran-Aydintug, Candan
Asst Prof of Sociology
Dykhouse, Pamela Ledeboer
Art Teacher
Eberhardt, David R.
Political Science Instructor
Elliott, Robert Greer
JROTC Instructor
Ellsworth, Harold Richard
Social Studies Teacher
Erger, Catherine M.
English & Journalism Teacher
Estrada, Vickie Jean (Poague)
ESOL Teacher
Evans, Paulette Garrison
7th & 8th Grade English Tchr
Ewer, Michelle Berndt
Orchestra & Band Director
FeKete, Anita M.
Accounting Professor
Feldbush, James Martin
Guidance Counselor
Fengler, Daryl Wayne
Math Teacher
Ferguson, Charles Andrew
Sr Instructor of Biology Dept
Field, Daniel
Graphic Design Instructor
Foster, James Michael
Leadership Dev Dept Chair
Foster, Pat E.
Science Teacher
Fox, Ronald Charles
Music Director
Franks, Joyce S.
German & English Teacher

DENVER (cont)
Friedrich, Phil M.
Assistant Principal
Garceo, Mamie Pope
Science Teacher
Garcia, Delia M.
Diversity Achievement Coach
Gathman, John J.
AP American His & Psych Tchr
Gilbert, Paula Louise (Ruzicka)
HS Vocal Music Teacher
Glazier, Lisa Layne
English & Speech Teacher
Glenn, Kerry Lee
Mathematics Teacher
Goggin, Shelly Dawn Dalton
Electrical Engrng Asst Prof
Golembeski, Betty Stapp
8th Grade Social Studies Tchr
Gonzales, Frank N.
Principal
Goodnight, Gary Warren
Science Teacher
Gordon, Judy J.
Fifth-Sixth Grade Teacher
Gosman, Sue
Sr HS Spanish Teacher
Goss, Patricia Elizabeth
Social Studies Teacher
Grant, Judith Wilson
Eng Teacher & 8th Grd Advisor
Greaves, Barbara J.
Amer Govt, Law, World His Tchr
Greenlee, Lewis C.
History Teacher
Grenawalt, Jay A.
Intnl Baccalaureate Pgm Instr
Grull, Paul A.
6th Grade Teacher
Guerrero, Connie N.
Fourth Grade Bilingual Teacher
Hagen, Monys A.
History & Women's Studies Prof
Hammond, Timothy Michael
Science & Physical Ed Teacher
Hart, Richard L.
Economics Professor
Hartman, Douglas Bruce
President of CO Fed of Tchrs
Heath-Klinger, Mary Susan
History Teacher
Hess, Alison Ross
Assistant Professor of Acctng
Hill, Carol (Monahan)
English Teacher & Yearbook Adv
Hockenbury, Robert D.
Accounting Professor
Hogan, Patrick Brian
Chemistry & Physics Teacher
Huber, Frances Fay
High School Math Teacher
Huber, Martin Emile
Asst Prof of Physics
Humphrey, Amparo Ramos
Spanish & French Teacher
I, Jesse Cheng-Fan
Professor of Chemistry
Ingram, Dennis L.
Principal
Jagoe, Paulette Hill
6th Grade Teacher
Janes, Craig Robert
Assoc Prof of Anthropology
Johnson, Ann
English & GED Professor
Jones, C. Robert
Biology & IPS Teacher
Kerstiens, Deline M.
Spanish Teacher
Kimbrough, Doris Renate
Chemistry Professor
King, Patricia Ramsey
Instructor of Accounting
Kinghorn, John Gordon, III
English Teacher
Kinney, Dick Joseph
Biology & Physical Ed Tchr
Kirwan, Carol A. (Stanojev)
HS ESOL Teacher
Kitzmiller, Stanley Phillip
Fourth Grade Teacher
Knauber, David Lawrence
Professor
Knighton, John Andrew
Physics Teacher
Koester, Evelyn G.
Elem Physical Education Tchr
Koester, Rich D.
Fourth Grade Teacher
Kos, Dennis Steven
Industrial Tech & Math Teacher
Kourse, Lauralee Dale
Chemistry Teacher
Kovoor-Misra, Sarah
Management Professor
Kramer, Andy Thomas
Chemistry Teacher
Krauss, Louis W.
Social Studies Teacher
LaCroix, Jane Simmons
Fourth Grade Teacher
Lander, Joanne Methner
Fourth Grade Teacher
Langford, Andrew
Associate Professor of Biology
Lawlor, Greta Veselik
Mathematics Teacher
Lee, Patsy Linn
Associate Professor
Lehtinen, Joanna K.
Third Grade Teacher
LeMasurier, Wesley Ernest
Geology Professor
Linan, Pamela
Pgm for Pupil Assistance Tchr
Linville, Susan E.
English & Film Stud Professor
Loftus, Susan M.
Fourth Grade Teacher
Luttrull, Caroline Wilson
Staff Developer
Mac Carter, Stephanie S.
College Counselor
Macdonald, Patricia Lynn (Davis)
Fifth Grade Teacher
Maes, Kathryn Gonder
Associate Professor of Theatre
Martin, Loraine (Krings)
4th Grade Teacher
Martin, Steven Michael
Dean of Students & Sci Teacher
Mays, John Rushing
Professor of Civil Engineering
Mc Call, Ron
Fourth Grade Teacher
Mc Ginnis, Michael J.
Mathematics Teacher
McHenry, Scott R.
Business & Computer Teacher
Meagher, Christopher Morgan
Psych & US History Teacher
Medema, Steven George
Economics Prof & Dept Chairman
Mehring, W. Darryl
Instructor of Philosophy
Mendelsberg, Andy Ray
English Teacher
Meras, Joanne
French Teacher
Michaud, Kathleen J.
Instrumental Music Teacher
Milavec, James Lee
Science Teacher
Miles, Mary Ann
Library Media Specialist
Mills, Carolyn Louise
First & Second Grade Teacher
Mitchell, Doug
Math Teacher
Monsour, William Michael, III
Communication Professor
Moone, Charles L.
Professor of Fine Arts
Moriarty, Viola Rose
Eng as Second Lang Tchr, Coord
Mowery, Candis Delzell
Teacher
Murphy, Brendan C.
Social Studies Teacher
Murphy, Terri Lee
Math Teacher
Myers, Charles Bernerd
Technical Education Teacher
Neiman, Bennett Robert
Assoc Prof of Architecture
Obstfeld, Diana Taberski
Mathematics Teacher
Olson, Ann
French & Spanish Teacher
Ott, Larry Ann Ortiz
Biology Teacher
Parrott, Craig H.
Bible & English Teacher
Pawlowski, Cheryl Joyce
Professor
Paxton, Wesley Freeman
Teacher & Coordinator
Payne, David Michael
Theatre Teacher
Peden, Troy Duane
Stud Abroad Coordinator
Peters, David Tate
History & Economics Teacher
Pfenning, Jacqueline Hammelmann
Music Teacher & Choir Director
Phillips, Timothy J.
Instructor of German
Phillips, Vickie K. Fuller
Science Teacher
Pinar, Libby Smith
Dietetic Professor Emerita
Pointer, Marsha Gentry
Assistant Principal
Porterfield, Susan Smart
Counselor
Potts, Barbara Anne
English Dept Chairman
Powell, Deborah Totten
Middle School Art Teacher
Price, Michael Eugene
Social Studies & Business Tchr
Qualteri, Brenda Louise
Consumer & Family Stud Tchr
Quansah, George Kojo
Economics Professor
Quigley, Mo Monahan
Site Coordinator
Razani, Ata R.
PE Teacher
Redford, Duane Robert
Industrial Arts Teacher
Redford, Kyle Larson
History & English Teacher
Ritter, Joyce Ilene (Bradley)
4th Grade Teacher
Roach, Abby B.
HS Art Teacher
Rosen, Ted
English & Theater Teacher
Saltar, Mary Maureen Robert
US History Teacher
Sanchez, Patricia Delaney
Third Grade Teacher
Sanders, Richard Wayne
Professor of Music Engineering
Savage, Marjory J.
English Teacher
Saveliev, Alexei N.
Assistant Professor of Russian
Sawyer, James Robert
Social Studies Teacher
Schaap, Judith Anne
Classroom Teacher
Schaefer, Lyle L.
Dept Chairman & History Tchr
Scheck, Suzanne Didier
5th Grade Teacher
Schnicker, Heidi Schoen
Math Tchr of Gifted & Talented
Schroeder, Marcia Holm
4th Grade Teacher
Schutt, Elizabeth N.
Substitute Teacher
Sen, Pankaj K.
Electrical Engineering Prof
Shikes, Patricia Ann
French & Spanish Teacher
Siefkes, Keith Henry
Math & Physical Ed Teacher
Simington, William Robert
Science Teacher
Simons, Shirley Ann
Third Grade Teacher
Singer, Eric J.
German Teacher
Singer, Sherry L.
2nd Grade Classroom Teacher
Smit, Janice Marie-Jaax
Third-Fourth Grade Teacher
Smith, Denise Lorraine
High School Mathematics Tchr
Smith, Judiith Miller
Secondary Science & Math Tchr
Smits, Donna Afman
Second Grade Teacher
Snelling, Thomas Allan
6th Grade Teacher
Springer, Scott C.
Instrumental Music Teacher
Starck, Pamela Peters
Art Tchr & Stu Activities Dir
Stilman, Boris
Professor of Computer Science
Stocker, Candace Gressett
Social Studies Teacher
Streeter, Daniel Robert
Social Studies Teacher
Sullivan, Mary Rose
English Professor
Suter, John L.
US History Tchr & Tennis Coach
Swiney, Kenneth W.
Sociology Instructor
Thomas, William C.
English Teacher & Lecturer
Thorpe, Judith Kathleen
Assoc Prof of Art & Chprsn
Timmons, Katherine Yeager
Dir of Ger Studs & Stud Act
Tisdell, Barbara Lynn
4th Grade Teacher
Tricarico, John Nicholas
Mathematics Teacher
Trickel, Donald D.
AP Coll American His Teacher
Tucker, Elaine Deacon
Lit, Math, Speech & Span Tchr
Van Deman, Brenda Teter
English Teacher
Venters, Kathleen Mary
Religious Education Director
Wagner, Flo Stephens
Student Advisor & Teacher
Walker-McDowell, Sally Virginia
Counselor
Weber, James H.
Mathematics Professor
Weese, Jennifer Carol
7th & 8th Grade Science Tchr
Wehlage, Frank Carroll
Physics & Mathematics Teacher
West, Shermita Gray
Second Grade Teacher
Whitehead, Roger
Psychology Professor
Wiener, Sarah Elizabeth
Fourth Grade Teacher
Wolf, James B.
Professor of History
Wurst, Linda Hochevar
English Teacher
Young, Kathy Hill
Adjunct Faculty
Zaidins, Clyde Stewart
Professor of Physics

DILLON
Agone, Camille Licciardi
Elementary School Principal
Wynne, Margaret Levitt
Fifth Grade Teacher

DOLORES
Melvin, Charles Edward
Science Dept Chairperson
Powell, Charles W.
Math & Cmptr Sci Instr
Tompkins, E. Sue (Van Camp)
HS English & French Teacher

DOVE CREEK
Buffington, Jim Glen
History Teacher & Athletic Dir
Odette, Bert Leon
Math & Science Teacher
Rice, Edward James
Secondary Agriculture Teacher
Soper, Kenneth L.
PE, Wt Trng & Soc Stud Tchr

DURANGO
Aten, K. Kevin
Graphics & Media Advisor
Blue, Thomas Ralph
Organizational Behavior Prof
Cano, Miguel F.
Full Professor
Coleman, Judith Fernekes
Mathematics Teacher
Dare, Byron D.
Prof of Political Science
DeNier, Barb Wolfe
Counselor & Coach
Jeep, Lola J.
Social Studies Teacher
Kendall, Deborah M.
Professor of Biology
Kendrick, Carolyn L.
Art & Ceramics Teacher
Kraemer, Dale Alan
Sci, Math, Hlth & Eng Tchr
Mann, Rochelle (Ryder)
Music Professor
Martinez, Clair
Counselor
McClain, Alice Ann
English Teacher
Mosher, Nicole Marie
Associate Professor of French
Myers, Jolleen Ann (seculo)
Sixth Grade Teacher
Peterson, Carroll V.
Professor of English
Raso, Amy Heather
Physical & Alternative Ed Tchr
Schultz, Debora Frazier
Spanish Teacher
Wood-Patterson, Mona L.
Theatre Director & Teacher
Yoast, Karen M.
2nd Grade Teacher

EAGLE
Stanish, Kasey Elizabeth
Hlth & Physical Education Tchr

EATON
Preston, Ronald Lee
Ag Ed Instr
Trotter, Thomas Michael
Social Studies Teacher

ELBERT
Carothers, Rick Dean
Physical Ed & Health Teacher

ELIZABETH
Culver, David W.
Technology Education Teacher

ENGLEWOOD
Adair, Mindy Heather
Math & Science Teacher
Anderson, Belinda Dyan
Social Studies Teacher
Anderson, Lynn Allen
HS Mathematics Teacher
Archer, Patricia Wagner
Kindergarten Teacher
Bader, Michael T.
Chemistry Teacher
Bagwin, Lilette Stella (Levy)
Math & Computer Science Tchr
Barber, Daniel Wynn
Social Studies Teacher
Bradley, William J.
English & AP Art History Tchr
Bristow, Roberta MC Millen
English & Forensic Teacher
Brown, Mary Glass
Hlth Occupations Instr & Coord
Carlson, Diane Diack
Third Grade Teacher
Collins, Edward Lawrence
Math Teacher & Dept Chair
Cooper, Benjamin Evans
English Department Co-Chair
DeAntoni, Karen D.
English Teacher & Dept Chair
Doyle, Renae Louise (Blather)
Third Grade Teacher
Gilchrist, Jerry B.
Science Teacher
Gilford, Charles Andrew, Jr.
Dean of Students
Goldsberry, Mark Stephen
High School Health Teacher
Gumbay, R. Steven
Biology Teacher
Heath, Jayne Walker
General Music Teacher
Hitchens, Barbara Steiner
Junior High School Teacher
Hodgkinson, Joan Sidle
Math Teacher
Jacoby, Don William
Economics & History Teacher
Kempton, Theodore Luce
US History Teacher
Liden, Norm
Mathematics Instructor
Lofaro, Verna
French Teacher
Manceaux, Faye
Drama & English Teacher
Messer, Linda Rood-Hurd
Reading Specialist
Moore, Jefferie Jean Haynes
HS English & Social Stud Tchr
Nichols, Christine C.
Physics, Chem & Earth Sci Tchr
O Neil, J. Lee
Social Studies Teacher
Owen, Raylene Mc Williams
Biology Teacher
Paynter, David Ray
Biology Teacher
Poole, Shawn Patrick
Fourth & Fifth Grade Teacher
Prichard, Donna Katherine
Dean of Students
Rencehausen, Mark Charles
Sixth Grade Teacher
Ridgley, Donald James
Mathematics Tchr & Dept Chair
Rivet, Edmond-Joseph Matthias
Technology Coordinator
Rottmann, Mary Lou
Retired Sr Instr of Biology
Ryan, Ann Lane
Third Grade Teacher
St Peter, Lily Diaz
Spanish Teacher
Sanger, John M.
English & Physical Ed Tchr
Saracino, Jim M.
Secondary Math Teacher
Scruggs, Monique Christine (Benson)
Math Teacher
Selby, Frederic A.
Band Director
Siemers, Kaye L.
History Teacher
Stender, Margot Elizabeth (Ehler)
Third Grade Teacher
Streeter, Patricia Latimer
English Teacher
Talich, William Charles
Ninth Grade Physical Sci Tchr
Torrance, Gregory David
4th-5th Grade Classroom Tchr
Walton, Michael Gene
English Teacher
Wanger, Rhonda Primack
Mathematics Teacher
Weber, Paul Joseph
Art Teacher
Wischmann, Pat J.
Physical Education Teacher

ERIE
Bain, Leonard Rodney
Science Teacher
Binkley, David Hugh
Math, Physics Tchr & Coach
Gaetzke, Karen A. (Koss)
9th-12th Grd Mathematics Tchr
Lienert, Patricia M.
Middle School Math Teacher
Vogel, Elaine Jane Leinweber
Social Studies & German Tchr

ESTES PARK
Bradford-Richardson, Nancy S.
Fifth Grade Teacher
Brown, Laura S.
Spanish & English Teacher
Johnson, Robert Bruce
8th Grade English Teacher
LaMarsh, Marilyn Patrice
Teacher, Trainer & Mentor
Tucker, Karen Dee
7th Grade Language Arts Tchr
Varilek, Chuck F.
Director of Bands

EVERGREEN
Brant, Sally Schwartz
1st Grade Teacher
Brown, Susan Elizabeth
Fifth Grade Teacher
Griffin, Kerry Marie
Social Studies Teacher
Jackson, AnnaMarie
Intermediate Classroom Teacher
Jennings, Marion Miller
Teacher
Loper, William E.
Band & Choral Director
Lukich, Thomas Russell
Soc Studies Tchr & Dept Chair
Lyon, Evelyn DeLafose
Former Business Teacher
Reese, Linda Jean J.
Consumer & Family Studies Tchr
Tenney, Susan Ann (Bruce)
Language Arts & Soc Stud Tchr

FAIRPLAY
Rzepka, Steve L.
Counselor

FLAGLER
Bode, Carol Williams
High School Math Teacher

FLORENCE
Anderson, Robert Ronald
Mathematics Teacher
Caricato, Josephine Gemma
8th Grade Language Arts Tchr
Heid, Larry E.
Fourth Grade Teacher
Lemmon-Oliver, Lynn Cherie
History & Psychology Teacher
Miller, Fran (Jackson)
English Tchr & Yearbook Tchr
Odom, Cynthia Johnson
Fourth Grade Teacher

T CARSON
inney, Karen Lee (Oliver)
& 5th Grade Instructor
ed, Paul Aaron
Grade Algebra & Math Tchr
T COLLINS
n, Carol Lee (Green)
lish & Speech Teacher
sek, Alexandra
Professor of Economics
y, Jeffrey Lehman
nce Teacher
Don H.
hematics Teacher & Coach
n, Sally Jane
guage Arts Teacher
nan, Joyce Hamilton
n School Counselor
ensen, Scott Ervin
Instructor
er, David Ross
h & Physical Science Tchr
ova, Manuel A.
h Grade Physical Ed Tchr
Steven Eugene
n Grade Teacher
oza, Tony
nish Teacher
r, Mark Brian
Prof of Human Anatomy
Ann M.
ech Communication Professor
Patricia Lee
ondary English Teacher
nan, Nathan Samuel
or High English Teacher
n, James L.
rth Grade Teacher
on, Neil A.
9th Grd Music Teacher
Scott Phillip
nish Teacher
im, Kurt R.
Social Studies Teacher
t, John Duris
mistry Teacher
n, Eric Baker
covery Teacher
Margarita Maria
essor of Accounting
Marc S.
al Studies Teacher
n, Lisa R. (Dunkin)
dergarten Teacher
eal, James E.
ductor & Orchestra Teacher
Patrick Alan
dance Counselor
n, Richard Reu
tical Science & His Tchr
an, Janet K.
hematics Instructor
n, Edward Norman
red Instrmntl Music Tchr
neir, Judy Rae
Technologies Instructor
nard, Erik Allen
cipal & Teacher
rford, Lisa Ruth (Schultz)
nish & German Teacher
tz, Norman Otto
oc Prof of Accounting
er, William F.
D Special Education Instr
, Thomas Joseph
oc Prof of Civil Engrng
, Michael
d Director
, Patti Ann (Cumings)
care Fnds Prgm Instructor
, Teresa Irene
unct Faculty
, Jim M.
n Grade Instructor
Ronaldd H.
nselor
r, Beverly J.
ch, Anthropology & His Tchr
er, Mary L.
f of Bus Commnctn & Mgmt
n, William Lewis
ner HS Instr
svick, Carl Lee
lish Teacher & Debate Coach
, Jill Klyn
Grade Teacher
T LUPTON
on, Roberta
s Educator & Coach
ts, Donna Lee
lish Teacher
ng, Dan L.
sical Education Teacher
lo, Salvador Sam, Jr.
mistry & Physics Teacher
T MORGAN
bell, Gene Matthew, Jr.
hematics Teacher
th, Judith Ellen
h School English Teacher
, Julie Meng
h Grade Teacher
vig, Gail Russell
sical Therapist
nerer, Donald James
ial Studies Professor
, Virginia A. (Ruzicka)
red Teacher
Connie S.
nissions & Retention Dir

Pope, Jeff Scott
MS Health & Physical Ed Tchr
Thompson, Linda Ann Esquibel
Spanish Teacher
Westhoff, Sandra Weimer
Second Grade Teacher
FOUNTAIN
Eckert, Michelle Fredeen
1st Grade Teacher
Kalish, John Harry
Art Instructor
Maiurro, Michael Anthony
HS Social Studies Teacher
Paddock, Christopher Warren
American Government Teacher
Torbet, Masha (Bartley)
English Instructor
FOWLER
Mercer, Gail Robbins
Second Grd Teacher
Paublits, Timothy Lee
District Media Specialist
FREDERICK
Graham, David Charles
Mathematics Teacher
Hancock, Tara
Music Teacher
Kunches, Linda Rae
High School Counselor
Peitz, Daryl Eugene
Assistant Principal
FRISCO
Adams, Ed
Science Teacher
Bowers, Robert Eldon
Social Studies Teacher
Cooper, Jayne Christensen
9th-12th Grade English Teacher
Frazier, Anne Carole
Language Arts Teacher
Keeling, Mary Winquist
Spanish Teacher
McBride, David P.
Dir Enrichment Ed & Eng Tchr
Montijo, James H.
Math Teacher
Palmer-Moloney, Jean
Latin & Geography Teacher
Reinking, Christy A.
Science Teacher
Shannon, Peter N.
Chemistry Teacher
Wallace, William Creighton
Math Teacher & Dept Chair
FRUITA
Costello, Jack Duane
Chemistry & Physics Teacher
Falsone, Lisa Burns
Language Arts Teacher
Felix, Marty S.
7th Grade Language Arts Tchr
Gugat, Sharmin Brollier
4th Grade Teacher
Henry, Shanna E.
English Teacher & Dept Chm
Karly, Gregory Dean
Director of Bands
Kidder, Barbara Jean
7th Grd Soc Stud & Rdng Tchr
Meyer, Dallas Lee
Mathematics & Computer Teacher
Sandoval, Richard
Spanish Teacher
Schlager, Jami D.
German Teacher
Stites, Max D.
Eighth Grd US His & Rdng Tchr
Thomas, Gary Eugene
Mathematics Teacher
GALETON
Asbra, Gatha Williams
4th Grade Teacher
GILCREST
Eckhardt, Tracy Tuttle
Fifth Grade Elementary Teacher
Fedie, Pam Hopf
German Teacher
Pearson, Judith Kaiser
HS Mathematics Teacher
GLENWOOD SPRINGS
Brickell, Guy Warren
Soc Stud Dept Chm & Teacher
Kelley, Robert Daryl
Professor of Biology & Math
Lambert, Keith J.
Education Instructor
Starnaman, Craig Daniel
History Anthropology Instr
Vidakovich, Michael Anthony
4th Grade Teacher
Wescott, Annette
Lang Arts & Soc Stud Tchr
GOLDEN
Atwater, Judith Wheeler
Fourth Grade Teacher
Boian, Judythe Ann
English & Social Studies Tchr
Cawthra, Michael Erle
Sixth Grade Teacher
Cooper, Debra Anne
Counselor
Deselms, Gaylen R.
Physical Education Teacher
Ensminger, Mary Janice Cestkowski
American History Teacher
Juran, Heidi Hauser
Third Grade Teacher
Kinsey, Robert A.
Soc Studies & AP His Teacher

Leonard, Karen Kopp
Substitute Teacher
Martynuska, Jan Hall
Mathematics Teacher
Mc Kellips, Briant Wayne
Physics Teacher
Mummert, Charles E.
Dean
Munson, Thomas John
6th Grade Teacher
Myers, Roger Bradley
Social Studies Teacher
Northway, Robert A.
Jr & Sr High School Counselor
Panasewicz, Karen Marie
Dance Instr & Choreographer
Poveda, Linda Geike
Spanish Teacher
Shibly, Janet Jungmeyer
Vocal Instrumental Music Tchr
Sohrweid, Roberta Lee Maurer
Library Information Specialist
Steele, Lisa Ann
Student Outreach Administrator
Strong, Rosemary H.
Sixth Grade Teacher
Wahl, Lisa Marie
Social Science Teacher
GRANADA
Grasmick, Steven Bryan
Industrial Studies Teacher
Huffman, Robin Michelle
English Teacher
James, Renny P.
7th-12th Grade Science Teacher
GRANBY
Cherrington, Calvin
Physical Ed & Health Teacher
Cherrington, Tami J.
Physical Education Teacher
GRAND JUNCTION
Arroyo, Leslie Goodner
English Second Language Tchr
Baker, Boyce Allen
Science Teacher
Becker, Darrell Gene
Humanities Teacher
Cameron, Sandra Leah Bird
High School Teacher
Champion, Virginia Godfrey
Teacher of Gifted & Talented
Condit, Daniel W.
Tech Ed & Driver Ed Instructor
Cypher, Susan Marie
Private Vocal Teacher
Dearden, Dennis William
Assistant Principal
Egebrecht, Paula J. (Salerno)
Literature & American His Tchr
Elliott, Carol Ann
Physical Education Teacher
Fricke, Karen
Third Grade Teacher
Frisby, Linda Marie (Wood)
French & English Teacher
Garner, Demi Arapkiles
Alternative Education Teacher
Goetz, Anna Sperber
English & Speech Teacher
Goldsworthy, Christopher
Social Studies & Reading Tchr
Gugat, Terence Michael
Social Studies Teacher
Gurule, Laurence Manuel
Physical Education Teacher
Guth, Karen
Middle School Math Teacher
Haerle, Cynthia Louise
6th Grade Teacher
Hejny, Marcia Lynn
Business Teacher
Hokanson, Janet Pool
Third Grade Teacher
Hughes, Christopher Adam
Band Director
Ingram, Larry Charles
US History Teacher
Joseph, Kathy A.
High School Band Director
Kane, Mary Ann
Middle School Teacher
Kerr, Charles F.
English Teacher
Krueger, Michael John
Eighth Grade Science Teacher
Laase, Andrew Eric
Elementary School Principal
Lee, Kerry Dane
Language Arts Teacher
Leggero, Catherine Babicki
8th Grade Teacher
Lisco, Thomas Joseph
Tchr of Talented & Gifted Pgm
Loehr, Cristal Ann
English Teacher
Mac Donald, Rod Grant
Coach & Physical Ed Teacher
Matchee, Sally Meyer
Philosophy Professor
McClurg, Dannie Jones
Math Teacher
Mc Lennan, Raymond S.
Math Teacher
Moschetti, Tanya Eliz
7th Grade Teacher
Mottram, Claude William
Mathematics & Physics Teacher
Murray, Paul Belnap
Math Teacher

Myers, Toots C.
Bible & English Teacher
Newton, Mark Anthony
Journalism Tchr, Newspaper Adv
Perry, Leonard
Instrumental Music & Band Tchr
Pollert, Ned
Spcl Ed Resource Tchr
Polson, Houston Hardin
Business Professor
Rexroad, James Arthur
Math Teacher
Rinderle, Linda Watts
Lang Arts & Soc Stud Teacher
Salas, Salvador Valentino
Art Teacher
Schafer, Terri L.
Vocal Music Teacher
Schoenbeck, C. J. Dupps
9th Grade Counselor
Schrader, Lyle L.
Automotive Technology Instr
Seaman, Ted L.
Math & Science Dept Chair
Streeter, Robin Elaine
8th Grade Teacher
Thompson, Lorena Ann
English & Language Arts Tchr
Walker, D. John
English & Reading Teacher
Wells, Jeffrey Scott
Administrator
GREELEY
Ackley, Robert Steven
Comm Disorders Prof & Chprsn
Ayers, Kristin Jo Higgins
Special Ed Teacher & Counselor
Ballman, Terry Lynn
Assoc Prof of Span & Ed Tchr
Bjork, Lawrence Roy
Science Teacher
Blanding, Cindy Wyn
Assoc Professor of Recreation
Bohrer, Paul E.
Professor of Accounting
Burgess, Virginia L.
HS Counselor & Teacher
Canales, Genie
Psych & Hispanic Studies Prof
Clinebell, Sharon (Wyers)
Assoc Prof & Mgmt Dept Chrmn
Clukey, Lory
Nursing Professor
Condon, Ethel
Fourth & Fifth Grade Teacher
Copley, R. Evan
Professor of Music
D'Amato, Rik Carl
Prof, Dir of Schl Psych & Neun
Darrough, Galen Paul
Professor of Choral Music
DeHoogh-Kliewer, Michelle Marie
Counseling & Psych Grad Stud
Elliott, Kathy Ann
Health Teacher
Elsea, John Edward
Professor of Accounting
Farmer, Jeff D.
Asst Professor of Mathematics
Fentiman, Karen Kauffman
Vocational Education Tutor
Fernandez-Balboa, Juan-Miguel
Associate Professor
Fuchs, Richard
Professor of Violin
Galovich, Cynthia S.
Associate Professor of Physics
George, Hermon, Jr.
Professor of Africana Studies
Haefeli, John W.
Social Studies Educator
Hagerty, Patricia J.
Associate Professor
Hanson, Kathleen Ann
Mathematics Teacher
Hoffman, Eugene
Assoc Professor of Visual Arts
Hopkins, Kenneth Donald
Geology Professor
Hyslop, Richard Michael
Professor of Chemistry
Jackson, Catherine G. Ratzin
Kinesiology Professor
Jenkins, Virginia Ann
Assoc Prof of Visual Arts
Jones, Waldo Rosebush
Lang Arts, Thtr & Drama Instr
Kalu, Anthonia Chinyere
African Studies Professor
Karlin, Nancy J.
Assoc Professor of Psychology
Kastner-Wells, Peter
German Professor
Kiefer, Rita Brady
English & Women's Studies Prof
Klug, James R.
Vocational & Technology Tchr
Korth, Pamela R. Hanson
Vocal Music Teacher
Leafgren, Rita Rotunno
Instr of Earth Sciences Dept
Leichliter, Mark H.
English Instructor
Leners, Debra Woodard
Nursing Professor
Lenhart, Kay J. (Anderson)
Social Studies Teacher
Mc Beth, Sally
Assoc Prof of Anthropology

MIles, Diane Sari
Junior High Art Teacher
Minton, Sandra Cerny
Dance Program Coord & Prof
Prichard, David F.
Band Director
Reichel, Philip Lee
Sociology Professor
Rowe, Gail Stuart
History Professor
Siu-Runyan, Yvonne
Associate Professor
Smeltzer, Joe H.
High School Spanish Teacher
Spatz, Nancy K.
History Professor
Thomas, Karen Ann (Littlepage)
4th Grade Teacher
Trimberger, Linda Archibeque
5th Grade Teacher
Van Dyken, Ronald Lee
4th Grade Teacher
Vigil, MaryAnn
Third Grade Teacher
Warner, Linda Ann
Master Teacher
Warren, Steven D.
Gifted & Talented Specialist
Willis, Courtney W.
Associate Professor of Physics
Wilson, Mike Woody
Industrial Technology Teacher
Worrall, Janet Holasek
History Professor
GROVER
Babb, Katherine Bailey
Music & Chapter I Tchr
Healey, Patrick E.
History & English Teacher
GUNNISON
Bromley, Patricia Ellen
Physical Education Instructor
Coleman, Marta Jo
12th Grade English Instructor
Cooper, Craig Howard
Seventh Grd Mathematics Tchr
Rasche, Holly
Math & Science Teacher
Stegmaier, John Franklin
Science Dept Chair & Teacher
GYPSUM
Bujnowski, Nancy Ann
French, German & English Tchr
Vogel, Charles Arthur
Instructor & Soc Sci Dept Head
HAYDEN
Moos, Steven Andrew
Business Teacher
HENDERSON
Wides, Aaron Nathan
Fifth Grade Teacher
HIGHLANDS RANCH
Barker, James Hal
History & Pol Sci Teacher
Barnhardt, David E.
Social Studies Teacher
Beauchamp, Randy F.
French Teacher
Cohan, Daniel C.
Mathematics Teacher & Coach
Dolan, Robert Patrick
Physical Education Teacher
Flink, Ernest William
Psychology Teacher
Hall, Laura Shelton
Athletic Director
Hamulak, Dwana Diane
Seventh Grd Language Arts Tchr
Hart, Don G.
7th Grade Language Arts Tchr
Juniel, Cheryl Lynn
Spanish Teacher
Kirsch, Linda Hermsen
6th Grade Teacher
McCord, James Russell
Geography Teacher
Moore, Malcolm P.
Social Worker
O'Hara, Rindy S.
Life Management Teacher
Perry, India Lee
French & Spanish Teacher
Peterson, Gilbert Alan
Counselor & Educator
Reiling, Sharon Ward
Fourth Grade Teacher
Samuels, Barbara Jean
8th Grade Language Arts Tchr
Vincelette, Pete A.
Mathematics Teacher
Wallace, Michael John
Mathematics Teacher
Wille, Lisa Margaret
Spanish & ESL Teacher
Williamson, Christine Henry
Third Grade Teacher
Wynn-Gavel, Kathleen W.
Math Teacher & Dept Chprsn
HOLLY
Bland, Deborah (Dennis)
Science Teacher
Burns, Jackie Kalma
Math & Cmptr Sci Teacher
Fowler, Diane Olander
Fourth Grade Teacher
Roup, W. Bruce
Science & Amer Problems Tchr
HOLYOKE
Rafert, Ann L. (Smith)
HS Math & Computer Teacher

HOLYOKE (cont)
Watson, Daniel Ray
HS Math & Computer Teacher
HOTCHKISS
Reed, Robert Eugene
Social Studies Teacher
Schelle, David Christian
English & History Teacher
HUDSON
Gigliotti, Angela A.
Second Grade Teacher
HUGO
Meyer, David Brian
Art & Annual Teacher
HYGIENE
Esarey, Dallis Duane
Fifth Grade Teacher
IDAHO SPRINGS
Spencer, Cherri Thompson
Mathematics Teacher
IDALIA
Chamberlain, Dixie R.
Math & Reading Teacher
Mansfield, Gail Wingfield
Reading, English & Art Teacher
Moellenberg, Betty E.
Music, Band, Choir & Sci Tchr
Rittenhouse, James J.
Social Stud Tchr & Dept Chm
Soehner, Judith Ann
Second Grade Teacher
Weyerman, Cyndie Osbahr
K-12th Grd Special Education
IGNACIO
Billings, Jacqueline Pluzynski
Reading Teacher
Salazar, Laurie Harris
Math & Reading Teacher
Searle, Howard E.
Music Teacher
Smith, Rick Kevin
Computer Instructor
Somers, Julia Combs
Science Teacher
Swilling, Sheryl Rutt
Social Studies & English Tchr
ILIFF
Brandsted, Janice M.
Mathematics & Computer Teacher
INDIAN HILLS
Kuehster, Laura Hicks
5th & 6th Grade Teacher
JOHNSTOWN
Palmer, Howard M.
Chem, Physics Tchr & Sci Coord
Pasqua, David A.
Music Director
York, Alice Berg
English, Rdng & German Instr
JULESBURG
Williamson, Jean
Computer Tchr & Library Supvr
KEENESBURG
Gigliotti, Catherine F.
Reading & Social Studies Tchr
Hoke, Brenda K.
Social Studies Teacher
Jakel, Larry Wayne
Biology Instructor
KERSEY
Churchill, Linda Ruler
Retired History & English Tchr
Lauck, Mary Elaine
English & Journalism Teacher
Warden, Shirley Ann
Third & Fourth Grade Teacher
KIM
Fletcher, Susan Fair
English Teacher
KIOWA
Bozarth, Phyllis Mehard
First Grade Teacher
KREMMLING
Cameron, Kimberly Colburn
7th-8th Grd Soc Stud Teacher
Pesch, Jackie Valance
Business Teacher
LA JARA
Crowther, Brian
Business Teacher
Richardson, Marty
Building Trades Instructor
LA JUNTA
Gray, Joel L.
Chemistry Instructor
Hetrick, Terry L.
Dean of Instructional Svcs
Maik, Mike Paul
7th-8th Grade Science Teacher
Smith, Kelly Jo
Speech, Drama & English Tchr
Vialpando, Abel V.
English & Foreign Lang Prof
LA SALLE
Rains, Darrell E.
Retired Instrmntl Music Supvr
Rice, Mark Robert
8th Grade Physical Sci Teacher
LA VETA
Johnson, Robert Wayne
Language & Visual Arts Teacher
LAFAYETTE
Jones, Judy Markee
Music Teacher
Nihan, Amy Lauterbach
First Grade Teacher
Sanger, James R.
Phys Ed Teacher & Coach
Upczak, Francis John
Fifth Grade Teacher

LAKEWOOD
Bason, Linda C.
Kindergarten Teacher
Bauer, Linda Ann (Schardt)
Third Grade Teacher
Becker, Irene Colvin
Reading & Computer Teacher
Black, Niki E.
Department Chair & Instructor
Camy, Ann Lorraine
English Instructor
Chaney, Venita L.
3rd-4th Grade Teacher
Church, Kelly (Ward)
High School English Teacher
Eastman, Ben B., Jr.
Teacher
Filson, Jay Gordon
Art Teacher
Haddad, Donald F.
Mngmt & Mrktg Prof, Dept Chair
Hagebak, Gwendolyn Nylene
Second Grade Teacher
Hogue, Bruce David
Physical Science Teacher
Joy, Carla Marie
History Professor
Kaye, Steven John
Professor of Biology
Konstantakos, Zoi Konstantin
English Teacher
Kusulas, Elaine S.
4th Grade Teacher
Olson, Scott S.
Environmental Compliance Instr
Porter, Becky Ann
English Teacher
Ryan, Gordon D.
Math & Science Teacher
Sanchez, Fil H.
English, Speech & Drama Tchr
Sawyer, Kenneth Vern
Instrumental Music Director
Sellon, Katherine Hinkel
5th-6th Grade Multi-Aged Tchr
Spillyards, Joey
Drafting & Design Instructor
Watwood, Mary Jo Cochran
Language Arts & History Chair
Wright, William F.
High School History Teacher
LAMAR
Baer, Cynthia Lynn (Parsons)
Alternative Learning Ctr Dir
Coghill, Amos E.
Psych, Sociology & His Tchr
Easton, Dawni JoLynn
Marketing Instructor
Elarton, Mary T.
4th Grade Teacher
Heger, Janet Olinger
Mathematics & Cmptr Sci Tchr
Neal, Delores (Osteen)
Consumer & Family Stud Tchr
Scheuerman, Carole Walker
High School English Teacher
Washburn, G. Anne
Third Grade Teacher
LAS ANIMAS
Koenig, Gregory A.
High School English Teacher
Montoya, Michael Ray
Math Teacher & Athletic Dir
Spinden, Carl E.
English & Social Studies Tchr
Tanner, Nancy Fleming
History Teacher
LEADVILLE
Fattor, Melissa Mc Farland
Multi-Age Classroom Tchr
LIMON
Bailey, Don Alan
Biology Teacher
Bailey, Janet Kathleen Brown
French & Spanish Teacher
Grimes, David
Physical Ed & Health Teacher
Larson, Stacy Anger
Mathematics Teacher
Phillip, Amy (Wyckoff)
Science Teacher
Vratil, Jan
Third Grade Teacher
Vratil, Scott
Social Studies Teacher
LITTLETON
Akerfelds, Daniel Gene
Secondary Teacher
Alexander, Clark Earl
Psychology Professor
Andres, Leland G.
Vocal Music Teacher
Asleson, Sue Ellen (Weber)
4th Grade Teacher
Baca, Tina Lynn
Mathematics Teacher
Barron, Leonard Ray
Social Studies Dept Chair
Bloemen, Crystal L. (Chaffin)
8th Grade Science Teacher
Boehm, Bill W.
His, Anthropology & Ec Teacher
Boldman, Sandra Louise (Phillips)
Language Arts Teacher
Bond, Bruce
Social Science & PE Teacher
Bowser, Marilyn Gibson
Retired Elementary Teacher
Brenner, Janette Ann (Hailey)
Business Education Teacher

Brown, Sandra Jane
Sci, Human Growth & Dev Tchr
Cannava, Edward Salvatore
Band Director & Music Teacher
Cansler, Charm Taylor
Business Education Teacher
Carpenter, Jeanette Pedrotti
Chemistry Teacher
Chapman, Robert Charles
Music Teacher
Chase, Harriet Jane
Retired Fifth Grade Teacher
Collins, Ryan L.
9th-12th Grade Counselor
Comeaux, Linda Fay
Med Lab Tech Instr & Pgm Dir
Cummings, Peggy A. (Paynter)
7th Grd Soc Studies Teacher
Dampier, Robert Randall
Physical Ed & Health Teacher
Davis, Pamella Flansburg
Sixth Grade Teacher
Dinmore, Kathy A.
High School Science Teacher
Dinwiddie, George A.
High School Math Teacher
Dolan, Patrick Thomas
Full Member English Dept
Dorais, Roger
Energy Manager
Drury, Mark Joseph
English Teacher
Emsing, Lawrence John
Social Studies Teacher
Farrell, James DeArey
Director of Vocal Music
Filipiak, Ann Rogers
Math Teacher
Fitch, Thomas Patrick
Science Teacher
Gentry, Gregory Reid
Choral & Orchestral Music Dir
Goddard, Robert Melvin
Fourth Grade Teacher
Goorman, Joan W. Retzlaff
Retired English & Drama Tchr
Graf, Galen Kim
Mrktg, Bus Ed & DECA Coord
Hampshire, Mark Douglas
Secondary Teacher
Hardwick, Sally J.
PE & Aeronautics Teacher
Hardy, Timothy Briant
Mathematics Teacher
Hart, Gayle Madsen
Second Grade Teacher
Havens, Terry
HS Math Teacher & Coach
Hawthorne, Ray Clarence
US History & Law Teacher
Herring, Katherine B.
World History Instructor
Hicks, Tonya Anita
Spanish & Russian Teacher
Hightower, Janice M. (Korber)
1st Grade Teacher
Hirsch, Cynthia Lee
Consumer Family Studies Tchr
Hitchens, Joan Keene
High School Art Teacher
Huff, Elaine Esther
Retired Elementary Teacher
Hyland, Peter Ryan
Science Teacher
Johnson, Jim
Counselor & Articulation Cnslr
Kay, William Terry
Science Teacher
Keesecker, Wallace Leland
Advanced Placement Chem Tchr
Keller, Kimberlee Ann (Clary)
English & Religion Teacher
Lettes, Charles S.
Language Arts Teacher
Linkhart, Brian Dwight
Science Teacher
Lonnquist, Stephanie Tinan
High School English Teacher
Lovitt, Sharon K.
Spanish Teacher
Luther, Barbara Maywald
Art & Journalism Teacher
Mann, Erin G.
Chemistry & Science Teacher
Marcum, Della Mae
Retired Elementary Teacher
McClelland, Virginia Faye
Seventh Grade Teacher
Mc Connell, Carole Gehrke
Fifth Grade Teacher
McCune, Jeanne Marie
8th Grd Social Studies Tchr
McGrath, Baree Lynn
4th & 5th Grd Multi-Age Tchr
Meagher, Patricia Ursini
8th Grade Mathematics Teacher
Molzer, Ann Stanko
Science Teacher
Narracci, Albert Joseph, Jr.
High School Teacher
O'Dell, Jean Priest
French Teacher
Osborne, Pamela Allen
Spanish Teacher
Parnell, Rebecca Stewart
Amer & AP US History Teacher
Pfeiff, Otto Lewis
Prof of Eng & Philosophy
Poole, Scott Edward
Lang Arts & Soc Stud Teacher

Ribelin, Michael L.
Vocational Coordinator
Roberts, Donna J.
Counselor
Rogers, Birgit Christine
German & English Teacher
Rosentrater, Gwendolyn Henry
Dist Coordinator for GATE
Russell, Lindsay G.
Mathematics Teacher
Sadler, Glenda R.
High School Math Teacher
Samson, Carol Reese
AP English Teacher
Schneider, Carole Grotz
Math & Science Teacher
Semin, Dennis Dale
Stu Act Dir & Math Teacher
Skarda, Bryan Douglas
Mathematics Teacher
Sneddon, George Allen
Earth Science Teacher
Sonnkalb, Marilyn Miles
Bus, Technology & Math Teacher
Stahlhut, Barbara McElroy
Mathematics Teacher
Stephens, Ramona Attig
Second Grade Teacher
Summers, Sharon Frances
English Teacher
Sweetland, Thomas G.
Second Grade Teacher
Trammell, Victorine Mae
Instructor of Biology
Trelfa, Eugenia Marie
6th Grade Teacher
Troxel, Dan
Technology Education Teacher
Vlasin, Judy Zimmerman
Secondary English Teacher
Vucich, James Joseph
PE & Health Teacher
Wanty, Virginia
Assistant Principal
Webster, Armistead Churchill Gordon
Principal
White, Ronald Leonard
Mathematics Teacher
Wilborn, Verna R.
Social Studies Teacher
Williamson, Cindy Calhoun
5th Grade Teacher
Wirsbinski, William Francis
High School Math Teacher
Zajicek, Gladys Harvey
Business Technology Instructor
LOMA
Hoelscher, Joan C. Walker
Ret 6th Grd Sci & Math Tchr
LONGMONT
Adams, David Edward
World & American History Tchr
Adams, Diana P.
US History Teacher
Baranway, Phyllis Kay Schaefer
English & Amer History Tchr
Bergamo, Michael Scott
Social Studies Teacher
Blackwood, Lois Burchett
1st & 2nd Grade Teacher
DeSantis, Emilio
Chemistry & Physics Teacher
Fisher, Janice Arbaugh
Math & Biology Teacher
Fisk, Patsy R.
Kindergarten Teacher
Gaudio, James Joseph
C P Chemistry Teacher
Greene, Karen Ann
First Grade Teacher
Henson, Timothy John
Science Teacher
Huck, Albert Richard
High School Science Teacher
Johnson, John Doug
Mathematics Teacher
Kelsch, Sharon Ann
Retired Teacher
Kennelly, Lila Marie (Romolo)
1st Grd Biling Ed Teacher
Main, Karen Culver
Accompanist
Martenson, Shannon Stromquist
English & Forensics Teacher
Moeller, Dianne B.
English & Forensics Teacher
Mysyk, Jeanne Sparling
6th-8th Grd Soc Studies Tchr
Nagelkirk, Joy Allyn
Mathematics Teacher
Niccore, Madeline Droitcourt
Bio & Environmental Sci Tchr
Rieser, Linda Neill
8th Grd Language Arts Teacher
Sargent, Robert G.
Mathematics Teacher
Schultz, Paul James
Principal & 5th-8th Grade Tchr
Stephens, William A.
Ath Director & Tech Teacher
Stricklin, Patricia Naples
Language Arts & Forensics Tchr
Tanner, Thomas E.
Physical Education Teacher
Tinius, Karen Sue
Kindergarten Teacher
Underwood, Robert Dean
English Teacher
VanWinkle, Barbara Lee
5th Grade Teacher

Ward, Terri M.
Physical Education Teacher
Williamson, David Allen
World Geog, His & Ec Teacher
Woods, Kent Edward
Science & Physical Ed Teacher
LOUISVILLE
Arnold, Beth
Fifth Grade Teacher
Crnkovich, Christine Jones
Third Grade Teacher
Hendricks, Lloyd J.
Retired Chem & Physics Teacher
Tilley, Joanne Engel
Honors Math Teacher
Woolley, Edwin Lee
Retired Teacher
LOVELAND
Anderson, Devin F.
Industrial Sci & Tech Teacher
Beans, Troy Scott
Athletic Director
Berry, Robert S.
Soc Stud Teacher & Admin Asst
Black, Marcus Edward
English & Journalism Teacher
Breidenbach, Anita Clementz
Third Grade Teacher
Brown, Nancy Kay
Title I Teacher
Burns, Marilyn Baird
Seventh Grade Lang Arts Tchr
Coleman, Jeanie Ann
Fourth Grade Teacher
Cowan, David Howard
High School Counselor
Davis, Carrie Kiehn
8th Grd Language Arts Teacher
D'Orazio, Joseph
Spanish & Mathematics Teacher
Dunkin, David Bruce
Music Teacher
Evans, Leland E.
Mathematics Teacher
Fehl, David Allan
Science Teacher
Felton, Michael Scott
Ninth Grade Civics Teacher
Gabbert, Timothy Alan
Eighth Grade Teacher
Giauque, Linda M.
Math Teacher
Glasgow, Patricia Edgerton
Fifth Grade Teacher
Glover, Gary A.
English Teacher & Dept Chair
Gutowsky, Wayne R.
Soc Stud & US History Teacher
Halvorsen, Douglas Brian
High School Chemistry Teacher
Hansen, Craig William
Elementary Principal
Jaramio, Frances Ann (Thomas)
English Dept Chr & Vice Prin
Johnson, Stephan Charles
Earth Science Teacher & Coach
Kniese, Valerie Marcene
Third Grade Teacher
Kowalski, Tom Albert
High School Counselor
Lange, Christopher Wade
Language Arts Instructor
Ludwig, David Lloyd
World History Teacher
McCormick, Ronald Jack
US History Instructor
Mc Laughlin, Bruce Alan
7th Grd Social Studies Teacher
Metcalfe, Leona Kay
Second Grade Teacher
Neigherbauer, James John
6th Grade Social Studies Tchr
Santomaso, Cindy M.
Third Grade Teacher
Short, Gerrianne
Sci, Bio, Genetics & Chem Tchr
Smith, Phyllis Marlene
5th Grade Teacher
Theilgaard, Jann Marie
Choir Teacher
Walter, Susan K.
Business Instructor
Welker, Claudia Mainard
French & Spanish Teacher
Whitcomb, Ellaine Oliver
Art Teacher
Williams, Anna Mae Stuben
Spanish Teacher & Dept Head
Williams, Harold F.
Math & Science Teacher
Wishon, Cindy Long
Third Grade Teacher
Ziesche, Barbara D. (Mecher)
German Teacher
LYONS
Cinnamon, Ken R.
Dean to Students
Kirby, James Douglas
Band Director
MANITOU SPRINGS
Astley, Stevie Kay Fouts
6th-12th Grd Choral Director
Barnett, Judith Kay
Social Studies Teacher & Coach
Barrera, Leona Rae
Spanish Teacher
Hokanson, Delrae Ruth
Head Coach & Coordinator
Johnston, Ron V.
Ath Dir & Psychology Teacher

ITOU SPRINGS (cont)
ag, Diana Lynn
lish & French Teacher
rew, Sharon G.
rd of Prgms for GATE Stdnts
Phil R.
ondary Math & Science Tchr
, Russ
rth Grade Teacher
ZANOLA
, Russell J.
sical Ed Teacher & Coach
cek, Ted Robert
ness Teacher
CLAVE
Nancy Jane Tucker
d Grade Teacher
r, Terry Michael
al Studies Teacher
D
w, Shari Smith
guage Arts Teacher
KER
, Mary Elaine
h & Social Studies Tchr
TURN
herty, Cheryl Ann
Grd Lang Arts Teacher
TE VISTA
r, David Eugene
h Teacher
, Ruth Ward
red Music Teacher
tt, Arlene
red Teacher
, Laura Lynn (Lopez)
ond Grade Teacher
adden, Alan D.
rnet Instructor
on, Mary Catherine (Romero)
nish Teacher
son, Cheri Ann
Grade Earth Science Tchr
nson, Gary Lynn
h School Science Teacher
, Eric
al Studies Teacher
TROSE
nan, Kenna Rae
eer Options Seminar Pgm Dir
er, Hans R.
al Science Instructor
Jan Kerr
h Grade Teacher
Beverly Bond
red 5th-6th Grade Teacher
y, Paul Patrick
& 9th Grade Soc Stud Tchr
Shawn
d Director
ermott, Carol Carmody
lish Teacher
n, Dan A.
red Science & Math Teacher
is, Richard George
h School History Teacher
an, Sheila J.
Grade Teacher
a, Carla R.
hematics Teacher
rs, Joan M.
red Elementary Teacher
ar, Lora H.
rth Grade Teacher
UMENT
kelman, Jane Thornley
5th Grade Teacher
n, Allan Dale
ach & English Teacher
Frederic Louis
guage Arts Instructor
edy, Karen C.
ma Teacher
Donald S.
hematics Teacher
pson, Sharon A. Manaugh
nselor
ks, Reid A.
nselor & Coach
RISON
s, Jerry A.
Grade Teacher
CA
rts, Yvette Bernadette
lish & Social Studies Tchr
ERLAND
nson, Kathleen Ann
nish & PE Teacher
ll, David W.
g Arts & Soc Stud Teacher
CASTLE
ur, Jack J.
lish & Reading Teacher
RAYMER
sen, Roger
h & Computer Instructor
THGLENN
n, Joyce Lipovsek
h Grade Teacher
es, Cindy J.
h, Sci & Soc Stud Teacher
, Linda Anna
guage Arts Teacher
WOOD
n, Thomas P.
red Teacher
e, Lea Roy
red Mathematics Teacher

NUCLA
Sandefur, Denice Cary
Science Chairperson & Instr
OAK CREEK
Johnson, Robert Morris
Physical Education Teacher
OLATHE
Pleau, Mary Lucas
Fifth Grade Teacher
Ready, Lance C.
High School Science Teacher
Sullivan, Russ Bruce
Mathematics Teacher
ORDWAY
Fosdick, Jacque Grooms
AP Eng, Speech & Drama Tchr
Gavin, Troy
Physical Ed & Soc Stud Tchr
Wise, Gregory Thomas
Jr High Science Teacher
OTIS
Samber, Susan Kraich
English & History Teacher
OURAY
Fagrelius, Eric Walter
Science & Math Teacher
Hughes, Lonnie
5th Grade Physical Ed Teacher
Rushing, Diane Paul
English Instructor
OVID
Killifer, Kathleen M.
Mathematics & Computer Teacher
PAGOSA SPRINGS
Charles, Kahle Robert
Social Studies Teacher
PALISADE
Cameron, Robert Monroe
Biology Instructor
Conaway, Ann
High School Mathematics Tchr
Vogt, Scott L.
Language Arts Teacher
PAONIA
Curtice, Brent Allan
Principal
PARACHUTE
Cain, Michael Scott
Industrial Arts Teacher
PARKER
Bartok, James Allen
History Teacher
Brinker, Margaret Maud
Physics & Math Teacher
Byrne, Tara C.
8th Grd Language Arts Teacher
Crock, Bret L.
Mathematics Teacher
Davies, Linda Ann
Art Teacher
Durbin, Geri Lee
PE Teacher & Coach
Grantier, Patricia Mann
Counselor
Iovino, Linda Matney
English Teacher
Johnson, Cynthia Lee (Gray)
Counselor
Morgan, Bruce Phillip
Fourth Grade Teacher
Puga, Charles A., III
Social Studies Teacher & Coach
Randall, John Clifton
History Teacher
Rauh, Don W.
Industrial Arts Teacher
Rauh, Kimberley Nephew
Soc Stud Teacher & Dept Chair
Sabec, Janet Kathleen
English & Speech Teacher
Simpson, Bob
Mathematics Teacher
Stanton, C. Danelle
Spanish Teacher
Stump, Timothy Joe
English & Journalism Teacher
Tabola, Toby J.
Psychology & Sociology Teacher
Thompson, Linda Kannegieter
Special Education Teacher
PEETZ
Bickel, Shirley Ann
Mathematics Teacher
PENROSE
Cook, Katherine Anne (Merchant)
7th Grd Span & Lang Arts Tchr
PEYTON
Carmody, Shaun
Mathematics Teacher
Phillips, Carol A.
English Teacher
Ross, Raymond Foster
Special Education Dir & Cnslr
White, Marni Rychener
Third Grade Teacher
PLATTEVILLE
Enright, Kristan Shane
Eighth Grade Mathematics Tchr
Schaffer, Patricia Salberg
Language Arts & Reading Tchr
Thomass, Signe L
3rd Grd Tchr
PUEBLO
Armijo, Peggy Ann
Language Arts & Jrnlsm Tchr
Aronosfky, Suzanne
High School Biology Teacher
Barnett, Janet Heine
Assoc Professor of Mathematics

Beeman, Carl Edward
Agricultural Sciences Instr
Benfield, Arthur Merrill
Social Studies Teacher
Betz, Kay Hedrick
Third Grade Teacher
Blea, Alice Romero
Spanish Teacher
Bonacquista, Joseph Martin
US & Colorado History Teacher
Borton, John Miles
Assoc Prof Cmptr Info System
Bottini, Patrick W.
Assoc Prof Industrial Sci
Brotherton, Tim Dale
American History Teacher
Burke, Devon (Periman)
Science Teacher
Chenoweth, Janice Danti
Social Studies Teacher
Chorak, Michael Gene
Social Science Teacher
Cody, Deborah Bollendorf
French Teacher
Cooper, Doyle Lynn
8th Grd Social Studies Teacher
Cowen, Elizabeth L.
Eng, Speech & Drama Teacher
Epstein, Susan B.
Speech Communication Instr
Fajt, Albert Ray
Mathematics Teacher
Gallegos, Geraldine Hilda (Rivas)
High School Counselor
Gallegos, Salvador Lawrence
9th-12th Grd Lang Arts Tchr
Genova, Charles P.
Social Studies Teacher
Genova, Wayne D.
Choir Director & Dept Chair
Gramstorff, Chris
Assistant Principal
Gribben, Tom J.
Biology & Chemistry Teacher
Haley, H. Robert
Physical Education Teacher
Hansen, Darwin Duane
Marketing Education Teacher
Herrmann, Scott J.
Professor of Biology
Holder, Gary Eugene
Theatre & Lang Arts Teacher
Kaumeyer, Alvin Gregory
Teacher
Krueger, Judie Pelmear
LD Teacher Assistant
LeFebre, John L.
Spanish Teacher
Leonard, Barbara Jean (Chatham)
Science Teacher
Levy, Patricia Anne
Assistant Prof of Psychology
Longoria, Randall G.
Spanish Teacher & Coach
Lujan, Leonor Lucrecia
Honors English & Spanish Tchr
Martinez, Ulfredo Luther
4th Grade Teacher
McConnell, Allan D.
Adjunct Instructor of Business
Medve, Patricia Anna Marie
Assistant Principal
Muniz, Shirley Amore
High School Math Teacher
Nelms, Chlide Alan
Marketing Ed Tchr & Coord
Nogare, Mario A.
History & Psychology Teacher
Parlapiano, Mary M.
Title 1 Reading Teacher
Poole, Rita DeSimone
Language Arts Instructor
Post-Gorden, Joan Carolyn
Psychology Professor
Pounds, JoAnne Tomsick
Mathematics Tchr & Dept Chair
Presley, Dorothy L.
Retired Teacher
Proctor, Kristina Gae
Chem Prof & Dept Chair
Riesner, Rich H.
Mathematics Teacher
Rottinghaus, William S.
Biology Instructor
Roybal, Judith Arellano
Spanish Teacher
Ruiz, Deneen Marie (Noga)
Physical Ed & Health Teacher
Ryan, John
Professor of Teacher Education
Schmaltz, Mary Olive (Porco)
Retired Math Teacher
Schuster-Ward, Sandy G.
Teacher on Special Assignment
Sherman, Mary Jo (Steinbach)
Reading & Language Arts Tchr
Spade, Beatrice
Assoc Professor of History
Taylor, Cynthia Hinkel
Assistant Professor of English
Van Buiten, Lauren
Visual Arts Teacher
Weiler, Karen A.
Mathematics & Computer Teacher
Weiler, Russell
Science & Mathematics Teacher
White, Katherine M.
Home Economics Tchr & Chprsn
White, Patricia (Karg)
Social Studies Teacher

RANGELY
Thorsby, Kathleen Elizabeth
Math, Reading & Health Teacher
RIDGWAY
Lindsey, Gayle Atwell
Language Arts Teacher
RIFLE
Auxter, Susan M.
5th Grade Teacher
Balch, Christine Alice
Fifth Grade Teacher
Cotton, Joel B.
Teacher
LeMoine, Shirley Heck
District Coord of GATE
Mc Connell, Kelly Ann
Marketing Teacher
Scoggins, Mary Marilyn Miller
Fifth Grade Teacher
Skinner, Brad
Director of Student Services
ROCKY FORD
DeLeon, Doris Roybal
Kindergarten Teacher
RUSH
Keller, George Ray
Social Stud, PE & Hlth Tchr
RYE
Grenfell, Mary-Jo
Music Director
SAGUACHE
Duncan, Warren Stephen
Science & Mathematics Teacher
SALIDA
Butacan, Wilson Vern Ely
Mathematics Teacher & Coach
King, Steven Wayne
Phys Sci & Applied Math Tchr
Miller, Dale Eldon
Business Teacher
Phillips, Greg
4th Grade Teacher
SAN LUIS
Quintana, Linda Joyce
Voc Business & English Teacher
SANFORD
Hall, Robert Charles
Science Teacher
SEDALIA
Mc Cormack, Staci Cull Cull
Day Care Director
Reynolds, Stephanie Mary (Jakopovic)
Third Grade Teacher
SHERIDAN
Meadows, Roland Earl
Physical & Earth Sci Teacher
SHERIDAN LAKE
Fees, Ruth Anna
English & Spanish Teacher
SILT
Gates, Louayne Olson
Fifth Grade Teacher
SILVERTON
Fluckey, Alan R.
Spanish & English Teacher
O'Leary, Janet
Science, Art Tchr & Dept Head
Timbrell, Daniel William
Music Teacher & Coach
SIMLA
McClelland, Darrell James
Science Teacher
Schmidt, David Roland
Industrial Arts & PE Teacher
SPRINGFIELD
Bambor, Ralph Thomas
Business & Computer Instructor
Lacy, Verva Ann
First Grade Teacher
Mc Neal, Mary E.
4th Grade Teacher
STEAMBOAT SPRINGS
Ford, Kevin B.
Science Teacher
Johnson, Michael G.
5th Grade Teacher
Mc Kelvie, William R.
US History & Geography Teacher
Talle, Karen Noren
Third Grade Teacher
Wilderman, Lisa Hoehn
English Teacher
STERLING
Amen, Ken E.
Instructor of Equine Sciences
Donaldson, Gail A.
Ornamental Horticulture Coord
Gillham, Carol Watson
Kindergarten Teacher
Horsford, James
Business Instructor
Kaiser, Richard Eugene
Life Science Teacher
Perry, John Steven
Driver's Education Teacher
Schmale, Cindy R.
English Teacher
Wagner, Robert Charles
English & Speech Professor
STRASBURG
Ames, Merci Skiles
Biology & Anatomy Teacher
Deffenbaugh, Lawrence David
Social Studies Teacher
Ehrhorn, Kimberlee Dawn
Jr High Sci & HS Span Tchr
Schoonover, Mary Ellen
English, Speech & Drama Instr

STRATTON
Webb, Darryl Ernest
HS Science Teacher
SWINK
Bartolo, Kyle Teresa
Social Studies Teacher
Blanc, Al
HS Social Studies Teacher
Grossen, Bonnie Ruth (Shipman)
English Teacher
Stork, DeeAnn Merritt
Art Teacher
Wheeler, Donna Krout
Language Arts Teacher
THORNTON
Bleier, Jay Stuart
Math Teacher
Brown, Val L.
Psychology & US History Tchr
Egbert, Laurie A.
Counselor
June-Roppo, Mary Elizabeth
High School Teacher
Keiser, Bryan Paul
Spanish Teacher
Kerr, Jacquelyn Elaine (Nixson)
Vocal & General Music Teacher
Maenpaa, Ruth Elaine (Pettit)
English Teacher
Modrell, Jody
Counselor & English Teacher
Roth, Susan C.
High School Counselor
Thiel, Sharon Asato
Fourth Grade Teacher
Walsh, Margo
5th Grade Teacher
Wood, Kathy
English Teacher
TIMNATH
Skaflen, Eileen Ann
4th Grade Teacher
TRINIDAD
Aragon, Lou Ella
Business Teacher
Bachoroski, Vicki
Fourth Grade Teacher
Cihura, James Edward
Science Department Chair
Durland, William R.
Prof of Philosophy, His & Govt
Evans, Gregory
Dir of Stu Act & Instr of Eng
Gonzales, Verlie F.
Second Grade Teacher
Gurule, Ernestine Mestas
Third Grade Teacher
Huhn, Patricia Joan
Prof of English & Journalism
Leonetti, Robert
Psychology Professor
Lopez, Richard David
Soc Stud Tchr, Driver Ed Instr
Mason, Jennifer Sanchez
Secondary English Teacher
Miller, Kirk A.
Spanish Teacher
Mincic, Michael Anthony
Assoc Prof of Civil Engrng
Rino, Louis S.
English Teacher
USAF ACADEMY
Bogard, Judy Ann (Geer)
English & Speech Teacher
Davis, Lisa
French Teacher
Derr, Lee Stoner
Biology & Chemistry Teacher
Flygare, Jeff
English Teacher
Kim, Peter
Chemistry & Mathematics Tchr
Lafreniere, Kaye Loudon
Fourth Grade Teacher
Madden, Kimberly Ann
Math & Social Studies Teacher
McHenry, Barbara J.
Mathematics Teacher
Miller, Maria Virzi
Spanish Teacher
Newburn, Mary Lou
English & Social Studies Tchr
Palmer, Christine Kingsolver
English Teacher
Robran, Conrad John
Social Studies Teacher
Williamson, Judy M.
Mathematics Teacher
VAIL
Compton, Oliver K.
Mathematics & Science Teacher
WALSENBURG
Martinez, Juan O.
Spanish Teacher
Rodriguez, Dolores E. (Vigil)
ESL Teacher
WALSH
Buckhaults, Texas D.
7th & 8th Grd Mathematics Tchr
Carlson, Dennis Howard
Industrial Arts Teacher
Horner, Sigrid Wagner
German & English Teacher
Lancaster, Robert Carl
Science Teacher
WESTCLIFFE
Wilson, Barbara Newman
K-12th Grades Counselor

WESTMINSTER
Baldwin, Patty Ross
High School French Teacher
Clark, Marilyn Snethen
Mathematics Teacher
Colin, Anita Marie
Adjunct Biology Professor
Cooper, Linda Lee Dalk
Prof of English Communication
Cronk, Jerry A.
HS Science Teacher
Daniel, Jean Marie Kilpatrick
Political Science Instructor
Denman, Carrie Chinn
English Teacher
Doland, Suzanne Clavel
Kindergarten Teacher
Glade, Rosaline Joan Diaz
5th Grade Teacher
Hill, Thane Clayton
Professor of Biology
Knapp, Patricia Keenan
6th Grade Math Teacher
Loveless, Thomas A.
Social Studies Teacher
Macaya, Dominic
Counselor
Manry, David Edward
Adjunct Instructor
Noonan-Morrissey, Nancy B.
Art History & Humanities Instr
Novy, Donald John
Mathematics Instructor
Preston, Stephen Charles
Fifth Grade Teacher
Rears, Lorraine Greco
Third Grade Teacher
Sullivan, John William
English & Humanities Professor
Thorton, Lisa Harper
Spanish Teacher & Dept Chprsn
VanLieu, Douglas Lynn
Engineering Tech & CAD Instr
Wood, Jean Crews
Business Teacher
WESTON
Degurse, Nancy Hiebert
Superintendent of Schools
WHEAT RIDGE
Adams, Frances Holloway
Language Arts & Science Tchr
Mesplay, Gail Graeber
World History Teacher
Plungy, Barbara Reis-McCarthy
Honors English & Jrnlsm Tchr
Smith, Mary Hayes (Scott)
Retired Eng & Soc Studies Tchr
Stokes, Carolyn L. (Rysta)
Fourth Grade Teacher
Wilson, Joan Stoeckle
English & Music Teacher
WIGGINS
Bruntz, Gary Dean
High School Math Teacher
Kuczala, Michael Scott
Music Teacher
Ritzdorf, Barbara Martin
Principal
WILEY
Patton, Lenna
Mathematics & Computer Teacher
Robinette, James G.
Mathematics Teacher
WINDSOR
Balerud, Laurie Ann
HS Physical Education Instr
Hoffner, Lori A.
Third Grade Teacher
Pratt, William L.
Spanish Teacher
Stoffer, Jill Marie
Second Grade Teacher
WOODLAND PARK
Bartlett, Robert Clark
Mathematics Teacher
Cavera, Robert Michael
Physical Education & Hlth Tchr
Cutting, Spence
Computer & Social Science Tchr
Hoffman, Marta Singer
Chemistry & Science Teacher
Koldenhoven, Robin Eileen
Math Teacher
Leonard, Scott G.
English Teacher
Mc Pherson, Kevin B.
Geography & History Teacher
WRAY
Linehan, David W.
Social Studies Teacher
YODER
Jenkins, Donna Sherman
K-2nd Grade Teacher
YUMA
Harper, Dianne Hervey
Teacher & Curriculum Director
O'Brien, Kevin Patrick
High School Art Teacher
Wingfield, Jolene K.
Fourth Grade Teacher

CONNECTICUT

ANSONIA
Balouskus, Richard A.
Science Teacher
DeGennaro, Virginia Wolfe
6th Grd Language Arts Teacher
Mc Girr, Bernadette Berwick
Eighth Grade Teacher
Ornstein, Avi
Science Teacher & Educl Dir
Sabulis, John Paul
History & Technology Ed Tchr
AVON
Dennis, Roger W.
English Teacher
Fenelon, Leonard G.
Program Director
Gomes, Joel J.
Earth Science Teacher
LaRocque, Kenneth H.
Provost
Usich, Nancy Calandruccio
Second Grade Teacher
BERLIN
Calise, Joseph Edward
English & Humanities Teacher
Hallbach, Carol Ann
American History Teacher
Kucharski, Frank W.
7th Grade Science Teacher
Read, Robert Vernon
Fifth Grade Teacher
BETHANY
Amento, Janet
Mathematics Teacher
Bialicki, Cornell J.
5th Grade Teacher
Liberman, Rosette Belle
English Teacher
Tremaglio, Robert C.
Social Studies Dist Chairman
Trench, Alberta Conte
Foreign Lang & French Teacher
BETHEL
Chapman, Pamela
English Teacher
Dansdill, John P.
English Teacher
Hartsburg, Susan C.
English Teacher
Kearney, Cynthia Aguilar
Former Jr HS Teacher
Pompa, Daniel Thomas
Guidance Counselor
Rayner, Patricia Ann
Science Teacher
Russo, Donna Daniel
Assistant Principal
Van Geons, Loretta Coppola
Second Grade Teacher
Whiting, Gregory Robert
Pastor
BLOOMFIELD
Trzcinski, Richard
Math Dept Head & Teacher
BRANFORD
Beccia, Nancy LaMotte
Eighth Grade English Teacher
Brink, Sylvia Corley
3rd-4th Grade Teacher
Caruso, Carmelina Siena
Second Grade Teacher
DeCaprio, Judith LaVorgna
8th Grade Social Studies Tchr
Mac Kinnel, Sharon Rudden
Kindergarten Teacher
Schwanfelder, John Martin, III
Social Studies Teacher
Spear, Susan H.
Fourth Grade Teacher
von Hofe, Harold Edward
Horizons Teacher
BRIDGEPORT
Amiot, Roxanne Montarro
Automotive Instructor
Autuori, Michael J.
Professor of Biology
Burns, Marleni Brown
Social Studies Teacher
Caciopoli, Robert A.
English Teacher
Cadelina, David Jonathan
Math Teacher
Cavanaugh, Virginia Waterman
Social Studies Teacher
Coppolella, Biagio
Assoc Professor of Accounting
Council, Marilyn Williams
Fourth Grade Teacher
Donnelly, Ann Marie Degaetano
Jr HS Language Arts Teacher
Edwards, Marie Byrne
4th Grade Teacher
Fernandes, Cynthia Dixon
Evaluation Staff Mediator
Forte, Francis Carmine
Physics Teacher
Fusco, Leona Jean
Mathematics Teacher
Gallagher, Joan Nagy
Bus Admin Chair & Professor
Garrison, Phyllis Susan
Career Education Coordinator
Gockley, Angela Green
Science Teacher
Greenspan, William Edward
Professor of Business Law
Gutowski, Phyllis Jean
Associate Professor of Science
Hayward, Adam Patric
English Teacher
Hickey, Jeffrey Charles
Social Studies Teacher
Joines, Keith Perryman
Guidance Counselor
Maloney, Maureen Murphy
Instructor of Psychology
Mandel, Michael R.
Business Professor
Martin, Neoklis John
History Teacher
Martinez-Strubbe, Elizabeth
Tchr of the Talented & Gifted
Moran, Kenneth Paul
Mathematics Teacher
Morris, Elizabeth Carol
English & Reading Teacher
Neri, Rosanne
ESOL Teacher
Olivera, Igdalia
Guidance Counselor
Orloski, Sharon Gloria
Biology Teacher
Peck, Orion Noble
Chemistry & Physics Teacher
Pifko, Patricia Gillespie
Assoc Prof of Mathematics
Poulin, Mary J.
Science Teacher
Schaff, Robert A.
Assoc Prof Mrktg & Intnl Bus
Selski, William E.
Architectural Drafting Teacher
Simon, Michael Alan
Physics & Math Professor
Vas, Jose Maria
Social Studies Teacher
Vazquez, Pedro, Jr.
Mathematics Teacher
Vincenzi, Joseph Perry
Spanish Teacher & Admin Asst
Yatsinko, Mary Ann
Sixth Grade Teacher
BRISTOL
Barlowski, Nancy Mackiewicz
High School Math Teacher
Clauss, Sandra Ryan
Second Grade Teacher
Engels, Eileen O'Brien
Fifth Grade Teacher
Fournier, Karen K.
Science Teacher
Kaczmarczyk, Barbara Brochu
Chem, Hlth Tchr & Dept Chprsn
Lefevre, Darlene Bartucco
7th Grade Reading Teacher
Morache, Denise Marie
Span Tchr, Frgn Lang Dpt Chpsn
Moylan, Eileen Ricci
6th & 7th Grade Science Tchr
Rietze, Patricia Muratori
Spanish & French Teacher
Smith, James Michael
Drama Director
Varricchione, John Robert
7th Grd Geography Teacher
Weisman, Edward L.
Fifth Grade Teacher
Zimbouski, Harriet
Sixth Grd Soc Studies Teacher
BROOKFIELD
Asselta, Nelly
Spanish Teacher
Brightly, Charles M.
Biology Tchr & Sci Dept Chair
Cloutier, Cynthia Hendrickson
Foreign Language Dept Chairman
BURLINGTON
Bentley, Paul
English Teacher
Dennis, Judith E.
English Teacher
Knight, Merle M.
6th-12th Grd Soc Stud Coord
CANTERBURY
Shea, Joanne St. Martin
First Grade Teacher
CANTON
Aksamit, Scott F.
Martial Artist
CENTRAL VILLAGE
Ericson, Melanie A.
High School Social Worker
CHAPLIN
Graber, Elise J.
English Teacher
Leonard, Anne Marie
Business Teacher
CHESHIRE
Andrews, Valerie Warner
Fr Tchr & Frgn Lang Dpt Chprsn
Connor, Marguerite Pezzullo
French & Spanish Teacher
Dugan, James F.
History Teacher
Kern, Barbara Mae (Hutchinson)
High School Guidance Counselor
Lutes, Carole Linn
7th Grade English Teacher
Maturo, William Donald
Sixth Grade Teacher
Mrowka, William Francis
Chemistry Teacher
Shirk, Renee Hunsberger
Social Science Teacher
White, Angela R.
Chair of Sci Dept & HS Tchr
CHESTER
Drake, Linda Kerwin
Sixth Grade Teacher
CLINTON
Aguzzi, Robert Thomas
Physical Ed Teacher & Coach
Eriksen, Jane Reynolds
English Department Chairperson
Grippo, Joseph Anthony
Mathematics Teacher
Herbst, June Alexander
2nd & 3rd Grade Teacher
Lampe, John Lawrence
Music Teacher
Mc Conville, Garry Owen
Fourth & Fifth Grade Teacher
Musacchio, Olga
French Teacher
O'Brien, James Edward
Chem Tchr & Sci Dept Chm
Peterson, Carol Lynn
High School English Teacher
Schutz, Kalli Joy
Adapted PE Teacher & Coach
COLCHESTER
Champagne, Gregory John
Business & Computer Teacher
Dart, Peter M.
8th Grd Science & English Tchr
COLLINSVILLE
Glasgow, Brennan
Fourth Grade Teacher
Rogalski, Signe
Sixth Grade Teacher
COLUMBIA
Giggey, Diane
Spanish & French Teacher
Howard, Nancy N.
US His & Mathematics Teacher
COVENTRY
Alkire, Cynthia Bayne
Science Teacher
Ayer, William Lloyd
Math, Social Stud & Rdng Tchr
Clark, Susan Jessie
Family & Consumer Sci Tchr
Maneggia, Peter, Jr.
Softball & Volleyball Coach
Scopino, Aldorigo Joseph, Jr.
8th Grade American His Teacher
CROMWELL
Grandazzo, Aline M.
High School Art Teacher
Helgeson, Donna Sandburg
Former Math Tutor
Horton, James Christopher
K-12th Grd Hlth Ed Tchr, Coord
Huffstetler, Charles Frederick
World Civilization Teacher
DANBURY
Albritton, Nada Little
Second Grade Teacher
Allen, Vera Maren Taylor
Hlth, Fam Life, Cnsmr Sci Tchr
Barratt, Susannah Patt
History & Social Studies Tchr
Calhoun, John Terry
High School Teacher
Cesca, Sharon Ann
Second Grade Teacher
Craw, Terence L.
US History Teacher
DeMayo, Donna Marie
High School English Teacher
Dunleavy, Kevin M.
Dean of Students & Sci Instr
Evans, Roger L.
Guidance Counselor
Goethals, Susan Claire
Schl Admin & Science Teacher
Granata, William Edward
Spanish Teacher
Hall, Alden B., Jr.
Jr & Sr High Teacher
Hammer, John J., Jr.
4th Grade Teacher
Hansberry, Kenneth Michael
History Department Chair
Harris, Richard A.
English Teacher
Heyd, Suzanne H.
11th-12th Grd English Teacher
Hochsprung, George Werner, III
5th Grade Teacher
Jugler, Brian
Eighth Grd Amer History Tchr
Kisver, Anne Nachbar
Spanish Teacher
Montgomery, Melody Warke
8th Grd Amer His Teacher
Morton, Susan Elias
Mathematics Teacher
Purcell, Thomas Edward, Jr.
Psychology Teacher
Riley, Robert Thompson
Amer & Mid East Studies Tchr
Salem, Timothy Joseph
History Teacher
Sanches, Clemente Vaz
Spanish Teacher
Santora, Frank Joseph
Asst Pastor & Algebra Teacher
Sanzeni, Kenneth Alan
9th-12th Grade Math Teacher
Sniffin, Allan D.
English Teacher
Stence, Deborah C.
English Teacher
Swanson, Connie Labbadia
Music Teacher
Toscano, Ralph A.
English Teacher
Trudel, R. I.
Social Studies Teacher
Villella, Patricia Maria
Spanish, French & Italian Tchr
Webber, John S.
6th Grd Social Studies Teacher
Wisniewski, Charlotte Castronovo
English Teacher
DANIELSON
Aleman, Frank
Business Professor
Baron, Edward S.
English Teacher
Depasse, Colleen Mc Dermott
Principal
Johnson, Sheila Fogarty
English & Journalism Teacher
Marcotte, Chuck
History Teacher
Richards-Schmit, Jan
English Teacher
Robey, Judy Sochor
Spanish Teacher
Rose, Irene Caron
French & Latin Teacher
DARIEN
Tierney-Buchanan, Patricia
Reading & Study Skills Teacher
DEEP RIVER
Anderson, Janet Thompson
Third Grade Teacher
Mahoney, Helen Schwartz
7th & 8th Grade English Tchr
DERBY
Baczek, Linda Antinozzi
Sixth Grade Teacher
Castiello, Frances Dobek
Fifth Grade Teacher
De Francisco, John P.
English Teacher
Faroni, Mary-Ellen Simko
Spanish Teacher
Keefe, Carol Pastore
4th Grd Self-Contained Teacher
Romano, Linda-Marie Mascolo
Social Studies & ESOL Teacher
DURHAM
Balletto, Theresa
Mathematics Teacher
Delvecchio, Susan Lombardi
Second Grade Teacher
Roberts, Martin Philip
Physics, Chem & Earth Sci Tchr
EAST GRANBY
Sponzo, Elaine Dineen
Mathematics & Science Teacher
EAST HAMPTON
Friedman, Edward
Music Teacher
LaFave, Richard P.
French & Spanish Teacher
Peloso, John Richard, III
Chief Instructor
Seydewitz, Linda Rancourt
Chemistry & Phys Science Tchr
Sprague, Lois Vitelli
Music Teacher
Tabacinski, Elaine Bigelow
Chemisty & Physics Teacher
Wyllie, Robert B.
Photography & Graphic Art Tchr
EAST HARTFORD
Cyr, Roderick J.
Retired Counselor
Juleson, Mary Ramey
Family & Consumer Sci Instr
LeBeau, Gary D.
US History Teacher
Monahan-DiNoia, Kelly Ann
Latin Teacher
Sansing, Louise Berbrich
Math Teacher
Smernoff, Ina Kaplan
Teacher of GATE & Pgm Leader
EAST HAVEN
Carr, John W.
Fourth Grade Teacher
Della Pietra, John
English Teacher
DeStefanis, Giancarlo
French Teacher
Ginnetti, Antonia M.
Latin & Business Ed Teacher
Keller, Cheryl Shaymow
Spanish Teacher
Mannion, Barbara A.
Social Studies Teacher
Mc Garry, Catherine Ann
Art Teacher
Savo, Phyllis
School Psychologist
Schwolow, Erna Emma
Third Grade Teacher
Vasaturo, Annette M.
8th Grade Teacher & Asst Prin
EAST LYME
Liniak-Bodwell, Mary Ann
Vocal & Music Teacher
Sherman, Rick
Physical Education Teacher
EAST WINDSOR
Cezus, Joseph James
9th, 11th & 12th Grd Eng Tchr
Soutra, Marcus Stanford, Jr.
Sociology & Psychology Teacher
ELLINGTON
Stack, Susan A.
Kindergarten Teacher
ENFIELD
Alaimo, Esther
Professor of Accounting
Beauregard, Kenneth G.
Eighth Grade Teacher
Bourassa, Guy Jean
Technology Instructor

IELD (cont)
n, William George
rth Grade Teacher
erman, Donna
ructor of Sociology
, Cheri A.
f of Management & Mktg
r, Linda Gale
cial Education Teacher
k, Barbara Long
ence Teacher
ak, Tophie Katherine
Grade Teacher
ette, Thomas Peter
tory Teacher & Dept Chprsn
er, Gary
h Grade Teacher
ham, Edwina Ann
ociate Professor of English
ent, Richard Louis
th Grade Teacher
FIELD
nam, Patricia Ann
lish Teacher
a, Lucille Mary
ior High School Teacher
arik, Andrew F.
ence Teacher
er, Robert Raymond
n & English Teacher
ad, Lawrence J.
hematics Teacher
ford, Kim Suzanne
ociate Professor of English
Raymond T.
hematics Teacher
er, Mary-Anne Nufrio
nish & ESL Teacher
el, Paul Peter
lish Teacher & Dept Liaison
Doris Christenson
rth Grade Teacher
ur, Richard Edward
cational Consultant
Margaret M.
tory & Religion Teacher
cel, Eileen D.
nish Teacher
engack, Edward
h Teacher
o, Richard Joseph
ial Studies Teacher
sman, Sheila C.
istant Professor of Nursing
n, Helen Hughes
t Grade Teacher
s, Marie Royce
nch Teacher
man, Harvey F.
ctrical Engineering Prof
y, John H.
logy Teacher
son, William M., Jr.
h School Health Ed Teacher
s, Colleen A.
cher, Cmptr Sci & Tech Dir
an, Jeffrey Thomas
gion Teacher & Dept Chair
itay-Balogh, Claudia Elizabeth
h School English Teacher
ll, Theodore John
ptr Assisted Drafting Instr
olland, Betty Jane Rupe
ond Grade Teacher
r, Elizabeth Willis
nch Teacher
ing, Carol Walakiewicz
rth Grade Teacher
, Edward J.
hematics Teacher
lph, Mark Raymond
h Grade Teacher
rdote, Thomas Joseph
ial Ethics Teacher
, Eve Gorham
ddle School Math Teacher
f, Margo Lynn
nish & French Teacher
is, Nicolina
Grade Rdng, Lang Arts Tchr
, Robert Michael
rd Grade Teacher
n, Edward Roger
ad Director
, Patricia Ann
erature & Soc Studies Tchr
LS VILLAGE
, Amy
ial Studies Teacher
rt, Audrey Lynn
siness Teacher
MINGTON
se, Constance P.
glish Teacher
Diane Deane
st Prof of Allied Dntl Prgm
rs, Ronald Russell
hropology & Sociology Instr
burn, David Roger
Grade Teacher
ic, Edward J.
fessor of English
len, Renana Robkin
glish Teacher
tch, Louise F.
cial Studies Teacher
on, Janice Ehlers
ired Elementary Teacher
il, Frances L.
fessor of Psychology

Pasanen, Jack M.
English Teacher
Sullivan, Rebecca Jeanne
Assoc Prof of Allied Dental Ed
GALES FERRY
Dickenson, David Alan
Health Teacher
Plotnick, Frances B.
5th Grade Teacher
GLASTONBURY
Blain, Mary Perron
Physics Instr & Sci Dept Head
Galuska, MaryAnne Aronson
High School Guidance Cnslr
Keilman, Christine Rawley
Mathematics & Science Teacher
Marshall, James Hilton
HS Social Studies Teacher
Pilz, Linda M.
English & Theater Teacher
Rust, Patricia
Third Grade Teacher
Waterhouse, John Almon
Head Teacher
GREENS FARMS
Roll, Joseph
Latin & Philosophy Teacher
GREENWICH
Abbot, Marie Passaro
Fourth Grade Teacher
Anderson, Anton S.
English Teacher
Barnes, Kathy Harris
English Teacher
Brody, Thomas Cobb
Ninth Grade English Teacher
Bushell, Esther Simon
High School English Teacher
Dietzel, Sharon Lake
Dean of Students
Epstein, Mark Steven
Social Studies Teacher
Hoffman, Adele Katzowitz
Elementary & MS Strings Tchr
Lowe, Terence A.
Mathematics Teacher
Lyon, Kenneth Albert
Geology, Anatomy & Psych Tchr
Piotrzkowski, Richard Alan
Chemistry Teacher
Roberts, Elizabeth Hausner
Fifth Grade Teacher
GROTON
Buttermore, Sidney P.
Seventh Grade Teacher
Congdon, Christopher
Lecturer in English
Frink, Madelyn B.
English Teacher
Henderson, Douglas Leslie
English Teacher
Leivers, Kathleen A.
Teacher
Marsh, David Charles
Physical Education Teacher
Nasser, Bernard Samuel
Eng & Creative Writing Tchr
GUILFORD
Bennett-Hayes, Joan St Clair
Mathematics Teacher
Dillon, Lois A.
8th Grd Language Arts Teacher
Hart, Joanne S.
6th Grade Math & Rdng Teacher
Heckman, Ruth Wasinger
Bio, Anatomy & Physiology Tchr
Hicks, Norman W.
6th Grade Science Teacher
Houlihan, Sheila M.
Latin Teacher
Kennedy, Margaret Wolf
HS Home Economics Teacher
Kingsley, Jane Wheaton
English Teacher
Litevich, John A., Jr.
HS Social Studies Teacher
Lund, Carrol Gagliardi
Speech Pathologist
Mikulak, David Thomas
English Teacher
Moumen, Rosemary Thompson
Third Grade Teacher
Nettleton, Ruth Alexander
Retired First Grade Teacher
Peluso, Joseph Frank
Social Studies Teacher
Russo, Louis Harry
Social Studies Teacher
Sawyer, Robert Carl
PE & Earth Science Teacher
Scarpa, Carol Tramontano
Secondary English Teacher
Sharpe, Kathleen
Social Stud Dept Chprsn & Tchr
Tucker, Joyce B.
Spanish Teacher
Urban, Shirley Genhle
Chemistry & Physics Teacher
HAMDEN
Avallone, Patricia Liberatore
Elem Admin
Boni, Lorenzina Sagnella
First Grade Teacher
Brockway, Susan Palmer
Fourth Grade Teacher
Buongirno, Carol Aranci
6th Grade Tchr
Calamita, Marion Vermiglio
Kindergarten Teacher

Canell, Beverly J.
Foreign Language Dir & Tchr
Ciulla, Louise Marcelle
Fourth Grade Teacher
DeCaprio, Dorothy Torello
6th-8th Grade Math Teacher
DellaCamera, Paula Maria
High School Italian Teacher
Farley, John Gilbert
Science Teacher
Gagliardi, Richard A.
Athletic Dir & Math Teacher
Garfield, John M.
Dir of Stud & His Teacher
Harlow, Elizabeth Mary
Vocal General Music Teacher
Kelly, Leo J.
Educational Coordinator
Loro, Lauren Marguerite
Instrumental Music Director
Merkle, William Gotthilf
History & Mathematics Teacher
Mungiguerra, Carl
Chemistry Teacher
Nitkin, Risa M.
11th-12th Grade English Tchr
Oddie, Donna-Jeanne Mary
8th Grd Sci Tchr & Team Leader
Pfeffer, William H.
Social Studies Teacher
Quintin, Ellen Bontempo
Spanish Teacher
Rascati, Diana Polce
Italian & Spanish Teacher
Reiber, Barbara Mae
History Teacher
Richardson, Anne Ostro
English Tchr & Dean of Stdnts
Semenza, Robert A.
Assistant Prof of Accounting
Skrzyszowski, Claire Jean
Italian & Spanish Teacher
Topitzer, Mary Jane Lynch
Retired English Teacher
Wayne, Carolyn Setaro
7th & 8th Grd Spanish Teacher
Zaretsky-Croll, Ruth Gail
First Grade Teacher
HARTFORD
Amaio, Carole B.
High School English Teacher
Beasley, Juanita Duncan
6th Grade Teacher
Biggs, Susan J.
HS Chem & 8th Grd Sci Tchr
Brick, Arline Roth
Biology & Psychology Teacher
Buch, Marcia
Art Teacher
Buksbaum, Ronald Walter
Professor of Fine Arts
Callahan, Leon E.
Philosophy & Logic Teacher
Callo, Lynda
English Teacher
Campbell, Mandlyn Cerysse
Special Ed Paraprofessional
Cosker, Barbara S.
Math Teacher
Daniels, Cheryl Stone
President
de Ramos, Aida Fernandez
Spanish Teacher
DiCicco, Dominick William
Technology Teacher
Felder, Cheryl McGee
Math Teacher
Jackson, Marjorie A.
Science Teacher
Kearse, Lorraine Hart
English Instructor
Knight, Herbert Lindsay
English Teacher
La Penna, Janice Pietrycha
Physical Education Teacher
Lester, Florence Thomas
Chem Teacher & Sci Dept Head
Mangiafico, Salvatore A.
French Teacher
Misenti, Nicholas Charles
Asst Prof of Acctng & Bus Law
Powers, Clinton H.
Math Teacher
Raffalo, Robert George, Sr.
Physical Education Teacher
Rodney, Nancy Hartman
Therapeutic Foster Mother
Rosen, Edward
Mathematics Teacher
Skowronski, Richard Michael
6th Grade Teacher
Slade, Farlina Wilson
Social Studies Teacher
Smith, Thomas Gordon
Teacher
Somma, Michael
Art History Teacher
Vania, David C.
Mathematics Teacher
Viviano, Anthony S.
College Counselor
Wagar, Charles C.
Mathematics Teacher
Wentzel, Connie Russo
7th & 8th Grd Math & Sci Tchr
Williams, Mattie Louise (Harris)
Dir of Pre-Nursing Prgm
HEBRON
Iacovelli, Nicholas
History & Social Studies Tchr

Localio, William
Guidance Counselor
Mirakian, James Edward
High School Music Teacher
Weiss, Bruce J.
HS Social Studies Teacher
Yankowski, Linda Jean Pilver
Science Teacher
HIGGANUM
Dupre, Karen Cote
French & Spanish Teacher
Keck, Barth Allen
HS English & Journalism Tchr
Tencza, James A.
Mathematics Teacher
JEWETT CITY
Atkins, Patricia A.
Phys, Sci, Chem & Bio Teacher
Brycki, Catherine Provencher
English Teacher
Frizzell, Mark Edward
Technology Education Teacher
Jerbert, Marilyn Baker
Business Teacher
Johnson, Dawn Neville
Spanish & French Teacher
Whitford, Patricia Anne
Spanish Teacher
KENT
Adams, Bruce K.
6th-8th Grd Social Stud Tchr
Goodwin, Peter H.
Sci Dept Chm & Physics Tchr
KILLINGWORTH
Quamma, Carole Nestor
Fifth Grade Teacher
LAKEVILLE
Crain, Walter J.
Math Teacher & Dean of Stdnts
Davis, Edward Ronald
Biology & Limnology Teacher
Frankenbach, Charles Henry
English Teacher
Laurence, Ronald Frederick
AP & Honors Chemistry Instr
Morrill, James Martin
Bio & Environmental Sci Tchr
Tracy, James
History Instructor
LEBANON
Burns, Virginia Zimmerman
Retired Elementary Teacher
LEDYARD
Douglass, Bruce Linwood
Chemistry Tchr & Sci Dept Chm
Holland, Carden
Art Teacher
Madison, Ellen L.
English Teacher
LISBON
Belisle, Kathleen Kane
First Grade Teacher
LITCHFIELD
Bogosian, Robert G.
Science Teacher & Dept Head
Geci, Gerald G.
Language Art Dept Chairman
Kissko, John Martin
Social Studies Teacher
Niehoff, Karissa Lynn
Health & PE Coordinator
Perkins, Frances B.
English Teacher & Hum Chair
MADISON
Hermonat, Sue Krenning
Sixth Grade Teacher & Team Ldr
Hershnik, Mark Karl
English Teacher
Marcinkiewicz, Marian Filkoski
First Grade Teacher
Muggleston, Patricia Greene
Language Arts Specialist
Muzer, Frederick Carl
Fifth Grade Teacher
Phelps, Julianne Jacobsen
Media Specialist
Van Dyke, Fay Deane
Art Teacher
MANCHESTER
Campbell, Katherine M. L.
Language Arts Teacher
Duffy, Joseph William
History Instr & Guidance Cnslr
Hillyer, Diane Carol
Associate Professor of Math
Paterna, Joan Osipowitz
Asst Professor of Psychology
Sandhu, Parminder Singh
Engineering & Tech Asst Prof
Stafford, Carl Jay
Hotel, Food Svc Mgmt Asst Prof
Wynn, Jean Boris
Anthropology & Psychology Prof
MANSFIELD CENTER
Satriano, Anita Guardo
Retired Kindergarten Teacher
MARLBOROUGH
Colavecchio, Anthony Phillp
Physical Education Teacher
Kania, Sarah Hodge
Reading Coordinator
Ledoux, Bruce
6th Grade Teacher
MERIDEN
Brandt, Irene H.
HS Mathematics Teacher
Curry, Maureen C.
Math & Computer Science Tchr
Marsh, Robert Andrew
Mathematics Teacher

Miller, Joseph A.
Mathematics Teacher
Ogorzalek, Margarita Parrilla
Language Arts Teacher
Papandrea, Marianne Petrus
English Chair
Wisneski, J. Jerrold
Social Studies Teacher
Woods, Mary Lou Dioguardi
Second Grade Teacher
MIDDLEBURY
Coffin, Bruce Metcalf
English Teacher
MIDDLEFIELD
Sage, Lawrence T.
5th Grade Teacher
MIDDLETOWN
Digiulio, Daniel Arthur
Director & Tchr of Voc Ag Ed
DiMauro, Patricia Ann OBrien
Pre-School Teacher
Grasso, Virginia M.
Reading & Lang Arts Consultant
Hoisl, Andrea DeVito
Campus Ministry Dir & Rel Tchr
Jackson, Karen Pennypacker
Mathematics Teacher
King, John R.
Mathematics Instructor
Malone, Barbara Marshall
Second Grade Teacher
Torcello, Mary Jo
Biology Teacher
Vallee, Anita Gomez
Cooperative Work Coord & Tchr
MILFORD
Betzig, James Walter
8th Grd Math & Algebra Teacher
Bevino, Jeffrey F.
Head Coach & Dir of Athletics
Dodd, Alan Charles
Art Teacher
D'Orsi, Irene Karajanis
5th Grade Teacher
Elmo, Lin J.
Art Teacher
Eustace, Thomas Joseph
Biology Teacher
Galligan, Mary J.
Fourth Grade Teacher
Gibson, Donna McNeill
English Teacher
Marottoli, Vincent
Foreign Language Tchr
Murray, Colleen M.
Middle School Teacher
Nelson, Betty Falco
6th-8th Grd Science Teacher
Parcella, Mary McPoyle
Spanish Tchr & FL Chprsn
SantaBarbara, Barbara Cantore
Second Grade Teacher
Shiffrin, Lawrence L.
Physics Teacher
Simmons, Margaret (Flynn)
Business Education Teacher
Smith, Anthony J.
Heat, Vent & AC Dept Head
Testagrossa, Peter Michael
Mathematics Teacher
Waldron, Jill Murphy
Business Teacher
MONROE
Cianciolo, Anthony James
Technology Education Instr
Gangi, Robyn Joseph
Choral Activities Director
Garofolo, Nancy Gombas
First Grade Teacher
Halliwell, David Dean
Science & Language Arts Tchr
Lipeles, Enid Singer
Schl Dept Chair & Chem Teacher
Piurck, John S.
High School History Teacher
Shubert, Jonelle M.
Business Education Teacher
MOODUS
McGinnis, Thomas James
French & Spanish Teacher
Shepard, Bion
Sixth Grade Soc Stud Tchr
Tabacinski, William George
Agriscience Instructor
MOOSUP
Breton, Eleanor Virginia
Office Assistant & Tutor
MORRIS
Allen, William C.
Fifth Grade Teacher
MYSTIC
Goldberg, Edward Michael
Language Arts Teacher
Solar, Neil S.
Mathematics Teacher
Zezulka, Charles
MS Developmental Reading Tchr
NAUGATUCK
Allen, Nancy Niehoff
English Teacher
Carroll, Maureen FitzMaurice
English & Social Studies Tchr
Friend, Scott Leslie
Instrumental Music Director
Gallo, Kimberly H.
Assistant Principal
Giannini, Vito Stephen
Mathematics Teacher
Grady, Nancy DiMaria
Fifth Grade Teacher

NAUGATUCK (cont)
Kirkby, Michael Ross
History Teacher
LaGrave, Nancy Goodwin
Special Education Teacher
Mc Knack, Jayne Woods
Guidance Counselor
Moran, Diana Whalen
Biology Teacher
Pappano, Carol Ann
Mathematics Teacher
Piola, Robert C.
Special Education Teacher
Rubbo, Lena Santomenno
HS Child Care Teacher
Shapiro, Denise DeCarlo
Art Teacher
Solomito, Mark
6th Grade Mathematics Teacher
Tarantello, Guy
Earth Science & Physics Tchr
Wesche, Kevin James
Technology Education Instr
NEW BRITAIN
Argazzi, Paul D.
Math Tchr & Team Adv
Burke, Barbara Kusek
Teacher of the Gifted
Colon, Marybelle B.
Bilingual Special Ed Teacher
Eberhardt, Nancy M.
8th Grade US History Teacher
Gilmartin, Mary Ellen Gerner
Fashion Technology Instructor
Light, Marcy Bradley
English Teacher
Luchansky, Barbara Pilecki
HS English Instructor
Spence, Joanne Frances
Fifth Grade Teacher
Unwin, Robert C.
Sci & Math Gifted Prgm Teacher
NEW CANAAN
Johnson, Diane Deroche
5th Grade Teacher
Mastroianni, John Frank
Director of Bands
Tomasello, Leonard A.
Principal
NEW FAIRFIELD
Balsley, Christopher Barry
Earth Science & Biology Tchr
Castaldi, Jeffrey M.
10th Grade Biology Teacher
LaPorte, Karen Ann
Chemistry Teacher
Lopes, Patricia Aires
Spanish Teacher
NEW HAVEN
Axtell, Robert Stockton
Prof of Exercise Sci Dept
Brajkovic, Henry
History Teacher
Broga-Norton, Sandra
Professor & Pgm Coordinator
Brownstein, Michael Mark
English Teacher
Caliendo, Richard J.
Instructor of Humanities
Ceraso, Michael Matthew
English & Magnet Resource Tchr
Chase, Cynthia Sargent
Assistant Athletic Director
Cherry, Tarah S.
4th Grade Teacher
Coggins, Rose B.
Magnet Resource Teacher
Cohen, Milton R.
Retired English Teacher
Cole, Susan Letzler
Eng Prof & Dramatic Stud Dir
Couden, Linda Burns
Eighth Grade Teacher
D'Ambrosio, Sandra Ann
Seventh Grade Teacher
Davis, Hugh H.
History Professor
Dawidoff, Maria Gerschenkron
English Teacher
Doval-Oetting, Marie
Spanish Teacher
Erkerd, Ivory Dansby
History Teacher
Fehm, Margaret Quinn
4th Grade Teacher
Feinberg, Susan Elconin
English Teacher
Frost, Betty Ann Miller
Biology Instructor
Giamatti, Toni Smith
English Teacher
Gibson, Robert Alfred
History Teacher
Grandfield, Maria L.
Language Arts Teacher
Gurga, Rosemary
Spanish Teacher
Hamilton, Julia
Associate Professor
Hartwig, Michael J.
Ethics Professor
Jooss, Mark Edward
Seventh & Eighth Grd Sci Tchr
Jooss, Patricia (Clifford)
4th Grade Teacher
Kaufman, Minna P.
Health Occupations Teacher
Kearney-Mc Fadden, Linda
5th Grade Teacher
Mc Dougald-Campbell, Rita A.
English Teacher
Mininberg, Mary Ellen Murhy
English Tchr & Stu Cncl Adv
Moore, Jimmy-Lee
4th-7th Grd Resource Room Tchr
Morico, Lawrence Francis
Guidance Counselor
Naples, A. Richard
Math & Science Teacher
Neighbors, Shirley Moss
Bio, Anatomy & Physiology Tchr
Petuch, Carol Ann
English Teacher
Rebeschi, Lisa Cirillo
Assistant Professor of Nursing
Rienzi, William Robert
History Teacher
Ross, Carol Frost
Latin Teacher
Saxon, Burt
Teacher of the Gifted
Schaeffer, Ingrid Mary
7th & 8th Grade Drama Teacher
Stamborsky, Phillip
Assoc Prof of Eng & Dept Chm
Thorpe, Linda Darnell
Fourth Grade Teacher
Totman, Lisa Farrel
Third Grade Teacher
Velanno, Elayne Buccino
Honors English Teacher
NEW LONDON
Dizigan, Dorothy Svab
Fifth Grade Teacher
Hasse, Wilma Hahn
English Professor
Pescatello, Nancy Nolin
Sixth Grade Teacher
Tortora, Anne Halloran
Director of Music
Urtz, Jill
HS Mathematics Teacher
NEW MILFORD
Abraham, Michael A.
History Teacher
Knipple, William F., Jr.
Mathematics Teacher
Kraft, Dawn Bovais
Teacher & Director
Martin, Gilda Salvio
Spanish Teacher
Partelow, Susan M.
French Teacher
Putnam, Brock
History & English Teacher
Rittman, Ellen M.
Second Grade Teacher
Shaffer, David Robert
Mathematics Teacher
Vallombroso, Ann M.
HS Social Studies Teacher
Viau, Jules G.
Retired Teacher
NEWINGTON
Aros, Andrew S.
Social Studies Teacher
Begin, David G.
Music Teacher
Blake, Jean (Grafe)
3rd Grade Teacher
Brossart, Patricia Louise
Lang Arts & Soc Studies Tchr
Cottone, Gloria Lipscomb
Sixth Grade Math Teacher
Mallia, Paul Patrick
Math Tchr & Coach
Marchetti, Kathleen Rose (Bironi)
Spanish Teacher
Mc Kernan, Anne T.
Social Studies Teacher
Nagy, Joan B.
Vocational Education Teacher
Nardine, Angela Wagner
Lang Arts & Soc Studies Tchr
Nichols, Lesli Farnham
English Teacher
Nichols, Scott Thomas
History Bible Teacher & Coach
Pepin, Linda Sayward
Spanish Teacher
Perotti, John Alfred
English Teacher
Platt, Myra Schneider
Language Arts Teacher
Poorman, Judith (Skwira)
Mathematics Teacher
Roberts, Judy Bryant
English Teacher
Siano, Denise Smith
Physical Education Teacher
Treggor, Josef Philip
Marine Biology Instructor
NEWTOWN
Gardner, Deirdre Ryan
Retired English Teacher
Powlter, Nelson M.
Eighth Grade Math Teacher
NORTH BRANFORD
Kramer, Carolyn Elizabeth
French & Spanish Teacher
NORTH FRANKLIN
Connell, Joan Elizabeth
First Grade Teacher
NORTH GROSVENORDALE
Pizzarella, Paul Frank
High School Art Teacher
Weimann, Peter J.
English & Psychology Instr
NORTH HAVEN
Angeletti, Joseph John
Retired Principal
DeMayo, Bette J.
Mathematics Teacher
Greco, Anita (Campaniolo)
Fourth Grade Teacher
Morrissey, Charles Richard
5th Grade Teacher
O'Neill-Burns, Sheila
8th Grd Lang Arts & Rdng Tchr
Tangney, Patricia Amy
English Teacher
Wronski, Stephen John
Fifth Grade Teacher
NORTH STONINGTON
Willson, Frederic Austin
Spanish Teacher
NORWALK
Adams, Spencer E., Jr.
Science Teacher
Aucar, Hilda-Judith A.
Span Tchr & Lang Dept Chprsn
Bergquist, Jane Brewer
Third Grade Teacher
Block, Joel Warren
Science Teacher
Costabile, Mary Jo Croce
Fifth Grade Teacher
Cutuli-Block, Deborah A.
English Teacher
Girard-Couture, Glenn R.
Physics Teacher
Kemeny, Cheryl E.
President & Prof Voice Teacher
Morris, Martha
Social Studies Teacher
Peterson, Laurel S.
Adjunct Writing Instructor
Seaburg, Kyle Bruce
High School History Teacher
Trifore, Robert Edward
Biology Teacher
Wax, Angela LaBruzzo
Mathematics Teacher
Webster, Joan Palumbo
Mathematics Teacher
Wiggins, Charles
US Government & History Tchr
Wilson, Donald Glen
Math Dept Chair & Teacher
NORWICH
Bernardini, Brett Andrew
Performing Arts Director
Brunetti, Steven Lucian
Science Department Lead Tchr
Cook, Deborah Ferra
Assistant Principal
Donato, Gary Roland
Adjunct Instructor of History
Enright, Mary Ann Malone
Second Grade Teacher
Heffernan, Joan Elizabeth
Integrated Day Teacher
Jennings, Careen Schmidt
HS English Teacher
Levanto, Regina Dzialo
US History Teacher
Maulucci, Anthony Sebastian
English & Humanities Professor
Misiorek, Thomas
Fourth Grade Teacher
Ochs, Robert L.
Science Teacher
OAKDALE
Carter, Robert Thomas, Jr.
World His & Morality Tchr
Chick, Ann Holowaty
4th Grade Teacher
Lamperelli, Robert Nicholas
Social Studies Dept Chairman
Latman, Joel
United States History Teacher
Murphy, Jerome
Eng, French Teacher & Ath Dir
Waring, Richard Dana
Technology Education Teacher
OAKVILLE
Austin, Marilyn Elizabeth (Marano)
Third Grade Teacher
OLD LYME
Burbank, Alice M. K.
High School English Teacher
Murphy-Cranston, Donna Lee
Special Education Teacher
OLD SAYBROOK
O'Leary, Patricia Ann
Science Teacher
ORANGE
Anderson, Carol Fucci
Fifth Grade Teacher
Cerino, Ruth Ann O'Hara
Fourth Grade Teacher
OXFORD
Grappone, Karen Foster
7th Grade Lang Arts Teacher
Ryan, Gerald Joseph
Mathematics Teacher
PAWCATUCK
Palmer, Henry Robinson
Seventh Grade Math Teacher
PLAINFIELD
Stoll, Constance Darnowski
Guidance Counselor
Sweatt, Ronald B.
Jr HS Dept Chair & Team Leader
PLAINVILLE
Birdsall, Cindy Ann
HS Phys & Health Ed Teacher
Bogdan, Frank John
Social Studies Teacher
Feltt, Gary William
Sixth Grade Teacher
Hook, Frank Joseph, Jr.
2nd Grade Teacher
Rogers, Janice Lyons
First Grade Rdng Recovery Tchr
Zarzycki, Karen
4th Grade Teacher
PLANTSVILLE
DiMaio, Vicky P.
French & Spanish Teacher
Hughes, Suzanne Rao
French Teacher
PORTLAND
Avery, Maria Rose
8th Grade Teacher
Miles, Robert C.
9th-12th Grade English Instr
PRESTON
Gilbert, Judith Macbeth
French & Lang Arts Teacher
PROSPECT
DuBois, Mary Mulligan
Science & English Teacher
Lawlor, Janet Schiavone
6th Grade Teacher
Orintas, Bernadine Claire
Second Grade Teacher
PUTNAM
Sward, Ross Andrew
Music Director
REDDING
Derwin, Eleanor DeCapua
English Teacher
Morros, James A.
Health & Physical Ed Teacher
RIDGEFIELD
Bollenback, Dirk F.
Soc Studies Tchr & Dept Chm
Ginty, James Patrick
English Teacher
Gordon-Land, Carrie W.
Counselor
Jaslow, Jeffrey
Teaching Assistant Principal
RIVERSIDE
D'Antona, Joseph Peter
Science Teacher
ROCKY HILL
McMahon, William E.
English Teacher
O'Brien, Patricia Wood
English Teacher
Vijayasekar, Jaya Devarajan
Fr, Span Tchr & Team Ldr
Watson, Richard L.
Fifth Grade Teacher
SALISBURY
Menconi, Ralph Joseph, II
Eng Dpt Chm, Sr Mstr & Ec Tchr
SANDY HOOK
Ridarelli, Carol Marie
History Teacher
Schwartz, Elaine D.
Guidance Counselor
SEYMOUR
Bomba, Carol Ann
Third Grade Teacher
Branco, Danielle Rivard
Mathematics & SAT Prep Teacher
Desmond, John Edward
Science Teacher & Team Leader
Michaelson, Wendy Deegan
Chemistry & Physics Teacher
Sabatini, Patricia Malec
Fifth Grade Teacher
SHELTON
Clifford, Barbara O'Neil
Stu Assistance & Guid Cnslr
Driscoll, Karen Eileen
Kindergarten Teacher
Driscoll, Susann R.
Second Grade Teacher
Johnson, Beverly A.
Art Teacher
Moore, Theresa DePasqua
English Teacher
Moriarty, Jeffrey M.
English & Drama Teacher
Ostrosky, Barbara (Miranti)
Fourth Grade Teacher
Ritter, Darlisa Pivola
First Grade Teacher
Tokarski, Lorraine (Jarusinsky)
Tchr of Gifted & Talented
Weston, Raymond
8th Grade US History Teacher
SIMSBURY
Archibald, Robert A.
English & French Teacher
Clement, Nancy Glahn
1st Grade Teacher
Delo, Dirk Andrew
Mathematics Teacher
Ehrhardt, Margaret Finn
Mathematics Teacher
Gelineau, Catherine Rose (Cersosimo)
English Teacher
Gesualdi, Susan Anne
Social Studies Teacher
Groff, John William
Eng Dept Chm & Teacher
Leonard, Michael Heaton
English Teacher
Marco, Gregory David
Science Department Chair
Mickewicz, William D.
Science & Math Teacher
Mullane, Roberta M.
English Department Supervisor
Nelson, Patricia Mora
Spanish Teacher
Orsene, Mark Steven
Mathematics Teacher
Perillo, Susan Joan
Mathematics Teacher
Urner-Berry, Nancy Grahame
Chemistry Teacher
Winiarski, Benedict
Mathematics Teacher
SOMERS
Henderson, Barbara Lawton
7th & 8th Grd Rdng Consultant
Kmon, Patricia DelNegro
7th Grade Language Arts Tchr
Malone, Thomas Michael
English Teacher
Mayo, Michael James
Business Teacher
Mooney, Stephen Vincent
School Social Worker
Tyler, Jane M.
Sixth Grade Science Teacher
SOUTH KENT
Beebe, Jaye Howard
Assistant Headmaster
SOUTH WINDSOR
Bourn, Maureen Eddy
Third Grade Teacher
Cloutman, Arthur Rhodes
Mathematics Teacher
Crawford, Eileen Wilkos
Music Teacher
Duclos, Edward B., Jr.
Scndry English Education Tchr
Field, Cynthia Cyrkiewicz
Eighth Grade English Teacher
Glickman, Jeffrey Loren
Rabbi
Hagedorn, Deborah Collins
First Grade Teacher
Kinsloe-Byers, Susan
Art Teacher
Mealy, Ginger Zito
Coop Work Experience Coord
Moran, Sharon Ann
AP Government Teacher
SOUTHBURY
Fappiano, Virginia Greatorex
Art Teacher
Leavitt, Monita R.
Project Explore Enrchmnt Tchr
Lewbel, Samuel Robert
7th Grade Social Studies Tchr
Niestemski, Joyce A.
HS Teacher
Skowronski, Joyce M.
First Grade Teacher
Walker, Shirley Cintorino
Business Education Teacher
SOUTHINGTON
Benjamin, Deborah Ann
English Teacher
Carta, Joseph Raymond
Assistant Professor
Chiero, Nancy Taglia
Special Education Teacher
Isner, Karin Krauland
Mathematics Teacher
Kolakoski, David Frank
Social Studies Teacher
Mc Kernan, William Henry
Physical Science Teacher
Paradis, Karen Dutton
Teacher of the Gifted
Scadden-Remirez, Ellen Elizabeth
Spanish Teacher
Schilling, Eva Grzella
English, ESL & German Teacher
Schwartz, Rochelle Ann
Science Department Chairperson
Shea, Donna Papini
Sixth Grade Teacher
Victor, Stephen Michael
Math Teacher
Willis, Mildred Kashima
Fifth Grade Teacher
STAMFORD
Banks, Brenda Carol
2nd Grade Teacher
Burnich, Rodger
English Teacher
DeFeo, James Vincent
English Teacher
DeGennaro, Raymond Peter
High School Mathematics Tchr
Ferri, Louis J.
Mathematics Teacher
Gallagher, Rosemary Murphy
Support Services Director
Kenna, Colleen Frances
High School English Teacher
Kinberg, Bernard D.
Physics Teacher
Kriz, Thomas Edward
English Teacher
Kweskin, Helen Truss
English Teacher & Dept Head
Linton, Barbara Ann
Religious Studies & Psych Tchr
Marini, James Thomas
Spanish Teacher
Post, Robert John
Spiritual Director
Rinaldi, Michael F.
7th Grade Social Studies Tchr
Scott Ricco, Brenda Joy
Special Education Teacher

MFORD (cont)
ick, Patrick J.
ilosophy Teacher
mon, Cynthia Sherman
anish Teacher
i, Mary Lou Jerman
ench & Spanish Teacher
couch, Tim D.
emistry Teacher
ner, Sandra M.
mputer & Math Teacher
RRS MANSFIELD
, Ingrid Dzenis
athematics Teacher
lle, Audrey Lee
sociate Dean
l, John William
cial Studies Teacher
ATFORD
gnani, Gloria Riseley
th Grade Teacher
s, Peter Edwin
ysics Teacher
oks, Carolyn Elizabeth
cial Studies Teacher
azo, Linda Charak
cond Grade Teacher
richsen, Richard Peter
glish Teacher
nan, Linda Bukoff
cond Grade Teacher
chotte, Paul A.
hnology Education Teacher
g, Mary Neri
ndergarten Teacher
na, Lyn M.
rd Grade Teacher
er, Louise P.
-6th Grade Teacher
, Susie Hunter
thematics Teacher
in, Rosemary Elizabeth
glish Teacher
icotte, Joy M.
st Grade Teacher
er, G. James, III
sic Director
, Robin B.
guage Arts Teacher
on, Craig Robert
h Grade Teacher
er, Grace Rethartha
rary Media Specialist
a, Francis John
ired Language Arts Teacher
, Mary Betsy
English & Journalism Tchr
aidlin, Gary Bryon
cher & Coach
aidlin, Sandra Kondrasko
guage Arts Teacher
lewski, Charles S.
dance Counselor
accino, Sandra Romano
sic Teacher
k, Patricia Ann
n Language Arts Teacher
FIELD
e, Ronald Emery
Grade US History Teacher
nette, Linda
glish Teacher
FFVILLE
ominicis, Paula J.
ond Grade Teacher
RYVILLE
ylik, Edward S., Jr.
h School Science Teacher
MASTON
c, Veronica Mary
e Principal & Teacher
, Kimberlee Julia
-11th Grade English Teacher
r, John Michael
rth Grade Teacher
MPSON
avson, Eric Paul
ory Dept Chm & Ath Dir
ward, William Gerard
Dept Head & Sci, Rel Tchr
ra, Keith Armstrong
lish & Spanish Teacher
LAND
sito, Stephanie (Horinek)
logy Teacher
e, Roger
ector of Computer Education
ki, Karen Wells
ond Grade Teacher
RINGTON
one, Wendy Lee
-12th Grd Mathematics Tchr
ce, Richard Frank
hematics Teacher
er, Kevin Charles
ctronics Instr
, Susan B.
ence Teacher
, Eileen Kennedy
h School English Teacher
ins, Marie Katherine
cial Education Teacher
rry, Mary K.
lish Teacher
Karen E.
d Grade Teacher
Victor Joseph
lish Teacher

TRUMBULL
Bair, James F.
English Dept Chair
Berescik, Susan J. (Knechtel)
English & Journalism Teacher
Blank, Patricia Neidrauer
Sixth Grade Teacher
Bonaventura, Louis J., III
School Counselor
Brennan, Carol J.
MS English Teacher & Team Ldr
Cairns, Kristen Smith
French & English Teacher
Carusello, Richard James
Earth Science Teacher
Clyons, Katherine Helfrich
Kindergarten Teacher
Coughlin, Joan Damon
Fourth Grade Teacher
Danaher, Jane Winfield
First Grade Teacher
Davis, Patricia Murphy
Mathematics Teacher
Dawson, Sandra J.
Agriscience Instructor
DeCesare, Vincent Edward
Math Teacher
Farnen, James Joseph
Social Studies Teacher
Hamilton, Joyce Bartoli
Math Teacher
Lombard, Michael S.
Fourth Grade Teacher
Mc Auley, Edward J.
Social Studies Teacher
Murphy, Jean Trojanoski
5th Grd Lang Arts & Rdng Tchr
Neger, Nial E.
Mathematics Dept Chairman
Odoardi, Joseph M.
English Teacher
Pezzullo, Barbara Diane (Ondecko)
Library & Media Specialist
Schickler, Patricia Pallotto
English Teacher
Seidell, Donna Fuimara
Reading Consultant
Stern, Nan L.
Reading Consultant
Timpanelli, Lucinda A.
Foreign Languages Dept Chair
Tomscheck, Jacqueline A.
Third Grade Teacher
Trudeau, Isabel Lois
Third Grade Teacher
UNCASVILLE
Lamoureux, Arthur F., Jr.
Director of Athletics
Pagliuca, Richard
Guidance Counselor
Sharples, Douglas B.
Anatomy, Physiology & PE Tchr
Smith, Frederick Stanton
English Teacher
VERNON ROCKVILLE
Carlson, Linda DeRose
Guidance Counselor
Lessoff, Stanley
Business Ed & Soc Stud Tchr
Lewis, Jennifer E.
Special Education Teacher
Lord, Anna Coughlin
First Grade Teacher
Mangione, Michael
Social Studies Teacher
Martello, James Lawrence
English Teacher
Miller, Virginia Yaskulka
First Grade Teacher
Novak, Scott C.
HS Social Science Teacher
Ruggles, Kathleen Cormany
Fourth Grade Teacher
VOLUNTOWN
Kotzan, Holly Wills
Fourth Grade Teacher
Woronik, Stanley Ricahrd
7th-8th Grade Science Teacher
WALLINGFORD
Bailey, Darlene Cannata
Middle School Teacher
DeLucia, Maureen Murphy
Kindergarten Teacher
Hull, John R., Jr.
7th Grd Math, Geog & Rdng Tchr
Hutchinson, John Fuller, Jr.
Community Service Director
Lavalette, Cindy Greider
English Teacher
Marcello, Claudia Orsini
Vocational Agriculture Ed Tchr
McCormack, Gail G.
Medical Careers Pgm Coord
Menon, Konthath Kunhirama
English Teacher
Pauley, Mary-Ann Melchionda
Transitional Teacher
Troccolo, Joan Munley
Sixth Grade Teacher
Valentine, Ralph Burnet
Head of Music
WASHINGTON DEPOT
Adolphson, Thomas Joseph
History & Humanities Teacher
Buckley, Robert Thomas
English Teacher & Dept Chm
Kazanjian, Carla Elise
HS Social Studies Teacher
Olivea, Charles Laurence
History Teacher

Spooner, Rick Stephen
Assistant Headmaster
WATERBURY
Accuosti, Sue M.
Social Studies Teacher
Albino, Lori Ann
High School English Teacher
Barnes, Patricia Quinn
Foreign Lang Dept Chair
Carini, Dominic Joseph, Jr.
Social Studies Department Chm
Carini, Mary Albanese
English Teacher
Carrington, Barbara Ciriello
Vice Principal
Cummings, Del F.
Indstrl Envrnmtl Mgt Asst Prof
Cyr, Gilman Joseph
Science Teacher
DaSilva, Elizabeth Martin
Biology & Chemistry Teacher
Dawson, Penelope Baldwin
Asst Prof & Dir of Equine Mgmt
Decheine, Phyllis J.
8th Grade Teacher
Drewry, Walter J.
Social Studies Teacher
Estrada, Ann Beland
Theology Teacher
Griffin, Rosalie M.
Mathematics Department Chprsn
Hays, Nancy Gunther
8th Grade Science Teacher
Holden, Maryellen Rossvall
Frgn Lang Chpsn & Span Tchr
Hoodbhoy, Ozden Karakurum
Chemical Engineering Professor
Houlihan, Gail Lynn
Special Education Teacher
Hudson, Pennie Holley
Fifth Grade Teacher
Huxley, Sharon Jones
Associate Prof of Accounting
Jacobs, Tim
Anthropology & Sociology Instr
Jacovino, Joseph John, Jr.
Music Director
Johnson, Kathleen R.
Teacher
Kelly, Charles
Social Science Instructor
Killer, Kenneth Marsh
Honors Bio Tchr & Dept Chair
Kohanow, Carol Polletta
Social Studies Teacher
Kwon, Annie
Assistant Professor of Art
Labagh, Cheryl Christine
Spanish & ESL Teacher
Lecours, Dorothy Alice
First Grade Teacher
Lorusso, Tina Marie Elena
Music Teacher & Choral Dir
Marold, Mary Ann Sullivan
Acting Supervising Vice Prin
McCarthy, Rita A.
Technology Dept Chprsn & Tchr
Meisel, Harriet Kaplan
Second Grade Teacher
Mierzejewski, Mark Michael
Science Teacher
Murphy, Christopher Anthony
Social Studies Teacher
Nordone, James Paul, Jr.
Adjunct Instr of Psych Dept
Okwu, Austine S. O.
Professor & Director
O'Neill, Barbara LeRoy
Science Teacher
Orso, Joyce Grosso
5th Grade Teacher
Pitblado, Colin B.
Professor of Psychology
Pond, Gloria Dibble
Professor
Ponzillo, Louis R., Jr.
Social Studies Teacher
Purcaro, Michael Joseph
Chemistry Teacher
Rieger, Samuel L.
Professor of Chemistry
Saukas, Mark W.
Soc Stud Tchr & Dir Stu Act
Scully, Linda Lanese
Kindergarten Teacher
Sheehy, Midge
MS Language Arts Teacher
Stein, Marsha E.
Associate Prof of Marketing
Wick, John R.
Career Counselor
WATERFORD
Christensen, Howard G.
US History Teacher
Haney, Roslyn Pacifici
Retired Sixth Grade Teacher
Hoye, June M.
English Teacher
WATERTOWN
Barone, Stephen Nicholas
Health Teacher
Bernon, Jonathan Robert
Math Teacher
Bisselle, Andrew Philip
History Teacher
DuBois, Louis Peter, Jr.
Chemistry Teacher
Galvin, John Brett
Mathematics Teacher

Hawley, George Joseph, Jr.
Music Teacher
Hostage, David W.
Director & Sci Dept Head
Krantz, Joan Sczawinski
English Teacher
Monti-Bovi, Louisa Nora
English Teacher
Nicholson, William G.
English Teacher
Zwyner, Grace Eleanor
Mathematics Teacher
WEST HARTFORD
Bornstein, David Stuart
English Teacher
Brasher, Deborah E.
History Teacher
Cottone, Joseph Rauol
Physical Education Teacher
Juda, Patricia S.
HS English Teacher
Lynch, Patricia A. (Henigin)
English Teacher
Pennington, Galinda Ostrinski
Russian & Spanish Teacher
Reilly, Brendan
Accounting Professor
Sweetland, Raymond David
History Teacher
WEST HAVEN
Bartolotta, Ardell Mathews
Third Grade Teacher
Bartosz, John
Teacher
Bellmore, Patricia Thomson
English as a Second Lang Tchr
Bonn, Kathy Kadish
Spanish Teacher
Carriuolo, Ralf Eugene
Professor of Humanities
Castelot, William Lawrence
HS & Coll Mathematics Tchr
Celone, Jim
High School Mathematics Tchr
Clifford, Patrick James
Guidance Counseling Director
Corraro, Dominic J.
Foreign Language Dept Chair
DeCaprio, John Anthony
Freshman Social Studies Tchr
Della Rocco, Felix Carlo
Sixth Grade Teacher
Deppen, Catherine Cummings
Fifth Grade Teacher
Erickson, Roger Craig
8th Grade Reading Teacher
Evangelista, Barbara Poppendick
English Teacher
Fortino, Joseph G.
Soc Stud, Rdng & Rel Tchr
Gabriel, Ann Louise
Library-Media Specialist
Goldberg, Steven David
Asst Professor of Management
Grady, Jacqueline J. Stuckey
Social Worker
Hawley, Lester Edward
Assistant Principal
Iliescu, Sorin
Asst Prof of Fire Sci Dept
Janeczek, Mary
Mathematics Teacher
Koutsospyros, Agamemnon Demetrios
Assoc Prof of Environ Engrng
Langello, Laura Cianci
7th & 8th Grd Choral Director
Marks, Joel Howard
Professor of Philosophy
Mathews, Linda Roth
First Grade Teacher
Maxwell, David A.
Prof of Law & Criminal Justice
Miller, Marianne Giordano
Fourth Grade Teacher
Paolino, Frank J.
4th Grade Teacher
Rossi, Michael J.
Asst Prof of Bio & Environ Sci
Suster, Zeljan E.
Economics Professor
Toole, Audrey Medley
4th Grade Teacher
Torro, Patricia Lewis
Fifth Grade Teacher
Warner, Mark Mosher
Acting Dean & Assoc Professor
Whitley, William Thurmon
Professor of Mathematics
WEST SIMSBURY
Flaherty, Patricia Chudecki
Fourth Grade Teacher
Morency, Bertram Anthony, III
Sixth Grade Teacher
WESTON
Billus, John E.
French Teacher
Ehrhard, Joseph A.
Science Dept Chair & Tchr
Trent-Fraser, Jan Ann
Reading Consultant
Wroe, Patricia Pettigrew
6th Grade Teacher
WESTPORT
Garrick, Barbara Georgia
3rd Grade Teacher
Lazaroff, Michael Jonathan Vieira
High School Biology Teacher
Luster, Judy Ann
English Teacher

Rhodes, Stanley Williams
Physics Teacher
Wright, Marcia Kornblum
Fifth Grade Teacher
WETHERSFIELD
Brown, Nancy Gilbert
6th Grade Teacher
Farrelly, Delphine Johns
Guid Cnslr & Career Ed Coord
Hulse, Sharon A.
Fourth Grade Teacher
Korp, William Michael
Math Teacher
Prouty, Nancy Zumwalt
Sixth Grade Teacher
Skinner, Kathleen Ann
Special Education Teacher
Steinmetz, Shirley Wenning
English as Second Lang Tchr
Sticka, Gloria Morris
Sixth Grade Teacher
Tralli, Rosemary Haraburda
Resource Teacher
Wachtelhausen, Susan Johnson
English Teacher
WILLIMANTIC
Abbott, Mary Milligan
9th-12th Grade English Tchr
Gable, Michael Francis
Professor of Biology
Mazzola, Michael
Instructor & Dept Chairperson
Skoog, William Elliott
High School English Teacher
WILLINGTON
Houle-Madden, Lee
Sixth Grade Teacher
WILTON
Crowley, Donald Christopher
Sixth Grade Science Teacher
Dumser, Patricia Mahoney
English & Soc Studies Tchr
Fagan, Genevieve Taylor
2nd Grd Tchr & Tech Instrl Ldr
Flocco, Angela Farina
5th Grade Teacher
Gawle, Frank Edward
Dean of Students
Henry, Sheila Callan
High School English Teacher
Hughes, Jacqueline Luciani
Retired Elem School Teacher
Jacobs, Robert S.
Chemistry Teacher
Lasala, Jeff A.
Science Teacher
Mc Donald, Ann Brubaker
6th-8th Grade Teacher
O'Grady, Terence J.
Geography & Soc Stud Teacher
WINDSOR
Adler, Lori Robin (Prague)
Business Educator
Belzer, Barbara Bloom
Third Grade Teacher
Byrne, Pamela Hyde
9th-12th Grd Mathematics Tchr
Deshais, Thomas Francis
Science Teacher
Doyle, Carolyn Fletcher
Social Studies Teacher
Franklin, Katherine Courtney
8th Grade Social Studies Tchr
Hymes, Patricia Edith
Violence Preventn Educl Coord
Joffray, Donald Marshall
Math Teacher
Landin, Keith
Technology Teacher
Savage, Peggi Benner
Explorer Teacher
Scanlon, Jeffrey M.
English Teacher
Thurber, Bert Henry
History Teacher
Van Ausdall, Diane Sullivan
Social Studies Teacher
Williams, Mark C.
History Teacher
WINSTED
Barber, Frances (Cox)
Family & Consumer Sci Edctr
Crameri, Gregory Peter
Music Teacher & Dir of Bands
Ejzak, Kristy Foley
Fifth Grade Teacher
Jassen, Alison Putnam
Instructor of Chemistry & Bio
Mossman, Claudia
HS Business Education Teacher
Murray, Karen J.
Mathematics Teacher
Welcome, Maryann D'Amico
History Dept Chair & Teacher
WOLCOTT
Bagioni, John Joseph
HS Science Teacher
Blair, William
English Teacher
Del Cioppo, Victor
8th Grade Math Teacher
Veneziano, Joan Pesce
Mathematics Teacher
WOODBRIDGE
Adams, Linda Moran
Math & Comp Teacher
Blozzon, Susan Cortina
Chemistry Teacher
Bonomi, Marilyn Alkus
American Literature Tchr

WOODBRIDGE (cont)
Concilio, Alan J.
Teacher & Dist Science Coord
Duffy, Susanne M.
History & Government Teacher
Gibbons, Richard Paul
Psychology Teacher
Gibbons, Vicenta Calzadilla
Spanish Teacher
Grammatico, Regina Bowler
French Teacher
Hovey, Arthur
Physics Teacher
Hunt, Dennis Charles
History Teacher
King, B. Diane Coleman
3rd Grade Teacher
Miranda, Carolina Henriques
Spanish Teacher
Parsons, Patricia Brooks
Math Teacher
Redmond, Nancy Dunn
Sr HS Mathematics Teacher
Schmidt, William Howard
Bus & Technology Dist Dept Chm
WOODBURY
Casagrande, Louis Angelo, Jr.
History & Social Studies Tchr
Hall, Patricia Mary
Computer Instructor
Thomson, Alexander L.
Agri-Sci & Tech Dept Dir
WOODSTOCK
Colburn, Devra L.
Mathematics Teacher
Susla, Jeffrey J.
English Teacher

DELAWARE

BEAR
Arterbridge, Denise Belinda
8th Grade Teacher
Aubrey, Alison Adams
Rdng, Lang Arts & Civics Tchr
Keller, Beverly Darlyne Jones
Third Grade Teacher
LaBarbera, Thomas Joseph
Scndry Soc Studies Teacher
Lewandowski, Mary Ann Harris
Second Grade Teacher
Norris, Rhonda Joyce
Jr High English Teacher
Owens, Vicki Daffara
Art Teacher
Robson, David James
English Teacher
BRIDGEVILLE
Christian, Drew Mitchell
Secondary English Teacher
CAMDEN WYOMING
Layton, Theodore Glenn
Agriculture Science Teacher
Livingston, Kimberly Ann
English Teacher
Marsh, Melinda Ray
Choral Dir & Gifted Prgm Coord
Mills, Susan Shatzer
Business Education Teacher
Noble, Nadine Morse
Fr Tchr & Frgn Lang Dept Chair
Rathbun, Allan L.
Ag Tchr & Dept Chairman
Reinhart, Joanne D.
8th Grade Language Arts Tchr
Richards, Allison Browning
Latin Tchr
CLAYMONT
Crum, John William
History Department Chairman
D'Angelo, Louis Phillip, Jr.
Mathematics Teacher
Ifkovits, David John
Director of Choral Activities
Manerchia, Thomas Evans
Biology Teacher
Pomeroy, Patricia Waldron
Bio, Chem Tchr & Dept Chmn
DELAWARE CITY
Breffitt, Steven Wayne
Bands Director
Henry, Mary Colette
Middle School Health Teacher
Paolillo, Lorianne
Eighth Grade Algebra Teacher
DELMAR
Johnson, Stan Allan
Business Teacher
Speicher, Denise Culver
English Teacher
DOVER
Adams, Cheryl Anne (Kirkner)
Parent & KDG Cmptr Teacher
Andres, Linda
Advanced Composition Teacher
Angstadt, Ginger
Language Arts & Drama Teacher
Barlett, Elizabeth Habecker
Fifth Grade Teacher
Berns, Brian Keith, Sr.
PE & Health Teacher
Caldwell, Marion Milford, Jr.
Former Instructor
Dean, Thomas Eugene
Choral & Asst Band Director
George, Ted Daib
US History & Law Teacher
Gieske, Frank H.
8th Grd Earth Science Teacher
Gregory, Frank R.
History Teacher
Harrington, Mitzi B.
Kindergarten Teacher
Kirk, Jan Boechler
Biology Teacher
Layton, Walter John
Associate Principal
Mundell, Charles Leo
Program Director & Instructor
Nadel, Colleen Diane
8th Grd Social Studies Tchr
Oncay, Barbara Sharp
German & French Teacher
Quirk, James Edward
Public Services Dept Chairman
Rigby, Susan Hickey
Remedial Reading Teacher
Simon, Gina Ann
Second Grade Teacher
Voshell, Sharon P.
Seventh Grade Lang Arts Tchr
Wagner, Nancy H.
English Teacher
FELTON
Boyd, Michael P.
English Teacher
McCartney, Lorrie Kay
High School Art Teacher
Moffett, Doris Hendricks
School Nurse
Szajewski, Mary (Marshall)
Eng, Jrnlsm Tchr & Dept Chprsn
FRANKFORD
Adkins, Anita E. Schaab
English Teacher
Milspaw, Thomas Henry
Physical Science Teacher
Steele, James Raymond
Mathematics Teacher
West, Sabrina Lavella
Business Teacher
GEORGETOWN
Burton, Becky Albert
Fifth Grade Teacher
Di Sabatino, Phillip Anthony, Jr.
Physical Ed & Health Teacher
Dix, Marguerite Elizabeth
Fifth Grade Teacher
Donaway, Frances J.
English Teacher
Gum, Susan Edwards
Pub Relation Coord & Yrbk Tchr
Hunt, Carole MacGregor
English Teacher
Hurdle, Elizabeth Conroy
Basic Skills Teacher
John, Michelle Hand
Math Teacher
Jones, Adele Lisa
Math Teacher
Lathbury, Allen Franklin, Jr.
Science Teacher
Smith, Karen Carroccia
Evening Instr of Bus Admin
Ward, Nancy Hanna
English 2nd Language Teacher
HARRINGTON
Jerman, Elizabeth Faye
5th Grade Teacher
Ridgely, Debrah Wuthnow
First Grade Teacher
Riser, Jamila Qaissaunee
7th Grade Math Teacher
HARTLY
Allen, Denise DiSabatino
Elementary School Librarian
Johnson, Morei Banks
Kindergarten Teacher
HOCKESSIN
Ahlborn, Patricia L. (Horn)
Math Teacher & Department Head
Stephens, Jami Leigh
Social Studies Teacher
LAUREL
Crouse, Michael Thomas
History & English Teacher
Elliott, Helen E.
7th Grade Social Studies Tchr
Lewis, Robert K.
Band & Drama Teacher
Moore, Lynn Wilson
Social Studies Teacher
Rosen, Jennifer Paysse
Bio & Phys Sci Tchr
Whaley, Donna M.
School Nurse
Whaley, Sharon Wheatley
3rd Grade Teacher
LEWES
Eisenhour, Michael U.
Math Department Chairman
Hilton, John Martin
Physics Teacher
Peterson, Vicki Pierce
3rd Grade Teacher
Tull, David A.
High School Math Teacher
LINCOLN
Beebe, Robert D.
English & Spanish Teacher
O'Bier, Mary Louise Long
First Grade Teacher
MIDDLETOWN
Boyer, Ted
Business Teacher
DeSalvo, David Paul
Mathematics Teacher
Koster, Mary M.
6th Grade Science Teacher
Murphy, Byron Girard
Mathematics Tchr
Perrine, Veronica Beader
Choral & Drama Director
Robinson, Lovell
USAF JROTC Instructor
Shaffner, Vickie Anne
6th Grade Language Arts Tchr
Thomas, Jeffery Joseph
Mathematics Teacher
MILLSBORO
Messick, Edward Burton
Pre Algebra & Math Teacher
MILTON
Webster, Ronald Sanford, III
Language Arts Teacher
NEW CASTLE
Ambrose, Alan A.
Bible Teacher
Brittin, Beth Ann
Middle School History Teacher
Campbell, Ivy Meadows
Sixth Grade Teacher
Davis, Sarah Olinda
Fourth Grade Teacher
Durkee, Sharon Seiders
Biology Teacher
Guidry, Gail Keith
Math, PE & Hlth Teacher
Johnson, Jenny Ehren
English Teacher
Kassees, Martha Cadoura
Social Studies Teacher
Morris, Lida M.
5th Grade Teacher
Reynolds, Bruce C.
History Teacher & Coach
Trotter, Rosa Snow
Kindergarten Teacher
Wells, Phyllis Coccia
Teacher of the Gifted
Young, Melody Gyles
Spanish Teacher
NEWARK
Albright, Lester E.
Math Teacher
Antes, Carol Lynn (Mickel)
Third Grade Teacher
Atchley, Steven Wayne
Criminal Justice Instructor
Baldwin, Charles William
Assoc Naval Science Instructor
Bolden, Stephanie Teresa
Business Education Teacher
Cavanaugh, John Charles
Interim Assc Provost Grad Stud
Christy, Charles W., III
Dept Chm Ind Engineering Tech
Cornish, Annette Holliday
HS Counselor & Student Advisor
Davies, Harry Russell
Counselor & Chairperson
Doughty, Beverly (Ingersoll)
Eighth Grade Lang Arts Teacher
Fredricks, Karen Chapman
Third Grade Teacher
Freidly, Mark S.
Telecommunications Teacher
Hammonds, Jay A.
Soc Stud Tchr & Dept Chprsn
Hester, Eugene William
Science Teacher
Hite, Mary Simms
Business Education Teacher
Huff, Charles C.
Assistant Principal
Janeka, Rhonda Roark
Science Educator
Janis, Joann Bramble
Business Teacher
King, Lloyd Eugene
English Teacher
Klopfer, Ronald G.
Prof of Anatomy & Physiology
Macera, Rosaria
Orchestra Director
Maio, James Albert
Technology & Drafting Teacher
Miller, Susan Dawson
Mathematics Teacher
Pepekanos, George
Teaching Assistant
Phipps, Carol Swales
Secondary Social Stud Teacher
Posatko, Sheila Finan
English & Latin Teacher
Reeves, Rodney
Counselor & Intnl Students Adv
Ross, Lloyd H.
Director of Bands
Rudisill, David A.
7th Grade Social Studies Tchr
Sheppard, Ami Holland
Secondary English Teacher
Shoemaker, Anne W.
English as a Second Lang Tchr
Swann, Beverly Mitchell
Business Teacher
Tini, Kathleen A.
Industrial Engrng Tech Instr
Toccafondi, Barbara L.
Instructor in French
Vance, Linda S.
Spanish & French Teacher
VanWickle, David Thomas
Mathematics Instructor
Young, Phyllis Arlene
Physical Education Teacher
OCEAN VIEW
Grise, Deborah Waldin
Fifth Grade Teacher
Hitchens, Grace Williams
Fourth Grade Teacher
REHOBOTH BEACH
Roe, Lori Ann (Butler)
6th Grade Math & Science Tchr
SAINT GEORGES
Toler, Charles Robert
Mathematics Teacher
SEAFORD
Dufour, Carol Tallon
English, Typing & Math Teacher
Fletcher, Kathi L. Harris
Bus Tchr & Occupations Coord
Labor, John J.
Asst Admin & Band Dir
Mc Intyre, Dina Helene
7th Grd Social Studies Teacher
Moore, Stephanie Lois (Davis)
Social Studies Teacher
Pegelow, Thomas Ray
Special Ed Teacher & Coach
Ritts, Samuel Donald
Technology Education Teacher
Sirman, Marsha Stein
German & ESL Teacher
Treherne, Brenda O'Neill
Social Studies Teacher
Weyhe, Jill Elaine
Fourth Grade Teacher
Wills, Melissa Wright
Elementary Multi-Age Teacher
SELBYVILLE
Farrell, Michael R.
7th Grade Life Science Teacher
Truitt, Cheryl Lynne
6th Grade Science Teacher
Twisselmann, Diane Meredith
8th Grade Earth Science Tchr
SMYRNA
Prillaman, Derek Vincent
10th-12th Grd Soc Studies Tchr
Smith, Robin W.
Business Teacher
Wolbert, Stephanie Ann
Math, Sci & Soc Stud Teacher
WILMINGTON
Bainbridge, Lisa Donna
Cheerleading Coach
Bellezza, Nina H.
Life Science Teacher
Borleske, Barbara Lesh
Chemistry Teacher
Bounds, Shirley Watson
Associate Principal
Brazill, James Edward
Physical Education Teacher
Brown, Lorna Mauriz
Reading Teacher
Buccio, Deborah K.
Eleventh Grade English Teacher
Burke, Barbara Ramsey
History Teacher
Carlton, John Ryland
Sci Dept Chm & Biology Tchr
Carrell, Anthony Joseph
Social Studies Teacher
Christoph, Margaret S.
Chemistry Teacher
Ciuffetelli, Anthony
Spanish & Italian Teacher
DePace, William Frederick
Secondary Math & Bible Teacher
Doran, Laurie Kirkpatrick
Art Instructor & Dept Head
Downs, Donna Lynn
Art Teacher
Emerick, Linda Cowgill
English Language Arts Teacher
Eshleman, Ronald Eugene
Chem Teacher & Sci Dept Head
Euganeo, Kathleen Doran
Allied Health Instructor
Flowers, Margaret M.
Business Teacher
Giansiracusa, Michael
Theology Teacher
Good, Peter J., Jr.
Math Teacher
Goodell, Dianne Lee
Human Svcs & Social Sci Prof
Hamilton, Battle M.
Dean of Students & His Tchr
Heiss, Ralph E.
Counselor
Highfield, Harlan Edward, Jr.
Social Studies Teacher
Hodges, Ann Taylor
Second Grade Teacher
Ingram, W. Bruce
Theology Teacher
Kegelman, Bernadette
Biology Teacher
Knotts Moyer, Edith Claude
Math Specialist
Lambert, Charlene Jane
Spanish & French Teacher
Larkin, Gail Graber
Bus Ed Dept Chprsn
Lombardozzi, Patrick Enrico
Social Studies Teacher
Love, Annamarie Moschella
9th-12th Grd Math Tchr & Chair
Lowther, Martha H.
Mathematics Teacher
Lukaskiewicz, Robert Paul
Theology Teacher
Mark, Ellen S.
Spanish Teacher
Markham, Barbara Niccolo
Social Studies Instr & Chprsn
Mazzio, Robert Joseph
Math Teacher & Dept Chair
Mc Connell, Joan (Basilio)
Spanish Teacher
Mc Laughlin, William Francis
English Teacher
Mc Monigle, Francis Marie, SND
Art Teacher
Moore, Clare Peoples
Social Studies Tchr & Dpt Head
Novak, Walter Joseph
Technology Education Teacher
Oberholtzer, William Irving
Senior Army Instructor
Page, Elma May
Sixth Grade Science Teacher
Parets, Paul L.
Director of Bands
Petruzzelli, John Paul
History Teacher
Pieslak, Judith Staples
English & Literature Teacher
Poliski, Lisa M.
Social Studies Teacher
Quann, Thomas K.
9th-12th Grd Soc Stud Teacher
Renshaw, John Hubert
US History Teacher
Rimmer, Mary Bontempo
Spanish Teacher
Roewe, Barbara Clancy
HS English & Journalism Tchr
Ruth, George Allen
Art Education & Drama Director
Sharps, Howard Edward
Fine Arts & Mathematics Tchr
Shreve, Angela Pollard
Early Childhood Ed Professor
Sianni, Mary Ann C.
English Teacher
Slater, Elizabeth A.
English Teacher
Smith, James F.
English & Drama Teacher
Stanley, Mary Montgomery
Business Dept Chairperson
Stemniski, Michael Andrew
Chemistry Teacher
Teaf, Louise Spitzner
7th Grade Mathematics Teacher
Thomas, Benjamin L.
Language Arts Teacher
Thomas-Holder, Susan A.
Physics & Chemistry Teacher
Tilghman, Kathy Quinn
Stu Advisor, Stu Relation
Toombs, Jean Carter
Home Economics Teacher
Vassalotti, Wayne
Technology Education Dept Chm
Vavala, Phillip D.
Science Dept Chair & Bio Tchr
Vye, Rebecca Wittmeyer
English Teacher
Wahl, Megan Lynn
7th Grd Earth Sci Tchr & Dean
Walker, Dennis Patrick
Health & PE Teacher
Walls, Stacy Lynn
World History Teacher
Welch, Mary Newell
English Tchr & Dept Chprsn
White, Estella M.
Academic Advisor
Whiting, Janet Subers
US His & Philosophy Teacher
Wiesel, Mary Helen
English Teacher
Wilkinson, Eileen Frances
Amer His Teacher & Dept Chair
Williams, Carolyn A.
HS English Teacher
Williamson, Kathleen Hines
Vocational Teacher
Williams-Young, Diane L.
Accounting & Computer Teacher
Wilson, Eleanor Kelly
Mathematics Teacher
Wolanski, Anthony S.
Math Teacher
Young, Valerie Secor
English Teacher & Dept Chair
Ziemianski, Michele M.
2nd Grade Teacher
WOODSIDE
Babbitt, Lucienne Carter
Social Studies Teacher
Curry, Bruce Oxley
Aerospace Science Instructor
Davis, Roger William
Science Teacher
Shaffer, Timothy D.
Criminal Justice Instructor
Sombar, Rose
Nursing Instructor
Stoner, Sarah Lisa (Maupin)
Business Education Teacher

STRICT OF
OLUMBIA

HINGTON
rre, Maria Sophia
nomics Professor
d, Joyce Deans
dance Counselor
, Sandra Alex Denise (Mills)
hematics Teacher
, Emelda Siri-Ntinglet
nputer Professor
niswami, Anthony
hematics Teacher
d, Richard Leroy
hematics Teacher
., Susan Mc Callum
logy & Science Teacher
on, Richard S.
ory & English Teacher
r, Josephine C. (Johnson)
h Grade Teacher
r, Curtis H.
Instructor
ett, Betsy Kraus
hematics Teacher
arour, Zahia
fessor
nd, Patricia Ann
et Mistress, Tchr & Coach
, Llewellyn l., III
lio Production Instructor
, Marie
h Grade Teacher
rs, Michael Everett
Stud Dept Chprsn & Instr
son, Patricia McEwan
glish Teacher
oe, Frank William
sical Education Teacher
n, Carolyn Cosby
Grade Teacher
ck, Barbara Jean
h Grade Teacher
, Larry Glenn
n
on, William Patrick
n Grade English Teacher
on, Richard Carroll
, Greek His & Drama Tchr
on, Margaret Mulkey
cher
bers, Bettye Thomas
ian Teacher
lin, Hattie Daniels
j Dir of Tutorial Vol & LiB
, Steve Han-Hoy
gineering Prof & Asst Dean
stian, Judy Ann
st Dean, Coll of Arts & Sci
ell, Larry Winfred
glish Teacher
, Robin LaVerne
ncipal
er, Elizabeth Anne
ial Studies Dept Chprsn
er, Kenneth Peter
igion Teacher
n, Richard William
siness Admin Dept Chair
kett, Beverley Anne
Grade English Teacher
s, Martha Louise
, Rel Tchr & Librarian
le, Donald Paul
thematics Teacher
ng, Marsha Jean Tyson
tory Professor
, Sarah Miles
5th Grade Music Teacher
aney, Shirley Booth
ucation Specialist
ze, Donna Emile Marie
glish Teacher
nis, Susan Selena
cial Studies Teacher
er, Caroline Elizabeth
st Professor of Classics
k, Eileen Marie
th Grade Teacher
sti, Mahmood N.
th & Cmptr Science Teacher
gherty, John Martin
cial Studies Teacher
n, Mildred Hall
athematics Teacher
on, Kitty L.
glish Instructor
t, Frances Levenstein
urth Grade Teacher
n, Marcia Moten
ology Teacher
on, Ethel Speight
Grade Teacher
ey, Patrick James
nptr Information Sys Dept Chm
Judith Banzer
ofessor of English
, Rita
L & Russian Teacher
man, Martin Robert
emistry Professor
uson, Delphine David
xth Grade Teacher
is, Lorraine Catherine
nguage Arts Teacher
er, Dwayne Edward
glish Teacher

Fullard, Barbara Lois
English Teacher
Garland, Kenneth Warren
Pgm Dir, Aviation Maint Tech
Garner, Ernest
Secondary Mathematics Teacher
Garrett, Clayton W.
Professor
Goggins, Deborah Stringfellow
Teacher
Gordon, Murielene Elizabeth
Art Teacher
Graham, Sharon L.
English Teacher & Dept Chprsn
Griffin, Christopher Gerald
Teacher
Griffin, Sandra Anita
Mathematics Teacher
Guinyard, Fayetta Lafton
Health & Physical Ed Instr
Gultneh, Yilma
Associate Professor of Chem
Guyton, Constance Gaines
English Teacher
Hallums, Brenda Reynolds
6th Grade Math Teacher
Harris, Mary-Louise
Professor
Headen, Robert James
PE Teacher & Athletic Dir
Henderson, Jean Victoria
Sixth Grade Teacher
Hermosillo, Carmen
Spanish Teacher
Heroux, Richard Donald
Professor
Hillery, Sharon Stewart
Chem Teacher & Sci Dept Chair
Horne, David Charles
Music Teacher
Horvath, Laura Hutchison
Research Asst & Univ Supvr
Hottel, David Timothy
Professor of Business
Hubsch, Tristan
Physics Professor
Hudrlik, Paul F.
Chemistry Professor
Hufford, Terry Lee
Professor of Botany
Isa, Geneva A. Cooper
Science Resource Teacher
Jackson, Basil P.
Cmptr Information Systems Prof
Jacobowitz, E. Lunn
Assistant Professor
Johnson, Cassandra Ann
English Teacher
Jolin, Martin John
Asst Professor of Theatre Arts
Jones, Bryan David
Biology Teacher
Jones, Paula Crawford
1st Grade Teacher
Jones, Shirley Winder
Sixth Grade Teacher
Jones, Thomas Wright
Professor of Education
Jones, Zainabu Netosh
Educator
Kabes, Marianne Otilia
French Tchr & Lang Dept Chprsn
Katz, Vera J.
Professor
Kearney, Lynn
Social Stud & Humanities Tchr
Keels, Carl Eugene
Science Teacher
Kelley, Peter E.
Math Department Chair
Kelly, Christopher Michael
Principal
Kimbrough, Rennae H.
Asst Prin & Lang Arts Teacher
King, Unity Macklin
Business Education Teacher
Knox, Barbara A.
Mathematics Teacher
Lacy, Consuella Frazier
Senior Counselor
Ladd, Culver S.
Classroom Teacher
Latney, Carleen Marie Lewis
English Teacher
Lee, Don Franklin
Chemistry Teacher
Leonard, Charles Brown, Jr.
Dept of Biology Assoc Prof
Levinson, Lynn
High School Humanities Teacher
Lewis, Kathleen Ann (Myers)
English Teacher
Lewis, Ned L.
Music Teacher
Logan, Gwendolyn Runnels
Science Teacher
Macy, Thomas Lawrence
Humanities Teacher
Maisch, Christian Joaquin
Assistant Professor
Mann, Kathleen Comedy
Fourth Grade Teacher
Mansour, Elsayed Ahmed
Department Head of CIS
Marchitelli, Anita Marie
Assoc Prof of PE & Recreation
Martin, Deborah Eileen
6th Grade Teacher
Marvin, James Paul
Drama Teacher

Matthews, Elaine Hardy
Health & Physical Ed Teacher
Mattingly, Catherine Schulz
English Teacher
Mattison, Gary Allen
Campus Dean
Mc Aleer, Brenda Oates
Campus Dean
Mc Cahill, Dennis F.
Director of Construction Pgms
Mc Carthy, Joan Kane
History Teacher
Mc Nair, Erick Donnell
Anatomy & Hnrs Gen Bio Teacher
Metze, Charles Levi, II
Literature Professor
Misra, Prabhakar
Associate Professor
Moore, Elaine
Social Studies Teacher
Moore, Eva Annette
Second Grade Teacher
Moore, Janice Alexander
Mentor, Tchr & Spiritual Adv
Moore, Ronald Cullen
Cmptr Information Systems Prof
Mostoller, Cynthia Scholz
Soc Stud & Amer His Tchr
Murphy, Christine S.
English Dept Chairperson
Murphy, Edward Jerome, Jr.
Senior Army Instructor
Murphy, Katherine Ann
Religion Teacher
Murrell, Daisy Mae (Goolsby)
Business Education Teacher
Nafisi, Rasool
Dept of General Studies Chprsn
Naughton, Ingrid Emelda
English Teacher
Neale, Margaret Dukes
United States Government Tchr
Nguyen, Charles C.
Professor of Electrical Engrng
Nyang, Sulayman Sheih
African Studies Dept Professor
Oxendine, Elnora Coley
Music Teacher & Coord of GATE
Palmer, Melvin L.
Spanish Teacher
Parker, DeWayne Gordon
6th Grade Teacher
Parks-Lee, Barbara Evans
9th & 11th Grade Teacher
Pelosi, Delora Mary
Latin Teacher
Pelton, Caroline Brown
Secondary English Teacher
Pemberton, Gladys Fitzhugh
Business Teacher
Perry, Juanita Lambright-Linder
Fifth Grade Teacher
Peters, Antonia Mari
Assistant Principal
Powe, Karen Denise Marcia
Physics Teacher
Prince, Eugene V.
English Second Language Tchr
Pushia, Alfrieda Cooper
4th Grade Teacher
Ragan, Wallace Bennett
Chair of Classics
Rasmussen, Olga Rodriguez
Religion Department Chair
Reidy, George H.
Math Teacher & Dept Chair
Rice, Angela Swanson
English Teacher
Rice, Gene
Prof of Old Testament Lang
Rice, Theodore Delano
Pre K-6th Grade Art Teacher
Rice, William Stantley, III
Mathematics Professor
Richardson, John Edwardo
Graphic Arts & Printing Tchr
Roane, Lillian E.
Math Teacher
Roberts, Sadie Jones
English & French Teacher
Rogovski, Elizabeth
Assistant Professor
Ruf, Frederick John
Assoc Professor of Religion
Russell, Shirley Deck
Reading Teacher & CBC Chprsn
Satyshur, Rosemarie Frances DiMauro
Asst Prof & Child Hlth Nurse
Saunders, Cynthia Ann
Cheerleader Coach
Savoy, Doris Jean Hurd
Spanish Teacher
Schlagel, Josephine Regar
French Instructor
Schlief, Marilyn Nagano
Senior Program Officer
Schuhart, Arthur Lovis
English Teacher
Scott, Betty Jo Ann
Heatlh & Physical Ed Tchr
Scott, Russell Bert
Professor
Scott-Hunter, Judith
Communications Coord
Shannon, Mary Suing
7th-8th Grd Lang Arts Tchr
Shea, Remee Hausmann
English Professor
Sheppard, Bettie Hall
Business Educator

Siegel, Frederic Richard
Professor of Geochemistry
Simpson, Yvette LaShon
Scndry Social Studies Teacher
Slaughter, Janice
Elementary Teacher
Slocumb-Bradford, Alesia B.
Geometry & Algebra Teacher
Snead, Lala F.
Mathematics Teacher
Starosta, William J.
Human Comm Studies Professor
Stephenson, Jeffrey Earl
Former Teacher
Sutter, Judith Anne
Academic Dean & Professor
Sutton, Augustus
English Teacher
Taylor, Alfred Overton, Jr.
Assistant Dean
Taylor, Clarence Leroy, Jr.
High School Chemistry Tchr
Tesmer, Floyd Stephen
Social Science Professor
Thornton, Alvin
Professor
Thurber, James Allen
Professor of Political Science
Tolbert, Effie Ann Footman
Fifth Grade Teacher
Tollo, Richard Paul
Assistant Professor of Geology
Tucker, Pamela J.
Mathematics Teacher
Twitty, Geraldine Williams
Professor of Biology
Vaile, Jonathan Reed
English Teacher & Dev Director
VandeHei, Richard Paul
Senior Army Instructor
Walton, Mary Frances
Science Teacher
Weitzel, Ronald L.
Social Studies Chairman
Welters, Lynn B.
Dance Chairperson
Whitfield, Stephen Venard, Sr.
PE & Health Teacher
Wickersham, Tilney
Social Studies Teacher
Williams, Carol Margretanne
Second Grade Teacher
Williams, Ella Marilyn M.
Mathematics Teacher
Williams, Veronica Elizabeth
Science Teacher
Winn-Ritzenberg, Mark Olin
English Second Lang Teacher
Winters, Wendy Russell
Sociology Professor
Wood, Herbert Thomas
Math Teacher
Yarborough, Davey S.
Instrumental Music Teacher
Yates, Cara Chamberlain
Third Grade Teacher
Young, Frank J.
Teacher & Coach
Zobenica, Lindsay
Foreign Language Chair

FLORIDA

ALACHUA
Ayres, Jonathan David
Science Teacher
Carlisle, Casey Allen
Chemistry Instructor
Curtis, Mattie Lattrell
English Teacher
Davis, Valinda Charmaine
6th Grd World Cultures Teacher
Jackson, Bessie Gautier
High School Media Specialist
Priscott, Sandra W.
Second Grade Teacher
Sims, John E.
Teacher & Department Chairman
ALTAMONTE SPRINGS
Abbott, Debra Byrne
Gifted & AP Chemistry Teacher
Blake, Robert L.
Dean of Students
Branum, Cynthia Ann (Edgerton)
English & Art Teacher
Carpenter, Kevin W.
Exceptional Education Teacher
Cotto, Gisela
English Teacher
Cutler, Charles Stanley, III
Physics Teacher
Fawcett, Virginia Carroll
Teacher of Gifted
Gilliam, Pattie Pittman
Retired Kindergarten Teacher
Hauptkorn, George Edward
8th Grade English Teacher
Jarrett, Janice Hauk
Second Grade Teacher
Johnson, Mary Nan Howard
English Teacher
Mills, Joe B.
Assistant Principal
Nieto, Shirley
Teacher
Rigby, Carol Ann
Mathematics Teacher

Smith, Gary John
Drivers Education Teacher
Spoon, Donald Wayne
K-5th Grade Physical Ed Tchr
Sullivan, Tracey L.
Peer Counseling Teacher
ALTHA
Williams, Millie Jo
English Teacher
ALTURAS
Carroll, Clare Needham
Third Grade Teacher
APALACHICOLA
Butler, Denise Dosal
Teacher & Activities Director
Clayton, Valerie Seyforth
Journalism & Computer Sci Tchr
Faircloth, Annada Shaw
5th Grade Teacher
Jones, Teresa Ann (Brown)
History Teacher
Theis, Rita Barnett
Diversified Coop Trng Coord
APOLLO BEACH
Rothenbush, Polly Churchill
Fourth Grade Teacher
APOPKA
Aguas, Michael Gabriel
Biology Teacher
Barnard, Barbara Annette
7th Grade Science Teacher
Buckman, Mary Ann
Fourth Grade Teacher
Edstrom, Evelyn Julie Sinclair
Mathematics Teacher
Fulbright, Rodney Joe
HS Physical Education Teacher
Grabowski, Mary Meyer
Latin Teacher
Johnson, Stephanie Beary
Academic Advisor
Kampe, Lanny Terrance
Chemistry Teacher
Kelley, Darlene Ehman
Home Economics Teacher
Kendall, Nancy Elizabeth
English Teacher
Klenk, Theodore C.
High School Science Teacher
Lynn, James C.
Mathematics Teacher
Mc Leod, Sarah Margaret
English Instructor
Mercer, Gwyn Orme
Sixth Grade Teacher
Myrold, Sharon Whitworth
Fifth Grade Teacher
Nash, J. Michelle Mathis
9th & 11th Grade English Tchr
Nelund, Martha Elizabeth
Spanish Teacher
Perry, Douglas Dale
Band Director
Poole, Joyce Sluss
English Teacher
Sanford, Mary Ann Dickens
First Grade Teacher
Shepherd, Mary S.
6th Grade Math Teacher
Stephens, Larry Ben
Guidance Dir & Religion Tchr
Zeek, Judy Nix
Mathematics Teacher
ARCADIA
Faison, James Lee, III
7th Grade History Teacher
Mc Elroy, Sue Hill
6th Grade Science Teacher
McQuay, Carol Adranna
Instrumental Music Teacher
Wildt, James Lewis
Social Studies Teacher
Yost, Dorothy Cash
Vocational Health Instructor
ARCHER
Moore, Lynda Brunson
Fifth Grade Teacher
AUBURNDALE
Johns, Quinton Downer
Fourth Grade Teacher
Johnson, Denise Clary
Third Grade Teacher & Chprsn
Kilpatrick, Charlene Flach
Fifth Grade Teacher
AVON PARK
Bettich, Heinrich Robert
English Professor
Carlisle, Betty Lou
Counselor
Craft, Dale L.
Mathematics Professor
Davis, Gordon Taylor
Sci & Physical Education Tchr
Farmer, William Edward
Principal
Hitch, Ledon
Mathematics & Chemistry Tchr
Locke, William F.
Coord Stu Support Services
Moldrik, Ruth Margaret
Second Grade Teacher
Szeligo, John Richard
Adj Instructor of His & Govt
Zesch, Jeannette Mc Donald
English & Journalism Teacher
BABSON PARK
Orphanoudakis, Nikos G.
Prof of Mgmt & Bus Dept Chair

BAGDAD
Willis, Elaine Cook
Technology Coordinator
BAKER
Barton, Mary Beth B.
Social Studies Dept Chair
Bolton, Rodney Lawrence
MS Business & Math Teacher
Harrison, Kimberly Ranae
Physical Education Teacher
Humphrey, Brian Kenneth
Science Teacher
Josey, George Robert
Senior Army Instructor
O'Neal, Roger D.
7th Grd World Geog Teacher
BARTOW
Allison, Eleanor Adele
Anatomy & Physiology Teacher
Calandros, Patricia Murphy
English & Leadership Teacher
Cobb, Marnee Coryell
Math Teacher & Athletic Dir
Coolman, Jan Darrell, Jr.
Band Director
Cross, Faye Thames
MAPS Coord
Frost, Terry Phillips
English Teacher
Salgado, Tamara
Spanish Teacher
Smith, Lonnie William
Social Studies Supervisor
Smith, Nancy Carol
Fifth & Sixth Grade Teacher
Steele, Deborah J.
4th Grade Teacher
BELL
Dorsey, Kelly Oliff
Band Director
BELLE GLADE
Bolden, Melanie L.
Spcl Lrng Disabilities Tchr
Gallo, Judith Adams
English Instructor
Williams, John E.
Fifth Grade Teacher
BELLEVIEW
Anderson, Edward Christopher
High School Teacher
Ballas, Jacqua Lynne
7th Grade Science Teacher
Dennis, Patricia Thompson
Teacher of the Gifted
Kreutchic, Jack Leonard
Technology Coordinator
Popp, Timothy James
5th Grade Teacher
Reeder, Spencer Dwain
Speech & Environmntl Sci Tchr
Ridenour, Joseph V.
Fifth Grade Teacher
Savage, Sherelyn Sue (Cook)
English & Drama Teacher
Stewart, S. Linda
Math Teacher
Tanner Ward, Gwenda Adams
English Teacher
BLOUNTSTOWN
Hall, Ann Booth
6th Grd Math & Sci Teacher
Henderson, Quentin Ray
Science Teacher
Joyner, Tamaria Elizabeth
Former Teacher
Leonard, Joseph H.
Social Studies Teacher
Marshall, Rhonda Pitts
Language Arts Teacher
Miller, Mary Bailey
English Teacher
Sheard, Geraldine B.
Media Specialist
BOCA RATON
Aguila, Susan Donath
English Learning Specialist
Anderson, David J.
English Teacher
Andrew, Jan
University School Instructor
Aparicio, Maria del Carmen
Physics Teacher
Bare, Patricia Kelly
Head Athletic Trainer
Bernardo, Madeline Ann
Computer Science Teacher
Bjorkland, Mark Louis
Physics & Astronomy Teacher
Blanco, Candice Gartel
Spanish Teacher
Boerstler, Barbara DuBose
Eng, Hum & Speech Teacher
Castillo, William John
Band Director
Cross, Lorraine D.
Assoc Prof & Music Specialist
Curl, Donald Walter
History Dept Chair & Professor
Darman, Laurie Thayer
Literature Teacher
Davidson, Leah Sprick
Social Studies Coordinator
Devick, Susan G.
Science Teacher
Dietter, Denise Haneberg
Marketing Teacher & DECA Adv
Di Figlio, Thomas C.
Soc Stud & Psychology Teacher
DiRenzo, Lisa Weiss
Social Studies & Psych Teacher
Durnell, Nannetta Yvette
Asst Prof of Comm
Faraci, Mary Elizabeth
Associate Professor of English
Gehrig, Donna Ann
History Teacher
Geraldi, Robert
Professor
Glines, Marsha
Dean & Professor of Education
Glynn, Simon V.
Assoc Professor of Philosophy
Goebel, Donald William, Jr.
Chemistry Associate Professor
Gosser-Esquilin, Mary Ann A.
Latin American Assistant Prof
Gould, Staci Olivia
Physical Education Teacher
Graham, Patricia Maria
Business Education Teacher
Grasso, Marie Teresa
Physics Professor
Gray, Margaret Hughes
English & Social Studies Tchr
Hahn, Dan F.
Dept of Communication Prof
Hamm, Carol L.
Teacher's Aide
Harris, Michael Scott
Anthropology Professor
Hasko, Jacquie Bolling-Pepper
Drama & Adv Placement Eng Tchr
Holland, Michael Brooks
Psychology & US History Tchr
Horner, Thomas L.
5th Grade Teacher
Ivy, Russell Lee
Geography Professor
Johnson, Sandy Chidgey
4th Grade Alternative Ed Tchr
Kac, Barbara Kelly
7th-8th Grade English Teacher
Kagan Persin, Susan Miller
Spanish Teacher & Dept Chprsn
Keaton, Ken
Associate Professor of Music
Klager, Stewart
Social Studies Teacher
Lewis, Elaine Gutel
Kindergarten Teacher
Mc Clelland, Mary Ann
Second Grade Teacher
Miller, Elizabeth Powell
PE Teacher & Health Instructor
More, Kane J.
Sci Dept Chm & Life Sci Tchr
Murley, Mary F.
Gifted & AP Soc Studies Tchr
Musser, Karen Frederick
SLD & English Teacher
Negyessy, Arpad Anthony
World History Instructor
Nicole, Donald J.
Frgn Lang Dept Hd & Span Tchr
Niemczyk, Kim Parker
Senior Instr of Communications
Owen, Frances Virgin
Eng Teacher & Publications Adv
Pagano, Colleen Feeney
Artistic Director
Persin, Ronald Charles
Math Dept Chair & Teacher
Podhurst, Burt
English & Social Stud Tchr
Schilling, Richard Allen
Earth Science Teacher
Schoenhut, Anne Clark
Kindergarten Teacher
Scott, Rutha G.
Business Education Teacher
Smith, Sean
History & Political Sci Tchr
Sparks, George Ed
Professor of Music
Staggs, Steven Thomas
11th Grd Amer History Teacher
Stavrakos-Sigalos, Stephanie
French & ESOL Teacher
Tsurutome, Sandra Higa
Director
Wershoven, Carol
Communications Professor
Wright, Matthew H.
Assistant Professor of Theatre
BONIFAY
Clemmons, Timothy
Mathematics Teacher
Dixon, Paula Driver
English Teacher
Hudson, Geretha Locke
Primary Curriculum Coordinator
Parish, Tami Porter
Math Teacher
West, Jimmy Wade
Third Grade Teacher
Wheeler, Thomas Anthony
PE Teacher & Head Ath Dir
BONITA SPRINGS
Bradley, Jean Irene
Seventh Grade Math Teacher
Clase, Ron E.
Social Studies Teacher
Hegner, Alfred O.
Science Teacher & Director
Muench, Kenner Sloan
Language Arts & Reading Tchr
Truax, Bennie Statham
Emeritus Conductor, Prof Music
BOYNTON BEACH
Castaldi, Laraine Shepard
Instr of Family & Consumer Sci
Duberstein, Carol M.
Frgn Lang Tchr & Chprsn
Johnson, Sandra Chillson
Third Grade Teacher
Kayne, Carol H.
Retired Teacher
Love, Cherie Tatum
Media Specialist
Merkle, Edward Raymond
Social Studies Teacher
Sippel, Mary Cochran
Eighth Grd Guidance Counselor
Spyker, Harry Asbury, III
Band Director
BRADENTON
Aldrich, Michael R.
World History & Economics Tchr
Anderson, Frank G.
English & Journalism Teacher
Andrews, Richard James
Social Studies Teacher
Barrios, Tina M.
Tech Coord & Science Teacher
Belcher, Deborah Ann
Title One Reading Teacher
Brady, Chris Aaron
Math Teacher
Brown, Amy K.
Jr & Sr HS Science Teacher
Bruce, James Robert
Director of Bands
Burnette, Larry R.
Senior Army & JROTC Instr
Cover, Ellen Catherine
Full Professor of Biology
Davis, Janet Ruth Hosley
4th Grade Teacher
Dixon, Wanda Gordon
2nd Grade Teacher
Dzurak, John Stephen
Adjunct Faculty Legal Asst Pgm
Fleet, Candi L.
Secondary English Tchr & Coord
Gilpin, Joseph Arthur
Associate Administrator
Green, Daniel Clayton
9th Grd Amer Govt & Law Tchr
Hartzog, Lorette J.
2nd-3rd Grade ESOL Teacher
Harvey, John Luther
Fifth Grade Teacher
Kerley, Janet Riley
English Teacher
Lyon, Micheal Bruce
Physical Education Teacher
Mc Combs, Baron
9th-12th Grade Teacher
Murray, Barbara Rankin
French Teacher
Niesiobedzki, Andrew
Associate Professor
Okonkwo, Louis Obi
Professor of Business Admin
Papa, Joan Geske
First Grade Teacher
Petschel, Sally Jane Neff
Group Co-ordinator & Ed Asst
Pitt, Cynthia Inez
9th-12th Grd Montessori Tchr
Price, Erin Michelle
Physical Education Teacher
Rigo, Tibor, Jr.
HS Social Studies Teacher
Rohrer, Jill Leonard
PE Teacher & Dance Team Dir
Rudacille, John L.
Band Director
Santaniello, Michael J.
Bio & Chem I Honors Teacher
Schoch, Robin Bryant
Science Teacher
Snyder, Archie Glenn
Director of Choral Music
Snyder, Jeffrey Robert
Instr of Health, PE & Wellness
Stencik, Joan Wofford
Family & Consumer Sci Instr
Temple, Robert Michael
Instructor of English Dept
Tessier, Danielle Danette
7th Grade Math Teacher
Townsley, William Wendell
Science Dept Chairman & Tchr
Trafford, Elizabeth Tucker
Life Science Teacher
VandePol, Daniel Gene
Fifth Grade Teacher
Welch, Linda Olsen
Guidance Counselor
Whelan, Patrick B.
History Department Chairman
Wubben, James A.
Mathematics Teacher
Yotsuda, David
ESOL & Yearbook Teacher
BRADENTON BEACH
Paul, Karen Marie
Third Grade Teacher
BRANDON
Albers, Deborah Marie
PE, Sci, Band & Cmptr Teacher
Brady, Margaret Gill
8th-9th Grade English Teacher
Calhoun, Susan L.
8th Grade Teacher & Coach
Castelli, Arlene Stefanadis
Administrative Asst-Attendance
Colen, Lisa Price
8th Grade Science Teacher
Fernandez, Susan C.
Teacher of GATE & Science
Forrest, Linda Dotts
8th Grd American History Tchr
Fussell, Patricia M.
Tchr, Dancerette & Clrgrd Spon
Hall, Robert Dale, Jr.
Math, Physics & HS Supervisor
Harrell, Virginia Granstrand
Math Dept Head & Teacher
Harris, Kathy Baxter
Technology Teacher
Iarosis, Sondra Lynn
Assistant Principal
Mancini, Marsha (Wilder)
English & Journalism Teacher
Mc Cann, Sharon Wall
First Grade Teacher
Mc Goldrick, Robert Daniel
Science Teacher
McNair, Elizabeth Cherry
Algebra Tchr
Owens, Jacqueline Joanne Honrath
Eng Tchr of Advanced & Gifted
Plaire, Tommi Sue
Physical Education Teacher
Reifenberg, Susann Lynn
Law Studies & Math Teacher
Scionti, Richard Abthony
Marketing Teacher
Shaw, Cindy
Teacher of Gifted
Suarez, Carolyn Zucker
Lit, Religion & Geog Teacher
Thompson, Jane Adams
Third Grade Teacher
Williams, Jacqueline Foster
English Teacher
BRATT
Thomas, Mary Alice
9th-11th Grd Soc Studies Tchr
BRISTOL
Capps, Sonya M.
English Teacher
Evans, Sunae
Mathematics Dept Chprsn & Tchr
Muza, Melissa Boykin
2nd Grade Teacher
BROOKSVILLE
Ahrens, Frederick Peter
Agriculture Teacher
Bauer, Peggy Simpson
Teacher
Clark, Daniel H.
Science Teacher
Donataccio, Dean M.
Band Director
Emerson, Joan Coppedge
Guidance Counselor
Gates, Kathy T.
3rd Grade Teacher
Granger, Shirley VanEyck
Kindergarten Teacher
Hays, Suzanne Johnson
4th Grade Teacher
Maggard, Katina Starr
Girls Var Bsktbl Coach & Tchr
McLeod, Elizabeth Storm
English Teacher
Miller, Glenn A.
Retired Choral Music Director
Percevecz, Walter Dennis, Jr.
History & World History Tchr
Pickard, Pamela M.
Teacher of Gifted Ed
Sampson, Norma Jean (Allen)
3rd Grade Reading Teacher
Summerall, JoAnn Ingram
Kindergarten Teacher
Tucker, Carol Bryan
11th-12th Grd Hum & Eng Tchr
Vonada, Rebecca LeAnn (Quickle)
Science Teacher & Dept Chprsn
Weeks, Donna Johns
Third Grade Teacher
Williams, Kristen Ann (Rippingille)
6th Grade Physical Ed Teacher
BUNNELL
Bond, James Kelly
History Teacher
Haller, Deloris Chapman
HS Mathematics Teacher
Honigman, Gerald Alan
8th Grade Science Teacher
Kuypers, Jorjann Bone
7th Grade Science Teacher
Mittelman, Canna Jo
Home Economics Teacher
BUSHNELL
Peterson, Jacqueline Revels
English Teacher
Petty, Richard Alden
Sci Dept Chm & Bio Teacher
Roberts, James Edward
US History Teacher
CALLAHAN
Grant, Sherrie Lowry
Spanish Teacher
Hicken, Jane Brophy
Life Management Skills Teacher
Humphrey, Twyla Sharise
Soc Stud Tchr & Dept Head
Lee, Nancy Tew
Math Teacher
Seaborne, David
7th & 8th Grd Sci & Math Tchr
CANTONMENT
Gideon, Idella Banks
2nd Grade Teacher
CAPE CORAL
Brown, Rita B.
Librarian
Ellis, Ann Marie
Principal
Kelly, Mark Edward
Earth Science Teacher
Kramer, Sharon Rae
English Teacher
Lease, Mary Mundy
Honors Eng II & AP Lang Tchr
Lewis, Cecilia M.
Teacher
Minich, Jacqueline Hutton
Science Teacher & Dept Head
O'Connell, Tommy E.
Asst Prin for Student Affairs
O'Hare, Russell James
Senior Army Instructor
Smith, Christopher Bell
Director of Guidance
Stagner, B. J.
Social Studies Teacher
Vaughn, Sue Liddle
Language Arts Teacher
Woolbright, Hannah
ESE Teacher
CASSELBERRY
Bennett, Tracy Candler
Fifth Grade Teacher
Chavers, Mary A.
Computer Literacy Teacher
Diesbourg, Jon Aloysius
Fourth Grade Teacher
McKenzie, Connie Weyeneth
4th Grade Teacher
CENTURY
Ikner, Grace Jackson
Third Grade Teacher
CHATTAHOOCHEE
Davis, Pearl Hospedales
English & Lang Arts Teacher
Scott, Joyce M.
Social Studies Teacher
CHIPLEY
Ellis, Linda Harrison
Second Grade Teacher
CHULUOTA
Vick, Patricia Meyer
Second Grade Teacher
CITRA
Bailey, Brian Allison
8th Grade Science Instructor
Butterfield, Jan
Teacher of the Gifted
Freimuth, Cheryl Daniel
Anatomy & Zoology Teacher
Garrett, James Lee
Lang Arts Tchr
Greiger, Constance King
Teacher
Hubbard, Sarah Johnson
High School Teacher
Pilcher, William Johnston
PE Teacher & Head Ftbl Coach
Wayte, George Ronald
Drafting Teacher
White, Pamela
Science Teacher
CLEARWATER
Boylan, Patti Heischman
Marine Biology Teacher
Ceraolo-O'Donnell, Rosemarie A.
Language Arts Teacher
Cummings, Mary Voigt
Guidance Coordinator
Daskarolis, Stavria
Humanities & Fine Arts Prof
Di Maggio, Pamela Thatcher
DECA Teacher
Dunn, Carol M.
Retired Language Arts Teacher
Dyck, James Michael
Ethics & Religion Teacher
Dye, Janet Stephens
Retired STARS Teacher
Elser, Sammie Halstead
Interpreter Trng Prgm Instr
Falls, Timothy Sean
Social Studies Teacher
Ford, James Ray
Chem Tchr & Sci Dept Chprsn
Hayes, Carol Anne
Second Grade Teacher
Henry, Jonathan F.
Prof of Natural Science
Hinz, Timothy Conrad
World History Teacher
Johansson, Mary Lynn Winfree
2nd Grade Teacher
Lersch, John David
High School Science Teacher
Neal, William Cheston
Retired Teacher
Percifield, Michael Edward
Math Teacher
Reinhart, Cathy Talbitzer
High School Science Teacher
Renner, Vicki A.
Physical Education Teacher
Riggs, Linda Clark
Science Teacher
Rivera, Carrie Ann
Math Teacher
Roche, Margo Schriver
Reading Teacher

RWATER (cont)
er, Susanne Diane
Grade Teacher
rio, Cynthia Carlberg
ematics Teacher
, Harolbelle Tomey
ed Elementary Teacher
, Jane Fichthorn
uage Arts Teacher
Frances Anna Briggs
ed Elem Teacher
r, Lissette
ish Teacher
MONT
roft, Patsy Short
, Sci & Soc Stud Teacher
VISTON
, Cheryl Louise
ness Teacher & DCT Coord
, Isabelle M.
ed Home Economics Teacher
Gerena Gail
nce Teacher
Edith Marie
Secretary & Bookkeeper
ld, Jane O'Sullivan
ish & ESOL Teacher
s, Wanda Sue
nce Teacher
Johanna Tertinek
nematics Teacher
anice
of Students
l, Jean (Barker)
Grade Mathematics Teacher
grove, Beverly Wilkinson
ing Exceptionalities Tchr
A
Carla Doughten
d Grade Teacher
Thomas W.
of Chem & Sci Dept Chair
y, Richard M.
essor of Biological Sci
on, Katherine Hagan
Instr & Project Coord
Kenneth Guy
nce Teacher
e, Halbert George
nematics Department Chair
e, Heather Foland
ond Grade Teacher
Patricia Anne
stant Professor of English
her, Ann Marie (Bride)
n Teacher & Dept Chair
on, Andrew Leonard, Jr.
nematics Teacher
Lynn William
al Science Teacher
lothin, Dale Chemerys
Grade Teacher
ier, Anna Clemmons
ish Teacher
Alexandra Marie
ospace Education Curr Coord
son, Christina Neese
lish & Drama Teacher
er, Anne Friedman
anced Placement Eng Tchr
oen, Mark A.
nce Teacher
er, Craig Wayne
stant Professor
in-Kun
Prof of Social Sciences
ams, Ann Wilson
Grd Language Arts Teacher
ONUT CREEK
Peggy Wright
rof of Soc & Behaviorl Sci
ro, Dora Y. Marron
ructor of French & Spanish
artz, Jerry
n of Bus Admin & Ec Prof
PER CITY
r, Jay
Grd Sci Tchr & Team Ldr
lstaedt, Diane D.
h Teacher & Dept Chprsn
Gloria Land
d Director
AL GABLES
y, Deanna Bieck
h Grade Teacher
Dennis Koon Ming
f of Music Theory & Comp
ery, Charles H.
fessor
AL SPRINGS
ner, Jay Harrold
unct Science Teacher
av, Diana Paris
glish Teacher
r-Pearson, MaryAnn
ence Teacher
egan, Ronald Vincent
rld History Tchr of Gifted
er, Melanie Diane
Science Teacher
man, Debby L.
glish Teacher
lolfi, Cary Cruz
anish Teacher
man, Beth A.
bate & English Teacher
n, Vinette Boyd
glish Teacher
er, Ann Markham
His, Art & Photography Tchr

Muir, Hyacinth Douglas
English Teacher
Serianni, Mary Trapasso
Spanish Teacher
Snyder, Patricia Penrose
HS Mathematics Teacher
Stone, Eileen
Special Education Teacher
COTTONDALE
Jones, Tammy Marie
English I & III Teacher
Myhill, Joseph F.
History Teacher
CRAWFORDVILLE
Allen, Wallace Lyle
Teacher
Cooper, Walter
Music Teacher
DuBois, Michael Henry
7th Grd Math & Science Tchr
Franklin, Vicky Johns
English Teacher
Griffin, Rhonda Metcalf
Math Teacher
Stewart, Mike Hayward
Assoc Naval Science Instructor
Thomas, Rebecca Browne
8th Grd Rdng & Lang Arts Tchr
Whaley, Dennis O'Neil
Math Teacher
CRESTVIEW
Bolton, Dorothy Roberts
Guidance Counselor
Callahan, Pamela Robinson
Family & Consumer Science Tchr
Falvo, Dianne T.
Honors Biology I Tchr
Hester, Tim
Social Science Teacher & Coach
Mc Sween, Judy Ann
First Grade Teacher
Meade, Shirley Thomas
World Geography Teacher
Roberts, Donna C.
Fourth Grade Teacher
Robinson, Glenda N.
Fourth Grade Teacher
Willoughby, Caroline Collins
6th Grade Social Studies Tchr
Zant, Susan E.
American History Teacher
CROSS CITY
Davidson, Betty Ann (Williams)
Health Occupations Instructor
Featherston, Gary Alfred
Chemistry, Physics & Bio Tchr
Mc Kinney, Laura Elizabeth Suggs
Kindergarten Teacher
CRYSTAL RIVER
Amundson, Karl Edward
Employability Specialist
Farrell, William L.
Curriculum Specialist
Hamilton, Gregory Allen
Physical Education Teacher
Hulett, Othella S.
Business Education Teacher
Positano, Priscilla Carroll
Psychology Professor
Pullar, Phyllis DePriest
Guidance Counselor
Reed, Kenneth A.
English Instructor
Weaver, Naomi Sharon
Gifted Education Teacher
DADE CITY
Boles, Stanley Richard
Govt, Economics & US His Tchr
Buzzy, Cynthia Louise
Family & Consumer Science Tchr
Carter, Barbara Hill
Lab Coordinator & Instructor
Craig, Barbara Mahaffey
Assistant Professor of Nursing
Dillard, James Ed
Agriculture Ed Teacher
Garcia, Ronald Paul
Mathematics Teacher
Hillen, Matthew Thomas
Financial Aid Cnslr & Instr
Jones, Margaret Arnold
Math Teacher & Dept Chairman
Kamps, Robert A.
7th-8th Grade Science Teacher
Lepisto, Susan Ewing
Vocational Teacher
Phillips, Ann Marie
Spanish & French Teacher
Rosenglick, Sonya Brooks
Business Education Teacher
DANIA
Stinchcomb, Jeanne B.
Consultant
DAVIE
Leonardo, Joseph
Pres, Dir & Addiction Spclst
Levy, Mitchel
Associate Professor
Melograno, Gail Lucarelli
Third Grade Teacher
DAYTONA BEACH
Ampiaw, Joseph Akyene
Rel & Philosophy Assoc Prof
Butler, Lorine
Criminal Justice Instructor
Carlton, Donna Searle
Fourth Grade Teacher
Chuven, Jamie T.
TV Production Instructor

Clowers, Edwin Lee
Music Teacher
Collins, Thadeus La Ronnie
Kindergarten Teacher
Cupick-Matz, Linda S.
Asst Prof of Legal Assisting
Curtis, Connie DeFrazer
Spanish Professor
Davis, Elizabeth Baum
First Grade Teacher
Davis, Thomas F.
Prof of Mathematics
Dellavalle, Jacques Alexander
Professor of Visual Arts
Delos Santos, Teri
Prof of English & Humanities
DeLuca, Rosemarie Ciulla
Tchr of Gifted Social Studies
DeRosa, Joseph Peter
School Resource Officer
Dorbad, Leo J.
Professor of English
Dowdy, Linda Ann (Windjack)
Director of Guidance
Duncan, Margaret Evelyn
Professor & Coordinator of Eng
Ekpo, Efremfon Frank
Associate Professor
Enget, Treva Lee Lewis
Peer Facilitator Coordinator
Ennis, Patricia D.
Asst Prof of Cultural Arts
Fuqua, Muriel Avant
Assistant Professor of English
Griffith, Randy Ray
Assoc Prof of Avionics Tech
Guthrie, John J., Jr.
Associate Prof of History
Hay, Jonette M.
Theatre Educator
Holt, Norman William, II
Prof of Legal Assisting Pgm
Humphrey, Betty Templeton
Algebra Teacher
Johnson, James Russell
Professor
Jones, Paula McMillan
Journalism Professor
Kelder, Alice Flouhouse
Fourth Grade Teacher
Krajewski, Molly
Mathematics Instructor
Lancio, Jerry W.
Dir of Resource Center
Lynn, Mark Wayne
Theology Tchr & Dept Chairman
Martin, William A.
Aeronautical Science Professor
McBroom, Carol Elizabeth
Vocational Department Chprsn
McFarland, J. Larry
Social Science Instructor
Mcneeley-Bouie, Barbara
Humanities & Music Instructor
Miller, David J. L.
Behavioral,Human & Soc Sci Chr
Miller, Jake Charles
Emeritus Professor
Miller, John David
Geometry & Calculus Teacher
Minks, Shawn Allen
Sixth Grade Teacher
Mootry, Russell, Jr.
Professor of Social Sciences
Munns, Harry C.
Business Professor
Murray, Barbara Roberts
Professor of English
Nethery, Darcie Jayne
Radiography Education Pgm Dir
Newnam, Hollie Marie
Physical Education Specialist
Odu, Michael
Associate Professor
O'Neill, Nancy M.
Assoc Prof of Nursing Program
Picott, Jerry Lee, Jr.
Teacher & Band Director
Porter, Richard Edwin
Professor of Aeronautical Sci
Raborn, Sandra Lynn
Professor in Health & Fitness
Rea, Suzanne Stewart
Spanish Teacher
Rogers, Michael D.
Physics Professor
Rogers, Richard William
Professor
Sadowski-Carr, Melissa
English Teacher
Sen, Shukdeb
Professor of Biology
Session, Willie Mae (Edwards)
Assistant Professor of Nursing
Sivasundaram, Seenith
Mathematics Professor
Snyder, Roberta Sexton
Math Department Chair
Swanson, Gerald Carl
Chemistry Professor
Thompson, Keturah Vernanchell
Assistant Principal
Vendon, Mark
Physics & Chemistry Teacher
Vitale, Michael A.
Professor of Biology
von Krumreig-Hill, Eric
Prof of Aerospace Engrng
Ward, Holly Reddick
Drama & Gifted Lang Arts Tchr

Wharton, Demetrius Matthews
Speech Communications Instr
Williams, Mike M.
Professor of Economics
DE LAND
Brown, Rodella (Ennis)
Assoc Professor in Mathematics
Patrissi, Lewis Art, Jr.
Elementary PE Tchr
DEBARY
Ealy, W. John
Former Science Teacher
DEERFIELD BEACH
Almario, Antonio N.
Resource Teacher
Christina, Mary Ann
Mathematics Tchr & Dept Head
Landis, Marnie Sutton
World His, Psych & Soc Tchr
Mullins, Eddie Keith
Seventh Grade Geography Tchr
Murtha, Barbara Jean
PE Teacher & Asst Athletic Dir
DEFUNIAK SPRINGS
Anderson, Cynthia Chandler
French Teacher
Harrison, Glen H.
History Teacher
Retzlaff, Dorothy Ross
English Teacher
Whayne, Leslie Kissling
English Teacher & Dept Chair
Willcox, Billy Ray
High School Math Teacher
DELAND
Bear, Lynn E.
Retired Latin Teacher
Bruten, Richard, Sr.
Retired Science Teacher
Bush, Barbara Lathrop
English Tchr of the Gifted
Butler, Vera W.
Assistant Principal
Clements, James Olin, Jr.
Drop Out Prevention Teacher
French, James J.
English Teacher
Highsmith, Jane M.
Business Teacher & Advisor
Huss, Debra Lynn (Hanna)
Physical Education Teacher
Kroh, Bernice Hook
Mathematics Teacher
Reddish, Barbara Waters
Guidance Counselor
Ryan, Janie Tiller
Dance Teacher
Sharpe, William G.
Art Tchr & Performing Arts Chr
Smith, Ellen Hurt
Associate Professor of English
Staudt, Paula Shane
6th Grade Tchr of Gifted
Wallis, Lisa Suzanne
6th Grade Teacher
Wolf, Jean Lowry
English Teacher
Wright, Margaret Tapley
Biology Teacher
DELRAY BEACH
Adams, Barbara Middendorf
Fifth Grade Teacher
Baum, Susan Diane
High School Math Teacher
Buliung, Ralph J., III
ESOL Coord & Chairperson
Christopoulos, Susan Irene
High School ESOL Teacher
Freeman, David T.
Speech & Mass Media Teacher
Goldsmith, Richard I.
Administrative Asst Principal
Kruppenbacher, Martin Francis
5th Grade Teacher
Ostaffe, Joy Anderson
Teacher of Gifted English
Scherer, Beverly
Retired Teacher
Veasey, Carolyn Roberts
Teacher
Wesley, Carl Gene
Band Director
DELTONA
Batie, Twila Ann
6th Grade Teacher
Brandt, Lori M.
English Teacher
Fielding, John E.
Retired Social Studies Teacher
Frank, James Thomas, II
High School Science Teacher
Gawriluk, James Wesley
Driver's Ed Teacher & Coach
Griffiths, Mickey Dolan
Drama Teacher
Hall, Rhae H.
Graduation Assurance Teacher
Holland, John A.
8th Grade Math Teacher
Johnson, Celeste Gauthier
6th Grade Teacher
Long, Thomas Rodney
Language Arts Teacher
Manion, Lisa Kay
Chorus & Keyboard Teacher
Morris, Arthur E.
Nature Photographer
Navarro-Rivera, Lydia
Spanish Teacher

Nenno, Barbara A.
Social Studies & History Tchr
Norris, Gigi Roushdi
Eighth Grade Lang Arts Tchr
Perry, Terri Lynn
English Teacher
Rowell, Cynthia Kay
Tenth Grade Honors Eng Teacher
Shaffer, Mark Ellis
Physical Science Teacher
Shott, Douglas A.
Amer His & Law Studies Tchr
Snyder, Teresa Ann
Guidance Counselor
Thomas, Cephas P.
Science Teacher
Turner, Virginia Willis
5th Grd Teacher of the Gifted
Viret, Marc
Elem & HS Cmptr Science Tchr
Wagner, Richard S.
Business Education Teacher
DESTIN
Cass, Janet Ridgely
Kindergarten Teacher
DUNEDIN
Black, Elizabeth Moore
Mathematics & Computer Teacher
Bytheway, Charlotte Bragg
Dept Chprsn & English Teacher
Cole, Danny L.
AP History & Economics Teacher
Eberts, John Jacob
Social Science Teacher
Harper, William Pierce
Retired Teacher
Loscalzo, Norman Louis
HS Social Studies Teacher
Martin, Ellen Moore
Classroom Teacher
Sharpe, Bonnie Rose
Teacher of the Gifted
Winship, Susan Ely
Physical Education Teacher
DUNNELLON
Hoekstra, Marcia Vance
8th Grade Mathematics Teacher
Johnson, Robert Cecil
Biology & Biotech Teacher
Love, Debbra Reid
Science Department Chair
Payne, Phyllis S.
Social Studies Teacher
Reulbach, Veronica (Rodriguez)
Spanish Teacher
Smith, Rosetta B.
Third Grade Teacher
EAGLE LAKE
Parker, Jimmy Lawrence
Band Director
EGLIN AFB
Ashley, Lanie
Guidance Counselor
James, Georgia Banks
Second Grade Teacher
ELFERS
Crawford, Jane
5th Grade Teacher
ENGLEWOOD
Jones, Margaret Jane Atkins
Third Grade Teacher
Lock, Frank Daniel
Chemistry Teacher
Moon, Isabel Myers
First Grade Teacher
Payne, Michael D.
English Teacher
Ragan, Sherie Lynn
Theatre Teacher & Director
ESTERO
Raykovics, Lawrence Edward, Jr.
TV Production & Drama Teacher
Sommer, Jeff Wayne
Teacher & Coach
Turner, Monica L.
Mathematics Teacher
White, David Hughes
Art Instructor
EUSTIS
Kinney, Susan Calvin
English Teacher
Powers, Cynthia Bowles
Science Teacher
Swett, Arthur H.
Minister of Music & Teacher
FERN PARK
Mark, Janet LaForest
Third Grade Teacher
Porter, Meta Burgess
Fifth Grade Teacher
Price, Martha Sue
4th Grade Teacher
FERNANDINA
Almers, Candace Crocker
8th Grade Math Teacher
Carver, Sandra Beard
US History & Pre-Algebra Tchr
Cline, Marcia Ann (Mc Donald)
Math Teacher
Day, Ruth G.
8th Grade Reading Teacher
Hess, Margaret Courtland
Science Teacher
Hickman, Frank W.
Math Teacher
Johnston, Elinor Shaw
Art Teacher
Kline, Carol Dupree
Spanish Teacher

FERNADINA (cont)
Maxwell, Nancy Bridges
Guidance Counselor
Pendleton, Sylvia Anita
Chemistry & Biology Teacher
Rodeffer, James Dickens
English & TV Production Tchr
Rogers, Lillie Marie Dority
Hlth Careers & Mdcl Sklls Tchr
FORT LAUDERDALE
Adams, Jill Beiter
English Teacher
Adams, Nathan A., III
Eng, Jrnlsm & Crtve Wrtg Tchr
Alexis, Alister M.
Guidance Counselor
Alioto, Suzanne Grotjohan
Journalism Teacher
Amato, James Randall
Law Professor
Amos, Janette G.
English Teacher
Amreihn, Raymond F.
Mathematics Teacher
Anderson, Andrew James
5th Grade Teacher
Andrews, Mary Shaw
Eng Tchr & Pgm Specialist
Armstrong, James Robert
JROTC Instructor
Bass, Amy Greenberg
Mathematics Teacher
Bass, Kenneth B.
Social Studies Teacher
Bauer, Jerry H.
Physical Education Dept Head
Behrend, John A.
6th Grade Mathematics Teacher
Belafonte, Denise L.
College Instructor
Bevilacqua, Mary N.
English Teacher
Birge, Beverly Harrington
High School Psychology Teacher
Blanton, James Anthony
World Civilization Teacher
Blosch, Charles S. (Stan)
Choral Director
Bonshoff, Andrea Regina
Amer Govt, Ec & Amer His Tchr
Boudreau, Barbara Helen
High Tech Lang Arts Teacher
Boyett, Dave
Mathematics Teacher
Boyles, Freda Robinson
Business Technology Instructor
Breslin, Maureen Linda
English Teacher & Dept Head
Brown, Cheryl Enid
Math Teacher
Bryant, Leon Carl
Art Teacher
Burnes, Steven Ashley
Music Director
Carlson, Lori Van Nus
Choral Music Teacher
Caruso, William Ralph
Industrial Arts Teacher
Charles, Israel
Band Director
Chinn, James Albert
Professor of Mathematics
Christian, Rosa Mc Griff
Home Economics Teacher
Clark, Zenobbie Hammond
Curriculum Facilitator
Cossio, Mattie Roig
Assistant Prof of Biology
Cunningham, Delania Williams
Tenth Grade English Teacher
Cunningham, Marcia G.
English & Journalism Teacher
D'Andrea, Minerva A.
8th Grade Amer History Teacher
Davis, Gary Alan
English Chairman
Davis, Michael Wayne
Theology Department Chairman
Day, Barbara Tong
Kindergarten Teacher
Delp, John Edward
Business Education Professor
De Sadier, DeAnale Titus
HS Health & Aerobics Teacher
De Santis, Mark Louis
Psych Prof & Dir of Remediatn
DiNicola, David
Physical Education Teacher
Dunham, Laura Harland
Art Teacher
Elder, James Dennis
Social Studies Teacher
Ewan, Diane DiLuzio
Spanish Teacher
Forsyth, Sharon R.
French & Spanish Teacher
Foster, Mary Alice
English Teacher
Gaus, Claire Chamberland
Private Consultant & Tutor
Geiger, Mary J.
English Teacher
Gillam, Paula Sample
Art Instructor
Gonando, Carolyn Noreen
Span, ESL Tchr & Frgn Lang Chm
Gonzalez, Joseph Frank
Assoc Dir of Comm Sci
Gouin, John Pierre
Fifth Grade Teacher
Grasso, Mary Ellen Cipolla
Prof & English Dept Head
Gray, David John
Chemistry Teacher
Greenblatt, Gladys Liebman
5th Grade Teacher
Greenstein, Phyllis Googel
Math Teacher & Dept Chair
Guild, Jeffrey Kirk
Mathematics Tchr
Hall, David Earl
Director of Bands
Hanken, Etta Lou
Mathematics Teacher
Hayes, William L.
Comp High-Tech Algebra Tchr
Hensley, Peter Henry
Seventh Grade Teacher
Hesse, William Allen
Biology Teacher
Holcroft, Samuel J.
Science Teacher
Jackson, Angela DiBenedetto
High School Chemistry Teacher
James, Patricia Ann
Hlth & Physical Education Tchr
Johnson, Denise Mc Guire
English Teacher
Johnson, Elease Hughes
Assoc Prof of English
Johnson, M.E. Evelyn
Instructor, Coord & Lecturer
Jones, J. Preston
Professor of Management
Jones, Willie Edward
Assistant Principal
Jordan, Judith A.
Mathematics Teacher
Joyner, Pamela Maynard
6th Grade Lang Arts Teacher
Joynt, Robert Harger
US History Tchr & Dept Chprsn
Kalicharan, David Harry Chand
Business & Marketing Instr
Kalvaitis, Lee H.
7th & 8th Grd Gifted Sci Tchr
Keen, Richard Eugene
Earth Science Instructor
Kennedy, Greg Robert
Marketing Teacher
Kennedy, Toni Ketchel
Tchr Spclst of Early Chldhd
Kiger, Davis Joseph
Economics Teacher
Kimble, Nancy
Mathematics Teacher
Kirschner, Marguerite Imperial
Foreign Languages Dept Chprsn
Koontz, Larry Steven
Junior High Teacher
Kramer, Andrea Kinbar
Fifth Grade Teacher
Kulhanek, Patricia L.
5th Grade Teacher
Landen, Pamela K.
Kindergarten Classroom Teacher
La Rosa, Kathryn Denise
Choral Director
Lashbrook, Bonnie Hayes
Peer Counseling Coordinator
Levitt, Stephen Ross
Asst Prof of Legal Studies
Loe, Diana Button
Fifth Grade Teacher
Lovarco, Patricia Marie
8th Grade Science Teacher
Love, Kim Woods
Health Tchr & Var Vlybl Coach
Mages, Anthony George
Finance Professor
Mahon, Thomas Edward
Teacher & Football Coach
Maines, Donald Kevin
Psychology Teacher
Marini, Alfred James
Soc Stud Department Chair
Mashal, Ed
Audio Instructor
Mc Cartney, Timothy Osborne
Clincial Psych, Assoc Prof
McCoy, Gloria House
English Teacher
Mc Donald, Beverlene Elaine-Dawes
Social Studies Teacher
Mc Dowell, Clarence Lee
Asst Varsity Coach & Sub Tchr
Melillo, Sandra Mansfield
Fine Arts Teacher
Miller, Douglas Lane
Economics & Government Tchr
Mills, David M.
Audio Instructor
Minor, Thomas Mc Swain, Jr.
Honors Chemistry Teacher
Moore, Evelyn Comminos
Fashion Marketing Dept Instr
Moran, Elena Marie
Soc Stud & Religion Teacher
Mustacchio, Bruce
History & Geography Teacher
Newton, David C.
Adjunct Professor of Acctng
Noland, Sheryl L.
Magnet Program Coordinator
Nusbaum, Diana I. (Riccio)
Social Studies Teacher
Orcutt, Scott Eugene
Physics & Bible Teacher
Ott, Paul David
Senior English Teacher
Park-Clemons, Tiffany
Math Teacher & Asst Ath Dir
Pate, Boyd Alan
Art Teacher
Pawela, Susan Judith
Instructor of Music
Perez-Cubas, Carlos
Teacher & Activities Director
Perkins, Alicia Conlon
French, German & Latin Teacher
Petik, George Andrew, Jr.
Head Baseball Coach
Pick, Ellyn Gordon
High School Science Teacher
Pickett, Damian Carl
History Teacher
Pierson, Glen William
Chemistry & Earth Science Tchr
Pietrzak, Brian William
Social Science Teacher
Pinder, Loretta Louise
English Teacher
Plant, Vicki Lynn
Adj Prof of Law Related Tchng
Potter, Dorene Helen
Fifth Grade Teacher
Raffensperger, Susan Wheeler
Social Studies Teacher
Reis, Victoria Jean (Evranian)
English Teacher
Riefler, Diane Mary
English Teacher
Roberts, Beverly Diane
Fifth Grade Teacher
Rogers, Scott Christopher
Geography Teacher
Rogow, Bruce Sylvan
Law Professor
Rooney, Michael David
Fifth Grade Teacher
Rose, Arthur E.
Career Research & Dev Teacher
Rosenberg, Mitchell Douglas
6th Grade Math Teacher
Rosenthal, Juliette Ann
Political Science & His Prof
Ross, James S., Jr.
Principal & Coach
Ryan, Dorothy Montuori
Fifth Grade Teacher
Sacks, Harold
Intnl Law & Global Ec Prof
Sallette, Delores
8th Grade Hi-Tech Sci Teacher
Sanderson, Rita Marye
US History Teacher
Sayres, Olga Cadilla
Geometry Teacher
Scherperel, Loretta Fox
Professor of Music
Sefferly, Mary
HS ESOL Teacher
Shaaban, Hisham H.
Academic Dean
Shealy, Charles
Social Studies Teacher
Sherry, Thomas Joseph
Senior Broadcasting Instructor
Smith, Dennis Bruce
Math Teacher
Sniegocki, Mary Furda
Fifth Grade Teacher
Spereno, Deborah Smith
English Teacher & Dept Chair
Spereno, Robert William
Industrial Arts Teacher
Stanislawski, Antoinette
Sixth Grade Teacher
Steinberg, Arlene G.
Fifth Grade Teacher
Steiner, Marcia Ilene
5th Grade Teacher
Stigler, Lois Isaacs
7th Grade Geography Teacher
Stitsky, Leo Jay
Art Instructor
Stoddart, Scott Frederick
Assoc Prof of Lbrl Arts
Sun, Junping
Assistant Professor
Tamayo, Pura Ortiz
Spanish Teacher
Taylor, Erica Lynn
Speech & Lang Clinician
Theiss, Cynthia S.
Hnrs English II & German Tchr
Toth, Sharon Lee
Fifth Grade Teacher
Treloar, Georgette K.
Science Dept Chair
Tromans, Mark A.
Behavioral Sciences Dept Head
Truitt, Elizabeth Caruso
English Teacher
Urbano, Sandra E.
HS Math Teacher
Van Lehn, Rachel Wheeler
1st Grade Teacher
Venters, John Mac Kenzie
Interior Design Instructor
Waligunda, Kari Schabo
Family & Consumer Sci Teacher
Wanton, Dorothy Baxter
Mathematics Teacher
Watson, Matthew A.
Physics Teacher
Wilbur, Colleen Cooney
Third Grade Teacher
Winrow, Linda Grobstein
English Tchr & Curr Coord
Wolfson, Rona Schindler
Fifth Grade Teacher
Wood, Lorenzo Charles
Social Stud & US History Tchr
Wright, Davette L.
Fifth Grade Teacher
Wruble, Carol Elizabeth
Amer His & Law Studies Tchr
Zaslofsky, Steve
Dean of Students
Zislin, Joan Cristeen
Varying Exceptionalities Tchr
FORT MC COY
Andry, Kae
Kindergarten Teacher
FORT MEADE
Mullen, Michael Patrick
Social Studies Teacher
Williams, Rhonda Ann
English Teacher
FORT MYERS
Ackord, Marie Mallory
Mathematics Teacher
Arya, Mahmoud P.
Economics Professor
Blue, Michael Robert
Second Grade Teacher
Bress, Christopher J.
Math Teacher
Burnside, Carl Clifford
Assistant Principal
Burwash, Margaret M.
2nd Grade Teacher
Caldwell, Carol E.
Language Arts Teacher
Camp, Carol Frederick
12th Grade British Lit Teacher
Conley, Ingela VanEssen
High School French Teacher
Cook, Jan Hope
Tchr of Hearing Impaired Stdnt
Crux, Linda
Intnl Baccalaureate Teacher
Dahlberg, Mark L.
High School Music Educator
Der Hagopian, Cynthia Mercier
History Instructor
Dewey, Bobbie Cunningham
Athletic & Activities Director
Donnell, Dwayne LaVelle
9th-12th Grd Science Teacher
Eberle, Susanne Fisher
Soc Studies Tchr & Dept Head
Ellis, Lanny E.
Teacher
Erickson, Jennifer Folland
Fifth Grade Teacher
Fain, Bob
Chemistry Teacher
Fain, Marcia Staggers
Mathematics Teacher
Fellerman, Marilyn Joy
English Teacher
Ficherski, Nancy Gaukier
Literature & Composition Tchr
Fitzpatrick, Michael Dennis
Tchr of the Gifted
Girard, Joan Ebert
Professor of Mathematics
Glass, Mary Elizabeth (Mirro)
Biology Teacher
Grace, Lynn W.
Pgm Dir, Acctng & Taxation Ed
Green, Kathleen M.
Drama, Newspaper & Eng Tchr
Hale, Myra Patricia
Prof of Speech & Communication
Hatcher, Phyllis Ann
Mathematics Teacher
Hefty, Catherine Kane
Social Studies Teacher
Hewitt, Robert Grant
Prof of Criminology & Ed
Hildebrand, Robert L.
Physical Education Teacher
Hill, Mary Louise (Cissna)
English Department Chairman
Hinkle, Lynn D.
Mathematics Teacher
Jekel, Donna Gainer
Middle School Teacher
Johns, Donna Lee
Second Grade Teacher
Krupo, Edwin J.
Technology Specialist
Lewton, Richard L.
Science Teacher
Ludwig, Diane Kudra
8th Grade Math Teacher
Mc Gillicuddy, Frances Crank
Fourth Grade Teacher
Middlebrooks, James A., Jr.
Professor of Mathematics
Miller, Jack Reece
Retired Teacher & Team Leader
Morriss, Stephen Edward
Science Teacher
Nadeau, Beverly Moriarty
Math Teacher
Nicoletti, Robert Anthony
Science Teacher
Norman, Anita Diaz
Third Grade Teacher
Orlando, Karen Schurr
6th Grade Science Teacher
Perry, Skip
Band Director
Plappert, John Charles
French & German Teacher
Quattrucci, Louis Anthony
Fourth Grade Teacher
Ragland, Anne Wells
Eng, Jrnlsm, Publications Tchr
Rosenberg, Sally LaRue
Math Teacher
Ryan, Jack
11th Grd Computer Tech Tchr
Schrecongost, Dorothea V.
Mathematics Teacher
Scoppettuolo, Robert V.
Fourth Grade Teacher
Sell, Jacqueline Bensing
Kindergarten Teacher
Shepard, Scott Charles
Biology & Driver Ed Teacher
Simms, Levon
Art Instructor
Smith, Susan Nanette (Blazier)
Lead Science Teacher
Warburton, Irene Teresa
Professor of Nursing
Weaver, Elizabeth Brenneman
Former English Teacher
Wert, Jack D.
HS Math Tchr & Adj Math Prof
Wheeler, Rosalind W.
Eng Teacher & Dept Chairperson
White, Richard Woodward, Sr.
Professor of English
Wicktor, Gregg Charles
Biology Teacher
Wildermuth, Maggie Eldridge
6th Grade Science Teacher
Yordy, Winifred Barrett
Third Grade Teacher
FORT PIERCE
Arnold, Donna F.
Business Professor
Ayres, Robert Bruce
High School Mathematics Tchr
Bennefield, Alicia Lavette
Business Education Teacher
Boudrot, John Michael
Social Science Teacher
Brown, Judith Conner
Music Teacher
Burga, Shellene Wyrick
Spanish Teacher
Caddigan, Deirdre Ann
7th Grade Life Science Teacher
Campbell, Mark Edward
Mathematics Teacher
Crenshaw, Neil W.
Professor of Biology
Crocco, Karen
Band Director
Gray, Richard Kenneth
Soc Stud, His Tchr & Dept Chm
Hanlon, Gill Temple
Ret Soc Stud Tchr & Dept Chair
Kadzis, Barbara Jones
Sci & Eng Tchr & LA Dept Chm
Lee, Mary Louise-Cherry
Language Arts Teacher
Lynch, John Joseph
Athletic Dir & Math Teacher
McLam, Barbara Woodyard
Math & Computer Teacher
McManus, Doris A.
English Teacher
Middlebrooks, Ann Ervin
Former Chemistry Teacher
Redic, Barbara Bulgin
Med Skills & Hlth Tchr
Roberts, Margaret Ann
Computer Science Teacher
Santmier, Dewey James
Teacher & Coach
Taylor, Kristen Lee
Drama, Debate & Speech Teacher
Waugh, Kimberley Sue
Sci Dept Chm & Instructor
FORT WALTON BEACH
Anderson, Elaine Carr
Counselor & Minority Liaison
Austin, Sally Ann (Baldwin)
Rhythm & Keyboard Teacher
Barnes, Mary Whitten
Second Grade Teacher
Brock, Kay Dunn
Social Studies Teacher
Burden, Mayra Yadira
Spanish & Latin Teacher
Chisolm, William Mc Kinley, III
Teacher & Coach
Chubb, Valerie Lynn
Mathematics Teacher
Craig, Kevin M.
Teacher & Girls Bsktbl Coach
Crowder, Marjorie Ann (Eby)
Alternative Education Tchr
Durrett, Sondra Rae (Bynum)
World Cultures Tchr & Dept Chm
Evanchyk, Linda Patrick
HS English & Jrnlsm Teacher
Ferguson, Deborah Hattaway
Economics Teacher
Gentry, Marilyn Hobbs
PIB & Honors World His Tchr
Grady, Dianne Chustz
Math Teacher
Hagan, Elaine J.
Sci Dept Chair & Bio Tchr
Henderson, Donald Leroy
Biology Teacher
Heyse, Rebecca Lang
Mathematics Teacher
Hicks, Ann Willson
Speech, Debate & English Tchr

WALTON BEACH (cont)
gton, Sandra Mc Arthur
nd Grade Teacher
i, Cathy Race
stant Prin for Instruction
s, Alton Russell
in Disciplinarian
, Eugene Lewis
stant Aerospace Sci Instr
on, Terry
School Counselor
Bess Bartholomew
ish Teacher & Dept Chair
e, Cynthia C.
ish Teacher
Judy Brightwell
ntnl Bacc & US Hist Tchr
Martin, Nancy Jane Leonard
ish Teacher
ngham, Damon Lamon
nselor & Coach
od, Beth Louise
ner Teacher
el, Adela J.
h Teacher
, Billy Wayne
her & Coach
, Katie Elizabeth
h Grade Science Teacher
n, Randall C.
ds Director
ls, Janice Louise
nce Teacher
son, Joseph James
hematics Teacher
olds, Jerry L.
Psych & Prof of Cnslng
ers, Karen Ann
Grade Language Arts Tchr
, Gerald B.
h Teacher & Team Leader
, Cheryl Rinita
ogy & Chemistry Teacher
an, Suzanne Bourgeois
ond Grade Teacher
r, Donna Williamson
h Teacher & Team Leader
ki, John Edward
mistry & Biology II Teacher
land, Jennifer Ann
ish Teacher
, Connie Russell
lish Teacher
EPORT
e, Nancy Ellen
h Grade Teacher
Sandra King
, Hum, Speech & Drama Tchr
th, Carla Fredenburg
n, French & English Teacher
TLAND PARK
ams, Lois Mc Clellan
Grade Teacher
NESVILLE
n, Kay H.
sic Teacher
ckle, Linda J.
istant Prof of Ceramics
Donald D.
fessor of English
dano, Alejandro
nish Teacher
nia, Nazanin
hematics Professor
er, Terry Bain
t Grade Teacher
Sanford V.
tinguished Svc Prof Ec
man, Melissa Kish
e & Gifted Science Teacher
ning, Ted Price
hematics Teacher
oun, Betty Jean
ence Teacher
i, Abdol
sociate Professor
-Harper, Eva
atomy & Physiology Instr
h, Henry M.
h Grd Hnrs World His Tchr
h, Leon W., II
fessor & Associate Chairman
slow, David Albert
onomics Professor
e, Dirk David
Stud, Performing Arts Tchr
olsky, Evan Bruce
ology & Physical Sci Instr
oit, Brian Murray
thropology Professor
ards, Barry Michael
glish Instructor
Coy, Norman G.
sistant Professor
er, John Frederick
Grade World History Tchr
am, Elizabeth Peeler
ofessor of Voice
en, S. Liane
ology Teacher
ell, Carolyn W.
glish Teacher
ry, Charmaine Brown
source Teacher
sley, Theresa Locklear
junct Math Instructor
ing, Willie Marie
athematics Instructor
land, Robert Joseph
ology Teacher

Hughes, Holly Elaine
Associate Professor of Piano
Hummel, Rolf E.
Professor in Engineering
Hyatt, Lou Warriner
Music Teacher
Jessup, James Vernon
Assistant Professor of Nursing
Jones, Gregory Ray
Theatre Professor
Jones, Griffith
High School Physics Teacher
Kauwell, Gail Abbott
Nutrition Professor
Keller, Corinne Conlon
Language Arts & Reading Tchr
Kelso, William Alton
Political Science Professor
Kiester, Jane Bell
English & French Teacher
Kushner, David Zakeri
Music History Professor
Kynast, Gregory Joseph
Spanish Teacher
Ledbetter, Richard Scott
Chemistry & Physics Professor
Lehman, Amalia Alvarez
Spanish Teacher
Lowe, Marilyn B.
Retired Kindergarten Teacher
Lucas, Patricia Loomis
Bus Cmptr Applications II Tchr
Macdaid, Melissa Anne
Accounting Faculty
Mc Rae, Stuart I.
Chairman Dept of Anthropology
Mc Tureous, Rochelle Waters
8th Grade Mathematics Teacher
Moretta, Jo Lois
English Teacher
Najafi, Fazil Tawab
Associate Professor
Owens, Claude Sylvie
Spanish Teacher
Park, Chang-Won
Engineering Professor
Peace, Carol L.
Art Teacher
Pickren, Wade Edward
Professor of Psychology
Powers, Patricia
English Teacher & Dept Chair
Remshardt, Ralf Erik
Assistant Professor of Theatre
Reynierson, Sarah Sharp
English Teacher
Rienzo, Barbara A.
Professor Dept of Hlth Sci Ed
Robinson, Russell L.
Professor of Music
Rodrick, Gary Eugene
Professor of Food Sciences
Sabatella, Joseph John
Professor of Art
Sanders, Michele Anne
Mathematics Teacher
Sankar, Bhavani Vaidyanathan
Prof of Aerospace Engineering
Schall, Jan Thorsness
Art History Professor
Schultz, Denise Pendlebury
Special Education Teacher
Scully, Judith Ann
Assistant Professor of Mgmt
Skiles, Sharon Smittle
Sci Dept Chm & Teacher
Smith, Karen Cole
Social Science & His Chprsn
Smith, Nancy Trantin
English & Humanities Teacher
Smocovitis, Vassiliki Betty
Asst Professor of History Sci
Stepp, Jonita Elaine
Spanish & French Teacher
Stone, Sarah Lipford
Instr of Anatomy & Physiology
Strickland, Elizabeth Hayward
Librarian & Media Specialist
Thieke, Robert J.
Assistant Professor
Thornton, Paula Elizabeth
Band Director
Towers, Daniel Lee
Veterinary Care Mgr
Waldorf, Joseph Carl
AP Social Studies Teacher
Whitney, Julie Desjardin
Nursing Instructor
Williams, Linda
Family & Consumer Science Tchr
Yariv, Louise Fried
ESOL Teacher
GIBSONTON
Chandler, Stephen O.
Biology Teacher
Lota, Lynnette B.
Drama Instructor
Mc Dermott, Nancy Bachman
Science Dept Head & Teacher
Ratayski, Robin L.
High School English Teacher
Worten-Fritz, Anna Ruth
US History Teacher
GLEN SAINT MARY
Brown, Cheryl Showalter
Band Director
Cobb, Elizabeth R.
English Teacher
Floyd, JoAnn Truett
World Geography Teacher

Pelham, Gary E.
Life Management Skills Teacher
GONZALEZ
Bryan, Sharon McElhaney
Family & Consumer Sci Tchr
Colon, Robert L.
Bands Associate Director
Hall, Annola Ferguson
Math Tchr & Dept Chair
Lael, Linda Elizabeth
Mathematics Teacher
McCorkle, Sam Blaine
Coach & Physical Ed Teacher
Queckboerner, Susan K.
Visual Arts Instructor
Varner, Michael David
Science Instructor
Welch, Lynn W.
Language Arts Teacher
GRACEVILLE
Burdeshaw, Julie Wilson
HS Social Studies Teacher
Cook, William F.
New Testament, Greek Asst Prof
Davenport, RIchard Lee
Band Director
Davis, Dorothy Ponds
Science Teacher
Lee, Jerry Wallace
Prof of Old Testament
Malone, Patrick R.
Music Dept Chair & Assoc Prof
Mixson, Louise Turner
Social Studies Teacher
Odom, Donald R.
Music Professor
Olds, Mary Smith
Third Grade Teacher
Wright, Paula Turner
Science Teacher
GREEN COVE SPRINGS
Barber, Anne Steart
Spanish & English Teacher
Cassidy, Myra Linville
Health Careers Teacher
Fore, Stacee R.
Amer History & Journalism Tchr
Garner, Barbara W.
First Grade Teacher
Henry, Michael Sherwood
HS Social Studies Teacher
Hopkins, Michele Lynn
8th Grade Social Studies Tchr
Kinnear, Sylvia Kauffeld
4th Grade Teacher
Koblitz, Ronald Dean
Math Teacher
McIntosh, Emily Walls
French Teacher
Reape, James Patrick
History & Psychology Teacher
Riddle, William Ronald
PE Teacher & Coach
Robinson, Karen Landers
Media Specialist
Veschio, Jane
Director of Guidance
Wise, Sherry Hulsey
High School English Teacher
GREENSBORO
Robinson, Calvin Orentheal
Mathematics Instructor
GREENVILLE
Dean, Annie Blake
8th Grade Reading Teacher
GROVELAND
Bordenkircher, Dave
High School Dean
Boyack, Michael E.
Soc Stud & Amer His Teacher
Campbell, Pamela Catrett
English Teacher & Chairperson
Cherry, Lother C.
Kindergarten Teacher
Cox, Benjamin R., III
Ec & AP European His Tchr
Crawford, Michael Elon
Social Studies Teacher & Coach
Haeck, Robert Douglas
High School Geometry Teacher
Jones, Jon
Baseball & Soccer Coach
Kilcrease, Bobbie Gail
Math Teacher & Dept Chprsn
Mc Griff, Lucressie Dugans
Family & Consumer Sci Tchr
Miller, Annette (Baker)
First Grade Teacher
Thomas, Sandra Barwick
6th Grade Science Teacher
Webb, Ruby Nell
Rdng, Eng & Soc Studies Tchr
GULF BREEZE
Bryant, Betty Woodham
Foreign Language Dept Chair
Faklis, Andrea G.
10th Grade English Teacher
Henderson, Sharon Kenerleber
Geography Teacher
Lord, Pamela Webb
Family & Consumer Sci Tchr
Luucella, Helen Hogg
Fourth Grade Teacher
Mazenko, Ann Adams
Art Specialist
Mills, Douglas Hundley
American History Teacher
Parsons, Jo Ann
Chemistry Teacher

Weinstein, Marian Davis
Language Arts Teacher
HAINES CITY
Cranston, Robert William
World History & German Teacher
Fie, Denise Marie
Teacher
Minshew, Nancy Elizabeth
Social Science Teacher
Simons, Carl Wayne
History Teacher
Streeter, James William
Mathematics Teacher
HALLANDALE
Blanco, Carmen Jimenez
Spanish Teacher
Kaut, Patricia Chrise
Eng Tchr, Lang Arts Dept Chair
Peyton, Naomi Dominguez
English Teacher
HAVANA
Anderson-Smith, Cora Shuler
Alternative Education Teacher
Browning, Regina Michelle
Civics & African Amer His Tchr
Knight, Gina L.
History & English Teacher
Knoblauch, Cynthia M.
Former Elementary Ed Teacher
Ulrich, April Wood
Librarian & Testing Coord
Williams, Lelia Caldwell
Social Science Teacher
HAWTHORNE
Waters, Milton Buford, Jr.
Dean of Students
HIALEAH
Alvarez, Luis Ramon
Work Experience Coordinator
Behrman, Robin Pollak
5th Grade Tchr & Dept Chrprsn
Benford, Jimmy Lee
JROTC Teacher
Borcz, Patricia Jean
English Teacher
Brown, Duane Edward
Mathematics Instructor
Butler, Eugene, Jr.
Special Instruction Coord
Catalano, Maria Rosa Diaz
Computer & Mathematics Teacher
Cline, DeeAnne
Drama Instructor
Cotilla, Rebeca Quiros
Retired Third Grade Teacher
Cryer, Cathy Sue
6th Grade Science Teacher
Cummings, Cheri Lee
Physical Ed & Health Teacher
Donohue, John Joseph, Jr.
Anatomy Teacher
Essex, Peggy M.
Band Director
Fernandez, Maria
Religion Teacher
Fletcher, Nartha Bernadetta
8th Grade Social Studies Tchr
Foley, Joy Myers
English Teacher
Garneff, Raisa Canet
Social Studies Teacher
Garner, Shelley Bowen
English Teacher
Green, Carol Litman
12th Grade English Teacher
Ivy, Michelle Bushey
Government, Ec & Law Teacher
Jenkins, Daniel James
Psychology Teacher
Johnson, Glenn Eugene
7th Grade Social Studies Tchr
King, Stephanie
World His & Law Studies Tchr
Llerena, Framberto J.
Mathematics Dept Chairman
Lopez, Lylliam
English & Speech Teacher
Martin, DeeAnne Cline
Drama Instructor
Martinez, Darliny
Teacher
Martinez, Giselle Rodriguez
Math Teacher
Mc Kenzie, Karen Marie
Life Science & Biology Teacher
Mensinger, Nancy Lynn
Geometry Teacher
Mobley, Madeline Beatrice
Health Occupations Ed Tchr
Nelson, Ronald Alfred
Director of Bands
Padron, Rosa Lourdes
Spanish Teacher
Ringler, Michael A.
ESOL Department Chair
Rivero-Leon, Maria D. C.
Principal
Russo, Michael James
Foreign Language Teacher
Smith, Linda Fuller
Business Technology Teacher
Spingler, Kevin Charles
Science Department Chairperson
Steinberg, Sandra Shubin
Counselor
Sullivan, Ruth Hardin
Fifth Grade Teacher
Torres, Lucy Catani
Fourth Grade Teacher

Traviesas, Berenice Rodriguez
Spanish Teacher
Treadwell, James Anthony
Biology Teacher
Van Duser, Kevin Joseph
Orientation & Health Teacher
Willenborgh, James
Physical Education Teacher
HIGH SPRINGS
Gallop, Cindy Westmoreland
Tchr of Gifted & Tutoring Adv
HILLIARD
Kirkland, Brenda Sue (Platt)
Business Education Teacher
HOBE SOUND
Blaske, Dolores Schuster
Retired 1st Grade Teacher
Mc Elwain, Randall Dean
Music Professor
Mc Elwain, Sue Rediger
8th Grade Teacher
Wright, Kathleen White
English Teacher
HOLIDAY
Elwell, Catherine Ann
Teacher
HOLLY HILL
Beaver, Ruth Anne Gust
Eighth Grade English Teacher
Hilderbrandt, Timothy John
5th Grade Classroom Teacher
HOLLYWOOD
Andrews, Steve
8th Grade History Teacher
Bell, Bernard Clayton
9th Grade Geography Teacher
Burgess, Mary V.
Former Teacher
Clark, Frank S., Jr.
Math Dept Chair & Teacher
Donehoo, Dorothy Jean
Science Tchr & Academic Chair
Ferraro, Florence Fischermann
Family & Consumer Sci Chprsn
Gesin, Stephen R.
Science & Math Teacher
Gulla, Frank E.
Math Dept Chairman
Hilyard, Dirk B.
Freshman English Teacher
Jones, Laurie-Lynn L.
Science Teacher
Marsh, Judith Dozier
Ninth Grd Eng & Jrnlsm Teacher
McCann, Bobby E.
Principal
Mc Carthy, Norma Parchment
Spanish Teacher
Mc Master, Jeffrey Scott
Soc Sci Dept Head & His Tchr
Miller, Constance Johnson
Physical Education Teacher
Morse, John A., Jr.
Dean of Students
Paris, Terry
Physical Education Teacher
Parnham, Lesa Updegrove
Peer Counseling Coordinator
Sasse, Tab A.
Social Studies Teacher
Sercey, Icesilyn Poole
Fourth Grade Teacher
Shurak, Elizabeth Fernandez
ESOL Teacher & Dept Head
Stephens, Barbara Ann
English & Speech Teacher
Weber, William Charles
Seventh Grade Science Teacher
Wilson, Linda Edmiston
KLAS Program Co-Coordinator
Yeater-Villa, Paula
Physical Education Teacher
HOMESTEAD
Arnett, Lynn Joiner
8th Grade Language Arts Tchr
Bachmeyer, Steven A.
Tech Ed Tchr & Dept Chm
Burton, Linda Kramer
Mathematics Instructor
Hudson, Alan
Orchestra Teacher
Israel, Linda Townley
Family & Consumer Science Tchr
Martelly, Diana
Natural Science Chairperson
Mc Donald, Jean Baird
Gen Studies Dept Chairperson
Pesina, Ernestina DeLeon
ESOL Teacher
Rodriguez, Nilda M. Maury
Spanish Teacher
Shipp, Don C.
AP Government & Ec Tchr
Tohulka, Mark Daniel
Biology Teacher
HOMOSASSA
Calzaretta, Mildred Anderson
Retired Primary Teacher
Colson, Lauretta B.
5th Grade Math & Science Tchr
Lester, Jack Eugene
Curriculum Specialist
HUDSON
Bishop, M. Ann G.
English & AP English Teacher
Bloomer, Nancy Clark
Kindergarten Teacher
Brown, Debbie Foster
First Grade Teacher

HUDSON (cont)
Byrne, Kathleen Allen
Early Childhood Education Tchr
Cella, Jeanne Attwood
Teacher of the Gifted
Cottingham, Ruth Ann Sharber
5th Grade Teacher
David, Mary
Language Arts Teacher
Fisel, Dianna Lawton
6th Grade Science Teacher
Greene, Richard Joseph
Seventh Grade Geography Tchr
Holbrook, Anthony W.
7th Grade Mathematics Teacher
Neymour, Derek Joseph D., Sr.
High School Teacher
Phillippi, Susan M.
Third Grade Teacher
Pollock, Ernest Johnston, Jr.
Mathematics Teacher
Quinn, Sheryl Galbraith
Science Teacher & Dept Head
Taranto, Clarence Paul
Senior Army & JROTC Instr
Wolbert, Elin Virginia
Social Studies Teacher
Zielinski, Dolores Zasucha
Fourth Grade Teacher
HURLBURT FIELD
Davis, Wesley Donald
Psychology Professor
Tunder, Mary Lerch
Early Childhood Ed Tchr
IMMOKALEE
Fenton, Michael Justin
English Teacher
Harvey, Ian Michael
High School English Teacher
Johnson, Melissa Ann
Eighth Grade Art Teacher
Miller, Lynn Robertson
Math Teacher
Possell, Elaine H.
English Teacher
Shippy, Jenny V.
Business Teacher
INDIALANTIC
King-Paddock, Deborah B.
Mathematics Teacher
Sawczyn, Cynthia Carveth
English & History Teacher
INTERLACHEN
Broadrick, Monica Bankhardt
3rd Grade Teacher
Carr, Marcia Ann
Pre-Vocational Business Tchr
Price, Nina Osborn
7th Grd Language Arts Teacher
Weaver, Libby Boshell
English Teacher
INVERNESS
Anderson, Barbara Watts
Curriculum Specialist
Crandall, Stephen E.
8th Grade Math Teacher
Jamison, Jerry Wayne
High Schl Social Studies Tchr
Keiper, Thurman M., Jr.
Guidance Counselor & Math Tchr
King, Richard Allen
8th Grd American History Tchr
Myer, Charlotte Smith
Fifth Grade Teacher
Niceley, Charlotte B.
English Teacher
Patton, Douglas A.
Marine & General Biology Tchr
Ruble, Katherine Goins
Fourth Grade Teacher
Schmidt, Fabian F.
Chorus Teacher
Schnee, James Ronald
Bio, Anatomy & Physiology Tchr
Stokes, Tracie J.
English Teacher
Taylor, James A.
Kindergarten Teacher
Walker, Priscilla Rooks
Kindergarten Teacher
Williams, Angela S.
Business Technology Instructor
Zay, Dorothy Leta
Spanish Teacher
JACKSONVILLE
Adkins, Carmen S.
Hnrs English & Debate Teacher
All, Geraldine Still
Retired English Teacher
Anderton, Cheryl Morrison
Third Grade Teacher
Andrews, Penny Maditz
Fourth Grade Teacher
Antone, Mary Jo
Lead Tchr & Pub Svc Magnet
Arnold, Susan Shipes
Tchr of Gifted Stdnts & US His
Austin, Clarence W., Jr.
English Teacher
Bagby, Matilda Gumm
Language Arts Teacher
Ballard, Pamela Marlean
Pre-Kindergarten Teacher
Barfield, Robert E.
Band Director
Barker-Johnson, Bonnie Louise
Pre-Kindergarten Teacher
Baum, Teresa May
Anatomy & Zoology Teacher
Belk, Michael N.
Junior High School Principal
Bertsch, Jeffrey Curtis
Religion Professor
Bladel, Dianne Nuckolls
Communications Professor
Bogar, Larry P.
Teacher
Bonteski, Robert Richard
Mathematics Teacher
Bounds, Amanda Mc Right
Professor of Computer Science
Bowers, William R.
Naval Science Instructor
Brantley, Margaret Lordi
Latin Teacher
Brennick, Layne Anthony
Dean of Stdnts & Religion Tchr
Brown, Douglas Anthony
American History Teacher
Brown, Ellis Garnett, Jr.
African-American History Instr
Brown, Neil A.
Tchr of Exceptional Ed Stdnts
Brown, Tanny La'Vern
Social Studies Teacher
Bullen, Laurie Hammack
Substitute Teacher
Burnette, Sharon Kennedy
5th Grade Teacher
Burns, Kimberly Tomlinson
Third Grade Teacher
Burton, Marc McCall
Adjunct Professor of ESL
Calhoun, William Groves
Soc Stud Teacher & Dept Head
Campbell, Evalyn Nesmith
Government & Economics Tchr
Campbell, James Taylor
Global Studies Teacher
Campbell, Roger Colin
8th Grade US History Teacher
Cherney, James Robert, III
Life Mngmt & Peer Cnslng Tchr
Clark, Dorothy Evans
Retired Teacher
Closs, Howard Joseph
Chemistry & Physics Teacher
Cohen, Mosetta Sykes
Professor
Crandall, G. Patterson
English & Journalism Teacher
Cummings, Anita Taylor
Fifth Grade Teacher
Dagenais, Wayne Eugene
Retired Science Teacher
Davis, Karen Reeves
2nd Grade Teacher
Debs, David Murphy
Social Studies Teacher
Denton, Wanda Byrd
Guidance Counselor & Math Tchr
Devoe, Dorothy Sirmans
Third Grade Teacher
Donaldson, Matthew Scott
Guidance Counselor
Donavan, James Reynolds, Jr.
Math Teacher
Dumas, Mary Smith
Third Grade Teacher
Dunn, Clifford H.
Math Teacher
Dupree, Rene
Elementary School Teacher
Dyster, Janene Perrin
Spanish & English Teacher
Edwards-Roine, Pamela Ann
Social Studies Teacher
Flemirs, Robert Mark
Physical Education Teacher
Forrest, Roy Ashley
Science Teacher
Fowler, Jolene Jeannette
Third Grade Teacher
Fowler, Unita Barnes
Project EDGE Teacher
Gardiner, Karen Lynn
6th Grade Teacher
Gasque, Diane Tiffany
Math Department Head
Gil, S. Sam
Caribbean & Latin Am Stud Tchr
Givens, Kathleen Bukaty
7th Grade Math Teacher
Goode, Martha H.
Bus Tchr & BCE Coord
Gunter, Wayne Stephen
Fourth Grade Teacher
Hale, Marilyn Marrero
Spanish & Social Studies Tchr
Haley, Agatha Henry
Biology Teacher
Halloran, Sharon Kathryn
Science Teacher
Hanks, Karen Mc Kay
Business Tech Tchr & Dpt Chair
Hardwick, Hariett A.
Fourth Grade Teacher
Harm, Judith Banck
Science Department Head
Harmon, Charles Victor
Dir of Studies & Acad Dean
Hazzard, Nancy LeMacks
Science Dept Chair & Teacher
Helwig, Patricia Crosby
8th Grade English Teacher
Hendricks, Virginia Lopez
Humanities Professor
Hicks, Deborah Turner
Spanish Teacher
Howard, Betty Henderson
Retired Teacher
Howard, Bunny Ruth
Cmptr & Ofc Systm Tech Prof
Huber, Thomas W.
Graphic Technology Teacher
Jefferson, Verdell Mc Donald
Kindergarten Teacher
Jiles, Florence Bennett
5th Grade Teacher
Johnson, Ethel Mae
Retired 2nd Grade Teacher
Johnston, Karen Lee
Psychology Instructor
Jones, Jacquelin Mary
Eng & Creative Writing Chprsn
Keezel, Debbie Kyle
Band Director
Klein, Karl M.
Science Teacher & Dept Chair
Knight, Sandra Moody
2nd Grade Teacher
Larsen, John Alexander
Chorus Director
Larson, Harry M.
4th Grade Teacher
Layman, Katie Ann Shadden
English Teacher
Lee, Betty Meadows
Kindergarten Teacher
Lee, Chew-Lean
Professor of Physics
Lewis, Orzie Lorraine
Family & Consumer Sci Dept Chr
Lipsky, Iris J.
Language Arts Teacher
Marsh, Kathy Gill
Language Arts Teacher
May, M. Cristina Murphy
Third Grade Teacher
Mc Clure, Rufus Raymond
Emeritus Chr Eng & Humanities
Mc Coy, Sandra Johnson
Honors English I Teacher
Mc Gill, Donna Hotchkiss
First Grade Teacher
Mc Hone, Lynda Martin
English Teacher
Mc Kinney, Bruce Douglas
Computer Applications Teacher
Mc Millan, Beverly Townsend
Eighth Grd Tchr & Vice Prin
Mc Queen, Carol W.
Band Director
Mead, Ramsay Oliver
English Teacher
Medley, Kenneth Dean
Fifth Grade Teacher
Milam, Linda Meeler
Algebra & Science Lab Teacher
Mitchell, Jessie Heck
Fifth Grade Teacher
Morgan, Eddie E.
Physical Education Teacher
Morris, Elaine Carroll
Fifth Grade Teacher
Newkirk, Judy O'Neal
Vocational Business Tech Tchr
Nugent, Sue Ellen B.
First Grade Teacher
O'Connor, Paul Joseph
History Teacher
Ortagus, Terri Leitman
Resource Teacher
Paschall, Edith B., SSJ
10th Grd Religion Educator
Patterson, Phyllis Bett
English Teacher
Penney, Phyllis A.
Dance Dept Chairperson
Perry, Maggie Ola
Amer History Tchr & Dept Chair
Pierce, Robert Gehry
Eng & Creative Writing Tchr
Piltz, Susan Colleen Davis
Elementary School Teacher
Ponder, Lee T.
Band Director
Price, Frances Waltz
Art Teacher
Raesemann, Shirley Hurn
Eighth Grade English Teacher
Rambach, Denise Ann
English Teacher
Ranch, Kelley Anne
English Teacher
Reaves-Williams, Machele Devon
8th Grade Algebra Teacher
Reed, Isa Now
Fifth Grade Teacher
Reed, Rosemary Pinkney
Mathematics Teacher
Respess, Steven Murray
English Teacher
Roberts, Cynthia Broussard
Mathematics Instructor
Robinson, Vernell Watkins
Guidance Counselor
Rush, Jodi Lynne
High School English Teacher
Sacerdote, Kevin Richard
Social Studies Dept Chprsn
Sacks, Shirley Gough
Theatre Arts Director
Sapp, Jimmy Durell
5th Grade Teacher
Scott, J. Mark
Choral Director
Seidelmann, Susan Elaine
History, Physical Ed, Art Tchr
Sellers, Henry Lee
JROTC Teacher
Shaw, Robert Myers
Fifth Grade Teacher
Shawver, Jerry Edward, II
Math Teacher
Shepard, Emily Gaye Phillips
5th Grade Teacher
Shinn, Laureen Mary
Spanish Teacher
Shirey, Benton Drew
Sci & PE Teacher
Shirkey, Brenda Tetrick
Elementary Teacher of Gifted
Shockley, Ronald James
Physical Education Teacher
Skinner, Connie Turner
Vice Principal
Sloth, Ingrid Stevens
11th Grade English Teacher
Slupski, Vivian Lahuniak
4th Grade Teacher
Smith, Franklin LaVaughn
Student Activities Director
Smith, Rodney L.
Geometry Teacher & Coach
Sneed, Emily I'Anson
Math Teacher
Stampalia, Rhonda
Director of Ballet
Stanton, Bob
Professor of English
Stewart, Carole Keys
5th Grade Teacher
Strickland, Pamela Canty
Third Grade Teacher
Sullivan, Frances Halliburton
Health Teacher
Switzer, Annette M.
Sculpture Teacher
Taber, Winnie Pearson
HS Home Economics Tchr & Supv
Tackett, William Dale
Language Arts Instructor
Thompson, Donna Ruth
Learning Disabilities Teacher
Thompson, Earl James
Choral Music Teacher
Turner, Linda Wolf
Mathematics Teacher
Wade, Beatrice (Parrish)
Mathematics Teacher
Walker, Gloria Outler
Business Professor
Wallis, Susan Marie (Jones)
Mathematics Teacher
Warren, Daniel Wayne, Jr.
World History Teacher
Warren, Stephen Scott
Humanities Teacher
Waters, Alex Chapman, III
Marine Science Teacher
Waugh, Candace C.
AP Psychology Teacher
Webb, Debra Lee
Dance Teacher
Wenzel, John Stanley
Graphic Arts Teacher
West, Carl L.
Dean of Boys
West, Carmen Atkins
Special Education Teacher
Whaley, Julie Yvette
Language Arts Teacher
Williams, Joyce D.
Family & Consumer Science Tchr
Williams, Suzy Dean
Kindergarten Tchr & Curr Dir
Willoughby, Richard Glenn, Sr.
Social Studies Teacher
Wilson, Benjie Eddleman
Math Teacher
Yarber, Nancy Thomas
8th Grade Teacher
Yedlicka, Karel Edward
Mathematics Instructor
Young, Elizabeth Caswell
Spanish Teacher
Young, Lona Karen
Language Arts Teacher
JACKSONVILLE BEACH
Antone, Joe
Mathematics Teacher
Bailie, Frances Walsh
Science Teacher & Athletic Dir
Feins-Snow, Kim
Teacher of Gifted Soc Studies
Spraggins, Rosemary Racine
Principal
JASPER
Davis, Ferman Edward
Social Studies Teacher
McIver, Delores Gwendolyn
Family & Consumer Science Tchr
Pinello, Philip H.
Technology Coordinator
JAY
Roggenbuck, Elaine Jones
Elem Music Teacher
JENNINGS
Blair, James Billy
Retired Sci & PE Tchr & Coach
JUNO BEACH
Miller, Annette Y.
Retired Fifth Grade Teacher
JUPITER
Carleton Bryant, B.
Assistant Principal
Headlee, Mark R.
Supervising Science Teacher
Hendricks, Josephine
Fourth Grade Teacher
Hickel, Deborah Osika
K-5th Grade Music Teacher
Johnson, Lydia Knowles
Second Grade Teacher
MacKenzie, Carolyn Bailey
Science Teacher
Moran, Nancy Ledwin
Gifted Language Arts Teacher
Niemeier, Donald L.
Math Teacher
Reppel, Charlie Hilbert, Jr.
Physical Ed & US His Teacher
Tanner, Jo Seitz
Team Leader & English Teacher
Whalen, Lorraine Ann
6th-8th Grade Science Teacher
KEY BISCAYNE
Hawkins, Alvin C.
Maritime Science Asst Instr
Kolb, Janet Ruesink
Health Teacher
Moreland, Nancy Cotton
Aquatics Instructor
Skinner, Paulette Anne
5th Grade Teacher
Wright, Linda Huttunen
Family & Consumer Sci Ed Tchr
KEY LARGO
Ganim, Roseann Mc Grath
Middle School Math Teacher
Garrison, Catherine May
Language Arts & Reading Tchr
Willich, Inge (Oding)
Teacher of the Gifted
KEY WEST
Cook, Sue
Reading Teacher & Team Leader
Fant, Nancy P.
Environmental Science Teacher
Monroe Nugent, Susan
Coordinator of English Dept
Wise, J. A.
Health Teacher
KEYSTONE HEIGHTS
Grant, Michele Elizabeth (Sheese)
10th Grd World History Teacher
Green, Nancy Estridge
First Grade Teacher
Lee, Virginia Craft
Secondary Math Teacher
Martin, Norma Valldejuli
Counselor
Parrish, Donna N.
Gifted American History Tchr
Smith, Vina Crews
6th Grade Eng & Spelling Tchr
KISSIMMEE
Barclay, Donnelly J.
Professor of English
Beckel, Lonnie L.
Vocational Education Teacher
Briner, Cindy M.
Third Grade Teacher
Bryan, Brenda Barrett
Elementary Media Specialist
Delgado, Amneris
8th Grade Language Arts Tchr
Dunwoody, Laurie Pickren
Math Teacher
Evans-O'Connor, Norma Lee
Psychology Teacher
Henley, William Thomas
Band Director
Holmes, Janis Ann (Schaffer)
Eng, Jrnlsm Tchr & Dept Chair
Jones, Beverly Anne
History & English Teacher
Liesch, Donald Arthur
AFJROTC Aerospace Sci Instr
McGowan, Edward Roberts, III
Naval Science Instructor
Mundinger, Barbara K. Schendel
3rd Grade Teacher
Nash, Heidi Mullendore
High School Math Teacher
Pugh, Shirley Ann
Language Arts Instructor
Rahiya, Shelley Lange
Business Education Teacher
Ridenour, David Eugene
Athletic Director
Ritzmann, Janet Adkins
5th Grade Teacher
Savickis, Rodney Frederick
Drama Teacher
Steele, Joyce Rogers
English Teacher
Thackston, Elaine Janet
8th Grade Algebra Teacher
Tilson, Deborah Ann
Marine Bio & Oceanography Tchr
Tuthill, Donald Leroy
English & Humanities Professor
Wakefield, Laura Wallis
Social Studies Teacher
Warner, Susan J.
English Teacher
Watkins, Norman D.
Ecology Teacher
Yates, Robert Wayman
Third Grade Teacher
Zelenak, Pamela S.
Chemistry Teacher
LABELLE
Andrews, Darryl Glenn
Band Director
Williamson, Joel Edward
Athletic Director

: ALFRED
r, Claudia H.
nd Grade Teacher
: BUTLER
Renae J.
uctor & Science Dept Chm
eal, Jerry Duane
her
; CITY
man, Barbara K.
her & Program Coord
Dawn O'Connor
1 Teacher
nan, Jill Davis
culture Teacher
and, Lorraine LeCrann
her of Gifted
, Roberta Keeny
ond Grade Teacher
tosh, Gloria Newsome
nistry Teacher
ts, Clara Davis
ors English Teacher
s, Clara Orander
nentary Teacher
on, Gary Rodney
Grade Math Teacher
n, Bobie Thomas
lish Teacher
E MARY
k, Ronald William
Grd Amer His Teacher
er, Linda G.
guage Arts Teacher
na, Minerva
nish Teacher
is, Julius Edward
istant Principal
er, Patricia Ann
ence Teacher
Virginia Marcile
ch, Sociology & Ldrshp Tchr
Robert Edwin
cher of Gifted Mathematics
abb, Grace Keiko
Risk Teacher
, Diane Thrasher
er Government & History Tchr
day, Vera Eugenie
ial Studies Teacher
, Martha T.
iness Education Teacher
fer, Mark R.
ence Department Chairman
erman, Marcia Choper
nish Teacher
chein, Kathleen Joyce
nch & Latin Teacher
e, Susan Boder
cher of Gifted Lang Arts
Mary Ellen (Wilson)
og, Alg I Hnrs & Gifted Tchr
E PARK
ne, Bonnie Spencer
Grade Teacher
E PLACID
ingham, Karen Kenyon
Grade Teacher
n, Joan Crankshaw
siness Education Teacher
in, Dennis Clair
th Teacher & Principal
an, Donna Stalls
Grade Teacher
es, Kenny H.
rld History, Psychology Tchr
ker, Mary T.
: Studies Teacher
e, Troy Wade, Sr.
tr of Soc Stud & Dept Head
ney, Kevin E.
th Teacher
KE WALES
yn, Carrie Morgan
Grade Teacher
ards, Barbara Baker
urth Grade Teacher
ning, Sam Luther, III
story Teacher
, Angela Yancey
ence Teacher
ring, Terri Lynn
athematics Teacher
s, Cindy Pera
glish Teacher
KE WORTH
e, Keith Edward
ble Teacher
ee, Rebecca Patterson
ndergarten Teacher
ks, Debra Jackson
t Teacher
cinski, Connie Parker
hird Grade Teacher
om, Jane Carol (Caserta)
usiness Education Instructor
don, Florencia Mills
th Grade English Teacher
apetta, Cynthia Ann
ology Teacher
e, Robert
rktg Oper & Productions Coord
k, Peggy Herrington
h Grade Science Teacher
tello, Patricia
athematics Teacher
rtemanche, Tambra Ann
pecial Education Teacher
gen, Regina Marie
djunct Communications Instr

Dingman, Caryl Joscelyn
Music Teacher
Drinkwater, Sherry Lee
Spanish Teacher
Duxbury, Alice Thorp
Sr Instructor
Fine, Marsha Cranman
Health Teacher
Finn, Gretchen Thomas
Aerobic & Dance Teacher
Flamer, Marc Phillip
Guidance Director
Fowler, Ethel M.
Sr Instructor & Program Leader
Gattozzi, Karen Brown
Associate Professor
Goffe, Jerri
Band & Chorus Director
Grabinski, Jeannie M.
First Grade Teacher
Gunnels, Patricia Kay
HS English & Speech Teacher
Hamblin, Gillian Crosbie
Occupational Specialist
Hoff, Karren Roncadori
Mathematics Tchr & Dept Head
Hutchens, Ruth Mc Vey
Retired Kndgtn & Elem Tchr
Jackson, Bryan Keith
Science Teacher
Kalt, James Thomas
English Teacher
Kass, Mitchell
Assoc Professor of Sociology
Kaysen, Kerry Bruce
Earth & Science Teacher
Lobdell, Andrew Scott
Law & Psychology Teacher
Lord, Jean Forman
5th Grade Teacher
Lowry, Diane Finley
High School Math Teacher
Mc Tier, Ardell Hughes
Second Grade Teacher
Miles, Susan Denise
Math Teacher & Dept Chair
Mooney, Suzanne Elizabeth
Biology Teacher
Parbhoo, Ernest
Asst Professor of Journalism
Parry-Sanchez, Kelly A.
Teacher
Passman, Scott David
ESOL Coordinator
Scheurer, Vicki Freund
Instructor of English & Lit
Slygh, Carolyn V.
Biology Teacher
Spence, Lana E.
Business Education Teacher
Thompson, Mary Elizabeth
Lang Arts Chprsn & Teacher
Thompson, Susan M.
Business Professor
Thorsen, Deborah Lynn
Economics Professor
Vacco, Dianna Marie
Science Teacher
Violette, Eileen Cody
Assistant Professor of Nursing
Vrouhas, Dorothea
English Teacher
Wasserman, Bruce M.
Guidance Counselor & Ath Dir
Weidenhamer, Gary C.
Chemistry Teacher
Wells, B. Scott
Guidance Counselor
Whitaker, Jane Mullen
English Teacher
Yinger, Richard Ervin
Prof & Pgm Ldr of Soc Science
LAKELAND
Ambrose, Ana Morejon
Spanish Teacher
Armstrong, Audrey Jean
9th-10th Grd History Teacher
Asbridge, Cathy Pike
Biology & Chemistry Teacher
Blount, Carla Ruth
9th Grd Physical Science Tchr
Bonnichsen, Gail Lindstrom
English Teacher
Brekke, Janice M. (Heiden)
First Grade Teacher
Bridges, Janice T.
Fifth Grade Teacher
Calloway, Wanda Joyce (Kirkland)
Scndry Social Studies Teacher
Claycomb, Jeanne Marie
8th Grade Science Teacher
Craig, Peggy L.
English & Debate Teacher
Dence, Denise Kay
English & Journalism Teacher
Dittmer, Gladys M.
Kindergarten Teacher
Doddy, Shirley St John
7th Grd Lang Arts Teacher
Doerr, Cynthia Lee
6th Grade Reading Teacher
Dunne, James Robert
Eighth Grade Science Teacher
Everett, Sandra Sharp
Business Teacher
Fallin, Cynthia Morris
Multi-Age Classroom Teacher
Fitzgerald, Elayne Thoman
HS Business Education Teacher

Floyd, Kelly O'Connor
Geography Teacher
Fritz, Robert A.
English & Drama Teacher
Gargan, Laura Anne
English Teacher
Garnham, Jane Aspinwall
Retired Teacher
Genzel, Nancy DeJulius
Principal
Gibble, June Byers
Teacher
Giles, Charnell Clark
Exceptional Student Ed Teacher
Gulledge, Frances P.
Spanish Teacher
Haskins, Jodi Ann
Orchestra & Chorus Teacher
Haskins, Robert Craig
Eighth Grade History Teacher
Hewitt, Kathryn Boomer
AP & Honors Government Teacher
Hollen, Evelyn Kirsch
Assistant Principal
Hutto, Deborah K.
Biology Teacher
Johnson, Laureen Teresa
French Teacher
Keers, Steven Grant
Physics Teacher
Kelly, Dana Kay
K-5th Grade Gifted Educator
King, Gwendolyn Vivian
Guidance Counselor
Lanier, Audrey Davenport
6th Grade Teacher
Lee, Nannette Lyman
Fifth Grade Teacher
Long, Richard Dean
Secondary Spanish Teacher
Losch, Christine Failing
Math Teacher
Lowry, Jody Miller
Hlth Occupations Tchr & Dpt Hd
Morgan, Bruce A.
Social Studies Teacher
Moseley, Lisa Lent
Psych & World History Teacher
Norman, Tex
Jrnlsm & Creative Writing Tchr
Osthoff, Pamela Bemko
Spanish Teacher
Privett, James Everett
Science Teacher
Radford, Susan Widdowson
Home Economics & Jrnlsm Tchr
Reagan, Nancey Vogler
Guidance Counselor
Reeves, Rosemary Antoinette
Spanish Teacher
Reynolds, Gwen Craig
Guidance Counselor
Riley, Edward Wayne
High School Teacher
Riley, Milissa Hammond
Business, PE Teacher & Coach
Robare, Michelle Perez
Social Studies Department Head
Rudman, Karen Jo Heald
Third Grade Teacher
Salcedo, Iris Johnson
Span Tchr & Frgn Lang Dept Chm
Sansome, Gail Lynn
Fifth Grade Teacher
Starling, Sharon Godwin
Music Dept Chm & Piano Tchr
Sylvester, Betty Ruth (Moore)
Fifth Grade Teacher
Thomas, Holly
Asst Prof of French & Spanish
Townsend, Diana Bloodworth
Third Grade Teacher
Waibel, Faith Kohatsu
Fifth Grade Teacher
Williams, Yvonne Speed
Kindergarten Teacher
Woods, David M.
HS Mathematics Chair & Teacher
Zamzow, Dale Allen
Chemistry Teacher
Ziolkowski, Claire Lynn
Science Teacher
LAND O LAKES
Chapman, Saybra Rice
High School Guidance Counselor
Daly, Donna Lee
Reading Specialist
Gleaton, Rebecca Brown
High School Guidance Counselor
Guss, Nancy Nason
Language Arts Teacher & Chprsn
Hundt, Jay Charles
Geography Teacher
Mc Dermott, Caryn L.
Language Arts Chairperson
Paver, Shannon Metcalf
Math Teacher
LANTANA
Cannon, Robin R.
Personal Tutor
LARGO
Barber, Cynthia Gary
Lit, Lang Arts & Religion Tchr
Beck, Michael Dee
PE Teacher & Coach
Boyd, Chantal Woel
Science Teacher
Branch, Mary Abel
Gifted Mathematics Teacher

Bush, Lynn Gardner
Humanities & English Teacher
Gavin, Kathryn Mayes
Family & Consumer Sci Tchr
Graf, Joan
Fifth Grade Teacher
Haight, Thomas Charles
Bus Ed Instr & Swim Coach
Hart, Cathy Collins
Chorus Teacher
Hartley, Mark Edward
Bible Teacher
Horn, Mary S.
Algebra I & 8th Grd Math Tchr
Jensen, Sara
Teacher of GATE, Drama & Rdng
Keller, Margaret Jeanne
K-12th Grade Spanish Teacher
Lara, Star Richards
Library Information Specialist
Lops, Diane N.
Executive Internship Pgm Coord
Lowry, Christine Ossenberg
Resource Teacher
Marina, Jonathan DuVaul
Science Teacher
Minchey, Marilyn O'Dell
Mathematics Tchr, Stu Govt Adv
Oliveros, Barbara Franco
Spanish Teacher
Reed, Susan Walworth
ESP & 1st Grade Teacher
Riel, Ruth Ellen
Drop-Out Prevention Specialist
Spradlin, Marilyn Beasley
Math Teacher of the Gifted
Starner, Rob Alan
Guidance Counselor, Psych Tchr
Talmadge-Logan, Elizabeth M.
French Teacher
Ward, Kelly Elizabeth
Elem PE Tchr
Wiggins, Quitman, Jr.
Social Studies Teacher
Willis, Lucinda Webster
Teacher
LECANTO
Badger, Andrew
English Department Chair
Chytka, Ann Couch
Mid Level Tchr & Curr Coord
Clark, Robert Lindsay
Physical Education Teacher
Jackson, Robert Edward
Mathematics Dept Chairman
Kupovics, Aranka Mester
English Teacher
Stokes, Patricia Ryan
Title One Teacher
Taylor, Sheryl Z.
Spanish Teacher
Torricelli, Ben L.
Social Studies Teacher
Venezio, Allen J.
Band Director
LEESBURG
Dillinger, Austin Carey, Jr.
Mathematics Instructor
Harris, Adrienne Ginette
First Grade & Spec Rdng Tchr
Harvard, Gloria Moore
English Instructor
Hostetler, Donald L.
Biology Teacher
Lang, Corrine Randolph
2nd Grade Teacher
May, Dennis Eugene
Physical Education Teacher
Mularsky, Fredrick Ray
Economics Teacher
Symonds, Joyce
Kindergarten Teacher
Wright, Kathryn A.
Gifted Eng & Soc Studies Tchr
Zeis, Anne Hahn
Retired Teacher
LEHIGH ACRES
Barlow, Linda Ellen
Guidance Counselor
Gribble, Noel
Language Arts Teacher
Jamison, Greg N.
Curriculum Assistant Principal
Johnston, Nancy Joan
Specific Lrng Dsblts Teacher
McFee, Eric Joseph
Spanish Teacher
Mullings, Ceclyn Dennis
Mathematics Teacher
Oakes, Lynne Wilson
Teacher of Gifted & Reading
Roberts, Lynne Diane Martin
2nd Grade Teacher
Shelton, Kimberly Dianna
Physics & Chemistry Teacher
Wagner, Kristen Jane
Third Grade Teacher
LITHIA
Stevens, Alon Morgan
Third Grade Teacher
LIVE OAK
Boggus, Tamara G.
Secondary Science Teacher
Brinson, Terry Joe
8th Grade US History Teacher
Brothers, William Lindsay
Agriculture Teacher
Jacobs, Charlie
Naval Science Instructor

Law, H. Randolph
American History & Hum Tchr
Maguire, Jane Bancroft
Fifth Grade Teacher
Woodrum, Melissa Grabe
12th Grade English Teacher
LONGWOOD
Alexander, Diannetta Williams
Fifth Grd Elementary Educator
Backel, Michelle P.
Drama Teacher
Barnes, John Thomas
Chemistry Teacher
Barnes, Patsy H.
English Teacher
Berry, Peter Benjamin
Coop Diversified Ed Coord
Braverman, David L.
ESOL Teacher
Finke, Fredrick John
Biology & Computer Teacher
Gorman, Peter Cregg
High School Principal
Harris, Michael
American History Teacher
Heck, Jean Condon
10th-11th Grade English Tchr
Hooper, Rebecca Stalvey
Biology Teacher
King, Allan Louis
Learning Disabilities Teacher
Lecky, Kit Nelson
Amer & World History Teacher
Nosal, Dorothy Sadloch
Art Teacher
Quiles, Cynthia Roe
Kindergarten Tchr & Team Ldr
Rochefort, Doreen Gruber
Assistant Principal
Sperrazza, Susan Santarpia
Kindergarten Teacher
Thompson, Janice Moore
English & Geography Teacher
Walker, Joyce Taylor
Teacher of Gifted English
LOXAHATCHEE
Lake, Cathlene Sue
Physical Ed Teacher
LUTZ
Joiner, Teresa Daniels
Second Grade Teacher
Thompson, Donald Neal
Retired Mathematics Teacher
LYNN HAVEN
Boss, Beverly
History Teacher
Collins, Thomas Worthington
Physics Instructor
Cooley, Judith Neill
5th Grade Teacher
Jordan, Melissa Bertrand
Business Education Teacher
Kimball, Susan Cavelli
Spanish Teacher
Land, Margaret DePuy
Fifth Grade Teacher
Reeve, Scott Alan
Art Instructor
Wixted, Clayton Lee
Art Teacher
MACCLENNY
Giles, Sue Thrift
Guidance Counselor
MADISON
Aikens, Katrina Ann
Second Grade Teacher
Benjamin, Nancy Lee
HS Physical & Drivers Ed Tchr
Crutcher, Juanita Marie
Science Teacher
Holmes, Robert L.
Geography Teacher
James, Gale Turner
Spanish Teacher
Killingsworth, Benjamin Franklin
Assistant Principal
Lankford, Steve
Economics & Physical Ed Tchr
Mc Cauley, Barbara Lynne
Instructor
Proctor, David Annis
History Instructor
Sargeant, H. Brooks, III
Retired Amer Govt & His Tchr
MAITLAND
Bauer, Raymond
Physical Science Teacher
Clark, Sandy K. (Clark)
English Teacher & Dept Chm
Helms, Jackie
Math Teacher
Hotaling, Doris Ridgeway
K-5th Grade Music Teacher
Miller, Richard A.
History & Government Teacher
Rolph, Arleen Gregory
English Teacher
Rosario, Bethsaida P.
Cosmetology Teacher
Sheldon, Sandra J.
Orch Dir, Stu Assistance Coord
Somarriba, Sarah Bernhardt
Soc Studies Teacher & Yrbk Adv
MALONE
Hatcher, Patte Nettles
Economics Teacher
MARATHON
Hawes, Stephen Ellis
WIN Teacher

MARATHON (cont)
Howard, Janyth Stewart
Social Studies Teacher
McFaddin, Peggy Jane
Cosmetology Teacher
MARGATE
Gotha, Kathleen Campbell
Fourth Grade Teacher
Tyson, Josephine Rose
Second Grade Teacher
Upmeyer, Jeanie
Third Grade Teacher
MARIANNA
Almand, Howard Warren, Jr.
English Instructor
Almand, Lydia Moore
English Department Chairman
Bondurant, Pamela Melvin
Chemistry, Bio & Physics Tchr
Cavin, Rose Mobley
HS Math Teacher
Crouch, Brenda Smalley
Science Teacher
Faircloth, Charmin Proctor
5th Grade Teacher
Laramore, Carol Ann
Amer History & Government Tchr
Malloy, Amenda Marguerite
Social Science Teacher
McClendon, Charlotte Tatum
Third Grade Teacher
Mulder, Lynne Sluis
Kindergarten Teacher
Pforte, Dorothy Ellis
Fifth Grade Teacher
Walker, Jane Peacock
Coordinator
MELBOURNE
Abdo, George Edgar
Associate Prof of Applied Math
Belcher, Susan Krebs
Latin Teacher
Bolton, Susan Rae
Science, Ocngrphy & Bio Tchr
Brennan, Karen
Math Teacher
Brown, James Brunson
Mathematics Professor
Cocke, Robert Hagan
Science Teacher
Coffman, Robert Dale
World History Journalism Tchr
Curtiss, Glenda Lynne
5th-6th Grade Teacher
Demming, Suzanne Leigh
Biology Honors & Comp Sci Tchr
Dickinson, Rhonda Dalton
Fourth Grade Teacher
Dyer, Sean S.
High School English Teacher
Earhart, Brenda J.
English & Journalism Teacher
Forget, Julie Ann
Gifted Studies English Teacher
Freeman, Carol Lawton
Art Teacher
Galiszewski, Michael Robert
Science Rsrch & Phys Sci Tchr
Gelder, Kathleen Dillon
Substitute Teacher
Holdsworth, John Wilbur, Jr.
American History Teacher
Jury, Joyce Marie
Latin Teacher
LaChappelle, William Gaylord, III
Psychology Instructor
Lee, Randolph Melvin, Jr.
Assistant Principal
Mc Cullough, Marguerite T.
K-6th Grade Resource Teacher
Mc Ginnis, James Daniel
Social Studies Teacher
McLaren, Robert Thomas, Jr.
Social Studies Dept Chprsn
Meyer, Barbara Ward
Director of Guidance
Neill, Tanya Ferguson
Art Teacher
O'Connell, Ann Williams
English Professor
Osborne, Jack
Science Teacher
Pacheco, Carol Anne
Secondary English Teacher
Parrish, Linda Carol
Associate Professor of Math
Patterson, Joy Bacon
English Department Chair
Pedlow, Pamela J. Scannell
10th-12th Grade English Tchr
Pekich, Joseph
Chem & Science Research Tchr
Reynolds, Jeffrey Warren
Professor of Music
Roach, Julia Roach
Teacher of Gifted English
Ronman, Peter E.
Professor
Sampere, Roberta Farley
English Adjunct Instructor
Santangelo, John Anthony
8th & 9th Grade Math Teacher
Schultz, Sarah Rice
Fourth Grade Teacher
Sepri, Paavo
Assoc Prof of Mechanical Engr
Slaughter, Beverly J.
Assoc Prof of Comms & Coord
Smith, Scott Wayne
Instrumental Music Teacher
Stevens, Robert Edward
His Tchr & Soc Stud Dept Chm
Tramontana, Nicki
English Teacher
Tucker, Janice Elaine
Life Management Skills Teacher
Vanderveer, Ron
Science Teacher & Dept Chm
Viglianco, ELissa Soda
French Teacher
Walker, Patricia Hughes
Secondary Mathematics Teacher
Warren, Lori Ann
Eighth Grade Science Teacher
Waters, Abanne
English & Acting Professor
White, Gerald Franklin
Physical Education Teacher
Williamson, Tamara L.
Math Teacher
Wolfe, Gary K.
Oceanogrphy & Marine Bio Instr
MERRITT ISLAND
Ahlgreen, Charline G. Kitchen
Drama & English Teacher
Bounds, Arleen Leigh
Social Studies Teacher
Bryant, Jerry Fred
Marketing Teacher
Elliott, Suzanne Smith
Guidance Counselor & Coach
Fehl, Felicia Alexandra
English Teacher
Ferrie, Bertram William
JROTC Instructor
Garr, Alfred Bruno
Science Teacher
Guerra, Rich Lee
Prsnl Ftns & Life Mgmt Teacher
Hall, Rowland Lowe, Jr.
Secondary English Teacher
Harris, Julie Hall
6th-8th Grd Soc Stud Tchr
Kaleel, Lesa Ochab
American & World His Tchr
Kirker, Barbara Ann
Second Grade Teacher
Lober, Skippy Z.
English Teacher
O'Neal, Donald Rogers
Photography Teacher
Ramos, Alice White
Language Arts & Soc Stud Tchr
Rossi, Cheryl C.
5th & 6th Grade Science Tchr
Thaden, Jacquelyn P.
Family & Consumer Sci Instr
Warren, Cheryl M.
Business Teacher
Young, Gerald Norman
6th Grade Math & Science Tchr
MIAMI
Abercrombie, Stacey Macks
Journalism Teacher
Abrahams, Mark
Substance Ed Specialist
Adair, Jane Britton
7th Grade Science Teacher
Adderley, Oddette Pitter
Social Studies Teacher
Adjouadi, Malek
Engrng Prof & Dir of GATE Ctr
Alexander, Anthony C.
English Teacher
Alexander, Dimitry Nicholas
Professor of Law & Business
Alexenberg, Mel
Dean of Visual Arts
Alford, Debbie
Math Teacher
Allen, Evit L.
Music Teacher
Allison, Alba Tur
Spanish Teacher
Allsopp, Michael E.
Theology Professor
Alvarez, Blanca Figueredo
Associate Professor of French
Alvarez, Hector, Jr.
Computer & Math Teacher
Alvarez, Jose
Athletic Director
Alves, Lisette Marichel
English Teacher
Alzaga, Florinda
Span & Philosophy Professor
Amparo, Robin Faith
Magnet English Teacher
Angell, Carl Henry
Physical Education Teacher
Angelucci, Patrick
Former Principal
Arango-Montero, Frances
World Geography Teacher
Ashley, Silas Edward
History Teacher
Atkins, Carol Patricia
Ninth Grade English Teacher
Azrikan, Joel
5th Grade Teacher
Baker, Louise Coleman
First Grade Teacher
Balch, Donald James
Fifth Grade Teacher
Bales, Virginia Carol Henley
10th Grade English Teacher
Banks, Susan Leean
Associate Professor of Art
Barakat, Nemtalla H.
Seventh Grade Math Teacher
Barrios, Andres Javier
Physics Instructor
Barry, Roy Alexander
Professor of Social Science
Bear, Robert M.
Professor
Bellamy, Marilyn F.
English Teacher
Benz, Stephen Lee
English Professor
Berger, Francine Blake
Forensics Dir & Debate Coach
Berman, Marcee Meyers
6th Grd Gifted Lang Arts Tchr
Bigley, Robert Franklin
Music Director
Bistrong, Sylvia Rae
Interior Space Planning Tchr
Bohm, Jeanne Metzger
Retired Elementary Teacher
Bohr, Teresa M.
Biology, Anatomy & Sci Tchr
Borges, Mike D.
Hnrs Science Phys Tchr
Bostic, Donald R.
Physical Education Teacher
Boudreau, George Raymond, OP
Theology Professor
Bowers, Bradley Roy
Assistant Professor of English
Boyd, Glendie Watson
Science Teacher & Chairperson
Brandt, Gregory Alan
English Teacher
Braun, Marcia Delich
ESOL Teacher & Dept Chair
Bremer, August William, Jr.
Senior Army & Jr ROTC Instr
Brennan, Cynthia Norwood
Guidance Counselor
Brown, Elaine Ann
Chprsn, Prof of Paralegal Stud
Brown, Isabella Hopkins
Retired 5th & 6th Grd Teacher
Brown, Linda Hiles
Family & Consumer Sci Teacher
Brown, Mary Holmberg
Govt & American History Tchr
Brown, Tyrone A.
High School History Teacher
Brown-Major, Tanya Renee
Assistant Principal
Brumfield, Charlotte Allent
High School English Teacher
Bryant, Jimmie L.
Bus Educ & Math Teacher
Buitrago, Myriam Herrera
Spanish & Humanitites Teacher
Bullard, Mary Marie Baity
Family & Consumer Sci Tchr
Butler, Ruby Vaughn
5th Grade Teacher
Bynes, Marvin LeVent
Fifth Grade Teacher
Cabrera, Rose Marie
8th Grade Language Arts Tchr
Cadieux, Kathryn Kelly
Special Ed Tchr & Dept Chprsn
Calkins, Robert Brian
High School Teacher
Callaghan, Lillian P.
Spanish Teacher
Carpenter, John A.
Professor
Casademunt, Vivian R.
ESOL Teacher
Casero, Cristina Ramirez
Speech & Writing Teacher
Castaldi, June Page
Science Dept Chair & Teacher
Castello, Carmen M.
Teacher & Newspaper Advisor
Castillo, Tomas Franklin
Science Teacher
Cayocca, Maria Larrauri
First Grade Teacher
Ceballos, Melba P.
Business Technolgy Ed Teacher
Chait, Phillip Howard
American & World History Tchr
Chavarry, Alexander G.
Mathematics Teacher
Chewning, Mae Kelly
Business Technology Teacher
Choi, Jung Min
Sociology Prof
Clifton, Carol Cleland
English Teacher
Colon, Dolores Richard
Visiting Lecturer
Constantine, Edward C.
Chemistry Teacher
Copeland, Diane Cantwell
Dance Teacher
Cortes, Sara Montiel
Theology Teacher
Cortina, Leda Lynn
Dance & Aerobics Teacher
Covin, Paulette Delise
Language Arts Teacher
Cox, Kim Williams
Assistant Principal
Crarey, Hugh W.
5th Grade Mathematics Tchr
Crawford-Martinez, Joyce L.
Dean of Inter American Center
Crespo, Susana Rachel
Arch, Draft & CAD Instructor
Crockwell, Alan Lord
Science Dept Head
Cruz, Ana Margarita
Asst Prof of Accounting & Tax
Cuevas, Peggy D.
Science & Math Teacher
Curtis, Blannie M.
Secondary School Principal
D'Agati, Suzanne Snook
Occupational Therapy Professor
Daire, Sandra Arguelles
Math Teacher
Dallas, Catherine Lamberti
Middle School Counselor
Davis, Maggie
Lead Teacher
Davis, Martha Yelina
Drama Teacher
Davis, Roderick M.
Artistic Dir of Dance Dept
Davis-Rolle, Josephine Marie
Sixth Grade Teacher
Deal, Betty J.
Fifth Grade Honors Teacher
del Castillo, Myriam Perez
Spanish Teacher
Delsalle, Maria Jofre
Spanish Professor
Devieux, Robert
Economics Professor
Diaz, Hilda Eliza
ESOL Teacher
Diaz, Nestor
Mathematics Teacher
Diaz, Saturnino
Advanced Academics Eng Instr
Dispenza, Frank Joseph
Third Grade Teacher
Doan, Scott L.
Dean of Students & Teacher
Dorsett, Tony Lloyd
Teacher
Douce, Rhonda Ray
4th Grade Teacher
Downum, Kelsey R.
Assoc Prof & Dir of Grad Prgm
Drummonds, Janis Denise
Fitness Teacher
Duchatelet, Martine N. J.
Ec & Finance Assoc Prof
Dugard, James Thomas
10th & 12th Grd Theology Tchr
Edwards, Charles
5th Grade Teacher
Edwards, Paul Eric
Religion Dept Chair & Teacher
Ellis, Gilbert E.
Asst Professor of Physiology
Esquivel, Carlos A.
Mathematics Teacher
Evans, Christine Sherley
Interim Associate Dean
Fairchild, Susan S.
Assistant Professor of Nursing
Falco, Julia Wilcox
Fifth Grade Teacher
Faulmann, Roger Ray
Instrumental Music Director
Faz, Rina Maria
Span Tchr, Frgn Lang Dept Head
Fernandez, Alexandra Romero
Music & Spanish Teacher
Fernandez-Toledo, Guillermo
Theology Professor
Festa, Paula Carney
Math Teacher
Field, Charles H.
Head Football Coach
Figueroa Sierra, Ana Maria
Ninth Grade English Teacher
Fine, Joyce Caplan
Reading & Language Arts Prof
Fisher, Ronnie H.
Psychology Professor
Flax, Stanley
Intnl Bus & Mrktg Professor
Fleming, Jermaine V.
Teacher & Band Director
Floyd, Genevieve Latrice
Mathematics Teacher
Forgan, Ruth Beazell
Computer Teacher of Gifted
Fortuna, Alina
Resident Teacher
Fragin, Dayle Marlyn
6th Grd Elementary Instructor
Freijo, Grisselle
High School Spanish Teacher
French, Vivian Russell
4th Grade Teacher
Furton, Deborah Fries
Teaching Assisting Teacher
Futch, Sherri M.
Business & Computer Instructor
Garcia, Leticia R.
Eighth Grade Lang Arts Teacher
Garcia, Manolo
Psychology Professor
Garland, Edward J.
Mathematics Teacher
Gehr, Maria Leal
5th Grade Teacher
Genendlis, Margaret Ann
Eighth Grade Honors Teacher
Gibbons, Erin Anne
English Teacher
Gilham, James Stewart
Bio, Sci & Music App Teacher
Giner, Magaly
Spanish Teacher
Giro, Marcia M.
Third Grade Teacher
Glick, Sharon Scotch
Teacher of Gifted
Goffe, Peter
Associate Prof of Marketing
Goldstein, Ronni C.
Exceptional Student Ed Teacher
Gomez, Ofelia
Spanish Teacher
Gonzalez, Pablo
Math Teacher
Gooding, Rosiland Dunn
English Teacher
Gottlieb, Jo Ann Kelly
Assistant Professor of Nursing
Grace, Kenneth Lee
Science Dept Chairman
Graham, Robin Michelle
5th Grade Teacher
Grieper, Sandra Rose
Second Grade Teacher
Grizzle, Gary L.
Asst Professor of Sociology
Grof, Andrew P.
Adjunct Professor of English
Gropper, Idania Rojas
Professor
Gutting, Richard
History & Humanities Teacher
Guttman, Michael
Chemistry Professor
Haatvedt, Leslie Blair
Guidance Counseling Director
Hall, Virginia Jane
AP Chemistry Teacher
Harris, Barbara Carnegay
5th Grade Teacher
Harris, Jamie Rae
Psychology Professor
Harris, Myriam
Dean
Hart, Stephen Warren
Fifth Grade Teacher
Hawkins, Joretta Wallace
Language Arts Teacher
Haynes, Merry Renee
3rd Grade Teacher
Hazelton, Carolyn Easley
Fifth Grade Teacher
Hegner, Paul Allen
Art Instructor
Heisserer, Gary
Theatre Professor
Heneks, Sandra Marshall
Exceptional Student Ed Tchr
Henson, Donald Mason
Program Instructor & Eng Tchr
Hernandez, Gloria Haydee
Spanish Teacher
Hess, Linda Bowers
Physical Education Teacher
Heyman, Shari Danziger
Fifth Grade Teacher
Hill, JoAnn Golatt
5th Grade Teacher
Hill, Sharon Redden
Fourth Grade Teacher
Hollinger, Martha Reese
Mathematics Teacher
Holmes, Dianne Theresa
Psychology & Biology Teacher
Holmes, William Jacob
Mathematics Teacher
Host, David J.
5th Grade Teacher
Houstoun, Ogden King, III
Latin & World History Tchr
Hoyos, Carmen Marcela
7th & 8th Grd Science Teacher
Huff Lowe, Danna Lynn
Kindergarten Teacher
Hughes, Lee Thomas
Director of Bands & Orchestra
Hunt, Helen Yarochowicz
AP Wrld & European His Teacher
Iglesias, Caridad
Sr High School Spanish Teacher
Ingraham, George Albert
Choral Dir & Key Board Instr
Jensen, Marilyn A.
Fifth Grade Teacher
Jones, David Spencer
Physics Teacher
Jones, Jacqueline Marcia
World History Teacher
Joseph, Betty Jean Felton
Owner
Kalb, Christopher Adam
Business Teacher
Kaplan, Donna J.
Computer Teacher
Kell, James A.
Mathematics Professor
Kelly, Laura Ann
Assistant Professor
Kendall, John A.
Language Arts Department Head
Kidd, Andrea Roth
Drama Teacher
Kimbro, Lenyta Joanella
Kindergarten Teacher
Kirby, Esther Marie
Family & Consumer Science Tchr
Kirkpatrick, David Wesley
AP Physics & Engineering Tchr
Kjeldsen, Joan Bromhall
Acad Dean & Dir of Coll Cnslng
Klein, Elizabeth Ann
Professor
Kroll, James Michael
PE Dept Chair & Bus Ed Tchr

MI (cont)
us, Terry E.
nce Teacher
, David M.
essor of Theatre
, John Gray
al Studies Teacher
, Saralee Smith
al Studies Teacher
n, Maricela
ding Specialist
k, Lisa Rene
chology Instructor
iere, Peter Roderick
of Math & Cmptr Sci Dept
ence, Keitha Denise
erican History Teacher
ulius Travis, Jr.
ma Teacher
Muriel Lewis
Grade Teacher
en, Lili
-11th Grd Eng Teacher
s, Teresita Padron
hematics Teacher
, Veda Mara
& Creative Writing Tchr
Harriet
dance Counselor
n-Dorsey, TMay Green
& Asst Prof Eng & Dev Stud
, Jean Roberdeau
rth Grade Teacher
, Myra Sachs
cher of the Gifted
necker, Barbara Duskus
h Grade Teacher
, Frances
IS English Teacher
, Marcia
Grade Teacher
, Deborah Lynn
h Department Chairperson
-Smith, Regina Pamela
t Principal
, Roger William
arch & Biblical His Teacher
, Rosemarie
glish Teacher
, William Alan
ence Teacher
, Alberta
glish Teacher
den, David Paul
nd Director
, Brunda Russ
-6th Grd Acad Excl Pgm Tchr
r, Betty A.
Grade Science Teacher
onado, Jose Dolores
thematics Teacher
golis, Jeffrey Eric
evision Production Instr
glio, Francine Patricia
gh School English Teacher
on, Patricia Summers
nily & Consumer Science Tchr
shall, Cynthia Young
siness Vocational Ed Tchr
inez, Agustin D.
glish Teacher
inez-Ramos, Alberto
story Teacher
sin, Joyce Carol
glish Instructor
, Rosalyn
tired 8th Grd Algebra Tchr
Crimmon, James Allen
nguage Arts Teacher
Cutcheon, Maura Ann
cial Studies Teacher
Kham-Gilkes, Catherine Denise
usic Teacher
Kinley, Scott Allen
agnet Art & Design Lead Tchr
Lean, Thomas John
orld History & Geography Tchr
Quay, Joseph D.
st Dir of Univ Relations
chum, Henry J.
ience Teacher
eros-Blanco, Ana
eatre Arts Instructor
gar, Miguel
str & Head of Cmptr Business
adez, Jesus
ssociate Professor of History
adoza, Manuel Gonzalez
ofessor of Social Science
stre, Teresita Gonzalez-Abreu
S Math Teacher
ler, Ida L.
ocial Studies Teacher
ler, Sharon
ysical Education Teacher
ar, Mariejean Collado
am Chprsn & Art His Teacher
ntgomery, Valerie Juanita
acher of the Gifted
ntpellier, Lily
mer His, Govt & Ec Teacher
ore, Christopher Robert
anguage Arts Instructor
rales, Juan Carlos C.
erman & Japanese Teacher
rris, Janice Rivero
hem & Environmental Sci Tchr
rton, Martha Ann
nglish Teacher

Moss, Helen Richardson
Health Svc Occupations Tchr
Mudd, Laura Mary
Assistant Professor of Biology
Muench, Karl Hugo
Professor of Medicine
Muhlig, Frederick Charles
HS Math Teacher
Munoz, Yolanda
6th-8th Grd Sci & Math Tchr
Murdock, Sue Schultze
Physical Education Teacher
Musco, Douglas Paul
HS History & Government Tchr
Mustell, Ann C. Marshall
Fifth Grade Teacher
Nanney, Barbara Payne
5th Grade Teacher
Neira, Laurie Louise
3rd Grade Elementary Teacher
Nieves, Luis, Jr.
JROTC Instructor
Nobil, Andrea Valerie
Language Arts Teacher
Oaken, Marilyn Nierenberg
2nd-3rd Grade Teacher
Ojala, Joan Susan
Second Grade Teacher
Olesky, Doris Jacobs
Retired Teacher
Orihuela, Lawrence Roy
Third Grade Teacher
Ortega, Josefina Rodriguez
Mathematics Teacher
Owens, Tom
Elementary Education Professor
Oxar, George Edward
Biology & Chemistry Teacher
Palermo, Maureen Walsh
4th Grade Teacher
Palmer, Naomi Yvonne (Hanna)
Teacher
Parker, Maria Beal
Science Teacher
Patterson Grafton, Teresa
French Teacher
Penny, Donna Praier
Math Teacher
Perez, Arturo
Social Studies BCC Teacher
Perry, Eugene John
High School Science Teacher
Phillips, Patricia Ann-Thomas
English Teacher
Pickard, Carolyn Rogers
English Teacher
Pino, Elena Patten
ESL Lab Instructor
Ponce, Mary Doyle
Spanish Teacher
Portocarrero, Nestor de J.
Accounting & Finance Professor
Price, Donna J.
Professor of Biology
Rad, Rita Maria Chica
Bus Adm Assoc Prof & Chair
Ramsey, David Morgan
Social Studies Teacher
Range, Henry B., Jr.
World Geog & Amer His Teacher
Rashkind, Robin Shane
Kindergarten Teacher
Redman, Myra J.
Associate Professor of ESL
Redway, Fiona Arundel
Asst Prof of Biology
Remis, Maria R.
High School Spanish Teacher
Revilla, Mercedes Gonzalez
Mathematics Tchr & Dept Chprsn
Ricardo, Edward Paul
Former Gen Business Lecturer
Riley, Sandra
English & Drama Teacher
Rivas, Lourdes Lopez
Kindergarten Teacher
Rivas, Martha Beatriz
Reading & Vocabulary Teacher
Robinson, Cathy Meng
Violinist Instructor
Robinson, Patricia Ann
Family & Consumer Sci Tchr
Robledo, Iraida Castillo
ESL Tchr & Dir of Student Act
Roche, Liana M.
7th Grade Science Teacher
Roda, Nanci Rogenscky
Fifth Grade Teacher
Rodriguez, Carlos Rene
Chem, Physics & Phys Sci Tchr
Rodriguez, Margarita Valeria (Pestana)
Spanish Teacher
Rodriguez, Pamela Keeley
6th Grade Teacher
Roig, Gustavo A.
9th Grade History Teacher
Rojas, Francisco Javier
Leadership Skills Teacher
Roman, Nilda
Employment Specialist
Rosbury, Patricia F.
Counselor & Journalism Teacher
Rose, William F.
Music Teacher
Rosenblatt, Eric D.
Science Teacher
Rosenblatt, Evelyn Bahn
9th & 10th Grd Biology Teacher
Roundtree, Gailyn P.
Chemistry Teacher

Rozanski, Frank
Social Studies Teacher
Rubin, Lawrence C.
Assistant Professor
Ruenes, Gladys E.
Fourth Grade Teacher
Ruiz, Andres J.
4th Grade Teacher
Ryan, Regina Joseph
Theology & French Teacher
Sacher, Ana Comas
Spanish Teacher
Safreed, Daryl Leroy
English Teacher
Salinero, Martha I.
Physical Education Teacher
Sample, Althea Merritt
Orchestra Teacher
Sampson, Carol Randle
Chemistry & Physical Sci Tchr
Sanborn, Allen Francis
Professor of Biology
Sanchez, Alina Maria
Biology Teacher
Sanders, Rubye Peterson
Fifth Grade Teacher
Sang, Diane Pou
Medical Assistant Professor
Santino, Tom Vincent
High School Band Director
Saunders, Anthony William
Acctng & Computer Teacher
Scherker, Steven Marc
Lead Teacher
Schmatolla-Brooks, Nicole
Language Arts Teacher
Schneider, Robert B.
United States History Teacher
Schwartz, Barbara Chak Shugerman
Chemistry Teacher
Schwartz, Glenn David
Mathematics Teacher
Schwindler, Mimi P.
Law Professor
Sciabarassi, Marie Ellen
Elem Computer Teacher
See, Jeffrey Glenn
Regular, Honors & AP Ecs Tchr
Shane, Erik
English Teacher & Debate Coach
Sharland, Alexander Peter
Asst Prof of Intl Marketing
Shaw, Constance Boone
Guidance Counselor
Shepardson, Philip C.
Prof & Coord of Comm Arts Pgm
Shepherd, Philip Lynn
Bus Environment Assoc Prof
Sicius, Francis Joseph
History Professor
Sickinger, Denise Ann
English Teacher
Siegfriedt, Maria Praderio
Science Teacher
Singer, Ellen A.
English Teacher
Siplin, Pamela Fuller
Assistant Principal
Sklaroff, Dorothy Chauveron
English Department Chair
Skop, Ray S.
Anatomy Teacher
Smith, Arthur L.
Chemistry Teacher
Smith, Cheryl Clayton
Family & Consumer Science Tchr
Smith, Deborah Gaines
Sixth Grade Teacher
Smith, Lois Faulkner
7th Grade Language Arts Tchr
Smith, Robert Walton
Sixth Grade Teacher
Smith, Sandra Sue
Family & Consumer Science Tchr
Smith, Timothy James
Seventh Grd Soc Studies Tchr
Snell, Bernadine Lisane
Reading Instructor
Solomon, Robert Lee
Physical Education Teacher
Soltz, Joan Frances (Snell)
Tchr of Intnl Stud Gifted Prgm
Sosa, Martha Santiago
Media Specialist
Souter, Larry Edward, Sr.
Bargaining Agent Rep
Stayman, Andree Bourgault
Retired Coord of Fr Lang Instr
Stechschulte, Agnes Louise, OP
Professor of Biology
Stepanenko, Sara Yolanda
Rel & Human Sexuality Tchr
Stephens, Robert Stanley, Jr.
US Govt & Economics Teacher
Stevens, Merle Braveman
Fifth Grade Language Arts Tchr
Stirrup, Bonnie Newbold
Kindergarten Teacher
Stock, Stephanie
International Projects Coord
Suarez, Marilda Herrera
Science & Computer Teacher
Suarez, Susan Croche
Math, Computer Tchr & Coord
Suarez, Yamile Fernandez
Spanish Teacher
Sweeney, Christopher Robert
Former Music Teacher
Symonette, Barbara Carr Rivers
1st Grade Reading Teacher

Taboada, Jose A.
SCSI Instructor
Tall, Lambert
Dept of Civil Engrng Prof
Tavel, Norma Lugo
Spanish Teacher
Taylor, Rennina Lynn
High School Language Arts Tchr
Testa, Ronald Joseph
Psychology Associate Professor
Thomas, Janice Mintze
6th Grade Math Teacher
Thompson, Ray
Program Administrator
Toledo, Angel
Science Professor
Trzecieski, Eugene
Philosophy, Hum & Eng Teacher
Tucker-Griffith, Gail Susan
Science Teacher
Tullis, Jeanette Young
Fourth Grade Teacher
Turk, Marian Kuffler
10th-12th Grade English Tchr
Tyler, Michael Lewis
Assistant Professor of Acctng
Valdes, Ernesto
English Professor
Valdes, Lourdes (Ballina)
Fourth Grade Teacher
Valencia, Ruben Dario
History Teacher
Valledor, Blanqui
English Teacher
Valls, Alicia Cruz
Math Teacher
Vazquez, Hector Manuel
Assoc Prof of Music & Hum
Venezia, Frank J.
Theatre Arts & Production Tchr
Warner, Alan
Marketing Instructor
Watson, Elaine Thaggard
Adult Special Ed Teacher
Weeks, Opheila Inez
Assoc Prof of Anatomy
Weiss, Julia A.
6th Grade Language Arts Tchr
Welch, Reina Kanarek
Professor of Languages
Wentworth, Pamela Jane
Science Teacher
Whidden, Bruce Edward
Chaplain, Bible Tchr & Cnslr
Whitney, Kaye Beth
Eng, Jrnlsm & French Teacher
Wild, Thomas L.
Physical Education Teacher
Wiley, Kimberly Sherrie
Computer Education Teacher
Williams, Dennis R.
Mathematics Teacher
Williams, Elizabeth Taggart
Hlth & Physical Education Tchr
Witten, Dana Robert
Social Studies Teacher
Wronge, Keith Michael
Adj Professor of Communication
Yahara, Mae L.
Asst Professor of Phys Therapy
Zacholski, Richard David
Health Teacher & Coach
Zack, Linda Rabinowitz
Teacher of Resource Gifted
Zamorano, Martha Bianca
Associate Professor of English
Zhao, Fang
Assistant Professor

MIDDLEBURG

Gilmore, Barry Thompson
Gen Math & Pre Algebra Tchr
Gossett, Marianne Lowe
English Teacher
Lyons, Willam Roy
10th Grade World History Tchr
McDonald, David James
Principal
Moyer, Marion Stewart
Composition, Eng & Speech Tchr
Powers, Dawn R.
English Teacher
Smith, Dianna Berry
4th Grade Teacher
Waybright, David Michael
Art Teacher
Wright, David Allen
Biology Teacher

MILTON

Butler, Carolyn Fairfield
Second Grade Teacher
Duncan, Cathy Carr
5th Grade Teacher
Hickman, James Andrew
Science Teacher
Loudon, Alexander
Mathematics Teacher
Payne, Tamara Leigh
Family & Con Life Sci Tchr
Roberts, Jean Ellen
Associate Professor of English
Salter, Linda Beasley
Home Economics Teacher
Taylor, Timothy Joseph Andrew
8th Grd US History Teacher
Watts, Janice Kay
Lang Arts & GT Teacher
Whidby, Nannette Robinson
Dance Teacher
Worrell, Tracey Jordan
Mathematics Teacher

Youngblood, Clark Joyner
High School History Teacher

MIMS

Edwards, Carl Rudy
PE Teacher
Mc Cartney, Susan Ann
5th Grade Teacher

MIRAMAR

Beggs, Jan M.
English Teacher
Costa, Kevin S.
Social Studies Teacher
Elicker, Charles G.
Economics Teacher
Lang, Albert Leon
Mathematics Teacher
Magana, Vivian A.
6th Grd World History Teacher
Murray, Ella Denmark
English Teacher
Ragone, Lydia Mary
10th-11th Grd English Teacher
Theis, Barbara Rose
Media Specialist

MONTICELLO

Patterson, Patricia Keith
5th Grade Teacher

MONTVERDE

Moore, Anna McLaughlin
English Teacher & Dept Head

MOORE HAVEN

Bartley, Wanda Pugh
Business Education Teacher
Hevner, Lisa Marie
Science Dept Chprsn & Teacher
Randolph, Ben
Agriculture Teacher

MOUNT DORA

Carter, Lisa Lipford
Marine Bio & Earth Sci Teacher
Hill, Antoinette Goudeau
Eng, Art & Bible Teacher

MULBERRY

Manfready, Gary Martin
Chemistry & Science Teacher
Scott, Rodney Pitt
US History Teacher

NAPLES

Borth, George Edward
Math Teacher
Branson, Jeffery Mark
Band Director
Bruno, Rick Anthony
Social Studies Teacher
Camp, Sharon Suzanne
3rd Grade Teacher of Gifted
Demarest, Patricia Perez
Frgn Lang Dept Hd & Span Tchr
DuVall, Nancy Wallace
Language Arts Teacher
Eaton, Roy Joseph
Mathematics Teacher
Fornes, Kathleen West
Language Arts Teacher
Friedland, Carole Ann Pace
English & Language Arts Tchr
Gorence, M. Joy
HS Eng Teacher & Dept Chair
Gutierrez, Marisela
Health & Personal Fitness Tchr
Honig, Sheryl L.
Kindergarten Teacher
Johnson, Carl Walter, Jr.
Prof of Science & Cmptr Sci
Landi, James G.
Headmaster & English Teacher
Miller, Kathia Linda
English Composition Professor
Purdy, Charles H.
World History & Hum Teacher
Rapelye, Cynthia P.
Math Teacher
Roll, Ardis McCowan
7th & 8th Grd English Teacher
Sadelfeld, Joe Robert
Latin & Health Teacher
Sapere, Kathryn Leigh-Terry
Math Teacher
Soto, Maria Cristina
Counselor
Stump, David John
Social Studies Teacher
Tracy, MaryJo Hoover
English Teacher
Walters, Valerie Koziol
French & English Teacher
Watson, Judith Novak
Second Grade Teacher
Weinland, Linda Sue
Bio Professor & Faculty Chrmn
Westberry, Jory Smith
Language Arts & Reading Tchr
Willets, Sondra Burris
Seventh Grd Language Arts Tchr
Wilson, Cynthia Ann
Second Grade Teacher

NAVARRE

Adams, Laura Wise
Third Grade Teacher
Wallace, Julie Russell
4th Grade Teacher

NEPTUNE BEACH

Coker, Marsha Linder
First Grade Teacher
Lynch, Debra Williams
Mathematics Teacher
Nunn, Mattie Thomas
Fourth Grade Teacher

NEW PORT RICHEY
Adair, Catherine Moberly
Chemistry Teacher
Albrecht, William G.
Associate Professor of Math
Angeliadis, Maria
Tchr of Emotionally Handicap
Ardizzone, Richard
8th Grd American History Tchr
Bellak, Sharon Lee
Math Tchr & Dept Chprsn
Blair, Gerald Bryan
Cooperative Education Tchr
Boots, William Byron
Art & Photography Teacher
Braddy, Edwin Arnold
Science Dept Chairperson
Brannan, Gary E.
Professor of Biology
Capaz, Nelson
Computer Programming Professor
Cash, Linda
High School Math Instructor
Colen, Mickey D.
Mathematics Teacher
Cooper, Lucy Yeiser
High School Guidance Counselor
Corbin, Jacqueline Kubena
Cooperative Training Coord
Currelly, Anne Murphy
French Teacher
Diederich, Gail Shepherd
Third Grade Teacher
Driscoll, James L.
Adjunct Instructor
Egan, Susan D. (Collins)
5th Grade Teacher
Erickson, Timothy John
Drama Teacher
Ewell, Calvin E.
6th-8th Grade Science Teacher
Fenton, Karen Brooke
Science Teacher
Gibson, Sara Thing
Latin Teacher
Hazelief, Patricia Cobb
8th Grade Science Teacher
Hudak, Lori Eytcheson
1st Grade Teacher
Huling, Barbara Crawford
Elementary Music Teacher
Huling, Darrell Edward
World His, Geog & Music Tchr
Keller-Augsbach, Linda Jean
Fourth Grade Teacher
Line, Dennis L.
High School Band Director
Livermore, Renee Pollock
4th Grade Teacher
Lofton, Ethel Cooley
Reading Specialist
Marlin, Michael Andrew
Tchr of Learning Disabilities
McNeil, Renee Pollock
4th Grade Teacher
Mohr, Kathleen Conover
Comprehensive Science Teacher
Mooney, Katherine Wordal
High School Mathematics Tchr
Morrell, Randi Ann
Language Arts Tchr & Prin
Mortner, Harry J.
Business Education Teacher
Nickels, Frank L.
Professor
Padovano, Chris
MS Graphic Arts Teacher
Palma, Alfred John
Assistant Principal
Parzik, Joyce (Wagner)
Biology Teacher
Perez, Ignacio J.
American History Teacher
Plyer, Rita Sue
Adjunct Instr of Nursing
Ryan, Dennis Joseph
Professor of Language Arts
Salerno, Steven Vinci
US History Teacher
Schlosser, Michele A.
Teacher
Snead, Sharon O'Keefe
8th Grd American History Tchr
Starkey, Barbara Tormala
English & Honors I Teacher
Stevens, Starr Strever
Algebra & General Math Teacher
Swenson, Steven C.
Biology Teacher
Tehan, Cynthia Spear
Journalism Teacher
Tennant, Victoria Kinsey
Vocational Home Economics Tchr
Thomas, Nancy L. (Jackson)
4th Grade Teacher
True, Donna Jean
Substitute Teacher
Vanek, Carol Thompson
Media Specialist
Vien, Susan Mattone
Physical Education Teacher
Virgadamo, Sherry Beth
Business Ed Instr & Dept Chmn
Watson, Carolyn J.
7th Grade Language Arts Tchr
Watson, Stanley Floyd
3rd Grade Teacher
Wildey, Cathern J.
English Dept Chair & Teacher
Wolfe, Darlene Shnider
Television Production Instr
Zantop, Karen Featherly
English Teacher & Dept Chprsn

NEW SMYRNA
Brannon, Lala Kaye
6th Grade Teacher of Gifted
Cooper, A. Burdett
Kindergarten Teacher
Galliano, Rosa Maria
Span Tchr & Frgn Lang Dept Chm
Kehoe, Kevin Andrew
TV Production, Mass Media Tchr
Rehling, Betsy (Hough)
Sixth Grade Teacher
Zemaitis, Raymond Bernard
Physical Science Teacher

NEWBERRY
Rummel, Raymond Howard
High School Mathematics Tchr

NICEVILLE
Adams, Lourdes Camman
Tchr & Foreign Lang Dept Head
Bryan, Jonathan Russel
Instructor
Bullard, Mary Jean Gillis
Third Grade Teacher
Clark, Patricia Stewart
Language Arts Teacher
Cones, Claire Harvey
Spanish Teacher
Dugan, Thomas J.
Social Studies Teacher
Dye, Cheryl Barttelt
Choral Director
Dye, Michael Nelson
Choral Director
Eaves, Lisa Gayle
Lit, PE Teacher & Coach
Edwards, Natalie E.
Business Instructor
Fisher-Blain, Lainie Michelle
Social Studies Teacher
Hernandez, Richard Allen
Social Science Teacher
Houp, Sharon Mace
8th Grade Mathematics Teacher
Howard, Shirley Ann (DeShazo)
Mathematics Instructor
Johnson, Sharon McWaters
English Teacher
Kuritz, Helen Angelas
Fourth Grd Project Child Tchr
Mann, Deborah W.
English Teacher
Peavy, Joan Foster
Family & Consumer Science Tchr
Peyton, Tracy Arnold
English Instructor
Plank, Diane Loux
Social Studies Teacher
Ray, Nancy Gettinger
Retired Sixth Grade Teacher
Ritter, Darryl P.
Biology Instructor
Sandlin, Beverly Harvey
Child Dev Instructor & Coord
Schelling, Mary H.
Family & Consumer Sci Teacher
Skinner, Gale Ellis
English Teacher
Stroehl Crist, Shawna
Project Child Reading Tchr
Sublette, Julia Wright
Applied Piano Instr & Hum Tchr
Taylor, Kimberly Nihill
Art Teacher
Yarnall, Joy Parrish
English Instructor

NORTH LAUDERDALE
Boggess, Paul
Computer Science Teacher
Duggan, Linda Ann Cline
ESOL Teacher
Gerson, Linda
Math Teacher
Goldfarb, Susan Schorr
Peer Counselor Coordinator

NORTH MIAMI
Oxar, Mary Grace
Professional Potter

NORTH MIAMI BEACH
Das, Sudip Kumar
Pharmaceutical Sci Asst Prof
Groseclose, Edye E.
Professor of Biochemistry

NORTH PALM BEACH
Gill, Susan Giordano
3rd Grade Teacher

NORTH PORT
Robinson, Lori Ellen
1st-3rd Grade Teacher
Schuette, Betty Hall
Fourth Grade Teacher

OCALA
Arnold, Gloria Gordon
5th Grade Language Arts Tchr
Baker, Mary Katherine Levitt
HS PE & Dance Teacher
Baumann, Keith E.
English & Drama Teacher
Bernhardt, Jana Mastin
Counselor & Adjunct Instructor
Boele, Lynne L.
Eng & Humanities Assoc Prof
Brown, Irvin, Jr.
Psychology Professor
Burrell, Rebecca Ann
Business Teacher
Butler, Betty Dorsey
Retired Kindergarten Teacher
Byrd, Shirley Harrell
Fifth Grade Teacher
Cantrell, Kathleen Peironnet
American & World History Tchr
Collins, Thomas Francis
Assoc Professor of Accounting
Dexheimer, Larry J.
Science Dept Chair & Teacher
Eubanks, Carol J.
8th Grd Physical Science Tchr
Evans, Frank Kinsey
Chemistry Teacher
Fleming, Barbara Leona
ESE Teacher
Freeman, Bertha Lelah
Science Instructor
Fry, Pamela Parker
7th Grade English Teacher
Griffin, Deloris Kinsler
Fifth Grade Teacher
Gruendyke, Robert Daniel, Jr.
Mathematics Teacher
Gufford, Patrick W.
10th-12th Grd Honors Eng Tchr
Haisten, Judy Aurich
Spanish Instructor
Hartley, David Lee
Director of Theatre
Holton, Mary P.
Dean of Math, Sci & Wellness
Hudgins, Stephani Jo
Math Teacher
Jaye, Harold Seymour
Professor of Philosophy & Hum
Kanoy, Diana K.
Speech Communication Professor
Kilcrease, Kathy Lynne
Associate Professor of Science
LaMarra, Garrett John
High School Mathematics Tchr
Lindsey, Deana Shull
School Board Member & Instr
Little, Yvonne Clark
Media Specialist
Lowe, Revetta LaRenee
Physical Education Teacher
Loyd, Sharon B.
Dean, Bible Tchr & Counselor
Macdonald, Hilery Paige
Acting Teacher
Markham, Timothy Doyle
Social Studies Teacher
Mathews, Edgar Hugh
Electronic Teacher
Mc Clellan, Jane M.
English Teacher
Mc Grath, Katie Marie (Keirnan)
Teacher of the Gifted
Meunier, Judy Kaye
Third Grade Teacher
Miller, Susan G.
Technology Coordinator
Moorhead, Jack Phillip
English Teacher
Moreno, Orlando Julio
Dean of Communications
Morrison, Lou P.
American History Teacher
Murphy, Randy Earl
Curr, Tutor Coord & Adj Prof
Nobles, Patricia Duncan
Agriculture Teacher
Pendarvis, Richard Olin
Chemistry Associate Professor
Peters, Donald Scott
Criminal Justice Instructor
Phillips, Margaret Crouse
Teacher of Gifted
Saxon, Ben L.
8th Grd American History Tchr
Schildwachter, Paul John
Biological Science Teacher
See, Betty Gebhardt
Retired Teacher
Shawver, Lynnda Sparh
English Teacher & Yearbook Adv
Shelley, Janet Charter
Marketing Ed Teacher & Coord
Smith, Richard Scott
Math Instructor
Stowers, Gary Wayne
Mathematics Teacher
Swartz, Kim Phillips
HS English, Language Dept Head
Vazquez, Debra Allen
English Instructor
Weaver, Thomas L.
Dir of Testing & Honors Prgm
Westol, John Lloyd
6th Grade Teacher
Wilkinson, Mary Ann Kelly
Eng & Creative Writing Tchr
Wyckoff, Earl Albert
Mathematics Teacher
Zorich, Mary Kay
Fifth Grade Teacher

OCOEE
Benson, Rebecca Marie
Teacher, Coach & Ath Trainer
Brown, Richard E.
Band Director
Gray, Stuart Christopher
Social Studies Dept Chair
Martin, Bobby John
Physical Ed Tchr & Asst AD
Neilson, James E.
Dir Admissions & History Tchr
Nostro, Deborah Tarter
7th Grade Language Arts Tchr
Postell, Francine Coleman
Eighth Grd Social Studies Tchr

ODESSA
Johnson, Dale Elizabeth Dickson
Math, Sci & Lang Arts Tutor

OKEECHOBEE
Alexander, Sarah Autrey
Assistant Principal
Clark, James A., III
High School Guidance Counselor
Egolf, James Edward
History Instructor
Gerren, Georgia Barger
Sixth Grade Teacher
Jolicoeur, Jerry Scott
Chemistry I & II Teacher
Mc Bride, Glenda Marlene
Preschool Special Ed Teacher

OLD TOWN
Davidson, Watson Perry
Kindergarten Teacher

OLDSMAR
Brown, Pamela W.
Athletic Director & Coach
Diss, Keith W.
Second Grade Teacher

OPA LOCKA
Adlerberg, Peter B.
English Teacher
Berman, Carol
Lead Teacher
Brown, Leslie, III
Theology Teacher
Bryant, Terry Jones
First Grade Teacher
Cavanaugh, Casey
English Teacher
Challacombe, Wesley
Technology Teacher
Collins, Arthur
Physical Education Teacher
Eaddy, Catherine Smith
Lang Arts & Soc Stud Teacher
Hernandez, Leonel
Mathematics Teacher
Hinson, Al Joseph
Math Teacher
Hunt, Shenita Renee
Chorus & Piano Instructor
Jehovah, Paulette Sills
Fifth Grade Teacher
Kelly, Rosemary Gencarelli
Director of Guidance
MIller, Mary-D Spencer
Media Specialist
Mucha, Jeanette Marie (Sattler)
Biology Teacher
Mulder, Robert
English Department Chairperson
Owens, Cortel Hanks
Third Grade Teacher
Posey, Patty
Stu Act Dir & Government Tchr
Selwood, Ethel Marie
4th Grd Alternative Ed Teacher
Smith, Cyril Joseph
Academic Dean & Teacher
Smith, Joyce Cox
Title I Teacher
Sweeney, Carma Dambrosio
Fifth Grade Teacher
Tolbert, Donna Neely
Chorus, Piano & Gen Music Tchr
Tolbert, Paula Wayne
Third Grade Teacher
Van Dyke, Florence Walker
Alternative Education Teacher
Vazquez, Teresita deLosAngles
Math Teacher
Walker, Willie L., Sr.
Alternative Education Teacher

ORANGE CITY
Arnold, Ann Woodruff
Physics Teacher & Asst Chprsn
Dunbar, Philip Craig
English Teacher
Fair, Fred P.
Economics Teacher & Curr Coord
Hernandez, Kristina Kati
English Teacher
Holubecki, Chester John
Karate & PE Instructor
Houdeshell, Jennifer Thomas
Visual Arts Instructor
Lail, Nancy M.
Technical Studies Facilitator
Radigan, Patricia Dunlap
Social Studies Teacher
Taylor, Brit A.
Journalism & English Teacher

ORANGE PARK
Abshire, Margaret Whitaker
World & Amer History Teacher
Callahan, Steven Wendell
Advanced Science Teacher
Chasey, Virginia Wilbanks
Science Teacher
Cushey, Dennis Robert
Instructional Technology Adv
Denton, Barbara Quick
Community Relations Specialist
Devine, Catherine Carol
Chemistry & Anatomy Tchr
Fiedler, Patricia I. (White)
Business Education Teacher
Haase, Kimberly Starling
Physical Ed & Typing Teacher
Herx, Fred C.
Teacher of the Gifted
Jarvis, Jeffrey Bruce
Educational TV Exec Producer
Johnson, Laura Acre
Mathematics Teacher
Kmiec, Deborah Mc Daniel
Fifth Grade Teacher
Kung, Mary Rose Wang
Mathematics Teacher
Lamphier, George Allen
Music Director & Teacher
Lancaster, Larry Ray
Assistant Principal
Layton, Norma Lonberg
Family & Consumer Science Tchr
Linkous, Gayle Hogan
Second Grade Teacher
Loehr, Vicky Kissinger
Marine Biology Teacher
Lykins, Marge H.
Fourth Grade Teacher
MacNichol, Marianne
Humanities, Art, Lit Professor
Martz, Karen Elizabeth
Junior High Science Teacher
Nelson, Betzy McDaniels
HS Bio & Life Mgmt Teacher
Nulty, William Harry
Social Studies Teacher
Rangeo, Cathy Moore
9th Grade Life Mgmt Teacher
Rinker, Elizabeth Hargreaves
Bio Prof & Sci Dept Chrmn
Schad, James Paul
English Teacher
Skelton, Jerry Dean
Professor of Chemistry
Walters, Caroline Scott
English Teacher
Woolard, Anna Louise
Choral Director

ORLANDO
Aebischer, Cynthia Trisler
Reading Teacher
Alarcon, Martha Matamoroos
1st Grade Bilingual Teacher
Allen, Alicia Venita (Roach)
Fourth Grade Teacher
Andrews, Cindy Baumann
Math Tchr & Stu Cncl Spon
Ashmen-Wright, Suzanne
Chemistry Teacher
Babir, Melanie Jan
Sixth Grade Teacher
Banks, Sandra Kay
Mathematics Teacher
Barber, Elizabeth Ann
Tchr of Learning Disabilities
Barrows, Roger Edwin
English & Humanities Teacher
Barton, Terry A.
5th Grade Teacher
Batchelor, Laureen G.
English Teacher
Becker, David Clarence
High School Mathematics Tchr
Bonatis, Valerie Baumrind
Social Studies Teacher
Bragg, Robert Mitchell
Technology Resource Teacher
Brennan, Linda Hanley
9th-12th Grd Biology Teacher
Brown, Patricia Sykes
Business Technology Teacher
Brusick, Nancy Lois
Music Director
Bush, Wendy Elana
Math & Statistics Professor
Byerts, Wendy Irvin
English Teacher
Bynes, Norma Jean (Smith)
English Teacher
Caldwell, Sandy Pelser
English Teacher
Carey, Eethel Grady
6th-8th Grade Physical Ed Tchr
Chambless, Jack Andrew
Economics Professor
Charlton, Kathleen Sellards
Social Studies Teacher
Cox, Sandra Cleek
Business Technology Teacher
Cravens, Bradley Joe
Psychology Teacher
Crouse, Maryon Smith
Art Teacher
Davis, Don M.
World History Teacher
Davis, Joanne Hanvey
7th Grade Life Science Teacher
Davis, Karl Benjamin
Retired Tech Ed Drafting Tchr
DeVoss, July D.
ESOL & Social Studies Tchr
Diaz, Aida Esther (Font)
Spanish Professor
Dietrich, Jennifer Rowe
Title I Teacher
Dixon, Roger Weldon
Humanities & World His Tchr
Doering, Pamela Brady
MS Social Studies Teacher
Drake, Kathryn Riley
High School Math Teacher
Duncanson, Carolyn S.
High School ESE Teacher
Dvis, Tasha
English Teacher

NDO (cont)
, Enid L. Crooks
titute Teacher
er, Lynne Horovitz
ish & Drama Teacher
ten, Lori Gamble
School English Teacher
e, Marty Thompson
ors Biology Teacher
n, Benita Cherry
hematics & Dance Teacher
, Craig S.
stant Principal
Raymond P.
oc Professor of Marketing
n, Georgette Cynthia
g Arts Chprsn & Eng Teacher
sbee, Kathy Story
ce Teacher
, Kathleen Ward
gh English Teacher
David I.
or Mathematics Instructor
r, Claudius
stant Principal
r, June Esther
Grade Teacher
nstar, Laura Kirkland
lish Teacher & Dept Chair
alez, Nicole B.
nish & French Teacher
en, Kathryn Furlow
al Studies Teacher
, Earl Alexander, II
ine Biology Teacher
, Joal Fekete
lia Specialist
e, Veronica Williams
Grade Teacher
ke, Marsha A.
nology Coordinator
, Lorraine Edwinna
Tech Ed & Mrktg Ed Instr
son, Angela Wilson
Grade Teacher
, Amy Sullivan
r of Specific Lrng Dsblts
ito, Suliveras
enth Grade Teacher
stra, Louis, Jr.
ld Geography Teacher
stine, Linda Winslow
lish Teacher of Gifted
ngsworth, Elaine Marie
stensen)
Grade Mathematics Teacher
Kenneth Arnold
mistry Tchr & Sci Dept Chm
Nancy Hartmann
nch Teacher
ard, Janice Ann
ministrative Dean
er, Luther E.
ial Studies Teacher
Dorothy Elizabeth
homore English Teacher
ston, Greg Albert
Mathematics Teacher
ston, Sharon Paramore
rning Specialist
ston, William Harris
glish Tchr & Lang Dept Head
s, Karla Maxine
cond Grade Teacher
s, Robert D.
th Grade Biology Teacher
er, Marsha Mason
Grade Mathematics Teacher
, Deborah Eliza
mer Instructor
y, Gerard Hilary
HS Theology Teacher
y, Susan Thigpen
story Teacher & Chairperson
p, Helen-Sue Hurley
th Teacher & Dept Chprsn
ting, Kurt Ernst
rman Professor
n, Patricia Dingess
alth & Physical Ed Tchr
roix, Suzanne Michelle
ceptional Education Teacher
ne, Michael Allen
ramics Instructor
g, James D.
th Professor
Janine Ranelin
ministrative Dean
g, Mary Nell
ciology Professor
non, Stepanie Ann
th Ed Tchr & Head Ath Trnr
is, Diana Lynn
acher of the Gifted
is, Kenneth
CJROTC Instructor
ort, Glenn Michael
hemistry Teacher
gino, Sarah
onors Biology Teacher
asco, Sharon Stanley
nglish Department Chairperson
et, Arthur R.
hemistry Professor
lar, Ronald G.
erospace Sci Chm & Instr
sh, Lisa L.
hysical Education Teacher
Caffery, Roberta Chance
nglish Teacher

Mc Clellan, Jane E. (Bennett)
Social Studies Teacher
Mc Ginn, Michele Fogerty
11th Grade English Teacher
Mc Glone, J. Anthony
Administrative Dean
Mc Nair, Trudy Elizabeth
Professor of Humanities
Miller, Suzanne W.H.
Coordinator of Technology
Miller, Tommie Kay
2nd Grade Teacher
Millsap, Leroi Victor
English & Drama Teacher
Minton, Sheryn Hicks
Counselor
Mitchell, Debra Hall
American Government Teacher
Mitchell, Marie Cairns
History Teacher
Mitchell, Martha Myrick
Lang Arts Teacher & Dept Chair
Moody, Sallye Harper
English & Speech Teacher
Moore, Marlene Beter
Lang Arts & Writing Tchr
Mroczkowski, Harry Potter
Math & Computer Science Tchr
Mullin, Thomas A.
Chair & Associate Professor
Murgia, Louis Anthony
Fifth Grade Teacher
Nelson, Jane Sponholtz-Bray
Physics Teacher
Nemec, Drew William
Social Studies Teacher
Nolin, Laura Holcomb
Second Grade Teacher
Norton, Patrick A.
English Department Chairman
Oswald, Eileen De Feo
Communications Professor
Page, Mary Ellen Schmidt
Spanish & Humanities Professor
Pappa, Rita Beasley
Missionary in Guatemala
Parker, James Anthony
Ag Science & Tech Instructor
Parsons, Romana Christina
High School English Teacher
Pawlak-Kerivan, Grace T.
Marine Biology & Chem Teacher
Pelletier, Kelly Anne (Wiggins)
Mathematics Teacher
Perkins, Marsee Gay
History & Spanish Teacher
Phillips, Kenneth Lee
Chemistry Teacher
Ponce, Regina R.
Curriculum Resource Teacher
Prochnow, Jean Elizabeth
Kindergarten Teacher
Puyana, Ann Bush
English as Second Lang Prof
Quarles, Toni Eichhorn
US History Teacher
Rainey, Margaret Mozley
Second Grade Teacher
Raver, Marianne J.
Lang Arts & Journalism Teacher
Rawls, E. Neil
Choral Director
Rene, Pierre T.
Professor of Self Defense
Renfroe, Jane Vincent
English Professor
ReVoir, Karen Elizabeth
Third Grade Teacher
Reyes, Elizabeth
Spanish Teacher
Richardville, Kathleen Smith
Classroom Teacher
Roberts, Malcolm William
Naval Science Instructor
Robinson, Eugenia Love
English Teacher & Drama Coach
Robinson, Shawn Henri
Mathematics Professor
Rozzi, James Francis
Instrumental Music Teacher
Rumney, Donna Hewett
Kindergarten Teacher
St John, Terri
English Teacher
St Lawrence, Kathleen Bulkley
6th & 7th Grade Math Teacher
Samuelson, Andrew Lauritz
Fourth Grade Teacher
Saulsby, Janice Patterson
Media Specialist
Scanlon, Elizabeth Ann
ESOL Teacher
Schemer, Arriean Aders
English Teacher & Dept Chprsn
Scherr, Deborah Ann
Phys Ed Tchr & Dept Head
Seaman, David Scott
Seventh Grade Math Teacher
Settle, Bart J.
Spanish Teacher
Sheridan, Barbara H.
Chemistry Teacher
Shuttleworth, L. DAvid
Biology Teacher
Simms, Francis Moss-Weir
Asst Prin & Athletic Dir
Sinclair, Gail D.
Amer Lit & English Teacher
Sisler, Marcella Hutchinson
Tchr of Mentally Handicapped

Smisek, James John
Band Director
Smith, Timothy Andrew
Assistant Principal
Snoles, Susan Elaine
Fourth Grade Teacher
Sowers, Deleigh Davidson
Secondary Social Studies Tchr
Stephenson, Geri Berkowitz
Eng & Language Arts Teacher
Taylor, James S.
Professor of Engineering
Thompson, Barbara Elaine
Business Seminar Instructor
Toulgoat, Maryse Annie (Renault)
French Teacher
Trimble, Wesley Todd
Administrative Dean
Truelove, Margaret Kohr
5th Grade Teacher
Tucker, Herman Charles
Instructor
Vandermast, Roberta J.
Prof of Interdisciplinary Stud
Vazquez, Edith E.
Spanish Teacher
Vincent, Carol A.
Computer Tchr & Coordinator
Walsh, Karen Quinn
Former Teacher
Wanielista, Betty Kusmierz
Office Systems Technology Prof
Wassatt, Lynne M.
Science Dept Chair & Teacher
Watkins, Sonya E.
Mathematics Teacher
Wells, Lois Joan
Kindergarten Teacher
West, Diane Sizer
ESE Vocational Teacher
Widick, Mary Ham
Mathematics Teacher
Williams, Kevin Wayne
Chem Tchr & Science Dept Chair
Wilson, Paul A.
Director of Bands
Wray, Carole J.
Language Arts Teacher
Zastrow, Kathleen Plawin
9th Grd Eng & Tchr of Gifted

ORMOND BEACH

Althouse, Lianne F.
Fourth Grade Teacher
Bryson, Sherry Haynes
Former Teacher
Harwood-Hawkins, Elaine
8th Grade Science Teacher
Hill, Plemon Agnuie, Jr.
Physical Education Teacher
Hutchinson, Betsy A.
Language Arts Teacher
Mudrey, Judith Arnold
7th & 8th Grade Teacher

OSPREY

Goffard, Lucien Henri
French & Latin Teacher
Gould-Olson, Stephanie
Teacher of Gifted Science
Krause, Thomas John
English & Speech Teacher
Mitchell, Robin Lee (Ringo)
MS & HS Language Arts Tchr

OVIEDO

Buntz, Viola Tarrant
Resource Tutorial Teacher
Cadwallader, Donald C.
English Teacher
Cioffi, Diane Harper
AP English Teacher
Gasthoff, Karlin Fayne
World History Teacher
Hall, Gilbert Charles
7th Grade Life Science Teacher
Hurst, Karen Sue
Guidance Counselor
Johnson, Theresa Anne
High School Chemistry Teacher
Keogh, Susan Simpson
Second Grade Teacher
Labreche, Beth M.
Science Teacher of the Gifted
Lustok, Elisabeth
Math Teacher
Mahr, Angie Jeanette
6th Grade Science Teacher
Mathews, Kevin Thomas
PE Teacher & Athletic Trainer
Mathews, Sheri Lynn
High School English Teacher
McAuley, Gerald Keith
Guidance Director
Mc Carthy, Anna Bartlinski
Assistant Principal
Norton, Edward V.
English Teacher
Pabon-Castaner, Milagros
AP Spanish Teacher
Pence, Jackie S.
US History & World Geog Tchr
Poole, Dorothy Willcox
Gifted English Teacher
Rector, Joy Ziegler
Mathematics Teacher
Register, Gregory S.
9th-12th Grade Math Teacher
Rodriguez-Ayala, Magali
ESL Teacher
Sincebaugh, M. Lynn
Pre-Kindergarten Teacher

Strzalko, Cindy Drabik
Math Teacher
Warner, Maureen Morrissey
AP English Teacher
Yentz, Susan M. Smith
English Teacher

PACE

Beard, William T., II
Applied Mathematics Teacher
Bitely, Claire Gilfoyle
Teacher
Haynes, Sandra J.
Business Education Teacher
Mc Fee, Michael George
Physics & Math Teacher
Mc Kenzie, Richard Sidney
Alternative Education Teacher
Nelson, Cathy Jenell
Fifth Grade Teacher
Overby, George Frederick, Jr.
6th-8th Grade Phys Ed Teacher
Pool, Angela Maria Guidy
Mathematics Teacher
Riddles, Howard Carlton
English Instructor
Riggs, David Allen
Band Director
Royston, Kenneth James
NJROTC Instructor
Sessions, Celene Amelia
English Teacher
Shell, Bryan Stephen
Teacher & Dean of Students
Smith, Bruce Clinton
9th-12th Grd English Teacher
Wessinger, Elizabeth Gay
First Grade Teacher

PAHOKEE

Burroughs, Jeannette Manning
ESOL Coordinating Teacher
Harrell, Tracy Lynette
Social Studies Teacher
Mawali, Carolyn Davis
Sixth Grade Teacher
Palm, Jack Raymond
Senior English Teacher
Shreffler, Michael R.
English Teacher
Talbert Smith, Nancy
Teacher of the Gifted

PALATKA

Brown, Marcellus
Modern Dance Instructor
Caillouet, A. Allen
Prof of Economics & Sociology
Crook, Alma Slothouber
2nd Grade Teacher
Embree, Mary Evelyn
English & Humanities Teacher
Humerick, Rosalind Wharf
Chemistry Professor
Hunter, Phyllis Clark
English Teacher
Kalmbacher, Nancy Anne
Fr Tchr & Foreign Lang Chair
Landis, Sandi Sheldon
Humanities & Composition Instr
Lewis, Annie Jean (Hicks)
8th Grade English Teacher
Purinton, Shann Garrett
Vice President of Stu Affairs
Roberds, Gene Allen
Fine Arts Professor
Rothschild, Jerome Joseph
Professor of Biology
Virnstein, Elisabeth Lane
English Teacher
Wagner, Judith Stuart
Humanities & English Professor
Whitaker, Albert W.
Instructor
Wiltse, Gail Gamble
Instructor of Mathematics

PALM BAY

Barnwell, Margaret A.
Assoc Prof, Off Systems Tech
Benton, Louella
Third Grade Teacher
Caufield, Frank Earl
Sixth Grade Science Teacher
Cottle, Shirley Marie
Adjunct Instructor Comm Tutor
Dalton, Penny E.
Second Grade Teacher
Glover, Laura Jane
8th Grd Mathematics Teacher
Martin, Paul A.
Technology Coordinator
McCrudden, Teresa Susan
Third Grade Teacher
Platt, Cheri Yvonne
1st Grade Teacher
Ramsey, Debborah Bowers
World History Teacher
Shiley, Andrea Gail (Henry)
Choral Dir & Vocal Music Instr
Whitlow, Jerri Chappelear
Third Grade Teacher
Wright, Cathy Stinner
Title 1 Teacher

PALM BEACH GARDENS

Amedee, Terianne Bottomley
Teacher of Gifted Students
Baptiste, Charlemagne
ESOL & Mathematics Tchr
Castillo, Ann Kingsbury
ESOL & Spanish Teacher
Daniel, Tanya
11th-12th Grade English Tchr

DeArmas, Ana Porro
Mathematics Senior Instructor
Eisen, Jerrilyn Marks
Art Educator
Fagan, Richard
Latin & ESOL Teacher
Holloway, Elizabeth Farris
11th Grade US History Teacher
Jackson, Phillip R.
Division Chair
Kilpatrick, Diana David
English Professor
Kinard, Nancy Watkins
Math Tchr & Pre-Med Mgnt Coord
Kissel, Karen Audia
Health Occupation Instructor
Liebman, Brian Jay
Social Studies Teacher
Nelson, Wende Lee
First Grade Teacher
Neubecker, David
ESOL, Soc Stud Tchr & Asst Chm
Packwood, Gary Darnell
Dir of Choral & Vocal Stud
Percy, Elizabeth Coutant
Voc Home Ec Tchr & Dept Chprsn
Trainor, Cheryl A.
SLD English Teacher
Yonkers, Cathy Godwin
Drama, Eng & Soc Bahavior Tchr

PALM CITY

Phillips, Jeanette Andrews
3rd Grade Teacher

PALM COAST

Lea, Jeanne Evans
English Professor

PALM HARBOR

Antozzi, Jeri James
Eighth Grade Teacher
Booth, Robert LeRoy
Third Grade Teacher
Felos, Kimberly
Humanities Professor
Fletcher, Frederick Orton, Jr.
Geography Teacher
Goddard, Joyce Carol
Fifth Grade Teacher
Hern, Paula Kangas
French Teacher
Johnson, Ginny Trusler
5th Grade Teacher
McGonegal, Randy Clay
Intnl Baccalaureate Bio Tchr
Olson, Michelle Louise
Teacher of the Gifted
Payne, Barbara B.
Third Grade Teacher
Plunkett, Allen F., Jr.
Assoc Prof of Ethics & Logic
Smith, Angela Cicero
Speech Communication Professor
Spillers, Rita Seabridge
Fifth Grade Teacher
Stambaugh, Timothy Hollingsworth
Fourth Grade Teacher
Wallis, James A., II
Associate Professor of Nat Sci
Zebley, Calista Ann
Band Director

PALMETTO

Davis, Gwenard F.
Fifth Grade Teacher
Mc Kinney, Carol Lewis
Math Teacher
Parker, Betsy Thomas
American History Teacher

PANAMA CITY

Baker, Kim Amann
Kindergarten Teacher
Baugh, Anna Marie
Asst Prof of Nursing
Biletnikoff, Brenda Harris
High School English Teacher
Boutwell, Jeaneen Parsons
10th Grd AP European His Tchr
Cantwell, Anna Buranosky
Math & Leadership Teacher
Creamer, Michael B.
Ninth & Eleventh Grd Eng Tchr
Danford, Howard Richard
Technology Education Teacher
Ellis, Vicky Dye
Associate Prof of Chemistry
Funk, Anne Devereaux
Language Arts Teacher
Gainer, Mona Catherine
Geometry Teacher
Garcia, Mario
Fifth Grade Teacher
Garner, Carolyn Larkins
4th-5th Grd Teacher of Gifted
Gorman, Barbara H.
English & Speech Teacher
Grimes, Sue Koontz
Coordinator of Grants
Hadley, Starla Thompson
Learning Disabilities Teacher
Hawk, Robert Eugene
Physical Sci & Biology Teacher
Hazard, Cynthia Burns
Foreign Language Dept Chair
Helms, Leah Grant
Fourth Grade Teacher
Hunter, Anita Mc Intyre
Fifth Grade Teacher
Hurd, Cynthia Ann
Guidance Counselor
Inman, Barbara Canterbury
6th Grd Eng Tchr

PANAMA CITY (cont)
Jacques, Monica Greder
Fifth Grade Teacher
Kennedy, Michael Rodgers
Special Assignment Teacher
Massey, Donna Caswell
Math Department Chair
Mc Keithen, Diane Phillips
7th & 8th Grd Lang Arts Tchr
Olson, Jean Lundberg
Chemistry Teacher & Dept Head
Pace, Michael Miller
English Teacher
Palmer, Clark Allan
Algebra & Pre-Algebra Teacher
Parker, Gwendolyn Evon
Third Grade Teacher
Posnansky, Gary Ross
Communication Professor
Riviere, Judy Broome
Art Department Chairperson
Sanders, Bonnie Gilbert
Math Teacher
Simonson, Joy Powers
Teacher
Simonson, Robert T.
Math Teacher
South, Donna B.
Math Teacher
Sparks, Mary Alma Hamlin
Elem Teacher & SLD Consultant
Surber, George Daniel
Biology Teacher
Therrien, Lamar C.
Law Studies Teacher
Wilherspoon, Gretchen Schmaltz
Teacher of the Gifted
PARKLAND
Cordova, Denise Lombino
Spanish Teacher
Park, Cynthia Louise
Educational Consultant
PAXTON
Hogg, Shawneen Berry
English Teacher
PEMBROKE PINES
Castillo, Joe
Mathematics Professor
Grant, Sandra Thompson
8th Grd Lang Arts Teacher
Kirsner, David Michael
Spanish & Education Professor
Martin, Laurie Krupa
Gifted & Regular Soc Stud Tchr
Nightingale, Barbra Evans
Associate Professor of English
Watnik, Steven Michael
Mathematics Professor
Willingham, Maria E.
Music Teacher
PENSACOLA
Ables, Linda Bomberger
Marine Biology Teacher
Adams, Dianne M.
Biology Teacher
Arnold, Barry Raynor
Assoc Prof of Philosophy & Rel
Barnes, R. Reiko
Former 6th Grade Teacher
Bates, Robin Jeanne
Middle School Director
Beechem, Michael H.
Administrative Dir
Bond, Ronald Thomas
Biology Teacher & Coach
Boone, Nora Ruth
Physical Education Teacher
Bowen, William R.
Political Science Instructor
Broxton, Randall
History Professor
Brune, Steven Donald
Science Teacher
Bump, Vanessa Goldbach
Social Studies & Jrnlsm Tchr
Burk, Kathleen Bailey
Associate Prof of Mathematics
Byrd, Minnie Clark
Mathematics Teacher
Cagle, Sheree Diane
Curriculum Coordinator
Calhoun, Michelle Denise
Guidance Counselor
Carvalis, Linda F.
Business Tchr & BCE Coord
Corley, Sherry Lee
Mathematics Teacher
Coward, William Reginald
Math Teacher
Csuros, Csaba
Associate Professor of Science
Di, Xu
Assoc Prof in Educational Fnds
Drennen, James Douglas
Asst Prof of Adv Tech
Droubay, Melvin Staples
Asst Professor of Geography
Duby, David Gerard
History Teacher
Dysart, Jane Ellen
Associate Professor of History
Enfinger, Mary Fields
Pre-Kndgtn Classroom Tchr
Evans, Ronald V.
Professor of English
Ferguson, Shirley Evans
Third Grade Teacher
Fitzgerald, Isabel Wilson
Business Technology Teacher

Frame, Marcia Dozier
Biology Teacher
Franklin, Godfrey
Associate Professor in Ed
Freckmann, Fred Henry
Philosophy Adjunct Instructor
Gamble, Linda L.
Business Technology Dept Chair
Gott, Linda S.
Health Professions Coordinator
Griffith, Peggy Rookstool
Business Tech Ed Teacher
Gulley, Walter
Amer & African-Amer His Tchr
Hammock, May
5th Grade Teacher
Haynes, Debra Richardson
6th Grade Teacher
Hendrix, Charles Avery
Health Occupation Teacher
Hicks, Beatrice B. Simmons
Administrative Dean of Girls
Hill, Luann Rudder
Math Teacher & Dept Head
Horacek, Patricia Carey
Associate Professor
Howe, David P.
4th-6th Grd Vice Principal
Howe, Lawrence W.
Dept of Philosophy Chair
Hurley, Jackie Goodson
Kindergarten Teacher
Imatt, Donna
Integrative Curr Tchr & Writer
Jernigan, Sharon Jean
Fifth Grade Teacher
Jernigan-Bobe, Karen Renee
Family & Consumer Sci Teacher
Jolly, Natalie Adams
Algebra & Geometry Instructor
Karp, Patricia Parker
Retired Teacher
Katona, Sharon Wilson
Mathematics Teacher
Kennedy, Sidney G.
Dean, School of Liberal Arts
Keough, Peggy H.
Amer Sign Language Instr
King, Hugh Garrett
Lang Arts & Soc Studies Tchr
Kintz, Mary Lou
First Grade Teacher
Krostag, Kelly Perkins
English Teacher & Debate Coach
Kuhn, Richard Herbert, Jr.
Intnl Baccalaurate Pgm Coord
Langford, Constance Hathaway
4th Grade Teacher
Lanier, Gregory Warren
Chrmn & Assoc Prof of English
Lindsey, Ernest L., II
Third Grade Teacher
Long, Steve
Asst Professor of Psychology
Lynn, Dorinda Mae Dellinger
Accounting Associate Professor
Markey, Linda Cunningham
Tchr Ed Instr, Practicum Supvr
McCartan, Michael J.
Physical Education Teacher
McGovern, James Richard
Professor of History
Mc Leod, Stephen Glenn
Adjunct English Instructor
Miller, Daniel E.
Assoc Professor of History
Mountcastle, William Wallace, Jr.
M.L. Tipton Prof of Philosophy
Mowe, Doris Jean
Second Grade Teacher
Murphy, Mary Jeanette Lea
5th Grade Teacher
Neff, Susan Ballard
6th Grade Teacher
Page, Virginia Mason
Economics & Amer Govt Teacher
Pearson, Carolyn
Associate Professor
Pete, Evelyn Long
Assoc Professor of Business
Petruska, Mary Anne Chandler
Adjunct Instr of Mathematics
Pierce, Wilma D.
Business Technology Teacher
Porto, Kathryn Bihary
K-2 Multi-Age Teacher
Reser, Francoise Lucy
Art Teacher
Ross, Michael William
Business Tech Ed Teacher
Sansone, Frank Anthony
Social Work Professor
Saunders, Martha Dunagin
Public Relations Professor
Schuler, Charles G., Jr.
His, Lang & Philosophy Instr
Sermons, Etoyle Meadows
Prof of Art & Pgm Coord
Sherrill, Michael Lee
Head Football Coach
Simmons, David M.
Music Teacher & Choir Director
Soule, Margaret Meyer
Religion Teacher
Stolhanske, Linda Hanson
English Instructor
Stone, Alonzo Thomas
Agriscience Teacher
Stopp, Margaret Thomas
Legal Administration Professor

Sue, Janney
HS Math Teacher & Dept Chair
Suggs-Booker, Lane
Fifth Grade Teacher
Walker, Warren H., Jr.
Latin Teacher
Ward, James E.
Professor of Mathematics
Ward, Kevin Charles
HS Photography Teacher
Warren, Rhoda G.
Family & Consumer Science Tchr
Webb, John Floyd
Choral & Guitar Teacher
Wernicke, Marian O'Shea
Associate Professor of English
Whitfield, Toni Selena
Comm Instr & Forensics Dir
Woolam, Alice Anne
Assoc Prof of Devl Math
Young, Lawrence Everett, Sr.
Band Director
PERRY
Harvey, Ruth Taylor
Secondary Language Arts Tchr
Patrick, Ramona Sonnier
11th-12th Grd Social Stud Tchr
Powers, Deborah Bader
Reading Teacher
Rollings, Estic LeVonne
9th & 10th Grd English Teacher
Thompson, Michael Reynog
Dean
Titus, Shirley York
8th Grade Teacher
Trofemuk, Virginia M.
Fifth Grade Teacher
Wheeler, Lucy Kate
Science & Lang Arts Teacher
Woodfaulk, Flora Williams
Seventh Grade Lang Arts Tchr
PIERSON
Ancona, Peter Leonard
World History Tchr & Dept Chm
de Lane, Ana Maria
5th & 6th Grd Combination Tchr
Rock, Timothy Kasimir
Mathematics Teacher
Worthington, Rebecca Barnes
Govt, Ec & Amer His Teacher
PINELLAS PARK
Benedict, Gail Cleveland
Music Specialist
Bliss, Joan H.
Human Svcs & Hlth Mngmt Instr
Boyd, Cindy A.
English & Yearbook Teacher
Hodson, David S.
Nursing Instructor
Holte, Betty C.
Professor of Nursing
Mc Fee, Laurie Jean
Primary Multi-Age Teacher
O'Hare, Deborah Kay
Primary Multi-Age Teacher
Sepe, Annette M.
Executive Secretary & Teacher
Stone, Marcia Tucker
Assistant Principal
PLACIDA
Holleran, Francis John
Guidance Counselor
PLANT CITY
Alderman, Robert Edward, Jr.
Agriculture Education Teacher
Amick, Kathy
Mathematics Teacher
Baird, Jeanne A.
Professor of Mathematics
Floyd, Thomas B.
Orchestra & Vocal Teacher
Guerre, Thomas Joseph
English Teacher
Hill, Mary Lou Hinson
Second Grade Teacher
Honer, Patricia Ann
English Teacher
Motika, Linda Borbath
Science Teacher
Wilson, Yvonne Fabian
Business Technology Ed Teacher
POMPANO BEACH
Abrams, Linda Anne
Oceanography Teacher
Amaker, Rendolyn Williams
Seventh Grd Language Arts Tchr
Bagnoni, Dan
Calculus Teacher
Basso, Sheryl Lyn Jerome
Nursing Instr & PN Chairperson
Beans, Teresa Kay
HS Dance, Math & PE Tchr
Bell, Grantis
Guidance Counselor
Bell, Lisa Marie
Antmy, Physiology & Bio Tchr
Canamucio, Michele Lynn
Biology & Chemistry Teacher
Davis, Theodore E.
Science Teacher
DeSanti, Janis Ann
Fifth Grade Teacher
Detwyler, Cynthia Reddick
Business Education Teacher
Dorn, Patricia E.
English Teacher
Dunham, Cheryl Ives
Fourth & Fifth Grade Teacher
Dussel, Daniel Carl
High School Teacher & Coach

Goodwyn, Michael H.
Drama Dir, Founder & Director
Gordon, Sheila Berman
Stu Govt Spon & Peer Cnslr
Groleau, Maeying Yuen
Science Teacher
Gulbrandsen, Caroline
Eng Tchr & Peer Cnslng Coord
Halberg, Jeanne Newman
Music Teacher
Hayes, Mary Evelyn
Physical Education Teacher
Howell, Deborah Prochaska
1st-2nd Grd Multi Age Teacher
Idone, Beverly Abaid
Kindergarten Teacher
Johnson, Blanche M.
Kindergarten Teacher
Kessler, Kim L.
Chemistry Teacher
Kessler, Tony Dominick
Teacher
Knowles, Maxine Bradish
Fifth Grade Teacher
Kramer, William H.
History Teacher
Lashman, Brenda K. (Dix)
Science & Math Teacher
Ledbetter, Barbara Garson
5th Grade Teacher
Magnetta, Laura Sue
8th Grd American History Tchr
McConnell, Kimberly Anne (Baxter)
Vocational Home Economics Tchr
McKee, Madelrine Armistead
Support Specialist
McManus, Lorraine Sara
Vocational Ed Dept Head Tchr
Michaelson, E. Richard
Hnrs Ec, Govt & Psych Teacher
Nunn, Barbara E.
Math & Chem Teacher
Rubinstein, Harriet Berenfield
Math Dept Chair & Teacher
Silvergerg, Nancy Fysh
Social Studies Teacher
Smith, Larry Thomas
Math, Art & Bible Teacher
Sobol-Colton, Estelle Rozensky
High School Teacher
Spiller, Linda Martruse
Seventh Grade Geography Tchr
Wainwright, Ann Howard
5th Grade Teacher
Walker, Jessie Collins
Social Studies Teacher
Washburn, Linda S.
Third Grade Teacher
West, Patricia Ann
Assistant Principal
Wonn, Florence Tallman
Pre-Kindergarten Teacher
PONTE VEDRA
Blue, Kelvin Bernard
Dean of Stdnts & Act Coord
PORT CHARLOTTE
Francis, Denise Marie
Science, Art & Math Teacher
Fritz, Linda Marie Gerhard
English Teacher
Gonzales, Barbara Rockefeller
Third Grade Teacher
Gravelin, David P.
Middle School Math Teacher
Johnson, Robert W.
World Religions Teacher
Leighty, Martha L.
8th Grade Social Studies Tchr
Mut, Thomas Michael
Science & PE Teacher
Orobello, Natala
English Teacher
Place, Nancy White
8th Grd Language Arts Teacher
Thomas, James Frank, Jr.
Physical Education Teacher
Tornwall, Judith Heiss
Honors & AP Biology Teacher
PORT ORANGE
Chesley, Cynthia Carolyn
8th Grade Algebra Teacher
Gyarfas, Alexander
Media Specialist
Hilderbrandt, Elizabeth Rosa
Third Grade Teacher
Hughes, Patricia Ann
Math Teacher
Kuiper, Dirk William
Drama Teacher
Palmer, Todd Winston
Senior English Teacher
Ridgdill, Jefferson Henry
Social Studies Teacher
Salerno, Cheryl Roberts
Speech, Critical Thinking Tchr
Sorensen, David D.
Psychology Teacher
PORT SAINT JOE
Lowrey, Patricia Edwards
Language Arts Instructor
Rainwater, John Victor, III
Science Teacher
Riley, Laurel Whitfield
Social Studies Teacher
PORT SAINT LUCIE
Adams, John Ellery, Jr.
English Teacher
Baylow, Jocelyn Kinney
Human Development Teacher

Brooks, Evanne Sinclair
Retired Teacher
Fields, Denise E.
Second Grade Teacher
Kittrell, Julie Ann
First Grade Teacher
Motto, Anthony Robert
7th Grade Geography Teacher
Neuberg, Mike
Bio & Oceanography Teacher
Port, Domenic T.
Biology Teacher
Reeder, Susan Kay
AP, Hon Amer His & Ec Teacher
Willis, Maria T.
Science Tech Prep, Ldrshp Tchr
PUNTA GORDA
Desjardins, Margaret M.
Eng & Critical Thinking Prof
Dunn, Thomas Adam
Chemistry Teacher
Durkee, Raymond E.
Drama & Theater Tech Teacher
Foster, Angela M.
Fourth Grade Teacher
Grizzaffi, Karen
Mathematics Teacher
Martin, Edith Anne
Mathematics Professor
Mc Laughlin, Becky
Assistant Principal
Rankin, Ann Michie Ono
7th Grd Language Arts Teacher
Rankin, Kenneth Rhodes, Jr.
7th Grade Pre-Algebra Teacher
Russell, Dale V.
Life Management Skills Teacher
Seay, Pamella A.
Law Professor
Stein, Roger R.
Industrial Technology Teacher
Widmeyer, Donna F.
Guidance Counselor
QUINCY
Bryant, Ann Clark
Fourth Grade Teacher
Colston, Leroy
Choral Music Teacher
Edwards, George H., Jr.
English Teacher
Holland, Annie Moten
Business Teacher
Johnson, Marva Austin
Sixth Grade Teacher
Simpson, Mary Caryl
4th Grade Teacher
REDDICK
Northcott, John Louis
Physical Education Teacher
RIVERA BEACH
Collins, Stephen C.
5th Grade Teacher
RIVERVIEW
Ford, Joey Douglas
Senior Bible Teacher
Freeman, Andrew Jerome
Fifth Grd Basic Subjects Tchr
ROCKLEDGE
Bowen, Billy A.
Science Teacher
Ferguson, Barbara Hiers
7th Grade Language Arts Tchr
Funk, Thomas C.
History & Sociology Teacher
Gannon, Carolynn Louise
Drafting Teacher
Grace, Joan A.
English & Math Teacher
Holmes, Margaret P.
English Instructor & Chair
Johnson, Cynthia Schaefer
Choral & Orchestra Music Dir
Milbourne, Melinda Dedman
Science Teacher
Moore, Kathy Lynn
Teacher of Hearing Impaired
Stockton, Charles Wayman
Health, Drivers Ed & PE Tchr
Twiss, Carl R.
Social Stud Tchr & Dept Chair
RUSKIN
Lamb, Deborah Kickliter
Kindergarten Teacher
Pierce, Michael Jack
Second Grade Teacher
SAFETY HARBOR
Buckley, Ramita Kay
Vice Prin & Sixth Grd Teacher
Davis, Catherine Keeler
First Grade Teacher
Jablonski, Walter
Physical Education Teacher
Lindsay, George W., Jr.
Sixth Grade Earth Science Tchr
Powers, Susan Dault
Science Teacher
Wickstrom, Marilyn Ruth
Teacher of the Gifted
SAINT AUGUSTINE
Bateman, Terry Tyner
8th Grade Reading Teacher
Bergstrom, George Henry, III
Bio, Anatomy & Physiology Tchr
Bond, Nancy Jane Precobb
Fifth Grade Teacher
Dodd, Jeff
Music Teacher
Esser, Denise Manley
Teacher of the Gifted

AUGUSTINE (cont)
Kenneth W.
Science Teacher
'l Clark
Studies Teacher
ara Wigginton
h Teacher
ndrea Meaux
matics Teacher
enneth M.
ade Amer History Teacher
Paul C.
matics Instructor
Mark Irving
Studies Teacher
, R. Joan
h & Russian Teacher
Judith Oliver
h Teacher
, Ann Browning
mic Counselor
, Michael John
& Clinical Soc Worker
homas R.
h Teacher
Lauren E. (Firth)
3rd World His Honors Tchr
Mary Grady
Studies Teacher
Mark Alan
Professor
Lisa Jane
h Department Chairperson
, Stephen Pitts
iate Professor of Psych
CLOUD
, Laura Patrice
ematics Tchr & Dept Chair
, Patricia Donegan
a & Speech Teacher
ton, Pamela Ann
age Arts & Jrnlsm Teacher
Margaret A.
cs & Chemistry Teacher
m, Steve
ican History Teacher
mon, Martha MacAuley
rade Soc Studies Teacher
k, Minerva DelaPaz
e Biology Teacher
, Barbara R.
l History Teacher
Ronald Griffen
istry Teacher
, Bonnie Riedl
Teacher
PETERSBURG
y, Elaine Marie
inary Technology Instr
amp-Willis, Mary
tant Professor of English
, Dennard F.
Dept Chairperson
Angelean Smith
tant Principal
Barbara
disciplinary Honors Tchr
, Lisa Anne
Grade Biology Teacher
gane, Esvicloria Ellis
ematics Teacher
Charlene Burke
al Studies Teacher
nus, Donald J.
r History & Govt Teacher
r, Patricia B.
a & Journalism Teacher
, Deane R.
al Studies Teacher
, Leslie Yearick
ance Coordinator
bill, Timothy Robert
umental Music Director
llo, Anthony Raymond
c Prof of Political Sci
Gail Reynolds
ciate Professor
, Sally Day
h Teacher
ut, Daniel Atwood
ematics Teacher
h-Smith, Diane M.
ram Counselor
y, Walter James
ram Dir of Natural Science
tt, Barbara Swope
ness Technology Educator
ord, Lu Ann
h Grade Teacher
l, Sheila M.
ematics Teacher
, Samuel Lee
History Teacher
sky, Gary E.
ory Teacher
, Rita Barbara (James)
Grade Teacher
las, Lynne Koster
red Teacher
ing, Claudette Rietveld
Grade Sci Tchr & Moderator
nt, Betty Lewis
lish & Speech Teacher
man, Ivy J.
nch Teacher
Jill Branham
e Arts Dept Chairperson
, Chris-Ann Ercius
Stud Tchr & Dept Chair

Falde, Daryl Gene
Math Tchr & Dept Head
Ferguson, Pam
Kindergarten Teacher
Ferrara, M-J
Assoc Prof of Communications
Fischer, Debbie F. (Rotstein)
BCE & Coord
Fishman, Mark Brian
Assoc Prof of Computer Science
Flaherty, Michael Gregory
Professor of Sociology
Franck, Sharon DiBello
Kindergarten Teacher
Fultz, Nancy C.
4th Grade Teacher
Galiger, Sara M.
English Teacher
Gamble, Shirley Ham
English Teacher
Garrison, Marcia Rowsey
9th & 11th Grd English Teacher
Geiger, Theresa Baker
Mathematics Instructor
George, Marilyn Presnall
Language Arts Teacher
Geraghty, Kathryn Subbert
Social Science Teacher
Griffin, Evelyn Nan
French Teacher
Guarino, John Michael
Professor of Strategic Mgmt
Hallinan, Veronica
Fifth Grade Teacher
Heidt, Sandra Mae
Biology Teacher
Henderson, Donna Fritchman
Learning Disabilities Tchr
Hicks, Steven Paul
High School English Teacher
Hilderbrand, Paula Jean
Business Education Teacher
Hoest, David Alden
English Teacher
Hoge, Monte Allen
Teacher & Coach
Horn, Gabriel
Writing & Literature Instr
Horning, Anthony Clark
4th & 5th Grade Teacher
Horton, John Wayne, Sr.
Mathematics Professor
Howard, Graham Charles
Theater Teacher
Hughes, Martha Dowdy
Chemistry Teacher
Jackson-Evans, Gussie Jones
Fourth & Fifth Grade Teacher
Keiser, Lynn Marie
PE Teacher & Dept Chairperson
Kerr, David William
Mathematics Professor
Kostreva, Donna Marie
Writing Demonstration Teacher
Koufas-Wilcox, Katherine L.
Fine Arts Teacher
LaBrant, Kenneth Richard
Science Teacher
Lancraft, Thomas M.
Professor
La Rose, Judy Hope (Storer)
Psychology & English Teacher
Layton, Polly Kersker
Third Grade Teacher
Lewis, Margaret Knouse
Language Arts Teacher
Lindsay, Stephen Parsons
Teacher
Lofton, Mary Jane Dunsworth
Social Studies Teacher
Masciotra, Janet Marie
Social Studies Teacher
Mason, David Bruce
Band Director
Mc Clendon, Sandra Grayson
3rd Grade Teacher
Mc Kenzie, Barbara Ann
Fourth Grade Teacher
Miller, Claudia Francis
Varying Exceptionalities Spec
Miller, Laurance W.
Visual Arts Teacher
Miller, Myron Michael
Social & Behavioral Sci Dir
Mintz, G. Murray
Drama Teacher
Moore, Gloria Susan
Nursing Skills Instructor
Naylor, Terri Costantini
Fine Arts Teacher
Nelson, Rebecca Bohne
Mathematics Teacher
Nesbitt, Reuben
Mathematics Teacher
Nicholson, Judith Ann
Math Teacher
Nuccio, Michael Paul
Athletic Dir & Science Teacher
Oberg, Peter G.
Chemistry I Honors Teacher
Oescher, John Calhoun
HS Mathematics Teacher
Pittman, Keturah Drayton
Guidance Coordinator
Pollak, Paul Anthony
Social Studies Teacher
Prendergast, Barbara Podemski
English Teacher
Prosynchak, Michael Paul
MS Language Arts Teacher

Redding, David Lyn
Math, Computer Teacher & Coach
Reed, Marijon Crusemeyer
Middle Schl Lang Arts Teacher
Reeves, Yvette Moore
Physical Ed & Goals Teacher
Reynolds, John Elliott, III
Prof of Marine Sci & Biology
Robinson, Jean Estey
Social Studies Teacher
Rowe, Timothy M.
Reading Teacher
Rutledge, James Joseph
Mathematics Instructor
Sartor, Connie May (Snyder)
Business Tech Education Tchr
Scheier, Karen Meuser
Fourth Grade Teacher
Shannon, Andrew Gerard
Campus Mnstr & Rel Dept Chprsn
Shapiro, Marty
Physics & Research Teacher
Shedd, Paul Russell
Spanish Teacher
Slomback, Ronald George
8th Grade Phys Sci Teacher
Stadler, Jerry A.
American History Teacher
Stevens, Sarita Louise
Spanish Teacher
Stitt, Nancy Sneed
6th Grd Earth Science Teacher
Streszoff, Denise Grams
Spanish Teacher
Strickland, Bruce Loring
Chaplain & Teacher
Szelistowski, William Alan
Biology & Marine Science Prof
Templin, Donna Hanley
Marine Biology Teacher
Thomas, Barbara E.
Sixth Grade Teacher
Townsend, Robert Charles
Mathematics Teacher
Tuchol, Mary Ann (Carlock)
English Teacher
Tucker, Wayne Thomas
Fifth Grade Teacher
Vann, Karen F.
English Teacher
Vozne, Richard William
Social Studies Teacher
Weiskopf, Mardi F.
Second Grade Teacher
Wharton, Donald Russell
Vocal & Instrmntl Music Tchr
White, Donna Hayes
High School Theatre Teacher
Wiand, Christopher John
Social Studies Teacher
Wikoff, Marjorie-Anne Smith
English Teacher
Williams, Elaine
Nursing Instructor
Wilson, Winnie Shreve
High School Science Teacher
Witham, Wallace Fernald
History Instructor
Wynn, Julius Leonard
7th Grade Mathematics Teacher
Younkin, Sharon Louise
Director of Counseling Center
Zavadil, Kathy Anne
Physics Teacher
SAINT PETERSBURG BEACH
O'Berry, Linda Webber
Kindergarten Teacher
SAN MATEO
Lee, Karen Hall
5th Grade Teacher
Sevearance, Sylvia G.
4th Grade Teacher
SANFORD
Ackerson, Anthony Dean
American Government Teacher
Ackerson, Tami Leigh
AP Calculus Teacher
Bailey, Beverly W.
English Instructor
Beal, Lawrence Paul, Jr.
Social Studies Teacher
Brown, Betty Louise
Teacher & Math Dept Chprsn
Cabell, Mary Snoke
Anatomy & Physiology Teacher
Carli, Debby M.
9th Grd Honors English Teacher
Caughell, William Warren, Jr.
Economics Instructor
Copeland, Amy Brough
Fifth Grade Teacher
Cragar, Mary Casto
Tech & Cooperative Ed Instr
Cullum, Laura Lynn
Media Specialist
Epps, Jane F.
Drama & Speech Teacher
Fitzgerald, John Patrick
Philosophy & Video Prod Prof
Francis, Rudene Elder
School Liaison
Herring, Cheryl Lynn
Elementary Teacher
Holbrook, Larry Edward
Reading Teacher
Hoover, Michael H.
Political Science Instructor
Hunnicutt, Barbara Isert
Honors Dir & Biology Prof

Jones, James Clinton
Science & Music Teacher
Jordan, Jeff
Director of Bands
Knight, Donalyn P.
Life Management Skills Teacher
Lowery, Nancee Plickebaum
Computer Lab Teacher
Mead, Deborah Lyn
Chemistry Instructor
Miller, Debbie J.
Health Science Teacher
Minor, Gary Carlton
English Instructor
Park, Carolyn Aven
Child Care Assisting Teacher
Powers, Michael Covington
Biology Teacher
Rapalje, Robert John
Professor of Mathematics
Reid, Susan M.
Health Occupations Teacher
Sackett, Brian Donald
Third Grade Teacher
Shober, Lynne Shockey
Fourth Grade Teacher
Taylor, Michael Steven
English Teacher
Turner, James Swift
Professor of Biology
Vickers, Paula Cain
English Teacher
Weber, Pamela Poole
Legal Studies Program Manager
Williams, Andrew Denis
Social Studies Dept Chair
Williams, Robert Howard
7th Grd World Geography Tchr
Woodruff, Arthur D.
Physics & Journalism Teacher
Wright, Stephen Caldwell
Professor of English
SARASOTA
Ansley, Katherine Clark
Fifth Grade Teacher
Arndt, Susan
Biology Teacher
Askins, Diane Mc Elveen
8th Grade English Teacher
Baker, Charles Doug
Assistant Principal
Bates, Margaret Louise
Professor of Political Science
Benjamin, Denise Verheul
Music Teacher
Black, Wallace William
Bio, Chem & Research Tchr
Bozarth, Robert Douglas
American History Teacher
Bryan, Deb Torine
HS English Teacher
Campbell, Viola Edwards
Fourth Grade Teacher
Cook-Flynn, Linda
Teacher Trainer
Danis, Cynthia C.
Lang Arts & Soc Stud Tchr
Goodwin, Patricia Evon
8th Grade Science Teacher
Halbert, Gary R.
Mathematics Teacher
Hankinson, Ann Howie
Mathematics Teacher
Harshman, James Paul
Chemistry Teacher & Sci Chair
Hervieux, Norman Edward
Interior Design Dept Head
Hill, Sandra Kay
4th Grade Teacher
Johnson, JoAnna
Mathematics Dept Chairperson
Johnson, Mary Ann
Social Studies Teacher
Jones, Ruben Earle
HS Biology & Science Teacher
Keil, Jane
3rd Grade Teacher
Kiser, Shane S.
Dean of Students
Kresek, Laurence Victor
Illustration Instructor
Kuno, Ernest Lewis, Jr.
Spanish Teacher & Coach
Leiby, Zera Christian
ESOL Teacher
Lovegrove, Carl Buck
Law Studies Teacher
Lynch, Curtis Michael
Math & Science Department Chm
Mitchell, Morris C.
Fine Arts Instructor
Murtland, Gary Lee
Physics Teacher
Pizzuto, Johntimothy Charles
Foundations Instr of the Arts
Porter, Henry L.
Principal
Rector, Carolyn S.
Language Arts Teacher
Rogers, Betty Bouknight
English Teacher
Schleifer, Neal
Senior Honors English Teacher
Simmons, Stephanie Dean
Social Studies Teacher
Skelly, Ladd Murdoch
Instructional Technology Supvr
Stapleton, Linda Larsen
AP French Teacher

Vannucci, Richard A.
Religion Teacher
Walck, Sonid R.
Third Grade Teacher
Walker, Margaret Juan
Mathematics Teacher
Warrington, Ralph Edward
English Teacher & Dept Chm
Waterman, Deborah Fitzgerald
5th Grade Teacher
Weber, Donna Heckroth
Fourth Grade Teacher
Wheeler, Kitty Landress
Retired 3rd & 4th Grade Tchr
Wilson, Ned B.
Chief Exec Officer & Provost
Winemiller, James Mitchell
4th Grade Teacher
Yoder, A. Jerome
Science Teacher
SATELLITE BEACH
Baisley, Angela Johnson
English Teacher
Blanchard, Glenn A.
9th Grade History Teacher
Boan, Stacel Barney
Mathematics Teacher
Brewer, Sara Hayes
English & Speech Teacher
Burch, William Carman
Guidance Director
Clayton, John Myhrel
2nd Grade Teacher
Dubois, Mary Farr
Spanish Teacher
Geronimo, Sandra H.
Senior English Teacher
Hall, Judith Johnson
High School English Teacher
Kinder, Anne W.
Language Arts & Jrnlsm Tchr
Miles, Judith C.
2nd Grade Teacher
Ryan, Ellen M.
Teacher
Schledorn, Mark Frederic
English & Journalism Teacher
Spell, Alfreda
9th Grd Eng Teacher of Gifted
Stamm, Marjorie Faith
Social Science Teacher
Wiese, Danal C.
Sixth Grade Teacher
Yatauro, Louise
Mathematics Teacher
SEBASTIAN
Douglas, Lydia Davis
10th-12th Grd English Tchr
Stutzke, Edmund Michael
Intnl Baccalaureate Instructor
Thomas, Angela Janine
Spanish Teacher
SEBRING
Allard, Leslie Harrington
Agriculture Instructor
Hamilton, Barbara Mills
Sixth Grade Tchr & Elem Dean
Jordon, Marshall Edward
Admin Dean & Sci, Math Tchr
Rosenbaum, Cheryl Schmalzriedt
English Teacher
SEFFNER
Kessler, Patricia Ann
Latin & Spanish Teacher
Resciniti, Angelo George
English & Teacher of Gifted
Saladino, Tony
Physical Education Teacher
Silver, Denise Knox
Science Teacher
Thie, Genevieve Ann Robinson
Mathematics Tchr & Dept Chm
SEMINOLE
Bennett, Evelyn
Spanish Teacher
Gernaat, Mary Galante
Spanish & French Teacher
Ham, Edward E.
Mathematics Teacher
Shrum, Lester William
Veterinary & Animal Sci Instr
Stewart, John F.
English Teacher
Vaughn-Grantges, Laurie
Science Teacher
SHALIMAR
Adams-Bush, Martha
Third Grade Teacher
DeCoux, Nancy Stephens
Choral Director
Holley, Netta Tutwiler
Alternative Education Tchr
Scalion, Gloria June
Retired 2nd Grade Teacher
SILVER SPRINGS
Hutchison, Karen Wright
Elementary Learning Specialist
SNEADS
Gammons, Darey DeWitt
Mathematics Teacher
Harley, Dorothy Adams
Second Grade Teacher
Stoutamire, Thomas Bowen
Voc Agricultural Teacher
Tucker, Susan Howell
Curriculum Specialist
SOUTH DAYTONA
Biggs, Ruth D.
Retired Teacher

SPARR
Bondank, Teula Perkins
Junior First Grade Teacher
SPRING HILL
Campbell, Claude Whitner, Jr.
Air Force Jr ROTC Instructor
Davenport, Clifford
Physics Teacher
Horn, Marie Carl, SSND
5th & 7th Grade Teacher
Piccinich, Victoria Bait
Fourth Grade Teacher
Stenstrom, Debbie Goller
English Teacher
Thomson, Margo Ann Ruth
Business Teacher
Vonada, William James, Jr.
Business Education Teacher
STARKE
Allen, Scott Wayne
History Teacher
Harris, Ronney
Amer Govt & Economics Teacher
Sakezles, Regina Radonis
Mathematics Teacher
Sheffield, Linda Faye
8th Grade Language Arts Tchr
STUART
Arnold, Charles
Personal Fitness Tchr & Coach
Bartholomew, Stephen Anthony
Asst Headmaster & Dir of Dev
Carson, Patricia Louise
Dir Of Admission & Curr Coord
Casey, Janice Rae Wilcox
1st Grade Teacher
Davis, Doris Halpin
Varying Exceptionalities Tchr
Evans, Dan James
English & Journalism Teacher
Featherstone, Ginger Gardner
Anatomy & Physiology Teacher
Flanagan, Joe
Director of Bands
Hall, David Irvin
Science Teacher
Herd, Kristine Gaiser
English, Math & Dance Tchr
Klett, Kathryn V.
Math & Science Teacher
Krueger, Albert R., IV
Sci Dept Chair & Physics Tchr
Lombari, Rory M.
Social Studies Teacher & Coach
Newell, Lois Seymour
Substitute Teacher
Reamer, M. J.
First Grade Teacher
Tatje, Kenneth Robert
Guidance Director
Tick, Stewart
Chemistry Teacher
Vitale, Charlotte Newsom
Biology Teacher
Wells, Barbara Cloud
Computer Teacher
Wetzl, Joanne Lockley
High School Teacher
Wetzl, Thomas W.
Art & Photography Instructor
SUMMERLAND KEY
Hanagan, John Joseph
Philosophy Emeritus Professor
TALLAHASSEE
Ahlquist, Jon Elling
Associate Prof of Meteorology
Anderson Darling, Carol
Prof of Family & Child Science
Ayoub, April M.
Home Ec & Life Mgmt Teacher
Baker, James E.
Physics Teacher
Barrett - Hayes, Debi Paige
Professor of Art Education
Beaumont, Sharon Hood
English Teacher
Bensko, Donna Anderson
Math Teacher
Bentley, Yvonne Baxter
Physical Education Teacher
Blanche, Scott Adam
Mathematics Instructor
Blomberg, Thomas Gunnar
Criminology Professor
Booth, Jeb
Art & Humanities Teacher
Branch, Lisa Wilson
Exceptional Student Ed Teacher
Bridger, Carolyn Ann
Prof of Piano & Chamber Music
Broen, Priscilla Lindsey
English Teacher
Brown, Patrick Arnold, Sr.
Army JROTC Instructor
Bryan, Dana Ostlund
Third Grade Teacher
Burleigh, John R.
High School History Teacher
Burroway, Janet G.
English Professor
Causseaux, Linda Van Schuyver
Librarian & Earth Science Tchr
Clarke, Karen Bast
Professor of Music
Clendinning, Jane Piper
Assoc Prof of Music Theory
Coleman, Pamela Tanner
5th Grade Teacher
Colombo, Sue Crawford
Assoc Prof of English & Hum
Cox, Laurie Lawson
Physical Education Teacher
Cramer, Carla Barber
Social Studies Teacher of GATE
Crews, Judy Young
Fine Arts Department Chair
Croft, James Edwin
Dir of Bands & Prof of Music
Crowley, Melinda S.
Media Coordinator
Dailey, Sarah Ann Gibson
First Grade Teacher
Dietrich, Karen B.
Kindergarten Teacher
Drew, Jodi Hoffman
Music Teacher
Dunlap, Janice Dickens
English Teacher
Folkner, Janet Dean
4th & 5th Grade Teacher
Friedlander, Steven Leonard
Mathematics Teacher
Gavin, Kirk Erwin
Dean of Students
George, Joey Franklin
Associate Professor of IMS
Goldstein, Stanley Bruce
Mathematics Teacher
Grosvenor, Susie Sadler
Business Education Teacher
Hanna, Xanthippi Hassadis
English & Philosophy Teacher
Harsanyi, Janice Morris
Professor of Voice
Hatcher, Bettie J.
English Teacher
Hodges, Barbara Sue Harvey
Kindergarten Teacher
Hollis, Fred D.
Band Director
Hosford, Thomas DeCarr
Middle School Phys Edctr
Isaac, Shayne Alexander
Head Swimming & Diving Coach
Johnson, Leisa V.
Secondary English Teacher
Jones, Shirley Ann
Mathematics Teacher
Jones, William Darryl
Choral Director
Jungling, Alice Diana
4th & 5th Grade Teacher
Kemper, Kirby Wayne
Professor of Physics
Klees, Don R.
Supervisor of Developmental Ed
Lambert, LaVerne Craig
Retired 2nd Grade Teacher
Lightfoot, Jeffrey L.
Math Teacher & Dept Chair
Lubitz, Steve
Social Studies Teacher
Lundberg, Leslie Grant
Spanish Teacher & Coach
Magdziak, Mary
Chemistry Teacher
Major, Don L.
Intnl Bus Strategic Mgmt Prof
Mathis, Dennine Annette
Band & Chorus Director
Maurice, Ingrid L.
Family & Consumer Sci Teacher
Mc Lellan, Margarete Suzanne Powell
Agriculture Teacher
Merickel, Victoria Powers
AP English & Teacher of Gifted
Moore, Stephanie Nance
English Teacher
Moscoso, Elizabeth Marie
Biology Teacher
Noel, Karen Simpson
2nd Grade Teacher
Obrecht, Michael D.
Admissions Asst Dir & Eng Tchr
Obrecht, Steven E.
English Teacher
Parramore, Susan Kay
Assistant Professor of Math
Parrish, Christine H.
Spanish Teacher
Payne, Margaret Banocy
English & Reading Teacher
Phelan, Pat B.
English Dept Chair & Tchr
Rinehart, Betty Wright
Third Grade Teacher
Roberts, Mary Warren
Professor of Music
Robertson, Mary Lee B.
Science Teacher of Gifted
Rodgers, Kathleen Louise
Fifth Grade Teacher
Scott, Kathryn Elizabeth
Dean of Students
Seaton, Douglas
Professor
Shepard, Deborah True
English Teacher
Skelly, Danley Robinson
Mathematics Teacher
Skelton, Tom A.
7th Grade Mathematics Teacher
Smith, Doris Jacobs
Social Studies Teacher
Spears, Barbara E.
Drama Teacher
Standley, Jayne Marsh
Music Therapy Professor
Stephens, Janet Strickler
Math Tchr of Gifted Children
Stickle, Charles Edward
Soc Studies & Psychology Tchr
Story, Martha Knight
Music Teacher
Teague-Rogers, Linda
AP Psych & Hnrs World His Tchr
Terrell, Levon
Amer & African Amer His Tchr
Thomas, Leesther
Assistant English Professor
Trowbridge, Roberta Yantz
Third Grade Teacher
Twomey, Fred M.
Social Studies & Religion Tchr
Vertuno, Beville Geyer
French Teacher
Weathers, Darryl L.
Assistant Principal
Wells, Mary Kay K.
Mathematics Teacher
Werdesheim, Gary
Professor of Music
Williams, Henry L.
Mathematics Professor
Wood, Margaret Clagett
Exceptional Education Teacher
TAMPA
Adams, Susan Kay
Occupational Therapy Assistant
Adkins, Claudia Kangas
Professor of Nursing
Alfieri, Sandra L.
Spanish & Italian Teacher
Allison, Pamela A.
Mathematics Dept Chm & Tchr
Alvarez, Mario
French & Spanish Teacher
Andrews, Milton Odell
American Govt History Teacher
Artal, Karen Sue (Mason)
Sixth Grade Teacher
Aubel, Joseph Lee
Physics Professor
Bachman, Gregg Paul
Asst Prof of Communication
Bailey, Darlene Kay
English Teacher
Bailie, Helen Grace
Second Grade Teacher
Baillou, Theresa Milligan
Fourth Grade PEP Teacher
Baker, Steven M.
Bible Teacher
Baldwin, Maryann Powell
Secondary Guidance Counselor
Barringer, James Evan
History Professor
Batianis, Thomai
10th-12th Grade French Teacher
Bernstein, Bobby C.
Tennis Coach
Bramblett, Robin Davis
Sixth Grd Language Arts Tchr
Brightman, Barbara Bembeneck
Gifted Education Specialist
Brinkley, Susan Forson
Associate Prof of Criminology
Brundage, Rita Sibucao
Reading Recovery Teacher
Brust, Peter John
Economics Professor
Buntin, Jeanette Bowen
Fifth Grade Teacher
Campbell, Elizabeth Anne
Allied Medical Science Teacher
Cardoso, Vincent D.
Spanish & ESOL Teacher
Carey, Annie Mae
5th Grade Teacher
Carpenter, Jane Watkins
Fifth Grade Teacher
Carte, Patricia Delany
5th Grade Teacher
Carter, Douglas Oral
Psychology & Peer Cnclng Tchr
Chouinard, Pauline Anne
French & Spanish Teacher
Courtney, Kevin Francis
Information Systems Asst Prof
Cox, Dee L.
English Tchr & Yearbook Spon
Crowder, Donna Sue
Teacher of the Gifted Program
Cummins, Sandi Schafer
HS Math & Physics Teacher
D'Agostino, Dorinda Diaz
ESOL & Resource Teacher
Dargel, Jan Kay
Assoc Prof of Political Sci
Dominguez, Christine Schebell
Language Arts Teacher
Downs-Lombardi, Judy Rollins
Asst Prof of Education & Eng
Duncan, Debra Brown
6th Grade PEP Teacher
Duncan, Jody L.
Dean of Students & Eng Teacher
Duncan, Roger L., II
Dean of Boys
Edberg, Judith Patterson
Professor of Music
Edwards, Tammie L.
HS Mathematics Teacher
Ehringer, J. Nicholas
Professor of Biology
Elles, Pamela (Nardo)
Spanish Teacher
Ellis, Walter Randolph
Sociology Professor
Evans, Jean Frazier
Social Studies Teacher
Fabiano, Vicki Rae
Eighth Grade Literature Tchr
Farnham, John Francis
Adjunct Prof of His & Pol Sci
Flowers, Linda D.
English Teacher & Curr Coord
Floyd, Theodore Vincent
American Govt & History Tchr
Fogg, Dana Thayer
Management Professor
Forbes, Stuart Cameron
Economics Professor
Fordham, Teresa Ann
Nursing Instructor
Formy-Duval, Kathryn Schlenker
Science Department Chairperson
Fox, Liana Fernandez
Professor of Mathematics
Foxx, George J.
8th Grade US History Teacher
Galanopoulos, Christos D.
Adjunct History Professor
Gammill, Emmett R.
Professor of Earth Sciences
Garcia, Bonnie Sullivan
Fourth Grade Teacher
Geraghty, Susan Joan
Fifth Grade Teacher
Giancola, John A.
Communication Professor
Golomb, Gary Lee
Teacher & Media Specialist
Grant, Bettye Jackson
Reading Teacher
Grimaldi, Sonya Eileen
Acad Cnslr & Asst Dir
Hammer, Karen Sue
Criminal Justice Teacher
Hammer, Kathryn J.
Mathematics Teacher
Hanks, Kenneth Byron
Music Professor
Hart, Michael Douglas
Director of Bands
Henderson, Edward Melvin, Jr.
Social Studies Teacher
Hickman, Hugh Vernon
Physics Professor
Hill, David Joseph
Chemistry Teacher
Hoerbelt, Susan Harvey
Sociology Professor
Hope, Elizabeth Moritz
Professor of Computer Science
Hutton, Alice Heiss
Humanities Professor
Ingalls, Marie-Joele Wagon
French Teacher
Irmis, Terry
Second Grade Teacher
James, Mary Elizabeth
Second Grade Teacher
Jankowski, Joel R.
Assoc Prof of Finance
Jarrett, Beverley Roye
Psych Tchr & Stu Cncl Sponsor
Joeb, Joseph Martin
Critical Thinking Skills Tchr
Johnston, Michael H.
Tech Coord & Math Teacher
Kapono, M. Malia
English & Journalism Teacher
Kearney, Maureen
World His & Religion Teacher
Kelly, Je Nanne K.
Science & Math Teacher
Kendricks, Vivian Davis
Former Professor
Ketcham, Beverly Lynn
Associate Professor of Biology
King, Debra Whitmer
Senior Counsel & Con Law Instr
Kinney, Jill Ledford
Science Teacher of Gifted
Klinck, Dana Scott
Physics Professor
Kratzer, Colleen Gold
Retired English Teacher
Laboy, Oscar Daniel
Physical Ed Tchr & Coach
Lairsey, Marilyn P.
Program Manager & Assoc Prof
Lambert, Katherine Davies
8th Grade Math & Religion Tchr
Leaverton, Paul E.
Epidemiology Biostatistic Prof
Le Blanc, Sonny
Head Softball Coach
Lennon, Susan Taylor
Dance Professor
Lennox, Edna David
Fmly & Cnsmr Sci Dept Head
Little, Paul Robert
Agi-Technology Instructor
Loechler, Ruth M.
Professor of English
Logan, William Patrick
Language Arts, Lit & Math Tchr
Lono, Luz Paredes
Frgn Languages Professor
Madeo, Nicole
High School Reading Teacher
Mansour, Cynthia Strong
Mathematics Professor
Mathews, Richard B.
Professor of English
Mc Caskill, Rachel W.
Chemistry & Biology Teacher
McDermott, Robert James
Professor
Mc Farland, Deborah Holmes
English Teacher
Mc Kee, Archibald Sturdivant
Science Teacher
Mc Kee, Jane Macchia
9th Grade Reading Specialist
Mecha, Marlyn
ESOL Teacher
Metzger, Joan
Art & Humanities Adj Instr
Michaels, Robert S.
American Government Teacher
Miletta, Susan Chattan
HS Science Teacher
Morgado, Melissa Astorquiza
Spanish Teacher
Morris, Rochelle Yaeger
Counselor & Psychology Prof
Mueller, Luan Fechter
Scndry Instrumental Music Dir
Myers, Barbara White
Mathematics Teacher
Myers, Ellamae M.
Gifted Program Teacher
Nelson, Karen Marra
Radiation Therapy Instructor
Nelson, Lespy, II
Assistant Principal
Oline, Larry W.
Professor
Osburn, L. Lee
Mathematics Teacher
Osterman, Maxine Schrager
Lang Arts, Drama & Peer Cnslng
Osterman, Michael George
Mathematics Teacher
Page, Dean Edwin
Life & Physical Science Tchr
Paloumpis, Athanasios A.
Secondary Social Studies Tchr
Partridge, E. Durene
Teacher of Gifted Math & Sci
Paschal, Hugh Holliday
English Professor
Perez, Antonio
Biology Teacher
Perrino, Carol Marie
Health Occupations Teacher
Pickett, Jane Graham
Assistant Prof of Math
Pividal, Gayle Dabney
4th & 5th Grds Tchr of Gifted
Pressner, David M.
Academic Dean
Price, William Wayne
Professor of Biology
Pritchard, Odalys Gordillo
8th Grade Language Arts Tchr
Punzo, Fred
Dana Professor of Biology
Pushkin, Jodi B.
English & Journalism Teacher
Pusins, Dolores J.
Pgm Mgr & Cmptr Sci Professor
Quinn, Philip Francis
Criminology Professor
Rackauskis, Joyce Marie
Medical Asst Prgm Dept Chair
Ramsay, Colin M.
History Instructor
Rhodes, Jan F.
Mathematics Teacher
Richards, Donald
Math Teacher & Swim Coach
Rimbey, Anne Giles
English & History Teacher
Rizzi, Sandra Alas
French & Spanish Teacher
Robertson, Doris A.
Second Grade Teacher
Rock, Margo Barrera
Professor of Accounting
Romeo, Gertrud Kuntz
German, Latin & French Teacher
Rosete, Philip
Physics Teacher
Ross, Brenda B.
English Tchr & Dept Chm
Rowland, Louis William
English Teacher
Rozman, Jacquelyn West
Tech Teacher & Consultant
Rustogi, Hemant
Marketing Professor & Chairman
Sanford, Evelyn Trice
3rd-6th Grd Teacher of Gifted
Sarbacker, Donald L.
Economics & Business Professor
Sarrett, Sylvia G.
English Teacher
Schlueter, Raymond A.
Professor of Biology
Scudder, Sallie Elizabeth
Mathematics Teacher
Seeders, Michele Lorraine
6th Grd Math & Sci Tchr
Shropshire, Trisha Cypher
Middle School Teacher
Sibol, Janet Marguerite
Mathematics Instructor
Smith, James Lynwood
History, Soc Studies & Ec Tchr
Smitson, Marlene Frances
English Teacher
Stahl, Stephanie Meeks
8th Grade Teacher
Streater, John Baxter
Algebra Teacher

(cont)
soon Park

.rthur Joseph
Studies Teacher
gh, Eugene L.
sy Prof of Ind Hygiene
ai, Manuel Alfonso
Studies Teacher
Eduardo Emiliano
of & Adv of Stu Org
on, Dale Lee
' Physics & Astronomy
Debbie M.
r Dir & Asst Prof Mrktg
renda May
n Teacher
Mary Beth
ate Professor
Phyllis Laverne
age Arts Teacher
Elaine Margaret
Grade Teacher
nckeren, Kathryn
' Eng & Creative Writing
Patricia Lynn
lary Mathematics Teacher
James Matthew
sor of Criminal Justice
Vesta L.
y Teacher
Delores Moten
ess Technology Teacher
Edward C., Jr.
rofessor
s, Patricia
ess Technology Teacher
Charles Dwayne
Arts Director
user, Robert Michael
ade Science Teacher
Jimmy Ronald
h & Humanities Teacher
Maria Santayana
Lit & Honors Gifted Tchr
Mary M.
n Relations Specialist
gh, Douglas Bond
y of Knowledge Teacher
g, Dorothy E.
d Grade Teacher
ofer, Tom
Teacher
man, David Walter
Physical Education Tchr
N SPRINGS
on, James Robert
n & Physical Ed Teacher
Lucia Batstone
Dept Chair & Teacher
Lee W.
r Education Tchr & Coach
aan, Charles
l Music Director
Mary Garrigan
y & Consumer Sci Dept Chm
ond, Lori Anne
ce Teacher
ad, Marilyn Louise
ce Teacher & Dept Chrprsn
n, Steven T.
er
Anna Pauline
uage Arts Teacher
Manny John
& Anthropology Instr
ow, Richard Lee
istry Teacher
r, Brad Joseph
merican History Teacher
ws, Hrisa Kalodoukas
sh Teacher
nell, Robert Michael
Studies Dept Chm & Teacher
ff, Greg J.
al Studies Teacher
oanne M.
ner Assistant Coordinator
t, Vicki L.
ematics Teacher
:, Joyce
ematics Tchr & Dept Head
ker, Linda Ann
ice Teacher
RES
ng, Charlie Will, Jr.
ical Education Teacher
Adrian Headquist
ical Education Teacher
, Martha T.
Arts & Theatre Arts Tchr
Mary Williams
School English Teacher
sner, Leslie Carrol
al Studies Teacher
on, William J.
nematics & Science Teacher
RNIER
, Pamela S.
Grade Teacher
Rafael
Alternative Ed & Math Tchr
PLE TERRACE
ns, Larry Luther
essor of Chemistry
y, M. Thaxter
avioral Science Professor
Thomas Edward
ech Prof & Dir of Forensics

Hunter, Carleton Brent
Assoc Prof of Communications
Jenkins, Ferrel Ferrell
Chairman of Biblical Studies
Johnson, Laura Elliott
English Teacher
Pickup, Martin Craig
Biblical Studies Professor
Thayer, Norene R.
English Instructor
THONOTOSASSA
Dafeldecker, Cheryl Temple
Assistant Principal
TITUSVILLE
Abdel-Al, Fayek H.
Gifted Math & Science Teacher
Adams, Kay Marie
HS Guidance Counselor
Andritz, Leah J.
Art Tchr & Yearbook Advisor
Ball, Karen Evans
Social Studies Dept Chprsn
Ball, R. N., Jr.
Social Studies Teacher & Coach
Barnette, Jackie Kee
Language Arts Teacher
Blankenship, Rebecca Farr
Physical Education Teacher
Blanner, Deborah E.
German Teacher & Dept Chair
Bowman, Mary Pat Bourgeois
Third Grade Teacher
Boye, Pamela Hoopingarner
Choral Activities Director
Bragg, Kim Kenwood
Science Department Chairperson
Calhoun, Charles Todd
Science Teacher
Cleavenger, Eldon Daniel
High School Teacher
Clifford, Evelyn A.
Fourth Grade Teacher
Clift, Barbra (Cook)
United States History Teacher
Coveney, Bernard Burdell
American History Teacher
Davis, Thomas Paul
Choral Activities Director
Dearborn, Linda Moody
Choral Music Director
Demmon, Charles E.
In Schl Suspension Coordinator
Deters, Anna Friend
Sixth Grade Teacher
Diesel, Daniel E.
Biology Teacher
Donnelly, Judith Setnicka
Mathematics Teacher
Donovan, George P.
Sr High School Guidance Cnslr
Freeman, Pat S.
Humanities & English Teacher
Gadappe, Brett Ronald
Ninth Grade English Teacher
Joynt, Julie Elaine
Drama Teacher
Kahle, Patricia Leigh
Social Studies Teacher
Kenney, Mary Hannigan
Social Studies Teacher
King, Sheila Sue
Music Teacher
Kinker, Leila M.
Business Teacher
Kling, Carol J.
6th Grade Teacher
Mc Donald, Theresa Thornbury
World Geography & History Tchr
Metz, Gloria Lee
Teacher
Nevins, Kathleen Lowry
Kindergarten & Technology Tchr
Nickolenko, L. Margaret
English Teacher
Nielsen, Mary Tanzy
Assoc Prof of Communications
Nolan, Frances Caton
Business Education Teacher
Owens, Kathy Pauline (Pipho)
Sixth Grade Teacher
Rush, Patricia Mc Clay
President & Teacher
Sorensen, Brenda Mudrak
Mathematics Teacher
Sparkman, Tim
Ec Tchr, Ath Dir & Act Coord
Sumner, Betty Ann Sirmons
Pre-Algebra & Business Teacher
Tharpe, Wendy Yvonne (Post)
Science & Health Teacher
Tucker, Linda Smith
English Teacher
White, Jeffrey Scott
Drafting Design Tech Instr
Wilkinson, Mary E.
Mathematics Dept Chairman
Zack, Joseph William
French Teacher
TRENTON
Broker, Steven F.
Agriscience Teacher
Cook, John L.
Computer & Communications Tchr
Wilson, Richard Carlton, Jr.
High School Biology Teacher
UMATILLA
Loveday, Beverly Berthelot
Teacher
Morgan, Donna Bateman
Science Teacher

Surber, Susan Lynn
ESE Teacher & Coach
Trenfield, George Stanley
Agriscience-Agribusiness Tchr
Woodall, Harold Wilson
Math Teacher & Dept Chair
VALRICO
Aardrup, Tim D.
9th-12th Grade Science Teacher
Fernandez, Dilia A.
Span Tchr & Frgn Lang Dpt Chr
Gammill, Betty Trowbridge
Senior English Teacher
Herzog, Bonnie B.
Social Studies Teacher
Hope, Ted M.
Band Director
Mathews, Delores Mashburn
English Teacher
Meyer, Karen Marcos
Art Department Head & Teacher
Peters, Linda Antis
English Teacher
Ramsey, Barbara C.
AP US History Teacher
Sutherland, Beverly G.
Choral & Orchestra Director
Wright, Juliana Nicole
English Teacher
VENICE
Biller, Jerry Lynn
Mathematics Teacher
Brinkman, Fran Dahm
Retired Teacher
Carter, Randy Manolt
World History Teacher
Di Giacomo, Anthony Charles
Guidance Counselor
Good, Gwen Bierstedt
Third Grade Teacher
Hallstein, Julia Graham
Family & Consumer Sci Tchr
Johnson, Marlene Reno
English & Journalism Teacher
Lambert, Jack Robert
Geography & History Teacher
Lersch, Elaine L.
Third Grade Teacher
McQueen, John R.
Fourth Grade Teacher
Swain, John P.
8th Grade Math & Algebra Tchr
Thorsen, Jerry Eugene
American Government & Ec Tchr
Turgeon, Jack L.
EH Teacher
Vihlen, Sally Puncke
Renaissance Coordinator
VERNON
Bush, Sally A.
English Teacher
Parish, L. C., Jr.
Sixth Grade Teacher
VERO BEACH
Alexander, Wendy Daniels
Teacher of the Gifted Program
Barenborg, Teri Gotts
Media Spec & Sci Resource Tchr
Carlsen, Patricia Bryant
French & Spanish Teacher
Cassara, Virginia Buker
5th Grade Teacher
Eliot, Barklie W.
English Teacher
Fore-Moran, Jeanne
Former 5th Grade Teacher
Fox, Joan Paula
2nd Grade Teacher
Gibbons, Morris A., III
English Teacher & Testing Dir
Henderson, S. Hiram
Pre & AP Calculus Teacher
Hewitt, Steven Dale
Automotive Technology Instr
Howard, Jennie Murphree
Fourth Grade Teacher
Ingram, Margaret Myrick
Fourth Grade Math & Sci Tchr
Mayes, Geraldine A.
First Grade Teacher
McCarthy, Thomas K.
Physics Teacher
Mezzina, Frank
English Teacher & Dept Chair
Miller, Barbara Angell
Teacher of Gifted
Moorehead, Virginia Allene
First Grade Teacher
Willis, Gloria Bagley
Fourth Grade Teacher
Wright, Ossie, Jr.
Music Teacher
WAUCHULA
Bryan, Karen Summers
Guidance Counselor
Daggett, Richard Lewis, Jr.
Dist Technology Resource Tchr
Knight, Barbara Gayle
4th Grade Teacher
Mc Candless, Lawrence Ray
Science Teacher
Orwig, Bette Manis
Teacher
Saddler, Peggy C.
High School Counselor
Shayman, Linda J.
English & Humanities Teacher
Shayman, Robert Alan
Band Director

Thiesen, Michael Lewis
Life Management Teacher
Vance, Belva Lee
Mathematics Teacher
Womack, Linda Jean
Social Studies Teacher
WEST PALM BEACH
Arrington, Jennifer Moorman
Chemistry & Physics Teacher
Baker, Carolyn Price
Math Teacher
Banks, Carolyn Jeanette
Acting Asst Prin of Stu Svcs
Barton, Barbara LeAnn
Spanish & Latin Teacher
Bates, Patrisha Lucinda
Fourth Grade Teacher
Campbell, Carmen-Ann
Social Studies Teacher
Carroll, Debbie Styron
English Teacher
Cavanaugh, Michael James
World American History Teacher
Cinquino, Michael A.
Chemistry Teacher
Clarke, John Felix
Stu Activities Dir & Chrpsn
Colarulli, Rosemary
Asst Principal for Curriculum
Cote, Margarita Leonor
Spanish & ESOL Teacher
Cotton, Laurie Willson
History Teacher
Cox, John Dennis
Anatomy & Physiology Teacher
Cunningham, Thomas Nelson
History Teacher
Dame, Glenn William
TV Production Instructor
Drake, Shirley Ann
Math Teacher
Elhilow, Laurice Bou Salem
6th Grd Reading Teacher
Evans, Janice M.
Mathematics Teacher
Frizzell, Colleen Williams
Family & Consumer Science Tchr
Gardner, Ron
Science Teacher
Gibson, Sally McCall
English Department Chair
Girard, Daniel Rheal
Mathematics Teacher
Grandusky, Jane Josey
Dean of Visual Art Department
Hebard, Kevin Marshall
High School Math Teacher
Heers, Richard L., II
American Govt Teacher
Hof, Elizabeth D.
Elem Teacher & Director
Holderby, Amy Lea
Academic Dean
Iglesias, Teresita Aragon
Advncd Sci Tchr & Dept Chprsn
Johnson, Mercedes Baldwin
Mathematical Teacher
Knapp, Kay Lynn
Social Studies Teacher
Knoll, Linda Crawford
Science Teacher
Kramer, Nona B.
7th-8th Grd Teacher & Gftd Eng
Lawrence, Sarah Robinson
9th-12th Grd Bus Tech Teacher
Leal, Rosa B.
Spanish Teacher
Lee, Linda Bravakis
First Grade Teacher
Leonhardt, RoseMarie Leonardo
Drama Teacher
Link, Antonia Powell
MS Faculty Coord & Consultant
Long, David Harry
Amer His & Law Stud Teacher
Long, Kathy Knuth
Art Teacher & Dept Chair
Medlock, William Kenneth
Business Technology Ed Tchr
Miller, Clydena Synoria
3rd & 4th Grade Teacher
Morse, Nanci Hubbard
Intnl Baccalaureate Teacher
Noble, Elsa Rose
4th Grade Teacher
O'Brien, Kevin Fleming
Social Studies Teacher
Opper, Marilynn Pedek
Chem Tchr & Science Dept Chair
Oser, Mary S.
Band Director & Music Teacher
O'Toole, Barbara Ann
Specific LD & Inclusion Tchr
Persek, Elaine
Magnet Coordinator
Petuch, Linda Joyce (Sellard)
Kindergarten Teacher
Rafter, Alicia Barrett
English II & III Teacher
Renault, Alexis Eileen
First Grade Teacher
Sharon, Robert Barry
Performing Arts Division Chair
Steffes, Arthur William
Religious Studies Teacher
Stout, Sara L.
Ec & Political Theory Teacher
Thomas, Renee J.
Teacher

Tracy, Sandra Craft
Tchr of Learning Disabilities
Trotsky, Tadziu
English & World History Tchr
Walter, William A.
Art History Teacher
Watson, Jary Todd
Social Studies Teacher
Wells, Jonathan David
Fifth Grade Teacher
Williams, David Edward
Mathematics Dept Chairman
Williams, M. Gai
Mathematics Teacher
Williams, Nancy D.
5th Grade Teacher
Wilson, Cynthia Oliver-Baumann
HS English Tchr & Coll Instr
Wright, Velma Gene
Physical Education Teacher
WILDWOOD
Hampton, Richard Bryan
Business Ed & DCT Coord
Hampton, Sherri Christina
High School Mathematics Tchr
WIMAUMA
Fernandez, Shirley Wagner
Fourth Grade PEP Teacher
Gordon, Stephen Nichols
6th Grade Teacher
WINDERMERE
Conger, Robert Brian
Band Director
Quinn, Diane Kardynski
8th Grd Physical Science Tchr
WINTER GARDEN
Bethmann, Jan Friederich
8th Grd Physical Science Tchr
Clark, Cynthia G.
SAFE Coordinator
Gessner, Robert Frank
Biology Teacher
Hudson, Glyniss Ann
Science Instructor
Johnson, Maude S.
English Teacher
Mercer, Susan Beth
English & Peer Mediation Tchr
Robinson, Wanda Gail
Mathematics Teacher
Stebbins, Rebecca Scott
Social Studies Teacher
Zubricky, Rudolph
Technology Education Teacher
WINTER HAVEN
Anderson, Susan Hunter
8th Grade Math Teacher
Beasley, Beth Ann
4th Grade Teacher
Bindschadler, Benjamin S.
Biology Instructor
Braxton, Letha Owens
8th Grade Math Teacher
Bruner, Sandra J.
Professor
Curry, Sheena Lucas
Teacher
Farthing, Mildred E.
Teacher & English Dept Chair
Fortney, Sarah
8th Grade Science Teacher
Henry, Valarie Walker
Third Grade Teacher
Hobbs, W. Pearl
Computer Teacher
Joiner, Judy S.
History Teacher
Kerner, Howard Alex
Prof of Eng & Communications
Love, Harold Sanford
Professor of Chemistry
Morgan, Thomas Benjamin
Video Production Chairperson
Murphy-Rivera, Maria C.
Reading Teacher
Myers, Ana Maria Gutierrez
Professor of Spanish
Powell, Jane Woods
Teacher of Gifted Students
Rackelman, Marilyn Turner
Art Instructor
Reed, Jennifer Hardage
History Instructor
Reynolds, Jean Rafenski
English Professor
Richardson-Brinson, Charlene Angela
Assistant Principal
Roess, Dolly Lee
Spanish Teacher
Sepi, Michael Thomas
Jr Reserve Ofcr Trng Corp Tchr
Wells, Sherry Trent
Business Education Teacher
Williams, Patty Clements
Lifetime Fitness Professor
Worthington, Dorothy Jean Hicks
Retired Teacher
WINTER PARK
Barden-Sullivan, Claudia
Teacher of Gifted World His
Bouch, Cecily Hopkins
Math Teacher
Bouch, Davin Michael
Mathematics Chairperson
Carpineto, Joseph Thomas
Asst Prin, Sci Tchr & Ath Dir
Cole, Brenda Mc Guire
9th-12th Grd Lit & Comp Tchr
Craig, Teddy Lynn
Math Teacher & Baseball Coach

WINTER PARK (cont)
Daye, Rebecca Cranston
Social Science Teacher & Dean
Denicole, Carol Louise
Math Instructor
DeToma, Carmela Maria
7th & 8th Grd English Teacher
Dionne, Dana Gayle
Academic Dean & Science Tchr
Everson-Hendryx, Sarah
Spanish Teacher
Folsom, Barbara Shafer
High School Guidance Counselor
Fortuna, Kevin Charles
Physics Teacher
Frazier, Deloris Diane
Third Grade Teacher
Furo, Stephen Michael
Language Arts & Math Teacher
Grimm, Jack H.
Govt & Economics Teacher
Guillemette, Rebecca Giles
Guidance Counselor
Hawkins, Marilyn Atkins
Fr Tchr & Frgn Lang Dpt Chprsn
Hayden, Annie Green
Director of Special Education
Heidelberg, Arnetta Jean
Mathematics Teacher
Ivey, Charles T.
Psych & Thry of Knowledge Tchr
Kinsler, Joanne Anderson
Second Grade Teacher
Krolik, Marybeth Sorbello
Anatomy Teacher
Lewis, Terry Thayer
Spanish Teacher
Luciano, Joanna Margaret
Health & Physical Ed Teacher
Marini, Kelly Sands
Peer Mediation Coord & Teacher
Maurer, Lynn
Math Teacher
Munoz, Jacqueline Andrews
Math Teacher
Pinder, Altamese NiBlack
English Teacher
Prokes, Donald Richard
Teacher & Swim Coach
Siry, Joseph Vincent
Asst Prof of Envrmntl Stu
Thornhill, Gary Lee
Associate Naval Science Instr
Townsend, Don
Math Teacher
Vierling, Ronald John
Senior English Instructor
Warren, Sharon L.
English & Social Stud Teacher
Wooten, Karen Paula
Applied Math Teacher
Wright, Mary Jane
Mathematics Teacher
WINTER SPRINGS
Fallon, Sharlyne Ihara
Fourth Grade Teacher
Ginn, Arlene Jones
Fifth Grade Teacher
Higgins, Naragaret Murphy
Resource Teacher of Gifted
Horner, Helen Epstein
Physical Science Teacher
Mc Donald, Pamela Dawn
Primary Multi-Age Teacher
Shyrock, Sharon Webb
8th Grd Pre-Alg & Algebra Tchr
ZEPHYRHILLS
Burdick, Gregory David
English & Theater Arts Instr
Connell, Renny Michael
Retired A P Amer His Instr
Csanadi, Joyce Sharrett
Third Grade Teacher
Davis, James T.
Principal
Fones, Raymond Wendell
Reading Resource Specialist
Frazier, Ophelia
Spanish Teacher
Gillars, Deborah Marie
Visual Arts Teacher
Hines, Rebecca Campbell
Spanish Teacher
Hube, Cindy Felentzer
Third Grade Teacher
Jones, David Russell
Drop Out Prevention Teacher
Knecht, Elizabeth Lewis
Retired Teacher
Martin, Linda Pogue
Family & Consumer Science Tchr
Melquist, Donna Messing
Music Teacher
Milham, Peter
English Teacher
Nelson, Diane Calvert
Mathematics Teacher
Reynolds, Gail Andrea
HS & Adjnct Comm Coll Eng Tchr
Robison, Sharyl Bishop
Continuous Progress Team Ldr
Sinaguglia, Philip Leonard
English & Journalism Teacher
Steuart, C. Paul
Band Director
Summerhill, Elaine Ann
Music Teacher
Woodham, Laura Heller
Mathematics Teacher

Younglove, Doris E.
Fifth Grade Teacher
ZOLFO SPRINGS
Kelly, George C.
Director
Roberts, Pamela Jo
Migrant Pre-Kindergarten Tchr

GEORGIA

ACWORTH
Mc Coy, Randall Wheeler
Business Instructor
McFather, Jeff Thomas
5th Grade Teacher
ADAIRSVILLE
Cornett, Kevin E.
Special Ed Teacher & Coach
Crews, Sally C.
Math Teacher & Dept Head
Moncus, Edward M.
HS Agriculture Teacher
Pyle, Michael Charles
HS Rdng & Pre-Algebra Tchr
Silvers, Joan R.
Social Stud Department Chair
Simonds, Steve W.
Health & Physical Ed Teacher
Smith, Gregory William
High School Math Teacher
Walker, Faires Lynn
Science Teacher
ADEL
Barnes, Billie Ballek
Mathematics Teacher
Batchelor, Julia Hendrix
Math Teacher
Best, Portia Belinda
Seventh Grd Life Science Tchr
Bradley, Deborah J.
Director of Bands
Davis, Lori Barfield
Third Grade Teacher
Godwin, Jan Baldree
Science Teacher
Greeson, Ray A.
Agriculture Education Teacher
Harris, Rebecca Patten
Third Grade Teacher
Lavender, Marguerite T.
2nd Grade Teacher
Meadows, Linda Ward
Social Studies Dept Chairman
Morris, Dawn Green
7th Grd Social Studies Teacher
Rutland, Mattie Brumblow
Preschool Teacher
Williams, Ota Ken
6th Grd Social Studies Teacher
ALAMO
Collins, Melissa Spradley
Mathematics Tchr & Dept Chair
Ford, Gail Thomas
Media Specialist
ALBANY
Arrington, Elnora Jones
Sixth Grade Math Teacher
Bacon, Kathy Warren
Math Teacher
Battle, Sharlotte Yvette
English Teacher
Bowman, Joan Catresia
Chemistry Instructor
Cable, Ron L.
Cmptr Applications & Ec Tchr
Cody, Carlos Bernard
Principal
Coleman, Durie Royal
Writing Lab Instructor
Collier, Barbara Yeager
English Teacher
Cone, Harriett
Eighth Grade Government Tchr
Davis, Jimmie Nell
Fourth Grade Teacher
DeLoach, Michael Odell
Bible Teacher
Dinkins, Carol Deen
Third Grade Teacher
Engram, Ann T.
Prof of History & Geography
Floyd, Jacqueline Jones
8th Grade Science Teacher
Gay, Juanita E.
Science Teacher
Greenia, Jean Tice
MS Science & Math Teacher
Harris, Lorene Latson
Mathematics Teacher
Hodge, Linda S.
Social Studies Teacher
Horton, Elza B.
Language Arts Teacher
Inman, Uysel, Jr.
Asst Aerospace Science Instr
Jones, Evelyn Campbell
English Teacher
Jones, Linda Hunter
Math Teacher
Jones, Merita Cromartie
First Grade Teacher
Jordan, Medarine
In-Schl Suspension Prgm Coord
Kooti, John G.
Professor & MBA Coordinator
Lane, JoAnn Reddick
English Teacher

Lovejoy, Giles
8th-9th Grd Eng & Bible Tchr
Mathis, Marcus Lee
Secondary Mathematics Teacher
McKinney, Laura M.
Teacher
Mc Lendon, Barbara Jordan
Assoc Professor of Mathematics
Miller, Hannah Allen
French & Spanish Teacher
Moultire, Ferrell Tyrone
Mathematics Teacher
Mowery, Clinton A.
Retired Biology & Health Tchr
Nelson, Mamie Ruth
Sixth Grade Teacher
Postell, Irene Freeman
4th Grade Teacher
Roberts, Ann T.
Third Grade Teacher
Shelton, Linda Mc Cloud
Middle School Teacher
Sibley, Robin Eliza
Lang Arts & Soc Stud Teacher
Smith, Debra Hutchinson
Middle Grds Teacher of GATE
Smith, Lamar
Music Professor & Band Dir
Staker, Karen Lee
Social Studies Teacher
Taylor, Margaret Lee
English Teacher
Walker, Myra E.
4th Grade Teacher
Whiting, Laura Watt
6th Grade English Teacher
ALMA
Burkett, Amy Johnson
School Counselor
Carden, Kevin
Social Studies Teacher
Davis, Shirley Harper
Algebra Teacher
Hall, Sherman Edward
Science Teacher
Roberts, Debra J.
Business Education Teacher
ALPHARETTA
Bidegain, Marie Claude
French Teacher
Boddie, Joyce M.
Science Teacher
Coleman, Beverly Durden
5th Grade Teacher
Crum, Jane Gilbert
Math Teacher
DeBellis, Shirley Ann
High School Math Teacher
Edwards, Alice F.
Teacher of Gifted Education
Free, Christine Geraci
Math Teacher
Greeson, Bonnie Dorton
Tchr of Talented & Gifted Sci
Jacques, Cynthia Rebecca
Science Teacher
Jones, Allison Leigh
Orchestra Teacher
Kahn, Stuart E.
English Teacher & Asst Coach
Kolkka, Steven W.
6th-8th Grd PE Teacher
Laird, Marcia Howard
Director of Bands
Lang, Diane Teed
English Teacher
Matthews, Joseph Samuel
Health & PE Teacher
Phillips, Lori Leigh
Art Teacher
Pratt, Christie Posey
Multi Age Intrdscplnry Teacher
Robinson, Donna Maddox
Cooperative Bus Ed Coord
Saunders, Amy Harris
Spanish Teacher
Schmidt, Carol Meyer
Retired Teacher
Searle, William Coleman, Jr.
US History Teacher
Snee, Susan S.
Teacher of Gifted Education
Spiess, Jennifer Amerson
7th Grade Science Teacher
Umeck, Judy K. (Hill)
English & Journalism Teacher
Wells, James W., Jr.
President
AMERICUS
Boggs, Jane Leigh
English Teacher
Brochu, Lloyd David
Social Studies Tchr & Ath Dir
Chapman, Alma J.
ISS Teacher
Davis, Gail Crutchfield
Algebra & Pre-Algebra Teacher
Douglas, Frederick
Health & PE Teacher
Dowdell-Pope, Linda M.
Vocational Home Economics Tchr
Ferguson, Timothy Andrew
5th-8th Grade History Teacher
Glanton, Ronnie Leroy
Physical Education Instructor
Hoxsie, Carol Chappell
AP Eng Comp Tchr & Hnrs Chm
Hurst, Joseph Richard
Biology & Phys Science Tchr

Kinnamon, Karen Wommack
English Teacher
Kluball, Jeffrey L.
Band Director
Martin, Linda L.
Fifth Grade Teacher
Maxwell, Willie P.
Science Teacher & Dept Chair
Owsley, Joyce Long
Science Dept Chair & Chem Tchr
Parker, Susan Cobb
English Teacher & Yrbk Adv
Paschal, Eloise Richardson
Middle School Media Specialist
Pirkle, Gina Michele
History Teacher
Spann, Judith Walker
Special Education Professor
Stovall, Patricia Spann
Second Grade Teacher
Streeter, Emmarene
Counselor
Stribling, Maxine N.
Business Ed Teacher
Thomas, Mae Belle
Junior-Senior Counselor
Welch, Susan Parker
US History Tchr & Dept Chm
Whitten, Elayne Diane Kinloch
Teacher of Gifted & Enrichment
APPLING
Moore, Geniene Carter
Third Grade Teacher
ASHBURN
Mathis, Nell T.
8th Grade Language Arts Tchr
Robison, David Marvin
Social Studies Teacher
ATHENS
Bailey, John Michael
Business Manager
Bamford, Jack K.
Mathematics Teacher
Boggs, Matthew Patrick
History Teacher
Bouldin, Sandy Martin
Math Teacher
Bufford, Harry Eugene
PE Teacher
Burns, Malcolm V., Jr.
Eighth Grade Science Teacher
Burwell, Warren
Mathematics Teacher
Campbell, Constance Louise
Costume Technician
Clark, Leigh McNeal
Band Director
Colbert, Larry D.
Band Teacher & Director
Coley, Linda Marie
Mathematics Teacher
Cummings, Timothy A.
Social Science Teacher
Daniel, Shirley Moore
High School Counselor
DuBose, Jed E.
World History Teacher
Flatt, William P.
D. W. Brooks Distngd Professor
Freeman, Sanford Lee
Studies Teacher
Fulcher, Earl H., Jr.
Clinical Education Director
Guy, Robert Arthur
Science Teacher
Hern, Leigh Ann
Undergraduate Advisor
Howell, Carolyn Tallman
Spanish Teacher
Huthmaker, Roland Terry, Jr.
Orchestra Director
Kaminski, Sandra Jean (Denero)
Marketing Teacher
Kurtz, Mary Bates
Lang Arts & Special Ed Tchr
Longman, Ruth Farstrup
Teacher
Mack, Paul Douglas
Former AP Biology Teacher
Malone, Abbie Shearry
English Teacher
Morgan, Nancy French
8th Grade Social Studies Tchr
Myers, Carol Anne
Instr of English & Dev Studies
Nofsinger, Alisa J.
Fifth Grade Teacher
Paguio, Ligaya Palang
Associate Professor
Pappas, Elaine Andris
Mathematics Teacher
Picas, Anita Ribo
Spanish Teacher
Poss, Brenda Arrington
Piano & Music Theory Teacher
Postell, Joan Yvonne
First Grade Teacher
Raines, Janis Cash
English Teacher
Rosser, Evelyn Crawford
Literature & Composition Tchr
Sandor, Edward P.
Professor & Assoc Dir of Music
Schneider, Margaret Lex
Science Dept Chair & Teacher
Schneider, Scott Evans
Humanities & Drama Teacher
Scott, Wilder Pattillo
Retired Undergraduate Coord

Skeen, Patsy
Prof of Child & Family Dev
Stoffel, Candace Rike
Middle School Choral Director
Stowe, Janice Sheridan
Asst Prin & Math Tchr
Wade, Dorothy Sutton
6th Grade Teacher
White, Carol Lord
Health Sciences & Chem Instr
ATLANTA
Abron, Christine Boddie
Math Teacher
Adams, Frances Danette
Vocational Coordinator
Adams, Robert Eugene
Hospitality Admin Dept Chair
Adley, Stephen Patrick
HS Social Studies Teacher
Akpan, Okon Hanson
Assistant Professor
Archuleta, Benjamin R.
Physical Education Teacher
Armour, Edna Coble
Bio & Ecology Tchr
Asemota, Cathy Jean Brown
Third Grade Teacher
Bagby, Jessica L.
English Dept Head & Teacher
Barksdale, Marcellus Chandler
Professor of History
Bauman, Mark Keith
History Professor
Beach, Jill E.
Science Teacher
Beard, Linda Bradley
High School Counselor
Becker, Verla Gardner
Choral Director
Betts, Jennifer Leah
History Teacher
Binnicker, Pamela C.
Assoc Prof of Pharm Sci
Birdsey, Ralph Talmadge
Middle School Tchr & Cnslr
Blackbourn, Barbara L.
French Professor
Blair, Donald W.
Architectural Pgms Director
Bolster, Livija Rieksts
Journalism Teacher
Boonyapat, Boon C.
Science Department Chairman
Borders, Bessie Sanders
Fifth Grade Teacher
Box, Betsy E.
Director
Bradley, William W.
Soc Sci & Law Related Ed Tchr
Brasher, Julia Trotter
First Grade Teacher
Bridges, Paul Anthony
Special Ed Tchr & Bsktbl Coach
Briggs, Nancy Bowers
Special Education Teacher
Brothers-Ogbuwa, Edith S.
Bus Ed Dept Chprsn
Brown, Macquelyn
English & Literature Teacher
Brown, Mamie M.
Third Grade Tchr & Chairperson
Browning, Gail Fort
Chemistry Teacher
Bryant, Robert Louis, Jr.
Band Director
Bryant, Vista Huguley
Assistant Professor of Health
Cabine, Rebecca Taylor
Assistant Principal
Cahill, Mary Ragan
First Grade Teacher
Cahn, Eileen Margaret
ESL Teacher
Carter, Jeannette Tarver
Mathematics Teacher
Carter, Peggy E.
7th-8th Grd Soc Stud Teacher
Cathcart, Shirley Brandon
Teacher of Gifted
Charles, Karen Long
Mathematics Teacher
Clark, Curtis
Assoc Prof of Math
Colbert, Natalie Fisher
Orchestra Director
Crecraft, Helen
Tutor
Crider, Berenecea Johnson
Dir Ctr for Acad Support
Crowe, Nell Dahlberg
Ret Latin Teacher
Curtis, Thomas Benjamin
Bible Department Chrmn
Cushman, William Claybrook
World & US History Teacher
Cutler, Stephen John
Asst Professor of Pharmacy
Dailey, Maceo Crenshaw, Jr.
Associate Professor
D'Andrea, Stephen Franklin
Art, Photography & Jrnlsm Tchr
Davis, Diane Barefield
6th Grade Teacher
Davis, Michael David
Religion & Philosophy Teacher
Deane, Mildred Woods
Third Grade Teacher
Delaney-Lawrence, Ava
Ninth & Tenth Grd English Tchr

TA (cont)
re, Cristina
h Professor
Cynthia Y.
chool Art Teacher
Sheppard, William H.
Studies Dept Chairperson
Darlene Johnson
Grade Teacher
Frances Segall
Teacher of GATE
Connie
rative Bus Ed Coord
ye, Mustapha A.
Prof & Chm of Bio
oone, Dorothea Bateman
Grade Teacher
an Patrick
e Teacher
m-Zadeh, Susan Dean
h Teacher & Dept Head
Peter Ukuku
ant Professor
, Tilford Tyrone, Sr.
& Physical Ed Teacher
avetta Glover
& Teen Dev Teacher
ynda Mixon
siness Education Teacher
oot, Annie
Arts Instructor
Pamela Cathcart
Honors Biology Tchr
Valerie
Prof of Anthropology
Arthur Weldon
h & Speech Teacher
ick, Patrick E.
gy Teacher
ory, April Majett
Dir & Strings Specialist
d, Donna Ann
Teacher
Stan T.
Intnl Studies Teacher
Alyce Ringer
sh Teacher
n, Willene Smith
rade Teacher
Sherry Denise
ian Education Professor
, Thomas P.
Studies Teacher
Wanda
Science Teacher
Ella Lou Butts
n Grade Teacher
d, Cornelia L. (Denson)
Professor of Chemistry
William Gerard
Professor of Economics
ez, Carmen
Learning Art Teacher
, William Murray
ematics Instructor
Thomas Harris
Sci Instr & Dept Chprsn
Rosia Lee (Burke)
rade Teacher
Bernice Parks
rade Teacher
steen, Louise Dunaway
Grade Teacher
Elizabeth Savage
h Grade Math Teacher
Miyokia Morris
e Language Teacher
Robin Collins
ndary English Teacher
arah Lovett
Lang Arts & Soc Stud Tchr
er, Nancy Funderburk
ctor of Studies & Eng Tchr
, Alice Kimbler
ematics & Physics Teacher
Brit Lamar
Grade Language Arts Tchr
Gwendolyn P.
r & Coll Orientation Instr
, Mark Edwin
al Studies Teacher & Coach
on, Valerie Garrett
ling Consultant
y, Linda Sawyer
nce Teacher
s, John Kermit
ckard Prof of Sci, Bio Chm
Marty A.
al Studies Instructor
r, Anthony J.
of Industrial Engineering
s, Robert Nash
sical Education Teacher
Stacy Marie
lish Teacher
Betty Walton
stant Professor of Math
, Mark Robert
ner Band Director
n, William R.
Grade Math Teacher
rd, Peggy Wise
dergarten Teacher
rd, Sheila Camille
ia Specialist
on, Sterling Henry, III
uty VP Acad Affairs & Dean
Jessica Karoliszyn
hematics Teacher

Hyde, Gregory Allen
English Teacher
Jacobs, Sylvia Alexander
Special Events Director
Johnson, Arnold L.
Counselor
Johnson, Luke Timothy
Prof of New Testament
Johnson, Marilyn B.
Marketing Coordinator
Johnson, Willie Pierce
Registrar
Jones, Andy
High School Mathematics Tchr
Jones, Yolanda Mallory
Fourth Grade Teacher
Jones-Webb, Sharon Baldwin
Technology Laboratory Manager
Kadaba, Prasanna Venkatrama
Associate Professor
Katz, Robert Britton
Assistant to Vice President
Keiller, James Bruce
Vice President & Academic Dean
Keith, Susan Reuter
English Teacher
Kelly, Marian Patricia
Language Arts Chairperson
Key, Carol Hamock
Language Arts Teacher
Kilgore, Shirley C.
Instructional Coordinator
Kim, Gyuheui
Mathematics Professor
Kimball, R. Bruce
History Teacher
Kimble, Celeste Seace
Teacher
Kimbrough, Marjorie L.
Asst Prof of Rel & Philosophy
Klister, Charleen Ann
English Teacher
Koff, Robert Allen
Math Dept Chairman & Teacher
Kohn, Suzanne A. Geffroy
French Teacher
Kolesky, Walter Stephen
Science Dept Head
Konneh, Augustine
Assistant Professor of History
Lammers, Matthew John
Bio Tchr & Soccer Coach
Landers, Judith Joyner
Mathematics Teacher
Latham, William Douglass
Social Studies Teacher
Lechner, Frank J.
Assoc Prof of Sociology
Ledbetter, Peggy G.
Guidance Counselor
Lee, Don E.
Music Dept Chm & Band Dir
Lee, Rebecca Kirkland
Administrator
Lee, Robert Burgin
Assoc Prof of Education & Dir
Lee, Willie E.
Pre-Algebra & Science Teacher
Leopold, Marlene
Teacher of the Gifted
Lester, Mamie Mc Crary
Mathematics Teacher
Lester, Willie Bernard
Social Studies Teacher
Lindsey, Philip M.
Physical Education Teacher
Lisbon, Carolyn Craft
Language Arts Teacher
Liss, Cheryl Robin
Guidance Counselor
Loyd, Page Riley
Retired Teacher of the Gifted
Maddock, Dean E.
Principal
Maksimowski, Rosemary Ezzo
Fifth Grade Teacher
Mapp, Linda J.
Vocational Home Economics Tchr
Marcus, Alan Stewart
Tchr of Talented & Gifted Pgm
Marine, Steve Murphy
English Teacher
Mathews, Edith W.
7th Grd Tchr & Soc Stud Chm
Mau, Eric William
Biology Teacher
May, Deborah Lynne
Former HS Math Teacher
May, James S.
Math & Cmptr Sci Teacher
Mc Donald, Deborah Alyse
Mathematics Teacher
Mc Gee, Darlene Toran
Social Studies Teacher
Mc Kinney, E. Helen
Asst Prof of French & Spanish
Mc Swain, Georgia Haygood
Language Arts Tchr
Metcalf, Dwyer Douglas
History Teacher
Metzger Haugh, Suzanne
Publications Advisor
Miller, Holland Lee
Math Teacher
Mills, Joyce Hunter
Mathematics Tchr
Minick, Diane Sanford
Biology Teacher
Mitchell, Ella Pearson
Professor of Homiletics

Molbey, Joy Lashea
General Music & Choral Teacher
Moor, Stan W.
Comm Service Coord & Span Tchr
Moore, Gwen Bailey
Title I Liaison Teacher
Moore, Judy Raggi
Italian Prof & Dir of Stud Pgm
Moreland, Lois Baldwin
Political Science Professor
Mote, Patricia Taylor
Teacher
Mugg, Marsha Raymond
Math Dept Head & Teacher
Murty, Komanduri Srinivasa
Assoc Professor & Dept Chm
Myers, Johnnie Dumas
Criminal Justice Prof & Chair
Mynatt, Mary Bernice
Eighth Grade English Teacher
Nabangi, Fabian Kafuko
Asst Professor of Accounting
Nichols, Heather Chandler
Math Teacher
North, Barbaralaine Ross
ESOL Specialist
Odom, Myrtle Von Johnson
Business Department Chprsn
Okoh, Fred I.
Associate Professor & Chair
Okpala, Mattie Mays
Math Teacher
Onabanjo, Babs Olusegun
Assoc Prof of Computer Science
Onukwuli, Francis Osita
Computer Science Professor
Orr, Debra Mc Keon
Learning Lab Teacher
Overstreet, Thomas Anthony
Assistant Principal
Papp, Barbara Ann
English Teacher
Parker, Burma Tucker
Science Teacher
Parker, Gary Alan
VP & Dir of Accounting Svcs
Patterson, Jamie E.
Social Studies Teacher
Patterson, Lillie Rochelle
Physical Education Teacher
Payne, John M.
Math Teacher
Pearson, Nanci Laura
English Department Chairperson
Peavy, Deborah Dixon
French Teacher
Pedescleaux, Desiree Selma
Asst Prof of Pol Sci
Pickens, William Garfield
English & Linguistics Prof
Pierre, Dwight Anthony
Math Teacher
Poole, Bryant Alexander
Band Director
Porter, Diana Browner
Culture Area Studies Teacher
Powers, Helen W.
Science Teacher
Prince, Larry Evans
Social Studies Teacher
Prybylski, Andrea Allio
Biology Teacher
Pryor, Julia Boone
Writing To Read Teacher
Pryor, Patsy Jackson
Science Department Chairperson
Quattrocchi, Teresa K. (Fields)
History Teacher
Rahman, Ajile A.
World & African History Tchr
Rau, Kenneth V.
Latin & Classics Instructor
Raybourn, Carole A.
English Instructor
Reed, Randy
Mathematics Teacher
Reese, Kenneth Edward
Physical Education Teacher
Reid, Gail Patrick
Teacher
Respess, Barbara Calvert
10th-12th Grd Eng Tchr
Riddle, Rosetta Lawson
Spanish Teacher
Ritchie, MaryJane Long
Principal
Roberts, Lillian I.
Science Teacher
Roberts, Mary Pat
Mathematics Teacher
Robinson, Steven C.
Computer Programming Teacher
Rockett, Julia Elizabeth
English Teacher
Romm, Tracy
Intnl Baccalaureate Coord
Roth, Mary Alice Hughes
Second Grade Teacher
Rubino, Stephen John
US History Teacher
Runnels, Brent Michael
Concert Pianist & Private Tchr
Sanders, Gloria Jean
English Teacher
Sargent, Charles Jackson
Assoc Professor of Homiletics
Sarullo, Angela M.
4th Grade Teacher
Scheer, Wayne
Assoc Professor of English

Schroeder, Mona Freeman
English Teacher
Schroer, Donald Paul
Associate Professor
Sgrosso, Greg
Mathematics Teacher
Shaheed, Stanley F. H.
Mathematics Teacher
Shea, Barbara O'Keefe
Teacher of Disorders
Sheftall, Willis B., Jr.
Professor of Economics & Chair
Siegel, Roger John
Physics Teacher
Siler, Glen B.
English Teacher
Simpson, Alan P.
Assistant Teacher
Simpson, Niki Nichols
English Teacher & Drama Dir
Sims, Deborah Lyde
School Counselor
Singletary, Clara Haynes
Social Studies Teacher
Smiley, Dave B.
Art & Photography Teacher
Smith, Eric Dale
Geography Teacher
Smith, Julian K., Sr.
French & Spanish Teacher
Smith, Olivia Cotton
5th Grade Teacher
Smith-Scott, Wanda
10th Grade English Teacher
Stajich, Gregory Victor
Assoc Prof of Pharmacy Prac
Stephens, Gloria Lockhart
High School Math Teacher
Stewart, Ethel Marie
5th Grade Teacher
Storms, Tommie Lynn
Instr of Broadcast Media
Stovall, Juliett Viola
Social Worker
Tarvr, Margaret Conner
Chemistry Teacher
Thomas, Earnestine Lester
Gifted Program Facilitator
Toro, Gina Harris
Eighth Grade Science Teacher
Toth, John W.
English Teacher
Townsend, Richard Wayne
Biology & Physical Sci Tchr
Tribble, Alton Joseph, III
History Teacher
Troy, Carolyn Hankins
History Teacher
Turner, Paula Vanessa
Former Assistant Professor
Tyree, C. Dale
Intnl Stud Magnet Prgm Teacher
Vacca, Marilyn Mahoney
6th Grade Teacher
Valeri-Gold, Maria Teresa
Associate Professor of Reading
Vermilya, Wright
Teacher
Vest, Donald S., Jr.
Asst Prof of Intrnl Bus
Vogtner, Karen Ponatoski
Asst Prin & Technology Coord
Volkert, George A.
High School Latin Teacher
Vyas, Ashwin G.
Assoc Prof & Grad Coord
Waith, Terry Isabel
First Grade Teacher
Walker, Patricia Loeb
Mathematics Teacher
Wallens, Michael Gary
Chaplain
Wa Ng, Chung
Asst Prof of Computer Science
Ware, Nedra R. (Gambrell)
Earth Sci & Rdng Tchr
Ware-Brazier, Rhonda A.
Assistant Principal
Warren, LaVerne Chapman
English Teacher
Watkins, Audrey Newsome
First Grade Teacher
Weaver, Delsandra Hill
English Teacher
Wexler, Robin Ann
8th Grade Teacher
White, Clementine J.
HS Mathematics Teacher
Whitfield, Bettye L. Mc Clendon
Math & Computer Tech Teacher
Williams, Cynthia A.
French Teacher
Williams, Emily Allen
English Professor
Williams, Glenda
Career Education Teacher
Williams, Judith Ann
Fourth Grade Teacher
Williams, Roselee Gross
Second Grade Teacher
Williams, Valjean
Fifth Grade Teacher
Williams, Virginia
Mathematics Teacher
Wilson, Jasper
Assistant Professor of Busines
Wilson, Robert, III
Health & PE Instructor
Wimberly, Anne Streaty
Assoc Prof of Christian Ed

Wokatsch, Jurgen
German Teacher
Womick, Susan Ary
French Teacher
Woods, Elizabeth Bradford
Mathematics Teacher
Wright, Diana Albritton
English Dept Chprsn & AP Tchr
Wu, De Ting
Mathematics Professor
Wynn, Rheanolia Mc Graw
Biology & Chemistry Teacher

AUBURN

Spiler, Chip
Fifth Grade Teacher

AUGUSTA

Alexander, Regina DeBow
Teacher
Andrews, Teresa Letitia
Assistant High School Prin
Arena, John William, Jr.
Computer Programming Teacher
Barinowski, Rhonda Dickerson
Chemistry Teacher
Barnett, Catherine Anne Becker
Director of Guidance
Battles, Jan Warren
HS Mathematics Teacher
Beaird, Roxane Rodgers
Math Teacher
Bean, Linda Dacus
Fifth Grade Teacher
Berger, Jennifer Garvey
Literature Teacher
Birdseye, James Havens
History Instructor
Bland, Tracey Adams
Language Arts Teacher
Bradshaw, Martha Melton
Nursing Asst Professor
Brigham, Debra Conrad
Mathematics Teacher
Bullock, Alystene Bush
First Grade Teacher
Carlyle, Gussie Hurt
Math Teacher
Carmichael, Stanlye Whitman
Language Arts Teacher
Caudle, Herbert Addison, Jr.
French Teacher
Clemons, Aleksandriya Bonner
Electro-Mechanical Teacher
Clifford, Connie M.
Language Arts Dept Chairperson
Dasher, Samuel Douglas, Jr.
Eighth Grade Science Teacher
Deal, Donna R.
Language Arts Teacher
Dickert, Floride Clarkson
Mathematics Teacher
Didley, William A.
Registrar
Dinkins, Janice Marie Whorley
Eng & Lang Arts Tchr, Team Ldr
Dunn, Richard Alan
Secondary Math Teacher
Durst, Caroline Elizabeth
Language Arts Teacher
Easler, Vivian Smart
General Music & Chorus Teacher
Estroff, Andrea Rich
French Teacher
Fahnoe, Carol Hudson
Language Arts Teacher
Fellows, Catherine Kleen
Bible, Art Teacher & Librn
Fields, Carlotte Lester
Mathematics Teacher
Fortson, Barbara Hammett
Kindergarten Teacher
Galvin, Stephen Christopher
Mathematics Teacher
Gardner, Brenda Cummings
Fourth Grade Teacher
Garrard, Ruth Sandiford
Math & Pre-Algebra Teacher
Gerlach, Mary Jo Mirlenbrink
Asst Prof of Adult Nursing
Graham, Geraldine Parker
Language Arts Teacher
Green, Neatie Smith
Pre-Kindergarten Teacher
Hair, Bonnie Lynn
Secondary Counselor
Hamrick, Kathy Barr
Mathematics Professor
Hancock, Finetta Graves
History Teacher & Asst Prin
Harp, Irell Smothers
Mathematics Teacher
Hatmaker, Debra Dawson
Assistant Professor of Nursing
Henry, Helen Simmons
Seventh Grade Lang Arts Tchr
Heppert, Mary Donnan
Elementary Art Teacher
Howard, Jeania Carr
Tchr of Spec Lrng Disabilities
Hughes, Laura Martinez
Teacher of the Gifted
Joe, Cara Linn Cole
ESL Teacher
Johnson, Alesia Greenaugh
8th Grd GA History Teacher
Johnson, Craig LaVergne
History Teacher
Jones, Carol Algeo
Pre-K Tchr & Head-Lower Schl
Kanavage, Tara Cooper
High School Art Teacher

AUGUSTA (cont)
Kelley, Sandra Williams
HS Social Studies Teacher
Kelton, A. Earl
In School Suspension Teacher
Kelton, Earl
In Schl Suspension Teacher
Kennedy, J. Franklin
Latin Teacher
Land, David L.
HS Civics, Ec Teacher & Coach
Latigue, Dolores Gray
Mathematics Teacher
LeRoy, Mary-Margaret Weatherby
Eng Tchr of Dev, Pub Relations
Mabray, Stacey Nicole
Science Educator
Manly, Richard Henry
Chemistry & Physics Teacher
Mason, Henrietta Ingram
Data Processing Coordinator
McCall, Mark Douglas
His, Ec & Anthropology Tchr
McElreath, Mary Helen
Health, PE Teacher & Coach
Mc Ree, Melody Jennings
5th Grade Teacher
Mealing, Amy Spivey
Science Teacher
Melchior, Jonathan Michael
Bible & Theology Teacher
Owens, Kathryn Rhodes
4th Grade Teacher
Pavonarius, Mary, DC
HS Religion Teacher
Peterson, Karen Sanders
Science Tchr & Dept Chair
Pettit, Mary M.
History Teacher
Polite-Miller, Chiquita
Language Arts Teacher
Pousman, Cynthia A.
Science Teacher
Puryear, Joan Copeland
Gen Ed Chprsn & English Instr
Rensch, Kira Volz
English Teacher
Rouse, Arbernice
Science Teacher
Saxon, Patricia Martina
Language Arts Teacher
Sherer, Marcheta Bohannon
Science Dept Chairman & Tchr
Sistrunk, Janette
Mathematics Teacher
Smith, Joel Stephen
Asst Principal for Student Act
Smith, Melissa Renae
Mathematics Teacher
Smith, Susan Medford
Chemistry Teacher
Spurr, Melissa Jernigan
Asst Prof of Adult Nursing
Stutts, Rosanne
Visual Art Teacher
Sullivan, Lawrence Robert
Forensic Chemist
Tanner, Anita Marie Woodruff
Social Studies Teacher
Tanner, Ernest Grier, Jr.
Fifth Grade Teacher
Tanner, Wendell Ray
Retired Social Studies Teacher
Tolbert, Patricia Larkin
Fifth Grade Teacher
Tompkins, Geoffrey Richard
Assistant Professor
Turner Jackson, Bettie M.
Special Instrl Asst Tchr
Tutt, Brenda Brown
8th Grd Lang Arts & Rdng Tchr
Velez-Cruz, Vanessa
Spanish Teacher
Vella, Helen Lynn
HS Social Studies Teacher
Walker, Angela Stockton
Science Teacher
Wallis, Alberta J.
English Teacher & Dept Coord
Ward, Pamela Starkey
Mathematics Teacher
Welch, Christopher W.
Assistant Professor
Whaley, Margaret Rosemarie
Title I Program Coordinator
Wilcox, Nancy Morgan
5th Grade Teacher & Coach
Wright, Margaret Ganster
Spanish Teacher
Yarborough, James Timothy
Social Studies Teacher
Zimmerman, Coleen
Respiratory Therapy Instructor

AUSTELL
Allen, Marilyn Hames
Assistant Administrator
Barfield, H. Gregory
French Teacher
Boggs, Rhonda Rayborn
Chemistry & Phys Sci Teacher
Hammett, David Edward
Mathematics Teacher
Jackson, Charles Ray
Band Director
Wahlmeier, Bruce Edward
High School Science Teacher
Wierengo, Sarah Jane
Art Teacher
Williamson, Jo
English Teacher

AVONDALE ESTATES
Carter, Patricia Hollis
Reading Consultant
Hammond, Scott Joe
Orchestra Director
Jackson, Donna Jane
Fifth Grade Teacher
Shearer, Diane Jones
English Teacher

BAINBRIDGE
Allen, Terry L.
Social Studies Teacher
Beers, Joan Stagner
English Teacher
Benton, Lillian King
Third Grade Teacher
Bius, William M.
Agricultural Education Teacher
Carpenter, Pamela Herndon
Kindergarten Teacher
Elrod, Teresa Cox
Math Teacher
Hinson, Ronald Edward
Teacher
Huskey, Donald S.
Assoc Prof of Electronics
Jeter, Lisa Richardson
Business Education Teacher
Johnson, Peggy Mitchell
Kindergarten Teacher
Mc Diffitt, Rebecca Riggins
Personal Safety Coordinator
Murrah, Barbara Bolden
High School Math Teacher
Ragan-Martin, Bronwyn
High School English Teacher
Smith, Greg S.
Director of Choral Activities
Strickland, Alice White
Mathematics Teacher
Thomas, Jan Skipper
5th Grade Teacher
Vickers, Robin Musgrove
9th-12th Grade English Teacher
Ward, Paschal A.
Director of Bands

BALDWIN
Kimbrell, Charlotte Wade
Fifth Grade Teacher

BARNESVILLE
Allen, Susan Dean
Kindergarten Teacher
Finley, Denise Milner
Kindergarten Teacher
Hightower, Christopher
English Teacher
Jackson, Daniel Joseph
Associate Professor of Chem
Parnell, Carl S.
8th Grd GA History Teacher
Wright, Robert Monroe
Assistant Principal
Young, Douglas Parker, Jr.
Asst Prof of Political Science

BAXLEY
Ammons, Wanda A.
Retired 4th Grade Teacher
Davis, Charles Allen
English Teacher
Dominy, Sandra Taylor
Social Studies Teacher
Folsom, Tamela Tanner
School Counselor
Nails, Juanita Brookins
Assistant Principal
Page, Lisa Hutchison
Special Education Teacher
Riddle, Joyce Lewis
Secondary English Teacher

BELLVILLE
Whiten, Ann Keels
High School Science Teacher

BLACKSHEAR
Clough, Melanie Smith
Seventh Grade Lang Arts Tchr
O' Steen, Judith Bowen
Math Dept Chair & Teacher
Treadwell, Angelia Maron
7th Grd Life Science Teacher
Waters, Marilyn Clough
Spcl Ed Dept Chair & SLD Tchr

BLAIRSVILLE
Bryner, Renny Floyd
PE Teacher
Collins, Sheila Tritt
Fifth Grade Teacher
Davenport, Martha Ledford
Kindergarten Teacher
Hughes, James Robert
Science Teacher & Coach
Kell, Curtis Cliff
PE Teacher
Knight, Carol Roberts
Secondary Mathematics Teacher
Thomas, Betty Erwin
Psychoeducational Tchr

BLAKELY
Drew, Cecelia Hale
Science Teacher
Ferry, David Michael
Band Director
Ford, Veita Blue
Title I Math Teacher
Harris, Glynda Mills
8th Grade Mathematics Teacher
Hollinger, Alma Shephard
Curriculum Director
Howard, Lisa Easom
HS Math Teacher
Langley, Sandra Mc Griff
High School English Teacher
Megahee, Hazel Moulton
Math Teacher
Yarbrough, Priscilla Graham
Business Teacher

BLUE RIDGE
Burlingame, Sandra L.
Mathematics Teacher
Collins, David Russell
Science Teacher
Craig, Robert W.
Social Studies Teacher
Dillard, James Terry
Algebra Teacher
Parris, Cheryl L.
Sixth Grade Reading Teacher
Paul, Michael Raymond
PE Teacher & Basketball Coach
Phillips, Paul Steven
Science Teacher
Welch, Sherry Scholes
Fifth Grade Math Teacher

BONAIRE
Griffin, Barbara Conley
Kindergarten Teacher
Hopkins, Catherine Gail
Fourth Grade Teacher

BOWDON
Davis, Stanley Hughes
Health Teacher
Wynn, Jane Parham
Multi-Age Reg Classroom Tchr
Young, Peggy Entrekin
Title I Teacher

BOWERSVILLE
Martin, Becky F.
Second Grade Teacher

BREMEN
Burrell, Regina Holbrook
First Grade Teacher
Dobbs, Cassandra Jones
6th Grade Teacher
Hughes, Carol Mc Whorter
Special Education Teacher
Phillips, Lisa Blackmon
Business Education Teacher
Phillips, Robin James
Math & Science Teacher
Powell, Robert L. W.
8th Grade Social Studies Tchr
Threadgill, Sheral Brown
6th Grade Math Teacher

BROOKLET
Barber, Sandra Lee
Science Teacher & Dept Chair
Grooms, Sheri Boyd
Mathematics Teacher
Newell, Anne Shelburne
Science Teacher
Oliver, Phillip Hayes
World History Teacher
Shaw, Mary K.
Mathematics Teacher

BRUNSWICK
Altman, Margaret Jones
Chemistry Teacher
Barber, Debra Lynn
HS Social Studies Teacher
Barber, Gwen Mc Quade
Assistant Prof of Mathematics
Bartkovich, Sharon Lee
Assistant Prof of Humanities
Blasko, Frederika Carn
Kindergarten Teacher
Brown, Donna T.
Asst Prof of Bus & Office Tech
Bumgardner, Vickie Lynn
8th Grd Math & Algebra Teacher
Butler, Judith Ann
Science & Language Arts Tchr
Carithers, Robert Hugh
Social Studies Dept Head
Carver, Carolyn
Assistant Professor of Nursing
Cason, Diana (Singletary)
Eng Tchr, Lang Arts Dept Chair
Cowden, Susan West
Fourth Grade Teacher
Cox, Polly B.
Biology Teacher
Dunn, Shirley Joyner
Fifth Grade Teacher
Durham, Lori Butler
English Teacher
Freeman, Brenda J. Robinson
Business Teacher
Hendrix, Todd Alan
Science Teacher
Hubsch, Kathleen Ann
PE & Health Teacher
Knight, Anne S.
Assistant Professor
Lyde, Catherine Erlene
Chemistry Teacher
Maasha, Ntungwa
Phys, Geology & Astrnmy Inst
Mellana, Linda Rae
English Teacher
Metz, Ingrid C.
Latin Teacher
Pittman, Catherine Sylvia
Social Studies Teacher
Powell, Teresa Tozzi
Senior English Teacher
Randolph, Edith E.
School Counselor
Trobaugh, Karla N.
Mathematics & Lang Arts Tchr

BUCHANAN
Griffith, Beleta S.
8th Grade Math & Algebra Tchr
Jones, Kathryn Joy Crosthwait
3rd Grade Teacher
Momon, Clovis Kate Biggers
Retired Sixth Grade Teacher
Whitton, Bobby J.
Special Education Teacher

BUENA VISTA
Brown, Stacey Cornelious
Physical Science Teacher
Chapman, Hallianna
7th Grade Teacher
Dennis, Virginia Blackmon
Retired Teacher
McCorkle, Richard Rogers
History Teacher
Mc Glaun, Sandra Simpson
First Grade Teacher
Tidwell, Glenn
Biology Teacher
Welch, Margaret Brodnax
Health Occupation Teacher

BUFORD
Bonds, Suzann K.
Gifted Program Teacher
Crawford, Judy Sanders
Gifted Program Teacher
Gailey, Stephanie Joy
7th Grade Language Arts Tchr
Hopper, Gerald P.
Mathematics Dept Chairman
Jones, Dale Allen
8th Grade Algebra Teacher
Nash, Pat Roebuck
11th Grade English Teacher
Newman, Ashley Giddens
Teacher
Perry, Natalie Bailey
Choral & General Music Tchr
Tarpkins, Crystal Wood
Physical Education Teacher
Timbes, Michelle Elizabeth
Math & Social Studies Teacher

BUTLER
Smith, Steven E.
Mathematics Teacher

BYRON
Arrington, Jamie Leigh
Math & Science Teacher
Hart, Carol Sellin
Third Grade Teacher
Henley, Mattie La Verna Jackson
Social Science Teacher
Johnson, Dianne M.
Language Arts Teacher

CAIRO
Donalson, Tammy Cook
Mathematics Teacher
Ezell, Mary M. (Dunagan)
Mathematics Teacher
Maxwell, Tanya Wells
At-Risk Intervention Teacher
Murphy, Connie Gainous
Business Education Teacher
Ray, Robert Martin
Kindergarten Teacher
Turner, Cynthia Drew
2nd Grade Teacher
White, Erin Evans
World History Teacher

CALHOUN
Bailey, Judy Webb
Youth Apprenticeship Director
Buchanan, Karen Cope
Eighth Grade Science Teacher
Burton, Susan Schollenberger
Social Studies Teacher
Burton, William Speight
Social Studies Department Chm
Coe, Deborah Loftis
Spanish Teacher
Davis, Wanda Sue
Math Department Chairperson
Enloe, David Donaldson
Band Director
Farmer, Gina Spriggs
Mathematics Teacher
Fry, Shelly Ritz
History & Government Teacher
Glover, Gregory R.
8th Grade Science Teacher
Guider, John Payton
HS Math Teacher
Harris, Angela Batson
10th-11th Grade English Tchr
Hayes, Brad E.
American Government Teacher
Holland, Winifred Hollis
Teacher of Gifted
Krusac, Irma Christina
Kindergarten Teacher
LaMountain, Jennifer A.
Music Director
Leming, Patricia Netrick
English & Latin Teacher
Lempke, Bonnie Ann
ISS Supervisor
Lloyd, Renee Denise
CBE Coordinator & Bus Instr
Palmer, Pamela Michelle
HS Mathematics Teacher
Satterfield, Gail
English Teacher

CAMILLA
Clay, Rebecca Williams
Pre-Kindergarten Teacher
Dover, Janine Gambill
PE Teacher & Dept Chm
Edwards, Deborah Kay
Speech & Language Pathologist
Harding-Davis, Charlotte Ray
Third Grade Reading Teacher
Hicks, Vicki Eunette
Kindergarten Tchr & Tech Coord
Luke, Susan Davis
Biology Teacher
Ragan, Jackie Tinsley
Rgstrd Nurse & Dir of Nrsng
Robinson, Beverly Wheeler
6th Grd Reading Specialist
Woodams, Gary Allen
Mathematics Teacher

CANTON
Andes, Pamela Ray
Mathematics Teacher
Bowen, James Lamar
Biology Teacher
Bragg, Rick A.
English Department Chairman
Bryant, Sande Shreve
Third Grade Teacher
Buice, Susan Melissa
6th Grade Teacher
Cagle, Janie L.
Health & Sex Education Teacher
Carnes, Richie Louie
English Teacher
Cline, Letitia Anne
Second Grade Teacher
Cole, Glenda Jean
Science Teacher
Conley, Richard Lester
English & Drama Director
Corbett, Peggy Maynard
Advanced Placement Eng Teacher
Crowe, Susan Ray
Third Grade Teacher
Fincher, Elaine Langston
5th Grade Teacher
Forsh, Frederick Douglas
Vocal Music Director
Gaddis, Pamela Hamilton
Sixth Grade Teacher
Heintz, Peter
9th Grade Physical Sci Tchr
Hill, Joan Jack
Counselor
King, Rosemary Lees
Spanish Teacher
Kohler, Debbie M.
Mathematics Teacher
Levine-Male, Karen
Spanish & French Teacher
Lewis, Janice Dye
Theatre & English Teacher
Lowery, Fran Holcomb
Second Grade Teacher
Martin, Rickey Alfred
Social Studies Teacher
Nelson, Ron
Social Studies Teacher
Palmer, Nanette Jernigan
Mathematics Teacher
Parker, Gerald Luther
HS Language Arts Teacher
Phagan-Kean, Mary
Vision Education Specialist
Puckett, Peggy Hines
Family & Consumer Sci Teacher
Ransom, Stephen Joe
Eighth Grade Eng & Lit Teacher
Ratcliff, Reeca Chastain
Fifth Grd Tchr
Sheffield, Laurel Newbold
Retired Teacher & Yrbk Co-Adv
Sims, Russell Reeves
Mathematics Teacher
Smith, Betty Cavaliere
Interrelated Spec Ed Teacher
Stouder, Cassandra Connolly
Spanish Teacher
Tatum, Carolyn Rose
Advanced Placement Eng Teacher
Todd, Martha Seay
3rd Grade Teacher
Warren, Frances Witherington
Math Teacher & Department Head
Williams, Cindy Blalock
1st Grade Teacher
Williams, Teresa Wilson
English Teacher

CARNESVILLE
Brooks, Donnie James
Band Director
Coile, Latana Fitts
Social Studies Teacher
Floyd, Jennifer Lucille
7th Grade Science Teacher
Kerr, Judy Walsh
Eighth Grade Lang Arts Tchr
Phillips, David Calvin
Technology Teacher
Truesdale, Leigh Ann
Biology & Human Anatomy Tchr
Young, Cheryl Hill
Kindergarten Teacher

CARROLLTON
Ayers, Penny W.
Science Teacher
Bailey, Billy R.
Economics & History Teacher
Cetti, Marsha Cosby
Language Arts Teacher
Clanton, Cynthia Lynn
History Teacher
Cook, Julie Nichols
Art Dept Chair

LLTON (cont)
, Thomas Jack, Jr.
Middle Grds Education
Richard Lee
Teacher
William Lee
ant Principal
Scarlett
Grade English Teacher
homas Harold
e Teacher
Jane W.
n Teacher
atricia Hall
ade Math Teacher
arolyn (Wilson)
matics Teacher
thy Robinson
Grade Teacher
ohn Michael
ud & Special Ed Tchr
on, Alice B.
& Teacher of Gifted
David Greg
Teacher
Clare V.
ce Learning Facilitator
Martha H.
al
Gail M.
Grd Earth Science Tchr
, Rebecca Hammock
age Arts Chairman
Darlene Stewart
Grade Teacher
RSVILLE
Jan Alverson
d Grade Teacher
ght, Charles Eldon
c Arts Teacher
, Carol C.
Grade Teacher
ladine Willis
rative Bus Ed Coordinator
ik, Drew T.
gy Teacher & Coach
, Amanda Ward
Arts & Applied Comm Tchr
, Brenda Ann-Hudson
al Education Teacher
Melissa Lynn
th Grade Science Teacher
Linda Hensley
Grade Teacher
l, Neal A.
Director
Martha Elaine
matics Teacher
Stephen Michael
Director
t, Mary White
ade Teacher
e, Ellen Currier
sh Teacher
June Harris
Grade Teacher
Donald Gary
Teacher
, Diane K.
sh Teacher
Scott
ance Counselor
ier, Angee K.
Specialist
SPRING
Diane Stinchcomb
sh & Language Teacher
RTOWN
athy Hood
Grade Teacher
Jeff J.
l Studies Teacher
Juanita Veasley
rade Teacher
n, Elaine David
nd Grade Teacher
Canzada Bryant
Economics & Health Tchr
ERVILLE
, Joy Colquitt
a Specialist
Betty Willis
School Guidance Counselor
BLEE
n, Verna Jean
d History Teacher
n, Brenda Deily
sh Teacher
, Martha Reed
her of the Gifted Students
Barbara C. (Coffey)
Chem Teacher
s, Mary Churchill
sh Teacher
an, Valerie Kimpson
ish Teacher
sky, Nancy Wiley
ish Teacher
SWORTH
ng, Susan Brooks
nce Teacher
tt, Timothy Alan
al Studies Teacher
on, Virginia Harris
nd Grade Teacher
rd, Jonathan Franklin
Grd Social Studies Tchr
rd, Timothy R.
al Studies Teacher

Loughridge, Nell Davis
Home Economics Teacher
Lunsford, Linda Ganelle
Eng & 10th Grd Coll Prep Tchr
Mc Neill, Janice S.
Latin Teacher
Parson, Randal Phares
9th-12th Grd Science Teacher
Pritchett, Monica Leigh-Ann
French & ESOL Teacher
Quarles, Peggy Delores
English Teacher
Ridley, Jerry E.
7th Grade Teacher
Sampson, Larry
Assistant Principal
Sosebee, Sharon Elizabeth
Bio, Chem Tchr & Sci Dept Chm
Sylvester, Fred Angus, III
High School Band Director
Tranum, George W.
7th Grade Mathematics Tchr
Young, Samuel Lynn
8th Grade Science Teacher
CHESTNUT MOUNTAIN
Cash, Dianne Hayes
Third Grade Teacher
England, Katie Irene
Second Grade Teacher
CHICKAMAUGA
Boyd, Ted J.
Applied Mathematics Teacher
O'Kelley, Mary Ann Gillespie
Teacher of the Gifted
Phillips, Jayne Stout
Biology Teacher
Pollard, Julie Marie
Math Teacher
CHULA
Barber, Patti H.
High School Science Teacher
Light, Christie Carlynn
Mathematics Teacher
CLARKESVILLE
Ausburn, Mark Eugene
6th-8th Grd PE & Health Tchr
Gaines, Betty Maness
Second Grade Teacher
Jennings, Dale Barron
4th Grade Teacher
Riggins, Maxine Caswell
SIA Teacher
Williams, Rick
Health & Physical Ed Teacher
CLARKSTON
Dalton, Sandra Tina
Nursing Instr
Davis, Daisy Walker
Mathematics Instructor
Fenster, Kenneth R.
Assistant Professor of History
Flowers, Thomas Jones
History, Govt & Economics Tchr
Michelich, Virginia Jean
Associate Professor of Biology
Moore, Darrell Glenn
Physical Ed Teacher & Coach
Sams, Linda Willis
Bio, Anatomy & Physiology Tchr
Shearod, Marva Jean
4th Grade Teacher
Sherer, Margaret Pearcy
Social Studies Teacher
Sporborg, Ann J.
Assoc Prof of Humanities
Thompson, Georgina Francois
Nursing Assistant Instructor
Venable, Margaret H.
Asst Professor of Chemistry
CLAXTON
Glass, Lisa Michelle
6th-12 Grd Music & Chorus Tchr
Lewis, John Stephen
Sr Eng Tchr & Dept Chairman
Mc Gahey, James Todd
School Counselor
CLAYTON
Coan, Cynthia Adair
Sixth Grade Teacher
Lesley, Cynthia Fair
Substitute Teacher
CLEVELAND
Adams, LaMerle Ann
2nd Grade Teacher
Aiken, Sandra W.
Science Teacher
Blalock, Linda Freeman
First Grade Teacher
Collins, June Cash
1st Grd Tchr of Gifted
Conley, Shaun Burl
Middle Schl Mathematics Tchr
Davis, John Corrado
Administrative Director
Franks, Eddie (Faye)
3rd Grade Teacher
George, David Neal
Fine Arts Division Chairman
Gerrin, Sherri R.
Middle School Science Teacher
Harland, Katherine Wronek
Second Grade Teacher
Harris, Kevin Joe
Political Science Instructor
Herrin, Jon Andrew
Asst Prof of Eng & Dev Stud
Hicks, Darcy Simmons
HS English Tchr & Debate Coach
Huff, Fred Mercer
Science Teacher

Jordan, Tommy Wayne
Theology & Speech Instructor
Kennedy, Sara Burnett
Teacher of the Gifted
Lewis, Patsy D.
11th & 12th Grd Eng Tchr
Mc Cullough, Howard Smith
Professor of Biology
Pruitt, Trilla Dorsey
Counselor
Shippey, Robert Clifford, Jr.
Associate Prof of Theology
Smith, Vivian Ann
Anatomy & Physiology Professor
Valko, William Jay
Psychology Instructor
Weaver, Fiorella Beltrani
Asst Professor of Fr & Span
Winger, Alexis P.
English Instructor
COCHRAN
Beier, David Jay
Professor of Political Science
Caldwell, Thomas Andrew
Associate Professor of Psych
Carter, Alice Fordham
Family & Consumer Science Tchr
Coody, Kathy S.
Second Grade Teacher
Cranford, Shelly Lane
Physical Education Teacher
Davis, Catherine Mitchell
Mathematics Professor
DeLorenzo, Ronald Anthony
Chemistry Professor
Dykes, Phyllis Gordon
Family Service Coord
Evans, Debra Cooper
3rd Grade Teacher
Friedman, Frank H.
Vice President of Acad Affairs
Garvin, Brett Allen
Economics & Government Teacher
Keller, Mark Alan
English Professor
Lowery, Annette Fennell
Health Occupations Instructor
Makaya, Peter B.
His, Pol Sci & Sociology Prof
Meadows, Wendy Mullis
Elementary Gifted Teacher
Pasto, John D.
Professor of Biology
Reff, David C.
Assistant Professor of Biology
Rhodes, Robert Allen
Chemistry Professor
Sullivan, Troy Vincent
Computer & Accounting Prof
Wilson, Mary Ellen
Associate Professor of History
COHUTTA
Killcreas, Suzanne R.
1st Grade & Lead Science Tchr
COLBERT
Stone, Gail Voiles
Fourth Grade Teacher
COLLEGE PARK
Brakefield, Paul Traylor
Voc Acad Ed Coord & Tchr
Brodie, Charles G.
Director of Bands
DeLuca, Robert Edward
Instructional Lead Teacher
Eaton, Marian Balams
Chemistry Teacher
Fullwood, Betty Mapp
Physical Sci & Biology Teacher
Hood, Joan Nelson
English Teacher
Lamfalusi, Suzanne Elizabeth
AP Ec & Hnrs US History Tchr
Lamont Hudson, Lori A.
2nd Grade Teacher
Legg, Tammy Crowe
Social Studies Teacher
Logan, Beth Tesch
English Teacher
Love, Miriam Wilson
Mathematics Teacher
Mosley, Michael Dale
Counselor
Teets, Cheryl Jackson
7th & 8th Grade English Tchr
Thompson, Daisy Lewis
English & Drama Teacher
COLLINS
Small, Annie Jackson
7th Grade Science Teacher
COLQUITT
Darley, Deborah Paul
Eng, Drama & Journalism Tchr
Phillips, Debra W.
English Teacher
Spooner, Bill H.
Agriculture Teacher
COLUMBUS
Arnold, James Austin
Director of Bands
Austin, Susan
Spanish Teacher
Bergeron, Audrey H.
Business Ed Tchr & Tech Coord
Bickerstaff, Ellen Rambo
Second Grade Teacher
Bonaker, Patricia W.
Choral Director
Boone, Oliver Carter
Director of Bands

Boothe, Charles O.
Biology & Physiology Teacher
Bovaird, Patricia Anne
Mathematics Instructor
Boynton, Kimberly Brown
English Instructor
Brock, Kelly Dawn
Business Teacher
Brown, Joseph
English Teacher
Bruner, Melanie Gail (Burnette)
Drama & English Teacher
Bryan, Brenda Givens
8th Grade Social Studies Tchr
Burden, Jeffrey Keith
Art Department Chair
Burns, Sandra Hardegree
Family & Consumer Sci Tchr
Byrd, Wilburn L.
Dept of Mathematics Instructor
Cargal, VerDel Marie
Kindergarten Teacher
Cason, Kimberly W.
English Teacher
Chuites, Shepherd Johnston
French Teacher
Clarke, Barrie Eugene
Social Science Teacher
Cockrell, Tim
Technology Education Teacher
Craig, Eugene L.
Retired Elementary Principal
Cross, Tina Renee
Bio Tchr
Davis, June Pratt
Biology Teacher
Davis, Mary Willetts
Social Studies Dept Chprsn
Decker, James Martin
8th Grd Language Arts Teacher
Devery, Rebecca Ramirez
Spanish & English Teacher
Dillard, Patricia Spratling
Third Grade Teacher
Dore, Fred T.
Social Studies Teacher
Douglas, Anna H.
Business Education Teacher
Douglas, Mary Ann
7th Grade Mathematics Teacher
Dowdell, Charlie Thomas
Physical Education Teacher
Dowis, Dorinda Lee
Criminal Justice Instructor
Drew, John Joseph, Jr.
Economics Teacher
Earls, Gail Morris
Fifth Grade Teacher
England, James Warren
7th Grade World Cultures Tchr
Fike, Jo Marie
Fifth Grade Teacher
Fry, Laura Fleet
Band Director
Fullerton, Faye (Tapley)
Media Specialist
Galloway, Quovadis Walker
Guidance Director
Gemes, Anne Gammage
Math Teacher
Gillis, Dianne Henson
Language Art Dept Chairperson
Gilmore, Virginia Davis
Adult Education & Sub Teacher
Gilstrap, Sidney J.
Fitness & Health Teacher
Green, Michael Dale
PE Teacher & Coach
Green, Richard
Special Education Teacher
Hadley, Linda Upshaw
Asst Professor of Finance
Harding, Wendy Wecht
Spanish Teacher & Dept Chrm
Harrison, Carol A.
7th Grd Social Studies Teacher
Henry, Peggy Ann
Teacher
Hudson, Janice Lucille
Physics Teacher
Jackson, Nora Algracie
Science Teacher
James, Sherry Faye (Young)
Fourth Grade Teacher
Johnson, Edgar Allen
Science Teacher
Jones, Helen H.
Counselor
Kaeserman, Charlotte Trevena
Guidance Director & Counselor
Kimsey, Carmen
Georgia Studies & 8th Grd Tchr
King, Marie Daniell
2nd Grade Teacher
Kirby, Jean M.
Marketing Teacher & Coord
Kirkland, Cathy Trigg
Language Arts Teacher
Lang, Miriam Anne
Mathematics Tchr & Dept Head
Latham, Jacquelyn Christensen
Kindergarten Teacher
Lee, Joyce Marie
Math & Sci Tchr
Lester, Anise Joyce
Triad Resource & Instrl Lead
Lewis, Jewell Mays
Home & Family Mngmt Tech Tchr
Lowe, Helen Hess
5th Grade Teacher

Marsh, Faye Wilcox
English & CAI Teacher
Mc Bride, Betty Thomas
Senior Counselor & Class Spon
Mc Bridge, Betty Thomas
HS Senior Cnslr & Class Spon
Medley, Donis Carroll
Algebra & Geometry Teacher
Melendez, Mark Edward
High School Teacher
Mion, Zaiga Polis
German & French Teacher
Mitchell, Ocle Talley
Retired Kindergarten Teacher
Murphy, Elizabeth B.
English Teacher
Norah, Patricia Ann
Choral Director
Ogle, Rose M.
1st-7th Grades Art Teacher
Onye, Nkolika Ajakwe
Science Teacher
Owens, Laurene (Peacock)
English Teacher
Patrick, Cathy
Band Director
Pierce, Alberta Howard
Language Arts II Teacher
Popp, Ronald Stephen
Fourth Grade Teacher
Powers, Karen Elizabeth (Alves)
High School Math Teacher
Querna, Margaret Bushree
Human Anat & Physiology Tchr
Ralph-Doctrie, Gladys Varnell
7th Grade Life Science Teacher
Reese, Richard L., II
Mathematics Teacher
Reynolds, Cassandra Otanback
Secondary Instructor
Robertson, Lynn Baldwin
Integrated Science Teacher
Robinson, Julie A.
9th Grade English Teacher
Rowell, Barbara Poindexter
Third Grade Teacher
Shearouse, Susan Fife
English Teacher
Sneed, Cynthia Elaine
World & US History Teacher
Sneed, Susan Rae
Science Teacher
Starling, Ginger Lee
Spanish Teacher
Stokes, Glenn Daniel
Bio Assoc Prof, Sci Assoc Dean
Stone, James Richard, Jr.
Secondary Math Teacher
Strickland, Amy C.
Business Education Teacher
Taliaferro, Tandie Tivera
Georgia & US History Teacher
Thompson, Tangela Felicia
High School Math Teacher
Vann, Elaine
English Teacher
Vinson, Alicia Hartford
Choral Director
Walker, Bernice Morgan
5th-6th Grade Teacher
Wall, Jerry Kent
Senior Army Instructor
Walton, Felix
Physical Education Teacher
Watson, Beverly Shull
Third Grade Teacher
Watson, Sue E.
Social Science Teacher
Williams, Burma Dene
Fifth Grade Teacher
Williams, Valerie Hall
Lead Parenting Title I Teacher
Wingard, Carol Etheridge
English Teacher
COMMERCE
Pritchett, Edith Gayle
English Chairperson & Teacher
CONYERS
Abbott, Cathy Lancaster
US History Teacher
Anderson, Becky Bowen
Kindergarten Teacher
Bell, David Brian
Health & Physical Ed Teacher
Biddy, Dolores N.
Family & Consumer Science Tchr
Brown, Patsy Bowling
Fifth Grade Teacher
Carter, R. Lance
Mass Media Technology Teacher
Crenshaw, Robert Earl
Marine ROTC Instr & Tchr
Crooks, Laurie L.
Teacher of English & Gifted
Dean, Sherry Wilkes
First Grade Teacher
Edwards, Hamilton Oliver, Jr.
Teacher of the Gifted
English, Deborah Jayne
Social Studies Teacher
Fain, Judy Simmons
Chemistry Teacher
Gajownik, Gregory Robert
Band Director
Goss, Nancy Powell
10th Grade English Teacher
Graff, Sharon Bobo
Math Teacher
Hodges, Richard Dwight
Cooperative Business Ed Tchr

CONYERS (cont)
Ingle, Carol Brodnax
Family & Consumer Science Tchr
Jenkins, Jimmie Byington
8th Grade Math Teacher
Jones, Cheryl Ellington
Biology Teacher
Knight, Kenneth William
Biology Facilitator
Mobley, Beth T.
Business Education Teacher
O'Neill, Arthur Vincent
Social Studies Teacher
Purcell, Peggy R.
Second Grade Teacher
Rowser, Jeffrey Orlenda
Band Director
Russell, Debra Aull
Biology Teacher
Stamps, Susan C.
English Teacher & Cadet Instr
Stephenson, Marcia Speer
English Department Head
Storar, Linda (Yarger)
High School Math Teacher
Supple, Mary Stevens
English Teacher
Tarr, Lawrence Roy
Physics Teacher
Thomas, Stephen Matthew
History & Bible Teacher
Weil, Celestia Raulerson
Chemistry Teacher
Young, Laura Jean
Seventh Grade Teacher
COOLIDGE
Jones, Eva J.
Retired Teacher
CORDELE
Booker, Pearle Phillips
School Counselor
Deriso, Bettye Hamilton
Language Arts Teacher
Gay, Gayla Sheffield
Language Arts & Soc Stud Tchr
Spires, Denise Tate
HS Mathematics Teacher
CORNELIA
Dalton, Loretta Westbrook
Seventh Grade Mathematics Tchr
Davis, Jean Davis
6th Grade Teacher
Epperson, Carol Ann
First Grade Teacher
Tench, Lynn Barnett
Media Specialist
Whitworth, Tammy Barrett
Computer Technology Teacher
COVINGTON
Anderson, Anita Williams
HS Social Studies Teacher
Brown, Huanne Moore
Chemistry Teacher
Carver, William Michael
Soc Stud Tchr & Dept Chm
Cooper, Angela Danner
High School Science Teacher
De Gay, Jeannine Chipoulet
French Teacher
Denman, Dannette Daniel
Third Grade Teacher
Fitzpatrick, Jane Franklin
First Grade Teacher
Greer, Pamela Peppers
English Teacher
Grim, Mary Gaynor
Spanish Teacher
Hall, Nancy L.
Fifth Grade Teacher
Johnson, Judith H.
Language Arts & Jrnlsm Teacher
Marra, Jean Anne Mc Allister
Principal
Patel, Nilesh C.
Chemistry Teacher
Peters, Jane King
Math Teacher
Smith, Shelley Kae
7th Grade Teacher
Strong, Davidlyn P.
Seventh Grade Math Teacher
Willard, Dean Cleveland
Lang Arts Tchr & Newspaper Adv
Wimberly, Margaret Bostick
Language Arts Teacher
CRAWFORDVILLE
Chatman, Marvin
Principal
CUMMING
Austin, Judy Mundy
English Teacher & Yearbook Adv
Banker, Teresa G.
Mathematics Teacher
Benson, Patsy B.
Business Teacher
Bishop, James William, Jr.
Physical Education Teacher
Bramblett, Sid J.
Collision Repair Teacher
Gravitt, Marcy S.
8th Grade Teacher
Harris, Patricia Wilson
8th Grade Math Teacher
Hicks, Patty Lynn
8th Grade English Teacher
Mashburn, John Byron
Music Director
McMullan, Kit B.
Math Teacher
Meadows, Carolyn Nan
History Teacher
Muehlbauer, Daphne Holcombe
8th Grade Language Arts Tchr
Phillips, Sherrie
Span Tchr & Chair Frgn Lang
Reid, Elizabeth Ann (Lassetter)
English Teacher & Dept Chair
Richardson, William H., Jr.
Science Teacher
Rohacek, Katherine Frances
8th Grd Earth Sci Tchr & Coord
Smith, Bonnie Bracewell
Drama Coach & English Teacher
Tatum, Jane Holland
Mathematics Teacher
Ward, Keating B.
English Teacher
Weldy, Kimberly Dawn
8th Grade Math Teacher
CUTHBERT
Gilbert, Crispin Carter
Health & Physical Ed Professor
Hardwick, Margaret Holder
Tchr & Coord of Gifted Program
McFather, Jim David
Teacher & Coach
Sabree, Yahya Agin
Music Teacher & Band Director
Smith, Kimberley Michelle
High School Science Teacher
Swinson, Sue Whitlow
Latin Teacher
DACULA
Berryman, Michele Whittington
AP English Teacher
Bugg, Rebecca B.
Biology Teacher
Burleson, Lisa Sitton
Gifted Program Teacher
Caudell-Glassman, Nancy L.
Seventh Grade Teacher
Dobbs, Vicki Lynn
Science Teacher
Farr, Dale Robert
Health & PE Teacher
Gilbert, Robert L.
Health, PE Teacher & Coach
Hall, Diane Lindsay
Fifth Grade Teacher
Howard, Nancy Sprouse
7th Grade Teacher
Keefer, Tracy Lyn
Health & Physical Ed Teacher
Mason, Mary Teague
Social Stud Tchr & Dept Chair
Nygaard, Sandra Glover
6th Grade Math & Sci Teacher
Palmer, Margaret Ann
7th Grade Teacher
Pollock, Michele Joanne
Seventh Grade Teacher
Taylor, Annalisa
Art Teacher
Thornton, Lisa M.
Chemistry & Biology Teacher
Verdi, Kristy Causey
Pol Systems & World His Tchr
Watts, Christy Cates
French Teacher
DAHLONEGA
Davis, Thomas Cohen
Director of Admissions
Ferguson, Barbara G.
Cooperative Business Ed Coord
George, Gary David
Asst Prof, Dept of Chemistry
Justus, Laura Gail
Secondary English Teacher
Souders, Joan Bennett
English Teacher
DALLAS
Abbey, Linda Lee
7th Grade Math Teacher
Bell, Marcia Winn
Family & Consumer Sci Teacher
Carter, Mary Ruth
Eighth Grade English Teacher
Davies, Debbie Moore
Band Director
Earwood, Julianne Bray
AP & World History Teacher
Edwards, Lisa A. (Landman)
Social Studies Teacher
Gilbert, Martha Wilson
High School English Teacher
Harris, Eric James
Health Teacher
Hudson, Dawn M.
Biology Teacher
Johnson, Jay H.
Business Education Teacher
Katzowitz, Ellen C.
Health Occupations Teacher
Lee, Deborah Hardman
English Teacher & Dept Head
Maurer, Dawn DeBenedetto
8th Grd Communications Teacher
McDaniel, Jay Nell
English Teacher
McLeod, Carol Smith
English & History Teacher
Padgett, James Michael
Instructor of Visual Art
Shuster, Traci Leigh
High School English Teacher
Steele, Barbara Schumacher
4th Grade Teacher
Vollenweider, Betty Henley
Math & Social Studies Teacher
Wilson, Jean George
6th Grade Language Arts Tchr
DALTON
Adams, James Kevin
Assistant Professor of Biology
Adams, Rosemary D.
Fifth Grade Teacher
Allen, Charles Everette
Physical Education Teacher
Bagby, Paul C.
Social Studies Teacher
Baker, Lisa Seymour
Home Economics Teacher
Beesley, Bernard Franklin
Asst Professor of English
Boyatt, Louis M.
Teacher & Coach
Bramblett, Ginger Lee
Language Arts Teacher
Broadrick, Patricia Ann
Former Teacher
Callahan, Reva Phelps
5th Grade Teacher
Carson, Christina Denise
Remedial Reading Teacher
Chapman, Doris Reynolds
Fourth Grade Teacher
Davis, Sara Creswell
3rd Grade Teacher
Elakman, Erik Joseph
8th Grade Science Teacher
Freeman, Deborah Pollock
Teacher of the Gifted
Gaddis, Charles Ronnie
Band Dir & Fine Arts Dept Chm
Gallmon, Sylvia Corn
Business Education Teacher
Gray, Russell Eugene, Sr.
Science & ESOL Teacher
Harris, Rick W.
Principal, Bible & Span Tchr
Headrick, Vivian Hayes
6th Grade Math Teacher
Helton, Mark Wane
Lang, Drama & Speech Teacher
Higgins, Vicki Rogers
Lrnng Disabilities Therapist
Mahoney, Kelley K.
English Instructor
Meagher, Teddi Mallory
Tchr of Orthopedically Imprd
Oxford, Joyce Murrell
First Grade Teacher
Phinney, Jennifer Martin
English & Drama Teacher
Russell, Kenneth Wayne, II
Social Studies Teacher
Sheikh, Gail Ewton
Third Grade Teacher
Sisson, Perry W.
Math & Pre-Algebra Teacher
Thompson, Robert Gray
English Teacher
Turner, Deborah Bliss
Retired English Teacher
Ward, Becky Adams
First Grade Teacher
DAMASCUS
Dozier, Martha Hoover
Art Department Head
Gibbs, Anngene Culbreth
English Teacher & Counselor
Houston, Claire J.
Journalism & English Teacher
Swift, Ann Hasty
Literature & Soc Studies Tchr
Warrick, Mary Jane
Fourth Grade Teacher
DANIELSVILLE
Carey, Renee
9th-11th Grade English Teacher
Clark, Lynn Weingartner
Third Grade Teacher
Freeman, Linda Williams
English Teacher
Harrison, Stephanie Ann
12th Grade English Teacher
Hayes, Cindy Aaron
Bio Teacher & Sci Dept Chair
Scarsborough, Karol Andrea
His Tchr & Soc Stud Dept Chair
Shepherd, Sherry Wilkes
6th Grade Social Studies Tchr
Shirley, Christopher Glenn
Eighth Grade Earth Sci Tchr
DARIEN
Abrahamsen, Hege Thiis
Spanish Teacher
DAWSON
Benjamin, Lila M.
Business Education Teacher
Kendricks, Melva Jean
Literature Teacher
Moore, Emma Jones
Language Arts Teacher
Stafford, Dorothy Jean
Social Science Teacher
DAWSONVILLE
Allen, Sherry Harper
Teacher of the Gifted
Browning, Sherry G.
English Teacher
Burlack, Marsha
Business Education Teacher
Kirton, Charlotte Marie
Life Sci & Soc Stud Teacher
Miller, Deidre Thomas
HS Mathematics Teacher
Smith, Della Combs
Assistant Principal
Voss, Evangeline Norris
History Teacher
DEARING
Story, Jean
Second Grade Teacher
DECATUR
Adler, Kenneth Martin
Social Studies Teacher
Alexander, Barrett Dion
Band Director
Blitz, Rick
HS Social Studies Teacher
Bobo, Linda Ann
Science Teacher
Brock, Rose Merry
Counselor
Brown, Leonard Alvin
History Teacher
Cagle-Wimpey, Carolyn A.
Teacher of Gifted & Talented
Chadwick, Bill
AP US & European History Tchr
Clark, Lillie Reynolds
Sixth Grade Teacher
Deas, Yolanda Yvette
3rd Grade Paraprofessional
Dessables, Mireille M.
French Teacher
East, John Michael
PE Teacher & Coach
Fortune, Christine Daniell
Mathematics Specialist
Furnace, Mikhail Damone
Spanish Teacher
Garner, Sharon Pendleton
First & Second Grade Teacher
Gilmer, Mark Anthony
Chemistry & Physics Teacher
Hall, Obelia Harper
English Teacher
Harris, Lillian Lewis
Fifth Year Teacher
Huckaby, Scott Allan
Sci Chair & HS Headmaster
Jones, June Hawkins
7th Grade Science Teacher
Jordon, Alice Orleans
8th Grd Earth Science Teacher
Junot, Gail E.
Mathematics Teacher
Kettering, Paul T., III
English Teacher
Knapp, Amy Lyn
English Teacher & Yrbk Advisor
Lane, Johnnie M.
World History Teacher
LeBlanc, JoAnn Hall
Third Grade Teacher
Lee, Barbara Milton
Mathematics Teacher
Leissa, Angela Crumpton
Instructional Lead Teacher
Lewers, Regina Pawlak
English Teacher
Lewis, Adrienne Yvonne
Secondary English Teacher
Locklear, Reva Freeman
Elementary Teacher
Lummus, Rose Maria
Senior English Teacher
Lunsford, H. Eugene
Naval Science Instructor
Maddox, Sarah A.
English Teacher
Mc Clinic, Joshulyn P.
Science Department Chairman
Mc Entire, Debora Self
Fourth Grade Teacher
Medwick, Lee N.
Health & Phys Education Tchr
Morris, Cynthia McGuire
Reading Specialist
Nelloms, Krystal Kaye
7th Grade English Teacher
Okafor, Martin Okechukwu
Inter-Discipline Dept Coord
Ostrenko, Linda Bottoms
11th Grade English Teacher
Owens, Suzi Green
8th Grade English Teacher
Payton, Gerald L.
ISS Teacher
Pinka, Patricia Garland
Professor of English
Quirouet, Amy Carver
Eng Dept Chprsn & Cadet Instr
Reed, Elmira
English Teacher
Rhodes, Jane Dean
Media Specialist
Rigler, Sharon Elaine
English Teacher
Robinson, Mary Joyce (Lundy)
8th-10th Grd Science Teacher
Scruggs, Darlene Smith
Sixth Grade Teacher
Sethi, Asha Kohli
Sixth & Seventh Grade Teacher
Thomas, Susan M.
Associate Professor of English
Thornton, Jerelean Troutman
5th Grade Teacher
Turner, John Mc Coy, Jr.
Biology Teacher
Tyler, Casey Eugene
11th Grade Chemistry Teacher
Ubriaco, Susan D.
Science Teacher
Ward, Randi Darelle
High School English Teacher
Warthan, Patricia
Science Teacher & Dept Chair
Whorton, Monique Louise
Teacher of Gifted
Word-Rogers, Altha B.
Third Grade Teacher
DEMOREST
Gardner, Mark Lawrence
Economics Professor
Kassem, Cherrie Lou
Asst Professor of Education
Kibler, Madge Holden
Assistant Professor of Ed
Pleysier, Albert Jan
Professor of History
Quarles, Connie Coker
Fifth Grade Teacher
Simmons, Garen
History Professor
Vance, Cynthia Lynn
Psychology Professor
Whited, Stephen Rex
Assistant Professor of English
DOERUN
Kimbrell, Myra G.
Pre-Kindergarten Teacher
DONALSONVILLE
Bryant, Cynthia Claire
Business Education Teacher
Franklin, Gloria Roberts
English Teacher
Godwin, Kevin Lamar
MS Phys Ed Teacher
Ponder, Mary Lou
Former Social Studies Teacher
Register, Martha H.
Science Teacher & Dept Chm
DORAVILLE
Knapp, Cecilia Cleveland
7th Grade Math Teacher
DOUGLAS
Bedford, Lee Ann
Emtnl & Behavior Disorder Tchr
Dykes, Martha Wood
Mathematics Teacher
James, Grace M.
Professor of Health & PE
Josey, Jean Wright
Teacher of the Gifted
Lawrence, Robert Lee, Jr.
Jazz Band Instructor
Nye, Roger D.
Prof of Criminal Justice & Soc
O'Brien, John Bernard
Director of Bands
Rivers, Wanda Jean
Math Dept Chair
Taft, Deidre Lott
English & Applied Comm Tchr
Tinsley, Billy E.
Director of Agriculture
Tipton, Juanita Ensley
English Teacher
Worth, Junell
2nd Grade Teacher
DOUGLASVILLE
Adams, Betty W.
Coord of Voc Acad Education
Alford, James Robert
English Teacher
Arrington, Billy Rodney
Administrative Asst & Ath Dir
Arrington, Sue Ellen
7th Grade Science Teacher
Bogo, John P.
English & Russian Teacher
Brantley, William Michael
HS Vocational Ag Teacher
Brewer, Susan Segars
English Teacher
Brook, Leslie Cole
Family & Consumer Sci Instr
Bruner, Jim
Drafting & Design Teacher
Chaffin, Laura Ann
Math Teacher
Clay, Roxanne
Theatre & English Teacher
Clay, Sheryl Thigpen
Director, Owner, Head Instr
Droke, Galen Ross
Mathematics Dept Chairperson
Dugan, Marla Gill
Biology Teacher
Hale, George Ronald
Bio, Anatomy & Physiology Tchr
Hall, Mary Hugh M.
Teacher & Dept Chairperson
Heavner, Howard Hoke
Social Studies Teacher
Holloway, Charles Keith
US History Teacher
Jones, Heather Hall
Business Teacher
Macoy, Virginia Jenkins
Math & Algebra Teacher
Nolin, Judith Lynn
Title I Teacher
Petty, Richard Merton, Jr.
Social Studies Teacher
Prickett, Harvard Pittman, Jr.
Retired Social Studies Teacher
Scott, Sherri Elizabeth
Language Arts Teacher
Sleek, Judith Anderson
English Teacher
Steadham, Zan Marie
World & European History Tchr
Teal, Casey Darnell
9th Grd Physical Science Tchr

ASVILLE (cont)
›n, Kim Richardson
al Ed & Health Teacher
renda Carroll
ı Teacher of Gifted
RANCH
Ada Rose Reese
Grade Teacher
N
ena Scream
Grade Math Teacher
Cecelia Broadway
ss Education Teacher
ith Wayne
Grade Science Teacher
ndra Grace
d Social Studies Tchr
, Sue Ann Shaw
chool & Coll Eng Tchr
, Susan Darling
er of Gifted & Lang Arts
, Terry McMillan
stry Teacher
etty Ann
d Grade Teacher
ean Floyd
ade English Teacher
Mary Jane Smith
ng Teacher
Aurelia R.
h Teacher
Jameson Miguel
Teacher
ucille M.
Physical Education Tchr
s, Jeffrey Scott
cial Studies Teacher
d, Thomas Alexander
Instructor
Y
Kathy Kitchens
ade Teacher
H
inda Cain
rade Teacher
, Vicki Boles
al Education Teacher
JoAnn Culpepper
istry Teacher
one Andrew
age Teacher
William Preston
Studies Teacher
k, Sabrina Cox
matics Teacher
ead, Elaine Renfroe
ratory Teacher
Rebecca Edwards
School Theater Teacher
Carole
gy Teacher
Billy Edward
Dept Head & Sci Tchr
Michael D.
Studies Teacher
Vendy S.
rd Physical Science Tchr
nnell, Peggy Howard
ath Teacher
, Kirsten Kaufmann
ematics Teacher
Mary Pickard
rade Teacher
and, Michael
y US His, Fnd of Ed Instr
Ginger Horton
omics & History Teacher
Bernadete Moody
y & Consumer Science Tchr
, Pamela Mozelle
ergarten Teacher
OODY
James Arthur
of History & Geography
Marcia Mitchell
ciate Professor of English
Kathleen Bailey
sh Instructor
Barbara Jones
tant Professor of English
, Tina Moowey
c Professor of Economics
oltzer, Sheryl Fanning
ciate Professor of Biology
POINT
, Ellen Thomas
her of Gifted
czak, Kimberly Portwood
ation & History Professor
Foster, Lywonnis Price
Grade Lang Arts Teacher
ons, Jamesena Hall
Grade Science Teacher
n, Ralph G.
essor of English
MAN
ws, Jane Bonner
ergarten Teacher
, Johnny Lee
TC Instructor
Gina Williams
E Coord & Yrbk Sponsor
Brenda Faye
n Teacher
l, Ruby Lee
nselor
m, Carolyn Eagerton
hematics Teacher
Susan White
Speech & Debate Teacher

West, Cheryl L.
Consultant
EATONTON
Allen, Robin E.
Social Studies Teacher
Edwards, Connie Abel
Sixth Grade Teacher
Hunter, William James
Music Teacher
Jones, Pamela Wilder
Phys Sci, Bio & Chem Teacher
Pascavage, Darren
Science & Mathematics Teacher
Sheppard, D. J.
Agriculture Teacher
Todd, Kimberly Cook
8th Grade Teacher
EDISON
Ginn, Virginia H.
Mathematics Dept Chairperson
ELBERTON
Adams, Sandy Duncan
PE Coord & Cross Cntry Coach
Duncan, Martha Coleman
English Teacher
Eckler, Ann Robinson
English Department Chairman
Floyd, Tammy Childs
DCT Work Pgm Coord
Glidewell, Joseph William
History Teacher
Jones, Karen Fitzgerald
English Teacher
Mc Ferrin, Thomas Sumner
Athletic Director
ELLAVILLE
Wurtz, Patti Dillard
6th & 7th Grade English Tchr
ELLENWOOD
Belfrom, Philip Ishmael
Mathematics Teacher
Decuir, Michael
Band Director & US His Teacher
Lottie, Joanne Harvey
Foreign Language Dept Chair
Mc Kee, Lynda Diane
Mathematics Teacher
Rasar, Cathy Dunn
Second Grade Teacher
Treadwell, Oleria Carr
Elementary Teacher
ELLERSLIE
Kimber, Louis Wesley
5th Grade Teacher
Walker, Alma Goodwin
Media Specialist
ELLIJAY
Burnette, Linda Anderson
7th Grd Soc Stud & Rdng Tchr
Calhoun, Gwendolyn J.
Remedial Specialist
Calhoun, Stephen E.
Music Coordinator & Band Dir
Hils, Ralph John
Ind Researcher & Consultant
Huff, Renee
5th Grade Teacher
Hyde, Gary C.
Science Teacher
Kincaid, Sharon Southern
Third Grade Teacher
Mayfield, Leonard Eugene
Physical Education Teacher
Mc Clure, Saundra Renee
First Grade Teacher
Ottinger, Tom
Math Dept Chair & Tech Spclst
Overstreet, Kathleen A.
First Grade Teacher
Pettit, Mark A.
Health & Physical Ed Teacher
Pritchett, Lynne Gheesling
Home Economics Teacher
Rainey, Anne Thompson
Third Grade Teacher
Snider, Samuel Lee
Physical Education Teacher
Spears, Nancy S.
English Teacher
Sweat, Louise Andrew
SIA Teacher
Thomas, Anita Ruth
Seventh Grade Teacher
Thomas, Myra Crane
First Grade Teacher
Vail, Marylyn Kirkpatrick
Counselor
Webb, Sidney A.
Director
EMERSON
Denney, Kevin Scott
6th-8th Grade Gifted Teacher
Rutland, Peggy Blenis
Sixth Grd Sci & Lang Arts Tchr
EVANS
Alford, Deborah Zobel
First Grade Teacher
Anderson, Marsie Bentley
Social Studies Teacher
Blau, Linda Downing
Coll Prep Tchr & Jrnlsm Adv
Boggus, Betsy R.
High School English Tchr
Boyd, Cynthia Blankenship
Biology Teacher
Bryant, Roselyn Glasgow
Art Teacher
Carraway, Rosalie Sandlin
Spanish Teacher

Cleveland, Mary Hoover
9th-12th Grade Math Teacher
Crislip, Belinda Machen
High School Mathematics Tchr
Daniel, Deborah B.
English Teacher
Dobson, Jill Anne
Chemistry Teacher
Dollander, Glenda Buckingham
AP English & Speech Teacher
Easler, Timothy N.
Teacher of the Gifted
Ferko, Catherine Farabaugh
Spanish Teacher
Gaddy, Janet Starkel
Seventh Grade Life Sci Tchr
Glenn, Janice Gordon
7th Grade Life Science Teacher
Graham, Suzanne Marie
PE & Health Teacher & Coach
Gray, Rosemary Faulk
High School Science Teacher
Greenway, Paul Howard
His Tchr, Ftbl & Track Coach
Guinn, Mae Kilpatrick
High School Guidance Cnslr
Hall, Mary Reid
Middle School Band Director
Hall, Trace Eric
Math Teacher
Hancock, Sheila J. Stephens
CBE Coordinator
Howard, Rhonda Lynn
Former Soc Stud & Fr Teacher
Massengill, Kathy M.
HS Mathematics Teacher
O'Brien, Stephanie Mortensen
Business Education Instructor
Peebles, Betty L.
Anatomy Teacher & Dept Chm
Quinn, Henry Lewis
Social Studies Dept Chairman
Rachels, Jennifer Wood
Science & Social Studies Tchr
Russell, Robert L.
Drafting Teacher
Segraves, Christopher Robin
PE Teacher & Coach
Van Sant, Brenda B.
Teacher
Varner, Marsha Jewell
Spanish Teacher
Williams, Jennifer Lee
8th Grade Teacher & Math Coord
FAIRBURN
Arnold-Wallen, Vinie Delores
MS Language Arts Teacher
Dawson, Joanna Cavan
French Teacher
Dearin, J. David
French & Science Teacher
Enlow, David Michael
Science Teacher & Coach
Harper, Earnest Gregory
Composition & Literature Tchr
Hughes, Cheryl M.
Mathematics & Bible Teacher
Marsh, Nancy Grayson
Rdng Recovery & Remedial Tchr
Mays, Larry Michael
High School English Teacher
Pendergrass, Larry Lee
Senior Army Instructor
Stevens, Elizabeth Martin
Counselor
Titus, Mike
Math Department Chair
FAYETTEVILLE
Alldredge, Laura Robinson
Spanish Teacher
Barnes, Judith Ann (Smith)
7th Grade Life Science Teacher
Beard, Kenneth Franklin
Band Director
Borders, Donna Turner
Fourth Grade Teacher
Byars, Jason William
History Teacher
Drewry, Robin Hutchins
Choral Director & Music Tchr
Farr, Evelyn Bailey
Collaborative Reading Teacher
Garcia, Margaret Taylor
Fifth Grade Teacher
Godbois, Gay Speed
Child Care Teacher
Gray, Julie Prather
Science Teacher
Green, Janis S.
HS Social Studies Teacher
Hannon, Jane Turner
8th Grd Mathematics Teacher
Jeffcoat, Kimberly Gregory
7th Grade English Teacher
Kuykendall, Keith Shane
AP Chemistry Teacher
Langley, Beth Ray
HS Mathematics Teacher
Leatherwood, Sheila Foster
Fourth Grade Teacher
Moulton-Wright, Sharon
Family & Consumer Sci Tchr
Munsey, Daire Hubert
Math Teacher
O'Shields, Paula Fulford
Mathematics Teacher
Overstreet, Priscilla Ann
English Teacher of the Gifted
Penland, Richard Holliday
Biology & Chemistry Teacher

Proctor, Dianne Guthrie
Social Studies Teacher
Turner, Susan Stone
Fifth Grade Teacher
Underwood, George Anthony
HS History & Phys Ed Teacher
Wasson, Winton Lann
History Teacher
Whitaker, Sandra R.
Speech, Drama & English Tchr
FITZGERALD
Cunningham, Lisa Stone
Computer Exploratory Teacher
Frye, Melanie Thomas
9th-12th Grd Soc Stud Teacher
Garber, Rebecca Elizabeth
8th Grd Earth Science Teacher
Lewis, Charles Wesley
Registrar
Stanley, Crimora Walker
Computer Instructor
Whitley, Brenda Sue Ross (Parks)
Advanced Placement Eng Teacher
Wilder, Patricia Childers
Math Teacher
FLINTSTONE
Chapman, Marlene Craig
Kindergarten Teacher
FOLKSTON
Edwards, Dorothy S.
English & Journalism Teacher
Lairsey, John Delman
Principal
Mudd, Peggy A.
SLD Teacher
Staeger, William Frederick
Social Studies, Lang Arts Tchr
Sulzberger, Cynthia Lynn
Band & Asst Director
FOREST PARK
Alfaro, Cheryl Frost
High School Spanish Teacher
Blose, Nancy L.
Math Teacher & Coach
Campagnone, Ernest Rosario
AF Jr ROTC Instructor
Moreland, Terri Hanes
Seventh Grd Mathematics Tchr
Ortt, Debra Duggan
Lead Teacher
Ross, Mary Susanne
Antmy, Physiology & Bio Tchr
Taylor, Marsha L.
ESOL Teacher
White, Gail Hood
8th Grade Mathematics Teacher
Williams, Angelyn Stewart
Business Education Teacher
FORSYTH
Anderson, Helen E.
Teacher of Gifted
Bazemore, Julie A.
English Teacher
Berner, Catherine Leslie
High School Teacher
Curry, Carol Cooper
Elem Music & English Teacher
English, Lauren Jackson
French Teacher
Henderson, Shirley Kendall
Social Studies Tchr & Chprsn
Hoyt, Nora Mulligan
Former Homeschooling Teacher
King, Rayceen H.
Guidance Counselor
Mathis, Delores Curry
4th Grade Teacher
Shurling, Nancy O.
Mathematics Teacher
Speir, Cornelia Johnson
English & Writing Teacher
Stewart, Rodney
Science Teacher
Tuttle, Lisa Milam
Teacher
Wangerin, Hollie N. H.
AP US History Teacher
Wilson, Casaundra Byrd
HS Mathematics Teacher
Wilson, Rhonda Leigh
Instruction Asst Principal
Worthy, Dorothy Vaughn
Sixth Grade Teacher
FORT BENNING
Blanchard, Lorri Stevens
Music Director
Cunningham, Kimberly Faulkner
Literature & Lang Arts Tchr
Dent, Mary Joyce
Science Teacher
Jones, Patricia Pridgeon
Amer History & Civics Teacher
Reasoner, Michelle Ann (McCune)
7th Grd Lang Arts & Lit Tchr
Shaw, Anne Tamblyn
Indstrl Arts & Tech Ed Instr
Tuggle, Cathy Parker
First Grade Teacher
FORT GAINES
Daniels, James Monroe
Parent Coordinator & Teacher
Glaze, Georgia Salary
Fifth Grade Teacher
Hartley, Bess
7th Grade Teacher
FORT OGLETHORPE
Anderson, Larry Woodward
Science Dept Chair & Teacher
Carlock, Brenda Rollins
Fourth Grade Teacher

Coe, Brenda Kaye
K-6th Grade Gifted Teacher
Forester, Shirley Bridges
Asst Prin & Vocational Dir
Greene, Willa K.
English Teacher
Hunt, Reese Thomas, Jr.
Biology Tchr & Wrestling Coach
Liner, Chip
Hlth & Physical Education Tchr
Richardson, Christie Renee
English Teacher
Souders, James A.
Band Director
Stephens, Carla Morgan
AP Senior English Teacher
FORT STEWART
Cabbage, James Richard
Religion & Philosophy Prof
Floyd, Billie G.
Teacher of the Gifted Program
FORT VALLEY
Adadevoh, Charles Olywatoyin
Computer Sci Asst Professor
Arora, Sanjeev
Assistant Professor of Physics
Barrett, Gary Doyle
Chemistry & Physics Teacher
Bellamy, Donnie D.
Regents Professor of History
Canty, George, Jr.
Emeritus Assoc Prof of Chem
Davis, Frances Wells
Fourth Grade Teacher
Felton, Annette Frances
Homebound Teacher
Fineran, Amy Henry
English Teacher
Fitchben, Susan Pauline
Tchr of the Visually Impaired
Gatliff, Susan Sheffey
Social Studies Teacher
Harris, Virgie Nobles
Assoc Prof of Speech & Drama
Heslin, J. Alexander, Jr.
Assoc Prof of Computer Science
Holloway, Anna Rebecca Wallace
Associate Professor of English
Hunt, Sharon K.
Assistant Professor
Jackson, Birdelle Martin
Sixth Grade Math & Sci Tchr
Jenkins, Carolyn Mallard
Third Grade Teacher
Jones, Yvonne Louise (Rumph)
Eighth Grade Science Teacher
Kicklighter, Teresa Kay
Teacher & Sci Dept Chprsn
Prevost, Michele Renee
Biology Teacher
Terrell, Marion
Associate Professor
Ward, Lillie D.
Computer Science & Math Prof
Wilson, Richard
Economics Professor
FORTSON
Parrish Johnson, Mary Sellers
Retired Middle School Teacher
FRANKLIN
Quinn, Hydie Johnson
English Teacher
Scott, Betty Holloway
Sixth Grade Teacher
Smith, Phillip Ballard
Fifth Grade Teacher
Worley, Robin Warren
Middle School Teacher
FRANKLIN SPRINGS
Edmonson, James H.
History Prof & Sci Dept Chair
Holcombe, Joan Robinson
Dept of Teacher Ed, Assoc Prof
Moon, Tony Gordon
Christian Ministries Professor
Peden, Ralph Kenneth
Professor of Education
GAINESVILLE
Anderson, Kelly M.
Band Director
Anthony, Jeffrey Neal
Computer Technology Teacher
Bagwell, Susan Brown
Principal
Bell, Lilla Daniels
Fifth Grade Teacher
Bell, Sylvia Stewart
First Grade Teacher
Bolding, Deborah Reynolds
Assoc Professor of Mathematics
Boring, Diane W.
Fifth Grade Teacher
Britton, Linda Borie
Guidance Counselor
Brown, Jan L.
Retired Fourth Grade Teacher
Bryant, Marion Randolph
Fourth Grade Teacher
Bryant, Pam Adams
Math Teacher
Buffington, Shelly Garner
Special Education Teacher
Byrne, Lynda Terrell
English Dept Chair, Curr Coord
Clendenning, Lee Roy, Jr.
Asst Prof of Mathematics
Cook, Diane Brothers
Asst Professor of Psychology
Crandall, Dale Sherman
Foreign Language Dept Head

GAINESVILLE (cont)
Duck, Mary Faye M.
8th Grade Mathematics Teacher
Dunn, Carlene Martin
Math Dept Chairman & Teacher
Dunn, Mark D.
Social Studies Teacher
Elliott, Bradley Eugene
9th & 10th Grade Teacher
Elrod, Carol Ann
Mathematics Professor
Emery, Joseph William
Art Instructor
Foster, Beverly Jean
Health & Physical Teacher
Garrett, Cristie D.
Cooperative Bus Ed Coordinator
Greear, Delbert P. T.
Mathematics Tutor
Hall, Beverly Hogan
English Teacher
Hamilton, John Michael
Associate Professor of Biology
Harkins, Barbara Jean
Math, Soc Stud & Lang Arts
Hayes, Judith Lane
English Teacher
Hebda, Piotr W.
Assistant Professor of Math
Hendrickson, Andrew Gerard
Drafting Teacher
Hermann, Barbara Jean
Assoc Prof of Behavioral Sci
Hughes, Jo Ellen Albertson
Third Grade Teacher
Husby, Sue Duff
Fifth Grade Teacher
Johnson, Shelbie Carter
English Instructor
Jones, Andrea R.
High School English Teacher
Jonick, Christine A.
Asst Professor of Bus Admin
Lee, Hilda Gilleland
First Grade Teacher
Lynn, Lois E.
Assoc Professor of Bus Admin
Martin, Clara Morris
Mass Media Specialist
Mas, Carmen A.
Assoc Professor of Psychology
Mayhew, Edmond A.
Professor of Biology
McEachin, Nina Beggs
Sixth Grade Teacher
Mc Leod, Glenda Wall
English Professor
Mills, Robert M.
Health & PE Teacher
Moore, Peggy
Media Specialist
Morgan, Stacey Henson
8th Grade Science Teacher
Morrison, Louise E.
Math Teacher & Chair
Moulder, Maureen V.
Special Education Teacher
Mullis, Karen Leigh
Physical Education Teacher
Newberry, Margaret Pierce
History Professor
Nicholson, Karen Shea
12th Grade English Teacher
Nix, Montey Walters
First Grade Teacher
O'Kelley, Diane Hally
Kindergarten & 1st Grd Tchr
Pastorino, Ellen
Assoc Prof of Psychology
Prescott, Rita Palumbo
High School English Teacher
Prezel, Jean C.
Chemistry & Science Teacher
Ray, Betty J.
Second Grade Teacher
Roark, Joe D.
Construction Teacher
Schaap, Eve English
Counselor
Sharpley, Marilyn A.
First Grade Teacher
Shockley, Charles Lewis
Fifth Grade Teacher
Smith, Elizabeth Robertson
Gifted Program Teacher
Smith, Randall Markham
8th Grade Teacher
Smith, Rebecca Sewell
Social Studies Teacher
Stewart, Melissa E.
Secondary Mathematics Teacher
Stover, Lisa D.
Choral Director
Thom, Robert James
Spcl Ed Services Chm
Tolbert, Debbie N.
4th Grade Teacher
Watson, Elaine Halley Strickland
Proj Success Intrlk Math Instr
Watts, Annette Culberson
Science Teacher & Coach
White, Hanna Ashford
Third Grade Teacher
Wilkes, Marsha Dalton
Mathematics Teacher
Williams, Claire Foster
Retired Kindergarten Teacher
Williams, Sheryl Leverett
Assoc Professor of Chemistry
Wolf-Smith, Jane Hills
Prof of Sociology & Soc Work
Yamilkoski, Loretta Watkins
Second Grade Teacher
Zaun, George Herman
Military Academy Staff
GARDEN CITY
Melvin, Timothy Scott
8th Grade Social Studies Tchr
GIBSON
Garner, Dale M.
6th Grade Teacher
Moss, Eileen Ganci
Fourth Grade Teacher
GLENNVILLE
Blocker, Judy Thompson
Second Grade Teacher
Dykes, Betty J.
Assistant Principal
Porter, James Logan
English & History Teacher
Porter, Miriam Barnard
Math & Music Teacher
GRAY
Altman, Frances Jones
6th Grd Mathematics & Sci Tchr
Bowden, Linda Hilburn
Spanish Teacher
Briley, Debra Farmer
Business Education Teacher
Combs, Curtis
Secondary English Teacher
Dufford, Constance I.
Math Teacher
Faulkner, Jody Childs
1st Grade Teacher
Freeman, J. Lavane Paramore
Fourth Grade Teacher
Hamilton, Cynthia Gail
Special Education Teacher
Jones, Martha Lee Sorrow
Rdng, Eng Tchr & Team Leader
Scott, Linda Jordan
Social Studies & English Tchr
Starr, Nancy Yawn
School Counselor
Svensson, Debra Rose Mc Mahon
Art Tchr & Self-Defense Instr
GREENSBORO
Lovin, Bruce Griffith
Science Teacher
Rainwater, Davilyn Loving
Art Teacher
GREENVILLE
Geer, Sue Burt
Business Education & CBE Coord
Samuels, Muriel Shelton
Math Teacher
Terry, Dora Gates
Media Specialist
Tigner, Frank Hill, III
World Studies Instructor
Tigner, Suzanne Stukes
Multi-Age Class Teacher
GRIFFIN
Barrett, Joyce D.
Retired Elementary Teacher
Beaton, Richard Joseph
Latin Teacher
Benz, Todd David
Latin & English Instructor
Brown, Retha Hollis
4th Grade Teacher
Canterbury, Hugh Franklin
AP Psychology Teacher
Champion, Georgia Luckett
Lrnng Disabilities & ESL Tchr
Craft, David Michael
Social Studies Teacher
Daniel, Myra McKinney
History Teacher
Doane, Michelle Helton
8th Grade Lang Arts Teacher
Dunham, Frances Glorioso
US History Tchr & Dept Chair
Graves, Elaine Harvey
6th Grd Math & Science Teacher
Hanes, Clark
World History Teacher
Harris, Elizabeth Piper
English Teacher
Hiers, Grace M.
Chemistry Teacher
Kimble, Virginia Fears
Chorus & Music Apprec Tchr
Lipper, Stephen Wayne
Former French & Speech Tchr
Manley, Anne Hilger
Teacher of Gifted
Nash, Barbara Blackmon
5th Grade Teacher
Reynolds, Edward Howell
Georgia History Teacher
Snell, Wiley Edward
Asst Principal
Whitley, Janet Curlee
Health Occupations Teacher
Williamson, James Paul
Science Teacher
Williamson, Rachel Anne DiGioia
Biology Teacher
GROVETOWN
Akins, Lois Bradley
Violin Teacher & Director
HAHIRA
Hutchinson, Kenneth R.
Social Studies Teacher
Touchton, Chandler Mc Caskill
Science Teacher
HAMILTON
Davis, David E.
Music Teacher
Hubbard, Carla Ingalls
Social Studies Teacher
Johnson, Phyllis N.
Health Occupations Teacher
Midgette, T. Michelle
English Teacher
Morgan, William Franklyn
Tchr & In Schl Suspension Dir
Thomason, Melanie Whitten
Amer Lit Tchr & Coach
HARLEM
Born, Debbie Anne
MS PE, Health Tchr & Coach
Bradshaw, Patty Thomas
High School English Teacher
Campbell, Mary Bennett
Social Studies Dept Head
Floyd, Judith Starr
Home Economics Teacher
Hollands, Mary Clackler
Science Teacher
Kitchens, Pamela Jean
Science Teacher & Dept Head
Mitchell, Athena Diane Dorn
AP, CP Eng Tchr & Dept Head
Perez, Dietmar Felix
History Teacher
HARTSFIELD
Howell, James Douglas
Principal
Strickland, Julie (Poole)
Media Specialist
HARTWELL
Carroll, Pam Sanders
4th Grade Teacher
Certain, Janice Bond
Fifth Grade Teacher
Fennell, Donna Pruitt
First Grade Teacher
Hulme, Martha Ann
Lit Teacher & Eng Dept Chair
Mann, Frank
Physics, Chem Tchr & Dept Head
Mize, Suzanne Holbrook
English Teacher
Pitt, Tammy Hicks
1st Grade Teacher
Stephens, Michelle A.
Agriculture Teacher
Washko, Sandra Elizabeth
First Grade Teacher
HAWKINSVILLE
Hill, Judith Moore
Mathematics Teacher
HAZLEHURST
Bowen, Karen Collins
Counselor
Daniel, Donna Lynn
Coll Prep Eng Tchr & Chprsn
Hurley, Martha Carol
English Teacher
Miles, Denise L.
High School Math Teacher
Mills, Leslie Pearson
Mathematics Teacher
Moore, Jacklyn Williams
Business Education Teacher
Ryles, Arlene T.
Kindergarten Teacher
Toole, Connie Douberly
Family & Consumer Science Tchr
HELENA
Routh, Catherine O'Connor
Former Teacher
HEPHZIBAH
Cofer, Barbara Golden
Art Teacher
Hankinson, Brenda Johnson
8th Grade Lang Arts Teacher
Harrell, Barbara T.
Math Teacher
Hicks, Terrie Lynn
Physical Education Teacher
Joiner, Todd Andrew
History Teacher
McKie, Ronald
Eighth Grade Literature Tchr
Norris, Thomas James
7th Grade Math Teacher
Sisler, Bonnie Carter
Mathematics Teacher
HIAWASSEE
Berrong, Angela Anne Kitchens
Title I Reading Teacher
Flanagan, Irma Plott
English Teacher
Flanagan, Thomas William, Jr.
History Teacher
Withers, Mary Cresent
K-12th Grade Music Teacher
HINESVILLE
Baker, Lily H.
Health & PE Teacher
Brock, Leigh Woodward
Band Dir & Fine Arts Dept Chpr
Chalker, Linda Reddish
Tchr of Mildly Disabled
Culver, Lester Albert, Jr.
Diversified Coop Teacher
Durden, Amanda Ashburn
Choral Director
Dutton, Catherine
6th Grade Reading Teacher
Ellis, Raymond R., Jr.
Choral Director
Etheridge, James Ralph
Advanced Placement Teacher
Everett, Virginia Peterson
Mathematics Teacher
Ginn, Ray Lavon
Health & Physical Ed Teacher
Golden, Lillie Jones
8th Grade Earth Science Tchr
Kelly, Lillie
Health, PE Teacher & Coach
Mixon, Susan Dollar
Social Studies Teacher
Patterson, Lilla Durden
Elementary Math Resource Tchr
Patterson, Paige Lilla
English Teacher
Podmore, Walter Eugene
Science Teacher
Remppel, Joanne Marie
Visual Arts Teacher
Sandoval, Jeannie Askew
Art Teacher
Scott, Jerry L.
Science Teacher
Scott, Patricia Jan
7th Grd Composition & Lit Tchr
Seale, Robert Christopher
Pre-Kindergarten Teacher
Shumans, Edward T.
Math Teacher & Dept Head
Smitherman, Maggie Jackson
Science Teacher
Tatum, Karen Elaine
Science Teacher
Walker, Barbara C.
5th Grd Lang Arts Tchr
Washington, Ethel Smith
Mathematics Teacher
Watson, Merle Harriett (Prim)
History Teacher
Williams, Carolyn Carr
Biology & Anatomy Teacher
Wright, James Michael
Youth & Sports Director
Yancey, Stanley Allen, Jr.
Business Teacher
HOGANSVILLE
Curtis, David Stevens
Physics Teacher
Trammell, Sue Hannah
Business Education Teacher
HOLLY SPRINGS
Anderson, Tracie Teague
Fifth Grade Teacher
Gay, Deborah Stanfield
6th Grade Teacher
HOMER
Marlow, Harold Dennis
Physical Education Teacher
Standridge, Warren Dean
Hlth & Physical Education Tchr
Vaughn, Connie V.
High School Math Teacher
HOMERVILLE
Leccese, Jean Jones
English & Business Ed Teacher
Meltz, Victoria
Science Teacher
Tison, Pamela H.
1st Grade Teacher
IRWINTON
Knight, Mary Hall
Eighth Grade Teacher
Preyer, Lillie Joyce
Government & Economics Teacher
Reece, Lisa Mc Donald
4th Grade Teacher
Stanley, Susan Brinson
5th Grade Teacher
JACKSON
Lunsford, Carole L.
Mathematics Teacher
Redding, Gladys Thompson
4th Grade Teacher
JASPER
Davis, Janet Holmes
DCT Coordinator
Duff, Daniel Ellis
PE Tchr & Ftbl Coach
Fountain, Jerry Denton
Fifth Grade Teacher
Hermann, Suzette Mc Taggart
Mathematics Teacher
Pickering, Kathy Pearce
Title I Teacher
Schlenke, Debra Keener
Science Teacher
Young, Anthony William
World History Teacher
JEFFERSON
Fitzpatrick, Sandra Sailors
Teacher & Coord of the Gifted
Goodman, Oscar Anderson
Assistant Principal
Schwartz, Janet Cline
English Tchr & Dept Chairman
JEFFERSONVILLE
Gantt, Amanda Jones
Remediation Teacher
Johnson, Don L.
Science Teacher
Rich, Lisa Maureen
English Teacher
Stanley, Allene Flagg
9th-12th Grd Business Teacher
JESUP
Blash, Kermit T.
Math Teacher
Denty, Jamie Ruth
Eng & Jrnlsm Tchr
Galvin, James G.
Agricultural Instructor
Moseley, Tina Howard
Seventh Grade English Teacher
Odum, Sharlene Mc Intyre
Lang Arts & Soc Studies Tchr
Thomas, Richard Alexander
Athletic Director
Voyles, Denise Dukes
Teacher of Gifted Education
Williams, John Wayne, Jr.
Chemistry Teacher
JONESBORO
Adams, Debbie Grethen
Third Grade Teacher
Ball, Rubye Harris
7th Grade Language Arts Tchr
Byrom, Donald Lamar, Jr.
Georgia History Teacher
Cox, Diane Crane
English Teacher
Crane, Celeste Vinson
Fourth Grade Teacher
Croft, Clara Susan
English Teacher
Cunningham, Lovely Charlene
Special Education Teacher
Curry, Gregory L.
Hlth, Sci & Computer Tech Tchr
Ferguson, Cynthia Wendling
Mathematics Teacher
Fleming, Janelle Smith
Social Studies Dept Chprsn
Fox, Joan R.
Tchr of Academically Gftd Pgm
George, Cindy Schell
Instructional Lead Teacher
Hudson, Julee Sams
English & Latin Teacher
Jackson, Cynthia Diane
Physiology & Human Antmy Tchr
Johnson, Connie Whitehead
3rd Grade Teacher
Martin-Podobnikar, Martha Ame
Fifth Grade Teacher
May, Sandra Kae
First Grade Teacher
Mixon, Jean Cobb
Senior English Teacher
Moon, Ashby Joe
Eighth Grade Math Teacher
Newton, Lurline
Coord, Cooperative Bus Ed Tchr
Olivier, Leon Louis, Jr.
Chem & Prin of Tech Teacher
Parish, Wanda Manning
Second Grade Teacher
Puckett, Michael Neal
Director of Bands
Richard, Susan Carol
First Grade Teacher
Salter, Sherrill Chandler
Fourth Grade Teacher
Scruggs, Bernadette Butler
Orchestra Teacher
Sigler, Cynthia Marie
Dance Teacher
Steiner, Peg Horne
English Teacher
Stillions, Gregory Wayne
Health Teacher & Coach
Stokes, Gloria Bryant
Latin Teacher
Sweeney, Lorena Foster
2nd Grade Teacher
Vickery, Janice Swain
Second Grade Teacher
Zimmerman, Michelle M.
9th-12th Grd Science Teacher
KENNESAW
Attaway, Dennis Bryant
Mathematics Teacher
Balentine, Jeannie Cannon
Mathematics Teacher
Barras, Patricia Anne
English Division Head & Tchr
Biggers, Cliff D.
English Teacher
Bowman, Michelle Therese (Szum)
High School Mathematics Tchr
Brown, Elsa Osiris Villarreal
Spanish Teacher
Brown, Reva M.
Sixth Grade Language Arts Tchr
Bruner, Marie Castro
Spanish Teacher
Burke, Barbara Barton
Teacher of Gifted
Burton, Elizabeth Dorsett
Physics Teacher
Butts, Cathy Clark
French Teacher
Carroll, Beverly Moulder
Third Grade Teacher
Dickens, Michael Sean
Business Education Teacher
Dukes, Alan Lynn
US History Teacher
Fennell, Susan Hathcock
High School Math Teacher
Fuchko, Linda Deasy
K-8th Grade Teacher
Gandolfo, Paul F.
Eighth Grade Math Tchr & Coord
Hagemann, Betsy Downer
English Teacher
Hagerty, Linda Grocott
Academic Dean
Hawkins, Christina F.
Secondary Science & PE Teacher
Hightower, Edward Holman, Jr.
Special Education Tchr & Coach

SAW (cont)
Van Lee
nics Teacher
, Candy Clymer
y & Government Teacher
, Willie Ray
ad Dept Chair & Teacher
andra Presley
er of the Gifted
di
r 3rd Grade Teacher
David M.
h & French Teacher
Paula Weyl
n Comm & English Teacher
on, Linda Uram
udies Tchr & Dept Chair
Andrea Medlock
d Social Studies Tchr
o, Alex Russell
n Teacher
a C.
ade Science Teacher
d M.
Professor of Chemistry
d, Pamela
School Teacher
David Lee
World History Teacher
tricia Carnation
h Teacher
Edwin Robyn
Bus Owner
n, Claudia Holmes
Dept Chairman & Teacher
t, Melanie Elizabeth
ud & Behavioral Sci Tchr
r, Robert Gene
or of Bands
on, Thomas Gene
Studies Teacher
George Wade
Astrnmy & Earth Sci Tchr
an, Mary G.
istry Teacher
man, Edwin Frank
d & Vocal Director
, Kim Escoe
matics Teacher
on, Carol Jo
ant Professor of Spanish
e, Margaret Wilder
rade Teacher of GATE
Herman Edward, Jr.
istry Teacher
BAY
Noel E.
of Education & Dev Stud
ld-Wilson, Gwendolyn Sue
ct Professor of History
ed Donovan
ssor of English
SLAND
nd, Josephine Keeter
or of Gifted Education
e, Patricia Chapman
ce Teacher
ne Miller
rd Algebra & Lit Teacher
n, Teresa L.
Teacher
Mary Donna Linton
Chemistry Teacher
Barbara Howard
sh Instructor
ghter, Mary Ann Todd
Grade English Teacher
tz, Jessie Thomas
sh Prof & Asst Dean
ris C.
ematics Teacher
ski, Kathy Pounds
Grade Language Arts Tchr
n, Charles Dwayne
Grade US History Teacher
Diane Williams
uage Arts Teacher
s, Wayne F.
Director
orn, Linda L.
ner of Gifted
STON
Carol Lynn
Grade Teacher
YETTE
, E. Jean
sh Teacher
ee, Judy Young
Hlth Occupations Instr
Betty Haynes
ematics Teacher
gwe, Pamela Suttles
ogy Teacher
aney, Charles Kevin
al Studies Tchr & Ath Dir
s, Sandra Gilreath
Grade Teacher
t, Stacy Jill
ial Education Teacher
, John Larry
ematics Department Chprsn
ANGE
ht, Jewell Corbitt
Grade Math Teacher
John Joseph, Sr.
ematics Teacher
son, Norma Jane
Grade Teacher
, Cynthia Moore
d Grade Teacher

Beckom, Yolonda Cruz
Math Teacher
Benjamin, Faye Patricia
PE Teacher & Coach
Brown, Vee S.
Assistant Professor of Art
Cain, Carol Diane
English & Drama Teacher
Cammon, Dorothy D.
Eng Tchr & Tchr of Gifted
Carwell, Jane Garrett
Social Studies Teacher
Cone, Gordon B.
History Teacher
Cook, Sandy Guy
History Teacher
Denney, Louise Sloan
Math Teacher
Ellis, Barbara Kirby
Science Teacher
Faucette, Tippi Anne
Spanish Teacher
Frazier, Robert Tyndall
Math Teacher
Gaddy, Elizabeth Ann
Social Studies Teacher
Gaffney, Martha Davis
Choral Music Teacher
Gooden, Anderson, Jr.
Administrator
Harris, Timothy Martin
AP English Tchr & Drama Dir
Hart, Brenda Godfrey
10th Grd World History Teacher
Holloway, Linda Ann Potts
5th Grade Teacher
Hood, Wilton Clayton
In-Schl Suspension & Lead Tchr
Johnson, Raymond Edward
High School Band Director
Leverett, Laurie Kathryn
Kindergarten Teacher
Lucas, Dan Matthew
Social Studies Teacher
Mc Cook, Elaine Laster
5th Grade Teacher
Moncus, Andrea Noble
Creative Writing Teacher
Moncus, Michael M.
Asst Principal & History Tchr
Newman, Mary Seay
High School Art Teacher
Olney, Nancy Helen
Art Instructor
Phillips, Jacqueline S.
Bus Ed Tchr & CBE Coord
Teaster, Jane Teaster
Guidance Counselor
Trask, Mary Jo
Eighth Grade Algebra I Tchr
Ward, Gary Kenard
Hlth, Physical Ed Tchr & Coach
Yancey, Jimmy L., Jr.
Social Studies Teacher
LAKE PARK
Curtis, Nancy Ruth Harris
2nd Grade Teacher
LAKELAND
Brantley, Gloria M. Alexander
6th Grade Language Arts Tchr
Cowart, Joy Ganas
5th Grd Language Arts Teacher
Downs, Barbara Lynn
8th Grade Mathematics Teacher
LAWRENCEVILLE
Bahn, Gary Arnold
Assistant Principal
Burnham, Jill Schwartz
Early Childhood Education Tchr
Busby, Sandra Hurst
Language Arts Teacher
Collins, Thomas William
Biology Teacher
Collum, Patricia High
6th Grade Teacher
Fite, Rosa N.
Math & Science Teacher
Handwork, Joyce Marie
Instr of Developmental Math
Hill, Ranelle Crosby
Business Education Teacher
Hollstein, Kip Gene
Science & Social Studies Tchr
Jones, Lee Brewer
Assoc Prof Developmental Eng
Lingo, Patricia Glover
Former Teacher
Lyon, Carol Schumacher
Second Grade Teacher
Madsen, Carolyn Peetz
Assistant Principal
Manson, Valerie Lowe
Assistant Principal
Mathison, Regina Parnell
Fifth Grade Teacher
Moon, Brenda Berry
Tutor
Murray, John Marshall, III
Social Studies Teacher
Panimdim, Nilva Sucano
Missionary Teacher
Paxton, Jerry
Teacher
Reavis, Bonnie Simpson
7th Grade Life Science Teacher
Reed, Laura Lane
Fifth Grade Teacher
Spencer, Shirley D.
6th Grade Teacher

Whitten, Diane Quattlebaum
6th Grade Science Teacher
Wilson, Cheryl Jean (Avery)
Principal
Wilson, Frances Bailey
ESOL Teacher
LEESBURG
Benton, Amy Timmons
Science Teacher
Bowling, Cynthia K.
Science Teacher
Davis, Kimberly Paul
High School Algebra Teacher
Davis, Robert Lee, Jr.
English Teacher & Theatre Dir
Hayes, Judy P.
Fourth Grade Teacher
Joiner, Vicki E. (McGraw)
Sixth Grade Teacher
Jones, Linda R.
Mathematics Teacher
Justice, Barry Walton
4th & 5th Grd HOTS Tchr
Massey, Janet Klages
Georgia Studies Teacher
Mears, Suzanne Summers
Fourth Grade Teacher
Mears, Tim
Counselor & Coach
Melvin, Gail Stevenson
Instructional Supervisor
Pennington, Rosemond Russ
Kindergarten Teacher
Ruckel, Elaine Neal
English Teacher
Scozzari, Sherri Long
Physical Education Teacher
Smith, Margaret Joan
7th Grade English Teacher
Turner, Susan Perry
8th Grd Georgia Studies Tchr
Ward, Michael Henry
Biology Teacher
Watts, Hugh Stanley
In School Suspension Teacher
Wilkinson, Thad H.
5th Grade Teacher
Williams, Andrew Michael
Band Director
LEXINGTON
Ammons, Cynthia Rhea (Hudson)
Mathematics Teacher
Jackson, Joanna F.
School Counselor
Winchester, Tammy Annette
Health & Physcial Ed Teacher
LILBURN
Bailey, Michael Paul
English Teacher
Block, Jeselyn Creasy
Family & Consumer Science Tchr
Broucek, Carolyn Bennett
Honors Biology Teacher
Bryant, Brandi Graham
Mathematics Teacher
Buchanan, Marlene Ratledge
Counselor
Burkhalter Page, Stephanie
Gifted Resource Teacher
Cahoon, Jane E.
Language Arts Instructor
Cantrell, Nancy Lynn
Second Grade Teacher
Childs, L. Kay
1st-2nd Grade Teacher
Cleckler, Melodie Gail
Mathematics Teacher
Cox, Denise Svajko
Kindergarten Teacher
Creed, Frederick Henry
Mathematics Instructor
Crum, Sheryl Simmen
Mathematics Teacher
Harrison, Katherine Bolinger
First-Second Grade Teacher
King, Carla Maxwell
Math Teacher
Lane, Peggy
Fifth Grade Teacher
Leach, Deborah Dickinson
Language Arts Teacher
Leeks, Alexis Bryant
8th Grade Social Studies Tchr
Leetch, John Dougal
High School Bible Teacher
Lucy, Joanne Peterson
9th-12th Grd Biology Teacher
Mann, Doris Petrea
ESOL Teacher
Mc Adams, Sandra Jones
Mathematics Teacher
Medwick, Debra Lou (Graff)
Special Education Teacher
Moody, Debra Tatum
Teacher of Gifted Program
Morris, Marilyn Fairrel
Mathematics Teacher
Parks, Rosalie Rottler
Math & Georgia History Teacher
Pierce, Arthur John
Sixth Grade Teacher
Powell, Wendy Weigle
Spcl Education Tchr & Chprsn
Purvis, Carolyn O'Neil
Former Teacher
Roach, Dick E.
8th Grade Math Teacher
Robinson, Patsy Welborn
Social Studies Teacher

Sarfaty, Jack Edward
High School Math Teacher
Schwartz, Karrie Ann
Honors World His & Debate Tchr
Sheldon, Janie Galloway
Lang Arts Tchr & GF Pgm Coord
Stacks, Nona Wood
Eighth Grade Science Teacher
Stromie, Dennis Edward
Social Studies Teacher
Totten, Dan
HS English Teacher
Traylor, Sharon Dollar
Eighth Grade Teacher
Werner, Alice Marilyn
Language Arts Teacher
Wilson, Patti Simonides
First Grade Teacher
LINCOLNTON
Beale, LuAnn Parks
US History Teacher
Edmunds, Trudy B.
Mathematics Tchr & Dept Chprsn
Garnett, Mamie Louise
11th Grade English Teacher
Hogan, John Robert
Science Tchr & Dept Chairman
Olson, Carol Williams
Fifth Grade Teacher
Rhodes, Helene Kathren
Spanish Teacher
LINDALE
Gillespie, Timothy Eric
Language Arts Teacher
Harkins, Julie Ayer
English Teacher
Mann, Nancy Stripling
Language Arts Teacher
Paredes, Kellie Baumgartner
Spanish Teacher
Pinson, John Franklin
History Teacher
Silver, Gail Eden
Social Studies Teacher
Tunnell, Kimberly Hill
Music Teacher
LITHIA SPRINGS
Greene, Paul E.
Science Department Chairman
Hardnett, Helen Beryhill
4th Grade Teacher
Hector, Homer Lee
High School Teacher & Coach
Hedges, Rachel Lee
Social Science Teacher
Hood, Camilla R.
AP US His & Journalism Tchr
Jimenez, Ann Barbara
Gifted Education Teacher
Johnson, Mandy Sparks
Business Education Teacher
Nixon, Ginger Lin
Business Teacher
Sears, Ilse Navas
High School Spanish Teacher
Spence, Paul W.
Earth Science Teacher
Trout, David L.
HS Mathematics Teacher
Waller, Lynda Nix
Home Economics Tchr & Dept Chm
White, Georgia Pelter
5th-6th Grd Math & Sci Tchr
Wisehart, Michael Scott
8th Grade Teacher
LITHONIA
Adams, Jimmie L.
Science Teacher
Arnold, Debra
French Teacher
Atkins, Denise Johnson
Third Grd Tchr & Comp Spclst
Birdseye, Maria Felicia (Bittner)
7th Grade Science Teacher
Bissell, Rand Lee
Social Studies Dept Head
Connally, Linda Dee
Math Teacher
Davis, Lorraine Daye
In-School Suspension Instr
Fletcher, Laurie
Seventh Grade Teacher
Gambrell, Cheryl M.
Mathematics Teacher
Hawkins, Hope J.
High School Math Teacher
Hays, Tara Atkinson
Language Arts Teacher
Hudnall, Catherine Ruth
Orchestra Teacher & Director
Huey, Patsy Decker
English Teacher & Dept Chair
Jones, Ivan Dunlavy, III
High School History Teacher
Jones, Thomasena Griffin
Third Grade Teacher
Jordan, Charlie F.
PE Tchr & Head Ftbl Coach
McDonald, Cynthia Strickland
Spanish Teacher
Moore, Mary-Frances Montano
8th Grade Spec Ed Teacher
Musick, Angela Wood
Fifth Grade Teacher
Penn, Janna Darlene
Mathematics Teacher
Pharr, Irish Mc Collum
6th Grade Math Teacher
Poppe, Pamela Elizabeth
Mathematics Tchr & Dept Chair

Printz, Becky
Social Studies Teacher
Sery, Linda Andrews
Pre-Algebra Teacher
Stewart-Reese, Alice
Guidance Counselor
Tichelaar, Kay Altman
High School Counselor
Vander Velde, Todd F.
Technology Education Teacher
Walter, Beckey Ardd
6th Grd Teacher
Ward, Nancy Avriett
9th Grd Language Arts Teacher
Ware, Katherine Pepper
Anatomy & Physiology Instr
LOCUST GROVE
Robinson, Jane Little
Fifth Grade Teacher
LOGANVILLE
Doster, George W., Jr.
Chemistry & Physics Teacher
Greene, Gina Minton
Frgn Language Teacher
Harwood, Frank W.
High School Biology Teacher
Rutter, Karen Lord
Family & Consumer Science Tchr
LOOKOUT MOUNTAIN
Yonts, Jane Allen
5th-6th Grade Science Teacher
LOUISVILLE
Armstrong, Ve'Ester Tooks
Science Teacher
Arnold, Stacy Raley
English & Journalism Teacher
Brown, Nancy Mullins
Mathematics Teacher
Farmer, Ellen V.
Counselor
Fields, Michael Wayne
History Teacher
Holbert, Patricia Linville
Assistant Principal
Holbert, Robert Lee
Social Studies Teacher, Chprsn
Johnson, Gregory
5th Grade Teacher
Joslin, Rebecca J.
Secondary Mathematics Teacher
Mack, Eunice Paradise
Business & Technology Teacher
Silver, David Louis
Director of Bands
Swint, Edna Braddy
Business Education Teacher
LOVEJOY
Adams, Priscilla Anne
English Teacher
Brunn, Fran Foster
7th Grade Math Teacher
Corwin, Frederick Scott
Social Studies Teacher
Federovitch, Dianne (Wall)
AP English Teacher
Ivey, Nelle Murray
Secondary Mathematics Teacher
Johnson, Sandra R.
Instructional Lead Teacher
Jones, Louann
United States History Teacher
Marr, Sharon Martinez
High School Science Teacher
Re-Darling, Domini
High School Art Teacher
Schultz, Jennifer Ann
German Teacher
Simich, Susan Mc Cranie
Dance, Drama & Speech Teacher
Stone, Shirley Ann
Chemistry Teacher
Stroup, Lorabeth Fisher
French Teacher & Dept Chair
Stumpf, Brenda F.
10th Grd Biology Teacher
Thompson, Jackie Duckworth
Lang Arts & Soc Stud Tchr
Williams, Owen Brian
Choral Director
LUDOWICI
Kennedy, Rhonda Williams
English Teacher
Madray, Libby Warner
7th Grade Mathematics Teacher
LULA
Griffin, Karen Brock
Second Grade Teacher
Justus, Sarah Harris
Fifth Grade Teacher
LUMPKIN
Barrett, Anna Laura Mayo
Pre-Kindergarten Teacher
Hart-Williams, Tresa
System Wide Art Teacher
Moses, Patterson Leroy
World History Teacher
Perrymond, Fannie L.
Instr & English Dept Chprsn
LYONS
Brigman, Michelle Palmer
Algebra II Teacher
Fleury, Tanya Graham
Span Teacher & Drama Director
George, Robert W., Jr.
11th-12th Grd US History Tchr
Hart, Martha Mc Cullough
Fourth Grade Teacher
Kelhear, Mary Gibbs
Fourth Grade Teacher

LYONS (cont)
Mayo, Betty Anderson
Second Grade Teacher
MABLETON
Blair, Christopher William
12th Grade English Teacher
Grimes, Debbie Beal
High School Science Teacher
Hayes, LaJuan (Lawrence)
Learner Support Strategist
Jackson, C. Dean
English Teacher
Keeton, Katherene Zay
Learner Support Strategist
Morgan, John Thomas
Math Teacher
Scar, Teresa L.
High School Math Teacher
Tucker, Rose Marie Perez
Classroom Teacher
Wheeler, Jeanette Blount
8th Grade Earth Science Tchr
MACON
Abel, Floyd Smith, Jr.
Health & Physical Ed Teacher
Abore, E. Randolph
English Teacher
Adeboyejo, Queen Valerya
Eighth Grade Math Teacher
Ashley, Christine Mc Clinton
Second Grade Teacher
Bikus, Rita Jones
World, Amer His & Latin Tchr
Bivins, Angela Rena
Kindergarten Teacher
Booker, Gwendolyn Stroud
Biology & Chemistry Teacher
Bowens, Cheryl Gadson
Eighth Grd Language Arts Tchr
Braswell, Joann Grantling
Seventh Grade Teacher
Campbell, Sharon Denise (Moore)
Eighth Grd Language Arts Tchr
Chapman, Nelda Madge
Choral Director
Childers, Rita Wilson
Fourth Grade Teacher
Childs, Joseph Floyd
Social Studies Teacher & Coach
Cleghorn, Deborah Gail
7th-12th Grd English Teacher
Copelan, Ashley Amos
Span Tchr & Cheerleading Coach
Cubit, Gregory
Art Teacher
Davidson, Chip
History Teacher
Davis, Beth Parker
Second Grade Teacher
Davis, Brenda Kelley
Vocational Supervisor & Tchr
Decker, James David
Political Science Professor
Dermatas, Amelia Bambalis
Biology Teacher
Drumm, Cheryl Gill
Third Grade Teacher
Durand, Robert C.
Assistant Professor of History
Eisel, Charlotte Stallworth
English Teacher
Felder, Ishmell
Administrative Asst & Teacher
Fobbs, Darrell Jennings
7th Grade Teacher
Funderburk, Jeffery S.
Choral Director
Gaines, Gwendale Deloris
8th Grade Social Studies Tchr
Garvin, Michael Joseph
High School Math Teacher
Giles, Leonard Arnold
Band Director
Glover, Selender Tatman
Sixth Grade Teacher
Gonzalez, Dale A.
Spanish Teacher
Grace, Emilie Kemp
Social Studies Teacher
Greene, Elaine White
English Teacher
Greer, Kay Smith
Latin Teacher
Haley, Anne Rigby
Foreign Lang Dept Chair & Tchr
Hall, Carolyn James
Mathematics Teacher
Harnsberger, Charles Whitfield
Assistant Professor of Biology
Hicks, Sandra McGhee
6th Grade Teacher
Hilburn, John Ragan
Physical Education Teacher
Hill, Willie D., Jr.
8th Grade Teacher
Hinderleider Mead, Diane
Art Dept Chair
Hood, Shirley
Career Planning Teacher
Hubbert, Rita Jane
8th Grd Earth Science Teacher
Hunt, Joseph Lee
6th Grade Teacher
Jarvis, Debra Sammons
Science Teacher
Jenkins, Pat Carter
Ninth Grade English Teacher
Johnson, Dorothy Purnell
First Grade Teacher
Johnson, Janice Yvonne
Sixth Grade Teacher
Jordan, Ida Glover
English Teacher
Jordan, Lorice Stewart
Middle School History Teacher
King, Wanda Bryant
2nd Grade Teacher
Kirby, Christopher Scott
Eng, Drama & Humanities Tchr
Lane, Linda Jones
1st Grade Teacher
Lavender, Debbie Marlin
Spanish & Chorus Teacher
Lewis, Gail Randall
Science Dept Chairperson
Long, Julie Selman
Mathematics Teacher
Maier, Darin Michael
Social Studies Teacher
Malone, Keela Whymms
Assistant Principal
Manard, Julia Phillips
English & Drama Teacher
Marsh, Regina E.
Kindergarten Teacher
Mc Call, Patricia Alene
Orchestra Teacher
McDuffie, Virginia Blanks
Sixth Grade Teacher
Mc Gee, Harry H., III
Psychology & Bible Teacher
Moehrbach, Kathleen Carter
Spanish Teacher
Montgomery, Jim L.
Language Arts Teacher
Moore, Judith Bonnette
Mathematics Teacher
Morris, Geraldine Rentz
Fourth Grade Teacher
Murphy, Edward J.
Assoc Prof of Pol Sci, Pub Adm
Nirenstein, Connie Jackson
Elementary Teacher
Nixon, Brenda Ashley
Soc Studies & Lang Arts Tchr
O'Brien, Carol Braren
History Teacher
Pace, Sandra McMillen
Science Teacher & Chprsn
Parker, Kirk Douglas
History Teacher
Prince, Jennifer Taylor
English Teacher
Reid, Carol Perkins
Biology Teacher
Roberts, Cynthia Mills
Social Studies Teacher
Roberts, Dianne Deese
Fifth Grade Teacher
Robinson, Irene Scales
K-8th Grd Teacher of Gifted
Rodgers, Diana Palmer
Gifted & Talented Teacher
Sams, Mary Davis
Counselor
Sheftall, Margaret Rucker
School Counselor
Sherwood, Donald T.
Math Teacher
Smith, Ann Harper
Instructor of Accounting
Smith, Suzann Waddell
Language Arts Teacher
Spann, Benjalyn
Science Lab Resource Coord
Sun, Eric L.
Asst Prof of Biology
Swint, John William, Jr.
Senior Social Studies Teacher
Tobias, Scott C.
Bands Director
Tucker, Marilyn M.
Spanish Teacher
Ussery, Sally Dominey
Fifth Grade Teacher
Wallace, Mary Little
First Grade Teacher
Ware, Cheryl Ethridge
Second Grade Teacher
Warren, Audrey Price
Elementary School Counselor
Watts, Darlene Appling
Fifth Grade Teacher
Webster, Pamela Fried
Inter-Related Resource Teacher
Weston, Gwen Johnston
Speech & Writing Teacher
Wilcox, Edward Talmadge, Jr.
Assistant Administrator
Wilson, Martha A.
Associate Professor of English
Woolfork, Paula Denise
Fourth Grade Teacher
Wright, Kathy Janann
Social Studies Teacher
Yarbrough, Patricia Holt
American History Teacher
Young, Gwenever Davis
Science Teacher
MADISON
Batchelor, Rhonda Ruark
Seventh Grade Teacher
Brewer, Emily Harper
Math Teacher
Duff, Julie Brown
8th Grade History & Govt Tchr
Holbert, Sara Lynn P.
Director
Jordan, Sylvia Ingram
8th Grade Teacher
Martin, Karen Lee (Rigsby)
5th Grade Teacher
Peek, Minnie Shepherd
7th Grade Science Teacher
Woods, Clarice Davis
Third Grade Teacher
MANCHESTER
Byrd, Emily Reid
History & Social Science Tchr
Robbins, Jennifer Snow
English Teacher
Tomlin, Patricia Tumlin
Bus Ed Tchr & CBE Coord
MANOR
Arnold, Deborah Hersey
Chemistry & Biology Teacher
MARIETTA
Adams, Andrew Powell
History Teacher
Adkins, Shirley Saunders
English Teacher
Afsharpour, Salman
Anatomy & Neurosci Asst Prof
Agee, Lizbeth Luke
7th Grade Social Studies Tchr
Alston, Katrina Ford
Kindergarten Teacher
Back, J. Michael
Assistant Band Director
Baker, Norman Allison
Technology Teacher
Baldree, Carolyn Price
Algebra & Pre-Algebra Teacher
Barrett, Cynthia Smith
Fifth Grade Teacher
Beck, Dexter Eugene, Jr.
Instructor
Beck, Lisa Anne
Assistant Dean
Bialko, Mary Rebecca
Family & Consumer Sci Teacher
Billington, Beth Akers
6th Grd Language Arts Teacher
Blackman, Rebecca M.
Social Studies Teacher
Bockhold, Heidi Marie
Technique Instructor
Bonza, Tracy Strange
Biology Teacher
Bridges, Kathy Coleman
High School English Teacher
Brooks, Loraine Clayton
Fifth Grade Teacher
Bryan, Harold Edward, Jr.
Social Studies Teacher & Coach
Bunte, Betsy Martin
Middle Schl Lang Arts Teacher
Camara, Diane Staubus
Spanish Teacher
Cantrell, Ann Bailey
4th Grade Teacher
Carpenter, Bonnie Cooper
Math Teacher
Cherry, Lisa Diane
Secondary Ed English Teacher
Clark, Frances H.
High School English Teacher
Clayman, Ruth Elaine
English Teacher
Coats, Jonnell Rowland
English Teacher
Cook, Lori Sue
Asst Prof Of Indstrl Engrng
Cook, Sherry J.
Management Professor
Cooke, Jerry Edward, Jr.
Science Teacher
Coursey, Joy (Pearson)
8th Grade Earth Science Tchr
Crowder-Eagle, Lynnda Bernard
Assistant Principal
Curington, Rosalyn Patterson
Music Teacher
Deavers, Edward Daniel
Theatre Teacher
DeSantiago, Luis E.
Spanish Teacher
Desenberg, Kenneth Charles
Air Force Jr ROTC Instructor
Dial, Mary Beth Liberto
English Teacher
Dobbs, Sandra Henderson
French Teacher
Douglas, Lillian Yvonne
Middle School Counselor
Durr, Ravan I.
Assistant Band Director
Dutter, Joan Anascavage
Sci Dept Chair & Physics Instr
Dye, Julia Ross
Vocational & Academic Ed Coord
Eaton, Jacqueline Gwen
MS Social Studies Teacher
Edwards, Linda G.
Spanish Teacher
Empie, Alice Winter
Upper School Principal
Eubanks, Nancy Stamey
Third Grade Teacher
Evans, Laverne
Learner Support Strategist
Ewing, Greg A.
Latin Teacher
Fleenor, James Gregory
English Teacher
Floyd, Rodney Keith
World History Teacher
Freeman, Lynn Morgan
Elementary Gifted Specialist
Freeman, Robin Minick
4th Grade Teacher
Frey, Gloria Anderson
Economics & Business Law Tchr
Frost, Lawrence D.
Geography & History Teacher
Fuller, Ted E.
8th Grade Algebra Teacher
Galli, Doreen Lynn
Assoc Prof of Computer Science
Gerhold, Gary Earl
Drafting Teacher
Gillis, Leslie Myers
Choral Director
Goldberg, Paul Aaron
Clncl Nutrition, Pub Hlth Prof
Goolsby, Beth Davis
Language Arts & Reading Tchr
Gribble, Gary Dale
High School Band Director
Hahn, Robert Allen
Senior Government Teacher
Hall, Julie Haydon
8th Grd Language Arts Teacher
Hansard, Annette Gibbs
Social Studies Teacher
Hawkins, William Joseph
Earth Science & Biology Tchr
Hayes, Beverly Coleman
Ninth Grade English Teacher
Heil, John Allen
Physics Teacher
Herron, Frances Burk
Second Grade Teacher
Hoefer, Michael T.
Asst Dean of Undergrad Schl
Hood, Northrup L.
Science Teacher
Hoomes, Eleanor Wolfe
Teacher of Gifted
Hoyum, Jerry Lee
Second Grade Teacher
Hughes, Dale Richard, Jr.
Phys Ed, Bible Tchr & Ath Dir
Humphreys, Karen K.
8th Grade Science Teacher
Hutcherson, Edwin Bailey
Health Educator
Hutton, Cristin C.
8th Grd Earth Science Teacher
Ireland, Theresa E.
Latin Teacher
Jenkins, Robin G.
Anatomy, Physiology & Bio Tchr
Jenks, Noel LeBaron
Latin Teacher
Johnson, Carolyn Hardee
4th Grade Teacher
Johnson, Don Garrett
Senior English Teacher
Keller, Jean Starr
5th Grade Teacher
Kellogg, Mary Marjorie
College Intervention Coord
Kelly, John Patrick
Physical Science & Chem Tchr
Kimberlin, Lynn T.
English & Reading Teacher
King, Lyn Melvin
Teacher of the Gifted
Knox, Ansley Moring
Seventh Grade Teacher
Lanxton, Kristi Milam
Learner Support Strategist
Lemco, Gary Robert
Associate Professor of English
Leong, Donna Ewing
First Grade Teacher
Lile, Margaret Bryington
7th Grade Math Teacher
Lile, Robert
Owner & Manager
Lowe, Pamela Harris
Art Teacher
Lund, Christopher Michael
Chemistry Teacher
Lyons, Sara A.
Social Studies Teacher
Mac Leod, Edward
Mathematics Teacher
Markham, Garland Euel
Instrumental Music Supervisor
Martin, Dawn Adams
7th & 8th Grd Tchr of Gifted
Martin, Jeanette Lucido
9th-12th Grd Tchr of Gifted Ed
Martin, Laura Renegar
6th Grade Science Teacher
Mathews, Angela Dorrough
English Teacher
Mc Afee, Joan Keogh
Theatre Teacher
Mullins, Michael Smylie
Teacher of At-Risk
Neal, Dianne Littlefield
8th Grade Social Studies Tchr
Neal, Kathryn Ann (Vaughn)
Mathematics Teacher
Newton, Patricia Greenlee
First Grade Teacher
Nodar, Jane Scally
5th Grade Teacher
O'Brien, Kaye Carter
Fourth Grade Teacher
O'Dell, Debra Clark
Kindergarten Teacher
Ohberg, Robert Nils
Chemistry & Physical Sci Tchr
Parkhurst, Donald Robert
Chemistry Teacher
Patton, Alice Cowan
7th Grade Life Science Teacher
Paule, Nancy Carson
Assistant Principal
Peery, Beth Archbold
Instructional Lead Teacher
Pezold, Emily Sue
Mathematics Teacher
Pool, Margaret Freeman
Eighth Grade Math Teacher
Pritchard, Howell Scott
HS Social Studies Teacher
Ralin, Dennis B.
Associate Professor of Biology
Reed-Smith, Susan
Fifth Grade Teacher
Rhoades, Sandra Jonas
Sci Dept Chair & Physics Tchr
Rhyne, Bruce Trimble
Biology & Anatomy Teacher
Rivers, Faye Letterman
English Teacher
Robertson, Robbie
Health & PE Teacher
Robertson, Theresa Rushton
Eighth Grade Teacher
Rossi, Armand Michael
Assistant Professor
Scarbrough, T. Brandon
Social Studies Teacher
Scherer, Mary F. Williamson
Secondary Mathematics Teacher
Schott, Kevin Frank
French, German Tchr & Coach
Seelman, Carol Ann
Third Grade Teacher
Shaw, Mary Jane Brabham
7th Grade Social Studies Tchr
Shook, Billie Higdon
Chorus & Music Teacher
Shue, Tamara Rellis
Instructor of English
Siegel, Murray H.
Mathematics Specialist
Smithweck, Marie Barfield
Preschl Asst & Music Teacher
Spaeth, Karen Gruber
HS Science Teacher
Stanford, Leslie Charles
Fourth Grade Teacher
Stathas, Vicky C.
Bio, Anatomy & Physiology Tchr
Stephens, Scott Alan
Latin Teacher
Stoddard, Jane Waters
Second Grade Teacher
Swann, James Rocky
Social Studies Teacher
Taylor, Bonnie I.
Third Grade Teacher
Taylor, Gregory
Science Teacher
Taylor, Patricia Bruce
8th Grd Teacher of Gifted
Thomas, Walter, Jr.
Textile Engrng Tech Professor
Thomasson, Cheryl Denise
Chem Teacher & Sci Dept Head
Thornton, Carla Coleman
Sixth Grade Math Teacher
Tippens, Scott Joseph
Electrical Professor
Titlow, Beverly Price
Latin Teacher
Todaro, Barbara Iversen
Social Studies Teacher
Tromblee, Sue Cantrell
Middle School Orchestra Dir
Tucker, Bruce Arnold
Campus Pastor & Teacher
Tynes, Joy Lynn
French Teacher
Underwood, Melissa Nelson
Teacher of the Gifted
Viger, William Joseph
Health Ed & Geography Tchr
Vilcoq, Judith Ann
5th Grade Teacher
Walker, Cathy Hallman
8th Grd Language Arts Teacher
Williams, Orren W.
Prof of Mechanical Engrng Tech
Willis, Gary L.
Assistant Professor
Wilson, Margaret Stump
Special Instrl Assistance Tchr
Wiseman, Thomas Lynn
English Associate Professor
Wooten, Nell Myers
First Grade Teacher
Youmans, Kenneth Byron
Visual Arts Teacher
Young, Donald Francis
Assoc Prof of Mathematics
MARTINEZ
Colberg, Bonnie Huckaby
History & English Teacher
Easter, Benny Ray
Band Director
Hawkins, Julie Armstrong
High School Spanish Teacher
MC DONOUGH
Barajas, Nancy H.
Spanish Teacher
Bodle, Amy Ballard
Art Teacher
Bradford-Hunt, Kristie
Chemistry Teacher

NOUGH (cont)
wanda Auzenne
ess Teacher
Tracey L.
sh Teacher
Dave Samuel
rd Math Tchr of Gifted
y Tuggle
ess Education Teacher
argaret M.
dary Mathematics Teacher
Teresa Guenther-Parramore
ce Teacher
Katherine Harvin
Studies Teacher
Janice Poulson
ome Economics Teacher
h, Ethan Joe David
sh Teacher
Alice Harding
Grade Teacher
, Adra Diane
Theatre & Jrnlsm Tchr
ity, Rita Parker
n Grade Teacher
vs, Betty Foster
School Spanish Teacher
wei, Suzanne Foster
School English Teacher
Gina H.
Tchr & Performing Arts Dir
, Barbara Ann
ematics Teacher
n, Debra Edwards
ematics Teacher
, Beverly A.
ematics Department Chair
Joyce Hayes
Grade Teacher
, George Russell, Jr.
ematics Teacher
Linda Kay
ce Teacher
AE
, John P.
ology Teacher
ulia E.
er & Bus Ed Dept Chrpsn
ns, Kim Wynell
y Services Coordinator
Timothy B.
l Studies Tchr & Dept Hd
s, Inez Marchant
Grade Teacher
ck, R. Scott
2th Grd Hlth & PE Tchr
l, Susie MC Rae
h Grade Teacher
, Coleen Watson
nth Grade Mathematics Tchr
, Carla Yvette
sh Teacher
Eva Clyde
ergarten Teacher
O
r, Carole S.
le Grades Teacher
d, Carolyn Wall
Arts & Soc Studies Tchr
ER
, Hilda Jarriel
Grd Teacher
, Joy Sarah
ry Teacher
tson, Terry Jean
rade Sci & Math Teacher
ndon, Teresa W.
sh Teacher
, Karen Lynn
selor & Teacher of Gifted
AY
, Shirley
ial Education Teacher
EDGEVILLE
John F.
ership, Ed & Training Tchr
, Ann Muhs
Mathematics Dept Chair
, Charles E.
nselor
ss, Deana Wills
ation Explorer Teacher
ay, Grace B.
essor of Education
son, Nancy Bacon
c Professor of English
Alonzo
uage Arts Instructor
an, John Arthur
& Drama Tchr, Dance Dir
s, Karen Knight
l Studies Teacher
, Lydia Sans
ish Teacher
y, Nancy Carlisle
ematics Teacher
on, Evelyn
Grade Language Arts Tchr
on, Robert Kendall
ory Teacher
Sherrill Crowell
entary School Principal
Susan Haynes
ch Teacher
dy, Nancy Crumbley
ish & History Teacher
, Peter Allen
Grade Teacher
Martha Thornton
essor of English

Moore, Linda W.
Associate Dean of Academics
Peevy, Dinah Clemons
Biology Teacher
Ragan, Gordon B.
English Teacher
Schwarz, Wanda C.
Instructor of Biology
Stewart, Cecelia Gunter
High School Counselor
Taw, James S.
History Professor
Thornton, John Curtis
History Instructor
Washington, Martha Odum
Seventh Grade Teacher
Watson, Janice H.
CVAE Interlocking Teacher
White, Jannie Dryer
7th Grade Mathematics Teacher
MILLEN
Boyer, Ann Dwelle
Gifted Program Coordinator
Deal, Janine
8th Grd Language Arts Teacher
Johnson, David Timothy
Health & PE Teacher
Wilkey, Benny
Social Studies Teacher
Wilkey, Delores Green
Kindergarten Teacher
MONROE
Brady, Cheryl Foster
Fifth Grade Teacher
Cabe, Donna P.
English & French Teacher
Cates, Betsy
Family Services Coordinator
Dial, Agnes Hancock
First Grade Teacher
Ervin, Barbara Sosebee
Fourth Grade Teacher
Garrett, Devin Misean
English Teacher
Hill, Paul C.
Physical Education Teacher
Juett, JoAnne Crum
English Department Chair
Meredith, Kathleen Dixon
Mathematics Teacher
Peters, Sharon Payne
K-5th Grade Teacher of Gifted
Pope, Tammy Lee
English Teacher
Tiencken, Denise Stansell
5th Grade Teacher
Tuggle, Diedra Marshall
Social Science Teacher
White, Robert Alton, Jr.
Rsrch Entomologist Coll Instr
Whitfield, Susan C. Williamson
7th Grade Language Arts Tchr
MONTEZUMA
Blue, Earlene Bland
Science Teacher
Carter, Norman
Teacher & Band Director
Cornett, Charles Bryant
Athletic Director & PE Teacher
Cullers, Consiwilla C.
School Counselor
Grey, Walter Forrest, Jr.
Biology & Chemistry Teacher
Rumph, Annie Rachel
Title One Teacher
Warnock, Lucy Williams
Head Librarian
MONTICELLO
Caldwell, Mary Pittard
Media Specialist
Giles, Linda Beyer
Fourth Grade Teacher
Nisbet, Gregory Alan
Seventh Grd World Geog Teacher
Parham, Sandra Clemons
Bus & Cmptr Ed Teacher
Threlkeld, Catherine Davis
HS Mathematics Teacher
MORROW
Crawford, Micky Diane
6th-8th Grade Health Teacher
Gillette, David F.
Bible, Science & Math Teacher
Hurley, Joleen H.
Biology Teacher
Hyder-Williams, Tammy D.
5th Grade Teacher
Jacobs, Vicki
Fifth Grade Teacher
Kent, Sandra Anne
Fourth Grade Teacher
Kotler, Elaine Almon
World History Teacher
Massey, Barbara Brown
Fifth Grade Teacher
Music, Carol Grizzard
Health & PE Dept Chairperson
Nelson, Sharon Diane
6th Grade Teacher
Starbuck, James Carlton
Social Studies Teacher
Stivers, Judith C.
Choral Director
Stone, Troy Lee
Mathematics Teacher
Thurston, Melodie B.
Spanish Teacher
Wofford, Rhonda Yaughn
Educational Therapist

MOULTRIE
Bledsoe, Mary Jo
English Teacher
Bollinger, Lynn Ransdell
English Teacher
Caldwell, Bill
Choral Director
Carr, Marietta Marie
Eighth Grade Science Teacher
Childs, Sally Adams
Mathematics Teacher
Dunlap, Sharon Stanley
Fifth Grade Teacher
Graham, Vickie
Mathematics Teacher
Hamby, Rena B.
6th-8th Grd Tchr of Gftd Math
Hill, Trudie M.
Spcl Ed Dept Head & Teacher
Johnson, Constance Remona
English Teacher
Mc Lendon, Richard Charles
Band Dir & Instrumental Coord
Ryce, Glendora Pearson
Retired Elementary Teacher
Thompson, Gail Darby
Family & Consumer Science Tchr
Was, Ruth Elgin
Seventh Grade Teacher
Wear, Jana Spain
History Teacher
MOUNT AIRY
Allen, Kimberly Taylor
Mathematics Teacher
Ausburn, Kathy Marie
Economics & Amer History Tchr
Bragg, Timothy Phillip
Weight Trng & Drivers Ed Tchr
Bush, Janet Mc Entyre
Mathematics Teacher
Childs, Ted L.
Counselor
D'Agata, Dale Ann
History Teacher
Finelli, Stacy Enzor
French Teacher
Galati, Rhea Nichols
11th Grd Lang Arts Tchr
Hull, Cherrie Ann
English Teacher
Johnston, Jane White
Math Teacher
McClure, Susan M.
Honors Mathematics Teacher
Nix, Cheryl
English Instructor
Staples, Kimberly Brown
Theatre & English Teacher
Williams, Marcia Wright
Fifth Grade Teacher
MOUNT VERNON
Altman, Jennifer Schroer
Teacher & Staff
Brewer, Faye DeLoach
Social Studies Teacher
Caudle, Anita Louise
Biology Instructor
Edenfield, Deborah Sharpe
Physical Ed & Health Teacher
Fathi, Michael Masha
Assoc Prof of Bus Admin
Headley, Phillip Anthony
Womens Basketball Coach
Jossey, Laurie A.
Physical Education Professor
Rhoades, Charles Vance
Assoc Prof of Psych & Cnslng
Spurlin, John Henry
Vocational Education Teacher
Toll, Larry Allen
Asst Professor of History
Weber, Vierow-Lynn McClelland
Director of Education Programs
Wilcox, Brian Kenneth
Religion Professor
MOUNT ZION
Wieck, Melinda Stewart
Chemistry & Physics Teacher
NAHUNTA
Harper, Anne J.
English Tchr & Lang Arts Chm
Meldey, Stuart
EBD Teacher
Thrift, Sharron Woodard
CBE Coordinator
Tucker, John Hudson
Physical Ed & Science Teacher
Woods, Josephine Caliendo
Spanish Teacher
NASHVILLE
Cornelius, Angie Allen
Social Studies Teacher
Hendley, Faith Scarborough
High School Counselor
Lee, Deborah Royal
Counselor
Postell, Amy Jones
Former 6th Grd Soc Stud Tchr
Register, Brenda Rackley
Kindergarten Teacher
Stoker, JoAnn Langford
Teacher
Strickland, Debbie Dorminey
7th Grade Math Teacher
Suber, Elizabeth Brogdon
Science Teacher & Dept Chair
Tomberlin, Carol R.
High School Math Teacher
Young, Don Van, Jr.
Social Science Teacher

NEWNAN
Aiken, Lorraine Harmon
7th Grd Teacher & Team Leader
Allen, Tisa A.
English Teacher
Arons, Christiane H.
French Teacher
Bass, Alice M.
Kindergarten Teacher
Camp, Helen Moore
8th Grade Science Teacher
Campbell, Steve
Science & Math Teacher
Cotton, Jean Hubbs
Seventh Grade Teacher
Davis, Jeffrey Mark
Tchr, Coach & Soc Stud Chm
Hall, Peggy Tinsley
Mathematics Teacher
Harrison, Diane Carrington
Business Education Teacher
Jones, Johnnie Grimsley
7th Grade Lit & Reading Tchr
Kendrick, Barbara J.
Assistant Principal
Lang, Beverly Smith
Science Teacher & Dept Chair
Madden, Teresa Highsmith
6th Grd Sci Tchr & Team Leader
Mann, Stacia Atkinson
Fifth Grade Teacher
Moseley, Karen Howard
Chorus Director
Reeve Morgan, Frances Ann
Seventh Grd Lang Arts Teacher
Smith, Harvey Richard
Senior English Teacher
Smith, Susan Powers
Chemistry Teacher
NICHOLLS
Nobles, Bobbie Lightsey
Fourth Grade Teacher
NORCROSS
Almon, Kenneth Neal
Fifth Grade Teacher
Altman, Melanie Hood
Business Education Teacher
Ball, Timothy Allen
Life & Phys Science Teacher
Barrett, Sallie Louise
7th Grade Science Teacher
Blackman, Jane B.
Tutorial Support & ESOL Tchr
Block, Leigh Spencer
High School English Teacher
Boldt, L. Thomas
Bible Teacher
Eley, William A.
HS Chemistry Instr & Coach
Espinosa, Jaime A.
Counselor
Gambill, Stephen Franklin
HS Social Studies Teacher
Gamez, Kristina Lindsey
Mathematics Teacher
Goff, Johnny Darrell
Physical Education Teacher
Griffis, Julia Lovell
8th Grade Science Teacher
Gross, Richard Thompson
Social Studies Dept Chairman
Harris, Susan Williamson
Special Education Teacher
Hayes, Virginia Warren
Fifth Grade Teacher
Henderson, Andrea Prickett
Sixth Grade English Teacher
Kaufman, Howard Marc
Science Enrichment Specialist
Kelly, Timothy J.
Social Studies Teacher
Kunka, Michael Jerome
Chemistry Teacher
Lewis, Dorothy A.
Mathematics Tchr & Dept Chair
Long, Barbara Clark
Language Arts Educator
Luthart, Scott David
Science Teacher
Lynch, Peggy Hunt
First Grade SIA Teacher
Mason, Pamela Anne
Mathematics Teacher
Mc Devitt, Susan Stanley
6th Grade Sci & Soc Stud Tchr
Neuman, Susan Blackerby
Mathematics & Science Teacher
Nichols, Eunice A.
Mathematics Teacher
Pharris, William J.
Director of Bands
Pierce, C. Wayne, Jr.
Health Teacher
Reid, Angelene Yvonne
HS Language Arts Teacher
St John-Wacker, Courtney L.
Comp Sci Tchr & Tech Coord
Shelton, Kristy Lou
Physical Education Teacher
Smith, Jeffrey L.
Biology Teacher
Suiter, Betty Bledsoe
8th Grade Language Arts Tchr
Swift, Karen V.
Biology Teacher
Waggener, John Woolfolk
Social Stud & ESOL Teacher
Yearout, Thomas William
Mathematics Teacher

NORMAN PARK
Ruffin, Ronnie Jerome
Elementary Physical Ed Tchr
OAKWOOD
Barrett, Judy S.
English Teacher
Bartlett, Marie Day
Seventh Grade Teacher
Burruss, Benita Bower
Math Teacher
Ecke, Laura Bailey
8th Grade Teacher
Gale, Timothy Carnell
Choral Director
Harrison, William D.
Hlth & Phys Education Teacher
Merritt, Traci Lawson
English Teacher
Meyer, Jacqueline Tolley
Second Grade Teacher
Roberts, Brad
Social Studies Teacher & Coach
Stover, Sharon Kelley
English Teacher
OCILLA
Stringer, Jeffrey Todd
First Grade Teacher
OGLETHORPE
Jackson, Brenda Hill
Speech & Language Pathologist
OXFORD
Baker, Steven Curtis
Assistant Prof of Biology
Carpenter, Lucas Adams, III
Professor of English
Kendall, Regina Braxton
Second Grade Teacher
Wood, Charlotte Hollis
1st Grade Teacher
PATTERSON
Garner, Mattie Eady
Reading & Math Teacher
PEACHTREE CITY
Belvedere, Damian Thomas
Social Studies Teacher
Burnette, Dawn Colbert
English & Journalism Teacher
Gilbert, Carole C.
English Teacher & Dept Chprsn
Gividen, Laurie Hicks
7th Grade Language Arts Tchr
Guice, Susan E.
High School French Teacher
Holbrook, Judith Anne
2nd Grade Teacher
Humphrey, Craig Blount
Economics & Humanities Teacher
Moore, James Alan
Chemistry & Physics Teacher
Perrin, Sandra June
School Counselor
Stout, Thomas Edward, Jr.
Science Teacher
Tiller, Jana L.
Mathematics Teacher
PEARSON
Carver, Laverne Mc Donald
Business Education Teacher
Daniel, Paul William
Eighth Grade Tchr & Var Coach
Stone, Brenda Davis
4th-12th Grd Teacher of Gifted
Trapnell, Michele B.
High School Spanish Teacher
PELHAM
Todd, David C.
Mathematics Teacher
PEMBROKE
Boone, Randell Edward
Teacher
Butler, Lawrence Edward, Sr.
World History Teacher
Turner, Gwen Coleman
Title I Reading & Math Teacher
York, Melanie Jayne
9th-10th Grd English Teacher
PERRY
Beeland, Glynelle Ellis
5th Grade Teacher
Claxton, Argene
Agriculture Education Teacher
Massey, James Lee, III
Government & Economics Teacher
Mc Dow, Rita Small
Counselor
Nunn, Janet Norton
Second Grade Teacher
Pope, Alvalyn Hutto
9th-12th Grd Economics Teacher
Pund, Amelia Ann
Rdng Recovery & Title I Tchr
Ridley, Glenda Anne Smith
Science Teacher
Sexton, Thelma Dianne
Eighth Grade Math Teacher
Shelton, Katherine Orlovich
Earth Sci & Soc Studies Tchr
Soles, James Henry
Math Teacher
Williams, Linda Bassett
8th Grade Language Arts Tchr
PINEHURST
Reynolds, Beth Thompson
Reading & Spelling Teacher
Wood, Roberta Guy
Math Teacher & Dept Chairman
PITTS
Patterson, Pamela Whitehead
Instructional Specialist

PLAINVILLE
Land, Marilyn Fite
Instructional Coordinator
PORTAL
Clark, Debra H.
English Teacher
POWDER SPRINGS
Blackmon, Cynthia Salley
English Teacher & Div Chair
Buchanan, Barbara Ann
Social Studies Teacher
Caplan, Robert Michael
6th Grd Lang Arts & Rdng Tchr
Clayton, Don Russell
Social Studies Teacher
Colquitt, Sheila Walsh
English Teacher
Conn, LeAnne Green
Biology Teacher
Fleming, Pamela Ingram
Teacher of the Gifted
Fowler, Sheryl June
Health, PE Teacher & Coach
Gossett, Keith Eugene
English Educator
Grable, Vivian Tate
HS Chemistry Teacher
Hansard, R. Deana
7th Grade Math Teacher
Jordan, Sharon Dukes
Business Education Teacher
Lenihan, Linda D.
Fourth Grade Teacher
Maugans, Ella Ruth Odom
Biology Teacher
Mc Mullen, Ed
Geog Tchr & Soc Stud Dept Chr
Medford, Gary Lee
7th Grd Social Studies Teacher
Michalke, Douglas Walter
Chemistry Teacher
Padgett, Stephen Eric
English Teacher
Paul, Deborah Anne
Teacher of the Gifted
Reece, Terri Freeland
Target Teacher
Savage, Linda
Business Education Teacher
Sawyer, Simone Seamon
Seventh Grade English Teacher
Semenas, Cathy (Wokwicz)
7th Grd Science & Reading Tchr
Taylor, Randy L.
Anatomy, Physiology Tchr & Dir
Wahl, Gerald Lewis
Biology Tchr & Sci Dept Head
QUITMAN
Baggett, Moiya M.
English Teacher
Huss, Christina M.
Band Director
Scott, Robert L.
World History Teacher
Wakefield, Beurena Hunter
Business Education Teacher
Wall, Emily Strickland
Elem Tech Instr & Lit Coord
RABUN GAP
Beaver, Nancy DuPuy
English Teacher
Cook, Michael Oscar
English & Journalism Teacher
Cook, Sandy Sluder
Mathematics Teacher
Fowle, Daniel Steven, Sr.
ESL Coordinator & Teacher
Malot, Woodrow
Science Teacher
Rosa, Lisa (Gibilisco)
Eng & Creative Writing Teacher
Saino, Elaine Spellman
English Teacher
Stiles, Billy Joe
Senior Master Archivist
REDAN
Colson, Valerie Van Landingham
Second Grade Teacher
Gordon, Mark Bryce
Elementary School Counselor
Hodo, Chinita Macon
Elementary Teacher
Kefetew, Pamela Harris
Sixth Grade Teacher
REIDSVILLE
Corbitt, Cindy Avant
Family & Consumer Science Tchr
Hassol, Douglas A.
Biology Teacher
Kicklighter, Jerry Asbury, Jr.
Chemistry Teacher
Maybin, Joyce Lanier
Sixth Grade Teacher
Smith, Brenda Cowart
Coordinator of the Gifted
RESACA
Mc Entyre, Judith Clement
Kindergarten Teacher
REX
Daniel, Jane Young
Sixth Grade Math Teacher
Davis, William Edward
Band Dir & Fine Arts Dept Chm
Rhoades, Allison Bosco
Orchestra Director
Thomason, Tammy Bynum
GA His Tchr, Soc Stud Dept Chm
RICHMOND HILL
Barnes, Alice Porter
Math Teacher & Department Head
Bayens, J. Mickey
World Geography Teacher
Bond, Gail Smith
English & Literature Teacher
Freeman, Lisa Baumgardner
8th Grade Science Teacher
Griffin, Michelle Burgoon
HS Chemistry & Physics Teacher
Johnson, Kathryn E.
Mathematics Teacher
Justice, Susan Mills
Lead Teacher
Mc Grath, William Joseph
Health, PE Tchr & Coach
Scott, Debra Janis
7th Grade Science Teacher
Shuman, Kenneth David
Math Teacher
RINCON
Sikes, Betty Allen
Lead Teacher
RINGGOLD
Baker, Marjorie Parham
Health Occupations Teacher
Bayne, Mitzi Diane
French Teacher
Brady, Jeanne La Rue
Span Tchr & Lang Dept Chprsn
Brown, Belinda White
Assistant Principal
Brown, M. Modena Penland
English Teacher
Harper, Sandra Reynolds
English Teacher
Henderson, Pamela Sue (Kenley)
Mathematics Teacher
Hilley, Angela Jean
English Teacher
Leonard, Julia D.
Social Science Teacher
Newell, Jeanne Bailey
Art Teacher
Potts, Susan Parker
Mathematics Teacher
Proctor, Zelma Diane
Counselor
Roddy, Keith Allen
High School Science Teacher
Sharrock, Gregory Todd
Graphic Arts Instructor
Spurgeon, Leland
Senior Army Instructor
Watts, Barbara T.
Retired Third Grade Teacher
Woodham, John Michael
Junior ROTC Instructor
RIVERDALE
Farr, Sonya Brady
Kindergarten Teacher
Frisbie, Jane Bridges
Second Grade Teacher
Hill, Brenda F.
Bus Ed CBE Coord & Teacher
Johnson, Chrisanda Oetting
Fourth Grade Teacher
Knight, Gail Henderson
5th Grade Teacher
Pittman, Dorothy Diane
Spanish & English Teacher
Terry, Scott Stanley
Social Studies Teacher
Young, Melinda Elton
Gifted Program Teacher
Zimmerman, Vickie Teal
Rep, Title I Paraprofessional
ROBERTA
Bassett, Patricia Jones
Math Teacher
Byram, Tony Glyn
Amer History Teacher & Coach
Crutchfield, Lucius Rodney
History Teacher
Moss, Barbara Allen
Assistant Principal
Perry, Pam Joyner
Art Teacher
ROBINS AFB
Hardin, Nancy McCullough
K-6th Grd Computer Specialist
Mitchell, Florence Johnston
Sixth Grade Teacher
ROCHELLE
Harden, Carol Keene
English Dept Head & Teacher
Titshaw, Ann Braziel
Math Teacher
ROCK SPRING
Haslerig, Ann
Fourth & Fifth Grade Teacher
ROCKMART
Edwards, Carol Swint
2nd Grade Teacher & Dept Chair
Lumpkin, Dena Thomas
English Teacher
Malone, Sharon Norman
Kindergarten Teacher
Miller, Lynn A.
Middle School Teacher
Wilson, Charlene Hutchings
6th Grd Tchr & Math Dept Head
ROCKY FACE
Hill, Thomas Kelly
English & Reading Teacher
Meeks, Jane Garrett
4th Grade Teacher
Sorrell, Mark Stephen
Algebra & Georgia History Tchr
Taylor, Lisa H.
Sixth Grade Teacher
ROME
Awsumb, Elizabeth Breytspraak
Dir of International Students
Baltzer, Samuel W.
Associate Professor
Barge, John David
English & Journalism Teacher
Benson, Aaron Lee
Visual Art Professor
Berry, Virginia Gaines
Second Grade Teacher
Black, Suzanne DuPuy
Psychology Professor
Boggs, Lynda Lovell
Reading Instructor
Brock, Edwin Harold
Former History Teacher
Bugg, William Adolphus, III
Director of Publications
Camp, Sandra Hughley
Fifth Grade Math Teacher
Carswell, Michael David
Residential Life Director
Chesnut, Joanna L.
8th Grade English Teacher
Cochran, Susan Shelton
Language Arts Teacher
Cole, Valarie Kendrick
English Teacher
Cox, Beth Perkins
Speech & Language Pathologist
Cromer, Janie M.
Fifth Grade Teacher
Culberson, Lila Frances
Seventh Grade Teacher
Cunningham, Gary Steven
11th Grd Amer History Tchr
Darville, Robert H., III
Division of Bus Chair
Davis, Margaret Sewell
Mathematics Professor
DeAngelus, Ronald Louis
Physical Education Teacher
Dillard, Philip E.
Professor of English
Duke, Johnny I.
Assistant Professor of Math
Durham, Susan Fuqua
Choral Director
Gibbons, Mark
AP Calculus & Math Teacher
Green, Melanie Moore
Second Grade Teacher
Griffith, Tamara Lynn Chamlee
Math Teacher
Hagerstrand, Martin A., Jr.
Mathematics Teacher
Hall, Loren Wilson
Professor of Humanities
Hall, Thelma R.
Prof of Eng & Chair of Hum
Hamer, Diana Hixon
Second Grade Teacher
Harmon, Mary H.
English Teacher
Hodges, Thomas Christopher
Art Instructor
Holcomb, Mary Siegel
Mathematics Teacher
Hollaran, Anna S.
Second Grade Teacher
Ingis, Gene
Band Director
Inglis, Gene
Band Director
Johnson, Alberta Clark
Psychology Professor
Jones, Barbara Ann
Instructional Assistant
Kerce, Raymond Dempsey
Social Studies Teacher
Lewis, Melinda Shell
7th Grd Lang Arts & Sci Tchr
Long, Christina (Clay)
Biology Teacher
McCormick, Julie Walton
Biology Teacher
Mc Coury, William Bryan
HS Social Science Teacher
McKenzie, Janet Butler
8th Grade Lang Arts Teacher
Mendence, Don Joseph
Head Rec Mngmt Degree Prgm
Miller, Dale R.
Practical Nursing Instructor
Morris, Terry Ray
Honors Program Director
Murray, Raymond B.
English Teacher & Coach
Nance, Mary Hancock
8th Grade Counselor
Ratledge, John
Director of Choral Activities
Reichel, Sharon Werfelmann
French Teacher
Rice, Herbert William
Associate Professor of English
Rice, Linda Myers
Spanish Teacher
Rickman, Debbie Fowler
Math Teacher
Rucker, Phyllis J.
Third Grade Teacher
Saunders, Lewis Syester, Jr.
English Teacher
Smith, Susan Myers
English Teacher
Spoon, Gregory J.
AP Lang Comp & Journalism Tchr
Taylor-Colbert, Alice Fay
Soc Sci Div Chprsn & His Prof
Thomas, Diane Connally
School Counselor
Travis, Milt Louis
Health Teacher
Tucker, Michael David, Sr.
6th Grd Tchr & Wrestling Coach
Walker, Eileen Dooley
Instructor
West, Martha Myrick
Education Professor
Williams, Tabatha Zachery
Georgia Studies Teacher
Wingard, Sara B.
English Professor
ROOPVILLE
Denney, Ronnie Lynn
Speech-Language Pathologist
Huckeba, Emily Causey
First Grade Teacher
ROSSVILLE
Bilbrey, Jane Hughes
Third Grade Teacher
Burt, Ann Elizabeth
Fifth Grade Teacher
Cornelius, Judy Warren
Home Economics Teacher
Davis, Elizabeth Anne
Eighth Grade Science Teacher
Prichard, Lona Ann Harris
First Grade Teacher
Ragon, Judith Ann
English Tchr & Dept Chair
Stephens, Jerry Dean
Science Teacher
Thomas, Carlton
Gifted Facilitator
Unger, Larry Thomas
Science Teacher
ROSWELL
Bauman, Carol Jean
Fourth Grade Teacher
Born, Gayle F.
Principal
Burrell, Maryellen Z.
Science & Math Teacher
Clark, Martha D.
Teacher of the Gifted
DeShazier, Sandra Childs
Assistant Principal
Doughty, Barbara Burrows
Third Grade Teacher
Eachus, Lynette Combs
Middle School Lead Teacher
Feight, Linda Lee
1st Grade & Rdng Recovery Tchr
Gramith, Dale S.
Physics Teacher
Hauenstein, Glen Alan
Assistant Principal
Hundley, James Douglas
English Teacher
Huntley, SaraBeth B.
HS Tchr of Gifted & Talented
Mazur, Martha S. (Hammond)
AP Chemistry Teacher
Paul, Linda W.
Business Education Teacher
Pittman, Ira W., Jr.
HS Choral Music Teacher
Rymer, Gary Lee, Sr.
9th-10th Grade Biology Teacher
ROYSTON
Gaines, Zadie Pruitte
Kindergarten Teacher
RYDAL
Bishop, Gina King
Fifth Grade Teacher
SAINT GEORGE
Ross, Heather Jane
Sixth Grade Teacher
SAINT MARYS
Bird, Jo Beth Hinson
Assistant Principal
Harrison, Jeremiah Dwain
4th Grade Science Teacher
Jest, Leatha (Lester)
Career Connection Teacher
SAINT SIMONS ISLAND
Darby, Rose McDonald
Fifth Grade Teacher
Rogers, Sonja Olsen
Second Grade Teacher
Wood, Evelyn Gowen
Third Grade Teacher
SANDERSVILLE
Brown, Marcia Gerrald
7th Grade Reading Teacher
Grant, Catherine Mountain
Mathematics Teacher
Jenkins, Lillian Brinkley
Health Occupations Ed Tchr
Lehr, Michael William, Jr.
Sixth Grd Soc Studies Teacher
Mathis, Dianne Holmes
Media Specialist
Mathis, Leslie Doolittle
Seventh Grade Math Teacher
Pharis, Denise Dollar
Algebra Teacher
Smith, Cheryl Brown
Biology & Biochemistry Tchr
Smith, Roy Leon
Assistant Principal
Smith-Bryan, Paula Young
Guidance Counselor
Veal, Mary Kaye
5th Grd Language Arts Teacher
Whitfield, William Henry, Jr.
8th Grd Soc Stud Teacher
Wiley, Terri Michele
Band Director
Wilkerson, Mary Newsom
Math Dept Chair & Teacher
Youmans, Mercedes Norris
Reading Teacher
SAVANNAH
Aaron, Wayne Bradford
Technology Coordinator
Alley, James Pinckney, Jr.
Professor of Graphic Design
Aquadro, Jeana Lauren
Graphic Design Professor
Begrowicz, Alan Nicholas
Mathematics Department Chm
Bess, Betty Frazier
I A Teacher
Best, JoAnne Osinski
English & Humanities Teacher
Blanchard, Annette Allene
High School Teacher & Coach
Bowen, Olufunke
Criminal Justice Professor
Brewer, Lora Lee
Mathematics Professor
Broome, Mary N. (Van Alstine)
English Teacher
Brown, Brenda Jane (Boyette)
First Grade Teacher
Brown, Gail LaVerne
Science Teacher
Brown, Margaret Belinda (Sullivan)
Pre-Kindergarten Teacher
Bryan Heath, Matilda
History Teacher
Bryant, Thelma Truedell
Mathematics Teacher
Burke, Cecile Johnson
Mathematics Teacher
Callahan, Lisa L.
Chemistry Teacher
Calloway, Mildred Scott
Business Education Instructor
Chandra, Kailash S.
Professor & Dept Head
Chandra, Sushma S.
Fourth Grade Teacher
Chetty, Chellu Sreeramulu
Professor of Biology
Chewning, G. Dean Crawford
First Grade Teacher
Clarke, Jane Godfrey
Kindergarten Teacher
Coursey, Roger Warren
NJROTC Naval Science Instr
Coward, Patricia Ann
Assistant Principal
Cowart, Jackie Adams
Retired Business Teacher
Crawford, Emily Maxine
Asst Professor of Marketing
Cummings, Delores Briggs
Transition Resource Specialist
Davies, Karen Elizabeth
Fine Art Professor
Davis, Dwan Porter
English Teacher
Davis, Joyce Washington
Mathematics Teacher
DeLettre, Angela Cheryl
Mathematics Teacher
Dillon, Donna
Fifth Grade Teacher
Duren, Kelly Evans
English & Drama Teacher
Eke, Joy Grimes
Pre-Kndgtn & Family Svc Coord
Falk, Denise Bowman
Prof of Painting & Dept Chair
Finlay, Terry Margaret
Spanish Teacher
Finnegan, Rosalyn Kirkendoh
Mathematics Teacher
Fischer, Thomas Jeffrey
Professor of Art & Photography
Forrest, Larry W.
Professor of Art History
Frasier, Theta Johnson
Sixth Grade Science Teacher
Gaskin, Carol Hadsell
Seventh Grade Math Teacher
Gearing, Colin
Professor of Graphic Design
Godawa, Emma Kay
Art Tchr & Fine Arts Dept Chr
Gough, Charlene Elizabeth
Mathematics Teacher
Gray, Jacqueline Wilson
Health & Physical Ed Professor
Griffin, Jeanette Cribbs
Business Teacher
Griffis, Teresa M.
Eng Prof & Chair of Lbrl Arts
Hahn, William G.
Assoc Dean & Prof of Mgmt
Hardwick, Marietta Carter
Fifth Grade Teacher
Hart, Addie Scott
8th Grd Science Teacher
Heath, Barbara Wilhite
First & Second Grade Teacher
Hester, Rebecca Wise
Marketing Management Instr
Holdren, Bradley Herbert
Head Rowing Coach
Holmes, Robin Enyce
Composition Teacher

NAH (cont)
Fernandez, Sachiko
sor of Fashion
Chaohui
iate Professor of History
Lucilla Potter
ter Art Professor
ey, Cindy Page
h Teacher
istopher
al Science Professor
Fredda H.
matics Teacher
, Julie Marie
h Teacher & Yearbook Adv
, Cynthia Carlyle
y Teacher
, Darrell Jerome
sor of Art
, Susan B.
al Studies Dept Chairman
itin
Professor of Biology
arol Quincy
h Teacher
anah Cordelia
f Soc Work & Policy
, Ronald Boulware
stry Teacher
ana Gordon
etry & Precalculus Teacher
d, Barbara Card
omputer Coord & Teacher
Lloyd B.
can Studies Professor
, Arlene
Teacher
Martha Dell
Studies Teacher
ll, Frank J.
ogy Instr & Drama Teacher
Golden, Barbara Ann
Grade Teacher
Yvonne Hooks
iate Prof of Humanities
kle, Sandrae Jenness
h Grade English Teacher
-Brown, Shirley A.
ce Department Chairperson
Angela Yvonne
athematics Teacher
Patricia Jenkins
d Language English Tchr
, Betty Louise Greene
age Arts Teacher
Ben Currie
lations & Fashion Prof
on, Virginia Young
rgarten Teacher
Deborah Cherry
ation Professor
son, Dorothy Davis
ssor of Mathematics
, Emma Katrina
rade Tchr & Vice Prin
, Mohamad Adel
of Civil Engineering Tech
ar, Govindan K.
ssor & Head
, Karen B.
sh Teacher
hirley Leech
ess Teacher
n, Eileen Wages
sh Teacher
, Jeffrey Scott
ous Studies Teacher
ch, Joseph Anthony
ematics Teacher
, John Manson, III
r Army Instructor
Ganesh Mangesh
unting Professor
oung Ryong
outer Info Systems Prof
eorge N.
cal & Social Sci Instr
uis, Robert Dolan
ssor of Sequential Art
t-Hutchins, Sylathea Renea
c Dept Chair & Teacher
Eunice Levy
Grade Teacher
Sandra Jean
ssor of Painting
Kimsherion Phezette
ce Teacher
Judith Lange
ssor of Architecture
dson, Joseph P.
ne Biology Professor
ski, Judith Cerbone
al Studies & GA His Tchr
Xuhong
dation Professor
Jackie
ematics Teacher
n, Gloria A.
stant Professor
ard, Gwendolyn Passmore
ergarten Teacher
ey, Donald Kent
l Science Instructor
Tom
ssor of Interior Design
, Patricia Groover
rade Social Studies Tchr
Roger H.
Tchr, Frgn Lang Dept Chair

Steinmetz, Mary Boskwick
Prof of Historic Preservation
Stevens, Craig G.
Photography Professor
Stewart, Alma Jean
First Grade Teacher
Sutlive, John Lawrence
English Teacher
Swinford, Thomas Reese, III
Guidance Counselor
Tapp, Carol Dysart
Computer Information Sys Prof
Temple, Michael D.
History Teacher
Thurman, Dianne Sailors
Fourth Grade Teacher
Toney-White, Cynthia
Comp Lit Teacher
Washington, Katrina Tacita
Mathematics Teacher
Washington, Terry Ann
Life Science Teacher
Weaver, Crystal Dawn
Professor of Interior Design
Weber, Adam Scott
Science Teacher
Wesolowski, Anthony P.
Cmptr Prgrmng & Robotics Tchr
West, Nancy Griffin
Mathematics Teacher
Williams, Robin Brentwood
Architectural History Chrpsn
Woods, Timothy Joseph
Professor
Worsham, Sharon Elizabeth
Georgia History Teacher
Wright, Deborah Ann (Gordon)
Chemistry Teacher
Wright, Theresa Leona (Murray)
Consumer Home Economics Tchr

SCREVEN

Fuller, Juanita Boykin
Adult Literacy Instructor

SHARPSBURG

Thomas, Karen
Kindergarten Teacher
Thompson, Scott Douglas
Chemistry Teacher

SILOAM

Morgan, Jane Bryan
Business Education Teacher

SMYRNA

Banks, Melinda Ann
School Counselor
Brown, Lila Mitchell
SIA Developmental Specialist
Buchan, Jean Nicholson
8th Grade Math Teacher
Ervin, James Frederic
Administrative Assistant
Goodrum, Marlene Roach
Math & English Teacher
Grainger, Yancey Hansberger
English Teacher
Hogan, Michael Clifford
Coach
Jones-Grayson, Iris Denise
Guidance Counselor
Mc Clure, Randy Odell
Science Teacher
Moffitt, Barbara Jane
Owner & Admin of Pvt Schools
Nicely, Alan Ross
Soc Studies Tchr & Ath Dir
O'Connor, Judi Pera
Fourth Grade Teacher
Romanchuk, Judith Kay
English Teacher
Shields, Rose Boyd
Teacher
Taylor, Clayton Davis
Special Education Teacher
Taylor, Sherry Ann
Third Grade Teacher
Tighe, Helen Marie
Middle School Guidance Cnslr

SNELLVILLE

Burgess, Robert Arthur
Latin Teacher
Cannon, Fred Thomas, Jr.
Senior English Teacher
Carr, Patricia Faye (Amos)
Bio Teacher & Sci Dept Chprsn
Christian, Linda Thorne
Business Education Teacher
Crawford, Sally Hemstreet
Kindergarten Teacher
Crocker, Cindy A.
8th Grade Math Teacher
Curl, Donna Armstrong
Fifth Grade Teacher
Edgar, James William, II
8th Grade Teacher
Garrison, Joe Lowell
Math Teacher
Gudger, Felicia Brisbay
Social Studies Teacher
Guy, Vicky Wagner
HS English Teacher
Hulme, Gavin Mell
Math Teacher
Jahner, David J.
German Teacher
Love, Sharon Beasley
Fifth Grade Teacher
Melvin, Marlene Elmore
Law & World History Teacher
Newman, Katharine Louise
8th Grade Algebra Teacher

Peters, Betty Moon
1st Grade Teacher
Phillips, Rebecca F.
Eighth Grade Teacher
Reynolds, Stanley Thomas
Spanish Teacher
Roberts, Sheila Smith
Fifth Grade Teacher
Robinson, Karen Mc Daniel
Frgn Lang Dept Chm & Span Tchr
Shue, Michael Edward
Social Studies Teacher
Smith, Margaret Alayne
Broadcast Journalism Teacher
Taylor, Stewart Lee
American Government Teacher
Waters, Paul Todd
Social Studies Teacher
Watkins, Leslie Ann Strickland
Language Arts Teacher
Westaway, Cynthia Crawford
Language Arts Teacher
Wilson, Ohlen Rudolph, Jr.
Director of Bands
Wood, Richard Alan
HS Biology & AP Biology Tchr

SOCIAL CIRCLE

Broussard, Ernestine Gonzales
American His, Govt & Ec Tchr

SOPERTON

Edge, Mitchell J.
Social Studies Teacher
Gillis, Justine Lawton
High School English Teacher

SPARTA

Behne, Tina Todd
Math Teacher
Bell, Patricia Williams
First Grade Teacher
Birdsong, Stephanie King
High School English Teacher
Carswell, Elnora R.
Second Grade Teacher
Gardner, Betty Jean
Third Grade Teacher
Johns, Lynn Reich
Business Education Teacher
Youngblood, Sylvia Reese
Fourth Grade Teacher

SPRINGFIELD

Coombe, Laurie L.
Math Teacher
Helmly, Slade F.
High School Math Teacher
Martin, Ronald Urbano Keith
World History & Geography Tchr
Palmer, Rebecca Jill
Spanish Teacher
Truluck, Rebecca Fulton
Business Education Teacher

STATENVILLE

Bezona, Ronald Edward
His, Soc Sci Dept Chm & Tchr
Carter, Mary Lou
English Teacher
Tefft, Sylvia Staten
2nd Grade Teacher

STATESBORO

Anderson, Kay Carmichael
Mathematics & Lang Arts Tchr
Butler, Judy Riner
English Teacher
Cowart, Jean Dwelle
Fourth Grade Teacher
Davenport, John Wayne
Professor
Downs, Alan Craig
History Professor
Edwards, Anne Milton
Middle School Soc Stud Tchr
Jones, Mary Roche
Mathematics Teacher
McKenna, Donna Torielli
4th & 5th Grade Teacher
Moore, Stacey Lee
Spanish & German Teacher
Pullen, Susan Spires
Mathematics Teacher
Rushing, Nan Shealy
Seventh Grd Language Arts Tchr
Sparks, Robert Michael
Mathematics Professor
Stallworth-Clark, Rosemarie
Reading Asst Professor
Vargo, James A.
Assistant Prof of Mathematics
Zhang, Jie
Sociology Professor

STILLMORE

Collins, Betty Karen
Science Teacher

STOCKBRIDGE

Beshiri, Barbara Wallace
8th Grade GA Studies Teacher
Clifton, Frank Todd
Health Teacher
Creasman, Gwen U.
Second Grade Teacher
Creasman, Michael Richard
US History Teacher
Crutchfield, Cynthia
8th Grade Math Teacher
Hamilton, Lori S.
1st Grade Teacher
Henry, David Warren
Band Director
Holcomb, Linda Reagan
Fifth Grade Teacher
Johnson, Annie Noble
Fifth Grade Teacher

King, Scott D.
Asst Band Director
Leader, Ginny Wright
8th Grade Language Arts Tchr
Mc Berry, Thomas Ray, Jr.
Admin & History Professor
Penland, Carolyn Jane
Biology & Physical Sci Teacher
Rhodes, Lynne Beason
Kindergarten Teacher
Sorrell, Joyce Barr
Retired Math Dept Chair
Spicer, Felecia Vinson
Fifth Grade Teacher
Sponsler, Laurie Kandt
HS Health & PE Teacher
Steiner, Debra Amy
Science Teacher
Thomas, Jennifer Leigh
Counselor

STONE MOUNTAIN

Anderson, Jeanie Denton
Second Grade Teacher
Ash, Yvonne Overton
First Grade Teacher
Barry, Elizabeth Ashlin
French Teacher
Bell, Joan Carson
English Teacher
Black, Monica Renee
Mathematics Teacher
Brewer, Brenda Neal
Social Studies & History Tchr
Cassan, Margaret Black
Spcl Education Resource Tchr
Crawford, Jim Dan
Science Teacher
Davidson, Sylvia Roberts
Engish Teacher of Gifted
Deighton, Jacqueline Sara
Marketing Teacher
Dixson, Frances Booker
9th-12th Grd Guidance Cnslr
Doss, Gregory Stone
Choral Director
Doster, Rachel Gwendolyn
US History Teacher
Dupree, Odessa B.
Business Education Teacher
Flowers, Herman, Jr.
Aerospace Science Instructor
Frost, Chanta Garrett
High School Science Teacher
Goodspeed, Johnnie (Barnhill)
Reading Specialist
Harvey, Angela Bair
5th Grade Teacher
Henderson, Harold
Physical Ed Teacher & Coach
Hill, Ruth Ann Martin
7th Grd Language Arts Teacher
Hodges, Melvin J., Jr.
Director of Bands
Holland, Jeffrey Brad
High School History Teacher
Houston, Bernadette Marie Burke
English Teacher
Ifill, Madaline P.
Social Studies Teacher
Johnson, Linda Evans
English Teacher
Knowles, Cheryl H. Glenn
Science Teacher
Knowles, Patricia D.
English Teacher
Lewis, Martha Bell
Latin Teacher
Lyons, Rita Heflin
Second Grade Teacher
McKenzie, Frank Hubert
HS Mathematics Teacher
Moon, Selina Carol (Thedford)
Mathematics Teacher
Nabers, Crystal Dawn
Science Teacher
Niehaus, Jennifer Elise
Math Teacher
Osborn, James M.
Emeritus Math Prof
Pitts, Kathryn C.
7th Grade Teacher
Randolph, Mavis Athelean
Third Grade Teacher
Rayford, James
Mathematics Teacher
Shriver, Shannon Kyl
History Teacher & Athletic Dir
Stallworth, Betty A.
7th Grade Life Science Teacher
Stephansen, Stephanie Brown
Secondary Mathematics Teacher

SUCHES

Ashurst, James Ray
Counselor
Wood Chapman, Elizabeth Ann
Elementary Teacher

SUMMERVILLE

Allred, Donna Honea
Math Teacher
Mintz, Katrina Hunter
English & Drama Teacher
Perry, Alan Eugene
English & Journalism Teacher
White, William Rodney
English Teacher

SUWANEE

Benson, Robert Alan
Mathematics Teacher
Detweiler, Sharon Burns
History & Law Teacher

Fletcher, Diane Phillips
Spanish & English Teacher
May, Sue Ellen S.
Lang Arts & Journalism Teacher
Winn, James E.
Language Arts Instructor
Zayas, Teddi Thornburg
Science Teacher
Ziecker, Lorraine (Lauer)
Choral Teacher

SWAINSBORO

Andrews, Bobby
In-School Suspension Coord
Ashcroft, Margaret Hughes
Language Arts Chair & Teacher
Baker, George Marvin
Professor of Biology
Bennett, Jean
World History Teacher
Bolton, Virginia Faulkner
Mathematics Teacher
Bridges, Charlotte Nizzi
Phys Sci, Bio & Chem Teacher
Tanner, Horace Randall
Ag Ed Teacher
Youmans, Debora Jo
United States History Teacher

SYCAMORE

Belflower, Carla Williams
4th Grade Teacher

SYLVANIA

Kemp, W. Burton, Jr.
Soc Stud Chm & Amer Govt Tchr
Rewcastle, Melanie Bazemore
In School Suspension Teacher

SYLVESTER

Bean, Craig Baylor
Band Director
Bridges, Keith S.
Mathematics Teacher
Brock, Melissa Milton
EBD Teacher
Burdette, Dedra Cerfus
Economics & Geography Teacher
Cravey, Sarah Elizabeth
Science Teacher
Drawdy, Blake D.
Science Teacher
Haney, Wylene A.
Computer Technology Teacher
Kirkbride, Wayne Alvin
Senior Army Instructor
Monahan, Patricia Gonzalez
French & Spanish Teacher
Terry, Steve R.
6th Grade Math & Reading Tchr

TALBOTTON

Ellison, Betty Daniel
French Tchr & Rdng Specialist
Riley, Ernestine
Middle Grades Teacher

TALLAPOOSA

Brooks, David J.
9th-12th Grd Mathematics Tchr
Chester, Karen Smith
Eng, Latin Tchr & Chair
Connell, Norma Jean Bell
Fourth Grade Teacher
Howle, John S.
English Teacher
McKibben, Ilana (Machelle)
Biology Teacher
Norton, Ravonda G.
7th Grade Mathematics Teacher
Ramsey, Paul Randall
Band Director
Ward, Tammy Mauk
Counselor
White, Gwen W. Mc Intyre
4th Grade Teacher
Wilburn, R. Allen
Project Success Coordinator

TAYLORSVILLE

Hudson, Joyce V.
Fourth Grade Teacher

TENNILLE

Haywood, Dale Lord
First Grade Teacher
Raley, Carol Williams
Third Grade Teacher

THOMASTON

Bailey, Margaret Johnson
Media Specialist
Brown, Ann M.
Spanish & Journalism Teacher
Brown, Roy Bradley
Math Teacher & Coach
Craft, Alida C. M.
Data Processing Coordinator
Douglas, Cynthia Nash
Second Grade Teacher
DuBose, Dianne L.
English Teacher
Elder, Carey Gatlin
Fourth Grade Teacher
Gill, George Gary
History Teacher
Holloway, Beatrice Hester
Sixth Grade Teacher
Hunter, Daniel
English Teacher
Husak, Elsie Jerez
Mathematics Teacher
Kring, Gary Dean
Science Teacher
Pasley, Linda Grier
Sixth Grade Teacher
Rogers, Jo Ann Franklin
Third Grade Teacher

THOMASTON (cont)
Rogers, Peggy Johnson
Kindergarten Teacher
Short, Angela Warren
Math Teacher
Siclari, James D.
Technology Instructor
Simmons, Jan Nipper
Third Grade Teacher
Thomas, Joan Elizabeth
Choral Director
Timms, Terrance Farrell
History Teacher
Vaughan, Lynn Torbert
Mathematics Teacher
Watts, Sheryl Taylor
Spanish Teacher
Weathers, Patricia A.
Fifth Grade Teacher
THOMASVILLE
Coleman, Evelyn
Retired Second Grade Teacher
Crispell, Brian Lewis
Geography Teacher
Fairman, N. Kyle
Band Director
Farrell, Dean D.
Chemistry & Physics Teacher
Goff, Michael W.
School Counselor
Jamison, Janice Simpson
8th Grade Math Teacher
Massey, Keith Alan
Mathematics Teacher & Tech Dir
Pope, Raquel VanDerPoll
Frgn Lang Dept Chprsn & Instr
Stowers, Lynn Ramsey
English Teacher
Taylor, Margaret Christine
High School Mathematics Tchr
Taylor, Shamane Hall
English Teacher
Voyles, C. Palmer
USAF JROTC Instructor
THOMSON
Barnett, John Hix
Social Studies Tchr & Dpt Head
Barnett, Kimberly Blevins
Mathematics Teacher
Brown, Christy Hawes
English, Speech & Drama Tchr
Kay, Dorothy Shields
8th Grd Science & History Tchr
Pinson, Claire Lynne
English Teacher
Powell, Joyce Rawlins
English Teacher
Smith, Steven Lee
8th Grade Math Tchr & Dept Chm
Zwemer, John Thomas
History, Math & Science Tchr
TIFTON
Barber, Ray Neal
Professor of Biology
Boyd, Debra Dowler
High School English Teacher
Brodie, Ginger Lawson
Tenth Grade English Teacher
Byers, Martha Cheryl
7th Grade Language Arts Tchr
Coates, Donald Bradsher, Sr.
Assistant Professor of Music
Daniel, Bertha Becton
Asst Prof of Criminal Justice
Dorsey, Shirley G.
Guidance Director
Duffey, Tammy Youngblood
Mathematics Teacher
Evans, John Dell
Spanish Professor
Graves, Debra Garrett
7th Grade Eng & Soc Stud Tchr
Hammons-Bryner, Sue
Assoc Prof of Social Science
Hampton, Danny Lamar
Assistant Professor of Biology
Hudson, H. Glenn
8th Grade Mathematics Teacher
Jones, Wayne P.
Assistant Professor of Music
Lang, Cynthia Moore
Spanish & French Teacher
Marchant, Lea Stoner
Retired Teacher
Massey, Donald Leroy
Assoc Professor of Mathematics
Mc Millan, Gina Bailey
Home Economics Teacher
Miller, Paul William
Asst Prof of Mngmt & Mrktg
Parson, Raleigh
10th & 11th Grade Science Tchr
Payne, Richard Lee
Associate Prof of Wildlife
Pfeiffer, Charlotte S.
Professor of English
Saxon, Elizabeth Merle
Mathematics Teacher
Scott, Nancy Mitchell
Asst Prof of Business Admin
Seagle, Eddie Dean
Associate Prof & Dept Head
Shurley, Joy B.
Assistant Professor
Sumner, JoAnn Troyer
Associate Professor of Nursing
Thornhill, Lynn Doss
Economics Assistant Professor
Thornton, Vann C.
Music Instructor
Webb, Ina Claire (Watson)
Biology Teacher
Weeks, Kay Dukes
Asst Prof of Speech & English
Wetherington, Marcia Mc Allister
Occupational Child Care Tchr
TIGER
Foster, Chuck
Guidance Counselor
Streible, Catherine McRae
Science Teacher
TOCCOA
Cash, Vivian Poole
First Grade Teacher
Clifton, Jennie K.
French & Latin Teacher
Elrod, Linda Addison
Fifth Grade Teacher
Gibson, Evelyn Sue
Fifth Grade Teacher
Miller, Rosemary
Fifth Grade Teacher
Morgan, Sue Stovall
Biological Science Teacher
Presley, Anthony F.
Chemistry Teacher
Razhoff, Beverly Shultz
Dir Instr & Asst Prof Speech
Sanders, Cynthia Cadwell
Teacher of the Gifted
Stephenson, Mary Stephens
Mathematics Teacher
Wilcher, Gregory Scott
Band Director
TOCCOA FALLS
Bellefeuille, Barbara Kae
Asst Professor of Teacher Ed
Harris, Jon R.
Asst Prof of Chrstn Cnslng
Harvey, David P.
Assoc Professor of Missiology
Hayner, Phillip Avery
Director, School of Music
Matthews, Carol Ann
Psychology Professor
Matthews, Douglas Kent
Assistant Professor
O'Brien, Michael Dennis
Professor of Communication
Sprinkle, Joe Melvin
Assoc Prof, The Old Testament
TRENTON
Ambrose, Kim Daniels
8th Grade Science Teacher
Bell, Kristyn Jenness
Sixth Grade Teacher
DeFriese, Kelli Cathleen
Health Occupations Teacher
Emmett, William E.
Math Teacher
Hamilton, Ronda Irvin
8th Grade Teacher
Mc Carty, Faith Ann
8th Grade Teacher
Scoggins, Amelia June
High School English Teacher
Slater, Dale Ballard
Mathematics Teacher
Smith, Samantha (Slater)
Seventh Grade Teacher
Taylor, Pat Thomas
English, Drama & Latin Tchr
TRION
Ward, Marijayne
GA History & Govt Teacher
TUCKER
Burks, William Winthrop, Jr.
Physical Education Teacher
Douglas, Chatta Gibbs
6th-7th Grade Math Teacher
Ralston, Susy R.
Retired Teacher
Vidal, Leonetta Butler
Mathematics Teacher
TUNNEL HILL
Bryan, Coylee Dykes
English Teacher
Collins, Susan E.
Language Arts Teacher
Griffin, June Dianna
Kindergarten Teacher
MIller, Selina Joy
Choral Director
Scull, Faye Mc Entire
French & English Teacher
Strong, William Allen
Chemistry Teacher
TWIN CITY
Clark, Debbie Boatright
Fourth Grade Teacher
TYRONE
Ballard, Kevin Wade
7th Grd Life Sci, Rdng Tchr
Bohlke, Jeffrey Richard
8th Grade GA History Teacher
Clough, Sandra Craighead
English Teacher
Coleman, Randall O.
Band Director
Finch, Jeannie Carson
Business Teacher & DCT Coord
Gibby, Carol C.
English Teacher
Gies, Stephen C.
Physics & Chemistry Teacher
Kilburn, Krista Rea
English & Speech Teacher
Murphy, Cathy Craton
English Teacher
Murphy, Julie Stempinski
Teacher of Gifted Children
Sconyers, Jeannette D.
Business Education Teacher
Smith, Karen Gil
US His & Govt Teacher
Snider, Cynthia Deniston
Tchr of Gifted & AP English
UNADILLA
Dhuart, Doris
Ret Elementary School Teacher
VALDOSTA
Busch, David Truett
Assoc Prof of Psychology
Chatelain, Margie Baird
Family & Consumer Sci Tchr
Colson, Ona Cheryl Cook
Secondary Mathematics Teacher
Craven, Glynis Ruth (Croft)
Business Education Teacher
Drossos, Narci J.
English Teacher
Drummonds, Deborah Keil
Nursing Instructor
Fender, Margaret Eve
Social Studies Teacher
Golivesky, Frances Hackel
US, World History & Govt Tchr
Googe, Betty Phillips
Sr English Tchr & Acad Dean
Gray, Brenda Dees
First Grade Teacher
Griffin, Karen M. (Algier)
Social Studies Teacher
Hall, Donna Taylor
English Teacher
Hare, Barbara Roxanne
Spanish Teacher & Dept Chprsn
Hayes, Sharon Hester
RVI Specialist
Hearn, Matthew Galen
English Professor
Henderson, William Larry
Science Teacher
Hjort, Nancy Parker
World History Teacher
House, Daniel H.
Honors US History Teacher
Hunt, Kaye Chastain
Kindergarten Teacher
Ipina, Ricardo R.
Drama Director
Iverson, Patricia Spencer
Counselor
Ji, Jun
Assistant Professor of Math
Kenney, Carole M.
Secondary Mathematics Teacher
Lassiter, Samuel D.
Social Studies Teacher
Logan, Carol Ann
Business Education Teacher
Lowther, Roosevelt, Jr.
Biology & Science Teacher
Mc Cranie, Margaret Yarbrough
8th Grade English Teacher
Meghabghab, George Victor
Associate Professor
Miller, Patricia A.
Associate Professor of English
Moran, Dorothy Thomas
Writing To Read Teacher
Mulkey, Terry Shiue Strausbaugh
Mathematics Teacher
Nienow, James A.
Associate Professor of Biology
Nolan, Debbie Hanson
Kindergarten Teacher
Odom, Rebecca Anne
Kindergarten Teacher
Parker, Rhenda Faye
Music Teacher & Choral Dir
Parten, Aaron Eugene
Vocational Agriculture Teacher
Pate, William H.
History Teacher & Coach
Pitchford, Thomas Neal
Technology Education Teacher
Rayford, Essie Pennington
Home Economics Teacher
Ruddle, Carmen Julia
Spanish Teacher
Ryan, Judith Wheeler
Science Teacher
Shepard, Beth Nix
Biology Teacher
Spencer, Norma Gail
English Teacher
Stalvey, Nancy Y.
Health Occupation Instructor
Strickland, Tina Boyett
Math Teacher
Tarpley, Jeane Broyles
Math Teacher
Todd, Charles E., II
Band Director
Townsend, Michael
Drafting & Design Tech Instr
Valencia, Willa Ferree
English Professor
Whitesell, Tallulah Long
English Teacher
Wingert, Debra Steedley
4th Grade Teacher
VIDALIA
Bellamy, Sally Toler
Science Teacher
Joiner, Rubye Doris Faison
Second Grade Teacher
Lambert, Peggy Mc Collum
Media Specialist
Oliver, Lisa Morris
Math Teacher
Padgett, Robert D.
Reading & English Teacher
Seabolt, Betty Jenkins
English Teacher
Sharpe, John Edwin, Jr.
Social Studies Teacher
VIENNA
Cason, Kay Herndon
Kindergarten Teacher
Harrell, Jodie W.
Kindergarten Teacher
Jordan, Margaret Taylor
Middle Grades Teacher
Stephens, Barbara Ann
8th Grd GA History Teacher
Tippett, Wilma Faircloth
Retired 3rd Grade Teacher
VILLA RICA
Best, Claudia Day
High School English Teacher
Ryals, Nan
Second Grade Teacher
Stephens, Rhonda Maxwell
Spanish Teacher
Thornton, Valencia Solita
6th Grade Language Arts Tchr
WADLEY
Rutland, Mary Delores
Principal
WALESKA
Edlund, Sherry C. Korthase
Associate Professor of English
England, Jane Cantrell
Prof of His & Political Sci
Lindsey, Harriett Almond
Assoc Professor of Education
Parrish, Arminda (Ingram)
6th Grade Math Teacher
Robertson, Eddie B.
Professor of Biology
WARM SPRINGS
Gill, Kelley E.
Pre-Kindergarten Teacher
WARNER ROBINS
Adams, Jane Wilson
High School Math Teacher
Atcheson, Monica Redmond
Kindergarten Tchr & Tech Coord
Avery, Bruce Alan
8th Grade Teacher
Baxley, Sidney Joseph
Biology Teacher
Beason, Angela Bolden
Mathematics Teacher
Bell, Carol Schlafer
Mathematics Teacher
Bell, Susan G.
English Teacher
Blaylock-Few, Geralyn Y.
Middle School Teacher
Blount, Katie Stringer
Elementary Art Teacher
Borek, Michele Pasco
French Teacher
Buller, Sylvia Burtis
Retired Teacher
Byrd, Laura Pinaud
AP Chemistry Teacher
Chambers, Toni Tononi
Middle School Mathematics Tchr
Clopton, R. Terry
6th Grd Math & Science Teacher
Comeau, Michael D.
Sixth Grade Mathematics Tchr
Cook, Jamie Barton
Latin Resource Tchr for Gifted
Crider, Karen Wiley
Third Grade Teacher
Crosby, Peggy Faye
Fourth Grade Teacher
Dean, Sharon Askew
7th Grade Mathematics Teacher
DeLaigle, Christina Taulbee
Seventh Grade Science Teacher
Emminger, Jane S.
Reading Teacher
Ennis, Lamar Wallace
English Teacher
Ferguson, Julie Golladay
Fifth Grade Teacher
Ferris, Gloria Partridge
4th Grade Teacher
Fluellen, Eula Watkins
Third Grade Teacher
Fuqua, Dianne Landers
6th Grade Teacher
Gore, Mary Ann (Burke)
Mathematics Teacher
Hamrick, Tracie Haynes
Spanish Teacher
Hinnant, Sherin C.
Lead Resource Tchr of Gifted
Hobes, Margaret Sanks
8th Grade Math Teacher
Jennings, Barbara M.
Middle Grades Honors Sci Tchr
Jerles, Dawn Daniel
French Teacher
Jones, Vicki Carreker
Biology Teacher
Joyner, Sharon Shiver
Cooperative Business Ed Coord
Kelly, Daniel Brendan
Economics & US History Tchr
Lacey, Faye Tharpe
Media Specialist
Mangrum, Bevelry Sanders
Middle Grades Teacher
McConnell, Beth Parker
School Counselor
Mc Rae, Ernest Cornell, Sr.
5th Grade Teacher
Molyson, Margaret
Science Department Chairperson
Murchison, Susan Harper
English Teacher
Ogletree, Patricia Colley
Mathematics Teacher
Peavy, C. H. Bobby
4th Grade Teacher
Peavy, Gregory Wayne
Band Director
Phillips, Susan Michelle
Science Teacher
Poythress, Laura Stafford
English Teacher
Scott, Dee Schewe
8th Grd Math & Soc Stud Tchr
Scudellari, Cheryl Ann
Graphic Communications Teacher
Simmons, Kay Boyette
6th Grade Math Teacher
Stocker, Bonita Swarts
Math Tchr & Dept Chairperson
Stoica, Patricia Morgan
Media Specialist
Stupke, Sylvia Ann
Level I Adult Literacy Teacher
Swartz, Sidney R.
Honors Science Teacher
Taylor, Gwendolyn Blasingame
Assistant Principal
Turpin, Robert Gene
Aerospace Science Instructor
Vizzini, Carol Lay
Third Grade Teacher
Warnock, Larry E.
Teacher & Coord of Mrktg Ed
Washington, Gretchen Natasha
Sixth Grade Teacher
Westman, Charles
Director of Bands
White, Willie Marie
4th Grade Teacher
Williams, Ronald
Sixth Grade Teacher
Zinicola, Debra Courtney
1st Grade Teacher
WARRENTON
Parrish, Meredith Bauknight
High School English Teacher
WASHINGTON
Guin, Belle Johnson
Math Teacher & Dept Chair
Lindsey, Debbie Brown
First Grade Teacher
Melton, Mark A.
7th Grade Teacher
WATKINSVILLE
Baldwin, June M.
Retired 3rd Grade Tchr & Prin
Boswell, Mary Parham
Math Teacher
Bowie, Sherry Shuler
7th Grade Mathematics Teacher
Cain, Randall G.
8th Grade Math Teacher
Cheeley, Kim Boswell
Kindergarten Teacher
Della Torre, Joseph Peter
Health, PE Tchr & Dept Chm
Dickens, Brian Charles
9th-12th Grd Hlth & PE Teacher
Gay, Dianne Smith
6th Grade Teacher
Green, Patricia Huff
Middle School Counselor
Hall, Hazel Diane
Business Education Teacher
Hansen, Carolyn Parkerson
Teacher of Gifted
Kennon, Pamela Canerday
Fourth Grade Teacher
Russo, Joseph Leslie
Social Studies & Reading Tchr
Shanks, Cris Grogan
7th Grade Social Studies Tchr
Southers, Lucy Johns
Kindergarten Teacher
Stoneburner, Ellen Hansen
Sixth Grade Teacher
Varner, John J.
English Teacher
Walker, Jamie Berryman
Math Teacher
Williams, Linda Rowley
8th Grade English Teacher
WAYCROSS
Arnold, Joyce Bandy
1st Grade Teacher
Comer, John Fletcher
10th Grade English Teacher
Cranshaw, William Raymond
Teacher
Fields, Pamela Fridell
Third Grade Teacher
Flowers, Thomas Edward
Math Teacher
Godwin, Sandra Donna
Social Science Teacher
Harris, Ted C.
Acting President
Helms, James M.
Assoc Professor of Mathematics
Hyers, Jill Sprague
English Teacher

ROSS (cont)
, Liz Davis
e Teacher
, Edith Keaton
h Teacher & Chairperson
obin Denise
aphy Teacher
ary Ann
th Grd Tchr & CVAE Coord
ames D., Sr.
h Teacher
Betty Craven
Grade Teacher
, Amy Leigh
age Arts Teacher
l, Virginia Everitt
n Teacher
Alice Thomas
d Second Grade Teacher
hard Byron
y & Political Sci Prof
Debra Gill
y Teacher
ara E.
h Instructor
Carol Taylor
gy Teacher
nsy O.
al Science Teacher
Lynda Gayle
Grade Teacher
ESBORO
an, John Allen
rce JROTC Instr
Joyce Lake
e & Earth Science Tchr
and, Jan D.
er & Coach
Jackie
Studies Teacher
, Carolyn Williams
ade Teacher
Renee Mc Clellan
Grade Teacher
Beth Bennett
h Teacher
Frances Vereen
Grade Teacher
GREEN
ack, Betty Sue Dyal
ade Teacher
COOCHEE
ose Hester
Specialist
ason, Myrtice Perkins
er I Teacher
ER
, James Marcellus
ysical Science Teacher
ship, Carleen S.
h Dept Chair & Teacher
rne, Shelia Calhoun
Occupations Teacher
n, Cynthia Young
matics Teacher
, Katherine Jill
age Arts & Math Teacher
Carol Robinson
ce Dept Chairperson
l, Claire Patricia
sh Teacher
orothy Towler
h Grade Teacher
son, Shadie Howard
l Studies Teacher
, Jane F.
matics Teacher
TON
s Amidon, Bonnie Bailey
Grade Teacher
BINE
o Ann Lasseter
rade Teacher
BURY
n, Robert Wayne
Headmaster & Law Prof
OSTOCK
Barry H.
eacher & Basketball Coach
t, Nancy B.
selor
, Karen Marie (Chance)
School Math Teacher
an, Alma Rogers
PE Teacher
D'Laine Doyle
rd Special Education Tchr
, Rebecca Mc Brayer
ergarten Teacher
Brenda C.
Grade Teacher
nough, Jean Michaud
School Art Instructor
, Carole Shuler
nced Placement Dept Chair
, Penny
Gifted Program Teacher
Deborah Day
th Grade Teacher
, Patricia Stever
sh & Drama Teacher
n, Dorothy Hendren
School Biology Teacher
son, Patricia Reddick
nce Teacher
, James Curtis
& Physical Education Tchr
NS
r, Beverly Law
Grade Teacher

WRIGHTSVILLE
Hunt, Nadine M.
CBE Coord, Ed Dept Head & Tchr
YOUNG HARRIS
March, B. Lee
Professor of Political Science
ZEBULON
Flemister, Brenda Clarice
Teacher
Hammond, Cheryl Dunn
English Teacher & Dept Chair
Willis, Lonnie Jean
Sixth Grd Social Studies Tchr
Woods, Geneva M.
Biology Teacher

GUAM

AGANA
Flores, Christina Franquez
6th Grade Art Teacher
Guerrero, Connie Perez
School Program Consultant
AGAT
Carnegie, Gedell Marie
Bio, Anatomy & Physiology Tchr
BARRIGADA
Cruz, Loring Santos
PE Teacher
Herriage, Dan
Science Teacher
Schlosser, Mark Todd
Math, Science & Computer Tchr
MANGILAO
Balakrishnan, Narayana Swamy
Professor of Chemistry
Cruz, Dorothy Flores
Cmptr Sci Prof & Dept Chprsn
Cunningham, Lawrence Joseph
Adjunct Professor
Fernandez, Carmen Frances
Dir of Ctr for Continuing Ed
Hamilton, Persis Mary
Nursing Professor
Kosky, Leslie Johnson
Tourism Professor
Lobban, Christopher Simon
Professor of Biology
Platt, Donald Leland
Associate Professor of History
Pobocik, Rebecca Susan
Assoc Prof of Nutrition
Raulerson, C. Lynn
Biology Teacher
Sauget, Clyde Raymond
Marketing Professor
Seay, William J.
Assoc Prof & HPERD Dir
Skipper, Richard Knox
Marketing Instructor
Smith, Barry Dale
Service Coord & Biology Instr
Tangye, Ronald M.
Professor of Marketing
Tydingco, Daisy Marie Dezell
Instructor
Whippy, Helen J. Dalmaso
Mathematics Professor
Wolf, Ione M.
Asst Professor of Elem Ed
PALAU ISLAND
Polloi, Justa Franz
Religion Teacher
PITI
Estampador, Gloria Dionio
Science Dept Chprsn & Tchr
SINAJANA
Aguon, Gloria Crisostomo, FSPA
Third Grade Teacher
Dydasco, Rosalind Pilar Paulino
Retired Teacher
TAMUNING
Crisostomo, Jose Atoigue
Human Anatomy, Physiology Tchr
Cummings, Maria Manalo
Chemistry Teacher
Figirliyong, Dana Akers
Science Teacher
Hardy, William Robinson, Jr.
English Teacher
James, Geraldine Sablan
High School Math Teacher
Jones, Cynthia Simmons
Guidance Counselor
Umagat, Carlotta Blaz
Retired HS Soc Stud Teacher
Watabayashi, Karen Lee
Language Arts Dept Chairperson
Willemsen, Craig R.
Guidance Counselor

HAWAII

AIEA
Abrazado, Paula Cyran
Math, Speech & Computer Tchr
Carmody, Harriet Okubo
Language Arts & G-T Teacher
Castillo, Richard Joseph
Assoc Prof of Psychology
Cox, Darrel Harvie
Retired Sixth Grade Teacher
Falgout, Suzanne
Assoc Prof of Anthropology
Haruno, Jeanne M.
Second Grade Teacher
Herman, Louis Gershone
Assistant Professor
Nakano, Helen Tsugiyo
Second Grade Teacher
Petersen, James K.
Social Studies Teacher
Savage, Adam Jason
Professor of Business Admin
Tadaki, Jeanne Nashiwa
Retired Elementary Teacher
Wong, Cindy Sachie
Japanese Teacher
Yap, Naomi Hamasaki
Teacher of Gifted Students
CAPTAIN COOK
Kaku, Julie Ann Rocha
First Grade Teacher
Mc Coy, Shirley Layaoen
Success Compact Resource Tchr
EWA BEACH
Armstrong, Heidi Wilkens
Fourth Grade Teacher
Enomoto, Jenny Sumie
First Grade Teacher
Hood, Teresa Rodriquez
English Teacher & Dept Chair
Kimura, Sara Ann Michie
Secondary Health Teacher
Mersberg, Aaron Kanekawaiola
English Teacher
Nash, Allen Garnet
9th-12th Grd Photography Tchr
Nosaka, Barbara Ann
Dir Peer Ed Pgm & Coord
Oda, Eleyne K.
School Counselor
Palmer, Ernest Elvin
Retired Eighth Grd Teacher
Rogers, Robert Agard
HS Social Studies Teacher
Rosengrant, Robert L.
Social Studies Teacher
Sato, Stacy Kazuo
Prin, Tchr, Ath Dir & Coach
Watanabe, Carol Ann B. S.
Second Grade Teacher
Whiteley, Bobby Conway
Social Studies Teacher
HANA
Paisley, Ariel Michael
Math & Science Teacher
HILO
Arthurs, Barbara Ann
Instructor & Counselor
Bailey, H. Robert
Instructor of English
Chow, Jay Morse
Calculus Teacher
Corella, Charlotte Vierra
US History & Sociology Teacher
Farmer, John Baring
Social Studies Teacher
Gorman, Mary Lee Simons
Kndgtn & 1st Grade Teacher
Haiku, Sandra Charlene
Science Teacher
Hees, Karl F.
Secondary English Teacher
Kelly, Audrey Archer
Art Teacher
Kobayashi, Liza Toshiko (Shigeta)
Science Teacher
Kojima, Sheri Igawa
Secondary Business Teacher
Kunimoto, Yvonne Mc Rae
Japanese Lang Tchr & Vice Prin
Lino, Timothy K.
Vice Prin & Head Ftbl Coach
Miura, Carole
Professor in Mathematics
Morton, Peter Collister
Seventh Grade Math Teacher
Nahm-Mijo, Trina
Professor of Psychology
Nakagawa, Janice Matsumoto
Kindergarten Teacher
Nakanishi, Roy Mitsuo
Science Teacher
Narimatsu, Gwen Tanabe
Kindergarten Teacher
Richardson, Patricia Lee
French Teacher
Sager, Jon Patrick
Science Teacher
Shindo, Rene Tanaka
Biology Teacher
Soares, Judith Olsen
English Teacher
Stembridge, Melodie Weeks
Instructor of Nursing
Urasaki, Jasmine (Okada)
HS Mathematics Teacher
Uyeda, Kelly Okuma
US His Tchr & Chrldng Coach
Wong, Jeanette
Biology Tchr & Sci Dept Chprsn
Yamamoto, Donn T.
Business Education Teacher
Yoshimura, Arleen E.
Retired Business Ed Teacher
HONOKAA
D'Amico, Kathleen Louise Logan
Vice Principal
Nakachi, Rachelle Mattos
English Teacher
Washburn, Gary Scott
Music Director
HONOLULU
Abe, Gregg Koyei
Band Director
Aki, Dorothy Yoshida
Counselor
Asato, Michael K. T.
Mathematics Teacher, Dept Head
Ashimine, Tanya Celeste
Biology Tchr & Sci Dept Head
Austin, James Serenous, Jr.
Asst Prof of History & Ed
Bailey, Lisa Preston
Russian Teacher
Baldwin, Katherine Moon
12th Grade Mathematics Teacher
Barry, Elizabeth Gandy
Geog & Wrld Civilizations Tchr
Barton, Nancy Lee
High School Music Teacher
Bauer, Theresa Lukenich
Science Teacher
Behr, Marlene Stevens
Human Development Teacher
Cantley, Timothy Owen
Math Teacher
Char, Linette Lee
Mandarin Teacher
Ching, Susan L.
English Teacher
Chow, Saralyn Leilani (tollefsen)
Fourth Grade Teacher
Chu, Micheal
Behavior Coordinator & Admin
Clark, Michael David
ESLL Teacher & Coordinator
Collier, Edward William
Performing Arts Dpt Chm & Tchr
Colte, Michelle Carlson
Language Arts Teacher
Cook, Robert Lee
Social Studies Teacher
Dik, Ibrahim E.
Economics Professor
Domalavage, Albert James
Hawaiian Regional Stud Instr
Eldredge, David Pinkham Ka'iana, III
Hawaiian Studies Tchr & Coach
Endo, Barbara Lois Hasegawa
5th Grade Teacher
Fee, Larry Leo
College Lecturer of Physiology
Field, Susan Jane (Cooling)
Mathematics Teacher
Fleischer, Joseph
French Teacher
Fontes, Randall Guy
Science & Social Studies Tchr
Fuchs, Gaynell MC Auliffe
English Teacher
Fujii, Daphne N.
English Teacher
Fujinaka, Francine Nobue
Japanese Lang Teacher
Fukumoto, Laura Maxine
Fifth Grade Teacher
Gaydos, Gregory George
Political Science Professor
Gefroh, Daniel Joseph
Asst Professor of Mathmetics
Goong, Leora Wong
Second Grade Teacher
Gorsky, Susan Rubinow
Dean of Students & Eng Tchr
Haas, Valerie S.
Latin Teacher
Hackler, Jeffrey M.
History Teacher
Hall, Sally Cooper
English Instructor
Heen, Marilyn L.
Art, Photography & Yrbk Tchr
Hefner, Carl J.
Anthropology Professor
Helbling, Joan Halldorson
Second Grade Teacher
Herring, Jennifer
Art Methods Instructor
Higa, Susana Mieko Che
Social Studies Teacher
Higuchi, Elaine K.
Japanese Teacher
Hom, Diane Hill
AP English Teacher
Hornsby, Debbie M.
English Teacher
Hu, Sophia Fei
Science Teacher
Jones, Samuel Lawrence
Associate Naval Sci Instructor
Jung, C. Sue Jean Ching
Second Grade Teacher
Kahawaiolaa, Christmas Napua
Teacher
Kaito, Robyn Kaneshiro
Sixth Grade Teacher
Kakugawa, Frances H.
Retired Teacher
Kam, Sandra C. L. (Hee)
Mathematics Teacher
Kam, Thomas K. Y.
Asst Prof of Accounting & Fin
Kamimura, Irene Hiroko
5th Grade Teacher
Kanada, Gary Nobyuki
Japanese & Hawaiian Lang Instr
Kaninau, Clayton K.
Resource Teacher
Katz, Daniel Steven
English Teacher
Keawe, Robyn Kaleilani Holland
Counselor
Kim, Christopher Kaniala
Hawaiian Lang, Cult & His Tchr
Kim, Su Chon Lee
Retired Teacher of GATE
Kimura, Jane Okamura
Fourth Grade Teacher
Kobata, Marilyn M.
Second Grade Teacher
Komori, Rusty
Tennis Professional
Kunishige, Lynn Kimura
Computer Science & Math Tchr
Lange-Otsuka, Patricia A.
Asst Prof of Nrsng & Acad Coor
Lee, Charles S.K.
JROTC Dept Head & Instr
Leong, Herman S. H.
Mathematics Teacher
Levinson, Lynn Gehler
English Teacher
Luckenbach, Barry Brent
Fifth Grade Teacher
Makagon, Jill Abbott
Instructor of English
Masuda, Melvin M.
Associate Professor of Law
Mathis, Susan Elouise (Patrick)
Math Teacher
Matsumoto, Timothy
Mathematics Teacher
Matsuo, Roy Takashi
Business Education Instructor
Mc Cutcheon, Susan Catherine
Chemistry & Physics Lead Tchr
Merrifield, Monica M. (Letoto)
Economics & Japanese Teacher
Messer, William G.
English & Latin Teacher
Meyers, Victor
Computer Science Instructor
Minami, Maydeen Tsuruda
School Improvement Plan Coord
Miyamoto, Georgeanne Keiko
English & Speech Teacher
Miyamoto, Mark Toshiichi
Sixth Grade Teacher
Moore, Edward Parsons, Jr.
English Teacher
Murakami, Gail Piilani
Physical Education Teacher
Nagashima, Yuka
Acad Sci Tchr & Internet Coord
Nakakura, Jeanine Tamiko Sao Wai
Science Teacher
Nakashima, Debra Yumi
High School English Teacher
Nelson, Jeanne Tyler
Mathematics Teacher
Nishiki, Amy Yamamoto
Retired 6th Grade Teacher
Nylen, Cynthia Behr
Soc Studies & History Teacher
Odo, Carol Uyehara
First Grade Teacher
O'Keefe, John F.
Instructor of English
Okimura, Cyrenne Hisae
Ballet & Jazz Instructor
Ostrowski, Bernard Edward
Psychology Instructor
Palmore, Paul Duncan
Director of Drama
Park, Michael Thomas
Mathematics Teacher
Pascua, Stephen James
Biology & Chemistry Teacher
Pavelle, James Restle
Instructor of Management
Pine, Ronald C.
Prof of Logic & Philosophy
Prevedouros, Panos D.
Assoc Prof of Civil Engrng
Psak, Jamie L.
Special Motivation Teacher
Rahsaan, Umar
US History Teacher
Rathyen, Cristina Campbell
AP English Teacher
Reginelli, Marcy Muellner
Fine Arts Department Chair
Retherford, Robert Dennis
Senior Fellow
Richards, Leon
Dean of Instruction
Rogers, Barbara
Science Dept Chair & Teacher
Romines, Gregory Dee
Academy Choral Director
Rudometkin, John David
Religion, Health & PE Tchr
St John, Karen Cavanagh
Assistant Professor of Psych
Savini, Bette Wellnitz
Fourth Grade Teacher
Sawai, Dahleen
Japanese Teacher
Schnackenberg, George Emil
Tchr & Alternative Ed Cnslr
Seamon, Neal Irving
Lecturer of Cooperative Ed
Sera, Jean Harimoto
Retired Elementary Teacher
Sheridan, Mary Stoebe
Associate Professor of Psych
Sibley, Gay Palmer
Associate Prof of English
Siegmund, Peggy Anne Gilcher
HS Performing Art Dir & Tchr
Strawn, Christopher Winfield
Latin Teacher
Suehiro, Cynthia
Secondary Math Teacher

HONOLULU (cont)
Sugimura, Lori-Lei M.
Japanese Teacher
Sumner, William Alexander
Biology Teacher
Suzuki, Matthew
Dir of Stu Acts & His Teacher
Tabije, Robert Charles
Secondary Social Studies Tchr
Takeshita, Patricia Yuki
English Teacher
Tamura, Victoria Ishida
Preschool Teacher
Teixeira, Tracy Lee Y. H.
Counselor & Asst Admin
Teter, Bill
12th Grade English Teacher
Teves, Rodi Jane Manaois
Science Teacher
Tjarks, Mark Damon
Instructor of English & Lit
Tottori, Jane Hirata
5th Grade Teacher
Trautwein, Ronald Dean
School Administrator
Wagner-Wright, Ron
English Professor
Welte, Mary Elizabeth
Freelance Writer
Wesolosky, Jacquelyn Guillaume
Biology Teacher
Wong, Dominica Malia
Church His & World Rel Tchr
Wong, Harry Cheong-Yung
TV Station Volunteer Dir
Wong, Joyce Baker
High School Bible Teacher
Yokoyama, Lane Shigeru
Graph Comm & Draft Tech Instr
KAHULUI
Adams, Patricia Kerr
English Instructor
Fujimoto, Yvonne Iris
Science Teacher
Harrowby, Kathleen Cosgrove
HS Language Arts Teacher
Hasenpflug, Nancy Anne (Miller)
Counselor
Kunitake, Rita Maeshira
1st-5th Grade Math Teacher
Ogata, Linda Murakami
Science Teacher
Omura, Janyce M.
Secondary Social Studies Tchr
Ueki, Michael H.
Math & Science Teacher
KAILUA
Akaka, Jonah Hau'Oli
Hawaiian Teacher
Campbell, Kathy F.
Special Education Teacher
Estes, Mary-Jo Ellen
Third Grade Teacher
Everest, Charles Marvin
Mathematics Teacher
Kapepa, David Stanley
Sixth Grade Teacher
Kawauchi, Frances Takahama
Retired Kindergarten Teacher
Kent, Patrick Ray
Eighth Grade Math Teacher
Neal, Monty
Business Education Teacher
Nishihira, Jerry M.
Mathematics Dept Chairman
Okamura, Karen
Student Activities Coordinator
Russell, Francine Diane (Cambra)
English Teacher
Spencer, Bruce F.
Student Activities Coordinator
Stewart, Leslie Shannon Keliilauahi
Community Quest Director
Terauchi, Madge Akao
Substitute Teacher
Teruya, Margaret Ann
English Teacher
Voss, Alfred D.
Mathematics Teacher
Yoshimori, Regina Emi (Goya)
Business Teacher
KAILUA KONA
Matsukawa, Nancy Fujikawa
7th Grade Mathematics Teacher
Orme, Sara Mae
Reading Specialist
KAMUELA
Goodwin, Debbie Anne
Science Teacher
Saito, Jean Kawaguchi
Retired Elementary Teacher
Young, Peter Thomas
Business Math Teacher & Coach
KANEOHE
Albert, Rosetta Young
Social Science Teacher
Cyboron, Sheila Anne
Science Teacher
Jenness, Cynthia Gibson
Peer Education Prgm Coord
Kalauokalani, Naomi L.
Fourth Grade Teacher
Kobayashi, Elsie Shiotani
Sixth Grade Teacher
Lee, Carol Ann
Senior English Teacher
Loo, Ronald J.K.
Philosophy Professor
Mc Gurk, Margaret Isbister
American Literature Teacher
Menor, Mercedes Basa
Teacher of Gifted & Talented
Miura, Elise Keiko
Family & Consumer Sci Instr
Reilley, Mary E.
7th-8th Grd Honors Eng Teacher
Sugitani, Susan Yuri
Social Studies Teacher
Tom, Joseph R.
PE, Hlth Tchr & Guid Dept Chm
KAPAA
Baldridge, Laurel Jane
Math Teacher
Bruns, Terry W.
Science Teacher
Caspillo, Carol A.
Mathematics Teacher
Morris, Cheryl Hamamura
7th-8th Grade Art Teacher
Stuart, Kimberlee Anne
10th Grade Biology Teacher
Sugimoto, Blanche H.
High School Teacher
Ward, Joseph William
English & Special Ed Teacher
KAPAAU
Park, Rodney Keith
Industrial Arts Teacher
KEALAKEKUA
Hickcox, Anna Aikue
English Teacher
Kanai, Therese Marie
Math Department Chair
Kerr, Priscilla Darlene
Mathematics Instructor
Leslie, Milton Michael
Educational Specialist
Mandelman, Hersh
Social Studies Teacher
Mosson, Edward James
Math Teacher
KIHEI
Bandonis, Diane Staiger
Eng & Oral Comm Teacher
KILAUEA
Maddock, Mike
Technology Coordinator
KUALAPUU
Helm, Kimberly Kuuipo Tomie
Physical Education Teacher
LAHAINA
Catanzaro, Douglas L.
English Teacher
Harbaugh, Amy Sue
Mathematics Teacher
Miller, Jay R., Jr.
Social Studies Teacher
Okemura, Audrey Y.
Science Teacher
Standish, Greg P.
English Language Arts Teacher
Wakida, Anna Pennell Seaver
12th Grade English Teacher
Zimmerman, Kathaleen Iacampo
7th Grade Science Teacher
LAIE OAHU
Barton, Susan Dale
Associate Professor of Math
Burnett, Keith R.
Professor of Education
Gali, Kari Basa
Special Education Professor
Hammond, Dale Alden
Professor of Chemistry
Han, Sherman H. M.
Professor of English
Harper, Jana Lynn
Lecturer
Havea Tolutau, Viliami Asipeli
Ceramics & Sculpture Professor
Haynes, C. Beth
Assoc Professor of Economics
Jonassen, Jon Tikivanotau Michael
Political Science Teacher
Kehoe, Dan G.
Director of Counseling Service
Kongaika, 'IsiIeli Tupou
Dean of Students
Mc Arthur, Janice R.
Asst Prof of Elementary Ed
Peterson, Keith S.
Assistant Professor of English
Spickard, Paul Russell
History Professor
Taylor, John E.
Prof & Hospitality Tourism Chm
Underwood, Grant R.
Professor of Religious Studies
Wells, Richard Delos
Art History Professor
Winstead, Roy
Education Professor
LAUPAHOEHOE
Seely, Naomi Kushi
Math Teacher
LIHUE
Inouye, Cherylyn Zane
Enrichment Teacher
Kong, Dewayne George
Business Education Teacher
Mc Millan, Pamela Knauss
Tenth Grade English Teacher
Meister, Arnold
Director
Oyama, Mark
Chef Instructor
Tokita, Lane T.
Senior Social Science Teacher
Uyematsu, Betsy Sakoda
Mathematics Teacher
Yamamoto, James Tetsuo
World His Tchr, Computer Coord
MAKAWAO
Buczynski, Sandy C.
Biology Tchr & Sci Dept Chm
Haldeman, Gary Allen
Foreign Language Dept Chair
Sanches, Margaret Livingston
Fourth Grade Teacher
Van Amburgh, Todd
Arts Chrmn & English Teacher
MILILANI
Chiang, Chenfu
Math, Drafting & Bible Teacher
Hiyane, Curtis Yoshio
Band Director
Kimura, Ann Yamashita
Second Grade Teacher
Lai, Leslie S. S.
Secondary Social Studies Tchr
Lau, Sherilyn Senaha
Secondary Business Ed Teacher
Moore, Andrea Beth
Secondary Language Arts Tchr
Niimi, Gail Tatsuko (Nakashima)
Japanese Teacher
Sproles, Kathleen Saiki
Former Fourth Grade Teacher
Teraoka, Irene Kanda
First Grade Teacher
NAALEHU
Johnson, Victoria Lynne
Third Grade Teacher
PAHOA
Niimi, June Amy
Mathematics Teacher
Oliverio-Caldwell, Ann L.
Science Dept Chair & Tchr
PEARL CITY
Amano, Esther Leialoha
6th-8th Grade Teacher
Burns, Tim
Assoc Prof of Physics & Engrng
Fujishima-Lee, Karen Yuriko
Mathematics Instructor
Kimura, Alison Jenny Chiaki
High School Mathematics Tchr
Koyama, Hope Kotoshirodo
Teacher
Matsunaga, Milton Toshio
Instr, Pgm Coord & Acad Adv
Moser, Michael
Math & Science Lecturer
Muranaka, Charlotte S.
Teacher
Nishigaya, Linda Eiko
Professor of Sociology
Reese, Michael T.
Chemistry Teacher
Tomoyasu, Faith Naomi Tachino
5th Grade Teacher
WAHIAWA
Arai, Betty Keiko
HS French & Guidance Teacher
Chun, Sue Ann Pacheco
Social Studies Teacher
Dowd, Constance Magata
Reading & Lang Arts Teacher
Fernandes, Dawn M.
Registrar
Fukumoto, Keith Makoto
Band Instructor
Hanaoka, Lois Hinazumi
Sixth Grade Teacher
Molina-Sagon, Fay
Spanish Teacher
Momiyama, Shirley Radcliff
MS Rel & Soc Stud Teacher
Nakayama, Keith Kenji
Band Director
Okamoto, Nelson Hisashi
Industrial Arts Teacher
Roldan, Phyllis Jean
ESL Social Studies Teacher
Sato, Lance Yukio
World History Teacher
Yoshizaki, Lynn Megumi
Lead Teacher
WAIALUA
Kawachi, Noel Susumy
Athletic Director
Kawamoto, Susan Miyoshi
English & AP Comm Teacher
WAIANAE
Bland, Bobbie Brown
Business Teacher
Chun, Mary A.
Social Studies Teacher
Ferris, Ruth Ann (Farmer)
Social Studies Teacher
Goya, Curtis
Vocational & Technology Tchr
Matsuda, Beth Anne
Health Teacher
Terada, Linda Emi
1st Grade Teacher
Watson, Michael
US History Teacher
WAILUKU
Boteilho, Charlotte Ann
Lang Arts Instr & Forensic Adv
O'Brien, Kevin John
World Civilizations Teacher
Omura, Diane Shinkal
Tenth Grd Hlth & Guidance Tchr
Razo, Tracy Mamiya
Business Dept Chairperson
WAIMEA
Ibara, Linda Toyama
7th Grd Social Studies Teacher
Nitta, Glenn T.
Special Education Teacher
WAIPAHU
Felmet, Adrienne Mc Pherson
Choral Director
Fukuda, Denise S.
High School Math Teacher
Pangilinan, Gloria DeVera
ESL & Social Studies Teacher
Sandobal, Beverly Keiko
Principal
Tonaki, Ann Nakamura
Sixth Grade Teacher
Yamashita, Lorraine Hayashi
Second Grade Teacher

IDAHO

ABERDEEN
O'Brien, Janet Johnston
Family & Consumer Sci Teacher
Wilson, Michael Jon
English Dept Chairman
AMERICAN FALLS
Bowman, Carol A.
7th Grd Sci Tchr & Team Ldr
Erlandson, Debra Marie (Banister)
7th-8th Grade Special Ed Tchr
Johnson, Jesse Nielson
Physical Education Teacher
Kruckeberg, Margaret Gabardi
First Grade Teacher
Rowland, Connie Payne
English Teacher
Smith, Kevin D.
Social Studies Teacher
West, Kimberly Jean
Home Ec Tchr & Yrbk Adv
Wiles, Greg B.
PE Teacher & Coach
Zelus, Kathryn Elyse
High School Counselor
ARCO
Taylor, Richard Cardan
Secondary History Teacher
ARIMO
Armstrong, Bradley J.
Business Teacher
Gillman, Gordon Lynn
Agriculture, Sci & Tech Instr
Mc Farland, Dale
Social Studies Teacher
Morris, Sherrill Stephenson
Math Teacher
Oslund, Mary Lou
Tech & Photography Teacher
Smith, Cheryl L. (Elsass)
English Tchr & Newspaper Adv
ASHTON
Eidinger, Jeannette Bessey
4th Grade Teacher
Sharp, Lin Hintze
Spanish & Art Teacher
BANCROFT
Christensen, Diane Gail
7th & 8th Grd English Teacher
Larsen, Aileen
Asst Prin & English Dept Chrmn
Olorenshaw, Anne Harris
Music Teacher
Peterson, Ralph W.
Science & Math Teacher
Pristupa, David William
Ag Science Technology Instr
BLACKFOOT
Baguley, Barbara Stark
English Teacher
Baguley, Lance W.
Language Arts Teacher
Blain, Jeff
High School Teacher
Campbell, Natalie Steffler
Kindergarten Teacher
Cashmore, Thain M.
Physical Science Teacher
Chapman, Cleon
High School Teacher
Cramer, Constance C.
Spanish & French Teacher
Crumley, Aartje
Gifted & Talented Facilitator
Dalton, James Michael
Drama, TV Jrnlsm & Law Ed Tchr
Dayley, Tammi Alverson
Reading Recovery Teacher
Elison, Loah
Fourth Grade Teacher
Hansen, Dennis George
Earth Science Teacher
Hansen, Leora Kay (Rider)
Forensics Dir
Hughes, Ellen Tsuchiyama
English Teacher
Jackson, Edward Neese
5th Grade Teacher
Jensen, Linda Yost
Teacher
Jenson, Delward LeRoy
Retired Mathematics Teacher
Johnson, Vicki L.
Physical Ed & Peer Ldr Teacher
Martin, Julie W.
Fifth Grade Teacher
Merrick, Nancy Bithell
First Grade Teacher
Merritt, Harold Hugh, Jr.
7th Grade Geography Teacher
Nacheff, Judy Ann
6th Grade Teacher
Rawson, Glenn Jay
LDS Seminary Teacher
Reese, Karen Hall
4th Grade Teacher
Scott, Mary S.
Business Department Chair
Spinner, Mary Margaret
Middle School Counselor
Torgerson, Theda Palmer
Fourth Grade Teacher
Wasia, Valerie
US Government & His Teacher
Wright, Thal V.
Soc Stud Tchr & Track Coach
BLISS
Sauer, Robby C.
History & Government Teacher
BOISE
Ah Fong, Richard James
English Teacher
Andersen, Michael Thomas
Fifth Grade Teacher
Anderson, Bonnie Marie
Science Teacher
Axtell, Shelley Miller
Second Grade Teacher
Bahruth, Robert Edwin
Professor of Elementary Ed
Baker, Richard L.
6th Grade Teacher
Bear, David Logan
Band Dir & Music Dept Chrmn
Berner, Mardell Edna
Retired Teacher
Block, William T.
English Teacher
Branton, Constance Chrest
Vocal Music Teacher
Brigham, Dean E.
Principal
Cameron, Daniel Harold
Professor of Chrstn Ministry
Centanni, Russell Joseph
Professor of Biology
Chehey, David James
Mathematics Teacher & Dept Chm
Chournos, Kathaleen Rowley
Physical Sci & Earth Sci Tchr
Clark, Robert B.
United States History Teacher
Cook, Jacki Leigh
Creative Commnctn & Spch Tchr
Crawford, Kathy Hegstad
First Grade Teacher
Cunningham, W. Patrick
Language Arts Dept Chair
DeWane, Marian Hallock
Chemistry Teacher & Chair
Doty, Glenn L.
Reading & Health Teacher
Douglass, Donna Kay
Second Grade Teacher
Eck, Pamela Tomkins
5th Grade Teacher
Ellis, Robert W.
Professor of Chemistry
Erickson, William Glenn
Sixth Grade Teacher
Falk, Dennis G.
Teacher
Farley, Jeffrey Bryon
Mathematics Teacher
Ferrel-Mc Moran, Bonnie Porter
7th Grade Mathematics Teacher
Firman, Robert G.
Math Teacher
Fisher, Paula (Wood)
English Teacher
Foristiere, Michael Anthony
Speech & English Teacher
Fullmer, Bonnie
English Teacher
Gerhardt, Claudia Joan
Debate & English Teacher
Gilchrist, Kaye Griffiths
Theatre Arts Teacher
Graves, Jerry J.
US History Teacher
Griggs, Roy Edward
Educl Services Supervisor
Handley, Kristine Diane
Earth Science Teacher
Harden, Imogene D.
9th Grade English Teacher
Hensley, Gerald L.
Theater Arts Tchr
Hill, Lynette Hehn
ID Eng Lang Arts Consultant
Hill, Ronald R.
Earth Science Teacher
Hixon, Vernon James
Geography Teacher
Holmquist, Barbara J.
Reading & Journalism Teacher
Hranac, Kathleen A.
Sixth Grade Teacher
Hultstrand, Roger C.
Social Studies Teacher
Husted, Sally Hanson
French Teacher
Johnson, Daniel Dean
Band Director
Johnson, Patricia L.
Language Arts Teacher
Kennings, Marilyn
English & Latin Teacher
Kluksdal, Gary E.
Calculus Tchr & Bsbl Coach

(cont)
Dick
rade Teacher & Asst Prin
J. Michael
ology Teacher
ws, DeDe D.
Grade Teacher
lum, Molly Jo
Photography Teacher
Rex Robert
2th Grd Army ROTC Teacher
ff, Claudia Grout
Grade Teacher
n, Sharon Lynn
Grade Teacher
, Richard William
entary School Principal
nd, Chris Ann
sh Teacher
amilton, Barbara Frances
uage Arts Department Chair
Darla D.
rade English & Lit Tchr
z, James B.
gy Teacher
William David
Prof & Pub Admin
s, Vernon Lewis
h Educator
k, Hollis B., Jr.
Director
g, Daniel Lee
istory & Journalism Tchr
Tamsen Baker
School Biology Teacher
Craig Allen
ssor of Music
, Julianne Curtis
ematics Teacher
a, B. Jon
ematics Teacher
Darly Steven
rade World History Tchr
, Peter Michael
h & Physical Ed Teacher
, Sandra Shea
l Studies & History Tchr
t, Linda Elliott
al Music Teacher
, John Scott
rade Physical Sci Teacher
Linda Sipila
Science Teacher
, Todd A.
ssor
Georgia Mae
th Grade History Teacher
Ron George
Educator
nder, Jon S.
8th Grade English Tchr
Chuck
her
Eric Anthony
gy & Anatomy Teacher
s, Edmund M.
istory & Govt Teacher
son, Tina Dickey
Grade English & Rdng Tchr
, Maria Helen
sh Teacher
za, John Joseph
rade Math & Science Tchr
, Mary Ellen Johnson
sh Teacher
Cotton D.
Grade English Teacher
ERS FERRY
Marcella Elston
Grade Teacher
, Harry Edward
ematics Teacher
ds, Teddy Eugene
h Grade Science Teacher
Robert Oliver
ematics & Science Teacher
Wendy A.
sh Teacher
EAU
ter, Connie Flamm
ce & Math Teacher
ide, Cheryl Lynn
sh Tchr & Yearbook Adv

her, Paul Jonathan
th Grd Tchr & Headmaster
Shar
nd Grade Teacher
n, Carla Anne
School English Teacher
n, Gary Dean
English Teacher & Coach
g, B. Eileen
Grade Teacher
y, Kathleen Thompson
Grd Earth Science Teacher
, Robert Lee
d Grade Teacher
EY
ta, Theresa Lee
Grade Teacher
an, Linda Rose
Grade Teacher
Karin M.
2th Grade Supervisor
ll, Morus O.
Tchr, Athletic Dir & Coach
n, Sherry Lynn
rvisor

Judd, Cynthia Spreier
Music Teacher
Leone, James Skip
Eighth Grade Earth Sci Tchr
Lindsay, Richard Thomas
Band Director
Merrell, Kathy Tylene
Third Grade Teacher
Parkin, Colleen Mary
Geography & World History Tchr
Spencer, Miriam Judith
Physical Science Teacher
CALDWELL
Attebery, Louie Wayne
Eyck-Berringer English Prof
Frank, Robert Carmen
9th Grd Earth Science Teacher
Free, Joel Martin
6th-7th Grade Art Teacher
Haynes, Diann Hurd
7th Grade Language Arts Tchr
Hovey, Marcia Stone
Third Grade Teacher
Ireland, Richard Elton
Auto Mechanics Tech Teacher
Leake, Robert Bruce
Math & Computer Science Tchr
Lytle, Carey John
Art Teacher & Yearbook Advisor
Martin, Beverly Jean
Physical Education Instructor
Mc Cormick, Elaine Johnson
Pre-School Teacher
Perkins, David Harrison
Prof of Accounting & Finance
Pfost, Lanetta Carol
2nd Grade Teacher
Rember, John V.
Assistant Prof of Eng & Jrnlsm
Sasaki, Leland K.
Jr High Mathematics Teacher
Sasaki, Michael Duaine
Sixth Grade Teacher
Scott, George Marshall
American Government Teacher
Smith, Samuel Whitney
Langroise Trio Cellist
Smithers, James R.
Graphic Communications Teacher
Tanikuni, Gary L.
US History Teacher
Thiel, Sharlene Kaye
3rd Grade Teacher
Tilzey, Winston Gary
Chemistry & Physics Teacher
Tucker, George Byron
Mathematics Teacher
Warnke, Carla S.
7th Grd Language Arts Teacher
CAMBRIDGE
Ertel, Barbara Anne (Sullivan)
7th Grade Teacher & Principal
Horn, Corringa Owen
Counselor & Computer Teacher
CAREY
Cordell, Joni Lawrence
Principal
Jolley, Vernon Ferril
7th-12th Grd Math Teacher
CASCADE
Wise, Sally
Math Teacher
CASTLEFORD
Howard, Laurie Jean (Gandiaga)
Mathematics & PE Teacher
Nolevanko, Linda Gill
Science Teacher
Wiseman, Andrew David
Principal
CHALLIS
Bradshaw, L. Keith
6th Grade Teacher
Skeen, David Earl
HS Teacher
COCOLALLA
Keene, Pamela Rinebold
Science Teacher
Vann, Janet Nordin
5th Grade Teacher
COEUR D'ALENE
Andrea, Dawna Louise
Instr of Bus & Prof Programs
Astroquia, Rosie Sinclair
Vice Principal
Belmont, Laureen Metzger
Instructor of English
Bieber, Eileen
English Teacher
Blank, Russell Scott
Marketing Education Teacher
Bloem, Bob
Communications Teacher
Bridges, Cory Stephen
Physical Education Teacher
Brower, Judith
Mathematics Professor
Clifford, Gayne A.
Business & Statistics Instr
Couser, Carl Andrew
6th Grd Tchr & Dept Chm, Coach
Duarte, Victor Manuel
Instructor of Psychology
Duman, Lloyd Paul
Eng & Intensive Eng Teacher
Federici, Peggy D.
Education & Sociology Prof
Gray, David Bruce
Algebra Teacher
Hamilton, Jeanne Sutton
4th Grade Teacher

Hyatt, Judy
English Teacher
Jones, Terry Morgan Lewis
Music Instructor & Band Dir
Kay Gomes, Pamela Diane
Science Teacher
Klinger, Ramona Hayes
Speech Comm Instructor
Knox, Sheila Stephens
Elem Technology Facilitator
Mann, R. David
Instructor
Mathes, Gerard John
Music Instructor
Mc Carty, Carol Moorhead
Biology Teacher
Melton, Melody Lynn
Speech Media & Sociology Tchr
Minkler, James Elton
Instructor of Philosophy
Proser, William Sloane
English Teacher
Rodriguez, David Charles
Science Teacher
Sacheck-Kramer, Marcia Ann
Health & Phys Ed Teacher
Wild, Kynne Marie
Computer Teacher
COTTONWOOD
Stubbers, Kathleen Jenny
Music Educator
COUNCIL
Huter, Judith Ann Swanson
Fourth Grade Teacher
Stovner, Danna Katzenberger
Elementary Teacher
DAYTON
Connerley, Richard Dennis
Director of Bands
La Bonty, Nancy
Business Teacher
Wareham, Kenneth L.
Sci Dept Chm & Phys Instr
DECLO
Rigby, Tanya
PE & Health Teacher
DIETRICH
Hoffman, Russell Bruce
Health, PE Tchr & Title 1 Dir
DOWNEY
Brim, Linda Pugmire
Third Grade Teacher
DRIGGS
Graves, Gary Bret
Science Teacher
Ross, Janine D.
Music Teacher
EAGLE
Lehosit, Merrilyn Featherstun
7th & 8th Grd Math & Sci Tchr
Mapp, Lynn Blackwell
Fourth Grade Teacher
Robertson, Noelle
English & German Teacher
Thomas, Adelle
Kindergarten Teacher
ELK CITY
Nelson, Michael Lee
3rd-4th Grade Teacher
EMMETT
Alder, Judy O.
English Teacher
Davis, Joanne M.
Advanced Eng & GATE Teacher
Dean, William J.
Ag Science & Technology Instr
McKie, Linda McLinn
2nd Grade Teacher
Nutile, Jean L.
English Teacher
Pawlick, Peter H.
Computer Coord & Sci Tchr
Presley, Judene C.
5th Grade Teacher
Schneider, Allan R.
Reading & Drama Teacher
Wayenberg, Richard Allen
Language Arts Teacher
FAIRFIELD
Ballard, Clell Gaskill
Soc Studies & Frgn Lang Tchr
FILER
Crooks, R. Moreen
Second Grade Teacher
Davis, Jean Roberts
English Teacher
Huitt, John Michael
His Tchr & Head Ftbl Coach
Lammers, Suellen Nelsen
History, English & Arts Tchr
Patrick, Afton E.
Fourth Grade Teacher
FIRTH
Pratt, Mark Blaine
Ag Science Technology Teacher
Smith, Lane D.
7th & 8th Grade English Tchr
FRUITLAND
Baines, Konnie Irene
Business & English Instructor
Carter, Pamela K.
Family & Consumer Science Tchr
Eitemiller, Glen Thomas
HS Biology Teacher
Greif, Michael Irvin
8th Grade Science & Tech Tchr
Hotchkiss, Darlene Noe
English Teacher
Rowley, Ralph S.
7th Grade Science Teacher

Wright, Troy S.
Agriscience & Technology Instr
GENESEE
Bielenberg, Cheryl Elizabeth
4th Grade Teacher
Caldwell, Kelly
K-12th Grade Music Teacher
GLENNS FERRY
Hance, Rick Dean
Ag Sci & Tech Teacher
Neal, Kay Russell
English, Speech & Spanish Tchr
GOODING
Cabbage, Nelly Petra Kristine Nerhus
Family & Consumer Sci Teacher
Eisinger, Patsy C.
Retired English Teacher
Hollifield, Lisa M.
Elementary Counselor
Jones, Ty Elton
History Teacher
Schmitt, Arden Joseph
Art Teacher
Skabronski, Annette
4th Grade Teacher
GRACE
Gummersall, Hilda Pearson
English Teacher
Kingston, Paula Stock
3rd Grade Teacher
Olsen, Dawna Karine
Government & World His Teacher
Smith, Dina Downs
5th & 6th Grade Teacher
Yamauchi, Ray W.
Mathematics & Economics Tchr
GRANGEVILLE
Wemhoff, Raylene Annette Baune Kasper
5th-6th Grade Teacher
GREENLEAF
Morse, Ellen Perry
5th-12th Grd Music Director
HAILEY
Bailey, Bart C.
Band & Choir Director
Dominick, Lynn Anne
First Grade Teacher
Laughlin, J. Stanley
Mathematics Teacher & Chair
Manweller, Matthew Shon
Economics & Amer Govt Teacher
Miller, Carolyn R.
4th Grade Teacher
Miller, Charles Melvin
Science Teacher
Peck, John M.
Business & Office Ed Teacher
Renaud, Michael John
8th Grd Social Studies Tchr
Seals, Mark Allen
Secondary Science Teacher
HANSEN
Hall, Lucinda Berriochoa
Business Teacher
Remaley, Renea Hamby
Health & Physical Ed Teacher
HAYDEN LAKE
Spencer, Nancy Eddy
Administrator & Teacher
HAZELTON
Reed, Dahl Wesley
Retired English Teacher
HOMEDALE
Greeley, Michael William
Industrial Technology Teacher
Hoff, Jody Gotsch
HS Math & Economics Teacher
Mendelsohn, Leo James
Secondary & Health Teacher
Nash, Ardis Elizabeth
9th-10th Grade Lang Arts Tchr
Skeen, Wayne Lavern
Fourth Grade Teacher
IDAHO CITY
Mc Farlane, John Earl
MS Biological Sciences Tchr
IDAHO FALLS
Caffaro, Rosalie Cooper
English Teacher
Carosone, Heather Johnson
English Teacher
Case, Wanda L. Schaures
Sr Literature Composition Tchr
Childs, Joyce Miller
German & French Teacher
Christensen, La Ralph
6th Grade Teacher
Christensen, Patricia Boyle
Grammar & Literature Teacher
Christensen, Vickie J.
English Teacher
Cook, Wendy Mc Une
Journalism & English Teacher
Dunn, Johlyn
Theatre Arts & Comms Teacher
Eaton, Leo David
5th Grade Teacher
Elser, Dalee Ann
English Teacher & Yearbook Adv
Fauver, Jodi Brandon
Science Teacher
Gillespie, Pam K.
Math Teacher
Goeken, Glenna Maurine
English Teacher
Green, Nikie
English Teacher
Haroldsen, G. Eric
World History Teacher

Harris, Donnelly LeRoy
Journalism Instr & Advisor
Herbst, Judy Lynne
Second Grade Teacher
Hincks, Evva N.
English Teacher
Hostert, Linda Jackson
Physical Education Instructor
Johnson, Marsha E.
Career Ed Coord & Center Dir
Jones, Nancy L.
Career Education Coordinator
Kakacek, Steven Jacob
7th Grade Math Teacher
Keating, John E.
Mathematics & Soc Stud Tchr
King, Ruth Ellen
Health Occupations Teacher
Kopp, Edward Ferrel
Welding Instructor
Leatham, Douglas A.
Govt, Psych & Sociology Tchr
Mac Donald, Karen Louise
7th Grade Reading Teacher
Marler, Anne
English Teacher
Mays, Kelli Kathleen
English & Reading Teacher
Mc Coy, Jeanie Robson
English Teacher
Monson, Cindy Wilson
Family & Consumer Science Tchr
Moore, Craig Allan
Computer Teacher
Moratcka, Esther Iverson
History Teacher
Murphy, Shirley Griffin
English Teacher
Neal, Robert L.
Health & Physical Ed Teacher
Oloff, James L.
Sixth Grade Teacher
Payne, Kay K.
Title I Math Tutor
Perkins, Maridee Hill
English & Speech Teacher
Peterson, Robert Scott
US History Teacher
Phillips, Sheryl Bingham
Sixth Grade Teacher
Pickett, Vicky Lynn
Psychology & Sociology Teacher
Portrey, Renee D.
Speech & Drama Teacher
Potter, Nancy Irene
Third Grade Teacher
Rice, Kay (Zimmer)
Fifth Grade Teacher
Roberts, Lorna
Math & Computer Teacher
Schlechten, Jamie Lynn
Algebra & Geometry Teacher
Scott, Lisa Nukaya
Fourth Grade Teacher
Sestero, Shanna Kirkham
French Teacher
Smith, Richard Alan
8th & 9th Grd Soc Stud Teacher
Storms, Honore Melissa Hendrickson
Soc Studies Tchr & Dept Chair
Taylor, Joyce Hart
English Dept Chair & Teacher
Thomas, Richard David
Mathematics & Science Teacher
Toole, Kelli Diane
Second Grade Teacher
Waite, Randy Glen
Chemistry & Physics Teacher
Wisner, Suzanne Proulx
Mathematics Teacher
Wolf, Kim Mc Cabe
First Grade Teacher
INKOM
Becker, Viola M.
1st Grade Teacher
Marshall, Connie F.
6th Grade Teacher
Roberts, Elizabeth Toone
4th Grade Teacher
IONA
Wood, Grant E.
5th Grade Teacher
JEROME
Bradley, Kurt
Math Teacher
Enos, Judy Ann
4th Grade Teacher
Hatmaker, David Peter
Fifth Grade Teacher
Miller, Robert Michael
History & Government Teacher
Samuels, Kathleen Marie
Third Grade Teacher
Scofield, Marla L.
8th Grade Math & Algebra Tchr
Shank, L. Arlene Garrison
Kindergarten Teacher
Trail, Janet Arlene Walker
Third Grade Teacher
KAMIAH
Squires, Robert Larry
Proj Dir Adult & Stu Lit Pgm
KELLOGG
Amos, Shawn M.
Business Teacher
Baillie, Teresa Lea
7th Grade Language Arts Tchr
Dickinson, Richard K.
Instrumental Music Director

KELLOGG (cont)
Haller, Ph.D., Ann Cordwell
Science Instructor
Lowe, Ralph Wesley
Activities Director
Seaton, James Allen
8th Grade American His Teacher
KENDRICK
Bradley, Clarke
Social Studies Teacher
Wolff, Lisa Vallem
Girls Basketball Coach
KETCHUM
Stansberry, John L.
4th Grade Teacher
KIMBERLY
Hall, Vinnie Jan
Advanced Health & WTS Tchr
Hogan, Gordon
Scndry Math Tchr & Chair
Mc Adams, George Alan
Soc Stud & Body Dev Teacher
Miller, John Samuel
Govt & World History Teacher
Shawver, Jean (Fagan)
Media Specialist & Rdng Tchr
Sorensen, Jim L.
Agriculture Instructor
Young, Judy Gott
Fifth Grade Teacher
KOOSKIA
Lewis, Greg Vincent
Art Teacher
Spencer, James, Jr.
K-8th Grd Counselor
Weeks, Steve W.
Fifth Grade Teacher
KUNA
Bergdoll, Brenda
Mathematics Teacher
Bosserman, Sherrie D.
Teacher of Gifted & Talented
Delaney, Terrence Patrick
Math Teacher & Dept Chair
Garden, Camille Cruise
Language Arts Teacher
Lilienkamp, Ken Richard
Assistant Principal
Lyons, Connie Jean
Second Grade Teacher
Smith, Gordon Paul
Band Director
Snider, Toni
2nd Grade Teacher
LAPWAI
Scott, Sheila Reid
English, Comm & Drama Teacher
LEADORE
Sharp, Kim Nelson
Business & Computer Teacher
LEWISTON
Caudron, Cordell Robert
English Teacher
Hill, Crag Allen
Language Arts Teacher
Mathewson, Lasinnda Machell
Marketing Teacher
Moore, Pam Schubach
English Teacher
Patterson, John W.
Art Teacher
Taylor, Gwen Ensly
Associate Professor of Reading
Tiede, Glen
Math Tchr & Chairperson
Trout, Douglas Michael
Mathematics & Science Teacher
White, Patricia Earlene
6th Grade Teacher
Wicks, Jimmy Ellis
Biology & Forestry Teacher
MACKAY
Roche, VerNon D.
Vocational Agriculture Instr
MALAD CITY
Brimhall, Roslyn C.
Secondary PE & English Teacher
MALTA
Wight, Elmoine Orr
First Grade Teacher
MARSING
Muntean, Kathy A.
English Teacher
Pfeifer, Edward C.
HS Social Studies Teacher
MC CALL
Carrico, Ted L.
Musical Director & Teacher
Gans, Kathy C.
Math Teacher
Sheldon, Toni Couch
3rd Grade Teacher
Staup, Debra Kaye Mousetis
Sixth Grade Teacher
MC CAMMON
Cobia, Elaine
Sixth Grade Teacher
Gunter, Jill Rowe
5th Grade Teacher
MELBA
Durbin, Robbie J. (Taylor)
Third Grade Teacher
Hoagland, Mark W.
HS Math Teacher
Knapp, Alfred Arthur, Jr.
Middle School Teacher
Mangum, David Sellman
5th Grade Teacher & HS Coach
Mangumj, David Sellman
Elementary PE Teacher
Ober, Phyllis Ann
Fifth Grade Teacher
Stirm, Heidi Smith
Family, Consumer Sci & Ec Tchr
Strong, Darla K. (VanNortwick)
Third Grade Teacher
MENAN
Taylor, Deidre Ann
Fifth Grade Teacher
MERIDIAN
Alger, Brent Lee
Physics & Algebra Teacher
Ascuena, Vikki Pepper
English Teacher & Dept Chm
Babcock, Karen Wohlrabe
Mathematics Teacher
Brokaw, Kristie McAllister
Fourth Grade Teacher
Cowley, Jerry B.
English & Journalism Teacher
Fischer, Kelli Powell
Phys Sci Tchr & Dist Sci Coord
Fout, Randy D.
History Teacher
Foxall, Elaine
8th Grade English Teacher
Hall, Lannice Budge
Math Teacher
Hannity, Mary Murphy
American History Teacher
Hoseley, Jeffrey Gordon
Economics & US History Tchr
Kassens, Zola I.
Retired Cnslr & GATE Faciltr
Mc Cathron, Penny Anne
Second Grade Teacher
Spaulding, Allen
Business Education Teacher
Wertz, Marva Lea
Biology Teacher
Wyke, Janet Evans
Third Grade Teacher
Young, Greg
6th Grade Language Arts Tchr
MIDDLETON
Brown, J. Michael
English Teacher
Garwick, Gail Fillmore
Physical Education & Hlth Tchr
Georgeson, Yvonne LeCler
HS Eng Tchr & Newspaper Adv
Harris, Lisa Jeanne
Third Grade Teacher
King, Sandra Young
English Teacher
Morley, Sylvan Howard, Jr.
Spanish Teacher
Nau, Richard A.
Mathematics Dept Tchr & Chair
MONTPELIER
Burdick, Judi Penrod
6th-12th Grade Choir Teacher
MOSCOW
Admassu, Wudneh
Chemical Engrng Associate Prof
Burnham, Jocene Jones
2nd Grade Teacher
Carson, Catherine Joan
Mathematics Teacher
Cooke, Marcia K.
Drama & English Teacher
Finn, Calvin L.
Assoc Prof of Elec Engineering
Fletcher, Janice Williams
Child Dev & Family Rel Prof
Ford, Martha J.
Mechanical Engrng Sr Instr
Gill, Rick
Prof of Mechanical Engineering
Guenthner, Joseph F.
Agricultural Economics Prof
Hallgren, Karen L.
English Teacher
Jones, Elaine Garrison
Third Grade Teacher
Kittell, Ellen E.
Assitant Professor of History
Morris, Linda Joyce
Marketing Professor
Murray, Vince
English Teacher
Myers, Marla Ann
Assistant Professor of Acctng
Nance, James Brian
Secondary Math & Science Tchr
Niles, Marcia Selden
Asst Prof & Assoc Dept Head
Noren, Kenneth Vincent
Asst Prof of Electrical Engrng
Passanante, Joy Cathey
English Professor
Popiel, Elizabeth Mowrer
Asst Prof of Teacher Education
Spencer, Tom Hart
Principal
Struble, Wesley Hopping, Jr.
Science Teacher
Woods, Tina Miller
2nd Grade Teacher
Young, Jeffrey L.
Asst Prof of Elec Engineering
MOUNTAIN HOME
Cherry, Heather Hrrett
English Teacher
Graves, Karen Lee Popplewell
Guidance Counselor
Herrboldt, Robert W.
Industrial Arts Teacher
Martin, Susan Johnston
Journalism & English Teacher
Thomas, Beth Wilkins
Reading & French Teacher
Wagner, Janet K.
Special Education Teacher
Williams, Jennifer Lynne
Secondary Art Teacher
NAMPA
Ashley, Tami
4th Grade Teacher
Brackett, Ruby J.
Gifted & Talented Facilitator
Burton, Fred Thomas
Mathematics & Physics Teacher
Fastabend, Gloria J.
Government & Psychology Tchr
Gratton, Joseph Michael
Secondary Teacher
Hauge-Mikkelson, Paula
6th Grade Teacher
Hokenson, Peggy
Counselor
Jamison-Eubanks, Glenda Reed
English Teacher
Kern, Ralph M.
High School Principal
Lawson, Linda Laws
1st Grade Teacher
Loughmiller, Donald Ray
Mathematics Instructor
Lundergan, Laurie Hills
First Grade Teacher
Nettinga, Robin L.
9th Grade Reading Teacher
Richardson, Bonnie Jean
English Teacher
Russell, Brad R.
High School Drafting Instr
Slabaugh, Gerald Lee
8th Grade US History Teacher
Taylor, Thomas Rusty
Secondary Science Teacher
Tucker, Sandra Sue (Sasaki)
Fourth Grade Teacher
Wood, Greg
Reading & Study Skills Teacher
NAPLES
Adamson, James Evans
Fifth Grade Teacher
Benda, Norma J.
Second Grade Teacher
NEW MEADOWS
Budler, Brenda Lee (Martin)
Family, Cnsmr Sci & Bus Tchr
NEW PLYMOUTH
Beutler, Ronald Kenneth
English & Reading Teacher
Davis, Kimberly Gail
Science Teacher
NEZPERCE
Higgins, Steven Douglas
History, Govt & PE Teacher
OLA
Sutton, Gloria Harrison
Multi-Grade Classroom Teacher
OROFINO
Jarolimek, Tammy Ann
Health & Physical Ed Teacher
Wilson, Cindy P.
Social Studies & English Tchr
Wilson, Shannon Scott
Consumer, Ec, Psych & Soc Tchr
PARMA
Freeman, James Karl
Mathematics Teacher
Webster, Shari Robison
Office Occupations Instructor
PAUL
May, Sheryl Crane
Science Teacher
Mayes, Elaine Spencer
Third Grade Teacher
Norton, James P.
Jr HS Assistant Principal
Workman, Laura Ann (Dietz)
Sixth Grade Teacher
PAYETTE
Christian, Deborah H.
Business Instr & Cmptr Coord
Davila Levson, Margaret E. (Greif)
PE & Health Tchr
DeBord, Marilyn Anne
English I & 9th Grd Teacher
Hash, Peggi Roxene
Kindergarten Teacher
Heater, Suzan R.
1st Grade Teacher
Moss, Aaron David
Classified Music Aid
Thomas, Marion N.
Science & Computer Teacher
PINGREE
Turpin, Sharon Lynne (Yancey)
First Grade Teacher
POCATELLO
Andersen, Beverly N.
Mathematics Teacher
Anderson, Scott Eric
Director of Choral Activities
Anderson, Stephen B.
Fourth Grade Teacher
Balsai, Scott S.
9th Grade Reading & Eng Tchr
Banning, Matt James
4th Grade Teacher
Chandler, Dianna Saylor
Literature & Composition Tchr
Chase, Paul Capps
Social Science Teacher
Coe, Cathy
English, Speech & French Tchr
Couch, Doris Graves
2nd Grade Teacher
De Jesus, Karl
Chemistry Professor
Dilweg, JoAn Kisling (Falter)
Drama Director
Fisher, Carol J.V. Vreeland
Mathematics Instructor
Frost, Chris
Physical Education Teacher
Frost, James C.
CIS Instructor
George, Patricia Dengler
Flute Professor
George, Thom Ritter
Professor of Music
Gunning, Linda M.
English Teacher
Haws, Byron Lee
Mathematics Teacher
Hildreth, Delbert H.
History & Science Teacher
Hopkins, Becky Bowser
6th Grade Teacher
Jarman, Susan Bishop (Manly)
First Grade Teacher
Jensen, Rosalie K.
Fifth Grade Teacher
Jeppson, Richard Joel
Biological Science Teacher
Johnson, Christine Nelson
PE & Health Teacher
Kinloch, MaryLou
Physical Ed Tchr & Coach
Loftin, John Allen
HS Biology & Zoology Teacher
Mayes, Marie Nash
4th Grade Teacher
McAleese, Mary Voupel
6th Grade Teacher
Mc Curdy, Marlys I.
Biology Teacher
Nichols, Rebecca Elaine
Biology & Geology Teacher
Noakes, Sandra Dee
Assistant Professor of PE
Olds, Karen Reed
9th Grade English Teacher
Owens, Grace Wittig
Spanish & Frgn Lang Tchr
Peterson, Deborah K.
French & English Teacher
Robinson, Jean Pile
Earth Science Teacher
Ronk, Jay Herbert
Band & District Music Coord
Sarraf, Shirley A.
Eng Dept Chprsn & AP Tchr
Self, Sharon Sucharda
First Grade Teacher
Sondag, Rebecca Michelle
English Teacher & Track Coach
Steed, Larry Wayne
Sixth Grade Teacher
Stenson, Edwin C.
English Teacher
Tallant, Alexander G. S.
English Teaching Assistant
VanPelt, Tamise J.
Professor of Critical Theory
Whitaker, Warren
Gen Business & Economics Tchr
POST FALLS
Berg, Gregory Edward
Chemistry & Physics Teacher
Coffin, Jon W.
Junior High Teacher
Corbeill, Dave Vance
Economics Teacher
Cossette, Gregory Russell
Biology & Geology Instructor
Foster, Jack William
8th Grade Social Studies Tchr
Gay, Dolores Parkhurst
Special Ed Para Professional
Hall, Marjorie Kay
Fifth Grade Teacher
Koetter, Kurt Warren
Science Dept Chm & Teacher
Merrill, Karla Sue
Student Assistance Pgm Coord
Newton, Craig W.
US History & Government Tchr
Nipp, Dan D.
Technical Drafting Teacher
Peterson, Lynda Raye Ross
Kindergarten Teacher
Williams, Susan Diane
Jr High English Teacher
PRESTON
Anderson, Julie
Scndry English & Reading Tchr
Williams, D. Brent
Chemistry & Physics Teacher
PRIEST RIVER
Benson, Sheila
HS English & French Teacher
RATHDRUM
Martinson, Teresa R. Brown
6th Grade Teacher
Willford, Deborah Anne (Hiatt)
Piano Teacher
REXBURG
Andrus, Alyn Brown
History Professor
Barnhill, William Charles
Professor of Design & Drafting
Barzee, Ellen Furness
Kindergarten Teacher
Beesley, Judy K.
English Department Chair
Benson, Bruce Lynn
Speech & Debate Teacher
Bergstrom, Robyn Hill
Communication Professor
Black, Darvil Kim
Professor of Horticulture
Burgie, Dona Jeanne (Berry)
English & Art Teacher
Christensen, Maribeth
Home Economics Teacher
Fisher, Rex Neil
Engineering & Tech Instr
Gordon, Harold James
Family Science Professor
Gray, H. JoAnn
Business Instructor
Green-Hacberle, Elena
English Teacher
Griffeth, Melvin
Professor of Biology
Haeberle, James Daniel
History Teacher
Hansen, Sharon A.
Teacher Ed Dept Chairman
Hibbert, Larry Eugene
Professor of Anatomy
Hunt, Murray Watson
Instructor of English Dept
Ingoldsby, Bron Barnett
Professor of Family Science
Ivers, John Joseph
Instructor of Spanish
Keller, Rodney Dean
Eng Instr & Dir of Composition
Knighton, Sandra Kay
Physical Ed & Health Teacher
Lewis, Shawna C.
Elementary Teacher
Lloyd, Linda F.
Professor of Education
Mangum, Lyle E.
German Tchr & Wrestling Coach
North, Danny L.
Director of Bands
Patterson, Keith Frank
Accounting Professor
Robertson, Blaine P.
Teacher Education Professor
Satterfield, Bruce Kelly
Religion Teacher
Seamons, Rhonda
Education Professor
Strong, Brent Marvin
Foreign Language Dept Chm
Terry, Steven Spencer
Mathematics Chairman
Terry, Vivian Hickman
Math Teacher
Thomas, Daniel C.
Math & Comp Programming Instr
Thomason, Bonnie Carlsen
Fifth Grade Teacher
Ward, David Lee
English Professor
Wightman, Philip C.
Religious & Family Living Chm
Winmill, Nancy Muhlenbruch
High School Math Teacher
Woolf, Laurene Harrison
Government & Psychology Tchr
RIGBY
Carollo, Natalie A.
English & History Teacher
Clark, Leon D.
Anatomy & Physiology Tchr
Hawkes, Richard Reed
Industrial Technology Teacher
Jones, Sharon A.
Student Counselor & Eng Tchr
Lambert, Pamela J.
Tech Prep Business Instructor
Miller, Allen Louis
Mathematics Teacher
Owen, Cathy Stenersen
Business & Marketing Teacher
Parrish, James E.
Health Teacher & Track Coach
Whitworth, Lisa
PE & Health Teacher & Coach
RIGGINS
Fitch, Buck
Math Teacher
ROBERTS
Cutler, Amy
Sixth Grade Teacher
ROCKLAND
Dean, Bill
Math Teacher
RUPERT
Amen, Karyn Marie
Former Math Teacher
Arritt, Kelly Ray
Business Education Teacher
Bodensteiner, Teresa Bergin
Jr High Counselor
Eskelsen, ElRay
Dir of Guidance & Cnslng Svcs
Gibson, Karan Ingersoll
First Grade Teacher
Gregory, Tamra J.
Family & Consumer Science Tchr
Hoebelheinrich, Anita Schieffer
4th Grade Teacher
Hyde, Tamara
English & Journalism Teacher
Kontos, John William
Counselor

T (cont)
Shelley Elizabeth (Charlton)
more Counselor
odie Hegstad
y Teacher
ary N.
ator of the GATE
Harriet Shupe
Grade Teacher
n, Jana Marie
d Grade Teacher
, James K.
Geography Teacher

nita Wirthlin
r Band Director
ANTHONY
Betty M.
ator of GATE Program
ort, DelRay S.
ant Principal
Marvin O.
onal Agriculture Teacher
Regena J.
High School Counselor
er, James D.
matics Teacher
Norma F.
d 6th Grade Teacher
Lori Ann
h Teacher
Gloria Anderson
Grade Teacher
MARIES
ate, Charlotte (Welz)
d Grade Teacher
Miriam Kathleen
School English Teacher
aymond Joseph
elor
atheryn J.
h Teacher
ht, Steve
ade Teacher
Ryan Eric
gy, Economics & His Tchr
N
, Helen Mary
glish Teacher
Grant Lee
Studies Teacher
dorf, Linda Allsup
h & Home Economics Tchr
ance R.
arts Teacher
OINT
on, Tom E.
matics Teacher
ll, Jon L.
th Grade Choral Director
ayne E.
& Comp Programming Tchr
aymond K.
th Grade Business Tchr
Edna Colliander
Science Teacher
Shirley Ann (Henriksson)
h Teacher
Daniel Kenneth
acher
Barbara Iva
Photography & Yrbk Tchr
Daniel C.
h Teacher & Coach
ouglas Roy
rade Science Instructor
Thomas S.
Director
atrick A.
Teacher
EY
ald, Terrence Everett
acher
, Darrel Chancy
Science Teacher
g, Carolyn Marie
9th Grade English Tchr
Kelli Shumway
Team Advisor
n, Lana
r Education Teacher
Jennie Lyn
Home Economics Teacher
, Eldon Stan
Grade Teacher
erold L.
gy Teacher
etty J.
rade Teacher
ra, Janine Barker
& Earth Sci Teacher
, Cindy Reid
Grade Teacher
son, Sandra Jane
ematics Teacher
Vincent
ctor of Chemistry & Ger
HONE
ay, JaNene Johnson
uage Arts Specialist
SPRINGS
Leslie Summerkamp
ch Therapist
ton, Sabrina Jean
& Psychology Teacher
nson, Richard Lee
h Grade Math Teacher

Welles Mae Henderson
ed Teacher

SUGAR CITY
Butikofer, Margaret A.
Mathematics Teacher
Keller, Janice Jeanselme
4th Grade Teacher
Kinghorn, Donna Jean
English Teacher
Loosli, Lucy M.
Sixth Grade Teacher
Schultz, Kevin G.
English Teacher & Dept Chair
Stumme, Gloria Hollingsworth
Speech, Drama & Eng Teacher
Williams, Nedra Ricks
US & Idaho History Teacher
TWIN FALLS
Anderson, Kent Charles
Assistant Elementary Principal
Braga, Sandi Sheppeard
Instructor
Bryan, Jay D.
Art Teacher
Federico, Mike Anthony
Psychology Teacher
Fields, Marypat Donnelly
Associate Professor of Nursing
Gerrish, Philip Alan
9th Grade Alg & Geometry Tchr
Golding, Fran M.
Professor of Biology
Gooding, Jo Anne Watson
English Teacher
James, Ronald Lloyd
World Geography Teacher
John, William Neivell
Asst Professor of Office Tech
Jones, Julie Morris
History & German Teacher
Knight, Roger James
Equine Instructor
Mannen, Tony
Asst Prof of Speech & Drama
Miller, Howard
Theater Teacher
Mosley, James Daryel
World Geography Teacher
Mottern-High, Janis T.
English Teacher
Petersen, Tamara Marie
Kindergarten Teacher
Pfefferle, Reid Wyman
American Government Teacher
Ploss, Carrie Lynn
Marketing Teacher
Reed, Miriam Rawls
Second Grade Teacher
Scherer, Frank D.
Counselor
Schlund, Kathy Human
Third Grade Teacher
Selelyo, Pat Ann
Professor of Life Science
Smack, G. Richard
Choral Music Director
Studebaker, Judy K.
Librarian
Sugden, Mark A.
Associate Professor of Biology
Tanner, Fran
Chm Dept of Speech & Drama
Vannoy, Deann Williams
Counselor
Williams, Norene Fumiko
Math Teacher
Woebke, Connie Lytle
Eng & Creative Writing Teacher
Wright, N. Darlene Ward
9th Grade World Geography Tchr
UCON
Mackay, Caroline Simmons
Fifth Grade Teacher
WALLACE
Adams, Janet E.
English Teacher
Bardelli, Frederick Ketchell
Art Teacher
Bokekman, Darlene Ann
5th Grade Teacher
England, Douglas Raymond
Science Teacher
WEISER
Bayley, Lyle J.
Teacher & Coach
Bradley, Loretta S.
Counselor
Knight, Kevin P.
Social Studies Teacher
Mac Donald, Laurel A.
English Teacher
WENDELL
Harbaugh, Louise Rast
English & Reading Teacher
Newton, Sherry L.
4th Grade Teacher
Powell, Jeanne Varin
Retired Elementary Teacher
WILDER
Varner, Catherine L.
Second Grade Teacher

ILLINOIS

ABINGDON
Landon, George O.
High School Math Instructor
ADDISON
Biske, Jeff L.
Graphic Communications Instr
DeBoni, Joseph Leonard
Professor
Frank, Zbigniew
Electronics Professor
Goliber, Donna Gardner
Asst Dean of Evening Programs
Green, Frederick T.
Retired High School Math Tchr
Holland, Sally A. Griffith
Director of Guidance
Jares, Daniel John
Social Studies Teacher
Khan, Ahmed S.
Senior Professor
Krudel, Sharon Janis
Cosmetology Teacher
Kupkowski, Gary P.
Biology & Chemistry Instr
Lee, Sang M.
Electrical Engineering Prof
Link, Robert
Senior Professor
McBride, Eileen West
Reading Professor
Mocek, Nancy Rowinski
Associate Professor of English
Moore, Sharon L.
8th Grd Reading & Writing Tchr
Parker, Laraine Yurcho
Reading & Religion Teacher
Parpet, Paul F.
PE & Drivers Ed Teacher
Racki, Timothy Gerard
English & Speech Tchr, Coach
Schumacher, Shawn Allen
English Professor
Smith, Katy A.
English Teacher
Waterman, Steven J.
Senior Professor
ALBANY
Nowak, Shirley Hall
Second Grade Teacher
ALBION
Borowiak, Jackie Lovins
Art Teacher
Dewig, Toni J.
First Grade Teacher
Ellis, Gary L.
Social Studies & Lang Teacher
Endsley, Vickie Enlow
6th-8th Grade Math Teacher
Kinsey, William R.
Social Stud & Driver Ed Tchr
Lowe, Linda Diane (Hadsall)
Junior HS Science Teacher
Novara, Leonard Edwin
Driver Education Teacher
Oxby, Linda K.
Physical Ed & Health Teacher
Ritchey, Carol Moore
5th Grade Teacher
Shupe, Karen S.
Home Ec & Economics Teacher
Wallace, Barbara J.
Retired Humanities Teacher
Weiler, Judith Lynn
5th Grade Teacher
Willis, Gregory Keith
Social Studies Teacher
ALEDO
Artcher, Mark Robert
Social Science Instructor
Chausse, Michael G.
Ag Ed & Vocational Instructor
Eastin, Bonnie Haymaker
Retired English Teacher
Johnson, Victor Otis
Elementary Principal
Ricketts, Lois Stevens
Spanish Instructor
ALEXIS
Clute, Marilyn M. (Hennenfent)
Retired Third Grade Teacher
Kozelichi, Tony
English & Speech Teacher
ALGONQUIN
Bertram, Jon
7th Grade Science Teacher
Carnes, Sharon K.
Mathematics Teacher
Chemelewski, Mary Roccaforte
Vision Training Teacher
Davis, Randy Dean
Social Studies Teacher
Dietrich-Reineck, Doreen
4th Grade Teacher
Fricke, Ralph J.
Chemistry Teacher
Gullickson, Nancy Kehr
Spanish Teacher
Haraburda, David E.
Sci Dept Chm & Bio Tchr
Johnson, Julie Ward
English Teacher
Jones, Barbara Laird
5th Grade Teacher
Katzenmayer, Mary Sue
German Teacher
Krueger, Paula Jane
Third Grade Teacher
Mc Mahon, Kathleen French
Principal
Schertz, Wilbur Lynn
Chemistry Teacher
Siebeck, Elizabeth Parker
Spanish Teacher
Sinclair, Deborah L.
Orchestra & 8th Grd Drama Dir
ALHAMBRA
Cain, Anita K. Johnson
Third Grade Teacher
ALPHA
Crapnell, Jane Friichtenicht
Second Grade Teacher
Currier, William George
Teacher
Herges, Patricia Graham
Substitute Teacher
ALSIP
Conboy, Phillip Joseph
Math Department Chairman
Heinen, Leona Zahn
First Grade Teacher
Sweeney, Mary Lu Sweeney
First Grade Teacher
ALTAMONT
Casper, Lyle S.
American History Teacher
Heiden, Diane Kay (Bunting)
Jr High Math Teacher
Koester, Dana Kay
Business Teacher
Kollmann, V. Suzanne (Bell)
Sixth Grade Teacher
Lading, Carol Ann
High School Guidance Counselor
Niehaus, Wayne Charles, Jr.
Tech Coord, Cmptr & Spch Tchr
Poe, Susan Margaret Spence
Third Grade Teacher
Weber, Carol
Title I, PE & Kndgtn Tchr
Weiss, James D.
Jr HS Teacher & Asst Principal
Wilson, Jami Elizabeth
High School Biology Teacher
ALTON
Bentley, Ray Thomas
Title I Basic Skills Teacher
Bricker, Wilma Jean
Business Education Teacher
Caffey, Vernetta Greer
English Teacher
Calcari, Reno Louis
High School Business Teacher
Conrad, Joan Hollenbeck
History & Government Teacher
Drillinger, David Wayne
Director of Bands
Eardley, David Russell
English Teacher
Gentelin, Joseph James
Environmental Science Teacher
Goode, Vickie Hunt
Kindergarten Teacher
Hill, Jane Ready
French Teacher
Jarden, Timothy George
Band Director
Kasten, Cathryn Meade
Computer Literacy Teacher
Klaus, Ruth Diak
English & Speech Teacher
Macias, Felix
Driver Education Teacher
Miller, Mary Elaine
Third Grade Teacher
Phelps, Suzer
Math & Computer Instructor
Rose, Cathy Newcome
Third Grade Teacher
ALTONA
Larson, Karen L.
Principal & Teacher
AMBOY
Johnson, Ray R.
Social Studies Teacher
Jones, Gary Robert
Physical Education Instructor
Knutson, Gregory E.
Director of Instrumental Music
Marsili, Dennis E.
Science Teacher
Mool, Gordon Eugene
Driver Education Instructor
Watkins, Craig Allen
Fifth Grade Teacher
ANNA
Bailey, William O.
Physics, Chem & Math Teacher
Dillow, Wanda R.
4th Grade Teacher
Hayden, Jeffrey Louis
Health & Math Teacher
Heidinger, Bonnie Osman
Secondary Social Studies Tchr
Pommier, Richard Louis
English Teacher
Shoemaker, Bob G.
Business Tchr & Dept Chair
Wise, Jean Koelling
3rd Grade Teacher
ANNAWAN
Earl, Douglas Kent
Mathematics Teacher
ANTIOCH
Alm, Roger L.
Mathematics & Computer Instr
Bush, Earl L., Jr.
Jr High Band Director
Curtis, James Morgan
Social Studies Teacher
Hargrove, Lauri Ann (Baker)
Health Education Teacher
Kakacek, Phyllis Ann (Mc Millen)
English Teacher
Logan, Judith Hebenstreit
English Teacher
Marshall, Jay Henry
Science Teacher
Mason, Janice M.
5th Grd Science, Computer Tchr
Owens, Wes Lee
7th Grade Teacher
Schmitt, Suzanne Gerasch
English Teacher
ARCOLA
Eskridge, Judith Ann (Blain)
Title I Teacher
McQueen, Marcia Willamon
6th Grade Teacher
Sapp, Kathy Jones
Second Grade Teacher
Sluder, Darla Lee
Art Teacher
Typer, Janis Crawford
Business Education Teacher
ARGENTA
Diercks, Cheri A.
Business Education Instructor
German, Henry Edward
Business Teacher
Kahila, Roger F.
Science Teacher
May, Pamela Jean
High School Art Instr
Woods, Troy Wayne
Social Science Teacher
ARLINGTON HTS
Barrigar, Lynn Williams
English Teacher
Bellito, Michael John
English & Speech Teacher
Boehm, John H.
High School Mathematics Tchr
Bolsinger, Katherine Ann
Second Grade Teacher
Borghoff, Kent
Social Studies Teacher
Brodnan, Kathleen Zigman
7th Grade Mathematics Teacher
Darr, Carmelle
Second Grade Teacher
Englbrecht, Elizabeth Jane
Chemistry Teacher
Ferrero, David John
English & Social Studies Tchr
Figlewicz, John Joseph
7th Grade Earth Science Tchr
Gabryszewski, Michael P.
Geography Teacher
Glover, Bruce Lee
Mathematics Teacher & Coach
Kleinschmidt, Linda Lamson
Counselor for Gifted Program
Konkolowewski, Jeanine Fermo
Physical Ed Teacher & Coach
Metzger, Robert Allen
Social Studies Teacher
Moon, Edward C.
English & Drama Teacher
Nall, Thomas
History Teacher
Novak, John B.
High School Mathematics Tchr
Rhinehart, Robert Arthur
Seventh & Eighth Grade Teacher
Rogowski, Richard A.
Chemistry Teacher
Sattler, Jeanne Anne Ellis
Religious Studies Teacher
Smith, Lee William
Math & Computer Teacher
Smith, Susan M.
Junior High English Teacher
Taborsky, Patricia Ann
English Teacher
Van Wiel, John Edward, CSV
Science Dept Chair & Teacher
Zaletanski, Beverly Remaly
Rdng & Writing Resource Tchr
ARMSTRONG
Gasick, James D.
HS Social Studies Teacher
ARROWSMITH
Maupin, Charlene Builta
Second Grade Teacher
ARTHUR
Crane, Rita Irene Schmitter
Business Education Teacher
Marks, Glenda Kay
7th-8th Grd Science Teacher
Plank, Jim H.
Supervisor & Principal
Reynolds, Michael Lynn
Indstrl Tech Ed & Geog Teacher
ASHKUM
Eimen, Theresa Clark
Third Grade Teacher
Kuipers, Mary Jane Lee
First Grade Teacher
ASHLAND
Barnhart, William David
Art Teacher
Pfaffe, Jeffrey Carl
Chemistry & Physics Teacher
Ten Eyck, Cheryl Ann (Kincaid)
English & Lang Arts Teacher
ASHMORE
Walters, Connie Pierce
4th Grade Teacher
ASSUMPTION
Abell, Linda Lee (Adkins)
Elementary Principal
Smail, Carol Ann
Sixth Grade Teacher

ASTORIA
Perdew, Rosemary Chilstrom
High School Math Teacher
Stambaugh, Jennifer Brewer
HS Spanish & History Teacher
ATHENS
Basso, Lisa Primm
Sixth Grade Teacher
Curry, Francene Anderson
Third Grade Teacher
Curry, John Wesley
HS Math & Computer Teacher
Miller, Karen Loeffler
English Teacher
Miller, Philip
Counselor
Porter, Sharon M.
Business Teacher
ATWOOD
Gardner, Judith Ann (Willoughby)
Social Studies Teacher
Shirley, Steven Lynn
High School Biology Teacher
Simpson, Charles Wade
Mathematics Teacher
AUBURN
Howard, Amy Sue Phalen
Art Teacher
Krell, Marla Atchison
English Teacher
Madison, Angela Dorks
2nd Grade Teacher
Wargo, Deborah DeWall
Third Grade Teacher
Young, Raymon Dwaine
Grammar & Composition Teacher
AUGUSTA
Hopper, Janet Sue
English Teacher
Reuschel, Roger N.
Math Teacher
AURORA
Abhalter, Peggy J.
Foreign Language Dept Chair
Anderson, Monica Marie
Guidance Dept Chairperson
Arthur, Mark Wesley
Physical Ed Tchr & Asst Coach
Baker, Kathy Abel
French Teacher
Bataille, Vincent Paul
Spanish Teacher
Beach-Elsbree, Catherine Palmer
6th Grade Teacher
Bouldin, Janet C.
English Teacher
Bowman, William P.
English Teacher
Bright, Doris Marie Otterbein
Reading Resource Ctr Director
Bubb, Janet Zitney
Mathematics Teacher
Butler, Patricia Clifford
Mathematics Dept Chair
Calvert, David Andrew
Soph English & Theatre Teacher
Cervenka, Eldonna Willrett
Science Teacher
Corlew, Michelle M.
Science Teacher
Davidson, Donald Edward
Bible Teacher, Ath Dir & Coach
Davidson, Matthew Jeremy
HS History & Bible Teacher
Didos, Mary Anne Abdnour
Business Teacher
Dodillet, Diane Ruth
Music Teacher
Dods, Richard F.
Chemistry Team Leader
Dollinger, Joan Riedl
Vocational Coord & Bus Teacher
Dover, Ruth
Math Teacher
Ebeling, Richard F.
Science Chair & Chemistry Tchr
Eddins, Susan Kohn
Mathematics Teacher
Edwards, Steven
High Schl Physical Ed Teacher
Erickson, Beverly Eggimann
English & Speech Teacher
Evert, Colleen Finnerty
Social Studies Chair
Ferguson, Marian Brown
Junior High Schl History Tchr
Flosi, Karen Zajac
English Teacher
Frerich, David Dean
Retired 5th Grade Teacher
Geistler, Renee Sherman
Sixth Grade Teacher
Giangrego, Frank Vincent
Campus Minister-Theology Instr
Gilbert, James A.
Middle School Science Tchr
Gilliam, Patrick Thomas
High School English Teacher
Goodman, Dana Richard
English Teacher
Grosshuesch, Clayt Emerson
Guidance Counselor
Hanson, Ann Marie (Hames)
Mathematics Teacher
Hanus, Raymond Charles, II
HS Science Teacher
Heckel, Lucille Anne Wehrle
Fifth Grade Teacher
Heintz, Karen Ann
Jr High Science Teacher
Helvie, DiAna Lynn-Tuel
Kindergarten Teacher
Hemmens, Margaret Blais
Fourth Grade Teacher
Herbert, Heidi Hult
Junior High Teacher
Herbert, Susan Ascott
First Grade Teacher
Hinkebein, Kathryn Flavin
Algebra & English Teacher
Holinger, Richard Lange
Teacher & Writer
House, Collette Ranelle
Mathematics Tchr & Ath Trainer
Hunt, Jeffrey L.
Planetarium Director
Kersey, Alan Robert
Physics & Chemistry Teacher
King, Laura Eileen
Ret Secondary English Teacher
Krawczyk, Lonetta Fross
Fourth Grade Teacher
Leitner, Virlyn Herley
Social Studies Teacher
Lemp, Anne-Marie Elizabeth
Physical Education Teacher
Leonard, Karen Sue (Mierkiewicz)
High School Counselor
Licandro, Jann Hawkins
Tchr of Gifted Math & Science
Loret de Mola, Paula M.
Kindergarten Teacher
Luedtke, David Christopher, Jr.
History Teacher
Malone, Mary Margaret
7th Grade Reading Teacher
Margerum, Timothy
Physical Education Teacher
Martini, Mary Catherine
Science Dept Chprsn & Teacher
Maxwell, Judith Ann (Wallin)
Home Ec & Child Dev Teacher
Mc Carthy, Mary Beth Constance
Conductor & Music Teacher
Mc Glynn, Jacqueline Marie
Mathematics Teacher
Mc Williams, Patrick
English Teacher
Mentgen, Dwayne
Mathematics Teacher
Nagis, Cynthia Marsh
Mathematics Teacher
Nardone, Nancy E.
Junior High School Teacher
Olsen, Diane Bryscan
High School Spanish Teacher
Orland, Stephen Patrick
Director of Bands
Papadolias, Meg Blazier
Vocal Music Teacher
Pensyl, Clifford George
Ath Dir & Mathematics Teacher
Perez, Traci L.
Business Teacher
Plachetka, Beth Benjamin
Rel Tchr & Campus Minister
Rebenstorf, Robert Louis
English Teacher
Richards, Marlene Liesse
Fourth Grade Teacher
Richmond, Nathan Nile, Jr.
Dean of Students
Rippinger, Joel Anthony
AP American History Instructor
Rozanski, Norbert Anthony
Asst Principal & Dean
Schindel, Dick
Business Education Dept Chair
Schmidt, Carolyn
Fifth-Sixth Grade Teacher
Shaw, Donna Ann
Business Education Teacher
Short, Dennis James
Business Education Teacher
Spencer, Kathryn Curran
World History & Latin Teacher
Sriver, Tracy Lynn (Boll)
English Teacher
Staley, Charles W.
Band Director
Taylor, Bonnie Elizabeth
Science Teacher
Tornabene Coleman, Mary T.
English Teacher
Van Hooser, Rebecca Sue
2nd Grade Teacher
Vavrinek, Ronald
Math Team Ldr & Dept Chair
Wallin, Susan M.
Fifth Grade Teacher
Weiss, Dorothy Marie
Sixth Grade Teacher
White, Jackie
English Instructor
Williams, Don Aulton
History Teacher
Williams, Kathleen S.
Mathematics Teacher
Wilson, Carol Douglass
English & Reading Teacher
Wredling, Carl Lawrence, Jr.
Performing Arts Teacher
Wyeth, Joel Ryan
Social Studies Teacher
Yanisch, William F.
High School Math Teacher
Zajac, Karen M.
English & Literature Teacher
AVISTON
Hostmeyer, Phyllis Huelsmann
Lang Arts & Computer Teacher
AVON
Naslund, Beverly (Ogle)
Business Tchr & Computer Coord
BARRINGTON
Andruss, Jeffrey Scott
Fourth Grade Teacher
Baum, Cynthia Anne
Health Education Teacher
Benas, Tobey Lee
Spanish Teacher
Engle, David C.
Art Instructor
Heath, Laura Ann
Fifth Grade Teacher
Kallenbach, Michael Phillip
Sixth Grade Teacher
King, Joan (Cutter)
Retired Teacher
Littwin, James Patrick
English Teacher
Mastroianni, Anthony John
Psychology & Sociology Teacher
Moony, Thomas John
Soc Stud, US His & Econ Tchr
Pitluck, Kay Blosten
Social Studies Teacher
Smith-Peace, Judith
Substitute Teacher
Watson, Penny Rebecca
8th Grade Amer History Tchr
Zenner, Colleen Ann
Physics Teacher
BARRY
Barnes, Mary A.
Agriculture Teacher
Carlson, Carl Bertil
5th & 6th Grd Split Class Tchr
BARTELSO
Sauer, Jack E.
Social Studies Chairman
Schroeder, Dianne Kampwerth
Fourth Grade Teacher
BARTLETT
Broeker, Carol Ann
Fifth Grade Teacher
Hill, Sue Glos
Fifth Grade Teacher
Kredich, Evelyn Margret
Second Grade Teacher
Nemmers, Georgia Kay
First Grade Teacher
Wietzke, Judith M. (Heckert)
Former Teacher
BATAVIA
Bauer, Susan Robison
Mathematics Teacher
Brozenec, Susan (Diehl)
Fourth Grade Teacher
Cange, Edwin Charles, Jr.
Soc Science Dept Chair & Tchr
Flannigan, Sandra F.
English Teacher
Gilman, Barry L.
Fifth Grade Teacher
Heath, John Robert
Director of Bands
Jenkins, Kalah A.
1st Grade Teacher
Karstens, Virginia
Eighth Grade Teacher
Kettering, William J.
Government Teacher
Mandele, Michael John
Health & Physical Ed Teacher
Wielunski, Susan Brown
Math Instructor
BAYLIS
Shover, Luanne M.
Former Teacher
BEACH PARK
DeBennette, Patrick John
History & Literature Teacher
Lonchar, Betsy Podboy
7th-8th Grade History Teacher
Meissner, Donald Wayne
8th Grade Life Science Teacher
Rompella, Elaine Dracos
8th Grd Lang & Lit Teacher
BEARDSTOWN
Mc Queen, Stacy Lynn (Sperling)
Special Education Teacher
Smith, Donna Burmood
First Grade Teacher
Sommer, Gena Helton
English Teacher
Studer, Cathy Lynch
Coordinator of Gifted
Vermillion, Kathy Warden
Music Director
BECKEMEYER
Riegel, Pat Hogg
Kindergarten Teacher
BEECHER CITY
Baker, Diane Wicklein
Science & Biology Teacher
Walk, Alan Joseph
Social Studies Teacher
BELLEVILLE
Barth, Roberta Tate
Music Teacher
Bartlow, Mary Jo
English Teacher
Belt, Margo Jean
English Teacher
Benivegna, Maria Theresa
Spanish Teacher
Bernier, Sheree Luna
3rd Grade Teacher
Blaes, Donald A.
Psychology & Philosophy Instr
Blistain, Margaret Louise
Math Teacher & Dept Chprsn
Bolen, Susan Coffey
Speech Instructor
Bolesta, Christine Ann
Vice Prin for Student Affairs
Brewer, Patricia Anne
Anatomy & Physiology Instr
Brown, Jacquelyn Mary
Nursing Instructor
Cadell, Barbara Ann
Religion Teacher
Caswell, Curtiss Ray
Business Education Teacher
Dickenson, Randy D.
High School History Teacher
Dismukes, Patricia A. (Noser)
4th Grade Teacher
Donnelly, Mary Ruth
Instr of Eng Lit & Composition
Dyer, Laura Ann
Mathematics Instructor
Edwards, Janet Dukes
Math Department Chairman
Epperson, Mary Dressler
Third Grade Teacher
Fornero, Candice Darlene
Art Teacher
Frerker, Jeffrey Carl
US History Teacher
Galvin, Nova (Lee)
Retired 8th Grade Teacher
Ganey, Mary Jo Feder
Former Tutor
Gessford, Bonnie Lowe
Biology Teacher
Graville, Sharon Cox
English Instructor
Grodeon, Christine Wandling
Chemistry & Phys Sci Teacher
Gushleff, William L.
Social Studies Instructor
Harris, Karol Troutt
English Teacher
Hart, William Roger
English Teacher
Hoercher, Barbara Kutz
Fifth Grade Teacher
Kassebaum, Robert Irvin
Mathematics & Physical Ed Tchr
Keim, James Lee
Social Studies Teacher
Lowery, Daniel A.
Art Professor
McGarrity, Rebekah Ann (Shryock)
English Teacher
McGinnis, Carol Ann
Second Grade Teacher
Metzger, Dian Rable
Fifth Grade Teacher
Millas, Lynelle Dee
Biology Teacher & Coach
Mueller, Betty Dehn
English & Reading Teacher
Mueller, Joseph Henry
Retired Social Studies Tchr
Obenchain, Larry Orville
Civics Teacher
Park, Connie Odle
HS Mathematics Teacher
Phillips, Aaron W.
Mathematics Instructor
Range, Rose Marie
Jr High Lang Arts Teacher
Reaves, Pamela Ann (Thompson)
Third Grade Teacher
Reyes, Jennifer Kanle
Spanish Teacher
Rodman, Charles Goodnow
High School English Teacher
Schmidt, Trudy Taylor
Chemistry Teacher
Sparn, Dennis E., Sr.
Counselor
Steinhaus, Richard Frederick
Sociology Instructor
Stone, Kerry E.
Math Teacher
Struze, Mary Ellen Beedy
Secondary Eng & Reading Tchr
Thomas, Barbara Victory
Sixth Grade Teacher
Thompson, Susan Annette
PE & Health Educator
Tinoco, Patricia Ann
Junior High Teacher
Vick, Karen Koesterer
Second Grade Teacher
Voll, Margaret L. (Taylor)
L D Resource Teacher
Weyhaupt, Charles Richard
Instrumental Music Teacher
Wiemerslage, Leslie Joseph
Biology Instructor
Wilder, Merle Francis
Spanish Teacher
Williams, Linda Hayes
Retired Science Teacher
Wimmer, Cheryl Scandrett
Art Teacher
Woesthaus, David Allen
Art Teacher
Zorko, Ronald W.
Computer Teacher
BELLWOOD
Biggs, Bernice Golson
6th Grade Teacher
Humphrey, Valarie Anne
Mathematics Teacher
Noel, Bernice K. (Williams)
First Grade Teacher
Patch, Milton Roland, Jr.
Building Assistant
BELVIDERE
Cross, James Gavin
Chemistry Teacher
Faul, Jane Rosalie
Retired Spanish & English Tchr
Gibson, Kathleen K.
Eng, Debate & Oral Comm Tchr
Groh, Patricia A.
German Teacher
Larkin, John S.
Rdng Specialist & Title I Dir
Lay, Robert G.
Teacher
Luhman, Janice Lewis
Kindergarten Teacher
Luthin, Mark Alan
Earth & Environmental Sci Tchr
Mc Mahon, Janet Lynn
8th Grd Physical Science Tchr
Morris, Janet J.
Math Teacher
Page, Michael Charles
HS Social Studies Teacher
Rudolph, Evelyn M.
Retired Sixth Grade Teacher
Salley, Brad A.
Spanish Teacher
Schwebke, Mary Lou
Retired Elementary Teacher
Smith, Shirley Oberts
Fifth Grade Teacher
Swanson, Kenneth B.
6th Grade Elementary Teacher
BENSENVILLE
Anderson, Timothy James
High School Science Teacher
Becker, Martha Conway
Third Grade Teacher
Ewert, Roger Frank
Seventh Grade Lang Arts Tchr
Falco, Nick M.
Head Soccer Coach
Fitzgerald, Jill M.
Chemistry Teacher
Goldberg, Barby Kleinerman
ESL & French Teacher
Hodges, Robert A.
US History Teacher
Howard, Walter J., III
9th-12th Grade English Teacher
Koenig, Pamela (Palmer)
Third Grade Teacher
Lehmann, Gregory Jay
Business Ed Teacher & Coach
Oelslager, Virginia Alexander
Family & Consumer Science Tchr
Olsen, Den
Tech Education Dept Chprsn
Pabst, Gina
High School Spanish Teacher
Randolph, Stanley P.
Industrial Arts Teacher
Roepke, Diane Woodsum
HS Social Studies Teacher
Trainor, Sandra Kay
Guidance Counselor
Walsh, Jean Ann
2nd Grade Teacher
Yarke, Susan Lois
Third Grade Teacher
BENSON
Norman, Margaret L. (Bone)
Retired Elementary Ed Tchr
BENTON
Alexander, Gene R.
Retired Elementary Principal
Carlile, Wilma Jean (Baker)
Second Grade Teacher
Frick, Joe E.
Drafting & CAD Teacher
Giacone, Anna Marie Mayeski
English & Amer History Teacher
Kimball, Pamela Johnson
Speech & Drama Teacher
Mc Graw, Kandis A.
Second Grade Teacher
Miller, Jackie S.
English Teacher & Dept Chair
Nimtz, Robert Paul
Social Science & PE Teacher
Owens, Kaye Hargrove
Retired Teacher
Page, James William
Vocational Teacher
Shaw, Annetta Dougherty
Second Grade Teacher
West, Beckie
7th Grade English Teacher
BERWYN
Barth, Carol Bergin
6th Grade Teacher
Bauer, Mary J.
Science Tchr & Asst Principal
Daniels, Tom
Seventh Grade Teacher
Delach, James Ignatius
HS Teacher & Coach
Fator, Diane M. Rezek
Third Grade Teacher
Fotias, Evangeline Metanias
English Teacher

'N (cont)
Maryann
ade Teacher
ames I.
ic Arts & Comm Tech Instr
, Ronald F.
or of Bands & Orchestras
, Donna Jean
Development Teacher
Michele Filishio
d Tchr
, Barbara Joyce
nce Counselor
oseph H.
h Teacher
ti, Susan
ade Teacher
, Maree A.
al Education & Hlth Tchr
Sharon Sine
Economics & Business Tchr
ky, Richard Joseph
d Social Studies Teacher
on, Rosann Cicchetti
Language Arts Teacher
, Mary Kathryn
BD Resource Teacher
, Onofria
Teacher
e, George D.
rial Technology Teacher
Mary Ann
Teacher
Richard James, Jr.
story & English Teacher
Melissa Gail
School English Teacher
Steven W.
School Mathematics Tchr
ALTO
Bernadette Geralyn
d Grade Teacher
acqueline Jean
Grade Teacher
tier, Michael Avery
al Ed & Health Teacher
y, Robert Eugene, Jr.
er & Principal
an, Danny Lee
ath Teacher & Dept Chprsn
, Donald John
ology & Special Ed Tchr
ANY
g, David John
sh Teacher
Amy Jo
Grade Teacher
arlone L. (Albert)
ce Teacher
ce, Jim
ematics Teacher
, Margaret A.
n Grade Teacher
enise Fults
& Computer Teacher
OCK
an, Roy A.
h Science Teacher
VILLE
son Aaron
ocial Studies Teacher
as, Cherry Galusha
eacher
etti, Ronda Sue
istry Teacher
all, Ledith Snyder
of Early Chldhd Hndcppd
ARCK
r, Anna Beth
rade Teacher
i, Barbara Kay Eppley
rade Teacher
MINGDALE
-Alford, Judi Lynn
rade Language Arts Tchr
on, Delaine Bird
rade Math Teacher
Vicki Elena (Siambra)
rade Gifted English Tchr
MINGTON
on, Mark Louis
rafting & CAD Instr
-Marcusiu, Eva
ng Instructor
Melissa Ann
2th Grd Spanish Teacher
r, Charlotte Ryan
Grade Teacher
y, Kenneth David
ronics Teacher
Mark
ematics Teacher
ell, Janet Tobin
nology Teacher
ark, Stacie Renea (Rose)
ssor of Biology
Mark E.
nce Professor
, Bodo
of Hum, German & French
rry L.
nglish & Speech Teacher
a, Sharon Maria
School Mathematics Tchr
ff, Linda Sue
h Grade Teacher
rs, Cindy Sands
stant Principal
as, Keith A.
cal Science Instructor

Joyce, Janette Walker
First Grade Teacher
Kindle, Otis Thomas
Teacher & Baseball Coach
Lawrence, John C.
Business Education Teacher
Lazzaretti, Ann Peterson
Office Technology Professor
Lowry, Pamela E.
Asst Professor of Economics
Nixon, Peggy L.
Spanish & English ESL Tchr
Paulson, Kathryn Joan (Haselhuhn)
Hotel Teacher
Schlickman, Janel Jacobs
English & Speech Teacher
Scott, Janenne Kay
Third Grade Teacher
Smith-Williams, Katie Lynn
Professor
Thomas, Lisa Ragsdale
English Instructor
Tosh, Terry
Sixth Grade Teacher
Tracy, Carla Barker
Fourth Grade Teacher
Wendling, Hal R.
Instructor of Economics
Wenum, John Dale
Emeritus Professor
Wilson, Tonya Loree
English Teacher
BLUE ISLAND
Alfano, Michelle
Bilingual Teacher
Charters, Cynthia (Beckett)
Math Teacher
Natonek, Stan A.
Physics Teacher
Oriente, Connie Palomo
Rdng, Lang & Soc Stud Teacher
Peters, Richard John
9th-12th Grd History Teacher
Phillips, Steve Brady
Amer & World History Teacher
Stevens, Arlene L. (Brown)
Business Teacher
Van Loo, Carmen E.
Science Teacher
Walder, Gregory Scott
Math Teacher
Zic, Karen Marie
Home Economics Teacher
BLUE MOUND
Rappe, Sheila Brame
Seventh Grade Science Teacher
Wiles, Linda Mc Clerren
Second Grade Teacher
BLUFORD
Dalby, Russell Irvin
Social Studies & English Tchr
Johnson, Christine J.
English Teacher
BOLINGBROOK
Acton, Phil
Business Teacher & Coach
Acton, Sara Jane Adams
4th Grade Teacher of Gifted
Coaker, Susan K.
8th Grade English Teacher
Dombrowski, Donna
2nd Grade Teacher
Eischen, Deborah Ann (Wawrzyniak)
Language & Science Teacher
Greever, Wrenne Stockard
Lang Arts & Soc Stud Teacher
Hannigan-Wiehn, Christine Anne
Special Education Teacher
Harvey, James Patrick
Assistant Principal
Hinchliffe, Barbara Shepherd
7th Grade Math Teacher
McClenahan, Beth Enz
5th Grade Teacher of Gifted
McGrath, Kimberly Ann
7th-8th Grade Math & Sci Tchr
Pezze, Jurate Elena
Hnrs Lang Arts & Soc Stud Tchr
Schoob, Roger Steven
Biology Teacher
Shaw, David Robert
English Teacher
Swinkunas, Sandra Sue
3rd Grade Challenge Teacher
Sykora, Deborah Lynn (Acree)
Sixth Grd Math & Science Tchr
Wallin, John
7th Grade Math & Sci Teacher
BONFIELD
Mahoney, Randy Lee
Fourth Grade Teacher
Monferdini, Susan Schultz
Second Grade Teacher
BOURBONNAIS
Brooks, Beulah A. (Christensen)
Retired Fifth Grd Tchr
Erazmus, Thomas R.
5th Grade Teacher
Ross, Catherine Meier
Sixth Grd Lang Arts Tchr
Sandusky, Jon L.
Law Enforcement Teacher
Schweigert, Delores Cullick
Travel Tourism Instructor
Wilhoyt, Joseph Michael
6th-8th Grade Science Teacher
BRACEVILLE
Wise, Evon
First Grade Tchr

BRADFORD
Gorham, Kelley Brown
Mathematics Teacher
BRADLEY
Dykstra, Connie Jean
English Teacher
Gruber, Marilyn Walsh
8th Grade Math Teacher
Hassett, John Bernard
Science Instructor
Lilienthal, Linda Ruth
Fifth Grade Teacher
Lystila, David Scott
Math Dept Chair
McCarthy, John Joseph
Amer, World His & Geog Teacher
Severson, Stephen Allen
Principal
Tracy, Charles Lee
6th Grade Math Teacher
BRAIDWOOD
Browning, Diana Zolecki
8th Grd Lang Arts & Sci Instr
Hogan, Melinda O'Brien
Family & Consumer Science Tchr
Jennette, Jane Anderson
Eighth Grade Science Teacher
Johnson, Donna Grumish
1st-5th Grade Science Teacher
Jones, Carl James
Psychology & Sociology Teacher
Lane, Jeffrey Michael
Biology Teacher
Lockwood, Todd Alan
8th Grade Social Studies Tchr
Murphy, Eileen Marie
High School Science Teacher
Novy, Laurie James
English Teacher
Padilla, Roderick Carl
ComSci & Physics Teacher
Simon, Mark David
English Teacher & Coach
Spiezio, Joseph R.
Assistant Principal
Voris, John B.
TASC Coordinator
BREESE
Aliste, Myriam L.
Spanish Teacher
Bagby, Richard E.
English Instructor
Bailey, Pamela S.
English Teacher
Cook, Jim
Seventh Grade Teacher
Falconio, James R.
Visual Art Instr
Fuchs, Alan L.
Physical Science Teacher
Garcia, Stephanie A.
Jr High Language Arts Teacher
Holzinger, Bonnie Lakenburges
English Teacher
Kampwerth, Judith Kniepmann
Religion Teacher & Dept Chair
Litteken, Dennis Anthony
Asst Prin & Head Ftbl Coach
Ostrom, Donnie Charles
Superintendent
Otrich, Christine Noel
Bio, Earth & Phys Sci Tchr
Rohr, Lucille DePaul (Washford)
Math Teacher
BRIDGEPORT
Cummins, Michael Eugene
Principal
Drury, Debra Lynn
English & Latin Teacher
McMillen, Julie Bowen
English Teacher
Miller, Timothy
Sixth Grade Teacher
Rea, Jane Behagg
French & English Teacher
BRIDGEVIEW
Burk, Mary Wojdygo
Sixth Grade Teacher
Jarad, Fuzia Rashid
Jr HS, HS Eng & Rdng Teacher
BRIGHTON
Sessions, Faye Ann
Sixth Grade Teacher
Sullivan, Sue Rosenthal
5th Grade Teacher
Winslade, Mary Carr
Fifth Grade Teacher
BRIMFIELD
Bonczyk, Mike J.
Govt Teacher & Athletic Dir
Reem, Daniel Wayne
History & French Teacher
Warner, Dennis Jay
HS Math Teacher
BROADLANDS
Rothermel, Judy Sancken
Girls Basketball Coach
BROADVIEW
Antonelli, Joseph K.
Music Educator
BROOKFIELD
Belcher, Marilyn L.
Social Studies & Health Tchr
Prack, Barbara Anne
Intermediate Lang Arts Teacher
BROOKPORT
Christiansen, Debbie Hammack
Kindergarten & Sixth Grd Tchr
Donaldson, Ada Elliott
Second Grade Teacher

Kindle, Carolyn Meadows
Principal
Sawyer, Marna Vancil
8th Grade Teacher
BROWNING
Cox, Glenna M.
Retired Lang Arts & PE Teacher
BROWNSTOWN
Beckel, Harlan Lowell
HS Math & Physics Teacher
Thoele, Craig J.
Counselor
BRUSSELS
Kiel, M. Dorothy D.
Math Teacher
BUDA
Albrecht, Donna L.
Spanish Teacher
Bechtold, Lynne Parker
English Teacher
Litherland, Victori Ann
Physical Ed & Health Teacher
McBride, Lawrence J.
Special Education Teacher
Smith, Vicki Lynn
Mathematics Teacher
Stetson, Deborah Marie (Sprowls)
Business Teacher
BUFFALO
Crowe, Debra Doerfler
Spanish & English Teacher
Danner, Karen Anne
Vocal Music Teacher
Hubbell, Trudy Lee (Gamel)
Fourth Grade Teacher
Scheibe, Diane Marie (Swengrosh)
7th-12th Grade Art Teacher
Shumaker, Harold E.
Science Teacher
BUFFALO GROVE
Bonk, Lawrence Edwin
Social Studies Teacher
Cherpak, Cynthia Podosek
Fifth Grade Teacher
Collins, Ann Banta
First Grade Teacher
Elder, Barbara Callahan
1st Grade Teacher
Ikenn, Steven
Asst Principal
Jackson, Sharon Sackrider
Math & Biology Teacher
Lind, Pat A.
7th & 8th Grd Art Teacher
Loeb, Wendy Gartenberg
7th & 8th Grade Math Teacher
Mohr, Carolyn L.
Science Teacher
O'Reilly, David E.
High School Guidance Counselor
Panagakis, Bonnie Conner
Language Arts Instructor
Ploplys, Saulius V.
Honors & AP Physics Instructor
Singsank, Ellen A. (Burger)
Second Grade Teacher
Wilson, Nancy
8th Grade Math Teacher
BUNCOMBE
Hogue, Brenda Kay (Jones)
4th Grade Teacher
BUNKER HILL
Bieser, Judy Suppiger
English, Spanish & Speech Tchr
Doerr, Sue S.
Fifth Grade Teacher
Hanks, Nancy L. (Oehler)
Jr High Eng Tchr & Media Spcl
Moody, Michelle Ann (Godar)
Biology & Chemistry Teacher
Sparks, Virginia MacKenzie
Volleyball Coach
Wilson, Charlotte Jewell
Retired Chem, Hlth & Sci Tchr
BURBANK
Bakanas, Andria Brigita
Mathematics Teacher
Brouillette, Robert N.
Director of Guidance
Burk, Mary Foerner
Mathematics Teacher
Cruse, Joyce Mary
Social Studies Teacher
Cunningham, Rosemary Chimpoulis
Music Coordinator
Dahlman, Judith G.
Business Education Teacher
DeStefano, Carmel Theresa
English, Speech & Theatre Tchr
Donoghue, Vincent Joseph
Christian Living Teacher
Faires, Catherine Ann
Spanish Teacher
Finnegan, Joan Quinlan
English Teacher
Flowers, Phyllis Schofield
Kindergarten Teacher
Fowler, Patrick Gilbert
Mathematics Teacher
Glanzmann, Edward J.
Sophomore Theology Teacher
Gorman, Thomas Edward
English Teacher
Holy, Francine Matthes
Junior High Teacher
Houston, Charlotte Sopkowicz
Mathematics Teacher
Janecyk, Geraldine Theresa
High School Mathematics Tchr

Janik, Patricia Ann
Third Grade Teacher
Johnson, Walter Thomas
Jr HS Language Arts Teacher
Kaufmann, Marguerite Taylor
Junior High Teacher
King, Joycelyn Mosby
Scripture Teacher
Kirwin, Susan Wolfe
Junior High Language Arts Tchr
Klein, James C.
English Teacher
Larmon, Linda
Spanish Teacher & Dept Chair
Laude, Maureen Hanafin
Mathematics Teacher
Lunn, Deana Regan
Social Studies Teacher
Lynch, John Robert
English Department Chairman
Maas, Renee Marie
Mathematics Teacher
Mahoney, Thomas C.
English Teacher
McLean, William M.
Computer Science Dept Chm
Mc Sharry, Barbara Parlin
Jr High Math Teacher
Merrick, Michele Traficante
French & Spanish Teacher
Miller, Carol Sacks
1st Grade Teacher
Murphy, Terrence J.
Social Studies Teacher
Paprocki, Joanne (Grabarczyk)
Curr Coord & English Teacher
Paxton, Pamela M.
Physical Education Teacher
Poropat, Judith Oblak
Second Grade Teacher
Quinn, Mark A.
Religious Studies Teacher
Rezek, Thomas Anthony
History Teacher
Rokaitis, Virginia Lynne
Junior High Lang Arts Tchr
Scott, Mark Stonewall
Art Tchr & Dir of Student Act
Smith, Michael Edward
Physical Ed Teacher & Coach
Stawicki, Barbara T.
Fourth Grade Teacher
Stearns, Steve Mark
Physical Education Teacher
Tracy, Jim
Teacher, Coach & Sports Coord
Werner, Patricia Brice
Sixth Grade Teacher
Wright, Rita Bauer
Physical Science Teacher
Zitlow, Judith A.
US His, Sociology & Psych Tchr
BURLINGTON
Gilliland, Dave Dodd
English Teacher & Dept Chair
Keil, Andrea Marie
Mathematics Teacher
Kimmel, Phyllis Ann
Head Counselor
Mytych, Paula Marie
Math, Sci Teacher & Supvr
Van, Terry Wayne
Music Teacher
Wendt, Debbie Holze
Math Teacher
BURR RIDGE
Bolas, William James
English & Literature Teacher
Eskey, Richard C.
6th & 7th Grd Soc Studies Tchr
Esposito, Deborah Dykema
Math Teacher & Curr Coord
BUSHNELL
English, Timothy M.
Third Grade Tchr
Myers, D'Ette Bourell
First Grade Teacher
Sorrill, James Michael
HS Soc Stud Teacher & Coach
BYRON
Adler, John Daniel
6th Grade Writing Teacher
Baker, Robert A.
English Teacher
Beem, Ronald R.
Journalism & History Teacher
Diehl, Susan M.
High School English Teacher
Ferb, Gary John
Chemistry Teacher
Kilmer, Maureen
Media Center Assistant
Riney, Charley P.
Public Recreation Director
Ryder, Nancy J.
Media Director
CAHOKIA
Abell, Benjamin Francis
Professor of Meteorology
Andres, Richard Mathias
Professor of Aerospace
Besse, Penny Jo (Falkenbury)
Music & General Music Teacher
Davis, Donna K.
Physiology & Bio Chem Teacher
Eble, Joseph R.
German Teacher
Geppert, Martha S.
English & Journalism Teacher

CAHOKIA (cont)
Gharabagi, Roobik
Electrical Engineering Prof
Harvell, Susan Marie
Math Teacher
Hopper, William Alexander
Associate Professor
Kamm, Richard Walter
Professor of Aerospace Tech
Latta, Carolyn Fantini
English & Social Studies Tchr
Manor, David
Aerospace Engineering Prof
Roseboom, Roberta Jean
Fourth Grade Teacher
Sherlock, Barry Graham
Associate Professor
Stone, Clara V. (Schaefer)
6th & 8th Grade Math Teacher
Wegner, Edward William
8th Grade Science Teacher
CALEDONIA
Seeber, John Joseph
Sixth Grade Teacher
CALUMET CITY
Grenchik, George J.
Jr High Teacher
Hybert, Diana Sasic
L D Resource Teacher
Lessner, Faye Christensen
7th-8th Grade Science Teacher
Lilly, Nancy (Swannie)
Substitute Teacher
Webb, Carl H.
Science Teacher
Weber, Jeffrey Barron
Social Studies Teacher
CAMBRIDGE
Alhorn, Ron
HS Agriculture Teacher
McAvoy, Michael F.
English Instructor
Swanson, Barbara J.
English Teacher
CAMP POINT
Anderson, Peggy Davidson
High School English Teacher
Arnold, Pamela Kelso
Counselor
Bower, Beth Ann
Bus, Comp Tchr & Tech Adv
Brickman, Roger D.
Physical Education Teacher
Brown, Keela J.
Science Teacher
Cox, Donita Foster
English & Psychology Teacher
Creek, Patricia (Sprick)
PE & Health Teacher
Frese, Barbara K. (Sapp)
1st Grade Teacher
Hood, Karen Kunkel
Second Grade Teacher
Houston, Rod
High School Mathematics Tchr
Lillard, Denise
High School Business Teacher
Long, Matt G.
Social Studies Teacher
Walter, John Carl
High School History Teacher
CAMPBELL HILL
Bennett, Rose L.
English Teacher
Eldridge, Sue Smith
Fourth Grade Teacher
Goetz, Charlotte Sue (Stanley)
Family & Consumer Science Tchr
Martin, Roger Brian
Art Teacher
Phoenix, Esther Pulcher
Fifth Grade Teacher
Speith, Gerald Ray
Music Teacher
Weithorn, Julie
Math Teacher
CANTON
Beam, Sherry A.
High School English Teacher
Beam, Terry A.
Physics & Math Teacher
Bloyd, Jeanine (Standard)
Instructor of Psychology
Culbertson, Karen J.
Second Grade Teacher
Dare, Cheryl Pennington
Fourth Grade Teacher
Flannigan, Peggy Simmons
Associate Dean of Nursing
Francis, Joseph E.
Electronics Instructor
Gomes, Crystal Ann
8th Grade Math Instructor
Gorg, Robert F.
Speech & Theatre Teacher
Graham, Candie Russell
German & Amer History Teacher
Hardy, Jan Jones
English & Composition Instr
Harland, Robert Lee
Retired Teacher
Harms, Frederick Joseph
Dept Chair & Soc Stud Teacher
Htwe, Win Tha
Physics Professor
McGrew, C. Eugene
Agriculture Instructor
Melton, John Riley
Vocational Teacher

Reavis, Kevin L.
Middle School Band Director
Roman, Joseph P.
Band Director
Sondgeroth, Byron Luke
Assistant Principal
Sparhakel, Janice R.
Sixth Grade Teacher
CANTRALL
Turek, Kathleen Rose
1st Grade Teacher
CARBONDALE
Asaturian, Suzanne Marie (Bales)
Biology Teacher
Barbeau, Debbie J.
Accounting Lecturer
Basi, Bart A.
Professor of Taxation
Bateman, Marianne Webb
Prof of Music & Organist
Beintema, Mark Bruce
Mathematics Professor
Brandt, Janis E.
Marketing Professor
Bruce, Cicero
Graduate Assistant in English
Bruner, Gordon Carl, II
Associate Prof of Marketing
Craven, Martha Joyce
Assistant Professor
Cross, Daniel Curtis, Sr.
9th-12th Grd Vocal Music Dir
Dyer, William Gerald
Professor & Associate Dean
Evans, David A.
Lecturer & English Dept Chair
Flesher, Jeffrey W.
Training & Development Prof
Grabowski, Richard
Professor of Economics
Gregory, John
Mathematics Professor
Gregory, Yolonda Johnson
Lang Arts & Soc Stud Teacher
Grimmer, Patricia Andresen
Social Studies Teacher
Grimmer, Ronald Calvin
Mathematics Professor
Hagan, Mary M.
Principal
Howell, Suzanne Firmin
English & Humanities Teacher
Hudson, Cleothus Charles
Art Teacher
Hughes, Marilyn Lu
Seventh & Eighth Grade Teacher
King, Maryon Frederick
Asst Professor of Marketing
Koster, Mary Dolores
Biling Prgm Coord & ESL Tchr
Kulkarni, Manohar R.
Prof of Mechanical Engineering
Lippert, Lance R.
Graduate Teaching Assistant
Lowe-Dupas, Helene
Assistant Professor of French
Major, Judy
Math Teacher
Malik, Fazley Bary
Professor of Physics
Mathur, Lynette Knowles
Asst Professor of Marketing
Mavigliano, George J.
Assoc Prof of His & Amer Art
Mc Eathron, Scott J.
Assistant Professor of English
Nicolai, Albert Thomas
English Teacher
Ravat, Dhananjay
Geophysics Professor
Sari, Mouna
Research Assistant
Sasse, Mary Hawley
Writer & Consultant
Shidler, Jon A.
Asst Prof of Advertising
Wade, David R.
Assoc Professor of Physiology
Wright, Michael David
Jr High English Teacher
CARLINVILLE
Card, Andrea Lou
Guidance Counselor
Lohnes, Bradley E.
Director of Guidance
Miller, Victor "Jake" Alan
Psychology Professor
Witham, Craig R.
Biology Teacher
Zalisko, Edward J.
Professor of Biology
CARLOCK
Myers, Scott Neil
Fourth Grade Teacher
CARLYLE
Reinhard, Brian K.
Spanish Teacher
Wiegmann, Lisa Ann
Business Tchr & Vocational Dir
CARMI
Garrett, Donald Lee
Chemistry Teacher & Sci Chm
Hughes, Carl Dean
HS Social Science Teacher
Mitchell, Arla Meler
High School Teacher
CAROL STREAM
Berglund, Charles Alfred
Speech Arts Dept Chm

Boyer, Lucy Ann (Barrett)
Sixth Grade Teacher
Chamberlain, John Smith
High School Science Teacher
Choice, Penny K. Means
Gifted Program Coord & Teacher
Crowley, W. Randall, III
Fifth Grade Teacher
Dall, Roger W.
Retired Elementary Teacher
Drendel, Paula Rae
French & Spanish Teacher
Johnson, Laura Stichnoth
Choir Director
Krasno, Gary Stephen
English Teacher
Loynachan, Brian Keith
Science Teacher
Miller, Mary S. Ashley
German Teacher
Partyka, George
Sixth Grade Teacher
Pucciani, Donna
English Teacher
Schraft, William Robert
Music Dept Chair & Band Dir
CARPENTERSVILLE
Bogue, Richard H.
High School English Teacher
Brown, Joan Marie Burkart
English Teacher
Court, Anita Kotarba
Counselor
Davis, Michael C.
Social Studies Teacher
Ehrhardt, Myrna M.
Kindergarten Teacher
Gorman, John M.
Music Dept Chm & Band Dir
Havard, Audrey Frasen
Spcl Programs Coord & Fr Tchr
Maher, Dennis R.
American History Teacher
Mendro, Lynn (Weber)
Mathematics Teacher
Ostewig, Patricia M.
Art Teacher
Utterback, Nita Ruth
2nd Grade Teacher
VanMeter, Margaret Thomas
Fifth Grade Teacher
Vokac, Nancy Jean
Third Grade Teacher
CARRIER MILLS
Grace, James Arza
5th Grade Teacher
Richey, William Jeffrey
Superintendent
CARROLLTON
Caldwell, James Matthew
English Teacher
Ficker, Ruth Ann (Brauer)
Business Education Teacher
Hamann, Richard G.
History & Geography Teacher
Kiger, Rhonda (Price)
Physics & Algebra II Teacher
Thatcher, Mary Jo Hundley
Biology Teacher
CARTERVILLE
Bradley, Carla Mosby
Assoc Prof of Cmptr Infrmtn
Bush, H. Ray
Machine Shop Teacher
Carl, Kathleen Dwyer
Associate Professor of English
Childers, Bruce E.
Social Studies Teacher
Clark, Rebecca Noel
English Teacher
Gayer, Bill Terry
Associate Professor
Humble, Louise
8th Grade Literature Teacher
Jackson, Phyllis Kobler
Assoc Prof of Secretarial Stud
Johnson, Paulette Loyd
Bus Instr & Spcl Projcts Coord
Martin, Kerry Bryce
HS Soc Studies & US Govt Tchr
Mc Cowen, Mickey Vinsavage
Associate Professor of Health
Minton, Jane Templeton
Instructor & Counselor
Obliboni, Thomas Joseph
History Instructor
Parker, Elaine S.
Prm Coordinator & Counselor
Racey, Tracy Jo
Reading Recovery Teacher
Trammell, Janice Crain
2nd Grade Teacher
Wright, Pamela Piper
5th & 6th Grade Science Tchr
CARTHAGE
Brownlee, Ingrid Elizabeth
English Teacher
Dion, Joseph J.
Guid Counselor & Coop Coord
Flesner, Connie J. (Logan)
Biology & Science Teacher
Hoeher, Gregory G., Sr.
High School Social Stud Tchr
Mc Gaughey, Marcia Gorman
Spanish Teacher
Waggoner, Reford William
Science Teacher
CARY
Lundstrom, Kristin K.
Biology Teacher

Mootz, Terrance M.
Science Teacher
O'Meara, Mary Moriarty
Home Ec Tchr, Hlth Dept Chprsn
Otto, David Paul
Mathematics Teacher & Coach
Overheu, Arlene Joy
Sixth Grade Teacher
Popp, Susan Robinson
Soc Science Tchr & Dept Chair
Roti, Karen Bailey
English Teacher
Tuber, Henry Brian
Director of Bands
Wojtach, Alan A.
Junior High Math Teacher
Youel, Therese J.
Physics & Chemistry Teacher
CASEY
Haines, Steven Edwin
Mathematics Teacher
Lee, Marsha McVey
HS Math Teacher
Richards, Patty
Speech, Eng & Media Teacher
Throneburg, Denny J.
Science & Health Instructor
CATLIN
Huchel, Karen Swigart
English Teacher
Trask, Vicki Crawford
First Grade Teacher
CENTRALIA
Ackerman, Neil L.
Geography & Ecology Instructor
Ackerman, Pamela Ann (Taveggia)
Eighth Grade Reading Teacher
Allen, Marie Melton
Band Director
Bill, Terry
Accounting Coordinator
Brinkman, Penny Lou
Radiology Program Director
Coers, Alvin E.
Mathematics Instructor
Fark, Judy Ann (Mabry)
High School Mathematics Tchr
Francois, Sharon Sweitzer
Adult Education Instructor
Gadel, Sandy
Math Teacher
Gibson, Jody Chase
8th Grd Eng & Reading Teacher
Gillmore, Hala Marie (Groff)
First Grade Teacher
Krumrey, James I.
English Teacher
Lippman, Douglas Arthur
World History & Govt Tchr
Marquardt, Sharon Noel
English Teacher
Mayer, Dee Ann Carter
Teacher
Scheurich, Mark Q.
Superintendent
Stein, Stephen A.
English Instructor
Suarez, Tina Marie
Child Care Coordinator
White, James Edward
Social Studies Teacher
Wiedman, James E.
Science Instructor
Wilimzig, Eileen Byrne
French Teacher
CERRO GORDO
Arseneau, Anthony James
High School Math Teacher
Ozier, Barbara Anne
Band Director & Music Teacher
Young, Angela J.
French Teacher
CHAMPAIGN
Aldridge, Suzanne Meek
English & Drama Teacher
Allen, Louisa Semrdjian
Fifth Grade Elementary Teacher
Blair, John Philip
Biology Teacher
Chambers, David Lee
Dean of Students
Ellis-Nelson, Janet Connor
Collaborative Consultant
Eubank, Shari
Teacher & Education Coord
Fleming, Alfred John
Science Dept Chair & Teacher
Gross, Stacey
Art Instructor
Henthorn, Judith Elaine
Co-Dir of Dental Hygiene Prgm
Jones, Roberta S.
Math Dept Head
Kirby, Schelli (Harrold)
Social Studies & Science Tchr
Lavender, Sheila Fallon
Fifth & Sixth Grade Teacher
Moore, John Edward
Associate Professor
Pearson, Minnie Hemphill
First Grade Teacher
Pickard, Karen Kracher
Seventh Grade English Teacher
Quinlan, Kevin Michael
Social Studies & English Tchr
Seed, Sara Sue
Physical Education Teacher
Stirrett, Philip D.
Business Ed Teacher & Coach

Stover, Judy Ann
Fourth Grade Teacher
Tancig, David Ramier
Professor of Computer Science
Thom, Gregory
Accounting Professor
Travaglini, Catherine Helen
Professor of Chemistry
Wallace, Sally Foster
Professor of English
Way, Jeremy John
Chem, Bio & Physics Teacher
Whetstone, James R.
Criminal Justice Program Dir
Wilhour, Reo
International Student Advisor
Wyatt, Marian Kuethe
Choral Director
Yanchus, Stan
English Teacher
Zimmerman, Faith Erickson
Retired Third Grade Teacher
CHANNAHON
Davisson, Sarah (Miller)
Sixth Grade Reading Teacher
Ewing, Kathleen L.
2nd Grade Teacher
CHARLESTON
Ankenbrand, Larry J.
Professor & Associate Dean
Ankenbrand, Maureen Kelly
Business Chairperson & Teacher
Augustine, Kathryn Singer
Junior High Math Teacher
Bodine, Paul G.
Fine Arts Professor
Carey, Janelle
English Instructor
Crawford, Donald Paul
English Instructor
Dell, Carl W., Jr.
Speech Pathology Professor
DiBianco, Douglas Robert
Professor of Music & Fine Arts
Everett, Rick Dean
Social Studies Teacher
Gochanour, Robert Denby
Sixth Grade Teacher
Griffith, Clyde Mitchell
Fifth Grade Teacher
Hills, Robert L.
Director of Choral Music
Keiter, Ellen A.
Professor & Chem Dept Chair
Manfredo, Joseph
Director of Bands
McArthur, Joseph Andrew
Band Director
Mc Collum, Timothy David
Science Instructor
Mc Gaughey, James
Assistant Professor of Botany
Mc Ginness, Leslee Lance
English Teacher
Reven, Linda Marie
Associate Professor
Satterwhite, Marcy L.
Business Instructor
Simons, Sheila Renee
Professor of Health Studies
Spencer, Boyd
Professor of Psychology Dept
Swim, Tina Marie Grissom
Biology Teacher
Treadway, Shirley Adams
Math Teacher
Walz, Mary Ann Kinkin
5th Grade Language Arts Tchr
Webb, Patricia Ann (Leu)
French Teacher
White, Andrew Martin
Asst Prof of Math & Cheerteam
Wiley, Dan L.
Fourth Grade Teacher
Woods, Susan Lerch
Prof & Hlth Stud Dept
CHATHAM
Baumann, Tadd Kent
Soc Stud Tchr & Dept Coord
Correll, Sally Kohl
Science Teacher & Dept Chm
Cox, Kerry (Grubb)
5th Grade Teacher
Kennedy, Rosemary Vieira
Fifth Grade Teacher
Korte, Julie J.
Science Teacher
Martin, Pamela Joyce (Kelly)
Secondary Math Teacher
O'Brien, Marilyn
High School Math Instructor
Rentfrow, E. Kay (Morgan)
Fifth Grade Teacher
Root, Tina Norris
Social Studies Teacher
Singer, Rita Deutch
Biology Teacher
Smith, Norman R.
Guidance Dept Coordinator
Theobald, Judy Clark
English Department Chairperson
Van Alstine, Pamela Ann
Teacher
Woodruff, Rebecca Manning
Mathematics Teacher
CHENOA
Bare, Diane Maguire
Pre Vocational Coordinator

TER
in, Cynthia Anne
ergarten Teacher
enin, Donna Monfredini
& Computer Teacher
anell Dianne
irade Teacher
Linda Cash
sh Teacher
Melissa Kay
Grade Language Arts Tchr
ostel, Darlene M.
ness Teacher
AGO
nsky, Howard
essor of Criminal Justice
an, Marcie (Shapiro)
ent Support Services Tchr
Jill Kinley
ry Teacher
, Donald Ray
Math & English Teacher
on, Michelle Shelton
ing Teacher
Bobbie Jean
TC Instructor
son, Ernest Edward
itectural Drafting Teacher
, Victor Kodzo
c Professor of Math
ze, Justin Kanayo
ics Professor
Ellen (Stewart)
ace Teacher
ge, Earl L.
hysical Education Teacher
ader, Marlena Acerhart
sh Teacher
, Michael
al Studies Teacher
do, Rene
c Dir of Admin & Fin Aid
raal, Brenda Bysterveld
nced Placement Eng Teacher
Sandy M.
ipal
son, Betty A.
r Grade Lang Arts Teacher
son, Mark Joseph
ematics Teacher
son-Moon, Darlene Yvette
urce Specialist
ny-Perez, Bobbie C. M.
nology Professor Emeritus
e, Jacqueline Marie
ol Improvement Facilitator
opoulos, Kathy
nglish & Reading Teacher
, Fred David
essor of Finance
r, Phyllis Falls
tion Teacher
y, Diane
th Grade Science Teacher
d, Ismay Rose
of Eng, African Amer Stud
, Ron
ed States History Teacher
Eugene Jonathan
al Worker
Rosemary
sh & Journalism Teacher
Lawrence S.
ematics Teacher
Carmen Maria Velez
gual & Soc Studies Tchr
Gracy Ann
School English Teacher
Kathleen Pasquale
sh Teacher
Johnson, Doris Weeks
Grade Teacher
wski, Mary Eileen Niemiec
Cnslr & Theology Tchr
d, Alice Alicia
Chairman & Lang Arts Tchr
, Lorene Taylor
sh Tchr & Options Coord
t, Annie Coleman
Prgmr & Stu Acts Dir
p, Linda Vitacco
8th Grd Mathematics Tchr
, Katie Elizabeth Evans
her
ill Lauren
ry Teacher
, Erik Matthew
al Studies Teacher
, Jose Luis
sh Teacher
rs, Retha Britton
th Grade Teacher
Joan Marie
th Grade Teacher
Gwendolyn Estelle
ergarten Teacher
d, Cynthia Maria
sh Teacher
t, Solomon Frederick
ner of Gifted Program
Martin Barry
essor of Biology
ann, Joseph B.
h & Sociology Teacher
Faye Bernd
nth & Eighth Grd Eng Tchr
Barbara H. Mc Gee
d Grade Teacher
Sandra Bea Roach
entary Teacher

Berry, Thomas Dale
Associate Professor
Bicknell-Hentges, Lindsay Pugh
Assistant Professor of Psych
Bigane, Meg M.
English Teacher
Billingsley, Mary Louise
High School History Teacher
Billups, Christine Alice
Theology Teacher
Blackburn, Darlene Yvonne
Physical Educator
Blake, Kelly Ann
French Teacher
Blohm-Hamlet, Jessie B.
Curr Lead Teacher & Admin Asst
Blumberg, Judith K.
Accounting Instructor
Boarden, Latanza Walton
Mathematics Teacher
Bogumil, Scott A.
Guidance Counselor
Boivin, Kenneth Daniel
JROTC Instructor
Boldovici, Lumi
Social Studies Teacher
Bonner, William Paul
English Teacher
Bosch, Jerome James
Spanish & English Teacher
Boucek, Barbara Walsh
HS Social Studies Teacher
Boyer, Stanley D.
Professor of Biology
Bradley, Charles R.
Dept Head
Brake, Christopher Lynn
7th & 8th Grade Math Teacher
Brewer, Jacqueline Ann
5th Grade Teacher
Britton-Wheeler, Marcia Jane
Teacher
Brown, Elizabeth Bonnie Hampson
Campus Minister
Brown, Grafton Reed, III
Spanish Teacher
Brown, M. Shaina
English Teacher
Brown, Michael, Sr.
Advanced Math Teacher & Admin
Brown, Rose Marie
Mathematics Professor
Brownstein, Dorothy Spreitzer
Business Teacher
Buchanan, Bertha Paul
Attendance Coordinator
Buckley, Julia Rohaly
English Teacher
Budow, Norman Edward
Prof of Geography & Sociology
Burks, Michael Odell
Principal
Burrage-Couch, Patricia
English Teacher
Burt-Bradley, Della A.
Professor of English
Bush, Martin E., Jr.
Science Teacher
Bush, Sandra Anita
Sixth Grade Teacher
Byrd, Maria Becki
Horticulture Teacher
Byrd, Prentiss Nelson
Assoc Prof of Cnslng & Instr
Cage, Cheryl Eileen Abernathy
Tchr of Learning Disabilities
Cameron, Theresa Millie
English Teacher
Campbell, Mary B.
Associate Prof of Education
Canepa, Patricia Lenihan
Lang Arts & Soc Stud Tchr
Cappitelli, Mary Kay Philbin
English Tchr & Newspaper Adv
Carr, Mae
Chem Tchr & Sci Dept Head
Carter, Artisha Collins
Assistant Principal
Caruso, Rita Wenckowski
Junior High Language Arts Tchr
Caruso, Ronald Ralph
K-9th Grd IASA Science Coord
Casey, Peggy Sue Snyder
Director of Bands
Castilleja, Veronica
College Counselor
Cavanaugh, Thomas Alan
Science Teacher
Cebrzynski, Pamela Mary (Borowski)
Seventh Grade Teacher
Califoux, Kristine Howes
Instructor of English
Chandran, Satish Raman
Professor of Anatomy & Bio
Chapman, Shirley Ann
Assistant Principal
Chappell, Robert B.
High School History Teacher
Chibe, Lisa Michele
Social Studies Teacher
Chierico, Robert James
Professor of Spanish
Childress, Jacqueline Harris
MS Lang Arts Teacher
Chinn, Betty Heath
Teacher & Librarian
Chishty, Muhammad R. K.
MBA Pgm Director & Assoc Prof
Choi, Sang Joon
Associate Prof of Electronics

Cissom, Lynn Wilbert
Administrative Assistant
Civik, Pam Thompson
Sixth Grade Teacher
Claiborne, Etta Liddell
English Teacher
Clendenen, Avis
Assoc Prof of Religious Stud
Coen, Mae Z.
Social Science Teacher
Coffey, Paul Bruno
Adj Professor of First Yr Pgm
Coffman, Nathaniel Ward
Dean of Stdnts & History Tchr
Cohan, Barbara Ann (Ulman)
High School English Teacher
Coleman, Krisha Rogers
Spanish Teacher
Collias, Christopher Nicholas
Journalism & English Teacher
Collins, Aretha Ryan
Chicago Mentor Tchr & Dept Chm
Connors, Sally J.
Science Teacher
Conway, James Michael
Assistant Principal
Cooper, Paul, Jr.
English Teacher
Costello, Matthew John
Assoc Prof of Political Sci
Covalcic, Ina
Spanish Teacher
Crandall, Arlene R.
Bilingual Lead Teacher
Crockett, George Ephraim
Social Studies Teacher
Cummings, Miriam Patrick
Vice Principal
Curnow, Barbara Ann
Special Education Teacher
Cutcher, Barbara R.
Resource Teacher
Czaja, Darlene Feret
English & Drama Teacher
Daniel, Wilbur Nathan
Math Lab Teacher
Daniels, Marvin Anthony
Cnslr & Yth Outreach Prgm Dir
Davenport, Joni
Teaching Assistant
Davenport, Willimethra Reed
Biology Teacher
Davis, Carl Edward
Middle School Science Teacher
Davis, Joseph
French & Spanish Teacher
Davis, Mary (Slack)
Resource Teacher
Davis, Sylvester
Dean of Students & Ath Dir
Dean, Rosamary Slater
Teacher
DeBow, Nancy J. (Cobb)
Computer Coordinator
Deitelhoff, Catherine Mary
Math Teacher
Delane, Hilda
Second Grade Teacher
Delk, Annie Ruth
Eighth Grade Teacher
Denning-Golden, Patricia Paul
HS English & Journalism Tchr
Derza, Andrzej Euzebiusz
Math Teacher
Deutscher, Ronald Walter
Jr HS Social Studies Teacher
Devane, Catherine Foley
Retired Jr HS English Teacher
Devience, Alex (N), Jr.
Associate Professor
Diaz, Claudio, Jr.
Spanish Teacher
Dickerson, Chester Lee, Jr.
English Teacher
DiFonzo, Judith Buick
Kindergarten Teacher
Ditkowsky, Deborah Jean
Science Teacher
Ditkowsky, Judith Goodman
Chemistry Teacher
DiVito, Arthur N.
Mathematics Professor
Dobbins, Ernestine Tucker
English Teacher
Dodsworth, Scott Thomas
Social Studies Teacher
Doig, Donald Clarke
Music Prof & Dept Chair
Dormin, Patricia Cassidy
7th-8th Grade Lit Teacher
Doulgeris, Marianne Georgia
English & Literature Teacher
Dowling, Daniel P.
Teacher & Coach
Dring, Mark
Physics Teacher
Dulewski, Sharon Lynn (Buczak)
7th-8th Grade English Teacher
DuMez, Berniece Ruth Anderson
Retired K-3rd Grade Teacher
Dust, Margaret C.
Assistant Professor of Psych
Duvall, David Eric
English Department Chairman
Dziak, Jennifer Marie
Family & Consumer Science Tchr
Eckert, Stacy A.
Assistant Professor of Music
Einoder, Camille Popowski
Chemistry & Biology Teacher

Ekpenyong, Boniface Esong
Instructor in Physics
Eliakopoulos, Angeline
Eighth Grade Teacher
Ellis, James Edward
French & History Teacher
Enstrom, Laura Ann
English & ESL Teacher
Evers, Fran
Sixth Grade Science Teacher
Evins, Charles B.
Elementary Teacher
Fabian, Robert Paul
7th & 8th Grade Teacher
Fager, Slavka Djekich
Recruitment Director
Falkowska, Aleksandra
Polish Bilingual Teacher
Farmans, Spencer Michael
English Teacher
Farver, Steven C.
French Teacher
Fech, Barbara Neitz
Assistant Principal
Fiaoni, Jean A.
Sixth Grade Teacher
Figuracion, Marcelina DeJoya
English Teacher
Filan, Alan P.
Business Teacher
Filipski, Barbara Ehrmann
Reading Specialist
Fine, Jim
Instr of Paralegal Studies
Fisher, Berry William, III
Mathematics Instructor
Fisher, Roberta Moore
Media Specialist
Fitzgerald, James Richard
Law Instructor
Fitzgibbons, John Joseph
Programmer
Fitzgibbons Fox, Rita
Social Science Teacher & Chair
Fitzhugh, James
Social Studies Teacher
Florek, Donna Frances (Gaida)
Physical Education Teacher
Forbes, Christina Catherine
Focus English Teacher
Fosco, Susan (Alderson)
Physical Education Teacher
Fowler, C. Randal
French & Spanish Teacher
Fox, Dorothy Jane Lehman
Seventh & Eighth Grade Teacher
Foxwell, Betsy M.
7th & 8th Grd Tchr of Gifted
Franklin, Sharon Althiea (Mc Neal)
HS Special Education Instr
Frazier, Minnie Louise
Reading Specialist
Fredericks, Elisa
Adjunct Professor
Freeman, Linnie Welch
Retired Teacher
Fuller, Clarence
Art & Photography Teacher
Funk, Janet Mallo
4th Grade Teacher
Gabelnick, Helene Seeder
Prof of Physical Science Dept
Garbacz, Margaret Mary
Dir of Religious Education
Garcia, Elaine M.
Fourth Grd Language Arts Tchr
Gasior, Dawn Marie (Slowinski)
Second Grade Teacher
Gaus, Joanne T.
Second Grade Teacher
Gavin, Gail Swanson
HS Horticultural Sci Tchr
Gawlik, Laura Snow
Theology Tchr & Retreat Dir
Gawlik, Robert A.
Eighth Grade Teacher
Gbur, Alan Theodore
Cmptr Information Systems Prof
Geleerd, Jennifer Goodhart
History Teacher
Georgiopoulos, Spyridoula Roula
Soc Studies Dept Chair & Tchr
Gerber, Ian Marcus
Drama Director
Gervais, Mark G.
Athletic Dir & PE Dept Chrmn
Gianotti, Sharon M.
Language Arts Teacher
Gibbons, James R.
English Teacher
Glab, Stephen Anthony
High School Math Teacher
Glennon, Owen Gerard
Mathematics Teacher
Gogins, Alan Jerome
Band & Orchestra Director
Goldman, Robert Craig
Social Studies Teacher
Gomez, Josephine
Biology Instructor
Gonzalez, Jose Luis
Bilingual Teacher
Goodkind, Allan Samuel
English Teacher & Dept Chm
Goodman, Virginia-Ellen Jones
Associate Professor of Reading
Goodson, Phyllis Moore
Science Teacher & Dept Chprsn
Gossmann, Gerlinde Jochum
English as a Second Lang Tchr

Goulding, Laura Weiner
3rd Grade Teacher
Goutis, Nikki Ann
Spanish Teacher
Grace, Claude
Art Teacher
Grafner, Peter Vincent
History Teacher
Grange, Janet Lenore
Accounting Professor
Grant, Raymond R.
World His & Ec Tchr
Gray, Leslie Anne
History Teacher
Green, Lolita Davenport
Assistant Principal
Green-Powell, Sharon Yvette
English & History Teacher
Griffin, Mattye Anderson
First Grade Teacher of Gifted
Gross, Susan Olendzki
High School English Teacher
Hafner, Mary E.
Asst Principal & Athletic Dir
Haley, Helena Sengstacke
Head Teacher
Hall, Bruce William
High School Eng & Jrnlsm Tchr
Halliday, Valentina Grigoriev
Environmental Ed & Span Tchr
Hamberlin, Keith Yvonne
Music Teacher
Hammond, Stephen E.
7th-8th Grade Science Teacher
Handler, Evelyn
Social Studies Dept Chprsn
Hanna, Roger Ralph
Physics Instructor
Hanrahan, Theresa Marie
Dir of Stu Act
Hansra, Monpreet Kaur
Mathematics Teacher
Hare, Ethelene Kearney
Chemistry Teacher
Harley, Laura
Teacher
Harvey, Faith Lorraine
Fine Arts Coordinator
Hasan, Tanweer
Assistant Professor of Finance
Hau, Joan Marie
Assoc Prof of Nursing
Hayes, Patrick Sean
Physics Teacher & Science Chm
Hayes, Tamlyn Grimes
Elementary School Counselor
Hecker, Roy C.
7th & 8th Grade Reading Tchr
Heider, Anne Harrington
Assoc Prof & Dir Choral Music
Heinze, Michael Ernest
8th Grd Teacher
Henderson, JoAnne Mc Kinney
Reading Resource Teacher
Henderson, Vantasta
Sixth Grade Teacher
Henning, MaryLee Love
Seventh Grade Teacher
Henry, Barbara J.
English Teacher
Henry, Caroll Easter
Prof & Chprsn of Bio Science
Herrick, Deborah A.
English Teacher
Higgins, Diane Mary
Co-Programmer
Hill, Allan P.
Teacher & Assistant Principal
Hill, Nancy Thorley
Accounting Professor
Hill, Richard L.
History Teacher
Hillard, Dorothy Lee
Senior Counselor
Hillsman, Juanetta Elaine
Pre-K School Teacher
Hirdler, Kenneth Edward
Tchr & Social Studies Chprsn
Hogan, Michael Thomas
Foreign Lang Chair & Span Tchr
Hogg, Betty T.
History Teacher & Coordinator
Holder, Natalie June
English Teacher
Holland, Rita Therese
High School English Teacher
Hollins, Anthony
Founder & Artistic Director
Hong, Jai Woo
Industrial Technology Prof
Hoover, Ronald H.
Theology Teacher
Horsham, James Edward
Political Science Professor
Hoskins, Patricia Annette
HS Business Education Teacher
Hoth, Cheryl
Guidance Director
Houston, John Leonard
Finance Professor
Howard, Sarah Gail
Social Studies & History Tchr
Hudson, Christine
Teacher
Hudson-Lucas, Nicole Cherese
HS Mathematics Teacher
Hulseberg, Henry M.
Science Teacher
Hulsebus, Barbara Pfuhl
Mathematics Teacher

CHICAGO (cont)
Hunt, Atha
Associate Professor of Finance
Hunter, Carolyn Faye
Computer Science Teacher
Husband, Roberta Wheeler
Mathematics Teacher
Ihde, Thomas F.
Education Instructor
Inge, Aretha DuPree
Guidance Counselor
Inzinga, Joseph
Dean of Students
Isackson, R. J.
Dir of Bridge Pgm & Eng Instr
Jachna, Virginia L. (Kemper)
Assistant Professor
Jackowiak, Mark Richard
Mathematics Teacher
Jackson, Mary Lewis
Eighth Grade Teacher
Jackson-Ivy, Marvis Bonita
Intermediate Teacher
Jacoby, Daniel Andrew
History Teacher
Jaffe, Miriam Sokol
Judaic Studies Teacher
Jamerson, JeTaun Farley
Social Studies Teacher
James, Rochelle Donna
Science Instr & Lab Teacher
Jann, Lynda Gail (Jones)
Reading & Art Teacher
Jennings, Karen Saikins
Chemistry Teacher
Jimmar, Alfred James
5th Grade Teacher
Johannessen, Larry Richard
English Professor
Johnson, Dennis E.
Biology & Zoology Teacher
Johnson, Rose Marie
Drama, Speech & English Tchr
Johnson, Slyvester
Seventh Grade Teacher
Jones, Claudia Artis
Mathematics Teacher
Jones, Jimmie T.
Retired HS Graphics Arts Tchr
Jonscher, Margaret Breitenreiter
Tchr of Gifted & 8th Grd Math
Joseph, Andrew Phillip
US History Instructor
Joyce, Edward Alan
Latin, Greek & English Prof
Juarez, Lisa Adrienne
Sixth Grade Classroom Teacher
Kadas, Frances Ann
First Grade Teacher
Kamberos, Patricia
4th Grade Teacher
Kazmier, Henry E.
Anatomy & Physiology Prof
Kenny, Emily Florence
Fourth Grade Teacher
Kerr, Lisa Godde
Learning Assistance Counselor
Khula, Dolores Diane
Spanish Teacher
Killingsworth, Cicely
Seventh Grade Teacher
Kirley, Jacqueline Paulette
Social Science Professor
Kirstein, Peter
Professor
Kisicki, Michael John
Asst Principal & English Instr
Klebes, Robert E.
Dean of Students
Klein, Joan McCastland
Associate Professor of Nursing
Klein, Patricia Judith
Retired Fourth Grade Teacher
Klug, Brian
Assoc Prof & Phil Dept Chrmn
Knepper, William Frank
Eighth Grade Math Teacher
Knitter, Linda Mary
French Teacher
Knox, George W.
Professor of Criminology
Koegler, Karen Kinsella
Science Teacher
Kolak, Czeslawa Kardas
Teacher & Bilingual Coord
Komai-Thompson, Loisjean
English & Reading Professor
Koob, Nadine Nader
Social Studies Teacher & Chair
Kowalski, MaryJane Schram
Span Tchr & Foreign Lang Dept
Krall, Beverly Easterday
English Teacher
Kramer, William F., CFC
Lang Dept Chprsn & Span Tchr
Kratzer, Thomas A.
Management Professor
Kritzberg, Barry
English Teacher
Kubik, Thomas Michael
Chemistry Teacher
Kuhn, Karl Zachary
Former Teacher
Kun, Steven John
6th Grade Teacher
Kurek, Linda (Baro)
PE Teacher & Coach
Kurland, Jeanine
Junior HS Religion Teacher
Kurtz, Nancy Ann
Piano Teacher
Lach, Michael C.
Science Teacher
Lamar, Christine (Horn)
Math Teacher
Laschober, Patricia Ann Kelly
Eighth Grade Teacher
Lee, Pauline Mytrice
Guidance Counselor
Leffner, Helen Joseph
Frosh, Soph Cnslr & Registrar
Lehman, Dennis Dale
Professor of Chemistry
Lenczycki, Ruth A.
French Teacher
LePore, Lin M.
Spanish Teacher
Lewis, Dorothy L.
Social Science Teacher
Lewis, John Wesley
PE Teacher & Head Bsktbl Coach
Liebenow, Franklin Eastburn, Jr.
Associate Professor of English
Link, Joseph Patrick
Mathematics Teacher
Lipson, Jo B.
Counseling Department Chair
Lodl, Albert Peter
Biology Tchr & Sci Dept Chprsn
Lofton, Shirley Falconer
5th-6th Grade Teacher
Longo, Michael Sharkey
Rel Teacher of Faith Dev Dept
Longstreet, John C.
Professor
Lowe, Rita Johnson
Assoc Prof Cmptr Infrmtn Sys
Lucas, Annette B.
Reading Resource Teacher
Lumpkin, Carolyn Neal
7th & 8th Grade Reading Tchr
Maccagnano, Vincent Philip
Physics Teacher
Mackrill, Kathleen Ellen
Eighth Grade Teacher
Maebane, Clairellen Toney
8th Grade Science Teacher
Malecki, Emelyn
Asst Principal & Remedial Tchr
Malito, Lawrence W.
English Dept Chairman
Mallek, Frank Alan
Junior High Teacher
Manna, Frank Joseph
Band Director
Manno, Andrew S.
Biology Teacher
Mariotti, David L.
Seventh Grade Teacher
Markulin, Beverlee Jancy
Pub Relations Dir & Yrbk Adv
Martin, Diane Burrage
Home Economics Teacher
Martin, Patrick Michael
Mathematics Instructor
Martinez, Joaquin O.
Former Science Teacher
Mason, Sharon L.
Band Director
Mason-Johnson, Janice
MS Social Studies Teacher
Matonich, Linda K. (Hood)
Fine Arts Instructor
May, Edgar D.
8th Grade Teacher
Mc Abee, Catherine A.
Schoolwide Resource Teacher
McAuliffe, Janice J.
English Teacher
Mc Carthy, Clare Kobald
7th-8th Grd Math Teacher
Mc Carthy, Thomas Raymond, OSA
Pastoral Dir & Theology Tchr
Mc Cloud, Aminah Beverly Thomas
Islamic Studies Professor
MC Cray, Deborah Wigfall
First Grade Teacher
Mc Dermott, Daniel Joseph
6th Grade Teacher
Mc Donnell, Mary Ryan
English Teacher
Mc Enroe, John Edward
Amoco Professor of Accountancy
McFarlane, Victor Manuel
8th Grade Bilingual Teacher
Mc Govern, Carolyn Ann
Spanish Teacher
McHugh, James Thomas
Asst Prof of Political Science
Mc Intyre, MaryAnn
Computer Coordinator
Mc Knight, Katherine Siewert
English Teacher
McKwartin, Dan B.
Assoc Prof of Political Sci
McNicholas, Walter Francis, OSA
Freshman Guidance Counselor
Mc Rae, Cheryl Maria
Second Grade Teacher
Mc Tigue, Robert J.
Dir of Stu Acts & History Tchr
Meade, Mary Therese (Harmon)
Science Coordinator
Meltzer, Sharon Bittenson
Professor of English
Merritt, Adrienne Darcelle
Physical Education Specialist
Mesa, Virginia
Former Bilingual Teacher
Meyer, James Lee
Dean of Students
Michaels, Pamela A.
Asst Professor of English
Michalak, Melanie S.
Choral Director
Mielke, David E.
Dean & Counselor
Milkie, Michael E.
Mathematics Teacher
Miller, Betty Jean
Coalition Essential Schl Coord
Miller, Gwendolyn Samuel
High School Guidance Counselor
Mizerka, Patricia Miceli
Seventh Grade Teacher
Moffett, Ann George
Second Grade Teacher
Molenda, Don
Chemistry Instructor
Molinaro, Ann Lewis
Jr High Math Teacher
Montgomery, Shirley Cherie
Departmental Math Teacher
Moody, Willard A., III
Assoc Prof of English
Moravec, Alan Mark
Choir Director
Morrison, William Richard, III
Admissions Counselor
Morrow, Robert Irvin
Asst Professor of Biology
Moseley, Juanita Major
Professor of Speech
Moses, Judith Wager
German & ESL Professor
Mowatt, Leatrice Mc Clain
Assistant Principal
Moy, Jun
Math Teacher
Moy, Soo Lon L.
Cantonese Biling Lead Tchr
Moyzis, Virginia Spurney
Retired Eighth Grade Teacher
Muller, Richard C.
Mathematics Tchr & Dept Chair
Mundo, Rick L., Jr.
High School History Teacher
Naddy, Candace Freyer
Challenge Program Teacher
Naegele, Elizabeth Faul
Professor of Sacred Music
Nah, Bok-Hi Lim
Director & Principal
Nangle, Eleanor
Social Studies Teacher
Narasimhan, Lynn Colburn
Assoc Dean of Lbrl Arts & Sci
Nasko, Nancy Cullinan
Vice Principal & 8th Grd Tchr
Nayak, Manmath K.
Mathematics Professor
Neary, Judith Flynn
English Teacher
Nelson, Brett F.
Social Studies Teacher & Coach
Nelson, Pratibha Varma
Professor of Chemistry
Nelson, Roberta J.
Mathematics Teacher
Nemsick, Theresa Marie
Theology Teacher
Nesterowicz, Paul John
English & ESL Dept Chairperson
Newkirk, Jean Allen
Business Tchr & Dept Chprsn
Newman, James J.
Music Teacher
Newton, John Edward, OSA
Theology & World History Tchr
Nichols, Peter John
Science Teacher
Nolan, Becky Ann
Drama & Religion Teacher
Novak, Paul E., OSM
Religious Studies Instructor
Nunn, David Ray
Psychology & Sociology Teacher
O'Callaghan, Darlene Czop
Asst Dean of Nursing Pgm
O'Conner, Johnetta Gwendolyn
Spanish Teacher
O'Donnell, Sandra M.
Associate Prof of Public Admin
Ogorzaly, Michael A.
Associate Professor of History
O'Keefe, Robert Daniel
Prof of Marketing & Assoc Dean
Olson, Matthew John
High School Science Teacher
Onofrey, Robert Earl, CPPS
Priest & Religion Teacher
Osaghae, Vincent
Accounting Professor
Osterman, William Ralph
Fifth Grade Teacher
O'Toole, Eileen
Science Teacher & Chairperson
Page, Larry LaMorris
History Teacher
Pales, William Andrew
8th Grade Teacher
Palm, Dylester C.
English & Math Teacher
Palubiak, Laura Lynn
Math Teacher
Pappas, Judy Piergalski
8th Grade Teacher & Asst Prin
Pappas, Magdaline Berchos
Counselor
Passi, Anthony Michael
US & World History Teacher
Paul, Seena Brodnax
Science & Music Teacher
Perez, Larry W.
Chemistry Teacher
Perlman, Bella Beach
Lang Arts & Social Stud Tchr
Perry, Theresa Alexander
History Teacher
Peterson, Lynn Marie
Math Dept Teacher
Petrak, Cliff Matthew
Math Teacher & Asst Librarian
Pickett, Edgar Mitchell, Jr.
Math Tchr of Gifted Students
Pociask, Rosalie
Kindergarten Teacher
Podesta, Marie Victoria, SP
Teacher & Assistant Principal
Pohl, Joyce Ziwisky
6th & 7th Grade Teacher
Poll, Diana Ginsburg
Professor of Education
Pollard, Otto Carl
Seventh Grade Teacher
Poole, Mattie Weems
High School English Teacher
Porch, Danielle Lorraine
HS History Teacher
Portney, Chad Paul
Math Teacher
Postiglione, Corey Michael
Art History & Theory Professor
Postone, Moishe
Dept of History Assoc Prof
Potocki, John S.
Asst Principal
Powell, Dwight E.
Associate Professor
Pratt, Therese Greeley
French & ESL Teacher
Predl, Robert George
Engineering Graphics Instr
Pretkelis, Algird Casmir
Assitant Principal
Pugh, Bertha M.
Special Education Teacher
Pukelis, Larry
Art Tchr & Fine Arts Chprsn
Pye, Sandra Ann
Social Science Teacher
Quaintance, Susan M., OSB
English Teacher
Quinn, James Joseph
Prof of Music & Humanities
Rainey, Anthony George
Assistant Principal
Raja, Shanker
Mathematics Professor
Randle, Mary Thomas
Assistant Principal
Rapp, Mary F. (Allen)
English Teacher
Rave, Sheila Murray
Theology Teacher
Raymond, Melzine
Teacher & Librarian
Reamon, Karen Kankelborg
Scndry Schl English Instructor
Reeves, Sherri Valentine
English Teacher
Reilly, Timothy Joseph
Asst Prin & 7th Grade Teacher
Reist-Jones, Bernice Stephanie
Soc Stud & Anthropology Tchr
Reospopovich, Beth
Athletic Director
Reynolds, Robert David
Nutrition Professor
Rhinehart, Celeste Lois
Health Occupations Teacher
Rhodes, Mary Kay
Kindergarten Teacher
Richardson, Charles Phillip
Eighth Grade Math Teacher
Rigney, Kevin
Math & World History Teacher
Riley, Patricia Ann
Chemistry Teacher
Rivera, Concepcion Millet
Bilingual Chemistry Teacher
Rivera, Luis R.
Associate Prof of Theology
Robinson, Bettye Jean
Fifth Grade Teacher
Robles, Michael
Electronics Teacher
Roche, Eloise O'Connor
9th-12th Grd Science Teacher
Romba, Mary O'Grady
Assoc Professor of Nursing
Roos, Maryanne Lippner
1st Grade Teacher
Roper, Barbara Golding
Accounting Professor
Ross, Pamela Jefferson
Fourth Grade Teacher
Ross, Susan Mary (Skonieczny)
Junior High Teacher
Rottman, Mary Rose
Fourth Grade Teacher
Rucker, Jessie Breashears
Science Teacher
Ruskamp, John Arthur
Executive Assistant Principal
Russell, Milicent De'Ance (Lavizzo)
Assistant Principal
Russo, William
Dir of Contemporary Amer Music
Ryan, Edward John
5th Grade Teacher
Ryan, Michael Patrick
Algebra Tchr & Athletic Dir
Sablan, Robert Gill Fernandez
Senior Army Instructor
Sailes, Michael Edward
Teacher & Coord of Bus Dept
St Leger, Sidney Collins
Assistant Professor
Sampson, James Edward
8th Grade Soc Sci Teacher
Samuel, Arthur William
Science Teacher
Samuel, Marie Antionettee
Eighth Grade Teacher
Samulis, Pamela
Math Lab Resource Teacher
Sanchez, Blanca Lucero
Science Department Chair
Sanders, Willette Marie
Fourth Grade Teacher
Saucedo, Maria Guadalupe
High School Math Teacher
Schaffner, Trudy Michele
Junior High Math Teacher
Schanel, Mary J.
Math Teacher & Dept Chair
Schill, Fred M.
American Literature Teacher
Schmeelk, Alice Bruno
Science Dept Chairperson
Schmid, Lynn Ann
Teacher
Schmidt, Joseph G.
Principal
Schmidt, Katherine A. (Puerschner)
English Teacher
Schmitz, Richard Frank
Physics & Chemistry Teacher
Schulz, Robert L.
US History & Economics Teacher
Schust, Judith Ann
Assoc Prof Child Development
Schwartz, Lois Weinrib
English as Second Lang Tchr
Scotese, Karen Frank
Sci Dept Chair & Teacher
Scully, Mary Eileen
Director of Guidance
Sebestyen, Donald Erich
Assistant Principal
Segler, Keith Brian
Social Studies Teacher
Sellers, Rodney E.
HS Social Studies Teacher
Semmes, Adrienne Davis
7th Grade Teacher
Seputis, Thomas J.
Business Teacher
Serrano, Juan S.
Teacher
Shaffer, Edward L.
English Tchr & Athletic Dir
Sharrow, Debra Bartgen
Kindergarten Teacher
Shedd, Valerie Ann (Hudson)
Bus & Special Ed Teacher
Shegog, Barbara Faye
Computer Education Teacher
Shibayama, Tamara Valda
Chemistry Teacher
Simmons, Margaret Jones
English Teacher
Simone, Sarah Talbot
Jr High Math & Science Teacher
Simpson, Robert L.
Social Studies Teacher
Sims, Paul Anthony, CR
Religion Teacher
Skowronski, Michael G.
Admissions Director
Smith, Anthony Joseph
History Teacher
Smith, Barbara Thomas
Guidance Counselor
Smith, Cynthia Susan
English Teacher
Smith, Dorothy King
Mathematics & Science Teacher
Smith, Mildred House
8th Grade Teacher
Smith, Ronald Forrest
History & Humanities Teacher
Smith, Sibyl Amaryllis
English Teacher
Smyrniotis, Bess George
Third Grade Teacher
Sochacki, Tina Marie (Spirakes)
HS French & Spanish Teacher
Stack, Patricia Marie
Third Grade Teacher
Stallings, Cheryl Turner
Art Teacher & Dept Chair
Stark, Ola M. Draper
Business Education Teacher
Starling, Clarence William
Drafting Tchr & Voc Dept Chm
Stavrakas, Joanne Chronis
High School Math Teacher
Stawicki, Jody Hanley
8th Grade Lang Arts Teacher
Stecich, Rita Fahey
English Tchr & Co-Dir Rdng Lab
Stelmack, Gloria Joy
Language Arts & Math Teacher
Sternberg, Joel B.
Assoc Prof Dept of Mass Comm
Stewart, Andrea Louise Stingley
Soc Studies Dept Chprsn & Tchr

:AGO (cont)
kal, James L.
erintendent
:, Marianne (Nawrocki)
ndance Coordinator
r, Micheal Anton, Sr.
sical Education Instructor
Marian Laura
h Teacher
se, Kenneth R.
mistry & Biology Tchr
), Mary G.
h Teacher & Social Worker
ney, Catherine Ann
Stud Tchr & Dept Chprsn
ney, Juanita Idalia Valdes
Grade Bilingual Teacher
zer, Catherine
urer & Writing Faculty
n, Lisa J.
al Studies Teacher
wski, Edward B.
'ting Teacher
k, Susan M.
or High Teacher
anksi, Miroslaw
igual Teacher of Math
, Donald Joseph
guage Arts Teacher
Daniel William
or High Science Teacher
, Olufemi
oc Professor of Philosophy
r, Herbert David
ogy Teacher
Mildred Patton
ent Advisor
r, Arlene
Mathematics Teacher
, Joel
ociate Professor of Physics
, Alfred W.
th Grade Reading Teacher
', Priscilla Dean
stant Principal
starovic, Lisa
Professor of Economics
n, Sadako
red Second Grade Teacher
son, Brian Craig
opean & World His Tchr
sky, Frank Joseph
ic Teacher
, Rosetta B.
ish Teacher
as, Mary Alice
n Teacher
as, Rogetta Margerum
Teacher
as, Willa Mae Tyler
ish Teacher
as-Price, Janice Coreen
th Grade Teacher
Iaz, Sydney
of Visually Impaired
oson, Kenneth Roy
ociate Professor of Mgmt
oson, Martin C.
nce Teacher
ton, Geoffrey Vincent
Teacher of Gftd & Tlntd
r, Dorothy R. Bennett
d Grade Teacher
, Sheila Wenzel
English Teacher
Mary
ory & Womens Studies Prof
t, Oleevia Adams
ness Ed & Computer Teacher
kins, Leonia Tompkins
ish Teacher
', Christine Annette
ish & Journalism Teacher
, Carolyn Ann
th Grade Teacher
ni, Frank E.
or High Teacher
Terry Lee
l & Classroom Music Teacher
ll, Jeffrey R.
Calculus Tchr & Curr Dir
Pauline Lau
ese Bilingual Teacher
s, Genevieve Campasano
igual Teacher
ki, Chester Henry
ish & Journalism Teacher
rama, Manuel Santos
ish Teacher
z, Rosa
igual Coordinator
urme, Carol Quagliano
ish Dept Chair & Teacher
verbeek, Gerald Joseph
ner Teacher
n, Taylor
th Grade Teacher
, Carson Ward
ish Professor
juez, Gloria DeLeon'
3rd Grd Biling & Span Tchr
Camille Serritella
d Grade Teacher
ra, Mary, O.P.
th Grade Teacher
go-Perez, Shirley A.
igual Voc Resource Teacher
ry, Janice Marshall
ource & Disciplinarian Tchr

Vinci, Mark Thomas
Math Teacher & Dept Chprsn
Vogler, Candace Arlene
Asst Professor of Philosophy
Vogt, Stephen Carl
Assistant Professor of Finance
Vonnie-Buehlander, Mandy C.
High School Mathematics Tchr
Walas, Renata Jagodzinska
Bilingual Polish Teacher
Walczak, Anthony Michael
School Disciplinarian
Walk, Gloria Chizever
Options Prgm Basic Skills Tchr
Walker, Girod Cassell
Director of Guidance
Waller, Kevin Edward
Govt & US History Teacher
Walton-Todd, Linda
Business & Computer Teacher
Ward, Ellen Maria
English Teacher
Ware, Joseph Edward
Physical Education Teacher
Washington, Beverly Leonard
English Teacher
Washington, Velma
Social Studies Teacher
Wasson, Pamela Reyes
Special Ed Bilingual Teacher
Watson, Lawrence William
Math Instructor
Watts, Celestine
Music Department Chair & Tchr
Weaver, Angela Dawn (Wald)
Biology Teacher
Webb, James Franklin
HS Math & Computer Teacher
Webster, Bonnie Lee
Mathematics Teacher
Weems, Antoinette DuPree
8th Grade Science Teacher
Weinbrenner, Leroy
Chemistry & Physics Teacher
Weiner, Lynn Y.
History Professor
Weiner, Patricia S.
Fifth Grade Teacher
Wells, Pamela (Hampton)
Tchr of Learning Disabilities
Welsch, Thomas Alan
Asst Professor of Accounting
Wenger, John C.
Professor of Mathematics
West, Michael
Counselor
West, Victor Herbert
Chemistry Teacher
Westergren, Gene Frank
High School English Teacher
Wethers, Kandi Bryson
Teacher of Gifted Literature
White, Gregory Paul
Teacher
White, Robert Joseph
HS Music Teacher & Guitar Dir
White, Sylvia Rhodes
7th Grade Teacher
White, Vanessa Marie
Second Grade Teacher
Whited, Wendy Kay
Eighth Grade Teacher
Whitker, Carolyn Miller
Instructional Coordinator
Wilkins, Barbara Jean
Third Grade Teacher
Williams, Alice Stewart
7th-8th Grade Science Teacher
Williams, Carol Traynor
Professor of Humanities
Williams, Cathryn Anette
Professor
Williams, Richard
Professor of Mathematics
Williams, WJ
Assistant Professor
Williams-Elliston, Eleanor Geraldine Key
Assistant Principal
Willis, Reginald Erwyn
Electronic Music Instructor
Wimpffen, Otto R.
Assoc Prof of Bus & Math
Wingert, Mary Catherine
Principal
Winters, Anna Noble
High School English Teacher
Wipachit, Ferdinand
AP Biology Teacher
Wiseman, Kevin J.
8th Grade Teacher
Wittbrodt, Elizabeth Stratton
Associate Professor
Wojton, Gary W.
Physical Education Teacher
Wolen, Arnie
Social Science Teacher
Wolter, Marlene Helen
7th & 8th Grade Teacher
Woolley, Michael F.
History Teacher
Wright, Robin
Prof of Eng & Dir Women's Stud
Wright, Stacy Dione
Third Grade Teacher
Xavier, Searphine Josephraj
Science Teacher
Yates, Elouise Donaldson
7th-8th Grd Language Arts Tchr
Yates, Lottie Turner
Biology Teacher & Dept Chprsn

Yavetsky, Andre N.
Spanish Teacher & Dept Chprsn
Yoksas, Theresa M.
Social Studies Teacher
Young, David James
7th-8th Grade Teacher
Young, Pamela Debra
Physical Education Teacher
Zajac, Judith Mary
English Teacher
Zajicek, Jeronym
Professor of Music
Zambrano, Kathleen Thielemann
English & Business Teacher
Zarnowski, Robert Anthony
7th-8th Grd Teacher of Gifted
Zayid, Hanan Khalil
Fifth Grade Teacher
Zehren, Linda
Kindergarten Teacher
Zevallos, Bettyann (Bervid)
Teacher
Ziencina, Thomas Robert
6th Grade Teacher
Zonsius, Judith
Theology Dept Chair & Teacher
CHICAGO HTS
Anastasia, Lena Rizzo
HS Spanish & Italian Teacher
Baader, Gerladine M.
Grant Director & Comm Liaison
Barrett, Reuben Edward
Assistant Professor of Biology
Boudreau, Kerry L.
Physical Science & Bio Teacher
Centanni, Ronald Paul
Counselor & Dir of Guidance
Clegg, Jantina Dykster huis
Reading & Language Arts Tchr
Dieckman, Sherry
Chemistry & Humanities Teacher
Ferro, Karen S. (Tomnaszewski)
English Teacher
Gliottoni, Cathy S.
Biology & Computer Teacher
Hatfield-Simpson, Nancy Aileen
Mathematics Teacher
Holmes, Nancy R.
Foreign Language Dept Chprsn
Hunt, Pauline Walters
Eighth Grade Soc Stud Tchr
Kneeland, Alexis Y.
PE Teacher
Kowynia, Lisa Marie
English Teacher
Lloyd, Velda Frick
English Teacher
Luna, Evangelina Garza
Kindergarten Teacher
Marwick, Judith D'Arcy
Assoc Prof Math & Dept Chair
Mc Guire, Peter Joseph, Jr.
US History & Sociology Teacher
Mirocha, Nancy Ann (Robeson)
Choral Music Director
Paul, Alvin, III
Professor of Math
Perna, Richard
Dean of Students
Pietrzak, Tony F.
PE & Driver Ed Teacher
Quas, Marilyn E.
Assoc Prof of Physical Sci
Raftery, Michael Patrick
High School English Teacher
Rayon, Marshall Singleton
English & Social Studies Tchr
Sadus, Eugene Frank
Social Studies Teacher
Segert, Richard Ray
Junior High School Teacher
Smith, Sheryl Overheidt
English & Humanities Teacher
Taylor-Drake, Rubye J.
English Professor
Tischauser, Leslie Vincent
History Professor
Vara-Pohlman, Irene Marie
Spanish Teacher
Wilson, Thurman Emory
Professor of Biology
Wright, Judy Ann (Perkins)
Mathematics Teacher
CHICAGO RIDGE
Dahlberg, Patricia Toczek
Reading Teacher
Drew, Carol Marie (Homerding)
Social Studies Teacher
Socha, Maureen O'Connell
Sci, Soc Studies & Eng Tchr
Stein, Kathleen Cassidy
Jr High Teacher
CHILLICOTHE
Dearman, Scott Gregory
Secondary Mathematics Teacher
Flagg, Charles Lee
Art Instructor & Dept Chrmn
Goodin, Antoinette Gill
English Teacher
Howell, Robert C.
Assistant Principal
Kennedy, Diane C.
First Grade Teacher
Lane, Charlotte Anne
7th Grd Soc Stud & Math Tchr
Mercer, Paul LaVerne
Physical Ed Teacher & Coach
O'Boyle, Dennis Stephen
HS PE, Health Tchr & Coach

Stoyak, Daniel P.
High School German Teacher
CHRISMAN
Anglen, Donald Edgar
Math Department Chairman
Good, Shelley S.
6th-8th Grades Math Teacher
Means, Eleanor Webb
First Grade Teacher
Parkinson, Jeffrey Allan
Industrial Technology Teacher
Riggen, Vicki Henry
High School English Teacher
Sims, Debra Throneburg
Vocal Music Teacher
Wright, Diana Lee (Sanquenetti)
Kindergarten Teacher
CHRISTOPHER
Gossett, Jeffrey Dale
Social Studies Instructor
Wheeler, Thomas D.
Physical Education Teacher
Williams, Rita L.
Lit & Gifted Lang Arts Tchr
CICERO
Antus, Robert Lawrence
English Teacher
Blondin Bruton, Mary Ann
Sixth Grade Teacher
Bluemer, Judy E.
Professor of Biology
Boyer, Jane Kay
Sixth Grade Teacher
Carens, Mary Elizabeth
Math Teacher
Cosimano, Carole J.
English & Reading Teacher
Crockett, Janet Kardelis
Instructor of Chemistry
Fenelon, John Edward
Social Studies Teacher
Hanzlik, Joseph S.
Math Teacher
Harris, Deborah Ann
ESL Teacher & Recreation Dir
Ioli, Barbara Auriene
Family & Consumer Sci Tchr
Leitgeb, Paul Fred
High School Teacher
Lucca, Mary Nancy
Sixth Grade Teacher
Martinez, Rito
History Bilingual Teacher
McDaniel, Pamela Harris
Eighth Grade Teacher
Miller, Kimberley Kohnlein
American Studies & Eng Tchr
Murray, Michelle A.
Social Worker
Nawara, Christine M.
Jr HS Teacher & Asst Principal
Pedryc, Wayne Richard
Jr High Social Studies Teacher
Prazak, Bessmarie Kolar
Life Science Teacher
Reynolds, Jane Tomisek
Teacher & Music Department Chm
Schumacher, Barbara Pietras
Kindergarten Teacher
Sheridan, Michael P.
Eng, Speech Tchr, Gifted Coord
Spring-Hodges, Patricia Ellen
Kindergarten Teacher
Sylvester, Marcia Gwen
Jr High Social Studies Tchr
Tanski, Therese M.
High School English Teacher
Turk, Lucia Luchetti
Second Grade Teacher
Volk, Ellen S.
Math Teacher
Watson, Arlene Johnson
English Teacher
CISNE
Keck, Garland Dean
Social Studies Teacher
Liston, Kim Courtright
Jr High Science Teacher
Mooney, Ruby Kathleen
Third Grade Teacher
CISSNA PARK
Lynch, Ron G.
Vocational Agriculture Teacher
CLARENDON HILLS
Gallagher, Sheila S.
Asst Principal & Soc Stud Tchr
Otto, Kathy Jean
Fourth Grade Teacher
CLAY CITY
Patridge, Daniel Joseph
Science, PE Teacher & Coach
CLIFTON
Davidson, Carol I.
Mathematics Teacher
Kohn, Martin Steven
HS & MS Band Director
Krizan, Kathy Ostrowski
English Teacher
Schroeder, Clara Doorn
Combination Pub & Schl Librn
Townsend, Norman P.
10th-12th Grd Soc Studies Tchr
CLINTON
Bowman, Carl David
Bio, Phys Sci & Physics Tchr
Cors, Steven Scott
Mathematics Teacher
Gullone, Gary Paul
Assistant Principal

Jones, D.Ann Moore
Fine Arts Dept Chair & Tchr
Lighthall, Loretta Dixon
Fifth Grade Teacher
Milton, Terry Eugene
Sixth Grade Teacher
Monts, Billiemarie Marshall
High School English Teacher
Wollet, Judith Ann
Fourth Grade Teacher
Zartler, Steven John
Social Studies Teacher
COAL CITY
Crawford, Carol J.
8th Grd Language Arts Teacher
Duffin, Suzanne Mary
English Teacher
Holler, Joyce Guderjan
First Grade Teacher
Magnuson, Martha Ann
Physical Education Teacher
Marizza, Sharon Sue
Retired Sixth Grd Reading Tchr
Quinzio-Zafran, Anna
First Grade Teacher
Smith, Jason
Physics Teacher
Swinney, Jane E.
Chemistry & Mathematics Tchr
Vigna, Dean J.
History Teacher
COAL VALLEY
Matthews, Elaine Sahs
Basic Education Teacher
COFFEEN
Macon, Sheila M. Claybrook
1st Grade Teacher
Rappe, Rose Millburg
Fifth Grade Teacher
COLCHESTER
Bentzinger, Kimberly Rexroat
6th Grade Teacher
Murfin, Max E.
History & Physical Ed Tchr
Nelson, Kristen D.
Science Teacher
Paul, Teri Lynn
Elementary PE Instructor
Shipman, John Duane
Research & Development Shop
COLFAX
Hagenbruch, Louis Francis
HS Mathematics Teacher
Meiner, Paula Keighin
6th Grade Gifted Teacher
Smiley, Marcia Payne
Home Economics Teacher
COLLINSVILLE
Allaria, Jill Patrice
5th Grade Teacher
Beebe, Ellen Tippett
United States History Teacher
Biesendorfer, Robert James
Eight Grade Teacher
Brueggeman, Gail Shadewaldt
Math Teacher
Eschman, Elbert Edward
Physical Education Teacher
Fritzsche, Gail Forshee
Fifth Grade Teacher
Hamilton, Richard A.
Mathematics Teacher
Hotson, Trudie Beth
Social Science Teacher
Huber, Sarah Jane Roberts
Retired Elementary Teacher
Kinder, Sandra Sue (Williams)
Sixth Grade Teacher
Kotras, Donna M. Rice
Academic Coordinator
Lahue, Francis Roma
Retired Teacher
Lang, Alberta Roseboom
English Teacher
McChristian, Timothy S.
Social Studies Teacher
McGarrahan, Catherine Manning
Principal
Nelson, Mark William
Speech, Drama & Sociology Tchr
Ostanik, John Ronald
Business Teacher
Patton, Julia A.
Spanish Teacher
Reichmuth, Sharon Kay
First Grade Teacher
Rincker, Keith Eric
8th Grade Teacher
Santel, Dorene Otte
2nd Grade Teacher
Scogin, Helen L.
Retired Teacher
Sheahan, David Michael
Elementary School Principal
Templeton, Tammie Matthews
Eighth Grd Amer History Tchr
Timko, Richard P.
Counselor & Dept Chair
Tucker, Thomas H.
6th Grd Tchr & Act Coord
Wescoat, Charles S.
Teacher & Coach
Winney, Dianne (Schuette)
Math Teacher
COLONA
Miller, Carol Jean-Wilson
Reading & English Teacher
Yazbec, John Stephen
7th & 8th Grade Science Tchr

COLUMBIA
Burd, Darrell Edward
PE Tchr & Var Bsktbl Coach
Huwer, Dale Lloyd
Health Teacher
Kuni, Rita Marie Niemann
High School Mathematics Tchr
Lanoue, Richard Russell
Chemistry Teacher
Leonard, Debra Elizabeth
Amer, Contemp Lit & Drama Tchr
Maus, Linda Lee
Assistant Public Librarian
Wehrenberg, Jonathan Frederick
Eighth Grade History Teacher
CONCORD
Breese, Stephen Bernard
5th-6th Grade Social Stud Tchr
West, Charles Samuel
Math, Physics & Chemistry Tchr
CORNELL
Morrissey, Marcia Wilson
Fourth Grade Teacher
COTTAGE HILLS
Halliday, Beverley Raye (Weigel)
Second Grade Teacher
COULTERVILLE
Albers, Herman J.
HS Language Arts Teacher
Malott, Amy B.
Fourth Grade Teacher
COUNTRY CLUB HILLS
Anderson, Keith Anthony
Band & Chorus Director
Cappel, Thomas Joseph
Social Studies Tchr & Coach
Carnaghi, Joseph John
Band Director
Egan, Thomas Donald
Science Teacher
Exo, Amy (Dolan)
Mathematics Teacher
Henry, Mary Stancy
Mathematics Teacher
Hughes, Joanne-Elizabeth Davis
Retired Junior High Schl Tchr
Kendrick, Gladys G.
Junior High Counselor
Vickery, Michael
Science Teacher
COWDEN
Conlon, Michael Joseph
HS Social Studies Teacher
Russell, Elizabeth Ann
1st Grade Teacher
CRETE
Barraca, Lynda Roberts
Biology Teacher
Browning, Mark N.
Computer Aided Drafting Tchr
Franze, Wayne
Fourth Grade Teacher
Hickey, Kathleen Dore
Mathematics Teacher
Moore, Stephen E.
English & Humanities Teacher
Stucke, Patricia Ann (Zysk)
High School Science Teacher
Taylor, Marcia Bailey
8th Grade Science Teacher
Thomas, Loretta Tisdel
3rd Grade Teacher
CRYSTAL LAKE
Daly, Mary M.
8th Grd Lang Arts & Rdng Tchr
DeWig, Marge
Fourth Grade Teacher
Hicks, Frances B.
7th Grade Life Science Teacher
Kronewitter, Karen Sipes
6th Grade Teacher
Ludwig, Ronald Patrick
Middle School Principal
Min, Ann Marie Halwix
Math & Science Teacher
Noshay, Linda Henderson
Spanish Teacher
Persky, Scott
Coord & Instr Comp Information
Sayles, John Edward
Chemistry Teacher
Serio, Gus Anthony
Mathematics Teacher
Shearer, Anne Fosler
English & Social Studies Tchr
Stumpf, Donald E.
Health Teacher & Coach
Szalaj, Steven John
Music Teacher & Chorus Dir
Weisman, Mary C.
Mathematics Teacher
CUBA
Falk, Douglas Robert
Agricultural Education Teacher
Harr, Martha A. (Smith)
English Dept Chprsn & Teacher
CULLOM
Mortensen, Elaine Bottcher
Home Economics Teacher
DAKOTA
Hoefle, Margaret Baile
First Grade Teacher
Zaleski, Mary Ann Breske
4th Grade Teacher
DALLAS CITY
Phillips, Carolyn Robinson
Science Teacher
DALZELL
Fanti, Connie L.
1st & 2nd Grade Teacher

DANVILLE
Blue, Nancy Carolyn
Second Grade Teacher
Burns, Gary L.
Science & Bible Teacher
Cornelius, David L.
Mathematics Teacher
Downing, Stephen Michael
Economics Instructor
Eaton, Paulette Houchin
Information Systems Instructor
Hall, Sharon Elizabeth
Latin Teacher
Haurez, Phyllis Dahlquist
Retired Third Grade Teacher
Mickelson, Carol D.
Math Instructor
Miller, Donna Hunley
Language Arts Teacher
Miller, John Mark
History Teacher
Miller, Patricia Ann
Sixth Grade Teacher
Muench, Ann M.
Science Division Instructor
Oakwood, Sharon Sheetinger
Junior High Literature Teacher
Parker, David W.
Sixth Grade Teacher
Pascal, Freddie Stewart
2nd Grade Teacher
Reid, Winifred Simpson
Jr HS Mathematics Teacher
Skaggs, Randy Dean
Physical Education Teacher
Taylor, Christopher Allen
English Teacher
Turner, Judy Kay (Lind)
English Teacher
Weilmuenster, Deborah Letlow
Third Grade Teacher
DARIEN
Brucato, Judy Therese
Spanish Teacher
Camasta, Susan Fullett
Science Teacher
Charters, John R.
English Teacher
Donelan, Kathleen Ann
Third Grade Teacher
Doyle, Linda Kay
Second Grade Teacher
Gianotti, Darlene Ann (Giovanazzi)
5th & 6th Grade Science Tchr
Hanley, Carol Wulfers
Spanish Teacher
Holt, Shelley Johnson
Guidance Counselor
Huber, Judith A.
English Teacher
Kampa, William Dale
English Teacher
Kendrick, Bruce Michael
HS Mathematics Teacher
Kinder, Carol Berglund
Tchr & Dir of Gifted Prgrmng
Kot, Marianne Kathleen
Chemistry Teacher
Lichter, Robert J.
High School Biology Teacher
Malloy, Thomas M.
Social Studies Teacher
Matozzi, Michael Robert
Dean of Students
Maupin, Susan Marmon
Mathematics Department Chair
McDonnell, Suzanne M.
English Teacher
Scott, June Kallal
Counselor & Teacher
Smith, Elizabeth Rose
First Grade Teacher
Stefanos, Elaine Danos
HS Math Teacher
Sweet, Julie Ann
Mathematics Teacher
DE KALB
Abrams, Barbara Krohner
Third Grade Teacher
Bazeli, Marilyn Weerts
Instructional Technology Instr
Cliffe, Daniel P.
Mathematics Teacher & Coach
Engstrom, R. Ellen
Retired 3rd Grade Teacher
Grant, A. J.
English Instructor
Grubb, Daniel D.
Mathematics Professor
Kersten, Bonnie Kerchner
Mathematics Teacher
King, Albert Sidney
Professor of Management
King, Kenneth Paul
Sci Methods Instructor
Lessen, Elliott
Prof & Acting Associate Dean
Merrill, Chris
Technology Education Teacher
Modloff, Jan E.
Spanish Teacher
Moremen, Robin Daralyn
Sociology Professor
Overbeck, Deborah Schroeder
Second Grade Teacher
Richoz, Arthur Vernon
PE Teacher & Athletic Director
Smith, Jay Alan
Physics Teacher

Solomon, Gregory Paul
Speech & English Teacher
Ward, James Philip
Instructor of Management
Wright, Katherine Chatas
Graduate Adv & Instr of Eng
DECATUR
Bartison, Barbara Sue
Fifth Grade Teacher
Bayler, Angela M.
Former Teacher
Berger, Ellen S.
First Grade Teacher
Bodamer, William G.
Professor of Religion
Bolser, Chad Michael
American History Teacher
Bryant, Janice B.
7th-8th Grd Eng & Lit Teacher
Burke, John T.
Chem & Phys Sci Tchr & Coach
Burras, Christine Duggan
5th-8th Grade Science Teacher
Buzan, Beverly Hogan
Nursing Instructor
Cadieux, Marie-Aline
Assistant Professor of Music
Davenport, Stephen M.
English Professor
Davis, Sara Joanne
English Teacher
Donovan, Susan Stogsdill
Elementary Teacher
Downey, Dennis J.
HS Social Science Teacher
Edmonson, Joel Frank
Health, Science & PE Teacher
Farris, Cinda W.
5th-8th Grade Science Teacher
Ferry, Richard E.
Professor of Education
Frazier, Mary Schmidt
Fourth Grade Teacher
German, Phyllis Ann
Elementary Principal
Godin, Diane Evelyn
Professor of Biology
Good, Hugh
HS History & Economics Tchr
Hagenbach, Maryrose Delaney
Principal
Harris, Peter Michael
Middle School Band Director
Jones, James D.
Instructor of Mathematics
Keller, Diane M. Langevin
Theology & Remedial Rdng Tchr
Keller, Kurt A.
Biology, Phys Sci Tchr & Coach
King, Mary Wrigley
Second Grade Teacher
Klaven, Marvin L.
Professor of Art
Lauderdale, B. Jo Putt
English Teacher
Likins, Carolyn Virginia (Lemen)
Asst Professor of Mathematics
Long, Melanie Reed
Stu Assistance Pgm Cnslr & Ldr
Lowry, Gregory R.
Language Arts Teacher
Mc Afee, Nancy Ditmars
First Grade Teacher
McGee, Luegeanes
Asst Professor of Sociology
McMullen, Phillip Allen
Biology, AP & Zoology Instr
Mc Reynolds, Nancy Marie (Bauer)
English & Speech Teacher
Moore, Malcolm W., Jr.
8th Grade Social Studies Tchr
Moyer, James Arthur
Assistant Professor of Music
Myers, Denise
Assistant Professor of Theatre
Nelson, Vickie Haws
Fifth Grade Teacher
Norman, Jeanelle (Tulloss)
Rdng & African-Amer Stud Prof
Parriott, Sherry Fry
German Teacher & Dept Chair
Paul, Dennis Don
Social Studies Teacher
Pressnall, Lonn A.
Professor of Speech & Theatre
Propst, Marilyn Lewis
Math Teacher, Dept Chairperson
Rauff, James V.
Mathematical & Cmptr Sci Prof
Reinhardt, Mary Margaret
Fourth Grade Teacher
Robertson, Marianne Willey
Assistant Professor of Biology
Runnells, Lee Anne
7th-8th Grade Math Teacher
Rusk, Michael L.
Teacher & Soc Studies Dept Chm
Salmi, Lyle J.
Adjunct Asst Professor of Art
Schultz, Katana Lea
Parent Liaison & Counselor
Scott, Milton Elliott
Director of Choirs
Setina, Marilyn Larson
Elementary Education Teacher
Shelton, Ronald Myron
Mathematics Professor Emeritus
Slifer, Carolyn Lowery
Biology Teacher

Smith, Joseph Orpheaus
2nd Grade Teacher & HS Coach
Sperry, Joanne Galloway
Kindergarten Teacher
Thacker, Randall
Principal & Administrator
Tower, Marjorie Emshoff
First Grade Teacher
Valdahl, Cheryl Jean (Ganley)
First Grade Teacher
Vasquez, Susan Habing
Social Studies Teacher
Walczyk, Sarah Jean
Band Director
Wenger, Steven Paul
Fifth Grade Teacher
Wiersig, W. Dan
Principal
Wilks, Mike
Math Teacher & Coach
Williams, Julie Ann (Johnson)
Mathematics Teacher
Wilson, Brenda Sue
Math Teacher
Yonan, Edward Albert
Griswold Distngd Prof of Rel
Zemaitis, Rose Mary (Krolak)
Latin Teacher
DEERFIELD
Doubet, Marvin Eugene
Mathematics Department Chair
Flanagan, Michael James
Computer Lab Director
Foucault, Helen Crowley
History Teacher
Hollenbeck, Donald Tarrence
English Dept Co-Chair
Marks, Lori Ellen
English Journalism Teacher
Moorhatch, Jennifer Johnson
Christian Music Industry Buyer
Rasmussen, Lynda Ann (Nuetzel)
8th Grade US History Teacher
Ritter, David E.
Fine & Applied Arts Dept Chair
Severns, Kay Smith
English Teacher
Weatherby, Linda M.
English Teacher
Wick, Marti Cogen
High School Math Teacher
Williams, Clifford
Philosophy Teacher
DELAVAN
Brown, Robert H.
HS & Jr HS Technology Teacher
Cameron, Marlena Hutton
Librarian
Carr, Sanish LaRay
Math Department Chairman
Meeker, Marcia Schertz
Fourth Grade Teacher
Schroeder, Earlene Hidlebaugh
HS Special Education Teacher
DEPUE
Bachio, Carol Anne
Fourth Grade Teacher
Cocking, Susan Jean (Rietgraf)
English Teacher & Librarian
Gonzalez, Reyes C.
Pre-K at Risk Prgm Tchr Aide
Mc Kee, Larry Everett
Mathematics Teacher
DES PLAINES
Anderson, Sue Marie
Prof of Anatomy & Physiology
Arnold, Annette J.
Eighth Grade Science Teacher
Carman, Terri Spreckman
Elementary School Principal
Dowdy, Luther Earl
Prof of Student Development
Drezdzon, William L.
Professor of Mathematics
Goldstein, Sandi Lee
Second Grade Teacher
Harper, Randall A.
History Teacher
Jerit, Lynda M.
English & History Professor
Kipp, Derril Herbert
Teacher & Coach
Kraft, Robert H.
Lang Arts & Soc Studies Tchr
Majcen, Dawn Karinn
HS Mathematics Teacher
Mc Clure, Matthew K.
Social Science Dept Teacher
Neff, Miriam Janette
High School Counselor
Olsen, Karen Sue
9th-12th Grade PE Teacher
Smith, Richard Frank
Eight Grade Teacher
Tomski, Joel Christopher
Mathematics Teacher
Trotter, Andrew
Mathematics Teacher
Wood, John Charles
Lead Teacher of Art Dept
Zimmerman, Linda Lanoff
Asst Prof of Student Develop
DIETERICH
Brovont, Robert Michael
Fifth Grade Teacher
Hinterscher, Ray Lawrence, Jr.
Math Teacher
Hortenstine, Monique Albert
English Teacher

DIX
Quick, Peggy Wimberly
Asst Principal & 4th Grd Tchr
DIXON
Buzzard, Rothell Dean
Science Teacher
Bzdon, Marcianne
Principal
Clementz, Betty May
French Teacher & Dept Chair
Fletcher, Harry W.
Basketball Coach
Gentry, Rockton Lee
Math Teacher
Heuck, Dale John
Chemistry Professor
Koesler, Donald Steven
Math Instr of Gifted Students
Kuhn, Jeffrey Roger
US History & Government Tchr
Lessner, Patrick R.
Business Education Teacher
Schmelcher, D. Gerald
Social Studies Teacher
Semetis, Ronald S.
Psychology Teacher
Swartz, Ann Kellen
Third Grade Teacher
Upstone, Shirley J.
Third Grade Teacher
Vivian, Shirley F.
Jr High Lang Arts Teacher
Weaver, Jane Cook
High School Counselor
DOLTON
Baker, Suzanne Markvart
Mathematics Teacher
Barclay, Fitz
English Teacher
Baumgart, Edwin
Science & Math Teacher
Brucki, Patricia Trusk
English Teacher
Canik, Orrel Kauffman
French Teacher
Hanson, Sheryl Lynn (Kohlberg)
English Teacher
Nelson-Mc Kenzie, Kristen Marie
High School Science Teacher
Primozic, Janice Koss
Mathematics Teacher
Prince, Darrell L.
Accounting Teacher
Shirley, Terrence James
Physical Ed Teacher & Coach
Simpson, Aimee C.
Retired Spanish Teacher
Stockdale, William O.
Mathematics Teacher
Talley, Lee Robert
HS Radio, TV & Film Instr
Unander, Jane M.
Sixth Grade Teacher
Werling, Margaret L.
Social Studies Teacher
DONGOLA
Woodney, Angie D.
English Teacher
DONOVAN
Klinefelter, David E.
US History & English Teacher
Walker, James Alva
Economics & American Govt Tchr
DORSEY
Schelp, Keith Allen
6th-8th Grd Teacher & Prin
DOW
Taylor, Virginia Lynn
Third Grade Teacher
DOWNERS GROVE
Blonn, Karen Ann
Dance Instructor & Studio Dir
Buckie, Mary B.
Soc Studies & Lit Teacher
Burkle, Pamela Kasch
Middle School Counselor
Christensen, Janice Dayon
Spanish Teacher
Cornwell, Lynn Ann
Spanish Teacher
Cox, Terry L.
HS Social Studies Teacher
Dewbray, Maryalice Maloney
Fifth Grade Teacher
Dinelli, Judith K.
8th Grd Lang Arts & Rdng Tchr
Fiene, Joanne Lynn
Fifth Grade Teacher
Gonciar, John Steven
Mathematics Teacher
Green, Sharon C. (Groh)
Sixth Grade Teacher
Harrold, John Richard
English Teacher
Heggerty, Thomas Michael
First Grade Teacher
Jacobson, Barry
Social Worker & Soccer Coach
Josephson, Colleen Carey
French Teacher
Kayse, Michael Lee
History & Geography Teacher
Keller, Anthony Christian
Social Studies Teacher
Krueger, Jack
Mathematics Tchr & Dept Head
Kunzler, Judith Angone
Fourth Grade Teacher
Loftus, Rita Ann
Science Teacher

IERS GROVE (cont)
ıski, Kathleen Marie
gy Teacher
Sandra Alice Bohn
h Grade Teacher
:, Walter Phillip
l Studies Teacher
c, Diane Kowalski
eacher & Coach
Ronald F.
ce Teacher
), Gail Ruth
eacher & Athletic Director
Jon
Grade Teacher
:, Nancy Sue
nd Grade Teacher
Patricia F. (Bowes)
ergarten Teacher
Mary Lou Sally
ıer of Behavior Disorders
Valerie Dearborn
sh & Acting Teacher
ıal, John Joseph
rade Social Studies Tchr
, Terrett McBrayer
tor of Bands
en, Judith Less
nd Grade Teacher
Robert Scot
sh Teacher
or, Paul Joseph
tor of Bands
IS
de, Mark J.
ry Dept Chair & Teacher
n, Barbara Schafer
ry Teacher
son, Marybeth Newman
sh Teacher
IS
er, Nancy Kay
ce, Math & Soc Stud Tchr
OIN
Barbara Ritter
rade Teacher
ell, Larry A.
h & PE Teacher
Stuart Leon
ipal & Teacher
r, Sarah Lowery
a Specialist
Mae (Maxton)
ry Media Specialist
l, Allan Glenn
peaking, Drama & Eng Tchr
ary, Stephen Michael
& Jr HS Girls Vlybl Coach
e, Ramona Lemmon
Counselor
, Jane Ellen
School Spanish Teacher
rt, Faye Irene
8th Grd English Teacher
, Johanna Ernst
rade Teacher
Kathy Joann
ocial Studies Teacher
Lori Reierson
nd Grade Teacher
AP
gton, John Aaron
cience Teacher
David E.
2th Grade Band Director
ill A.
& Choral Director
s, Arlan D.
Teacher
Elizabeth Love
sh Teacher
Linda J.
sh Teacher

ian, Norma V.
l Science Teacher
Beverly Ann
ness Teacher
, Gary S.
Jr HS PE Teacher
C. Denise Hoffman
al Education Teacher
son, James Crandall
l Studies Teacher
ND
Kathryn Marlo
& Language Arts Teacher
feld, Christian James
ocial Studies Teacher
s, Kathryn Anderson
& Theatre Teacher
ellan, Patricia Goodwin
rade English Teacher
HT
, Carol Ann
sh Teacher
g, Paula Smith
Grade Teacher
John Ronald
Teacher
ve, Roxanne Marie (Tanner)
th Grade Lang Arts Tchr
, Dolores Joann Simmons
ed Teacher
Karen Lea
Con Sci Tchr & FHA Adv
on, Thomas H.
sh Teacher
baum, Linda Jean
nd Grade Teacher

White, Julia Mary (Ryan)
3rd Grade Teacher
EAST ALTON
DiPaolo, Marcella K.
7th Grade Teacher
Harrison, Deanne Elizabeth Adams
Health, Lit & Science Teacher
Roberts, Karen Louise Kissack
Fifth Grade Teacher
EAST MOLINE
Cumberworth, Tiffany Jean
8th Grade Langauge Arts Tchr
De Meulenaire, Janet Ann
Science & Art Teacher
Diaz, Jose V.
Dean of Students
Ertel, Constance M.
Jr HS Social Studies Teacher
Gellerman, Gary E.
Mathematics Teacher
Golby, Martin Jay
English & Speech Teacher
Hagg, Jeanne Rosczyk
Third Grade Teacher
Hunter, Scott
Physical Education Teacher
Peterson, Marsha Lyons
English Teacher
Simmons, Hugh F.
Business Ed Tchr & Tech Coord
Stiegel, Helen Jannes
Business Teacher
Tyler, Theodore R.
Physics Teacher
Wiborg, Daniel E.
Art Teacher
EAST PEORIA
Armon, John Anthony
Mathematics Instructor
Baker, Roger K.
Prof of Bus & Information Syst
Barr, Verona (Marx)
Biology Instructor
Becker, Susan Schwandt
Professor of English
Cimadevilla, Maria V.
International Business Instr
Dwyer, Margaret Ann
English Teacher
Emerson, Cheryl Renee
Earth Science Professor
Estes, T. Scott
8th Grade US History Teacher
Gasparovich, Sandra Augsberger
Sci Tchr
Hoffmann, Richard Lee
Emeritus Professor of Chem
Hofreiter, Dierk Lewis
Physics Instructor
Holmes, Tubal C.
Professor of Music
Jacobson, Kristen Anna
Biology Instructor
Jarboe, Gerald Neil
Physics Professor
Karcher, Jan
First Grade Teacher
Kelch, Denise Marie (Hager)
Speech Communication Instr
Lyle, Valeska Terry
Academic & Adult Re-Entry Adv
Ostrowski, Ralph John
Professor of Accountancy
Pagel, Mark A.
Middle School Math Teacher
Pederson, Mary Beth Maurer
Mathematics Assistant Prof
Resutko, Lawrence
Geography Teacher
Rush, Stanley William
Electronics Instructor
Sandoval, John Michael
High School Mathematics Tchr
Sheldon, Robert
Band Director
Strasma, Kip D.
Assistant Professor of English
Swayne, James Richard
Professor of Computer Science
Walker, Champ E.
US & World History Teacher
Westler, Lin Susan
Biology & Physiology Teacher
Witherell, Andria Lane
Physical Education Teacher
Zaiser, Susan Ann
Business Teacher & Coordinator
EAST SAINT LOUIS
Brimm, Wardell Clifford
English Teacher
Chatman, Glenda Reed
Title 1 Teacher
Fentress, Angela
Early Chldhd Education Instr
Griffin, Lorelei Warren
Choral Music & Spanish Teacher
Griffin, Luereatha Jones
1st Grade Teacher-in-Charge
Griffin, Rose Marie
2nd Grade Teacher
Humphrey, Gracie L.
WECEP Coordinator
Massenburg, Doris Evelyn
English Teacher
Mayes, Mary Ann (Kovachich)
English Teacher
Nelson, Alonzo Ellery, Sr.
Math Teacher
Packer, Ida M. (Fields)
Business Education Teacher

Peterson, Mary Elizabeth Stein
2nd & 3rd Grade Teacher
Ransom, Charles Edward
Mathematics Teacher
Shaw, Evelyn Smallwood
American History Teacher
Smith, Leslie
High School Mathematics Tchr
Swiener, Rita Rochelle
Professor of Psychology
EDGEWOOD
Sherrick, Sally Metzelaars
4th Grade Teacher
EDINBURG
Jones, Kenneth D.
Math Teacher & Coach
EDWARDSVILLE
Elzinga, Laurel Susan (Hill)
Educational Consultant
Hansen, Linda Louise (Filippi)
Second Grade Teacher
Hastings, Kathleen Gutzler
3rd Grade Teacher
Lipe, David T. J.
English Teacher & Tennis Coach
Lybarger, Susan Elaine
Sixth Grade Teacher
Motley, Kate Richards
English Teacher
Nungesser, Christine Bachman
Eighth Grade Teacher
Peterson, Carol Ann Hackworth
Second Grade Teacher
Stallings, Maria
English Teacher
Swalley, Gary W.
Jr High Social Studies Teacher
Swanner, Jeanne Hannon
Former Biological Sci Tchr
Symanski, Joseph A.
Psych & Global Studies Teacher
Waldo, Michael Ray
Special Education Teacher
Wappelhorst, Alexandra Ellouise
Counselor
Wheat, Kenneth Ray
Biology Teacher
Whittaker, Sharon A.
7th Grd Eng & Soc Stud Teacher
Woelfel, Charnell Hudgens
Spanish Teacher
Wolf, Susan Lemanis
Fourth Grade Teacher
EFFINGHAM
Brown, Kent D.
Speech Teacher & Video Dir
Collins, Janie L.
8th Grd Eng & Lit Teacher
Fatheree, Joseph G.
History Instructor
Groothuis, Monte
Substitute Teacher
Hawkins, Phil
English Teacher
Klosterman, Robin A.
English Teacher
Koester, Irene Scmidt
Religion Teacher & Dept Chair
Luchtefeld, Judy Wilkens
6th-8th Grade Lang Arts Tchr
Pickett, Marlene Brumleve
French Teacher
Pickett, Steven Harold
8th Grd Lang Arts & Rdng Tchr
Rubach, Wayne Dale
Vocational Teacher & Coach
Shull, Sharon Mc Mechan
English Teacher
Tuman, Tracy Long
Spanish Teacher
Warner, Nina Happe
Fifth Grade Teacher
Willsey, Raymond Richard, Jr.
Band Director
Wood, Mary Patricia (Owen)
Reading & Soc Studies Teacher
EL PASO
Lindsey, Jennifer Rose
Fourth Grade Teacher
Loper, Lucy Stevenson
Frosh & Soph English Teacher
Musick, Marilyn Sampson
6th-12th Grd Vocal Music Tchr
Tipler, Daisy Finney
Fourth Grade Teacher
ELDORADO
Cox, Jeffrey Dale
Art Teacher
Roberts, Deb Starnes
Middle School Art Teacher
Simpson, Linda Sue Bundren
5th Grd Social Studies Teacher
ELGIN
Arnet, Robert Charles
Bio & Environmental Sci Tchr
Bertrand, Christine Frances
First Grade Classroom Teacher
Blaus, Robert A.
Chemistry Teacher
Brown, David Lanier
Honors Bio Tchr & Admin
Brown, Judith Cain
5th Grade Teacher
Buckley-Hunter, Brenda
Theatre Arts Dir & Assoc Prof
Cerio, Carol Lynn
High School Guidance Counselor
Craig, Melissa Mc Millin
8th Grade Teacher

DePue, Carol E. (Hamann)
Family & Consumer Science Tchr
Dix, Kevin
Business, Ec & Govt Teacher
Duffy, John L.
Latin Tchr, Eng & Reading Chm
Grabenkort, Susan Stoneall
Sixth Grade Teacher
Grohs, Gary Robert
HS Mathematics Teacher
Haefliger, Donald Jerome
English Dept Chairman & Instr
Hamachek, Laurie Ann
Spanish Teacher
Hawkins, James Alan
School Social Worker
Henry, Sharon A.
Associate Professor of Nursing
Himley, Barbara (Stoll)
English Teacher
Klatt, William Lynn
Mathematics Teacher
Kummer, Loretta (Holm)
Mathematics Teacher
Lamdfear, Mollie Ehle
Family & Consumer Sci Tchr
Lapetina, Maggie Hunt
English Teacher
Larson, Richard Joseph
American Studies Teacher
Lindert-Vazquez, Nancy Ann
Spanish Teacher
Mahoney, Doreen Erin
Math Teacher
Marciniec, Peggy Van Leirsburg
Third Grade Teacher
McGlothlen, Elvera Tegnelia
Bilingual Teacher
Meaney, Thomas Joseph
Business Teacher & Coach
Mendro, Al
Math Teacher
Miller, Betty Madsen
US History & Reading Teacher
Monkemeyer, Joy Joanne
6th-8th Grade Teacher
Newton, Gary Bruce
Chemistry Teacher
O'Kelley, Connie Mc Intosh
Math Teacher
Olofson, Steven A.
Sixth Grade Teacher
Ostwald, Ray E.
Orchestra Director
Pellicore, Joyce Marie
8th Grade US History Teacher
Perkins, Margaret Ruth
Fifth Grade Teacher
Peters, Sandra Ormsbee
Special Education Teacher
Peto, Carole Loman
8th Grade English Teacher
Price, William Ralph
English Teacher
Przybylski, Brian E.
Math Teacher
Rhode, Mark Paul
Chemistry Instructor
Rich, Linda Arrington
Fifth Grade Teacher
Roll, M. Jane (Cope)
English Teacher
Roome, Bernice Helene
English Teacher
Rothlisberger, Jeanne Miller
Math Teacher
Saiz, David
Physics Teacher
Schmidt, Gary Paul
Mathematics Teacher
Sellers, Laura Kloss
Guidance Counselor
Springer, Carolyn A.
AP Biology Teacher
Steinbach, Robert Dale
Professor of Biology
Swanson, Carol Linnell
First Grade Teacher
Tabbert, Jacquelyn Farrell
Home Economics Teacher
Takacs, Erika Porer
German Teacher
Thomas, Richard Clayton
Psychology & Economics Teacher
Thorne, Susan Kuriga
Orchestra Director
Tombaugh, Paul
Science Teacher
Tuin, Jon Allen
Fifth Grade Teacher
Turnquist, Jerry L.
Science, Math & His Teacher
Wallace, Juli Whitmer
4th Grade Teacher
Wascher, Barbara Royer
Professor
Whitmer, Lisa Ann
High School English Teacher
Wilson, Patrick James
Geography Teacher
Wince, Richard D.
Dir of Pupil Personnel Svcs
Zuniga, Elizabeth Hampton
English Teacher
Zurek, Christine S. (Malocha)
Mathematics Teacher
ELIZABETH
Brown, Donna Limage
2nd Grade Teacher

Farral, Shari A.
English Teacher
ELIZABETHTOWN
Hastie, Rita Suits
Kindergarten Teacher
Humphrey, Tim
Jr HS Social Studies Teacher
Ledbetter, Patricia Pearson
Substitute Teacher
ELK GROVE VILLAGE
Berner, Dennis Joseph
Humanities Teacher
Blasucci, John T.
Humanities & English Teacher
Brackney, Kathryn Herbert
Fifth Grade Teacher
Brown, Robert S.
6th Grade Teacher
Fraser, Jane V.
Eng Tchr, Writing Center Coord
Gould, Jill Kay (Driggs)
7th Grd Language Arts Teacher
Johnson, Linda Barkoo
Literature Dept Chair
Krzywicki, Joanna Infantino
7th & 8th Grd Lang Arts Tchr
Presley, LaVonne Theis
Fourth Grade Teacher
Rosenstein, Marianne Prefer
Mathematics Teacher
Spangler, Raymond I.
5th Grade Teacher
Trent, Richard
Chemistry Teacher
Vance, Karen Johnson
Second Grade Teacher
ELKHART
Gleason, Karen Marie (Svenson)
First Grade Teacher
Radtke, Mary Ann (Gasaway)
Third Grade Teacher
ELKVILLE
Piper, Donna F.
HS Cheer Coach & Supt Sec
ELLIS GROVE
Hughes, Lynn Montroy
Former Lang Arts Tchr
ELMHURST
Anstett, Thomas C.
Eng Tchr & Var Bsktbl Coach
Arado, Marilyn Sereno
Retired Elementary Teacher
Bachr, Marie
Associate Professor of Physics
Bassett, Larry Charles
Electrncs Instr & Co-op Coord
Bredehoft, David Paul
Music Director & Minister
Carr, Lorraine Grandys
Third Grade Teacher
Caruso, Christine
Ret Lang Arts Tchr & Chprsn
Coons, David Michael
Industrial Technology Teacher
Franz, Jean May
4th Grade Tchr
Medema, Richard Andrew
Guidance Counselor
O'Fallon, David Edward
Assistant Professor of Music
Payne, Michael James
Asst Prof of Communication
Peterson, Margaret L.
Art Dept & Photography Tchr
Poltrock, Naomi E.
Eighth Grd Soc Studies Tchr
Salvo, Bonnie Margaret
School Social Worker
Thomas, Cindy Marie (Wojcik)
High School English Teacher
Tice, Michael D.
Social Science Teacher
Torney, Michael D.
HS Social Studies Teacher
Venetucci, David Alan
Jrnlsm & Speech Comm Teacher
Wetta, David Paul
English Teacher
ELMWOOD
Charlesworth, Kent E.
Math & Computer Sci Teacher
Welch, Lynette Ann
Spanish Teacher
ELSAH
Glen, John Mason
Assistant Professor of History
ERIE
Alepra, Anne Murphy
English Teacher
Ludwig, William Charles
English Dept Chm & Teacher
Windish, Laura Denaque
HS Spanish Teacher
EUREKA
Barth, Joe
Assoc Prof of Physical Ed
Ewan, Sue A.
Science Teacher
Griffith, Richard F.
Chemistry & Physics Teacher
Hartter, Beverly Jo (Stock)
Associate Professor of Math
Hohulin, William S.
Social Studies Teacher
Houch, Debra Ahrens
Third Grade Teacher
Knapp, Edie Schaffer
Science Teacher
Logsdon, Loren L.
Professor of English

EUREKA (cont)
Mc Collum, H. Warner
Assoc Prof of PE & Ath Dir
Small, Paul Keith
Associate Professor of Biology
Spanbauer, Jeffrey Alan
Social Studies Teacher
Sweitzer, Karen Marie
Assoc Prof of PE & Coach
Vijitha-Kumara, Kanaka
Computer Science Professor
EVANSTON
Albiani, Ronald M.
Retired Psychology Instructor
Berry, Melvin Lorenzo
Math Teacher
Berry, Neidra Ellen Webb
Kindergarten Teacher
Brady, Charles Anthony
History & Social Science Tchr
Broadbelt, Linda J.
Asst Prof of Chem Engrng
Carlini, James
Adj Prof of Telecommunications
DeWald, Renee Demetra
Science Teacher
Doud, Dennis Adair
Humanities & History Teacher
Eddy, Bruce L.
US History Teacher
Fernandez, Marta
Spanish Teacher
Fodor, David B.
Music Teacher
Giles, Jeffrey Robert
Self-Contained & Math Teacher
Goranson, Linda Sayka
English & Reading Teacher
Gordon, Julie Peyton
Executive Director
Hill, Christopher
Science Teacher
Kreutzer, Cynthia L.
4th & 5th Grade Teacher
Larson, Mark A.
High School English Teacher
Lieberman, Syd
English Teacher
Mitchell, Bruce Eardley
English Teacher
Ngoi, Mephie K.
AP Chemistry Teacher
Onofrey, David Charles
Junior High Language Arts Tchr
Ratner, Mark A.
Professor of Chemistry
Stern, Malcolm E.
English Dept Chair
Taylor, Clayton Embry, Jr.
History & Social Studies Tchr
EVERGREEN PARK
Fagerstrom, Sherrie Smith
Former Elem Tchr
Olson, Robert Michael
Technology Coordinator
O'Neill, Patricia Donati
Substitute Teacher
EWING
Goss, David E.
Soc Studies & Lang Arts Tchr
Rountree, Sue R. (Stover)
Fourth Grade Teacher
FAIRBURY
Butts, Jeffrey Kimbro
Athletic Dir & Health Teacher
Loy, Christy Wolfer
English Teacher
Quinn, Michael John
Guidance Counselor
Ropp, Darren Lee
Agriculture Teacher
FAIRFIELD
Aldrich, Monty Kenth
Business Tech & English Tchr
Brewer, Julia Elizabeth
English Teacher
Doty, Kathy Runyon
Business & Economics Instr
Helm, Brenda K.
Success Network Advisor
Kinney, Loretta
English Teacher
Leighty, Marc
Social Studies Teacher
Liston, Steve
Science Teacher
Queener, Mary Julian
Former Fifth Grade Teacher
Robbins, Pamela Stewart
Fam & Consumer Sci Teacher
Spence, Forrestine Warren
Third Grade Teacher
Warkins, Mardi Holtkamp
Computer Coordinator
Zimmerman, Karen Johnson
Fourth Grade Teacher
FAIRVIEW HEIGHTS
Akridge, MaryEllen A. Miller
Social Studies & Lit Teacher
DeMerath, Marta (Palen)
4th-8th Grade Band Director
Frazier, Nancy L.
Retired 5th & 6th Grd Eng Tchr
Fuhrhop, Mary (Toler)
Kindergarten Teacher
Holland, Paul M.
Soc Stud Tchr, Dean of Studnts
Lucarelli, Mary Anne
Second Grade Teacher
Quain, Beth Conroy
Speech Language Pathologist
FARINA
Burgess, Steve
Driver, Consumer & Phy Ed Tchr
FARMER CITY
Brackenhoff, Darby Eubank
Retired High School Teacher
Cribbett, Gwen Marie
History & Social Studies Tchr
Drake, Patricia Reilly
English Tchr & Tech Prep Coord
Hawkins, Lynn Allen
Guidance Counselor
Hawn, Jerry W.
High Schl Bible & Math Teacher
Hendricks, Michael Hall
Chemistry & Physics Teacher
Luck, Mary Rowland
Retired Primary Grades Teacher
Springer, Kathleen Rae
Spanish Teacher
Vaughan, Susan Jill
High School Biology Teacher
White, Allison Hoffmeyer
Principal
FARMERSVILLE
Harms, P. Gale
5th-6th Grd Tchr, Co-Principal
FARMINGTON
Bruniga, Marianthe Gartelos
Speech, Eng & Drama Teacher
Duchardt, Linda A. (Williams)
Kindergarten Teacher
Ellberg, Hazel L.
English Teacher
Faralli, M. Kay (Nichols)
Fourth Grade Teacher
Hickenbottom, Loren W.
Agriculture Education Instr
Sullivan, Ann M.
Biology & Anatomy Teacher
FINDLAY
Baker, Stephen Andrew
Sixth Grade Tchr & Pgm Coord
Bruyn, Shari L. Traughber
Math Teacher
Ryan, W. Kaye
Fifth Grade Teacher
Wilson, Ann
Business Teacher
FISHER
Musson, Robin Lynn
Biology & Math Teacher
FITHIAN
Anderson, Norma Kiifner
Spanish & Biology Teacher
Clow, Deborah Elaine
Chemistry & Physics Teacher
Lee, Timothy E.
Social Studies Teacher
FLANAGAN
Hart, Beverly Ann
High School English Teacher
Kapraun, Peg A.
Mathematics Teacher
Peterson, Gregory Jay
Biology, Health Tchr & Coach
FLORA
Healy, Julie Michelle
Biology Teacher
Koontz, David Howard
Junior High Band Director
McQuiston, Christine J.
HS English & History Teacher
Upton, Debbie L.
Jr High Math & Algebra Tchr
FLOSSMOOR
Boettcher, David George
English & Theater Teacher
Bonavia, Jill Marie
English Teacher
Chasey, James Charles
Economics Teacher
Du Bois, Frank J.
Guidance Counselor
Golich, Mary Ellen
French Teacher
Kelley-Fernandez, Nancy
English & Journalism Teacher
MacLean, Lynn (Billmeyer)
Junior High English Teacher
Moschel, Richard Leonard
US His Tchr & Dean of Stdnts
Mosher, Nancy Ann
Science Teacher
O Keefe, Thomas H.
English Teacher
Pries, Kenneth
English Teacher
Rezny, Karen S.
English Teacher
Simpson, Donna Monique
Mathematics Department Chprsn
FOREST PARK
Brod, Charles W.
Teacher & Assistant Principal
Carlisle, Marie Johnson
Title I Teacher
Fedorski, Mary Halpin
First Grade Teacher
LeFevour, Dee Kiley
Fifth Grade Teacher
Saunders, David Russell
6th Grade & Soc Stud Teacher
FORRESTON
Asp, Sharon Zumdahl
Art Teacher
Mc Morris, Donald Gene
High School Counselor
FORSYTH
Parrish, L. Kathleen
First Grade Teacher
FOX LAKE
Baron, Thomas F.
Mathematics Teacher
Cittadino, Frank, Jr.
HS His Tchr & Athletic Dir
Garlanger, Andrea L.
Biology Teacher
Hofeldt, Glenn Arthur
Science Teacher
Kapraun, David Francis
Industrial Tech Teacher & Dean
Kennedy, James S.
5th Grade Teacher
Klippert, Brian Allen
Math Teacher
Multra, James Carl
Social Science & English Tchr
Murphy, Karen Leah
Math, Sci Tchr & Div Chprsn
Schuenemann, Sandra J.
Lang Art Tchr & Curr Dir
Vida, Diane
Dir of Hum & Gifted Coord
FOX RIVER GROVE
Bruhn, Kenneth L.
Retired Educator
FRANKFORT
Coughlin, Kimberly Ann (Luce)
5th-8th Grade Band Director
Davis, Aimee Lynn
English Teacher
Griffith, Kathleen Gerrity
Specialized Instruction Tchr
Hattendorf, Diane L.
First Grade Teacher
Heilman, Jeannine Marie
Mathematics Teacher
Holmquist, Darrell G.
US History Teacher
Hopper, Colin Lee
Honors American History Tchr
Huddleston, Ronald Duane
Eng Tchr & Asst Dean of Stdnts
Kohlbacher, Pamela Fiocca
Fourth Grade Teacher
Lopez, Susan Crowley
6th Grade Teacher
McCormick, Jillene Ann
Biology & Chemistry Teacher
Pesavento, Paul Anthony
Western Civilization Tchr
Schaefer, Pamela Joan
Fourth Grade Teacher
Scheer, Bridget J. Whelan
10th Grade History Teacher
Stipanovich, Mary Jane
Foreign Language Teacher
Thompson, Laura Lynne
Spanish Teacher
Thompson, Patricia A.
English Teacher
Weber, Tracy Dawn
Mathematics Teacher
Yos, Jennifer Gail
English Teacher
FRANKLIN
Morris, Jonathan Eugene
Ag & Horticulture Instr
Pearson, Laura Lee
Sixth Grade Teacher
Smith, Rick W.
Math Teacher & Athletic Dir
FRANKLIN GROVE
Dillon, Dolores C. (Schafer)
Retired Third Grade Teacher
Kleinmaier, Bruce Joseph
HS Social Studies Teacher
FRANKLIN PARK
Duffey, George L.
Physical Education Teacher
Kibiloski, Eileen F.
Family & Consumer Science Tchr
Liesz, James Allen
English Teacher
Lilly, Christopher James
Eng III Hnrs & AP Teacher
Masters, Tom M.
English Teacher
FREEBURG
Bayers, Jack R.
Physical Education Teacher
Butcher, Gordon Wayne
Social Studies Teacher
Elkins, Don Robert
History & Drivers Ed Teacher
Fahrner, David Michael
High School Science Teacher
Frerking, Gregory Allan
Mathematics Teacher
Glaus, Marilyn A.
Home Economics Teacher
Greenlee, Renee (Smith)
High School English Teacher
Heidenreich, Elaine Marie
Fifth Grade Teacher
Hughes, Sammy L.
Driver's Ed Tchr & Track Coach
Mitchell, Kimberly Terece
Former Teacher
Nash, Karen Rae
Mathematics Teacher
Opperman, Brenda Sue
MS Science & History Teacher
Reavis, Dale Dean
Eng Dept Chprsn & Instructor
Smithson, James Michael
Tchr of Industrial Technology
FREEPORT
Bangasser, Vi E.
Math & Computer Science Instr
Barger, JIll Schiesser
English Teacher
Bausman, Darryl W.
Retired Teacher
Benoit, A. Douglas
English & Drama Teacher
Bicker, Mary Alice (Plager)
Third Grade Teacher
Budden, Kevin
Math, Computer Teacher & Coach
Buss, George A.
Life Science Teacher
Connors, Timothy R.
Director of Speech & Theatre
Currier, Judy Burchett
4th Grade Tchr of Gifted
Daniels, George William
Band Director
DeGraw, W. P.
Fifth Grade Teacher
De Hahn, Jean
5th Grade Teacher
Dittmar, Susan Jane (Kottke)
Business Education Teacher
Everding, Paul Robert
History & Journalism Teacher
Felder, Sheila Kennerly
Orchestra Director
Finch, Edward F.
American Studies Instructor
Firebaugh, Douglas B.
Chem Teacher & Sci Dept Chm
Friedenbach, Penni Drosopoulos
Third Grade Teacher
Juergens, Harlan Keith
Third Grade Teacher
Kiser, Kenneth Paul
Social Studies Instructor
Kolcharno, Richard J.
Principal & Supervisor
Marquard, Joan Ellen
Retired 1st Grade Teacher
Marske, Linda Patrick
English & Speech Tchr
Martin, Thelma Crawford
6th Grade Teacher
Mikkelsen, Kathleen Boggs
French Teacher
Nason, Christine Lorreen
Fifth Grade Teacher
Niles, William T.
Teacher of Gifted
Regan, Diane Marie (Ballard)
US History & Spec Ed Teacher
Roemer, Terri Lyn
Biology & Chemistry Teacher
Schirmer, Patricia Harring
English Teacher & Librarian
Soukup, Norman Lee
Mathematics Professor
Tellefson, Roberta Andrews
High School Mathematics Tchr
Tellefson, Steven K.
Physics, Chem & Aviation Tchr
Wendt, Phyllis Jeanette
Third Grade Teacher
Zulke, Shirley Maxwell
Co-Chair of Development
FULTON
Cornelius, Sandra K.
Math Teacher & Dept Chairman
Goodenough, Lisa Kay (Ottens)
Spanish Teacher
Johnson, Tamara Kay
Business & Computer Teacher
Koehn, Ronald Herman
Social Studies Instructor
Martinez, Jack D.
Band Director
Widbin, Nancy J.
English Teacher
GAGES LAKE
Jankovich, Donald Dean
Special Education B D
GALENA
Cording, Deanna Sue
English Teacher
Howard, Linda J.
English Teacher
Sciutto, Michael Lynn
Guidance Counselor
GALESBURG
Andersen, Roy Robert
Timme Professor of Economics
Armstrong, Gary Michael
Fifth Grade & Computer Teacher
Banks, Sandra Kay
German & Mathematics Teacher
Brown, Robert Odell
Instructor
Burgess, Joe Franklin, Jr.
Principal
Bushnell, Cheryl K. Buckingham
Comp Instructor & Lib Director
Coleman, Rena Marie (Griffin)
Title I Outreach Coord
Corpuz, Isabel Navasca
Third Grade Teacher
Devore, Hal
Soc Studies Tchr & Dept Chair
Ehrenhardt, Deborah Ann (Anderson)
Home Living Teacher
Eisemann, Rosemary Godsil
Mathematics Teacher
Ferguson, Steve R.
Art Teacher
Gold, Penny Schine
History Professor
Graham, James M.
Political Science Professor
Henley, Fran (Bradburn)
Fourth Grade Teacher
Jacobs, James Vernon
5th Grade Teacher
Johnson, Susan L.
Social Science Instructor
Kerber, Rob M.
Physical Education Teacher
Kessler, John L.
Retired Math Dept Chairman
Lacy, Jared W.
Jr High Art Instructor
LaDage, Janet Peterson
Business Instructor
Lytle, Barry Thomas
Art Teacher
Maurizi, Kenneth Rudolph
Biology Teacher
Morgan, Robert Lee
Retired PE & Health Teacher
Myers, Tammy Walker
Third Grade Teacher
Nicely, Eunice Deffenbaugh
Retired Third Grade Teacher
Perry, Shirley Tucker
3rd Grade Teacher
Qualls, Tamera Lee
English Teacher
Rubinfeld, Judith Ann (Cotton)
Second Grade Teacher
Schulz, Faye Diament
Mathematics Teacher
Spencer, Bruce Edward
Sci Dept Chm & Chem Tchr
Todd, Thomas Davidson
Coord of Criminal Justice
Wessels, Becky Mitchell
Fourth Grade Teacher
Willy, Patricia Clayton
Science Teacher
Wujek, David Stephen
Biology Instructor
GALVA
Milroy, Amy Beth
Social Studies Teacher
GARDNER
Coulter, Julienne E.
English Teacher
Egleton, James Joseph
Science Teacher
Rinehart, Debra Caspary
Jr High Language Arts Teacher
Siders, Richard Dean
High School English Teacher
GENESEO
Benson, Colleen L.
Teacher & Frgn Lang Dept Head
Durian, Pamela Jane (Hasselbusch)
Junior High English Teacher
Dwyer, Joy Asplund
Third Grade Teacher
Garlick, Serena Sue
Assistant Principal
Gronski, Tammy Alan
HS Business & Computer Teacher
Heiberger, Elizabeth Susan
Chem Teacher & Sci Dept Chair
Kalscheur, Jean Antoinette
Retired 5th Grade Teacher
Lo Giudice, Mary Oberle
Spanish Teacher
Roeder, Linda Susan
Third Grade Teacher
Sieben, Marilyn Kay (Maynard)
English Teacher
GENEVA
Dispensa, Cheryl Britton
Science Teacher
Gannon, Kevin
Science Dept Chair & Bio Tchr
Krieger, Julie Eckstrom
High School English Teacher
Schaus, Jon Michael
Phys Ed & Driver Ed Teacher
Thostenson, Gib John
English Teacher
GENOA
Crabel, Richard
Physical Education Teacher
Dorn, Gary William
Sixth Grade Teacher
GEORGETOWN
Brackney, James Ray
Social Studies Teacher
Hall, Jane Knowles
Cross Cat Teacher
Trahan, P. Jestin
Retired French & English Tchr
Wasko, Dolores Hughes
8th Grade Language Arts Tchr
Wright, Mark Stanley
Ag Education Teacher
GERMAN VALLEY
Bruning, Lucille Phyllis
Elementary Private Tutor
GERMANTOWN
Albu, Raymond
5th Grade Teacher
Buller, Cathleen Duncan
PE & Teacher of Gifted
GIBSON CITY
Petersen, Cindy Adreon
Kindergarten Teacher
Titus, Frank Michael
Band Director

ESPIE
kamp, Alice Smith
ed Home Economics Teacher
oy, Kay Jean
lle & High School Teacher
o, Cindy Wilde
uage Arts Teacher
er, Vickie Jackson
ness Teacher
rt, Suzanne Salic
l Music Instructor
RD
Sharon Kaufman
8th Grd Language Arts Tchr
s, Dorothy Dorband
ed Elementary Teacher
Rick E.
ish Teacher
rs, Robert L.
ance Counselor & Hlth Tchr
, Deborah
nce Teacher
hs, Melba J.
ed Teacher
, David Lance
ematics Teacher
James L.
ematics & Computer Teacher
Patricia Ann
ness Teacher
Leonard Stephen
al Studies Teacher
ELLYN
an, Deborah
c Professor of English
ht, Mary Lou McKay
Grade Teacher
son, Barbara Jean (Kleist)
ciate Professor of Biology
icks, Laura Riley
c Prof of English
logun, Adenuga Olatunde
c Prof of Engrng & Physics
n, Lesli Barger
stant Prof of Anthropology
s, Brian
tsng & Design Instructor
, Susan K.
Teacher
d, Mark Timothy
nan Teacher
aura Gillette
ogy & Chemistry Teacher
ord, Cindy Boyd
ory Instructor
Jeffrey Nicholls
ography Chair & Professor
man, Lynda Joyce
ogy Instructor
A. Valerie
uctor
veld, Paul John
ematics Instructor
aum, Charles Otto
ropology & Religion Prof
aum, Gail Mattson
Math, Eng & Gifted Teacher
gi, Rita Anne
d Grade Teacher
y, Sandra Rohlfing
Grade Teacher
er, Bill
nce Teacher
, Henry Charles
US History & Ec Tchr
nstedt, Robert Joseph
& Psychology Instructor
Raymond J.
ematics Teacher
Ellen Jo (Szabad)
ish & PBL Resource Tchr
s, Laurie
c Prof of Travel & Tourism
v, Douglas M.
Department Chairperson
Becky Campbell
Grade Teacher
Jeffrey Alan
ciate Professor of Physics
, Gina M.
ram Director
, Daniel Richard
ic Teacher
, Christine N.
8th Grd Language Arts Tchr
, Robert L.
essor of Psychology
s, William Frederick
al Science Instructor
s, Stephanie Sophia (Bezanes)
Vocal Music Teacher
rove, Alice M.
ors Pgm Coordinator
, Mark A.
cial Ed Tchr & Dept Chair
erilyn Ann
& PE Dept Chair
lani, Bert Howard
uctor of Biology
Eileen Moriarty
c Professor of Humanities
um, Steven Edward
ish Teacher & Drama Coach
ane Jaijing
stant Professor of History
ICOE
Suzanne M.
Grade Teacher

GLENDALE HEIGHTS
Martello, Debra Ann
Science & Language Arts Tchr
Mayer, Matt A.
Art Teacher
GLENVIEW
Cadwell, Kathleen Holland
2nd Grade Teacher
Davis, John Raymond
Physical Education Teacher
Fiorio, Lee G.
Technology Teacher
Glazer, Evan Michael
Mathematics Teacher
Gregory, Gail Ann
Home Economics Teacher
Herzog, Paul H.
HS Guidance Counselor
Hussmann, Benedict Julian
History & Humanities Teacher
Kennedy, Dell
Radio Broadcasting Teacher
Koller, Emmerich
German Teacher
Lebryk, Dianne Reuter
Science Instructor
Leibowitz, Susan Lauri
French & Russian Teacher
Quinones, Donna M.
Former Teacher
Rounds, Julie Ward
Teacher & Coord of Child Dev
Steilen, Marybeth Schmidt
HS Health & Physical Ed Tchr
Weissenstein, Steven E.
Business Education Teacher
Whipple, Matthew Robert
Social Studies & English Tchr
Wolke, Barbara Linda
Fifth Grade Teacher
Young, Edward H.
Hlth Ed Tchr & Peer Group Sup
GLENWOOD
Lagger, Frank Charles
Physical Ed & Social Stud Tchr
GODFREY
Carpenter, Adele Johnson
English Professor
Edwards, Lana Barnett
Instructor
Holloway, Paula Puckett
Professor of Biology
Mihalich, Nancy Masinelli
Adjunct Instr Bus Division
Price, James Coleman
Asst Professor of History
Schwartz, Joan Triplett
Lang Arts & Literature Teacher
GOREVILLE
Asbury, Mary Mighell
Retired Teacher
GRAND CHAIN
Clark, Lynn Ray
Spcl Ed Learning Facilitator
Cross, Linda Gordon
Second Grade Teacher
GRAND RIDGE
Hynd, Nancy Mann
4th Grade Teacher
GRANITE CITY
Bucatch, Judith Annette
8th Grade & PE Teacher
Carli, Larry
Mathematics Teacher
Cook, Harry E.
Retired Govt & History Tchr
Grote, Barry Dane
High School Math Teacher
Halbrook, Russell Haywood
Ath Dir, Coach & Scoutmaster
Jessee, Sandra Finke
Mathematics Teacher
Kopsky, Patricia Mills
Art Teacher
Lignoul, Terry Millikin
Fifth Grade Teacher
McClain, David A.
Chemistry Teacher
Mc Givern, Mary Beth O'Connor
Head Directress & Teacher
Messick, Jean France
6th Grade Teacher
Messick, Karen Lurton
Eighth Grade Team Leader
Prazma, Diana Lynn (Holmes)
High School Science Teacher
Rahn, Dan David
Speech & Language Pathologist
Randall, Thelma K.
Math Teacher
Sullivan, Joyce Richardson
Sixth Grade Teacher
Tate, Norbert Dale
Assistant Principal
Varadian, Barbara Koch
6th Grade Teacher
Weiss, Ida Schellhardt
Retired Teacher
Zukas, Michele A.
Eighth Grade Math Teacher
GRANT PARK
Guertin, Mary Fillman
Fr, Rdng & Eng Teacher
Johnson, Colleen Kay (Cellarius)
Fourth Grade Teacher
Ohm, Sharilyn Hamann
Teaching Assistant Principal
Shipman, Fredrick William
Phys Ed & Driver Ed Teacher

GRANVILLE
Bluemer, Ronald Glenn
Earth Sci & Soc Sci Teacher
Shimkus, Lynette Boers
Kindergarten Teacher
GRAYMONT
Wasson, Dawn Elaine (Freed)
Intermediate Teacher
GRAYSLAKE
Byers, Karen S.
English Teacher
Chikos, Kelley Callahan
Middle Schl Lang Arts Teacher
Coleman, Lucille Deloise
Assistant Professor of Nursing
Hemmelman, Mary Kay
Jr HS Sci Tchr, Asst Principal
Kindsvater, Connie S.
Journalism Instructor
Martin, Lawrence
Teacher
Miller, Jeffrey Willard
Language Arts Teacher
Park, Wing M.
Math & Computer Science Prof
Parker, Robert J.
High School Computer Sci Tchr
Pederson, Joyce E.
Mathematics Teacher
GRAYVILLE
Baker, Curry Jay
Retired Band Director
Luthe, Gary Wayne
Industrial Arts Teacher
Millar, Thomas Kent, Jr.
Mathematics Department Chair
GREEN VALLEY
Poelker, Brian
Eighth Grade Science Teacher
Rahn, Tammy (Easterly)
8th Grade Mathematics Teacher
Schmidt, William E.
Art & English Teacher
GREENFIELD
Jones, Amy Hawkins
Business Teacher
Trump, James Richard
Health & Phys Ed Teacher
GREENVIEW
Cameron, Janet Sue
High School Business Teacher
Lowe, Jacqueline Marie
HS Mathematics Teacher
Steinhauser, Judith Wilkinson
English Department Chairman
Wilson, Susan Mc Cabe
Gifted Coord & Writing Instr
GREENVILLE
Ahern, William B.
Prof of Biology & Dept Head
Harnetiaux, D. Mike
6th Grade Teacher
Heilmer, Steven Lee
Adjunct Professor of Art
Reeves, Deanna M. Schanfelberger
Math & Language Arts Teacher
Schmidt, Sandra Salguero
Professor of English
Shepherd, Michael Joseph
Social Studies Instructor
Starr, Lawrence A.
Professor of Mathematics
Stonebraker, Thomas B.
Psychology Professor
Weiss, Louise Guthals
Music Instructor
Willis, Larry Zakary
Asst Rel Prof, Ath Dir & Coach
GRIGGSVILLE
Pulliam, Betsy
High School Math Teacher
Smith, Rebecca J. (Woodworth)
Business & Computer Teacher
GURNEE
Bandman, Michael Ray
Band Director
Beckwith, Thomas Lyman
Director of Bands
Cummings, Kim C.
Biology Teacher
Ferrell, Sean Patrick
Secondary English Teacher
Garrison, Lari Helene
Mathematics Teacher
Gilbert, Roxane
English Teacher
Hanlon, Debra Laskonis
High School English Teacher
Jelinek, Jamie Susan
Spanish Teacher
Neal, James Edward
6th-8th Grade Drama Instructor
Nohr, Barbara Allen
Social Studies Teacher
Popp, Deborah Glogovsky
9th-12th Grd Business Ed Tchr
Raywood, Philip Harris
High School Spanish Teacher
Ricker, Lisa Fasolo
English Teacher
Strosin, Lisa A.
Spanish Teacher
Tatgenhorst, Bob Alvin
Social Studies Tchr & Coach
Walgren, Jay Nelson
High School Science Teacher
HAMILTON
Dion, David Arthur
Business Teacher

Dion, Elaine Markovich
Language Arts & Lit Teacher
Golemo, Camilla Veith
Fr, Span, & Adult Living Tchr
Howes, Roberta Foley
Retired 5th Grade Teacher
Reed, Tena (Morley)
Guidance Counselor
Short, Edward Charles
Mathematics Teacher
HAMPSHIRE
Campbell, Dirk R.
English Teacher
Collins, T. Michael
Soc Stud Chair & His Teacher
Herrmann, Guy Christopher
Economics, Govt & US His Tchr
Nilsen, Kris A.
Spanish Teacher
HANOVER PARK
Schmidt, Lenaye Suzanne
First Grade Teacher
HARDIN
Tucker, Kay S.
Mathematics Tchr & Dept Chair
HARRISBURG
Beal, Sue Ellen Melton
College Instructor
Harbison, Jerri Ann
Math Teacher
Hathaway, Tonja Marie
Business & Drivers Ed Teacher
Johnson, Tamara Barger
High School Teacher
Keasler, Karen L.(Bard)
Business Science Division Chr
Sullivan, Cathy McMullough
English Teacher
HARVARD
Bowers, Ann Farrell
High School English Teacher
Jordan, Dennis R.
6th-8th Grd Soc Stud Tchr
Listebarger, Edna Jane
Driver Education Instructor
Ploenzke, Andrew David
Mathematics Teacher
Umland, Kathleen (Story)
Third Grade Teacher
Warren, Colleen Eyrich
English Teacher
Warren, Jason Robert
Mathematics Teacher
HARVEY
Averyheart, Benjamin Collins
Math & Science Teacher
Brooks, Elaine Rose
Special Education Teacher
Franklin, Linda Knowles
Social Studies Teacher
Gouwens, Mark David
History Teacher
Graham, Nina
Science Teacher
Miller, Charlene Marie (Hairston)
Spanish & ESL Teacher
Quandt, Lynn Brennan
Math Tchr
Randall, Helen L. Garner
K-6th Grade Counselor
Smith, Loretta White
Third Grade Teacher
Spain, Jennie L.
Second Grade Teacher
Stevens, Ingrid Alyce
Coordinator of Gifted & Tchr
Vallort, Shirley A.
Mathematics Teacher
VanderVelde, Roxanne R.
HS Mathematics Teacher
Van Horn, Lisa Bathalter
Sixth Grade Teacher
White, Julie Ann
Second Grade Teacher
HAVANA
Gerdes, Stephen Kent
Instructor
Gilson, Jennifer S.
Math Teacher
Heller, Rebecca Burgard
Second Grade Teacher
Hohn, Kristine M.
Second Grade Teacher
Lounsberry, Richard
Athletic Director & Coach
Schroeder, Michael F.
Sixth Grade Teacher
Stadsholt, Brenda
High School Counselor
HAZEL CREST
Brink, Theresa Hanks
Junior High Math Teacher
Lloyd, Edna Marie (Banks)
Sixth Grade Elementary Teacher
Looby, Ruth Harrell
Fifth Grade Teacher
Strezo, Francis Anthony
Junior High Teacher
HEBRON
George, Timothy A.
HS Mathematics Teacher
HECKER
Hodapp, Leo John
7th-8th Grd Teacher & Prin
HENRY
Bazyn, Richard William
Physics & Math Teacher
Cluskey, Brian C.
English Teacher

Mc Cracken, Jay Kent
5th Grade Teacher
Orsborn, Carolyn J.
Spanish & Psychology Teacher
HERRICK
Dona, Sandra Faye (Revisky)
7th & 8th Grd Lang Arts Tchr
Shaffer, Sandra (Walden)
Sixth Grade Teacher
HERRIN
Bondioli, Mary Elizabeth (Korte)
Rdng Recovery & Resource Tchr
Collins, Mark Gerard
Biology Instructor
Lockridge, Martha Washington
First Grade Teacher
HERSCHER
Briggs, William Edgar
English & Journalism Teacher
Livesey, Rick Alan
Biology & Env Science Teacher
Lloyd Mau, Janet Rachel
Spanish Teacher
Rezba, Willis Eugene
Speech & English Teacher
Schluter, Anita Louise
Fifth Grade Teacher
Shank, Ronald Michael
Dean of Students
Splear, Wanda Feller
Business Teacher
Thomas, Frostine Rachelle Miller
Mathematics Teacher
HEYWORTH
Wentworth, Cathy
Language Arts Teacher
HICKORY HILLS
Charles, Janet Miles
English Teacher
Dalzell, Bruce David
7th & 8th Grade Science Tchr
Demma, Judith Spoto
Retired Teacher
Dudzik, Carol Joanne (Blake)
Art & Health Teacher
Trepac, Wayne
Social Science Teacher
HIGHLAND
Armbruster, Irene Clarkin
Math Teacher
Brave, Kimberly Ellen (Foster)
MS Science Teacher
Campbell, Kim Rae
Middle School Instructor
Deets, Michelle
Spanish Teacher
Duncan, Margaret Knebel
HS Mathematics Teacher
Genczo, Kathryn A.
First Grade Teacher
Govero-Yann, Laura
7th & 8th Grd Lang Arts Tchr
Harnetiaux, Judith Haake
6th Grade Teacher
Iftner, Larry L.
Math Teacher
Jimenez, Ada Wiegand
Fourth Grade Teacher
Jones, Larry Kent
Agriculture Dept Chm & Instr
Kuper, Tamara Lynn
Fifth Grade Teacher
Miener, Judith L. Marinko
6th Grade Teacher
Monken, Glenn A.
6th Grade Teacher
Monken, Susan Mary
Fifth Grade Teacher
Murphy, Luanne (Blasting)
Music Teacher
Nelson, Linda Kramper
English Teacher
Probst, Carol Jean (Jeanie)
Math Instructor
Schmitz, Donald F.
Agriculture Teacher
HIGHLAND PARK
Berg, Carl Russell
5th Grade Teacher
Carlsen, Wendy M.
English Teacher
Downey, David Michael
Humanities Instructional Assoc
Ewert, Deborah Joy (Baileys)
Vocational & Business Ed Tchr
Freer, Ruth M.
English as a Second Lang Tchr
Ott, Bryan M.
History Tchr & Bsktbl Coach
Rosenzweig, Cathleen Case
English Teacher
Rosenzweig, Michael David
A P History Teacher
Schaffel, Sheldon
High School Counselor
Schwartz, Jody G.
English & ESL Teacher
Scurto, Margaret Ann Sims
2nd Grade Teacher
Slavick, Ann Friedman
High School Art Teacher
Wentz, Eric John
English Teacher
Williams, Glenn Carl
Director of Bands
HIGHWOOD
Victor, Mary Jo
Primary Teacher

HILLSBORO
Albracht, Robert D.
Assistant Principal
Boston, Leslie Crandall
Math Teacher
Dawson, Pamela Susan (Flori)
Third Grade Teacher
Deabenderfer, Ronald Earl
English Teacher
Hewitt, Barbara Childs
English Teacher
Leitheiser, Kevin James
Fifth Grade Teacher

HILLSIDE
Alcorn, Marlene Frances
Family & Consumer Science Tchr
Astling, Duane K., Jr.
Marketing Ed & Coop Coord
Batka, Daniel Joseph
Health & Physical Educator
Bean, Matthew Dale
Director of Bands
Bry, Eilene Cohen
Second Grade Teacher
Clish, Richard J.
English Department Chair
Emmett, Sheila Glaczenski
Physiology Teacher
Hemminger, Lora R.
English Teacher
Joslyn, Bruce Elliott
Science Teacher
Joslyn, Nedra Boyer
Third Grade Teacher
Kunas, Dieter
Mathematics Teacher
Lima, Samuel S.
Mathematics Teacher
Stelter, Robert Walter
Science Department Chairman
Strater, Angela
Spanish Teacher
Thomas, Debra Dianna
Spcl Ed Tchr & Bsktbl Coach
Tye-Spytek, Jennifer
High School Mathematics Tchr
Wallace, Alexis Palm
English & Drama Teacher
White, Antoinette Louise
First Grade Teacher

HINCKLEY
Kross, Connie Benson
Second Grade Teacher
Mc Grath, Daisette Amanda
English & Sociology Teacher
Peterson, Judy R.
High School Guidance Counselor

HINSDALE
Baran, Marion S.
Retired Biology Teacher
Dempsey, Mary Fleming
Science Teacher
Dorrance, Thomas Patrick
Mathematics Teacher
Feeney, Linda S.
Fourth Grade Teacher
Ferrone, Christine Brinckerhoff
9th Grd World History Teacher
Freiler, Christopher William
History Teacher
Hesslau, Jean Mc Manus
Fifth Grade Teacher
Hill, Gregory James
High School Math Teacher
Johnston, Brent A.
Driver Education Instructor
Lindon, James R.
English Teacher
Meyers, Terry
French Teacher
Newcomb, Ellen Lehtonen
4th Grd Tchr & Rdng Specialist
Pascual, Kharolynn J
Rel, Eng & Work Prcssng Tchr
Quaintance, Richard C., Jr.
Counselor
Radcliff, Evelyn D. (Lawrence)
7th Grade French & His Teacher
Sculley, Marla Mc Murray
US His, Lit & Religion Teacher
Wieder, Raymond Charles
English Tchr & Rdng Specialist

HOFFMAN ESTATES
Brown, Carolyn Boyd
English & Journalism Teacher
Gentes, George Howard
Choral Dir & Music Dept Chm
Habisohn, Mary Herrig
Former Fifth Grade Teacher
Hill, Frank Philip
English Teacher
Mack, Denise E.
Social Science Teacher
Mc Claughry, Jill Schrader
Retired Fourth Grade Teacher
Mc Ginn, Kari Eckert
Life & Family Studies Teacher
McLaughlin, Dona Olson
Second Grade Teacher
Phillips, Katherine Cirella
English & Speech Comm Teacher
Riley, Mary Jane
Teacher of the Gifted
Rucks, Jim
Driver Education Teacher
Spaletto, Mary Ann Pecucci
Kindergarten Teacher
Wandro, Kathleen M.
English Teacher

HOMER
Tighe, Pamela Hoag
Jr High Social Studies Tchr

HOMETOWN
Baitis, Carolyn Jean
Retired 5th Grade Teacher

HOMEWOOD
Carney, John
Eighth Grade English Teacher
Majetich, Sharon
Lang Arts & Soc Stud Tchr
Pudlewski, James
Science Teacher
Weiss, Gregory J.
Speech & Drama Teacher
Wood, Frank Prout
Math Teacher

HOOPESTON
Duffin, Linda Kay (Rector)
Physical Education Teacher
Tolch, Rita Woesthaus
Honors English Teacher

HUDSON
Patkunas, Wayne Anthony
Retired Substitute Teacher

HUMBOLDT
Tolle, Debra Randolph
4th Grade Teacher

HUME
Allen, Dianna (Dee)
Mathematics Teacher
Allen, R. Steven
Guidance Director
Belobraydic, Billijeanne Harvey
History Teacher
Coartney, Carole Sue
Jr High Math & Soc Stud Tchr
Garst, Cheryl Allison
Kindergarten Teacher
Hammond, Kelly Stockberger
English Teacher
Miller, Sue E.
Business Teacher
Wood, Helen Powers
Reading & English Teacher

HUNTLEY
Leggee, C. William
Retired English Teacher

ILLINOIS CITY
Fuhr, Janet Flaherty
First Grade Teacher

ILLIOPOLIS
Butcher, Karla Joell
Vocal Music Teacher
Lessen, Jill D.
HS Math Teacher
Maske, Barbara Hohenstein
5th Grade Teacher

INA
Beasley, Sharon Kay
Nursing Instructor
Bennett-Minor, Patricia B.
Nursing Instructor
Benns, Deborah Jones
Assoc Professor of Nursing
Capps, Sarah
Art Instructor
Davenport, Barbara Jean
Anatomy & Physiology Teacher
Hoar, Rosalie Abdallah
Developmental English Instr
Howard, Therese Melena
Art Instructor
Kennett, Stephen Allen
Psychology & Philosophy Instr
Kuberski, Christina R.
English & Speech Instr
Mc Cowen, Daniel
Automotive Instructor
Nimtz, Lynn E.
Reading Instructor
Page, Linda Bean
Teacher & Instr of Gifted
Schuessler, David Lee
Computer Science Instructor
Sickmeyer, Kent Allen
Agriculture Business Instr
Stewart, Carolyn Reed
Assoc Prof of Soc Sci Dept
Tomlin, Susan Santoro
Instructor of Sociology
Volk, Lisa Reed
Assoc Prof of Biological Sci

INDUSTRY
Erlandson, Nancy Jean
Social Studies Dept Head

INGLESIDE
Kesser-Anderson, Jeanne
Math Teacher
Simon, Karen (Richard)
Third Grade Teacher

IRVINGTON
Brown, Robert William
6th-8th Grd Soc Sci Tchr

ITASCA
Kaspar, Rose Lach
6th-8th Grade Math Teacher
Lorenz, David Earl
6th-8th Grade Teacher
Tison, Jack
Junior High Teacher

JACKSONVILLE
Anderson, E. Charlene
7th Grade Social Studies Tchr
Armour, Gary Allan
Professor of Biology
Chance, Paula Amann
High School Composition Tchr
Cooper, Randy
Principal & Teacher
Decker, Philip Hunt
W F Short Prof of Eng & Drama
Denny, Leslie A.
Spanish Teacher
English, Kathleen Romang
English Teacher
Groce, David C.
Director of Bands
Hahn, Naomi Elizabeth
Associate Professor of English
Hansmeier, Barbara Jo
1st Grade Teacher
Headen, Diane Jones
Eng, Special Ed & LD Tchr
Jerry, E. Claire
Asst Professor of Humanities
Johns, Beverly Holden
Program Supervisor
Kerr, Robert Lynn
English Teacher
Kiesow, Maureen Kepner
Third Grade Teacher
Lemley, Patricia Arthur
Dir & Asst Prof of Deaf Stud
Marshall, Mary Kerr
Assistant Professor of Math
Mc Cord, John
Math & Science Teacher
Mulhern, Donald Gerard
Physical Education Instructor
Nicolet, Toi Louise
7th Grd Math Tchr & Dept Chair
Olson, Craig Dean
5th-6th Grade Elem Teacher
Preston, Edward Allan
Amer His & World Geo Teacher
Robinson, Nancy A.
5th Grade Teacher
Ryan, Aleta S.
2nd Grade Class Room Teacher
Saunders, Lynn William
Communications Professor
Stewart, Brenda Minor
Word Processing Tchr
Stewart, Roberta J.
Asst Prof of Philosophy & Rel
Sweatman, Sandra Ann De Frates
1st Grade Teacher
Szczepanski, Nadine Marie
Chemistry Professor
Tendick, Rita Nobis
Coordinator of Gifted Programs
Thaxton, Clifford L.
Counselor
Thompson, Dixie Henderson
Second Grade Teacher

JERSEYVILLE
Beauchamp, Brett Alan
English & Broadcasting Teacher
Bone, Vicki Linn
Business Education Teacher
Clendenny, Gary A.
Retired Teacher & Counselor
Davis, Kimberly Sue (Schroeder)
High School Science Teacher
Driesner, Cynthia Beach
French Teacher
Evans, David G.
Math Teacher
Halemeyer, Margaret Schudel
Kindergarten Teacher
Robinson, Shelly Davis
Business Education Teacher
Shaffer, Mary Lou Mills
Science Teacher

JOHNSONVILLE
Brashear, Janice R.
First Grade Teacher

JOHNSTON CITY
Bauernfeind, Karon Sullivan
Fourth Grade Teacher
Eli, Paul Stephen
Art Teacher
Ellis, Linda Sue (Farthing)
General Math & Algebra I Tchr
Hubbard, Lona Lee (Davies0
Third Grade Teacher
James, June Griffin
Fifth Grade Teacher
Kee, Roger
8th Grade Lang Arts Teacher
Mooneyham, Michael Lee
7th Grade Soc Stud & Eng Tchr
Zanotti, Patti Jo
Math Teacher

JOLIET
Alexander, Grant
Mathematics Professor
Arendt, Daniel Raymond
Social Studies Teacher
Bankston, Marion (Redmond)
History Teacher
Bennett, Barbara Ann
Second Grade Teacher
Bias, Sophronia Maria
5th Grade Teacher
Black, Debra Peck
4th Grade Teacher
Blasing, Noel L.
Social Studies Teacher
Booras, April
3rd Grade Teacher
Brandon, Ann Wagner
Physics Teacher
Brewer, Karen E. (Holliday)
Mathematics Teacher
Brown, Judith Germain
6th-8th Grd Soc Stud Tchr
Burns, John Michael
Social Studies Teacher
Chamberlain, Jeffrey S.
Assistant Professor of History
Cherry, Douglas E.
Mathematics Teacher
Clark, Sean T.
English Instructor
Clarke, Lucy A.
Fifth Grade Teacher
Clarke, Mark Edward
7th-8th Grd Soc Stud Teacher
Contos, Anthony B.
Guidance Counselor
Crump, Larry T.
Professor of Biology
Davis, Sharlene Stevenson
Communication Arts Teacher
Diab, Salim M.
Professor of Chemistry
Disera, Catherine L.
Student Assistance Coordinator
Douglas, Vanessa Ravin
Assistant Director & Teacher
Eberhart, Lucille Kegley
5th Grade Teacher
Edwards, Gerald
Jr ROTC Instructor
Gatons, Janice Marie
Mathematics Teacher
Golf, Mary Lou
French & Latin Teacher
Grider, Nancy Chambers
Retired Coll Bound Eng Teacher
Gura, Marlene Mc Intyre
Jr High Language Arts Tchr
Hatten, Lillie Norman
Math & Science Teacher
Hunnewell, Patricia Reavley
4th Grade Teacher
Johnson, Walter Lee, Jr.
Secondary Social Studies Tchr
Juozaitis, Joy Roarty
English & Science Teacher
Jursinic, Kathryn Ireland
Elementary Principal
Krieger, Dee C.
Education Dept Adjunct Faculty
Lakota, Margaret Mary (Kukla)
Mathematics Teacher
Lewis, Jerry E.
Fine Arts Department Chairman
Liley, Thomas L.
Professor of Music
Lutz, Michael L.
Tech Prep US History Teacher
Maisonneuve, Joseph F.
Mathematics Teacher
Malloy, Julia Danahay
Retired Educator
Mankowski, Marsha Ann
Math Teacher
Marzec, Marcia Smith
Professor of English
Mattai, Bansraj
Sociology Professor
Mc Carthy, Cheryl
9th-12th Grd Math Teacher
Mc Dowell, Bobby
Cmptr Information Systems Prof
McGirr, Vincent K.
Marketing Education Teacher
Mines, Pamela Ann (Wilson)
Language Arts & Soc Stud Tchr
Neary, Leonore M.
Professor of Biology
Parks, Barbara Fahrner
French Teacher & ACT Coord
Paul, Patrick F.
Junior High Teacher
Penhale, Tandy Cash
Fifth Grade Teacher
Perignon, Barbara Jean (Colberg)
7th Grd Commnctn Arts Teacher
Porter, Susan Jane
Lang Arts & Soc Studies Tchr
Prendergast, Jack
Speech, Eng & Photography Tchr
Prola, Donald John
Dist Dir of Aths & Stu Acts
Rinehart, Kathleen Kelly
English Teacher
Rodeghero, Joseph Steven
History Teacher & Coach
Sallie, Stella Holmes
English & Reading Teacher
Sameck, Susan Shepich
Lang Arts & Soc Stud Tchr
Scott, Linda Ann
Assistant Principal
Semrov, Beatrice A.
Social Studies Teacher
Shaw, Larry Mayfield
Accounting & Computer Teacher
Smith, Ann Semin
Anatomy & Physiology Instr
Stoiber, Marguerite Veras
HS Art Teacher
Swarthout, Mary Sue
Kindergarten Teacher
Tunney, Teresa Mary
History Teacher
Vivanco, Liduvina (Paramo)
Bilingual Science Teacher
Vojnovich, Christine M.
English Teacher
Walker, Kathryn (Kocielko)
Seventh Grade Teacher
Wallace, Helen Elaine
Resource Specialist
Waxweiler, Paula Emery
Career & Voc Ed Division Chm
Wissbroecker, Raymond Joseph
Science & Chemistry Teacher
Wolff, Marie W.
Chemistry Professor
Zabrocki, Emily Kolar
Professor of Nursing

JONESBORO
Dallas, JoAn Koelling
3rd Grade Teacher
Lehr, Robert Powers, III
PE & Health Teacher
McCloud, Linda Faye
4th Grade Teacher
Miller, Beth Ann (Bell)
First Grade Teacher & Coach
Phillippe, Philip
Jr High Science Teacher
Rendleman, Susan Schuster
Third Grade Teacher
Schramka, Lawrence P.
Jr High Social Studies Teacher

JOPPA
Lambert, Susan Nicole
Band Dir & General Music Tchr

JOY
Campbell, James R.
Chemistry, Physics & Math Tchr
Louck, Mickey Owen
Elem PE Tchr & HS Coach
Neeld, Jeannette L.
9th-12th Grade PE Instructor

JUNCTION
Baltimore, Carolyn Ann
Junior HS Soc Stud Teacher
Davis, Nancy M.
World His, Span, Music Teacher
Downen, Cheryl Angela
Special Education Teacher
Hernandez, Linda McConnell
Third Grade Teacher
Vargo, Stephen Michael
7th-8th Grd Lang Arts Teacher

JUSTICE
Du Praw, Alice
Principal
Young, Margaret Anne
Title I Reading Teacher

KANKAKEE
Baspineiro-Edwards, Sonia
Spanish Dept Chair & Instr
Branson, Robert Dean
Div of Religion Chrprsn
Clasberry, Genevra A.
School Social Worker
Denault, Helen Faye (Nelson)
Kindergarten Teacher
Doenges, James David
Math Teacher
Du Voisin, Cathy Lynn
6th Grade Teacher
Ellwanger, Charles William
Professor of Theology
Frogge, James Lewis
Science Department Chairman
Gay, Margaret Mary
Language Arts Teacher
Gianotti, Francis Joseph
Sixth Grade Teacher
Grant, Jill Berghouse
Sixth Grade Teacher
Heil, John Omer
8th Grd Teacher & Athletic Dir
Hensley, Chuck E., Jr.
HS Theatre & English Teacher
Hermes, Joan Garvey
English Teacher
Kinnersley, Richard Lewis
Reading & Language Teacher
Kupcikevicius, Kazys
Social Studies Teacher
Mack, Pamela R.
English Instructor
Neyhart, Kathleen Patrice (Nagy)
Science & Math Teacher
Paul, James Francis
History & Philosophy Instr
Schrock, Lee C.
Professor of Psychology
Schultz, Lana Kay
First Grade Teacher
Shadid, Susan
Fourth Grade Teacher
Simington, Lorrie Rae
Business Education Teacher
Sotak, John Joseph
History Teacher
Tate, Alice Margaret
Psychology Instructor
Weedon, Leslie Alan
Electronics Program Coord
Zullo, Sandray Kay
Chemistry Teacher

KANSAS
Carwell, Lucille Bartimus
Home Ec, Psych & Health Tchr

KELL
Luschen, Nancy K.
Math & Social Studies Teacher
Malone, Jeannie Wooldridge
Kindergarten & Music Teacher

KEMPTON
Frantz, Lois Odendahl
4th Grade Teacher

KEWANEE
Anderson, Carolyn Kay
Professor
Christakos, Gregory William
Science & PE Teacher
Gleason, Marcia A.
Principal & Fifth Grd Tchr

ANEE (cont)
aula Dea
ness Information Tech Prof
, Sara Jane Westerdale
Grade Teacher
Linda Vandemore
ish Teacher
, Verna M. Bloomquist
ed 4th Grade Teacher
Suzanne (McGaughey)
Schl Home Economics Tchr
ootegem, James Edward
ness Education Teacher
AID
, Gary Duane
ish & Lang Arts Teacher
h, Linda L.
d Grade Teacher
h, Michael David
Grade Teacher
d, Cheryl L.
ish Teacher
o, John Jerome (Jerry)
2th Grd Math Teacher
S
stad, Dennis Gene
th Grade Teacher
z, Ronald Wayne
, Sci & Geography Teacher
UNDY
, Terry Jane
Grade Teacher
LAND
ller, Charles Eugene
al Studies Teacher
n, Connie Lou (Benson)
ish Teacher
VILLE
erdon, Philip M.
a Specialist
er, Michael
School Math Teacher
ody, Colleen Ann
Grade Teacher
Lynne J.
ish Teacher
RANGE
son, Bradley Ray
ish Teacher
d, Luke A.
th Grade Teacher
vich, Beth Ann, SSSF
logy Teacher
Robert Alexander
al Director
, Glen H.
ish Teacher
oell, Jane Blackburn
School English Teacher
ecki, Donna Michels
ch Teacher
Catherine Kay
ematics Tchr & Dept Chprsn
ckson, Lin Margaret
Arts Dept Chair & Tchr
e, Nan C.
Teacher
tt, Norma Easter
ish Teacher
, Tom
ace Chairperson & Director
ldi, Annamarie
ish Teacher
Lucretia Jo
nan & World History Teacher
erschmitt, Carolyn Catherine
th Grade Teacher
bek, Joseph Arthur
ogy & Science Teacher
d, Ginny Gabe
uage Arts Teacher
lin, Diane Lynn
School Guidance Counselor
s, Donna N.
tre Teacher
o, William L.
ance Counselor
y, Robert Eugene
l Director
al, Claudia Drozd
Dept Chair & Spanish Tchr
Beverly Ann
uage Arts Teacher
, Jana (Sykes)
3rd Language Arts Teacher
el, Jeanne L. Freudenberg
Grade Teacher
asek, Deborah Ann
pus Minister & Teacher
lewski, Lori E.
ish & German Teacher
Kimberly Anne
ch & Drama Teacher
ck, Scott George
School Math Teacher
RANGE PARK
on, Lorana Kauffman
ed Eng Tchr & Dept Chair
ARPE
, Mildred Suerrette
titute Teacher
, Richard Lee
ory & Government Teacher
ALLE
ri, Maria De Los Angeles
nish Teacher
, Mark William
nematics Teacher
ery, Cathy Brate
Biology Instructor

Johnson, Susan Clair
Foreign Lang Dept Chair
Kosciewicz, Sue Elizabeth
History Teacher
Mercer, Daniel Raymond
German & World History Teacher
Sarver, Gregory Stephen
Science Teacher & Coach
Tomsha, Kathleen P.
Math & Science Teacher
Unzicker, Janet Martha
Science & Math Teacher
Zeman, Debra Marie (Bernard)
English Teacher
LAFOX
Fowler, Tom G.
Dean of Men
Kunitz, Edward Joseph
Science Dept Chair & Instr
Stark, Michele Anne
Music Director
LAKE BLUFF
Volpe, Elsie Vienne
Second Grade Teacher
LAKE FOREST
Enright, Thomas Francis, Jr.
HS Social Studies & Rdng Tchr
Forst, Margaret Grauff
English Teacher
Hawkins, David Roger
English Teacher
Kellerman, Vanessa Jeanne
Mathematics Teacher
Krouse, Ann Wolk
High School English Teacher
Kurowski, Elizabeth Korn
Music Director
Lindsay, Dennis R.
Director of Bands
O'Steen, Abby
English Teacher
Scheiber, Richard
History Teacher
Zarob, Virginia M.
Soc Stud Chair & History Tchr
Zeller, Marilyn Cornish
English & Lang Arts Teacher
LAKE VILLA
Anderson, Michael David
Science Teacher
Schwager, Louise Mohr
German, Eng & Soc Studies Tchr
Welch, Anna Estep
Mathematics Teacher
LAKE ZURICH
Beauprie, Karen Ann
Health & Physical Ed Teacher
Biondi, Joanne Linda (Gettleman)
Special Education Teacher
Bivin, Jeffrey L.
Mathematics Teacher
Egizio, Mary Ann C.
5th Grade Teacher
Eiserman, Mary Ann Calusha
English Teacher
Ellis, Steven Mark
High School Math Teacher
Hopkins, Anne Ruth
High School Biology Teacher
Hoss, Kathy
MS Teacher
Hughes, Deborah Keys
Spanish Teacher
Jaskier, Janine (Anderson)
Reading & Lang Arts Teacher
Perkins, Kathryn Jenkins
Fifth Grade Teacher
Peterson, Elizabeth Bowman
Director of Bands
Rash, Roy
Principal
Stanko, Philip W.
Science Teacher
Szady, Patrick Joseph
7th-8th Grade Sci Tchr & Chm
Weber, William John
Art Teacher
LANARK
Feltmeyer, Darcie Frye
Second Grade Teacher
Hartman, LeAndra Landt
Home Ec & Consumer Ed Tchr
Majors, Beverly Ann Smith
Third Grade Teacher
Pierce, Kristy Ritenour
Physical Education Teacher
Wheeler, Sarah Seitner
4th Grade Teacher
LANSING
Anderson, Joy H.
Dean of Students
Bobos, Kenneth Allen
6th Grade Social Studies Tchr
Brady, Susan Heintz
Kindergarten Teacher
Carr, Deborah Jean
School Social Worker
Cushing, G. Michael
6th Grade Math Tchr
Hertz, Henry Louis
Drama & English Teacher
Klain, Jeannine Bunce
Special Education Teacher
Kompier, Timothy Peter
7th Grade Science Teacher
Miller, Patricia Evans
Third Grade Teacher
Nederhood, Mary Lou (Steigenga)
Second Grade Teacher

Padjen, Janet Shallcross
Third Grade Teacher
Posewick, Joan F.
Junior High Teacher
Schweitzer, Beverly Brinkman
English & Computer Teacher
VanDrunen, Milton Jay
Social Studies Teacher
Yannakopoulos, Helen Alex
Business Education Teacher
Zeuner, Richard Paul
Sci & Art Dept Chair & Tchr
LAWRENCEVILLE
Magee, William Harold
Band Director
Pulleyblank, Larry K.
English Teacher
Rice, Theresa Dunkel
Librarian
Scott, Jerry R.
Math Teacher
LE ROY
Chancellor, Shirley Jean
Sixth Grade Teacher
Small, Margaret Wilson
Retired Social Studies Teacher
Straub, Sandra Kay
English Teacher
LEBANON
Mc Chesney, Robert
Professor of Marketing & Mgmt
Thom, Dian L. (Dill)
Adjunct Professor
LELAND
Beck, Barbara J.
HS PE Teacher
Cavanaugh Smith, Laura Beth
1st-12th Grade Art Teacher
Chapman, Mary Jane (VanDuzer)
Special Education Teacher
Doolin, James Patrick
Superintendent
Elder, Kathleen S.
High School Mathematics Tchr
Goetsch, Raymond Paul
Industrial Arts Teacher
Inman, Richard L.
Driver Education Tchr & Coach
LEMONT
Albrecht, Albert G.
Driver Education Coordinator
Conlon, Martha Perry
Teacher of the Gifted
Dick, Janet Lingeman
Sociology & English Teacher
Dosen, Maryann
Math Teacher & Dept Chair
Fisher, Diana
HS Science Teacher
Garibaldi, Janet Kent
Business Ed Tchr & Dept Chprsn
Melei, Patricia Mary (Herr)
High School English Teacher
Naiden, Jude Marie
Rel Stud Dept Chair & Teacher
Prangen, Richard Charles
History & Government Teacher
Sklom, E. Michael
Physics & Astronomy Teacher
LENA
Bussian, Susan K. Gorz
Former Substitute Teacher
Laity, Richard James
Mathematics Teacher
Stronhecker, Jerilyn K.
English & Social Studies Instr
Thill, Mary Beth Loring
Jr HS Phys Ed Teacher
LERNA
Reed, Sandra Sterchi
Kndgtn & Reading Recovery Tchr
Spaniol, Connie Hickenbottom
Third Grade Teacher
LEWISTOWN
Bennett, Gregory Wayne
Social Studies Teacher & Coach
Ellis, Colleen Whitehead
Eng Tchr & Media Specialist
Graham, Ned Duane
Mathematics Teacher
Litchfield, Rita Madsen
Sixth Grade Teacher
Rhodes, Janet Wilcoxen
Social Sci Dept Chm, Hist Tchr
White, Daniel Harrison
Retired Chemistry Teacher
LEXINGTON
Baker, Rick
Math Teacher & Asst Principal
Kirby, Beverly Ann
English Teacher
Wisdom, Sondra Mc Euen
Eng Tchr, Chorus & Play Dir
LIBERTY
Brooks, Charles William
Band Director
Buyck, Steve C.
Agriculture Education Teacher
Roberts, Brenda Jeanette
First & Second Grade Teacher
Taylor, Jenice
Eng, Language Arts & PE Tchr
LIBERTYVILLE
Brenner, Richard Allan
Mathematics Teacher
Bush, Michael E.
Physics Teacher
Goodwin, James Edmond
High School Math Teacher

Johnson, Robert Bruce
English Teacher
Larson, Patricia (Hughes)
7th Grade Soc Stud Tchr
Leone, Matthew John
Earth Science & Physics Tchr
Locke, Cynthia Jones
Middle School Counselor
Mahoney, Kathleen Marie (Vanson)
Social Studies Teacher
McKenzie, Jeffrey John
Team Leader
Schneider, Barbara Pedian
Public Info Liaison & Teacher
Tarczynski, Marie Forte
4th Grade Classroom Teacher
Trzyna, Christine Ann
PE & Asst Athletic Dir
Weber, William C.
Freshman English Teacher
Williams, Beatriz Sampedro
Spanish Teacher
LINCOLN
Anderson, Jean (Rankin)
8th Grade Lang Arts Teacher
Buffington, Bill J.
Associate Professor of Music
Dumouchel, Jean A.
4th Grade Teacher
Fulcher, James W.
Hum, English Professor
Griffin, Charlotte Schumm
Tchr of High Ablty & Remedial
Hackett, Joseph Paul
Fifth Grade Teacher
Harberts, Betty Cantrell
Physics & Mathematics Teacher
Howard, Debra Fletcher
Mathematics Teacher
Litherland, Erwin
Science & Language Arts Tchr
Litherland, Kathleen Bahe
Seventh Grade Lang Arts Tchr
Mc Evers, Claudia
Social Studies & Reading Tchr
Sackett, Glenn Charles
Prof of Christian Ministries
Stoltzenburg, Anne Shanle
Jr High Math Teacher & Coach
Stoltzenburg, Gary L.
Sixth Grade Teacher
Trommer, Linda Carol (Hart)
2nd Grade Elementary Teacher
LINCOLNSHIRE
Biesiada, Mark J.
History Teacher
Bolger, John Mark
AP United States History Tchr
Cousins, Monica Nicole
History Teacher
Dagro, Caryl Jo
Jrnlsm, Eng & Rdng Tchr
Durham, Debbie Fulghum
Associate Music Director
Feurer, James M.
Teacher & Work-Study Coord
Fischer, Dolores Helen
Mathematics Instructor
Foltin, Robert J.
Guidance Counselor
Heckel-Oliver, Christine
English Teacher
Johansen, Richard Alan
Technology Ed Instructor
Knapp, Theresa Klug
Biology Teacher
Latka, Kenneth P.
Science Teacher
Lyons, Robert E.
High School Soc Studies Tchr
Martinez, Lino
Spanish Instructor
Maxwell, Elizabeth Payne
English Teacher
Nuteson, Alice Lynn
Choral Music Director
Plank, Margaret Roseli
German Teacher
Rauch, Catherine Kerkes
Math Teacher & Team Coach
Reimer, Michael Paul
Chemistry Teacher
Schenk, Bob L.
Phys Ed Teacher & Coach
Silbert, Ellen
ESL Coord & Teacher
Singer, Susan Lynne Jacobs
British Literature Teacher
Swan, Paul
Mathematics Teacher
Ward, Robert P.
High School English Teacher
LINCOLNWOOD
Perino, Gordon
5th Grade Teacher
LINDENWOOD
Bell, Loretta Long
Science Teacher
Magnuson, Ann Elizabeth
Third & Fourth Grade Teacher
Palmer, Martha Kobel
Math & Social Studies Teacher
LISLE
Beato, Eric W.
English Teacher
Biel, Joseph Francis
Assoc Prof of Philosophy Dept
Collins, Kristi G. Koehler
Family Child Care Provider

Dawson, Frank Joseph
Jazz & Commercial Guitar Instr
Dennerlein, Donald T.
Chemistry Tchr & Science Chm
DiMarco, Lisa Hurst
English Teacher
Fiore, Beverly Hatfield
Speech Comm & Drama Teacher
Fogarty, James M.
English Teacher
Green, Donald Jon
Driver's Ed & PE Teacher
Honeysett, Michelle Lynn
Mathematics Teacher
Peters, Timothy Justin
Science Teacher & Dept Chair
Townsley-Kulich, Lisa
Mathematics Professor
Truemper, Martha T.
English Teacher
Weber, Mary Johnson
Seventh Grade Reading Teacher
Willman, Fred Dale
7th Grd Social Studies Teacher
LITCHFIELD
Boutcher, Alison Joy (Evans)
Special Education Teacher
Brakenhoff, Nancy A. Dellamano
K-8th Grade Substitute Teacher
Gray, Bruce Wayne
Automotive Technology Instr
Hott, Thomas A.
Chemistry & Physics Teacher
Newkirk, Daniel D.
Physical Education Teacher
Scobbie, Dennis James
Biology Teacher
Stock, Patrice Lisa
6th-12th Grade Music Teacher
LOAMI
Neubauer, Nancy A.
Fifth Grade Teacher
LOCKPORT
Bernard, GayAnn Simpson
Family & Consumer Sci Teacher
Boylan, Judith Williams
Teacher
Burke, Richard E.
7th-8th Grade Science Teacher
Callis, Eric J.
Social Science Teacher
Casey, Mary Faye Gildea
Fourth Grade Teacher
Kalchbrenner, Jane Stockment
Language Arts Teacher
Kimble, Ivan Albert
Science Department Assoc Chm
Kuhn, Daniel Joseph
English Teacher
Mason, Melvia
Social Studies & Math Teacher
Mlecko, Brian Edward
Science Teacher
Morris, Colleen D.
5th Grade Teacher
Nash, Christine Kukla
Reading & Spanish Teacher
Nelson, James Lee
Aerospace Science Instructor
O'Brien, Thomas P.
English Teacher
Ortmann, Jeffrey David
5th Grade Gifted Teacher
Paukstis, Susan Marie (Rupcich)
Fifth Grade Teacher
Speaker, Karen Clavenna
Guidance Counselor
Tully, Sharon Lee (White)
Principal
VanOss, Joyce M.
English, Theater Dir & Tchr
Veerman, Virginia Lucas
English Teacher
Young, Kathy Principato
Instructional Aide
LOMBARD
Bakkum, Barclay William
Associate Professor of Anatomy
Barnhart, Claudine Cygan
8th Grade Science Teacher
Bartley, Carol Marie
Second Grade Teacher
Cain, Constance M.
English Teacher & Jrnlsm Adv
Curtis, Micheline
Govt, US His & Ec Tchr
Darby, Susan Anderson
Associate Professor of Anatomy
Eberhard, David Aaron
Geography Instructor
Elder, Terry Matthew
Instructor
Ferri, Daniel Jon
Teacher of the Gifted
Ganas, Betty Ann
Math & English Teacher
Garcia, Christa N.
Foreign Language Instructor
Grumbles, Carl E.
6th Grade Teacher
Heuser, Adele Martha
First Grade Teacher
Huntoon, Robert Leroy
Mathematics Teacher
Johnson, Beth Dotson
Math & Language Arts Teacher
May, Joanne Thalia
Orchestra Director
Meyer, Patricia Adams
English Department Chair

LOMBARD (cont)
Nance, Karen Doyle
5th Grade Teacher
Nathan, Marsha A.
Spanish Teacher
Ro, Chae-Song
Anatomy Professor
Schillerstrom, Martha Morris
French Teacher
Schwarze, Janice Colburn
English Teacher
Scott, Harold James
Retired Latin Teacher
Scott, Michael H.
Mathematics Teacher
Stieglitz, Roger Henry
Woodwork & Arch Drawing Tchr
Tobin, Cathy Mary
Mathematics Teacher & Coach
VanDenBerg, Christopher J.
History & Geography Teacher
Webb, Gay Lynn
Kindergarten Teacher
Young, Dorothy D.
Math & Science Teacher
LONDON MILLS
Boughton, Theresa Clardy
French & English Teacher
Bultemeier, Odette Manuel
Fourth Grade Teacher
Kellogg, Radine Stucky
Chemistry & Biology II Teacher
Mc Kinley-Balfour, Stephanie Ann
Director of Libraries
Tasker, Robert Eugene
History & Government Teacher
LOSTANT
Anderson, Rhonda Carol
Second Grade Teacher
Mann, Gladys Marie (Haun)
Retired School Teacher
LOVES PARK
Anderson, Timothy William
English Teacher
Bronzi, Lois Ann
English, Math & Religion Tchr
East, Jennifer Lee
Former Math Teacher
Lunsford, Sandra J. (Towles)
Business Education Teacher
Medearis, Douglas William
6th Grade Teacher
Pelley, Frederick Lawrence, Jr.
PE Teacher
Theisen, Mary Wetzel
Math Teacher
Wilburn, Camilla Carlson
2nd Grade Teacher
LOVINGTON
Casteel, Linda Kay (Webner)
Math & Chemistry Teacher
LYONS
Alexander, Suellen M.
Third Grade Teacher
Orozco, Gale Evans
Math Teacher
Sergesketter, Andrew Franklin
Social Studies & Think Teacher
MACHESNEY PARK
Benson, Nancy Jo
Spanish Teacher
Cain, Sandra Doll
HS Choral Music, Drama Teacher
Dredge, William Robert
High School Mathematics Tchr
Drennan, Susan Furster
Curriculum Coordinator
Fiepke, Julie Oswald
Graphic Arts Teacher
Flick, Michael
Special Education Teacher
Gunn, Melody
English Teacher
Hanrahan, Kerry Kathryn
English Tchr
Hayes, Jane DeNier
French & English Teacher
Heimer, Sharon Rich
Mathematics Teacher
Jacobs, Wayne S.
Marketing & Entrepreneur Tchr
Kaffenbarger, Timmie J.
Advanced Chemistry Teacher
Leisure, Paul Lyle
Spcl Ed Teacher & Case Mgr
Letourneau, Ellen Teevan
English & Communications Instr
Pape, Denise Mary
Biology & Chemistry Teacher
Paulsen, Mark L.
Guidance Counselor
Peterson, Paul Dennis
Psychology & US His Teacher
Primuth, Andrea L.
High School Counselor
Ramsey, Jack Robert
Driver Ed Tchr & Dept Chprsn
Schultz, Connie Steffen
High School English Teacher
Stockwell, Karen (Eissens)
Home Economics & Family Tchr
Whiteman, Roger Russell
Drafting Teacher
Zapke, Clifford F.
HS Economics & US History Tchr
MACKINAW
Boston, Tina Colette
Mathematics Teacher

MACOMB
Adkins, K. Dake
Recreation Professor
Brakefield, James Thomas
Management Professor
Bushmire, John Anthony
Fifth Grade Teacher
Combs, Colleen J.
Assistant Professor of Spanish
Combs, William Lee
History Professor
Crawford, Wayne
Assistant Professor of English
Creger, Donald Wayne
Manufacturing Engineer Prof
Curtis, Joanne De May
8th Grade Language Arts Tchr
Dively, Lois
English & Home Ec Instructor
Dooley, Cindy June (Huls)
Elem Ed Asst Professor
Egler, David George
Professor of History
Elia, Nada
Asst Prof of Postcolonial Lits
Frazer, June Martin
Professor of English
Hallwas, John Edward
Professor of English
Harris, Karen Sears
Psychology Professor
Jensen, Mary Murphy
Professor
Lemon, Hallie S.
Composition Teacher
Lindsay, Sherry Crane
Spanish Teacher
Majeres, Raymond Leonard
Professor
Marshall, Judith Duffy
5th Grade Teacher
Mortier, Sandra Jean
Third Grade Teacher
Palm-Gessner, Catherine Ann
Science Teacher
Parker, Rebecca Peroshek
Asst Prof of Dept of Comm
Rippey, Phyllis Farley
Interim Dean
Rittenmeyer, Steven D.
Law Professor
Rutledge, Essie Manuel
Sociology Professor
Setser, Sharon Grassmyer
English & Speech Teacher
Simmons, John Kent
Dept of Philosophy Prof
Stegall, James Clayton
Director of Choral Activities
Sullivan, Kellee Kessler
6th Grade Math Teacher
Sunday, Betty R.
Biling & Eng Second Lang Prof
Sutton, Robert P.
Professor of History
Vos, Morris
Professor of German
Watkins, Thomas H.
Professor of History
Wozniak, John Francis
Associate Prof of Sociology
MACON
Berg, Steven Robert
History Teacher
Bugg, Sondra Gaskill
English Teacher
Hurst, Margie Griffin
English Teacher
Mahone, Janis Stewart
Mathematics & Physics Teacher
Moore, Donna Adams
Business Education Teacher
Wand, Brian A.
Music Teacher
MADISON
Brazil, Lois Marie (Crawford)
Third Grade Teacher
Cox, Barbara Anne
Media Specialist
Hogg, Cheryl J. Moye
Spanish & English Teacher
Kolakowski, Cynthia A.
High School Guidance Counselor
Williams, Yolanda Michele (Washington)
Sixth Grade Teacher
MAHOMET
Drew, Robyn Kuperus
6th Grd Language Arts Teacher
Gardner, Beth Emerson
Retired Teacher
Koeberlein, Geralyn Ransone
Math Teacher
Sattazahn, M. Jean (Pitrat)
7th Grade Lang Arts Teacher
Tilford, Michael Ray
Social Studies Teacher
Zimmerman, Lori Bowald
Third Grade Teacher
MALTA
Busse, Ann Elizabeth
Speech & Philosophy Instructor
Gruber, Linda Janus
Instructor of English
Kramer, Patricia Ann
English Instructor
Martenson, Debra Marie Chapman
Science Teacher
Martin, Terry Ross
Comm Coll Biology Instructor

Mason, John Robert
Soc Sci & Svc Learning Teacher
Olsen, Anne Pico
Office Systems Instructor
Thor, Alan D.
Cad Instructor
Walters, Mary Lynn Goode
Nursing Instructor
MANHATTAN
Burich-Cox, Robin Maree
Junior High Math Teacher
Creasey, Kimberly Marie
Junior High English Teacher
Kent, Janice Kay (Norene)
7th & 8th Grade Teacher
Nagra, Timothy John
Fourth Grade Teacher
MANITO
Abbott, Elizabeth Heinkel
Fifth Grade Teacher
Blair, Jay Childers
High School Science Teacher
Gren, Linda M.
Librarian & Teacher
Heinhorst, Teresa Ann (Van Fossan)
Secondary Social Studies Tchr
Steele, Jeffrey L.
Science Teacher
Switzer, Rebecca J.
Business Teacher
MAPLE PARK
Blankenship, Donna Sue Danley
Fifth Grade Teacher
Dickson, Katherine Applebey
First Grade Teacher
Nelson, Elaine Cheris
Spanish Teacher
Nowicki, Richard Wesley
Biology & Chemistry Teacher
Sheetz, Patrick Christopher
7th Grade Life Science Teacher
MAPLETON
Ness, Sharon Maureen (Farley)
Third Grade Teacher
MARENGO
Hoch, Amy Moss
4th Grade Teacher
Hoffert, Corinne P. (Will)
Teacher & Music Director
Hoffert, Ric
8th Grade Teacher
Mathiesen, Laurie B. (Heinsohn)
Biology Teacher & Coach
Mathis, Jay Buchanan
Spanish Teacher
Mc Knight, Steven C.
Mathematics Teacher
Peters, J. D.
HS English & Lang Arts Teacher
Reed, Thomas Henry
Lang Arts & Humanities Teacher
Stimes, Joseph David
Jr High Social Studies Teacher
MARINE
Boyce, Mitchel Alan
Language Arts Teacher & Coach
Hogue, Jackie Lynn (Holler)
5th Grade Teacher
MARION
Bradshaw, Jo Jayne
French & Art Teacher
Butler, Dennis Ray
Drafting Teacher
Edwards, Daniel Dale
Eigth Grade American His Tchr
Ellison, Rebecca Anne
Speech & English Teacher
Ferris, Kay Francis
5th Grade Teacher
Forbes, Dana Ann (Dycus)
Math & Physical Education Tchr
Grant, Chris
School-to-Work Coordinator
Jackson, Charles Robert
Retired Art Instructor
Koller, Barbara A.
Director of Guidance
Lindquist, Thomas Bernard
Art Teacher
McSparin, William Stephen
Eighth Grade Teacher
Minnis, Linda Fae (Barnett)
Physical Education Teacher
Pauls, Carol (Davison)
Retired 4th Grade Teacher
Poole, Melanie Kaye
English Teacher
Schoen, Barbara Chamness
Eng, Jrnlsm Tchr & Dept Chair
Smith, Pamela Dungey
4th Grade Teacher
Wall, R. Mark
Mathematics Teacher
MARISSA
Gibbons, James B.
Music Instructor
Monbrum, Joan M.
Business Teacher
MAROA
Holmes, Jeffrey Dean
High School Principal
Weis, Kathy Myers
Spanish Teacher
Zimmerman, Kathleen Picchietti
High School Art Teacher
MARSEILLES
Ballerini, Dale Victor
Middle School Science Teacher
Harvey, Kay Ann
Retired Fifth Grade Teacher

MARSHALL
Bear, Becky Rene
Biology Teacher
Bolinger, Kay Rennels
English Teacher
Gateley, Timothy Gene
Freshman English Teacher
Johnson, Troy Lee
PE Teacher & Coach
Meehan, Vickie Soppi
Fifth Grade Teacher
Pomatto, Michael A.
Social Studies Instructor
Smith, Daralea Harlow
Second Grade Teacher
MARTINSVILLE
Liggett, Dale L.
Retired 5th Grade Teacher
Redman, Carol Ann Newtson
Spanish & English Teacher
MARYVILLE
Gasawski, Bonnie L.
Kindergarten Teacher
MASCOUTAH
Harris, John
High School Biology Teacher
Harris, Karen Ann
Home Economics, Health Teacher
Marchioro, Robert P.
5th Grade Elementary Teacher
Parks, Barry Timothy
High School Mathematics Tchr
Simpson, Charles Dean
Science Teacher
Stokes, Leila Horton
Cooperative Ed Coord
Thoeming, Jorene Marie
8th Grade Math & Algebra Tchr
Vahlkamp, Julia Vasquez
Retired Third Grade Teacher
MATTESON
Lewis, L. Jean
Art Teacher
Markey, Mary Baldelli
Fifth Grade Teacher
Roberts, Willadeane Clayton
Tchr of Gftd, Lang Arts & Math
MATTOON
Adelman, Deborah Susan
Nursing Instructor
Allen, Joyce Yandell
Psychology Instructor
Bell-Adkins, Jill Ann
1st Grade Teacher
Conlon, Steven Joseph
8th Grade History Teacher
Darimont, Lynn M.
HS English Teacher
Englund, Michelle Marie (Strong)
Fifth Grade Teacher
Fessel, Marilyn Kay Moore
Elementary Teacher
Gebben, Christopher James
6th Grade Teacher
Goodwin, Kelly Curry
Chapter I & Rdng & Math Tchr
Gourley, Sandra J.
Instr & Coord of Human Svcs
Hendrix, William Robert
4th Grade Teacher
Henry, Janet Koch
Office Technology Teacher
Hortenstine, Salisa L.
Speech Comm & English Instr
Horton, Lucinda L.
Biology Instructor
Houston, Sam
Mathematics Professor
Kearney, Jim
Math Teacher
Martinez, Bethany Jill
Spanish Teacher
Miller, Richard Alan
Instructor & Tutor
Norberg, Ann (Cole)
Physical Education & Hlth Tchr
Parker, Jerry
Mathematics Teacher
Parker, Marcia Hinkle
Guidance Counselor
Ragle, Benny Ray
Coordinator of CIS
Rohlinger, Marion Elizabeth
Microbiology Instructor
Sampson, David Raymond
Zoology & Biology Teacher
Schaal, Laverne F.
Sixth Grade Teacher
Self, Clyde Craig
6th Grade Teacher
Sinclair, Michele Nance
Mathematics Teacher
Smith, Susan Ohm
Sixth Grade Teacher
Sundheim, Pamela Point
French Teacher
Swartzbaugh, Dorothy L. Stoeppelwerth
GATE & Language Arts Teacher
Thurn, Rebecca Lynne
High School English Teacher
Warnsing, Kent Randy
John Deere Ag Tech Instructor
Warrem, Margaret Cecelia (Gaseor)
Biology & Chemistry Teacher
Wright, Kathy Jones
4th Grade Teacher
Yelk, Ronald Benton
Sr Army & JROTC Instr

MAYWOOD
Beidas, Edward S.
Physics Teacher
Bellezzo, Cynthia Lenore
Jr High Science Teacher
Bozer, Teresa Marie (Holmes)
Spanish & French Teacher
Conley, Mary Ellen
Office Education Coordinator
Glover, David Ross
Physical Education Teacher
Lid, Glenn David
Chemistry Teacher & Coach
McCants-Young, LaVern Ranita
Counselor & Consumer Ed Tchr
Morrison, Jelena Savic
Mathematics Teacher
Murphy, Terrence Wayne, Sr.
Biology & General Science Tchr
Packer, Aldine LaJoyce
Lang Arts Teacher & Stu Coord
Phelps, Veneeta Brewster
Math & Sci Tchr of Gifted Pgm
Robinson, Mattie Scott
US History Teacher
Warren, Rosella May
Social Studies Instructor
Watts, Maryann Thomas
Jr HS Social Studies Teacher
MC HENRY
Beaudoin, Lisa Meiers
Chemistry Teacher
Bosman, Janice Elaine
Business & English Teacher
Hauck, William Jack
Science & Reading Teacher
Lillibridge, Marilyn White
6th-8th Grade Band Director
Miller, David John
Social Studies Teacher
Schnelker, Lynn M.
English Teacher
Shelton, Kevin Patrick
English Teacher
Trembly, Gary Lee
Mathematics Teacher
MC LEAN
Thompson, Crystal
6th Grade Teacher
MC LEANSBORO
Endicott, Karen Kay (Kreher)
Kindergarten Teacher
Hopper, Gary Ray
8th Grd Special Education Tchr
Miller, Jane Wilson
Fifth Grade Teacher
MEDIA
Thomas, Tamyra Rae
Sci Tch & Instr of Gifted
MEDORA
Clark, Rosemary L.
Second Grade Teacher
MELROSE PARK
Burke, Kathleen M.
Second Grade Teacher
Nendge, Janet O.
Physical Education Teacher
Opel, Elizabeth Ann
English Teacher
Richards, Roberta J.
Fifth Grade Teacher
Ward, Linda Cheryl
Lang Arts & Soc Stud Teacher
Zuffante, Dawn Marie Kessling
Junior High Science Teacher
MENDON
Kreinberg, Mary Ann
7th-8th Grade English Teacher
Lask, Richard Raymond
Music Instructor
MENDOTA
Atherton, Jerilynn Dickey
Counselor
Garthe, William Charles
8th Grade Biology Instructor
MEREDOSIA
Franklin, Janet M. Waitkus
Science Teacher
METAMORA
Bachfischer, Peter John
German Teacher
Coon, John A.
Language Arts Teacher
Crow, Mary Jo Ann Williamson
Science Teacher
Doty, Alana S.
Jr High History & Civics Tchr
Fehl, Linda Sue (Kapraun)
Spanish Teacher
Hicks, Kevin S.
History & English Teacher
Hnilicka, Greg
Physics Teacher
Jones, Gene
Guidance Counselor
Toniny, David Paul
Physics & Chemistry Teacher
Wagner, Kathryn S.
High School History Teacher
Whitfield, Sally Lauterbach
English Teacher & Dept Chair
METROPOLIS
Artman, Vickie Ann Williamson
Third Grade Teacher
Bremer, Sue E.
Mathematics Teacher
Downing, Janice Mae
Third Grade Teacher
Glass, Kelly Wayne
Physical Education Teacher

ROPOLIS (cont)
an, Brent Alan
Grade Basketball Coach
Roger D.
stant Special Ed Teacher
, Marilyn Croach
ish Teacher
Marty (Johnson)
man Teacher
, Dorothy Ledsinger
3rd Language Arts Teacher
ghby, Thomas Edward
ness Teacher
, Donna Mason
ish Teacher & Dept Chrpsn
OTHIAN
ziak, Lynne Cione
Grade Teacher
brosio, John Dominic
ish Teacher
Susan D.
School English Teacher
Jeffrey Scott
al Studies Teacher
an, Margaret
th Grade Teacher
Jane Blew
ogy & Plant Science Tchr
d, Deborah Victoria
h Grade Teacher
s, Michele Santos
Teacher
eley, Kathleen
ematics Teacher
nhall, Marcia M.
Teacher
ton, Michael Joseph
al Studies Teacher
n, Diane Davis
nce Teacher
ns, Corinne Anne
nce Teacher
d, Susan Marie
Grade Teacher
ORD
g, Sam W.
Teacher
Barbara L.
ish Teacher
EDGEVILLE
art, Randall Lee
ogy & Chemistry Teacher
STADT
Frederick Albert
ed Teacher
pf, Sandra Schmidt
h Grade Teacher
NK
Brian Patrick
ocial Studies Teacher
Sue Alice
Grade Teacher
all, Barbara Emm
ness Education Teacher
James R.
nce Teacher
OKA
no, Kathy Ann (Folz)
d of Gifted & Talented
Richard A.
Instructor
Judith Marie (Adams)
al Studies Teacher
Erick David
al Science Teacher
ns, Daniel Shaun
d & Cultures His Tchr
Martha Portegys
gh Art Teacher
, Kathy Etherton
uage Arts Teacher
Ken
Tchr
el, Kimberly Scholtes
l Director & Teacher
Glenda Rogene
ory & Government Teacher
Phil B.
Grade Teacher
r, Angela Kathleen
ch & Drama Teacher
ENA
man, Rob
Arts Teacher
, Vickie Jean Markham
th Grade Teacher
der, Rita Ann (Rubas)
Grade Teacher
Mary Jane
Grade Language Arts Tchr
NE
s, William S.
ting Teacher
cht, Timothy Charles
ness & Marketing Ed Coord
, Joseph
hman & Sophomore PE Tchr
n, John David
Bio & General Sci Tchr
ry, David Lynn
ish Professor
er, Leo
Grade Geography Teacher
gh, William George
strial Technology Instr
-Camper, Sherry Aman
ematics Teacher
s, David Raymond
ish Teacher

Craver, Barbara Reis
7th & 8th Grade PE Teacher
Crouch, William Ronald
Cooperative Education Coord
Curtis, Sally B.
Assistant Prof of Chemistry
Dodd, Sharon Reedy
Fourth Grade Teacher
Gibbs, Marilyn Kay
First Grade Teacher
Krueger, Nancy Lee (Mason)
Business Education Teacher
Maguire, Kenneth Edward
Assoc Prof of His & Sociology
Mahieu, Marty Andrew
Health Educator
Miley, Karla Krogsrud
Professor
Nitzel, Michael George
Social Studies Teacher
Pitz, Arthur Hugo
History Professor
Pitz, Paul Nicholas
English, German & Hum Teacher
Pleshe, David L.
Fine Arts Chairman
Pleshe, Rebecca Leinen
4th Grade Teacher
Ratkiewicz, Susan Illingworth
1st Grade Rdng Recovery Tchr
Roberts, Kevin R.
English Instructor
Rung, Gail Rubin
English Professor
Schauenberg, Susan Kay
Professor & Counselor
Schmidt, Mary Beth
6th Grade Teacher
Schwaegler, Steven Robert
Band Director
Smith, Susan L.
Learning Skills Counselor
Spriet, Jill Hoener
Fifth Grade Teacher
Tipton, Patricia Jean (Buchmeyer)
Third Grade Teacher
Verbeke, Tammy Seitz
7th-8th Grd PE & Hlth Teacher
Weigel, Janet
Assoc Prof, Behav & Sci Dept
White, Robert Keith
Speech Professor
Ybarra, Joseph Daniel
8th Grade History Teacher
MOMENCE
Collins, Sylvia Smith
Third Grade Teacher
Danish, Charles William
Fourth Grade Teacher
Degitz, Richard Louis
Vocal Music Tchr & Choral Dir
Dvorak, Linda Jameson
Social Studies Teacher
Frank, Stephen William
Geometry Teacher & Counselor
Rehmer, Ellen Milstead
Music Teacher
MONMOUTH
Baker, Marie Erspamer
Math & Computer Sci Instructor
Connell, Michael L.
Asst Prof of Economics
Kusnerick, Christopher Martin
Social Studies Teacher
Lariviere, Nancy Ann
Asst Professor of Psychology
Li, Chenyang
Assistant Prof of Philosophy
Pieper, William John
Science Teacher & Dept Chm
Symington, Garnet Earl, Jr.
Vocational Agriculture Tchr
Urban, William L.
Lee L Morgan Prof of History
Van Arsdale, Susan
English & Journalism Teacher
Watts, Christine A.
Mathematics Tchr & Dept Chm
MONTGOMERY
Mc Carron, James P.
Fifth Grade Teacher
Reilly, Lynne R.
Principal
MONTICELLO
Handley, Jeanne M.
Guidance Counselor
MOOSEHEART
Kreitzer, Julie Kaye Swanson
Kindergarten Teacher
MORRIS
Dergo, L. George
Special Needs Teacher
Doyle, Sherry L. (Drum)
Third Grade Teacher
Ehteshami-Afsher, Kristin Sauter
English Teacher
Hankins, Christine Geden
Art Teacher
Henson, Vicki Barth
French & Substitute Teacher
Hussey, Kelly J.
Guidance Counselor
Jensen, Linda Brancato
Kindergarten Teacher
Locke, David L.
Social Studies Teacher
Michael, Deb S.
Health Teacher
Miller, Judith Goodwin
English & Speech Teacher

Petric, Janine M.
Math & Social Studies Teacher
Pinkstaff, Bob
Retired Math Teacher
Rath, Barbara Reas
Business Education Teacher
Shaw, Herbert Ralph, III
Industrial Technology Teacher
Spirek, Lawrence James, Sr.
Biology Teacher
Wren, Dawn Bukes
7th Grade Math Teacher
MORRISON
Bean, David Howard
High School Band Director
Blunt, Marjorie Kapper
French & English Teacher
Hibbeler, Eric Allen
Vocal Music Director
Williams, Janice Jean
General Studies Instructor
MORRISONVILLE
Montgomery, Della Amos
3rd Grd Tchr & Gifted Coord
MORTON
Combs, James Edward
Sixth Grade Teaching Team
Durham, Eveline Myers
High School Counselor
Highbanks, Sherry J.
Family & Consumer Science Tchr
Hildebrand, Shirley Rumold
Chemistry Teacher
Klein, Steven Joe
Mathematics Teacher
Owen, Gail Simpson
Language Arts Teacher
Stimpert, Dan P.
HS Math Teacher
Zuck, Andrew F.
Social Studies Teacher
MORTON GROVE
Daiberl, Richard Joseph
7th Grd Social Studies Teacher
Emanuel, Steven John
PE & Health Educator
Wicinski, Juli (Main)
3rd Grade Teacher
MOSSVILLE
Dunn, Kay L.
First Grade Teacher
Pullen, Peggy
Fifth Grade Teacher
MOUNDS
Weston, Edward Eugene
Social Studies Teacher
Wohlwend, Holly Derickson
Family & Consumer Sci Teacher
MOUNT CARMEL
Adams, Gary Hite
Chemistry & Biology Instructor
Bayne, Victoria Akers
Foreign Language Dept Chair
Brown, C. Allen
Instructor of Mathematics
Burns, Bonnie Jean
Mathematics Instructor
Buss, Kelly Marie (Neuman)
Fifth-Eighth Grd Hlth Tchr
Corwin, Jerry J.
Industrial Technology Instr
Gruca, Deborah Hatfield
Math & Social Studies Teacher
Kepley, Linda Walter
8th Grd Amer His Teacher
Owens, Patricia Ann
Instructor of History
Phegley, Brenda Acree
Composition Instructor
Schafer, Beverly M.
English Teacher
Shoaff, Richard E.
Social Science Teacher
Stein, Jill E.
Chemistry Teacher
Storckman, Cynthia Schimp
LD Resource Teacher
Wallar-Henegar, Marylin Lee
Substitute Teacher
Wilderman, David M.
Lead Instructor of Marketing
Youngs, Charles Ronald
Sci Dept Chprsn & Bio Tchr
MOUNT CARROLL
Hartman, Daniel Ray, Jr.
Agriculture Advisor
MOUNT MORRIS
Crain, Terri L.
Choral Dir & Music Specialist
Lawton, Michael F.
Social Studies Teacher & Coach
MOUNT PROSPECT
Eigenfeld, Peter B.
Math, Sci Tchr & Coord
Golob, Jeff H.
4th Grade Teacher
Leapley, Kurt Allen
Teacher & Assistant Principal
McGinnis, J. Milton
Teacher
Price, Robert Earl
8th Grd Biology & Physics Tchr
Ware, Elease Harris
Spanish & PE Teacher
MOUNT STERLING
Ramsey, Les Robert
Math, Physics & Spanish Tchr
Riden, Scott Charles
Agriculture Education Instr

MOUNT VERNON
Beene, Burl Vance
English Teacher
Kabat, John Thaddeus
Ag & Cooperative Ed Teacher
Lacey, Stephen Lee
Science Teacher
Mason, Judy Schultz
Art Teacher
Morris, Steve Walker
Asst Regional Supt of Schls
Nottmeyer, Diane Meyer
High School Mathematics Tchr
Pulley, Paula Jean
Mathematics Teacher
Quinn, Ted G.
English Teacher
Shifflet, Dorothy Kneer
High School Spanish Teacher
Tickner, Scott D.
Hlth Ed Tchr, Hd Wrstlng Coach
Tomlin, Bob
Physics & Electronics Teacher
Wells, Andrew Lee
Social Studies Teacher
Wiman, Ferrell Frank
Guidance Counselor
MOUNT ZION
Britton-Garrett, Lois
Kindergarten Teacher
Browning, David Robert
Biology & Physical Sci Teacher
Brush, Sandra J.
Guidance Counselor
Johnson, Marcia Rittmueller
English & Speech Teacher
Marshall, Victoria Lenore (Addison)
High School Mathematics Tchr
Oakes, Nancy W.
French & German Teacher
O'Brien, Marciann Raczek
HS Mathematics Teacher
Richardson, Sally Longmuir
HS Math Teacher
Russell, Joyce Cecilia
Spanish Instructor
Shaw, Susan Reed
Home Economics Teacher
Tilton, Judith Albin
First Grade Teacher
MOWEAQUA
Caplinger, Ben F.
Mathematics & Physics Teacher
Caplinger, Donna Kay
Biology Teacher
Laymon, Richard O.
5th Grade Teacher
McGartland, Steven R.
Instrumental Music Director
MULBERRY GROVE
Dooly, Thomas Charles
Industrial Arts Teacher
Grigg, Barbara Ann
Fifth Grade Teacher
Neathery, Dianne Marie
Social Studies Teacher
MUNDELEIN
Acosta-Carmona, Jose Felipe
Spanish Teacher
Alloian, David Sarkis
Fourth Grade Teacher
Barker, Marianne Duellman
Chemistry & Earth Science Tchr
Chorazy, Linda Kostich
8th Grade Teacher
Dolph-Smith, Susan Diane
Director
Duncan, Pamela Sue
Instructor of Science & Math
Franco, Jennifer Biel
English & Speech Teacher
Girard, Ronald G.
Psychology & Journalism Tchr
Green, Glen Lee
Physics Teacher
Green, Scott Alan
Mathematics Teacher
Halford, James
Psychology Teacher
Harry, William Joseph
President
Hartwig, Barbara Ellen
PE & Health Teacher
Henke, Gloria Smith
Mathematics Teacher
Kuykendall, Robert Martin
English Teacher
Ladd, David Scott
Director of Choral Music
Mayer, John C.
Art Teacher & Coach
Phillips, Sheri Lynn
High School Business Teacher
Sager, Elaine Spivak
Fourth Grade Teacher
Santi, Mary Beth Frainey
Reading & Composition Teacher
Strutzel, Lynne G.
English Department Chairman
Wirt, Jodi Ladwig
English Teacher
MURPHYSBORO
Beggs, Lynne Anne
Math Teacher
Berry, Alice Allen
Choral Music Director
Bisaga, Richard Henry
Retired 6th Grade Teacher
Cramer, Loraine Rebstock
Retired Teacher

Mikulay, Mark
HS Band Director
Pugh, Donna Garver
4th Grade Teacher
Rathjen, Lillian
Guidance Counselor
Roberts, Gwen Lofquist
Guidance Counselor
Rosenberger, Terry Ray
Metals Instructor
MURRAYVILLE
Mc Carty, Janet Butler
Kindergarten Teacher
NAPERVILLE
Andre, Donald M.
Fourth Grade Teacher
Bee, Martin
Guidance Cnslr & Asst Ath Dir
Bruce, Laura Ann
Mathematics Teacher
Bucher, David Edward
PE & Health Ed Teacher
Bushman, John F.
Agriscience Instructor
Caron, William Gerard
Dean of Students
Costopoulos, James G.
Humanities Teacher
Dolan, Patrick Michael
HS American Studies Teacher
Duncan, Gary L.
8th Grade Science Teacher
Durham, Gary David
8th Grade Soc Stud & Eng Tchr
Elenbaas, Judith Thoma
Physics Teacher
Favreau, Catherine Louise
Latin Teacher
Golff, Kathleen Pederson
Jr High Lang Arts & Rdng Tchr
Grover, Ardith Gaylord
8th Grade English Teacher
Haas, Brent
HS English Teacher
Hamilton, James Evans
Fifth Grade Teacher
Jones, Richard Carl
English Teacher
Kane, Linda Louise (Schiesser)
English Tchr & Newspaper Adv
Kasten, Lewis Scott
Fourth Grade Teacher
Keating, Janet Sue
Chemistry Teacher
Kennedy, Laurel Jane
Guidance Counselor
Kenton, Patricia Readey
Chemistry Teacher
Kluckman, Tim L.
Law & History Teacher
Kramen, Rita E.
Reading Teacher
LaBianca, Kiki
Gifted Language Arts Teacher
Lademann, Lon Darryl
History & Literature Teacher
Lee, Holly Hildenbrand
World History Teacher
Lemanski, Karen A.
Health Teacher
Lipari, Russell Joseph
Band & Music Coorinator
Marek, Lee Robert
Chemistry Teacher
Mazzarella, Steven Gerard
Health Education Teacher
Moody, Jim
Social Studies Teacher
Pease, Kathy Waldo
Administrative Assistant
Raab, Richard John
Sci Teacher & Swim Coach
Rosenthal, Edward L.
Science Teacher
Savage, William Kevin, Jr.
Proj Arrow Math Tchr of Gifted
Sikula, Melody Cepek
Second Grade Teacher
Somers, Michael J.
7th Grade Science Teacher
Thompson, Jane A.
Comparative Religions Teacher
Torsberg, Susan Ann
English Teacher
Tschopp, Barbara Classon
Resource Teacher
Ulbrich, Thomas E.
English, Theatre Teacher & Dir
Wall, Douglas F.
Math Teacher
Waterman, Beth Ann
Biology Teacher
Wilkins, Michele Merrick
College Instructor
Yarbrough, James P.
HS Vocal Music Teacher
Young, Kenneth Allan
Social Studies Teacher
Zaininger, Gayle Gasick
HS Communication Arts Teacher
NAUVOO
Candido, Salvatore A.
English & Religion Teacher
Ferguson, Elaine Chapin
Sixth Grade Teacher
Jacobs, Janice Massa
Vocal & Instrumental Instr
Lake, Connie Becker
Teacher

NAUVOO (cont)
Stambach, Stan Lee
Jr & Sr Science Teacher
NELSON
Henderson, Rick
5th & 6th Grade Teacher
NEOGA
Cohorst, Sally Sheridan
Math Teacher
Davis, Kirby Duane
Counselor
Gidcomb, Barbara Jean (Unkraut)
Jr High Language Arts Tchr
Kenneaster, Donna K.
Business Teacher & Comp Coord
Mc Clure, Douglas S.
Music & Drama Teacher
Powell, Michael Duane
7th & 8th Grade Math Teacher
Short, Linda Baker
Language Arts Teacher
Snyder, Michael Wayne
Resource Teacher
NEW ATHENS
Houshmand, Emma Lambdin
JR HS & HS School Art Teacher
Lawrence, Jill West
Junior High English Teacher
NEW BADEN
Horstmann, Elaine Varel
Elementary Teacher
NEW BERLIN
Buffington, Rosemary
7th-12th Grade Art Teacher
Escorcia, Christie Marie
Second Grade Teacher
Kimball, David Arlen
High School Math Teacher
NEW LENOX
Aiu, James A.
High School Math Teacher
Babcock, Paul Andrew
Social Science Teacher
Bennett, Jacquelyn Faye
Chemistry Teacher
Bernhard, David C., Sr.
Mathematics Instructor
Blasing, Eilen Brennan
English & Speech Teacher
Brown, Jeffrey Paul
Drafting & CAD Teacher
Bultman, W. Michael
Music Teacher
Casey, Kathleen Mc Mahon
Chemistry Teacher
Clark, Susan Joy
3rd Grade Teacher
Dolak, Jayne Gardner
8th Grade Math Teacher
Gardner, Michael Lawrence
Principal
Graham, Michelle L.
US History & Civics Teacher
Healy, Keith Albert
Physical Education Teacher
Hollingsworth, Jennene Sciabica
Fifth Grade Teacher
Houston, Paul B.
Soc Studies Tchr & Act Dir
Immel, Judith Hill
Business Teacher
Ludwig, Kelly Edward
Bio, Anatomy & Physiology Tchr
Malone, Karen Hordesky
Amer Civics & Sociology Tchr
Mandella, Richard Kenneth
Coll Counselor & Bsktbl Coach
Maza, Christopher John
French Teacher
McHenry, Rebecca Schweitzer
6th Grd Social Studies Teacher
Moser, William Daniel
English Teacher
Mostyn, Margie Irwin
Math Teacher
Mudrock, James Lee
Mathematics Teacher
Mudrock, Jennifer Sward
Mathematics Teacher
Niznik, Ernest Gaylord
Geology Teacher
Paisley, Lorna Ann
Chemistry Teacher
Pritchard, Rosemary Clare
Fifth Grade Teacher
Rabbers, Kathleen D.
English Teacher
Rassman, Michael R.
English Teacher
Romadka, Robert G., Jr.
Mathematics Instructor
Spagnola, Margaret Anne
Theology Tchr & Dept Chprsn
Thompson, Tim David
Psychology Teacher
Tighe, Patricia Kaufman
High School Mathematics Tchr
Torkelson, Erik Paul
General Music Teacher
Warning, Eleanor L.
English Teacher
Wilhelmi, Richard Thomas
HS Mathematics Teacher
Windish, Elizabeth Lynn (Klepper)
HS Math Teacher
NEWARK
Jorstad, Priscilla Kmiecik
Jr High Language Arts Teacher
Knutson, Joan Evans
Teacher's Aide
Nordstrom, Paul Robert
Fourth Grade Teacher
Schobert, Mary M.
HS Home Economics Teacher
Skelton, Dale Allen
Phys Dev Instr & Ath Director
NEWTON
Pasero, Peter Joseph
Chemistry & Physics Teacher
Sharpe, Carol Jean (Mc Elhiney)
Physical Education Teacher
Wiman, Loretta Lovelace
Eng Dept Head & Speech Tchr
Zerrusen, Joseph Anthony
Agriculture Instructor
NIANTIC
Long, Susan Jane Craine
English Teacher
Miller, Marta Lane
Art Teacher
Rhodes, Mark Lee
Physical Ed Teacher & Coach
Waller, Joanne Garnett
English Educator
NILES
Cochrane, M. Kathleen
Science Dept Chair & Teacher
Dawidczyk, Angela Orlando
Social Studies Teacher
Hennessey, Michael Joseph
Enrollment Mgr & Asst Dean
Jennings, Kurt M.
Director of Br Andre Schlr Pgm
Kelliher, Thomas G., Jr.
American History Teacher
Moran, Judith Ann
HS Math Teacher
Moscatello, Anthony D.
English Teacher
O'Connor, Mary Karris
English Teacher
NOBLE
Herndon, Terry Lynn
Language Arts Teacher
Stallard, Brenda Lea
Business Education Teacher
NOKOMIS
Klinefelter, Barbara Colonius
English Teacher
Tosetti, Maxine Bradley
Retired Vocal Music Teacher
NORMAL
Bellich, Patick James
Third Grade Teacher
Blodgett, Celeste Kankowski
Supervisor
Blum, Pamela P.
Assoc Prof & Art Fndtns Coord
Boyd, John Rupe
French Teacher
Chizmar, John Francis
Economics Professor
Cordero, Rogue
Distngd Prof of Music Emeritus
Dean, Dorothy Lynn
Business Education Instructor
DeSouza, Eros R.
Physchology Professor
Embry, Chris
Agricultural Science Teacher
Farrell-Stroyan, Sue Patricia
Second Grade Teacher
Fitzgibbons, Dale Edward
Assoc Prof of Management
Freeman, Robert B.
Art Instructor
Graham, Sandra McCommis
Secondary Level Bus Ed Tchr
Grogg, Patricia M.
Prof of Bus Comm & Assoc Dean
Hill, John I.
Mathematics Professor
Lammers, Lucille E.
Professor of Accounting
Lindahl, Jama Lynn
Spanish Teacher
Morgan, Lauren Grace
English & Communication Tchr
Nagle, Daniel James
Fifth Grade Teacher
Neisler, Joe Wilson
Professor of Horn
Noles, Scott Preston
Technology Education Instr
Otto, Albert Dean
Mathematics Professor
Parsons, Gerald Anthony
Faculty Associate Emeritus
Payne, Harriette F.
Science Teacher
Pereira, Kim
Professor
Reinholz, Randy S.
Assistant Professor
Thomas, Sally A.
Fifth Grade Teacher
Virlee, Michael R.
Biology Teacher
Wallace, David Charles
Information System Dev Prof
NORRIDGE
Lupo, Robert J.
Curriculum Director
Michelon, Mariella
Italian Teacher
NORRIS CITY
Gray, David Orley
Physical Education & Hlth Tchr
Griffin, Jane Healy
Fifth Grade Teacher
Hobbs, Roger
High School Teacher
Sutton-Phillips, Kimberly Dawn
Spanish Teacher
Taylor, Mary Ludene
3rd-12th Grade Art Teacher
NORTH AURORA
Reynolds, Jan Kay
2nd Grade Teacher
NORTH CHICAGO
Friedes-Craig, Judith A.
Mathematics Teacher & Liaison
Johnson, Cathy J.
Librarian
Johnson, Glenn Solomon
Fifth Grade Teacher
King, William James
Coord of Ath & Activities
Porter, Susan Marie
Spanish Teacher
Whitaker, Vernell
Dean of Students
NORTHBROOK
Belluomini, Ronald Joseph
Lang Arts & Soc Stud Teacher
Berdick, Ruth James
ESL & English Teacher
Collins, Frank
Math Teacher & Dept Head
Collins, Julie Willbanks
Chemistry Teacher
Doebler, Judith Novak
Art Teacher
Drozdoff, Nicholas P.
Honors Physics & Science Tchr
Helfrich, Katherine Hale
Retired 6th Grade Teacher
Jackson, Martha Frame
Mathematics Teacher
Kruzic, Robert Paul
English Teacher
Mathieu, Bud
Science Teacher
Mc Pherrin, James Sterling
History Instructor
Owens, Lea Ferguson
Kindergarten Teacher
Piskel, Michael James
High School Science Teacher
Powers, Kristi Jean (Snider)
High School Math Teacher
Rhodes, Burt
US His, Geog & Urban Stud Tchr
Schulz, Karin M.
Rdng, Lang Arts, Soc Stud Tchr
Spak, Helene Savage
Gifted Rdng & Lang Arts Tchr
Terdich, Catherine Ann (Slosar)
Integrated Language Arts Tchr
Unterman, Nathan
Physics Teacher
Vroman, Julie Anne
8th Grd Language Arts Teacher
Ware, Jeffrey Allen
Spanish Teacher
NORTHLAKE
Knox, Brian A.
3rd Grade Teacher
O FALLON
Bickel, Richard S.
Ec, US His & Intnl Issues Tchr
Cordon, Ray Lewis
Teacher & Speech Dept Chair
Cosmano, Vincent James
Instrumental Music Teacher
Cotts, Jane Ellen (Friedrich)
Algebra Teacher
Day, Michael E.
US History & Citzenship Tchr
Deets, Patricia A.
High School Math Teacher
Edgar, Anthony Wayne
8th Grd Boys Basketball Coach
Estes, Kelly Austin
English Teacher
Herrington, James Patrick
Mathematics Instructor
Jackson, Mary Ellen Courter
English Teacher
Jones, Beverley A. C.
Second Grade Teacher
May, Daniel S.
Social Studies Teacher
Santos, Pamela S.
Business Teacher & Coordinator
Schaub, Sylvia Lynn
Retired Math Teacher
Smith, Linda Marie Keserauskis
Fourth Grade Teacher
Toenjes, Norman Raymond
Social Studies Teacher
Voellinger, Arthur Charles
English Instructor
OAK BROOK
Haley, Mary L.
Social Studies Teacher
Sabbagha, Hope Barnes
Former Teacher
OAK FOREST
Benes, Helen Bell
Computer Teacher
Dieskow, Laurel
Chemistry Teacher
Griffith, Patricia Taliefero
Fourth Grade Teacher
Moroz, John Louis
Mathematics Teacher
Ryder, Sandra L.
Amer His & Global Stud Tchr
Schwaighart, Kathleen Margaret
Philbrook
Jr HS Soc Studies & Rel Tchr
Smith, Saundra Jo
Mathematics Teacher
Snider, Judy Ann
8th Grade Language Arts Tchr
OAK LAWN
Arneson, Amy J.
Home Economics Teacher
Atkins, Scott A.
Biology Teacher
Carlson, Jan Ristow
High School Guidance Counselor
Carrier, Arlene Lerro
English & Spanish Teacher
Chilvers, Charles James
Physical Education Teacher
Deitemyer, David
Music Teacher & Band Director
Egan, Mary B.
Student Assistance Coordinator
Fiscella, Theresa Janulis
7th & 8th Grade Math Teacher
Folliard, Julie Ann
4th Grd Tchr & Sftbl Coach
Gath, Robert Edward
8th Grd LA & Reading Teacher
Hash, Georgia Lower
Spanish Teacher
Hill, Maureen A.
High School English Teacher
Johnson, Pamela R.
Sixth Grade Teacher
Joyce, Janet Brown
4th Grade Teacher
Kantola, Denise Kathleen
Speech & English Teacher
Kilroy, Clare Dempsey
5th Grd Lang Arts & Hmrm Tchr
Koenig, Paul Ronald
Scndry Soc Studies Teacher
Kunde, Robert William
History Teacher & Coach
Laskowski, Joanne Dolores
Sixth Grade Teacher
Lawson, Charles R.
Science Teacher
Leable, Marjorie A.
English Teacher
Levy, Rhonda M.
Art Teacher
Malloy, Eleanor R.
HS Social Studies Teacher
Morisette, Cheryl Palaggi
Special Education Teacher
Motley, Cora Beamon
English Teacher
Persson, Jodi Robin
Mathematics Teacher
Rekruciak, Thomas A.
Business Department Teacher
Riordan, Michael James
Science Teacher
Scheman, Nicholas John
Science Teacher
Schubrych, Barbara Ann Marie
6th-8th Grade Teacher
Smenos, James J.
Math Teacher
Sulek, Jan
Chem Tchr & Sci Dept Chair
Sullivan, Eugene Edward
Social Studies Teacher & Coach
Termuende, Edwin A.
Chemistry Teacher
Troy, Cherryl A.
Spanish & French Teacher
Wax, Alan Samuel
French Teacher
Whiteaker, Barbara J.
English Teacher
Woulfe, Yvonne E. Kenney
Sixth Grade Teacher
Zenz, Mary Ann A.
Third Grade Teacher
OAK PARK
Arellano, Andrew Michael
Speech & English Teacher
Averbach, Micheal Kent
History Division Chairman
Aylesworth, Jim
1st Grade Teacher
Black, Todd Mitchell
Physical Education Teacher
Blackburn, Richard Jay
Eng Lit & Hum Teacher
Bonney, Richard H.
Mathematics & Cmptr Sci Tchr
DePaldo, Michael George
English Teacher
Farmar, Margaret DeFily
8th Grade Mathematics Teacher
Fiene, Judy M.
Fifth Grade Teacher
Gambro, John M.
Classics Dept Chm & Latin Tchr
Goldstein, Lois
Mathematics Teacher
Granias, Joseph Thomas
Language Arts Teacher
Harken, Bruce R.
Social Studies Teacher
Hayes, Charles Thomas
Choral Dir & Vocal Music Tchr
Honkomp, Clinton P.
Theology Teacher
Jones, Alan Leon
5th Grade Teacher
Kerr, Robert W.
Teacher
Langenderfer, Duane Lee
Instructor of English
Lindon, Linda Cantrell
High School French Teacher
Lordan, Gerald Francis
Social Studies Dept Chair
Metropoulos, Miraflor Luistro
Fourth Grade Teacher
Polka, John Dean
Sci Dept Chm & Biology Teacher
Roe, JoAnne
Spanish Teacher
Scotty, Helen Lawson
Retired 1st Grade Teacher
Urbanski, Marie Jezik
Biology Teacher
Vyborny, Terrieann Susin
Physics Teacher
OAKLAND
Hawkins, Patricia Ann (Tibbs)
Math Teacher & Guid Counselor
Roll, Lee Isaacson
English Teacher
Schneider, J. Scott
Social Studies Teacher
Stites, Marijon Anna Goekler
Life Science Instructor
OBLONG
Lange, Margaret Eileen (Medler)
Fifth Grade Teacher
Mowrer, Kurt Clinton
Industrial Technology Teacher
Sweat, Karen Williamson
Fifth Grade Teacher
ODELL
Ehrhardt, Marjorie Anne (Masching)
Seventh & Eighth Grade Teacher
ODIN
Jackson, Rick J.
6th Grade Teacher
Miller, Sara (Pearson)
Rdng, Spelling & Math Teacher
OGLESBY
Anderson, John D.
Mathematics Teacher
Mueller, Robert James
English Instructor
OKAWVILLE
Fox, Joy Bohlebea
1st-2nd Grade Teacher
OLNEY
Barndt, Darren William
High School History Teacher
Bishop, Susan Lynn
Seventh Grade English Teacher
Huffman, George W.
Math Teacher
Kolb, James Herdis
Principal
Pampe, Lisa K. Hasewinkle
Trig, Calculus & Physics Tchr
Steber, Mark A.
Agriculture Teacher
Wallace, Nancy Stevens
LD Inclusion Teacher
OLYMPIA FIELDS
De Pasquale, Thomas August
History Teacher
Dusa-Day, Margaret Marie
Social Studies Teacher
Fash, Gregory Andrew
CADD, Automotive, Voc Ed Instr
Goods-Cherry, Sharman
Spcl Education Coordinator
Martin, Barbara J.
Guidance Cnslr & Algebra Tchr
Pluta, Maria E.
Physics Teacher
Ross, John Charles
HS Mathematics Teacher
Rostron, Larry Allen
Guidance Counselor
Wessendorf, James A.
History, Ec & Philosphy Tchr
ONARGA
Covey, Richard H.
Social Studies Teacher
ONEIDA
Davis, Donna K.
Elem Supvr & Jr High Principal
Main, Rodney Edward
Agriculture Education Teacher
Mohr, Carol Y.
English Department Teacher
Mottaz, Janet R.
English Teacher
Redfern, Penny S.
Art Teacher
Vittone, Joseph James
Amer History Teacher
ORANGE PARK
Larrabee, Ronald Paul
Tire Sales Manager
ORANGEVILLE
Mc Cabe, Jim E.
Social Studies Tchr & Ath Dir
OREANA
Collis, Virginia Mallory Hall
Third Grade Teacher
OREGON
Armbruster, Sandra Arndt
English Teacher
Eddington, Kelly Gaye
High School Art Teacher
Gatz, Julie Marshall
Home Ec & Soc Studies Teacher
Lauer, Mitchell William
Band Director

ON (cont)
nstry, Byron
al Dir & Music Chprsn
, Patsy Donohue
ish Teacher & Stu Cncl Adv
hoven, Brenda Joyce (Harris)
sh & French Teacher
n, Kathleen Lolita
Mathematics Teacher
, Mary Alice Quick
ish Teacher
N
a, Beverly Moody
ed Math Instructor
, Jay
ish & Communications Tchr
Rhonda L.
ematics Teacher
, Stephanie K.
Grade Teacher
son, Janice Garrity
ergarten Teacher
rg, Karin Buehler
& 12th Grd English Tchr
-Martinez, Martin Sean
ral & Vocal Music Teacher
ms, Todd Michael
rl Tech Tchr & Head Coach
rink, Travis Dale
culture Teacher & Coach
AND PARK
lomew, Jim
ish Teacher
rs, Ray Glenn
ounting Teacher
, Cathleen Ann (Coleman)
dance Counselor
elle, Scott
Grade Science Teacher
racki, Gregory G.
ematics Teacher
Harry A.
ogy Teacher
on, Daniel A.
d Director
s, Alice Czwornog
nish Teacher
rt, Bill
ish Teacher
, Donna
ogy Teacher
rd, Patricia (Bigoness)
ish Instructor
Janet E.
her & Consultant
a, James C.
ructor
en, Wayne Gregory
nce Teacher
on, Karen J. (Hoffman)
Grade Language Arts Tchr
an, Peggy Slattery
h Grade Teacher
, Cari Ann
nce Teacher & Coach
l, Jerry R.
anities Department Chair
EGO
, James Warren
Grade Lang Arts & His Tchr
, Carole Johnson
nce & Language Arts Tchr
, David A.
Grade Teacher
son, Michael James
ral Director
g, Grant Barry
Grade US His & Govt Tchr
, Linda Lee (Wright)
Teacher & Coach
ance, Russell Joseph
n School Math Teacher
r, Howard S.
istrial Technology Teacher
s, David Charles
Dept Head & Teacher
Jean Kendall
lish Teacher
s, Margene Kirkwood
d Director
as, Robert
erican History Instructor
able, Mike E.
Grade Teacher & Coach
e, John Robert
h Grade Teacher
AWA
n, Harry F.
lish Teacher
-Buinickas, Laureen J.
guage Arts Teacher
e, Margaret Roloff
red 4th Grade Teacher
er, Barbara Jean
Grade Teacher
er, Michael Steven
cial Education Teacher
enberger, Linda M.
lish Teacher
, Linda Schultz
nch & English Teacher
Patricia Connelly
ence Teacher
ood, E. Joseph
, PE Instr & Ath Trainer
g, Patty Lynn
rth Grade Teacher
David Raymond
istant Principal

Olsen, Bill E.
Chemistry Teacher
Reckmeyer, Sarah Anne
Band Director
Reuther, Marsha Jean
English Teacher
Riley, Clarence Dean
Retired Coach
Smith, Matthew Terrence
World History Teacher
Vaughan, Harry William
Improvement Consultant
Williams, Christopher Gerard
Sixth Grade Teacher

PALATINE

Anderson, Gary L.
English Teacher
Artrip, Jim Reid
Fifth Grade Teacher
Bachrodt, Michael
High School Chemistry Teacher
Boehm, Janette Ruth
Math Teacher
Chamberlain, Charles Michael
Dean of Students
Corliss, Kathleen (Bradish)
Middle School Teacher
Froelich, Karen Schuler
Assistant Prof of Mathematics
Gilbert, Jacquese Latonia
Physical Education Teacher
Harris, Jane Pazderka
ESL & Intnl Student Advisor
Healy, Mark L.
Economics Professor
Held, Robert George
Accounting Professor
Herriges, Greg Charles
English Professor
Herzog, Mary M.
Comprehensive Music Teacher
Hickey, Barbara Butler
English Professor
Jansa, Marjorie
Algebra & LD Teacher
Jedlicka, William Joseph
Professor
Kraft, Gary Edward
Chemistry & Gifted Ed Tchr
Lang, David G.
Associate Band Director
Lang, Margaret Ann
High School English Teacher
Mc David, Sally Lee
Teacher
Mottla, LeRoy Joseph
Professor of English
Neuhauser, Carol Czarnota
Early Childhood Education Prof
Njus, Barbara Simon
Associate Professor of English
Ostrowski, Michael V.
Prof & Chm of Psych Dept
Palmer, Kevin Clark
Social Studies Teacher
Pass, Stephen K.
Guidance Counselor
Petricca, Joseph A.
Health, PE Tchr & Coach
Radebaugh, Barbara Ann
Chair of Ed Dept, Prof of Mngt
Richards, Jane E.
Business Ed Teacher
Ryan, Kathleen M.
Fifth & Sixth Grade Teacher
Siegel, Steven Jeffery
Physics & Astronomy Professor
Sipiera, Paul Peter, Jr.
Prof of Geology & Astronomy
Sobeski, Kathryn Joan
English Teacher
Stephens, LaVerne Langmann
Language Arts & History Tchr
Tippens, Jack Duane
Prof of Art & Dept Chair
Trethaway, R. Denise Rinovato
High School English Teacher
Weaver, James Francis
English Teacher
Wilcox, Claire Jayne
Associate Prof of Chemistry
Willis, Mary Jo
Prof of Speech Theatre
Zelman, Mark E.
Assistant Prof of Biology

PALESTINE

Catt, Mark Douglas
Math Teacher
Kelley, CArolyn M.
Social Studies Teacher

PALMYRA

Andrews, Lorie
LD Resource Teacher
Daley, Dawn Dee
Spanish & English Teacher
Griffith, Joseph H., III
High School Math Teacher
Holloway, Beverly Grimmett
HS English & Speech Teacher
Jackson, Rodney Shane
Fifth Grade Teacher
Metcalf, William Douglas
Science Teacher

PALOS HEIGHTS

Alderden, Joan E.
PE & Hlth Tchr
Anderson, Sandra L. (Strege)
Kindergarten & 4th Grade Tchr
Baros, Gregory Vincent
Secondary Spanish Teacher

Biggs, Charon Lorene
Family & Consumer Science Tchr
Carnell, Christine Hicks
Fifth Grade Teacher
Coffman, Fay Ellen Huetson
High School English Teacher
Collins, Thomas G.
Social Studies Teacher
Dunleavy, Edward Patrick
Sixth Grade Teacher
Gardner, James Justin
Physical Sci & Biology Teacher
Heinz, Michael J.
Science Teacher
Hiscock, Charles Glenn
Art Teacher
Mc Kee, Carole S. (Baron)
Mathematics Teacher
Meyer, Gary G.
English Teacher
Nikolas-Gulino, Paris S.
English Teacher
Palmisano, Jeanne Bleeker
French & Spanish Teacher
Patterson, Diann Twait
Math Teacher
Proske, Stephanie Ann
English Teacher
Smith, Jeanine Katherine
Science Teacher
Van Kampen, Kenneth A.
Business Ed & Religion Teacher
Wojciechowski, Linda
Bio, Anatomy & Physiology Tchr
Zadkovic, Lynn Cooper
English Teacher

PALOS HILLS

Amelio, Barbara J.
Physical Education Teacher
Churchill, Mark Edward
Assistant Professor of Chem
Czworniak, Carol Joan
Social Studies Teacher
DeVillez, Randy
Prof of Lbrl Arts & Sciences
Dillon, Bob
English Tchr & Softball Coach
Dziallo, Paula Janiak
German Teacher
Fett, Joy D.
Mathematics Professor
Grider, Roy Lee
History Teacher
Kirvaitis, Joanna Sheivys
Professor of Chemistry
Marino, Marilyn Jane
Third Grade Teacher
Maxwell, Mary Allen
Psych Tchr & Comm Svc Coord
Mc Guire, Ann Marie Lawler
Chemistry Teacher
Reifsnyder, Robert
Music Professor
Sajewich, Patricia Kenney
Mathematics Teacher
Spajer, Kenneth Carl
Adj Instr of Lbrl Arts & Sci
Stark, Peggy Louise
Mathematics Teacher
Tabak, Valerie
Sociology Instructor
Vaccarello, Charles
Band Director
Zike, Raymond John
High School Mathematics Tchr

PALOS PARK

Bliss, Rodney Allan
Biology Teacher & Coordinator
Clark, Donna J.
6th Grade Teacher
Durkin, Jacqueline Vanucci
Kindergarten Teacher
Laratta, Rebecca Mickelson
8th Grade US History Teacher
Lawler, Susan George
Fifth Grade Teacher
Malito, Sharon Fitzgibbons
Teacher of Gifted
Morgan, Sandra Ann Domico
Fifth Grade Teacher

PANA

Matamis, Magdalene
Mathematics Teacher
Maziarz, Susan Spinner
5th Grade Teacher
Vaughn, Jennifer A.
English Teacher
Voudrie, Nancy Jane
Math Teacher
Warren, Barbara Nell
Volleyball Coach

PARIS

Bergdolt, Barbara Lindsey
Language Arts Teacher
Berry, Allen
Chemistry Teacher
Doris, Ronald
Math & Physics Teacher
Gosnell, Rick Ray
Driver's & Physical Ed Teacher
Jobst, James S.
Science Teacher
Meister, Dave D.
Social Studies Dept Chair
Milavickas, David V.
Math Tchr & Head Ftbl Coach
Propst, Angela Clapp
Home Economics Teacher
Ray, Carolyn Swackhamer
Kindergarten Teacher

Schwinghamer, Cynthia Ann
Algebra & Geometry Teacher
Wacaser, Sharon Ann
7th-8th Grd Title One Teacher
Wright, Sharon du Pont
Teacher of Gifted & Talented

PARK FOREST

Dalke, Carl D.
Pupil Personnel Services
Dexthorn, Bob
Teacher
Giddings, Ruby Jean (Dennis)
Fourth Grade Teacher
Johnson, Dale M.
In Schl Suspension Supervisor
Matyasec, Maryann Magero
Seventh Grade Mathematics Tchr
Ulreich, Douglas C.
Choral Music Dir

PARK RIDGE

Aduddell, Linnea Liken
Retired 5th Grade Teacher
Anderson, John
Math Teacher
Angioletti, Mary Grant
School Social Worker
Bondi, JoAnn Gaeke
HS History & Lead Teacher
Chidester, Joanne Muessle
High School English Teacher
Deger, Christopher L.
Social Studies Instructor
Dieter, Lynn P.
English Teacher
Englebert, Barbara Maud
Spanish & French Teacher
Greenbaum, Susan Culp
Eng as a Second Language Tchr
Guilfoil, J. Scott
Physical Education Teacher
Hunt, Robert H.
English Teacher
Irwin, Harriet Lucille (Snyder)
Fourth Grade Teacher
Krockover, Mark Allen
Chemistry Teacher
Lampert, Joan Buttrick
Social Worker
Lorenz, Eva Maria
HS German Teacher
Madden, Eileen
English Teacher
Mastrolonardo, Michael Angelo
High School Art Teacher
Nica, Magdalena Maria Muntean
High School French Teacher
Papreck, Sue (Yow)
Psychology Teacher
Reeves, Mary Ellen
Gifted & Math Curr Specialist
Salefski, Douglas A.
Biology & Physics Teacher
Sweetwood, Jill Koncel
Mathematics Teacher
Tyler, John Edward
Counselor

PATOKA

Jones, Carol Mitchell
Fifth Grade Teacher
Watkins, Dale Wayne
Math Teacher

PAWNEE

Clarke, Teri Mary T. Boarman
Elem Physical Education Tchr

PAWPAW

Eichelkraut, Laurel Lynn
Sci, Math & Soc Stud Teacher

PAYSON

Carey, Shaun Patrick
Junior High Science Teacher
Corso, Robert Charles
Spanish, Soc Scis & PE Teacher
Eidson, Barry L.
Agriculture Education Instr
Frye, Linda Louise
Accounting & Computer Teacher
Mena, Lacinda Speckhart
Fifth Grade Teacher
Morrison, Carla Nelson
History Teacher
Ohnemus, Janet Kay (windoffer)
Mathematics & Physics Teacher
Sparks, Carol Lynn
7th Grade Language Arts Tchr
Wottman, Vivian M. Olker
Science Teacher

PEARL CITY

Heidenreich, Kristine Marie
Mathematics Teacher
Vohwinkle, Mary Carroll
English & Social Studies Tchr

PECATONICA

Lucas, Patricia E. (Tucker)
6th-8th Grade Math Teacher

PEKIN

Braun, Jan
School Improvement Consultant
Bushue, Ronald D.
Retired Teacher
Clinch, Rebecca S.
Third Grade Teacher
Fryman, Carol Ann
1st & 2nd Grade Teacher
Graf, Patience Brownfield
Kindergarten Teacher
Henry, Mark
Advanced Bio & Phys Sci Tchr
Ingram, Mary Jane (Vincent)
Second Grade Teacher

Matuska, Jan A.
Health Occupations Teacher
Orrick, Kelly Klein
Science Teacher
Patton, David Dale
Physical Education Teacher
Peckham, Diana Maurer
Publications Adv & Eng Teacher
Polson, Barbara R.
Spanish Teacher
Ries, Rhonda S.
Mathematics Teacher
Schwader, Shauna Berry
Secondary Mathematics Teacher
Steiner, Jarvis Loren
Fifth Grade Teacher
Stokowski, Linda Betzelberger
Music Teacher
Truckenmiller, Mary Ann
Mathematics Teacher
Weakley, Susan Elizabeth
Third Grade Teacher
Westfall-Taylor, Kendra Jan
Fifth Grade Teacher
Wetzel, Linda Lou (Abrahamson)
First Grade Teacher
White, Richard Lee, Jr.
History Tchr & Dept Chair

PEORIA

Adams, Carol P.
Reading & Social Studies Tchr
Adams, Kristin Anthony
Mathematics Teacher
Al-Khafaji, Amir Wadi
Civil Engrng Prof & Chprsn
Al-Manaseer, Akthem
Civil Engineering Professor
Alwan, Sandra Hastings
Third Grade Teacher
Bachelor, Robin Lynn
Span Tchr & Frgn Lang Chprsn
Bahnsen, Karen Amundson
6th Grade Teacher
Barnett, Cheryl Lynne (Fishel)
Math Teacher
Baylor, Julie Sweety
Assistant Professor
Behrens, Irene E.
Biology Teacher
Blick, Rodger W.
High School Principal
Blickenstaff, Wendy Croslin
Counselor
Brenton, Dorothy Gillis
HS Math Tchr & Chrldng Coach
Brignadello, Patricia Colgan
Second Grade Teacher
Brooks, Donna Jobe
Teacher & Counselor
Bryant, Kenneth Lee
Third Grade Teacher
Burash, Larry E.
Science & Computer Teacher
Burgauer, Debra Laaker
English Lecturer
Camp, Gregory Duane
Mathematics Teacher
Caster, Gary C.
Chaplain & Religion Teacher
Clark, Cindy A.
High School Math Teacher
Conley, Patrick Kevin
Social Studies Tchr & Coach
Cummings, John Mark
His Tchr & Soc Stud Dept Chm
Dannehl, Charles R.
Asst Prof of Political Sci
Delgado, Paul
Math & Science Teacher
Dempsey, Gary L.
Asst Prof of Electrical Engrng
Diamond, Ronald L.
High School English Teacher
Drassler, Laura Jane (Humphrey)
English Teacher
Drew, Sara Stoyke
English Teacher
Dzapo, Kyle Jean
Assistant Professor of Music
Efinger, Marilyn Gilbert
Science Teacher
Ewan-Skorczewski, Martha Elaine
German Teacher
Fay, John Everett
His, Govt & Economics Teacher
Fink, Susan Colleen
Chemistry Teacher
Flohr, Eric Joseph
Principal
Funke, Kelly Jo Monahan
HS Mathematics Teacher
Garrison, Bruce Ernest
Physics Instructor & Sci Chm
Gillett, John W.
Accounting Professor
Gilmer, James R.
Social Studies Tchr & Coach
Ginn, Judith Day
English Teacher
Graham, Lesley Patricia
Associate Professor
Grzanich, Susan D.
Science Teacher
Harris, Janet (Latimer)
Bus, Health & Science Teacher
Harris, Stanley W.
Mathematics Teacher
Hayden, Deborah Cummings
Former Teacher

PEORIA (cont)
Heinemann, Wayne S.
Music Director
Heiser, Barbara Lee Wenzel
Jr High Science Teacher
Higgins, Rudy Alan
Band Director
Hubert, Eileen Ann (Gramlich)
Eng & Speech Tchr & DIV Ldr
Irwin, George Wendell
Teacher & Coordinator
Jenkins, Larry Dean
English Teacher
Johnson, Gay Taylor
Math Teacher
Johnson, James E.
Science Teacher
Kassel, Paul S.
Asst Professor of Theatre Arts
Keach, Janet Douglas
Retired 1st Grade Teacher
Kellerman, Lawrence Robert
Assistant Professor of Elem Ed
Kennedy, Patricia Havens
Math Teacher
Klopfenstein, Rhoda K.
Computer Tchr & Athletic Dir
Knowles, Elizabeth Leigh
Art Professor
Konradi, Donna Beth
Assistant Professor of Nursing
Kupper, Tracey E.
Second Grade Teacher
Lacy, Thomas E.
Mathematics Teacher
Laird, Thomas Leonard
English Teacher
Lane, Maria N.
English Teacher
Lawrence, Betty Jane Cromwell
Lecturer of Comm Dept
Link, OSF, Barbara Marie
Religion Teacher
Lord Robinson, Julie Christine
Mathematics Lead Teacher
Mack, Bonnie Jean
United States History Teacher
Maier, Joseph P.
English Teacher & Head Coach
Manos, Mary Ann
Assistant Professor
McCann, Bonni R.
Assoc Dir Court Reporting Dept
McCann, Louise Ann
Mathematics Teacher
Mc Caw, Larry L.
Educator
McCaw, Teddi Helena
Jr High Math & Science Teacher
McDaniels, Carol Lynn
5th Grade Teacher
Mooney, Leslie Scruby
Junior High Teacher
Moore, Michael James
7th & 8th Grd Science Teacher
Morris, James Michael
Choral Music Teacher
Moutoux, Gregg Elden
Jr High Math Instructor
Myers, Janet Rae (Pierson)
Business Education Teacher
Myers, Lana May
Math & Computer Teacher
Nelson, Maria Valdescruz
Spanish Teacher
Nix, Myrna Lee Miller
Accounting Instructor
O'Brien, Kevin Michael
Asst Professor of Economics
Patel, Geeta C.
Dir of Travel & Tourism
Pilcher, June J.
Professor of Psychology
Rashid, Jerry Ralph
English Teacher
Reents, Larry G.
Debate & English Teacher
Ricca, Edward J.
Mathematics Teacher
Risinger, Lana Kay
English & Communications Instr
Robinson, Rose Henderson
First Grade Teacher
Rouse, Ruth Dennis
Fourth Grade Teacher
Rowe, Kathleen Burgard
Jr High Science Teacher
Ruck, Jerrie Dean
8th Grd Language Arts Teacher
Runkle, Marcey
English Teacher
Sansom, Diane (Gantt)
8th Grd Lang Arts & Art Tchr
Schifeling, Scott Bradley
Social Studies Teacher
Schneider, Christine Grace
Kindergarten Teacher
Schoenheider, Peggy Ridgway
7th-8th Grd Literature Teacher
Schoon, Timothy W.
High School History Teacher
Sexton, Lisa Marie (Cain)
Second Grade Teacher
Shahbodaghlou, Farzad
Assoc Prof of Civil Engr
Smith, Annette Taylor
Title I Pre-Kindergarten Tchr
Smith, Marvin Francis
His Tchr & Head Sftbl Coach
Sprenger, Marilee Broms
Language Arts Teacher
Stetzler, Kenneth Lee
Mathematics Teacher
Stowell, Gail Mushovic
Spanish, Art & Soc Stud Tchr
Strasma, Linda
Communication Instructor
Strickler, Dorothy G.
Spanish Teacher
Stroup, Donald R.
Third Grade Teacher
Suhr, Barbara Gilbert
French & Spanish Teacher
Sullivan, Paula Marie
Kindergarten Teacher
Taylor, Carolyn Maudeen (Reliford)
Social Science Teacher
Templeton, Rosalyn Anstine
Assistant Professor
Thomas, William Charles
German Teacher
Tony, Susan Kelly
Science Teacher
Truho, Gail L.
Middle Schl Science Teacher
Tyree, Nancy Nesmith
Retired Math & Algebra Teacher
Venturi, Pamela Brucken
Bus Tchr, Dept Chr & Tech Prep
Wendle, Tim
Residntl Life & Judicial Dir
Wessler, Max Alden
Professor of Mech Engineering
Willingham, William James
Math Teacher & Track Coach
Wojcikewych, Joan Harris
Principal
Wyman, Annie Marie Sullivan
English Teacher
Zant, Bernard Joseph
Chair Admin of Crim Justice
Ziegler, Constance J.
Seventh Grade Teacher
Zuza, Anne M.
Teacher
PEORIA HEIGHTS
Dunn, Teri Murphy
Mathematics Staff Developer
PEOTONE
Anderson, Winona Townsend
English Teacher
Andriano, Jody Weger
English Instructor
Cline, Bunni Peterson
Third Grade Teacher
Cyr, Charles Edward
Agriculture Instructor
Kibelkis, David Joseph
Hlth, Physical Education Instr
Rue, Nancy Ellen
French Teacher
Sippel, Todd Ernest
Chemistry & Physics Teacher
Smith, Jane
Spanish Teacher
PERRY
Galle, Jeff Edward
Coord & Instr of Swine Mngmt
PERU
Strassburger, Mark Frederick
Band & Choral Director
PESOTUM
Hall, Ellen Kimery
First Grade Teacher
PETERSBURG
Coleman, Edith Plate
Third Grade Teacher
Cox, Kris Tumbleson
Band Director
Denton, Emma Lou Ann
Retired Elementary Teacher
Koelling, Charlene E. (Prosse)
Science Teacher
Malinak, Janet Lorton
Speech & English Teacher
PHOENIX
Schaeflein, Barbara A.
7th Grd Social Studies Teacher
PIASA
Alderman, Jeffrey Dale
Physical Ed & English Teacher
Drury, Barbara M.
Family & Consumer Sci Teacher
Eldred, Polly Boydstun
History, English & Lit Teacher
Emerick-Smith, Donna Marie
Sixth Grade Teacher
Pace, Roger
Guidance Counselor
Pranger, Barbara L.
High School Math Teacher
Schmidt, Susan Chiolero
English Department Chairperson
Sweetman, Laurel Velliquette
High School Art Teacher
Williams, Gary Lee
Biology & Chemistry Teacher
PINCKNEYVILLE
Barge, Cynthia Ann Foster
Junior High Lang Arts Tchr
Cannedy, Stephen Darrell
High School Band Director
Filipsic, Shirley Ervin
6th Grade Teacher
Johnson, LInda L.
Business Teacher
Klingenberg, Linda K.
6th Grade Teacher
Kulenkamp, Roy R.
English Teacher
Mc Pheeters, George M., Jr.
Science Teacher
Shepard, William Mark
Soc Stud Teacher & Coach
Wisniewski, Lisa Czerwinski
English Teacher
PIPER CITY
Schantz, Denise
Jr High PE Teacher
PITTSFIELD
Acuff, Rebecca Watson
English, Speech & Drama Tchr
Boren, Michael Bruce
World History Teacher
Carnes, Sandra Spellman
Jr High Literature Teacher
Evans, Debbie Lynn
Third Grade Teacher
Fischer, Tamara Ward
Second Grade Teacher
Guthrie, Beatrice Eileen
Title I Reading & Math Tchr
Haskins, Sherolyn Biddle
8th Grade Mathematics Teacher
Hoover, Jean
Principal
Ideus, Karen Kay
6th-7th Grade Math Teacher
Peak, Ellen Lashmett
Jr High Generalist
Schultz, John Joseph
Business Teacher & Coach
Shields, James R.
Amer Govt Tchr & Ath Director
Woods, Gary Kent
Trig & Calculus Teacher
Zimmerman, Cheryl Lee
Home Economics Teacher
PLAINFIELD
Capps, George William
Principal
Ellis, Lawrence Willliam
Retired Math Teacher
Hunt, Adele Pitts
Spanish Teacher
Klaas, Lisa M.
Health & Wellness Teacher
Magruder, Gary L.
Retired American Lit Teacher
Mc Carthy, Loretta Lind
English Teacher & Drama Dir
Moore, Terry Anne
High School Choral Director
Riederer, Steven Vincent
K-6th Grd Physical Ed Tchr
Wauthier, Larry Alan
Science Teacher
Williams, Michael Joseph
Driver Education Teacher
Zehringer, Vickey Lynn
Geology & Earth Sci Teacher
PLAINVILLE
Schwartz, Goldnita Oitker
Retired Kindergarten Teacher
PLANO
Benton, Joel C.
Middle School Principal
Chernick, John Paul
Mathematics Teacher
Cummins, Kenneth W.
Industrial Arts Teacher
Green, James C.
Mathematics Teacher & Coach
Gruidl, Al
US & World History Teacher
Ingles, Elizabeth Lastell
Title I Reading Teacher
Mc Coy, Barbara Ann Hughes
Biology & Chemistry Teacher
Stoyak, Ronald Thomas
English Teacher
Tyler, Timothy Thomas
Math Teacher
PLEASANT PLAINS
Brownback, Anna Jane
English Teacher
Lee, Linda Gayle
Biology Teacher
Martin, Carol Svoboda
Band Dir & Music Theory Tchr
Yates, James W.
Eng, Sociology & Psych Tchr
POCAHONTAS
Evans, Frank James
Science & Social Studies Tchr
POLO
Allison, Nel Dietrich
Concert Clarinet & Piano Tchr
Cheek, Deborah Lynn
Math & Computer Teacher
Ebert, Betty Jean (Rebuck)
Home Economics Teacher
Hall, Dale B.
Guidance Counselor
Jenkins, Eleanor Marie (Quayle)
Retired 4th Grade Teacher
Maggi, Gail Bryant
Second Grade Teacher
McGuire, Julie Gilbert
English Teacher
Reece, Donald Fredrick
Social Studies Teacher
Taylor, Lowell A.
6th Grd English & Reading Tchr
Welty, Tom C.
Language Arts Teacher
PONTIAC
Dowdy, Betsy Engelhorn
Home Economics Instructor
Frickey, Linda Louise
Sixth Grade Teacher
Heinrich, Vicki Stevenson
Fifth Grade Teacher
Levin, Linda Donnell
English Instructor
Oberholtzer, Norma Franzo
Fourth Grade Teacher
Peterson, Mick
High School PE Teacher
Raube, Dee Dee (Carls)
Fifth Grade Teacher
Schulz, Kathleen Hoerner
1st Grade Teacher
Thorson, Gail Lynn (Dietz)
Home Economics Teacher
POPLAR GROVE
Bristol, June Worley
Physical Education Teacher
Ellingson, Jacqueline Meyers
Guidance Counselor
Key, Patricia Kay
3rd Grade Teacher
Oliveri, Michael Paul
Math Teacher
Sepich, Kim Anne
Elementary Principal
Troller, Christine Loveland
Junior HS Soc Stud Tchr
PORT BYRON
Apicella, Andrew
Biology Teacher
Fortney, Gordon Ray
6th Grade Teacher
Peasley, Margaret Louise
French Teacher
Thomas, Linda
Science Teacher
Weaver, Cindy Weber
HS English & Psychology Tchr
Yackle, Kelly Jean
Sixth Grade Teacher
POSEN
Hinkle, Dorothy Nell Brooks
Fifth Grade Teacher
PRINCETON
Church, Brian
Guidance Director
Gewin, Jean Chase
8th Grade English Teacher
Kiser, Marty Fogel
English Teacher
Laesch, Phillip L.
Retired German Teacher
PRINCEVILLE
Dorrington, William P.
HS Social Studies Teacher
Ramos, Rogelio Ibarra
Title I Migrant Teacher & Dir
Romane, Marjorie Slane
Retired Teacher
Stanley, Susan Diane (Gilmore)
Rdng, English & Soc Stud Tchr
Stromberger, Connie Aschenbrenner
High School Math Teacher
PROPHETSTOWN
Wagenecht, Ann Marie
Retired Second Grade Teacher
PROSPECT HEIGHTS
Labant, Elizabeth Malee
Junior High Teacher
QUINCY
Bergman, Rachel Scanland
Journalism Teacher
Bergman, Sarah Ann
Assoc Professor of Physical Ed
Breyley, James Kendall, Jr.
MBA Dir & Assoc Prof of Bus
Brown, David L.
Art & Art History Teacher
Capalbo, Kenneth Michael, OFM
Asst Professor of History
Chase, Michael Lee
Associate Prof of Psychology
Connell, William James
Physical Science Teacher
Cooper, Jody Dieker
Fourth Grade Teacher
Cooper, Stephen Charles
11th Grd US History Teacher
Culbertson, Jerry Dean
Chair of Natural Sciences
De Voss, Karen Kenady
4th Grade Teacher
Dickens, Christie Elizabeth (Pence)
Third Grade Teacher
Dolan, Doris Ann (Bergman)
1st Grade Teacher
Elbe, Michael Lewis
Student Life & Athletics Dir
Ellerman, Terry Joseph
Guidance Svcs Coordinator
Emeka, Ekemezie Joseph
Associate Professor of Math
Fuhr, Susan Wand
Scndry Lang Arts Teacher
Fulte, Lon Raymond
Principal
Gage, Ann P.
Principal
Hadley, Eric Morton
Biology & Zoology Instructor
Harris, Debbie D.
Home School Teacher
Hayes, Margaret A.
Biology Teacher
Hermann, Gail B.
Chem Tchr & Sci Curr Comm Chm
Hoebing, Phil Joseph
Retired Assoc Prof of Phil
Howell, Susan Elaine
Eng, Rel, Soclgy & Psych Tchr
Huelsmeyer, Jane D.
Earth Science Teacher
Humphrey, Michael C.
High School English Instructor
Kelly, John D.
Building Manager & Coach
Knorr, Susan Nudo
Science Teacher
Larner, Ronald Philip
Business Teacher
Lask, Patricia (Kratochvil)
English Teacher
Leach, Roger Dale
6th Grade Teacher
Lohmeyer, Nancy Moore
English Teacher
Mc Ginley, Patrick M.
World History Tchr & Dept Chm
Meyer, Macklin Leo
7th Grade Language Teacher
Meyer, Marilyn Meier
4th Grade TAG Teacher
Moore, Mark William
Chemistry Instructor
Pryor, Peggy Ann
HS Physical Education Teacher
Quintero, Jose Joaquin, Jr.
Spanish Teacher & Coach
Richmiller, Donna Mary
8th Grade Teacher
Rigg, Dana Spratt
Chemistry Teacher
Selby, Margaret Carol (Meier)
Third Grade Teacher
Shiraki, Tatsuo Steven
Sixth Grade Teacher
Stewart, Jackie Sue
Chemistry Teacher
Stewart, Richard Lee
Government Teacher
Stewart, Sarah Burke
Science Teacher
Wagner, LaWanda Joyce
6th Grade Teacher
Wittler, Karen Sarver
Spanish Teacher
RAMSEY
Harris, Linda Lee
Jr High Science Teacher
Lau, Michael Edward
Mathematics Teacher
Mc Clure, Joy Alexander
Librarian & Media Director
Stephens, Clarice Humphres
Home Economics Teacher
RANTOUL
Burk, Gregory L.
Algebra I Teacher
Caldwell, Camille Marie (Franzen)
5th Grade Teacher
Duitsman, Susan Kay (Babb)
Business Teacher
Frizol, Herbert J., Jr.
Retired Bus Ed Teacher
Johnson, Nancy L.
Span III & IV Teacher
Kruse, Diane Marie
English & Mathematics Teacher
Muhr, Esther Towey
Art Teacher
Newkirk, Diane (Hendrickson)
Reading Teacher
Rauch, Barbara Cover
Sixth Grade Teacher
Rauch, Frederick Rogers
6th Grade Teacher
Schingel, Robin A.
Business Teacher
Scott, Rose Ellen Rehm
Chem Tchr & Sci Dept Chprsn
Walsh, Mary Swift
7th-8th Grade Math Teacher
RAYMOND
Jones, Dennis Michael
Band Director & Music Teacher
Lamore, Margaret DeMartini
Spanish Teacher
Miles, Judith Ann Snell
6th Grd Rdng & Science Teacher
RED BUD
Belter, James Edward
Fourth Grade Teacher
Fahey, Kristie (Horrell)
Eighth Grade Teacher
Franklin, Linda Kay (Hale)
High School Art Teacher
Lesinger, Myra
High School Math Teacher
Mc Cutcheon, Debra Sue (Wegener)
English Teacher
Snyder, Ronald A.
8th Grade Teacher
REDDICK
Wancho, Amy Clark
3rd Grade Teacher
RICHMOND
Dodd, Mark William
High School Lang Arts Teacher
Jones, Larry Curtis
Dean of Students
Peterson, Linda Frautschy
English Teacher
Wood, Richard G.
Math & Physics Teacher

TON PARK
d, Mary Wood
lish Teacher
wick, Deborah Livermore
ness Teacher
, Cheryl Vittorio
ory Teacher
, Sandra E.
nish Teacher
k, Madeline Marie-Cecilia
ond Grade Pub Schl Teacher
ey-Bell, Bridget
nish Teacher
R FOREST
n, Barbara Ann
d Grade Tchr & Asst Prin
ese, Richard Joseph
Arts & Comm Stud Chprsn
l, Carol Martin
man Teacher
William J.
ology Teacher
, Marilyn McNichols
ology Teacher
Marcia Lynn
mentary School Principal
, Margaret L.
h Grade Teacher
r, Mary Ann
nish Tchr & Campus Minister
k, Barbara G.
al Studies Chprsn & Tchr
n, Paulette Iversen
nce Department Chairperson
s, Dorathea Jean
ondary Math Teacher
, Mary Blaney
ector of Guidance
, Laura S.
no Teacher
R GROVE
y, Rosalie E.
hematics Department Chair
r, Daniel David
cipal & Teacher
rtniak, Robert Louis
Cnslr, Psych & Math Prof
ee, Betsy
lish Teacher & Yearbook Adv
ng, Cheryl Fae
ial Science Teacher
r, Mary Ann
h School English Dept Chair
gan, Terry L.
d Director
r, Ann Marie Maffiola
h School English Teacher
a, Mary Ann (DiNovi)
ciality Programs Coord
lar, Thomas F.
cipal
, Thomas Henry
ial Science Teacher
, John Fredric
ounting Instructor
ERSIDE
berg, Jan D.
ial Studies Teacher
vsky, William Michael
ial Studies Dept Chm
, Carl F.
cher & Science Chair
Renee K.
hematics & Dance Teacher
rt, Sarah Diane
-12th Grd Soc Stud Teacher
ERTON
Helen Marie
hematics Teacher
n, Susan Elaine
ence Teacher & Coach
on, Jilinda A. (Pfeiffer)
siness & Computer Teacher
, Nancy Muir
unselor
NOKE
tsen, Rolf Arnold
ustrial Technology Instr
BINS
ers, Joseph Jeffrey
Grade Teacher
INSON
l, Dale E.
nior Guidance Counselor
kman, Kelly A.
ysical Education Teacher
lson, David Charles
ecommunications Instructor
son, Karen Lee Twigg
Science Teacher
son, Wayne Keith
ology, Zoology & Antmy Tchr
aid, Nancy Hughes
ementary Counselor
cher, Searoba Deisher
of Learning Skill Ctr
rd, Janelle Kaye
glish Teacher
, Maria Strelka
acher of Learning Disabled
Anurdha
e Science Professor
ey, Cynthia Mefford
athematics Teacher
CHELLE
erson, Bruce Wylie
cl Ed Dept Chair & Teacher
on, Richard Lee
chnology Teacher

Carlson, Rosemary Lacko
High School Chemistry Teacher
Cole, Julie Ann
Third & Fourth Grade Teacher
Corkery, Jean Marie (Fitzpatrick)
Math Teacher
Craven, Richard Jamison
Dean of Students
Graber, Daniel L.
Sixth Grade Teacher
Hilgert, Pamela Ann
Gifted Ed Pgm Dir & Instr
Hintzsche, John E.
High School Agriculture Tchr
Johanning, Debra Irene
7th-8th Grade Math Teacher
Kenney, Diane Pelinski
Third Grade Teacher
Kessen, Nancy Spencer
Fifth Grade Teacher
Mayes, Joanne E.
Retired HS English Tchr
Merema, Steven J.
Fifth Grade Teacher
Rice, Ann P.
Title I Reading Teacher
Steinbrenner, Glenn Alan
Principal & Jr High Teacher
Toohey, Karen Marie
Mathematics Teacher
Weidmann, Carol Lynn
Eng Instructor & Theatre Dir
White, Ellen Erickson
Social Studies Teacher
ROCHESTER
Butcher, Mark William
Science Teacher
Gibler, Laurel Lee (Heitzler)
Spanish Teacher
Grimm, David H.
HS Teacher
Jacobs, David Michael
Physical Educator
Leach, Nancy Bischoff
Mathematics Teacher
Ratliff, Malinda Ann (Wiemers)
7th Grade English Teacher
Rutherford, Elizabeth Townes (Cole)
Eng, Comm Tchr & Dept Chprsn
Verner, Helen Deloris
English Teacher
Woodruff, Thomas William
Chemistry Instructor
Zobrist, Deidre Ann
German Teacher
ROCK FALLS
Abney, Robert L.
Bus, Math & Consumer Ed Tchr
Cassady, Zoe Scheidecker
Media, Spch, Drama & Eng Tchr
Davis, Frank L.
6th Grd Social Studies Teacher
Deibert, Carol Shoup
Art Teacher
Deibert, S. Ray
Soc Stud Tchr & Dept Chm
Dolan, Gregg Allan
Biology Teacher
Grennan, Donna Bressler
5th Grade Teacher
Moran, Joan Jensen
Physical Ed & Health Teacher
Rouse, Monica Siperly
English Teacher
Simester, Pat Maxey
Retired 5th-6th Grade Teacher
Thome, Judy M.
Eng, Speech Tchr & Co-Dept Chm
Wahl, Cristela Rodriguez
Spanish Teacher
ROCK ISLAND
Adams, Jesse Edward
Art Teacher
Ahlstrand, Phyllis Thorne
English Teacher
Anderson, Darryl Dean
PE Teacher & Athletic Director
Bustard, James Michael
Consumer Economics Teacher
Dakin, Deborah
Instructor of Music
Dear, Margaret Coleman
Third Grade Teacher
Denten, Donald R.
Retired Social Studies Teacher
DiIulio, Joanne A.
Spanish Teacher
Jacobs, Alice A.
Business Education Teacher
Kline, Joane Lincke
Literature Teacher
Lafrenz, Jill Smith
Business Teacher
Menke, Michelle L.
Mathematics Teacher
Miller, Keith E.
Chemistry & Biology Teacher
Moline, Janet Ahlstrom
Global Biology Teacher
O'Brien, Katherine Jean (Doty)
English Teacher & Drama Coach
Shirk, Grace Diaz
9th-12th Grade Spanish Teacher
Sias, Janice Wollenburg
3rd & 4th Grade Teacher
Troll, Ralph
Professor of Biology
Vize, Susan M.
English Teacher

Walters, Darla R. (Larimore)
6th Grade Teacher
Wee, Rebecca
Assistant Professor of English
Wehner, Lois McCreight
Mathematics Teacher
Wood, David Richard
Mathematics Teacher
ROCKFORD
Anderson, Francis E.
English Teacher
Anderson, Roger David
Math Teacher
Auman, Linda M.
High School Art Teacher
Austin, Jane Stewart
Fifth Grade Teacher
Basile, Louise Broghammer
History Teacher
Bennett, Debra Dew
Assistant Professor of Ed
Bennett, Marjorie A. Flannery
Retired 3rd Grade Teacher
Benson, K. Drake
Instr of Government & Latin
Bergstrom, Mary Vivian
Third Grade Teacher
Bertrand, Diane J.
1st Grade Teacher
Bessler, Linda Dittberner
Title I Reading Teacher
Biavati, Kathryn Schopf
Algebra & Geometry Teacher
Bjork, Barbara G.
Jr High Tchr & Asst Prin
Blake, Penelope LeFew
Professor
Bodner, Thomas Andrew
Social Studies Teacher
Bost, Thomas H.
English & Drama Teacher
Boyer, Karen Anderson
English Teacher
Buhl, William George
Science Teacher
Canter, William Benjamin
History Teacher
Carlson, Leland John
6th Grade Teacher
Carson, William Bates
Chemistry Lecturer
Carter, Janet S.
5th Grade Teacher
Cassioppi, Peter James
Mathematics Teacher
Caton, Ann Charlotte
Education Professor
Caton, Gerald Lee
Math, Cmptr Sci Prof & Chair
Cook, Jerry
British & World Lit Teacher
Cotelleso, Anthony Vittorio
High School Math Teacher
Coupar, Brigitte Marianne
German Teacher
Criscimagna, Angela (Gravlin)
Creative Dance Teacher
Currier, Janet Geiger
Eng & 4th Grade Teacher
Davies, Gerald Thomas
Math Tchr & Dept Chair
Dinges, William B.
Govt & Honors Amer His Tchr
Dunn, Susan Armstrong
Tchr of Gifted Social Studies
Ervin, Nearo J.
Instructional Implementor
Fahrenwald, Jeffrey William
Assoc Prof of Business
Fedeli, Shirley A. Martignoni
Social Studies Chair
Ferguson, Reid Edward
Psychology & English Teacher
Fieldhouse, Ronn K.
Chemistry Teacher
Finley, Janis Gail
Mathematics Teacher
Fisher, Scott Michael
English Professor
Fouch, Hertha Gesine
6th Grade Teacher
Gaskin, Michael David
Math Teacher
Gavan, Mary Margaret
English Department Chair
Godin, Anne M.
English Teacher
Grimes, Norman
Chem, Biology & Science Tchr
Groth, Eric David
Youth Minister
Gustafson, John D.
American History Teacher
Halom, Vickie Kuhs
Elementary Art Teacher
Hartz, Linda M.
7th Grade Science Teacher
Haugen, Lorna Dorothy
English Teacher
Heal, Barbara A.
Dept Chair of Education
Heffner, Dennis Gene
History & Government Teacher
Heideman, Linda T.
French Teacher
Heimer, Jane M. (Brede)
English Teacher
Heisel, Kathryn Kalivoda
English Teacher

Heuer, Beth Lee
Instrumental Music Director
Hicks, Stephen
Philosophy Professor
Holman, Rhonda Greer
Third Grade Teacher
Huang, Liang Jiao
Mathematics Professor
Hulme, Nancy Berggren
High School History Teacher
Hulstedt, Linda L.
British Lit & Spec Ed Tchr
James, Robert Harold
Eng Tchr & Publications Adv
Johnsen, Deborah Kramme
Mathematics Teacher
Johnson, Dennis J.
US History Teacher
Johnson, Richard Lewis
5th Grade Teacher
Jurgens, Raeann E.
Mathematics Teacher
Jurgens, Richard L.
Mathematics Teacher
Kauffmann, Ruth Annette
Assistant Professor of Spanish
Keyzer, Bruce E.
Physics Instr & Sci Dept Head
Kluck, Rhonda S.
Math Department Chair
Kobylas, Joseph G.
Spanish Professor
Kohl, Barbara Houghton
1st Grade Teacher
Kohlwey, Martin R.
Spiritual Life Director & Tchr
Kuhn, Floyd George
High School Economics Teacher
Larsen, Leonor
Mathematics & Spanish Teacher
Larson, Dale P.
Science Teacher & Tennis Coach
Lauger, Paul Stephen
Computer & Aided-Drafting Tchr
LeFeure, Steven Wayne
Seventh Grade Teacher
Lendman, Christy Ann
Education Professor
Lindner, Ronald Edward
History Teacher
Longhenry, Carol Carroll
English & Latin Teacher
Longhenry, John Charles
World History Teacher
MacKay, Rose Marie
3rd Grade Teacher
Magee, D. B.
English & Journalism Professor
Martindale, Jim Wayne
5th Grade Teacher
Mc Cormick, Michael Joseph
Freshman Softball Head Coach
McKinney-Alberts, Lou Ann
Performing Arts & Dance Tchr
Mertz, Darryl H.
German & Geography Teacher
Messersmith, Shirley Anne
1st-3rd Grd Montessori Teacher
Moderson, Christopher Paul
Enrollment Mngmt VP
Monarski, Francis Joseph
Religion Teacher
Mucha, Patricia Carlson
Spanish Teacher
Myers, Denise Lower
Sixth Grade Teacher
Nelson, Carol H. Johnson
Retired Montessori Teacher
Nunez, Robert
Driver's Ed Teacher & Coach
Nyquist, Barry Bryant
Theatre Teacher
Papich, Anita Kracik
Math Teacher & Dept Head
Parris, Jennifer Karen
Chemistry Teacher
Pasch, Gary Warren
4th Grade Teacher
Patterson, Janet Louise
History Teacher
Pettera, Jeffrey R.
HS Science Teacher
Pinzarrone, Rebecca Downing
Art Instructor
Pontious, Carol Ann
Mathematics Teacher
Potter, Coleen Elizabeth
Biology & Zoology Teacher
Powell, Sharon Yeater
Mathematics Teacher
Reder, Mary E.
Science Teacher
Reese, Nancy Hollingsworth
English Teacher
Rehnberg, Janice Carlson
Counselor
Reynolds, James Robert
Industrial Technology Teacher
Rimbey, Robert S.
Fifth Grade Teacher
Rudie, John Walter
US History Teacher
Rydberg, Elizabeth Alden
Elementary Art Teacher
Sanders, Mary Katheryne
English Professor
Scheuer, James Andrew
English & Journalism Teacher
Schlueter, Dean John
Physical Education Teacher

Schmelzle, Joan Mary
Cheerleading Coach
Schultz, Nancy Hemeyer
Student Support Services Coord
Sherman, Verne Patrick
Principal & 5th-8th Grd Tchr
Skoglund, Jon Barton
Band, Choir & Jazz Teacher
Slife, Linda L.
5th Grd Teacher of GATE Stdnts
Stewart, Minnie Smith
Biology Teacher & Mentor I Ldr
Stockton, David
Soc Science Teacher & Coach
Strang, Gayle M.
Prof of Physical Education
Strothoff, Marcia Dresser
8th Grade Algebra Teacher
Thompson, Robert H.
Principal, Teacher & Coach
Toppe, Richard Iven
Second Grade Teacher
VanHowe, Karen F.
French Teacher
Vaughan, Charlene Anne
First Grd Rdng Recovery Tchr
Voigt, Mary Jean Meads
Psychology Teacher
Walhout, Justine (Simon)
Professor of Chemistry
Weckerly, Ronald Roy
8th Grade US History Teacher
Weidman, Barbara A.
Business Teacher & Dept Crprsn
Weislo-Campbell, Susan
Fr Tchr & Frgn Lang Dept Chm
Whealler, Susan C.
Associate Dean
Whinna, George W. R., III
History Teacher
Whitfield, Debbie DeWild
Physical Education Dept Chm
Williams, Judy Rhodes
English Department Chairman
Wolfgram, Steven Scott
Music & Math Teacher
Yurkew, Penny Snyder
English Teacher
Zavadil, Barbara (Shaw)
History Dept Chairman
ROCKTON
Carleton, John Charles
Program Improvement Coord
Frailey, Jane K.
Environmental Sci & Bio Tchr
Gonet, David Mark
Speech, Theatre & English Tchr
Gregoire, Eugene Harold
Director of Bands
Krajco, Terese Jean
Chemistry Teacher
Mc Donnell, Shirley Harrod
Ret Soc Stud Tchr & Dept Chair
Mc Larty, Ray
Biology Teacher
Muldowney, Kerry P.
Psychology & Sociology Teacher
Neumer, Kristy Blackwelder
Mathematics Teacher
Polaski, Thomas Brian
US History & Economics Tchr
Radke, Linda K.
Spanish Teacher
Sennerud, David Scott
Social Studies & English Tchr
Sughroue, Timothy J.
Math Dept Coord & Teacher
Washburn, Linda C.
5th Grade Teacher
Webster, Richard Perry
English Teacher
Zimmerman, Brian D.
Science Teacher
ROLLING MEADOWS
Benes, Gregory Edward
AP European & World His Tchr
Block, Allen L.
7th & 8th Grade Teacher
De Keyser, Monica Dupont
English Teacher
Dilger, Laine Gurley
Biological Sciences Teacher
Duellman, Michael
Mathematics Teacher
Friedrich, Mary Kay Straub
English & Literature Teacher
Leece, William Joseph
HS English Teacher
Meyer, Mary Elizabeth
History Teacher
Nestor, Daniel E.
Math Teacher
Raak, Diane K.
Fifth Grade Teacher
Robertshaw, Rick
Math Teacher
Runyan, Luann Marie
Third Grade Teacher
Sheridan, Rita Johnson
Gifted Ed Tchr & Consultant
Strongin, Bonnie Lynn
English & Literature Teacher
Tirado, Nancy
Lit, Cmpstn & Soc Stud Tchr
Weidner, Art
Computer Technology Instructor
ROMEOVILLE
Clehouse, Rita E.
Middle School Honors Teacher

ROMEOVILLE (cont)
Irwin, Thomas Joseph
Jr HS Mathematics Instructor
Rompa, Delphine Dorothy
Third Grade Teacher
Santas, Elizabeth Jane
Nursing Instructor
Smith, Mary Cerceo
Jr HS Literature & Eng Teacher
Waitkoff, Barbara
College of Nursing Asst Prof
ROSCOE
Kobischa, Linda L.
First Grade Teacher
ROSELLE
Alexander, Donna J.
Physical Ed & Health Teacher
Bergen, Thomas
Physical Education & Hlth Tchr
Gard, Timothy John
Mathematics Teacher
Heyen, Jennifer Rebecca (Miller)
English Teacher
Lovelace, Donald C.
Driver Education Teacher
Mccarter-Lovelace, Kathleen M.
Science Teacher
Moshure, Pamela P.
Reading Specialist
Papa, John Joseph
Driver Ed Teacher & Dept Coord
Safranek, Andrea Lynn
Math Teacher
ROSEVILLE
Crippen, Tamara Stone
English Speech Teacher
ROSSVILLE
Anvick, Susan Mader
Third Grade Teacher
Bibb, Joanne Timmons
5th Grade Teacher
Musgrave, Mary J.
Literature Teacher
Tracy, Christina L.
Chemistry, Physics, Cmptr Tchr
Watson, Tracey Jean
High School English Teacher
ROUND LAKE
Dempsey, Kevin R.
PE & Drivers Ed Tchr & Coach
Edge, Gary Adam
History, Ec & Geography Tchr
Logan-Burnhorst, Kora Lee
Sixth Grade Teacher
Marchiori, Lane K.
Dean of Students
Prochnow, Janet C.
Head Librarian
Starosto, Kimberly A. Bond
Third & Fourth Grade REI Tchr
Starzynski, Daniel Edward
Third Grade Teacher
Starzynski, Mary Peterson
Second Grade Teacher
ROXANA
Abbott, Pamela S.
Chemistry Teacher
Buehrig, Janet Raley
High School Spanish Teacher
Ciccorelli, Susan Fitzpatrick
First Grade Teacher
Clark, Randy Ramon
Math Teacher
Clark, Virginia (Highlander)
3rd Grade Teacher
Goodson, Nancy Kay
Home Ec Tchr, Vocational Coord
Griggs, Shelly Rene
HS Mathematics Teacher
Harbke, C. Murray
Soc Sci Tchr & Hum Coord
Kunz, Gene Terry
Mathematics & Science Teacher
Morgan, Dan D.
Co-op Coord & Auto Tech Tchr
Royse, Laura J.
English Teacher
Slusser, Darla Kay (Bold)
English Teacher
Vinyard, Mary K.
Business Education Teacher
Welker, Jeffery Lynn
History Teacher & Coach
RUSHVILLE
Merritt, Mary Sue
Fifth Grade Teacher
Ogden, Beulah Utter
Retired 6th Grade Teacher
Shepherd, James Terry
Business Teacher
Sillars, James Richard
High School Science Teacher
Sprehe, Suzanne Nix
6th Grade Teacher
Thomas, Charles Paul
English Teacher
Tucker, Richard H.
Physical Science Instructor
Van Brooker, Angela Harris
Science Teacher
SAINT ANNE
Beatty, Karen L.
Teacher
Cotton, Deborah Lou Medler
Second Grade Teacher
SAINT CHARLES
Adams, Stephen Vance
Science Teacher
Beckmann, Beverly Bublitz
Child Care Instructor
Brazell, Sonja Ann
HS English Teacher
Brens, Kathleen Frothingham
Speech & Amer Lit Teacher
Cordier, Ken T.
Eighth Grade Teacher
Cox, Linda L.
4th Grade Teacher
Davis, Ronald P.
Retired Mathematics Teacher
Dockum, Melissa Monroe
Student Assistance Coordinator
Drawer, Sena Cirese
Mathematics Teacher
Feddern, Martha Dawson
Home Economics Teacher
Feiza, Linda Millage
Spanish Teacher
Felbinger, Rosemary Kamin
Fourth Grade Teacher
Hackett, Kimberly J.
Mathematics Teacher
Hauser, Audrey D.
Mathematics Department Chair
Heyer, Jennifer Louise
Health Teacher
Kaiser, Kathleen Jeananne
Director of Instruction
Kling, Deborah S.
Art Teacher
Leavey, Jeffrey Allen
Sociology & World History Tchr
Leitsch, Sandra Stevens
Math Teacher
Martines, Robert M.
Technology Teacher
Moreau, Joseph John
Business Education Teacher
Overton, Amy R.
Social Studies Teacher
Powers, Michael Thomas
Math & Computer Sci Teacher
Redmer, Bonnie Kay
Biology Teacher
Rhoades-Moran, Kathryn
High School English Teacher
Ricke, Dennis F.
Computer Teacher
Roderick, Thomas N.
Mathematics Teacher
Sears, Vicki Kabichis
Second Grade Teacher
Stock, John L.
5th Grade Teacher
Trauth, Carole Ann (Brassington)
Retired Fifth Grade Teacher
Werbach, Judith Rae
Coord & Math ADAPT Teacher
Wininger, William Joseph
Retired Mathematics Teacher
Zimmer, Kathryn Gwen
Spanish Teacher
SAINT DAVID
Tucker, Kendall Evan
Eng, Rdng, Spelling & PE Tchr
SAINT ELMO
Oliver, Janet E.
Business Education Teacher
SAINT JACOB
Estes, Sharon Lee (Thompson)
Spanish Teacher
Gerstenecker, Janice Johnson
English & Journalism Teacher
Haynes, Marla Lynette
English Teacher
Hill, Bonnie C.
Math & Physics Teacher
Packard, Patricia Dunn
Business Education Teacher
Sargent, Sherrie Allen
Dean of Students
SAINT JOSEPH
Hillman, Carol Koehn
Retired Music Director
SAINT MARIE
Kaufman, Francis E.
Junior High Math Teacher
SALEM
Baggett, Benjamin M.
Retired Teacher & Coach
Baldridge, Sheila W.
Teacher & Soc Studies Chprsn
Basnett, C. Jan
English Teacher
Buck, Ruth R. Mc Neilly
Retired Teacher
Cartwright, Debbie A.
6th Grade Social Studies Tchr
Davis, Gary R.
Third Grade Teacher
Gruenkemeyer, Gregory L.
Assistant Principal
Liddle, Craig Alan
Eighth Grade Science Teacher
Mc Cowan Sager, LeaAnn Satterfield
Kirsch
Second Grade Teacher
Smudrick, Connie Lynn
Business Teacher
SANDOVAL
Vogt, Mary Altadonna
1st Grade Teacher
SANDWICH
Blackwell, Samuel M., Jr.
History Teacher & Dept Chair
Fraley, Darla Johnson
Mathematics Teacher
Pax, Bob
Physical Education Teacher
SAVANNA
Franzen, Mark Jonathan
Social Studies Teacher
Taylor, Kathleen Stretton
High School Math Teacher
Tippett, Judy Ann Stark
Savanna District Librarian
Titus, Joseph
Band Director
White, Wayne C.
Indstrl Arts & Drivers Ed Tchr
Wright, Kathleen Vorwald
Second Grade Teacher
SCALES MOUND
Downs, Dennis Dwane
Social Studies & PE Teacher
SCHAUMBURG
Albamonte, Mary Kay
English Teacher
Anderson, Barbara Elizabeth
English Teacher
Anderson, J. Keith
2nd-3rd Grade Teacher
Anderson, Jane Ellen
English Teacher
Arizpe, Efrain
Spanish Teacher
Ary, Jack M.
Driver Education Teacher
Bawden, Marlene Kay
Fourth Grade Teacher
Bethurem, Robert Van
7th Grade Language Arts Tchr
Blasucci, Carmein Jannotta
3rd & 4th Grd Tchr of Gifted
Breunlin, R. James
Math Teacher & Dept Chair
Cassert, Leonard H.
Social Studies Teacher
Danello, Germaine Karen
Kindergarten Teacher
Donehey, Maureen
Spanish Teacher
Everett, Karen (Weger)
English Teacher
Gillette, Gregory Thomas
Economics Tchr & Track Coach
Gray, Rebecca Susan
Second Grade Teacher
Grebasch, Gail Ellen
7th-8th Grd Lang Arts Teacher
Hays, Judy Meyer
Music Teacher
Hornor, Renee R.
Mathematics & Science Teacher
Jackson, Jim
5th Grade Tchr
Kandl, Loretta Colban
Fourth Grade Teacher
Kasper, Timothy A.
Math Teacher
Kupkowski, Daniel D.
Training Support Supervisor
Malmquist, Joseph Richard
Orchestra Teacher
Mc Coy, David L.
AP Micro Ec, Govt & Psych Tchr
Mc Donald, Judith Ann
Soc Studies Dept Chair & Tchr
Miller, Kevin J.
Band Director
Minnick, Deborah
Eighth Grade Tchr & Math Chair
Noce, Susan Guthrie
Math Teacher & Dept Chair
Pree, John H.
Math Teacher
Proska, Deborah Katheryn
Elementary Art Teacher
Putnam, Shirley DeMarke
English Teacher
Reed, Donna Moran
English & Speech Teacher
Rivera, M. Angelo
High School Science Teacher
Rubin, Howard J.
US History Teacher
Sack, Nancy Condon
High School English Teacher
Schroeder, Loring W.
Special Education Teacher
Stordahl, Jean Weigt
First Grade Teacher
Thorsness, Bob A.
High School Business Teacher
Tomaso, Maribeth Gottemoller
5th Grade Teacher
Turner, Ken L., Jr.
High School Chemistry Teacher
SCIOTA
Vogel, Thomas Vincent
Biology Chairperson
Zimmerman, Barbara Ann
Eng Tchr & Media Specialist
SENECA
Babcock, Derek L.
Third Grade Teacher
Downes, Bonnie C.
English Teacher
Helton, James W.
7th-8th Grd Soc Science Tchr
Hobbs, Lawrence A.
Industrial Arts Teacher
Houchin, Kirk Anthony
Counselor
Keech, Tanya M.
Science Teacher
Maierhofer, Jeffrey Alan
Agriculture Education Teacher
Marshall, Moira Delarosa
Chemistry & Physics Teacher
Martin, Mary Patricia
Spanish Teacher
Miller, Rosemary I.
Health Occupations Instructor
Mitchell, Carol Swanson
Mathematics Teacher
Nagle, Patricia Ann
First Grade Teacher
Olsen, Wyman Leslie
Music Teacher
Stahl, Gregory Alan
Jr High PE Teacher
Weber, Kent Douglas
Agriculture Teacher
SERENA
Martin, Jeanie Gura
High School English Teacher
Struna, Fran
High School History Teacher
SESSER
Downs, Glenda Faye (Gilliam)
10th-11th Grade English Tchr
SEWARD
Huntley, Cynthia Alice
Fourth Grade Teacher
SHABBONA
Dawson, Ken S.
Teacher
Hunt, Ronald Gene, Jr.
English Teacher
Jefcik, Ronald R.
Bio, Anatomy & Physiology Tchr
Kuntz, Jan Marie
High School English Teacher
Tyler, Gloria A.
Art Teacher
SHANNON
Cornelius, Jerry Carl
Social Studies Teacher
SHELBYVILLE
Burns, Patrick James
High School Counselor
Burrell, Dixie West
Business Teacher
Eberspacher, Jacqueline Dunaway
7th & 8th Grade Math Teacher
Fedrigon, Becky Wooters
Second Grade Teacher
Lookofsky, Betsy Elam
Biology Teacher
Niestradt, Kathy Lynn
English Teacher
Rood, Thomas L.
3rd Grade Teacher
Shoaff, Brenda Brown
Kindergarten Teacher
Wilhelm, Nancy Hulick
English Teacher & Counselor
SHELDON
Maleske, Kris Matthew
Art Teacher
Pittman, Richard Dwight
Fifth Grade Teacher
Skrobul, Guy Gerard
Geography Teacher
SHERMAN
Kuhnke, Carolyn F.
Third Grade Teacher
SHERRARD
Coon, Lori Ann
Business Teacher
Newton, Susan Lee
High School Mathematics Tchr
Shaffer, Gregory Harold
Math Teacher
Swegle, Charles Thomas
French Teacher
Tyler, Vicki L. Hostetler
HS PE & Health Instructor
Watkins, Thomas Sheldon
English Department Chair
Weese, Jack L.
History & Indstrl Arts Teacher
SHIPMAN
Davis, Paula C.
4th Grade Teacher
SIDELL
Knott, Barbara Ringo
Retired Teacher
Marno-Martin, Mari D.
K-12th Grade Dist Art Teacher
SIGEL
Tegler, Christina
Tutor
SKOKIE
Ahmed, Samira A.
English Teacher
Asaro, Joseph Francis
Biology Teacher
Belkind, Edith P.
ESL & Hebrew Teacher
Benitez, Pamela J.
Spanish Teacher
Biondi, Katherine Anne
Fifth Grade Teacher
Bruce, Judy Paxton
Junior High School Art Tchr
Christie, Peter Joseph
Accounting Instructor
Connelly, John R., Jr.
Social Studies Teacher
Eisele, Elton L.
Director of Bands
Elegreet-DeSalvo, Nora
7th-8th Grd Lang Arts Teacher
Geismann, William F.
English Teacher
Grabowski, Dennis
Art Instructor
Gregerman, Daniel Paul
Choral Director
Hammer, Joyce Leviton
Math Teacher
Hendrix, Pamela Marie
Orchestra Director
Johns, Michelle Mustybrook
English Instructor
Josephson, Barbara
Spanish Teacher
Keegstra, Bruce H.
Social Studies Teacher
Kelley, Kevin J.
High School Business Teacher
Kuehn, Karen Lynn
PE Teacher & Coach
Lencioni, Judie Miller
Art Teacher
Lupi, Guillermo
Spanish Teacher & Tennis Coach
Miller, Yvonne
Counselor
Musleh, Conrad Yusuf
Physics Teacher
Pasternak, Albert A.
Science Teacher
Robertson, Elizabeth Perez
Spanish Teacher
Roschmann, Dennis
Field Service Director
Schenewerk, Karen L.
High School Biology Teacher
Schinto, Donna M.
Librarian
Schuffert, Patricia A.
Math Teacher
Schutt, Robert Andrew
HS English Teacher
Schwarz, Jacqueline
Mathematics Teacher
Sweeney, James Arthur
English Teacher
Wilkins, Susan Franklin
Social Studies Teacher
Youstra, Greggory Albert
Health & PE Teacher
SMITHTON
Bean, Susan Lynn
Third Grade Teacher
Giliberti, Karen Boltinghouse
7th-8th Grade Teacher
Procasky, John David
Science Teacher
SOMONAUK
Bulkley, Michele Jane
7th-8th Grade Jr HS Math Tchr
Cofer, Della Frazier
English Teacher
Hall, Michael Steven
Soc Stud Tchr & Ath Dir
Hickey, Charles H.
Math Teacher
Kember, Karen Marie
Physical Education Teacher
Wright, Susan Margarethe (Wilson)
Art & Biology Teacher
SOUTH BELOIT
Martin, Gregory Darrel
Physical Ed Teacher & Coach
Sievers, Kathleen Jones
Second Grade Teacher
SOUTH ELGIN
Thompson, Phyllis Darlene (Yount)
Third Grade Teacher
SOUTH HOLLAND
Beaver, George Robert
Science Department Chairman
Beno, Marybeth Zagotta
Mathematics Instructor
Brand, Smith V.
Instructor of Speech
Bushor-Gardner, Sandi
Prof of Bio & Educl Consultant
Bytnar, Ronald James
Acctng Instructor & Pgm Coord
Chappelle, Richard C.
US Teacher
Eberhardt, Kathryn Melin
Instr of Occupational Therapy
Jones, Melvin Richard
English Teacher
King, Jill M.
Business Instructor
Kulycky, Michael N.
Instructor of English
Kuyper, Virginia Alamsha
Retired Fifth Grade Teacher
Linz, Andrea Lynn
8th Grd & Algebra Instructor
McCarthy, Carol A.
Office Admin & Tech Instr
Naegele, William Gregory
Mathematics Professor
O'Connor, John Patrick
Guidance Counselor
Pinkard-Avant, Rita E.
HS Counselor
Sanfilipp, Ronald Joseph
Business & History Teacher
Shields, Richard Leonard
Mathematics Teacher
Small, Linda Marie
Business Teacher
Swentko, Wallene M.
4th Grade Teacher & Asst Prin
Wachel, Michael
Fourth Grade Teacher

H HOLLAND (cont)
Mary Griffin
ctor of Recruitment
ra, Suzette Markancek
stant Office Manager
H PEKIN
, Suzanne Jones
r High English Teacher
H ROXANA
stein, Janet Stahlschmidt
K Teacher
r, David W.
Grade Teacher
H WILMINGTON
Linda Wallace
gtn & Rdng Recovery Teacher
TA
, Walter
Grade Teacher
, Carolyn Sue (Ernsting)
Arts & Soc Studies Tchr
, Marilyn Bruns
ematics Teacher
Gary L.
, Physics Tchr & Dept Chm
h, Janet S.
al Studies Teacher
s, Claudia M. M.
her
Mark Hilton
Stud Tchr & Dept Chm
gton, Lynn Pirtle
Grade Lang Arts Teacher
worth, Laura Grah
Grd Language Arts Teacher
NG VALLEY
t, Eric Christian
h Teacher & Coach
one, Teresa Denise
lish Teacher
, Jean Marie
hematics Teacher
s, Philip Ray
sical Sci & Biology Teacher
NGFIELD
, Elizabeth Blackwell
enth-Eighth Grade Teacher
rson, Rachell N.
essor
Michael George, Jr.
rumental Music Instructor
p, Donna L.
red Fifth Grade Teacher
r, Daniel Robert
sics & Math Teacher
rdi, Barbara Ann
essor of Biology
lt, Don
m, Physics & Math Instr
idge, Denis P.
hematics Instructor
er, Edwin R.
munications & Lit Instr
nger, Barbara Hansch
h Grade Teacher
Wanda Wright
ence Dept Chairman
on, Pamela Lynn
h School Choir Teacher
ano, Carlo S.
Grade Mathematics Teacher
ress, Susan J. (Eaglen)
guage Arts & French Teacher
ell, Cecilia Stiles
istant Professor of History
in, Anne L.
oc Prof of Legal Studies
hart, Kathryn Elaine
t Prof in Legal Stud Dept
, Michael Roy
Stud Tchr & Asst Prin
e, Judith B.
Tchr & Science Supv
, Arlene Morosi
rd Grade Teacher
Jane Pervinich
th Grade Teacher
igoni, Mauri Monihon
soc Prof of Visual Arts, Dir
rd, Terri Leigh
s Ed Teacher & Dept Head
s, Dorothy Elizabeth
rketing & Finance Professor
berg, Kelly Renee
nds Dir & Music Theory Instr
en, Bradley Gifford
mer His, Govt & Ec Tchr
en, Mary Jo
glish Department Chair
ebrand, Barbara Drusendahl
tructor of Psychology
censmith, Christa M.
sistant Professor of Chem
omb, Maria Teresa
anish Professor
son, Sheila
Grade Science Teacher
mark, Gloria Santowski
High Science Teacher
a, Lois Joan
junct Asst Professor
hard, Marcellus Julian
st Prof of English
, Cheryl Montooth
operative Education Teacher
e, Jennifer Christine
emistry Instructor
ura, Jack Joseph
of of Art

Meister, Suellen N.
Nursing Professor
Miller, Tim Ralph
Professor of Mgmt
Morrison, Linda J. (Mills)
4th Grade Teacher
Pringle, Marla Mc Cormick
Retired Fifth Grade Teacher
Rathke, Greg Dean
PE & Health Teacher
Redick, Robert Alan
Instructor of Business Admin
Sanders, Rick Dale
Vice Principal
Simpson, John C.
Private Music Lessons Instr
Squibb, John R.
History & Pol Sci Instructor
Stewart, Tambra Hagan
Vocational Teacher
Stremsterfer, Gary W.
Jr High Social Studies Tchr
Tolan, Helen Roth
Regional Superintendent
VanderKloot, Carol Dallmann
Math & Language Arts Teacher
Van Der Slik, Jack R.
Professor of Political Studies
Van Dyke, Annette Joy
Asst Prof of Intrdsplnry Stud
Volkman, Barbara Helfert
Spanish Teacher
Walch, Janet Logal
Mathematics Teacher
Walk, Sheila K.
Speech, Drama & English Tchr
Wheeler, Mary Elaine
Composition & Literature Instr
Wilcox, Marie
Math Teacher
Williams, Richard Ray
Prof of Comm & Lit
STANFORD
Bellas, Connie Hirst
Middle School Lang Arts Tchr
STAUNTON
Hawkins, Linda J.
English & Speech Teacher
Lamore, Dave
Science Teacher
Malone, Bruce Allen
Social Studies Teacher
Mansholt, Connie
Jr High Language Arts Teacher
Ruehrup, Donna Jo
Physical Education Teacher
STEELEVILLE
Harding, Natalie Christine
English Teacher
STEGER
Matthies, William Herbert
6th Grade Teacher
Rogers, Cynthia C.
Jr HS Eng Tchr
Simone, Anthony Gerard
Asst Prin, Eng & Rdng Tchr
STERLING
Altenburg, Tod J.
English & Spanish Teacher
Baker, Maurice Jesse
Biology Tchr
Beaty, J. Mark
Choral Director
Bohlin, Susan
Teaching Assistant
Boone, Kenneth A.
Investment Representative
Booth, Barbara Ann
Math Instructor
Ebbens, Wendell Todd
Sixth Grade Teacher
Eubanks, Michael Henry
Social Studies Teacher
Faber, Cheryl Gerken Riess
First Grade Teacher
Gatz, Elisa McGee
Physics Teacher
McCue, Deborah J.
HS & MS Counselor
Mc Ginn, Nancy Grennan
Religion Teacher
Papoccia, Michael Thomas
Athletic Dir, PE & Health Tchr
Pfundstein, Pamela S.
Mktg, Mngmt & Distrbv Ed Instr
Robinson, Cheryl McGhee
Third Grade Teacher
Siebert, Donna Rae
Second Grade Teacher
Wurmle, Nancy K.
Home Economics Teacher
STEWARD
Eckhardt, Jacqueline Beardsley
Mathematics & Amer His Tchr
STICKNEY
May, Frances Burgess
6th-8th Grd Soc Stud Tchr
STILLMAN VALLEY
Beem, Christine Ann
English Teacher
Bratta, Kathleen J. (Grennan)
First Grade Teacher
Cassinelli, Lydia Faith
Trans Prgm Instruction Teacher
Lorbinenko, Nina
French & World History Teacher
Meves, Sharon Bromley
English & Lang Arts Tchr

STOCKTON
Sertle, Terry G.
Guidance Counselor
Werner, Jeffrey B.
5th Grade Teacher
STONINGTON
Covington, Jeannine Anne
Second Grade Teacher
STRASBURG
Curry, Lucy
First Grade Teacher
Oyer, Donald Ray
Retired 6th Grade Teacher
Ray, Lynda Sue (Enterline)
Visual Arts Teacher
Wascher, Mark Frederick
Business Ed Tchr & Bsbl Coach
STREAMWOOD
Beard, Kathleen M.
Math Teacher
Chmielewski, Joanne
Math Teacher
Garcia, Jaime Daniel
Principal
Gudeman, Helen Sutter
English Teacher & Dept Chm
Kalsow, Kathryn M.
General Music & Chorus Teacher
Kyle, Candida Passeri
6th Grade Teacher
Lackey, Linda Grimes
English Teacher
Lamberti, Thomas M.
Social Studies Teacher
McCarty-Fulton, Marilyn Fornall
7th Grd English & Speech Tchr
Meade, Glenn Louis
English Department Chairman
Phillips, Carol L.
Mathematics Teacher
Robin, Carol B.
Home Economics Teacher
Searcy, Rupert T.
Dean of Students
Sindelar, Carol Lynn
Physical Education Teacher
Wallace, Bruce Dale
Fifth Grade Teacher
Wallace, Linda Ann (Schmidt)
Hlth Occupations Tchr & Coord
STREATOR
Abry, Constance Joan
Fifth Grade Teacher
Adrian, Carol Louise (Rush)
1st Grade Teacher
Birins, Jane Glass
Second Grade Teacher
Bublitz, Kenneth Irvin
Social Studies Teacher
Cave, JoAnn Hatzer
Eighth Grade Teacher
Helfers Riss, Pam
Math & Science Teacher
Horton, Debbie Ann
German Teacher
Johnson, Clyde G.
Guidance Counselor
Johnson, Henry C.
PE Teacher & Athletic Director
Johnson, Sally J.
Business Department Teacher
Kolb, Larry D.
Agriculture Teacher
Leonard, Bryan Donald
Chemistry & Physics Instructor
Le Rette, Jacqueline Ann
4th Grade Teacher
Robbins, Barbara Zurlinden
6th Grade Teacher
Russell, Gail Jeanine
Sixth Grade Teacher
Timmerman, David Owen
Soc Stud Tchr & Dept Chprsn
Vandemark, Gerald G.
Math Teacher
Wargo, Edw J.
Retired Teacher
STRONGHURST
Blender, Jay Mark
Physical Education Teacher
Clifton, Richard W.
Retired Teacher
SUGAR GROVE
Denault, Gary L.
Emergency Medical Technician
Hauser, Raymond Edward
His Instr & Honors Prgm Dir
Matousek, Cherie Rose
Art Appreciation & His Teacher
May, Robert G.
Assoc Prof Criminal Justice
Otto, Gloria Grill
Anatomy & Physiology Instr
Port, Ruth Kaiser
English Assistant Professor
Staas, Beth Zahn
College Instructor
SULLIVAN
Buxton, Claudette Oliver
English Teacher
Lawson, Rebecca Lynn
English Teacher
Seelhoefer, Leroy Bermard
High School Mathematics Tchr
Terrell, Amy Sue
Spanish Teacher
SUMMIT ARGO
Farley, Linda Marie
Third Grade Teacher

Findley, Dan J.
HS Bio Tchr & Sci Dept Chair
Giuriati, Nancy Weytkow
HS English Teacher
Good, Vincent Robert
High School Band Director
Johnson, David W.
English Teacher
Konkol, Pamela Jane
Radio & TV Teacher
Lilly, Mandy Williams
Social Work Specialist
Panfil, Paula Jahnke
Science Teacher
Peterson, Donald Arthur
Choral Music Director
Piwnicki, William Raymund
English Instructor
Remes, Deanna C.
English Teacher
Tsenes, Sammy Ellen Vallos
Home Economics Teacher
SUMNER
Czemski, Anthony Joseph
Social Studies Teacher
Frohock, Brenda Stallins
Language Arts Teacher
SYCAMORE
Johnson, Yvonne A.
5th Grade Teacher
Jordan, Joseph Michael
Driver Education Leader
Meadowcraft, Helen Jackson
Fourth Grade Teacher
O'Neil, Patricia Ann
Dean of Students
Schumacher, Jamie
English Teacher
Toles, John C.
Chemistry Teacher
TABLE GROVE
Bowton, Lisa Diane (Sailer)
Grammar & Literature Teacher
Lafary, Karen Rhea
English Teacher
Meyer, Daniel J.
Industrial Technology Teacher
TAMMS
Leatherman, Nancy Jane
Secondary English Teacher
Mc Crite, Danny Ray
Agriculture Teacher
Young, Raynell Welch
Kindergarten Teacher
TAMPICO
Cooper, Debra Sue
HS Math Teacher
Hagan, Pamela Sue
Fifth Grade Teacher
Kelly, Kathryn A.
4th Grade Teacher
TAYLOR RIDGE
Bischoff, Pamela J.
HS Mathematics Teacher
Downey, Barbara J.
English Teacher
Morgensen, Larry F.
English & Speech Teacher
Ontiveros, Ranelle Downey
Spanish Teacher
Potthast, David Raymond
Social Studies Teacher
Smith, Roma Reed
HS His & Soc Stud Teacher
TAYLORVILLE
Banko, M. Marcia
Third Grade Teacher
Bertauski, Nancy Ann Fruin
Third Grade Teacher
DeCourcy, Eunice Grabble
4th Grade Teacher
Freese, Suzie W.
Choral Director
Johnson, Carol J.
Math & Physical Education Tchr
McVey, Deloris Marie
English Teacher & Dept Chair
Metzger, Jacqueline Reid
Health Sciences Teacher
Walters, Donna Wylder
Spanish Teacher
Westrick, Carol Rupert
1st Grade Teacher
TEUTOPOLIS
Drone, Mark Alan
Physics & Chemistry Teacher
Fisher, Sandra Bigard
Jr HS Language Arts Teacher
Probst, Kent M.
Lit, Math Tchr & Title 1 Dir
Runde, Barbara
Fourth Grade Teacher
THOMPSONVILLE
Kee, Yolonda Cardwell
Retired Language Arts Teacher
Phillips, Donita Kay
Kindergarten Teacher
TINLEY PARK
Ambrose, Jennifer M.
Counselor
Anderson, Ellen
English Teacher
Beckmann, Arthur H.
Director of Bands
Bennett, Ruth Hodgson
Office Ed Coord & Bus Tchr
Broccolo, Louis J.
8th Grade Social Studies Tchr
Buell, Carole S.
Fifth Grade Teacher

Finfrock, Pamela J.
Mathematics Teacher
Hoffman, Karen Burdi
Retired 1st Grade Teacher
Kirk, Letitia Ann
Associate Principal
Kramer, Susan Whaley
PE Tchr & Sports Coord
Lipowski, Edwin Anton
HS Social Studies Teacher
Maday, Larry
Mathematics Instructor
Michael, George Franklin, III
Mathematics Teacher
Nettle, Sean Christopher
Language Arts Teacher
Ogrodowski, Diane M.
Teacher
Pallissard, Theresa Nolan
English Teacher
Pickert, William Robert
Mathematics Teacher
Pries, Margaret Ann
Junior High Language Arts Tchr
Rapinchuk, Peter David
High School Physics Teacher
Rhoades, Jane A. (Frees)
Sci Dept Chair & Physics Tchr
Rose, Richard Scott
English Instructor
Shanahan, Jeri
Fifth Grade Teacher
Stanioch, Iris A.
English & Latin Teacher
Valant, Tracey Kathleen
High School Math Teacher
Wennberg, Maria Wilhelm
German & English Teacher
TOLEDO
Anderson, Roger Kent
Soc Stud Instr & Dept Chair
Blade, Robert Olin
Jr High Lang Arts Tchr
Hollis, Stacy Marie (Hammond)
High School English Teacher
Miller, James Allen
Science & Health Teacher
TOLONO
Herriott, Diana Fey
HS Science Teacher
Himone, Robert L.
Math Teacher
Wallis, Evelyn Antey
Social Studies Teacher
TOWER HILL
Oller, Linda M.
Jr High Math Teacher
TREMONT
Hopkins, William Robert
Mathematics Teacher
Moyers, Debby Ann
English Teacher
Ramsey, Steven A.
Teacher
Schaidle, Dale Francis
Technology Education Instr
Strifler, Pete
Social Studies Teacher
Stuckwisch, Shelly
Business Teacher
Zumstein, Ray Theodore
Advanced Chemistry Teacher
TRENTON
Brinkman, Terry Lee
Mathematics Teacher
Cryder, Steven Joseph
Media Spec & Research Instr
Lane, Steven Bruce
American History Teacher
Satterfield, Phyllis Medcalf
First Grade Teacher
Shute, Terry Estel
Principal
Stone, Ralph
Industrial Arts Teacher
Thole, Mary Lee (Jansen)
1st Grade Teacher
Washburn, Rodney E.
Band Director
Welz, Neal Anthony
Retired Teacher & Coach
TROY
Frey, Tammy Lynn (Bernreuter)
Physical Education & Hlth Tchr
Ingersoll, Linda Edwards
Language Arts Teacher
TUNNEL HILL
Akins, Mona Reeder
First Grade Teacher
TUSCOLA
Chamberlain, Elizabeth Ann
Chemistry & Phys Sci Teacher
Eiben, Warner G.
English Teacher
Miller, Sherry
First Grade Teacher
ULLIN
Anderson, Kathy Webb
School Improvement Coordinator
Holm, Carolyn Vinson
Speech, Eng & Literature Instr
Murley, Robert F.
Social Studies Teacher
Oros, Frances Jean
Science Instructor
Sander, Phyllis J. (Propst)
Business Professor
Somers, Peter William
Math & Science Professor

ULLIN (cont)
Stewart, Lisa Lynn
Elementary Principal
Thompson, Carmen Wright
Jr-Sr English Teacher
UNIVERSITY PARK
Chang, Lisa L.
Mathematics Education Prof
Dave, Jagdish P.
Professor of Psychology
Genevich, Maureen Bailey
Psychology Professor
Hildebrand, Susanne Yohnka
Communication Disorders Prof
Johnson, Elizabeth Jean (Black)
University Lecturer
Katz, Marsha
Management Professor
Koutouzos, Patricia L.
Prof of Eng & Secondary Ed
Mc Master, Michele
Communications Professor
Osuch, Barbara Byrne
English Instructor
Panic, Milan
Linguistics & Lit Lecturer
Peterson, Karen Myhra
Elementary Education Professor
Potempa, Nancy Mae (Papesh)
University Lecturer
Segal, Eli
Media Communication Professor
Wei, Anthony Yueh-shan
Prof of Philosophy & History
URBANA
Beckrum, Karen Kathleen
Elementary Teacher
D'Angelo, John P.
Professor
Fuller, Dorothy L.
English Teacher
Gingold, Phyllis Kay
HS English Teacher
Hebert, Sherry Bedeaux
English Second Language Tchr
Kesler, Darrel J.
Associate Professor
Mazurek-Suslick, Adele
English Teacher
Meister, Diane Bier
Sixth Grade Teacher
Micele, Lisa R.
Counselor
Miller, Robert Earl
Emeritus Professor
Nelson, Jeffrey H.
Social Studies Teacher
Portnoy, Esther
Associate Prof of Mathematics
Prescott, Ronald Walter
Retired Teacher
Presley, Janice Allen
Spanish Teacher
Procter, Patricia Trowbridge
Third Grade Teacher
Rimington, James Earl
Instructor
Rogers, Paula A.
High School Math Teacher
Summerville, Willie T.
Choral Music Director
Suslick, Adele Mazurek
English Teacher
Yarber, Ann Theresa (Harris)
9th Grade Physical Ed Teacher
VANDALIA
Cliff, Michael D.
Physical Science Teacher
Heinzman, Jerry Lee
English Teacher
Patrick, Michael Lee
HS Social Studies Teacher
Rohlfing, Tracy Dolores
7th Grade Lang Arts Teacher
Staff, Billye B.
Retired Fourth Grade Teacher
Watkins, Mary Louise Stefano
Home Ec & Child Care Teacher
Wollerman, Julie (Lee)
Project Coordinator
VARNA
Darnell-Rock, Beth
Music Teacher
VENICE
Alexander, Annette
HS Principal
Arons, Leonard Frank
World History Teacher
VERGENNES
Fletcher, Jan Abernathie
5th Grade Teacher
VERNON HILLS
Bock, Louise Powell
6th Grade Math Teacher
Castellano, Mary
7th & 8th Grd Soc Stud Teacher
Cosmano, Lesley Madelon Leise
5th Grd Sci & Lang Arts Tchr
Koch, Thomas A., Jr.
7th Grade Soc Studies Teacher
Kuehl, Timothy Arlen
8th Grd Mathematics & PE Tchr
Rizzolo, Anne B.
Jr High Science Teacher
Rudolph, Barbara Bowden
Fifth Grade Teacher
Worman, Kathleen Marie Herman
Junior High English Teacher
Wotman, Meredith Louise
7th Grade Math Teacher
VIENNA
Bedwell, Vera L.
Mathematics Teacher
Bremer, Jeff
Science Teacher
Faulkner, Mary Jaye (Hunsaker)
Spcl Ed, Psych & English Tchr
Hight, Corby Todd
Biology Teacher
Kreuter, Brenda D.
American Lit & Speech Teacher
Miller, Teri Sue
Title I Teacher
Ray, Max Gordon
Retired Elem Tchr & Coach
Reichert, Richard Coleman, Jr.
Industrial Technology Teacher
Sherwood, Cindy Kay
Physical Education Instructor
VILLA GROVE
Aden, Nancy Lee
Business Tchr & Tchr Coord
Dilliner, Linda Archibald
Second Grade Teacher
Granse, William F., Jr.
5th Grade Teacher
Krejci, Ann Schnitz
Soc Studies Dept Head & Tchr
Pritchard, Mary Ann Helm
5th Grade Teacher
Shadwick, Linda Icenogle
HS Science Teacher
Sigler, Joyce Anne
Junior High Reading Teacher
VILLA PARK
Amelio, Ralph J.
English & Humanities Instr
Becvar, Carol Will
4th Grade Teacher
Burton, Therese Mondek
Mathematics Teacher
Calaway, Kenneth A.
English Teacher & Asst Prin
Contorno, Joseph Shane
HS English Teacher
Devine, Faith E.
Tutor
Drennan, Carol F.
Theatre Arts & English Teacher
Gehrt, Vicky Edwards
Writing & English Teacher
Gerut, Charles Joseph
HS Physics Teacher
Heise, Nancy M.
French Teacher
Jacoby, Carol Lynne
Dance & Phy Education Teacher
Knoebber, David Thomas
Art Teacher
Lyons, Maureen Montague
Math Teacher
McCurdy, John Thomas
Mathematics Teacher
Montgomery, Peter James
Social Studies Teacher
Sejnost, Roberta L.
Rdng Dept Chm & Title I Dir
Smith, David James
Math & Cmptr Programming Tchr
Tyler, Ronald Miles
Counselor
VIRGINIA
Bennett, Jeffrey Russell
Social Science Teacher
Dean, Carol Dawdy
Spanish & English Teacher
WARREN
Balbach, Susan Kay
Second Grade Teacher
Bourquin, Susan Gallo
K-12th Grd Vocal Music Teacher
Holland, Steven John
Instrumental Music Teacher
WARRENSBURG
Brodbeck, Nancy Negley
English Teacher
Burckhartt, Fred G.
PE, Health & Drivers Ed Tchr
Green, Craig Steven
Former Professor
Hurst, Ronald Raymond, Jr.
Mathematics Teacher
Janvrin, Winnie Ann
English & Social Studies Tchr
Kiick, Debbie Mc Feeters
Health, PE & Drivers Ed Tchr
Ryterski, Camella (Parrett)
Middle School Science Teacher
WARRENVILLE
Mitchell, Amber Lynn (Bechtlofft)
Music Teacher
Timson, Mary
Fifth Grade Teacher
Wondrow, Carolyn
Third Grade Teacher
WARSAW
Bertucci, Thomas Eugene
7th-12th Grade Principal
Finton, Daniel J.
Retired Teacher
Snowden, David Ross
English & Spanish Teacher
WASHBURN
McCleary, Nicole E.
Mathematics Teacher
Taylor, Katherine Ann
French, Spanish & English Tchr
WASHINGTON
Arnett, Tina Sikula
Business Tchr & Dept Chprsn
Coughlin, Patrick M.
Guidance Counselor
Essington, Mary Landon
Fifth Grade Teacher
Jones, Patricia Louise
Language Arts Teacher
Neakrase, Paul M.
Biology Instructor
Schroeder, Vickey Sue Peak
First Grade Teacher
Shempf, Lisa Petry
6th Grd Language Arts Teacher
Witt, James A.
Math Dept Chair & Instructor
WATERLOO
Babbs, Jerry Ray
High School Social Stud Tchr
Birchler, John Alexander
Director of Music
Corzine, Diane Lynn
Fine Arts Dept Head
Downing, Mary Ann Stewart
Second Grade Teacher
Freund, Elaine
Literature Teacher
Gregson, David Michael
Computer Teacher
Haberl, Chris A.
Junior High Science Instructor
Maguire, Donna Carlene
English Teacher
Matson, Judith Kay
First Grade Teacher
Souchek, Terry Ray
Junior High School Teacher
Speck, Gelea Karraker
English Teacher
Wacker, Betty L.
Business Teacher
Wilkinson, Judy Ann
Family & Consumer Science Tchr
Yagge, Linda S.
8th Grade Math Teacher
WATERMAN
Martin, Sherrie Marlene
Third Grade Teacher
WATSEKA
Hartke, Stephanie Bedinger
Freshman English Teacher
Newlin, Monte A.
Guidance Counselor
WAUCONDA
Doetzel, Beverly Berra
Second Grade Teacher
Ezel, Kathleen Ketchum
3rd-5th Grd Gifted Rdng Tchr
Hartman, Melba M.
Physical Education Teacher
Price, Karl Jay
High School Math Teacher
Thornton, Daniel G.
Math Teacher
WAUKEGAN
Adler, Elaine Bader
English Teacher
Barsky, Linda Gauger (Ryden)
Comm & Soc Stud Tchr
Burckhalter, Patricia Ellgen
English Teacher
Cherry, Ella Marie Williams
Third Grade Teacher
Clyne, Amy
Math Teacher
Cusick-Acosta, Jodi Lea
Spanish Teacher
DiPierro, Barbara Ross
English as Second Lang Teacher
Franz, Robert C.
High School Mathematics Tchr
Gillespie-Walser, Jamie
French Tchr & Coll Stud Coord
Grossberg, Terry Craig
Band Director
Guttman, Arnold Robert
Chemistry Teacher
Hauser, Goldie Stillson
Biology Teacher
Jarrell, Steve
Psychology Teacher
Laino, Jean Fitzgerald
Retired Teacher
Lynd, Steven Michael
Fifth Grade Teacher
Mathias, Susan Zillig
High School History Teacher
McKenzie, Debra J.
Secondary English Teacher
Merzlicker, William Frank
Business & Computer Teacher
Oeffling, Laura Kathryn
Mathematics Teacher
Peterson, Michele Colette (Saniuk)
English Teacher
Reiher, Cynthia Jean (Shaver)
8th Grade Communications Tchr
Rohlwing, Vicki K. (Scott)
Fifth Grade Teacher
Sabourin, Gloria Katoll
5th Grade Teacher
Scott, Deborah Aikens
5th Grade Teacher
Taylor, Christine P.
HS Science & Math Teacher
Townsend, Louise
Business Education Teacher
WAVERLY
Hoots, Diane Kay
French & Language Arts Teacher
Lawler, Marilyn Budde
Elementary Principal
Stahr, Ellen Marie
English & French Teacher
WAYNE
Brown, Donna Loretta Forke
Third Grade Teacher
Corso, Kathleen Anne (Mc Lachlan)
Third Grade Teacher
WAYNE CITY
Medder, David La Vern
Eng, Soc Stud & PE Tchr
Wilson, Hollie Ann Morgan
Health Occupations Teacher
Wilson, Jerry Wayne
HS English & PE Teacher
WENONA
Gehm, Victoria Lynn (Coley)
Former Teacher
WEST CHICAGO
Bachkor, Robin
5th Grade Teacher
Blume, Nancy Ann
Business Teacher
Burzynski, Frank Michael
Math, Computer Science Teacher
Coughlin, Nancy Ann
Principal
Daneels, Mary Ellen
Social Studies Teacher
Euler, Andrew Joel
Bible Teacher
Fisher, Helen Ann (Szalay)
English Department Head
Hudock, Christine F.
Language Arts & Reading Tchr
Johnson, Dan
PE & Health Department Chair
Kammes, Diane Holm
Retired Kindergarten Teacher
Mason, Mark Alan
7th-8th Grd Soc Stud Teacher
Parks, Carol Ann Snabb
Chemistry Teacher
Pederson, David Martin
Media Representative
Perez, Elizabeth
Bilingual & ESL Teacher
Radunzel, Nancy Sheila
2nd Grade Teacher
Reimer, Todd Connelly
History Teacher
Rubini, David A.
6th Grade Teacher
Tunt, Jo-Ann Espelage
Science Department Chairperson
Wrobleski, Steven Ronald
American History Teacher
WEST FRANKFORT
Blackwood, Sheila Kay
Math Dept Chairman
Carney, Randall G.
College Professor
Dimmick, Danella Meanovich
5th Grade Teacher
Hutchins, Polly Miner
Second Grade Teacher
Karoski, Mike S.
Amer Govt & Zoology Teacher
Pagano, Helen Urban
Seventh & Eighth Grade Teacher
Wayer, Mark R.
HS Band & Chorus Director
WEST SALEM
Arvin, Gail Weightman
Sci, Eng, & Tchr of Gifted
Luthe, Leslie J.
Second Grade Teacher
WESTCHESTER
Camp-Allen, Monica Rose
Art Department Chairperson
D'Andria, Claudia Therese
English Teacher
Franceschini, Louis P.
Mathematics Teacher
Kripas, Karen (Meisner)
Mathematics Teacher
Riley, Bill L.
English Teacher & Asst A.D.
Schultz, Judith Vachata
First Grade Teacher
Vitha, Margaret Ann
Math Teacher
WESTERN SPRINGS
Bermier, Anne Marie
8th Grade Teacher
Cepek, Charleen S.
ESL & English Teacher
Cunningham, Bea Agnes
Lang Arts Dept Chair & Teacher
Dutton, Phyllis Robbins
Retired Second Grade Teacher
Gale, Judie Trocchia
Kindergarten Teacher
Simak, Barbara Bayles
Mathematics Tchr & Dept Chair
WESTMONT
Gaul, Roxane Rosy
Speech & Language Pathologist
LeBeda, Catherine Anne
Fifth Grade Teacher
Loescher, M. Richard
Math Department Chairman
WESTVILLE
Kotcher, Peggy Jane
2nd Grade Teacher
WHEATON
Ashland, Diane Smith
Fourth Grade Teacher
Athos, Melissa J.
7th Grd Language Arts Teacher
Baldus-Strauss, Susan
Coach
Bingham, Anita
Sixth Grade Teacher
Blomberg, Janet R.
Assoc Director of Educl Svcs
Botha, Graham Derek
Lit, Writing & Soc Stud Tchr
Cherry, Robert Douglas
HS Math Teacher & Chairman
Duff, Sheryl Kay
Junior High Science Teacher
Harper, Michael
Social Studies Teacher
Harrington, Julie Wilson
Foreign Language Teacher
Havertine, Dianne C.
Home Economics Teacher
Healy, Michael Patrick
Business Teacher
Himmel, Marilyn Louise
Fifth Grade Teacher
Huck, Sharon Sweeney
Retired English Teacher
Johnson, Karna S.
High School English Teacher
Josephson, Donald A.
Assoc Professor of Mathematics
Koenitz, Susan L.
French Teacher & Dept Chairman
Krauspe, Gordon Stevens
Dir of Fine & Performing Arts
Kuharik, Jessie Hamilton
Intermediate LD-BD Tchr
Kustak, Joan O'Mara
Math Teacher & Dept Chair
Latta, Gloria Dondero
Biology Teacher
McCleary, John Mark
Science Teacher
Mc Lean, Maxine Hallberg
Kindergarten Teacher
Morrow, Lyle Warren
Mathematics Teacher
Nicholas, Kimberly Lynn
High School Spanish Teacher
Parisek, Bonnie
First Grade Teacher
Polino, Jill Marie
Social Stud & Lang Arts Tchr
Russell, Wayne John
Guidance Counselor
Ryder, Deborah Krug
4th Grade Teacher
Schultz, Candice (Kane)
Mathematics Teacher
Stankevitz, James Henry
Physics Teacher
Sulek, Thomas Michael
Director of Bands
VanderNaald-Johnson, Sue
Literature & Lang Arts Tchr
Volkmer, Karen Tylwalk
7th Grd Reading & Writing Tchr
Wegscheid, Joanne Wallden
Orchestra Director
Wiesman, Jeff L.
High School Math Teacher
Wolf, Delores Sheridan
Second Grade Teacher
WHEELING
Black, James Henry, III
Director of Orchestras
Cushing, Judy Clara (johnson)
Language Arts & Reading Tchr
Maxwell, Mark Scott
High School English Teacher
Pardun, Jim Joseph
Math Teacher
Saylor, Mark W.
Physical Education Teacher
Schwartz, Linda Kohn
5th Grade Teacher
Wickersham, Donald N.
Physical Education Teacher
WHITE HALL
Paslay, Rodney J.
Physical Education Instructor
Steckel, Susan L.
Science Teacher
Woods, Carla Sue
Biology Teacher
WHITE HEATH
Whetstone, Elizabeth Ann
First Grade Teacher
WILLIAMSFIELD
Garst, Patrick Michael
Math Teacher
Pistorius, Carolyn Fox
Biology Teacher
Wight, Connie
Fifth Grade Teacher
WILLIAMSVILLE
Allison, Kathleen Bollinger
HS Coll Bound English Teacher
Hoffek, Karen King
Guidance Director
Kaitschuk, Janet Ann
Eighth Grd Language Arts Tchr
Lemme, Kathleen Benner
Home Economics Teacher
Pruitt, David R.
Instrumental Music Tchr
Runge, Betty Garrett
Substitute Teacher
Stier, David A.
HS Physics & Chemistry Teacher
WILMETTE
Allworth, Verna Wallace
English Instructor

ETTE (cont)
Robert P.
h & Latin Teacher
Kathleen G.
sh Teacher
d, James Edward
gn Teacher
, Najwa Baidas
12th Grade Chemistry Tchr
baugh, Marianne Minnis
ematics Teacher
t, Judith Pavell
ematics Teacher
erty, Mary Katherine
logy Teacher
on, James M.
Dir of Information Svcs
atricia Tobin
ematics Teacher
alli, Deborah A.
logy Dept Chairperson
Barbara Leonard
logy Teacher
Bernadette Ortegel
ice Teacher & Dept Head
, Diane Sue
selor
on, Jack M.
h Grade Social Stud Tchr
on, Donna L.
ish Teacher
wski, Joan Marie, OP
uctor
nt, Mary Mungovan
logy Teacher
, Geraldine Gail
sh Teacher & Stu Cncl Adv
r, Jerry William
Helping & Ldrshp Dev Tchr
k, Kevin John
School Math Teacher
nor, Marion
al Studies Teacher
ky, William Charles
ics Teacher
Faye Morse
ch & Theatre Teacher
, Suzanne M.
ctor of Music
enberger, John G.
Grade Teacher
ie, Donald E. C.
ors Program Director
Rebecca Clauss
h & English Teacher
INGTON
Linda Spellman
d Grade Teacher
Richard P.
al Science & US His Tchr
es, Karen Lynn
th Grade Teacher
ann, Roberta Madsen
3rd Amer History Teacher
s, Jeff James
& Health Teacher
, Lisa Jean
ool Social Worker
HESTER
Cara Sue Fraser
Grade Teacher
, Cheri Christine
nce Teacher
Kay Bossarte
ish Teacher & Drama Coach
rough, Shirley Louise
lish Teacher
, Cheryl Bradshaw
lish Teacher
, Janet M.
nish Teacher
, Tamara Jo Culp
h School Business Teacher
es, Carol Dwyer
Teacher,Co-Op & Tech Coord
DSOR
s, Marie E.
ogy Teacher
NEBAGO
n, Margaret Samorian
ource Tech Specialist
es, Carol Scelonge
nce Dept Head
son, Lenore C.
ence & Math Teacher
ning, Melissa Ramsey
dergarten Teacher
ell, Lisa M.
hematics Teacher
Brian Andrew
nish Teacher
NETKA
Alan Arthur
sics Teacher
n, Mary K. Wermerskirchen
th Grd Music & Choral Dir
erina, Christopher John
sics Teacher
er, Timothy A.
lish Teacher
, Cheryl Ann
graphy & Computer Teacher
, Larry N.
ial Studies Teacher
er, Anthony John David
ence Teacher
Judy A.
cial Education Teacher
ence, Andrienne Kane
nch Teacher

Levin, Andrea
Social Studies Teacher
Lupfer, Kimiko Koga
High School Japanese Teacher
Mac Kinney, Daniel Ivan
Spanish Teacher
Mewhort, Julie Kempf
Social Studies Teacher
Meyers, Charles J.
Social Studies Tchr
Munley, Gerald Robert
Chemistry Teacher
Randolph, Paul Kevin
History Teacher & Dept Chair
Rhoad, Richard Arthur
Mathematics Teacher
Rosenberg, Jay Stanton
English Teacher
Rosheger, Peter David
Orchestra Teacher
Wagner, James R.
Chemistry Teacher
WINTHROP HARBOR
Koffs, Marianne Richards
7th-8th Grd Lang Arts Teacher
Morzuch, Robert Eugene
Junior HS Science Teacher
WITT
Irvine, Margie A. (Yeske)
Fourth Grade Teacher
Kiefer, Patricia Ann (Powers)
Math Teacher & Ath Dir
Miller, Larry Wayne
Science & Ag Teacher
Munsell, Nancy Anne (Lyskawa)
Second Grade Teacher
Stockstill, Cheryl T.
Mathematics Teacher
WOLF LAKE
Matthews, William Gene, Jr.
Social Studies Dept Chair
Shock, Nancy White
Business Education Teacher
WOOD DALE
Stitzel, Jane L.
Physical Education Instructor
Wyman, Deborah A.
7th Grade Mathematics Teacher
WOOD RIVER
Stamps, Kim Michele
Vocal Music & Visual Arts Dir
Thompson, Carole Rhoades
Eng, Comm Tchr & Hum Div Chm
WOODHULL
Brown, Dennis R.
Guidance Counselor
Petrie, Scott Preston
Math Teacher
WOODLAND
Crabtree, Janie Ellen
4th Grade Teacher
WOODLAWN
Gualdoni, Ronda Sue
Third Grade Teacher
WOODRIDGE
Tait, Alicia Cordoba
Oboe Teacher & Musician
WOODSTOCK
Armstrong, Jean Wagner
Elementary Art Teacher
Bailey, Carolyn Louis
Kindergarten Music Teacher
Belonger, Steve L.
Social Studies Teacher
Cebrzynski, Stan Gerard
Chemistry & Physics Teacher
Donato, William C.
Science Teacher
Goodwin, Catherine Craner
Art Teacher
Headley, John
Psychology & Sociology Teacher
Kresse, Mary Kate
French & English Teacher
Mather, V. Gay Stevenson
Fourth Grade Teacher
Mc Camman, Joanne Roberta Zimmer
Principal
Miller, Dorothy Maye (Symens)
Music & Reading Specialist
Reinhard, James E.
High School English Teacher
Unverzagt, Virginia Tyler
Religious Studies & Math Tchr
WORDEN
Lybarger, Len W.
Retired Health Teacher
Pulliam, Carolyn Fiegenbaum
Fifth Grade Teacher
Sievers, Bertha Mueller
Kndgtn Teacher & Asst Prin
WORTH
Paulson, Ron
Principal
XENIA
Hosick, Suzanne Shaeffer
Third Grade Teacher
YATES CITY
Sherman, Sharon White
English Teacher
YORKVILLE
Anielak, Elaine L.
Third Grade Teacher
Barrett, Christa Lynn
Speech Language Pathologist
Bennett, George Arthur
Earth Science Teacher
Conklin, Joyce Shonesky
Spanish Teacher

Cryder, Diane Wayne
Fifth Grade Teacher
Gierzynski, Susan
Lrng Disabilities Teacher
Grant, Peggy Scharoun
5th Grade Teacher
Knowles, Daniel Craig
Science Teacher
Konop, Colleen Carlson
English Teacher
Mandle, Linda Lou
Social Studies Teacher
Mayo, Suzie Kunberger
6th Grade Language Arts Tchr
Nelson, Chris Allen
Math Dept Chairman & Teacher
Pecka, Linda Sandstrom
Spanish & German Teacher
Schmelzle, David C.
Social Studies Teacher
Schumm, Karen Rebecca
6th Grade Teacher
Steinwart, Kimberly Ann
Physical Education Teacher
Thompson, Sheila R.
HS English Teacher
Trumble, Peg J.
General Music & Choral Teacher
ZEIGLER
Simpson, Gary Wayne
HS Social Studies Teacher
Wexstten, Gerald H.
English Teacher
Williams, C. Jay
English Dept Co-Chair
ZION
Belmont, Alice Schafer
Choral Director
Bozin, Sofia
Third Grade Teacher
Byrd, Maurice Elton
Music Teacher
Grabnik, Sandra DeVore
5th Grade Teacher
Gray, Sheryl Porter
8th Grade Reading Teacher
Hall, Katherine A.
Chemistry & Phys Science Tchr
Johnson, Delores Curtis
Fifth Grade Teacher
Kwiek, Mary Morehouse
Fifth & Sixth Grade Teacher
Murphy, James F.
12th Grade Social Studies Tchr
Oates, Richard William
7th & 8th Grd Ind Arts Teacher
Powell, Jason B.
Physics Teacher
Ramlose, Herbert V., Jr.
English Teacher
Rinehart, Mary Kathleen
English & ESL Teacher
Rymer, Victoria (Aeem)
5th Grade Teacher

INDIANA

AKRON
Landis, Wayne Lee
7th Grade Math Teacher
ALBION
Jones, Vera J.
Science Teacher
Knopp, Cathy S.
English Teacher
McWhorter, David Bruce
Middle School Principal
Sievers, Darwin Russell
English & Soc Studies Teacher
ALEXANDRIA
Abernathy, Melissa Ann
English Teacher
Cone, Garth Fred
MS Phy Ed & Health Teacher
Gordon, Martha Sue
English Teacher & Dept Chm
Phipps, A. Hugh
School Counselor
Ray, Barbara Lou Rinker
First Grade Teacher
AMO
Collier, Mary Evans
Third Grade Teacher
ANDERSON
Airhart, Diane Kendall
Staff Development Coordinator
Alexander, Daniel Eugene
4th Grade Teacher
Aukerman, John H.
Assoc Prof of Christian Ed
Binkerd, Kraig S.
Math Teacher
Bitner, Ted R.
Professor of Education
Boehm, Carl R.
Finance Professor
Bradley, James William
Associate Dean
Burnett, Fred Wayne
Rel Stud & Philosophy Prof
Caldwell, Maurice
Tri-S International Assoc Dir
Callen, Barry L.
Religion Professor
Chase, Vicki L. (Howard)
Science Tchr & Softball Coach
Clark, Ronald Keith
English & Drama Teacher

Clark, Sandra Stephens
Professor of English
Cookman, Linda Ruth
English Teacher
Dean, Janice D.
5th Grade Teacher
Dixon, Shirley Theis
Kindergarten Teacher
Duc, Joan Lynn
Journalism Adv & English Tchr
Dugan, Kathleen Mary
Adjunct Professor of Art
Engel, Donald James
Asst Professor of Acctng & Fin
Farmer, Roberta Ann
Eighth Grade English Teacher
Foley, Pamela Sokol
Office Ed Tchr & Coord
Fox, Kathy Holding
English Teacher
Harris, George A.
8th Grd Soc Stud & HS His Tchr
Heyen, Bruce Jay
Chemistry Professor
Hitz, Barbara J.
Math Teacher
Holder, Douglas R.
Mathematics Teacher
Ivy, Robert Eugene
Retired Sixth Grade Teacher
Janutolo, Delano Blake
Professor of Biology
Johnson, Michael Wayne
Science & Mathematics Teacher
Jones, Margot Dawne
Prin & Tchr of Select Subjects
Keller, Teresa Blain
Instr of Admin Office Tech
Kennedy, JoEllen Theresa
Assoc Professor of Sociology
Knaus, Betty Kose
2nd Grade Teacher
Koontz, Charles Benton
Asst Professor of Computer Sci
Kousari, Ehsan O.
Fine Arts Teacher
Lain, Melanie R.
Social Work & Sociology Instr
Lamey, Teddy Jean
Fourth Grade Teacher
Lawvere, Nickolas B.
Science Teacher
Malone, Carolynn Joy
Looping Teacher
Mc Clead, Janet Curts
Second Grade Teacher
Miller, Deborah M.
Writing Instructor
Minnick, Rhea Dawn
Speech Therapist
Moody, Ronald Lee
Math, Science & Computer Tchr
Mullarkey, Susan Frohman
English Teacher
Nicholson, Soteria Pancol
5th Grade Teacher
Parnell, Mary Ann (Pierce)
Kindergarten Teacher
Peck, Cynthia Lash
Assistant Prof of Accounting
Penhorwood, Lucinda Jean
Nursing Instructor
Plank, Wanda Jean
Math & Reading Resource Tchr
Porter, Jerry
Mathematics Teacher
Prieshoff, Ann-Marie
Art Teacher & Dept Chairperson
Rable, George C.
Professor of History
Radaker, Kevin Paul
English Professor
Rector, Neal W.
Health Teacher
Rhule, Imogene Tate
Eng Instr & Writing Ctr Dir
Rooks, Barbara Jean
English & Speech Teacher
Shearer, Elizabeth H.
Mathematics Teacher
Shively, Fredrick Harold
Professor of Religion
Shulmistras, Sally Jo
Associate Professor of French
Spears, William Jack
Drafting & Arch Design Tchr
Sumner, Miriam Eileen
Business Teacher
Torongeau, Melba Trimble
Eng Tchr, Lang Arts Dept Chair
Vermillion, Douglas Minshal
Soc Stud Dept Chrprsn
Wendling, Joyce K.
Fourth Grade Teacher
Wilburn, Carol A.
Mathematics Teacher
Williams-Boyd, Linda Marie
Physical Education Teacher
Womack, Joe K.
Social Work Professor
ANDREWS
Lawyer, Venita Lee
4th Grade Teacher
Myers, Paula Galbraith
1st Grade Teacher
Price, Bonita Seibold
Kindergarten Teacher
ANGOLA
Bertram, Vince M.
Physical Education & Hlth Tchr

Clary, Julia Kay (Ahlersmeyer)
Third Grade Teacher
Crain, Steven D.
Assistant Principal
Dennison, Amy L.
3rd Grade Teacher
Dobbert, Duane Lloyd
Criminal Justice Studies Prof
Enneking, Thomas J.
Engrng Assoc Prof & Dept Chm
Hendricks, Troy Gerald
English Teacher
Hoolihan, Barbara Hutchins
Elementary Librarian
Hostetler, Judy Ann (Pierce)
Third Grade Teacher
Kirkton, Rick L.
Social Studies Teacher
Koenig, Robert W.
HS Teacher & Admin Pastor
Lenaburg, Ronald Stephen
Eighth Grade Algebra Teacher
Mentzer, Natalie R. (Hinkle)
Math Teacher
Milleman, Jon Arley
High School Director of Bands
Pinkham, Chester Allen
Professor of Chemistry
Rice, Ann M.
6th Grade Teacher
Richards, Von Lee
Asst Prof of Mechanical Engrng
Rider, Julia Somers
Art Teacher
Rodman, Jerry Lee
High School Science Teacher
Snyder, David K.
Teacher
Thomas, Jill Hardwick
Fifth Grade Teacher
Van Rie, Debra Ann
Associate Professor of Math
Wagner, John Eric
Asst Prof of Chemical Engrng
Wilson, Andrew James
Chm & Prof of Chem Engrng
Wright, Tony Gene
Science Teacher
ARCADIA
Herndon, Richard L.
Math Department Chair
Volz, Joy Ellen
English Teacher
ARGOS
Hourigan, Becky Lynn
Mathematics Teacher
Kitch, Devon Dale
7th-8th Grade Teacher
Van Duyne, Timothy J.
Fourth Grade Teacher
ATWOOD
Graney, Daniel P.
6th Grade Teacher
AUBURN
Armstrong, Catherine E. (Cobler)
5th Grade Teacher
Bassett, Tina Squier
1st Grade Teacher
Lemons, Kellie Rachelle
Junior-Senior High His Tchr
Schaefer, Lola Marie
4th & 5th Grade GATE Teacher
Wever, Mark Wayne
Administrator
AURORA
Bowers, C. Todd
Science Teacher
Rullman, Patty Hileman
English Teacher
Schallhorn, Mark Brian
Principal & Teacher
Ullrich, Judith Carroll
Second Grade Teacher
AUSTIN
West, Mary Jo Shields
High School Librarian
AVON
Mace, Carole J.
Third Grade Teacher
Trout, Rilla Mae Hybarger
Lang Arts, Bible & Math Tchr
BATESVILLE
Amrhein, Michael Albert
Principal
Burton, Melissa Kay
Fifth Grade Teacher
Cochran, Steve W.
Mathematics Teacher
Dickson, Cindy Neal
1st Grade Teacher
Enneking, Leon William
MS Choir & General Music Tchr
Ferguson, Mark E.
Athletic Director
Harrelson, Donna Jean (Kessens)
1st Grade Teacher
Hoeing, Donna Lamping
Mathematics Teacher
McKinney, Deidre Carol
Eng Teacher & Lang Arts Coord
Raver, Ronald George
Chem & Anatomy Tchr
Thornton, Terri L. (Carrier)
Family & Consumer Sci Teacher
Voegele, Louella A.
PE & Health Teacher
Zimmerman, Charles L.
Biology Teacher

BATTLE GROUND
Kubiske, Annette Marie
Soc Stud, PE & Health Teacher
BEDFORD
Coats, Marylss Hopper
English Teacher & Adjunct Prof
Cosner, Karen Steele
English Teacher
Faubion, Kae Hatfield
Second Grade Teacher
Gabbard, Mary Louise
Math Dept Chair & Tchr
Goodwine, Karen Ann
Health Teacher
Horner, Pamela Ann
6th & 7th Grade Lang Arts Tchr
Jones, David A.
Electronics Instructor
Nickless, Andrea Sue
Second Grade Teacher
Paledino, Cate Jackson
Social Studies Chair
Porter, Lynn Elizabeth
Elementary Teacher
Raab, Linda Collins
Language Arts & Jrnlsm Tchr
Sanders, Linda Irby
English Department Chairperson
Simmerman, George Jacob
Math Teacher
Snapp, Rebecca Acton
Fifth Grade Teacher
Sprinkle, Rebecca R.
Director of Guidance
Walker, Gregory Dale
Vocational Agriculture Teacher
BEECH GROVE
Cahill, Michael Edward
High School Math Tchr & Coach
McNew, Dawn Denise
PE & Drug Ed Teacher
Ott, Jeffrey Kent
Social Studies Teacher
BERNE
Brehm, Lori Gail-Yeates
7th Grd Eng & Jrnlsm Tchr
Cook, Sheryl Kay
English Teacher
Rinker, Steven Lee
Industrial Tech Teacher, Coach
Tatman, Steve
English, Speech & Drama Tchr
Tooley, Kathleen Bauman
2nd Grade Teacher
BICKNELL
Blome, Mary Kathy
2nd Grade Teacher
Holscher, Lola J.
English Teacher
McClure, John Ralph
Social Studies Teacher
BIRDSEYE
Bruner, Pat Leonard
Retired Teacher
Hodges, Wesley Gene
Principal
Smith, Franklin B.
Retired Eng & Ch I Cert Tchr
BLOOMFIELD
Clouse, Chrislyn A.
Kindergarten Teacher
Dean, David Marshall
Science & Math Teacher
McBride, Jeannine J.
Math & Chemistry Teacher
Rogina, Brenda K.
Jr HS English & GATE Teacher
Stallons, Melbo R.
Language Arts Teacher
Wikle, Stephen Rex
Scndry Geography Tchr & Chprsn
BLOOMINGTON
Ackerson, Scott L.
Ceramics Instructor
Adams, William Richard
Director of Zooarchaeology Lab
Bartel, Charles John
Electronics Program Chair
Bellessis, Martyna Ryder
Elementary Art Teacher
Beyers, Criss
Health & Safety Teacher
Brancart, Evelyne
Assoc Professor of Piano
Chafin, Karen Schwomeyer
Mathematics Teacher
Curry, Sherrill Lindsey
Art Teacher
Elkins, Kay
4th Grade Teacher
Gibson, Linda Jill
2nd Grade Teacher
Ginger, Laura Ann
Associate Professor of Bus Law
Gouker, Jane Ann
Orchestra Teacher
Grady, Barbara Kretzinger
English Teacher
Hanks, Lawrence J.
Political Science Professor
Haven, Betty Haley
Asst Professor of Kinesiology
Hill, Carol R.
Third Grade Teacher
Hitchings, Linda Flebotte
Home Education Consultant
Horning, Debora Bridges
HS English Teacher
Jolivette, Sandra Wade
Third Grade Teacher
Jones, Mary Ann (Verbeeck)
Retired Teacher
Judah, Barbara Jean Jewel
Speech & Language Pathologist
Krumpe, Norman Joseph
Associate Instructor
Miller, Nancy Smith
Kindergarten Teacher
Monts, Michael Max
5th Grade Teacher
Morgan, Jill Busick
Spcl Ed & Inclusion Eng Tchr
Nicholson, Daniel Thomas
Business Teacher
Nolan, Edwynna Dean
Family & Consumer Sci Tchr
Pierro, Lou M.
Instructor
Powell, Brian
Professor of Sociology
Reising, Deanna Lynne
Nursing Instructor
Riggle, Michael D.
Principal
Schaffer, Claire
English Teacher
Skirvin, Don
8th Grd Social Studies Teacher
Smith, David Lee
Sixth Grade Teacher
Stucky, Karen J.
Math & Science Teacher
Tate, Helen
Assistant Instructor
Tilton, Timothy A.
Prof of Political Science
Veselack, Ellen Mosher
Kindergarten Teacher
Wicinsky, Beverly Broehm
National Trainer
Wilson, Patricia Jane (Vance)
Social Studies Dept Chairman
BLUFFTON
Baker, Steven Thomas
High School Math Teacher
Carpenter, Gary Alan
Sixth Grade Teacher
Dilley, Deborah Ann (Feher)
Fourth Grade Teacher
Gehrig, Marilyn Vizard
Fourth Grade Teacher
Lesh, Bruce Alan
5th Grade Teacher
Lux, Douglas Craig
Math Teacher
Neuenschwander, Ted Kenyon
Fifth Grade Teacher
Rodgers, Lyn L.
1st Grade Teacher
Shively, Sally Gerber
Sixth Grade Teacher
Weldy, Tina Kallimani
First Grade Teacher
Worman, Linda Kay (Bergman)
5th-7th Grade Japanese Teacher
Yake, Nan Elaine (Pearson)
Language Arts Teacher
BOONE GROVE
Flood, Jerry N.
Business Education Teacher
Hahn, Philip Edwin
Computer Applications Teacher
Snow, Kenneth G.
Science Dept Chprsn & Bio Tchr
BOONVILLE
Bertram, John Charles
English Teacher
Crane, Donald M.
Art & Ceramics Teacher
Green, Marla Hendrickson
Secondary LD Resource Teacher
Hart, Anita Carol
High School Teacher
Kline, Sylvia J.
Cross Country Track Coach
Little, James R.
Social Studies Teacher
Long, Albertis Gene
Computer Science Teacher
Stevens, Michael Gene
Sixth Grade Teacher
Stilwell, Bonnie Lee
Family & Con Sci Dept Head
Vile, Francis Elwyn, Jr.
Director of Bands
Wilson, Steven Kevin
Jr HS US History Teacher
BOSWELL
Scherer, Gail Sondgerath
4th Grade Teacher
BOURBON
Beam, Janet Gail
Fourth Grade Teacher
Carpenter, Jack Lee
Fourth Grade Teacher
Reese, Laura Louise
Fourth Grade Teacher
BRAZIL
Caraboa, Thomas James
7th Grd Social Studies Tchr
Connors, Joanna Thomas
Home Economics Teacher
Harris, Jean
5th Grade Teacher
Mc Cullough, Caroline G.
Science Dept & Life Sci Chair
Nees, Joyce Elaine
Sixth Grade Teacher
Penry, Kathryn Pritsch
Seventh Grd Language Arts Tchr
Pfrank, Stephen Robert
Social Studies Teacher
Pliskin, Harlean K.
Spanish Teacher
Sayers, Jeffery D.
Physics & Mathematics Teacher
Switzer, Victoria Miser
K-3rd Grade Title I Teacher
BREMEN
DeSantis, Frank Andrew
Certified Athletic Admin
Dumph, Faydene Ruth (England)
Teacher & Private Counselor
Hassel, Jill Lynn (Deller)
Technology Coordinator
Holmes, Ron
6th Grd Math Teacher
Jankowski, Geoff L.
Chemistry Teacher
Mark, Lana M.
7th & 8th Grade Math Teacher
Tjernagel, Ellen Radewahn
Kindergarten & English Tchr
BROOKVILLE
Armstrong, Bruce Harold
Guidance Counselor
Barker, Norman Glen
Mathematics Teacher
Chaddon, Beth Bentz
English Teacher
Cotherman, Steven Robert
Phys Ed, Health Tchr & Coach
Geiss, Melissa Ann
Spanish & English Teacher
Hausman, Marcia Robbins
Math Teacher
Jobe, Donald Morris
Biology Instructor
Lehman, Cathy Marie (Cook)
Sixth Grade Teacher
Mc Kay, Gloria Ann
6th Grade Teacher
Mc Lane, Mark Dennis
English Department Chm
Midlam, Sherry Langley
Math, English, Reading Teacher
Moster, Mary Ann
Second Grade Teacher
Renaker, Loretta Elizabeth (Hartung)
Third Grade Teacher
Seiter, Bonnie W.
Sixth Grade Science Teacher
Steiner, William F.
Science Teacher
Sun, Elvira G.
Frgn Lang Dept Chair & Teacher
Tafelski, Patrick Edward
US History Teacher
Thackery, William Franklin
Athletic Director & Sci Tchr
Wade, Beth Thomas
English Teacher
BROWNSBURG
Adkins, Billie Myers
4th Grade Teacher
Bellville, Linda Walls
7th Grd Mathematics Teacher
Clark, Susan (Durbin)
Junior High Teacher
Corn, Randall A.
English Teacher
Corn-Siefert, Betty Lou
Second Grade Teacher
Dearringer, Paula K.
Art Teacher
Griffin, Sean
German Teacher
Guthier, Julie
Principal
Joiner, Robert Scott
Mathematics Teacher
McClain, Maggie Turk
MS Social Studies Teacher
Prather, Deborah Ilgenfritz
HS Vocal Music Director
Reynolds, John William
Economics & Bible Teacher
Roll, Georgia Terry
English & Etymology Teacher
Salmon, Jeffrey John
Speech & Vocal Music Instr
Semenick, Steven J.
Biology Teacher
Slack, Gerald K.
Math Teacher & Dept Chair
Stucker, Joe E.
Psych, Sociology & Cmptr Tchr
Swango, Colleen Jill
Science Teacher
Thurman, Wayne Glenn
US History Teacher
Wilson, Brenda Kay
Teacher of Gifted Ed
BROWNSTOWN
Bachmann, Raymond E.
Third Grade Teacher
Cutter, Barry Dean
HS Earth Science Teacher
Otte, Laberta
Fourth Grade Teacher
Willey, Jan Leslie
Vocal Music Teacher
BUNKER HILL
Baker, Nancy Jayne
First Grade Teacher
Beall, David W.
Social Studies Teacher
Bradbury, Pamela Gene (Seward)
6th-8th Grade Science Teacher
Hanlon, Barbara Ann (Deegan)
English Teacher
Oatess, Janet Sue
English Department Head
Peters, John Paul
Biology Teacher
Roller, Kathy Ann
French Teacher
Smith, Nancy L.
Science Teacher
BUTLER
Beck, Duane J.
7th-12th Grd Choral Director
Bowman, Connie Jo (Howard)
Math Teacher & Dept Chair
Everhart, Janet Sebert
First Grade Teacher
Fetters, John Wayne
Mathematics Teacher
Fiedler, Michael Duane
Social Studies Teacher
Hollabaugh, Donna J.
Secondary English Teacher
Moughler, Bobbie Lynn
Bus Dept Chprsn & Teacher
Randinelli, Kimberly Ann
Instrumental Music Director
Wagner, Merle William
Math & Physics Teacher
Willard, Aaron C.
Physical Ed & Health Teacher
CAMBRIDGE CITY
Casey, Joan Roberta
Home Economics Teacher
Ervin, Mark Randall
Social Studies Teacher
Musial, Dennis A.
Band Director
Oliger, Ted
Social Studies Teacher
Seidner, Gregory Wayne
Secondary Science Teacher
CAMPBELLSBURG
Deaton, Greg L.
Fifth Grade Teacher
Hopkins, Beth Ann Marshall
Kindergarten Teacher
Mc Donald, Barbara Sipe
Mathematics Teacher
Mitchell, Tina Albers
Chemistry & Math Teacher
Pruett, Donna Vilet
HS Spanish & English Teacher
Toothman, Susan Archer
Language Arts Tchr
CANNELTON
Harris, Lowell Ray
English & Social Studies Tchr
CARLISLE
Ramey, Mike Douglas
Fourth Grade Teacher
CARMEL
Baker, William Edward
Earth & Space Science Tchr
Barcio, Bernard Francis
Latin Teacher
Benz, Paul J.
Teacher & Math Dept Chair
Blackwell, Gregory James
Bus Ed Tchr & Prof Dev Coord
Brown, Janice Elaine (Secor)
Mrktg Ed Tchr & Coordinator
Burrell, Joyce Mott
Drawing Instructor
Butz, Suzanne Elaine
5th Grade Teacher
Dick, Thomas Oliver
Orchestra Director
DUtton, Lisa K.
Art Teacher
Estell, Doug A.
English Teacher
Fiedler, Janis Latella
Physical Education Teacher
Fiedler, Keith A.
Science Teacher
Flowers, Patricia Jane
English Department Chair
Gallagher, Karen Cockrell
Resource Teacher & Dept Chprsn
Gordon, Bruce Edward
Social Studies Teacher
Gossard, Greg
Government & Sociology Teacher
Gutzwiler, Donna Marie
Spanish Teacher
Hellems, Ronald Dean
Vocal Music Teacher
Hill, Nancy Meek
Gifted & Talented Teacher
Jones, Angela Y.
English Teacher
Knowles, Kenneth H.
English Teacher
Law, Joy Zarse
Business Education Teacher
Lustig, Marcia Linder
Sociology Teacher
Maxam, Thomas Edward
AP Bio, Sci Composition Tchr
Reece, Virginia J.
Family & Consumer Sci Teacher
Rott, Stephen Ross
Biology Teacher
Schoeller, Thomas Harry
Radio Station WHJE Gen Manager
Shiffer, Helen Elliott
English Teacher
Tryon, Terry T.
Building Trades Instructor
Weaver, Cathy Clouser
4th Grade Elementary Teacher
Weaver, Mark Robert
Science Dept Chm & Teacher
CARTHAGE
Rozzell, Mark Allen
Sixth Grade Teacher
CAYUGA
Carli, Pamela Kay (Porter)
Technology Director
Corey, Donald Edward
6th Grade Teacher
Dunavan, Eva Louise
1st Grade Teacher
CEDAR GROVE
Hollins, Donna Kay Walker
K-8th Grd Music Teacher
CEDAR LAKE
Ash, Christine (Piech)
Adv Biology Teacher
Dawson, Robert Michael
Fourth Grade Teacher
Halvorson, Virginia Gillson
French Teacher
Kirk, Jean Ann Wozniak
Home Economics Teacher
Krol, Robert John
Bio, Chemistry & Physics Tchr
Kwasny, Frank J.
6th Grade Math Teacher
Landis, Steven Jacob
9th-10th Grd English Teacher
Rajchel, Gene
English & Speech Teacher
Rausei, Carol V.
Fifth Grade Teacher
Sumner, Cliff W.
6th Grade Teacher
Whitestine, William George
Business Teacher
CENTERVILLE
Baumer, Kathie Cox
First Grade Teacher
Kean, Sherry Therrien
L D Teacher
CHANDLER
Christmas, Connie Sue
6th Grade Teacher
Davidson, April Anne (Temme)
Music Teacher
Hurt, Richard L.
6th Grade Teacher
Shelton, Linda Pauden
Fourth Grade Teacher
CHARLESTOWN
Berry, Barbara Ann
English Teacher
Cross, Robert Layne
Fifth Grade Teacher
Hall, Michael Douglas
Marketing Educ & Business Tchr
Horvath, Judith Kay
Sixth Grade Teacher
Hoyland, Dolores M.
7th Grade Lang Arts Teacher
King, Amy Lynn
Writing Teacher
Knight, Jerri Lynn
Sixth Grade Math Teacher
Money, Melody S.
English Teacher
Watson, Kenneth Roland, Jr.
7th Grade Science Teacher
CHARLOTTESVILLE
Darling, Diana S.
Gifted & Talented Coordinator
Hilton, Steven A.
Fifth Grade Teacher
Holmes, Ken
Mathematics & Physics Teacher
Ray, Nichola Turner
Second Grade Teacher
Thompson, Richard Eugene
German Teacher & Cmptr Coord
CHESTERTON
Brandenburg, David George
Soc Studies Tchr & Dept Chprsn
Campbell, Jack Eugene
PE Instructor
Didelot, Linda Mc Combs
7th-8th Grd Comm Teacher
Hayduk, John Matthew
English & Journalism Teacher
Johnson, Patricia Wriing
English Teacher
Keammerer, Sandra Ziegeler
English Teacher
Kilander, Linda Ebert
Spanish Teacher
Schaudt, Lorene Swanson
1st Grade Teacher
Schaudt, William E.
Biology Teacher
Smith, Robert Brown, Jr.
Fifth Grade Teacher
Thoms, Jennifer Lynn
Counselor
Welkie, LaRue Schlene
Third Grade Teacher
CHILI
Friend, Judy Myers
Fifth Grade Teacher
Gottschalk, David A.
English, Speech & Drama Tchr
Jackson, Marilyn Snyder
Mathematics Teacher
Spear, Philip Charles
Art Instructor
Sroufe, Alice Barts
Fifth Grade Teacher

I (cont)
ɛnson, James F.
World His & Ec Teacher
r, Jeraldine Roseanne (Ginsburg)
ish & Composition Teacher
lesey, Howard L.
ral & General Music Instr
n, Jane
ss-Categorical Teacher
RUBUSCO
, Gary D.
lish & Driver Ed Teacher
on, Sherry L.
lish Teacher
, Karen (Delaplane)
nish Teacher
am, Linda Diane (Bassett)
Grade Teacher
ll, Donna Simonetti
rumental Music Director
arson, Duane R.
h Grade Teacher
, Gary R.
Social Studies Instructor
r, Daniel J.
lth & Physical Ed Teacher
RO
Donald Robert
ial Studies & Bible Teacher
RKSVILLE
inger, Cheryl Schultz
t Grade Teacher
nan, Robert A.
ence Teacher
, Tamara Flock
sic Teacher
ner, Sonia Oczypok
Grade Teacher
ein, J. Frederick
Tchr & Cross Cntry Coach
e, Myrl Dunham
mentary Counselor
an, Phyllis Wayman
Grade Teacher
er, Jerilyn
Science Tchr & Dept Chr
Donald P.
ial Science Teacher
Y CITY
Jeff H.
hematics Teacher
ting, Jerry Wayne
Grade Teacher & Asst Prin
nan, Karla Mc Cullough
st Grade Teacher
YPOOL
sly, John Dennis
Grade Teacher
YTON
a, Stace Lee
logy & Anatomy Teacher
s, Rosalyn Marie (Marsh)
sical Ed & Health Teacher
s, Patricia A.
thematics Teacher
r, Darrin John
siness Education Teacher
, Diane
glish & Latin Teacher
in, Steven W.
afting Teacher
h, Linda Litz
siness Education Teacher
NTON
n, Vicki Joy
th Grade Teacher
per, DeAnn
cational Business Teacher
se, Harold V.
operative Education Director
o, Stephen John
chnology Teacher & Dept Head
ring, Nancy Lehe
th Grade Teacher
on, Marlene J.
tired Third Grade Teacher
e, Kent L.
nerican History Teacher
OVERDALE
son, Pamela Kay
arning Disabilities Tchr
an, Milton B.
tired Assistant Principal
mpson, Deborah J.
oral Director
ner, Maureen J.
ench & Government Teacher
LUMBIA CITY
y, Martina Fox
cond Grade Teacher
ch, Mary S.
source Teacher
y, William Joseph
ience Teacher
r, Janet Elaine
ddle School Teacher
key, Ronald Dean
athematics Teacher
le, Carol Phyllis (Watson)
mputer Lab Supervisor
ney, Patricia
nguage Arts Teacher
ger, Scott Wayne
ience Teacher
zger, Linda S.
ementary School Counselor
lendore Oliver, Jayne (Mullendore)
glish & Literature Teacher
lett, Susan White
glish Teacher

Myer, Ronald C.
8th Grade Math Teacher
Nelson, James H.
Fourth Grade Teacher
Perry, Candice S. Cooper
Former 3rd Grade Teacher
Steill, Laurel Carlson
English Teacher & Dept Chair
Warner, Roger L.
Drafting Teacher
Wood, Tom Dean
Health & Substance Abuse Tchr
COLUMBUS
Clark, Mary Evelyn
Fourth Grade Teacher
Davis, LuAnn Wehmeier
Guidance Counselor
Doty, David Allan
Eighth Grd Language Arts Tchr
Ferguson, Jim
Sixth Grade Teacher
Fribley, David Karl
US History Teacher
Gemberling, Roger Alan
7th Grade Mathematics Teacher
Giovanini, Sandy M.
Mathematics Teacher
Harney, Joyce Ann
Dir of Health & Human Services
Jesse, Karen Adora
Jr HS Science & Religion Tchr
Johnson, Darin Lynn
Industrial Technology Teacher
Karwacki, Cynthia L.
Spanish Teacher
LeBlanc, Ray J.
Retired Teacher
Lowe, Karen Burkett
French Teacher
Niespodziani, Edward J.
Social Studies Teacher
Nowak, Jeffrey Andrew
Science Teacher
O'Neal, Florence S.
Fifth & Sixth Grade Teacher
Patterson, William Charles
High School English Teacher
Riggle, Scott Brian
Tennis Coach
Smith-Herron, Janet Nading
6th Grade Teacher
Sturgis, Cynthia Henny
English Teacher
Tews, Larry Nelson
Fifth Grade Tchr & Band Dir
Walters, Sue Ellyn (Carmichael)
Gifted & Talented Teacher
Wasmuth, Sara M.
Biology Teacher
Wilson, Jonathan Harris
Visual Communications Instr
COMMISKEY
Baugh, Kay Ellen (Ford)
Fifth Grade Teacher
CONNERSVILLE
Burchett, Ralph Edward
Business Ed Teacher & Chair
Clemons, E. B.
Sixth Grade Teacher
Coleman, Brenda Kay
Fifth Grade Teacher
Girot, Linda G.
5th-6th Grade GATE Tchr
Henry, Carol S.
Science Teacher
Hughes, Patricia Ann
Second Grade Teacher
Krebs, Sylvia Ann
High School English Teacher
Ledman, Douglas Andrew
Psychology Teacher
Mc Henry, Carol Lorraine
5th Grade Teacher
Miller, Donald R.
Counseling Coordinator
Myers, Eric Lee
High School Math Teacher
Rosenberger, Linda A.
Business Teacher
Rowley, Frank, Jr.
Economics & World Geog Teacher
Sanders, Helen Burkart
Math Teacher
Siebert, Douglas Scott
5th Grade Teacher
Sowder, Nancy Hamilton
Kindergarten Teacher
Stull, Janet Marie (Baker)
Scondary English Teacher
Tritle, Jim Edwin
Soc Stud, PE & Bible Teacher
CONVERSE
Helms, Margaret Jane
High School Band Director
CORYDON
Goerres, Susan Terrell
9th & 12th Grd English Teacher
Hammond, Phyllis J.
English Teacher
Shearn, Sandra R.
English Teacher
Uhl, Michael Joseph
HS Mathematics Teacher
COVINGTON
Crumrin, Patricia Trott
Fourth Grade Teacher
Davis, Carolyn Sue
Family & Consumer Science Tchr
Field, Terry Lane
Mathematics & Physics Teacher

Myers, Scott A.
Agriculture Education Teacher
Stidham, Deborah S.
Speech & English Teacher
Watt, Joyce Ellen
English Teacher
CRAWFORDSVILLE
Allen, Curtis Edward
US His & World Cultures Tchr
Balch, Sue Danforth
Second Grade Teacher
Boone, William E.
Latin & English Teacher
Brunton, Jolinda (Hinds)
Fifth Grade Teacher
Dove, Elena Perez
High School Engligh Teacher
Frees, Steven Wayne
Fourth Grade Teacher
Gonzarow, Anthony Theodore
Science Teacher & Coach
Hallett, Ruth Hester
English Teacher & Dept Chm
Hoke, Judy L.
First Grade Teacher
Howard, Deborah Wright
Second Grade Teacher
Hudson, Helen Mundy
Honors English Teacher
Lefebvre, Mary Hill
2nd Grade Teacher
Lowe, Mary Ann (Johnson)
3rd Grade Teacher
Mosbaugh, Gary Ray
Agricultural Sci Dept Chm
O'Connell, Teresa J.
Choral Director
Patrick, Randy Roy
Geology Teacher
Richardson, William Charles
Teacher
Rubenstein, William D.
Middle School Lang Arts Tchr
Switzer, Jane Anderson
Second Grade Teacher
Turner, Beverley White
Nutrition & Foods Teacher
Warner, Kimberly Ann (Hulsman)
Substitute Teacher
Wiatt, Glenn L.
Mathematics Department Chm
CROTHERSVILLE
Maxie, Linda Myers
Agriculture Sci & Bus Tchr
Sweany, Sandra R.
Substitute Teacher
CROWN POINT
Buczek, Nada (Peyovich)
First Grade Teacher
Cole, Grace Nance
Social Studies & Spanish Tchr
Cross, Arlene E.
Retired Elem Teacher
Cuffia, Deborah Taylor
English Teacher & Dept Chprsn
Edwards, Marilynn P.
Science Teacher
Fodemski, Delores Dickson
6th Grade Teacher
Gullett, Diana L.
Fifth Grade Teacher
Hutchison, Randall L.
Math Teacher
Iddings, Floyd Keith, III
Mathematics Teacher
Johnson, Linda Susan Johnston
Language Arts Teacher
Miklosy, Nora M. (Fagen)
HS Mathematics Teacher
Rose, Karen Lynn
Sixth Grade Teacher
Shaffer, Peggy S.
Director of Bands
Underwood, Barbara Jean
3rd Grade Teacher
Wilson, Carol D.
High School English Teacher
CULVER
Benner, Vickie Sanders
English Teacher & Dept Chair
Boswell, Rex Allen
English Instructor
Colvin, Craig Elliott
Sr Instructor in Chemistry
Garzon, Jose Manuel
Master Instructor
Kline, Nancy Ellen
Second Grade Teacher
Lawson, Latham Lane
Soc Stud Dept Chair & Tchr
Little, Edgar M., III
Director of Horsemanship Prgm
Lyman, Joyce Ann Morrison
Elementary Art Tchr, Drama Dir
Mc Clendon, Garrard O.
English Teacher
Miller, Theresa Warnez
Science Teacher
Urbin, Jean Brandt
1st Grade Teacher
DALEVILLE
Beard, David A.
Elem Tchr of Gifted & Talented
Burrell, Diane Lynn Tuckerman
Art Teacher
Keogh, Patricia Darlene
Media Specialist
DANVILLE
Burdsall, Michael Joseph
Biology Teacher & Coach

Burrows, Richard
High Schl Social Studies Tchr
Cassady, Stephen Milton
Life Science Instructor
Cole, Pamela Kay (Northern)
7th Grade Mathematics Teacher
Hammons, Terry J.
Math & Health Teacher
Vitosky, Stephen David
English, Speech & Drama Tchr
DAYTON
Thomas, Marilyn G. Natvig
Third Grade Teacher
DECATUR
Geist, Richard George
Vocal Music Director
Germann, Kenneth Ralph
Learning Disabilities Teacher
Grogg, Julia Therese
Visual Arts Teacher
Heimann, Janice (Schamerloh)
German Teacher
Hisner, Cheryl Linn
Second & Third Grade Teacher
Miller, David Charles
6th Grd Tchr & HS Girls Coach
Reynolds, Janice Marie
High School Band Director
Stanley, Joseph R.
Business Dept Head & Teacher
Tuckey, Philip L.
Biology & Chemistry Teacher
DECKER
Nolting, Harry Wallace
Principal
DELPHI
Brettnacher, Patricia L.
Scndry Eng Tchr & Yrbk Adv
Le Page, Danny William
Math Teacher & Athletic Dir
DEMOTTE
Shank, John F.
Fifth Grd Tchr & Asst Prin
DONALDSON
Baki-Hashemi, Saeid
Assoc Prof of Sci & Math
Bayless, Charles Eugene
Prof of English & Dept Chair
Buchanan, Thomas Wayne
Assistant Professor of History
Greifer, Mary Dolores, PHJC
English Prof & Dir of Alumni
Kunkel, Johnel
Special Assist to President
Niebrugge, Agatha
Sociology Instructor
DUBOIS
Elliott, Roger Craig
English & Phys Ed Teacher
Klawitter, Kathleen Ann
Teacher & Curriculum Director
Meredith, Diane K.
English Teacher
Schroeder, James Anthony
Math & Social Studies Teacher
Seger, Charlotte (Denu)
School Counselor
Wibbeler, Kathy Heldman
3rd Grade Teacher
DUNKIRK
Cheek, Terrence L.
Jr High Language Arts Teacher
DUPONT
Zehren, John R.
6th Grade Teacher
DYER
Gilbert, David Ellis
8th Grd US History Teacher
Katic, Milan
Physics & Chemistry Teacher
EAST CHICAGO
Anderson, Myra G.
Spanish Teacher
Anderson, Verdell
6th Grade Teacher
Cataldi, Mary Anne
High School Art Teacher
Daronatsy, Jeanette Shirley (Fratter)
Second Grade Teacher
Fisher, Kenneth D.
Dept Chair
Gillis, Cytheria Artis
Business Education Teacher
Goode, Bennetta Shelley
HS Special Education Teacher
Josvai, Wayne Joseph
Chemistry Teacher
Molnar, Kathleen (O'Malley)
Mathematics Teacher
Rainford, Elizabeth N.
French Teacher
Sander, Susan Heins
Reading Teacher
Tobin, Mary Beth
Kindergarten Teacher
Whitaker, Barbara Tonkovich
Title I, Rdng & Math Tchr
EAST ENTERPRISE
Barbour, Sharon Ann
5th & 6th Grade Reading Tchr
EDINBURGH
Snyder, Brenda S.
Fifth & Sixth Grade Teacher
EDWARDSPORT
Hill, Matthew Bartlett
8th Grade History Teacher
ELBERFELD
Yates, Ken W.
Principal

ELKHART
Bass, Marsha Kay Burson
Dean of Stu Affairs & Yrbk Adv
Berndt, Cheryl Marie
US His Tchr & Soc Studies Chm
Boren, Nancy Ann
Middle School Counselor
Bunn, Kay Frey
Elementary Principal
Byrd, Kathy Denise
High School Guidance Counselor
Collins, Donald Lee
Retired 6th Grade Teacher
Farrer, Don C.
Social Studies Dept Chair
Faunce, Gayle Devon
Adjunct Professor
Ferro, Mildred Irene
Sr English Teacher & Chprsn
Filpus, Jean (Allen)
Home Ec & Keyboarding Teacher
Fowler, Chuck J.
8th Grade PE & Hlth Teacher
Gaff, Lyle Arden
Sixth Grade Teacher
Heater, Jacqueline Marian
Art Teacher
Heeter, Garnett M.
English Teacher
Hixon, H. Thomas
Principal
Hoover, Helene A.
Admin Office Technology Instr
Horein, Bruce L.
Science Teacher
Horn, Don
High School Science Teacher
Hummel, Elsie McGlosson
Mathematics Teacher
Kauffman, Linda Nofziger
Third Grade Teacher
Klassen, Marilyn K.
Retired Teacher
Koester, Cheryl A.
Language Arts Teacher
Kominowski, Barbara Micinski
4th Grade Teacher
Komins, Joseph Allen
Mathematics Teacher
Larimer, Stanley E.
Biology Teacher
Menzel, Cheryl Anne
English Teacher
Mickels, Andrew Joseph
United States History Teacher
Montgomery, Michael Kenton
5th Grade Teacher
Nadon, W. Irene
4th Grade Teacher
Peat, Rita Taylor
3rd Grade Teacher
Raval, Rita J.
Dept Chprsn & Spanish Teacher
Roggeman, William C.
Physical Ed & Health Teacher
Rupe, Vickie S.
4th Grade Teacher
Sharkey, Randy P.
Math Teacher
Sheline, Timi L. (Reed)
English Teacher
Stutsman, Kristie Kurth
Science Teacher & Dept Chair
Werbiansky, Matthew
PE & Mathematics Teacher
ELLETTSVILLE
Ledbetter, Marla Kay
Third Grade Teacher
ELNORA
Lee, Susan L.
HS English Teacher
ELWOOD
Boyer, Eugenia Forst
6th & 7th Grade Lang Arts Tchr
Drummond, Sherry Muir
HS English & Drama Teacher
Harlan, Faith M.
Middle School Band & Choir Dir
Holaday, Tracy Anderson
English & Journalism Teacher
Huffman, Howard Lee
Health Teacher & Coach
HUffman, Julia (Mc Gill)
Third Grade Teacher
Kirkwood, Brian Scott
Physical Education & Hlth Tchr
Simmons, Paula Irene
Music Director
EMINENCE
Nyce, Darren Troy
Math Teacher
Watson, Scott John
Social Studies Teacher
ENGLISH
Megenity, Mark A.
4th Grade Teacher
EVANSVILLE
Alcorn, Bonnie Below
High School English Teacher
Allen, David R.
Sixth Grade Teacher
Ambrose, Bonnie Zint
Language Arts Teacher
Apka, Barbara Heim
Skills Advancement Math Instr
Bailey, Sandra C.
Pgm Chair of Business Admin
Barnthouse, Marsha L.
Counselor

EVANSVILLE (cont)
Bartelt, William E.
History Teacher
Beard, Doris Jean
Mathematics Teacher
Bender, Mary Beth Farny
Teacher
Blice, Sylvia A.
German Tchr & Frgn Lang Head
Blohm, Wendell Edwin
Photography Teacher
Boyer-Johnson, Pamela
Ger, Japanese & Span Teacher
Caldwell, Larry W.
Associate Professor of English
Carrell, Judith Witte
German Teacher
Caton, Barbara H.
PE, Health & Biology Teacher
Combs, Steven Bradley
Mechanical Design Tech Instr
Couture, Emma Jean Elpers
Jr High Math Teacher
Covert, Douglas C.
Assoc Prof of Mass Commnctn
Denner, Anne Greer
Biology Instructor
Denner, Melvin
Professor
Dennis, John D.
PE Teacher & Coach
Dubber, Colleen W.
5th Grade Teacher
Duncan, Sharon Ann (Drier)
Instructor
Everett, Shirley Watkins
High School English Teacher
Flandermeyer, Cleone Elaine (Hladky)
Fourth Grade Teacher
Fortune, Jeanne Kathleen
Mathematics Teacher
Fox-Keller, Jennifer Bugher
First Grade Teacher
Freeman, Donald Mc Kinley
Igleheart Prof of Pol Science
Funkhouser, Cheryl
English & Speech Teacher
Garland, Virginia Steinhauer
Fourth Grade Teacher
Glaser, Josephine Indrani
Chemistry Teacher
Griepenstroh, Larry Irvin
Mathematics Teacher
Hamby, Alma Dean (Wilson)
Elementary Teacher
Harris, Jerrie Hargis
Second Grade Teacher
Hawkings, Ted R.
Mathematics Teacher
Heard, Michael Norman
Science & Computer Teacher
Hensley, Lee R.
Headmaster
Hollon, James Max
Sci Dept Chm & Chem Teacher
Hopkins, Joseph Henry
Assistant Professor of Music
Hughes, Marlissa Kay
English Teacher
Isvik, Lynn Barnes
Adjunct Business Instructor
Jones, Barbara Power
French Teacher
Jones, Jerry Ilbern
6th-8th Grd Math Teacher
Kelley, Michael K.
Physics Teacher
LaMastus, James Wade
US History Teacher
Lammers, Mark Paul
Automotive Technology Chrmn
Lasher, Sandra Beard
English Teacher
Ligon, Carol Lynne
Medical Assistant Instructor
McKeag, Christine Lowry
Accounting Instructor
Miley, Les
Professor of Art & Dept Chair
Millay, Gloria Jean
Fifth Grade Teacher
Miller, Kristi Carnahan
HS Vocal Music Teacher
Mintner, Dennis Steven
High School Science Teacher
Mitchell, Timothy Jerry
8th Grd Soc Studies Teacher
Modesitt, Alyson Gaisser
Kindergarten Teacher
Moon, Gretchen Kaye
Medical Assisting Instructor
Motz, Steffanie Wood
MS Social Studies Teacher
Neufelder, Rosemary
Former 6th Grade Teacher
Niehaus, Michael Allen
Electronics Program Chair
Oatis, Carolyn S. (DeJean)
Microbiology & Lab Tech Instr
Potter, Kathie Olson
Mathematics Instructor
Rapp, D. Neil
AP Chemistry Teacher
Recker, Terrance Patrick
English Teacher
Rickerby, Ian J.
Soc Stud Instr & Coach
Roberts, Nancy Morris
Department Chair
Russell, Richard Alan
English Teacher
Sater, Pearl Helen
8th Grade English Teacher
Schmitt, Kathy Rappee
Homeroom & Science Teacher
Schwenk, Katie Marie
Third Grade Teacher
Shipley, Kathleen LaVon (Miller)
French Teacher
Smith, Lori L.
Instructor
Stewart, Debra Lyles
First Grade Teacher
Szabo, Bret Stephen
History Teacher
Theriac, Linda Bauza
French Teacher
Tuggle, Sharon Bush
Retired English Teacher
Vire, Jane Tyring
Skills Advancement Chair
Volkman, Lowell William
Math Teacher
Walling, Brenda Craig
Spanish Teacher & Dept Chprsn
Weber, JoAnn Mayer
Jr HS Math & Literature Tchr
Weinzapfel, James A.
Algebra Teacher & Math Coord
Wilson, Alan Ray
French Teacher
Wiseman, Lino Kent
8th Grade Science Teacher
FAIRLAND
Crock, Molley Molen
Family & Consumer Science Tchr
Davis, Jerome Edward, Jr.
Boys Bsktbl Coach & Math Tchr
Fussel, Joseph Michael
Health & PE Teacher
Huey, Marbey Anne
English & Yearbook Teacher
Noel, Nancy K.
Business Teacher
Pringle, Larry Richard
Assistant Principal
Tresslar, Debra Gustafson
First Grade Teacher
Wilson, Jeffrey Wayne
High School Mathematics Tchr
FAIRMOUNT
Bragg, Linda L.
Counselor
Earnest, Martin Leon
Chemistry Tchr & Sci Dept Chm
Hiatt, Bette Leisure
Third Grade Teacher
Hull, Melody Summers
English Teacher
Lamb, Donald Ray
Director of Bands
Martin, D. Terry
Biology Teacher
Summers, Jeffrey L.
HS Industrial Arts Teacher
Williams, Pamala Jane
Junior High Art Teacher
FARMERSBURG
Burns, Paula Jean
1st Grade Teacher
Faught, Patricia Kay
Jr High Language Arts Teacher
Liston, Nancy Gayle
Science Teacher
Willard, Walter Jerry
Mathematics Teacher & Coach
FERDINAND
Beach, Thomas Allen
5th Grd Lang Arts & PE Tchr
Beach, Vicki Denbo
1st-12th Grd Span & PE Tchr
Cornwell, Gary Scott
5th & 6th Grade Science Tchr
Dall, Mary Roman
1st Grade Teacher
Drach, Rita C.
Soc Studies & Reading Teacher
Ellison, Kathy D.
Librarian & Latin Teacher
Harmeier, Mary Francis
Physical Education Teacher
Hoppenjans, Diane Elizabeth
5th & 6th Grade Teacher
James, Kathleen A. (Faulkenberg)
Second Grade Teacher
Mehling, James Ernest
Scndry Math Tchr & Dept Chprsn
Mitchell, Carla M.
Retired Fr & Math Teacher
Rasche, Tara Bonifer
English & Speech Teacher
Tenbarge, Larry Bernard
German Teacher
FISHERS
Armstrong, Mary Emily
English Dept Chair & Teacher
Beier, Wm. C.
Drafting & Engineering Teacher
Braden, Carol Anne
History Teacher
Butt, Lee Davis
6th Grd Language Arts Teacher
Carson, Mary Armstrong
8th Grade Math Teacher
Fork, Jeri Louise
English Teacher
Harrold, Nancy E.
English Teacher
Karcasheff, Rick Vasil
7th Grade Language Arts Tchr
Noble, Larry B.
Third Grade Teacher
Randall, Kathleen A.
Mathematics Teacher
Stoner, Natalie Ledkowsky
7th Grade Math Teacher
Wong, Susan Knueven
Mathematics Teacher
FLORA
Dillman, Glen Dean
8th Grd Social Studies Instr
Miller, Michael Eugene
US History & Sociology Teacher
FLOYDS KNOBS
Bixler, Kathy Nye
HS French Teacher
Cecil, Rusty
Mathematics Teacher
Hottell, Penelope
Math Teacher
Krammes, William Gene, II
Math & General Sci Educator
Little, Thomas R.
Mathematics Teacher
Neely, Michael D.
Ret Chrl Dir & Music Thry Tchr
Neely, Phyllis Davis
French Teacher
Newkirk, Michael D.
Secondary English Teacher
O'Rear, Barbara K.
Business Education Teacher
Taylor, Alan G.
HS Industrial Technology Tchr
FORT BRANCH
Bengert, Patrick Thomas
Psych, Sociology & Govt Tchr
Bertram, Michael Wayne
Math & Physics Teacher
Buck, LuAnn Holderbaugh
Math Teacher
Donohoo, Brenda Sue (Purkiser)
Math Teacher
Spradley, John Albert
Computer Applications Teacher
Stansberry, Don Wayne
English Teacher
FORT WAYNE
Allen, Rick G.
5th Grade Teacher
Amick, Elizabeth Martin
English & French Teacher
Amt, Philip M.
Principal & Teacher
Backofen, Mary Kay (Fremion)
Latin Tchr, Frgn Lang Dept Chm
Bahr, David M.
Mathematics Teacher
Baker, Jack
Business Ed & Economics Tchr
Barnes, Marc W.
Psychology Professor
Barone, Jeanne Tessier
Instructor of Communication
Beebe, Eric D.
English Teacher
Belknap, Sue H.
First Grade Teacher
Boggs, Barbara Joan (Green)
Fifth Grade Teacher
Bowman, Diane Ridley
3rd & 4th Grade Teacher
Boyer, Joan S.
English, History & Ec Tchr
Brubaker, Phyllis Johnson
1st Grade Teacher
Butler, Darleen R.
Soc Stud Teacher & Dept Head
Butler, Sally Benjamin
Retired 8th Grd Amer His Tchr
Carey, William E.
Mathematics Teacher
Catalano, Gary John
Assistant Principal
Ceder, Vernon L.
Dir of Technology & Registrar
Clements, Roland F.
Earth Sci, US History Teacher
Crawford, Gary Allen
Economics & Government Teacher
Crawford, Gordon Leon
6th-12th Grade Music Teacher
Croft, Tod
Mathematics, Computer Sci Tchr
Crum, Stanley Kent
Physics Teacher
Dew, David Charles
Social Studies Tchr
Diek, Lenore (Bek)
Early Childhood Consultant
Downs, Philip G.
8th Grade Social Studies Tchr
Duchovic, Ronald Joseph
Asst Prof & Dept of Chemistry
Fettig, Vernell Gehron
8th Grd Language Arts Teacher
Flott, Robert Leslie
Adj English & Commnctn Instr
Frick, Karl George
Fifth Grade Teacher
Furiak, Laura L.
Math & Dance Teacher
Garcia, Khristina
Math & Spanish Teacher
Garvin, Madeline Marcelia
English & Career Dev Teacher
Gatson, Derrell, Sr.
Mathematics Teacher
Gaughan, John Francis
Asst Dir of Diocesan High Schl
George, Reva A.
Spanish & English Teacher
Gerig, Wesley Lee
Prof of Bible & Theology
Gordon, Kathleen D.
Fifth Grade Teacher
Graf, Conrad Josef
History Teacher
Gray, Richard Lawrence
Asst Prof of Urban Ministry
Green, Gussie L.
Mathematics Teacher
Gremaux, Ronald Joseph
8th Grade Math Teacher
Griffin, Roderic B., Jr.
Spanish & French Teacher
Haffner, Katherine
Asst Prof of Psych
Hart, Ruth E.
Director
Hebel, Susan Koehlinger
English & Journalism Teacher
Hines, Maria Ricciardi
Practical Nrsng Dept Assc Prof
Hipskind, Mindy Rodgers
English & Literature Teacher
Hockemeyer, Phyllis Ann
Third Grade Teacher
Hole, Franklin Delano
HS Biology & Botany Teacher
Hollenberg, William B.
Chemistry Teacher
Holmes, Ronald Eugene
Social Studies Teacher
Hopewell, Thomas Martin
Social Studies Dept Chairman
Huls, Richard Arthur
Music Teacher
Isaacs, Russell, Jr.
Bus Tchr & Head Ftbl Coach
Jackson, Mary Ann
English Instructor
Joyner, Rex W.
Assistant Professor of Physics
Kamp, Suzi E.
Dental Careers Instructor
Keathley, Michael W.
Latin Teacher
Kennedy, Patricia Emrick
Music Teacher
Kerwin, Mary McDonagh
Third Grade Teacher
Kierstead, Richard
Practical Nurse
Kim, Seung Hyun
Asst Prof of Engineering Tech
Kleber, Beth Bartkus
8th Grade Science & Math Tchr
Knopf, Linda A. (Rahdert)
Second Grade Teacher
Knorr, David William
Science Teacher
Knudson, Thomas Alan
Science Teacher
LaFontaine, Patricia Jo
French Teacher
Lambert, James Wilson
Industrial Technology Teacher
Lesh, Larry Noel
Science Teacher
Letizia, Frank James
7th-8th Grd Soc Studies Tchr
Levy, Debra Cantwell
Assistant Professor of English
Liang, Wilson Zhongming
Engineering Technology Prof
Long, Stephen Michael
Physics & Biology Teacher
Mallers, William Charles
Business Teacher
Manning, Marianne
English Teacher
Maraldo, Sandra Angela
Science & Social Studies Tchr
Martin, C. Joseph
Assoc Prof of Psych & Cnslr
McClintock, Robert Vincent
Social Studies Teacher
Medsker, Anita L.
Preschool Teacher
Mergenthal, Sondra K.
Language Arts Teacher
Merkel, Eva Gankiewicz
Biology & Chemistry Teacher
Meyer, Nancy Kay
First Grade Teacher
Meyer, Robert Wayne
Guidance Counselor
Miller, Diane Nark
Nursing Instructor
Mills, Scott E.
HS Youth Minister
Moss, April Evans
Social Studies Teacher
Mueller, Barbara Mary
Kindergarten Teacher
Murray, Charles E.
Science Teacher
Myers, Barbara Gail
HS Religion Teacher
Narang, Ramesh V.
Indstrl Engrng Tech Asst Prof
Nichols, Donn J., III
Language Arts & Computer Coord
Norton, Donald Alan
Physics Teacher
O'Reilly, Pamela S.
Journalism Adv & English Tchr
Parrish, Glenn Franklin
Business Manager
Patterson, Dennis Robert
Social Studies Teacher
Ping, Robert (Marshall)
Physical Ed & Science Teacher
Polhamus, Lisa Ann
Anatomy & Genetics Teacher
Pruse, Robert R.
Instructor
Ramsey, Yvonne (Akers)
English Instructor
Reeder, Rebecca Glock
Teacher of Gifted Talented
Reinking, Timothy John
Religion Teacher
Roberts, Barbara Sue
Kindergarten Teacher
Rochford, Nancy Jean (Croll)
Fourth Grade Teacher
Rodenbeck, Edith Fay (Knake)
First Grade Teacher
Romary, Thomas G.
Mathematics Professor
Root, Jana Lee
Music Teacher
Schmidt, James Robert
Social Studies Teacher
Scholz, Carl F.
Mathematics Teacher
Scudder, David Carl
United States History Teacher
Shaw, Dan Lee
Industrial Tech Teacher
Shullenberger, Daniel F.
Asst Professor of Chemistry
Slavens, Dean Albert
Advanced Biology Teacher
Squadrito, Kathy
Assoc Professor of Philosophy
Steinbronn, Patricia Burckell
Social Studies Teacher
Stimson, Peggy Beth
HS English Teacher
Stoner, Sarah Slyby
5th Grade Teacher
Suvar, Jaylene Ann (Case)
Junior High Literature Teacher
Tannas, Daniel Deal
Latin & Aeronautics Instructor
Taylor, Craig Allen
English & Reading Teacher
Taylor, Karen Remington
Science Teacher
Temte, Mark Clifford
Assoc Prof of Computer Science
Tobias, Janice Walmsley
Math Teacher
Tone, J. Fred
Principal
Turner, Roger Andre
Fourth Grade Teacher
VanFossen, Judith Robinson
Cooperative Education Coord
Weiss, Ronald William
Teacher & Coach
Wesley, Lisa Carol
Math, Geometry & Algebra Tchr
Wilson, Meg Chaney
Assistant Professor of Nursing
Windom, Lawanda
Sixth Grd Social Studies Tchr
Wyss, Bonnie Anderson
English Teacher
Zent, Jerry
Physical Education Instr
FORTVILLE
Beaver, Joyce Ann Burton
Math Teacher
Beeson, Terry Michael
Math Teacher
Brooks, Vickie Lynn
English Teacher
Brown, Brock Alan
Social Studies Teacher
Campbell, Bernard Russell
Assistant Principal
Doddridge, Bob Allen
English & Spanish Teacher
Flanagan, Mary Beth Bolander
Language Arts Teacher
Fry, Kenneth Wayne
Mathematics Teacher
Smith, Judy Diane
Former 4th Grade Teacher
Smith, Steven Craig
HS Social Studies Teacher
Thomas, Darrell H.
Principal
Wendelboe, Linda Watts
Chemistry Teacher
FOUNTAIN CITY
Cooper, Patricia Charles
Second Grade Teacher
Haynes, Linda Louise (Retter)
Kindergarten Teacher
Lower, David Allen
Eng & Lang-Composition Teacher
Snell, Kathryn Jane (Myers)
Sixth Grade Teacher
Yaroch, Lu Ann Hankins
9th-12th Grd Math Teacher
FOWLER
Dearth, Frances
Third Grade Teacher
FRANCESVILLE
Srull, Karen Ellen
English & Psychology Teacher
Stevens, Joanne Stefanich
Business Teacher

NCISCO
on, Thomas Earl
guage Arts Teacher
NKFORT
, Patricia Sayers
Grade Mathematics Teacher
sma, Stephanie Shue
hman Biology Teacher
, William E.
History Teacher
rd, Bruce A.
Grd Social Studies Teacher
well, Debra Ann
lish & Yearbook Teacher
er, Ronald Eugene
red His Tchr & Ath Supvr
erd, Ronald L.
Studies Tchr & Dept Chair
r, Ruth Pickel
ond Grade Teacher
NKLIN
oel, Carol Gettelfinger
ond Grade Teacher
h, Douglas Alan
graphy & Mathematics Tchr
es, Robin Gardner
h Grade Teacher
ck, Gloria P.
mistry Tchr & Sci Dept Head
, Kathleen Ann (Fetz)
anese Teacher
NKTON
ingham, Jennie M.
h Grade Teacher
Ruth E.
nish & English Teacher
, Lola Hobbs
th Grade Teacher
holder, Donald James
hematics Teacher
MONT
han, Daniel F.
mistry & Physics Teacher
, Gayle Sears
rth Grade Teacher
npion, Patricia Mitchell
rth Grade Teacher
, Robert N.
thematics Teacher
a, Merry Nelson
dergarten Teacher
nell, David Anthony
ial Studies & Eng Tchr
st, Roger Julius
ondary Social Studies Tchr
z, Ken W.
ior High Science Teacher
NCH LICK
es, Jane Sumner
ired Kindergarten Teacher
h, Wilbert J.
siness & Social Studies Tchr
TON
haney, Rebecca Jacks
g Instr & Lang Arts Chair
, Mary Sadowsky
sh Eng, Jrnlsm & Spch Tchr
VESTON
ertson, Roslyn Ratliff
st Grade Teacher
RRETT
er, Suzon Lynne
athematics Teacher
bower, Matthew Ray
High Guidance Cnslr
k, Rebecca Cathleen
ath & Physics Teacher
on, Deb Jo (Hile)
th Grade Teacher
nkamp, Brenda Conley
th Grade Teacher
ker, Alan D.
emistry & Physical Sci Tchr
per, Kathy Emmert
HS & HS Mathematics Teacher
y, Robert Joseph
edia Specialist
s, Linda Buttell
glish, Speech & Drama Tchr
ler, Patti
n Grade Math Teacher
f, Mary Haynes
s & Intrdscplnry Coop Coord
RY
ulaleem, Sulaiman Binyakub
athematics Teacher
hanapalli, Bala G.
ssociate Professor of Finance
er, Patti J.
urth Grade Teacher
ks, Barbara Shivers
uidance Counselor
wn, Theodore H.
and Director
cher, Frances Mc Kee
rst Grade Teacher
son, Alice I.
of of Basic Eng Skills
, Gregory DeLane
nited States History Teacher
k, Pamela Elaine (Childress)
athematics Teacher
hran, Cynthia Barron
ysics & Physical Sci Teacher
aire, Lydia Roselia
gebra & Geometry Teacher
eman, Patsy Ann
n Grd Math Teacher
per, Rachel Berry
ath Dept Chprsn & Teacher

Dailey, Eleanor Tysall
English & US History Teacher
Dakich, Roberta Elizabeth
Third Grade Teacher
Daniels, Sadie M.
Science & Biology Teacher
Dawson, Walter Edward
Retired Teacher
Dorsey, Charlotte Arletha
Fifth Grade Teacher
Eastland, Vivian Fitzpatrick
Fourth Grade Teacher
Emmons-Kirk, Monica L.
Counselor
Fabian, Alfred Edward
Senior Instructor & Pgm Adv
Farkas, Harriet Bard
Kindergarten Teacher
Fisher, Ethel Page
3rd Grade Teacher
Flint, Linda Smith
MS Math & Algebra Teacher
Florios, Joann Maria
First Grade Teacher
Foffin, Donald A.
Assoc Prof of Economics
Gonzalez-Pierce, Carmen Maria
Spanish Teacher
Grubl, Cynthia Kvachkoff
1st Grade Teacher
Gyurko, Charlene Wozniak
Instructor of Nursing Program
Harper, Joyce Peterson
Social Studies Dept Chprsn
Hazelett, Rochell
Math & Computer Teacher
Heard, Patricia J.
First Grade Teacher
Henley, Janet Maxine (Wallace)
Fourth Grade Teacher
Hill, Anita Wheat
Music Teacher
Hobson, Charles Jeffrey
Assoc Professor of Management
Horne, Saundra Jean
Practical Nrsng Chm & Faculty
James, Mary Ann (McGown)
10th Grade English Teacher
James, Teresa Elaine
Mathematics Teacher
Johnson, Bettye Marte Evans
Eighth Grade Mathematics Tutor
Johnson, Brenda Terry
Social Studies Teacher
Johnson, Cheryl Clayborne
Business Ed & Computer Tchr
Jones, Carol Robinson
Spanish Teacher
Jones, Henry L.
Science Teacher
Keehn, Jeffrey James
Secondary Mathematics Teacher
Kimbrough, Faye Crowder
Mathematics Teacher
King, Gloria K.
6th Grd Rdng & Soc Stud Tchr
Kini, Ranjan Bailur
Business Administration Prof
Knapp, Judith Ann (Nagel)
Assoc Prof of Data Processing
Knight, Harriette (Scott)
7th-12th Grd Math Teacher
Kolarik, Peggy Ann
Third Grade Teacher
Korellis, Ann
French Teacher
Kouvelas, Dorothy
Government & Economics Teacher
Levander, Mitzi Ann
Fourth Grade Teacher
Marshall-Ligon, Ava Renee
Kindergarten Teacher
Martin, Melonie Joyce
8th Grade Language Arts Tchr
Masson, Scott Alan
7th Grade Mathematics Teacher
Mc Crady, Carolyn Jean
English & Journalism Teacher
Mitchell, Gail L.
8th Grd Lang Arts Teacher
Montgomery-Toppin, Patricia Diane
Physical Education Instructor
Nickoloff, Mary Ann Luberda
Middle School Science Teacher
Noble, Phyllis Protho
Dean of Students
Paczolt, Sandy
Mathematics Teacher
Powers, Elaine Phelps
9th-12th Grade Spanish Teacher
Raby, JoEllen Brink
Soc Stud Tchr & Admin
Rasheed, Jamal Raheem
Soc Stud, Hlth & Safety Tchr
Roberts, William Theodore
African American History Tchr
Ross, Jacqueline Dixon
Biology Teacher
Schiefelbusch, Lary
Assoc Professor of Mathematics
Schulz, Anna Ulrich
Special Education Teacher
Scott, Cuthbert Loraine, III
Management Professor
Sefton, Jan Sudroff
English Teacher
Sheldon, Mark
Philosophy Professor
Shivers, Mary J. Hayes
5th Grade Teacher

Siggers, Jacquenette Carter
High School Mathematics Tchr
Smith, Danise Vossos
12th Grade English Teacher
Smith, Treacie Bradley
Spanish Teacher
Stewart, Eugene Russell, III
Art Dept Chprsn & Instructor
Tauber, Jerry Joseph
Math & Cmptr Programming Tchr
Turner, Sandra Davis
3rd Grade Teacher
Vazquez, Omar A.
Physical Education Teacher
Villalobos, Kathleen
Fifth Grade Teacher
Vincent, Carl
Vocal & Instrumental Teacher
Vincent, Juanita Parsons
Middle School Vocal Music Tchr
Walls, Nancy Krebs
Biology Teacher
Weaver, Aurelia Ann
French Teacher
Williams, Joan McDaniel
Language Arts Teacher
Williams, LarGlendal
English Teacher
Yuhasz, Kathryn Ann
Speech Teacher
Zimmerman, Joseph James
4th & 5th Grd Sci Tchr
GAS CITY
Anthony, Donna Welch
Fifth Grade Teacher
Barker, Steven J.
Biology Teacher
Beall, Michael P.
Sixth Grade Teacher
Campbell, Dix Ann
Math, Lang Arts & Health Tchr
Crawford, Dorothy E.
Childcare Director
Gill, Tammie Buchanan
High School Business Teacher
Haggerty, Wilbur Ernest
English Teacher
Kammeyer, Rebecca Jones
Marketing Ed Tchr & Coord
Lorenzano, Vincent Mario
Business Teacher
Mc Phail, Steven David
World & US History Teacher
Muchmaw, Keith
Biology Teacher & Coach
Taylor, Jan
Family & Consumer Science Tchr
Terhune, Florence Marcum
Lang Arts, His & Cmptr Tchr
Willey, Ann Chapman
8th Grade Language Arts Tchr
Willey, Janet Sprinkle
5th Grade Teacher
Wilson, Pam
Bus Tchr & Coop Ed Coord
GASTON
Cullum, Amy J.
Spanish Teacher
Howell, Kenneth James
Biology & Chemistry Teacher
Meier-Fisher, Pamela Beiser
High School English Teacher
GENEVA
McKean, Linda Reusser
Fourth Grade Teacher
GOSHEN
Aschliman, Kathryn A.
Kindergarten Dir & Teacher
Blickenstaff, Marvin Ray
Music Teacher
Cartwright, Diane Lee (Thomas)
English Teacher
Cheek, Charles C.
Eighth Grade US History Tchr
Crawford, Judy Ellen
Third Grade Teacher
Detweiler, Jerry R.
Mathematics Teacher
Graves, James L.
German & ESL Teacher
Hershberger, W. Frank
Fifth Grade Teacher
Keyser, Dori E.
Stu Assistance Dir & Peer Cnsl
Linton, Mary Catherine
Professor of Biology
Ogle, Donald R.
Health Educator
Schrock, H. Devon
11th-12th Grade English Tchr
Smith, Daniel A.
Asst Professor of Chemistry
Thiery, Timothy Allen
Science Teacher
Vermeulen, Diana Lynn
Secondary & MS Sci Teacher
Wittrig, Ruth Ann Miller
Fourth Grade Teacher
Yost, Marcia Elaine
Choral Director
GRANGER
Conrad, Alecia Luna
5th Grade Teacher
Merrill, Mary Mancuso
Computer & Math Instr
O'Hara, Kathryn Scott
Retired Teacher
GRAYSVILLE
Badger, Judith Stone
Elementary PE Teacher

Miller, Pam S.
Third Grade Teacher
GREENCASTLE
Berry, Amy S.
French Teacher
Berry, Robert Joseph
Visual Arts Instructor
Bryant, Rachel E.
English Teacher
Cary, William Riley
Science Teacher
Evans, Sharon C.
6th Grade Teacher
Fallis, John
Math Teacher & Coach
Gibson, Michael V.
Instructor of Computer Science
Hile, Glenn R.
Social Studies Teacher
Huber, Connie Dee Porter
Elementary Music Teacher
Lawrence, Marilyn Carnegie
Fifth Grade Teacher
Miller, Douglas W.
Mathematics Teacher
Newman, David Michael
Associate Prof of Sociology
Shumaker, Randall
Eng Tchr & Lang Arts Dept Chm
Wildman, Mark L.
Counselor
GREENFIELD
Gardner, Thomas Dean
Sixth Grade Teacher
Grube, Linda Carpenter
First Grade Teacher
Holzhausen, Nancy Jones
First Grade Teacher
Kress, Kevin Michael
7th Grade Social Studies Tchr
Murphy, William D.
History & Science Teacher
Oden, Judith Collins
Third Grade Teacher
Ross, R. Keith
Bio & Gen Sci Tchr
Spivey, Kathy Ann (Draper)
3rd Grade Teacher
Strickland, Joyce Hyatt
6th Grade Teacher
Todd, Susan Clehouse
Literature Teacher
Wolf, Cynthia Ann
Fifth Grade Teacher
GREENSBURG
Cruser, Deb Hensley
7th & 8th Grade Counselor
Hartman, Martha L.
Principal
Hickey, Jean Wesley
Third Grade Teacher
Hoffman, Jean Marie
English Teacher
Reynolds, Diane Gulley
Media Specialist
Sellers, John Adrian
Secondary Science Teacher
Wilson, Dennis
Physics, Math & Cmptr Sci Tchr
GREENTOWN
Kirkman, Jennifer Hainlen
Assistant Band Director
Nicholson, Paul L.
Sixth Grd Math & Soc Stud Tchr
GREENWOOD
Bales, Carol Stark
Music Teacher
Ball, Jill Lynn
Media Specialist
Davis, Karen S.
English Teacher
Gill, Kim Dunwiddie
Spanish Teacher
Hayes, Carolyn A. (Agee)
Biology Teacher
Hoff, Sharon Sue
English Teacher
Jones, Joyce Lynn Brinsom
Spanish Teacher
Kehler, Rebecca Terpstra
Biology Teacher
Manship, Teri Hines
Former Elementary Educator
Meyer, Linda (Pepmeier)
Second Grade Teacher
Newton, Denise Ann
Journalism & English Tchr
Smith, Victor Brian
8th Grade Mathematics Teacher
Stephens, Susan Margedant
Scndry Voc Bus Tchr
Templeton, Elizabeth Bales
Retired Elementary Teacher
Todd, James William
Physical Ed Tchr & Swim Coach
GRIFFITH
Bowron, Joan
Third Grade Teacher
Carpenter, Janis Watkins
4th Grade Teacher
Dye, Barbara
Elementary Teacher
Giba, Barbara Ann
Second Grade Teacher
Keithley, Margie Ellen (Wimer)
Family & Consumer Sci Tchr
Lazzaro, Sherry Marie
Sixth Grade Teacher
Lukmann, Lynn Frances
7th & 8th Grade Teacher

Rincon, Harriet Murdock
Fourth Grade Teacher
Shiperek, Briget Furticella
Sixth Grade Teacher
Veneziano, David Alexander
Junior HS Soc Stud Tchr
HAGERSTOWN
Bradway, Stephanie Renee
Kindergarten Teacher
Dilley, Jean Ann
Third Grade Teacher
Lebo, Suzy F. (Workman)
Bus Tchr & Cmptr Tech Coord
Morton, Janis Kay (Pattison)
5th Grade Teacher
Moyer, Sandra Bronnenberg
Speech & Language Pathologist
Watson, Jorgena Kay Evans
Gifted, Talented Coord & Tchr
HAMILTON
Mc Cann, Jeffrey Eugene
HS Mathematics & Physics Tchr
Mc Cann, Marsha A.
Sixth Grade Teacher
Shoemaker, Randy L.
Fifth Grade Teacher
Stackhouse, Susan Lash
Language Arts Teacher
HAMLET
Brems, Julie Marie (Beem)
Mathematics Teacher
Carmichael, Nancy L. David
English & Social Science Tchr
Flaugher, Donna Moore
High School English Teacher
Rose, Lynda Howard
Science Dept Chairman
Underwood, Marilyn Sue
Sixth Grade Teacher
HAMMOND
Allen, Jerome Lemont
5th Grade Teacher
Arnold, Mary Ellen Deardorff
Third Grade Teacher
Behling, Irene Dianne
7th Grd Reading & Spanish Tchr
Berg, Catherine Rider
English Teacher
Bigheart, Terri Rae
Director of Student Activities
Burrell, Marles Ann
First Grade Teacher
Conley, Elizabeth Fredericksen
Debate, Comm & PE Teacher
Craig, Elaine Krasowski
HS Mathematics Teacher
Csigas, Karen Marie
Kindergarten Teacher
Culp, Gary R.
Sociology Instructor
Cummings, Grace Stranc
Theology Teacher
Dakich, Barbara Jayne
Teacher of Gifted & Talented
Daronatsky, Aram R.
English Teacher
Daronatsy, Aram Robert
High School English Teacher
Davis, D. Deanna
Third & Fourth Grade Teacher
Demantes, Bill, Sr.
Gen Math & Pre-Algebra Tchr
Demantes, Linda Lee
4th-5th Grade Teacher
Domsich, Karen Lynne (Yonke)
5th-8th Grade Teacher
Dowd, Lesa Ann
Chemistry Teacher
Duffala, Michele Kaye
Business Teacher
Edmondson, Christopher David
8th Grade Math Teacher
Fies, James David
8th Grade Mathematics Teacher
Figi, Matthew L.
Math & Cmptr Programming Tchr
Graban, Garry Michael
Social Studies Teacher
Greenberg, Christine Irene
Literature Teacher
Hedges, Mary Curtis
Fifth Grade Teacher
Hedges, Peter James
Middle School Science Teacher
Howell, Janice C.
Journalism Teacher
Huber, Kevin Richard
Campus Ministry Director
Hunt, Mary Rodgers
Teacher
Ivers, Betty Sikora
English Teacher
Johnston, Nancy Lynn
Fourth Grade Teacher
Jones, Emanda Archie
English Teacher & Dept Chprsn
Kepchar, Barbara Ann (Dominguez)
Special Ed Inclusion Teacher
Kepler, Frederick
Health & Safety Teacher
Kessler, Martin H.
Secondary Mathematics Teacher
King, Juliana Sredno
Family & Consumer Sci Teacher
Kish, Julius Steven
Chemistry Teacher
Kolanowski, Darlene Batwin
8th Grd Math & Algebra Teacher
Kostopoulos, Lynne Ackermann
German Teacher

HAMMOND (cont)
Maka, Lawrence John
Mathematics Teacher
Makely, Pamela Jean
Fifth & Sixth Grd Math Tchr
Mastej, Mary Ellen
Reading & Literature Teacher
Mayer, Barbara M.
Journalism & Eng Teacher
Mc Callister, Doug
High School Math Teacher
Mc Guire, Claudia June (Skinner)
Home Economics Teacher
Melby, William Todd
Mathematics Teacher
Miller, Robert Daniel
HS Social Studies Teacher
Murphy, Alma
First Grade Teacher
Nelson, Kathy Jean
Third Grade Teacher
Nestich, Stephen Richard
Language Arts Teacher
O'Connor, Mary Beth
Assoc Prof of Communication
Perrine, Diane
Music Teacher & Choir Director
Popplewell, Shawn Brust
Physical Education Teacher
Quinn, Nancy E.
Math Teacher
Robison, Mary Elena Giglio
English Teacher
Romano, Constance Pikula
Math & Psych Tchr
Safstrom, David Lee
English & Drama Teacher
Schiralli, Marsha Browne
Art Teacher
Schultz, Kathleen Boyle
3rd Grade Teacher
Schwegman, Mary L.
HS Physical Education Teacher
Sever, Darlene Kuruzovich
7th Grade Social Studies Tchr
Small, Christine E. Wierzbicki
Third Grade Teacher
Smith, JoAnn
5th Grade Teacher
Sunny, Michael J., Jr.
Social Studies Teacher
Trelo, Barbara Buksar
First Grade Teacher
Tutacko, David Martin
Social Studies Teacher
VanRennes, Pamela Ann
Middle School Counselor
Vavrek, Jennifer Joyce
Sixth Grd Math & Science Tchr
Walczak, Barbara Ann
4th & 5th Grade Teacher
Wilson, Laura Kessler
German Teacher
Wilson, Roberta Mae
Substitute Teacher
Wolak, Deane L. (Groszewski)
Child Care Instructor
Zelencik, Mary Joan
4th Grade Teacher
Zuidema, Beverly J. Van Drunen
Teacher of Academically Gifted
HANOVER
Orrill, Jennifer A.
English Teacher
Poindexter, Ruth Kay
Language Arts Teacher
Waller, Robert Michael
Chemistry Teacher
HARTFORD CITY
Adams, John S.
Art Department Chm & Coach
Clossin, Michael Joseph
Drama & English Teacher
Janicki, David P.
Health Teacher
Kline, Kenneth Richard
American Government Teacher
Richardson, Michael J.
Social Science & Psych Tchr
HAUBSTADT
Kahle, Ronnie Lee
Social Studies Teacher & Coach
HAYDEN
Sullivan, Patrick L.
Sixth Grade Teacher
HEBRON
Dowdy, Marianne Terzes
5th Grade Elementary Teacher
Fisher, Tobi J.
Second Grade Teacher
Huber, Peggy Ann
Kindergarten Teacher
Kirkman, Bette S.
Fourth Grade Teacher
HENRYVILLE
Cole, Paula Robbins
Third Grade Teacher
Schroeder, Jeffrey Stephen
Eng, Speech & Jrnlsm Teacher
HIGHLAND
DeVaney, Cynthia Ann (Burner)
4th Grade Teacher
HOBART
Agnew, Charles Arthur
Teacher
Bartlett, Brian Edward
Band Director
Brandenburg, Jamie Enrico
Fourth Grade Teacher
Cline, Darrin O.
Chemistry & Mathematics Tchr
Hooks, Kathy Seegers
Science Teacher
Kicinski, Patricia Lee
Swim Coach & Vice Prin Sec
Lain, Richard William
6th & 8th Grade Teacher
Loverich, Barbara L.
Psychology & Geography Teacher
Mumaugh, Shirley Ann
Speech, Theatre & English Tchr
Reygaert, James A.
Math Teacher
Richardson, Kennard James
Principal
Rykovich, Kristine Sippel
Spanish & French Teacher
Shinovich, Barbara Jean Polizzotto
Spanish Teacher
Whiting, J. Kirk
Social Studies Teacher
Wielgus, Andrew A.
Asst Prin & US History Teacher
HOPE
Blomenberg, Janeen Miller
Art Teacher
Grimes, Todd R.
World History & Psych Teacher
Johnson, Barbara Sue
Third Grade Teacher
HOWE
Bauman, Roger Scott
Math Dept Chairman & Teacher
Kimball, Reed James
Physics Teacher & Headmaster
Morgan, Philip
Chaplain & Rector
HUNTERTOWN
Shamanoff, Gloria Ann
Elementary School Principal
HUNTINGBURG
Himsel, George E.
5th Grade Teacher
LaGrange, Ronald Glenn
Assistant Prin & Health Tchr
Ring, David R.
Agribusiness Teacher
Younker, Keith Carson
English Teacher
HUNTINGTON
Arnold, George H.
Science Teacher
Brown, Phyllis Fluke
Third Grade Teacher
Burley, Gloria Darlene Mc Clain
Fourth Grade Teacher
Duling, Connie S.
English Teacher
Evans, Delores Stumbo
Middle School Vocal Music Tchr
Flora, Robert Alan
Chemistry Teacher
Herzog, Frank Robert
Social Studies Teacher
Hippensteel, Scott A.
Band Director
Hotchkiss, James B.
English & Math Teacher
Kline, Arthur H.
Science Teacher
Lewis, Judith Lyna
Eng, German, Lang Culture Tchr
Lippe, Jon Karl
Physics & Astronomy Teacher
Matheny, Patty Ann
Kindergarten Teacher
Mc Elhaney, Douglas A.
6th-8th Grade Band Director
Morton, Anita Renee (Farmer)
Chemistry & Phys Sci Teacher
O'Donnell, James Maurice
Assoc Prof of Business
Sherlock, Jeffrey Fred
Instructor of Business
Smekens, Brady
Jrnlsm Tchr & Publications Adv
Smelser, Jerry L.
Industrial Technology Teacher
Smith, Shirley Irene (Stites)
2nd Grade Teacher
Snively, Elizabeth Swan
English Teacher
Spenner, Richard Lee
Drama & English Teacher
Stoffel, Wallace James
Mathematics Dept Chairman
Teusch, Kristine Thomas
HS Math Teacher
Updike, Connie Carroll
Asst Prof of Recreation Mgmt
Walker, Bill
Radio & Television Teacher
Wilcoxson, Scott Brady
High School Math Teacher
Wright, Samuel L.
English & Journalism Teacher
INDIANAPOLIS
Abebe, Solomon
Education Professor
Adams, Susan Adams
Fourth Grade Teacher
Adcock, Karen S.
7th Grd Sci & 9th Grd Bio Tchr
Adrianson, Jena Jones
Vocal Music Teacher
Allbright, Troy Devan
Band Director
Allen, Diane Maurer
Fifth Grade Teacher
Anderson, Helen Esther
History & Political Sci Instr
Andzer, Steven Craig
Sixth Grade Math Teacher
Armao, Ruth Heider
Preschool Teacher
Armstrong, Tony
English Teacher
Banks, Jamyce Curtis
Teacher & Team Leader
Baughman, Terry Alan
Director of Choirs
Bevis, Karen L. (Mohr)
Principal & Administrator
Blair, John Paul
Teacher & Vocal Coach
Blase, David K.
Biology Teacher
Boebinger, Carol M.
Fifth Grade Teacher
Bolinger, Thomas William
Business Professor
Booker, Jill
Asst Professor of Psychology
Boone, Diann Endres
Gifted Elementary Teacher
Borden, Kenneth D.
Professor of Chemistry
Bowles, Stephen Reese
English Teacher & Yearbook Adv
Braun, Mary Jane Pickard
Elementary Counselor
Brendel, Gary O.
HS Biology Teacher
Brooks, Dennie W.
5th Grade Teacher
Brooks, Pamela Sue
English Teacher
Brown, Kimberly Ann
5th Grade Teacher
Brown, Leslie Anne
Sixth Grade Science Teacher
Brown, Paul J.
Mathematics Instructor
Brown, Teresa Williams
6th Grade English Teacher
Browne, Pat Myers
Supvr of African Mltculturl Ed
Bui-Brown, Lan Thu
Mathematics Teacher
Bunting, Lawrence Eugene
Adj Instr of Cmptr Inf Systems
Burdine, Linda Sharon
Secondary Business Ed Teacher
Byram, Laura Hedges
Dance Dept Coordinator
Cain, Jerry D.
Mathematics Teacher
Castino, William
6th Grade Science Teacher
Christian, Daniel Robert
Band Director
Clark, Daniel Wayne
Math Instructor & Dept Chprsn
Clawson, Thomas William
Hum Interdisciplinary Stud Dir
Clevenger, Penny
Commercial Food Teacher
Coahran, Elizabeth Sievers
Tchr of Learning Disabilities
Collins, Rose (Baumgart)
Spanish Teacher
Colvin, Bessie Epps
Vocal Music Teacher
Cook, Patricia Ann Parker
Professor of Education
Crismore, James B.
Orchestra Director
Crumlin, Angela (Lime)
Math Teacher
Darko, Alexander David
Chemistry Teacher
Darnell, Margaret E.
Human Services Instructor
Davidson, Debbie Richhort
Business Teacher
Davison, Lisa Maureen
History & Geography Teacher
DeJong, Karen Switzer
4th Grade Teacher
Dickerson, Mary Ann
Cosmetology Instructor
Disney, Brian R.
Math Teacher
Dodds, Linda (Finn)
Language Arts Teacher
Doucette, Richard Lloyd
Religious Studies Chairperson
Douglas, Joseph Michael
MS Science Teacher
Dowden, Sheri Lynn Hessong
Mathematics Teacher
Draving, Mary Beth Walsh
English Teacher
Dunkle, Robert Hudson
Psychology Professor
Earle, Rebecca Schiller
Guidance Counselor
Edmondson, Russell D.
5th Grade Math Teacher
Edwards, Donita J. (Honey)
First Grade Teacher
Eley, Myles D.
English Teacher
Elliott, Desiree Marie
English & Communications Tchr
Ellis, Stanley Eugene
Soc Stud Tchr & Dept Chair
Elmore, Richard K.
Mathematics Teacher
Ewing, Deborah Ann (Hanneken)
Art & Gifted Humanities Tchr
Fadely, James Philip
Dir of Admissions & His Tchr
Fallis, Kenneth Clark
Retired Amer Literature Tchr
Farlow, Lorelei R. Pokral
1st-12th Grd Orchestra Teacher
Farrell, Grace
American Literature Professor
Fiddler, Janet Lynn Price
Kindergarten Teacher
Fidler, Marcia Light
History Teacher
Fields, Gary Lee
Band Director
Fischer, Carol P.
English Teacher
Fischer, Pamela Ann
High School English Teacher
Fisher, Susan Morgan
6th Grd Language Arts Teacher
Folco, Angelika Heise
German Teacher
Frankum, D. Mark
Math Teacher
Franzman, Leslie Voltz
Physical Education Teacher
Frazier, Edward L.
Biological Science Dept Chrmn
Fronczek, James Louis
Choral Director
Fulford, Phyllis Lee
Choral Music Teacher
Galley, Danielle Bessette
English & Journalism Teacher
Gentry, Marshall Bruce
Associate Professor of English
Gholston, Pearla Mae Owens
Humanities & English Teacher
Gilbert, Shirley Margaret
Humanities Magnet Teacher
Gilkerson, Marlene Patterson
First Grade Teacher
Gilmartin, William Aloysius
Latin Teacher
Godan, Linda R.
Third Grade Teacher
Gorball, Clifford Lee
Math Department Chairman
Gramer, Ellie Poe
Fourth Grade Teacher
Grayson, Jerry W.
Theatre Dept Chair
Greathouse, William L.
Hotel & Rest Mgmt Prog Chair
Green, Paige (Bates)
Fifth Grade Teacher
Greenlee, John R.
Mathematics Teacher
Greer, Vernal Pierce
Seventh Grade English Teacher
Guanajuato, Edward Rudolph
Band Teacher
Guffin, Jan A.
Curriculum Coordinator
Hall, Stanley O.
Chemistry & Physics Teacher
Hamilton, Cheryl Louise
Fourth Grade Teacher
Hamilton, Jeffrey Milton
7th & 9th Grd English Teacher
Hamrick, Jeffrey
English Teacher
Hannan, John Charles
English & Journalism Teacher
Hannigan, Bonny Carolyn (Bryant)
Counselor
Hannon, Donald Lee
Chemistry Teacher
Hard, Jody Kay (Plotner)
Fifth Grade Teacher
Harris, Georgette Saba
Mathematics Teacher
Hartshorn, Cynthia Lewis
Music Department Head
Haviland, Rex L., Jr.
Theatre & Speech Teacher
Hawk, Linda Joyce
Mathematics Teacher
Hayden, Bettie Green
Language Arts Teacher
Haydock, Thomas Kyle
Fourth Grade Teacher
Heady, Ronald
Secondary School Advisor
Heckman, Carol Haffner
German Teacher
Heiniger, Steven Roby
6th Grd Social Studies Teacher
Helms, Robert D.
Social Studies Teacher
Hensley, Krista Metheny
English Teacher
Hensley, Lori Henson
Mathematics Teacher
Herre, Norma Schroeder
6th-8th Grd His & Music Tchr
Hess, Jeffrey Stephen
Choral Director
Hignite, Robert E.
Retired SAP, Coord & Teacher
Hobson, David Lee
Eighth Grade History Teacher
Hollenberg, Krista
Paralegal Instructor
Holmes, Brad Scott
Art Teacher
Hornback, Sally J.
Assoc & Adjunct Writing Instr
Hoskins, James W., Jr.
Social Studies Teacher & Coach
Hougesen, Cara Dawn Wilson
Language Arts Teacher
Hougham, William Bryan
Industrial Technology Teacher
Hruban, Sally Swinford (Beeson)
5th & 6th Grd Literature Tchr
Hubbard, Ruth Delight
Amer Literature & Bible Tchr
Hudson, Janet B.
Mathematics Teacher
Hurley, Karen Jeanne
Language Arts Tchr & Curr Rep
Hutslar, Paul Thomas
Mathematics Teacher
Ilardi, Jimmie
Vocational Electronics Teacher
Jablonski, Barbara Powell
Media Director
Jablonski-Polk, Terri Lynn
Human Services Program Chprsn
Jegen, Lawrence A., III
Professor of Law
Johnson, David Lee, Jr.
7th Grd Language Arts Teacher
Johnson, Paul Wayne
Director of Music
Jones, Harvey Wayne
Math & Sci Dept Chair
Joseph, Denise Ann
French Teacher
Kass, Mary Jane (Sharpe)
French Teacher
Keel, Gary Louis
Social Studies Teacher
Keller, Carol Skierkowski
Middle School Teacher
Kellison, Eric Thomas
US History & Soc Stud Tchr
Kelly, Larry Joe
Social Studies Teacher
Kelly, Sandra J.
Fifth Grade Teacher
Kelsay, Rhonda Davis
High School Art Teacher
Kern, Susan (Humbarger)
Art Teacher
Kerr, William Andrew
Law Professor
Khan, Jehan Zeb
Mathematics Teacher
Kidwell, Sharon Anne
Lang Arts Teacher & Asst Prin
Kin, Ann McMillan
English Teacher
Kinghorn, Kathy
Teacher of Hearing Impaired
Kirkham, R. Gregory
Government & US History Tchr
Kissling, Deborah Ann (Shaw)
Kindergarten Tchr
Kivela, David A.
History Department Chairman
Kixmiller, Jane Marutz
Kindergarten Teacher
Koors, Lucille Marie
Chemistry Teacher
Koudou, Nicolas Ahile
Marketing Professor
LaFave, Sherry L.
Biology Teacher
Lang, Grace (Wollersheim)
Religion Teacher
Langdon, John H.
Associate Professor of Biology
Lausch, Carolyn France
Asst Prin & AP Eng Teacher
Lawlis, Sandra Brown
US His & Amer Studies Teacher
Leax, Alice Elva (Joswig)
Consumer & Family Sci Tchr
Lerch, Kathryn Wilsey
History & German Teacher
Lewis, Carla Ross
Language Arts Teacher
Litts, Glenn Stanley
MS Visual Arts Specialist
Lord, William Herman
Performing Arts Dept Chairman
Lupear, Ellen Marie
French & German Teacher
Lyday, Jill Ferris
English Teacher
Lynch, Debbie Sue
Chemistry Teacher
Mack, Wallace John
Math Department Chairman
Madden, Elisha Onelyous
Assistant Principal
Mason, Maxine J.
Business Teacher & Dept Chm
Massela, Mary Ann
Biology Teacher
Mc Clure, Sylvia Dennis
Second Grade Teacher
McCormick, Larissa Trenette
English Teacher
McCowen, Teresa Anne
Chemistry Lecturer
Mc Farland, Betty Pollard
7th & 9th Grd Lang Arts Tchr
McGeath, Kennita Dunbar
Fifth Grade Teacher
Mc Ghee, Johnnie Sawyer
Fourth & Fifth Grade Teacher
Mc Gill, Daniel K.
Science Teacher
Mc Grath, Michael LeRoy
7th Grade Language Arts Tchr

APOLIS (cont)
e, Stephen
natics Teacher
ey, Philip R.
s Tchr & Sci Dept Chm
en, Debra J.
Grade Teacher
B. Jeanne
h Teacher
ton, Lynda Smith
lary English Teacher
ger, Carolyn Martin
age Arts Teacher
hall, Gordon L.
y & Human Genetics Tchr
Barb E.
lary Visual Arts Teacher
Nicole L.
and & Orchestra Director
Barbara L.
h Teacher
Dawn Powell
ng Recovery Teacher
mery, Debra Ann (Overbey)
age Arts Teacher
mery, Mark Everett
n Anatomy, Physiology Tchr
William Ernest
ade Teacher
M. Etta
ess Education Teacher
n, Deborah Floyd
Studies Teacher
k, Larry
h Tchr & Football Coach
Barbara (Baldwin)
ations Teacher
, Karen Van Buskirk
Grade Teacher
Mark Dennis
sh Teacher
horst, Debra Sue
d Grade Teacher
Diana Snider
Lab Director
Angela Joyce
istry Educator & Pvt Coach
, Carl Vincent
Schl Advisor & Teacher
C. Rebecca
al & Performing Arts Dir
Florence Bremen
Grade Teacher
Richard A.
sh Teacher
k, Elizabeth Shute
sh Teacher
Karen L.
istory Teacher
, Sharon
Grade Teacher
obert H.
c Dean of Acad & Stu Prgms
, George
d History Teacher
Sandra Denise (Hall)
e School Advisor
Peggy Hattiex
ly & Consumer Science Tchr
Shawn Charles
al Director
Charles Edward
g, US & World His Tchr
elli, Timothy Angelo
of Studs & Religion Tchr
n, Joseph Lee
al Studies Teacher
y, Martha Jane
ager
Kate Duffy
oc Faculty, Dept of Engrng
e, Lars Edward
nology Teacher
an, Betty Louise
nish Teacher
Gwendolyn Carter
hematics Teacher
s, Beverly Wiley
ral Lrning Ldr & Dept Chair
Cynthia Shelley
, Advanced Composition Tchr
es, Mark Christopher
al Studies & Religion Tchr
Barbara A. (Martin)
lish Teacher
Donald R.
fting & Computer Teacher
Holly Harding
ech & Drama Teacher
ardson, Julie Hennegan
ond & Third Grade Teacher
ardson, Ronald Dale
dio Visual Dir & Teacher
ardson, Virginia Gowland
ector of Student Life
, Diana L. Heintzelman
ool Counselor
ins, Kathleen Oliverio
-3rd Grd Classroom Teacher
nson, Beverly Mc Neil
ational Counselor
, Deborah Regina
English Teacher
, Cheryl Ann
gh School Chemistry Teacher
, Janis Alsager
th Grade Science Teacher
, Lucia
th & Science Instructor

Sander, James F.
Accounting Area Coordinator
Sanders, Anne Elizabeth
High School Choral Director
Sanders, Wesley E.
Staff Development Consultant
Scering, Debra (Nease)
Hlth Prof, Dental Asst Teacher
Schaaf, Mark
Spanish Teacher
Schaefer, Christine C.
Fourth Grade Teacher
Schmid, Dionne Betcher
Second Grade Teacher
Schrepferman, Jan M.
Geog & Social Studies Tchr
Schuch, Marla Stankey
Math Teacher
Schwenn, Lou Anne
9th-12th Grade Counselor
Sheridan, Patricia Kazer
2nd Grade Teacher
Simonton, Peggy Smith
Special Education Teacher
Smiley, Gregory Allan
Guid Cnslr & Soc Stud Teacher
Smith, Candace Russell
Language Arts Teacher
Smith, Erik Richard
HS Math Teacher
Smith, Esther Chesebro
Fourth Grade Teacher
Smithburn, Susan Hughes
7th Grade English Teacher
Sparks, W. Cody
Social Studies Tchr & Ath Dir
Spencer, Alberta Arlene Montgomery
Composition Instructor
Staffieri, Edra Pauline
Foreign Language Teacher
Stauffer, Nancy B.
Mathematics Teacher
Steffel, Nancy Oster
Asst Professor of Literacy Ed
Steinmetz, Mark Allan
Science Teacher
Stokes, Lillian Gatlin
Associate Professor
Stoneburner, Michelle Ann
Associate Professor of French
Strain, Greg
Social Studies Teacher
Strange, Wanda Jacobs
English & Journalism Teacher
Striby, Gerard M.
Religion Teacher
Stroup, Daniel Warren
Jr High Bible Teacher
Stumpf, Georgia Ann
English Teacher
Stuteville, Lannae Lynn
English & Speech Teacher
Sullender, Joy Barkman
Third & Fourth Grade Teacher
Sutton, Susan Buck
Professor
Sydnor, Barbara Baker
Second Grade Teacher
Taylor, Judy King
Fifth Grade Teacher
Toffolo, Nancy Watson
Teacher
Turner, Rhonda Lee
5th Grade Teacher
Unruh, Jeffrey Karl
Civics & English Teacher
Van Riper, Christina
High School English Teacher
Vest, Jeffrey Allan
Secondary Social Studies Tchr
Voigt, Kristin Hoyt
French Teacher
Voris, Jack Holmes
Advanced Biology Teacher
Walpole, David B.
High School Math Teacher
Walsh, Maria Rivert
Chemistry Teacher
Washburn, Brian H.
Bible Tchr & Schl Admin
Watson, Robert Lee
Advanced Placement Teacher
Webb, Jody E.
5th Grade Teacher of Gifted
Webster, Doris Anne Wagner
Spanish Teacher
Wheeler, Arlene E.
5th Grade Teacher
White, Linda L.
Fifth Grade Teacher
Wiggins, Andrew John
Social Studies Teacher
Williamson, David Michael
Director of Student Programs
Witmer, Dana Day
Marketing Ed Coordinator
Wolfe, Elaine Claire Daughetee
Science Teacher
Wray, David E.
Sixth Grade Teacher
Wright, Bradley Jon
Director of Theatre
Wright, Mary Jo J.
Fifth Grade Teacher
Yedinak, Mary Ann (Hensley)
Humanities & Lang Arts Teacher
Young, Sheilah Lyles
4th Grade Teacher
Yumang, Adoracion Zapanta
1st-2nd Grd Montessori Teacher

Zimny, Rick
Mathematics Teacher
Zimny, Sally Bender
Business Education Teacher

IRELAND
Kluemper, Janet Lubbers
Fifth Grade Teacher

JAMESTOWN
Busenbark, Nancy Ann
Fourth Grade Teacher
Kelly, Jill Davis
Kindergarten Teacher
Randle, Linda Kay (Vickrey)
6th Grd Language Arts Teacher

JASONVILLE
Gorby, Donna M.
English & Journalism Teacher
Hobbs, Rick
Sixth Grd Math & Science Tchr
Salter, Linda Keaton
Second Grade Teacher
Thorlton, Cynthia Baugh
Math Tchr & Dept Head

JASPER
Bennett, Stella Fischer
First Grade Teacher
Flamion, Randall L.
Math Teacher
Fromme, Clara M.
12th Grade English Tchr & Chm
Hendrickson, Anita Jane
English Teacher
Jochum, Gayle Ann (Couch)
Family & Consumer Science Tchr
Kavanaugh, Irma R.
Fifth Grade Teacher
Kieffner, Mary Ann
Second Grade Teacher
La Grange, Timothy Louis
HS Social Studies Teacher
Leinenbach, Claudette Ann (Frommie)
Third Grade Teacher
Lents, Sonny Allen
Teacher
Rebstock, Therese Mary
Adjunct Instructor
Rohleder, Linda Lou
Math Teacher
Schaeffer, Joan Ernst
High School Mathematics Tchr
Schum, Thomas Allen
Fine Arts Dept Chairman
Smith, Richard Neal
Science Teacher

JEFFERSONVILLE
Beard, Julia A.
Third Grade Teacher
Campbell, Carol Cuernsey
7th Grade Social Studies Tchr
DiNoto, Frank
Arch Drafting Design Tech Tchr
Farr, Larry Edwin
Chemistry Teacher
Haire, Arthur Allen
Teacher
Halter, LeRoy William, II
8th-12th US History Teacher
Isaacs, David Lee
Math Teacher
Leavell, Sharon Handley
Pre-Primary Teacher
Miller, Kenneth L.
8th Grade Social Studies Tchr
Platt, Lisa Chamberlain
8th Grd Physical Science Tchr
Rose, Greg
English Teacher
Schickel, George Thomas
Fifth Grade Teacher
Smith, Ruth Leonard
6th Grade Teacher
Stanley, Janice M.
Latin & World History Teacher
Stemle, Allison Ann
English Teacher
Trice, Veoletta Oby
Fifth Grade Teacher

JONESBORO
Biggs, Thomas R.
5th Grade Teacher

KENDALLVILLE
Grawcock, Jack Brent
Mathematics Teacher

KENTLAND
Molter, Karen Sue
English Teacher

KINGMAN
Bush, Patricia Louise
Retired English Teacher
Woodrow, Miriam Rusk
Retired Teacher

KNIGHTSTOWN
Miller, Gregory Samuel
Physical Education Teacher
Smith, Patricia Van Dyke
Admin Asst Curr & Instruction

KNOX
Allen, Gerald
Pastor & Principal
Poindexter, John Michael
Eng Tchr
Wilson, Carol Lee (Pawlik)
Math Teacher

KOKOMO
Atkins, Gary Lee
8th Grade Language Arts Tchr
Bailey, Janice L.
Business Division Chair
Comer, Russena
Assistant Principal

Goodrich, Jo (Johns)
Fifth Grade Teacher
Hall, Larry Ray
Automotive Tchr & Prgm Chrmn
Hockney, Daniel William
General Education Dept Chair
Kay, Sue Buell
English Teacher
LaGrave, Stephen E.
Business Instructor
Lindgren, Randy A.
6th Grade Teacher
Monnot, Gregory A.
6th & 7th Grade Teacher
Parsons, Rick Alan
Biology & Envrnmtl Ed Tchr
Rebuck, William David
Chemistry Teacher
Sandifur, Lorene H.
Math Curriculum Supvr & Tchr

KOUTS
Benham, Sue Ann (Rankin)
Bus Ed Tchr & Dept Chprsn

LA PORTE
Adkins, Nancy Douglas
Third Grade Teacher
Applegarth, Debra Sue
Fifth Grade Teacher
Biggerstaff, Patricia Maloney
Physics Teacher
Birkholz, Martha Coram
Sixth Grade Mathematics Tchr
Bransford, Margaret Rambo
6th Grade Reading Teacher
Briggs, Martin Scott
Fourth Grade Teacher
Burger, Ronald Gregory
Science Teacher
Carter, James Michael
Math & Chemistry Teacher
Fairman, Sandra Burke
8th Grd Language Arts Teacher
Fruth, Gregory Alan
High School English Teacher
Grimes, Marilyn Jane
4th Grd Tchr & Cmptr Coord
Lindeman, Paul David
Genetics & Biology Teacher
Long, Karen Hart
Art Teacher
Marquis, Peter A.
Sixth Grade Lang Arts Teacher
Otwinowski, Melinda Ludwig
5th Grade Teacher
Peterson, Dale Richard
Science Department Head
Schroeder, Linda Kay
Third Grade Teacher
Shott, Katherine Margaret
4th Grade Teacher
Stisher, Mickey D.
Director of Music
Upp, Larry Scott
Social Studies Teacher
Wippich, David DeLloyd
PE Teacher & Athletic Advisor
Zeisig, Rodney Alan
Seventh Grd Geography Teacher

LADOGA
Williams, Steven Owen
Sixth Grd Tchr & Asst Prin

LAFAYETTE
Adams, Jason Thomas
Religion Teacher
Beck, Debra Franks
Science Teacher
Butz, Leo Robert
Rel & Etymology Latin Teacher
Camilotto, Louis Dennis
Geography Teacher
Carmin, Kathy Sue (Henderson)
Health & Physical Ed Teacher
Conner, Denny
Science Teacher
Dolphin, Mary Jane Gregan
Choral Music Teacher
Eckert, Linda Smith
Associate Instr of Business
Esgar, Sandra Christian
Third Grade Teacher
Frauhiger, Lori Barnes
Fifth Grade Teacher
Gascho, David L.
Mathematics Teacher
Griffith, Linda Mattingly
6th Grd Language Arts Teacher
Gripe, Gail (Clippinger)
English Teacher
Jackson, Gracie Lou
German Teacher
Kinsey, Daniel Alan
English Teacher
Milligan, Sharon Vrabec
Fifth Grade Teacher
Montgomery, Glade T., II
Mathematics Teacher
Parham, Lugenia Rae White
Secondary Soc Studies Teacher
Poelstra, Stanley William
Physics & Aerospace Teacher
Sherry, Peter A.
US History Teacher
Simpson, Suzanne Mae (Lindsey)
Kindergarten Teacher
Smith, James George
Instructor
Snodgrass, Lisa Lambert
English Teacher
Toth, Debra Tribbett
Science Dept Chairperson

Wheeldon, Sandra Hughes
Consumer & Family Science Tchr

LAGRANGE
Beuret, Kevin Paul
7th & 8th Grade English Tchr
Booth, William Printiss
Health & Physical Ed Teacher
Brown, Gloria Fae
Third Grade Teacher
Bykowski, Sara Buss
5th Grd Math, Social Stud Tchr
Hammer, Rick Alan
Math & Pre-Algebra Teacher
Hayes, Atta Bradford
6th Grd Math & Soc Stud Tchr
Jaeger, Lori Piper
Sixth Grade Teacher
Keim, Marthe Wright
First Grade Teacher
Newman, Stephen D.
8th Grade Science Teacher
Rigg, Patricia Eileen
Scndry Eng Tchr & Dept Chprsn
Schmidt, David Joseph
Spcl Ed Dept Chair & Geog Tchr
Shroyer, Jae Ann
HS Mathematics Teacher
Stiller, Janet Jackson
Math & German Teacher

LAKE STATION
Craigin, Sarah Jane Geisen
6th Grade Teacher
Fleming, Olga Hodko
Fifth Grade Teacher
Plotner, Charlene Kay
Mathematics Teacher
Plotner, Jon D.
Business Teacher
Williams, Fred Niell
6th Grade Teacher

LAKE VILLAGE
Ekstrom, Marilyn Louise
Kindergarten Teacher

LAKEVILLE
Dennie, Lee David
US History Teacher
Grummell, Larry A.
Mathematics Teacher
Laub, Bonnita M.
English Teacher
Olson, Margaret M. (Bullis)
Middle School Mathematics Tchr

LAMAR
Dilger, Elmer
6th Grade Teacher

LANESVILLE
Arnott, Phyllis M.
Fourth Grade Teacher
Fewell, Phillip Steven
Chemistry Teacher
Reisenbichler, Robert Dean
Prin & 7th-8th Grade Teacher
Richards, Lance Allen
English Teacher
Thieneman, Robin Monroe
Title 1 Prgm Admin

LAPEL
Birge, Jean Jackley
Business Education Teacher
McDermit, Sharon Schuyler
Physical Ed & Health Teacher
Scott, Gregory R.
Band Teacher

LAUREL
Barricklow, Jacqueline Sue
Teacher of the Gifted
Wolfe, Monte E.
Science Teacher

LAWRENCEBURG
Arnold, Peter K., Sr.
English, Speech & Hum Tchr
Blackwell, Dorothy Jean
Mathematics Teacher
Bowell, Gerald Carr
Biology Teacher & Chairman
Cleary, Bonnie Jo
English & Journalism Teacher
Cook, Sally Irene
Third Grade Teacher
Dadosky, Paul David
Computer Systems Instructor
Kline, Lorinda Dawn
Mathematics & Physics Teacher
Mc Kee, Cynthia Margaret
6th Grade Math Teacher
Ziegler, Janice McCullough
Library Media Specialist

LEBANON
Dettmer, Beth Bush
Fourth Grade Teacher
Fleetwood, Faith E.
Language Arts Teacher
Goodwin, John Charles
Soc Studies Tchr & Dept Head
Gould, Robert Dean
English Teacher
Heck, Debra York
Math Teacher
Immel, James Franklin
Industrial Technology Teacher
Ison, LaRonda Lyn
Mathematics Teacher
Jacobs, Beth Mc Cammack
Business Teacher
Linton, Elizabeth Cruce
Science Teacher
Lohsl, Matthew John
Math & Comp Sci Teacher
Pedersen, Barbara J.
CLASS Director

LEESBURG
Kinsey, Judy Anne
Fourth Grade Teacher
Starner, Jane L. (Harley)
Former English Teacher
LEO
Boleyn, Bruce G.
Fifth Grade Teacher
Sell, Daniel Duane
4th Grade Teacher
Zech, Carol Hatton
4th Grade Teacher
LEOPOLD
Dickerson, William Ray
Accounting & Economics Teacher
Fischer, Carmen E.
Third Grade Teacher
Goffinet, Carroll R.
Secondary Math Teacher
Kranning, Antoinette Roebuck
5th Grd Tchr & Tchr of GATE
Linne, Robert Warren
Secondary Mathematics Teacher
Spence, Barbara Ellen
English Teacher
Spence, Rodney Glen
Social Studies Teacher
Wagner, Terry Paul
Industrial Technology Teacher
LIBERTY
Starr, William J.
English Teacher
Thompson, Sue Ann
Secondary School Educator
Van Frank, Constance Paglione
Junior High Language Arts Tchr
LIGONIER
Blank, Michelle Denise
English Teacher
Lamble, Carolyn Morris
Middle School Art Teacher
Shepherd, Brian Steve
4th Grade Teacher
Wellman, Jane A.
First Grade Teacher
LINCOLN CITY
Compton, Robert Lee, Jr.
Jr HS Science Tchr & Coach
Heneisen, Shirley Albin
Spanish Teacher
Hess, Larry E.
Math Teacher
Lifke, James Michael
Health & Drafting Teacher
Painter, Richard Allen
World History Teacher
Wade, Callie Doraine
English Teacher
LINTON
Boyd, Douglas Q.
Jr High Math Teacher
Long, Linda McCullough
Business Teacher
Sloan-Miller, Agnes M.
Retired English & Lit Teacher
Wellington, Rick Dale
Elem PE Teacher & HS Coach
LIZTON
Emmert, Marjorie Ellen (Hines)
English Teacher
Haste, Mark V.
Physical Education Teacher
Hufford, Marguerite Dine
English Teacher
Williams, Steven W.
High School Chemistry Teacher
LOGANSPORT
Carvey, Gloria Bartleman
Manager of Student Services
Cole, David A.
Band Director
Davis, Jeffrey Scott
English Teacher
Gundrum, Boyd Arthur
Mathematics Teacher
Reed, Gregg Alan
Music Teacher & Speech Coach
Sellers, Marla Sue
Second Grade Teacher
Sullian, Jayne Rosalyn Decker
1st Grade Teacher
LOOGOOTEE
Ackerman, Ann H.
HS Social Studies Teacher
Johnson, Gregory O.
Speech & English Teacher
Poehlein, Steve
World History Teacher
Wininger, Regina (Steiner)
6th Grade Teacher
LOWELL
Buchko, Marian L.
Elementary Principal
LYNN
Mahuron, Judith Ann (Back)
Spanish & AP English Teacher
Moore, Peggy (Hollingsworth)
First Grade Teacher
Stevens, David Christopher
Fifth Grade Teacher
LYNNVILLE
Christmas, Barbara Woolsey
Business Education Teacher
Crooks, Elaine F. (Hayden)
English Teacher
Harvey, Elmer Morris
Art Dept Chairperson & Teacher
Oxley, Kevin Ray
English Tchr & Bsktbl Coach
Oxley, Leslie
Art Teacher
MADISON
Cummins, Brenda A. (McCormick)
7th-12th Grd Math Pgm Leader
Erickson, John Leonard
Science Professor
Ison, Gregory Loren
Sixth Grade Teacher
Sebree, Betty Mitts
Guidance Director
Steinert, Bethel Jean
Geography & History Teacher
Stephens, Emily A.
Cmptr Information Sys Chair
Strohl, Lloyd David, II
Science Dept Chair & Teacher
Tereshko, Lynne
Girls Swimming & Diving Coach
MARENGO
Beals, William Edward
Industrial Arts & PE Teacher
Brown, Richard Allen
Sixth Grade Teacher
Colvin, Donna Jean (Fridman)
Third Grade Teacher
Oxley, Dennie Ray, Sr.
Hlth, PE & Drivers Ed Tchr
MARION
Adams, Janice Battle
Assistant Professor
Bartley, David Daniel
Assoc Prof of His & Pol Sci
Bence, Clarence L.
Prof of Historical Theology
Carr, Judith Hoskins
Cello Instructor
Clark, Lisa Ann
Mathematics & Ind Studies Tchr
Crouch, Michael Duane
Psychology Instructor
Curfman, Robert A.
Asst Prof of Art & Photography
Elder, Marjorie J.
Professor of English
Elliott, Raymon P.
Retired Chemistry Professor
Ellis, Malcolm Eugene
Professor of Philosophy & Rel
Fisher, Susan Dianne
Associate Professor of Ed
Fratus, Teresa Nelson
Spanish Teacher
Fratzke, Betty Jane
Psych Prof
Glenn, Ann Etsler
6th-7th Grd Lang Arts Teacher
Goff, Albert M.
Professor of Biology
Lakes, Terry Wayne
English Teacher & Coach
Lennox, Stephen John
Asst Professor of Religion
Lessly, Chris Ann
Assistant Professor of Music
Lobdell, Cathy S.
Middle School Math Teacher
Maher, John G.
Professor of Music
Mazellan, Ronald R.
Assistant Professor of Art
Millage, Philip John
Professor of Business
Miller, Phillip Ed
Chemistry Teacher
Mitchell, Larry Bradley
Assistant Professor
Peters, Leeann Burns
First Grade Teacher
Ray, Thomas Edward
Principal
Reed, Janice S.
Second Grade Teacher
Ross, Margaret K.
English Teacher & Chair
Schwartz, Carolyn Breedlove
Fourth Grade Teacher
Shaffner, Winnie Clement
Librarian
Sylte, June (Hurlbut)
Math Teacher
Watson, Sandra Lee
Home School Teacher
Webb, Burton J.
Assistant Professor of Biology
Williams, Wilbur Glenn
Associate Professor
Yocum, Kenneth Alan
Jr HS Social Studies Teacher
MARSHALL
Crowder, Cathryn Ellen Pyle
Voc Family & Consumer Sci Tchr
Hinshaw, Gwendolyn Sue (McGee)
Second Grade Teacher
Lester, Patricia S.
Social Studies Teacher
McMullen, Jane Dawes
Elementary PE Teacher
Russell, Janie S.
English & Speech Teacher
Stutler, Karen Ruth
Technology Director
MARTINSVILLE
Bowlen, Eric Vincent
Social Studies Teacher
Burden, Debbie S.
German Teacher
Burkhart, Kathryn L.
English Tchr & Lang Arts Chair
Cline, Frederick Arlen
Jr & Sr HS English Teacher
Elliott, Patsy Towe
Kindergarten Teacher
Fendley, Janet R.
Fifth Grade Teacher
Hadley, Clark G.
7th-8th Grade Science Teacher
Harmon, Robert Hugh
HS Counselor
Hartzler, Rhonda Burpo
Second Grade Teacher
Heacock, Richard L.
Assistant Principal
Keller, Jill Nutter
English Teacher
McClain, Andrew Allen
Earth Science Teacher
Miller, James V.
8th Grd US History Teacher
Parker, Susan Whitaker
High School English Teacher
Staggs, Robert K.
Business & Drivers Ed Teacher
Weddle, Rebecca Tidd
Principal
MEDORA
Beavers, Mary Hill
Teacher
MENTONE
Barr, Beth D.
HS Speech, Eng & Drama Tchr
Buss, Lois Ann
French Teacher
Eiser, Kimra Yvonne
1st Grade Teacher
Screeton, William Terence
Mathematics Teacher
MERRILLVILLE
Angelidis, William G.
Biology Teacher
Antal, Donna
Geography Teacher
Battistini, Maryanne Burke
Guidance Counselor
Bergeson, Robert D.
Business Teacher
Clay, Mary Sue
Director of Bands
Covaciu, Lorraine M. (St Aubin)
English Teacher
Crist, Sharon Meyer
Elementary Honors Teacher
Dust, Lori Lynn
High School Physical Ed Tchr
Galanis, MaryAnn
HS Social Studies Teacher
Graham, Barbara A.
Third Grade Teacher
Hamilton, Raymond Dale
Ger Tchr & Frgn Lang Dept Chm
Hutchison, Carl Max
High School Mathematics Tchr
Kobza, John R.
Elementary Physical Ed Teacher
Melnik, George Joseph
Sixth Grade Teacher
Mohr, Patricia Dudak
Science Department Chairperson
Nicolini, Gail Marich
Mathematics Teacher
Owens, Mark Edward
History Teacher
Peller, Thomas Leo
Math Teacher & Coach
Pete, Judith
German Teacher
Shoshoo, Mary
High School Math Teacher
Stanford, Jean E. (Gill)
Journalism & English Teacher
Styrna, Marilyn Wielgus
First Grade Teacher
Sulich, Michelle Rae (Kurfman)
Teacher of Disabilities
Terpstra, Richard L.
English Teacher
Timmerman, Barbara L. Smeltzer
Orchestra Director
Vermillion, James O.
Physics Teacher
Woods, Bruce L.
English Teacher
Yelton, Jeffrey S.
Biology Teacher
MICHIGAN CITY
Boysel, Sharon Held
English Teacher
Cannon, Patrick Joseph
Social Studies Chairman
Golday, Christina Hovermale
First Grade Teacher
Jones, Jon P.
Biology Teacher
Jones, Judy A.
First Grade Teacher
Kissinger, Laure Ann
Language Arts Teacher
Laux, Paul Allen
Speech Teacher
Manuel, Carolyn Gwen
First Grade Teacher
Novak, Donna Miller
4th Grade Teacher
Tilden, Byron D.
Mathematics Instructor
Villoch, Iris L.
Consumer & Family Science Tchr
MICHIGANTOWN
Siegfried, Barbara Kitchen
English & Spanish Teacher
MIDDLEBURY
Augustine, Ellen Louise (Fisher)
Language Arts Instructor
Lantz, Ted Randall
Third Grade Teacher
Priem, Stephanie J. L.
Language Arts Teacher
Thomas, Lynn Marie
English & Language Arts Tchr
MIDDLETOWN
Bramlett, Robert Edward
Social Studies Teacher
Brown, David Edward
German & English Teacher
Drake, William Theodore
Fifth Grade Teacher
Harter, Billie Ann
3rd Grade Teacher
Hittson, Kenneth Joe
Science Teacher
Hornaday, Theresa (Wilson)
Fourth Grade Teacher
Hunter, Dallas Gene
Retired Teacher
Penn, Rick
English & Government Teacher
Woodard, Lloyd Ervin
Art Instructor
MILAN
Brookbank, Bob
High School Science Tchr
Reale, Thomas George
9th-12th Grd German Teacher
MILFORD
Stookey, David Allen
Fifth Grade Teacher
MILLERSBURG
Ediger, Kaylene Yoder
Fourth Grade Teacher
Leer, Debra Jo
Elementary Music Teacher
MISHAWAKA
Anderson, W. Marquis
Teacher
Andreae, Thomas E.
Visual Arts Instr & Dept Chair
Burns, Mark Duaine
Counselor
Burton, Daniel Joe
Assistant Band Director
Chlebek, Michele Marie
Art Teacher
Clason, Steven Robert
Director of Technology
Coddington, John Francis
Certified Athletic Trainer
DaKoske, Amy Mendenhall
English Teacher
Diltz, Judith Ann
English Teacher
Doi, Wesley Allen
8th Grade English Teacher
Flora, Linda Sue
9th-12th Grd Math Tchr of GATE
Frazier, Michael William
German Teacher
Garrett, James L.
HS Finance Teacher & COE Coord
Gordon, Sheri Flint
Dance Teacher
Harper, Sheryll Lynch
Principal
Hess, Brendan Fitzgerald
8th Grade Social Studies Tchr
Jumper, Marjorie Lee
Mathematics Teacher
Kayser, Martha Jade
English Teacher
Lancaster, Scott C.
History Teacher
Lauck, Julie Kay
English Teacher
LeRoy, Bob S.
Sixth Grade Teacher
Manningham, Bonnie Ellen
High School English Teacher
McKenna, Marie Rose Jacqueline
French & Spanish Teacher
Murphy, Jan M.
Fifth Grade Teacher
Owens, Rhonda Lynn
Integrated Studies Eng Teacher
Pawlik, Lisa Hale
Guidance Counselor
Pierce, Erin Byrne
Theology Teacher
Robertson, Chris Randall
Marketing Education Teacher
Ruhe, Frances
Retired Fifth Grade Teacher
Schulz, Caroline Garcia
Physical Ed & Health Teacher
Shearer, Rick
Biology Teacher
Sissell, Carla Lewis
Mathematics Teacher
Smith, Alvin R.
Soc Stud Tchr, Wrestling Coach
Snavely, Rebecca Rodriguez
6th-8th Grade Band Teacher
Stout, Margaret Ann (Compton)
Retired Primary Teacher
Stratford, Lynn Ann
High School Counselor
Stump, Sharon K.
Sixth Grade Teacher
Szumski, Thomas G.
Unit Leader & Teacher
Toth, Joe B.
Social Studies Teacher
Wegner, Charles Lowell
Mathematics Teacher
MITCHELL
Abner, Melissa Le Anne
Teacher of Mildly Disabled
Bennett, Larry D.
Science Teacher
Caudell, Paula J.
Health & Physical Ed Teacher
Deckard, Brett C.
Jr HS Health & PE Teacher
Dorsett, Stephen Wayne
8th Grade Social Studies Tchr
Dyke, Daniel William
Science Teacher
Fields, Marc L.
Government & Economics Teacher
Fountain, Jerry L.
Fourth Grade Teacher
Giggy, Kevin M.
French & English Teacher
Hewetson, Julie Johnson
Guidance Counselor
Purlee, Bradley J.
Chemistry Teacher
Purlee, Lee A. Richards
Mathematics Teacher
Reynolds, Danny Eugene
Industrial Technology Teacher
Tieken, Melinda Lund
Language Arts & Amer Stud Tchr
Tolliver, Gerald W.
Teacher
Tolliver, Kathy Mae
7th Grd Language Arts Teacher
Williams, Evelyn J.
4th Grade Teacher
MODOC
Morris, Linda Roman
Eng, Math Tchr & GATE Coord
Palumbo, Patrick Louis
Instrumental Music Director
Shore, Randy
Bio, Chemistry & Physics Tchr
Wehneman, Joyce Duty
Sixth Grade Teacher
Wiley, Harold
English Teacher
MONON
Peterson, Vicki S.
Business Teacher
MONROE
Egley, Nancy Miller
Business Ed Tchr & Voc Dir
Flesch, Karen Schlosser
Elementary Art Teacher
Goulet, Jayne Lynn
Fifth Grade Teacher
Miller, Randall Wayne
HS Math Teacher & Coach
Mosser, Rodney K.
Technology Teacher
MONROEVILLE
Lehrman, Dean Elwin
High School Mathematics Tchr
Mergenthal, James E.
Choral Music Director
Price, C. Eugene
Social Studies Teacher
MONROVIA
Garrard, Sandra L.
Coach, PE & Health Teacher
MONTEZUMA
Bonini, Barbara
Special Education Teacher
Britton, Jami Malone
6th Grade Teacher
Lunsford, Michael Joseph
English & History Teacher
Woodard, Sue
7th & 8th Grade English Tchr
MONTGOMERY
Holt, Mark Leon
Mathematics Teacher
Knepp, Maria Duncheon
Language Arts Teacher
Mangin, Gerald Leo
Fifth Grade Teacher
Myers, Judy Frederick
Fourth Grade Teacher
Price, Arthur V.
Biology & Chemistry Teacher
Wirtz, Gloria Townsley
Health & Physical Ed Teacher
MONTICELLO
Haselby, Gary Eugene
Fifth Grade Teacher
Willbanks, Susan Marie (Wilson)
Guidance Counselor
MONTPELIER
Cline, Brian Jeffery
Math Teacher
Stewart, Toni Beth
First Grade Teacher
Strickland, Sandra Jo
Fourth Grade Teacher
MOORES HILL
Ranck, Carol A.
Music Teacher
MOORESVILLE
Abbott, Donna K.
Elementary Principal
Beebe, Joel Arlan
English Teacher
Brewer, Cynthia Foster
Third Grade Teacher

ESVILLE (cont)
, Amy Elizabeth
e & High Schl Band Dir
heryl Ann (Giltner)
stra Program Director
yce Shadday
ment & Psychology Tchr
, Norbert Lee
Teacher & Admin Asst
ent, Duana Magoun
n Grade Choir Director
arole Brunson
Grade Teacher
n, Judy Wagner
d Grade Teacher
lizabeth Z.
h Teacher
CCO
Nancy Johnson
Language Arts Teacher
ISTOWN
an, John Alfred
matics Teacher
lark Alan
ade Teacher
Deborah Ann
sh Teacher
T SUMMIT
Paul Howard
sh Teacher
ury, Eric John
or of Bands
Michael Allen
tic Director & Asst Prin
as, Robin Jean (Dulc)
Grade Teacher
T VERNON
Barbara Ann
& Director of Vocal Music
David Marc
High Math Teacher
ane Ann
Grade Teacher
Jody Weintraut
tor of Testing
r, Paul E.
School Science Teacher
Terry Douglas
sh & Journalism Teacher
Brian Thomas
d Teacher & Dept Head
IE
Claire Anne (Diercks)
istry Instructor
g, Keith D.
Teacher
n, Dale Edward
School Guidance Counselor
Beverly Kay
& Etymology Teacher
Donna L.
ematics Instructor
r, Jack Alan
sh Teacher
ebecca
ch & English Teacher
an, Patricia I.
Grade Teacher
n, Kathy
Prof of Educational Psych
ey, Mary Hanna
uctor of Philosophy
Karen Threewits
nistry Teacher
, Sam John
Grade Teacher
Ronald Lee
ogy Teacher
n, Dixie Faye
uctor
bower, John Charles
uctor of English
, Fred
an Svcs Pgm Chair & Instr
y, Augustine
ndary English Teacher
Rogene Barbara
d Grade Teacher
, Kathleen Farr
8th Grd Language Arts Tchr
Kimberly Ann
ructor of Mathematics
Melinda Jill
ir of Math & Phys Science
er, Donna Holladay
rth Grade Teacher
n, Todd Edward
ld History & Govt Teacher
, Howard R.
ial Studies, Gifted Ed Tchr
y, Joy Edith
d Grade Teacher
es-Snyder, Laura
lish Instructor
aud, Sue Joyner
nch Instructor
Stephen Wade
lish Instructor
ell, Alice Florence
m Art Teacher
s, Bill
emistry Teacher
s, Richard Roy
glish Education Instructor
es, James Calnan
manities Instructor
drix, Jon Richard
f of Biology & Science Ed
, Michael
nguage Arts Teacher

Huggins, George Wilbur
Art Teacher
Johnson, Louis E.
8th Grade Science Teacher
Kaufman, Richard Charles
Social Studies Dept Chair
Leichty, Neysa Kaye (Christy)
French Teacher
Masters, Beverly Sue (Bowen)
English Teacher
Mc Kee, Mark Howard
Bible, History & PE Teacher
Meade, Ronald Raymond
9th-12th Grd Latin Teacher
Meyer, Kimerlee Lin (Riggin)
Tchr of Learning Disabilities
Miller, Glenda D.Henry
Fourth Grade Teacher
Miller, Kandice Powell
4th Grade Teacher
Missair, Liliana
Instructor
Moore, Patricia Ann (Barkoull)
Art Instructor
Murray, Sandra (Alexander)
4th & 5th Grade Teacher
Niles, Edward L.
4th Grade Teacher
Orchard, Paul Joseph
US, World His, Hlth & PE Tchr
Osborne, Charles
Fifth Grade Teacher
Parkison, Joyce Hale
English Teacher
Phillips, John David
Science Teacher & Coach
Police, David G.
Mathematics Instructor
Poulakidas, Andreas K.
Assoc Prof of Eng & Lit
Ranieri, Lynn Austin
Language Arts & Science Tchr
Rankin, L. Kay
Business Education Teacher
Reed, Cara Lynn (Caldieraro)
Middle School Math Teacher
Richard, Janice Braun
Second Grade Teacher
Robbins, Bruce Anthony
Social Studies Instructor
Rogers, Heather Hobar
Russian Instructor
Scagnoli, Joseph Richard
Prof of Music & Dir of Bands
Schmaltz, Kathleen Conn
High School Choral Director
Smith, Brien Nelson
Associate Professor
Smothers, Cheryl Justin
HERD Coordinator
Swartz, Benjamin Kinsell, Jr.
Professor
Talbert, Linda Absher
US History Teacher
Thomas, Jody Lynn
Fourth Grade Teacher
Wallen, Charles Kennith
5th Grade Teacher
Warrner, Robert Andrew
Social Studies Teacher
Wells, Grant Joseph
Prof of Finance & Real Estate
White, Susan Marie
Mathematics Teacher
Whitehead, Karen Allen
Math & Comp Sci Division Chair
Zhang, Min
Chinese Teacher
Zimpfer, Arlene Newton
English Teacher
MUNSTER
Blocher, Carolyn Reppa
Third Grade Teacher
Brandt, David R.
Eighth Grd Tchr & Music Dir
Douglas, Ginger Joan
Director of Bands
Dykstra, Jodi Ellen
Mathematics & PE Teacher
Fratzke, Laura Vitikapa
6th Grade Teacher
La Reau, Paul J.
Teacher
Mihalo, Olga Arends
Retired 5th Grade Teacher
Moisoff, Teresa C.
First Grade Teacher
Pavlovich, Donna Stackhouse
6th-8th Grade Math Teacher
Weiss, Jody L.
High School English Teacher
Whiteley, Anne Brisco
Spanish Teacher
Witt, Nina L.
MS Language Arts Teacher
NAPPANEE
Bauer, Julie Kay (Rogers)
English & Speech Teacher
Cannaday, Bruce Dale
Industrial Technology Teacher
Germann, Peggy Dean
Third Grade Teacher
Julian, Deb J.
English Teacher
Myers, Fredrick Allen
Physical Education Instructor
Newcomer, Carla Dee (Steffey)
Teacher of Gifted & Talented

NASHVILLE
Bartels, Patricia Rhoden
Art Teacher
NEW ALBANY
Bitzegaio, Barbara Stephens
4th Grade Teacher
Buerger, John R.
Economics & US Presidency Tchr
Buescher, Harvey M.
Kindergarten Teacher
Christie, Samuel Henry, III
Chemistry Teacher
Combs, Bonnie Pamplin
Fourth & Fifth Grade Teacher
Dewey, Donald Lee
Teacher & Counselor
Duffy, Louis A., Jr.
Sixth Grade Classroom Teacher
Gast, Doris Austin
Junior High Math Teacher
Hutchens, Ronald Paul
American Civics Teacher
Kaiser, Michael Bruce
Sixth Grade Teacher
Kupferer, N. Jean
Mathematics Teacher
Lambert, Aaron Kirk
Band Director
Largent, Dora H.
Business Education Teacher
Linnert, Glenn Robert, Jr.
Seventh Grade Science Teacher
Poteet, Ruth (Jolly)
Second Grade Teacher
Railey, Mark S.
Professor of Philosophy & Bio
Rayl, Randall Scott
Art Teacher
Sprinkle, Judith B.
Math Teacher
Willman, John Robert
Assistant Principal
NEW CARLISLE
Beebe, Harry James
Health & PE Teacher
Moffitt, Brenda Cox
5th Grade Teacher
NEW CASTLE
Bell, Robert Curtis
Physical Education Teacher
Dye, Mary Jane Hostetler
Teacher of Gifted & Talented
Fisher, Sharon Marie
Fourth Grade Teacher
Hampton, Dorothy Ann
Fourth Grade Teacher
Huffman, Harold Duane, Jr.
Sociology & Anthropology Tchr
Shortridge, Pamela Kay Kutter
Child Care Teacher
Taylor, Maribeth Burton
Kindergarten Teacher
Thompson, John Douglas
Chemistry & Physics Teacher
Vanderleest, Stephanie Stephenson
French Teacher
NEW HARMONY
Wilson, Connie Rose
Second Grade Teacher
NEW HAVEN
Benak, Sue Wickemeyer
Title One Teacher
Lake, Matthew R.
HS Science Teacher & Coach
Nietert, Henry N.
Mathematics Teacher
Pitcher, Paula D.
Math, PE & Drivers Ed Teacher
NEW MARKET
Claypool Coats, Donna Sue
Fourth Grade Teacher
Shirk, Janice Clare
Third Grade Teacher
NEW PALESTINE
Alter, John Allen
Science, PE & Health Teacher
Clements, Ginnette (Dunwell)
Former MS Math Teacher
Hercamp, Miles Allen
High School Math Teacher
Jones, Deborah Horvath
English & Literature Teacher
Kehrt, Brian Lee
HS Mathematics Teacher
Seifert, Darlene Lynn (Shields)
Biology Teacher
NEWBURGH
Bagby, John R.
Indstrl Tech & Drafting Tchr
Barnett, Sari Anne (Jones)
7th-8th Grade Math Teacher
Childress, Carol O'Cull
Sixth Grade Teacher
Cook, Carole Patricia
Third Grade Teacher
Gibson, Brian Thomas
English Teacher
Hagmann, Robert John
Industrial Technology Teacher
Harris, H. David
Social Studies Teacher
Kemp, Judith Anne (Reed)
Mathematics Teacher
Northern, Glenn Eric
Instrumental Music Teacher
Odom, Sharon A.
Teacher
Reese, Jerry Wayne
Director of Bands

Renschler, Connie Brammer
Kindergarten Teacher
Rowe, Kathy DeKemper
History Teacher
Shelby, Jesse Ray
Math Teacher
Trafton, Elaine Kennedy
English Teacher
Wambach, Richard Keith
Science Teacher
NOBLESVILLE
Atkins, V.A. A., III
Health & Substance Abuse Tchr
Beardshear, Carolyn Harnisch
German Teacher
Dudgeon, Joyce Lou (Couden)
English Dept Chair & Tchr
Franciosi, Jeffrey L.
Hlth & Substance Abuse Edctr
Fulton, Karen Holt
Second Grade Teacher
Hitchcock, Gerald Bruce
Social Studies Tchr & Chprsn
Huffine, Deborah Peters
6th Grade Teacher
Knotts, Thomas C., II
US His Teacher & Sftbl Coach
Mitchell, Scottie M.
Middle School Supervisor
Purvis, David Lee
English Teacher
Shoemaker, Alice Amick
English Teacher
Snyder, Sherri G.
English Teacher
Spalding, Jeannie Bolitho
First Grade Teacher
Towle, Richard Winslow
Seventh Grade Science Teacher
Welch, David L.
Teacher of Gifted & Talented
Whitlock, Kimberly Linn
Mathematics Teacher
NORTH JUDSON
Archer, John Earl
Music & Art Teacher
Jones, Lewis Cliff
Math Teacher
Rausch, Barbara Vogel
Fifth Grade Teacher
Stewart, Kenneth Ray
Business Ed & Journalism Tchr
Watts, Tom
Science Teacher & Dept Chair
Worst, Todd Elisha
HS Math & Science Teacher
NORTH LIBERTY
Gordon, Marilyn Ann (Runyon)
Second Grade Teacher
NORTH MANCHESTER
Clevenger, Janet E.
Kindergarten Teacher
Huntington, Benjamin Everett
Physics, Phys Sci & Math Tchr
Manges, Deborah Lantz
Fifth Grade Teacher
McLaughlin, Michael James
5th Grade Teacher
Meeks, Carol Jean (Ludwig)
Second Grade Teacher
Miller, Edward G.
Chemistry Professor
Naragon, Steve
Philosophy Professor
Onyeji, Benson Chinedu
Political Science Professor
Sponseller, Kay (Browning)
English Department Chairperson
Strode, Scott K.
Prof & Chair of Commnctn Dept
Welborn, Barbara Ann
Second Grade Teacher
Wilkins, Teresa R.
Business & Computer Teacher
NORTH VERNON
Daeger, Tony
Health & Physical Ed Teacher
Hughes, Gayle Mills
Health & PE Teacher
Ison, Barb L. Asher
Art Teacher
Losey, Tricia M.
Math Teacher
Moore, Sherida Burgmeier
English Department Chairperson
Mull, Tammie Sue
6th Grade Teacher
Stone, Eric Alan
Principal
NORTH WEBSTER
Willaman, Mitchell Lee
Fifth Grade Teacher
NOTRE DAME
Bederman, Gail
Assistant Professor of History
Lucchesi, Linda Flosi
Visiting Asst Prof of Italian
Schoen, Suzanne Thorsen
Associate Professor of English
OAKLAND CITY
Asa, Robert Lynn
Professor of Religious Studies
Atkinson, Michael Joe
Associate Professor of Biology
Buyher, Phillip A.
Mathematics & History Teacher
Delhomme-Cutchin, Claudine
History, French, English Instr
Jump, James Edwin
Dir of Associate Degree Prgms

Low, Douglas A.
Assoc Professor of Rel Stud
Marley, Bernard M.
Dean, Schl of Education
Marley, Linda G. Mahan
Assistant Prof of Education
Phillips, Judy Black
Sixth Grade Teacher
Schafer, Patricia Day
Hlth & PE Ed Dept Chprsn
OLDENBURG
Deardorff, Constance Wanstruth
Social Studies Teacher
Ertel, Pat Fledderman
Science Teacher
Gillman, Mary Ellen
Music Teacher & Chair
OOLITIC
Spires, Rick Wayne
Jr High Health & PE Tchr
ORLEANS
Gilmore, Susan Kay
Sixth Grade Teacher
Hudelson, Karen Mc Cart
English Teacher
OSGOOD
Eaton, Judith S.
English Teacher
Ruble, Ernest Lee
Social Studies Teacher
Westerman, Eugene L.
Math & Physics Teacher
OSSIAN
Gilbert, Michael Lee
Vocational Business Teacher
Harkless, Judith Ann (Dietrich)
Third Grade Teacher
Jones, Howard E.
Science Instructor
Marshall, Peter P.
Spanish Teacher
Mc Collum, Clara I.
Secondary Math Teacher & Coach
Murphy, Anna Mary (Bennett)
Math Teacher
Snyder, Victoria
Physical Education Teacher
Vogt, Don D.
English Teacher
Willits, JoAnne Hommel
Lang Arts & Soc Stud Teacher
OTTERBEIN
Delks, Brian Kirk
Sixth Grade Teacher
OWENSVILLE
Benson, Reba Emerson
Language Arts Teacher
Braselton, Lois G. Newkirk
Second Grade Teacher
Gentry, John Arthur
Art Teacher
Johnson, Ruth Spray
First Grade Teacher
Krohn, Martha Prusz
Home Economics Teacher
OXFORD
Blad, Deborah Lynn
Family & Consumer Sci Tchr
Davis, Nancy A.
Mathematics Teacher
Doeden, Carolee A. (Rooze)
Math Teacher
Doyle, Patrick Allen
Health, PE Teacher & Coach
Hatke, Jayne Ann
Third Grade Teacher
Hinkel, David Lee
8th Grd Physical Science Tchr
Lange, Gail Gilbert
Coord of Gifted & Talented Ed
Madden, Sylvia (Gornicki)
English Teacher
Massie, Dennis Keith
Art Teacher
Purcell, Ronald Roy
Science Teacher
Rathert, Michael John
Biology Teacher
Rogers, Linda
Spanish Teacher
Santon, Bridget Ann (Sondgerath)
Visual Arts Teacher
Skinner, Jolie Linn
Spanish Teacher
Versyp, Sharon Kathleen
High School Teacher & Coach
Wolford, Ronald Wayne
US History Teacher
PAOLI
Laughlin, William C.
Director of Bands
Noble, Tamera Stalker
8th Grade English Teacher
Stuckwisch, Thomas Joe
Math Teacher
PARKER CITY
Davis, Helen Voiles
High School Librarian
Huffman, Molly A.
Spanish Teacher
Lee, Barbara Robison
Science & Math Teacher
McQueen, Kathy Marie (Carter)
Art Teacher
Morgan, Russell-Don Glenn
Principal & Teacher
Proctor, Preston George
Social Studies Teacher
Ruble, Joyce Louene
Third Grade Teacher of GATE

PARKER CITY (cont)
Williamson, Cheryl L.
French & English Teacher
PEKIN
Sullivan, C. Frank
English Teacher
PENDLETON
Adamiak, Sandra K.
English Teacher
Adams, Stephen L.
Amer His Tchr & Team Leader
Bartmas, Mark K.
4th Grade Teacher
Bellessis, Christine
High School English Teacher
Byers, Linda Norris
8th Grade Math Teacher
Dietrick, Christi Wagner
Third Grade Teacher
Farr, Marcie Harvey
Third Grade Teacher
Gennett, Mary Lou (Saul)
Speech & Language Pathologist
Hudson, Robert Edward
Sixth Grade Teacher
Hutton, William L.
Assistant Principal
Kuskye, Lamonte Allen
Choral Dir & Music Dept Head
Medler, Patrick Neil
Physics Teacher
Noggle, James Allen
Trigonometry & Algebra Teacher
Rhoades, John Raymond
Algebra Teacher
Sheward, Lois (White)
Speech & Language Pathologist
Smith, Mark A.
Social Studies Tchr & Team Ldr
Sporinsky, Susan Donaldson
English & Speech Teacher
Stock, Ann Bradnick
Fourth Grade Teacher
Stoner, Larry A.
Mathematics Teacher
Thompson, Jane Gustafson
History & French Teacher
Turner, Karen G.
English Tchr & Newspaper Adv
Wallace, Dennis E.
US History Teacher
Wilson, Brenda Jean (Boss)
Teacher of GATE & Coordinator
PERU
Alexander, Janet Rae Gustafson
Third Grade Teacher
Anderson, Bill
Middle Schl Technology Teacher
Berryman, Louanne Schlotterbeck
5th Grade Teacher
Bickel, Kimberley Alderfer
Business Teacher & FBLA Adv
Carlson, Lyle Eugene
Biology Teacher
Coblentz, Michael James
History & Government Teacher
Glassburn, Deana Alice
4th-5th Grade Teacher
Johnson, Walter Donald
Math Teacher & Dept Chprsn
Keller, Richard Lee
Industrial Arts Teacher
Kimpel, Kent M.
Social Studies Teacher
Nowling, Janice Marie
Consumer & Homemaking Ed Tchr
Powell, Bart L.
Assistant Volleyball Coach
Rudolph, Zelma Thomas
5th Grade Teacher
Schwartz, John Robert
5th Grade Teacher
Seiler, Carolyn Marie (Young)
Second Grade Teacher
Vollmer, Fred L.
Technology Instructor
PETERSBURG
Barrett, Elaine Susan
Physical Ed Tchr & Coach
Fears, Betty J.
Business Teacher
Hays, G. Vance
Choral Music & Drama Teacher
Hill, Vesper Lee
Math Teacher
Kincaid, David Michael
Mathematics & Physics Teacher
Krause, William Edward
9th-12th Grade Drafting Instr
Stewart, David Joe
Mathematics Teacher
Stuckey, Roger O.
High School English Teacher
Whitten, Mike Vern
Math Teacher
PITTSBORO
Davis, Gil
Fourth Grade Teacher
PLAINFIELD
Carpenter, Teresa Kay
HS Mathematics Teacher
Glidden, Winston Robert
English Teacher
Melevage, Raymond Paul
Art Teacher
Peters, Stacey E.
High School Mathematics Tchr
PLYMOUTH
Bowers, Jeffrey Scott
Jr HS & HS Math & Science Tchr
Condon, Thomas
Physical Education & Hlth Tchr
Geist, Sandra Scott
3rd Grade Teacher
Liechty, Anna L.
English Dept Chair
Wagoner, Cynthia Rowe
Instrumental Music Dir
PONETO
Hartman, Chris Pearson
Computer & Math Teacher
PORTAGE
Drake, Ruth Ann
English Teacher
Greer, Nellie
8th Grade English Teacher
Johnson, Kay Dianne (Remington)
First Grade Teacher
Kravas, Shirley Black
Kindergarten Teacher
Lemond, Linda Noble
High School English Teacher
Martz, James Allen
Social Studies Teacher
Marvin, Mark Charles
7th & 8th Grd Soc Stud Tchr
Milner, Terry Melvin
Hlth & Physical Education Tchr
Norman, Dennis J.
English & Speech Teacher
Sanidas, Tom G.
English Teacher
Shrader, Kathryn J.
Math Teacher
Vinzani, Dina Lee
2nd Grade Teacher
Waite, Karen Sue
Third Grade Teacher
PORTLAND
Humbert, David Lee
Band Director
Meinerding, Thomas Jerry
World & US History Teacher
Miller, Deborah Ann
Science Teacher
Selvey, Lea E.
Biology Teacher
Stephens, Dolphus L.
Dept Chair & Tchr of English
Stith, Ronald Lesslie
Social Studies Teacher
Vogler, Peter John
Band Director
POSEYVILLE
Anderson, James E.
Math & Physics Teacher
Phipps, Judy E.
Business Department Chairman
Reising, Linda Kay
8th Grade English Teacher
PRINCETON
Cloin, Robert H.
Audio-Visual Dir
Gilbert, Malinda Lu
Eight Grade English Teacher
Hauger, Steven E.
Assistant Principal
Kiesel, Charles Ray
5th Grade Teacher
Mason, Dale A.
Fifth Grade Teacher
Neidigh, Dianna Lynn
1st & 2nd Grade Teacher
Pressley, Lisa Gail
Junior High School Teacher
White, Debbie Giese
English & Speech Teacher
White, Mari Celesta
Literature Teacher
RAMSEY
Martin, Larry Allen
Health & PE Teacher
Shewmaker, Gary F.
Social Studies Teacher
REELSVILLE
Crosby, J. Todd
Principal
RENSSELAER
Henady, Jill M.
Math Dept Chair & Teacher
Marchand, James Claude
Middle School Counselor
Post, Bernice Koesters
6th Grade Math Teacher
Roeschlein, William Earl, Jr.
Art Teacher
Thiel, Robb G.
Prof of Music & Dir of Bands
Washburn, Judith Merchant
7th Grade Math Teacher
RICHLAND
Freeman, Connie Jo (Brauns)
Second Grade Teacher
Hodges, Thomas Eugene
4th Grade Teacher
RICHMOND
Berrier, Peggy A.
College Instructor
Bond, Idris A.
Program Chair of Medical Asst
Burkhardt, Eric R.
8th Grade Lang Arts & Lit Tchr
Cobine, David
English Teacher & Dept Chprsn
Craig, Judith E.
Latin & English Teacher
Crawford, Paul M.
Math & Science Teacher
Eyler, George Alan
Food Svc Instr & Pgm Chprsn
Graesser, William Mc Connell
Pgm Chair, Math & Sci Teacher
Graf, Joyce Nevins
Spanish Teacher
Hartsough, Michael R.
Science Teacher
Hollingsworth, Michael S.
Spanish Teacher
Lewis, Nancy Stilwell
Instructor
Moore, Sandra C.
Retired Resource Tchr of GATE
Pace, Mary Jo
Mathematics Teacher
Routson, Susan Hutchins
Executive Director
Sparks, Susan Eileen
Christian Education Director
Steininger, Barbara Ann
Practical Nrsng & Med Asst
Stewart, Aleasia White
Title I Director
Stoner, Robert G.
Applied Physics & Bio Teacher
Williamson, Ruth W.
Retired Eng Teacher
Wilson, Marc Lundy
Composition Instr, Lang Arts
RIDGEVILLE
Burkett, Cheryl Burk
Third Grade Teacher
RILEY
Cahill, Kay A.
Second Grade Teacher
Elliott, William Porter
Fifth Grade Teacher
RISING SUN
Gray, Grace Brown
Retired Teacher
Kittle, Eunice Cunningham
Music Teacher
ROACHDALE
Gottschalk, Patricia Hogan
Spanish Teacher
ROANOKE
Braun, Susan Barnett
Elementary Teacher
ROCHESTER
Berdine, Cedric Leroy
Retired Vocal Music Tchr
Moore, Joe F.
5th Grade Teacher
ROCKPORT
Thomas, Neal
Social Studies Teacher
ROCKVILLE
Horney, Carolyn Harris
Retired Fourth Grade Teacher
Lohrmann, Patricia Kay
English & Composition Teacher
Phillips, Michael Ray
Soc Stud Tchr & Dept Chm
Vandevoorde, Carl Joseph
Fifth Grade Teacher
ROME CITY
Baker, Brad David
Mathematics Teacher
Claussen, Richard L.
Science & Health Teacher
Keil, Edward A.
7th & 8th Grd Soc Stud Tchr
Kissinger, Lisa Sprunger
Fourth Grade Teacher
ROYAL CENTER
Munson, Sharon R.
Business Teacher & Dept Chprsn
Riise, Erik Spencer
United States History Teacher
Scheffer, Cheryl Ann
Mathematics Teacher
RUSHVILLE
Buckley, Sharon A. Miller
Fifth Grade Teacher
Cumberworth, Richard A.
Algebra & General Math Tchr
Personett, Diane Zinkan
Business Teacher
Porter, Don R.
Social Studies Teacher
RUSSIAVILLE
Eveland, Cynthia D. C.
5th Grade Teacher
Hoppes, Patricia Jones
Kindergarten Teacher
Suffield, Judith Kreutz
English Teacher
SAINT JOE
Fox, Lori (Raub)
5th-6th Grade Science Teacher
SAINT JOHN
Ballou, Cynthia Brasel
Spanish Teacher
Birmingham, Jack Lee, Jr.
Social Studies Teacher
Brannock, Dennis Dean
Voc Automotive Tech Teacher
Bugaski, Don F.
Mathematics Teacher & Coach
Clark, Thomas Edmund
US History Honor Teacher
Hewlett, Shirley Miller
HS Publications Advisor
Holden, Jacqueline Marie
Tchr of Learning Disablities
Laskey, Rita Marie
Spanish Teacher
Lewis, Michael Thomas
High School Music Teacher
McCaslin, Jason Kyle
English Teacher
Miller, Pamela Benda
High School English Teacher
Ossanna, Richard R.
English Teacher
Patellis, Scott J.
Fifth Grade Teacher
Phillips, Marjorie Jean (Feddeler)
First Grade Teacher
Stemp, Marcy Mary
Mathematics Instructor
Svetanoff, Wayne Walter
English Teacher & Coach
Tokoly, Penny Hanrath
English Dept Chair
Vassar, Timothy Myles
Special Education Teacher
Wright, Sandy Jones
High School Counselor
SAINT MEINRAD
Mueller, Noel
English Literature Teacher
Ring, Dennis Gill
Philosophy Professor
Werne, Stanley J.
Philosophy Professor
SALEM
Allen, Debra Hayes
Acctng & Comp Pgmng Tchr
Day, Richard Charles
Teacher & Coach
Doyle, Debra Jean
Business Education Teacher
SCHERERVILLE
Backe, Robert E.
Science Teacher
Conley, Sandra Louise
Third Grade Teacher
Fesenmyer, Kathy Kelly
Kindergarten & 1st Grade Tchr
Geras, Cheryl
Literature & Math Teacher
Jansen, Dorothy Ann (Cook)
Retired Soc Studies & Rel Tchr
Ondra, Carol Burch
Choral & Handbell Director
Saunders, Barbara Seremet
Jr HS Social Studies Teacher
Schweitzer, David Warren
Mathematics Department Chair
Starcevich, Stephen Anthony
Fifth Grade Teacher
Sumner, Gary Dean
Fifth Grade Teacher
Vinzant, Greta Elisabeth
Second Grade Teacher
Vogel, Thomas J.
Biology Teacher
SCOTTSBURG
Jerrell, Susan Deenese (Tower)
English & Journalism Teacher
Judd, Jerry Leland
6th Grade Math Teacher
Phillips, Jean
Health Teacher
Wright, George Stephen
High School Language Arts Tchr
SELLERSBURG
Eckert, Albert Thomas
Computer Applications Teacher
Heiligenberg, Evelyn Smith
Spanish Teacher
Johnson, Sandra L.
Medical Assistant Instructor
Newman, Susan Ann
Pgm Chair & Math Instructor
Paro, William Herbert
Varsity Bsktbl & Soccer Coach
Rawles, Deborah Dene
Medical Assistant Pgm Chair
Sprigler, Gail Bennett
Nursing Instructor
VonKanel, Robert Lee
Assoc Sci & Nursing Instr
Winslow, Marion Diack
English, Journalism & Art Tchr
SELMA
Beard, Judith Ann (Wine)
Eng Dept Chair & Teacher
Jones, Sarah L. (Sally)
Third Grade Teacher
Kirklin, Charles Bryan
Math & Physics Teacher
Nieman, John Jacob, Jr.
6th & 7th Grade English Tchr
Scott, Sandra L.
5th Grade Teacher
Truax, John C.
History Teacher
SEYMOUR
Baker-Schneider, Debra Ann
Latin Teacher
Goodman, Sharon Leach
Second Grade Teacher
Jenkinson, Rosemary L.
Asst Principal
Johnson, Tom Gregory
Fourth Grade Teacher
Jones, Marsha Ozbun
Psychology & Lang Arts Teacher
Jones, Thomas M.
US History Teacher
Leclerc, Kristine Kunz
4th Grade Teacher
Lucas, Angie Runge
Math Teacher
Roth, Kenneth F.
Fifth Grade Teacher
Schwartz, Cheyl Donovan
Special Education Teacher
Sexton, Robert Alan
Technology Teacher
SHARPSVILLE
Croxford, Carol Ann
English Teacher
Dearth, Gary A.
Sixth Grade Science & Eng Tchr
SHELBYVILLE
Chesser, Linda Read
7th Grade Geography Teacher
Cooper, Nanette Marie
Fifth Grade Teacher
Creed, Annette Weintraut
Fifth Grade Teacher
Crosby, Myra (Montgomery)
Music Teacher
Davis, Thomas William
Latin Teacher
Davis, Virginia Webb
English Teacher
DeLuna, Michele Miller
Spanish Teacher
Evans, Helen Stewart
First Grade Teacher
Harris-Rausch, Cheryl D
Math & Computer Teacher
Hewitt, Caroline Janet
English Teacher
Howell, Linda Myrastacia
Fourth Grade Teacher
Howell, Phillip Lothair
Fifth Grade Teacher
Meyer, Jan Renee
Elementary Counselor
Murphy, William R.
Mathematics Teacher
Nickel, Jacquelyn Long
Elementary Teacher
Page, Perry Robert
9th-12th Grd Math Teacher
Rice, Jerry Ken
Foreign Language Dept Coord
Schwickrath, Kris
Latin Teacher
Shreves, Sheila Annette Kinder
Second Grade Teacher
Slater, James P.
8th Grd Sci Tchr & Dept Chprsn
Smith, Russell Omer
Instrumental Music Director
Titus, Jonathan Ray
High School English Teacher
Wildman, Elizabeth Gail
Art Teacher
Zerr, Kathy Linne
1st Grade Teacher
SHERIDAN
Cook, Alan L.
Industrial Technology Teacher
Dunn, Joan
Mathematics Teacher
Haskell, Jim C.
Director of Bands
Perkins, Joan Arthur
Retired 1st Grade Teacher
Wiete, Shirley R.
Math & Computer Teacher
SOUTH BEND
Alspaugh, Michael
Mathematics Teacher
Baim, Betty J. (Isza)
Fifth Grade Teacher
Baldwin, Carolyn S.
Sixth Grade Teacher
Baldwin, William David
Auto & Body Technology Instr
Bayak, Wendy LeAnn
Categorical Resource Tchr
Besinger, Richard L.
PE & Weight Training Tchr
Blockson, Beverly Richmond
Teacher
Bovenkerk, Scott Lee
PE Teacher & Head Ftbl Coach
Breedlove, William L.
Sociology Assistant Professor
Burgess, Carol L.
Social Studies Teacher
Chandler, Henry Bruce
Social Studies Teacher
Chiszar, Bonnie Cheever
5th Grade Teacher
Clark, Jay Ransom
Math, Cmptr & Ceramics Teacher
Cohen, Sharon (Hugdahl)
Bus Ed Tchr & Dept Head
Coomes, Rosemary Ieraci
Business Education Teacher
Cwidak, Paulette Emily
English Teacher & Dept Chair
DeFreeuw, Marsha Ann
Third Grade Teacher
Demmon, Terri Lynn (Wallace)
Comp Information Systems Prof
DeRue, Albert Fredrick
English Teacher
Early, Thomas Michael
Head Ldrshp Dept & ROTC Instr
English, Patricia L.
Math & Basic Skills Teacher
Fizdale, Barbara Zomick
Adult Edctr & Homebound Tchr
Flowers, Herbert Gary
Math Instructor
Fox, Diane Margaret
English Teacher
Gates, Burt J.
Biology Teacher
Gerencher, Thomas A.
English Teacher

BEND (cont)
Marilyn Kay
age Arts Teacher
, Michael Robert
y, PE Tchr, Athletic Dir
atricia Arehart
sh Teacher
n, Allan Lee
Studies Teacher
, Celeste Moore
sh Teacher & Yearbook Adv
udith Susan Schymanski
ematics Teacher
Patrick Robert
Grade Teacher
n, Randall M.
ational Psychology Prof
Jack M.
eacher & Dept Chair
Mary Martin, FDC
h Grade Teacher
mer, Adele Stepien
ipal
Carol Ann
entary Building Principal
ski, Mary Jane
h Grade Teacher
n, James William
rade Language Arts Tchr
ski, Marta Pinnyei
ng Instructor
, Kenneth Daniel
Grade Teacher
Jill Van Camp
Grade Science Teacher
Babette C.
her & Counselor
an, Dorothy Sebelski
rade Teacher
y, Janice
nce Department Head
n, Amy Humphrey
uage Arts Teacher
son, Eva Latrelle
ish Teacher
on, Mary Ann
her
, Casimer A.
Teacher
otto, Rosemary (Lashenik)
ish Teacher & Dept Chair
Catherine Anne
8th Grade Science Teacher
Sue Ann Lyle
ond Grade Teacher
ugh, Betty Vergon-Slabaugh
ram Chair of Accounting
s, James Allan
His & World Geography Tchr
ns, James Reid
ign Language Dept Chairman
ff, Joan G.
nematics Teacher
owski, Susan Kuester
h Grade Teacher
ker, JoAnn Pennington
ish Teacher
Beverly R.
nish Teacher, Adj Asst Prof
r, Joseph A.
ogy Teacher
TH WHITLEY
Clara Marie
red Third Grade Teacher
, Kevin
culus & Physics Teacher
on, Cheryl J. (Blanchard)
ond Grade Teacher
Nancy Woolsey
lish & French Teacher
ki, Walter
h School Art Teacher
ey, Laura Shepherd
English Teacher
NCER
Kirk, Francey L.
h Grade Teacher
, Brent P.
h Teacher
orn, Scott David
logy & Earth Science Tchr
ELAND
p, Rosemary Miller
rd Grade Teacher
NGVILLE
s, Karen L.
rd Grade Teacher
AUGHN
oka, Elizabeth Rooney
ebra Teacher
LIVAN
, Francie Colleen
alth, Family, Cnsmr Sci Tchr
eatt, Jo Linda
arning Disabled Resrce Tchr
ips, Betty Golish
mily & Consumer Sci Teacher
fler, Karen Risley
ndry Soc Sci & Eng Teacher
oe, Don R.
achine Trades & Welding Tchr
et, Lela Gambill
ddle School Science Teacher
et, Robert Wayne
ncipal
MAN
is, Karen S.
3 Title I Reading Teacher
ler, Valerie McFall
cond Grade Teacher

SWAYZEE
Ertel, Sarah Ann
First Grade Teacher
Jung, Debbie Hutton
Fourth Grade Teacher
SWITZ CITY
Borders, Janice Riggs
English & Speech Teacher
Lentz, Marsha Sue (West)
Business Teacher
Terrell, Michael R.
Biology Teacher & Vllybl Coach
SYRACUSE
Aalbregtse, John Randolph
World Civilizatn, Careers Tchr
Bruce, Nance L.
Spanish Teacher
Harris, Kristi Anne Boyer
8th Grade Math Teacher
Iden, Terry Allen
English & Psychology Teacher
Kitson, William Kay
Chemistry Teacher
Koble, Carol F.
Fifth Grade Teacher
Lant, Janet P.
English Teacher
Metcalf, Philip Leslie
Mathematics Teacher
Zolman, Kem S.
High School Math Teacher
TASWELL
Smith, Mary Jo
Sixth Grade Teacher
TAYLORSVILLE
Jackson, Debra Lynette
Pupil Service Teacher
Wools, Glenna Tellman
Fifth Grade Teacher
TELL CITY
Brewer, Marty Carrington
7th Grade Language Arts Tchr
Fischer, Mickey
5th Grade Teacher
Goffinet, David Neal
Eighth Grade Mathematics Tchr
Lacy, Dan
Social Studies Teacher
Thomas, Renee Kuntz
Head of Sci Dept & Bio Tchr
TERRE HAUTE
Adler, Theresa Ann
Science Teacher
Aird, Debra Walls
World His & Civilizations Tchr
Allen, Marianne Mazely
English Teacher
Archer, Barbara Schomer
First Grade Teacher
Banghart, S. Brad B.
Aviation Director
Boehler, Charles S.
Voc Tech Tchr & Dept Chm
Brewer, Jill Brewer
General Music & Strings Tchr
Brink, Terrie Ann
Fourth Grade Teacher
Cantrell, LaDeena Jean
Nursing Instructor
Carty, William Brian
Fifth Grade Science Teacher
Cottrell-Smudde, Debby
First Grade Teacher
Douglas, Max Edward
Professor of Management
Gasway, Pamala Kay
English & Dramatics Teacher
Graham, Jeanne Ann
Senior Instructor
Harmless, Malcolm D.
Electronics Tech Instr & Chr
Harrison, Hobie Steele
Education Coordinator
Hile, Nancy A.
Biology Teacher
Horrall, Bettina Galey
English Teacher
Howard, Carol Alter
First Grade Teacher
Huxford, Teresa Odum
Special Education Teacher
Kemp, Jacqueline L.
Coord of Credit Outreach
King, Deanna L.
Accounting Instructor
Kirby, Gary L.
Fifth Grade Teacher
Kjonaas, Richard Allen
Professor of Chemistry
Layton, Martha Jackson
Foreign Language Teacher
Lingenfelter, Stephen R.
Computer Teacher
Mann, James Richard, II
8th Grade Social Studies Tchr
Marshall, Steven L.
Biology & Math Instructor
Matherly, Linda Handlin
Tchr of Learning Disabilities
McKee, Nancy Jane
Assoc Dean for Acad Affairs
Meyers, Ward F.
Geography & Government Tchr
Reed, Rhonda Gastineau
Nursing Instructor
Richards, Donald Gordon
Associate Professor of Ec
Sauer, Nancy R.
Dance Teacher

Spurgeon, Myrna Beth (Cloud)
Third Grade Teacher
Swindell, Warren C.
Professor
Turner, Donald Eugene
Art Teacher & Dept Chprsn
Webster, Barbara Kay
1st Grade Teacher
Webster, Janice Marie (Wailly)
Quality Sci Instr & Prgm Adv
Young, Joyce A.
Marketing Professor
THORNTOWN
Engle, Amy L.
Secondary Mathematics Teacher
Harris, Rebecca Ader
Math Teacher & Dept Chair
Johnson, Jane L.
Fourth Grade Teacher
O'Conner, Tammylyn
Director of Bands
Smith, Willie C., Jr.
8th Grade Mathematics Teacher
TIPTON
Borders, Rodger Lee, II
Fifth Grade Teacher
Cole, Amy Rae (Atchley)
7th-8th Grade Math Teacher
Everidge, Mary Lowry
Retired Fourth Grade Teacher
Flook, Susan Lynn
Choral Dir & Gen Music Tchr
Harbit, Mary Ann (Belmore)
English Teacher
Meyer, Nancy Irwin (Good)
Retired Fourth Grade Teacher
Morgan, Phillip Mark
Social Studies Teacher
Rushton, Joseph Wayne
Mathematics Teacher
Waddell, Phillip Eugene
HS Physical Ed Teacher & Coach
Weaver, Lisa Heflin
Third Grade Teacher
Weismiller, Debbie
English Teacher
TOPEKA
Auer, Carol Ann (Frazier)
Family & Consumer Sci Teacher
Tooker, Nancy Ann
High School Math Teacher
TRAFALGAR
Bratton, Robin Elaine
9th Grade English Teacher
Goen, Sherry Miles
Fifth Grade Teacher
Hankins, David Matthew
Business Teacher
LaFary, Linda L.
First Grade Teacher
Lancaster, Randall Jay
Biology Teacher
Martin, Scott A.
Mathematics Teacher
UNION CITY
DeHaven, Phillip Dean
Social Studies Teacher
Edwards, Alice Marie
Third Grade Teacher
Hinshaw, Mary Huffman
Third Grade Teacher
Murphy, Joy Delee
Fifth Grade Teacher
UNION MILLS
Chrobak, Stephen L.
Mathematics Teacher
UPLAND
Chechowich, Faye E.
Asst Professor of Religion
Denton, Margaret Jane (Love)
4th Grade Teacher
Fuller, Carolyn
Fifth Grade Teacher
Hubbard, Jackie Lockler
Principal
Lay, Robert Franklin
Associate Prof of Chrstn Ed
Lee, Twyla F.
Director of Social Work Ed
Parker, Richard Allen
Professor of Music & Ed
White, Lori Nadene
Associate Professor of Voice
VALPARAISO
Anderson, Teri
HS Mathematics Teacher
Austin, Benjamin Lee, Sr.
Physics Teacher
Baker, Anne LaForce
Soc Studies Dept Chair & Tchr
Barber, Ann Marie
Secretary
Beltz, Kay E. (Vanderhoff)
English Teacher
Bien, Joyce Ailes
Business Dept Head & Yrbk Adv
Byrne, Pamela Benner
English Teacher
Chase, Tammy Elizabeth
General Music Tchr & Choir Dir
Dixon, Christine R. (DeWell)
Business Education Teacher
Drake, Cheryn (Kelley)
Eng Tchr & Dept Chair
Floran, David K.
English Teacher
Gross, Gary Paul
3rd Grade Elementary Schl Tchr
Guyer, Susanne (Conrad)
School Psychologist Intern

Hanson, Marilyn C.
Art Teacher
Hardebeck, Carolyn
Guidance Counselor
Harnish, David Charles
Chemistry Teacher
Hirstein, Paul Dean
5th Grade Teacher
Hornung, Mary Carolyn (Fitch)
6th-8th Grd His & Sci Teacher
Jones, Joanne H. (Smith)
First Grade Teacher
Keller, Karl W.
Fifth Grade Teacher
Kleist, Deborah (Lauridsen)
Guidance Counselor
Lebryk, Judith Diana
Secondary English Teacher
Levandoski, Kathy (Mc Kibben)
Special Education Teacher
Moore, Sandra Sue
Associate Instructor
Needham, Darlene
Choral Director
Polizotto, Heidi Marie Wuchner
German & French Teacher
Punter, Robert Allen
Math Teacher & Coach
Rodenbarger, Linda Skinkle
2nd Grade Teacher
Schoenfelder, J. H.
Dept Chair of Bus Technologies
Strayer, Jane Patrice
6th Grd Language Arts Teacher
Terhune, Vickie Ruth
Secondary Math Teacher
Turley, Betty June Youngblood
RISE Teacher
Yelkovac, Penny
Fourth Grade Teacher
Ziegler, Timothy David
Advanced Math & Computer Tchr
VAN BUREN
Wright, Dale Lynn
6th Grade Teacher
VEEDERSBURG
Halladay, Danny Guy
Ec, Psych & Sociology Teacher
Taylor, Jerry Eugene
Aquatic Director
Whitington, Judith A.
Sixth Grade Teacher
Younker, BeAnn Johnson
Govt & US History Teacher
VERSAILLES
Avedissian, Janice Aikins
Science & Social Studies Tchr
Bates, Jeffrey Lee
Social Studies Teacher
Brawner, David Wayne
Sixth Grade Teacher
Ester, Beverly Farrow
Office Technology Teacher
Mohr, Troy Alan
High School Math Teacher
Ploeger, Wanda M.
High School Math Teacher
Speer, Janet Morningstar
Latin & English Teacher
Vankirk, Julie Biltz
English Teacher
VEVAY
Fancher, Bonnie Jean Barger
Chemistry & Physics Teacher
Headen, Sarah Baggett
Art Teacher
Hendricks, Janet Miller
English Teacher & Dept Chair
Jackson, Denny Carroll
Social Studies Tchr & Chprsn
Jessup, Gerald
Business Education Teacher
Seaver, Debbie Goffe
Business & Computer Ed Teacher
Weales, Richard D.
Math Teacher
VINCENNES
Alsobrooks, John Lewis
Funeral Svc Ed Chairman & Prof
Amers, Betty Jo
Business Teacher & Dept Chair
Battles, Kreg Scott
Chemistry Teacher
Blome, John B.
6th Grd Language Arts Teacher
Clausman, Hope Lynn
Assistant Prof of Psychology
Dohner, Cary Lee
Assoc Prof of Law Enforcement
Fabyan, E. Joseph
Chair & Prof of His & Pol Sci
Goodman, Dean R.
Associate Prof of Sociology
Grow, Susan J.
Professor of Physics
Harmon, Dennis Allen
Assistant Professor
Henderson, Kay Alldredge
English Teacher
Hollars, Mary Johnson
Asst Professor of Accounting
Jackson, Sharon Sue
Associate Professor of Music
Kaskus, Andrea J.
English Teacher
Kiteka, Sebastian F.
Assoc Prof of Cmptr Prgmng
Marchino, Lori Cullop
Professor of Hospitality

Marsh, William Joseph, Jr.
Band Director
Nead, Morris James
Professor of Management
Negley, Phillip
Asst Prof of Commercial Art
Otten, Esther E.
Third Grade Teacher
Penn, Charles S.
Assoc Prof of Education
Phillippe, Carol Abendroth
Assoc Prof, Sociology & Soc Wk
Richardson, Phyllis A.
Assistant Professor
Rode, Susan Kaye
Kindergarten Teacher
Schaefer, Hugh Scott
HS Soc Stud Tchr & Dept Chair
Simonds, Maria Jacqualine
4th Grade Language Teacher
Smith, Joan
Mathematics Department Chair
Snyder, Barbara Boehm
7th-8th Grade Math Teacher
Sweeney, Shirley Steffey
Professor & Department Chair
Tevebaugh, Steve
Biology Teacher
Thompson, Michael Allen
Social Studies Teacher
Toy, Stephen Gerard
English Teacher
Tucker, Linda Foncannon
Professor of Music & Voice
Vieck, Jana (Klein)
Associate Professor of Nursing
Wagner, Andy D.
Professor of Physics & Engr
Wayman, Mark A.
Band Dir & Music Dept Chm
Willis, Lisa Michelle (Rueter)
Third-Fifth Grade Teacher
WABASH
Beamer, Richard Donald
5th Grade Teacher
Bolinger, Mark Lowell
High School Teacher & Prin
Cole, Rodney James
Math & Pre Calculus Teacher
Gerger, Ida Mae Eddingfield
Second Grade Teacher
Herbert, Cornelia McLeod
High School English Teacher
Howes, Sharon Delight
Fine Arts Teacher
Keefer, Susan Hornaday
Vocal Music Teacher
Livergood, John Eldon
Industrial Technology Instr
Rapp, Diana Hegel
Fourth Grade Teacher
Schenkel, Deb Welker
4th Grade Teacher
Sparling, Rosa Marie (Bridegroom)
Family Science Teacher
Terrel, Toni Young
Biology Teacher
Uggen, Tony G.
US History & Geography Tchr
Warren, Mary Kent
Social Studies Teacher
Woodward, Ronald Lee
Social Studies Teacher
WADESVILLE
Davis, Nancy Louise (Ours)
Second Grade Teacher
WAKARUSA
Lanting, Esther A.
Coord for EASE & Bible Tchr
Stubbs, Jacqueline Whiting
2nd Grade Teacher
WALKERTON
Hostrawser, William David
Business Teacher
Schmeltz, Beth Irwin
High School Counselor
WALTON
Ayers, John E.
Social Studies Dept Chairman
Bauer, Mike Jude
Ind Technology & PE Teacher
Boe, Patricia Bruner
Third Grade Teacher
Bower, Joyce Stover
2nd Grade Teacher
Isenburg, Larry L.
Math Teacher
Krug, Don L.
High School Band Director
Metz, Mark Lewis
Chemistry Teacher
Sarber, Jane-Ann
Guidance Counselor
Shriver, Anita Sue
Fifth Grade Teacher
Southern, Gordon Thomas
Earth & Environmental Sci Tchr
WARREN
Moreland, Ruth Hanby
5th Grade Teacher
WARSAW
Bartels, Barbara
Admin Offc Tech Coord & Instr
Basden, Jill Richards
Sixth Grade Teacher
Bieber, Robert L.
HS Art Teacher
Blunk, Deb Lynn
Physical Ed & Aquatic Teacher

WARSAW (cont)
Boyer, Ron L.
Vocational Business Teacher
Burch, Linda L.
7th & 8th Grd Math Tchr
Ciula, Peggy Jeffers
HS Biology Teacher
Clevenger, Shirlee Ann
Spanish Teacher
Conlon, Joseph Martin
English Teacher
Cook, Keith C.
7th Grade Mathematics Teacher
Dyba, Diana Schroeder
1st Grade Teacher
Erwin, Renatta Thomson
HS Latin Teacher
Fisher, Terry A.
Pastor
Foster, Christine M.
English Teacher
Hamilton, Traci Lynn
Chemistry & Microbiology Tchr
Harris, Paula Marie
Language Arts & Lit Tchr
Hoy, Linda Mattern
Business Education Teacher
Mohler, Gary M.
Sixth Grade Teacher
Neumann, Michele Kathryn (Dearth)
Learning Disabilities Teacher
Nunez, Carolyn Jeannette (Schultz)
Kindergarten Teacher
Raft, David William
Marketing Education Coord
Shepherd, Jennifer Mitchell
Theatre Teacher & Director
Wolff, Raphael Gustave
High School English Teacher
WASHINGTON
Arnold, Mark W.
7th & 8th Grade Science Tchr
Bennett, Mary F.
Foreign Lang Dept Head
Engleman, Misha Carroll
English Teacher
Fry, Sue Lynn (Davis)
English Teacher
Mc Lin, Christine Watland
French Teacher
Mercer, Michael S.
Sixth Grade Teacher
Price, Cheryl June (Alford)
K-6th Grade Music Teacher
Reller, Dale
English Teacher
Rink, Rose Wright
Choral Director
Smith, Brenda J.
Third Grade Teacher
Spillman, Donald Crane
Social Studies Teacher
Stevens, Holly Jean
English Dept Chair & Teacher
Traylor, L. Michael
English Teacher
Wade, Gordon L.
Social Studies Dept Chair
Wafford, Joseph E.
Naval JROTC Instructor
Webb, Suzanne Marie
High School Theology Teacher
Whittaker, Patricia Gerber
Retired 5th Grd Tchr
Wilkerson, Larry W.
Sixth Grade Teacher
Worland, Madonna Sue
Junior High Mathematics Tchr
WATERLOO
Fleming, Dennis Robert
Mathematics Instructor
Gearhart, Marilyn Kaye
Geometry & Algebra II Teacher
Gordon, Tita
Biology Teacher
Hardesty, Joseph James
7th Grade Language Arts Tchr
Heminger, Dottie Jones
English Teacher
Karkosky, Richard Duane
Bands Director
Metelko, Barbara Allen
English Teacher
Nagel, Gerry
Speech, Debate & Photo Tchr
Voors, Tina Linn
German Teacher
Weber, Josie A.
English Teacher
Ziebell, Cynthia Brines
English Teacher
WAVELAND
Petry, Richard Lee
6th Grade Teacher
WEST LAFAYETTE
Bortoletto, Daniela
Physics Professor
Davenport, Brent Allen
Teacher & Coach
Eiff, Mary Ann
Asst Prof of Aeronautical Tech
Ellison, Elaine Krajenke
Mathematics Teacher
Fenn, Mary Ann
Director & Title I Teacher
Jeffries, Arliss Richard
English, Speech & Drama Tchr
Karberg, Suzanne Kay
Comm Spec & Civil Engr Tchr
Krockover, Gerald Howard
Professor of Science Education
Laskowski, Louie
Art & Photography Teacher
Montgomery, Tracy L.
Spanish Teacher
Nimmer, Kathy Ann
English & Speech Teacher
Schilawski, John Todd
Social Studies Teacher
Schoorman, Dilys
Graduate Instructor
Scott, Jimmy Mark
Economics & US History Tchr
Wood, Leonard E.
Professor of Civil Engineering
WEST LEBANON
Barry, John M.
Math & Science Teacher
Comer, John David
Social Studies Teacher
Moore, Brian Scott
Life Science & Biology Teacher
Peterson, George Walter
Instrumental Music Instructor
Shackleton, Wilma Knoop
HS Social Studies Teacher
Taylor, Fran Williams
Math & Accounting Teacher
Turner, Jeffery Kyle
Mathematics & PE Teacher
Wright, Jill Johnson
5th Grade Teacher
WEST TERRE HAUTE
Beasley, Edward L.
Math Dept Chm, Physics Teacher
Daniel, John Alexander
Retired Social Studies Teacher
Dyer, Debra Jean
Learning Disabilities Teacher
Edwardson, Tonya Lake
Mathematics Teacher
Ferres, Laura Lynn
8th Grade Language Arts Tchr
Gummere Jackson, G. Catherine Moreland
Retired Elementary Teacher
Hatcher, Faith Anne Neddo
Health & Physical Ed Teacher
Hayden, John Christopher
Eighth Grade Science Teacher
Hensley, Sharon M.
Third Grade Teacher
Johnson, Lois Ann
4th Grade Teacher
Miller, Kathleen J. Strole
Family, Con Sci & Lead Teacher
Newton, Rosetta Siner
Ret Lang Arts & Reading Tchr
Skinner, Timothy Dale
Economics & Government Teacher
WESTFIELD
Borgnini, Susan Heine
Cnslr & Administrative Asst
Davis, Nikki S.
English & Journalism Teacher
Denari, Robert John
Biology Teacher
WESTVILLE
Keldsen, Glenn Lloyd
Associate Professor of Chem
WHEATFIELD
Abel, Peggy Jo
Eighth Grade Science Teacher
Benham, Stephanie
High School Art Teacher
McKinney, Kathy Fasel
English & Journalism Teacher
Orsburn, H. William
High School Mathematics Tchr
Slaby, Kristi Lynn
Biology Teacher
WHITELAND
Canary, Rebecca Jordan
Cnsmr & Fam Serv Teacher
Conner, Sharon H. MIller
Counselor, Gftd Ed & Eng Tchr
Croy, Todd A.
Science Teacher
Curry, Lorilee Deer
Academically Talented Tchr
Eccles, Mark E.
Chemistry & Physics Teacher
Loop, Martha Ann
Language Arts Teacher
Price, John Garfield
Sixth Grade Teacher & Ath Dir
Reynolds, Phyllis Beck
Mathematics Teacher
Venter, John Bradley
Math Teacher
WHITING
Bachmann, Donald
Math Instr & Head Tennis Coach
Bobby, Rosalie Skertich
English & Literature Teacher
Ciciora, Therese Marie Sutkus
Fourth Grade Teacher
Gandolfi, Lisa A. Graves
Physical Education Teacher
Guaccio, Betty Jane
English Teacher
Karagys, Linda Bublis
Fifth Grade Teacher
Lemon, Gail A.
Business Education Teacher
Marks, Georgianna Ellen
Vocal Music Director
Montalbano, Pasquale
Math & Cmptr Programming Tchr
Reinke, Fran Kasperek
Sci Educator & Dept Chprsn
Williams, John S.
Dir of Tech & Instructor
WILLIAMSPORT
Foster, Robin H.
5th Grade Teacher
WINAMAC
Murray, Rita J.
6th Grd Social Studies Teacher
Nellans, Gary D.
4th Grade Teacher
WINONA LAKE
Callighan, David Eugene
Social Studies Teacher
Gaerte, Dennis E.
Assoc Prof of Education
WINSLOW
Mason, Ivan V., Jr.
Third Grade Teacher
WOLCOTT
Hintzman, Charles A.
Chrmn of English & Tech Dir
Jackson, Penny Lorae Lashbrooks
Former Teacher
Stitz, Jean Ann (Nist)
Mathematics Teacher
Streitmatter, Rebecca Lynn (Rupe)
English Teacher
WOLCOTTVILLE
Cords, Eunice Ketchum
6th Grd Lang Arts & Math Tchr
Grossman, Deborah Jean (Phares)
Kindergarten Teacher
WOODBURN
Foust, Diana Lee Hebner
3rd Grade Teacher
Mull, William R.
Government & Economics Teacher
YORKTOWN
Evans, Joan Barshes
First Grade Teacher
McGalliard, David L.
K-5th Grd GT Coordinator
Winkle, Kelli Ann
Spanish Teacher
ZIONSVILLE
Eddy, Kimberly Jo (Harris)
Former Teacher
Eggers, James Stephen
Psych Tchr & Soc Stud Dept Hd
Fendley, Linda R.
English Teacher
Grabianowski, Mary Scifres
Government & Economics Tchr
McCormack, David Lee
Math, Cmptr Tchr & Dept Head
Peter, Faye Weeks
2nd Grade Teacher
Rodgers, David G.
Amer Lit & US His Teacher
Rutledge, Marian Colvin
Lang Arts & Soc Stud Tchr
Tikijian, Kimberly Ann
Former English Teacher
Treadway, Cindy DeWitt
Health & Life Skills Teacher

IOWA

ACKLEY
Huff, Virginia Illene
Second Grade Teacher
ADAIR
Bond, Gary
Art Instructor
Wesack, Sheryl Lea
Sixth Grade Teacher
ADEL
Harpster, Teresa L.
Language Arts Teacher
Weems, Della Miller
High School English Teacher
AFTON
Hancock, Bryant William
HS Social Studies Instructor
Kneller, Deborah Jessen
Second Grade Teacher
Loeffler Rose, Lois Ann
English & Speech Teacher
AGENCY
Lunkley, Mary Ellen Bircher
Retired Teacher
AKRON
Frerichs, Sharon Rae
Business Education Teacher
ALBERT CITY
Schmidt, Allan John
Mathematics Teacher
ALBIA
Allgood, Bernard H.
Instrumental Music Instructor
Jones, Judy Blomgren
5th Grade Teacher
Kellar, Stephen Glenn
Band Director
Lindberg, Hjalmer August
Guidance Counselor
ALBURNETT
Hicks, Catherine Marie
Scndry Eng & Psychology Tchr
Lebeda, Larry Leo
Anatomy & Physiology Teacher
Meadows, Vicki Herr
Band Director
Wander, Lauralea (Leonhart)
Jr & Sr High Teacher
ALDEN
Ford, Kenneth D.
Industrial Technology Teacher
Smith, Dennise Kay (Huston)
Fourth Grade Teacher
ALGONA
Burrow, David Michael
Mathematics Teacher
Connick, Brian J.
World History Teacher
Froehlich, Kathleen Bestenlehner
Principal
Herbst-Ulmer, Todd John
Vocal Music Director
Kadow, Eileen F.
High School Math Teacher
Kohlhaas, Kathy Neumann
8th Grade Math Teacher
Kueck, Lynn R.
Mathematics Instructor
Mc Call, Mary Therese
English Teacher & Dept Chair
Mertz, Linda D.
Vocal Music Teacher
Wigley, Paul Edward
Vocal Music Teacher
ALTA
Boelter, Victoria Ruth (Hamik)
Fifth Grade Teacher
Brubaker, Marilyn Elizabeth
First Grade Teacher
Sherkenbach, Joan Marie (Anderson)
5th-6th Grade Teacher
Still, Darlene Conover
Family & Consumer Sci Tchr
ALTON
Fischer, Lorraine Foley
6th Grade Teacher
Le Tendre, Beth Ann
8th Grade English Teacher
ALTOONA
Blue, Betty Lou (Fretty)
3rd Grade Teacher
Morris, Phyllis Wilson
5th Grade Teacher
AMANA
Merritt, Beverly (Andersen)
Retired Fifth & Sixth Grd Tchr
AMES
Ahrens, Franklin Alfred
Professor of Pharmacology
Beisser, Sally R.
Instruction of Ed
Bergeson, Kenneth Lynn
Assoc Prof of Civil Engrng
Bishop, Michael A.
Philosophy Professor
Brannon, James Haggard
Sixth Grade Classroom Teacher
Carlson, Samuel Keith
English Teacher
Hanson, Marilyn Stafford
Math Teacher & Dept Coord
Hoiberg, Karen Bush
Fifth Grade Teacher
Johnston, Gail
Mathematics Instructor
Knight, Jennifer Hart
US History Teacher
Knox, Margaret Hopkins
1st Grade Teacher
Lambert, Carolyn Ann
Coordinator & Teacher
Larson, Louise Paysen
Third Grade Teacher
Mendenhall, Jack James
Physical Education Teacher
Mitra, Ambar Krishna
Assoc Prof of Aerospace Engr
Mitzel, Gwendolyn Smith
Sixth Grade Teacher
Mohapatra, Prasant
Assistant Professor
Munson, Bruce Roy
Prof of Aerospace Engineering
Nespor, Angela Marie (Quint)
General Music Teacher
Ness, Thelma J.
Fifth Grade Teacher
Porter, Max L.
Civil Engineering Professor
Windsor, Charles Walter
Physics Teacher
ANAMOSA
Algoe, Bob C.
Science Teacher
Cooley, Rebecca Stuczynki
Media Specialist
Gehring, Lizabeth Ann
Language Arts Teacher
High, Barb Kay
Third Grade Teacher
Johnson, Dale Bruce
Secondary Mathematics Teacher
Ketelsen, Margret Downing
Retired Teacher
Oltmann, Donna Marie First
Second Grade Teacher
Otting, Gary John
Language Arts Teacher
Stanaway, Richard Earl
Instrumental Music Teacher
Van Der Millen, Scott
High School Teacher
ANDREW
Everding, Robert James
Mathematics Teacher
Manders, Vicki R.
Science Teacher
Peterson, Don D.
Guidance Counselor
ANITA
Knuth, Andrew Jon
Spanish Teacher
Swim, Donna (Lloyd)
Transtn Coord & Resource Prsnl
ANKENY
Bevis, Darrell
Assistant Professor of Music
Brix, Jeff D.
Spanish Teacher
Dyer, Karen Hanna
Second Grade Teacher
Fields, Robin Frances
Lang Arts & Journalism Teacher
Fuller, Gerry Kay David
English Teacher
Hood, Elaine Sue
9th Grade Geography Teacher
Hoogland, Verlyn John
Instrumental Music Instructor
Houghton, Myron James
Department Chair
Huber, Ronald Lee
Language Arts Instructor
Johnson, Jennie L.
HS Language Arts Teacher
Jones, Susan Henderson
5th Grade Teacher
Krull, Dennis Wayne
Physical Education Teacher
Markos, Beth Kristen
English & Spanish Teacher
Parker, Linda Delbridge
Teacher of Gifted & Dept Chair
Rosenberger, Twyla Pelley
Retired Elementary Teacher
Seifert, Joyce A.
6th Grade Math Teacher
Thorson, Arlan John
Research Technology Instructor
ANTHON
Kirchgatter, Scott K.
Science & Computer Teacher
APLINGTON
Lumley, Marlys Ulfers
Third Grade Teacher
ARCADIA
Weitze, Kathleen Ann
Sixth Grade Teacher
ARLINGTON
Reynolds, Carol Anne
HS Language Arts Teacher
ARMSTRONG
Larsen, Jon Montgomery
Social Studies Dept Chrpsn
ATLANTIC
Christensen, Nancy Grebert
3rd Grade Teacher
Hansen, Bruce O.
Fourth Grade Teacher
Hansen, Lael Lowden
1st Grade Teacher
Hansen, Paulette Christensen
Sixth Grade Teacher
Hendrickson, Dennis Paul
Choral Activities Director
Johnk, Bruce Carol
Agriculture Education Teacher
Larsen, Catherine Hjortshoj
6th Grade Teacher
McCaskey, Cheryl Kay
Guidance Counselor
Morenz, JoAnne M.
Secondary English Teacher
Wiley, Tony Michael
Social Studies Instructor
AUBURN
Lesle, Dale
Retired Teacher
AUDUBON
Lang, Jason Allen
Science Teacher
Lynch, Kaye Abbott
Kindergarten Teacher
Wagner, Donald J.
Mathematics Tchr & Dept Head
AVOCA
Hardisty, William L.
Language Arts Dept Chairman
Merriam, Dan Stephen
Social Studies Teacher
Rock, Patricia O'Neill
Third Grade Teacher
Weddum, Kim Michael
Social Science Instructor
BADGER
Gord, Arlene Hanson
Retired Third Grade Teacher
BATTLE CREEK
Brown, Steven Ray
Social Studies Tchr & Ath Dir
Conley, Janelle
K-8th Grd Vocal Music Teacher
Ehler, Enid Dornbrack
First Grade Teacher
BAXTER
Akins, Donna Marie (Cole)
English & Spec Ed Teacher
Dralle, Eric D.
MC Resource Teacher
Hoskins, Jeffery John
Secondary Social Studies Instr
Loupee, Michael Alan
Science Teacher
Robinson, Tim
English & Spanish Teacher
Stanley, Patricia Osborne
Fourth Grade Teacher

D
on, Laurie Rippentrop
h Grade Science Teacher
PLAINE
n, Valerie Strom
sh Teacher
'VUE
Robert K.
er
Kenneth A.
Studies Teacher
, Priscilla Kay
Reading Teacher
d, David W.
structor
o Brockhage
e School English Teacher
ack
ath & PE Teacher
nn, Nancy Schreurs
Grade Teacher
, Marcia Davis
& Computers Teacher
OND
James W.
Grade Sci & Math Tchr
, Charlotta
School English Teacher
kloth, Jon P.
School Art Instructor
ENDORF
ch, Gabriele Maria
an & French Teacher
Pamela Misfeldt
d Health Dept Coordinator
Carlita Gillmeister
Grade Teacher
en, Peter G.
cs Teacher
William O.
oor Education Teacher
onte Leonard
Teacher
Candace Heuer
Stud & Concentration Tchr
o, Sally Tellez
Grade Teacher
el, Stephen Michael
cs & Chemistry Teacher
Stephen Douglas
l Stud Dept Chair & Tchr
Paul Edwin
h Teacher
Linda Lee
Grade Teacher
Michael James
Director
an, Ethel Sanderson
ary Media Specialist
, Joyce Sue
entary Guidance Counselor
n, Donna Petras
h Grade Teacher
Joan A.
ish Teacher
Carol Angerer
Grade Teacher
k, Marianne Galitz
of Tlntd & Gftd Stdnts
ds, Phyllis Anne
rd Language Arts Teacher
Judith Gilbert
d Grade Teacher
, Jeffrey B.
3rd Soc Stud & Rdng Tchr
INGHAM
, Shirley Wilson
ed Teacher
RSBURG
r, Lisa Anderson
ily & Consumer Science Tchr
KESBURG
s, Beverly Conrad
n, PE & Computer Teacher
lge, Dennis Michael
th Grade Teacher & Coach
GRASS
ollam, Donna Louise
red 3rd Grade Teacher
APARTE
Kathy McKim
dergarten Teacher
OURANT
n, Edward Robert
nce Teacher
n, Sally Rhinehart
n School English Teacher
NE
an, Donna Mae
red Second Grade Teacher
, Jeanne Carlson
ector of Guidance
wold, Susan Dankel
cher of Talented & Gifted
vig, Janice Greiman
cial Education Teacher
eman, Marian Knox
th Grade Asst Principal
r, Donald L.
Grade Teacher
r, Alice Shekleton
red Teacher
, Timothy Paul
h Teacher & Dept Chair
, Matthew Hill
h Grade Teacher
eler, Roberta Ann
lish Teacher
ardson, David Joe
h School Band Director

Walczyk, Jon Henry
French & Spanish Teacher
Wells, Jeff
Math Teacher & Coach
BOYDEN
Cox, Marcene Boertje
5th & 6th Grade Teacher
BRIDGEWATER
Bauer, Debra Ann
Kindergarten Teacher
Faga, Kelly Jo-Krogh
Elementary Guidance Counselor
BRITT
Sanger, Linda Rose
HS Business Education Teacher
BROOKLYN
Grimm, Charles Allen
Eng, Speech, Span & Drama Tchr
Munson, Duane Stanley
Secondary Principal
Scott, Inez M. (Ranfeld)
First Grade Teacher
BURLINGTON
Abel, Dennis Dean
Social Studies Teacher
Anderson, Larry E.
Mathematics Teacher
Barnholdt, Mary Jo Parsons
Third Grade Teacher
Bohlen, Clair Ervin
Mathematics Teacher
Burman, Louise Clover
Third Grade Teacher
Davidson, Jim B.
Business Education Teacher
Davis, Geane Elizabeth
7th Grade Language Arts Tchr
Dillon, Richard Lynn
Seventh Grade Mathematics Tchr
Fenton, Theodore J.
8th Grd Amer Studies Teacher
King, James L.
Welding Instructor
Shacklett, Larry Joe
Industrial Technology Teacher
Smith, Kathryn Lynn
Associate Director of Bands
Smith, Tina Lundeen
5th Grade Teacher
VanBuskirk, Chan Blair
American History & Govt Tchr
Wilcox, Janice Anne Dolmage
5th Grade Teacher
BURNSIDE
Gilson, Kirk Richard
Mathematics Teacher
Hoffmann, Robert Paul
High School & 5th Grd Band Dir
BUSSEY
Dobernecker, Susan Lynn
Third Grade Teacher
Dykstra, Shannon J. Folger
Instrumental Music Teacher
CALMAR
Donlon, Cheryl Brinkman
Science Instructor
Kirby, Kenneth Harold
Instrumental Music Instructor
CAMANCHE
Dawson, Pat Rosenow
Second Grade Teacher
Henry, Sheryl Boysen
6th Grade Teacher
Letchford, Roy LaVern
Mathematics Teacher
Metzger, Brenda Hugunin
Math Teacher & Track Coach
Montgomery, Janie Lou
Physical Ed & Health Teacher
Struck, Danette Cavanaugh
Third Grade Teacher
CARLISLE
Johnston, Roger Stewart
Sixth Grade Teacher
CARROLL
Burrack, Frederick William
HS Instrumental Music Tchr
Geelan-Potthoff, Winnifred
Spanish Teacher
Halverson, Joani E.
Art Instructor
Hogan, Dick Edward
High School Guidance Counselor
Lee, Kimberly Kolacia
Spanish Teacher
Paulsen, Tom Howard
Ag Ed Instr & FFA Advisor
Peters, Mark Wayne
Sixth Grade Instructor
Shields, Kimberly Marie
Third Grade Teacher
CARTER LAKE
Andersen, Paul William
5th Grade Teacher
CASCADE
Takes, Larry L.
Math & Physics Instructor
CEDAR FALLS
Baumhover, Marlene Kennett
Fifth Grade Teacher
Butler-Nalin, Kay
Computer & Composition Spec
Copeland, Jeffrey Scott
Eng Lang Tchr & Lit Dept Head
Davison, Judy Tracy
Intnl Project Coordinator
DeMoss, Marguerite Donaldson
HS English Teacher
Engel, Dianne Dale
HS Geography & History Teacher

Engel, Richard James
Drivers Education Teacher
Graber, Linda Bundt
Instructor of Science Ed
Groote, Velda Fleshner
Sixth Grade Teacher
Halupnik, Dirk Alan
Biology Teacher & Coach
Haurum, Carolyn Cummings
Retired Teacher
Houts, Timothy Layton
Fourth Grade Teacher
Johns, Tracy E.
Special Education Teacher
Nelson, Phillip J.
Asst Professor of Teaching
Port, Marty Mc Nutt
Secondary Counselor
St Pierre, Eileen Foley
Finance Professor
Sellers, J. Thomas
8th Grd Life Science Teacher
Spore, Cindy K.
Fifth & Sixth Grade Teacher
Tandy, Don J.
Science Teacher
Williamson, Janet L.
Sixth Grade Teacher
CEDAR RAPIDS
Allwardt, Ruth Lorraine
Early Childhood Teacher
Asigbee, Emmanuel M.
Economics Professor
Battin, Patricia Ann
Language Arts Teacher
Begalske, Catherine Meyer
Sixth Grade Teacher
Bender, Sharon Brown
Chemistry Teacher
Berry, James Kelly
Choral Activities Director
Boggs, Darlene M.
1st Grade Teacher
Bogguss, Joann Gerdes
Mathematics Teacher
Boston, Richard Allen
World His & US Govt Tchr
Bradley, Diane K.
HS Mathematics Teacher
Burwell, Hope Elizabeth
Asst Professor of English
Conrad, Richard Lee
Middle School Math Teacher
Danker, Lora Duffy
Reading Specialist
Danskin, Claire Murray
French Teacher
DeKock, Margaret Ladd
Math & Soc Stud Tchr
Efting, James Charles
Social Studies Teacher
English, Susan Boyd
Associate Professor of English
Ernster, Thomas J.
English Instructor
Fearing, Kennard D.
Mathematics Coordinator
Feuerhelm, Heather Merrick
Language Arts Teacher
Fitzpatrick, Mary LaVon Brashaw
Math Teacher
Fogle, Thomas V.
English Teacher
Foster, Mary Anderson
Former Elementary Teacher
Gaddie, Joyce K.
German Teacher
Gano, Gwendolyn Minor
6th Grade Teacher
Gano, Rocky Lynn
5th Grade Teacher
Garris, Marylin Mallinger
Third Grade Teacher
Goodlove, Jay C.
Business Education Teacher
Hampton, Tom E.
Fifth Grade Teacher
Hatcher, Ruth E.
Eighth Grade Teacher
Henderson, Jeff William
Chief Administrator
Herkelman, Bill
Math Teacher & Dept Head
Horton, Marlene Rammelsberg
Math Teacher
Johanson, Roger Phillip
Assoc Prof & Chm of Tchr Ed
Johnston, Gail Thompson
Fourth Grade Teacher
Karns, Dean Meredith
Associate Prof of Music & Math
Kvach, Janet Secor
6th Grade Teacher
Lauer, Mary Lou
Assoc Prof of Microbiology
Law, David John
Band Director
Lindsay, Gary Donald
Journalism Teacher & Pub Adv
Lippert, Thomas L.
Choral Music & Fine Arts Dir
Lueck, Leon Anthony
Gifted & Talented Pgm Manager
Martin, Charlotte Joy
Asst Prof of Religious Studies
McCollum, Sarah-Elizabeth E.
High School Science Teacher
Mc Donald, Lucinda Ritenour
6th Grade Teacher

McVay, Jenifer James
Vocal Music Director
Michels, David H.
Math & Personal Dev Teacher
Mueller, Mark S.
Physical Education Teacher
Nekvinda, Terrene Cumberlin
Fourth Grade Teacher
Nesmith, Bruce F.
Asst Prof of Political Science
Newland, Ronald J.
Physics & Chemistry Teacher
Norburg, Angela Marie
English Teacher & Drama Dir
Norris, Linda L.
8th Grade Science Teacher
Oberbroeckling, Mary Jean
Extended Learning Program Mgr
Oberfoell, Amy Marie
English Teacher
O'Brien, James Richard
Industrial Technology Tchr
Oliver, Eric Lloyd
Eighth Grade Teacher
Olson, Virginia F.
Retired Intermediate Grd Tchr
Peitz, Michael J.
Language Arts & Theatre Tchr
Perkins, Janet Marie
Spanish Teacher
Phelan, Frances LaNoce
Theology Dept Chairperson
Rhine, Dan E.
Math Teacher
Roup, Julie Lynne
7th Grade Teacher
Russell, Steve D.
8th Grade Science Teacher
Santee, Leslie R.
8th Grade US History Teacher
Sauser, Mary E.
First Grade Teacher
Schons, Dianne Marie
Middle School Teacher
Sepulveda, Christine L.
Fifth Grade Teacher
Shireman, Joyce Richardson
Associate Professor of Nursing
Stauffer, David R.
Biology Teacher
Stiers, Alan Leon
PE Teacher & Coach
Tack, Ann L.
Second Grade Teacher
Tafoya, Corey Gibson
Spanish Teacher
Thiessen, Joanne O'Brien
English Teacher
Tonsfeldt, Lori Ann (Bennett)
Seventh Grade Teacher
Trachta, Marie Hansen
History Teacher
Tungesvik, Jennifer L.
Spanish Teacher
Van Zile, Cheryl St. Germaine
6th & 7th Grade Teacher
Wagner, Betsy Vickery
Social Studies Teacher
Weinbrenner, Donna Washington
K-1st Grade Teacher
White, Carol Schutte
German Instructor
White, Ruth Elaine Trotter
Humanities Teacher & Acad Adv
Wilden, Mark Allen
Special Education Teacher
Wilkinson, Harold R.
Student Facilitator
Wilson, Barry Robert
Industrial Technology Teacher
Wortman, John Elliott
Professor of History
Yeager, Leslie A.
Lang Arts & Amer His Tchr
CENTER POINT
Sackett, Zelda Kirchner
Retired 5th-6th Grade Teacher
Stonerook, Sue Narmi
Elementary School Counselor
CENTERVILLE
Campbell, Roger Allen
Dean of Stdnts & Athletic Dir
Denning, Justine
Elementary School Teacher
Frevert, Beverly McCartan
Third Grade Teacher
Huston, Stanley Max
Freshman English Teacher
Miller, Russell A.
Scndry Earth Science Teacher
Moorman, Anne Marie
First Grade Teacher
Sacco, Gary Allen
Seventh Grade Science Teacher
Wehrle, Melissa Anderson
5th Grade Teacher
CENTRAL CITY
Butters, Vicki Holleen
2nd Grade Teacher
CHARITON
Dawson, Patricia Merchant
Fourth Grade Teacher
Hamilton, Cynthia Jean
Teacher & Coord GATE Program
Vandevenne, Tamara Shay
Fourth & Fifth Grade Math Tchr
Wolverton, Todd Farrell
Scndry Soc Stud Tchr & Coach

CHARLES CITY
Bode, Allan Floyd
Spanish Teacher
Brant, Linda Jean
English Teacher
Mulcahy, Judith (St Clair)
Social Studies Teacher
Pearson, Carl J.
Life Science & Geography Tchr
Petersen, Dennis L.
Visual Art Teacher
Rasmussen, Beverly Waller
Fourth Grade Teacher
Schafer, Cherie Cobet
First Grade Teacher
Troutman, Janice L.
Teacher of Talented & Gifted
CHARTER OAK
Hardy, James Darius
Social Science Instructor
McCool, Robert Ray
Business Education Teacher
Urwiler, William L.
Industrial Technology Teacher
CHEROKEE
Berigan, Betty Meisinger
5th-6th Band Director
Christensen, Lee Ann Marie (Siegfried)
Work Study Instructor
Sarchet, Amy Roed
Math Teacher
Zelle, David Arthur
High School Mathematics Tchr
CLARENCE
Hayes, Kenneth G.
HS & MS Business Teacher
Krall, Karina Kae
Span, Yrbk & Newspaper Tchr
CLARINDA
Carper, Joelene Beth
Business Teacher
Gowing, Jolinda Lee
Third Grade Teacher
Gransow, Karla Faye
History & Sociology Teacher
James, Martha Lou
Title I Reading Teacher
Kramer, Jane-Marie Gifford
Hlth, Sci & Project Wild Tchr
Lawrence, William Dale
English & Government Teacher
Mc Nees, Kimberly Honette
Fifth Grade Teacher
Nichols, Jeffrey L.
Athletic Director
Norris, Tammy Juanita
Middle School Math Teacher
Price, Janet Byron
Kindergarten Teacher
Richardson, Connie Johnson
MS Social Studies Teacher
Wagoner, Mary Lou Reddel
Second Grade Teacher
Wilson, Lynette
Aftercare Coordinator
CLARION
Cramer, Cathy L.
2nd Grade Teacher
Funnell, Sylvia Kelly
Spanish Teacher
Golbuff, Linda Wellman
Fourth Grade Teacher
Warnke, Craig Alan
Industrial Technology Instr
CLARKSVILLE
Coleman, Trudy J.
High School English Teacher
Rudebeck, Kathy Joy
Title 1 Reading Instructor
Van Gorp, David Eric
Second Grade Teacher
CLEAR LAKE
Erhardt, Karen Walker
Former 2nd Grade Teacher
Ertz, Phyllis Ann (Borud)
Consultant
Schumacher, Beth Ann (Herker)
Soc Stud Dept Chair & Teacher
CLEGHORN
De Stigter, Julie
Administrative Assistant
CLEMONS
Berrey, Bonnie Louise
First & Second Grade Teacher
CLINTON
Boyd, Joan Carole
Language Arts Depart Chair
Craig, Douglas R.
High School Science Teacher
Doughty, Judy Ann (Whiteside)
Math Teacher
Gaulrapp, David A.
Dir of Bands & Music Coord
Hensey, Lisa Kent
Education Teacher
Hess, Suzanne Mc Laughlin
English & Jrnlsm Instructor
Horst, Patricia A.
Fifth Grade Teacher
Johnson, Marion Schafer
Sci Div Chair & Chem Instr
Krogman, Georgene Helen
Second Grade Teacher
Oakley, Stacy Hansen
Drama Dir & Lang Arts Teacher
Remy, Donita M. (Wiederholt)
Language Arts & Jrnlsm Tchr
Rohwer, Karl F.
Choral Music Director

CLINTON (cont)
Rump, Harriet
Music & Voice Teacher
Saladino, Gene Francis
Former Teacher
Schrunk, Odelia E.
Math Tchr & Dept Chprsn
Searles, Elizabeth (Elitreby)
Humanities Division Chair
Temple, Laurie Adolph
English & Tech Writing Tchr
Ullrich, Margaret Joan (Bergman)
Guidance Counselor
Wall, Suzanne Marie (Mc Guiness)
Special Education Teacher
Wegehoft, Irene E. (finger)
Middle School Teacher
Witt, Debra Arvidson
Spanish & English Teacher
CLIVE
Cooley, Ryan Sean
8th Grade Mathematics Teacher
COGGON
Aden, Marilyn Russell
Spanish & Speech Teacher
Blin, Keith Ray
Math Tchr & Athletic Dir
Oberbroeckling, James J.
Soc Stud & Lang Arts Tchr
COLESBURG
Goedken, Joan E.
Fourth Grade Teacher
COLFAX
Murillo, Cindi R.
3rd Grade Teacher
Price, Connie Sorensen
Business Teacher
Schmitt, Anita (Novak)
Fifth Grade Teacher
COLLEGE SPRINGS
Athen, Shannon Lee (Sims)
6th-8th Grd Lang Arts Tchr
Irvin, Connie
Kindergarten Teacher
Strong, Glenna Elaine (Williams)
English & Spanish Teacher
Wheeler, Carl Leland
Science Teacher
COLUMBUS JUNCTION
Helscher, Stephen Andrew
Band Director
Wilson, Mary Masonholder
English Teacher
CONRAD
Ehn, Jeanne Marie (Nelsen)
English, Speech & Drama Tchr
Johnson, Debra Jolene (Davison)
Family & Consumer Sci Teacher
Johnson, Kay B.
English Teacher
Lee, David LeRoy
Bio & Environmental Sci Tchr
COON RAPIDS
Slater, Diane Lyons
Spanish Teacher
Stablein, Joseph Edward
English Teacher
Tipton, Thomas Ray
High School Biology Teacher
Zanders, Shawn
Business Educator
CORALVILLE
Grieves, Deborah Seieroe
Reading Recovery Teacher
CORNING
Davis, Dianne G. Smith
Family & Consumer Sci Instr
Drake, Christy L.
6th Grade Teacher
Maitlen, Susan Ryan
Sixth Grade Teacher
Morris, LeAnn Grundman
Gifted, Talented Coord & Tchr
Nett, Andrea Leigh (Carter)
HS English Teacher
Nett, Peter Joseph
English & History Teacher
Quinn, Helen E.
Retired Reading Teacher
Stielow, Percy William
Math Instructor
Winter, Sandra F.
Health & Physical Ed Teacher
CORRECTIONVILLE
Anderson, Susan M.
Eng, Speech Tchr & Drama Coach
Jordan, Bonnie Fendrick
Teacher of Talented & Gifted
Leuschen, Richard A.
Social Studies Teacher
Wych, Ruby Jeanne
HS Mathematics Teacher
CORWITH
Fuhrman, Mark W.
Business Teacher
Sohl, Merle L.
Industrial Technology Tchr
Wagner, Keith Matthew
K-12th Grade PE Teacher
CORYDON
Olson, Diane Louise
Jr HS English Teacher
Sinclair, Charles Thomas
Guidance Counselor
COUNCIL BLUFFS
Addison, Michael Benjamine
8th Grade Amer History Teacher
Allmon, Joann Oberreuter
Fifth Grade Teacher
Ankenbauer, Joseph Michael
Mathematics Tchr & Tech Coord
Barnett, Todd Michael
High School Social Stud Tchr
Buhrman, Brian W.
Mathematics Professor
Burgart, Rebecca Watson
Child Dev Assoc Professor
Cochran, Barbara Stotts
Fourth Grade Teacher
Crawford, Lynn Dianne
Instructor in Sign Language
Cupp, Jo Birdsall
English Teacher
Fancher, Jane Ann
Office Occupations Assoc Prof
Fink, Christine Martine
Science Lead Teacher
Forsee, William Anthony
Biology Teacher
Gepner, Mary (Matthews)
Acad & Hnrs World His Teacher
Gibson, John Robert
Drama, Speech Dir & Chairman
Giles, James F.
Orchestra Director
Grosvenor, Kathy
Adjunct Instructor
Hagar, Trisha Lee
High School Math Teacher
Hans, Paul
Psych & Human Relations Tchr
Hardiman, Rhonda Kleckner
Business Teacher
Howard, Jane Ann
English Tchr & Dept Chprsn
Hudek, Albert D.
Mathematics Teacher
Hughes, Mary MacPherson
Asst Prof of Child Development
Kennedy, Kathy Dee (Swain)
1st-6th Grades Music Teacher
Kermoade, Barbara Falk
Math Teacher
Leaders, Sandra Larson
English Teacher
Ranslem, Barbara Ann Hyde
5th-6th Grade Lang Arts Tchr
Richter, Nicholas Kent
Fifth Grade Teacher
Rosmann, Marilyn Sanada
Assistant Professor of Nursing
Rutz, Timothy Andrew
7th Grade World Govt Teacher
Smith, Colin Patrick
Social Studies Teacher
Smith, Mark Allen
Counselor
Snipes, Linda Fenton
Bible, Math & Spanish Teacher
Socolofsky, Lowell Edward
Computer Programming Prof
Spinharney, Sharon D.
Teacher
Synhorst, Wanda Lee
Science Teacher
Tettenborn, Deb Kleinschmidt
Business Education Teacher
Tipton Biggs, R.
Professor of English & Drama
Wahl, Rick R.
Meteorology Teacher
Weiss, Ronald Dean
Biology & Chemistry Instructor
Wymore, Steven E.
7th Grade Soc Studies Teacher
CRESCO
Beckmann, Raymond Henry
7th Grade Life Science Teacher
Eckhardt, Skip D.
K-6th Grd Tlntd & Gifted Tchr
Hovden, Judith Anderson
Sixth Grade Teacher
LeFebvre, Karen Kaye Anderegg
Junior High Vocal Music Instr
Lentz, Christopher P.
Industrial Technology Teacher
McConnell, Jill Marie
HS Multi Resource Teacher
Mc New, Robert Dean
HS Physical Education Teacher
Mikkelson, Sandy Stopperan
Kindergarten Teacher
Numedahl, Paul Joseph
Science Teacher
Obermann, James Milton
High School English Teacher
Zajicek, James Edward
Junior High Teacher
CRESTON
Bishop, Patricia Healey
Retired Teacher
Christensen, Loy Laurine
8th Grade Mathematics Teacher
Irelan, Sharon Lee
Math, Science & TAG Teacher
Stults, Dee Ann Stine
Mathematics Instructor
CRYSTAL LAKE
Curley, Jeffrey John
Business Education Teacher
Granger, Leslie William
Social Studies Department Head
Kanauss, Kent R.
Music Director
CUMBERLAND
Struthers, Evon Rosewall
Retired 6th Grade Teacher
CUSHING
Bagenstos, Debra Rae Ellerbusch
2nd Grade Teacher
Suhr, Pearl Evelyn (Bayer)
First Grade Teacher
CYLINDER
Kalsow, Susan Christensen
Educational Consultant
DALLAS
Bauer, Cindy Knust
5th Grade Teacher
Bronzynski, Karla Beth Sneller
Multi-Age Classroom Teacher
Crozier, James Floyd
5th & 6th Grade Teacher
DALLAS CENTER
Sales, Steven Earl
Composition & Lit Instructor
Shepherd, Jean M.
Language Arts Teacher
Stammerman, William T.
Science Teacher
DANVILLE
Murrell, Mary Beth
Secondary Mathematics Teacher
DAVENPORT
Bates, Gary Robert
High School Business Teacher
Beat, Mary R.
English Teacher
Becker, Bartholomew Powers
Secondary Counselor
Bernatz, John D.
Director of Bands
Bodayla, Mary Ann Mraz
Asst Professor of History
Bovee, Michael L.
Professor of Clinical Science
Breneman, Dean Edward
Mathematics Teacher
Buttleman, Deborah Aller
Lang Arts & Journalism Teacher
Campbell, Beth Ann
Media Specialist
Cockrell, Linda P.
Third Grade Teacher
Cullinane, Kathleen
First Grade Teacher
Currence, Glennda Kay
Elementary Counselor
Dailey, Dorothy Ann
French Teacher
Denner, Patricia Sue
PE & Jr High Health Teacher
Draper, Carolyn Susan
Act Dir, French & Geo Teacher
Flaherty, Patricia Lane
Elementary Mathematics Teacher
Green, Thomas
Fifth Grade Teacher
Grimoskas, Marjorie Kasten
Retired Jr HS Counselor
Howard, Georgia Chanez
Math Teacher
Hudson, Gwen Grange
Fifth Grade & Lang Arts Tchr
Keester, Mary Lou Nebel
Math Teacher
King, Jack B.
Retired Band Director
Lipnick, Barbara Olsen
Spanish & French Teacher
Luton, Janet Kainz
Assistant Professor of English
Mahieu, Carollyn Barker
First Grade Teacher
Mayhew, Garvin Edward
Physics Teacher
Mc Aleer, Joanne M.
Secondary Spec Education Tchr
Mc Cartney, James Robert
Band Director
Mc Millin, Ruth Ann
Frgn Lang Chprsn & Span Tchr
Mekow, Craig Larry
Assoc Prof & Chprsn of Anatomy
Miller, Kathleen Hayes
English, Speech & Drama Tchr
Minard, Larry Eugene
Language Arts Tchr & Dept Chm
Moe, Bruce Lee
Social Studies Teacher
Redeker, Katherine R.
Language Arts Tchr & Yrbk Adv
Richter, Mark J.
Physics Teacher
Robinson, Cyrus Edwin
Physical Education Teacher
Robinson, Lynda Stratman
Assoc Professor of Education
Ruebbelke, Kathleen Marie
Chiropractic Unit Director
Salter, Lauralie Pilcher
Second Grade Teacher
Schmiedel, Gilbert O.
Anatomy Professor
Scott, Julie Hein
Mathematics & French Teacher
Searle, Katherine McLeod
7th & 8th Grd English Teacher
Skarr, Pamela J.
Fifth Grade Teacher
Sohr, Sandra Miller
History & Govt Teacher
Stensrud, Diane Boyd
Third & Fifth Grade Teacher
Stites, John Scott
Director of Campus Hlth Center
Stoltenberg, Jan (Scott)
German Teacher
Sullivan, Christine Gravino
Music Teacher
Theissen, Marilee Vierkant
Third Grade Teacher
Vogel, Linda Hafner
Second Grade Teacher
Walker, Diana Hall
Social Studies Teacher
Walton, Judith Jordan
Math Teacher
Zimmerman, Jodi Dye
Psychology & History Teacher
DAYTON
Doran, Jean Anne (Gifford)
MS Language Arts Teacher
DE SOTO
Parton, Cheri Lynn
Fifth Grade Teacher
DECORAH
Brown, Randall Hale
Physics Professor
Crookshank, Karen M.
Reading & Social Studies Tchr
Daywitt, Jean E.
German & Language Arts Teacher
Edman, Laird Roy Oakes
Psychology Prof & Honors Adv
Kelly, Mary Brian
1st Grade Teacher
Meyer, David Joseph
Special Education Tchr & Coach
Natvig, Holly Hanson
Clinical Instructor of Ed Dept
Ringdahl, Shirley Cocker
Retired Elementary Teacher
Spilde, Jeanette Nelson
Orchestra Director
Twedt, Rick
HS Agri-Science Instructor
Vyverberg, Jere Michael
Associate Principal
Wangsness, Clayton Elvin
Agriculture Teacher
Wenthold, Bonnie Rothmeyer
English Secondary Teacher
DELHI
Folsom, Terry G.
High School Mathematics Tchr
Foster, Gary Carl
High School Biology Teacher
Hoekstra, Roger G.
7th-8th Grade Science Teacher
Poynor, Mary Ann (Stanaway)
Mathematics Teacher
DENISON
Boddicker, Artis Ralston
First Grade Teacher
Burchfield, Jeffrey Jon
Language Arts Teacher & Coach
Reddel, Donna Jayne
Second Grade Teacher
Schon, David Curtis
American History Teacher
DENVER
Johnson, Diane Marie
Art Educator
Niemann, Ruth A.
First Grade Teacher
Ruiter, Randy L.
Social Studies Instructor
DES MOINES
Ahrendt, Laura
Journalism Teacher
Arnold, Betty Ann
Third Grade Teacher
Bailey, Beth Ann-Graff
Teacher of Behavior Disorders
Baker, Carla Sue
Spanish & Math Teacher
Barnett, Mary Lee
HS Vocal Music Teacher
Bennett, David Wayne
Physical Education Teacher
Bennink, Carroll L.
Vocal Music Instructor
Blenderman, Shirley (A.) Grimmius
Business Education Teacher
Bockelman, Byron B.
7th-8th Grd Soc Stud & Prin
Borich, Vickie L.
Mathematics & Computer Teacher
Bravard, Susan Lynn (Haugen)
Physical Therapy Instructor
Cawthorne, John Malcolm
Span & African Amer Stud Tchr
Conlon, Peg Mary
7th & 8th Grd Science Teacher
Crook, Susan Jane
4th Grd Tchr & Comp Specialist
Darge, Diana Lunette (Bessinger)
Social Studies & Reading Tchr
Driscoll, Anne Anderson
1st Grade Teacher
Ellerhoff, Jean G.
High School English Teacher
Elliott, Clive
Artist in Residence
Fant, Laureen Hall
Fourth Grade Teacher
Fincham, Allen Lee
Physical Education Teacher
Flesch, Cindy Ann (Miller)
Business Education Teacher
Foshe, Kimber Lee
English & Psychology Teacher
Goldsmith, Vicki Lynn
English Teacher
Harms, Dena Allen
Algebra Teacher
Harned, Ollis Hayes
Elem Physical Education Tchr
Havnen, Judith Robertson
Fifth Grade Teacher
Henderson, Dan L.
Secondary Principal
Hendrick, Donna R.
8th Grade Teacher
Hogan, Patricia Polking
MS Language Arts & Asst Prin
Hubbard, Naomi Anderson
4th Grade Tchr, Asst Principal
Hutzell, Laurence A.
Chemistry Teacher
Keasey, Barbara Jo
English Teacher
Kever, Mary Jo Mehalovich
First Grade Teacher
Lynch, Jeffry Gerard
6th-7th Grade Social Stud Tchr
Lytle, Marlene Gail
Child Development Careers Tchr
McCormick, Trudy Ann
Kindergarten Teacher
McManus, Walter Roy, Jr.
Deputy Industrial Commissioner
Miller, Michael Andrew
Debate Teacher
Murphy, Jeffrey O.
Elementary Math Teacher
Nelson, Lorene K.
ESL Teacher
Noah, Anne Flynn
Language Arts Teacher
Olson, Pamela Haroldson
Third Grade Teacher
Perschau, Donald James
Science Teacher & Dept Chair
Person, Steven Orlan
English Teacher
Peterson, Mark Alan
Instructor of Education
Petree, Jane Elizabeth
7th Grd Rdng & Lang Arts Tchr
Petree, Sandra Kay
Reading & Language Arts Tchr
Pose, Joanna Danos
Third Grade Teacher
Prey, Bette Jayne
English Teacher
Schlafke, Steven Edward
Former HS Science Teacher
Schneckloth, Tim J.
Math Teacher
Schumann, Lois Gerke
1st Grade Teacher
Shambaugh, Mary Beth Kiernan
Art Teacher
Slickers, Vikki
Music Teacher
Smith, Debra Lynn Eason
HS Math Teacher
Springer, Giles William
Radio Production Teacher
Starostka, Katie Rood
Assistant Principal
Storm, Ronald H.
Mathematics Teacher
Thompson, Karen Fay Nihart
Mathematics Teacher
VandenBranden, Mary P.
Elementary Teacher
Vickroy, Joyce (Howe)
Physical Education Teacher
Wadden, Marilynn
Principal
Walag, J. Michael
Vocal Music Director
Ward, Sherry Mulcahy
Middle School Math Teacher
Wierson, Christine Terry
Retired Elementary Teacher
Woods, Miriam Jodine
Science Teacher
DEXTER
LaVonne, Linda
Dance Studio Owner, Dir & Tchr
DIKE
Juhl, Richard H.
Retired Industrial Tech Tchr
Paar, Sara Ann (Laube)
Spanish Teacher
DONNELLSON
Coffin, Daryl Eugene
Middle School Music Teacher
Dodds, Mary Jane Jury
5th Grade Teacher
Grimes, Miriam Kae (Long)
High School Math Teacher
Lind, Deanna Hennies
Teacher of Talented & Gifted
Mickelson, Chris Benner
Middle School Volleyball Coach
Sheerin, Michael Blaise
6th Grd Language Arts Teacher
Wilson, Dianne C.
Math Teacher
DOUDS
Gilchrist, Janet Dooley
Third Grade Teacher
DOW CITY
Hartman, Steven John
Industrial Arts Instructor
Sliefert, Gaylord
Mathematics & Social Stud Tchr
DOWS
Hoelscher, Virginia Ailes
English Teacher
Muhlenbruch, Melissa Jane
Home Ec & Health Teacher

UE
Christopher King
ant Professor of Biology
ey, Robert Miles
Global History Teacher
o, Frank Patrick
ion & Psychology Prof
nan, Jared Micah
s & Chemistry Teacher
Margaret Mary, BVM
ion Assistant Professor
, Susan Fleming
age Arts Teacher
, Thomas Gene
e Teacher & Coach
Virginia (Colby)
er & Drama Director
, Thomas John
e Teacher
Ed P.
Teacher
, Frank James
iate Prof of Business
Norman Charles
sor of Philosophy
elt, Katherine Murray
iate Professor of Nursing
Shirley Ann Bonfig
e Teacher
andra Kathryn
ations Adv & Eng Tchr
Stephen P.
Grade Teacher
y, Dennis P.
School Language Arts Tchr
, Robert Earl
osition & Literature Tchr
Mary Carol Cameron
f Speech Communication
, Coleen R. (Schaefer)
e Teacher
sen, Edward A.
of Business & Economics
Barbara Jeanne
rgarten Teacher
Debra Meyer
nce Counselor
Jerald Lee
ematics Teacher
dy, Mary Conlan
School English Teacher
ohn F.
rade Teacher
eanna Danielson
sh Teacher
s, Mary Lynn L.
of Speech Communication
Patricia
sh Teacher
an, Paul William
ed Teacher
, Michael J.
ematics Teacher
on, Lloyd David
mental Music Teacher
, Dawn Miller
rade Teacher
s, David Stringer, Sr.
of Pol Sci & Legal Stud
Philip Robert
ematics Instructor
er, Paul Frederick
8th Grade Math Teacher
dt, Judith M.
sh Teacher
, Mary Lou
ergarten Teacher
l, Virginia Mary
hology Professor
auser, Robert Joseph
Grade Science Teacher
an, Vicki Marie
Grade Teacher
, Janet Ann
d Grade Teacher
Teri
Teacher
r, Cheryl Ann (Grap)
ning Resource Center Tchr
nbusch, Sue Ann
gh Language Arts Teacher
ann, Mary Ann
essor of Religious Studies
AP
ll, Sue Ann
5th Grd Math Tchr
nd, Kimberly Ann
d Instr
ANT
, Nancy Lee (Madsen)
Rdng & Computer Tchr
e, Loretta Graham
th Grade Teacher
, Robert Glenn
al Studies Teacher
Adria Meeks
dergarten Teacher
RSVILLE
y, Carrie Ann
ish Teacher
, Patrick Robert
Stud, His & PE Tchr
n, Kay Krapfl
th Grade Teacher
ann, Mary Kay (Gonner)
ebra Teacher
ART
ns, Richard Ernest
ld History & Cultures Tchr

EAGLE GROVE
Baum, LeRoy B.
Director of Bands
Becker, Jerry K.
History Teacher
Gearhart, Roi Anne
Music Teacher
Larson, Bradley Alan
Computer Instr & Tech Coord
Lilly, Mary Anne
English & Speech Instructor
Manues, Patricia Henning
7th-8th Grade Reading Teacher
Nelson, Bonnie Dooley
Third Grade Teacher
Schultz, Helma K.
Kindergarten Teacher
EARLHAM
Adkins, Christopher George
Biological Sci Instr
Williams, Tyler Ray
4th Grade Teacher
EDDYVILLE
Fenton, Tony L.
Business Teacher
Fisher, Jerry
Literature Teacher
Mc Clenthan, Cean Elizabeth
Media Specialist
Sheesley, Connie Ray
4th Grade Teacher
Vermeulen, Gale Courtney
Chemistry & Physics Instructor
EDGEWOOD
Johnson, Arthur Allen
Science Teacher
Martin, Hazel Anne
Multicategorical Resource Tchr
Smith, Scott Evard
Spanish Teacher
ELDON
Coffman, Priscilla Chapman
5th Grade Teacher
Knowles, Jean Beemblossom
Business & Marketing Teacher
Peyton, Jana Rae Page
Fourth Grade Teacher
ELDORA
Baker, Annette Hansen
High School English Teacher
Sogard, Donna Wearda
5th Grade Teacher
ELDRIDGE
Chapman, Cecil
Junior High Vocal Music Tchr
Hartman, Marcia Smith
High School Math Teacher
Scott, Don
HS Social Studies Teacher
ELGIN
Bonte, Kent M.
Social Studies Instructor
Lyngaas, Lowell Dean
Coach
ELK HORN
Redman, Joyce Rosenhauer
5th-8th Grd English Teacher
ELKADER
Gnagy, Susan Keenan
English Teacher
Moyna, Judy Bender
Business Education Teacher
Reimer, Arlene
Language Arts Teacher
Webber, Thomas Charles
Art Teacher
EMMETSBURG
Blake, Mary Kane
Sixth Grade Language Arts Tchr
Brennan, Michael Wayne
Physical Education Teacher
Felderman, Mark Thomas
Social Studies Building Chair
Hoobler, Sharon Hermansen
4th Grade Teacher
Welander, Linda Laeupple
Spanish Teacher
EPWORTH
Bowers, Rodney Patrick
Instructor of Theology
Elgin, Daniel Richard
High School Teacher
Findley, Steven K.
Business Education Teacher
ESTHERVILLE
Sanders, Diana J.
Sixth Grade Teacher
EVANSDALE
Wolfe, Calvin Russel
Art, Photo & Comp Grphcs Tchr
EVERLY
Haberman, Roger Frederick
Mathematics Dept Head
Heikens, Allyn M.
High School Science Teacher
Jones, Connie Kramer
Math Teacher
Peterson, Jeffrey L.
English Teacher
Vander Broek, Marsha Page
Fourth Grade Teacher
EXIRA
Larsen, Kristine Lou-Moore
K-12th Grade Art Teacher
FAIRBANK
Buhr, Debra Lynn (See)
Third Grade Teacher
Peine, Linda Ann (Davis)
Voc Family & Consumer Sci Tchr

Warnke, Sandra Heiserman
High School English Teacher
FAIRFIELD
Bradley, Betty Lemke
Chemistry Teacher
Cochran, Rosalie J. (Martin)
Seventh Grade Science Teacher
Edgeton, James William
Band Director
Flinspach, Sharon Carlson
Math & Cmptr Programming Tchr
Marker, Dian Whitney
High School English Teacher
Miller, Gail Lindfield
Multicategorical Resource Tchr
Mitcheltree, Linda Young
Vocal Music Teacher
Openshaw, Ronald Edwin
Asst Prof of Physics
Septer, Marvin Leland
Physical Science Teacher
Witzenburg, Joyce Berlin
Calculus Teacher
FARLEY
Noonan, James Edward
8th Grade Math Teacher
FARMINGTON
Bumgarner, Freda Catherine Mohr
Fmly, Consumer Sci & Hlth Tchr
Morgan, Amy Marie
Social Studies Teacher
FARNHAMVILLE
Albert, Ann L.
Middle Schl Literature Teacher
Hammen, Mary E.
8th Grade English Teacher
FARRAGUT
Deter, Christine Wilkinson
Secondary Resource Teacher
Holmes, Jennifer Anne
High School Math Teacher
Wilson, Douglas Bruce
Govt, Amer & World His Tchr
Wilson, Jane Elizabeth Nielsen
French & Spanish Teacher
FAYETTE
Beane, Robert Lowell
Chair Div of Bus, Instr Acctng
FENTON
Bennett, Vickie Irene
Spanish Teacher
Brown, Paul Douglas
Art Teacher
FONTANELLE
Benton, Deborah Miller
English Teacher
Lisk, Myra Rowedder
Jr High Teacher
Means, Larry D.
7th & 8th Grd Guid Counselor
Raasch, Connie Rose Smith
Art Teacher
Wood, Dale Marion
Band Director
FOREST CITY
Church, Paulette Adams
Ed & Developmental Stud Prof
Hartman, Mary Jo
Professor of Biology
Kuns, Bonnie Bjelland
Retired Elem Teacher
Raupp, Edward Robert
Business & Economics Professor
Williams, Susan Leffel
Asst Professor in Music
FORT DODGE
Adam, Richard A.
Theology Tchr & Spiritual Dir
Armstrong, Carol Phillips
Science Instructor
Bahrenfuss, Trish O'Connor
Math & Computer Teacher
Beck, Nancy Nitzke
Mathematics Teacher
Cole, Steven D.
Associate Science Professor
Elberg, Joann Lee (Umstead)
Nurse Educator
Evers, Donald Robert
Asst Professor of Chemistry
Galbraith, Gail (Miller)
Language Arts & German Teacher
Galbraith, Stan Ray
German Teacher
Humburg, Dawn Ann
Accounting Instructor
Inman, Richard M.
Instructor of Social Science
Lack, Philip Keith
Advanced Instr of Lang Arts
Lanning-Ventura, Suzanne
Special Education Instructor
Lehmkuhl, William T.
Western Civilization Instr
Linney, Joseph Orion
Business Education Instructor
Mitchell, Linda Sue
Sixth Grade Teacher
Niceswanger, Betty Jean
Second Grade Teacher
Nilles, Katherine Prohaska
6th Grade Teacher
Payne, Judy Sollie
Business Education Teacher
Rathermel, Danielle Ann Dooley
Third Grade Teacher
Robertson, Joan VanHoozer
Bus Admin & Offc Tech Instr
Snell, Roger Duane
Spanish Instructor

Stripling, Craig Michael
Earth Science Teacher
Stuart, Katherine Caloud
Medical Lab Tech Instructor
Vogt, Melanie (Polking)
English Teacher
Wozniak, John F.
Chemistry Instructor
Wright, James Timothy
Band Director
FORT MADISON
Campbell, Albert Carl
At Risk & TAG Teacher
Helling, Bernadette Therese (Haden)
Vocal Dir & Music Teacher
Pepple, Diane
English Teacher & Librarian
FREDERICKSBRG
Meier, Donald H.
Business Tchr & Elem Principal
FREMONT
Cook, Laura Rice
MS Math & Social Studies Tchr
GARDEN GROVE
Alley, Brant Lee
Business Teacher
GARNAVILLO
Claude, Leonard Harold
Math & Computer Instructor
GARNER
Mestad, Gary Allen
Social Studies Teacher
GARWIN
Koster, Sue M.
TAG Teacher
GEORGE
Bleeker, Leola Adell (Jurrens)
First Grade Teacher
Hoing, Beverly Groth
English Instructor
Johnson, Michele Allen
Math Teacher
GILBERT
Geist, Pauline Henryson
Kindergarten Teacher
Stratton, Mary Galvin
Fifth Grade Teacher
GILBERTVILLE
Palmer, Ruth Bunt
Language Arts Teacher
Schulte, Myron U.
Science Teacher & Dept Chm
Strempke, Stacey Olson
Biology & Mathematics Teacher
GILMAN
Devlin, John T.
Instrumental Music Teacher
GLENWOOD
Portrey, Leon Paul
HS Business Teacher
Trager, Craig Dean
Mathematics Teacher
Walters, Doris Harper
Second Grade Teacher
GLIDDEN
Feldman, Tim Allan
Mathematics Teacher
Hodges, Kathleen Jo
4th-6th Grade Science Teacher
Jensen, Beverly Kay Christenson
Kindergarten Instructor
Lamp, Dean Leslie
Director of Instrumental Music
Mathine, Gerald Donald
Bus Ed Tchr & Tech Coord
GOOSE LAKE
Burke, Pamela Lensing
Spanish Teacher
SChneden, Phyllis Kay
Kindergarten Teacher
Schoon, Kendell Ray
Industrial Technology Instr
GOWRIE
Egger, Mary M.
Vocal Music Instructor
Kruse, Don D.
Industrial Arts Teacher
Peterson, Lisa Johnson
Spanish Teacher
GRAETTINGER
Ebeling, Kenneth Elmer
High School Science Teacher
GRAND MOUND
Blake, Wendy Wentworth
Second Grade Teacher
GRANGER
Emery, Elwin Louis
Retired Middle School Sci Tchr
Smyser, Ellen Jane (Baker)
Third Grade Teacher
GRANVILLE
Schueder, Jean M.
Fifth Grade Teacher
Willman, Scott Arthur
Social Studies Teacher
GREENE
Juhl, Timothy P.
Instrumental Music Teacher
Landers, Donita Hook
High School Science Teacher
Muhlenbruck, Milo D.
High School Business Ed Tchr
GREENFIELD
Auten, Kristy Williams
Kindergarten Teacher
Baier, Donna Faubel
Fifth Grade Teacher
Clark, John Gilbert
Science Teacher

Glade, Rana Chapman
6th Grade Social Stud Teacher
Riley, Barbara (Wehrspan)
HS Math & Accounting Teacher
Riley, Larry Gene
Industrial Tech Tchr & Coach
Swanson, David B.
HS Eng, Rdng Teacher & Coach
Weber, Phil L.
5th Grade Teacher
Wildt, Tonia C. Stupp
Spanish Teacher
GRIMES
Dixon, Tami Jo Wagner
4th Grade Teacher
Klocke, Gary Lee
Science Teacher
Kopecky, Julie Morgan
Guidance Counselor
Korporal, Esther Renate
Kindergarten Teacher
Slauson, Cindy Sue
Fifth Grade Teacher
GRINNELL
Abarr, David Trent
4th Grade Teacher
Bachman, Marsha Hawkinson
Second Grade Teacher
Buter, Diana Dinkel
Language Arts Teacher
Dobbs, Brenda Ann
Spanish Teacher
Doonan, Jerry La Verne
7th Grade Life Science Teacher
Grant, Terese Baker
French Teacher
Kenealy, Larry Joseph
Drop Out Prevention Prgm Dir
Kunce, Nancy Joan Muckler
First Grade Teacher
Manly, Debra Yellick
Art Teacher
Schneider, Leroy Paul
High School Science Teacher
Shults, Frank
Assistant Principal
Wagner, Joyce Vales
HS English Teacher
GRISWOLD
Mortensen, Richard Carl
Technology Coordinator
GRUNDY CENTER
Hosch, Kathy Janssen
Secondary Language Arts Tchr
Williams, Frank C.
Fifth Grade Teacher
GUTHRIE CENTER
Blass, Pauline Parker
Third Grade Teacher
Hesse, Marie Nesselroad
Retired Second Grade Teacher
Wessling, Sharon Walstrom
Mathematics & Physics Teacher
GUTTENBERG
Andregg, Janice Lee Kolker
Social Studies Teacher
Bryant, Bruce Arthur
Speech & English Teacher
Connelly, Kathy Bouska
Kindergarten Teacher
Feldman, Kimberly Marie
2nd Grade Teacher
Hubbell, Howard James
Soc Stud Instr & Ath Dir
Streich, Mary Elizabeth
1st Grade Teacher
HAMBURG
Lueth, Beth Kellogg
English & Drama Teacher
HANLONTOWN
Reeder, Carolyn J.
Fourth Grade Teacher
Thede, Jay R.
Math & Science Teacher
HARLAN
Barry, Jeffrey A.
English Teacher
English, Robert E.
United States History Teacher
Lawson, R. Steve
Band Director
Leinen, Daniel Joseph
High School Ag Education Tchr
Ludwig, Nancy Blobaum
Tchr, Coord of Tlntd & Gftd
Sprague, Kenneth Wayne
Math Instr & Computer Coord
HARTLEY
Steinbeck, Mary L.
Spanish Teacher
Trost, Donald Dean
Industrial Technology Teacher
HASTINGS
Delisi, Robert Joseph
HS Social Studies Teacher
HAWARDEN
Fox, Gary Eldon
Chemistry & Physics Teacher
Halligan, Steven F.
PE & Economics Teacher
Johnson, Steven Murray
American Government Teacher
HIAWATHA
Mc Carty, Marjoria Mae
Retired Teacher
HINTON
Hermsen, Arlene Marie
Spanish Teacher
Johnson, Julie O'Meara
English Teacher

HINTON (cont)
Rusk, Garie William
Social Science Teacher
HOLSTEIN
Baier, Jodi Hester
High School Spanish Teacher
Barringer, Dale Gary
Science Teacher
Struck, Linda Wilkie
Mathematics Teacher
Witten, Arthur Lee
Physics & Chemistry Teacher
HUDSON
Allen, Nancy Lynn
Vocal Music Teacher
Petersen, Lynn Allen
Social Studies Teacher
Remy, Robert Wayne
Fifth Grade Teacher & Coach
HULL
Barkel, Daniel James
Vocal Music Director
Kooiman, LaVern H.
Business Teacher & Ath Dir
Wright, Dennis William
Soc Stud Tchr & Athletic Dir
HUMBOLDT
Christiansen, Merlin Earl
6th Grade Teacher
Jennings, Jill Janina
Spanish Teacher
Miller, Timothy Allen
Band Director
Sawyer, Kenneth L.
Retired Social Studies Teacher
Van Langen, Orin D.
8th Grade Mathematics Teacher
Wickett, John Charles
Biology Teacher
HUMESTON
White, Susan Johnson
Second Grade Teacher
HUXLEY
Telford, Gary Dean
Eighth Grd Earth Sci Tchr
IDA GROVE
Brown, Kurt D.
Business & Computer Teacher
Groote, Sheldon Howard
Social Studies Teacher
O'Tool, Jane A. (Banowetz)
High School Math Teacher
INDEPENDENCE
Hosch, Lyle Robert
Varsity & Junior High Coach
Sheets, Rhonda Amfahr
High School Business Teacher
Short, Harriet Mason
Gifted & Talented Resrce Tchr
INDIANOLA
Bushby, Michelle Lang
High School English Teacher
Eady, Arthur R.
Adjunct Professor of History
Herring, Kay (Snethen)
English Teacher
Horn, James Andrew
Agricultural Education Teacher
Kelley, Jerry Lyons
Teacher of Gifted & Talented
Rose, Steven William
Asst Professor of Ed
Wonderlich, Kathy
5th Grade Teacher
INWOOD
Denekas, Kenneth D.
Jr HS Mathematics Instructor
Martinson, Marsha Lynn
2nd Grade Teacher
Moen, Pamela Neuharth
Third Grade Teacher
Rozeboom, Jay
Elementary Resource Teacher
Smith, Glennie Sue
Kindergarten Teacher
Stai, Mary Coughlin
Biology Teacher
IOWA CITY
Alvarez, Pedro Jose
Environmental Engineering Prof
Anthony, Tas
History Teacher
Aunan, Thomas William
Fifth-Sixth Grd Sci Tchr
Bohnsack, Jan Kaye
Extended Learning Program Tchr
Brashier, Ann Day
English Teacher
Brems, Bob
Jr High Mathematics Teacher
Finken, Helen Goodell
Soc Stud Teacher & Dept Chair
Fridrich, Kirk L.
Associate Professor
Garton, Gary L.
Bio & Advanced Hnrs Bio Tchr
Gommels, James H.
Global Studies Teacher
Gommels, LeDonna Knack
Fourth Grade Teacher
Grove, Gregory Alan
Vocal Music Director
Henning, David Fredrick
Band Director & Music Prof
Herren-Wegman, Dawn Elaine
Third Grade Teacher
Hollis, Janet Keefer
Mathematics Teacher & Coord
Klink, Judith
Language Arts Teacher
Koepnick, Kevin
Biology Teacher
Kurtz, Alice Kaufman
5th-6th Grade Teacher
Mitchell, William Paul
Language Arts Teacher
Muilenburg, Gregory J.
Science Teacher
Phillips, Carole Rae
English Teacher
Reilly, Barbara
Science Tchr & Dept Chair
Robinson, Janet Bond
Former HS Chem & Physics Tchr
Schmidt, Patricia Last
Director & Teacher
Skay, Jayme Joseph
Math Teacher & Coach
IOWA FALLS
Augspurger, Debra Sue (Ross)
Music Director & Instructor
Bromann, Warren Alan
Chemistry Tchr
Brown, Daniel W.
Prof & Agriculture Head
Dirks, Darvin Richard
Sixth Grade Teacher
Neumann, John Robert
Social Studies Teacher
Phipps, Patricia Kay
Learning Center Teacher
Santee, JoAnn Ohling
Third Grade Teacher
Smith, Nicolette (Schaup)
Equine Management Instructor
VanBuskirk, Peg Sonichsen
Prof of Office Occupations
IRWIN
Reddell, Don J.
Social Studies & Reading Instr
JANESVILLE
Ehmen, James E.
Sixth Grade Teacher
Fleckenstein, Judith Rae (Treloar)
Instr of Talented & Gifted
Gifford, Robert M.
Social Studies Teacher
Henriksen, Karen Kay (Mennen)
Title I Reading & Math Tchr
Johnson, Fredrick Albert
HS Social Studies Teacher
Squires, Jennifer Elizabeth
Mathematics Teacher
Stufflebeam, Roger Eugene
Secondary Science Teacher
JEFFERSON
Lawson, Lois (Dukeshier)
Retired Elementary Teacher
JESUP
Ammon, Jennifer Leyden
English & Journalism Teacher
Emick, Kraig Robert
Music Director
Flaharty, Danny Lee
High School Math & Health Tchr
Gearhart, Robert Jeffrey
History & Business Teacher
Kies, Mary E.
Vocational Home Ec Teacher
Levendusky, Maria Warrenburg
Fourth Grade Teacher
Munger, Mary Ann Knief
Second Grade Teacher
Thomas, Lawrence Dean
Science Teacher
JEWELL
Jacus, Ann M.
Mathematics Teacher
Paulsen, Darrell Eugene
Third Grade Teacher
JOHNSTON
Donahue, Brian
8th Grade Eng & French Teacher
Henkenius, Cheryl Greiman
Associate Principal
Moermond, Mary M. Ohaver
French Teacher
Paul, Kathy Moderow
Tchr, Coord of Gftd & Tlntd
Schwartz, Nancy Bergeman
Vocal Music Teacher
Smith, Steve Lee
High School Mathematics Tchr
Vos, Michelle Lee (Laverenz)
Business Education Teacher
KALONA
Brenneman, Mary Forney
English Teacher
Conaway, Laura Ann Anderson
Reading & Language Arts Tchr
Hancock, Richard Anthony
Language Arts Teacher
Rhodes, Dean E.
Spanish & Sociology Teacher
Smith, Rolland Perry
Geometry & Religion Teacher
KEOKUK
Anderson, Phyllis Lichtenberg
7th Grade Science Teacher
Breshears, John William
Math, Physics & Cmptr Instr
Hardy, Linda Kay
Art Dept Chair & English Tchr
Huls, Kathy Lynn
5th Grade Teacher
Kiedaisch, Deverie Peterson
Mathematics Teacher
Little, Amy Morrison
Substitute Teacher
Strong, Pamela Jean
Business Education Teacher
Struck, Randy Alan
PE & Social Studies Teacher
Turner, Doris Strunk
Math & Science Teacher
Vandenberg, Jim
Social Studies Teacher
Wendt, David Allen
Speech, Eng & Drama Teacher
KEOTA
O'Connor, Lynell Jeanette
Math & Elem TAG Teacher
KNOXVILLE
Hanifan, Marjorie Jane
Former 1st Grade Teacher
Johnson, Joel John
High School Business Teacher
Lane Florez, Sheri Kayleen
English Teacher & Athletic Dir
Phillips, Lloyd Keith
9th Grd Physical Science Tchr
Scott, Larry Michael
High School Art Teacher
Sloan, M. Jane Mc Cauley
2nd Grade Teacher
LA PORTE CITY
Gingrich, Craig Alan
Biology & Human Anatomy Tchr
Slessor, Ellen Boes
Life Skills & Health Instr
Wigg, Bruce Jay
Social Science Teacher
LAKE CITY
Devine, M. Jeanne (Haugen)
Title I Reading & Math Teacher
Jacobs, Julia Schacherer
Business Ed, Cmptr Aplctn Tchr
Schaefer, Mark Steven
Biology Instructor
Von Glan, Donna
Math Teacher
LAKE MILLS
Aamodt, Julie Hillman
4th Grade Teacher
Grotewold, Brad Erling
Guidance Counselor
LAKE PARK
Richardson, Gary A.
HS Principal
Trow, Nancy Shultz
Math Teacher
LAKE VIEW
Mitchell, Sharon Peterson
High School English Teacher
Waggie, David Layne
Science Teacher
Willems, Arlan L.
English & Journalism Teacher
LAKOTA
Hill, Larry David
Principal & Ed Consultant
LAMONI
Anders, Steven Lee
Prof of Ec & Soc Sci Div Chair
Dauzvardis, Shirley M.
Asst Professor of Nursing
DeBarthe, Linda M.
Asst Prof of Acctng & Bus Admn
Evans, Billie Griffin
Eng, Speech & Journalism Tchr
Hawley, James F.
Professor of Mathematics
Henson, Peggy Anderson
Kindergarten Teacher
Horstman, Joey Earl
Instructor of English
Hunter, Suzanne
K-12 Music Teacher
Mesle, C. Robert
Prof & Chair of Phlsphy & Rel
Parkes, Brenda Armstrong
Professor of Nursing
Sherman, Stu Russell
PE Prof & Coach
Warner, Craig L.
Assistant Professor of Art
Waterman, Carole Lee
Speech Instructor
LANSING
Morgan, Peggy Pearce
7th-12th Grade Schl Counselor
LATIMER
Brown, Barbara Hyde
Literature & Lang Arts Tchr
LAURENS
Darrow, Lori Peterson
Mathematics & Computer Teacher
LAWTON
Lang, Thomas George
Science Teacher
Law, David E.
Mathematics Teacher
Peterson, Ronald G.
Science Teacher
LE GRAND
Hildebrandt, Willis Harvey
High School Art Teacher
LE MARS
DeKoster, Tom L.
5th Grade Teacher
Horan, Gale R. (Solheim)
Spanish Teacher
Isebrand, Cory Virgil
6th Grade Teacher
Rohlfsen, Georgia Lee
Language Arts Teacher
Tonsfeldt, Jolynn Marie
9th-12th Grd German Teacher
LENOX
Bearden, Lana Sue
Prin & K-12th Grd Curr Dir
Bertelle, Patty J.
Business Teacher
LEON
Griffieon, Michelle Ellis
Elementary Teacher
Helton, Ronald L.
Chem, Physics, Electronic Tchr
Horn, Mary Hutchison
English & Speech Teacher
LETTS
Colton, Peggy Lee
Sixth Grade Teacher
Vantiger, Thomas Robert
Math Teacher
LIBERTY CENTER
Scullen, Cathy (Manning)
High School Science Teacher
LIBERTYVILLE
Wells, Carol Teeter
Third Grade Teacher
LINDEN
Humphreys, Arlone Hughes
Third Grade Teacher
LINEVILLE
Marolf, Patricia Stiles
Language Arts & Soc Stud Tchr
LINN GROVE
Landsness, Phyllis Jane (Sewalson)
Lang Arts & Soc Stud Tchr
LOGAN
Muxfeldt, Laura Varnum
Rdng, Speech & Drama Tchr
LOST NATION
Hamdorf, Vicki
7th-8th Grade Math Teacher
LOWDEN
Buck, Cynthia Fae
Fifth Grade Teacher
LYTTON
Mc Neil, Jan
Mathematics & Health Teacher
MACEDONIA
Hummel, Helen H. (Boege)
4th Grade Teacher
MADRID
Christensen, Loa Marie
Consumer Teacher
Polich, Annette Madison
Third Grade Teacher
MALLARD
Gehrt, Joy Kingdon
Retired Teacher
Kapustynski, Peter John
Science Teacher
Yilek, Michael James
6th-8th Grd Social Stud Tchr
MANCHESTER
Bramman, Hank S.
7th Grade Math & Science Tchr
Dighton, Carol Thomas
5th Grade Teacher
Gaskill, Darla Herman
High School English Teacher
Hagelberg, Annette Bahlmann
Mathematics Teacher
Johansen, Brad
8th Grd Science & History Tchr
Keith, Joe
Social Studies & Math Teacher
Schultz, David Michael
Social Studies Teacher
Wallace, Karen Klaus
Math, Art & Soc Stud Tchr
MANILLA
Lewis, Phyllis North
Speech, Eng, TAG & Media Tchr
Smith, Fay G. Nelson
High School English Teacher
MANLY
Anderson, David William
Jr High Sci & Geography Tchr
Kloster, Vaugn Willard
HS Mathematics Instructor
Pratt, John Irving
Social Studies Tchr & Ath Dir
MANNING
Shannon, Lori Ann (Hekter)
English & Speech Instructor
MANSON
Jimmerson, Jerrold Phillip
Instrumental Music Tchr
Kistenmacher, Kristin Johnson
Vocal Director
Zinnel, Jeffery Lynn
English Teacher
MAPLETON
Johnston, Mark Aaron
High School Social Sci Tchr
MAQUOKETA
Ott, Jim
School Psychologist
MARENGO
Hardie, Scott Kevin
Social Studies & History Tchr
Simmons, Linda Calkins
Instr of Gifted Ed & Coord
MARION
Bodensteiner, Margie Kruse
Elementary Teacher
Edaburn, Mary Lou Quinte
Second Grade Teacher
Ehlinger, Diane Marsh
Music Teacher
Goldstein, Kathe A.
Spanish Teacher
Hakanson, Harry D.
HS English & Humanities Tchr
Hills, Diane Brazell
4th-6th Grade Teacher
Kacere, Dee Parks
Family & Consumer Science Tchr
Kordick, Connie J.
Mathematics & Lang Arts Tchr
Menken, Debra Lynn
6th Grade Teacher
Miller, Ernest Virgil
7th Grd Lang Arts Teacher
Olson, J. Steve
Math Teacher
Piche, Kimberly A.
HS Mathematics Teacher
Pratt, Judith L.
5th & 6th Grade Teacher
Soukup, Sheri Hildebrand
Fifth & Sixth Grade Teacher
Turner, Jeanne (Hammen)
High School Social Stud Tchr
Young, Joan Elizabeth Crogham
Business Education Teacher
MARSHALLTOWN
Bell, Tim R.
Associate Principal
Fitzgerald, Mary Kelly
7th Grade Language Arts Tchr
Hanson, Gloria Beemer
Vocal Music Teacher
Ketchum, Karen Seastrum
5th Grade Teacher
Lamb, Susan Leith
Teacher of the Special Needs
Lang, Julie Jontz
Fourth Grade Teacher
Mogard, Connie Maureen
7th Grd Language Arts Teacher
Peterson, Donald Dean
World Cultures Teacher
Rakowicz, Jerry Lee
7th Grd Social Studies Tchr
Rozell, Richard L.
Mathematics Teacher
Wagaman, Samantha Conte
Third Grade Teacher
Whitver, Kevin Dean
Language Arts Teacher
Wooster, Stan
8th Grd American History Tchr
MASON CITY
Balk, Gene Anthony
10th Grade Biology Tchr
Christianson, Steven Alan
Spanish Teacher
Edel, Meri Schoer
Spanish Teacher
Everist, Joel Jonathan
Director of Choral Activities
Foster, Barbara Kay
Mathematics Teacher
Grommesh, Laura Lynn
9th-12th Grd German Teacher
Harris, Ellen (Hill)
Retired Language Arts Teacher
Hugo, Steven Douglas
PE Teacher & Swim Coach
Johnson, Robert Wayne
8th Grd Sci & Soc Stud Tchr
Klemas, John Lee
Director of Instrumental Music
Krull, Cynthia Edwards
Journalism & English Teacher
Kuhlman, Ann Bullock (Davis)
Ethics & Philosophy Instructor
Larson, Kacy LuAnn (Bohach)
Office Technology Instructor
Lichman, Laurie Ann (Fountas)
Fifth Grade Teacher
Luker, Rohn
Art Teacher & Team Leader
Nyhus, Gary L.
Math Teacher & Dept Chairman
Olson, Paul Buxton
Government Teacher
Perrin, Charles Austin
Math & Pre-Engineering Instr
Rezab, Ava Smith
Math & Social Studies Teacher
Rosenberg, Dale N.
Pyschology Instructor
Ryan, Rosie
Fifth Grade Teacher
Slaven, Tim
Theatre Instructor
Sloan, Kay Block
5th Grade Teacher
Stattelman, Leo William
Latin Teacher
Tacheny, Rita Catherine
5th Grade Teacher
Taylor, Jean Evelyn
Resource Teacher
Vega, Raymond Michael
Spanish Teacher
Vix, Katharin Ann (Finn)
Alg, Pre-Alg & Commnctns Tchr
Yarrow, Keith P.
Math Curriculum Specialist
Zoellner, Craig Allen
Professor of Natural Sciences
MASSENA
Lage, Lance Lynn
Social Studies & PE Teacher
MAYNARD
Burke, William Raymond
Science Teacher
Palas, David L.
Math & Computer Science Instr

APOLIS
ı, Dave Alan
rade Teacher
Joyce Charbonneaux
er Sixth Grade Teacher
an, Ralph O., III
School Biology Teacher
nnell, Lyle Denton
Teacher & Ath Dir
, Jill Hardin
h Grade Teacher
Cerwin D.
trial Technology Teacher
, Elon A.
ce Teacher
, Thomas LeRoy
ch & English Teacher
HER
oger Dean
Arts, Speech & Drama Tchr
ORD
s, Gregory Robert
uage Arts Teacher
O
Scott Bradley
le Schl Lang Arts Teacher
OURI VALLEY
, Mitch M.
Music Teacher
Nancy Patricia
Grade Teacher
s, Catherine Schall
School English Teacher
Cynthia Neujahr
nth Grade Teacher
OAMIN
Kimberly Michelle
Grade Teacher
ori Lynn (Weiland)
rade Teacher
ONA
ell, Mary Engelhardt
nan Teacher
us, James Dean
nce Teacher
n, Peter Newland
Grade Teacher
Shirley Jean (Hauan)
ish Teacher
ROE
Jacqueline Ann
ish & Journalism Teacher
na, Kathy Allen
ish Instructor
Todd Linden
Biology & Physiology Tchr
ris, Eileen Lundy
ness Ed Teacher
oud, Linda Maria (Garrison)
Arts & Mass Media Teacher
er, Leslie Joe
strial Technology Teacher
TEZUMA
son, Phyllis Randels
red Teacher
, Darrell Gene
ndary Principal
on, Rick Joe
business Instructor
ch, Ronald Eugene
hematics Department Head
TICELLO
, Lucy Mae
ding Teacher
hy, Denise Elizabeth
th Grade Teacher
z, Dea William
School Lang Arts Tchr
, David W.
Teacher
TOUR
James G.
& 5th Grade Teacher
RHEAD
d, Timothy Michael
strial Technology Teacher
h, Kreg Andrew
sical Ed & History Teacher
AVIA
, Georgia Mae
ish Instructor
LTON
tt, Marilyn Jane (Klum)
cial Ed & Vocational Tchr
n, Glenda Burns
rth Grade Teacher
Kathryn Marie
ond Grade Teacher
NT AYR
nan, Marcia Ridnour
red 2nd Grade Teacher
n, John Arthur
hematics Teacher
on, John Paul
Teacher
ring, Linda Pittsenbarger
r High Librarian
le, James E.
ial Studies Teacher
nkamp, James J.
lish & German Teacher
NT PLEASANT
Marilyn Rae
ired 6th Grade Teacher
on, Kirby D.
Grade Teacher
orth, Thomas Robert
Grade Teacher
rd, Jeanne Kay
ond Grade Teacher

Litwiller, Calvin J.
Science Teacher & Dept Chm
Lowe, Betty Utsler
ESL Tchr & At Risk Coordinator
Osborne, Karen Anne (Viebrock)
Sixth Grade Teacher
Speidel, Sandra Kay
5th Grade Teacher
White, Carolyn Kay
9th Grade English Teacher
MOUNT VERNON
Michaud, Ruth Marie
English Teacher
MOVILLE
Grau, Daniel Neil
Chem, Physics & Calculus Tchr
Greene, Jane Annette
HS Science Teacher
Hubert, Carla J. (Beeler)
Middle Schl Language Arts Tchr
Manker, Kelly Robert
HS PE & Keyboarding Teacher
Miller, Larry Dean
6th-8th Grade Math Teacher
MURRAY
Luttenegger, Greg John
HS Math & Computer Sci Teacher
MUSCATINE
Brooker, Bruce Bentley
Science Teacher
Browne, Gregory Michael
Geograpy, US His & Govt Tchr
Clark, Chris Graham
ESL Teacher
Fillman, Heather Cynthia Hedtke
French & Physical Ed Teacher
Fowler, Christel Elaine Anderson
5th Grade Teacher
Harvey, Sarah Halligan
Mathematics Teacher
Hasson, Jerry Lee
Social Studies Teacher
Holland, Stephen Thomas
English & Journalism Teacher
Holler, Herb
PE Teacher & Dept Chair
Kaufmann, Jeffrey Allen
History Professor
Laviada, Diane Senne
First Grade Teacher
Meerdink, Louise Ann Forbes
Second Grade Teacher
Niederer, William G.
Choral & Vocal Music Director
Phillips, Janet McMillin
Music Teacher
Rivera, Matthew E.
Teacher of Behavioral Disorder
Teel, Jerry Ray, Jr.
Special Education Teacher
Velasquez, Charles Thomas
5th Grade Teacher
NASHUA
Edson, Connie S.
Kindergarten Teacher
Seamans, Patricia Edson
First Grade Teacher
Smith, Lorraine Hummel
Retired Teacher
NEOLA
Clausen, Arla Jo (Hildreth)
Vocal Music Teacher
Conway, Mary Vanderbur
HS Language Arts Instructor
Hornbostel, Larry William
Jr HS Social Studies Teacher
Krohn, Nancy Palmer
Kindergarten Teacher
NEVADA
Albers, Alton F.
Biology Teacher
Foley, Michael J.
Amer His Tchr & Track Coach
Schneider, William Lee
Mathematics Teacher
Swanson, Marlys R. (Wycoff)
Third Grade Teacher
Upchurch, Joni Madsen
High School English Instructor
NEW HAMPTON
Colvin, Barbara Thomas
Math Teacher
Conlon, Alice Meyer
Principal
Felton, Thomas F.
HS Physical Science Teacher
Fliris, Rachel Ann
Fourth Grade Teacher
Fredrichs, Nadean E.
Reading Teacher
Gage, Bonnie Wolfe
First Grade Teacher
Hugh, Linda Ann Langin
Sixth Grade Reading Teacher
Kubesh, Donald Joseph
Physical Education Instructor
Meyer, Joan Shonka
Seventh & Eighth Grade Teacher
Prehm, David
HS Visual Arts Teacher
NEW LONDON
Coberley, Ronald D.
Instrumental Music Director
NEW SHARON
Alexander, Vance E.
Industrial Technology Teacher
Gruber, Olganida Ziegler
First Grade Teacher
Hodgeman, Lynn Norton
HS Special Education Teacher

Strobel, Sherrill DeJong
Speech & Engligh Teacher
Sullivan, Mary Jane (Kohler)
6th Grd Math, Sci & Lang Tchr
Winegardner, Patricia Louise
Family & Consumer Sci Teacher
NEWELL
Caradine, Phyllis Nelson
Bus Ed & Social Studies Tchr
NEWHALL
Sankey, Kenneth T.
Seventh-Eighth Grade Teacher
NEWTON
Bartels, Mary Beth
First Grade Teacher
Bergeson, Sharon Kay
6th Grade Teacher
Caldwell, Jeanne Myerscough
Orch Dir & Music Dept Chprsn
Clayton, Russell D.
Retired Teacher
Delgado, A. Charlie
Spanish Teacher
Dunham, Leonard Wayne
Industrial Technology Teacher
Eckhart, Mary Ann
Language Arts & Speech Teacher
Else, Dina Ryan
Vocal Music Director
Ergenbright, Ed Paul
MS Resource Teacher
Fitzgerald, Patricia Kout
Fourth Grade Teacher
Gutz, Ann Louise
Language Arts Teacher
Kramer, Carol Annette
Sixth Grade Teacher
Lloyd, Larry Lee
Sixth Grade Teacher
Mullan, Mary Angstman
Sixth Grade Teacher
Mullan, Steven G.
Lang Arts & Speech Comm Instr
Quanbeck, Marie Hagene
Lang Arts, Rdng & Span Tchr
Shirley, Trudy Highfill
Counselor
Simpson, Gloria Petersen
French Teacher
Stone, Andrew C.
Sixth Grade Teacher
Tisdale, Thomas Joe
7th Grade Social Studies Tchr
Ward, Doree Maxine
Psychology & Sociology Teacher
Wiley, Clyde Leon
Amer Government & History Tchr
NORA SPRINGS
Ghere, Mikel William
English & Drivers Ed Teacher
Hoffman, Randy Douglas
Teacher & Coach
Zbornik, Layton R., Jr.
Language Arts Teacher
NORTH LIBERTY
Powers, Leigh Mc Intosh
Former English Teacher
NORTHWOOD
Dakken, Deborah Hustad
Family & Consumer Sci Teacher
NORWALK
Hinders, Lonnie Lee
HS Physical Ed & Resource Tchr
Nielsen, Lori Ann (Burgin)
Vocal & General Music Teacher
OCHEYEDAN
Slagter, Corwin James
Jr High Teacher
ODEBOLT
Becker, Glenn Raymond
HS Business Education Teacher
Schmidt, Alan Lee
High School Science Teacher
OELWEIN
Kurt, Mary
Third Grade Teacher
Levin, Alanna Boyle
Fourth Grade Teacher
Mc Farlane, Douglas Evert
Band Director
Nederhoff, Dixie Kasemeier
Family & Consumer Science Tchr
Schwemm, Steven James
8th Grade Social Studies Tchr
Sivertsen, Tom
Journalism Teacher
OGDEN
Bardole, Richard Allen
Middle School Music Teacher
Stull, Gordon O.
History Teacher
OLIN
Achenbach, Sandi Smith
Fourth Grade Teacher
ONAWA
Humrichouse, Douglas Derek
Industrial Technology Teacher
Kersten, C. Kirk
Bio, Physiology, Life Sci Tchr
Kingsbury, Vicki Cose
English Teacher
Mc Laughlin, Robert Dean
Fifth Grade Science Teacher
Petersen, Joan Belfrage
Tchr, Gifted & Talented Coord
ORAN
Moeller, Dorlin
Math Teacher

ORANGE CITY
Bundt, Joel D.
HS Math Teacher
Elgersma, William Peter
English Teacher
Geurts, Marlene Louise
Language Arts Teacher
Koets, Paul Duane
Retired Fifth Grade Teacher
Miedema, Barry Alan
PE & Bible Teacher
TeGrotenhuis, Linda Juffer
First Grade Teacher
Wielenga, Larry Alan
Bible & Thelogy Teacher
Wiersma, Rachelle Kramer
English Teacher
ORIENT
Shallenberger, Billy Dean
MS Language Arts Instructor
OSAGE
Huegli, LeRoy Ervin
Computer & Mathematics Teacher
Kirkpatrick, Jeffrey DeWayne
Director of Bands
Knudtson, Mark Allen
Fourth Grade Teacher
Masmar, Pamela J. Stumberg
Fifth Grade Teacher
OSCEOLA
Ashley, Mildred Maxine
Retired 4th Grade Teacher
Riley, Frank W.
Math Dept Chair
Van Werden, Dotti Gene
First Grade Teacher
OSKALOOSA
Burrichter, Lorene E.
5th Grade Teacher
Burrow, Paul Irving
Spanish & Social Studies Tchr
Dieleman, Edwin D.
7th & 8th Grade Math Teacher
Hatch, Gerald Everett
Retired 7th Grd Soc Stud Tchr
Hoch, Eleanor May (Anderson)
Retired First Grade Teacher
Johnson, Clark Thomas
Social Studies Teacher
Johnson, Debra Latham
5th Grade Teacher
McClure, JoLynn
Resource & Spec Services Tchr
Rogers, David Royal
Sixth Grade Teacher
Sarver, Kristen Dye
English Teacher
Shuman, DeLores Rank
First Grade Teacher
Slofkosky, M. Kathleen
English Teacher
Smith, Suzanne (Dooley)
Mathematics Teacher
Swim, Donald E.
Math Dept Chair
Van Hooser, Gayle
Vocal Music Instructor
Wright, Randall Mark
English Department Chair
OTTUMWA
Altfillisch, Heidi Hanna
Bookkeeping Instructor
Buttel, Theodore Lyle
Science Instructor
Carlson, Kay Vetterick
Retired Supvr of Student Tchrs
Cox, Cheryl Kinder
English Teacher
De Moss, Leland Charles
Art Instructor
Fisher, Colette Marie
Health & Home Economics Tchr
Flournoy, Douglas Stewart
Instructor of Chemistry
Hendred, Jeffrey Dale
Principal
James, Crystal Carr
9th Grd English & Speech Tchr
McGinity, Kevin Brian
Science Teacher
Mc Williams, Mike
History Civilization Teacher
Miller, Cherie L.
Fourth Grade Teacher
Miller, H. Stephen
Instrumental Music Instructor
Parsons, Jean
English Teacher
Patrick, Lloyd A.
Math Teacher
Peck, Ana Hernandez
10th-12th Grade Spanish Tchr
Rainey, Richard J.
US His & Govt Tchr
Schuck, Julie Critchlow
Spcl Ed Tchr
Seddon, Marcia Kay (Pettit)
Social Science Instructor
Slaymaker, Vernon Forrest
Advanced Chemistry Teacher
Stahlhut, Karen Willhite
Algebra Teacher
Starcevich, Patricia Landis
Kindergarten Teacher
Vogt, Linda Wallin
Counselor
Warren, Bob
Social Studies Teacher
Wright, Sarah Cross
5th Grade Teacher

PACKWOOD
Calvin, Patricia J.
English Teacher
Dickey, Suanne Adam
2nd Grade Teacher
Sathoff, Art M.
Secondary English Teacher
Van Voorst, Harlan Jacob
Math Instructor
Witzenburg, Robert Keith
Math & Science Teacher
PARKERSBURG
Garbe, Susan Mary (Olson)
HS Math & Computer Teacher
PARNELL
Gronlund, Carol Clark
Teacher of Gifted & Talented
PAULLINA
Brasser, Kevin Jay
Life Science Instructor
Vige, Dana Konrad
History Teacher
PELLA
Carter, D. Lester
Chemistry & Physics Teacher
Hartman, William
Bible & American History Tchr
Hoekstra, Wilma Damhof
Retired First Grade Teacher
Kooi, Fred Earl
Music Teacher
Muether, Charles Alexander
English Teacher & Chairperson
Olsthoorn, Brenda Veenstra
Third Grade Teacher
Robinson, Thomas Earl
Special Education Tchr Assn
Ryken, Edie (VanderLinden)
6th Grade Language Arts Tchr
Schulte, Matthew Lee
High School Mathematics Tchr
VanderLeest, Dorothy VandeKrol
Integrated Lang Arts Teacher
Vande Voort, Pamela Simmons
Adjunct Instructor
VerMeer, Jerry Lee
History & PE Teacher
Visser, Ann Mutti
English & Journalism Instr
Vos, Judy A. De Jong
Curriculum Dir & TAG Coord
Weld, Jeffrey D.
Biology Instructor
Westerkamp, Nancy Eileen
Fifth Grade Teacher
Willis, Barbara DenOuden
7th Grade Lang Arts Teacher
PEOSTA
Brimeyer, James Leon
English Teacher
Hughes, Rosalie Garrett
Coord of Hlth Occupations
PERRY
Irwin, Marilyn Ulfers
Third Grade Teacher
Moore, Mary Kathleen
Eighth Grade Language Teacher
PLAINFIELD
Frost, Alan Dean
Physical Education Teacher
Haberman, Joyce Schluter
Math Teacher
Klapperich, Barbara Purcell
Art Tchr, Tchr of Gftd & Tlntd
Lines, Christi Abbas
MS Language Arts Teacher
PLEASANT VALLEY
Hatfield, Kevin John
4th Grade Teacher
Hodge, Dalen Dwain
7th-9th Grade Math & Sci Tchr
Kuebrich, Janelle Marie
Family & Consumer Sci Instr
Moross, Linda D.
Biological Sciences Teacher
PLEASANTVILLE
Adreon, Tom E.
Industrial Technology Teacher
Betterton, M. Glenadean Van Zee
Kindergarten Teacher
Heimer, Joseph Vincent
English Educator
POCAHONTAS
Gruber, Richard C.
Middle School Social Stud Tchr
Kibbie, Kay Myers
Health & Biology Teacher
Rude, Margaret J.
Fourth Grade Teacher
Schott, Jane Frerk
2nd Grade Teacher
POMEROY
Bevan, Robert S.
Soc Stud Speech & Drama Tchr
POSTVILLE
Bossom, James Donald, Jr.
Bio, Anatomy & Physiology Tchr
Campbell, Mona A.
Middle School Math Teacher
PRAIRIE CITY
Bird, Michelle Frank
7th Grade Language Arts Tchr
Elrod, Mary Bone
Fourth Grade Teacher
PRESTON
Frost, Joel Allen
Ag Ed Instr & FFA Adv
Larson, Denise Renee
K-12th Grade Art Teacher

PRESTON (cont)
Stewart, David Wayne
Social Studies & English Tchr
PROTIVIN
Chyle, Arlene Sobolik
Elementary Teacher
RADCLIFFE
Barber, Donald Vernon
Social Studies Teacher
Nehring, Linda Jo
5th Grade Teacher
READLYN
Bruns, Patricia Ann (Warrick)
Seventh & Eighth Grade Teacher
RED OAK
Button, Jeff
7th Grd Social Studies Teacher
Deter, Robert A.
Business Teacher
Elliott, Tracy Lynn
7th Grade Mathematics Teacher
Gilbert, Mike
High School English Teacher
Godbout, Ronald D.
Eighth Grade Math Teacher
Johnson, Kathleen Prichard
Biology & Anatomy Teacher
Spangenberg, Angela Ridnour
HS Social Studies Teacher
REDFIELD
Frantum, Marla Jean
Middle School Counselor
REINBECK
Bailey, Pattie Petersen
5th Grade Teacher & Coord
Hild, Roxine (Hoeppner)
Mathematics Teacher
REMBRANDT
Skelton, Kristin Jones
Kindergarten Teacher
REMSEN
Elkins, Carol Ann
English Teacher
Feilmeier, Curt H.
Business Tchr & Ath Dept Dir
Groetken, Alan Leo
Math & Social Studies Tchr
Kahler, Kevin Michael
Theology & Government Teacher
Klein, Susan M.
Elementary Computer Instructor
Nacke, Peg Meacham
Mathematics & Religion Teacher
Shostak, Barbara Janssen
Junior High Instructor
RICEVILLE
Beelman, Gary E.
K-8th Grade PE Teacher
Grady-Mans, Ellen Marie
5th-6th Grd Eng & Rdng Tchr
Larson, Thomas A.
Junior High English Teacher
RIDGEWAY
Adamec, Evelyn Grace (Sobolik)
Sixth Grade Teacher
ROCK RAPIDS
Keizer, Angela Rae (Kopsas)
4th Grade Teacher
Snyder, Daniel Paul
7th Grade English & Lit Tchr
ROCK VALLEY
Kelderman, Robert Gene
Social Studies Teacher
ROCKFORD
Halsted, Doug Victor
Guidance Cnslr & Athletic Dir
Higby, Ronald Eugene
Business & Computer Teacher
Shultz, Kent Joel
Social Studies Teacher
ROCKWELL
Sheriff, Doug W.
5th & 6th Grade Teacher
Storey, Cheryl Ann (Houck)
Mathematics & Computer Instr
Twedt, Mark H.
Secondary Science Tchr & Coach
ROCKWELL CITY
Albinger, Jean Ann
Family & Consumer Sci Teacher
Wintz, Diane Kay
Music Teacher
ROLFE
Cook, Sharyn Kirsch
Voc Mus, TAG & MS Teacher
ROWLEY
Krone, Richard Allen
Fifth Grade Teacher
RUNNELLS
Anderson, Tracy Colleen
Secondary English Instructor
Bauer, Lowell Dale
Mathematics Instructor
Bredlow, Charles W.
Amer History & Success Tchr
Brill, Kirk L.
High School Biology Teacher
Elrod, Hugh Ernest
Senior High Mathematics Tchr
Horton, Joseph Michael
Eng Tchr & Wrestling Coach
Horton, Michael William
Industrial Technology Teacher
Pevestorf, Kevin Loren
Science Teacher
Pitkin, Richard V.
English Teacher
Schilling, Tracey Timmerman
American History Teacher

Svendson, Ray James
Principal
Wood, Mary Vasbinder
Eighth Grade English Teacher
SAC CITY
Birkhofer, Segna Grace
English Instructor
Fischer, Michael Francis
Sixth Grade Teacher
Seieroe, Thomas E.
Math & Physics Teacher
Sorensen, Larry Eugene
Language Arts Teacher
Youll, Thelma Richards
Retired Teacher
SAINT ANSGAR
Brodersen, Shirley Ann
High School English Teacher
Fell, Cynthia Meinen
Coord & Teacher of GATE
SANBORN
Bosma, Karen K. (Nederhoff)
Jr High Language Arts Teacher
Cougill, Kimberly Kay
Fifth Grade Teacher
Jacobsen, Marla Simdorn
6th Grade Language Arts Tchr
SCRANTON
Murphy, Karen Barr
4th Grade Teacher
Whitver, Rebecca Farley
First Grade Teacher
SERGEANT BLUFF
Friedmann, Ken John
Science Dept Chprsn & Bio Tchr
Ruble, Mary Cartmell
5th Grade Teacher
Zarbano, Dane Tonner
Spanish & Special Ed Teacher
SEYMOUR
Doggett, Dennis Neil
Business & Marketing Teacher
Parker, Mary Waelder
Director of Vocal Music
SHEFFIELD
Borgie, Kristin Ann
English Teacher
Morey, Patricia Jane
Elementary Counselor
SHELBY
Lippold, Joanne Joyce
Retired Elem Teacher
SHELDON
Adams, Mary Ann (Hellman)
Family & Consumer Sci Tchr
Gildehaus, Lisa Jane
Lang Arts, Jrnlsm, Speech Tchr
Gude, James Anthony
8th Grade Science Teacher
Hillary, David Osborne
Math, Sci & Social Stud Tchr
SHELL ROCK
Garth, Greg Paul
6th Grd Lang Arts Tchr
SHENANDOAH
Beery, Pamela Jean (King)
Vocal Music Teacher
Briese-Le Fever, Patricia
English & Social Sci Teacher
Dilks, Jeffery Lynn
9th Grd Physics & Science Tchr
Henderson, Linda Turner
Language Arts Teacher
Hinz, JoAnn Fender
Science Teacher
Merical, Todd Charles
Sixth Grade Teacher
West, S. Doyle
Sixth Grd Math & Science Tchr
SIBLEY
Bradfield, Joseph Francis
High School English Teacher
Earll, Michael Dean
Agricultural Ed Tchr & FFA Adv
Koerselman, Cornelius Gerrit
High School Guidance Counselor
SIDNEY
Eitzmann, Roger Neil
PE, Life Sci & Bio Tchr
Jorgenson, Sarah Strong
Sixth Grade Teacher
Williams, Tammy
English Teacher
SIGOURNEY
Edmundson, Lois Masterson
Retired Teacher
Gilliland, Fred
HS Social Studies Teacher
SIOUX CENTER
Ellis, Jean Gant
7th-12th Grd Physical Educator
Franken, Vicki L.
Counselor
Grimm, Norman Russell
Vocal Music Director
Schut, Donna Sue (Intveld)
Fourth Grade Teacher
Tacke, Dennis G.
High School English Teacher
Van Kley, Dennis Lee
Fifth Grade Teacher
Wiekamp, Gerald Eugene
Science Teacher
Wierda, Martin A.
Social Studies Teacher
SIOUX CITY
Bergeson, Donna Schirck
Third Grade Teacher
Busker, Jean A.
Choral Director

Campbell, Connie Jo
6th Grade Teacher & Elem Supv
Dillman, Kristin Lee
Instrumental Music Teacher
Eichhorn, Laurin Edward
Math Teacher
Ericson, Ginny M.
Fifth Grade Teacher
Flom, Larry James
History Teacher
Greene, Susan
2nd Grade Teacher
Hanson, Mary Curry
Business Instructor
Hantla, Ruth Grindberg
Fifth Grade Teacher
Henderson, Robert James
Mathematics Instructor
Herman, Douglas Carter
Biology Teacher
Hickman, Kim Marie (Vinopal)
Fifth Grade Teacher
Holder, Ruth Campbell
Language Arts Instructor
Hoye, Elena
Religious Education Director
James, Anne Niemer
English & Reading Teacher
Loffswold, Norma Fischer
Eighth Grade Math Teacher
Mc Williams, Deb Tjebben
Third Grade Teacher
Murphy, Margaret Teresa
Theology & History Teacher
Poston, Thomas H.
English Professor
Rogers, Michael Jordan
Vice Principal
Steunenberg, John Eric
5th Grade Teacher
Stone, Gayle Kloeppel
5th Grade Teacher
Strayer, Janet Myers
Life Science & Geography Tchr
Tingle-Crozier, Sheri L.
Business Education Teacher
Trysla, Margaret Hartnett
Language Arts Teacher
Washington, George
Phys Sci Tchr & Acad Chprsn
Wassell, Ric Wayne
Earth & Biology Teacher
Young, Janet Marie (Liibbee)
Mathematics Teacher
SIOUX RAPIDS
Mc Clatchey, Lynn Groen
Science Teacher
Rachuy, Kendall Dean
High School Mathematics Tchr
Westergaard, Bobbie Brand
French Teacher
SLATER
Wierson, Kim Thompson
Fourth Grade Teacher
SLOAN
Greder, Todd Gordon
Mathematics Teacher
Kendall, Jean D.
Secondary Language Arts Tchr
Smith, Cheryl Shook
Secondary Math Instructor
SOLON
Berry, Ed. D.
HS Math Teacher
Hanes, Jeanne Marie
Second Grade Teacher
Nettleton, Karen Weis
Mathematics Teacher
SOUTH ENGLISH
Grice, Linda Elaine (Britten)
Consultant of Gifted-Talented
SPENCER
Bruning, Marc Christopher
Spanish Teacher
Frank, Mary Hazen
English Tchr & TAG Coord
Hecht, Lori Ann
Choral Director
Koppen, Diana Doocy
4th Grade Teacher
Rath, Arla H. (Proehl)
High School English Teacher
Waggoner, Dale Allen
MS Social Studies Teacher
SPIRIT LAKE
Purdy, Janice Baker
Third Grade Teacher
SPRINGVILLE
Ball, Mark Earl
Fourth Grade Teacher
Blackwell, Rick L.
Principal
Medberry, Susan Cassaday
English & Spanish Teacher
Read, Alan Scott
PE, Health Tchr & Ath Dir
Weber, Vickie F.
English Teacher & Dept Chair
Wilig, David Roger
High School Art Instructor
STANTON
Eklof, Patricia Kay
Bus Ed & Cmptr App Tchr
Mead, Karen Marie
Fourth Grade Teacher
Nelson, Marla German
K-12th Grade Vocal Music Tchr
Stephens, Gary Douglas
Jr Sr High School Principal

STANWOOD
Hunt, David Arthur
HS Social Studies Teacher
Lange, Sarah Colleen
High School Mathematics Tchr
STATE CENTER
Burroughs, Natalie Allen
7th Grd Rdng & Lang Arts Tchr
Hoskey, Vickie Wright
English Teacher
Van Weelden, Kimberly Dianne (Lindblad)
6th-12th Grd Vocal Music Tchr
STORM LAKE
Anderson, Nancy Lee
Lang Arts & History Teacher
Blanchard, John David
Computer Educator & Coord
Bochtler, Stanley Edwin
Professor of Ed
Brostad, John Charles
8th Grade Mathematics Teacher
Cole, Sarah Marie
English & Religious Ed Teacher
Cone, Cynthia Lea
Secondary Speech & Drama Instr
Fields, Marilyn
High School Mathematics Tchr
Gadeken, Cheryl Buss
HS Mathematics Teacher
Gill, Mary Margaret
Communications Professor
Haack, Duane Glen
Asst Prof of Composition & Lit
Higley, Wayne M.
Accounting Professor
Inglis, Laura Lyn
Phlsphy, Rel Asst & Assoc Prof
Lewis, Dee Dunham
Third Grade Teacher
Madsen, John
Assoc Prof of Bus & Corp Comm
Mc Daniel, Timothy Elton
Asst Prof of Math & Statistics
Mc Kenna, Janet Beenken
Third Grade Teacher
Miller, Jay L.
Retail Specialist
Nichols, James Alan
History Teacher
Nicholson, A. Dean
8th Grd Physical Science Tchr
Parkhurst, Donald Dean
Scndry English & History Tchr
Peterson, Rose Hainline
Spanish Teacher
Redding, Dorothy Jean
Family & Consumer Science Tchr
Seitz, Susan M.
Associate Professor of English
Ullerich, Stanton G.
Economics Professor
STUART
Bauch, Nancy (Hendren)
Speech, Drama & Eng Teacher
Broman, Tod Arthur
Biology Teacher
King, Jacqueline J.
English & Spanish Teacher
SULLY
Hubbard, Taylor Kuhlman
Science & Math Teacher
Robidoux, Jim H.
Spanish & English Teacher
SUMNER
Helmers, Patricia Jo
Science & Health Teacher
Smothers, Berle Wayne
Retired English Tchr & Prin
Smothers, Margaret Ann (Burr)
Retired Choral Director
VanDeBerg, Joanna M.
Band Director
Walke, Gary D.
HS Social Studies Teacher
SWEA CITY
Friedow, William Joseph
HS Counselor & French Teacher
Kaufman, Stephanie Marie
Director of Bands
TABOR
Malcom, Daisy Berry
English Teacher
Roberts, David Lee
Middle & HS Science Teacher
Wood, Michael Howard
Jr High Math Teacher
TAMA
Hanna, Bruce C.
Mathematics Teacher
Masters, Terry Joe
Art Educator
Mills, Jan Owen
Vocal Teacher
TERRIL
Byers, Brian Keith
Social Studies Teacher & Coach
THORNBURG
Bell, Nancy Lewis
Second Grade Teacher
Blair, Kevin Earl
Agricultural Education Teacher
THORNTON
Heitland, Alice Elaine
6th Grade Teacher
TIFFIN
Farrell, Mary Wagner
Business Teacher & MOC Coord
Maas, Kurt Edward
High School Teacher

Mustaine, Donna Lynch
Science Teacher
TIPTON
Leighty, Kay Hasselbusch
Second Grade Teacher
White, Jeanne Pohlmann
First Grade Teacher
TOLEDO
Clemens, Gary Louis
8th Grade Math Teacher
Heller, Terri Dunlap
8th Grade Reading Teacher
TRAER
Crawford, Kenneth Ronald
Business Educational Teacher
Halupnick, Janice Mary
Family & Consumer Sci Tchr
Lindaman, Jennifer Frazell
Secondary Mathematics Teacher
Vesely, Rick Dean
Var Vlybl, Pastor & Youth Dir
Wiges, Leland Earl
Science Teacher & Coach
TREYNOR
Owens, Steven John
Social Studies Teacher
TRIPOLI
Kehe, Teresa Ann
Physical Education Teacher
TRURO
Baethke, Eugene
English Teacher
Busby, Jane (Martin)
Sr HS Science Instructor
Trieff, Barbara Ahnen
English Teacher
UNDERWOOD
Benzing, Nick
Govt Ec & World Cultures Tchr
Handbury, Julie Ann
MS Language Arts Teacher
Minssen, Tamera Ann Andersen
MS Math & Computer Teacher
Prewitt, Beverly A.
First Grade Teacher
Spiegel, Ray Allen
Biology & Physical Ed Teacher
UNIVERSITY PARK
Cooper, Floyd L.
Retired Teacher
DeVore, Kathryn Cooper
Frosh Compstn I & II Instr
Mills, Stephen Louis
History Professor & Chairman
Sprunk, Ralph
Retired Professor
URBANDALE
Burns, Mari Miller
English Tchr & Asst Drama Dir
Dubberke, Gail McArthur
Fifth Grade Teacher
Lerner, Deana Van Engelen
English Teacher
Monson, Brent Allen
English & Journalism Teacher
Peters, Gloria L.
HS Earth Science Teacher
Schreck, Dana S. Bowstead
Sixth Grade Teacher
Sorensen, Lana Hughes
English Teacher
Sweeney, Robert Lynn
Fifth Grade Teacher
Urich, Laura Jill Sporer
Counselor
UTE
Keating, Mary Ellen Schulte
Fifth Grade Teacher
VAN HORNE
Logan, Donald Dean
Psychology Teacher & Counselor
Peitz, Linda Hellyer
English Teacher
Rohlena, Bonnie Modracek
Family & Consumer Sci Teacher
Thomae, Martin
Sixth Grade Teacher
VAN METER
Druery, Wendy Elizabeth
English Teacher
McPherren, Marcia Hoos
Span Composition & Jrnlsm Tchr
Tapps, David E.
HS Math & Computer Teacher
VENTURA
Pierce, Brian Keith
Secondary Language Arts Tchr
Stewart, Bonnie LaRue
Vocal Music Teacher
VICTOR
Collingwood, Lori Maschmann
4th Grade Teacher
Cummings, William Howard
High School Math Teacher & Chm
Larkin, William Curtis
K-12th Grade PE Tchr & Coach
Nelson, Patricia Sue
First Grade Teacher
Prottsman, Jon Edward
Jr & Sr Science Teacher
Roe, Robert Andrew
Science Teacher
VILLISCA
DeVore, Matthew James
Mathematics Teacher
Nook, Teresa J.
English Teacher
VINTON
Frost, Jeffrey
High Schl Social Studies Tchr

N (cont)
Dorla Lyons
Grade Teacher
, Sharyl Eden
ocial Studies Instructor
OTT
Michael Dale
cal Education Teacher
Christine K. (Harper)
Arts & Reading Teacher
Thomas Anthony
ry & Language Arts Tchr
ER
ester, Victoria M.
d Grade Teacher
UT
n, Paulette Nielsen
y & Consumer Sci Instr
INGTON
n, Carolyn Van Houweling
Instructor
, Sandra L.
9th Grade Math Teacher
s, Max Lesley
Teacher & Track Coach
Monte James
cal Education Teacher
, Arlene R.
ess Teacher
, Michael James
man Science Teacher
usan Troutman
Teacher
Michael
rd Sci & Soc Stud Teacher
RLOO
e, Laura Winter
ducator
, Earlene
l Studies Teacher
ong, Daniel David
ematics Teacher
Marlan L.
ed Science Instructor
Bette Rae
nstructor
, Janice L. (Rippenkroeger)
ish Teacher
rth, Marcia Bockes
ergarten Teacher
g, Renee (Meyers)
I Rdng Recovery Teacher
wski, Brian Edward
ical Education Teacher
Edgar A.
c Department Chairperson
Roger John
essor
Bruce Dean
estra Director
y, Deretha J.
Grade Teacher
, Lydia Gurrero
entary Teacher
n, Kenneth Joseph
School Spanish Teacher
, Kenneth L.
stant Band Director
s, Carole O'Neill
Grade Teacher
an, Roger Lee
e Teacher
, Jeanne Judge
ish, Jrnlsm Tchr & Adv
Nancy Leigh
ish Teacher
ka, Thomas R.
guage Arts Teacher
Amy Betsworth
guage Arts & Math Teacher
, Kevin Eugene
Grade Math Teacher
, William John
nematics Teacher
ck, Sharon (Schmidt)
c & Preschool Teacher
n, Barbara Joan (Bacich)
nestra Teacher
ough, D. Patrick
ish & GATE Teacher
Dahlgreen Engel, Janis
lish Teacher
s, Anthony William
ness Education Teacher
os, Anne White
th Grade Teacher
er, Barbara Irene
nish Teacher
n, Ann Bader
h School Science Teacher
r, Lois A.
Grade Teacher
itt, Susan Elizabeth
Grade Teacher
l, Paulette Marie
al Science Tchr & Dept Hd
, Anjean Elizabeth
dergarten Teacher
er, Robert Dean
ence Teacher
lino, Michael Anthony
Science Instr & Coord
g-Kent, James Ernest
h, Gifted Ed Tchr & Coach
ERVILLE
on, Nancy Lopp
rth Grade Teacher
Kenneth Lee
cipal & PE Teacher

WAUKEE
Ferrell, Lorraine Lundgren
High School English Teacher
Krefting, Denise Herbel
Computer Teacher & Tech Coord
Tigges, Mark
HS Biology Teacher
WAUKON
Erion, Randy Jay
High School Physical Ed Tchr
Hay, Kathy Lee
Third Grade Teacher
Mindham, Leon Russell
8th & 9th Grade Science Tchr
Sawyer, Nona BetsCel
Fourth Grade Teacher
WAVERLY
Arns, David A.
Mathematics Teacher
Black, Daniel W.
Assistant Prof of Phys Sci
Duneman, Gary Donald
HS Social Studies Teacher
Egli, Pamela J. (Wehrkamp)
4th Grade Teacher
Hagen, Alan John
High School Choral Director
Harrison, Jane Ann
7th-8th Grd Eng & Math Teacher
Janssen, Sandra Dee Marsh
First Grade Teacher
Montague, Lynn Anthony
Art Dept Chair
Peters, Arthur Lynn
Social Work Professor
Ramthun, Susan L. (Buck)
Mathematics Teacher
Schneider, Richard John
Slife Professor in Humanities
Thorson, Sally Lynn (Odell)
Social Studies & TAG Tchr
West-Lentz, Teresa Lynn
English Teacher
WEBSTER CITY
Arras, Joyce Perotka
First Grade Teacher
Brock, Patsy L. Anderson
Teacher of Talented & Gifted
Bucknam, Nan Rudolph
Social Studies Teacher
Cramer, Melanie Peterson
French & Spanish Teacher
Haberman, Al F.
Business Education Teacher
Hansen, Rae Lavone
English Teacher
Jansen, Larry G.
US History Teacher
March, Mary Hoffman
Fifth-Sixth Grade Teacher
Nelson, Jerita Kay
Title One Reading Teacher
Nielsen, Larry Reese
Life Science Teacher
Oppold-Blessman, Bev
HS Business Education Teacher
Webb, Dennie Lyle
Third Grade Teacher
Zahn, John George
Science & Mathematics Teacher
WELLMAN
Brinning, Margaret Huber
First Grade Teacher
McClenahan, Craig Christopher
Instrumental Music Director
Schweinfurth, Susan Marie
High School English Teacher
WELLSBURG
Hansmann, Laura R.
English Teacher
Janssen, Larry D.
Business Education Teacher
Larson, Mary Ann Hazelhoff
Public School Music Teacher
WEST BEND
Besch, Ruby Zaugg
Retired 3rd-4th Grade Teacher
Grimm, Gilbert Lee
Mathematics Teacher
Larson, Richelle Stockton
Business Education Teacher
Metzger, Mary Fouts
4th Grade Teacher
Nelson, Barbara Lundy
Fam & Con Sci-Health Tchr
Wek, Anita Laurel
HS English, Journalism Teacher
Winkelhorst, Loren Jon
Industrial Technology Teacher
WEST BRANCH
Anderson, Carolyn Walker
Math, Science Tchr & Adm Asst
Arp, Jeffrey Wayne
4th Grade Teacher
Beatty, Cary Ross
High School English Teacher
Houser, Pamela Ann
Instrumental Music Instructor
Ibarra, Hector
Science Educator
Murphy, Bonnie Lemley
Reading Teacher
WEST BURLINGTON
Beaman, Ray Lee
HS Mathematics Teacher
Evans, James William
Guidance Counselor
Krekel, Donald Lee
Mathematics Instructor

Reid, Dan G.
Physical Ed Teacher & Coach
Sandberg, Barbara Marie
7th Grd Lang Arts & Rdng Tchr
Schach, Ann
Science Teacher
Schach, Margaret Ann
Science Teacher
WEST DES MOINES
Abrahamson, Kent B.
Language Arts Teacher
Brooks-Bentley, Hope Diana
5th Grade Teacher
Christiansen, Margaret A.
Sci, Chem & AP Biology Teacher
Cookman, Jay Preston
Counselor
Eklof, Jane Drobnich
Instrumental Music Teacher
Fitzgerald, Kathleen Teresa
HS Social Studies Teacher
Hendel, Marc E.
Mathematics Teacher
Hepburn, Jeffrey Blaine
Chemistry Instructor
Matthias, Nicole Ann (Knippel)
Math Teacher, Volleyball Coach
Mc Donald, Philip Grant
Social Studies Teacher
Mc Lean, Kathleen Monica
Chemistry & Physics Instructor
Meyer, Susan Kay
Language Arts Instructor
O'Brien, David Joseph
Theology Teacher
Olson, Judith F.
Language Arts Tchr & Dept Chm
Sanders, Kimberly Ann
Third Grade Teacher
Slemp, Dorothy M.
Mathematics Teacher
Thornton, John Edwin
European History Teacher
WEST LIBERTY
Carter, Thomas A.
Ec, Wrld Culture & Soclgy Tchr
Elder, Barbara Ann
5th Grade Teacher
Grady, Karla K.
Self-Contained Third Grd Tchr
Sutton, Sara L.
8th Grd US His & Reading Tchr
WEST UNION
Poppen, Douglas Alfred
7th-12th Grd Music Teacher
Scott, Robert John
Mathematics Teacher
Straate, Mary Elizabeth
Jr & Sr Eng Instr
WHEATLAND
Clough, Barry K.
Agriculture Education Instr
Drowns, Glenn Jay
Science Teacher
Knoll, August E.
HS Band Director
Williams, Debra Jo
Scndry Math & Psychology Tchr
WHITING
Forbes, Eudean
English, Speech & Span Tchr
Rodman, Robert Keith
Activities Dir & PE Teacher
Thatcher, Lori Kay
Art Teacher
WILLIAMSBURG
Kleinmeyer, Claudia Norton
2nd Grade Teacher
Mayer, Garwood R.
History Teacher
Mayer, Patricia Sue (Polich)
Sixth Grade Teacher
Wyatt, Beverly Elliott
Scndry Eng Tchr & Dept Chprsn
WILTON
Guss, Barbara Morse
10th & 12th Grade English Tchr
Hoekstra, Constance Lynn
Communications & Drama Teacher
Lawrence, John H.
Social Studies Teacher
Nolte, Donna Covell
Fourth Grade Teacher
WINFIELD
Hardy, Carolyn Ann (Wilkinson)
Computer Teacher
WINTERSET
Pope, Dona Butler
Art Teacher
Vogt, Barry Jay
Fourth Grade Teacher
Wheeler, Julie Ellen
First Grade Teacher
WINTHROP
Quint, Mary Ann Connolly
7th & 8th Grd Whole Lang Tchr
Short, Janice Miller
Middle School Literature Tchr
WOODWARD
Cupp, Jeffrey Robert
High School History Teacher
Pooler, Sally Marie
6th-12th Grade Guidance Cnslr
Werner, Jill Marie
Math Teacher
WYOMING
Greenfield, Daniel Paul
HS Science & Math Teacher

KANSAS

ABILENE
Cearley, Rex Lee
6th Grade Teacher
Foltz, Jane A. (Miller)
Parent Educator
ADMIRE
Johnson, E. Suzanne
Music Teacher
Stukey, Loretta
Fifth Grade Teacher
ALMA
Ayers, Avery Vanessa
Art Teacher
Jensen, Julie Beth Sheik
High School Math Teacher
Reinert, Barbara Kay (Dietz)
Music Teacher
Ronnau, Louise Roos
Elem Schl Physical Ed Tchr
Williams, Martin
Drafting Instructor
ALTAMONT
Crain, Karla Barnes
English Teacher
Gerdes, James Arthur
Social Science & Science Tchr
Holroyd, Richard M.
Industrial Arts & Tech Ed Tchr
Leake, Jack Kenneth
8th Grade Social Science Tchr
Milks, Warren Andrew
Automotive Technology Instr
Sauer, Rhonda Kay (Waller)
Teacher of Hearing Impaired
Semonick, Gary Martin
Social Science Instructor
Tongier, Joan Carter
Speech & Language Pathologist
Warren, Martin Lloyd
Electronics Instructor
Witty, Clinton Lyle
Secondary Mathematics Teacher
ALTOONA
Meier, LaRonna Kay (Hall)
Mathematics & Reading Teacher
AMERICUS
Cottenmyre, Denise Marie
Social Studies Teacher
Taylor, Brenda Ann (Richards)
3rd Grade Teacher
ANDALE
Alexander, Elizabeth Ann
English Teacher
Mounts, Alice May (Schippers)
Mathematics Teacher
ANDOVER
Hollenbeck, Michelle Dawn
6th Grade Tchr & Admin Intern
Humburg, Julia Kay (Reynolds)
5th Grade Teacher
Johnson, Richard E.
English Teacher & Bsktbl Coach
Lovelace, Skyler
Dir of Ctr for Learning Excl
Regehr, Donovan G.
Computer Science & Math Chm
Schrock, Deborah Lynne
Biology Instructor
Smith, Suzann Kinkead
8th Grade Social Studies Tchr
Thomas, Roberta Phillips
Facilitator of Gifted
ANTHONY
McLarty, Pamela Jean
Second Grade Teacher
ARGONIA
Adams, Gregory Allen
Secondary Math Teacher
ARKANSAS CITY
Allen, Bart W.
Business & Computer Professor
Culbertson, Kenneth
Biology Teacher & Coach
Eaton, Terry Hodkin
Dev Math Instructor & Coord
Gackstatter, Gary Lee
Band Director
Grunder, Beverly Jarboe
Accounting Instructor
Hallford, Randall L.
Instr of Chemistry & Physics
Hargrove, Ed G.
Director, Instructor & Coach
Harvey, Richard A.
Math Teacher
Hatfield, Elvin Morris
Criminal Justice Studies Prof
Head, Larry Dale
Director of Aeronautics
Hendricks, Cathy S.
Social Science Instructor
Hill, Sharon Yarbrough
Humanities Instructor
Juden, Reatha Bruner
Physical Education Teacher
Land, Shannon L.
Special Education Teacher
Moore, Suzanne Henry
Communications Teacher
Nittler, Deb Lee
Social Science Instructor
O'Hair, Steven Lee
Teacher
Paton, Peggy I.
Business & Office Tech Teacher
Phillips, Linda Brooks
Third Grade Teacher

Queen, Judith H.
Dir of Single Parent Program
Raines, Randy R.
Director of Bands
Rohr, Tony Edward
Math Teacher
Scram, Barb Lynne Rakestraw
Kindergarten Teacher
Sleeper, Lana Dee
Dance & Cheer Coach
Stinemetze, David Ray
Chemistry, Physics & Math Tchr
Stirnaman, Paul H.
History & Geography Instructor
Tidwell, D. Jean
Social Science Instructor
Young, Eugene A.
Adjunct Biology Instructor
Young, Ronald Eugene
Technology Coordinator
ARMA
De Armond, Patti Jo
K-12th Grd Vocal Music Instr
ASHLAND
Heath, Dan G.
English Teacher
ATCHISON
Albright, Marilyn Megli
Kindergarten Teacher
Anthony, Elizabeth Ann (Green)
6th Grade Reading Teacher
Ball, Terri Moyer
Business & English Teacher
Bradford, Lawrence
Associate Professor of Biology
Carrigan, Celine
Associate Professor of English
Fellin, Jo Ann, OSB
Math Dept Chair & Prof
Foster, Stephen Paul
HS Teacher of Gifted Program
Homan, Thomasita
English Professor
Hyland, William Patrick
History Professor
Jackson, Dan A.
English, Speech & Drama Tchr
Kaveler, Lu Ann
English Teacher
King, Max L.
Visual Arts Teacher
Noll, Marcia Arensberg
Interrelated Resource Teacher
Nowell, Irene, OSB
Community Formation Director
Oliver, Nancy Lee (Barker)
Second Grade Teacher
Palmer, E. Noelle
Science Dept Chair
Ridgeway, Margery Elisabeth Burleigh
Psychology Teacher
Rockey, Jusy Williams
First Grade Teacher
Stammers, Jon Michael
Title 1 Math Teacher
Stillings, Kelley Low
English & Journalism Teacher
Theis, Charles W.
Associate Professor of Music
Voysey, Jennifer Bednar
Soc Stud, Eng & Religion Tchr
Warner, Tod Iley
9th Grd General Science Tchr
Wiesner, Loretta, OSB
Retired Principal
ATTICA
Mc Diffett, Danton J.
High School English Teacher
ATWOOD
Bliss, Thomas Charles
Social Science Teacher
AUBURN
Miller, Sharon Cowell
Fifth Grade Teacher
AUGUSTA
Box, Linda L.
8th Grade History Teacher
Bradford, Ann (Stephens)
High School English Teacher
Conrady, Keith Wayne
Math Dept Chairman & Teacher
Hess, Richard C.
Social Studies Teacher
Kidd, Irma Eileen
Fifth Grade Teacher
Lawlor, Peter E.
Counselor
Nickel, Cindy L.
7th-8th Grd Lang Arts Teacher
Pavlicek, Kelli J.
Mathematics & Science Teacher
Pazzie, Steven Ray
Sr HS Drafting & Tech Tchr
Reed, Merita A.
8th Grade Science Teacher
Reichardt, Joan Mayers
HS History Teacher & Coach
Sayler, Larry Dayle
Physical Science Teacher
Stanyer, Jeri L.
Counselor
Stevens, Nathan T.
Science Teacher
AXTELL
Broxterman, Lisa A.
English Teacher
Wenz, James E.
Principal

BAILEYVILLE
Zimmerman, Charles Leon
Title I Teacher
BALDWIN CITY
Botkin, Richard Donald
Asst Professor of Philosophy
Cink, Calvin Lee
Professor of Biology
Dorsey, Stuart B.
Bus & Economics Dept Chair
Harris, Martha West
Associate Prof of Business
Honomichl, Virginia Ruth (Roglin)
Science Teacher
Schnitker, Thomas J.
Vice President of Student Svcs
Stuber, Gayle M.
Assistant Prof of Education
BASEHOR
Rodenbaugh, Sheila K.
Mathematics Teacher
BAXTER SPRINGS
Bough, Faye Jean
Elementary Counselor
Crotts, Linda Lee
5th Grade Teacher
Dillon, Daniel R.
English Teacher
Kissel, Greg Strong
HS US His & Government Teacher
Smittle, Ena S.
Spanish & French Teacher
Zordel, Susan Lynn
High School Mathematics Tchr
BELLE PLAINE
Coats, Leota Janzen
English Teacher
Happy, Judy Kaye
Sixth Grade Teacher
Kobbe, Roberta
4th Grd Lang Arts Tchr
McVeigh, Jason Leon
Bio, Anatomy & Physiology Tchr
Nicholas, Kevin S.
Technology Instructor
Rivers, Kristy Gentz
Language Arts Teacher
Taylor, Sherra S.
7th & 8th Grd Lang Arts Instr
Wellman, Martha Wilson
Fourth Grade Teacher
Williams, Terry Nolan
History Teacher
BELOIT
Boyd Tice, Helen Earlene
5th-8th Grade Counselor
Daniels, Dolores Shields
Math Teacher
Jorgensen, Janet Jean
Third Grade Teacher
Smith, Larry Eugene
Math & Computer Teacher
Tarrant, Kimberlee Crighton
Lang Arts & Soc Studies Tchr
BERN
Alfers, Julia Maxton
At-Risk Coordinator
Beachler, Wes C.
Health & PE Teacher
BERRYTON
Davis, Roxie Crouch
Second Grade Teacher
Weir, Lori Witt
4th Grade Teacher
BIRD CITY
Beougher, Barbara A.
Language Arts Instructor
Samson, Bernadine L.
Math & Physics Teacher
BISON
Stos, Lynnette Kay
English Teacher
BLUE RAPIDS
Gould, James David
Teacher
BOGUE
Pennington, Mary Lou
Retired Teacher
BONNER SPRINGS
Chandley, Martha Patterson
Family & Consumer Sci Instr
Decker, Ann Stengel
Mathematics Instructor
Engquist, Linda Vazquez
Kindergarten Teacher
Fernau, Marita Ann (Motacek)
Sixth Grade Teacher
Henry, Connie J.
Latin & English Teacher
Makona, John N.
Amer & World History Teacher
Matlock, Johnny Clay
Choral Music & Theater Dir
Mc Graw, Jane Heckart
HS Social Studies Teacher
Melius, Patricia Ann (Molid)
Spanish Teacher
Nelson, Marsha L.
French Teacher
Tate, Victoria A.
7th Grd Language Arts Teacher
Wood, Christine Tweedle
English Teacher
BREWSTER
Depe, Delores M. (Fixsen)
Lang Arts Instructor
BROOKVILLE
Brannon, Lorene Michele
English Teacher
Wulf, Kathryn
Librarian
BUCKLIN
Heier, Beverly A.
High Schl Social Science Tchr
Linn, John Charles
Business Teacher
Wiseman, Susan Bartlett
English Instructor
Wyrick, Gregory Dean
Physical Education Teacher
BUFFALO
Moews, Dawn Van Tuyl
English & Speech Teacher
BUHLER
La Force, Brona Joleen
Third Grade Teacher
Petty, Crystal Denise
Business Teacher
Porter, Charles C.
Physical Ed & US His Teacher
Swanson, Donna J.
Second Grade Teacher
BURDEN
Dennett, Susan Mae (Jones)
Business Instructor
Keplinger, Dorothy Hawley
Math Teacher
McCutcheon, Patricia Joan (Morgan)
English & Speech Teacher
Rivers, Priscilla Liebau
Sixth Grade Teacher
BURDETT
Walker, Joel Edward
MS Sci & Amer His Teacher
BURLINGAME
Buche, Tamara L.
6th-8th Grade Math Teacher
Curtis, Sheila Anne Godderz
English & Journalism Teacher
Rankin, Donna Hutton
English & Language Arts Tchr
BURLINGTON
Elson, Julie Dawn Sherraden
Elementary Counselor
Smith, Wendy Brown
LD Resource Room Teacher
BURR OAK
Curtis, Robert Grant
High School Science Teacher
Parton, Seresa Ann
Business & Computer Teacher
BUSHTON
Deighton, Dale Larry
Govt, Sociology & PE Teacher
CALDWELL
Bruey, Gail Ann
Fourth Grade Teacher
Cornejo, Karen Walcher
Language Arts Teacher
Ginn, Peggy Pettigrew
Vocal Music Teacher
Jamison, Alan D.
Jr Sr High Schl Soc Stud Tchr
Roberts, Kenneth Howard
Math Teacher
Struble, Veda Ann Bunch
Third Grade Teacher
CANEY
Collins, Betty Gower
Fifth Grade Teacher
Gordon, Shirley Joan (Jarvis)
Retired 4th Grade Teacher
Jensen, Julie K.
High School Computer Teacher
Stelfox, Rajean Taylor
Second Grade Teacher
Van Winkle, Diana Mc Burney
Second Grade Teacher
Warnock, Joseph Louis
Third Grade Teacher
Wright, Michele Marie
Music Teacher
CANTON
Koehn, Jack C.
History & Multi-Media Instr
CARBONDALE
Fockele, Linda J.
Third Grade Teacher
Marquart, Allan Paul
Spanish Teacher
Ricklefs, Sharon Dell Nesbitt
4th Grade Teacher
CAWKER CITY
Armknecht, Henry L.
Science & Computer Teacher
McKinnie, Shari Shellenberger
English & Journalism Teacher
Stroh, Sherry Lee (Emerson)
Span & Applied Commnctn Tchr
CEDAR VALE
Hass, Glendon Lee
Social Science Tchr & Coach
Seral, Goff Otis E., Jr.
Industrial Arts Shop Teacher
CENTRALIA
Bourne, Melvin E.
Bio Sci Tchr, Ath Dir & Coach
DeBord, Margaret Joyce
English & Psychology Teacher
CHANUTE
Allen, Pat Updegraff
Counselor
Babb, Charles Henry
Computer Science Instructor
Cadwallader, Linda Park
Third Grade Teacher
DiLisio, Michelle Specht
Physical Education Teacher
Keller, Barbara Ann
Retired Teacher
LaRue, Joan Kipp
Nursing Instructor
Nelson, Colletta Myers
Retired Nursing Instructor
Petersen, Barbara Gail
6th Grade Teacher
Robertson, Eileen Wulf
English Teacher
Swender, Lesta Irene (Hedman)
Psychology Instructor
Woods, Dixie Kay
Third Grade Teacher
CHAPMAN
Divel, Lisa Kessinger
Speech, Drama & Forensics Tchr
Stout, Patricia Gail (Roberts)
English Teacher
CHENEY
Gillett, James E.
Jr HS Mathematics Teacher
Mareda, Jim W.
Instrumental Music Teacher
CHEROKEE
Coles, Lori Smith
Sci Chairperson & Instructor
Kohley, Janice Myers
Business Teacher
Varsolona, John L.
Teacher
CHERRYVALE
May, Ronald K.
Mathematics Teacher
Smith, Charles Hoyt
Vocational Agriculture Instr
Wadman, Sharon Renee
Biology, Health & PE Teacher
CHETOPA
Slater, Larry John
Mathematics Teacher
CIMARRON
Smith, Thomas P.
Social Studies Teacher
Stucky, Celia Beth
Second Grade Teacher
Vlcek, Cindy
Business Teacher
CLAFLIN
Stephens, Rita Pekarek
Mathematics Teacher
CLAY CENTER
Cromwell, Esther Irene
Kindergarten Tchr
Smith, J. Kathy
Computer Technology Teacher
CLEARWATER
Harris, Amy Hanquist
English & Lang Arts Teacher
Harris, Drew
HS Mathematics Instructor
Hensley, Christy Miller
4th Grade Teacher
Solter, Deanna Lee
Social Studies Instructor
CLIFTON
Bechard, Bill
English & PE Teacher
George, Barbara Jean (Hamel)
Eng & Speech HS Teacher
CLYDE
Blaha, Irma Jean
Business Instructor
Jones, Nicholas Martin
Art Teacher
COFFEYVILLE
Amos, Gretchen Carol
5th Grade Teacher
Corle, Betty Lea Tuck
Instr & Asst Coord Dev Stud
Gard, Mark A.
Secondary Vocal Music Teacher
Hartzell, Peri Van Tassel
French & German Teacher
Herrell, Susan Kay Copeland
Fourth Grade Teacher
Kengle, Marietta
History Tchr & Soc Stud Chprsn
Lippoldt, Vaughn
Choral Activities Director
Martin, Artonza Louise
Business Teacher
McCurry, Claudia Jo (Smith)
Sixth Grade Reading Teacher
Merry, DeAnn M.
English, Speech & Drama Tchr
Morris, Alice F. Schneider
7th & 8th Grd Vocal Teacher
Partridge, Sharon Bever
Family & Consumer Sci Tchr
Patterson, Thelma Marie (Steeby)
Retired Teacher
Reed, DeLisa Francine
Business & Computer Teacher
Roland, Frankie Genette
Fourth Grade Teacher
Speer, Michael Wayne
Algebra Teacher
Staudt, Carolyn Sue
English Teacher
COLBY
Allison, Dennis L.
Director of Criminal Justice
Baker, Douglas Lee
Fifth Grade Teacher
Burlew, Jonathan W.
Director of Mass Communication
Craghead, Kent Lee
Mathematics Instructor
Erickson, Patricia Ann (Walker)
Dir of Phys Therapist Asst Pgm
Fishel, Pauline Dean
Mathematics Instructor
Flanagin, Karen Gilchrist
Business & Computer Instructor
Groom, Juliann
Director of Bands
Hooker, Paul Derek
Chemistry Instructor
Jones, Linda L. (Bennett)
HS Language Arts Teacher
Lupton, Janis Lussmyer
English Instructor
Malcolm, James Vernon, Sr.
Chemistry & Physics Instructor
Myers, Janet Pollnow
Nursing Instructor
Oelke, Victor C.
Instructor
Pickerill, Max E.
Chemistry Professor
Reichert, Tricia Ann (Park)
Instructor
Schrick, Christina Garcia
Nursing Instructor
Shuman, Philip L.
Choral Music Professor
Sprenkel, Mike D.
Math Instructor
Stueve, Carlene Ann (Letcher)
HS Language Arts Teacher
Thyfault, Delila Burrell
Home Economics Instructor
Turrell, Patricia Heaton
Title One Math Teacher
Wente, Mary Smith
1st Grade Transitional Teacher
Zimmerman, Lynn Dible
Biology Teacher
COLDWATER
O'Hair, Jeanette Sue (Peck)
Vocational Home Economics Tchr
COLUMBUS
Alvested, Donna Lee
English & Journalism Teacher
Armstrong, Teresa Ann (Parise)
Math & Computer Instructor
Atkins, Paul Dewitt
Agriculture Instructor
Bruce, Polly Vietti
Business, Cmptr Voc Ed Teacher
Edmondson, Rebecca Lou (Stice)
Voc Business Teacher & Coord
Green, James Michael
Social Studies Teacher
Herron, Elaine Kay
6th Grd Language Arts Teacher
Hodgson, James Edward
HS & Jr High Wood Tech Tchr
North, Darrell G.
Jr HS Soc Stud Tchr
Simpson, Barbara Marie
Kindergarten Teacher
Smittle, E. John
Art Teacher
COLWICH
Brown, Kay McNulty
Lang Arts & Amer His Teacher
Yaeger, Janice Petz
Kindergarten Teacher
CONCORDIA
Esslinger, Shirley LaRue
Bus Ed Instr & Dept Chairman
Foster, Anthony B.
Instructor & Acad Advisor
Hobson, Tony
Business & PE Instr
Kaufman, Jack Francis
Art Instructor
Schmitz, Kathy Barr
Art Teacher
Schmitz, Ted V.
Health, PE Tchr, Adv & Coach
Sutton, Susan Lyn
Director of Humanities
Wilkens, Ruth Spurling
English & Literature Teacher
CONWAY SPRINGS
Kimple, Jean Ann
Math Teacher
Lange, Theresa Kay
Second Grade Teacher
Mack, Karen F.
2nd Grade Teacher
Sanders, Michael Sean
Social Studies & Health Tchr
COPELAND
Alexander, Deanne Matkin
Third Grade Teacher
COUNCIL GROVE
Landgren, Larry Leon
Geometry & Earth Science Tchr
Riedel, Cynthia Seaman
Journalism Teacher
Selby, Dona Jean (Foltz)
Title I Reading Teacher
Williams, Eloise Ann (Cowan)
Math & Human Sexuality Teacher
COURTLAND
Saunders, Linda Youngblood
5th Grade Teacher
CUBA
Crist, Steven Anderson
Science Teacher
CUNNINGHAM
Johnson, Gregory Scott
Choral Music Instructor
Lane, Kasey Lynn
Foreign Lang Tchr & Yrbk Spon
Sillin, Brad D.
Counselor
DE SOTO
Bogardus, Gayle Lorraine
Vocal Music Dir
Bruns, Roger Lee
7th Grade Science Teacher
Copeland, Mary Etta E.
Choral Director
Draper, Robbin J.
Instrumental Music Teacher
Farmer, Carol Ann
Journalism Teacher
Hodges, Jeffrey L.
Director of Bands
Montgall, Bonnie L.
English Teacher
Opdycke, Vergie Dean
First Grade Teacher
Petersen, Joyce Ann (Mauer)
Health & PE Dept Chair
Reddy, Kathy Ann
Language Arts Instructor
Wall, Karen (Hind)
American History Teacher
Wootton Lucas, Linda Hind
Family & Consumer Science Tchr
DEERFIELD
Facklam, Kristin Heidi Quayle
Physical Education & Hlth Tchr
Hill, Tony
K-12th Grd PE Teacher
DELIA
Jackson, Laurel Stone
7th & 8th Grade Teacher
DERBY
Buzzi, Robert K.
History Tchr & Wrestling Coach
Davis, Tamera Seibel
Special Ed Inclusion Teacher
Dunn, Glenn A.
8th Grade Science Teacher
Everhart, Pamela Horn
Special Ed Inclusion Teacher
Harris, Darlene J. (Anderson)
English Teacher
Heller, Brenda Heins
English & Language Arts Tchr
Jenkins, Penny L. (Stevens)
English Teacher
Lollar, Lonnie Allen
US & World Geography Teacher
Lymer, Barbara Ann (Kennedy)
English & Literature Teacher
Rebel, Sherrie Ann
Fifth Grade Teacher
Slade, Lisa Federinko
Seventh Grade English Teacher
Tauer, Sandra Selm
Science Teacher
Vigil, Jose B., Jr.
Chemistry Instructor
Wilkerson, Gary Dwaine
Kindergarten Teacher
DEXTER
Haden, Dorothy S.
Business Teacher & QPA Coord
McFall, Alice Jane (Austin)
3rd Grade Teacher
DODGE CITY
Albrecht, Ronald Gordon
Chemistry & Physics Professor
Amawi, Hala Aidi
Associate Professor
Barnett, Shirley A.
7th-8th Grd Math Teacher
Burke, Larry Keith
History Professor
Doussa, Christopher George
History Teacher
Ewy, John L.
Mass Commnctn & Broadcast Prof
Fawcett, Chris Franklin
Biology Instructor
Feist, Jacquelyn Kaye
Social Studies Dept Chprsn
Kaiser, Charlotte Anne
Theatre Dir & Forensics Coach
Katzenmeier, Claudette (Mc Cammon
Debate & Speech Instructor
Keeley, Bill James
Biology Teacher & Coach
Kenton, E. Van
Associate Professor of Math
Kinnan, Trisha E.
Business Instructor
Kolb, Dan R.
Admin Intern & English Teacher
Moore, Cindy Ann
Journalism Teacher
Powers, Robert G.
7th Grade Science Teacher
Reichenborn, Dan L.
8th Grd American History Tchr
Rogers, Sue
7th & 8th Grd Eng & Rdng Tchr
Ronen, Jean Marie
5th Grade Teacher
Wood, Goldie Ford
11th & 12th Grade English Tchr
DORRANCE
Thielen, Susan Marie
4th Grade Teacher
DOUGLASS
Baldridge, Judy Fronterhouse
High School Science Teacher
Lowe, George F.
History, PE Teacher & Coach
Mc Cluggage, Angela Jean
Second Grade Teacher

Susan Golladay
s Teacher
ry Lee
e Arts Teacher

Volara Ann
Teacher
ON
oberta Lee (Shinn)
ade Teacher

ori Kay
h Grade Teacher
HAM
Susan Keck
atics Teacher
ynn Rogers
arten Teacher
, James A.
& Biology Tchr & Coach
, Glenda Sims
rade Teacher
Eileen Marie
rade Teacher
ADO
William Granville
or of Eng & Mass Comm
inda Diane
Adjunct Prof of Psych
onnie Duane
ial Technology Tchr
Marvin Lee
nics Instructor
Pat C. (Gross)
pt Chair & Teacher
orra Leigh
Grade Teacher
William Dean, Jr.
nctn & Amer His Tchr
obert Brad
Teacher
ow, Shirley Nelson
ss Instructor
everly (Rudicel)
ade Teacher
er, Marsha K.
Teacher & Spanish Instr
, Gary Wayne
al Education Teacher
obert Dean
nics Instructor
ennifer Lynn
ss Instructor
Beverly J.
rade Teacher
s, Stephen Lee
Science Teacher
Gaynell Mc Fadden
d Fourth Grade Teacher
, Karlene Gann
nting Instructor
Raymond Eugene
h Grade Sci & Math Tchr
, M. Jane (Weigel)
osition & Literature Tchr
rank Robert
eacher
Yvonne
Grade Teacher
G
on, Mark David
School Business Teacher
Mae Marshall
h Grade English Teacher
z, A. Leroy
athematics & Physics Tchr
Beverly Sue Stucky
mental Director
Lewis Richard
ry & Health Teacher
ART
der, Karen Sue
nd Grade Teacher
y, George A., Jr.
ance Counselor
, Patricia Ilene
ce Teacher
WORTH
Dawnae Urbanek
alism Teacher
meyer, Duane Lee
gy & Chemistry Instructor
OOD
Nancy Sue Juhl
Grade Teacher
Murla Cunningham
uage Arts Teacher
RIA
s, Jay D.
al Studies Teacher
, Thomas Clay
essor of Political Science
n, Terry J.
ic Professor
ell, Sandra Kaye Schrant
hology Teacher
r, John A.
R Assoc Prof & Ath Trainer
nquist, Richard Lee
nce & Physical Ed Teacher
Linda Sue
ch Teacher
tt-DeVito, Myrna M.
munication Professor
ge, Ann Holmgren
Grade Social Studies Tchr
y, Bartlett J.
agement Professor

Gustafson, Philip Edwin
Mathematics Professor
Henrikson, Jerilynn
Language Art Teacher
Howland, Clarence E.
Retired Science Teacher
Johnston, Paul Leo
Professor of Geology
Karst, Ronald Hubert
Rehabilitation Svcs Ed Coord
Kirchhefer, Dan Robert
Art Professor
Krueger, Marilyn Trudelle
Counselor
Luedtke, Mark Chase
Physical Education Teacher
Lyons, Barbara Kepka
First Grade Teacher
Maricevic, Beverly Zirnstein
First Grade Teacher
Mauney, Connie Pat
Dir of Public Affairs Program
Mc Junkin, Myoan Swilley
Primary Teacher
McKinney, Susan F.
Language Arts Teacher
Mehring, Tes
Dean
Nichols, Joan Wilson
Ins}r, Dir of Insurance Ed Ctr
Obiakor, Festus E.
Assoc Prof of Psych & Spec Ed
Phillips, Jill Mitchell
Math Teacher
Queen, Carla Palmer
Mathematics Teacher
Reeves, Kenna Pearson
Instructor of Communication
Rich, John Carr
Associate Accounting Professor
Samuelson, William George
Professor of Education
Saunders, David Kent
Assistant Professor of Biology
Schwarm, Larry W.
Associate Professor of Art
Schwenn, John O.
Dean of Grad Stud & Research
Sherman, Gregory Patrick
Asst Prof of Inst Dsgn & Tech
Somer, John Laddie
Professor of English
Thompson, Kenneth Wayne
Earth Sci Dept Asst Professor
Trahoon, Kari Michelle
Special Education Instructor
Turner, Steven R.
Soc Stud Teacher & Asst Prin
Van Sickel, Patricia Lucille
French Professor
Weatherholt, Betty Lynn (Barger)
Eighth Grade English Teacher
Weaver, Kenneth Andrew
Assoc Professor of Psychology
Wheat, Jane Pearson
Coordinator of Group Piano
Wright, Candace Ann
Accounting Instructor
Wright, Rose Louise (Feeney)
Third Grade Teacher
Wyatt, Gary
Assoc Prof, Dir Univ Hnrs Prgm
Wyrick, Herb
7th Grade English Teacher
ENTERPRISE
Bragaw, Timothy R.
Boys Dean, Coach & PE Tchr
ESKRIDGE
Shumate, Carol L.
Secondary Social Science Tchr
EUDORA
Hughes, Ruth Anderson
Third Grade Teacher
Kobza, Martin James
HS Social Studies Teacher
Warren, Carolyn Collins
Sixth Grade Teacher
EUREKA
Argabright, Michael Dal
Physical Education Teacher
Collinge, Pamela J.
Fourth Grade Teacher
Flock, Carol Ann (Storrer)
Family & Consumer Science Tchr
Mariani, Marlene Adams
Inter Related BD & LD Teacher
Mc Guire, Rosemary Gilkison
5th Grade Teacher
Pitko, Pamela Ann
PE & Health Teacher & Coach
Powell, Marty Lee
Math & Computer Science Tchr
Sanders, Linda Pape
Lang Arts & Family Sci Tchr
Twaddell, Douglas Oren
Instrumental Music Teacher
Veale, Nancy Graham
Secondary English Teacher
Wichman, Janell M.
Language Arts & Geog Teacher
EVEREST
Wenger, Eli J.
7th-8th Grade Social Stud Tchr
FORT SCOTT
Antonetti, Landia Eileen (Swope)
Third Grade Teacher
Campbell, Bobbi Ferraro
High School Algebra Teacher
Coffman, Robert Wayne
Technology Teacher

Dulgarian, Mark Richard
Social Science Teacher
Hearn, W. Kyle
Agribusiness Instructor
Hilger, Geraldine Ann
English Teacher
Kendrick, Ellen
Photography & Art Teacher
Klassen, Kenneth Guy
Physics, Calculus & Chem Instr
Klassen, Ronald Nick
Latin Instructor
Miller, Norman Dan
American History Teacher
Regan, David Lee
Sci, Hlth, & Basic Skills Tchr
Swanwick, Nancy Austin
Home Economics Instructor
Ward, Lisa DiNardo
Business Instructor
FOWLER
Bartlett, Ruth Ann (Travis)
Former Kindergarten Teacher
Wise, Debbie Howell
Title I Teacher
FRANKFORT
Gallion, J. D.
K-12th Grd Vocal Music Instr
Gunter, Bruce Michael
HS Social Science Teacher
Roeder, Linda M.
Math Instructor
FREDONIA
Blackwell, Anthony Allan
Middle School Science Teacher
Blackwell, Carla J. (Bowers)
Soc Stud & Lang Arts Tchr
Bruner, Genea Lynn
Language Arts Instructor
Morrow, Carolyn S. Stewart
English, Speech & Rdng Teacher
Schoolcraft, Twila K. (White)
Second Grade Teacher
Spohn, Diana Lee (Scott)
Title I Math Teacher
FRIEND
Jacques, Susan Parry
6th Grade Science Teacher
FRONTENAC
Borchardt, Rosie (Parker)
Communication Teacher
Miller, Leon P.
Physical Education Teacher
Tener, Mick G.
Counselor & Psychology Instr
GALENA
Anderson, Evelyn Farmer
Computer Science Teacher
LaTurner, Mark G.
Jr High Social Science Teacher
Outt, Dennis B.
Science Teacher
GALESBURG
Tromsness, Debra Renee (Trim)
3rd Grade Instructor
GALVA
Becker, Mark Alan
Math & Physical Education Tchr
Decker, Jeanne
Fourth Grade Teacher
GARDEN CITY
Ackerman, Linda G.
Computer Science Teacher
Almos, Sandy Troxel
Associate Principal
Anderson, Richard Thomas
Vocal Music Teacher
Blyn, Therese Grilliot
Mathematics Instructor
Caruthers, Clifford M.
High School English Teacher
Claassen, Jeanette Ruth
Librarian
Dague, Emma Elizabeth
Math, Science & Soc Stud Tchr
Dale, Julia Ann
Counselor & Teen Parent Coord
Fox, Jan Schneider
Mathematics Teacher
Glende, Christy Merrie
Math Teacher
Gutierrez, Gilbert G., III
Math Teacher
Hauschild, Barbara A.
Middle Schl Soc Stud Teacher
Hembd, Leigh Ann
English Teacher
Herod, Ann M.
Family & Consumer Science Tchr
Hooker, Maureen K.
Business Education Teacher
Loyd, Suzanne Keeler
8th Grd Comm & Civics Tchr
Mc Millan, Mary Ogle
Kindergarten Tchr
Mc Nutt, Shelby V.
Communications Teacher
Meyer, Deron J.
7th Grade Social Studies Tchr
Nolan, Shonda R.
HS Phys Ed Teacher & Coach
Nyberg, Kevin Dale
Latin Teacher
Olson, John Robert
Physics Instructor
Romero, Traci Papineau
ESL Coord & Lang Arts Teacher
Senkbeil, Dale
Health & Physical Ed Teacher

Smith, Dale Alan
Mathematics Teacher
Smith, Steven Michael
Fourth Grade Teacher
Sowers, Nancy Eileen
Second Grade Teacher
Tolbert, William Jeffery
World History Teacher
Travers, Jamila Nadine
English as a Second Lang Tchr
Weatherly, Bill D.
HS Health Tchr & Asst Ath Dir
Whitehill, Judy Welp
Social Science Instructor
GARDEN PLAIN
Durham, Carolyn Louise
Third Grade Teacher
Papke, Janice K.
Language Arts Teacher
GARDNER
Berg, Douglas Harvey
Vocal Music Teacher
Jones, Teresa Mae
First Grade Teacher
Kirgan, Barbara Kathleen
Fourth Grade Teacher
Meyer, Malcolm Edwin
Band Instr & Dist Musc Supvr
Simmons Lee, Terry Dianne
Drama & Speech Teacher
Stewart, Nancee Gayle
History Teacher
GARNETT
Bakken, Vicki Lynne
English, Theatre & Speech Tchr
Gigstad, Marti Ann (Pense)
Third Grade Teacher
Peters, Alvin
English & History Teacher
Strickler, Shelly A.
7th-12th Grd Cnslr & Eng Chair
GENESEO
Donley, Terry Robert
Middle School Teacher
Renollet, Laura Cooley
First & Second Grade Teacher
GIRARD
Leonard, Sharon Huff
Business & Computer Ed Teacher
Mitchell, Lorene E. Tarpy
4th Grade Teacher
Shade, Shely Sharp
Computer Teacher
GLASCO
Tatro, Sherry L.
Third Grade Teacher
GLEN ELDER
Martin, Debbie J. (Lackey)
7th & 8th Grade Algebra Tchr
GODDARD
Criss, Darlene Edwards
Lang Arts Dept Chm & Teacher
Foltz, Jim David
Math Teacher
Fredrickson, Nancy Lee
Art & Drama Teacher
Gingraux, Daniel M.
Physical Ed Teacher & Coach
Goering, Don
Middle Schl Science Instructor
Loomis, Sally Van Dyne
Second Grade Teacher
Phox, Kimberly S.
Math & Science Teacher
Pratt, George Jr.
6th Grade Teacher
Robert, Christi M. Hubbell
HS Art Instructor
Schartz, Barry Lynn
Science Teacher & Dept Chair
GOESSEL
Nikkel, Joan Carol (Reimer)
Librarian & Media Specialist
Stucky, Bruce J.
Math & Science Teacher
Toews, Jerry D.
5th-12th Grd Instrumental Tchr
GOODLAND
Berringer, Jan Ochsner
Fourth Grade Teacher
Frazier, Mary L.
5th & 6th Grade Teacher
Gillette, Kelly Brian
Social Studies Instructor
Gregory, Sharon Lea (Jackson)
Language Arts Teacher
Hurley, Landra Jean
Second Grade Teacher
Mc Kee, Linda (Mc Dougal)
Third Grade Teacher
Palmquist, Sharon M.
10th Grade English Teacher
Porterfield, Mary M.
Spanish Teacher
Shank, Gaylene (Hayden)
Mathematics Instructor
GRAINFIELD
Beougher, Marilea Johnson
Retired Business Teacher
Parker, Merle L.
Industrial Arts Teacher
GREAT BEND
Adams, Ann C.
German Teacher
Barrows, Mary Osburn
English & Literature Professor
Bealer, Richard T.
Psychology Instructor
Berens, Ronald J.
Math Teacher

Bittel, Linda L.
Art Teacher
Chrisler, Marilyn Ann
Business Teacher
Clapsaddle, Alice A.
Coord of Child Care & Guidance
Compton, Wm Michael
Director of Bands
Cross, Crystal Kaye
Senior College Prep Eng Tchr
Daniel, Deborah Kay (Gerstenkorn)
Third Grade Teacher
David, Menter Haniel
Professor of Microbiology
Dennis, Elizabeth K. Chadd
Assistant Principal
Dudek, Steve E.
Instructor of Art
Gotsche, Linda Sue (Wilson)
First Grade Teacher
Holaday, Patty Lynn
EMH & TMN III Teacher
Howard, Jane Johnson
Accounting Instructor
Hullman, Helen Arnoldy
2nd Grade Teacher
Johnson, Rachel Dalene (Kraus)
English & Literature Professor
Kaiser, Todd Eric
Physical Education Teacher
Kenyon, Gary Eugene
Instructor of Social Science
Kern, Kayleen Hertel
First Grade Teacher
Kottas, Kathleen Wedel
Nursing Clinical Educator
Kruckenberg, Homer
Teacher
McCaffery, Linda Fox
Social Science Instructor
Mc Naney, Grace Ann (Pollard)
Business & Computer Teacher
Mink, Ronald Dean
Instrumental Music Coordinator
Richter-Baxter, Susan Stambaugh
Vocal Music Instructor
Robinson, Kay S.
Instructor of Communications
Saskschewsky, Shirley Noble (Metzger)
Fifth Grade Teacher
Schultz, Jacqueline Dritley
First Grade Teacher
Sheikh, Bahar
Chemistry Instructor
Stoskopf, Lilbourn Roy
Vocational Education Instr
Tinkler, David N.
Computer Teacher
Tranbarger, Gary D.
Professor
Vincent, John Michael
Science Department Chairman
Watson, Barbara Denise (Sharp)
Speech, Eng & Drama Teacher
White, Avalon Marie
Business Instructor
Wolf, Kurt Alan
High School Art Teacher
GREENSBURG
Crites, Donna Mae
Kindergarten Teacher
GRIDLEY
Johnson, Patricia (Ott)
PE & Language Arts Teacher
Lingenfelter, Carol Sue
Eng, Speech & Forensics Tchr
GRINNELL
Dold, Paul Anthony
Science Teacher
Heinz, Marilyn L.
Soc Stud, Title I & PE Teacher
Tweed, JoAnn Price
1st Grade Teacher
GYPSUM
Edwards, Bradley Craig
Fourth Grade Teacher
Katzenmeier, Phil R.
Math, Science & PE Teacher
Kolzow, Jerry (Dee)
Jr-Sr High Math Teacher
HALSTEAD
Bodecker, Jane I.
Spanish & English Teacher
McKay, H. Ralph
Instrumental Music Teacher
Sigmund, Cynthia Marie
Art Teacher
HANOVER
Hatesohl, Rebecca Ann (Baker)
Fifth & Sixth Grade Teacher
HANSTON
Lee, Myra Coleman
Math & English Teacher
HAVEN
Brown, Mark Andrew
Mathematics Teacher
Lee, Robert E.
Band Director
Savaiano, Emil F.
History Teacher
Vogel, Bradley Dean
Vocal Music Instructor
Wiese, Angeline K. (Warneke)
Preschool Program Dir & Tchr
HAVILAND
Roher, Thad Joseph
Jr High English Teacher
Troyer, Rosie (Slaven)
Fourth Grade Teacher

HAYS
Anderson, Leota L.
German Teacher
Billinger, Richard L.
English Teacher
Blurton, Jill Ann (Reitz)
Health, PE Instr & Dept Chair
Boldra, Sue Holloway
Social Studies Teacher
Brull, Carol Dinkel
Lang Arts & Soc Stud Teacher
Caprez, Judith V.
Asst Professor of Social Work
Clough, David Otis
Computer Studies Dept Chm
Cooper, Donna Steele
Bio Tchr & Sci Dept Chprsn
Davidson, Harvey Leonard
Cnslr, Guid Dir, Adult Ed Tchr
Dinkel, Shirley A. Gnad
5th Grade Teacher
Firestone, Ruth Hartzell
Professor of German
Flax, Brian E.
Substitute Teacher
Flood, Diane Hoisington
Vocal Music Teacher
Ganstrom, Linda Marie (Bunker)
Asst Prof of Art in Ceramics
Grogan, Jacqueline Plummer
Social Studies & French Tchr
Hafliger, John A., Jr.
Special Ed Teacher & Dept Chm
Hassett, Charles Michael
Cmptr & Information Sys Instr
Humphreys, Alice Gould
Practicum Coordinator
Jilg, Michael Florian
Art Professor
Kuchar, Kathleen
Professor of Art
Kuhn, Cathy Ann
Home Economics Teacher
Lovett, Christopher Charles
History Professor
Lucas, James B.
Athletic Director & Coach
Luehrs, Robert Boice
Prof of History & Intrm Chair
Malmberg, Virginia A. (Wood)
Marketing Instructor
Marshall, Delbert Allan
Chemistry Professor
Mc Clure, Ann L.
Assoc Prof of Business Law
Mc Kemey, Dale Richard
Business Admin Assoc Professor
Moore, Rager Harrell
Director of Choral Activities
Murphy, James Lawson
Prof of Music & Dept Chair
Niernberger, Gail (Pratt)
Interrelated Special Ed Tchr
Nolte, Steven F.
Instructor of Ldrshp Studies
Nuss, Mark Douglas
Instructor of Communication
Parker-Price, Susan Jane
Professor of Psychology
Plymell, Darlene Grossardt
Mathematics Teacher
Rupp, Dan G.
Professor of Economics
Salien, Jean-Marie
French Professor
Schonthaler, Susan Towns
Third Grade Teacher
Sekavec, Twylia McSpadden
Chem & Applied Physics Teacher
Selbe, Nancy Sue
University Instructor
Stramel, Phyllis Dinkel
Third Grade Teacher
Taylor, Kathleen J.
Social Sci & Journalism Tchr
Teeter, Kent
Physical Education Teacher
Towns, Cheryl Hofstetter
English Instructor
Urban, Gerald Lee
Language Arts & Science Tchr
Wagoner, Kathy Hime
English Teacher
Washburn, Cindy Karlin
Kindergarten Teacher
Wilson, Raymond
Professor of History
Wilson, Sharon Raye
Instructor of English
Windholz, David James
Technology Instructor
Zakrzewski, Martha V.
Fifth Grade Teacher
HAYSVILLE
Campbell, Jana Nutter
Middle School Tchr of Gifted
Hertel, Eloise
Principal & Teacher
HEALY
Dreiling, Keith Marvin
Mathematics Teacher
Heier, Mark Philip
Industrial Arts & Tech Tchr
HESSTON
Baehler, Karen Frankamp
Social Studies Teacher
Boesker, Marjorie M.
Retired Educator
Clark, LeAnn D.
Third Grade Teacher
Cox, Dana E.
English & Yearbook Teacher
Dahlsten, Mark Edward
Math Teacher
Goertzen, Michael D.
Science Teacher
Harder, Kurt Allen
History & Humanities Teacher
Jacobs, Marcia
Science Instructor
Miller, Marcia G.
Computer & Business Ed Tchr
Regehr, Wesley J.
7th-8th Grade Teacher
Sildus, Tatiana I.
Russian & German Teacher
Waltner, John D.
History & Government Teacher
Weaver, Phyllis Diane (Miller)
Facilitator of the Gifted
HIAWATHA
Eisenbise, Irene Elizabeth
Language Arts Teacher
Heise, Rhoda Margie (Sider)
Retired Second Grade Teacher
Jury, Karen Swanson
Assistant Librarian
Rake, Darlene F. (Smith)
English Teacher
HIGHLAND
Church, Sharon Kay
Psychology Instructor
Gormley, Esther (Magie)
College Teacher
Shelton, Ronald E.
History & Geography Teacher
Winchester, Susan Kay (Boos)
Business Instructor
HILL CITY
Crippen, Donald Eugene
Retired Elementary Teacher
Crippen, Doris Binder
Retired First Grade Teacher
HILLSBORO
Boldt, Dennis E.
Business & Computer Teacher
Frenzen, Donald H., Jr.
Science Instructor
Friesen, Bonnie D.
Sixth Grade Teacher
Hiebert, Allen G.
Chemistry Professor
HILLSDALE
Conner, Beth Romine
Fifth Grade Teacher
Rowe, Cheryl Evans
4th Grade Teacher
HOISINGTON
Irvin, Lonnie B.
7th Grade Soc Studies Teacher
Johnson, Tina Marie
Physical Ed Teacher & Coach
HOLCOMB
Kemper, Mary Catherine
Theatre Arts & Speech Teacher
Turley, Vicki Cornett
Interrelated Resource Teacher
HOLTON
Alley, Lyle Richard
Social Science Chairman
Anderson, Marilyn Sue
Second Grade Teacher
Anderson, Severt A.
High School Counselor
Beam, Alan B.
Amer His & Soc Stud Teacher
Dolsky, Jerome R.
Business Teacher
Hummel, Rick L.
Business & Computer Teacher
McAsey, Jacqueline Hutfles
American History Teacher
Nightingale, Terry Steele
HS Math Teacher
Spade, Debra McDougal
Scndry Soc Stud, Hlth, PE Tchr
Stous, Karen Ann
English & Speech Instructor
Van Donge, Nancy Lee (Proctor)
6th-7th Grade Science Teacher
White, Joni Gilliland
9th Grade English Teacher
HOPE
Wedel, Debbie (Mercer)
Kindergarten Teacher
HORTON
Kirschner, Rod L.
Physical Education Teacher
Pottroff, Larry Lee
Agriculture Education Teacher
HOWARD
Smith, Kevin E.
English Teacher
HOXIE
Bergin, Kathleen A.
Science Teacher
Emerick, Joanne Pfannenstiel
HS Social Science Teacher
Hague, Beverly Elling
5th-6th Grd Soc Studies Tchr
HOYT
Gustin, Chris Wiseman
Business & Computer Tech Instr
Holthaus, Kenneth F.
Social Studies Teacher
Ronnebaum, Beverly Homolka
HS Mathematics Teacher
Williams, Bonnie S.
English Teacher
HUGOTON
Brecheisen, Tracy (Cox)
Former Teacher
Seaman, Judy Sinnett
HS Language Arts Teacher
Seaman, Kevin Joseph
English & Journalism Teacher
Sosa, Annette (Meier)
English Teacher
HUMBOLDT
Dexter, Kent D.
Biology Teacher
Honas, Linda Frederick
3rd Grade Teacher
Mauk, Kelly Lorraine
5th Grade Teacher
Wilhite, Allen
Publications Advisor
HUTCHINSON
Barker, Joyce L.
Professor of Biology
Broxterman, Roy
Accounting Teacher & Coord
Dillon, Marcia Marie
HS History & Religion Teacher
Dreiling, Ron Dean
English Instructor
Enfield, Janet Sue
Sixth Grade Teacher
Graber, Melanie Cavenec
Junior High & High School Tchr
Guengerich, Ruth Lapp
Counselor
Hallford, Janet A.
Journalism Instructor
Hirst, Walter Allen
Biology Instructor
Horton, Dawna Sue
Elem & Jr High Counselor
Hunter, Bev Claassen
Adjunct Professor of Speech
Hutter, Jeannie D.
Math, Comms & Drama Teacher
Marcoux, Helene Elizabeth
College Counselor & Instructor
Masterson, Nancy Keens
Art Instructor
Miller, Dena Saunders
Third Grade Teacher
Miller, Rosemary Falconbridge
Library & Media Specialist
Moore, Kenneth B.
Social Science Instructor
Morrell, John Edmund
Computer Science Instructor
Neufeldt, David E.
Psychology Professor
Pelischek, Jeffrey B.
Director of Bands
Pinkston, Elaine Lavonne (Merritt-Moore)
Special Education Teacher
Seck, Elynor M.
Microcomputer Teacher
Smith, Ann White
Math Instructor
Stafford, Jeane W.
Psychology Instructor
Switzer, Edwin L.
Science Teacher & Dept Chair
Torres, Ivan
Tchr of Learning Disabilities
Unruh, Stephanie Schroeder
Mathematics Instructor
Williams, Stephen Erick
Journalism Advisor
Wingfield, Karen L.
Office Technologies Pgm Coord
Young, Rita Basgall Birzer
Social Stud & Lang Arts Tchr
Yowell, Laura Elaine
English Teacher
INDEPENDENCE
Boner, Connie Kaye
2nd Grade Teacher
Bowersock, Garry James
Retired 6th Grade Teacher
Boyer, Rick Dean
Elementary Principal
Douglas, Alice Henry
7th Grd Math & Computer Instr
Kawulok, Jo Ann Crane
Office of Technology Instr
Kurucz, Jane Thomas
Third Grade Teacher
Main, Susan E. (Thornton)
Humanities Instructor
Rothgeb, Donna M.
Language Arts Teacher
Watson-Boyer, Sharon Chism
School Counselor
Webb, Scott Brian
Eighth Grade Science Teacher
Williams, Glenn
Mathematics Instructor
Winslow, Mark William
Physics Instructor
Zito, Concetta
Math & Spanish Teacher
INGALLS
Harris, Judy Lea
HS Language Arts Teacher
Harris, Mitchel D.
Physical Education Teacher
Kliewer, Wylene K.
Third Grade Teacher
IOLA
Buller, Connie Heiman
Second Grade Teacher
Caillouet, Laura Jane
Second Grade Teacher
Farmer, Anne Stadler
English Instructor
Houser, Donna Snyder
7th-8th Grd Eng & Drama Tchr
Houser, Raymond E.
Social Studies Teacher
Lacy, Mary Ann
Psych, Soc & Life Adjust Tchr
Raines, Susan McCrate
Speech & Drama Teacher
Sager, Janet Hopkins
Physical Education Teacher
Stout, Jane Hemphill
Business Teacher
Stricker, Julie Ann
5th Grade Teacher
Young, Regina Arlene
8th Grade Math & Algebra Tchr
IUKA
Schrepel, Susan Frederick
Learning Disabilities Consltnt
JENNINGS
Carter, Julie Ward
English Teacher
Gallentine, John K.
English Teacher
Reaves, Craig Thomas
Social Studies & PE Teacher
Wagoner, Lesley (Kersenbrock)
Business & PE Teacher
JETMORE
Whipple, Mary E. (Pfannenstiel)
Mathematics Teacher
JEWELL
Greene, Susan C.
Family & Consumer Sci Teacher
JOHNSON
Clare, Nanon Bird
Retired Adv Plcmnt Eng Instr
Cullen, Judy Ann (Lechtenberg)
English Teacher
Terpstra, Wendi Weinmaster
English Teacher & Voc Supvr
JUNCTION CITY
Foster, Patricia Kay
6th Grd Math & Lang Arts Tchr
Jensen, Erick James
Hiv, Aids Counselor & Educator
Johnson, Susan Ondie
Spanish I & II Teacher
Korte, Matt L.
Algebra I Teacher
Kugler, Roger K.
Senior Army Instructor
Malec, Karen Elaine
4th Grade Teacher
Moloney, Judith Jochems
Language Arts Teacher
Moore, Nan Keaton
6th Grd Science & Math Teacher
Nigro, Joan Rose
Secondary Family Teacher
Pelcak, Kay Diane (Shalla)
Fifth Grade Teacher
Reynolds, Sarah Bowling
7th Grade Sci & Health Tchr
Sanders, Rob Steven
Elementary Band Instructor
Seely, Cynthia E.
Science Teacher
Sidesinger, Mark T.
9th Grade Biology Teacher
Sislo, Lynnetta D.
German Teacher
Skinner, Theresa Marie
7th Grade Math Teacher
Wewer, Randy Lee
Mathematics Teacher
Wild, Caroline Ann
Family & Consumer Science Tchr
Young, Lawrence R.
8th Grade Science Teacher
KANSAS CITY
Anderson, Virginia R. (Pitts)
Sixth Grade Teacher
Angilan, Ione
Art Teacher
Archer, Terry D.
Counselor
Born, Paul L., Jr.
7th Grade Life Science Teacher
Boyd, Sandra Jean
Business Teacher
Brown, Robert Loyd
9th Grade Social Science Tchr
Chinn, Latoria Jean
Professor of Business & Hum
Christopher, Teresa Chapman
Kindergarten Teacher
Clough, Deborah Joy
Psychology Teacher
Collins, Barbara Ruth
Reading & Social Studies Tchr
Conklin, Scott Matthew
Social Studies Teacher
Cook, Virginia Holmes
8th Grd Social Studies Teacher
Cooper, Marlin Duane
Director of Instrumental Music
Custer, Lance Alan
French Teacher
Daniels, Joan Spangler
German & French Teacher
Delich, Michael Craig
Social Science Teacher
Dotson, Dottie Wolfrom
Third Grade Tchr & Acting Prin
Dowd-Turkovic, Lori
Business Education Teacher
Drysdale, Barbara Lockerby
4th Grade Teacher
Eighmey, J. B.
Social Science Dept Chm
Elashkar, Sam
Microbiology Professor
Freeman, Caren Banks
English & Journalism Instr
Garrett, Doris M.
Second Grade Teacher
Generaux, Dale Anne (Riden)
Art Teacher
Gerstenberger, Terry Wayne
Asst Principal & Act Director
Gibson, Elizabeth
English & Journalism Teacher
Goheen, Ruth Ann
Counselor
Golubski, Linda Reynolds
High School Librarian
Gordon, Todd Leslie
Biology Teacher
Green, Joyce Elaine
First Grade Teacher
Haney, Jeffrey Lynn
Theatre, Debate & Forensics
Harding, Benton A.
Amer His & Pre-Algebra Tchr
Hassig, Robert M.
Social Studies Teacher
Heffron, Terry Anne (Browne)
3rd Grade Teacher
Henry, Sharon Calloway
Eng & Coll Composition Teacher
Hill, Ann E.
Reading, Writing & Math Tcher
Hoffman, Candee Gaunce
Librarian
Horner, Harriette Jane
Art Teacher
Huffstutler, Carol L.
Lang Arts & Jrnlsm Teacher
Ishum, Marcella Luckett
6th Grade Social Studies Tchr
Jackson, Melanie
Coordinator & Instructor
Jacob, Norma Bertha
Retired 3rd-4th Grade Teacher
Kenner, Beverly J.
Third Grade Teacher
Kimbrough, Michael Jerome
Director of Media Services
Konrade, Nancy (Kingry)
Seventh Grade Teacher
Lacy, H. Christopher
Professor
Larive, James Alan
Counselor
Lewis, Wesley Clyde
Teacher
Linck, Martha Ann, CSJ
Art Instructor
Link, Charyl (Kress)
Math Instructor
Litzen, Kelly Lynn
Physical Education Teacher
Louis, Pamela Margaret
American Literature Instructor
Martin, Betty Clune
Administrator
Mayfield, Connie E.
Instructor of Music
Mc Combs, Rick R.
Math & Reading Teacher
Meade, Robert Joseph
Desktop Publishing Teacher
Meditz, Josef Pat
High School Teacher
Mercer, Stephen W.
Algebra Instructor
Monroe, Norma J. (Banks)
7th Grade Teacher
Mosley, Charles William
Chemistry Teacher
Murphy, Lenore Griffey
Driver Education Assistant
Myers, Charlotte Susie
Rec Therapy Dept Instr & Coord
Naylor, Judy
Physical Education Teacher
Netzer, Barbara Sue
5th Grade Teacher
Nowakowski, Daniel Francis
Engineering & Drafting Teacher
Oland, David Eric
Social Studies Teacher
Park, Donald R.
Mathematics Teacher
Parra, Sylvia M.
Spanish Teacher
Ramirez, Carol Tripkos
English & Journalism Teacher
Ressler, Thomas Allen
English & Debate Teacher
Robertson, Curt Daniel
Drama & English Teacher
Roland, Gary Lynn
Drafting Technology Instr
Russell, Linda S. (Wilks)
High School Counselor
Ryan, John Patrick
History Teacher
Schnewels, James Phillip
Religion Teacher & Coach
Sheble, Sandra K.
History Teacher
Smith, Curtis Vinicio
Professor of Microbiology
Smith, Douglas
Math Teacher

S CITY (cont)
Duane Richard, II
ctor of Mortuary Sci
mes Howard
Studies Teacher
Deborah Eldridge
ce Instructor
Jean Ann
ng Instructor
an, Todd Jerome
matics Instr
en, Pennie H.
ience Dept Chair & Tchr
Anita J.
elor
B. Kaye
stry Instructor
Kathryn S.
Bible, Speech & Comp Tchr
-Dodd, Linda (Weinert)
Teacher
Kay (Stollman)
ctor of Math & Astronomy
Virginia Rose
ess Teacher
Gwendolyn Williams
dary Counselor
Valdenia Camille
of History & Pol Science
Lewis W.
sh Teacher & Mentor
Bill D.
of Electronics Tech
Kay Ann
& Coord of Mrktg & Mngmt
Roderick L.
& Orchestra Director
NGTON
Shelia Kay
ry Media Specialist
el, Butch E.
ng Teacher
MAN
Leon Doyle
ct Technology Coord
y, John D.
Teacher
William F.
tor of Instrumental Music
Colleen Ruthrauff
rgarten & First Grd Tchr
Mike Ray
ematics Teacher
endruber, Timothy J.
h Grade Science Teacher
EY
e, Galen Ray
h & Lang Arts Teacher
ona Dell (Conley)
ce Teacher & Counselor
A
l, Marcia Diane
Grade Teacher
on, James Dean
ocial Studies Teacher
ET
Troy S.
l Studies Tchr & Coach
s, Clifford Leslie
sh Teacher
ROSSE
, Marion Jerry
ndary English Instructor
atricia Ann (Foos)
nd Grade Teacher
N
s, Donald Roy
, Ec & Amer His Teacher
Blain Eldon
rican Government Teacher
ASTER
gham, Denise Carol
Grd Title I Teacher
son, Joyce Marie
Grade Teacher
NG
rnold Martin
ematics Teacher
, Bianca Lynn
th Grade Teacher
, Robert Christopher
ical Education Instructor
myre, Rita Medill
cipal
Linda (Higley)
bra II Instructor
rr, Helen C.
ogy Teacher
, Errol L.
hology Teacher
sti, Priscilla Anschutz
th Grade Teacher
n, Helen Chatburn
ed Mathematics Teacher
ngs, Greg
Science Teacher
Ronald Joseph
l Music Instructor
ger, Mary Alice
ch & Writing Teacher
Virginia Gayle
guage Arts Chair
l, Carla Y.
atre & Language Arts Tchr
ED
y, Jerald Joe
ogy Instructor
Richard Dean
umental Music Director

Jacob, Philip Charles
Science Teacher
Lytle, Cheryl R.
4th Grade Teacher
Snyder, Joseph Edward
Psychology & Amer His Teacher
Williams, Harold Eugene, Jr.
Band Teacher
Zahn, Noel Edward
Substitute Teacher
LAWRENCE
Antonio, Robert John
Sociology Professor
Bailey, Patricia A.
Social Studies Teacher
Ball, Shirley Galinski
6th Grade Teacher
Born, David Gilbert
Prof of Human Development
Brookshire, Jack E.
Band Director
Carr, Troy Douglas
Graduate Student Instructor
Chaput, Cheryl Post
Secondary Mathematics Teacher
Earles, Roma Jean
Gifted Education Advisor
Evans, Daryl Paul
Associate Prof of Sociology
Fangohr, Pamela Blatchford
Mathematics Teacher
Hamm, Virginia Green
Kindergarten Teacher
Lyerla, Karen D.
Teacher & Consultant
Mellen, Benjamin Lee
Computer Teacher
Pasik-Duncan, Bozenna J.
Professor of Mathematics
Polcyn, Jayne Woolley
Elementary Teacher
Rabiola, Samuel Charles
English Teacher
Renick, Lynne M.
English Teacher
Roddis, W. M. Kim
Associate Professor
Rogers, Lisa Rogers
Former Art Teacher
Schaumburg, Teresa Gayle
Media Teacher & Coach
Shawn, Margaret Anne
Latin Teacher
Souza, Martha L.
Spanish Teacher
Thornburg, Betty Jean
Retired Fourth Grade Teacher
Vining, David A.
Assistant Professor
Weiss, Thomas Joseph
Professor of Economics
Wiley, Edward Orlando, III
Prof of Systematics & Ecology
Williams-Boyd, Patricia
Music Teacher
Wolfe, Judith Bowles
Mathematics Teacher
Zehr, Philip J.
Former Teacher
Zimmer, Peter John
Graduate Teaching Assistant
LE ROY
Jones, Edward
Business, PE Teacher & Coach
Kloefkorn, Mary Jane
English Teacher
LEAVENWORTH
Cowger, Lawrence Ray
Chemistry Teacher
De Rousse, Judith Ekmark
English Department Chair
Doll, Pete Anthony
High School Mathematics Tchr
Frierson, Flavia Ann
German & English Teacher
Jackson, Jane
Social Studies Teacher
Jackson, Susan Dorr
English Teacher
Lauxman, Larry A.
Art Teacher
Massoth, Arthena C.
Kindergarten Teacher
Mauton, Ivonne Perez
Spanish Teacher
Moran, Patrick Eugene
Math Teacher
Morrisey, Rebecca D.
Mathematics Teacher
Murphy, Susan Sernus
Language Arts Teacher
Notter, Frank Arthur
Jr Rsrve Offcr Trng Crps Instr
Pulem, Gayle Ann
Gifted Program Consultant
Rankin, Debra Lynn
Mathematics Teacher
Robben, James Allan
Junior ROTC Instructor
Schmidt, David Alan, Sr.
World & American History Tchr
Simpson, Raymond Leon, Sr.
Math Teacher
Strano, Tamra Gayle
Health & PE Instructor
Vest, Tracy Pederson
Elementary Art Teacher
Williams, Joyce Sandra
High School Guidance Counselor

LEAWOOD
Amos, Joseph Glenn
Social Studies Teacher
Burkindine, Timothy Neil
English Teacher
Colwell, Thomas B.
Amer His & Sociology Teacher
Cummings, Jeanne Marie
Latin Teacher
Cyr, Jan K.
Science Teacher & Dept Chprsn
Gilcrest, Telia Sebaugh
Enrichment Specialist
Hazlett, David L.
Science Teacher
Hill, Larry E.
Speech & Drama Teacher
Jenkins, Kay K.
English Teacher
McGeehan, Donna Luisa
Spanish Teacher & Vllybl Coach
Migneron, Kathy Ann
English Teacher
Morris, Diane Reichart
English Teacher
Nagel, Judy Schwartz
6th Grade Teacher
Pintar, Liliane
Mathematics Teacher
Roberts, Marion King
Instrumental Music Director
Simpson, Dava Sue
First Grade Teacher
Wimmer, Linda Ann
English & Speech Teacher
Young, Denise Lynn
Math & Computer Teacher
LENEXA
Demo, Thomas E.
Educational Specialist
Kostus, Marcia Rae
6th Grade Teacher
LENORA
Reinhardt, Patricia Lindemann
Business Education Teacher
LEOTI
Ames, Leah Juanita
Language Arts Teacher
Aschenbrenner, Stephen A.
Amer His & Govt Teacher
Johnson, Cheryl Dutton
Third Grade Teacher
Lane, Grant Jay
Social Studies Teacher
LIBERAL
Argo, Calvin Elton
Science Department Chair
Cornelsen, Gary W.
HS Physical Education Teacher
Goodman, Martha Susan
Seventh Grade Mathematics Tchr
Loucks, John Chester
Instr & Hum Division Chair
Marsh, Gary William
Middle School Art Teacher
McConnell, Jack Darril
Biologist Instructor
Miles, Donna Glass
Jrnlsm Adv & English Teacher
Nix, Elaine Templin
Retired 2nd Grade Teacher
Parker, Darin Rex
Vocal Music Directer
Perkins, Mark Chrisman
IRC Tchr & Gifted Facilitator
Shandy, Robert Keith
Counselor
Tillman, L. M. Casey
4th Grade Teacher
Witherspoon, Terry L.
9th-12th Grd World His Teacher
LINCOLN
Brockett, Fae E.
Retired Teacher
Hayworth, Kae Marie (Ray)
Art Teacher
Schmeidler, Darrell
Industrial Technology Teacher
LINDSBORG
Johnson, Kristin Brase
Fourth Grade Teacher
Lewis, Linda M.
Associate Professor of English
Myers, Jay H.
Social Science & Jrnlsm Tchr
LINN
Blaha, Frank H.
Retired Business Teacher
Friedrichs, Diane Kay
Scndry Eng & Speech Tchr
Savage, Michael Dale
Social Studies Teacher
LITTLE RIVER
Ellwood, Douglas
History & English Teacher
Hodgson, Helen Elizabeth
Retired Kindergarten Teacher
Myers, Beth Wood
K-12th Grade Art Instructor
Prickett, Toni Lee
Mathematics Teacher
LOGAN
Berg, Debra States
Fourth Grade Teacher
States, Freida M. (Hofaker)
First Grade Teacher
LONG ISLAND
VanKooten, Donna Fae (Godfrey)
Retired School Teacher

LONGFORD
Van Scoyoc, Evelyn Oberdick
3rd & 4th Grade Teacher
LONGTON
Crowell, Nancy Jo
Business & Computer Tech Tchr
Young, Juli Jontra
Mathematics Teacher
LOST SPRINGS
Broce, Bill Eldon
Science Teacher
Webb, Alan Dale
English & Communications Tchr
LOUISBURG
Best, Pamela L.
Business Teacher
Bradbury, Mary Elizabeth (Hix)
Home Economics Teacher
Cates, Beth (Johnson)
7th-8th Grd Math & Sci Tchr
Cisetti, John Domenic
Band Director
Guetterman, Lisa (Perry)
Third Grade Teacher
Hill, Bonnie Sue
Learning Disability Teacher
Pease, Danna M.
Facilitator of Gifted
Winters, Nancy S.
Third Grade Teacher
LURAY
Spears, Gaylene Louise
Fourth Grade Teacher
LYNDON
Gales, Lori Catron
Jr High Math Teacher
LYONS
Dumler, Larry Dean
Technology Education Instr
Feldman, Rhonda (Cory)
2nd & 3rd Grade Classroom Tchr
Peak, Janice Mai
Elementary Music Instructor
Wall, Lola Mae
Coord of the Gifted Ed Program
MACKSVILLE
Adams, Lyndel Schmalzried
K-12 Grade Counselor
George, Lelin Haskell
HS English Teacher
Hemphill, Mary Ann Tompkins
Second Grade Teacher
Miller, Yolette Sue (Rehmer)
Special Education Teacher
Zachman, David Mark
Social Studies Teacher
Zachman, Debbie Ann
Kindergarten Teacher
MADISON
Bolen, Dale M.
Language Arts & Soc Sci Tchr
MAIZE
Ashby, Kathleen A.
German Teacher
Bergkamp, Stanley Eugene
Physical Science Teacher
Blazek, Joan Pottore
Drama Teacher
Borrego, Christine Warner
English Teacher
Crow, Randy L.
Fifth Grade Band Teacher
Elder, Sherry S.
Spanish Teacher
Faulkner, Michael Scott
Health & PE Teacher
Heger, Lori Corinne
Physical Education Teacher
Hughbanks, Nancy Ann
6th Grade Teacher
Martling, Steve W.
Math Teacher
Oakman Kraybill, DaVonna
US History & Economics Teacher
Rogers, Cynthia Pauline
Social Science Teacher
Sroufe, Julia Duckworth
Kindergarten Teacher
Welsh, Polly Ann
English Teacher
MANHATTAN
Babbar, Sunil
Management Professor
Bogart, Mickey L.
History & Social Studies Tchr
Burke, Richard Kent
Dir of Grad Studies & Instr
Burton, Esther Hoehn
Tutoring & Substitute Teacher
Clark, Stevan Dion
Sixth Grade Teacher
Cook, Sarah Virginia
Graduate Teaching Assistant
Cowan, Thaddeus McKelvey
Professor
Davis, Olga Idriss Sneed
Asst Prof of Rhetorical Stud
Dehon, Claire L.
French Professor
Deines, Dan S.
Associate Prof of Accounting
DeVault, James E.
Electrical Engineering Prof
Dukas, Stephen P.
Assistant Professor
Dyer, Ruth Geis
Assoc Prof Elec & Cmptr Engrng
Fatemi, Ali M.
Department Head of Finance

Freeby, Scott R.
Band Director
Hagedorn, Tami Jo
4th Grade Teacher
Haller, Wayne Roger
Substitute Teacher
Hoerman, Rose Marie
Sixth Grade Teacher
Hope, Jeanell Wynn
English Teacher
Irelan, Frances J.
Third Grade Teacher
Isom, Steven Warren
VP for Academic Affairs
Kaweck, Patricia Paskiewicz
High School Art Teacher
Krebs, Paul Samuel
Asst Prof of Kinesiology
Kujawa, Raymond Lawrence
Mathematics Teacher
Leach, Joyce Ann (Crill)
First Grade Teacher
Lenhert, Anne
Assistant Professor
Miller, Ruth Douglas
Electrical Engrng Professor
Morcos, Medhat Mourad
Assoc Prof Electrical Engrng
Mueller, Delbert Dean
Biochemistry Professor
Mueller, Paula B.
Learning Disabilities Teacher
Niehoff, Brian Patrick
Management Professor
Ostrom, Janet Parker
Title I Parent Outreach Coord
Paddock, Wesley T.
Assoc Prof of Old Testament
Paukstelis, Maria Krassoi
Director of Academic Services
Prins, Harald E.L.
Anthropology Professor
Roberts, Karen Louise (McDaniel)
Gifted Education Facilitator
Shea, James Douglas
Soc Stud & Advanced Bible Tchr
Sorensen, Christopher M.
Physics Professor
Swihart, Nancy L.
English Professor
Tracz, Frank Carl
Band Dir & Assoc Prof of Music
Warren, Virgil
Theology Professor
West, Angela Graham
Asst Prof of Mrktg & Intl Bus
Wilson, Scott A.
Psychology Teacher
Wilson, Susan Foxley
First Grade Teacher
Yetter, David N.
Associate Professor of Math
MANKATO
Becker, Robert L.
Secondary Social Science Tchr
Bradley, Vic L.
Science & Math Instructor
Daniels, Sherill
English Teacher
Menhusen, Rosalie D.
Science & Math Teacher
MAPLE HILL
Loomans, Alan Leonard
Science Teacher
MARION
Connell, Dean Michael
Band Director
Meyer, Mark Wayne
Agriculture Education Teacher
Padgham, Shari Addison
Third Grade Teacher
Smith, Lois A. (Dreiling)
Comp Applications & Bus Tchr
MARQUETTE
Challans, Joyce L.
Fifth Grade Teacher
Holmquist, Thomas Nathaniel
Social Studies Teacher
MARYSVILLE
Dittmar, Lona (Davis)
Speech, Media Teacher & Coach
Edwards, Brenda K.
4th Grade Teacher
Etelamaki, Gordon Gene
Mathematics Instructor
Gross, Dora E.
HS Math Teacher & Dept Chair
Harmer, Sheri Lea
Business Teacher
Knott, Linda Kay (Bade)
7th Grade Life Science Teacher
Pillard, Gary Raymond
Jr & Sr HS Art Instructor
Schwarz, Annga Lynn
Algebra I & Math Tchr
Stone, Stephen Thomas
11th Grd American History Tchr
Tilley, J. Roxanne Welch
Learning Strategies Teacher
Wehling, Stanley Henry
6th-8th Grd Principal & Tchr
MAYETTA
Geiger, Linda C.
Science & Technology Tchr
Morris, Sandra Nelson
Title I Reading Teacher
MC CUNE
Cooper, Steve
Lang & Social Studies Teacher

MC DONALD
Wilkens, Anita Klepper
Fourth Grade Teacher
MC LOUTH
Gardner, Garon Gale
Secondary Social Science Tchr
Wagner, Charlene Marie Kempa
Keyboarding & Soc Sci Tchr
MC PHERSON
Dodson, James M.
Associate Professor
Fenwick, Marsha L. (Becker)
Fifth Grade Teacher
Ferguson, Carole (Persin)
HS English Instructor
Ferrell, Linda Rae Griffith
Kindergarten Teacher
O'Dell, David Arthur
Accounting & Business Prof
Overman, Tim
Social Science Instructor
Parker, Sherilyn E.
Facilitator of Gifted Ed
Pauls, Leon W.
Teacher & Department Chair
Peck, Gordon Wayne
Physical Ed Tchr & Coach
Smith, A. Herbert
Prof of Philosophy & Religion
Stroup, Lorna Lehmberg
Former Teacher
MEADE
Holmes, Merlin J.
Science Teacher
Thomas, Colette A.
English Teacher
Wiens, Waldo K.
Former 4th Grade Teacher
MEDICINE LODGE
Miller, Dean Chamberlain
Media Specialist
Parker, Devra Diane
10th-12th Grade English Tchr
MELVERN
Snyder, Brenda J.
Family & Consumer Science Tchr
Wallace, Stuart
Social Studies Teacher
MERIDEN
Bruton, Leslie Ann (Keil)
Math Teacher
Bush, Jacqueline Rae
First Grade Teacher
Johnson, Janine Coleman
Kindergarten Teacher
Lawlor, Jolene Marie
Mathematics Teacher
MINNEAPOLIS
Atkinson, Phyllis Hess
Kindergarten Teacher
Grosshans, Meryl E.
Retired Spanish Teacher
Mc Cullick, Julie (Comfort)
English Teacher
MINNEOLA
Lang, Ronald E.
Fourth Grade Teacher
MISSION
Chatelain, Carol Brumfield
Former Music Teacher
MONTEZUMA
Crump, Beverly Musselwhite
Mathematics Teacher
Gillespie, Kelly Patricia
Assistant Principal
Koehn, Kathleen V.
Counselor & Teacher
Lupton, Mary Evans
Fifth Grade Teacher
Watkins, Thomas Gregory, IV
Science Teacher
MORAN
Beene, Mike D.
Agriculture Education Instr
Sager, David Michael
Life Science & Biology Tchr
Smith, Ron
Counselor
Storrer, Joyce Lynn
Fourth Grade Teacher
MORROWVILLE
Leakey, Richard Donald
Teacher
Noll, Steven Louis
Social Studies Teacher
MOSCOW
Broaddus, Cindy Bressler
4th-5th Grade Teacher
MULLINVILLE
Hayse, Monica Mc Fadden
Retired Biology Teacher
MULVANE
Channell, Gary W.
Chemistry & Physics Teacher
Fisk, Karen Anderson
Gifted Facilitator
Johnson, Joe W.
Biological Science Teacher
Kraft, William Earl
Social Studies Teacher
Mason, Charles Allen
English & Drivers Ed Teacher
Webster, Jennifer L.
Family & Consumer Sci Teacher
NEODESHA
Clifton, Judyth Elaine
Fourth Grade Instructor
Gassaway, Denise H.
Language Arts Teacher

Martin, Paul C.
Director of Educational Tech
Schoenfeldt, Melinda Webb
Lang Arts Teacher
NESS CITY
Blakeslee, Kent G.
Agriculture Education Instr
Depperschmidt, Mari Ann
Principal & Teacher
Meis, Lora Jean Rohr
Language Arts Educator
Parker, Juanita Kay (Pember)
Business Education Teacher
NEWTON
Cowan, Sondra Patton
1st Grade Teacher
Cranston, Sharon Wells
French Teacher
Dick, Darlene Klassen
Senior High English Teacher
Jones, Barbara Jean
Second Grade Teacher
O'Banion, Sally M.
High School English Teacher
Pallucca, William Michael
English Teacher
Perbeck, Deborah D.
Schl Improvemnt, Staff Dev Dir
Rucker, Nute Patrick
Agriscience Instructor
Saab, Jan E.
English Teacher
Smith, Mary Rebecca
Secondary Math Teacher
Smyth, Robert D.
Physical Education Teacher
Supernois, Joanne Lee (Spade)
Business Tech Instr & Coord
Thull, Shelley Schreuder
Math Teacher
Voth, Wynette Flickner
Technology Teacher
NICKERSON
Colle, V. Renae (Bailey)
4th Grade Teacher
Fulton, Eric Todd
PE & At Risk Teacher
Henke, Judy Van Loenen
Home Economics Teacher
Hodgson, Robert George
Retired Physical Ed Teacher
Shores, Brad Jay
Instrumental Music Teacher
Summerrill, John Charles
Athletic Director & Govt Tchr
NORTH NEWTON
Friesen, Duane K.
Professor of Bible & Religion
Graber, Gladys Caroline
Assoc Professor of Accounting
Hart, Julie Putnam
Asst Prof of Sociology
Kasper, Kathryn Dick
Assoc Professer of Voice
Sprunger, Keith L.
Professor of History
NORTON
Burns, James B.
3rd Grade Teacher
Green, James L.
Science Teacher
Sebelius, Nancy Gruver
Teacher of the Gifted
Wetter, Margaret Ann
2nd Grade Teacher
NORTONVILLE
Sheeley, Grace Newman
4th-6th Grade Teacher
OAKLEY
Keenan, James Michael
Bus Instr & Activities Dir
OBERLIN
Dejmal, Candace Sue
Computer Instructor
Dorshorst, Patricia Jo (Miller)
Mathematics Teacher
Sand-Breth, Brenda
English & Journalism Teacher
OLATHE
Ackerson, Sandra Stephens
History Teacher
Ater, Gwen Wright
Sixth Grade Teacher
Banks, Maryellen Cline
7th Grd Unified Studies Tchr
Barnett, Douglas Scott
History Teacher
Birch, Candy S.
English & Journalism Teacher
Blake, John Tyler
English Professor
Bush, Jane Anderson
Science Teacher
Case, Steven Bassett
Biology Teacher
Colson, Edwin L.
Director of Bands
Crago, Barbara Rice
Kindergarten Teacher
Craig, Jana Marie
Staff Development Specialist
DeRodes, Deven
Math Teacher
Doolittle, Carolyn Ruth
Assistant Professor of Ed
Elsey, Tamara J.
Mathematics Teacher
Epp, Garrett Wayne
Choral Director

Fales, Jennifer Lea
Family & Consumer Science Tchr
Fine, Larry Douglas
Prof of Philosophy & Religion
Golub, Janet J.
Math Teacher
Gorman, Kathleen
Fourth Grade Teacher
Gough, Mike
Business Administration Chair
Greiner, Linda Jefferson
English Teacher
Grigsby, Penney Farnell
Kindergarten Teacher
Haffey, Larry Joe
Assoc Prof of Computer Science
Hampton, Linda Kay (Melvin)
Mathematics Teacher
Harris, Nick L.
Health & Physical Ed Instr
Heinrich, Lisa Ann
Spanish Teacher
Henning, Douglas Dayn
Psychology Prof & Dept Chair
Hoffman, Mickey Scrogham
Spanish Teacher
Kifer, Gregory L.
Physics Teacher
Kirschner, Debbie Janice
Speech, Drama & English Tchr
Kraft, Michael Gene
Ninth Grade Life Science Tchr
Landis, Judith Kay
Intnl Lang Chprsn & Span Tchr
Lang, Jacqueline R.
Social Science Teacher
Largent, Donna M.
PE Teacher & Coach
Lerner-Sexton, Marie Kraus
Choral Music Teacher
Limes, William E., Jr.
Chemistry & Biology Instructor
Matthews, Janet Hulse
6th Grade Teacher
Mc Cullough, Carol A.
Social Studies Teacher
McIntire, Melissa Leiker
Sign Language Teacher
McRoberts, Nancy Reed
Family & Consumer Sci Teacher
Meeker-Miller, Anne
Choral Teacher
Mittenmeyer, Diane Dickson
Junior HS Social Studies Tchr
Norman, Mary Jane J.
French Teacher
Oberhelman, Tim Allen
Biology Teacher
Packard, Clifford Montel
Third Grade Teacher
Palmberg, Edith Ann
ESL Tchr
Pope, Ramona Myers
Biology & Life Science Teacher
Porterfield, Sherri Lou
Choral Music Director
Reglin, Russell Ray
Assistant Professor of Psych
Reusser, Jean Humphrey
Language Arts Teacher
Ricci, Mary Beth
Spanish & Italian Instructor
Ring, Beverly A.
Science Teacher
Rogers, Leigh Anne
Second Grade Teacher
Rossiter, Philip Wylie
4th Grade Teacher
Royer, Stephanie Melander
6th Grade Teacher
Schafer, Virginia Rae
Assistant Professor of Nursing
Sill, Vivian A. (Johnson)
Gifted Education Facilitator
Simmons, Nila Kay
English Teacher
Smith, Barth C.
Practical Theology Professor
Smith, Katheryn Jeanette
Music Professor
Sperry, Mlee Annette
Cmptr Tchr & Bldg Sys Operator
Staudenmaier, Andrea Meyer
Math Teacher
Taylor, William LLoyd
Prof Emeritus of Chemistry
Tharp, Peggy A.
Facilitator of Gifted Children
Tidd, Steve W.
PE Teacher
Trapp, Deanna Hobbs
Art Teacher
Ulmer, Gary Dean
Business Teacher
Van Der Stelt, Sheryl Linette
Mathematics Teacher
Wehmeyer, Willadee Stewart
Professor of Business Admin
Wilder, Mary Jane Whitehead
Voice Professor
Wilson, Lisa Yvette
English Tchr & Newspaper Spon
Worth, Julie Anne (Probasco)
HS Guidance Counselor
Zeligman, Carolyn Pickett
French & Spanish Teacher
ONAGA
Barth, Mary Jane Frederick
MS IRC & Inclusion Teacher

Clark, Jolene J.
Secondary English Teacher
Hermreck, Dennis M.
Secondary Social Studies Tchr
Sauvage, Sandra Kaye
Middle School Generalist
Suther, Anne O'Shea (Heptig)
Middle School Science Teacher
Switzer, Marilyn M.
4th-5th Grade Teacher
OSAGE CITY
Gallagher, Renee
English Tchr & Forensic Coach
Karmik, Cynthia Neumeier
Spanish Teacher
OSAWATOMIE
Ingle, Carl D.
American History Teacher
Kuder, Donneta Kimball
Social Studies Teacher
Madden, Ruth M. (King)
Substitute Teacher
Maring, Tracy Rae (Letterman)
Eighth Grade Math Teacher
Vilgiate, Joy Janell
Director of Bands
Williams, Kinda Erkenbrack
Business Teacher
Woolery, Nancy Ann
Elementary Counselor
OSBORNE
Draayer, Stephanie G.
Kindergarten Teacher
Hutchinson, Pamela Jean (Stemsrud)
Spanish & English Teacher
Ubelaker, Douglas James
Secondary Social Studies Tchr
OSKALOOSA
Ellis, Ronald Burrton
Jr High Social Science Instr
Miller, Robert D.
HS Social Studies Teacher
Niemann, Mary Ann
Business Teacher
Twombly, Matthew Wayne
Science Teacher
OSWEGO
Jessee, Patty J. Crossland
Community Service & Art Tchr
Redburn, Kristin A.
Spanish & French Teacher
Schenker, Jennifer Nelson
HS Mathematics Teacher
Wittmer, Rodney Scott
Business Teacher
OTIS
Bechard, Matthew William
Physical Ed & Health Teacher
Goodheart, Mark
HS Principal
Heinen, Edward Ralph
Math & Cmptr Programming Tchr
Stottlemire, Rodney Ray
Social Science Teacher
OTTAWA
Bushman, Kay Parks
Lang Arts Dept Chr & Eng Tchr
Criqui, R. Cheryl Mc Call
Fifth Grade Teacher
Geiss, Susan G.
History Teacher
Hart, Kirk Mc Grew
Elementary Principal
Kimes, DeeAnna P.
Computer Instructor
Kimes, Ronald Richard
Junior & Senior Counselor
McClaran, Carol Sue Miller
7th-8th Grd Soc Studies Tchr
McCullough, Charles Raymond
Technology Education Teacher
Saueressig, Becky Sue (Lyman)
Third Grade Teacher
Spigle, Edward Ammon
Business Education Teacher
Stevens, Marjorie L.
First Grade Teacher
OVERLAND PARK
Ackelson, Maggie Harlow
College Instructor
Akkam, Mazen
Engineering Instructor
Bernard, Rene E., Jr.
Band Teacher
Black, Brian D.
Asst Prof of Religion
Buckner, Virginia Lester
Instructor of Biology
Bundons, Albert Richard
Acad Dir of Bus Admin Pgm
Calvin-Law, Sandra K.
English Instructor
Carden, Glenda Kay
American History Teacher
Carpenter, Nancy Heffner
Math Instructor
Cotter, Julia Anne
Fashion Merchandising Instr
Davis, Charles Isaac, Jr.
Former Chemistry Teacher
Duffey, Donna Bedsworth
Instr & Career Pgm Facilitator
Dussair, Merejo Noellsch
Retired Spanish Teacher
Ellis, Dave W.
Counselor
Frailey, Carl David
Instructor of Science
Franzoi, Kathleen Carson
Former Counselor

Gerson, Steven Marc
English Professor
Gould, Marion White
Middle School Teacher
Harpst, Jean Jensen
Mathematics Instructor
Hendrikse, Robin Rosenthal
Manager & Owner
Janis, Gretchen VanGalder
German & English Instructor
Kester, Renee L.
Social Studies Teacher
Kim, Paul
Instructor of Economics
Langdon, Harry Norman
Humanities Professor
Leibham, Karla Bender
Principal
Miller, Janet Benner
Elementary Teacher of Gifted
Morman, Mark T.
Instructor of Speech Comm
Omundson, Michelle Floren
First Grade Teacher
Plummer, Maurice Lee
Retired Teacher
Purtle, Dorothy (Mc Gehee)
Music & Home Economics Teache
Rodriguez, Carol Duff
Instr in Office Systems Tech
Sawyer, Charis Christensen
Reading Instructor
Seibel, David Edwin
Life Science Instructor
Stringer, Gayle Ann
Former MS Facilitatr of Gifted
Uryasz, Ann Jeffrey
Former Teacher
Wiegraffe Gaar, Marilyn Audrey
History & Pol Science Instr
Wolkenfeld, Lloyd
Science & Math Teacher
OXFORD
Bales, Anita M.
Spanish Teacher
Browning, Terri L.
High School English Teacher
Camp, Paige Hower
Instrumental & Voc Music Tchr
Lundy, Ann Stephens
Bus Inst & Multi Media Tech
OZAWKIE
Baker, Christopher Allen
History & Study Skills Teacher
PAOLA
Fassold, Marsha L.
4th Grade Teacher
Morris, Jeff L.
Counselor
Nichols, John Dean
High School Ag Science Teacher
Ransom, William Allen
Biology & Gen Science Teacher
Reaka, Phillip B.
Business Education Teacher
Sims, Cristie Lynn
Social Studies Teacher
Tillman, Leon D.
Seventh Grade Teacher
Walters, Gretchen Ann Guenther
Physical Education Teacher
PARSONS
Baker, Barbara Anne
Fifth Grade Teacher
Barrett, Robert Galen
Retired Teacher
Burris, LeAnne L.
Biology Teacher
Fabrycky, Glenna Jean
Elementary Title 1 Teacher
Friess, Mary Saliba
Science Teacher
Hill, Theodore Lynn
Mathematics Teacher
Mayberry, Mark Douglas
Math & Science Teacher
Newbery, Jeanie Marie
Retired Teacher
Patton, Susan Womack
7th & 8th Grade Math Teacher
Rapalino, Pamela Auman
Business & Computer Teacher
Thompson, Jody LaMonte
PE Prof, Coach & Ath Director
Vance, Jack Lynn
Chemistry & Physics Teacher
Viranda, Karla K.
Social Science Tchr & Coach
Wolverton, Debora L.
High School Art Teacher
Yoakam, Patricia Senechal
Fifth Grade Teacher
PAWNEE ROCK
Wagner, Marcy L.
Math & Science Teacher
PEABODY
Hughes, Rebecca Ann
Director of Bands
Loganbill, Kelly Renee (Brockus)
Journalism & Lang Arts Teacher
Moddelmog, Christopher Dean
Social Science Teacher
Pippin, Margaret E.
Fourth Grade Teacher
Rucker, Dorothy Ann
Language Arts & Jrnlsm Tchr
Silvers, Cathy Sue
Family & Consumer Sci Teacher

Y
Stephanie Dow
h Grade Science Teacher
Charles John
cal Education Teacher
ter, Marvin Wayne
ocial Studies Teacher
e, Susan Geoffrion
al Services Teacher
.IPSBURG
e, Holly Jolene
cal Ed & Health Teacher
Iichela Jean
ol Counselor
h, David Michael
le School Health Teacher
e, Don E.
School Science Instructor
Jeffrey L.
cal Education Teacher
on, Jody A.
sh Teacher
BURG
us, Gary Wayne
ematics Teacher
on, Thomas F., Jr.
selor & Soc Sci Teacher
Julie Cagle
er Teacher
-Taylor, Vicki Purl
rian
g, Margaret S. Fry
Arts & Soc Stud Tchr
e, Robert Lee
tant Professor
ersley, Christine B.
ner
Patrice
h Teacher
, Edward L.
ndary Science Teacher
lly, Christy Jones
th Grd & HS Jrnlsm Tchr
, Lynda Lea
ish Teacher
Robert Tyler
School Special Ed Tchr
, Janie Marie
Grade Teacher
uez, Jesus J.
& Chairman of Printing
ski, Connie Smittle
nstructor
, Robert Alan
ics Engrng Tech Professor
Barbara Lavon
h Grade Teacher
Valarie Susan
Grade Teacher
er, John Thomas
Teacher
ki, Paul W.
essor of Political Science
NS
k, Louise Abbott
uage Arts Teacher
NVILLE
, Shari Eisiminger
ature & Spelling Teacher
nel, Jon F.
ndary Math Teacher
nel, Wanda Deges
Grade Teacher
ONA
, Beth Briles
ed Elementary Teacher
T
n, Karen Shaw
nematics Instructor
Jane Harris
ch, English & Jrnlsm Tchr
m, Carol Goss
nistry Instructor
, Michael Wayne
Grade English Teacher
Tamera Sue (Peterson)
ish Instructor
Wanda K.
ounting Instructor
, Monette E. (Kumle)
uctor of English
n, Mary A. (PFeiffer)
uctor of Bus & Cmptr Tech
n, Patrick Ellis
g Ed Coord & Small Bus Dev
mb, Helen Louise
Course Coord for Nrsng Pgm
Kari Lynn
nentary Physical Ed Teacher
Vance Edward
stant Basketball Coach
ey, Stephen Lee
erican History Teacher
k, Marsha Gates
Instructor
ow, Steve Roy
h & Computer Science Tchr
rhaus, Michael D.
essor of Biology
and, Gene
lio Arts Instructor
TTY PRAIRE
on, Jon Edward
al Studies Teacher
TECTION
Janice Huck
ily & Consumer Science Tchr
, David Lee
istrial Ed Instructor

Hill, Gregory Len
K-12 Grd Physical Ed Teacher
Jarvis, Sandra Haywood
Eng Instr & Forensics Coach
Puderbaugh, Joyce Baldwin
Fifth Grade Teacher
QUINTER
Bray, M. JoAnne (Hanks)
Spcl Ed & Gifted Facilitator
Crist, Carole Huffman
English Teacher & Chairperson
Herzog, Phyllis Day
Third Grade Teacher
Hoover, Roxanne Ritzel
Life Science Teacher
Look, Linda N. (Poore)
Kindergarten Teacher
Ochs, Leah Smith
4th Grade Teacher
Tebo, SueAnn A.
Jr High Eng & HS Debate Tchr
RANSOM
Roths, Cindy Sue
Substitute Teacher
REXFORD
Schultz, Leanna L.
MS Language Arts Teacher
Weiner, Edward Allen
Science Teacher
RICHMOND
Erisman, Bobby Dean
Assistant Principal
Getty, Gerry Roeder
Fifth Grade Teacher
Getty, Steven R.
Computer Instructor
Perry, Liza Jane
English & Physical Ed Teacher
Reynolds, Samuel E.
Art Teacher
RILEY
Lewis, Kathy S.
High School English Teacher
Shorman, Carol M.
Fifth Grade Teacher
Whitesell, Clarice (Crispin)
7th-8th Grd Math Teacher
RIVERTON
Cole, Sherry Baker
Biology & Chemistry Teacher
Cox, Claudia Thomas
MS Science Teacher
Davis, Sara E.
Mathematics Teacher
Hunt, James M.
HS Social Studies Teacher
Lloyd, Pamela Kitch
Guidance Counselor
ROBINSON
Hankins, Robert M., Jr.
Science Teacher
Soden, Jean M.
Math Teacher
ROLLA
Courtney, Mary
Fifth Grade Teacher
Raff, Howard R.
Math & Science Teacher
ROSALIA
Hanson, Deborah
Business Teacher
Kane, Alice Louise
7th-12th Grade Science Teacher
ROSE HILL
Annuschat, James Vogt
Social Science Teacher
Covey, Freema Deck
5th Grade Teacher
Gilbert, Clarence H., Jr.
Eng Tchr & Newspaper Adv
Leete, Beverly Barnes
6th Grade Science Teacher
Smith, Sally Ann
8th Grade Social Studies Tchr
Tallman, Vernelle Ruth (Busenitz)
HS Family & Consumer Sci Tchr
ROSSVILLE
Foote, Cathy L.
Science Instructor
Schmidt, Melly Karst
Eng, Speech, & Debate Tchr
Willits, Delores Wallace
Science Teacher
ROZEL
Artaz, Jay Dee
Phys Ed & Biology Teacher
RUSSELL
Cross, Melinda A.
Spanish & English Teacher
Lueth, Martin Steven
Instrumental Music Tchr
Renz, Lisa Stoner
Honors English & AP Teacher
SABETHA
Burger, Scott Leon
HS Business Education Teacher
Hall, Randy F.
Mathematics Teacher
Herbster, Connie S.
Art Teacher
Plattner, Sheryl Schmidt
Fifth Grd Rdng & Writing Tchr
Remmers, David W.
8th Grd Physical Science Tchr
Scarbrough, Jan Marie
Second Grade Teacher
SAINT FRANCIS
Kinen, Patricia A. Gallagher
Retired Eng & Journalism Tchr

SAINT GEORGE
Beam, Michael Lynn
PE & Health Instructor
Dille, Tammy Morgan
District Technology Specialist
Nicholson, Jay K.
Chemistry & Physics Instructor
Shreve, Mark
Counselor
SAINT JOHN
Bennington, Jane Wiles
Soc Stud Dept Head & Teacher
Clausing, William Wolfgang
Instrumental Music Teacher
Dickson, Carolyn Wilcox
Third Grade Teacher
Friesen, Cynthia DeAnn
Physical Education Teacher
Hullman, Michael Loren
Business Ed Teacher & Coach
Wibright, Eddy Ann
Language Arts Instructor
SAINT MARYS
Sullivan, Colleen Ann
Physical Education Teacher
SALINA
Bell, Jeffrey Lee
Middle Level Teacher
Blagg, Rosann Marie
High School Religion Teacher
Brown, David Alan
7th-8th Grade Teacher
Burch, Jean A. (Mortimer)
Retired Elementary Teacher
Butler, David Michael
Math Teacher
Caselman, Stephen Franklin
English Teacher & Coach
Claassen, Tom H.
Technology Teacher
Clark, Joseph Lewis
Science Teacher
Claus, Tony Lynn
Vocal Music Instructor
Curchy, Stefani Lea
Health & PE Teacher
Drevets, Roma Kibler
Counselor & English Teacher
Elbl, Robert Stephen
Chemistry Teacher
Ferwalt, Katrina Alene
10th Grd English Teacher
Fitzpatrick, Raymond Lynn
English Teacher & Dept Chprsn
Hickel, Michael L.
Elementary Counselor
Hutton, Melva Dean Tucker
Kindergarten Teacher
Johnson, Sheri R.
English Teacher
Kasselman, Robert L.
Mathematics Teacher
Kukula, Pauline Louise, CSJ
Religion Teacher
Loersch, Rachel Stucky
6th Grade Teacher
Martin, Sharon K.
Journalism Instructor
Mc Daniel, Brenda Joyce
Social Studies Teacher
McMillen, Gayle Conner
Band Director
Mobley, Karol Hubbard
Third Grade Teacher
Morissette, Barbara A.
5th Grade Teacher
Murphy, Steven Dean
Eighth Grade Life Science Tchr
Olson, Karen Kay Hubbard
5th Grade Teacher
Reed, Jo
English Teacher
Shivers, Karen Lewick
Teacher of Learning Disabled
Steele, Llona J.
Fr, Span Teacher & Dept Chair
Straub, Camille Kaiser
Science Teacher
Yantes, Scott David
Mathematics Teacher
SATANTA
Apsley, Joyce Borg
Math Teacher
Bynum, Becky Ann
English Teacher
SCANDIA
Cox, Richard Eugene
Social Science Teacher
SCOTT CITY
Cupp, Deva (Duff)
English & Social Studies Tchr
Doll, John G.
Government Teacher
Mason, Julie Ann
Fifth Grade Teacher
Stoppel, Sherree Smith
Vocal Director
Walter, Gaylon L.
Indstrl Ed & Technologies Tchr
SEDAN
Colvin, Kermit Scott
English & Drama Teacher
Shoup, Christine Suzette
7th Grd Life Sci Educator
Wilson, John G.
Business & Computer Teacher
SEDGWICK
Armbrister, Pamela Jean (Beisel)
School Counselor

Cummings, Dwayne Scot
5th Grade Teacher
Duft, James Steven
Industrial Arts, Tech Teacher
Eftink, Deborah Kay Edens
Dance & Baton Teacher
Fleming, Gary Dean
Jr HS Math & HS Ec Tchr
Gilbert, Connie Chestnut
6th & 8th Grade English Tchr
Humphries, Nancy Todhunter
Art Teacher
Hymer, Martha Amburn
5th Grade Teacher
Niles, Rae (Koch)
Curriculum Director
Ralston, Andy Wallace
PE Teacher & Athletic Director
Roberts, Becky A.
English Teacher
Shepherd, Steve L.
Business Dept Chair & Tchr
Turner, Peggy A.
Family & Consumer Sci Teacher
SELDEN
Baker, Richard Reno
Math & Science Teacher
SENECA
Hughes, Carol Wiesedeppe
Science Teacher
Meyer, Sharon Holeman
Mathematics & Computer Teacher
SHARON SPRINGS
Daily, Jori Faye
High School Math Teacher
Hennick, Peggy (Short)
1st Grade Teacher
Swanson, Lucretia Ann
Family & Consumer Sci Teacher
SHAWNEE
Nave, Marie Herbst
Home Economics Teacher
SHAWNEE MISSION
Adams, Mary Noble
Retired Third Grade Teacher
Adkins, George Micheal
HS American History Teacher
Allen, Carol Duran
Fourth Grade Teacher
Allen, Keith Michael
English Teacher
Alley, Mary Frances
Science Teacher
Alpaugh, Donald R.
Business & Computer Teacher
Armenta, C.J.
Mathematics Teacher
Armstrong, Lisa Bailey
English Teacher
Beardsley, Marcia Hininger
Retired Sixth Grade Teacher
Bennett, Everett G., Jr.
8th Grade Language Arts Tchr
Benson, Stacy Van Der Tuuk
8th Grade Social Studies Tchr
Bowen, Mary Ann Schneider
English Teacher
Bower, C. Kay Howard
Sixth Grade Teacher
Brecheisen-Pribyl, Linda Rae
Secondary Language Arts Tchr
Britton, Stacy Lynn
HS Social Science Teacher
Brown, Paul B.
Business & Physical Ed Instr
Brown, Tom
Automotive Technology Instr
Buckner, Susan Dutoit
7th Grd Language Arts Teacher
Camburako, Sophie Gerras
7th Grade Science Teacher
Cawley, Janet K.
Math, Albebra & Rel Teacher
Conley, Cheryl Parrette
Sixth Grade Teacher
Cormack, Gerald Lauran
Social Studies Teacher
Creach, William Joseph
Social Studies & Theology Tchr
DeBarthe, Paul N.
Anthropology & Archlgy Tchr
DeLuna, Carla Angela
English Teacher & Soccer Coach
Diebold, Scott G.
Industrial Technology Teacher
DiNitto, Allyson Ann
Middle School Counselor
Eller, David Roy
Phys Ed & Health Teacher
Esfandiary, Jennifer Sue
Fourth Grade Teacher
Fabiano, Ted F.
High School English Teacher
Farnan, Phil E.
English & Theology Teacher
Fletcher, Douglas G.
Sixth Grade Teacher
Frisby, Albert Vernon, II
Advanced Bio II Honors Tchr
Fuchs, Craig Alan
Band Director
Galvin, Valerie K.
Seventh Grade Science Teacher
Garrett, Christine Winters
6th Grade Teacher
George, Clara A.
Teacher & Math Dept Chprsn
Gibson, M. Sue
Science Teacher

Giokaris, James Daniel
History Teacher
Glenn, Deborah S.
Debate Teacher & Coach
Green, Daniel Eugene
Sixth Grade Teacher
Guillen, Sally S.
Spanish Teacher
Hammons, Chuck L.
Biology Teacher
Hazelbeck, Gregory Martin
Industrial Arts Teacher
Heitmeyer, Sharon MacPherson
Kindergarten Teacher
Henry, Michael F.
Reading Specialist
Henry, Sandra Borcherding
English & Literature Teacher
Herdoiza, Fabiola Carmen
Spanish Teacher
Herrelson, Cheryl Tackett
Tchr of GATE, Mentorship Prgm
Hills, Mark Christian
Math Teacher & Division Coord
Hilscher, Jerome A., V
English Teacher
Holland, Barbara Jeanne
Third Grade Teacher
Holt, Dennis W.
8th Grade Amer History Tchr
Hughes, Nancy J.
7th Grade Math Teacher
Hunter, Tami Mize
2nd Grade Teacher
Huppe, Mark Thomas
Social Studies Teacher
Jantsch, Beth Anne
European His & Amer Govt Tchr
Johnston, Cynthia Freeman
Fifth Grade Teacher
Jones, Mary Louise Hoover
Orchestra Teacher
Kelly, Erin Kathleen
Eng Teacher & Drill Team Coach
Kessler, Penny Perme
French Teacher
King, Sharon Hayes
American & World History Tchr
Kipper, Theresa Buzzard
Honors & Pre-Algebra Teacher
Knight, Karen Heath
8th Grd American History Tchr
Lane, Robert William
English Teacher
Larkin, Karen
Facilitator of Gifted Ed
Lubin, Mitchell Sinclair
US His & World Geography Tchr
Lucas, Becky S.
Journalism Teacher
Lucito-Copenhaver, Julie A.
7th-8th Grade English Teacher
McCathen, Evelyn Ross
Fifth Grade Teacher
McClatchey, Margaret Baxter
Theatre Teacher
Mc Cormick, Connie Sue
Sixth Grade Teacher
Mc Vey, Linda Myers
English Teacher
Meador, Darrell Thomas
Biology Teacher
Michels, Zelma Marie
Sixth Grade Teacher
Morton, Kathleen Eisele
Sixth Grade Teacher
Mulvany, Timothy P.
Development Dir & Bsktbl Coach
Murray, Cheryl Ann
Voc Fashion Careers Instructor
Naster, Mike B.
His Tchr & Head Track Coach
Nelson, Barbara Jo
High School Vocal Music Instr
Nelson, Cynthia G.
Seventh Grade Lang Arts Tchr
Nickum, Judy Carr
German Teacher
Parrish, Leslie Alan
6th Grade Teacher
Pearson, Kevin Dwayne
Biology Teacher
Pennington, David Earl
Social Studies Teacher
Poe, Carita D. (Hammond)
Child Dev & Education Teacher
Poplau, Ronald Wayne
Social Science Instructor
Prendergast, Shawn Francis
Religion Teacher
Pribyl, Rick R.
English Teacher
Puett, Karen Lanette
Chemistry & Adv Biology Tchr
Rames, Doe (Meyer)
5th Grade Teacher
Reed, John Thomas
Physical Education Teacher
Ricker, James Benjamin
History Teacher
Roper, Kenneth E.
Physics Teacher
Rousselo, Pamela Ann
4th Grade Teacher
Royer, Richard S.
High School Mathematics Tchr
Rutherford, Paul Mason, Jr.
Physics Teacher
Ryan, John M.
Social Studies Teacher

SHAWNEE MISSION (cont)
Schaaf, Deanna (Gerdes)
Business Education Teacher
Scott, Jacqueline Winsky
Third Grade Teacher
Seevers, John Charles
Sociology & Psychology Teacher
Shadonix, William Andrew
5th Grade Teacher
Snow, Truman Leo
Science Teacher
Southwell, Shelley C.
Math Teacher
Spratlin, Karen Spakes
Sixth Grade Teacher
Stafford, Brenda Trent
German Teacher
Stern, Stanley Bernard
Teacher of Gifted
Summers, Norma Lee
Fifth Grade Teacher
Sutton, Cynthia Ann
High School Art Teacher
Tarbutton, Kathy Hill
Div Coord Intnl Languages
Temple, Rachel Gaynor
Spanish Teacher
Trupp, Susan Claire
Family & Consumer Science Tchr
Unruh, Sherry Louise (Johnson)
English Instructor
Veer, Phil
High School Athletic Director
Vrabac, Elizabeth
American History Teacher
Wentz, Mark A.
Science Teacher
Wilson, Nancy
English Teacher
Wilson, Phillip G.
English Teacher
Wolff, Susan Richardson
Computer & Business Teacher
Woodhead, Devena M.
Business & Computer Teacher
Wuller, Nan Marlin
5th & 6th Grade Teacher
Young, Dean Arthur
World Geog Classroom Teacher
SILVER LAKE
Bonine, Patricia Ann
English & Spanish Teacher
Craig, Robert C.
Mathematics Teacher
Cunningham, Alan Lee
Math Department Chairman
Davis, Tina Ann
Special Education Teacher
SOUTH HAVEN
Greenlee, Wayne Alan
Special Education Instructor
Metzinger, Virginia Klingman
Sr HS English & Span Tchr
SOUTH HUTCHINSON
Hewitt, Christopher Keith
Sixth Grade Teacher
SPEARVILLE
Dick, Kenneth Richard
Science Teacher
Mc Daniel, Tim
Comm & Social Studies Teacher
SPRING HILL
Booth, Elaine Samuel
Spanish & French Teacher
Jochims, Lynda Marie
HS Learning Disabilities Tchr
Ludwig, Stephen M.
Eng, Speech & Forensics Tchr
Madison, Claude John
Biology Teacher
STANLEY
Jones, Jill Johnson
7th Grade Mathematics Teacher
Kissing, Pamela Kathleen
Family & Consumer Sci Teacher
STERLING
Beecham, Curtis Michael
Associate Prof of Chemistry
Burgess, Sheila Bailey
Third Grade Teacher
Keith, Thomas F.
Associate Prof of Psychology
Long, William Rudolf
Professor of History & Govt
Mc Cullers, P. Douglas
Associate Professor of Math
VerSteeg, Mary Louise
Physical Education Asst Prof
Williams, Donald Lester
Asst Prof of Bio & Premed Adv
STILWELL
Apel, David Svensson
Social Studies Teacher
Braun, Jennifer Ann
Computer & Math Teacher
Dunlap, Martin H., Jr.
Band Director
Fryer, Sandra J.
Counselor
Gregory, Deborah Annette (White)
Mathematics Teacher
Hare, Larry L.
Science Teacher
Harris, Patricia Sanders
Fifth Grade Teacher
Katstra, Joyce Timmer
English Instructor
Lemons, Anita L.
Spanish Teacher & Dept Chm

Lerner, Robin M.
Math Teacher
McDonald, Harry Eugene, III
Biology Teacher & Coach
Nixon, Karen Frazer
Mathematics Teacher
Oliva-Martinez, Heather Kristine
Spanish Teacher
Osier, Ruth Frances
Latin Teacher
Riffer, Christopher John
Debate & Speech Teacher
Schultz, Rebecca G.
Learning Strategies Educator
Tate, Diana (Swickard)
English Teacher
STOCKTON
Gish, Angela Cordo
Family & Consumer Science Tchr
Jenkins, Connie Poore
Kindergarten Teacher
Latham, Darrell D.
Math & Physics Teacher
Lindsey, Lee William
Math & English Teacher
Pettijohn, Sharon M.
Spanish & Social Sci Teacher
Reishus, Connie Gale
Music Teacher
Van Eaton, Quentin Eugene
Social Science Teacher
SUBLETTE
Boutwell, Dot Welter
Speech & Debate Teacher
Brown, Kevin W.
HS Social Studies Tchr & Coach
Lehning, Jane Elizabeth Schmeidler
Business & Computer Instructor
Trigg, C. Paul
Social Studies Teacher
SYRACUSE
Lewis, Selola Belle (Wilson)
Retired Teacher
TECUMSEH
Appelhanz, Charlie A.
HS Social Studies Teacher
Bartel, Lila Waltner
Coordinator of Gifted Program
Buchanan, Patrick E.
Social Studies Teacher
Dibbern, Gaylene D.
8th Grade Amer History Teacher
Glaser, Kent A.
Mathematics Teacher
Hay, Douglas Robert
High School Science Teacher
Henry, Mark Thomas
Business Teacher
Hinkel, Deborah Beal
Family & Consumer Science Tchr
Jarboe, Mark E.
Physics & Astronomy Teacher
Kelley, Kate E.
Secondary Language Arts Tchr
Mead, Karen Rae
Family & Consumer Science Tchr
Mickens, Bradley J.
7th Grade Math Teacher
Nelson-Bova, Linda D.
Art Teacher
Pitman, Connie Brack
Facilitator of GATE
Swafford, Diana (Laurence)
Language Arts Instructor
Syverson, Elizabeth Ann
Spanish Teacher
Van Meter, Janis Kay (Fowler)
Art Teacher
Van Petten, Jackie Baker
Journalism Teacher
Wells, Bob
Chemistry Teacher
Wisdom, Michael B.
8th Grade Mathematics Teacher
THAYER
Aikins, Steven Ray, Sr.
5th Grade Teacher
Wagner, Jim Alan
Industrial Arts & Tech Ed Tchr
Young, Donald Leroy
Retired Classroom Teacher
TIPTON
Baker, Gerold Dean
Physical Education Teacher
TONGANOXIE
Arevalo, Pamela Ann (Phillips)
Spanish Teacher
Cackler, Vickie Barnett
College Bound English Teacher
Fritz, Beth Knoebber
Fourth Grade Teacher
Gilner, Andrew Thomas
Soc Sci, Driver Ed Tchr, Coach
Herron, Christopher Alan
Earth Science Instructor
McClellan, Michael B.
9th Grade Social Studies Tchr
Plaschka, Russell E.
Agriculture Ed Teacher
TOPEKA
Adams, Paul Matthew
Social Studies Teacher
Alksnis, Gunnar
History Professor
Allen, Susan Buettner
Gifted Education Coordinator
Altman, Joanne D.
Psychology Professor
Angel, Stephen Arthur
Asst Professor of Chemistry

Ash, Ronald Joseph
Professor of Biology
Asklund, Marilyn Lou
American Studies Teacher
Asselin, Connie Jean
Kindergarten Teacher
Barton, Beverly Ann (Milton)
First & Second Grade Teacher
Bissey-Lowdon, Pamela
Orchestra Director
Booher, Lori J.
Amer His Tchr & Dept Chair
Bossell, Bobbi Ann
6th-8th Grd Soc Studies Tchr
Bradley, Mary Jane (Logan)
English Teacher
Brooks, Dan A.
Middle School Teacher
Bruch, Gerald Mark
Energy Manager
Bunyan, William Price
5th Grade Teacher & Coach
Burbridge, Carol A.
Library Media Specialist
Buscher, Sharon Katherine
7th & 8th Grade Science Tchr
Calderwood, Robert A.
English & Amer History Teacher
Cann, Steven J.
Prof & Political Sci Dept Chm
Carter, Lesia Darcel
Social Worker
Chamberlain, Barbara Lynn
Language Arts Teacher
Clark, Nora Eastman
Assistant Professor of Nursing
Clark, Paul Francis
English & Photography Teacher
Collins, Timothy Oliver
English Teacher
Cowen, W. Edward
8th Grade Science Teacher
Daeschner, Judith Adele
Sixth Grade Teacher
Dalton, Mark E.
Geometry & Intro to Alg Tchr
Eley, DeAnn
Third Grade Teacher
Ensley, Pamela Sayler
5th Grade Teacher
Ensley, Ted G.
American History Teacher
Evans, Barry Eugene
Director of Bands
Evans, Lucinda Marie
American History Teacher
Fusaro, Nancy Moffitt
Kindergarten Teacher
Gifford, Donald E.
Social Science Instructor
Gish, Roseann C.
Dean of Comm & Jrnlsm Tchr
Goehring, Michael R.
World Geography Teacher
Greiner, Sarah Jane
Third Grade Teacher
Groves, Gary A.
Elementary Principal
Gustavson, Robert Lloyd
Professor of Economics
Hagan, Jill Ewing
5th Grade Teacher
Hageman, Anne Marie
Computer Teacher
Heisler, Robert Joseph
Biological Sciences Teacher
Holden, Adam Charles
English Teacher
Holloway, Diana Kay
Mathematics Teacher
Hull, Robert M.
Assoc Prof Business Finance
Hunter, Mardine L.
Elementary Teacher
Janousek, Lynn Wargo
2nd Grade Teacher
Jernigan, Sue Stiefel
First Grade Teacher
Johannsen, Shirley Ann
5th Grade Teacher
Keiss, Connie Sue
8th Grd American Studies Tchr
Kelly, Patrick Timothy
Music Educator
Kickhaefer, Scott L.
Theatre Instructor
King, Cindy Ileen
Vocational Rehabilitation Tchr
King, Theresa Ellis
Chem Tchr & Sci Dept Coord
Knight, Billie-Renee
Spanish Instructor
Lady, Richard Alan
Science & Health Teacher
Latimer, Larry Bruce
US & World History Teacher
Lee, Elisabeth M.
English Teacher
Manley, Donald C.
Retired Elem School Teacher
Manson, Tony James, Sr.
Administrative Asst & Teacher
Martin, Loanne Bouman
Asst Prof of Nrsng & BSN Coord
Mc Carthy, Mary Beth (Needham)
Retired Speech Debate Tchr
Mc Comas, Barbara Wilde
Second Grade Teacher
Mc Donald, Brenda Joyce
First Grade Teacher

Mc Ginnis, Connie Archer
Lang Arts & Drama Instr
Mc Greevy, Patricia Nash
Freshman Religion Teacher
Middendorf, Carolyn Yvonne Brockhoff
Assistant Professor of Nursing
Miller, Dianne Kay
Fifth Grade Teacher
Miller, Tondra Ann Smith
1st Grade Teacher
Mitchell, Michael R.
Mathematics Teacher
Navone, Edward
Professor of Art
Neuman, Kelly Suzanne
Publications Advisor
Norris, Peggy J.
Business Teacher
Nunley, Patricia Mc Guire
Music Specialist
Ockree, Kanalis Anne
Accounting Professor
Ohm, Kenneth R.
Lecturer
Padget, Barbara J.
Jrnlsm & Photography Teacher
Pence, Gerald William
Business Teacher
Pieplow, Susan Jean
6th & 8th Grade Teacher
Pyles, Diane
Fifth Grade Teacher
Rao, Lalitha Kondabolu
Asst Professor of Nursing
Rues, Alicia Anne
Lrng Disabilities & CWC Tchr
Sandquist, Arthur H.
Dept Chprsn & Biology Tchr
Schaefer, Margaret Fay
Seventh Grade Teacher
Schlicher, Jane Elizabeth
Kindergarten Teacher
Schreiner, Cheryl Lynn
Former English Teacher
Schroeter, Elaine Murphy
Third Grade Teacher
Serino, Anthony A.
Assistant Professor of Biology
Shamburg, Barbara Manke
Classroom Teacher
Sharp, James LeRoy
Band Director
Sittenauer, Susan Mannoni
Social Studies Teacher
Slimmer, Barbara Marie
Kindergarten Teacher
Smith, Loran B.
Political Science Professor
Smith, Maureen Joanell
Science Dept Chair & Tchr
Smith, Ronald D.
Agriscience & FFA Instr
Stumbaugh, Kathy Richard
Substitute MS Teacher
Swearingen, Paul Lee
Language Arts & Spanish Tchr
Tinkum, Marsha Williams
Social Studies Teacher
VanMeter, David Eugene
Industrial Arts Teacher
Walker, Joann Louise
Chemistry Teacher
Warner, Catherine Patricia
Assistant Principal
Waters, Shari Lynn
Psychology & Soc Science Tchr
Wilson, Peggy Holeman
Math Teacher
Zimbelman, Gary Lee
6th Grade Teacher
Zimmerman, Kerry Guy
Anatomy & Physiology Teacher
TOWANDA
Pyle, Linda Kay
English I & American Lit Tchr
Strong, Ronald James
Math Teacher
TROY
Bond, Charles Thomas
Coach
Koelsch, Cheryl
Mathematics Teacher
Reynolds, Bruce L.
Social Studies & Business Tchr
TURON
Mc Kinney, Betsy Lynn
6th-8th Grade Teacher
UDALL
Kratochvil, Lara Jean
Math Teacher
ULYSSES
Battin, Gloria Mc Farland
Seventh Grade English Teacher
Cole, Dale M.
Biology Teacher
Hastert, Vernon Ray
Business Teacher
Perez, Juan L.
Social Science Teacher
UTICA
McNinch, Kimberly O'Daniel
Secondary Science Teacher
VALLEY CENTER
Brown, Jan Weaver
Third Grade Teacher
Carey, Melissa Kathleen
Biology Teacher
Fonseca, David Michael
Visual Arts Educator

Fortna, Elizbeth Ann
9th-12th Grd Eng & Rdng Tchr
Gleason, Thomas W.
Science Teacher
Graham, Jon E.
8th Grade Amer History Teacher
Mittman, Gregory Douglas
Teacher of Behavior Disordered
Murphy, Karen S.
6th Grade Language Arts Tchr
Seery, Anita Maureen
First Grade Teacher
Sells, Delores J.
6th Grade Teacher
Svaty, Monica L.
Mathematics Teacher
Williams, Debra A.
Sixth Grade Science Teacher
VALLEY FALLS
Bunde, Rodney Alan
Science & Physical Ed Teacher
Burns, Larry
PE & Health Teacher & Coach
Conser, Anna Elizabeth
Fourth Grade Teacher
VICTORIA
Engel, Bruce Kevin
Industrial Technology Teacher
Werner, Ivan Edward
Math, Science & Computer Tchr
Werner, Verda L. (Goetz)
First Grade Teacher
WA KEENEY
Collins, Doris Marie
English Instructor
Durr, Marcia Jo (Gilg)
Business Ed & Computer Teacher
Scott, William M.
Physical Science Teacher
WAKEFIELD
Laha, June Kuck
4th Grade Teacher
Seirer, Rocky
PE, Health & Drivers Ed Instr
WALLACE
Pearce, Louise Mae Evans
Retired Multi Grd Clsrm Tchr
Short, Patsy L.
Math & Science Teacher
WAMEGO
Callender, Terry Michael
Biology Teacher
Klein, Tim Allen
7th Grd Math & Ag Class Tchr
Langston, Patricia Johnston
Seventh Grade English Teacher
Morton, Cleion Whitebread
8th Grd Language Arts Teacher
Rush, Judy Duncan
English Teacher
Sunley, Barbara Bauer
Family & Consumer Sci Tchr
Webb, Gregory Wayne
Mathematics Teacher
Zahn, Martin E.
5th Grade Teacher
WASHINGTON
Baskerville, Roger Alan
Superintendent & French Instr
Colgrove, Margaret Marie (Bieker)
Sixth Grade Teacher
Hebert, Celeste Monique
French Teacher
Mallean, Bill Robert
HS Guidance Counselor
Wehling, Mary Beth Becker
Fifth Grade Teacher
WATHENA
Burks, Sarah Jane
Social Studies Teacher
Hyatt, Jill Janesko
High School English Teacher
WAVERLY
Davison, Phil J.
Science Technology Teacher
WELLINGTON
Arndt, Linda McCoy
Third Grade Teacher
Ginn, Dee Ann
Third Grade Teacher
Hatcher, Patricia Barker
7th Grade Language Arts Tchr
Leslie, Dorothy Louise
English Teacher
Mc Nett, Patsy Lou (Ports)
Kindergarten Teacher
Mc Vay, Pam (Robinett)
Math Teacher & Dept Chair
Miller, Laverne Ann (Van Kooten)
Third Grade Teacher
Pettigrew, Sandra Reno
Fifth Grade Teacher
Turner, Ronald Bruce
Counselor
WELLSVILLE
Adams, Madlyn Jo
Physical Education & Hlth Tchr
Rutledge, Charles E.
Math & Strength Trng Teacher
Savage, Timothy Scott
English & Psychology Teacher
WESKAN
Befort, Jake
Math Teacher
WESTPHALIA
Quaintance, Alan Lee
Junior High Educator
Schulte, Jane A.
4th Grade Teacher

PHALIA (cont)
Wilma K.
Arts & Soc Stud Tchr
er, Melvin Laverne
d Teacher
ORE
Deborah Renay Merritt
al Education Teacher
TA
rdt, Danny E.
& US History Teacher
ald, Tracy Ann
sh Teacher
oe Patrick
Studies Teacher
Sandra J.
sh Teacher
Joel D.
ples of Technology Tchr
, Martin M.
sh Teacher
Sherri Leigh
& Physical Science Tchr
Patricia Jo (Miles)
sh Teacher & Team Leader
, Leigh A.
Tchr & Frgn Lang Chair
J. Scott
gy Instructor
Frances Monnat
uage Arts Teacher
, Jeffrey Scott
mental Music Director
Jeanette Marie
Tchr & Gifted Facilitator
Nancy Lynne
istry & Physics Teacher
oach, Kathy Knolla
tud & Am History Tchr
Delano John
er
, Henry Lee
selor & Teacher
Kenneth Winfield
ssor
e, Marvelyn R.
ector & Graduate Coord
ynn E.
School English Teacher
hirley Louise (Towns)
rs English III Teacher
Stephen Wesley
and Orchestra Director
William Robert
ssor of Chemistry
Jen-Chi
omics Professor
ong Woo
ssor of Economics
mb, Cindy Bugner
tant Professor of Mrktg
ly, Julie Wright
ector & Adjunct Professor
, David Allen
ipal
Judith Drummond
Arts, Math & Alegbra Tchr
Denise Grohwin
sh & Spanish Teacher
azadeh, Mohammad
c Prof of Mngmt Info Sys
Barbara Sue (Hilton)
uage Arts Teacher
Charles Edward
eacher
M. Kay Miller
istory Teacher
, Karen Rietcheck
c Dir of Legal Asst Prgm
a, Deema
Professor & Director
ch, Bryan David
ish Teacher
en, Janet Wolcutt
c Dir & Instr Ec Ed
r, Mark Gordon
nce & Real Estate Prof
Margaret Lee
agement Professor
, Kris Alan
ory Teacher
, Renee Osborne
sh Teacher
Miriam Bonnie
ematics Instructor
l, Matt
ness & Computer Teacher
, Kenneth Eugene
sportation Tech Teacher
, Jim Ray
nce Teacher
s, Angela Fagan
ish Teacher
Nancy Hurt
red Elementary Teacher
asture, Judy Ashmore
ish Department Chair, Tchr
e, Sandra Annette
uage Arts Teacher
on, Randall Bennett
rman & Prof of Economics
r, Cheryl Larimore
Grade Science Teacher
ng, Reni J.
Grade Language Arts Tchr
n, Jean (Winning)
l Conductor
Tonya
c Prof of Ed

Hudson, Ronald Emory
Management Consultant
Hull, Raymond H.
Prof of Communicative Disorder
Huxman, Susan Schultz
Assoc Prof of Communicaton
Jackson, Gayle Mc Gilbray
HS Language Arts Teacher
Jackson, Randy Joe
Physical Education Teacher
Jones, Sarah Louise
French Teacher
Keane, Rebecca Mae (Waddell)
Secondary Mathematics Instr
Kehoe, Virginia Ward
Lang Dept Chm & Latin Tchr
Kerns, Robert L.
Army Instructor
King, Monika Middleton
Biology Teacher
King, Susan Hagerman
Asst Prof of Mathematics
Koeller, Pamela Sue
Journalism Teacher
Kramer, Joseph Ray
Science Teacher & Dept Chair
Krueger, Ruth Patricia
Sophomore English Teacher
Laflick, Bill
Math Teacher & Athletic Dir
Lake, Jean Marie
HS & Coll Science Teacher
Lamkey, Victoria Thynne
Zoology & Biology Teacher
Lamoree, Jan Fitzpatrick
English Teacher
Leary, Diane
Assoc Prof of History & Coach
LeBaron, Mariam Sanderson
Retired Teacher of Gifted
Ledy, Cara Prange
9th-10th Grade Lang Arts Tchr
Lewis, Alice Foster
Language Arts Tchr
Lindsey, Wanda Goldsmith
Teacher & Computer Coordinator
Long, Roland C.
Sci Dept Chm & Biology Teacher
Maurer, Michael D.
Mathematics Teacher
Mc Clain, Donna Sue (Abraham)
Business Education Teacher
Mc Coy, Michael Wesley
Weight Training & Sports Instr
Mc Donald, Keven Mark
High School English Teacher
McGuire, Cathy J.
Math Teacher
McKenney, James William
Assoc Prof & Dept of Pol Sci
Millerskow, Duane
Physics Teacher
Morgan, Vernell
7th & 8th Grade Teacher
Most, Valerie Lynn
Business Teacher
Moutray, Nila Lambert
7th Grade Math Teacher
Murphy, David Scott
Science Teacher
Murphy, Deana Kay
1st Grade Teacher
Myers, Eustasia
Senior Honors English Teacher
Nance, James Warren
Science Teacher
Nickens, Denise Darnell Kennedy
8th Grade Social Studies Tchr
Nighswonger, Darren Lee
History Teacher
Nitcher, Louise Jordan
Physical Education Teacher
Nixon, Jerry L.
Instructor of History
O'Daniel, Herbert Julian
English Teacher
Orchard, Brock Neill
Geography & US His Tchr
O'Shaugnessy, Michael Coffey
Social Studies Teacher
Otte, Bryan D.
Science Teacher
Palmer, Janice L.
High School Math Teacher
Perline, Martin Michael
Professor of Economics
Pfannestiel, Maurice
Associate Prof of Economics
Poelma, William Theodore
Multi Age Teacher
Powell, Jonathan Orr
4th-5th Grade Teacher
Rapp, Judy Hardman
Peer Coach
Ratzlaff, Harriet Elizabeth
US History & Amer Lit Tchr
Richardson, Gail M. (Lake)
Special Education Teacher
Riley, Ronald Gene
High School Assistant Prin
Riney, Cecil J.
Division of Fine Arts Chairman
Routon, Martin Wayne
Fine Arts Dept Chairperson
Ruder, Janet Sunderland
Biology & Botany Teacher
Saar, Kathy A.
HS Social Studies Teacher
Sanders, Kyle Richard
Phys Education Teacher & Coach

Schaake, Sherri S.
Biology Teacher
Schainost, Susan Hendrix
Middle School Director
Schommer, Marlene Ann
Assoc Prof of Educl Psychology
Scoville, Michael John
8th Grade Teacher
Sell, Steven K.
Art Teacher
Sherman, Mary K.
Second Language English Coord
Sherman, Twyla G.
Asst Prof of Elem Science Ed
Shockley, Kathy
Business Teacher
Shubert, David C.
Professor of Chemistry
Smith, Susanne Tanner
Fifth Grade Teacher
Sorensen, Tina Middlebrooks
High School English Teacher
Stegman, Dorothy Irene (Wilson)
English & Publications Teacher
Stewart, Jimmie D.
Mathematics Teacher
Stubby, Robert L.
Site Specialist & Teacher
Swaney, Linda Laird
Associate Professor in Nursing
Sweney, V. Ann
Psychology Lecturer
Taggart, Priscilla Ann (White)
Peer Coach & Soc Stud Tchr
Terrell, William Theodore
Economics Professor
Torkelson, Liana Albers
Counselor
Trechak, Andrew
Assistant Professor of Piano
Trimble, Constance Rathke
Social Worker Supervisor
Unruh, Mark W.
Soc Science & Journalism Tchr
Valdez, Stacie Phillips
Language Arts Teacher
Van Boer, Bertil
Professor of Music Comp
Veith, Margaret A.
Math Coordinator & Teacher
VonMerveldt, Mary Howse
Former Eng & Gifted Teacher
Wade, Patricia Rae
Second & Third Grade Teacher
Wagner, Ruth (Prueter)
Sales Assoc & Bridal Consult
Ward, Doye Diann
Physical Education Teacher
Weber, W. David
Professor of Voice
Weed, Doris Zogleman
Third Grade Teacher
Wentz, Steven Bradley
Psychology & US History Tchr
Wesolowsky, Joan C.
Computer Laboratory Coord
West, Andrea Denise (Lamon)
Eighth Grade Algebra Teacher
Whittemore, Kimme Young
Band & German Teacher
Williams, Eva K.
Principal
Wood, Deborah A.
10th Grade English Teacher
Woods, Florianne Staatz
Spanish & French Teacher
Zemanick, Walter
Math Teacher
Zoller, Peter T.
Assoc VP of Acad Affairs
WILLIAMSBURG
Coppoc, Frances Mae
Retired Eng, Fr & Typing Tchr
WINCHESTER
Newmann, Stacy Lynn (Miller)
Vocal & Instrmntl Music Tchr
WINFIELD
Barrier, Sherry Clements
Social Science Teacher
Bonham, Dawn Marie
Kindergarten Teacher
Buffum, Marilyn J.
Retired Language Arts Teacher
Cain, Nancy Rabel
Language Arts Teacher
Feinstein, Sandy
Associate Professor of English
Hanna, Joan Spicer
Kindergarten Teacher
Rhodes, Gary L.
Principal
Schotte, Mark L.
Principal & Teacher
Tuttle, Carla M.
Second Grade Teacher
Watt, Virginia Nichols
Retired 4th Grade Teacher
Yount, Sandra June
Elementary Teacher
WINONA
Johnson, Sheila I
High School Math Teacher
Moorhous, Kathleen (Lehmann)
7th & 8th Grade Teacher
YATES CENTER
Carpenter, Donna Kay
Business Teacher
Mabeus, Sue Lundgren
English Teacher

ZENDA
Vierthaler, Larry J.
Seventh Grade Teacher

KENTUCKY

ALBANY
Armstrong, Louis Elliott
Art Teacher
Beard, Michael
Social Studies Teacher
Craig, Debra Brown
US History Teacher
Grider, Deborah Lynn
Child Ed Teacher
Little, Paula Stockton
Writing Specialist
Stearns, Alfreda E.
Business Technology Teacher
Upchurch, Beverly Brown
8th Grade English Teacher
ALEXANDRIA
Blair, Ruth Hedges
Primary Teacher
Cochran, Matthew Scott
Mathematics Teacher
Dilts, Melody Roberts
HS Mathematics Teacher
Doll, Sylvia Loechle
HS Religion Teacher
Gosney, Bruce Joseph
5th Grade Teacher
Hart, Reeda Stamper
3rd-4th Grade Teacher
Heim, Donna Kremer
Hebrew Scripture Teacher
Juengling, Barbara P.
English Teacher
Lamb, LeeAnn
Guidance Counselor
Levermann, Mary Carol
Fifth Grade Teacher
Long, H. Phillip
Biology Teacher
Manker, Donn Ray
Math Teacher
Manley, Kelly Sato
English Teacher
Mc Cormick, Gary Wayne
Graphic Arts Teacher
Menetrey, Patti Buchert
Homebound Teacher
Ravenscraft, David Charles
Language Arts Teacher
Riley, Joetta Lynn
Math & Computer Prog Teacher
Sandlin, David Wayne
HS Guidance Counselor
Seiter, Robert B., Jr.
English Teacher & Athletic Dir
Warren, Kyle Shaw
English Teacher
Wilbers, James Joseph
Social Studies Teacher
Williams, Ted Neal
Director of Bands
ALLEN
Aiken, Ramona B.
Language Arts Teacher
Allen, Emily Martin
4th Grade Teacher
Comstock, Diane Morgan
Kindergarten Teacher
ANCHORAGE
Mc Kinley, Jane Leming
Primary Teacher
ARGILLITE
Montgomery, Linda H.
Fifth Grade Teacher
Robinson, Sharri Tolliver
Guidance Counselor
ARY
Grubb, Pamelia Jones
7th-8th Grd Language Arts Tchr
ASHLAND
Adams, Anna Traylor
Chemistry & Physics Teacher
Allemang, Thomas Albert
Assoc Professor of English
Blevins, Marsha Fain
Business Teacher
Boyd, Kathy Frasure
Fifth Grade Teacher
Campbell, Michael R.
Choral Director
Chandler, Kathleen Adams
Retired 1st Grade Teacher
Cochran, Jenny K.
Seventh Grade Science Teacher
D'Aoust, Jean-Jacques J.
Associate Professor
Duncan, Shelia Foster
Spanish Teacher
Felty, Kathy Smiley
Social Studies Teacher
Fielding, Beverly N.
Social Studies Teacher
Fluty, Christel Collins
MS Human Services Teacher
Gehringer, Rebecca Davis
Asst Prof of Health & PE
Gillum, Martha Blair
History & English Teacher
Griffith, Anita Evans
Biology Teacher
Hanni, Kelly Jo
Mathematics Teacher

Hilterbrand, Angela C.
Eng Assoc Prof & Writing Coord
Howard, Clarence Paul, Jr.
Mathematics Teacher
Klaiber, Linda Gail
English Teacher
McDowell, Linda Guyette
Secondary Mathematics Teacher
Mericle, Margaret Elizabeth
Assoc Prof of Political Sci
Poteet, Amy Jo
Assoc Prof of Communications
Renfroe, John Mark
World History Teacher
Rigsby, Douglas Lee
Anthropology Teacher
Scott, Robert Dennis
Mathematics Professor
Shields, Bennie Johnson
Chemistry Teacher
Sloan, Patricia Whitt
5th Grade Teacher
Spears, Cheryl Nunley
Primary Teacher
Stucker, Susan Bernstein
Spanish Teacher
Sullivan, Cynthia Miller
Vocal Music Teacher
Swanson, Uma G.
Professor of Psychology
Thacker, Betty Arnold
Family & Consumer Science Tchr
Washington, Elizabeth B.
Scndry Math & Phys Sci Teacher
Watts, David Lee
Science Teacher
Wellman, Joyce Riddle
German & English Teacher
Wellman, Tandy Floyd
4th Grade Teacher
Wente, Janet Brown
Elem Schl Guidance Counselor
Zornes, Clyde Leo
Drafting Teacher
AUBURN
Asbridge, Linda Linzy
Lang Arts & Computer Teacher
BARBOURVILLE
Bingham, Mary Ann Cornett
Social Studies Teacher
Blakley, Cathy Elaine Rhoden
English & Journalism Teacher
Buchanan, Joyce Campbell
Retired Teacher
Martin, Gina Smith
Business Education Teacher
Mc Farland, Thomas J.
Professor of Music
Merida, Gary Kim
High School Business Teacher
Merida, Vada Warren
Fourth Grade Teacher
Michalak, Daniel Arthur
Education Professor
Pope, Susan Joe
Seventh & Eighth Grd Eng Tchr
Shelton, Linda Wilson
7th-8th Grade Reading Teacher
Smith, Jesse Harold
Integrated Sci & Bio Tchr
Stallard, Mary Juanita (Helton)
English Teacher & Dept Chair
Unthank, Judith Callebs
English Chprsn
West, Karen Gayle
Secondary English Teacher
BARDSTOWN
Barnes, David Coleman
Alternative School Director
Brown, Mark Edward
US History Teacher
Campbell, Rosa Marie
Physics, Astronomy & Chem Tchr
Finch, Steve Anthony
7th & 8th Grade Math Teacher
Glass, Michael Stephen, Jr.
Agriculture Education Tchr
Jones, Estella Francis
Am His, Psych & Sociology Tchr
Lasure, Ralph Carter
Senior English Teacher
Mc Dowell, Connie Hutchins
Biology Teacher
Stone, Kenneth Gene
Physical Education Teacher
Warner, Bonnie Gayle
Educational Evaluator
Williams, Thomas Grant, Sr.
Health & Physical Ed Teacher
Williamson, Hobert
Eighth Grade Teacher
BARLOW
Bowles, Jan Nave
Art Teacher
Dunn, Margaret Pittman
History Teacher
Evans, Rebecca Ann (Hicks)
Spanish Teacher
Fraser, Marlene Barrow
Business & Office Instructor
Harris, Aleta M.
Biology Teacher
BAXTER
Lawson, Nancy H.
Jr High Teacher
Lynch, Joanie L. Murphy
Teacher
Smith, Robert Franklin
Principal

BEATTYVILLE
Burch, Kelly Calvert
History & English Teacher
Land, David
Technology Education Teacher
Stickler, Jamie Lee
English Teacher
BEAVER DAM
Cardwell, Kathryn Curtis
Classroom Teacher
Rowe, Camilla June Gatewood
Retired Elementary Teacher
BEDFORD
Davis, Sheila Loraine
Director of Special Services
Dawson, Charlotte Lynn
Soc Stud, Rdng & Hum Teacher
BEECHMONT
Reynolds, Marcia Mercer
6th Grade Teacher
BELFRY
Booth, Elizabeth Frances
History & English Teacher
Fite, Tamela Shawn
Chemistry Teacher
Gannon, Teresa L.
Algebra, Cmptr & German Tchr
West, Bennett
Geography Teacher
BELLEVUE
Brennan, Ronald W.
Psychology Teacher
Dosch, Janet Grant
Jr HS Math Tchr
Floyd, George, Jr.
Physical Education Teacher
Klopp, Judy Fosdick
Vocational Business Teacher
Klopp, William A., Jr.
Mathematics & Physics Teacher
Puglielli, Mary Jo
6th Grade Teacher
BENTON
Adams, Charles Hafford
Science Teacher
Bradley, Stacey Bruce
Chemistry & Physics Teacher
Brien, Phyllis Flatt
First Grade Teacher
Brooks, Valera Wyatt
MS Social Studies Teacher
Chambers, Kelly M.
Fourth Grade Teacher
Chiles, Dianne Holland
Senior English Teacher
Clark, Kathryn Lorraine
Mathematics Teacher
Coakley, Patricia Vaughn
Gifted Education Teacher
Congiardo, Michael Todd
Band Director
Cothran, Barbara T.
3rd Grade Teacher
Coursey, Susan Harris
Speech & Language Pathologist
Griffy, Toni F.
Third Grade Teacher
Jordan, Donna Carol
English Teacher
Lovett, Jeanne Meadows
World Civilization Teacher
Lyles, Doug
Biology Teacher & Bsktbl Coach
McElwain, Connie (Turner)
Media Specialist
Prater, Jacqueline Mitchell Morgan
Second & Third Grade Teacher
Watkins, Kay Dassinger
Fourth Grade Teacher
Wood, Phyllis Park
English Teacher
York, Donna Ann
Science Teacher
BEREA
Boggs, Glenda Harrison
Reading Teacher
Gilliam, David Glen
Marketing Teacher
Hutcherson, Gayle Purple
English & Spanish Teacher
Lahamer, Amer Said
Assistant Professor of Physics
Lambert, Brenda Holt
English & Journalism Teacher
Lynch, William Travis
Social Studies Teacher
Mardon, Mary Bascom
Biology Teacher
Maupin, Amy Beth
English Teacher
McAninch, Vivian Durham
Biology Teacher
Montgomery, Linda Holbrook
MS Mathematics Teacher
Stewart, Marcia Devere
Fourth Grade Teacher
Whitaker, Janie Powell
Primary Teacher
BETSY LAYNE
DeRossett, John B.
9th-12th Grade LD/MMD Teacher
Huffman, Patricia Allen
Family & Consumer Science Tchr
Prater, Paul W.
College Prep Mathematics Tchr
Vanover, Lou
English & Literature Teacher
BEVINSVILLE
Johnson, Judith Lynn
Primary Teacher
Slone, Genevee Gibson
Primary Teacher
BLEDSOE
Slusher, Linda Hensley
Fourth Grade Teacher
BLOOMFIELD
Wheeler, Margaret Hatfield
8th Grd US History & Lit Tchr
BONNIEVILLE
Bowman, Joyce Frye
Primary Teacher
Kelly, Mary Lee
Title 1 Teacher
Taylor, Martha Line
Counselor
BOONEVILLE
Spence, Brenda Johnson
Business Education Teacher
BOWLING GREEN
Alverson, Charlotte Yvonne
Special Education Teacher
Briley, Kevin E.
Band Director
Burkeen, Phillip Cardwell
Driver Ed & Soc Stud Tchr
Cole, Stacey
Mathematics Teacher
Cooke, Wanda J.
5th Grade Teacher
Cottongim, Cynthia Webb
Business Education Teacher
Davneport, Vonda S.
English Teacher
Emberton, Dana Faye
Bio Tchr & Cheerleading Coach
Evans, Mary Motley
Gifted Stud Ctr Program Coord
Harlow, Dana Pedigo
Elementary Teacher
Harris, Rick L.
Band Director
Hightower, Sarah M.
Primary Teacher
Johner, Carole M.
Physics & AP Calculus Teacher
Martin, Betty Mc Knight
Fourth Grade Teacher
Meier, Faye Marie
Former English Teacher
Padilla, Anne Hardle
English & Spanish Teacher
Pesterfield, Lester L.
Asst Professor of Chemistry
Reese, Randy
Math Tchr & Head Ftbl Coach
Riggsbee, Debra Jean (Fuller)
8th Grd Language Arts Teacher
Romagnoli, Donna Grant
English Teacher
Rudloff, Melissa Irene
Physics Teacher
Scott, Patricia Finnell
English & History Teacher
Sisney, Shirley Ann Pace
Sixth Grade Language Arts Tchr
Sledge, C. Elaine
High School Math Teacher
Tarrence, Stacey Massey
HS Mathematics Teacher
Thomison, Susan Stambro
Business Teacher & Dept Chair
Thrasher, Barry Lloyd
Sci, Lit & Remedial Stud Tchr
Tolbert, J. Todd
Social Studies Department Head
Townsend, Angela Lewis
English Teacher
Turley, Louis W.
Associate Professor of Mrktg
Utley, William F.
Counselor
Wassom, Melissa Scott
English Teacher
West, Linda Hendricks
8th Grade English Teacher
White, Rhonda Lynn
7th & 8th Grade Math Teacher
Winstead, Elaine Poole
HS English Teacher, Dept Chair
Wolff, Clarence Neal
Physics Professor
Yonts, Jana Vaughn
Social Studies & English Tchr
BRANDENBURG
Adams, William Kelsey
Science Teacher
Bruington, Bettyruth Frymire
Enrichment & Research Teacher
Campbell, James Robert
Honors World Civ Teacher
English, Michelle Charbonneau
English Teacher
Esarey, Andrea O'Bryan
Fifth Grade Teacher
Flamm, Dawn Marie
Spanish Teacher
Gentry, Rebecca Cooper
Assistant Choral Director
Jones, Shirley Pollitt
Choral Director
Lyons, Kimberly Peveler
Business Education Dept Chair
Meadows, Jeff
Asst Band Director
Melloy, Linda Berry
8th Grade Math Teacher
Mills, Eleanor
Primary Teacher
Mills, Gwendolyn Worley
English Teacher
Powers, Janet Embrey
Reading Teacher
Roberts, Pamela Marie
Chemistry & Physics Teacher
Taylor, Alison J.
Chemistry Teacher
BRODHEAD
Williams, Dottie Sensabaugh
Intermediate Teacher
BROOKSVILLE
Appleman, Mary Beth
Mathematics Teacher
Jefferson, Carrie Appelman
Business Teacher
Kalb, Sally C.
Secondary Business Ed Tchr
Klapheke, Daniel E.
English Teacher
Maddox, Robbie Lynn
Math & Science Teacher
Morgan, Barbara Korner
Fifth Grade Science Teacher
Whitt, Linda (McKibben)
Guidance Counselor
BROWNSVILLE
Campbell, Yvonne Houchin
English Teacher
Carnes, James Oscar, Jr.
History & English Teacher
Jackson, Kevin Lynn
Secondary Guidance Counselor
Sturgeon, Anna Doyle
Spanish & English Teacher
BUCKHORN
Bishop, Edward
Social Studies Chairman
Sandlin, Eugene
Eighth Grade Teacher
Turner, Janice Kimberlin
Primary Teacher
BUCKNER
Carey, Richard M.
HS Mathematics Teacher
Combs, Kevin C.
Physical Education Teacher
Goodman, Fred
Health Teacher & Coach
Hart, Pam Sullivan
English & History Teacher
Neikirk, Andrea Woods
Biology & Chemistry Teacher
Newton, Dee A.
English Department Chairperson
Schultz, William Gregory
Social Studies Teacher
Sheeley, Sally Guelda
Special Education Teacher
Vajner, Deborah Ann (Skiscim)
Social Studies Teacher
BUFFALO
Sutherland-Flanders, Ann
Retired First Grade Teacher
BURDINE
Maynard Brown, Elizabeth Hopkins
Fourth Grade Teacher
BURKESVILLE
Hammer, Ruth Ann (Wilson)
Secondary Business Ed Teacher
BURLINGTON
Hicks, Susan Schrock
Fifth Grade Teacher
Troutt, Susan Jane (Zeigler)
Fourth Grade Teacher
BURNSIDE
Duncan, Beth Lamkin
Primary Teacher
BUTLER
Case, Monte Earl
Sixth Grade Teacher
Chaplin, Craig Larry
Guidance Counselor
Jones, Christy Habermehl
Preschool Teacher
Polley, Janice Ramsey
Fifth Grade Teacher
Pribble, Margie Moore
Retired First Grade Teacher
Stahl, Janet Turley
Title I & Rdng Recovery Tchr
CADIZ
Hale, Amy E.
Marketing Education Teacher
Harrison, Zelma Sue
Health Occupations Teacher
CALHOUN
Enoch, Marhsall
Technology Education Teacher
Hoover, Vonda Loyd
Middle School English Teacher
Prow, William Francis
Senior Army Instructor
Whitaker, Stephanie Kay
Mathematics Teacher
CALVERT CITY
Bock, Donald Frank
7th-8th Grd PE & Math Teacher
Madison, Vicki Dunkerson
K-8th Grade Music Teacher
Martin, Catherine Spencer
Science & Career Teacher
Parish, Carla Williams
Science Teacher
Rudolph, Carol Ann
Enrichment Teacher
Smith, Judy (Jones)
Language Arts Teacher
Tucker, Sharon Elizabeth
Language Arts Teacher
Vaughn, Janice Annette
Math & Social Studies Teacher
CAMP DIX
Nolen, Lois J.
4th-6th Grade Teacher
CAMPBELLSVILLE
Akridge, Jacqueline Louis Wilson
English & Journalism Teacher
Eastridge, Darlene Romine
Assistant Prof of Social Work
Eastridge, Jessica Davenport
Biology Teacher
Evans, Patty Gilbert
Marketing Education Instructor
Kearney, Lynn
Health & Physical Ed Teacher
Mattingly, Phyllis Louise
Social Studies Teacher
Newton, Shirley Goodin
English & Psychology Teacher
Rodgers, Patricia A.
Business Teacher
Rogers, Diane Nichols
Biology Teacher
Scott, Deanna Judd
HS Math Teacher
Smith, Vonda Davis
Teacher of Gifted & Talented
Ware, Peggy Allen
Earth Science & Home Ec Tchr
Warren, Perri Ann
Health & Physical Ed Teacher
Willis, William Larry
English Teacher
Wiseman, Herb D., II
Special Education Teacher
CAMPTON
May, Gwen Tyra
Mathematics Teacher
CARLISLE
Baird, Anne Skees
Kindergarten Teacher
Gardner, Melissa England
English Teacher
Hayes, Jack R.
English & Media Teacher
Hendricksen, Anita Litton
Mathematics Teacher
Simons, Linda Lynn Wilson
Reading Rcvry & Title I Tchr
CARROLLTON
Edelen, Linda Hooser
Director & Lead Teacher
Garvey, Michael M.
World History Teacher
Kelley, LaVerne Hartman
5th Grade Teacher
O'Neal, Donna Reed
Teacher
Shelton, Carol Louden
Ninth Grade English Teacher
Wise, Gerda Ford
Fifth Grade Teacher
CATLETTSBURG
Lester, Ronna Sutton
4th Grade Teacher
Naughgle, Cindie B.
5th Grade Teacher
CAWOOD
Stewart, Janice Ann
Social Studies Teacher
CECILIA
Brewer, Paula Spaulding
High School English Teacher
Conway, Jane P.
Spanish & English Teacher
Cruse, Sharon Jones
Business Teacher
Kinney, Michael Walton
Social Studies Teacher
Russo, John G.
JROTC Instructor
Sweat, Michael Francis
Chemistry Teacher
Townsend, Dan C.
Business Education Teacher
CENTRAL CITY
Lancaster, Ellanee Bidwell
Primary Teacher
Reno, Deborah Ann (Blake)
2nd & 3rd Grade Teacher
CLARKSON
Mollyhorn, Carol Cheal
Elem Teacher
CLAY CITY
Akins, Wanda Jean
Math & Algebra Teacher
CLINTON
Armbruster, Robert E.
Senior English Teacher
Bizzle, Becky Edwards
Second Grade Teacher
Brawley, Joan Pruitt
Sixth Grade Teacher
English, Sarah Byers
Fifth Grade Teacher
Johnson, N. Todd
Jr High & HS History Tchr
Roberts, Sheri Hurd
Writing Consultant
CLOVERPORT
Hamilton, Jeff M.
Choral Director
Hensley, Michael Ray
Guidance, Pupil Personnel Dir
Lasley, Richard Allan
High School Math Teacher
Litherland, Gayle Weiss
Primary Teacher
Powers, Gayle
Primary Teacher
Renfrow, Glendon Ray
Social Studies Chairman
Smith, Deborah Mc Coy
Fifth Grade Teacher
Tindle, Neal Ray
Technology Education Instr
Tinsley, Michelle Mc Brayer
Business Education Instructor
Turner, Lynda Lois
English & German Teacher
COLUMBIA
Bradshaw, Judy Fann
Primary Teacher
Burton, Nancy Turner
Eighth Grade Lang Arts Tchr
Coomer, Bobbie Powell
Early Childhood Coordinator
Cox, Kathy Keltner
Preschool Teacher
Foust, Pamela Hurt
Choral Director & Music Tchr
Goodin, Judith Ann
Title 1 Math & Science Teacher
Hagan, Richard Patrick
Cmptr Information System Instr
Huddleston, Janella Brockman
Math & French Teacher
Minton, Susan Knight
Communications Instructor
Pourheydarian, Mohammad
Assoc Professor of Business
Powell, Gary Michael
Asst Prof of His & Pol Sci
Rigney, John Russell
Prof of Cnslng & Psychology
Taylor, Margaret Loy
8th Grade Teacher
Troutman, Patricia E.
Spanish Teacher & Dept Chair
Williams, Rickie L.
Mathematics Instructor
CORBIN
Aills, Lynda Borders
High School English Teacher
Bezold, Mary L.
Montessori Teacher
Burchette, Carcille Carloftis
Math Tchr & Dept Chair
Collins, Karen R. Adkins
Business Teacher
Conyers, Tamara Crouch
Biology & Physical Sci Tchr
Cox, David Bret
8th Grade Social Studies Tchr
Daniel, Brenda Hughes
Art Teacher
Hammons, Penny Pennington
6th Grade Social Studies Tchr
Harris, Nicole
Mathematics & Chemistry Tchr
Jones, Sharon Laws
Bus Ed & Journalism Teacher
Mc Burney, Darlene Hammons
Health Teacher
McCarty, Timothy Paul
English Teacher
Mitchell, Diane Miller
Writing Resource & Jrnlsm Tchr
Pendergraft, Gwendolyn Bacon
English Teacher
Perkins, Janna L.
HS Librn & Media Specialist
Phipps, Jennifer Wells
Eighth Grade Teacher
Rice, Heather Mc Falls
Mathematics Teacher
Shelton, Warren Thomas
Welding Instructor
Stewart, Janice Trett
Fifth Grade Teacher
Tinsley, Cheryl Steele
Jr High & HS Teacher
Tompkins, Luane LeGore
Health Science Instructor
Wilson, Polly Pennington
Fifth Grade Teacher
Young, George Kenneth, Jr.
JROTC Teacher
CORYDON
Dixon, Sammie Ray
Retired 1st Grade Teacher
COVINGTON
Bingman, Greg A.
Director of Bands
Clark, Janet Louise
Business Education Teacher
Haggard, Deborah K.
Sci Dept Chm & Chemistry Tchr
Kusch, Kelly
Teacher & Frgn Lang Dept Chair
Owens, Jerry W.
Stu Assistance Cnslr & Coord
Parks, Dara Lynne
Mathematics Teacher
Stein, Sue Spradling
4th, 5th, 6th Grade AP Teacher
Watts, Theresa E.
Science Teacher
COXS CREEK
Trent, Barbara Ann
2nd Grade Teacher
CRAB ORCHARD
Goode, Rebecca Howard
Technology Teacher
Walker, Mabel Cooper
Fourth Grade Teacher
CRESTVIEW HILLS
Bensman, Andrew Louis
History Professor

WOOD
aniel Kenneth
& Sociology Tchr & Cnslr
Cathy Warden
n Teacher
William Roger
Studies Teacher
, Joseph James
e Arts Instructor
Sylvin Janice
Director
Leeann Bryan
ss Teacher
effrey Lance
Studies Teacher
, Richard Dennis
e Teacher & Team Leader
, Evelyn Campbell
eacher
, Nancy Kerr
Tchr & Frgn Lang Dept Chr
RLAND
bert S.
ate Professor of English
Terry Thomas
Program Coordinator
Carlton Wayne
Prof of Communications
, Astor Lee
rof of Sociology & Psych
Jamie H.
rofessor of Accounting
IANA
Susan R.
d Language Arts Teacher
, Marion Lee
ne Tool Technology Tchr
ones, Cynthia Axford
h Grade Science Teacher
Debbie L.
uter Teacher
Inez Toohey
/ & Consumer Science Tchr
oann Kathleen
h Teacher
immy Lee
Grade Teacher
ngela Gayle
/ & Consumer Science Tchr
, Sandra Reid
Teacher
, L. Louise
dary Business Teacher
, Amie L.
Director & Piano Tchr
Winifred Kay
matics Teacher
Sylvia Lewis
ntary Resource Teacher
, Gordon E.
dary Science Teacher
Ellie Marshall
Sciences Instructor
, Erika Crafts
sh Teacher & Speech Coach
n, Faye B.
chr & Asst Ath Director
Leslie Anne
ce & Social Studies Tchr
LLE
Lin Walter
f Archtctrl Technology
, Jim W.
ean & Amer His Tchr
n, Margo Endres
h Teacher
on, Sarah Frances
Teacher
Brenda Stevens
ry Teacher
, Ralph K., II
e School Science Teacher
, Kathy B.
ry Teacher
Elaine Hunter
n & 1st Grd Teacher
an, Kaye Ellis
y & Consumer Science Tchr
ON
, Rosann Frances
Teacher
, David T.
rade Mathematics Teacher
STON
Sonja Cox
h & Fifth Grade Teacher
TT
d, Glenna Helton
puter Lab Teacher
N
, Regina A.
Grade Eng & Jrnlsm Tchr
ll, Ann Dodson Veazey
sh Teacher
, E. Carolyn Brown
ultant & Instructor
RIDGE
rson, Jesse Carter
sh Teacher
Barbara Fay
rd Language Arts Teacher
Jerry Wayne
ce & Math Teacher
son, James David
gy Teacher
INGTON
Patricia Tucker
ary Teacher
, Elizabeth Mc Dowell
5th Grade Teacher

EAST BERNSTADT
Collins, Diane Lowe
Kindergarten & First Grd Tchr
Helton, Elaine Lowe
2nd & 3rd Grade Teacher
Kesler, Andrea Reed
Fourth Grade Teacher
Reid, Janice Henderlight
Title I Coordinator
EASTERN
Bowling, Janet L. (Varney)
Home Economics Teacher
Hall, Karen Duff
Teacher
Spurlock, Kevin G.
Geography Teacher & Coach
Turner, Wava Eileen
Sixth Grade Teacher
EDDYVILLE
Buchanan, Ruth Ann
4th Grade Teacher
Burchett, Marina J.
English Teacher
Litchfield, Mary Freeman
7th & 8th Grade English Tchr
Swinny, Judith Walston
Home Economics Teacher
Whittington, Sally Hayes
Sixth Grade Teacher
EDMONTON
Kindred, Teresa Bell
History Teacher
Moran, Harold W.
Coord Middle School ESS
Rascoe, Steven Eugene
Math & Chemistry Teacher
VanMeter, John Davis
Computer Applications Teacher
EKRON
Board, Darlene Tate
Fourth Grade Teacher
ELIZABETHTOWN
Davis, Jimmie F.
Assistant Principal
Eicher, Katrina Marie
Assoc Prof Commnctn & Theatre
Finney, Gail Hamilton
Associate Prof of Nursing
Goodman, Bennie r.
Mathematics Teacher
Gott, Tim
Dist Math Resource Teacher
Hayes, Connie J.
8th Grd Lang & Soc Stud Tchr
Hopman North, Ruth
Instructor in Dental Hygiene
Hornback, M. Carla Collard
Assistant Prof of Comm
Lewis, Jennifer Haselwood
7th Grade English Teacher
McCracken, Daniel M.
Fourth Grade Teacher
Mollett, W. Maurice
Bus Ed & Criminal Justice Tchr
Redel, Ruth Falk
Professor
Stoltzfus, Carl L.
Principal
Wooldridge, Bill, Sr.
5th Grade Teacher
Young, Bonnie Johnson
Schl to Work Coord & Bus Instr
ELKHORN CITY
Bevins, Judy Ford
MS Social Studies Teacher
Cantrell, Geneva Ratliff
8th Grd Language Arts Teacher
Martin-Looney, Carolyn S.
Primary Teacher
Venters, Rebecca Anderson
Seventh Grade English Teacher
ELKTON
Davey, Marjan Healy
High School English Teacher
Groves, Darlene Powell
Art Teacher
Kelly, Doris Martin
Art Teacher
Shanks, Billy Ray
Social Studies Teacher
EMINENCE
Baird, Joyce Kilgore
Business Teacher
Hensley, Dewey Douglas
English Teacher
Westrick, Charles Bryan
5th-6th Grade Science Tchr
ERLANGER
Althoff, Carolyn A.
Art Department Chair & Teacher
Brauch, Scott Lawrence
Mathematics Tchr & Guid Cnslr
Brewer, Peggy Schneider
Religion Teacher
Brown, Frances Wells
Retired Elementary Teacher
Doan, Virginia Massie
Kindergarten & First Grd Tchr
Dunaway, Katherine Ann
Business Teacher
Durham, Ronald Wayne
Choral Music Teacher
Faust, David Thomas
Algebra & Business Teacher
Hartman, Rose Anne
8th Grade Teacher
Rosenhoffer, John Jay
8th Grade Science Teacher
Rymarquis, Barbara Wolsing
English Teacher

Schmeing, Martha Louise
Assistant Principal
Stryffeler, Jam
History Teacher & Coach
Warner, Jacqueline Jean Vater
HS Individualized Ed Supvr
EUBANK
Childers, Jill Roy
Kindergarten Teacher
Livesay, Jayne Sandidge
Primary Teacher
McWilliams, Mary Jo Anderson
Primary Teacher
Slone, Ralph
Fifth Grade Teacher
Trowbridge, Rodney
Retired Agriculture Teacher
EVARTS
Browning, Tammy Robinson
Business & Computer Teacher
Luttrell, Gurney Clay
Teacher
McLain, Polly Lloyd
Ninth Grade English Teacher
Neace, Marsha Kay
Physics & Math Teacher
Robertson, Ernest Wayne
Technology Education Teacher
FAIRDALE
Anderson, Anita Gholson
Mathematics Teacher
Elder, Joseph Todd
Band Director
Schneider, Erin Murphy
Mathematics Teacher
Schneider, Gregory Scott
Chemistry & Physics Teacher
Sheeley, Bennie Jo
French Teacher
FALMOUTH
Bertram, Janice King
First Grade Teacher
Browning, Mark
Guidance Counselor
Carson, Joyce Mains
Sixth Grade Teacher
Cordray, Susan Renee
Fourth Grade Teacher
Courtney, Bettie Grow
Sixth Grade Teacher
Crowley, Michele Barton
7th-8th Grade Math Teacher
Harpe, Cathy McDowell
Primary Teacher
Holland, Debra Howe
Band, Choral & Music Teacher
Hughes, Cheryl Griner
Special Education Teacher
Owen, Bill Carl
Retired Teacher
Puckett, Millie M.
Lang Arts, Speech & Drama Tchr
Sargent, Brenda Courtney
Lang Arts & Soc Stud Tchr
Seever, Shirley Miller
Fifth Grade Teacher
Smith, Everett Keith
Marketing Education Teacher
Spegal, Susan Dotson
Primary Title One Rdng Tchr
Sullivan, Sandra Fields
Chemistry Teacher
West, Linda Sharp
Math Teacher
Ziegler, Teri Carol
Science Teacher
FANCY FARM
Barton, Susan Morgan
Jr HS Sci & Lang Arts Tchr
FARMINGTON
Conklin, Elizabeth Anne
Guidance Counselor
McClain, Joyce P.
5th & 6th Grade Teacher
Rodgers, Joann Newsom
Fourth Grade Teacher
Wilford, Joyce Ann
Teacher
FEDSCREEK
Fuller, Jennifer Carleen (Meade)
French & English Teacher
Fuller, Randy Blake
Secondary US History Teacher
FLAT LICK
Bargo, Nancy Spring
Primary Teacher
Mills, Linda Gregory
English Teacher
FLATWOODS
Hopkins, Ruth Greene
Fifth Grade Teacher
Miller, Donna Ramey
5th Grade Teacher
FLEMINGSBURG
Beckett, Mona Carpenter
Primary Teacher
Burton, Julie Douglas
English Teacher
Bussell, Gwendolyn Flora
Allied Health Occupations Tchr
Christman, Angela Kay
Home Economics Teacher
Clark, Terri Bottom
Special Education Teacher
Dials, Rita T.
Home Economics Teacher
Hurd, Ramona Fern
Biology Teacher

FLORENCE
Ackley, Carol Riley
Advanced Placement Bio Teacher
Atha, Wanda Poore
Retired Third Grade Teacher
Baker, William Franklin
High School Principal
Breitholle, Sheree Mc David
Primary Teacher
Claypool, Sharon Hayes
French Teacher
Daniel, Susan B.
Social Studies Teacher
Deatherage, Judi E.
Acctng, Finance & Banking Tchr
Johnson, T. J.
Visual Arts Teacher
Meyer, David Joseph
Fourth Grade Teacher
Powell, Ben Carl
English Teacher
Redding, Donna Jean
Business Education Teacher
Siler, Thomas Eugene
6th Grade Mathematics Teacher
Sorrell, Linda Hanson
Fourth Grade Teacher
Stidham, Deborah K. (Smith)
Mathematics Teacher
Walton, Laurie A.
6th Grade Science Teacher
FORDSVILLE
Coomes, Barbara Ann
4th Grade Teacher
FORT CAMPBELL
Austin, Jamie Sue (Smith)
Music & Band Teacher
Doughman, Sherry Wells
5th Grade Teacher
Dowlen, Kathy Marguerite
High School English Teacher
Fox, Catherine Porter
Science Teacher
Greene, Patricia Ann
English & Journalism Teacher
Izzo, Deana Jo
1st-2nd Grade Teacher
Johnson, Marsha Bolen
Sixth Grade Teacher
Karrigan, Bonnie L.
English Teacher
Lange, Leon L.
Science Department Chairman
Loucks, Iris Rita
German Teacher
Rey, Patsy Watson
Science Teacher
FORT KNOX
Aulbach, Teresa Davis
Rdng Recovery & Improv Tchr
Hester, Berna Harris
Reading Recovery Teacher
Hill, Gwendolyn DuVall
Mathematics Teacher
Isham, Pamela Knox
English Teacher
Jackson, Mary Lowe
8th Grd Lit & Math Teacher
Jones, Mabel Hinson
9th-12th Grd Eng & Jrnlsm Tchr
Long, Michael V.
Mathematics Teacher
Speck, Clancie Atherton
Eng, Jrnlsm Teacher & Chm
Thompson, Bobby Gene
JROTC Instructor
Wahlberg, Felice Jan
History Teacher
Yundt, Betty Brandenburg
Sixth Grade Teacher
FORT MITCHELL
Abney, Jerry Eldon
Computer Applications Teacher
Barth, Susan Albers
Fourth Grade Teacher
Brown, Brian Ross
Band Director
Caudill, Cathy Darlene
Business Teacher
Christensen, Linda Beck
Third Grade Teacher
Eovaldi, Cheryl Shook
English & History Teacher
Hart, Timothy R.
8th Grd Language Arts Teacher
Jameson, Christopher
Language Arts Teacher
Miller, Glen Alan
District Tech Coordinator
Oliver, Alissa Chandler
Speech, Theater & English Tchr
Osborne, Gail S.
8th Grade Science Teacher
Raker, Mary Diane Bailey
Science Teacher
Rauch, John D.
Biology Teacher
Releford, Susan Brownfield
Math Teacher
Roberts, Priscilla M.
Drama, English & Speech Tchr
Stoll, John Robert
History Teacher
Wuellner, Kathleen D. (Pritchard)
Eng, Jrnlsm Tchr & Dept Chair
FORT THOMAS
Burns, Michael George
Social Studies Teacher
Gracey, Linda L.
Sixth Grade Teacher

Heil, M. Stephen
English, Speech & Debate Tchr
Juett, Joseph Kent
Social Studies Teacher
Keller, Charles Michael
Eng & Amer Studies Teacher
Klembara, Linda Nolan
Mathematics Teacher
Long, Ross Edwin
Teacher of Gifted & Talented
Mueller, Dale Richard
Math Teacher & Activities Dir
O'Brien, Barbara Stevens
9th & 11th Grd English Teacher
Shields, Marie E.
Sixth Grade Teacher
Simon, Gary L.
7th Grade Social Studies Tchr
Skop, Kathy Prince
Art Dept Chair
Stephenson, Judith Klappert
Fifth Grade Teacher
Toner, Donna Hoffman
Sixth Grade Teacher
Willig, Janet Jennings
Teacher of Gifted & Talented
FRAKES
Partin, Belinda Leigh
Primary Teacher
FRANKFORT
Adams, Sally Brown
8th Grade Lang Arts Teacher
Bator, John S.
Coord of Art Dept & Asst Prof
Bibbins, Paul Edward, Jr.
Division of Math & Sci Chprsn
Billiter, Kathleen Hopkins
Sci Dept Head & Bio Tchr
Bolen, Anita
Math Teacher
Booker, Philip, Jr.
Social Work Professor
Bowker, Linda Whiteside
English Teacher
Boyd, Lee Longmire
Retired Bio & Genetics Tchr
Bright, Venita
Bio-Ecology Tchr & Dept Chair
Bullock, Elizabeth Ramos-Graulau
Consultant
Caspani, Guido Edmond
Asst Prof of Romance Languages
Chase, Jerald Lloyd
Math Department Chairman
Collett, Sharon Childers
Business Education Teacher
Coomer, Michelle Lynn
Span Tchr & Chrldng Coach
Crowe, Joni Napier
Sixth Grade Teacher
Dowler, Tami Lewis
Instruction & Prof Dev Dir
Duncan, Lou Jean Richardson
Language Arts Teacher
Elrod, Cynthia Lee Thurman
Math Teacher
Farley, Nancy Cook
Instructional Counselor
Finney, Nancy Lewis
Math Teacher
Fitzgerald, Barbara Davis
Substitute Teacher
Gambill, Judith Rose
English Teacher
Geoghegan, Barbara Hart
Spanish & Latin Teacher
Green, Gayle Ann
English & Business Ed Teacher
Grubbs, Leslie Noell
Mathematics Teacher
Hammond, Harold Thomas
7th Grade Social Studies Tchr
Hines, Lydia Smith
Primary Teacher
Hodgkin, Mary Lee Bryan
Teacher
Jackson, Tonya Potterfield
Reading & Literature Teacher
Johnson, Elaine Heaton
Retired Third Grade Teacher
Johnson, Kathrine A.
Asst Prof of Criminal Justice
Johnston, Gayla Harrison
4th Grade Teacher
Jones, Barbara Mitchell
Retired Teacher
Judge, Barbara Ellen
High School Guidance Counselor
Kaul, Karan
Professor of Biology
LaChapell, Barbara Johnston
6th-8th Grade Science Teacher
Landy, Tucker
Liberal Studies Professor
Logan, Tierelee Reed
4th Grade Teacher
Magel, E. Terry
Cmptr & Tech Sci Division Chm
Mason, Lara Lee
Mathematics Teacher
Mefford, Valerie Yagel
Biology & Anatomy Teacher
Merritt, Brent E.
Choral Dir & Music Teacher
Murphy, Ernestine M.
7th Grade Math & Reading Tchr
Nemeth, Carolyn Madison
English Teacher
Oder, Susan Smith
Assistant Principal

FRANKFORT (cont)
Pearson, Patricia Annette (Bradley)
Associate Professor of History
Peters, Joan Todd
Primary School Teacher
Reagan-Wallin, Nancy
Assistant Professor of Biology
Robinson, Bennie C.
Social Work Division Chprsn
Scruggs, Brenda Valentina
Mathematics Teacher
Shelton, Roosevelt Orinthal
Div of Fine Arts Prof & Chprsn
Shields, George W.
Philosophy Professor & Chair
Smith, Sherri L.
English & Journalism Teacher
Smith, Sherrill Grant
Pupil Personnel Director
Stepp, Greg N.
Band Director
Stivers, Susan Mc Cubbin
Human & Environmental Sci Tchr
Strickland, Marva Yvonne
Asst Prof of Pol Sci
Tao, Deh Chang
Professor of Math & Sciences
Trammell, Jerry Powell
Associate Professor of English
Trammell, Sandra Martin
English Professor
Turner, Judith Wilson
Language Arts Teacher & Admin
Unuakhalu, Michael
Computer Science Asst Prof
Viel, Cheryl Lynn
Mathematics & Latin Teacher
Weathers, Mary Cosby
Associate Professor
Weeks, Dennis L.
Associate Professor of English
Wells, Kathryn Williams
English & Journalism Teacher
Williams, Margaret Sullivan
6th Grade Science Teacher
Woelfel, Marty
Assistant Professor of Biology
FRANKLIN
Chaney, Linda H.
High School English Teacher
Hughes, Norm E.
Assistant Principal
Powell, Jacqueline Caudill
Primary Teacher
FRENCHBURG
Tackett, Joan L. (Ratliff)
Social Studies Teacher
Willoughby, Dianne Stull
Consumer & Family Life Teacher
FULTON
Brown, Judy Barnes
Jr High Language Arts Teacher
GAMALIEL
Collins, Julie Downing
Kindergarten Teacher
GARRISON
Collins, Marsha Bentley
Primary Teacher
GEORGETOWN
Allen, Rosemary Alice
Associate Professor of English
Apple, Lindsey
History Professor & Chair
Bridges, Kim Mitchell
8th Grade US History Teacher
Chi, Keon S.
Professor of Political Science
Cook, Margaret Hall
8th Grade Language Arts Tchr
Curry, Gwen Cranfill
Dept of English Chair
Dougoud, Kitty Watson
Fifth Grade Teacher
Edwards, Richard Bryan
Mathematics Teacher
Gillespie, William L.
Professor & Chair
Godsey, Linda Lorene
High School Spanish Teacher
Gregory, Evelyn (Steele)
Adult Reading Coordinator
Greynolds, Margaret Thornton
Fine Arts Prof & Dept Chprsn
Haddad, Zahi Daoud
Professor of Bus Admin & Chair
Hoyle, Lydia Huffman
Professor of Church History
Johnson, Mark Colwell
Assoc Prof of Biological Sci
Kleinhenz, Emma LouRhea
Math & Physics Teacher
Kruschwitz, Robert Bruce
Philosophy Professor
Lunceford, Joe Elbert
Professor of Religion
Matthews, Linda Jeanette
7th Grade Language Arts Tchr
May, Steven W.
Professor of English
Means, Virginia Smith
Family & Consumer Science Tchr
Moore, Janice Allen
Fifth Grade Teacher
Nash, Karen Denise
Business Teacher
Perry, Wanda Faye
Retired Science Teacher
Taylor, Tracy H.
Business Teacher
Turner, Faith VanHuss
Business Teacher
Woosley, Rebecca Carol (Wade)
Jr-Sr English Teacher
GLASGOW
Angstrom, Anne Lewis
English & Drama Teacher
Bailey, James Wilson
Agribusiness Education Teacher
Belcher, Johnny D.
Guidance Counselor
Billingsley Greer, Joy
Science Teacher
Blevins, Ellen Elizabeth
Math Teacher
Brown, Carmina Fornaris
Spanish Teacher & Dept Head
Bunch, Jan D.
4th Grade Teacher
Burris, Janet Yvonne
Science Teacher
Coomer, M. Joan Calvert
Spanish Teacher
Irving, Marianna Martin
Fourth Grade Teacher
Johnson, Brenda Landrum
English Teacher
Lowe, James M.
Teacher & Auditorium Director
Mc Cloud, Susan W.
GATE Resource Specialist
Spillman, Harry Wayne
Social Studies Teacher
Wilson, Cindy White
Fifth & Sixth Grade Teacher
GLENDALE
Hayden, Foster Todd
8th Grd Social Studies Teacher
Lee, Daniel Owen
Social Studies Teacher
GORDON
Bradley, Merlin
Retired Teacher
Bradley, Reneva Sparkman
Retired Teacher
GOSHEN
Fawbush, Stanley Keith
Primary Teacher
GRAYSON
Caudill, Diane Gritton
Prof of Bus Admin & Comp Sci
Curtis, Sherry Lynn
Vice President of Student Life
Damron, Donald Marshall
Eighth Grade Science Teacher
Damron, Donald Reid
History Professor
Fielding, Ruth Ann
Mathematics Teacher
Ford, Karen Creamer
Professor
Franks, Melanie Wentz
Family & Consumer Sci Tchr
Green, Cora Crabtree
Title I Primary Teacher
Hatfield, Margaret Mc Laughlin
Soc Work Prgm Dir & Asst Prof
Knight, K. Fawn
English Professor
Knight, Leonard Charles
Prof & Dir of Counseling Svcs
Kouns, Harriett Susie
Health & PE Teacher
McCoy, Pat Gallion
Fourth Grade Teacher
Morgan, Joanne Ramey
Language Arts Teacher
Plummer, Lisa Graves
7th Grade Science Teacher
Porter, Jeffrey Louis
HS Math & Physics Teacher
Ruffner, Kail Daniel
Dept of Tchr Ed Chprsn & Prof
Ruffner, Rosalyn Burton
Professor & Stud Tchr Coord
Sammons, Fred A.
9th-12th Grade German Teacher
Steele, Ada Shaffer
Biology & Anatomy Teacher
Wilcox, Verla A.
Primary Teacher
GREENSBURG
Cowherd, Jerry Elliott
Soc Stud, Psych & Soclgy Tchr
Cox, Tammy Lynn
Seveth Grade Mathematics Tchr
Edwards, Beverly Bloyd
Mathematics Teacher
Ellis, Casandra Humble
Elementary Teacher
Hartson, Anne Finch
French Teacher
Phelps, Kenneth Allen
Art Teacher
Squires, Jayne Smith
8th Grade Lang Arts Teacher
GREENUP
Baldridge, Bill J.
Supvr in-School Susp & Coach
Carter-Hunter, Rebecca J.
Sr English & Journalism Tchr
Collier, Cindy Rae
Biology Teacher
Ferguson, Melanie Wallace
Mathematics Teacher
LeMaster, Barbara Lyons
English Teacher
Riley, Robin Angela
English Teacher
Sizemore, Tammy Graham
Biology Teacher
Waller, Rosemary Armstrong
High School English Teacher
Ward, Randy
Physical Education Teacher
Whitt, Shirley Gayhart
10th Grade English Teacher
GREENVILLE
Ashley, Traci Melton
Seventh Grade Math Teacher
Cosby, Anna M.
Mathematics Teacher
Freeman, W. Lee
Social Studies Teacher
Hancock, Patricia Anne
9th-12th Grd English Teacher
Hawkins, Jane Gary
English Teacher
Lovell, Regenia Faye
English Teacher
Mc Carraher, Edward L.
HS Biology & AP Biology Tchr
Neal, Michael Bruce
Geography & Law Teacher
Oliver, Philip Martin
Mathematics Teacher
Peters, Terri Dean (Osborn)
Life Science Teacher
Smith Lampton, Debra Lynn
English & Social Studies Tchr
Sparks, Steven Grant
History Teacher
Stewart, Leigh Ellen
High School Art Instructor
GUTHRIE
Martin, Jane Slack
Fourth Grade Teacher
HAGERHILL
Blair, Sharon Kaye (Conley)
Lang Arts & Science Teacher
HALLIE
Shuffler, Delilah Faye
7th-8th Grade Teacher
HANSON
Osburn, Mary Zachary
Primary Teacher
HARDINSBURG
O'Reilly, Anne Mary (Saleski)
Retired Math Teacher
O'Reilly, Paul F.
Retired HS Social Studies Tchr
HARDY
Maynard, Joetta Johnson
Retired Mathematics Teacher
HARDYVILLE
Dudderar, Brenda Russell
Kindergarten & 1st Grade Tchr
HARLAN
Bailey, Deborah (McFarland)
Science Teacher
Holcomb, Pamela Fay
HS Math, Speech & Drama Tchr
Medlar, Paul D.
Gifted Education Teacher
Powell, David W.
Earth Science & Geography Tchr
Roark, Mary Faye
High School Librarian
Wills, Glenn Allen
Driver Ed & Safety Ed Teacher
HARNED
Henderson, Patrick M.
Agriculture Teacher
Hildenbrandt, Walter Lee
Chemistry & Physics Teacher
La Grange, Denny
Health Teacher & Coach
O'Reilly, Bryan Patrick
Biology, Chem & Physics Tchr
Pelton, Pamela Owens
Span Tchr & Frgn Lang Chair
Smiley, Leon
Agriculture Tchr & FFA Adv
HAROLD
Chaffins, Linda Allen
Primary Teacher
Stevens, Milford Lee
Fourth Grade Teacher
Ward, Bonnie
Seventh Grade Teacher
HARRODSBURG
Burns, Sheila Vaught
Math & Psychology Teacher
Camic, Roxie Stratton
4th Grade Teacher
Culp, Evelyn Bennett
Fifth Grade Teacher
Davis, Marianne Malone
Biology & Physics Teacher
Davis, William Robert, Jr.
Business Technology Instructor
Downey, Sandra Lee
English Teacher
Durr, Marsha Moore
Kindergarten Teacher
Fegenbush, Donna Horn
Language Arts Teacher
Hammons, Kenneth Duane
Math Teacher
Parker, Cindy L.
HS Eng & Speech Teacher
Patrick, Twana Jean
High School Art Teacher
Smith, William M., Jr.
HS Social Studies Teacher
Yerian, Dale
Technology Coordinator
HARTFORD
Coppage, Angela Hale
Math Teacher
Fackler, Regina Petett
8th Grade Lang Arts Teacher
Grant, Ronnie Dean
PE Teacher & Coach
Mayes, Amy E.
Language Arts & Drama Teacher
Moredock, Regina Paulette
2nd & 3rd Grd Primary Teacher
Phipps, Charles Bradley
High School Science Teacher
Russell, Patricia Moss
Family & Consumer Sci Tchr
Todd, Mina L.
9th Grade Health Teacher
HAZARD
Asher, Laura Grace
High School Biology Teacher
Brown, Wanda
Mathematics & Journalism Tchr
Caldwell, Venita Morgan
Asst Professor of Education
Collins, Debbie Baker
High School Teacher
Feltner, Jeanne Lou (Ritchie)
Secondary Mathematics Teacher
Klinglesmith, Kendra L.
Spanish Teacher
Mackin, Reid David
Asst Prof of Communications
Melton, Anthony
Math Teacher
Phipps, Sandra Kaye Combs
Assoc Professor of Psychology
Riestenberg, Patricia Lynn
Pastoral Associate
Shackelford, Carlene Willoughby
Retired Teacher
Shostell, Joseph Mark
Professor of Biology
Smith, Tammy
Accounting Professor
Strong, Ella Jean
Assistant Professor
Teague, Linda Jenkins
English & Drama Teacher
Weaver, Barbara Ann
Science Teacher
HAZEL GREEN
Brown, Rhonda Lindon
Primary Teacher
HEBRON
Alig, Susan
English Teacher
Challis, Helen Emily Krumpelman
French & A P English Tchr
Estenfelder, Joanne Collins
Math Teacher
Gardner, Laura Lee
English & Latin Teacher
Harshbarger, Lauri Gouge
Mathematics Teacher
Hinton, P. Dawn Hamilton
Biology & Math Teacher
Hitzfield, Timothy William
Science Educator
Hughes, Nancy Ellen
Visual Art Teacher
Mc Glasson, Les F.
5th Grade Teacher
Mc Intosh, Michele Collord
Sixth Grade Science Teacher
Meither, Nancy Lee
Voc-Tech Health Sci Instr
Michael, Amy
Algebra Teacher
Musselman, Alice Faye
Guidance Counselor
Santos, Delma Lucas
Biology Teacher
Shipley, Wayne K.
American Government Teacher
Stellman, Thomas John
AP US History Teacher
HENDERSON
Alvey, Eva Mae (Shouse)
Third Grade Teacher
Conley, Cary Neil
Science Teacher
Di Pietro, Michael
Mathematics Teacher
Duncan, Karen (Ellis)
Special Education Teacher
Ellis, Robert H.
Director of Choral Activities
Farley, Jon S.
Social Studies Teacher
Houchin, Vicki Green
5th-6th Grade Teacher
Leigh, Janice F.
8th Grd Language Arts Teacher
Mathias, Johnnie Wayne
Landscaping Teacher & FFA Adv
Mc Intosh, Darice Ellen
Science Teacher
Reed, Janna Charlein (Hubbard)
Fourth Grade Teacher
Smith, Debra Lynn
Primary Teacher
Stenger, Brenda Lovell
French & Spanish Teacher
Stevens, Lisa Ploeg
Health Sciences Teacher
Tennyson, Timothy Lee
Math Teacher
Thurman, Susan Sommers
English Teacher
HI HAT
Stegall, Billie Jo
Art Teacher
HIGHLAND HEIGHTS
Admas, Michael Charles C.
Professor of History
Amburgey, Valeria
Asst Prof of Math & Cmptr Ed
Andersen, Barry Walter
Professor of Art & Photography
Boyd, Stephen Dean
Communications Professor
Cate, Thomas Henry
Economics Associate Professor
Chukwudolue, Charlie Esokwu
Asst Prof of Justice Studies
Dunevant, David Lynn
Associate Professor of Music
Giesmann, Larry Allen
Professor of Biology
Goddard, Perilou
Assoc Professor of Psychology
Hamm, Durell Dexter
Asst Prof of Speech Comm
Hewan, Clinton George
Asst Prof of Intnl Studies
Jenisch, Russell A.
Assistant Professor
Marquis, Linda Mills
Associate Professor Accounting
Neely, Sharlotte Kathleen
Professor of Anthropology
Painter, Sue (Brown)
Fifth Grade Teacher
Ramage, James Alfred
Professor of History
Rambo, Thomas Clough
Prof of Biological Sciences
Reno, Beverly A.
Associate Professor of Nursing
Sheffield, Linda Jensen
Math Education Professor
Steely, Will Frank
Professor of History
Thomson, J. Michael
Assoc Prof of Political Sci
Wallace, Robert K.
Professor
HINDMAN
Childers, Tammy Vance
Anatomy & Biology Teacher
Cobb, Jay S.
Pol Sci Tchr, Ath Dir & Coach
Hall, Tommy Curtis
History Teacher
Hall, Willma Jean
PE & Television Workshop Tchr
Webb, Scelinda Handshoe
Biology & Phys Science Teacher
HODGENVILLE
Wright, Jane Reeves
Family & Consumer Sci Tchr
HOPKINSVILLE
Cowan, Sherry Haile
Social Studies Teacher
Ezell, Portia Aldridge
English & Theater Arts Tchr
Hancock, Kathryn Rose
Biology Teacher
Hill, Faye Carr
Primary Classroom Teacher
Huddleston, Lisa Newton
High School Mathematics Tchr
Johns, Shirley Collins
Retired Elementary Teacher
Joiner, David Lee
PE Tchr & Head Baseball Coach
Kaler, Benna Sue
Chemistry Teacher
King, Dianne Brown
Mathematics & Physics Teacher
Martin, Donald Lee
Band Director
McReynolds, Mary Lou
Professor of Biology
Robertson, Gary Dean
Math Teacher
Sansom, Marsha Lynn
Spanish Teacher
Scott, Susan Collins
HS Math Teacher
Smith, Gladys Adams
English Teacher
Suddeath, Sharon A.
Assistant Principal
Thorpe, Mary Peters
1st & 2nd Grade Teacher
Tipton, Valery Sullivan
Retired Elementary Teacher
HORSE BRANCH
Flener, Loreca Jane
Sixth Grade Teacher
HORSE CAVE
Dick, Samuel Ellsworth
Science Teacher
Melloan, Barbara Gail
6th Grade Teacher
HUSTONVILLE
Brown, Susan M.
Elementary Counselor
Coffey, Donna Hoskins
5th-6th Grade Lang Arts Tchr
HYDEN
Asher, Mary Feltner
Anatomy & Chemistry Teacher
INDEPENDENCE
Baldwin, Bert Bowling
Retired Elementary Teacher
Boyle, Karen Raque
Library Media Specialist

PENDENCE (cont)
yne, Teri L.
mediate Elementary Tchr
acqueline Malone
:h Teacher
ı, Mary Anne Elander
ary Teacher
an, Ina Vahlsing
ing Teacher & Yrbk Advisor
art, Virginia Henderson
ish Teacher
, Diana
2th Grade Math Teacher
hn, Carolyn Joan
ird Language Arts Teacher
Rodney Edward
uage Arts Teacher
son, Ruth Tidwell
irade Algebra Teacher
gi, Gerard Anthony
ıstructor & Athletic Dir
der, Janet Cheniae
:h & Spanish Teacher
man, Carissa Bradley
ish Teacher
, Martha K.
nistry Teacher
ı, Susan Moore
nth Grade Science Teacher
Janice Ferner
'eacher
, Daniel Alan
bra Teacher
, Gary Lee
ɔgical Science Teacher

ly, Donna Callaham
ness & Office Teacher
ly, Michelle Stepp
ıce Teacher
Sharon Preece
ly & Consumer Science Tchr
IE
nond, Linda FLeenor
ish Teacher
Melissa Galloway
:h Teacher
rson, Valerie Raye
Grd Language Arts Tchr
s, Jeanette Moore
ary Teacher
Ronald
Dept Chairman
IGTON
ıder, Patricia Lawson
th Grade Teacher
James G.
ıce Teacher
, Ruth-Gail Claycomb
ary Teacher
rson, Mary Jane
ary Teacher
SON
ıg, Linda Jo (Combs)
Grade Teacher
Akhter Saeeda
uctor of Chemistry
Margaret E.
ıce Teacher
Gillum, Joannie L.
School Mathematics Tchr
man, Joyce Watts
stant Professor of English
ook, Dora Ann
ed Primary Teacher
Richard Earle
stant Professor of History
on, Mary Sue
th Grade Teacher
ermilk, Robert Elbert, III
of Rel & VP of Admin
e, Arthur Jackson
stant Professor
, Marcia Kay
ish Professor
, Carol L.
French & Spanish Teacher
r, Bradley Ernest Pitt
gion & Orientation Prof
Mary Jo
ociate Professor of Comm
n Smith, Leila
oc Professor of Business
tian, Eugene
uctor of Education
man, Irton
nology Education Teacher
ıs, Melanie Val (Gross)
ıematics Teacher
rt, Sherri Rae (Thomas)
culture Teacher & FFA Adv
, Brenda Sue (Turner)
2th Portfolio Resource Tchr
CTION CITY
n, Susan Jones
ı Grade Teacher
PER
ston, Shirlene Justice
d Grade Teacher
LEY
ıs, Ludora Feese
Grd Contained Class Tchr
ENTER
n, Mary Louise
red 2nd Grd Tchr
RANGE
, Karen Berg
Grade Teacher

LANCASTER
Baker, Jewell Wells
Title I Teacher
Black, Judy Gay
8th Grade Science Teacher
Brogli, Anne H.
Retired Second Grade Teacher
Compton, Jerry Thomas
Mathematics Teacher
Hammons, Brenda Ruth
Vocational Home Economics Tchr
Hester, Jeffrey Clay
Hlth & Phys Ed Teacher
Hooper, Cheryl Lyne
Family & Consumer Science Tchr
Logan, Carmen Carico
Primary Teacher
Noe, Carolyn Barclay
Title I Math & Reading Tchr
Poore, Sherry J.
Guidance Counselor
Richardson, Karen Elizabeth
Special Ed Tchr
Rogers, Cindy Edgington
Language Arts Teacher
Turner, Jean Bailey
Teacher of Gifted & Talented
LATONIA
Barker, Tommy
Exceptional Education Teacher
Bedford, Julie Ann
History Teacher
Fox, M. Patricia
English Teacher
Ginney, Mary Ellen
Fifth Grade Teacher
Hyde, Peggy Perkins
US History Teacher
Manahan, Sean Thomas
Mathematics Teacher
Martin, Patricia Ann
Spanish Teacher
Motsinger, J. Maureen
French Teacher
Moyers Works, Mary Elizabeth
Elementary Principal
Norton, Bryan Scott
9th Grd Health & PE Teacher
Orcutt, Thomas Leslie
History Teacher
Osborne, Marcia Arnold
Word Perfect, Keyboarding Tchr
Pennington, Linda (Leach)
Chemistry Teacher
Richardson, Jane Elizabeth
4th Grade Teacher
Schlarman, Susan Eifert
High School English Teacher
Taylor, Becky Ann
Math Teacher
Whalen, Teena Tanner
Physical Education Teacher
LAWRENCEBURG
Baker, Jean Page
Fourth Grade Teacher
Bee, Laurie Sprague
6th Grade Science & Rdng Tchr
Mills, Cherry Leigh
English Teacher
Powell, Christine I.
English Teacher
Riley, Delisa League
Former Teacher
Thompson, Ginny Newberry
8th Grade Science Teacher
Tinsley, Sadie Sea
Primary Teacher
Vaughn, Eva Kidwell
Retired Elementary Teacher
LEATHERWOOD
Hall, Mickey Lynn
Literature & Science Teacher
LEBANON
Black, Nancy Barnett
Health Science Instructor
Farris, Lynn Davis
7th & 8th Grade Teacher
Gibson, Laura Bernice
English Teacher
Griffith, Mike
Physical Education Teacher
Hamilton, David Wayne
Psych & Political Sci Teacher
Hogan, Jayne Eubank
English & Journalism Teacher
Lanham, Jan Weaver
K-8th Grd Tchr of the Gifted
Matney, Shirley Kilby
Spanish Teacher
McDonald, Sondra Lanham
Fourth Grade Teacher
Myers, Terry Enzweiler
8th Grd Lang Arts & Sci Tchr
Ortego, Kayren Fontenot
English Teacher & Cheer Coach
Raley, Vickie Wright
Librarian
Sexton, Mendy Brown
Eighth Grade Math Teacher
Ward, Jennifer Phillips
Biology Teacher
LEITCHFIELD
Carman, Debbie Fulkerson
Health Service Instructor
Logsdon, Gary Vance
High School Visual Arts Chair
McKinney, Lonnie Edwin
Electronics Technology Instr
Meredith, C. Lynne Hale
Business Ed Teacher, Dept Head

Moudry, Thomas Franklin
High School English Teacher
Parker, Gary L.
Director of Bands
Pence, Deloris Hart
High School English Teacher
Perkins, Deborah Kinslow
Fourth Grade Teacher
Smith, Cynthia Renee
Marketing Education Teacher
Stikeleather, Glen Alan
8th Grade Science Teacher
Taylor, Karen Nolan
High School English Teacher
LETCHER
Blair, Manis
Health & Physical Ed Teacher
LEWISBURG
Bailey, Joe Kenneth
Math & Art Teacher
Riley, Sarah England
Fifth Grade Teacher
Wells, Janet Strader
Physical Education Teacher
LEWISPORT
Coffey, Frank Lyle
English Teacher
Gatton, Therese Evelyn
English Teacher
Hawkins, Christina M.
Secondary Mathematics Teacher
Hobbs, David Lee
Director of Bands
Lasley, Mary Szemethy
Spanish Teacher
Price, Eddie
Soc Stud Tchr & Dept Chair
LEXINGTON
Adcock, Lucy Lanier
Social Studies Teacher
Akers, Lyn Formau
Experience Based Career Coord
Allen, Claudette M.
Social Studies Teacher
Andrews, Jennifer M.
8th Grd Language Arts Teacher
Apple, Judy Young
Art Teacher
Arvin, Joyce Handy
Retired Teacher
Barber, Cynthia Eberhardt
Mathematics Professor
Barber, Jeffrey Lynn
7th Grd Life Sci Teacher
Bell, Donald Scott
History Teacher
Bowen, Jane G.
Title I Rdng Lang Arts Tchr
Bowles, Denna Faith-Cox
Preschool & Kindergarten Tchr
Bray, Conrad Joseph
Chaplain & Bible Teacher
Brooks, Melanie Peavler
Math & Computer Sci Tchr
Bryant, Ron D.
Instructor of History
Bullock, Angela Tweel
Psychology & Economics Teacher
Byrum, Douglas
7th Grd Life Science Teacher
Caldwell, Rose H.
Math Department Co-Chair
Cantrell, Timothy Alfred
Professor of Political Science
Cassity, Danny R.
Exprnce Based Career Ed Tchr
Champe, Teresa Martin
High School Mathematics Tchr
Chittenden, C. David
Division Chairman
Cornish, Craig Steven
Band Director
Crouch, Dianne Gabbert
High School Guidance Counselor
Davin, Jean Kasper
Junior High Science Teacher
Davis, Jennifer Mink
High School Mathematics Tchr
Elrod, Betty Lewis
6th Grade Language Arts Tchr
Embry, Nolen Ulysses
Assoc Prof & Division Chprsn
Emerson, Alyce Sterling
Social Studies Teacher
Erminger, H. Wayne
English Teacher
Evensen, Grace Elizabeth
Elementary Science Teacher
Farmer Higdon, Karen S.
Math Teacher
Feese, Natalee M.
Mathematics Coordinator
Flanary, Patricia Cardinal
Assistant Professor of English
Frisbie, Molly Crandall
Assistant Professor of Biology
Garten, Patty King
English Teacher
Gil, Caroline
Chemistry Teacher
Gill, Karen Vinning
Physics Teacher
Gill, Scot Aaron
Physics Teacher
Go, Robert J.
Physics & Astronomy Professor
Green, Rita Dayton
4th Level Teacher
Greer, Nellie Witt
Home Economics Teacher

Gregory, Kimberly Mae
HS Social Studies Teacher
Groleau, Sally Villa
Assoc Professor of Mathematics
Guffey, Roger L.
High School Math Teacher
Hall, Ada Mae Mc Cray
5th Grade Classroom Teacher
Hanley, Carol Diane
Chemistry & Biology Teacher
Hardy, Charles Eugene, Jr.
Staff Assistant
Harned, Colleen Barry
Second Grade Teacher
Harper, Teri Stein
Social Studies Teacher
Horine, Jim
Religious Studies Dept Teacher
Howard, Keene Collins
Physical Education & Hlth Tchr
Huber, Barbara Jean
Primary Classroom Teacher
Humpert, John Eric
German Teacher
Jones, Rande Wayne
Math & Computer Science Tchr
Kikuchi, Elizabeth Jarvis
Chemistry Teacher
Lamirande, James Howard
Welding Instr
LaVey, Rebecca Harper
Project Transition Soc Worker
Lee, Earlyse Brown
Retired Social Studies Teacher
Lefler, Patricia
Asst Professor of Psychology
Legere, Charlene Frances
Mathematics Teacher
LeGrand, Mari K.
High School English Teacher
Liles, Tammy Jo
Professor of Biology
Lillich, Kathleen O'Brian
High School French Teacher
Little, Charles Fuller, Jr.
Band Director
Livingston, Jane Coventry
English Teacher
Madison, Sharon K.
English & Speech Teacher
Martin, Diane W.
Assistant Professor of English
Matthews, Rene K.
English Teacher
Mazurek, Joan Stevens
Sixth Grade Science Teacher
Mc Clure, Shirley Clark
Primary Teacher
Mc Euen, Melissa A.
History Professor
McGrath, Lenora Ann
High School Mathematics Tchr
Meaux, Dolores H.
Guidance Counselor
Miller, Marcia S. (Raupe)
Spanish Teacher
Montgomery, Lisa Segneri
Mathematics Teacher
Moran, Ann Grinton
4th Grade Teacher
Murphy, William Kevin
Architectural Tech Assoc Prof
Nash, Martha Taylor
7th Grade Life Science Teacher
Newby, Sarah Clark
Third Grade Teacher
Oatley, Douglas Wayne
Band Director
O'Brien, Janet J.
11th-12th Grade English Tchr
O'Melia, Kathy Marie
Math & Study Skills Teacher
Omlor, Dan W.
American Literature Teacher
Owens, Denise Asher
Chemistry Teacher
Papandria, John Robert
Bands Director
Pocholik, Ted, Jr.
Health & Phys Education Tchr
Powell, Charles Norman
Business Teacher
Purdue, Susan Gabbett
Science Teacher
Quinesberry, Rosetta Lucas
Social Studies Teacher
Ransdell, Traci G.
English Teacher
Rickenbacker, Elizabeth Hendricks
Math Teacher
Ripley, M. Bret
History Professor
Roberts, Gloria M.
8th Grade Math Teacher
Sallee, Jonel Curtis
English Teacher
Schmidt, Ann Currie
Chemistry Tchr & Science Chr
Settle, Mickey Levy
English Teacher
Shearer, Robin Deering
Eighth Grd Lang Arts Tchr
Shelton, Pat
Biology & Phys Science Teacher
Simpson, Elaine Hamilton
Social Studies Teacher
Sims, Marian Moore
English & Health Teacher
Sirles, Linda Troutman
Jr HS Religion & English Tchr

Stayton, Lisa Cross
Social Studies Teacher
Stevens, Paul Harman
Biology & Physical Sci Teacher
Stevens, Sally Wallace
Mathematics Teacher
Stivers, Earl
8th Grade Mathematics Teacher
Sutherland, Joy Lynette
Social Studies Teacher
Taylor, Dr. Ronald David
Psychology Professor
Travelbee, Cynthia Norman
Assoc Professor of Psychology
Underwood, Dale N.
Associate Professor
Underwood, Nancy Lockyer
Fourth Grade Teacher
Ward, Barbara Parks
English Teacher
Warren, Jo
High School English Teacher
Wesley-Gill, Sharron A.
Business & Marketing Teacher
Wheaton, Jo Cartwright
English Teacher
Whitescarver, Shirley A.
Biological Sci & Nursng Instr
Wilgus, Linda Louise
Nursing Instructor
Wood, Rebecca Adelle
Mathematics Teacher & Chprsn
Woods, D. Kay
Social Studies Teacher
Woods, Diana W.
Principal
Young, Gretchen Kay
Speech, Debate & Drama Teacher
Zourakis, Joyce Macdonald
Spanish Teacher
LIBERTY
Buis, James Rodney
Mathematics & Comp Sci Teacher
Coffey, Lydia Sweeney
MS Language Arts Tchr
Douglas, Imo Jane
Business Education Teacher
Elmore, Randy E.
High School Mathematics Tchr
Hoskins, Beverly G.
Eng, Journalism & Speech Tchr
Hughes, Hayward Taggart
His Dept Head & Teacher
Overstreet, Marvetta Douglas
English Teacher
Patton, Nancy C.
Science Teacher
Pennington, Aubrey El
HS Soc Stud & History Teacher
Terry, Leah Dawn
Computer Application Teacher
Tucker, Sandy Rigney
English Teacher
Ware, Brent
Agriculture Teacher
Williams, Roma J.
English Teacher
LITTCARR
Richardson, Shirley Holliday
3rd-4th Grade Teacher
LIVERMORE
Sutherlin, Shirley Davis
Retired 5th Grade Teacher
LONDON
Adkins, Sheila Denise
6th Grade Social Studies Tchr
Bailey, Janna (House)
Mathematics Teacher
Blankenship, Gloria Faye
Elem Schl Guidance Counselor
Bowling, Darlene Greene
High School English Teacher
Bush, Sharon Parrett
Business Teacher
Cheek, James E., II
VP of Acad Affairs & Acad Dean
Claiborne, Carla Clark
Primary Teacher
Cornett, Gary Lane
8th Grade History Teacher
Davis, Jamie Stidham
Secondary Mathematics Teacher
George, Jeannie Hensley
Primary Teacher
Gregory, Carolyn Ruth (Wells)
English Teacher
Grigg, Lindell Ray
JROTC & Aerospace Sci Instr
Harris, Lonnie
4th & 5th Grade Teacher
Hensley, Ruby (Langdon)
Mathematics Teacher
Henson, Vivian Reams
English Department Chair, Tchr
Hill, Larry Wayne
Math Teacher
Hodges, Betty Mae (Reynolds)
Coord of Gifted & Talented
Hopkins, Emmie Daugherty
Business Teacher & Co-op Coord
Irwin, Rebecca Rush
Social Studies Teacher
Jackson, Karen S.
High School English Teacher
Johnson, Elizabeth Cupp
Mathematics Teacher
Kennedy, Deborah Black
US & World History Teacher
Kennedy, Timothy Burch
Band Director

LONDON (cont)
Mc Abee, Michal Holmes (Phelps)
Title I Resource Teacher
McCowan, Suzanne Fiechter
English Teacher
Mc Sweeney, Gene
Soc Sci Prof & Dept Chair
Mills, Billy Maithlan, II
HS Mathematics Teacher & Coach
Mobley, Judy Haywood
Kndgtn & First Grade Teacher
Mosley, Billy Ray
Social Studies Teacher
Mullins, Betty Jo Anders
Primary Teacher
Owens, Pamela Williams
Social Studies Teacher
Phelps, Kimberly Baxter
Marketing Teacher
Powell, Joan Sizemore
English Teacher
Proffitt, Janet Lowe
Third Grade Teacher
Reed, Jeffrey Lee
8th Grade Science Teacher
Robinson, Ruth Johnston
Fifth Grade Teacher
Siebert, Mae M.
Librarian
Smallwood, Ty Ruth
English Teacher
Smith, Monica Feltner
High School Guidance Counselor
Vaughn, Vickie L. Davis
6th Grade English Teacher
Weierich, Andre' Jean
Adjunct Professor of Biology
Weierich, Mary Baumer Young
Asst Prof in Rel & Philosophy
Yaden, Gary Richard
Social Studies Teacher

LOUISA
Cline, Judy Coleman
Seventh Grade English Teacher
Compton, Carol Ann Jones
Science Teacher
Frazier, Anna Narue
Science & Math Teacher
Hayes, Doris Rejean
Former Second Grade Teacher
Kelley, Margie Stumbo
Remedial Teacher
O'Brian, A. Jene Turner
Secondary Teacher
Pigmon, Delores Miller
Reading Teacher
Spicer, Wilma Mc Clure
Primary Teacher
Young, Glenna Blevins
English Teacher

LOUISVILLE
Aberli, David Anthony
Religion Teacher
Allen, John Matthew
Latin, Bible & Typing Teacher
Anderson, LeRoy, Jr.
Social Studies Teacher
Andrada, Norma Jean
Bus Information Processing Tch
Ansback, Joey
English Teacher
Arbogast, Leonard Michael
Chemistry Teacher
Arnold, Kenneth Steven
Technology Education Teacher
Baar, Robert Lewis
Chemistry Teacher
Baker, Janice Faye
Mathematics Teacher
Baker, Martha Louise (Thorpe)
Scndry Business Education Tchr
Bannon, Lisa Wine
7th-8th Grade Science Teacher
Barnes, Shirley L.
High School English Teacher
Barto, Calvin Walter, III
PE & Health Teacher
Bauer, Susan Milburn
Community Liaison
Bennett, Marsha Lentz
7th & 8th Grd English Teacher
Berthold, Dudley Giro
Marketing Education Teacher
Bhaskar, Nageshwar Rao
Associate Professor
Biasiolli, Pamela Sue Sloan
Assistant Prof of Nursing
Bickel, Ted, Jr.
Chemistry Teacher
Blake, Joey Higgs
English Teacher
Blandford, James Robert, Jr.
Religion Teacher
Bloyd, Roger Allen
Business Instructor
Blue, Bonnie Lee (Dallas)
Kindergarten Teacher
Bock, Sherri Lenberger
5th Grade Teacher
Bohannon, Julie M.
Choral Music & Math Teacher
Bosemer, Cathy Carrier
English Teacher
Bosley, Gabriele Weber
German Professor
Brandon, Alice B.
Biology Teacher
Brewer, Harlan Woodrow
Eighth Grade Lang Arts Teacher
Brown, Kevin Kendall
Chemistry Teacher
Brown, Marianne Dunfee
English Teacher
Bundrent, June Marie
5th Grade Teacher
Bush, Susan Burgess
Math Lit & Religion Teacher
Butler, Donna Ross
Eighth Grd Soc Studies Teacher
Butsch, Richard Anthony
Assoc Prof of Eng & Dept Chair
Byrne, Bill
Comp Drafting & Theatre Tchr
Camenisch, Johanna
Fourth Grade Teacher
Carroll, Jean Gray
High School Mathematics Tchr
Chancellor, Michael Lee
Mathematics Teacher
Chasteen, Beverly Joan (Bennett)
Jr High Lang Arts & His Tchr
Christensen, Jean Marie
Music His Prof & Dept Chair
Clark, Donna Foushee
8th Grade Teacher
Clements, James L.
Mathematics Teacher
Coker, Claudia LaNette
Orchestra Teacher
Cole, Rickie W.
7th Grd Language Arts Teacher
Coleman, Jerusha Moseley
Excptnl Chldrn Ed Tchr & Chair
Conboy, Jane M.
History Teacher
Conway, Candace Nunn
Marketing Teacher
Cowden, F. Lamont
Theater Design & Dept Chm
Crawford, David Morgan
Math & Biology Tchr
Crone, Julie Hauswald
Anatomy & Physiology Teacher
Curd, Regine Maria (Tannhoff)
German & English Teacher
Dennis, Kenneth Allen
Social Studies Teacher
Dennis, Margaret B.
First Grade Teacher
Dickens, Lisa Kay
High School Band Director
DiGiovanni, Frederick Matthew
Art Teacher
Diminnie, Patricia Jaworski
English Teacher
Dobson, Rita Lanham
Junior High Teacher
Drew, Donald Edward
Military Science Teacher
Drucker, Claire Freeman
4th-5th Grd Adv Prgm Tchr
Dunbar-Demaree, Margaret
ECE Teacher
Esterle, Dennis Lee, Sr.
Math Teacher
Farris, Gloria Davis
Business Teacher
Faulls, Anne Wille
English & Theater Arts Teacher
Fischer, Kate Greer
11th Grd US His & Geog Tchr
Fletcher, Mary Morley
Kindergarten Teacher
Frank, Marita A.
Director of Cooperative Ed
Franklin, Beverly Johnson
High School Guidance Counselor
French, Dolores (Pfaadt)
Middle School Teacher
Fugate, Myra Karr
English & Humanities Teacher
Garing, Bernard Shaun
Geography Teacher
Garner, Sandra H. Morrison
Retired Mathematics Teacher
Garrett, Kennethia Lee
Math Teacher
Gibson, Peggy Collins
Guidance Counselor
Graham, Jean Sage
Retired 3rd & 4th Grd Teacher
Green, Catherine Carson
English as Second Lang Teacher
Greene, Ron
Social Science Teacher
Gregory, Kathleen Kay (Royster)
Former Intermediate Teacher
Grigsby, R. Karen
Second & Third Grade Teacher
Grosz, Clinton Edward
Asst Principal & Violin Instr
Hall, Brenda G.
English & Drama Teacher
Hall, Rebecca Allen
English as a Second Lang Tchr
Hamilton, Carol Hawkins
Math Teacher & Dept Chprsn
Harkleroad, Patricia Cross
Kndgtn & Remediation Tchr
Harris, Sharon Elaine
HS Biology & Chemistry Teacher
Harris, Sonda Berry
Dean & 6th Grade Teacher
Harrison, Leo
6th Grade Math Teacher
Hash, Michael Douglas
Substitute Teacher & Coach
Hayes-Nichols, Cynthia Ann
Math Teacher
Helton, Ann Mc Donald
Student Assistance Counselor
Hennessy, Kimberly Kyser
Computer Teacher & Tech Coord
Hnat, William Patrick
Assoc Prof Mechanical Engrng
Hockenberger, Susan Jane
Dean & Nursing Professor
Hodapp, Kathleen Crawford
Adv English I Teacher
Horowitz, Barry R.
Prof of Elec & Biomed Engrng
Hughes, John C.
History Teacher
Hultz, Brian Jeffrey
Band Director
Hunt, Charlotte Risner
Mathematics Teacher
Irwin, Marilyn Baldwin
Mathematics Teacher
Jackson, Joyce Wagers
Teacher
Jones, Jane Housman
Math & Cmptr Programming Tchr
Jones, Neysa Barbour
HS Composition & Lit Teacher
Jones-Earley, Cathy L.
Frosh Honors English Teacher
Jordan, James A.
Mathematics & Physical Ed Tchr
Karem, George Frank
6th & 8th Grade Soc Stud Tchr
Kee, Brenda Eltrine
Associate Professor of Piano
Kitchen, Nancy B.
High School Art Instructor
Klapheke, Steven Lee
United States History Teacher
Kline, Daniel Thomas
Assoc Professor of English
Koch, Raymond A.
Social Studies Chairperson
Kulp, Brian Burdan
World History & Govt Teacher
Lattimore, Kirk Byron
Assistant Principal
Lattimore, Sharis Miller
Math Teacher
Lete, Vicki Duckworth
Biology & Anatomy Teacher
Lin, Stephen Houng Tze
Vocal & Choral Music Teacher
Lincoln, Angela Lea
Theology Teacher
Lindsay, Betsy B.
School Support Resource Tchr
Lococo, Anthony John
Teacher
Love, Geraldine
Social Studies Teacher
Lucchesi, Peter Joseph
Comm & Computer Science Tchr
Maddox, Marjorie Ann
Associate Professor of Nursing
Madeya, John
Biology Teacher
Magruder, Daniel Anthony, Jr.
Chemistry Instructor
Maguire, Ceci Mc Kiernan
Middle School Teacher
Mahin, Vickie Smith
6th Grade Language Arts Tchr
Major, Mark Edward
Bio, Anatomy & Physiology Tchr
Manuel, Donna Marie
Fifth Grade Teacher
Matter, Curt Heuer
Social Studies Teacher
Mattingly, Mary Smith
Sixth Grade Teacher
Mattingly, Robert Andrew, Jr.
Anatomy & Physiology Professor
May, Jean Ann
Asst Prin & Math Resource Tchr
May, Karen Cain
Adv World History Tchr
McClanahan, Cia White
English & Journalism Teacher
Mc Hugh, Phyllis Meadows
Mathematics Teacher
McNabb, William Michael
Biology Teacher
Meagher, Ava Lardner
Religion Teacher
Medley, Charles Francis, Jr.
Mathematics Teacher
Milam, Stephen D.
US History Teacher
Miller, Carol Martin
English Teacher
Miller, Linda
Jr HS Language Arts & Lit Tchr
Montgomery, Ronald Clell
Broadcast Communcations Tchr
Moody, Harry Allen
Math Teacher
Mull, Alfred William
Primary Teacher
Murphy, Naniene Hammond
Jr HS Soc Stud & Lit Teacher
Nation, Pamela Grace
Biology, Science & Math Tchr
Nefouse, Barbara S.
Principal
Nichols, M. Celeste C.
Assistant Professor of English
Niemi, Rhonda C.
8th Grade Mathematics Teacher
Nuss, Donna Lee
Chemistry & Biology Teacher
O'Bannon, Shawn
Health & Fitness Teacher
Oerther, Deborah Lee
Primary School Teacher
O'Toole, Martin M.
Chemistry Teacher & Coach
Owen, Deborah Smith
Biological Sci Tchr
Paris, Richard LeCompte
Chemistry Teacher
Peacock, Joseph V.
English Teacher
Pendleton, Sarita Lynn
Spanish Teacher
Perkins, Joan Brissman
French Teacher
Pickett, Mary L. (Kendall)
4th Grade Teacher
Porta, David James
Asst Professor of Biology
Probus, Laura Ann
Religious Activities Director
Protenic, James C.
Amer His Tchr & Athletic Dir
Rademaker, Marianne Einars
High School Mathematics Tchr
Raines, Robin Edwards
Eighth Grade Math Teacher
Ralph, Mary Margaret
Religion Teacher & Dept Chair
Rapley, Gay M.
English & Humanities Teacher
Redd, Joyce Childress
5th Grade Teacher
Reddington, Bill Charles, III
Calculus, Finite & Stats Tchr
Reynolds, Denise Garrard
Travel & Tourism Teacher
Richardson, Janet Wright
High School Biology Teacher
Roelofsen, Amparo Mollica
Spanish Teacher
Rostel, Richard Thomas
Spanish Teacher
Rowan, Linda Cox
Fifth Grade Teacher
Rudolph, James Edward
Biology Teacher & Coach
Sadolsky, Theresa G.
Computer Teacher
Schiller, Marcia Werle
Counselor
Schmidt, Brenda Benton
Acting Magnet Coordinator
Schueler, Susan Brawner
Retired 8th Grd Lang Arts Tchr
Servino, Charles Louis
Social Studies Teacher
Sidebottom, Suzanne Sharpe
Visual Arts Tchr & Dept Chprsn
Simmons, Barbara Hagan
Religious Studies Teacher
Sisler, Susan Fae
Math Teacher
Smith, Andrea Elizabeth
Spanish & English Teacher
Smith, Patty Redman
Primary Teacher
Snyder, Jennifer Ellard
7th & 8th Grade Lang Arts Tchr
Spagnolo, Joe
Science Teacher
Speck, Frederick Alan
Music Professor
Spurr, Sally Ann
College Counselor
Steffen, Pamela Bray
English & German Teacher
Stewart, Katherine Cross
Art, Photography & Yrbk Tchr
Stigger, Patricia Hester
English Teacher
Stinson, Deborah Jarboe
Business Technology Teacher
Stites, James Franklin
Technology Teacher
Sutton, Faye C.
Prof & Job Search Trainer Dir
Terrell, Michael Edward
Primary Teacher
Terry, Norman Lee, Jr.
Spcl Needs Teacher
Tinch, Marsha Pullem
7th Grade Language Arts Tchr
Tingle, Glennda Hagan
English & Theater Teacher
Trice, Jennifer Kaye
Primary Teacher
Turner, Jill Michelle
English & History Teacher
Tuttle, Rebecca H.
Mathematics Teacher
Twaryonas, Kay Ellen
English & Humanities Teacher
Van Nostrand, Gloria Joan
Math & Science Teacher
Vogedes, Glenn Allen
Social Studies Teacher
Vogel, Sandra L.
5th Grade Teacher
Waiters, Sandra Alexine
Vocal Music Specialist
Walker, Jennifer Kaye
High School English Teacher
Walker, Kathy Lynn
7th & 8th Grade English Tchr
Walsh, Alice A.
7th & 8th Grade Teacher
Wantland, Bonnie Turner
Chemistry Teacher
Warden, Patricia Kurtz
Fourth Grade Teacher
Weatherbee, Harriette Halter
Retired 4th-5th Grd Tchr
White, Tom
High Technology Specialist
Whitehouse, Ruth Ann
Teacher & Coach
Wiegand, Deborah Roman
7th Grd Lang Arts & Sci Tchr
Willman, Robert Wayne
English Teacher & Coach
Wilson, Tonya Milby
Tenth Grade English Teacher
Winkler, Linda Cornett
English & Journalism Teacher
Wisman, Jackie Boone
Mathematics Teacher
Wong, Julius P.
Professor of Mechanical Engrng
Wood, J. Gayle
Elementary School Counselor
Works, Victoria Lynn
English & Theater Teacher
Wright, Tammy Dennis
Veterinary Science Teacher
Wright, Wanda
Associate Prof of Business
Yancy, Fronda Kellum
Seventh Grade Teacher
Young, Christine Evans
English Teacher
Zierer, Carolyn Blandford
Sixth Grade Teacher
Zippin, Beth Taylor
English & Journalism Teacher

LOWES
Hargrove, Sandra Lyonhurst
7th-8th Grade Math Teacher

LOYALL
Cain, Julia Hickey
Fourth Grade Teacher
Lynn, Sandra D.
Primary Teacher
Parsons, Bill
5th Grade Teacher
Toll, Joyce (Mc Daniel)
Primary Teacher

LUCAS
Stewart, Marla Furlong
Third Grade Teacher

LUDLOW
Kidwell, Bill Larry
Band Director
Rohlman, Vickie Reeves
Health & PE Teacher

MACEO
Conklin, Dot Robertson
Retired Primary Teacher

MADISONVILLE
Alexander, Betty C.
Counselor
Ashby, Deanna Duvall
Guidance Counselor
Ashby, Fred Neal
Band Director
Barnett, Timothy H.
Instrumental Music Tchr
Clayton, Donald Owen
Assoicate Professor of Math
Davis, Susan Knapp
Associate Professor of Nursing
Gooch, Virginia Allen
Fifth Grade Teacher
Gower, Virginia Pratt
Asst Professor in Nursing
Hoskins, Charles Herbert, III
English Teacher
Lowery, Michael Douglas
Soc Studies & Gifted Prgm Tchr
Nygaard, Timothy
Assoc Prof of Accounting
Oglesby, Sarah Mc Gregor
Associate Professor
Pace, Debra Lea
English Instructor
Seibert, Allen Gail
Marketing Education Instructor
Shifflett, George Michael
Assistant Professor of Physics
Simmons, Patricia Lynn
Associate Professor of Nursing
Sizemore, Andrea Beth
Pharmacy Technician Pgm Dir
Walters, Patricia Harris
English Teacher & Dept Chair
Weatherford, Susan Hayes
English Teacher
West, Ann Elizabeth
Communications Professor
Whitfield, Barbara Frances
Math Teacher & Dept Chm
Williamson, Thomas C.
Social Studies Teacher
Wilson, Aya Leah
8th Grade US History Tchr
Winstead, B. W.
History Instructor
Wright, Debbie L.
Assoc Professor of Accounting

MANCHESTER
Murray, Christine (Caudill)
Secondary Art Teacher
Roberts, Glenna Rae Gregory
Fifth Grade Teacher
Short, Bettye Moore
Fourth Grade Teacher

MARION
Benningfield, Mark Christopher
Band Director

ON (cont)
Larry Allen
ulture Education Instr
Teresa G.
rade Language Arts Tchr
, Mary Helen
ematics Teacher
vell, Linda Foster
l Studies Teacher
len, Rhet
cal Education & Hlth Tchr
Lori Brown
2nd Grade Teacher
, Jeanette Margaret
rd Literature & Sci Tchr
Outland, Phyllis Anne
Grade Teacher
IN
indy Speaks
rd Homerm & Soc Stud Tchr
Coley
ce Teacher
Kenneth Wayne
Studies Dept Chprsn
IELD
ong, Sandra Simpkins
r Exploration Dir & Tchr
, Jodie Anne
School Math Teacher
Stephanie Beth
er
Mary Vick
r English Teacher
y, Jay Francis
chr & Head Ftbl Coach
ion, Henry Clifton
ed Teacher
, Fran Louise
selor
n, Tony Lee
ry Teacher
Marcie Willett
sh Teacher
, Mary Ellen Dyar
Civilization Teacher
n, Lana Kaye
sh & Journalism Teacher
in, Jill Summerville
Grade Teacher
, Barbara Bogle
ess Education Teacher
ll, Angela Widener
ive Writing Teacher
, Christy H.
ess Teacher
l, Eddie Lee
History Tchr & Dept Chair
, Martha Hendon
urce Teacher
rd, Barbara Gumm
th Grd Mathematics Tchr
n, Stephanie Dawn (Williams)
Teacher
, Robert Eugene
ra I & Eng III Tchr
, Rim Anthony
of Students
Mary Jean
ance Counselor
IELDON
, Belinda H.
gh Math & Sci Tchr
VILLE
l, Douglas K.
Director
od, William Wallace
sh Instructor
, Laura C.
Prof of Accounting
ay, Linda Smith
ciate Professor of Nursing
indy Fidler
sh Professor
ohn Robert
ssor
r, Phyllis Weber
nd Grade Teacher
OWELL
Karen Stumbo
sh Teacher
Geraldine Karen
ary Teacher
EE
Paul H.
rade Teacher
Brenda Harrison
World History Teacher
Doris Ann Harrison
ness Teacher
Keith Noel
ance Counselor
, Lonzo
ce Teacher
n, James R.
rican History Teacher
Janine Lewis
mistry & Biology Teacher
, Douglas Vee
Science Teacher
IN
ok, Linda Mullins
ance Counselor
LEBURG
, Lorene Hill
ary Teacher
LESBORO
Mary Winston
her
n, Kenneth Ray
umental Music Director

Turner, Wanda
Teacher
MIDWAY
Houp, Katherine Hanke
Professor of Biology
MONTICELLO
Abbott, Gary Lynn
Service Learning Coordinator
Ball, Doris Robinson
Health Services Instructor
Chaney, Gregory
Alternative Classroom Teacher
Hurt, Winfrey Lee
Agriculture Teacher
Kelsch, Marla Kay
Business Education Teacher
Owens, Gary Wayne
English Teacher
Radford, Gale S.
Science Dept Chprsn & Bio Tchr
Ryan, Shirley Linville
High School Math Teacher
Smith, Emily Clay
AP English IV Teacher
Stamper, Edwin P.
Technology Education Teacher
MOREHEAD
Bumgardner, Charlotte Fraley
Teacher of Gifted Students
Burton, Brenda Catron
French Teacher
Clark, Melissa Clay
Earth Science Teacher
Hall, Betty Lathram
Retired Teacher
Helphinstine, Frances L.
Professor of English
Jones, Rhonda Gay
Primary Teacher
Knipp, Sandy Diano
Family Literacy Prgm Teacher
Kunz, Michelle B.
Assistant Professor
Mains, Patricia Skaggs
7th Grade Science Teacher
Ramey, C. Victor
Science Associate Professor
Rose, Evelyn Brown
Dev Occupations & Wrk Exp Tchr
Stidom, Sharon Newman
Vocational Home Ec Tchr & Chm
Tuerk, Craig
Assistant Biology Professor
Walke, Dianna Teater
English Teacher
Walke, Ronald Lee
American History Instructor
MORGANFIELD
Belt, Leilani Gresham
Spanish Teacher
Chambliss, Cathy Davis
English Teacher & Media Spon
Ciecorka, Matthew Richard
Mathematics Teacher
Davidson, George Russell
Middle School Teacher
Dickens, Tana Shea
English Teacher
Edmondson, Bonnie Kearney
English Teacher
Gill, Janet Daniel
Family & Consumer Sci Tchr
Greenwell, Robin Quinn
Math Teacher
Jenkins, Beverly Brown
Primary Teacher
Paris, Charlie Bob
Ath Director & Health Teacher
Plum, Anita Jane Fuller
4th Grade Teacher
Shelton, Teresa Thompson
English Instructor
Smith, Linda Mooney
8th Grd Language Arts Teacher
Vaughn, Jeanne Edmonds
Secondary French Teacher
Zollinger, Rita Karen
Fourth Grade Teacher
MORGANTOWN
Baseheart, Lisa Jean
Mathematics Teacher
Crafton, Laura Smith
Primary Teacher
Davis, Byron Keith
Math & Social Studies Teacher
Young, James Rice, IV
English Teacher
MORNING VIEW
Talbert, Beth Busemeyer
Former 6th Grade Teacher
MOUNT OLIVET
Jones, Jennifer Thompson
Primary Teacher
MOUNT STERLING
Barnes, Kimberley Renee
English & Yearbook Teacher
Brice, Sally Tripp
Elementary Teacher
Brown, Lucy Marie
Mathematics Teacher
Clemons, Mary Gay
Language Arts Teacher
Forgy Mc Intosh, Jennifer Turnbull
English & Drama Teacher
Gray, Cavanah Paige
Sixth Grade Math Teacher
Manley, Mary Caudill
4th Grade Teacher
Rawlings, Julia Davis
Science Teacher

MOUNT VERNON
Allen, Ruth Brown
English Teacher
Belcher, Mary Hamm
Guidance Counselor
Bustle, Trina Gayle
High School Math Teacher
Lynch, William Junior
Psychology Teacher
Martin, Pamela Cummins
Social Studies Teacher
Roark, Michael David
Fifth Grade Teacher
Short, Cathy
Special Education Teacher
Wells, Janet Johnson
Library Media Specialist
Whitaker, Dale Vaughn
High School Guidance Counselor
MOUNT WASHINGTON
Brooks, Harriet R.
Media Center Director
Maggard, Frances Collier
Language Arts Teacher
Scott, Christal Stallings
Business Teacher
MUNFORDVILLE
Adams, Tommy
HS Coach & Tchr of Spec Ed
Beams, Bobby Gene
Social Studies Teacher
Cvitkovic, Cindy Roberson
Algebra & Pre-Algebra Teacher
Cvitkovic, Dean Anton
Physical Education Instructor
Day, Deidre Barger
Secondary English Teacher
Edmonson, Gary L.
History Teacher
Line, Brenda Porth
Business Teacher
McCoy, Mary Ann
HS Physical Education Teacher
Murray, Renee Logsdon
Language Arts Teacher
Shoulders, Betty Jones
Biology Teacher
Thompson, Faye D.
Language Arts Teacher
Turner, Bonnie Walton
Family & Consumer Science Tchr
Winstead, Barbara Powell
Business Education Teacher
MURRAY
Barksdale, Charlotte Allen
English Teacher
Bates, Kay Gardner
Associate Professor of Music
Bohannon, Toni Burchett
3rd Grade Teacher
Coleman, Lynda Kelso
Department Chairman & Eng Tchr
Colson, Carolyn Hendon
Second Grade Teacher
Conley, Libby (Woods)
Asst Prin & English Teacher
Darden, Don J. D.
Marketing Teacher
Darnall, Sherry Shutt
Art Teacher & Guidance Cnslr
DeVoss, Linda McCuiston
English, French & Psych Tchr
Dill, Michael
Driver Education Tchr & Coach
Douglas, Elizabeth Sims
Title I Math Teacher
Elder, Rose Ross
HS Math Teacher
Foley, David L.
Science Teacher
Futrell, Ruth Ann
Honors English Teacher
Green, Melissa Miller
Science Teacher
Hasty, Lloyd
Chemistry Teacher
Johnson, Wanda Garrett
Social Studies Tchr & Dept Chm
McGaughey, Robert Howe, III
Dept Chairman of Journalism
Milner, Cheryl Holsapple
First & Second Grade Teacher
Mitchell, Billy
Health & PE Teacher
Mullins, Gary J.
Band Director
Patterson, Diane Rhoades
4th Grade Teacher
Pyle, Yvette Watson
Sci Dept Chprsn & Chem Tchr
Robinson, Reita Ladd
4th Grade Teacher
Simmons, Vicki Edwards
Business & Math Teacher
Spann, Sue M.
French Teacher
Stubblefield, Kathy Jo
Junior & Senior English Tchr
Wyatt, Stephanie Lynne
Science Teacher
NEBO
Adcock, William Kennedy
Language Arts Teacher
Beshear, Jim
Social Studies Teacher
Parker, Alice Lowery
English Teacher & Dept Chprsn
Stanley, Alan O'Neal
Jr HS & HS Special Ed Tchr

VanCleve, Sharon S.
Mathematics & Science Tchr
Womack, Jerry Lynn
Bio, Gen Sci & PE Teacher
Yarbrough, Nell Pendley
English & Psychology Teacher
NEON
Johnson, Mark Anthony
German & Psychology Teacher
Sturgill, Paul David
Math & Science Teacher
NEW CASTLE
Gilley, Cheryl Ann
Counselor
McCardwell, Michael Thomas
Art & Humanities Teacher
Smith, Ruthie L.
8th Grd Language Arts Teacher
NEWPORT
Brown, Robert Grady
Science Teacher
Carothers, Karen M.
First Grade Teacher
Frakes, Linda Voelker
Seventh Grade Math Teacher
Herald, Sara G. (Deaton)
Social Studies Teacher
Krebbs, Mark James
Social Studies Teacher
Pence, Helen Kathleen
English & History Teacher
Shearer, Mary Hislop
Primary Teacher
Spence, JoeAnn
Preschool Teacher
Wagner, Daniel James
Health & Career Choices Tchr
Young, James W.
Science Teacher
NICHOLASVILLE
Boggess, Bronnaja
8th Grade Science Teacher
Boggs, Daniel Wayne
Sixth Grade Teacher
Buchanan, Anne Frances
Science Teacher
Clem, Janet Hall
5th Grade Teacher
Colliver, Becky Montgomery
Guidance Counselor
Crawford, Tony Douglas
Guidance Counselor
Cruce, William Robert
Industrial Tech Teacher
Daniel, Denise Pippin
English Teacher
Holobek, Gary Lyle
Teacher & Basketball Coach
Ison, Louis Charles
Science Teacher
Jones, Kay (Coody)
English Teacher & Dept Chprsn
Leitch, Martha Terry
Business Teacher
MacGregor, Lois Berry
Drama & Speech Teacher
Martin, Sam L.
English Teacher
Nichols, Nancy Smith
Mathematics Teacher
Rice, Dennis C., Jr.
8th Grade Social Studies Tchr
Robinson, Jennifer Christian
8th Grade Science Teacher
Roher, Lee Alan
Mathematics Teacher
Smither, Arlene Moccia
Mathematics Teacher
Vass, Frank Raymond
English Teacher
NORTONVILLE
Brooks, David Gene
8th Grade Language Arts Tchr
Hinton, Melinda Rudolph
6th Grade Teacher
Moore, Shannon Cooper
Math Teacher
Moore, Twila Oglesby
7th Grade Math Teacher
Scott, Teresa Lynn (Howton)
Secondary Mathematics Teacher
OIL SPRINGS
Bailey, Sarah C.
Kindergarten & 1st Grade Tchr
OLIVE HILL
Brown, Kevin Lee
Social Studies Teacher
Carter, Linda Oakley
Fourth-Fifth Grade Teacher
Greene, Bert
US History Teacher
Henderson, Kathy Karen
Business Teacher
Rose, Wilma Jean
HS Math Teacher & Dept Chm
Salyers, Debra Hamilton
Language Arts Teacher
Stark, Jenny Callihan
Primary Teacher
OLMSTEAD
Kemp, Cynthia Mason
Preschool Teacher
ONEIDA
Powell, Ruth Ann
5th Grade Teacher
Robinson, David
Assistant Principal
OWENSBORO
Abschier, Katherine Stephens
English & Humanities Teacher

Adams, Faye Litsey
Third & Fourth Grade Teacher
Ahnell, Emil G.
Professor of Music
Allen, Janet Renee
High School Band Director
Armendarez, Peter X.
Professor of Chemistry
Barrette, Craig R.
Professor of English
Belcher, Larry Allen
Tech Instructor & Dept Head
Bittel, Ruth Ann
Spanish & French Teacher
Boehmann, Margaret Raibley
2nd & 3rd Grade Teacher
Bouvier, Fumie (Nakaguki)
Teacher
Britton, Joe S.
Prof of English & Dept Chprsn
Brown, Iris Moreno
Assistant Professor of Spanish
Burns, Linda Dawn
Language Arts Teacher
Chelgren, Beverly Wolf
Science Department Chairperson
Church, Phyllis Stone
English Teacher
Clark, Deborah Sparks
English Teacher
Clark, Susan Conrey
Business Education Teacher
Combs, John Raymond
Professor of English
Conkright, Laura Daum
Mathematics Teacher
Corden, Stephen Denton
Associate Professor
Coy, Marisue Stevens
Asst Professor of English
Depp, Sheila Taylor
Coordinator of Gifted
Dick, Timothy Thomas
Associate Professor of Biology
Durbin, Brenda Carol
4th Grade Teacher
Ellis, Julie L.
Community Relations Dir
Firkins, Robert Scott
Mathematics Teacher
Fritz, Jeffrey Paul
Mathematics Educator
Givens, Jacqueline Ann Raymond
Business Teacher
Grimsley, Thomas Jacob
High School Art Teacher
Ham, Franklin Stephen
Amer History & Sociology Tchr
Hartgrove, Rob John
Biology Teacher
Heffelfinger, Dayton Hicks
US History Teacher
Hicks, Judith Martin
English & Psych Teacher
Hohiemer, Suzanne Simmons
Title 1 Consultant
Howell, Dorothy A.
Spcl Svcs & Collab Sci Tchr
Jennison, Marla Horner
Associate Professor of English
Jones, Grace Carter
Business & English Instr
Kelly, Sharon L.
Third Grade Teacher
Kesler, Nancy Ann
French Teacher
King, Rick Lee
Science Teacher
Lanham, Donna M.
Alternative Education Director
Lee, Amy Austin
C P Biology Teacher
Luckett, Martha J.
HS Teacher & Counselor
Maltby, Marc Samuel
Associate Professor of History
Mann, Julie McGehee
Computer Keyboarding Instr
McIver, Robert Hugh
Music Director & Professor
Miller, Francy E.
Primary Teacher
Minks, Lawrence Claud
Division Chair & Prof of Bus
Mowers, Kathy Ann
Assoc Professor of Mathematics
Naas, James Frederick
Associate Professor
Nall, Donald E.
United States History Teacher
Nall, Ora Thompson
Amer His Tchr & Soc Stud Coord
Nicholson, Miriam K. Curtis
7th & 8th Grd Science Teacher
Oetinger, David Frederick
Professor of Biology
Pride, Wanda Wedel
Mathematics Teacher
Purdy, Cheryl A.
Math, Computer Science Teacher
Reeves, David Michael
Teacher & Coach
Rhodes, Donald Bartlett
Science & History Teacher
Robinson, Ginger Holcomb
Spanish Teacher
Rocco, Steve
English Teacher
Rogers, Thomas
Ret Prof of Rel & Philosophy

OWENSBORO (cont)
Rumage, Linda Mayfield
Biology Teacher
Sallan, Veena Bhardwaj
Associate Professor of Biology
Sandifer, Douglas Scott
HS PE Teacher & Coach
Schmeal, Nancy King
Physical Ed Tchr & Dept Chprsn
Sears, Helen DuBois
Academic Coach
Self, Danny Dale
8th Grade Science Teacher
Settle, Marsha Hunter
4th Grade Teacher
Shrewsberry, Lyllis W.
Media Specialist
Sims, Jan Mitchell
7th Grade Math Teacher
Sullivan, Sharon, OSU
Asst Prof of Ed & Spec Ed
Taylor, David Preston
Teacher
Taylor, Deborah Vinecke
Elementary Principal
Taylor, Tim
Counselor
Thompson, Gail Hodskins
Third Grade Teacher
Thomson, Belinda Collings
Asst Prof of Speech & Drama
Tiahrt, Chris Andrew
Asst Professor of Mathematics
Valdez, Jake Armando
Retired Spanish Teacher
Wilson, James A.
Health & Physical Ed Teacher
Woodward, Nicole Girvin
Language Arts Teacher
Worth, Judy Humphrey
Fifth Grade Teacher
Yeckering, Marilyn Maden
Primary Teacher
OWENTON
Bush, Barbara Kay
Business Teacher
Harrod, John Patton
Gifted & Talented Teacher
Marcum, Timothy Lee
Seventh Grade Math Teacher
Skaggs, Mike L.
Mathematics Teacher
Stewart, Bethany Dee
Title I Reading Teacher
Stowe, David Roy
12th Grade English Teacher
Webster, Kim A.
Home Ec & History Teacher
Williams, Kathy Baxter
English Teacher
Wooten, Carol Cobb
5th Grade Teacher
OWINGSVILLE
Adams, Robert Tate
Agricultural Education Teacher
Bailey, Shella Manley
Vocational Consumer & Sci Tchr
Beck, Sue Rawlings
Math Teacher
Brosseit, Brenna O'Hara
Tchr of Functionally Disabled
Childers, Sheliah Marie
Language Arts & German Teacher
Counterman, Michele Broeg
Spanish & French Teacher
Coyle, Brenda Staton
Second & Third Grade Teacher
Holder, Brenda Adams
Business Education Teacher
Huber, Judy S.
English Teacher
Jeanes, Janet Anne
Band Director & Music Teacher
Prater, Peggy P.
Math Teacher
Staton, Pashia R.
Lang Arts & Wrtng Prtfls Tchr
PADUCAH
Adkins, Rhonda Griffey
Mathematics Professor
Anderson, Sherry Mattingly
Prof & Business Pgm Coord
Arant, David W.
High School Math Teacher
Bell, Karen Anne
Span Tchr & Foreign Lang Chm
Cecil, Mary Jude
French & Religious Ed Teacher
Cook, Jeannie Butler
Kindergarten Teacher
Davis, Arthur F.
Instrumental Music Teacher
Dukes, Lisa Hinrichs
Math & Algebra Teacher
Freels, Mary Ann
Professor of Office Systems
Freeman, Nelta Horton
Biology I & II Teacher
Fuqua, LaDonna (Haltom)
Primary Teacher
Green, Donna S.
8-12th Grade Choral Director
Harned, Paige Alleyne
Teacher of Hearing Impaired
Harper, Daralea Franklin
Business Teacher
Hook, Haley Lee
HS English & Psychology Tchr
Knoth, Marilyn B.
Nursing Professor

Lambert, Laura Jane
History Teacher & Dept Chprsn
Masden, Deborah Cheryl
Mathematics Teacher
Massey, Becky Slusmeyer
2nd & 3rd Grade Teacher
Mc Elrath, A. Jamon
French & English Teacher
Morris, Ginger Smith
7th & 8th Grade Math Teacher
Moss, Debbie Steele
Kindergarten Teacher
Mullen, Susan Wilson
English & Journalism Teacher
Nall, Michael R.
English Teacher
Ramer, Linda Guess
English Teacher
Reed, Diane Thompson
4th Grd Tchr & Guidance Cnslr
Robertson, John E.L.
Prof of Economics & History
Senn, Cindy Young
6th Grade English Teacher
Steele, Linda Edwards
1st Grade Teacher
Thomason, Dorcas Coil
Fourth Grade Teacher
Underhill, Teresa Ray
English Teacher
Underwood, Betty Roberts
First Grade Teacher
Ward, Janet Yates
Biology Teacher
Washburn, George William
Electronics Technology Instr
Werner, Lynn Boyd
G & T Social Studies Teacher
PAINT LICK
Dickerson, Judith Norris
Retired Primary Teacher
Kinnaird, Patricia Bowling
5th-6th Grade Teacher
PAINTSVILLE
Ailiff, William Michael
History Teacher
Burchett, Dwight
Middle School Science Teacher
Carpenter, Tonya Puckett
Language Arts Teacher
Chafin, Shirley R.
English Teacher & Dept Chprsn
Collins, Nila
Mathematics Teacher
Crace, Mary Anna
Science Teacher
Gullett, Cathy Goble
English & Journalism Teacher
Howard, Bonnie Susan
Biology & Anatomy Teacher
Jones, Connie Renee
Chemistry Teacher
Lafferty, Homer
8th Grd Amer History Teacher
Little, Jeffrey L.
Math & Science Teacher
McKenzie, Terry Samuel
8th Grade Math Teacher
Preston, Tina G.
Speech & Drama Teacher
Robinson, Virginia Conley
Fine Arts & Humanities Teacher
Spencer, Carolyn Price
High School French Teacher
Sturgill, Anita Ruth
American History Teacher
Van Hoose, Jimmy Dean
Mathematics Teacher
Van Hoose, Tammy Bryant
High School Math Teacher
Watson, Betty A.
Mathematics Teacher
Williamson, John R.
Curriculum Director
Wireman, Phillip
Attendance Coord & PE Teacher
PARIS
Barcol, Kelly Todd
Technology Education Teacher
Buchanan, J. David
Teacher & GATE Coordinator
Mc Combs, Suzann Shaver
Science Teacher
Roseberry, Kenney Shropshire
English Teacher
Sosby, John Anthony
Business Teacher
Umfress, Lynda J.
Teacher of Gifted
PARK HILLS
Armbruster, Nancy Carol (Kostner)
Anatomy & Physiology Teacher
Durkee, Steven Irving
Religion Teacher
Eckerle, Thomas Gene
Religion Teacher
Gleeson, Mary Jean
French & Spanish Teacher
Greife, Ronald Frederick
Social Studies Teacher
Gunkel, Sue Gerding
High School Mathematics Tchr
Hertsenberg, Al Joseph
Religion Teacher & Dept Chair
Horton, John Charles
Social Studies Teacher
Krumpelbeck, William Thomas
Bio Tchr & Bsbl Head Coach
Lewis, Mary Leigh
Bio Chem & IPS Teacher

Ruth, Diane Lynn (Thornton)
English Teacher
Spencer, Nora Ryan
HS Religion & English Tchr
Timmerding, Diana M.
English & Journalism Teacher
PAYNEVILLE
Benock, Karen Egolf
Primary Teacher
PHELPS
Mercer, Sandra P.
Guidance Counselor
PHILPOT
Blandford, Mark Alan
6th-8th Grade Teacher
Rearden, JeanAnn Aud
Third Grade Teacher
PHYLLIS
Harris, Okeh Luke
Eighth Grade Teacher
PIKEVILLE
Adkins, Beverly Venters
Science Teacher
Banks, Angeline Elizabeth
Biological Science Teacher
Duncan, Victoria Gwynn
Primary Teacher
Fletcher, Colleen Conway
Primary Teacher
Ford, Jeffrey Dale
General Sci & Phys Ed Teacher
Ford, Thomas Charles
Biology Teacher
Hall, Zelda Newsom
Physics Teacher
Hunt, Doris Kay (Thompson)
Teacher
Justice, Phoebe Coleman
Family & Consumer Teacher
Little, Linda Thornsbury
High School Math Teacher
Lowe, Linda Justice
Math Dept Chm & Teacher
Maynard, Brenda Stanley
English Teacher
Mueller, Catherine J.
Alumni Dir & Counseling Asst
Pinson, Cherry Lynn
English Teacher
Searcy, Thomas Alden
High School Tech Ed Teacher
Slone, Lauren Thompson
Social Studies Teacher
Syck, Jennifer Church
Language Arts Teacher
Thompson, Patricia Dotson
Biology & Anatomy Teacher
Tussey, Tammy
Physical Education Teacher
Williamson, Jeanne
Language Arts Teacher
PILGRIM
Collins, Brenda Preece
Fourth Grade Teacher
PINE KNOT
Jones, R. Howard
Retired Soc Studies Tchr
PINEVILLE
Brock, Susan Sharpe
English Teacher
Bush, Sharan Lovell
Social Studies Teacher
Dunn, Sylvester
Agriculture Teacher
Poore, Toby Ann
Biology Teacher
PINSONFORK
Maynard, Marlene
Retired Lang Arts Teacher
Parsley, Coletta Ann
Language Arts Teacher
PIPPA PASSES
Bentley, Charlene Reynolds
English Instructor
Gilmore, Samuel K.
Professor of Biology
Jukes, Pamela Morris
Asst Professor of Education
Mitchell, Kossuth Mayer
Professor of Business Admin
Sanders, Duane D.
Assistant Professor of Biology
Walford, Gerald A.
Physical Education Dept Head
Wilson, Stephen Douglas
Professor of History
POWDERLY
Grundy, Ann H.
8th Grade Math & Science Tchr
Vincent, Robert Alan
Social Studies Teacher
PRESTONSBURG
Briggs, Judith Gutteridge
Assistant Professor of Nursing
Dye, Patricia Balsley
7th Grade Math & Sci Teacher
Hammonds, Gwendolyn Stumbo
Eighth Grd Soc Studies Tchr
Heywood, Timothy George
Assistant Professor of Math
Mauk, Craighton Stiles
Assistant Prof of Biology
Mc Aninch, Robert Danford
Professor
Reynolds, Kimberly Wiley
Media Specialist & Librarian
Robertson, Charles S.
Physics Professor
Schuster, Betty Lenora
Guidance Counselor

Shepherd, Anna Whitaker
Kindergarten Teacher
Smallwood, Kathy Clark
Assoc Prof Economics & Bus
Vierheller, Thomas Leslie
Asst Prof of Biology
Watts, Randall Leo
Mathematics Professor
PRINCETON
Benton, Paula Sanders
Math Teacher
Cash, Betty Laudeman
World Civilization Teacher
Coursey, Marlene Brown
Science Teacher
Dyer, James Robert
Physics & Chemistry Teacher
Giordano, Al D.
Retired Coach
Hart, Deborah Hinton
Seventh Grade Mathematics Tchr
Hughes, Richard Anthony
Physical Education Teacher
King, Reece A.
Band Director
Scott, Robin W.
Science Teacher
PROSPECT
Dockstader, Mildred Kemp
Former Choral Dir
RACELAND
Barker, David A.
Band Director
Blair, Doris Starr
English Teacher
Lamblin, Marilyn F.
History & Geography Teacher
Rose, Janet Warnock
Business Education Teacher
Van Der Hoof, Randy D.
Business Education Teacher
RADCLIFF
Bright, Bob O.
Library Media Specialist
Daniel, Tonya S.
Chemistry Teacher
Ellis, R. Dwayne
11th-12th Grades English Tchr
Emberton, Gary Lee
Resource & Spec Ed Tchr
Gray, Paul Clell
JROTC Instructor
Hodge, Iris Davis
Advanced Placement His Tchr
Johnson, Peterson Martin
Science Department Chairman
Lee, Teresa Crawford
7th Grade Math Teacher
Lirot, Patricia Irmgard
Business Educator
Lowery, Gerald William
Advanced Placement Bio Tchr
Moore, Robert Lee
Mathematics Teacher
Senninger, Marsha Rae
Spanish Teacher
Thompson, Gregory Dale
Counselor
Turner, Robert Ray
Business Education Teacher
Wethington, Mary Rebecca
Teacher
Wheeler, Dawn Marie
Business Education Teacher
Wilkinson, Shelia Hardin
HS Mathematics Teacher
RICHMOND
Aghajanian, Doreen Jane
Former Fourth & Fifth Grd Tchr
Bayer, Estelle Park
Latin Teacher
Bertram, Dixie Ramona
Language Arts Teacher
Boewe, Joan Pierce
Professor of Music
Brockman, Stacy Leigh
Eighth Grade English Teacher
Brosi, George Ralph
English Instructor
Cahill, Timothy C.
Swimming Coach
Combs, Martha Prewitt
Retired English Teacher
Cook, Erika M.
Mathematics Teacher
Core, Deborah L.
Professor of English
Daugherty, Vicki Reedy
Fourth Grade Teacher
Freeman, Marsha Smith
Health Sciences Instructor
Fryman, Sandra F.
Biology Teacher
Fultz, Gina Witten
Health Teacher
Graves, Sharon Farthing
8th Grd Social Studies Teacher
Hisle, Eva Murphy
Retired Primary Teacher
Hopton-Jones, Pamela Dayle
Music Education Professor
Isaacs, Judith A.
Art Teacher & Assistant Prof
King, Amy C.
Professor of Mathematics
Mac Kethan, Philip Pack
High School Math Teacher
Marken, Dory Scholand
Assoc Prof of Occ Therapy

Mills, Kay Baker
Ret Soc Stud & Reading Teacher
Moberly, Vickie Fritz
Mathematics Teacher
Powell-Mc Coy, Tracy Lee
Middle School Science Teacher
Silver, David G.
Marketing Education Teacher
Skepple, Rose Gilmore
Biology Teacher
Tennant, Raymond Frederick
Mathematics Professor
Turpin, Ann Taylor
12th Grade English Teacher
RINEYVILLE
Gardner, Derotha Garrison
Fourth Grade Teacher
ROBINSON CREEK
Damron, Marian Abbott
Primary Teacher
Mullins, Evelyn
Elementary Teacher
ROCKHOLDS
Carroll, Rita Kay
Primary Teacher
Perkins, Lana Ruth
6th Grade Teacher
ROGERS
Mc Whorter, Mary Burton
Primary Teacher
RUSSELL
Frame, Karen McBrayer
English & Reading Teacher
Mc Donald, Garland Wayne
Drafting Teacher
RUSSELL SPRINGS
Antle, Tracey Roy
English Teacher
Cardwell, Joy Gosser
Business & Office Teacher
Keene, Janice Carol
Science Tchr & Dept Chair
Taylor, Lynn Earldon
Soc Stud & US His Tchr
Troutman, Elizabeth Lee
8th Grade Language Arts Tchr
RUSSELLVILLE
Atkins, David W.
Math Teacher
Burnett, Bobbie Jean Cook
Retired Elem Teacher
Christmas, Rebecca Campbell
English Teacher
Dockins, Sharon McLarty
Oral Comm & Drama Teacher
Estes, Norman Bryan
Agriculture Teacher
Holliday, Jan Barnes
Scndry Voc Home Ec Teacher
Myers, Touria Abou
Spanish Teacher
Reynolds, Jean Sosh
Fourth Grade Teacher
Rogers, Brenda Mitchell
Fourth & Fifth Grade Teacher
Toon, Alisa Thompson
Home Economics Teacher
Webb, Paulette Lapointe
Fourth Grade Teacher
Wright, Nancy Brown
High School Mathematics Tchr
SAINT CATHARINE
Britt, Jeff L.
Education & PE Instructor
Chancellor, Madonna Gamble
Associate Professor
Sauer, Lyda Parker
Assoc Professor of Psychology
Urekew, Robert S.
Prof of Religion & Philosophy
Ward, William Terry
Assoc Prof of Rel Studies
SALYERSVILLE
Adams, Donna May
English & Oral Comm Teacher
Adams, Justine
Retired English Teacher
Bruce, Brenda Sue
Social Studies Tchr & Chprsn
Culbertson, Lucy Jenkins
7th Grd Language Arts Teacher
Fletcher, Dottie
Primary Teacher
Helton, Nora May
High School History Teacher
Howard, Diana Lykins
Reading & English Teacher
Joseph, Phillip R.
Assistant Principal
Patrick, Gwendolyn Estep
Business Education Teacher
Prater, Stella Salyer
Business Teacher
Rice, Sheila Kaye (Slone)
8th Grade Math Teacher
Sparks, Cathy Rowe
High School Home Ec Teacher
Stamper, Vera Connelley
French, Eng & Jrnlsm Teacher
Stapleton, Kimberly Jo (LeMaster)
Computer Science Teacher
SCOTTSVILLE
Kiene, Melanie Jones
Language Arts Teacher
Marsh, Carol Deane (Sapp)
Scndry Home Economics Educator
Meador, Beatrice G.
Retired Fifth Grade Teacher
Oliver, Ferrell Ray
Agricultural Teacher

TSVILLE (cont)
, Adonica Lavonne
keting Teacher
Lanna Jo Stinson
& Oral Communications Tchr
EE
y, Bettie M.
ed 2nd Grade Teacher
LIA
Louis R.
th Grade Social Stud Tchr
BYVILLE
, Marti Anzinger
ster
Jill S.
ance Counselor & Teacher
Nellie Roberts
ish & French Teacher
Mary Elizabeth
ematics Tchr & Dept Chair
David Bruce
Teacher
Susan Manning
sh & Spanish Teacher
obin Roberts
bra & Geometry Teacher
d, Barry Rice
ent Assistance Coordinator
, Hubert Ray
selor
, Vickie Gumm
ish & Pre-Algebra Teacher
HERDSVILLE
, Janice (Horrell)
th Grade Teacher
osh, Leslie Bruner
& Social Studies Teacher
Mary Bartsch
ary Teacher
Nancy Ann (Quaack)
Service Technology Instr
Glenda Faye
Grade Math Teacher
s, Melanie J.
nce Teacher
Joan K.
c Teacher & Band Director
R
Wanda Faulkner
d Grade Teacher
Naomi Ruth (Smith)
3rd Sci & Lang Arts Tchr
ER GROVE
n, Donald Norman
cipal
r, Linda Kay
ish & Social Studies Tchr
SONVILLE
n, Elissa Hatcher
ary Teacher
l, Gail Grebe
ary Teacher
IP
Jimmy Ray
ed 6th Grade Teacher
HLAND
ese, Deborah Lynne
Jrnlsm & Pol Sci Tchr
Rena Hall
Grade Teacher
, Nancy Gail
Teacher
ERSET
e, Robin Lane
3rd Science Teacher & Ldr
, John William
Stud Tchr
, Mary Jane Burton
lem Solving Teacher
ne, David Cody
3rd Social Studies Teacher
tt, Georgia Price
ness Teacher
ell, Donna F.
ory Teacher
, Anita Hurt
guage Arts Teacher
, Frances Combs
nmntl Sci Tchr & Dept Chm
d, Mark Elliot
raft Maintenance Instr
ord, Arthur Ray
Department Chairman
erry, John H.
ory Professor
er, Susan Eldridge
ness Education Teacher
erald, Nelva Sue
th Grade Teacher
r, Yvonneda Byrd
ness Teacher
r, Douglas E.
Tchr & Basketball Coach
r, Alyce A.
Professor
Jane H.
School English Teacher
Ronald Wayne
keting Instr & DECA Advisor
l, Charles Valentine
Prof of Ed & Philosophy
y, Anna Faye
lish Teacher
Lisa Ann
keting Teacher
ison, Melinda Sue
ral Director
s, Kristi Lee
lish & Journalism Teacher

Keith, Danny Litton
Agriscience Instructor
Lee, Esther Catharine
Spanish Teacher
Martin, Marsha Bolton
Choir Director
Mc Daniel, William C.
Asst Prof of Psych & Sociology
Mikel, Becky
Secondary Math Teacher
Muse, Scott Allen
Fifth Grade Teacher
Phelps, Lori Wiles
Librarian
Prather, Hilma Skonberg
Principal
Reynolds, Raymond M.
College Counselor
Rogers, Sharon Kay (Morrow)
Assoc Professor of Psychology
Roy, Lela Fay
English Teacher
Shaw, Darrell Keith
Sixth Grade Science Teacher
Simpson, Tammie Taylor
English Teacher
Smith, Karen Robertson
Algebra Teacher
Stringer, John Gary
Social Studies Dept Chair
Sullivan, Jim
English Teacher
Wilson, Russell Darrell
Junior ROTC Instructor
Withers, Robert Ira
Mathematics Teacher
SOUTH SHORE
Carver, Carolyn S.
Primary Teacher
Hieneman, Nancy Adkins
Guidance Counselor
Martin, Tamala Morgan
Primary Teacher
Purtee, Georgia Dodd
Science Teacher
Sipple, Sherri Dupuy
Eighth Grd Language Arts Tchr
SOUTHGATE
Iden, Sharyl Hughes
7th & 8th Grd Math & Sci Tchr
SPRINGFIELD
Craig, Donna R.
Agriculture Teacher
Crum, Richard Clark
Science Tchr & Acad Team Coach
Gabhart, Patricia Royalty
Biology Teacher
Hutchins, Malissa Gayle
Special Education Teacher
Malone, Shirley Tatum
Fifth Grade Teacher
Reinle, John F.
Principal & 7th-8th Grd Tchr
Shewmaker, Doris Cheser
Retired Primary Teacher
Spaulding, Mary Jane
Fourth Grade Teacher
Stanford, Rhonda Birdwell
English Teacher
White, Monika P.
HS Mathematics Teacher
STANFORD
Atwood, Judy D.
Primary Teacher
Belcher, Janet Sue Playforth
Primary Teacher
Candler, Catherine McAlister
Business Education Teacher
Cox, Pamela Hobbs
Primary Teacher
Durham-Speaks, Laura Lee
First Grade Teacher
Harris, Billy Reed
Seventh Grade Math Teacher
Howard, Ryan Tyler
Social Studies Teacher
Mattingly, Crystal Pendygraft
Mathematics Teacher
Munday, Myra Swope
Title I Resource Teacher
Pence, Jacqueline Marie
Health & Physical Ed Teacher
Pendygraft, Douglas Calvin
Sci Teacher
Rankin, Carolyn Sue (Sparks)
Business Teacher & Dept Chprsn
Sims, Debbie Johnson
7th Grd Social Studies Tchr
Snow, Carolyn
Head Supervisor
Stewart, Morris Allen
Assistant Principal & Ath Dir
Underwood, Ray Stuart
Choral Director
Underwood, Sheila Kester
Elem Resourse Teacher
Watts, Debra Gale
General & Choral Music Teacher
STANTON
Bradley, Bonnie Berryman
Business & Office Tech Tchr
Crabtree, Danny Clay
Guidance Counselor
Duff, Deana Williams
Math & Spanish Teacher
Duff, Kevin Wayne
6th Grade Math Teacher
Hall, Jimmy Daryl
Science Teacher

Hampton, Mary E.
High School Mathematics Tchr
Stokley, Candrea Baker
Math Teacher
Townsend, Cathryn Richardson
High School Biology Teacher
STEARNS
Douglas, Pamela Brown
Chemistry Teacher
Hubbs, Christopher Alan
Choral Director
Manning, Sandra Lavonne Staley
Math Tchr of Lrng Disabilities
Wilson, Doris Nevels
Health Sciences Instructor
STEPHENSBURG
Mattingly, Anna Catherine
7th & 8th Grd Lang Arts Tchr
STURGIS
Littrell, Richard Lee
Fifth Grade Teacher
SUMMER SHADE
Harbison, Blanche Kay
5th Grade Teacher
Mc Murtrey, Rita A.
Principal
Shaw, Bonnie McIntyre
Primary Grade Teacher
Wilson, Dane Petett
Primary Teacher
SWEEDEN
Wingfield, Beckey B.
Title I Reading Teacher
SYMSONIA
Jones, Jenifer Fowler
Language Arts Teacher
TAYLORSVILLE
Smothers, Mary Audrey Lanham
Business Teacher
TOLLESBORO
Ferguson, Bonnie M.
Substitute Teacher
Wagner, Jeri Sloas
Science & Health Teacher
TOMPKINSVILLE
Chapman, Sondra Crowe
Home Economics Teacher
Curtis, Sandra Burris
Spanish Teacher
Emberton, Shelia Sherfey
Preschool Teacher
Hammer, Betty D.
Retired Elementary Teacher
Myers, Judy Wilson
6th-8th Grade Science Teacher
Pare, Dorothy Lyon
Primary Teacher
Walden, Janice Carter
Health & Physical Ed Teacher
UNION
D'Adamo, Stephen Vincent
Social Studies Teacher
Dawson, Donna L.
High School English Teacher
Fulmer, Kenneth Denver
Hlth & Physical Education Tchr
Henry, Jo Anne Schmitt
English Teacher & Dept Head
Kanabroski, Carol Van Luvanee
Calculus & Trigonometry Tchr
Kepf, Constance Grimme
Spanish Teacher & Dept Chprsn
Ogden, Stephen Michael
Mathematics Teacher
Perkins, Deborah Stephens
Biology Teacher
Ryan, G. Russell
Physics Teacher
VANCEBURG
Cook, Edwin Samuel, III
Principal
Gilbert, Joseph Harold
Earth Science Teacher
VANCLEVE
Finney, Gale Wayne
Biblical Studies Instructor
VERONA
Kirk, Peggy Richardson
Fourth Grade Teacher
VERSAILLES
Dowell, Susan L.
Primary Teacher
Fannin, W. Kyle
Social Studies Teacher
Rodgers, Wanda Chynoweth
Drama, Oral Comm & Eng Tchr
Terry, Terry Fitzpatrick
Science & Mathematics Tchr
Tuttle, Bertie Stamper
Retired Elementary Teacher
VILLA HILLS
Burden, Therese Urbain
Rel Chprsn & Soc Studies Tchr
Clements, Nancy Sue (Sproull)
English Teacher & Dept Chprsn
Rabe, Mary
AP Bio Chem Phys & Math Tchr
Rodenkirchen, Shelly Wimmers
Mathematics Teacher
Steinker, Marcia Williams
Spanish Teacher
Stuempel, Kenneth Russell
Soc Stud, His, Ec & Govt Tchr
VINE GROVE
Cantwell, Terry E.
Physical Ed Teacher
Dennis, Lonnie W.
7th Grade Science Teacher
Wilson, Susan L.
Eighth Grade Teacher

VIRGIE
Hall, Renina Little
Art Teacher
Jarrell, Verla Sue (Bartley)
Seventh Grd Language Arts Tchr
Wright, Rodney
Eighth Grade Teacher
WALLINS CREEK
Carter, Helen Marie Craig
English & Reading Teacher
WALTON
Boyle, William Lewis
Assistant Superintendent
Compton, Amy Hammonds
Spanish & English Teacher
Feagan, Layna Cheesman
HS Mathematics Teacher
Gayle, John Richard
7th-8th Grade English Teacher
Strilka, Robert J.
English Tchr
WARSAW
Aulick, Neal Douglas
Soc Studies Tchr & Dept Head
Schudder, Judy Klette
Owner & Manager
WAYNESBURG
Deatherage, Ronald Wayne
Elementary Principal
Foster, Brenda Peavler
4th Grade Teacher
Horton, Judy Rector
Title I Teacher
WEST LIBERTY
Lacy, Michael Rex
Administrator
Lykins, Sheila Lewis
Home Economics Teacher
Oldfield, Mary Alice
Sixth Grade Teacher
Risner, Pamela Reed
6th Grd Language Arts Teacher
WEST PADUCAH
Davis, Sheri Smith
High School Biology Teacher
Humphrey, Jane Harrison
Special Education Teacher
Mc Cuiston, Kent
Agriscience Teacher
Mc Ginty, Barbara Wilson
English & Yearbook Teacher
Record, Regina Mathis
6th Grade Teacher
Weaver, Gale E.
English & US History Teacher
WEST POINT
Matthews, Rebecca Cain
Teacher
WHITE MILLS
Mc Coy, Frances Hornback
Primary Teacher
WHITESBURG
Combs, Tammie Bates
Primary Teacher
Earls, Sandra Stallard
5th Grade Teacher
WHITESVILLE
Haynes, Christina Marie
English, Drama & Spanish Tchr
Howard, Alice Aud
Second Grade Teacher
Williams, Katie (Ward)
High School Teacher
WHITLEY CITY
Perry, Bessie H.
Special Education Teacher
WILLIAMSBURG
Adair, Paula Estes
Mathematics Teacher
Anderson, Beverly E.
United States History Teacher
Baker, Christopher Blake
Special Education Teacher
Bennett, Douglas Brad
Spanish Teacher
Bird, Virginia Moore
Business Teacher
Black, James Vincent
History Teacher
Bowling, Sheila Siler
Fifth Grade Teacher
Campbell, Michael Todd
Physical Education Teacher
Chitwood, Dana Shoun
Chemistry Teacher
Couch, Amon Wesley
Scndry History & English Tchr
Cox, Sharon (Warfield)
Home Economics Teacher
Dirrim, Jenny Lee
Title I Teacher
Douglas, Angela Mary
Business Teacher
Faught, Kenneth Lyle
Asst Professor of Religion
Head, Robin Earlene (Davis)
Sixth Grade Teacher
Hensley, Lee Powers
Primary Teacher
Hill, Lena Chandler
Biology Teacher
Jaynes, Mary Susan
Title One Teacher
Peace, Roy L.
Special Education Teacher
Rains, James Lee
Biology Teacher
Rains, Veronica Carr
Kindergarten Teacher

Roaden, Jill Wilder
Mathematics Teacher
Rose, Jerry Clayton
Writing Resource Teacher
Sears, Regina Bunch
Biology & Chemistry Teacher
Shelton, Sharon Woody
English Teacher
Smith, Donna Jones
Counselor
Stanfill, Gary G.
High School Science Teacher
Stroud, Geraldine Parks
Fifth Grade Teacher
Wake, Eric L.
His, Pol Sci Dept Chair & Prof
Wilson, Roger D.
Social Studies Teacher
Wilson, Ronald Preston
English Teacher
WILLIAMSTOWN
Crowley, Kyle Anthony
Social Studies Teacher
Perry, Jill Burd
Fifth & Sixth Grade Teacher
WILMORE
Joy, Robbie B.
Retired Elementary Teacher
Spann, Howard Glen
History Professor
Whiteman, Darrell LaVerne
Prof of Cultural Anthropology
WINCHESTER
Burkhead, Don Richard
Mathematics Teacher
Castle, James Langley
Biology Teacher
Christiansen, David Jon
AP Biology Teacher
Cox, Shannon Joel
7th Grade Social Studies Tchr
De Capio, Terry Leslie
Health & Physical Ed Tchr
Detring, Robbyn Spencer
7th Grade English Teacher
Fields, Ketsy Lee
8th Grade Reading Teacher
Hall, Sharon R.
6th Grade Reading Teacher
Hicks, Judy (Horne)
Bus Ed Teacher & Dept Head
Hoffman, Anne Stanley
Counselor
Huff, Barbara Ann
Primary Teacher
Jacobs, Audeen Pace
Learning Disabilities Teacher
Jacobs, Lydia M.
Fifth Grade Teacher
Lisle, Yutanna Woods
Physical Education Instructor
Lowe, Richard Thomas
Science Teacher
McCarty, Jenny Sowder
Career Dev Tchr & Coord
Noplis, Bonnie P.
Fourth Grade Teacher
Reed, Rachel Taylor
Primary Teacher
Sharp, Debra Kay
Mathematics Teacher
Shoemaker, Terry Blackburn
Biology & Chemistry Teacher
Snell, David Henry
Social Studies Teacher
Thornberry, Ruth Huff
Chrldr Coordinator & Coach
Whitaker, Jodie
Health & Physical Ed Teacher
White, Douglas Dale, Jr.
Scndry Social Studies Teacher
White, Sue Hobbs
Secondary English Teacher
Willian, Lewis Mansfield
Chemistry Teacher
Young, Linda D.
Math Teacher
WINDSOR
Campbell, Yvonne Yaden
6th Grade Teacher
WINGO
Brown, Patti Mc Manus
Language Arts Teacher
Wood, Barbra Hord
Primary Teacher
WOOTON
Coots, Douglas
Fourth Grade Teacher
WORTHINGTON
Biehle, Harriet Jo Cornwell
Fourth Grade Teacher
WURTLAND
Jordan, Pamela Mauk
7th Grade Math Teacher

LOUISIANA

ABBEVILLE
Barras, William Andre, III
11th Grade American His Tchr
Baudoin, Olita Broussard
English & Speech Teacher
Bourque, Ann Lori Langlinais
Math & Psychology Teacher
Ducharme, Rachel Domingue
Math Teacher
Gayneaux, Peggy O'Bryan
Fifth Grade Teacher

ABBEVILLE (cont)
Gregoire, Therese G.
HS Math Teacher
Le Boeuf, Sherline Mire
Eng Teacher & Dept Chairperson
Leggette, Paula Boudreaux
Retired Teacher & Dept Head
Mc Cann, Julia Martin
6th Grd Social Studies Teacher
Mouton, Richard Wayne
Agriscience Teacher
Vallee, Joseph Gabriel
Amer His Tchr & Acad Counselor
Vincent, Rebecca Boggs
Librarian & Media Specialist
ABITA SPRINGS
Barnes, Jeanine H.
8th Grade English Teacher
Hudson, Nancy Mohlke
Title I Rdg & Stud Skills Tchr
Jones, Gloria Bradley
Assistant Principal
Kety, Karen Mathies
Guidance Counselor
ALBANY
Collins, Linda Kay (Washburn)
English Teacher
Cox, Michael David
HS Chem, Physics & Math Tchr
Tupper, Curtis V.
Math Teacher
ALEXANDRIA
Allgood, Patricia Dufreche
Chemistry Teacher
Blackburn, Kay Callihan
Scndry Math Teacher
Bradford, Dianne Beauregard
Fourth Grade Teacher
Brasher, David Andre
Athletic Director & Teacher
Brian, Vicki Lee (Erickson)
Fifth Grade Teacher
Carter, Denese Edwards
Fifth Grade Teacher
Cathey, Sue (Melder)
6th Grade English Teacher
Dupar-Gatson, Iradean
Counselor & Business Teacher
Fall, Wally Ray
Special Education Teacher
Harris, Tylitha Via
Dir After Schl Prgm, Schl Bd
Hobbs, Irene Silas
Business & Office Ed Teacher
Howell, Donna Walker
English Teacher
Ingalls, Edith Cox
Physics, Earth & Phys Sci Tchr
LaCaze, Melba Sciortino
Speech & Debate Teacher
LaCombe, Margaret DiStefano
1st Grade Teacher
Lemons, Yvonne Young
High School English Teacher
Looper, James Armon
World History Teacher
Mott, Sue R.
Business Education Teacher
Nixon, Jackie Ann
Retired HS English Teacher
Rachal, Alfred
Science Teacher & Coach
Roach, Gail Holloway
K-5th Grade Music Teacher
Sexton, Geri Haworth
Teacher of Visually Impaired
Simmons, Judy Lytle
Teacher of Gifted
Smith, Robert Lewis
Social Studies Tchr & Dept Chm
Smith, Susie Cooper
Principal
Tabor, Catherine Ann
English Teacher
Thurman, Rhonda Irene
Spanish Teacher
Tyler, Connie Owens
Physical Sci & Biology Teacher
Welch, Kelli Carruth
PE Teacher & Cheerleader Spon
Wiederholt, Joseph James
Asst Prin & Religion Coord
Wilder, Linda Geoffroy
Mathematics Teacher
AMITE
Dees, Marilyn Kent
Teacher
Jackson, Lionel
Social Studies Teacher
Lawson, Tommy Gene
High School Math Teacher
Newton, Vivian Schmidt
5th & 6th Grade Math Teacher
Tracie, Ada Simmons
Social Studies Teacher
Vining, Mark Dillan
Physical Science Teacher
ANGIE
Pendarvis, Donna K. Haddox
Counselor
ARABI
Bohlke, Gretchen Mary
Middle School English Teacher
Dauphin, Mary Marquer
Fourth Grade Teacher
Mitchell, Carmelite Labruzzo
Kindergarten Teacher
Montz, Jocelyn Barrosse
Curriculum Coord & Teacher

ARCADIA
Ambrose, Susie Moseley
Second Grade Teacher
Moore, Susan Butler
Business Teacher
ARNAUDVILLE
Brinkhaus, Celeste L.
Eng III & World Geography Tchr
Davis, Jessie Pavy
High School English Teacher
DeJean, Gwendolyn J.
Freshman & Senior Counselor
Duplechain, Mary Maxine
English Teacher
Fontenot, Gary K.
Physical Education Teacher
Lanclos, Marie Dalfrey
Mathematics Teacher
ATHENS
Cole, Peggy Thibodeaux
Social Studies & French Tchr
BAKER
Achord, Kyle Christopher
Physical Education & Hlth Tchr
Long, Robyn Marie
English Teacher
Pocorello, Ronnie Pete
Marketing Coordinator
Stuppeck, Sandra Breland
Art Teacher
BALDWIN
Sherman, Sarah Mitchell
First Grade Teacher
BALL
Gray, Barbara Brouillette
1st Grade Music Teacher
BASILE
LeJeune, Darrel Brice
English & Social Stud Teacher
BASKIN
Lyles, Debbie
Business Education Teacher
BASTROP
Colvin, Gene
Amer His & Louisiana His Tchr
Doty, Marilyn Diane (Foshee)
World History Teacher
Hackleroad, Jean Clark
English & Psychology Teacher
Harrison, Barbara
Business Education Teacher
Heckford, Tammy Garrett
Math Teacher
Kendrick, Debra Keene
Fourth Grade Teacher
Lewis, Debbie Hern
Computer Science Educator
Rodgers, Tammy K.
English Teacher
Shank, Patricia Jean
Applied Algebra Teacher
Taylor-Whaley, Patricia Ann
Business Teacher
Tyler, Sherrie Gray
Business Education Teacher
White, Mary Jayne
12th Grade English Teacher
BATON ROUGE
Abraham, Penny Carlisle
Library Media Specialist
Ales, Jo Dale Hill
Biology & Environ Sci Teacher
Allen, Josephine Ann
Mathematics Teacher
Allums, Claudia Tanner
Mathematics Teacher
Anthony, Monica Louise
School Counselor
Armstrong, Prince W.
Professor of Mathematics
Arvie, Beatrice Joseph
Technology Teacher
Ayo, Jacqueline Lorio
Science Teacher
Baal, Kathryn Marie
Biology & Anatomy Teacher
Babb, Libbie Lowe
Middle School Soc Stud Teacher
Bean, Miltonia Evans
Kindergarten Teacher
Bellemin, Bredna Collins
Algebra II Teacher
Berry, Carla Kennedy
First Grade Teacher
Biggers, Ann P.
Eng & Creative Writing Tchr
Bosworth, Jennifer Spradley
English Teacher
Branton, David C.
Computer Science Teacher
Buckner, Cornelia C.
Fourth Grade Teacher
Bueche, Kenneth Dairon
Louisiana History Teacher
Cannon, Gail Rowland Wood
Jr HS Science Teacher
Caputa, Dean Joseph
Amer His & World Geog Tchr
Carter, Clyde L.
Naval Science Instructor
Cavalier, Daniel Paul
Biology Teacher & Coach
Clayton, Marjorie Isaac
9th-10th Grade English Teacher
Cleveland, Elinda Foshee
First Grade Teacher
Cowan, Christine Ciembronowicz
Instructor of English Dept
Daly, Janet Burnside
English Dept Chair

Davis, Leah Corkern
Business Education Teacher
Dawan, Hashim Arcene
Gymnastics Coach & PE Teacher
Delacroix, Stephen Louis
English & World History Tchr
Domino, Cheryl Lynn
Teacher
Dyer, Geraldine Shanklin
Mathematics Teacher
Eldringhoff, Crystal Vinning
Religion Teacher
Ellis, Ava Williams
Second Grade Teacher of Gifted
Evans, Jerraldine Lewis
Social Studies Teacher
Evans, Sandra Hernandez
Art & Computer Graphics Tchr
Fawley, Karen Tominello
Religion Coordinator & Teacher
Frazier, Carolyn Fields
Title I Reading & Math Tchr
Frazier, Ellen Smith
AP & Honors English Teacher
Frazier, Howard Wayne
Band Director
Freshney, Pamela Sue
English Teacher
Fryoux, Jean, CSJ
Biology Teacher
Garcia, Caesar
Gymnastics Teacher
Garnett, Dorothy Jackson
Mathematics Teacher
Gendron, Janel Gremillion
High School Math Teacher
Giles, William Elmer
Assoc Prof, Dept of Mass Comm
Gordon, Carolyn Aaron
Music Teacher
Gordon, Ralph, Sr.
JROTC Instructor
Graham, Annette Neames
Physics & Physical Sci Teacher
Grand, Sharon (Koch)
Mathematics Teacher
Halbert, Colleen M.
Math Teacher
Hamilton, Mary Kelson
Chemistry Teacher
Harelson, Ursula
Chemistry Teacher
Harich, Jane Yeager
5th Grade Teacher
Harrelson, Clyde Lee
Seventh Grade English Teacher
Harris, Julia White
MS English & Speech Teacher
Harrison, Donna Robertson
Science Teacher
Harrison, Lafayette, Jr.
Fifth Grade Teacher
Harrison, Sandra June
Title I Reading Teacher
Hecker, Catherine Mayne
5th Grade Teacher of Gifted
Henderson, Rosa H.
Assistant Professor of Math
Herrera, Armantina Salido
Spanish Teacher
Higgins, Geraldine Braxton
English & Journalism Teacher
Hilton, Audrey Dunbar
Math Teacher
Hoffman, Barbara Shuman
5th Grade Teacher of Gifted
Hollins, Rosa Lemons
First Grade Teacher
Hopkins, David Walter
Mathematics Instructor
Hurst, Sonia Dauzat
3rd Grade Teacher
Johnson, Ann
Fourth Grade Teacher
Juneau, Charmaine Hebert
8th Grd English & Jrnlsm Tchr
Kaufman, Kristin Lynn
English Teacher
Key, Nora Bader
5th Grade Teacher
Khan, Marcia Leah
5th Grade Teacher
Lee, Ellen Bogan
Mathematics Dept Chairperson
Lignos, William
Retired Teacher
Louding, Delores Ann
MS Teacher & Coach
Mathews, Sharon Walker
Dance Director & Teacher
Mattox, Christopher Abbott
Latin Teacher
McHardy, Roberta
Graduate & Undergraduate Instr
Mc Kell, Gretchen Jackson
Fifth Grade Teacher
Mc Mahon, Anise Perkins
Teacher
Mc Murrian, Micala H.
English & Journalism Teacher
Mc Murtry, Carol Jeanine Aldridge
High School Math Teacher
Meares, Kathleen Daigre
Academic Coord & Registrar
Mendoza, Kathleen A.
Librarian
Milligan, Valerie Jones
Bio Tchr & Chprsn Sci Dept
Mitchell, Jo Anne (Marrs)
English Teacher

Mitchell, Randy Joseph
History Teacher
Morello, Katherine Hebert
Physics Teacher
Morrison, Una Hurst
Fifth Grade Teacher
Muhoberac, John Lamar
Soc Studies Chair & His Tchr
Murrell, Eugene E.
Science Teacher
Newman, Shirley Haugen
Language Arts & French Teacher
Nutt, James Kevin
Biology Teacher & Bsbl Coach
Osborne, Cynthia Jones
Teacher of Gifted & Talented
Oufnac, Marilyn Barber
Chem Tchr & Science Dept Chm
Oulton, Grace Dieter
English Teacher
Palmer, Wilhelmina Terhoeve
Science & Biology Teacher
Payer, Debra E.
Social Studies Teacher
Piha-Paul, Roger A., Sr.
World & AP European His Instr
Plain, Gloria Hawkins
French Teacher
Poche, Patricia Hoff
11th & 12th Grade English Tchr
Potts, Sylvia Sue
History & Geography Teacher
Price, Marline Mire
4th Grade Teacher
Rivault, R. Michael
Social Studies Teacher
Robson, Shirley D.
6th Grade English Teacher
Rogers, Mary Morales
Religion Coord, Dev Dir & Tchr
Ruddick, Buddy
Social Studies Teacher & Cnslr
Ruzicka, Louise Stowell
French Teacher
Saia, Benny A.
Ath Dir, Ftbl Coach & PE Tchr
Sances, Charlotte Williams
504 Coord & Soph Eng Teacher
Sanford, Erma Parker
Reading & Social Studies Tchr
Schmeeckle, Frances C.
6th Grade English Teacher
Scott, Charlene Cannon
Biology Teacher
Sept, Hazel Fowler
Math & Peer Helpers Teacher
Sherlock, Ronnie Clelie
Band Director
Shirley, Patty Mc Gee
American His & Humanities Tchr
Sinanan, Martha Collazo
HS Spanish Teacher
Sivils, Kevin Christopher
Athletic Dir & PE Teacher
Smith, Gloria Stephanie
Senior English Teacher
Snellings, William E.
Civics & American History Tchr
Sones, Floyd F.
Band Director
Stamper, Mark Edward
American & Louisiana His Tchr
Starks, Lucretia Kay Butler
First Grade Teacher
Stelly, Willis
Health & Physical Ed Teacher
Stockett, Estelle Lorraine
Fourth Grade Teacher
Strickland, Theresa Parsons
Earth & Marine Science Teacher
Thomas, Bobbye Lynne
PE, Hlth, Dance & Gym Teacher
Thomas, Grelyn
Computer Science Teacher
Tiberghein, Daniel Charles
Theater, Sci & Sign Lang Tchr
Tolbert, Charles M.
Professor of Sociology
Turner, Albert Charles
Teacher & Athletic Director
Turner, Mallalieu Caldwell
Studio Class Piano Teacher
Veck, Leah Brock
Language Arts Teacher
Vidaurreta, Alicia C.
French Teacher
Vucasovich, Robert Stephen
High School Math Instructor
Ward, Mary Kenelly
Home Economics Teacher
West, Patricia Leggett
Eng, Literature & Film Teacher
Weydling, Yuri Paula
Latin Teacher
Whitten, Olivia Jane
Math & Algebra I Teacher
Wilkerson, Debra Ann
Business Education Teacher
Williams, Maurice Antonio
Physical Science Teacher
Williams, Ronell Davis, Sr.
Director of Bands & Jazz Stud
Yigletu, Ashagre Awoke
Economics Professor
BELCHER
Carter, Sylvia Hayden
Social Studies Teacher
Hergenrader, Pamela Gill
Third Grade Teacher

BELL CITY
Fontenot, Dina M.
Math Teacher
Lewis, Felicia A.
Business Instructor
Nunez, Richard Scott
PE & Health Ed Teacher
BELLE CHASSE
Leger, Susan B.
Computer Based Lang Arts Tchr
Long, Martha Williams
Louisiana History Teacher
Richards, Lana Monteverde
Kindergarten Teacher
BELLE ROSE
Gilmore, Alice Mary Picou
Third Grade Teacher
BENTON
Beagley, Ted James
MS & HS Director of Band
Carroway, Scott
His & Free Enterprise Tchr
Carson, Ricky Lynn
English & Reading Teacher
Lewis, Jeanette D.
7th Grade Math Teacher
Nelson, Cheryl Long
10th Grade English Teacher
Turner, Joy Rose Thomas
Adaptive Physical Ed Teacher
BERNICE
Bennett, John H.
Science Teacher
Simpson, Carol Hageman
English Teacher
BERWICK
Busbice, Deborah L.
Fourth Grade Teacher
Mc Elroy, Cheryl Lopez-Lemoine
English & Speech Teacher
Minchew, Beverly Jiles
Eighth Grade English Teacher
Mire, Lisa Jones
Eng & Publications Teacher
Scheuermann, Glenn Michael
Band Director
Thibodeaux, Mona D.
Fifth Grade Teacher
Watson, Sandra Naquin
Retired 8th Grade LA His Tchr
BOGALUSA
Cyrus, Bessie Mae
Retired Teacher
Frazier, JoAnna Spann
7th Grade Math Teacher
Gaddy, Harold Edwin
History Teacher
Gaddy, Maureen Elizabeth
English Teacher
George, Jennifer Germany
Math & History Teacher
Jackson, Bobby E.
8th Grade LA History Teacher
Leggitt, Barbara Fairley
Science Teacher
Magee, Susan Knight
French Teacher
Merritt, Beverly Lawrence
English Teacher
Stewart, Jeri Purdy
Social Studies & Eng Teacher
Tanner, Lisa Hamilton
Spanish & English Teacher
Williams, Marilyn Jamie (Hooper)
Retired 4th Grade Teacher
BOSSIER CITY
Bamburg, Jean
Math Instructor
Brabham, Wray
Psychology Professor
Brock, Belvia Mary
English & Honors Hum Tchr
Cann, Doretha King
Math, Sci & Soc Stud Teacher
Critton, Gladys Montgomery
Second Grade Teacher
Dauenhauer, Ann James
Biology Teacher
Densmore, Donna Bordelon
Mathematics Instructor
Engi, Claudia Atkins
8th Grade Language Arts Tchr
Graves, Vickye Long
Second & Third Grade Teacher
Gray, Rebecca Gene
English Teacher
Heidecker, Ruth Urfis
1st Grade Teacher
Holland, Ann Hamilton
Teacher of the Gifted
Jackson, Henry R.
Civics & Ec Tchr
Jones, F. Sylvia
Instructor of Science Dept
Kelly, Eugene James
Director of Surgical Tech Prgm
Kittler, Ann Frances (Jones)
6th-8th Grade Lang Arts Tchr
LaBarbera, Constance S.
Health & PE Professor
Lee, Rodger Darryl
PE Teacher & Coach
Manuel, Kathleen Bond
Psychology Professor
Mercer, Carolyn Lombardino
1st Grade Teacher
Monzingo, Freida Haynes
Dean of Community Education
Morrison, Charlene Grace
6th Grade Teacher

IER CITY (cont)
, Ronald I., Sr.
essor of History
ıy, Lee Girtha Williams
Grade Teacher
ls, William Lyman, Jr.
ructor
eri, Anthony Joseph
sical Education Teacher
ll, Mona Hughen
nce Teacher
, Judy Robe
guage Arts Teacher
our, Dan
avioral Science Instructor
l, Kim Kelly
ech Commnctn Instructor
Marijane H.
ructor
, Denise Davenport
hematics Teacher
RG
der, Karen Ann (Ayo)
iness Teacher
is, Earl Stan
ti Media Research Instr
n, Cynthia LeJeune
hematics Teacher
n, Jeanette Marcel
dance Counselor
TTE
lon, Rebecca Rae
lish Teacher
x, Marion Mary
al Studies Teacher
et, Susan Rae
cher of Talented Drama
, Elizabeth Smith
culus Teacher
thal, David Arthur
d Director
pson, Jan Heurtin
hematics Teacher
, Barry Christopher
n, Drama, Dbte & Span Tchr
THWAITE
y, Tina Molero
nce Teacher
AUX BRIDGE
hard, Allen
h Teacher
sard, Deborah Guidry
hematics Teacher
n, Ann Newland
nce Teacher
es, Carolyn Morvant
ech & Lang Therapist
ney, Mary Margaret
d Grade Teacher
nt, Bradley Kent
nce Teacher
USSARD
aussee, Linda Thibeaux
aking Skills at Risk Tchr
haux, Linda Cassidy
rth Grade Teacher
ers, Pamela Thompson
Grd Earth Science Teacher
, Stacey Guillory
ic & Youth Director
ord, Helen Martien
arian
SLY
geois, Joanne C.
ancement Program Teacher
Norma Jean Bellar
iness Education Teacher
s, Althea Hughes
& 8th Grd Math Tchr
t, Gary Paul
ory & Geography Teacher
KEYE
n, Linda Kramel
lish Teacher
nore, Carol Ringler
, French Tchr & Counselor
ord, Dianne Kay
ory Teacher
KIE
elon, Sheila Taylor
sics & Prin of Tech Tchr
ston, Dexter J.
d Director & Math Teacher
he, Susan Ducote
erican History Teacher
oard, Diana Lewis
f Development Coordinator
AS
son, Alberta Guidroz
nputer Education Teacher
Royce Elaine Elliott
lish & Speech Teacher
Petey-Jo Lask
t Grade Teacher
an, Lois Achee
h School Librarian
ncon, Paula Coon
iness Teacher
HOUN
man, Tracie Bidwell
hematics Teacher
Sonja Heidenreich
ond Grade Teacher
, Carolyn Jackson
rd Grade Teacher
Nova Smith
guage Arts Teacher & Coach
nter, Terri Crenshaw
& 8th Grd Eng Tchr

Sullivan, Vicki Barkley
Sixth Grade Mathematics Tchr
CALVIN
Dupree, Linda Harris
English Teacher
CAMERON
Trahan, Danny Michael
Assistant Principal
CAMPTI
Bonier, Mary Williams
English Teacher
Burns, Abiah Utter
Spanish & English Teacher
Gandy, Bryant Ray, Jr.
Social Studies Teacher
Haser, Sharon Bell
Science Teacher
Spiller, Rhonda Davis
Typing Teacher
CARENCRO
Broussard, Lisa Moore
Language & Reading Tchr
Richard, Cheryll Patin
Consumer & Family Scis Tchr
CECILIA
Autrey, Mickey Burt
World Geog & Civics Teacher
Beebe, Lottie Polozola
Special Education Teacher
Dupuis, Carolyn Pecoraro
Mathematics Teacher
Kidder, Jewell Landry
English Teacher
Narcisse, Myra Yvonne Dugas
Business Teacher
Sonnier, Janice Herring
Mathematics Teacher
Stevens, Jean Helen
Art & Keyboarding Teacher
Thibodeaux, Denice Doucet
Health & Physical Ed Teacher
CENTERVILLE
Payton, Sandra Proche
Instruction Specialist
Rome, Angela Ann
Business Ed Instr & Dept Head
CHALMETTE
Audler, Angela Barcelona
Instructor
Bassett, Martha Bush
Teacher of Academically Gifted
Bauer, Calvin Roy, Jr.
Social Studies & LA His Tchr
Briley, Bonnie L.
Administrator
Carty, Michael Nicholas
French & Speech Commnctn Instr
Coulson, Jennifer Outlaw
Biological Sciences Instructor
de Blanc, Lester, SSND
Reading & English Teacher
Deckelmann, Carla Dagro
Academic School Counselor
Dier, Lynne Michele
High Schl Social Studies Tchr
Dugger, Thomas F.
English Department Chairman
Gegenheimer, Robert P.
Health & PE Teacher
Hampton, Marie Cure
Private Tutor
Huff, Kathleen Martin
Special Educator Teacher
Jeandron, Carol Adragna
Arts & Sciences Division Chrmn
Jones, Alan Michael
Mathematics Teacher
LaBauve, Pamela Picone
English Teacher
Lemoine, Barry A.
High School English Teacher
Lux, Michaele A.
English Teacher & Dept Chprsn
Romaguera, Dawn Suarez
Asst Prof of Office Careers
Simpson, Paul Waymon
Air Force JROTC Instructor
Tillman, Dirk Robert
12th Grade English Teacher
Williams, Claudia Ann
General Science Teacher
CHATAIGNIER
Fruge', Valli Marie
English Teacher & Librarian
CHATHAM
Jones, Dale Pipes
High School Science Teacher
CHAUVIN
Authement, Lisa Chauvin
Sixth Grade Language Arts Tchr
Beasley, Lorraine Breazeale
8th Grade Math Teacher
Peltier, Betty Moreno
Principal
CHOUDRANT
Cox, Cathi
Science Teacher
Crouch, Jeanette Rinehart
K-6th Grd Coordinating Teacher
Hyams, Marilyn Orr
Math & Science Teacher
Lamkin, Cheryl Skains
Health, PE Teacher & Coach
CHURCH POINT
Magee, Michael Kenneth
Social Studies Teacher
Miller, Ann Fuselier
Fifth Grade Teacher
Olivier, Patsy Benoit
Social Studies Teacher

CLINTON
Gordon, Earnestine D.
Social Studies Teacher
Harvey, Nancy Soule
4th Grade Teacher
Jensen, Katherine Ann
Mathematics Teacher
Record, Rebecca Magee
Chemistry & Physics Teacher
COLFAX
Andrews, Erin McCain
Third Grade Teacher
COLUMBIA
Carnahan, Ruby Allen
English Teacher
Chappell, Sandra Beach
English Teacher
Isca, Andy R.
Director of Bands
Larson, Joan Parker
Fr GATE Tchr & Dyslexic Prgms
Richmond, Tim
Social Studies Teacher
CONVERSE
Lee, Phyllis Loupe
Family & Consumer Sci Teacher
COTTON VALLEY
Smith, Beverly Pyles
Business Education Teacher
COTTONPORT
Coco, Betty Ducote
Fifth Grade Teacher
Joffrion, Kathy A.
First Grade French Teacher
COUSHATTA
Crow, Barbara Ann
Fourth Grade Teacher
Horton, Patricia Hayden
4th Grade Teacher
Longino, Evelyn Blanchard
Teacher of Gifted
Walters, Betty Lou
Fourth Grade Teacher
COVINGTON
Albright, Angelle Fournier
English & Journalism Teacher
Craig, Jon A.
Science Department Chairman
Fitzmorris, Tawnya Foust
Span Tchr & Foreign Lang Chm
Flynn, Pam Mueller
6th Grade Teacher of Gifted
Hladky, Lynne L.
Reading Specialist
Koss, Susan Annette Lauver
Elem Computer Lab Teacher
Mabile, Tammy Ellis
Chemistry Teacher
Moore, Martha P.
History & Reading Teacher
Olinger, Barbara Carlene
Civics & Free Enterprise Tchr
Palliser, Darlene Young
Reading & Language Arts Tchr
Poche, Deborah Cieutat
Eighth Grade Teacher
Schilling, Anita Howard
English & Psychology Teacher
Smith, Allie V., III
Biology & Phy Ed Teacher
Stroud, Melissa Hope
Guidance Counselor
CREOLE
Brasseaux, Elizabeth Woodgett
4th Grade Teacher
Rogers, Stephanie Procell
English Teacher
CROWLEY
Amiot, Leodore Mathew, Jr.
Science Teacher & Dept Coord
Ancelet, Peggy Vining
High School Business Teacher
Butler, Connie Y.
Guidance Counselor & Math Tchr
Gates, Cynthia Going
Guidance Counselor
Mire, Sydney Gauther
Secondary English Teacher
Parker, Regina Hill
English Teacher
Richard, Janet Leger
English Teacher
Thomas, Laura Seilhan
English & Resource Teacher
CROWVILLE
Brooks, Linda Wade
Middle School Teacher
Futch, Cynthia Bryan
Teacher of the Gifted
CUT OFF
Bruce, Sandra Comeaux
5th Grade Teacher
DELCAMBRE
Delcambre, Michael Allen
World Geog Tchr & Ath Director
DELHI
Black, Dennis Leland
4th Grade Teacher
Christman, Caroline Smith
Mathematics Teacher
Doles, Glenda Coleman
French I & II Teacher
Stroud, Lou Dean
Counselor
DENHAM SPRINGS
Crawford, Virginia H.
Life Science Teacher
Gurley, E. Frank
Junior High School Teacher

Mc Carty, Wanda Watts
Teacher
Richardson, Dianne Piggott
4th Grade Reading Teacher
Varnado, Terri E.
Technology Education Teacher
DEQUINCY
Bonin, Milford Keith
Special Education Teacher
Chapper, Gwendolyn Simien
First Grade Teacher
Clement, Margaret Williams
2nd Grade Teacher
Cooper, Melonee Van Winkle
Choral Director
Cooper, Nancy Trahan
Agriscience Teacher
Dever, Michael S.
Science Teacher
LeBouef, Beverly Ann
First Grade Teacher
Peterson, Jeanette K.
Ger by Satellite Tchng Partner
DERIDDER
Archer, Linda West
4th Grade Spanish Teacher
Burnett, James B., Jr.
Art Teacher
Caldwell, Charles William
7th-8th Grd Science Teacher
Iles, James Michael
8th Grade History Teacher
Miller, Donna M.
Kindergarten Teacher
Petty, Dana Johnson
Biology Teacher
DESTREHAN
Benoit, Lisa Gautreaux
Fifth Grade Teacher
Griffis, Marcia Wilson
7th & 8th Grd Lang Arts Tchr
Pharr, Madeline Breaux
1st Grd Reading Recovery Tchr
Tyler, Karen Burnside
Sixth Grade Teacher
Ward, Stefanie Babin
English & Journalism Teacher
DEVILLE
Winbery, Sarah Ann
Teacher of Gifted
DODSON
Miles, Melinda Murphy
PE Teacher & Coach
DONALDSONVILLE
Aysenne, Sue Chenevert
Math Teacher
Babin, Reine Legendre
Social Studies Teacher
Bolotte, Julius Richard, Jr.
Biology Teacher
Hollins, Henry Huddleston, Jr.
Music & Computer Teacher
Marco, Donna McBride
English Teacher
Mast, Janis Soroka
In-School Suspension Pgm Tchr
Young, Dianna Whitley
English Teacher
DOWNSVILLE
Daniels, Jo Annette Pardue
Mathematics Teacher
McDonald, Ritchie Todd
Agriscience Teacher
Roberts, Betty L.
Stu Affairs Dir & English Tchr
DRY PRONG
Futrell, Elizabeth V.
English Teacher
Simmons, Mary Willett
American History Teacher
DUBACH
Key, Vicky Skains
Coordinator & Librarian
Pylant, Judy Payne
First Grade Teacher
DUSON
Cook, Faye D.
1st Grade Teacher
Lear, Catherine Gale Grossie
4th Grade Teacher
Sam, Edith C.
First Grade Teacher
EAST POINT
Easley, Cecil Franklin, Jr.
Principal & Math Teacher
EFFIE
Barnhart, Connie Dauzat
Third Grade Teacher
Morgan, Anita J.
First Grade Teacher
ELM GROVE
Mansueto, Jane F.
Gifted English & Reading Tchr
ELMER
Havens, Lana Jarrell
Language Arts Teacher
Jackson, Lenard
Teacher & Coach
Mc Neely, Marguerite Verret
Secondary Science Teacher
ELTON
Goebel, Rose Vilardi
6th-8th Grade Reading Teacher
Putnam, Helena Miller
French Teacher
ERATH
Shiner, Teilla Broussard
Speech, Drama & French Teacher

EUNICE
Arceneaux, Jules Menou, II
Religious Ed Teacher
Ardoin, Brenda Ann
Guidance Counselor
De Rouen, Sheila Herrod
Civics & Accounting Teacher
Devillier, Louis Oliver, III
Counselor
Dupre, Joyce Christ
Teacher of the Gifted
Fisher, Anthony
French Teacher
Frank, Judy Martin
5th Grade Teacher
Fuselier, Carole Mc Cauley
English Teacher
Guillory, Harland Dale
Associate Professor of Biology
Jodon, Dwight Robert
Band Director
Johnson, Louise Bellon
HS French Teacher & Coach
LeJeune, Susan Gardiner
Associate Professor of English
Robichaux, Renee Hazelton
Instructor in Biology
Sanders, Jackie Trichel
Junior High Language Arts Tchr
Schambough, Mary Ann Williams
Librarian & Teacher
Stutes, Ellen G.
Asst Professor of Mathematics
Tatman, Deborah Elliott
World Geography & Civics Tchr
Thompson, David Anthony
Mathematics Teacher
FARMERVILLE
Burton, Debra Lynn
Sixth Grade Teacher
James, Debra Leichman
High School Science Teacher
FERRIDAY
Bailey, Cordell
Teacher & Coach
Cade, Betty Lee
Teacher, Cnslr & Site Supvr
Carnette, Patricia Gallender
French Teacher
FOREST
Prine, Florence Booth
HS Science Teacher
FRANKLIN
Abraham, Delores Madison
English Teacher
Bourgeois, Trudy P.
Family & Consumer Sci Teacher
Bourliea, Sheila Marie
Biology Teacher
Delahanty, Sean E.
Mathematics Teacher
Garrison, Gary
Social Studies Teacher
Lockley, Andre Lazar
Special Education Teacher
Milius, Sarah H.
French Teacher
Miller, Linda Vappie
American History Teacher
Mitchell, Anthony Reed
Seventh Grade Reading Teacher
Sonnier, Dennis Irving
Sixth Grade Teacher
FRANKLINTON
Alvear, Maggie Schroeder
7th Grade Math Teacher
Brumfield, Mercer Riche
Spanish & Biology Teacher
Carpenter, Renee Stogner
Algebra Teacher
Crowe, JoAnn M.
English Teacher
Freeman, Jackie Turnage
Pre-School Teacher
French, Johnette Osborn
Science, Reading, Math Teacher
Junkins, Phill Stirling
Jr HS History Teacher
Lewis, Roxann Marie
Math & Social Studies Tchr
Magee, J. Hallene Smith
Fifth Grade Teacher
Mc Kenzie, Carol Ann Crain
Second Grade Teacher
Richardson, Pam
Spanish Teacher
Stafford, Cindy Parker
Elementary Counselor
Thomas, Mazina Ann Williams
Lang Arts Tchr & Eng Dept Chm
Wood, William Gerald
History Teacher
Young, Beverly A.
Principal
FRENCH SETTLEMENT
Holmes, Myra Myers
Bio & Environmental Sci Tchr
GALLIANO
Guidroz, Joey A.
Special Ed Tchr & Coach
Lefort, Michael Joseph
Counselor
Schiro, Eddie L., Sr.
Band Director
GEISMAR
Braud, Allison Speligene
Teacher of Academically Gifted
Gaudin, Angelique Hebert
8th Grade Science Teacher

GEISMAR (cont)
Labbe, Kathleen Nola
7th Grade Language Arts Tchr
Mire, Liz Delaune
8th Grade LA History Teacher
GEORGETOWN
Pendarvis, Doris W.
Third Grade Teacher
GIBSON
Thibodaux, Gayle Toups
4th Grade Teacher
GILBERT
Bufkin, Martha Lou T.
English Teacher & Librarian
GLENMORA
Halliburton, Sue B.
First Grade Teacher
Speir, James Bradley
Math Teacher & Coach
Sutton, Michael R.
Sci Dept Chm & Tchr
Weatherford, Emily James
Business Teacher
GOLDEN MEADOW
Anselmi, Laura R.
Family & Consumer Science Tchr
Duet, Norma Faucheux
Computer Lab Teacher
Rousse, Glenn Anthony
7th Grade Science Teacher
GONZALES
Bacala, Lisa Faucheux
Spcl Ed Content Mastery Tchr
Blanchard, Tammy Nickens
Counselor
Landry, LLoyd John
Science Teacher
Lukse, Heather Crawford
Business Teacher
Moak, Lynn Davies
7th-8th Grd Language Arts Tchr
Stewart, Louise Price
In School Suspension Presider
GRAMBLING
Blake, Zinnia L. Livingston
Psychology Instructor
Boyd, David Thomas
Assistant Prof of Accounting
Brown, Joyce M.
Speech & Theatre Professor
Butler, A. Phillip
Professor
Coleman, Floyd
English Associate Professor
Deberry, Clyde Edward
Assoc Prof of Criminal Justice
Dorsey, Waneene Coffey
Assistant Professor of Biology
Edward, Kathaleena
Asst Prof of Cmptr Information
Foster, Ray W.
Psychology Professor
Friedman, Shirley Siegman
Asst Prof of Spanish
Garner, Lawrence Edward
Assoc Prof of History
Hosseini, Mahmoud H.
Assistant Professor
Humphries, LeRoy, Sr.
Associate Professor of Music
Johnson, Betty Williams
Psychology Professor
LalehParvaran, Parvin
Assistant Professor
Lewis, David Lee
Asst Prof & Criminal Justice
Negm, Hossam A.
Prof of Biological Scis Dept
Nelson, Jerrell Lanone
Assistant Professor
Nwokoma, Anele
Computer Instructor
Reddy, Y. B.
Associate Professor
Sanders, Velora Scott
Assistant Professor
Smiley, Ellen D.
Assistant Director
Terrell, Barbara Rucker
English Teacher
White, Yolande Evans
Journalism Teacher
Williams, LaWanna Gunn
Professor & Acting Chairperson
GRAND COTEAU
Cain, Carmen de Moya
Alumni Dir
GRANT
Hahler, Sharon Ritchie
Math Teacher
GRAY
Brown, Stella Chauvin
GATE Amer His, Govt & Ec Tchr
Matherne, Cynthia Ann
High School English Teacher
Olivier, Bridget Schexnayder
Biology & Chemistry Teacher
Poole, Marsha Trosclair
Mathematics Teacher
GREENSBURG
Bush, Hollis, Jr.
Mathematics Teacher
Chaney, Patricia Bishop
HS Biology I & II Teacher
DeVance, Edna Gordon
8th Grade Teacher
Stringer, Louise Smith
English Teacher
GRETNA
Benoit, Joyce Smith
6th-8th Grd Soc Stud Tchr
Bordlee, Anna Victoria
Fifth Grade Teacher
Brandt, Diana Budzine
Visual Art Teacher
Brock, Jane
Middle Grades Teacher
Dennison, Suzanne Templeton
World Geography Teacher
Derhake, Judiann
Montessori Teacher
Jackson, Leola Wells
Science Teacher
Mithun, Mary Kevin Cahill
Algebra Tchr & Assistant Prin
Pilet, Geraldine Shaver
Math Teacher
Richard, Nevelyn Ann
Guidance Counselor
St Pierre, Marilyn Tomino
Assistant Principal
Siegel, Suzanne Oberkirch
Kindergarten Teacher
Wartelle, Amy Campbell
Sci Teacher & Curr Coord
GUEYDAN
Abshire, Janice L.
6th-7th Grade Reading Teacher
Adams, Wayne J.
Social Studies Tchr & Dept Chm
Gardiner, George Logan, III
Vice Principal
Heard, Mary Baker
Fourth Grade Teacher
Hensgens, Melanie Trahan
Mathematics Teacher
Richard, Linda Stansel
Science Teacher
Sirmon, Carolyn Cayton
High School Counselor
HACKBERRY
Baker, Mary H.
Business Teacher
Broussard, Lloyd J., Jr.
English Teacher
Ross, Sherry Duplechain
Mathematics & Cmptr Sci Tchr
HAHNVILLE
Gomez, Shirley Doucet
4th Grade Mathematics Teacher
Smith, Evan Edwards
Director of Music
HAMMOND
Baker, Jeffrey Duane
Asst Professor
Barbera, Frances Fertitta
Assistant Prof of Management
Bellavia, Michelle Cheramie
Instructor of English
Bissonnette, Victor L.
Assistant Prof of Psychology
Cross, Eartha Cyprian
Louisiana Studies Teacher
Cudd, Mike
Finance Professor
Delony, Willis Lane
Associate Professor of Music
Doolittle, Peter E.
Educational Psychology Prof
Edie, Richard Dale
Asst Prof of Mathematics
Eleser, Chris Bivona
Assistant Professor
Elliott, Scott Maxwell
Asst Prof of Communication
Frederick, Larry Joseph
Associate Professor of Biology
Gaydos, Shelly Carter
Math Teacher
Gray, Larry Allen
Prof Emeritus & Artist
Hale, Robert Legan
Criminal Justice Professor
Harper, Karin WIlliams
Biology Instructor
Hilliard, Newton Parr, Jr.
Chemistry Instructor
Hyde, Samuel Claiborne, Jr.
Assistant Professor of History
Jacob, Shirley Woods
Assistant Professor
Jenkins, Susan McMichael
Math Instructor
Johnson, Susan Fagan
Instr of Developmental English
Kerber, Patrick Conrad
Adj Prof of Classical Guitar
Laurent, Dianna Marie
English Instructor
Levi, Danilo
Visiting Asst Prof
Li, Ken
Mathematics Professor
Marshall, Margaret Maryanne
Associate Prof of French
May, Jerome Gerard
Chemistry Instructor
Miller, Terri Louise
Communication Instructor
Milton, Grace A.
English Teacher
Mitchell, Kenneth L.
English Professor
Mohs, Matthew Christian
American History Teacher
Nauman, Ann Keith
Prof of History & Philosophy
Nichols, C. Howard
Professor of History
O'Hara, Bradley Shawn
Dir MBA Pgm & Assoc Prof Mrktg
O'Neill, Tommy W., Jr.
7th Grade Reading Teacher
Owings, Addison D.
Botany Professor
Ozazaki, Robert Koichi
Biological Science Professor
Ratcliff, Ellen Hildebrand
Instructor
Rogers, Ashley Eckbert
History Instructor
Schrock, Scharmal K.
Professor of Voice
Shaffer, Teri Root
Marketing Professor
Simoneaux, Dolores Pesek
Assistant Professor in Tchr Ed
Sineshaw, Tilahun
Education Professor
Strahan, David William
Art Instructor
Sullivan, Monica Pohl
English Teacher
Trahan, Wanda A.
Assistant Professor of Psych
Tucci, Jack Eugene
Assistant Professor
Vance, Charley Keith
Theatre Teacher
Vartanian, Hasmig B.
Art Professor
Wellman, John F.
Professor
Wells, Eleanor Dixon
Assistant Professor in Nursing
HARRISONBURG
Mayo, Mary Carrico
Family & Consumer Sci Teacher
HARVEY
Arnondin, Steve Joseph
Science Teacher
Bailey, Charlene (Whitaker)
English & Mythology Teacher
Barras, Carolyn Arlette
English & Newspaper Teacher
Fortmayer, Carroll John
Aerospace Science Instructor
Lewis, Margery M.
Spanish Teacher
Marks, Betty Finch
Teacher of Gifted
Milam, Cheryl Perilloux
Instructional Pgms Consultant
Sagona, Barbara Burton
Mathematics Teacher
Zappulla, Brenda Margaret
Third Grade Teacher
HAUGHTON
Blasingame, Larry L.
Science Dept Chairman
Prudhomme, Brenda Lewis
2nd Grade Teacher
Prunty, LeeAnn Marsiglia
Teacher of Academically Gifted
Shaw, Kelli Collins
Speech & English Teacher
Watters, Margene Ray
Third Grade Music Specialist
Wimbrough, Penny Dawn Hudson
Science Teacher
HAYNESVILLE
Durham, Jane Bourn
7th-8th Grd Math Teacher
Harson, Martha Odom
Science Teacher
Waits, Margaret Ann Newsom
Counselor
HOLDEN
Blount, Tinita Sykes
Business & Office Ed Dir
Dufrene, Valarie Dillon
English Teacher
HOMER
Tinsley, Louise Wallace
Math & Computer Lit Teacher
HOUMA
Brock, Della Ann
Kindergarten Teacher
Champagne, Betty Folse
Fifth Grade Teacher
Cortez, Martin Lynn
Assistant Principal
Dagenhardt, Glynn Anthony
Band Director
Duplantis, David L.
7th & 8th Grd Prevention Coord
Dupre, Karen Luc
Business & English Teacher
Evans, Judith D.
Family & Consumer Sci Teacher
Ferguson, Susan Brumfield
Spanish Teacher
Hebert, Linda Schexnayder
Guidance Counselor
Hebert, Timothy Ray
Physics & Biology Teacher
Kolb, Alfred
Senior English Teacher
LeBlanc, Nancy P.
English IV Teacher
Pierce, Eve B.
Parent Literacy Teacher
Robichaux, Byron James
Social Studies Tchr & Dept Chm
Smart, Linda Duplantis
Third Grade Teacher
Smith, Etta Norman
Sixth Grade Teacher
Songe, Diana LeBlanc
Health Occupations Teacher
Theriot, Helen S.
English Teacher & Jrnlsm Instr
Trussell, Shirley McIlveene
6th-7th Grd Teacher of Gifted
INDEPENDENCE
Morales, Sheryl Hein
Mathematics Teacher
IOTA
Bearb, Phyllis Benoit
7th-12th His Tchr & Yrbk Adv
Garner, Rachelle Rougeau
Business Teacher
Miller, Daniel Ray
Elementary Physical Ed Teacher
Phillips, Susan
English Teacher
IOWA
Leger, Keith E.
SS Chprsn & Amer His Tchr
Leonard, Linda Lapearous
English & Speech Teacher
Natali, Ursula Zaunbrecher
School Guidance Counselor
Prather, Linda Conner
First Grade Teacher
Primeaux, Winnie Leger
3rd Grade Teacher
Strasburg, Otto R.
History Teacher
JACKSON
Price, Charles Edward
Science & Mathematics Teacher
Scott, Jessica Patterson
Sci Dept Chairperson & Teacher
JEANERETTE
Lapeyrouse, Judy Powell
French Teacher
Little, Barbara Lockette
Master Teacher
Robin, Cecile L.
American History Teacher
Trahant-Champagne, Andree
English & Yearbook Teacher
JEFFERSON
Fonte, Harold Joseph, Jr.
Science Teacher
Lusignan, Kevin David
High School Teacher
Sylvas, Maggie Viola (Holloman)
English Teacher
JENA
Burgess, Gawan L.
Biology Teacher
Johnson, David Evan
Industrial Arts & Math Teacher
Mayo, Deborah Bailey
Fifth Grade Teacher
Seward, Tracy Shane
Spcl Education Teacher & Coach
JENNINGS
Benoit, Lillian R.
5th Grd Science & Reading Tchr
Doucet, Suzanne Parker
English Teacher
Lasserre, Donna Cayce
Reading Lab Instructor
Marcantel, Jean Rougeau
Jr High Teacher
Rose, Leslie Paige
Band Director
JONESBORO
Brown, Judy McConathy
First Grade Teacher
Hagan, Brenda
Special Education Teacher
Hough, John David
Science Teacher & Dept Chprsn
JONESVILLE
Kirby, Kerry E.
Alternative Education Teacher
Shively, Cary Stephen
Physics & Algebra Teacher
Swayze, Susie Smith
Family & Consumer Science Tchr
KAPLAN
Couvillon, Julian S.
HS Advanced Math Teacher
Dubois, Eve Greene
8th Grade English Teacher
Faulk, Kendal James
Band Dir & Music Teacher
Meaux, Deborah Mouton
English Teacher
Melancon, Timala Hair
Speech Teacher
Mire, Patrice Q.
Science Teacher
Sonnier, Jennifer Meaux
Hlth & Physical Education Tchr
Touchet, Francis, Jr.
Biology II, Hlth & PE Tchr
KEITHVILLE
Boone, Rosetta Claire
Family & Consumer Science Tchr
Freeland, Shirley Barnes
2nd Grade Elementary Teacher
Hays, Laura
Math & Computer Literacy Tchr
Jackson, Anna Morris
7th Grd Rdng & Lang Arts Tchr
KENNER
Bell, Sharon Bowers
Kindergarten Teacher
Campbell, May Elizabeth
Physical Education Teacher
Dillehay, Deborah Lotz
Dance Teacher & Artistic Dir
Harmeyer, Julie Prestia
Social Studies Teacher
Hobaugh, Mariea Arlene
Fifth Grade Teacher
Jackson, Henry, Jr.
Fifth Grade Teacher
Pelitire, Brendaline O.
Special Education Teacher
Smith, Richard Lee
Air Force Jr ROTC Instructor
KENTWOOD
Bankston, Pamela H.
English Teacher
Sanders, Shirley Larry
1st Grade Teacher
Trappey, Cynthia Ann
Spanish & Amer History Teacher
Wells, Fochia Edwina
Teacher & Administrative Asst
KINDER
Botley, Barbara Kirklin
Business Education Instructor
Doumite, Susan Hall
Ninth Grade English Teacher
Manuel, Carolyn Smith
Fifth Grade Math & Sci Tchr
Miller, Patrick
Health & Civics Teacher
Whittington, Rick Glen
World History Teacher
LA PLACE
Bazile, Lydia M.
Second Grade Teacher
Boe, Coy Michael
Algebra I Honors & French Tchr
Bourgeois, Larry Joseph, Jr.
MS Soc Stud Tchr & Asst Prin
Fisher, Robert
9th-12th Grd Art & Jrnlsm Tchr
Knight, Barbara Poche
History Teacher
Melancon, Terrell Paul
Religion & Accounting Teacher
Montz, Jeffrey Michael
Religion Teacher
Roussel, Angela Mc Donald
7th & 8th Grade Math Teacher
Stein, Patricia A.
English & Drama Teacher
Vanderbrook, Susan
Social Studies Teacher
Walton, Paula Anderson
English Teacher
LACOMBE
Gorman, Elise Mary
Former Elementary Teacher
LAFAYETTE
Aguillard, Karen Wyatt
Mathematics Teacher
Aucoin, Larry Dale
Indstrl Arts & Driver Ed Tchr
Barry, Cynthia Shaffer
French Teacher
Bartig, Rhonda McCullough
Health, Phys Ed Tchr & Coach
Baudoin, Elaine Rozas
Chorus Teacher
Baudoin, Marcella Lee (Alpha)
Math Teacher & Dept Chairman
Bearb, Katy Marie
Journalism & English Teacher
Berard, Christine E.
English Teacher
Blair, Deborah Gage
Art Educator
Bourque, Christina Lanie
High School Math Teacher
Broussard, Sandra Laborde
Speech & Drama Teacher
Broussard, Stephanie Ann
Asst Principal
Cabes, Blair Bowden
English Teacher
Cahanin, Eurella D.
Secondary Mathematics Teacher
Campbell, Barbara Waddell
Retired Fourth Grade Teacher
Cannon, D. Jeanie Moore
Second Grade Inclusion Teacher
Carmouche, Pearl Melody Hewitt
Retired Teacher
Chlan, Caryl Anne
Assistant Professor of Biology
Church, Leah Suggs
Mathematics Teacher
Colbert-Cormier, Patricia Ann
Bio & Molecular Genetics Tchr
Couvillon, Clelie Dubuisson
7th-8th Grd Soc Stud Teacher
Dalme, Ann Bell
Teacher of the Gifted
Fogleman, Kathryn Marcantel
Retired 5th Grade Teacher
Ford, Cynthia Richard
Mathematics Teacher
Fortenberry, Alicia Dazet
Fourth Grade Teacher
Frank-Senegal, Patricia Dianne
Business Teacher & Chairperson
Grau, Brenda L. (White)
Biology Tchr & Sci Dept Chair
Green, Juanita Sexton
First Grade Teacher
Grizzaffi, Emanuel Joseph
Former Teacher
Guidry, Gayle Paul
HS Guidance Counselor

YETTE (cont)
au, Brenda Richard
l Geography Teacher
on, Carolyn Robertson
ergarten Teacher
Martha Callahan
tud Dept Head & Teacher
son, Sara Deshotels
rd Math & Sci Teacher
er, Russell Charles
ssor
Randy Ray
ing Assistant
l, Beverly Hernandez
Grade Teacher
nd, Leslie Nelson
ctor of Chemistry
e, Donna M.
ce Teacher of the Gifted
, Yvette Primeaux
ematics Teacher
orio, Marilyn H.
ora II Teacher
l, James Frederick
ology Education Teacher
Gloria Brock
urce Teacher
ey, Catherine Talbot
ergarten Teacher
, Albert C.
ner
on, Laura
ion Teacher
l, Joyce Landry
Music Teacher & Choral Dir
Mary Jane
istry Teacher
Deanna Taylor
nd Grade Teacher
a, Deborah Yount
iana History Teacher
omery, Veronica Poullard
rade Language Arts Tchr
n, Kathy Q.
ndary English Teacher
Barbara R.
Lang Arts Teacher
, Sharon Johnson
sh Teacher
Paula S.
rade Science Teacher
a, Marlene Landyr
Grade Teacher
, David L.
sh Teacher
aux, Amy G.
urce Teacher
o, Jan Braquet
ican History Teacher
o, Nancy Bradford
ndary English Teacher
Laurie Gail
ce & Comp Literacy Tchr
, Philip Roy Harper
puter Science Teacher
and, Susan Andrus
Math Teacher
, Lyla Wham
ce Teacher
Ann Martin
ciate Professor of English
Wanda Campbell
ess & Spec Ed Teacher
George B.
rs Chemistry Teacher
eaux, Jody J.
logy Teacher
r, Mary Elizabeth
h & Physical Ed Teacher
erry, Anthony
Mechanics Teacher
Cinde Raye
rian
Carol Ann (Morello)
Ed & Social Studies Tchr
aux, David G.
ature Associate Professor
eaux, Patricia Broussard
sh Teacher
l, Greg
ace Teacher
Michael Wayne
logy Teacher
, Laura Guirovich
Enterprise & English Tchr
s, Becky Letteer
ctor of Campus Ministry
, Jack
ical Science Teacher
r, Paula Dunning
School Mathematics Tchr
y, Cynthia Ann
ical Education & Hlth Tchr
Ellen Kay (Viator)
Art & Communications Tchr
ARTHUR
Katherine Jester
ness & Computer Teacher
CHARLES
a, Linda Baier
ish Teacher & Dept Chprsn
Bijaya Nandy
ish Teacher
d, Denise Leveque
Grade Teacher
o, Frank James
rican History Teacher
Sandra H.
al Studies Teacher

Conley, Judy Mouhot
Instructor of Mathematics
Corbello, Mary McCatherine
Physical Education Teacher
Courville, Alicia Dulaney
Physics, Chem & Phys Sci Tchr
DeFelice, Brenda Quigley
Leadership Mathematics Teacher
De Witt, Sandra Lawson
Applied Technology Teacher
Dublin, Melinda Bailey
Business Teacher
Duhon, Deanna DiGiglia
English Teacher
Dunham, Melinda Louise
English Teacher
Fontenot, Kendall Wayne
7th-8th Grd Soc Stud Teacher
Fontenot, Mary Etheridge
11th Grade English Teacher
Fuselier, Cheryl Reed
Teacher
Goodaker, Dianne M.
English Teacher & Dept Head
Goode, Margaret Gain
Instr of Academically Gifted
Gorrell, Carmel Walters
American Literature Teacher
Grigsby, Suzanne Allison
English Teacher
Guillory-Lueckenhoff, Linda
Teacher of Gifted & Talented
Harris, Pamela Thibodeaux
First Grade Teacher
Hearn, Barbara Chapman
Physics & Chemistry Teacher
Hoffpauir, Elizabeth Doolan
Business Tchr & Dept Head
James, Sharon Eaglin
Mathematics Teacher
Jenkins, Jassaland Kelly
Eng & African Amer Stud Tchr
Keller, Belinda Marie
Social Studies Teacher
Kingery, Kathryn Ann
Spanish Publications Teacher
Kohler, Julie Cagle
11th Grade Social Studies Tchr
Lacefield, Mary Ann
French & Spanish Teacher
Landry, Brenda Houston
Eng & Creative Writing Tchr
LaPointe, Alva K.
Guidance Counselor
Le Fevre, Helen
Hlth & Physical Education Tchr
Lemelle, Carla Yvette
English Teacher
Mallet, Sharon Waters
Eng & African Amer Lit Teacher
Malone, Yasmin Cyiark
Second Grade Teacher
Malveaux, DeBorah
5th Grade Teacher
Miller, Liz Walla
First Grade Teacher
Murphy, Diane Berry
7th Grd Language Arts Teacher
Paris, Anne Marguerite
8th Grade Language Teacher
Peavy, Brenda C.
Counselor
Pete, Dorothy Gray
4th Grade Teacher
Pete, Thail Fontenot
Chemistry Teacher
Powell, Kathy LaComb
Social Studies Teacher
Reynolds, Amy Peet
English Teacher
Richardson, Laura Perkins
American History Teacher
Ringo, Marve Robinson
Algebra & Geometry Teacher
Ritchie, Janet Green
7th Grade Life Science Teacher
Rivet, Laura Lee Dille
Fourth Grade Teacher
Sanford, Janice Mayfield
Retired Teacher
Saucier, Patrice Pruitt
4th-5th Grd Rdng & Sci Tchr
Shumaker, Linda Gail Sonnier
Chemistry Teacher
Simon, Catherine Reado
Language Arts Teacher
Smith, Brenda Taylor
English & Home Ec Teacher
Spain, Pinelle Sias
6th-8th Grd Reading Consultant
Steen, Kristi Danielle
English Teacher
Storer, Courtney Jackson
Third Grade Teacher
Strasburg, Jo Ann (Brown)
Former Teacher of the Gifted
Strong, Kathy Williams
Fifth Grade Teacher
Stutes, Christina Marie
Tenth Grade English Teacher
Taylor, Nancy Toussaint
Fourth Grade Teacher
Vallee, Joan E.
Asst Professor of Chemistry
Walker, Andrew Thomas
5th Grade Teacher
White, Vicky Allison
Math & PE Teacher
Wilson, Phillip Ray
Sr Army Instr & JROTC Dept Chm

Woodward, Shirley Castete
Fourth Grade Teacher
Wyche, Charlyne Smith
English III & IV Teacher
Young, Brenda Demary
Business Teacher
LAKE PROVIDENCE
Batchelor, Jeanette Mc Pherson
Third Grade Teacher
LAROSE
Lasseigne, Carolyn Sandras
First Grade Teacher
Plaisance, Michelle R.
Physical Education & Hlth Tchr
LAWTELL
Davis, Doris Chachere
7th Grd Soc Stud & Math Tchr
Fontenot, Lucille Joubert
First Grade Teacher
LECOMPTE
Duck, Linda Hardy
Physical Education Teacher
LEESVILLE
Ashworth, Elsee
Curriculum Director
Avant, N. Thomas, III
Biology & Science Dept Head
Beck, Deborah Stamp
Eng & Career Exploration Tchr
Boren, Lynda Sue (Schoenberger)
English Tchr of the Gifted
Bosley, Johnny Leland
Algebra Teacher & Coach
Browning, Cheryl Van Dine
Eighth Grade Lang Arts Tchr
Cart, Barbra Lynell
Vocational Teacher
Davis, Renita Goins
Business Teacher
Ellias, Maxine Murphy
Business Education Teacher
Folse, Raphael James, III
English & Social Studies Tchr
Fulks, Melissa Haymon
Third Grade Teacher
Green, Iva Reed
Language Arts Teacher
Jonson, Leigh Wood
Spanish Teacher
Krenek, Tamara C.
5th Grade Teacher
Langton, Marsha Lynn
1st Grade Teacher
Leonard, Henry E.
Jr High Math Teacher
Lewis, G. David
Advanced Math Teacher
Mc Cloud, Harry E.
Sr Army & JROTC Instr
Menedez, Dannette Cruz
Spanish Teacher
Morgan, Michael Baron
Band, Choir Dir & Music Tchr
Smith, Debbie Bailey
Business Teacher
Thomas, Phillisia Cooper
English Teacher
Werner, Amparo G.
Spanish Teacher
LENA
Allen, Gwendolyn Clark
Life & Earth Science Teacher
Hamberlin, Barbara M.
5th Grade Teacher
Tadlock, Odell Roshton
Science Teacher
White, Gary Wade
Sixth Grd Math & Science Tchr
LILLIE
Phillips, Diona Norman
8th Grade Teacher & Librarian
LIVINGSTON
Bartlett, Donnie Jones
English Teacher
Miller, Charles C.
Guidance Counselor
LOCKPORT
Le Blanc, Jeffrey J., Jr.
Principal
Prados, Mary Foret
Erly Intrvntn-Infant Prgm Tchr
Rome, Joan Landry
Second Grade Teacher
LOGANSPORT
Harrell, Frances Lovington
Jr High Language Arts Tchr
LONGVILLE
Herrington, James Grady
Principal
Johnson, Jacquelyn Chapman
Kindergarten Teacher
Newsome, Jean Brand
6th Grade Lang Arts Teacher
Pharris, Alvie
Mathematics Teacher
LOREAUVILLE
Joseph, Lucille Darby
Fifth Grade Teacher
Larson, Norma Hebert
English I Teacher
LULING
Lawson, Virginia Olive
Third Grade Teacher
LUTCHER
Hoover, Eugene H.
High School Teacher & Coach
MADISONVILLE
Frederick, Lee Forrest
Science Teacher

Rapp, Jamie P.
Second Grade Teacher
MAMOU
Fontenot, Christopher Stuart
7th-8th Grade English Teacher
Fontenot, Patrola Ann (Savoy)
5th Grade Teacher
Frank, Donald Ray
Soc Stud & Detention Clnc Tchr
MANDEVILLE
Allan, Christa Bassil
English Teacher
Bernard, Hilly J.
Tchr & Enhancement Pgm Coord
Boudousquie, Anne Henry
Third Grade Teacher
Decker, Laura Elizabeth
Biology Teacher
de Mauriac, Gwenn R. B.
Teacher of Gifted English
Disher, Fay Ann Houves
Math Tchr of Gifted Stdnts
Fields, Virgie C.
Business Education Teacher
Flettrich, Judy Whitman
Louisiana History Teacher
Gaines, Walton Jay
Assistant Principal
Gilvey, Regina Weldon
Art Teacher
Hebert, Wanda Lorentz
7th Grade Mathematics Teacher
Mac Donald, James Craig
Tchr of Gifted Soc Stud Stdnts
Mathison, Terri Jackson
Science Teacher
Patron, Sandra Acomb
Seventh Grade Math Teacher
Plesh, Melanie Anne
English Teacher
Sandoz, Jackie Sparacio
Reading & English Teacher
Sullivan, Elizabeth M.
Fifth Grade Tchr of the Gifted
Wilson, Lonny Lee
Guided Group Study Program Dir
Wood, Sharon Bodie
8th Grd Tchr of Gifted English
Woodworth, Robert Newton, Jr.
Environmental Science Teacher
MANSFIELD
Hunter, Kay Smith
Gifted Resource Teacher
Junkin, Carol Laffitte
Computer Teacher
MARINGOUIN
Kolb, Judy Crousillac
Fifth Grade Teacher
MARKSVILLE
Gaspard, Robby Joseph
Science Teacher
Laborde, Errol Joseph
Teacher
St Romain, Charlotte G.
Science Teacher
MARRERO
Albarado, Joan Terrebonne
Second Grade Teacher
Allan, George W., Jr.
Social Studies Teacher
Anderson, Elizabeth Harrison
Spanish Teacher
Angeles, Kree Ann (Lilley)
Resource Teacher of GATE
Ardeneaux, Elaine D'Angelo
English Teacher
Begg, Michael J.
Asst Development Director
Beoubay, Lois Larose
Biology Teacher
Carr, Chenelle Elaine
Speech & Sociology Tchr
Chin, Gaye Stiglets
6th Grade Teacher
Clark, Evelyn Johnson
Business Education Teacher
Conway, Michael James, SDB
Youth Ministry Coordinator
Crochet, Grace Ledet
Retired Primary Grade Teacher
Cruice, Michael E.
Math Teacher & Dept Head
Cruice, Shelley Graham
Mathematics Teacher
Culverson, Elizabeth H.
Eng, Speech & Comm Tchr
Drake, LaQuerita Richard
High School Teacher
Fallon, William Robert, Jr.
Social Studies Teacher
Felder, Dell Metoyer
Asst Prin & Lang Arts Tchr
Flattmann, Julie Brechtel
8th-9th Grade Reading Teacher
Florent, Beauty Nell Jackson
High School English Teacher
Fugler, Rebecca Elizabeth
English Teacher
Hourcade, John E., Jr.
Physical Science Teacher
Hunt, Lance Ware
Asst Aerospace Science Instr
Lally, Vilma Rivera
Second Grade Teacher
Lazare, Bryan Michael
Mathematics Teacher
Matthews, Karen Sue
Instrumental Music Educator
Mesa, Elida Lopez
HS Spanish Teacher

Miller, Suzanne
Freshman Theology Teacher
Naquin, Neal Gregory
Band Director
Ory, Thomas Joseph
Assistant Principal
Perez, Berchmans Jennings, III
Assistant Principal
Petitjean, Sylvia T.
Mathematics Teacher
Plauche, Deborah Navarre
Fourth Grade Teacher
Rabig, Jeanne Pat
ESL Teacher
Segura, Melba Elizabeth
English Teacher
Spano, Anthony Joseph
History Teacher & Coach
Steel, Carolyn Daigle
Bus Ed Teacher & Dept Chprsn
Sweeden, Debra Miceli
Science Teacher & Principal
Thibodeaux, Shannon E.
Science Teacher
Thompson, Hilda M.
Physical Education Teacher
Trentcosta, Norman Arthur
Science Teacher
Vedros, Denise Taulli
Math Teacher
Verret, Thomas K.
Tech Ed Prep Site Facilitator
Witte, Sharon T.
Fifth Grade Teacher
MATHEWS
Foret, Karen Knight
Math Teacher
MAUREPAS
Vicari, Alesia Stilley
English Teacher
MAURICE
Franques, John M.
Science Teacher
Frederick, Denise Falcon
Fifth Grade Teacher
Trahan, Charlene Frederick
Math Teacher
MER ROUGE
Williams, Alvin Troy
Mathematics Teacher
MERAUX
Darcey, Duane P.
English Teacher
Krause, Paulette L.
Senior Counselor
Pou, Daniel E.
Senior Physics Teacher
Roebuck, Kendahl Alan
World History Teacher
MERRYVILLE
Franks, Cynthia Wylie
Teacher & Admin Assistant
Lilley, Mary Craft
Librarian
METAIRIE
Aguiar-Netto, Harriet G.
Sci Dept Head
Babineaux, Philip Joseph
Counselor
Baisier, Maria Davis
English Teacher
Barton, Sherri Lewter
Religion Teacher
Beckman, Eileen Kolb
English Department Chair
Bordelon, Cheryl Delatte
English Teacher
Brown-Darbon, Barbara Ann
Math Teacher
Bucher, Shawn Larrieu
French Teacher
Burns, Ray Nell
Eighth Grd Social Studies Tchr
Cain, Mary Alice Legendre
Earth Sci Teacher & Dept Chair
Capaci, Brenda Trosclair
Business Education Teacher
Casey, Jan Bourgeois
Social Studies Teacher
Charles, David Christopher
Law, Psych & Amer History Tchr
Cooper, Raleigh Ernest, III
Aerospace Science Instructor
Culver, Mary Margaret
Lobanov-Rostovsky
Social Studies Teacher
Dauterive, Janie W.
7th-8th Grade Literature Tchr
DiBartolo, Elvina Vivien
Mathematics Teacher
Drez, Mary Beth Remes
Assistant Principal
Firmin, Mark J.
Mathematics Instructor
Fourroux, Katherine Mipro
English Teacher
France, Kevin Charles
Asst Dir & Soc Stud Dept Chm
Frigo, Anthony T.
Head Band Director
Genevay, Michael Eugene
Band Director & Asst Principal
Gravois, Peggy G.
5th-6th Grade Rdng Lang Tchr
Guerin, Merle Higgins
Civics & Economics Teacher
Guichet, Otis P.
English Teacher
Holmes, Willie Evelyn
Business Education Teacher

METAIRIE (cont)
Jackson, Hazel Truluck
Title I Teacher
Jones, Elizabeth Strong
English Teacher
Jongbloed, Barbara Nunes
Second Grade Teacher
Klein, James Herbert
6th-8th Grade Science Teacher
Klock, Sandra Slaten
Soc Stud Chprsn & Tchr
LaCour, Yvette Vezina
Campus Minister
Lapre, Thomas Joseph
English Teacher
Le Bon, J. Walter, Jr.
Physics Teacher
Lewis, Fay Harthcock
Biology Teacher
Malone, Marilyn G.
Math & Latin Teacher
Maloney, Rebecca Scudari
Science Teacher
Manceaux, Mary Ann
Parish Coord & Band Dir
Mason, Sandra Riggs
Gifted Resource Teacher
McGuire, Michael Martin
Physical Ed Coord & Teacher
Miller, Carolee Brophy
Art & Gifted English Teacher
Moak, Mary Jane Whitfield
Fine Arts Department Chairman
Nicholson, Sheila Ann
Social Studies Teacher
O'Brien, Esther Phelps
Algebra I Teacher
Penter, Elizabeth DeWitt
Fourth Grade Teacher
Perdomo, Elena Todini
Foreign Language Dept Chprsn
Peters, Frankie Horton
Gifted Biology Teacher
Pisciotta, Erin Marie
Art & Fine Art Apprec Teacher
Rainey, Patrice Cheramie
Eleventh Grade Teacher
Richard, Arthur John
Ninth Grade Algebra Teacher
Riess, Kathleen Markey
Eng, Spch & Theatrcl Arts Tchr
Rosato, Laurie Stewart
Chemistry Teacher
Rost, Lois Anne
Vice Principal
Schuber, Margaret Beacham
Head of Middle School
Smith, Ann S.
5th & 6th Grd Mathematics Tchr
Smith, Roberta O'Dell
Retired Assoc Prof of Bio Sci
Spears, Sylvia Austin
Dept Chprsn & Rep Teacher
Suprean, Connie Lynn
Physical Education Teacher
Tadlock, Susan Melady
Mathematics Teacher
Torrence, Diann Howard
Mathematics Teacher
Trower, Kevin Francis
Latin & English Teacher
Tynes, Patricia Ann
Physical Education & Hlth Tchr
Voltz, Pamela Pigott
4th Grade Teacher
Wagner, Samuel, V
High Schl English Teacher
Waldrop, Martha Troxler
8th Grade English Teacher
Wall, Carol O.
2nd Grade Teacher
Ware, Elizabeth Cambre
Math & Science Teacher
Weidenbacher, Albert Frank, Jr.
Ath Dir, PE & Driver Ed Instr
Westholz, Frances Carroll Daly
Resource Teacher
Wilbert, Kathleen Kirk
Second Grade Teacher
MIDLAND
Leger, Bradley Allen
Agrisci & Agribusiness Instr
MINDEN
Belton, Martha Louise
Teacher of Academically Gifted
Harman, D. J.
Band Director
Jones, Judy Penny
English Teacher
Stevens, Iantha Hampton
Business Teacher & Counselor
Wright, Gloria Pickrom
English Teacher
MONROE
Allen, LaRue A.
10th-12th Grade Biology Tchr
Baldwin, Michelle Silvy
English Teacher
Barron, Judith M.
Teacher of Gifted Sci & Math
Breard, Janet Williams
Spanish Teacher
Bristo, Daniel Gene
Biology & Bible Teacher
Brock, Margaret Small
Retired Guidance Counselor
Burkett, Sharon Roberts
French Teacher
Butler, Bobbie Lawrence
Bio & Chem Tchr of the Gifted
Chardkoff, Joan Corb
French Instructor
Ciccone, Mary Frances
GATE English & Reading Tchr
Coats, Lyneta Beth
Eng, Cmptr & Sociology Tchr
Coleman, Michelle Lenard
Spanish Teacher
Conway, Maurice Hall
Teacher
Dante, Jules C.
Chemistry Teacher
Davis, Brenda Smith
6th Grade Mathematics Teacher
Dayton, Dianna Victoria
Fine Arts Dept Head & Art Tchr
Edmondson, Susan Bosso
Mathematics Teacher
Ernst, Annice Newman
Jr High Math & English Tchr
Fields, Beverly Ann Johnson
Third Grade Teacher
Fleming, Mildria West
LD Resource Teacher
Galle, Jo Kuhn
English Assistant Professor
Graham, Dianne Allen
English & Psychology Teacher
Graham, Judith Anne
8th Grd Eng Teacher & Chrprsn
Gremillion, Elizabeth Marie, DC
Sixth Grade Teacher
Harris, Lula Rodgers
Biology Teacher
Harrod, Rebecca Huenefeld
English & Amer History Teacher
Hill, Betty J.
Administrative Coordinator
Howard, Chrys
Special Services Teacher
Huey, Margaret A.
Advanced English I Teacher
Johnson, Sharon White
Mathematics Teacher
Jones, Elaine Arrant
Advanced Placement Eng Tchr
Kelly, Dorothy Parra
Language Arts Teacher
Kemner, Cheryl
Mathematics Teacher
Kennedy, Katherine Gardner
Geometry Teacher
Landrum, Shirley Curry
English Teacher
McClelland, Mary Anne
English Department Head
Mc Kee, Sadie Joseph
Sixth Grade Teacher
McNeal, Dorothy Glover
Social Studies Teacher
McPherson, Caron Tullos
Special Education Teacher
Medley, Karen Hemphill
High School Art Teacher
Menyweather, Mary
Kindergarten Teacher
Moore, Betty Clay
7th Grade Amer History Teacher
Oliver, Mona Acosta
Asst Professor of English
Olson, Kay (Farrar)
English Teacher
Overturf, David J.
Instr of Hlth & Human Perfmnc
Paris, Judy Ewbank
Former Math Teacher
Payne, Bobbie Mc Innish
4th Grade Teacher
Rogers, James Robert
Math Department Tchr & Chair
Shackelford, Kim Hawkins
Mathematics Instructor
Sharp, Karen Dean
Art Department Chair & Tchr
Smith, Bessie Grossley
Biology Teacher
Tao, Ye
Orchestra Director
Tatum, Maxine M.
Fifth Grade Teacher
Thomas, Barbara Gilliam
Science Teacher
Tucker, Mary Helen (Price)
Ninth Grade English Teacher
Walker, Samuel Etta
French & English Teacher
Walters, Denny Ray, Jr.
Mathematics Teacher
Webb, Paula Bauer
Teacher of Gifted & Talented
Weedman, Grace Lindsey
Gifted English Teacher
Wheeler, Darren Lee
PE Teacher & Coach
White Gunter, Nedra G.
First Grade Teacher
Worthington, Nancy Cozort
Music Teacher & Orchestra Dir
Zykan, Linda Diane
Reading & Earth Science Tchr
MOORINGSPORT
Golden, Lucy Ouzts
First Grade Teacher
Mc Manus, Michele Dickerson
Special Education Teacher
MOREAUVILLE
Armand, Christine Tassin
Math Teacher & Counselor
Moreau, Mary Tyler
English Teacher & Chairperson
MORGAN CITY
Autrey, Pat Swiber
English Teacher
Bagwell, Teresa T.
US History & Psychology Tchr
Chauvin, Cindy (Clayton)
Third Grade Teacher
Dinger, Mary Herrington
English & French Teacher
Dupre, Susan Vining
English Teacher
Frederick, Juanita G.
1st Grade Teacher & Asst Prin
Galler, Tina Bergeron
Teacher
Henry, Melanie Latanya
Business Teacher
Holcomb, Catherine Provost
English & Journalism Teacher
Johnson, Shannon Blaine
Pre-Algebra Teacher
Lewis, John C.
Science Teacher
Martin, Diane Theriot
English Dept Chair & Tchr
Myers, Jerry John
Math Dept Chprsn & Teacher
Pennison, Patrick Thomas
Social Studies Teacher & Coach
Stadalis, Joseph Martin
Physics & Physical Sci Teacher
Thomas, Mary Roy
5th Grade Teacher
Tregle, Alfred Francis
Athletic Director & PE Teacher
Wamble, Robert B.
Earth & Life Science Teacher
MORGANZA
Robertson, Gary P.
Social Studies Teacher
Stafford, Elizabeth Pearce
English Teacher
Terrance, Helen George
7th & 8th Grade Reading Tchr
Williams, Juliet Taylor
American History Teacher
MOUNT HERMON
Thomas, James Troy
Vocational Agriscience Teacher
Toney, Sandy Wilcox
Third Grade Teacher
Vernon, Onshella Magee
English Department Chairperson
Williamson, Charles T.
Math & Physics Teacher
NAPOLEONVILLE
Blanchard, Melanie Susan
7th-8th Grade Reading Teacher
Fussell, Sandy Bergeron
Accounting Teacher
Hausknecht, Sharon Ann
Family & Consumer Sci Tchr
Simoneaux, Paul James
Gifted & Talented Instructor
NATCHITOCHES
Beier, Nahla M.
English Teacher
Blend, Benay D.
History & English Instructor
Clay, Louise Wilcox
Retired 5th Grade Teacher
Ebarb, William Lawrence
Director of Fiscal Affairs
Elvestrom, Michael David, BSG
Art Teacher
Evans, Christina Lloyd
Teacher of Gifted Program
Findley, James Lee
Humanities Teacher
Flanagan, Essie Ruth
Home Economics Teacher
Garcia, V. Carol Barnidge
Chem Tchr & Sci Dept Chprsn
Gleason, Linda Ruth
Mathematics Instructor
Gregory, Bob
Math, Cmptr Sci Tchr, Dept Chm
Hall, Elizabeth Zakarison
Latin Teacher
Harkrider, Millard Travis
Computer Science & Math Instr
Hebert, Carol Hicks
Business Teacher
Ingram, Brenda Stanford
Supervising Teacher
Jones, Charles Howard
Arts Dept & Piano Instructor
Laborde, John Leslie
High School Guidance Counselor
Martinetti, Anthony James
English Instructor
McBride, William G.
His Instr & Hum Dept Head
Mc Grath, Michael Ross
Mathematics Teacher
Pinet, William T., III
Computer Science Instructor
Roach, Linda Easley
Asst Prof Of Sci Ed
Sampson, Clinton J.
PE Tchr, Asst Basketball Coach
Song, Xiang-Ning
Physics Instructor
Straham, Robin M.
English Teacher
Taylor, Terry Lynn
History Instructor
NEGREET
Funderburk, Sharlee Salter
Business Education Teacher
Savell, Donna Cummings
JR HS Mathematics Teacher
NEW IBERIA
Babineaux, Marilyn D.
Guidance Counselor
Brantley, Rae Duchesne
World History & Geography Tchr
Daspit, Toby Allan
Teacher of the Gifted
Joseph, Jennifer B.
Principal
King, Brenda W.
Computer Science Teacher
Meech, Sally Borque
5th Grade Rdng & Spelling Tchr
Rapp, Anne Hynes
Honors Social Studies Teacher
Vice, Peggy C.
Second Grade Teacher
NEW ORLEANS
Adams, Saundra Stallworth
Health Occupations Teacher
Agan, Jennifer Howe
8th-10th Grd Mathematics Tchr
Albert, Margaret Pereira
Middle & High School Educator
Alexander, Nathalie Sherman
Mathematics Teacher
Alexander, Tommie Mason
Staff Development Teacher
Alfaro, Lorraine Wright
Coordinator of Vocal Studies
Allen, Stella Thompson
Chemistry Department Chprsn
Allende, Amy Viso
Former Mathematics Teacher
Amedee, Rita JoAnn
Sixth Grade Teacher
Anderson, Beverly Ann
Instructor of Nursing
Andrews, William N.
Principal
Arnolie, Juanita Mc key
Sci & Louisiana Studies Tchr
Augustin, Sheila Ann
Kindergarten Teacher
Autin, Nancy Pellerin
Acad Asst Prin & Math Teacher
Bailey, Blake
Teacher of Gifted Lang Arts
Barzon, Marie Thomas
Kindergarten Teacher
Bennett, Helene Mary
1st Grd Transitional Teacher
Blanchard, Patricia J.
Dir of Chrstn Life & Eng Tchr
Bonin, Raphael Robert
5th Grade Teacher
Boucvalt, Catherine Johnson
Physical Life Science Teacher
Bourgeois, Carolyn Blanche
Asst Professor of Education
Brechtel, Rebecca U.
Gifted Social Studies Teacher
Broadway, Ruby Lindella
Associate Professor of Biology
Brody, Weekee Wong
Music Professor & Grad Coord
Broussard, Francis Peter
Adjunct English Instructor
Brown, Gwendolyn Joseph
Adjunct English Professor
Brown, Leola Smith
English Teacher
Bryant, Earle Vincent
English Professor
Buckner, Vivian Portia (Fuller)
7th & 8th Grade Teacher
Buisson, Jeanne Roussel
HS Math & Science Teacher
Burrell, Brenda
Assoc Professor of Special Ed
Butcher, Kathryn
Coord of Eng as Second Lang
Butera, Lydia Ann
Literature Teacher & Principal
Byrne, Patricia Warren
Mathematics Teacher
Carlson, Elizabeth Doxsee
English Instructor
Carter, Jane Burr
Assoc Prof of Classical Stud
Carter, Patricia Gabriel
Teacher
Carter Ellis, Janice Elizabeth
English Teacher
Cashner, Robert
Professor
Choudhury, A. Shameem
Director of Honors Program
Clay, Janice J.
Cooperative Office Ed Tchr
Cola, Quintella Boult
Social Studies Teacher
Condiff, Donna Marie
Kindergarten Teacher
Cook, Beverly Ruth
High School Art Teacher
Cook, Helen Cassimere
Third Grade Teacher
Coutin, Vivian Deschapelles
Span Tchr & Frgn Lang Dept Chr
Criddle, Beverly Baham
English Teacher
Danielson, Susan Nussbaum
Mathematics Instr & Acad Cnslr
Dapremont, Valerie Hewlett
Fourth Grade Teacher
Davis, Verna McCormick
8th Grade Math & Science Tchr
Dean, Frances Smith
Math & Cmptr Literacy Tchr
DeGruy, Patricia Vagas
Sixth Grade Teacher
Depreo, Eileen Spicuzza
Social Studies Chairperson
Doll, Mary Aswell
Prof of English
Draper, David Elliott
Professor of Music
Druhan, Erin Donahoe
9th-12th Grd Art & Yrbk Tchr
Dugger, Richard Charles
Asst Prof of Music Education
Eberle, V. Joyce Lapiana
Second Grade Teacher
Elfman, Julia Ann Youngblood
Teacher of Gifted Resource
Elliott, Tabeika Lynett
Teacher
Farrelly, Judith Ann
Spanish Teacher
Favre, Beverly C.
Social Work Professor
Fitzpatrick, Elizabeth Butera
Math Teacher
Fortenberry, Carole Jackson
Health & Physical Ed Teacher
Fox, Earl Jacob, Jr.
Band Director
Francois, Edna Woods
English Teacher
Frank, Zelma Lloyd
Dir of Student Support Svcs
Gage, Ethel Barber
Kindergarten Teacher
Ganitsky, Joseph
Professor of International Bus
Gentry, Judith Johnson
Asst Prof of Clinical Nrsng
Gibson, Brian Keith
Mathematics Teacher
Gourrier, Valerie Prevost
Art Teacher
Granier, Sandra Vicknair
Pub Relations Director
Greco, Bonita Marie Stables
Algebra I & Geometry Teacher
Griffith, Bernard Wayne
Asst Prin & Economics Tchr
Grossimon, L. A.
Math & Comp Literacy Tchr
Gruenig, Shawn Sigl
Teacher of Gifted
Guma, Ginger
MS Drama & English Teacher
Hadley, Charles D.
Research Prof of Political Sci
Halpern, Katherine Kay
Associate Professor of Nursing
Hammond, Donald Heath
Assoc Prof of Management
Harris, Wilbert David
11th-12th Grd Soc Studies Tchr
Hawkins, Clifford Jerome
Sixth Grade Teacher
Herbert, Joseph Gilbert
Music Professor
Herring, Sarah Marshall
Lang Arts Tchr & Dept Chair
Hess, Michael David
Gifted Social Studies Teacher
Holmes, Linda George
Kindergarten Teacher
Hoover, David William
Theatre Professor
Horne, William Phinazee
Music Professor
Hosch, Gordon Adolph
Professor of Accounting
Howard, Byron, Sr.
Fifth Grade Teacher
Huck, Margaret Mary
Chemistry Teacher
Hudson, Sharon Marie
Fifth Grade Teacher
Ieronimo, Giuliano Celestino
HS Visual Arts Teacher
Jackson, Carolyn Robertson
Teacher & Dean of Students
Jackson, Lizzie Williams
Ninth Grade Science Teacher
James, Felix
History Professor
Jefferson, Patrick O'Neal
Administrative Asst to Pres
Jett, Nancy Marie
Fourth Grade Teacher
Jimenez, Roberto Ortega
Spanish & Religion Teacher
Johnson, Charles Conrad
Spanish & English Teacher
Johnson, Edward Fields, Sr.
Fifth-Sixth Grade Teacher
Johnson, Karen Marie
Geometry Teacher
Johnson, Shelia Eugene
Pre-Kindergarten Teacher
Johnston, Lynda Kay
Math Dept Chair & Algebra Tchr
Jones, Sterling Anthony
Teacher
Jordan, Bettyrae Ives
Asst Professor of Nursing
Karnell, Phillip E.
Professor of Drama
Kinchen, John Dawson, III
Prof of Music Theory of His
Lacy, Pharris
Teacher

ORLEANS (cont)
irault, Suzanne Dright
lish Teacher
st, Bonnie White
lish Teacher
erson, Sharon Ryan
lish Teacher
y, Rita Lorraine
Teacher
an, Charles Clifton
lish Teacher
nont, Michelle Ann
Grd Language Arts Teacher
oseph Huan
h Teacher
n, Lew Edward
hematics Professor
ine, William B.
ebra Teacher
man, Peter J.
tical Science Professor
n, Sharon O'Quinn
ence Dept Chair & Teacher
e, Peggy L.
h Teacher
ha, Jacquelyn Lynn
Grade Math & Science Tchr
Daphne
ounting Professor
onado, Judith Helmke
dance Counselor
use, Judith B.
ond Grade Teacher
, Meredith A.
hematics Instructor
nall, C. Pierson
mistry Teacher
Patricia Angeles
8th Grade Sci & Span Tchr
, Aldor Loring
n & Educl Tech Dept Chm
artney, Jewell Smith
dle Grade Team Leader
arty, Kathleen Gaines
lish Department Instructor
ullough, John Edward
nish Teacher
sker, Diane Steinert
ors American History Tchr
wain, Susan Gingold
ogy & Chemistry Teacher
overn, Daniel G.
h Teacher & Disciplinarian
in, Gloria Crawford
ence Teacher
, Chester St. H.
ociate Professor
ell, Iola Gordon
Grade Teacher
L'genia Joffrion
al Studies Teacher
ey, Frankie Galmon
ce Business Education Tchr
Leanna Blackman
English Teacher
one, Mary Napoleon
Grade Teacher
gomery, Elwanda Morgan
h Grade Teacher
mer, Roy
cipal
er, Gerald Joseph
lth Education Instr & Coach
hy, Kay A.
lish Instructor
k, Tommye Gail
Dir of African Amer Stud
n, David Lowell
sic Professor
kov, George John, Jr.
ministrative Assistant
nnell, Cynthia Katherine (Petrusek)
Arts Chprsn & HS Art Tchr
man, Kathleen Ann
oc Prof of Religious Stud
, Nchor Bichene
rd & Asst Prof of Pol Sci
ettle, Heather Cruickshank
hematics Teacher
ma, Washington Ije
ed Math Teacher
an, Raj
mistry Professor
r, Arlie Quincy
lish Teacher
r Jackson, Audrey Lee
Grade Teacher
ns, James Calvin
lish Teacher
Janice Mary
h Grade Teacher
cki, James A.
n & Video Teacher
, Yvonne Spear
hematics & English Teacher
s, Lois Ewell
dance Counselor
, Aelita Jurjevics
fessor of Biological Sci
exter, Judith Cecelia
mistry & Biology Teacher
Arvilla Miller
& 8th Grd Lit Teacher
st, Margery Yvonne
rd-Sixth Grade Teacher
an, Phyllis Toups
lish Teacher
Zhaoming
fessor

Randall, Wanda Francois
Third Grade Teacher
Rice, Patricia Wegmann
High School Counselor
Riemer, Terry Edmund
Assoc Prof Electrical Engrng
Roberts, Janie Herbert
Middle School Teacher
Robertson, Betty Smith
Language Arts Teacher
Robinson, Doris Samuels
Principal
Ross, Brenda Marie
Gifted Resource Teacher
Rossi, Ronald C.
American History Teacher
Rouillier, Michael John
Lecturer of History
Saizan, Carmel Rose
Teacher & Asst Principal
Salise, James Peter
Instructor of CADD
Sander, Stephanie Ann
Teacher & Admin Asst
Sanders, Charles Edward
Asst Prof of Business Mngmt
Sanders, Jane
Social Studies Teacher
Schiller, Susann Rutledge
Principal & Eight Grade Tchr
Schock, Peter A.
Associate Professor of English
Schuth, H. Wayne
Professor
Senegar, Leon
Language Arts Teacher
Shay, Diane Indest
Guidance Counselor
Shirer, Patricia Ann
English Teacher
Smart, Ann D.
Science Dept Chprsn & Teacher
Smith, Donna Adams
Mathematics Teacher
Smith, Young William
Eng & Creative Writing Instr
Sneed, Barbara Follins
French Teacher & Dept Chair
Somervill, Winona Robertson
Assoc Professor of Sociology
Spencer, Brenda
6th Grade Teacher
Spinella, Faith Ann
Assistant Professor
Spitzfaden, Thomas Joseph
Theology Teacher
Stephens, Sharon Kaye
NASA Training Site Director
Steward, Betty Nolan
Sixth Grade Teacher
Stirgus, Michael J.
Math Chairperson
Strassel, Audrey M., MSC
Math Teacher & Librarian
Stroup, Gerald L.
Graduate Student
Taulli, Janice Ann
Asst Prof of Clinical Nursing
Taylor, Herbert G.
History Teacher
Terry, Tyrone Kenneth
2nd & 3rd Grade Teacher
Theriot, Catherine Jarboe
Secondary Mathematics Teacher
Thomas, Mary
Mathematics Teacher
Tinguee, Tracy Johnson
4th Grade Teacher
Torregano, Michael James
Band Director
Triche, Karen Miller
Computer Literacy Teacher
Tu, Shengru
Asst Prof in Computer Science
Tucker, Stephen R.
Social Studies Dept Chair
Tuckerson, Audrey Patterson
HS Mathematics Teacher
Turner, Kathleen J.
Communication Professor
Tyson, Toni-Lynn O.
Supervisor & Asst Principal
Vaccaro, Sue Borne
Third Grade Teacher
Valdin, Robin Rotherham
English Teacher
Vance, Timothy Allen
Asst Professor of Psychology
Verdigets, Michelle Michelet
English Teacher
Villemarette, David Paul
Science Teacher
Villere, Cheryl B.
Third Grade Teacher
Vincent, Darryl Alphonse
Health Sciences Teacher
Vinnett, Dorothy Brown
First Grade Teacher
Voigt, Lydia
Professor of Sociology
Wagner, Pamela Gorum
Staff Development Teacher
Ward, Barbara Anne
Teacher of Gifted English
Ward, Patricia Ann
Language Arts Teacher
Watson, Ernie Lee
Marine Corps Jr ROTC Instr
Weber, Flora Gordon
Fourth Grade Teacher

Welch, Robert
Mathematics Teacher
Wellhousen, Karyn Rhea
Early Childhood Education Prof
Williams, Gaynelle Foe
English & Speech Teacher
Williams, Lelia Georgia
Special Ed Teacher
Williams, Meaurex Martin
Pre-Kindergarten Teacher
Williams, Mollie Marie
2nd Grade Teacher
Williams, Stella Campbell
Computer Sci & Math Teacher
Wolfe, George Cropper
Art Teacher
Wood, Guy Charles
Band Dir & Instrmntl Mus Tchr
Woodward, Ralph Lee, Jr.
Professor of History
Wright, James David
Professor of Human Relations
Wu, Wanda
Nursing Instructor
Ybos, Cynthia SHank
Clinical Instructor
Zell, Randal James
Biology Teacher & Student Adv
Zimmerman, Lenora Chandler
Teacher of Academically Gifted
Zimmerman, Michael Edward
Professor of Philosophy

NEW ROADS
Atkinson, Edith Sterling
Science Teacher
Henderson, Mary Ostarly
4th Grd Language Arts Teacher
LeBlanc, Bonnie Sue Aguillard
Second Grade Teacher

NORCO
Bienvenu, Peggy Flynn
Computer Teacher
Matherne, Brian Anthony
Teacher

OAKDALE
Fitzgerald, Chris Holman
Science Teacher
Reed, Karen Creel
Principal
Whitman, Sharon Wright
Elementary Vocal Music Teacher

OBERLIN
Pearce, Zollie Tyrus
Principal

OPELOUSAS
Bainter, Mary Oge
Resource Teacher
Bergeron, Debbie Flanagan
Mathematics Teacher
Davis, Carolyn Allen
Eighth Grade Reading Tchr
Duplechain, Glenda Joubert
Second Grade Teacher
Gaines, Anna C.
Biology & Chemistry Teacher
Gordy, Mary Ross
Junior High Language Arts Tchr
Hunt, Priscilla A. Green
English Teacher
Jones, Emma George
Librarian & Reading Teacher
Pollingue, Charmaine Verrette
High School Science Teacher
Preston, Richard Paschal
Science Teacher
Reynolds, Beverly Handy
8th & 9th Grd English Teacher
Ryder, Brenda Quebedeaux
Third Grade Teacher
Skrantz, Emery
Fifth Grade Teacher
Stephen, Joseph Eugene
English & Fine Art Teacher
Stevens, Floyd Charles
Social Studies Teacher
Tolson, Jacquelyn Young
Retired 5th Grade Teacher
Urban, Donna Young
Mathematics Teacher
Washington, Matthew, Sr.
8th Grade Math Teacher
Watson, Catherine G.
Spanish Teacher

PARADIS
Gaudin, Rhonda Hotard
Eighth Grade Math Teacher

PATTERSON
Byrne, Lisa A.
12th Grade Teacher
Gouaux, Robbi Lirette
8th Grd Math & Computer Tchr
Governale, Jean Carol
Jr HS Social Studies Teacher
Hidalgo, Judith Bergeron
9th-12th Grade Science Teacher
Trevor, Evelyn Jay
Secondary Teacher

PAULINA
Bergeron, Barbara Hymel
6th-8th Grd Soc Stud Tchr
Dufresne, Cathy Millet
Second Grade Teacher

PEARL RIVER
Beaushaw, William Miley
Social Studies Teacher & Coach
Fandal, Amy Nix
English Teacher
Howard, Russell Anne Foti
Family & Consumer Science Tchr

King, Tiffini Ann
Bio & Environmental Sci Tchr
Lunsford, Virginia Moncada
Art Teacher
Messina, Darlene Addison
Band, Chorus & Music Teacher
Smith, Ronnie L.
Physical Education Teacher

PIERRE PART
Sedotal, Brenda Ann
Math & Adult Ed Teacher

PINE PRAIRIE
Johnson, Judith Elaine
English & Civics Teacher

PINEVILLE
Barnes, Levenia Maxwell
Professor of Education
Barnes, Ted D.
Art Professor
Brumfield, Madeliene Fortino
5th Grade Teacher
Cofer, Bruce Ray
Assoc Professor of Economics
Cofer, Judy B.
English Teacher
Crain, Louise Toney
K-5th Grd Tchr of the Gifted
Dabbs, Jennifer Burns
Dept Coord Sociology Soc Work
Davis, Sylvia Yancy
English Teacher
Guy, Debra Howell
Fourth Grade Teacher
Hanson, Gretchen Loewer
Asst Professor of Biology
Henry, Bonnie Thiels
2nd Grade Teacher
Hollis, Freida Hale
Title I Teacher
Howell, Thomas
History Professor
Kelly, Vickie Young
Dir of Assist Student Success
Lundy, Dianne H.
Family & Consumer Science Tchr
McAllister, Ann Motte
Social Work Program Director
McKee, Linda Gilbert
Jr High Language Arts Teacher
Mc Pherson, Karen Lanoue
Former Elementary Educator
Normand, Bonnie Longino
Teacher of the Gifted
Prince, Dorothy Griffin
Third Grade Teacher
Simpson, William M.
Professor of History
Valley, Linda Faye
Third Grade Teacher
Watson, Dennis R.
Chm of Natural Sci & Math Divs
White, Karen Gaspard
Teacher
Williams, H. Davis
Band Director
Yang, Ben H.
Associate Professor of Music

PITKIN
Avant, Ramona Copeland
Science, Biology & Chem Tchr
Babcock, Charlene Perkins
3rd Grade Teacher
Britt, Connie Perkins
English Teacher
Richmond, Elsie Anding
Mathematics Teacher

PLAIN DEALING
Jones, Ronald Ray
High School Math Tchr & Coach
Lamb, Janice Olive
Math & Creative Writing Tchr
Walding, Terri
Special Education Teacher

PLAQUEMINE
Allain, Blanche Dupre
Math & Computer Science Tchr
Carroll, Gloria Dean
Seventh & Eighth Grade Teacher
Williams, Alison Bains
Social Studies Teacher

POLLOCK
Mc Kay, Debbie Kees
Third Grade Teacher
Sparks, Ann
Third Grade Teacher

PONCHATOULA
Crovetto, Mary Beth Link
English & Speech Teacher
Grigas, Stephen Allen
American History Teacher
Welch, Vickie Shaffer
3rd Grade Teacher

PORT ALLEN
Beverly, Willie Mae
8th Grade Lang Arts Teacher
Kennedy, Willie F.
Principal
Washington, Gloria Warner
Kindergarten Teacher
Wilson, Barbara Batiste
5th Grade Math Teacher

PORT SULPHUR
Moreno, Delia Hernandez
First Grade Teacher

PRAIRIEVILLE
Blackwell, Deborah Lee
Teacher of Gifted Students
Harvey, Rhonda Evalyn
Acad Gifted Resource Tchr

Johnson, Dorothy Jordan
Third Grade Teacher
LeMaire, Charmon Gail
6th-7th Grade Soc Stud Teacher

PRINCETON
DeFreese, Jane Case
8th Grade LA Studies Teacher
Hewitt, Barbara C.
8th Grd Language Arts Teacher
Leon, Debra Trombetta
6th Grade Language Arts Tchr
Perry, Patrice Townsend
Teacher of Gifted Education

PROVENCAL
Kay, Ruth Sepulvado
Principal

QUITMAN
Freeman, Jacqueline D.
High School Science Teacher
Pierce, James R.
Social Studies, H & PE Teacher
Shovan, Steven Ray
Mathematics Teacher

RACELAND
Pitre, Ray Anthony
Instrumental Music Teacher

RAYNE
Doucet, Margaret Leger
Kindergarten Teacher
Harris, Candace B.
Fifth Grade Teacher
Proctor, James Wilbert
Principal
Touchet, Barbara Potier
4th Grade Teacher

RAYVILLE
McPherson, Diann Collie
Jr High Science Teacher
Schwich, William Joel
History Teacher & Coach
Thomason, Sarah A.
English & Spanish Teacher

REEVES
Land, Barbara Doiron
Kindergarten Teacher
Monceaux, Dave James
Athletic Dir & Speech Tchr

RESERVE
Donaldson, Joy Chopin
English Teacher
Ernewein, Philippe
Special Education Teacher
Gauthier, Marjorie Louise (Paulsen)
Soc Stud & Lang Arts Tchr
Nicholson, Ervin
Former Technology Teacher

RINGGOLD
Beatty, Bruce Edward
High School English Teacher

ROANOKE
Zaunbrecher, Teresa Germany
Language Arts Teacher

ROSEPINE
Brown, Mark Thomas
Algebra I & II Teacher
Calhoun, Linda
Librarian
Cole, Frances Morrow
Gifted & Talented Student Tchr
Granger, Melinda A.
English Teacher

RUSTON
Andrews, Ann Denton
Life Science Teacher
Barham, Barbara Ann
English Teacher
Barron, Randall Franklin
Prof of Mechanical Engr Dept
Burton, Rickey Lee
Social Service Facilitator
Dick, Linda Wright
Lang Arts Tchr of the Gifted
Huth, Suzanne Childers
Assistant Professor
Johnson, Elaine Childers
Geometry Teacher
Johnson, Jerald Eugene
Fourth Grade Teacher
Lewis, Mary Jane Mc Elrath
High School Art Teacher
May, Shirley Hoof
Teacher of At Risk Students
Mayfield, Marilyn Mc Intyre
Sixth Grade Teacher
McDowell, Michelle Phillips
High School Spanish Teacher
Milstead, Pamela Toms
Mgmt Information Systems Instr
Overstreet, Sarah A.
Mathematics Teacher
Potts, Ruth Collins
English Teacher & Dept Chair
Pyles, Sue Holland
Associate Professor of Nursing
Sanders, Joan Elizabeth
Curr, Instr, Ldrshp Asst Prof
Silver, Debbie Thompson
Site Coordinator
Smith, Charlotte Welch
Eighth Grade English Teacher
Stewart, Howard D., Jr.
Physics Teacher
Strother, Joseph Willis
Director School of Art
Talley, Amy Riley
Chemistry & Phys Science Tchr
White, Donna Hightower
Chemistry & Physics Teacher

SAINT AMANT
Baker-Brown, Yvonne Bell
Reading, Eng, Art & Lit Tchr
Blanchard, Beverly R.
Secondary Math Teacher
Hebert, Lucille A.
Social Studies Teacher
LaCaze, Lynette B.
Business Education Teacher
Landry, Darlene Frances
Special Education Teacher
Landry, Sandra Rickner
English Teacher
Oubre, Alice Dornier
Secondary Teacher
Oubre, M. Alice Dornier
Secondary Math Teacher
Poirrier, Veronica W.
English Teacher
Schexnayder, Carl J.
Band Director
Schexnaydre, Deenie Wright
6th Grade Language Arts Tchr
Tullier, Iva Lambert
Fifth Grade Teacher
SAINT BENEDICT
Foley, Augustine Edward, OSB
Philosophy Teacher
SAINT BERNARD
Buras, Susan Connell
Social Studies Teacher
Guerra, Regina Misuraca
English Teacher
Harvey, Patricia Ann
Fifth Grade Teacher
Mc Reynolds, Georgia Wood
English Teacher
SAINT FRANCISVILLE
Baker, William Theodore
Naval Science Instructor
Hughes, Leigh Brummett
Teacher of Gifted
King, Peggy T.
Spanish Teacher
Ramshur, Colleen Dickey
Choral Director
Stewart, George Calvin
Naval Science Instructor
Webb, Mary Ann
Social Studies Teacher
SAINT JAMES
Beard, Lane Buren
Agriscience Teacher
Ezidore, Barbara Winchester
Social Studies Teacher
Ezidore, Judy Joyce
Biology Teacher & Counselor
Gauthreaux, Kermit Joseph
Chemistry & Physics Teacher
Harris, Clara Mae
Teacher
SAINT JOSEPH
Blanche, Tonya Lewis
Math, Sci & Soc Stud Teacher
SAINT MARTINVILLE
Alexander, Dorothy Wiltz
Kindergarten Teacher
Brosius, Nancy L.
Social Studies Teacher
Courville, Similian James
Sci, Math & Lang Arts Teacher
Guidry, Cathy LeBlanc
Third Grade Teacher
Hartman, Diane
Guidance Counselor
Olivier, Karen Talley
Librarian
SAINT ROSE
Maddox, Joseph Michael
7th Grd Lang Arts & His Tchr
SALINE
Madden, Douglas Felton
Agriscience Teacher & Coach
Martin, Debra Warren
Cnslr & Bus Ed Tchr
SCOTT
Bertrand, Virginia Young
6th Grade Science Teacher
Cormien, Irene Watson
Third Grade Teacher
Fogleman, Shirley Theriot
8th Grd French & English Tchr
Gilbert, Pat Thibodeaux
Math & Computer Literacy Tchr
Hebert, Charlotte Credeur
Third Grade Teacher
SHONGALOO
Benefield, Kaye Jester
English Teacher & Librarian
Flynn, Jeanne Dean
7th-12th Grd Math Teacher
Lyons, John Whitlock
Soc Studies Dept Chm & Teacher
SHREVEPORT
Alford, Robert Lee
9th Grade Algebra I Teacher
Bates, Betty Mosley
Fifth Grade Teacher
Beauchamp, Jesse Louis, Jr.
Mathematics Teacher
Begnaud, Pamela W.
HS Dance Tchr & Danceline Spon
Bell, Murrilline Burnette
Assistant Professor of Math
Bissell, Mary Kent
Geometry & Algebra Tchr
Boyd, Cynthia Morgan
1st Grade Teacher
Boyd, Joe Edward
Physical Education Teacher
Brooks, Julia Hall
Third Grade Teacher
Brown, Georgia R.
Assistant Professor of Biology
Brown, Margaret Lynn
Eng Tchr & Asst Sftbl Coach
Bryant, Wayne Henry
University Counselor
Burford, Sharon Porter
4th Grade Language Arts Tchr
Clark, J. Stephen
Assoc Professor of Classics
Clark, Paul
JROTC Instructor
Conger, Lucy Youman
Secondary Math Teacher
Cowdin, Barbara Lieber
First Grade Teacher
Cox, Evelyn Sue
English Teacher
Cunningham, Shannon Jay
Spcl Ed Tchr & Head Bsbl Coach
Dawson, Omerror Consalina, III
Math Teacher
Degenhart, Karen Sue
Business, Mrktng Tchr & Coord
Douglas, Evelyn Marie (Myles)
Ninth Grade English Teacher
Ellerbe, Rebecca Ann
8th Grade Math Teacher
Escude, Bobby Hammons
7th Grd Amer History Teacher
Evans, Darryl Keith
Director of Bands
Ezernack, Patsy D. Smith
6th-8th Grd Vocal Music Tchr
Fair, Darlene Portier
Second Grade Teacher
Gallant, Kathryn Powell
Eng, Jrnlsm Tchr & Admin Asst
Gant, Carl Ellis
Early Childhood Professor
Giles, Shirley Jewell Moore
Fifth Grade Teacher
Gilmore, Larry
Librarian & Media Specialist
Grassi, Augustine Michael
Senior Army & JROTC Instr
Gruettner, Mark Martin
Assistant Professor of German
Grunes, Rodney Arthur
Prof of Political Science
Guerrero, Kevin Keith
Assistant Principal
Harper, Sandra Poss
2nd Grade Teacher
Hinze, Carrie Mc Clelland
Teacher of Academically Gifted
Holoubek, Stephanie Coffman
Computer Coordinator & Teacher
Howard, Marian Elizabeth
High School Math Teacher
Hunt, Dee Germany
Middle School PE Teacher
Hunton, Clara Carr
Curriculum Coordinator
Igbokwe, Emmanuel Chukwuemeka
Anatomy & Physiology Professor
Johnson, Dorothy Jean (Auston)
Teacher & PE Dept Chairperson
Joshua, Percy
English Teacher
Keene, William Roy
American History Teacher
Kennedy, James Robert
Physics & Phys Sci Teacher
Knuckles, Micheal
English, Speech & Drama Tchr
Kress, Dana Alan
Assistant Professor of French
Lamkin, Michelle M.
English Creative Writing Tchr
Loyd, Sheila Rene
8th Grade Reading Teacher
Mahoney, Jackie Corn
Math Teacher
Malmay, Sherri D.
Biology I Teacher
McCollough, Kathryn Stall
Lecturer & Staff Accompanist
Mc Michael, Charles Ernest
Social Studies Teacher
Mc Pherson, Alvadus Bradley
Professor of Biology
Meehan, Camille Johnson
French Teacher
Morehead, Deborah Betts
GATE World Literature Teacher
Nectoux, Joseph John
Middle School Teacher
O'Neal, Kathy W.
Teacher & Department Chair
Osment, Sylvia Ann Moore
Teacher
Owen, Vicki M.
Health & PE Teacher
Pederson, William David
Political Science Professor
Peek, John Michael
Assoc Prof of Political Sci
Penuel, Patricia Forbes
Spanish Teacher
Porter, Stephen Duane
Middle School Art Teacher
Rettelle, Kathryne Weferling
String Instrument Specialist
Rolinger, Rosetta Gregorio
Third Grade Teacher
Salone, Mary Burton
9th Grade English Teacher
Sandifer, Cheryl Beatty
World Geography Teacher
Schmidt, Pamela Powell
GATE Language Arts Teacher
Shea, Jane Stillwell
LA His Teacher of the Gifted
Shepherd, Samuel Claude, Jr.
History Professor
Simmons-Brown, Rubenstene
Keyboarding Teacher
Slay, Shirley A.
Social Studies Teacher
Sledge, Cathy Whitten
GATE Dept & English Teacher
Smith, Peggie George
Algebra Teacher
Sowders, Delbert Dwayne
Science Teacher
Stewart, Kathy S.
Mathematics Teacher
Taylor, Pecola
Reading Recovery Teacher
Thomas, Sheryl Anita
Biology Teacher
Thompson, Charles Chester
JROTC Instructor
Tisby, Anita Lind
Former Music Teacher
Trahan, Jeffrey F.
Professor of Physics
Vowels, Mitzi Hauser
First Grade Teacher
Walker, Bobbie Burnell
First Grade Teacher
Walmsley, Mary Clay
Teacher
Welch, Patricia Hansen
Preschool Special Ed Teacher
Whitehead, Barbara Ann
Social Studies Chprsn & Tchr
Williams, Nathan Paul
Science Teacher
Yaz, Yvonne Ilke
Mathematics Professor
SIMPSON
Keathley, M. C.
Social Studies Teacher & Coach
SIMSBORO
Ferrel, Sherri Barfield
Science Teacher
Gaudet, Gloria Elaine
Fourth Grade Teacher
Sims, Kathy Conville
Second Grade Teacher
Smith, Daisy Powell
Third Grade Teacher
Taylor, Freda Nash
Second Grade Teacher
SINGER
Beckcom, Jeanez L.
Science Teacher
SLIDELL
Barrett, Thomas Joseph, III
Science Teacher
Bonnette, Melody D.
History Teacher
Bougere, Shirley Speeg
English & Social Studies Tchr
Braud, Theresa Ellen
Chemistry Teacher
Brooks, Janice Danna
Elementary Teacher
Chimento, Dale Bernard
Mathematics Teacher & Coach
Cooper, Denise (Selby)
Social Studies Teacher
Cunningham, Janice Mayfield
Math Teacher
Dailey, Shirley Bastian
Computer Science & Math Tchr
Deane, Margaret Davis
First Grade Teacher
Duhon, Charlene Hayton(Layburn)
Counselor
Eades, Marian Brandt
Health, PE Teacher & Coach
Eades, Robert N.
Physical Ed Tchr & Coach
Ellinwood, Ellen Nunez
Math Teacher
Eversull, Jill Anders
Second Grade Teacher
Fischtziur, Joanne Stanley
Math Dept Chair & Teacher
Frechou, Paul Aloysius
Band Director & Fine Arts Tchr
Gatlin, Linda Pickering
Biology Teacher
Guste, Henrietta Vinas
Spanish Teacher
Hernandez, Elise Fritchie
High School Math Teacher
Hess, Naomie LaBurthe
Math & Pre Algebra Teacher
Hobson, Joanne Kaupp
Science Teacher
Jacobs, Jean Guedry
Math Teacher
Katz, Joan Mc Cleary
Retired Teacher
Klos, Donald Eugene
Religion & English Teacher
Kondas, Janet Calongne
French & English Teacher
Kraus, Patricia Wade
Fourth Grade Teacher
Ladner, Norma Foley
History Teacher
Le Normand, Kathleen Bader
English Teacher of the Gifted
Meyers, Karen Altmann
Fourth Grade Teacher
Mohr, Janice Douglass
American History Teacher
Morris, Elizabeth Matherne
English Teacher
Moyle, Judith Baisler
Rdng & Lang Tchr of the Gifted
Pansano, Virginia Clark
Second Grade Teacher
Ponson, Joseph Albert
Guid Cnslr & Drivers Ed Tchr
Prendergast, Anne Mayfield
Brdcstng & Career Orntn Tchr
Pressley, Ann Wright
8th Grd English & Reading Tchr
Reynolds, Jane Baer
Assistant Principal
Richard, Jill Alford
8th Grade Science Teacher
Sager, Kim Culotta
Physical Ed Tchr & Coach
Schexnayder, Manfred Jean
Latin Instructor
Schmidt, Misty Cutrer
LA Studies Teacher
Schmit, Sharyn Kearney
Mathematics Department Chair
Schneider, Timothy William
Director of Bands
Scott, Angela Magee
Band Teacher
Severs, Joan Sasseen
Social Stud & Lang Arts Tchr
Sheffield, Patsy Elaine
Speech Teacher
Shumaker, Shelly Ruiz
Science & Bible Teacher
Sisson, Linda Kateri
Math, Community Ed Coordinator
Smith, Rene C.
Earth Science Teacher
Soileau, Dorothy Jumonville
Fifth Grade Teacher
Soniat, Diane Duhon
Gifted Math Teacher
Spiehler, Jeralyn Page
Freshman Counselor
Swalm, Renee Bellows
English Teacher
Thomas, William Moore
Physical Education Teacher
Urreta, Denise Dolores
LA Stud & Lang Arts Tchr
VanZandt, Gloria T.
Tchr of Gifted Social Studies
Vogt, Denise Sabrio
Teacher of Gifted Social Stud
Yeates, Cheryl Whittington
Mathematics Teacher
Yohe, Margaret M.
Math Teacher & Dept Chair
SPEARSVILLE
Burns, Emma Lee U.
Retired First Grade Teacher
SPRINGFIELD
Briggs, Rose Demonica
Science & Math Teacher
Kuhn, Thomas Joseph, Sr.
Assistant Principal
SPRINGHILL
Applegate, Karen Vest
Math Teacher
Carpenter, Joan R.
Language Arts Teacher
STERLINGTON
Ransom, Carol Ullman
English Teacher
STONEWALL
Stanley, Shelba S.
Itinerant Teacher of Gifted
SULPHUR
Bonsall, Kathy Gaskin
Chemistry & Biology Teacher
Clark, Kathy Simmons
Second Grade Teacher
Farrar, Anne
Retired Eng Tchr of Gifted
LeBlanc, Joann Dias
Assistant Principal
Perkins, Lora Livengood
Latin Teacher
Richardson, Craig Stephen
Fifth Grade Teacher
Schanz, Dale Beglis
Louisiana Studies Teacher
Texada, Linda Edwards
Resource Teacher
Thomason, Thomas Stuart
World Geography Teacher
SUMMERFIELD
Harris, Vicki Henry
Business Education Teacher
SUNSET
Arnold, Rosa Lee
8th Grade English Teacher
SWARTZ
Embanato, Karen Sibley
Fourth Grade Teacher
TALLULAH
Dailey, Walter
History Teacher & Coach
Esters, Lucille Toldson
Math & Science Teacher
Fort, Bobbie Moore
English & Sociology Teacher
Magoun, Louise Testa
English Teacher
Moreland, Hattie Jean-Williams
Reading Teacher
Powell, Dava Annette
Voc Ed & English Teacher
Watts, Patty Fairbanks
Algebra Teacher
Williams, Geneva Guy
Reading Teacher
THIBODAUX
Beslin, Scott Jude
Mathematics Professor
Bonvillain, Gina Hebert
Preschool Special Needs Tchr
Bonvillain, Shirley Kraemer
Business Education Teacher
Boudreaux, Laurie Legendre
Instructor of Mathematics
Bouterie, Karen Hebert
Kindergarten Teacher
Chiasson, Lloyd Ernest, Jr.
Professor of Mass Comm
Dennis, John H.
Associate Professor of History
Didier, Raymond Ernest, Jr.
Head Volleyball Coach
Duet, Rick Joseph
Assistant Professor
Fairchild, Joseph Virgil, Jr.
Professor of Accounting
Folse, Earl J.
Psych & Cnslr Ed Dept Head
Guidry, Michele Dantin
Accounting Instructor
Harrist, Ronald Anthony
Religion Tchr & Key Club Adv
Jack, Lenus, Jr.
History & Geography Dept Head
Janusa, Michael Albert
Asst Professor of Chemistry
Jordan, Anne Falgout
7th & 8th Grade Science Tchr
Kooros, Syrous K.
Prof of Economics & Finance
LaFleur, Charles Paul
Associate Professor
LaFleur, Elizabeth Kerley
Associate Professor of Mrktg
Mandhare, Keshav S.
Chemistry Professor
Menezes, Doris D.
Reading Coordinator
Middleton, David Edward
Distngd Svc Prof of Eng
Morton, Mary L.
Professor of English
Oncale, Linda Terracina
Hnrs Calculus & Adv Math Tchr
Phillpott, Denise Landeche
Math Teacher
Rosser, Betty J.
Instructor
Stilling, Erik Andreas
Asst Prof of Mass Commnctn
Stroud, J. B.
Professor of Accounting
Thibodeaux, Ruth Gros
English Teacher
Toups, Stephen L.
Band Director
Trahan, Anne Boudreaux
Assistant Professor of English
Weber, Richard C.
Agriscience Instructor
Weimer, John Louis
Associate Professor of Bus Law
Worthington, Janet Evans
English Professor
TIOGA
Carey, Joyce Fryar
Tenth Grade English Teacher
Carpenter, D. Karl
Dir of Bands & Music Dept Chm
Despino, Theresa Rosier
Physical Education Teacher
Lindsay, Elizabeth Quinn
Math Teacher & Debate Coach
Lott, Sandra Carrier
English Teacher
Wiley, Darrell Glenn
Social Studies Teacher & Coach
URANIA
Walters, Charles K.
Amer His & Earth Sci Teacher
VACHERIE
Bolden, Fannie Williams
Reading & Social Studies Tchr
Jacobs, James, Jr.
Retired Band Director
Lassere, Iris Moses
Guidance Counselor
VENICE
Vaughn, Patricia Nations
Home Economics Teacher
VIDALIA
Bacon, Willie Mae
Business & Computer Ed Teacher
Costantini, Diane Osborne
Math & Computer Science Tchr
Grimble, Mildred Jennings
Mathematics Teacher
Hilton, Pamela Edwards
Seventh Grd Mathematics Tchr
Marsalis, Dorothy Alexander
Business Education Teacher
Webster, Josephine Sanders
Sixth Grade Reading Teacher
VILLE PLATTE
Ardoin, Virginia Smith
Social Studies Teacher
Hamlin, Bobby Max, Jr.
Science Dept Chariman & Tchr

E PLATTE (cont)
ı, Rella Marie
ling & English Teacher
ie, Gene A.
ish Teacher
er, Phyllis Mire
ith Grade Reading Teacher
Kay Ortego
d Grade Teacher
as, Regina O'Conner
riculum Coordinator
ON
, Ruby Higdon
ily & Consumer Science Tchr
erson, John C.
ness Education Teacher
el, Mitchell Wayne
al Studies Teacher & Coach
el, Roxanne Miller
h & Computer Science Tchr
ovich, Lori Young
ogy Teacher
AN
gton, Laura Clementi
nish & French Teacher
, Herman G.
y JROTC Instructor
, Robert Lloyd
ness Education Teacher
ow, Charlotte Tyson
Ed & English Teacher
at, Jesse
hematics Teacher
KER
haw, R. K.
ogy Teacher & Coach
Nona Allen
mistry Teacher
rs, Beth Fitzgerald
ding Teacher
, Jean
al Studies Teacher
an, Rebecca Howze
dergarten Teacher
et, Colleen Colter
hematics & Science Teacher
orn, Donna Jean
ironmental Science Teacher
SON
son, Patsy Bunyand
cipal Designee & Teacher
, Mary Christian
t Grade Teacher
d, Cindy F.
nth Grd Eng & Math Teacher
r, Robert Glenn
lish Teacher
ent, Laurie Callahan
mistry & Biology Teacher
dle, Anita Jones
cipal
SH
Darlene Edgar
iness Education Teacher
rde, Nathan Peter
iscience Teacher
e, Tonna K.
ence Teacher
nomme, Clarence Joseph
ebra I & General Sci Tchr
T MONROE
ns, Dianne bodron
r of the Hearing Impaired
ard, Mary C.
enth Grade English Teacher
, Billy Wayne
Grade Earth Science Tchr
ks, Jamie Rene Berry
cher of Gifted & Talented
dson, Rissa Eley
Grd Teacher of Gifted Math
a, Mary Linda
th Grade Teacher
Kathryn Traweek
glish & Language Arts Tchr
erson, Queen E.
cial Education Teacher
Linda Manyweather
urth Grade Teacher
oway, Dona Smith
Grade Teacher
ston, Glenda Owens
th Grade Lang Arts Tchr
ston, JoNell G.
th Teacher
lon, Carol G.
th Grade Teacher
nor, Nancy Baker
st Grade Teacher
nnis, Margaret Miles
Grd Gifted Lang Arts Tchr
Manus, Deborah Thompson
fted Mathematics Teacher
vanger, Delia H.
ench Teacher
is, Carolyn Martin
urth Grade Teacher
esbee, LaVon Barnes
ence Dept Chair & Tchr
rd, Frances Anne Miller
cond Grade Teacher
hney, Mary Kathryn
rld History Teacher
erts, Susan Willey
g Tchr of the Gifted Prgm
ı, Aurelia Ann Shields
st Grade Teacher
mons, Terry Lynn
orld Geography Teacher

Sistrunk, Carolyn Hinton
Mathematics Teacher
Stephens, Marjo Chaney
Sixth Grade Teacher
Traweek, Sharon Auttonberry
Journalism Teacher
Warner, James
Soc Stud Chm & Amer His Tchr
Williams, Lori Harrist
Fifth Grade Teacher
WESTLAKE
Buchholz, F. Elaine Russell
Physical Education Teacher
Caldarera, Frank Max
PE & Drivers Education Tchr
Crick, Lee R.
Social Studies Teacher
Ecker, John Jacob
Band & Choral Director
Hungerford, Chris L.
6th-8th Grade Band Director
Richardson, Karen Kaye Sigler
English Teacher
WESTWEGO
Blackwell, Karen Elaine
Band Director & Music Teacher
Damare, Connie Schneider
English Teacher & Asst Prin
Dares, Melissa Higgins
7th & 8th Grade History Tchr
Feehan, Laura Hatcher
Kindergarten Teacher
Knighten, Karen Brooks
Fourth Grade Teacher
Larkin, Mark Bruce
Social Studies Teacher
Pinney, Jean Long
Title I Facilitator
WHITE CASTLE
Selmon, Betty Johnson
Mathematics Teacher
Trepagnier, Stella Chiek
Science Teacher
WINNFIELD
Carroll, James Lee, Jr.
Band Director
Joe, Lee Edward
Business Education Teacher
Vines, Steve
Vocational Agriculture Teacher
WINNSBORO
Beasley, Mary Ann Givens
Fifth Grade Teacher
Cagle, Janie Taliaferro
6th Grade Math Teacher
Cordill, Naomi Causey
High School Teacher
Mohl, Sladen John
Senior Army Instructor
YOUNGSVILLE
Le Doux, Rita Tate
Classroom Teacher
ZACHARY
Anderson, Vivian Norsworthy
Drama Teacher
Brown Stevenson, Sue
Fifth Grade Teacher
Carter, Brenda Bennett
Special Education Teacher
Cole Black, Stephen
SR Army Instructor
Kline, Donna Bradley
English Teacher
Mc Hugh, Catherine Bondurant
Math & Computer Science Tchr
Shipp, Renee Foshee
Health & Phys Ed Teacher
Thomas, Cynthia Nobles
Choral Director & Piano Tchr
ZWOLLE
Leggett, Cara Parsons
Home Economics Teacher
Remedies, Stephen Lamar
Physical Education Teacher
White, Ramona
Seventh Grade Teacher

MAINE

ATHENS
Mitchell, Scott Nathan
Middle Level Tchr & Asst Prin
Moulton, Tammy Lynn Frith
Science & Mathematics Teacher
AUBURN
Appleby, Penny Ligler
Literacy Speclst & Drama Coach
Jacobs, Ethel Bowden
Instructor of Communications
Ogg, Karen Hand
Art Teacher
Shore, Meredith Mann
Math Teacher
Stauffer, Anne E.
Fourth Grade Teacher
AUGUSTA
Cole, Nancy Clifford
Early Chldhd Occupations Instr
Desmond, Mabel J.
State of Maine Representative
Donar, Robert Anthony
Bus Ed Tchr & Coach
Fitzgerald, Betsy Forrester
History Dept Head
King, Lynne Fonieczko
Associate Prof of Nursing
Lachance, Elaine Estelle
5th-6th Grade Teacher

LaPointe, Laurence Arthur
English Instructor
Neighoff, Carolyn Sue
Physical Ed & Hlth Dept Head
Porath, Sheila Nadile
English Teacher
Rudnick, Isidore Leslie
Music Professor
Schlenker, Jon Arlin
Sociology & Anthropology Prof
Towle, Dennis G.
English Teacher
BANGOR
Clain, Janice Lee
Spanish Teacher
Cowan, William F.
Scndry Social Studies Teacher
Dube, Lorraine G.
Math Teacher
Halkett, Sandra True
Sixth Grade Teacher
Hodge, Maureen A. (Doyle)
Guidance Counselor
Jones, Fred G.
English Teacher
Millett, Nadine M. Orski
Business Ed Tchr & Chairperson
Rice, Marilyn Ann
Physical Education Teacher
Wall, Kathleen Ann
Anatomy & Physiology Professor
Willette, Wayne A.
Alternative Education Tchr
BATH
Haney, Eleanor Humes
Retired Humanities & Rel Prof
Legere, David E.
8th Grade Science Teacher
Tiemann, Maryli Kenoe
English & Fine Arts Teacher
BENTON
Hathaway, Marilyn Mandoff
Fifth Grade Teacher
Otis, Janet E.
Third Grade Teacher
Smith, Whendolyn
Reading Recovery Teacher
BERWICK
Sullivan, John William
Math Teacher
BETHEL
Bean, Karen Gulbrandsen
7th Grd Language Arts Teacher
Keane, Steven
Health Teacher
Morton, William Harold
History Teacher
Tornrose, Russell T.
Eng & Theatre Arts Teacher
BIDDEFORD
Caron, Elaine M.
Assistant Prof of Nursing
Cote, Susan L.
Home Economics Teacher
Danforth, Peter Gregory
Chemistry Teacher
Goulet, Madeleine J.
Hlth, Phys Educator & Coach
Houghton, Ruth B.F.
Mathematics Teacher
Larrivee, Steven E.
Math & Comp Science Teacher
Lizotte, Thomas P.
Band Director
Mc Cann, James E.
11th-12th Grd English Teacher
McDonough, Paul Francis
Social Sci Tchr & Dept Head
Montembeau, Jeanne A.
Sixth Grade Teacher
Mullin, Jerome L.
Associate Prof of Chemistry
Stebbins, Timothy Paul
Social Science Teacher
BINGHAM
Rollins, Gloree M.
6th Grade Teacher
BLUE HILL
Andy, Emil J., Jr.
Asst Headmaster & Math Teacher
Bennatti, Roger Joel
Teacher & Sci Dept Chprsn
Kane, Daniel Joseph
Physical Ed Tchr & Coach
BOOTHBAY HARBOR
Blake, Marcia Sayward
4th Grade Teacher
Cook, Karen Atwood
First Grade Teacher
Deetjen, John H., Sr.
Math, Reading Tchr & Ath Dir
Landry, David E.
French Teacher
O'Connell, Eugenie
Music Teacher
Pinkham, I. J.
Math Teacher & Bsktbl Coach
Saunders, Chris R.
Social Studies Teacher
Williamson, Michael Mason
English Teacher
BRIDGTON
Shane, Elizabeth Harrigan
6th Grade Teacher
BROWNFIELD
Leeder, Rochelle Leslie
Multi-Age Teacher
BRUNSWICK
Audette, William Everett, Jr.
Math Teacher

Callahan, Sharon Linda
8th Grd Language Arts Teacher
Gordon, Marilyn Baumann
Retired Teacher
Haggerty, Mary Kathleen
Fourth Grade Teacher
Hunter, Jerry Leroy
Business Administration Tchr
Jalbert, Sandy
Eng Dept Chair & Writing Tchr
Morris, Andrew Xavier
7th Grd Soc Studies Teacher
O'Donnell, James C.
English Dept Chair & Teacher
Rawson, Pamela Morin
Mathematics Facilitator
Spencer, Jill
Teacher
Wilson, Richard Edward
7th & 8th Grd Soc Studies Tchr
Wright, Lenna Morris
Retired Elem & HS Teacher
BRYANT POND
Szente, Christopher Jon
5th Grade Teacher
BUCKSPORT
Carter, Michael Raymond
Physical Education Teacher
Clapp, Kathleen Lyons
Math Teacher & Dept Chair
CALAIS
Duplissea, Lynda A.
English Teacher
Sanford, Elinor Minnick
Home Economics Teacher
CAMDEN
Moro, Stephen M.
High School English Teacher
Vail, R. Garrett, Jr.
English Teacher
CAPE ELIZABETH
Brewington, William A.
Science Teacher
Brownell, Elaine Jordan
Mathematics Teacher
CARIBOU
Atcheson, Kenneth W., II
Social Studies Teacher
Laraia, Ann Levesque
Third Grade Teacher
Thibodeau, Carol H.
Biology Teacher
Thompson, Roger P.
7th Grade Teacher
CARMEL
Hunt, John H.
7th & 8th Grd Science Teacher
CASTINE
Fegley, Stephen Robert
Associate Prof of Marine Sci
Monberg, Alden Gates
Associate Professor of Math
Otto, Fred Bishop
Associate Professor of Physics
Pilot, Christopher H.
Physics & Mgmt Science Prof
Willmann, Jeffrey Scott
Mathematics Professor
Young, F. Michael
Engineering Professor
CUMBERLAND CENTER
Fordham, Wayne Robinson
Biology Teacher
Thomas, Janice Mischel
Choral Director
DAMARISCOTTA
D'Amico, Anne-Marie
Instrumental Music Teacher
DEER ISLE
Flagg, William R., Jr.
Math & Science Teacher
Grindal, Clare Fifield
English Instructor
DEXTER
Canning, Mary Gerrish
Choral Director
Krauss, Diana S.
English Teacher
Ranagan, Joseph Andrew
Physics Teacher
Schottenfeld, Daniel M.
History Teacher
White, Martha Page
English Teacher
DIXFIELD
St John, William Hugh
English Teacher
DOVER FOXCROFT
Withee, Paul J.
Mathematics Teacher
EAGLE LAKE
Lovley, Barbara S.
Special Education Teacher
EAST LEBANON
LaBranche, Shirley Louise
English & Social Studies Tchr
EAST MILLINOCKET
Conroy, Timothy Lee
Math, Science & Cmptr Teacher
Marks, Ronald Paul
Teacher & Athletic Director
Michaud, David Raymond
Business Teacher
EAST WATERBORO
Wood, Priscilla Ann Bernier
Sixth Grade Teacher
EASTON
Nichols, Mary Ruth Cyr
French Teacher & Librarian

Wright, Bryan R.
Science Teacher
ELIOT
Gaspar, Charles E.
Math Teacher & Dept Head
Oliver-Green, Nancy
English Teacher
ELLSWORTH
Giunta, Maureen Prenda
English Teacher & Dept Chair
Lynch, Teresa Day
2nd Grade Teacher
Thomas, Brenda Ray
Second Grade Teacher
ETNA
Fortier, Gregory K.
Social Studies Teacher
FAIRFIELD
Andrews, Charles Everett
Earth Science Teacher
Gates, James Stearns
Drafting Instructor
Malady, Kevin John
Science Teacher
Marcoux, Joey Albert
7th Grade Math & Science Tchr
Marcoux, Marc Paul
Physics & Chemistry Teacher
Mc Gee, Michael Patrick
PE Tchr & Hd Boys Bsktbl Coach
Spear, Sylvia Niles
English Teacher
Voisine, Ronald Arthur
Social Studies & Math Teacher
Wheeler, Karrie Lynn
English Teacher
FALMOUTH
Herrick, Christopher L.
HS Physics & Math Teacher
FARMINGDALE
Johnson, Peter Hassell
Social Studies Teacher
FARMINGTON
Cyr, Karen Mary
1st-2nd Grade Teacher
FORT FAIRFIELD
Albert, Cindy Lee
Early Multiage Teacher
Dunsmore, Cathy Coats
Early Multiage Experience Tchr
Mc Kenney, Jay Anthony
Third Grade Teacher
Peters, Jeanette Nevers
Health & Physical Ed Teacher
FORT KENT
Chouinard, Donald Peter
English Teacher
Closser, Charles E., Jr.
Prof of Oral Communication
Grant, Paul Q.
Mathematics Teacher
Murphy, Irene E.
Biology Teacher
Plourde-Ouellet, Valerie A.
History Teacher
Sevigny, Scott Dana
Social Studies Teacher
FREEPORT
Dixon, Kimberly Laurene
3rd & 4th Grade Teacher
Irish, Allen M.
Chemistry, Science Topics Tchr
LaForge, Margaret Hanson
Director of Choral Music
FRYEBURG
Condello, Charles Anthony
Instrumental & Gen Music Tchr
Cote-Crosskill, Scott Andrew
Life Science Teacher
Gibson, James C.
8th Grade Science Teacher
McClellan, Anette
Fourth-Twelfth Grade Supvr
St Pierre, James Francis
English Teacher
Strom, Gregory Lawrence
Fine Arts Dept Head & Instr
GARDINER
Young, Patty Ann Levasseur
Spanish & French Teacher
GLEN COVE
Bourke, Mary E.
Art Teacher
Jennings, Kathryn M.
Head Teacher
GLENBURN
Wallace, Rebecca Larkin
7th-8th Grade Reading Teacher
GORHAM
Hannigan, Susan M.
Physical Ed Teacher & Coach
Martin, Peter John
Professor of Music
Pierce, Derek Scott
English Teacher
GOULDSBORO
Boulrisse, Mona Bouchard
Business Education Teacher
Whitney, Charles Dana
Science Teacher
GUILFORD
Dyer, Margo Busque
Art & US History Teacher
Emrich, Robert Keith
Soc Stud Teacher & Dept Chair
HAMPDEN
Elliott, Diane Beaulieu
Special Education Teacher
Mc Connell, Linda Kay
7th Grd Lang Arts & Math Tchr

HAMPDEN (cont)
Morris, Serena J.
Biology & Chemistry Teacher
Stevens, Gifford Maxim
English Teacher
HARRINGTON
Paulson, Charlane Susan (Mc Daniel)
Seventh Grade Teacher
Ramsay, Joan Levasseur
Secondary French Teacher
HARTLAND
Crowley, Osmond E.
7th Grade Math Teacher
HEBRON
Craig, Jennifer Lynn Scaife
Teacher
Moore-Leamon, Silver
Studies Director & Math Tchr
Valeriani, Gino Paul
Science Instructor
HIRAM
Consalvo, Marilee O.
Latin & English Teacher
HOLDEN
Christie, Thomas William, Jr.
Middle School Teacher
Doyle, Elaine Beecken
Seventh Grade Teacher
HOULTON
Carr, Peter Edwards
Bandmaster
Fagnant, Joseph Albert
Instrumental Teacher
Fitzpatrick, Brian Paul
Social Studies Teacher
Inman, Joann Nasuta
English Teacher
Jordan, Carol DeLong
Language Arts Teacher
Kinens, Lee Ann N.
Third Grade Teacher
Snell, Shawn Anita
French & Spanish Tchr
Wade, Heidi Mitchell
English Teacher
West, Darren A.
US History Teacher
ISLESBORO
Conover, Vicki L.
Computer & Business Teacher
JAY
Chase, Raymond Earl
Eighth Grade Science Teacher
Fitzgerald, Robert Patrick, Sr.
Mathematics Teacher
Mitchell, Karen Folsom-Tilton
Chemistry Teacher
Taylor, Robert M.
Science Teacher
JONESPORT
Robinson, Barbara Chamberlain
Kindergarten Teacher
KENNEBUNK
Mitchell, David E.
Math Teacher
Moody, Timothy Robert
Sixth Grade Teacher
Murphy, Thomas William, Jr.
Amer Govt, Ec & US His Tchr
Strickland, Bridget Frances
Math Teacher
KENTS HILL
Turner, Eric James
Social Studies Teacher
KINGFIELD
Kusmin, Jessica Byrne
English & Drama Teacher
KITTERY
Little, Sheryl G.
Social Studies Teacher
Sanborn, Brian Albert
Chemistry Teacher
LEBANON
Zaviskas, Jenny
Fifth Grade Teacher
LEWISTON
Bazinet, James Richard
Fifth Grade Teacher
Beaudin, Doris Pintal
Third Grade Teacher
Belisle, Sally Frank
Retired Teacher
Brackett, Marilyn Janice
Nursing Instructor
Brookhouse, Phil
8th Grade Science Teacher
Burke, Aaron Herbert
Retired Teacher
Courchesne, Michel Maurice
8th Grade French Teacher
Dufour, Louise Ella
Religion Dept Chairperson
Dulac, Elizabeth Ann
8th Grade Language Arts Tchr
Given, Madelyn Kenniston
First Grade Teacher
Goodwin, Rosemarie Levesque
Retired 8th Grd Lang Arts Tchr
Henault, Louise Bernier
Third Grade Teacher
Letourneau, Darlene Anne (Lauziere)
Third Grade Teacher
Levasseur, Dawna L.
8th Grade Eng & Lit Teacher
Marcoux, Carol Gee
Special Education Teacher
Martel, David H.
US History Teacher
Moore, Ann G.
Science Department Chairperson

Reissfelder, Tyson Paul
Biology Teacher
Siragusa, James J.
English Teacher
Ward, Crystal D.
Soc Stud Dept Head & Govt Tchr
LIMESTONE
Gould-Leighton, Susan
Math Teacher
LINCOLN
Emery, Evelyn Peck
Adult Education Teacher
Przystup, Donna W.
7th & 8th Grd Soc Stud Teacher
White, Roberta Weinhauer
Spanish & Latin Teacher
LISBON
Stevens, Gretchen Jane
Fourth Grade Teacher
LISBON FALLS
Crouse, Marsha (Kirtley)
Reading & Science Teacher
Hall, Dean B.
Social Studies Teacher
St Peter, Florence S.
Librarian
White, Barbara Higgins
Language Arts & Reading Tchr
LIVERMORE FALLS
Beedy, Ronald Bradford
History Teacher
Keane, John Patrick
8th Grade Science Teacher
St Pierre, Susan White
History Teacher
Stevenson, Susan York
English & Journalism Teacher
MACHIAS
Sinford, Robert Fred
PE Teacher & Athletic Director
MADAWASKA
Marshall, Edward P.
Physical Education Teacher
MADISON
Blake, Rachel Norton
Language Arts & French Teacher
Doody, Linda Marie (Goodridge)
Fifth Grade Teacher
Stevens, Wilma Brown
Fourth Grade Teacher
MECHANIC FALLS
Tucker, Edward
Social Studies Teacher
MEDWAY
Hanley, George H.
8th Grade Teacher
MEXICO
Batherson, Joanna Park
Second Grade Teacher
La Pointe, Stephen Michael
Social Studies & Language Tchr
Morse, Donna Marie
Teacher
Petrie, Linda Jean Epps
Fourth Grade Teacher
Rouleau, Ann F.
Seventh Grade Teacher
MILFORD
Bernier, Stephanie
Social Studies Teacher
Morrison, Nancy L.
Second Grade Teacher
MILLINOCKET
Ingerson, Bradford I.
Assistant Principal
Metropoulos, Adam Peter
Chemistry Teacher
MILO
Decker, Madeline S.
Spanish & French Teacher
MONMOUTH
Amero, Richard A., Jr.
Business Teacher
Fairchild, Ann Dowe
Third Grade Teacher
MOUNT DESERT
Kerwock, Paul William
French Teacher
MOUNT VERNON
Beedy, Lois Mahon
Sixth Grade Teacher
NAPLES
Bolduc, Karen A.
Earth & Environmental Sci Tchr
Clark, Brian
Biology Teacher
Foye, Jane Libby
Kindergarten Teacher
NEW SHARON
La Bree, Lynda Goodwin
Retired Teacher
Price, Holly Welch
Coord of Gifted & Talented
NEW SWEDEN
Morgans, Ellen Cleaves
7th Grade Teacher
NEWCASTLE
Ebert, Janet Gill
Business Education Teacher
Sims, Patricia S. Taylor
English Tchr & Dept Chprsn
NEWPORT
Dyhrberg, Geoffrey M.
Social Studies Teacher
Lind, Dianne
High School English Teacher
Oakes, Gene
Guidance Counselor
St Lawrence, Diane Marie
Tchr of Deaf & Hard of Hearing

NORRIDGEWOCK
Carter, John William
Ninth & Tenth Grade Teacher
NORTH ANSON
Carbone, Nancy Moody
Fourth Grade Teacher
Lahti, Susan Ainaire
Social Science Teacher
NORTH YARMOUTH
Jack, Stephen Douglas
Fifth Grade Teacher
NORWAY
Gatchell, Lynette Titus
Third Grade Teacher
OAKLAND
Allen, Sharon L.
Third Grade Teacher
Baker, Marshalyn Elaine (Wing)
Mathematics Teacher
DelGiudice, John Michael
Ice Hockey Coach
Kemper, B. J.
English Teacher
Whitcomb, Cornelius James
Owner
Wright, Gerry Linwood
Vocal Music Director
OLD ORCHARD BEACH
Kerry, Jane Elizabeth
High School English Teacher
OLD TOWN
Dube, Julie Lynn
English Teacher
Lucas, Bernie A., Jr.
Fourth Grade Teacher
Pullen, Nancy Fogg
Social Studies Teacher
Walsh, James Richard
Social Studies Teacher
ORLAND
Adamo, Karen L.
7th & 8th Grade Teacher
ORONO
Blair, Farnham
English Teacher
Chilelli, Christopher Jay
6th Grade Teacher
Glueck, Richard D.
Sixth Grd Mathematics Teacher
Landis, Eric Nichols
Civil Engineering Asst Prof
Scott, Linda Kane
Instructor
ORRINGTON
Flood, Pamela Sue
Math, Reading & Lang Arts Tchr
PEMAQUID
Meyers, Karen Hall
Second Grade Teacher
Nilson, Linda Maxson
Reading Support Teacher
PEMBROKE
Luginbuhl, Ann
Resource Room Teacher
PERU
Cox, David Emery
Hlth & Physical Education Tchr
PHILLIPS
Perez, Christine Morales
Special Education Teacher
PITTSFIELD
Treadwell, Julia E.
Dean of Students
PORTLAND
Anderson, Candace L.
Senior English Teacher
Blattstein, Deborah Ann Rothwell
First Grade Teacher
Conlogue, Ruth A., RSM
Science Department Chair
Edwards, Thomas Steven
Asst Prof of Eng & Amer Stud
Frenzilli, Rocco Joseph, III
Physical Education Teacher
Gough, Miriam
Director of Travel & Tourism
Grant, Reginald T.
HS Guidance Counselor
Gurney, Henry J.
Bus, Accounting Dept Chair
Johnston, Jamie
Assoc Professor of Woodworking
Kress, Richard Michael
Latin & English Teacher
LaFond, John Philip
Biology Teacher
Morrison, Donna Lee
Math Teacher
Morrow, Raymond Allen
Director of Jazz Ensembles
Nickerson, Mary Davis
Vice President of Academics
Novey, Judy
Art Teacher
Pappas, Carol Schmouth
9th-10th Grd World His Teacher
Plouffe, Lorraine Patricia
Medical Division Dept Chair
Rowe, Howard Arthur
English Teacher
Santa Lucia, Gaetano Francis
English Teacher
Sears, Anne Cribby
First Grade Teacher
Sproul, David Walter
Science Teacher
Wheeler, Kathleen Garvey
School Social Worker
Whidden, Elsie S.
High School English Teacher

POWNAL
Clukey, Sue Hartford
Fifth Grade Teacher
Phillips, Mark O'Hara
Eighth Grade Teacher
Pinkham, Alison Duckett
7th-8th Grade Teacher
PRESQUE ISLE
Barnes, Jennifer Ann (Irving)
Mathematics Teacher
Chelewski, Ray Edward
Agriscience Instructor
Davidshofer, Claire H.
French Instructor
Lisco, John Fitzgerald
Recreation Professor
Lisnik, Donna Bell
Mathematics Teacher
Lord, Richard Newell, Jr.
Biology Teacher
Mc Lennan-Smith, Nancy
Social Science Teacher
Olore, Timothy Mark
8th Grd Social Studies Teacher
Osgood, Ann Flewelling
Business Instructor
Prescott, Timothy Raymond
Secondary Physical Ed Teacher
Schmidt, Winifred VanPell
Teacher & Volunteer Coord
Scott, Robert Edward, Jr.
Business Instructor
York, Jennifer S.
5th Grade Teacher
PRINCETON
LeTourneau, Carol Ann
Title I Coord & Literacy Spec
RANGELEY
Aylesworth, Chris Robert
HS Science Teacher & Chprsn
RAYMOND
Gorham, Frank
6th Grade Teacher
READFIELD
Ellis, Martha Alden
Math Teacher
ROCKLAND
Bryant, Daniel J.
Computer Teacher & Coordinator
SABATTUS
Allen, Erlene (Hagan)
Business Ed Teacher
Murphy, Kimberly Janet
Music Director
Potvin, Paul
Classroom Teacher
Sherman, Helen Steele
Physical Education Teacher
SACO
Hansen, Michelle Louise
Music Teacher
LeBlanc, Mary Flynn
Dir of Rel Ed & Yth Ministry
Parker, Richard Myron
Chemistry Teacher
SAINT AGATHA
Cyr, Elaine Marie
Secondary Resource Teacher
SAINT FRANCIS
Johndro, Marcia Mae
History Teacher
SANFORD
Kezar, Wanda Leigh
Eighth Grade Science Teacher
Perry, John S.
Mathematics Department Chair
SANGERVILLE
Patten, Darlene Dufault
First Grade Teacher
SCARBOROUGH
Hanscom, Stacie Jane (Shoppell)
Biology, Geography & Sci Tchr
Hayward, Chris
Mathematics Teacher
Murphy, Michael Joseph
6th-8th Grade Multi-Age Tchr
Petras, Ruth Yeaton
Mathematics Teacher
SEARSPORT
Groening, Leanne McLellan
Social Studies Teacher
SEBAGO LAKE
Lucy, Ellen Louise Gowen
Third Grade Teacher
SHERMAN STA
Grady, Rachael Emmons
History Dept Chairperson
SKOWHEGAN
Crowell, Arthur Paul
Chemistry Tchr & Dept Head
Susi, Katherine C.
First Grade Teacher
SOUTH BERWICK
Clinton, Dana Gail
Fr Tchr & Frgn Lang Dpt Chprsn
Ferguson, Michael William
5th & 6th Grade Science Tchr
Petrie, Lee A.
8th Grade History Teacher
SOUTH PARIS
Jordan, Kyle A.
Director of Bands & Orchestra
Knightly, David S.
Teacher & Administrator
Lynch, Nancy Ellen
Mathematics Teacher
MacLeod, Eva-Marie Cunsolo
English Teacher
Mc Kay, Robert Francis
Business Education Teacher

Trebilcock, Caroline M.
High School English Teacher
Tyrrell, Nancy Holmes
Business Ed Dept Chprsn & Tchr
SOUTH PORTLAND
Allen, Margaret Elizabeth
4th-5th Grade Teacher
Baker, Ruthann King
Fifth Grade Teacher
Foster, Margaret Carey
English Teacher
Herbert, William John
Instructor of Law Enforcement
Leary, Aline LeBrun
Language Arts & US His Teacher
Mc Claran, William B.
Law Enforcement Tech Teacher
Roberge, Richard W.
Third Grade Teacher
Towle, Michael Thomas
World Geography Teacher
SOUTH THOMASTON
Baum, Lynda Sprague
Second Grade Teacher
STANDISH
Aronica, Michele Teresa, RSM
Associate Prof of Sociology
Boyd, M. Eunice
Chm & Prof of Nat Science Dept
Clark, Brooks Alexander
English Teacher
Davey, Lynn F.
Psych Prof & Dept Chair
Doyle, Phyllis Louise
Eng Dept Chair & Asst Prof
Hannaford, Arthur G.
Mathematics Teacher
Hoyt, William Chester
Chemistry Professor
MacWilliams, Elizabeth Ulrickson
Science Teacher
Olore, Gina Marie
Business Teacher
Reese, Theodore I.
English Tchr & Wrestling Coach
Rielly, Edward James
Eng Prof & Dean of Distance Ed
Staley, Alene
Business Admin Dept Chair
Sunderman, Marilyn A., RSM
Religious Studies Asst Prof
Turner, Adrienne Barringer
Earth Science Teacher
SURRY
Barrett, Joanne L.
Middle Grades Teacher
THOMASTON
Damian-Marvin, Lisa M.
Science Teacher
Eaton, Mariellen Lucas
English Teacher
Marcoux, Philip James
Sci, Math & Tech Coord & Tchr
Vail, Benjamin P.
Vice Principal & US His Tchr
THORNDIKE
Cross, Arthur Burton, Jr.
Physical Education Instructor
Schultz, Donald Carl
Social Studies Teacher
Wright, Anita D.
9th & 11th Grd English Tchr
TOPSHAM
Baker, Linda Lawson
English & Language Arts Tchr
Brooks, Jeanne Nadeau
French Teacher
Chapman, Chris Priscilla
Art Teacher
Franklin, Barbara A. (Blackmon)
Choral Director
Graffam, Allen Clinton
Band Director
Schlaack, Margaret Landry
6th Grade Teacher
Stilkey, Stewart R.
Biology Teacher
TURNER
Cifelli, Christopher T.
Social Studies Teacher
Fairbanks, Stephen
7th Grade Language Arts Tchr
Leavitt, Duane L.
Chemistry Instructor
Rose, Joyce Lynne
English & Writing Lab Teacher
UNITY
Knupp, David Murray
Assoc Prof Environmental Prgm
Ramsey, Sari
Assistant Professor
Sanborn, John Newell
Professor of English
UPPER FRENCHVILLE
Chase, Mary May (Dionne)
Health Occupation Instructor
VAN BUREN
Belanger, Sharon Lawson
English & Jrnlsm Tchr of GATE
Madore, David Joseph
Business Education Teacher
Michaud, Patricia Ouellette
Fourth Grade Teacher
WALDOBORO
Durgin, Nancy E.H.
US His, Rdng & Eng Teacher
Goddard, Paula C.
Junior High Teacher
Haynes, Randall Walter
Eng, Cmptr, His & Bible Tchr

OBORO (cont)
Margaret Miller
& Science Teacher
o, Karen B.
h, PE Teacher & Coach
Linda Marie Dolloff
uage Arts Teacher
BURN
ry, Elizabeth Adams
rian & French Teacher
Sue Henderson
, Physics & Calculus Tchr
Joan Wallace
& Social Studies Teacher
RBORO
, Andrea M.
ess Education Teacher
s, Mayvella R.
sh Teacher
Mary Law
rd Language Arts Teacher
s, Winthrop T.
School English Teacher
ds, Betty B.
tor of Guidance
Jonathan David
rade Teacher
RVILLE
Martha E.
ce Teacher
ve, Daniel J.
rd US History Teacher
Carole Cutliffe
c Teacher
g, Anne D.
sh Teacher
g, Thomas Elton
sh Teacher
n, Gayle T.
h & Family Studies Tchr
eld, Lawrence Eben
h Grade Teacher
Shannon Scully
Grade Teacher
Rosemarie King
ce Teacher
Darlene R.
ish & Math Teacher
S
, Harriette Gavaza
ter I Reading Teacher
od, Daniel Cole
ical Ed Tchr & Act Dir
, Jay
ness Education Teacher
SUMNER
s, Clarissa Richardson
ing Teacher
BROOK
ari, Cynthia F.
nce Teacher
Frances Mollica
Chldhd Occupations Tchr
Todd Lester
ing Instructor
, Maryanne Shapazian
d Grade Teacher
s, Ronald
gtn & Rdng Recovery Tchr
, Douglas W.
ish Teacher
EFIELD
lm, Beth Ann
rature & Writing Teacher
ON
, Robin Brasier
& 2nd Grade Teacher
, Donna Chick
ding Rcvry & Title I Tchr
Ruth Browning
ner Teacher
HAM
s, Eliza Jane
dance Counselor
, Ruth Louise
mistry Teacher
uil, Terrilynn Barden
Teacher & French Tutor
ey, Leslie M.
cher & Coord of Gifted Ed
lin, Jeffrey Scott
ond Grade Teacher
ton, Harold Clifton, Jr.
Grade Social Studies Tchr
Debora Reynolds
rth Grade Teacher
tt, Carole Dunbar
Grade Math Teacher
tt, John
h Dept Chairman
n, Donna Jean
Grade Teacher
tford, Martha Thurlow
lish Teacher
rson, Richard George
ral Music Director
Rand, Anna Marie
h Grade Teacher
, Barbara Foote
& Music Director
ers, Estelle Watson
lish Department Head
ni, Anne Thibodeau
h Grade Teacher
SLOW
er, Kathy Bowman
rarian & Renaissance Coord
Linda Rasmussen
Grd Reading & English Tchr

Wendell, Dolores G.
Science Teacher
WINTER HARBOR
Weaver, Mary Lou (Burt)
K-8th Grade Art Teacher
WINTHROP
Edwards, Robert K.
Physics, Math & Computer Tchr
Geyer, Virginia E.
Physical Ed & Health Teacher
WISCASSET
Liebmann, David W.
Assistant to the Director
WOODLAND
Towle, Kevin Arthur
Hlth, PE Tchr & Stu Ath Coord
WOOLWICH
Striewski, Edward P.
Fifth Grade Teacher
YARMOUTH
L'Heureux, Donald Christopher
Schl Counselor & 5th Grd Tchr
Tarbox, Anne W.
Art Teacher
Webster, Elaine Gerber
History Teacher
YORK
Randolph, Susan I.
History & Psychology Teacher

MARYLAND

ABERDEEN
Brown, George William, Jr.
Retired 6th Grd Soc Stud Tchr
Corbin, Stephanie Ann
English & Journalism Teacher
Mc Bee, Andrew Avery Digges
English & Drama Teacher
Thompson, Dolores Bak
Business Teacher
Ward, Patricia Lynne
4th Grade Teacher
ACCIDENT
Bulka, Thomas Michael
Computer Science Teacher
Coburn, Lynn Ann
English Teacher
Derlan, Sharon E.
English & Theater Teacher
Farrar, Rick
Lead Science Teacher
Harman, Yolanda Michelle (Forno)
10th & 12th Grd Bio Instructor
Himmler, Charles Joseph
Coordinator of USST Program
Hinebaugh, Donna Buckel
4th Grade Teacher
Langley, Denise Blank
Mathematics Tchr & Dept Head
Law, Barbara Doyle
Child Care & Home Ec Teacher
Martin, Joanny Jones
Guidance Counselor
Martz, Homer B.
Automotive Technology Teacher
Martz, Kelly Ann (Riley)
English II Teacher
Mosser, Von William
Physics Teacher
Roberts, Teresa L.
Art Teacher
Settle, Sharon E.
Language Arts Teacher
Sherwood, Rosanne Evans
5th Grade Teacher
Stough, Scott David
Drafting & Technology Teacher
Vent, Thomas E.
AD, Football Coach & PE Tchr
ACCOKEEK
Glyda, Bonnie Rae
Foreign Lang Tchr & Dept Chair
Sobnosky, Carol Ann (Frantz)
Fifth Grade GATE Teacher
Van Natta, Richard C.
4th & 5th Grade Math Teacher
ANNAPOLIS
Ariola, Kelly Marie
Business Education Teacher
Bell, Virginia Russell
Elementary Physical Ed Teacher
Block, Laurence Erwin
Teacher & Dept Chairman
Connell, Royal W.
Naval Science Instructor
Crosier, Sandra Kay
Mathematics Teacher
Curry, Lee Martin
Outdoor Education Director
Deterding, Christopher David
Mathematics & Cmptr Sci Tchr
Flanagan, Charles M.
English & History Dept Chm
Haas, Katherine Hsu
4th Grade Teacher
Hamrick, Kimberly Kae
Math Teacher
Honey, Erin Ellen
Psychology & World His Tchr
Johnson, Agnes Franklin
Substitute Teacher
Johnson, Debra Ann (Vaultz)
Fifth Grade Teacher
Knisely, Linda Sue
Chemistry & Physics Teacher
McMullen, Timothy Michael
Honors Ec Instr

Moochler, Olive Parsons
5th-7th Grade English Teacher
Morony, Rosemarie E.
Eng Chprsn & AP Hnrs Instr
Peckham, Diana J.
English Teacher
Penn, Larry Darnell
Administrator
Poisson, Terry Eiseman
8th Grade His & Lang Arts Tchr
Scher, Helena Ellinghaus
Assistant Principal
Stevenson, Allan Charles
Psychology Teacher
Sullivan, Carol Benjamin
French Teacher
ARNOLD
Dabrowski, Lawrence John
Science Teacher
Halberstadt, Avis (Levy)
Math Teacher
Iyengar, Sridharan S.
Professor of Chemistry
Larsen, Paul M.
Assistant Professor of Biology
Luby, Thomas Aquinas, Jr.
Radiolgc Tech Prof & Dept Head
Majer, John M.
Psychology Adjunct Professor
Marlowe, Jamie E.
Prof of Radiation Physics
Rau, Grace Ann Henderson
Instructor of English & Speech
Rosen, Susan A. C.
Assistant Professor of English
Sherer, Maureen Alexa
Chemistry Professor
Sloss, Henry E.
Associate Professor of English
BALT COUNTY
Guchemand, Margaret Kelso
Assoc Prof Music & Dept Head
Stahl, Donald L.
Geography Professor
Stearns, Ann Kaiser
Professor Dept of Psychology
BALTIMORE
Abdur-Rahman, Laura
6th-8th Grd Teacher
Adams, Chrystie Larson
General & Vocal Music Teacher
Ambrose, Cattie
English Teacher
Amiss, Christine Elizabeth
Intnl Baccalaureate Coord
Ayala, Homeretta M.
Library Media Specialist
Bafaro, Joanne L.
Reading Teacher
Baker, Janice Herman
English Teacher
Barrett, Kenneth Brandon
Guidance Counselor & Teacher
Batzer, Deborah Moxey
Science Teacher
Baxter, Cynthia Lynn
8th Grade English Teacher
Bayne, Lois Merchant
Social Studies Dept Chairman
Belzner, Charles Joseph
Guidance Counselor
Berkeley, Muriel V.
Director
Berry, Margaret Elaine
English Teacher & Dept Chair
Binko, Naomi K.
Third Grade Teacher
Blinke, John David
US History Tchr & Dept Chm
Blumenthal, Tatiana S.
Russian & Spanish Teacher
Boone, Kevin Earl
Physics, Bio & Earth Sci Tchr
Borah, Ken Roy
Biology, Chem & Physics Tchr
Bosley, Joseph William, III
Social Studies Teacher
Bowman, Donna Rae
Science Teacher
Brennan, MaryEllen Feeley
5th Grd Teacher & Asst Prin
Brooks, Reginald D.
Athletic Director
Brown, Marguerite J.
Fifth Grade Teacher
Bruner, Michael Stephen
English Teacher
Bryan, Thelma Jane
Professor of English
Brzozowski, Edward Joseph, Jr.
Am Govt & World History Tchr
Bucher, Richard David
Professor of Sociology
Buckingham, Patricia Dorothy
Business Education Teacher
Burns, James Arthur
Business Teacher
Burwell, Beverly Kyler
Adv Acad & Consulting Teacher
Cain, Leona Marie
7th-8th Grade Math Teacher
Cain, Rosa Marie
Assistant Professor
Calvert, Katherine Reno
Substitute Teacher
Campbell, Jean A.
Tchr & Lwr Schl Head Asst
Carnahan, Amy Martin
Assistant Professor

Carpenter, Elizabeth Wixted
Physics Teacher
Cartwright, Willie Quinton
Vice Chair & Assistant Prof
Casciero, Thomas
Associate Professor
Casey, Kathleen Louise
Fr Tchr & Frgn Lang Dpt Chrpsn
Cayer, Jane
English Teacher
Chikeka, Charles Dhiri
Associate Professor
Cichowicz, Ann Marie
Science Teacher
Ciesla, Betty E.
School Assistant Professor
Clanton, Patricia Dickens
Language Arts Teacher
Clay, Etta Stein
English Teacher
Cobb, Joan E.
Dir, Acad Adorsement Center
Cole, Delysia Lassiter
Chem, Anatomy, Physiology Tchr
Collier, Elise Herrington
Special Education Teacher
Collins, Ronnie Leon
Linguistics Professor
Cooper, Cecelia Chesley
Consulting Teacher
Cox, Jacob Thomas
Science Teacher
Craig, Willie Edward
Mathematics Teacher
Crandol, Cynthia Morings
Business Education Teacher
Culbertson, Gordon Lee
Mathematics Coordinator
Cuneo, Anthony Leo
Jr High Language Arts Teacher
Daneker, Sarah Masterson
Frgn Lang Dept Chair & Tchr
Davidson, Kenneth W.
Chemistry & Physics Teacher
Davis, Betty Louise
English Professor
Davis, Carolyn J. Smith
Eng, Lang Arts & Drama Tchr
Devlin, Judi Callanan
Assistant Principal
Devorah, Stephen Richard
12th Grade English Teacher
Dietrich, Marlyn Rose
Eng, Spelling & Math Teacher
Diggs, Nancy Goodwin
Education Professor
Diggs, Vanessa Juanita
Fourth Grade Teacher
Dimaio, Patricia Ann
English & Theater Arts Teacher
Disharoon, Richard Alan
Music Dept Chair
DiStefano, Anthony Robert
Mathematics Teacher
Domanico, Jerry
Chemistry Teacher
Doster, Harvey M.
Catalyst Theatre Director
Dotterweich, Patricia Lee
Fourth Grade Teacher
Dowling, Dorothy Woodward
Social Studies Tchr & Team Ldr
Dunbar, Elizabeth S.
English Teacher
Dykstra, Jason A.
Mathematics Department Chm
Ehrbaker, Richard George
Science Teacher
Ehrman, Elizabeth Keyes
English Teacher
Enders, Ruth Rathgeber
Fifth Grade Teacher
Engle, Ronald John
English Teacher
Ercolano, Phyllis Maria
French Teacher
Evans, Ellen Dean Crawford
2nd Grade Teacher
Ezeka, Hyacinth A.
Assistant Prof of Accounting
Falcone, Susan Hull
Family Studies Teacher
Feit, Marilyn Ruth
Art Dept Chprsn & Teacher
Fick, Brenda Stevens
English Instructor
Finkelstein, David Mark
Judaic Teacher
Fisher, Donna Lynn
Scndry Eng Tchr & Yrbk Adv
Fisher, Sherri Williams
Educational Specialist
Flohr, Patricia Miles
Administration & Geog Teacher
Floyd, Sharon Elizabeth
Dept Chair of Special Ed
Flynn Low, Bernadette
Professor of English
Forcellese, Cesare Augusto
Biology Teacher
Foreman, Johnnie L.
Asst Ath Dir & PE Dept Head
Freeman, Doris Patricia
Middle School Mathematics Tchr
Frey, Ruth Lazetta
History Teacher
Fry, Clarence Arthur
Lecturer of Ind Engineering
Frye, Wini Hoffman
Spanish & French Teacher

Galbreath, Cycrel C.
Retired Fifth Grade Teacher
Galla, Nelida M.
Spanish Teacher
Garner, Leah Lorraine
Sci & Math Ldrshp Tchr
Gartner, Leslie Paul
Anatomy Professor
Gates, Nancy Lee
Intermediate English Teacher
Gilbert, Deborah Lynn
High School Math Teacher
Giro, Alicia Godoy
Spanish Teacher
Gittings, Patricia Yvonne
Fifth Grade Teacher
Goeller, Stephen Bryan
Social Studies Teacher & Chair
Gottschalk, Elaine Moyer
Mathematics Teacher
Grabenstein, Carole M.
Elementary Teacher
Grauer, Marie Charles, SSND
HS English Teacher
Gray, Frances Thomas
Retired Second Grade Teacher
Gray, Winston Robert
Vocal Music Teacher
Greene, James Augustus, Jr.
8th Grade US History Teacher
Greenfield, Marsha Diane
1st Grade Teacher
Greenwalt, Mary Carol
Mathematics Teacher
Gudenius, Barbara Hamaker
English Department Head
Guenther, Kathy R.
Home Economics Teacher
Hall, Eleanora T.
Social Studies & Spec Ed Tchr
Hall, Linda R.
Music Educator
Hall, LuJean E.
Math Teacher & Associate Head
Hall, Wade
8th Grade Social Studies Tchr
Hammond, Roselyn Brown
College Biology Professor
Hanson, Susan Jane
Social Studies Department Chm
Harvey, Aminifu R.
Assistant Professor
Harvey, Gloria Marie
Music Teacher
Hastings, Katherine Klinefelter
High School Math Teacher
Hecht, Richard
Seventh Grade Science Teacher
Heller, Harland Edward
7th-8th Grade Teacher
Helmrich, Earl Spencer, Jr.
Social Studies Teacher
Henderson, Brian, FSC
Assistant Prin & Sr Rel Tchr
Henn, Carolyn (Branagan)
Principal
Hilliard, Eunice Purnell
Guidance Department Head
Hoffman, Eugene William
Health Ed, Math & PE Tchr
Holloway, Rosalind Davis
5th Grade Teacher
Holter, Norma C.
Assoc Prof of Acctng & Auditng
Hooe, Tom Norman
Professor of Biology
Hunter, Donald Scott
Instructor & Coord
Hutzley, Carol Jo
Frgn Lang Dept Chair & Fr Tchr
Ivey, Jessica
Physical Education Teacher
Jackson, Gustav E.
Prof of Environmental Studies
Jackson, Preston, Jr.
Air Science Teacher
Jacobson, Jonathan Lee
Arts & Humanities Acad Leader
Janishefski, Victor Frank
Art Teacher
Jones, Sarah Ann (Crawley)
Art Teacher
Jones, William Irving, III
Eng & Creative Writing Teacher
Jose, Cheryl Ann
Foreign Language Dept Chm
Kanis, Sharon, SSND
Religious Studies Asst Prof
Karsner, Anna Joan (Wagner)
2nd Grd Tchr & Primary Coord
Kehring, Lee A.
Art Department Chairperson
Kelbaugh, Ross J.
Social Studies Teacher
Kelleher, Joseph Edward
Instructor
Kenney, Nancy Elizabeth
Algebra Teacher
Ketchum, Andrew Scott
Science Teacher
Kimbrow, Ruby Eulola
Bus Ed Tchr & Dept Chprsn
Koch, Philip Frederick
Professor of Fine Arts
Kolb, Mary Louise
Math Teacher
Krich, Ellen Bernhard
English & Public Speaking Tchr
Krolczyk, Francesca
Former Business Manager

BALTIMORE (cont)
Kuchta, Linda Zaccari
Sixth Grade Teacher
Kuzsma, Marilyn Mushalko
Chem Dpndncy Cnslng Asst Prof
Kwarteng, Charles Owusu
Political Science Asst Prof
Laird, Louis Calvin, Jr.
MS Social Studies Teacher
LaPerriere, Michelle L.
Instr of Drawing & Painting
Lassen, Lolita White
Foreign Language Dept Chair
Lassiter, Ernest Lee
Journalism Professor
Latchford, Mary-Margaret Kardian
Social Studies Teacher
Lathroum, Marcia R.
Guidance Chairperson
Leddy, Stephanie Miranda
English Department Chair
Lee, Linda Yvette
Teacher
Leroy, Paul G.
Math & English Teacher
Lesh, Bruce Allyn
Social Studies & History Tchr
Lewis, Deborah Lee
Third Grade Teacher
Lo Presto, Charles Thomas
Associate Professor of Psych
Lukehart, Barbara J. Brady
Soc Studies Tchr & Dept Chair
Macauley, Francis John
Professor of Criminal Justice
Macie, Mary Jones
Substitute Teacher
Maggio, Raymond Patrick
Religion Teacher
Magrogan, Heather Michele
Guidance Counselor
Mainolfi, Ann
Drama Teacher
Makela, Maria Martha
Art History Professor
Mallery, Barbara Lou Belle
5th-6th Grade Teacher
Malstrom, Kathleen Anne
French Teacher
Manu, Franklyn
Assoc Professor of Marketing
Marriott, Salima Siler
Soc Work & Mental Hlth Prof
Marshall, Robert Hulings
Physics Teacher
Martin, Michael Thomas
Dir of Adm & Rel Stud Tchr
Maskell, Kathleen M.
9th-10th Grd Rdng Specialist
Mathura, Clyde Bradman
Assoc Prof, Applied Psych Chm
May, Patrick Joseph
Instructor of Geog & History
Mayer, Jennifer Ann
High School Teacher
McCleary, Louise Sharps
First Grade Teacher
Mc Laughlin, John Grover
Math Chair
Menefee, Selitha Meacham
French Teacher
Merritt, Marlene Jannette
Youth Coordinator
Meyerl, Gary T.
Campus Minister, Religion Tchr
Miller, Michael M.
Religion Teacher
Mitchell, Glendora White
First Grade Teacher
Moore-Green, Donna Marie
Fifth Grade Teacher
Moran, Sean Patrick
History Teacher
Morgan, Branch, III
French & Spanish Teacher
Morgan, David Lee
French & German Teacher
Morgan, Josephine Anne (Dill)
English Teacher & Dept Chair
Morse, Patricia Stanley
7th-8th Grade Science Teacher
Mortimer, Elizabeth Ann
French Teacher
Murphy, Christopher John
Latin & World History Teacher
Murphy, Donna Hurst
Guidance Counselor
Murray, Jacqueline Nicholson
5th Grade Teacher
Murray, Mabel Lake
Human Growth & Dev Stud Coord
Muskauski, Judy Morrash
Fifth Grade Teacher
Myers, Ellinor Elizabeth
English Teacher
Nachby, Helen Gomberg
Art Teacher
Neverdon-Morton, Cynthia
Professor of History
Newkirk, Jack Angle, II
Business Education Teacher
Nichols, Susanne Albert
Art & Computer Teacher
Nixon, Lois Torrence
Special Education Professor
O'Boyle, M. Paula Mc Namara
Social Studies Teacher
Odell, Kathleen Louise
Project Counselor
Offer, Sharon Jones
History Teacher
Orem, Waltyne Brooks
Fifth Grade Teacher
Orendorff, Laurence F.
Guidance Director
Ostrov, Lyn K.
Art Director
Pacheco, Debra Insley
Dance Teacher
Park, Sechoul
Accounting Professor
Parker, Wendy Ann (Mc Namee)
5th-6th Grd Language Arts Tchr
Perkoski, Rikki Diane
English Teacher
Petchik, Marian
High School Math Teacher
Peters, Sam
Printmaking Instructor
Polk, O. Elmer
Assoc Prof & Acting Chrmn
Potter, Mark J.
Teacher
Potts, Patricia Finnegan
Mathematics Teacher
Powell, Kathleen Scee
Multi-Age Classroom Teacher
Quinn, Lee Emerson
English Teacher
Raden, Eva Rosenberg
Judaic Studies Teacher
Ragin, Jean Bush
Math & Sci Curr Coordinator
Raval, Sushila Navnit
Psychology Professor
Reichart, Kelly Anne
United States History Teacher
Rhoads, Ann Claire
Middle School Teacher
Richmond, Deborah Ann
Social Studies Teacher
Rickels, Donald Lee
K-5th Grd PE Teacher
Riggs, Yvonne Holmes
Chem Tchr & Sci Dept Chprsn
Riley, Gloria Berarducci
Pgm Dir, Prof Dental Hygiene
Rivkin, Toby
French & Spanish Teacher
Roberts, Randolph Wilson
Health & Sciences Chair
Roberts-Gaither, Jennifer L. Jones
Language Arts Teacher
Robinson, Mary Elizabeth
7th-8th Grade Math Teacher
Robinson, Michael Edward
English Teacher
Robinson, Retiana Branch
Mathematics Teacher
Rocca, Celia-Ann Maria Genuardi
English, Drama Teacher & Dir
Roeder, Nancy Katherine
Professor of Fine Arts
Rogers, Donald Francis, Jr.
High School Math Teacher
Roseman, Maria Spears
5th Grade Teacher
Russell, Shirley Kathleen (Brown)
Mathematics Instructor
Sacks, Paul N.
Theatre Magnet Dir & Eng Tchr
Scherr, Arlene Cohn
Art Teacher & Yearbook Advisor
Schmidt, Gloria Paolini
Second Grade Teacher
Schuyler, B. Kay
Reading Specialist & Eng Tchr
Schuyler, Kathleen T.
PE Teacher & Athletic Director
Sedlak, Valerie Frances
Associate Professor of English
Seward, Alan Bruce
Guidance Counseling Svc Dir
Shaw, Frances C.
Social Studies Teacher
Shawen, Deborah A.
Dir of Lower School Admissions
Shields, Jeffrey Franklin, Sr.
Assistant Professor of Acctng
Shields, LaMarr Darnell
Spanish & History Teacher
Silversmith, Ernest Frank
Chemistry Professor
Simmons, Bryan Keith
Math Teacher
Skunda, Kathleen Myers
1st Grade Teacher
Smith, Deborah Verplanck
English Teacher
Smith, Harry E.
Allied Human Svcs Dept Chm
Smith, Heather Anne
Secondary English Teacher
Smith, Mary Anne, RSM
Admissions Dir & Span Tchr
Smith, Susan Taylor
American Literature Teacher
Soboleski, Melvin
Science Teacher
Spahr, Susan Jean
Family Studies Teacher
Sprinkle, Maggie
Business, Computer & Math Tchr
Spry, Janet Denise (Richburg)
Assistant Professor
Sriram, Ven
Associate Prof of Marketing
Stange, Gilbert William, III
Social Studies Teacher
Stansbury, Clayton C.
Honors Program Director
Starks, Marion Redmond
Pre K Teacher & Coordinator
Stebbins, Richard Vaughn
Social Studies Teacher
Steele, Iris Clarke
Assistant Principal
Steele, Susan Jane
8th Grade Science Teacher
Stern, Susanna Burger
History Teacher
Stevenson, Victoria E.
Mathematics Teacher
Stoddard, Raymond Michael
Social Studies Dept Chprsn
Strunk, Bruce Richard
HS Physical Education Teacher
Stukes-Maurice, Joan
English Teacher
Summerson, Ann Mc Aneny
Art Teacher
Swengosh, Michael Edward
Chemistry Teacher
Szymanski, Frank T.
Retention Specialist & Cnslr
Tamberrino, Jeanne Haffner
Physical Education Teacher
Tarr, Jennifer Hoover
Third Grade Teacher
Taylor, Elias L.
Sociology Professor
Taylor, Joan Patterson
English Instr & Program Dir
Taylor, Susan E.
Science Teacher
Terry, Richard Milton
Asst Professor & Coordinator
Thompson, John Robert
Mathematics Department Chair
Thompson-Cager, Chezia Brenda
Professor of Literature & Lang
Thom-Woodson, Amanda
Dance Director
Tisa, Ken
Fine Arts Dept Teacher
Tuten, April Borum
Math Teacher
Ukpong, Leo U.
Finance Professor
Vance, Theresa Alfano
Spanish & French Teacher
Varvaglione, Kathleen Grace
Business Education Teacher
Vaughan, Nancy H.
English Teacher
Veasel, William Edward
Electrical Tech & HVAC Teacher
Vendetti, Dina Carol
Choir Director
Wagoner, M. JoAnn
Middle & High School Teacher
Wann, Donald Carlton
Physical Ed & Health Teacher
Warner, Roland John, OFM
Pastoral Associate
Watkins, Kathleen A. R.
Acting Science Dept Chprsn
Wenker, Bernard John, Jr.
High School English Teacher
Weston, James K.
Chemistry & Physics Teacher
Wetzel, Deborah Alex
Spanish Teacher
White, Richard Albert, Sr.
Asst Prof of Human Services
Wieprecht, Charles Thomas, Jr.
Music Tchr & Rdng Dept Coord
Williams, David Ronald
Spanish, French & ESOL Tchr
Williams, Olivia Lee
Mathematics & Futures Teacher
Wilson, Barney Joe
Associate Professor
Wolk, Morris
Art Teacher
Wright, Pamela Powell
Physical Education Teacher
Wright, Sandra Louise
Chemistry Teacher
Wyatt, Quentin
Teacher
Wyskiel, Louisa Jamison
Middle School Mathematics Tchr
Young, Lauretta Dorsey
Voice & Diction Teacher
Young, LeRoy James, Jr.
Adjunct Professor
Younger, Robert George
Biology & Health Teacher
Zentz, Richard Charles
Social Studies Teacher
Zuskin, Ronald Edward
Clinical Instructor

BARNESVILLE
King, Suzanne S.
Soc Studies, Math & Eng Tchr

BARTON
Miller, Linda Clark
First Grade Teacher

BEL AIR
Bernstein, Jules
PE Teacher & Dept Head
Chapman, Danielle Renee
Spanish Teacher
Conner, Pamela Provins
6th Grd Language Arts Teacher
Cooper, Valerie Lanette
Health Teacher
Dean, Jane Amoss
Assistant Principal
DeMarco, Carla Ann
English Teacher
Dempsey, Douglas Mark
Fifth Grade Teacher
DiBiase, David Alan
Fourth Grade Teacher
Downes, Lilli Matesig
Assoc Professor of Sociology
Gradsihar, Susan Clor
Mathematics Teacher
Greenstreet, Michael Bradley, Sr.
Fifth Grade Teacher
Handy, Robert Alan
Soc Stud Tchr & Dept Chair
Hastings, Sally Harbaugh
8th Grade Language Arts Tchr
Heckler, Donald Warren, Jr.
Social Studies Teacher
Heinly, Sharalyn Roberts
Pre-School & Sign Lang Tchr
Heitz, Judith Mearns
Third Grade Teacher
Heitz, Michael Wilford
Chemistry Teacher
Herzog, Robert Mark
Science Teacher
Hughes, John Edward, Jr.
Eng & Sci Teacher
Kunkel, Janice Lorayne
Math Instructor & Dept Chair
Lang, William Frederick
Bus Law, Persnl Fin & Ec Tchr
Pickard, James E.
History Teacher
Randle, Brian Scott
HS Social Studies Teacher
Riley, Bruce Robert
HS Mathematics Teacher
Roberty, Paula C.
Choral Director & Music Tchr
Rudolph, Robert Arthur
Amer Govt Tchr & Dept Chm
Smith, David Joseph
Asst Prof of Paralegal Stud
Smith, Elvira Maria
French & Spanish Teacher
Svilar, Lorraine Eva
English & Journalism Teacher
Wainwright, Terri A.
Eng & Creative Writing Instr
Walstrum, Wendy Sue
Third Grade Teacher
Walter, Cynthia Benson
English Teacher
Whitehurst, James Patrick
Social Studies Dept Chair
Wise-Gladwell, Lucy L.
French Teacher

BELTSVILLE
Alexander, Sarah A.
Vice Principal
Berndt, Lillian Jean
HS English Teacher
Braxton, Sheila Melinda
English Teacher & Dept Chprsn
Bryant, Bernardine Althea
Mathematics Teacher
Covington, Leatriz Dellahoussaye
History Teacher
Dibler, Eileen Mc Cauley
English Teacher
Eckenrode, Robert Bruce
9th-12th Grd Math Teacher
Green, Leigh
Drama & English Teacher
Matthiesen, Steven
English as Second Lang Tchr
Mc Cool-Hennessy, Alysia Grace
English & Journalism Teacher
O'Brien, Gloria Norat
ESOL Teacher
Raveling, Gordon Reynolds
English & Speech Teacher
Schwartz, Norman David
Social Studies Teacher
Sibert, John Winston
Social Studies Teacher
Sondak, Abbey Ronald
Math Teacher
Stewart, Denise Bosworth
Math Teacher
Wasserman, Nadia L.
French Teacher
Welsh, Elizabeth Kay
Math Teacher
Whitlow, Doreathea Sims
Cooperative Voc Ed Tchr, Coord
Yablon, Shelly Beth
English Teacher
Young, Raymond L.
Mathematics Teacher

BERLIN
Andrews, Patricia A.
English & Mythology Teacher
Berquist, Stephen Barrett
Stud Skill & Career Exp Tchr
Cofiell, Monica Elise
Science Teacher
Ebelein, Dawn Marie
Mathematics Teacher
Larimore, Dora Trader
Math Teacher
Schott, Lawrence W.
Mathematics Teacher
Short, Brenda Figgs
Math Teacher
Turner, Valerie L.
Self-Contained Classroom Tchr
Vathis, James B.
History Teacher

BETHESDA
Abramo, Wren Moorefield
8th Grade English Teacher
Butler, Robert Dalton
Resource & Social Stud Tchr
Davidson, Jeffrey Howard
High School Choral Director
DePinho, Mary Voegeli
French & Literature Teacher
Diamond, Jean Rosenberg
Art Teacher
Dickerson, Martin
Mathematics Teacher
Dunston, Gregory Alan
Mathematics Teacher
Flynn, Christopher Albert
Special Education Tchr & Coach
Garran, Christopher S.
Social Studies Teacher
Giblin, Kevin Raymond
Algebra & Religion Teacher
Hodziewich, Gabriel Anthony
Biology Teacher
Kanagy, Michael T.
Mathematics Resource Teacher
Kearns, Ronald Edwin
Instrumental Music Teacher
Kleppner, Amy M.
English Teacher
Kroeger, Vickie Peterson
Honors & AP Chemistry Teacher
Levin, Lawrence Alan
Science Teacher
Mc Crady, William F.
English & Special Ed Teacher
MC Intosh, Nancy Ziegenfus
Ceramics Art Teacher
Oliver, Darlene Hooker
High School Mathematics Tchr
Overton, Dorothy Jean
Biology Teacher
Pax, Julianna B.
Chem & Nutrition Sci Teacher
Ryback, Susan King
English & Humanities Teacher
Scott, Marjorie Davis
Art & Photography Teacher
Shawaker, Carolyn Heckert
Social Studies Teacher
Shifrin, Stuart D.
Science Resource Teacher
Silberman, Sydelle Baron
HS Math Teacher
Sorkin, Steven Bruce
Mathematics Teacher
Sumner, Alton Elliot
History & Government Teacher
Tortosa, Manuel Ramon
ESOL Teacher
Williams, Everett Pendleton, Jr.
Choral Music Teacher
Wilson, Janice Fiscus
ESOL & Resource Teacher
Wright, Martha Elizabeth
Second Grade Teacher
Yack, Marguerite Dettlinger
Third Grade Teacher
Zukas, Rhona Gorsky Reiss
Director of Education

BLADENSBURG
Adami, Carolyn Johnson
Resource Room Special Ed Tchr
Billups, Harriet Gurley
French Teacher
Klapper, Margery Mahler
English & Journalism Teacher
Kovach, Sandra
Health Occupations Instructor
Manseau, Lani, DC
Old Testament Teacher
Ross, Charles W., Jr.
Science & Chemistry Teacher
Scoulios, John A.
Mathematics Instructor
Sullivan, Susan L.
Health & Biology Educator

BLOOMINGTON
Shook, Rebecca Ann
Fourth Grade & Spec Ed Tchr

BOONSBORO
Crowl, April Ann
English Teacher
Ecton, Jeanne Marie
Proj Challngr & TAG Teacher
Jamison, Marjorie Ann
US Soc Stud Tchr & Dept Chm
Lemonakis, Steve Frank
High School English Teacher
Nave, JoAnne Pennesi
High School English Teacher
Reineck, Drenna L.
Elementary Principal
Steiner, Barbara Janus
French Teacher
Sturniolo, Gary F.
Mathematics Teacher
Tolerton, Ty Daniel
5th Grade Teacher
Woodring, Deane Carson
Social Studies Teacher

BOWIE
Andrulonis, Richard George
Social Studies Teacher
Benbury, Karen Zak
Assoc Professor of Mathematics
Bennett, Kathleen Joyce
English Teacher

IE (cont)
, Oberia Burge
nematics Instructor
Ruth Stetler
e Economics Teacher
ing-Chung
puter Science Professor
o Clarke, Anita Griffin
3rd Eng Tchr & Dept Chprsn
y, Sarah Cowgill
ish Teacher & Yrbk Adv
burg, Donald Lee
a School Mathematics Tchr
Ada Maria
& Coordinator of Guidance
man, Julie Ann
al Studies Teacher
, Julian Rodney
h Teacher
mith, Frances Puryear
nematics Teacher
Monika E.
stant Professor of English
a, Eleanor Niles
red Elementary Teacher
ins, Renee Dela Vega
Grade Health Ed Teacher
, Michael Scott
Placement US His Tchr
es, William Edward
hematics Teacher
, Marion Bartlett
Stud Tchr & Coord
ton, Thomas Edward
anteer Coordinator
eau, Julia Louise
mistry Teacher
lon, Joan S.
nputer Science Professor
ers, Eileen Dimon
e Principal
ews, Juanita Franklin
red First Grade Teacher
nley, Joanne May
lish Teacher
lanus, Mary Hairston
lish Professor
ord, Gail Stewart
t Prof of Spch Comm & Thtre
r, M. Sammye
fessor of American History
eafor, Cosmas Uche
nmunication Professor
ville, Kathleen V.
n & French Teacher
mond, Anita Smith
h Grade Teacher
ck, Katherine Virginia
rd Grade Teacher
n, Joanna E.
cial Education Teacher
n, Valeria Ann Lomax
Grade Science Teacher
ens, Mark lloyd
estling Coach
bauer, David S.
val Science Instructor
ington, J. Charles
oc Professor of English
e, Doris Oliver
st Grade Teacher
erman, Marion Eberman
ond & Third Grade Teacher
Wei-hsiung
glish Professor
g, Swazette Dickason
ial Studies Teacher
NDYWINE
ler, Jeanne O'Connor
Grade Reading Teacher
OKLANDVILLE
ph, Holly Gaumnitz
thematics Teacher
nan, Stanley Virgil
tory & Philosophy Teacher
owitz, Howard Craig
glish Teacher & Theatre Dir
storf, Paul S.
ddle School Math Teacher
ee, Sandra Sundquist
glish Dept Chairman
Susan Greenfield
sistant Principal
one, Carol J.
glish Teacher
n, Wendy Emerson
glish Dept Chair
ton, Marla Ullrich
anish & French Teacher
en, Peter Dana
manities Tchr & Dept Chair
NSWICK
th, Frank S., Jr.
glish & Journalism Teacher
zo, Joyce Belt
me Economics Teacher
tin, Jeffrey Stephen
usic Teacher
s, Thomas Edward
ience Teacher
sker, Doris G.
aillist & Student Assistant
sada, Bernard
glish Teacher
h, Carol S.
ealth, PE Teacher & Ath Dir
es, Lori Hobbs
ience Department Chairperson

BURTONSVILLE
Brenner, Mary Jo (Rotili)
Family & Consumer Science Tchr
Garratt, Mary Kathleen
Kindergarten Teacher
Goepfert, Sandra
Guidance Counselor
Goldman, John Patrick
English Teacher
Leffler, Pamela Smith
Anatomy & Physiology Teacher
Mitchell, Christine Dixon
Vocal & Gen Music Teacher
Mostow, Robert Alan
Theatre, Television & Eng Tchr
CAMBRIDGE
Gullette, E. Anne
First Grade Teacher
Walters, Laura Travers
First Grade Teacher
CAMP SPRINGS
Roberson, Valerie Spooner
6th Grd Lang Arts & Rdng Tchr
CAPITOL HEIGHTS
Brenner, Scott A.
7th Grade English Teacher
Curtin, Michelle Blahut
High School Biology Teacher
Johnson, Gloria Faye
Vocal Music Teacher
Johnson, Jan Melaine
Sixth Grade Teacher
Johnson, Vaughn Monroe
Art Teacher
King, Carrie Lynn
Spanish Teacher
Libby, Kara Miley
Social Studies Teacher & Coord
Nameth, Joseph Louis
Aerospace Instr AF JROTC
Peterson, Donnell Ricardo
English & Journalism Teacher
Shattuck, Blaine De Vere
History Teacher
Thomas, Philomenia Jones
Mathematics Teacher
Vargo-Sidney, Linda
English Teacher
CATONSVILLE
Dingle, Frank Joseph
Prof of Printing Mgmt & Comm
Drees, Dedree A.
Art Prof & Cmptr Grphcs Coord
Fetter, Dian E.
Professor of Arts & Humanities
Michel-Moyer, Edna R.
Associate Professor of Nursing
Tyson, Joy
Assistant Professor
Wilkins, David Benjamin
Former Teacher
Zwingelberg, William C.
Prof of Art & Dept Chair
CENTREVILLE
Larrimore, John Wayne
Guidance Counselor
Schultz, Gretchen Ruth
English Teacher
Stahl, Debra Dawn
English Teacher
Wilhelm, Mark Andrew
Elementary Physical Educator
CHESAPEAKE BEACH
Hall, Beryle Francine
Fifth Grade Teacher
Lorton, Barbara Ferguson
Teacher of Gifted & Talented
CHESAPEAKE CITY
Kline, A. Bruce
US History & Govt Teacher
CHESTERTOWN
Parks, Lanetta Wolfe
Librarian & Lang Art Tchr
Wright, Christina Tarbutton
Mathematics Teacher
CHILDS
Pare, Marilyn Warren
8th Grade Teacher
CLARKSVILLE
Adkins, Sandra Kay
Vocal Music Director
Boyan, Kitty Stein
5th Grade Teacher
Dockeray, Kathleen Croake
Fourth Grade Teacher
Holihan, Deborah Dawn
6th Grade English Teacher
Hoyer, Lawrence Coswell
Science Teacher
Kogut, Violette Kara
French Teacher
Vazzana, Stephen S.
Seventh Grade Teacher
Whorton, Barbara Young
6th-7th Grade English Teacher
CLEAR SPRING
Barvinchack, M. A. Roman
Business Education Teacher
Cornett, Margaret Kershner
Retired Fourth Grade Teacher
Dorsey, Lottie Gisriel
Spanish Teacher
Jessee, Linda Crampton
5th Grade Teacher
Mowbray, John Scott
PE Teacher
Saur, Janice Snyder
Family Life & Con Sci Tchr
Tabler, Debra (Griffith)
Math Teacher & Dept Head

Teach, Karen L. (May)
Business Education Instructor
CLINTON
Baukman, Christabell V. Bates
Intensity IV Teacher
Harris, Stephanie Fara
6th & 7th Grade Teacher
Heintzelman, David G.
Chemistry Teacher
Prince, Tawanda Elayne
English Teacher
Scott, Aree Jackson
Testing Coordinator
Scott, Juanda Davis
Mathematics Teacher
Vaughan, Sheila Gaither
Curriculum & Instruction Coord
Villano, Christina Zikkos
Spanish & English Teacher
Wanner, Paul Michael
Elem Physical Education Tchr
COCKEYSVILLE HUNT VALLEY
Blevins, Isabel Rosendale
MS Teacher
Houseman, Barton L.
Prof of Chemistry Emeritus
Willis, Karen Amanda
Music Teacher
COLLEGE PARK
Chi, Albert Yu-Ming
Professor
Fontana, Maxine Attea
Instructor
Green, Martrice
6th Grade Math Teacher
HIggins, William Joseph
Associate Professor of Zoology
McIntosh, Wayne V.
Political Science Professor
Neal, Sandra H.
5th & 6th Grade Teacher
Pease, John Alan
Associate Prof of Sociology
Povisil, Mary-Jo
Adjunct Prof of Women's Stud
Ranallo, Jean Emrick
Language Arts Teacher
Sanner, Robert Michael
Asst Prof of Aerospace Engrng
COLUMBIA
Adams, Joseph John
Art Teacher
Allera, Lynda Grace
French & Spanish Teacher
Amato, Leah Ashendorf
Fifth Grade Teacher
Barnes, Dawn Cooper
Asst Prof of Performing Arts
Bates, Althea Thompson
Media Specialist
Bell, James Edward
Professor of Psychology
Belt, Leesa Carole
Sr HS Speech & English Tchr
Brickman, Barbara Felsenstein
Speech & Fine Arts Teacher
Brodsky, Caryn Gottlieb
HS Spanish Teacher
Brown, Linda Sue
Sixth Grade English Teacher
Burke, Jack Ollie, Jr.
Soc Stud & World His Tchr
Conlon, James G.
Social Studies Teacher
Finley, Patrick L.
Hlth Scis Division Assoc Prof
Goode, Lamont Edward
Social Studies Department Chm
Gross, Linda Holmes
English Teacher
Hahne, Reginald Allan
Computer Science Chair
Jefferson, Cheri Tyler
English Teacher & Dept Coord
Jewett, Barbara Joanne
Sci Dept Chprsn & Chem Tchr
Jones, Carrye Bowers
Gftd & Talented Resource Tchr
Kirkley, Donna B.
Professor of Speech
Kutz, Arlene Clarke
English Teacher
Law, Judith Ann
Office Technology Professor
Madaras, Lawrence Higgins
Prof of His & Political Sci
Mason, Pamela L.
Special Ed Department Chair
Micka, Paula B.
Foreign Lang Dept Chprsn
Morris, Zelena Mc Fadden
English Teacher
O'Brien, Tim
Social Studies Teacher
Orlosky, Janet Ann
Resource & Math Teacher
Petering, Jennifer Marie
Science Teacher
Rappoport, Cherry Karl
Assoc Prof of Nrsng
Rawlings, Ross Scott
Vocal Music Director
Rucker, Kenneth Hewitt
Social Studies Teacher
Saunderson, Patrick Joseph
World History Teacher
Schlossberg, Robin Flax
First & Second Grade Teacher
Schneider, Adelia
Spanish & Italian Teacher

Steelman, Ann Margaret Sullivan
9th Grd Earth Sci & Bio Tchr
Stewart, Tebbie Willis
ESOL Teacher
Vitagliano, David Harold
English & Journalism Teacher
Wallace, Rodney E.
Math Dept Chairperson
Webster, Forrest Graydon
Government & History Teacher
West, Herbert Lee, Jr.
Social Studies Teacher
White, Karyn Adelia
Guidance Counselor
Winer, Jane M.
Prof of Art, Art History & Hum
Zachmann, Kenneth Dwight
Science Department Head
CRISFIELD
Cody, Michael Thomas
8th Grade Mathematics Teacher
Sterling, Donna Mills
Language Arts Teacher
CROFTON
Gruber, Linda Sara
Second Grade Teacher
CUMBERLAND
Andrews, Patricia S.
Professor of Biology
Berry, James Edward
8th Grade English Teacher
Brown, Beth Lee
Spanish Teacher
Brown, Roberta Ann
Fifth Grade Teacher
Buser, Sally Schoenbeck
Foreign Language Teacher
Clark, Helen Madden
Fifth Grade Teacher
Cramer, Eugene Dale
School Guidance Counselor
Dawson, George E.
English Teacher
DeLaney, Marc William
Social Studies Teacher
Dressman, Rita, OSU
Religious Education Dir
Dunn, Edwin James
Biology & Chemistry Teacher
Eberly, Charles Francis
Health & Phys Ed Instructor
Etchison, Craig
Associate Prof of English
Feck, Terry Lee
Dir of Communication Media
Fuller, Mary Baker
Chemistry Instructor
Hendrickson, Gary Lee
Mathematics & Physics Teacher
Henson, Kim Allen
Guidance Counselor
Jackson, Larry Thomas
Band Director
Ketterman, Linda Ann
US History Teacher
Lattimer, Sara Vastine
9th-12th Grd Spanish Teacher
Lease, Joseph Francis
Social Studies Teacher
Lloyd, Carol Lannon
Pre-K Teacher
Logsdon, John Wayne
First Grade Teacher
Mattingly, Kathryn Cecelia
Math Teacher
Merrill, David Royce
Science Tchr & Head Ftbl Coach
Morgan, Sharon Lynn
Second Grade Teacher
Neely, Carolyn Burkey
K-12 Art Teacher
Nolan, Edward L.
9th Grd Govt & Earth Sci Tchr
O'Brien, Lee Ann Atwood
Instrumental Music & Span Tchr
O'Rourke, Mary Jane J.
English Teacher & Dept Chair
Paulus, Kim Smith
English & Journalism Teacher
Phebus, Debra C.
Computer Science Instructor
Ratchford, Linda M. (Stewart)
French & Religion Teacher
Shore, Mark Andrew
Mathematics Professor
Sisca, Rodger Franklin
Anatomy & Physiology Professor
Smith, Larry John
Social Studies Teacher
Smith, Marcia Babcock
Business Education Teacher
Stangel, Jo Ann
Amer Lit & SAT Prep Teacher
Stevens, Jay Arthur
Social Studies Teacher
Stimmel, Robert Bryan
Science Teacher
Wallace, Kevin Alexander
Science Teacher
Watkins, Mildred Louise
Mathematics Teacher
Weaver, Joseph Henryh
Professor of History
Weaver, Patrick Francis
Mathematics Teacher
Winterberg, James Joseph
6th Grade Teacher
Wiseman, Earleen Humbertson
Spanish Teacher

Workman, Amarylis Jarrell
Chemistry Teacher
Zamagias, Constantine James
Social Studies Teacher
DAMASCUS
Baker, Lisa
High School English Teacher
Conway, Maria Trementozzi
Social Studies Teacher
Crumley, Kristie Caldwell
Mathematics Teacher
DeGraba, Michael Joseph
Mathematics Teacher
Eilers, Robert Bruce
Cabinetmaking Instructor
Lang, Erick Joel
Music Teacher
Murdock, Kathryn A.
Social Studies Teacher
Redos, Vicki Carter
English Teacher
Silvio, Nancy Schapp
Tchr & Frgn Lang Dept Chair
Weinberg, Marsha Henderson
English Teacher
DARLINGTON
Kennedy, Ruth L. (O'Diam)
Fifth Grade Teacher
DELMAR
Brewer, Tamara Joan (Wootten)
Former Mathematics Teacher
DENTON
Kohler, Patricia Hargadon
Music Teacher
Loveless, Carol Miller
3rd Grade Teacher
Parsons, Linda
Second Grade Teacher
Ross, Else Adelhelm
Sixth Grade English Teacher
Wolcott, Connie Meredith
MSPAP Teacher Specialist
DERWOOD
Ahearn, Rebecca Birt
Spanish Teacher
D'Anna, Michael Dominick
English & Theater Teacher
Dicken, Dania Haller
Business Teacher
Foster, Pamela Gail
5th Grade Teacher
Kirkpatrick, Allan K.
Choral Music Teacher
McGeehin, Roseann Eroh
Mathematics Teacher
Mulholland, Kathleen Ann
Fine Arts Teacher
White, Martha Burton
5th Grade Teacher
Whitehouse, Elizabeth King
English Teacher
DISTRICT HEIGHTS
Abbott, Paola (Antonelli)
Latin & Italian Teacher
Ashpes, April Allen
7th Grade Intnl Studies Tchr
Burnette, Cykeithia
AP Biology & English Instr
Carter, Evelyn Adkins
English Tchr
Disney, Donald Bruce, Jr.
Naval Science Instructor
Fax, Jesse Stewart
English & Speech Teacher
Fear, Don W.
Photography Teacher
Hance, Alta Ann Myers
Second Grade Teacher
Kochansky, Mary Cooper
Chemistry Teacher
Kuhl, Judith Annette
Science Teacher
Lacey, Kevin Patrick
Social Studies Teacher
Mosley, Rogee Yvette
Earth Science & Biology Tchr
Reese, Lyvita Deonna
Fourth Grade Teacher
Spivey, Natasha
Mathematics Teacher
Thompson, Karol Margery
Instructor Emeritus
Zentz, Melissa O.
Spanish Teacher
DUNKIRK
Kozik, Francis X.
Former Teacher
EASTON
Craig, Mary Acker
5th Grade Teacher
Depuy, Deborah Luciano
Spanish Teacher
DeShields, Charlene Caldwell
First Grade Teacher
Guth, Howard
Earth Science Teacher
Hutchison, Alice LeeAnn
Science Teacher
Jones, Linda L.
Teacher
Reitz, David K.
Biology Teacher
Thomas, William Richard
Music Teacher
Volante, William
Guidance Dir, US History Instr
Willoughby, C. Stephen
Third Grade Teacher

EDGEWATER
Condon, Gail Ann
English Teacher & Dept Chair
Edelmann, Dorita Martinez
Spanish Teacher
Hopkins, James R.
Mathematics Teacher
Rodriguez, Jacqueline (Cosby)
Mathematics Teacher
EDGEWOOD
Gallagher, Richard James
Eng Dept Chm & Cmptr Lab Coord
Grant, Sherry Colby
Spanish Teacher
Guhr, Beth Timmons
German Teacher
Lamb, James Thomas, III
HS Biology & Physics Tchr
Lynn, Deborah Ann
Physical Education Teacher
Mollock, Clarence B.
Art Teacher
Pavlik, Michalyn C.
French Teacher
Watson, Eileen Murnin
Special Education Teacher
Weber, Patricia Ann (Lohr)
Secondary Art Teacher
ELKTON
Buck, Barbara Mc Kee
English Teacher
Carrion, Richard Peter
Earth & Environmental Sci Tchr
Lenhoff, Margaret Rees
German Teacher
Schneider, Jacob C.
Instrumental Music Teacher
Teoli, Judith Ladd
8th Grade Reading & Lit Tchr
ELLICOTT CITY
Ahlbrand, Nikki Rosky
Jr HS Math & Science Teacher
Astri, Robert
Physics & Chemistry Teacher
Begeny, Nancy Zahn
First Grade Teacher
Borowski, Kelly Simon
Psychology & Sociology Teacher
Churchill, Paul G.
Latin & French Teacher
Clem, Vicki Kearton
French Teacher
Davis, Patricia Ann
Spanish & Latin Teacher
Ditman, David Brent
Assistant Principal
Doyle, Deborah Zemanick
Spanish Teacher
Dunlop, Karen B.
Howard Cty Ed Assn President
Dutterer, Myron A.
Theater Instructor
Elder, Carol Brehm
Spanish Teacher
Feldmesser, Linda Borkan
Resource Teacher of G&T
Gardner, Rick Alan
HS Art Instructor
Gershman, Andrea Clayman
Resource Teacher
Glenn, David Samuel
Counselor & Guidance Dept Chm
Heck, Karen Miller
Business Teacher
Holshue, Edward Joseph
Biology Teacher
Holshue, Martha Ann
Art Teacher & Dept Coordinator
Jones, Nancy Jane
Social Studies Teacher
Kinnear, Diane Lash
Fifth Grade Teacher
Klingner, Ronald W.
Gifted, Talented & AP Bio Tchr
Lambros, Margo Bourdosis
Teacher
Mc Caslin, Rodney Kimbel
History Teacher
Meitl, Claire Wagner
Sixth Grade English Teacher
Novotny, Joseph M.
Technology Teacher
Petrovich, Michael
Seventh Grade Science Teacher
Ricker, Jennie Anne
Dance Teacher
Riegel, Bruce David
Site-Based Management Chrprsn
Sankey, Thomas Lee
High School Math Teacher
Swartz, Eugene Robert, Jr.
Director of Choral Activities
EMMITSBURG
Heath, William Ralph
Professor of English
Mitra, Indrani
English Professor
Sollenberger, Michael George
Assoc Prof of Class & Mod Lang
Stanton, Timothy James
Assoc Professor of Economics
FALLSTON
Harvey, Craig Stephen
Director of Bands
FEDERALSBURG
Pierce, Christy Ann
Teacher Specialist
FLINTSTONE
Heavner, Lee Perry
Agricultural Education Teacher

Hoopengardner, Marion Rice
Third Grade Teacher
Raley, James M.
Technology Teacher
FORESTVILLE
Beach, Jennifer Anne
English Teacher
Bohrer, Robert Lee
Math Teacher
Brenneman, Josephine Hartmann
Biology Tchr & Sci Dept Chair
Brown, Ethel Luciel
Sixth Grade Teacher
Cassidy, Suzanne Ruth
Biology Teacher
Davis, Ruby C.
Physical Education Teacher
Gray, Mary Regina
English & Language Arts Tchr
Hunt, Michael Lee
Band Director
Kazimer, Denise Lynn
Sports Medicine Instructor
Naugle, Judith (Pulliam)
Mathematics Teacher
Sanford, Katana Kimberly
English Teacher
Saunders, Janette
English Teacher
Seyedkhalili, Saiedeh
Physical Sci & Chemistry Tchr
Smalling, Barbara Washington
High School Teacher
Treichel, Clare Marie
Guidance Director
Williams, Lauretta
English Specialist
Wockley, Marilyn Hahnefeld
Spanish Tchr & Dean of Women
FORT MEADE
Durrett, Doris Oakcrum
Language Arts Teacher
Garrigan, Thomas Edward
Social Studies Teacher
Haas, Richard M.
Mathematics Teacher
Herring, Barnelle Robinson
Bus Ed Teacher & Coordinator
Jepsen, Kathleen Hagerty
English Teacher
Leydorf, Janet Ruth
Language Arts Teacher
Markowitz, Michael David
Music Teacher
Micklos, Charles Richard
Sixth Grade Teacher
Sargent, Alexis Helynne
French Teacher
Schult, Anne Bourgeois
Dept Chrpsn & Guidance Cnslr
Stewart, Kelly Lynn
7th Grd Language Arts Teacher
FORT WASHINGTON
Barton, William Thomas, III
English Teacher
Bilinski, Kathleen Miller
French & Latin Teacher
Brown, Ronald
Music Department Chm & Teacher
Coley, Helen Alston
Math & Science Coordinator
Dolesh, Gloria Decker
English Teacher
Funka, Serena Hecht
2nd Grade Teacher
Gill, Bonnie S.
Teacher
Harrison, Beverly M.
Seventh Grade Geography Tchr
Jones, Dan Ethel
Math Instr & Dept Chair
Lambert, Normand Leo, Jr.
HS Social Studies Teacher
Leino, Patricia West
Biology & Physiology Teacher
Lynch, Robert Joseph
Social Studies Teacher
Mc Elfish, Donald Albert
Geography & US History Teacher
McMillin, Katharine E.
Physics Teacher
Morris, Roy Anthony, Jr.
Naval Sci Instr
Powell, Karleen Dyson (Moore)
Guidance Counselor
Sheppard, William
Middle School Math Teacher
Torbic, Carol A.
4th Grade Teacher
White, Dennis A.
Vice Principal
Williams, Celeste Carr
Science Dept Chair
FREDERICK
Babb, Cathlyn Borggaard
Teacher of the Deaf
Boyd, Ann Lewis
Dean of Graduate School
Boyd, Michael D.
Associate Professor
Campagnoli, Kathy J.
English Teacher
Coblentz, Wayne Albert
Social Studies Teacher
Commito, Ann E.
Associate Prof of Mathematics
Connar, Meredith Lynn
Teacher of Gifted Students
Crum, William Lee
Chemistry Teacher

Dacus, Judy McLellan
Science Dept Chair & Prof Bio
Ernstedt, Barbara Jean
Sixth Grade Mathematics Tchr
Evans, Natalie Ann
English Teacher
Fenwick, Bonnie Jean
High School Mathematics Tchr
Fisher, Kimberly Ann
Mathematics Teacher
Fitzpatrick, James Donald, Jr.
Social Studies Teacher
Foster, Vicki Staley
First Grade Teacher
Gamble, Hal Walter
English Teacher
Gearhart, Pamela Osburn
Child Development Teacher
Gearinger, Mary Ann Brush
Third Grade Teacher
Haller, Norma Rae
Fourth Grade Teacher
Harding, Charles Douglas, Jr.
HS Chemistry & Physics Teacher
Hershwitzky, Patricia Ann
Math & Social Studies Teacher
House, Kathleen Burke
Mathematics Dept Chairman
Joyner-Giffin, Sally B.
Adj Instr of Psychology & Ed
Lartigue, Dannette Elizabeth
Social Studies Teacher
Lovato, Vanessa Lynn
Nursing Professor
Martin, Anthony J.
Computer Science Teacher
Martin, Cynthia Welty
Business Teacher
Mc Donald, Mary Kathryne
German Teacher
Mc Donough, James Richard
English Teacher
Mc Glynn, Michele Hanni
Retired Teacher
Moore, William L.
Mathematics Teacher
Nee, Joann Wheeler
Vocal Music Teacher
Newbold, Ardith Hanson
1st Grd Tchr of Gifted Stdnts
Noffsinger-Spurrier, Lois Baumgardner
Kindergarten Teacher
Paugh, Mark Lee
Associate Professor
Phillips, Aaron Dwayne
Assistant Principal
Reeves, Mary Ryan
Visual Arts Teacher
Shaw, Pamela Ann
Biology Teacher
Shobe, Charles William
Art Teacher
Smith, Esther Ruth (Horst)
Math & Chemistry Teacher
Spencer, Rita A.
High School Science Teacher
Swaiko, Nancy Marie
Reading & English Teacher
Thomas, Mary Lynne C.
Mathematics Teacher
Williams-Kennedy, Cherri Dawn
Mathematics Teacher
Wilson, Teresa Schmitt
French Teacher
Wood, Katherine Watson
Associate Prof of Human Svcs
Wright, Benjamin Franklin
Physical Education Teacher
FREELAND
Klasnic, Kathleen Carroll
3rd Grade Teacher
Mc Cabe, Lynn Johnson
Fifth Grade Teacher
FRIENDSVILLE
Glotfelty, Melvin Ross
5th Grade Teacher
FROSTBURG
Eisel, Stanley Patterson
Guidance Counselor
Smith, Betty Parker
Fifth Grade Teacher
FRUITLAND
Hensley, Susan Wollet
Second Grade Teacher
Ritter, Ross Wesley
Physical Education Director
GAITHERSBURG
Ahalt, Susan James
Foreign Language Dept Chair
Arce, Luis G.
ESOL Teacher
Bescher, Arthur F., Jr.
Social Studies Teacher
Busche, Leon Frank
Social Studies Department Head
Ciotti, Carol A.
First Grade Teacher
Donovan, Joan Lauer
Fourth Grade Teacher
Flowers, Pearl Wilson
Mathematics Dept Chairperson
Fogleman, Robert Tyson
Instrumental Music Teacher
Gainor, John Wesley, III
Naval Science Instructor
Hobson, Stephen Charles
World Studies Teacher
Kail, Ronald
Science Resource Teacher

Kesler, Kathleen Harmon
English Teacher
Larsen, Phyllis Hamilton
6th Grade Classroom Teacher
Mannino, Laurie Sue
Social Studies Teacher
Masal, Jan C.
Second Grade Teacher
Mc Aneny, Sally
Science Teacher
Nolan, Edward Charles
Mathematics Teacher
Piechocinski, Michael Neison
Art Teacher
Pye-Timko, Jennifer
Social Studies Teacher
Redinger, Janice C.
Home Ec & Child Dev Teacher
Roe, Donald Winston
Physics Teacher
Strubel, Elizabeth Brill
Assistant Principal
Thompson, Gilbert Ross
Math Teacher & Coach
Townsend, Traci Vernon
Science Teacher
Unger, Nancy Sesler
4th Grade Teacher
Vestal, Phyllis Chicano
English Interdisciplinary Tchr
White, Rae Myles
English Teacher & Dept Chprsn
Wise, Shirley Timmons
Principal
Yuspa, Eleanor Hecht
HS Photography Teacher
GAMBRILLS
Chapman, Kathleen Paschal
Mathematics Teacher
Deshields, June M.
Fifth Grade Teacher
Fellona, Christine Marie
HS Physical & Health Ed Tchr
Hubbard, Randy Allen
Physics, Zoology & Bio Instr
Rains, Dale Russell
Math Teacher & Dept Chprsn
Rogers, Lee M.
Physical Educator
Schaeffer, Jo Ann Blickenstaff
Science Teacher
Trimnal, Wanda Lee
English & Journalism Teacher
Yannuzzi, Paul Michael
Sci Dept Chprsn & Bio Tchr
GERMANTOWN
Abrams, Debra Josephson
Assistant Professor of English
Arlen, Barbara Goldsmith
HS Mathematics Teacher
Bradley, Kitty Lea
Drama Dir & Newspaper Advisor
Burrall, Charles S.
High School English Teacher
Charuhas, Jeffrey Maury
Chemistry Teacher
Cohen, Phyllis
English Teacher
Cromwell, Pamela Ann
Elementary Teacher
Duffield, Judith L.
English Teacher
Duffy, Margaret Kitzinger
Third Grade Teacher
Fulwiler, Arlen L.
Professor & Chair of Rdng, ESL
Hartle, Brian L.
Instrumental Music Director
Joyce, Ellen
Instructional Support Teacher
Martin, Martine Kent
Career Awareness Teacher
Mc Cormick, Christine JoAnn
Spanish Teacher
Schmetz, Beth Scheffflin
Mathematics Teacher
Sereno, Edgel E.
Mathematics Professor
Smith, Thelma Cheryl (Cromartie)
Assistant Principal
Surette, Richard James
Eng & Creative Writing Tchr
Thompson, Catherine Perry
Math Teacher
Williams, Debra Jones
Physical Ed & Health Teacher
Witte, Bill Thomas
Assoc Prof of Cmptr Applctns
GLEN BURNIE
Buckley, MaryAnn Doll
Science Teacher
Conley, Kimberly Sweigart
Kindergarten Teacher
Foster, David Eugene
Biology & Physical Sci Tchr
Grimmer, Jolene Michele
German Teacher
Hawkins, Gwendolyn Gail
English Teacher
Keating, Margaret DeAngelo
Second Grade Teacher
Kump, Lisa S.
9th-12th Grd English Teacher
Miller, Sue Bowers
Sixth Grade Teacher
Moore, Joseph Sean
Physics Teacher
Oravecz, Julia Lookabill
High School English Teacher

Perry, Yolanda Burkeen
French Teacher
Wheatley, Elaine Lippy
French Teacher
Wilson, Bradley Leroy
Health & Physical Ed Teacher
GLENCOE
Jennings, Elizabeth Louise
Director of Alumnae Affairs
Jensen, Sven
Social Studies Dept Head
Weeks, Anne Macleod
Coll Guid Dir & Eng Tchr
GLENELG
Berlin, Mary Wobbeking
Math Teacher
Bishop, Linda Goon
Math Teacher
Cambell, Jane Ross
English & Film Arts Teacher
Davis, Mary Pitt
Biology Teacher
Sutton, Ivan Clark
Chemistry Teacher
Volrath, Roger L.
Physics Teacher
GLENWOOD
Painter, Alice Maney
First Grade Teacher
GRANTSVILLE
Downton, Mary S.
Admin, Math & History Teacher
Perkins, Marlene Kay
Third Grade Teacher
GREAT MILLS
Berg, Leslie Renea
Mathematics Teacher
Jarczynski, Mary Ann Dooley
HS Bus & Social Stud Teacher
Moore, Lowell Cornelius
Physical & Business Ed Teacher
Weber, Maria B. (DiGiovanni)
English & Remedial Rdng Tchr
Wortman, Claudia G.
Biology Teacher & Dept Chmn
GREENBELT
Ball, Donna D.
Pom Squad Coach & Sponsor
Burr, Candie
Spanish Teacher
Carrington, Richard James
AP US History Teacher
Congleton, John Michael
Math Teacher
Coon, William Aaron
Guidance Counselor
Dowler, Karen Lewis
Tchr of Deaf & Hard of Hearing
Duff, Catherine Flynn
Chemistry Teacher
Hanson, Michelle Alward
English & Yearbook Teacher
Harrison, Dorothy Dunsen
Vice Principal
Horn, T. Scott
Chemistry Teacher
Kallas, George Christ
Special Education Teacher
Kyte, Julie Evans
English Teacher
Lewis, Sharon Lowe
Peer Mediation Teacher
Lindo, Marcus William
Social Studies Teacher
Linn, Terry Ann Noffsinger
Mathematics Teacher
Magin, Joan Helman
Social Studies Teacher
Manion, William Paul
English Teacher
Marryat, Jennifer Stephens
English Teacher
Mc Fadden, Paul Edward
Math Teacher
McGlew, Kathleen McFeaters
Television Productions Teacher
Mc Rae, Michael R.
High School Math Instructor
Murphy, Patrick Michael
Guidance Counselor
Myers, David R.
Science Dept Chair & Teacher
Paschyn, Kwitoslawa Saluk
English Teacher
Roe, Glenn William
Science Teacher
Samordic, Michael George
Math & Computer Science Tchr
Sommerville, Robert J.
Government Teacher
Strachan, George Hugh
Physics & Earth Science Tchr
Wagner, Sally Sterrett
High School Band Director
Watson, Linda Ann
Business Education Dept Chprsn
GREENSBORO
Cook, Barbara Helms
Kindergarten Teacher
HAGERSTOWN
Allen, Douglas Tyler
Mathematics Teacher
Beecroft, Thomas Kenneth
Professor of Psychology
Blank, Nancy Crossley
Art Department Head
Cassutto, George Henricus
Secondary Soc Studies Teacher
Chatkin, Dorothea Carbaugh
12th Grade English Teacher

RSTOWN (cont)
ns, Thomas G.
ry Professor
via, Tracy Tischer
sh & Journalism Teacher
aly, Salif
ish Teacher
an, Vicki Hutzell
cience & Chemistry Teacher
er, Darwin Lamar
essor of Accounting
Vaughn Dana
essor of Psychology
ert, Samuel Stewart
ish Teacher
son, Jan O'Brien
th Grade Teacher
le, Jack Murray
hology & Sociology Teacher
William Ditto
essor of Biology
art, Aaron Gregory
'chr, Coach & Ath Dir
n, Mary Williams
ish Teacher
r, Wanda Grace
nce & PE Teacher
t, Nina Adrienne (Rihard)
Grade Math Teacher
rd, Kathy Saunders
ish Department Chair
G. Archie
Grd Social Studies Teacher
, Douglas Edward
nematics Teacher
, Michael Gerard
ciate Prof of Humanities
ecker, Charles Robert
hology & Government Tchr
, Edgar
red Math & Economics Tchr
t, Judith Kennedy
c Prof & Clinical Coord
Cecil Lynn
nce Teacher
ett, Rebecca Shuttleworth
her of Gifted & Talented
ry, Kathleen Claire
cipal
n, James David
hematics Department Chair
, Harold L., Jr.
in Asst & Economics Teacher
Sandra Loree
na, Eng & Span Teacher
w, Valerie Austin
stant Principal
ay, John Henry, Jr.
nce Dept Chm & Teacher
er, Marlys Ann
' of Health & Physical Ed
nberger, Howard Wilmer
rd of Auto Tech & Collision
Bonnie Kormos
lish Dept Chair & Teacher
, John Michael
History Teacher
ones, Bienvenida E.
ence Teacher
er, Kerry Ann
h Teacher
Kellie Bowers
h Grade Teacher
y, Ginger Hutzell
Grd Social Studies Teacher
ling, Linda Gore
t Grade Teacher
mgen, Denise Monn
sm Instr & Kndgtn Tchr
, Regina Dawn
t Principal
nan, Pamela Noreen
h Grade Teacher
er, Curtis Barrett
oral Director
, Gregory Edward
sical Ed & Health Teacher
, Diane Marie
ar of Behavioral Disorders
nhill, Kathy Ann
glish Teacher & Dept Chprsn
er, Kay Harner
rth Grade Teacher
enfeltz, David John, Jr.
th Teacher & Dept Chair
ner, Ann Elizabeth
gh School Physical Ed Tchr
MPSTEAD
rs, Leslie Carolyn
Grade Science Teacher
, Patricia Cooke
Grade Language Arts Tchr
haar, Emma Formwalt
athematics Tchr & Chairperson
RWOOD
m, Sarah Cowan
athematics Teacher
wles, Carolyn Birch
athematics Teacher
icki, Joline DeHart
glish Dept Chair
r, Bonnie
siness Teacher & Dept Chprsn
VRE DE GRACE
ler, Catherine C.
sistant Principal
ki, Dennis Michael
idance Counselor
ncer, Jo Ann Jones
idance Counselor

Wensell, Georgia
Mathematics Teacher
HELEN
Adams, Cheryl Palonis
Pace Language Arts Teacher
Carney, Britt Maria
Mathematics Teacher
Dankulich, Cheryl Wysong
Language Arts & Reading Tchr
HUNTINGTOWN
Dargan, Carol Wiant
Reading, Eng & Soc Stud Tchr
Jones, Joan A. Johnson
Fourth Grade Teacher
Momberger, Sherry M. Sherwood
Reading & English Teacher
HURLOCK
Bowens, Elva Marie
Former MSPAP
Groton, Jacquelyn McCall
Social Studies Teacher
Jackson, James Henry
Sixth Grade Science Teacher
Lake, Janice Jones
Language Arts Teacher
Steward, Sabra Corbin
Choral & General Music Teacher
HYATTSVILLE
Barton, Roger E.
United States History Instr
Donegan, Sue A.
ESOL Content & Soc Stud Tchr
French, Barbara Jean
ESOL Teacher
Gravel, Claude J.
Religion & Math Teacher
Lucas, Sheila White
English & Reading Teacher
Mendosa, Doris Kurscheid
Eighth Grade English Teacher
Roper, James Stephen
Assistant Band Director
Smith, Patrick Sean James
Eng Tchr & Basketball Coach
Suazo, Gaby Montoya
ESOL Teacher
Vogel, Susan Gramsky
Social Studies Teacher
Weir, Merlene J.
Fifth Grade Teacher
Williams, Charlene Davis
Sixth Grade Teacher
IJAMSVILLE
Hinkley, Brian David
Band Director & Music Teacher
Olow, Frances Adams
8th Grade Mathematics Teacher
Reickel, Eric James
English Teacher
INDIAN HEAD
Barbour, Henry J.
Social Studies Educator
Dyson, Arnetha Lyndell
Third Grade Teacher
Gilbert, Charles L.
Aerospace Science Instructor
Kavlick, Kathryn Ann
Second Grade Teacher
Mazzeo, Michael Joseph, Jr.
Social Studies Teacher
Mc Ghee, R. Faye Mc Callum
Choral Music Teacher
Morris, Kathleen Foy
Language Arts & Rdng Teacher
Overholtzer, David Craig
Instrumental Music Teacher
Roan, Lou Wright
Guidance Counseling & Chair
JEFFERSON
Remmert, Jean Bogdonski
Second Grade Teacher
JESSUP
Mc Swain, Patrick Edward
6th-8th Grade Band Director
Plitt, Vickie Lynn
Physical Educator
JOPPA
Barowski, Renee Isabel
Spanish Teacher
Biscotti, Sharon Lois
Third Grade Teacher
Kaniecki, Linda Pinchot
Mathematics Teacher
Karminski, Barbara Kay
Computer Teacher
Komondor, Gregory
Geography & Government Teacher
Schuhart, Benjamin A.
Music Department Chairperson
KENSINGTON
Cofino, Josefina Gonzalez
Frgn Lang Chprsn & Span Tchr
Edwards, Catherine Fairley
Guidance Counselor
Flanagan, Patricia Ann
Social Studies Teacher
Schlie, Jamie
Science Dept Chair & Teacher
Stathes, Deborah Deems
English Teacher
KINGSVILLE
DeNike, Amy Patricia
3rd Grade Teacher
Piraino, Catharine Miller
Retired First Grade Teacher
KITZMILLER
Brady, Elsie Ilene (Burrell)
Retired Elementary Teacher

LA PLATA
Ayers, Phillip Dennis
Technology Education Instr
Bodamer, Timothy Baun
Band Director
Geason, Marian Caster
Vocal Music Teacher
Getgen, Teresa Cisney
Health & PE Teacher
Headley, Russell Matthew
English Teacher
Hugel, Julie Mc Coy
Home Economics Teacher
Osborne, Hilda Barnes
English Teacher
Prevas, John
Latin Teacher & Greek Lecturer
Reichard, David Carl
Prof of Engineering & Math
Rudy, Linda Mae
Mathematics Teacher
Simpson, Judith Garner
Social Studies Teacher
Sinkey, Henry Anthony, Jr.
Fifth Grade Teacher
Wade, Mary Ann
Guidance Counselor
Warren, Cynthia Douglas
Social Studies Teacher
Wilkerson, Kathryn H.
Business Ed Tchr & Dept Chprsn
LANDOVER
Lipiano, James Joseph
Visual Arts Teacher
Mateer, Anita K.
English Teacher & Dept Chair
Pitts, Rhonda Gray
Vice Principal
LANHAM
Carter, Dian (A.) Leake
English Teacher
DeRoo, Helen Pynn
English & Language Arts Tchr
DuCharme, Carol Ann
English Teacher
Konrad, Carol J.
Mathematics & History Teacher
Mather, Frances Twohig
Chemistry Teacher
Mitchell, Melodye A.
Science Teacher
Shelton, Gloria Gordon
Art Teacher
Targan, Eric Gabriel
English & History Teacher
Williams, Elaine Louise
English Teacher & Coordinator
LARGO
Bassette, Lorraine Pratt
Prof of Business Management
Ferguson, Paul Warren
Counselor
Goldfaden, David Louis
English & Philosophy Professor
Hunt, James Christopher
Science Department Professor
Smith, Rosemary Teresa
Associate Professor of Lit
LAUREL
Adams, Peter A.
Social Studies Teacher
Cecil, Robert Anthony
Sixth Grade Teacher
Ekstrand, Sharon Klein
High School Counselor
Fisher, Umbrenda Herrington
Mathematics Teacher
Fitzwater, Diana C. (Sines)
Art Teacher
Galloway, Leirdre Clements
Social Studies Teacher
Gottsman, Earl Eugene
Vice Pres of Acadamic Affairs
Grant, Nona Turner
5th Grade Teacher
Hobbs, Lorra Rhodes
Guidance Counselor
Littlefield, Virginia Lucas
Adjunct Professor
Masonis, Kathleen Todd
Former English Teacher
McFarland, Deborah Scott
Administrator
Miller, Robert Wayne
Band Director
O'Brien, Paul James, Jr.
Religion Teacher
Overton, Winnifred Helen
Physical Education Teacher
Shry, Hob
8th Grd Math Tchr & Team Ldr
Silverman, Jay Harry
Math Teacher
Speer, Sharon Elizabeth
Univ & Comprehensive Eng Tchr
Stancliff, Melanie Deitz
Cosmetology Teacher
Vergers, Charles A.
Prof of Elect Engrng Tech
LEONARDTOWN
Andrewson, Rosemarie Beth
Biology & Chemistry Teacher
Foley, Tracy Aumann
9th & 11th English Teacher
Henderson, Robert Bruce
History Teacher
Krafty, Diane Werkheiser
High School Mathematics Tchr
Krafty, Joseph John
Social Studies Teacher

Leopold, Eunice Zippermann
Fine Arts Dept Chm, Choral Dir
Shea, John James
Eighth Grade Lang Arts Tchr
Taylor, Phyllis A.
Instructor
Zona, Andrea
Math Teacher
LEXINGTN PARK
Cross, Robert Edward
8th Grade Mathematics Teacher
King, Karen Banville
Science Teacher
LIBERTYTOWN
Shanholtz, Melinda Main
Third Grade Teacher
LINTHICUM HTS
Punte, Audrey Bowen
Junior High Teacher & Coord
LONACONING
Boord, James Edward
Music Teacher
Dye, William Edward
English Teacher
Llewellyn, Marvin Thompson
Algebra & Trigonometry Teacher
Martin, William Louis
History Tchr & Dept Chprsn
Mc Dowell, Robin Lynn (Dorsey)
Computer & Business Teacher
Moffatt, Barbara Braskey
Second Grade Teacher
Vogtman, Thomas Allen, Sr.
Mathematics Teacher
Walton, Virginia A.
Fr, Latin Tchr & Dept Head
Williams, James Dale, Sr.
World History Teacher
Winters, Lori Ann (Engle)
Choral Dir & Music Dept Chprsn
LOVEVILLE
Cox, Judith Ann
Fifth Grade Teacher
Sachs, Michelle Mykulyn
Mathematics Teacher
LUSBY
Roof, Kimberly Hall
Athletic Dir, Hlth & PE Tchr
LUTHERVILLE
Fernando, Chandra Cooray
Academic Dean
LUTHERVILLE TIMONIUM
Huebler, Kitty
Third Grade Teacher
Hundley, Rita P.
1st Grade Teacher
Shank, Helen Hilleary
2nd Grade Teacher
MARDELA SPRINGS
Brahosky, Adam C.
HS Social Studies Teacher
MC HENRY
Crawford, Joan Bielau
Dir of Enrllmnt Dev & Eng Prof
Glotfelty, Thomas Austin
ABE & GED Instructor
Luers, Beth Hurley
Professor of Social Sciences
Mitchell, Lillian Lee
Academic Affairs Dean
Skidmore, Ronald Keith
Professor of Art
MECHANICSVLLE
Kastner, Roxanne Lee
Fourth Grade Teacher
Tyler, Gail Fain
Music Specialist
MIDDLETOWN
Bohn, Brenda Williams
Sixth Grade Lang Arts Tchr
Grim, Valerie Pearce
Science Teacher & Coach
McCumber, Linda M.
Science Teacher
Rupert, Gary Lynn
Director of Bands
MILLERSVILLE
DeVore, Janet Pressman
Business Ed Tchr & Coordinator
Frankhouser, Richard Edward
Physical Education Teacher
Jernigan, Prince David
History & Social Studies Tchr
Landers, Bernard Joseph, Jr.
Music Tchr & Dept Chprsn
Poist, Brenda Lorraine
Biology & Physiology Teacher
Schachter, William Norman
Band & Orchestra Director
Swanson, Sean Arthur
High School English Teacher
Wagner, Virginia E. (Solano)
Spanish Teacher
MONKTON
Benson, Gordon C.
7th-8th Grade Science Teacher
Medwin, Maria Carmen
French & Spanish Teacher
Peterson, Kathleen Detorie
Art Teacher
MONTGOMERY VILLAGE
Bellman, Allan Edward
Math & Computer Science Tchr
Brown, Louise Elaine
English Teacher
Bucher, Patricia Lawrence
Math & Computer Teacher
Drake, Jerry Francis
Band Director & Dept Chrmn

Fassett, Lorraine Hilma
Medical Careers Teacher
Howard, Joanna
English Composition Assistant
Pevey, Cathy Devoll
English Teacher
Rockwell, Phoebe
Choral Music Teacher
Sampselle, David William
Senior High English Teacher
MORGANZA
Adair, Janine Mahaley
Theatre & English Teacher
Asher, Donald Francis, Jr.
Biology Teacher
Costner, Barbara M.
Latin & Mathematics Teacher
Ensminger, Karen Marie
Mathematics Teacher
Fickes, Carrie Ann Enicks
Fine Arts Chairperson & Tchr
Santee, Marck N.
English Teacher
Young, Cindy Mc Kay
English Teacher
Younkins, James E.
Mathematics Teacher & Chm
MOUNT RAINIER
Shaver, Richard Clayton
Third Grade Teacher
MOUNT SAVAGE
King, Sandra Lee
Business Ed Tchr & Dept Chprsn
Strietbeck, Elizabeth
French Teacher
NEW MARKET
Fleming, LeRoy Duke
Social Studies Teacher
Motter, Melissa Mary
Fifth Grade Teacher
Richardson, Linda Adele
Language Arts Teacher
Shipman, Janet VanZoest
8th Grade Language Arts Tchr
NEWARK
Cannon, Geneva
Instruction & Cnslng Svcs Supv
NORTH EAST
Allison, Edna
Mathematics Teacher
Arrante, Michelle Denise
Secondary Math Teacher
Bauer, Paul Franklin
Philosophy Professor
Henderson, Marsha Jane
Fourth Grade Teacher
Krasman, Albert James, Jr.
Carpentry Instructor
Lake, Becky Brenda
Science Teacher
Porter, Michelle Catington
Art & Photography Teacher
OAKLAND
Beard, David C.
Civics Teacher
Biggs, Harry Lee, Jr.
Social Studies Teacher
Cosner, Stephen Edward
Electronics Instructor
Durst, Donna Wojciechowski
Algebra Teacher
Fleming, Linda Teets
Principal
Foley, Patricia Ault
First Grade Teacher
Freyman, William David
Vocational Drafting Teacher
Gilbert, Elizabeth Rees
6th-8th Grd Classroom Teacher
Graham, Vera Gibson
Business Education Teacher
Grove, George Wade
Mathematics Teacher
Grove, Virginia Morris
Fifth Grade Teacher
Hamill, Marjorie Railey
Retired 4th Grade Teacher
Harvey, William Scott
Social Studies Teacher
Hinebaugh, Debra K.
Title I Resource Teacher
Janoske, William E.
Science Teacher
Lambert, Joan Wirtz
German Teacher
Leitzel, Lowell Leslie
French Teacher
Mayfield, David Wayne
Geometry & Physics Teacher
McBride, John Daniel
Alternative Program Teacher
Miller, Maxine Klink
Assistant Principal
Newcomb, Glenda Dale
Fourth Grade Teacher
Pratt, Sonia L.
Art Teacher
Ramsay, Pauline English
8th Grade Language Arts Tchr
Rettel, Cherie J.
School Enrichment Pgm Tchr
Slagle, Elsie Sisler
Allied Health Teacher
Smith, Cheryl Lorena
Third Grade Teacher
Spiker, Robin Jean
English Teacher
Taylor, Athena L.
Business Education Teacher

OAKLAND (cont)
Yommer, Bonnie Jane
Sixth Grade Math Teacher
Zollner, Michelle Lois
Health Teacher
ODENTON
Barker, Joyce Elizabeth
Fifth Grade Teacher
Brasoveanu, Alexandra
Mathematics & Physics Teacher
Hays, Laurel Ann
Secondary Coordinator
OLDTOWN
McElfish, Shawnee Lee
Social Studies Teacher
Parsons, Cynthia Hayden
Fourth Grade Teacher
Swauger, James Edward, Sr.
Sixth Grade Teacher
OLNEY
Bidinger, Kay Lazio
Social Studies Teacher
Cumberland, Kathleen Cascio
Fifth Grade Teacher
LaPadula, Bonnie Watson
Teacher
LeRoux, Lynne Anne Spellman
First Grade Teacher
OWINGS
Clites, Robin Rae
Chemistry Teacher
Daugherty, Lori Perry
Psychology & Sociology Teacher
Evans, Sharon Mertz
Spanish Teacher
Hall, James E.
Social Studies Teacher
Kelley, William Michael
Mathematics Teacher
Martin, Kathleen Podlesny
Sixth Grade Teacher
Minderlein, James Lloyd
Naval Science Instructor
Pittman, Jimmy Lee, Sr.
Art Teacher
Ray, Dawn Maureen
9th-12th Grd Spcl Ed Teacher
Travers, Janet Barrett
English Teacher
Venezlani, Tricia O'Neill
Drama & English Teacher
Weber, Charles Richard
Dean of Freshmen & Ath Dir
OWINGS MILLS
Barr, Mona Joyce
Mathematics Teacher
Chidester, Joseph Paul
Physical Science Teacher
Cox, Cynthia Ann
English Teacher
LeBarron, Therese Ann
HS Special Education Teacher
Lutz, Sharon Figinski
English & Theater Arts Teacher
Mahon, Robert Joseph, Jr.
Science Teacher
Mc Kibbin, Martin Howard
AP US History Teacher
Rundel, Wendy J.
Guidance Counselor
Shapiro, Yehoshua
HS Assistant Principal
Smith, LouAnne Walkling
Latin Teacher
Smoot, Robert Clarence, IV
Science Teacher
Wolf, Elise R.
English & History Teacher
OXON HILL
Abbott, Philip Keenan
High School Spanish Teacher
Baker, Laverne H.
Math Teacher
Belanger, Donald Joseph
Biology Teacher
Benns, Eddie L.
Aerospace Science Commandant
Boatman, Dwight
Peer Mediation Teacher
Bogan, Claud E.
Air Force JROTC Teacher
Charnock, Felicia Persinger
4th Grade Teacher
Chesser, Phillip Jerome
English Teacher
Comerford, Joan K.
Biology Teacher
Courtemanche, Margot Suzanne
Ninth Grade English Teacher
Dickson, Audrey Elva
Magnet Coordinator
Fenton, David Christian
Technology Teacher
Foster, Jan Strickland
Business Teacher
Haliburton, Brenda Wood
Six Grade Math & Lang Teacher
Johnson, William Leander
8th Grade Teacher
Jones, Diana Brandt
Science Teacher & Coordinator
Kouame, Sheila Pulley
Spanish Teacher
Lange, Linda Diane
Lang Arts & Reading Teacher
Linthicum, Erlena Claudette
Sixth Grade Teacher
Norwood-Dobbins, Cornelia LeVon
Business Teacher
Pickens, Geneva Moore
English Teacher
Spinks, Cloyce Isaac
Social Studies Teacher
Thomas, Venita Ruth
6th Grade Teacher
Vance, Beatrice Elizabeth
Math & Science Teacher
Vance, Robert Carroll
Math & Science Teacher
Wemple, Jonathan Barent
English Teacher
Williams, James, Jr.
Multi Level Voc Dev Teacher
Wilson, Viola Washington
Instructional Resource Teacher
Zeman, James A.
Mathematics Teacher
PARK HALL
Wilson, Delores Harris
Lang Arts & Soc Stud Teacher
PARKTON
Harding, Sandra T.
Physical Education Teacher
Migliarini, Cheryl S.
Advanced Physics Teacher
Mundie, Tammy Louise
Math, Computer Science Teacher
Roth, John Martin, Jr.
High School Guidance Counselor
Zacharko, David M.
Spanish & French Teacher
PASADENA
Buchan, James Bruce
English Teacher
Cappellini, Laura Reno
4th Grade Teacher
Flythe, Nancy Parker
Fifth Grade Teacher
Gottlich, Henry
Zoology, Chem & Bio Tchr
Hackett, Arleatha Walston
Second Grade Teacher
Irvine, Carole Walter
4th Grade Teacher
Kraning, Tom
Physical Ed Teacher & Coach
Metrinko, Paul Walter
Tchr & Social Stud Dept Chair
Pair, Glenn Cleveland
Social Studies Teacher
Pfeffer, Judith Stern
Mathematics Teacher
Reynolds, Craig A.
Assistant Principal
Rhodes, Karen S.
Vocal Music Teacher
Richards, Cyndee Ann
Marketing Teacher & Coord
Routh, Delores Capel
Second Grade Teacher
Triolo, Audrey P.
Math Teacher
White, Noel Jean Dunker
Secondary Soc Studies Teacher
Zemke, Donna Lynn
Mathematics Teacher
PERRYVILLE
Connelly, Kevin M.
Computer Sci & Biology Tchr
Lathrop, Constance Cook
French Teacher
Nacrelli, Cathy Singleton
Language Arts Teacher
PHOENIX
Karwacki, Margaret Wolski
Retired First Grade Teacher
PITTSVILLE
Mc Kelvey, Maxwell George
4th Grade Science Teacher
Purnell, Cynthia Adams
First Grade Teacher
POCOMOKE CITY
LaCurts, Carvel Lee
Math & Computer Science Tchr
Springle, Terry Wade
Mathematics Teacher
Stewart, Peggy Watson
Guidance Counselor
Wells, M. Emily
Social Science Educator
POMFRET
Brinjak, Raymond
Earth & Space Science Teacher
Bryant, Stephanie Elaine
Social Studies Teacher
Gibson, Lessie (Walton)
Business Teacher
Harclerode, Beth Diane
High School Art Teacher
Horsey, Major Franklin
Fourth Grade Teacher
Mc Phaul, Mary F.
Mathematics Teacher
O'Neill, David
Social Studies Teacher
Roberts, Paula M.
High School Mathematics Tchr
Rogers, Joan Tompkins
Business Education Teacher
Scanlan, Jane Overton
English Teacher
Searfoss, Beth
English Teacher
Stattel, Philip James
Vocal Music Teacher
POOLESVILLE
Hennessy, Laura Jean
PE & Health Teacher
Kissinger, Lori Ann
Foreign Language Dept Chairman
Schultz, Jan D.
Soc Studies Tchr & Dept Chprsn
Tabachnick, Patricia Ann
English Resource Teacher
POTOMAC
Clark, Ross James
Soc Studies Tchr & Dept Chrpsn
Cutler, Elaine Cooper
Fifth Grade Teacher
Hibbs, Michael Edward
English Teacher
London, Douglas
Principal
Ravenscroft, Elizabeth Werres
Retired Soc Studies & Rel Tchr
Rebman, Eileen S.
History Teacher
Weinberger, Linda Welsh
Kindergarten Teacher
Wieand, William George
Social Studies Teacher
PRESTON
Sturtz, Agnes Leonard
Librarian & Admin Assistant
PRINCE FREDERICK
Bramble, Gloria Maxine
Secondary Math Resource Tchr
Briscoe, Rosslyn Michelle
Business Teacher
Brown, Andrew Jackson, Jr.
Counselor
Clark, Joseph Theodore
English Teacher
Evans, Vaughn Dale, Sr.
Reading & Lang Arts Teacher
Fisher, Daniel Craig
English Teacher
Keosseian, John Mark
English Tchr & Mentor Pgm Dir
Lister, Dawn Sheetz
Social Studies Teacher
Mc Coy, Charlie Lorenzo
Associate Naval Science Instr
Moore, Sheila Goodman-Council
Business Teacher
Murray, James Phillip
Computer Programming Instr
Wallace, Lucy Ann Parker
Kindergarten Teacher
PRINCESS ANNE
Anderson, Mignon Holland
Eng & Modern Lit Lecturer
Brooks, Carolyn Branch
Dean & Associate Professor
Carter, Ralph Donald
Asst Prof of His & Soc Sci
Christian, Sandra Hart
Visiting English Lecturer
Coursey, Leon N.
Health & Physical Ed Prof
Dienhart, John
Chairman
Drechsler, Terry Ann
Mathematics Tchr
Eisenberg, Beverly S.
Interior Design Educator
Gill, Cynthia Holder
Lecturer of Physical Therapy
Herzins, Charlene Mason
Guidance Counselor
Herzins, Frank James, Jr.
Social Studies Teacher
Hymon-Parker, Shirley
Acting Chair
Johnson, Della Dameron
Drama Professor
Kaup, Shekhar Shetty
Prof of Bus Administration
Kollehlon, Konia Tweninmii
Assoc Professor of Sociology
Mc Neil, Rachel Eaddy
English Teacher
Middleton, Suzanne Marie (Swis)
Math Teacher
Morant, Mervalin Anderene
Asst Prof of Plant Pathology
Noble, Annette
Mathematics Professor
Verbeke, Karen A.
Assoc Prof of Spec Education
PYLESVILLE
Gant, Paul J.
English Teacher
Goetz, Arletta West
Seventh Grade English Teacher
Greve, Phillip Thomas
Band Director
Heinly, Mark David
4th-12th Grd Orchestra Dir
Holdaway, Stacey Taranto
Mathematics Teacher
Johnson, John Clinton
Math Teacher
Westberry, Douglas Bruce
Music Teacher & Choral Dir
QUANTICO
Kelly, Sharon R.
First Grade Teacher
QUEENSTOWN
Dawson, Sandra Petty
Teacher
RANDALLSTOWN
Hamstra, Jodi Grosser
Spanish Teacher
Hemler, Mary Patricia
Mathematics Teacher
Tillery, Juanita Tynes
Diversified Occupations Coord
REISTERSTOWN
Jester, Kelly Wilson
Social Studies Teacher
Maistros, Harry Constantine
Art Department Chair
Mc Henry, Catalina Maria
Spcl Education Dept Chairman
Whitman, Barbara Carr
Tchr of Eng Gifted & Talented
RIDGELY
Counell, Sherry Phillips
Instructor of Hlth Occupations
Knight, Margie J.
Physical Education & Hlth Tchr
Moore, James
Assistant Principal
Robinett, Robena D.
Lead Science Teacher
Shaffer, Keith Laverne
English Teacher
Stockman, Maureen DiLaura
Mathematics Teacher
RISING SUN
Bannister, Lois Cameron
Eighth Grade Reading Teacher
Duff, Barbara R.
6th-8th Grade English Teacher
RIVERDALE
Ashendorf, Robert Scott
Art Teacher
Brooks, Lisa Diane
High School Band Director
Brown, Phyllis Taylor
Sixth Grade Teacher
Gray, Cheryl Christine
Fifth Grade Teacher
Shorr, Sandra B.
Health Education Chairperson
Zachry, Shirley Mc Clanahan
ESOL Teacher
ROCK HALL
Mullikin, Terri Evetett
Seventh & Eighth Grade Teacher
ROCKVILLE
Baker, Dana Louise
Student Development Professor
Barber, James Allen
PE Tchr & Bsktbl Coach
Bennett, Rhoda G.
English Teacher
Blum, Carol Kramer
Eng Teacher & Lit Magazine Adv
Boratenski, Matthew John
English Teacher
Boyar, Gail Tucker
History Teacher
Breslin, Deborah Kay
Mathematics Teacher
Broadman, Sandra Kaplan
Mathematics Teacher
Brown, Carole Thayer
World Studies Teacher
Brown, Clinton Harvey
Chemistry Teacher
Brown, Virginia Judith
AP Biology Teacher
Chiariello, Joan Szewczyk
English Teacher
Cooney, Frieda DiGiorgio
Home Ec & Health Educator
Davies, Diane Oliver
English & Computer Teacher
Dempsey, Lance
World Studies Teacher
DeRosa, Anthony Mark
Foreign Language Resource Tchr
Dosh, Deborah Ann
Third Grade Teacher
Earenfight, Richard Huntington
8th Grd English Teacher
Edwards, Kamala
English Professor
Evans, Wayne Curtis
5th Grade Teacher
Fernandez, Yolanda de la Pena
Spanish Teacher
Galvin, Aloysius C., SJ
Math Teacher
Garcia, Judith Gann
Choral & General Music Teacher
George, Robert Meredith
PE Teacher & Head Coach
Goetz, C. Jon
Physics Teacher
Goldsmith, Paula Levendorf
English Teacher
Goodwin, Alan S.
English Department Chairman
Grant, Warren Herbert
Professor of Chemistry
Hanley, Joni Barbara
Kindergarten Teacher
Hanrahan, Barbara Moran
Retired High School Teacher
Henderson, Elizabeth Karina
Professor
Hluch, Kevin Andrew
Associate Professor of Art
Homes, Phyllis R.
Guidance Cnslr & Coll Adv
Humphrey, Jean Whitcomb
French Teacher
Jackson, Carmen Longo
Biology Teacher
Jannotta, Doreen Patricia
Volunteer Substitute
Kador, Suellen Anderson
Chemistry Teacher
Kaldahl, Brad G.
Electronic Imaging Professor
Kimble, Kay Joyce Smith
English Teacher
King, George Curtis
AP Eng, Lit & Composition Tchr
LaRuffa, Nancy Fritz
Teacher & Math Dept Chprsn
Laycock, Robert T.
Professor of Accounting
Leary, John Daniel
Spanish Teacher
Leonard, Robert E.
Mathematics Teacher
Liszka, Joseph John
Math Teacher
Lynch, Lisa Decktor
French Teacher
Maiberger, Merry Porter
History & Science Teacher
Metz, Elinor Daschbach
Teacher
Metz, Nancy J.
Instruction Specialist
Milne, Henry U.
Sci Dept Chairperson & Teacher
Morgan, Cheryl Ann
PE & Health Ed Teacher
Napolitano, Daniel C.
Dept Regligious Stud Faculty
Niewiaroski, Trudi Osmers
Social Studies Teacher
Okulski, Gloryia Lenzi
Literature Teacher
Olexik, William A.
Professor of Biology
OuYang, Benjamin T.
Resource Counselor
Peebles, Monica Louise
History Teacher
Petrides, Bette Cowden
English & Journalism Teacher
Price, Woody
Prof of Visual Communications
Restorff, Kathleen Ann
Physics Professor
Saunders, Sheila Mae Lewis
Special Education Teacher
Scozzafava, Rose T.
9th-12th Grade Music Teacher
Shire, Maria Gallaccio
French & Spanish Teacher
Sindall, Robert St Clair
5th Grade Teacher
Skalet, Linda H.
History of Art Profesor
Smith, Virginia Baer
English Professor
Swift, Stephen E.
English Teacher
Switzer, Daniel Leland
Associate Principal
Symister-David, Cathalene Elizabeth
Fourth Grade Teacher
Taubman, Nancy Beth
English Teacher
Thomas, Diana Jones
Assistant Professor
Trettel, Joseph Francis
Instrumental Music Teacher
Watts, John Marvin
English Department Professor
Wehrle, John George
History Teacher
Wendrich, Barbara Anne
Second Grade Teacher
Wilson, Brian Scott
History Department Chair
Wright, Nancy Mazis
11th Grade English Teacher
SAINT JAMES
Meehan, Charles George, Jr.
Mathematics Teacher
SAINT MARYS CITY
Byrd, Jeffrey J.
Asst Professor of Biology
Daugherty, Helen Ginn
Professor of Sociology
Ebenreck, Sara V.
Philosophy Professor
Froom, David
Associate Professor of Music
Glaser, Michael S.
Professor of English
Hicks, Louis
Sociology Professor
Kozak, Andrew Frank
Associate Prof of Economics
Lasane, Terell Prince
Asst Professor of Psychology
Martin, Stefan
Asst Professor of English
Nguyen, Ho N.
Professor of Economics
Stabile, Donald Robert
Economics Professor
Watts, Christina James
Education Instructor
Wilson, Bruce M.
Eng & Comparative Lit Prof
SAINT MICHAEL
Bridges, Patricia Ross
Mathematics Teacher
Kinlock, Steven F.
Psych & Government Teacher
Whiteley Distler, Carolyn de Sales
Guidance Counselor
SALISBURY
Ball, Marchan Rawlins
8th Grd World History Teacher
Briscoe, Patrick Morris
Conflict Resolution Counselor

BURY (cont)
Keith Eugene
ematics Teacher
, Anne Louise
istory Teacher
dins, Philip A.
ce Teacher
vanna, Augustine Gaspar
ssor of Biology
, Jennifer Steptoe
& 12th Grd English Tchr
Debra Jane
nd Grade Teacher
, Paola Judith
sh Teacher
Marion Lee Gordy
d Culture & History Tchr
Rosemary Pataky
Department Chairman
ss, Raymond
ary Arts Instructor
as, Thomas Franklin
ed Professor
n, Deborah Henshall
Grade Teacher
Ellen Meyer
Science Teacher
, Suzanne Knox
ematics Teacher
David Lee
ronics Technology Tchr
aumer, Jill D.
sh Teacher
, Charles Benton
, Gen Music & Drama Tchr
Jeffrey Allan
ogy & Physiology Teacher
es, Carla Nelson
Professor of Mathematics
ter, Glenn O. B.
h Grade Math Teacher
-Clute, Elaine Cullen
ch & English Instructor
Susan Miller
& Creative Writing Teacher
, Dollie Claiborne
l Music Teacher
an, Dorothy Ann
-12th Grade English Tchr
Y SPRING
r, Mary Elizabeth
al Studies Teacher
man, Jeffrey Alan
ish Teacher
eitha Sue (Snodgrass)
Teacher
, Malinda Maurie
ish Teacher
as, Robert Swan
al Studies Teacher
RN
son, Cathy S.
Grade Teacher
anni, Mary Linda
tr Sci & Bus Dept Chair
Linda Marlene (Runk)
Grade Teacher
Constance Adelle
, Science, Spanish Teacher
, Thomas Edward
pus Minister
RNA PARK
Lillian Elizabeth
ory Teacher
Susan Mc Clay
h Teacher
es, Paula Cadogan
Grade Science Teacher
, Robert Charles
Grade Teacher
onnell, Karen Sims
ach & Spanish Teacher
rland, Paula Wiise
ach Teacher
aughlin, Claudia
g Dept Head & Span Teacher
, Barbara Ward
mistry Teacher
ts, Anita Claire (Miller)
chment Teacher
on, Lillian Weekley
sical Education Teacher
, Barbara Hottel
ior Ballet Teacher
ER SPRING
estein, Eliot Josef
chology Teacher
r, Jack F.
Principal & Lead Teacher
, Roberta Dana
Tchr & Dept Chprsn
bell, Tamitha Fisher
h School English Teacher
r, Ayanna-Patricia Taylor
cher & Computer Specialist
man, Nancy Louise
erdisciplinry Resource Tchr
ihan, Darlyn Joyce
gnet Mathematics Teacher
, Anne-Marie
dance Counselor
r, Jody L.
ma & Vocal Music Teacher
mbrosio, Judith Rega
dergarten Teacher
Stanley Currier, Jr.
History & POTC Teacher
efano, Mark Paul
glish Teacher

Dismuke, Roy Eugene
Computer Science Teacher
Dyas, Nannette
Mathematics Teacher
Ehrhardt, Cathleen Hecht
Science Teacher
Felhuhn, Susan Baylin
Biology Teacher
Glynn, Ed
Dean of Academic Affairs
Green, Thomas Frank
Physics Teacher
Griffith, Thomas Calvin
Social Studies Teacher
Groomes, Warren Edward
Mathematics Teacher
Grossman, Shana R.
ESOL Teacher
Haber, James Frederick
Computer Science Teacher
Hinkle, Brian Daryl
9th-12th Grd Soc Stud Teacher
Hofman, Barbara Hartung
Mathematics Teacher
Johnson, Charles William
PE Teacher
Jones, Stephanie Wright
10th-12th Grade Health Ed Tchr
Kravitz, Michael Stanley
Chemistry Teacher
Kroeger, Paul E.
Science Resource Teacher
Landefeld, Kyle Carson
HS Social Studies Teacher
Lane, Ronald Dale
Special Education Teacher
Lang, Amye Roache
Team Ldr & MD Tomorrow Pgm
Lockard, Karen Oberheim
English Teacher
Lopes, John F.
Retired Teacher
Mannino, Louis Anthony
Mathematics Teacher
Mc Intosh, Edward Leon
Anatomy, Physiology & Bio Tchr
Menke-Fish, Sarah Frances
Hum & Comm Magnet Pgm Coord
Michal, Susan Lynn (Castelluccio)
Media Production Magnet Coord
Miltner, Daniel Scott
Mathematics Teacher
Moore, Martha Adele
English Teacher
Moser, Patricia Judge
Biology Teacher
Natonick, Marlys-Jean Schiller
Third Grd Teacher & Asst Prin
Negro, Frank Joseph, Jr.
Science Teacher
Nogay, Brian Michael
Science, Biology & Chem Tchr
Olinger, Lester Lee, Jr.
Retired Social Studies Teacher
Palmer, Bonnie Hancher
English Teacher
Redding, J. Patrick
ESOL & Resource Teacher
Reeks, Daniel M.
Social Studies Teacher
Reichard, Gary Gilbert
Mathematics Teacher
Richardson, Virginia Mapp
English Teacher
Rowe, Paula Peck
Science Teacher
Sandoval, Doris Simmons
Chemistry Teacher
Schultz, Phyllis Ann
Eighth Grd Tchr & Asst Prin
Shay, Daniel Brandt
Art Instructor
Shropshire, Jacquelyn Ann Bond
Business Teacher
Tarner, Laurie Ann(Desch)
Eighth Grade English Teacher
Tile, Michael David
Oral Comm & English Teacher
Tomayko, Carole Anne
Eng & Creative Writing Tchr
Touzeau, Jeanne Marie
French Teacher
Tracey, Robert Michael
Social Studies Teacher
Vinik, Bruce
Upper School Principal
Weiner, Christiana M.
Math Teacher
Wire, Colleen Frances Hogan
Science Teacher
Wolfe, Pamela Kline
Soc Stud Dept Chair & Teacher
Zucker, Mordechai
Judaic Studies Teacher
SMITHSBURG
Everett, Patricia Anne
7th Grade Language Arts Tchr
Fowkes, William James, Jr.
Biology Teacher
Getz, Brian David
Health & Life Skills Teacher
Paci, Jamie Amato
Spanish Teacher
Shanholtz, Shirley Day
First Grade Teacher
SNOW HILL
Pennewell, Margaret Anne
Eng, Psych & Journalism Tchr
Slacum, Rosemary Ehlinger
10th Grade English Teacher

SPARKS GLENCOE
Hollingshead, Ophelia Ensor
Retired Physical Ed Teacher
STEVENSON
Diaconis, Linda
Nursing Instructor
STEVENSVILLE
Zajac, Elise Tanner
Second Grade Teacher
SUDLERSVILLE
Henckel, George Lee
Principal
Iverson, Gregory Allen
Math & Science Teacher
SUITLAND
Elborne, Kathy Jeanne (Yohe)
Fifth Grade Teacher
Hansen, Sandra Mueller
5th Grade Teacher
Pelzer-Brower, Rose Vernita
Magnet Coordinator
SYKESVILLE
Cicone, Carl
6th-7th Grd Social Stud Tchr
Delise, Thomas J.
English Teacher
Eber, Bryan Andrew
Instrumental Music Director
Fazenbaker, Charles Robert
Social Studies Dept Chprsn
Foote, Gary E.
Science Teacher
Hevener Miller, Susan Gene
German & Spanish Teacher
Hooper, Dale Thomas
Career, Drafting & CAD Teacher
Hoover, Michael Jay
Language Arts Teacher
Horn, James Bernard
Social Studies Teacher
Johnson, Kenith R.
PE Teacher & Coach
Jones, Lynn Alice
Chemistry Teacher
King, Kevin B.
Choral Director
King, Patricia Ann
English Tchr & Dept Chprsn
Langrall, James E.
Business Education Teacher
Lotz, Lucille Tucker
4th Grade Teacher
Perouty-Byrne, Cynthia L.
Biology I & II Instructor
Phelps, Virginia Taggart
English Teacher
Schaefer, Missie Hodges
Latin Teacher
Schneehagen, Ruth Gorey
Second Grade Teacher
Shank, Lacye Koons
English & Speech Teacher
Vaughn, Courtney Colleen
Physical Education Teacher
Weaver, Wendy Jane
Third Grade Teacher
TAKOMA PARK
Ahlstrom, Edwin Arthur
Professor of Art
Alignay, James Neil
Chemistry Teacher
Ayub, Jamshed
Chemistry Professor
Bennett, Glen Howard
Associate Professor of Biology
Gabele, Susan Elaine
English Teacher
Gearon, Estelle Kathleen
Prof of Chem & Dept Chair
Gurubatham, Gladstone P.
Professor of Social Sciences
Hammond, Carol Howard
Fourth-Fifth Grade Teacher
Khiel, Marie O'Connell
Instructional Assistant
Leitma, Grant G.
Psychology Professor
Melbourne, Bertram Lloyd
Department of Religion Chair
Melbourne, Cavel Andrea (Beckford)
Junior High School Teacher
Paradis, Pixie Bergez
Second Grade Teacher
Roberts, Lee Melvin
Assistant Professor of Chem
Thompson, Phillip J.
Associate Professor
Tripp, Donald Ray
Bible Teacher & Dept Chrmn
Truitt, Ostein Barnes
Associate Prof of Microbiology
Vandervort, Ronald Charles
Science Teacher
Waxman, Randi Joy
Associate Prof of Business
Wheeler, Joe Lawrence
English Department Chair
TANEYTOWN
Cummings, Cynthia Huggins
Third Grade Teacher
TEMPLE HILLS
Berryman-Singleton, Tracey Lynne
5th Grade Math Teacher
Braxton, Marshall Sandra
Social Studies Teacher
Brown, Ira Hugo
Guidance Counselor
Brown, Wondel Everett
Chorus Teacher

Butts, Clara C.
English Teacher
Davis, Wanda Anderson
Eng, Speech & Drama Teacher
Dixon, Marjorice Thomas
Business Education Teacher
Glenn, Doris Swiggett
Math Teacher
Hite, Ann M.
English Teacher
Langley, Catherine A. Nixon
Mathematics Educator
Marshall, Grayson Bernard
Retired 6th Grade Teacher
Mathis, Louphelia Brown
Science Coordinator & Chprsn
O'Malley, Martin
History Teacher
Paupe, Mary Joann (Coyle)
RN & Hlth Occupations Instr
Ryans, Edward O'Neal
English Teacher
Speight, Martha M.
US History Teacher
THURMONT
Beavan, Robert Allan
HS Agriculture Teacher
Drenning, Charles Dahl
Social Studies Teacher
Forman, Carol J.
Mathematics Teacher
Kehne, David Andrew
English Teacher
Myers, Linda Sayler
6th Grd Lang Arts & Math Tchr
Styers, Nancy Haifleigh
Second Grade Teacher
Thomas, David Alan
Chemistry & Physics Teacher
Williams, Douglas James
PE Teacher
TIMONIUM
Fanto, Elizabeth Cuppett
English Teacher
Hedberg, Jacqueline Hope
Social Studies Teacher
Jones, Kathleen Anne
English & Journalism Teacher
Laferty, Craig W.
Math Dept Chair
Lehmer, Elsie Joyce Durham
Contemp Amer & US Hist Tchr
Philips, David Wendell
History Teacher
Smith, Harold Edward, Jr.
Fine Arts Department Chairman
Wajbel, Patricia K.
Math Teacher
White, Mourine Elliott
Physical Ed & Health Teacher
TOWSON
Baker, Jean Harvey
History Professor
Bardaglio, Peter Winthrop
Associate Professor of History
Bergfeld Mills, Dr.
Professor of Psychology
Delahunty, George
Prof of Biological Sciences
Dundes, Lauren
Assistant Professor
Free, Anne Rebecca
Instructor in Theatre
Gould, Barbara Woodruff
Professor of Education
Horn, David E.
Professor of Chemistry
Kaplan, Laurie Smith
Associate Professor
Levy, Nancy R.
Education Professor
Morton, Joe
Professor of Philosophy
Mussina, Mark Andrew
Sports Talk Show Host
Woodson, Amanda
Associate Professor of Dance
UNION BRIDGE
Totten, Leo Mark
Physical Education Dept Chair
UPPER MARLBORO
Ahluwalia, Usha
French Teacher
Anderson, Cynthia Silvis
Physical Education Teacher
Bashoor, Janetta Taylor
HS Math Teacher & Guid Cnslr
Bragg, Giles G.
Retired Teacher
Brown, Patty Mosley
High School English Teacher
Cameron, Judy Phillips
Sixth Grade Teacher
Carson, Janita Dechvan
Mathematics Teacher
Cowan, Frances Headley
Vice Principal
Cunningham, Lisa Anne
Middle School English Teacher
Dingle, Patricia Ann
High School Art Teacher
Fowble, Leah Ruth
Home Economics Teacher
Gahagen, Amy Linn
French Teacher
Goldman, Wendy Singer
9th-12th Grade Art Instructor
Goldsmith, Marilyn Mc Near
Special Education Teacher

Horton, Johnnye Marie
Inter Disciplinary Math Tchr
Hummel, Randy Michael
Social Studies Teacher
Hyde, Kathleen Scully
Peer Mediation Coordinator
Jensen, Pamela Marie
HS Speech, Drama & Debate Tchr
Lingenfetter, William M.
Fifth Grade Teacher
Lucas, Melba
Dance Teacher
Maddox, Charles E.
Mathematics Teacher
Marchizza, Michael Joseph
AP Biology Teacher
Mc Cullough, Phyllis A.
Mediation Specialist
Mc Ginnis, R. Chuck
Chem & Physics Tchr, Ath Dir
Mc Guinn, Patrick James
HS Govt & History Teacher
Mentzer, Jayne Marie
Former Director & Coach
Morrison, Eddie Ray
Spanish Teacher
Murphy, Jeremiah Nathaniel
Vocal Music Teacher
Reeves, James C.
Health Education Teacher
Ryan, Jeffery Thomas
High School Science Teacher
Salisbury Blair, Dana Yvette
English Teacher
Saverino, Philip N.
Social Studies Teacher
Stuckey, Ronald W.
Guidance Dir & Dean of Acad
UPPERCO
Lorenz, Judith Anne
Fourth Grade Teacher
Taylor, Phyllis Ulrich
Physical Education Teacher
VIENNA
Webb, Jeffrey Lynn
Fifth Grade Teacher
WALDORF
Babiak, Robert Joseph
8th Grd Social Studies Teacher
Bateman, Toni Chichester
Physical Education Teacher
Beierle, Jean Steinbach
Spanish Teacher
Bilmanis, Andris, Jr.
High School Track Coach
Blizzard, Nancy Snyder
Language Arts Teacher
Callahan, Polly Clark
Soc Stud Teacher & Yrbk Adv
Callahan, Richard Stuart
Earth Science Teacher
Donoghue, Terry L.
Health Teacher & Coach
Frick, Gary Wayne
Mathematics Teacher
Gaertner, Stephen Andrew
Service Representative
Greer, Vicky Lee (Swope)
Vice President
Irwin, Rebecca Suit
Second Grade Teacher
Jochum, Bridgett Whittaker
Third Grade Teacher
Krush, Christopher Paul
Art Teacher
Morrison, Jennifer Lyn Dydo
English Teacher
Pekala, Dorothy Olsen
Mathematics Teacher
Perriello, Kathy Goldsmith
Spanish Teacher
Reilly, David W.
Coach
Richards, Cheryl Mello
Fifth Grade Teacher
Sanders, Sandra Lee
English Teacher
Sherrod, Margaret
PE & Health Teacher
Silkworth, Sandra J.
Business Education Teacher
Strickland, Deborah Ann Cover
First Grade Teacher
Thoman, Jane FitzSimmonds
Fifth Grade Teacher
Walsh, James Matthew
Theater Teacher & Director
White, Janet Gleason
Reading & Lang Arts Teacher
WALKERSVILLE
Harman, Abbe Click
Third Grade Teacher
Powell, Katharine Jenks
HS His Tchr & Dept Chair
Roller, Gloria W.
Sixth Grade Language Arts Tchr
WESTERNPORT
Fogle, Judy Lancaster
Kindergarten Teacher
Freeman, Rosalee Calemine
Reading & English Teacher
Himmler, Suzanne Paletta
English & Reading Teacher
Kiddy, Keith Russell
MS Guidance Counselor
Mosser, Willeda Wilson
Fourth Grade Teacher
Ward, Kenneth Vandiver
Chemistry Teacher

WESTMINSTER
Baile, Carole Richardson
Mathematics Teacher
Barnhart, Patricia Read
Fourth Grade Teacher
Beard, Gary W.
Academic Advisor & Eng Tchr
Berry, Catherine Clagett
English & Reading Teacher
Braune, Mabel Brown
Retired Elementary Teacher
Campbell, Mark Allen
Assistant Pastor
Dorsey, Shirl Elaine
High School English Teacher
Dotterweich, Patrick Timothy
7th Grd Social Studies Teacher
Handley, Charlene Ballard
Sign Language Teacher
Holt, John R.
English Teacher
Jenkins, Melinda Ann
Math Teacher
Jones, Diane Wheeler
Elem Vocal Music Specialist
LeGates, Gary A.
Latin & French Teacher
Matthews, Arthur Clay
Social Studies Teacher
Mc Cullin, Francis Matthew
Eighth Grd Math & Algebra Tchr
Mied, Judith Maude
Biology & PE Teacher
Moore, James Edward
7th Grade Language Arts Tchr
Pilachowski, K. Joann Donnelly
Assistant Professor of English
Potts, David Keith
Sixth Grade Math Teacher
Powell, David Joseph
Life Science Teacher
Pyles, Sherry Gordon
Pupil Personnel Worker
Richardson, Randolph Gary
History Teacher
Wells, Beverly J.
HS Choral Director
Whitney, Timothy Leroy
Spanish & German Teacher
Wood, Ralph Bernard
Asst Professor of Mathematics
Wright, K. Siobhan
Assistant Professor of English
WHITE HALL
Wimer, Sharon Ann
Fifth Grade Teacher
WHITE PLAINS
Davis, Kathleen Gaines
English Teacher
WILLARDS
Dettbarn, Shirley Joseph
First Grade Teacher
WILLIAMSPORT
Baer, Margaret Ann
Spanish Teacher
Holder, Charles Richard
Social Studies Teacher
Johnston, Pamela Kuhn
Biology Teacher
Parks, Lori K.
English Teacher
Ridenour, Ruth Ann
Music Chprsn, Choral Music Dir
Strelser, Jennifer Jacobs
Chemistry & AP Biology Teacher
WOODBINE
Gaither, Helena Theresa
Retired First Grade Teacher
WORTON
Dize, Karen M.
French & English Teacher
Fell, Michael J.
HS Math Teacher & Dept Chair
Mac Leod, Elizabeth Donovan
Science Teacher
Maloney, Sylvia Romanoski
Mathematics Chair
Shorter, Brenda Willie
Eng & Creative Writing Teacher
WYE MILLS
Lednum, Florence Nash
Biological Sciences Professor
Marchand, Jean-Louis G.
Psych & Sociology Professor

MASSACHUSETTS

ABINGTON
Kamb, William D.
CAD Department Manager
Phillips, Jane S.
Retired Mathematics Director
Powers, Nancy Spencer
Biology Teacher
Stenerson-Reynolds, Margaret
Chemistry Master Teacher
ACTON
Chateauneuf, John E.
English Teacher
Mc Grath, Jean
1st Grade Teacher
Mc Inerny, Joseph C.
Fifth Grade Teacher
Michelson, Susan S.
Spanish Teacher
Murphy, Neil P.
English Teacher
Smith, Mark Francis
Soc Stud, Psych & US His Tchr
Veley, Nina Gould
Mathematics Teacher
Wilson, Dianne Anderson
Academic Support Coordinator
ACUSHNET
Tapper, Louise Connor
First Grade Teacher
ADAMS
Bigelow, Sally Tetlow
8th Grade English Teacher
Bushika, Joan Maynard
Third Grade Teacher
Chapman, Judith Ann (Polak)
English Teacher
Dynes, James H.
Soc Stud Team Leader & Tchr
Fuller, Abigail M.
Elementary Art Teacher
Lennon, David James
7th-8th Grd Soc Studies Tchr
Rossbach Mc Shane, Nancy Bourassa
Third Grade Teacher
AGAWAM
Crean, Anna DeMichele
Second Grade Teacher
DeFilipi, Janice Ann
English & Reading Teacher
Joseph, Richard H.
Biology Teacher
Lester, Evelyn Cole
Teacher of the Gifted
Nigri, John, III
Social Studies Teacher
Orefice, Vladimiro
Italian Teacher
Pulaski, David Walter
High School Math Teacher
Sasso, Linda Beecher
Spanish Teacher
Spiro, Louis Marshall
Fifth Grade Teacher
Thomas, Irene West
High School English Teacher
Zabielski, Joseph Steven
Acting Principal
ALLSTON
Lewis, Gregory W. J.
Rel & Soc Studies Dept Chair
AMESBURY
Bailey, Rose Marie Bernier
2nd Grade Teacher
Horan, Tom
High School Musical Director
Manoloff, Brett A.
High School Science Teacher
AMHERST
Carew, Dale Maxson
Fifth Grade Teacher
Emery, Christopher
Physics & Electronics Teacher
Feldman, Robert Stephen
Psychology Professor
Hannum, Thomas Patrick
Assc Band Dir-Percussion Instr
Kelly, Robert J., Jr.
Social Studies Teacher
McNamara, Brian J.
Sixth Grade Teacher
McSweeney, Terence James
Jr HS Social Studies Teacher
Rabin, Monroe S. Z.
Professor of Physics
Wallace, Roger Lawrence
Sixth Grade Teacher
Whitbourne, Susan Krauss
Professor of Psychology
ANDOVER
Anderson, Stephen S.
Biology & Chemistry Instructor
Beckwith, Clyfe
Instructor of Physics
Byrne, Michael Joseph
Latin & Cmptr Appl Teacher
Chivers, John Patten
German Teacher
Cook, Kathleen Doyle
Art & Interdisciplinary Tchr
Costello, James Francis
ESL Teacher
DeFlorio, Patricia Ann
ESL Teacher
Evans, Richard Mark
High School English Teacher
Fitzgibbons, Janice Mazzotta
French & Spanish Teacher
Germain, Edward Barnard
English Instructor
Han, Yuan
Chinese Department Chairperson
Henrick, Kenneth Albert
High School Guidance Counselor
Hodgson, Thomas Salkald
Philosophy & Rel Stud Dept Chm
Iworsley, Arthur William
Physical Education Teacher
Kalkstein, Paul
English Instructor
Kolbe, William Andrew, Jr.
Spanish Teacher
Lyons, Thomas Tolman
History Instructor
Mc Cann, Harrison F.
Span Tchr & Intnl Stu Coord
Mc Cann, Rebecca Downey
Spanish Teacher
O'Brien, Brenda Halstead
Health Education Program Coord
Parker, Chandler B.
History Teacher
Quattlebaum, Edwin G.
History & Social Science Instr
Redmond, James Joseph
Eng Tchr & 6th Grd Team Ldr
Shulins, Susan Soule
English Instructor
Simpson, Craig Bonham
Interdisciplinary Teacher
Spanos, Joe James
Business & Technology Teacher
Tabor, Denise Lynne (Ostrow)
English Instructor
Terrile, Paul Edward
Mathematics Teacher
Tomlinson, Louise
English Teacher
Zaeder, J. Philip
Instructor in English
ARLINGTON
Amrod, Claudia Marie
Mathematics Teacher
Burt, Lucile D.
English Teacher
Cleveland, Joelita C.
Librn & 8th Grd Earth Sci Tchr
Deeley, Jo-Anne Marie
Biology & Chemistry Teacher
Doyle, Kathleen Mary
English Teacher
Emmet, Brian Miles
Headmaster
Finberg, Pauline Esther
9th-12th Grd Art Teacher
Foisy, Arthur Joseph
English Teacher
Foley, Paula Christine
Fifth Grade Teacher
Folsy, Arthur Joseph
English Teacher
Graham, Margaret Mary
Consumer & Life Stud Teacher
Guerra, Rebekah D.
History, Lit & Algebra Teacher
Karlson, Joyce V.
First Grade Teacher
Leen, Marie D. Pazola
French Teacher
Manning, Barbara
English & Communications Tchr
Naughton, William B.
English Teacher
Orlando, Maryann Joan
English Teacher
Puckerin, Richard Kent
School Counselor
Reed, Loretta A. Muise
Mathematics Teacher
Russo, Stephen S.
Mathematics Teacher
Seminara, Jane C.
Theology Teacher
Shufro, Pamela Reed
Special Education Teacher
Smith, Raymond Joseph
Dept Lead Tchr & Latin Istr
Vazquez, Martin John
Computer Science Teacher
ASHBURNHAM
Adams, Christopher Gerard
Span Teacher & Dean of Stdnts
Berner, Kelly Ann
English Teacher & Coach
Di Geronimo, Linda Jane (Seretto)
Dean of Students
Dowling, Mark John
Science Educator
Lawrence, Donald Jeffris, Jr.
Biology & Chemistry Teacher
Lee, Margaret Healey
Eng as Second Lang Dept Chair
Manser, William E.
Technology Educator
Rasmuson, Nancy L.
Fifth Grade Teacher
Romano, Margaret Membrino
Sixth Grade Teacher
ASHFIELD
Patch, Alyson L.
6th Grade Teacher
ASHLAND
Farry, Mary E.
English Teacher
Heaton, Renate R.
5th Grade Teacher
Mason, Jane Ellison
Fifth Grade Teacher
Morrison, Ruth M.
History & English Teacher
ATHOL
Davidson, Edward P.
Latin, Spanish & French Tchr
Donham, Susan Vaughn
Title I HOTS Teacher
Goudie, Kathleen Donovan
English Teacher
LaBombarde, Patricia Ann (Barnicle)
Social Studies Tchr & Team Ldr
Lajoie, Donna Ranae Herk
High School Business Teacher
Louzonis, Helena P.
Science Teacher
Telicki, Thomas David
High School English Teacher
ATTLEBORO
Boudreau, Richard M.
Electrical Instructor
Cousens, James Blaine, Jr.
Visual Arts Teacher
DeOliveira-Kashtan, Paulette
Private Piano Teacher
Drazek, Diane Rarus
6th Grade Teacher
Flavin, Paul Stephen
Alternative Education Teacher
Forde, Mary Francis
Comm & Inclusion Teacher
Hebert, Katherine Campbell
English Department Head
Moynihan, Jerome Daniel
Adj Instr of Economics & Bus
Paulo, William David
Information & Technology Tchr
Powers, Claire Mahoney
Science Teacher
Stevens, Kathy
English Teacher
Teixeira, Ann M. Montagano
Graphic Design Teacher
Toner, Janet Larkin
Special Education Teacher
AUBURN
Amend, Kenneth C.
Chemistry Teacher
Barringer, John H.
English Teacher
Brunell, Arthur B., Jr.
Social Studies Teacher
Degon, Nancy McGowan
High School Chemistry Teacher
Farley, Joellen
High School English Teacher
Hurley, Joseph
Science Teacher
Lauder, Thomas A.
PE & Health Teacher
Loosemore, Marie Kathleen
Mathematics Teacher
Redding, Linda Gail
Mathematics Teacher
Schoenfeldt, Sandra Lee
Fifth Grade Teacher
AVON
Mc Grath, Patricia Louzan
Mathematics Teacher
AYER
Capodilupo, Phillip
5th-8th Grd Phys Ed Teacher
Deamer, Patricia Mulvany
Third Grade Teacher
Garvin, Nancy E.
Science Teacher
Noga, Paula
Second Grade Teacher
BALDWINVILLE
Ewing, Diane Brazawskis
Math Teacher & Dept Head
Jasinski, John S.
Vice Principal
Morris, Kathleen Anthony
English Department Chairperson
BARNSTABLE
Comeau, Katherine Sullivan
Third Grade Teacher
BARRE
Grandone, Roberta Maki
World Language Dept Head
Lorge, Barbara Cash
Soc Stud Dept Chair & Teacher
Sawyer, Winslow Allen
Director of Music & Tchr
Twarog, Susan Crombie
Fourth Grade Teacher
BEDFORD
Beams, Cynthia Ruprecht
Adj Prof of Social Science
Bladon, Mariluci T.
Assoc Prof of Biotechnology
Crowley, Kenneth B., Jr.
Medical Lab Science Professor
Gleason, Phyllis Suzanne
Associate Prof of Humanities
Haney, James E.
Theatre Department Chairman
Hunt, Gary S.
High School Mathematics Tchr
Mahler, Philip Henry
Mathematics & Cmpter Sci Prof
Meagher, Linda Daryl
Humanities Professor
Reynolds, John Dennis
Pol Sci & US His Teacher
Sergi, Rose Anne
Journalism Professor
Trounstine, Jean R.
Humanities Professor
BELCHERTOWN
Austin, Eileen C.
Third Grade Teacher
DiPilato, Nancy M.
World Language Teacher
BELLINGHAM
Dalpe, Leo Paul
American History Teacher
Trocchio, Josette T.
French, Latin & His Teacher
BELMONT
Coleman, John M., Jr.
High School History Teacher
Commoss, Susan Harriet
5th Grade Teacher
Firenze, Wega Sconzo
Spanish Teacher
Pisano, Rosemary Hoey
Fourth Grade Teacher
Seeley, George Wheeler
History Teacher
BERKLEY
Costa, Jake Francis
Vice Principal
BEVERLY
Boutin, Pauline Pereira
Fifth Grade Teacher
Brown, Miriam Mac Donald
Third Grade Teacher
Dunbar, Diane
History, Eng & Rdng Teacher
Dunn, Robert W.
English Teacher
Levesque, Shirley Pisani
Foreign Language Teacher
Pilanen, Carolyn L. (Doherty)
Choral Director
Rand, Mark W.
World Geography Teacher
Robertson, Margaret Borge
Var Bsktbl Chrldng Coach
Smith, Merelyn Elizabeth
Mathematics Teacher
Taylor, Linda Sue
Teacher of Deaf Students
BILLERICA
Ahern, Barbara Forand
Coordinator of Health Programs
Biagiotti, Deborah A.
High School Mathematics Tchr
Breen, Kathleen Holland
English & Amer History Teacher
Fowler, Meredith Anderson
French & Spanish Teacher
Fuccillo, Cheryl-Ann
Third Grade Teacher
Giroux, Judith Maxwell
English Teacher
Molloy, Linda Dankese
English Teacher
O'Brien, Thomas Francis
Assistant Principal
Smith, Paul A.
Business Technology Instructor
Tsoukalas, George Christos
Chemistry Teacher
Tucceri, Robert Gene
High School Math Teacher
Whalley, David A.
Science Department Chair
Winchell, Elaine (Foley)
Band & Elem Instrumental Tchr
BLACKSTONE
Keough, Andrew William
Vice Principal
Maloney, Kevin Edward
Guidance Counselor
BOLTON
Dahl, Winthrop H.K.
Latin Teacher
Mianulli, Susan Impress
Choral Music Director
Peterson, Carolyn
Biology Teacher
Williams, Loretta Kean
English Teacher
BOSTON
Aswell, Jane Furca
Professor of Biology
Bajdek, Anthony Joseph
Assoc Dean & Sr His Lecturer
Berger, Mark
Spanish & French Teacher
Bertello, Andrew Angelo
Alumni Coordinator
Bifano, Thomas Gary
Professor
Binkoski, John Philip
Latin & Greek Teacher
Bitzas, Penelope Elaine
Assistant Professor of Voice
Born, Jeffery Allen
Associate Professor of Finance
Browning, Robert J.
Prof of Eng as Second Language
Camara, Joan Ellen
Paralegal Studies Instructor
Carr, Oyeshiku Burgess
History Teacher
Chambless, Sylvia
Piano Instructor
Charnas, Fran E.
Theatre & Musical Theatre Prof
Condry, Florence M.
English Professor
Correll, Linda Conway
Advertising Professor
Cottrill, Michael David
Accounting Professor
Fernandes, Elise M.
Law Professor
Fernandes, Roseanna Marie
Music Teacher
Fitzpatrick, David Joseph
Adjunct Instructor
Folan, Mary Teresa
Associate Professor of Nursing
Gallivan, Stephen Joseph
German Teacher
Gomez, Susan L.
Computer Education Teacher
Green, Harvey
Professor of History
Griffith, John L.
Adj Prof of Human Resources
Guimond, Robert W.
Professor of Biology
Habibullah, Mohamed
Assoc Prof in Coll Bus Admin
Holzman, Gary Neil
College Instructor

ON (cont)
stein, Mark N.
rical Engrng Assoc Prof
, Dalia Skudzinskaite
nistry Teacher
on, Viola Tolbert
ndary English Teacher
lis, James A.
essor
David Richard
stant Professor
, Cornelia A.
stant Head Master
ocke, Maureen Elizabeth
ege Instructor
seur, Doris Lecuyer
y Childhood Ed Professor
, Jack
ology & Criminology Prof
, Michael R.
of Piano & Artistic Dir
zoni, Vivian Maria
th Grade Teacher
n, Janet H.
d & Undergrad Ed Supvr
lister, Ronald J.
essor of Sociology
be, Charles Joseph
ory Teacher
nnell, Steve
essor of Theatre Arts
ormick, Richard Joseph
ology & English Teacher
er, Diane
ociate Professor of Math
li, Jean Ann
lish Teacher
en, Donna Henderson
Ed & Sr Homeroom Tchr
ri, Natalie Anne
nmunication Department Prof
Daniel William
h Teacher
ier, Dennis
of External Outreach
n, John Michael
ior English Master
Don R.
ance Professor
guez, Kyrsis Raquel
essor of Science
, Norma Silverman
d Specialist & Ed Cnsltnt
ettos, John Nicholas
essor of Mechanical Engrng
ge, John David
istant Professor of Science
tz, Gina Jane
iness Professor
artz, Lloyd
lish Professor
Lewis
tng & Bus Admin Prof
Mary A.
cient Language Teacher
nsen, Erl
iness Statistics Professor
et, Alan Francis
atomy & Physiology Tchr
van, Elena Negmatullaeva
mer Lecturer
ey, Paul J.
tory Teacher
naga, Yasuko
airperson of Dance Division
an, Emery Anthony
ance Professor
er, Raymond E.
of Math & Sci Tech Chair
Winkle, Prudence Bridges
g Dir of Early Chldhd Ed
a, Nagagopal
soc Prof of Neurology
on-Wortzel, Heidi
ofessor of Management
ein, Harvey
ordinator of Educl Svcs
serman, Moe
ectrical Engrng Assoc Prof
e, Sonya Renee
ing Teacher
g-Ho, Ivy Yau-wah
sic Teacher
LSTON
nwald, Neil
alth, PE Teacher & Coach
AINTREE
avanel, Lynn Rae
acher
n, David C.
athematics Teacher
pbell, Priscilla Barry
ird Grade Teacher
ey, Ann Crehan
ird Grade Teacher
ovan, Donald J., Jr.
ience Teacher
ko, Michael Richard
ysics Teacher
y, Stephanie Jepson
rst Grade Teacher
zier, Robert E.
ocial Studies Teacher
derburk, Jane Mc Bain
emistry Teacher
ung, Mary J.
urth Grade Teacher
dman, Michael C.
athematics Teacher

Grigas, Deborah Ann (Duran)
Science Teacher
Kendall, William Walter
Math & Computer Teacher
Larkin, Perry
Guidance Counselor
Leminen, William Rafael
5th Grade Teacher
Shea, Michael Patrick, III
English Dept Head & Instr
Sullivan, Noreen Yee
English as a Second Lang Tchr
Svensen, Diane D.
English & French Teacher
Toma, Deborah Veronica
First Grade Teacher
Toohey, Susan Alice
Physical Education Teacher
Whalen, Mary Louise
History Teacher
Wilson, David G.
English Teacher
BRIDGEWATER
Bowens, Keith Karnell
Guidance Counselor
Casabian, Joan Ando
PE Tchr & Field Hockey Coach
Cushing, Alan David
Social Studies Teacher
DeLisle, Lucille Fortunato
Assistant Professor of History
Jones, Eugene
Bsktbl & Sftbl Coach
Keenan, Mary L.
Third Grade Teacher
Kostka, Robert Raymond
Social Studies Teacher
Mantell, Nora Margaret
English Teacher
Martin, Linda Cicchetti
English Teacher
Marvelle, John David
Associate Prof & Chrmn of Ed
BRIGHTON
Gheridian, Maria
Spanish & Bilingual Teacher
Kalista, Nancy Concannon
ESL Teacher
Lee, William R.
Senior Instructor
Nguyen, Thieu Trung
Social Studies Tenured Teacher
BROCKTON
Anania, Kenneth Joseph
Professor of English
Ayers, Ann Merrigan
Professor
Brosius, Janice DeJesus
French & Latin Teacher
Demers, Robert A.
Professor of Chemistry
Elliot-Smith, T. P.
Humanities Professor
Goldberg, Joan Crosby
Third Grade Teacher
Issa, Joseph G.
Fifth Grade Teacher
Jorgensen-Kimball, Marion
English Teacher
Kelleher, John Thomas
Business Education Faculty
Lincoln, Mark Joseph
English Teacher
Lipper, Denise Frances
Elem Kdg Tchr
Marble, Patricia Ann
English Teacher
Mott, Nancy Fraser
Sixth Grade Teacher
O'Brien, Richard Larence
English Teacher
OReilly, H. Gordon
Professor
Paul, Leslie Berry
Third Grade Teacher
Purnell, John C.
Sixth Grd Teacher & Asst Prin
Thompson, Anne
Educational Technology Teacher
Warnock, Linda DeTommaso
Spanish Teacher
BROOKLINE
Bacote, Denise Whitehead
English Teacher
Burbank-Schmitt, Priscilla
High School Math Teacher
Chirban, John T.
Psych Prof, Human Dev Dept Chm
Christman, Robert L.
1st-12th Grade Music Teacher
Conway, Dean Joseph
English & Social Studies Tchr
Cook, Nancy M.
Hotel & Restaurant Mgmt Instr
Cornish, David Freeman
Director
Cradle, Toni J.
Guidance Counselor
Gibb, Reen Dorothee
Science Curriculum Coordinator
Gonnerman, Madelyn Jones
Latin & French Teacher
Gutmann, Nancy
English Teacher
Hadge, Kenneth Michael
Marketing Professor
Howard, John Loughery
Science Teacher
Howard, Nancy Mallison
Bio Tchr & Acad Team Ldr

Lantos, Steve D.
Teacher
Leverich, Joseph Terrel
Mathematics Teacher
Markell, Linda Beth
History Teacher
Mastandrea, Mary T.
Drama & English Teacher
Quitt, Deborah Lobsenz
History Teacher
Schnipper, Sydra
Mathematics Teacher
Tobin, Maurine Motter
English Teacher
White, Roseann
Assoc Dept Chair of Legal Stud
BURLINGTON
Beaumont, Richard Alan
Human Physiology & Chem Tchr
Bransfield, Rosemary
Child Development Teacher
Bullock, Maura Nestor
English Teacher
Carroll, Richard L.
Eighth Grade Science Teacher
Ferretri, Nancy
Choral Director
Ferretti, Nancy Ann
Choral Director & Music Tchr
Field, Kevin Lloyd, Sr.
English Teacher
Imbriglio, Thomas F.
HS Pupil Services Chairman
Kagan, Marlin R.
Mathematics Teacher
Lovell, Matthew S.
Music Teacher
Luther, C. David
Bio & Envrmntl Sci Plant Tchr
Macione, Paula Kirby
Chemistry Instructor
Nash, Mildred J.
BEAM Teacher
Nolan, John Robert
Mathematics Teacher
Panciera, Carla Marie
English Teacher
Phelan, Michael Robert
Computer Teacher
Saxe, Jean T. (Meranda)
HS Mathematics Teacher
BUZZARDS BAY
Butler, Richard Arthur
7th Grade History Teacher
Cartier, Penny Weldon
First Grade Teacher
Coughlin, Jack A.
Guidance Counselor
Valeri, Carole G.
First Grade Teacher
BYFIELD
Allen, Linda A.
Program Coordinator
Gosse, David Ronold
Mathematics & Computer Tchr
Lovering, John Henry
Enrichment Coordinator & Tchr
CAMBRIDGE
Ball, Alison Coles
Choreographer, Dancer & Tchr
Caragianes, William James
Mathematics Teacher
Carroll, Susan Elliot
English Teacher
DeSimone, Michael Paul
Social Studies Teacher
Dollard, Catherine Anne
Biology Teacher
Fisher, Hersha S.
Retired History Teacher
Gendreau, Marianne
Business Dept Chprsn & Tchr
Gienapp, William E.
Professor of History
Griffith, Karen C.
HS Business Education Tchr
House, Carol Elaine
Mathematics Teacher
Kelley, Lynne Dhionis
Chinese Biling & ESL Teacher
Lawlor, Susan Dunphy
Fifth Grade Teacher
Mead, Morgan Noyes
Dean of Students & Eng Tchr
Miceli, Elaine Marie
French & Spanish Teacher
Payack, Christine A.
Amigos Prgm & 6th Grd Eng Tchr
Queen, Christopher Scott
Dean of Students
Rice, William Craig
Expository Writing Preceptor
Richards, Judith Johnson
Third & Fourth Grade Teacher
Skinner, Amy Woo
Jr HS Language Arts Teacher
Sumner, Donna Cellucci
Mathematics Dept Chprsn & Tchr
Weinstein, Alan James
Teacher & Leader
CANTON
Barbour, Nancy C. (Meneely)
Art Teacher
Duffy, Arthur Joseph
Social Studies Teacher
Gaudet, Joseph Edward
Mathematics Instructor
Heine, Judith G.
Social Studies Teacher

Kilroy, Mary Crowley
Department Head & Teacher
Schauble, Bruce
K-12th Grd English Coordinator
Staiti, Richard Robert
Science Teacher
Sullivan, Charles Edward, Jr.
5th Grade Teacher
CARVER
Hiller, Susan
Social Studies Teacher
Marzelli, Cameron L.
English Teacher
Moreno, Patrick Anthony
World Languages Dept Chair
Simeone, Wendy Matheson
English Teacher
CENTERVILLE
Eckes, Mary Kelly
Retired Biology Teacher
CHARLESTOWN
Boudreau, Annmarie M.
Social Studies Teacher
CHARLTON
Bostock, William Francis
Data Processing Teacher
Dhembe, Albert Frank
Physical Education Instructor
Maywalt, Joann Johns
Culinary Arts Instructor
McNamara, Robert P.
Social Studies Teacher
Savage, Michael Victor
Chemistry & Physics Teacher
Stietzel, Ronald D.
Sixth Grade Teacher
CHATHAM
Avery, Jean (Carmell)
Chemistry & Physics Teacher
CHELMSFORD
Simorellis, Christos
Social Studies Department Head
CHELSEA
Gagnon, Jacqueline Anne
English Teacher
CHESHIRE
Leitch, Amelia Graziani
Fourth Grade Teacher
CHESTNUT HILL
Barry, Ann Marie Seward
Communication Professor
Bronson, Martha B.
Assoc Prof of Early Chldhd Ed
DiMattia, Philip Anthony
Assoc Prof & Dir of Education
Friedman, Audrey Valade
Adj Assoc Prof of Education
Hauser-Cram, Penny
Associate Professor
Herbeck, Dale A.
Communications Professor
Hughes, Mary Joe (Bregenzer)
Adj Assoc Prof of Humanities
Kenney, Margaret J.
Professor of Mathematics
Mc Kinney, Lynda R.
Public Relations Professor
Ruggles, Jeanne-Francoise Peter
French Teacher
Smith, Gerald E.
Professor of Marketing
CHICOPEE
Bobala, Chester Peter, Jr.
Guidance Counselor
Canales, Maria-Cristina
Associate Professor of French
Chelte Ph.D., Judith Segzdowicz
English Teacher
Coderre, Bette-Jean
Junior High Teacher
Collins, Gloria Michalski
Second Grade Teacher
Corridan, Paula Marie
Science Teacher
Costello, Cecilia Lonczak
English Teacher
Crandall, Maureen Nadeau
First Grade Teacher
Currier, Katherine A.
Prof & Dept Chair of Paralegal
Czelusniak, Judith Tyminski
Spanish Teacher
Czerwiec, Irene Theresa (Matuszek)
6th-8th Grd Tchr of Gifted
Dachowski, Thomas Joseph
Science Teacher
Davis, William G.
Social Studies Teacher & Coach
Donofrio, Nancy Mercier
Junior High Teacher
Dumont, Barbara A. Bailey
Moderate Special Needs Teacher
Harrison, Anne Elizabeth
Education Professor
Joseph, Victoria Therese
Associate Professor
Karkut, Anne
Peer Mediation Facilitator
Keating, Sharon Flynn
Fifth Grade Teacher
Kendra, Jeffrey Laurence
Mathematics Teacher
Kisiel, John Charles
Sixth Grade Teacher
LaFlesh, LeRoy William
Eighth Grade Math Teacher
Londraville, Charles William
Physical Ed & Health Teacher
Love, Adelle Lodzia
ESL Teacher

Lyons, Joanne Coppola
Second Grade Teacher
Macanka, William John
Assoc Prof of Chemistry & Math
Moriarty, Thomas F.
Professor of History
Oleska, Carla Marie, SSJ
Coord of Spcl Pgms & Adj Asst
Powers, Patricia Mc Donnell
4th Grade Teacher
Powers-Lagac, Virginia
Director of Weekend Coll
Wohl, Matthew deForest
Social Studies Teacher
CLARKSBURG
Maroni, Mary Ann Pratt
Jr HS Lang Arts & Math Tchr
CLINTON
Bloom, Sharon Daigle
Family, Consumer Tchr & Admin
Lent, Claire F. Mc Intyre
English Teacher
Moynihan, Judith Tomolo
7th Grd Math & Science Teacher
COHASSET
Duffy, Maureen M.
Family & Consumer Sci Tchr
Hughes, Corinne Suzan
Audio Video Technician & Coach
CONCORD
Bradley, Peter James
Division Head & Math Teacher
Carter, James R., II
9th Grade Russian His Teacher
Dentino, Alfred William
Director of Bands
Katz, Cynthia
Photography Instructor
Mc Namara, David L.
Chemistry Teacher
Pollack, Richard David
VP of Rsrch & Information Tech
Powers, Albert L.
Science Teacher
Yun Jeong, Mark
Mathematics Teacher
CONWAY
Laffond, Wanita Sioui
Sixth Grade Teacher
CUMMINGTON
Swider, Louise Pictrowski
Fourth Grade Teacher
DALTON
DiNicola, Kathleen Cady
Fifth Grade Teacher
Winters, Rae-Ann
Fourth Grade Teacher
DANVERS
Brown, Kerry Michael
HS English Teacher
Camilli, Daniel Anthony, Jr.
Social Studies Teacher
Corkery, Antoinette Jugon
High School English Teacher
Davis, Gina Paglia
5th-6th Grade Teacher
Hey, Shirley Stahler (Childs)
7th Grade Language Arts Tchr
Jeong, Joyce Chih-Chen
Engineering Assistant Prof
Klein, John M.
English Chairperson
Lewis, Nancy F.
Prof of English & Coordinator
Logan, Madelyn Esposito
Natural Sciences Prof & Chair
Mc Donald, Jane Russell
Mathematics Teacher
McLaughlin, John Lawrence, III
English Teacher
Moulton, Donna Carvotta
High School Math Teacher
Muhilly, Maryann
English Teacher
Needham, Donna L.
English Teacher
Paul, Timothy, CFX
Assistant Principal
Persenaire, Suzette Wadsworth
Reading Specialist
Petelle, Linda F.
Spanish Teacher
Ponticelli, Richard James
Professor of Math & Dept Chair
Smith, Dana Frederick
History Teacher
Sullivan, F. Russell, Jr.
Professor of Philosophy & Math
Wermers, Patricia Lynn
Computer Science Professor
DEDHAM
Atkinson, Meredith O.
English Teacher
Bullerwell, Lornie David
Biology Teacher
Corcoran, Andrew Joseph
Chemistry Teacher
Drake, Mary M.
French & Spanish Teacher
Jones, Ann L.
Teacher of Gifted Talented
Payne, Richard W.
High School Teacher
Sheehan, Pauline Walsh
Third Grade Teacher
Sicuranza, Linda Machell
Science Teacher
Vacirca, Joanne Marie
High School Math Teacher

DEDHAM (cont)
Ziemian, Carol Ann
English & Journalism Tchr
DEERFIELD
Cumming, William Gordon
Chemistry Tchr & Fin Aid Dir
Hindle, Peter Gage
Mathematics Teacher
DIGHTON
Patten, Brenda Lussier
Sixth Grade Teacher
Paynton, Krista I.
Animal Science Teacher
Sullivan, Timothy Lee
Fifth Grade Teacher
DORCHESTER
Abdul-Tawwab, Najwa
1st-2nd Grd Tchr & Sci Coord
Barry, Elaine Sullivan
Third Grade Teacher
Cohen, Roberta
Advanced Work Class Teacher
Cook, Leah Hutten
Computer Science Teacher
Florentine, Margaret Toomey
Social Studies Dept Head
Garlington-Carrier, Barbara Mc Allister
Early Childhood Teacher
Johnston, Sandra
Third Grade Teacher
Keane, Kathleen M.
English Teacher
Maguire, Michael J.
Latin Teacher
Reardon, Mary Teresa
Social Studies Teacher
Smith, Joy S.
English Teacher
DOVER
Cannon, Donald E.
English Department Head
Libenson, Lois Jane (Aaronson)
Third Grade Teacher
Powers, Ralph
Physical Education Teacher
Preiser, JoAnne L.
English Teacher
DRACUT
Davis, Olga Natsios
French Teacher
Donahue, M. Robert
Biology Teacher
O'Leary, Michael Paul
Guidance Counselor
Przybyla, Joseph A.
Mathematics Department Chprsn
Przybyla, Therese Roy
Spanish Teacher
DUDLEY
Downs, Lawrence Douglas
Assoc Prof of Mrktg & Chair
Earp, Carolyn Velier
Business Education Teacher
Prouty, Timothy J.
Technology Education Teacher
DUXBURY
Meier, Carl W.
Social Studies Department Head
O'Brien, Margaret K.
Chemistry Teacher
Phillips, Alton Freeman, III
5th Grade Teacher
EAST BOSTON
Amara, Vincent H.
Science Teacher
Cardullo, Maria Ann
Sci Dept Chairperson & Teacher
DeRosa, Heidi Louise
Travel & Tourism Tech Teacher
Sullivan, Gerald Joseph
English & Latin Teacher
Tsiotos, Nicholas
Second Grade Teacher
EAST BRIDGEWATER
Brindle, Karen Barbara
Kindergarten Teacher
Bryan, Dorothy C.
Drama Director
Carlson, Lisa Anne
Foreign Language Teacher
Cronin, Patrick Lawrence
English Teacher & Curr Coord
Gillespie, Barbara J. Long
French Teacher & Stu Act Coord
Illsley, Arthur E.
Social Studies Teacher
Kofton, Diane Wisneski
4th Grade Teacher
Ladouceur, Regina Quealy
Literature Teacher
Mc Cabe, George C., Jr.
Social Studies Curr Coord
Smith, William Paul
Social Studies Teacher
Teahan, Kathleen Mary
Teacher
EAST BROOKFIELD
Zaring, Vicky Lynn
Resource Room Teacher
EAST DOUGLAS
Sokol, Mary
Physical Education Teacher
EAST FALMOUTH
Brennan, Corinne A. (Buechs)
6th Grade Teacher
Possel, Corinne Denise
First Grade Teacher
EAST FREETOWN
Lopes, Regina Maria
Retired Music Teacher & Dir

EAST LONGMEADOW
Barry, Deborah J.
5th Grade Classroom Teacher
Burke, Marilyn J. Kearney
Social Studies Teacher
Cleavall, Marilyn A.
Special Educator
Leib, Ronnie R.
English Teacher
O'Hearn, James B.
English Teacher
EAST LYNN
Catalucci-Nicosia, Linda
Third Grade Teacher
EAST SANDWICH
Evans, Harry Dager, III
English Teacher
Follett, Phyllis V.
French Teacher
Hackett, Donald W.
6th Grd Math & Sci Tchr
Hebditch, Daralyn Duquette
Eighth Grade English Teacher
Orrico, Amy Willson
English & Theatre Arts Tchr
EAST TAUNTON
Bettencourt, Helen Guthrie
3rd Grade Teacher
Dewey, Robert Thomas
Seventh Grd Soc Stud Teacher
Everidge, Nancy Mulrooney
5th Grade Special Educator
Hyland, Mary Lou
Head Science Teacher
O'Brien, Gregory Michael
Art Teacher
EAST WEYMOUTH
Anderson, Bryant Thomas
Arch & Structural Drftng Tchr
Bertolino, Linda Wingard
Cheerleading Coach
Clark, George A., Jr.
Biology Teacher
Cowie, Estelle Marie
Family & Consumer Science Tchr
Creedon, Vincent J.
Business Education Teacher
Cunningham, Sandra Ann
Second Grade Teacher
Devlin, Patricia Conrad
Fourth Grade Teacher
Hoffman, Marilyn Patricia
Guidance Counselor
Marinos, Patricia A.
Social Studies Teacher
Murray, Eleanor L.
Foreign Language Teacher
Player, George Henry
Spanish Teacher
Porter, Edward A.
Russian Teacher
Vincent, Susan Hanian
Math Teacher
Worcester, Marie
English Teacher
EASTHAMPTON
Black, Gail Patricia
Soc Stud, Sci, Lang Arts Instr
Curtin, Diane M.
Fourth Grade Teacher
Franceschina, Mona Jean
Math & Science Teacher
Lipp, Alan
Mathematics Department Head
Maiorano, Betty Bradley
Math Teacher
Parent, Robert C.
7th Grd Math & Science Teacher
Sonerson, Paul
Language Arts Teacher
Tenczar, Maureen St Martin
Teacher
Turner, Benjamin Curtis
Physics Teacher
EVERETT
Colachico, Ronald Charles
Chemistry Teacher
Colosi, Ronald J., Sr.
Bio, Anatomy & Physiology Tchr
Goldberg, Anita
English Teacher
Harrington, William Thomas
Submaster
Hickey, Laurel Guarino
Special Education Teacher
Larkin, Frances Bolla
Special Education Teacher
Shaw, Dennis Daniel
Social Studies & Science Tchr
FAIRHAVEN
Henriques, Michael Alan
8th Grd Life Science Teacher
Kaner, Carol Elias
French & Spanish Teacher
Medeiros, David
English Teacher & Athletic Dir
Perry, Kraig Streeter
History Teacher
Young, Bryan Alan
Band Director & Music Teacher
FALL RIVER
Andrade, Suzette M.
French & Portuguese Teacher
Bennett, Timothy Joseph
Fifth Grade Teacher
Boardman, Nancy (Sayward)
Fourth Grade Teacher
Byron, Nancy J.
Eighth Grade Teacher

Caine, Lorraine Smith
English & Literature Teacher
Chovinard, Donald Raymond
Counselor
Costa, Joyce
High School Math Teacher
Daley, Patricia
Health Careers Teacher
D'Ambrosio, Madeline
1st Grade Teacher
Fayan, Anne Marie M.
Mathematics Teacher
Grillo, Paul Stephen
Portuguese & Spanish Teacher
Grillo, Paula Occhiuti
Chemistry Teacher
Kochanski, Denise Turcotte
Junior HS Teacher
Lacroix, Roland Andre
English Teacher
Lanyon, Susan Ward
Fourth Grade Teacher
L'Heureux, James Michael
Admissions & Pub Relations Dir
Marchand, Sharon E.
Mathematics Teacher
Massoud, Donald Peter
Guidance Counselor
Mc Mahon, William Edward
Social Science Teacher
Pesce, Carol Anne
Math Teacher
Robinson, Dennis Sean
Music Teacher & Band Director
Rose, Nancy Silvia
French & Spanish Teacher
Saulino, Alphonse F., III
Fifth Grade Teacher
Silvia, Susan Gregory
Foreign Language Dept Chprsn
Sousa, Nancy Ann (Wrobel)
Kindergarten Teacher
Strickman, Leo
Drama Director
Theriault, Caryl Ann
First Grade Teacher
Willis, Jean Marie
5th & 6th Grade Teacher
Zwierchowski, Walter
High School Religion Teacher
FALMOUTH
Branco, Maria Clotilde
Spanish Teacher
Cali, Paul V.
Principal
Cotton, Martine Bindler
French Teacher
Craig, Kathleen Carney
Guidance Counselor
Cummings, Dorothy Lacerda
Special Needs Educator
Holcomb, Joanne Hurley
English Teacher
Hussey, George Ernest
Chem & Earth Sciences Teacher
Mc Cauley, Joseph H., III
Math & Science Teacher
Ozug, Charles David
English Dept Chprsn & Tchr
Stephens, Barbara
High School English Teacher
Wheeler, James Ide
US History Teacher
FEEDING HILLS
Brown, Susan Carol
Music & Chorus Teacher
Delevo, Doris Britton
Developmental Reading Teacher
Montesi, Fred Joseph
4th Grade Teacher
Quinn, William M.
Social Studies Tchr & Coord
Walsh, Douglas Timothy
English Teacher
FISKDALE
Hackenson, Cheryl Heske
Business Educator
Sawyer, Nancy Menanson
English Teacher
Wilson, Mark Christopher
Ninth Grade Teacher
FITCHBURG
Allard, Donna Marie
Music Teacher & Choral Dir
Bahde, Stephen James
English Dept Chairman
Barney, Janice G.
Science Teacher
Chakemian, K. Kenneth
Foreign Language Instructor
Conlee, James Richard
Social Studies Teacher
Economou, Catherine Fanos
4th Grade Classroom Teacher
Fitzpatrick, Karen A. (Boudreau)
Kindergarten Teacher
French, Deborah Ann (Du Phily)
Fourth Grade Teacher
Grier, Margaret Maynard
6th Grade Teacher
Hennessey, Thomas H.
Teacher
Hotchkiss, Anita Pruzan
Psychology Professor
Jablonski, Michael Jude
Social Studies Teacher
Kennedy, Jane A.
Reading Teacher
Lorenzen, Louis Otto
Full Prof of Fine Arts

Shao, Lawrence Peter
Assoc Prof Business Admin
Telicki, Dianne Galipeau
High School English Teacher
Thomas, Tamara Jane
Special Educator
Tulli, Stephen Michael
Chemistry Instructor
Woods, Christopher Beaumont
Guidance Cnslr & Track Coach
Zeiner, Diane Elizabeth
English & Journalism Teacher
FOXBORO
Bridges, Robert Arthur
History Teacher
Martinelli, Jack B.
Health & Physical Ed Teacher
Roy, Gerald Allen
Art Teacher
FRAMINGHAM
Buell, Donald A.
A P Biology Teacher
Ciocca, Camellia Kurt
High School Art Instructor
Citino, Donna
Social Studies Teacher
Crowe, Nadine Senecal
Mathematics Instructor
Elmont, Maxine
Professor of Social Sciences
Faiman, Bonnie Margolin
Language Arts Teacher
Foster, Gita Hakeren
Science Teacher
Herlihy, Gerard Walter
English Dept Chairman
Judge, Christine M.
English Teacher
Mc Carthy, Desmond Fergus
Assistant Professor of English
O'Brien, John Joseph
Retired Social Stud Dept Head
Sudmyer, Ronald Paul
Social Studies Teacher
Tredeau, Louis
Guidance Counselor & Eng Tchr
Vodoklys, Michael J.
8th Grade Lang Arts Teacher
Yang, Karen M.
High School Mathematics Tchr
FRANKLIN
Alexander, Dorothy Jean
Child Studies Instructor
Ashettino, Elaine (Gordon)
Asst Prof of Communication Art
Bardol, Joyce Saster
6th Grade Teacher
Bloom, Nancy Stawicki
Business & Technology Teacher
Dean, Richard Marshall
Assistant Professor of Art
Geysen, Thomas Francis
English Teacher & Coach
Hoar, Timothy John
Physics Instructor
Kramer, Charles Marvin
Professor of Economics
Missler, Charles W.
High School English Teacher
Palladino, Joan Phelps
Professor & Dance Pgm Coord
Powers, James Bradford
Professor of Sociology
Ratkevich, George D.
Art Teacher
Rich, Susan J.
Child Studies Program Coord
Richardson, Linda Szymanski
Business Education Teacher
GARDNER
Astor, Diane
Business & English Teacher
Beauregard, David Francis
Bio & Environmental Sci Tchr
Caci, Kathryn Mary
Third Grade Teacher
Doyle, Jane G.
Assistant Professor of Nursing
Fanos, Christine
Fourth Grade Teacher
Filteau, Ardath Mills
Science Teacher
Gearan, Janice Walendziak
Instructor of Psychology
Kozlowski, Edmund Edward
Math Teacher
LaCava, Michael M.
Music & Band Director
Lariviere, Blair J.
Art Teacher
Markham, John Thomas
Social Science Dept Instructor
Murray, Judith L. (Enman)
Lang Arts Teacher, Dept Chprsn
Natalizia, Elena Maria
Criminal Justice Instructor
Rahaim, Catherine Leger
World & US History Tchr
Troest, Donna Marie
Fourth Grade Teacher
Weitze, Teena Cowan
Biology Teacher
Wojtukiewicz, Carla J.
Kindergarten Teacher
GEORGETOWN
Baglio, Rose Anne Brinkley
Business Education Teacher
Bennett, Bernard George
Teacher & Dept Chairman

Pechilis, William C.
High School Mathematics Tchr
Sinibaldi, Carol Chase
Retired 5th Grade Teacher
GLOUCESTER
Finacey, Carol Jean
French & Spanish Teacher
Fuller, Kathleen Wile
French Teacher
Konaxis, Antoinette
English Teacher
Lafond, Jada Mc Rae
Biology & Health Teacher
McMahon, Christina Marie
Biology & Ocean Studies Tchr
Munroe, Norma Goyetche
Fifth Grade Teacher
Neill, Margaret Daugherty
Third Grade Teacher
Parady, Roger James, Jr.
High School Soc Studies Tchr
Pike, Douglas Snow
Special Education Case Manager
Proposki, William J.
Math Teacher & Cmptr Specialst
Smith, David B.
Pgm Leader of Soc Stud Dept
Waterhouse, Joan L.
English Teacher
GRAFTON
Caputo, John Richard
Business Dept Chair & Teacher
Tite, John Gregory
Math Dpt Chr & Calculus Instr
GRANBY
Blake, Clifford Joseph, Jr.
English Dept Chairman
GRANVILLE
Thompson, Robert W.
Principal
GREAT BARRINGTON
Armstrong, James J.
7th-8th Grade English Teacher
Beacco, John A.
Social Science Dept Chm
DelPlato, Joan
Instructor of Art History
Dupee, Sharyn Marie (DeSanty)
7th-8th Grade English Teacher
Hurlbut, Bruce Alan
Business Education Teacher
Jillson, Jill
3rd Grade Teacher
Vining, Ted
Teacher
GREENFIELD
Meese, Cynthia Ekblad
Music & Theater Teacher
Ruiz, Lillian
Instructor of English
Singley, Judith Greene
Recreation Coordinator
GROTON
Lyons, John Louis
History Teacher
Moore, Laura Rogerson
English Teacher
GROVELAND
Daley, Ann Mary
Fourth Grade Teacher
HADLEY
Duseau, Michael James
Science & Math Teacher
HAMPDEN
O'Sullivan, Cynthia Ellen
First Grade Teacher
HANOVER
Barker, Barbara U.
Retired Teacher
Palmer, Sandra Cira
7th Grade Science Teacher
Sanders, Wilma Jocelyn
Second Grade Teacher
HANSCOM AFB
Duffy, Christine
Third Grade Teacher
HANSON
Blauss, Wesley
6th Grade Teacher
Brady, Kathleen Patricia
Art Teacher
HARVARD
Besold, Stephen Gerard
Social Studies Teacher
Pierce, Deborah A.
Biology Teacher
HARWICH
Anderson, Janice Pearson
Retired Elementary Teacher
HAVERHILL
Barberio, Cynthia Malynn
English Teacher
Barron, Carol Talbot
Assoc Prof of English
Cunningham, David E.
Computer Teacher
DiBurro, Joseph P., Jr.
8th Grade Social Studies Tchr
Donovan, Nancy Romeos
Fourth Grade Teacher
Dufresne, Roger
Accounting Professor
Gosbee, Judith Ann (Gauthier)
English & Journalism Teacher
Metthe, Esther (Grillo)
8th Grade English Teacher
Moll, Angela Marie
Latin, Classical Greek Teacher
Mooney, Susan P.
High School Science Teacher

HILL (cont)
Carol Ann
l Director & Music Tchr
os, Maria
eacher
John Edward
Drafting Teacher
Joan Marie
matics Teacher
AM
Kenneth F.
al Psychologist
hi, Barbara L.
gy Teacher
Dennis Howard
matics Teacher
nne Duggan
sh & French Teacher
Claudia A.
Teacher
ROOK
Walter William
matics Chairperson
a, Pamela Brown
HS Science Dept Chair
EN
oy K.
gy Teacher
Jennifer Decelles
cal Education & Hlth Tchr
Jack F., Jr.
istory & Government Instr
d, C. William
pal
te, Vivianne L.
Teacher
ds, Joseph R.
sh Teacher
ISTON
ano, Janet Rascoe
eacher
y, Susan Duponte
rade Teacher
, Raymond F.
Teacher
gs, JoAnn Consoletti
rgarten Tchr
Mary Sheila
Coordinator & Teacher
Joseph Philip
gy Teacher
ahan, John Dowd
rade Math & Science Tchr
Ronald Michael
ce Teacher
, Robert B.
l Studies Teacher
OKE
y, Roberta Kelly
ipal
nd, Marion Wilson
ssor of English
ra, Brenda Lee
ergarten Teacher
, Carolyn Whitenett
ness Teacher
i, Judith Authier
d Languages Dept Chair
on, Patricia Hamel
Grade Language Teacher
ndes, Anthony R.
al Studies Teacher
, Rosellen E.
ter I Teacher
, Diane Marie (Pepin)
th Grade Math Teacher
owski, Maureen Kennedy
Arts, Latin & Span Tchr
Elizabeth Ann Oparowski
, Lang Arts & Rel Tchr
ee, Maureen Downing
Grade Teacher
n, Candace Young
stance Abuse Prvntion Tchr
owski, Charlene
hematics Teacher
, Joseph Dominic
ish Teacher
elian, Melva Strong
ish Teacher
Jack Joseph
essor of Psychology
rty, Kevin John
al Studies Teacher
, Lorene Ann (Laplante)
lish Teacher
a, Marlene M., SSJ
Tchr & Dept Chair
nor, Anne L.
Grade Teacher
nor, Edwin Joseph
iness Teacher
r, Judith K.
ily & Consumer Sci Teacher
Diane Jendrysik
ond Grade Teacher
, Richard J.
Arts Teacher
evant, Virginia Ann
rning Specialist
van, James Michael
Grade US History Teacher
van, Patricia
logy & Physiology Teacher
, Harold Thomas, Jr.
derate Special Needs Teacher
EDALE
so, Thomas Ralph
h Grade Teacher

Fielder, Janice Laraine
Mathematics Teacher
Morgan, Lynne Paul
Spanish Teacher
Whitten, Francis, III
Health & Psychology Teacher
HOPKINTON
Fleming, Michael
European & World His Tchr
Kiley, Eva Celularo
History Teacher
Mc Gonigle, Patricia
English Teacher & Dept Coord
Mecagni, Carol
High School Art Teacher
Porth, Christopher Francis
Choir & General Music Director
Scanlon, Michael Joseph
Physics Teacher & Sci Coord
HUDSON
Johnson, Paul Robert
Drama & Choral Director
Mac Queston, Carole Beaumont
French & Spanish Tchr
Mishley, Joseph J.
8th Grade Science Teacher
Murtagh, Linda Christine
7th Grade Science Teacher
Sullivan, J. Bryan
Mathematics Teacher
HULL
Cahalane, Joan A.
2nd Grade Teacher
HUNTINGTON
Cangro, Marilyn Bingham
Third Grade Teacher
Fisk, Stephanie Lauren
Var Girls Bsktbl & Sftbl Coach
HYANNIS
Caldwell, Frederick Jackson, Jr.
Mathematics Tchr & Dept Chair
Diaz, Consuelo Antona
Spanish Teacher
Mc Clelland, James Warren
Biology Teacher
Oberman, Diana Bound
English Teacher
Presbrey, Janice Mattson
English Teacher
Reed, John L.
Social Studies Teacher
Regan, Margaret Manahan
Admin Asst & English Teacher
Sides, Barbara A.
Second Grade Teacher
HYDE PARK
Long, Sandra M. Kube
Social Studies Teacher
IPSWICH
Beaudoin, Pamela Anne
High School History Teacher
Dion Faust, Debra
English Teacher & Drama Adv
Dolan, Gerald John, Jr.
Band Director
JAMAICA PLAIN
Chan, Fernadina How-Ching
Dance Program Dir & Teacher
Mc Nabb, Edward Joseph, Jr.
US History Teacher
JEFFERSON
Kumpey, Marie Doherty
Fourth Grade Teacher
KINGSTON
Carl, Catherine (Walsh)
Mathematics Teacher
Goldberg, Eunice Meier
English Teacher
Hybertson, Beverly Blaisdell
Elementary Teacher
Jordan, Margaret L.
Spanish Teacher
Kohout, Dolores, CDP
Religion Teacher
Mahtesian, Valerie Ann
Computer Teacher
McEwan, John Francis
Principal
Mutrie, Martha Christian
English Teacher
Provenzano, Diane Louise
Science Teacher
Record, Luci Deborah
English Teacher
Stanghellini, Mary Ellen (Tower)
Chemistry Teacher
Woodhouse, Carol B.
Latin Teacher
LAKEVILLE
Bienvenue, Janet C.
Economics Teacher
Homen, Peter John
Social Studies Dept Chair
Lamoureux, Denise Marie
Biology Teacher
Ledwith, Edward J.
Instrumental Music Teacher
LANCASTER
Moeckel, Ilona Cislak
Fifth Grade Teacher
LAWRENCE
Adamopoulos, Charles Arthur
Business Education Teacher
Barbagallo, Phyllis Manzi
Counselor
Beninato, Paul Phillip
Music & Choir Director
DiStefano, Brenda
HS ESL Teacher

Fillipon, Elaine M. (Vallante)
English Teacher
Harrison, Joyce DeCesare
Fourth Grade Teacher
Kelley, Terri
French Teacher
Meehan, David Paul
Arts & Humanities Teacher
Moore, Susan
Reading Teacher
O'Sullivan, Peter Vincent
Mathematics Teacher
Post, Barbara Wilbur
Sci Dept Chair & Chem Teacher
Roedel, Robert R.
Senior Army Instructor
Rosen, Carol A. (Nardozza)
Math Teacher
Sullivan, Christopher Francis
English Teacher
Sullivan, Joyce Ann
Jr High Mathematics & Sci Tchr
Troianello, Vina Marie
Teacher
LEE
Lomaglio, Alexander A.
7th Grade Science Teacher
LEICESTER
Comer, Diana Houde
Dir of Early Childhood Ed
Dutton, Nancy C.
English & Lang Arts Teacher
Kane, Barbara Morrison
Associate Professor of English
Krauss, Art J.
Prof & Coord of Communications
Lucier, Edward H.
Professor of Biology
LENOX
Brunette, Beverly Jane
Biology Teacher
Jones, Marcia Vern
Latin & Mathematics Teacher
Moore, Donna Negrini
5th Grade Teacher
Vincent, Shirley Jones
English Teacher
LEOMINSTER
Buss, Angela R.
11th Grade English Teacher
Hay, Scott
High School English Teacher
LEXINGTON
Comenetz, Marian
German & Spanish Teacher
Fruscione, Albert A.
Biology Teacher
Good, C. Edward
Math Department Head
Kelley, Joseph Gerard
English & History Teacher
Kelly, Kevin A.
Mathematics Teacher
Zetarski, Robin Ann
Math & Programming Instr
LITTLETON
Coburn, Barbara Puppel
9th-12th Grd Soc Stud Teacher
Downing, M. Gail Fitzgerald
Third Grade Teacher
Hoffrage, Phoebe Ann
4th Grade Teacher
Pizza, Dominic A.
Physical Science Teacher
LONGMEADOW
Donoghue, Ruth Ellen
Teacher
Freed, Virginia Kelly
Asst Prof & Academic Dev Dir
Mc Cormick, Linda Mc Carthy
Fourth Grade Teacher
Merritt, Ronald J.
Science Chairperson
Pantuosco, John Joseph
Business & Special Ed Tchr
Peters, Susan Berry
Mathematics Teacher
Therrien, Jean Randall
Middle School Teacher
LOWELL
Agostini, Hector P.
Prof of Bus Admin
Aste, Mario
Professor of Languages & Hum
Atkinson, Jay Michael
Adjunct Professor of English
Bergeron, Dean Joseph
Professor of History
Boisjoly, Claudette Elaine (Houle)
French Teacher
Boisjoly, Ronald Francis
French Teacher
Bolianites, Charles
Mathematics Teacher
Borst, James Robert
US History Teacher
Burke, William Joseph
Professor of Legal Stud Dept
Catallozzi, John Joseph
Professor of Educl Psychology
Cielakie, Antonina Mary
6th Grade Teacher
Clark-Apel, Joanne M.
7th Grade Teacher
Cullen, Lois Carter
6th Grd Lang Arts & Rdng Tchr
Curran, Barbara A.
8th Grade Language Arts Tchr
Das, Mitra
Professor of Sociology

Del Llano, Patricia A.
Art Teacher
De Profio, James A.
Health Teacher
Descheneaux, Ernest Joseph
English Teacher
Doesschate, Judith Everett
Art Teacher
Donahue, Stephanie Quinn
Secondary School History Tchr
Dorr, Margaret Gallagher
Third Grade Teacher
Dunkley, Yvonne Brown
Personal & Career Counselor
Earle, J. Michael
Biology Teacher
Eby, G. Nelson
Professor of Earth Sciences
Freimiller, Jane
Asst Professor of Philosophy
Gomes, Luis Augusto
Portuguese Teacher
Gore, Richard Z.
Assoc Prof of Earth Science
Hallissy, Sheila Mary
English Teacher
Hawkins, Mary Pendergraft
Family & Consumer Science Tchr
Healy, Ann Considine
English Teacher
Heines, Jesse M.
Assoc Prof of Computer Science
Isaks, Martin
Assoc Professor of Chemistry
Kannenberg, Lloyd Chambers
Professor of Physics
Kelley, Judith Anne
Chemistry Professor
Kennedy, James Joseph, Jr.
Math Teacher
Kramer, Mary Duhamel
Full Professor of English
Kudzma, Thomas George
Assoc Prof of Math & Engrng
Kunzendorf, Robert Godfrey
Psychology Professor
Lindeke, William A.
Professor & Department Chair
Mac Dougall, John
Professor of Sociology
Maia, Philip C.
Spanish Teacher & Track Coach
Maille, Lorraine R.
Guid Cnslr & Admissions Dir
Mandell, Charlotte C.
Professor of Psychology
Martineau, Irene Marguerite
Religion & Language Arts Tchr
Marx, Kenneth Allan
Chemistry Professor
Mayotte, Gail Anne
Principal
McCormack, Arlene Smith
Dept Sociology Chairperson
McDonough, Carole Fadden
English Teacher
Mil'Shtein, Samson
Professor of EE Department
Murphy, Daniel Patrick
High School Teacher
Nelson, Joan M.
Third Grade Teacher
Parker, Jill Marie
HS Social Studies Teacher
Pennell, Melissa Mc Farland
Associate Professor of English
Pho, Hai B.
Professor of Political Science
Ritchotte, Michelle Marie
Spanish Teacher
Rivera, Ezequiel R.
Prof of Biological Sciences
Rubinstein, Harry
Professor of Chemistry
Sheldon, Eric
Physics Professor & Honors Dir
Tartaglione, Louis C.
Full Prof of Civil Engineering
Tripathy, Sukant K.
Provost & Prof of Chemistry
Turpin-Petrosino, Carolyn
Asst Prof of Criminal Justice
Verreault, Kathryn Mary
Coll of Mngmt Interim Dean
Walsh, Nancy Sherman
Kindergarten Teacher
Wilk, Ann Rousseau
Math Teacher
Wooding, John Charles
Associate Professor of Pol Sci
LUDLOW
Hogan, Donna Berte
English Department Chairperson
Koch, Cynthia Jean
Instrumental Music Teacher
Lavoie, Alice Anna
5th-8th Grade Religion Teacher
Lynes, Daniel Paul
Mathematics Tchr & Dept Chm
Mancuso, Toni-Marie Mendes
Assistant Principal
Marino, Betsy Marie
Special Education Teacher
Mazzocco, Diane Kensicki
English Teacher
Nunes, Lucille Sousa
Second Grade Teacher
Rheault, Michael
Music Teacher

Sheehan, Mary Jane M.
Sixth Grade Teacher
LUNENBURG
Davis, Karen Ann
3rd Grade Teacher
Gearin, Dawn Ducharme
Science Teacher
LaMothe, Ronald Robert
Social Studies Teacher & Coach
Masse, Ann Walker
English Teacher
Robbins, J. Wayne
Social Studies Professor
LYNN
Barrett, Paul F.
English Instructor
Briggs, John A.
Retired Social Studies Teacher
Brown-Breckenridge, Charlotte R.
Distributive Education Teacher
Coolidge, Richard F.
Lead Social Studies Teacher
Durgin, Belinda Tracy
Fourth Grade Teacher
Fahy, Marietta R.
Lang Arts & Literature Tchr
Gately, Lorraine M.
Biology & Health Teacher
Griffin, Carol M. (Carluccio)
Mathematics Teacher
Kontoules, Charles James
Reading Teacher
McHugh, William P., Jr.
Chemistry Teacher
Mulholland, Mary Jane
English Dept Director
Rappa, William Newton, Jr.
Fifth Grade Teacher
LYNNFIELD
Lambert, Stephen E.
7th Grade Mathematics Teacher
Macadino, Ritamarie Frasca
Teacher & Specialist
Mc Mahon, Margaret (Miano)
4th Grade Teacher
Robins, Margie Ann Westberg
First Grade Teacher
Sullivan, Kathleen Marie
Science Teacher
MALDEN
Brauer, Mary Elizabeth
Fifth Grade Teacher
Cooper, Alana Gail (Wartell)
Sixth Grade Teacher
Glionna, Joseph Michael
Eighth Grade Reading Teacher
Hines, Robert Joseph
English Teacher
Low, Charles Malcolm
Biology Teacher
Matthews, Maureen T.
Third Grade Teacher
Mc Carthy, Elaine M.
Sixth Grade Teacher
Melvin, Noreen M.
World Language Teacher
Murphy, Jane Zampitella
Classroom Teacher
Newman, Marie A.
5th Grade Teacher
OHearn, Maureen Ann
1st Grade Teacher
Quist, Robert Mark
Guidance Counselor
Rodwell, Richard Charles
Elem Assistant Principal
Trabucco, Mary A.
Fifth Grade Teacher
Vatalaro, Susan
Principal
Walsh, Miriam
Principal
MANCHESTER
Gandolfi, M'Lena
Phys Ed & Health Teacher
MANSFIELD
Caouette, Anne M.
Health, Human Development Tchr
Carl, Ethel Elizabeth
Second Grade Teacher
Hayward, Sandra Tracy
Math & Computer Science Tchr
Pontes, John A.
English Teacher
Wood, Pamela M.
Science Teacher
MARBLEHEAD
Dana, Gregory Scott
Mathematics Teacher
Farrell, James J.
Senior High Art Teacher
Horgan, Michael H.
Health & Spanish Teacher
Leaver, Ann McCarthy
English Teacher
Page, Harriet
Science Teacher
Patch, Richard C.
Physics Teacher
Tyrrell, Sally Byrne
ESL Teacher
Williams-Lord, Mary Marcia
5th Grd Tchr & Enrichmnt Coord
MARLBOROUGH
Anastas, George Michael
Social Studies Tchr & Coach
Anusavice, Bernard
Drafting Teacher
Barter, Deborah Anne (Lyttle)
Fourth Grade Teacher

MARLBOROUGH (cont)
Cares, Philip Stephen
Seventh Grade Mathematics Tchr
Collins, John Francis, Jr.
Director of Instructional Svcs
Downes, John F.
Mathematics Teacher
Giorgi, Andrea C.
Social Studies Teacher
Giorgi, Mary A.
English Teacher
Ludgate, Judith
Bus Ed & Tech Prep Coord
Moorman, Janet Bouteiller
HS Social Studies Teacher
Nicalek, Kenneth A.
Health & Physical Ed Instr
O'Brien, Caren Schmidt
French Teacher
O'Connell, Shirley Tuttle
4th Grade Teacher
Pare, Brian Joseph
Dean of Students
Rigney, William F.
Biology Teacher
Russo, John Joseph
Music Teacher
Terry, Richard Robert
Science Department Chairperson
Vassel, Mary J. (Lynch)
4th Grade Teacher
MARSHFIELD
DeAguiar, Susan P.
Fourth Grade Teacher
Kauffman, Mary Ann
Mathematics Teacher
Price, John Nicholas
Mathematics Teacher
MARSTONS MILLS
Clarke, Keith
Counselor
MATTAPAN
Germany, Wilma Flakes
Science & Social Studies Tchr
Lee, Robin L.
Speech Pathologist
MATTAPOISETT
Meehan, Barbara Aileen
Guidance Counselor
MAYNARD
Benham, Daria Setzco
First Grade Teacher
Klepadlo, Shirley J.
Chemistry Teacher
Stebbins, Allen H.
History & Social Studies Tchr
Wirzburger-Seymour, Rita Ann (Brine)
Third Grade Teacher
MEDFIELD
DeSorgher, Richard Paul
US History Teacher
Mc Kechnie, Claire Collins
Fourth Grade Teacher
MEDFORD
Barry-Sutherland, Jean
4th Grd Tchr & Asst Prin
Carpenter, Calvin L.
History Teacher
DiCarlo, Rita Scaramuzzo
Foreign Languages Teacher
Doumanidis, Charalabos C.
Professor of Mechanical Engrng
Generazzo, Arlene Diamond
Fourth Grade Educator
Green, Susan A.
Second Grade Teacher
Jewett, Franklyn Wayne
Health & Physical Ed Teacher
Kane, Margaret Ann Mac Donnell
English Teacher
Martin, Paula DePasquale
English Teacher
Mc Adam, John J.
Social Studies Teacher
Rutstein, Barbara A. (Lerner)
Mathematics Teacher
Skane, Marie A.
Second Grade Teacher
Terrano, Robert John
Science Teacher
Vogel, Richard Mark
Associate Professor
Walker, Pauline Sullivan
Sixth Grd World History Tchr
MEDWAY
Andreoni, David N.
Social Studies Teacher
Brown, Arlene Barbara
Mathematics Dept Chairperson
Kelley, Carolyn Getz
Guidance Counselor
Phelan-Swan, Lorraine H. (Soltys)
English Teacher
MELROSE
Buckley, Susan E.
Fifth Grade Teacher
Coughlin, Robert Charles
US History Teacher
Dwyer, Marianne Jean
Special Needs Teacher
Flint, Mark Francis
Jr HS Coord & Eighth Grd Tchr
Hassett, Robert Andrew
Science & Biology I & II Tchr
Kaplon, Kerry L.
Mathematics Teacher
Usher, Nancy Spear
English Teacher
MENDON
Pearlman, Paula Schwartz
Fourth Grade Teacher
MERRIMAC
Campbell, Roy M.
Sixth Grade Teacher
METHUEN
Balavitch, Carolyn Kudla
5th Grade Teacher
Bates, Cynthia A.
Spanish Teacher
Blomgren, Gustave Eric, Jr.
Fourth Grade Teacher
Clark-Warne, Brenda Ruth
Track & Cross Country Coach
Crane, Elaine Marie (Kazanjian)
Secondary English Teacher
Cuoco, Marion
Language Arts Teacher
Dubois, Suzanne Evelyn
Theology Teacher
Ferrara, Ann Kilcoyne
English Teacher
Hammond, Kathleen M.
Middle School Associate Prin
Hiller, Judith Susan
Mathematics Teacher
Houle, Mark Steven
School Psychologist
Kemp, Lori Meese
Former English Teacher
King, Dennis F.
Science Teacher
Lane, Gary Michael
English Teacher
La Voice, Vickiann Deschamps
HS Math & Science Teacher
Lynch, Neil Samuel
9th-12th Grd ESL & TBE Teacher
MacDougall, Susan Murphy
Sixth Grade English Teacher
McHugh, Catherine B. (Noonan)
7th Grd Language Arts Tchr
Molchan, Jane Banker
Sixth Grade Teacher
Pellegrino, Diane Elaine (Perrett)
High School Nurse
Rapisardi, Frank
Science Teacher
Shaheen, Rosemary Licata
Second Grade Teacher
Spence, Corinne Lafrenier
Computer Facilitator
Woodbury, Stephen W.
Lang Arts & Soc Stud Tchr
MIDDLEBORO
Bizinkauskas, Charlene Cassiani
Special Needs Teacher
Card, Amy Clay
Former 2nd Grade Teacher
Cummings, Susan
Third Grade Teacher
Hanley, Michael P.
Reading Teacher
Jessop, Kathleen Duggan
English & Language Arts Tchr
Martin, Joyce Marie
Fourth Grade Teacher
Nickerson, William Whitman
8th Grade Science Teacher
Venice, Janet I.
Art Teacher
MIDDLETON
Murphy, Martin Vincent
Teacher
Worth, Paul Edward
Science, Math & Phys Ed Tchr
MILFORD
Campbell, Harriet Laverne
Math Teacher
Coffey, Francis G.
Fifth Grade Teacher
Crescenzi, Joanne Binks
English Teacher
Friedner, Eva Marie
Former Teacher
Jablonski, Francis James
Biology & Human Anatomy Tchr
Mazzarelli, Dolores M.
First Grade Teacher
Pirro, Kathleen Bianchi
Third Grade Teacher
Rose, Steven A.
Mathematics Teacher
Spivack, Roberta Frank
Reading Specialist
MILLBURY
Chiras, Carole Amour
Principal
Genese, Eugene J.
Business & Soc Stud Teacher
Sutphen, Mark Albert
8th Grade Physical Sci Teacher
MILLIS
Bradford, Bonnie J.
Third Grade Teacher
Dooling, William Paul
HS Social Studies Teacher
Guinta, Melodie Dickerson
Pvt Voice Instr & Choir Dir
MILLVILLE
DuRocher, Joan Teresa
Science Teacher
MILTON
Baino, William A.
Fifth Grade Teacher
DiManno, Dorria L.
Communications Professor
Fatouros, Vasiliki
Professor of Business Mgmt
Hilgendorf, Mark Steven
High School History Teacher
Jennings, Robert M.
United States History Tchr
Lanigan, Jack
Sixth Grade Teacher
Piotrowicz, Paul
Varsity Soccer Coach
Tart, Stephen Mortimer
High School English Teacher
Tyler, Robert Stephen
Chemistry Teacher
MONSON
Devine, William T.
Art Teacher
Renaud, Richard Henry
English Dept Chprsn & Teacher
MONTAGUE
O'Riley, John George
Secondary English Teacher
MORGANTA
Bailey, Robert Pendleton, Jr.
8th Grd Social Studies Teacher
MOUNT HERMON
Petroff, Theodora Mc Geoghan
Art Teacher
NANTUCKET
Blair, Helene Roche
English Teacher & Dept Head
Kuhl, David Schuyler
Computer Science Teacher
NATICK
Ash, Gerald Ernest
HS Band Director & Hum Tchr
Buckley, John Thomas
Math Teacher & Department Head
Cull, Christopher John
Acting Teacher
DeGuzman, Patricia Wholihan
Lang Arts & Humanities Teacher
Mac Beth, Jan
English Department Chair
ONeil, Mary A. OKeefe
English Language Teacher
Plunkett, Marie Sarris
Bio, Anatomy & Physiology Tchr
Rylko, W. Russell
Earth Science Instructor
Saladino, Jean Elizabeth
Director of Vocal Studies
Sand, Jacquelyn M.
Frgn Lang Chprsn & French Tchr
Schell, Jessie Rosenberg
Creative Writing Dept Chair
NEEDHAM
Fitzgerald, T. Kern
Bio Tchr, PE & Athletic Trnr
Lubar, Phyllis L.
Speech & Language Pathologist
Schwimmer, Elaine D.
Modern Languages Dept Chair
NEEDHAM HEIGHTS
Candlen, Frances Larkin
Third Grade Teacher
NEEDHAM HGTS
Panich, Diane
Fine & Performing Arts Dir
Rizzitano, Jane Elizabeth
Spanish Teacher
Rousse, Valerie
German Teacher
NEW BEDFORD
Baptiste, Kathryn Russo
Math Teacher
Barrett, Richard Joseph
Automotive Tech Instructor
Cabral, Paul Anthony
Gen Music Teacher & Choral Dir
Caron, Albert W., Jr.
English Teacher
Constant, William Paul
Math Teacher
Demers, Ann Marie Kresge
Related Cosmetology Teacher
DePina, Barbara L.
Social Studies Teacher
Edmundson, Lawrence George
Social Studies Teacher
Ferreira, Bonnie M.
Secondary Sciene Teacher
Fraga, Stephen
English Teacher
Garrison, Robert, Jr.
Sixth Grade Teacher
Gilchrest, Priscilla (Tripp)
Fifth Grade Teacher
Hamlet, Wayne L.
Biology Teacher
Lamontagne, David Leo
Elementary Health Specialist
Lavigne, Barbara Tavares
7th & 8th Grd Sci & Math Tchr
LeBlanc, Therese Fecteau
Fourth Grade Teacher
McFall, Marvin Edward
Data Processing Instructor
Medeiros, Richard Alan
Sixth Grade Teacher
Oliveira, Anne Marie
Science Teacher
Pina, June Marie
First Grade Teacher
Sasseville, Eugene Henry
Electronics Teacher
Souza, Teresa Ann
Third Grade Teacher
Strittmatter, John
Chemistry Teacher
Suarez, Ruben
Adult Christian Education Tchr
Walker, Steven A.
HS Science Teacher
Winn, Dennis Michael
Assistant Principal
York, Margaret Chagaruly
Chemistry Teacher
NEW SALEM
Santner, Marcia Cunningham
Third-Fourth Grade teacher
NEWBURYPORT
Politis, Jane Gwyn
History & Ldrshp Seminar Tchr
NEWTON
Benjamin, Penelope Smith
Third Grade Teacher
Cella, Jean Demma
Instructor of Legal Studies
Delay, Richard James
PE Teacher & Coach
Donatio, Diane Marie
English Instructor
Fitzsimmons, Barbara Smith
Assoc Prof of Early Chldhd Ed
Haddad, Mark H.
Music Teacher
Heffernan, Kerrissa Jane
Assoc Prof & Director
Kosakowski, Joanna C.
Mathematics Professor
Landis, Lisa Shadovitz
Assistant Director
Leach, Todd Joseph
Associate Prof of Business
Mitchell, Robert William
Teacher
Montgomery, Marjorie A.
8th Grade Social Studies Tchr
Moore, David Edward
History Teacher
Newman-Levy, Sandra S.
Fashion Instructor
O'Beirne, Marguerite J.
Former Principal
Panchuck, Paula DeAngelis
Dir of Early Chldhd & Elem Ed
Reilly, Suzanne Sweeney
Senior Lecturer
Ruopp, Faye Nisonoff
Mathematics Educator
Scavone, Sarah Baker
Assistant Prof of Business
Solomon, Catherine F.
Program Dir of Human Services
Vallone, Maria Libera
Italian Teacher
Van De Carr, Theresa Joanne
Professor of Education
NEWTON CENTER
Bronson, Vinson
Physics & Chemistry Teacher
Dias, Jeffrey E.
Special Education Teacher Aide
Eisenhauer, Elaine Cerul
Russian Teacher
Gonson, Dorothy Rose
English Teacher
Kantrowitz, Betty
Mathematics Teacher
Markin, Esta B.
English Teacher
Mc Graime, Judith M.
French Teacher
NEWTON CENTRE
Archambault, Leo Zak
Retail Merch & Bus Prof
Carter, William R.
Associate Professor
Forde, Patricia Ann (Joyce)
College Instructor
Kane, Robert Joseph
Sr Instructor of Mortuary Sci
Sims, Joanne Magaldi
Associate Prof of Textiles
NORFOLK
Henrich, Christine Rossetti
8th Grd American History Tchr
Rice, James Michael
7th Grade Math Teacher
Walkins, Virginia Burns
6th Grade Teacher
NORTH ADAMS
DeGiorgis, Jacqueline Mailhot
Biology Teacher
Flaherty, Frances Bachand
Eighth Grade US History Tchr
Jenkins, Carl H.
Music & Band Director
LeSage, Paul Edward
Assoc Prof of Journalism & Lit
Noel, Edward John
Mathematics Teacher
O'Connell, J. Brian
Principal
Pecor, Donald Joseph
Social Studies Teacher
Swain, Carol Murphy
1st Grade Teacher
Tarsa, Barbara J.
9th-12th Grd Bus Info Sys Tchr
NORTH ANDOVER
Bassett, R. Diane (Perry)
Mathematics Teacher
Baylies, Susan Michel
5th Grade Classroom Teacher
Bennett, Robert Clay
Sci Dept Chm & Physics Tchr
Bradley, Michael John
Assoc Prof of Math & Cmptr Sci
Del Gaudio, Richard
Dean of Business
Dwyer, Kevin Francis
Assoc Prof of Religious Stud
Grady, Raymond F.
AP American History Teacher
Gregoire, Mary Julie (Connor)
High School English Teacher
Han, S. Bruce
Asst Professor of Management
Hanson, Donald T.
Assoc Prof of Acctng & CPA
Kim, Chong Rae
Mathematics Professor
Leibowitz, Jodie Plimley
Former Spanish Teacher
Longsworth, Ellen Louise
Art History Prof & Dept Chrmn
Mahoney, MaryKay Anne
Assoc Prof of English Dept
Mc Carthy, Kevin F.
Sixth Grade Teacher
Montella, Ennis Joseph
Mathematics Professor
Nicolaisen, Elena Petrella
First Grade Teacher
Powers, Mark Richard
Guidance Counselor
Pressman, Sylvie
French Professor
Rueda, Norma G. (Graciela)
Assistant Professor of Math
Schruender, Edward
7th Grade Math Teacher
Shine, Margaret Eileen
Retired Teacher
Wass, Russell David
Accounting Professor
NORTH ATTLEBORO
Bergeron, Normand A.
English Teacher & Hum Coord
Carey, Elizabeth Catherine
English Teacher
Fisher, Sheila Brennan
Life Science Instructor
Keaney, Kathleen Carbon
Math Teacher
Leonard, Violet Elva
5th Grade Teacher
Murphy, Joan Murphy
3rd Grade Teacher
Pasquine, Marilou Carey
English Teacher
Thibault, Phyllis S.
Latin Teacher
Thompson, Jean (Cavanagh)
English Teacher
Vito, David Robert
Biology Teacher
NORTH BILLERICA
Mc Caffrey, Jane
First Grade Teacher
Tobin, Patricia Anne Gendron
Elementary School Principal
NORTH CHELMSFORD
Bradman, Robert R.
High School Math Teacher
Defilippo, Dana H.
Coach
Doherty, Jeffrey Daniel
Emerson House Dean
Hazzard, Barry David
English Teacher
Hoover, Eric Douglas
Advncd Plcmnt Studio Art Tchr
Leite, John Joseph, Sr.
K-4th Grd Music Specialist
Marshall, Bruce Thomas
Physical Education Teacher
Silva, Janice Lynn
English Teacher
NORTH DARTMOUTH
Barry, Sharon (Schlosser)
English Teacher
Christie, Suzanne M.
Music & Drama Director
Fortier, Joanne Mendes
High School English Teacher
Grant, Rose Guindon
Science & Health Teacher
Hart, William T.
Athletic Director & Math Tchr
Howe, Elizabeth Miller
3rd Grade Teacher
Martin-Fortin, Jane
Mathematics Teacher
McCarthy, Joseph F.
HS Computer Science Teacher
Mc Dermott, Thomas Edward
Health Teacher
Mc Donald, James Thomas
US History Teacher
O'Brien, Michael Patrick
Dean of Students & His Tchr
Pierce, Bradford Irving
Mathematics Teacher & Dept Chm
Regan, James P.
Mathematics Teacher
Revil, Jean L.
Religious Studies Teacher
Robinson, Judith D.
English Teacher
Rodrigues, Douglas Mark
Religious Studies Teacher
Silva, John
Physics Department Instructor
Tolley, Linda Ann
Spanish Teacher
Winey, W. Fred H.
Science Dept Chairman & Tchr

H DIGHTON
Villiam Joseph, Jr.
l Studies Dept Chair
avid Lewis
cs Teacher
Linda Rose
tive PE Teacher
H EASTHAM
, David A.
ance Counselor
Selena Fraser
2th Grd English Teacher
ob
ry & Social Sciences Tchr
H EASTON
Francis Vincent
d Language Department Chm
rank
Grade Teacher
, Hazel M. Luke
al Studies Chair
, Manuel David
ogy Teacher
H READING
M. Judy
panish & French Teacher
HAMPTON
ee, Maria Nemcova
essor of Russian
er, Yvonne Ruth
& German Teacher
ed, Karl Paul
ster & Theology Educator
George Morrison
essor of Chemistry
o, Sandra
ogy Teacher
an, Lynn Cleare
nstructor
G. Frederick, Jr.
ol Counselor
Susan B.
osophy Professor
Malgorzata Zielinska
essor of Physics
t, Denise
ociate Professor of French
t, Robert D.
nistry Teacher
zinski, John Charles
3rd Math Teacher
THBOROUGH
it, Mary Ann
n Teacher
r, Eleanor Braley
stitute Teacher
n, Joan Fitzgerald
ond Grade Teacher
, Kathleen
al Studies Teacher
, Martha A.
sics Teacher
ox, Frederic Richard
lish Department Chairman
our, Robert Joseph
nce Teacher & Dept Chair
Mary Aiken
rdisciplinary Curr Coord
er, Eileen Costello
Grade Teacher
THFIELD
oe, Ralph Cornelius
sics Teacher
ey, Robert Jacobs
lish, Greek & Latin Tchr
elly, Margaret Wetherbee
nanities Coord, English Tchr
dge, Stuart Allyn
hropology & World His Tchr
, Nick
lish Teacher
edy, Dennis William
lish Teacher
en, Richard E.
ory & Social Sciences Tchr
Mahon, Sabina Leigh
hematics Teacher
ian, Kerry F.
glish & Social Studies Tchr
os, Starr Jean
nish Teacher
ick, Elizabeth Anne
tory Teacher
ts, Audrey Hathaway
glish Teacher
ck, Wendolyn T.
tory & Classics Teacher
tcheff, Michael
thematics Teacher
nger, James Francis
th Teacher
uk, Kathleen Page
ector of Academic Resources
RTON
odica, Kathleen Anne (Murphy)
gh School Science Teacher
g, Gloria Bzdula
ird Grade Teacher
in, Diane (Neville)
ence Dept Chm & Bio Teacher
z, Saundra Trova
glish Teacher
ly, Elaine
glish Teacher
ell, Lorna Smithers
ench Teacher
es, Deborah Honhan
urth Grade Teacher
or, James E.
glish Teacher & Counselor

NORWELL
Sullivan, James E.
English & Social Studies Tchr
NORWOOD
Czyryca, Michael Thomas
Principal
Dalzell, Kenneth F.
Jr HS Science Teacher
Grazado, Robert William
Guidance Counselor
Malachowski, Ann Mary
Elem Art Coordinator
Mooney, Joseph Patrick
6th Grade Teacher
OAK BLUFFS
Agnoli, Jeffrey Michael
English Teacher
Donald, David H.
Chemistry Teacher
Dripps, Craig R.
Math Teacher
Morris, Sidney Brock
Technology Coordinator
Weintraub, Elaine Cawley
Social Studies Teacher
ORANGE
Grzesik, Karen L.
Physical Education Teacher
Holmes, Helene
5th Grade Teacher
Mitchell, Bruce C.
Science Coordinator
ORLEANS
Hall, Nancy Marvin
Writer & Consultant
Masterson, Robert Patrick
6th Grade Math Teacher
OSTERVILLE
Hyde, Robert Livingston
Humanities Instructor
West, Michael Edwin
Phys Tchr & Outdoor Pgm Coord
OTIS
Skrocki, Jody E.
5th Grade Teacher
OXFORD
Allaire, Britta Elisabet (Broman)
Sixth Grade Teacher
Boulay, Barbara J. LeBlanc
5th Grade Teacher
Cooney, James Henry
5th Grade Teacher
Theros, Joan
Second Grade Teacher
PALMER
Dougal, John A.
English Teacher
Lapointe, Gary Joseph
Heating, AC & Refrig Tchr
Mac Donnell, Brendan Jude
Assistant Principal
Roy, Alicia M.
English Department Chair
PEABODY
Baberadt, Stephen Jay, Jr.
High School Music Director
Colozzi, Diane M.
Foreign Language Dept Head
Costa, Donna Marie
Electronics Tchr & Dept Head
Farley, John E.
11th & 12th Grd Soc Stud Tchr
Forsey, Barbara Finegan
Third Grade Teacher
Galluzzo, Carolyn Marcotte
English Dept Chair & Teacher
Gibbons, Eileen Ann
Math Teacher
Kokoras, Victoria
Ret Elementary School Teacher
Kuzara, Linda Marie
Math & Computer Teacher
Lampropoulos, Peter J.
US & World History Teacher
Metropolis, Andrew Murray
Social Studies Teacher
Osterfield, Barbara Connick
Biology Teacher
Rollins, Eileen Catherine (Nally)
English Teacher
Rollins, Philip Clark
Industrial Technology Teacher
Ryan, Marguerite Mastrianni
Third Grade Teacher
Shafner, Betsy Walker
Math Teacher
Skerry, Helene Hickey
Principal
Sutera, Stephen Anthony, Sr.
English Teacher
Terlizzi, James Vincent, Jr.
Science Department Head
PEMBROKE
Anti, Peter N.
Level Six Teacher
Arsenault, Joseph Ernest
Sixth Grade Teacher
Moreland, David S.
Social Studies Teacher
PEPPERELL
Donnelly, Helen-thomas Ritchie
8th Grade Social Studies Tchr
Morin, Holly Jean
Director & Teacher
Smith, David Albert
Retired Teacher
PETERSHAM
Buron, Robert W.
Sixth Grade Teacher

Kirousis, Linda
Second Grade Teacher
PITTSFIELD
Avalle, Linda Rapkowicz
School Psychologist
Bell, Barbara T.
US History AP & Honors Tchr
Canfield Border, Karen
Anthropology & His Professor
Canning, Kathleen A.
Latin Teacher
Carey, Thomas P.
Professor of Allied Health
Chilla, Benigna
Professor of Art
Everest Wojtkowski, Anne
Professor of Engineering
Frazier, William J.
Guidance Counselor
Haff, Julie M.
Director of Public Relations
Hammann, Ralph R.
Drama & Film Instr
Healy, Daniel Joseph
Math Instructor
Ketcham, Sandra Roberts
Assistant Professor
Lauzon, Lorraine Marie
Art Teacher
Mancivalano, Joseph Charles
Soc Studies Tchr & Dept Chprsn
Marinaro, Vincent Paul
5th Grade Sci Specialty Tchr
McWhorter, Jane Brill
Coordinator of College Graphic
Mulholland, William Daniel
Professor of Business
Murphy, Kathleen Ann
Mathematics Dept Chairman
Reynolds, Fayette A.
Adj Instr in Human Anatomy
Weeks, Joshua N.
9th Grd Human Dev & PE Teacher
PLAINVILLE
Mazzeo, Cheryl Ann
Second Grade Teacher
Rush, Lionel G.
International Sales Director
PLYMOUTH
Bradley, Judith S.
Seventh Grade Science Teacher
Collins, Jake Henry
Housemaster
Collins, Paula Govoni
1st Grade Teacher
Draghetti, Janet A.
English Teacher
Fancy, Brenda Lee
Housemaster
Kahrl, Benjamin Richards
Social Studies Teacher
Lindberg, Charles Aaron
Science & Math Teacher
Martin, Karen A.
English Teacher
Miller, Debra Ann (Bunker)
Moderate Special Needs Teacher
Preskenis, Anne M.
English Teacher
Sholtanis, Catherine Keefe
First Grade Teacher
Simpson, Amy Taylor
6th Grade Teacher
Wolf, Ann Elizabeth
Chemistry Teacher
QUINCY
Ambraziejus, Rimas Marius
9th-12th Grade History Teacher
Cantelli, Stephen J.
5th Grade Teacher
Carnabuci, Catherine Solomita
Music Department Head
Clarke, Madeline Fleming
6th Grd English & Reading Tchr
Clover, Susan E.
Instr of Practical Nurse Pgm
Couture, Dawn Titus
Govt & Criminal Justice Instr
Galante, Maryanne O'Connell
Jr HS Mathematics Teacher
Glaser, Susan Aborn
Vocal Music Director
Gralton, Mary (Regan)
Mathematics Teacher
Hanna, Mary King
Mathematics Teacher
Koelsch, Ralph Gerald
Math Teacher
Manoli, Cheryl Ellen
HS Mathematics Teacher
Miceli, Leonard
Western Heritage Teacher
Milluzzo, Kathleen A. O'Leary
Assistant Director
Mitchell, Corinne F.
English Teacher
Mulready, Sean Michael
English Teacher
Palmer, Gale L.
Biology Teacher
Pegg, Ann M.
5th Grade Math & Science Tchr
Praetsch, Pamela M.
Librarian & College Counselor
Quintiliani, Gerald Carmine
Business & Computer Teacher
Sheehan, Janet Frances
Office Technology & Bus Tchr
Smales, Sandra L.
Coordinator of Paralegal Prgm

Taylor, Leslie M.
English Teacher
Walsh, Milton James
Aerospace Science Instructor
Welch, Barbara
English Professor
White, Paul F.
Criminal Justice Director
Whitehouse, Raymond Charles
Biology Teacher
Wilson, Mary Vaughn
Math, Science & Religion Tchr
RANDOLPH
Edwards, Thomas Broderick
Computer Technology Teacher
Klusas-King, Paula A.
Spanish Teacher
Lane, Ellen R.
First Grade Teacher
O'Brien, William Henry
Physics & Mathematics Teacher
Todd, Edward H.
HS Chemistry Teacher
Tuite, John J.
Math Teacher
Vellante, Anthony C.
English Teacher
Ward, Patricia M.
English & Humanities Teacher
RAYNHAM
Oliveri, Joseph
Social Studies Teacher
Voller, Kathleen Grignon
Classroom Teacher
READING
Andruchow, Elaine
Third Grade Teacher
Bowen, Warren John
Retired Social Studies Teacher
Burne, Janet (Sharpe)
English Teacher
Gramling, David Karl
Social Studies Dept Chm & Tchr
Hichborn, Peter Cooper
Middle School Eng Dept Chair
Maradei, William F.
Physical Sci & Algebra Teacher
Marnik, Elia D.
Asst Prin & Rdng Specialist
Segal, Ina M.
3rd Grade Teacher
Stone, Roger F.
Foreign Languages Dept Chm
REHOBOTH
D'Agostino, Anne Donnelly Rogers
Second Grade Teacher
Egan, Jack
Math Teacher
Sullivan, Janice C.
Sixth Grade Teacher
Vickery, Sherran Hower
Second Grade Teacher
REVERE
Cella, Michael Andrew
Physical Education & Hlth Tchr
Collar, Corinne Melinda (Capano)
First Grade Teacher
Coscia, Wayne Anthony
Chemistry Teacher
Feldberg, Philip L.
6th Grade Teacher
Fleury, Marguerite DeSimone
First Grade Teacher
Gaudet, Mary I.
Sixth Grade Teacher
Haney, Carol Anne
Mathematics Teacher
Kamlot, Frances Lopilato
Fifth Grade Teacher
Lomanno, Domenic
English Teacher & Soccer Coach
Pedi, Mary Cataldo
Language Arts Teacher
Randazzo, Frances Amanda (Marcotte)
Seventh & Eighth Grade Teacher
Testa, Ronald M.
Fifth Grade Teacher
ROCHESTER
Despres, Gina Louise
English Teacher
Francis, Robert C.
House & Mill Carpentry Instr
Hesketh, Thomas
Science Teacher
Riley, Paula Gamache
Cmptr Information Tech Instr
ROCKLAND
De Mello, Mary Ann
HS Sci Tchr & MS Curr Coord
Fredericks, Richard James
High School Mathematics Tchr
Isaac, Patricia
Art Teacher
Johnson, Kenneth R.
Biology Teacher
Looney, Kathleen Mc Carthy
English Teacher
Rossetti-Bailey, Donna L.
Art Teacher
Washburn, William Henry
Mathematics Teacher
Woodward, Peter Michael
English Teacher & Coach
ROSLINDALE
Harrington, Majorie Henderson
French & Spanish Teacher
Skoler, Naomi Nason
Reading Teacher

ROXBURY
Eason, Norma Bervinda
Special Education Teacher
Jackson, Neelia Thompson
7th Grade Mathematics Teacher
RUTLAND
Jordan, Janet E.
Fourth Grade Teacher
SALEM
Cacace, Irina R.
Frgn Lang Dept Head & Teacher
Davis, Marie Kielbasa
4th Grade Teacher
Donofrio, Dolores De Simone
French & Spanish Teacher
Doron, Barbara Kingsley
6th Grade Teacher
Emmith, William H.
Math & Science Teacher
Flibbert, Joseph Thomas
English Professor
Grant, Robert Maynard
Retired Principal
Kehoe, Deborah L.
Special Education Head Teacher
Labrecque, Marguerite
7th Grade Teacher
Leonard, Frank D.
Hawthorne Program Coord & Tchr
Seeley, James Leo
Honors English Teacher
Thibeault, Robert H.
English Teacher
SANDWICH
Driscoll, David E., Jr.
Math, Sci & Soc Stud Tchr
Laughton, Virginia Harrison
8th Grd Mathematics Teacher
SAUGUS
Ahern, Ronald Joseph
Social Studies Teacher
Bontempo, Michael Thomas
Technology Education Tchr
Bryan, Barney Frederick
Math Teacher, Work Study Coord
Masucci, Judith Dorothy
Guidance & Tech Facilitator
Sacco, Robert Anthony
Elementary Art Specialist
Waxman, Laurie Golan
Mathematics Teacher
SCITUATE
Berman, Christine Morin
English & Social Studies Tchr
Deakin, Patricia Smith
6th Grade Language Arts Tchr
Nord, Peter Dalby
English Teacher
Shacochis, Norman F.
History & Soc Sci Dept Chm
SEEKONK
Babiec, Edwina M. (Gugel)
4th Grade Teacher
Morrill, Ann Cassidy
First Grade Teacher
SHARON
Berkowitz, Stuart M.
Social Studies Teacher
Bruns, Eric W.
Physics Teacher
Conely, John L.
English Teacher
Duff, Paul S.
History Teacher
Gattone, Lynn
English Teacher
Howie, Alan C.
PE Teacher & Coach
Kaiser, James F.
Science Teacher
Kay, Linda L.
English Teacher
Lampert, Sheryl Levine
High School Math Teacher
Norton, Emily Fine
Science Teacher
Picheny, Janet L.
English Teacher
Turner, Kathleen Mae
French Teacher
SHEFFIELD
Merrill, Norman W.
English & Latin Teacher
Peron, John C.
World Langs Curr Chair
SHELBURNE FLS
Newell, Judith (Sweet)
7th Grade Mathematics Teacher
Ross, Robert Jon
Social Studies Teacher
SHREWSBURY
Black, Lisa Dorner
Spanish Teacher
Kavanagh, Justine
8th Grade English Teacher
Lahey, Michael Edward
English Teacher
Mead, G. Michael
Mathematics Teacher
Riley, Neal Anthony
Fourth Grade Teacher
Vilandre, David A.
English Teacher & Dept Chm
SOMERSET
Auclair, Fernand C., Jr.
Social Studies, Lang Arts Tchr
Brezinski, Richard Anthony
Psychology Teacher
Cabral, Catherine Elizabeth (Mello)
Mathematics Teacher

SOMERSET (cont)
Costa, Roxanne Ferreira
Social Studies Teacher
Crouch, Robert William
HS History Teacher
Goulart, Amy E.
Art Instructor
Lanneville, Madeleine Lavoie
Fourth Grade Teacher
Mc Manus, Paul M.
Curriculum Specialist
Michalewich, Richard Paul, Sr.
7th Grade Math Teacher
Peachy, Irene Pappianou
Reading Teacher
Peachy, Nicholas
English & History Teacher
Pimeault, Robert Walter
Business Teacher
Relle, Laura Jean (Estrella)
Alternative Education Teacher
Salmon, Marcia (Zapasnik)
Health Educator
Silvia, Edward J.
Fifth Grade Teacher
Toomey-Carroll, Maureen A.
Science Teacher
SOMERVILLE
Cardillo, Antonio
High School ESL Teacher
Hyde, Anthony John
Band Master & Dir of Bands
Lyver, Julie Cecilia
Eighth Grade Teacher
Rudolph, Dorothy Elia
Eighth Grade Teacher
Strauss, Sarah Ann
Former Social Studies Teacher
Watson, Andrew Compton
Former English Teacher
SOUTH BOSTON
Davis, Thelma Duncan
English Teacher
Lydon, Frances T. Macchia
Biology & Chemistry Teacher
Odom, Patricia A.
7th Grade Teacher
Thompson, Margaret
Physics & Chemistry Teacher
SOUTH DARTMOUTH
Pierce, Susan Frates
5th Grade Teacher
SOUTH DEERFIE
Gamlin, Patricia A. (Murley)
First Grade Teacher
SOUTH DEERFIELD
Furtek, Barbara Ann
English Teacher
Heston, Frank Craig
Social Studies Teacher
Smith, Robert Francis
English Teacher
Taylor, Paul M.
Soc Stud, Jrnlsm & Eng Tchr
SOUTH DENNIS
Keith, Thomas A.
Eighth Grade Science Teacher
Melnick, Andrew Dimitry
6th Grade Teacher
SOUTH EASTON
Costa, Mary Ann T.
High School English Teacher
Dawe, Joseph Randall, III
Social Studies Teacher
Deady, Linda Augusto
Mathematics Teacher
Degan, David Michael
Baking & Pastry Arts Teacher
Edson, Lynda Kaake
English Instr & Curr Developer
SOUTH HADLEY
Ramsey, Patricia Gale
Education & Psychology Prof
SOUTH HAMILTON
Butler, Catherine Mary
Second Grade Teacher
Daniels, Harry A.
Mathematics Department Chair
Kotch, John Paul
Science Teacher
SOUTH LANCASTER
Francis, Joan Annette
Professor of History
Ghosn, C. Josef
Business Professor
Laing, Stephen Brian
Vice Principal & History Tchr
SOUTH WEYMOUTH
Crosby, Linda Estes
Special Education Teacher
Cummins, Alexis Kechris
9th Grade Social Studies Tchr
Tully, Jeanne A.
English & Literature Teacher
SOUTH YARMOUTH
Peace, William E.
Biology Teacher
SOUTHBOROUGH
Brewitt, LeeAnn Adele
Second Grade Teacher
Martin, Julie A.
Biology Teacher
SOUTHBRIDGE
Jowett, Linda Langevin
Geography Teacher
Julian, Ralph David
French Teacher & Dept Head
Kruczek, Thomas Paul
Instrumental Music Teacher

Lehner, Raymond Albert, Jr.
Science, Math & Physics Tchr
Loconto, Teresa Carmen
English & Law Teacher
Marona, Rebecca
Sixth Grade Reading Teacher
Olson, Donna Marie
Arts Educator
Pedisich, Dina
Spanish Teacher
SOUTHWICK
Arduini, Kathleen Moore
5th Grade Teacher
Dieni, Dominick Joseph
American Government Teacher
Fontaine, Carolyn Eddy
Second Grade Teacher
Fouche, Sharon Leahy
Language Arts Teacher
Jacobs, Paula
Social Studies Teacher
SPENCER
Benjamin, Geraldine L.
Home Economics Teacher
Bouchard, Eugene U.
Bio Genetics Microbiology Tchr
Crosbie, William F.
Math, Science Tchr & Dept Head
Flynn, Kathy L.
Mathematics Teacher
Garber, George Andrew, Jr.
Director of Bands
Higgins, Jane Edgington
Art Teacher
Jyringi, Craig Aarne
Human Anatomy, Physiology Tchr
Lavoie, Paul A.
Psychology Teacher
Lehner, Raymond Albert, Sr.
Chemistry & Biology Teacher
Nelson, Mary Campbell
Social Studies Teacher
SPRINGFIELD
Belhumeur, Catherine Harkins
English Teacher
Bellucci, Meg
Accounting & Finance Professor
Bennett, Mary Morrison
Professor of Biology
Bennett, Richard P.
Social Studies Teacher
Bowler, Sheila Mary (Harrington)
Health & Human Services Prof
Brock, Kevin L.
Mathematics Teacher
Brouillard, Diane Trybulski
First Grade Teacher
Bugbee, E. John
Chemistry Professor
Carey, Walter Henry, III
Anatomy & Physiology Professor
Carithers, James Franklin
Mathematics Teacher
Chartier, Karen Motta
Fifth Grade Teacher
Cleland, Thomas Edward, Jr.
Aerospace Sci Dept Chairman
Costa, Carol A.
School Psychologist
Cremonini, Michael P.
English & Theater Arts Teacher
Cressoti-Bugbee, Elsa
Chem Prof & Dept Chairman
Cressotti, Deanna Ray
French Teacher
De Carvalho, Maria-Filomena Fidalgo
Spanish Teacher
Dinnie, Craig D.
English Teacher
DiVenuto, Michael Joseph
Italian Teacher
Dunn, Gail Pederzoli
Professor of English
Dupont, Carole H.
Professor of Biology
Felix-Fournier, Carmen
Spanish Teacher
Flynn, Kathleen T.
Prof & Surgical Tech Dept Chm
Ford, Terry Michael
High School History Teacher
Gagne, Kathleen Dunne
Humanities Communications Tchr
Gintowt, Cecilia S.
Office Systems Teacher
Goonan, Mary Fatima
Math & Religion Teacher
Gouthro, Barbara Norton
Vocal & Drama Teacher
Gross, Barbara Mary
Eighth Grade Teacher
Hale, Stephen Michael
Campus Ministry Director
Hallen, Bettie S.
Writing & English Teacher
Harrington, Linda Shea
Professor of English
Hood, Barbara Landers
Kindergarten Teacher
Jones, Thomas Marsden
Retired Teacher
Kawa, John Stanley
Fifth Grade Teacher
Kirsch, John
Associate Director
Kjergaard, Sonia Prado
Bilingual Social Studies Tchr
Krupa, Rita Christine
Religion Teacher

Labonte, Jacqueline Anne
Fifth Grade Teacher
Leslie, George Jerome
Professor of Biology
Lukas, Cheryl A.
Graphic Arts Technology Prof
Luxton, Richard Neil
Assoc Prof of Human Studies
Mackie, Diane DeRosier
English & American Stud Tchr
Magalhaes, Suzana Joao
Medical Radiography Professor
Mariani, Terri
Nursing Professor
Martin, Regina Brady
Junior High Science Teacher
Masciadrelli, Gary John
Mechanical Engrng Tech Prof
Mastronardi, Elaine Marie
Art Teacher
Mayfield, Walter Patton
Professor of English
Mc Carthy, Kevin Michael
Social Studies Dept Chprsn
McClure, Patricia Crowley
Prof of Acctng Fin & Statistic
Mc Donald, James Anthony
Professor of Mathmatics
Mc Kinnon, Margaret Connor
English Teacher
Miller, Carol Dee
Third Grade Teacher
Miller, Robert E.
Fr & Computer Lab Title I Tchr
Mitchell, Jimmie F.
Teacher
Moran, Anna (Ladue)
Social Studies Teacher
O'Connor, Matthew J.
Junior Religion Teacher
O'Donnell, Marjorie Maziarz
Professor of Office Admin Dept
Olio, David Michael, Jr.
English Teacher
Plunkett, Paul H.
US His & American Govt Tchr
Poirot, Anne Cichy
Chemistry Professor
Rappoport, Nancy Dicke
Professor
Robitaille, Jane Kinlock
Biology Teacher
Rosario, Oscar
Spanish Teacher
Rossi, Rose E.
7th Grade Math Teacher
Saex, Lawrence K.
Algebra & Pre-Algebra Teacher
Schumann, Nancy Fatzinger
Art Dept Chair & Teacher
Sears, Josephine Ryan
Professor of Nursing
Slozak, Linda Skidmore
US History Teacher
Smola, Daniel John
Environmental Technology Prof
South, Ted Johnson
Assistant Professor of History
Sullivan, Carol P.
Psychology & History Teacher
Taft, Raymond Francis
High School Science Teacher
Tenerowicz, Elaine Frydryk
11th Grd Social Studies Tchr
Thomas, Jimmie Elaine
Associate Prof of English
Touchette, Martin John
History Teacher
Tuttle, Holly Christina
High School Art Teacher
Tuttle, Sally Gagnier
Retired Teacher
Tyminski, Claire Nixon
Clinical Instructor
Urbanowski, Martha Ann Garabedian
Spanish Professor
Veronesi, Mara M.
Religions Education Teacher
Verville, Richard F.
Professor of Marketing
Wcislo, Susan T.
Music Teacher
Whitney, Matthew Charles
Business & Mathematics Teacher
Wilk, Adeline Jones
Adjunct Professor of Math Dept
Williams, Donald Clyde
Government Professor
Winsper, W. David
Prof of Eng & Dept Chprsn
Wozniuk, Vladmir
Assoc Professor of Government
Yawin, Robert Arthur
Math Professor
Zagarins, Juris
Professor & Dept Chairman
STERLING
Beliveau, Robert
Second Grade Teacher
STOCKBRIDGE
Leisk, Eloise Carlson
Fifth Grade Teacher
STONEHAM
Aastrup, Rondi Suzanne
English & Journalism Teacher
Bent, Sandra Diane
Science Department Head
Burke, Margaret Connarton
Fourth Grade Teacher

Hampton, Lisa Marie
English Teacher
Jarmusik, Therese Riley
Principal
O'Brien, Linda Jean Velardocchia
Kindergarten Teacher
STOUGHTON
Cabral, Edward M.
Mathematics Teacher
Catalano, Roseleen Ward
2nd Grade Teacher
Clark, James A.
English Teacher
Clough, Russell Dean
Science Teacher
Erickson, Ann Marie
6th Grade Teacher
Fontecchio, Thomas A.
Gymnastics Teacher & Coach
Gasior, Florence Therese
Mathematics Teacher
Gay, Kenneth Paul
6th Grade Teacher
Griffin, John L.
Administrative Principal
Iacobacci, Philip Joseph
Mathematics Teacher
Keppel, John Charles
Social Studies Teacher
Krol, Janet Charubin
Mathematics Teacher
La France, Maureen Murphy
Fifth Grade Teacher
Weiner, Ruth Shatz
English Teacher
STOW
Mc Carthy, Julie
Fifth Grade Teacher
STURBRIDGE
Baron, John David
6th Grade Sci & Soc Stud Tchr
SUDBURY
Conti, Daniel R.
English Teacher
Hilton, Marjorie Sylvia
Kindergarten Teacher
Mahoney, Mary Hawes
Teacher & Literature Comm Chm
McCarthy, Carmen Carrasquillo
Spanish Teacher
Wong, Bella T.
Science Teacher
SUTTON
Lamontagne, Paul Leo
Latin Teacher
SWANSEA
Burke, John Anthony, III
English Teacher
Cote, Paul D.
Social Studies Teacher
Da Rosa, Luis Gonzaga
Span Tchr & Dept Head
Davis, Linda Witmer
Science Teacher
Eddy, Robert J.
Biology Teacher
Hood, R. Elizabeth Paquin
8th Grade Science Teacher
McCann, Brian John
English & Journalism Teacher
Rioux, Margaret Anne
Math, Science & Reading Tchr
Shaker, Charles Nasib
K-12th Grade Computer Director
Whittemore, Maureen Austin
Fifth Grade Teacher
TAUNTON
Allenchey, Joan M.
Biology Teacher
Bourque, Mary H. (Carreiro)
Kindergarten & Preschl Teacher
Burns, Mary Catherine
Math, Physics Tchr, Dept Chair
Hull, Leonard Emerson, Jr.
Social Studies Teacher
Purcell, Roberta Kirk
Teacher of the Special Needs
Roth, Barbara Ann (Alfonso)
Spanish & French Teacher
Tripp, Lynda Hendricks
English Dept Chairman & Tchr
TEMPLETON
Kazinskas, Victoria Hunter
Kindergarten Teacher
TEWKSBURY
Berube, Judith Kane
Applied Arts Teacher
Gropman, Richard
Anatomy Teacher
LeProhon, Joseph Arthur
Science Teacher
Levine, Steven Barry
Physical Education Instructor
Sutliff, Nadine B.
American History Teacher
TOPSFIELD
Daly, Mary Wellington
German Teacher
Pierce, Donald A.
Spanish Teacher
Rasner, Elena
French & Russian Teacher
TOWNSEND
Blunt, Bess
Eighth Grade English Teacher
Champigny, David Paul
English Teacher
Franciosi, Peter Michael
Chemistry Teacher

Horgan, Judith Marcia (Harris)
First Grade Teacher
Manetta, Louis
High School Music Teacher
Mastandrea, Diane Marie
Spanish & Latin Teacher
Mountain, Carleton John
US History & Government Tchr
O'Brien, Maura Kennedy
HS Social Studies Teacher
O'Malley, Patrick Edward
Math Teacher & Computer Coord
Richard, George Charles
Social Studies Teacher
Richard, Lee Twarog
High School English Teacher
Sweatman, Jon Scott
Biology & Ecology Teacher
Tornikoski, Kathleen Vera
English Teacher
TURNERS FALLS
Avery, Robert A.
Guidance Counselor
Dahowski, Nancy Carpenter
Family & Consumer Sci Teacher
TYNGSBORO
Beati, Mark Anthony
PE & Health Teacher
Bolling, Suzanne Schryver
Dean of Students
Buczek, Ann Marie Margaret
Mathematics Teacher
Chadwick, Joy Carpenter
Kindergarten Teacher
Coddaire, Ann Romilda
Music Teacher
Doulamis, Katherine
Mathematics Dept Chairperson
Dumoulin, Julann
Spanish Teacher
Keefe, Mary C.
Mathematics Teacher
Marti, Susan Kay
Jr HS Health Teacher
Mc Laughlin, Donna C. Lorden
US History & Psych Teacher
Mc Niff, Marie Paula
Literature Tchr, NHS Moderator
Nickerson, Lucy Elizabeth
Math Teacher
Puma, Frank Joseph
Biology Teacher
Ragwar, Joanne DiDonato
Guidance Counselor
Taylor, John William
Cosmetology Instructor
Vergados, James
Biology Teacher
Webber, Ruth
Fourth Grade Teacher
UPTON
Bracebridge, Edward Lee
Culinary Arts Instructor
UXBRIDGE
Lane, David Michael
Technology Education Teacher
WABAN
Panaggio, Janet Leone
2nd & 3rd Grade Teacher
WAKEFIELD
Blanchard, Daniel Frank
Social Studies Lead Teacher
Brodeur, Virginia Chambers
Lead Teacher of Science Dept
Caranfa, Janice Chase
Accounting Teacher
Chaplick, Mary Virginia Goodhue
English Teacher
Cronin, Patricia K.
Vice Principal
Davis, Claudia Mary (Frampton)
Sixth Grade Teacher
Deveney, Dorothy A. Giardino
Mathematics Teacher
Eckman, Sandra Nagle
Music Tchr & Choral Director
Gleason, Beverly Anderson
Sixth Grade Teacher
Mc Donough, Susan
English Teacher
WALPOLE
Brainard, Susan L.
Assistant Principal
Brown, Thomas James
Physics Teacher
Calf, Penelope Schneider
Latin Teacher
Colvin, Linda Benedict
Computer Education Coordinator
Lind, Eleanor Radzwill
Math Coordinator
Pearson, Lisa Mara
Mathematics Teacher
Quinn, Tammy Tower
Math Teacher
Stapleton, James Michael
Social Studies Teacher
Sullivan, Mary Beth
English Teacher & Jrnlsm Adv
Tompkins, William Lewis, Jr.
PE Teacher & Coach
Watters, Sally B.
7th Grd Social Studies Teacher
Weikel, William Eugene
Mathematics & Accounting Tchr
WALTHAM
Cox, John Warren
History Teacher
Ditri, Robert H.
Social Studies Teacher

IAM (cont)
ks, Donna Jean
Studies Teacher
ne, Sarah A.
School Counselor
n, Alan Joel
School Guidance Counselor
vs, Barbara Ward
h Teacher
n, Karen Piazza
gy Teacher

Peter James
Studies Dept Chairman
Christina Moulson
School English Teacher
ki, Mary Clare
ng & Religion Teacher
uk, Julianne E.
ce Teacher & Dept Chprsn
rth, Sharyn A.
rade Teacher
HAM
, Linda Constance
sh & Portuguese Teacher
n, Deborah Anastasia
sh Teacher
rtain, William Patrick
nglish Teacher
Mary Jane J.
n & Physical Ed Coord
lcides F.
School Guidance Counselor
Jonathan G.
d States History Teacher
EN
Clifford Wayne
n Grade Math Teacher
om, Peter Allan
trial Technology Teacher
s, Victoria A.
ematics Teacher
ICK
Barbara Johnson
& Second Grade Teacher
RTOWN
, Mariann
rade Teacher
Phyllis Skahan
sh Teacher
AND
er, Jay
ce Teacher
Shirley Gernhardt
Teacher
TER
John Lawrence
h Teacher
Blanche Nadeau
Grade Teacher
, Donaldine P.
sh Teacher
nd, Craigin Bartlett
sh Teacher
, Stanley John
l Studies Department Head
wski, Barbara J.
Teacher
wicz, John H.
ry Director
os, Donna Defusco
Grade Teacher
, Olga
her
arczyk, Denise M.
sh Teacher
Beatrice L. (Pion)
Dept Chairperson
ESLEY
on, John Wilson
sh Dept Head
Martha C.
sh Teacher
s, Linda Marie
essor of Law
y, Marisa Gori
ed English Teacher
ffe-Boogs, Colette D.
ical Education Teacher
ls, Linda Garber
uctor in Science
, Kathleen M.
nistry Tchr & Sci Dept Head
o, Ronald Seth
hematics Instructor
nan, Robert L.
ish Composition Professor
bert P.
nistry Professor
HAM
, Thomas A.
essor & Chair of History
on, Gary David
n of the Chapel
n, Marvin Russell
of Biblical & Thlgcl Stud
T BARNSTABLE
de, Charles Pires, Jr.
ness Law Professor
shian, Helen Wade
essor of Psychology
g, Minxie
hematics Instructor
Phyllis Anne
ech Communications Prof
zenski, Michael Felix
nposition & Lit Professor
e, Theodore
neering & Mathematics Prof

WEST BOYLSTON
Gustafson, David Bruce
English Dept Program Leader
WEST BROOKFIELD
Alexander, Barbara
Primary Resource Room Teacher
WEST DENNIS
Cooper, Phyllis Viall
Third Grade Teacher
WEST LYNN
Hegan, Michael K.
Sixth Grade Teacher
Vocke-Mc Govern, Ann
Fifth Grade Teacher
WEST NEWBURY
Clark, Norman Grant
Chemistry Teacher
Dakos, Minas James
Seventh Grade Soc Studies Tchr
Foss, Robin H.
Reading Specialist
Rostosky, Dorothy Anna
Middle School English Teacher
WEST NEWTON
Etre, Thomas Anthony
4th Grade Teacher
O'Connell, Daniel C.
Staff of Spiritual Dev
WEST ROXBURY
Bernard, David F.
Computer Graphics Teacher
Buckley, Brian Burke
Art Department Chair
Hurley, Joseph D.
English & Latin Teacher
Obel-Omia, Michael Charles
English Tchr & Dean of Stdnts
Papahagis, Sandra L.
Third Grade Teacher
Tegan, Robert Francis
Guidance Counselor
WEST SOMERVILLE
Aili, Robert Steven
Math Teacher
Damian, Patricia M. (Re)
Lang Arts Tchr & Dept Chair
Foss, Alexandra
Guidance Counselor
WEST SPRINGFIELD
Cosentini, Marianna Rettura
Italian & Spanish Teacher
Cote, Diane Newman
Fourth Grade Teacher
Gumlaw, Elayne (Kraverotis)
English Teacher
Herman, Donna Cook
Second Grade Teacher
Ryan, William Lawrence
English Teacher
Tolpa, Chris Ann
English Teacher
WESTBOROUGH
Burritt, Mary Ann
Elementary Guidance Counselor
Corbosiero, Susan (Bachofner)
Math & Business Dept Head
Fields, O. Eugene
Biology Teacher
Poole, Robert Alan
MS Guidance Counselor
Reinstein, Susan M.
6th Grade English Teacher
Sharpe, Carl M.
English Teacher
Spinney, Charlotte C.
Social Studies Teacher
Trahan, Emile Roger
English Teacher
Young, David Robin
Third Grade Teacher
WESTFIELD
Bartley, Eugene Anthony
Instrumental Music Director
Burnham, Robert J.
English Teacher
Clark, Lynn Laux
Physics Teacher
Hagan, Christine Genovese
English Teacher
Klorer, Alison Elizabeth
Autism Specialist
Krok, Thomas B.
Guidance Counselor
Lewis, Philip
Second Grade Teacher
Matthews, Patricia Donovan
8th Grd Language Arts Teacher
Palmer, Kathleen Ann
3rd Grade Teacher
Pelletier, Deborah Jean
Physical Education Teacher
Quinn, Anita Marie
Seventh Grade Teacher
Reed, Marcy J.
Mathematics & Computer Teacher
Salvidio, Nanci Mahoney
Assoc Dir of Acad Advising
Shepardson, Richard P.
Government Teacher
Snyder, Marion Tebo
Retired Fourth Grade Teacher
Wheeler, George Raymond
5th Grade Teacher
WESTFORD
Brady, Shelagh Ann
Language Arts Teacher
Parent, Michael J.
High School Special Needs Tchr

WESTMINSTER
Nussey, Michaelina (Quarella)
First Grade Teacher
WESTON
Maloney, Cheryl Ryan
History Teacher
Taylor, Lori Lyn
History Teacher
Williams, John Charles
History Teacher & Dept Chm
Wood, Robin Benensohn-Rosefsky
Theatre Department Head
WESTPORT
Camara, Pauline Francoeur
Business & Finance Acad Coord
Dybowski, Jane
Science Teacher
Holt, Peter A.
7th-8th Grade Science Teacher
O'Hara, James D.
Social Studies Teacher
Ouellette, Lynette (Landry)
French Teacher
Silvia, Gail Marie
HS Social Studies Teacher
WESTWOOD
Dillon, Brendan Edward
High School History Teacher
Madden, Kathleen J. (Raymond)
Retired Teacher
Mc Kinney, Heather Ruth
English & History Teacher
Staiti, Jo Ann Johnson
Chemistry & Biology Teacher
WEYMOUTH
Donovan, Thomas C.
Sixth Grade Teacher
Phillips, Margaret A.
Social Studies & Reading Tchr
Sansone, Ramona Jean
Vocational & Substitute Tchr
WHITINSVILLE
Johnson, Linda Elin
Middle School Math Teacher
Miller, Judith Ann
Sixth Grade Teacher
Muradian, Andrea Lynne
English Teacher
Van Tol, Jerry Leroy
English Teacher
Vriesema, John Kenneth
Bible Teacher & Guid Cnslr
WHITMAN
Anderson, Beth Stone
English Teacher
Daily, Cheryl A.
Spanish & French Teacher
Delaney, Matthew Michael, III
Instructor of Fine Arts
McCann, Linda H.
Business Education Curr Coord
Niemi, Peter Andrew
Rdng & Lang Arts Specialist
WILBRAHAM
Brewer, Mary Lou
History Teacher
Dugre, Nancy A. (Closson)
Mathematics Teacher
Heiney, Diane L.
English & Drama Teacher
Jeserski, Diane D.
Business Teacher
Kulig, Linda Cole
Reading Recovery Teacher
Sirois, Barbara J.
Mathematics Teacher
WILLIAMSTOWN
Dailey, Martha La Croix
History Teacher
Dodds, Richard Delano
English & AP English Teacher
Nickerson-Plock, Paula
5th Grade Teacher
WILMINGTON
Boudreau, Frances Kazalski
Business Education Teacher
Smith, Susan Beth
7th Grade Mathematics Teacher
WINCHENDON
Boccardy, Steven John
HS Civics Teacher
Dellasanta, Louis Richard
Assistant Principal
WINCHESTER
Cronan, Beverly M.
English Teacher
Smith, Laurence Martin
Physics Teacher
WINTHROP
Cyr, Paul Ronald
English Teacher
Mulligan, Joseph Paul
Music Director
Nimblett, James F.
Mathematics Teacher
Puopolo, Nicholas Ralph
Educational Consultant
WOBURN
Callahan, Sean Michael
Technology Teacher
Celi, Janet Lyn
Spanish Teacher
Cooper, Richard P.
English Teacher
DeStefano, Karen Marie
Fourth Grade Teacher
Elanjian, Dorothy Elizabeth
English Teacher
Grant, Joanne O'Neill
Third Grade Teacher

Lynch, Edward Richard, Jr.
7th Grade English Teacher
Maltacea, Joseph Paul
11th Grade Health Educator
McEachern, Joan E.
Second Grade Teacher
Murphy, Gayle Richardson
11th Grade English Teacher
O'Donnell, Patricia Lee
5th Grd Tchr & Building Asst
Suchecki, Wayne
Social Studies Teacher
WORCESTER
Albano, Leonard D.
Civil Engineering Professor
Alberghini, Helen
Religion & Social Studies Tchr
Andersen, Roy Stuart
Emeritus Professor of Physics
Barrows, Mary E. (Klemetti)
Physics & Math Professor
Bechan, Barbara Bucinskas
Rdng Specialist & Eng Instr
Bergassi, Pauline Elizabeth
English Teacher
Bush, Jodi M.
7th & 8th Grd Sci & Math Tchr
Chadwick, Christina Page
Teacher for the Deaf
Crocker, Elli Barbara
Assistant Professor
Daly, Daniel James
Hotel & Restaurant Mgmt Coord
Damian, Radu Alexandru
Visiting Assistant Professor
Dennison, Deborha Wiland
Fourth Grade Teacher
Derrell, Craig Anthony
High School Religion Teacher
Donohue-Berthiaume, Nancy
Director of Vocational Ed
Ennis, Kathleen Macridis
Humanities Teacher
Erickson, Karen L.
Professor of Chemistry
Fegreus-Reynolds, Mary Elizabeth
Instr of Anatomy & Physiology
Ferderer, J. Peter
Economics Professor
Ferrari, Inez Iolanda
Asst Prin & Science Teacher
Frederickson, Kathy Ann
English Professor
Freeberg, Priscilla Marie
Music Teacher
Gannon, Donald Francis
2nd Grade Teacher
Garczynski, M. Roberta, CSFN
Science Teacher
Gareau, Charlotte Ann
English Teacher
Giacomelli, Marion Wood
Social Studies Department Head
Glispin, Patricia J.
Athletic Administrator & Coach
Gravel, Leo Raymond
Mathematics Dept Chprsn
Greenaway, Frederick Thomas
Chem Prof & Dean of Grad Stud
Healey, Lisa Battista
High School Math Teacher
Heeder, Ruth Samson
World History & French Teacher
Johnson, Kallin A.
Director of Music
Karaska, Gerald James
Professor
Kirk, Kevin Edward
English Teacher & Dept Chair
LePain, Cheryl Turturro
Social Studies Depart Chair
Lucas, Paul
Assoc Prof of European History
Manzi, Susan Lillian
Kindergarten Teacher
Martello, Carolyn A.
English Teacher
Mc Dermott, James E.
Eng Tchr & Dept Head
Miller, Mark Carlton
Assistant Professor of Govt
Nolan, Thomas J.
Secondary English Teacher
O'Brien, Brian Andrew, Sr.
English & Computer Sci Teacher
O'Sullivan, Michael
English Teacher
Pakaluk, Michael
Associate Prof of Philosophy
Pappas, Thomas Francis
Assistant Principal
Patenaude, Dan Robert
College Placement Counselor
Pavlik, James William
Chemistry Professor
Polito, Marilyn
Assistant Principal
Rappaport, Jonathan Charles
Arts Curriculum Liaison
Rayner, Janice Lee
English Teacher
Reilly, Judith G.
Physical Science Professor
Rodrigues, Donna Ghize
Dir of Univ Park Campus Schl
Ross, Robert Jon Sanford
Department Chair of Sociology
Rubert-Lopez, Luz E.
Student Support Services Dir

Sabulis, Ann Hawkesworth
English Teacher
Simi, Richard Andrew
PE Tchr & Athletic Director
Smith, Ruth Lynette
Assoc Prof of Religion
Spedding, Richard David
6th Grade Teacher
Starr, Susan Dunn
Education Specialist
Sultan, Stanley
Professor of English
Thoms, Frank R.
Middle School History Teacher
Treese, William Sherratt
English Teacher & Dept Chm
Ulbrich, Mary (Steinbach)
English Tchr & His Dept Chair
Valerio, Lucilia M.C.
College Lecturer
Vaughan, Virginia Mason
Professor of English
Watson, Diana Michaels
Director of Theater
Wicklund, Bonnie-Lou
Adjunct Mathematics Professor
WRENTHAM
Fradkin, Amy Lynn
Chemistry Teacher
Sumner, David Mason
Design Technology Teacher

MICHIGAN

ADA
Bierling, Neal
Bible & History Teacher
ADDISON
Ellis, Bud
Bio, Chem Teacher & Dept Head
Stevick, Mary Beth
English Teacher
ADRIAN
Bleam, Sheri Reeves
Prof of Communication Dept
Carpenter, Wayne S.
Mathematics Teacher
Champion, Jeff L.
School to Work Coordinator
Crosley, Diane Gorman
Advanced Science Teacher
DeRemer, Cathleen A. Smith
Language Arts Teacher
Fox, Dennis Lee
Special Education Tchr & Coach
Goddard, James Edward
Physics Teacher
Hanke, Grace Gruenwald
Retired Teacher & Principal
Harvat, Patricia, OP
Formation Dir & Theology Tchr
Henningfeld, Kenneth G.
Mathematics Educator
Jaimes, Celeste A.
Business Teacher
Johns, Francis George
Substitute Teacher
Mattson, Teresa
High School English Teacher
Rawlins, Linda L.
Social Studies Teacher
Roberts, John M.
English & Speech Teacher
Schultz, John Edward
Principal & Teacher
Schwartz, Cecelia Marie
Fifth Grade Teacher
Twining, Lathan Elwood
High School Mathematics Tchr
Weigel, Richard Arthur
Music Teacher & Dept Chprsn
ALBA
Zimpfer, Judith Louise
Math, Eng Teacher & Prin
ALBION
Bradley, Naomi Daggett
Eighth Grade Physical Sci Tchr
Egnatuk, Mary Ann Stokes
Social Studies & Math Teacher
Patrick, Joyce Elaine (Karger)
Bus, Cmptr Tchr & Dept Chair
Valdes, Ruth
English & History Teacher
ALGONAC
Bade, Sandra Pearsall
English Teacher
Osadchuk, Karen Elizabeth
Fourth Grade Teacher
Shafer, Daniel Raymond
Commnctns Instr & Track Coach
ALLEGAN
Buese, Susan Girodat
English, Speech & Drama Tchr
Dalm, Debra Hopper
Third Grade Teacher
Dalm, Harry Patrick, III
Principal
Ellis, Gary Lynn
Social Studies Teacher
Miller, Rhonda Shelley
Math Teacher
Sterner, Chesterine Jane Oszustowicz
Retired Elementary Teacher
ALLEN PARK
Abercrombie, James Eugene
Teacher & Soc Studies Dept Chm
Bochenek, Elizabeth Ann
4th Grade Teacher

ALLEN PARK (cont)
Compton, Mari
English Dept Chair & Teacher
Cookinham, Diane K.
Senior English Teacher
Griffiths, Patrick John
Bible Teacher
Kempf, Lorry A.
English Dept Chair
Kraatz, Mark Edward
Science & Physical Ed Teacher
Loyd, Robert Lawrence
History Teacher
Murtha, Pamela Berry
English Teacher
Stasiw, Maria M.
English Teacher & Dept Head
Towler, Martie J.
Fourth Grade Teacher
ALLENDALE
Hyatt-Druart, Constance
Vocal Music Teacher
ALMA
Eggenberger, Kristina Brendel
HS Social Studies Teacher
Engel, Gregory Scott
Science Teacher & Dept Chair
Goecker, Theresa Ann
Music & Movement Teacher
Kooiman, Mary Jane
HS English & Humanities Tchr
Massanari, Rhoda Nyce
3rd Grade Teacher
Mc Donald, Sharon Mae (Foster)
Business & English Teacher
Timmins, Deanna Lynn
8th Grade Teacher
ALMONT
Martin, Mary Anne
English Teacher
ALPENA
Davis, Sharyl (Mohr)
Sixth Grade Teacher
Frey, Norman Leo
High School Counselor
Henry, DeLysle L.
Instructor of Law & Government
Herman, Vicki Riebeling
Science Teacher
Hubbard, MaryAnn Begian
Instrumental Music Teacher
Jacques, Patrick Francis
English & Political Sci Tchr
Kaye, Elizabeth Ann
German & Social Stud Educator
Knowlton, Herbert C.
Chemistry Instructor
Krans, Gerald D.
6th Grade Teacher
Lewis, Carol S.
HS English Teacher
Meharg, Michael Charles
Fifth Grade Teacher
Meyer, David Joel
Teacher & Principal
Rasmussen, Jeanne Ann (Moffat)
Choral Music Educator
Rosebush, Charley M.
Math Instructor
Zinsli, Maurice Michael
German Teacher
ANCHORVILLE
Pollock, Mary Louise Zuccaro
Third Grade Teacher
ANN ARBOR
Armstrong, Steve
Physics & Math Teacher
Askew, Marcus Zonnechris
Math, Reading & Soc Stud Tchr
Batell, Mark Franklin
Mathematics Teacher
Behmer, Kevin Shea
Secondary Mathematics Teacher
Behrendt, Linda S.
Psychology Professor
Bellers, Clifford M.
Accounting Department Chair
Bricka, Mary Jane (Pierucki)
Lang Arts & Soc Studies Tchr
Carduner, Isabelle M.
Fr Tchr & Frgn Lang Dept Chm
Creal, Colleen R.
Social Studies Teacher
Crippen, Caroline Gibson
Retired Second Grade Teacher
Dahl, Claire Kitchin
Social Stud & AP US His Tchr
DePree, Alyce Benoist
11th Grd Principal & Eng Tchr
Dever, Nancy Kay
Lang Arts & Soc Stud Tchr
Dittmar, Larry Edward
Director of Orchestras
Ennes, Steven Mark
Sales & Marketing Instructor
Fuehrer, Paul Fredrick
Physical Education Teacher
Glass, Michael Kent
Intnl Acad Advisor & Instr
Greely, Sharon H.
4th Grade Teacher
Grigely, Joseph
Visiting Assoc Prof of Art
Haines, Jennifer Shikes
Third Grade Teacher
Heise, Anne
Instructor of Biology
Kahn, Steven Jeffrey
10th Grd Principal & Eng Tchr
Kunec, Jennifer Jelinek
History Teacher
Lewis, William Alfred
Mathematics Teacher
LoCiero, Lisa Maria
Spanish Teacher
Lockard, Jon Onye
Professor of Art & Humanities
Long, E. Daniel
Director of Orchestras
Mac Donald, Janet Hastings
Mathematics Instructor
MacMillan, Steven L.
Teacher
Mangan, D. David
Mathematics Teacher
Marschke, Paul O.
History Professor
Newcomb, W. Edward
Instructor
Nordmeyer, Richard Cleo
Principal
Robert, James Patrick
History Teacher
Roberts, Stephen Edward
Band Director
Scheider, Walter
Physics Teacher
Scott, Carolyn Ann (Speer)
Seventh Grd Life Science Tchr
Showalter, Martha A.
Professional Faculty
Starr, Jan Neff
5th Grade Teacher
Still, Susan O'Connor
4th-5th Grade Teacher
Strahilevitz, Michal
Assistant Professor
Thomas, David Philip
Geology Professor
Vogel, Terence A.
Latin & English Teacher
Warner, Elizabeth R.
Instr of English & Reading
Weber, Constance E.
4th-5th Grade Teacher
Westfield, Bryan J.
Biology Teacher & Coach
White, Karin Windisch
Vocal Music Teacher
Whiteford, Priscilla Sharon
Professor
Wilson, Patricia Ann
Fourth Grade Teacher
Winkler, Noel Ann
Media Specialist
Wise, Mary Lee
Chemistry Teacher
ARMADA
Merillat, Calvin Lee
Principal & Supervisor
Pollock, Christopher Paul
High School Mathematics Tchr
Wahl, Richard W.
Coll Prep, Math Instructor
ATHENS
Draheim, Craig B.
Geography & Mathematics Tchr
ATLANTA
Parsons, Samuel James
History Teacher
Ross, Earl A. C.
HS Math, Gov & Computer Tchr
ATTICA
O'Conell, Tamara Jean
Horticulture, Agriscience Tchr
AU GRES
Hahn, Craig L.
Sci, Drafting & Enging Instr
AUBURN
Broka, Thomas G.
Music Coord
Campbell, Carolyn Olsen
English Teacher
Clayman, Dorothy Plum
High School English Teacher
Jacqmain, A. Michael
Science Teacher
Janowicz, Thomas Edmund
HS US History Teacher
Marotzke, Kenneth Edward, Jr.
Instr of the Gifted & Talented
AUBURN HILLS
Chudnof, Mel
Mental Health & Soc Work Prof
Hall, Mary Anne
Third Grade Teacher
Johnson, Randy Thomas
Dean of Students
Lichty, Dawn Marie
Mathematics Teacher
Mason, Scott William
English Teacher
Nork, Laura M.
French Teacher
Pichel, F. Kipring
Accounting & Computer Teacher
AUGUSTA
Green, Joan Melges
Retired Science Teacher
BAD AXE
Byrne, Theresa Anne
Physical Education Instructor
Kasserman, Jean Anna
Title I First Grade Teacher
Lehrke, Lori Beth (Humm)
English & Language Arts Tchr
Rubringer, Edward Charles
Mathematics Teacher
BALDWIN
Jones, Faith Thomas
2nd-5th Grade Chapter 1 Tchr
Welford, Clyde Anthony
Psychology & Special Ed Tchr
BANGOR
Hoch, Dale Lynn
Freshman Science Teacher
Paquette, Deborah Lynn Fitz
HS Physical Education Teacher
BARAGA
Pepper, Linda Brown
Biology Teacher
BARRYTON
Drake, Doris Mary (Curtis)
Retired Second Grade Teacher
Waite, Holly J. (Hand)
Kindergarten Teacher
BATH
Anderson, Karen Kay (Tacia)
Media Specialist
Knoebel, Dixie A.
Retired Second Grade Teacher
Six, Donna E.
Retired Soc Stud Secondry Tchr
BATTLE CREEK
Austin, Donna (Poppen)
Assistant to Director
Baker, Corky
7th Grd General Sci Teacher
Britton, Linda Ann
Mathematics Instructor
Bush, Richard S.
History & Psychology Tchr
Cable, Cindy Truex
Language Arts Teacher
Churchill, Mary Faggan
Engish Instructor
Davis, Deland Mckay
Teacher
Davis, Sharon Holcomb
Mathematics Teacher
De Maso, Dora Dolores
Retired Elementary Teacher
Densmore, Ted Robert
CAD Instructor
Dunton, Thomas Lee
Fifth Grade Teacher
Evans, Jenny C.(Poot)
English Teacher
Frank, Stephen John
Teacher Specialist
Gifford, Brian Dale
Mathematics Teacher
Grosso, Kathy Mary
Specialist & Outreach Teacher
Guerra, Sheila Marie
Social Studies Teacher
Halbert, Stephanie Lynne
French Teacher
Hart, Dave
Science Teacher
Hermanson, Ralph Kent
Industrial Technology Instr
Horsman, Emily Lashmit
Hnrs Pgm Coord & Bus Instr
Howell, Catherine Stewart
Upper Elementary Teacher
Ingraham, Virginialee
3rd & 4th Grade Teacher
Ives, Peter Paul
Biology Teacher
Kent, Warren Franklyn, III
Publications Adv & Eng Teacher
Lawrence, Patricia L. Sebeson
English Teacher
Lee, Stephanie Marie
Teacher
Lewellen, James Matthew
Computer Science & Bus Teacher
Lindsey, Ruth Ann
Sixth Grade Teacher
Loftus, John W.
Adjunct Instr of Philosophy
Marks, Carrie Beth
Math Teacher
Matthews, Sheila Parker
Human Svcs Pgm Coord & Instr
Mc Gaghie, Thomas James
Political Science Instructor
Mc Nally, Barbara Ann Aldridge
5th Grade Teacher
Mikolajczyk, Patsy Ann
Third Grade Teacher
Minter, Denise E.
HS Choral & Piano Lab Tchr
Moran, Pamela Pedranzan
Kindergarten Teacher
Munther, Jan Bray
Art & English Teacher
Niemann, Frank Jeffrey
PE & Atheltic Director
Peters, Robert Charles
Director of Bands
Philo, Avril E. M.
Spanish Teacher
Rice, Tony Edward
Physics & Anatomy Teacher
Rizor, Kathy D.
Biology & Language Arts Tchr
Secrist, C. Robert R.
Math & Computer Sci Prof
Singleton, Mary Williams
First Grade Teacher
Sprague, William Howard
Fifth Grade Teacher
Sutton, Cynthia Weller
Spanish Teacher
Wendt, Martin J.
Adv Biology Instructor
Wilburn, Marva J. (Protho)
English Teacher
Wilson, William Ashley
Printing Instructor
Wortz, Marvin Dale
Math & Computer Professor
Zuk, Joseph Stanley
English Dept Chair
BAY CITY
Dewar, Therese Ann
English Teacher
Gabil, Diane Rapson
Primary Special Education Tchr
Hauser, Ronald Luther
Teacher & Music Coordinator
Heidtman, Mary A.
Fifth Grade Teacher
Hopp, Jerry
Principal & Teacher
Kellerman, Suzanne Elizabeth
Reading Specialist
Martin, Gregory Joseph
6th Grade Science Teacher
Packard, Richard E.
Science Teacher
Painter, Glen A., Jr.
Soc Studies, Quest & Art Tchr
Porchia, Dorothy Marie
Kindergarten Teacher
Schafer, Sandra Hayes
Chemistry Teacher
Scheiwe, Warren
Teacher & Minister of Music
Smith, John L.
Teacher, Counselor & Coach
Stamm, Mary Bertha
Teacher
Taylor, Carol Lee (Michael)
English Teacher
Trinklein, Rebecca Marie
Kindergarten Teacher
Yost, Judith Gregory
Fourth Grade Teacher
BAY PORT
Keena, Janet Patterson
4th Grade Instructor
BEAR LAKE
Matesich, Michael S.
HS Social Studies Teacher
BEAVERTON
Ewert, Jennie Robinson
Business Teacher
King, Dennis Gene
6th Grade Teacher
Lance, Jeffrey P.
Spanish Teacher
Locey, Bryan A.
Eng Teacher & Stu Asst Coord
Rodabaugh, Esther Keeley
English & German Teacher
BEDFORD
Goff, Kathrin Ann
Second Grade Teacher
BELDING
Miller, Kathy R.
English Teacher
Slater, Norrie Baker
Rdng Recovery & Title I Tchr
BELLEVILLE
Earl, Roberta R.
Teacher of Gifted & Talented
Gray, Kathleen Speir
Elementary Art Teacher
Larson, Angela Reaume
Art Teacher
Orr, Nancy E.
Bus Dept Chprsn & Co-op Coord
Smith, David Michael
Social Studies & Math Teacher
Smith, Paul K.
Sixth Grade Teacher
Somers, John R.
Mathematics Teacher
Villa, Samuel Scott
Physical Education Teacher
Williamson, Mary Louise
Employee Relations & Prsnl Mgr
Wolff, Delruss Rodney
Secondary Math & History Tchr
BELLEVUE
Everest, Jeaniemarie Skidmore
English Teacher
Hume, Michael J.
Athletic Director
Luneke, Martha Yahnka
Language Arts Teacher
Place, Ronald Lee
Government & PE Teacher
Willis, Betty R.
Sixth Grade Teacher
BENTON HARBOR
Anderson, Selene Seawood
Admissions Coord & Adj Faculty
Bruehlman, Lynne
Instr of History & Sociology
Claeys, Jill E.
Physical Education Instructor
Cox, Gerry Lee
Mathematics Professor
Mc Arthur, Marianne
Occptnl Therapy Asst Instr
Randolph, Lisa Shanda
Radiologic Technology Instr
Riley, Linet Hinds
English Teacher
Sharon, Janet C. (Depew)
Chemistry & Health Instructor
Stern, Edward Spiro
Psychology Instructor
Walker, Michael Lee
Mathematics & Computer Teacher
Wheeler, Timothy R.
Adjunct English Instructor
Whitfield, Alouch, II
Biological & Life Sci Instr
Wiggins, Shirley Jean
Speech Teacher
Wurz, Kevin P.
Theatre Instructor & Director
BENZONIA
Gehring, John Rowland
Biology Teacher
Rebone, Donna L.
HS Resource Room Teacher
BERKLEY
Blackwell, Megan Barker
HS Social Studies Tchr
Carey, Katie Schwarze
Fifth Grade Teacher
Jansen, Elizabeth Ann
English Teacher
Johnson, Calvin
Track & Football Coach
Sakalas, Marlene Virginia (Piet)
7th Grd Homeroom & Sci Tchr
Stephan, Marilyn Anderson
High School English Teacher
Suggs, Sherry Lynne (Locke)
English Teacher
BERRIEN SPRINGS
Boger, Dennis Neal
Science Teacher
Bolton, Susan Ayers
Fourth Grade Teacher
Bowser, Tamara VanderArk
High School Mathematics Tchr
Chadderdon, Bonnie Holmes
English Teacher
Denton, Paul H.
Associate Professor of Tchr Ed
Economou, Elly Helen
Prof of Biblical Langs & Rel
Gibson, Annetta Mae
Accounting Professor
Greig, Alexander Josef
Prof of Rel & Biblical Lang
Huttenstine, Gary D.
Science Teacher
Kilsby, Marcia Ann
Allied Health Dept Chair
Krantz, Nancy Batie
Fourth Grade Teacher
Ludeman, Robert R.
Professor Emeritus
Maier, Rudolf
Asst Prof of World Mission
Mc Kenzie, Nellie Douglas
Assistant Professor of Biology
Simmons, Timothy Scott
HS Social Studies Teacher
Thomas, Kenneth Edwin
Chairman of Mathematics
Wheeler, Cindy Davis
Special Education Teacher
White, Cleon Eugene
Mathematics & Chemistry Tchr
Young, John Wesley
Assoc Prof of Political Sci
BESSEMER
Partanen, James P.
Social Science & Business Tchr
Rowe, David Wesley
High School Science Teacher
Rowe, Tracy Halstead
Mathematics & German Teacher
Saari, Kim Huotari
Spanish Teacher
BIG BAY
Vargo, Laurie Henriksen
Speech, Lang & Hots Tchr
BIG RAPIDS
Clark, Steven Craig
Assoc Professor of Education
Crowe, Francis L.
Assoc Prof & Corrections Coord
Draysey, Carole Jean
English Teacher
Fogarty, Susan Laraine
Associate Professor of Nursing
Grannis, Sally Schaefer
English & Soc Studies Teacher
Hastings-Bishop, Susan Jane
Assoc Professor of Recreation
Hawkins, Richard T.
Assoc Dean, College of Bus
Horn, Gary C.
Comm Prof & Dir of Forensics
Keating, Michael Patrick
Optics Professor
Mattson, Renee Bernadette
HS Science Teacher
Mc Cullen, Matthew John
Math Teacher
Rye, Clayton B.
Television Production Prof
Schumann, Rachel A.
Associate Professor
BIRCH RUN
Barger, Barbara Zielinski
Science Teacher
Davis, Linda
Consumer Education Teacher
Franz, Kim
HS Counselor
Hadd, Curtis Jay
Global Stud, Govt & Ec Tchr
Laich, Mary A.
Fourth Grade Teacher

RUN (cont)
aals, Kathleen Sue
n Teacher
on, Janice Ethel
d Grade Teacher
NGHAM
athleen Toma
ade Teacher
, Ellen Mayfield
l Psychologist
Fred A.
ade Teacher & Asst Prin
Alice Ann
d Third Grade Teacher
Elizabeth Heckenhauer
h, Speech & Drama Tchr
FIELD
Peter E.
h Teacher
Mary Anne
ntary Teacher
MFIELD
Clinton H.
ade Mathematics Teacher
Ann C.
h Teacher
, Thomas W.
matics Teacher
ch, Christopher James
matics Teacher
ohn David
elor
eter James
istry Teacher
Catherine Corgan
eacher
er, Karen Hoffman
h Teacher
, Sandra Parker
sh Teacher & Dept Chair
c, Frank Joseph, Jr.
y Social Studies Teacher
rescott, Jay
ogy Teacher
Gregory Charles
Ath Dir & Physics Tchr
William B.
er & Coach
Emerly L.
entary Science Teacher
Lafayette
s Director
ndaro, John F.
ology Education Teacher
, Anne Murphy
h Grade Teacher
on, David Gordon
lum Dept Head & Chaplain
r, Sue Carol (Hahn)
ce Dept Head & Chem Tchr
Susan
istory & Math Teacher
MFIELD HILLS
, Marie Bell
ematics Professor
, Douglas Allan
l Studies Teacher
rd, Dave
cs Professor
MINGDALE
, Keith E.
School English Teacher

a, Frances Marilyn
ed Mathematics Teacher
E CITY
amer, Deborah Lynn
e Economics Teacher
n, Gale Paul
h Grade Teacher
KENRIDGE
, David J.
sh Department Chairperson
, Linda Ann (Robison)
l Music Teacher
HREN
David K.
rade Science Teacher
GEPORT
Clifford A.
nce Teacher
l, Larry Robert
th Grade Teacher
, Jacqueline Kay
sh Teacher
Cheri A.
th Grade Teacher
lace, June Siwula
l Teacher
r, Irene Sennowitz
nan Teacher
GMAN
Shirley Vonk
nd Grade Teacher
czyk, Daniel Joseph
Studies & Lang Arts Tchr
dt, Ruth Gerlach (Kunde)
Grade Teacher
r, Paul G.
4th Grade Teacher
HTON
nan, Sheila R.
d Grade Teacher
n, Gary James
Grade English Teacher
acken, Carol Kastner
red Elementary Teacher
t, Thomas L.
puter Teacher

Pethoud, Rick J.
Director of Bands
BRIMLEY
Harwood, Alice (Carpenter)
English & PE Teacher
Innerebner, James Robert
6th Grade Teacher
Johnson Cox, Susan
Discipline Rep, Ofc Tech Instr
La Course, John R.
Computer Dept Head & Instr
Noss, Deborah J.
4th Grd Language Arts Teacher
Olson, Penny Jean-Bolm
English Instructor
BRITTON
Musolf, Jon P.
English & Math Teacher
BRONSON
Dykman, Keith R.
Phys Ed & Health Teacher
Sybesma, Lana Mildred
Fifth Grade Teacher
BROOKLYN
Dickens, Michael Anthony
Science Teacher
Gulliver, Ted
Economics & Computer Teacher
Scheick, Robert LaVere
Biology Teacher
Schutter, Vernon Jacob
Fourth Grade Teacher
BROWN CITY
Carpenter, Judith Ann
Fourth Grade Teacher
Kreiner, Sheryl L.
History & Current Issues Tchr
Smith, Juanita M. (Welch)
Fourth Grade Teacher
Snyder, Robert C.
Junior HS Mathematics Teacher
Takacs, Sharron Lee
5th Grade Teacher
BUCHANAN
Bender, Steve
High School English Teacher
Marazita, Ernest Todd
High School Math Teacher
Mefford, Jacquelyn B.
Spanish Teacher & Dept Chprsn
BUCKLEY
Hornyak, James
Math Teacher
BURR OAK
Quertermus, Richard James
Science Teacher
BURTON
Armstrong, Allen Douglas
English Teacher & Principal
Ballge-Kimber, Pamela Jean
Fifth Grade Teacher
Bearden, Timothy James
English Teacher & Vlybl Coach
Carpenter, Daniel Jay
Science Dept Chair
Darby, Dayle Christine
High School English Teacher
DeMino, Betty Jeane
5th Grade Teacher
Hobolth, Michael Warren
Principal & Soc Studies Tchr
Hobolth, Ronald Craig
Economics & History Teacher
Hobolth, Traci Lee
Social Studies Teacher
Johnson, Michael Bruce
2nd Grade Teacher
Kilgore, Linda Mae (Mattson)
1st Grade Teacher
Rainear, Christopher David
Geometry & Algebra Teacher
Rusinek, Joan Marie (Hrinevich)
High School Science Teacher
BYRON
Warren, Sandra J. Schagane
Retired 5th Grade Teacher
BYRON CENTER
Merchant, Michael Lee
CAD & Technology Ed Teacher
Terpak, Dorothy Ann
3rd Grade Teacher
Wyn, Frances Ann
Fourth Grade Teacher
CADILLAC
Baker, Frances P.
2nd Grade Teacher
Bechtel, Marlene Kay
Math Teacher
Gussert, Renee Cousino
Sixth Grade Teacher
Hamilton, Robert Lee
Economics Professor
Mc Donald, Jeffrey
High School Guidance Counselor
McMahon, Karen S.
English Instructor
Meyers, Paula Jo
5th Grade Teacher
Monson, David Jonathon
6th & 7th Grd Health Ed Tchr
Neyer, Janet Anne
English Teacher
Palacios, MaryAnn Elian (Gagon)
Elementary School Principal
Pearce, David Michael
Medical Instruction Coord
Peterson, Eleanor M.
Retired Mathematics Instructor
Rooks, David L.
Technology Ed & Amer His Tchr

Sprague, Mary Beth
Fifth Grade Teacher
Van Alst, Kathleen J.
Mathematics Teacher
Van Dellen, Robert J.
Management & Marketing Prof
Whitley, Michelle Jordan
10th Grade Teacher
Whittum, Donna Lee
First Grade Teacher
CALEDONIA
Blain, Diane
Third Grade Teacher
Nykamp, Beth Ann
American Studies Teacher
Spencer, Stanley Wayne
HS AP Amer History Teacher
Wilson, Mike
High School Teacher
CALUMET
Bastian, Dennis M.
Drafting Teacher
Brumm, Phyllis Orthner
English & German Teacher
Cox-Adolphs, Janice Elaine
German & English Teacher
Ewert, Gary C.
Sixth Grade Teacher
Frantti, James Leonard
Physics & Computer Sci Teacher
Glinn, Daniel W.
Social Studies Teacher
Mellen, George Michael
Retired Teacher
Parsons, John G.
English Teacher
Pellegrini, Sherrie Lynn
4th Grade Teacher
CAMDEN
Lutz, Cynthia SuAnn (VanPelt)
7th-12th Grd Life Mgmt Tchr
Vallieu, Kenneth S.
Chemistry & Biology Teacher
CANTON
Belobraidich, Sharon Goul
1st & 2nd Grade Teacher
Brownlie, Barbara Jean
US & Western Civilization Tchr
Carroll, Mary Beth
English Teacher
Cizek, Carol Ann Bilbrey
Former K-12th Grd Art Teacher
Durow, Arthur c.
Biology & Ecology Teacher
Fox, Christel Johnson
Science Teacher
Gaines, Samuel Preston
Social Studies Chairman & Tchr
Goodrich, Bonnie
Kindergarten Teacher
Gorzen, Michael M.
Science Teacher
Howe, Laurie Houghton
Business Teacher
Huff, Deanna Marie (Green)
Spanish Teacher
Hussey, Maureen Beth
4th Grade Teacher
Hymes, Christopher William
Mathematics Teacher
Marshall, Barbara Lynn
Mathematics Teacher
McLean, Ann Margaret Schaaf
Math Dept Chair & Teacher
Monaster, Anthony S.
English & Reading Teacher
Paquette, Arlene Marie (Ward)
Social Studies Teacher
Plecha, Richard Stanley
4th Grade Teacher
Reeves, Paul Wayne
Principal
Schneider, Susan Ilene
English Teacher
Siedlik, Mark A.
Elec & Automtn Robotics Tchr
Van Westenburg, C. Elizabeth (Bennett)
High School Math Teacher
Williams, Stephen Scott
Philosophy Teacher
CAPAC
Cutler, Chris J.
French & Mathematics Teacher
Huss, Christopher Randall
Mathematics Teacher
CARLETON
Cunningham, Richard Lawrence, Jr.
HS Social Studies Instructor
Morrin, Carolyn Sara
Sixth Grade Teacher
Renton, Janette Kay
High School English Teacher
CARNEY
Safford, Alice Field
3rd Grade Teacher
CARO
Finkbeiner, Jan Glaspie
5th Grade Teacher
Jane, Constance Ruth
Chemistry & Physics Teacher
Pape, Helen C.
HS Biology & Science Teacher
Shay, Virginia Cogan
Third Grade Teacher
Thorp, Douglas Wayne
MS Math & English Teacher
Williams, Stephen K.
Social Studies Teacher

CARSON CITY
Deschamps, Donita J.
Life Skls Prntng & Drama Tchr
Richards, Patricia Fae (Flowers)
K-5th Grade Title I Teacher
Tasker, Bruce
Mathematics Teacher
CARSONVILLE
Fritz, William Russell
HS Art & Soc Stud Teacher
Humble, Brenda L.
First Grade Teacher
Nichol, Brenda Gough
Language Arts Teacher
Rowley, Robert M.
HS Social Studies Teacher
Ruebelman, Sonja Marlene (Matteson)
Special Education Teacher
CASEVILLE
Watts, Janet Dereadt
Principal
CASS CITY
Tuckey, Shirley Jean (Graham)
3rd Grade Teacher
CASSOPOLIS
Barr, Ada M.
English & Theater Teacher
Hari, Brooke Suzenne
Business Ed & Yearbook Advisor
Jamison, Lillie B.
Retired Teacher
Rogers, Cheryl Louise (Frost)
Sixth Grade Teacher
Zimmerman, David Wayne
Business Education Teacher
CEDAR LAKE
Carter, David Leroy
Chemistry & Anatomy Teacher
Peterson, Douglas William
Principal & Teacher
Reichert, Bruce Earl
History Teacher
CEDAR SPRINGS
Fox, Peggy Sue
Eighth Grade Science Teacher
Norkus, Tony
US History Teacher
Robuck, Robert Wayne
High School Band Director
Schumann, Mark Arny
4th-5th Grade Physical Ed Tchr
Vande Panne, David Edward
Economics & Government Teacher
CEDARVILLE
Postma, Ralph C.
HS Math Teacher
Schaedig, Randy E.
HS Science Teacher
CEMENT CITY
Dresselhouse, Penny Elizabeth
Fourth & Fifth Grade Teacher
Reimer, Kathie Eileen
6th Grade Teacher
CENTER LINE
Baron, Alice Stenger
Third Grade Teacher
Sommariva, Frank James
7th-8th Grd Lang Arts Tchr
Zaleski, Edward Lawrence, Jr.
Social Studies Teacher
CENTREVILLE
Carlisle, Maribeth Shirley
Mathematics Teacher
Hass, Larry Eugene
Accounting Professor
Smith, Sharon Lee
Business Professor
Swanwick, Norma J. Wellington
Am Govt & US History Teacher
CHAMPION
Ruspakka, Marvin Wayne
Third Grade Teacher
CHARLEVOIX
Glynn, James Richard
Physical Education Teacher
Henne, Betty Vermeesch
Library Media Specialist
Jinsky, James F.
Industrial Arts Teacher
Kanine, James Joseph
Seventh Grade English Teacher
Sharrow, Alice Lewalk
Retired Elementary Teacher
CHARLOTTE
Coe, Ann M.
Business Teacher
Cummings, Joy Lee (Barnett)
Fourth Grade Teacher
Duby-Smith, Jadine Suzanne (Gee)
Kindergarten Teacher
Johnson, Barbara Collinsworth
Speech & Drama Teacher
Mayes, John Dennis
Vocational Drafting Instructor
Moran, John Paul
Social Studies Teacher
Sullivan, Gary Thomas
Band Director
CHASSELL
Pyorala, Mildred M.
Retired Teacher
CHEBOYGAN
Hirschman, Betty H.
Retired Teacher
Veihl, Marsha Shields
Second Grade Teacher
CHELSEA
Andrews, Jonathan Burdette
English Teacher

Beard, William E., Jr.
Fourth Grade Teacher
Bower, Mary Lou Merriman
Retired Kindergarten Teacher
Carlson, Jill Maureen
Kindergarten Teacher
Caswell, Lisa Marie
Spanish Teacher
Kutschinski, Sandra Schock
High School Science Teacher
Mitchell, Lonnie H.
High School Math Teacher
Orlandi, Christopher Raphael
Mathematics Teacher
Ott, Marcy H.
Spcl Ed Consultant & Eng Tchr
Turok, Linda Carlton
Home Economics Teacher
Yelsik, Beverly Ann
Art, Speech & Drama Teacher
CHESANING
Bishop, Rebecca Joan
Spanish Teacher
Galm, Janet Kreager
Fr, Span & Eng Teacher
Maike, Lisa A.
US History & Geography Teacher
Miller, Christine A.
Pub Spkng, Media & Debate Tchr
Sheridan, James Robert
Science Teacher
Strait, Leonard LeRoy, Jr.
7th Grade Math & Health Tchr
Tithof, Judy Azelton
Fourth Grade Teacher
CLARE
Fultz, Roger T.
7th Grade Science Teacher
Johnson, Judith Marie (Freeland)
Business & Computer Teacher
Johnson, Robert Lee
Mathematics Teacher
Laskowsky, Lynn Fredrick
English & US History Instr
Marshall, Stevan Edward
Seventh Grd Soc Stud Teacher
CLARKSTON
Blanchard, Danielle R.
Jrnlsm, Music & Drama Teacher
Chapman, Clifford K.
Instrumental Music Teacher
Forbush, Stephanie Jeane (Forsten)
Cmptr, Typing & Bus Math Tchr
Hart, Victor E.
High School Counselor
Hartwell, Cynthia R.
History & English Teacher
Hine, Scott Aaron
Art, English & History Teacher
Howell, John Dee
Music & Bible Teacher
Lampkin, Barbara L.
Mathematics & Bible Teacher
Matheus, John Robert
English & Geography Teacher
O'Brien, Judy (Lee)
Retired Math Department Chair
Slayton, James Carroll
High School Science Teacher
Swartout, Richard Charles
High School English Teacher
Weil, Dalana Hunt
Teacher
Winters, Virginia Ann
Sixth Grade Teacher
CLAWSON
Bates, Joyce Morgan
Computer Instructor
Evans, Katy Angelo
First Grade Teacher
Henriksen, M. Sue
Retired Elementary Teacher
Oliver, Mary
English Teacher
Waddell, David Bruce
High School Math Teacher
Ward, Monica Terese
Government & English Teacher
Wentz, Alan William
7th & 8th Grade Math Teacher
CLAYTON
Bleecker, Helene Denise
Retired Orchestra Director
CLIMAX
Pierce, Ellen Irene (Pratley)
English Instructor
Robinson, Douglas Scott
Mathematics Teacher
Smith, Dale F.
Spanish & Social Studies Tchr
Wyant, Bradley Earl
4th Grade Teacher
CLINTON
Dunham, Ann Leary
English Teacher
Mc Gahey, Pamela A.
Professional Educator
Proctor, Linda Alexander
4th Grade Teacher
CLINTON TOWNSHIP
Anderlite, Anita L.
HS Mathematics Teacher
Azar, Marie Ann
English Teacher
Cardeccia, Ronald D.
6th-8th Grade Level Counselor
Crawford, Betty St John
English Teacher
Fluegge, David Norman
Science Teacher

CLINTON TOWNSHIP (cont)
Hite, Karen J.
Fifth Grade Teacher
Jacobson, Robert Paul
Chemistry Teacher
Kelley, William Richard
Math, Science & Reading Tchr
Miller, David M.
High School Mathematics Tchr
Miller, Elaine Rita
First Grade Teacher
Murphy, James P.
Work Stud Coord
Pitt, Celina Rolnitzky
High School English Teacher
Spanke, Timothy L.
HS Instructor & Coordinator
Sperrick, Susan Santilli
Sixth Grade Teacher
Wojcicki, Jacquelyn L.
English Teacher
CLIO
Carlson, Dennis Allen
Math & Industrial Ed Tchr
Hunjo, Jeri Ann
8th Grade English Teacher
Kerr, Eileen Wisniewski
4th Grade Teacher
Knapp, Diane Swart
First Grade Teacher
Logan, Arthur Paul
Chemistry Instructor
Nelson, Diane Kay
7th Grade English Teacher
Patton, Glenda Batey
Middle School Counselor
Refice, Kathy D.
French Teacher
Wilborn, Malcolm Mitchell, II
High School Art Teacher
Winberg, Richard Lawrence
Math Teacher
Wise, Alan William
5th Grade Teacher
COLDWATER
Ashdown, Marilyn Jill
Multi-Age Teacher
Burtch-Fetters, Mary M.
Retired 5th Grade Teacher
Carman, David Scott
Band Teacher
Crenshaw, Alice Fabian
Kindergarten Teacher
Dally, Mary Elizabeth Bodie
Elementary Teacher
Johnson, Douglas E.
Asst Principal
Kreiger, David
Fourth Grade Teacher
Mullally, Robert Charles
English Teacher
Nicely, Thomas William
MI History & 6th Grade Teacher
Olsen, Julie A.
German Teacher
Rodgers, William A.
US History Teacher
Smith, Susan Kelly
Third Grade Teacher
Spangler, Randy Earl
Math Teacher
Todd, Linda Diane Dunworth
Life Management Tchr & Chprsn
Wardwell, Waive Wilson
Retired Music Teacher
Yager, Nancy Thompson
Sixth Grade Science Teacher
Zuppann, Mechelle Owen
English Teacher & Dept Chair
COLEMAN
Bower, Mary Delores
First Grade Teacher
Jones, Carol Kay
Eighth Grade English Teacher
Ruckman, John Paul
Chem, Physics & Earth Sci Tchr
Sorensen, Marianne Cowell
English & Speech Teacher
COLOMA
Kellogg, Freeborn Anthony
English Teacher & Dept Chair
Prosper, Jolene Brimage
Dir of Parent-Tchr Involvement
Sieg, Alvin Paul
K-2nd Grade Teacher
Willmeng, Lori Wingert
High School Math Teacher
Zechiel, Elia Recuero
Spanish Teacher
COLON
Hendrickson, Dennis R.
Girls Basketball Coach
Kelley, Jane Schumacher
Life Management Educator
COMMERCE TOWNSHIP
Matson, Diane Johnson
Fifth Grade Teacher
Miller, Cynthia Gayle
Fifth Grade Teacher
Staryk, Susan Leone
6th Grade Resource Room Tchr
COMSTOCK
Bailey, Richard Nathan
Eng Tchr & Dept Chair
Daniel, Tracy Marie
Physical Education Teacher
Loichinger, Sharon Shaw
4th Grade Teacher
Welbourne, Susan Moyer
Second Grade Teacher
COMSTOCK PARK
Moore, Larry Carl
Director of Bands
Schneider, Harold Frank
Technology Teacher
Wier, David
Teacher
CONSTANTINE
Clark, Shari K.
English Teacher
Grunert, Fred Charles
Artist & Teacher
Grunert, Mary Ballagh
English & At-Risk Teacher
Strawser, Ethan Allen
HS Social Studies Teacher
COOKS
Carlyon, Peggy Marie Wangberg
Third Grade Teacher
Haindl, Carol Thora
Business & Geography Teacher
Miller, Paul Albert
K-9th Grd PE & World His Tchr
COOPERSVILLE
Renzema, Richard Lee
Algebra Tchr & Bsktbl Coach
CORUNNA
Brooks, Lyle Arnold
Band Director
Buysse, Bruce Lee
Biology Tchr & Sci Dept Chm
Clark, Keith Allen
Teacher & Coach
Constine, Leo L.
Biology Teacher
Douglass, Judy K.
1st Grade Teacher
Kuhn, Lizabeth Lewis
Second Grade Teacher
Labadie, Sally Zolkosky
Principal
Mathias, Pamela Jo
5th Grade Teacher
Riley, James Dale
Mrktg & Bus Tchr, Co-op Coord
CROSWELL
Geiger, Maryellen Pengelly
Fifth Grade Teacher
Walborn, Carol Sue
Kindergarten Teacher
CRYSTAL FALLS
Friestrom, Karen Talerico
Business Education Teacher
Sherby, Carol Jean (Brauer)
Art Teacher
Skelton, Stanford James
Eng & Environmental Sci Tchr
Stender, Thaddeus A.
High School Music Teacher
DANSVILLE
Thorburn, Stuart George
Economics & Psychology Teacher
DAVISON
Brown, Kevin Michael
Biology Teacher
Brown, Marilyn Inman
Retired Teacher
Eller, William Fredrick
Biology Teacher
Hartman, Alice Marie
Retired Teacher
Herfert, Bonnie M.
English Teacher
Mac Lean, Ray D.
Instrumental Music Director
Pugh, Martha Jayne
World Studies Teacher
Shears, Joan
English Teacher
Sproule, Mary Theisen
4th Grade Teacher of Gifted
Thornton, Judy Alchin
English Teacher & Comm Coord
Wells, Catherine
Computer Education Teacher
Wheeler, Dawn E.
High School Principal
DE TOUR VILLAGE
Reed, Angela Grochowalkski
Mathematics & Computer Tchr
DEARBORN
Anderson, Pamela Frances
8th Grd Language Arts Teacher
Azar, John C.
Philosophy Professor
Bacile, Carol Ann (Farino)
First Grade Teacher
Boron, Linda M.
US History & Economics Teacher
Brandt-Teeple, Linda
Biology & Genetics Instructor
Broderick, Patricia
Retired 5th Grade Teacher
Brown, Maria Canducci
Foreign Lang & Lang Arts Tchr
Burks, John L.
Adjunct Teacher
Ciocan, Ruth
English Teacher
Colter, Doris M.
College English Instructor
Dawson, Jeannine Kujava
Teacher
De Roo, Robert Wayne
Teacher & Principal
Gray, Gary James
Head Women's Volleyball Coach
Hashoian, Ralph G.
Teacher
Holman, Melissa Ann
Eng, Amer His & Jrnlsm Tchr
Honer, Peggy Jean Kruzel
Deaf Ed Teacher & Counselor
Horvath, Rebecca Badger
Instructor of Psychology
Hudak, Catherine Lukasiewicz
First Grade Teacher
Kelley, Donna J.
First Grade Teacher
Kiersey, Stephen Francis
English & Drama Teacher
Knisley, Karen G.
Social Studies Teacher
Kobeissi, Ali Hassan
Math & Computer Tech Teacher
Kostyshak, Michele Ann
French Teacher
Krol, Ed J.
Anatomy & Physiology Professor
Lawera, Kenneth John
High School Science Teacher
Linderman, Marianne Montgomery
Mathematics Teacher
Lo Proesto, Michael Charles
Instr of Physics & Astronomy
Machak, Duane Lee
Conflict Resolution Teacher
Martin, Kelly Lynn
Fifth Grade Teacher
Molyn, Carol Ann
5th Grade Teacher
Nadasen, Aruna
Professor of Physics
Nelson, Nancy Owen
Professor of English
O'Donnell, Mary Therese
8th Grade Language Arts Tchr
Otto, James Richard
Band & Orchestra Teacher
Popyk, Marilyn Kay
Instr of Bus & Ec Division
Priskorn, Craig S.
Lead Instructor
Pritchard, Karen J. Williams
Speech, Theatre & Lit Tchr
Renko, Melissa Maree
Science Teacher
Rietz, John
English Professor
Roumayah, Afaf
Bilingual Dept Math & Sci Tchr
Shaw, Carol (Shalda)
High School Biology Teacher
Shuraydi, Wafa Unis
High School Teacher
Silver, Charles N.
Mathematics Teacher
Skwarski, Suzanne Fink
English Teacher
Smillie, Andrea Lee
Tchr, Consultant, Adj Grad Fac
Spain, John Mason
Physical Education Teacher
Stockton, Ronald Ralph
Professor of Political Science
Thoin, Annette Irene
Elementary Teacher
Turner, Mildred Adams
Soc Sci Chair Pearson & Instr
Weisenthal, Fredrika Elman
English Professor
White, Paulette Childress
English Instructor
DEARBORN HEIGHTS
Barker, Carole L.
English Teacher
Bird, Michael Joseph
Physical Education Instructor
Boroditsch, Ira
Spanish Teacher
Campbell, Brian Chandler
Co-Director of Adolescent Pgm
Doty, Margaret Cooper
English Teacher
Johnson, Ollie
Sixth Grade Teacher
Kaniewski, Janet Catherine
2nd Grade Teacher
Matigian, Mary Ellen (King)
Fourth Grade Teacher
Messner, C. Thomas
Co-Op Coord & Bus Ed Teacher
Orr, Lydia Ervin
Social Studies Teacher
Ruivo, Marion (Cassar)
7th Grade & Math Teacher
Tait, Patricia Snover
Music Director
DECATUR
De Roo, David G.
Mathematics Teacher
Dick, Joseph Waldo
Mathematics Department Chm
Shroyer, Leonda Kessinger
English & Speech Teacher
DECKERVILLE
Blackburn, David Linn
English Department Chairperson
Cesefske, A. Gary
Fifth Grade Teacher
Rudduck, Charles W.
Trig, Chem & Computer Sci Tchr
DEERFIELD
Gonzalez, Carolyn Ortman
Second Grade Teacher
Johnston, Beth Hadden
Jr HS Math Teacher
Maples, Cathy A.
Spanish Tchr & Media Spclst
Shilling, Larry P.
Principal
Shoemaker, Jerry Charles
K-12th Grade Counselor
DELTON
Finedell, Richard Alvin
Automotive Instructor
Gibson, James Henry
Teacher & Coach
Mc Donald, Carolyn Jean
Second Grade Teacher
Rowgo, Linda Christine
Guidance Counselor
Smith, Gregory Allen
HS Social Studies Teacher
Vreeland, Linda A. (Slocum)
5th Grade Teacher
DETROIT
Adams, Denise Victoria
9th-12th Grd Dance & Hlth Tchr
Anandwala, Naquiya M.
Science Teacher
Apter, Katherine Barnes
Secondary Eng & Writing Tchr
Baker, Phyllis Macuga
Lang Arts, Rdng, Soc Stud Tchr
Barath, Dawn Marie
English, Speech & Drama Tchr
Barnes, Amos Randy
Senior Guidance Counselor
Barnes, Arlene Laura
Director of Guidance
Barwinski, Ronald J.
English Teacher
Bayer, Luanne L.
Library Teacher
Belfield, Kevin D.
Chemistry Professor
Benvenuto, Mark Anthony
Assistant Prof of Chemistry
Billiu, Anne-Marie
Language Arts Tchr & Ath Dir
Blankenship, Coy Lee
Senior Army Instructor
Bledsoe, Dorothy Barbara Ann
HS Social Studies Teacher
Booker, Sallie Thomas
Mathematics Teacher
Bradley, Cheryl Wright
French & Spanish Teacher
Brantley-Jackson, Terri L.
English Teacher
Bridges, Darryl Stanley
Language Arts & Science Tchr
Brown, Bettie Ann
8th Grade Math Teacher
Brown, Marvell Mc Cutcheon
Sixth Grade Teacher
Bryant-Phillips, Sharon
Spanish Teacher
Burkhalter, Sarah Anderson
Sixth Grade Teacher
Cadieux, Margaret Elizabeth
PE & Science Teacher
Calugar, Eugenia
Bilingual & Foreign Lang Tchr
Carney, Louis Joseph
English & Debate Teacher
Carter, Malcolm Spencer
Coordinator & Social Stud Tchr
Cason, Hattie Griffin
Assistant Principal
Chapman, Adrienne Therese
Math, Art Tchr & Fac Chprsn
Chapman-Sanders, Jan Sheron
Health & Physical Ed Teacher
Childs, Oraldine Mitchell
Language Arts Teacher
Conahan, Patricia Lynn
Middle School Coordinator
Connor, Edward McDonald
Spanish Teacher
Coomes, Paul
Mathematics Teacher
Cooney, Mary A.
High School English Teacher
Corbin, Matthew James
Commercial Art Instructor
Crudder, Frederick Howson
Former Assoc Prof of Phtgrphy
Crump, John L., Jr.
Teacher
Cunningham, Bertha Jackson
English Teacher
Davis, Sandra L.
Mathematics Instructor
Dean, Kelly Ann
Science Teacher
Dean, Norma Kelley
Middle School Counselor
Dennis, Lovie Hutchinson
Language Arts Teacher
DiBasio, Jan Lee
Kndgtn & Rdng Recovery Teacher
Dickens, Clarence Phillip
Art Teacher
Dinkins, Baynard Juan, Jr.
Science & Business Teacher
Dinkins, Bronte Craighead
English Teacher
DiPonio, Judith Connell
Eighth Grade Teacher
Divers, Arthur J.
Guidance Counselor
Dixon, Carolyn Miles
Second Grade Teacher
Dobrski, Diane
Secondary Mathematics Teacher
Dorchak, Gregory A.
Contract Administrator & Coach
Dowding, Lynda Lou
Mathematics Teacher
Duchene, Robert Ray
Social Studies Teacher
Dugas, Jean Richard
8th Grade Civics Teacher
Ecclestone-Boegler, Mary Ann
First Grade Teacher
Edelson, Joanna Grossman
HS English & Speech Teacher
Edwards, Betty L. (Dixon)
Business Education Teacher
Edwards, Carolyn L.
Title 1 Reading & Math Teacher
Ellis, Mary Reid
English Teacher
Evans, Mary Cleveland
Gifted & Talented English Tchr
Feinberg, David
Math & Philosophy Instructor
Fennell, John Thomas
Biology Teacher
Ford, Pamela Hunter
6th Grade Rdng & Soc Stud Tchr
Fox, Howard William
5th Grade Teacher
Furlow, Josephine Abshire
HS Counselor & Unity Minister
Gibney, Nancy Lorraine
Assistant Education Professor
Gibson, Jacqueline HUllum
English Teacher
Gipson, Emma Jean
Business Ed Teacher
Gold, Patricia Lillie
English Teacher
Gold-Livingston, Ernestine
Choral Music Director
Gonzalez, Franco, Jr.
Health & PE Teacher
Goston, Johnny L.
Counselor
Granderson, George
Science Dept Head
Graves, Nina Renee
Business Education Teacher
Green, Gaye Evelyn (Morris)
AP Literature & Jrnlsm Teacher
Greer, Edwina Currie
Fourth Grade Teacher
Griffin, Margaret Ann
Science Teacher
Guyer, Brad L.
English Teacher
Hafner, Denise Marie
Science & DAPCEP Teacher
Haldane, Patricia J.
6th-8th Grade Math Teacher
Hammond, Jimmy L.
Drop-Out Prevention Prgm Coord
Hand, Judith Rochelle
English Teacher
Hare, Rosemary Littleton
Social Studies Teacher
Harrell, Anita Bonnie
Technology Coordinator
Harris, Jay R.
5th Grade Teacher
Harrison, Karen Perkins
Supervisor & HS Science Tchr
Harvey, Pearl Marie
Ninth Grade Counselor
Haynes, Mary Lee
Professor
Hearn, Kendra Carter
English Teacher
Henderson, Sylvia Dolores
Dance Teacher
High, Arnetta Wilson
Sixth Grade Teacher
Hightower, Shirita Jeneen
English Teacher
Hinson, Tonya Renee
English Teacher
Hoetger, Thomas Joel
Social Studies Teacher
Holley-Foster, Victoria Ilene
Dance Teacher
Holmes, Mary Dawson
Science Teacher
Holmes-Gunter, Evelyn Dolly
Title One Teacher & Tutor
Hoover, William Franklin, Jr.
Science, Math & Health Teacher
Horst, Brenetta A. Dukes
Instrumental Music Teacher
Hosbach, Virginia Shaening
Clinical Nursing Instructor
Hosely, Harlan Gathal
Science Teacher
Howard, Pamela J.
Counselor
Hunt, Layne
Speech Teacher
Ingram, Ina Louise
Elementary Math Teacher
Jackson, Claude
Social Studies Educator
Jackson, Lodesta Mitchell
Language Arts Teacher
Jackson, Marilynn Burden
Middle Schl Sci Teacher
Jarvis-Height, Lennis Merica
4th Grade Homeroom Teacher
Jeanpiere, Severine Morris
Mathematics Teacher
Johnson, Charles Dyrel
Instrumental Music Ed Instr
Johnson, Dolores Yvonne
Assistant Principal

OIT (cont)
n, Sylvia S.
ly Living Teacher
n, Veronica
ness Teacher
n, Winnie
irade Homeroom Teacher
Ella Ray Eddins
l Grade Teacher
Jewel Johnson
er & Tech Ed Dept Head
Patty Burnette
ary Teacher
vic, Vladan
vare Management Professor
dy, Diana Willis
al Studies Teacher
, Ikhlas Sadik
gual Gym & Health Tchr
ofel, Dennis Frederick
rican History Teacher
Thomas Allen
ciate Professor of History
Sandra Sowell
Arts, His Tchr, Asst Prin
tt, Brian Stuart
l Director
, Jay Charles
nselor
, Elive Francis
Telecommunications Analyst
, Elaine Galinsky
Teacher
ston, Gail Toby
netology Teacher
y, Diann
nematics Teacher
kin, L. Marie Mitchell
8th Grd Language Arts Tchr
, Dorothy Georgene Clark
Grade Teacher
nder, Frederick William
puter Teacher
em, Walter C.
h & Computer Teacher
Evelyn D. Rias
ish Teacher
do, Gary A.
nish Teacher
ad, Marjorie Joy
Grade Teacher
erry, John Henry, Jr.
al Studies Teacher
rty, Jacqueline Fleming
d Grade Teacher
ormick, Marilyn G.
orming Arts Teacher
ormick, Marilyn G.
orming Arts Dept Teacher
arlin, Annie Johnson
hematics Teacher
esham, Audrey Coleman
Mathematics Teacher
il, Anthony Bernard
rmy Instr
apley, Roger D.
Grade Math Teacher
tt, Irene
nematics Teacher
ael, Pamela Ann
d Director
r, Deborah J.
Grade Social Studies Tchr
r, Luther, Jr.
h School Math Teacher
r, Melissa Marie
ce Teacher
ell Smith, Beverly A.
lish & Yearbook Teacher
e, Gladys Curry
lish Teacher
s, Dennis E.
h Teacher
olson, Willie Louise
hematics Teacher
s, Gina Linnet
cher & Counselor
ce, Felix Chukwuma
hematics Teacher
ist, Ina Ruth McKenzie
rd Grade Teacher
am, Mignon (Hayes)
glish Teacher
r, Herman Lee
em, Physics & Calculus Tchr
nan, Nito Dewitt
sical Education Teacher
ns, Rodger
siness Education Teacher
ch, Christine O.
Grade Teacher & Vice Prin
aw, Barbara Jean
glish Teacher
n, Delanor Haven
tory Teacher
ey, Elaine Margerite
glish Teacher
, Patrick John, SJ
n Lang Dept & Psych Teacher
ardson, Gilbert
Grade History Teacher
ardson, Olive-Cherie Young-Wyatt
gh School Counselor
ardson, Roberta Maxine-Collier
tology Instructor
e, Carolyn Jirkans
sistant Dean
rs, Ivanetta House
Grd Language Arts Teacher

Rizzo, Donald Charles
Professor of Biology
Robinson, Charlene Franshell
Social Studies Teacher
Robinson, Dena
English Teacher
Robinson, Lisa Renee
English Teacher
Robinson-Chambers, Linda Bernice
Math Teacher
Rodriguez, Anna Maria
Social Studies Teacher
Rome, Joyce Lawson
7th & 8th Grd Soc Stud Tchr
Royster, Sheila Anne
Mathematics Teacher
Sanders, Monica Kaigler
Reading Specialist
Sanford, Martin D.
Mathematics Teacher
Sapp, Carrie Joannita
Mathematics Teacher
Saunders, Harriet
English Teacher
Schwartzhoff, Maureen
Business, Vocational Dept Head
Scott, Barbara McGlockton
Counselor
Scott, Nina Ray
Choir Director
Shoshani, Jeheskel Hezy
Biology Lecturer
Sievert, Dolan A.
Counselor
Simon, Carolyn Jean
Dental Assistant Instructor
Slater, Linda-Carole Mosley
3rd Grd Tchr & Math Specialist
Smith, Jerome H.
English Teacher
Stachler, Duane R.
Band Director & Math Teacher
Stakley, Eric Christian
Commercial Photography Instr
Stamell, Rhoda B.
English Teacher
Steigerwald, Louis R.
English Instructor
Steward, Felicia
Assistant Coach
Stout, Faye J.
Science & DAPCEP Teacher
Street, Jeanette Murphy
English Teacher
Studenka, Carol A.
English Teacher & Yrbk Adv
Swayne, Ethel Lee
6th Grade Teacher
Tate, Sherita Ann
Mathematics Teacher
Taylor, Evelyn R.
6th Grd Language Arts Teacher
Terrell, G. Michael
Indstrl Tech & Drafting Tchr
Thompson, Valerie Marsae (Childress)
Librarian & Media Specialist
Thornton, Judith Elaine (Collier)
Mathematics Teacher
Tichik, Mel
English Teacher
Treadwell, Johna Andrews
Vocal Music Teacher
Tyler, Lorraine Wesley (Powell)
French Department Head & Tchr
Varner, Beverli Nealy
Psychology Instructor
Vileta, Estrella Monzon
Vice Principal & Jr HS Tchr
Waltz, Carolyn Jean
Spanish & English Instructor
Ward, Lorraine King
Mathematics Teacher
Wardell, Paula Renee
Mathematics Teacher
Washington, Rosie Bingham
Business Teacher
Wasson, Suzanne Streeter
Math, Science Tchr, Admin Head
Watts, Crystal Yvonne
Career Counselor
Weathers, Julaine Gaddis
Math Teacher
Wells-Smith, Deidra Petross
Mathematics Department Head
Wesley, Juanita Christine Whisenton
3rd Grade Language Arts Tchr
Wesley, Lawrence E.
Scndry Social Studies Teacher
White, ChyVon Thomas
6th Grd Rdng & Lang Arts Tchr
Whitmore, Bernestine
Mathematics Teacher
Wiley, Ruthie Reedy
Language Arts Teacher
Wilkins, Cathy Alfreda-Walk
Lang Arts & Sci Tchr
Williams, Gloria
Computer Programming Instr
Williams, Kenneth Lamont, Sr.
5th & 6th Grade Math Teacher
Williams, Margaret Diane
Modern Dance Teacher
Wood, Deborah Ann (Johnson)
Social Studies Teacher
Woolridge, Spencer Merle
Fifth Grade Teacher
Wyatt, Quincola
Sci, His, Govt & Ec Teacher
Wynn, Clarence
Health & Physical Ed Teacher

Young-Hamlett, Murdis R.
Language Arts Teacher

DEWITT

Darnell, David Ray
7th-8th Grade Math Teacher
Mc Cullen, William James
Social Studies Teacher

DEXTER

Brill, Ann Linder
Third Grade Teacher
Frederick, Frank H.
Physical Education Instructor
Hartman, Paige C.
5th-8th Grade Life Skills Tchr
Kessler, Cheryl Marie
Fourth Grade Teacher
Smith, Gerald R.
Math Teacher
Walsh, Susan Sortor
1st Grade Teacher

DIMONDALE

Heller, Virginia Pierce
Retired Instrmntl Music Tchr

DOLLAR BAY

Mattson, John A.
Teacher & Counselor
Salo, Carol Maki
Art & Living Skills Teacher

DORR

Kadwell, Charlotte Marie
Retired Elementary Teacher
Lakatos, Janine Hampel
1st Grade Teacher

DOUGLAS

Battaglia, Michael G.
Reading Specialist

DOWAGIAC

Chaddock, Diane K.
Math, Sci Instr & Dept Chair
Latourette, Ronald James
High School Math Teacher
Magyar, Annette Marie
Mathematics Instructor
Stanley, Ester J.
Spanish & English Teacher

DRYDEN

Borden, William George Eugene
Teacher

DUNDEE

Bockert, Cindy Haughey
Life Management Teacher
Hoffman, Ernest Edward
Sixth Grade Teacher
Jennings, Douglas Charles
Eighth Grade English Teacher
Jurasek, Marilyn Korican
Fourth Grade Teacher
Keeler, Marsha Felcyn
Math Teacher
Moskwa, John Henry
Fifth Grade Teacher
Nix, Sharon Ann
English & Spanish Teacher
Schultz, Scott William
Trans Director & Bsktbl Coach
Sedlar, Luan Marie
Physical Education Teacher
Stock, Gene
Guidance Counselor
Wickenheiser, Donna Marie Olmsted
Second Grade Teacher

DURAND

Hoisington, Stephen Paul
Tchr of Emotionally Impaired
Schultz, Keith P.
Math & Science Teacher
Widder, Linda Lee
5th Grade Teacher

EAGLE

Hollerback, Nancy Dee
Second Grade Teacher

EAST CHINA

Gilmore, Karan Olive
Third Grade Teacher
Hillier, Sharon Kota
Fifth Grade Teacher

EAST DETROIT

Scherer, Ronald David
8th Grade Teacher

EAST JORDAN

Leach, Cheryll Culver
Dir Discovery Science Teacher

EAST LANSING

Dennis, Frank George, Jr.
Professor
Hoppe, Patricia Bothwell
High School English Teacher
Howard, Susan F.
English Teacher
Jones, Cara Collier
Mathematics Teacher
Kazsuk, Jon David
Science Teacher
Lawrence, Beth Morley
English Teacher
Mc Aleer, Connie Hartman
English & French Teacher
Mitchell, Juanita
Science & Math Teacher
Pernell, Ida Yvonne
Second Grade Teacher
Smith, Jeff A.
Mathematics Teacher
Versluis, Arthur J.
Lecturer

EASTPOINTE

Allen, Marguerite Malko
Biology Teacher
Battaglia, Linda Williams
English Teacher

Bever, David Paul
Sixth Grade Teacher
Casey, Joanne Kimball
Fourth Grade Teacher
Clark, David William
Business Education Teacher
Domin, James Eugene
Physics & Chemistry Teacher
Emanuele, Joseph Scott
Health & Physical Ed Teacher
Slawinski, Judy Elaine (Moss)
First Grade Teacher
Szymanski, Paul Gerard
High School Math Teacher

EATON RAPIDS

Anderson, Jo Anita
Counselor
Bradish, Gwen Lakia
Science & Social Studies Tchr
Fox, Charles Daniel
Amer & Erpn History Teacher
Geisen, Mary E.
High School Teacher
Honsowitz, Joe Edward
Middle School Teacher
Moore, Cynthia Lawrence
7th Grade Soc Stud & Lit Tchr
Wyckoff, Carolyn D.
Student Svc Guidance Secretary

EAU CLAIRE

Cooper, Sharen (Bartels)
Second Grade Teacher
LaCourt, Marvin Richard
Retired 7th & 8th Grd Tchr
Melody, Karen
Fifth Grade Teacher
Miner, Timothy John
7th & 8th Grade History Tchr
Rygg, Pamela Miller
Business Teacher

ECORSE

Conn, Gloria M.
Fifth Grade Elementary Teacher

EDMORE

Woodcock, Nancy Ann
Kindergarten Teacher

EDWARDSBURG

Clase, Nancy Elson
French Teacher
Goldsmith, Donald Roger
Art Teacher

ELK RAPIDS

Parks, David Alan
Mathematics Teacher

ELSIE

Dahlke, Karl
Math Teacher
Holmes-Crocker, Rebecca Jo
Biology Teacher
Kora, Richard Michael
Psychology & Literature Tchr
Smith, Everett Ricky
Industrial Education Teacher

ERIE

Fortner, Melissa Stephens
Asst Dean, His & Govt Tchr
Leighton, Raymond Edward, II
Third Grade Teacher
Michael, John C.
Teacher & Coach
Voight, Nancy Lee
Former Teacher
Wood, LeRoy George
Eighth Grade Mathematics Tchr

ESCANABA

Bolek, Sally Bray
2nd Grade Teacher
Buckbee, Stephen
Sociology Teacher
DeRidder, Thomas James
HS Social Studies Teacher
Dollhopf, Karl H.
Fourth Grade Teacher
Libby, Gregory P.
Physics & Math Teacher
Lindstrom, Barbara J.
Retired 6th Grade Teacher
Lundin, Christine Marie
Instructor of Business Dept
Majestic, Sally Jeanne
Spanish Teacher
Mead, Barbara Minor
2nd Grade Teacher & Asst Prin
Myrick, Eileen
Retired Home Economics Teacher
Ouwinga, Stewart Allen
Biology I & II Teacher
Pascoe, Theresa Mae (Berube)
Physical Education Teacher
Swetkis, Candace Ann
8th Grade Science Teacher
Wiles, Tammy Marie (Severinsen)
English Teacher
Woolford, Karen R.
Second Grade Teacher
Ziemba, John Francis
Associate Prof of Chemistry

ESSEXVILLE

Barassi, Rodrigo Patricio
Spanish Teacher
Holdship, Candace Golding
Elementary Music Teacher
Johnson, Gary Joseph
7th Grade Science Teacher
Lanway, Dale Newton
Science Teacher
Smith, Thomas Hood
Speech & Drama Teacher

EVART

Eaton, Carol Ann
Business & Computer Ed Instr
Junker, Jeffrey Jon
Third Grade Teacher
Lehnen, Monica Ford
Second Grade Teacher

EWEN

Byrne, Nancy Stephenson
Science & Math Teacher

FAIRGROVE

Upton, Alocoa Draper
English, Jrnlsm & Band Teacher

FARMINGTON

Allen, Marjorie E.
Latin Teacher
Atchinson, Patricia Ann
Service Learning Coordinator
Calkins, Carim Raymond
Life, Phys & Cmptr Sci Teacher
Ciske, Robert W.
Math Teacher
Cunningham, Catherine Eve
Secondary Marketing Teacher
Dingeman, Kathryn E.
Physics Teacher
Dubb, Barbara Haas
Speech, Drama & Eng Teacher
Evasic, Thomas Stanley
Mathematics Teacher
Finney, David Dorsey, Jr.
American History Teacher
Gippert, Carl Alfred
Instrumental Music Director
Hagerty, Margaret Ellen
Third Grade Teacher
Harmon, William Robert
Art Teacher & Dept Chair
Harris, Dodie Pasman
4th Grade Teacher
Henderson, Marie Katheryn
Art Department Chairperson
Jones, Ronald Frederic
American History Teacher
Massey, Carole Ann
Swimming Dept Chair & Instr
Maxwell, Jerry H.
History Teacher
Mika, Frances
English Teacher
Morden, Joette Marie
Life Management Tchr & Chprsn
Mordenski, Janice E.
English & Speech Teacher
Pinnell, William Edward
Mathematics Teacher
Poelke, Wendy Ann
Special Education Teacher
Schumacher, John Doyal
Biology Teacher & Coach
Shaw, James A.
His & Interdisciplanary Tchr
Simpson, Jeffrey Paul
Mathematics Teacher
Smith, Barbara Weale
Religious Studies Teacher
Sparrow, Laura Halford
Eng, His & Humanities Teacher
Sutter, Robert John
Physical Education Teacher
Williams, Lori Olson
5th Grade Teacher
Wright, George H.
Religious Studies Teacher

FARMINGTON HILLS

Bennett, Carole A.
Tenured Faculty of Speech Comm
Cocar, Benjamin
Bib Theo Chrstn Stud Asst Prof
Cuthbertson, Duane G.
Professor of Psychology
Giddens, Charles Darwell
Asst Prof of Bible & Theology
Holmes, Zach E.
Instructor of Accounting
Nickel, Ann Marie
Literature Instructor
Steinhaus, Reta Ansell
Retired Teacher of GATE

FARWELL

Laverty, Mignon Earline (Mogg)
High School Librarian
Mc James, Margaret Ann
Mathematics & Dance Teacher
Paesens, Maxine Joyce Waalkes
Retired First Grade Teacher
Rau, Brenda Kay
Spanish Teacher
Thurston, Judy Kay
Art Teacher

FENNVILLE

Klosner, Michael Paul
11th-12th Grade English Tchr
Lopez, John, Jr.
Head Baseball Coach
Lugten, Blaine Alan
High School Math Teacher
Neubecker, Michael Charles
Secondary Science Teacher
Park-Mason, Susan Kay
8th-12th Grade Art Teacher
Sievert, Marilyn L.
Kindergarten Teacher
Snider-Gilliam, Karla D.
High School English Teacher

FENTON

Brown, Barbara E.
AP Am His, AP Lit & Comp Tchr
Bruder, Robert Charles
Math Tchr & Bsktbl Coach

FENTON (cont)
Leh, James A.
Science Teacher
Miller, Joseph Lee
Chemistry & Biology Teacher
Pilar, Charles Steven
8th Grade Social Studies Tchr
Van Effen, Nora
7th-8th Grd Tchr & Asst Prin
FERNDALE
Brown, Patricia Webb
First Grade Teacher
Carlson, David John
Upper Elementary Teacher
Dixon, John Phillip
Teacher
Downey, Rachel Anne
English Teacher
Francis, Robert Scott
Physical Education Instructor
Kaps, Helen Osborn
Kindergarten Teacher
Pennock, Peggy Ann
English Teacher
FERRYSBURG
Fisher, David James
6th Grade Teacher
FIFE LAKE
Costley, William J.
Bio, Chem, Physi & Eco Tchr
Gillooly, Mary R.
Lead & Head Teacher
High, Michael L.
High School English Teacher
FLAT ROCK
Bernaiche, Andre C.
Soc Studies Tchr & Dept Head
Dickinson, John E.
Biology Teacher
Douglas, Robert James
Counselor
Dulmage, Mary Jo-Ann
5th Grade Teacher
Ferstle, Marie Labo
English Teacher
Gambino, Carol Anne Daloisio
Guidance Counselor
Harrill, Thomas Joseph
Electronics Teacher
Hill, Thomas Paul
Social Studies Teacher
Huepenbecker, Rebecca Lynn
Special Projects Coordinator
Virgis-Henderson, Sally
English Teacher
FLINT
Allen, Judy Gallion
United States History Teacher
Armstrong, Sharon K.
K & 1st Grade Teacher
Bagley, Gayle Marie
Sixth Grade Teacher
Bean, Jeff A.
Hum & Social Studies Teacher
Berent, Chrsitina Ann
Eng & Communications Teacher
Brown, Richard Wesley
Social Studies Teacher
Burns, Avon Lorraine
Assoc Prof of Criminal Justice
Butzu, Ava Cybulski
English Teacher
Byers, Catherine Bennett (Pitts)
Geography Instructor
Chard, Clyde Philip
Senior High Guidance Counselor
Collins, Helen Kelley
Business Teacher
Collinsworth, Catherine Jean (Funsch)
Fourth Grade Teacher
Crowder, Earl D.
7th Grade Math Teacher
Davidek, John Clarence
Social Studies Teacher
Demps, Napoleon, Jr.
Assistant Principal
Drumm, Dennis
Mathematics Teacher
Duncan, Alfreda Michael
Vocal Music Teacher
English, Thomas Andrew
Math Teacher
Evans-Tutt, Rhonda D.
Counselor
Fonger, Thomas Mitchell
Industrial Electronics Prof
Forsythe, Thomas
Comp Information Systems Prof
French, James Elwood
English Teacher
Gaines, Gwendolyn Walker
Third Grade Teacher
Gerace, Dennis John
American History & Law Teacher
Green, Margaret Ellen
MS & HS Science, Biology Tchr
Haffner, Richard Foster
Chemistry & Physics Teacher
Harris, Bettye Hannah
Career & Technical Ed Teacher
Harris, Leola Jones
English Teacher & Dept Chair
Harris, Robert James
Science Teacher
Hayes, Joyce M.
English Department Chair
Hayes-Scott, Fairy C.
Prof of Eng & Interpreter Trng
Hibbs, Gary Lee
Guidance Counselor
Hodgers, Glenda Fay
Multi-Age Teacher
Holec, Robert John
Biology, Zoology Tchr & Coach
Hollingsworth, David Ledyard
Anatomy & Physiology Instr
Howard, Barbara A.
Teacher
Hughes, Myra E. Nichols
5th Grade Teacher
Jenkins, Lynn Grabozynski
Biology Teacher
Jerore, Jeanne Clothier
5th-6th Grade Teacher
June, Karen Marie
HS Math Teacher
Kells, Gordon Fraser
Professor of Geography
Kippe, Larrilee A.
5th Grade Teacher
Korhonen, Gail Anne
Mathematics Teacher
Lampley, Amos
Compensatory Ed Math Teacher
Lewis, Joanne Maxine
4th & 5th Grade Teacher
Londrigan, Paul James
Professor & Advisor
Molter, Karilynn Shaw
English Dept Chair & Teacher
Montpas, Patricia Dillon
Professor of Nursing
Moore, Mamie Elaine
High School English Teacher
Moorman, Pamela L. Plumb
Third Grade Teacher
Muench, Kathleen E.
6th Grade Teacher
Nassif, Jeanette Mary
English Teacher
Pavlovich, Joseph Michael
Science Department Chair
Petrich, Johnnie Sue (DeHoff)
Physics Teacher
Pierce, Susan Ann
Business & Technology Instr
Powell, Faye Kathleen
High School Math Teacher
Pratt, Sue Ann Hanton
6th & 7th Grade Teacher
Richards, Karen Adair
Teacher of Gifted & Talented
Rivard, Leila Knuuti
Teacher & Curriculum Coord
Rollins, Kathleen Flanagan
English Professor
Rose, Phillip William
Center Director
Ross, Darrell Wayne
English Instructor
Salazar, Carmelita Roman
Montessori Kindergarten Tchr
Scheidemantel, Marilyn Perkins
Biology Teacher
Settergren, Karol Ann
Music Teacher & Flute Instr
Smith, Barbara A. (Spann)
Counselor
Smith, Maureen Catherine
Accounting & Financial Instr
Smith, Verna Jo Herriott
5th Grade Teacher
Sperlich, Terryl Jo
HS Social Studies Teacher
Stratton, Margaret Fortino
Third Grade Teacher
Sullivan, Laura Lindahl
Asst Prof of Manufacturing Sys
Swirtz, Glenda Eiler
Eng Department Chair & Tchr
Trowt, Patricia E. Kelly
American Literature Teacher
Turner, Varnay Denise
Instrumental Music Tchr
Waner, James M.
Physical Science & Chem Tchr
Welch, William Joseph
Chemistry Teacher
White, Paul L.
Vocal Music & French Teacher
Wojtowicz, Alfred Michael
Mathematics Teacher
Zwiebel, Patricia A.
Math & Biology Teacher
FLUSHING
Coggins, Dale Patrick
Biology & Athletic Coordinator
Eavy, Janet Kay
1st Grd Reading Recovery Tchr
Evans, Mel A.
Social Studies & English Tchr
Gandolfi, Anthony
Social Studies Teacher
Gillam, Gregory Alan
Genetics & Biology Teacher
Grieve, Robert J.
Sixth Grade Teacher
Hinds, Donn Stephen
Advanced Bio Tchr & Sci Coord
Jekel, Carol Diane
Business Teacher
FORT GRATIOT
Airtene, Pamela Keelor
Language Arts & Speech Teacher
Eastman, Janet Irene Ritchie
History Teacher
Knapp, Patricia Ann
Business Teacher & Act Dir
Peltz, Edwin Lee
Spcl Ed Teacher & Consultant
Sommer, Susan Lynn
Second Grade Teacher
Teeple, Scott David
Instrumental Music Teacher
Wedge, Amy Joy
Speech & English Teacher
FOWLER
Edwards, Marie Byrne
First Grade Teacher
Powell, Beverly Ann (Smith)
Third Grade Teacher
Shauver, Annette Hannula
English & Reading Teacher
FOWLERVILLE
Frazier, Susan Grunn
English Teacher & Chair
Macklem, George P.
Science Teacher
Russell, Nancy Lee
French Teacher
FRANKENMUTH
Cataline, William Leslie
Psychology & Sociology Teacher
Kuske, Eugene Carl
Retired Jr HS Teacher
Schmidt, Christine Kostrzewa
First Grade Teacher
Schollmeyer, Robert C.
Sixth Grade Teacher
Szybala, Joann Lewandowski
English Teacher
Wellander, Ronald Ernest
Instrumental Music Director
Willis, Mary Natzelle
First Grade Teacher
FRANKFORT
Dost, Cheryl Kozan
First Grade Teacher
Hooker, James Ronald
Drafting, CAD & Gen Tech Tchr
Mollema, Wallace A., Jr.
Retired English & Speech Tchr
Pratley, Michael B.
English & Social Studies Instr
Zimmerman, Michael James
Math Teacher
FRANKLIN
Abello-Labiano, Nora Ines
Upper School Spanish Teacher
Becker, Barbara Harder
HS Math Teacher
Brough-Gresh, Sandra
Science & Physics Teacher
Cheff, Carol Ann
Latin Teacher
DiVizio, Robert Louis
Social Studies Teacher
Dixon, Susan K.
Sixth Grade Teacher
Gilman, Brad
Upper School Director
Guilmet, Judith W.
German & French Teacher
Houston, Ann Draper
Kindergarten Teacher
Lessenberry, Karen Marie (Oxley)
Social Studies Teacher
Leybourn, Judy J.
Dean, Math Chair & Tchr
Mac Dougall, James F.
Amer His, Hlth & PE Tchr
Warren, Dana Marie
Biology Teacher
Woodward, Robert Milburn
Math Teacher
FRASER
George, Donald S.
Soc Stud Teacher & Dept Chair
Kettonen, Frank Allen
Industrial Technology Chprsn
Murray, John Leslie
High School Business Teacher
Rorai, Cathy
High School English Teacher
FREELAND
Gale, Stephen Thomas
5th & 6th Grade Teacher
Miller, Christine C.
Govt & Economics Teacher
Parsch, Gary M.
Computer & Technology Teacher
Rahl, Janet Hargett
Elementary Principal
FREMONT
Bont, Ann Wagley
Special Education Dept Chair
Bultman, C. Baars
Senior Studies Instructor
Byland, Jody V.
Elementary Principal
Homsher, Laurene (Lautzenheiser)
Vocal Music Director
Lick, Steve J.
Instructional Manager
Luchies, Mary K.
Early Childhood Ed Instr
Luchies, Sandra Stefanich
Business Applied Tech Instr
Mc Grath, Timothy J.
Fourth Grade Teacher
Tompkins, Richard Diehl
Elem PE Teacher & HS Coach
Tower, Randy D.
Career & Tech Ctr Instructor
FRUITPORT
Clarke, Tom O'Brian
6th Grade Teacher
Hall, Doree Sue (Roudebush)
Math Teacher
Holden, Barbara Wilson
College Prep English Instr
Kingsley, Robert Karl
HS Social Studies Teacher
Nuyens, Kay Ann (Hurrell)
Counselor
Pohlman, Carl Walter
American Studies Teacher
Thomas, Cheryl Sue
Choir Teacher
Vivian, Mary E.
2nd Grade Teacher
GALESBURG
Coates, Kenneth E.
Fifth Grade Teacher
Edgerton, Janice Kay
Director of Bands
Moreland, Ed
High School Math Teacher
GALIEN
Amy, Cindy Anne
English & Spanish Teacher
Cangelosi, Brenda Collins
Second Grade Teacher
Cook, Brenda Sue (Marshall)
Earth Sci, Hlth & Civics Tchr
Longacre, Kay Dalrymple
Home Economics Teacher
Rabe, Marianne
5th Grade Teacher
Remmo, Matthew James
English Teacher
GARDEN CITY
Balazy, Pamela Gerber
Fifth Grade Teacher
Carter, Sara L.
Business Education Teacher
Chambers, Cynthia A.
9th-10th Grade English Teacher
Erickson, Jane L.
Teacher
Lasceski, John C.
Business Education Teacher
Maslij, Anna
Second Grade Teacher
Navoy, Betty Ann Nielsen
Fourth Grade Teacher
Orloff, Keith A.
Tech Consultant & Eng Tchr
Phillips, Robert Edward
Science Teacher
Tobias, Anne
First Grade Teacher
GAYLORD
Anderson, Steven D.
Drafting & Design Teacher
DiRosa, Jeffery W.
Vocational Director
Dutcher, Charles R.
Latin Teacher & Football Coach
Kaschalk, Susanne Margaret
Media Specialist
Krieger, Judith A.
English Dept Chair & Teacher
Soffredine, Russell Patrick
6th Grade Teacher
Sysko, Mitchell
5th Grade Teacher
GLADSTONE
Anderson, Sharon Anne (Kruggel)
Retired 8th Grade Math Teacher
Beranek, Susan Langer
Economics & Business Teacher
Bjork, Randolph Lee
6th Grade Teacher
Bolek, Stephen Joseph
English Teacher
Grondine, James David
Chem Tchr & Sci Dept Head
Harrison, Dennis C.
High School Math Teacher
Herioux, Lionel
Principal
Hubbard, James W.
Math & Cmptr Science Teacher
Lombard, Douglas W.
HS Social Studies Teacher
Salmi, Allen F.
Biology & Journalism Instr
Ulatowski, Kathaleen Ann (Harris)
Math Dept Chair
Young, Larry Allen
Woodworking Teacher
GLADWIN
Beyer, Paul J., III
High School Visual Arts Tchr
Dawley, Kari Lynn
Chemistry Teacher
Edick, Judy Haines
Fourth Grade Teacher
Laitner, Christine Mary
English Teacher
Robertson, James Calvin, Jr.
Vocational Bldg Trades Teacher
Robinette, Catherine Jean
Pom Pom Coach
Shellenbarger, Suzanne Marie
7th & 8th Grade English Tchr
Sleeper, David C.
Auto Mechanics Teacher
Talley, Michele Andre' (Henry)
Former Elementary Teacher
Wetmore, Clair L.
Advanced Math Instructor
GLEN ARBOR
Bell, Stephen Aldon
Govt, Ancient & Medievel Tchr
Wheeler, Norman Robert
Science & English Teacher
GLENN
Schmid, Erna Baehr
Retired Ger Tchr & Dept Chair
GOODRICH
Doerr, John William
Mathematics Teacher
Gath, Gerald Louis
Chemistry & Computer Teacher
Stojek, Bonnie Ann (LeVey)
Mathematics Teacher
GRAND BLANC
Bostwick, Mary Airato
3rd Grade Teacher
Braciak, Ted W.
Mathematics Teacher
Cornelison, Jan Christine (Jaksa)
Fifth Grade Teacher
Corrado, Carla
Science & Mathematics Teacher
Darnell, Lynn Elaine (Fischer)
Alternative Education Tchr
Hall, Diane L.
High School English Teacher
Jackson, Janice Sorokin
Spanish Teacher
Larpenteur, Nita Steward
French Teacher
Lemke, Laura Ann (Zarobinski)
Assistant Principal
Litten, Charlee Mae
Multi-Age Teacher
Miller, Ann Swink
Retired Fourth Grade Teacher
Oldham, Craig William
Biology Teacher & Coach
Perry, Deborah Barton
Reading & Language Arts Chair
Survant, Gerald Wayne
HS Counselor
VanderKooy, Susan D'Avignon
4th Grade Tchr & Cluster Ldr
Weadock, Thomas Ralph
Former Boys & Girls Golf Coach
GRAND HAVEN
Barry, David Allen
Associate Principal
Bedford, Carol Haas
Biology Teacher
Breen, Richard Jon
Social Science Teacher
De Vries, Lynnda Cain
French Teacher
Flahive, Craig Raymond
Director of Bands & Orchestra
Greinke, Paul Harold
Astrnmy Tchr & Planetarium Dir
Groenendyk, Wailand Ray
Middle Schl Bible & His Tchr
Horodyski, Steven
Bio & Physical Education Tchr
Larson, Kenneth L.
7th Grade Science Teacher
Nelson, Joseph Benton
Mathematics Teacher
Parks, Bradford J.
Math & Keyboarding Teacher
Pearson, David E.
Eighth Grade Science Teacher
Poulin, Connie Lee Wilkinson
Life Management Educator
Rodgers, Carrie OBrien
1st Grade Teacher
Schakel, Deborah Noe
8th Grade Drama Teacher
Smart, David Michael
7th Grade PE Teacher
Van Schelven, Connie
English Dept Chair & Teacher
Veneklasen, Diane
English Teacher
GRAND LEDGE
Harris, Sherleen Stahl
Communication Arts Teacher
Shay, Patrick
American History Teacher
Sweetland, Margaret (Trantham)
First Grade Classroom Teacher
Ward, MIke W.
Fifth Grade Teacher
Wilson, Carol Mc Gowan
Sixth Grade Teacher
GRAND RAPIDS
Abu-Lughod, Javad Ibrahim
Eng & Creative Writing Tchr
Aleski, Douglas Paul
Adjunct Faculty
Alexander, Kathleen Rudd
Fifth Grade Teacher
Baron, Wendy Jane-Smith
Life Management Educator
Becherer, Joseph Paul
Art History Assistant Prof
Bennett, Jeffrey King
Director of Band & Orchestras
Bergman, Lawrence Joseph
Mathematics & Science Teacher
Bernhardt, Barry Alan
Computer & Technology Teacher
Bradford, Barry N.
Teacher & Activities Director
Brechbiel, Frank
Science Teacher
Briggs, Milton, Jr.
English & PE Teacher
Carnevale, Gregory Charles
Latin & Classics Teacher
Cochrane, David Allen
AP English Teacher
Conrad, Shirley Korpi
Math Teacher

RAPIDS (cont)
Benjamin John
Teacher
, Lois Kroll
h Teacher
s, Roger
: Chair of Physical Sci
on, Gary Lyle
Teacher & Coach
a, Daniel George
graphy Teacher
k, Ann L.
ade Teacher
olski, David Lee
glish & Soc Stud Teacher
Elizabeth Holton
& English Teacher
, Paulette M.
ade Teacher
an, Carla Perry
ade Teacher
in Judson
Teacher
Marcia Beckwith
ade Teacher
h, Robert Bruce
ality Ed Div Chprsn
Marshall
ics Instructor
v, Thomas J.
Algebra & Comp Teacher
Marg
rgarten Teacher
errence Timothy
story Teacher
a, Jon K.
h Grade Teacher
l, Franklin Pierce
Dir & Music Dept Head
na, Carrie Leeser
Music Teacher
n, Nancy Patricia
h & Drama Teacher
, Marilyn Joanne
rade Teacher
mily Joanne
rade Teacher
ma, Ellen M.
h Teacher
mp, Donna Kamerman
an & English Teacher
ga, Jerry A.
Studies & Civics Tchr
ean Edward
Music Instructor
Guzman, Laura
rade Teacher
ski, Judith Ann
ology Teacher
Alese
Teacher
James Andrew
e School Teacher
ury, Nancy K.
matics Teacher
Donald Lee, Jr.
rade Teacher
a, Raymond G.
rade Teacher
Thomas Edward
gy Teacher
ek, Emma, OP
Arts & Literature Teacher
a, Adele
entary School Principal
er, Jerry L.
& Current Events Teacher
ear-Van Horn, Martha
eting & Communication Prof
John, Jr.
Teacher
ood, Walter L.
rof & Screenwriter
Ruth Anne Rudzinski
th-12th Grd Spec Ed Tchr
s, Thaddeus Michael
an & Business Teacher
David E.
sh Teacher
ve, Judith Kathryn
ance Dept Chair
, Betsy Van Noord
th Grade Teacher
rthy, Craig Alan
puterized Accounting Instr
rty, Barbara
istry Professor
Daniel Robert
ssor of History
eux, Mary Zamarripa
rade Teacher & GATE Coord
, Joshua D.
Dept Chprsn & Cmptr Coord
s, Jon Preston
s Director, Music Chrmn
s, William John
ish Teacher
Pearlie M.
0th Grade English Teacher
n, Angelique Rogers
Grade Teacher
Anthony John
her
, Irene Hill
sh & Humanities Teacher
, Elliott Roger
ematics Teacher
s, Ruthie
munication Teacher

Reeder, Ruby Arthettia Lowery
Reading Teacher
Rex, James Logan
English Teacher
Rogers, Mary Alice
2nd Grade Teacher
Rutherford, Joel David, Jr.
Psychology & History Teacher
Scott, Pearl Raak
Retired Elementary Teacher
Seif, Andrew Derk
HS Mathematics Teacher
Sellers, Pamela Cheetwood
English Teacher
Shaltz, Gregory Paul
Latin & Philosophy Teacher
Siegel, Robert William, Jr.
Intern Prin & 3rd Grd Teacher
Truskoski, Richard Joseph, Jr.
Bio, Physiology & Anatomy Tchr
VandenBosch, James
English Professor
VandenBroek, Jon H.
Director of Bands
Vandertol, Obe Jarig
Music & English Teacher
Van Enk, Peter James
Soc Stud Tchr & Act Dir
Van Pernis, Daniel Mark
Guidance Counselor
Videtich, Eva Miller
German Teacher
Vos, James B.
8th Grade History Teacher
Warners, Philip John
Sixth Grade Teacher
Webster, Brian Lee
Asst Prof of Bible & Religion
Wegener, Randall Elliott
English Teacher
Whalen, Rosemarie
Mathematics Teacher
Wierenga, Rebekah DeYoung
English Teacher
Wisnewski, James V.
Art Department Chairman
Yarrington, Martha Cox
4th Grade Teacher
Young, John Thomas
Retired Eng & AP Eng Teacher
GRANDVILLE
Barwacz, John Stanley
Fourth Grade Teacher
Bosscher, Jack
HS Mathematics Teacher
Huizinga, Hank F.
Economics Teacher
Lachniet, Melinda Ann
English Teacher
Stevens, Daniel Arthur
Drafting Teacher
GRANT
Dykema, Judy Kirkeby
6th Grade Math Teacher
Hyzer, Marilyn Lee
Life Skills Teacher
Jensen, Scott Randall
Fourth Grade Teacher
Minnema, Tena Vermeulen
Third & Fourth Grade Teacher
Stickney, James Scott
Social Studies Teacher
Thayer, Lorraine Foster
Biology & Health Teacher
Worfel, Paul Alan
Music Teacher
GRASS LAKE
Poertner, Larry Paul
Mathematics Teacher
GRAYLING
Davis, Lawrence M.
Retired Administrator
Finch, Curtis Ellsworth, Jr.
Assistant Principal
Glicker, David Mark
Eng, Drama & GATE Teacher
Ingvarsson, Martha M. Baker
Language Arts Teacher
Mesack, Judith P.
MS Language Arts Instructor
Spencer, Charles Steven
English Teacher
Stephan, Lacey Don, Jr.
Mathematics & Chemistry Instr
GREENVILLE
Cottingham, Michael Chad
Soc Stud & US History Teacher
DeBaar, Tammy Chase
Science Teacher
Gould, Susan Wiegandt
Band & Orchestra Director
Martin, William R.
Social Studies Teacher
Nichols, Eric E.
8th Grade Social Studies Tchr
Remus, Rita D.
Second Grade Teacher
Roys, Jerald Owen
Fifth Grade Teacher
Stasiuk, Jon Edward
Mathematics Teacher
GROSSE ILE
Ondick, Melanie Kiraly
6th Grd Tchr & Stu Act Dir
Schiebner, Ann Elizabeth
Biology Teacher
GROSSE POINTE
Apkarian, Dyanne Lynne
4th Grade Teacher

Bennett, Gary L.
Mathematics Teacher
Berschback, Thomas
Mathematics & Computer Teacher
Cleary, Mary Ellen E.
Retired Chemistry Teacher
Cook, Marcia D.
English Teacher
Duffield, Tamera N.
Homeroom Teacher
Ely, Jane Sparks
English Teacher
Fildew, Helen Lloyd
Foreign Lang Dept Chairperson
Fultz, Michael S.
Environmental Sci & Bio Tchr
Georgopoulos, Constance Deana
Retired Teacher
Jackson, Carla Renee
English Teacher
Keith, Cecil Gatlin
US Teacher & Soc Stud Chairman
Kiriazis, Irene Zervas
Retired Paraprofessional
Knaus, Louise Ann
Third Grade Teacher
LaSala, Peter L.
4th Grade Teacher
Manzella, Michael Matthew
Sixth Grade Math Teacher
McGaugh, Rufus J.
Social Studies Teacher
Morlan, Gordon Elliott
Chemistry Teacher
Pamerleau, Elizabeth Ruth (Gregory)
Instrumental Music Teacher
Schmidt, James Fredrick
Dean of Student Activities
Seagram, Janet L.
Counselor
Victor, Patrick Michael
Middle School Science Teacher
GROSSE POINTE WOODS
Dempsey, Susan Osip
5th Grade Teacher
GWINN
Blanck, John Jay
Industry & Tech Ed Teacher
Hyska, Francis D.
Science Teacher
Mettlach, Richard Joseph
Physical Ed & Biology Teacher
Parlato, Terry P.
Math Teacher
Ross, Thomas G.
Chemistry Teacher
HALE
Banks, Nancy K.
Band Teacher
Bromund, Alan D.
Mathematics Teacher
O'Farrell, Joni M.
Third Grade Teacher
Shellenbarger, Nelson Lyle
Physical Education Teacher
HAMILTON
Braschler, Douglas William
Mathematics Teacher & Ath Dir
Goodpaster, Jennifer Wilson
Global Studies Teacher
Higgs, Kent Christopher
Math Teacher
Hofman, Richelle Kortering
English Teacher
HAMTRAMCK
Brown, Harold Mark
8th Grade Social Studies Tchr
Green, Mary Dean-Culver
Teacher & Counselor
Hausner, Eleanore
Chemistry & Physics Teacher
Mellor, Susan
Mathematics Teacher
Stonchus, Edward William
Junior High School Teacher
HANCOCK
Miller, Richard Owen
Sr HS Math Teacher & Coach
Plippo, Walter Allen
6th Grade Science Teacher
Schourek, Kristin Raisanen
Biology & AP Biology Teacher
Warrington, Susan Bell
Chem Tchr & Sci Dept Chair
HARBOR BEACH
Block, James J.
Chemistry Teacher
Bowen, Phillip Edward
Sixth Grade Teacher
Dillon, John Daniel
Head Football Coach
Kennedy, Anne M.
K-8th Grade Teacher
Schelke, Troy Philip
Special Education Tchr & Coach
HARBOR SPRINGS
Morrison, Irene Diane Bach
Spanish Teacher
HARPER WOODS
Bernardi, Susan Lynn
French Teacher
Biondo, Deborah Rammalaere
Social Studies Teacher
Bucci, Elisabetta A.
Spanish Teacher
Dandy, Alice Housey
Teacher
Gaerlan, James B.
Athletic Instructor

Gay, Patricia Pucko
Social Studies Teacher
Jogan, Judith A.
American Literature Teacher
Kiefer, Marianne Schervish
Speech, Media & Comm Teacher
Kiepke, Cassandra Janette
High School Mathematics Tchr
Kiselica, John J.
His, Ger & Old Testament Tchr
Loewen, Mary Louise
Rel Stud & Stud Skills Tchr
Moser, Phyllis Marie
Secondary English Teacher
Robertson, Michele LaLonde
Secondary Social Studies Tchr
Rossi, Lillian
Retired Teacher
Stann, Nick C.
Campus Minister
Topel, Stanly Richard
Teacher
Wiese, Kathryn Marie (Staples)
Spanish & Geography Teacher
HARRISON
Alford, Bernard
English & Humanities Instr
Charboneau, Christopher Raymond
Director of Bands
Elden, Lucia Margaret
English & Humanities Instr
Ogg, Mary-Jane Henne
English & Psychology Teacher
Petrongelli, Michael Brian
7th Grade Science Teacher
Seymour, Violet I.
Health Education Teacher
HARRISON TOWNSHIP
Brennan, Bridget
English & Speech Teacher
HART
Borgeld, Theodore Alan
Science & Mathematics Teacher
Carter, Kathryn Heil
English Teacher
Saucedo, December Anne
3rd Grd Tchr & Drama Club Adv
HARTFORD
Boothby, Cheryl Lynn
State Federal Prgms Dir
Godlew, Carol L.
Interim Principal
HARTLAND
Bachman, Freida Dalton
Speech & English Teacher
Drafta, Cindy M.
Computer Teacher
Huber, Jeffrey Hal
5th Grade Teacher
Jagdfeld, Judy Harteay
Fitness & Health Teacher
Merrill, Ray W.
English & Drama Teacher
Merrill, Suzanne Kay (Zimmerman)
Classroom Teacher
Rea, Mary Elizabeth
First Grade Teacher
Ringvelski, Dennis F.
History Teacher
Steinberger, Anna Mae (VanVleet)
Fifth Grade Math Teacher
VanNocker, Barbara Damson
4th Grade Teacher
HASLETT
DuByne, Thomas
High School Science Teacher
HASTINGS
Buehler, Martin Richard
Integrated Science Teacher
Cooklin, Joyce Belliveau
HS Mathematics Teacher
Mann, Douglas William
Drafting Teacher
Melendy, Mary Martha (Potts)
English & Theater Arts Tchr
Merritt, John Frederick
5th Grade Teacher
HAZEL PARK
Stuef, Susan E.
Sixth Grade Teacher
HEMLOCK
Earle, Beverly Ann
Kindergarten Teacher
Hoffman, E. Ida Lyness
Kindergarten Teacher
HESPERIA
Bleiler, Steven Mark
Mathematics Tchr & Dept Chair
DeLong, Marjorie Louise
Retired English Teacher & Prin
Homan, Daniel J.
Biology Teacher
Smith, Kimberly Yates
Computer Teacher
Thompson, Mary Kraley
First Grade Teacher
Walch, Colleen Maynard
Third Grade Teacher
HIGHLAND
Buchta, Robert Wayne
Sci, Lang Arts, His, Comp Tchr
Hill, Judith I.
US His Tchr & Soc Studies Chm
Marinucci, Ronald E.
Government & History Teacher
Schreiber, Paul A.
Director of Bands
Schumann, Douglas Howard
Fourth Grade Teacher

HIGHLAND PARK
Chester, Lillian
Vocal Music Teacher
Franklin, Linda Sue
Scndry Career & Guidance Cnslr
Gardner, Oliver W., Jr.
4th-6th Grade Mathematics Tchr
Shepherd, Dolores Jean Frazier
Eng Instr & Facilitator
Shook, Patricia Diane (Weinstein)
Title I Rdng Tchr
Taylor, Sharon Cunningham
Mathematics Consultant
HILLMAN
Chappa, Lorraine Sharon
Kindergarten Teacher
Kenyon, Marjory James
Jr High Teacher
HILLSDALE
Bell, Kathryn Tamblyn
HS English & Journalism Tchr
Conner, Thomas Hayes
History Professor
Felix, Bradley J.
HS Math Teacher & Chairperson
Livingston, Robert Alan
Band Director
Miller, JoAnne Philipps
6th Grade Teacher
Pastula, Patrick
Reading & English Teacher
Roche, George Charles, IV
Exercise Physiologist
Vincent, William Boyden, Jr.
Retired Science Teacher
HOLLAND
Andree, Robert G.
Retired MS Math Teacher
Boersma, Joseph F.
Printing & Graphic Arts Instr
Bruns, Christi
Math Teacher
Calnin, Roland Frank
5th Grade Teacher
Dershem, Herbert L.
Professor of Computer Science
Dunn, Nicolette Tienstra
Third Grade Teacher
Eberly, Lorelle Stauffer
HS English Teacher
Emery, Wendell A.
Spanish Teacher
Foley, Patrick David
HS Theatre Teacher
Geister, Mark Vern
Business Teacher
Helder, William E.
High School Teacher
Holleman, Karen Ruth
Spanish Teacher
Krueger, Bonnie Hansen
Mathematics Teacher
McNitt, Michelle Ann
HS English & Lang Arts Tchr
Pennings, Timothy J.
Associate Professor of Math
Perez, Robert Anthony
Spanish Teacher
Permesang, John Robert
Science Teacher
Phelps, Charles Michael
PE Tchr & Athletic Dir
Spence, Karla L.
Math Teacher
Vander Kooy, Daniel
Biology Teacher
Vander Meer, James
MS Physical Ed Tchr & Coach
Van Iddekinge, Harold L.
Social Studies Department Chm
Wyckoff, Brent Preston
Social Studies Teacher
Zoerhoff, Georgianna L.
Retired Ger & Eng Teacher
Zwyghuizen, Melanie Anne
HS Span & Geography Teacher
HOLLY
Barton, Gayle Margery
Business Teacher
Dode, Tim E.
English Teacher
Hetherington, David A.
Biology Teacher
Leach, Beverly Jo
Mathematics Teacher
Majeske, Daniel Lee
9th Grade English Teacher
HOLT
Bell, Ruth Marie
4th Grade Teacher
Foy, David Scott
Chemistry Teacher & Coach
HOLTON
Haggart, Kenneth Lee
World Studies Teacher
Kasprzyk, David Joseph
Spanish & English Teacher
Koppenhofer, Beverly Brandt
High School English Teacher
Less, David Gordon
Biology Teacher
Mc Leod, Raymond Charles
6th Grd Sci Teacher & Ath Dir
Slayton, Kim Marie
Fourth Grade Teacher
HOMER
Blashfield, Holly Anne
Middle School Science Teacher
Cooley, Rick W.
Second Grade Teacher

HOMER (cont)
Grogg, Fred E.
Math Teacher
Ham, Frederick Lee
Physics Teacher
Norton, Nancy Ann
College Preparatory Eng Tchr
Peiffer, Betty Page
Third Grade Teacher
Sitkiewicz, Duane Michael
Director of Bands
Welch, Arthur Glen
World History & English Tchr
HOPKINS
Brown, Robert Harry
Ag & Earth Science Teacher
Engel, G. Yvonne Campbell
2nd Grade Teacher
Fein, Lois J.
English Teacher
Lowe, David Allen
Band Director & Soc Stud Tchr
Manchip, Nancy Jo
Spcl Ed Tchr & Stu Cncl Adv
HORTON
Dennison, Denise (Archer)
HS Social Studies Teacher
Nees, Donna M.
Sixth Grade Teacher
HOUGHTON
Anderson, Monica Marie
Graduate Teaching Assistant
Bagley, Susan Tuck
Associate Professor
Beckwith, Mary Ann Liss
Dept of Fine Arts Asst Prof
Chen, Jiquan
Assistant Professor
Daavettila, John Paul
Assoc Prof of Civil Engrng
Dassbach, Carl Henry August
Asst Professor of Sociology
Diehl, Jimmy Fredrick
Professor of Geophysics
Drummer, Thomas David
Statistics Professor
Erm, Greta Penrose
Media Specialist
Filer, Robert Francis
Professor
Gale, James Ray
Professor of Economics
Gilpin, Michael James
Mathematics Professor
Glime, Janice M.
Professor of Biology
Heckel, Richard W.
Metallorgical & Materials Prof
Hicks, Darrell Lee
Prof of Mathematical Sciences
Irish, Michael John
Associate Prof of Music
Jaszczak, John Anthony
Asst Professor & Adj Curator
Jayaraman, Gopal
Prof of Engineering Mechanics
Kim, Nam Kyun
Assoc Prof in Chem Engrng
Krishnan, Ajit C.
Teaching Assistant
Lukowski, John T.
Assistant Professor
Miller, David James
Asst Prof of Philosophy & Comm
Olson, David Alan
Mathematics Instructor
Olson, Tamara
Professor of Mathematics
Olsson, Milton Lee
Department Chair of Fine Arts
Passerello, Chris Edward
Professor of Engrng Mechanics
Paterson, Kurtis G. M.
Asst Prof of Envrnmtl Engrng
Pickens, James Bruce
Forest Management Professor
Rao, Mohan D.
Assoc Prof of Mech Engrng
Reed, David Doss
Professor of Forest Biometrics
Soldan, Alice Faye (Ravi)
Co-Dir Clinical Lab Sci Pgm
Subhash, Ghatu
Asst Prof in Mechanical Engrng
Turino, F. Walter
Algebra & Comp Pgmng Teacher
Walck, Christa L.
Professor of Orgnl Behavior
Weinmann, Sigrid Birke
Associate Prof of Lang & Lit
Wilson, Carol Marie (Monticello)
Second Grade Teacher
Young, Michael Francis
Mechanical Engineering Instr
HOUGHTON LAKE
Blasky, Barbara Lyn
Mathematics Teacher
Drogt, Eric L.
Math Teacher & Bsktbl Coach
Goll, Theodore
Eighth Grade Lang Arts Teacher
Jansen, Elaine Kay (Dieterich)
His, Soc Tchr & Dept Head
Pietchak, Wendell J.
Business & Drivers Ed Teacher
Thompson, Elizabeth Ann
Business Teacher
HOWARD CITY
Badge, Randy Ray
Drafting Teacher
Crosby, Lenore Craigie
8th Grd Lit & US History Tchr
Murphy, Maureen Margaret
Language Arts Teacher
Roberts, Jean Hitchcock
Fourth Grade Teacher
Rodgers, Donna K.
Home Economics Teacher
HOWELL
Dukes, John Roy
High School PE Teacher
Florida, Wayne
English Teacher
Grotenhuis, Bruce Gary
Science Teacher
Groth, Paul Edward
Seventh Grade Math Teacher
Hiller, Wendy Katz
English Teacher
Hirschman, Kathleen Mary
8th Grade Math Teacher
Horton, Richard Kenneth
7th Grade Science Teacher
Johnson, Judith M.
8th Grade Soc Studies Teacher
Noble, Marsha Gessas
Teacher
Rein, Marlene K. (White)
Business & English Teacher
Rivera, Beth Polakowski
High School Mathematics Tchr
Rosenquist, William S.
Accounting Professor
Rubin, Kathi K.
Language Arts Teacher
Saoud, Joanne D.
Speech & Drama Teacher
Shaw, Eric Gordon
Social Studies Teacher
Trader, Kathleen Yax
4th Grade Teacher
VandeBerg, Donna Vichcales
Special Education Teacher
Vertin, Roselyn Romo
Third Grade Teacher
Young, Rebecca Elaine
Science Teacher
HUBBARD LAKE
Schultz, Josephine A.
Retired Elementary Teacher
HUDSON
Storrer, Marcia A.
7th-12th Grade Counselor
Wilson, Rachel Spehar
Director of Bands
HUDSONVILLE
Davis, Robert Andrew
Social Studies & Bible Teacher
Duram, David Richard
HS History & Psychology Tchr
Elliott, Russell L.
5th Grade Teacher
King, Carol Jean
Eighth Grade Spanish Teacher
Laven, Russell John
Fifth Grade Teacher
Lidgard, David Alan
PE & Health Teacher
Reimink, Ronald L.
High School Biology Teacher
Sikkema, James Lee
Science, Chem & Physics Instr
Tovey, John M.
Instrumental & Vocal Teacher
Van Der Meullen, Bruce E.
Teacher & Coach
Van Dyke, Daniel Lee
English Teacher
Warren, Cheryl N.
English & Computer Teacher
IDA
Gianino, Mary Firestone
First Grade Teacher
Hayes, Janice
Fourth Grade Teacher
McCain, Susan Charlton
Kindergarten Teacher
Steffen, Roberta Hockstad
Math & English Teacher
IDLEWILD
Price, Daryl J.
American History Teacher
IMLAY CITY
DeClark, Tom Edward
Science Teacher
Gromak, Sheila A.
English & Publications Teacher
Mc Donald, Jill Blinn
At-Risk Program Coordinator
Topie, Louise Coscarelli
3rd Grade Teacher
INDIAN RIVER
Benn, Mark Hubert
5th Grade Teacher
Moore, Linda Kay
Kindergarten Teacher
Passino, Gail Warren
High School English Teacher
Sackett, Carolyn M.
6th Grade Teacher
INKSTER
Martin, Juanita Sanford
Principal
Mc Queen, Deborah Sharpe
Language Arts Teacher
INTERLOCHEN
Bushkova, Julia
Violin Teacher
Corum, Everett Eugene
Theatre Arts & Prfrmnc Tchr
Driscoll, Jack
Writer-In-Residence
Gaede, Jean Maraldo
Liberal Arts Division Chprsn
Gilb, Tyra Ellen
Flute Instructor
Hintze, Howard H.
English Instructor
Kamischke, Ellen J.
Mathematics Teacher
Montee, David D.
Theatre Arts Division Chairman
Murphy, Robert Henderson
Organ & Piano Instructor
Parsons, Jean Noble
Visual Arts Div Chair
Randall, Jack Alden
Chemistry Teacher
Randolph, Sharon Kay
Dance Div Chair & Ballet Instr
Ross, John Stanley
Conducting & Mus Theory Instr
Sears, William A.
Coord Jazz Studies & Sax Instr
IONIA
Ames, Orma Compton
English Teacher
Covell, Cynthia Louise
Math & Science Teacher
Daniel, Rose Marie
Choir Teacher
Hartman, Anna Ruby
Retired Teacher
Hesche, Keith W.
Teacher
Johnson, Rene Louise
Fourth Grade Teacher
Nevins, Vincent Neil
Political Sci & Psych Teacher
Trevan, Ken
High School Drafting Teacher
Voet, Barbara Morley
Kindergarten Teacher
IRON MOUNTAIN
Baiel, Linda Manner
Sixth Grade Teacher
Bailey, Timothy Joseph
History Teacher
Cavalieri, Francis R.
Middle School Math Teacher
Davidson, Robert Harry
Social Stud & PE Tchr
Feak, Paul Brian
7th-12th Grade Technology Tchr
Gardner, Marianne Lagina
Middle School English Teacher
Johnson, Connie Lou Manko
Third Grade Teacher
Novara, Charles John
Fourth Grade Teacher
Rossler, Elouise Germann
English & Journalism Teacher
Swan, Kenneth William
Fifth Grade Teacher
Wender, Cheryl Ann (Menghini)
7th Grd Rdng & Soc Stud Tchr
IRONWOOD
Holcombe, Linda Rundam
Vocal Music Director
Kerkes, George
6th Grade Teacher
Krznarich, James K.
Eighth Grade English Teacher
Niemi, Daniel W.
English Teacher
ISHPEMING
Boburka, Lawrence M.
Spanish Teacher
Chaperon, Juleen R.
Freshman English & French Tchr
Gauthier, L. Barbara Medlyn
Business Education Teacher
Hammar, Thomas Stephen
Mathematics Teacher
Huhta, Julianne Woitulewicz
Elementary Guidance Counselor
Nyman, Steven William
Chemistry Teacher
Ogea, Lois Lindholm
Science & Mathematics Teacher
Smetana, Sandra Kay
HS Mathematics Teacher
Upton, Martha VanderBrook
Seventh Grade Teacher
ITHACA
Buschle, Rosilyn Theisen
4th Grade Teacher
Evon, Darin Edward
Science Teacher
Kemler, John E.
Fifth Grade Teacher
JACKSON
Aikman, Rebecca Roush
French Teacher
Ambs, Donna LaFaive
Bus Dept Chprsn & Tchr
Berlet, Myrna Irene
Prof of Bio & Dept Chair
Bronson, Janet Ruth (DeWitt)
Chemistry Teacher
Brusseau, Cheryl Elizabeth
Mathematics Teacher
Burnette, Ronald Dean
Vocal Music & Drama Teacher
Chadderton, Colleen Daly
Associate Professor of Nursing
Cook, Randall J.
Principal
Cox, James R.
Data Processing Instructor
Crites, Elsie Collett
Retired Elementary Teacher
Crowley, Daniel Patrick
Business Education Teacher
Cryderman, Brent Daniel
Instrumental Music Director
Csage, Florence Nicita
Transitional First Grade Tchr
Daugherty, James R.
English Teacher
Dodge, Richard Norris
Prof of Math & Engrng Sciences
Falter, Carl Francis, Jr.
Theology Teacher
Gass, Thomas W.
English Department Chair
Gustwiller, Carter Paul
Assistant Professor
Haney, Susan Kay
Teacher & Counselor
Henderson, John William
Chemistry Professor
Hoyt, Mark R.
HS Social Studies Teacher
Kaiser, Duane Norbert
Physical Education Teacher
Klinger, Brian F.
Mathematics Teacher
LaMothe, Esther Gray
Educational Consultant
Larner, Yvonne Porkarski
High School Math Instructor
Marin, Fritz M.
Marketing Instructor
Mc Inerney, Jean, IHM
Spanish Teacher
Miller, Charles N.
Athletic Director
Murphy, Carolyn S.
Sixth Grade Teacher
Neville, Pat E.
Math Teacher
Niedzielski, Susan Byington
Fifth Grade Teacher
Pitts, Shirley Ann
10th-11th Grd English Teacher
Prus, Kathy Anne
Fifth Grade Teacher
Ramker, Mike Arthur
Teacher & Basketball Coach
Rathje, John Roy
Minister & Counsel to Families
Ross, Michael Stewart
Foreign Languages Chairman
Seal, Dale L.
English & Literature Teacher
Shaner, Joel K.
HS Music Teacher
Spitler, Shawn Charles
Social Studies Teacher
Tumey, Rita M. Carlson
7th Grd Language Arts Teacher
Ulstad, Samuel John
High School Math Teacher
Walker, Lisa Rachael
English Dept Chair & Teacher
Wilson, Wade A.
Sixth & Seventh Grade Teacher
Woodruff, Ron Allen
English & Journalism Teacher
JENISON
Adrianson, Gary L.
Chemistry Teacher
Clark, Brenda (Heykoop)
Marketing Instructor
Halliburton, Nancy Koop
Second Grade Teacher
Jautakis, Carl Anthony
Social Studies Dept Chair
Lancaster, Don R.
Tchr & Bldg Tech Coord
Peterson, Craig A.
Business & Social Studies Tchr
Wegener, Doreen Smith
Math Teacher & Dept Chprsn
JOHANNESBURG
Biehl, Kathryn Slat
Second Grade Teacher
Compton, Brian Richard
Chemistry & Physics Teacher
Davis, Fred Richard
Math & Computer Science Tchr
JONESVILLE
Loveless, John G.
Physics & Visual Arts Teacher
Watson, Nancy Nunn
Mathematics Teacher
KALAMAZOO
Angerman, Evelyn Carlson
Adjunct Professor of Music
Armstrong, Ervin Maurice
Physical Education Teacher
Babcock, Ralph E.
Science Studies Instr
Balmer, Cheryl A.
5th Grade Teacher
Bergman, Donald Lee
History Teacher
Blough, David John
Math Teacher
Burch, Ronald N.
English Teacher
Campbell, Donald G.
Instructor
Carlson, Daniel George
Mathematics Teacher
Cherpas, Patricia
English Instructor
Eckert, Lucille Smith
Substitute Teacher
Eenigenburg, Paul Jon
Professor of Mathematics
Ehlers, Anthony Raymond
Retired Teacher
Eichler, Victor B.
Coordinator of Med Asst Prgms
Elman, R. Amy
Asst Prof of Political Science
Evans, Julie Ann
Music Professor
Felkel, Barbara Ridge
Frgn Lang Dpt Hd & Latin Tchr
Fox, James Nelson
Drafting Instructor
Fox, Lyla
English Teacher
Gill, Pat
Associate Professor of English
Godfrey, Mary Noguess
Drama Teacher & Coach
Hamann, Richard J.
7th Grade Teacher
Hancock, Audrey Ann (Shields)
Fifth Grade Teacher
Haynick, Ann Walker
7th Grade Language Arts Tchr
Hess, Jeanne L.
Asst Prof of PE & Vllybl Coach
Kitzman, Joe Luke
English Instructor
Kloosterman, John
Retired Fourth Grade Teacher
Leonard, Jerry Alan
Fifth Grade Teacher
LeRoy, Sonja
Marketing & Computer Teacher
Mc Carthy, Michael William
English Instructor
Mc Cray, Kimberly J.
Fourth Grade Teacher
Mc Neal, Bertha Barbee
Vocal Music Tchr & Choir Dir
Mills, Karen M.
French Teacher
Mollhagen, Nancy Elizabeth
Art Instructor
Ogrin, Janene Sue Andersen
Mid & High Schl English Tchr
Roederer, Silvia
Associate Professor of Music
Rumph, Gail Searcy
Social Studies Teacher
Savicke, Gregory Joseph
Head Cross Country Coach
Schmeichel, Jean DeBoen
Asst Dir of Elem Spec Ed
Schrepper, Susan Modderman
Lang Arts & Soc Stud Teacher
Scripture, Douglas Paul
Adjunct Business Instructor
Steele, Brian Curtis
Middle Schl Math, Science Tchr
Stenger, Geneva Louise Smith
First Grade Teacher
Swearingen, Clyde Heenan
Retired Teacher
Swift, Robert Lee
Sixth Grade Teacher
Tod, Stephen Robert
English Teacher
Turner, James R.
Assistant Professor of Music
VerHey, Eric Eugen
Fifth Grade Teacher
Westra, Nicholas J.
Public Safety Program Manager
Williams, Stanford Earl
Adjunct Instructor
Wolf, Kathleen A.
Health & Biology Teacher
Zantjer, Angeline Speahar
Executive Director
KALKASKA
Fennell, James Matthew
Administrator & History Tchr
McAnallen, Sandra Lee
Spanish & English Teacher
Swoverland, Ricky David
HS Math Teacher
KEEGO HARBOR
Herman, James Frederick
Teacher of Gifted & Talented
KENT CITY
Evers, Jill M.
High School Science Teacher
McClintock, Steven William
Biology Teacher
Ross, Susan Cocola
Spanish & History Teacher
KENTWOOD
Klein, David Scott
Band Director
KINCHELOE AFB
Brood, Deborah D.
Title 1 Paraprofessional
Perry, Ellen Kline
Elementary PE Teacher
KINDE
Herford, Susan K.
1st Grade Teacher
KINGSFORD
Allis, Steven Don
Physics Teacher
Cummings, William John
Spanish Teacher
Davidson, Janet Kellenberger
Media Specialist
Maahs, Sharon L. (Maki)
Lang Arts & Soc Stud Tchr

FORD (cont)
ieber Arthur
Govt, Law & You Teacher
en, Robert John
School Science Teacher
Lorie Mileski
matics Teacher
aki, Susan Cox
Grade Math & Sci Tchr
n, Gina Marie
h Teacher
Mary Kay Backlund
ngmt & Business Teacher
TON
Marilyn Kapp
English Teacher
obert A.
ade Tchr
n, Paul Brent
Studies Teacher
CITY
rd, Sheryl Gregg
rgarten Teacher
n, Laura Elise
e School Counselor
LEELANAU
Ruth M.
Cheerleading Coach
LINDEN
d, Craig Arnold
Studies Teacher
ODESSA
y, Margaret Elaine (Custer)
Grade Teacher
ORION
ornelia Lewan
h Teacher
Michael
istry Teacher
regory M.
matics Teacher
, Ulla Egelhof
al Education Teacher
Ardis L.
h Grd Eng & History Tchr
uth Ellen
sh Language Arts Teacher
ch, Jan Elizabeth
sh Teacher
Kenneth Paul
h Teacher & Coach
n, Diane F.
on & Literature Teacher
Theo Francis (Tyre)
uage & Fine Arts Teacher
VIEW
, Nancy Beth
ematics & Biology Teacher
ll, Kathleen Cheever
School Guidance Counselor
Sharon K.
rade Teacher
ERTVILLE
Kathleen Ermish
n Grade Teacher
E
, Jane E.
Processing Teacher
s, Joyce Karen
sh Teacher
, Brian L.
intendent
Ellen Bakka
gh Language Arts Tchr
NG
shine, Linda Joan (Terry)
Grade Teacher
Alex
cs Professor
er, Terry Lynn
istry & Algebra Teacher
Lynn Nielsen
Management Educator
, Lori Ellen
Grade Teacher
on, Kathryn Marcinkowski
sh Teacher
on, Vicki S.
rade Basic Block Teacher
ell, Jill
Counselor
ion-Jones, Norma Ervin
Management Teacher
Whitney Jo
Teacher
on, Gregory J.
ness & Accounting Teacher
ad, William L.
o Tchr & Var Swim Coach
, Barbara Fox
nd Grade Teacher
rancine M. Libera
d History Teacher
atkowski, Pamela Cusick
ocational Teacher
ads, Peter Allen
essor of Humanities
, Johnnie Ruth Tillery
ish Teacher
James Riley
c Prof of Christian Ed
, Jane Brackett
ch, Theatre & Eng Teacher
Elizabeth Finnell
2th Grade Orchestra Dir
Samuel F.
n Tchr & Sci Dept Chprsn
r, Janice Hardesty
n & Orch Director

Gebhardt, Mary Lou Felter
Kindergarten Teacher
Ginther, Brenda VanGolen
Chemistry Teacher
Hartley, Eric E.
Mathematics Teacher
Herner, Susan Mc Neely
Mathematics Teacher
Hightower, Judith Ann
Social Studies Teacher
Hillman, Mary Richardson
Asst Prof of Business Careers
Holcomb, Grace L. Trisch
Graduate Student
Johnson, Gail Elaine
Design Instructor
Kamm, Sherry Ray
8th Grade Math Teacher
Kissling, Paul Joseph
Professor of Old Testament
Langdon, Gary Charles
Chemistry Teacher
Larson, Richard John
Hum, Art & Music His Instr
Lathrop, Mark Christopher
High School Physics Teacher
May, Shellye Regina
Social Studies Teacher
Mc Crae, Nancy Radtke
Fr Tchr & Frgn Lang Dept Chm
Mehaffey, Mark E.
High School Art Instructor
Miank, Timothy Alan
Professor
Mitchell-Withers, Myrna Jeanne
Global Cultures & US His Tchr
Paquet-Howard, Ann B.
Second Grade Teacher
Partlow, Kathy A.
History & English Teacher
Pentecost, Susan Cheadle
Science Teacher
Pogoncheff, Andon Blagoy
His Teacher & Sci Dept Chm
Pohlonski, Brent Allen
Mathematics Teacher
Quinn, Patrick Joseph
Bible Teacher
Robison, Norman L.
Fifth Grade Teacher
Rysztak, Marcia Poniers
Child Development Assoc Prof
Rzepecki, Beth Steadman
4th Grade Teacher
St George, Patricia Bon
Special Education Teacher
Savage, Elizabeth Lynn
Adjunct Instructor
Scheetz, Janet M.
5th Grade Teacher
Schultz, Mary Christine
Third Grade Teacher
Schuon, Mary Jane
Drama & English Teacher
Slater, Glenda Richmond
Volunteer Consultant
Small, Roger Steven
8th Grade World History Tchr
Stiles, James Richard
Retired High School Counselor
Studley, John Clarence
5th & 6th Grade Teacher
Walczak, Patricia Powell
Asst Professor of Accounting
Walker, Alfred Albert
Secondary Schl Vocational Adv
Warren, Joseph A., III
Professor of History
Wedel, Patricia Ann (Reichard)
Elementary Teacher
LAPEER
Bradley, Timothy Edward
Business Teacher
Dingman, Marilyn Holtkamp
Former Mathematics Teacher
Kowalski, Barbara J.
4th Grade Teacher
Namenye, Sharon M.
Math Teacher
Richardson, Barbara J.
5th & 6th Grade Math Teacher
Sabada-Davey, D'Ann
Language Arts Teacher
Shurkey, Patricia Cesefske
Third Grade Teacher
Supernault, Michael
Naturalist Teacher
Tessmer, Sarah Mc Kenzie
HS Mathematics Teacher
Wadsworth, Craig
7th-8th Grade PE & Health Tchr
Walker, Bradley G.
Chemistry Teacher
Warner, Peggy Weis
English Teacher
Weiss, Carl Joseph
Science Teacher
LATHRUP VILLAGE
Sullivan, Thomas William
Retired English Teacher
LAWRENCE
Dean, David Newell
High School Science Teacher
DeMink, Jane E.
6th Grade Teacher
Lottridge, Kimberly Gayle
Special Education Teacher
McCurley, Debbie (Williams)
Reading Specialist

Mickle, Susie Phillips
Retired Elementary Teacher
LAWTON
Bullock, Kris Alan
Teacher
Every, Calvin James
6th & 7th Grd Science Teacher
LELAND
Taylor, Joy M.
Third Grade Teacher
LEROY
Baker, Larry K.
Band Director
Burch, Cecil R.
6th Grade Teacher
Hunter, Ross M.
Third Grade Teacher
Mathews, Harriet R.
Kindergarten Teacher
Miller, Harvey G.
Eng, Jrnlsm Tchr & Dept Head
Snook, Kimberly Jane
Biology Teacher
Tuttle, George Lee
Mathematics Teacher
LESLIE
Sachar, Beverly Jean
French & English Teacher
Swaenepoel, Jane Coleen
Second Grade Teacher
Zimmerman, Robert Paul
Fourth Grade Teacher
LINCOLN
Syrett, Terry Douglas
World History Teacher
LINCOLN PARK
Dever, Anita Hill
English Teacher
Donovan, James Harold
High School Band Director
Gray, James Marion
Biology Teacher
Mittino, Judith Shaughnesy
Sixth Grade Teacher
Ostrowski, Lillian Margaret
Fourth Grade Teacher
LINDEN
Totzke, Cliff L., Jr.
Soc Science Dept Chair & Tchr
LINWOOD
Jameson, Bonnie BerBerick
Third Grade Teacher
LITCHFIELD
Hill, Lynn Ross
English Teacher
LIVONIA
Adamczyk, Jill Elizabeth
Social Studies Teacher
Booker, David Louis
Instrumental Music Teacher
Bowers, Athella-Anne, Jr.
Communication Arts Professor
Ciupek, Kathleen Garske
Preschool Tchr & Pvt Tutor
Davlin, Karen Yvonne
Fourth Grade Teacher
Florence, Frances Capoccia
Social Studies Teacher
Gay, Sibylle Voigt
German Teacher
Gugala, Kay Irene
Spanish Teacher
Hurick, Patricia Dianne
Counselor & Instructor
James, Beth Free
Fifth Grade Teacher
Karoub, James T.
Counselor
Kuratko, Louis G., Jr.
Junior ROTC Instructor
Ladd, Katherine Armstrong
English Teacher
Lesko, John Steven, Jr.
Professor of Physics
Love, Alisha Marie
Coach
Marmul, Laurel Barbara G. K.
Eighth Grade Teacher
Massucci, Lynn
Span Tchr & Frgn Lang Dept Chm
Muzbeck-Spence, Nancy V.
Sixth Grade Teacher
Quick, Ronald D.
English Tchr & Dept Chairman
Quinn, Barbara Dowdy
Psych Dept Chprsn & Assoc Prof
Rada0Levalley, Rose Ann
Fine Arts Dept Head
Salvati, Constance Wiland
Social Studies Teacher
Smith, Sherri L. (Copi)
HS Mathematics Teacher
Taylor, JuJuan Carolyn
Assoc Prof of Comm Arts
Tomlinson, James Brooksha
Teacher
Turnquist, Claudia Jeanne
High School Guidance Counselor
Udrys, Janina Radvila
Mathematics Professor
Valenti, Judith Bantle
Adj Asst Professor of English
Vance, Gary L.
Mathematics Tchr & Consultant
Williams, Larry Gene
Mathematics Professor
Wolf, Robert James
High School Science Teacher

LOWELL
Akers, Kenneth O.
History & Reading Teacher
Beachler, Christine Ann
Accounting & Computer Teacher
Frasier, Susan Meisner
Mathematics Chairperson
LUDINGTON
Burden, Mary Adele (Cordes)
5th Grade Teacher
Dennis, Michael Dean
Tchr of Trainable Mntlly Imprd
Erickson, Jon J.
English Teacher
Gancarz, Robert Walter
Eng, History & Geography Tchr
Genson, Dennis James
Mathematics Teacher
Kudwa, Thomas James
Calculus & Physics Tchr
Petersen, Michael Wayne
5th Grade Elementary Teacher
Quisenberry-Alvarado, April A.
Spanish Teacher
Rudy, Linda
5th Grade Teacher
Shank, Gene O.
Retired Social Studies Teacher
Thompson, Lynn Palmer
Retired 4th Grade Teacher
MACOMB
Adams, Bill
Counselor
Agnello, Bobbie Reichard
Sociology & Psychology Teacher
Baedke, Dianne Krentler
Child Care Teacher
Baranowski, Bonnie Jean
Science Teacher
Bunton, Roger H.
Technology Education Instr
Conachen, Cathleen J.
HS History Teacher
Cusenza, Daniel A.
6th-8th Grd Spec Ed Teacher
Ebert, Faith Barthel
World History & Health Teacher
Foor, Gerald Raymond
Social Studies Teacher
Grepke, Neil Michael
English Teacher
Kitchen, Ruth Long
Lang Arts, Soc Stud, Tech Tchr
Lanyi, Linda Kay
English Dept Chair & Teacher
Lesko, Thomas Paul
Mathematics Teacher
Palmeri, Patricia Ann-Norton
Child Care Teacher
Stroh, James E.
Drafting Teacher
Vrana, Joanne Puzzuoli
Foreign Language Teacher
Walker, Donna Jean
Third Grade Teacher
Wolf, Charles Harold
Chemistry Teacher
Young, Susan A.
Chemistry Teacher
MADISON HEIGHTS
Connelly, Catherine
Eng & Lang Arts Teacher
Kniivila, Louisa Ann (Hanna)
5th Grade Teacher
Leddy, William
Mathematics Teacher
Lowrie, Katherine Rachelle
HS English & Journalism Tchr
Maiuri, Richard Peter
Religion Teacher
Milch, Kenneth Harris
Director of Bands
O'Shea, Maryann DeLoof
Language Arts Teacher
Pricer, Wayne Francis
Director of Counseling & Guid
Ronney, Maureen Splane
French Teacher
Smith, David Earl
English & Journalism Teacher
Toma, James David
English Teacher
Uhlmann, Jamie Ann
PE & Social Studies Tchr
Wrobel, David A.
Science Tchr & Head Ftbl Coach
Zarro, Joan Schaack
Third Grade Teacher
MANCELONA
Nixon, Mark Edward
Industrial Arts Teacher
Reeves, Joel Scott
English Teacher
MANCHESTER
Diedrich, James L.
Industrial Technology Teacher
Jansen, Ronald Thomas
Health & PE Teacher
MANISTEE
Demeuse, Donald
Sixth Grade Teacher
Kelly, Jackie Mai
6th Grade Teacher
Laursen, Margaret Atkins
Third Grade Teacher
Peterson, Barry Russell
6th Grade Teacher
MANISTIQUE
Kahle, Richard E.
Retired Mathematics Teacher

Sablack, Rosemary Ann Leach
English & Pub Speaking Tchr
White, Susan Marie
Band Director
MANTON
Del Bello, Floyd L.
Social Studies Teacher
Schaaf, Gordon Ray
Business Education Instructor
MAPLE CITY
Bloch-Cox, Kristen Kaye
Business & Computer Ed Teacher
MARCELLUS
Afton, Daniel J.
Science Teacher
DeCou, David Paul
Ath Dir, Eng & Soc Stud Tchr
Holmes, Gary M.
6th Grade Teacher
McNamee, Kathleen Veronica
High School English Teacher
Mulnix, David G.
Fifth Grade Teacher
Orange, Tally (Cone)
Math Teacher & Dept Chrprsn
MARENISCO
Gulan, Jeffrey Roy
Social Studies Teacher
MARINE CITY
Bollivar, Kenneth Lee
Sixth Grade Teacher
Burmann, Penelope Elaine (Cagle)
Mathematics & Computer Teacher
Cavis, Anthony John
High School English Teacher
Drews, Beverly Howe
Mathematics Teacher
Maxwell, Timothy Joseph
Teacher
McClellan, Leslie M.
Reading & Language Arts Instr
Saunders, Alan F.
Mathematics Teacher
Schuett, Nicole Bonnette
Mathematics Teacher
MARION
Rice, Lynn Leslie
Fourth & Fifth Grade Teacher
MARLETTE
Clark, Rosann Timpone
Eighth Grade English Teacher
Lange, Duane N.
Curriculum Specialist
Sauder, Lou Ann
4th Grade Teacher
Wilson, Julie Ann (Woods)
Bio, Chem & Spanish Teacher
MARNE
VandenBerg, Daniel W.
Fourth Grade Teacher
MARQUETTE
Acocks, James Raymond, Jr.
Anatomy Teacher
Andresen, Jacqueline (Goad)
High School Teacher
Anthony, Robert Jeffery
Math Teacher
Balding, Richard Allan
Math Teacher
Brogan, James J.
Mathematics Teacher
Bullock, Ken
Social Studies & At Risk Tchr
Carr, Louis Orville
High School Swimming Coach
Coffey, Lauriann Gant
First Grade Teacher
Contois, Roger D.
6th Grade Teacher
Coombs, Richard Charles
Science Educator
Crotty, Bonnie Kay (Bittner)
Middle School English Teacher
Crowley, Carolyn Ann
Special Ed & Elem Tchr
Demboski, Richard Charles
Science & Social Studies Tchr
Donckers, Judy Luoma
Hnrs Span Tchr & Yearbook Adv
Etten, Linda Wendt
Teacher & Building Cmptr Coord
Humpula, Dennis Keith
Industrial Arts & Tech Tchr
Kotila, Peter Martin
Sci, Soc Studies & Rdng Tchr
Marchiol, Lou
Chemistry Teacher
Mc Kinney, Mary Tiziani
Sixth Grade Teacher
Murphy, Ruth Jensen
Third Grade Teacher
Nelson, Mary Louise
Mathematics Instructor
Norton, Janis Shier
Orchestra Director
Peterson, Nancy Thode
French Teacher & Dept Head
Phare, Scott Brian
Social Studies Teacher
Randell, Clyde Arnold
Social Studies Teacher
Raskin, Janalee Mary
English Teacher
Seeke, Thomas Roger
Mathematics Teacher
Smith-Potts, Kimberly Ann
Science Teacher
Striler, Brenda Lee
HS Art Teacher

MARQUETTE (cont)
Turenne, David S.
AP US History & Algebra I Tchr
Vezzetti, Deborah Rose Kangas
Fourth Grade Teacher
Wickstrom, Janice Fink
Fifth Grade Teacher
Wilson, Kevin Dale
Director of Bands
Witting, James Howard
Business, Voc Teacher & Coord
Wozniak, Carl Alan
Projects Coordinator
MARSHALL
Anderson, Kenton Victor
6th-8th Grade Teacher
Armstrong, Benjamin Earl
HS Business Teacher
Wingerter, Pamela Kay
English Teacher
MARTIN
Bogdan, Frederic A.
Band Director
Punches, Margery Shubel
English & Spanish Teacher
MARYSVILLE
Coe, Colleen Ann
11th Grade Amer Lit Teacher
George, David Michael
Chemistry & Physics Teacher
Jones, Kim Joseph
Art Teacher
Marshall, Thomas Robert
Mathematics Teacher
Meier, Barry Dean
High School Teacher
Nickonovich, Andrew Scott
Physical Science Teacher
Vonalt, Fred L.
English Teacher
Winston, Shawn Rodney
Government & At-Risk Teacher
MASON
Arnold, Brenda Susan
Second Grade Teacher
Campbell, William Edward, Jr.
Life Science Teacher
Coss, Thomas Allen
Social Studies Teacher & Coach
Fellows, David Charles
HS Assistant Principal
Hogan, Zoanne M.
English Teacher
Juall, Victoria Dorothy
Cosmetology Instructor
Messins, Elaine Messing
English Teacher
Riley, Donovan Patrick
8th Grd Earth Science Teacher
Warren, Scott William
Secondary Teacher
MATTAWAN
Cloney, J. Michael
Social Studies Teacher
Kuthe, Christine Powell
Math Teacher
Mills, David Lee
Math Teacher & Dept Chairman
Silber, Dean Barton
English & History Tchr
MAYVILLE
Ahrens, Mary Mindykowski
Second Grade Teacher
Bishop, Elizabeth Ann
Business Education Teacher
Bryan, Steven Scott
Missionary
Campbell, Marilyn Dean
Band Director
Collon, Dennis Ray
PE & Industrial Ed Teacher
Coopes, Lawrence M.
Middle School English Teacher
Kreger, Clare Lyle
HS Social Science Teacher
La Graff, John Martin
High School English Teacher
Tallman, Robert
Science Teacher
MELVINDALE
Hall, James E.
High School Counselor
Yeager, Barbara Jean
Social Studies Teacher
MEMPHIS
McNabb, Darin Lee
Band Tchr
MENDON
Lutz, Calvin Eugene
English Teacher
MENOMINEE
Karasti, John G.
Physics & Science Teacher
Ranzinger, Bruce Edwin
Science Teacher
Wills, John Michael
7th & 8th Grade Lang Arts Tchr
MERRILL
Curtiss, Michael Paul
Band Teacher
Devault, Theresa Lee
Learning Specialist
Ellis, William Duane
Social Studies Teacher
Franson, Chantal Merrill
Second Grade Teacher
Gardner, Anne M.
3rd Grade Teacher
Locke, Carol J. (Seres)
2nd Grade Teacher

Schomaker, Pamela Harper
Elementary Principal
MESICK
Roman, Richard W., Jr.
Elem Art Teacher
METAMORA
Spangler, Patricia Dailey
6th Grd Language Arts Tchr
MICHIGAN CTR
Coons, Deborah E.
Jr Sr High School Counselor
Curl, Gerry William
Second Grade Teacher
Griggs, Tony Wayne
Track Coach
Hritz, Marti C.
Vocal Music & Band Teacher
Stersic, Timothy Maxwell
Secondary Spanish Teacher
MIDDLETON
Andersen, Connie Jo
Business Education Teacher
MIDDLEVILLE
Domire, Joyce Marie
Life Skills Teacher
Miner, Phyllis Ann
5th Grade Teacher
MIDLAND
Adair, William Jay
Art Teacher
Bennett, Jeffrey Albyn
Acctng Dept Prof & Chairman
Blanchard, Constance Kelm
Spanish Teacher
Brooks, James Timothy
Administrative Assistant
Buller, Carol Harris
German Teacher
Chapin, Laurie Pinkham
Third Grade Teacher
Cooper, Robert G.
Mathematics Teacher
Dodge, Michelle Rene
Science Teacher
Farkas, Joan Theresa
Eng & Theater Teacher
Flaminio, Mary Ann Crispigna
Career Coordinator
Forbes, Daniel A.
Assistant Principal & Teacher
Karr, Carol Ann (Fritz)
Fifth Grade Teacher
Karr, Roger A.
PE & Social Studies Teacher
Kell, Delmar Arnold
4th Grade Tchr & Athletic Dir
King, Wendy Winters
Gifted & Talented Teacher
Krauss, Patricia Moeckel
Oral Communications Teacher
Maxwell, Jerene M.
Fifth Grade Teacher
Monroe, William Henry, II
Band Director
Nelsen, Stephanie Ewig
Business Education Teacher
Unkovich, Anna
7th-9th Grade Teacher
Whitehead, Larry Dale
High School Math Teacher
Williams, Thomas Harold
English Teacher
Wirsing, Gary A.
Mathematics Teacher
Yoder, Sarah Laylin
English Teacher
MILAN
Avery, Matthew Glenn
Computer Aided Drafting Tchr
Fahlstrom, Thomas Edward
Speech & English Teacher
Frank, Meredith Rose
English Teacher
MILLINGTON
Bickel, Elaine Carol (Petzold)
Eighth Grade Teacher
Dawson, Barbara Crumback
6th Grade Teacher
Giffels, Linda Sue (Stroope)
PE, Science & English Teacher
Klouse, Mary E.
Second Grade Teacher
Leach, Linda L.
Sixth Grade Teacher
Ruhanen, Marcia K.
6th Grade Teacher
MIO
Mc Falda, Timothy John
Industrial Tech & Math Teacher
Poff, John William
Substitute Teacher
Reed, Janet L.
Secondary English Teacher
MOLINE
Beute, Patricia Hoff
Fourth Grade Teacher
De Young, Karen
6th-8th Grd Language Arts Tchr
Sage, Clif E.
Social Studies Teacher
MONROE
Arrasmith, Mary de Aguiar
High School Soc Studies Tchr
Barron, Alan Gerard
Sixth Grade Teacher
Barton, Wanda Richeson
Third Grade Teacher
Berry, N. Kathleen
Math Teacher

Bezeau, Bruce
Biology & Science Teacher
Calkins, Linda Loonis
Art Teacher
Carollo, Paul Alan
Industrial Technology Teacher
Duvendack, Beth Gross
4th Grade Teacher
English, Gary E.
AP Biology & Anatomy Teacher
Evans, Ronald W.
Business Education Instructor
Felder, Mark Bernard
Band Director
Finzel, Diane Lynn
6th Grade Teacher
Finzel, Timothy Vernon
7th-8th Grade Science Teacher
Fiorani, Amy M.
French Teacher
Gray, Betty Jayne (Argo)
5th Grade Teacher
Hall, Mark V.
Counselor
Hendrix, Carolyn A.
Business Education Teacher
Henning, Eleanor Marie
Retired Elem Tchr & Principal
Hoppert, Scott David
Eighth Grade US History Tchr
Jones, Linda D.
First Grade Teacher
Kauza, Beverly Jean
Sixth Grade Teacher
Knapp, Garry Scott
Business & Social Studies Tchr
Kos, Susan Mae
7th Grade Teacher
Lauwers, Raymond E.
Theology Teacher
Lemerand, James S.
Police Officer & Coach
Meyers, Elva English
Third Grade Teacher
Pancone, John Publio
Kindergarten Teacher
Paquette, Anne Vernice
Retired Jr HS English Teacher
Pente, Julie A.
Mathematics Teacher
Pursley, Steven Neale
Third Grade Teacher
Raymond, John Edward
Fifth Grade Teacher
Ready, J. Edward
5th Grade Teacher
Roberti, Mary Teresa
Retired Comm Coll Instructor
Sandersen, Joseph H.
Math Tchr & Dean of Discipline
Schultz, Thomas F.
Criminal Justice Instructor
Servis, Mathew Alan
4th Grade Teacher
Servis, Robert Meier
Jrnlsm & Social Studies Tchr
Speare, Philip John, Jr.
Algebra & Geometry Teacher
Terrasi, Russ C.
Bus Dept Head & Mrktg Tchr
Vallade, James Kenneth
Mathematics Teacher
Villarreal, Lisa
Secondary English Teacher
Waggoner, David Lusher
Professor of Chemistry
Werner, Andrea Novak
Counselor & Stu Council Adv
Wilson, C. Gary
Associate Professor of Art
Wittscheck, Jacqueline Ludwig
First Grade Teacher
Woltmann, Jack August, Jr.
Assoc Prof of Resp Therapy
MONTAGUE
Dunn, Jeffery Allen
Bible Teacher
Watt, Timothy Alan
Director of Bands
MONTROSE
Juarez, Angela M.
Private Tutor
Paron, Terry Bigelow
6th Grade Writing Teacher
Smith, Helen Mary
Physical Education Instructor
Yokobosky, Joseph W.
Comp Tech Dept Chair & Teacher
MORENCI
Tursak, Rosemary Kennedy
HS English Teacher
Wilkins, Char-Lene Reinhart
High School English Teacher
MORLEY
Defrain, Scott Gerald
High School Science Teacher
Main, Kenneth H.
Mathematics & Chemistry Tchr
MORRICE
Young, Gregory Allan
Biology Teacher
MOUNT CLEMENS
Birch, Thomas Gary
7th & 8th Grade Science Tchr
Briggs, Curtis G.
Social Studies Teacher
Sargent, Denise Marie Crank
Biology Teacher
Schwark, Adelaide Schulte
8th Grade Language Arts Tchr

MOUNT MORRIS
Armentrout, Glenda Rose
Kindergarten Teacher
Boggs, Marlene Ann
Media Specialist
Brouillet, Sue Miller
Retired 3rd Grade Teacher
Craig, William Gordon, Jr.
Science Teacher
Forshee, Frederick Harold
Accounting & Computer Teacher
Forshee, Janice M.
English Teacher & Dept Chair
Hall, Mary Rateau
Mathematics Teacher
Harrison, Cynthia Harcourt
Science Teacher
Hendrickson, Annetta J.
Social Studies Teacher
Ingraham, Lillie Ware
Second Grade Teacher
Jean, Gary Raymond
Geography & Math Teacher
King, Gary D.
Fourth Grade Teacher
LaBelle, Michael Joseph
Fifth Grade Teacher
Rasmovich, Deborah Arnott
Kindergarten Teacher
Ratza, Carol F.
3rd Grade Teacher
Richards, James J.
Sixth Grade Teacher
Sventko, Kelly Ann
HS Life Mgmt & Health Ed Tchr
Vance, Doug
Spanish Teacher
Yuhasz-Pratt, Mary Margaret
Band Director
MOUNT PLEASANT
Baugh, Joyce A.
Assoc Prof & Chprsn of Pol Sci
Bensley, Loren B., Jr.
Health Promotion Professor
Bowen, Richard Douglas
Speech & English Teacher
Brockman, Roberta Ann Yehling
Retired Span & Govt Teacher
Brost, Lori F.
Video Production Professor
Buchanan, Austin John, II
Sixth Grade Tchr & Var Coach
Cooley, Nancy J.
Assistant Vice Provost
Cratin, Paul David
Professor of Chemistry
Current, David Harlan
Professor of Physics
Durocher, Phillip Joseph
Soc Stud Tchr & Dept Chair
Dwyer, Jean F.
Secondary English Teacher
Farley, Dennis Scott
Assoc Prof Hospitality Svc Adm
Hartshorne, Timothy Scotford
Professor of Psychology
Hayes, Randall Bryant
Professor of Accounting
Jose, Martha G.
Biology Teacher
Laskowsky, Audrey Joyce
Honors English Teacher
Lindahl, Robert Gordon
Music Professor
Martin, Lucinda Smith
Eng Subj Matter Specialist
Neurath, James H.
Accounting Instructor
Norton, Jerry
6th Grade Teacher
Phelps, Frederick Martin, III
Associate Professor of Physics
Quick, Alan Frederick
Dept of Tchr Ed Prof
Ranft, Patricia C.
Professor of History
Schiller, Susan A.
Associate Professor of English
Schneid, Daniel Louis
Associate Professor of Finance
Scukanec, Gail Kirkendall
Assoc Professor
Seiter, Patricia Ragley
Media Specialist
Somerville, Alan Howard
Asst Prof of Envrnmntl Rec
Steffel, Susan Bos
Asst Prof, Dept of Eng & Lit
Stuart, Kathryn J.
Biology & Adv Biology Tchr
Tucker, Allan Lee
Drafting Teacher
Williams, Samuel Wilbert
Assistant Professor
Willwerth, Paul Irvin
Emeritus Prof
MUNISING
Allen, Barbara Ann
Mathematics Teacher
DesArmo, Francis John
Math Teacher
Hendrick, Cathy Mutter
School Nurse & Coach
MUSKEGON
Adkins, Colleen Reck
Fifth Grade Teacher
Anderegg, Frankie Jean
Third Grade Teacher
Barber, Sharon Kay (Noble)
Fifth Grade Teacher

Boone, Sandra Elaine
Business Teacher
Brainard, Janet K.
Third Grade Teacher
Brichan, Marcia Kinney
1st Grade Teacher
Brooks, Kathy (Simms)
Sixth Grade Teacher
Buitendorp, Nancy Hillard
Second Grade Teacher
Campione, John Lee
English & Accounting Teacher
Carter, Jeri Tyler
6th Grade Teacher
Chappell, Constance Marie
Spanish & English Teacher
Charron, Debra M. (Panici)
High School Math Teacher
CLosz, Jeffrey M.
Third Grade Teacher
Coffin, Paula Ann (Noffz)
Elementary Resource Room Tchr
Davis, Margie David
First Grade Teacher
DeCoster, Daniel Allen
Fourth Grade Teacher
Deters, Ruth Wilkinson
Instr & Assoc Dean Surg Tech
DeWitt, Lanny H.
Social Studies Teacher
Doig, Gary Robert
6th Grade Teacher
Downing, Joyce Hilt
Mathematics Coordinator
Draeger, Gloria
Asst Dir of Career Services
Fairfield, Sally Mae
4th Grd Teacher
Farmer, Caron Marie
Spanish Teacher
Fleischmann, Roberta Schwalm
Geog, Sci & Life Skills Tchr
Fox, Linda Adamo
Kindergarten Teacher
Gallas, Russell Mark, Sr.
HS Religion & Comm Tchr
Gentle, Joseph James
Computer & Math Teacher
Gerard, Tod P.
Language Arts Teacher
Goodrich, Barney Steven
Cmptr Instruction Systems Tchr
Habetler, Steve
Sixth Grade Science Teacher
Hanger, Zen Clifford
Dept Chair of Business Dept
Hood, Linda Ruth
Dept Chair of Travel & Tourism
Hoogenstyn, Donald R., Jr.
Library Science Teacher
Jemerson, Tommie Sue
2nd & 3rd Grade Teacher
Kuch, James A.
Biology Teacher
Kurant, Kyle David
History Teacher
Kurdziel, Gail Boe
Fifth Grade Teacher
Langlois, Linda Vigeant
Fourth Grade Teacher
Luczyk, William McCormick
Professor
Lundell, John Proctor
Sixth Grade Teacher
Mercer, Patricia
5th Grade Teacher
Mohr, Beth Ann (Bowald)
Human Anatomy & Physlgy Tchr
Nash, John H.
Teacher & Coach
Parrott, Katherine Hayes
General Music & Strings Tchr
Potter, Susan Ireland
Spanish Teacher
Pratt, Elizabeth Maria (Hoffmann)
Math Teacher
Radel, Nancy Lou
2nd Grade Primary Teacher
Russell, Lynda Hanwell
Instructor of Business
Schiller, Ellen Swart
Fifth Grade Teacher
Six, Mitchell Tracy
PE & Accounting Teacher
Smith, Hayden M., Jr.
Mathematics & Physics Instr
Smith, Patricia Ann
Senior Learning Center Supvr
Sorauf, Linda Palmer
Varsity Softball Coach
Starr, Jesse Lewis, Jr.
Elementary Teacher
Thompson, Ida Willene
Compensatory Education Tchr
Williams, Harry Samuel
6th Grade Mathematics Teacher
Zorn, Robert A.
Retired Counselor & Teacher
NAPOLEON
Baxter, Donald A.
Mathematics Teacher
Ebinger, Christine Carrie
Third Grade Teacher
Golba, James E.
HS Chemistry & Biology Tchr
Murdie, Lynne Elsea
Third Grade Teacher
NEGAUNEE
Bell, Kevin H.
Computer Aided Drafting Tchr

AUNEE (cont)
:, Lisa Impola
ı Physical Education Tchr
, Karen Maureen
ish Teacher
man, Helen Hansen
nistry Teacher
ein, Connie S.
ish Teacher
Donald, Susan Stiles
Tchr, Frgn Lang Dept Head
ndt, Sharon Lynn
nematics Teacher
lind, Mark Stephen
nestra Director
rs, James E.
ish Teacher & Dept Chm
John Wendell
ness Teacher
BALTIMORE
Joseph Paul
atre Dir & English Teacher
ais, Larel L.
ness Teacher
ord, Douglas Frank
work Cabinetmaking Teacher
, Thomas Russell
cipal
, Gail Trebesch
ness Education Teacher
nan, Richard Jerome
keting Teacher
hford, Steven Edward
Aerospace Science Instr
BOSTON
er, Rodney Craig
Grade Teacher
uire, Kathleen A.
th Grade Lang Arts Tchr
rdson, Kim Suzanne
erleading Coach
lan, Patrick Joseph
hematics Teacher
d, Charles Gordon
ech & Language Therapist
BUFFALO
s, Deborah J.
nish Teacher
hill, Maria Ann
ond Grade Teacher
ey, John F., Jr.
Stud & World His Teacher
r, Terry Wayne
rature & PE Teacher
HAVEN
nan, Michael Henry Dortmann
Principal & Ath Director
ns, James Patrick
sical Education & Hlth Tchr
zar, Vivian Valentour
lish & Government Teacher
ns, Denise Mc Queen
al Studies Teacher
LOTHROP
k, Janeen Ann
Grade Elementary Teacher
ann, James V.
Grade Teacher
on, Arthur Donald
nmy, Metrlgy & Geolgy Tchr
AYGO
, Robert B.
ory & Science Teacher
enson, Kimberly A.
nce Teacher
BERRY
tt, Jeffrey John
m, Physics & Math Teacher
PORT
, Millie Franke
dergarten Teacher
va, Jayne Langton
rth Grade Teacher
'S
n, Barbara A.
h Grade Teacher
tert, Norman Louis
h Teacher & Dept Chair
l, Susan Victoria
dergarten Teacher
, Edward Walter
English Teacher
ke, Gregory J.
h School Mathematics Tchr
cki, Pauline Carol Czinski
mentary Teacher
, Kathleen Marie
lish Teacher
rt, Sheryl Kay
ech & Creative Writing Tchr
er, Susan Kay
hematics Teacher
van, Michael Robert
Grade Teacher
nas, Glenda Lee (Smith)
al Music Teacher
TH ADAMS
kins, Diane Marie
Grade Teacher
ckner, Mary Helen
cher & Coach
, Donna Michelle
h, Business & Cmptr Teacher
er, Robert Owen
Grade Elementary Teacher
TH BRANCH
, Carol Ann Galbenski
Grade Teacher
nen, Mark John
Dept Chm, Bio & Chem Tchr

Lott, Robert Gordon
Science Teacher
Ward, Ronald B.
Junior High Science Teacher
NORTHPORT
Roman, Karie Lee-Bensley
Fourth Grade Teacher
Wetherbee, Stephen James
Math Teacher
NORTHVILLE
Brown, Nancy L.
English Teacher
Dent, Douglas Michael
Humanities Instructor
Donahue, John Vincent
High School English Teacher
Henderson, Janice Stehney
4th-5th Grade Tchr of Gifted
Kammeraad, Judith DeVries
German Teacher
Schumacher, Darrel Charles
HS Math Teacher
Seiler, Karenda Sue
Spanish Teacher
Stringer, Patricia Hathhorn
Fourth Grade Teacher
Swift, Sally Hoener
Kindergarten Teacher
Warner, Cheri Pisani
Mathematics Teacher
NORTON SHORES
Hemingway, Susan L.
Former Teacher
NORWAY
Daley, Nancy M. (Wender)
7th-8th Grade English Teacher
Danielson, Shelley Fazer
Art Teacher
Grimes, Eveline W.
German Teacher
Krznarich, Milt J.
Social Studies Teacher
Recla, Timothy Lee
Band Director
Romick, Bruce Earl
Former Teacher
Tomasoski, Victoria Day
Sixth Grade Teacher
NOVI
Alex, Pauline Pierini
Fourth Grade Teacher
Crawford, Linda Johnson
English & History Teacher
Dean, Bridget Ann
Foreign Language Specialist
Harris, Susan Thomas
Vocal Music Teacher
Helmkamp, Rand W.
High School Science Teacher
Howard, Brian Jesse
Mathematics Teacher
Joyner-Clinard, Paula Ellen
Choral Dir & Musical Producer
Kaufman, Julie S.
Fourth Grade Teacher
Knight, Barbara Jean
Third Grade Teacher
Meyer-Garbovits, Lisa
Spanish Teacher
Pasquantonio, Katheleen Smedley
English Dept Chairperson
Prine, Ann J.
First Grade Teacher
Snyder, Shirley Hill
Third Grade Teacher
Sullivan, Dorothy Nett
Reading Teacher
OAK PARK
Clippert, Susan C.
Middle School Teacher
Goldberg, Sheila Rae Grossman
Classroom Teacher
Golding, Howard Barry
PE Tchr & Var Bsktbl Coach
Grady, Dennys Ann
Fifth Grade Teacher
Martin, Bradley Charles
Comp Tchr & Summit Prgm Coord
Miller, Gayle Foster
English Teacher
Muzzarelli, Doreen Michele
Secondary Mathematics Teacher
Newman, Conrad Thomas
HS Social Studies Teacher
Ruedisueli, Maribeth Arseneau
Sci Teacher
Surowka, Christine Laibinus
Math Teacher
Yono, Nameer Jamil
Bilingual, ESL & Math Teacher
OKEMOS
Clark-Lewis, Margery
French & Mathematics Teacher
Cockroft, Larry Gene
High School Math Teacher
Pendergast, Christine Marie
High School English Teacher
Porritt, Robert L.
Mathematics Teacher
Sterioff-Chamberlain, Debra Janice
Coordinator of Gifted Ed
OLIVET
Curtis, Norma Lynn
Asst Professor of Education
Hubbel, Michael Robert
Associate Prof of Insurance
Knapp, Leah Ruth
Dept of Ntrl & Phys Sci Chrpsn
LaRouech, Daniel Peter, III
Special Education Teacher

Peterson, Kristin Rouker
High School Math Teacher
Scott, Linda Jo (Samuels)
Prof of Eng & Hum Dept Chair
Smith, Randall R.
English & Mathematics Teacher
Stewart, Ann Marie
English Professor
ONAWAY
Abshagen, Charles E.
Government & World His Tchr
Anderson, Janet Richardson
Mathematics & German Teacher
Zdanowski, Brian Michael
PE Teacher & Coach
ONEKAMA
Burtch, John Vance
His & Social Studies Tchr
Eldridge, Barbara Jane
Fifth Grade Teacher
ONSTED
Fooks, Judy Hilton
Third Grade Teacher
Head, Steven Thomas
High School Soc Studies Tchr
Lauer, David C.
Social Studies Teacher
Rodenbeck, Doyle M.
Director of Bands
Small, Kim Anderson
Chemistry Teacher & Dept Chair
Tuttle, Patricia Ann
HS Mathematics Teacher
VanMeet, Debra Joyce
Sixth Grade Teacher
ONTONAGON
Brookins, Dana M.
English Teacher
Santini, Melissa D.
Chemistry & Physical Sci Tchr
ORCHARD LAKE
Castillo, Dennis Angelo
History & Theology Asst Prof
Mathison, Connie Ann
Mathematics Teacher
Stoppa, Thomas M.
Social Studies Tchr & Chairman
Zazaian, Deborah (Kachadurian)
Theatre Arts Teacher & Coord
ORTONVILLE
Griffiths, Mary Catherine
Fifth Grade Teacher
Knight, Cindy Bako
Kindergarten Teacher
Skauge, Bradford D.
His & Geography Scndry Tchr
OSCODA
Anderson, Thomas David
English Teacher
Bissell, Edward Jay
Sixth Grade Teacher
Ehle, Douglas Edwin
High Schl Bldg Trades Teacher
Hazelton, Robert Jay
Spanish & French Teacher
Kennedy, Robert Roy
Fifth Grade Teacher
Lindburg, Judith Jordan
English Teacher
Reynolds, Peresephone P.
English & French Teacher
Ross, Gary G.
5th Grd Math, Sci & Soc Stud
Rowell, Bonnie Hollman
English Teacher
Sanderson, Jane F.
Fourth Grade Teacher
OSSINEKE
Larson, Ilene Williams
Kindergarten Teacher
OTISVILLE
Avram, Wendy T.
Health Skills Teacher
Busick, K. Stephen
Retired Secondary Teacher
Chimento, Cliff
Amer History & Geography Tchr
Johnson, Donna Wrobel
Third Grade Teacher
Robarge, L. Jay
Social Studies Teacher
Smith, Sandra Barden
Business Teacher & Voc Coord
Wiggins, Charles Glenn
Science Teacher
OTSEGO
Collison, Susan Diane
Home Schooling Teacher
Kaechele, Teri VanPortFleet
1st Grade Teacher
Pearson, Roger Lynn
Psych & World Geography Tchr
Weaver, Londa J. (Peterson)
Junior High Teacher
OTTAWA LAKE
Bixler, Susan Crocker
Middle School Science Teacher
OTTER LAKE
Clark, Helen Irene (Simms)
Retired English Instructor
OWENDALE
Packard, Leslie David
Mathematics Teacher
OWOSSO
Carlson, Pamela Lynn
Second Grade Teacher
Engel, Janet Schroeder
Kindergarten Teacher
Hakken, Matthew Donald
Math Coordinator

Kain, Lynn LeClair
5th Grade Teacher
Melrose, Betty Jane (Garrett)
7th-12th Grd Chrstn Schl Tchr
Miller, Rozan Sinnott
7th Grade Eng & Soc Stud Tchr
Roecker, Darrell F. J.
7th Grd Teacher & Athletic Dir
Sheedlo, Colleen Ann (Merrill)
Third Grade Teacher
Tepper, Laura Burroughs
Coll Instr of English & Comm
Wallace, Leslie Jayne
Anatomy & Physiology Instr
OXFORD
Brown, Thomas Bicking
Science Teacher
Centers, Joy M. (Staats)
Spanish Teacher
Covault, Pamela D.
Retired Second Grade Teacher
Gelmine, Sherrill Lugers
English Teacher
Johnson, Suzann (Osentoski)
Third Grade Teacher
Johnstone, Marjorie C.
MS English & Soc Stud Teacher
Maddren, Diana Lynne
Fifth Grade LA & SS Teacher
Moore, Phillip
Director & Teacher
Rowland, William R.
Bible & History Teacher
Sargent, Daniel W.
Social Studies Teacher
Wilson, Lewis Newton
High School Counselor
PALO
Herrmann, Denise Weber
Third Grade Teacher
PARIS
Cross, Linda Lou
Principal
PARMA
Campbell, Sandra Kristine
Sr English Composition Tchr
Lazaroff, Michele Lorraine
Chemistry Teacher
Sutton, Anthony Thomas
Literature & Humanities Instr
PAW PAW
Barnes, Stephen David
Science Teacher
Swanson, Christine Mahnke
8th Grade Language Arts Tchr
PECK
Boursaw, George H.
Math Teacher
Jacot, Dixie Jean Brown
Mathematics Teacher
Jankowski, Louise Ann
Fifth Grade Teacher
Kredell, Janine Salchert
Band Dir & Jr High His Tchr
Moore, Dale Logan
Teacher
Rickett, Vickie Sue
Graphic Communications Instr
Soule, Judith M.
Sixth Grade Teacher
Vuylsteke, Thomas A.
English, French & German Tchr
Weyeneth, Vera Hamblin
Fourth Grade Teacher
PELLSTON
Farris, Jane G.
High School English Teacher
Fochtman, Paul Martin
Assistant Principal
PERRY
Catallo, Diana Marie
Third Grade Teacher
Church, Dee
Mathematics Teacher
Fitts, David Wm.
Director of Instrumental Music
Gayon, Donna M.
HS English Teacher
Kittleson, Stephanie Ortino
7th Grd Science & Health Tchr
Maurer-Westbrook, Paula
Second Grade Teacher
White, Sandra Kay
Biology Instructor
PETERSBURG
Dobberstein, Mary L. (Martin)
Fourth Grade Teacher
Loy, Susan Guenther
Mathematics Teacher
Mershon, John Pollock
6th Grade Teacher
Ratkowski, Joan (Witek)
Geography & Hlth Foods Tchr
Williams, Mike Lynn
9th-12th Grd Eng & PE Tchr
PETOSKEY
Bennett, Barry Lyle
Band Director
Brondial, Gerry E.
Music Specialist
Dickmann, Donald R.
Math, Physics Tchr & Dept Head
Fettig, Mildred Schaub
Retired Primary Teacher
Greene, Jeffrey Michael
Math & Science Teacher
Greyerbiehl, Eric John
Physical Education Teacher
Harvey, Roy Norman
6th Grade Math Teacher

Hice, Gary K.
Director of Athletics
Hoffman, Patricia Kay
English Teacher
Kelbel, Linda A. (Wieber)
Mathematics Teacher
Kolodziej-Mulhauser, Jo Anna Catherine
Psychology Professor
Murdick, John Francis
MS Social Studies Teacher
Ross, John William
Retired 6th Grade Teacher
Skinner-Linnenberg, Virginia
Comm & Humanities Dept Chair
Slanec, Therese Lynn(Koehler)
6th Grade Teacher
Smith, Janet Jacobs
4th Grade Teacher
Stoltz, April Pagarigan
English Teacher
Tamm, Matthew Anthony
HS History & Government Tchr
Vander Breggen, Roberta Louise (Rust)
Enrichment Coordinator
VanTreese, Linda D. Ten Have
Social Studies Teacher
PEWAMO
Bashore, Cary J.
Mathematics & Psychology Tchr
Kindsvatter, Lori Fedewa
Science Teacher
Wirth, Jerry M.
Crss Cntry, Track, Field Coach
PICKFORD
Hunter, Robert Alan
English Teacher
PIGEON
Grifka, Dale Joseph
Mathematics Teacher
PINCKNEY
Andrzejewski, Bernadine Ann
Fifth Grade Teacher
Craig, Joel D.
Science & Technology Teacher
Graham, Don
Third Grade Teacher
Jourden, John Edward
8th Grade Amer History Teacher
Meabon, Marcia Steensma
5th Grade Teacher
PINCONNING
Bishop, Helen deDoelder
Fifth Grade Teacher
Harris, Joan
Lead Secondary Teacher
Porter, Don M.
Eng, Psych & Jrnlsm Teacher
Tessmer, James F.
9th Grade Geography Teacher
PITTSFORD
Barber, Richard Joseph
Ace Learning Center Supervisor
Davenport, Lucy Kolivosky
English Teacher
Hart, Jean Ann
Title I Math Specialist
Irelan, John B.
Social Studies Teacher
Lovell, Scott Wilson
Social Studies Teacher
Neinas, Alger Herbert
Junior High Teacher
Perrin, Carla M.
12th Grade English Teacher
PLAINWELL
Cool, Scott Mark
Biology & Physical Sci Tchr
DuBois, John
Physical Education Teacher
Eicher, William Thomas
Director of Bands
Hope, Jacqueline Ann
English Teacher
Moulder, Mary Matrice
Spanish Teacher
Pennala, Dean Andy
Fifth Grade Teacher
PLYMOUTH
Bailey, Niran Mary Kheder
English & Social Studies Tchr
Fair, Patricia
Science & Geography Teacher
Gray, Richard H.
Eng, His & PE Teacher
Hecmanczuk, Barbara Ann
Sixth Grade Teacher
Robb, David James
High School History Teacher
Towers, Stanley Smith
Math & Science Teacher
Weycker, Joseph Calvin
Vocal Music Teacher
Williams, Thomas Scott
6th Grade Teacher
PONTIAC
Burroughs, Malissia Porter
Language Arts Teacher
Butler, Larry Calistus
Algebra Teacher
Cooper, Marsha Bower
Computer & English Teacher
Danis, Earlean Rutley
Student Advocate
Edwards, Geneva Flowers
English Teacher
Finley, Sharon Augusta
Ninth Grade Science Teacher
Hejhal, John Robert
Mathematics Teacher

PONTIAC (cont)
Phillips, Lorene Bessent
Language Arts Dept Chairperson
Spoor, Mary Lynne
Second Grade Teacher
Woodmore, Lori Renee
Math Teacher
Wroubel, Betty Ann
Health & Phys Ed Dept Head
PORT AUSTIN
Maurer, Tracy Lynn
Special Education Teacher
PORT HOPE
Hogan, Melissa L.
Eng, Journalism & German Tchr
PORT HURON
Burgess, Harry Thomas
History Teacher
Cameron, Linda H.
Teacher
Dickey, Cynthia Lynn
6th Grd Lang Arts & Rdng Tchr
Gourlay, Lea Mary (Tenbusch)
Eighth Grade Science Teacher
Grain, Terrie Anne Kathleen
Life Science Teacher
Huston, Mary Janet (Faulkner)
4th & 5th Grade Teacher
Kraft, Kenneth L.
German Teacher
Lakatos, William
Criminal Justice Professor
Lambert, Carol S. (Nickerson)
Mathematics Professor
Lardner-Erickson, Merle Lee Ann
Building Substitute Teacher
Lill, William H.
5th Grade Teacher
Martindale, Barbara Kirk
US History & Govt Teacher
Obee, Thomas Francis
Philosophy & English Professor
Pillsbury, Virginia Miller
Prof of Ger & Soc Svc Tech
Prout, Martin Jon Mark
Elementary School Principal
Singer, Debra C.
English & Amer Lit Teacher
Smith, Harley R.
Political Science Professor
Unger, John Edward
Instrumental Teacher
Voss, James David
Speech Communication Teacher
Wade, Cynthia Walton
Mathematics Professor
Weiss, Robert Keith
Chemistry & Biology Teacher
PORTAGE
Baker, John David
8th Grade Science Teacher
Baldwin, Bud
Counselor
Benedict-Kirshman, Lori J.
8th Grade Language Arts Tchr
Crankshaw, Karen E.
Gifted, Talented Tchr & Coord
Curtis, Sharon K.
Life Management Teacher
Esper, Renee Marie
Mathematics Teacher
Freeland, Dale
Physics Teacher & Dept Chair
Harmon, Charles Jay
Chemistry Teacher
Hazen, Richard Leo
Orchestra Director
Rajkovich, Richard Peter
Gifted & Talented Coordinator
Sang, Frederic P.
Elementary Music Teacher
Schaefer, Stephen Boon
9th Grade English Instructor
Schafer, James Atlee, III
Physical Education Teacher
Smith, Don J.
Physics Teacher
Stieve, Linda Diane
English Teacher
Swoboda, Gerald Lee
Mathematics Teacher
PORTLAND
Flate, Stewart
History Teacher
Johnston, Richard Wesley
Adult Education Teacher
Leak, Janice Louise
Third Grade Teacher
Longstreth, Barbara Winkel
Multi-Age Teacher
Rainey, Derek Rexton
World His, Psych & Art Teacher
Sanborn, Donalyn Kay
K-6th Grade Substitute Teacher
Thelen, Neil A.
Social Studies & His Teacher
POWERS
Busick, Mary R.
K-6th Grade Special Ed Tchr
PRESCOTT
Veruoort, Mary Jane Walch
Second Grade Teacher
QUINCY
Grace, Elizabeth Heitz
Fourth Grade Teacher
Gruner, Gregory G.
5th Grd Tchr & Bsktbl Coach
Olmstead, Kathleen French
Third Grade Teacher

Parzych, Andrew S.
Business Education Teacher
Stewart, Robert Thomas
US History & Civics Teacher
Wuori, Cindy Taylor
Third Grade Teacher
RAVENNA
Korson, Peter Mary
Principal & Teacher
READING
Hubbard, Mitch P.
Business Teacher & Coach
Jimenez, Bonnie VanAken
First Grade Teacher
Poikey, Laurie L.
English Teacher
Thompson, Susan Esterline
Physical Education & Hlth Tchr
REDFORD
Barnauskas, Geraldine Gushman
Middle School Teacher
Birecki, Shannon Brady
Fourth Grade Teacher
Doherty, Amy Gedman
English & Spanish Teacher
Green, Robert George
Vocational Drafting Teacher
Hoge, Ann Cancilla
Choir Teacher
Hunter, Audra Lee
English Teacher
Jenkins, James Michael
9th-12th Grade Art Teacher
Klettner, Molly A.
Math Teacher
LaLonde, Janet Arndt
Kindergarten Teacher
Lang, Joseph Anthony
High School English Teacher
Lund, Barbara Marie
Art, Soc Stud & Spelling Tchr
Mortimer, Susan C.
Teacher of Hearing Impaired
Papp, Kim Taylor
Science Teacher
Ragains, Kay M.
Second Grade Teacher
Rodriguez, Mike
Teacher & Coach
Schulte, Lawrence T.
Social Studies Dept Head
Sovinski, Kathryn Ann
Mathematics & Art Teacher
REED CITY
Vasicek, George John
High School Mathematics Tchr
Vermeulen, Garret Tolman
Physical Education Teacher
REESE
DuRussel, Annette Hecht
Math & English Teacher
Fuhrman, Mark Freemont
Social Studies Teacher
Weier, C. Timothy
High School Mathematics Tchr
Weier, Diana Hardy
Cmptr & Bus Education Teacher
REMUS
Berryman, Robert John
Counselor
Dague, Nancy Ann (Simmet)
Business Education Teacher
Lodes, Suellen Zuehlke
Special Education Teacher
Yarrick, James A.
Band Director
REPUBLIC
Podskalny, Darrin R.
Art Teacher
RICHLAND
Blackburn, Ronald William
Industrial Arts Teacher
Finn, Ed
History Teacher
Nott, Robin
Teacher & Director
Pelletier, Phyllis Burgwald
History Teacher
Rice, Denise G.
Sixth Grade Teacher
RICHMOND
Curtis, Peter M.
Mathematics Teacher
Hamblin, George Thomas
English & Speech Teacher
Ladd, Mark Anthony
Government Teacher
Olson, Doug
Mathematics Teacher
Sharpe, Judith Louise (Tarrant)
Vocal Music Instructor
Wood, Virginia Reed
Chemistry & Physics Teacher
RICHVILLE
Schiefer, Mark T.
6th & 8th Grd Tchr, Ath Dir
Wilke, Nancy Ellen
Third Grade Teacher
RIVER ROUGE
Gerlica, Dorothy L.
3rd-5th Grade Science Teacher
Howard, Viveca Yvette
Fourth Grade Teacher
Jacobs, Carole A.
First Grade Teacher
Koss, Gloria Ann
Reading & Drama Teacher
Marchio, Christine
Health Education Teacher

RIVERVIEW
Brown, Thomas Roy
United States History Teacher
ROCHESTER
Barner, Janie M.
German Teacher
Behler, Glenn William
Math Tchr
Blum, Phillip Ralph
Industrial Tech Teacher
Burch, Charles
Soc Stud Tchr & Dept Chair
Cheok, Ka C.
Professor of Engineering
Corteville, Janice Hickner
Literature Teacher
Domanski, Timothy Gerard
High School Chemistry Teacher
Fras, Micheal C.
Mathematics Teacher & Coach
Golemba, Adine (Salchow)
Spanish Instructor
Hahn, Stacey Layne
Associate Professor of French
Hartman, Gwyn Randall
9th-12th Grade History Teacher
Hawes, Thomas M.
History Teacher
Hogan, Geraldine Ann
MS Science & Lang Arts Teacher
La Grasso, Carolyn Papak
4th Grade Teacher & Sci Coord
Lawson, Ray H.
English Teacher
Lentz, Timothy Paul
Vocal Music Dir, Theatre Coord
Mathieson, Kieran
Professor of MIS
Mikula, Joseph Randall
Anatomy & Physiology Teacher
Murphy, Kevin James
Dept of Economics Chairman
Taylor, Jane Lohrman
4th Grade Teacher
Thoma, August John
Band Director
Topel, Timothy Lee
Science Teacher
Trahan, Marja G.
High School Counselor
Willis, Robin S.
French Teacher
Wismer, Joanne Genevieve
Retired Teacher
ROCHESTER HILLS
Bentley, Joe R.
Associate Professor of Music
Hyatt, Sharon Bell
Former Asst Admin & Eng Tchr
Kronewetter, Andrew David
Asst Prof of Communication
Noah, Benjamin V.
Asst Prof of Human Services
Reddick, Sarah Campbell
Asst Prof of Soc Work
Wheeler, Barry Wayne
Phys Ed & Health Professor
ROCK
Seymour, Robin Thompson
Third Grade Teacher
ROCKFORD
Beach, Craig J.
History Teacher
Cordeiro, Zelia M.
Mission-Vocation Director
Decker, Jacqueline Holland
English Teacher
Ensing, Andrea DeKuiper
Spanish Teacher
Eppink, James Albert
Earth Science Teacher
Longuski, Deborah A.
Counselor
Sagraves, Gregory Kenyon
Technology Education Instr
Sanders, Paula Norby
German Instructor
Smith, David Lawrence
English Teacher
ROCKWOOD
Burley, Joan Hesse
Government & Economics Teacher
Christiansen, Patricia Boblet
Teacher
Clemente, MIchael Albert
Science Teacher
Jones, Robert M.
Social Studies & PE Teacher
Pishlo, Michael David
Social Studies Teacher
ROGERS CITY
Allan-Marten, Kathi
Counselor
Bruder, Vivian Jane
Language Arts Teacher
Haselhuhn, JoAnna Jean
High School English Teacher
Little, Margaret Brown
Third Grade Teacher
Mertz, Susan Isabelle (Geyer)
First Grade Teacher
White, Danielle Renee
High School History Teacher
ROMEO
Johnson, Margaret (Corteg)
Mathematics Teacher
Nicholson, Martha Kay
Health, PE Tchr & Dept Chair
Webster, Mary Elizabeth (Ford)
French & Spanish Tchr

ROMULUS
Bayes, Ronald L.
Eng & Creative Writing Tchr
Kenyon, Darrell Rodney
9th Grade Science Teacher
Kruse, Richard August
Dir of Bands & Music Dept Head
Lassig, Paul Raymond
Math Teacher
Lockwood, Russell Lawrence
Mathematics Teacher
ROSCOMMON
Backlund, James David
Psychology Instructor
Ballard, Joyce Ann
Second Grade Teacher
Coulter, Veronica
Counselor
Diment, Linda Marie
Vocal Music Teacher
Ewald, Martin John
English Teacher & Coach
Farrell, Rosemarie Read
5th Grade Teacher
Giacobazzi, Frederic David
English Professor
Jacobs, Frances Roach
8th Grade English Teacher
Klein, Tim R.
PE Tchr & Head Ftbl Coach
Mc Clure, Timothy Earl
9th-12th Grade Art Teacher
Selon, Donald J.
Span Tchr & Dept Head
Thomas, Ted C.
Science Dept Chairman
Warren, Donald B.
Mathematics Instructor
ROSE CITY
Card, Kathryn Marie
Third Grade Teacher
ROSEVILLE
Conway, Peter J.
Mathematics Teacher
Eschenburg, Judy Rai-Oats
Sixth Grade Teacher
Herbertson, Joseph Robert
Social Studies Teacher
Holmes, Sharon J.
Spanish Teacher
Meyer, Mary Frances
3rd Grade Teacher
Tregembo, Paul S., Sr.
T & I Voc Coordinator
Turner, Tracey Minch
Director of Vocal Music
Wisnewski, Edward A.
Teacher
Wisnewski, Judy A.
Art Teacher
ROYAL OAK
Burr, Dale John
Health Teacher & Coach
Elmleaf, James R.
MS Mathematics Teacher
Emerick, Catherine Vissotski
Spanish Teacher
Fitzpatrick, James Joseph
Social Studies & English Tchr
Floyd, Rose Marie
Ballet Teacher
Heap, Anita O'Kulich
Second Grade Teacher
Korn, Justine
Fifth Grade Teacher
Mc Clanaghan, Barbara King
Lang Arts Dept Head & Eng Tchr
Mc Hale, Carol Gasperut
English Teacher
Stern, Judy Renee
Third Grade Teacher
Weiszbrod, Michael W.
8th Grd Teacher & Youth Dir
RUDYARD
Bickel, Ken L.
Jr High Social Studies Teacher
Monck, Debra Ann
HS Counselor
SAGINAW
Adams, Bill
Mathematics Teacher
Bennett, John Columbus
Science Consultant
Berg, Jerry Richard
Peer Counseling Coord
Bergant, Virginia Albers
Fifth Grade Teacher
Beson, Deanne Marie (Guy)
Music Teacher
Boehm, Jerry R.
Guid Dir & Trigonometry Tchr
Boyd, Jeraldine Day
Physical Education Teacher
Brantley, Sylvia Luzette
Special Education Teacher
Bushroe, John Anthony
6th Grade Teacher
Campbell, Jack Allen
7th & 8th Grade Math Teacher
Cheger-Timm, Cheryl Jeanne
Choir Dir
Clark, Donna Dyer
5th-8th Grade Teacher
Coleman-Dickens, Hurlette
Math, Sci, Tech & Drama Tchr
Cooper, James William
8th Grd Sci & History Teacher
Corcoran, Rea Braid
Multi-Age Teacher

DeGuise, Ann Therese
Principal
Dunham, Marie Stieve
Mathematics Teacher
Dusek, Carol Hammond
First Grade Teacher
Enszer, Robert M.
Chemistry & Biology Teacher
Fischer, Wendy K. W.
Social Studies Teacher
Gammon, Glenna Kay (Jordan)
Fifth Grade Teacher
Gase, Mary Ellen
6th-12th Grade Music Teacher
Giffin, Michael W.
Algebra Teacher
Grunwald, James R.
Math & Computer Science Prof
Hardy, Thomas Grey
Social Studies Teacher
Hoard, Robert A.
American Lit Composition Tchr
Holmes, Nancy Lounsbery
Fifth Grade Teacher
Hunter, Sharon Arnold
English Teacher
Hurd, James Allen
8th Grade Teacher
Jaksa, Stephen Peter
Athletic Director
Kern, Stuart C.
Teacher
Kleinbriel, Marjorie Wilson
Kindergarten Teacher
Kock, Norval Lauren
Professor
Kreucher, Kristen Maurine
7th & 8th Grade Drama Teacher
Lewis, Amy Marie
Math & Social Studies Teacher
Mehnert, Stephanie Lynn
Algebra & PE Professor
Miller, Leslie L.
Biology Teacher
Minda, Keith A.
Eighth Grade Teacher
Moore, Michele Rose Artecki
Fifth Grade Teacher
Nowak, Jonathan Lee
Substitute Teacher
Quinn, Jeanie Oberschmidt
Social Studies Teacher
Radina, Robert John
6th Grade Teacher
Reed, Demona Marie (Aldridge)
Traveling Vocal Music Teacher
Renko, Harry Joseph
Religious Teacher
Rummler, Mary Baranski
Psychology Teacher
Russell, Janet Ann
Biology Teacher
Sanders, James Charles, Jr.
4th-5th Grd Math & Sci Teacher
Schuler, William Charles
Fourth Grade Teacher
Smith, Cheryl Mc Coy
4th Grade Teacher
Stelter, William James
8th Grd Social Studies Teacher
Stephens, Sherry Stelzer
Middle Schl Math & Eng Tchr
Tack, Stephen Dennis
Mathematics Teacher
Tolley, Jan L.
High School Teacher
Torrey, Vicki
History Teacher
Ugartechea, Beatrice A.
Language Arts Department Chair
Valasek, David M.
Band Director
Warren, Beverly Regina
Special Education Teacher
Williams, Deborah Morris
Health & Life Skills Teacher
Williams, Patricia Baker
Science & Health Teacher
Wittig, Barry M.
Social Studies & Religion Tchr
Zill, Steven E.
Chemistry & Theology Teacher
SAINT CHARLES
Brownlie, Ronald Gene
English & History Teacher
Campbell, Susan Ann
6th-12th Grade Art Teacher
SAINT CLAIR
Hillier, Charles Frederick
Fifth Grade Teacher
Jobbitt, Renee Frances
Fifth Grade Teacher
Schreiber, Sheila Salloum
Sixth Grade Teacher
Shaw, Fred William
6th Grade Teacher
Thoel, Kenneth Roy
Industrial Technology Teacher
SAINT CLAIR SHORES
Boles, Penny R.
Chemistry Teacher
Colgan, Ellen Modelski
English Teacher
Crellin, George W.
Track & Wrestling Coach
Daly, John K.
Business & Vocational Teacher
Harris, Inge Anna
HS English & Art Instructor

CLAIR SHORES (cont)
:atherine Schoeninger
d & Third Grade Teacher
is, Robert David
School Eng & Drama Tchr
Pauline A.
History & Lit Teacher
, Kenneth James
istry & Physics Teacher
Betty Ceravolo
matics Tchr & Dept Chair
hirley Irene
Math, Drama & Chorus Tchr
Paula Ann (Kozentis)
Grade Teacher
IGNACE
y, Sean Patrick
School Math Dept Head
JOHNS
Dirk Alan
acher & Coach
andall Allan
Psych & Sociology Teacher
, Tom J.
:s Teacher
JOSEPH
on, Virginia Ruth
n & World History Teacher
o, Margaret R.
8th Grade Religion Tchr
Virginia Ann
High Science Teacher
Karla K.
d Teacher
y, Judith Ann
l Director
g, H. Ronald
d Instructor
LOUIS
, Steven J.
ess Teacher
atharine Gilbert
rgarten Teacher
f, Robert Lawrence
Studies Teacher & Coach
E
n, James K.
Studies Teacher
, Donald Gerard
nment, Sociology Educator
son, Beth C.
rade Teacher
Russ
rade Teacher
Suzanne Brodie
d Grade Teacher
rger, Jere A.
ematics & Physics Teacher
, David Bruce
r & Technical Ed Instr
n, David A.
rade Teacher
cott Thomas
Hlth Instructor
aub, Marlene R.
sh Dept Chprsn & Tchr
CREEK
, Mark R.
h Grade Math, PE Teacher
JSKY
, Marilyn Marie
e School Counselor
, Carole Berlin
sh Teacher
, Dean Eldridge
tor of Bands
r, Teresa Mosher
sh & Life Skills Teacher
ORD
obert Charles
trial Arts Teacher
NAC
berg, Dale Lynn
rade Science & Hlth Tchr
ATUCK
., Kathy Richards
Grade Teacher
SAINT MARIE
vich, Donna Blake
ematics Teacher
, Randall David
rade Teacher
Phyllis (Peake)
ed Teacher
Kathleen Ann (DeBusscher)
ematics Teacher
SAINTE MARIE
, Richard T.
Arts, Letters & Soc Sci
ore, Diana R.
: Professor of English
ER
e, Sandra K. (Dahlen)
hool Teacher & Director
OLCRAFT
Douglas K.
rd Science & Health Tchr
en, Cindy L.
Studies & English Teacher
TS
Elizabeth Hill
Grade Teacher
Janice Meyers
room Teacher
TVILLE
n, Denise E.
uctor of Social Sci Dept
d R.
, CAM & CNC Professor

Marshall, Rod D.
HS Learning Disabilities Tchr
Mc Kinney, Michael Alan
Professor of Biology
Meyers, Daniel Michael
Music Instructor & Director
Peterson, Shirley Kellan
Business Instructor
Richert, Thomas Mark
High School Teacher
Schumacher, Constance Marie
Business Professor
Svendor, Gerald Edward
Professor of Accounting
Van der Sluys, Norman Austin
Art History & Humanities Instr
Wojciechowski, Amy Rummel
Professor of Business
SEBEWAING
Kieser, Carl
Agriscience Teacher
Travis, Timothy Joseph
Mathematics & Physics Teacher
SHAFTSBURG
Dunckel, Pat Hewitt
Fifth Grade Teacher
SHELBY
Brimmer, Bruce Duane
Biology Teacher
Glerum, Jane Inbody
Language Arts & Span Teacher
Lewis, Jeremy Frederick
HS Government & Ec Teacher
SHELBY TOWNSHIP
Baas, Kathy J.
Instrumental Director
Bara, Norene N. Wnuk
6th Grade Teacher
Collins, Sandra Virginia
Freshman Cheerleading Coach
Davis, Shelley Lynn
HS Mathematics Teacher
Dybalski, Lynn Ann
Mathematics Teacher
Fox, Karen Marie
Vocal Music & Honors Eng Tchr
Luz, Kyle S.
Physics Teacher
Mann, Janice Maynard
Social Studies Teacher
Pfannes, Steven W.
Social Studies & Speech Tchr
Prill, Theodore F.
Secondary Mathematics Teacher
Schachinger, Linda Kuta
Spanish Teacher
Terry, Richard E.
Biology Instructor
VanHouten, Thomas Jay
Math Tchr & Dept Chprsn
Walsh, Cynthia Anne
Life Skills Teacher
Werner, Mark A.
Youth Director
SHEPHERD
Brock, Martin Roy
6th Grade Teacher
Burke, David Alan
HS Yearbook & PE Teacher
Dinkfeld, Robert Christopher
Elem Physical Education Tchr
Hamilton, William Edward, III
8th Grd Math & History Teacher
Kohrman, Cordelia Bingham
Teacher & English Dept Chair
Lehner, Clifford Leroy
Industrial & Technology Tchr
Lemmer, Claude Gerald
Band Director
Sneary, Kristine Renee
English Teacher
SHERIDAN
Beardslee, Gail Sue
Second Grade Teacher
Ledford, Anna Marie
Fourth Grade Teacher
SIDNEY
Spry, Sally Ann
Accounting & Bus Adj Prof
SIX LAKES
Hessbrook, Terry Scott
Alternative Education Teacher
SMITHS CREEK
Sharrard, David L.
US & World History Teacher
SOUTH HAVEN
Dustin, William K.
Science Teacher
Woodhams, Debra Harsch
4th & 5th Grade Teacher
SOUTH LYON
Overman, Kathleen Ann (Carey)
Lang Arts & Soc Stud Tchr
Soderquist, David Michael
Biology Teacher
SOUTHFIELD
Alameddine, Shirley J.
Special Education Teacher
Broderick, Ann C.
HS Biology & Chemistry Teacher
Burk, Steven Michael
PE Teacher & Health Dept Head
Chapman, Dianne
English Department Chairperson
Collins, Carol Shaw
American History Teacher
Fischer, Beth Ann
Jr High Teacher
Gerathy, Dennis B.
Scndry His & Soc Stud Tchr

Harris, Stanley Francis
Assoc Prof, Coll of Mgmt
Henderson, Irma Marie
Counseling Director
Hinzman, Rita Marie (Houn)
Chemistry Teacher
Howard, Thomas Elliot
Social Studies Teacher
James, Karen Susanne (Vosler)
Kindergarten Teacher
Johnson, Charlie Mae
English Teacher
Jones, Martha Momon
Ret Elementary School Teacher
Labuta, Claire Marie
Band & Orchestra Director
Lambert, Richard Stockton
Art Teacher
Lorenz, Sarah Birk
English, Speech & Yrbk Tchr
Maier, Ernest Louis
Marketing Professor
Martin, Mychelle Lynn
First Grade Teacher
Martin, Robert A.
High School Choral Teacher
Mavis, Wayne Arthur
High School Math Instructor
Mc Coy, Beth A.
Fourth Grade Teacher
McKenna, Thomas James
Professor of Business & Law
Mc Knight, Benjamin, Jr.
Instrumental Music Director
Mineweaser, Gayle Jackson
High School English Teacher
Mineweaser, Robert Lee
Science Teacher
Oshinsky, Leo Edward
Psychology & Government Tchr
Page, Patricia Green
7th-8th Grade Business Ed Tchr
Pellerito, Fred
Science Teacher
Shuman, William H., Jr.
Bible Teacher & Chaplain
Sullivan, Gwen Muhling
Jr High Math & Science Tchr
Teague, Rita H.
English Teacher
Teska, Jane Ellen
Chemistry & Physics Teacher
Traison, Datia T.
Spanish Teacher
Tulkki, Raymond John
Math Teacher & Dept Co-Chair
Ward, Peter lee
Mathematics Tchr & Dept Head
Watson, William Edward, II
Algebra Teacher
Wynn, Pamela Marshall
Special Education Teacher
Yee, Kingman Ethan
Assoc Prof Mechanical Engrng
SOUTHGATE
Anderson, Allan Joseph
Senior HS Mathematics Instr
Bankwitz, Kenneth George
Science Teacher
Guzman, Kenneth P.
Spanish Teacher
Ingram, Barbara Lynn
First Grade Teacher
Kotyk, Susan M.
Acad Dean & Science Dept Head
Martin, Ralph Peter
Automotive Tech & Science Tchr
Pauline, Patricia Ann
Mathematics & Science Teacher
Perry, Dorothy Louise
5th Grade Teacher
Peters, Frederick Emil
Biology Teacher
Robinson, Michael David
Spanish & Math Teacher
Sexton, David Rodney
Graphic Arts Teacher
Spivey, Regina Ann
Jr High Teacher
SPRING ARBOR
Ball, Thomas Michael
Professor of Communications
Boivin, Michael
Professor of Psychology & Chm
Johnson, Ruth Joy
Third Grade Teacher
Winters, Sara Lynn
Fifth Grade Teacher
SPRING LAKE
Clark, Sandra Race
English Teacher
Hagen, Diane Ensing
Math Teacher
Langs, Kevin William
7th Grd Social Studies Teacher
Reed, Rebecca Brick
Life Skills Teacher
Wolbrink, Paul H.
English Teacher
SPRINGPORT
Bradley, Karen Lee
Fifth Grade Teacher
Koval, Peter Paul
Life Science & Spanish Teacher
Layman, Peggy J. (Barber)
English Teacher
Lutzka, David Paul
Math & Art Teacher
Mariage, David Joseph
Social Studies Teacher

STAMBAUGH
Baker, Marquette M.
Third Grade Teacher
Cole, Patricia A.
English & French Teacher
Storti, James E.
Mathematics Teacher
STANDISH
Barnum, Carolyn Suzanne
High School Social Stud Tchr
Coquillard, Michael E.
Physical Education Teacher
STANTON
McConnell, Tina Janine
High Schl Language Arts Tchr
Payton, Brook W.
Math & Comp Programming Tchr
STANWOOD
Bross, Dorothy Jean
Third Grade Teacher
Douglass, Karin Johansen
4th Grade Teacher
STEPHENSON
Blair, Peter Edward
English & Speech Tchr
Dean, Nancy A.
Span, English & Amer Lit Tchr
Scott, Kimeen Karen
English Teacher
STERLING HEIGHTS
Barber, Christine Olane
High School Math Teacher
Barwick, Carolyn Jean
Fifth Grade Teacher
Beadle, Bosonda Lee (Hostottle)
1st Grade Teacher
Blain, Mary Conklin
French & Spanish Teacher
Burton, Zita Mc Grath
Fifth Grade Teacher
Carney, Tom
English & Newspaper Teacher
Cassidy, Thomas Richard
Counselor
Cassin, Christopher W.
Sixth Grade Teacher
Clippert, Richard John
6th Grade Teacher
Dundas, James Edward
Counselor
Dunlap, Dianne Jeter
5th Grade Teacher
Eggen, Gerald Thomas
Philosophy & Criminal Law Tchr
Garwood, Jeanne Middleton
Art, Drama, Speech & Eng Tchr
Green, Diane Marie
Second Grade Teacher
Hoenicke, Thomas Allan
Math Teacher
Jones, Fred R.
4th Grade Teacher
Julin, Marilyn Joyce
French & Spanish Teacher
Lancour, Karen Louise
Secondary Science Educator
Lutz, Kathleen Ann
French Teacher
Mandl, Marge
French & Spanish Teacher
Mc Alister, Kathleen
6th Grade Teacher
McBroom, Robert William
Speech Communication Teacher
Meyers, Gabriella Catherine
Sixth Grade Teacher
Miquel, Sharon Zimmerman
Kindergarten Teacher
Nitterhouse, Rick
Instrumental Music Teacher
Oleniczak, James Joseph
Comp Aided Manufacturing Instr
Oliver, Detta Loretta
Teacher
Platter, Donald R.
Director of Bands
Pogasic, Anthony J.
Math Teacher
Reagan, James Quentin
Math Teacher
Shaul, William Harry
History & Bible Teacher
Shaw, James Michael
Counselor
Smith, Patricia L.
Chemistry Teacher
Texter, Ronald Richard
Biology Teacher
Trzasko, Ann Marie Pauli
Medical Careers Instructor
Upper-Wilcox, Marion
High School Counselor
Waluk, Richard Charles
Science Teacher
Watterworth, R. Glenn
Eighth & Ninth Grd US His Tchr
STEVENSVILLE
Adler, Stephan Alan
Social Studies Teacher
Barnes, Karen Zantti
English Teacher
Davis, Diana Boelcke
Health Teacher
French, Heidi Ann
Fourth Grade Teacher
Kelly, David Allen
Second Grade Teacher
Lange, Barbara Mummaw
7th-8th Grade Math Teacher

Patzer, Ronald Lester
Lead Teacher
Poluhanycz, Chylon Lewis
5th Grade Teacher
Thompson, Susan Vinay
Govt History Teacher
Von Koenig, Lori Jewell
Director of Bands
Wark, Esther Stelter
Substitute Teacher
STOCKBRIDGE
Blankenship, Amy Beth
Band Dir
Channell, Karen Torrey
Third Grade Classroom Teacher
Tucker, Thomas A.
AP English Instructor
STURGIS
Brenneman, Mary Beth
French & Spanish Teacher
Downing, Gerald Gene
Mgmt, Mrktg & Cmptr Tech Tchr
Groebe, Jean Brighton
Second Grade Teacher
Peterson, Tim L.
Fourth Grade Teacher
Walters, Paulette Elaine
Mathematics Teacher
SUTTONS BAY
Capron, David C.
Chemistry Teacher
Fisher, Harold N.
Music Director
Gross, John C.
English Teacher
Nash, Joyce Riley
Retired Third Grade Teacher
Spearing, Kaye Jean
Third Grade Teacher
Venie, Lizabeth Ann
Mathematics Teacher
Wick, Nancy Marie
Third Grade Teacher
SWARTZ CREEK
Brown, Johanna Smith
Math, Sci Tchr & Tech Cntr Dir
Burk, Patricia Spillane
Fourth Grade Teacher
Halls, William Alford
High School Teacher
Olosky, Mary Kay
Fifth Grade Teacher
Rasmussen, Trudy Marie
Biology Teacher
Russ, Gayle Pettigrew
Middle School Counselor
Wingert, Diann L.
1st Grade Teacher
TAWAS CITY
Decker, Karen Anne (Stockwell)
Business Education Teacher
Reasner, Ann Lenore
Department Chairman & Teacher
Sass, Mary Terese
Reading & English Teacher
Wajda, George Leo
Fourth Grade Teacher
Wasylk, James L.
High School Math Teacher
TAYLOR
Dickelman, Charles E.
History Teacher
Freeman-Nied, Kathryn
Special Ed Teacher Consultant
Hayward, David John
JROTC Teacher
Herring, Donna Marie
English Tchr & Guidance Cnslr
Mc Cabe, Joyce Bagrowski
Allied Health Technology Tchr
Saffer, Peggy Greenspan
4th Grade Teacher
Sinnott, Judith Ann
Sixth Grade Teacher
Smith, Thomas H.
Band Director
Trent, Laura Maria
Assistant Principal
Wallace, Shirley Eggerding
Principal & Kindergarten Tchr
Watkins, Marcia Weatherby
Elementary PE & Music Teacher
Williams, Catherine Anne Karaffa
7th-8th Grade English Teacher
Winnie, Dennis Lynn
Band Dir & Media Class Teacher
TECUMSEH
Frenzen, Ronald G.
Art Teacher
Novak, Carl Maxwell
HS Mathematics Teacher
Rachwal, Theodore Arthur
Sci, Reading & Lang Arts Tchr
Staples, Alice Barrows
Multi-Age Teacher
Stevens, Victor Conrad
Advanced Algebra Teacher
TEMPERANCE
Bankowski, Edward Frederick
Jr HS Physical Ed Teacher
Buzene, J. Michael
6th Grade Science Teacher
De Boer, Annabelle
Sixth Grade Teacher
Duhaime, Gary Scott
Sr English Lit & Speech Tchr
Gerwin, Jean Adele
2nd Grade Teacher
Jenkins, Linda Garris
Third Grade Teacher

TEMPERANCE (cont)
Johns, Helen Marie (Deese)
High School Spanish Teacher
Koch, Ronald George
Instrumental Music Teacher
Kreft, Bonnie Rae (Bellville)
High School English Teacher
Smith, Mark F.
Teacher
Stanifer, Hillary
7th Grade Mathematics Teacher
Stanifer, Sue Karen (Clawson)
English & History Teacher
Stock, Linda Oberlin
Spanish & Phys Ed Instructor
Studer, Alan Lee
High School Biology Teacher
THREE OAKS
Chesnut, Alice Smith
Fourth Grade Tchr
Lee, Carol Chrestt
Fifth Grade Teacher
Ringler, Jane Anne
Fifth Grade Teacher
Sexton, Elizabeth L.
English Teacher
Snyder, Judy Kay
High School Math Teacher
Wicher, Sabine
German Teacher
Zombory, Dale Robert
Auto Technology Instructor
THREE RIVERS
Barnum, Wendy J.
English Teacher
Green, Bettie L.
Retired Elementary Teacher
TRAVERSE CITY
Baillie, Foy Edmond
English Teacher
Brian, Patricia Ann
9th Grade Mathematics Teacher
Campbell, Sandra Golaski
English Teacher
Daniel, Mark Jefferson
Assistant Director
DiPisa, Kathleen Jane (Lautner)
Science Teacher
Hansen, Lynn Alice
Music Educator
Hassett, Floyd B.
Fourth Grade Teacher
Hilbert, Lucy Leona
Retired Elementary Teacher
Homminga, Joseph James
Campus Minister & Rel Teacher
Hoth, Karen Lee (Farnan)
Sr HS Art Teacher
Kain, Karen Psaros
Respiratory Care Educator
Kenel-Truelove, Diane Lynn
K-6th Grd Lang Arts Consultant
LaCross, Gregory L.
Coll Instructor of Bio & Chem
Liske, Robert Louis
Administrator & Science Tchr
Nadeau, Rosalind Ann (Weesner)
Retired Math Teacher
Nelson, Harold Oscar
Biology Teacher
Nelson, Jean Marie
Elem Teacher
Racine, Linda Blair
Adj Instructor of Psychology
Smith, Horace Greeley
Adjunct Mathematics Instructor
Tester, William Charles
Biology Teacher
Williams, Cheri (Small)
English, History Tchr & Admin
TRENTON
Hipsher, Shirley S.
German Teacher
Piippo, Sue Crooks
6th Grade Teacher
Poindexter, James E.
7th Grade Life Science Teacher
TROY
Altemann, Sandra Yerke
English Teacher & Yearbook Adv
Balos, Emanuel Charles
Retired History Teacher
Bauer, Ted Charles
Biology Teacher
Benes, Geoffrey M.
Orchestra Director
Blugerman, Susan Page
5th Grade Teacher
Borden, Joan Louise
Mathematics Teacher
Charron-Hall, Heide
Marketing Teacher
Clark, Harriet Tresedder
Speech, Debate & Commnctn Tchr
Collins, Gary L.
Hlth & Physical Education Tchr
Cottone, Jerry James
6th Grade Global Studies Tchr
Epple, John Philip
Mathematics Teacher
Gagnon, Marcia Jane
Language Arts & Drama Teacher
Goslin, Joseph C.
English Teacher
Hammond, Jennifer Sue
Mathematics Teacher
Havrilla, Joseph William
Band Director
Jackson, Gilbert O.
Choral Music Educator
Johnson, William
AP English Teacher
Junod, Frederick Paul
Instrumental Teacher
Karazin, Ursula Schnieders
Mathematics & Biology Teacher
Koerner, Alfred W.
Substitute Teacher
Larpenteur, Richard J.
Photography & History Teacher
Lee, Gerri Harris
First Grade Teacher
Maurer, Peter J.
7th Grade Science Teacher
McKenny, Jane G.
8th Grd Language Arts Teacher
Osaer, Sandra J.
High School Science Teacher
Petersen, Hans Michael
Sixth Grade Teacher
Petrov-Shebowich, Natalie D.
Art Teacher
Pietrofesa, Cathy Joan
High School Guidance Counselor
Quattlebaum, Dennis Juan
Assistant Principal
Ramirez, Claudia Cobb
Spanish Teacher
Rosenman, Deborah Bohm
Fourth Grade Teacher
Schmittel, Melvin L.
Fourth Grade Teacher
Steltenkamp, Charles Joseph
English Teacher
Williams, Jeffrey W.
Chemistry Teacher
TUSTIN
Dietrick, Richard Gregory
5th & 6th Grade Teacher
TWIN LAKE
Polanyi, Thomas Stephen
Third Grade Teacher
TWINING
Botzau, Connie A.
Science Teacher
Flore, Michael Robert
Speech, Eng, Psych & Soc Tchr
Kearney, Janice May
Sixth Grade Teacher
Nickell, Janet Humerickhouse
5th Grade Teacher
UBLY
Elliott, Nancy Orr
Secondary English Teacher
Schneider, Marilyn E.
Retired Teacher
UNION CITY
Katz, Christopher Lewis
Comp Sci Tchr & Tech Dir
Knapp, Ronald Alton
6th Grade English Teacher
Smith, Carolyn Ann
English & French Teacher
UNIONVILLE
Schamber, Bonnie (Struck)
Third-Fourth Grade Teacher
UNIVERSITY CENTER
Bommarito, Mary Lynch
Health & Phys Ed Instructor
Eastland, George Warren, Jr.
Professor of Chemistry
Emond, Susie B.
Prof & Teacher of Education
Gorden, Berner J.
Professor of Chemistry
Hoffmann, William Stephany
History Professor
Jezierski, John Vincent
Prof of History & Geography
Kilar, Jeremy Walter
Professor of History
Mc Gaw, Richard Alastair
Speech Communication Professor
Rees, Jennifer Williams
Asst Professor of Psychology
Robinson, Janet K.
Professor of Psychology
Short, Catherine
English Instructor
Urbano, Charissa M.
Associate Professor
Weaver, David Roll
Professor of Political Science
Wiley, Sarah Elizabeth
Assistant Professor of History
Wolff, Janice M.
Asst Prof of English
UTICA
Brown-Ashley, Kathryn Olsavsky
Eng, Debate & Forensics Tchr
Duffy, Donna E.
English Teacher
Ensley, Jane Elizabeth
6th Grade Teacher
Ignasiak, Thomas Albert
High School Mathematics Tchr
Kammann, Linda Marie
German Tchr & Activities Dir
Marengo, Jan Lee
English Teacher
McElreath, Robert Dale, Jr.
High School Biology Teacher
Renshaw, Sharlene Luvelle Mc Cray
Third Grade Teacher
Schraufnagel, Beverly Jane
HS English & Math Tchr
VASSAR
Baldori, Dorothy A. Kutzer
First Grade Teacher
Carnes, Michael J.
HS Chemistry & Biology Teacher
Chapman, Clyde A.
History, Law & Govt Teacher
Hadley, Monica Oppenheimer
Second Grade Teacher
Killian, Robert Joseph
Industrial Ed Technology Tchr
Meier, Judith F.
Science & Social Studies Tchr
VERMONTVILLE
Kipp, Laurie McFarland
5th Grade Teacher
Smith, Manuel A.
History & Government Teacher
VESTABURG
Koutz, Larry C.
High School Math Teacher
VICKSBURG
Christie, Robert Lee
Humanities Teacher
Schramm, Keith Alan
Former Asst Prof of Chemistry
Smitley, Annette
Eng Tchr & Writing Consultant
Wills, Scott
Business Teacher
WAKEFIELD
Colassacco, Robert Gene
Math & Sci Teacher
WALDRON
Green, Clara Belle
English Teacher & Counselor
Oram, Mary Lee
Business Teacher
WALLED LAKE
Darnton, David Roy
English Teacher
Heath, Lawrence James
Mathematics & Computer Tchr
Jones, Barbara C. (Sobczak)
8th Grade Teacher
Marks, MaryKay
Biology & Ecology Teacher
Rexroat, Elizabeth Marie
Speech & Drama Teacher
Socks-Parker, Carol Glenna
Art, Fr Tchr & Frgn Lang Chm
WARREN
Bell, Alexander
English & Journalism Instr
Berlin, Jeri Herman
High School Lang Arts Tchr
Borza, Madalena Lamonica
Fifth Grade Teacher
Brazelton, Ned James
Phys Ed Teacher & Coach
Cencich, David Joseph
Mathematics Teacher
Cook, Keith
Chemistry Teacher
Custance, Thomas Neil
Psychology & Drama Teacher
Delia, Vito
Chemistry Teacher
Delis, Kathy Ann
Lang Arts & Social Stud Tchr
Dobrzynski, Richard W.
Physics & Cmptr Sci Instr
Dombrowski, JoAnn Legg
Art Teacher
Hohensee, Kelly Lynn
Pre-Algebra & Amer His Teacher
Igrison, Judith Zylstra
Fifth Grade Teacher
Jendrzejewski, Roxanne Marie
American History & French Tchr
Kearly, Barbara
Teacher
Kiracofe, Douglas Eugene
Marketing Instructor
Marks, Phyllis Cope
English Teacher
Marquardt, James Samuel, Jr.
US History & Crmnl Law Tchr
Mc Dowell, Barbara Jane
Third Grade Teacher
Metzler, Christine Majkowski
French Teacher
Mislivec, James Thomas
Fifth Grade Teacher
Newhouse, Kay Ellen
Sixth Grade Teacher
Perrin, Sandra Lynn
Religion Teacher
Potter, Barbara (Hammer)
English Teacher
Sadlowski, Lucia A.
Home School Teacher
Salminen, Len Walter
Auto Tech & Power Mech Tchr
Spear, Theresa H.
English Teacher
Stelmach, Carole Zlotohoski
Comp Sci & Technology Instr
Taft, Linda L.
5th Grade Teacher
Tokarski, Elaine Judith
Second Grade Teacher
Walrad, Phyllis Audrey
Psychology Professor
WASHINGTON
Dais, Lois Joyce
Retired First Grade Teacher
Fredal, Kathleen Mary
Former English Teacher
WATERFORD
Beardsley, Constance Sylvia
Lang Arts & Soc Stud Teacher
Burdette, Kay Sibley
Rdng Instr & Dept Chair
Davis, Lynn Marie
High School Spanish Teacher
DelPup, Dina M.
Spanish & English Teacher
Dostie, Lynn Marie (Kiple)
Span, French & Japanese Tchr
Garratt, Willis H.
Physics Teacher
Irish, Joan Cary
Counselor
Kinnunen, Frances (Spencer)
Language Arts & Honors Teacher
Knapp, Richard H.
Professor & Bio Sci Dept Head
Lerner, Rosemary Martin
Computer Science Teacher
Maher, Julie Rivero
First Grade Teacher
Meranda, John Arthur
Math Teacher
Miller, Harrison Edward, Jr.
Assistant Principal
Moon, Richard Louis
US History & English Teacher
Nottingham, Su
Human Relations Teacher
Scheiwe, William Arthur
Science, Math & PE Teacher
Spainhour, Ronald Elliott
Political Science Professor
VanHull, John E.
Soc Stud Tchr & Stu Ldrshp Dir
Zink, E. Marie
Retired Elementary Teacher
WATERSMEET
Peterson, George R., III
6th Grd Teacher & Athletic Dir
WATERVLIET
Johnson, William Lawrence
History Teacher & Athletic Dir
Newell, Edward Kent
Math Teacher & Principal
Waite, Michael Eugene
Industrial Arts Teacher
WAYLAND
Bollone, Brian Christopher
Advanced Placement Bio Tchr
Harcourt, Steven L.
Mathematics Teacher
Nelson, Sharon Kay
Physical Education Teacher
Salisbury, Jeffrey Louis
Eng, Jrnlsm & Desktop Pub Tchr
Steines, E. Lorraine Woodhams
Retired First Grade Teacher
Stephenson, Michelle Annette
Band Director
Wade, Sandra Kay
7th Grade English Teacher
Working, Steven L.
Band Director
WAYNE
DeLuca, Kal Ray
Science Teacher
Elsesser, Lynne Tuttoilmondo
Spanish Dept Head & Teacher
Marchi, Kevin
High School Spanish Teacher
Ping, Julie Sullivan
11th-12th Grd Social Stud Tchr
Wacksmuth, Susan Hubbard
Fourth Grade Teacher
WEBBERVILLE
Johnson, Jean
Fourth Grade Teacher
Showerman, Jeanne Lucas
Elementary Fine Arts Teacher
WEIDMAN
Snook, Judy Kaye
Retired Kindergarten Teacher
WEST BLOOMFIELD
Brody, Karen Sherck
HS Guidance Counselor
Brown, Louis R.
Support Teacher
Dorfman, Stephanie Biri
English & Humanities Teacher
Fornero, George V.
Principal
Friday, Joanne Marie
Language Arts & Soc Stud Tchr
Friday, Sean C.
Biology & Chemistry Teacher
Hilfiker, Anastasia Louise
HS Social Studies Teacher
Holtfreter, Timothy James
High School Math Teacher
Leider, Robert S.
Drama & Yearbook Teacher
O'Connell, Patricia Ann
Kindergarten Teacher
Ranke, Doris J.
Science Teacher
Rollinger, Susan Feldman
English Department Chair, Tchr
Watson, Patrick Arlo
Social Studies Teacher
WEST BRANCH
Dame, Frank Anthony
High School English Teacher
Roberts, Martha Payne
French, Spanish & English Tchr
WESTLAND
Deschaine, Thomas J.
Anatomy & Physiology Instr
Harmon, Gerald Edward
Math Teacher
Hinck, Barbara Ann
2nd-3rd Grade Teacher
Kitchen, Johnnie Lee
Special Education Teacher
Kliza, Nancy G.
Lang Arts Tchr & Dept Chprsn
Koenig, David Paul
Guidance Counselor
Loskowske, Esther Corinne
Second Grade Teacher
Roberts, Patricia Ann
Fifth Grade Teacher
Smiley, Clinton Adam
Assistant Principal
WHITE CLOUD
Frisbey, Bernadette Chien
Substitute Teacher
Mc Hattie, Anthony A.
Eng Tchr & Exploratory Instr
Taylor, Dawn Marie
Elementary Music Teacher
WHITE LAKE
Doyle, Eileen M.
History Teacher
Masson, Sherri Case
Fifth Grade Teacher
Montgomery, David Alan
Soc Stud & Mult Media Teacher
Ring, Theodore Edward
Teacher
WHITE PIGEON
Smith, Darryl Forrest
English Teacher
WHITE PINE
Makela, A. Eric
Mathematics Teacher
WHITEHALL
Brown, Deanna Marie
Chemistry & Biology Teacher
Malbouef, Andrew L.
HS Math & Physics Teacher
Mikkelson, Kirk Douglas
Math & Science Teacher
Rodriguez, David J.
Martial Arts Instructor
Zoellmer, Robert G.
Fifth Grade Math & Sci Tchr
WHITMORE LAKE
Krebill, Michael Edward
Science Teacher
Strauss, Kristen Tasch
Literature & Science Teacher
WHITTEMORE
Harrison, Samuel C.
Business Teacher
Sammons, Marilyn Walker
Scndry Speech & Eng Teacher
WILLIAMSTON
Pizanis, Takis S.
Teacher
WILSON
Harlan, Edwin A.
Teacher & Principal
Quillin, Randall Eugene
Outrch Coord & Gymnastic Coach
WIXOM
Berkey, Cheryl Leah
First & Second Grade Teacher
WOODLAND
Kinsey, Elizabeth Polzin
7th Grade Language Arts Tchr
Martin, Ronald Lynn
United States History Teacher
WYANDOTTE
Allison, James Robert
8th Grade Mathematics Teacher
Barber, Denise Ann
6th Grade Teacher
Bender, Edgar Leonard
Teacher
Boller, Yvonne Rose
Speech & English Teacher
Brennan, Susan Marie
Kindergarten Teacher
Butz, Margaret Ann (Holman)
Mathematics Teacher
Czarnota, Vivian Bojack
1st Grade Teacher
Dallos, Michael G.
Law Related Education Instr
Eshleman, Penny Clark
Technology Instructor
Gillum, Patricia
Fourth Grade Teacher
Glaza, Cindy Rose
English & Science Teacher
Gregory, Charlotte Anne
Special Ed Resource Room Tchr
Griswold, Millie Marie (Gall)
HS Social Science Teacher
Hauer, Nancy Ann
Home Economics & Art Teacher
Knoll, Karl Edward
9th-12th Grade English Teacher
Leizerman, Sylvan Phillip
English Teacher
Maher-Minor, Colleen
HS Physical Education Teacher
Nicholson, Daniel Mark
Mathematics Dept Head & Tchr
Ryniak, Gary James
5th Grade Teacher
Rzeppa, Charlene Serafinski
High School English Teacher
Simmons, David E.
HS Math Teacher & Dept Head
Smith, Barbara Blakeley
1st Grade Teacher
Wehner, David Joel
Biology Teacher & Dept Chm

DOTTE (cont)
cki, Glenda Lilburn
Studies Teacher
ING
Kayleen Joy
ant Professor of Music
, Barbara J.
Grade Teacher
Klay, Thomas D.
c Stud Tchr & Chairman
s, Renay Marie
Professor of Education
on, Elizabeth Ann (Koppinger)
th Grade Eng & PE Tchr
ANTI
a, Linda Rose (Kannam)
h Teacher
, Barry
sor of Art
Anne K.
sor of Education
ell, Thomas
er
Diane O'Brien
a & Music Teacher
e, Donald Andrew
f Math
, Larry J.
Dir & Algebra Teacher
a, Melvin Scott
er
Shirley Lesher
& Fourth Grade Teacher
John Kent
rade Teacher
Gary L.
unication Professor
velyn V.
Grade Teacher
Maude E.
pal
Carolyn L.
h Teacher
Timothy Gilbert
ra & Pre-Algebra Teacher
hwerdt, Rosanne Guttrich
Arts, Drama, Cmmnctn Tchr
Elizabeth Ann
tudies Tchr & Dept Chair
Edith Mac Lennan
ssor of Biology
orth-Rico, Alfonso
ant Professor
a, David Carl
ematics Education Prof
a-Ryles, Sharon Bluitt
rade Teacher
Zafar Ullah
Professor of Accounting
sser, George William
ce Teacher & Dept Chair
Roger Douglas
ry Professor
ewski, Deanna Karen
Grade Teacher
on-Harmon, Linda Rose
Studies Teacher
k, Karen Menke
ssor
eld, Richard Lee
Arts Dept & Art His Prof
, Natthi Lal
cs Professor
llene B.
ad Grade Teacher
Darryl Crawford
Arts Tchr & Dept Chair
uge, Silvia
ology Professor
n, Thomas Raymond
ciate Professor of French
m, Ron Mark
ssor of Sociology
ns, Regina Helen (Johnson)
Grade Teacher
AND
Michael Lee
rade Social Stud Teacher
n, Ivan Jay
& Science Teacher
ra, Nancy J.
cal Education Teacher
r, Rebecca Buning
sh Teacher
Robert C.
sh Teacher & Coach
Kenneth Robert
gy Teacher
Susan VanKoevering
Grade Math Teacher
ak, Steven Dale
Grade Teacher

NNESOTA

gton, Nathan Ray
culture Education Instr
gen, Karen Patricia (Ode)
ish & Business Ed Teacher
el, Joyce Stellon
Grade Elementary Teacher
IS
Larry Leroy
ndary Teacher

ADRIAN
Carr, James Francis
History, Social Tchr & Coach
Fritzemeier, Garret Lee
Mathematics & Physics Instr
Rother, Ronald Anthony
Vocal Music Teacher
ALBANY
Gardinier, Duane Gerald
Sixth Grade Teacher
Holt, Robin Kenneth
Math Teacher
Jepsen, Coy Roger
Spanish Teacher
Stromme, Steven Roger
Senior High English Teacher
ALBERT LEA
Heaney, Diane Mary
Choral & Vocal Music Director
Hintermeister, Gayle Janene
Spanish Teacher
Justesen, Dorothy Ellen
Third Grade Teacher
Larson, Paul Theodore
6th Grade Teacher
Lybeck, Richard Frederick
Sixth Grade Teacher
Morris, Brenda Moeller
Dean of Students
Skaar, Neal Alan
Senior Humanities Teacher
Sonnega, Michelle Marie
English Teacher
Zimmerman, Bernhard Gabriel
Math Teacher
ALBERTA
Gausman, Doris Feuchtenberger
Mathematics Teacher
ALEXANDRIA
Biegner, Chris P.
Social Studies Teacher
Crabtree, Joan Gerland
School Psychologist
Deitz, Steve
Vocal Music Director
Freborg, John Michael
English Teacher
Hanzlik, Stephen James
Bus Ed & Soc Stud Instructor
Johnson, Abby M.
Spanish & English Teacher
Kalpin, Dennis A.
Mathematics Teacher
Melby, Denis Lee
Math Instructor
Mork, DAvid Bryon
Science Teacher
Otterness, Benita D.
English Teacher
Prchal, Dawn Norlien
English Teacher
Raymond, Robert Alan
Physical Education Teacher
Rudolph, Dean R.
Elementary Teacher
Saeugling, Janet L. (Gisslen)
Eighth Grade Geography Teacher
Schnell, Bonnie Buhl
4th Grade Teacher
Syverson, Nancy Stewart
High School Math Teacher
Van Zomeren, Bernard H.
Agriculture Teacher
Warren, Thomas L.
Mathematics Teacher
Zieman, Julia Hanson
Gifted Education Tchr & Coord
Zinda, Dan R.
Biology Teacher & Sci Dept Chm
ANNANDALE
Force, Lorene Ann (Lemmerman)
Second Grade Teacher
ANOKA
Anderson, Janice Marie
English Teacher
Bohne, Brian Richard
Social Studies Teacher & Coach
Boo, Cindy L.
Math Teacher
Casey, Susan L. Gibbons
3rd Grade Teacher
Chamberlain, Sonja (Peterson)
Director of Choirs
Foster, Tirzah Jean
Vocal & Classroom Music Tchr
Gustafson, Scott John
Mathematics Teacher
Hagberg, Deborah E.
First Grade Teacher
Heck, Janice Kaye
Media Generalist
Hedin, Mark Arne
Math Teacher
Hill, Jeffery James
Math Teacher
Kowalchuk, Merry Mansfield
Third Grade Teacher
Leach, William John
English Teacher & Dept Chm
Marcy, Sherrie Gette
Sixth Grade Teacher
Phelps, Bruce Theron
High School Music Teacher
Rudzitis, Roland Talis
Band Director
Williams, Kate
Art Teacher
Zosel, David Timothy
7th Grade Life Science Teacher

APPLE VALLEY
Aase, Laura Luger
Reading Teacher
Altavilla, Robert Anthony
Physical Education Teacher
Becker, Bruce W.
Director of Choirs
Dahlstrom, Lorraine Marie Matuzak
8th Grade English Teacher
Eaves, Dee Ann
1st Grade Teacher
Egstad, Michael Charles
Social Studies Dept Coord
Gillard, Margaret Syverson
Social Studies Teacher
Helgeson, Robert John
Lang Arts & Humanities Tchr
Honrud, Susan Stephan
Mathematics Teacher
Jandro, Susan Marie
High School Math Teacher
Mc Cabe, William Frank
Teacher & Coordinator
Meyer, Lynne Stenerson
Fifth Grade Teacher
Miller, David Michael
Instrumental Music Teacher
Ogee, Charles K.
Communications Teacher
Randa, Keith E.
Science Teacher
Ruhmann, Wenceslaus F.
German, Russian & English Tchr
Ryan, Beverly Yvonne
English Teacher
Saathoff, Carole Gene
Academic Coordinator & Teacher
Zitur, Timothy S.
Mathematics Teacher
APPLETON
Tostenson, Renae Eloys
Kindergarten Teacher
ARLINGTON
Bienfang, Wyatt Lane
Third Grade Teacher
Hultgren, Mary Stallkamp
English Teacher
Ihrke, Alan Richard
Mathematics Teacher & Coach
Scott, Judith M.
Spanish Teacher
ASHBY
Kent, John Davy
Science Teacher
ATWATER
Aaker, Melissa Ryks
Language Arts Teacher
Huselid, Kathryn Kay (Kube)
K-12th Grd Vocal Music Instr
Reed, Steven Mark
5th Grade Elementary Teacher
Trooien, Philip E.
Biology Instr & Golf Coach
AUDUBON
Brooks, Laurie Dawn (Amundson)
5th Grade Teacher
Skaaland, Sam Gregg
Sixth Grade Teacher
AURORA
Klabechek, Thomas E.
Chem Tchr, Dist Sci Math Coord
AUSTIN
Anderson, Patricia S.
Fourth & Fifth Grade Teacher
Besel, Paul
Science & Social Studies Tchr
Clark, Carol
Family & Consumer Science Tchr
DeMars, Peter Leo
Calculus Teacher
Gale, Janine Pekas
Sixth Grade Teacher
Johnson, Brian Thomas
High School Vocal Music Tchr
Luehmann, Lloyd Luther
Principal & Teacher
Waterman, John Bradley
Mathematics Teacher
AVON
Kurilla, Joan Heurung
5th Grade Teacher
BABBITT
Hammer, Sylvia A.
Fourth Grade Classroom Teacher
BACKUS
Norlin, Diane Noll
5th Grade Teacher
BAGLEY
Brown-Colligan, Nancy Anne
Spanish & Speech Teacher
Sawyer, Darlene Gunelius
Secondary Language Arts Tchr
BARNESVILLE
Albright, Carol J. Schwandt
Art Teacher
Holm, Michael James
Social Studies Teacher
Loen, Nancy Joette
Ag Ed Instructor & FFA Adv
BARNUM
Hosmer, James Richard
Social Studies Teacher
Smith, Sue Johnson
Mathematics Teacher
BARRETT
Swanson, Keith Douglas
PE & Health Teacher
BEARVILLE NORTH
Bormann, Verna Scott
Home School Tutor

BEAVER CREEK
Siegfried, Mary Lee (Finke)
Third Grade Teacher
BECKER
Brandes, Victoria Ann (Casey)
Sixth Grade Teacher
Chirhart, Lonnie Keefe
K-12 Teacher of Gftd Education
Peterson, Robert Henry
Third Grade Teacher
Steinkraus, Julie Ann (Pederson)
Sixth Grade Teacher
BELGRADE
Schwarze, Larry Jon
Alg & Math Teacher
BELLE PLAINE
Callahan, Pauline DeMuth
Teacher
Moore, LaVonne Carlson
German Teacher
Wiley, Robert Devon
Band Director
BEMIDJI
Aalgaard, Ami Chari
8th Grade Science Teacher
Anderson, Richard Duane
Sixth Grade Math Teacher
Brandvik, Marylou Kittleson
English Teacher
Bruns, Susan L.
English Teacher
Falk, Lois V. Wicktor
Fifth Grade Teacher
Galarneault, Thomas Richard
A P European & World His Tchr
Lund, Jacquelyn Sterbenk
Chemistry & Biology Teacher
Reynolds, Pat Bridget
Fifth Grade Teacher
Sanders, John Ernest
Prof of Theology & Philosophy
Toward, Rick W.
8th Grade Social Studies Tchr
BENSON
Bradbury, Boyd Lee
Secondary Principal
Hamann, Emil Elmer
Science Instructor
Rois, Marjorie Ann (Loen)
Fourth Grade Teacher
BERTHA
Kelm-Maynard, Gail I.
HS Chapter I Math Teacher
Sutherland, James Martin
Soc Stud & Elem PE Teacher
Trisko, Thomas James
Business Instructor
BIG LAKE
Bjorklund, Barbara Johnson
Kindergarten Teacher
Bolin, Sandra Sommers
Soc Stud & World Geog Techr
Danner, Bruce John
3rd Grade Teacher
Danzel-Haskell, MaryAnn
Kindergarten Teacher
Roussin, James Lloyd
Lang Arts Tchr & Enrich Coord
BIGFORK
Lester, Joan Marie
Social Studies Teacher
Nathe, Margaret F.
English Teacher
BIRD ISLAND
Aumer, Dennis Lee
Physical Education & Hlth Tchr
BIWABIK
Herrmann, Leonard J.
Fifth Grade Teacher
BLACKDUCK
Bechtold, Stephen Mark
Secondary Mathematics Teacher
Johnson, Mark Robert
Fifth Grade Teacher
Liapis, Thomas James
Fourth Grade Teacher
BLAINE
Banghart, Joyce Ann
English Teacher
Bennett, Jeanne Dickman
Gifted Coord & Math Teacher
Bloom, Kellie Fae
Sixth Grade Teacher
Brucciani-Clark, Marcia A.
Secondary Social Studies Tchr
Buth, Delores Eide
German Teacher
Dunn, Gary L.
World History Teacher
Dunn, Jane Engh
Social Studies Teacher
Eggert, Karen Margaret
Mathematics Teacher
Gibson, Robert Millard
8th Grd Social Studies Teacher
Griggs, Patricia Ann
First Grade Teacher
Hokkanen, JoAnn E.
Mathematics Teacher
Lewis, Benjamin R.
9th Grade Physical Sci Tchr
Lider, Barbara R.
Educational Speech Lang Tchr
Lincoln, Lanice Lee
English & Humanities Teacher
Lips, Karen L.
7th Grade Math Teacher
Mann, Mary Dallman
Spanish Teacher & Drama Dir

Nelson, David Gregory
PE Tchr & Ftbl Head Coach
Samson, Rodney Dwight
Soc Stud Chm & US His Tchr
Willner, Kathryn M.
Spanish Teacher
Zemlin, Susan Carol
Vocal Music Director
BLOOMING PRAIRIE
Woehler, Charles Timothy
Science & Agriscience Instr
BLOOMINGTON
Adams, Walter F.
Acad Dean & Eng Dept Chprsn
Beatty, Suzanne Mary
Dental Instructor
Berg, Carol Sue Peterson
English Teacher
Borman, Charles Barry
Philosophy & Anthropology Tchr
Brenholdt, Nan
Kindergarten Teacher
Cavanaugh, Ronald Arthur
Business Teacher
Coulter, Cheryl M.
Math & Cmptr Sci Instr
Davis, P. Thomas
Research Investigator
Dunlap, Jeffrey Paul
Teacher
Fjelde, E. T.
World Cultures Teacher
Hayden, Colleen C.
Social Studies Teacher
Holsapple, Larry Urbin
Industrial Technology Teacher
Hudson, Nancy Ann (Schneider)
5th & 12th Grade Teacher
Johnson, Myles E.
Instructor of Psychology
Lyons, Earl James
English Teacher
Manne, Anita L.
Assoc Professor of Radiology
Mc Kay, Michael B.
Biology Teacher
Mislivec, Frank John
Fifth Grade Teacher
Otto, Beverly Jean
Second Grade Teacher
Peterson, Jerry B.
Student Act Coord & Teacher
Porter, Roger James
Fourth Grade Teacher
Ray, Jeffrey Paul
Math Teacher & Dept Chair
Schmidt, Karen Noelle
Social Studies Teacher
Schultz, Katherine Green
English Teacher
Specht, Donald
Media Specialist & Tech Coord
Spies, Thomas Peter
Math Teacher
Trenda, Roger Francis
American Literature Teacher
Tuchscherer, Mary Margaret
Science Prof & Physician
Wacker, Audrey Angeline
Retired Jr HS Science Teacher
Wallin, Barbara J.
1st & 2nd Grade Teacher
Wittich, Jane Elizabeth
Assoc Dean of Basic Sciences
Zachman, Zachary John
Associate Professor
Ziesemer, Jon Leslie
Seventh Grade Teacher
BLUE EARTH
Bly, Frankie Carl
5th Grade Teacher
Brandt, Bradley Allan
Band & Orchestra Director
Ellingsen, Mike
Vocal Music & Drama Teacher
Sullivan, Kathleen Marie (Skaro)
Span Tchr & Head Speech Coach
BRAHAM
Kaunonen, Arthur Neil
Soc Stud, His & Geography Tchr
Skarsten, Gary Phillip
Secondary Social Studies Tchr
Walker, Janelle Claire
Physical Education Teacher
BRAINERD
Anderson, Barbra Burres
Public Speaking Instructor
Bedard, Robert R.
Physics & Pre Engrng Instr
Belgum, Paul Charles
6th Grade Teacher
Blake, Kathryn Lee
College Mathematics Teacher
Christensen-Nelson, Ruth Ann
First Grade Teacher
Comstock, Joanne Halbmaier
First Grade Teacher
Eastman, Bruce Clyde
Professor of English
Eisenzimmer, Kevin Gene
Business Instructor
Jackson, Carol Ann Swenson
Sixth Grade Teacher
Langer, Michael Allen
Elem Special Education Tchr
Loney, Julienne E. Solheim
Fifth Grade Teacher
Mc Calla, Kelly Burt
Eng, Mass Communications Instr

BRAINERD (cont)
Moses, Marilyn Jane
English Instructor
Perlinger, Karen Cooper
English & Spanish Teacher
Phipps, Wayne LeRoy
8th Grade Earth Science Instr
Pruitt, Pamela Lynne
Math & Science Instructor
Smith, Carol Jean
Elementary Music Specialist
Smith, D. Michael
Vocal Music Teacher
Spradlin, Marion Elaine Graham
Speech & Theatre Instructor
Turner, Wendy Bletz
Psychology Instructor
Vogt, Karen Hugh
Sixth Grade GATE Tchr
Weiss, Kay Edgeton
Physical Ed Teacher & Coach
BRANDON
Peterka, Joleen A.
Mathematics Teacher
BRECKENRIDGE
Betsch, Patricia (Kunze)
7th-8th Grd Math Chptr I Aid
Hanneman, Dale Vernon
English Teacher
Mullin, Karen S. (Flynn)
Special Ed Para Professional
BROOKLYN CENTER
Solie, Konnie G.
Retired First Grade Teacher
BROOKLYN PARK
Balfour, Conrad George
Instructor of English
Crewe, Donna Lee
Counselor
Davis, Mary Proehl
Family & Consumer Science Tchr
Dovel, Gary C.
Health & Wellness Teacher
Foss, Matt
Mathematics Instructor
Hudson, Judy Fay
English Teacher
Johnston, Barbara Jean
Professor of Sociology & Chair
LePage, Peggy Lee
Prof of Biological Sciences
Lyons, Helen M.
ESL Paraprofessional
Miller, Karla Wiese
Choral Dir & Music Instr
Trooien, Roberta Peirce
English Teacher
Volk, Tatyana Michelle
Computer Science Instructor
BROOTEN
Halvorson, Carrie Kjellberg
6th Grade Teacher
Weimerskirch, Nancy R.
Administrative Assistant
BROWNSDALE
Gallaher, Mary Ann
Retired Teacher
BROWNTON
Crosby, Anita Louise
Eng Tchr & Media Specialist
BUFFALO
Eiynck, Nancy Jean
Spanish Teacher
Johnson, Jennifer Leah
French Teacher
Johnson, Michael W.
7th Grade English Teacher
Keifenheim, Charley Allen
Chemistry Teacher
Ramstad, Pamela Kay
Spanish Teacher
Rohl, Gerard Alan
Social Studies Teacher
Sonju, Patrick Lyndon
Biology Teacher
BUFFALO LAKE
Michelson, Eleanor Warner
Retired Elementary Teacher
BURNSVILLE
Cook, James Taylor
Technology Teacher
Daily, Lawrence W.
Chemistry Instructor
Dornfeld, Daniel John
Sixth Grade Teacher
Erickson, Dianne M.
Teacher & Environmental Edctr
Griffin, Mark E.
Business & Physical Ed Tchr
Gunderson, Veronica Paulson
Director of Bands
Hugstad-Vaa, Jennifer Jo
Bio Teacher
Ketcham, Steven Jon
English Teacher
Marshall, Marcia Jane
First Grade Teacher
Truitt-Petersen, Barbara Althera Parker
Spanish Teacher
Zetah, Elizabeth Fulmer
First Grade Teacher
BUTTERFIELD
Eichhorst, Jay Thomas
Dir of Instrumental Music Stud
BYRON
Beech, George Paul
5th Grade Teacher
Gehrking, Martha Syverson
9th-12th Grd English Teacher

Hodge, Alan L.
Mathematics Teacher
CALEDONIA
Denstad, Eileen Clauss
Spanish Teacher
Froehling, Mark Harold
Chemistry & Physics Teacher
Lapham, Mary Ellen Billhorn
First Grade Teacher
Medin, Howard Vernon
Mathematics Teacher
Olson, Harold Elvin
Grad Standards Site Director
Walcker, Carol Tiber
Fifth Grade Teacher
Zard, Joanne Scott
English & Speech Teacher
CAMBRIDGE
Ayen, Norman Dale
English Teacher
Burns, Edward John
Industrial Technology Instr
Hoffman, Kathleen Ann
English Instructor
Jakovich, Colleen Patricia
7th Grd Lang Arts & Comm Tchr
Johnson, Allyn Maynard
Environmental Science Teacher
Kittock, Claudia Jean
College Professor
Maikkula, Dwight Raymond
Social Studies Instructor
McGivern, Francis Patrick
English Teacher
Meyer, Jodi Renae
Health & Business Teacher
Newton, Timothy Philip
Bible Teacher
Reisdorf, Timothy
Math & Science Teacher
Renstrom, Lila M.
Business Teacher
Wedlund, Lynn Shafer
Band Instructor
CANNON FALLS
Downs, Colleen Freiborg
English Teacher
Erdmann, Jeff
Activities Dir & Civics Tchr
Johnson, Myron O.
Retired Music Teacher
O'Keeffe, David Patrick
6th Grade Teacher
Sahli, Michele Regina
Third Grade Teacher
Senjem, Patricia Lickteig
High School Counselor
Stary, Ronald Allen
High School Band Director
Wendelschafer, Darlene Alice
Retired 5th Grade Teacher
CASS LAKE
Schullo, Charlotte Elaine (Rich)
5th Grade Teacher
CEDAR
Pederson, Mickey Ray
6th Grade Teacher
CHAMPLIN
Bastian, Olivia Ann
English Teacher & Dept Leader
Block, William L.
Fourth Grade Teacher
Blomgren, Judy Ann
Music Teacher
Franson, Cheryl
Sixth Grade Teacher
Germanson, Susan Rae
Spanish Teacher
Grimm, Julie Kristen
Science Teacher
Idstrom, Thomas Uddo
9th Grade US Government Tchr
Johnson, Patricia
English Teacher
Lyons, Steven Gerard
Band Director
Meuers, Frank Anthony
6th Grade Teacher
Ogaard, Richard D.
Counselor
Shore, Cynthia Kaye
Mathematics Teacher
CHASKA
Hager, Derek Lyndon
Art Teacher
Rodrique, Kimberly Sue (Berhow)
Art Teacher
CHISAGO CITY
Mattson, LouAnn Marie
4th Grade Teacher
CHISHOLM
Abraham, Jon W.
Fifth Grade Teacher
Anderson, Kathleen L.
Fourth Grade Teacher
Charter, Rita Costanzi
Eng Instr & Media Generalist
Debever, Mary Sullivan
Social Studies Teacher
Hines, Beverly Kruchoski
Kindergarten Teacher
Jacobson, Linda Axelson
Science & Math Teacher
Kavlie, Evelyn Therese
Community Education Director
Snyder, Gerald L.
Band Director
Sushoreba, Marlys Anne
5th Grade Teacher

Varichak, James
6th Grade Teacher
CIRCLE PINES
Anderson, Jon Peter
Physics & Astronomy Teacher
Belich, Sharon Flokstra
Eng as a Second Lang Tchr
Bragg, Richard Joe
Science Teacher
Johnson, Scott R.
English Teacher
Perreault, Kathleen Ann
1st Grade Teacher
Sturlaugson, Craig T.
8th Grade Geography Teacher
CLARISSA
Hudalla, Cindy Iten
Kindergarten Teacher
Tuorila, Patricia Tracy
Fourth Grade Teacher
CLEVELAND
Grabow, Becky Skaar
K-12th Vocal Music Teacher
Kortuem, Cindy D.
Secondary English Teacher
Letts, Connie J.
Fifth Grade & Mentor Teacher
Rusch, James Alvin
10th-12th Grade Soc Stud Tchr
Swedberg, Douglas H.
Science Teacher
CLIMAX
Hastad, Rebecca Marie
7th-12th Grade English Teacher
Haug, John Paul
Secondary Science Teacher
Hayden, Ruth Marie
PE & Health Ed Teacher
CLOQUET
Gittings, Ronald Frederick
Sociology Instructor
Jirschele, Anthony Paul
Dir Bands, Instr & Dept Chair
Kronemann, Don M.
Fourth Grade Teacher
Lizotte, Gerald Lee
Retired Music & Band Teacher
Rose, Elizabeth Ann (Wilson)
Choral Director
Schmidt, Gail S.
Retired Teacher
COKATO
Ellis, Steven Patrick
Industrial Technology Teacher
Harmala, Joe
Accounting Instructor
Jensen, Mary Elizabeth Olson
English Teacher
Ring, Jonathan Paul
Mathematics Teacher
COLD SPRING
Athmann, Brian H.
K-8th Grade PE Teacher
Clapp, Karen Jean
Biology Teacher
Distel, Gary Max
HS Social Studies Teacher
Eisenreich, William Charles
6th Grade Teacher
Grundman, Denna Timboe
English Teacher
Karcher, Judith Ann
Spanish Teacher
Mergen, Jeffery Henry
Mathematics Teacher
Meyer, Linda Putz
Sixth Grade Teacher
Oscarson, Evan Charles
Business Education Teacher
Pasquerella, Frank Matthew
Director of Bands
Sell, Carol Dols
First Grade Teacher
Thompson, Susan Alexander
11th & 12th Grade English Tchr
COLERAINE
Gould, Marcella Mevissen
Span & Eng Tchr & Dept Chair
Greniger, Gary Duane
Social Studies Teacher
COLLEGEVILLE
Blanchette, Kevin Joseph
Mathematics Teacher
Cahoy, William John
Associate Prof of Theology
Cunningham, Anthony
Assistant Prof of Philosophy
Froehle, Peter H.
Physics & Mathematics Teacher
Martin, Marina
Associate Professor of Spanish
COLUMBIA HEIGHTS
Johnson, Nancy Marie
Health Teacher
Kordiak, Mary George
English Teacher
COMFREY
DeBerg, Gigi Gardiner
English Instructor
COOK
Maki, Robert Martin
Counselor
Popelka, Bonnie Lynn
English & Speech Teacher
COON RAPIDS
Adkins, Frederick Addison
Math Teacher & Head Coach
Biederman, James J.
Psychology Instructor

Brown, Stanley Howard
Sixth Grade Teacher
Carlson, Linda Marie
Lang Arts, Gftd & Tlntd Tchr
Ehlers, Susan Bumann
Mathematics Professor
Geiger, Patrick Charles
Vocal Music Director
Gramith, Charles Willis
8th Grade Geography Teacher
Jewell, H. Richard
English & Humanities Instr
Kittelson, Dale Allan
Science Teacher
Mattson, Drew E.
Economics Professor
Paulson, Patricia Caldwell
Sixth Grade Teacher
Reines, David Hershey
Fifth Grade Teacher
Riha, Michael William
Mathematics Teacher
Rover, Gary Glenn
Physical Education Teacher
Tracy, Sharon Layman
Hnrs English & Hum Tchr
Vickerman, Maureen Linnihan
German Teacher
Wax, Gordon Lee
Philosophy Teacher
COSMOS
Broderius, Sherri L. Ahlness
6th Grade Teacher
Herrick, Nyla Rowerdink
Second Grade Teacher
COTTAGE GROVE
Adams, Joseph Avery
Teacher, Supervisor & Admin
Armbrust, John G.
Secondary Social Studies Tchr
Beaudoin, Lesley Erickson
1st Grade Teacher
Bloom, Pamela Kay (Ulander)
Math Teacher
Boche, Cheryl R.
Business Education Teacher
Davies, Bud E.
Mathematics Tchr
Huelsmann, Thomas J.
Director of Bands
Johnson, Jill
First Grade Teacher
Krussow, Randy Kenneth
Principal & Teacher
Malicki, Patrick Damus
Junior High Mathematics Tchr
Patterson, Karen Breitbach
HS Mathematics Teacher
Peltier, Kay Quinn
6th Grade Teacher
Ryan, Corinne English
Vocational Teacher & Coord
Taack, Katherine A.
English Teacher
COTTON
Beaupre, Elisabet B. (Casserberg)
French & Social Studies Tchr
CROOKSTON
Bittner, Jon Victor
HS Social Studies Teacher
Cooley, Connie Kay
2nd Grade Teacher
Davidson, David Michael
English Teacher
Feltis, Jerome Donald
Lecturer of Ethics
Grove, Toni Jean
Business Teacher
Liebl, Caroline
Retired Teacher
Skanson, Daniel Curtis
Sixth Grade Teacher
Wagner, Leslie Alvin
Fourth Grade Teacher
Wesselink, Michael Dean
Mathematics Teacher
CROSBY
Christenson, James Michael
Science Teacher
Sharp, Gordon James
World History Teacher
DAWSON
Hanson, Paul W.
Band Director
DEER CREEK
StPeter, Bernard Leland
Fifth Grade Teacher
DELANO
Fitzer, John Andrew
Spanish Teacher
Wilson, Teresa Kuzinski
Music Teacher
DETROIT LAKES
Crawford, Lorren DeFloy
English Teacher
Ferris, Eric Kelly
Health & Physical Ed Teacher
Johnson, Therese Perrizo
Third Grade Teacher
Neff, Louise Rae
Junior First Grade Teacher
DODGE CENTER
Clapham, Linda Marie
Learning Disabilities Tchr
Peterson, Karen K.
Business Teacher
Schreiber, John Frederick
English & Theater Teacher

DULUTH
Bauer, Andrea Jane (Danisch)
1st Grade Teacher
Birnbaum, Lawrence John
Assoc Prof & Dept Chm
Burnham, Albert David
Retired History Tchr
Clark, Beth Marie
MS PE Teacher
Englund, Lee Robert
Art Dept Chairperson & Teacher
Gaard, Greta Claire
Cmpstn & Womens's Stud Tchr
Gordon, David R.
German Teacher
Gordon, Randall Allan
Associate Professor of Psych
Hornstein, Theresa Marie
Professor of Biology
Isbell, Tom K.
Assistant Professor
Jankofsky, Klaus Peter
Professor & Department Head
Johnson, Brian c.
Mathematics Teacher
Johnson, Joann Marlene
Professor of Physical Ed
Joseph, Barbara Fedder
5th Grade Teacher
Kovacovic, Milan
Associate Professor of French
Ley, Eugene Stephen
Prof of Health Education
Mickolajak, Tyce James
5th Grade Teacher
Muckala, Patricia Marie
English Teacher
Naslund, Karen Wagner
6th Grade Teacher
Olm, James F.
Vocal Music & Drama Teacher
Olson, Patti J.
English Teacher
Ostrofsky, Linda Ann
Business Education Teacher
Price, Marylina Hayden
Retired Third Grade Teacher
Priest, Donald Firmine
Mathematics Teacher
Rallis, Helen
Associate Prof of Education
Reich, Deirdre Mc Carthy
Mathematics Teacher
Rindal, Robert John
Retired 6th Grade Math Teacher
Ringsred, John Norman
Electronics Professor
Running, Susan Dahl
Fifth Grade Teacher
Severson, Laurie S.
Earth Science Teacher
Shermer, Jeanne Marie (Johnson)
6th Grade Language Arts Tchr
Van Mersbergen, Audrey Marie
Communication Professor
Vukelich, Joe Axel
Economics & US History Teacher
Waterhouse, Rebecca Lynn
German Teacher & Dance Coach
Winkelman, Winnifred Veronica
History Professor & Dept Chair
EAGAN
Bishop, Daniel Paul
Science Teacher
Block, Richard William
5th & 6th Grade Teacher
Cullen, Joan E.
8th Grd Interdisciplinary Team
Eiden, Kathleen Ascher
Spanish Teacher
Henderson, Judy DelPino
Social Studies Teacher
Kunze-Hoeg, Kari Alison
Spanish Teacher
Lee, Jane E.
High School Math Teacher
Nelson, Bruce Henry
Physical Education Teacher
Payette, Anthony D.
Fifth Grade Teacher
Remington, Michael V.
Mathematics Teacher
Sagen, Judy
Choral Activities Director
Schlink, Michael Jerome
American History Teacher
Welckle, H. Diane (Mager)
Language Arts Teacher
EAGLE BEND
Rapatz, Gabriel Louis
Science Teacher
Stevenson Olson, Lonna L.
English Teacher & Media Dir
EAST GRAND FORKS
Danielson, Donald B.
Retired Vocal Mus Tchr & Supvr
Marek, Michael John
Science Teacher
Oppegaard, Denise (Pulkrabek)
Math Teacher & Dept Chprsn
EDEN PRAIRIE
Anderson, Larry R.
Social Studies Teacher & Coach
Brettingen, Karen Lynn (Frisch)
Marketing Education Coord
Cwodzinski, Steven Allen
HS Social Studies Teacher
Ebert, Melanie Corrine
Art Dept Chair & Instructor

PRAIRIE (cont)
y, Karen Keup
irade Teacher
y, Peter J.
irade Math Teacher
Dean E.
al Studies Teacher
VALLEY
ds, Paul Scott
2th Grade Math Instr
RTON
ra, Calvin W.
Chem Instr & Sci Dept Chm
N
Scott Alan
ctor of Bands
RIVER
, Debbie Huso
ird Physical Ed Teacher
son, Kelli Brown
ird Mathematics Teacher
Varland Jay
h Grade Teacher
Diane LePage
ergarten Teacher
, Noel M.
irade Phys Science Teacher
WORTH
an, Lois Mae Romberg
nd Grade Teacher
RE
Stella Ullestad
ed Sixth Grade Teacher
d, Arlyce Johnson
Grade Teacher
ONS
, Scott John
gh Science Teacher
NE
Kay
gh English Teacher
k, Russel Edward
th Grd Soc Stud Teacher

on, Debra Jean (Jobin)
ndary English Teacher
SVILLE
Bonnie Marie
Grade Teacher
er, B. J.
ness Ed & Computer Teacher
ETH
n, Beverly Williams
rs English Teacher
Richard A.
ematics Teacher
, Jason C.
ness Education Teacher
Ann Marie
ch, English & Rdng Tchr
LSIOR
, Polly L.
Grade Teacher
A
, Paula L.
Health Teacher
, James Kenneth
irade Teacher
Ellen I.
uage Arts Teacher
, Karen Marie (Meyer)
ness Education Teacher
, Nancy Jean (Sorenson)
Grade Teacher
AX
, Randy Martin
th Grade Teacher
MONT
Pauline Carmen (Henschen)
titute Teacher
Bob
ol Counselor & Coach
, Cheri Schwaegerl
irade Teacher
, Harlan G.
al Studies Instructor
, Ronald L.
Stud Tchr & Bsktbl Coach
e, Robert Joseph
nd Grade Teacher
n, Joni Kohn
ctor of Youth Programs
e, David Mark
Tchr & Dist Tech Coord
er, Leon Vincent
ematics & Adv Algebra Tchr
n, Leonard O.
Grade Teacher
Bradley B.
d Grade Teacher
BAULT
, Cheryl Diane (Stendel)
ergarten Teacher
r, Franz John
ish Teacher
Barbara Bennett
al Studies Teacher
rald, Lydia Siefken
hology Teacher
enfield, Michael Raymond
ish Teacher
Gary Alan
Grade Teacher
n, Annie Rose (Adamczak)
Tchr & Girls Athletic Dir
happ, Richard Alan
h Grade Science Teacher
e, Rodney Scott
Grade Science Teacher

Madson, Charles Gary
English Teacher
Scheil, Deborah Kay
4th Grade Teacher
Schuldt, Harvey Robert
Mathematics Teacher
Zwagerman, Kelly Jo
Secondary Journalism Teacher
FARMINGTON
Franklin, Joan Beilharz
Former Science Teacher
Gottwig, Jeffrey Allen
Instrumental Music Director
Grawe, Tanya N. Chatfield
Physical Sci & Biology Teacher
Maxwell, Kim Linette
Business Teacher
Olwell, Jack
Elementary Physical Ed Teacher
Swanson, Felicia Kay (Balmer)
Elementary Special Ed Teacher
FERGUS FALLS
Carney, Paul C.
English Instructor
Egersdorf, Roberta (Ball)
English & Speech Teacher
Larrivy, Jean Marie
4th Grade Teacher
Mc Kenzie, Jean Johnston
Accounting Instructor
Michelson, Karen M.
English Instructor
Nikolas, Arlin D.lin
Instructor of History
Prischmann, Diane Kay
Senior High Language Arts Tchr
Pugh, Louise Williams
Instructor of Mathematics
Undseth, Steven P.
English Teacher
FERTILE
Affeldt-Boetcher, Denise Elayne
English as a Second Lang Tchr
Carlson, Laurie Ann
K-12th Grd School Counselor
Halvorson, Yvonne L.
Business Ed & Computer Coord
Wahlin, Shelly Robin (Christenson)
Vocal Music Teacher
Werner, Gary A.
Mathematics Teacher
FISHER
Mc Donald, Barbara Lovaasen
English Teacher
FLOODWOOD
Alexander, William C.
Music Studies Director
FOLEY
Bigger, Cindy Marie
Extension Edctr & Assoc Prof
Foote, I. Louis
Choral & Vocal Music Teacher
Gibbs, Sandra Bemis
Health & Drivers Ed Instructor
Grave, Scott Dennis
High School English Teacher
Hanson, Kevin James
8th Grd Earth & Space Sci Tchr
Holm, Perry Steven
Coach
Jansen, Coleen Lawrence
2nd Grade Teacher
Koester, Barbara Lynn
Spanish Teacher
Mc Intire, Barbara Kelsey
Guidance Counselor
FOREST LAKE
Bernauer, Michael F.
Language Arts Instructor
Buck, John Michael
Mathematics Teacher
Carlson, Mark Ryan
Mathematics Teacher
Dorsey, Matthew Allen
Tchr of Emtnl Behvr Disordered
Mc Donough, Judith M. (Bogie)
English & French Teacher
Onell, Carleen Peterson
Language Arts Teacher
Pearson, James Joseph
Science Teacher
Sapa, Michael Joseph
Fifth Grade Teacher
Stromberg, James E.
Teacher & Coach
Tillema, Sally Jean
Guidance Counselor
FRAZEE
Hesby, Frank James
Athletic Director
FRIDLEY
Ahrndt, Maria Ramalho
Art Teacher
Andrews, Jean Amundson
6th Grd Classroom Teacher
Cathey, Susan Hencir
6th Grade Teacher
Coburn, Peggy Lee
First Grade Teacher
Crofton, Michael Douglas
Physics Teacher
Drewes, Steven J.
High School Guidance Counselor
Ferguson, Jeffrey M.
HS Biology & Health Teacher
Galchutt, Adeline Wagner
Sixth Grade Teacher
Guzy, Grant Andrew
Mathematics Teacher & Coach

Harlan-Marks, Stephen Alan
English Teacher
Henry, Lori Ann
Family & Consumer Sci Tchr
Hoheisel, Ronald Gry
Industrial Technology Teacher
Johnson, Barbara R.
German Teacher
Munsterman, Adele Patricia
Spanish Teacher
Neiss, William Gregory
Emergency Health Care Instr
Nelson, Kathleen (Novak)
Math Tchr & Enrichment Coord
Nelson, Linda Yanka
8th Grade Earth Science Tchr
Petroff, Gail Batten
Fourth Grade Teacher
Reif, Robert Kevin
English Teacher & Coach
Rivard, Maureen Catherine
Spanish Teacher
Schleicher, Michael W.
Instrumental Music Instructor
Skjervold, Leanne Kay
Middle School Teacher
Witt, Jeffrey Alan
Chemistry Teacher
FULDA
Carlson, Loren George
Algebra Instr & Guidance Cnslr
Carroll, Harvey O'Dean
6th Grade Classroom Teacher
Holden, Judy Marie (Wanous)
Retired Kindergarten Teacher
Sandburg, Dale Lee
Sixth Grade Teacher
Skjong-Bakke, Nancy
English Teacher
GARDEN CITY
Enright, Deanna Faye
Geography & Literature Teacher
Schultz, David W.
Inst Music Teacher
GARFIELD
Nelson, Jan R.
Sixth Grade Teacher
GARY
Anderson, Jon Andrew
6th Grade Teacher
Ruud, Sandra Bratvold
Kindergarten Teacher
GAYLORD
Bergaus, Mary Lucille
English Teacher
Koffarnus, Dallas L.
Teacher & Principal
Marshall, Sharon (Haefs)
Sixth Grade Instructor
GILBERT
St Lawrence, Omar J.
Retired Elementary Teacher
GLENCOE
DeCorsey, Robert Charles
Physical Education Teacher
Eckhoff, Scott Donald
Earth Science Teacher
Hofferberth, Mary Mc Gee
Science Teacher
Wilson, Kay N. (Warner)
HS Vocal Music Director
Zaske, James H.
Chem & Phys Sci Tchr
GLENVILLE
Roisen, Sandra Dillavou
5th Grade Teacher
Staska, Robert H.
Mathematics Teacher
GLENWOOD
Bailey, Bill
Biology Teacher
Moeller, Gordon Elwyn
Choral Director
Swenson, Don Lee
Counselor
Wiirre, Beth Ann
Special Education Teacher
GLYNDON
Marquart, Paul Anthony
Social Science Teacher
Olson, Sally Ann
Second Grade Teacher
GOLDEN VALLEY
Holt, Eva Laurel
Science Teacher
Hunton, Janice A.
Music Teacher
Norwood, Nancy Stalnaker
Media Arts Teacher
GOODHUE
Stottler, Wade Alan
Secondary Social Studies Tchr
GOODRIDGE
Dahlen, Dave W.
Math Teacher
Moe, Connie Lynn
Third Grade Teacher
Peterson, Linda Anderson
Kindergarten Teacher
GRACEVILLE
DeGier, Gregory Alan
Band Director
GRANADA
Heidmann, Patricia Patterson
Health & Physical Ed Educator
GRAND MARAIS
Bushman, Sharon Ardys
Third Grade Teacher
Neal, Karen Kreitlow
Spanish Teacher

GRAND MEADOW
Moe, Janet Kirsten
K-8th Grade Music Teacher
Petzel, Lori Oehlke
Kindergarten Teacher
GRAND RAPIDS
Dodge, Katherine Taylor
English Teacher
Lehto, Sue K.
Program Director
Porter, Lana J.
Fifth Grade Teacher
Shaner, Robert Alan
Intnl Baccalaureate Chem Tchr
GREENBUSH
Schultz, Sharon (Kauth)
High School English Teacher
GROVE CITY
Kolle, Sharon Lynnette
Spanish & English Teacher
GRYGLA
Marquis, Avis Diane
Special Ed & Chapter 1 Teacher
HALSTAD
Carlson, Philip Allen
Science Teacher
HARMONY
Elston, Del Roy Wayne
Biology Teacher
Hokenson, Cynthia Jane
English & German Teacher
Markegard, Ann Catlin
Science Teacher
Mehus, Joni Christensen
English, Speech & Cmptrs Tchr
O'Reilly, Robert Roger
HS English Teacher & Play Dir
Schnabel, Jerry E.
Media Director
HASTINGS
Dahlberg, Thomas Martin
High School Mathematics Tchr
Dewall, John H.
Horticulture & Plant Sci Tchr
Gronquist, Gary L.
Graphic Arts Teacher
Johnson, Thomas G.
PE Instructor & Athletic Dir
Keller, Ronda Jane
7th Grade Language Arts Tchr
Miley, Mark William
Social Studies Teacher
Myers, Mary Jo Kranz
Social Studies Teacher
Obler, Michael W.
High School English Teacher
Welch, Russ A.
Sr HS PE & Health Teacher
Zywiec, Jim J.
5th Grade Teacher
HAWLEY
Clementich, DiAnn Wawers
Fifth Grade Teacher
Pasche, Steve Richard
Soc Stud Tchr & Bsktbl Coach
Pfingsten, Peggy Tangen
Art & Physical Education Tchr
Siegel, Roberta Jean
English Teacher
HAYFIELD
Fischer, James Stewart
6th Grade Teacher
Nute, Douglas Alan
Technology Education Teacher
Rueckert, Lisa Marie
Biology & Chemistry Teacher
HENNING
Johnson, Betty Erickson
Retired Third Grade Teacher
Trosdahl, Marie Carol (Westad)
Mathematics Teacher
HERMANTOWN
Martinson, Cindy Kay
Second Grade Teacher
HIBBING
Furlong, Kathryn McCormick
9th-10th Grade English Teacher
Galliford, John Edward
Psychology Instructor
Harkonen, Anthony Neil
Mathematics Teacher
Kearney, John M.
4th Grade Teacher
Milani, Kevin John
Chemistry Instructor
Miller, Patricia Middleton
Chemical Hlth Coord & Cnslr
Milner-Thomas, Donna K.
11th-12th Grade English Tchr
Moe, Carmen K.
English Instructor
Potts, Steve Jay
Professor of History
Stutzman, Paul Franklin
HS Social Studies Teacher
Warner, Mary C. (Bussey)
Science Teacher
HILLS
Huber, Dale
Social Studies Teacher
HINCKLEY
Baustian, Debra Rae
First Grade Teacher
Becvar, Karlajean
Acting English Teacher
Riley, Patrick William
Sr HS Studies Teacher
HOLDINGFORD
Bruns, Dale H.
Social Studies Teacher

Czarnowski, Sharon Chamberlain
Dev Reading & English Teacher
Harren, Linda Jean
First Grade Teacher
Killoren, Peggy
English, Speech & Drama Tchr
Odden, Michael E.
7th-12th Grade Art Teacher
Schoon, Steven Ray
Mathematics & Physics Teacher
Theisen, Linda Lou
Jr-Sr High Hlth & PE Coach
Yourlzek, Jerald John
Science Teacher
HOPKINS
Bates, Don Argil
Band Director
Byrnes, Mary Pat Paulson
Jr High Math & Science Teacher
Dahlquist, Katherine R.
Biology Teacher
Franke, Thomas Glenn
Science & Astronomy Teacher
Gieseke, Sharon Guggisberg
Mathematics Tchr & Dept Chair
Johns, C. Richard
Third Grade Teacher
Kleinman, Jane M.
Secondary Hlth Science Teacher
Len, Paula S.
Art Teacher
Marier, William J.
Second Grade Teacher
Mason, Martha Jean
6th Grade Teacher
Peterson, Patricia Briley
Vocal Music Director
Shoger, Kirk David
Science Teacher
Zachman, Deborah Ann
Gifted Education Specialist
HOUSTON
Markegard, Michael Lee
Math & Aviation Tchr
HOWARD LAKE
Weninger, James Lloyd
Agricultural Education Instr
HUTCHINSON
Elwell, Brian R.
Physical Science & Bio Teacher
Haberkamp, Sharon Ruth
First & Second Grade Teacher
Judd, Angela Kay (Ahlbrecht)
English Teacher
Kuusisto, Donna Marie
HS Mathematics Teacher
Lorenz, Lester Eugen
Mathematics & Science Teacher
Lueck, Kathleen Deitering
Learning Readiness Coordinator
Rostberg, Grady A.
Math Teacher & Football Coach
Scheer, Dan William
Sixth Grade Science Teacher
Sederquist, Dexter A.
English Teacher
INTERNATIONAL FALLS
Gruner, Wendy
Physics Instructor
Horner, David Charles
Math Instructor & Bsktbl Coach
Pearson, Mary Louise Miljonovich
10th-12th Grd Social Stud Tchr
Schmidt, Darrell M.
English & Foreign Lang Instr
Simon, Orin Lee
Math Teacher
Zika, Sharon Fisher
Title One Teacher
INVER GROVE
Bell, Hamilton Everett
Diversity Specialist
Glassel, Donald Michael
Director of Bands
Helfter, Jeffrey John
Computer Consultant
Kehr, Kenneth Gilbert
American History Teacher
Severson, John Byron
Chemistry Instructor
INVER GROVE HEIGHTS
Hillenbrand, Anna Margaret
Coordinator & Instructor
IRON
Blyckert, Judith Ann
French Teacher
Cackoski, Beverly J.
Science Teacher
Wiegert, Kathryn A.
Band Director & Music Edctr
ISANTI
Anderson, Mary Kay
Kindergarten Teacher
Anderson, Michael R.
Mathematics Teacher
Beaupre, Carl H.
Seventh Grade Science Teacher
Blakesley, Calvin T.
Middle School Art Teacher
Burleigh, John Scott
Eighth Grade English Teacher
Kreis, Cindy
Speech & Language Pathologist
Wilson, Dean George
Physical Education Teacher
ISLE
Becker, Kurt James
Fifth Grade Teacher
Searles, Jeffrey James
English Teacher

JACKSON
Walker, Mary Ellen Mc Gillivray
Medical Secretarial Instructor
JANESVILLE
Smith, Patricia Lynn
HS Hlth & Physical Ed Teacher
Straub, Vincent John
8th Grade Teacher & Principal
JASPER
Beckering, Marion Petersen
Retired Fourth Grade Teacher
JORDAN
Scheuble, Patricia Delubery
Special Education Teacher
Webb, Kathryn Breugger
Family & Consumer Sci Teacher
KARLSTAD
Eveland, Cheryl Lynn
Kindergarten & First Grd Tchr
Gust, Robert Douglas
English, Speech & Theatre Tchr
Johnson, Robert Allan
Visual Arts Instructor
Lutz, Georgine Rhoda (Engel)
Spanish Teacher
Rodahl, Kitty Anderson
First Grade Teacher
KASSON
Fredrickson, Marilyn H.
Art Education Instructor
Johnson, W. Clark
Vocal Music Teacher
KEEWATIN
Gunelson, Charlene Koski
Language Arts Teacher
KELLIHER
Guenther, Frank Louis
Geog Bus & Drivers Ed Tchr
Hughes, Patricia Dahlgren
English & German Teacher
Ross, Judith Marie (Baltes)
Vocal & Instrmntl Music Tchr
Smischney, Maureen Kristi
English & Psychology Teacher
KENYON
Berg, Sue Sundry
Third Grade Teacher
Braun, A. John
High School Math Dept Head
Kincaid, Richard H.
Advanced Biology Teacher
Senjem, Paul G.
English Teacher
KIESTER
Heaney, Mary R.
7th & 8th Grd Amer His Teacher
KIMBALL
Jensen, Larry Dean
Social Studies & PE Tchr
Linn, Michael Clayton
Art Teacher
Sandal, Angela Provost
Eng Dept Chair & Comm Teacher
LA CRESCENT
Briggs, Hollie Joyce
Second Grade Teacher
Guse, Dawn Marie (Nibbe)
8th Grade Geography Teacher
Little, James Alvin
Art Teacher
Mc Loone, Robert Michael
Social Studies & English Tchr
Moen, Cheryl A.
Eng & Advanced Placement Tchr
O'Connor, Darryle Diane
English Teacher
Peterson, James Charles
5th Grade Teacher
Trnka, Michael A.
Chemistry & Physics Teacher
Unangst, Thomas C.
Social Studies Teacher
Wilke, Ronald D.
Music Teacher & Band Director
Yates, Anita Louise (Colby)
Fifth Grade Teacher
LAKE CITY
Brown, Kevin John
Secondary Agriscience Instr
Chant, Barbara Marilyn Oliver
English as a Second Lang Tchr
Dahling, Roberta Jo (Ives)
English Teacher
Heise, James Arthur
History & English Teacher
Huppert, Gail Lynn
Elementary Music & Band Instr
Ritzenthaler, Stephen A.
Instrumental Music Director
LAKE CRYSTAL
Crane, C. Sue
Lang Arts & Lit Tchr
Hagen, Thomas P.
English & Social Studies Instr
Sieling, Norm L.
Voc-Ag Instructor
LAKE ELMO
Dymacek, Patricia Leverty
Instrumental Music Teacher
Johnson, Bruce Alton
7th-9th Grd Ind Tech Teacher
Klancher, Larry S.
7th Grd Social Studies Teacher
Strauch, Gary M.
9th Grade Civics & Law Teacher
LAKE PARK
Anderson, Evonne Annette
Science Teacher
Anderson, Thomas Jeffrey
9th-12th Grd Soc Stud Teacher
Ronken, Lewis
Technology Coordinator
Wichmann, Michael Kenneth
High School Science Teacher
LAKEFIELD
Zellar, Doyle
Administrator & Teacher
LAKEVILLE
Cybyske, Lynne Knoblauch
Fifth Grade Teacher
Gehlsen, Mary Leslie Flynn
Chemistry Teacher
Laubach, Mary Ann
Sixth Grade Teacher
Ostergaard, Julie Marie
French Teacher
Quinlan, Laurie Ann
Communications Instructor
Schmitz, Pamela Jo (Russett)
Bio, Anatomy & Physiology Tchr
Seldon, Julieanne Frawley
Math Teacher
Sender, Janis Richards
4th Grade Teacher
Villanueva, Wendy Kathleen
Spanish Teacher
Zeise, Mark F.
Biology Teacher
LAMBERTON
Furth, Deborah Kay
Family & Consumer Sci Tchr
Jacobson, Larry Joe
Chemistry & Physics Teacher
Martinson, Sharyn L.
Business Teacher
LAPORTE
Curb-Aitken, Margo Lynn
Business Teacher
LE CENTER
Davies, John Burton
Sixth Grade Teacher
Rostad, John Milo
Technology Coordinator & Instr
Smith, Dianna L. Moen
Lead Teacher
Zeiher, Ann Marie Reilly
High School Math Teacher
LE ROY
Anderson, Keith Erick
Sixth Grade Teacher
Fechner, Shirley Diane Alden
4th Grade Teacher
Rosedahl, Kyle Robert
Mathematics Teacher
Ryks, Kevin L.
Band Director
LE SUEUR
Aldrich, Bryan Lee
Chemistry Teacher
Anderson, Tamara Jane
Mathematics Teacher
Nieland, Sandra Marie
Communications Teacher
LEWISTON
Mills, Gary L.
Physical Education Teacher
Youngs, Nancy Thomson
Kindergarten Teacher
LINDSTROM
Birklid, Heather Moseman
Tenth Grade Biology Teacher
Filzen, Darlene Sharon
Middle School Science Teacher
Leyendecker, Constance M.
Language Arts Instructor
Lindeman, Jeffery Mark
Agri-Science Teacher
Quam, David Eugene
Chemistry & Physics Teacher
Ramola, Ambrose John
Mathematics Teacher
Wordelman, Donna Jean
4th Grade Teacher
LISMORE
Bullerman, Cynthia Jorgensen
Preschool Teacher
LITCHFIELD
Clites, Duane Dean
Retired HS Counselor
Loftness, Mary Hertsgaard
German Teacher
Springer, Thomas Michael
Third Grade Teacher
Thomes, Bruce John
Middle School English Teacher
Wanek, Richard Allan
Counselor
LITTLE CANADA
Hoskins, Juanita Walker
Assistant Principal
LITTLE FALLS
Auger, Elaine Marilyn (Johnson)
Fifth Grade Teacher
Haas, Jane Kristi
Health Instructor
Hemingway, Mark A.
Vocal Director
Hinnenkamp, Ronald L.
Secondary Education Teacher
Hircock, Bill
Electronics Teacher
Hoskins, Kevin Allen
6th Grade Reading Teacher
Kaddatz, Chad Donald
8th Grade Science Teacher
Ploof, Doug Robert
Agricultural-Science Teacher
Schmidt, Rhonda Marie
French & Spanish Instructor
Spofford, Gregory Byron
Coordinator of Volunteers
Strahl, Rebecca Jacobsen
High School Spanish Teacher
LITTLEFORK
Erickson, Leonard James
Principal
Stagg, Jane Mc Cullough
English Teacher & Counselor
LONG PRAIRIE
Evenson, Bradley Raynold
1st Grade Teacher
LONGVILLE
Lilyquist, Marilyn Louise (Welk)
Retired Fifth Grade Teacher
LORETTO
Schmidt, Kathryn Jacobs
Fourth Grade Teacher
LUVERNE
Bonnema, George H.
Business Education Teacher
Johnson, Michelle Lori
Computer Instructor
Swanson, Joel Lane
Mathematics Teacher
LYLE
Buntje, Mark Richard
5th Grade Teacher
Klemetson, Steven Bruce
Industrial Arts Teacher
Perry, Barbara B.
Home Economics Teacher
Plotts, Michelle Flatin
English Teacher
MADELIA
Lovett, Eleanor Lenz
Retired 6th Grade Teacher
Neiman, Gladys Marie
HS Science Teacher
MADISON
Koester, Ronald D.
Math & Science Teacher
Makepeace, Terry Joseph
Mathematics Teacher
Omland, Kim M.
Music Teacher
Schmidt, Nancy Davidson
Special Education Teacher
Walker, Richard J.
9th-12th Grade English Teacher
Wilkening, Anne Juul
English Teacher
MADISON LAKE
Fasnacht, Iverna Reintjes
Tutor & Substitute Teacher
MAHNOMEN
Amundson, Brent Stanford
Jr High English Teacher
Amundson, Judy Margaret
Second Grade Teacher
Hoppestad, Mary Lois (Kveno)
First Grade Teacher
Stock, Joyce E.
English Teacher
MANKATO
Arzdorf, Daryl Lee
Social Studies Educator
Askalani, Mohamed H.
Econometrics Professor
Beyer, Jerrold Arthur, Sr.
Asst Prof of Political Science
Brunz, Jane Elizabeth Pittman
Physical Education Teacher
Bryant, Antusa S.
Professor of Special Education
Burges, David Scott
Science Teacher
Fitterer, Alan R.
9th Grd American Studies Tchr
Gallup, Janice Seidl
Retired PE Teacher
George, Keith G.
English Teacher & Coach
Green, Kay Cline
Sixth Grade Teacher
Gullickson, Tedd Gonnard
Director of Bands
Haglin, David Jon
Computer Science Professor
Hanson, Roger E.
Biology Teacher
Hopkins, Layne Victor
Computer Science Professor
Jensen, Kathleen Ann (Burgess)
Business Ed Tchr & Dept Chair
Johnson, David August
Mathematics Teacher
Kessel, William B.
Professor of Social Sciences
Marburger, Bradley Thomas
Substitute Teacher
Miller, Cynthia A.
Geography Professor
Natvig, Harold O.
6th Grade Teacher
O'Clock, George Daniel, Jr.
Professor of Electrical Engrng
Oh, Jung R.
Chemistry Professor
Perkins, Carol Ortman
Assoc Prof of Womens Stud
Schostag, Jane Nordgren
English Teacher
Sipe, Michael John
His, Psych, Socilgy, Govt Tchr
Vieceli, Jacqueline Marie
Assoc Prof of Political Sci
Williams, Ned
Assoc Professor of Biology
Younge, Ronald John
Vice Pres for Academic Affairs
MAPLE GROVE
Randall, Bradley Nyborg
Science Teacher
MAPLE LAKE
Kalli, Bette Puncochar
Retired Teacher
Leiseth, Keith
Science Teacher
Thomas, Joseph John
Music Teacher
MAPLEWOOD
Belisle, Metta May
Former Teacher
MARSHALL
Ivers, Marcia Michalek
Business Education Teacher
Ivers, Wayne Paul
Band Director
Ochocki, James John
Industrial Technology Teacher
MAYER
Lane, David Marland
Mathematics Teacher & Coach
MCGREGOR
Cummings, Steven Walter
History Teacher
Mc Kenna, Karen Adair
Math Teacher
Schneider, Leonard A.
Science Teacher
MCINTOSH
Langan, JoAnn Olson
Secondary Teacher
Malmanger, Marilyn Annette
Third Grade Teacher
MEDFORD
Anderson, Diane Thorn
6th Grade Teacher
Hamner, Steven Carl
5th Grade Teacher
Riesterer, Kathleen Honor
Family & Consumer Sci Instr
Slarks, Judith Larson
First Grade Teacher
Slifka, James Anthony
Industrial Tech & Arts Tchr
MELROSE
Fahrner, Fulton James
Mathematics Teacher
Glasener, Vaughn Stuart
Social Studies Teacher
Heilig, Janis Kay
Third Grade Teacher
Molitor, Karen Meyer
English Instructor
Neuschwander, Dale Lawrence
English Teacher
Picha, Kenneth Albert
Social Studies Teacher
Pundsack, Susan Rose
Sixth Grade Teacher
MENAHGA
Farnam, Jennifer Eibes
English & Lang Arts Instr
MILACA
Christopherson, Allan Gregory
High School Mathematics Tchr
Mettling, Daniel Henry
Math & Physics Teacher
Sieve, Leon Joseph
Band Director
Taylor, James Marcus
Social Studies Teacher
MINNEAPOLIS
Anderson, Jonathan Franklin
Graduate Intern Counselor
Ashland, Myrna
Preschool Instructor
Barnes, Ann Marie
Third Grade Teacher
Bass-Aune, Jean
Fifth Grade Teacher
Bell, Carolyn Light
English Teacher
Berg, Paula Jean
Jr High Social Studies Teacher
Berge, Gwen Snipstead
Assistant Administrator
Bingham, Marjorie Wall
History Teacher
Blom, Connie R.
English Teacher
Boughton, Robert Randall
6th Grade Teacher
Brands, Vonda (Vander Pol)
Math & Science Teacher
Brown, Deane Eric
Geography Teacher
Connell, Thomas R.
9th Grade American Govt Tchr
Connor, Sharon
History & Language Arts Tchr
Cussler, Elizabeth Beidler
English Teacher
Debe, Dennis Wente
English Teacher
Debe, Ellen F.
English Teacher
Demetra, Kordopitoulas
4th Grade Teacher
Dentz, Harold DuWayne
Social Studies Teacher
Descombaz, Roberta Lee (Johnson)
Fifth Grade Teacher
Dymoke, Daniel F.
Psychology & Civics Teacher
Enderlein, Beverly (Bass)
Administrator
Erck, Elaine Pacy
Health Educator
Fawbush, Karla Winther
French & English Teacher
Fogelman, Sonia Dora Dickoff
HS English & Lang Arts Tchr
Foster, Scherrie Ann
Speech Communication Professor
Gill, Deborah Menken
Prof of Pastoral Ministries
Gillespie, Shannah Tinker
Kindergarten Teacher
Gomez, Cynthia Jean
Social Studies Teacher
Goodrich, Larry Allen
Professor of Education
Gorton, Anne Fredrickson
Chemical Health Specialist
Hallen, Diane Weiher
7th & 8th Grade Science Tchr
Hanson, R. Allyn
Social Studies Teacher
Henriksen, Dennis Lee
Chemistry Teacher
Heytens, Laura Lee
First Grade Teacher
Hielkema, Marilyn Ann VanDeRiet
1st Grade Teacher
Hodapp, Margaret Mary
Religious Studies Teacher
House, Benjamin George, Jr.
Secondary Mathematics Teacher
Isaacs, Gary Stark
Math Teacher
Isaacs, Paul Wayne
Instrumental Music Instructor
Johnson, Charlyne Alyce
6th-8th Grd Lang Arts Teacher
Judge, Jeffrey Francis
Spanish & French Teacher
Jump, Timothy Eugene
Science Teacher
Kasper, Lynne E.
6th Grade Teacher
Kassner, Scott Gerald
Instructor
Kauls, Guido Percy
Ger Instr & Var Soccer Coach
Kenney, Mark Daniel
PE, Religion & Soc Stud Tchr
Kirchdorfer, Faith McLain
German & Spanish Teacher
Kots, David Erwin
Math Teacher
Krueger, Diane Carol
Physical Education & Hlth Tchr
Kruppstadt, Gloria Ische
Mathematics Teacher
Leer, Debra Ann Holewa
5th Grade Teacher
Lysne, Shari Matelske
Special Education Teacher
Manahan, Nancy
Composition & Literature Tchr
Mc Keegan, Susan Orpha
Mathematics Teacher
Merrill, Lori Hasslinger
History Teacher
Monson, Ronald T.
Biology Tchr & Sci Dept Chair
Morris, Hugh James
Third Grade Teacher
Morris, Michael Thomas
Social Studies Teacher
Murphy, Daniel W.
9th Grade Science Teacher
Nelson, Daniel Ray
Assoc Prof of Behavioral Sci
Neubauer, Suzanne F.
Second Grade Teacher
Passmore, Lonnie Clinton
5th Grade Teacher
Pelinski, Debra Beyer
9th-12th Grd Drama Instructor
Priest, Owen Patrick
Former Teacher
Redmond, Peter Kelvin
Language Arts Teacher
Reed, Margaret A.
English Teacher
Roemer, Stephen
Conductor
Roff, Daniel J.
Physical Ed Teacher & Coach
Rye, Lisa Gruber
Physical Education Teacher
Saslow, Jeffrey M.
Multi-Age Teacher
Schwartz, Richard S.
Intnl Baccalaureate Pgm Coord
Scoggin, Kathy Book
4th-6th Grade Teacher
Sechrist, Sharon S.
Chemistry Instructor
Shelton, Jerry G.
Band Director & Jazz Education
Smelter, Jessie E.
English Teacher
Smith, Marilyn Klemt
Sixth Grade Teacher
Snaza, Rose Mary, SSND
Math Teacher
Studer, James A.
English, Speech & Hum Tchr
Sudo, Richard M.
7th-8th Grade Teacher
Trelstad Porter, Jim
Co-Coord of Study Abroad Prgms
Turnberg, Judy Juris
Third Grade Teacher

EAPOLIS (cont)
nd, Carol Ann Marie
ig Disabilities Specialist
Antoinette Mary Lanteri
gh English & Lit Tchr
court, Jennifer Wilson
Arts Coordinator
g, Myra Jean
er of Gifted & Talented
green, Lorraine Mary
ess Instructor
Linda Carlene
ive Writing Teacher
Margaret M.
f Intnl Ed & Chinese Tchr
, Richard T.
Grade Teacher
n, Tracey Jo Brixius
Dependency Cnslng Prof
, Connie Fourre
ion Teacher
ETONKA
son, Lori Jo
ematics Teacher
erg, Paula Andrist
Director
, Polly Boone
iology Teacher
EVIDEO
aier, Jeffrey Paul
Grade Math Teacher
n, Kevin Dean
ulture Ed Instructor
James Mark
ce Teacher
Ralph Norman
sh & Speech Teacher
Kathleen Hansen
nstructor
st, Darwin Russell
ematics Teacher
ss, Lee Alan
imental Director
erth, Myrtiss D. Heikes
rade Teacher
ater, Gerald V.
rade Science Teacher
GOMERY
Jerilyn Sue
sh Teacher
Cynthia K.
uage Arts & Speech Teacher
n, Lynn D.
gy Teacher
Janet Eide
rade Teacher
ssen, Donavan William
2th Grd Bus & Cmptr Tchr
ovich, Richard Peter
Grade Teacher & Coach
lt, Barry Jon
ultural Education Teacher
an, Beverly E.
Director
aard, Susanne K.
ematics Teacher
ICELLO
n, Thomas Lee
Grd Social Studies Tchr
David Charles
School German Teacher
Judith Ann Rivers
al Education Instructor
Peter Anthony
rade Math & Reading Instr
er, Dirk J.
ocial Studies Teacher
RHEAD
, Buzz Reed
Albegra II Teacher
Toni J.
selor
rg, Mary Erickson
ness Education Teacher
Mark W.
cs Professor
, Merrie Sue
of Speech & Theatre Arts
a, Shannon Mary
rade Teacher
, Janet Hagen
sh Teacher
ow, Kalan Mitchell
omics & US History Teacher
ean L.
ish Teacher
Mary Ann
rade Teacher
, I. Kenneth
ssor of History
n, Jay
an Teacher
E LAKE
David Ounet
eacher
A
ell, Jennifer Ungar
Grade Teacher
n, Steven Eric
S Soc Govt & His Tchr
RIS
Paul R.
ematics Instructor
ing, Barbara (Gust)
Grade Teacher
TAIN IRON
Donald David
l Studies Tchr & Coach
eb, Gary A.
nl & Behavioral Dev Tchr

Luoma, Charlene Diane
English Teacher
MOUNTAIN LAKE
Peters, Dolores Smith
Retired Kindergarten Teacher
Syverson, Kim (Rolfing)
English Teacher
NASHWAUK
Damjanovich, MaryJane
Language Arts Teacher
Ratai, Joe P.
9th-12th Grd Math & Cmptr Tchr
NEVIS
Sandmeyer, Jodi Lund
Mathematics & Science Teacher
Schroeder, Paul Terry
Third Grade Teacher
Shay, Louise Gunkel
Lead Special Education Teacher
Stennes, Gary J.
Music Teacher
Uscola, Rusty Jay
Science Teacher
Wolff, Marsha M.
English Teacher
NEW HOPE
Buetow, Tamara Ruth
English Teacher
Buffington, Sidney C.
Mathematics Teacher
Marks-Hildebrand, Lauren Alexander
Gifted Resource Specialist
Mc Alpin, Ann Carlson
Fifth Grade Teacher
Phleger, Gary Michael
Gen & Enriched Phys Sci Tchr
Stewart, Guy James
Eighth Grade Earth Sci Tchr
NEW PRAGUE
Puls, Daniel Lee
Social Studies Teacher
Tise, Karl J.
English & Language Arts Tchr
Tschimperle, Michael Matthew
Math & PE Teacher
NEW RICHLAND
Anderson, Terry Q.
Science Teacher
Flowers, LaDona Miller
Family & Consumer Science Tchr
NEW ULM
Barenz, John R.
Social Studies Instructor
Bute, Robert Todd
Social Studies Teacher
Dengerud, Mary A.
Computer Teacher
Hakes, Richard Allen
Math & Computer Teacher
Lambrecht, Diane Hanson
6th Grd Rdng & Lang Arts Tchr
Luepke, Wayne W.
Mathematics Instructor
Moran, Stephan Michael
Jr High Band Director
Sauers, Theodore John, Jr.
5th Grade Teacher
Schuette, Terri Freundl
Sixth Grade Teacher
Whaley, Cynthia Elaine
Prof of Ed & Stu Tchrs Supvr
NEW YORK MILLS
Brown, William H.
Director of Bands
NEW YORK MLS
Cassidy, Donald Andrew
Literature of Am West Teacher
Sorensen, Jay D.
Social Studies Instructor
NICOLLET
Hanson, Carmen Lynn Niemeyer
Social Studies Teacher & Coach
Lohmiller, Frederick Martin
8th Grade Teacher & Principal
NORTHFIELD
Dalgaard, Bruce Ronald
Professor of Economics
Fink, Karl Julius
Professor of German
Hagen, Shari Ann
Spanish Teacher
Morris, Ron O.
7th Grade Social Studies Tchr
Rogers, Marie Louise
Retired Teacher
Slegers, Kimberly Ann
Sr HS Hlth Ed Instr & Coach
Wiertsema-Miller, Kathy Jo
English Teacher
NORTHOME
Schneider, James Otto
Science Teacher
Struss, Jerry Edwin
Principal
NORTHROP
Patrick, Robert Brian
Music & Social Studies Tchr
NORWOOD
Berndt, Jerine Bakker
Sr High School English Tchr
Rain, David Duane
Band Director
Rieck, Jana Lee
Communications Teacher
Saxon, Carrie Budke
7th Grd PE & Hlth Ed Tchr
Simmons, Dottie Iverson
Fifth Grade Teacher
Stanek, Dennis David
HS English & Math Teacher

OAKDALE
Hei, Teresa L.
Mathematics Teacher
OGILVIE
Erickson, Joan Gens
English Teacher
OKABENA
Ohlmann, Candice A.
Principal & Teacher
OKLEE
Peterson, Karen E. Jensen
Science Teacher
Swenson, Michael Herbert
7th-12th Grd Commnctn Teacher
ORR
Kurz, Joy
English & Comp Sci Teacher
Kurz, Nancy Joy
Resource Center Director
Maki, Michele Holm
Counselor
ORTONVILLE
Danielson, Ryan Leigh
History & Drivers Ed Teacher
Rasset, Bonna Kay
Third Grade Teacher
Sandberg, Roger Lee
Science Teacher
OSAGE
Fondow, Connie Gellerman
Second Grade Teacher
OSAKIS
Benson, Saundra Kay
Fourth Grade Teacher
OSSEO
Anderson, Sheila Blehr
Eighth Grade English Teacher
Boyum, Gail Barnard
Sixth Grade Teacher
Elmquest, Jess Richard
Economics & Amer History Tchr
Gunderson, Richard Alvin
Fourth Grade Teacher
Holtorf, Daniel Berge
Technology Education Teacher
Johnsen, Janet E.
Ninth Grade English Teacher
Koenig, Paul Jerome
Biology Teacher
Maetzold, Sharon Pauly-Tripp
4th Grade Teacher
Manthey, William Edward
Language Arts Teacher
Nelson, Elaine M.
English as a Second Lang Tchr
Paske, Tim J.
Technology Education Teacher
Sackett, Mark D.
Earth & Science Teacher
Schierenbeck, Paul Allen
Bands Director
Wills, Laura Kling
AP Eng, Speech & Theatre Tchr
Yencho, Thomas John
Assistant Principal
OWATONA
Heiser, Michael Steven
Asst Prof of Biblical Studies
OWATONNA
Anderson, Marcia Ellen (Swanson)
High School Mathematics Tchr
Billings, Barbara Ann
Junior High Science Teacher
DuFrene, Ronald Oliver
Science Teacher
Giga, Vilnis John
Economics & Political Sci Tchr
Grabau, Merton John
Retired 5th Grade Teacher
Haberman, Margaret A.
Third Grade Teacher
Johnson, Lori Ann
Science Teacher
Kolbe, Douglas B.
Pol Sci, Ec, & Philosophy Tchr
Malin, Karen Lee
First & Second Grade Teacher
Noble, Michelle Wilker
Elementary Teacher
Seykora, Gary Joseph
High School Art Teacher
Thompson, Nels Frederick
Biology Teacher
Westra, Gary Jacob
9th Grd American Studies Tchr
Williams, Jeffrey Richard
Biology Teacher
Zishka, Maureen C.
German Teacher
PARK RAPIDS
Berry, Lynn Richard
Biology Instructor
Dierkhising, LouAnn S.
HS Vocal Music Instructor
Johnson, Kerry Woods
High School English Teacher
Kalahar, Shawn L.
MS Social Studies Teacher
Lueth, Karen Ufer
Fourth Grade Teacher
Novak, Larry Ray
High School Band Director
Oberstar, Ronald L.
Fifth Grade Teacher
Uscola, Linda Sue (Licke)
German Teacher
PARKERS PRAIRIE
Klaessy, John Dale
Language Arts Department Chair

Mesker, Kelly Marvin
Social Studies Teacher
PAYNESVILLE
Leitzman, Jane Norman
6th Grade Communications Tchr
Lura, Carol Lang
Senior High Art Teacher
PELICAN RAPIDS
Evenson, Connie Knutson
English & German Teacher
Fletcher, James Douglas
Art Teacher
Johnson, Elaine R. (Cluever)
ESL & Reading Teacher
PEQUOT LAKES
Guenther, David John
Visual Arts Instructor
Thaler, Rene Mayer
English Chairperson & Teacher
PERHAM
Hanson, Hans Jay
8th Grade Mathematics Teacher
Hatlestad, Robert Lynn
Art Instructor
Wielinski, Stanley P.
Language Arts & Speech Teacher
Wieser-Matthews, Sandra Jo
Speech & Mass Commnctn Tchr
PIERZ
Holbrook, Steven John
6th Grade Teacher
PILLAGER
Pietz, Rose Marie Carlson
4th Grade Teacher
PINE CITY
Clark, Carolyn Engrecht
Fourth Grade Teacher
Farguharson, Stephen Paul
Social Studies Instructor
Marenchin, Kathy Ann
Jr High Art & Civics Teacher
Oare, John Howard
Fifth Grade Teacher
Olson, Elizabeth Meyer
Fourth Grade Teacher
Ovick, Robert Victor
Alg & Advanced Math Teacher
Splittgerber, Lois Marie
HS Lang Arts Tchr & Dept Chair
Voce, Daniel H.
Geography & History Teacher
PINE ISLAND
Mc Phail, Donald W.
History & Soc Studies Teacher
Ringle, Jeanne Ann Coopersmith
Second Grade Teacher
Straudell, Douglas James
Choral Director
PINE RIVER
Miller, Thomas Darrell
Technology Teacher
Moen, Dian L.
Mathematics & Physics Teacher
Puleo, John Peter
Third Grade Teacher
Van Vliet, Linda Backora
Second Grade Teacher
PIPESTONE
Allmendinger, Diane Swenson
Spanish Teacher
Fish, Joy Mae (Reeve)
Elementary Multi-Grade Teacher
Groth, Harriett Iverson
Retired Kindergarten Teacher
Hayes, Charles Alan
Fifth Grade Teacher
Hulstein, Roberta Rose (Engel)
Fourth Grade Teacher
Kraft, Nyla (Stueven)
English Teacher
Stehlik, Margie Jean
Home Ec Dept Chair & Instr
PLAINVIEW
Cravath, Carol Marie
Elementary Educator
Fiskum, Donald Ray
Band Director
Fiskum, Janice Johnson
Vocal Music Teacher
Holst, Donna Jean (Kuhlmann)
5th Grade Elementary Teacher
Kiefer, James Michael
HS Mathematics Teacher
Luckstein, Donald Dean
German & Social Studies Tchr
Timm, Mary L.
English Teacher
PLUMMER
Walker, Paul D.
Mathematics Teacher
PLYMOUTH
Bergstrom, Kristi Therkelsen
Special Education Teacher
DeLapp, Meg Wigley
Social Studies Teacher
Guerrero, Mary Wasick
Science Teacher
Hegrenes, Odney Dean
Physics Teacher
Jewell, Suzanne M.
English Teacher
Johnson, Douglas Gene
5th Grade Teacher
Rumpca, Jill Marie
Sixth Grade Teacher
Tuura, Larry John
French & Spanish Teacher
PRESTON
Amundson, Sandra K. Graff
First Grade Teacher

O'Mara, Ann Bertler
5th-8th Grade Band Director
PRINCETON
Davis, Steven A.
Social Studies Teacher & Coach
Erickson, Sondra Koering
English & Journalism Teacher
Halverson, Jeffrey D.
Technology Ed & Math Teacher
Shish, Robert Russell
Social Studies Teacher
Tomsky, James Thomas
English Teacher
Vailliancourt, Howard V.
English & Lang Arts Teacher
PRINSBURG
Beekman, Irma Dykstra
Guidance Counselor & Teacher
Pluimer, Dennis Lee
Biology Teacher
PRIOR LAKE
Cade, Molly Flynn
Spanish Teacher
Ottoson, Carol J. Dixon
Senior HS English Teacher
RANDOLPH
Heski, Thomas Martin
6th Grade Teacher
Nygaard, Harriet Mayvis
First Grade Teacher
Schaffer, Nancy A.
Fourth Grade Teacher
RED WING
Danell, Alice Goelz
1st-2nd Grade Teacher
Nelson, Charley
Social Studies Teacher
Peterson, Richard Kurt
Director of Bands
Strusz, Karen Callstrom
Second Grade Teacher
REDWOOD FALLS
Ellingworth, Janet Huss
Senior High English Teacher
Erickson, D. Dale
Math & Career Exploration Tchr
REMER
Arnquist, Kathleen Buchanan
7th-12th Grd LD Teacher
Kitchenhoff, Jacoline Zwart
E, BD Instructor
Nyland, Roselyn Borene
Fifth Grade Teacher
RENVILLE
Abbas, Charlette Ann
Business & English Teacher
Kutter, Robert James
English Teacher
Mulder, Michelle Kay
Vocal & Instrumental Teacher
Purrington, Lois L.
German Teacher
Westby, Janet D.
Senior High Mathematics Tchr
RICE
Rajkowski, Edward Anthony
Elem Physical Ed Teacher
RICHFIELD
Abele, Marie Alena Isoherranen Maunula
Language Arts Teacher & Chair
Bartlett, Bob F.
Sr HS Theology Tchr & Cnslr
Berg, Patricia Anne
English & Mathematics Teacher
Kennedy, Kathleen Robertson
History & Social Science Tchr
Meyer, Stephen James
Chemistry Teacher
Mills, Steven Murray
Art Teacher
Sonday, Janice Neumann
ESL Teacher
Wickre, Carol Tointon
Kindergarten Teacher
Wickre, Paul N.
7th-8th Grd Tchr & Ath Dir
ROCHESTER
Bachman, Paul Lee
Science Teacher
Bailey, David Alan
4th Grade Teacher
Bothun, Darald Norris
Fourth Grade Teacher
Brehmer, Steven Lester
Physics Teacher
Carisch, David Robert
Instr of Anatomy & Physiology
Danielson, Karen Elizabeth
English Teacher
Davis, Christopher Allen
Professor of New Testament
Dealing, Bonnie Desmone
ESOL Teacher
Deines, Judy Snell
French Teacher
Elliott, Elissa Lien
Biology Teacher
Freudenburg, Kathy (Day)
First Grade Teacher
Glaser, Dallas R.
Sr HS Social Studies Teacher
Grandprey, Thomas Christian
Director of Bands
Grosso, Lorne A.
Latin & Italian Teacher
Gunnarson, Priscilla Berthelsen
Orchestra Music Teacher
Hoag, Jeffrey Alan
German Teacher

ROCHESTER (cont)
Johnson, Candi
Middle School Teacher
Kulzer, James J.
Thematic Coordinator
Lee, Jay A.
Law Enforcement Pgm Coord
Lunde, Jeffrey Alan
Social Studies & Psych Tchr
Mahle, Benj
9th Grade English Teacher
Mangano, Mark John
Professor of Bible
Mc Cormack, Neil Richard
Biology Teacher
Milburn, Barbara Kay (Orum)
English Teacher
Olson, Barbra J.
Guid Cnslr & Soc Stud Instr
Ondler, Douglas Lee
Science Teacher
Robbins, Dori Bremer
4th Grade Teacher
Russell, James Miller
History Instructor
Smith, Gerald Duane
Retired Vocal Music Teacher
Stanich, Joseph Eugene
5th-8th Grade Teacher
Styve, Paul D.
Math Teacher
Sullivan, Beverly Lynn Wacker
AP Eng, Speech & Drama Dir
Theismann, Marilyn Jane Kelly
Professor of English & Speech
Thompson, Pamela Jean
Elementary Principal
Vardsveen, Carol
Third Grade Teacher
Wetzel, Myron Emil
9th Grade Teacher
Willis, Larry C.
4th Grade Teacher
ROCKFORD
Davies, Susan Margaret
7th-12th Grade Art Teacher
Miller, Jay Charles
Business & Computer Teacher
ROCKVILLE
Heltemes, Gary P.
5th Grade Teacher
ROGERS
Dittrich, Denise Rene
Fifth & Sixth Grade Teacher
ROLLINGSTONE
O'Laughlin, Tammy Marie
Former Teacher
ROSEAU
Ross, Gary Charles
Fourth Grade Teacher
Ruud, Elwyn Olson
Third Grade Teacher
Vagle, Neil L.
Business Education Teacher
Wagner, William Harvey
Geometry & Calculus Teacher
ROSEMOUNT
Ball, Mark Edward
Math, Sci, His & Span Tchr
Buscho, Bruce Roger
German Teacher
Common, James L.
Guidance Counselor
Ellingson, LaRae A.
French Teacher & Dept Coord
Fondrick, Kyle Anton
High School Science Teacher
Groth, Barbara Jo (Sherman)
Business Teacher
Gundacker, Rosemary Nigon
Mathematics Teacher
Halvorson, James Mentor
Mathematics Teacher
Hanzlik, Kevin Patrick
Sixth Grade Teacher
Kachelmacher, Jon C.
Speech & English Teacher
Lewis, Lisa (Bauman)
English & Communications Tchr
Manther, Wanda Wittenberg
Communications Teacher
Rasch, Carroll H.
Teacher
Schema, Sue Ellen Dingman
Tchr of Deaf & Hard of Hearing
Strandquist, Patty Danielson
Language Arts Teacher
Strey, James Oscar
6th Grade Teacher
Trygestad, JoAnn Carol
Global Studies Teacher
ROSEVILLE
Ash, Robert William
Educational Methods Instructor
Huffman, Douglas Scott
Assistant Professor of Bible
Martin, J. E. Harvey
Professor of Christian Ed
Smith, Lawrence Ripley
Asst Prof of Communications
ROUND LAKE
Koller, John Leighton
Junior High Math Instructor
Miller, Paula Marie Kjellsen
Home Economics Teacher
ROYALTON
Malevich, Tony Charles
Senior High Social Stud Tchr
RUSH CITY
Bergeland, John Oliver
Third Grade Teacher
Laakso, Martin Louis
Fourth Grade Teacher
Nelson, Lori Ann
Fifth Grade Teacher
Schlagel, Robert Allen
Social Studies Tchr & Ath Dir
RUSHFORD
Leeman, William James
Social Studies Teacher
Moriarty, Michael Joseph
Lang Arts & Soc Studies Tchr
RUSSELL
Bender, Scott Allen
7th-8th Grade Soc Studies Tchr
SAGINAW
Dirksen, Kris Mary
4th Grade Teacher
Groves, Barbara Jean (Ceryance)
Fifth Grade Teacher
SAINT CHARLES
Karno, Stephanie Peterson
High School English Teacher
Mc Cready, Scott Paul
Math Teacher
Smith, Mike John
High School English Teacher
Staloch, Teri Anne
English & Humanities Teacher
SAINT CLAIR
Bromeling, Marcene Marzinske
Third Grade Teacher
SAINT CLOUD
Bischoff, Deborah Ann (Payne)
Science Teacher
Brobst, Del E.
Language Arts Teacher
Ellis, Kathleen Ann Monroe
Language Arts Teacher
Gerth, Steve Robert
Language Arts Teacher
Hall, David Cecil
Instrumental Music Teacher
Hancock, Martha Murray
First Grade Teacher
Hentges, Bruce L.
Activities Director
Klein, Robert E.
Chemistry & Physics Teacher
Koepp, Alan J.
High School Counselor
LaNave, Kevin Michael
HS Religion Teacher
Loch, Gary Basil
Art Dept Chairperson & Teacher
Meyer, Laurel Beth
Inclusion Facilitator
O'Brien, Dana Jerry
Work Experience Coordinator
Provinzino, Jannine Anne (Carlson)
Secondary Language Arts Instr
Rogosheske, Philip Roy
Health Teacher & Coach
Sieving, Robert W.
Choral Music Teacher
Trisko, Beth Ann
English & Speech Teacher
Wahman, John David
Seventh Grade Amer His Tchr
Young, Kathleen Kelly
Youth Service & Dev Coord
Zirbes, Norman Peter
Ninth Grade Science Teacher
SAINT FRANCIS
Carlson, Fran Ann
French Teacher
Erickson, Lee Donald
Mathematics Teacher
Mikrut, Michael Errol, Jr.
Earth Science Teacher
Nutter, Terry Morton
Physical Ed Teacher & Coach
Rau, Ellen A.
Spanish Teacher
Saba, Carol Alice
Eighth Grade Mathematics Tchr
Snead, Grace Holberg
4th Grade Teacher
Worcester, Richard William
Band Director
SAINT JAMES
Kaelberer, Jerome Theodore
6th-8th Grd Teacher & Prin
Larson, Robert R.
English Teacher
SAINT JOSEPH
Faulkner, Mara
Assistant Professor of English
Hope, Janet
Assistant Prof of Sociology
Hynes, Nancy J.
English Professor
Lamb, Deanna M.
Professor
Lierheimer, Linda Mei
Assistant Prof of History
McKenna, Anna Gibson
Assoc Prof of Chemistry
Mealey, Linda
Sr Lecturer of Psychology
Scipioni, Susan Kathleen
Principal
Wessman, Joann Phoebe
Prof of Nursing & Dept Chair
SAINT PAUL
Akervik, Susan Elizabeth
PE & Health Teacher
Amey, Marlene Lincoln
Math & Science Teacher
Anderson, David William
Professor of Education
Anderson, Juel E.
Health Teacher
Barry, Patrice Lorraine
Third Grade Teacher
Bassett, David Marvin, II
Asst Director & Science Tchr
Bland, Johnny
Science Teacher & Dept Head
Borgeson, Feryle
Math Teacher
Bostrom, Dennis Paul
Fifth Grade Teacher
Brabeck, Joan M.
Elem School Guidance Counselor
Brottem, Marc
Secondary Mathematics Teacher
Brown, Gerald Thomas
Mathematics Teacher
Burns, Maureen Joan
5th Grade Teacher
Butterfoss, Edwin J.
Professor of Law
Byron, J. Michael
Instructor of Theology
Carle, Elizabeth Ann (Schuneman)
English & Reading Teacher
Carlson, Gary Richard
Art Teacher
Cartier, Judith Bodey
Fourth Grade Teacher
Chandler, Betty Copeland
K-6th Grd Substitute Teacher
Clausen, Shelly Kay (Swenson)
Seventh Grd Lang Arts Teacher
Conrath, Patrice Lennae
Mathematics Professor
Devens, Jeffery Allen
Social Studies Teacher
Dukatz, Rose Mary Hirschey
Assistant Dean of Students
Egge, James Jennings
Biology & Chemistry Teacher
Eisele, Melodye
IB German & Psychology Tchr
Fields, Vivian Laverne
Third Grade Teacher
Flowers, William James
Pol Sci Tchr & Dept Chm
Freeman, Harryet Aronson
American History Teacher
Gavic, Rene' Lucey
Mathematics Teacher
Geistfeld, Annette Louise
High Potential Resource Tchr
Geroux, John Louis, III
Physical Science Teacher
Glau, Sandra K.
1st Grade Teacher
Gray, Robert Curran
6th Grade Teacher
Grunke, John Herbert
Mathematics Teacher
Hall, Thomas Frank
5th Grade Teacher
Harley, Jonathan K.
Mathematics & Computer Teacher
Herzog, Paul F.
Physical Ed Teacher & Coach
Hibbard, Howard A.
Middle School Counselor
Hickman, Roger A.
6th Grade Teacher
Huber, Norbert
German Teacher
Ingraham, Stacy Jean
Track Instructor & Coach
Jacobsen, Phyllis Ann
Third Grade Teacher
James, Cherie Lynn
Indian Studies Teacher
Jensen, Candace Kay (Vogel)
5th Grade Teacher
Jithendranathan, Shyamala
Chemistry Teacher
Johnson, Denise Renae
Science & Health Teacher
Johnson, Joanna Traver
Secondary English Teacher
Johnson, Scott Michael
6th Grade Teacher
Jones, Charles Weldon
Professor of Biology
Jones, Teresa Loeffler
Art Department Head & Teacher
Juaire, Dennis Leon
English Teacher
Jurney, Mary B.
Biology Teacher
Jurney, William Earl
Biology Instructor
Kallok, Richard A.
Asst Prin & Head Ftbl Coach
Kapoun, Barbara Ann
Fourth Grade Teacher
Keenan, Dean Alan
History Teacher
Klingberg, Steven Francis
Science Specialist
Krupich, Sally Ann (Clements)
Fifth Grade Teacher
Labuza, Theodore Peter
Prof of Food Sci & Engineering
Laska, Mike Thomas
Math Teacher
Lehmann, Melissa Ann (Rosga)
Sixth Grade Educator
Lewis, Sharon Stedt
Third Grade Teacher
Main, Michael James
English Teacher
McCrossan, Mary Alice
Fifth Grade Teacher
McFarland, Douglas Dale
Law Professor
Miller, Kathryn Munholand
11th Grade World History Tchr
Morton, Daniel Roland
Chem, Physics Tchr & Coach
Moynagh, Jack E.
American History Teacher
Mueting, Jean M.
4th Grade Teacher
Nichols, Mary Fanning
English Teacher
Obsatz, Michael
Assoc Prof of Sociology
Ochiagha, Rowena Jack
Assistant Professor
Olson, James Allen
PE Teacher & Coach
Paatalo, Joseph Eric
English Teacher
Peterson, Mary Plaszczewski
Social Studies Teacher
Peterson, Rosemary
Middle School Teacher
Polfliet, Susan Strasser
5th Grade Teacher
Quinn, George Michael
Guidance Director
Reymann, Joseph Alois
Sci Dept Chm & Biology Tchr
Richardson, Phillip K.
Director of Instrumental Music
Rosengren, John
English Teacher
Rouse, Marvin Arthur
Teacher of Handicapped Stdnts
Ruhberg, Liz
Science Teacher
Schumacher, Robert Michael
Science Teacher & Dept Head
Schwartz, Earl Bruce
Bible & Rabbinics Teacher
Sharma, Kamlesh Chandan
ESL Teacher
Sheppard, Carmen C.
Communications Specialist
Simpson, Camille Berry
Teacher of Gifted & Talented
Singer, Fern Dodge
Mathematics Teacher
Skie, Duane Anthony
High School Math Teacher
Smith, Barbara Lynn
Second Grade Teacher
Steffl, Stephen John
Social Studies Teacher
Swanson, Barbara Sorvik
6th Grade Educator
Swanson, Rebecca Sue
Third Grade Teacher
Swanson, Richard Pommier
Science Teacher
Swanson, Steven Richard
Professor of Law
TerEick, Jerald John
Teacher
Thacker, Susan Deitemeyer
Second Grade Teacher
Thompson, Christopher J.
Asst Prof of Moral Theology
Uemura, Joseph Norio
Professor of Philosophy
Vann, Arlene Theresa
Performing Arts Teacher
Varvel, Linda Elizabeth
American Literature Teacher
Villarreal, Roque John
Spanish Teacher
Wadell, Lourdes Rafaela
Spanish Teacher
Weber, Thomas Dale
English Teacher
Wicks, Joseph Leroy
High School Biology Teacher
Williams, Diane M.
Business Education Teacher
Young, Carole Joan
Assoc Professor of Psychology
Young, Melissa Dawn
Health, Phys Ed & History Tchr
SAINT PAUL PARK
Byhre, Carole Crane
Jr HS English Teacher
Fritsch, Gerald M.
Social Studies Teacher
SAINT PETER
Amamoto, Florence D.
English Professor
Amos, Eunice Paulson
Retired Family & Consumer Tchr
Behrenas, Mary Pederson
French Teacher
Halvorson, Marjorie Lind
First Grade Teacher
SANBORN
Sorensen, Karla (Heieie)
First Grade Teacher
SARTELL
Cooley, Donna Marie
First Grade Teacher
Kellerman, Jeffrey Fred
Physical Education Teacher
Kuhn, Thomas L.
Eng, Jrnlsm & Theater Teacher
Olson, Thomas P.
Physics & Physical Sci Teacher
Pantzke, Kathleen Victoria
Science & Communication Tchr
Rengel, Deborah Chirhart
Social Studies & Language Tchr
Thompson, Carla Kay
High School English Teacher
SAUK CENTRE
Boschee, Dana
English Teacher
Hartmann, Barbara Allen
English Instructor
Rosner, Sarah Vasquez
Second Grade Teacher
Ross, Jeffery Allen
Ninth Grade Civics Teacher
Super, James Joseph
Science Teacher
Uhlenkamp, Lois Elmes
5th Grade Teacher
SAUK RAPIDS
Allen, Daniel Ray
Physical Science Teacher
Engelhart, Michael D.
8th Grd Language Arts Teacher
Gainey, Ronald Joseph
Earth Science Teacher
Harris Walz, Anita Marie
Principal
Johnson, Mary Ropella
Social Studies Teacher
Madsen, Sheila Rosemary (Spier)
Sixth Grade Teacher
O'Brien, Katherine Jean-Mattison
Spanish & Math Teacher
Swanson, Thomas Clarence
Alternative Learning Teacher
SEBEKA
Brown, Ann Marie (Teigen)
Fourth Grade Teacher
Carlson, Bradley Paul
Math Teacher
Houle, Mark Scott
Fifth Grade Teacher
Pervine, Richard Lee
Social Studies Teacher
Pettis, Diane G.
5th-12th Grd Physical Ed Tchr
Wealot, Karen Wedman
Physical Science Teacher
SHAKOPEE
Arnett, Alene Mary
9th Grd English Teacher
Hanel, Linda Menden
Second Grade Teacher
Johnson, Neil I.
Mathematics Instructor
Leroux, Karen Rae
2nd Grade Teacher
Otto, James Robin
Sixth Grade Teacher
Weinzierl, Esther Theis
Substitute Teacher
SHERBURN
Bettin, Ross Jon
Social Studies Teacher & Coach
Branstad, Patricia A.
German Teacher
Carlson, Marsha Lynn
4th Grade Teacher
James, Timothy Paul
Art Teacher
Janke, Roxy Ann
English, Speech & Drama Tchr
Stenson, Rick Lynn
Soc Stud Tchr & Asst Coach
SHOREVIEW
Kenney-Adam, Kassy Mary
Admin & Language Arts Teacher
SILVER BAY
Yoki, LeRoy A.
Math Instructor
SLAYTON
Ristau, Steven Jon
HS Social Studies Teacher
Willadsen, Daniel John
English & TV Productions Tchr
SLEEPY EYE
Hansen, Larry Wayne
Sixth Grade Teacher
SOUTH SAINT PAUL
Egan, Ruth Dempsey
Special Education Teacher
Kaczmarek, Debra Dunn
Lang Arts Tchr & Speech Coach
Kuskovski, Vladimir David
Russian & German Teacher
Linnell, Susan Kaye
French Teacher
Peterfeso, Robert Jerome, Jr.
Biology Teacher
Schmoll, Janet Nelson
German Teacher
Smallidge, Ronald James
Fifth Grade Teacher
SPRING GROVE
Kapplinger, Kim D.
Science Teacher
Schieber, Susan Sorensen
Secondary Math Teacher
Sesker, Todd Curtis
Mathematics & Computer Teacher
SPRING VALLEY
Ascheman, Rick A.
HS Social Studies Teacher
Kappers, Kathleen Jones
Mathematics & Chemistry Tchr

GFIELD
an, Sharon Melby
Grade Teacher
ko, Lyle L.
r High Science Teacher
on, John Githens
nd Grade Teacher & Coach
BUCK
lson, Audrey Victoria
ed Elem Science Teacher
ARTVILLE
, Cindy R.
rade Civics Teacher
Marlene Kaye
sh Instructor
Brett Lee
l Science Teacher
Emily Bosse
Schl Mathematics Teacher
, Kurt Dennis
entary Teacher
er, Kris Martin
rade Teacher
WATER
n, James D.
estra Director
, Sharon Kay
nd Grade Teacher
s, Shelly
ce Teacher
George Leo
chr & Football Coach
DEN
er, Kenneth David
Grade Teacher
VILLE
ug, Steven John
ce Teacher
Dominic Francis
Social Studies Teacher
RIVER FALLS
, Charlie Bill
l Studies Teacher
Diane
sh Instructor
nd, Jack H.
ry & Geography Professor
n, Dennis L.
Asst & Philosophy Prof
n, Patti L.
Sci & Global Sci Teacher
, Delores Ulrich
le School Teacher
Eugene E.
Minority Student Svcs
ll, Diane Ryan
th & Eighth Grade Teacher
an, Dean C.
ematics Teacher
R
John O.
rade Teacher
Y
, Connie Elaine
h Grade Teacher
Chris M.
Director
AN
rom, Mary E. Nelson
Grade Teacher
an, Marilyn Sue (Belshan)
rade Teacher
rg, Linda K.
ce Teacher
eier, William H.
ematics Department Chm
mann, Wayne Earl
ech & Science Teacher
HARBORS
, Jill Ann Hultman
Music Director
bach, Dennis E.
gy Teacher
l, Greg C.
h Teacher
, Caren I.
rade Teacher
R
son, Janet Lee Osthus
sh & Social Studies Tchr
el, Randall George
sh & Speech Instructor
on, Kathleen Kramer
Director & Music Teacher

, Helga Kuasager
ce Teacher
LA
n, Patsy Stearns
ly & Consumer Science Tchr
AIS HEIGHTS
Ann Margaret
rade Teacher
NIA
nn, Patrick William
Adaptive PE Specialist
ansen, Wayne Gordon
sh & Spanish Teacher
Frank L.
School Counselor
esingh, Lutchmiparsad
ematics Instructor
n, Jeanette M. (Paukert)
ly & Consumer Science Tchr
, John Gerard
rade Teacher
Nancy Carolyn
His & World Studies Tchr

WABASHA
Seibel, Sharon Kay
Kindergarten Teacher
WABASSO
Dudgeon, Joel Wade
Second Grade Teacher
Johnson, Rick Alan
HS Social Studies Teacher
Klaers, William Lee
Agricultural Education Teacher
WACONIA
Hartwig, Sue Ann Moody
Family & Consumer Science Tchr
Johnson, Tracy Lee
Youth Development Coordinator
Kurtz, Kathryn Jean
Mathematics Teacher
Larson, Ronald James
Vocal Music Teacher
Luebke, Jon F.
Geography & Area Studies Tchr
Machtemes, Clark Thomas
Social Studies Teacher
Melchert, Pamela Jean (Gibson)
French Teacher
Mortensen, Wayne F.
Student Activities Director
Schellack, Polly B.
English Teacher
Singsaas, Sharon D.
Mathematics Teacher
WADENA
Guck, Janice Kay
First Grade Teacher
Larson, Joyce Stadum
Retired First Grade Teacher
Nelson, Jack Julius
5th & 6th Grd Title I Teacher
Palloch, Fred Michael
Senior High Mathematics Tchr
Westman, Byron Doyle
Social Studies Teacher
WALDORF
Schuldt, Darlene Schmidt
Social Studies Teacher
Witt, Fauniece Meyer
7th-8th Grade English Teacher
WALKER
Lindstrom, Jeffrey M.
Technology Coord & Instructor
WANNASKA
Storey, Walter Colby
Teacher & Principal
WARREN
Aafedt, Tom Allen
5th Grade Teacher
Beck, Elaine Rysavy
Life Science & Algebra Teacher
Corradi, Joseph A.
Social Studies Teacher
Nelson, Margaret Louise (Olson)
3rd Grade Teacher
WARROAD
Bengtson, Steven John
8th Grade Math Teacher
Furuseth, Lee Jonathon
Third Grade Teacher
Peterson, Robert Michael
Former Elementary Teacher
WASECA
Dufault, Richard A.
Retired Band Director
Hanson, John Charles
Social Studies Teacher
Seehafer, Carol Bitzer
Third Grade Teacher
WATERVILLE
Grugel, Ann Helene
Eng, European His & Psych Tchr
Wollin, David
Social Studies Teacher
WAUBUN
Dretsch, Marie Mae
6th Grade Teacher
Fabre, Marjorie A.
Retired Third Grade Teacher
Syverson, Edward Norman
Health, PE Teacher & Ath Dir
WAYZATA
Ivers, Jacqueline Jean
Elementary Teacher
O'Neill, Steven James
8th Grade Health Teacher
WELLS
Hagen, Dallas Ahrens
Adaptive Physical Ed Tchr
Prange, Melissa K.
Life Skills Teacher
Schlaak, Kelly Lee
Business Education Teacher
Schmidt, Gloria Jean
Mathematics Teacher
Thofson, Arlene Brenno
Third Grade Teacher
WESTBROOK
Arndt, Lynn Joy (Krahn)
Business & Social Teacher
Enstad, Carolyn Klima
Media Generalist & Teacher
Gundermann, Karla Kay
Kindergarten Teacher
WHITE BEAR LAKE
Abfalter, Sandra Jean
Spanish Teacher
Erickson, William Irving
Health Teacher
Frost, G. Douglas
Eng & Lang Arts Scndry Tchr
Gabrick, Robert William
History Teacher

Gerster, Patrick G.
Professor of History
Kimball, George Edmond
American History Teacher
Lacina, Jenny Marie
Fourth & Fifth Grade Teacher
Leleps, Vija Daina
College German Instructor
Nakasone, Edwin M.
History & Intnl Relations Prof
Nelson, Marilyn Dianne (Walsh)
MS Music, HS Theatre Teacher
Otis, Marlys Johnson
Mathematics Teacher
Rantanen, Robert H.
Band & Jazz Teacher
Travis, Carla Jean
Animal Science Teacher
Wiik, Susan Merrick
Communication & Lang Arts Tchr
Wilmot, Hampton L., Jr.
Communications & History Tchr
Zbikowski, Robert Paul
Science Instructor
WILLMAR
Hauser, Bonnie Hendrickson
Fifth Grade Teacher
Mc Donnell, Michael Joseph
Fifth Grade Teacher
Miller, Shelley Balkan
Dean of Students
Peper, George Thomas
Biology Tchr & Sci Dept Chair
Plotnik, Donna Mary (Sampson)
Fourth Grade Teacher
Steffen, Kathy Jane
Community College Instructor
Waskul, Dennis Donald
Professor Dept of Sociology
WINDOM
Kalash, Esther Ladehoff
Sixth Grade Teacher
WINNEBAGO
Dahms, Ramona C.
Retired 3rd Grade Teacher
WINONA
Anderson, Keith Ray
6th Grade Math Teacher
Anderson, Randy F.
Industrial Technology Teacher
Bailey, Melvin Clair
English Teacher
Beeman, Barbara Denine
Spanish & English Teacher
Blank, Sandra Ann
Biology & Anatomy Teacher
Boone, David Martin
Technology Coord & Math Tchr
Browne, Carol Ann Hoeppner
First Grade Teacher
Chick, Paul E.
Physics Teacher
Czaplewski, John Robert
Mathematics Teacher
Debnath, Joyati Chakraborty
Prof of Math & Statistics
Galleher, Kathleen Mary
Asst Professor of Psychology
Goldmann, Terry Ann
English Instructor
Gomsrud, Elise M.
Spanish Teacher
Hefel, Jeffrey Richard
Professor of Business Admin
Heydt-Nelson, Joan Elizabeth
Amer History & Psychology Tchr
Killion, Cindy Lou
Asst Prof of Mass Comm
Korte, Clare Ann
Professor of Biology
Kullman, Timothy Richard
Instructor of Sociology
Ludwigson, David N.
Fifth Grade Teacher
Manion, Andrew Patrick
Asst Prof of Psychology
Martin, Debra Joyce
Assistant Professor of Biology
Miller, Mariann Artaserse
Fourth Grade Teacher
Moeller, Janet Martin
Language Arts Instructor
Murtha, Timothy O'Hara
English Teacher
Ramos, Lilian Eva Maria
German & Spanish Professor
Ramsdell, Bruce D.
Concert Choir Director
Ryan, Heidi Guenther
Orchestra Teacher
Schild, Steven R.
Media Communication Dept Chair
Smith, Robert Joseph
Theology Professor
Sokolowski, David Paul
Assistant Professor of English
Vitek, Carolyn Rohrer
Biology Instructor
Whitney-Thrune, Karen
High School Counselor
Woyczik, Patricia Ann Boller
Special Education Teacher
WINSTED
Ebensperger, Marvin Lee
Math & Physical Sci Teacher
Schrandt, Dean Alan
Sixth Grade Teacher
Yaeck, Irene Storms
Business & Drivers Ed Teacher

WINTHROP
Roller, Carina Angelica
Spanish Teacher
Zellmann, Lowell Leslie
English Teacher
WOODBURY
Baldrica, James Robert
Elementary Band Teacher
Blake, Lisa M. Boland
Lead Instructor
Elliott, Karen Anderson
Math Teacher
Heinrich, Evelyn Rogers
Sixth Grade Teacher
Henton, Deborah M.
Social Studies Teacher
Hoge, Michael E.
Music Department Chairman
Rich, Wilma Thomason
Biology Teacher
Sommer, Andrew John
Spanish Teacher
Tannahill, Dwayne
10th-12th Grade Band Director
Travis, Susan W.
World Studies Teacher
Trepka, Judy Anderson
Chemistry Teacher
Westlund, Douglas Glenn
Social Studies Teacher
WORTHINGTON
Bastian, Vernon R.
Math Teacher
Evans, Francene E.
Psych Instr, Chair & Pgm Coord
Knutson, Brenda Alderson
Business Teacher
Lucht, Henrietta Le
Spanish Instructor
Mardesen, Mary Jane Harder
Eng, Speech & Theatre Instr
O'Neil, Alan L.
English & Speech Instructor
Regnier, Barbara K.
ESOL Teacher
WYOMING
Erickson, Thomas Bennett
Sixth Grade Teacher
Knox, Thomas Michael
5th Grade Teacher
Steichen, Patricia Jean
6th Grade Teacher
ZUMBROTA
Quiring, Kenneth Lee
Social Studies Teacher

MISSISSIPPI

ABERDEEN
Dodds, Kay D.
1st Grade Teacher
Holloway, Patricia B.
Business Education Teacher
Llewellyn, Nellie Kahl
Biology Teacher
ACKERMAN
Coleman, Frances Mc Lean
Teacher of Academic Courses
Curtis, Michael Davis
Diversified Technology Teacher
Davidson, Jessie M.
Bus & Comp Tech Tchr
Draper, John M.
Coach, Chem & Phys Sci Tchr
Scott, Shirley Parker
Sixth Grade Teacher
Stacy, Cheryl Long
English Teacher
Stidham, Barry Gwain
Vocational Counselor
Thomas, Bonnie Brown
Elementary Teacher
AMORY
Ashcraft, Natasha Vaughan
Third Grade Teacher
Duke, Burrell Blanton
Soc Studies & Driver Ed Tchr
Easley, David Ray
Math & Algebra Teacher, Coach
Ford, Elissa Diane
Eng, Writing & Speech Tchr
Griffith, Ruth M.
Mathematics Teacher
Hathcock, Sharon Cox
English Teacher
Herndon, Lisa Easley
Mathematics Teacher
Johnson, Melissa Dianne
Biology Teacher
Law, Angela DeJuan
Fifth Grade Teacher
Nesbit, Wanda Price
Secondary Mathematics Teacher
Parham, Mary Ann Goforth
Fourth Grade Teacher
Parker, Patricia Kennedy
4th-6th Grd Rdng & Math Tchr
Pearson, Bill Alan
Guidance Counselor
Sizemore, Monda Vaughan
Fourth Grade Teacher
Thrash, Patti A.
Business Education Teacher
Worthy, Loretta Roberts
High School Science Teacher
AVON
Clifton, Ann Dehne
History Teacher & Dept Chair

Lewis, Robert Daryl
Secondary History Teacher
BALDWYN
Gann, Richard Larry
Principal & HS Ath Director
Griffin, Robert David
Diversified Occupations Tchr
Pippin, Earnestine Miller
Bus Ed & Social Studies Tchr
BASSFIELD
Hitt, Martin T.
Fifth Grade Teacher
Hough, Eddie Delous
PE & Drivers Ed Tchr & Coach
West, Mary J.
Title 1 Lead Teacher
BATESVILLE
Bailey, Ruth Marett
HS Mathematics Teacher
Callihan, Betty Sue Burkhalter
Computer Teacher
Crawford, Libby Peeples
Guidance Cnslr & English Tchr
Dunaway, Sheila Ramsey
Gifted & AP US History Tchr
Estey, Melanie A.
Biology & Chemistry Teacher
Ginn, Janey G.
English Chair & Teacher
Grantham, Rebecca Shumaker
Mathematics Instructor
Wilkerson, David L.
Hlth & Drivers Ed Teacher
Wilkerson, Donna Smith
Occupational Child Care Tchr
BAY SAINT LOUIS
Blanchette, Jon E.
Retired Biology Teacher
Harris, Patricia Perniciaro
Mathematics Teacher
Lamb, Jane Viguerie
Vocational Coordinator
Maddox, Dana Morgan
Tchr of Behavior Disabilities
Mc Raney, Mary Ann
8th Grade English Teacher
Mehrtens, Joy Penny
Music Teacher
Modenbach, Patricia Fulkerson
Dir Dev, Pub Relations, Alumni
Robertson, Tanya Mitchell
English Teacher
Roche, Janet Hartt
Health Teacher
Schaferkotter, Michael Richard
Programmer & Analyst
Sokira, Anton
Senior Math Teacher
Switzer, John B.
Religious Studies Teacher
BAY SPRINGS
Rayner, Troy Lavelle
English Teacher & Bsktbl Coach
Russell, Noel
Secondary Social Studies Tchr
Sharp, Rosemary Sims
8th Grade Mathematics Teacher
BEAUMONT
Johnson, Evelyn Bolton
Fourth & Fifth Grade Teacher
Muscio, Patricia Turner
Tech Prep Instructor
Yates, Katie
Jr High Social Studies Tchr
BECKER
Sullivan, John Philip, Sr.
Soc Stud & PE Tchr
BELMONT
Chumbley, Joe Edward
Science Teacher
BELZONI
Body, Mattie Young
8th Grade Math Teacher
Brown, Marion L. Shamblee
9th-12th Grd Math Teacher
Reed, Gloria Helen
Teacher
Ross, Gester Dean
Social Studies Teacher
Rush, Martha Jayne
English & Spanish Teacher
BENTON
Ledbetter, Marion Subblefield
7th & 8th Grade Math Tchr
Moore, Teresa L.
Secondary Mathematics Teacher
Ringo, Hattie Ross
English & Reading Teacher
BILOXI
Barnes, Paul Zannoth
Senior Army & JROTC Instr
Bartels, Marie Powers
Span Ger Dept Chair & Teacher
Bond, Loretta W.
K-6th Grd Physical Ed Teacher
Caillavet, Sondra Parker
Mathematics Teacher
Campbell, Jeff W.
Business Education Teacher
Carter, Julia Strange
Retired Secondary English Tchr
Clement, Sheri L.
English Teacher
Comstock, Charles W., Jr.
Art I, II & III Teacher
Cummings, Betty Ann
Teacher of Gifted Education
Fayard, Brenda
Algebra & Calculus Teacher

BILOXI (cont)
Fields, Clementine
Bus & Computer Tech Instructor
Galloway, Linda Strange
English Teacher
Gardiner, Lisa Renee
Secondary Education Teacher
Gibbs, Woodrow J.
Marine Science Teacher
Gottsche, Myra M.
Curriculum Coord
Grant, Lori Brown
Third Grade Teacher
Hughes, Betty Jean
Latin Teacher
Jones, Beverly Kirby
Health Occupations Teacher
Killingsworth, Gloria Guyton
US & World History Teacher
Mattox, Carole L.
English Dept Chairman
McCarty, Diane DuRant
High School Choral Director
Mc Cool, Susan N.
Secondary Biology Teacher
Mc Dougall, Carolyn Vose
Art Teacher
Mize, Sandra Simpson
Mathematics Teacher
Mohler, Martha Howard
English Dept Chairperson
Nolan, Barbara Pittman
Fourth Grade Teacher
Roberts, Carlene Copeland
6th Grade Reading Teacher
Snipes, Lucinda Chandler
Spanish Teacher
Souza, Joseph M.
Air Force JROTC Instr
Thompson, Malia Hansen
Ninth Grade Biology Teacher
Veal, Mary Sue S.
English Teacher
BLUE MOUNTAIN
Bain, Douglas Cogburn, Jr.
Prof of Biblical & Assoc Stud
Brooks, JoAnne Biggers
Assistant Professor of Math
Cimon, Monique Rozenbaum
Prof of Modern Langs & Chair
Cockrell, Thomas D.
Chm Div of Social Sciences
Enzor, Sharon Ball
Chem Prof & Dept Head
Jackson, Estelle Raymer
Secondary English Teacher
Ludlow, G. Edward
Assoc Prof, Organ & Church Mus
Owen, Lou White
Professor
Quinn, Anna Jackson
Associate Professor of English
Washburn, Sarah Sims
Assoc Prof Dept of Social Sci
BLUE SPRINGS
Ivy, Mary Sappington
Mathematics & Oral Comm Tchr
Simpson, Barbara Gregory
3rd Grade Teacher
BOGUE CHITTO
Hodges, R. Michael
English Teacher
Hux, Barbara S.
Business Teacher
Willis, John Charles
Mathematics Teacher
BOONEVILLE
Akers, Bettie Raye Smith
Mathematics Teacher
Antillon, Christi Hamblin
Psychology Instructor
Bishop, Sharon Franklin
English & Journalism Teacher
Cox, Janet Taylor
Paralegal Instr & Head of Pgm
Davis, Reba Holley
Mathematics Instructor
Duckworth, Linda Mc Nutt
Instr of Mrktg & Mngmt Tech
Falkner, Carla Callaway
History Instructor
Hughes, Rocky Jay
Biology Instructor
Jackson, Carolyn Wallis
Retired English Teacher
Jones, Vickie English
Dental Hygiene Instructor
Kehoe, Deborah Pope
English Instructor
Long, Gerry Carmichael
HS Mathematics Teacher
Lucius, Debra Taylor
Chemistry & Physical Sci Tchr
Mattox, Johnny Lynn
Professor of Biology
McBride, Laurie Lynn
English & Speech Instructor
Mc Combs, Carolyn Greene
Fourth Grade Teacher
Moore, Tina Eaton
English Professor
Murry, Rita Goodwin
Medical Lab Technology Instr
Nabors, Larry Joe
Mathematics Instructor
Pardue, Barbara Brown
Computer Programming Tech Tchr
Ramsey, Vickie Quinn
Instr of Microcomputer Tech

Shadburn, Randy Glen
Astronomy & Physics Teacher
Ward, Patti Jumper
Science Teacher & Dept Head
White, Ann Hoover
English Instructor
Williams, Betty Windham
Vocational Business Ed Teacher
BRANDON
Cooley, Kristin B.
Geometry Teacher
Dunigan, Beth Barlow
Science Teacher
Emmons, Brenda Haralson
Third Grade Teacher
Evans, Valerie Rasberry
Biology Teacher
Gill, Mildred Wynelle
Venture Teacher of Gifted
Hinton, Thomas Montgomery
Teacher & Coach
Hollis, June Davidson
Social Studies Teacher
Jones, Christy Crowder
8th Grade English Teacher
Krebs, Phyllis Rhodes
Math Teacher
Livingston, Kelly Moreton
Third Grade Teacher
McSparin, Phillip A.
English Teacher
Oden, Marcia Archer
English Teacher
Sapen, Trina Patterson
Mathematics Teacher
Stewart, Terry Morgan
Kindergarten Teacher
Tullos, Rene Russell
Social Studies Teacher
Whittington, Millie Wyatt
Fourth Grade Teacher
BROOKHAVEN
Campbell, Sylvia N.
Advanced Math & Calculus Tchr
Creely, Charlotte Nell
Alg & Geometry Teacher
Crider, Arlene Frazier
Business Computer Tech Tchr
Dunn, Sondra McTaggart
Sixth Grade Science Teacher
Gardner, Diedrick Murray
Physics Teacher
Jordan, Alexine Duncan
First Grade Teacher
Land, Vicki A.
Art Teacher
Lloyd, Sarah Woodruff
Social Studies Teacher
Lucas, Jeanette Lowe
First Grd Tchr & Elem Supvr
Oberschmidt, Margaret Ball
Algebra II Teacher
Ogden, John Adams
Social Studies Teacher
Price, Carolyn Wesley
Algebra Teacher
Ratcliff, Richelle Adams
English Teacher
Reid, Katie McManus
Multi Age Teacher
Rutland, Amy Catherine
Biology Teacher
Smith, Janice Mullen
Fourth Grade Teacher
Spiller, Andrew
8th-10th Grd Soc Stud Tchr
Thurman, Myra Allgood
English Teacher
Vaughn, William Peck
Soc Stud & Hlth Tchr & Coach
Wallace, Phyllis Moore
Math Teacher
Waller, Johnny L.
American History Teacher
BROOKLYN
Breland, Harvey D.
Industrial Arts Teacher
Dolan, Lawrence Lovette, II
10th Grd World History Teacher
Emerson, Kay L.
Tchr of Intellectually Gifted
Green, Yvonne Daniel
7th-8th Grd Math Teacher
Lott, Carol McVay
5th-6th Grade Teacher
Minter, Barbara Tims
Advanced Placement Teacher
Rivers, Jerry Eugene
12th Grade Economics Teacher
Whitworth, Breck Howard
Biology & Physical Sci Tchr
BROOKSVILLE
Cullen, Reginald M.
Elementary School Principal
Jackson, Mattie Stewart
Retired Teacher
BRUCE
Burnett, Cheryl Seal
Librarian
Cooper, Beverly Overby
English Teacher
Gray, Nanci Murphree
Health Teacher
BUCKATUNNA
Austin, Martha Turner
First Grade Teacher
Chapman, Bettie Jean
8th Grade Teacher

BURNSVILLE
Adams, Betty Hall
Fifth Grade Teacher
McDuffy, Rhonda Lambert
7th & 8th Grd Mathematics Tchr
Robinson, Hubert Rhay
Retired Teacher
BYHALIA
Turnage, Cravin
RELAY Director
CALEDONIA
Carter, Christi Dendy
Social Studies Teacher
Luna, Rita
English & French Teacher
Reed, James Tabor
US & World His Tchr
Reed, Linda Hopper
Second Grade Teacher
Sellers, Annette Cabaniss
Mathematics Teacher
Sellers, Ronald Allen
Band Director
Sewell, Nancy Cash
Third Grade Teacher
Smith, Judy Evans
Social Studies Teacher
Whitney, Pamela J.
8th Grade English Teacher
CALHOUN CITY
Ferguson, Shelia Jenkins
Math & English Teacher
Garth, Hilda Marie Gladney
6th Grade Teacher
Inmon, JImmie Nell Scarbrough
English Teacher & Chair
Logan, Suzette Collins
Cooperative Education Coord
Perkins, Mary Lynn
Fifth & Sixth Grd English Tchr
Stewart, Billy Jack
History Teacher & Counselor
CAMDEN
King, Mary J. (Jackson)
English & Writing Teacher
McGraw, Tracey Cobb
English Teacher
CANTON
Canoy, Mistye Rhinewalt
Chemistry Teacher
Crump, Rodney Gerrard
French Instructor
Hand, Yancey Aldridge
Fourth Grade Teacher
Jiles, Eunice
Mathematics Teacher
Thigpen, Julia Williams
Home Economics Teacher
Thomas, Ernestine Davis
Language Arts Teacher
CARRIERE
Hoelzel, Karen B.
Mathematics Teacher
Ladner, Gwen P.
Bus Computer Applications Tchr
CARROLLTON
Harlow, Madelyn Slaughter
English Teacher
Nester, April Walker
Counselor & Psychology Teacher
O'Bryan, Lou Corley
Third Grade Teacher
O'Neal, Patricia Nell
First Grade Teacher
Turnipseed, Betty S.
5th Grade Teacher
CARSON
Holloway, Ira Tate-Sutton
Allied Health Instructor
CARTHAGE
Blocker, Kay Harrell
Secondary Math Teacher
Brown, Ginger Fulce
Counselor
Burns, Bruce Wayne
Social Studies Teacher
Cheatham, Tommie Kevin
Agricultural Education Teacher
Lewis, Grace Harris
Secondary English Teacher
Peoples, Pamela Tingle
Guidance Counselor
Spears, Wynnifred M.
Business & Computer Ed Teacher
CENTREVILLE
Holifield, Penny Caulfield
Science Teacher
Knight, Billie Springer
HS Algebra & Comp Math Tchr
CHARLESTON
Jones, Allene Houston
Librarian
Norphlet, John Fitzgerald
Mathematics Teacher
CLARA
Heathcock, Cindy B.
Jr High Science Teacher
CLARKSDALE
Barnes, JoAnne Hooper
Social Studies Teacher
Carter, Alberta Hall
4th Grd Social Studies Teacher
Duncan, Glynda J.
Journalism Instructor
Flautt, Jo Boswell
Fifth Grade Teacher
Fortenberry, Vickie Berryhill
English & Oral Comm Tchr
Gammill, Leslie Brewer
Secondary Mathematics Teacher

Griffin, Vera Seals
English Teacher
Harris, Jacqueline Ann
Alternative Teacher & Cnslr
Kincade, Ruby Anne Dunlap
Sixth Grade Teacher
Luckett, Francine Gardner
Math Teacher & Dept Chairman
Mitchell, Cheri Willis
Biology Teacher
Ratliff, Joyce Lyn Smith
7th & 8th Grade Math Teacher
Sawyer, Lucy Harris
6th Grd Lang Arts Tchr
Shelton, Julia Mc Knight
Business & Computer Tech Tchr
Simpson, Belinda Collins
Algebra I & II Teacher
Stapleton, Brenda Joyce
English Teacher
Taylor, Hattie Wright
Physics, Biology & Chem Tchr
Thomas, Beverley Winkel
HS Mathematics Teacher
Walker, Camille S.
English Teacher
Wilson, Patsy W.
Tenth Grade World History Tchr
CLEVELAND
Barnes, Linda Griffin
Sixth Grade Teacher
Bell, Carrie Ann
Science Teacher
Brown, Josephine Ferri
5th Grade Teacher
Buchanan, Mary Lenn
Voice & Opera Professor
Card, Robert Earl, Jr.
United States History Teacher
Clayton, Sam
10th Grade English Teacher
Daugherty, Kay Barrett
Mathematics Teacher & Dept Chm
Fioranelli, Beverly LaPresto
English Teacher
Griffin, Emma Swann
Reading & Mathematics Lab Tchr
Hamp, Annie R.
Second Grade Teacher
Holbrook, Arthur VanLuke
Technology Education Teacher
Isaac, Frances Smoote
English Teacher
Leach, Francis Orrin
Associate Professor of Music
Meek, Terry Young
Teacher of Gifted
Montesi, Patricia K.
English Teacher
Moore, Renee Alma
English & Journalism Teacher
Nisbett, Claudia Jackson
Headmistress
Odom, Mary Ann Bell
English Teacher & Dept Chm
Smith, Esther Hayes
Guidance Counselor
Smith, Ruth Janet
Business Teacher
Tate, William F.
Diversified Technology Instr
CLINTON
Bryant, Teresa Bell
1st Grade Teacher
Ford, Gayle Holcomb
Accelerated Eng & Span Teacher
Gibson, Linda Murray
6th Grade Teacher of Gifted
Lunceford, Robert Allen
9th Grade Teacher
Martin, Judith Johnson
5th Grd Language Arts Teacher
Moorer, Emily Hall
English Teacher
Parks, C. Dean
Chemistry Professor
Reynolds, Judith M.
English Teacher
Sholar, Lynda Boswell
Fourth Grade Teacher
Torrance, Penny Putnam
English & Journalism Teacher
Turman, Debra McDonald
English Teacher
Whitfield, Marijane Vickers
7th & 8th Grade Art Teacher
COFFEEVILLE
Franklin, Katherine Piner
English & Theater Teacher
Walton, Monroe, Sr.
Bio Sci Tchr & Dept Chrmn
COLDWATER
Collins, Sarah H.
5th Grd Eng & Spelling Tchr
McGraw, Connie Britt
Biology Teacher
Spiva, Wert Lee, Jr.
Health, PE Teacher & Coach
COLLINS
Hall, Sharon H.
Secondary Mathematics Teacher
Johnson, Lydia Kathlyn
Mathematics Teacher
COLLINSVILLE
Darnell, David Wayne
8th Grd Physical Sci Teacher
Herrington, Florence Jean (Espey)
Third Grade Teacher
Kinard, Faye D.
Physics & Chemistry Teacher

Mayatt, Jeffrey (Vincent)
Seventh Grade Math Teacher
Mayatt, Nettie Fretwell
Anatomy & Physiology Teacher
Vance, Brenda Joyce
Math Teacher
Williams, Jesse Charles
Assistant Principal
COLUMBIA
Davis, Barbara Brown
Fifth Grade Teacher
James, Lovalyn J.
Kindergarten Teacher
Lee, Evelyn Foster
Special Education Teacher
Mann, Karl C.
7th-8th Grade Principal
Pierce, Beth Ball
French Teacher
Rankin, Sharron A.
Art Teacher
Wright, Clara Riley
English Teacher
COLUMBUS
Albritton, Anna Marion
10th Grade Social Studies Tchr
Alford, John David
Art History Asst Professor
Allsup, Donna Carol
Algebra Teacher
Barham, K. Dawn
Performing Arts Educator
Bartlett, Sandra Hardison
History & Geography Instructor
Borden, Jackie Tubb
Kindergarten Teacher
Browning, Danny Richard
Science Dept Chairman & Coach
Brumley, Ellen Potter
2nd Grade Elementary Teacher
Cannon, Joni F.
Computer Science Teacher
Cheeseman, Robert Henry
Assoc Professor of Education
Cline, Cynthia Swift
Business & Computer Teacher
Coates, Sue S.
Div of Fine & Performing Art
Creel, Jo Anne
Home Economics Teacher
Davis, Connie Baldwin
5th Grade Teacher
Doty, Lillie Carson
Chemistry & Research Professor
Easley, Ruby Joyce
Mathematics Teacher
Eiland, Robert Louis
MS Assistant Principal
Ellis, Kathryn G.
AP English Teacher
Ezelle, Marya Rozowicz
1st Grade Teacher
Feeney, Lawrence Lee
Professor of Art
Gaither, Julia Sledge
Counselor
Gillespie, Linda Blake
HS English Teacher
Granderson, James Lee, Jr.
Teacher
Granderson, Lena Freeman
Teacher
Graves, Jeanette Johnson
Clincial Audiologist & Faculty
Gray, Dabney Smith
Assistant Professor of English
Halford, Michael Leon
Principal
Hazard, George Stephenson, Jr.
English Teacher
Hood, Laurie Stokes
Business Computer Tech Instr
Hunt, Barbara Gayle
Asst Prof of Grad Gifted Stud
Johnson, Ileana M.
Economics Teacher
Johnston, Grady L.
9th-12th Grd Soc Stud Teacher
Jones, Karen Murphy
Second Grade Teacher
Jones, Richard Lynn
AP Bio Teacher
Lancaster, Angela Jones
Art Teacher
Locke, Patricia Hopper
English & Journalism Teacher
Miller, Bonnie G.
SLD Teacher
Parker, William Skinker
Bio Prof, Sci & Math Div Head
Perry, Helen Davis
Advanced Physics Teacher
Ross, Janice Bradley
1st Grade Teacher
Ryan, Larry A.
5th Grd Math & Science Teacher
Shelton, Alecia Edmond
PE Teacher & Coach
Shepherd, Cary Gooch
5th Grade Teacher
Sheppard, Rhonda Fleming
Librarian & Media Specialist
Taylor, Luberta Phinisey
Math Teacher
Thomas, Jill Whitten
Science Teacher
Turner, Allie Ruth
Food Prod Mgmt & Serv Tchr
Turner, Jerry
Math Teacher

JMBUS (cont)
an, Nancy Hamilton
Grade Teacher
n, Dora Strickland
ond Grade Teacher
r, Addie Mitchell
I Math Teacher
ers, Deborah Pounders
nce & Math Teacher
Kathy Byrd
Grade Teacher
Toni Bouchillon
ish Teacher
ton, Jean Herrington
Grade Teacher
NTH
s, Betty Gwyn
Grade English Teacher
Linda Evans
entary Counselor
, Arrie Boswell
& 6th Grade Math Teacher
r, Janice M.
Teacher
n, Sandra Childs
ish & Business Teacher
ns, Vicki Berry
I & World His Teacher
ally, Angela Hubbard
ly & Consumer Sci Tchr
s, Pam Williams
nce Teacher of the Gifted
, Kona Street
bra I Teacher
y, Wanda Joy (Mc Creary)
ematics Teacher & Coach
, Fred Ronald
d Director
, Gina Rogers
al Science Teacher
son, Anne
nce Teacher
ons, William Arthur
& 9th Grd Soc Stud Teacher
TAL SPRINGS
s, Holiness, Jr.
nce Teacher
bell, Edward Wesley
3rd Social Studies Teacher
ALB
Wayne Morris
stant Principal
, Cleveland
d History Teacher
Mose
Teacher
Myra J.
her
, Pamela Feldman
School Mathematics Tchr
TUR
m, Linda Barnes
ish Instructor
s, Ann Hunter
ary Director
l, Judy Anne
ch & Theatre Instructor
Carolyn Johnson
ness Teacher
r, Lois B.
School Computer Teacher
r, Marcia Mason
nce Teacher
dy, James Bruce
Instr & Humanities Chprsn
, Shelby L.
of Math & Science Division
Jane D.
sing Instructor
Sheila Terrell
r & Spcl Populations Coord
ndon, Lucille Scoggins
cial Education Teacher
ullan, Lois F.
ematics Instructor
as, Sandra Towne
tical Nursing Instructor
pson, Kenneth Claude
3rd Pre-Algebra Teacher
V
uney, Larry Allen, Jr.
Social Studies Teacher
ANT
send, Andrew Lee
ndary Mathematics Teacher
J
r, Susan Norwood
& Applied Commnctn Teacher
, Brenda Huffstatler
Social Studies Teacher
, Debbie Edwards
hematics Teacher
SVILLE
s, Artie R.
d Director
ughs, Susie Watson
ory Instructor
son, Amy A.
igh Math Teacher
rd, Murrel Ralph
h Instructor
um, Lia Aultman
her of Gifted
all, Sherry Shows
8th Grade Tchr of Gifted
rs, Diann Cheeks
sical Ed & Science Teacher
, Sharline
Teacher

West, Mary Nell Hall
Third Grade Teacher
Wright, Sandra Morgan
Mathematics Teacher
ENTERPRISE
Frazier, Gloria Jean
Home Economics Teacher
Turner, Asline B.
Retired Mathematics Teacher
Walker, Patti Stone
11th-12th Grade English Tchr
Waltman, Cheryl Poole
English Teacher
ETHEL
Glaskox, Anna Cummins
Special Education Teacher
EUPORA
Long, Emma Embry
First Grade Teacher
Mason, Brenda Stewart
Mathematics Teacher
Mc Culloch, Ruth Chism
Social Studies Teacher
Walker, Harriett Embry
7th & 8th Grd Rdng Teacher
FALCON
Lomax, Ella Buckley
1st Grade Teacher
FALKNER
Boyd, Mary Goolsby
Business Instructor
Gray, Martha Louise Clemmer
Third Grade Teacher
FAYETTE
Berry, Gloria Coffie
Social Studies Teacher
Taylor, Lela Ann
Fifth Grade Teacher
Trimble, Mary Marie
Science & History Teacher
White, Levater Hayes
Third Grade Teacher
FLORA
Davis, Ruth Whitlock
Reading Teacher
FLORENCE
Bruce, Eunice Elizabeth
Junior High Art Teacher
Heinsch, Irmgard Niebuhr
Spanish & German Teacher
Ladner, Sandra Prisock
First Grade Teacher
Rushing, Sandra Hernbloom
English Teacher
FOREST
Allen, William Ronald
Social Studies Teacher
Arinder, Sandy Donald
Teacher of the Gifted
Caldwell, Irma Strong
Speech & English Teacher
Craig, Jerry L.
High Schl Mathematics Teacher
Herchenhahn, Chantelle
Science Teacher
Russell, Debbie Carol
Business Technology Instructor
FOXWORTH
Bochicchio, Jennifer Anne
English Teacher of the Gifted
Tynes, Lynn Evans
Second Grade Teacher
FRENCH CAMP
Hill, James Garrison
Music, Math & Science Teacher
Littlejohn, Larry W.
Asst Principal & Math Teacher
Nasekos, Paul Leo
Advanced Bible Teacher
FULTON
Beachum, Mary Loden
Kindergarten Teacher
Cox, Tanya Bruce
Community College Instructor
Franks, Judith Ann
Business Education Teacher
Hodge, Michelle South
Sociology Instructor
Lay, William E.
Biology Instructor
Loden, Susan Sheffield
Economics Professor
McLeod, Sandra T.
English Teacher
Miles, Sharon York
Biology Instructor
Montgomery, Elizabeth McGowan
English Instructor
Myers, Jeffery M.
Instructor of Music Education
Newsom, Elizabeth Watts
Admission Counselor
Partlow, Linda M.
Mathematics Instructor
Smith, Mary Ellis Perkins
Technology Instructor
Williams, Cy J.
Speech & Theatre Professor
Wiygul, D. L.
Furniture Technology Professor
GALLMAN
Ashley, Charlotte Pigg
High School English Teacher
Beach, Alison Graham
Language & Spelling Teacher
Day, Dorothy Ainsworth
Spanish & Psychology Teacher
Gaddy, Diane
Fifth & Sixth Grade Math Tchr

Henley, Rita D.
High School Science Teacher
Mackey, Mary Baylis
Computer Teacher
GAUTIER
Baggett, James Lamar, Jr.
Anatomy & Physiology Professor
Beard, Gwendolyn Marx
Principal
Brantley, Cindy Lou
Elementary Music Teacher
Fountain, Terry Price
Journalism Instructor
Haygood, Barbara Davis
Dev Stud Chprsn & Math Instr
Jones, E. Faye
Sociology Instructor
Koski, Reba Savell
Fourth Grade Teacher
Odom, Patricia Ann
Visual Arts Instructor
Sims, Kay Sanford
English Instructor
Timmons, Kathryn Hauck
6th Grade Teacher
Tringle, Sarah Taylor
Science Instructor
West, Patricia Scott
Communication Instructor
GLEN
Bowers, Linda Herald
Scndry Math Tchr & Dept Chair
Foust, Vera Jean
Eng, Fr Tchr & Eng Dept Chm
Houpt, Margaret Davis
Third Grade Teacher
Jeter, Rodney Eugene
6th Grade PE Teacher
Jobe, Stephen L.
Asst Principal
Little, Ann M.
English II Teacher
Mills, Carolyn Jobe
English & Speech Teacher
Nelton, Judy L.
Asst Band Dir & Chorus Tchr
GOLDEN
Swartzendruber, Debra Aven
Teacher of Gifted Education
GOODMAN
Bunch, Jan Reid
Choral Director & Voice Tchr
Burchfield, Michael Leonard
Science Instructor
Deaton, Steven Patrick
English Instructor
Gibson, Bobby E.
Engineering Technology Instr
Simpson, Janet Elkin
Music Professor
GREENVILLE
Ainsworth, Sherry Williams
Secondary English Teacher
Allen, Pearlie Davis
United States History Teacher
Batty, Sandra D.
4th, 5th & 6th Grade Teacher
Buchanan, Kaye Corder
First Grade Teacher
Byars, Martha Walker
Latin Teacher
Bynum, Jeannetta Huggins
Third Grade Teacher
Davis, Linda Donald
Algebra & Pre-Algebra Teacher
Glasgow, Linda Lea
Business Teacher
Hawkins, John
Chemistry Teacher
Jones, Patricia Smith
Spanish, French & English Tchr
Mc Clendon, Brenda Ikerd
Fourth Grade Teacher
Mc Gaugh, Sandra Low
Senior English Teacher
McKinnie, Zana McKelphin
Business Teacher
Moton, Barbara Taylor
7th Grade Social Studies Tchr
Nash, Louis Graves
Principal
Nash, Rose Conniff
Phys Sci, Chem & Physics Tchr
Parnell, Annette Lindsey
Third Grade Teacher
Preston, Earnestine Bender
Junior High Teacher
Rodgers, Ollie Freeman
Speech & Oral Comm Teacher
Sanders, Susannah Mc Cafferty
Second Grade Teacher
Sibley, Patricia Sanders
English I Teacher
Smith, Brenda Scott
English Teacher
Smith, Gladys J.
English Teacher
Taylor, Nina Palmer
English Teacher
Thomas, Majoice L.
HS Spanish & Japanese Teacher
Walker, Janice Dawson
HS Mathematics Teacher
Ward, Calvin E.
Chemistry Tchr & Bsktbl Coach
Williams, Mattie Neal
English Teacher & Dept Chprsn
Wilson, Dianne Ford
Science Teacher

Wuestenhoefer, Shirley Borganelli
Fifth Grade Teacher
GREENWOOD
Bailey, Esther Mays
Mathematics Teacher
Baylor, Patricia Young
Ret 5th-6th Grd Science Tchr
Clark, Kathryn M.
Math Dept Chairman & Teacher
Collins, Johnny L.
English Teacher & Asst Prin
Collins, Thelma Perkins
Ninth Grade English Teacher
Evans, Gwendolyn Dribben
Kindergarten & Resource Tchr
Hansbrough, Cassandria Baxter
English Teacher & Dept Head
Jennings, Warren Curtis
Art Teacher & Coach
Johnson, Marlene Leonard
Guidance Counselor
Jordan, Joyce Terry
English Teacher
Longstreet, Gloria Jean
Business & Computer Tech Tchr
McCoy, Hannah Littles
World History Teacher
Powell, Glory Moor
Third Grade Teacher
Powell, Percy
Algebra Teacher & Supervisor
Sullivan, Quentella Sneed
English Teacher
Welch, Sue Tribble
Chemistry & Phys Science Tchr
GRENADA
Collins, Joyce Morrow
Instructor of Business Tech
Hall, Mary Duncan Williford
Teacher & Coord of Gifted Ed
Hardy, Betty Jo (Spears)
Business Teacher
Harville, Myra Mitchell
Psychology Instructor
Honeycutt, Susan Snell
Math Teacher
Mayhan, Mary Ann Chamberlain
Business Technology Instructor
Ross, Irma Louise (Patterson)
8th Grade English Teacher
Tate, Debra Bills
Teacher of Gifted
GULFPORT
Adams, Susan Doty
Choral Music Supervisor
Bailey, June Jacqulyn
English Instructor
Breland, Leslie Bruce
Biology Teacher
Broadus, Jennifer Holder
Mathematics Teacher
Buckalew, William Glen
High School Band Director
Buckles, Evelyn Marie
Resource Teacher
Clark, Judy M.
Dept Chm & Soc Stud Teacher
Collins, Charlotte Simmons
9th Grd Bio & Phys Sci Teacher
Culpepper, Jack Thomas
Science Teacher
Dulaney, Timothy G.
United States History Teacher
Durbin, Sue
History & Math Teacher
Evans, Nettie Breland
7th Grd Eng Teacher & Team Ldr
Hammack, Phyllis Haywood
AP Eng Tchr to Gifted Stdnts
Hanser, Raymond Thomas, Jr.
English Teacher
Harden, Margaret Mack
Former 9th Grade History Tchr
Herbert, Karen Grigsby
Social Studies Tchr
Hollingsworth, Deborah Bennett
Band Director
Hollingsworth, Dwight N.
Band Director
Hoskins, Al
9th Grade Social Studies Tchr
Lawrence, Lisa Gayle
High School English Teacher
Lawrence, Vicki Lass
English Teacher
Lott, Donnie A.
Marine Biology Teacher
Lott, Ruby Holcomb
Second Grade Teacher
Marshall, Glenda Hamilton
English Teacher & Dept Chprsn
Mauffray, Katherine C.
Science Teacher
Maxwell, Constance Wilson
Chemistry Teacher
Mc Cary, Karla J.
Criminal Justice Professor
McCay, Barbara Rhea
Sixth Grade Teacher
Mc Kay, Paul G.
Mathematics Instructor
Moffett, Marguerite Wheat
Business Teacher
Moore, Kathy Mitchell
Guidance Counselor
Moulds, Peggy
Data Proc, Cmptr Applctns Tchr
O'Brian, Betty Sue
English Teacher

O'Connor, Cathy Patterson
Eighth Grade Science Teacher
Parks, Shelia Patterson
Fourth Grade Teacher
Redmond, Rosemary Warrick
Second Grade Teacher
Scott, Carolyn Hill
Business Education Teacher
Sinopoli, Paula J.
Instructor of Paralegal Tech
Swanier, Wendelyn Grace
8th Grade English Teacher
Waldorf, Elizabeth S.
Professor of Biology
West, Mary Whittemore
Sixth Grade Teacher
Williams, Arthur L.
Professor of Art
Williams, Brigitte Anne
French Teacher
Williams, Rosie
English Teacher
Wooten, Joan G.
Resource & Title I Teacher
HAMILTON
Robinson, Andlyn Sanders
Computer & Math Teacher
HATTIESBURG
Acker, Willie C.
Soc Stud Teacher
Anderson, Carmon Yvette-Bell
Algebra & Pre-Algebra Teacher
Bahm, Karl Franklin
Assistant Professor of History
Barner, Sandra L.
Math & Algebra I Teacher
Barthelme, Steven T.
Assoc Prof of English
Bates, Lucy Sharp
Assistant Professor of Nursing
Berry, Virginia S.
Speech & Hearing Sci Asst Prof
Bivins, John
Associate Professor of Music
Bosarge, Jane Kaden
Pre-Kindergarten Teacher
Bower, Janie Pittman
Jr HS Math Teacher
Boyd, Bettee Gandy
Director of Stdnt Tchng & Eng
Burkett, Vanneta Thompson
Fourth Grade Teacher
Cameron, Sandra Kay
Cooperative Education Teacher
Carpenter, Lucretia Brown
Science Teacher
Caston, Vicki Humphries
French Teacher
Chestnut, Allison Carol
Associate Professor of English
Coleman, Mary Pepper
9th Grade English Teacher
Cooley, Orville Forrest
Science Teacher
Cothen, Joe H.
Distngd Lecturer Biblical Stud
D'Arpa, Josephine A.
Associate Professor of Voice
Dickerson, Gale Sanders
Interior Design Associate Prof
Drummond, Jan Lee
Exercise Science Asst Prof
Elakovich, Stella Daisy
Chem & Biochemistry Dept Prof
Erickson, Keith Vincent
Chair & Prof of Speech Comm
Foster, Rene Wilford
5th & 6th Grd Lang Arts Tchr
Friedrich, Sharon Elizabeth, MSC
Principal
Gonzales, John Edmond
Emeritus Professor of History
Graham-Kresge, Susan
Community Health Instructor
Green, Frederick Paul
Asst Prof of Human Perf & Rec
Green Lee, Marsha Ann
Fourth Grade Math & Sci Tchr
Gupton, Sandra Lee
Assoc Prof, Educl Ldrshp Rsrch
Hamwi, Alex S.
Prof of Risk Mgmt & Insurance
Harris, Eleanor Liddell
Business Education Teacher
Harrison, Elizabeth Pittman
High School Mathematics Tchr
Herron, Sherry S.
Biology Laboratory Instr & Mgr
Hopkins, Bettye Jean (Lloyd)
Amer Govt & Applied Ec Teacher
Hubble, Susan Marie
Associate Prof of Recreation
Klinedinst, Mark Allan
Assoc Professor of Economics
Loncar, Miroslav
Guitar Professor
Lux, Mary Frances
Asst Prof of Clncl Microbiolgy
Martin, Fran R.
Family Nurse Practitioner
Mc Craw, Connie DeLong
Physics, Astronomy & Math Tchr
Mc Crory, Brian Ray
Art Teacher
Mc Daniel, Linda M.
Eng Tchr & Coord of the Gifted
Miller, Verna Ventress
Third Grade Teacher
Norris, Donald E.
Prof of Biological Sciences

HATTIESBURG (cont)
Owens, Katharine D.
Teaching Asst & Doctoral Stu
Richmond, Beth A.
Professor of Education
Rose, Ted Charles
Chairman of Art Department
Seyfarth, Benjamin Rayborn
Computer Science Professor
Sullivan, Aleta
Science Teacher
Sullivan, Ann Martin
Science Dept Chair
Swetman, GLenn Robert
Writer-in-Residence
Turner, Robert Waldo
Sociology Instructor
Waltman, Jerold Lloyd
Professor of Political Science
Weinauer, Ellen Mary
English Professor
Welch, Suzie
Mathematics Teacher
Whitecotton, Jerri Hatten
Social Studies Teacher
HAZLEHURST
Ashley, Janie Carole
Reading Teacher
Furnace, Judy Ann
Biology & Chemistry Teacher
Lewis, Cheryll Mc Clellan
Spanish & French Teacher
Littlejohn, John Thomas
8th-9th Grd English Teacher
Minor, Ida Peavie
Advanced Biology Teacher
HEIDELBERG
Ducksworth, Edna Broomfield
Third Grade Teacher
Johnson, Willie Jones
3rd Grade Teacher Assistant
Lowery, Davi Carlton
English Teacher
Mark, Artis, Jr.
Teacher & Coach
Prine, Angela Creel
English & Oral Commnctn Tchr
Windham, Cheryl Holifield
English Teacher
HERNANDO
Ferguson, Beth Butler
Language Arts Teacher
Haynes, Barbara Ann
English Teacher & Drama Tchr
HICKORY FLAT
Bennett, Kathy Thompson
Sixth Grade Teacher
Massengill, Belinda Barber
Science Teacher
HOLLY SPRINGS
Arafat, Elsayed S.
Division Chm & Chemistry Prof
Bost, Aileen A.
Math, Soc Stud & Rdng Tchr
Crain, Carey Rather
Science Teacher
Devore, Colet
Business Teacher
Johnson, Lillian
First Grade Teacher
LeSueur, Annetta Turner
English Teacher
Wells, Ila A.
English Professor
Williams, Julia Elizabeth
US History Teacher
HORN LAKE
Ferguson, James Myers, II
Math Teacher & Baseball Coach
Jolley, James Blake
Band Director
Mc Kinney, Rhonda L.
Biology Teacher & Coach
Mitchell, Jessica Jean
Mathematics Teacher
Nadgauda, Bridget
Spanish Teacher
Reid, Bonnie Manning
AP English Teacher
Riffe, Carolyn Payne
Preschool Teacher
Rodgers, Wanda Clois (Wilkinson)
Art Teacher
HOULKA
Easley, Carol Barnette
English Teacher
Luke, James Frank
Biology, Chem & Jrnlsm Tchr
HOUSTON
Chisolm, Cara Verell
Social Studies Teacher
Dallas, Rebecca (Langley)
Business Teacher
Furr, Annette E.
Teacher of Gifted & Talented
HURLEY
Anderson, Janice L. Smith
Biology Teacher
Baria, Jan H.
High School Counselor
Hollinghead, Brenda Barton
English Teacher
Long, Kelly L. Robinson
Govt, Economics & History Tchr
Morgan, Phillis M.
English Teacher
Watts, Hollie Jean
Algebra I & Pre-Algebra Tchr

INDEPENDENCE
Bowlin, Benjamin Franklin, Jr.
Biology Teacher & Ftbl Coach
INDIANOLA
Baird, Lucinda Roberts
History Teacher
Brindley, Mary Ruth
English Teacher
Brock, Doris Wilson
English Instructor
Calhoun, Hubert Eddye
World History Teacher & Coach
Cartlidge, Mildred Carter
7th-8th Grade English Teacher
Crespino, Joseph Hardin
11th Grade US History Teacher
Crigler, Sammie Wash
English IV Teacher
Gary, Toni Berryhill
Counselor
Hodges, Carrie C.
English Teacher
Jones, Barbara Stapleton
Assistant Principal
Kennedy, Linda Moffett
Mathematics Teacher
Lee, Annie L.
Retired Classroom Teacher
Richardson, Doris Hearon
Music Teacher
Riley, Roy Lanair, Jr.
Social Studies Teacher
Sims, Bettye A.
English Teacher
Spurlock, Patsy Hayes
Admin Asst & 7th Grd Tchr
Tabb, Vicki Clark
Mathematics Teacher
Tillman, Geraldine
6th & 7th Grade Reading Tchr
White, Tommie, Jr.
US History Teacher
ITTA BENA
Durham-Lacy, Lucille
Asst Professor of Social Work
Ero, Morgan Zan
Political Science Professor
Hicks, Anna L. I.
Assistant Professor of English
Hill, Mandy Williams
Math Teacher & Dept Chair
Hodge, Sheldon
Football Coach & Phys Ed Instr
Ikenga, Julius Obi
Asst Professor of Biology
Lee, Tazinski Patriece
Instructor of Criminal Justice
Lemon, Dianne Williams
Assistant Professor of Bus
Maxwell, Richard A.
Associate Professor
Moss, Orlando, Sr.
Coordinator of Vocal Studies
Ollie, Charles Tucker
English Department Chairman
Peaches, Barbara Baxter
English Teacher
Roundtree-Mc Coy, Joyce
University Counselor & Instr
Shores, James William
Prof of Criminal Justice
Singh, Elen Sakshaug
Prof & Coord of Pol Sci Pgm
Sitton, Jim
Educational Psychology Instr
Stewart, Maxine Perryman
Asst Professor of English
Thomas, Curlew O'Sullivan
Social Science Chprsn
Turk, Esin C.
Assistant Professor of Comm
Vaughn, Gwendolyn Annette
Instructor of Physical Ed
Washington, Barbara J. Powell
Eng Tchr & Honors Prgm Dir
Williams, Raymond
Professor of Cmptr Sci & Math
IUKA
Barlow, Jean Akins
Fourth Grade Teacher
Brown, Nancy Hartley
Mathematics Teacher
Haines, Mary D. D.
8th Grade English Teacher
Mc Clung, Dianne Dean
Fifth Grd Teacher
Pharr, Cindy Jones
Teacher of the Gifted
Rutledge, Suzanne Kelley
Mathematics Teacher
Smith, Corrine Rutherford
Biology & Phys Sci Teacher
Wallace, Kathy Shook
Computer & Business Teacher
JACKSON
Aeschliman, Terry Gene
US History Teacher
Albright, Billy Jade
Civics & History Teacher
Allen, Patricia Gail
Second Grade Teacher
Ball, Dee Cooper
Govt, History & AP Teacher
Barlow, J. B.
High School History Teacher
Barnett, Rebecca
Retired English Teacher
Beason, Mary Jane
Mathematics Teacher

Bishop, Loraine K.
History Teacher
Blakely, Clyde Henry
JROTC Instructor
Blue, Linda Patterson
Pre-Algebra Teacher
Bounds, Renee Parker
Economics & US History Tchr
Bradley, Charles Isaac
Band Director
Branning, Margaret Carol Crockett
Social Studies Dept Chairman
Brohough, Dana Mc Alpin
Jr High Science & Biology Tchr
Brooks, Jean Evelyn (Dingwall)
Assistant Prof of Soc Work
Brown, Christine
English Teacher
Campbell, Leon
Algebra I & II Teacher
Christopher, Clyde
Associate Prof of Computer Sci
Clark, Janis Durr
4th Grade Teacher
Clayton, Vashti Moore
Reading Recovery Teacher
Coker, Frances Heidelberg
Assoc Professor of Sociology
Cora, Spiro Pete
World History Teacher
Cornelius, Willie Jean
Geography Teacher
Creel, Sue Cloer
Eng & Creative Writing Teacher
Currid, John D.
Professor of Old Testament
Dedeaux, Marilyn G.
Accounting Teacher
Dungee, Darlene Washington
Associate Prof of Hlth & PE
Edon, E. Maxine
AP Calculus Instructor
Falco, Nikki Raye
English & Spanish Teacher
Farley, Jerry Michael
Professor
Foster, David Lee
Adjunct Instructor
Ganzerla, Michael C. (Lyde)
Art & Social Studies Teacher
Gaston, Ardella DeMyers
Biology Instructor
Gibson, Fredna Hudgins
Art Teacher
Gibson, Gina Mayfield
Algebra I Teacher
Gibson, Jerry L.
Social Studies Teacher
Graham, Nancy Bryan Meek
Honors Amer Lit Tchr
Guin, Irma Lollar
Retired Fifth & Sixth Grd Tchr
Hackman, Kenneth A.
AP & Honors Biology Teacher
Hale, Jerry L.
Soc Studies Tchr & Ftbl Coach
Hansford, Lucy A.
Teacher of the Gifted
Harvey, Maria Luisa Alvarez
Dean, Prof of Modern Frgn Lang
Hildebrand, Jane Taylor
Second Grade Teacher
Hill, Linda M.
Associate Professor of English
Hinton, Bonita Jackson
Biology Teacher
Hodges, Cheri Leninger
Math Teacher & Dept Chprsn
Hogan, Janice Susan Hughey
Math & Journalism Teacher
Holcomb, Elizabeth Turner
English Teacher
Howard-Reeves, Katrina F.
Spanish Teacher
Johnson, Jim H.
US Govt & Economics Teacher
Johnson, T. J., Jr.
Retired Science Teacher
Jones, Dianne Sigrest
Team Ldr & 7th Grd Eng Tchr
Jones, Ollie Faye (Mc Nair)
Fifth Grade Teacher
King, Rebecca Presley
High School English Teacher
Krolls, Sigurds O.
Chm & Prof Diagnostic Sci
Kursar, Valerie J.
Mathematics Teacher
List, Robert N.
Assoc Prof Eng & Mass Cmmnctn
Lollar, Linda B.
English & Speech Teacher
Loyacono, Rita Rudi
Span Tchr, Frgn Lang Dept Head
Mac Dowell, Kathryn C.
French Teacher
Martin, Barbria Haynes
6th Grade Teacher
McGee, Stephanie Stewart
Secondary English Teacher
McKay, Sandra K.
10th Grade English Teacher
McKnight, Sue Roberts
Sixth Grade Teacher
Mc Neece, Linda Jean
Algebra II Teacher
Miller, L. Wayne
Band Director
Milton, Alice Tyler
Business & Computer Tech Tchr

Mohamed, Iely Burkhead
Associate Professor of English
Moore, Michael Clarence
Physics & Chemistry Teacher
Moore, Twyla Boudreaux
Oral Comm & Journalism Teacher
Morrow, John Alex
Chemistry Teacher
Naylor, Bobbi S.
French Teacher
Neely, Barbara Busby
Science Department Chair
Nelson, Connie W.
Counselor
Noyes, Deanna Kuiper
Grad Assistant Professor
Owens, Jody E.
Teacher
Pan, Yi-Chuan
Professor of Mathematics
Park, James W.
Division of Business Admin Chm
Perkins, Rachel Thompson
Occupational Child Care Tchr
Perry, Wesley Frank
Education Director
Pickle, Jan Hammack
English Teacher
Price, Shirley A. Haynes
French Teacher
Richards, Arthur E., III
Advanced Geography Teacher
Richardson, Jeffrey Brian
World Geog Tchr & Bsbl Coach
Robinson, Patrick D.
Guidance Counselor
Ross, Susan Jordan
Senior Guidance Counselor
Sallis, Harrylyn Graves
Dean for Adult Learning
Scott, Ann W.
Fifth Grade Teacher
Self, Pamela Smith
9th-12th Grade Math Teacher
Sims, Preston Kendrick, Jr.
Mississippi Studies Teacher
Sims, Robert Dickson
Choral Director
Snyder, Brenda Hamill
Fourth Grade Teacher
Stelts, Beverly Self
Third Grade Teacher
Stroup, Susan Lynn
Fourth Grade Teacher
Stuart, Joyce Kelly
Occupational Child Care Tchr
Sullivan, Betsy Ann
Former Science Teacher
Tabb, Wanda Tew
K-5th Grade Teacher
Taylor, Mary Margaret
Fifth Grade Teacher
Terry, Greta Peyton
Principal
Tharp, Sidney Robert
Mathematics & Science Teacher
Thomas, Ada Chambers
US History & Economic Teacher
Tinnin, Janet Alexander
Mathematics Teacher
Turner, Teresa A.
Biology Teacher
Vaughn, Marlys T.
Professor & Dir of Stu Tchng
Waibel, Paul Richard
Assoc Prof of History
Walker, Annie Pearl
Fifth Grade Teacher
Walker, Windey Morrow
Science Teacher
Wallace, Gina Toney
Algebra Teacher
Washington, Arie, Jr.
JROTC Instructor
Washington, George Carver, III
Associate Prof of Biology
West, Barbara Bruce
Mathematics Teacher
Westerfield, Barbara Gregory
Economics Teacher
Westra, Raymond Nelson
Assistant Professor of Biology
White, Carolyn Brock
Sixth Grade Math Teacher
White, Carolyn Caldwell
Social Studies Teacher
Whittington, Jon H., Sr.
Professor of Art & Art History
Williams, Arleen Harrison
Computer & Business Teacher
Wilson, Mary Joyce
Mathematics Teacher
Wodetzki, Margaret Ann
Professor of Chemistry
York, Rice P., Jr.
Assistant Professor
Young, Mary Brown
First Grade Teacher
Young, Stella Robinson
Computer Teacher
KILMICHAEL
Austin, Charles L.
Guidance Director
Harrington, Gladys Goodman
Second Grade Teacher
McGee, Yoko Talmage
Soc Stud Teacher & Dept Chm
Miller, Earnestine Nolan
Business Education Teacher

Ratliff, Lula Eiland
Elem School Teacher
Thigpen, Mary Harvey
Fourth Grade Teacher
KILN
Ferrill, Jennifer Hilton
Mathematics Teacher
Ladner, Gary Lawrence
Government & Economics Tchr
Smith, Nancy F.
Counselor
Weiler, Frances Baird
Curriculum Coordinator
KOSCIUSKO
Boyette, Jeffrey Stone
Speech Pathologist
Mink, Rhonda B.
English Teacher
Pickle, Shelia Griffin
English Teacher
LAKE
Fedrick, Nancy Warren
Kindergarten Teacher
LAUREL
Biglane, Marilyn Blackledge
French Teacher & Dept Chairman
Buckler, Gary V.
Social Studies Teacher
Callahan, Mary Carol Stevens
English Teacher
Carter, Paula Young
Senior English Teacher
Carter, Troy Harold
Music Professor & Spanish Tchr
Compton, Lillian Louise Jordan
6th & 7th Grd English Teacher
Graves, Gary Jackson
Entrepreneurship Teacher
Robinson, Sherry D.
Principal
Rowland, Jeanne Bradford
7th Grade English Teacher
Simpson, Carole Ann
6th-7th Grd Soc Studies Tchr
Stennett, Kathy Bryant
6th Grade Teacher
Thatch, Brenda Pettigrew
10th Grade English Teacher
LEAKESVILLE
Brewer, Margaret Forsyth
Business & Computer Tech Tchr
Byrd, Dianna James
English Teacher & Annual Spon
Cobb, Margaret Hensarling
Lang Arts Dept Chr & Eng Tchr
Hough Williams, Mary Johnson
Family & Consumer Instructor
Webster, Marie Ryan
Library-Media Specialist
LELAND
Buckhaulter, Norma McIntosh
Sixth Grade Teacher
Lowe, Addie Morris
First Grade Teacher
Tucker, Nannie Hamilton
Multi Level Teacher
Wright, Velma Smith
Third Grade Teacher
LEXINGTON
Eiland, Carl
Science Teacher
Evans, Mattie Harris
High School Principal
LIBERTY
Harvey, Esther H.
ADM Assistant
Kreel, Nicholas Edward
JROTC Senior Army Instructor
Mabry, Joyce Jones
English Teacher
Scott, Johnny Marvin
Math Teacher
LONG BEACH
Bremenkamp, Douglas
US History Teacher & Coach
Chatham, Muzette Howard
English Teacher
French, Marcia Randall
11th & 12th Grade English Tchr
Haynes, Janet Roberts
Eighth Grade Reading Teacher
Kayes, Christine Harris
Chemistry & Physics Teacher
Lichtenberg, Josephine Mercer
Phys Science Tchr & Dept Chair
Martinez, Rosalyn Parker
Sixth Grade English Teacher
Matheny, Linda H.
Gifted Class Teacher
Matthews, Carolyn Perry
English Teacher
Mc Intyre, Anna Landon
Math Teacher
Paola, Carol Western
Teacher of the Gifted
Pike, J. B.
Principal
Rath, Patricia Ann
Science Teacher
Symmes, Laurie Dukes
7th Grade Teacher
Taquino, George E.
Guidance Counselor
Tincher, Jean Hagerty O'Neill
K-3 Special Ed Teacher
Ward, Vivian Lee
Oral Communication Teacher
Warner, Dorothy Susan
Teacher & Student Council Adv

AN
June Deloris
Prof of Food & Nutrition
Bernard
ssor of Politcal Science
Mary Ann Carter
ng Instructor
, Abram Henderson, Jr.
ssor of Biology
l, Darryl V.
of Biological Sciences
Kimberly Welch
Prof, Baccalaureate Nrsng
Joscelyn Ayodele
Prof of Math & Sci
e, Festus Sunday
ess Administration Prof
n, Alvin Tyrone
Prof of Psychology
Suresh Chandra
ssor of Agriculture
, Chunmun
ctor of Mathematics
ba, Benny Anigbogu
of Finance & Bus Admin
ba, Elizabeth Icheke
ematics Instructor
Kathleen Graham
of Bus Education & Mgmt
VILLE
Helen Wray
er Occupations Coord
Diane Taylor
School Math Teacher
, Julia Yarbrough
rade English Teacher
, Brenda Shamburger
istry Teacher & Dept Chair
, Linda Norfleet
h Grade English Teacher
l, Marcus Dee
l Studies Teacher
Carolyn Goss
d Grade Teacher
DALE
, Larry
ctor
Patricia Bryan
rade Social Studies Tchr
Larry Lavon
C Instructor
hern, Marie W.
ergarten Teacher
, Julia Mitchell
overnment & Economics Tchr
O. Michael
l Studies Teacher
Kathy Miller
h Grade Science Teacher
ERTON
Kenneth D., Jr.
Math, Chem & Physics Tchr
y, Jean S.
Specialist & Math Tchr
Kerrie Cowser
& Computer Teacher
son, Robert Bruce
Principal & History Tchr
N
, Barbara Bland
ce Teacher
N
, Pam L.
Grade Teacher
, Robert Lewis, Jr.
& 12th Grd Soc Stud Tchr
Robert Edward
h Grade Teacher
, Travis
ol Counselor
, Mildred Tate
rade Reading Teacher
Willie Smith
ess Technology Teacher
Ellsworth
l Studies Teacher
, Glenda F. Evans
er I Mathematics Teacher
, Carmen Kenagy
ergarten Teacher
ns, Sam
& Pre-Algebra Teacher
EN
Beth Freeny
h Grade Teacher
Judy Wallace
sh Teacher
d, Joe Philip
Math Tchr & Coach
SON
Donna Clarke
Department Chairman
l, Jillian Anthony
Grade Written Comm Tchr
s, Karen Dillon
Teacher
an, Leslie Robinson
d & US History Tchr
gton, Diana Gardner
Grade Math Teacher
Donna C.
r Counselor
, Patricia Allen
Grade English Teacher
Norma Carroll
l Grade Teacher
, Michael Evans
space Science Instructor
ood, Linda Hammett
ch Teacher

Isbell, Laura Gallagher
Commntn, Drama & Hnrs Eng Tchr
Kelley, Joan Doolittle
Tchr of Learning Disabilities
Little, Lonetta Wells
10th Grade Honors English Tchr
McKenzie, Loyce Cain
English Teacher
Miller, Deborah M.
7th Grade Science Teacher
Nolen, Rebecca
Anatomy & Physiology Teacher
Partridge, Leonard F.
Spanish Teacher
Rattler, Ethel Neal
Counselor
Robinson, Louella
World History Teacher
Smith, Gaye Gough
7th Grade Math Teacher
White, David L., Jr.
Director of Bands
Winkler, Bradley Mason
American History Teacher

MAGEE
Austin, Nan Swain
English Teacher
Floyd, Carol Yelverton
7th Grade English Teacher
Funchess, Charles Emmitt
Social Studies Teacher
Hayes, Esther Elaine
Kindergarten Teacher
Mangum, William Estus, Jr.
Voc-Ag Instructor
Meador, Tawesia Brooks
Teacher of the Gifted
Reed, Gloria Hughes
Second Grade Teacher
Sullivan, Deborah Barrett
7th & 8th Grd Math Tchr
Wendt, Dick Alan
Physics & Chemistry Teacher

MAGNOLIA
Dykes, Janet Janes
First Grade Teacher
Mallette, Barbara Felder
Retired Mathematics Teacher
Matthew, Janet Hayes
4th Grade Teacher
Mitchell, Alice Rhea
Teacher & Curriculum Coord
Paredes, Luis F.
Spanish Teacher
Pollan, Cecil Barrett
English & Drama Teacher

MANTACHIE
Gholston, Barbara Cromeans
First Grade Teacher
Gholston, Ronnie Wayne
Second Grade Teacher
Lollar, Kathy Wesson
English I and II Teacher
Painter, Bobby Rayvon, Jr.
11th-12th Grd English Teacher
Stembridge, Betty Yielding
Third Grade Teacher
Turner, Sarah Hill
Fourth Grade Teacher

MATHISTON
Echols, Jeffrey Milton
Biological Sciences Instructor

MAYHEW
Shaw, Ellen Poag
Tech Prep Coordinator

MC ADAMS
Moore, Bertha Carson
English Teacher

MC COMB
Bramlett, Judith Stevens
English Teacher
Burris, Lewis E., Jr.
Diversified Technology Teacher
Carruth, Jo Ann Cleveland
Bus Computer Tech Teacher
Coltrin, Wilda Cockerham
Retired Elementary Teacher
Holbrook, Helen Andrews
Retired Mathematics Teacher
Hutchison, Betsy W.
10th & 12th Grd English Tchr
Jones, Ida Simmons
Amer History, Eco & Govt Tchr
Kent, Christopher Eugene
Algebra I Teacher
Pannell, William Truett
8th Grd Amer His Teacher
Randall, Cherrie Barron
English Teacher
Simmons, Barbara Brent
English & Speech Teacher

MEADVILLE
Archie, Bernice Spiers
Third Grade Teacher
Scarbrough, Lugenia R.
Teacher of the Gifted
Smith, Mary Ann Malone
Health & Home Economics Tchr
Thompson, Mary Ross
Elementary School Teacher
Tillman, Carol Smith
Science Teacher

MENDENHALL
Dear, Linda Ann
Science & History Teacher
Magee, Betty L.
Spanish & English Teacher
Neely, Betty Lynn
Home Economics Tchr, Counselor

Redding, Paul Douglas
Mathematics Teacher

MERIDIAN
Abdella, Edward Samuel
History Teacher
Ammon, Sue Mc Alister
English Teacher
Arledge, Linda Taylor
Teacher of the Gifted
Baxter, Kathy Harmon
Pol Sci Professor & Acad Dean
Beckman, Jean Early
Academic Counselor
Berry, Laura Garren
Speech & Forensic Instructor
Burns, Annie Brown
English Instructor
Calderon, Beth Carver
Spanish Teacher
Crawford, Jim
Chemistry Teacher
Davidson, Nelda Mosley
Marketing Teacher
Davis, Betty Williamson
Nursing Instructor
Davis, Ray Prince
Mathematics Instructor
Dreyfus, Sylvia Williams
Mathematics Instructor
Etheridge, Virginia Hagwood
Tenth Grade English Teacher
Farmer, Terrie Lynn
Fourth Grade Teacher
Gambill, Hugh Thomas
Tchr of the Talented & Gifted
Gilmore, Melanie Laird
Nursing Instructor
Havard, Jeanne Spratlin
Business & Office Tech Instr
Hubbard, Dennetta Prentice
Fourth Grade Teacher
Hyche, Laura W.
11th Grd English & Jrnlsm Tchr
Ivy, Sabina Kay
Band Director
Ivy, Terry Dewayne
Band Director
Jones, Dale Harper
Biology Teacher
Lewis, Carole Hannah
Govt, Ec & Law Teacher
Matlock, Belinda Mc kee
Sci Tchr of Talented & Gifted
Mc Neal, Dorothy K.
Teacher
Michael, Liz Garner
English Teacher
Moore, John Wesley, IV
Band Director
Murphey, Jeannette Windham
Psychology Instructor
Naylor, Vivian Dixon
English Instructor
Nicholson, Margaret Lee
English Teacher
Parker, Cathy Dianne
Mathematics Teacher
Pouncey, Steve Collins
History Teacher
Price, Ingrid
Anatomy & Physiology Teacher
Rahaim, Rodgers
Government & Economics Teacher
Raymond, Alan Louis
International Coordinator
Risher, Ben F., Jr.
12th Grade English Teacher
Roberson, Bebe Hayden
5th & 6th Grd Soc Stud Tchr
Robinson, Kathy Gower
Dental Hygiene Instructor
Smith, Jan Reed
Cooperative Education Coord
Stokes, Deborah Bourrage
Assoc Degree Nrsng Prgm Coord
Tinsley, Glenda R.
Assoc Degree Nursing Instr
Webb, Cathy Tarver
Dir of Applied Learning Prgm
Webb, Peggy Maxey
Business Technology Instructor
Weir, ShaLayne Thompson
Science Teacher

MISSISSIPPI STATE
Abraham, Jimmy Wayne
Assoc Dean of Student Services
Binkley, Mark S.
Professor
Boling, Robert B.
Associate Professor of Health
Champlin, Franklin Ross
Assoc Prof of Microbiology
Flick, Hank Albert
Professor of Communication
Forde, John E.
Asst Prof of Communication

MIZE
Pruitt, Pamela Roberts
Sixth Grade Teacher

MONTICELLO
Dykes, Jane B.
Guidance Counselor
Ochenrider, James Larry
Chemistry & Physics Teacher
Polk, Rebecca D.
Eng & Intro Fine Arts Teacher
Stewart, Charlie Edward
Head Teacher
Sykes, Richard Terrell
Seventh Grade English Teacher

Tripp, Ruth Schooling
English Teacher

MOOREVILLE
Parham, Kathryn Langley
Fifth Grade Teacher
Pickens, Marie Chapman
Business Education Teacher
Rupert, E. Carol (Lummus)
English Creative Tchr
Stembridge, Jan Sheffield
Algebra II, Geo & Trig Tchr
Tally, Jeff L.
Health & PE Teacher
Tally, Lisa Merritt
Math Teacher

MOORHEAD
Abraham, Mary Magdalene
Anatomy, Physiology, Bio Instr
Ammons, John Fleet
Science Teacher
Bennett, Yvonne Smithhart
Language Arts Instructor
Brocato, Jacqueline Johnson
Medical Laboratory Tech Instr
Corley, Barry James
Agricultural Technology Instr
Davis, George Thomas, Jr.
Science Instructor
Free, Jimmy H.
Computer Programming Instr
Jones, Sherilyn Morris
Instructor of Sociology
Mc Cormick, Barbara Dupuy
English Instructor
Moore, Sandra Hobbs
Lang Arts Dept Chair & Instr
Sims, Margaret Church
English Professor
Strawbridge, James Robert
Chemistry Instructor
Webster, Theresa Gaines
Computer Science Instructor

MORTON
Barnes, Marsha Livingston
English & Speech Teacher
Lathem, Skip J.
Principal
Lovett, Teresa Smith
Third Grade Teacher

MOSELLE
Crosby, Terry Elaine (Fay)
Sixth Grade Teacher

MOSS POINT
Adams, Franklin John
Band Director
Burton, Margie Riley
Guidance Counselor
DeShields, Inez P.
Math Teacher & Dept Chair
Everett, Jackie Comeaux
Educl Talent Search Counselor
Street, Ada Abney
Marketing Coop Instructor
Wood, Rebecca Jolly
Restaurant Management Instr

MOUND BAYOU
Lloyd, Navie Irene
Algebra Teacher
Peterson, Carlene Tate
English & Written Comm Tchr
Sutton, Rose Merry (Gardner)
First Grade Teacher

MYRTLE
Craig, Janie Willard
Sixth Grade Teacher

NATCHEZ
Biglane, Jean Nosser
English Dept Chairperson
Daly, Astrid Gerry
Biology Teacher
DiNardo, Rita Joyce J.
Music Coord & Dir of Rel Ed
Edney, Lillian Clark
Biology & Chemistry Teacher
Falkenheiner, Phyllis Grant
1st Grade Teacher
Greene, Shirley A.
Computer Education Teacher
Hall, Mealnie Pintard
Physical Ed Tchr & Coach
Hinton, Jo (Moore)
Marketing Instructor
Johnson, Sue Laverne
PE Teacher & Coach
Kubera, Mary Beth
High School English Teacher
Lanier, Phyllis Hayes
Sci Dept Chprsn & Chem Instr
Lessley, Mary Berryhill
Bus Cmptr Tech I & II Instr
Madden, Kathy Cavin
Food Production Teacher
Murphy, Vounzell Causey
English Teacher
Nevill, Becky J.
Hotel & Rest Mgmt Tech Instr
Oliver, Georgia Collins
HS Social Studies Teacher
Rambin, Alice G.
7th-8th Grade Math Teacher
Reynolds, Sally M.
English Teacher
Smith, Evelyn Henry
Assistant Principal
Smith, Susan Gammill
Business Education Teacher
Terrell, Flora Green
Social Studies Teacher
Washington, Sandra Johnson
5th Grade Teacher

Williams, Brenda Hale
Spanish Tchr & Yearbook Adv

NETTLETON
Adams, Sharon Roberts
First Grade Teacher
Clayton, Kim Smith
High School Math Teacher
Hairald, Mary Payne
Cooperative Ed Tchr & Coord
Hill, Mary Mullins
English & French Teacher
Jones, Wanda C.
Biology Teacher
Rogers, Nan Coggin
Retired 4th Grade English Tchr
Welford, Betty Bailey
English Teacher

NEW ALBANY
Benjamin, Timothy M.
Superintendent of Education
Brownlee, Norma Watson
Business & Computer Tech Instr
Cook, Sarah W.
French & English Teacher
Eubanks, Billy
Band Director
Frazier, Tom
Biology Instructor
Goolsby, Judy Jackson
Teacher
Herrington, Tounia Swords
Science Teacher
Kimmons, Varnell Ford
Librarian & Media Specialist
Ratliff, Catherine Leigh
Biology Teacher
Tate, Diane Stroud
Creative Art Tchr of Gifted

NEW AUGUSTA
McCardle, Martha Ann
Secondary Science Teacher
Parkinson, Brenda Joyce
English Teacher

NEW SITE
Carroll, Ruth Evans
Family & Consumer Science Tchr
Miller, Karen Ruff
HS Science Teacher

NOXAPATER
Hudson, Mark Allan
Vocational Agriculture Tchr

OCEAN SPRINGS
Alderman, Carol Newton
Assistant Principal
Arender, Nina McDaniel
Sixth Grade Science Teacher
Blair, Stephanie Sison
Mathematics Teacher
Boswell, Melinda Phillips
Fifth Grade Teacher
Breland, G. Terry, Jr.
US History Teacher
Brune, Sally Lyttle
10th Grade English Teacher
Cacibauda, Joseph Anthony, Jr.
Fine Arts Dept Chairman
Crawford, Jean D.
Math Dept Chairperson
Ferrell, Bobby
Teacher
Hayes, Charlotte Davis
Bio, Anatomy & Physiology Tchr
Newby, Shirley
Band Director
Paslay, Jane Ann Burchfield
Chemistry Teacher
Payne, Rose Graham
Fifth Grade Teacher
Peresich, Mark Lee
US Government & Economics Tchr
Rich, Bettie C.
Retired Teacher
Sawyer, Mary Simmons
Choral Director
Stietenroth, Anne Carolyn (Berger)
French Teacher
Taylor, James K.
High Schl Social Studies Tchr
Wages, Mary Dene Sims
Third Grade Teacher

OKOLONA
Head, Juanita Buchanan
US His, Govt & Ec Teacher
Johnson, Zettie Moore
Guidance Counselor
Whitt, Elizabeth Diane Wilson
7th Grd Math & Science Teacher

OLIVE BRANCH
Cothren, Sharon Finch
Mathematics Teacher
Garrard, Diane Strange
10th-11th Grd English Teacher
Garrett, Brenda Higginbotham
5th Grade Teacher
Jamison, Cheryl Elder
6th Grade Math Teacher
Martin, Kelly F.
Social Studies Teacher
Mc Gee, Catharine Handlin
7th & 8th Grade Teacher
Neely, Norma
1st Grade Teacher
Stephenson, Martha Jackson
English Teacher
Wilson, William Andrew
History Teacher

OXFORD
Babb, Rebekah Beeler
Teacher of the Gifted Ed

OXFORD (cont)
Benson, Mary Them
Mathematics Teacher
Bryant, Georgia Patton
4th Grade Teacher
Cade, Ed
Asst Aerospace Science Instr
Collins, Linda Webb
6th-8th Grd Teacher of Gifted
Everett, Gabriella Marie
History Teacher
Howell, Frances Fletcher
Physical Education Teacher
Knight, Aubrey Kevin
Electronics Instructor
Lacy, Sarah Trotman
Advanced Placement Bio Teacher
Mixon, John Barry
High School Band Director
Murchison, Margaret Lynne
Advanced Placement Eng Teacher
Partridge, Linda Golden
5th Grade Teacher
Ramsey, Joan Mc Minn
Art Instructor
Schoenly, Victoria Arnold
Latin & Gifted Ed Teacher
Slate, Flora Johnson
Sixth Grade Reading Teacher
Thomas, Peggy W.
English Teacher
Webb, Diane Huckaby
Family Science Teacher
Whitwell, Martha Veazey
Chemistry & Physics Teacher
PASCAGOULA
Ball, Gerald Lee
District Music Coordinator
Booker, Sheila Clark
7th & 8th Grd English Teacher
Ellmer, Patricia Mallard
Remedial Instructor
Goldman, Darryl James
Diversified Technology Teacher
Masch, Barbara
English Teacher
McCormick, Susan Cumbest
Music Teacher
Merrill, Richard Timothy
Math Teacher & Coach
Moak, Rex R.
Chemistry Teacher
Sones, Phoebe Cary
Biology Teacher
Turner, Earl E.
Director of Bands
Turner, Natalie Welborn
Geography & Government Teacher
PASS CHRISTIAN
Callender, Karen Fuller
Career Center Technician
Herbert, Bill Joseph, Jr.
Science Instructor
HoughtalING, Bruce Hannum
Headmaster
Jordan, Linda M.
French & AP English Teacher
Mackay, David M.
Teacher & Coach
Necaise, Linda Love
First Grade Teacher
Ramsey, Michael Warren
Chem, Physics Instr & Dept Chm
Taylor, Madelyn Osborne
English Teacher
PEARL
Arledge, Ginger Nix
Chemistry Professor
Barnett, Woody
Biology Teacher
Blanchard, Alicen Anders
English Teacher
Butler, Sandra Kaiser
Asst Special Education Dir
Coleman, Lisa Renee
Social Studies Teacher
Cooper, Robert E.
Retired English Teacher
Lee, Dianne Woods
Spanish Teacher
Long, Eleanor Mashburn
History Professor
Neal, Valerie Hamilton
English Teacher
Nokes, Bert, III
9th-12th Grd History Teacher
Peacock, Sally Smith
Nutrition Instructor
Rogers, Patricia Dianne
4th Grade Teacher
Sansing, David G., Jr.
Social Studies Teacher
West, Randy C.
Biology Teacher & Ftbl Coach
Wise, Charles Hamilton
Department of Biology Chairman
Wood, Celia Farr
English Professor
PELAHATCHIE
Duvall, Jeffrey N.
History Teacher & Ftbl Coach
Flowers, Pearson F.
High School ROTC Instructor
PERKINSTON
Anderson, Brenda S.
Science Instructor
Batey, Brenda A.
Spanish Instructor
Hendry, Kathy Moran
Instructor

Jones, Pamela R. B.
Instructor of Child Dev Tech
Lee, Earl S.
English Instructor
Lewis, Jon Richard
Honors College Director
Mann, Noel Russell
Chemistry Instructor
Moody, Janet Gail
Science Instructor
Nalepa, Brenda Ragan
Professor of Biology
O'Neal, Barbara L.
Math & Computer Science Prof
Smith, Marilyn Porter
Choral Director
PETAL
Boler, Barry Kemp
Environmental Science Teacher
Brown, Christine Husband
English Teacher
Johnson, Ivette A.
English & Speech Teacher
Silkman, Brenda Draughn
English Teacher
PHEBA
Dobbs, Linda Boydston
Mathematics Teacher
Rogers, Earlean Smith
9th-11th Grade Math Teacher
PHILADELPHIA
Boler, Tanya Hillman
English Teacher
Bush, Sharmane Floore
English & Reading Teacher
Comby, Diane Malerich
Elementary Music Teacher
Cortines, Carolyn Chamblin
English Teacher
Jones, Jerry C.
History Teacher
Luke, Sue Huff
Retired Public Schl Music Tchr
Myers, Billie Herrington
English Teacher
Myers, D. Glenn
Science Department Chairperson
Pratt, Donald Clifton
Cooperative Education Coord
Shumaker, Frankie Mc Kay
Elementary School Principal
Skinner, Mike
6th Grade Teacher
Smith, Clarice M.
Third Grade Teacher
Thrash, Pamela Hicks
Computer Ed Teacher
Welch, Joe H.
Director of Bands
PICAYUNE
Fowler, April D. Mitchell
Physics Instructor
Griffith, Gail Diane
Mathematics Teacher
Jarvis, Charlotte Rouillier
Allied Health Instructor
Kirkland, L. Kent
Science Teacher & Coach
Shows, Rosemary Gregg
Algebra II & AP Calculus Tchr
Tate, Diane M.
English Teacher
Vaughn, Jacquelyn W.
Language Arts Teacher
Webb, Lisa Ann (Shivers)
Math Teacher
Williams, Mary Catherine
Sixth Grade Teacher
PINEY WOODS
Dampeer, Otis
Mathematics Teacher
Davis, Debra R.
English Teacher
Southers, Robert Lee
JROTC Instructor
PLANTERSVILLE
Wood, Martha Bright
Retired Scndry Eng Teacher
PONTOTOC
Barlow, Sue Laster
Teacher of Gifted & Talented
Hooker, Cristie Duncan
English Teacher
Jackson, Sandra Fulton
History Teacher
Long, Sharon Chittom
First Grade Teacher
McLarty, Michael H.
Band Director
Parks, Patrick Roberts
7th Grade Math Teacher
Williams, Pat Burkhalter
Gifted & Talented Teacher
POPE
Mills, Ann Mc Curdy
Third Grade Teacher
Sullivan, Kathy Benson
First Grade Teacher
POPLARVILLE
Alexander, Mary Addison
Fourth Grade Teacher
Easterling, Teresa Wilkinson
Business Technology Instructor
Grant, John A., Jr.
Instr of Phys, Math & Chair
Hollingsworth, Huelene Davis
English Teacher
McGill, Bobby
Art Teacher

Roberts, Hope Garrett
Diversified Occupations Tchr
Ruegger, Carolyn Maples
Mathematics Instructor
Windham, Brenda Loper
Business Technology Instructor
PORT GIBSON
Goldsberry, Vergia Aikerson
Retired Fourth Grade Teacher
Patten, Cynthia Reynolds
Teacher & Math Dept Chprsn
Reed, Janice Snyder
Chemistry & Physics Teacher
Thompson, Presandra Faye
Secondary Mathematics Teacher
Wilson, Pearl Myers
9th-10th Grade English Tchr
POTTS CAMP
Canerdy, Janice Potts
English Teacher
Mills, Billie Garner
Second Grade Teacher
Taylor, Jane Robbins
Assistant Principal
PRENTISS
Fails-Davis, Theresa Rose
English & Spanish Teacher
Hollingsworth, Sandra Polk
Spanish & English Teacher
Kerley, Margaret A.
Guidance Counselor
PUCKETT
Crawford, Betty Gray
Business Education Teacher
Jones, Jayne B.
Third Grade Teacher
O'Bryan, Jerry Johnson
Mathematics Teacher
Patrick, Margaret Jones
Career Discovery, Dev Rdg Tchr
PURVIS
Boone, Jeff
Agriculture Teacher
Lowe, Nelda Rouse
Mathematics Teacher
Pylant, Sarah Hensleigh
Math Department Chairperson
QUITMAN
Alford, Tammy Perritt
Computer Teacher
Harris, Lynette Herring
Technology Discovery Teacher
Holloman, D'Aunne
MS Stud & Ec Teacher
Ivy, Glynna S.
Fifth Grade Teacher
Mc Arthur, John Erwin
Band Director
McLendon, Jimmy D.
Biology Teacher
Moseley, Lynn
English III Teacher
Smith, Mary Eleanor
Mathematics Teacher
Sorto, Edgar R.
Geometry Teacher & Math Chair
Watkins, Kathy Donald
Computer Lab Teacher
RALEIGH
Thornton, Gwendolyn May
HS Home Economics Teacher
RAYMOND
Brooks, Sue Longest
Public Speaking Instructor
Duren, Paula Rebecca (Lick)
College Fine Art Instructor
Fields, Michael Leon
Physical Ed & Track Coach
Johnston, James Kenneth
Math Professor
Laster, Ann Appleton
English Professor
McCrorey, Charl McLain
English Teacher
Partin, Harry Johnson
Electronics Tech Dept Chair
Thompson, London Johnson
Federal Programs Director
Walker, Wanda Sumrall
Allied Health I & II Teacher
REDWOOD
Hanks, Linda Whitaker
Kindergarten Teacher
RICHLAND
Lara, Teresa Ferguson
Spanish Teacher
Varner, Barbara Smith
Fourth Grade Teacher
RICHTON
Anderson, Sylvia Edwards
2nd-6th Grade Tchr of Gifted
Goar, Lorraine
Fifth Grade Math Teacher
Malone, Liston Len
Junior High Math Teacher
Mc Donald, Betty Jean
5th Grade Teacher
Paige, Pinkie Howze
Mathematics Teacher
Ready, Mary Margaret
Home Economics Teacher
Smith, Annie Junia Walley
Retired Second Grade Teacher
Stennett, Marcus Arlo
Social Studies Dept Chprsn
RIDGELAND
Awad, James E.
Chemistry & Biology Teacher
Crawford, Sadie Magee
Third Grade Teacher

Gressett, William Howard
Microbiology Instructor
Jacobi, Barbara Stansbury
Retired 5th Grade Teacher
Kelly, Jeanne Smith
English Instructor
Luke, Mary Beth Blanchard
Third Grade Teacher
Smith, Ramona Lewis
Psychology Instructor
Stoddard, Diane
Mathematics Instructor
Switzer, John P.
History Instructor
RIPLEY
Akins, Pamela Walker
Health Cluster I & II Instr
Braddock, Rita Clemmer
Fifth Grade English Teacher
Cowan, Roger Lee
Science Teacher
Hill, Gail Henry
3rd & 4th Grade Teacher
Locke, Linda Jean
First Grade Teacher
Marsalis, Chris
Technology Discovery Teacher
Needham, Pamela Graves
Business Cmptr Tech Instr
Vaughan, James Timothy
Amer Govt & Economics Tchr
ROLLING FORK
Bennett, Connie Sue
English Teacher
Jackson, Barbara Davis
English Teacher
ROSEDALE
Hall, Linda Woodruff
Business & Computer Tech Tchr
Scott, George W., Jr.
9th-12th Grd Soc Stud Teacher
Shamblin, Lena Taylor
English III Teacher
RULEVILLE
Miller, Charlis
Business Teacher
SALTILLO
Covington, Charles Andrew
Biblical His & Soc Stud Tchr
Haddon, Helen Christine Cheatham
Third Grade Teacher
SANDHILL
Burge, Mary R.
Business Teacher
Mc Innis, Rosemary
Guidance Counselor
SARAH
Pigues, Dorothy LeSure
English Teacher
SARDIS
Gaines, Bennie Baker
Algebra Teacher
SAUCIER
Gill, Jonie Fore
Sixth Grade Teacher
SCOOBA
Cherry, Wynelia
Business Instructor
Cotton, Nancy Guy
Resource & Lead Title I Tchr
Landrum, Betty Quinn
Practical Nursing Instructor
Simpson, Linda Lindley
4th Grade Teacher
Tindal, Ann Magruder
Communications & Drama Instr
SEMINARY
Parker, Sue Clark
First Grade Teacher
SENATOBIA
Banham, Sandra Rodgers
English Instructor
Barnes, Farris Samuel
Science & Math Teacher & Coach
Bouchillon, Nancy Veazey
Business & Computer Teacher
Brown, Sandra F.
English Teacher
Carroll, Christy B.
Fourth & Fifth Grade Teacher
Champion, Sondra B.
Math Teacher & Dept Chairman
Clemens, Jeptha Clark
Paralegal Studies Professor
Darnell, Nancy Barham
First Grade Teacher
Grisham, Sandra H.
Instructor & Honors Director
Jubb, Carolyn Causey
Adv Eng IV Teacher
Lavender, Mary Melissa
Counselor
Patterson, James R.
Soc Studies Dept Chm & Coach
Poss, David Allan
Teacher & Coach
Reed, Nennie Carter
Second Grade Teacher
Russell, Bill W.
HS Basketball & Football Coach
Storey, Richard E.
US Government & MS Stud Tchr
Taylor, C. Douglas
English Professor
Williamson, Jane Waldrop
Business Teacher
SHANNON
Clay, Martha Jane
English Teacher

Mastin, Lynn Purdom
Science Teacher
Raper, Annette G.
English Teacher
Riley, Gladys Ann
Computer & Business Teacher
SHAW
Leach, John Burell
PE, Health & Drivers Ed Tchr
Towers, Gail Jones
Elementary Principal
SHELBY
Jordan, Hattie Robinson
Social Studies Teacher
Mc Gee, Tommie S.
Business Education Teacher
Morris, DeVoyce Campbell
Special Programs Supervisor
SMITHVILLE
Bowling, Dwight Glen, Sr.
Math Teacher & Head Ftbl Coach
SOUTHAVEN
Bond, Mary D.
6th Grade Teacher
Corey, Peggy Thornton
9th-12th Grd Spec Educ Teacher
Echols, John Lynn
Social Studies Teacher
Huckaby, Bettye Gnemi
Math Dept Chair & Algebra Tchr
Jeppe, Patricia Gant
7th Grade Math Teacher
Jones, Janet Mc Minn
Third Grade Teacher
Kahn, Marjorie Rhea
Home Economics Teacher
King, Lucian Clarence
Social Studies Teacher & Coach
Naquin, Richard O'Neal
Eighth Grade US History Tchr
Peterson, Phyllis Hallman
Band Director
Williams, David Wayne
PE & Drivers Ed Teacher
STARKVILLE
Avery, James Carroll
Senior Army & JROTC Instr
Bishop, Sandra Mc Bride
Sixth Grade Teacher
Butler, David E.
Science Tchr & Head Ftbl Coach
Carter, Angela Caldwell
Kindergarten PE Teacher
Hunt, Pamela Stafford
Social Studies Teacher
Johnson, Teresa Mantz
Soc Stud Teacher & Dept Chair
Kemp, Pam Garrard
Business Teacher
Krans, Kay Christensen
His, Geography & Bio Teacher
Kurtz, Karen Hammermeister
Mathematics Teacher
Laughlin, Sally Longest
Social Studies Teacher
Lusk, Jane Weygandt
Biology Teacher
Mabry, Paula Crockett
Pub Speaking & Drama Teacher
Mc Carty, Frances Reynolds
Eng & Creative Writing Tchr
Mc Coy, Mary Lambert
Fifth Grade Teacher
O'Bannon, Brenda Caraway
Math Teacher
Owens, Lula Townsel
3rd Grade Teacher
Parvin, Martha Ruth Malone
English Teacher & Tennis Coach
Rowan, Denise Rogers
Asst Director of Bands
Seitz, Mary Lynn Norris
3rd Grade Teacher
Sykes, Chanda Thomas
Spanish Teacher
Thweatt, Douglas B.
8th Grade English Teacher
White, Marcie M.
French & Spanish Teacher
Williamson, Norma Goff
Retired Communication Instr
Wright, Donna Luther
Fine Arts & Drama Teacher
STRINGER
Lester, Rachel Bush
Kindergarten Teacher
STURGIS
Sappington, Teresa Burge
Science Teacher
SUMMIT
Anders, Brenda Tribble
Teacher & Cheerleader Sponsor
Coney, Elaine Marie
Fr, Span, & Eng Cmpstn Instr
Ginn, B. Merrielyn
His Instr & Leadership Dev
Griffin, Carla J.
Anatomy & Physiology Instr
Guy, Mary Taylor
Chemistry Instructor
Turnage, Diane Nobles
Biology Instructor
Williams, Jeanne M. Wilson
English Instructor
SUMNER
Campbell, Bessie Ingram
6th & 7th Grade Math Teacher
SUMRALL
Hudson, Teresa Graham
First Grade Teacher

ALL (cont)
, Lynn Wendt
ora Teacher
, Janice
ipal
ck, Sharon Suzanne Nobles
sh Teacher
Patricia Curry
sh Teacher
RSVILLE
Barbara Jo
er
LA
an, Mattie Mae
ce Teacher
s, Paul Allen
Teacher
TON
, Faye Graham
ed Teacher
MINGO
Anthony Wayne
r Discovery Tchr & Coach
ead, Pam Pardue
tudies & English Teacher
ALOO
Ben E.
ssor of Music
ar, Giovina Draghi
ciate Professor of Biology
Mary Prittchette
tant Professor of French
Nimr F.
: Professor of Mathematics
, Johnnie Maberry
tant Professor
n, John, Jr.
sh Professor & Dept Chair
n, Richard Carl
: Prof of Philosophy & Hum
ra, Bam D.
ssor of Chemistry
Wilma D.
ematics Teacher
e, Olusola Ambrose
: Professor of Pol Sci
san, Asoka
ssor of Biology
e, Julie Ealy
Chair of Psych & Prof
erry Washington, Jr.
sh Professor
ONT
gham, Tammy Bates
sh Teacher
Sandra K.
ance Counselor
A
obert Earl
School Classroom Teacher
k, Bertha Black
Grade Teacher
O
Judy McKissick
ess Teacher
Amy Hudson
istry Teacher
Sharon L.
cs & Chemistry Teacher
Vicky Flowers
ad Grade Teacher
, Janice Kelso
a Specialist
Debby R.
re Teacher
, George Malcolm
tant Principal
, Jean Yancey
er of Talented & Gifted
Betty Mallard
al Education Teacher
lie Lasater
eacher
ston, Phyllis Pounds
sh Teacher
ty, Lou Ann Hartgraves
nced Placement Eng Teacher
skill, Eddie
& Human Anatomy Teacher
no, Raymond Clyde
d & US History Teacher
aul B.
entary School Principal
, Virginia Price
ematics Teacher
n, Jennifer B.
rade English Teacher
ge, Terry Smith
nd Grade Teacher
ers, Donna Lou
ora I Teacher
Bonnie R.
sh & Humanities Teacher
ks, Shirley J.
gy & Zoology Teacher
ks, Susan Harrison
ess Technology Instructor
ns, Frances Blakely
ry Teacher
RTOWN
, Karen Griffin
nglish & Spanish Teacher
Sandy Beard
Grade Teacher
berry, Mary Helen Ladner
Grade Teacher
Inita
ry Teacher
skill, Vernadette L.
Education Supervisor

Pigott, Jerry L.
Science Teacher
Soloman, Jacqueline Brumfield
Elementary Teacher
Sowell, Stephen Lynn
Band Director
Watts, William Henry
American Govt & Amer His Tchr
UNIVERSITY
Everett, George A.
Assoc Prof of Modern Langs
George, K. P.
Professor
Gold, Cindy
Assistant Prof of Theatre
Martin, Jeanette St. Clair
Asst Prof of Bus Communication
SAntry, Shirley Emilie (Wicks)
Assisstant Prof of French
Wilder, Wallace Mark
Accounting Professor
UTICA
Brown, Bessie Cole
English Instructor
Brown, Johnnie Ruth
Sixth Grade Teacher
Wilcher, Willie Hudson
English Teacher
VANCLEAVE
Henley, Stella Clegg
Retired 2nd Grade Teacher
VARDAMAN
Webber, Mary Wofford
Fourth Grade Teacher
Wright, Linda S.
Special Education Teacher
VICKSBURG
Athow, Susan Austin
High School Teacher
Bonelli, Andra Easley
5th Grade Teacher
Bonelli, Marla Mc Beath
Art Teacher
Britton, Lucy H.
English Teacher
Bruce, William David
Self Contained Teacher
Carpenter, Donna Taylor
English Teacher
Czaika, Sharon
Biology Teacher
Dodgen, Anthony B.
Math Department Chairman
Gold, Gary
Director of Bands
Gouras, Peggy Mayfield
Second Grade Teacher
Gullett, Elizabeth Carlisle
Math Teacher
Harden, Sharon Emery
Sociology Instructor
Harmon, Mary Clare
First Grade Teacher
Kelly, Andrew Phillip
English Teacher
Logue, Candance Holbrook
Teacher of Gifted & Talented
Long, Emily Hardin
Business Technology Instructor
Mc Elwee, Virginia Hawkins
English Teacher
McGee, Rhonda Nimmons
History Teacher
Monroe, Judy Lawson
3rd-4th Grd English Teacher
Myers, Bettye Fountain
Math Teacher
Otis, Bessie Barnes
French Teacher
Patin, Anna Christine Ducote
Theology Teacher
Rush, Shirley Fox
Social Studies Teacher
Stone, Sheila Werlein
English & Latin Teacher
Strahan, Fern S.
Fourth Grade Teacher
Stuart, Frances Brown
First Grade Teacher
Thomas, Dorothy Dixon
6th Grade Teacher
Toliver, Barbara Jones
Jr Remedial Reading Teacher
Turner, Linda Lee
Fourth Grade Teacher
Yarbro, Diane Emfinger
Math Department Chairman
WALLS
Lovelace, Carolyn A.
English Teacher
Washington, Gloria Hobbs
4th-5th Grade Science Teacher
WALNUT
Love, Sue
Biology Teacher
Meeks, Danny N.
Chemistry & Physics Teacher
Smith, Carol Johnson
4th-8th Grade Science Teacher
WALNUT GROVE
Bobo, Angie S.
Secondary Math Teacher
Rivers, Richard James
Mathematics Teacher & Coach
WATER VALLEY
Beard, Gayle Spradling
English Teacher
Cobern, Sammie Green
Mathematics Teacher

Hamilton, Karen Kuhnert
Pre-Algebra Teacher
House, Hubert
Social Studies Teacher
Westmoreland, Joan Little
French & Speech Teacher
Woodard, Doloris Black
Ninth & Tenth Grd Eng Tchr
WAVELAND
Bellone, Harriet Ann
Sixth Grade Teacher
Malone, Audrey Thomas
Third Grade Teacher
WAYNESBORO
Brewer, Rita Faye
Mathematics Teacher
Crager, Ginny Wingler
Teacher of Gifted & Talented
Doherty, Don P.
Asst Principal & Algebra Tchr
Graves, Barbara Martin
Fourth Grade Teacher
Hardee, Dinah Douglas
4th Grade Teacher
Hundley, KATHY Lynn
PE Tchr & Coach
Jordan, Naomi Lewis
Allied Health Instructor
Kendrick, Patricia G.
5th Grade Reading Teacher
McCarty, Mary C.
Social Studies Teacher
O'Dom, Gerald Wayne
High School English Teacher
Shoemake, Gail James
Fifth Grade Teacher
Staten, Ada M. Ward
Third Grade Teacher
Walker, Gay Mc Elhaney
Creative Writing Teacher
Walley, De Juan
Sr English Teacher
WEBB
Jordan, Myrtle Houston
Math Teacher
Williams, Patsy Tillmon
History Teacher
WEIR
Beard, Stewart Glen
Social Studies Teacher & Coach
Graham, Harold Wayne
Health & Physical Ed Tchr
WESSON
Brooks, Pegi Cline
Eng, Lit Tchr & Dept Chm
Brown, Geraldine W.
Psychology & Sociology Instr
Brown, Joann B.
Third Grade Teacher
Bush, Martha Berry
English Teacher
Cammack, Maurice Ervin
Computer Sci Instructor
Crews, Edna Earle Patridge
College English Instructor
Curtis, Shelley M.
Microbio & Biology Instructor
Daughdrill, Roy W.
Mathematics Division Chairman
Dykes, Jerry
Mathematics Teacher
Dykes, Nancy A.
English Instructor
Flynn, Linda Royals
Span & Speech Commnctns Instr
Grillis, Pamela Lea
English Instructor
Grimes, Judy Mc Alpin
Speech & Language Pathologist
Hammons, Brent
Technology Discovery Teacher
Huckaby, Susan L.
English I & Spanish I, II Tchr
Hughes, Lynda Rachell
Fifth Grade Teacher
King, Jeffrey Wayne
7th Grd Science & History Tchr
Lawson, Donny Lee
Science Instructor
Moon, Cindy Meeks
Science Teacher
Schexnayder, Douglas B.
Science Instructor
Sutton, Evelyn Portis
Humanities Instructor
Williamson, Ronald
Anatomy & Physiology Instr
WEST POINT
Armstrong, Lucille Deas
English Teacher
Busby, Anglyn Lytal
First Grade Teacher
Davidson, Vallie Washington
6th Grade Teacher
Davis, Willie Porter
Gifted Education Teacher
Dobbs, Zelda Patterson
Mathematics Teacher
Euer, Georgia Churchwell
Title I Language Arts Teacher
Green, Arnetta C.
Cosmetology Instructor
Mc Kinney, Eugene R.
Senior Army & JROTC Instr
Rice, Judy F.
Eng & Advance Composition Tchr
Sharma, Hari M.
Assistant Professor
Smith, Brenadett Larve
9th Grade Mathematics Teacher

Taylor, George Russell
Assoc Math Prof & Div Chrmn
Thomas, Patricia Anne
Assoc Prof of Business Tech
Tumlinson, Bobbie Martin
Mathematics Teacher
Westbrooks, Pearlie Greer
Reading & English Teacher
WHEELER
Moore, Charlotte Burcham
Sixth Grade Teacher
Murphy, Amanda Kay (Strange)
Third Grade Teacher
WIGGINS
Dedeaux, Clarice Bonnett
Soc Stud Dept Chair & His Tchr
Ladner, Carol Sue Bond
5th Grade Teacher
O'Quine, Vana Husband
US Govt & Economics Tchr
Shaw, Nina Campbell
Business Computer Tech Teacher
Young, Laura Mitchell
Second Grade Teacher
WINONA
Blaine, Annette
Business & Computer Tech Tchr
Bowman, Mindy Rae
Biology Teacher & Coach
Devine, Sammie C.
Sixth Grade Language Arts Tchr
Herring, Rebecca Whitmire
5th Grade Teacher
Latham, Vera J.
Mathematics Teacher
Lollar, Dwight Omar
Principal
Lollar, Judy Brooks
10th Grade English Teacher
Mc Gee, David Lee
Jr HS Social Studies Teacher
Phillips, Shirley Moore
5th Grade Teacher
Reed, Nanda Austin
Jr HS Social Studies Tchr
WOODVILLE
Boudreaux, Eva Anthony
4th Grade Teacher
Boyd, Sharon Elaine
Mathematics Teacher
Hurts, Arthur J., Sr.
Mathematics Teacher
Maiden, Marilyn Tjuanna
District Nurse
Payne, Bernetta Ezelia
Third Grade Teacher
Veals, Elnora
Social Studies Department Chm
YAZOO CITY
Brent, Aubry Noel, Jr.
Science Teacher
Moore, Rose Marie (Anderson)
Fifth Grade Teacher

MISSOURI

ADRIAN
Adkins, Sheila Swickhamer
English Teacher
Gepford, Shannon Dean
Science Department Chair
ADVANCE
Crader, Barbara Payne
Second Grade Teacher
Hindman, Patricia Allwood
English & Journalism Teacher
Jenkins, Liana Keller
Fourth Grade Teacher
Scott, Ida Jean Tilley
1st Grade Teacher
Vavak, Lois Faye (Revelle)
English, Speech & Drama Tchr
ALBANY
Holcomb, Kay
Algebra II & Mathematics Tchr
ALMA
Littrell, Gary D.
Principal
Rhoad, Emily Appelbaum
7th-12th Grade Science Teacher
ALTON
Strain, J. Darrell
Vocational Agriculture Instr
Vestal, Adria Karen
Librarian
ANDERSON
Fausett, Kathy Lann (Sprague)
HS Math Teacher
Francisco, Jerry R.
Math Teacher
Harper, Leanna Lankford
Elem Lang Arts & Reading Tchr
Harrell, Dale Kim
At-Risk Director
Hopkins, David Mark
High School Math Teacher
Johnson, Linda Smith
Business Instructor
Rogers, Janelle Lee
Family & Consumer Science Tchr
Secrest, Angie Barr
English Teacher
Sovereign, Mark Edward
Math Teacher & Coach
Whittenberg, Sally Price
English Dept Chairperson

ANNAPOLIS
Dinkins, Gerald Wayne
High School Guidance Counselor
APPLETON CITY
Marler, Theresa Gail
Family & Consumer Science Tchr
Moore, George William, Jr.
Industrial Arts Tech Teacher
Stevenson, Janice Elaine
Vocal Music Teacher
ARBELA
Kice, June (Palmer)
Retired Elementary Teacher
ARCHIE
Bartholomew, Tammy Parker
Agricultural Ed Instructor
Brown, Rhonda Marie (Hayes)
Band Director
Elsensohn, Mary K. (Brenden)
Curriculum & Instruction Coord
Hoyt, Shelly Renee (McCown)
Second Grade Teacher
ARNOLD
Andrus, Shirley Mae
5th Grade Teacher
Brengle, William L., Jr.
Math Teacher
Christ, Brenda A.
Kindergarten Teacher
Dill, Monica Beerman
Elementary School Counselor
Dunn, Darlene Kay
9th Grade Science Teacher
Farris, Cindy Tregent
Biology Teacher
Kasey, Arthur Robinson
Science Teacher
Kennon, Darrell G.
Fifth Grade Teacher
Kirberg, Mary Stolsek
First Grade Teacher
Maltagliati, Doris Jean (Alderson)
Third Grade Teacher
Thomas, Alyce Peeples
Retired Elementary Teacher
ASH GROVE
Herring, Sue Ellen
English & Journalism Teacher
ASHLAND
Ahlfield, Stephen E.
District Tech Coord & Teacher
Bard, Gene L.
Social Studies Teacher
Gilpin, Roxanne Marie
Fourth Grade Teacher
Lacy, Janine Dawn
Kindegarten Teacher
Mullen, Bonnie Anderson
HS Lang Arts Tchr & Dept Chm
Selby, Jean Elizabeth
6th Grade Teacher
ATLANTA
Brant, Melissa McCollum
English Teacher
AURORA
Bean, Sharon Baker
6th-12th Grade Vocal Music Dir
Colton-Millsap, Karen
Communications Teacher
Dial, Peggy Wyatt
English Teacher
Forester, Charle Kerans
K & 1st Grd PE & Music Teacher
Greer, Philip E.
Fifth Grade Teacher
Johnson, Daniel Lee
Eighth Grade Math Teacher
Meyer, Sherry Ann (Eden)
High School Media Specialist
Neyer, Eugene C., Jr.
Business Teacher
Woods, Charles Patrick
Math Teacher
AUXVASSE
Bell-Key, Julie L.
Fourth Grade Teacher
Crawford, Joy Horton
Science Teacher
Frey, Jeanie Sanders
1st & 2nd Grade Teacher
AVA
Adams, Howard W.
High School Math Teacher
Corder, Susan Eileen
1st Grade Teacher
Dickinson, Becky Bryan
Journalism & English Teacher
Eden, Tracy Lee
HS English, Speech, Drama Tchr
Gott-Stoecker, Shirley Jean
Spanish Teacher
Hall, Patricia Ann Morrison
Kindergarten Teacher
Heriford, Leigh Ann (Crain)
7th Grade Social Studies Tchr
Hunt, Ann Burris
HS English & Government Tchr
Streight, Judith Ann (Holt)
HS English Tchr & Dept Chprsn
AVILLA
O'Kelley, Frances Rochester
Fourth Grade Teacher
Still, Nila Gail
Kindergarten Teacher
BAKERSFIELD
Trick, Abel Jerry
Jr & Sr HS Mathematics Tchr
BALLWIN
Allen, Nancy L.
Physical Ed & Wellness Coord

BALLWIN (cont)
Barnhart, Dawna
Science Teacher
Blalock, John E.
Social Studies Teacher
Blassie, Dee Vonder Haar
Health Teacher
Bontrager, Kelly Krupp
English Teacher
Brown, Andrea Godfrey
English Teacher
Campa, Raoul Joseph, Jr.
Fifth Grade Teacher
Campbell, Patricia Jo Ann McCune
English Teacher
Castillon, Jerry R.
Biology Tchr & Sci Dept Chprsn
Conley, B. Patrick
Co-Chair of English Dept
Constantin, Susan Krebs
Fifth Grade Teacher
Coon, Donald Eugene
Mathematics Teacher
Cugier, David Gerard
Aerospace Science Instructor
Donnelly, Lenee Michele
Art Teacher
Elliott, Pamela Sue
Science Teacher
Farley, Cynthia Nelson
First Grade Teacher
Fridley, Shelley Lyn
Second Grade Teacher
Gaskill, Christena
Seventh Grade Math Teacher
Glenn, Jane
Mathematics Teacher
Grace, Jerre G.
English Teacher
Ham, Patricia Lynn
Math Teacher
Hardin, Irene Jane Marlault
Fifth Grade Teacher
Hawkins, Rita J.
5th Grade Teacher
Heller, Terri Gidley
Marketing Teacher
Hickenbotham, Barbara S.
Special Education Teacher
Hirth, Paul R.
English Teacher & Dept Chair
Hollerbach, Catherine Parker
Business Education Instructor
Hopkins, Michael Francis
English Instructor
Hoyt, Dixie Lee
Biology & Human Anatomy Tchr
John, Mary Syron
Mathematics Teacher
Jolly, Linda Harger
Physical Ed Tchr & Act Dir
Jones, Cathy Renae
Chemistry Teacher
Kelley, Sarah Jane (Welsh)
First Grade Teacher of Gifted
Kohl, Jane Mesnier
Second Grade Teacher
Lucas, Carolyn Sultzman
8th Grd American History Tchr
Luerding, Gina M.
French Teacher
Marnati, Donna Von Cloedt
5th Grade Teacher
Mazzola, Gary Salvatore
Interim Principal
Moore, Terri Bonita
Fifth Grade Teacher
Mueller, Mary Howell
Guidance Counselor
Neumann, Shirley Russell
Retired Third Grade Teacher
Ostermeier, Laurell Mays
English Teacher
Pinkstaff, Sandra S.
Business Education Teacher
Reardon, Daniel V., Jr.
Mathematics Teacher
Reeves, Donna Elizabeth
High School Mathematics Tchr
Ribbing, Don
English Teacher
Rivers, Joel Allen
8th Grd Homerm Tchr & Ath Dir
Rivers, Lisa Pfund
Third Grade Teacher
Rohan, David Joseph
4th Grade Teacher
Ryan, Rita A.
Biology Teacher
Schwieder, Marcia Fellows
Mathematics Teacher
Sehie, Dianne Vonder Haar
Elementary Teacher
Seibel, Gail C.
Fifth Grade Teacher
Shelton, Charlotte Haynes
Primary Teacher
Shepherd, Clifford Dale
Physical Education Teacher
Short, Patricia Moleski
English Department Chair
Smoot, Betty Davidson
Bus Teacher & Internship Coord
Stegmann, William Henry
Chemistry Teacher
Stoddard, Sally Carhill
English & History Teacher
Sykes, Gerri Foster
First Grade Teacher
Taussig, Lela Eunice
English Teacher
Tenholder, Florence Marie
Humanities & Asian Civ Teacher
Tinucci, Diane Marie
English Teacher
Volshteyn, Semyon Simon
Physics Teacher
Walton, Robert Joseph
English Teacher
Wardenburg, Robert Irvin
Music Teacher & Choral Dir
Weiman, Gloria J.
Fourth Grade Teacher
Weissman, Scott A.
Health & Physical Ed Teacher
Wharton, Dee Manuell
Assistant Principal
Wheeler, Gayle S.
Fourth Grade Teacher
White, Leola Anne (Burch)
GATE Teacher
Wright, Emilie Marie
Assistant Elementary Principal
BARNARD
Baumli, M. Evelyn Walden
Retired Elementary Teacher
BARNHART
Decker, Gloria Jean
Teacher of the Gifted
Grawitch, Kathy A.
Kindergarten Teacher
Mc Caffrey, Patricia Ellen
First Grade Teacher
BEAUFORT
Schuenemeyer, Darlene Alreta (Wright)
5th Grade Teacher
BELLE
Jeoffrey, Terri Lee
Physical Ed Tchr & Coach
King, Marlis Giedinghagen
Home Economics Teacher
Picker, Cathy Marie
Third Grade Teacher
Vrooman, Ingrid Haskell
First Grade Teacher
BELTON
Blake, Cathy Colip
Teacher of Gifted
Harrington, John Calvin
Social Studies Teacher
Hulsopple, Virginia Rene (Hummel)
Kindergarten Teacher
Kempster, Cynthia Hagan
Title I Math Teacher
Kendall, Sandra Butcher
Math Teacher
Knight, Glenn Howard
8th Grd Language Arts Teacher
McDonald, Mark Dean
Physical Education Teacher
Nelson, Linda Loomis
Library Paraprofessional
Norfleet, Sherry Jones
Second Grade Teacher
Parres, Kenneth Paul
Social Studies Teacher
Reese, Lynett Arashiro
Title I Language Arts Tchr
Robbins, Eloise Frisbie
Former Elementary Teacher
Schneider, Carol Huston
8th Grd English & Yrbk Tchr
Thomas, Patricia Hodge
Art Instructor
Webb, Diane Louise (Brines)
Mathematics Teacher
Wilckens, Linda E.
Math Teacher
BENTON
Creech, Marlene Anne Bouchard
Band & Vocal Music Director
Kielhofner, Donna Glueck
First Grade Teacher
King, Margaret Rose (Daniel)
Fifth & Sixth Grade Teacher
BERKELEY
Baudendistel, Donna Marie
Special Education Teacher
Ellis, Algeretta Carr
Language Arts Teacher
BERNIE
Brow-Hampton, Marta Ines
Spanish Teacher
Tanner, Jeanice Beacham
English Teacher
Zoll, Bill D.
Physical Ed Teacher & Coach
BETHANY
Epperson, Michael Keith
7th-9th Grade English Teacher
BEVIER
Belt, Rebecca Hunter
First Grade Teacher
Martin, Sue Thomes
English Teacher & Librarian
Yount, Debbie McVicker
Kindergarten Teacher
BILLINGS
Green, Michael Carl
K-12th Grade PE Teacher
O'Toole, Karen Lawley
Third Grade Teacher
Quigley, Ann Jones
Second Grade Teacher
Schott, Linda Steinmetz
Mathematics Teacher
BIRCH TREE
Gall, Janet Bearce
Language Arts & Math Teacher
BISMARCK
Lennon, Judy Katherine
Physical Education Teacher
Malone, Brenda (Anderson)
Family & Consumer Science Tchr
Wakefield, Kristi Williams
5th-6th Grade Math Teacher
BLOOMFIELD
Binford, Verlon Ray
Fifth Grade Teacher
Swindell, Marla Smith
Secondary Teacher of Gifted
BLOOMSDALE
Basler, Henrietta Marie (Bahr)
MS Mathematics Teacher
Kist, Donna Marie
Admin & 5th Grd Tchr
BLUE EYE
Parsons, Marilyn G.
Foreign Language Teacher
Settles, J. D.
Math Teacher
Stief, Edna Marie Green
Retired Teacher
BLUE SPRINGS
Alberg, Kimberly Crundeton
8th Grade Social Studies Tchr
Bailey, Beth
5th Grade Teacher
Beaird, Sharon Sue
Second Grade Teacher
Beal, Betty Gail
Science Teacher
Bolton, John Michael
Physics & Mathematics Teacher
Brock, Linda Marie
English Teacher
Brown, Jan Moss
Chemistry Teacher
Caywood, Melanie G.
Third Grade Teacher
Craig, Sue Ann
Third Grade Teacher
Dailey, Jay W.
Health & Physical Ed Teacher
Dannemiller, Jeff K.
English Teacher
Day, Douglas Lamont
Senior Psychology Teacher
DeShon, Kathryn Clair
6th Grade Teacher
Dod, Betty Wilson
Sixth Grade Teacher
Dowell, Randall Lane
Business Education Instructor
Eagle, Martha Jackson
Mathematics Instructor
Erneste, William H.
High School Math Teacher
Ernst, Rose Mary Henrich
Gifted & Talented Facilitator
Faris, Michael Boyd
8th Grade Social Studies Tchr
Fasciano, William Culp
Physics & Chemistry Teacher
Fulbright, Teresa Ankrom
English, Speech & Drama Tchr
Garrison, Gary E.
Intramural Sports Dir & Tchr
George, Deborah Ann
Mathematics Educator
Goldsmith, Danny Eugene
CAD Drafting Teacher
Gray, Debbie Smithee
Elementary Music Teacher
Grosser, Cheryl Summers
English Professor
Gurney, Robert Wayne
Biology Teacher
Hagmann, Timothy Donovan
Science Teacher
Hamilton, Jesse Ward
Social Studies Teacher
Harding, Troy Austin
Mathematics Teacher
Harlan, Sandy K.
7th Grade Math Teacher
Harmon, April Denise
6th Grade Social Studies Tchr
Hart, Michael Christopher
Social Studies Teacher
Hays, Ruth Jurgensmeyer
4th Grade Teacher
Hines, Marc Lawrence
Industrial Technology Teacher
Houser, Jo Ann
Physical Science Teacher
Hurd, Michael Don
Elem Prin & US History Teacher
Johnson, James Royal
Eighth Grade Earth Sci Teacher
Johnston, Christine Lee (Kanaba)
English & Spanish Teacher
Jones, Timothy Randall
Secondary Math Teacher
Jonson, Cheryl Jones
Second Grade Teacher
Keal, Fran Johnson
Comm, Speech & Drama Teacher
Kucharski, Denise Berard
Spanish Teacher
Langston, Jacquelyn E.
Speech & Forensic Instructor
Lankford, Deanna Mroz
Science Department Chair
Lapiska, Patricia Goslee
Chemistry Teacher
La Rosa, Rochelle Marianne
Spanish & French Teacher
Leabo, Barbara J. (Dickeson)
Seventh Grade Lang Arts Tchr
Leeper, Jerome Henry
6th-8th Grade Band Director
Lidman, Mark J.
Instructor of English
Manuel, Evan E.
Chemistry Tchr & Vlybl Coach
Marcum, M. Yvonne
5th Grade Classroom Teacher
Martin, Deborah L.
English Teacher
Mc Clanahan, Dennis James
Instrumental Music Teacher
Meals, Timothy Scott
History Teacher
Moran, Kathy Young
English Teacher
Morris, Carol-Rea Sciortino
Drama Teacher
O'Connor, John Anthony, IV
8th Grd Acad Applications Tchr
Owens, Pamela States
Social Studies Teacher
Ready, Carol I.
6th Grade Math Teacher
Reiff, Earlynn Horton
Sixth Grade Lang Arts Tchr
Round, Thomas Lane
Science Dept Chairman
Shover, Joan
Physical Education Teacher
Stephenson, Lindy Van Hemert
Sixth Grade Reading Teacher
Tede, Cathy L.
French Teacher
Theroff, Marvin W.
Biology Teacher
Watson, Lizabeth Jo
First Grade Teacher
Watts, Carl Douglas
Fine Arts & Band Director
Wilson, Kenneth Earl
ROTC Instructor
Wood, Cynthia Lee (Gates)
English & Spanish Teacher
Word, Jim
French Teacher
BOIS D ARC
Bader, Debby Ann
Third Grade Teacher
BOLIVAR
Brakebill, Carol J.
8th Grd English & Comm Teacher
Casebeer, Deanna Gentry
Fifth Grade Teacher
Denslow, Sharon Doran
High School Art Teacher
Derryberry, Joyce Nettles
Second Grade Teacher
Hagerman, C. Ed
HS Agricultural Ed Teacher
Maas, Jobeth Ellis
Fourth Grade Teacher
Otradovec, Jane Skarvan
Fourth Grade Teacher
Pufahl, Jean L.
Social Studies Teacher
Pursley, Grace
Retired Third Grade Teacher
Schrader, Todd Lee
Industrial Arts Tech Teacher
Stanton, Rhonda (Bogart)
High School English Teacher
BONNE TERRE
Brenon, Joan L.
Coordinator of Gifted Ed
Farr, Carol Ann (Major)
9th-12th Grade Math Teacher
Mitchell, Bart Allen
Mathematics Instr & Dept Chair
Wilke, M. Sue
English Teacher
BOONVILLE
Alexopoulos, Nicki Lee
English Teacher
Biesemeyer, Gina Louise
English & Math Teacher
Bradshaw, Janice Roberts
Vocal Music Teacher
Brimer, Sue Marie
Special Education Teacher
Draffen, Jacky Harper
Art Teacher
Heidenreich, Donald
History & Political Sci Instr
Mc Cush, Jacl D.
Physical Education Teacher
Scott, Lenora LaRose
Kindergarten Teacher
Smith, Annamarie Davis
Third Grade Teacher
Spence, Melissa Ann (Oswald)
Third Grade Teacher
Thorne, Patty Rapp
HS Physical Education Teacher
Whalen, Nancy Jaeger
Mathematics Teacher
BOURBON
Elliott, Kenneth Dean
Bio, Zoology & Anatomy Tchr
Hays, Genea Diane
English & Journalism Teacher
Klenke, Wendy (Klaeger)
Kindergarten Teacher
White, Sarah Elizabeth Sloan
Elementary Teacher
BOWLING GREEN
Brown, Carole Paap
Business Education Teacher
Fisher, Annette
First Grade Classroom Teacher
Foutes, Amy Ann Utterback
Seventh Grade English Teacher
Ingram, Deborah (Black)
Third Grade Teacher
Kemp, Cynthia Eckler
High School Math Teacher
O'Farrell, Elizabeth Ann
Language Arts Teacher
Shinn, Karen Elizabeth Korte
Sixth Grade Math Teacher
Williams, Pamela Fisher
Kindergarten Teacher
BRANSON
Aubin, David Lee
Science Teacher
Cheary, John M., Jr.
Band Director
Daugherty, Darlene (Springer)
7th & 8th Grd Tchr of Gftd Ed
Garner, Don
Social Studies Teacher
Helsel, Trisha Mills
English & Aerobics Teacher
Rains, Charlotte D.
High School English Teacher
Siegel, Marjorie Griffin
English Teacher
BRASHEAR
Erwin, Kathy Ann (Chandler)
Lang Arts & Elem PE Teacher
Fountain, Beth Haas
2nd Grade Teacher
Spase, Louis Duncan
Science Teacher
BRECKENRIDGE
Hulett, Melissa Dawn
Home Economics Instructor
Kimble, Sharon Hitchcock
Teacher
BRENTWOOD
Shephard, Maryann Weber
High School History Teacher
BRONAUGH
Sikes, Ada Ikerd
Eng, Speech, Drama & Span Tchr
BROOKFIELD
Cunningham, Marcia Kaye (Edgar)
Spanish Teacher
Moore, Betty Jean (Smith)
Retired Teacher & Adminstrator
BROSELEY
Clark, Charlotte Dreve
English Teacher
BRUNSWICK
Barry, Piper Y.
K-12 Music Instructor
BUCKLIN
Hawkins, Douglas C. J.
Physical Education Teacher
Lambert, Sue Frances
French & English Instructor
Ware, Valeta Ruth (Cattey)
Fifth Grade Teacher
BUCKNER
Coleman, Beverly Ann
Third Grade Teacher
Dike, Vicki Veseling
5th Grade Teacher
Oetting, Judy Sherman
5th Grade Teacher
BUFFALO
Autry, William Fred
8th Grade Amerian History Tchr
Beck, Sarah Carkuff
6th Grade Teacher
Cully, Carol Kay (Goode)
Business Education Teacher
Hostetler, Jill C.
English & Journalism Teacher
Mills, Sharyl G.
First Grade Teacher
Ramsey, Stacey Jo (Phillips)
Title I Teachers Aide
Smith, Joyce A. (Powell)
Business Teacher
BUNKER
McIntosh, Patricia Holland
Social Studies Teacher
Walker, B. Ann Baker
Title I Reading & English Tchr
Woolf, Virginia Innis
Second Grade Teacher
BURLINGTON JUNCTION
Blackford, Jill Wolken
Sixth Grade Teacher
Hann, William Irvin
High School Mathematics Tchr
Prather, David Eric
Science Teacher
Veatch, Pamela Kaye
Language Arts Instructor
BUTLER
Hannah, Sheryl Leigh
Seventh Grade English Teacher
CABOOL
Stringer, Frank R.
7th-8th Grade Science Teacher
CADET
Bone, Brenda K.
Middle School Math Teacher
Crumpecker, Norman Granville
Social Studies Teacher
Politte, Joyce Ann
Principal & Teacher
CAINSVILLE
Wilson, Lorrie Anne Shideler
Science Teacher

DONIA
Marilyn Vandeven
ness Teacher
IOUN
:, Brenda L.
Teacher
FORNIA
', Beth (Atteberry)
al Director
tter, Janet Burford
School Librarian
ell, Amy Huhmann
al Studies Teacher
s, Angela Sansbury
nd Grade Teacher
William Edward
cipal
DENTON
Corinne Atteberry
ergarten Teacher
gs, Beverly Ann (Butts)
nistry Teacher
, Janita Wood
ird Amer History Teacher
, Kim O'Brian
Instructor
Nancy Scheuerman
eting Education Coord
enzie, JoyceAnne A.
ematics Teacher
, Debra Hendrix
rade Teacher
ERON
, Kernan B.
& GED Teacher
he, Gwen Joyce Johnson
nistry & Physics Teacher
Steven Scott
ematics Teacher
, Mary Killgore
al Science Teacher
PBELL
bell, Kim Dean
S Sci & HS PE Teacher
rd, Pamela Kay
ish, Speech & Drama Tchr
, Jerry Philip
entary Teacher
Denise
S Eng & HS Jrnlsm Teacher
ws, Rick J.
Grade Teacher
TON
r, Candice Tomlinson
ergarten Teacher
r, Gael L.
nalism & Lang Arts Tchr
enneth Chiso
Professor of Economics
er, Kimberly Sue (Little)
ogy Teacher
, Gina Kratky
al Studies Teacher
Marcia Morgan
ish, Speech & Drama Tchr
GIRARDEAU
Trent
ning Specialist & Instr
er, Nancy Westrich
ish Professor
Leon C.
of Spanish & Scndry Ed
, Richard J.
Professor of Science Ed
nmyer, James A.
essor of Management
nan, Karen Ann
d Grade Teacher
an, Sharon Carr
nistry Professor
Dixie Lee Wilkes
ed Program Facilitator
Mark DeWayne
n Grade Teacher
boom, Sterling Page
artment of Music Chair
ston, Winona Lee (Trout)
Grade Teacher
n, Linda P. (Hedgecorth)
ogy Teacher
Roy Stanley
essor of Management
retchen Haas
ding Teacher
l, Linda Keena
inal Justice Instructor
r, Christina Lee
essor of Biology
r, Mitchel
ical Science Professor
Jin Kang
oc Prof of Chem
Mark
nce Teacher
Cynthia Wren
n Teacher
lin, Robert Wayne
essor of English
ton, Glenda Joan (Kirchdoerfer)
nth Grade Teacher
Thomas Bernard
ch Communication Prof
Helen Duerr
Prof of Computer Science
, Pamela Hindman
essor of English Dept
, Carolyn Lea (Jarrett)
ing Associate
Harvey E.
essor of English

Hooper, Jacqueline Rodell
Professor
Hopkins, Bill
Dir of Athletic Promotions
Johnson, Gary Gene
Assoc Prof of Accounting
Johnson, Patricia Robins
Home Economics Teacher
Kennedy, Linda Rogers
English & Publications Teacher
Kern, Ernest L.
Professor of Geosciences
Langenfeld, Mark
Associate Professor
Laudie, Drew T.
Recreation Professor
Lohmeier, Tracy Knight
Mathematics Teacher
Macke, Thomas E.
Retired Elementary Teacher
Mc Cowan, Brenda Schlimpert
Business Teacher
Moon, Scott Alan
Adjunct Instr of Philosophy
Nall, Cassandra Jones
Elementary Music Teacher
Overbey, Gail Ann Urhahn
Psychology Dept Asst Professor
Parette, Howard P., Jr.
Associate Professor
Pasborg, Lee A.
Social Studies Teacher
Peterman, Neal Frederic
Mathematics Professor
Pratt, Andrew LeRoy
Philosophy & Rel Dept Instr
Rademaker, Timothy Arnold
Physical Education Professor
Readnour, Mike
Chemistry Professor
Reutzel, G. Brett
Spanish Teacher & Coach
Ruark, Mark James
Assistant Principal
Santana, Mary Schrock
Second Grade Teacher
Schaffner, Steve B.
Orchestra Director
Seyer, Dennis C.
Assoc Prof of Speech & Theatre
Shell, Shelby Ann
Mathematics Teacher
Smith, Mimi Mecham
English & Reading Teacher
Smith, Ruth Brantly
First Grade Teacher
Snell, William E., Jr.
Psychology Professor
Spellman, Susan O'Rilla
Early & Special Ed Assoc Prof
Stepenoff, Bonnie Marie
History Assistant Professor
Stephens, Martha Elaine
French Teacher
Thompson, Joseph E.
Building Trades Instructor
Thompson, Sharon Sullivan
Principal
Train, Carl T.
Biology Professor & Dept Chm
Wiggs, Linda Henson
Associate Professor
Wright, Kathryn Oldsen
Chemistry Teacher
CARDWELL
Campbell, Rick Wayne
Asst Prin & Jr HS Sci Tchr
Davidson, Mary L.
Counselor
Kellums, Kimberly Phillips
Second Grade Teacher
Mc Minn, Jetta (Petty)
Business Education Teacher
McMinn, Johnny Wayne
Science Teacher
CARL JUNCTION
Bogart, LeAnn (Hight)
Language Arts Teacher
Jones, Eddie W.
Language Arts Instructor
Kirk, Keith Stanton
8th Grade American His Teacher
McGriff, Georgiana Lynn (Menapace)
Language Arts Teacher
Meyer, Eugene W.
Agriculture Educ Instructor
Nicolas, Anne E.
English Teacher
Owen, Sharon E.
Secondary Vocal Music Instr
Pim, Jacci Allgood
Vocational Business Teacher
Preston, Kenneth Mark
Industrial Technology Teacher
Rohr, Daniel T.
Sixth Grade Teacher
Wilson, Marianne Larson
7th & 8th Grade Math Teacher
Zumwalt, Bill Edward
6th Grade Mathematics Teacher
CARROLLTON
Hoffmeyer, Dianne Miles
Kndgtn Teacher
Jones, Joyce Grotjan
3rd Grade Teacher
Sullivan, Arnie Leslie
Math Teacher & Football Coach
CARTHAGE
Buchanan, Melfin Fasken
Geometry Teacher

Campbell, Don R.
Assistant Principal
Carmichael, Colleen Kloberdanz
Mathematics Teacher
Clement, James Arthur
Amer Govt & World History Tchr
Duncan, Kevin Lee
Agricultural Instructor
Frerer, Nancy Lauer
Fourth Grade Teacher
Gremling, Mary Ann
Biology Teacher
Hamilton, Nichol Dryton
Mathematics Teacher
Hazlett, James Lee, Jr.
American History Teacher
Johns, Alice J.
Spanish Teacher
Mc Afee, Diana Williams
Professor of Education
Meeks, Sylvia A.
Business Teacher
Phipps, Sherri Diane Austin
Language Arts Teacher
South, Howard E.
Fine Art Instructor
Streich, Edwin Lee
Assistant Principal
Taylor, Elizabeth Ann
Health & Physical Ed Teacher
Tubbs, Caroline K.
Language Arts Teacher
Youngworth, Andrew Carl
Psych & World History Tchr
CARUTHERSVILLE
Avis, Alexis Streete
Fifth Grade Teacher
Luye, Rita Gayle
Third Grade Teacher
Thatcher, Susan Young
Fifth Grade Teacher
Yarbrough, Gregg Alan
Assistant Principal
CASSVILLE
Shore, Christopher Todd
Physical Ed & Health Teacher
CEDAR HILL
Jung, Judith Miler
6th Grade Study Skills Teacher
CENTER
Birdwell, Malia Dawn
French Teacher
Hart, Phylicia I. (Schuchman)
English Teacher
Kassel, Amy Kathryn
Mathematics Teacher
Lewis, Pamela Louise (Bandelier)
Family & Consumer Science Tchr
Trower, Carolyn Little
Teacher of the Gifted
CENTERVIEW
Hagedorn, Karen Beasley
Sixth Grade Teacher
Metcalf, Barbara Dotson
Jr Sr HS Music Teacher
Smith, Caryee Sayer
English & Journalism Teacher
CENTRALIA
Evens, Keith Allen
Chaplain & Bible Teacher
Gillman, John Leroy
Science Teacher
Hort, Margaret N.
Math Teacher
Pedersen, James Carl
HS Social Studies Instructor
Price, Lawrence W., III
Science Dept Chairman & Tchr
CHAMOIS
Lawson, Barry Eugene
Social Studies Teacher
Paulsmeyer, Sabra Lynne (Witthaus)
HS Counselor & English Teacher
CHARLESTON
Harris, Lisa S.
Mathematics Teacher
Hoppe, Pamela Elizabeth
Tchr of Learning Disabilities
Sevic, Diane Bruenderman
English Teacher
Showmaker, Rosemary Renaud
First Grade Teacher
Zellars, Portia Morgan
Mathematics Teacher
CHESTERFIELD
Billing, Mary Hope
Music Teacher
Buckley, Allan J.
American & World History Tchr
Clark, Sally Wenzel
First Grade Teacher
Coldiron, Katherine Vuono
Former Teacher
Dobkin, Catherine Cox
Social Studies Teacher
Eisermann, David Jon
Physics Teacher
Ellis, J. Paul
Assistant Professor
Flaherty, Carol Lee
Assistant Principal
Fritschle, Sandra Ann
Spanish Teacher
Gerdes, Jane Galkowski
Language Arts Teacher
Gross, Patricia Motherway
Algebra Teacher
Hanks, Wanda J.
Computers Teacher

Harman, Lynne Vaughn
English Teacher
Jacoby, Sandy Sue
Math & Community Service Tchr
Jobst, Louis A.
English Teacher
Kohunsky, Mary Jo (Kuchan)
Physical Science Teacher
Lantz, Warren W.
PE & Health Teacher
Mertz, Valerie Brown
AP Biology Teacher
Nagy, Jan E.
English Teacher
Nolte, Alicia (Van Nevel)
4th-6th Grade Math Teacher
Overby, Lynna Schneider
Math Teacher
Phillips, Janice Arnold
Spanish Teacher
Richardson, Clare Lake
7th & 8th Grade Art Teacher
Ross, Mary Moore
Forensics Director
St Clair, Cyrus Frederick
Latin Teacher
Schneider, Ches C.
Teacher & Department Chairman
Shouse, Edward L.
Science Teacher
Skinner, Richard Duane
Sixth Grd Rdng & Lang Teacher
Smith, James Douglas
Science Teacher
Trimble, James Harold
7th Grade Mathematics Teacher
Zielinski, Kathleen Sarhage
Fifth Grade Teacher
CHILHOWEE
Schupp, Larry Elliott
Math & Physics Teacher
Willcockson, Kimberly D. (Holger)
6th-12th Grd Soc Studies Tchr
CHILLICOTHE
Coon, Mabel A. Cunningham
Vocational Business Instructor
Hinkebein, Jeanne Pfaff
Principal
CLARENCE
Wood, Ginger Daniel
Title 1 Teacher
CLARKSBURG
Hartman, Nancy Ellen (Robb)
Eng & Comp Literacy Teacher
CLARKSVILLE
Boyd, Helen Cook
Speech, Drama & Span Teacher
Lindsay, Edgar Lee
Ath Dir, Hlth & Driver Ed Tchr
Lovell, Mary Linda
First Grade Teacher
CLAYTON
Martin, Hiram Clay, III
Band Director
Martin, Stephanie Conboy
Spanish Teacher
Myers, Carolyn W.
Fifth Grade Teacher
CLEVELAND
Brown, Tamera Mae
Sixth Grade Teacher
Carder, Milton Douglas
Eng Instr, Ath Dir & Coach
CLEVER
Burch, Yvonne Elaine Etter
Social Studies & English Tchr
Swadley, Dan L.
Music Teacher
CLIFTON HILL
Lowry, Diana Lynn (Carter)
7th & 8th Grade Lang Arts Tchr
Seyer, Mary Ann
7th & 8th Grade Math Teacher
Williams, Roger G.
Soc Studies & Vocal Music Tchr
CLIMAX SPRING
Toole, Caroline King
Science Instr & Dept Chair
CLINTON
Bruns, Janet Faye
Third Grade Teacher
Dannels, Jack L.
High School Guidance Counselor
Dunning, Marie Howerton
First Grade Teacher
Ford, David Andrew
Instrumental Music Director
Goslin, Nancy R.
5th-8th Grd Math & Sci Teacher
Grimes, Mary Lynne
Business Teacher
Guernsey, John LeRoy
Mathematics Teacher
Hockenberry, Lynn Marie (Peterson)
ECSE Teacher
Johnson, Gayle H.
Kindergarten Teacher
Kiefer, Suzanne Green
5th Grade Teacher
Largent, Leslie Carroll
Social Studies & Jrnlsm Tchr
Litten, Sharon Lynn
Physical Ed & Health Teacher
Long, Mary Margaret Goth
7th & 8th Grade Teacher
Miller, Lisa D'Ann
Business Teacher & Soc Worker
Paschen, Nancy E.
Fifth & Sixth Grade Teacher

Snyder, Carolyn Sue (Bartimus)
Counselor
Stratton, Janet Brown
Third Grade Teacher
Weaver, Amy Diane
6th Grade Reading Teacher
Wright, Carol Welsh
Curriculum Dir & Coord
COLE CAMP
Gilbert, Michael James
Industrial Technology Teacher
Griffey, Cathy
Family & Consumer Sci Tchr
Meuschke, Tracy James
Physical Education Teacher
Rice, Brian D.
Sixth Grade Teacher
COLUMBIA
Adams, John Ewart
Assoc Professor of Chemistry
Ballard, Bruce William
Philosophy & Religion Prof
Barnhouse, Jack Bruce
Instructor of English
Bartlett, Beatrice Crowe
College Professor
Bichler, Lois Ann
Professor of Biology
Billings, Catherine Firestone
English Teacher
Bondeson, William Blaine
Prof of Phlsphy, Family & Med
Carrell, James E
Professor of Biological Sci
Clow, William Tracy
Production Coord
Dobbs, Sherry K.
English Teacher
Dulak, Janice
Dance Professor
Ellsworth, Pamela Sue
Voice Instructor & Choral Dir
Espinosa, Linda M.
Assoc Prof of Early Chldhd Ed
Greeson, Beverly Jo
Fourth Grade Teacher
Hardy, Cheryl-Ann
Assoc Prof of Psychology
Knepler, Robin A. Dotson
Art Teacher
Maiorino, Renata Ann
Director of Physical Education
Manian, Sabita
Asst Prof of Political Science
Markie, Peter Joseph
Professor of Philosophy
Mc Clure, Pamela Ardith
Adjunct Instr of Lang & Lit
Meyers, Cynthia Buchta
Nursing Instructor
Milligan, Dave
History Teacher
Mossman, Deborah Jean (McKechnie)
Associate Prof of Civil Engrng
Overeem, Phillip Michael
7th Grade English Teacher
Oxenhandler, Janet Joan
First Grade Teacher
Paulsen, Sandra Michele
Mathematics Teacher & Coach
Pettlon, Kimberly Kay
English Teacher
Prentiss, Brett
Actor, Teacher & Director
Price, Markita L.
Math & Comp Sci Professor
Pringle, Norma Jean Poarch
Instructor of Spanish
Rudroff, Linda Goodhue
First Grade Teacher
Sims, Wendy L.
Assoc Prof & Dir of Music Ed
Sisson, Marsha Correll
Seventh Grade English Teacher
Spate-Smith, Laurie Elizabeth
Eighth Grade English Teacher
Stallman, Sandra Jones
Tchr of Learning Disabilities
Stewart, Edward O'Neil
Art Teacher
Wehlburg, Catherine Wehlburg
Asst Prof of Psychology
Wells, Fran J.
Business Education Teacher
Zumwalt, Marilyn Wheeler
English as a Second Lang Tchr
CONCORDIA
Beerman, Janet Bethke
Fourth Grade Teacher
Beerman, John Wayne
English & History Teacher
Dahlke, James Edward
Religion & Social Studies Prof
Dunn, Norma Payson
Art Teacher
Inman, Carol Reinwald
3rd Grade Teacher
Oberbroeckling, Kristy Kay (Warnke)
Mathematics Teacher
Pfannkuch, Alyssa Kimball
HS Art & English Teacher
CONWAY
Mosley, Julie Lynn
Secondary English Teacher
Owen, Jonathan Daniel
Music Teacher & Fine Arts Chm
COSBY
Bartlow, Diana Allen
Chapter I Rdg Resource Tchr

CRANE
Crockett, Sandra Hellmann
High School Mathematics Tchr
CREIGHTON
Kelsay, James Ray
Jr HS Science & History Tchr
Mc Roberts, Christine (Kling)
First Grade Teacher
Price, Marlene N.
Business Educator
Yoder, Charla Johnson
Elementary Music Teacher
CREVE COEUR
Roberts, Karla Johanboeke
Lang Arts & World History Tchr
CROCKER
Bowling, Eddie Wayne
Social Studies Tchr & Coach
Carlton, Alice Hampton
3rd Grade Teacher
Morgan, James H.
HS Social Studies Teacher
Mullen, Karen Lynn
High School Art Teacher
CUBA
Barreca, Elaine Mildred Ballmann
Former 7th Grade Tchr
Barreca, Stephen Anthony
High School Art Teacher
Cape, Donna Jean (White)
HS Spanish & English Teacher
Dunn, Kimberlee G.
Fourth Grade Teacher
Grayson, Kimberly Ann
English Teacher
Gummersheimer, Allene Mc Cune
Learning Disabilities Teacher
Hunt, Dorothy Crump
Mathematics Teacher
Kinder, Kimberly Sue
Mathematics Teacher
Monda, Robyn Wells
Marketing & Journalism Teacher
Swindell, Sarah Ziske
High School Science Educator
Talley, Andrea Lea
Art Teacher
DE KALB
Sherard, Joy E.
Lang Arts Instr & Yrbk Adv
DE SOTO
Burkeen, Trisha Lee (Sauer)
Math Teacher
Cummings, Joel R.
English Teacher
Fallahi, Donna LuAnn
High School English Teacher
Masterson, Katherine Sue (Roth)
Business Education Instructor
Pierce, Linda Gail
4th Grade Teacher
Raisch, Diana Kay
Second Grade Teacher
Speropoulos, John
Mathematics Teacher
Wilson, Debra K.
Language Arts Teacher
Wyman, Juanita Rapp
Art Teacher
DEARBORN
Biermann, Daniel H.
Physical Ed & Health Teacher
Clemens, Lana Lee (Babcock)
High School Guidance Counselor
DEEPWATER
Cook, Virgilene Bartels
Business & Computer Teacher
O'Connor, Michael Xavier
High School Teacher
DEERING
Heller, Reba Pride
English & Soc Stud Teacher
DELTA
Blattel, Loretta A.
Fifth Grade Teacher
Helderman, Joyce Faye
Third Grade Teacher
Keirce, Betty (Mc Christian)
Math Teacher
Niswonger, Alice Cannon
2nd Grade Teacher
O'Reilly-Burton, Drenna Lee
Kindergarten Teacher
Weber, John Conrad
Social Studies Chairperson
DESLOGE
Hahn, Rosemary Vineyard
Retired High School Librarian
DEXTER
Brickhaus, Patricia Kay
7th Grade Mathematics Teacher
Clippard, Michael Mullen
Director of Bands
Cooper, Charles Thomas
Biology & Physical Sci Tchr
Copeland, Trevor Kyle
Biology & Chemistry Teacher
Crow, Debbie Koppman
Business Teacher
Freeman, Wayne
Instrumental Teacher
Goodwin, Donald F.
Social Studies Teacher
Hampton, Reeda Hardy
General Science Teacher
Hillis, Chris Y.
3rd Grade Teacher
Jennings, Tim Alan
Industrial Technology Teacher
Joyner, Anita Huey
8th Grd Math & Pre-Alg Teacher
Murphy, Lori Lee (Davis)
Learning Enrichmnt Facilitator
Rimel, Judy Evans
English Instructor
Wade, John Thomas
Science Department Chairperson
DIAMOND
Roark, Linda Foster
First Grade Teacher
DIXON
Barsby, Vaughn Earl
At Risk Teacher
Kulback, Anna Marie (Roberts)
Lang Arts & English I Teacher
Summers, Dennis Paul
Art Teacher
Williams, Jeff
Middle School Counselor
DONIPHAN
Anthony, Christine Marie
Social Studies Teacher
Barnett, Rhoda G. Collier
Spanish Teacher
Carrens, Anita L.
Math Teacher
Culbertson, Sandra Lea
Senior HS English Teacher
Dicken, Lisa Ellsworth
Chemistry Teacher
Johnson, Susan Murdock
First Grade Teacher
Mathis, Carol M.
Fifth Grade Teacher
Pepmiller, Joyce Braschler
Business Education Teacher
Whitwell, Brenda G.
Microcomputer Keyboarding Tchr
DORA
Barnett, Kathy Hall
Language Arts Teacher
DREXEL
Reynolds, Larry James
Mathematics & Physics Teacher
EAGLEVILLE
Hendren, Sue (Turner)
Language Arts Teacher
EAST PRAIRIE
Bowlin, Brenda Gaiser
English Teacher
Howell, Ann Bagby
Home Economics Teacher
White, Beverly Ann (Green)
Science Teacher
EDGAR SPRINGS
Herpich, John Clarence
Science & Physical Ed Teacher
Maples, Jenny Mutrux
Math Teacher & Computer Coord
EDGERTON
Hoeffner, Janey Lynn (Bockhaus)
Math Teacher
EDINA
Primm, Carolyn (Mayer)
Early Childhood Educator
Salmon, Jill Winner
Business Instructor
Tuman, Wes E.
HS Mathematics Teacher
EL DORADO SPRINGS
Abbott, Marcia Ann
Elementary Guidance Counselor
Andersen, Donald John
Chemistry Teacher
Burris, Christi Lynn
First Grade Teacher
Carter, Peggy Whited
Third Grade Teacher
Cooper, Becky L.
English Instructor
Hungerford, Rebecca Sue Miller
High School English Teacher
Mc Donald, Deborah Ann
2nd Grade Teacher
ELDON
Bachant, Fran
High School Counselor
Broeker, Debra Creed
Fifth Grade Teacher
Buster, Ronald Joe
Retired 7th Grd Sci Teacher
Campbell, Charles Edward
Marketing Instructor
Coulter, Harold Eugene
Electronics Instructor
Frye, Karen Enders
7th Grade Literature Teacher
Herren, David Christopher
Social Studies Teacher
Herren, Myrna Dunstan
Substitute Teacher
Hoffman, Mark David
Secondary English Teacher
Holder, Sharron Steen
4th Grade Teacher
Schler, C. Edward, Jr.
Eighth Grd Earth Science Tchr
Schulte, Samuel John
Collision Repair Tech Instr
Scott, Sharon Rose
Kindergarten Teacher
Steenbergen, Jackie Marie
6th Grade Teacher
ELLINGTON
Moore, Charlotte
Fifth Grade Teacher
Spradley, Gregory Raymond
Vocal Music Teacher
Wilson, Samuel Ray
Ecology & Biology Teacher
ELLSINORE
Crowley, Sandra F. Ferrell
Family & Consumer Sci Tchr
Francis, Roy Herbert
Elem Lib & Media Specialist
Leach, Willis G.
Psychology Teacher
Pippin, Sherry Ann
Science Teacher
Thompson, Denise Korenak
Jr HS Social Studies Teacher
Weathers, Beverly Bell
Junior HS Mathematics Teacher
ELMER
Jarman, Mary Evelyn Magers
Retired 1st & 2nd Grd Teacher
ELSBERRY
Griffon, Karen Roberta
Science Teacher
Howard, Mary Lynn Parks
Kindergarten Teacher
Lilley, Stephen Ray
High School History Teacher
Tillotson, L. Ezra
English Instructor
EMINENCE
Cook, Judy Hood
Sixth Grade Teacher
Gers, Linda Thornton
Family & Consumer Science Tchr
Hurt, Jennifer Jane Rayfield
High School Counselor
ESSEX
Bruce, Marrianne (Smith)
High School Science Teacher
Collier, Susan Lee (Lawson)
Business Tchr & Comp Coord
Hook, Kristi Hicks
Science Teacher
Lane, Karen Lynn (Polsgrove)
English & Journalism Teacher
EUGENE
Albee, Karen Alice
High School Art Instructor
Angerer, Shelly Anne
Mathematics Teacher
Bond, Jennifer Louise
Kindergarten Tchr & Principal
Farris, E. Douglas
Biology & Chemistry Instructor
Groose, Betty Jo
Retired Elementary Teacher
McDonald, Kevin Dwight
Elementary Physical Ed Teacher
Rehagen, Denise M.
Social Studies & English Tchr
EUREKA
Allmendinger, Susanne Erika
Drama & Language Arts Teacher
Barton, Mary Ann
Secondary Eng & Jrnlsm Tchr
Brown, William Lee, Jr.
Social Stud Tchr & Bsbl Coach
Carlisle, Russell
Soc Stud Tchr & Dept Chm
Coon, Billie Boucher
Language Arts Teacher
Curran, Greg
HS Guidance Counselor
Easton, Deanna Combs
Family & Consumer Sci Tchr
Goggin, William P.
American History Teacher
Hankins, Peggy Margaret Kearney
Reading & Language Arts Tchr
Johnson, Dianne Casey
Science Teacher
Lingle, Lisa Hurst
Mathematics Teacher
Linneman, Georgia Pyle
Business Education Teacher
Martin, Lynn Westerling
English & Comm Service Tchr
Parres, Suzanne Jean
Chemistry Teacher
Piedmont, Linda Noeller
Fourth Grade Teacher
Russell, Douglas Franklin
Learning Resources Director
Strecker, Robert Henry
College Prep English Teacher
Wasson, Sharon Steeves
PE, Drivers Ed & 1st Aid Tchr
Witt, Harry James
Lang Arts Tchr & Speech Spon
EWING
Lomax, Susan Lynn
Chem, Physics & Rsrch Teacher
Lueckenhoff, Mark
5th-6th Grd Soc Studies Tchr
EXCELSIOR SPRINGS
Admire, Rebecca C.
Mathematics Teacher
Andrew, Judith E. Bradley
Elementary Gifted Teacher
Armstrong, Barbara (Strobel)
7th-8th Grade Science Teacher
Brookshier, Linda Marie
Learning Disabilities Teacher
Craven, Margaret Ann (Berry)
Vocational Basic Skills Instr
Riley, Mercedes Ann
Home Ec Tchr & Dept Head
Snook, Sue Rinemuth
Fourth Grade Teacher
Welch, Mary Wenke
Science Teacher
EXETER
Cook, John C.
Science Teacher
Perry, Paul Anthony
Secondary Social Studies Tchr
FAIR GROVE
Kathka, Roger Anthony
Industrial Arts Teacher
FAIRFAX
Holtz, Judith Miller
Teacher & Librarian
Parker, Phyllis Acklin
Jr HS Mathematics Teacher
FARMINGTON
Bauche, Kurt Douglas
Instrumental Music Director
Bollinger, Jeffrey Lee
Industrial Technology Teacher
Gunder, Willis M.
Elementary Drug Ed & Hlth Tchr
Harris, Jane Boatright
Retired HS Mathematics Teacher
Huck, Linda A.
Assistant Band Director
Kellogg, Margaret A.
Middle School Teacher
Marler, Kevin Ray
Speech & Drama Teacher
Pinkston, Jackie L.
Social Studies Instructor
Ray, Linda Grindell
6th Grd Math & Science Teacher
Seufert, Susan (Todd)
Fourth Grade Teacher
FAUCETT
Campbell, Louise Cable
Sixth Grade Elementary Tchr
Grable, Victoria K.
Middle School English Teacher
Millard, Jennifer Malone
Band Director
Miller, Lori Pepple
Vocal Music Teacher
FAYETTE
Griffin, Sherri Holt
Assoc Prof of Early Chldhd Ed
Hirsch, Michael Lee
Assoc Professor of Sociology
Jones, Nancy Thompson
Associate Professor of Music
Kelly, John J.
Asst Prof & Dir of Theater
Melnyk, Julie Ann
Assistant Professor of English
Reece, Neva M.
Assoc Prof of Psychology
Robinson, O. A.
Professor of Philosophy & Rel
Rustemeyer, Maryann Hickman
Assistant Prof of Eng & Math
Vandelicht, Roy Dean, Jr.
Instrumental Music Director
FENTON
Bollinger, Gerri Lynn
Social Studies Teacher
Brader, Deborah Jean (Jackson)
Guidance Director
Casagrande, Trina Christine
Mathematics Teacher
DeArmond, William Garay
Fourth Grade Teacher
Deckelman, Eugenia Bolesina
4th Grade Teacher
Hults, Kathleen Sharon
Language Arts Instructor
Liggett, Bruce W.
Guidance Counselor
Meldurum, Todd R
6th Grade Reading Teacher
Rainey, Suzanne Rochelle (Ries)
Eng & Creative Writing Tchr
Rayfield, Annette Elizabeth
Grad Stu in Admin
Ruble, Charles Ray
Science Teacher
White, Mary Elizabeth
Orchestra Director
Wilson, Cathy
7th Grade Teacher
FERGUSON
Bruce, Judith Poleos
Vocal Music Specialist
Fague, Mary Katherine
Homeroom, Reading & Eng Tchr
Kendall, Rebecca Denise (Embick)
English Teacher
Kiehne, Judith Hammond
Second Grade Teacher
Maasen, Carla Schenewerk
7th Grade Teacher
Muehling, Sandra Verity
Sixth Grade Teacher
Roe, Jacquelyn Sue
Fifth Grade Teacher
Shelton, Kathy Rose Montrey
Fourth Grade Teacher
Spencer, Patricia Lonita Reese
Choir Director
Stade, Dorothy Frank
8th Grade English Teacher
Werner, Bradley Earl
Business Administrator
FESTUS
Akins, Marissa Greenfield
5th Grade Teacher
Comte, Bonnie Oehl
8th Grade Teacher
Cunningham, Carol Sewald
5th Grd Language Arts Teacher
Harper, Claudia Marie
Homeroom Teacher
Harris, Susan C.
6th Grade Teacher
Herting, Philip Martin
High Schl Math & Science Tchr
Hippert, Catherine Ann
Teacher of the Gifted
King, Linda Stephens
Fourth Grade Teacher
Korff, Donna Dowd
Art Teacher
Lewis, Leann Jeanette
Bus Instructor & Dept Chprsn
Mueller, Kathy Coleman
Science Teacher
Peeler, Raymond Lee
High School Science Teacher
Schmidt, Dana Long
Bio, Chemistry & Phys Sci Tchr
Shell, Richard L.
Band Director
Versemann, Shirley A.
8th Grade Homeroom Teacher
Whitener, R. Kay
Spanish Teacher
Wideman-Reid, Sharon Kay
6th Grade Science Teacher
Wood, Richard Alan
Social Studies Teacher
FLAT RIVER
Crews, Edwina Parks
English Instructor
Spengler, James Conrad
College Teacher
FLORISSANT
Allen, Ivy Martell
Orchestra Director
Argent, Kathy Smith
Third Grade Teacher
Barnicle, Michael W.
Math Teacher
Bekebrede, William W.
Physical Education Teacher
Best, Beverly Jean
K-6th Grd Gftd Education Tchr
Bhatia, Heidelies
9th-12th Grade German Teacher
Bolderson, David Alan
Religion Teacher
Brown, Patricia Ann
Mathematics Dept Chairperson
Bruder, Mary Lou Gisinger
Retired Commnctn Skills Tchr
Burkhart, Patricia Ellen
Mathematics Teacher
Carnagey, Russell Dean
Instructor & Vice President
Cassimatis, Lois Ann
Mathematics Teacher
Clark, Donna Drake
Fourth Grade Teacher
Coleman, Carrie Mae
Primary School Teacher
Conrad, Mary Flynn
Fourth Grade Teacher
Dames, Celeste Marie
Third Grade Teacher
Dell'Orco, Marilyn Montileone
Middle School Teacher
Dominguez, Christine Karwoski
Spanish Teacher
Dubis, Marian Jane
Health & AVID Teacher
Dylewski, Nancy Anne
Visual Arts Teacher
Foster, Cassie Stanton
Second Grade Teacher
Gillette, Celeste Jo
Family & Consumer Sci Tchr
Grieshaber, David Ralph
Health & Physical Ed Teacher
Harrison, Ann Daly
Mathematics Teacher
Heithaus, Eleanor Bono
Junior High Language Arts Tchr
Herbig, Doris Jean
2nd Grade Teacher
Hessell, Deborah S. (Griffey)
First Grade Teacher
Hodges, Barbara Karen (Brooks)
Third Grade Teacher
Huffmon, Barbara Ann Dotson
Business Education Teacher
Hutcherson, Elizabeth Young
Retired Teacher
Kemper, William R.
Social Studies Dept Chairman
Kern, Steven Charles
Health, PE & Drivers Ed Tchr
Kovarik, Phyllis Yates
Third Grade Teacher
Kralemann, William J.
Chemistry Teacher
Lane, Douglas Robert
English Teacher & Dept Chair
Lopez-Rosales, Aida M.
Spanish Teacher
Ludwig, Carol Kalinowski
6th Grade Teacher
Luetje, Lawrence Linton
Retired Band Dir & Dept Chair
Mantei, Mary Beth (Kuhn)
Retired 4th Grade Teacher
McEvoy, Shannon Patrick
Marketing Ed Teacher & Coord
Morgan, James M.
Industrial Technology Teacher
Neptune, Carol Ann
6th-8th Grade Religion Teacher

ISSANT (cont)
vorth, Kenneth Ray
al Science Teacher
, Florence Terry
d Grade Teacher
ı, Karen Werner
n Grade Teacher
t, Gary Lynn
ics Teacher
Norman J.
Aath Teacher & Ftbl Coach
dt, Charles A.
enship & 9th Grd Tm Tchr
n, Ray
al Studies Teacher
y, Deborah Davis
ish Teacher & Dept Chair
Darrick Alan
ematics Teacher
ki, Judith Gelmi
cipal
ger, Susan Lee (Gazda)
th Grade Teacher
ucci, Tricia Marie
ish Teacher
Collette Elaine
m Skills Dept Chm, Eng Tchr
, Carole Niemeier
ish Teacher
obos, Carol A.
ish & Japanese Cadre Tchr
o, Elana Christine
Teacher
ck, Ellenmaria Irene (Black)
l Director
ms, William Shane
ic Dept Chm & Dir of Bands
n, Roger Linden
th Grade Teacher
LAND
Janice Louise
ndary Mathematics Teacher
l, Evelyn I.Tedder
th Grade Teacher
, Norene Carol (Sparks)
ish Dept Chairperson
ix, Barbara Smith
ish Teacher
y, Geri Arleen (Mc Carty)
& French Teacher
YTH
n, Theodora A. (Smith)
ish Instructor
, William Floyd
al Studies Teacher
y, Phillip Lynn
l & Choral Director
Donald Marc
gh Science Teacher
LEONARD WOOD
lin, Judy Ann
a Coordinator
n, Michael Lee
n Grade Teacher & Coach
KFORD
, Charlene Tipton
entary Principal
KLIN
Charleen J.
ed 4th Grade Teacher
ERICKTOWN
Barbara LaBrot
Grade English Teacher
Connie S.
ish Teacher
man, James Allen
nselor
Wilma Lee
ish Teacher
, Alice Carol
l & General Music Teacher
Dale E.
nth Grade Mathematics Tchr
BURG
, Peggy Bax
nd Grade Teacher
, James J.
or
r, Linda Kathryn
8th Grade Teacher & Prin
ON
s, Christine Sinskey
cipal
Rebecca Jane Penrose
Teacher
og, Julian Arthur
Prof & Psych Dept Dir
er, Gary R.
ory Professor
William Joseph
stant Professor of Theatre
Mary Elizabeth
entary Art Teacher
ESVILLE
ese, Melanie Lynn
ness Education Teacher
Sidney
her & Coordinator
NA
, Ruth Lorraine (Provow)
h Grade Librarian
ATIN
n, Mark Andrew
School Social Sci Instr

ney, Dena Kay
ish Teacher
r, Robert Scott
nce Teacher

Fox, Phillip F.
Vocational Agriculture Instr
Jackson, Les Bryan
7th Grade Math Teacher
Shipley, Melody Jackson
HS Math Instructor
Shipley, Robert W.
Social Studies Teacher
GERALD
Horstmann, Jane Kristi
5th Grade Teacher
GILMAN CITY
Williams, John Bruce
HS Social Studies Teacher
GLADSTONE
Hallak, Ellen Anne (Huber)
Mortgage Underwriter
GLASGOW
Arni, Sherry Lou (Stober)
Language Arts Teacher
Drummond, Sara Walkup
English & Literature Teacher
Granneman, Eleanor J.
Title I Instructor
Meyer, Victoria Lynn
Soc Science Tchr & Dept Chair
GLENCOE
Blackford, Richard Dean
7th & 8th Grd Soc Stud Teacher
Blackmore, Kathy Morris
English Teacher
Luensmann, Allen Craig
Seventh Grade Geography Tchr
Nuelle, Sherry L. (Koehler)
Computer Room Specialist
Salazar, Irene
Language Arts Teacher
Sestrich, Jane Denise
Sixth Grade Language Arts Tchr
Sharp, Stephen Ray
Social Studies Chairman
GOWER
Ingle, Rosalie Dianne
English Teacher
Plackemeier, Sandra Schlueter
Kindergarten Teacher
Ruoff, Donna Jeanne
Fourth Grade Educator
Schottel, Eva Faye
Advanced HS Math Teacher
Wood, Cheryl Ann
English, Speech & Drama Tchr
GRAIN VALLEY
Maupin, Diane C.
English Teacher
Menefee, John J., Jr.
Chemistry Teacher
Morgan, Keiko
Japanese Lang & Culture Tchr
Schmidli, Lisa L.
English Teacher
Snyder, Kitty O'Grady
Family & Consumer Sci Teacher
Spina, Daniel B.
Director of Bands
Whitaker, Edwin K.
Social Studies Teacher
GRANBY
Clymer, Ada F. Clanton
Biology Teacher
Mason, Karen Taylor
Voc Family & Consumer Sci Tchr
Waynick, Janis Sue
Fourth Grade Teacher
GRANDVIEW
Black, Paula Sue (Alsop)
Fourth Grade Teacher
Bundy, Diana Lynn
English Teacher
Dunnington, Esther Cooper
Lang Arts Tchr & Dept Coord
Hayslett, Joanna Clark
HS Physical Education Instr
Myers, Richard
PE Teacher & Basketball Coach
Quick, Lawrence Kennedy
Language Arts Teacher
Ryan, Linda P.
Fifth Grade Teacher
Schuch, William Rod
Art Teacher
Staires, D. Clay
Tenth Grade Biology Teacher
Sutter, Yvonne E.
Debate & Speech Teacher
Wall, Carole L.
Dist Communications Coord
GRANT CITY
Coburn, Barbara Siddens
Science Teacher
Hayse, Katie Eisele
Sixth Grade Teacher
Mitchell, Elaine Winter
5th Grade Teacher
Spiers, James Richard
Vocal Music Teacher
Terry, Vanda Washburn
Retired 2nd Grade Teacher
GREEN CITY
Motley, Ernest Andrew, III
Music Director
GREEN RIDGE
Meyers, Sharon G. (Carter)
Jr High Math & Science Teacher
Smith, Karen Kaye
Librarian
Yunt, Mary
Kindergarten Teacher

GREENFIELD
Toler, Dawn
6th Grade Teacher
GREENVILLE
Barker, Deanise Bilbrey
Business Education Teacher
Carter, Tracy Lee
Jr High Lang & English Tchr
Howard, Judith (Goodman)
Third Grade Teacher
GREENWOOD
Branson, Petronella Hermina
Learning Disabilities Teacher
Gore, Patricia Lynn
4th Grade Teacher
Nielsen, Ginger Young
Kindergarten Teacher
Patton, Margaret Carol Martin
Remedial Reading Teacher
GROVER
Brown, Karen Thompson
Fifth Grade Teacher
Westbury, Cathy Lema
Elementary Guidance Counselor
HALE
Caughron, Jayme Bannan
Business Instructor
Gray, Steven DeVon
Science Instructor
Grossman, Christine M.
Music Teacher
HALF WAY
Gorden, Karen J.
Family & Consumer Science Tchr
Highley, Tammy Diane
English Teacher
LeJeune, Elaine (Singleton)
Sixth Grade Teacher
Pyle, Jody Lynn (Kempker)
Business Teacher
Stephens, Nathan Brian
History Teacher
Westfall, Sharon Douglas
Music Teacher
HALLSVILLE
Malancy, David Arthur
Tchr & Assistant Administrator
HAMILTON
Eaton, Ken
Agriculture Instructor
Milligan, Joyce A.
Business Teacher
Morrow, Elva Jean (Schulz)
MS Title I Teacher
HANNIBAL
Conrad, Michelle Ruth
Spanish Teacher
Cox, David D.
Spiritual Director
Immegart, Linda Rae
3rd Grade Teacher
Johnston, Beth Owens
First Grade Teacher
Krogmann, Connie Lee
8th Grade Teacher
Locke, Margaret A.
6th Grade Teacher
McNally, James P.
Mathematics & Journalism Tchr
Miller, Margaret Ann (DeBruin)
Social Studies Dept Chair
Morgan, Barry Erwin
Assoc Prof of New Testament
Mundle, Lionel Blane
Biology & Anatomy Teacher
Riley, Carole Jo (Lane)
Assistant Professor of Music
Roach, Marilyn Jean (Lampton)
Second Grade Teacher
St Clair, Mary Ann Walker
Psychology & World Stud Tchr
Schoonover, Vickie Lynn
3rd Grade Teacher
Snider, Lois Phillips
Bus Asst Prof & Dept Chair
Thomas, Sherri Elliott
English Teacher
Tuley, Shelia Beth
8th Grade Mathematics Teacher
Williams, Marian Leah
Assistant Professor of Math
Zahner, Jerauld Lee
Teachers Assistant
HARDIN
Balman, Everett E.
Agriculture Education Instr
Mansell, Sandra Sue (Jeffries)
2nd Grade Teacher
Mason, Susan C.
Family & Consumer Sci Tchr
Schmidli, Rick L.
History Teacher & Counselor
Waters, Judith L.
English, Speech & Drama Tchr
Wollard, Marjorie Janet (Ware)
Business & English Teacher
HARRISBURG
Glenn, Robert Randall
Music Teacher
Isaacs, Janie Marie (Stevenson)
Speech & English Teacher
Proctor, Lynn Kaiser
4th Grade Teacher
Yount, Kathie Gifford
English Dept Chair
HARRISONVILLE
Ferling, Karen M.
Second Grade Teacher
Garber, Dale M.
Physical Education Teacher

Hart, Aurora Lavery
9th-11th Grade English Teacher
Oetinger, Rosemary Stone
Kindergarten Teacher
Pfautsch, Donna Sue (Schmoll)
Gifted & Talented Teacher
Pike, Patricia Long
Guid Cnslr & Classroom Instr
Schrock, Carol Kay
Vocal Music Teacher
Swartz, Emma Kauffman
Principal
HARTVILLE
Adamson, Cindy Johns
Sixth Grade Teacher
Hardy, Billie Jo
Vocal Music Instructor
Huffman, Sherry Ryals
Elementary Principal
Mays, Joyce Ann (Swiney)
Business Teacher
Miller, Joel Ray
Mathematics & Physics Teacher
Whayne, Ramona Leyna (Salmon)
English & French Teacher
HAYTI
Byars, Timothy N.
Social Studies Teacher & Coach
DeBretto, Theresa Farmer
Business Teacher
Evans, Jerris Ann Reel
Language Arts Teacher
Griffin, Martha Lou Ellen
Language Arts Teacher
Howard, William Thomas
High School Mathematics Tchr
Reynolds, Glenda Sue (Sweeney)
2nd Grade Teacher
Suddarth, Kay Khourie
Remedial Math Teacher
HAZELWOOD
Bennett, Thomas Mitchell
Social Studies Teacher
Clark, Laura LaVerne
Fourth Grade Teacher
English, Sharon K.
Teacher
Geerlings, Janet Kaller
French & German Teacher
Kinder, Linda Johnson
Family & Consumer Science Tchr
Knarr-Ramming, Barbara Ann
Third Grade Teacher
Lanterman, Bonnie Lou Barron
First Grade Teacher
LeCroy, Patricia Ruth
English Teacher
Mangels, E. Jenni Pickel
Theatre Arts & Journalism Tchr
Mc Connaha, Scott Alan
English Teacher
Mincemeyer, Rebecca Inlow
Eighth Grade English Teacher
Pyatt, Mona Tallent
English Teacher
Rice, Constance Camille
Fourth Grade Teacher
Roades, Barry Howard
English Teacher
Sanick, Mary Jean (Grade)
Sixth Grade Teacher
Watson, Pamela Ann
Psychology & Japanese Teacher
HELENA
Ochse, Dennis Lee
Fifth Grade Teacher
HERCULANEUM
Franklin, Jane Carroll
Business Instructor
Williams, Jeffery A.
High School Counselor
HERMANN
Brooks, Jill (Cozort)
Science & Health Teacher
Draper, Doris King
Reading Recovery Teacher
Moritz, Christine Ann
Business Teacher
Speckhals, Allen Lee
6th-8th Grade PE Teacher
HERMITAGE
Berry, Maxine Mapel
Title 1 Lang Arts Teacher
Mitchell, Shirley J. Greer
Art Teacher
HIGBEE
Huckins, Sara Dawn Yell
8th-12th Grade Science Teacher
Kauth, Stephanie Ann
K-12 Vocal & Instrumental Tchr
Menius, David Christopher
7th Grade Teacher
HIGGINSVILLE
Bialczak, Jane Alexander
Elementary Music Teacher
Copenhaver, Barbara L.
Science Teacher
Davis, Cecile Ann
Physical Education Instructor
Jauss, Lanett Blunk
Science Dept Head & Teacher
Pace, Bob Scott
Amer His, Psych & Health Tchr
Simpson, Shelly Renae
Science Teacher
Slater, Sharon Kay
English & Journalism Teacher
Warren, Lorna (Clithero)
Physical Education Teacher

HIGH RIDGE
Bardon, Richard Alan
Retired Industrial Tech Tchr
Murphy, Kathleen Ann
Science Teacher
HILLSBORO
Barton, Terry Charlene
Vocational Business Ed Instr
Beahan, Pamela Arthette (Norton)
Writing Instructor
Bean, Lorie Tipton
Jr High Mathematics Teacher
Borgerson, Sara Thompson
French & Spanish Professor
Boyer, Darla Marie
Comp Information Systems Instr
Buschard, John Bernard
English Professor
Camp, Evelyn M.
Spanish Teacher
Cook, Linda (Hawkins)
Mathematics Professor
Dillon, Matthew W.
Soc Stud Tchr & Athletic Dir
Duntze, Robin Evans
Director of Veterinary Tech
Eimer, Mary (Means)
Nursing Associate Professor
Etchason, Rebecca Ann (Brockmann)
HS Business Teacher
Fritch, Margie Ann
Tech Prep Dir & Ed Prof
Ganey, Thomas James, Jr.
Philosophy Professor
Haggard, William Clifford
Teacher & Science Dept Head
Hutchings, William Jewell
Adj Professor of Economics
Joggerst, Sue A.
Acting & Communications Tchr
Johnson, Robert Swift
Accounting Professor
Johnston, Linda Mary
English Professor
Laird, Donna Crow
Second Grade Teacher
Levinson, Philip Joel
Professor
Loomis, Trish
English Prof & Honors Pgm Dir
Ludlum, Earl R.
Industrial Technology Teacher
Mc Craith, Joseph William, Jr.
Social Studies Teacher
McNeely, Pamela Lucas
High School Mathematics Tchr
Meyer, Bruce Joseph
HS Special Services Teacher
Mitchell, Dora Ann
Biology Instructor
Nausley, Steven Lee
PE & General Science Teacher
Pleimann, John Francis
English Instructor
Scott, Richard M.
Chemistry Teacher
Smith Walker, Nancy
Cmptr Information Systems Prof
Spencer, Karen Frances (Fuhrmann)
Mathematics & Physics Teacher
Sullivan, Jane Brouk
Speech & Theatre Professor
Sutton, Debra
English Professor
Thebeau, Marilyn Volkmann
Third Grade Teacher
Trautwein, Mark Walter
Instrumental Music Instructor
VanHouten, Jason Kyle
Biology & Science Teacher
Walker, Lynn
Cmptr Information Systems Prof
Wolfmeyer, Vern Lee
Prof of Chemistry
HOLCOMB
Wright, Sherri Lynn
Third & Fourth Grade Teacher
HOLDEN
Evans, Andrea
Mathematics Teacher
Kephart, James Russell
Agriculture Education Instr
McGraw, Cathy Case
Family & Consumer Science Tchr
Montgomery, Don Eugene
Eighth Grade History Teacher
Nelson, Bud W.
Elem PE Tchr & Coach
HOLLISTER
Goodwin, Janet F.
1st Grade Teacher
Kerns, Linda Gann
Third Grade Teacher
Peirce, Diana Kern
Third Grade Instructor
Pfister, Faye K.
High School Art Instructor
Shields, Paula Blair
Spcl Svcs Tchr & Dist Coord
Snelson, Illana L.
Former Science Teacher
HOLTS SUMMIT
Caldwell, Ingrid Hauser
Fourth Grade Teacher
HOPKINS
Cox, Ronald Dee
Spcl Ed, Writing & Rsrch Tchr
Wilmes, Ken Wayne
Vocational Agriculture Instr

HOPKINS (cont)
Wood, Sandra Sebacher
K-12th Grade Spanish Teacher
HOUSE SPRINGS
Betts, Susan Hiteshew
Resource & Diagnostic Coord
Cole, M. Renae
Art Teacher
Dohrmann, Vicki Mae
Elementary Music Teacher
Fischer, Roberta Ames
Mathematics Teacher
Fisher, Robert
Physical Science Teacher
Gullett, Kay Koerner
Business Education Teacher
Haug, Paul Edward
HS Phys Ed & Health Teacher
Hemenway, Patricia Myers
Third Grade Teacher
Hitpas, Daniel Edwin
Math Teacher
Joy, Deborah Shoff
Eng Teacher & Writing Coord
Kiel, Karen Marie
Fourth Grade Teacher
Knight, K. Sally
High School Asst Principal
Lutes, Denise Murphy
Chemistry Teacher
McGuire, Linda M.
Fifth Grade Teacher
Miller, Kimberly Pogue
2nd Grade Teacher
Navo, Sheila M.
Kindergarten Teacher
Paris, Judith A.
Math Teacher
Parkinson, Faye B.
Assistant Principal
Scharnhorst, Susan L.
7th Grade English Teacher
Schwandt, Mary Meyer
First Grade Teacher
Schweizer, Marilyn M.
HS Mathematics Teacher
Vaughn, Betty Arendell
Mathematics Teacher
Warren, Bernadette M. (Lintner)
Social Studies Teacher
Wedel, Barbara Rettinger
4th Grade Teacher
West, Dana M.
Accounting Teacher
Wyatt, Rebecca Biles
4th Grade Teacher
HOUSTON
Arata, John Ryan
Band Director
Campbell, Elaine Daile
HS & MS Enrichment Teacher
Fraser, Jane (Craft)
Language Arts Teacher
James, Debbie L.
Math & Social Studies Teacher
Jensen, Rita Douglas
7th-8th Grade Math Teacher
Reese, Mike K.
Science Teacher
Top, Onita Jane
Tchr of Learning Disabilities
HUGHESVILLE
Marsh, Debra Jean
English Teacher
Smith, Fred E.
Health, Drivers Ed & PE Tchr
HUME
Glynn, Dixie Lee Palmer
Lib Media Spclst & Eng Tchr
HUNTSVILLE
Baker, James Eldon
Mathematics Teacher
Gammon, Diane Eckenroad
Kindergarten Teacher
Haynes, Laurannah J.
Family & Consumer Sci Edctr
HURLEY
Faseler, Susan Kathleen
Family & Consumer Sci Instr
IBERIA
French, Vicki Jean
Mathematics Teacher
McPherson, D. Shayne
Social Studies & PE Teacher
Milbourn, Virginia Ruth
HS Mathematics Teacher
Trusty, Ralf Michael
Fifth Grade Teacher
Zink, Susan Lynn (Shackleford)
Soc Stud, PE Tchr & Coach
IMPERIAL
Berni, Mike
Civics Teacher
Brown, James Thomas
English Teacher
Brownfield, Eliza Bonham
7th & 8th Grade Math Teacher
Bryan, Patrice Marie
English Teacher
Butler, Bonnie Lee
First Grade Teacher
Carranza, Mauro James
American History Teacher
Easton, Daniel Allen
English Teacher
Ellington, Laura Cayse
Vocal Music Director
Kehr, Judith Ann
Foreign Language Teacher
Knaust, Kriston Whitledge
French & English Teacher
Leech, John Philip
English Teacher
Miller, Beth Ann
Vocal Music Teacher
Ponzar, Theresa Koppeis
Fourth Grade Teacher
Radvin, JoEllen Buchanan
Business Education Teacher
Stoecklein, Kelly R.
At-Risk Teacher
Taylor, Janet Sundstrom
Mathematics Teacher
Vaccaro, Pamela J.
Soc Stud Tchr & Dept Chprsn
INDEPENDENCE
Adams, Sheri Crawford
Math Dept Chprsn & Tchr
Anderson, Julia Church
English & Journalism Teacher
Baker, Elizabeth Ann
English & Religion Teacher
Baker, Lynne Stuver
High School Counselor
Beckmann, Carolyn Stark
Fifth Grade Teacher
Beggs, Stephen William
Secondary School Counselor
Benson, Bruce
Business Teacher
Bergner, Jane Holliway
English Teacher
Brand, Ellen
4th Grade Teacher
Brock, Sammy Joe
Math & Algebra Teacher
Brown, Gloria D.
Teacher
Brown, Jerry Harry
Art Dept Chairperson
Clemons, Ronald Dale
Communicative Skills Dept Chm
Comtois, Nancy Hannah
Elementary Librarian
Davidson, Sharon Kay (Niemeyer)
Second Grade Teacher
Demark, Thomas, Jr.
Health, PE Teacher & Coach
Dunbar, Richard Leroy
American History & Law Teacher
Ferguson, Charles Stephen
MS & HS Social Stud Teacher
Flanagan, Jane G.
Third Grade Teacher
Gregory, Clinton Lee, II
Instrumental Music Tchr, Coord
Griffith, Linda S.
English Teacher
Grubb, Henry L.
Social Studies Teacher
Hall, Mary Ann
English Teacher
Hammett, Susan Ann
Third Grade Teacher
Hood, Vickie Hein
Child Development Teacher
Hoppe, Gene Joseph
History Teacher
Inman, Jean Taylor
Retired Classroom Teacher
Johnston, Kenneth L.
Biology Teacher
Jones, Ron L.
8th Grd Earth Science Teacher
Kachur, Marylee Thompson
6th Grade Teacher
Keeland, Roy Lee
Retired History Teacher
Kelley, Margaret Netter
Third Grade Teacher
Kilgore, Antoinette Lee
5th Grade Teacher
LeVota, Sue Walters
6th Grade Teacher
Lewman, Katherine Whiting
Biology Teacher & Dept Chair
Long, Floyd Harrison
Social Studies Teacher
Lotz, Sharon Hogan
Business Department Chair
Lovelace, Joan
Fifth Grade Teacher
Maglinger, Gary L.
Art Director
Malott, Janice M.
Dist Art Dept Chair & Teacher
Mathews, Roberta Ann
3rd Grade Teacher
Meyers, Rosemary Gargotta
Second Grade Teacher
Miller, Donald Raymond
8th Grade Social Studies Tchr
Moad, Joy Bergman
5th Grade Teacher
Parker, Kimberly Kaye
Social Studies Teacher
Peck, Pamela Johnson
Spanish Teacher
Rees, Barbara Elaine (Jackson)
Chemistry Teacher
Resch, Paulette Votava
Music Teacher
Richardson, Ed A.
HS History & Govt Teacher
Sajna, Janette Rombach-Pintner
Second Grade Teacher
Schlotzhauer, Roger Lynn
Math & Indstrl Process Tchr
Schreiber, Steve M.
Fifth Grade Teacher
Schuler, John Rathbun
7th-8th Grade Art Teacher
Shrout, Brenda Whitebread
English Teacher
Smith, Debra Elaine Badder
Business Teacher
Steffens, Melissa Noelle
High School Mathematics Tchr
Stucker, Gary Alan
Bible Teacher & Athletic Dir
Thompson, Christina Westfall
5th Grade Teacher
Tucker, Kathleen Anne
Theatre Director
Waitman, Janice Kay
English Teacher
Winter, Sharon Jones
Kindergarten Teacher
IRONTON
Larkin, Patricia Hess
Family & Consumer Sci Instr
Lich, Douglas Wayne
HS Industrial Arts Teacher
Matthiesen, Randall Lee
Mathematics Teacher
Tate, Terry Queen
Sixth Grade Language Teacher
JACKSON
Cotner, James Lynn
High School Chem & Bio Tchr
Ellis, Nancy L.
Mathematics & Computers Tchr
Houchins, Darlene Green
French Teacher
Mirly, Timothy Scott
8th Grade Teacher
Smith, Patricia Winchester
First Grade Teacher
JAMESON
Sarver, Keith Milton
Music Math & Spanish Teacher
JASPER
Carter, Leona Jarmin
Business Education Teacher
Hummel, Steven Curtis
Ath Director & PE Instructor
Sample, Doris Hoover
Soc Stud Teacher & Dept Chprsn
JEFFERSON CITY
Abell, James L.
Math & Physics Teacher
Allen, Saundra Eileen (McGruder)
Elementary School Art Instr
Anderson, Kirk Gregory
Assistant Professor of English
Atkins, Carolyn Vaughn
Assoc Prof of Criminal Justice
Bardwell, Rosemary A. Wingate
English Teacher
Beza, Jabulani
Assoc Prof, Pol Sci & Crml Jst
Bowder, Russell E., Jr.
6th Grade Teacher
Boyer, Karen Sue
Speech & Language Pathologist
Buker, Sally B.
5th Grade Teacher
Cassin, John C.
Elementary PE Teacher
Doyle, Brendan Patrick
Religion Teacher & Counselor
Eggers, Pauline Kay Hammond
Math Teacher
Foster, James Robert
K-5th Grade PE Teacher
Gillespie, David Emanuel
Director of Choral Activities
Grissom, Susan M. (Lahr)
2nd Grade Teacher
Grout, Donna Mary
Associate Professor of English
Hake, Bradley Allen
9th-12th Grade Math Teacher
Halderman, Carolyn Schanzmeyer
Special Service Teacher
Haskamp, Mary Ann
Driver Ed & PE Teacher
Hassien, Frederick D.
Assoc Prof of Natural Resource
Hearn, Rosemary
Dean of Sciences & Eng Prof
Heckman, Linda (Forck)
Mathematics Teacher
Heermance, J. Noel
Professor of English
Hill, Michael Joseph
Mathematics Teacher
Horn, R. Edward
Adaptive Physical Ed Teacher
Hulley, Julia Maudlin
6th Grd Tchr of Tlntd & Gftd
Hunziger, Marsha Kay (Kinder)
Fifth Grade Teacher
Hutchcraft, Kay
French Teacher
Jones, Valerie Vislay
Language Arts & Religion Tchr
Jungmeyer, Roger L.
Assistant Professor of History
Kempker, Lori Ann
Business Education Teacher
Klein, Karen Buzard
5th Grade Teacher
Kucsik, Carol Ann (Link)
Business Technology Teacher
Logan, James E.
Asst Professor of Marketing
Lohner, Myra Spalding
World Civilizations Teacher
Loschky, Lynne Johnson
Professor of English
Mc Call, Richard Andrew
Asst Prof of Music & Bands Dir
Meredith, Steve
Associate Prof of Animal Sci
Miller, Herman T.
Professor of Chemistry
Mitchell, Robert Lee, Sr.
Professor of Music
Nichols, William Paul
PE Teacher & Education Dir
Noonan, Denise Bax
Junior High Teacher
Park, Chung Uk
Professor of Biology
Reidinger, Russell Frederick, Jr.
Adjunct Associate Professor
Rodeman, Connie Lea
Spanish Teacher
Savage, Richard Steven
Natural Resources Mgmt Instr
Schaefer, Joseph Lee
Mathematics Teacher
Schellman, Carol Ries
6th Grade Language Arts Tchr
Scroggs, Lisa Miller
English & Journalism Teacher
Snell, Susann Kenney
6th Grade Science Teacher
Ssekasozi, Engelbert
Philosophy Professor
Stappenbeck, Audrey Elaine
Mathematics Teacher
Stephens, Carey Gail
Business Education Supervisor
Thoenen, Rose Ann
PE Teacher
Thompson, Timothy Don
Mathematics Teacher
Wall, Patricia F.
History Teacher & Asst Prin
Wegman, Linda J.
Mathematics & Religion Teacher
Wenger, Bruce M.
Am History & Geography Teacher
West, Nancy Zemany
English Teacher
Wolters, Cathy
School Principal
Wyman, Linda
Professor of English
JOPLIN
Adkins, Laura Schooler
College Mathematics Instructor
Bartholet, Francis Leon, Jr.
Asst Prof & CADD Dept Head
Beals, Wiley A.
Radiologic Technology Dir
Brown, Barry Edward
Philosophy Professor
Brown, James Frederic
Associate Professor of English
Bruce, Debra Lee Smith
Science Teacher
Burch, Tammara Lynn
Behavioral Disordered Teacher
Burnett, Vonda Irene (Bland)
American Sign Language Instr
Carnahan, Vicki S.
Child Development Instructor
Cassens, Patrick
Professor of Mathematics
Crim, Loretta Gullette
Retired Vocal Music Teacher
Drouin, Dana Lorene
Elementary Guidance Counselor
Dworkin, Joy Stacey
English Professor
Fink, Clare F.
Second Grade Teacher
Goode, Larry Wayne
Associate Prof of Bus Admin
Hafer, Gregory Bruce
Professor of Communication
Jones, John Kenneth, Jr.
New Testament & Preaching Prof
Karimi, Mushabbar
CADD CAMT Instructor
LeRoy, Eunice Marie (Olson)
Second Grade Teacher
Markman, Joyce
7th Grade Science Teacher
McConnell, David H.
Assistant Professor of Ed
Meeks, Robert L.
Act Bands & Jazz Studies Dir
Miller, Richard B.
Professor of Sociology
Moore, Ines Avelina (Lausen)
Spanish Teacher
Moorman, Jay Rieley
Assoc Prof of Communications
Movic, Christine Roswitha
French & German Teacher
Myers, Janet Altendorf
Language Arts Teacher
Prichard, LaVietta (Comito)
Sixth Grade Teacher
Roy, Donald Kevin
History Teacher
Saltzman, Arthur Michael
Professor of English
Schurman, Bonnie L. Christeson
Drama Instructor
Scott, Mark Robert
Professor
Singleton, Anita Beth Clark
Associate Professor of Nursing
Squire, Karen Johansen
First Grade Teacher
Stausing, Leann Shivers
English Dept Chairperson
Tillman, David Lester
Associate Professor of Biology
Voss, Gerald Louis
Latin & Social Studies Teacher
Weber, Maryann
Assoc Prof of Communications
Wilcox, Loretta M.
Assistant Principal
Zustiak, Gary B.
Prof of Yth Ministry & Psych
KAHOKA
Harvey, Denise Lynette (Rockhold)
Mathematics Teacher
St Clair, Louise June Harvey
Fourth Grade Teacher
Wirsig, Ella Kennedy
Spch, Theatre & Lang Arts Tchr
Wirsig, Gregory V.
Language Arts Teacher
KAISER
Blackwell, Elizabeth Neukomm
History & Spanish Teacher
KANSAS CITY
Abraham, Jean E.
6th Grade Teacher
Ackerson, Jan Hay
Retired Third Grade Teacher
Adcock, Mary Jo
English & Journalism Teacher
Alexander, William David
Physics Teacher
Allen, Jean F. Shidler
Third Grade Teacher
Andersen, Marshall Lee
Prof & Dept Chair of Biology
Anderson, Amy Chastain
English Teacher
Anderson, Debbie Craycraft
Gifted Education Teacher
Anderson, Scott Ray
History & Leadership Teacher
Anstaett, David Edward
English Teacher
Banta, Nola Jean (Long)
English Teacher
Bargo, Betty L.
Counselor
Barlett, Paul Bruce
Undergraduate Studies Director
Barmann, Vicki New
French Teacher & Dept Chair
Bartlow, Terrence Overton
7th Grade Social Studies Tchr
Beale, Donna Jo
First Grade Teacher
Beatty, Barbara Lynn (Brady)
Second Grade Teacher
Becker, Larry Dean
Mathematics Teacher
Behrens, Joy Elaine (Dodd)
Family & Consumer Sci Instr
Bell, Harriet Gray
Teacher of Gifted Education
Benyo, David Michael
Elementary Principal
Bierbaum, Pamela Kay
English Teacher & Drama Dir
Blake, Christopher Steven
Spanish Teacher & Dept Chm
Blesi, Bonnie S.
Third Grade Teacher
Bradbury, Kathleen Black
Former 1st Grade Teacher
Bradford, Diane Cheadle
Teacher of Learning Disabled
Brady, Jules Malachi
Professor of Philosophy
Brandom, Vanessa Wormsley-Seals
Language Arts Teacher
Brewington, Katherine Anne (Mumm
Professor
Bridges, Helen Bright
English Teacher
Brooks, William C.
Mathematics Teacher
Brown, Chrisanthia
Assistant Professor
Brown, Joni Ketter
Title I Math Teacher
Brown, Sharon Sandifer
English Teacher
Brown, Steven Wesley
Psychology Professor
Buchli, Mary Kay (Porter)
6th Grade Science Teacher
Buford, Ronetta Marie
Vocal Music Instructor
Bullock, Donna Risan
Mathematics Teacher & Dept Chm
Byrne, Jan
Physical Education Teacher
Calvert, Donna Jean
Assoc Prof of Physical Therapy
Capra, Carl Joseph, Jr.
Asst Ath Dir & PE Instr
Carey, Rena Elizabeth
Accounting Professor
Carlson, Jo Ellen Crawford
Fourth Grade Teacher
Carlton, Judy Borton
Family & Consumer Sci Tchr
Carter, Howard Lee
Electronics Professor

AS CITY (cont)
, Michael Philip, SJ
l Prof & Dir of Campus Min
eld, Joan
ation Dept Chairman & Prof
an, James Martin
Professor of Chemistry
Sarah Jane
Grade English Teacher
Suzanne Julia
Teacher
an, Sherri R.
th Grade & Drama Teacher
s, Linda Carol
ng Communities Coordinator
ock, Janet Kuhlman
Grade Teacher
ughton, Marcia Marie
ory Teacher
ey-Buford, Ronetta
ctor of Choirs & Coach
-Scaggs, Patricia J.
Arts & Literature Tchr
ee, Don Eugene
usics Director
raft, Diane Susan
h Grade Music Teacher
ngham, Lisa Ann
ical Education Teacher
Constance E. (Smith)
c Prof of Telecmntns
port, Mary Ann
School Counselor
port, Michelle Ray
l Grade Teacher
son, Zeta Combs
ly Life Educator
Terrence
uctor of Biology
ng, Melanie Joan
nstructor
unay, Anne La Rose
essor of Voice
le, Francoise
ch Teacher
rtini, Mary Manning
Teacher
gton, Rita Shaw
ish Teacher
le, Randall
School Math Teacher
o, Cynthia Swindell
3rd Reading & English Tchr
son, Morssie L.
Grade English Teacher
Margaret O'Hara
ily & Consumer Science Tchr
, Margie Joann Grable
of Learning Disability
, Stacy Lynn
Grade Teacher
son, Russell K. Lee
urer
a, Jean Carroll
dle School Teacher
, Barbara Roberts
th Grade Teacher
ng, Mary Beth
guage Arts Teacher
ner, Frances Earlene
lish Professor
noy, James Alan
nce Teacher
, Johnna Young
al Studies Teacher
rick, Jennie
& Head of Art Dept
rick, Robert John
ory Teacher
nberg, Mark A.
& Interdisciplinary Instr
gher, Patricia L.
ial Science Teacher
n, Vicki Fats
Grade English Teacher
ner, Kathryn Trost
cher
ett, Marcia Joan Lehmann
y Childhood Teacher
nof, Ronald L.
m, AP Chem & Science Instr
n, Sharon J.
lish Professor
nola, Donald Robert
tory Teacher
nen, Carolyn Jacob
Grd Language Arts Teacher
er, Sue Ellen
hematics Teacher
es, Joan Elizabeth
cher
l, Larry W.
ial Studies Tchr & Ath Dir
ey, Ingrid Gates
nce Instructor
abedian, Thomas Mihran
uatic, PE Tchr & Divng Coach
ey, Jean M.
Dept Chair & Biology Tchr
erle, Jill C.
enth Grade Reading Teacher
mond, Marjorie Wood
ired Third Grade Teacher
ock, Curtis L.
losophy Associate Professor
en, Vicki' Jolene (Milner)
ading Teacher & HS Coach
ng, Rita Purkeypile
ond Grade Teacher

Harrington, Ralph Scott
Art Teacher
Harris, Loraine K.
Biology Teacher
Hartman, Gary Robert
Vocal Music Director
Haskins, Mary Frances
Associate Professor
Hawblitzel, Mary Ann
Fourth Grade Teacher
Hawthorne, Kara Avice
Math Teacher & Dept Chairman
Hedicke, Kenneth Charles
Math Teacher & Coach
Henry, Gloria Jean
Debate & Forensics Director
Hicks, Thomas Edward
History Teacher
Hill, Elizabeth
Speech Comm & Theatre Instr
Hilton, Marilyn L.
7th Grade Geography Teacher
Hogan, Jennifer Jon
Eighth Grade Science Teacher
Howe, Kyle Anthony
Social Studies Teacher
Howerton, Lisa Mc Pherson
Math Teacher
Hudson, Nancy L.
Drama Teacher
Hunter, Barbara Ann (McDaniel)
Health & Physical Ed Tchr
Hutchins-Lehman, Lois Elaine
Teacher of Gifted & Talented
Jackman, Dorothy Nell
Third Grade Teacher
Jackson, Randal Lynn
6th-8th Grade Speech Teacher
James, Deana Deakins
Spanish Teacher
Jeeninga, Emil C.
Business Education Teacher
Johnson, Mary Lou Kennedy
Math Teacher
Johnson, Tony
Fifth Grade Teacher
Johnston, Anne D.
Classical Lit Teacher
Jones, Aretas Rogan
8th Grd Social Studies Teacher
Jones, Linda Faye (Hill)
Earth Sci Teacher & Dept Chair
Jones, Linda Hayden
Health & Physical Ed Teacher
Jordan, Mario Rogelio
HS Visual Arts Instructor
Judd, Barbara Wessinger
US History & Government Tchr
Kane, Kathy Ann
Middle School Teacher
Kapral, George Edwin
English Teacher
Katz, Milton S.
Liberal Arts Prof & Chair
Keith, Penny Kloepfel
9th-12th Grd Hlth & PE Teacher
Kelley, Colleen Ellen
Primary Montessori Directress
Kernell, Robert Oliver
Marketing Education Coord
Khan, Rizwan
Physiology Asst Prof
Knipfel, Bruce Alan
Soc Stud Tchr & Dept Chair
Koch, Sharon Carlson
Assistant Principal
Kubic, Donna Williams
English Teacher
Kubis, Kit Alan
History, Govt & Economics Tchr
Kuenn, Marjorie Asp
Orchestra Director
Lamb, Kathleen Hodes
Lang Art Tchr, Intrdscplny Chm
Latta, Jill Noel
Amer His & Sociology Teacher
Lavin, Mary Ann
Art Teacher
Lawrie, Maureen Mc Nicholas
Fifth Grade Teacher
Lee, James Edward
Mathematics Teacher
Lindboe, Berit Roberg
English Department Chair
Lindsay, William Robert
Bio, Anatomy & Physiology Tchr
Long, Mark A.
CIS Professor
Longenecker, Dale
Computer Science & Math Tchr
Lopez, Albert
Wood Shop Teacher
Lusk, Milous Stanley
Counselor
Lynn, Carol Cotton
Retired 5th Grade Teacher
Maddick, Glenda Chaney
Business Education Teacher
Marshall, Maryvonne
French Teacher
Martin, Michael David
Religious Studies Teacher
Mathews, Marie Skutchan
7th Grade English Teacher
Mayhew, Stephanie
American History Teacher
Mayse, Steve
Asst Prof of Dsgn & Ilstrtn
Mc Carthy, Karen E.
High School English Instructor

Mc Murtrey, Carla Diane (Matthews)
Family & Consumer Sci Teacher
Mc Nabb, Kelly A.
Theater Instructor & Director
Meckel, Jim W.
4th Grade Teacher
Meyer, Cathy Anne (Miederhoff)
Spanish Teacher
Misra, Anil
Asst Prof of Civil Engrng
Moore, Terry J.
Mathematics Dept Chairman
Morrison, Patricia Padgett
Fifth Grade Teacher
Mreen, Rosemary Cambiano
3rd Grade Teacher
Murphy, Terry Ann
HS English & Journalism Tchr
Muschett, Richard Hunt
Biology Teacher
Nash, Marion F.
Jr High Teacher
Nelson, Barbara L.
Classroom Teacher
Nelson, Michael Scott
World History Teacher
Noelken, Carol Agne
Instructor in Chemistry
Nunn, William Sean
Science Teacher
O'Brien, Tom J.
Teacher & Coach
Ochoa, Joan Meadows
Reading Teacher
Oldani, Louis Joseph
Professor of English
Otto, Lucille Elizabeth
Biology Teacher
Owens, Kathy Carmichael
Office Tech Instr
Pace, Linda Lee
6th Grade English Teacher
Packett, Robert Lee
Soc Stud Dept Chm & His Tchr
Papadakos, Roger Alan
American History Teacher
Patterson, Michael Eugene
High School Counselor
Pennel, Cheryl Kay (Matthews)
Cosmetology Instructor
Pepple, Patrick Grable
Biology & Life Skills Teacher
Persell, Eathel McNabb
Fourth Grade Teacher
Peter, George Michael
Peace & Justice Teacher
Petitt, Pamela (Griffey)
English Teacher
Pinne, Christopher Patrick, SJ
Theology Teacher & Retreat Dir
Powell, Deborah Kay
Fourth Grade Teacher
Pratt, Linda Slade
English & History Teacher
Quinn, Kelly (Albright)
Pre-School Teacher
Ramos-Dodson, Lisette D.
Bio, Anatomy & Physiology Tchr
Ramsey, Donald R.
Speech & Debate Teacher
Raymo, Elaine M.
Third Grade Teacher
Reardon, Daniel Charles
Lecturer in English
Rethemeyer, Robert John
Social Studies Teacher
Richards, Judith Carolyn
Spanish & Womens Studies Prof
Roberts, Debra Lynne (Mingucci)
Jr HS Sci Tchr & Aftercare Dir
Robinson, Genevieve
History Dept Chair, Assoc Prof
Rogers, Craig Clifton
Social Studies Teacher
Rogers, Vonley Royal
First Grade Teacher
Rogers-Grantham, Mary L.
Language Arts Teacher
Russell, Jackie B.
Math & Leadership Teacher
Ryden, Donald Wilson
Assoc Prof Electronics & Math
Salsbury, Linda Daugherty
Biology Teacher & Dept Chm
Samples, Sherry L.
Vice Principal
Schroer, Michael Allen
Middle School Life Sci Teacher
Schuchman, Lynn Christine (Stolte)
Health Professions Teacher
Schuchman, Philip Melchor
Sociology Professor
Schulkin, Carl Roger
History Teacher
Setser, Lanus
Mathematics Teacher
Shelton, Thomas Alfred
Resource & Urban Studies Tchr
Sheppard, Barbara E.
Fifth Grade Teacher
Shipman, Elizabeth S.
Mathematics Instructor
Sieve, Charlena Jo (Sola)
Science Teacher
Sigler, Jeffrey Lee
Chemistry Teacher
Simmons, Carol F.
Mathematics Teacher
Skantz, Ann S.
Reading Resource Teacher

Smith, Canary Vivian
Teacher
Smithmier, L. Michael
English Teacher
Snelling, Troy Wayne
History & Philosophy Teacher
Starks, Sharon Micheal (Marsh)
Math & Algebra Teacher
Statz, Mary J.
Vice Principal & Soc Stud Tchr
Stein, Patricia A.
Sixth Grade Math Teacher
Stephenson, Lonnie Dean
Technology Teacher
Stevens, Terry
World History Teacher
Stewart, Emma D.
English Teacher
Sullivan, Donna Winkelman
American History Teacher
Sutton, Delvin Ray
Vocal Music Teacher
Taracido, Jorge Ezequiel
Spanish Teacher
Thompson, Mary Elizabeth
Cmptr Information Systems Prof
Toth, June Ann Hunt
Content Teacher
Towse-Roberts, Judith
Creative Writing, Art Dept Chm
Trainer, Russell Neal
Social Studies Teacher
Twyman, Deborah Anne
Service Learning Coordinator
Van Arsdale, Mary Bernadine
Fifth Grade Teacher
Vandepopulier, Cathy Ann
Family & Consumer Sci Teacher
Walker, Deborah Gibson
Fifth Grade Teacher
Warner, Todd Kenneth
Physical Education Teacher
Warren, Alicia Martin
Eng & Community Ed Teacher
Watkins, Judy Angeline
Second Grade Teacher
Weatherly, Lyn S.
First Grade Teacher
Weems, Clayden Grant
Math Department Chair
West, Wendy Lou
Multimedia Teacher
Wheeler, Clarke Downing
Seventh Grade Teacher
Wheeler, James Donlan
Professor of Chemistry
White, John Patrick
Instrumental Music Teacher
White, LaVera Jones
Language Arts Teacher
Wiley Dorch, Bettye JoEster
9th & 12th Grade English Tchr
Williams, Robert H.
Professor of Psychology & His
Wolken, Karen Forge
French Teacher
Wurtz, Vivian Adele
Mathematics & Religion Teacher
Yount, Joseph Jerome
Learning Disabilities Teacher
KEARNEY
Haahr, Scott Allen
Industrial Technology Teacher
Morrison, John Michael
Science Teacher & Coach
Rich, Greg L.
History Teacher
Taylor, Bryan A.
Vocal Music Teacher
KENNETT
Tate, Natalie
Social Studies Teacher
KEYTESVILLE
Clavin, Kristin Kuhn
HS Math Teacher
KING CITY
Shifflett, Laura Lynn (Larson)
K-12th Grade Art Teacher
KINGSVILLE
Schildknecht, Rita (Noble)
Voc Business Education Teacher
Schnakenberg, Linda Luetjen
Language Arts Teacher
KIRBYVILLE
Cobler, Charlotte Daugherty
Third Grade Teacher
KIRKSVILLE
Bahr, Sandra Helen
Biology Teacher
Carlisle, Judy Wade
Health & Physical Ed Teacher
Collins, Myra Schulze
First Grade Teacher
Colton, Linda Elam
Fifth Grade Teacher
Downing, Suzanna Marie (Moore)
Elementary Teacher
Harrison, Jacquelin Easley
High School Business Teacher
Hawkins, Cheryl Hightower
Computer Technology Teacher
Lovelace, Nancy Marie (Stewart)
English Professor
Mauck, Jane (Hollenbeck)
Language Arts Teacher
Morton, Wendy S.
Language Arts Instructor
Northdurft, Jennifer Spriggs
Biology & Physical Sci Tchr

Poston, Loretta Jean
Fifth Grade Teacher
Primmer, Thomas A.
Agriculture Ed Instructor
Robinson, Nancy Murdock
Spanish & English Teacher
Sanders, Nancy Kathleen
Assistant Professor of Biology
Wohler, Amy Christine
Math Tchr & Dept Chprsn
Wormsley, John William
Asst Prin & History Teacher
KIRKWOOD
Dauphin, Guy A.
Assoc Professor of Basic Sci
Illert, Walter Paul
Assoc Prof of Philosophy & Hum
Kilstrom, John Phillip
Assoc Professor of History
Larson, Judy Caryl (Fox)
Court Reporting Assistant Prof
Mc Donald, Virginia N.
Professor of Biology
Rueppel, Leonora Gray
Professor of Chemistry
Salmon, Harold Emerson
Counselor
Scroggins, Fredna Carlson
Coord & Teacher Education Prgm
KNOB NOSTER
Altis, Timothy Eugene
Social Studies Teacher
Cobaugh, Beth Ann
Library Media Specialist
Culbertson, Carol Durham
High School Mathematics Tchr
Dahman, Sheran L.
Kindergarten Teacher
Endel, Robert Eric
Sixth Grade Teacher
Miller, Wayne C.
High School Guidance Counselor
Resch, Tonda R.
Spanish Teacher
Robinson, David Gordon
Director of Bands
Roweden, Cheryl Bach
Mathematics Teacher
LA MONTE
Kizer, Mary Terresa
Speech, Theatre & English Tchr
LA PLATA
Bissey, Melvin Eugene
High Schl Mathematics Instr
Shelley, Samantha Louise
Art Teacher
LABADIE
Costello, Dolores A.
5th Grade Teacher
LADDONIA
Jaccarino, Emma Whalen
Computer & Technology Teacher
LAKE OZARK
Vogt, Rebecca Cochran
Speech, Drama & Debate Teacher
LAMAR
Burns, Barbara Armstrong
Superintendent of Schools
Foster, Charlene Howard
Learning Disabilities Instr
Fry, Harvey P., IV
Tchr of Severe Mental Disabled
Gordon, Patricia A.
Mathematics Teacher
Nutt, Frances Barton
Rdng, Math & Cmptr Teacher
Steward, David W.
Mathematics Teacher
Tuck, Don A.
8th Grd Science Tchr & Coach
Winter, Gail Gregg
6th Grade Teacher
LANCASTER
Smith, Betty Riley
Business Teacher
LATHAM
Whitson, Tena Potts
Principal & Teacher
LATHROP
Halter, Twila Pittsenbarger
High School Counselor
Hinderks Hardin, Barbara Culver
Fifth Grade Teacher
Smith, Jody M.
Mathematics Teacher
Tester, Deborah Jean
3rd Grade Teacher
LAWSON
Goss, Sandra Klingler
Fifth Grade Reading Teacher
Phillips, Dona Charlene (Baty)
6th Grade Teacher
Sloop, Nick
Elem PE Tchr & HS Track Coach
LEADWOOD
McNamara, Ann Olson
Eng Lang & Lit Teacher
Newcomb, Jean Raby
Librarian
LEBANON
Blair, William Chuck
10th-12th Grd Physical Edctr
Christal, Steward Regan
Civics, PE Teacher & Coach
Dudley, Paul
Social Stud Tchr & Asst Coach
Gottman, Tom
Ninth Grd PE & Hlth Tchr
Grimes, Betty Ringo
Fourth Grade Teacher

LEBANON (cont)
Palmer, Mike James
Physical Education Teacher
Sproat, Patricia Jo
4th Grade Teacher
Wheeles, Karen G.
Speech & Theatre Teacher
Wood, Rebecca R.
Social Studies Teacher
LEES SUMMIT
Althoff, Donna G. (Poe)
Third Grade Teacher
Barthold, Patricia Ann
Speech & Language Pathologist
Berlin, Russell E., Jr.
Dir of Orchestral Activities
Bobal, Christopher Thomas
Social Studies Teacher
Bock, Joyce K.
Second Grade Teacher
Borhan, Mehdi
Professor of Biology
Bowling-Benton, Tina
Spanish Teacher
Clark, Mary Kim
Third Grade Teacher
Edwards, Sylvia Boe
English Instructor
Eubank, Mary Kropf
College Instructor
Ferguson, Steve
Biology Teacher
Geoghegan, Andrew
Director of the Honors Program
Hall, Lucille Abraham
English Teacher
Halsey, Joyce Leslie
English Teacher
Hamsa, Sharon
Math Instructor
Hardy-Parcell, Cathy K.
Music Department Head
Harrison, Kevin B.
Mathematics Teacher & Coach
Heeney, Craig William
Biology Teacher
Holder, Bruce Kevin
Chemistry & Animal Sci Teacher
Hughes, Timothy James
Speech Instructor
Katzfey, Debbie Hettwer
Physical Ed Teacher & Dept Chm
Lillygren, Tricia Louise
Mathematics Teacher
Martin, Ben F.
Theatre Teacher
Mc Coy, Carol Pritchard
6th Grade Teacher
Miller, Marjorie (Brown)
Instructor of Office Systems
Nazworthy, James Matthew
Physics Teacher
Northrup, Marcia Jean
Family & Consumer Sci Edctr
O'Grady, Eileen Marren
English Teacher
Parsons, Jeanette M.
High School Art Instructor
Poindexter, Barbara Mulvaney
Instructor of Visual Arts
Roberts, Elizabeth A. S.
Former Social Studies Teacher
Simpkins, Sandra Cox
HS English Teacher
Theiss, Larry
Fourth Grade Teacher
Vaughn, Karen Elizabeth
Science & Horticulture Teacher
Warner, William M.
Physical Education Teacher
White, Candy Gardner
1st Grade Teacher
Whyte, Julie Proctor
Sixth Grade Teacher
Wilcox, Andrew P.
Biology Teacher & Coach
Williams, Manning
Art Teacher
Willis, Tony
Hearing Impaired Specialist
Wishon, Pamela Maria
5th Grade Teacher
LEETON
Meyer, Gail Adams
English Teacher
Rush, Kelly Jo
Learning Disabilities Tchr
LEOPOLD
Cooper, Teresa VanGennip
Sixth Grade Teacher
Jansen, Mary Zerrusen
Music Teacher & Chapter I Tchr
Nenninger, Jenny M.
Business & Home Economics Tchr
LESTERVILLE
Knight, Denis Peter
Science Teacher
Walker, Patricia Jean (Allen)
Librn & Family Cnsmr Sci Tchr
LEXINGTON
Brooks, Glenn Allen
Marketing Teacher
Craft, Douglas S.
HS Social Studies Teacher
Crosson, Timothy J.
Director of Vocal Music
Crump, Sharon Kalthoff
2nd Grade Teacher
Hofstetter, James A.
HS Social Sciences Teacher
Hofstetter, Juliann Pesek
Sixth Grade Teacher
Johnson, Patricia Lynn
Physical Education Teacher
Mc Crary, James Richard
English Teacher
Wene, Gregory Lance
Science Teacher
LIBERAL
Hall, Jill Marie
English & Journalism Teacher
Myers, Karen F. (Huffstutter)
Business Education Teacher
Williams, Robert Lee
Math Teacher
LIBERTY
Bertoldie, Forrest James
High School English Teacher
Brown, Elaine Kay (Smith)
Adjunct Flute Instructor
Brown, Jeffrey Robert
Social Studies Teacher
Chahos, Phyllis June (Newman)
Secondary Math Teacher
Chambers, Michael
Eng, Jrnlsm Tchr & Dept Chair
Cooper, Sharon Beard
Business Teacher & Dept Chprsn
Gasswint, Winona Marie (Woods)
Spanish Teacher
Howerton, Clara Eubank
1st Grade Teacher
James, Sally L.
Algebra Teacher
Johnson, Vonda Lankford
Retired Kindergarten Teacher
Mallams, Deanna Kay
Health & PE Teacher
McCollough, Gary Richard
Biology Teacher
Neal, Connie Ann
Family & Consumer Science Tchr
Older, Charles Edward
High School History Teacher
Price-Svehla, Cynthia Louise
Instrumental Music Teachr
Radio, Michele Louise
Language Arts Teacher
Rebori, David Michael
Health & Physical Ed Teacher
Rockhold, Randy Wayne
Teacher & Coach
Romisch, Dorothy Minnick
Vice Principal
Thoman, Darrel Ray
Mathematics Prof & Dept Chm
Truckowski, Richard H.
Mathematics Teacher
Warnex, Paul David
Director of Bands
Willett, Toni A.
Fifth Grade Teacher
LICKING
Rensch, Janis Gail
Second Grade Teacher
LILBOURN
Henderson, Brenda K.
Sixth Grade Teacher
LINN
Bower, Timothy Scott
Social Studies Tchr & Ath Dir
Broeker, Arlene M.
Former Office Tech Instructor
Burns, MaryAnn Wolfe
Principal
Dudenhoeffer, Susan Abel
Business Teacher
Gelven, Pansy Sue
Language Arts & Soc Stud Tchr
Hunt, Larry Lando
HS Social Studies Teacher
Krueger, Linda Orrick
Vocal Music Teacher
Lemmel, Scotti
Third Grade Teacher
Maassen, Linda Turner
Kindergarten Teacher
Mc Reynolds, Kelly Rikard
English & Literature Teacher
Samson, Mary Helen Baumann
2nd Grade Teacher
Smith, Veronica Jene (White)
Elementary Principal
Thoenen, Merilee Barnes
Family & Consumer Sci Teacher
LOCKWOOD
Hackney, Kenneth Craig
Industrial Technology Instr
Meents, Karen Renee Luallin
Fam & Consumer Sci Teacher
Shores, Cheryl Ann (Cook)
PE & Health Teacher
LONE JACK
Gafford, Angela Shepard
Former Teacher
LOOSE CREEK
Cockerham, Jeffrey Lee
Principal
LOUISBURG
Brewer, Don DeWayne
Welding Instructor
LOUISIANA
Hunter, David Russell
Chemistry & Biology Teacher
Pitney, Anetta Michael
Teacher of Gifted & Talented
Shepherd, Noveta Hayes
5th Grade Teacher
York, Margaret Calhoun
Second Grade Teacher
MACKS CREEK
Kinney, Mary May Kelso
History & English Teacher
Purtle, Kdendra Alayne (Erie)
English & Speech Teacher
MACON
Bennett, Larry Lee
Band Director
Carrender, Dena Van Slyke
English Tchr & Department Chm
Dixon, Donald Ray
HS Social Studies Teacher
Farmer, Jeffrey Wayne
Graphic Arts Teacher
Galucia, Marsha
Learning Disabilities Teacher
Harvey, Denise Elaine
English Teacher
Main, Myrna Joan (Morris)
Math Dept Chair & Instructor
Martie, Patricia Ann
Physical Education Instructor
McCollum, Robert Lane
High School Advanced Bio Tchr
Nuhn, Stephen Lynn
Principal & Teacher
Stark, Trisha Ann
Early Chldhd Special Ed Tchr
Stockham, Jay Bruce
High School Art Teacher
Trumper, Sharon Sue
Second Grade Teacher
MADISON
Groner-Davis, Theresa C.
Art Teacher
Moutray, John L.
Business Education Teacher
MALDEN
Darby, Susan Foster
Business & Social Studies Tchr
Luke, Kent DeWayne
Junior High Math Teacher
Norrid, Terry S.
Science Teacher
Rascher, Helen Arnold
English Teacher
MANSFIELD
Doherty, Freddie R.
Middle School Principal
Ghan, William Wesley
Retired Teacher
Probert, Pamela Helle
Science Teacher
Von Behren, Debbie Rush
Journalism Teacher
MAPLEWOOD
Hendrix, Sue Carr
Third Grade Teacher
MARBLE HILL
Dunivan, Eddie Dwayne
Physical Education Teacher
Helderman, Mary Beth Masters
Family & Consumer Sci Teacher
Jenkins, Linda Lee
LD & Gifted Teacher
Lowes, Debra Joyce Adkins
4th Grade Teacher
Markin, Kenneth Eugene
Jr HS Social Studies Teacher
Shrum, Lois I.
English & Home Ec Teacher
Wilkinson, Barbara Abernathy
Fifth Grade Teacher
Wilkinson, Jennings
Industrial Tech Teacher, Coach
Woeltje, Kathie Heitz
Sixth Grade Teacher
MARCELINE
Dixon, Patricia Ann
4th Grade Teacher
Park, Todd Anthony
Dir of Bands & Music Instr
MARIONVILLE
Arnold, Doug J.
Mathematics Teacher
Estep, Mark Randall
Agriculture Education Instr
Jones, Anne
High School Art Teacher
Laney, Candy
Counselor & Tchr of Gifted Pgm
Middleton, G. Boone
Jr High Social Studies Teacher
Rholman, Donna L.
Lang Arts & Speech Teacher
MARSHALL
Bleazard, Mary Elizabeth Vogel
Third Grade Teacher
Bredehoeft, Lavonne Marie
Frgn Lang Teacher & Dept Chair
Brennan, Michael David
Social Studies Teacher
Clark, Linda (Phillips)
Mathematics Teacher
DeVries, Christian
Instructor of Human Services
Ferguson, Charles Evans, Sr.
Instrumental Music Director
Gates, Lori A.
Assistant Professor of History
Grace, William R., III
Asst Prof of Business Admin
Gruber, Loren C.
Prof of Eng & Communication
Hoare, Timothy Douglas
Asst Professor of Religion
Kepner, Reed A.
Dean of Math & Science
Lines, Kevin Lee
Band Instructor
Ludwig, Rita M.
Associate Prof of Speech Comm
Malan, Diana Sue
Asst Prof of Music & Speech
Nelson, David Glenn
Advanced History Teacher
Porter, Mary Lou Carey
English Teacher
Shannon, John Randall
History & Drama Teacher
Sharon, Kathleen Dirks
6th Grade Team Teacher
Smith, Robert Lewis
Associate Professor of Theatre
Steinle, Jeffrey D.
Associate Professor of PE
Vazzana, Patricia Mc Graw
Associate Prof of Accounting
Woodruff, Joanne Esther (Spicher)
Science & Language Arts Tchr
Wright, Anita Cillane Walker
Language Arts Teacher
Wymore, Luann Courtney
Elementary Education Professor
MARSHFIELD
Bramer, V. Harlene
French & World History Teacher
Brewer, Joe Eugene
Social Studies Teacher
Bruffett, Rita Kay
History Department Chairperson
Clark, Diana Winslow
Secondary Mathematics Teacher
Cole, Suzan Diane (Layman)
High School Counselor
DeLozier, Sherri Rena
Assistant Band Director
Hanman, Cindy
Teacher
Herring, Lori Hutton
K-6th Grade Tchr of Gifted
Keeler, Betty Cantrell
1st Grade Teacher
Maples, Carol Jo
Jr High Communication Teacher
Turner, Norma Lynn (Perkins)
English Teacher
Turner, Richard Michael
English Teacher
Weaver, Dena Hyde
Third Grade Teacher
MARYLAND HEIGHTS
Beard, Richard Lawrence
Health Teacher
Clarence, Jerith Williams
High School Spanish Teacher
Cornwell, Pamela Hinton
Math Teacher
Fader, Harriet Schweisguth
Fifth Grade Teacher
Heggarty, Susan Doyle
English Department Chair
Henley, Carolyn Overturf
First Grade Teacher
Hilker, Silvia Julia
Spanish Teacher
Kramme, Theodore W.
Mathematics Teacher
Kurth, Mary Reed
Seventh Grade Teacher
Lacey, Velja Souders
History Teacher
Mc Guire, Louise Stone
Mathematics Teacher
Metz, Steven Edward
Mathematics Teacher
Miller, Judith Mitchell
Gifted Program Teacher
Perry, Ann Marie
Math Teacher
Peterson, Stephen Linn
High School Biology Teacher
Pugh, Allen Lewis
Physics Teacher & Sci Chair
Schrey, Kimberly Ann
Science Teacher
Thomas, Linda Helen
Physical Education Teacher
Weekley, Barbara Louise
Biology Teacher
Weiblen, Patrica L.
High School English Teacher
MARYVILLE
Barr, Rod
Agriculture Teacher
Chesnut, Robin Elizabeth
English & Reading Teacher
Funston, Carole Fields
Former Language Arts & Fr Tchr
Heeler, Philip J.
Chair & Prof of Cmptr Sci Dept
Henry, Carolyn Schacht
Retired Vocal Music Teacher
Hill, Kenneth Edwin
Psychology Professor
Howell, Kathy Jean
Youth Minister
Johansen, Eric
Math & Computer Sci Teacher
Keith, Rita Louise (Snively)
Learning Disabilitities Tchr
Matthews, Don Wayne
Social Studies Teacher
Matthews, Mary Walkup
5th Grade Teacher
Mauzey, Elizabeth Mowry
Chair Bus Dept & Tech Coord
Primm, David John
8th Grade History Teacher
Przybylo, Jeff F.
Dir Forensics & Comm Instr
Thomson, Michael Dean
Counselor & Coach
MAYSVILLE
Berry, Meridith Hembree
Facilitator of the Gifted
MAYVIEW
Glover, Mary Cetta
5th Grade Teacher
MEADVILLE
Singleton, Linda Schmidt
Business Instructor
MEMPHIS
Cottrell, Bill, Jr.
Agri Ed Instr & FFA Adv
Couch, Mary Ruth (Howard)
Language Arts Instructor
Mathes, Anna Jean Ketchum
Business Teacher
O'Donnell, Thomas Edward, II
5th & 6th Grd Soc Stud Teacher
Robinson, Richard John
Elem PE Tchr & Ath Coach
Sommers, Terry L.
HS Mathematics Teacher
Stephenson, Linda Faye
English Teacher
Yelton, Suzann
Business & Office Ed Teacher
MENDON
Holderieath, Evelyn Stoner
Business Teacher
Price, Kay Adams
First Grade Teacher
Switzer, Lynn Anne (Davis)
Math & Computers Instructor
MEXICO
Atkins, Susan E.
4th Grade Teacher
Baker, Nancy Piper
First Grade Teacher
Bryson, Judy (Lear)
Business Education Teacher
Craghead, Kathy
Journalism Teacher
Hurt, Cynthia Fletcher
Computer Teacher
Kasubke, Mary Ann Stahl
First Grade Teacher
Kirchner, Keith Curtis
Band Director
Kropf, James Arthur
Junior High Science Teacher
Mika, Daniel R.
Life & Earth Science Teacher
Miller, Betty Jo Newsom
Social Studies Teacher
Murphy, Mark Alan
Electronics Instructor
Norman, Jane Long
Art Teacher
Oldvader, Larry L.
English Instructor
Raney, E. G.
Guidance Counselor
Raney, Ginny Beavers
American History Teacher
Thomas, Renae Best
5th Grade Teacher
Twells, Richard Byron
English & ESL Teacher
MILAN
Montgomery, Teresa K. Morgan
Sixth Grade Teacher
Smolik, Stephen Douglas
Music Teacher
MILLER
Baker, Vicki Lynn
Business Teacher
Hunt, Sharon Sue (Johnson)
Administrator & Supervisor
Johnson, Rosemary Garner
English & Spanish Teacher
McGinnis, Brendan Ryan
Geography Teacher
Robertson, Cynthia Hopkins
Kindergarten Teacher
Scott, Dean A.
Vocational Agriculture Teacher
Spencer, Jane Rene (Craig)
Band & Choral Director
MOBERLY
Asbury, Connie Weimer
Language Arts & Speech Teacher
Bichsel, Terry Lynn
Practical Nurse Coord & Instr
Booth, Richard Dean
Principal
Brown, Kim Suzette (Kaiser)
Science & Math Teacher
Carter, Wendy S.
Gifted Program Teacher
Coyle, Arlene Campbell
Science Teacher
Eads, Cathy Ann
Librarian
Egesdal, Patricia Ann (Murphy)
CNA-CMT Instructor
Fowler, Terry John
7th Grade Social Studies Tchr
Greer, Barbara Smith
First-Fourth Grade Teacher
Herron, Barry Floyd
Chemistry Instructor
Hunter, Jerry David
American Literature Teacher
Jarboe, Mark Ellis
8th Grade Math Teacher

ERLY (cont)
Carla Stevens
i-Age Primary Teacher
nce, Carl W.
hology Instructor
, Gareth Lee
e Dept Head & Librarian
Robert Duane
tn Ministries & Bible Prof
olah, Lynn Browning
ology Professor
ANE
, Janet Marie
a School English Teacher
ck, Lola Cook
ondary Soc Studies Teacher
n, Kristeena Wherry
sical Education Teacher
ETT
Douglas C.
ogy Teacher & Athletic Dir
Marianne Loyd
nentary Counselor
son, Jeff Lee
Risk Coordinator
n, Traci Marrett
nnology Director
n, Nannette Weatherman
n Grade Teacher
orik, Mary Dominic
ner Principal
ers, Elizabeth Ann
Grade Teacher
ROE CITY
Sharon L.
h & Science Teacher
rd, Karen S.
ath Grd Language Arts Tchr
r, Ruth Ann Anderson
ond Grade Teacher
all, JoAnn (Gibbs)
d Grade Teacher
, Dede Yates
n Grade Teacher
TGOMERY CITY
ews, Jane Lynn
ence Teacher & Coach
rdson, Dennis M.
al Music Instructor
, Michael Irvin
ial Science Teacher
TROSE
r, Laberta J.
rd-Sixth Grades Teacher
on, Orval Donn
h, Physics & Chem Teacher
g, Nancy Mc Cullough
nish Teacher
RISVILLE
ders, Darin
sical Education Teacher
on, Betty J.
al Music Teacher
ND CITY
s, Randy A.
iculture Education Teacher
NT VERNON
, Rhonda G.
Grade Teacher
ngton, Susan Renee
Instructor
Rex Alan
hematics Teacher
, Jeanne Spradling
Home Ec Teacher
ck, Donald Edward
h Teacher
gon, Bonnie Copening
rth Grade Teacher
rts, Kathy Krick
st Grade Teacher
ell, Carol A.
cher of Gifted Student
npson, Cynthia Suzanne
thematics Teacher
hn, Janice Peck
ndergarten Teacher
UNTAIN GROVE
edo, Terry Andre
story Teacher
on, Debbie C.
th Grade Science Teacher
gore, Connie Bowling
glish & Journalism Teacher
sey, Michelle G. (Sehie)
siness Department Chprsn
nerly, Stacy (Skeen)
siness Teacher
rson, Bonnie Rae
emistry & Physics Teacher
h, Martha Barnes
Grade Teacher
npff, Marcia Peterson
ence Teacher
Leslie Ray
nguage Arts Instructor
UNTAIN VIEW
olson, Mary Kay (Sharp)
glish Teacher
nson, Methven Erskine
cial Science Teacher
RTLE
fitt, Pam J.
riculture Instructor
ELYVILLE
ris, Kathern J.
rst Grade Teacher
OSHO
n, ALva Jane (Cash)
cond Grade Teacher

Dean, Carolyn
Instr of French, Span, English
Fowler, Joe Earl
Health Tchr & Athletic Dir
Gibson, Nina M.
Social Science & Comm Instr
Goade, Charles Edward
Social Studies Teacher
Godfrey, Mike H.
PE Teacher
Goodlett, Debra Joy
English Instructor
Hively, Russell K.
English Teacher
Ingram, Cheryl Lynn
Mathematics Instructor
Messens, Diana Jessup
High School Business Teacher
Morehead, George F.
Mathematics Teacher
Mullin, Virginia Perkins
English Composition Teacher
Nelson, Mary Alice Hokill
Instructor
Nichols, Sally Louise
Bus & Office Admin Instructor
Parrish, Luann Houston
Instructor of English
Sides, Roger L.
Chem Tchr & Sci Dept Chair
Snow, Michael Ray
Wood Technology Instructor
Turner, Diane Mc Inturff
Elem Tchr of the Gifted
Warren, Gary George
Art Teacher
NEVADA
Aley, Shelley B.
Asst Prof of Eng & Jrnlsm
Baer, Sheryl L.
Mathematics Teacher
Beaver, Kathryn Elaine
Action & Computer Teacher
Bunton, Anne D.
College Professor
Fenske, Alfred
Professor of Drama & Speech
Goodwin, Ann Elizabeth
Band Director
Jones, Robert Lambert, III
Assistant Professor of Biology
McCullough, Patsy L.
8th Grd Language Arts Teacher
Mc Neley, Jodie Kay
8th Grade Science Tchr & Coach
Neu, Jane F.
Chemistry & Physics Teacher
Pendrak, Lois L.
Social Studies Teacher
Schulze, Ranea (Brooks)
Sophomore English Teacher
Townsend, Naömi Atkins
Computer & Journalism Teacher
Witt, Julie Beth
7th Grade Science Teacher
Young, Katherine Robertson-Howard
Reading & Speech Teacher
NEW BLOOMFLD
Haas, Wilda Pasley
English & Spanish Teacher
NEW CAMBRIA
Amen, Belita Elaine (Sappington)
Spanish & Kindergarten Teacher
Brinkley, John Edwin
Social Studies Teacher
NEW FLORENCE
Ellis, Mildred Fae (Powell)
Retired 2nd Grade Teacher
NEW FRANKLIN
Early, Terry D.
Language Arts Teacher
NEW HAVEN
Bounds, Carl Perry
Music & Spanish Teacher
Helling, Rhonda Gay
Lang Arts & Foreign Lang Tchr
Herzog, Ferne Rohlfing
Retired Third Grade Teacher
Spore, Kathryn Louise
English & American His Tchr
Strasen, John Charles
Mathematics Teacher
NEW MADRID
Brown, Janis Kay (Pearson)
First Grade Teacher
Hedgepeth, Lillian Ruth
Sixth Grade Teacher
Meadows, Barbara Jane
Second Grade Teacher
Ramsey, Susan LaPlante
Soc Studies Instr & Dept Chm
NEWBURG
Beasley, Anita Pfennighausen
3rd Grade Teacher
Brown, Margaret (Olson)
Science Teacher
Snider, Shelia Morgan
Jr High Science Teacher
NEWTOWN
O'Connor, Rowena Husted
English Teacher & Librarian
NIANGUA
Ahrens, Jennifer Ryser
First Grade Teacher
O'Connor, Sandy Warren
Industrial Technology Teacher
NIXA
Bough, Sharon Young
Elementary Computer Teacher

Christensen, Lue Anne Turner
English & American His Tchr
Gee, Judith Ann (Cook)
Teacher of the Gifted
Sorenson, Ruth
Music Teacher
Towe, Randy Lee
Social Studies Tchr & Coach
Townsend, Tracy Lovan
High School Math Teacher
NOEL
Kilby, Timothy Dean
PE & Health Ed Instructor
NORBORNE
Franklin, Susan Denise
Science Teacher
NORTH KANSAS CITY
Leimkuhler, Gus Ernest
Retired Librarian
NOVINGER
Johnson, Rick Douglas
Teacher of At-Risk
Keller, Allene Gordon
HS Band & Art Teacher
O FALLON
Allen, Joseph Michael
Social Studies Teacher
Baldwin, Jack Lee
Crisis Counselor
Bockhorst, Barbara Alice (Cox)
9th Grd Physical Science Tchr
Causey, Amanda Book
High School Art Teacher
Gaither, Linda Vanessa
9th-12th Grade Science Teacher
Gassel, Lora Marie (Julian)
English Teacher
Humphrey, Dana Creech
English Teacher & Dept Chair
Koeneker, Sharon J.
English Teacher
Kolb, Phyllis Hungate
8th Grade Language Arts Tchr
Rogers, Thomas W.
Spanish Teacher
Schark, Patricia Monterosa
English Teacher
Schmid, Ann Elizabeth (Werber)
Accelerated Education Teacher
Tharp, David L.
Chemistry Teacher
Thro, Lisa G.
Language Arts Teacher
OAK GROVE
Arnone, Larry M.
High School Mathematics Tchr
Daehler, Elaine
4th Grade Teacher
Loux, Catherine Lee
Guidance Counselor
McElligott, Timothy Patrick
HS Social Studies Teacher
Shields, Mary Ann Friedrich
7th Grade Civics Teacher
OAK RIDGE
Kurre, Jacqueline S.
2nd Grade Teacher
ODESSA
Holman, Gay Anderson
Business Teacher
Schrader, Robert Charles
Marketing Ed Teacher & Coord
Shields, Mike
English, Speech & Theater Tchr
OLIVETTE
Todd, Annie Pollard
Retired Teacher
ORAN
Kidd, Mary Jane Blattel
English Teacher
Nenninger, Vicki Sue
Mathematics Teacher & Coach
OREGON
Mc Comb, Betty Ann
Home Economics Teacher
ORRICK
Koerner, Karen S.
6th Grade Teacher
Wrisinger, Rick S.
Business Education Teacher
OSBORN
Haggard, Luanne Rae
Social Science Teacher
OSCEOLA
Platt, Don Ruel
Science & Social Studies Tchr
OTTERVILLE
Christian, Darrin R.
Business Teacher & Coach
Woodward, Reva M.
English Teacher
OVERLAND
Crowder, Kenneth Robert
Social Studies Teacher
Doering, Terry Paul
English & Social Studies Tchr
Golden, Denton Gerald
Fourth Grade Teacher
Magill, Mary D.
French Teacher
OWENSVILLE
Day, Paul Robert, III
PE & Weight Training Teacher
Duncan, Glen Ray
High School Math Teacher
Dunne, Shirley Mc Crary
Former Scndry Education Tchr
Eubanks, Linda Lee Henderson
HS Social Studies Teacher

Gauzy, Susan Maupin
Principal
Knight, Jean Louise
Former 8th Grade Science Tchr
Kosark, Randy L.
Sixth Grade Teacher
Steineker, Marilyn Kay
English & Journalism Teacher
Tayloe, Mary Margaret
Second Grade Teacher
Vogt, Bill Stephen
Director of Bands
OZARK
Ball, Gloria Anne Patterson
HS English Teacher & Chair
Dilsaver, John S.
Mathematics & Science Teacher
Estes, Joe
Sixth Grade Teacher
Harris, Laura Hasse
9th-12th Grd Math Teacher
McNabb, Tamra (Fears)
Family & Consumer Sci Tchr
Phillips, Deborah Dale
Family & Consumer Sci Teacher
Seidner, Jackie Farmer
High School Choral Director
Swick, Gregory A.
7th Grade Life Science Tchr
Toler, Charlene
Band Director
Turner, Donna Kay
Biology Teacher
Widmar, Rudy Joe
Industrial Arts & Tech Instr
PACIFIC
Appelbaum, Janie Gooch
Eighth Grade Science Teacher
Baker, Jennifer Lynne
1st Grade Teacher
Baker, Jim R.
Biology Teacher
Buersmeyer, Betty (Van Nice)
Math Dept Chair & Teacher
Dorenkamp, Michell Ann
6th Grade Math Teacher
Ellison, Brenda Lee Bartle
Spcl Ed Tchr & Sftbl Coach
Scheible, Duane H.
Athletic Director & Teacher
Thater, Nancy Peters
Social Studies Teacher
Yates, Gail P.
Technology Coordinator
PALMYRA
Bannon, Marquita L.
Fourth Grade Teacher
Bouchard, Frederick Louis
History Teacher
Brown, Donna Sue (Loy)
Sophomore English Teacher
Fleer, Martin Neal
HS Social Studies Teacher
Fore, Clarence
7th & 8th Grd Mathematics Tchr
Pugh, Della Kay
Secondary Mathematics Teacher
Stout, Richard L.
Social Studies Teacher
Thyson, Wendy Fay
Title I Rdng Tchr & Specialist
PARIS
Adams, Donna Elizabeth (Cannon)
Language Arts Teacher
Mitchell, James H.
Science & Physics Teacher
Olson, Jane Anne (Stone)
Business Education Teacher
PARK HILLS
Bates, Lisa Bradley
7th Grade Science Teacher
Berry, Jackie Evans
HS French & Business Teacher
Colwell, Sally (Zapf)
Chapter I & Study Skills Instr
Crum, Kimball Ray
English, Speech & Drama Tchr
Davis, John Philip
Science Teacher
Hardy, Mark Ferris
Fifth Grade Teacher
Hasty, Chuck M.
Social Studies Teacher
Layne, Dorothy Beck
Retired Fourth Grade Teacher
Martin, Cindy Crain
Health & PE Teacher
Mitchell, Martha Colleen
5th Grade Teacher
Morice, Donna Mc Coy
Retired Teacher
Pinkston, Gary Lee
7th & 8th Grd Soc Stud Teacher
PARKVILLE
Brecke, Ronald F.
Political Science Dept Chair
Mc Clelland, Patricia Hutchens
Assoc Prof of Education
Morgan, Marsha Marie
Theatre Department Chair
Noe, J. Mark
Comm Arts Dept Prof & Chprsn
Quemada, David V.
Associate Dean of Humanities
Schoof, Timothy Dale
Asst Professor of Biochemistry
Welborn, Charles Edwin
Asst Prof of Comm Arts

PARNELL
Gabbert, Kathy M.
First Grade Teacher
PATTON
Abernathy, Richard E.
Sixth Grade Teacher
Foltz, Traci Lee
Mathematics Teacher
Fulton, Lena Mae Hahn
Second Grade Teacher
Slinkard, Judith Ann
High School Science Teacher
PATTONSBURG
Gannan, Mary Kee
Science Teacher
PECULIAR
Allbright, Janine Henderson
Mathematics Teacher
Bloodworth, Ruth Jacobs
Language Art Teacher
Drury, Hillary Ann (Young)
Jrnlsm & Creative Writing Tchr
Edson, Jerry Charles
Chemistry Teacher
Genge, Jean Ann
Business Technology Teacher
Groom, Patsy Bruns
Social Studies & Math Teacher
Ingram, Barbara Ewing
English Teacher
Kimball, Jeffrey Paul
Math & Cmptr Programming Tchr
Pierson, Linda Kay
Instrumental Music Teacher
Robinson, Andy Lloyd
Varsity Soccer Coach
Williamson, Nancy Stephens
Adv Math Teacher & Dept Chair
PERRYVILLE
Finger, Kim Therese
Religion Teacher & Coordinator
Gremaud, Cathy Ruth (Hadler)
Mathematics Teacher
Heberlie, Nancy (Hotop)
Principal & Teacher
Lukefahr, Tammie Kluender
High School Biology Teacher
Meyer, Ellen T.
Fourth Grade Teacher
Norman, Crystal Kay (Vogel)
Second Grade Teacher
Oldham, John Rhett
Social Studies Teacher
Paulus, Mick
Social Studies Teacher
Prost, Thomas Lynn
Religion & English Teacher
Reisenbichler, Nancy Miesner
Business Education & Math Tchr
Rhodes, Carol Ann
First Grade Teacher
Richardson, Mary Cleary
Substitute Teacher
Sadler, Tammy Kay
Junior High Teacher
Schnurbusch, Virginia Lee
Elementary School Counselor
Schonhoff, Beverly Leadbetter
Art Teacher
Schuessler, Janet (Meier)
Algebra I & Geometry Teacher
Seibel, Eric H.
Assistant Band Director
Siegmund, Pamela Jean (Hotop)
Science Teacher
Streiler, Jennifer Ernst
Second Grade Teacher
PEVELY
Strauser, Sherri Faye
Third Grade Teacher
PHILADELPHIA
Clark, Shirley Miller
Fourth Grade Teacher
Johnson, Michael John
Sixth Grade Teacher
Sharpe, Carol Ann
Business Instr & Tech Coord
Spratt, Eric Kent
Math & Science Teacher
PIEDMONT
Morgan, Carmen Cook
Physical Ed Teacher & Coach
Schuller, Sheldon Vaughn
Sixth Grade Teacher
PIERCE CITY
Fenske, Benjy Allan
Business Teacher
Phillips, Patricia Anna
Science Teacher
PINEVILLE
Coffee, Debra Lee Cates
3rd Grade Teacher
Roark, Glen Paul
Fourth Grade Teacher
Stout, Laura Jean
First Grade Teacher
Tinsley, Waydene Cooper
Third Grade Teacher
PLATO
Crain, Shannon
PE Teacher & Athletic Director
Walker, Susan L.
Music Director
PLATTE CITY
Dunn, James
English Teacher
Hatfield, Kathy Sue
HS Physical Education Teacher
O'Brien, Christine Slattery
Middle School Reading Tchr

PLATTE CITY (cont)
Tarwater, James G.
Secondary Mathematics Teacher
PLATTSBURG
Armstrong, Beth Pearce
Algebra & Computer Sci Teacher
Collins, Connie Lowrance
English Teacher
Jackson, Marlene (Jones)
Business Teacher
Kennedy, Danny Leon
Middle School Principal
Masterson, Mickey Gerard
7th & 8th Grd Soc Studies Tchr
PLEASANT HILL
Hickman, Judy Irene
Fifth Grade Teacher
Keilholz, Michael Wayne
Vocational Agriculture Instr
Moulder, Karen Highfill
First Grade Teacher
Wickman, Troy Darrel
French & Spanish Teacher
PLEASANT HOPE
Agee, Debra Fesperman
Family & Consumer Sci Teacher
Bowser, Patsy Willis
Fifth Grade Teacher
Cordell, Yvonne Aschbrenner
5th Grade Teacher
Sukany, Todd A.
Sixth Grade Teacher
POINT LOOKOUT
Anderson, Ruth Gibson
Professor of Education
Bolger, Eric W.
Asst Prof of Philosophy & Rel
Eastman, Harold Dwight
Adjunct Professor of Sociology
Elmore, William Emory
Philosophy & Religion Prof
Garey, Duane George
Criminal Justice Professor
Horrell, William C.
Asst Prof of Humanities
Ingrum, Victor John
Assoc Prof of Graphic Arts
Keith, Herbert Ross
Assoc Prof of Ag
Kneeshaw, Stephen John
History Professor
Leftridge, Kay Sanders
Asst Prof of Ed
Lindquist-Mott, Janie L.
Asst Prof of Spanish
Martin, Suzanne G.
Professor of Nutrition
Pfister, Fred
Professor of English
Quiko, Edward
Professor of Political Science
Swearengen, Daniel Joseph
Associate Professor of Ag
POLO
Crouse, Gene
Science Teacher
Edwards, Norman Eugene
Music Director
Grove, Dorothy J.
Business Teacher
Hicks, Lori Ellen
First Grade Teacher
McQueen, Beverly Ann
Sixth Grade Teacher
POPLAR BLUFF
Black, Sandra Hulett
Comm Dept Chm & English Tchr
Blackwell, Vicki Harris
Second Grade Teacher
Crawford, James M.
Sixth Grade Science Teacher
Croarkin, Karen Hunsaker
Mathematics Instructor
Davis, R. Darlene
Business Education Teacher
Desgranges, Janice Garrett
Sixth Grade Teacher
Groves, Faith Colclasure
English Teacher
Holt, Debra Wylie
First Grade Teacher
Kaczmarek, Laurie Payne
Nursing Instructor
Lewis, Carol Swain
Professor of English
Malmstrom, Gerald H.
Biology Instructor
Million, Lisa Stott
6th Grd Math & Lang Arts Tchr
Newman, Tammie Lynne
Eng, Cmptr & Phys Ed Tchr
Potter, Judy Phillips
Fifth Grade Teacher
Rehkop, Joyce V.
Agricultural Business Instr
Ruhl, Helena (Watson)
Bus Div Chair & Acctng Instr
Sandlin, Lorenzo Lee
Elementary Principal
Scott, Darrin Jay
Mathematics Instructor
Stubbs, Carol Francis
Instr of Bus Admin & Acctng
Thatcher, Steven Michael
Social Science Instructor
Trotter, Edna Ruth
First Grade Teacher
Yeakley, Donna (Cloud)
Fifth Grade Teacher
Yeakley, Thomas Edward
Graphic Communications Instr
PORTAGEVILLE
Stevens, Linda K.
French & Spanish Teacher
POTOSI
Darling, Martha B.
HS English Teacher
Jackson, Susan (Richards)
English Teacher
Mims, Carol Lee Goodson
Learning Disability Teacher
O'Neal, Ina Dickey
Second Grade Teacher
Phelps, Connie Jean
Third Grade Teacher
Snyder, Joe
Sophomore Social Studies Tchr
Weiner, Roberta Wright
High School Guidance Counselor
Ziegler, Allen Wayne
Math & Gifted Education Tchr
PRAIRIE HOME
Beiri, Mary Lou
Vocal & Instrmntl Music Tchr
PRINCETON
Rinehart, Wanda Hembry
School Counselor
Scurlock, George C.
Soc Stud Tchr & Asst Prin
Swann, Linda Sue
Language Arts Teacher
PURDIN
Brown, Kate
Spanish & Publications Tchr
Monroe, John David
Counselor
Page, Jean N. Knight
Social Studies Teacher
PURDY
Dohn, Robert G.
Social Studies Teacher
PUXICO
Clinton, Ronnal Gail
Social Studies & PE Teacher
Grant, Leanne (Maxwell)
English & French Teacher
Parsley, Peggy S.
Art Teacher
Rowark, Charlotte Henington
Social Studies Teacher
Sifford, Ruth Anne
7th-12th Grade Counselor
Simpson, Deborah Ann
Social Studies & Jrnlsm Tchr
QUEEN CITY
Rowland, Geraldine Marie
English Teacher
RAVENWOOD
Henry, Kila Ann
Science Teacher
Lorance, Lavona Christine (Gardner)
Retired Third Grade Teacher
Scott, Gina Lynn (Hawk)
Physical Education Instructor
RAYTOWN
Davidson, Lauri May Chomyak
Journalism & English Teacher
Dyer, Debra Cockrell
Retired Teacher
Hilton, James Bruce
School Resource Officer
Lathrop, Gay Klippsten
Substitute Teacher
Locke, Donita Frazier
Substitute Teacher
Perry, Tanya Sue Talley
Home School Teacher
Sasse, Jill Lambert
Former Kndgtn & Preschl Tchr
Tacke, Diane Montgomery
Retired Kindergarten Teacher
Trundle, Sandra Kay
French Teacher
Wagner, MaryFrances Cusumano
English Teacher & Dept Chair
REEDS SPRING
Bloodworth, Julie (Gilmore)
English Teacher
Chance, Anna Griesemer
8th Grade Mathematics Teacher
Dorr, Terry Dale
Social Studies Teacher
Hole, Tina Louise (Beck)
5th-8th Grade Spec Ed Teacher
Kirsch, Jan
High School Counselor
RENICK
Gorham, John Richard
6th-8th Grd Language Arts Tchr
REPUBLIC
Ashley, Virginia Louise
English Teacher
Cummins, Harriet Deming
English Teacher
Howard, John Edward
Social Studies Teacher
Kendrick, Dorothy Jean
Fifth Grade Teacher
Mitchell, Gary Allen
High School Counselor
Ruckman, Laurie Montgomery
Kindergarten Teacher
White, Mary Ann
Math & Science Teacher
REVERE
Golden, Grace N.
1st-2nd Grade Teacher
RICH HILL
Davis, Paul S.
Music Teacher
Miller, David Wayne
Mathematics Teacher
Thompson, Newata Kay (Wimmer)
Sixth Grade Teacher
RICHLAND
Belshe, Sally Sue (Dustin)
Title 1 Math Teacher
Engle, Sheila Linzey
English Teacher
RICHMOND
Balman, Martha Cleaveland
Third Grade Teacher
Brown, Vickie Outersky
Kindergarten Teacher
Hamann, Billie Stoenner
Vocal Music Director
Hamm, Brenda Louise Williams
Sixth Grade Teacher
Jones, N. Jill
High School Theatre Teacher
Middleton, Hal James
8th Grade Social Science Tchr
Pointer, Erik E.
Instrumental Music Director
Richardson, Roy John
Business Ed Instr & Dept Chair
Speers, Elaine Maurer
Fifth Grd Teacher & Sci Chprsn
RIDGEWAY
Parman, Nancy Ronning
High School Principal
RISCO
Fortner, Alice Stobaugh
Second Grade Teacher
Murphy, Michael Emmett
Social Studies Teacher
ROCK PORT
Evans, Jamie Bryan
6th Grade Teacher
Miller, Jacqueline Bergman
Spanish Teacher
Mills, Kyra Rengstorf
Math & Science Teacher
Skillen, James David
Eng Tchr & Boys Bsktbl Coach
Stoltenberg, Del
Jr High Social Studies Tchr
ROCKY COMFORT
Dody, Amelia
Fourth Grade Teacher
Nichols, Carl
Jr HS Science & Math Teacher
ROGERSVILLE
Alexander, Rebecca Lea (Holt)
2nd Grade Teacher
Blakeney, Diana Schroder
Health & PE Teacher
Boyer, Kevin Dale
Soc Stud Tchr & HS Coach
Brake, Earl M., Jr.
HS Social Studies Teacher
Crandall, Ronald Wayne
Social Studies Teacher
Hurst, Sue Heinrich
6th Grd Reading & English Tchr
Mc Pheeters, Rick
Assistant Principal
Precise, Kathleen Ideker
Fourth Grade Teacher
Scruggs, Joseph Marion
Biology Teacher
Sell, Kathy Mc Vay
Fourth Grade Teacher
Talley, Nancy Jane (Lyons)
Business Teacher
Todd-Tull, Kathie D.
English Teacher
ROLLA
Bennett, Carol Bohannon
Kindergarten Teacher
Berkbuegler, Kathryn Mc Maffrey
Language Arts Teacher
Birman, Victor M.
Professor of Engineering
Bogan, James J.
Professor of Art
Brainard, Bonnie Boyle
Spanish Teacher
Cox, Georgia Law
English Teacher
Dearth, Julie Messmer
Remedial Math Teacher
Dinan, Jeff
Assistant Band Director
Haskell, Jane Marie
Sixth Grade Teacher
Jones, Elaine K.
Drama & Speech Teacher
Keltner, Kevin Roy
Mathematics Teacher & Coach
Lucian, Gayle Gene
Chemistry Teacher
Oster, Patricia Anne (Clark)
High School Math Teacher
Roller, Kathy Klingenberg
French Teacher
Stallcup, Scott Keith
Social Studies Teacher
Waldrip, Rod
Communications Teacher
Wempe, Virginia Volin
Spanish Teacher
Wityk, Linda McPheron
English Dept Chair & Teacher
ROSENDALE
Archer, Nancy Schmitz
High School English Teacher
RUSHVILLE
Lassen, Loretta Boatright
Sixth Grade Teacher
Sleeth, M. Gayle (Wright)
Fifth Grade Teacher
SAINT ANN
Burkhardt, V. Connie Wall
Hum Tchr of Gifted & Talented
Clauss, Elizabeth Ann Callaway
School Counselor
Fairchild, Gloria J.
8th Grade Mathematics Teacher
Le Bedun, Mark
Secondary Science Teacher
Mc Kinley, Tim
7th Grade Math & Reading Tchr
Morris, Mary Mullen
Math Teacher
Oster, Kathleen Rose
8th Grade Social Studies Tchr
SAINT CHARLES
Anderson, Michael Edward
Special Services Teacher
Aul, Jill Rubin
Kindergarten Teacher
Aull, Patricia Gipson
5th Grade Teacher
Ayyagari, Laxminarasimha Rao
Professor of Biology
Baker, Henriette Ingeborg
German Teacher
Barnes, Judy Sumner
Third Grade Teacher
Baxter, Audrey Holmgren
High School Spanish Teacher
Beard, Rita Freebairn
6th Grade Teacher & Coord
Bell, John David
Asst Prof of Eng & Frgn Lang
Berthold, Sandra Jean (Bush)
Social Stud Tchr & Dept Chair
Bhat, Kathleen Marie
Vocal & General Music Teacher
Bien, Carolyn Wilburn
Mathematics Dept Chm & Tchr
Biermann, Kenneth R.
8th Grade Math & Science Tchr
Blackwood, Christine Mitchell
6th Grade Social Studies Tchr
Boehm, Gerry Anthony
Environmental Studies Teacher
Bottoms, Ronald Royce
8th Grd American History Tchr
Brooke, George Alan
French Teacher
Buffa, Debra (Ellis)
8th Grade Social Studies Tchr
Campbell, Tracy (Cole)
4th Grade Teacher
Canale, Ann
Assoc Professor of English
Cella, Thomas A.
Mathematics Tchr & Ftbl Coach
Clark, Timothy E.
English Teacher
Coil, Kimberly Marie
Social Studies Teacher
Craig, Carol Myers
Teacher of Behavior Disorders
Dallas, Christopher Michael
HS Math Teacher
De Weese, Donna Netherton
High School History Teacher
Dillard, Jack David
Chemistry Teacher
Eagen, Gary D.
Physical Ed Teacher & Coach
Eernisse, Kathleen Murdoch
Math Teacher
Estes, Linda Allen
Associate Prof of Education
Flemming, Edward V.
Asst Prof of Sport Medicine
Freeman, Mildred Mangis
Business Education Teacher
Gianini, Kathleen Ann
4th Grade Teacher
Glover, Martha (Lutz)
Fourth Grade Teacher
Hargate, J. Grant
Professor of Fine Arts
Harrison, Louise Massie
Sixth Grade Teacher
Hartweger, Kaye Kovol
4th Grade Teacher
Hauser, Mary L. Hartwell
Third Grade Teacher
Hedges, Debra J.
Second Grade Teacher
Hengehold, Barbara Tiemann
Mathematics Teacher
Henley, Mark Ellis
Social Studies Teacher
Hennenfent, Mary Louise (Metcalf)
Science & Biology Teacher
Henrikson, Donna J.
Art & Publications Teacher
Hines, Janet Ann
Learning Disability Teacher
Hoffmann, Margo E.
Secondary Gifted Facilitator
Horn, Gayle Craig
Counselor
Hrdlicka, Michael J.
Assistant Principal
Jackson, Kay Pitts
Third Grade Teacher
Jones, Lisa A.
Secondary Math Teacher
Kelley, Michael Joseph
English Teacher
Kelly, Stephen Michael
Biology Teacher
Kendall, Joy Ann (Kelling)
Art Teacher
Kleinschimdt, Donna L.
Mathematics Teacher
Klutenkamper, Marilyn Sammelmann
Retired Third Grade Teacher
Lashley, Jessie Brown
Writing Instructor
Lay, Dorothy Hoekman
Fifth Grade Teacher
Lehmkuhle, Cynthia L. V.
Associate Professor of Math
Linder, Wayne M.
Drama Director
Loehrer, Cynthia Lee (Rash)
4th Grade Teacher
Lowry, Elizabeth Ann
Guidance Counselor
Mao, Kit M.
Assoc Prof Dept of Chemistry
Marshall, Alma H.
Family & Consumer Sci Teacher
Martin, Sue Janis
5th Grade Teacher
Mason, Michael Marvin
Coll Chaplain & Asst Prof
Medler, Martha Ann
7th Grade World History Tchr
Metzger, Melinda Marie
7th Grade Language Arts Tchr
Moody, Christopher E.
Mathematics Teacher
Morgan, Eileen Drescher
6th Grade Teacher
Mueller, Charles Edwin
Language Arts Teacher
Murdock, Linda Sue
Spanish Teacher
Needham, Deborah Sherrill
English Teacher
Nikonowicz, Barbara Catherine
8th Grade Teacher
Oehler, Sue Carol
Fifth Grade Teacher
Parker, Marsha Hollander
Dean of Fine & Performing Arts
Perrone, Anthony
Assoc Prof of Span & Italian
Peterson, Dorothy Marie
Mathematics Facilitator
Pingry, Joyce Marmillion
Sixth Grade Teacher
Pinkham, Scott B.
9th Grade Physical Sci Tchr
Pinson, Patricia Ann
Vocational Coop Coordinator
Postle, Mary L.
Physical Science Teacher
Prange, Glenn
Retired Teacher
Prinster, Diane Heinsz
Mathematics Teacher
Reeder, Bryan C.
Director of Theatre
Richards, Holly Davis
Fourth Grade Teacher
Ryan, Mary Ann (Amelung)
PE & Hlth Instructor
Sawyer, Jennie Lea
Sixth Grade Teacher
Schneider, Lorraine A. (Steinbach)
Sixth Grade Teacher
Sims, Kathy
Journalism Teacher
Smeltzer, MIchelle Curet
Math Teacher
Snyder, Joseph M.
Teacher & Math Dept Chprsn
Sommerville, Michael Lee
Tchr of Learning Disabilities
Steinhoff, Robin Ruth
Physical Ed Tchr & Coach
Steinmann, Rick M.
Assoc Prof of Criminal Justice
Stone, Jane Held
LD & BD Teacher
Stotts, Nancy Dammeier
6th-8th Grd Soc Studies Tchr
Suereth, Linda Markle
Third Grade Teacher
Talbott, Dale Ray
Acctng & Keyboarding Teacher
Thomlison, Clyde Dale
High School Chemistry Teacher
Thompson, Martha Statler
Science Lab Facilitator
Trupiano, Deoborrah Ellis
Asst Principal
Utley, Mary E.
Asst Professor of Psychology
Wall, Sharon Pavoggi
Physical Education Teacher
Wallace, Donna G.
Language Art Teacher
West, Eric James
High School History Teacher
Wheeler, Raymond E.
High School Science Teacher
Whelan, Thomas Michael, Jr.
Social Studies Teacher
Wion, Sandra Jostes
Librarian
Wootten, Laura Kay
Special Education Teacher
Wuertenberg, Mark Robert
8th Grd American History Tchr

T CHARLES (cont)
Berns, Lori Ann
al Studies Teacher
Jane E.
2th Grd Span & Fr Tchr
Brock, Pamela Jean
Tchr & Foreign Lang Chm
T CLAIR
Dennis Keith
culture Education Teacher
ey, B. Kay
School Art Teacher
T ELIZABETH
ane Volmert
al Studies Teacher
a, Virginia Bax
Grade Teacher
T GENEVIEVE
uster, Linda Hathaway
Grade Reading Teacher
Mary Gegg
nce & Mathematics Teacher
Dean Antonio
Stud Dept Chprsn
r, Nancy Ann
n, Physics & Anatomy Tchr
Lois J.
3rd Language Arts Teacher
an, Romaine
al Studies Teacher
Linda Kaye (Arnold)
ergarten Teacher
Carol Stranimeier
d Grade Teacher
uss, Mary Lea
ness Education Chairperson
Linda Sue
al Studies Teacher & Coach
r, Bob
ical Education Teacher
ner, Noel I.
12th Grade History Teacher
s, Richard Joseph
gion Teacher
T JAMES
no, Susan Daus
Grade Teacher
as, James Boswell
nce Department Chairman
Julian Marvin
12th Grade English Chprsn
T JOSEPH
s, Margaret Dills
red 6th Grade Teacher
Lynette Cole
position Teacher
n, Barbara Ann
3rd Language Arts Teacher
, Barbara (Renee)
Teacher
er, Barbara Lynn
Grade Science Teacher
ord, Sharon Estes
n Grade Teacher
t, Cathy A.
Grade Teacher
s, Lori Ann
guage Arts Teacher
n, Darin David
ral Director
, Anthony M.
Tchr & Strength Coach
ey, Randolph Joseph
History & Government Tchr
al, Connie Spiek
Grade Teacher
aus, Deborah Wright
ted States History Teacher
Randy H.
nth Grade English Teacher
man, Kassie F.
nish & French Teacher
Dennis Leroy
h Grade Teacher
y, Janell Wagner
h Dept Chair
nan, John Ray
matics & Oral Comm Teacher
aday, MaryJo Abey
lish & Journalism Teacher
, Elaine Kay
ond Grade Teacher
vell, Arthur LeRoy
ector of Bands
adin, Juanita Jones
erican History Teacher
aughlin, Charles William
emistry Teacher
ness, Denise Beaver
rth Grade Teacher
r, Wayne Keith
sical Education Teacher
en, Stacie M.
ademic Lab Coordinator
aup, Katherine Bolton
ial Studies Teacher
ien, Tom Leo
h School Math Teacher
, Melladee Kent
Grade Teacher
er, Jan Kauffman
nguage Arts Teacher
nger, Myra L.
nguage Arts Teacher
olds, Barry Lane
manities Teacher of GATE
ard, Deborah Stephens
Social Science Teacher
h, Melody Moss
glish Teacher

Smith, Susan Elisabeth (Schmidt)
Language Arts Teacher
Steeby, Marcia Renee
Science Teacher & Coach
Wang, Jinchang
Management Professor
SAINT LOUIS
Acton, Adele Cecilia
Third Grade Teacher
Adelani, Lateef Alabi
Assoc Professor of Mathematics
Adler, Richard Webster
Principal
Allen, Helen Marie
2nd Grade Teacher
Allen, M. Dale
Professor of Religion
Allen, Mona Onyemelukwe
Physical Education Teacher
Amen, Carolynn Burt
Vocal Music Director
Anderson, Barbara Ann
Family & Consumer Sci Instr
Anderson, Judith Lynne
Science Teacher
Anthony, Linda Brock
French & Spanish Teacher
Applegate, Sandra Kay (Johnson)
Math & Computer Teacher
Arico, James Anthony
Teacher & Coord
Armstrong, Kathleen Witscher
Language Arts Tchr & Eng Coord
Bagwill, Patricia Trotter
Instr of Eng & Newspaper Adv
Baker, Jean Marie (Bullard)
Elementary Teacher
Baker-Janis, Victoria Margaret (West)
Soph Coord BSN Prgm of Nrsng
Balderas, Barbara Ann
Assistant Principal & Educator
Baldini, Deborah Kristine (Suess)
Senior Lecturer in Spanish
Baldwin, Timothy Arthur
History Teacher
Bante, Robert Edward
8th Grade Teacher
Barber, Ann Eleanore
Counselor
Barber, Janet Kemmerer
3rd Grade Teacher
Barnes, Philip Victor
Classics Department Chair
Barnes, Rebecca Marie J.
Teacher of Gifted Education
Bartlett, Maria Cecelia
Assistant Professor
Bauer, Karen Michele
Fine Arts Teacher
Baumann, Jeri Start
8th Grade Math Teacher
Beabout, Gregory R.
Philosophy Professor
Beard, Marvin Earl
Eighth Grade Math Teacher
Beauchamp, Roger Thomas
Science Teacher
Behle, John H.
Assoc Prof of Mathematics
Beim-Esche, Clark
English & Fine Arts Teacher
Belcher, Linda Jones
Mathematics Teacher
Belcher, William Joseph
Mathematics Teacher
Bender, Carl Martin
Professor of Physics
Bender, Mary Henning
Mainstream Coord & Consultant
Bierwirth, Barry James
5th Grade Teacher
Bild, Karen Ann
Third Grade Teacher
Bishop, Mike
Math Tchr, Ath Dir & Coach
Biver, Diane Teresa
7th Grade Teacher & Tech Coord
Bland, Sheila Lane
Kindergarten Teacher
Blumenhorst, Christopher Frederic
Social Studies Teacher
Bock, Elizabeth Schelp
Chemistry Teacher
Boehlke, Keith William
Science Teacher
Bokamper, Susan Colletta
Junior High Soc Studies Tchr
Boley, Donna Offill
7th Grade Mathematics Teacher
Bollinger, Brenda R.
Eng, Debate, Pub Speaking Tchr
Boschert, Joyce (Voerster)
Remedial Reading Teacher
Bowen, Joann Owensby
Teacher, Coord & Asst Prin
Bowers, Steve Lee
PE Teacher & Asst Ath Director
Bowman, Kenneth Gordon
Dept of Sociology Instructor
Bowolak, Patricia Ann
Algebra & Language Arts Tchr
Bozich, Sara Ellen
Science Teacher
Brady, Beth Ann A.
Journalism Teacher
Brander, Janice Steinhauser
Fine Arts Teacher
Brandt, Randolph C.
Social Studies Teacher

Braun, Toni Hedden
7th Grade Lit & His Teacher
Brock, David Lindley
Advanced Placement Bio Teacher
Brotherton, Steve Jospeh
Assistant to the Principal
Brownfield, Stephen Paul
English Teacher
Buckey, Kimberly D.
US Studies Teacher
Buehler, Lester Kenneth
Social Studies Teacher
Bueneman, Janet Hanssen
English Instructor
Bull, Barbara Jenkins
Mathematics Teacher
Bunn, John Robert
Mathematics Instructor
Burroughs, Sharon Denise
Special Educator
Butler, Ray Lawrence
HS Principal, Coach & Ath Dir
Cacciatore, Jeffrey Michael
9th Grd Earth Science Teacher
Cain, Marie Tichacek
Social Studies Teacher
Callahan, Peggy
Gifted Education Teacher
Campbell, Carol Ann
Campus Mnstry Dir & Theo Tchr
Carlock, Cathy Lynn
Ninth Grade World His Tchr
Casey, Donald Scott
Teacher & Coach
Castelli, Michelle
English & Scndry Soc Stud Tchr
Causey, Maggie L.
Title I & Basic Skills Teacher
Chambers, Stan V.
Math Professor
Chrissos, Anna Marie Scott
Social Studies Teacher & Chair
Christensen, Emily Fast
Science Teacher
Clark, Donna Louise
English Teacher
Clark-Jackson, Ingrid
Assistant Principal
Clifford, Anne Niemeier
Cnslng Director & Coll Cnslr
Clinton-Gilleylen, Yvette
Computer Lab Specialist
Cochran, Paul Dean, II
9th-12th Grd Span & Eng Tchr
Colburn, David W.
Asst Professor of Child Care
Collins, Suzanne (Pundmann)
English Teacher
Conroy, Ruth M.
West Civilization Teacher
Cornford, Linda Hitchcock
Kindergarten Teacher
Corwin, Joan Sill
Retired Sixth Grade Teacher
Cox, J. Carlene
Guidance Counselor
Cox, Rhea R.
Eng Tchr & Guidance Counselor
Cox, Tamara Sue (Shepard)
Middle School English Teacher
Cradick, Thomas R.
Biology Teacher
Cramer, Patricia, CSJ
Biology Teacher
Creer, Gladys Z.
English Teacher
Crews, Jeanne Brader
Third Grade Teacher
Crowell, Kathleen S.
4th Grade Teacher
Currier, Dennis Mathew
Admissions Officer
Cusumano, Joseph D.
English Tchr & Rdng Specialist
Dabney-Gray, June Bosley
Vocal Music Teacher
Darst, Daniel Stephen
Religion Teacher
Davis, Evia L.
Preschool Coordinator
Deavens, Winifred Golliday
Math Curr Supvr & Adj Prof
De George, Julia Emrick
Comp, Crtv Wrtng & Drama Tchr
DeWulf, Helena L.
French Teacher
Dickinson, James Lewis, Jr.
History Instructor
Diggs, LaLinda Rose
Reading Specialist
Di Rollo, Fracesca
7th-8th Grd Dir of Students
Doherty, Cathy
Pastorial Associate
Doll, Stevan John
Soc Stud Teacher & Coach
Donaldson, Rhonda (Dudenhoffer)
Fifth Grade Teacher
Donelon, Angela Hunter
Art Department Head & Teacher
Donnelly, Susan Fort
Mathematics Teacher
Donohue, Richard Maurice
Theology Teacher
Downey, Ellen Speer
Chemistry Teacher
Dreessen, Charles Richard
Teacher
Drinkard, David Roy
Biology Teacher

Drysdale, Glenn
English Teacher
Dubelman, Judye Feinberg
Chemistry, Physics & Sci Tchr
Dudley, Beverly Jean Kemp
Kdgn Chairperson
Durso, Patricia Jean
Mathematics Tchr & Dept Chair
Duvall, Ellen M.
Resource Teacher
Dwyer, Kristine Zeiner
Art Instructor
Dyer, Elizabeth
French Teacher
Easley, Barbara Schaumberger
Social Studies Department Chm
Eaton, Leann
Assitant Professor
Edwards, Dossie Isom
6th Grade Teacher
Eilerman, Mary Elizabeth (Eaton)
Language Arts Teacher
Eilers, Denise Marie
Special Education Teacher
Epperly, E. Roger
Student Teacher Supervisor
Eppy, James William
Math Teacher
Everding, Sherry Nolan
Math Teacher & Dept Chm
Everding, Vicki Love
Speech & Language Pathologist
Eyre, Janice Arlyne (Poenack)
Math Teacher
Fernandez, Thomas John
Math Teacher & Dept Chair
Finn, Jacqueline Saia
Mathematics Teacher
Fisher, Judith L. Gaston
5th Grade Teacher
Flood, Kathleen Mary
Mathematics Tchr & Dept Chair
Fowler, Marti
Theatre Teacher
Francis, Michael Wright
Counselor & Tech Drawing Tchr
Frederiksen, Neal S.
Music Department Chairman
Friedel, Helen Brangenberg
Counselor
Frost, Odis Edward
Math Teacher
Fullenkamp, Barbara Bedford
Spanish Teacher
Fuller, Michael Jeffrey
Professor of Anthropology
Gale, Rosalie Garfinkel
Fourth Grade Teacher
Galloway, Alranzo
Physical Education Teacher
Galloway, Betty Hay
Physical Education Teacher
Gansner, George Andrew, Jr.
German Teacher
Garbow, Debbie (Bauer)
1st Grade Teacher
Garrett, John Levon
8th Grade Language Arts Tchr
Gatermann, Skip
Social Studies Teacher
Gautier, Michele Ann
Spanish Teacher
Georgieff, Katja
Professor of Music
Gerber, Carol Ann
Mass Media Teacher
German, David B.
Math Teacher
Gerondale, Carol A.
Theology Teacher
Gerren, Lucie Gaye
Counselor
Gervich, Tricia Peters
High School English Teacher
Gfeller, Jeffrey Donald
Associate Professor of Psych
Gibson, Karen Zehnbauer
French Teacher
Gieslemann, Todd
High School Guidance Counselor
Gill, Donald Keith
Vocal Music Tchr & Choral Dir
Glass, Dianne Gayfield
Third Grade Teacher
Glenn, Debra Ann
2nd Grade Teacher
Glover, Andrew
Band Director
Glover, Jane Roberts
Language Arts Teacher
Godefroid, William Anthony
Environmental Sci & Rel Tchr
Goldman, Elizabeth (Eubanks)
English Teacher
Gordon, Dolores Overstreet
Mathematics Teacher
Gordon, Evelyn Johnson
Fifth Grade Teacher
Goss, Constance Elaine
Social Studies Teacher
Graham, Ann-Marie
4th & 5th Grade Combined Tchr
Greene, Marvia Johnson
Literature Teacher
Greer, Alline Carter
Spanish Teacher & Dept Chprsn
Greer, Betty Vannatta
4th Grade Teacher
Greminger, Michael Leo
Biology Teacher

Griffin, Geraldine Denise
Math Teacher
Groneck, Beverly S.
Elementary Art Teacher
Grothe, James William
Mathematics Tchr & Registrar
Gruendel, George F.
Adjunct Professor
Guarino, Rosemarie Lagermann
Seventh Grade Teacher
Guilliams, Dennis Paul
Tchr, Coach & Dir of Admission
Guimon, R. Kyle
Chm of Natural & Health Scis
Hachegechog, M. Kathleen Beirne
English Teacher
Hadel, Richard Eugene, SJ
Freshman English Teacher
Hagerty, Bryan Ahrens
Political Science Teacher
Hake, Jon J.
Associate Professor of English
Hampton, Betty Joyce
10th Grade Social Studies Tchr
Hancock, Carole Patricia
PE Dept Head & Teacher
Hansen, William Lloyd
Math Teacher
Hardin, Neda M.
Social Studies Teacher
Harlan, Vernon
Instructor of Criminal Justice
Harned, Samuel F.
History Teacher
Harrell, Joyce L.
Teacher
Harris, Donna Troeger
HS Counselor
Harvey, Daisy L.
2nd Grade Teacher
Haux, Hadley Frederick
Director of Bands
Havener, Michael Raymond
Business Education Teacher
Hebert, Monica Leah (Hoffman)
Manager & Counselor
Hediger, Kent B.
Business Education Teacher
Heinrich, Jane Matenaer
Business Education Teacher
Henderson, Carol Elise
Accelerated Schls Coordinator
Hendrick, Angela Rodgers
Choral Director
Hendrix, Bobbie Jackson
9th-12th Grade Math Teacher
Henry, Betty Lee
Math & Pre Algebra Teacher
Herod, Loretta Tisdale
First Grade Teacher
Hesse, Lois A.
Sixth Grade Teacher
Heumann, Eric Gerard
Mathematics Teacher
Hill, Omega
6th Grade Teacher
Hodge, William Howard, Jr.
Social Science & Religion Tchr
Hodson, Carol Patricia
Associate Professor of Art
Hopkins, Gloria Davis
Remedial Reading Teacher
Hopkins, Rosemary Mason
History Teacher
Hopper, Clifton Earl
Biology Teacher
Horace, Thomas Vincent
Soc Studies, Govt & Law Tchr
Houston, Susan A.
Fifth Grade Teacher
Hubbard, Bill M.
Math Teacher
Hubbard, James Walter
High School Soc Stud Teacher
Huck, Susan
Science Teacher
Hughes, Pamela Anne
Guidance Counselor
Hurley, Andrew Joseph
History Professor
Hurley, Mary Elizabeth
Second Grade Teacher
Iezzi, Jean Mc Kenzie
Spanish Teacher
Irons, Sandra Mc Gahee
Mathematics Teacher
Jackson, Geneva
Resource Teacher of GATE
Jackson, Patrick Henry
Orchestra Director
Jackson, Sherra Colvett
Business Teacher
Jenner, Dorothy Mae
Fourth Grade Teacher
Johnson, Delwin Duane
Chemistry Professor
Johnson, Duncan Scott
History Teacher
Johnson, Gail A.
English Teacher
Johnson, John A.
Band Director
Johnson, Margaret Katherine
Assistant Professor
Jones, Donald L.
Associate Principal
Jones, Dorothea M.
Fifth Grade Teacher
Jones, Sandra Montz
4th-6th Grd Health & PE Tchr

SAINT LOUIS (cont)
Judy, G. Lee
Adjunct Prof & Clinical Instr
Kafura, Herman George
Social Studies Teacher
Kalbfleisch, Edith A.
Jr High Math Teacher
Kalmar, Albert G.
Dean of Faculty & German Tchr
Kampschroeder, Julie A.
Psychology Teacher
Katz, I. Norman
Professor & Department Chair
Kauffman, Mary Ann
Eighth Grade Teacher
Kavanaugh, John Francis, SJ
Prof of Philosophical Ethics
Keleher, Karlye Bennett
English Teacher & Coordinator
Kellogg, Deborah S. (Jesse)
Science Dept Coord & Teacher
Kerckhoff, Kenneth Keith
World History & Geography Tchr
Kernen, Linda Mueth
Fourth Grade Teacher
Kimble, Coral Wolff
Mathematics Teacher
Kimker, Anita Elaine Englehardt
Family & Consumer Science Tchr
Kinstler, Laurie Boesch
Elem School Counselor
Kirk, Ernestine Carr
Director of Choral Activities
Kirk, Paul J.
Adjunct Professor of Music
Knoedelseder, Kurt H.
Director of Theatre Arts
Knueppe, Sharon L. (Clayton)
Art Teacher
Koenig, Martin Clinton
High School English Teacher
Kofron, Patricia
Assoc Pastor & Dir of Adult Ed
Kohm, Linda L.
Math Teacher
Kolar, Carol Griffin
English Teacher & Dept Chair
Kralina, Linda M.
Physics & Chemistry Teacher
Kratky, Anna Ahrens
Civics Tchr & Soc Stud Chprsn
Kuegler, Diana Weldon
English Teacher
Kuenzle, Kathyjo W.
Kindergarten Teacher
Kwiatkowski, Christine V.
Jr High Social Studies Teacher
Ladd, Deborah Kay
Speech & Theatre Teacher
Lagunas, Marta R.
Span Tchr & Frgn Lang Chprsn
Lampe, Michael E.
Social Studies Teacher & Coach
Landau, Roberta Hornbein
Asst Prof of Physics
Lane, Doris Rogers
Counselor
Langefeld, Richard Alan
Science Dept Chm & Chem Tchr
Lathrop, Peggy Downey
Chemistry Teacher
Lawrence, Robert Lee, Jr.
Social Studies Teacher
LeFlore, Shirley Bradley
African-Amer Lit Assoc Prof
Lehman, Karen Burt
HS Child Dev Teacher
Lehr, Barbara Ann
Physical Education Dept Chprsn
Leser, Anne
Assistant Prof of Education
Levy, Robin Anne (Edghill)
Assistant Professor
Lewis, Florence J.
Dir of Admissions & Latin Tchr
Lewis, John Ballard
World Views Teacher
Liberstein, Jerold D.
Theology Teacher
Lind, Roberta Katharine (Hill)
Kindergarten Teacher
Linn, Mark Andrew
Director of Bands
Little, Martha B.
Fifth Grade Teacher
Lockhart, James R.
English Teacher
Lodato, Theodora
Instructor of Philosophy
Lodewyck, Ruth Gettinger
Math Teacher
Long, Martin Thomas
Eighth Grade Science Teacher
Long, Pamela Sue
Secondary English Teacher
Lonigro, Marilyn Mowry
Science Teacher
Loyet, Michael E.
Dean of Academics
Lundy, Mary E.
Guidance Counselor & Eng Tchr
Lungo, Philip Joseph
Advanced Biology Teacher
Luth, Lois Stuever
Retired Teacher
Mabrey-Lowry, Donna Gail
Spanish Teacher
Maclin, Rick
Asst Professor of Business
Maddock, Janet Ritz
1st Grade Teacher
Maggard, Donna Kathleen
7th Grade Science Teacher
Major, Edna
3rd Grade Teacher
Maley, Cathleen L.
Spanish Teacher
Mandelstamm, Ann
Learning Center Dir & Eng Tchr
Manita, Salvatore W.
8th Grade Social Studies Tchr
Manley, Diane Boden
Secondary Guidance Counselor
Manley, Shelli Godi
8th Grade Science Teacher
Margraff, Julia Ann Mc Dermott
Science Coordinator & Teacher
Marquez, Barbara Ann Daly
Third Grade Teacher
Martin, Dwight Richard
Special Education Teacher
Martin, E. Patricia
Visual Art Teacher
Martin, Paula Ashley
Choral Director
Matthews, Clifford Wayne
6th Grade Teacher
Maupin, Stephanie Zeller
French Teacher
Maxwell, Terry Wayne
Biology Teacher
McCarthy, Thomas Francis
Social Studies Teacher
Mc Clain, Curtis Keith, Jr.
Assoc Prof of Bible, Hum Chm
McClung, Johnny Wayne
6th Grade Science Teacher
Mc Collister, David
Social Studies Instr & Chair
Mc Cord, Laura R.
Eng & Journalism Tchr
Mc Cormick, D. Maxine
Music Director
Mc Glew, Mike
English Teacher
Mc Gough, Michael Kevin
Principal
Mc Gowan, Kendall
Sixth Grade Teacher
Mc Grath, Michael Stephen
Social Justice Issues Teacher
Mc Lard, Joyce L.
6th Grd Computer Science Instr
McLellan, Margaret Noelker
English Instructor
Mc Mullen-Hellwig, Patricia
Social Studies Teacher
Mc Murran, Michael Patrick
Athletic Dir & English Teacher
McVay, Peggy Schirmer
English Teacher
Melson, Brenda Hardin
College & Career Counselor
Mendelson, David
High School English Teacher
Meyer, Jacqueline Marie
Social Studies Teacher
Meyer, Judith Ann (Nesselhauf)
HS Math Teacher
Meyer, Lois Eggemeyer
Fifth Grade Teacher
Michaelis, Dale Harold
Industrl Tech Tchr & Dept Chm
Miller, Robert Layton, Jr.
Director of International Stud
Minogue, Pauline Kelly
Mathematics Teacher
Mitchom, Sheila P.
Second Grade Teacher
Moore, Eleanor L.
Spanish & Home Economics Tchr
Moore, Stanley Lee
Chemistry Teacher
Moore, Tammy Sue
Algebra Teacher
Morris, George Walter
Russian Teacher
Moushey, William J.
History & Chess Teacher
Muehlhauser, Susan Wright
Retired English Teacher
Mueller, Sandra Ross
Chemistry Teacher
Murphy, Earl Paulus
Professor of English
Murray, Ouima Slate
Counselor
Murray, Ruth Beckmann
Prof & Psychiatric Coord
Muth, Donat James
History Teacher
Nardie, Peter A.
Social Studies Dept Chair
Nasiatka, RoseMarie B.
Fifth Grade Teacher
Newton, Ronald Terry
Advanced Biology Instructor
Nunning, Paula Ann
College Newpaper Faculty Adv
Oehlert, Margaret Ann (Ritenour)
Fifth Grade Teacher
Olsen, Kenneth Charles
Advanced Biology Tchr & Chair
Olson, Barbara JoAnne
Art Teacher
O'Neal, Shereyl Hoskin
Kindergarten Teacher
Orange, Marion Smith
Fourth Grade Teacher
Ostlund, Karen Malouf
English Teacher
Owoc, Patricia (Cook)
Counselor
Pagano, Kathryn Bookstaver
Eighth Grade Math & Sci Tchr
Papin, Karen Ann (Kleppe)
Fourth Grade Teacher
Parato, Elizabeth Anne Unterreiner
BSN Prgm Dir & Prof of Nrsng
Parker, Michael Nay
Ethics & Psychology Teacher
Patterson, Constella Buren
Math Teacher
Paulsrud, Deborah Mae (Thompson)
Project Associate & Lecturer
Pautrot, JeanLouis J.
Associate Professor of French
Perkins, Benita
Fifth Grade Teacher
Perkins, Velmarie Diggs
Seventh Grade Teacher
Pessina, John Joseph
Sociology & Psychology Teacher
Peterson, Sheryl Joyce (Rosenberg)
Kindergarten Teacher
Petrillo, Mary Jeanette
Music Teacher & Band Director
Petru, Marianne
Mathematics Teacher
Pfefferkorn, Michael Gene, Sr.
Social Studies & Ethics Tchr
Pfefferkorn, Sandra Jo (Carter)
English Teacher
Pfund, Roy
Chemistry Teacher
Pieprzyca, Timothy Brian
Chemistry Tchr & Dorm Prefect
Pike, Susan Kay
High School Computer Teacher
Pittman, Doris Jane
Music Teacher
Popkin, Nancy Moore
Adjunct Instr Eng Composition
Popp, Tamara Thrasher
Mathematics Teacher
Povard, Vivian
History Teacher & Dept Chair
Powers, Shirley A.
Title I Mathematics Teacher
Prahlow, Donald August
Soc Stud Chprsn & History Tchr
Przada, Maria S.
9th & 12th Grd Religion Tchr
Puhr, Kathleen Marie
HS English Tchr & Dept Leader
Pulley, Marjorie Joyce
First Grade Teacher
Raglin, Vera Jean
English Tchr & Dept Chprsn
Ramming, Chris
Physics Instructor
Rank, Mark Robert
Associate Professor
Rauh, Shirley Perkins
Family Studies Chair
Rauscher, Gene Philip
Instrumental & Voc Music Tchr
Ray, Sandra L.
Mathematics Dept Chair & Tchr
Rayfield, Nancy Kay
Science Teacher
Rea, Barbara Andrea
Gifted Education Teacher
Reher, Dorothy C.
Fourth Grade Teacher
Reichert, Mary Joyce
Sixth Grade Teacher
Reilly, Timothy James
Math & Science Teacher
Rikili, Richard Lee
Jr HS Principal & Teacher
Riley, Barbara Ellen
Science Teacher
Ringo, Betty Jo
Special Education Teacher
Robben, Bob E.
Math Teacher
Robinson, Carol Dierkes
Spanish Teacher
Robinson, John Philip
Amer History & Psychology Tchr
Roble, James H.
Chemistry Teacher
Roby, Linda Thompson
Choral Director
Rockett, Wilhelmenia Howard
Social Studies Teacher
Rodgers, Thomas Edward
Physics Teacher
Roesch, Donna Eve (Disko)
English, Speech & Debate Tchr
Rosbrugh, Phyllis
Mathematics Teacher
Rosenthal, Howard Gary
Assoc Prof & Pgm Director
Ross, Nora Ann
Teacher
Ross-Fisher, Roberta Louise
Asst Professor of Education
Rossi, Patricia Anne
Social Studies Teacher
Rothermich, Beth Kay
Drama Teacher & Theater Mgr
Roti, Frank Victor
6th Grade Spanish Teacher
Rucker, Glendolene White
Sixth Grade Teacher
Ruddy, Thomas Michael
Professor of History
Ruebsam, Gail Ann
Kindergarten Teacher
Ruthmann, Marie Therese, VHM
English Teacher
Salomon, Wayne Mark
Dir of Theatre & Dept Chair
Schardan, Ronald Charles
Bio Tchr & Sci Dept Chm
Scharf, Margaret Mc Meel
Junior High Teacher
Schenk, Carla Horrell
Retired 2nd Grade Teacher
Scheve, Pearl Ann
Theology Teacher
Schilli, Richard J.
Campus Minister & Rel Teacher
Schmidt, Susan Cracraft
Jr HS Vocal Music Teacher
Schmitt, Linda Sue
5th Grade Teacher
Schmollinger, Connie S.
English Department Chairperson
Schoeffel, Georgia B.
Communication Skills Teacher
Schoonover, Carol Kruz
Third Grade Teacher
Schrappen, Virginia Hartlieb
Sales Associate & Former Tchr
Schroer, Jo Anna
Director of Physical Therapy
Schweitzer, Theresa Tarr
Enrichment & Art Teacher
Sciuto, Matthew C.
Religion Teacher & Coach
Scott, Lillyan Juliette
Math Teacher
Sczepanski, Etta Mae (Gregory)
Second Grade Teacher
Sebastian, Terry Linn
Instrumental Music Tchr & Dir
Seim, Richard F.
Social Studies Teacher
Sharp, Cecil T.
Physiology & Advanced Bio Tchr
Shaw, Andrew Dwight
Science Dept Chair
Shipps, Cecilia Ann
Vocal Music Teacher
Siebert, Jane Gulath
Mathematics Teacher
Skarda, Jean La Pacek
4th Grade Teacher
Smith, Donna L.
Social Studies Teacher
Smith, Frank Patrick
5th-8th Grd Sci Tchr & Coord
Smith, Jay Grantley
Fifth Grade Teacher
Smith, Joseph Martin
Asst Prof of Med & Biomedical
Spencer, Elizabeth Ann
Cmptr Coordinator & Math Tchr
Staed, Jennifer Keelan
9th-12th Grd English Teacher
Starks, Calvin Edmond
Assistant Principal
Stary, Frank E.
Chemistry Professor & Prgm Dir
Steiner, Michael Joseph
History Teacher
Stevens, James E.
Chemistry & AP Chemistry Tchr
Stewart, Roberta L.
Math Dept Chairperson & Tchr
Stockmann, Sharon Walsh
Art Teacher
Stokes, Lora Wilson
High School Mathematics Tchr
Stoller, Cheryl Lynn (Wilson)
Journalism Teacher
Stout, Arthur Madison, Jr.
Math Teacher & Tennis Coach
Stover, April M.
Chemistry & Physical Sci Tchr
Straatmann, Lisa Marie
Math Teacher
Strangman, George Herbert
Eighth Grade English Teacher
Straube, Kathee Meirink
Tchr of GATE
Strembicki, Stanley
Professor of Art & Photography
Strobach, Connie M. Travagliante
PE Teacher & Coach
Stuhlmann, Marvin A.
English Teacher
Sturgill, Darrel Gregory
Social Studies Teacher
Sullivan, Peggy A.
Family & Consumer Science Tchr
Sutton, Cynthia Johnson
Special Educator
Swatek, Marilyn Knaus
Seventh Grade Teacher
Tatlow, Holly Schafer
Homebound Teacher
Taylor, Harold R.
Math Teacher
Taylor, James Bertram
Associate Naval Science Instr
Terry, Lorraine Ann
5th Grade Teacher
Testa, Michael Angelo
Adjunct Prof of Religious Stud
Texier, Sue E.
Fourth Grade Teacher
Thies, Linda Killam
Mathematics Tchr & Dept Chair
Thompson, Dennis Charles
Soc Studies Tchr & Dept Head
Thompson, Leroy T.
English Teacher
Tiemann, Larry Gene
5th Grade Teacher
Tillmann, Vanita Denise
Fourth Grade Teacher
Tilly, Cindi Bach
First Grade Teacher
Torretta, Karen Bannister
Math & Gifted Education Tchr
Tran, Minh Thanh
ESL Teacher Assistant
Trenary, Mary Ann Colon
Sixth Grade Teacher
Troia, Elisabetta Collins
English Second Language Tchr
VanAusdall, Barbara Wass
English Teacher
Van Breusegen, Jennifer Chickering
English Teacher & Gifted Coord
Van Dyke, Karen
Associate Professor
Varley, Paul Charles, Jr.
Instrumental Music Teacher
Violetta, Marie Carol
Music Teacher
Walker, Terrell Nathaniel
School Counselor
Walsh, Kevin Patrick
Music Teacher
Weber, Janet Baugh
Junior High Language Arts Tchr
Weber, Jeanne Polonus
Senior High Spanish Teacher
Webre, Emory C.
Religion Teacher
Wehner, Richard Thomas
Theology Teacher
Weiss, Leslie Pabst
English & Language Arts Tchr
Welch, Patrick James
Economics Professor
Welschmeyer, Joe John
Former Teacher
Westphal, Mary Catherine
English Teacher
Weyer, Maurice
8th Grd Science & Math Teacher
Whalen, Patrick Joseph
Religion Teacher
Whitmore, Armetta Givens
Dir of Pathway Tchng Careers
Whitworth, Louise Royster
HS Family & Cnsmr Sci Teacher
Wilfred, Vasantha
Mathematics Professor
Wilkes, Christine Hoesch
4th Grade Teacher
Williams, Margaret Lea
Social Studies Teacher
Williams, Mark Ward
French Teacher
Williams, Tyrone
Social Studies Teacher
Williams, Yolander Davis
Chemistry Teacher
Wilson, Dianne
Mathematics Teacher
Winkler, Bertha Moore
Guidance Counselor
Wirtz, Jan D.
Art Teacher
Woehr, David Fredrick
Teacher
Wojak, Philip John
Physics Teacher
Wolf, Margaret Mueller
Teacher of GATE & Kindergarten
Woods, Audrey Mc Ghee
Sixth Grade Teacher
Woulfe, Ellen
Third Grade Teacher
Wright, Katie Harper
Associate Professor
Yates, Brian D.
Physics & Astronomy Teacher
Yost, Susan Ray
Dir Stu Support Svcs
Zimmerman, William C.
Chemistry Teacher
Zimmers, Gloria Koehler
5th Grade Teacher
Zitko, Dorothy Marie (Ellebracht)
Junior HS Math Teacher

SAINT PETERS
Ambruster, Ruth Lorraine
Assistant Principal
Cassibry, Wilma Linderman
English Teacher
Chandler, Calvin C.
Spanish Professor
Checkett, Lawrence
English Professor
Clemens, Michael J.
Principal
Curran, Kevin A.
7th Grade Social Studies Tchr
Curran, Laura Jane
Guidance Counselor
Deters, Kelly Marie
English Teacher
Ferguson, Larry W.
Fifth Grade Teacher
Goulden, Gordon H.
Asst Prof of Fine Arts
Groenemann, Jan
Art Instructor & Author
Gross, Janet Connor
Second Grade Teacher

' PETERS (cont)
;y, Susan Westenberger
ing Specialist
Carleen K. (Eichhorn)
2th Grade Health Ed Tchr
s, Kathleen Lyman
Grade Teacher
'heodore Judson
a Teacher
Wanda J.
ematics Professor
Helena A.
uage Arts Teacher
ton, Mary Angela
Grade Science Teacher
Karen K.
& Chprsn of Admin Off Mgt
, Diane Papageorge
'eacher
Denise Barnett
le School Music Teacher
rg, Robert
rtmental Teacher
ll, Jill Downen
Department Chair & Teacher
ki, Carol Ann Connor
d & Talented Facilitator
, Joseph Paul
al Studies Teacher
, Patricia A.
ch Comm & English Teacher
ever, Lisa Ann
nd Grade Teacher
ı, Ann Beene
of Life Sciences
ang, Barbara Yvonne (Taylor)
ematics Teacher
n, Carole Ann (Moniz)
School History Teacher
haus, Janiece M.
ention & Crisis Counselor
M
well, Jo Ann Snodgrass
ish Teacher
well, Lloyd E.
ematics Teacher
Randy Dewayne
nth Grade Teacher
r, Tana Jo (Green)
-England, Susan Jane
titute Teacher
& Learning Resource Instr
Kevin Glen
h Grd PE & Health Teacher
rs, Libby Sparling
& BD Resource Room Teacher
SBURY
on, Carole R.
d Director
, Madonna, SCL
Teacher & Ed Specialist
COXIE
on, Gay Lynne McDonald
th Grade Teacher
t, Janet Chrisman
ness Teacher
NNAH
son, Larry Wayne
th Grd Eng & Lit Teacher
ry, Debra Hutchcraft
School Biology Teacher
Kathleen J.
ch & Spanish Teacher
Retha Fern (Morrison)
guage Arts & Math Teacher
ence, Don Lloyd
of Schools
, Traci Waisblum
Instructor
William Randt
8th Grade PE & Hlth Tchr
William O.
ory Tchr & Acad Team Coach
, Sara Jane
th Grade Science Teacher
ELL CITY
m, Sheryl Jo (Bell)
ness Teacher
ngs, Maritza Teed
lish & Soc Studies Teacher
T CITY
, Martha Anne
rd Grade Teacher
ALIA
op, Mary Ellen
dergarten Teacher
l, Kendall Lee
Grade Mathematics Teacher
, Jeannine Allyson (Hinken)
dergarten Teacher
org, Britt Allen
m Music Teacher
en, JennaLee Martin
st-Second Grade Teacher
en, Bette Jo (Woodman)
siness Ed Teacher & Chprsn
er, Tommy Loyd
sical Ed Teacher
n, Donald Sangree, Jr.
r of Economics & Psych
oy, Frances Rifkin
nmunity College Instructor
ison, Matthew Brian
rketing Ed Teacher & Coord
ersbaugh, Eva Turner
guage Arts Teacher
ster, Julie Habing
enth Grade Math Teacher
ardson, Rebecca Martin
idance Counselor

Romig, Betty Ann
4th Grade Teacher
Taylor, Salome
Business Teacher
SENATH
Bailey, Jerry Dean
Industrial Arts Teacher
Clevenger, Charlene D.
HS Business Education Teacher
Raines, Alice Mitchell
High School Media Specialist
SENECA
Durbin, Sandra Schoen
Band Director
Hodge, Tom F.
Asst Prin & Athletic Director
Hunt, Jennifer Powell
Business Teacher
Miller, Dianne Striegel
Language Arts Teacher
Pattison, Ada Lee (Williams)
Third Grade Teacher
Vinson, Earl L.
Fifth Grade Teacher
Whitehead, John M.
HS Amer His Teacher & Coach
SEYMOUR
Coutchie, Valora Sue (Campbell)
Teacher of the Gifted
Humphrey, Tammy Lynne
8th-12th Grade Math Teacher
SHELBINA
Dandoy, Shawn William
Civics Teacher
Drummond, Charlotte Miller
Secondary Mathematics Teacher
Glover, Paula Keller
HS Language Arts Teacher
Kirby, Dee Ann Greening
Family & Consumer Science Tchr
Quinley, Denise Earlene
Library Media Specialist
Wieberg, Gregory Lawrence
Vocal Music Director
SHELBYVILLE
Geisendorfer, Mary Ann (Dodd)
Second Grade Teacher
Lund, D. Sue
5th & 6th Grd Lang Arts Tchr
Resa, Angela B.
Mathematics Teacher
Smoot, Diane Parsons
Bus Instr & Tech Coord
SHELL KNOB
Prewitt, Diane Burns
Guidance Counselor
SIKESTON
Baker, Gayle Godwin
Mathematics Teacher
Depro, Charles Robert
Social Studies Dept Chairman
French, Agatha Goehri
Orchestra Director
Lambert, Marla Bryant
Kindergarten Teacher
Lape, Melissa Harris
Second Grade Teacher
Moran, Sharon H.
Third Grade Teacher
Norton, Harold Oliver
Secondary Teacher
Pike, Carolyn Berry
Sixth Grade English Teacher
SILEX
Francis, James Keith Anthony
PE Tchr, Athletic Dir & Coach
Thompson, Helen Sledd
Retired First Grade Teacher
SKIDMORE
Everhart, Marian John
Second Grade Teacher
SLATER
Arni, Rick L.
History Teacher & Dept Chair
Clements, Connie
Biology & Ecology Teacher
Davis, Anna Catherine
HS Mathematics Teacher
Gonzalez, Robert E.
Soc Studies & PE Teacher
Humburg, Barbara Ann (Smith)
Junior High Science Teacher
Jones, Myra Shepard
Language Arts Teacher
Whiteaker, Denis Roi
Speech & Language Arts Teacher
SMITHTON
Cline, Judy Marie
4th Grade Teacher
Henley, Betty E.
High School Counselor
Pirtle, Jerry Lee
English & Speech Teacher
SMITHVILLE
Alagna, Kathy Lynn
Amer His, Geog & Pol Sci Tchr
Frazier, Cornelia Hartmann
5th Grade Classroom Teacher
French, Joyce Jane
Third Grade Teacher
Hayden, Leslie Schaefer
6th Grd Social Studies Tchr
Horton, James Michael
Science Teacher
Huke, Joseph Patrick
Mathematics Tchr & Co-Chm
Mast, Becky Lee (Brown)
Reading & Drama Teacher
Mayo, Alexis Miller
HS French & Spanish Teacher

Roesle, George Thomas, Jr.
4th Grade Teacher
Vitek, Scott A.
Technology Teacher
SOUTH WEST CITY
Ramsey, Kenny Dean
5th Grade Classroom Teacher
Slagle, Raymond Leroy
Math & Science Teacher
SPARTA
Hamilton, Harriet Wills
Middle School Teacher
SPOKANE
Farmer, Phyllis Lynn
High School Mathematics Tchr
Little, Helen Louise (Wilson)
Learning to Read Supervisor
Moore, Deloris Ann
Family & Consumer Sci Teacher
Nielsen, Laura M.
English Teacher
Rhoads, Angela Nickels
Business Teacher
SPRINGFIELD
Abramovitz, George Edward
Social Studies Teacher
Akaike-Toste, Janet Miyoko
Japanese Lang & Culture Tchr
Allen, Sandra Blackwell
Fourth & Fifth Grade Teacher
Ames, Jimmy Ray
Education Professor
Arnold, Forest Loyd
Associate Professor in Bible
Arnold, Virginia Lee
General Education Assoc Prof
Ashton, Kevin K.
English Teacher
Baker, Kevin Duane
8th Grd Amer His & Media Instr
Bauer, Kathleen Marie
8th Grade Teacher
Beard, Bobbi Mitchell
Assistant Professor of English
Beck, Julie Anne
Business Professor
Benson, Randi-Lyn Patricia (Proft)
Substitute Teacher
Berg, Jane Munson
Instructor of Voice
Berg, Robert Alan
Assoc Prof of Biblical Studies
Bowen, Jan Berry
Second Grade Teacher
Casalo, Gary Carlo
Art Instructor
Chesler, Sharon K.
First Grade Teacher
Church, Christy Roth
Band Director
Climer, Beth J.
Coord Instr Hlth Inf Tech Pgm
Clopton, Jo Akin
Retired Primary Teacher
Coffey, Lynn Daniel
Business Teacher
Colliatie, Janet Burkart
English Teacher
Collins, Wanda Sharp
Retired Teacher
Cooper Graves, Donna
Asst Professor of History
Cowin, Regina Maria
Third Grade Teacher
Daugherty, Caron Linelle
Academic Advisor
Davis, Debra Walden
Family & Consumer Sci Instr
Dingeldein, Verna Sue (Everett)
Elementary Teacher
Downs, Debbie L.
PE Teacher
Eastman, Valerie Hackmann
Asst Professor of Psychology
Ebert Shroyer, Judy Carole
3rd Grade Teacher
Edwards, Twila Brown
Assoc Prof of Biblical Studies
Fees, Louis Keith
Physical Ed & Health Instr
Fotsch, Frederick C.
Science Instructor
Gaines, Conita Cole
Former Third Grade Teacher
Gardner, James E.
Psychology Professor
Gasaway, Joan Duggins
Orchestra Director
Gillespie, Carolyn Sue
Teacher
Glover, Carolyn Kibby
Fifth Grade Teacher
Grabill, Dean Louis
Pastoral Ministries Assoc Prof
Gregg, Judith Ann
Social Studies Teacher
Gritz, Betty Melendy
Third Grade Teacher
Grover, Kathy J.
Mathematics Teacher
Gunnels, Wilma Menzies
Business Education Teacher
Haase, Lesa Conn
1st & 2nd Grd Multiage Teacher
Herman, Mary E.
Prof of Education & Dept Chair
Hinch, Steven William
Social Studies Supervisor
Howard, Charles Kenneth
Bible & Theology Professor

Hubbard, Willa Victoria
Mathematics Teacher
Huechteman, Earl Duane
Assoc Professor of Mathematics
Huechteman, Rebecca Kelly
Education Dept Chair & Prof
Jenkins, Robin Ann
Mathematics Teacher
Jones, E. Grant
Psychology Professor
Kavanaugh, Rosa (Kellner)
Instructor of Mathematics
King, Brian
Business Law & Pol Sci Instr
Lawrence, Edgar Dean
Special Ed Assoc Prof
Laws, Ron
Jr High & HS Teacher
Linn, Charles E.
Asst Professor of PE & Coach
Loudis, Anthony Alan
Broadcast Journalism Instr
Maslowsky, Sharon Ann
Business Education Teacher
Mc Clure, Nicholas Lee
History, Drama & Shop Teacher
McGee, Robin Marie (Shea)
French Teacher
McKiney, Diane Wilks
Multi Age Classroom Teacher
Meinhardt, Lynn Gerdemann
French Teacher
Menard, Kathleen Smith
4th Grade Teacher
Miller, Brett Alan
Speech & Debate Teacher
Morrow, Glenda Winkle
Associate Professor of Music
Morrow, Peggy Eutsler
4th Grade Teacher
Myers, Richard Lee
Prof of Microbio & Immunology
Nance, Lauren
Counselor
Nichols, Jimmy Washington
Mathematics Teacher
Parmenter, Jan Audrey (Perkins)
Asst Prof of Social Work
Piper-Schnapp, Becky
Tech In Living, Cmptr Sci Tchr
Prather, Belva Worthen
Associate Professor of Music
Prince, Lisa V.
English Dept Teaching Asst
Reed, Karen Gay
High School Biology Teacher
Reed, Sheila West
First Grade Teacher
Rooney, Sharon Westberg
Assistant Professor of English
Ryan, Debra Dianne
Language Arts Teacher
Sanders, Bryan H.
Assoc Prof of Govt, Legal Stud
Scheer, John Michael
Teacher of Gifted Resource
Sewell, James T.
Professor
Smith, David Edward
Asst Prof of Drama
Soetaert, W. James
Latin I & English IV Teacher
Sparkman, Teresa Elaine
Speech & Debate Teacher
Spear, Sylvia Ann (Chilcutt)
High School Biology Teacher
Spence, Jonathan Claude
8th Grade Social Studies Tchr
Stander, Linda Marie
Bus Ed Dept Head & Teacher
Stelplugh, Betty Overton
Retired Music Teacher
Straton, Joyce Remenar
Biology Teacher
Strunk, Gary Edward
Art Teacher
Swift, Karen Mitchell
Business Education Teacher
Taylor, Lisa Carole
Instructor of English
Tosh, Donald H.
Assoc Prof of Mathematics
Tummons, KayAnn Buckler
Seventh Grade Life Sci Teacher
Turnbull, Robert Bruce
Fr Prof & Hum Dept Chprsn
VanHook, Shirey A.
Instr & Peer Tutor Coordinator
Watson, David Glenn
Former Associate Professor
Watts, Wm. Kent
Schl Enrichment Facilitator
Wetteroth, Frank George
English Teacher & Coach
Wilson, Joyce Luna
Retired Teacher
Wubbena, Dennis R.
Professor
STANBERRY
Fisher, Kevin Dean
Mathematics Teacher & Coach
STEELE
Hollis, Linda Diane
French & English Teacher
House, Deborah Mc Carroll
Fourth Grade Teacher
STEELVILLE
Dicus, Lois Setzer
Retired Second Grade Teacher

Taylor, Carolyn Langston
Fourth Grade Teacher
STET
Saltsgaver, Mary Jane (Neswsom)
Mathematics Teacher
Shirley, Julie Bogda
English Teacher
STEWARTSVILLE
Heyde, Kevin Robert
Math Teacher
Holtzclaw, Stacy Lynn (Clark)
Business Education Teacher
Jones, Jay Robert
Band Director
Reed, John Blair
Principal & AD
STOCKTON
Carpenter, David Lee
Elem Physical Education Tchr
Cross, Gaila Mae
Sixth Grade Teacher
Keeton, Robert T.
Math Teacher
Martin, Marsha Sweaney
High School Counselor
Mayer, Jean Marie
Science Teacher
Randolph, Jack Lowell
Physical Education Teacher
Rutledge, Phyllis Ann
Second Grade Teacher
Stafford, Susie
Social Studies Teacher
Vahle, Leonard Charles
Math Dept Chair
Vahle, Shirley J. (Yazel)
English Teacher
Webb, Sue Price
Educator of the Gifted
STOUTLAND
Bentch, Mary Lou (Bucher)
Secondary English & Drama Tchr
STOVER
Stucker, Jodi Lorene
Vocational Business Teacher
STRAFFORD
Blevins, Freda Ann (Schreffler)
Speech, Theatre, Commnctn Tchr
Collins, John Keith
Physical Education Teacher
Goddard, Patricia Lee
Mathematics Teacher
Johnson, Ruth Ann
High School Guidance Counselor
Parkhurst, Becky Lynn
Fifth Grade Teacher
Zieres, Beverly Baker
English & Journalism Teacher
SUCCESS
Cook, Gary Wayne
Fifth Grade Teacher
SULLIVAN
Mincemeyer, Larrinda Ann
Fifth Grade Teacher
Scherrer, Cynthia L.
Special Education Teacher
Schuler-Brumley, Juanita Louise
High School Art Teacher
Weidenhaft, Mary K.
Social Studies Teacher
SUNRISE BEACH
Jones, Kathleen Frostrom Clark
2nd Grade Teacher
SWEET SPRINGS
Ferguson, Norma Jeane DeWitt-Libbey
Math, Gifted & Talented Tchr
Hill, Dan F.
Agriculture Ed Instructor
Reid, Nancy C.
Third Grade Teacher
TANEYVILLE
Bills, Garnet Pepper
6th-8th Grd Math & Comp Tchr
Swan, Denia Martin
Lit & Constitution Teacher
TARKIO
Clement, Lisa DeAnn
Fifth Grade Teacher
Palmeiro, M. David
Soc Stud, Span Tchr & Ath Dir
Schneider, Billie Faye
Social Studies Teacher
THEODOSIA
Hickman, Danielle Sue Allen
Business Education Teacher
TIPTON
Anderson, Mary L.
High School Soc Sci Teacher
Collier, Jo Ann Wittman
Fifth Grade Teacher
Hibdon, Carl Ralph
Elementary Principal
Strother, DeAnn Lynn
Science Teacher
TOWN COUNTRY
Beck, Mary Elizabeth
Special Education Teacher
TRENTON
Allison, Lesa Jo
Elementary Music Teacher
Arthaud, Fred Lee
Professor of Biology
Bain, Jack
Mathematics Instructor
Brassfield, Wayne E.
Cooper Occup, Ed Tchr & Coord
Campbell, Sara Skinner
Office Occupations Professor
Chasteen, Bonnie Lynn
English Teacher

TRENTON (cont)
Clough, Russell Edward
Math Teacher
Cooksey, Jane Ann
Third Grade Teacher
Cotton, Melissa Jayne
Office Occupations Instructor
Hannaford, Edward G.
Instrumental Music Director
Hannaford, Karla Allison
Rifle Line Sponsor
Hefley, Julie Stone
Business Management Dept Chair
Hudson, Lora Barnett
First Grade Teacher
Porter, Dorothy Wilhoit
Third & Fourth Grade Teacher
Sager, Pamela Lynne
Accounting Teacher
Skeed, Janet Gray
7th-8th Grade Science Teacher
Smith, Carolyn Sue Turnbull
Office Occupations Instructor
Stuber, Donna
Psychology Professor
Wimer, Betty Raney
Elem Gifted Education Teacher
Witten, Kimberly J.
Social Studies Teacher
TROY
Campbell, Janice Byers
Fourth Grade Teacher
Dascher-Harvath, Pat L.
Teacher
Hardy, Kathy L.
Kindergarten Teacher
Hartman, Sue Kuehle
Spanish Teacher
Lapinski, Michelle Lynn
LD & BD Teacher
Pohlman, Larry Lynn
Band Director
Roettger, Judy Atchley
HS Physical Education Instr
Roth, Audrey Stanek
Sixth Grade Teacher
TUNAS
Glor, Eva Marie
Retired Elem School Counselor
UNION
Arand, Christopher Joseph
Dir of Student Act & Coach
Cook, Judy Scheer
Comp Information Systems Instr
Dixon, Kevin Edward
Biology Instructor
Eads, Christy Kreft
Kindergarten Teacher
Ghasedi, Fatemeh
Chemistry Instructor
Huff, Dorothy Nadine
Dental Assisting Instructor
Malone, Doris Holtgreve
2nd Grade Teacher
Mechem, Glenn Alan
Social Studies Teacher
Prugh, Patsy Eloise
Accounting Teacher
Ruether, Bette Unnerstall
Secondary Phys Ed Teacher
Scott, Betty Jayne
Dental Assisting Coord & Instr
Shoemaker, Charles F.
Artist in Resident
Woolley, H. Patrick
Professor of Biology
UNION STAR
Crowder, Linda Clapham
Guidance Director & Teacher
UNIONVILLE
Mothersbaugh, Max Wayne
Social Studies Teacher
URBANA
Redies, Diana Lynn
Social Science Teacher
VALLEY PARK
Biffignani, Susan Marie (Henricks)
6th Grade Teacher
Gansler, Helen M.
Gifted Education Facilitator
VAN BUREN
Hager, Lana Kaye
Business Instructor
Miller, Susan Logan
3rd Grade Teacher
Tuttle, Elizabeth Sno
Second Grade Teacher
VANDALIA
Berry, Rebecca Diane
Art Teacher
Saladin, R. Randall
Athletic Director & Coach
VERSAILLES
Enowski, June Hlavacek
Mathematics Teacher
Hensley, John Lee
Health Teacher & Coach
Hughes, Beverly Ayres
English Teacher & Dept Chair
Mc Whirter, Jamila LeAnn
Vocal Music Teacher
Rhea, Marilyn S.
Science Teacher
Yoder, Rodney Lowell
Third Grade Teacher
VIENNA
Byrd, Mick J.
Social Studies Tchr & Coach
Melson, Michael R.
Agricultural Education Teacher

Wulff, Sharon Mae
Fourth Grade Teacher
VILLA RIDGE
Hogan, Ronalyn
First Grade Teacher
Wilson, Judith Phillips
Fifth Grade Homeroom Teacher
WALNUT GROVE
Baur, Alisha Burton
Band Director
WARRENSBURG
Allen, Densil Earl, Jr.
Professor of Agriculture
Bersin, Michael Dean
Associate Professor of Music
Heinrichs, Faith Janzen
Assoc Prof of Educl Dev
Robinson, Denise Jane (Stoner)
Vocal Music Teacher
Wille, Treva Kay (Whitfield)
Retired 4th-5th Grade Teacher
WARRENTON
Bradshaw, Donald D.
Ind Tech Teacher
Brandes, Sherry Lynn
High School English Teacher
Current, David E.
School Counselor
Current, Deborah Fouch
Fourth Grade Teacher
Gregory, Karen Dreyer
Elementary Principal
Kimball, Beverly J.
Math & Science Teacher
Mc Dowell, Katie (Frick)
Sixth Grade Teacher
Nolkemper, Sandra Anne
Speech, Drama & Eng Teacher
Rucinski, Kathryn Lewis
Third Grade Teacher
Shilharvey, Nancy Avis
Business Teacher
Stephens, Suzann K.
Speech & Language Pathologist
Wright, Karen Burris
Fifth Grade Teacher
WARSAW
Burnett, Kris Sims
Elementary Counselor
Campbell, Anita Arnett
English, Jrnlsm & Drama Tchr
Dixon, Don L.
Science Teacher
Mc Cubbin, Zane K.
Teacher
Simons, Elaine
6th-8th Grade Math Teacher
Southers, Carolyn Sutton
Sr HS Business Tchr
WASHBURN
Dye, Linda
Business Teacher
Epperly, Dennis Gale
Agriscience Teacher
WASHINGTON
Brown, Joyce Maune
Chemistry Teacher
Carter, Georganna Curtright
Elementary Teacher
Carter, John Sam
Physical Education Teacher
Carver, John Patterson
Vocational Guidance Counselor
Dawson, Karen Wilson
Art Department Chairman
Gildehaus, Dale John
Physical Education Teacher
Hannah, Frances Andrews
Teacher of Gifted & Talented
Jeske, Cheryl Stephens
Science Teacher
Koelling, Deborah M.
Vocal Music Director
Korte, Joann Marie
Counselor & Business Teacher
Parsons, Jeff S.
Social Studies Teacher
Schulte, Judy Noelke
Second Grade Teacher
Steffens, Theresa Maloy
Photography, Art & Jrnlsm Tchr
Vandecnocke, Robert Augustus
Teacher
Wiedemann, Marilyn Willmering
8th Grade Teacher
Wilson, June Arnote
Business Teacher
Wolff, Diann Lynn
Graphic Communications Instr
WAYNESVILLE
Beattie, Mike William
Speech & Drama Teacher
Belshe, Timothy Lee
American Government Teacher
Cagle, Phillip L.
Social Studies Teacher & Coach
Creel, L. Hope (Horne)
Chemistry Teacher
Hardman, Lula Mae
Social Studies Instructor
Huett, Nina Kathleen (Shore)
Art Teacher
Learmann, Judith S.
Journalism & English Teacher
Mathews, Rhea Anne Shryock
Eng & Gifted Ed Facilitator
Milbourn, Dennis Alvin
Math Teacher
Morgan, Nelson S.
6th Grade Teacher

Nickels, Adele Underwood
Fifth Grade Teacher
Powell, Warren Douglas
Biology Teacher
Skaggs, Dorothy D.
MS Sci & Health Teacher
Skaggs, James Richard
Industrial Technology Teacher
Slais, Daniel John
Earth Science Intructor
Zeman, Molly Belden
Language Arts Teacher
WEAUBLEAU
Hickman, Cal
Basketball Coach & PE Tchr
Lear, Charla Hoppens
Business Teacher
Vines, Patricia Ann (Kelley)
Science Teacher
WEBB CITY
Anderson, Amy Lynn (Munson)
Physics & Math Teacher
Bekebrock Davis, Rayma
English Teacher
Brown-Woolsey, Deanna F.
6th Grade Teacher
Deardorff, Rhonda Williams
Sixth Grade Teacher
Deardorff, Richard Neff
Fifth Grade Teacher
Francis, Pamela Clifton
First Grade Teacher
Hensley, Sylvai K. (Vik)
Fifth Grade Teacher
Holt, Matthew Kemp
Choral Director
Mosbaugh, Donald Roy
Aquatic Dir & Swim Instructor
Pittman, Marti Robins
Social Studies Teacher
Woods, Cynita Renee
Chemistry Teacher
WELLINGTON
Borgman, Mary Cunningham
Fifth Grade Teacher
McKee, Susan Kaye
English & Spanish Teacher
Smith, Jamie Charise (Stoner)
First Grade Teacher
Twente, David A.
Vocational Agriculture Instr
WELLSVILLE
Colter, Dorothy Rae (Schoening)
Elem Counselor & Psych Teacher
Gilmore, Harlan Eugene
Social Studies Teacher
Slovensky, John William
Mathematics Instructor
Smith, Joyce Wood
English Teacher
Vollertsen, Gary Lee
Sixth Grade Teacher
WENTZVILLE
Ayres-Salamon, Marilyn
Eighth Grade Teacher
Baber, Gregory D.
Seventh Grade Math Teacher
Baez, Dennis Edward
Mathematics Teacher
Cherry, Deborah Ann
2nd Grade Teacher
Clark, James Eugene
Assistant Principal
Coons, Janice Lynn (Edwards)
Third Grade Teacher
Green, Carol Steed
Chemistry Teacher
Holdinghaus, Michael Allen
Sixth Grade Teacher
Jacquin, Gerald Arthur
English Teacher
Jurotich, Edward John
8th Grade Mathematics Teacher
Keeran, Betty Ann (Wegener)
Vocal Music Teacher
Kulick, Janet M.
7th Grade Language Arts Tchr
La Manna, John Ercol
HS Physical Education Teacher
Langford, Deana Kay
5th Grade Teacher
Lauer, Deborah Sizemore
3rd-5th Grade PE Teacher
Luedloff, Ina Claypoole
Fifth & Sixth Grade Teacher
Mantione, Richard M.
Physical Education Instructor
Martin, Craig F.
Marketing Teacher
Rygelski, Barbara Egerer
Principal & 7th-8th Grade Tchr
Salamon, Rick
8th Grade Social Studies Tchr
Scanlon, Deborah Chesley
At-Risk Instructor
Simmons, Jack Wesley
Physics Teacher
Zollmann, Joyce Borgelt
2nd Grade Teacher
WEST PLAINS
Aid, Kathleen O'Neal
Gifted Facilitator
Beman, Elizabeth Lou
Retired Math Teacher
Bridges, Donna Yancey
2nd Grade Teacher
Bryant, Cynthia Watts
Mathematics Teacher
Carlson, Roger Alan
Anthropology Lecturer

Ford, Sabrina Mae (Plachy)
Instructor of Computer Science
Fugate, Rita Gilliam
Mathematics Department Chair
Griffin, Randall Lynn
Mathematics Instructor
Hawkins, Rita Joyce (Atkins)
Second Grade Teacher
Henry, Connie Jo
Chem Instr & Sci Dept Chair
Hessee, Pamela Hayes
Science & Computer Teacher
Hobbs, Linda Appel
Math Teacher
Holt, Donna K.
8th Grade English Teacher
House, Danette Cargill
Fourth Grade Teacher
Jones, Kelly Lea (Ryan)
Tchr of Learning Disabilities
Langston-Bowden, Janice LaFevers
Language Arts Teacher
Ledford, Barbara Cearley
Second Grade Teacher
Lindner, Mary John
Jr HS Tchr & Superintendent
Long, Bonnie Campbell
Physical Education Teacher
Long, Donald Larry
Sci & Physical Education Tchr
Mc Kinney, Edgar Duane
Asst Prof & His Dept Chrmn
Myers, Kenneth H.
Physical Education Instructor
Rackley, Janet Lynn
History Teacher
Rasor, Cynthia King
Fourth Grade Teacher
Rogers, Rhonda Michelle (Thompson)
Science Teacher
Simpkins, Gregory B.
Head Football Coach
Smith, Brenda M.
Family & Consumer Science Tchr
Surface, Lawrence D.
Sixth Grade Teacher
Thompson, Michael O.
Mathematics Teacher
Wright, Cynthia Ann
Integrated Sci Tchr
WESTON
Lynch, Bradley Dale
Chemistry Teacher
Wallace, Shawna Green
Fifth Grade Teacher
WESTPHALIA
Eads, Kay Duffin
Business Teacher
Fernandez, Sergio Manuel
Guidance Director
Heckman, Carol (Holterman)
English Teacher
Hoecker, Christine Brandt
Sixth Grade Teacher
Luebbert, Kim (Siebold)
Physics Tchr & Math Dept Chair
Orscheln, L. Linda Winkelman
Family & Consumer Sci Educator
Shemwell, Steven R.
Business Teacher
Sparr, Mary Helen
Phys Sci & Chemistry Teacher
WHEATLAND
Farmer, Peggy Jane
Science Teacher
Hotalling, Portia Murray
Kindergarten Teacher
Maddux, CarolSue Hume
Bus Ed Tchr & Cmptr Supvr
Warren, Patricia Breshears
Third Grade Teacher
WHEATON
Clair, Lavina Faye
Social Studies Teacher
Haynes, Edna Thomas
Elementary Principal
McInturff, Lowell Elton
Principal
Pumpkin, Charles B.
Science Teacher
Ray, Diane Lynn (Jones)
HS Science Teacher
Shepherd, Harold Robert
Cnslr & Dir of Spec Ed Svcs
WILLARD
Andrus, Bob
Technology Coordinator
Berry, Reuben Leonard
Geography & Economics Teacher
Chandler, Stephen Lee
High School Drivers Ed Tchr
Dennis, Dusty
Third Grade Teacher
Evans, Ronnie Dean
Mathematics Instructor
Foster, Rose (Wilson)
Math Tchr & Dept Chprsn
French, Candace Affolter
Choral Music Teacher
Lawrence, Lori Ayn
HS Physical Education Teacher
Martin, Karen Sue
Sixth Grade Soc Studies Tchr
Roth, Jay Brian
Math Teacher
Stout, Judith Helton
Science Teacher
Swann, Mary Eva Mc Lemore
Third Grade Teacher

WILLIAMSBURG
Austin, Patsy Jean
Kindergarten & Preschool Tchr
WILLOW SPRINGS
East, John Edgar
Band Director
Majors, Pansybelle Fay
Business Owner
WINDSOR
Lindsay, Denise R.
7th-8th Grd Soc Stud Tchr
McVeigh, Judy Penick
Family & Consumer Sci Tchr
WINFIELD
Alford, Roger Lynn
Drama Teacher
Henderson, Elaine Eversmeyer
Director of Services
Jones, Mary Anne Goodman
Math Teacher
WRIGHT CITY
Cook, David James
Agriculture Education Teacher
Freeman, Janet LeCrone
Guidance Counselor
WYACONDA
Cottrell, Cynthia Veerman
Business Education Teacher
Edgar, Judith Benson
Social Studies Teacher
Morrow, Jan Johnson
Mathematics Teacher
Padget, Sharon M.
Science Teacher
ZALMA
Rainey, Regina Corbin
Family & Consumer Sci Educator

MONTANA

ABSAROKEE
Boeck, Warren Joseph
6th Grade Teacher
Miller, Barbara Lynn
Vocal Music Teacher
ALBERTON
Gisselbeck, Candice Laura
Science, Math & PE Teacher
ANACONDA
Drescher, JoEllen Conwell
Media Specialist
Gallagher, William A.
8th Grd Soc Stud Teacher
Gossack, Bob T.
Science Teacher
Janosko, Jim Paul
Art Teacher
Laughlin, Robert C.
Chemistry & Algebra Teacher
Mc Carthy, Bea C.
First Grade Teacher
Solum, Janice Elaine
Psychology & World His Teacher
Tesson, Pierre E.
Business Education Teacher
ARLEE
Carney-Lammerding, Susan Marie
Physical Education Teacher
Fyant, Arthur Paul
Sixth Grade Teacher
Litzsinger, Hope Ann
Reading Recovery Teacher
ASHLAND
Fisher, Allen
Drug & Alcohol Pgrm Coord
Smith, Peggy Marie
Principal & Superintendent
BELGRADE
Buchanan, T.L. Buck
8th Grade Science Teacher
Dighans, Kay Marie
Third Grade Teacher
Rossman, Joseph Charles
Montana & US History Teacher
BELT
Byerly, Carol Lundeen
Business Education Teacher
Cummings, Craig Alan
Social Studies Teacher
DeVos, Leslie Rickey
Art Instructor
BIG SANDY
Genereux, Gaye Lynn (Keller)
Science Teacher & Dept Chair
Jespersen, Karen Ann
English Teacher
Pokorny, Cynthia Decker
Science & Computer Sci Teacher
Walker, Susan Dougherty
Music Teacher
BIG TIMBER
Beley, Marion A.
Third Grade Teacher
Braaten, Pam Crawford
3rd Grade Teacher
Bratvold, James A.
Vocal Music Teacher
LoPiccolo, Katherine Sipe
Social Studies Teacher
Mc Cullough, Kimberli Hart
Family & Consumer Sci Teacher
Ryan, Jane
Guid Cnslr & Hlth Enhncmt Tchr
Tulley, Kathleen Crosbie
English Teacher
BIGFORK
Aschim, Sid Robert
Vocational Education Teacher

ORK (cont)
eman, Catherine Bonham
e Assistant
n, Debra Osorio
sh Teacher
NGS
Sue Ellen
sh Teacher
ia, John R.
ish Teacher
Dottie Kay
th Grade Teacher
w, Dean Reuben
hematics Teacher
, Anneke-Jan
of Commnctn Arts Dept
, Doug S.
c Professor of Accounting
son, Wayne Darrel
l Music Director
ss, Donna Clark
ish & French Teacher
, Robert W.
ish Teacher
Oliver Y. K.
n, CS, STA Professor
Dorothy A.
ish Teacher
, Sandra Ward
ch Teacher
r, Thora Antoinette Focher
d Teacher
an, Rhonda Lynn
Professor of Chemistry
ey, Thomas Robert
Grade Geography Teacher
rds, Kevin Merrill
Grade Teacher
, Marilyn A.
ond Grade Teacher
n, Ralph L.
dle School English Teacher
Richard E.
Grade Teacher
Katherine Carlson
d Librarian
Kim Michael
Studies & Geography Tchr
er, Doyle
ial Studies Teacher
ara, Anne Mouat
Grade Teacher
ner, Peggy P.
Grade Elementary Teacher
ge, Randall G.
Prof of Eng & Philosophy
Duff R.
h & Cmptr Appl Tchr
f, Steve
lth Enhancement Teacher
erson, Ann Lochtie
Grd History Tchr & Librn
n, Lyle Dean
History Teacher
er, Candice Connis
Grade Teacher
mel, Cynthia Nash
man Teacher
on, Starla J. (Collum)
ior High School Teacher
n, Theodore Wayne
fessor of Spanish
, William Benedict
Grade Teacher
all, Maria Perico
nish Instructor
eel, Tasneem F.
, Graduate Stud & Rsrch
b, Susan D.
guage & American His Tchr
en, Tracy Anderson
th & Sixth Grade Teacher
ke, Denise L.
Grade Teacher
Ruey-Lin
fessor
er, Tracy Bernhardt
Instructor & Gallery Dir
, Russell H.
fessor & Department Chair
er, Christine Regina
sistant Professor of Biology
Fate, Richard Daren
ysics Teacher
Manus, Ronda Lee
rly Childhood Technician
heny, William M.
all Business Inst Director
er, Marcia Dombrowski
High Math Teacher
er, Kenneth Wayne
sociate Professor of Science
e, Jane Rogers
sistant Prof of Biology
oit, Charles B.
-Sponsor of Majorettes
ell, Larry Creston, Jr.
ath Teacher
rson, Nancy Weatherway
t & Ceramics Teacher
ue, Sheri Frisby
th Grade Teacher
d, Charles C.
n Grade Math Teacher
ater, Robin Pierce
d Grade Instructor
affer, Deborah Beth
ofessor of English
affer, Rachel
ofessor of English

Schwarz, Robert Joseph
High School English Teacher
Simmons, Carol Kercher
Enriched Junior English Tchr
Simmons, Richard Lee
History Teacher
Smith, Patricia C. (Allen)
English Teacher
Smith, Stephanie Reed
Specialist of Gftd & Tlntd
Solomon, Susan Wirtala
7th Grade Math Teacher
Staton, Jolene Kay
Fourth Grade Teacher
Suiter, Mary Howarth
Third Grade Teacher
Svec, Elaine Shiskowsky
Fourth Grade Teacher
Swander, Richard E.
Fifth Grade Teacher
Swoboda, Judith M.
English & French Teacher
Tangen, Gary James
Music Dept Coord & Band Dir
Tocci, Larry Raymond
Physical Education Instructor
Walkosz, Barbara J.
Assistant Professor
Warren, Peter Whitson
Professor of Art Dept Chair
Warwick, Rodger E.
7th Grade Life Science Teacher
Weik, Jeffrey L.
Amer Govt & World His Teacher
Whalen, Leslie A. (Erickson)
Secondary Teacher
Whitmer, Jerry Dean
8th Grd Physical Science Instr
Wickun, William G.
Chemistry Professor
Wise, Albert L.
History & Psychology Teacher
BONNER
Mc Culloch, Linda Harman
Schl Library Media Specialist
Strothman, Mary Ann Mullally
7th-8th Grd English Teacher
BOULDER
Kelly, Mark
Journalism & English Teacher
Piccolo, Linda Seeley
Eng, Drama & Speech Teacher
BOX ELDER
Antonich, Matt James
High School Science Teacher
Renaker, Pamela Isbell
Science & Biology Teacher
BOZEMAN
Ancell, William Winn
History Teacher
Bies, Kenneth Edward
Soc Studies & Lang Arts Tchr
Bruckner, Philip L.
Assoc Prof of Plant & Soil Sci
Clawson, Nancy Mc Nair
Retired English Teacher
Cooper, Jerry Dale
Science Teacher
Demetriades, Anthony
Professor of Mechanical Engrng
Durney, Michael J.
Eng Tchr & Writing Lab Dir
Francis, Gregory Evan
Physics Professor
Franklin, Nancy Evans
Special Education Teacher
Gnauck, Carol Zimmer
8th Grade Social Studies Tchr
Graves, John
8th Grade Teacher
Hawks, Jane Jennell
Fifth Grade Teacher
Hays, Sarah Strohmeyer
English & Algebra Teacher
Jelinski, Jack Bernard
Assoc Prof & Coord of Span
Kline, Sandra Eleanor
Sixth Grade Math & Sci Tchr
Landerdahl, Steve Arnell
Health Enhancement Teacher
Lee, Nancy C. (Buck)
Business Education Instructor
Mc Connen, Charmaine Staiger
Third Grade Teacher
Miller, Patricia McNelis
Adjunct Instructor
Nelson, Mark D.
Counselor Education Professor
Pierre, Michael Joseph
Seventh Grade Teacher
Reisig, Gerald L.
Physics Instructor
Sowell, Bok Forrest
Asst Prof of Range Science
Thompson, James Lee
English Teacher
Thompson, Patricia Dingwall
English Teacher
Waldorf, Thomas E.
Spanish Teacher
Wilson, Nancy G.
Music Teacher
Young, Gregory David
Music Professor
BRIDGER
Osborne, Ron
7th & 8th Grd Math & Sci Tchr
Svedberg, Rae Ann Jurak
English & Drama Teacher

VanSickle, Tammy Kunde
Music Teacher
BROADUS
Malyevac, Deanna Lynn
Math Teacher
BROADVIEW
Bymaster, Daniel Scott
Math & Advanced PE Tchr
Sipes, Allan D.
Elementary Teacher & Principal
Stiles, Janet Moody
High School English Teacher
BROCKTON
Stuber, Joel Ann (Geck)
Health & Physical Ed Teacher
BROWNING
Edwards-Vaile, Phyllis
Health & PE Teacher
Salois, Shannon (O'Regan)
Math Teacher
Woolf, Larry G.
Sixth Grade Math Teacher
BUTTE
Butler, Catherine
Spcl Ed & Chapter Tchr
Cameron, Douglas
Assoc Professor of Chemistry
Conklin, Carole D.
Legal Secretary Instructor
Connole, John Patrick
Govt & Current Events Teacher
Crossman, Maureen Geary
Retired First Grade Teacher
Daily, Terri A.
4th Grade Teacher
Douglas, Linda
Fifth Grade Teacher
Facincani, Linda Lombardi
English Dept Chair
Henrich, David Wayne
Sixth Grade Teacher
Howe, Maureen Theresa
Seventh Grade Reading Teacher
Jordan, Doc Stell
Retired Instructor
Kuecks, Ronald H.
Counselor
Lewis, Jane M. Rohret
2nd Grade Teacher
Liva, Robert J.
Math Teacher
Magnuson, Lloyd James, Jr.
8th Grd Earth Science Teacher
Mc Kay, Judy Sherwood
Mathematics Teacher
Mc Namee, Kathlene Youngren
Adjunct Instructor
Orr, Carol Whithorn
Sixth Grade Teacher
Osborne, William Jeffery
Asst Principal of Activities
Pedersen, Julie Tschetter
11th-12th Grade English Tchr
Pomroy, Cathy Bennett
Sixth Grade Teacher
Sager, Robert Darrell
4th Grade Teacher
Shea, Dennis Gerard
Automotive Instructor
Skinner, Jack Glen
School Guidance Counselor
Struznik, Denise Claxton
High School English Teacher
Walton, Sarah Pugh
Sixth Grade Teacher
Younkin, James A.
English Teacher & Yearbook Adv
Younkin, Marjorie J. (Priebe)
8th Grade Reading Teacher
CASCADE
Britton, Sharon Wilkins
1st Grade Classroom Teacher
Peterson, William Robert
Science Teacher
CHESTER
Tresch, Ramon Anthony
Lang Arts, His & Civics Tchr
CHINOOK
Bryson, Kathy Kay (Johnson)
Band Dir & Gen Music Tchr
Jacobson, Karen S.
Business Education Teacher
Kelley, Donald Patrick
Community Education Director
Miller, Donna Lynn
English Teacher
CHOTEAU
Facklam, Susan Inbody
11th & 12th Grd English Tchr
CLINTON
Kohler, Rohn Lee
6th-8th Grd Soc Studies Tchr
CLYDE PARK
Breitbach, Thomas Joseph
Science Teacher
COLSTRIP
Conroy, Lyndon R.
History Teacher
Davidson, Russ
Social Studies Teacher
Hayworth, Judith Workman
4th Grade Teacher
Johnson, Colleen K.
Eng & Communication Arts Tchr
Schneider, Gisela
High School Art Instructor
Will, Steven James
Math Teacher

COLUMBIA FALLS
Chestnut, Sandra Louise
English Teacher
Eddy, Sharon Renton
HS Health Enhancement & Coach
Knutson, Wesley E.
9th-10th Grade Health Teacher
Rossi, Norbert Guido
High School Choral Instructor
Smalley, Jerry L.
Science Teacher
Startin, Alexandra Shafizadeh
High School Mathematics Tchr
Thompson, John David
High Schl Earth Science Tchr
COLUMBUS
Campbell, Barbara Joy
County Superintendent of Schls
Walker, Fritzie
English Teacher & Counselor
CONRAD
Lockyer, Steven Scott
Science Instructor
Metz, John Arthur
Mathematics Teacher
CORVALLIS
Doolittle, Kathy Jeanne
7th Grade Social Studies Tchr
CROW AGENCY
Big Man, Beverly Wilson
Fifth Grade Teacher
Dittus, Merlin David
Sixth Grade Teacher
CULBERTSON
Gustafson, Jeri Gandrud
Speech & Drama Teacher
CUT BANK
Blair, Dawn M.
Band Instructor
Johnson, Jetta Mc Cain
4th Grade Teacher
DARBY
Gideon, Steve Alan
History & Government Teacher
DEER LODGE
Bradshaw, Clair D.
Math Teacher
Sorenson, Lynn Dee
Mathematics, Computer Sci Tchr
DENTON
Hassinger, Linda Snell
English, Speech & Drama Tchr
Mapston, Kenneth Dale
Agriculture Education Teacher
DILLON
Dickinson, Carol K.
Teacher
Hagenbarth, Laurie Garry
Choral Director
Jensen, Susan Boyd
Business Teacher
O'Neil, Debra Amelia (Carver)
Third Grade Teacher
Thumma, Doris Mayberry
Retired Third Grade Teacher
Valach, James John
Technology Education Teacher
DRUMMOND
Anderson, Donald Joseph
Soc Stud, Health & PE Teacher
Bradshaw, Mike L.
Sixth Grade Teacher
Wright, Lee Ann
Mathematics & Computer Teacher
EKALAKA
Mauch, Beth Brawner
Lang Arts, Math & MT His Tchr
EUREKA
James, David Robert
American History Teacher
Miller, Arvid C.
Sixth Grade Teacher
FAIRVIEW
Arndt, Fred R.
Science Teacher
Flynn, Julie Ann Johnson
Language & Title I Teacher
Karst, Arlene Ann Henderson
School Counselor
Shaide, Karen Martinez
3rd Grd Tchr & EES Prgm Dir
FLAXVILLE
French, Mark William
K-12th Grade Music Teacher
FLORENCE
Carlson, Bob C.
High School Mathematics Tchr
Horsens, Lois Weyers
First Grade Teacher
FORSYTH
Albertson, Dwayne
English & Social Studies Instr
Knoche, Craig E.
Science Teacher
FORT BENTON
Lulf, S. Colleen Dwyer
English Teacher
FORT SHAW
Reinhart, Myrna Stafne
School Counselor
FORTINE
Shay, Shelley Gwynn
First & Second Grade Teacher
FROID
Murphy, Karen A.
German Teacher & Librarian
Strauss, Irene Kachena
English Tchr & Guidance Cnslr

FROMBERG
Schara, LaRue Nelson Brumwell
Special Education Teacher
GARDINER
Riley, Patricia Lyn
English & Art Teacher
GEYSER
Birkoski, Stacy Jo
Kindergarten, PE & Art Teacher
GILDFORD
Amundson, Leif Lee
Tech Ed & Industrial Arts Tchr
GLASGOW
Girard, Kimberley Wilke
Mathematics Teacher
Girard, Norman Dale
High School Science Teacher
Glaser, Todd Nicholas
Physical Science & PE Teacher
Mires, Lawrence Elmer
Tech & Industrial Arts Teacher
Rusher, Katherine (Steen)
English Teacher & Dept Chm
Yoakam, Mark William
English Teacher
GLENDIVE
Carpenter, Verna Vossler
8th Grd Physical Science Tchr
De Beaumont, Jo Ann Burnham
English Teacher
Donnelly, Coralie F.
Third Grade Teacher
Fenton, Paige Marie
English Teacher & Coach
Geiger, Kolette Kukowski
2nd Grade Teacher
Gibbs, Lesley (Kettner)
English Instructor
Jacobs, Gerald A.
Math Instructor
Miller, Lee W.
8th Grade Math Teacher
Ohs, Carol Lynn
Third Grade Teacher
Schultz, James Donald
English Instructor
GRASS RANGE
Horyna, Sherry K.
Mathematics Teacher
GREAT FALLS
Alt, Arthur Lee
Professor of Natural Sciences
Anderson, Norman F.
Social Studies Teacher
Black, Donald Keith
Band Director & Music Chairman
Booth-Gilliam, Diane L.
Philosophy Professor
Castle, Arlee Tesinsky
English Teacher
Copeland, Gary
7th Grade Natural Science Tchr
Davis, Sherilu Jacobs
Math Teacher
Emett, Sharon Elizabeth
Third Grade Teacher
Garpestad, Lonny A.
Science Teacher
Gillespie, Katherine A.
3rd Grade Teacher
Ginalias, Anthony C.
Professor
Graham, Terry Loran
Math Tchr & Head Sftbl Coach
Halverson, Brian Glenn
US & World History Teacher
Howard, Michael M.
Science Teacher
Hungerford, Donald Wayne
Advanced Biology Teacher
Jacobson, Donna Joy
5th Grade Teacher
Kunka, James Charles
8th Grade Math Dept Head
Larsen, Ez
PE, Health & Aerobic Teacher
Larson, James D.
Advanced Biology Teacher
Linabary, Paulette Jean
Third Grade Teacher
Little, Dawn Elizabeth
German Teacher
Lydiard, Linda Rae
Orchestra Director
Matson, Joan Renee
English Teacher
Mattingly, Kirk Melvin
Drafting Teacher & Dept Head
Mc Intosh, Kathleen A.
Choral Director
Myers, Kathryn Luthin
English & Journalism Teacher
Nagengast, Angela Mc Lean
English Teacher
Nelson, Steven Dwayne
Associate Professor
O'Reilly, Betty Jane
Retired Reading Specialist
Perry, Kathleen Bethem
Life Skills Teacher
Rebich, Anthony Martin
Industrial Technology Instr
Rosenleaf, Patricia (Malcolm)
Eng & Honors Early Grad Tchr
Rossell, Charles H.
Humanities & English Teacher
Salonen, William Wesley
Principal
Soldano, Mary Lou
French Teacher

GREAT FALLS (cont)
Sprague, Teresa Ann (Ross)
First Grade Teacher
Stuckey, Richard Lewis
Teacher of the Deaf
Swanson, Jo-Ann Marie
Assistant Professor of English
Tarantino, Donna Gruel
5th Grade Teacher
Wallace, Gary Donald
American History Teacher
Walters, Kay Murphy
HS Teacher of the Deaf
Wavra, April Denning
Eighth Grade Mathematics Tchr
HARDIN
Fisher, Sally Lynn
Drug Free School Coordinator
Melville, Lillian Milonas
Kindergarten Teacher
Schultz, Melody Colleen
6th Grade Science Teacher
Sundheim, Laura Lee
High School Counselor
Thompson, Roger S.
K-5th Grade Music Instructor
HARLEM
Acher, Betty Marie
Fourth Grade Teacher
Faulkinberry, Kim Smith
Science Teacher
Kienenberger, Leona M.
High School English Teacher
Siemens, Matt
High School History Teacher
HARRISON
Carey, Margaret Ellen
English, Speech & Drama Tchr
Wilson, Randy Alan
Computer & Science Teacher
HAVRE
Bowman, Debbie Ann
Elementary Principal
Bymaster, Gladys Norris
Second Grade Teacher
Dierman, Sam J.
Special Education Teacher
Gilmartin, Brian George
Assoc Prof of Social Sciences
Hamilton, Brett Alton
Bio, Life Sci Tchr & Coach
Ita, John Bradley
AP History Teacher
Klarich, Duane Andrew
Chemistry & Biology Assoc Prof
Kologi, Ronald Stephen
Chemistry Teacher
Lockwood, Steve P.
Associate Professor of English
Sylvester, Stephen G.
Professor of History
Wolfe, Judith Carl
Science Instructor
HELENA
Abney, Michele
Second Grade Teacher
Burger, Jennifer Jude
Physical Education Teacher
Chenoweth, Joni Lynn
English Dept Coord
Dorrance, Debra A.
English Teacher
Harris, JoeAn Dallum
English Teacher
Hartman, Kathryn Barker
Fourth Grade Teacher
Mc Cauley, Cheryl Ann
5th Grade Teacher
Michelson, Steven Keith
Choir Director
Peach, Patricia Marlene
Sci & Lang Arts Teacher
Phillips, Paul Andrew
Chem & Advanced Chem Teacher
Sinnott, Danna Hintz
Spanish Teacher
Weingartner, Cynthia Lynn
Seventh Grade English Teacher
Whedbee, Linda
Spanish Teacher
HOBSON
Brottem, Kenneth Dwight
Music Educator
HOT SPRINGS
Kretzschmar, Susan Rae Gooch
K-12th Grade Music Teacher
Mirich, Rob
Chemistry, Math & CS Teacher
HYSHAM
White, Glen Allen
High School Mathematics Tchr
INVERNESS
Monilaws, Kenneth LeRoy
Retired 6th Grd Tchr & Prin
JOLIET
Schmidt, Lynn Peetz
Eighth Grade Classroom Teacher
Seaton, Dennis
HS Science Teacher
JORDAN
Mansfield, Barbara Burr
HS Science Teacher & Counselor
KALISPELL
Antonietti, Joseph Thomas
High School Science Teacher
Barragan, Jean Kellar
World & Amer His Tchr
Beyer, George A.
Social Science Dept Chm
Blood, W. Alexander
Earth Sci Instr & Dept Chair
Dudis, Rhonda Pettinah
English Instructor
Dunnehoff, Kathy Dunne
English Instructor
Fawcett, Matthew Michael
Sixth Grade Teacher
Hammond, Micki Lee
6th Grade Teacher
Harshbarger, Linda Jane (Hammond)
Advanced Eng & Geography Tchr
Hashley, David M.
Drama Director & Theatre Tchr
Hays, Pamella Paulin
English Teacher
Hodge, Patricia Sue
French Teacher
Jenkins, Paul Joseph
Principal & Superintendent
LaLum, Mark Duane
Ag Ed Teacher & Voc Chm
Lambright, Connie Smith
Math Teacher
Mahoney, Joanne Koslucher
Second Grade Teacher
McAllister, Frances Lynn (Vollhaber)
English & Social Studies Tchr
Mc Chesney, Robert Ernest
4th Grade Teacher
Miller, Deb
Sociology Instructor
Moser, Jeff L.
Sixth Grade Teacher, Principal
Moses, C. Jonathan
History & Political Sci Instr
Oliver, Jeanette Clements
Professor of Biology
Overly, Aliene Hyatt
English, Jrnlsm & Reading Tchr
Riley, Bruce Lee
Language Arts Teacher
Robinson, Sabrina Dee (Napper)
Mathematics Professor
Scalf, Lynn E. Hetrick
English Teacher
Schaus, Richard Harris
Physics & Mathematics Instr
Slater, Allen J.
Director of Bands
Stantus, Connie D.
Business Education Instructor
Streit, Robert Kirk
Social Studies Teacher
Thon, Janet Joan
Fourth Grade Teacher
Welder, Steven Terrence
4th-6th Grade Administrator
Wheeler, Eileen Mary
Habilitation Aide
KILA
Fischer, Phyllis Morgan
Retired Elementary Teacher
LAMBERT
Barnhart, Thomas Wade
Social Science Tchr & Cnslr
LAME DEER
Newsom, Nancy Bonner
Science Teacher
Tompkins, David K.
Instr of Alcohol & Drug Stud
LAUREL
Campbell, Linda Halligan
English Teacher
Colbrese, Dennis Eugene
Counselor
Edgmond, Brent Stanton
Physics, Bio & Chem Teacher
Langager, Harvey James
Business Teacher
Thompson, Katie Kammer
Fifth Grade Teacher
LAVINA
Grammens, Allen Joseph
Science Teacher
LEWISTOWN
Criswell, Mary Phillips
Retired Elementary Teacher
Feller, Victor John
High School Mathematics Tchr
Orr, Brian Robert
US History & Psychology Tchr
LIBBY
Kelsch, Brad J.
Fourth Grade Teacher
Kendall, Janet R.
Second Grade Teacher
Reckin, Gerald Eugene, II
Bio, Phys Sci & Computer Tchr
Schauer, Arthur Roy
Retired Lang Arts & His Tchr
LIMA
Gray, Rose Marie (Loveless)
English Teacher & Counselor
LINCOLN
Cyr, Fredrick LeRoy
Retired Fifth Grade Teacher
LIVINGSTON
Bray, Marla Neyl
7th Grd World Geo, MT His Tchr
Douglass, Elizabeth H. P.
US History & English Teacher
Gannon, John P.
Mathematics Teacher
Magalsky, Elaine M.
1st-12th Grd Home Schl Teacher
Peterson, Helen Bellach
6th Grade Math & Science Tchr
LODGE GRASS
Anderson, Della Jean
Business & Computer Instructor
MacDonald, Michael R.
English Teacher
MALTA
Demarais, Mardy Caves
High School Science Teacher
Wiederrick, Karen Ohs
Second Grade Teacher
MANHATTAN
Drusch, Nancy Matthews
4th Grade Teacher
Selles, Robert Dale
Science & Math Teacher
MARTINSDALE
Hereim, Barbara Anderson
Elementary Teacher
MEDICINE LAKE
Olson, Betty-Jean Clemons
Kndgtn Tchr & Elem Admin
Waller, Kathleen McWilliams
English, History & Jrnlsm Tchr
MELSTONE
Mattheis, Gary Edwin
Agricultural Education Teacher
MILES CITY
Carda, Michelle Malon
Home Economics Teacher
Gonzalez, Stephen
History & Technology Teacher
Nansel, Melody Van Atta
3rd Grade Teacher
Ogolin, Jamie Allen
Anatomy, Physiology & Sci Tchr
Peterson, Deana Devine
English Teacher
Raymond, Jack J.
9th & 10th Grd Lang Arts Tchr
Thorne, Nancy Kailey
Art Teacher
MISSOULA
Adcock, A. Daniel
5th Grade Teacher
Babcock, Waleen Johnson
Social Studies Teacher
Braun, Cyndy
Latin Teacher
Cracolice, Mark S.
Asst Professor of Chemistry
Curtis, Nancy Sacrison
Spanish & Journalism Teacher
DeLuca, Thomas Henry
Assistant Prof of Soc Sci
Duncan, K. Jane
Lang Art & Soc Stud Teacher
Elliott, Deni
Mansfield Professor of Ethics
Elsen, Carol Bowles
English Dept Chair
Fortmann, Brian Curtis
Mathematics Teacher
Gagermeier, Gary L.
Computer Coordinator
Ganser, Thomas Jay
Biology Teacher
Gillett, Gary Lee
Band Director
Hansen, Linda Gar
First Grade Teacher
Hawkins, Jonathan David
Third Grade Teacher
Hickethier, Reta Mae (Bach)
Social Studies Teacher
Jones, David C.
Science Teacher
Lousen, Elizabeth J.
English Teacher
Lukomski, Sharon Noble
English Teacher
Lukomski, Thomas
English Teacher
Lyons, Michael Lawrence
MS Title I Computer Teacher
Norberg, Jeffrey Owen
Science Teacher
Norman, Edward Carroll
Health Enhancement Teacher
Oberg, Todd Donald
Mathematics Teaching Assist
Olson, Paul Donald
Mathematics Graduate Student
Opsahl, Janice E.
Kindergarten Teacher
Palin, Angela Monaco
Second Grade Teacher
Perrin, Ronald Stewart
Science Teacher
Pilcher, Russ C.
Teacher & Department Chair
Ramsey, Ronald C.
Fifth Grade Teacher
Robson, Linda Maio
English Teacher
Ryan, Marilyn Jane (McCabe)
Former 8th Grd Amer His Tchr
Smith, Melodee Lynn (Singer)
5th Grade Teacher
Snyder, Jeffry John
Math & Physical Education Tchr
Stein, Gary Michael
US Governemnt & Psych Teacher
Stephens, Andrea G.
Biology & Earth Sci Teacher
Thane, Denis P.
5th Grade Teacher
Thomas, Maureen Wallace
Health & Physical Ed Teacher
Wilbur, Carol Anne
English Teacher & Yearbook Adv
NOXON
Groves, Mary A.
Business Education Teacher
PARK CITY
Dahlberg, Michelle Gunwall
Business Teacher
Rogers, John C.
Geology, History Tchr & Chair
PLAINS
Taylor, Betty Revier
K-12 Grade Counselor
PLENTYWOOD
Johnson, Harold Clifton
Science Teacher
Nielsen, James Allen
Retired Mathematics Teacher
Ralph, Jeffrey J.
Computer Instructor
POLSON
Briney, Paul Stephen
Social Science Teacher
Cox, John Garth
Third Grade Teacher
Mazurek, Robert John, Jr.
Instrumental Music Instructor
Thorsrud, Elizabeth S.
Third Grade Teacher
POPLAR
Anderson, Marie L.
Business Education Teacher
RED LODGE
Landsman Yakin, Nan Sherry
English & Spanish Teacher
ROBERTS
Mc Gregor, Cathy Olsen
Math & Physical Ed Teacher
Nelson, George Michael
Fifth & Sixth Grade Teacher
RONAN
James, Katie Engles
English Instructor
Jones, Linda Bond
7th Grade English & Lit Tchr
Stewart, Amy Diane
Second Grade Teacher
Watkins, Darlene Janssen
Teacher of Talented & Gifted
ROSEBUD
Welbes, Diane M.
English & PE Teacher
Woods, William John
Fourth Grade Teacher
RUDYARD
Williams-Tong, Julie Ann
Science Dept Chprsn & Teacher
SACO
Malone, Jay Barry
Science Teacher
White, Barbara Christiana
Kindergarten Teacher
SAINT IGNATIUS
Phillips, Jo Ann Harris
Business Education Teacher
SAINT REGIS
Graham, Cheryl Fredrickson
Business Teacher
Hill, Kenneth N.
6th-12th Grade Science Teacher
SAVAGE
Carlson, Arlinda Kay (Koschel)
Business & English Teacher
SEELEY LAKE
Carpita, Anne Marie
Ret Scndry Span & Eng Tchr
SHELBY
Cole, Barbara Tallent
4th Grade Teacher
Kinyon, Barbara Donnell
Second Grade Teacher
Kirkegaard, Leland C.
Choral Music Director
Meek, Gene Arthur
Chemistry & Physics Teacher
Mercer, Barbara Spiker
Third Grade Teacher
Robertson, Tammerah Berquist
Sixth Grade Teacher
Swoboda, Steven J.
Science Teacher
SHEPHERD
Lepley, William Leonard
High School Biology Teacher
Meryman, Susan Sandh
Math Teacher
Schaaf, Darwin Duane
History Teacher
Shannon, Vicki Lynn
English Teacher
Wiederrick, Traci Lee
English Teacher
SIDNEY
Bowers, Vicky Lynn
Resource Room Teacher
Kilsdonk, Lida Barber
Communication Arts Teacher
Leland, Tamra N. M.
Special Education Teacher
Ratliff, Lois Faye
3rd Grade Teacher
Zoanni, Richard James
Math Teacher
STEVENSVILLE
Meyer, Jay
Fourth Grade Teacher
Oliver, Joan Warner
Retired First Grade Teacher
Puccinelli, Joanne
6th Grade Teacher
Stanford, Wayne Frank
Sixth Grade Teacher
SUPERIOR
Martineau, Christopher Laureat
Science Teacher
St George, Janice (Peterson)
2nd Grade Teacher
Sevalstad, Blake E.
Social Studies Teacher
Sevalstad, Jackie Clouner
First Grade Teacher
Smith, Douglas Kent
Secondary Mathematics Teacher
Tull, Steven Gerald
HS English Teacher
THOMPSON FALLS
Hanna, Dianne Nissen
Title I Teacher
Kinkade, Rusty
Science Teacher
Nelson, R. Wade
K-12th Grade Art Specialist
THREE FORKS
Schwab, Susan Fogarty
English Teacher
Strickland, Jeffery Lee
Social Science & PE Teacher
TOWNSEND
Audet, Patrick Ronald
Biology, Phys Ed & Hlth Instr
Nugent, Terry E.
English Department Chairman
Robischon, Pete Charles
High School Science Teacher
TROUT CREEK
Newell, Doni Leonard
Principal
TROY
Arts, Joseph Gilbert
Third Grade Teacher
Arvish, Ellen Marie
Physical Ed & Music Teacher
Ferderer, Jeffrey A.
High School English Teacher
Kensler-Chiaverini, Andrea
French & English Teacher
Smith, Tony
History Teacher
TWIN BRIDGES
Dorseth, Verta Anne Basolo
Fifth Grade Teacher
VALIER
Durocher, J. Wayne
Mathematics Teacher
Mc Comb, Aileen Johnson
Retired Primary Teacher
VAUGHN
Gaskins, Nancy Rutten
1st Grade Teacher
WEST YELLOWSTONE
Lynn, Peggy Ann
Mathematics Teacher
Ritchey, Beverlie Sue Combs
First Grade Teacher
WHITE SULFUR SPRINGS
Bakken, Terry G.
8th-12th Grd Mathematics Tchr
Marks, Kenneth Charles
Physics, Chemistry & Sci Tchr
WHITEFISH
Braunberger, Pattie (Layton)
6th Grade & Science Teacher
Garberg, Linda Taylor
Third Grade Teacher
Heinrich, Klaus Karl
Retired Classroom Teacher
Helgath, Nancy Wilson
8th Grade English Teacher
Reading, Lini S. Hilbun
Varsity Girls Soccer Coach
Ryan, Kathie Mary
Business Owner
WHITEHALL
Getz, Garry Glenn
Sixth Grade Teacher
Robertson, Bobbie Stirling
Band Director & Music Teacher
Wheeler, Thomas Evan
Vocational & Technical Instr
WHITEWATER
Schulte, Susan Carole
English Teacher
WIBAUX
Abernethy, Rella M.
Second Grade Teacher
WILLOW CREEK
Frank, Lucy Ann
K-12th Grade Music Teacher
WOLF POINT
Wilson, D. Wayne Robert
Agriculture Education Teacher
Young, David W.
6th Grade Teacher
WORDEN
Burdett, Carmen Marie
First Grade Teacher
Dees, Rick Scott
High School Science Teacher
Fanyak, Charles Andrew
English Teacher & Coach
Hedrick, Vickie Gee
Fifth Grade Teacher
Smith, Michael C.
Spanish Teacher
Webb, Peggy Moore
Mathematics Teacher

BRASKA

S
, Thomas R.
& Computer Teacher
Dixie Lane
y & Consumer Sci Tchr
WORTH
effrey Craig
sh Teacher
Ruth Ann J. (Wall)
ematics Teacher
erg, Marilyn K.
mental Music & Hum Tchr
James Eugene
l Studies Teacher
Michael Dean
y Industrial Tech Instr
rf, Dale E.
Grade Teacher
ary Ann
nglish & Speech Teacher
ger, Pam Davis
cal Education Teacher
Paige Kay
sh & Journalism Tchr
Harv J.
ipal & Activities Dir
ON
son, Arne Ray
culture Education Teacher
a, Daniel L.
al Studies Teacher

rg, Deborah (Plejdrup)
Grade Teacher
n, Teresa Spellman
ergarten Teacher
N
Lloyd Richard
Director
e, Marcia Ann (Stamp)
ish & Social Science Tchr
ANCE
, Pamela Joella
School Art Teacher
s, Sherrie E.
uage Arts Teacher
r, Carolyn Marie Kloch
School Teacher
hew, Desiree Ingraham
bra & Accounting Teacher
n, Teresa (Chase)
nan & Earth Science Teacher
n, Stephen Mark
stant Principal
winkel, Mary Curtiss
ish Teacher
eits, Sheila Ann
8th Grd Mathematics Tchr
ll, Pamela J.
Science Teacher
ce, Tim
3rd Soc Stud Tchr & Coach
nan, Gloria Paulsen
th Grade Teacher
A
harms, Wayne Eugene
n Teacher
EY
, Jody Anderson
h Teacher
meier, DeLoy Allen
hematics Teacher
PAHOE
ig, Pamela J.
lish & Journalism Tchr
ausen, Karen A.
lish & Social Studies Tchr
ADIA
Mary E.
ence Teacher
r, Mary Anne
lish Teacher
INGTON
on, Steve Alan
h Grade Teacher
field, Gary Wayne
lish Teacher
, Jeff Kenneth
h School Business Teacher
OLD
ey, Michael Duane
ncipal
aniel, Michael Warren
h School English Teacher
LAND
ston, Kent James
t Prin & Act Dir
ra, Renee Kay (Steffen)
ddle School Literature Tchr
mann, James C.
-12th Grd Math Teacher
INSON
man, Tina Fisher
English & Speech Teacher
non, James M.
glish Teacher
, Michael J.
th & Science Teacher
URN
n, Caroline (Rhodes)
glish Teacher & Dept Chair
y, Dennis P.
& 8th Grd Science Teacher
hoff, Diana Meek
glish & Spanish Teacher
endall, Janet Marie (Nixon)
rd Grade Teacher

Kleine, Christian F.
Social Studies Teacher
Mc Mahon, Mark Anthony
Chemistry & Physics Teacher
Oliver, Mark Allan
World History & Geography Tchr
Peterson, Dianne Dietrich
K-5th Grade Elem Counselor
Reeves, Marcia Beth
Business Education Instr
Smith, Sally Harris
6th Grade Teacher
AURORA
Shaw, Robert LeRoy
Mathematics Teacher
AXTELL
Dimon, Bette Jane Schnabel
3rd Grade Elementary Teacher
Hinze, Douglas Wil
Physical Education Teacher
Oberg, Barbara J. (Homan)
Family & Consumer Sci Educator
Wendell, J. Rodney
Retired Music Teacher
BANCROFT
Hermelbracht, Lori Powley
Resource Teacher
BARTLETT
Miller, Henry Shayne
PE, Jr HS Sci Tchr & Coach
BASSETT
Camp, Steven Alan
Elementary Principal
Ford, Janis Bitterman
K-8th Grade Teacher
Troxel, Vicki Lawlis
6th Grade Teacher & Librarian
BATTLE CREEK
Masters, William L., Jr.
6th-7th Grd Teacher & Ath Dir
BAYARD
Lentz, Joseph Henry
Guidance Counselor
Tillman, Tamra K.
Math Instructor & Track Coach
BEATRICE
Dexter, Carmen M. Fletcher
Chemistry Instructor
Vetrovsky, Larry Joseph
Sixth Grade Science Teacher
Yocum, Lane
Agriculture Instructor
BEEMER
Bramble, Bonnye Lee
Retired Teacher
BELLEVUE
Beischel, Christine Lee
Assistant Professor
Braasch, Byron Paul
Band Dir
Branson, Patricia Brumbaugh
German Teacher
Cain, Stephanie Bednar
Speech & Language Pathologist
Denny, Patrick R.
7th Grd World History Teacher
Filloon, Michele McBride
7th Grade Life Science Teacher
Gehringer, Michele Louise
English Teacher
Gerbus, Louis Keating
Aerospace Science Instructor
Grow, Sabra Sue Brewer
Second Grade Teacher
Haburn, Ted M.
Math Teacher
Hargus, Ellen Hrbek
English Teacher
Hartel, Gregory J.
Biology & Ecology Teacher
Hester, Susan Kilbane
8th Grd Amer History Teacher
Hughes, Jeanne Toney
Retired Elementary Teacher
Lanham, Oprville E.
Associate Prof of Sociology
Lee, Oudious
Social Studies Teacher
Lehman, Karen Ann
Special Education Teacher
Lohman, Leonard Rocky
American History Teacher
Lucky, Rosemary Ann (Rottman)
English Instructor
Mc Andrew, Gerald Thomas
English Teacher
Mosser, Jerry Charles
Director of Athletics
Parente, Michael
Asst Aerospace Science Instr
Rauchut, Eward A.
Associate Professor
Sailors, Valorie Lynn
8th Grade Math & Computer Tchr
Scholar, Jacqueline Bifano
Natural Sci, Math Prof & Chm
Schraeder, Deborah (Cahoon)
Sixth Grade Teacher
Shank, Jerome M.
Social Studies Dept Chprsn
Sorensen, Julie A.
Career Center Coordinator
Stohlman, Bruce Richard
Aerospace Science Teacher
Suganuma, Guy T.
Assistant Professor
Sullivan, Diane Huebscher
Spanish Teacher
Sullivan, Roxanne L.
Psych & Womens Studies Prof

Tran, Phuoc Huu
Dept Chair & Assoc Prof Math
Trimpey, Barbara Lynn
Sixth Grade Teacher
Whitworth, Deborah Shay
English Teacher
BENEDICT
Gropp, Gail E.
Business Teacher
BENKELMAN
Ahrens, Larry E.
Mid Schl Math Tchr & Dept Chm
Hudson, Sally Hickert
Third Grade Teacher
Nelson, Troy O.
Teacher & Wrestling Coach
Zarkowski, Rob Paul
HS Social Science Teacher
BENNET
Stilwell, Gera Lou (Powers)
Kindergarten Teacher
BIG SPRINGS
Cooper, Timothy Joe
Science Teacher
Heimes, Matthew G.
Secondary Teacher
Sommerfeld, Janice Crouse
Mathematics Teacher
BLAIR
Brown, Diana
French & Spanish Professor
Limbach, Robert James
Drafting Instructor
Mallory, Fran Proskocil
Asst Business Professor
McAllister, Shirley A.
Asst Prof of Education & Psych
Michels, Therese Walter
Chemistry Instructor
Palmer, Richard Alan
Director of Choral Activities
Whitaker, Ellen Petersen
Sixth Grade Teacher
BLOOMFIELD
Cripe, Jim
Social Studies Teacher
Dooley, James R. X.
English Teacher
Pease, Esther E.
Eng, Speech & Yearbook Teacher
BLUE HILL
Norvell, Mark Edward
Mathematics Teacher
BRAINARD
Struebing, David Dean
Health & Phys Ed Teacher
Widick, Karmen Kay
English Teacher
BRIDGEPORT
Millette, Thomas Joseph, Jr.
2nd Grade Teacher
Worden, Maureen A.
English, Speech & Jrnlsm Tchr
BROKEN BOW
Meyer, Gary L.
6th Grade Teacher
BRUNING
Kluck, Frederick G.
Social Studies Teacher
Lemke, Marisa
Spanish Teacher
Monter, Gary William
Principal
Pohlmann, Debra Ann
Music Instructor
BURWELL
Goochey, Susan Henriksen
Spanish Tchr & Media Spclst
Hurlburt, Tim Duane
Industrial Technology Instr
CALLAWAY
Gardner, Brian N.
Counselor, His & Jrnlsm Instr
Miller, Teri Rhinehart
First Grade Teacher
Schuller, Ronald Lawrence
Teacher
CEDAR BLUFFS
Bowder, Lynn R.
Visual Arts Instructor & Coach
Dalton, Robyn Ann (Beller)
Speech, Drama & Eng Teacher
CEDAR RAPIDS
Braun, Linda Waskowiak
7th-12th Grd Math Teacher
CENTRAL CITY
Callahan, Karen Nazara
Third Grade Teacher & Coach
Robinson, Merlin Francis
Physical Education Teacher
Sealey, Barbara B. Majer
4th Grade Teacher
CHADRON
Butler, Shirley Strotheide
Elementary Teacher
French, Toni Kim Black
Head Teacher
Marshall, Mary Lou L.
Physical Ed Teacher & Coach
O'Connor, Jerry Paul
Assoc Prof of Speech & Theatre
Petersen, Sharon Schulz
Speech & Language Pathologist
Powers, Patrick Donald
Former Theology Teacher
Stein, Richard Ervin
Physical Education Teacher
CHAMBERS
Hixson, Lois Kay (Hadenfeldt)
Secondary Business Teacher

Remmers, Chyrel Roebke
English & Library Teacher
CHAPPELL
Davis, Mike
Ag Science Instructor
Franklin, George Denny
Instrumental Music Director
Freeman, Marge M.
Fourth Grade Teacher
CHESTER
Dunback, Mary Kathleen (Meyer)
English, French & Art Teacher
Pettigrew, Bud Dwaine
Social Studies Teacher
CLAY CENTER
Briggs, Jeanne Marie (Wolfe)
Kindergarten Teacher
CLEARWATER
Brummels, Jane Troyer
Sixth Grade Teacher
Rich, Lynda Statler
High School English Teacher
Schomberg, Betty Hales
Business Education Teacher
Sieh, Michael John
Principal
CODY
Miller, Jean Elizabeth
English, Speech & Health Tchr
Novicki, Patty Jo Beldin
Social Science Teacher
COLERIDGE
Hahne, Mary H.
5th-12th Grade Band Director
Kuchta, Vickie (Renstrom)
Secondary Science Teacher
Lentz, Margaret Frances (Claus)
First Grade Teacher
Widler, Thomas W.
Business Teacher
COLUMBUS
Bantz, Joseph Clarence
Mathematics Teacher
Brockhaus, Patrick John
High Schl Social Studies Tchr
Bryan, Debra Elayne
Third Grade Teacher
Dusel, Jane Marie
Chemistry & Physical Sci Tchr
Fuchs, Ann Belieu
Fifth Grade Teacher
Graf, Lynne Marie
5th-8th Grade English Teacher
Greenwall, Ronald Richard
English Teacher
Jahn, Steven L.
Seventh Grade Teacher
Larson, Barb Swanson
Business Teacher
Massman, David E.
Mathematics Instructor
Seckel, Sandra Strong
Second Grade Teacher
Slusarski, Margaret Milinar
English & Speech Instructor
Tooley, Janet Kay (Bornemeier)
7th-12th Grd PE Specialist
Went, Jan L. Rodehorst
7th-12th Grd Bus & Sys Oprtr
Woodrick, Patricia Ann (Waite)
4th Grade Teacher
COOK
Eichenberger, Robert A.
HS Science Instructor
Hahn, Teresa LuAnn
Business Teacher
Hiemer, Teresa L.
English Teacher
CORTLAND
Behrends, Dorothy Marie (Clare)
Retired Fourth Grade Teacher
Young, Ruth Latshaw
Retired Teacher
COZAD
Evertson, David Wade
Chemistry & Physics Teacher
Johnson, Norma Fiebig
First Grade Teacher
Mackowski, Stanley J.
Biology Teacher
Poore, David Scott
6th-7th Grade Science Teacher
CRAWFORD
Smith, John Wesley
Social Studies Teacher
CREIGHTON
Foner, Kathleen A.
Speech & History Instructor
Zepf, Kathy Schmidt
7th, 9th & 11th Grd Eng Tchr
CRETE
Fye, Eddie Ray
Coach & Recruiter
Gilbert, Jay Warren
Director of Instrumental Music
Johnson, James L.
Asst Professor of Mathematics
Lentell, John Douglas
Architectural Instructor
Mierau, Beth Ann (Propst)
Former Placement Coordinator
Muckel, Jean Dainton
First Grade Teacher
Muckel, Robert Dale
Professor of Biology
Palensky, Bob
Instrumental Music Teacher
Quinn, Kris Ann
5th Grade Teacher

VanDyke, Stephen Bruce
Amer His, Ec, & Govt Teacher
CROFTON
Hegge, Jacquelyn L.
6th-8th Grade Teacher
CULBERTSON
Kershaw, John Darren
History, Math & PE Teacher
Messersmith, Jeffrey Lyn
Mathematics Teacher
Schaeffer, Barry W.
Business Education Instructor
CURTIS
Rue, Karon (Dunbar)
Secondary English Instructor
DALTON
Kandel, Sue Ellen
English Teacher
DANBURY
Frecks, Pamela Lemaster
4th-8th Grade Teacher
DAVENPORT
Schoming, Holly L. (Grone)
Fifth-Sixth Grade Teacher
DAVID CITY
Griffiths, Kristi Kay (Krueger)
Business & Journalism Teacher
Hamling, Lisa Hemmer
Secondary Mathematics Teacher
Mandeville, Steven Joseph
Speech Teacher
Mimick, Ron
American History Teacher
Pohl, Carol
Vocal Music & Fine Arts Instr
Pokorny, Teresa A.
High School English Teacher
DAWSON
Fankhauser, Linnette S.
Guidance Counselor
Mason, Jan Harbour
1st-2nd Grade Teacher
Swanson, Chad Adam
Business Educator
DAYKIN
Oliver, Marilyn Heidemann
Art Teacher & Gifted Coord
Soukup, Kathy Matajka
Business Teacher
DE WITT
McMillan, Sue Guenther
English Teacher
Swarthout, Barbara Lea
Family & Consumer Science Tchr
DECATUR
Baker, Saranne Beard
Second Grade Teacher
DESHLER
Hasseldahl, Gregory Charles
Principal & Jr HS Teacher
Mroczek, Dave Joseph
Athletic Director
Pitts, Beverly Irene Brettmann
Business Teacher
Virus, Nancy Lee Smith
4th Grade Teacher
DODGE
Troska, Jeana M.
Spanish, Speech & English Tchr
Wieberg, Jeanette Wisnieski
Elementary Language Arts Tchr
DUNNING
Kennedy, Shirley Johnson
Jr High Eng & Resource Tchr
Ready, Rodney Eugene
Math Teacher
Rogers, Celeste Atherton
Business & Computer Teacher
EAGLE
Helsing, Nona Hansen
Fifth Grade Teacher
ELBA
Schmaderer, Linda S.
Art Teacher
ELGIN
Hoffman, Patricia
Math Teacher
Sweem, Terry Allen
English, Speech & Drama Tchr
ELKHORN
Bacus, John Wesley
Social Studies Teacher
Bastarache, Giselle Daigle
French & Spanish Teacher
Bischof, Stephen Joseph
World History Teacher
Clarke, Bradford George
8th Grade Science Teacher
Martin, Paul E.
Math Teacher
Nelson, Donna M.
Eighth Grd Language Arts Tchr
Sobota, Lynn Vosika
Instrumental Music Educator
Theis, Marilynn Ablott
Music, Art & Drafting Teacher
Torrens, Gene L.
Vocal Music Teacher
ELM CREEK
Scoville, Shirley M. (Blythe)
Classroom Teacher
EMERSON
Anderson, Cindy Morgan
5th & 6th Grades Teacher
Miller, Lynn Christian
High School Math Teacher
Wood, John Oliver
Science Teacher

EWING
Coy, Elsie May Cooper
Teacher
Jones, Gladys Loecker
Science Teacher
EXETER
Mahoney, Robert John
Social Studies & Math Teacher
FAIRBURY
Martin, Jerome T.
Chemistry & Physics Instructor
Stewart, Stanley Gaylen
Business Teacher & Tech Coord
Waldron, David Ross
Social Studies Teacher
FAIRFIELD
Kluver, Suzanne Finley
Sixth Grade Teacher
Krieger, Lynette Rae Davidson
German & English Instructor
Pernicek, Darrell William
Physical Science Teacher
Rose, Robert L.
Math Teacher
Ware, Ginny Dies
First Grade Teacher
FAIRMONT
Power, Allison Ann (Stables)
Business Teacher
FALLS CITY
Duerfeldt, Stacey Fritz
Third Grade Teacher
FARNAM
Dunlap, Bradley Charles
English Teacher
FILLEY
Titus, Rick
Mathematics Teacher
FIRTH
Ertl, Sheri Rohn
Spanish & English Teacher
Gibbs, Gregory Joseph
Theatre & Speech Teacher
Martin, Patricia Ann
Junior English Teacher
Severson, Phillip Ray
Mathematics Teacher
Votta, John Stephen
Social Studies Instructor
FORT CALHOUN
Boeka, Sarah Jane
Vocal Music Director
Jones, Mark Alan
Director of Bands
Thomas, Lola (Shreves)
Spanish & English Teacher
FRANKLIN
Dreher, Tom G.
Social Studies Teacher
Haussermann, Renee Henry
Science Teacher
FREMONT
Adamson, Thomas R.
Asst Professor of Business
Beightol, Debra A.
Physics Teacher
Boeck, Terry Dean
Teacher
Bristol, Rita Donahue
Asst Professor of Business
Campbell, James Linn
English & Journalism Teacher
Dodd, Cindi Pierce
Jr High Social Studies Teacher
Frey, Linda Teska
First Grade Teacher
Ganzel, Vicki Lynn (Reifschneider)
2nd Grade Teacher
Granger, Mary Mruz
Special Ed Teacher & Dept Chm
Martin, Lawrence Andrew
Biology & PE Teacher
Mc Mullen, John Charles
Psych Tchr & Staff Dev Coord
Muller, Jean Marie
Jr & Sr HS Eng & Drama Tchr
Parr, Roger A.
Business Teacher
Ronspies, Michael
Math & Computer Sci Teacher
Schomburg, Connie Custer
Asst Prof of Eng & Humanities
Schwaninger, Doyle L.
Journalism Teacher & Adviser
Wilshusen, Loren Wayne
Speech, PE Tchr & Ath Dir
Wojtkiewicz, Ginny French
5th Grade Teacher
FRIEND
Rasmussen, Margaret Geraldine
Retired Elementary Teacher
FULLERTON
Bassett, Joan Bretthorst
High School English Teacher
Bassett, Rodger Allen
Social Studies Teacher
Farrar, William Dee
Science Teacher
Ostransky, Shawn Adrian
Business Teacher
GENEVA
Wewel, Lori A.
English & Speech Teacher
GENOA
Dannelly, Marilyn Hayes
Art Teacher
Fehringer, Scott Edward
5th Grade Teacher
Jacobi, Linda Kay (Briese)
Business Teacher

Nelson, JoEtta
Sixth Grade Teacher
Rood, Randy Lee
English & Speech Teacher
Sass, Linda K.
English & Spanish Teacher
Smith, Richard R.
Physical Science Instructor
Westring, Kenneth W.
Counselor
GERING
Alvarez, Manuel, Jr.
Mathematics Teacher
Becking, Jerry Duane
High School Guidance Counselor
Couch, Scott Alan
7th-9th Grade Art Instructor
DeMaranville, Jason E.
History & Humanities Teacher
Eckerle, Jenell Dru
Multi-Age Teacher
Greenwood, Joy Ann
Jr High Counselor
Haun, Mary Kay (Heil)
Fifth Grade Teacher
Helgerson, Lilanie J.
Journalism & English Teacher
Peters, Gretchen J.
Art Instructor
Rueb, Kathy Jesson
Fourth Grade Teacher
Stukesbary, Robert Duane
Music Technology Theory Tchr
VanTilburg, Alan Keith
Publisher
GIBBON
Donnelly, Susan M. Curran
English Teacher
King, Stephen S.
High School English Instructor
GORDON
Kling, Jacqueline Jean
Sixth Grade Teacher
Kruger, Kay L.
Home Economics Teacher
GOTHENBURG
Mc Vay, Terry K.
Science Teacher
GRAND ISLAND
Brittin, Don R.
Second Grade Teacher
Burchess, Craig Clinton
9th American History Teacher
Casper, Nancy Rennecker
Retired Teacher
Chadek, William James
5th Grade Teacher
Clark, Joan Joyce
English Teacher
Colvin, Linda M. (Griffing)
Kindergarten Teacher
Colvin, Richard C.
Science Teacher & Coach
Cook, Alan James
Drafting Teacher
Dahlstrom, Linda Nichols
Fourth Grade Teacher
Dondlinger, Dennis Paul
5th Grade Teacher
Eirick, Kathleen Ann (Meyer)
Middle School Lang Arts Tchr
Fread, Ella M.
Retired Teacher
Hamner, Charles Lee
English Teacher
Haymart, Dawn Ann
9th Grade English Teacher
Howard, John K.
Scndry His Tchr & Soc Stud Chm
Killion, Karey Dillon
Mathematics Teacher
Krall, Pamela Anne (Chapman)
Speech, Drama & Rdng Teacher
Krolikowski, DeAnna Matthies
Math Teacher & JV Vlybl Coach
Magnuson, Guna Buss
6th Grade Elementary Teacher
Mc Cue, Kermit Clare
Eng Dept Chair & Jrnlsm Tchr
Miller, Marilynn Larson
Guidance Counselor
Moeller, Connie Louise Scheer
1st Grade Teacher
Nelson, Victor Harlan
Math Teacher
Newcomb, George Alfred
Math Teacher
Obermier, Duane A.
Communicative Arts Dept Chair
Peter, Victor K.
7th Grade Teacher
Sears, Paul Edward
Drafting Instructor
Suganuma, Guy T.
Economics Instructor
Urwiller, Stanley LaVerne
Math Department Chairman
Witt, Judy Eckmann
Middle School Science Teacher
Wolfe, Beverly Rother
6th-8th Grade Computer Teacher
GRANT
Tate, Diana Jean
English, Spanish & Speech Tchr
GREELEY
Lueck, Rebecca J. (Drake)
English & Speech Teacher
Williams, Bradley C.
Business Teacher

GRETNA
Beran, Richard J., Jr.
Social Studies Teacher & Coach
Boettger, Gregory Kent
Industrial Technology Teacher
Childs, Deborah Wieland
Biology Teacher
Haun, Jeffrey Wayne
11th Grade English Teacher
Huff, Patti Jean
Fourth Grade Teacher
Michl, Robert Wayne
English & Journalism Teacher
Oliver, James Scott
8th Grade Social Studies Tchr
Rhodes, John Arthur
HS & MS Mathematics Teacher
HAIGLER
Guernsey, Connie Sue Mendenhall
Third & Fourth Grade Teacher
HARRISBURG
Griffiths, Twila Pulver
Sixth Grade Teacher
Hillen, Jolyn
Math Teacher & Coach
Newland, Carol Rannells
2nd Grade Teacher
Rice, Kelley Jo
Substitute Music Teacher
HARTINGTON
Arens, Karen M.
Sixth Grade Teacher
Boehmer, Karen June
1st-12th Grd Vocal Music Tchr
HARVARD
Bohart, Patricia L.
High School Spanish Teacher
Colvin, Barbara Johnson
Family & Consumer Sci Teacher
Koehler, Karen Meyer
4th-6th Grade Lang Arts Tchr
HASTINGS
Babcock, Robert Sherburne
Assistant Professor of History
Bulas, Laura Ann
Business Administration Instr
Cafferty, Cathleen Jean
Fifth Grade Teacher
DeLaet, Joan Richter
Family & Consumer Sci Teacher
Hesselgesser, Vicki Hutchinson
Sixth Grade Teacher
Hunt, Betty Tratton
Business Teacher
Johnson, James D.
Instructor
Lloyd, Darrel W.
English Professor
McCarthy, Daniel Robert
Industrial Technology Teacher
Packard, David W.
English Teacher
Van Cura, Alan Ray
Mathematics Teacher
Vogel, James Patrick
German Teacher
White, Joy Johnson
6th Grade Teacher
HAY SPRINGS
Hiles, Judith (Dunbar)
Mathematics & Science Teacher
Houser, Douglas E.
Science Teacher
Olson, Francis
Industrial Technology Teacher
Rosche, Dorothy Janet (Hatt)
7th & 8th Grade Teacher
Sedivy, Luella
English & Speech Teacher
HAYES CENTER
Fornoff, Ann Lynnette (Hofman)
English & Journalism Teacher
HEBRON
Hoins, Richard L.
Math Instructor
Hoins, Sandra K. Foster
Speech & Comm Arts Teacher
HEMINGFORD
Ahrens, Cindy Jansen
Middle School Math Teacher
Hucke, Ramona Sue
Business Teacher
Lanik, Timothy Ray
Bio & Physiology Tchr & Coach
Zajic, Nancy Lea Roland
6th Grade Teacher
HENDERSON
Ernst, Tim L.
Counselor
HERSHEY
Madsen, Gail Allen
Math Teacher
HOLDREGE
Christensen, Bruce Maxon
Amer His & Driver Ed Tchr
Christensen, Milrae Jean
Math, Reading & Spelling Tchr
Durfee, Andrea Lee Sampson
Kindergarten & First Grd Tchr
Evans, Ronald Edward
Sixth Grade Science Teacher
Fagot, Pattie Nellor
Jr High Teacher
Gibbons, Judy Joslin
Business Education Teacher
Jeffery, Richard James
History Teacher & Coach
Kosmicki, Christy Lynn Bunger
Art Specialist

Oman, Mary Olsen
Fourth Grade Teacher
Sturtevant, Irene M.
Retired Elementary Teacher
Woythaler, Elaine
Retired First Grade Teacher
HOMER
Snyder, Kelley Faye
Biology Teacher
Thompson, Peggy Ann
English, Jrnlsm & Span Teacher
HOOPER
Moeller, Amy (Hirsch)
Fourth Grade Teacher
Mowinkel, Dan Henry
Agriculture Education Instr
HOWELLS
Devine, Kelli K.
Vocal & Instrumental Music Dir
Groene, Robin S.
Counselor
Jensen, Ken P.
History & PE Teacher
Kulhanek, Gene L.
Biology, Hlth & Ind Tech Tchr
Tichota, Paula Asche
Title I & Reading Teacher
Touil, Nancy Gatewood
Media Specialist
HUMBOLDT
Brettmann, Inez Irene (Gerdes)
English, Speech & Drama Tchr
Brodersen, Inga Marie
English, Span & Jrnlsm Tchr
Schnacker, Angela Sue
Kindergarten Tchr
Schnacker, Rick DeWayne
Social Studies Teacher
Schulenberg, Nancy Lee (Herrick)
Math & Computer Teacher
Volker, Sarah Zetterman
Music Teacher
HUMPHREY
Goering, Pamela J. (Milander)
K-12th Grd Vocal Music Teacher
Schumacher, Marlyn Frances
Second Grade Teacher
HYANNIS
Stillwell, Lynell Kime
English & Spanish Teacher
IMPERIAL
Bauerle, Jill Gibson
Jr HS English Teacher
Haneline, Richard D.
9th-12th Grade Art Instructor
Nelson, Lori Ann (Gieber)
Business Teacher
INDIANOLA
Roggenkamp, Les John
HS Agriculture Educator
Troester, Dennis Lee
K-6th Grd PE Director
JOHNSON
Placek, Ryan Laine
Vocal & Instrumental Director
Smith, Samuel E.
Mathematics Teacher
JUNIATA
Uden, Cindy Anderson
Multi-Grade Classroom Teacher
KEARNEY
Black, Ann Thompson
Secondary Resource Teacher
Davis, Gary L.
Associate Professor of Music
Dinsmore, Julie A.
Instructor & Dept of Cnslng
Eckloff, Maurine C.
Communication Professor
Francis, Connie (Dick)
10th & 12th Grade English Tchr
Froid, Rich W.
Political Science Teacher
Green, Jeffrey
Director of Theatre
Harris, Riley Kent
Math Instructor
Hoagstrom, George H.
Technology Teacher
Hullinger, James Lee
Assistant Prof of Speech Comm
Knipping, Ann (Ritzen)
8th Grade English Teacher
Livingston, Leslie F.
Bio & Physical Science Teacher
Mahalek, Dan J.
History Teacher
Mathieson, Roger A.
Amer History & Economics Tchr
McKenzie, Roberta Holt
Assistant Professor
Messersmith, Donaleen F.
Business Teacher
Mishou, Robert Francis
English Teacher
Patryla, Victoria M.
Associate Professor of Ed
Randolph, Lanna Petersen
Second Grade Teacher
Reiner, Darlene Marie
Fifth Grade Teacher
Schultze, Raymond W.
Professor of Art
Wolken, Daryl L.
Science Teacher
Zaruba, Gary Edward
Art Professor
KENESAW
Goelz, Diane Reiners
Family & Consumer Sci Teacher

Mc Bride, Lynn V.
English & Spanish Teacher
Schwenka, Linda Sue
K-12th Art Teacher
KIMBALL
Wallace, Diane Lynn (Gordon)
Reading, Lit & Lang Arts Tchr
LAUREL
Dahlquist, Mary C. Anderson
First Grade Teacher
Dvorak, Claudia Jane-Mallatt
Vocal Music Instructor & Dir
Hansen, Mary R. (Boyle)
Fifth Grade Teacher
Reinoehl, Patsy Lea
Mathematics & Cmptr Sci Tchr
Smith, Star Elaine (Dickey)
2nd Grade Teacher
LAVISTA
DeLoach, Bobbie Berry
District Challenge Facilitator
Witzki, Merry King
Fourth Grade Teacher
LAWRENCE
Troudt, Carroll LaVern
Math & Health Teacher
LEBANON
Kent, Margo C. (Kubik)
Business & PE Teacher
Rice, Peggy Gardner
Social Studies Teacher
Witte, Susan Carse
Counselor & Social Sci Teacher
LEIGH
Kabes, Beth Olson
Business Teacher
Meyer, Heidi Shoup
Science Teacher
Tyser, Donald William
Agricultural Education Instr
LEWISTON
Wilkinson, Corinne R. (Libal)
Third Grade Teacher
LEXINGTON
Ehlers, Patricia L. (Mc Bride)
7th-8th Grade Reading Teacher
Exstrom, Peggy Jean
Fourth Grade Teacher
Lindeman, Richard Eldon
Instructor of Biology
Nelson, Denise Lesley
Seventh Grade English Teacher
Page, Norma Jean
5th Grade Teacher
Reed, Jill Hueser
English & Journalism Teacher
Rutten, Stephanie (Leu)
Speech, Theatre & Bus Eng Tchr
Straka, Julie Cronk
Fourth Grade Teacher
LINCOLN
Baker, Mary A.
Math Teacher
Baker, Michael Lawrence
American History Teacher
Barth, Alana Gail
Fifth Grade Teacher
Beardslee, Thomas
Former Teacher
Bollinger, Kathy Hanson
7th Grade Teacher
Bowers, June Swanberg
Vocal Music Teacher
Bretz, Janice Cruse
English, Speech & Theatre Tchr
Butler, Mary Hunt
Mathematics Teacher
Christiansen, Cathy Mooney
English Teacher
Colon, Frances I.
Career Education Teacher
Connealy, Brien U.
ESL Teacher
Coulter, Mary Ann (Van Well)
Mathematics Teacher
Crew, James H.
Mathematics Teacher
Crews, Patricia Cox
Associate Prof of Textiles
Deemer, Lisette (Perez)
Vocal & Instrumntl Music Tchr
Dorn, Sandra S.
Gifted Facilitator
Dougherty, Daniel Dennis
Math Teacher
Doxtator, Brenda Sue
English Methods Instructor
Eddy, Arlys Joy
Spanish Teacher
Eisenbraun, Barbara Bakk
Reading & Literature Teacher
Elliott, Anita
Vocal Music Teacher
Epp, Dianne N.
Chemistry Teacher
Fangman, Michael Palmer
Coordinator & Science Teacher
Ferguson, Alida Robinson
Third Grade Teacher
Fraga, Melanie M.
French Teacher
Fredstrom, Kathy
Fourth Grd Teacher & Team Ldr
Freidline, Charles E.
Professor of Chemistry
Furse, Garold John
5th Grade Teacher
George, Clarence Ellis
World His & Soc Stud Teacher

LN (cont)
r, Alvin Henry, Jr.
nics & Bus Finance Instr
, Fayrene Lockhorn
ant Professor
, Jill Ondrak
h Teacher
, Donald W.
Teacher
eimer, Christy Froschheuser
Tchr & Frgn Lang Dept Chm
Eloise Beatrice
rade Teacher
ks, Ann B.
nting Instructor
z, Patricia Hazen
h Teacher
Jeffrey Gordon
2th Grd English Teacher
, Susan Elizabeth
nental Music Teacher
, Glen Oliver
sor
Sandra Jo
Grade Teacher
Thomas Michael
School Math Teacher
nne Reiter
ade Teacher
Kathryn Garrels
d Grade Teacher
aniel William
sor of Music
Dennis Alan
ce Teacher
Robert R.
Teacher
, Barbara Jean
pecialist
raffey, Robert Earl
& Philosophy Teacher
, Susan L.
l Studies Teacher
Sheree McCormick
y & Con Sci Dept Tchr
, Jane Osborne
gy Educator
or, Wendy L.
l Studies Teacher
Leona
ematics Teacher
ne, Therese Hill
gh Soc Studies Tchr
n, Betty J.
rade Teacher
n, Mandy Faripour
l Studies Teacher
s, Elizabeth
Prof of Hlth & Human Per
, Kirk Douglas
h Grade Teacher
ch, Michael Anthony
rer of Eng & Amer Lit
Mindy Schnegelberger
hysical Education Teacher
, Gail M.
sh Teacher
rdt, Jane Bredenberg
an Teacher
, R. Jane
ly & Consumer Science Tchr
berger, Bonnie Jean
Grade Teacher
n, Barry Thomas
neering Professor
der, Renee Puls
of Assc Degree Nrsng Pgm
ck, Judy Grove
rvisor of Student Teachers
era, Joe
her & Team Leader
ons, Richard Charles
nselor
, Tim
urer Dept of English
s, Annie N.
dance Counselor
Rebekah Sheely
ounting Professor
Ronald Lee
omotive Teacher
son, Kent Jay
erican History Teacher
seth, Scott Richard
agement Professor
pson, Gerald Everett
essor of Economics
Rhonda Dee
h Grade Teacher
ole, Peggy J.
iness & Computer Teacher
r, Gary Lee
ketball Coach
g, Russ
nomics Teacher
e, Robin E.
fessor of Biology
, Thomas Scott
ial Studies Teacher
er, Cathi Jean (Rosentrater)
al Music Teacher
n, Ruth Elaine (Janssen)
gical Tech Pgm Instr & Chm
, Annette A.
f of Txtls, Clthng & Dsgn
Donna Lynn
ence Teacher
miller, Johnson Meade
sics & Astronomy Teacher

Wolfe, Linda K.
Computer Teacher
Wysong, Linda Marie (Wright)
Director of U Career
Youker, Margo Couturier
Business Occupations Instr
Young, Linda Oltman
Lecturer & Director
Youngman, Nancy K.
Ger Mentor for Highly Gifted
LINDSAY
Schumacher, Russell Alan
Science Teacher
Uerling, Chris
Theology & Geometry Teacher
LODGEPOLE
Finkey, Kevin Dean
Physical Ed & Earth Sci Tchr
Stoll, Brent Eugene
7th-12th Grade Math Teacher
LOOMIS
Cruise, Nancy Joseph
Family & Consumer Sci Teacher
Gleason, Lanette Gardner
Mathematics Teacher
LOUISVILLE
Fitzgerald, William Parker
PE, Health & Drivers Ed Instr
Stock, Linda Green
6th Grade Teacher
White, Kevin Ross
Instrumental Music Director
LOUP CITY
Young, Garry A.
Math Teacher
LYONS
Brown, Floyd Iavn
History Teacher & Dept Chair
Farrens, Norma Bievins
Bus Ed & Language Arts Instr
Nelsen, Gene K.
Science Teacher
Toalson, Bobette Curry
English & Speech Teacher
MADISON
Gilson, Marty Michael
Physical Education Teacher
Tuckwe, Sandra Ourada
Math Teacher
MADRID
Hanson, Susan Kay
Art & Home Economics Teacher
Polson, William R.
Math Teacher
Reese, Troy L.
Science Teacher
MALCOLM
Tarr, Jack Louis, Jr.
Soc Studies Instr & Asst Prin
MAXWELL
Meyer, Carmen Lynne
Speech & English Instructor
MAYWOOD
Henry, Marvin C.
Industrial Arts Teacher
Jacobs, Connie Jorgensen
Sixth Grade Teacher
Johnson, Adrienne Joan (Shrago)
K-12th Grade Art Instructor
Johnson, Morris LaVerne
Science Teacher & Dept Head
Schultz, Judy K. (Walker)
Business Instructor
MC COOK
Bradley, Janet C. Schuler
Kindergarten Teacher
Garretson, James L.
Chemistry Instructor
Harms, Betty Lou (Aden)
Third Grade Teacher
Hueser, Joel A.
English Teacher
MEAD
Poltack, John Joseph
Science Teacher
Schnitzler, Julie Christensen
Language Arts Teacher
MERNA
Bargstadt, Debra A.
Business Teacher
Blakeman, Judith (Caldwell)
Spanish & Vocal Music Teacher
Gruszczynski, Carole Brune
4th Grade Teacher
MERRIMAN
Witt, Lisa M.
Elementary School Teacher
MILFORD
Burton, Mindy Sue Dahlgren
Art Teacher
MILLIGAN
Landenberger, Toni Michelle (Adam)
Business Teacher & Coach
MINDEN
Blum, Brian J.
Science Teacher
Miller, Jason W.
English Teacher
Thomsen, Julia Copley
English Teacher
MITCHELL
Chromy, Dan
Chemistry & Physical Sci Tchr
French, Karen Louise (Stenberg)
Fourth Grade Teacher
Hilyard, Linda K.
English & Reading Teacher
Pieper, LaVonne Wagner
Business & Computer Teacher

Ramig, Ellen F.
Business & Computer Instructor
Thacker, Blythe Maxine
Retired First Grade Teacher
Wagner, Marilyn M.
First Grade Teacher
MORRILL
Browne, Diane Carolyn
Fifth Grade Teacher
Cawiezel, Shirley (Onstine)
English Teacher
Hood, Mary Joyce
Science Teacher
Hughson, Jenny Moore
English & Journalism Teacher
Schlager, Carolyn Castiaux
Science Teacher
Steele, Sarah Cherry
Sixth Grade Teacher
MULLEN
Beyea, Nancy Whisman
Music Instructor
MURRAY
Garabrandt, Kathie Ann
Spanish Teacher
Wills, Todd S.
Social Studies Chairman
NEBRASKA CITY
Anthens, John
Keyboarding & Stu Skills Tchr
Cooper, John A.
Instructor & Music Director
Gogan, Edward A.
Assistant Principal
Johnson, Mary Helen
Family, Con Sci & Eng Instr
Kernes, Mary Beth (Lavigne)
His, Geog & Sociology Tchr
Varley, Louis Gordon
Math, Physics Teacher & Coach
NEHAWKA
Wilson, Sherri Shrader
Title I Teacher
NELIGH
Gilg, Ronald F.
9th-12th Grade English Teacher
Hauserman, Douglas J.
Instrumental Music Instructor
Miller, Laurel Smucker
Science Teacher
Petersen, Marlene Wood
Sixth Grade Teacher
Schindler, Robin Hayes
Mathematics Instructor
Steckelberg, Darrell Alan
Ind Tech Teacher
Timm, Darrel Ernest
Science Teacher
Trautman, Terry James
Social Stud & Government Tchr
Weinman, Donald D.
English, Journalism & PE Tchr
Wright, Tammy S. Marshall
Spanish Teacher
NELSON
Essink, Arnold Earl
Jr-Sr High Life Science Tchr
Spirk, Jaynie S.
Mathematics Teacher
NEWCASTLE
Myers, Kenneth L.
Secondary Mathematics Teacher
Thomas, Karma Janene (Anderson)
Guidance Counselor
NEWMAN GROVE
Davis, Dean John
Junior High Teacher
Kittle, Douglas Dean
Business Education Teacher
Seier, Mark Jerome
Science Teacher
NIOBRARA
Snowdon, Mary Colwell
Guidance Counselor
NORFOLK
Brummer, Marjorie Jean (Olson)
Second Grade Teacher
Doughty, Dixie L.
Marketing Educator
Fonder, Debra Joan
Art Teacher
Headlee, Marilyn J.
Remedial Reading Teacher
Henre, B. Vauri
English Instructor
Lindsay, Janis Fletcher
Sixth Grade Teacher
Mc Coy, Charles Edward
Biblical Studies Professor
Saltz, Elmer H.
Science Teacher
Schipporeit, Patricia (Peters)
English & Journalism Teacher
Timmer, Margaret Louise (Borgmann)
Art Instructor
Zessin, Ruth Fischer
Science Teacher
Zoucha, Douglas H.
History Teacher
NORTH BEND
Jelinek, Terri Lou
Mathematics Teacher
Watts, Danny Lee
Media Specialist & His Tchr
NORTH LOUP
Kluthe, Deborah S.
Principal & Physical Ed Tchr
Shafer, Connie Maxine Obermiller
Fifth Grade Teacher

NORTH PLATTE
Andre-Henn, Weston W.
Guidance Counselor
Broge, Linda Kay
Social Studies Teacher
Bruner, Thomas James
Guidance Director
Clements, Sydney Jo
Kindergarten Teacher
Darling, Sue E.
First Grade Teacher
Dickenson, Gwen E. Howitt
1st Grade Teacher
Erickson, Laura Mae
Substitute Teacher
Graves, Ray L.
Biology & Horticulture Teacher
Gulzow, Deborah Jorgenson
8th Grade History Teacher
Gulzow, Steven Kenneth
8th Grd Amer History Teacher
Hengen, Nadyne Long
Commnctn & Human Reltns Instr
Hirschfeld, Margo Mc Intire
Language Arts Teacher
Hopping, Vicki Lee
Physical Education Teacher
Kalblinger, William Lawrence
Voc Industrial Instructor
Kockrow, Elaine Oden
Nurse Educator
Larson, Lynn Ann (Miller)
1st Grade Teacher
Livingston, Kirk Richard
Social Studies Teacher
McAllister, Rebecca L.
2nd Grade Elementary Educator
Oltmanns, Larry Wayne
Math Teacher
Orcutt, Jim
Biology & Physiology Teacher
Peck, Sharon K.
Lang Arts & Soc Stud Teacher
Sawyer, Clissie Marie
Kindergarten Teacher
Sheesley, Daniel Leigh
US History & Sociology Teacher
Skillstad, Mark L.
Social Studies & History Tchr
OAKLAND
Johnson, Bryan R.
Band Director
McKillip, Beverly Dee (Herzog)
Biology Teacher
ODELL
Faulder, Myrna Boehmer
4th Grade Teacher
Wester, Stephen Lee
Science Teacher
ODESSA
Buesing, Farah Lea (Geer)
K-2nd Grd Multi-Age Clsrm Tchr
Gleason, Norma Jean
5th-6th Grade Teacher
OGALLALA
Ayres, LeAnn Kay
Spanish Teacher
Edens, Bev Christiansen
English Teacher
Kramer, Monica
Intern School Psychologist
OHIOWA
Reinsch, Sherri Matejka
Phys Ed Teacher
OMAHA
Abdouch, Gerald Lee
Technology Education Teacher
Adamski, Linda L.
Elementary Physical Educator
Allen, Robert Francis
Economics Professor
Anderson, Kristi Louise
HS English Teacher
Barker, Rex J.
Bands Dir & Music Dept Chm
Barry, Daniel Lee
7th Grd Mathematics Teacher
Baylor, Clare A.
English & Reading Teacher
Benak, Richard D.
Math & Computer Science Tchr
Benzel, Richard L.
Sixth Grade Teacher
Bergman, Roger Charles
Dir, Justice & Peace Stud Prgm
Bernardini, Larry Edward
Fifth Grade Teacher
Berner, Mary Mazzei
Kindergarten Teacher
Bluford, Michelle Angelina
Director of Bands
Bowers, Kay Margot
ESL Teacher & Dept Head
Brookhouser, Tamera Gade
Former Teacher
Buda, Nancy Schroll
French Teacher
Buggs, Ray Lee
Industrial Arts Teacher
Butler, Billy Ray
6th Grade Mathematics Educator
Butler, Janet Haynes
Business Teacher
Cain, David Allen
Sixth Grade Teacher
Camel, Marian, RSM
Principal & Administrator
Carmichael, Matthew Kelly
Early Childhood Spec Ed Tchr

Carroll, John T.
Science & Mathematics Teacher
Casey, Kathleen M. (Orr)
Fourth Grade Teacher
Cisar, Ronald James
Biology Teacher
Classen, Tamara Renee
Mathematics Teacher
Coates, Linda Jensen
7th & 8th Grade Math Tchr
Colony, Kip Stuart
English Teacher
Connelly, Daniel Joseph
Religion Teacher & Coach
Coppard, Brenda M.
Assistant Professor
Couture, Jane
Spanish Tchr & Academic Adv
Cunningham, Julie Seiko
Third Grade Teacher
Dahl, Rita Nielsen
Science Trainer
Dash, Alekha K.
Assistant Professor
Davis, Tim L.
Science Teacher
Deiml, Keith W.
Graphic Arts Instructor
Derry, Connie M.
8th Grade English Teacher
DeSimone, Edward Mario, II
Pharmacy Professor
DeWell, Elaine Kay
Fourth Grade Teacher
Dierks, Robert O., Jr.
Instr of Comp Pgm Tech
Dodd, William Henry, Jr.
Sociology & Black Stud Instr
Dornsife, Robert Stewart, Jr.
English Professor
Dow, David Charles
Chemistry Teacher
Dresser, Robert Francis
Human Services Instructor
Ecklebe, Kerry
Health Teacher & Dept Chprsn
Edwards, Norman Lewis, Jr.
Instrumental Music Teacher
Eickelman, Colleen Erin
Amer His & Lang Arts Teacher
Ellison, David J.
Accounting Professor
Ellison, Saundra Nelms
Spanish Teacher
Esser, Mary Kay
7th-8th Grade Math Teacher
Falcone, Jani McMullen
Guidance Counselor
Fanning, Alan L.
Economics Teacher
Farr, Jodie J.
English Teacher
Flagg, Richard O'Neill
Mathematics Instructor
Ford, Faye Janice
Biology Teacher
Fordyce, Victor Hayden
Ger, Eng & Bible Head Teacher
Fox, Gwen Hartman
Mathematics Teacher
Gabriel, Linda Lee
Asst Prof of Occup Therapy
Gabriel, Ron
English Teacher
Gleason, John Marquis
Professor of Decision Sciences
Glenn, Gregory John
History Teacher
Gnam, Mary Kay
2nd Grade Teacher
Goodrich, Carla Nugent
Former 6th Grade Teacher
Gradoville, Mary Alyce Hubschman
Fourth Grade Teacher
Gregg, Mary O'Brien
Junior High School Teacher
Griffith, Patricia Marie (Thommes)
5th Grade Religion Teacher
Grossman, Barry Scott
Dept Head of Paralegal Studies
Groth, Roger H.
9th-12th Grd Band Director
Haar, David L.
Social Studies Teacher
Haddad, Amy Marie
Ethics Associate Professor
Hall, Thomas J.
High School English Teacher
Hammer, Kim Anderson
Instrumental Music Teacher
Hanley, Dennis A.
Educational Technologist
Hansen, Betty Ann (Beelner)
5th Grade Teacher
Hansen, Mitchell James
English Teacher
Henning, Cindy Lou (Kardell)
5th Grade Teacher
Hermann, Rebecca A.
Computer Graphics Instructor
Hexum, Terry D.
Professor
Hill, Leslie Harris
School Counselor
Holt, Patricia Aitken
Office Skills Instructor
Holz, Craig
Physiology Tchr & Ath Trainer
Hood, Richard Eugene, III
Asst Prin & Athletic Director

OMAHA (cont)
Hoschar, Shawn R.
Social Studies Teacher
Hospodka, Ronald J.
Assoc Prof of Admin & Soc Sci
Houser-Foxworthy, Linda Marie
Middle Level Business Teacher
Houston, James Allan
Science Teacher
Hovorka, Theresa Schalla
Secondary Business Ed Teacher
Howe, Rodney Wayne
Journalism Instructor
Jackson, Mary Lou Olson
Vocal Music Teacher
Jensen, Mark Howard
English Teacher
Johnson, Johnny C.
Fourth Grade Teacher
Jones, Bruce Lynn
Amer Government Teacher
Kallhoff, Catherine
Instructor & Program Director
Kelly, Resa Marie
Chemistry Teacher
Kenagy, Molinda Dyan
Theology Teacher
Kier, Christine M.
Speech & Theater Teacher
Kinney, B. Dale
Teacher & Coach
Klosterman, Kathleen Tjaden
Elementary Counselor
Klug, Lori
Senior High Resource Teacher
Kocsis, Kathleen Peters
High School Guidance Counselor
Koger, Shawna Heldenbrand
Business Teacher
Konwinski, Maureen Kavanaugh
Social Studies Teacher
Kracher, Beverly
Asst Prof of Business Ethics
LaCroix, Karen Kreutzian
German Teacher
Lafontant, Julien J.
Prof of French & Black Studies
Laird, William Albert
Theology Teacher
Lamphier, Anne Margaret
Elementary Physical Ed Tchr
Langan, Steven M.
Lecturer in English
Leatherman, Mary Kay Mangus
Eng & Creative Writing Tchr
Lebeda, James F.
Principal
Leifert, Jo Ellen Weiss
Kindergarten Teacher
Levisay, Eunice Mithum
Retired Fourth Grade Teacher
Lewiston, Thomas Gene
Mathematics Instr & Dept Head
Lincoln, Velma Clawson
Second Grade Teacher
Littlejohn, Alonzo J.
Language Arts & Soc Stud Tchr
Lovgren, William Thomas
Biology Teacher
Lykke, Mary Johnson
American History Teacher
Machado, Gerardo H.
Spanish Teacher
Macklin, Shane Eric
Instrumental Music Teacher
Malchow, Carol Ann Rolfson
First Grade Teacher
Marne, Mildred Svagera
Third Grade Teacher
Matthies, Luann
Visual Communcation Arts Instr
Mc Creight, Sandra Schapiro
Biology Teacher
McKinley, Dierdre Denise (Jackson)
Physical Education Teacher
McQuade, Mary Clare
Theology Teacher
Means, Andrew V.
Social Studies Teacher
Merrigan-Potthoff, Juanita M.
Student Assistance Coordinator
Moeschler, Mary Egenberger
English Teacher
Moore, Julie Anne
Second Grade Teacher
Moore, Steven Glenn
Traveling PE Teacher
Morrissey, John Patrick
English Teacher
Mueller, Suzanne Shontz
High School English Teacher
Murphy, Susan Barry
3rd Grade Teacher
Murray, Wallace Jasper
Associate Professor
Nelson, Susan Louise
Mathematics Instructor
Nerud, Diane K.
English Teacher
Neumann, Thomas A.
Physics Instructor
Nixon, Nikki Anne
Third Grade Teacher
O'Brien, Phyllis Pieper
5th Grade Teacher
O'Donnell, Cheryl Marie
Fourth Grade Teacher
O'Donnell, Martin Joseph, Sr.
Social Studies Teacher
Orange, Thomas Arthur
Art Teacher
O'Rourke, Jeanne A.
Teacher
Ortman, Maria V.
French Teacher
Padilla, Rene L.
Asst Prof of Occup Therapy
Palmer, Darlene Rose
First Grade Teacher
Pane, Anthony Joseph
American History Teacher
Parker, Ginger Gay (Berkheimer)
Accounting Instructor
Petersen, Bonnie Jean (Getz)
Fourth Grade Teacher
Petersen, Patricia (Mc Laughlin)
7th Grade English Teacher
Peterson, Shannen Anderson
Health & Physical Ed Teacher
Peterson, Virginia Bourlier
Business Education Teacher
Pickens, Sara TeKolste
7th Grade Teacher
Plugge, Ted C.
Science Teacher
Policky, Charles Anthony
6th Grade Science Teacher
Pollak, Oliver B.
Professor of History
Portz, Bernard Joseph
Teacher
Pulverenti, Steven S.
Social Studies Teacher
Randall, Carolee Darden
Spanish Teacher
Rea, Roger
Chemistry Teacher
Redinbaugh, Larry D.
Strategic Marketing Mgmt Prof
Reed, Patti Jo Ann
Guidance Director
Robinson, Dennis Herbert
Associate Professor
Roder, Shirley C.
4th Grade Teacher
Rosenblatt, Ann Hermes
Office Skills Instructor
Rourke, Paulette Schlueter
7th-8th Grd Soc Studies Tchr
Salvador, Victorina Laperal
Eng & Creative Writing Tchr
Salzman, Sharon Louise
Business Education Teacher
Scheer, Denny
Industrial Technology Instr
Schettler, Lisa (Madigan)
English Teacher
Schmitz, Mary Jo Hoffmann
Vocal Music Director
Schumacher, Glen R.
4th Grade Teacher
Shinn, Bradley Wilson
Asst Prof of Pharmacy Practice
Shipley, David Craig
English Teacher
Sinnerud, James
Theology Teacher
Slobotski, Sandra Kay
Social Studies & Computer Tchr
Smith, Kathi M.
Science Teacher
Sokalsky, Joanne Placek
Spanish Teacher
Sonntag, Annette Schult
Head Teacher
Sova, Tamra Christensen
Family & Consumer Sci Teacher
Squires, Cathy Smith
English Instructor
Srb, Randal D.
French Teacher
Storm, Judy Marie
Special Ed Dept Chairperson
Stroope, D'Linda Patman
HS Family & Consumer Sci Tchr
Sturek, Mary Ann
English Instructor
Swanson, Constance Kawa
Fourth Grade Teacher
Tadros, Maher K.
C Prewett Prof Civic Engrng
Talbott, Jeanie Kaye
Physical Education Teacher
Todd, Mary Elizabeth
Fourth Grade Teacher
Trout, Donna Morseman
Math Teacher
Vesely, Maureen M.
Science, Math & Religion Tchr
Waldron, Gary Herbert
Marketing Teacher
Ward, Deborah Leah King
Publications Adv & Jrnlsm Tchr
Welch, Marti Rhea
4th Grade Teacher
Wells, Kathleen Marie
Math & World History Teacher
Williams, Robert Michael
Social Studies Department Head
Williby, Roseanne Lynette
Science Teacher
Willroth, Amy Louise
English & Speech Teacher
Wright, John Arthur
Instructor of Computer Pgmng
Zach, Rebecca Jane (Stevens)
MS Art Teacher & Yearbook Adv

ONEILL
Bahrij, Steven William
Mathematics Teacher
Brown, Steven W.
Social Science & PE Teacher
Brown, Teri D.
9th-12th Grd Spanish Teacher
Evans, Paula S.
Kindergarten Teacher
Hostert, Gary L.
Junior HS History Teacher
Maslen, Walt A.
Biology Teacher
ORCHARD
Cooper, Cathy A.
English Teacher
Leiding, Joanne Twibell
Fifth Grade Teacher
ORD
Augustyn, Diana Lynn (Stanley)
Fifth Grade Teacher
Drudik, Tonna Anderson
Fifth Grade Teacher
ORLEANS
Collins, Virginia A.
Title I Teacher
OSCEOLA
Ekart, James L.
Math Teacher
Teegerstrom, Marla Bean
English & Speech Teacher
OSMOND
Lemke, Gary Lee
English Teacher
OVERTON
Bacon, Gregory V.
K-12 PE, Hlth & Driver Ed Tchr
Kucera, David Joseph
Guidance Counselor
Simpson, Robby Dean
Sixth Grade Teacher
OXFORD
Rust, Johnny Alan
Mathematics & Ag Teacher
Siebels, Marilyn Jenkins
English & Journalism Teacher
Vahle, Sherida Lynn (Nohrenberg)
Math, Chemistry & Physics Tchr
PAGE
Dierks, Suzanne E.
5th-6th Grade Teacher
PALISADE
Knudson, Scot L.
Social Studies Teacher
PALMER
Lowe, Jane Bush
Third Grade Teacher
VanPelt, Mark Roy
Social Science Teacher
PALMYRA
Church, Charlynn Marie (Mathers)
Science Teacher
Horstman, Larry L.
Soc Stud, PE & Driver Ed Tchr
PAPILLION
Cronican, Karoline Kay
Youth Director
Cudly, Dean L.
Business Teacher
Draney, Bruce Gerald
7th Grd Soc Stud Teacher
Ferony, Astrid I.
Mathematics Teacher
Flock, Kathleen (Hobbs)
Special Education Teacher
Hennings, Gail E.
Fifth Grade Teacher
Kellett, William David
HS Instrumental Music Teacher
Linse, Dee Ann (Dishman)
9th Grade Science Teacher
Molzer, Kenneth A.
Band Director
Quick, Terrilyn Ann
Foreign Language Teacher
Sikes, Judith Estes
Family & Consumer Science Tchr
Slie, Larry James
English Teacher
Sommers, Janey Gildea
Eng & Amer Literature Teacher
Suhr, Gene H.
PE Teacher & Football Coach
Warner, Cheri Neal
Social Studies Teacher
Williams, Robert Rex
Mathematics Teacher
Wynn, Kevin Duane
8th Grd Amer History Teacher
PAWNEE CITY
Myers, Cindy L.
English & Jrnlsm Teacher
Schlender, Virginia Hazen
Fourth Grade Teacher
PAXTON
Elder, Kim H.
Director of Student Services
PENDER
Nelson, Tami Doht
Special Education Teacher
Norman, L. G.
Business Teacher
Olsson, Mary Ellen Kauth
Eng, Communication Skills Tchr
Smith, Patrick G.
Instrumental Music Teacher
Strom, Todd Allen
Life Sci, Bio Teacher & Coach

PETERSBURG
Hofeldt, Jeffery A.
Mathematics Instructor
PIERCE
Hoefener, Larry L.
Fifth Grade Teacher
Jessen, Constance Dianne (Heinz)
Vocal Music Teacher
Martin, Melinda Lee (Oetken)
Math & HS Geometry Tchr
Schwartz, Steven John
Sixth Grade Teacher
Weber, Marjorie Kay
First Grade Teacher
PLAINVIEW
North, Lois M.
Third & Fourth Grade Teacher
PLATTE CENTER
Tremain, Sally Ann
7th & 8th Grade Teacher
PLATTSMOUTH
Watt, Betty J.
8th Grd Earth Science Teacher
POLK
Cotter, Eugene D., Jr.
Fourth Grade Teacher
PONCA
Watchorn, David Clyde
Technology Teacher
Zimmer, Dave L.
English, Soc Stud & PE Tchr
POTTER
Brooks, Rebecca May
Kindergarten Teacher
Faden, Daria Anderson
High School History Teacher
Nielsen, Mary Frances
Math & Physics Teacher
RALSTON
Johnson, Diane Reye
Media Specialist
Johnson, Shirley
Fourth Grade Teacher
RANDOLPH
Heimann, Bill R.
Scndry Social Science Teacher
Morten, Ken L.
Math, Computer Science Teacher
RAVENNA
Beranek, Paul Francis
Art & Journalism Teacher
Grabowski, Janelle Marie Jahn
Junior High English Teacher
RAYMOND
Johnson, Dan R.
Speech Comm & Theatre Teacher
Marsh, James Mervin
Business Ed & Technology Coord
Schnell, David L.
Mathematics Tchr & Dept Chair
Trawinski, Pamela Merritt
Mathematics & Computer Teacher
RED CLOUD
McNeil, Donald Joseph
Science Teacher
Riemersma, Dennis
Mathematics Teacher
RISING CITY
Dunekacke, Mary Lou Kresha
Media Specialist
Habben, Jonathan Kent
Superintendent
RUSHVILLE
Dowding, Sharla Kay
7th-12th Grade Science Teacher
Gormish, Elizabeth
6th-8th Grade Teacher
Johnson, Candi L.
English, Speech & Drama Instr
Peters, Shirley Jean House
Fourth Grade Teacher
SAINT EDWARD
Harner, Jane Fry
Fourth Grade Teacher
Whidden, Virginia Hayes
Family & Consumer Sci Tchr
SAINT LIBORY
Watt, Lois Bader
Kndgtn-2nd Grade Teacher
SAINT PAUL
Schacht, Tom H.
Elem Physical Education Tchr
SARGENT
Poland, Carol Gruber
Counselor
Thamer, Carol Fries
Third Grade Teacher
SCHUYLER
Hagewood, Thomas Leslie, III
Biology & Cmptr Science Tchr
Knutson, Jon Eric
Social Studies Teacher & Coach
Lambley, Scott Q.
7th & 8th Grade Sci Teacher
Rittenburg, Mary L. (Wissink)
Language Arts Teacher
Zrust, Bonnie Kracl
Business Teacher
SCOTIA
Holmes, Karen Harvey
Mental Health Therapist
Medbery, Wilber D.
HS Mathematics Teacher
SCOTTSBLUFF
Edelbrock, Katherine Knowles
6th Grd Language Arts Teacher
Harrach, Sandra Haskell
6th Grade Math Teacher
Howard, Ron E.
Elementary Physical Ed Instr

Keszler, Deanna France
4th Grade Teacher
Moran, Mark Eugene
Social Studies Teacher
Nash, David Lloyd
Biology Instructor
Schlothauer, Loni Dale
Homeroom, Math & Speech Tchr
Schnell, Judy Moore
Div Chair of Math, Sci & PE
Wright, Kimberly Roemmich
English Teacher
Wylie, Guy Stephen
Human Service Program Coord
SCRIBNER
Hardesty, Lyle K.
English & Spanish Teacher
Svec, Mary Ann (Dillon)
Jr High Language Arts Teacher
SEWARD
Bauman, Kathy L.
Graduate Assistant of Math
Creed, D. Bruce
Asst Prof of Communication
Dolak, David E.
Prof of Psych & VP Acad Svc
Dynneson, Donald Lee
Professor of Art
Fiala, Maxine Bickel
Kindergarten Teacher
Frisbie, Daniel B.
Instrumental Music Teacher
Mannigel, David R.
Principal & Teacher
Meehl, Mark William
Assistant Prof of Theology
Moulds, Russell Glenn
Psychology Professor
Sloup, Deborah Hilton
Eighth Grade English Teacher
SHELBY
Lyons, Kevin Dean
Secondary Science Instructor
Scheele, Rebecca Jo (Rutledge)
English Teacher
SHELTON
Micek, Vicki Jo
English Teacher
Wehling, Linda Pruden
English Teacher
SHICKLEY
Boyer, Margaret Ogden
English Teacher
SIDNEY
Gottula, Alan Dale
High School Guidance Counselor
Johnson, Ella Berniece (Schnell)
Second Grade Teacher
Smith, Fran
Journalism & Photography Instr
SILVER CREEK
Anderson, Rose Beck
2nd Grade Teacher
Wilgocki, Susanne M.
Language Arts & English Tchr
SOUTH SIOUX CITY
Banks, Jules Kirk
Band Director
Davidson, Scott Fredrick
High School Math Teacher
Goedken, Keith
Language Arts Instructor
Huff, Patsy Hernandez
Fourth Grade Teacher
Koch, Helmut
Chemistry, Physics & Math Tchr
Rohde, Beth Ann
ESL & Biology Teacher
SPALDING
Gladem, Kathleen M.
Business Teacher
Hensley, Judy Ann
Fifth & Sixth Grade Teacher
Knust, Christine Walter
English Teacher
Mahoney, Martha Ruth Rassenfoss
1st & 2nd Grade Teacher
Socha, Eva Elizabeth Prickett
Elementary Teacher
Wagner, Loren Glen
Social Studies Teacher
SPENCER
Carlson, James Ivan
Sixth Grade Teacher
SPRINGFIELD
Jones, Lois Elizabeth
Speech & Drama Teacher
Kentsmith, Kitty
Gifted Coordinator
Pfeil, Kristine L. Smith
9th-12th Grd Business Teacher
SPRINGVIEW
Budnick, Thomas R.
Bus Ed, Cmptr Tchr & Coach
Sheffield, Paul Douglas
Math Teacher
STANTON
Waddington, Perry William
Mathematics Teacher
STAPLETON
Tool, Barbara Ann
Sixth Grade Teacher
STELLA
Furnas, Naomi Louise (Leakey)
K-12 Art Teacher
Hall, Philip Ross
Mathematics Instructor
STROMSBURG
Waller, Timm Owen
Math Teacher

Brenda Jo Fear
Speech & Drama Tchr
, Nancy Maria
acher
ena Stahlecker
arten Teacher
R
Ann Hensley
rade Teacher
rolyn Kay
rade Teacher
eri E. (Ryan)
l Education Teacher
Kenneth William, Jr.
rade Teacher
OR
eggy Louise (Applegate)
Grade Teacher
Fred C.
Instructor
ayna (Kuxhausen)
natics Teacher
ady Kae
& Language Arts Tchr
RLAND
uliann Rae
Teacher
n, Shannon Jolene
ss Education Instructor
William Charles
Counselor
rian R.
eacher
Michael Delno
al
N
John James
Performing Arts Instr
nes Charles
Grade English Teacher
, Thomas
ltural Education Tchr
rg, Stephen Robert
Drivers Ed Teacher
Mickey L.
Dept Chprsn & Teacher
USE
, E. K.
r
Dorothy Louise Gillispie
Grade Teacher
Monte C.
e Teacher
Ronald Mark
Language Arts Teacher
arbara Kay (Badberg)
l Grade Teacher
R
Kevin Paul
n & Speech Teacher
Cathy Ann (Hyde)
r & Coach
SEH
Ronald
th Grade Soc Sci Teacher
Marcee
matics Dept Chair & Tchr
TON
Rae Johnson
Grade Teacher
N
e Dwayne
ss Teacher
Eldon
dary Mathematics Teacher
S
Natalie Focken
tute Teacher
ON
er, Deb Lee
ealth & Drivers Ed Tchr
N
Alan Eugene
ocial Science Teacher
NG
ster, Maurine Sue Griffith
entary Teacher
TINE
, Ron R.
ce & Computer Teacher
Roy T.
Studies Teacher
Gregory L.
Dept Head & Media Spclst
n, Warren Dale
ematics Teacher
EY
Mary Jane (Convey)
sh & History Teacher
IGRE
oyce Ann
h Grd Art Teacher
Regina Rae
l Science Teacher
, James Allen, Jr.
cal Education Teacher
DO
, Connie Isaacson
a, Speech, Eng Tchr & Dir
, Wayne Clyde
Stud & Bus Math Tchr
EFIELD
, Coleen Papenhausen
th Grade Music Teacher
, Rod Dale
School English Teacher

WALLACE
Hunt, Mark Duane
Social Science Teacher
WALTHILL
Lawler, Patrick Wayne
Social Science Instructor
WATERLOO
Hammond, Sandra Hardy
Eng, Speech & Jrnlsm Tchr
WAUSA
Larson-Kaiser, LuAnn L.
English Instructor
Pfeil, Ann L.
English Teacher
Skala, Barbara L.
Physical Science Teacher
WAVERLY
Applebee, Keri B.
Secondary English Teacher
Bellinger, Murleen Felzien
Business Teacher
Curtis, Carrie Beth
English Teacher
Hollinger, Brent Lee
Chemistry & Physics Teacher
Kletchka, Kay Powell
Fourth Grade Teacher
Krieser, Dianne Cook
3rd Grade Teacher
Marquart, Catherine Ann
German Teacher
WAYNE
Hochstein, Dale Donald
Biology Teacher
Schafer, Judith Hodges
English Teacher
Youngerman, Lois Stigile
Retired Head Start Cncl Tchr
Zobel, Judith Ann
Science Teacher
WEEPING WATER
Franssen, John Paul
Instrumental Music Instructor
WEST POINT
Ortmeier, Joyce Ann
Fifth Grade Teacher
WESTON
Jonas, Janet Barry
Third Grade Teacher
WILBER
Brown, Sarah Dauphinee
English Instructor
Burger, Janet Lynne (Brickner)
German & English Teacher
Workman, Russel Howard
Band Director
WINNEBAGO
Calvillo, Mary Kimberly
Instructor
Chapman, Roland Royce
Computer Instructor
Posey, Margaret Ann
Communications Sociology Instr
Rice, Elaine Renee
Media Technician
WINSIDE
Hypse, Terri (Melena)
English Teacher
WISNER
Bockelman, Larry Allen
Science Teacher
Machacek, Darlene Novotny
Mathematics Teacher
WOOD RIVER
Heise, Peggy Jo
Life Science Teacher
Olson, Sandra Kay Bishop
Business & Computer Instructor
WYMORE
Bednar, Oren Lee
Mathematics Teacher
Brackhahn, Betty Louise
English Speech & Drama Instr
Hennecke, Kevin Leon
Industrial Tech Tchr & Coach
Pralle, Carol Lynn (Korgan)
Art Instructor
Wieden, Sheri Lynn (Horn)
Family & Consumer Sci Instr
WYNOT
Lee- Wiebelhaus, Debra Sue
Music Teacher
Tramp, Rhonda Masten
Resource Teacher
YORK
Brutto, Philip Antonio, Jr.
Art & Graphic Arts Instructor
Miller, L. Ray, II
Div of Natural Sci & Math Prof
Nixon, Gerald Eugene
Accounting Professor
Reetz, Janelle Kay
7th-12th Grd Vocal Music Tchr
Roush, Clark A.
Music Professor
Schulz, Dorris M. Lott
Assoc Prof of Psychology
Schulz, Thomas Neil
Professor of Biblical Studies
Simpson, David Scott
Asst Prof of Eng & Comm
YUTAN
Wilch, Lee Alan
K-12 Guidance Counselor

NEVADA

BATTLE MOUNTAIN
Dahl, Richard Lee
Fourth Grade Teacher
Grise, Martha Steenbergen
Home Economics Teacher
BEATTY
Isom, Floyd Richard
Teacher
BOULDER CITY
Backman, Brian Robert
Mathematics Teacher
Fullington, Peter Ross
Biology Teacher
Hafen, Linda Lee
Reading Specialist
Senko, Denise Marie
Science Teacher
Strachan, William Edward
Mathematics Teacher
Whitmore, Sharon Mc Ilrath
Retired 3rd Grade Teacher
CARLIN
Blinn, Jon Mark
Amer Govt & Economic Teacher
Tsunemori, Pat
Head Physical Science Dept
CARSON CITY
Bockman, Cherie Plouffe
High School English Teacher
Cannady, Charles Robert
Naval Science Instructor
Chacon, Joan G.
Spanish Teacher
Chandler, Karen Louise
Performing Arts Instructor
Clark, Terri K.
Biology & Human Anatomy Tchr
Coyle, Vincent Peter
Government & US History Tchr
Daniels, Jessica Barlow
8th Grade English Teacher
Dietrich, Bonnie Kay
Adapted PE Tchr
Findley, Leisa Park
Math & Computer Science Tchr
Fisher, Alice Bass
Fourth Grade Teacher
Gardner, Betty
3rd Grade Teacher
Johnson, Mark David
Mathematics Teacher
Keller, Charles Dale
Dean of Students
Lathrop, Peter S.
Biology Teacher & FFA Adv
Martinovich, Paul Andrew
History & Geography Teacher
Peebles, Stewart St Louis
Choral Director
Roosenberg, Rebecca Ruth
Art Teacher
Swain, John Q.
Biology Teacher
Thayer, Janet Marie
Second Grade Teacher
Valley, John Mac
Chemistry Teacher
Yerke, Shirley Ann (Bailey)
1st-5th Grd Reading Teacher
DAYTON
Fike, Claudia Henderson
7th & 8th Grd English Teacher
Moyle, Sean Steven
Assistant Principal
Volberding, Louis Earl, II
Occupational Teacher
Westerland, Lanette M.
7th Grd Eng & Soc Stu Teacher
EAST ELY
Conley, Keith Edward
Principal
Woessner, Annemarie
3rd Grade Teacher
ELKO
Aikenhead, Keith Kevin
Drafting Trades Teacher
Lee, Ruth Kramer
Vice Principal
Long, Patrick Jess
High School Art Teacher
Sweetwater, Sarah
Art Dept Chair & Educ Trvl Dir
Tutty, Kathryn Hazel Gilstrap (Miller)
Home Economics Teacher
Wallock, Jeff
Biology Teacher
Weeks, Fred Edwards
World His & Geography Tchr
Williams, Gerald Lee
Electronics Teacher
ELY
Beebe, Thomas H.
Dean of Students
Johns, Robin Baker
Early Chldhd Interventionist
Leonard, Leonard Gary
7th Grade Language Arts Tchr
Thornock, Dean Dean
US History & German Teacher
Wright, Joseph B.
Chemistry & Physics Teacher
Young, Jennifer Hales
Drill Team Coach & Dance Tchr
EUREKA
Moore, LeahRae Eske
Second Grade Teacher

Todd, Barbara J.
English, Math & Science Tchr
FALLON
Billett, John Lynn
AP US History & Govt Teacher
Cole, T. Keith
Social Studies Teacher
Combo, Daniel Raymond
Business Education Teacher
Craig, Kenna Booker
Computer Teacher
Duggan, Scott J.
Ag Teacher
Gentner, Merry J.
Spanish & Journalism Teacher
Guisti, Ursula Mohler
French & German Teacher
Hubbard, Sam J.
Mathematics Teacher
Hyatt, John Warren, Jr.
Vice Principal
Johnson, Steve D.
Chemistry Teacher
Jones, Lynn Apalategui
Second Grade Teacher
Keast, Dale A.
Math, Sci & Spelling Teacher
Marcoux, David John
Sr Deputy Juvenile Probtn Ofcr
McGowan, Catherine Manhire
Special Education Teacher
Montgomery, Eileen Hannifan
Third Grade Teacher
Moran, Joe
Jr HS Social Studies Teacher
Olson, Clara Jean
First Grade Teacher
Plants, Walter D.
Fourth Grade Teacher
Porterfield, Marie Jensen
Choral Music Director
Punchard, Nathan Glenn
English & Debate Teacher
Purrell, Victoria Rene
2nd Grade Teacher
Ranson, Steven Robert
Vice Principal
Smith-Ansotegui, Susan C.
Sixth Grade Teacher
Thompson, Pamela Beeghly
First Grade Teacher
Travis, Simmie Dee Cooper
English Teacher
FERNLEY
Case, Chris
German, Psych & English Tchr
Christensen, Patrick T.
History & Economics Teacher
Ghiringhelli, Fran
English Teacher
Kalousek, David
High School English Teacher
Rieger, Steven P.
Engineering & Technology Tchr
Van Parys, Alta Walker
English Teacher
GARDNERVILLE
Blanchard, Rod D.
Geography & English Teacher
Nelson, Jack Douglas
Science Teacher
Reynolds, Melinda Carole (Hansen)
2nd Grade Teacher
HAWTHORNE
Neville, Keith E.
Computer Tchr & Athletic Dir
Rogers, Marsha S.
English Teacher
HENDERSON
Aiello, Wendy Gross
Fifth Grade Teacher
Anderson, Robert Bruce
Science Teacher
Armstrong, Suzan Christine
Sixth Grade Life Science Tchr
Barclay, Kimberly Knorr
Choir Director
Bekaert, Jeri
Reading Teacher & Dept Chair
Bennion, David C.
Zoology & Biology Teacher
Braner, Gretchen Gaylord
World Geography Teacher
Cothrun, Esther Smalley
Business Teacher
Donley, Eleana Rachael
Spanish Teacher
Ebert, Jhone Marie
Mathematics Teacher
Echols, Susan Harris
English Teacher
Edgar, Susan Frances
English Teacher
Engel, Eileen Marie
French, German & Japanese Tchr
Fowler, Vaden L.
Social Science Instructor
Gronemeier, Martha Jean (Hubbard)
Private Violin Tchr & Prfrmr
Harris, Louis
Teacher of Gifted & Talented
Johnson, Syble L.
Mathematics Teacher
Kimball, Ira Gardner
Seventh Grade English Teacher
Kuzma, James Louis
Dean of Students
Lamph, Becky Lee
US His & Honors Govt Tchr

Luca, Carl U.
Biology Teacher
Meier, Christine Ann
Science Teacher
Newlon, Bradley Dean
Resource Room Teacher
Pechman, Cynthia McKay
Junior High Reading Teacher
Purtill, Toni Lynn (Oonk)
High School Teacher
Ryland, Carole Bill
Reading Teacher
Schofield, Jan Borum
Multi-Age Teacher
Sellers, Clayton D.
Adv Plcmnt Bio & Bio Tech Tchr
Steen, Karen M. (Rhoades)
English Teacher
Vecellio, Brenda Barnett
Fifth Grade Teacher
Wallace, John S.
US His & Amer Studies Tchr
INCLINE VILLAGE
Shipley, Anne
Art History Assistant Prof
LAS VEGAS
Adams, Elizabeth Ann Leigh
Child Development Professor
Alvarez, Joaquin, Jr.
Sixth Grade Math Teacher
Apfel, Patrick Joseph
Asst Prof of Radiological Sci
Arango, Alba
11th Grade US History Teacher
Arnold, Harry Bittner
Physics & Algebra Teacher
Arroyo, Patricia L.
Spanish & Japanese Teacher
Assane', Djeto D.
Assistant Professor
Bachellor, Marilyn Margaret (Mowbray)
Fifth Grade Teacher
Baker, Franklin Neil
Professor of Accounting
Ball, Larry Merle
Heating, Air Cond, Refrig Tchr
Banks, David James
Music Director
Barnett, Robert W.
Math, Bus & Cmptr Dept Chair
Beachley, DeAnna E.
Professor of History
Beal, Katherine Diane Steimle
Gftd & Talented Ed Specialist
Blizard, Susan Kennedy
Professor & Sci Dept Chair
Blockovich, Joe
Teacher & GATE Coordinator
Bluhm, Cheryl Dawn
Math Teacher
Boley, Wendell Howe
Vocational Drafting Teacher
Boyack, Steve Philip
Math Teacher & Head Coach
Boyle, Kim Ann
Business Education Teacher
Boyt, Thomas Eugene
Asst Prof of Marketing
Brasier, Donald Edwin
Geometry Teacher
Braun, William Henry
Math Dept Chairman
Broadhead, Marian Baldwin
Science Teacher
Burleson, Joy Concannon
Health & Physical Ed Teacher
Burns, Theo Anne
Dept Chair of Foreign Lang
Camero, Nancy J. McCoy
Third Grade Teacher
Cardwell, Denice Mitchell
Government & Psychology Tchr
Carroll, Stevi
Social Studies Teacher
Cazin, Cheryl Hackworth
Cmptr Sci & Publications Tchr
Chase, Dorothy Doreen
Reading Professor
Chesley, Kim L.
Fifth Grade Instructor
Costa, David G.
Mathematics Professor
Cox, Karen Elizabeth (Hauer)
Math & Business Teacher
Crego, William West
Math Teacher
Daneshvary, Nasser
Economics Professor & Chair
Davis, Gina Gonzalez
Physical Education Teacher
Delrosario, Giovanni Joe
Culinary Arts Professor
DeMaio, Geoffrey George
Marketing Teacher
Demeny-Hermes, Kimberly
High School English Teacher
Denson, Andre Brent
Assistant Principal
DePiazza, Nury Medina
Dance, Phys Edctr & Hlth Tchr
DiBlasi, Margaret Lindsay
Elementary School Librarian
Dill, Deana Cordeiro
Art Teacher
Dixon, Jennifer Strickler
First Grade Teacher
Duncan, Al
Anthropology & Psych Instr
Dunn, Joanne Pretty
Eighth Grade Teacher

LAS VEGAS (cont)
Ecklund, Barbara M. (Zaiger)
Health Occupations Teacher
Efthimiou, Diane O.
High School English Teacher
Eliopulos, Tina D.
Instructor of English
Elliott, Gary Eugene
History Professor
Elliott, Toni Farris
Rdng & Environmental Sci Tchr
Esperian, John H.
Prof of English
Essary, Bill
World & US History Teacher
Fama, Michelle Chi
French Teacher
Farris, Steven A.
English Instructor
Fernald, Leanne Odegaard
Special Assignment Teacher
Fewell, Douglas Martin
Health Teacher
Finocchiaro, Paul Edward
Dance Teacher
Foy, Margaret R.
Bus Ed Dept Chprsn & Tchr
Fullmer, Sue Gaisford
Family & Consumer Sci Tchr
Garman, Rebecca J.
Computers & Publications Tchr
Gerber, Charles A.
AP Calculus Teacher & Ath Dir
Gerber, Connie Kellen
Vice Principal & Spanish Tchr
Girard, Marie Anne Leman
French Teacher
Goertemiller, John C.
Teacher
Goodwin, Marques Anthony
Marketing Instructor
Granese, Judith Ann
Latin & English Teacher
Gratz, Jody Michels
English Teacher
Gresh, Stephen
Health Teacher
Grillo, Louis Anthony
High School Government Teacher
Grytdahl, Kim Howard
Mathematics Department Chprsn
Haines, Phillip LLoyd
Band Director
Hale, Gordon S.
Spanish Instructor
Halopoff, Greg Paul
Technology Specialist
Hanevold, Grant A.
7th Grade Math Teacher
Hansen, D. Parke
Physical Education Specialist
Hardigree, Donald W.
Inst Insurance & Risk Mgmt Dir
Harper, Anne E.
US History Teacher
Harrison, Lizette Marie
English Teacher
Hayes, James Charles
Mathematics Teacher
Heater, Karen Brew
Art Teacher
Henry, Nancy Jean
Math Teacher
Hicks, Martin E.
Professor of Biology
Hobbs, Jeffrey Dale
Life Science Teacher
Holland, Patricia Urie
History Teacher
Hollitz, John E.
Professor
Houdersheldt, Pamela Ellen (Paul)
Mathematics Teacher
Hovland, Diane M.
Anatomy & Physiology Teacher
Izzo, Joanne Gagich
Second Grade Teacher
Jacks, Lisa
College English Teacher
Jefferson, Jennie Brown
Title I Teacher
Johnson, Eric Paul
Geometry & AP Calculus Tchr
Johnson, Janie
English Teacher
Johnson, Norman A.
Science Teacher
Jones, Jo Anne
Special Education Teacher
Kabat, Gillian Simpson
Special Education Teacher
Kadoich, Stephen William, Jr.
Weight Training Teacher
Kelly, Christopher Pat
Dept Chair of Acctng
Klund, Renee Marie
Seventh Grade English Teacher
Lane, Marcella Smith
English Teacher
Lato, Anthony, Jr.
Assistant Principal
Lawrence, Deborah
8th Grade Algebra Teacher
Leavitt, Wayne Allen
High School Teacher
Lehmann, Mary Hansen
English Teacher
Leone, Jill Marie
Reading & English Teacher
Lestelle, Wende Susan
Earth Science Teacher
Lewis, Alan R.
Band Director & Biology Tchr
Lewton, Carolyn Minor
Sixth Grade Life Sci Tchr
Little, Diana Jacobs
Special Education Facilitator
Lobel, Kenneth Brian
Fifth Grade Teacher
Lou, Lillian Lim
Second Grade Teacher
Luberacki, Robert J.
Senior Army & JROTC Instr
Maguire, Bettyann
English Teacher
Maki, Rebecca Marie
Math Teacher
Manning, Elfie U.
Professor of French & German
Martin, Elizabeth S.
English Teacher & Dept Chair
Martinez, Anibal
ESL, Mathematics & Sci Teacher
Merritt Shade, Karla
Japanese Teacher
Michaels, Judith A.
Eng Tchr & Stu Cncl Advisor
Miller, Eleanor
English Professor
Miner, Janet Mae
Teacher & Facilitator
Miner, Kort A.
Earth Science Teacher
Morley, RosaLina Santiago
Kndgtn & 1st Grade Teacher
Myers, Carolyn Sue Balben
10th-11th Grd English Teacher
Niemiec, Joseph Ronald
Professor
Odle, Clifford James
Business & Physical Ed Teacher
Okeke, Charles Chukwurah
Economics Professor
Olin, Kenneth Duane
Physics Teacher
O'Neil, Ramona Ruiz
History Teacher
Orr, Linda Bryant
Chem Teacher & Sci Dept Chair
Ortis, Diane E.
Spanish Teacher
Painter, Patrick Allen
Teacher & Coach
Painter, Steven Lee
High School Math Teacher
Paterson, Mary Antoinette
Associate Professor
Pearson, Gary Arthur
Math Instructor
Percin, Mary Lou Moulton
Environmental Science Teacher
Perkins, Diana Loewenstein
Mathematics Teacher
Pinjuv, Annie
Geography Teacher
Presley, Daniela
German & English Teacher
Pribyl, Joan Lee Appleyard
Science Instructor
Prichard, Brenna D.
Biology Tchr & Sci Dept Coord
Quigley, Lynette (Davis)
Mathematics Teacher
Rafferty, Kevin A.
Professor of Ethnology
Ragland, John Howard
Religion & PE Teacher
Rahas, Peter
9th-12th Grd History Teacher
Regin, Charles E. W.
Asst Professor of Health Ed
Rich, Ray L., Jr.
Professor of Social Sciences
Roberts, Barrett Howard
Fifth Grade Teacher
Roberts, Judith Posner
11th-12th Grd English Instr
Romero, Anita Christine
Govt, Crime & Justice Teacher
Ross, Carmen Ann
Hnrs Bio & Earth Science Instr
Rycroft, Sally J.
A P His & Amer Govt Teacher
Sarbacker, Thomas Jeffrey
Mathematics Teacher
Sassenberg, Gary R.
Teacher
Scheele, Minka J.
Speech & English Teacher
Scott, Otilia Gandara
First Grade Teacher
Sibo, E. Lynette
English Teacher
Silvonek, Donna Angeline
English Teacher
Slayton, Brenda Joyce
Fifth Grade Teacher
Sobey, Teena Elaine
Home Economics Teacher
Stanley, Thomas E.
Social Studies Teacher
Steadman, Richard Thomas
Professor of Biology
Stephen, Anne DiIorio
Choral Studies Director
Stephen, Bud
Science & Mathematics Teacher
Stetts, Charles Edwin
9th-12th Grd Mathematics Tchr
Stetts, Sheila Carroll
English Tchr & Yearbook Adv
Stewart, Ingrid Gerda
Mathematics Instructor
Strauss, Paul E.
Lecturer in English
Suchy, Norma (Fetek)
Chemistry & Nutrition Prof
Thomas, William Henry
Military Science Instructor
Thompson, Kay Irene
Spanish Teacher
Tomlinson, K. Larry
Professor of Government
Toutovnji, Mindy Olson
Social Studies Teacher
Towner, Sharon
Orchestra Director
Trofholz, Daniel Ray
Third Grade Teacher
Turner, John Michael
HS Mathematics Teacher
Unrue, Darlene Harbour
Professor of English
Vernon, Hope Kanell
Eng I & II Teacher
Vining, Alma Garcia
Principal
Vollan, Rodney R.
Secondary Math Teacher
VonBehren, Thomas R., CSV
President
Vuillemot, Joanne Elaine
Community Coll Art Professor
Wallace, D. Kirk
History Teacher
Walo, Magel Irma (Hamm)
Retired Third Grade Teacher
Weinman, Susan Gail
Special Education Teacher
Wendt, Steven William
Director of MIS Labs
West, Louise L.
Retired Teacher
Wickliffe, Robert C.
Counselor
Willems, Claudette Anfinson
Eng as a Second Language Tchr
Williams, LaDawn Swallow
Amer Govt & US History Tchr
Wilson, Deborah Jean
Health Teacher
Wilson, Joyce Yvonne (Huskey)
Science Teacher
Winkler, Catherine Lee
Third Grade Teacher
Winston, Fannie M.
Second Grade Teacher
Wisusik, Marcia Kathleen
1st Grade Teacher
Wood, Benjamin
US History Teacher
Wood, John D.
Science Chairperson & Teacher
Wright, Lonnie Gene
Pgm Dir of Hotel Management
Wyatt, Michelle A.
Mathematics Professor
Young, Gayle Marie
Business Education Teacher

LAUGHLIN
Fermon, Benjamine Franklin
Soc Stud Tchr, Ath & Act Dir
Stitt, Richard R.
Theatre Teacher

LOVELOCK
Rowe, Patricia Hoysted
First Grade Teacher
Starr, Janie Quilici
5th Grade Teacher
Stewart, Larry R.
Social Studies Teacher

MC DERMITT
Jones, Michele Lynn
Second Grade Teacher
Pogue, Gary Lee
Counselor

MINDEN
Barnes, Debbie (Payne)
Math Teacher
Cordova, Theresa
High School Counselor
Cronin, Martin Anthony
Social Studies Teacher
Egan, Eric S.
3rd Grade Teacher
Mattison, Donovan M.
Secondary Science Teacher
Usher, Karen Marie
Agricultural Teacher

NORTH LAS VEGAS
Anderson, Lori Ann
8th Grade English Teacher
Arroyo, Sandra Montalvo-Pagan
English Teacher
Austin, Lorene Mislivec
Business & Computer Teacher
Bullen, Lisa (Dornak)
High School English Teacher
Burns, William John
College Counselor
Chen, Mark Paoming
Math Teacher
DeAngelis, Alfred Peter
English Teacher
Georges, Karla
ESL Teacher
Jackson, Tracy McCormick
English Teacher
Johnson, Freddie James
Bus Edctr & Work Exprnc Coord
Joseph, Jennifer Golden
English & ESL Teacher
LaFond, Gwen
English Teacher
Larsen, Diane Gail
Mathematics Teacher
Mc Clary, Marie Kathryn
10th-12th Grd Eng Instructor
McGuire, Michael Todd
Special Education Teacher
Rice, Jennifer A.
English Teacher
Seipel, Phyllis Jensen
English Instructor
Shriner, Joan Ward
English Teacher & Dept Chprsn
Smith, David Thomas
Choir & Orchestra Director
Stormer, Eugene E.
Retired Lit Teacher
Trombley, Susan Yeiter
English Teacher
Walton, Jennifer Palor
Mathematics Teacher
Weeteling, Terry R.
Photography Teacher
Williams, Faye Kiyomi
Science Teacher
Ziegler, David Anthony
Computer Science Teacher
Ziegler, Mary Lois
English Teacher

OVERTON
Genseal, Margaret Jeane
English Department Chair
Whitney, Sherrie Ann
Math Teacher

PAHRUMP
Calliet, Chris
HS Govt, Psych & US His Tchr
Rouse-Windholz, Sheila Marie
Second Grade Teacher

PANACA
Anderson, Michael Smith
Mathematics & Electricity Tchr
Louchard, Lorrell G.
First Grade Teacher

RENO
Albin, Leilani Palmer
Art Teacher
Austin, Carrath Ann
Teacher of Hearing Impaired
Baden, Larry Joel
Journalism Instructor
Bennett, Esther Laiola
1st Grade Teacher
Blackwell, Melinda Bourke
High School English Teacher
Bowles, JoAnn Holmes
Second Grade Teacher
Brook, Maria Elena (Sciarrotta)
Mathematics Teacher
Buhrmann, Kenneth Deane
English Teacher
Buzick, Tamera J.
Mathematics Teacher
Caviness, Linda Bryant
Principal
Cellucci, Sabrina
Drama Teacher
Christman, Sandra St John
English Teacher
Cirelli, Joyce Elaine
Fourth Grade Teacher
Clark, Joan Margaret
Bio, Envrnmntl & Phys Sci Tchr
Clyne, Robyn Munn
First Grade Teacher
Colbert, Douglas Mc Arthur
Mathematics Instructor
Craig, Maureen Elizabeth
Substitute Teacher
Crawford, Carol Annette
Dean of Students
Crawford, Sheri Faith
Western Traditions Instructor
Crosby, Lisa U'Ren
Mathematics Teacher
De Frutos, Gayle Lohse
Spanish Teacher
Denning, Susan Briggs
Eng Teacher & Schlsp Coord
Dugan, Kevin James
Professor of Psychology
Fabri, DeAnn Mc Gowan
Sixth Grade Teacher
Ferrell, Gail Small
Mathematics Professor
Fisher, Marjorie Bowers
Sixth Grade Teacher
Geyer, Mary Louise
French & Italian Teacher
Ghymn, Kyung-il
Mrktg & Intnl Business Prof
Halcomb, Daniel B.
English & Yearbook Teacher
Harris, Chris
Social Studies Teacher
Harris, Frederick Calvin, Jr.
Asst Prof of Computer Science
Hecimovich, Helen
Community College Professor
Hedrick, Georgia Carolyn
First Grade Teacher
Henderson, Phyllis Lee
Community College Professor
Heron, Lory E.
High School Science Teacher
Hess, Ruth M.
4th Grade Teacher
Hoover, Timothy James
Eighth Grd US History Teacher
Houk, William Lee
Physical Education Instructor
Hurren, B. Lee
Spanish Teacher
Hurren, Susan Emma
High School Counselor
Johnson, Bruce Paul
Prof of Electrical Engineering
Jones, Josette Frenzel
English, Speech & Debate Tchr
Kleppe, John Arthur
Prof of Electrical Engineering
LaForge, Laurence Edward
Asst Prof of Elec Engrng
Lambert, Jerry Wayne
HS Counselor
Lane, Kathy Heckman
6th Grade Teacher
LeMay, H. Eugene, Jr.
Chemistry Professor
Lindsey, Teresa Shiflett
9th Grade English Teacher
MacDonald, Michael Bruce
7th-8th Ger, Eng & His Teacher
Mancini, Roberto C.
Physics Professor
Manfredi, Nancy Petrini
English Teacher & Dept Chair
Martinelli, Eva Taverna
Retired Assistant Principal
Martinez, Frank John
US History & Government Tchr
McCreary, Kathy Tappe
First Grade Teacher
McGlinn, Rhonda (Swearingin)
1st & 2nd Grade Teacher
Melcher, Brett Warren
HS Physical Education Teacher
Mickey, Kathryn Reyman
Music Teacher
Milchak, Barbara Simmers
Integrated Multi-Aged Ed Tchr
Modolo-Parks, Michele
French & Spanish Teacher
Mohatt, Linda Rubin
5th-6th Grd Image Class Tchr
Moore, Dorothy Kay
6th Grade Teacher
Phenix, John William
Retired Fitness & Health Tchr
Preston-Baer, Paula K.
English Teacher
Reed, Phyllis Ann
Assoc Prof of Health Science
Roberts, Suzanne Thomson
First Grade Teacher
Rowberg, Lynne Francis
Spanish Teacher
Sambrano, Rosalio Flores
JV Basketball & Track Coach
Scheurer, Carla Coykendall
University Supervisor
Siegel, Richard Lewis
Political Science Professor
Smilanick, G. Phillip
Professor of Accounting
Sullivan, Robert Daniel
Principal
Tedford, Cynthia Gail
Business Department Teacher
Tripp, Carol A.
AP English Teacher
Trzynadlowski, Andrzej Maria
Prof of Electrical Engineering
Turner, Anthony George
Music Teacher
Valle, Linda S.
Spcl Ed Resource & His Tchr
Wiskerchen, Julie Cassinelli
6th Grade Teacher

ROUND MOUNTAIN
Harris, David Alan
HS Social Studies Teacher
Watts, Deborah Ann
English & French Teacher

SILVER SPRINGS
Senour, Joanne Marie
Fourth Grade Teacher

SMITH
Barton, LuVerne Alva
Math, Science & Drafting Tchr
Damele, John D.
Physical Education Teacher
Savidge, Maureen Patricia (Egan)
Third Grade Teacher

SPARKS
Allen, Mary Caddell
Home Economics Teacher
Anderson, Nancy Berdrow
School Counselor
Boulton, Dennis
9th-12th Grade Math Teacher
Branson, David George
Music Teacher
Cooper, Stan
Math Teacher
Feldman, Laurie Speth
First Grade Teacher
Gehr, Denton Smith, II
Soc Sci Tchr & Soc Stud Coord
Geyer, Ron Dee
Physics & Chemistry Teacher
Harrison, Corbett C.
High School English Teacher
Hildebrand, Douglas Alan
High School Teacher

; (cont)
r, Nancy Jean-Wood
th Grade Teacher
aul Michael
al Education Teacher
athy Smart
natics Teacher
W. Karl
s Ed Teacher
, Antonio
Grade Teacher
avid W.
story Tchr & Track Coach
Thomas L., Sr.
Instructor
ita J.
al Education Teacher
James M.
story Teacher
Earline
Teacher
Cathy J.
y & English Teacher
Ginny (keller)
Studies Teacher
LLEY
awrence Donald
Elementary Teacher
AH
au, Ted Charles
Teacher

e, Terry
ntary Counselor

Christopher Pal
Teacher
MUCCA
on Rex
Studies Teacher
arry P.
Teacher
GTON
len, Rod L.
Drama Instructor
ni, Steve W.
gy Teacher
e, Kay
Grade Teacher
nuth, Daron Casey
& Physical Education Tchr

V HAMPSHIRE

AD
, Robert L.
& French Teacher
, Taunya Purrington
sh Teacher
n, Ruth Lamb
d Art Teacher
otte, Barbara S.
8th Grd Mathematics Tchr
RST
Cheryl Milne
h Grade Teacher
H. Kirk
ematics Teacher
VER
ld, Randy John
ematics & Computer Teacher
AND
Elaine P.
ed French Teacher
ORD
Anthony Phillippe
ce Teacher
k, Barbara Ann (Smith)
Arts Curr Coord & Teacher
e, Peter O.
rade History Teacher
ONT
an, Vicki A.
h Grade Teacher
er, Steven W.
outer Coordinator
ns, Mary Ann
irade Teacher
e, Carol Pelzer
Grade Teacher
IN
, Hartson W.
ied Tech Dept Chair & Prof
o, Joseph John
ice Professor
old, Jacqueline Marie
an Svcs Pgm Professor
e, Margaret Bernadette
ish Teacher
Louise Filteau
ch Teacher
er, Marion Bierweiler
essor of English
on, Christine K.
Instr, Learning Specialist
, Sheldon Ellis
of Natural Resource Mgmt
, Michael Francis
red PE Teacher & Asst Prin

ais, Sandra E.
nth Grade Mathematics Tchr
ierczyk, Linda Mai
ic Teacher
, Susan Potter
ner English Teacher
arsh, Alexander William
el Services Dir & Coach

BRISTOL
Mills, Earl Allen
Science Teacher
Murphy, Natalie Ann
English Teacher & Dept Chair
CAMPTON
Hicks, Pauline E.
Social Studies Teacher
CANAAN
Blake, Carole I.
Instrumental Music Teacher
Ceplikas, Lynn Duffy
English Teacher
Grout, Nancy Fritz
English Teacher
Holm, Jennifer Susan
Science Teacher
CANDIA
Brown, Virginia Louise
Fourth Grade Teacher
Tonkin, Elizabeth Theresa
Music Teacher
CANTERBURY
Briggs, Janis Steinmetz
Music Teacher
Elliott, Ann Sharps
Second Grade Teacher
CENTER OSSIPEE
Hertzfeld, Elizabeth Nora
Elem Principal
CHARLESTOWN
Mates, Dona
Retired Teacher
CHESTERFIELD
Hood, Craig Robert
Social Studies Teacher
CLAREMONT
Bennett, John D.
Art, American Stud & Hum Tchr
Elders, Christopher A.
Professor of Science
Griggs, Shirley Kelly
Associate Professor of Nursing
Hall, Jacquelyn L. (Field)
Guidance Counselor
Lajoie, John Walter
English Teacher
Marashio, Nancy Feeney
Eng Prof & Gen Ed Dept Chair
Silva, Ralph E.
PE Teacher & Coach
CONCORD
Anderson, Terrance William
6th Grade Teacher
Curran, Kathleen Rosetti
Prof of Human Services
Denoncour, Mark T.
5th & 6th Grade Teacher
Fair, Dorothy R.
Title I Coord & Ed Consultant
Furlong, Cathleen Anne
K-2nd Grade Multi-Age Teacher
Gile, Mary Stuart Sinclair
Prof of Early Childhood Ed
Graf, Monique
Criminal Justice Professor
Greene, Benjamin Thomas
Music Teacher
Hunt, Martha Anne
Professor of Bus & Banking
Lewis, Judy Ouellette
8th Grd Language Arts Teacher
Martin, Philip Keith
Music Teacher
Mc Koan, Thomas Francis
Fifth Grade Teacher
McNamee, Jari G.
Life Studies Teacher
Mc Tague, Thomas Hugh
Prof of Alcohol & Drug Abuse
Metivier, Antoinette Poirier
Asst Prof of Dental Assisting
Morgan, Charles B.
English, Greek & Latin Teacher
Neiswenter, Phoebe Ann A.
Jewelry & Metals Teacher
Newman, F. David
English & Drama Teacher
Ohman, Sherri Lynn
7th-8th Grade Teacher
Osburn, Susan Bottorff
Spanish Teacher
Pavlidis, Anita Marie
Nursing Professor
Richardson, Daniel N.
Curr Facilitator & Span Tchr
Sherrill, Edmund Knox
Dean of Chapel & Hum Teacher
Smith, Karen Burgess
Art Dept Chair & Gallery Dir
Walton, Thomas Gay
Health & Related Fitness Tchr
Warde, Robert M.
Math, German & History Teacher
CONTOOCOOK
Houston, Tyrus C.
MS Geography & History Teacher
Mc Home, Jennifer L.
Spanish Teacher
CONWAY
Blanchard, Andrew Scott
Physical Education Teacher
Broomhall, Charles H., II
Phys Ed & Adventure Teacher
Chane, Richard Leo
Curriculum Coordinator
Franke, Karen Sims
Science Teacher
Freedman, David Brian
Sixth Grade Teacher

Hadam, Jack J.
Biology Teacher
Hamlin, Michelle Sparre
Mathematics Teacher
Judge, Jon Charles
Social Science Teacher
Mackey, Joseph Leonard
Social Studies Curr Coord
Mason, David George
Math Teacher
Steele, Helen Read
Chemistry Teacher
DANVILLE
Gustavson, Elisabeth Bustard
Fourth Grade Teacher
DEERFIELD
Tatulis, Edith E.
Fifth Grade Teacher
DERRY
Cain, Timothy Thomas
English Teacher
Collins, Laurie Boyle
Second Grade Teacher
DeCosta, Linda Marie (Donahue)
Scndry English & Comm Teacher
Gaucher, Peter Stanley
English Teacher
Hardman, Patricia Lynn
Math Teacher
Harrington, John Francis
Band Director
Labella, Victor
Vocational Teacher
Packard, Harvey B.
History Teacher
Pendergast, Judith O'Neil
Second Grade Teacher
Roberts, Walter Ernest
PE Teacher & Coach
Sellner, Linda M.
High School Counselor
Tartarilla, Susanne M.
English & Public Speaking Tchr
Trahan, Therese P.
English Teacher
West, Ann Garland
English Dept Chairman
DOVER
Allen, Sally J.
Art Teacher
Boulanger, Michele Jeanne
Music Director
Brewer, Martin John
English Teacher
Buckley-Harmon, Mary Francis
English Teacher
Donovan, Brian Richard
English Teacher
Falcione, Arnold M.
History Teacher
Fournier, Lisa M.
8th Grade Science Teacher
Genakos, Maureen E. Danahy
9th-12th Grade Math Teacher
Johnson, Janet Reissfelder
Fifth Grade Teacher
Mc Glynn, Audrey Elizabeth
Junior High Teacher
Pancost, Lois Elaine
Mathematics Teacher
Prince, Charles E.
Physics Tchr & Sci Dept Head
Rhoads, Michelle Renee
High School Math Teacher
Sanz, Michael Leo
Biology Teacher
Taylor, Ann I.
Dept Chair & Associate Prof
Zelonis, Joan Millett
3rd & 4th Grade Teacher
DUBLIN
Chisholm, Shawntel Marie
Substitute Teacher
DURHAM
Dodge, Elizabeth Leyon
English Teacher
Johnson, Sheila Susan
7th-8th Grade Science Teacher
Nadori, Barbara Gentile
Third Grade Teacher
Rief, Linda (Gustafson)
Language Arts Teacher
Smith, Susan Charlotte
French & Spanish Teacher
Tappan, Richard Charles
English Teacher
EAST SWANZEY
Kuhn, Gerald Jerome, Jr.
Technology Education Teacher
O'Brien, Cathy A.
Foreign Language Dept Chprsn
Raffelt, Toni Brown
First Grade Teacher
EPPING
Wheelock, Cynthia
English Teacher
EXETER
Ball, William David
Jr High English Teacher
Brochu, Denis O.
Dean Acad Affairs & Fr Instr
Cahalane, Carol
Health Educator & Dept Chair
Carlisle, Marcia R.
History Instructor
Coder, Hilary Hall
PE Teacher & Track Coach
Ekstrom, Frances Hovey
Science Teacher

Kilgore, Mary Spruill
Mathematics Instructor
Knowles, Harvard Vaughan
English Teacher
Kushner, Stephen
Music Dept Chair
McGuinn, Rex Alexander
English Instructor
Passero, Wendy Nokes
Spanish Teacher
Rossetti, Pamela Hammond
Fifth Grade Teacher
Shannon, David Kevin
Physical Education Teacher
StJean, Christine M.
Social Studies Teacher
Tilden, Gary M.
Social Studies Teacher
Wooley, Allan
Dept Classical Lang Chair
FARMINGTON
Lagueux McIntyre, June Marie
Home Economics Teacher
Malcolm, Jeffery J.
Economics & Civics Teacher
Taylor, James Franklin
Mathematics Teacher
FRANKLIN
Sawicki, Mary Murphy
Retired Social Studies Teacher
GOFFSTOWN
Blair, Margaret S.
English Teacher
Bracy, MarySue
Math & Earth Science Teacher
Lane, Ava-lynn Sonsky
Art Educator & Dept Chrmn
Lukasiak, Robert F.
Mathematics Teacher
Mc Coy, Ann-Marie Alosky
High School Biology Teacher
Miller, Kirk A.
Phys Sci & Geology Tchr
Montplaisir, Rene Edward
8th Grade Science Teacher
Osborn, David Francis
Guidance Counselor
Paul, James J.
Fifth Grade Teacher
Rosenthal, Lester Alan
Media Generalist
Singer, Mary O. Douglas
English Teacher
GORHAM
Mac Donald, Jane Abbott
Fourth Grade Teacher
HAMPTON
Hughes, Bridget Mary
Special Education Teacher
Tarbox, Patricia (Stansfield)
9th-12th Grade English Teacher
Whitney, Bernadette
7th & 8th Grd Lang Arts Tchr
HANOVER
Bohi, Charles Wesley
Social Studies Teacher
Collier, John P.
Professor of Engineering
Collishaw, Judith Ann Ahlin
Social Studies Teacher
Green, Ronald Michael
Director & Ethics Institute
Hammond, William Sandin
Mathematics & English Teacher
Henning, Albert Karl
Adj Assoc Professor of Engrng
Mansell, Darrel
English Professor
Mook, Delo Emerson
Prof of Physics & Astronomy
Samwick, Andrew Alan
Economics Professor
Stone, Frances Adams
Retired Fourth Grade Teacher
Swanson, Steven Jon
Womens Soccer Coach
Sylvester, Suzanne Tompkins
English Teacher
HILLSBORO
Brown, Donald O.
Industrial Technology Teacher
Dubreuil, George Leonard
French Teacher
Dubreuil, Jed L.
HS French Teacher
Kelly, Suzanne Boyd
Reading Specialist
Otterson, Sharon R.
Reading Specialist
Roth, Jonathan Dean
Music Teacher
HINSDALE
DeLong, Linda DiLuzio
6th Grade Teacher
HOLLIS
Ward, David Leigh
Third Grade Teacher
HOOKSETT
Hedrick, Richard W.
Middle School Art Teacher
HOPKINTON
Meinzer, Harry Valentine
Retired Art Dept Coord & Tchr
HUDSON
Arvanitis, James G.
Computer Education Chairperson
Curtis, John Louville, Jr.
Sixth Grd Language Arts Tchr
Daniels, Anne Marie
Language Arts Teacher

Dolphin, Michael Dennis
Director of Counseling
Inderbitzen, Marjorie Mohr
Chemistry Teacher
Meyer, Ann Elizabeth
English Teacher
Miller, Leonard M.
English & Drama Teacher
Proulx, Rita Marie
Music Teacher
Ray, Sandra Glinka
Mathematics Teacher
Rioux, Suzanne Marie
HS Mathematics Teacher
Varsoke, Deidre Karem
7th Grade Lang Arts Teacher
JAFFREY
Clark-Kevan, Margery Ann (Clark)
Biology & Chemistry Teacher
Corriveau, Beatrice Hatfield
English Teacher
Emerson, John G.
7th Grade Mathematics Teacher
Gilmartin, Joyce Eleanor
Social Studies Teacher
Hart, Beverly Ann
Mathematics Teacher
Howard, Jane C.
French Teacher
Pride, Jeanne M.
Family & Consumer Science Tchr
Thibodeau, Catherine Ellen (Mazzola)
Eighth Grade Teacher
KEENE
Allen, Timothy Thorpe
Assistant Professor of Geology
Brennan, Robert Timothy
Elem PE Coord & Tchr
Caldwell, Jennifer J.
Social Studies Teacher
Dauphinais, Donna M. (Franciusi)
Science Teacher
Falk, Virginia Knox
Fifth Grade Teacher
Hansel, Elizabeth Anne
Learning Disabilities Teacher
Jobin, Dorothy Martin
Kindergarten Teacher
Lawlor, Timothy James
5th Grade Teacher
Miller, Theodore Ray
Soc Stud Tchr & Dept Head
Odgers, John Abbott
Science Teacher
Sintros, Thomas Michael
Biology Teacher
Summe, Rachael Marie
Social Studies Teacher
Tremblay, Barbara Stanford
Principal
White, Thomas Michael
HS Social Studies Teacher
LACONIA
Ashworth, Bonnie L.
Science Teacher
Bishop, Jeanne Cotter
Business Teacher
Borchers, David Whitney
Science & Mathematics Teacher
Fellona, Edward James
Technology Education Teacher
Johnson, Nancy Fournier
Fourth Grade Teacher
Kline, Edwin
6th Grade Teacher
O'Mara, Daulette Pestonji
Retired 4th Grade Teacher
Saunders, Laurie Ann
3rd & 4th Grd Multiage Tchr
LANCASTER
Carr, Laurie Anne
8th Grade Physical Sci Teacher
LEBANON
Beach, Debra Wright
Physical Education Teacher
Forward, Judith B.
School Nurse
Kerr, Lois Jean Courtemanche
HS Social Studies Teacher
Wetmore, Thomas L.
Special Educator
LISBON
Heath, Mary
Guidance Director
LITTLETON
Pinkham, Barbara M.
English Teacher
Weaver-Flynn, Vicki Lynn
English Teacher & Dept Chair
Willey, Wilbur W.
Retired English Teacher
LONDONDERRY
Bastien, Gerard Emile
Music Edctr, Band & Chorus Dir
Belbin, Edward L., Jr.
HS Social Studies Teacher
Denno, George Raymond
6th Grade Teacher
Gosselin, Christopher Martyn
Biology Teacher
Iosue, Marilyn Terjesen
First Grade Teacher
Mattson, Paula Jo J.
English & Science Teacher
Sheehan, Dennis Patrick
US History & Civil War Teacher
Wolff, Fred S.
Elementary Curriculum Coord

LYNDEBOROUGH
Hopkins, John Goodwin
Retired Teacher
MANCHESTER
Allaire, Ellen Fox
Social Studies Teacher
Anderson, Barbara Jeanne
Second Grade Teacher
Ayer, Karen E.
High School Soc Studies Tchr
Blaine, Judith M.
Business Teacher
Bresnahan, David Charles
Band Director
Burgatti, Joseph C.
Social Studies Teacher
Cantin, Lucille J., CSC
Associate Prof of Education
Carrier, Celine Ann (George)
Seventh Grade English Teacher
Clancy, James P., Jr.
Junior High Mathematics Tchr
Confessore, Robert Joseph
Prof & Exercise Sci Pgm Coord
Couture, Linda Jane
Fourth Grade Teacher
Dennis, Nancy Clemons
Specialist
Duffy, Joseph Bradley
English Teacher
Dugan, Carolyn Jane
Eng Tchr, Interactive TV Coord
Duhaime, Susan Lillian
5th-6th Grade Science Teacher
Egan, Eileen Wesolowski
Teacher & Assistant Principal
Ewell, James FLoyd, Jr.
7th Grade Social Studies Tchr
Gregorious, Carol Ann
English Teacher & Dept Coord
Gustafson, Kraig L.
US History Teacher
Janelle, Diane L. St. Cyr
Former Third Grade Teacher
Kelso, David J.
Physical Science Teacher
Kenney, Michelle D. St Hilaire
Social Studies Teacher
Kieffer, Marita Greiner
Sixth Grade Teacher
LaBonte, Emily E.
Theology Professor
Lamarche, Ruth Richard
7th Grade Mathematics Teacher
Lanctot, Michele Marie
6th-8th Grade Science Teacher
Landry, Jean E.
Assistant Prof of Art
Larkin, Kimberly Morton
Spanish Teacher
Lloyd, Wilfred
English Teacher
Lord, N. Jane
English Teacher
Martin, Colleen Louise
German Teacher
Messier, David Charles
Principal
Michael, Robert Erlking
Distinguished Svc Prof of Eng
Mueller, Carol A.
Instr of Hosp & Culinary Ed
Mulvey, Michael Patrick
English Teacher
Nordle, Dolores Richard
Jr High Teacher
Perreault, Bruce M.
Social Studies Teacher
Peterson, Susan Kennedy
Child Development Instructor
Philippy, Gary
Math Teacher
Plante, Jeannette Therese, CSC
Professor of History & Latin
Ray, Donna Flanagan
Second Grade Teacher
Rice, Eugene Donald
Chairman of Liberal Arts
Santerre, Paul Anthony
Dir of Bands & Music Tchr
Sapienza, Alfred, Jr.
Mathematics Teacher
Scollin, George F.
Counselor
Sipka, Ann MacLean
Mathematics Professor
Spencer, Kathleen Raczka
Cheerleading Coach
Tessier, Marc John
English Teacher
Tetrault, Wendy L. (Schmid)
Fifth Grade Teacher
Thissell, Merrilee Ann
1st Grade Teacher & Asst Prin
Tishkevich, Frances Mary
Professor of Mathematics
Walsh, Thomas David
Composition Adjunct Faculty
Weilbrenner, Pam Kirk
Readiness Teacher
Willikens, Ingrid Norman
Social Studies Teacher
MARLBOROUGH
Martin, Mary Ann
Retired Teacher
MEREDITH
Hoefs, Mona Rae Bartlett
Elem Instrumental Music Tchr
Lapierre, George Omer, Jr.
English Teacher
Lorch, Lisa Stott
Sixth Grade Teacher
Meier, Kelly A.
1st Grade Teacher
Robinson, Joan Dianne
First Grade Teacher
MERRIMACK
Bruce, Rae Cota
Eng Tchr & Write Rm Consultant
Clark, Rodney Lynn
Biology Teacher
DeNutte, Barbara Allen
Fourth Grade Teacher
Dodge, Betty Wilcox
Reading Teacher
Lemay, Allen Blaine
Social Studies Teacher
Robinson, Thomas Frank
Science Department Head
Scannell, Timothy F.
Social Studies Teacher
MILFORD
Chrisenton, Virginia Hoeper
Computer Teacher
Coakley, Susan Gantz
ESL Teacher
Garnham, Kenneth Joseph
11th Grade US History Teacher
Holt, Barbara P.
Latin & French Teacher
Mamone, Denise Brisson
French Teacher
Murphy, Kevin James
Fourth Grade Teacher
O'Brien, Jeanne Petra
Physical Education Teacher
Roberson, Charles William
Computer Teacher
MILTON
Bacon, Bruce Crocker
Biology Teacher
Buzzell, James Richard
Mathematics Teacher
Carver, John Preston
Varsity Basketball Coach
MONT VERNON
Curtis, Rosemary Palmucci
Lang Arts & Soc Stud Tchr
NASHUA
Adams, Joyce M.
Sixth Grade Teacher
Albert, Pauline L.
PE & Health Teacher & Coach
Boisvert, Ronald Sheridan, Jr.
Sixth Grade Teacher
Borison, Maria Vejar
Spanish Teacher
Burgess, Norman Joseph
7th Grade Social Studies Tchr
Burns, Marie T. (O'Neil)
9th Grade English Teacher
Campbell, John K.
Telecommunications Professor
Carlton, Cecile M.
Mathematics Educator
Claffey, Neil Everett
HS Social Studies Teacher
Cunningham, Paul Francis
Psychology Professor
Dean, Sharon L. Welch
Professor
Desrosiers, Philip Charles, S.C.
Music Teacher
Dolan, Jeremiah J.
Assoc Prof of Philosophy Dept
Faiia, Marjorie Marcoux
Assoc Professor of Sociology
Gagnon, Jane Marie
Business Education Teacher
Geer, Bruce M.
Principal
Goulet, Karen Mc Afee
5th Grade Teacher
Griswold, Robyn Hallowell
Social Studies Teacher
Gruytch, Gail Hurley
English Teacher
Guerra, Clara Tiernan
Physics & Chemistry Teacher
Harrington, Louise Drapeau
Biology Teacher
Hilliard, Nancy
Social Studies Teacher
Jacob, Christina F.
Sixth Grade Teacher
Kaliski, Janice Graham
Physics Professor
Kaloudis, George
Associate Professor
Kelliher, Janet Sanford
Sixth Grade Teacher
Kemper, Linda Webster
Asst Professor of Education
Kreick, Elizabeth Laplante
English Teacher
Larrabee-Bell, Gretchen
Director of ESL Programs
LaSalle, Cathy L.
Education Professor
Lessard, Jan R.
English Teacher
Lyle, Anita Argust
HS Mathematics Teacher
Mahoney, Michael Joseph
8th Grade English Teacher
Majoy, Peter William
English Teacher
Marandos, Lynda L.
First Grade Teacher
Mastas, Sandra M.
4th Grade Teacher
Mc Enany, Shawn Arthur
Religious Studies Teacher
Michaud, Leona Fournier
French & Spanish Teacher
Migneault, Deborah R.
Social Studies Teacher
Muscott, Howard Steven
Assoc Prof of Ed & Spec Ed
O'Grady, Mark Daniel
Assoc Prof of Art & Chprsn
O'Neil, Terry Mc Guimess
Biology Teacher
Oswald, Mary Goodman
Learning Specialist
Pagano, Annette Mayo
Instructor
Peters, Armand Joseph
Voc Graphic Comm & Prntng Tech
Post, Ruth-Ellen
Paralegal & Legal Studies Prof
Provencher, Jeanne Stansfield
English & Womens Studies Tchr
Reynolds, Margaret A.
Social Studies Teacher
St John, Michael John
Earth Science Teacher
Stawasz, MaryAnn Willis
Reading Specialist
Tardif, Donald Oscar
Math Teacher
Viggiano, Theresa Kluska
Second Grade Teacher
Wefers, MaryLou L.
Fifth & Sixth Grade Teacher
Yates, Carolyn Herrington
English Teacher
NEW BOSTON
Dodge, Betsey Caroline
Former Teacher
NEW CASTLE
Share, Diane Lieberman
Early Childhood Educator
NEW IPSWICH
Corriveau, Kevin D.
HS English Teacher
NEW LONDON
Anderson, Patrick Donald
Humanities Prof, Dept Chairman
Calder, Lendol G.
History Professor
Clement, Marc A.
Prof of Social Sciences Dept
Coonley, Don E.
Dir of Comm Stud & Prof of Hum
Ewing, Janice Kryski
Child Development Professor
Hruby, Joseph C.
Graphic Design Assoc Professor
Springsteen, Kathryn Rose M.
Chemistry Professor
Taylor, Deborah A.
Psychology Professor
Teach, Nancy
Director of Academic Advising
NEWPORT
Bott, Kathy Hicklin
Art Teacher
Elliott, Jane Rauscher
Fifth Grade Teacher
Grumman, Robin Sykes
7th & 8th Grade Teacher
NEWTON
Bourdelais, Jill Denise
Third Grade Teacher
Mosca, Jeni A.
Athletic Director & PE Tchr
Raskow, Marion Marie
First Grade Teacher
NORTH CONWAY
Ayers, Deborah
Art Teacher
Dyrenforth, John Charles
Fourth Grade Teacher
NORTH HAMPTON
Elliot, Wayne I.
Retired Teacher & Asst Prin
NORTH HAVERHILL
Roy, Regis Jason
Fifth Grade Teacher
NORTH STRATFORD
Coppinger, Andrew James
Soc Stud Tchr & Asst Principal
NORTHWOOD
Colby, Rebecca Morrill
Special Education Teacher
Daigle, David C.
Mathematics Teacher
PELHAM
Desautels, Peter F.
9th-12th Grade Technology Tchr
Fox, Linda E.
Eng Tchr & Humanities Team Ldr
Mohr, Dorothy Ann
English & Journalism Teacher
Rivard, Carol Morris
Third Grade Teacher
PEMBROKE
Barnea, Anne M.
English Teacher
Frye, Harry Alfred
Science Teacher
Hutchinson, Susan M.
Physical Education Teacher
Kazakavich, Judith Emerson
Business Teacher
Lamos, Susan Marie
Biology Teacher
Mc Garrigle, Maureen E.
English Teacher
Parker, Alysson B.
English Teacher
PENACOOK
Anderson, David William
Math Teacher & Dept Chair
Bailey, Raymond E.
English Teacher
Piroso, Beth Angwin
Sixth Grade Teacher
Riker, Raymond
6th Grade Teacher
PETERBOROUGH
Alexander, Patricia Bourgoine
Business Education Teacher
Bartsch, Stephen Leonard
Science Teacher
Boggis, Donald Earl, Jr.
Physical Education Teacher
Davidson, Frank Edward
Special Education Teacher
Giovannangeli, Arthur Joseph, Jr.
Chemistry Teacher
Hunt, David Miles
Substitute English Teacher
Longworth, Patricia Enfield
6th Grade Teacher
Trust, Deborah Anne
Family & Consumer Science Tchr
PIERMONT
Sandell, Nancy
Fifth & Sixth Grade Teacher
PITTSFIELD
Vahey, Mary C. (Clancy)
Bio, Chem & Anatomy Teacher
PLAISTOW
Bigelow, Elizabeth Xaros
Computer & Economics Teacher
Binaghi, Giulio Paul
Spanish Teacher
Burns, Noreen Clark
Mathematics Teacher
Constantineau, Eric Robert
High School English Teacher
Donnellan, Daniel
Social Studies Teacher
Hayward, Thomas E.
7th Grade Math Teacher
Hodgkins, Patricia Marion
French Teacher & Dept Head
Mc Queen, Kevin Michael
Math Teacher
Nye, Dianne A.
Parks & Recreation Director
Pajak, Louise Bears
Orchestra Director
Pond, Martha Forsyth
Bio & Life Sci Electives Tchr
Rowinski, Pamela Anne (Letoile)
8th Grade Teacher
Simmons, Phyllis Keezer
Fourth Grade Teacher
Stackpole, Peter
Science Dept Head
Stone, Patricia T.
Tech Div Chr, Ec & Mngmt Tchr
PLYMOUTH
Bergstrom, Kenneth Iver
Lecturer in English
Cantor, Patricia Rogers
Education Dept Instructor
Donahue, Katherine Curtis
Anthropolgy Professor
Estes, Gisela Behrendt
Instructor of German
Estes, Paul L.
Professor of Mathematics
Fistek, Michelle Anne
Assoc Prof of Political Sci
Fraser, Grace Morth
Assoc Professor & Asst Chrmn
Govoni, Wendy Byrne
Language Arts Teacher
Graff, Carleen A.
Professor of Music
Grieve, Johanna Marie
Science Teacher
Gulick, Peter L.
Social Studies Chairman
Haight, David Frederick
Professor
Harding, Edward
Business Professor
Hoey, Ann Marie
College Instructor
Kelley, Emily Roorbach
Science Teacher
Lindberg, Patricia Lynn
Assistant Professor
Lockwood, Joanne Smith
Lecturer of Mathematics
Lyman, Richard Burr
English Teacher
Mc Cormack, Louise Samaha
Associate Professor
Mc Dougall, Duncan C.
Assoc Professor of Business
Moore, Denise Ellen
Health Teacher
Neikam, William Charles
Professor of Chemistry
Peterson, Meg Joanna
English Assistant Professor
Rudzinski, Jeanne (Marion)
Counselor
Santore, Jonathan Conrad
Asst Prof of Music Theory
Switzer, Alan Alexander
Physical Education Teacher
Tedeschi, Beverly A.
Science Teacher
Wiseman, Douglas Carl
Assoc Dean of Acad Aff & Prof
Zehr, David
Associate Professor of Psych
PORTSMOUTH
Arnstein, Joe
Latin & Spanish Teacher
Cook, Carol A.
Director of Curriculum
Daubney, Thomas James
Project Adventure Coord & Tchr
George, Doreen Eleonora (Raymon
Teacher
Hartwell, Susan Clark
Business Education Teacher
Squires, Sylvia Cunningham
8th Grd English Teacher
Theille, Anthony
English Teacher
Wentworth, Stephen Michael
English Teacher
York, Rosemary E.
Frgn Lang Dept Chprsn & Tchr
RAYMOND
Aylward, Christopher Michael
Sixth Grade Teacher
Boucher, Patricia Nardone
Law, Psych & History Teacher
Champagne-Jones, Marlene
First Grade Teacher
Clark, Kimberly Brennan
Social Studies Teacher
Fosher, Mary Jane
English Curriculum Director
Hall, Jon Michael
Science Teacher
McDonough, Shawn P.
Computer Educator
Moquin, Lynn Gerrish
Sixth Grade Teacher
Paquette, Paul Roger
8th Grade Social Studies Tchr
Scantlin, Euphemia Emanuel
English Teacher
Shelley, Amanda Margaret (Jones)
Music Teacher
Sheridan, Thomas Michael
9th-12th Grade Math Teacher
Willis, Craig C.
Social Studies Teacher
RINDGE
Harris, Wayne Russell
Fifth Grade Teacher
ROCHESTER
Houston, Jooanne
Music Director
Hyde, Elise Connelly
Secondary Soc Studies Teacher
Kaligian, Peter Leo
Physical Education Teacher
McCabe, Carolyn Carley
English Teacher
Wintje, Martin
French, Span Tchr & Dept Chair
RYE
Dining, Janet Taylor
English Teacher
SALEM
Angelini, Diane Bergeron
High School Math Teacher
Balaguer, Barbara Walker
1st Grade Teacher
Barbieri, Joseph Gene, Jr.
Science Teacher
Beninati, Rino
Seventh Grade Science Teacher
Broadhurst, Sandra A. Thornton-Shi
Fifth Grade Teacher
Bursaw, Norma Kenyon
Biology Teacher
Butler, Charlotte C.
Eighth Grade Social Stud Tchr
Christie, Katie Babcock
HS Special Education Teacher
Codding, Elaine (Simpson)
Fifth Grade Teacher
Courtois, Michael George
Biology Teacher
Epps, Janice Sherman
Elementary Art Teacher
Flanagan, Robert William
Science Teacher
Foley, Jack J.
Fifth Grade Teacher
Glaude, Mimi Wardwell
Fifth Grade Educator
Huard, Paul G.
English Teacher & Curr Coord
Hutchinson, Frederick Everard
6th Grade Teacher
Kalman, Gerda D.
History Teacher
Lake, Albert Clark, Jr.
Science Teacher
Lane, Kathy L.
Media Generalist
Mac Arthur, John Willand
Social Studies Teacher
Maestranzi, Patricia Lukas
6th Grade Teacher
McCue, Martin Joseph
Television Production Teacher
Mc Cune, Rhonda N.
English & Art Teacher
Mulligan, Janet H.
1st Grade Teacher
Murray, Kathleen Galvin
Child Care Teacher

(cont)
llo, Frank
y Teacher
ancy Kelley
Grade Teacher
eleste Chasse
n & French Teacher
, Robert John
can & Global Studies Tchr
athleen Marie
h Teacher
Linnea Thorp
h Teacher
Harold
ant Principal
M. Coleen Driscoll
ade Language Arts Tchr
dith Blades
ant Principal
Edward Joseph
& Drafting Teacher
RNVILLE
on, Cindy L.
e Teacher & Drama Coach
James A.
Grade Teacher
WN
Sharon Lee
ade Teacher
, Mady Allen
Grade Teacher
OOK
Patricia Backer
Grade Teacher
RSWORTH
Bruce John
h & Social Studies Tchr
, Robert H.
er
k, Joanne Tufts
Grade Teacher
, Luise Caroline
ce Teacher
HAM
u, Ronald C.
ant Professor
, Karen A.
ng & Allied Health Chprsn
EE
Laura E.
h & Spanish Teacher
, Marcia Carpenter
Studies Teacher
OOK
Laurie Fey
rade Teacher
N
nn, Arthur Walter
mics, Cmptr & Math Tchr
e, Daniel Scott
Studies Teacher
ke, James
uidance Counselor
e, George Douglass, Jr.
istry Teacher & Coll Cnslr
ER
Charlotte Fowle
Grade Teacher
E
Heather Shaw
School Biology Teacher
Deborah Lynne
cal Ed & Health Teacher
Connie K.
sh Teacher
Donald R., II
ce Teacher
, Laura Swertfeger
l Studies & English Tchr
, Susan Margaret
Cruelty Investigation
er, Donna E.
Dept Coord & Teacher
Matthew
ematics Teacher
MORELAND
Donald A.
ce Teacher
EFIELD
ac, Marge Adeline
Grad Yth Job Specialist
Helen Tucciarone
sh Teacher
ON
Daniel B.
al Studies Teacher
Rhonda Catherine
Grade Teacher
Judith Patterson
Teacher
HESTER
tadter, Peter Julian
ish & Communications Tchr
dy, Jean C.
ish Teacher
HAM
Eleanor
uctor
s, Jane Baines
ness Instructor
n, Lauri Dunn
Teacher & Athletic Director
FEBORO
dge, Robert M.
ish Teacher
Bruce
cultural Science Instr
n, Claire
al Studies Educator

Isabelle, Linda Lee (Bell)
Health & Human Services Instr
Kelley, Frank J.
Science Specialist & Team Ldr
Lee, William Joseph
English Teacher
Lush, Mark
HS Social Studies Teacher
Niiler, Kristine Carlson
Math Teacher
Stewart, Sally Anne
7th & 8th Grade Math Teacher
WOODSVILLE
Corzilius, Pauline Hollos
Science Teacher
Leafe, Francis William
Physical Education Teacher

NEW JERSEY

ABSECON
Coleman, Johanne Epifanio
G&T Teacher & Coordinator
de Ruyter, Carol Ann
8th Grade Mathematics Teacher
Desiderio, Patricia Ann (Di Bartolo)
Science Teacher
Emmanuel, Ernest
Science Teacher
Fanelli, Michael
Band Director & Music Teacher
Garrison, Charles Joseph
Drama & Media Comm Tchr
Gross, Kathleen Frances
Mathematics Teacher
Kelly, Barbara Wilson
Basic Skills Teacher
Kendall, Sherrie R.
7th-8th Grade Comm Arts Tchr
Lavery, Kristen Holt
Chemistry Teacher
Love, Alyce Ann (Salomone)
Spanish Teacher
Patrick, Carol A.
English Teacher
Price, Denise G.
English Teacher
Schiavo, Michael Scott
History & Religion Teacher
Spina, Bernadette Aleli
Religion Teacher
Walsh, Patricia A.
Second Grade Teacher
ALLENDALE
Brotschul, Diana
Computer Teacher
Doris, Cecilia Sulpizii
Spanish Teacher
Farrell, Gail A.
Teacher of Gifted & Talented
Mastropoalo, Rosemarie Sorrentino
Latin Tchr & Technology Coord
McDonald, Gregory Scott
Mathematics Teacher
Mugno, Albert Mark
Industrial Technology Coord
Murray, Patricia Calvin
Vocal Music Teacher
Russo, Christopher
Physics & Physical Sci Teacher
Scorese, Dianne Miller
Latin Teacher
ALLENTOWN
Folino, Lynn Anne
Mathematics Teacher
Mistretta, Antoinette Carrea
Math & Algebra Teacher
Snook, Joann Pierce
English Teacher
ALPHA
Caroprese, Ann
6th-8th Grade Teacher
ANNANDALE
Artz, David S.
German & Social Studies Tchr
Benson, Kathleen J.
Biology Teacher
Crawford-Jones, Carol
Business Education Instructor
Lockart, David R.
District Music Dept Chairman
Sakelarides, John
Art Teacher
Schmidt, Charles Arthur
Social Studies Teacher
Schumann, Christopher Scott
History Teacher
ASBURY
Riddle, Charles Henry
7th-8th Grd Soc Stud Teacher
ASBURY PARK
Abdul-Ghafur, Sharon A.
6th Grade Teacher
Adelson, Ellen Dee
Third Grade Teacher
Cooper, Joan Berton
Math Teacher
Harris, Harriet
Second Grade Teacher
Lord, John R.
English Supervisor & Teacher
Major, Caricella
Music Teacher
Mitchell, Donna Taborn
English & Social Studies Tchr
Moyer, Luther Samuel
Mathematics Teacher

Stradford, Georgia A.
5th-8th Grade APOGEE Teacher
Zakutinsky, Jonathan David
Judaic Studies Teacher
ATCO
Blatherwick, Charles A.
Science Teacher
Bresani, Jane Marie
Biology Tchr & Science Chprsn
Bruner, Gale Sneed
Hlth & Physical Education Tchr
Deering, Leslie Ellen
English Teacher
DeJoseph, Albert, III
Soc Stud Tchr of Gfted & Tlntd
LaPella, Maria
Spanish Teacher
Lee, Laura
English Teacher
Lewis, Carol D.
Band Director
Patterson, Marilyn Amy
English Teacher
Schrider, Patricia Rainey
Second Grade Teacher
Schweizer, Mark Robert
Bio Psych Astronomy Tchr & Dir
Shepherd, Robert Lee
Science Teacher
Tomasello, Marcy Bradwell
Business Education Teacher
Valenti, Betty Ann De Lucca
Second Grade Teacher
ATLANTIC CITY
Arsenis, Agnes Lemoniotis
Chemistry Teacher
Garbutt, Robert
Cmptr Assisted Drafting Tchr
Kyle, Merle Hurst
Kindergarten Teacher
Liddy, Mary Ann
School Counselor
Manos, Ted Peter
United States History Teacher
Mazzoni, Theresa Bagnell
Third Grade Teacher
O'Donnell, Timothy Michael
HS Math Teacher & Coach
Spinelli, Paul F.
Social Studies Teacher
ATLANTIC HIGHLANDS
Pomponio, Ann M.
Fourth Grade Teacher
AUDUBON
Gainer-Cecchini, Gail L.
Social Studies Teacher
Hurff, Richard Paul
English Teacher
Skrabonja, John Michael
English Creative Writing Tchr
AVENEL
Celeste, Jean Kane
Guidance Counselor
Fratterolo, Joanne Ferioli
8th Grade Mathematics Teacher
Wayne, Debra Ann Catanzaro
8th Grade Study Skills Teacher
Zilai, James W.
History Teacher
AVON BY THE SEA
Nappo, Vincent
Physical Ed & Health Teacher
Sanderson, John Michael
6th-8th Grade Sci Dept Chm
Sardoni, Phyllis Lamanna
8th Grade Teacher
BARNEGAT
Brown, Catherine Margaret (Edenfield)
Physical Education Teacher
Cordisco, Mary Ellen Fuller
Substance Awareness Coord
BARRINGTON
Hibbs, Linda Colangelo
6th-8th Grd Math Teacher
McPhee, Lawrence Joseph
7th-8th Grade Soc Stud Teacher
BASKING RIDGE
Devlin, Siobhan Anne
Health & Physical Ed Teacher
Giglio, William Vito
Business Education Teacher
Hess, Paul
High School Art Teacher
Retzko, Barbara Yulick
Choral Director
Slapin, Jann A.
Art Teacher
BAYONNE
Boyle, Alice T., SSJ
English Teacher
Cicconetti, Yvonne Elia
Instr & Coord of Allied Health
Connelly, Maryann Barry
Eighth Grade Teacher
Coulston, Theresa Auriemma
Sixth Grade English Teacher
DeFilippo, Cydney A.
Social Studies Teacher
Dittrich, Charlotte Ryer
7th-8th Grade English Teacher
Doyle, Enid
Art Teacher
Doyle, Fran
Student Assistance Coord
Eckert, Olivia Morreale
Kindergarten Teacher
Farley, Annjulie Bogatch
Math & Soc Stud Teacher
Furrevig, Karen McGrath
Business & Computer Ed Tchr

Gazzillo, Irma Ann
Music Teacher
Giouinazzo, Maryanne Cistaro
Eng & Creative Writing Tchr
Gironda, Joseph A.
Social Studies Dept Chairman
Gonzalez, Zoe M.
English Teacher
Graham, Terri
Art Teacher
Hrychynszyn, Carol Ponterdolph
Speech Therapist
Jones, Laura Orzechowski
Sixth Grade Teacher
Kobryn, Paula
Special Education Teacher
Koster, Rhina
Elem Social Studies Teacher
Lempa, Patricia Campbell
Sixth Grade Reading Teacher
Longo, Patricia M.
Physical Education Teacher
Lynch, Michael P.
7th & 8th Grade Math Teacher
Macalush, Jean Conahan
Fifth Grade Teacher
Malevris, Theodore
Instrumental Music Teacher
Megale, Lydia
Vocal Music & Theory Teacher
Mercier, Meghan Sullivan
High School Religion Teacher
Moallem, Filomena Viscardi
English Department Chairperson
Moloney, Mary F.
High School Math Teacher
Nisivoccia, Patricia (Rosace)
7th-8th Grade English Teacher
Olkiewicz, Diane Platania
English Teacher
Panayiotou, Anna Stephanou
Teacher
Parks, Maryanne
Fifth Grade Teacher
Patti, Cheryl Ann White
Fifth Grade Teacher
Pfund, Mary Ann, SSJ
Religion Teacher
Pisciotti, Alfred R.
Industrial Technology Teacher
Poruczynski, Christina Marie
Fine Art Teacher
Ruane, Nancy Jeanne
Reading & Writing Teacher
Samarat, Marie Cerbone
English Teacher
Sari, Marion Fama
Fourth Grade Teacher
Schreiner, Dawn Marie
Special Education Teacher
Schultz, Eileen Saulnier
Social Studies Teacher
Signore, Angela C.
Mathematics Teacher
Squitieri, Joanne Marie (Smyth)
Social Studies Teacher
Stabile, Maryann Ohalek
English Teacher
Sucharzski, Lois Parks
English Teacher
Szymczak, Barbara K.
High School Math Teacher
Tehrani, Alex
Science Teacher
Treonze, Richard
Physical Education Teacher
Trepko, Jo-Ann G.
Seventh & Eighth Grade Teacher
Wanko, Justine Dworzanski
Dev Child & Parenting Ed Tchr
Ward, Daniel J.
Social Studies Teacher
Wendroff, Varda Wasserman
French & German Teacher
Wierzbicki, Judith Duane
6th Grade Math Teacher
Wodzanowski, Kenneth John
Religion Teacher
Zervoulis, Donna Hurley
High School English Teacher
BAYVILLE
Burley, Christine L. Wargo
Child Dev & Basic Foods Tchr
Carfora, Lolita S.
Spanish Teacher
Guillen, Richard F., Jr.
Band Director & Music Teacher
Hubschman, Gail Gronau
6th Grade Teacher
Kerr, Maureen Reilly
Mathematics Teacher
Pasternak, Carol DeaKyne
8th Grade Language Arts Tchr
Thatcher, Cynthia MacQuaide
High School English Teacher
Thievon, Jay
Biology Teacher
Topoleski, Janice Marie
Second Grade Teacher
Waldron, William Alexander
Chemistry Teacher
BEDMINSTER
Thorpe, Betty Rawles
Health Educator
BELFORD
Generelli, Denise
Third Grade Teacher
BELLE MEAD
Coyle, Bernadette Downes
Social Studies Teacher

Fenster, Robert Michael
Social Studies Teacher
Furmato, Taryn Jayne
High School Biology Teacher
Jablonski, Marie Lorini
English Teacher
Leachey, John D.
Music Teacher
Manno, Christopher Michael
Mathematics Teacher
Schoof, James David
Industrial Education Teacher
Senesky, Linda Grow
Spanish Teacher
Singer, Vera Teutonico
Retired Math Teacher
Stanik, Leokadia Stawick
Art Teacher
BELLEVILLE
Albanese, Linda Borella
Spanish Teacher
Cerreto, Lucille J.
Cosmetology & Voc Ed Teacher
D'Ambola, Joseph
Industrial Ed & Tech Teacher
D'Angelo, Rita
Pre-Kindergarten Teacher
DeLuisi, Maria (Peluso)
Third Grade Teacher
Graves, Richard David
K-12th Grd Soc Stud Supvr
Harris, Vincent Andrew
Chemistry Teacher
Johnson, Carl
Mathematics Teacher
Kirsh, Francene K.
Spanish Teacher
Kraemer, Joseph Gerard
Performing & Fine Arts Supvr
Pugliese, Patricia Maucione
Social Studies Teacher
Richardi, Donna T.
English Teacher
Richter, Irene Bernardo
French Teacher
Shapiro, Sharon R.
Seventh Grade English Teacher
Worley, Grace Casale
Physical Education & Hlth Tchr
BELLMAWR
Gallo, Angelo Fred
Seventh Grd Lang Arts Tchr
Gallo, Jacqueline Knecht
Third Grade Teacher
Green, Sandra A.
Acad Talented Class Teacher
Perreca, Paul Mercedes, IHM
Eighth Grade Teacher
BELMAR
Carr, George Thomas, III
Industrial Arts Teacher
Dunkley, Paulette Shim
Spanish Teacher
Funderburk, Joan Tepoorten
Mathematics Teacher
Gallagher, Catherine Berardini
Advanced Placement Bio Tchr
Ganey, Dennis Bartholomew
Religious Studies Tchr & Coach
Gavaghan, Margaret
Teacher & Counselor
Gifford, Barbara Handschuh
5th Grade Teacher
Grausso, Kathleen Gray
English Teacher
Hillman, Barbara Hall
Sixth Grade Teacher
Imperato, Billie Jean
English Teacher
Jelliff, Evelyn Gail Nutt
First Grade Teacher
Klinek, Lucy Trebino
Spanish Teacher
Lawler, Alice S.
English Department Chairman
Manning, Diana Gallo
High School Religion Teacher
Marrone, Joseph Robert, Jr.
Industrial Education Teacher
Oberlander, Lois Berlin
Guidance Dept Chairperson
Winters, Thomas Joseph
Guidance Counselor
Zitarosa, Celestine Jessie
English & Drama Teacher
BELVIDERE
Courtright, Janice L.
English Teacher
Givler, Floyd C., Jr.
US History & Sociology Teacher
South, E. Wayne
Sci & Environmental Ed Teacher
Weaver, Kurt Charles
Science Teacher
BERGENFIELD
Bennington, Douglas R.
Social Studies Supvr & Teacher
Bruen, Charles James
Secondary Mathematics Tchr
Kupp, John Charles, III
Orchestra Director
Mandalakis, Stratos John
High School Choral Director
Mendler, Peggy-Ann Brush
Second Grade Teacher
Pennell, Kent John
Instrumental Music Teacher
BERKELEY HEIGHTS
Donnelly, Julia Ann
Fourth Grade Teacher

BERKELEY HEIGHTS (cont)
Fernandez, Ronald Joseph
Social Studies Teacher
Hooper, Barbara
European & US History Teacher
Moscowitz, Marlene Dobrin
Spanish Teacher
Penna, John Peter
Honors & AP Chemistry Teacher
BERLIN
Chiumento, Arlene DiMeglio
Third Grade Teacher
Davis, Cheryl Rose
Computer Teacher
BERNARDSVILLE
Delli Santi, Dolores D.
Drama Dir & English Teacher
Lawrence, Steven Raye
Vocal Music Director
Taber, Thomas Jay
English Dept Chair & Teacher
BEVERLY
Battaglia, Judith Foster
Elementary Art Teacher
BLACKWOOD
Berger, Claire Nachlis
Assistant Professor of English
Cohen, Jack A.
Psychology Professor
Coons, Adrienne
Associate Professor of Biology
Dellolio, Lawrence
Associate Art Professor
Eiding, Lynn Caniglia
Clinical Instructor
Einstein, Mark Tennyson
History Teacher
English, Marie Antoinette
Psychology Professor
Fallon, Thomas Tracey
6th Grade Teacher
Fanelli, Mary Sanderlin
Seventh Grade Math Teacher
Fiscella, Edward Phillip, Jr.
Language Arts Teacher
Hauser, William F.
Health & PE Teacher
Hepner, Mary Kay Mooney
Third Grade Teacher
Hoopes, Scott Michael
Guidance Counselor
Jackson, Margaret K.
History Teacher
Jankowski, Madelyn Ann
Art Teacher
Joynes, Betty Brown
Asst Prof & Fac Coord
Keating, Mary Malan
Math Teacher
Leff, Jeanette Borbe
Reading & Language Arts Tchr
Matsinger, Elizabeth Ann
Third Grade Teacher
Pesda, John Lawrence
History Professor
Quinn, Nancy Sharon
Language & Writing Teacher
Schmidt, Franklin Thomas
Middle School Biology Teacher
Smith, Richard Mount
Retired Choral Activities Dir
Vernon, Trudy Goode
Hlth & Physical Education Tchr
BLAIRSTOWN
Hough, Cheryl Moore
Fine Arts Teacher
Ivins, Ronald Tracy
Math & Computer Teacher
Jackes, Kathleen Mc Court
Fourth Grade Teacher
Maiella, Daniel Joseph
Retired 4th-8th Grd Teacher
Miller, Martin Stephen
History Teacher
Sliker, Trent W.
Agriculture Teacher
Smith, Tammy Ann
Health & Physical Ed Teacher
Usinowicz, Victor Paul
Seventh Grade Teacher
Vachris, David Robert
History Teacher
Wieboldt, Robert William
Social Studies Teacher
BLOOMFIELD
Ates, Kenneth Hogan
Social Science Teacher
Beatrice, Robert John
Teacher & Coach
Berry, Thomas
Mathematics Teacher
Califano, Ronald
Chemistry & Physics Teacher
Card, Kenneth Robert
Biology Teacher
Cenicola, Thomas
Industrial Arts & Tech Tchr
Dieterle, Jeff
Instrumental Music Teacher
Ehret, Kirby
Industrial Arts Teacher
Faller, Elaine Celia
Sixth Grade Teacher
Flynn, Mary Setow
Teacher
Fortkiewicz, Diana Brzezinski
Biology Teacher
Gabriel, John David
Teacher, Priest & Yth Minister
Garth, Al M.
6th Grade Teacher
Hopkins, Jean Ann
Junior High Math Teacher
Kenney, Virginia E.
First Grade Teacher
Kotcho, James P.
HS Social Science Teacher
Lopez-Espina, Gil J.
Visual Art & Photography Instr
Manzella, Linda Rusignuolo
Mathematics Teacher
Metzler, Thomas James
English Teacher
Noble, Eli Sidney, Jr.
Vice Principal
Parker, Thomas M.
Social Science Teacher
Pastorino, Linda Schlegel
Fifth Grade Teacher
Shanagher, John Michael
US History Teacher
Tucker, Michael Stuart
History Teacher
Zweben, Minnette Needle
Visual Arts Teacher
BLOOMINGDALE
Conger, Grace L. (Demarest)
Retired 5th Grade Teacher
BLOOMSBURY
Frankenfield, Neil A.
Assistant Principal
Lockard, Lynn Fahringer
Third Grade Teacher
BOGOTA
Braun, Audrey Haustveit
Business Ed Dept Chairperson
Insley, Lawrence David
Social Studies Supervisor
Smith, Kathleen Francis
Fourth Grade Teacher
Yannotti, Angela Lauren
Fifth Grade Teacher
BOONTON
DiNola, Janice Memering
Language Arts Teacher
Fordyce, Robert Allen
Science Dept Head & Ath Dir
BORDENTOWN
Johnson, Barbara Kender
Family & Consumer Science Tchr
Tafrow, Theresann C.
Third Grade Teacher
BOUND BROOK
Donahue, Dennis J.
English Supervisor
Donahue, Judith Gerber
English Teacher
Emhoff, Janet A.
Latin Tchr & Frgn Lang Chprsn
Young, Nancy Southard
French & World History Teacher
BRANCHVILLE
Cunningham, Richard
Math Teacher
Jaeger, Alfred Adams
6th-8th Grd Lang Arts Teacher
Lussier, Barbara Kerans
Science Teacher
Post, Douglas T.
Fifth Grade Teacher
Schroth, Caroline Ward
Tchr of Gifted & Talented Prgm
BRICK
Caci, Gerald F.
Social Studies Teacher
Caravella, Jayne Fiorella
English Teacher
Cooke, Patricia Fennelly
Science Teacher
Czarnecki, Doris Christie
Soc Stud & Lang Arts Teacher
Dunn, Patricia Brown
Hlth & Physical Education Tchr
Emmons, Charlotte M., RSM
Assistant Principal
Esposito, Alyce
Fifth Grade Teacher
Hankins, Vernon Harrison
Art Teacher
Karatz, Carol Straka
English, Rdng & Soc Stud Tchr
Kozikowski, Leona (Malinowski)
3rd Grade Teacher
Kraft, Deborah Dunkle
Business Teacher & CBE Coord
Logan, Lynn Johnstone
High School Guidance Counselor
Palladino, Roseanne M.
Social Worker & Counselor
Richardson, Maureen Milligan
Teacher of Gifted & Talented
Sanders, Tammy J.
Former Health & PE Teacher
Smith, Susan B.
English Teacher
Tarnowski, Ann Marie
HS Social Studies Teacher
Tierney, James H., Sr.
US Air Force JROTC Instr
Tompkins, Christy Lynn
Drama Teacher & Choral Dir
Tunis, Amelia Latori
Curr & Instruction Supervisor
Woolley, Mary Lou
Biology Teacher
BRIDGETON
Ballinger, Kay H.
Physical Education Teacher
Bilderback, Kristine Arriviello
Mathematics Teacher
Burris, Sheila R.
Assistant Prin & Math Teacher
Crilley, James Patrick, Jr.
History & Social Studies Tchr
Esposito, Donna Marie
High School Math Teacher
Francis, Dann
History Teacher
Furtek, Howard Leon
Physical Education Teacher
Gerson, Rosalind
Business Education Teacher
Kelsey, Michael Anthony
Special Ed, Health & PE Tchr
Laster, Carole Ann Hursey
Assistant Principal
Lingo, Felton, Sr.
Health, PE Teacher & Coach
Loder, M. Ayako
Fourth Grade Teacher
Mayhew, Rachel I.
Mathematics Teacher
Messore, Joseph Anthony
English Teacher
Moncrief, Dolores Tyler
First Grade Teacher
Parmenter, Fredrick A.
Culinary Arts Instructor
Rainear, Douglas Michael
Business Education Dept Chair
Ricards, Lynda Dawson
Seventh-Eighth Grade Teacher
Santoro, Frank
Computer Teacher & Tech Coord
Smith, Robert Oakford
Seventh Grd Language Arts Tchr
Ushler, Frederick C.
Social Studies Teacher
Whalen, Linda Russo
Fifth Grade Teacher
White, Cheryl Martin
Math Teacher
BRIDGEWATER
Bosco, Marjorie Abrams
French & Italian Teacher
Cimpko, Denise
English Teacher
Crop, Thomas J.
Social Studies Supervisor
Dorish, Barbara Ann
High School English Teacher
Drake, Joyce Williams
Eighth Grade Reading Tchr
Gentilucci, Theodore C.
Physical Education Teacher
Hart, Jean Krauss
High School Science Teacher
Indeck, Dorothy Zeidman
Retired Teacher
Jeffries, John E.
8th Grade Social Studies Tchr
Lane, Barbara T.
English Teacher
Neumann, Carolyn A.
Mathematics Teacher
BRIELLE
Apito, Pamela Norman
Teacher of Gifted & Talented
Holland, Kathleen Shecke
Resource Ctr & Spec Ed Tchr
BRIGANTINE
Dalessio, Elizabeth Bailey
Fifth Grade Teacher
DiLullo, Anita M.
Instrumental Music Teacher
BROWNS MILLS
Adams, Marcia Louise Williamson
Science Teacher
Cimino, David M.
Guidance Counselor
Cinnamond, Judith Ann
Mathematics Teacher
Fitzpatrick, Kathryn Ann (Manlove)
Social Studies Teacher
Hagan, Theresa Jean
Secondary English Teacher
Hoffman, Christina C.
Business Education Teacher
Pannone, Joseph John, Jr.
English Teacher
Perotti, Matthew Paul
World Cultures Teacher
BUDD LAKE
De Voe, Thomas Elliott
History Teacher
Ginsberg, Robert
6th Grade Social Studies Tchr
Mocik, Wayne Kenneth
Science Instructor
Rubin, Dorothea R.
Language Arts Teacher
Stanziale, Christine Torre
8th Grade English Teacher
Wallace, Maryanne C.
Social Studies Teacher
Wozniak, Sandra Stroud
Environmental Ed Tchr
Zola, Joan W.
French Teacher
BUENA
Butterfield, John C.
Science & Math Teacher
Dickett, Pamela
HS Special Education Teacher
Mc Carville, Alma N.
English Teacher
Meyrick, Barbara Ann (Appleby)
Health & PE Teacher
Monastra, Richard J.
US History, Psych & Soc Tchr
BURLINGTON
Barton-Willis, Paula Ann
Biology & Chemistry Teacher
Donohue, Robert Thomas
English Teacher
Forst, Ronald Harrison
Math Dept Chprsn & Teacher
Gumienny, Sherrie A.
English Department Chairperson
Lorenz, Irma Vela
ESL Teacher & Coordinator
Mc Farland, Jean Ramsay
7th & 8th Grd Lang Arts Tchr
Richards, Marie Baldorossi
6th Grade Teacher
Richardson, Sandra Mary
Art & Computer Education Tchr
Samsel, Jeannie N.
Sixth Grade Teacher
Tubman, JoAnne Morris
English & ESL Teacher
BUTLER
White, Sharon VanOrden
Media Specialist
CALDWELL
Berisso, George Eugene
Science Curriculum Specialist
Clinton, Peggy Ann, OP
Religious Studies Teacher
Gurkf, Elizabeth
Third Grade Teacher
Kolis, Maureen Elaine
Guidance Counselor
Malinak, Robert Charles
5th Grade Teacher
May-Lesh, Lois M.
Fine Arts & Jewelry Teacher
CALIFON
Paulson, Stanley Albert
Math, Science & Tech Teacher
CAMDEN
Ash, Stanley
Administrative Assistant
Butler, Jacqueline Jarvis
Teacher
Daaliya, Shareef Akbar
Computer Science Teacher
Garcia, Ana E. Perez
Spanish Teacher
Gooch, Cheryl Renee
Asst Prof of Communication
Grefe, Bruce Paul
Art Teacher
Hanson, Thomas Ray
Social Studies Teacher
Haskins, Alyce L. Hilton
First Grade Teacher
Holland, Nan Cobbs
English Teacher & Dept Chprsn
Kaufman, Carol Felker
Assoc Prof of Marketing
King, Richard
English Teacher
Labuda, Stanley Stephen
Global Studies Teacher
Lippert, Robert Lee
Assistant Professor of Finance
Miller, Allie F.
Asst Professor of Accounting
Nwaeze, Emeka T.
Accounting Professor
Porter, Gayle
Asst Professor of Management
Troiano, Donna Marie
ESL Tchr & Biling Dept Chprsn
Verdile, Vincent Narpone
Mathematics Teacher
Weiss, Martin J.
Physics & Sci Research Teacher
Williams, Bernice Cohen
10th Grade Biology Teacher
CAPE MAY
Clark, Mary Donaldson
Biological Sciences Teacher
Merrill, John Arthur
Amer, US & World History Tchr
Noe, William Leeds
Special Education Teacher
CAPE MAY COURT HOUSE
Bryan, Theodore Benjamin
Social Studies Teacher
Chew, Donald P.
Mathematics Teacher
Haines, David L.
At-Risk Teacher
Heslinga, Virginia Riposta
3rd-5th Grade Teacher
Lauriello, Gladys Anne
Vocal Music Teacher
Merryman, Robert Earl
History Teacher
CARLSTADT
Biamonte, Lynne Adrienne
Fifth Grade Teacher
CARNEYS POINT
Goehringer, Frederick, III
Business Professor
CARTERET
Abello, Joann Patruno
Language Arts Teacher
Bobel, Joseph, Jr.
Seventh & Eighth Grade Teacher
Bodnar, Linda
3rd Grade Teacher
Di Sarro, Nicholas
Mathematics Teacher
Galvanek, Sharon Brechka
Family & Consumer Sci Teacher
Grace, Lynne R.
English Teacher
Grobe, Ronald S.
High School Science Teacher
Hays, Carol Lynn (Baksa)
History & Psychology Teacher
Holleuffer, Leslie Patterson
French Teacher
Krugman, Dorothy Stein
History Teacher
Lombardi, Judith Ann Tomczuk
Art Teacher
Singura, Lydia
Home Economics Teacher
Sysock, Nicholas George
7th-8th Grd US History Teacher
CEDAR BROOK
Lancaster, Judy Marie (Garland)
First Grade Teacher
Moore, Armand L.
4th Grade Teacher
CEDAR GROVE
Arluna, Virginia
Language Arts Teacher
Kay, Kathy Dee
English Teacher
LaScala, Merrily Handelsman
Mathematics Teacher
Mc Bride, Joseph Thomas
English Teacher & Track Coach
Mc Guire, Marie Marra
Guidance Department Chairman
Santoro, Yvonne Michele
English Teacher
VanderMay, Ray Evan
PE Instructor & Coach
Wynne, Robert W.
Retired Teacher
CHATHAM
Cohen, Harvey Jay
Teacher & Ice Hockey Coach
Freiberger, Steven Z.
Social Studies Supervisor
Gagliardi, Cynthia Coster
English Teacher
Johnston, Dorothy Carr
Resource Center Teacher
Karpinski, Benjamin Thomas
Social Studies Teacher
Wetzel, Christina Jennifer
Physical Science Teacher
CHERRY HILL
Bass, Christine C.
Director of Choral Activities
Belchikoff, Teresa Emma
Mathematics Teacher
Boswell, Carol Lynn
English Teacher
Burgess, Craig Edward
Spanish Teacher
Canzanese, Robert Paul
High School English Teacher
Carr, Matthew Jay
English Teacher
Cooper, Wayne M.
Elementary Teacher
Esposito, Barbara Patrizi
Spanish & English Teacher
Farrow, Rosemarie Taylor
US History Teacher
Feeley, Ruth Engel
English Teacher
Forrest, Camille Walton
Principal
Greenberg, Susan Baim
Social Studies Teacher
Hauss, Maryann E.
Biology Teacher
Hu, Helen Li-Jen (Chang)
Mathematics & Cmptr Sci Tchr
Kerr, James R.
Social Studies Teacher
Kohlhaas, Donald N.
Biology Teacher
Levin, Robin Jacobs
Mathematics Teacher
Lopez, Teresita (Martinez)
Spanish Teacher
Mazzeo, Frank Arthur
Professor of Saxophone
Parish, Marian Mayer
Science Teacher
Pecker, Marsha Jurnovoy
Assistant Principal
Rocchino, Rosanne
AP English II Teacher
Sachson, Theresa
Religion Teacher
Sadar, Timothy G.
Mathematics Teacher
Sharp, William
Psychology Teacher
Sipp, Anthony Fred Hooker
English & Journalism Teacher
Van Note, Constance Arrom
First Grade Teacher
Veith, Calvin J.
Science Teacher
Vranich, Vladamier
10th-12th Grade Biology Tchr
Young, Albert L.
Physical Science Teacher
Zinke, Nancy C. (Snyder)
Spanish Teacher
CHESTER
Barba, Suzanne
Ath Trainer, Health & PE Tchr
Brennan, Margaret M.
English Teacher

ER (cont)
'rank M.
try & Physics Teacher
nes E.
Teacher
Janet Goudie
y Teacher
Robert James
de Social Studies Tchr
avid
chool Biology Teacher
Vincent J.
Activities Director
ohn A.
nmental & Physics Tchr
u, Maria Buranovsky
e Teacher
MINSON
obert E.
ade Teacher
alerie Lovell
Grade Teacher

rlene Clair (Crescenzi)
a Teacher
n, Leslie Catherine
e Teacher
John Joseph, Sr.
stry Teacher
ancy Osborne
n Teacher
Patricia S.
y & Geography Teacher
llan Joseph
& PE Teacher
ty, Susan M.
n Teacher
art E.
n Teacher
, Leanora Ilardo
h Teacher
Jo-Ann Marcone
h Grd Mathematics Tchr
an, San D. Schoenfeld
acher
A. Gloria (Mosca)
Teacher
, Rita Litwack
Grade Teacher
Mary Clare Bahrt
e School Science Teacher
Susan Robichaud
uperintendent of Schls
Mary Zipf
er of Gifted & Talented
William Russell
ntary Principal
aren D.
y & Lang Synthesis Tchr
ON
Andrea Lynn
age Arts Teacher
effrey E.
ology Education Teacher
ny, Michael John
nce Director & Counselor
, Janice Anne
h Grade Science Teacher
oseph T., Jr.
Teacher
Marie L.
er
, Marc Philip
acher
tino, Linda Schwerdtmann
ess Teacher
, Joan Belman
matics Teacher
ENTON
Maureen V. Casper
d Grade Teacher
roto, Joyce A.
y Teacher
Joanna Russo
matics Teacher
ati, Rita Murphy
ology Teacher
, Lauren Sue
rade Teacher
o, MaryAnn Sadlik
sh Teacher
e-Lewis, Adrienne Denise
eacher
no, Charles
sh Teacher
rmott, Kim Marie
al Education Teacher
, Kathleen Ann (Berenato)
Economics Teacher
-Cotey, Rita
sh Teacher
SIDE PARK
ere, Catherine Coane
ry Teacher
adis-Libecci, Georgette
h Grade Teacher
no, Christina C.
uage Arts & Reading Tchr
zzo, Thomas
l Studies & Bus Ed Supvr
no, Michael A.
ce Chairperson
Donna Anne
Director
, Joan Marie
ess Education Teacher
Jennifer J. (Smith)
School English Teacher

CLIFFWOOD
Nosti, Anna Marie Teres
Fifth Grade Teacher
CLIFTON
Agresti, Arlene Cappelle
7th-8th Grade Math Teacher
Anzaldi, Salvatore Paul
Principal
Baskinger, MaryAnn S.
Art Teacher
Blake, Gayle Elaine Larkin
Fifth Grade Teacher
Brach, Kathie R.
Mathematics Teacher
Bravaco, Joseph
English Teacher
Cannata, Beverly
4th Grade Teacher
Cardell, Grace Cassidy
Hlth Occupations Tchr & Coord
Carpinelli, Donna
Chemistry Teacher
Casey, Diane R.
Guidance Counselor
Celmer, Janice Mueller
Elementary Teacher & Vice Prin
Collins, Joan P.
Math & Homeroom Teacher
Cunha, Anna Marie Burke
8th Grade Lang Arts Teacher
Currie, Olive
English Teacher
D'Andrea, William R.
Language Arts Instructor
Decker, Walter Stuart
Chemistry Teacher
De Giau, Bette J.
High School Counselor
Dinino, Roslyn
Pre-K Teacher
Drake, Diane Ellen
Sixth Grade Teacher
Flynn, Elaine Samona
Language Arts Teacher
Gaccione, Anne Marie Calise
Social Studies Teacher
Gallagher, Lynne Anderson
Tchr of Perceptually Impaired
Generalli, Genevieve Tamburr
Third Grade Teacher
Giaconia, Julieanna Crowley
Business Teacher
Goodwin, Maryann
9th-12th Grd PE Teacher
Hall, Dianne Margaret
Teacher
Harmon, Carol Del Tufo
Art Teacher
Harris, Ruth Ann Sudol
Second Grade Teacher
Hart, Silvia Mary (Salvi)
Kindergarten Teacher
Hartmann, Sandra Hornby
US History & Anthropology Tchr
Hauck, Anne Branca
Teacher of Gifted & Talented
Hier, John Stephen
Eleventh Grade English Teacher
Hollingsworth, Madeline Kelly
Third Grade Teacher
Kelly, James P.
Comm Art & Science Trng Instr
Kensicki, Sandra A. LaCorte
English Teacher
Kroll, Lorraine Stein
Fourth Grade Teacher
LaDuke, Richard Martin
Physical Ed Teacher & Coach
Laskey, Frances Pollack
English Teacher
Lucarelli, Rosemary
Lang Arts & Frgn Lang Teacher
Mc Cann, Dorothy Gangi
Fifth Grade Teacher
Morgan, Robert D.
HS Band Director
Morrissey, Helen Larkin
Substitute Teacher
Mullen, Robert
Grammar & Composition Teacher
Orlando, Anthony Paul
Phys Ed & Health Teacher
Pignatello, Paul
HS Physical Education Teacher
Pontes, John
Health Teacher
Ritchie, Meryl (Milanese)
Learning Disabilities Cnsltnt
Routsis, Jeannie
Fourth Grade Teacher
Saddik, Orly Evon
English Teacher
Salerno, Jacqueline Festa
Social Studies Teacher
Seczawinski, Mary Farinella
Retired HS Span & Fr Tchr
Seppentino, Robert John
5th Grade Elem Teacher
Shagawat, Diana Sokasits
Seventh Grade Teacher
Stalbaum, Bernardine Vasel
English Tchr & Rdng Specialist
Stefanelli, Ellen McFadden
Seventh Grd Social Stud Tchr
Tobey, Jean
High School Science Teacher
Travers, Linda A.
Middle School Teacher
Van Den Berg, Barbara C.
6th Grade Teacher

Voigtlander, Walter Robert
Social Studies Teacher
Volonnino, Marianne
Language Arts Teacher
Waller, Jerry
Computer & AP Accounting Tchr
Zschack, Robert
Biology Teacher
CLOSTER
Knanishu, JoAnne Marie
Kindergarten Teacher
COLLINGSWOOD
Brown, Molly
English Teacher
Bruno, Joanne D'Allesandro
2nd Grade Teacher
Cianci, Scott D.
Mathematics Teacher
Combie, David
Latin, Fr & Ancient Greek Tchr
DiCicco, Mark Louis
Soc Studies, Sci & Art Teacher
Florig, Nancy Mac Donald
Sixth Grade Teacher
Menzel, Susan Magee
4th Grade Teacher
Paglione, Lori
French Teacher
Poland, Miriam S.
English Teacher & Dept Chair
Williams, Russell David
Mathematics Teacher
Wojdon, Francine Lutz
Fifth Grade Teacher
COLONIA
Chmiel, Thomas John
Bus Tchr & Bus Dept Staff Ldr
Endler, Susan
Middle School Math Teacher
Foster, Catherine Keating
5th Grade Math & Science Tchr
Gaspar, John
HS Mathematics Teacher
Greffer, Chantel Marie
Biology Teacher
Hollender, Diane Feigenblum
Spanish Teacher
Kaminski, Frank W.
History Teacher
Lerch, Rochelle Mosak
Elementary Teacher
Meade, Rosemary
Chemistry & Physics Teacher
Sheehan, Lynn Campbell
Health Teacher
Sobel, Sandra Gail
English Teacher
Strack, Richard Nicholas
English Teacher
COLTS NECK
Glemming, Patricia Reynolds
Reading & Language Arts Tchr
Pesce, Linda D.
Spanish Teacher
COLUMBUS
Balog, Jacqueline
Art Teacher
Coleman, Joseph
HS Social Studies Teacher
Massi, Carol-Anne Reese
Secondary Mathematics Teacher
Platt, Sharon Alban
English Teacher
Rein, Grace Logay
English Teacher
Robinson, Leila M.
Chemistry Teacher
Roman, George A., Jr.
Social Studies Teacher
Schneider, Jennifer Beth
7th & 8th Grd Science Teacher
Spence, Gerry
Technology Ed Teacher
Walter, Dennis H.
Band Director
CRANFORD
Bailin, Karen Lee
English Teacher
Boughner, Martha Reed
Elementary Band Teacher & Supv
Hilborn, Jennifer Lynn
English Teacher
Huff, George Anthony
High School Guidance Counselor
Phillips, Richard A.
Business Education Teacher
Rheem, Beth Ann
Chemistry Dept Adjunct Prof
Sbaratta, Christina (Courouniotis)
Fourth Grade Teacher
Schneider, Margaret Doyle
Retired English Teacher
Siemoneit, Regina Paliulis
Professor of Psychology
Singer, Mark D.
Criminal Justice Professor
Wilde, Joan Carol
Assistant Principal
CRESSKILL
Levy, Dennis Ira
Business Ed Dept Chm & Tchr
Morris, Marguerite Mary
Social Studies Teacher
Murphy, Ann Marie Callahan
Language Arts Teacher
Pagonis, Louis
Teacher
Perfetto, Janice Pedoto
Sixth Grade Teacher

Statuto, Wendy Rand
Business & Technology Teacher
Valli, Robert
PE & Health Teacher
DEMAREST
D'Ambra, John R.
High School English Teacher
DeLuccia, Kathryn Emily
Fine Arts Teacher
Dunne, Patrick Frank
Social Studies Teacher
Krauser, Joel
Related Arts Supervisor
Robey, Mary Frances Huth
High School History Teacher
Walter, Kevin Joseph
History Teacher
Wright, Charles Edward
Art Teacher
DENNISVILLE
Bonnet, Robert Lockwood
Eighth Grade Life Science Tchr
DENVILLE
Doyle, June Audrey
Art Teacher
Mc Grath, Mary Gordon
Mathematics Teacher
Racine, Steven R.
Sociology & Economics Teacher
Ruggeri, Jo Ann Zipko
High School Mathematics Tchr
Stanton, Elizabeth Matko
Educl Media Spec & Librn
Zemzicki, John Edward
Wrestling Coach
DOROTHY
Lopez, Phyllis Rundio
Seventh Grade Teacher
DOVER
Adams, Maxine Ann (Kowalchik)
Second Grade Teacher
Bolden, Evelyn Matthews
Business & Technology Supvr
Bottone-Randazzo, Patricia A. M.
Foreign Lang & ESL Teacher
Brady, Sharon A.
Former Earth Artist & Teacher
Byrnes, Robert William
English Teacher
DeBlase, Helen
First Grade Teacher
Mains, Robert Louis
Middle School Computer Teacher
Meyer, Gary Stephen
Mathematics Teacher
Nazzaro, Edward Michael
World Languages & ESL Tchr
Thomson, Harriet Marcia Shenk
HS Mathematics Teacher
Troha, Robert Anthony
Architectural Drafting Instr
Worthington, Deborah Eckhardt
English & Journalism Teacher
DUMONT
Cullen, Rosemary Crawford
High School English Teacher
Lakefield, Pamela Ann (Nobel)
English Teacher
Mahon, Mary Enders
K-6th Grd Art Teacher
Mantineo, Joseph Louis
Italian Teacher
Martensen, Kathy Pinella
Mathematics Teacher
Mc Whirr, Albert H.
Industrial Ed & Tech Teacher
Polomski, Raymond A.
Physics Teacher
DUNELLEN
Gallo, Leonard J.
Spanish Teacher
EAST BRUNSWICK
Beck, Aileen Kahrar
6th Grade Social Studies Tchr
Benish, Linda Sender
Eng, His & Jewish Studies Tchr
Bland, Amy Louise (Hando)
HS English Teacher
Botros, Nagy Hemaya
Mathematics Teacher
Boyle, Dennis Francis
Choral Director
Bravman, Jeffrey H.
Third Grade Teacher
Burke, James Vincent
High School Counselor
Christensen, Edward R.
Math Teacher
Doran, Arlene DeSimone
Eighth Grade Teacher
Gulick, Debra Edelkraut
Mathematics Teacher
Lajeskie, Jill Bracey
Teacher of Gifted & Talented
Lane, Melissa Ann (Kunze)
High School Art Teacher
Mangino, Deborah Lundin
Physical Education Teacher
Markot, Michael
Mathematics Teacher
Mc Evoy, Kevin Thomas
High School History Teacher
Moran, Daniel
English Teacher
Peil, Manfred Heinz
English Teacher
Perez, Mark David
Band Director
Porvaznik, Susan Joseph
Seventh Grade Teacher

Rabii, Gail Thomas
Science & Social Studies Tchr
Read, Shirley Zakrzewski
Science Teacher
Richards, Kelly Anne
8th Grade Social Studies Tchr
Schweizer, Jo Ann Merli
Home Economics Teacher
Unice, Lynne Volpe
5th Grade Teacher
Winters, Elizabeth
Italian Teacher
EAST HANOVER
Britez, Helen Ferrante
HS Choral Director
Lurz, Kimberly Juliano
High School Math Teacher
McNally, Eileen (O'Donnell)
4th Grade Teacher
Ponos, Olha Basarab
French & German Teacher
EAST ORANGE
Bligen, Edith J.
English Link Teacher
Brewington, Louise Taylor
Guidance Counselor
Butler, Florence C.
Fourth Grade Teacher
Ciamillo, Marie Eleanor
First Grade Teacher
Cieremans, Barbara Mills
HS Social Studies Teacher
Coleman, Charmaine N. Yanek
English Teacher
Gay, James M.
Vocal Music Director
Hale, Gary
High School English Teacher
Leshnoff, Susan K.
Art Teacher
Mc Cree, Joyce Winn
Technology Teacher
Paolella, Patricia Mullis
7th & 8th Grade English Tchr
Patel, Suryakant C.
Science Teacher
Rupinski, Charles Anthony
Mathematics Teacher
Ryan, Michael G.
Mathematics Teacher
Simpson-Chaney, Evette R.
9th-12th Grade Spanish Teacher
Stanley, Norman
Assistant Principal
Tascoe, Sue Deborah
Second Grade Teacher
Trotman, JoeAnna C.
Business Tech Tchr & Coord
Wilkerson, Jessie Morris
Retired English Teacher
Zanone, Patricia
2nd-3rd Grade Science Teacher
EAST RUTHERFORD
Bratowicz, John William
Social Studies Teacher
Calvanico, Jonna
English & Drama Teacher
D'Andrea, Robert Michael
Social Studies & Cmptr Teacher
Grasso, Florence
HS Reading & English Teacher
Haviland, Dorothy Maggio
Biological Sciences Teacher
Krupp, Marlene Costa
Mathematics Teacher
Lazerwitz, Roberta Joff
Kindergarten Teacher
Pedersen, Dolores Weller
Fifth Grade Teacher
Siri, Walter Alan
Science Teacher & Chairperson
EATONTOWN
Avella, Aristide A.
Guidance Counselor
Cannon, Leslie Galle
Mathematics Teacher
Cervone, Carmela Realmuto
6th Grade Teacher
Colangelo, Patricia Ann
Fourth Grade Teacher
Frantzen, Julie Haverty
Second Grade Teacher
Kanzler, Barbara A.
US His & World Cultures Tchr
Keetley, Janice Barbara (Noble)
Third Grade Teacher
Madonna, Sue Schneider
Physical Education Teacher
Mast, Susan Plancey
Sixth Grade Teacher
Oshin, Richard Kent
Instrumental Music Teacher
EDISON
Acciani, Lawrence N.
Art Teacher
Annand, Carl F.
Instrumental Music Teacher
Babich, Kathleen Simko
Family & Consumer Sci Tchr
Bamdad, Carol
English Teacher
Barrett, Nora M.
Assistant Professor
Burgess, Gilbert G.
5th Grade Teacher
Chmara, Van
American History Teacher
Daley, Jamie T.
English Professor

EDISON (cont)
DeFranzo, Frances Inzano
Assistant Principal
de Geneste, Leslie C.
Science Teacher
DeSena, Mary Elizabeth
High School English Teacher
Dudics, Maureen Mallon
Chemistry Teacher
Epstein, Ellen Davis
English Teacher
Frahme, Nina Hovell
Art Teacher
Freier, Audrey Werner
Dental Hygiene Professor
Gadek, Barbara Ann
English Teacher
Galbraith, Phyllis Laskey
Retired English Teacher
Gibson Burozski, Billie Eliza Ruth
5th Grade Teacher
Goldfarb, Ronald C.
Acctng & Legal Stud Dept Chm
Gould, Robert Andrew
Science Dept Head & Teacher
Grippaldi, Denise M. (Kozinski)
Math Teacher
Harris, Trudi
Assistant Professor
Haumacher, Joseph Charles, II
World & US History Teacher
Hrevnak, Matthew J.
Mathematics Teacher
Hughes, Winston
Fine Arts Department Chairman
Kupcha, Joseph Richard
Chemistry & Physics Teacher
Kushinsky, Jeanne Rothenberger
Second Grade Teacher
Lowenstein, Karen Lynne
Spanish & AP Lit Teacher
Montgomery, Rae Brinkley
Third Grade Teacher
Murphy, Maryann
Sixth Grd Mathematics Teacher
Nienburg, Gordon William
9th Grade Science Teacher
Nolan, Joseph A.
Latin Teacher & Dept Chprsn
Petersen, Susan Hamilton
ESL Teacher
Rak, Frances Bonarrigo
Social Studies Teacher
Rebovich, Elsie Rinaldi
Staff Development Specialist
Rockmore, Miriam Miller
Second Grade Teacher
Savner, Elizabeth Mary
Sci Dept Chair & Physics Instr
Schon, Gregory Paul
Human Sexuality Educator
Sochor, Mary Ellen Doyle
Math Teacher & Dept Chprsn
Soncuya, Marlene
Science Teacher
Stedronsky Fernandez, Louise E.
Sixth Grd Mathematics Teacher
Stolt, Ruth Allen
Science & Computer Teacher
Sudall, Dana D.
Math & Physics Teacher
Sudock, Eileen M.
4th Grade Teacher
Tillotson, Lucia E.
Biology Instructor
Tooker, Dorinda M.
Mathematics Teacher
Voloch, Lilian Aizman
Spanish Teacher
Wions, Diane Berg
Music Teacher
EGG HARBOR CITY
Cramer, Gail (Walczak)
English Teacher
Dawson, Christine
Reading, Math & Algebra Tchr
Hladky, Carolyn Welch
First Grade Teacher
Holland, Jonathan Perry
Music Director
Reynolds, Constance Marie
Chem & Advanced Sci Teacher
EGG HARBOR TOWNSHIP
Arthur, Wendy Jacqueline
English Teacher
Bailey, Dinita A.
Mathematics Teacher
Beninati, Margaret Ann
Business Teacher
Boyd, Peggy-Ann Bastiaans
German Teacher
Brooks, Warren Holland
Retired Physical Sci Tchr
Burke, Florence Lee
Retired Latin Teacher
Carey, Donna Vasquez
Sixth Grade Teacher
Cicali, Theresa Anne
Social Studies Teacher
Craig, Keith
English Teacher
Gartner, Rochelle Presser
Third Grade Teacher
Horan, Mike
Oceanography Teacher
Lamborne, Joan Chernuka
Mathematics Tchr, Cmptrs Supvr
Matthews, Linda Estok
High School Mathematics Tchr
Panetta, Judith M.
Special Education Teacher
Roeske, Joan N.
Business Education Teacher
Ruff, Amy Fischer
10th Grade Health Teacher
Sorrentino, Elaine
Biology Teacher
Throckmorton, Dennis A.
Teacher & Director
Wasserman, Wendy Ellen (Brown)
LRC Teacher
Willett, Francis Merrill, III
Social Studies Teacher
ELIZABETH
Aklonis, Raymond John
High School History Teacher
Bochenek, Paul Barton
Teacher
Brewer, Janice Nickens
French Teacher
Burke, Barbara S.
Fifth Grade Math Teacher
Carolan, Josephine M.
Guidance Counselor
Coakley, Jane Mazza
Reading Facilitator
Connelly, Edmund James, Jr.
Senior Marine Instructor
Cradle, Ronald Jotez
7th-8th Grd English Teacher
Fabiano, Maria Stillitano
English & Journalism Teacher
Fiano, Pilar Maria
Elementary School Counselor
Friedman, M. Douglas
Social Science Teacher
Greenagel, Heather Arling
English Dept Chairman & Tchr
Haase, Charles Paul
Director of Bands
Huebsch, Sue Alexander
English Teacher
Kenny, Rosemary
Kindergarten Teacher
Lauerman, Linda Rose Sanchez
Guidance Counselor
Mancini, Mary Ann
Relgn, Math, Eng & Rdng Tchr
Martino-Avella, Margherita
3rd Grade Teacher
Masin, Patricia Carol
Physical Education Teacher
Mautone, Robert Joseph
Psychology Teacher
Mc Nelly, Charles Wesley
Music Teacher
Mendello, James Peter
French Teacher & Dept Chairman
Moley, Edward C.
Science Department Chairperson
Munsky, Terry L.
Special Education Teacher
Palumbo, Jill A.
English Teacher
Papetti, Janet Gais
Guidance Counselor
Parisi, Phyllis DiMaria
Second Grade Teacher
Paterek, Pamela Ann (Sigloch)
Amer History II Teacher
Renzulli, Mary Ann
Science Teacher
Rota, Jerry
High School Math Teacher
Runfolo-Mc Cormack, Maria
Guidance Counselor
Saliba, Akhee
Computer Science Teacher
Sims, Yvette Patricia
Kindergarten Teacher
Smith, Thorton
World Civilization Teacher
Sterio, Anthony Angelo
HS Mathematics Teacher
Turner, Amelia Joanne
Basic Skills Math Teacher
Walsh, Eileen Elizabeth
Theatre Teacher
Winfield, Clifton Elwood
Social Studies Teacher
Wyner, Sybil
Social Studies Teacher
Young, Shona S.
Mathematics Teacher
ELMER
Mc Call, Donald Charles
Soc Stud Tchr & For Lang Supvr
Mortimer, Carolyn G.
High School Art Instructor
Stewart, Debora Jean (Rambone)
Special Education Teacher
ELMWOOD PARK
Lenetti, Angelo J.
Industrial Arts Teacher
ELWOOD
Spare, Margaret Ann
Sixth Grade Teacher
Strawn, Regina G.
Math Teacher
ENGLEWOOD
Battista, Carmine P.
History Teacher
Davignon, Paul Maurice
French Teacher
Minnicozzi, Donna Jill
English Teacher
Nies, Barbara
4th Grade Teacher
White, Jane Giegengack
Lang Dept Chair & Latin Tchr
ENGLISHTOWN
Hagany, Judith Marie
8th Grd Mathematics Teacher
Kwaak, Barbara Gower
Basic Skills Reading Teacher
Petrizzi, Suzanne C. Rakoczy
Teacher of the Handicapped
Richmond, Lawrence David
8th Grade Social Studies Tchr
Sawyer, Joanne Jandrowitz
Tchr of Academically Talented
Sferra, Dianna Marie
Mathematics Teacher
White, Naomi Corts
Science Teacher
FAIR HAVEN
Burgess, N. Jean Badida
5th Grade Teacher
Egan, Patricia Mary
6th & 7th Grd Soc Stud Tchr
Rothstein, Mark
Retired US History Teacher
Zakanych, Andrew
8th Grade Science Teacher
FAIR LAWN
Appel, Margaret Denise (LeFebore)
Secondary Education Teacher
Cooney, Joanne
English Teacher
Cullari, Claudia
Business Teacher
De Paola, William
Science Teacher
Fisher, Gordon Harl, II
Instrumental Music Director
Friedman, Howard
Physics Teacher
Heitmann, Jonathan Eric
Special Education Teacher
Kuhn, Marjorie Ann
6th Grade Teacher
Lapsley, Kristen Beth
High School Science Teacher
Levine, Ilene Joy Rose
Scndry Schl Spanish Teacher
Levy, Leonard Harold
5th Grade Teacher
Lustgarten, Ann Wakefield
5th Grade Teacher
O'Neill, Thomas Eugene
Art, Crafts & Photography Tchr
Palinkas, Alexis M.
6th Grade Teacher
Papoula, Manny
Middle School Mathematics Tchr
Pasuit, Mary Ann T.
6th Grade Teacher
Rood, Karen L.
Math & Cmptr Science Teacher
Sawyer, Susan Lutwyler
Guidance Counselor
Semendinger, Paul Russell
History Teacher
Stanley, Perry
English Teacher
Tolep, Marcia L.
Teacher in REACH
VanKoolbergen, Gerard A.
Guidance Counselor
Weiner, Eleanor R.
United States History Teacher
FAIRFIELD
Lozo, Ellen Cybuch
Fourth Grade Teacher
FAIRTON
Ganci, Debra Ruberti
Senior Learning Center Supvr
Strittmatter, Christine Marie
Second-Third Grade Tchrs Aid
FAIRVIEW
Garulli, Kathleen Ann
Language Arts & Homeroom Tchr
FARMINGDALE
Clayton, Barbara Ann
Special Education Teacher
Dague, William C.
English Teacher
D'Apolito, Kimberly Ann Woolf
Spanish Teacher
Gosewisch, Steven A.
Choral Music Teacher
Green, Donna Marine
French Teacher
Jannarone, Jane
English Teacher
Keegan, Kathleen Dunshee
Social Studies & Psych Teacher
Kuper, Susan D.
Eng & Humanities Instructor
Margulis, Greta Schwartz
Spanish Teacher
Martucci, Anthony Robert
Social Studies Teacher
O'Brien, Kathleen Deacon
8th Grade Language Arts Tchr
Petry, Dawn Carol
Social Studies Teacher
Pietrucha, Holly
Latin Teacher
Porter, Geraldine F.
Fourth Grade Teacher
Santorini, Victoria Anne
English Teacher
Scott, Kathleen Elizabeth
7th Grade Mathematics Teacher
Sninski, Frank G.
Social Studies Teacher
Strollo, Michael Angelo
Social Studies Teacher
Vernieri, Susan Jean
Business Admin & Tech Teacher
Williams, Robert Michael
5th Grade Teacher
Wolny, Howard A.
History Teacher
Zicker, Paul Steven
History Teacher
FLANDERS
Berry, La Rue
Art Teacher
Galley, Lisa Ann
Secondary History Teacher
Hart, Kenneth E.
Language Arts Dept Chairperson
Haun, Catherine Mary
High School Guidance Counselor
Kendall, Judith Townsend
Fourth Grade Teacher
Lyons, Bonnie Spencer
Third Grade Teacher
Middleton, Steven A.
Science Teacher
Newbold, Terrie Lee (Ward)
Fifth Grade Teacher
Percussi, Linda A.
Math Teacher
Sisto, Linda
Spanish Teacher
Stanton, Terry Laing
Second Grade Teacher
FLEMINGTON
Clymer, Karen Lynn
Psychology Teacher
Gibson, Janet c. Stevens
Teacher of GATE
Greaney, Debra S.
Math Teacher
Kelber, David Robert
Broadcast Comm Coord & Tchr
Kotcher, Kenneth James
Social Studies Teacher
Loreti, Daniel
Health & Physical Ed Teacher
Murphy, Michael Francis
Mathematics Teacher
Schultz, Jack Robert
Social Studies Instructor
Strauss, Linda Brower
Science Teacher
Tormey, Richard John, Jr.
Eighth Grade Science Teacher
FLORENCE
Tannenbaum, Audrey
Athletic Trainer
Tapley, Larry Ray
French & US History Teacher
Varela, Karen Ann (Giteles)
English Teacher
FORDS
Taborosi, Mary-Julianne
Sixth Grade Teacher
FORT LEE
Foster, Linda Porter
Vocal Music Teacher
Treacy, Kathleen Marie
Mathematics Teacher
FRANKLIN
Mc Nicholas, Eugene F.
7th-8th Grade Science Teacher
Platukis, Barbara Wynn
Principal
FRANKLIN LAKES
Bitten, Henry
Economics & Writing Teacher
Okin, Jason
History Teacher & Debate Coach
Schopp, Kenneth David
Social Studies Teacher
Smith, Amy K.
English Teacher
Turro, Stephen J.
English Teacher
FRANKLINVILLE
Alven, Gina Suzanne
English & Drama Teacher
Berkey, John Charles, Jr.
English Teacher
Coia, Lou V.
Seventh Grade Mathematics Tchr
Di Gregory, Nicholas A.
Social Studies Teacher
Heyel, David Craig
Athletic Trainer
Higgins, Deanna J. Frank
English Teacher
Kobik, Henry Nels
World History Teacher
Mc Culley, Frank J.
Physics Teacher
Propert, Madeline Burger
English & Pub Speaking Teacher
Rafferty, James Joseph
Sociology & History Teacher
Uznanski, Louise Quinn
High School Guidance Counselor
Williams, Kathryn Ann
Health & Physical Ed Teacher
FREEHOLD
Bizzigotti, Edna Becker
Retired Second Grade Teacher
Caruso, Sharon Marie
Social Studies Teacher
Cipriano, Julia Mary
First Grade Teacher
Forman, Reynold S.
Honors English Teacher
Juffey, Angela Nina
7th-8th Grd Computer Teacher
Kavin, Donna Galvanek
Music Teacher
Koba, Stanley Joseph
Social Studies Teacher
Patterson-Vaiti, Teresa VanAtta
Social Studies Teacher
Prencipe, Arundahti
Science Teacher
Summonte, Mary Therese O'Grady
First Grade Teacher
Wessel, Sharon Stewart
Home Economics Teacher
Whichello, Carol Diane
Social Studies Teacher
FRENCHTOWN
Glick, Debbie Hillegass
Instrumental Music Teacher
Karabinus, Cynthia Miller
Soc Stud & Psych Tchr
Smith, John Clifford
Supervisor of Social Studies
GARFIELD
Barbier, Robert A.
English Teacher
Barnhart, Frank H.
Mathematics Department Head
Cizon, Linda Rzegota
8th Grade Teacher
DI Piazza, Kathryn Brunetti
First Grade Teacher
Gut, Florence T. Serafin
Business Ed Coord & Teacher
Hanclich, Mariann E.
Fourth Grade Teacher
Notar, Joan
Third Grade Teacher
Passucci, Frank Martin
Principal
Richardson, Susan M.
Social Studies Teacher
Russo-Baron, Frances
Gifted & Talented Svcs Dir
Taormina, Rebecca Debra
Kindergarten Teacher
Velardi, Doreen M.
HS Science Teacher
GARWOOD
Bernosky, David Joseph
Social Studies Teacher
Druzek, Patricia A.
Second Grade Teacher
GLASSBORO
Gallon, William J.
TV Teacher & Production Coord
Gwalthney, Frank James
Math Dept Chair
Hoffman, Florence Anne Doherty
First Grade Teacher
Madden, Marjorie E.
Reading Coord of Basic Skills
Osler, Kathy A.
Spanish Teacher
Watson, Mary Ann Dievendorf
Choral Music Teacher
GLEN GARDNER
Harrod, Lois Marie
English Teacher
Lukas, Ann Marie
Home Ec & Child Care Teacher
McIntyre, Richard A.
Music Teacher
Mohan, Jude Franci
English Teacher
Tucker, Stephen Alfred
Supervisor
GLEN RIDGE
Hearn, Dolores Ann (Dolgas)
High School English Teacher
GLEN ROCK
Blake, Scott James
Science Teacher
Caine, Dana M.
High School Mathematics Tchr
Chenoweth, Okey Everett
Drama & English Teacher
GLOUCESTER CITY
Barth, Dennis
Baseball & Basketball Coach
Beckerman, Annette S.
Cooper Bus Ed Teacher & Coord
Chalmers, Joan Bove
Mathematics & Science Teacher
Chambers, Mary Jane E.
Social Studies Teacher
Gorman, Rose M.
History & English Teacher
Heim, Anne (Fatkin)
Tchr & Math Dept Chprsn
Lydon, Eileen Oxley
Fifth Grade Teacher
McKenna, Joseph Anthony
Religion Teacher
Murphy, Patrick M.
Business Teacher
Principato, Peggy Mendoza
Kindergarten Teacher
Rafferty, Joseph G.
American & World History Tchr
Sassano, Samuel J.
Teacher
Schairer, Robert F.
English Teacher & Supervisor
Tabasco, Denise
Mathematics Teacher
GREAT MEADOWS
Lockwood, Deborah E.
Literature Teacher

DELL
Maryann Walsh
the Gifted & Talented
ancis Thomas
Teacher
, A. Joseph
al Education Teacher
WICH
Kenneth Channing
g Teacher
NSACK
Carol Madeline
rts & Soc Stud Teacher
, Grace A.
Grade Teacher
Anthony M.
chool Math Teacher
o, Natalie Gatto
Grade Teacher
Robert Kern
s Teacher
, Anthony Paul
ade Teacher
Fred R.
Language Dept Chairman
, Emmanuil
s Teacher
, Valerie Jane
ss Education Teacher
gh, Kevin
ce Counselor
an, Robert Eric
rch, Bio & Psych Instr
e, Steven Robert
Studies Teacher
hn, Robert Louis
ang & Driver Ed Teacher
ark A.
rade English Teacher
r, Christopher
ealth & Bible Teacher
nita D. Sanders
Teacher
g, Katherine Vaughan
Grade Teacher
dalena Mancuso
natomy & Physiology Tchr
TTSTOWN
Bernard Thomas
th & Fine Arts Supvr
eeana Dawn
h Teacher
Rose Laudicina
Kindergarten Teacher
obert John
Prof of Eng & Intl Stud
Bonnie Burns
matics Supervisor
David Charles
Director
Kimberly Keyek
Teacher
Frank M.
Teacher
nathan Thomas
Studies Teacher
, Anthony L.
Professor of Philosophy
Melissa
Grade Teacher
ON HEIGHTS
, Scott B.
glish Tchr & Theatre Dir
anice Marie
High Science Teacher
tricia Campagna
ss Education Teacher
, Stephen Frazier
y & Bible Teacher
s, Joan M.
sh & SAT Prep Teacher
ONFIELD
ed
Arts Teacher
ks, Patricia Mary
h Teacher & Chairperson
Marion Hackman
d Sixth Grade Teacher
uger, Marilyn
h Teacher
ussell L.
pal
o, Gina
Teacher & Guidance Cnslr
, Joanne Monaco
School Religion Teacher
on, Mary Lou Furgione
on Teacher
SPORT
obert W.
al Education Teacher
Elizabeth Marker
Grade Teacher
OON
oel H.
ry & English Teacher
s, Mila V.
ce Teacher
, Jeanette Reed
h Grade Teacher
ak, Edith Ann
sh Teacher & Chairperson
, Richard E.
h & Physical Ed Teacher
ald, Michele
al Education Teacher
, Roy R.
cal Ed & Health Teacher
macher, Christopher Jon
istry & Physics Teacher

HAMBURG
Harris, Michael S.
Social Studies Teacher
Jurkouich, Carol Ann
Business Education Teacher
Kane, James P.
Superintendent
Parrott, Lori Marie
Social Studies Teacher
HAMILTON SQUARE
DiBongrazio, Donna Lacy
Third Grade Teacher
Rockhill, Constance Everett
Home Economics Teacher
HAMMONTON
Boswell, Jeffrey D.
Fifth Grade Teacher
Dedrick, David Lee, Sr.
Civics & Geography Teacher
Paul, Charles H.
Music Teacher
Shaner, Judy Ann
Biology Teacher
Volpe, Teckla Anne
English Teacher
Wiessner, John
English Teacher
HAMPTON
Cuccio, Carol Ann Samela
Math & Science Teacher
Hogan, Diane Utoft
6th Grade Teacher
HARRISON
Doffort, Alan Robert
Social Studies Teacher
Moore, Patricia G.
PE, Health & Drivers Ed Tchr
Pace, Karen Greene
Fifth Grade Teacher
HASBROUCK HEIGHTS
Bate, George Donald
5th Grd Math & Science Teacher
Fitzgerald, Robert Patrick
Performing Arts Coordinator
Healey, Carolynne Earl
Mathematics Teacher
Hicswa, Kathleen Donna (Hrobak)
Biology Teacher
Kresch, Jeffrey Scott
Health, PE Teacher & Coach
Luff, Marilyn K. Arcuri
5th Grade Math & Sci Teacher
Meyer, Doris Brower
English Teacher
O'Brien, Angela Altilio
Mathematics Teacher
Sayer, Dennis Gary
Chemistry Teacher
Schneeweiss, Erin Murphy
Eng, Theatre, Comm & Speech
Spino, Diane DiModugno
7th & 8th Grd Soc Stud Teacher
Stine, Robert Nelson
Physics Teacher
Tomesco, Lori Ann
First Grade Teacher
Valanzola, Diane Louise
Fourth Grade Teacher
HASKELL
Colefield, Bernice
Principal
Jaworski, Nancy Lynn
First Grade Teacher
HAWTHORNE
Banks, Patricia Ann
Language Arts Teacher
Gonzalez, Virginia Tanis
Spanish Teacher
Hanik, Gerald H.
Middle School Science Teacher
Horan Kneis, Sharon Teresa
Reading & Social Studies Tchr
Lakefield, Bradley Ronald
Sci, Math & Computer Supvr
Mac Leod, Donald William
English & Public Speaking Tchr
Monda, Karen Ann
MS Sci & HS Chem Teacher
Niznik, Judith Powell
Mathematics Teacher
Olsen, Gary Alan
Mathematics Teacher
Peterson, Ann Marie Guidelli
5th-8th Grd Social Stud Tchr
Robinson, Gail A.
Mathematics Teacher
Spreen, Judith A.
Fourth Grade Teacher
Zagatta, Rosanne Mandara
Social Studies Teacher
HAZLET
Crayton, Carol
English Teacher
Jelagin, Barbara Zliceski
Social Studies Teacher
Neri, Anthony Joseph
Biology Teacher
Sharma, Sushma
7th-8th Grade Science Teacher
Znaiden, Stephen Michael
History Teacher
HIGHLAND PARK
DeBaylo, Barbara Anne (Schraven)
Art Teacher
Gallino, John Frank
History Teacher
Krupinski, Sandra Jean
Chemistry Teacher
Paskewich, Brooke Vaccarino
Health & PE Teacher

Riley-Reid, Trevar D.
English Teacher
Solberg, Rona (Bernstein)
Sixth Grd Language Arts Tchr
Williams, Janel Powell
Special Education Teacher
Wolff, Mary T.
Biology Teacher
HIGHLANDS
Downey, Valerie
Mathematics Teacher
Fronzo, Joanne Claire
History & English Teacher
Johns, Carol Roma
English Teacher
McDonald, Cheryl Ann
Marine Biology Instructor
Senos, Rosa Maria
Spanish Teacher
HIGHTSTOWN
Boardman, Kenneth P.
Social Studies Teacher & Supvr
Britton, Raymond George
Hlth & Physical Education Tchr
Drucker, Susan
First Grade Teacher
Fowler, Diane Marie
Language Arts Teacher
Gartner, Mark Gorham
Math, Physics & Comp Sci Tchr
Guarino, Danita Cronin
Tchr of Multiple Handicapped
Horta, Theresa Chiappone
Mathematics Teacher
Miller, Judith Woodward
German Teacher
Nichols, James Flint
Health & Physical Ed Teacher
Petri, Christine Ann
Choral Music Director
Ratner, Donna Strumeyer
Spanish Teacher
Rose, Richard W.
TV Production Teacher
Ruhl, F. Marcia (Morawick)
HS Mathematics Teacher
Thom, Binnie J.
Fifth Grade Teacher
Tolley, Janice Basler
4th Grade Teacher
Wilson, Dwight Lamont
Executive Director
HILLSDALE
DeCaro, Laurence T.
Health Teacher
DiBartolo, Cosmo
Mathematics Teacher
Kaye, Maxine Tipton
Retired Teacher
Robinson, Valerie A.
Instruction Supvr & Guid Dir
HILLSIDE
Adams, Armelia M.
Fourth Grade Teacher
Clark, Zende Larmar
Mathematics Teacher
Dierolf, Evelyn Laura
Physical Education Teacher
Francis, Catherine
Math Teacher & Guidance Cnslr
Grace, Betty Mc Koy
Second Grade Teacher
Kleiman, Stephen Harris
History Teacher
Kosakowski, Eugene David
Fourth Grade Teacher
Lynch, Victoria Evone
5th & 6th Grade Teacher
Mancinelli, Angela
English Teacher
Porper, George Francis
Fourth Grade Teacher
Robinson, Sara Lucas
Business Education Teacher
Tatum, Gregory A.
Vice Principal
HOBOKEN
Cordes, Jennifer Ann
Engineering Professor
Duff, Frances Fusco
Reading Specialist
Farnese, Rosanna
Spanish Teacher
Grimaldi, Alfonsina Albini
French & Italian Teacher
Laccetti, Silvio R.
Professor of Humanities
Lynn, Gary S.
Assoc Prof of Mngmt Engrng
Martin, Bernard Francis
Latin Teacher
Matthews, Charles
Basic Skills Teacher
Noce, Gene
Head of High School
Sansevere, Sandra Ann
Literature & Math Teacher
Schwarz, Walter Ronald
Asst Prof of Mechanical Engrng
Shin, Jung Gil
Assoc Prof Electrical Engrng
Thangam, Siva
Professor of Mechanical Engrng
Tuazon, Fe L.
8th Grade Teacher
Wray, Gilbert Andrew
Research Professor
HOLMDEL
Boueil, Colleen Ann
Latin Teacher

Bryer, Patricia Gale
HS Social Studies Teacher
Carnevale, Diane DeBiase
7th-8th Grade Math Teacher
Clayton, Buddy
Math Teacher
Dougherty, Jerelyn M. Sklenar
Chemistry Teacher
Foster, James H.
Religion Teacher
Griesbach, Daniel Peter
9th-12th Grd Science Teacher
Kalman, Marcia Zarachoff
Social Studies Teacher
Nilsen, Adrienne Preteroti
Latin & English Teacher
Procopio, Judith Ann
Secondary English Teacher
Sanecki, Douglas Peter
Social Science Teacher
Sanecki, Judith Ann Cumbia
Science Teacher
Schwartz, Mary Marino
Mathematics Teacher
Waack, Ronald
Guidance Director
HOPATCONG
Conway, Janet Susan
High School Mathematics Tchr
Hradil, Barbara Elizabeth
8th Grd Language Arts Teacher
Levine, Carol
First Grade Teacher
Marino, James Ivor
American History Teacher
Mc Nulty, Rowena Catherine
Special Education Teacher
Ryder, Jeffrey
Social Studies Teacher
Sabol, Judith Malenowski
Fourth Grade Teacher
HOPEWELL
Alexander, Robert Wm.
6th Grade Teacher
Hartmann, Susan
Fifth Grade Teacher
HOWELL
Bohen, Marion Rita
Sixth Grade Teacher
Clarkson, Luann Davis
Spanish Teacher
Fine, Cathryn J.
Vice Principal
Gerritse, Kathleen Marie, CR
Math Coord & Teacher
Lashley, Barbara Reiner
Second Grade Teacher
Osepchuk, Deborah Churchill
Middle School Art Teacher
Wechter, Eileen Toffel
Principal
IRVINGTON
Allen, Patricia A.
Sixth Grade Teacher
Champion, Richard G.
History Teacher
Falco, Joseph James
Social Studies Teacher
Fields, Geraldine
History Teacher
Gould, Bruce Allan
Electronics & Drafting Teacher
Hawkins, Marvin Curtis
7th Grade Teacher
Luciani, Brian Thomas
History Teacher
Orbann, Carol A.
Reading & Basic Skills Teacher
Pellegrino, Josephine L. (Cevetto)
Sixth Grade Teacher
Steele, Teresa Ann
Social Studies Teacher
Weiss, Eileen Catherine
Social Studies Teacher
Wilson, Ezzard Sylvester
Science Teacher
ISELIN
Andreski, Richard W.
Mathematics Teacher
Behrmann, Linda Diane
Fourth Grade Teacher
Botti, Arlene Cwiekalo
High School Spanish Teacher
Capp-Saccocci, Carole Anne
French Teacher
Darytichen, Frank Joseph
Biology Teacher
Frederick, Richard D.
Amer His & Government Tchr
Gurkin, JoEllen Zygo
First Grade Teacher
Kiernan, Patrick Thomas
Psychology Teacher
Martin, Marcella Tabisz
High School Guidance Counselor
Newmark, Leslie Paul
Math Teacher
Rico, Maria Elena Ann
Dance Instructor, Dir & Owner
Russo, Judith
Home Economics Teacher
Tedesco, Laura Mistretta
Special Education Teacher
Wilson, Marianne Niehold
Music Teacher
ISLAND HEIGHTS
Kinstler, Cynthia (Behr)
Teacher & Counselor

JACKSON
Aires, Al
Health & Physical Ed Teacher
Allaire, Bobbie Carol
HS Art Teacher
Chase, Mary Fran
Choir Dir & Piano Lab Tchr
Conrad, Marion T. (McPolin)
Mathematics Teacher
Cucci, Susan Ruff
5th Grade Teacher
DeSimone, Elizabeth
Family & Consumer Science Tchr
Esparra, Rafael, Jr.
Spanish Teacher
Handfield, Angela Hernandez
Reading Specialist
McCormick, Anne Marie
Chemistry Teacher
McLaughlin, Lisa Marie
Social Studies Teacher
Mitchell, George Frederick, Jr.
Technology Education Teacher
Recht, Christine Baskin
Algebra Teacher
Romano, Patricia Campbell
Eighth Grade Science Teacher
Silverman, Cathy Leffler
English Teacher
Terranova, Laura Wilson
Eng, Speech Arts & Drama Tchr
Wheeler, William Robert
AP & Honors Biology Teacher
Wyer, Eileen
Soc Studies & Psychology Tchr
JACOBSTOWN
Gilbert, Kathleen Erickson
Math, Civics & Economics Tchr
Prewitt, B. JoAnne Hill
Elementary Teacher
JAMESBURG
Heinz, Harold J.
Language Arts Instructor
Jernigan, Janice Redmond
Business Education Teacher
Shamy, Robert
Teacher & Museum Director
JERSEY CITY
Azzarto, Anthony Joseph, SJ
Chaplain & Teacher of Religion
Bailey, Joan Weisenfeld
Associate Professor
Barone, Barbara Magnane
Vice Principal & 8th Grd Tchr
Barugel, Alberto
Professor of Modern Languages
Bautista, Justo Bautista
Math Dept Chprsn & Teacher
Bender, Judith Anne
Asst Prof & Dir Med Asst Prgm
Bennett, Deborah J.
Assistant Professor of Math
Boyce, Dolores Wilson
English Teacher
Brookins, Sharon Marie
Math & English Teacher
Camacho, James, Jr.
Mathematics Asst Professor
Catania, Patricia A.
Kindergarten Teacher
Cruz, Camilo
Chemistry Professor
DeLorenzo, Carl S.
12th Grade History Teacher
DelPiano, Doreen O'Neill
7th Grade Teacher
DiAngelo, Louis Philip
English Teacher
Di Ferdinando, Frank Anthony
Mngmt & Mrktg Dept Coord, Inst
Donohue, Kathleen Frances
Science Specialist
Donovan, Oliver Michael
Associate Professor of Biology
Duncan, Frances Marie, OSF
Chemistry & Physics Tchr
Emerick, Robert William
Adj Psychology Prof & Director
Esposito, Irene M.
7th Grade Teacher
Evanoff, Miriam Anne, SC
8th Grd Tchr & Vice Principal
Ferrigno, Nicole
Mathematics Teacher
Finstein, Marilyn LaIacona
Associate Professor of Biology
Flores, Lorena Alexi
Bilingual HS History Teacher
Fortuna, Myrna Zayas
Eighth Grade Teacher
Francin, Robert Dominick
Mathematics Teacher
Gabriel, Janet Florendo
High School Math Teacher
Gardner, Eileen Kaufman
Dept of Nursing Chairperson
Gaydos, Carol Wysokinski
8th Grade Teacher
Gibney, Ellen M.
English Dept Chairperson
Gillio, Geraldine
Social Studies Teacher
Goldstein, Shoshana
Adjunct Assistant Professor
Goss, Geraldine Charles
Third Grade Teacher
Gourhan, Maria Molinari
English & World Teacher
Greenberg, Robin S.
Social Studies & Reading Tchr

JERSEY CITY (cont)
Haddad, Alham S.
Mathematics Teacher
Hansen, Rich C.
Director of Athletics
Hynes, John Patrick
High School Soc Studies Tchr
Joffe, Patricia Dempsey
Assistant Professor
Johnston, Kellie E.
Resource Room English Teacher
Jones, Bessie Miley
Tech Coord & Computer Teacher
Kane, Richard David
History Professor
Kim, Min
Asst Prof of Piano & Theory
Lazzaro, Maria Ammerata
Art Teacher
Lebron, Miriam
8th Grd Teacher
Lynch, Jane Catherine
Retired Teacher
Mahoney, Lynda Radulich
Guidance Counselor
Marchitelli, Marguerite Meluso
First Grade Teacher
Massey, Veronica
Prof of Eng as a Second Lang
Matthews, Terence S.
9th Grade Guid Cnslr & Ath Dir
Mc Nutt, Robert Scott
AP US History Teacher
Messina, Anthony James
Jr Level Cnslr, Hum Antmy Tchr
Miragliotta, Sandra Anne Kaubek
Seventh Grade Teacher
Needham, Richard John
Social Studies Teacher
Ngatchou, Jean-Claude N.
Assistant Prof of Computer Sci
Noga, Andrew F.
Latin Teacher
Nu'Man, Vivian Seidah
Middle Grades Teacher
O'Connor, Marleen Tredy
Guidance Counselor
Oliver, Sandra Fowlkes
Seventh Grade Teacher
Oziemblo, Joanne Marie
Vice Principal & 8th Grd Tchr
Perlmutter, Barry
Professor of Geoscience
Politis, Catherine Nicole
Language Arts & Reading Tchr
Rabin, Sheila J.
Assistant Professor of History
Ratteray, Rose
Technology & Media Teacher
Reilly, Kathleen Murphy
Third Grade Teacher
Russo, Barbara Caiezza
Chemistry Teacher
Shelton, Frances M.
Language Art Teacher
Sica, JoAnn
Mathematics Teacher
Silkowski, Lillian Mary, SC
8th Grd Tchr & Vice Principal
Sims, Verna Crayton
Title I Teacher
Slawinski, Barbara Pesanello
6th Grade Math Teacher
Spagnoletti, Paula Ann
8th Grade Math Teacher
Stokes, Belinda E.
Math Teacher & Dept Chair
Thurston, Donna
4th Grade Teacher
Tuite, Kathleen A.
Religion Teacher
Vroom, Charlotte Mc Cormack
English Teacher
Woodger, Betty Lois
Assistant to the President
Zuckerman, Phyllis Rita
Third Grade Teacher
JOBSTOWN
Dunker, Eleanor Vaughn (Quay)
Kindergarten Teacher
KEANSBURG
Battista, Joseph L., Jr.
HS Music Teacher
Egan, Karen Donovan
Compensatory Education Teacher
Kochman, James Vincent
7th-8th Grade Math Teacher
Martucci, Patricia Pocsaji
Guidance Counselor
Miller, Kathryn Swenson
Head Counselor
Stark, Thomas Daniel
HS Tech & Indstrl Arts Teacher
Sterling, C. Gale
English Teacher
Strauch, Dawn
Mathematics Teacher
KEARNY
Babinski, Karen V.
First Grade Teacher
Bielefeld, Irma
German Teacher
Cella, Elvira Kohlhammer
Mathematics Teacher
Connell-Harper, Phyllis Claire
Social Science Teacher
Connor, Dorothy Edwards
Second Grade Teacher
Costello, Lynn Hammer
English & Drama Teacher
Crivello, Rita Levine
Chemistry Teacher
Culp, Marilyn Elizabeth (Samson)
Chemistry Teacher
Ficeto, Gerald J.
Instrumental Music Teacher
Howell, Jacqueline Dunphy
Eighth Grd Mathematics Tchr
Humphrey, Roseann Santangelo
Curr & Testing Supervisor
Iamonte, Bruno
Science Teacher
Kurta, Ann Mason
Fourth Grade Teacher
Lazaro, Dina Marie
Biology Teacher
Levy, Bonnie L.
7th & 8th Grade Math Teacher
Millar, John Allan
Physical Ed Teacher & Coach
Moehn, Juliette Marie
High School Science Teacher
Monaco, Arthur John
Tchr of Learning Disabilities
Policano, Joseph
8th Grade Social Science Tchr
Ragnoni, Patrick P.
Music Chairman
Rice, Agnes M.
Retired Kindergarten Teacher
Ridley, Vincent William
Physics & Earth Science Tchr
Romano, Virginia Buoye
Mathematics & Cmptr Sci Tchr
Schwab, Richard
Teacher of Art Enrichment Prgm
Tarnacki, Mary Ellen Laux
Teacher & Vice Principal
Tsien, F.
Computer Programming Teacher
Villella-Cole, Priscilla Fascia
Fourth Grade Teacher
Wancevich, John Hugh
Eng, Speech Arts & Drama Tchr
Whetstine, Thomas Robert
Social Studies Teacher
KENDALL PARK
Kedian, Mary Carden
Second Grade Teacher
KENILWORTH
Barnes, Donna Shallcross
Third Grade Teacher
KEYPORT
Behrman, Lynn Grover
Business Education Teacher
Bell, Janet Cooperman
K-8th Grade Teacher
Cattani, Caroline Mancini
Third Grade Teacher
Chretien, Ellen Masi
5th Grade Teacher
Connolly, Joni Herschenhorn
Student Assistance Counselor
Cornell, Cathy Campbell
Kindergarten Teacher
Kennedy, Linda (Sappah)
Third Grade Teacher
Kooistra, Susan Balmer
Home Economics Teacher
Muller, Charlotte Anne
English Teacher
Nagrosky, Joyce
English Teacher
Sutton, Linda Masiello
Mathematics Teacher
Walling, Elizabeth Erickson
Second Grade Teacher
KINNELON
Heeney, Helen Culleton
English Supervisor
Lorenzoni, Barbara
Resource Center Teacher
LAFAYETTE
Callahan, Dorothy Monahan
Teacher & Coord of GATE
LAKE HOPATCONG
Hardy, Brooke D.
Fifth Grade Teacher
LAKEHURST
Firetto, Mel Viola
Fourth Grade Teacher
Lilley, Patricia Anne
Stu Assistance Cnslr & Coord
Mac Phee, Daniel R.
Science Teacher
Mc Cann, Maureen
Health & Physical Ed Teacher
Rudeen, Dorothy J.
French Teacher
Statuto, Toni Marie
6th Grade Teacher
Wirth, Donald Edward
President
LAKEWOOD
Clark, Lawrence Thomas, Jr.
Assistant Professor of Ec
Cummings, Susan G.
Associate Professor of Biology
Deutsch, Warren Neal
Professor of Social Studies Ed
Doak, Nancy Ann
Mathematics Teacher
Feltz, Catherine Marino
Asst Professor of Special Ed
Franey, Shaun
Asst Professor of History
Guy, Ava Greene
English Teacher
Hackett, Debra Anne
Special Education Teacher
James, Linda S.
Professor of Psychology
Krol, Nancy J. (Bower)
7th-8th Grd Health & PE Tchr
Lloyd, Linuel Parker, III
Lecturer in Business Admin
Mc Carthy, Colleen
Fifth Grade Teacher
Mc Carthy, Mary-Theresa
Professor of French
Mc Lean, Nancy
7th-8th Grd Biling & ESL Tchr
Mc Mahon, Patricia A. Carroll
Assistant Professor of Spanish
Pilgram, Suzanne Phelps
Fine Arts Professor
Schroepfer, Joseph
Math, PE & Religion Teacher
Scro, Cheryl Mc Dowell
First Grade Teacher
Sessa, Sandra Ann
Associate Professor of Psych
Smorra, MaryAnn
Professor of Education
Sutton, Robert H.
Dept of Ed Supvr
Thomas, Mary Joyce Paproski
English Teacher
Velasquez, Geraldine Khaner
Professor of Art
Walsh, Joseph G., Jr.
English Teacher
Yezilski, Suzanne Lundsten
Social Studies Teacher
Young, Claribel (Mele)
History Professor
LANOKA HARBOR
Besante, Julia Donnelly
Home Economics Teacher
Brunson, Doris Holmes
Computer & Business Teacher
Dorso, Thomas Raymond
School Social Worker
Hamilton, Thomas Michael
High School Vice Principal
Ryan, Susan Jean
Physics Teacher
Schureman, Frank Eugene
Music Teacher
Warren, Susan Walrand
Fifth Grade Teacher
LAURENCE HARBOR
Gallagher, Alison Watson
Fifth Grade Teacher
LAVALLETTE
Ferraro, Joseph Peter
PE & Math Teacher
Hopson, William Albert
Head Teacher
Weiss, Nancy Anne Walters
First Grade Teacher
LAWRENCEVILLE
Atlee, Benjamin Champneys
English Instructor
Carroll, Anne Marie
Finance Professor
Confoy, Jane K.
English Teacher
Deschamps, Karin
German Teacher
Gauvin-Tharney, Denise Ann
Mathematics Dept Chair & Tchr
Giampetro, Theresa
Social Studies Teacher
Gusciora, Richard W.
Science Department Chairperson
Hamill, Leita Voss
English Teacher
Henkel, Karen Lynn
English Teacher
Ibe, Patrick Nneibe
Chemistry Teacher
Liptak, Mary Ann Elizabeth
Dean Acad Affairs
Marinari, Melissa M.
Spanish Teacher
Materna, Linda S.
Assoc Professor of Spanish
Poreda, Edward John
Cross Country Coach
Proctor, Robert Bruce
Science & Soc Studies Teacher
Schiel, John Edward
Mathematics Teacher
Sheats, John Eugene
Professor of Chemistry
Torres, Oscar, Jr.
Spanish Teacher
LAYTON
Seely, Maribeth Walsh
5th Grade Teacher
LEBANON
Moller, Judy O'Rourke
Third Grade Teacher
LEONARDO
Barclay, Nancy Burdge
Third Grade Teacher
Kouvel, Maureen
Head Guidance Counselor
Miller, Susan G. (Thomas)
French & Spanish Teacher
Stiffler, Dale Turner
Teacher of the Gifted
LEONIA
Franceschini, Vanessa Frangiosa
First Grade Teacher
Silverman, Lawrence I.
Band Director
Trotter, Gary J.
Physics Teacher
LINCROFT
Bryant, Andrew L.
MLT Pgm Dir & Prof Med Tech
Hayden, Mary Elaine
First Grade Teacher
Hudzinski, Deborah
Third Grade Teacher
Jones, Christian
Math Tchr, Dept Chm, Asst Prin
Koch, Garry R.
History Teacher
Lynch, Martha Miller
Third Grade Teacher
Matson, Jeffrey C.
History Dept Chair
McManus, Collette Gartner
7th & 8th Grade Science Tchr
Richards, Thomas Franklin
Political Science Prgm Chair
Templeton, William L.
Instructor of Biology
Wang, Linda C.
Mathematics Instructor
Watkins, William John
Professor of Humanities
Weigand, Bernardine S.
1st Grade Teacher
LINDEN
Boyd, Edith J. Major
8th Grade Social Studies Tchr
Chmielak, James J.
History Teacher
Cleary, Denise
Science Teacher
Foley, Francis Timothy
Eng Lit & Jrnlsm Teacher
Lemansky, Janet R.
Orchestra Director
Leonard, Bruce Raymond
Fifth Grade Teacher
Leone, Morris Anthony
Language Arts Teacher
Mehalick, Wayne
Biology Teacher
Richardson, Brenda Hauser
German Teacher
Tartivita, Patricia Christina
English Teacher
Wilk, Patricia Savage
High School Mathematics Tchr
LINDENWOLD
Brown, Mitchell Robert
Health & Physical Ed Teacher
LINWOOD
Becker, Christine Anne
Spanish Teacher
Burke, Donna L.
Sixth Grade Math Teacher
Caccavale, Sal, Jr.
High School Mathematics Tchr
Chojnacki, Barbara Pecher
Reading Specialist
Dampier-Cook, Julie
Former English Teacher
Harlan, Rebecca Jane
11th Grade Social Studies Tchr
Helmer, Jean Marie
Psychology Teacher
Penza, Charles, Jr.
High School English Teacher
Yakopcic, Michele Terese
Special Education Teacher
LITTLE EGG HARBOR
Dohanick, Ronald G.
4th Grade Elementary Teacher
Thulin, Kathleen Norton
3rd Grd Tchr of Gifted
LITTLE FALLS
Brown, Sheryl Benita
Math Liaison & Teacher
Frasche, Raymond M.
Music Teacher
Malone, Kenneth R.
Mathematics Teacher
Mc Guire, Kathleen Kocis
English & Art Teacher
Mercadante, James N.
Art Teacher
Sperrazza, Michael James
Drama Director
LITTLE FERRY
Aguilar, Sharon Marie (Rudd)
Seventh Grade Teacher
Lagerman, Harry M.
8th Grade Teacher
LITTLE SILVER
Hardison, Brandon Kieth
Minority Studies Director
Mac Lean, Kenneth Iain
High School Band Director
Otrupchak, Robert P.
High School Psychology Teacher
LIVINGSTON
Acquadro, Stephanie Nicholas
English Teacher
Bramhall, Roberta
English Teacher
Kastner, Mary E.
English & Debate Teacher
Knapp Webster, Donald
Honors, AP & IB Chem Tchr
Lamb, Gerald E.
Mathematics Teacher
Provost, Janine Michelle
High School Biology Teacher
SanGiacomo, Faye Ann
Career Planning & Dev Teacher
Smith, James William
TV Studio Director
Stoll, Kimberly Hvarre
Music Teacher
Tamburro, Barbara J. Boscaino
Conductor & Strings Teacher
LODI
Alagia, Margaret Rose
Secondary English Teacher
Cowan, Maybelle Ellen
English Teacher
LoPresti, Marilyn Warchol
English Teacher
Macri, Julie Illick
Director of Bands
Roma, Anna Marie Contino
High School Guidance Counselo
Schweitzer, Paula Ann
French & Spanish Teacher
VanBeveren, Abraham, Jr.
HS Social Studies Teacher
Wagner, Diane McCormack
Biology Teacher
LONG BRANCH
Arendt, Eileen D.
Mathematics Teacher
Billings, Kathleen Diane
Business Education Head Tchr
Borelli, Vincent J.
Head Teacher
Eibs, Charles Edward
Science Teacher
Fitzmaier, Gayle Gutheil
HS Guidance Counselor
Frost, Robert Alan
Social Studies Teacher
Rendish, Sandra Mary
English & Reading Teacher
Risden, Gerald Alan
Band Director
Roy, Carlether Polk
Retired Fifth Grade Teacher
Stansbury, Kevin Bradley
Engish Literature Teacher
White, Mary A.
High School Math Teacher
Youssef, Nadine Shalaby
Math Teacher
LONG VALLEY
Berger, Miriam G.
Social Studies & Reading Tchr
Blaufuss, Renee Prilop
Basic Skills Mathematics Tchr
Dickinson, Janet Keroher
8th Grade Language Arts Tchr
Domeraski, Vincent Paul
Computer Education Teacher
Hershfeld, Virginia W.
General Science Teacher
Robinson, Carole Ann
First Grade Teacher
Widmann, Wayne Bruce
8th Grd Language Arts Teacher
Wysocki, Linda Ann DiMarzo
Vocal & Instrmntl Music Tchr
Zarrello, Louis
Mathematics Teacher
LYNDHURST
Carpino, Elvira Ann
English Teacher
Carroll, Barbara Botto
Mathematics Teacher
Christensen, Betty Jane
5th & 6th Grd Math Teacher
Demetrician, Carol Ann Sesterak
Soc Stud & Language Arts Tchr
Ferrara, Susan
High School ESL Teacher
Fox, Charles Joseph
Science Teacher
Lanzerotti, Carol Ann
Kindergarten Teacher
Lees, Richard L.
Earth Sci Teacher & Supervisor
Torre, Nancy Ann
6th-8th Grade Math Teacher
Williams, Richard Wallace
Physics Teacher
MADISON
Boepple, Gale Klebosis
Math Teacher & Dept Chairman
Chemerka, William Ronald
Amer History & Ec Teacher
Fellows, Felicia P.
Social Studies Teacher
Gisoldi, Anne Marie
5th Grade Teacher
Gradone, Jeanne Marinaro
Math Teacher & Administrator
Lyle, Lisa Marie
Asst Dir of Residence Life
Malone, Lois Luke
Adjunct Prof & Dir Stu Svcs
Rondosh, Angela
4th Grade Teacher
Rose, Jonathan E.
History Professor
Sena, Mary Lee T.
French Teacher
MAHWAH
Adrion, Suzanne Napier
Assistant Professor of History
Blauvelt, Eileen C.
English Teacher
Chang, Anne Mikulas
Adjunct Professor
Harth, Marshall Stephen
Professor of Psychology
Hibbert, Errol Leroy
Adjunct Asst Prof & Acad Adv
Howenstein, Mark S.
Asst Prof of Law & Society

H (cont)
William Edward
ɔhy Professor
yra Lee
rts & Reading Teacher
William Edward
Professor of History
, Anthony T.
ɔr of Lit & Rel Studies
John Paul
Teacher
ɔlanda
or of Sociology
, Edward Bryan
eacher
ad Jim
ion Mgmt Professor
AWKIN
ancy Farese
rade Teacher
Mary Ann Antoinette
Ed Teacher
o, David Guy
Teacher
atricia Ann (Connolly)
Teacher
stan, Susan
Teacher
ank A.

ricia Yohn
& Consumer Sci Teacher
Ellen Hopp
chool Mathematics Tchr
, Robert Benjamin Lucas
h Grade German Teacher
White, Doreen L.
Physical Education Tchr
, Lorraine Pilger
ool Teacher
eanette M.
Educator
Nancy Robinson
the Gifted & Talented
, Ruth J.
y Teacher
QUAN
arianne Gallagher
acher
, Nancy Nye
h Grade English Teacher
Robert Francis
e Dept Chprsn & Teacher
chele Lynne
& Spanish Teacher
z, Steven Kelmore
ad Dept Chm & His Tchr
Richard M.
Studies Teacher
LLE
, Jane Margaret (sakal)
cal Music & Theatre Tchr
hn Joseph
Director
SHADE
ard, Linda Maslyn
y Teacher
Elizabeth Jones
Skills Teacher
Irene Kitzhofer
Grade Teacher
Michele Joy
n Language Teacher
WOOD
Sharyn L.
n Grade Teacher
ward F.
astics Director
n, Muriel
Grade Teacher
oward
h Teacher
uer, David E.
Studies Teacher
, Roger
ce Teacher
, Phyllis Agresta
rade Teacher
Kathleen A.
Teacher
s, Lillian Maria
Studies Teacher
in, David Howard
y & Sociology Teacher
ATE CITY
Thomas
sh & Literature Teacher
Cohen, Laureen M.
8th Grade Science Tchr
BORO
an, Sheila
Grade Teacher
in, Jane Lovi
sh Teacher
ianne Vanalesti
er of the Handicapped
mack, Jane E.
Studies Teacher
ald, Virginia Fiorito
er of Gifted & Talented
Arlene
sh Supervisor
nthuysen, Richard N.
ce Teacher
Kenneth F.
Grade Teacher
, Cathleen M.
sh Teacher
Larry
Counselor & Ftbl Coach

Zimmerman, Lorraine
Retired Teacher
MARLTON
Benedict, Joseph Park
8th Grade Science Teacher
Clemens, Karen Connors
Physical Education Instructor
Fadule, Alida Escalona
Spanish & Italian Teacher
Kloos, Sydney White
French Teacher
Kornhauser, Neil
Mathematics Teacher
Mayher, Catherine A.
English Teacher
Peraria, Melissa Kramer
English Teacher
Realdine, Dorothy S.
Secondary Mathematics Teacher
Roskey, Mary Louise Vogel
5th Grade Teacher
Ryder, Richard Carl
History Teacher
Schofield, Gerald C.
Humanities Dept Supervisor
Townsend, John C.
Industrial Education Teacher
Tsigounis, Pamela Ann
Spanish & Japanese Teacher
Weinert, Robert Joseph
Social Studies Teacher
MARMORA
Best, Dorothy DiLuzio
3rd-5th Grd Basic Skills Tchr
Cook, Mary Ann Farina
Third Grade Teacher
Graham, Gail Petras
Kindergarten Teacher
MARTINSVILLE
Abreu, Diana B.
Spanish Teacher
Berlin, Barbara Z.
Advanced Plcmnt Art His Tchr
Dineen, Susan Gilwood
English Teacher
Geacintov, Lydia B.
Director of Studies
Romano, Albert C.
Drama Teacher & Prgm Director
Thomson, Peter S.
Mathematics Teacher
MATAWAN
Dodi, Karol Demko
Seventh Grade Science Teacher
Geran, John James
Mathematics Teacher
Goldstein, Larry M.
Language Arts Dept Chprsn
Martucci, Joseph John
Assistant Athletic Director
Masiello, John J.
Social Studies Teacher
Mc Mahon, Robert Hugh
History Teacher
Quinn-Schymanski, Kathleen E.
Cosmetology Teacher
Sapir, Gary
Teacher
Smith, Patricia
English Teacher
Smith, Wayne Howard
Mathematics Teacher
MAYS LANDING
Bailey, Merrill-Jean Terry
Asst Professor of English
Braverman, Michael Alan
Sixth Grade Teacher
Clark, Lynn S.
English Teacher & Coordinator
Howell, Elizabeth Jean
Health & PE Teacher
Kingsdorf, Betty Glover
Retired Elem Teacher
Matlack, Harry Vernon, Jr.
High School Chemistry Teacher
Pomatto, Carmela Linfante
Seventh Grade English Teacher
Richert, George Daniel
Professor of Culinary Arts
Rosenberg, Milton
Professor of English
Rott, Carolyn Cade
Health & Physical Ed Teacher
Seigel, Andrew Mark
Music Teacher
Tobias, David ALlan
Director of Bands
MAYWOOD
Hrnciar, Angie Iorio
Fourth Grade Teacher
Hunt, Sue Heath
English Teacher
MEDFORD
Barrett, Joseph Charles, Jr.
English Teacher
Bieberbach, Yvonne Lathom
Retired Educator
Bowden, John
English Teacher
Buono, Frederick J.
Science Teacher
Coleman Kohn, Ann P.
World Geography & History Tchr
Corallo, Eleanor Klingerman
Instrumental Music Teacher
Curry, Clare Anita
8th Grade Math & Religion Tchr
Donlin, Brendon Michael
English Teacher

Mitchell, Edward J.
History Teacher
Murphy, David Thomas
English Tchr & Rdng Specialist
Norris, Joanne Ledone
Sixth Grade Teacher
Paul, Robert J.
Music Teacher
Polites, Olga Stavros
High School English Teacher
Sanferraro, Joanne Frances
Mathematics Teacher
Spitz, Robert Michael
HS Mathematics Teacher
Tortorelli, Joseph Anthony
English Teacher
MENDHAM
Bergman, Bruce Charles
High School Business Teacher
Matthews, Wendy Murphy
Mathematics Teacher
Orfe, Michael
Eng, US His, Hum & Soc Tchr
MERCHANTVILLE
Eisenmann, Francine Colangelo
Fourth Grade Teacher
Foys, Judith Caffrey
English Teacher
Mc Kay, Shawn William
Ornamental Horticulture Tchr
Quattrone, Mark Thomas
Skill Trades Teacher
Verner, Diana Denkman
Math Tchr of the Gifted
METUCHEN
Brown, Hilary M.
Humanities Teacher
Gasior, Florence E.
1st Grade Teacher
Kuenzel, Dianne Hunter
English Teacher
Madden, John F.
Religious Studies Chairperson
Martin, Craig Ronald
English Department Chair
Mc Groarty, Patrick P.
Mathematics Teacher
Rogers, Lynn
First Grade Teacher
MIDDLESEX
DeMarco, Helen Kinder
Literature & Lang Arts Tchr
Harrity, Linda (Dalziel)
English Teacher
Oliver, Marion Kercher
8th Grd Lang Arts Teacher
Ptaszynski, Martha
Tech Coord & Computer Teacher
Sivertson, Anita Kolinofsky
Seventh Grade Teacher
MIDDLETOWN
Austin, Jane Corson
Administrative Asst to Supt
Bisgrove, Donna Wood
First Grade Teacher
Colodin, Joseph Felix
Program Consultant & Writer
Couch, Philip George
Technology Teacher
Crowe, Marcella E.
Language Arts Teacher
Cusick, Thomas P.
HS Guidance Counselor
Diodato, Sherry Farwell
Eighth Grade English Teacher
Di Salvo, Carole Fairchild
Language Arts Teacher
Fidanza, Richard Joseph
Physics Teacher
Harper, Jimmie L.
Teacher
Hartnett, Marie Grisky
Math Teacher & Supervisor
Hendrickson, John T., Jr.
Social Studies Teacher
Jailer, Bernice Ponger
English Teacher
Jarusiewicz, Jane L.
Elementary Guidance Counselor
Killmer, Mary Grace Grall
Mathematics Teacher
Knodel, John J., Jr.
Mathematics Teacher & Coach
Kurzynowski, Kristen Patrice
Social Studies Teacher
Larrauri, Ileana Jaume
Spanish Teacher
Linaberry, Richard
Math Teacher
Mahoney, Geraldine Williamson
Eng Tchr & Tech Theatre Dir
Maisano, Anna C.
Foreign Language Teacher
Mc Alister, Susan Jean (Owen)
Elementary Vocal Music Teacher
Mc Andrew, Eileen
Mathematics Teacher
Mc Grath Thorpe, Ellen Hunt
Social Studies & Psych Teacher
Mc Namara, Dennis James
Biology Teacher
Pierce, Frances K.
Home Economics Teacher
Prisco, Lynn Thatcher
Fine Art Teacher
Quirk, Ellen Farrell
English Teacher
Steller, Robert Edward
Social Studies Instructor

Warren, Kenneth E.
High School Mathematics Tchr
MIDLAND PARK
Falkenheim, Rhea
English Teacher
Platter, Bonnie Fox
French Teacher
Tracy, R. Lee, Jr.
Health & Phys Ed Instructor
Varjian, Leon D.
Mathematics Teacher
MILLBURN
Barkovitz, Robert Walter
Physics Teacher
Bennett, Ruth Elizabeth
British & World Lit Teacher
Brener, Ellen Hock
Guidance Counselor
Brittner, Stewart E.
Biology Teacher
Krueger, Ellen
English Teacher
Meichsner, Kerry T.
History Teacher
Pitts, Michele Lill
High School Guidance Counselor
Sachsel, Gerard Richard
History Teacher
Selman, Carol
History Teacher
Urban, Peter F.
Social Studies Teacher
MILLINGTON
Longo, Mary Tassielli
Fourth Grade Teacher
MILLTOWN
Moglia, Allen William
7th-8th Grade Social Stud Tchr
MILLVILLE
Alston, Wanda Lyane Taylor
Second Grade Teacher
Andrews, Edward J.
Health & Physical Ed Tchr
Bell, Sylvia Mitchell
Mathematics Teacher
Brown, Sandra Monteleone
Teacher & Counselor
Camarata, Lyn L.
Social Studies Teacher
Fenili, Susan Porter
Third Grade Teacher
Kelly, Maxine Peterson
Mathematics Teacher
Mark, James D.
Director of Instrumental Music
Maul, Charles Bryce
Social Studies Teacher
Nagao, Carol Prichett
Art Teacher
Ponzetti, Janet Hassler
Math Teacher
Shaughnessy, William F., Jr.
Hlth & Physical Education Tchr
Smith, Denise Arrigo
Spanish Teacher
Thompson, Christy N.
Administrative Vice Principal
Vertolli, Audrey Mary
Second Grade Teacher
Webb, Robert George, Jr.
Technical Drafting Teacher
MINE HILL
Hackett, Elizabeth S.
First Grade Teacher
MINOTOLA
Hill, Ronald Salvatore
Special Education Teacher
MONMOUTH BEACH
Ginty, Karen Ladzinski
Kindergarten Teacher
MONMOUTH JUNCTION
Avard, Ralph Edward
Social Studies & History Tchr
Caffrey, Daniel
Mathematics Teacher
DeLucia, Vincent Richard
English Teacher
Gonzalez, April Lee
English Teacher
Hines, Florence Ellen
Business & Marketing Ed Tchr
Kreger, Patricia Di Bella
Art, Photo & Theatre Arts Tchr
Lott, Joyce Greenberg
English Teacher
Sanders, Rebecca Bonner
Physics Teacher
Sokol, Lisa Robin
Industrial Arts Tech Teacher
MONTCLAIR
Allen, Sheila M.
Social Studies Teacher
Antola, Andrea Maria
Science Teacher
Aquavia, James Michael
English Teacher
Cooper, William Thomas
Humanities Teacher
Coronis, Scott J.
Dean of Students
DeGennaro, Dorothy Jacobson
Jr HS Language Arts Teacher
Forbes, Patricia Fabritiis
English Dept Chair
Gipson, Joan AnnetteBoyd
English Teacher
Gugger, Gisela Machin
Spanish & French Teacher
Holley, Ezra John
English Teacher

Isidor, Julia Nawrocki
Theology & Ethics Teacher
Jennings, Mark A.
Assistant Principal
Jordan, Carlton Preston, Jr.
Language Arts Teacher
Lunario, Ross Anthony
Mathematics Teacher
Macaluso, Joseph Thomas
English Teacher
Natoli, Anne Lauraine Walka
Computer Creative Writing Tchr
Ozolins, Louise DeAngelis
Language Arts Teacher
Petersen, Maureen Jane McDonnell
Math Teacher
Schauble, Thomas J.
Drafting & Design Teacher
Springfield, Rebecca Blakeley
Social Studies Teacher
Svec, J. C.
Comm, Performance Instructor
Thornhill, Ann Troupe
Spanish Teacher
Tyson, Lorena E.
Sci Dept Chair & Chem Tchr
Velasco, Amparo
Mathematics Teacher
Ward, Stuart Groel
English Teacher
Washington, Courtney Willis
Mathematics Teacher
MONTVALE
Argeski, Bernard Gerald
Earth Science Teacher
DeCaro, Barbara Ann
Teacher
Donelly, Barry
English Teacher
Hagan, Ann J.
Third Grade Teacher
Hageman, Donald F.
Choral Director
Hediger, Donald
Supervisor of Science
Joseph, Arlene
Science Teacher
Lauro, Salvatore
Spanish Teacher
Russo, Richard A.
Science Coordinator & Teacher
Shust, Richard B.
English Teacher & Chairman
Talley, Glinda
Tchr of GATE & Enrichment
Wild, George F.
Math Teacher
Wilhjelm, Chris
Band Director
Williams, Karla B.
German & French Teacher
MONTVILLE
Bresnahan, Maureen Walsh
Student Assistance Counselor
Carroll, Stuart H.
High School English Teacher
Drozd, Stanley
Social Studies Teacher
Dyer, Hilde Rose
English & History Teacher
Holleran, Susan DeGennaro
Italian & Spanish Teacher
Kucher-Patenaude, Janice
Choral & Theater Dir
Meyer, Judith Willard
Fourth Grade Teacher
Moraes, Robert Llewellyn
Team Leader & Soc Stud Tchr
Regan, Donna Damiano
English Teacher
Robinson, Nancy Jean
Social Studies Teacher
Thayer, Adrienne B.
World Languages Teacher
Tolomeo, Johnna Annette
Health Teacher
Wetzel, Robert Charles
Physics Teacher
Williams, Michael J.
English Teacher & Supervisor
MOONACHIE
Salvatoriello, Sandra L.
1st Grade Teacher
MOORESTOWN
Boehmler, George Charles
Chemistry Teacher
Haag, Elizabeth A.
Orch String Instrumental Tchr
Heusser, John A.
Art & Art History Teacher
Marshall, Ruby Jean (Smith)
Life Science Teacher
Nelson, MaryLou Pickell
Retired K-2nd Grade Teacher
Pocius, Frank Leon
Mathematics Teacher
Rhody, David
Latin Teacher
Turnbull, Kinsa
English Teacher
MORGANVILLE
Cody-Howe, Patricia A.
Resource Center Teacher
Metz, Sheryl Felicia
Fourth Grade Teacher
O'Connor, Yvette Silver
Social Studies Teacher
MORRIS PLAINS
Callahan, Elaine Pasquarielo
Second Grade Teacher

MORRIS PLAINS (cont)
Cooper, David A.
Fifth Grade Teacher
Litwhiler, Mary Graves
Third Grade Teacher
MORRISTOWN
Bryant, Eunice Emily
Fifth Grade Teacher
Dodsworth, Jean
Math Dept Chair
Ingellis, Marian L.
Honors English Teacher
Keaney, Jonathan E.
Self Employed Agri-Business
Levin, Bette
Retired English Teacher
Pallante, Mary R.
Supervisor of Student Teachers
Rehm, Phyllis Andrea Chernoff
French & Italian Educator
MOUNT HOLLY
Bura, Claire Phillips
Math Teacher
Damico, Charles Alfred, Jr.
English Teacher
Gamel, Darren Matthew
English Teacher
Graf, Carol Coles
English & Journalism Teacher
Grocott, Dorene Mitchell
English Teacher
Hall, Donna Lynn
9th-11th Grade English Teacher
Harper, Pegeen Lee
Science & Mathematics Teacher
Havay, Stephen Lawrence
Navy JROTC Instructor
Latimer, James M.
Physics Teacher
Matarese, James D.
Spanish Teacher
Miller, Mary E.
3rd Grade Teacher
Minniear, Joseph C.
High School English Teacher
Mockus, John
Guidance Counselor
Sacks, Patricia Ann
Sixth Grd Tchr & Math Coord
Toppman, Evelyn Lea
Retired Lang Arts Teacher
Tresch, Gloria A.
Science Teacher
MOUNT LAUREL
Ballantyne, Elizabeth Knorr
Third Grade Teacher
Dooley, Jeanne Marie (Bradley)
7th Grade Mathematics Teacher
Golluscio, Gene
6th Grd Eng & Lit Tchr
Jeckot, John Joseph
MS Choral Music Teacher
Kochanski, Patricia Gale
Counselor
Noecker, Martha Ellen
Retired Third Grade Teacher
Smith, Darrell Wayne
History & Bible Teacher
Speidel, Byron D.
Science Tchr & Dept Coord
Terry, Vicki (Saas)
Fourth Grade Teacher
Uibel, Jennifer Mack
Language Arts Teacher
MOUNTAIN LAKES
Bond, Jeffrey Miller
Classics Teacher
Foster, Mary K.
English Teacher
Kaufman, Renie
Teacher & Coordinator
White, Patricia
English Teacher
MOUNTAINSIDE
Hine, Marie (Petgrave)
Retired Elementary Teacher
MULLICA HILL
Mc Dermott, Cynthia B.
English & Study Skills Teacher
NEPTUNE
Campbell, Jane K.
Mathematics Teacher
Newell, Sheila Schneidler
Retired Elementary Teacher
Pigut, Edward Anthony
English Teacher
Smith, Robert Reed
Retired 7th Grade Math Teacher
Stanford, Curtis Tillerson
Third Grade Teacher
Sullivan, Stephanie Samen
Former Teacher
NEW BRUNSWICK
Bronner, Stephen Eric
Professor of Political Science
Curry, Jane Elise
Fourth Grade Teacher
Davis, Ann S.
Seventh Grade Teacher
Davis, Frances Jones
Language Arts Teacher
Dobrowolski, Joan P.
11th-12th Grd English Teacher
Erath, Mary Regina
8th Grade Teacher
Flitterman-Lewis, Sandy
Assoc Prof Eng & Cinema
Gibson, Donald Bernard
English Professor
Gillespie, Angus Kress
Assoc Prof of American Studies
Gliserman, Martin Joel
Associate Professor of English
Martin, Marie T.
Guidance Counselor
Mitchell, Judith Unzicker
Third Grade Teacher
Richman, Kenneth A.
Instr of Philosophy & English
Schneider, Lee David
Dean of Students
Stinson, Anne D'Antonio
Teaching Asst
Ward, BJ
Poetry Instructor
NEW MILFORD
Colannino, Anthony
French, Spanish & Italian Tchr
DeNicolo, Patricia Nocetti
First Grade Teacher
Miller, Pam Van De Weghe
Mathematics Department Chair
Stanton, Susan Jeanette
Home Economics Teacher
Wilson, David W.
History Teacher
NEW MONMOUTH
Dickinson, Jeanne Marie
Mathematics Teacher
NEW PROVIDENCE
Brennan, Erin Marie
Math Teacher
Buccossi, Victor Louis
AP Psychology Instructor
Haness, Rosemary
Fine Arts Educator
Mac Burney, Christine Cleaveland
English Teacher
Tracey, Byron
History Teacher
NEWARK
Appling, Inez Gamble
Science Teacher
Ardito, John Anthony
Graphic Arts Teacher
Ballin, Kathryn Blizzard
Math Teacher
Berlinghieri, Mary
Eighth Grade Teacher
Best, Charles E., Jr.
8th Grade Teacher
Boyah, Paul B.
Mathematics Teacher
Bradley, Dolores Davidson
Guidance Counselor
Brown Jenkins, Daisy
Mathematics Teacher
Capalaran, Amelia Cortez
High School Math Teacher
Capik, Maria D'Agostino
Spanish Teacher
Caporaso, Jo-Ann
Freshman Teacher
Capriglione, Terese Montefusco
HS Guidance Counselor
Carrera, Rosely X.
Second Grade Teacher
Casey, Dorothy Floyd
Computer & Secretarial Teacher
Chamberlain, Robert J.
Asst Prof of Clncl Radiography
Conte, Lorraine F.
Substitute Teacher
DeValve, Dianne Grace
Professor of Counseling
DiGerlando, Salvatore Michael
Art Teacher
DiNola, Angela Jacangelo
Eighth Grade Teacher
Domenick, Anthony
Jr HS Rdng & Eng Teacher
Donohue, Kathleen A.
English Teacher
Ferrera, Victoria
English Teacher
Fischman, Judy Goldschmidt
Basic Skills Teacher
Freeman, Susan Nicole
Fourth Grade Teacher
Fricke, David John
Inst Music Teacher
Gallo, Michael Anthony
Health & PE Teacher
Garcia, Obdulia Lapis
First Grade Teacher
Garcia-Vazquez, Nelly Rafaela
Eighth Grade Teacher
Gironda, Marie Misita
English & Latin Teacher
Graves, June Merriweather
Technology Teacher
Hankerson, Robert
Mathematics Teacher
Hatcher, Shelia Parker
Elementary Science Teacher
Hewett, Sandra Lee
Health & PE Instructor
James, Linda D.
Resource Teacher
Kenyatta, Janice Green
Business Education Teacher
Koubek, Paulette Ann
English Instructor
Linner, Donald
Business Professor
Longmore, Paulette
English Professor
Lopes, Patricia Rufolo
Social Studies Teacher
Marinello, Elizabeth A.
Guidance Cnslr & Coll Coord
Mc Allister, Elizabeth Hevia
Ed Opportuity Program Cnslr
Mc Cray, Jerline F.
Mathematics Teacher
O'Brien, James O., Jr.
History & Government Teacher
O'Neal, Christian Michael
History Teacher
Pace, John P.
Professor of Mathematics
Pellegrino, Helenmarie
9th-12th Grd Art Teacher
Quinlan, Ronald Joseph
Social Studies Dept Chprsn
Repoli, Peter Michael
Math Teacher
Rey, Linda Ann
First Grade Teacher
Rhines, Jesse Algeron
Asst Prof of African Amer Stud
Richardson, Jean A. Tarantini
Kindergarten Teacher
Rosenbaum, Mimi Prawer
Educational Media Specialist
Salagaj, Deborah D'Alessio
Computer Programming Teacher
Samuelsen, Margaret Rooney
7th Grade Teacher
Sanders, Fred A., Jr.
Clinical Instr of Radiography
Solomon, Hattie Bennett
Guidance Counselor
Spruel-Thompson, Mollye E.
Fourth Grade Teacher
Stefanelli, Lisandra Anne Monetti
Accounting & Bus Law Tchr
Stridacchio, Donna Marie
Mathematics Teacher
Thomas, William Joseph
High Schl Mathematics Teacher
Tosun, Zeke
Spanish Teacher
Valitzski, Mary Cecilia
Principal
Walker, Finesia Dunovant
History Teacher
White, Ladylease Goodridge
Prof & Coord of Acctng Dept
Wigfall, Dorothy Brown
Reading & Language Arts Tchr
NEWFIELD
Cavagnaro, Susan VanHook
Social Studies Teacher
Elwell, Dorothy Marie
Third Grade Teacher
Fabrizio, Beatrice Grace
Sixth Grade Teacher
Fioresi, Veronica Monfardini
Kindergarten Teacher
Lawton, Thomas Joseph, V
Social Studies Teacher
NEWTON
Ancona, Francesco Aristide
Prof of English & Mythology
Bateman, Carl J.
Mathematics Supervisor
Bilby, Pamela Rencher
Social Studies Teacher
Carducci, Eleanor Whalen
Assistant Professor of English
Chase, Warren John
English Teacher
Crawn, Linda K.
Health & Physical Ed Teacher
Daniels, Pamela Bryant
German Teacher
DiGregorio, Robert Eugene
Fifth & Sixth Grade Teacher
Filipowski, Michael J.
English Dept Chair & Teacher
Gill, John Joseph, Jr.
High School Science Teacher
Hartemann, Ronald
German & Spanish Teacher
Kelly, Dirk Thomas
USI & World History Teacher
Kennedy, Philip Wayne
Elementary Schl Principal
Krupinski, Michael Steven
Supervisor of Instruction
Lengle, Larry Edward
English Teacher
McNabb, Nancy Grein
School Nurse
Morro, Thomas G.
Dev, Legal Studies Professor
Peattie, Patricia Kanouse
English Teacher
Pede, David William
Agriscience Dept Chprsn
Pomerantz, Kathleen Susan Laughlin
English Teacher
Rast, Judy Witman
Health & Physical Ed Teacher
Richards, Donna Riley
College Scheduler
Saba, Simon
Tech Resource Tchng Specialist
Scott, Arlene J.
English Instructor
Shuster, Douglas
Fourth Grade Teacher
Venable, Susan Gordon
Early Childhood Professor
Waite, William Foster
Asst Prof of Business Admin
Walborn, Sereno Bernard
English Teacher
Walton, Kurt George
Athletic Director
Yuhas, Sherri Lee-Lehmer
Varsity Cheerleading Coach
NORTH ARLINGTON
Cannell, Margaret M.
English Teacher
Chrzanowski, Chrystena Ann
English Teacher
Cordero, Patricia Wilmot
Fifth Grade Teacher
Da Cruz, Susy
Guidance Counselor
Fusco, Janet
English Teacher
Giovia, Donna Ann (Higgins)
Substance Awareness Coord
Hilla, Nancy
Eighth Grade Teacher
Ingraffia, Richard James, Jr.
Vice Principal for Discipline
Krista, Elizabeth Cole
8th Grade Teacher
Krista, Kevin Charles
History Teacher
Maisano, Alan A.
Social Science Dept Chprsn
Mc Ginnis, Paul F.
Director of Guidance
Mc Hale, Geraldine
Math Teacher & Dept Chair
Moran, James Martin
Religious Studies Teacher
Russell, Robert
Drama, Music & English Tchr
Santiago, Carl Michael
English & Religion Teacher
Toughmanian, Marguerite
French & Spanish Teacher
Touma, Stephen M.
English Teacher
NORTH BERGEN
Alonso, Lily
Fourth Grade Teacher
Costello, Joan F.
High School Guidance Cnslr
DeVincenzo, Madelyn Miller
Basic Skills Teacher
Haas, Marilyn Brickwedel
High School Science Teacher
Haviland, George Patrick
Band Director
Janesak, Mary Kody
Child Devlopment, Home Ec Tchr
Killeen, Thomas F.
English Department Chairperson
La Mastro, Louis Paul
Math, Comp & Science Teacher
Ludwig, Steven M.
Seventh & Eighth Grade Teacher
Romano, Diane Tuzzio
Eighth Grade Math Teacher
Rovelli, Joseph W.
HS Mathematics Supervisor
Rovere, Robert John
Chairperson Dept of Languages
Seyler, Mary Dolson
Math Teacher
Zink, Robert Donald
Retired History Teacher
NORTH BRUNSWICK
Ezdinli, Suzan
Italian & Latin Teacher
Jenner, Bryan H.
Band Director
Kaplan, Helen L.
Seventh Grd Mathematics Tchr
Obzut, Janet Caesar
Communications Teacher
Walshak, Alma Ippolito
French & Spanish Teacher
NORTH CALDWELL
Battershall, William H., Jr.
Hlth, Physical Education Tchr
Caruso, Robert F.
Social Studies & Drama Dir
Miceli, Virginia Colford
7th Grade Science Teacher
Monroe, David DuBose
Life Science Teacher
Sanelli, Anne
Biology Teacher
Schnauffer, Robert William
Health & Physical Ed Instr
Weig, Walter Frank, Jr.
High School Mathematics Tchr
Welfel, Linda Contursi
Mathematics Teacher
NORWOOD
Dinnell, Patricia Conway
Librarian
Johnson, Betty A. (Chiusolo)
Principal
Kriegel, Marion Newirth
Art Teacher
Mc Gee, Patricia Ellen O'Neill
7th-8th Grd Language Arts Tchr
Ricco, Bernadette Deierlein
Coord of Gifted & Talented
NUTLEY
Adubato, Gerard Michael
6th Grade Teacher
Betts, Stephen Christopher
Former Instructor
Chapman, Raymond
History Teacher
D'Ambola, Toby
High School Math Teacher
Foote, Elizabeth
Third Grade Teacher
Graziano, Nicolette
English Teacher
Kirsten, Miriam Joan
Spanish Teacher
Koci, Adele Katherine
Fourth Grade Teacher
Koci, Jan M.
7th Grd Tchr & Sci Dept Chprsn
LaReau, Susan C.
Second Grade Teacher
LaRocca, Fred Vincent
Retired Teacher
Masullo, Beverly Marino
Sixth Grade Teacher
Mullane, Ann Mary Mc Millan
Business Education Teacher
O'Hara, Carol Jeanne
First Grade Teacher
Reilly, Gail Sheridan
Second Grade Teacher
Rhodes, Gregory Lawrence
History Teacher
Sasso, Dennis Anthony
Teacher & Coach
Turturiello, Vincent Frank
Mathematics Teacher
Walker, John H.
Principal
OAK RIDGE
Eastman, Christopher J.
Audio Visual Dir & Ftbl Coach
Helfand, Scott E.
Social Studies Teacher
Jones, Virginia S.
Business Education Teacher
Masone, Sally
High School Spanish Teacher
Post, Earle M.
Biology Teacher
Staszak, Marci Ann
Social Studies Teacher
OAKHURST
Bio, Anna Maria Rosano
Italian Teacher
Olsen, Karen Nimal
Choral Director & Teacher
Sapnar, Susan Craig
English Teacher
Schlegel, Aurora Rini
French Teacher
Weiss, Elizabeth Tuchfeld
French & German Teacher
OAKLAND
De Freest, Kevin A.
Band Director
Fallone, Silvana
Vocal Music & Drama Director
House, Maxine B.
Latin & English Teacher
Ianacone, John A.
English Teacher
Kuzma, Daniel Franklin
Social Studies Teacher
Leicht, Joseph Peter
Mathematics Teacher & Coach
Peters, Anne
Teacher
OAKLYN
Hess, Linda Jane (Holloway)
Fifth Grade Classroom Teacher
Steffen, Patricia Jo
Third Grade Teacher
OCEAN
Day, Denise M.
Eng as a Second Lang Teacher
OCEAN CITY
Ghanavati, Kathleen
Chemistry Teacher
Margolis, Ida Moskowitz
Psychology & AP History Tchr
Peterson, Mary-Rodney Brooks
Ret Fam Lvng & Hum Sex Tchr
Soroka, Ronald T.
Computer Science Teacher
OCEANPORT
Falvo, Constance Difedele
Teacher of Gifted & Talented
Jeffrey, Nadine Woolley
Retired K & 1st Grd Teacher
OLD BRIDGE
Alfieri, Nancy J.
Math Teacher
Bosco, Simon Michael
English Teacher
Daganya, Rose A.
Physical Education Teacher
DeMarco, Zonia S.
Guidance Counselor
Lang, Louise L.
7th Grade Teacher
Lehrhaupt, Karen Kuechenmeister
Social Studies Tchr
McFadden, Charles Annice
6th-8th Grd Mathematics Tchr
Ogden, Melanie Anne
Student Assistance Counselor
Piscitelli, Michael
Accounting & Marketing Teacher
Rifkin, Alynn Sue
Math Teacher
Solomos, Rhoda
Director
OLD TAPPAN
Piper, Marjorie A.
Math & Computer Teacher
Roberts, Patrice Helen
Mathematics & Science Teacher
ORADELL
Drahouzal, Marlies
English Teacher

LL (cont)
oyce Lorayne
me Consultant
ouis W.
Computer Science Tchr
'homas Jude, CFC
al Studies & Math Tchr
, Kevin Michael
us Education Chprsn
haron Karp
Teacher
hirley Bassett
Elementary School Tchr
William
Chemistry Teacher
n, Robert George
chool Psych & His Instr
E
ahim, Zaimah
chool Mathematics Tchr
Robert Guy
eadership Program Dir
Candace Elaine Dixon
rade Teacher
ary Barnes
eader & Guidance Cnslr
Peter Richard
eacher
, Curtis L.
r
D
Marla Russick
rade Teacher
DES PARK
Harry
e Teacher
Robert
n Teacher
, Mary Abate
& Spanish Teacher
oris
ade Teacher
C. Lynn Hubert
natics Teacher
Jane M.
Grade Teacher
Barbara Margaret
h Grade French Teacher
Judith L.
Science & Tech Supvr
n, Ellen
n & Math Teacher
RA
Diane Calio
h & Latin Teacher
ni, Gene Paul
h Grd Soc Stud Instr
n, Linda A.
n Teacher
Kathleen Eck
y & Earth Science Tchr
Terry Lee
Grade Teacher
US
Debra DeFilippo
Psychologist
o, Robert John
sor of Biology
z, Jean Lavelle
glish Teacher
Walter, Jr.
matics Teacher
i, Edward Albert
Studies Teacher
k, Sidney R.
f Psych & Behavrl Sci
Gina Ricciardelli
Grade Teacher
Bruce Raymond
sor of Physics
le, Beverly Rose (Carnish)
y Teacher
Sandra E.
dary Social Studies Tchr
, Frank, Jr.
er of Gifted & Talented
, Katherine Theresa
d Teacher
Thomas Joseph
h Professor
arry
sor & Dir of Clinical Ed
. Arlene
Guidance Counselor
aum, Ruth
Professor of Mathematics
Stephen
h Teacher
, Mindy
ept Chair & Biology Tchr
Margaret M.
Studies Teacher
nn, Brenda R.
Grade Teacher
Adeline Paladino
Grade Teacher
, Ronald Jay
Teacher & Band Director
a, Richard G.
ce Teacher
, Edward Kevin
ssor of English
Jane E.
rade Teacher
Bruce
ogy Tchr, Campus Minister
Gary S.
ology Teacher
erg, Sandra S.
of Mathematics & French

Spreiregen, Harold M.
Accounting Professor
Tepfenhardt, Alice M.
Guidance Counselor
Thumm, Michael James
Guidance Counselor
Tichio, Anna
Guidance Counselor
Weisholtz, Anne Berchenko
English Teacher
Wolson, Karen Susan
Assoc Prof of Biological Sci
Yasin, Jon Abdullah
Professor of English
PARK RIDGE
Barnhart, Patricia Collons
Spanish Teacher
Bauer, Thomas Walter
Span Tchr & Frgn Langs Supvr
Donohue, James P.
French & Spanish Teacher
Finley, Patrick Daniel
Vocal Music & Music His Tchr
Langer, Norbert Joseph, II
German Teacher
Luce, Julia M.
French & German Teacher
O'Neill, Kevin
English Teacher
Popolizio, Rick John
Instrumental Music Teacher
Teagno, Marjorie
Sixth Grade Teacher
PARLIN
Castronovo, Jacqueline Ann
Special Education Teacher
Cifelli, Nicholas Joseph
Secondary Mathematics Teacher
Fitzsimmons, Beverly A.
Rdng Specialist & Title I Tchr
Gozora, Steve R.
History Teacher
Haltli, Patricia Defort
Business Teacher
Jegou, Gregory Charles
Health & Physical Ed Teacher
Kwiatkowski, Christine
Spanish Teacher
Lewis, Wayne Austin
5th & 6th Grade PE Teacher
Malara, Anthony Ignazio
7th Grd US History Tchr
Stricker, Kathleen Kapica
4th Grade Teacher
Suminski, Dolores Lasko
English Teacher
PARSIPPANY
Ahnemann, Gail Beatty
Second Grade Teacher
Bakker, Alice J.
Business Teacher
Bernabe, Joseph Michael
Band Director
Burek, Lynn Angelica
English, Speech & Theatre Tchr
Capsouras, John David
Business Education Teacher
Chuy, Deanna J.
Language Arts Dept Head
Clark, Marion J.
Guidance Counselor
Cocheo, Victor Paul
Special Education Teacher
Corigliano, Lynn Rae (Byrnes)
English as Second Lang Tchr
Curnow, Gary W.
Teacher of Gifted & Talented
DeVenezia, Ann M. (Lupardi)
English Teacher
Donaghy, Christine Ann
English Teacher
Ellenwood, Daniel Steven
Bible & PE Teacher
Foreso, Ronald Francis
Social Studies Teacher
Gihorski, Thomas Patrick
Health, Drivers Ed & PE Tchr
Golabek, Janet
Secondary Art Teacher
Heintjes, John P.
Social Studies Teacher
Kahn, Harold G.
8th Grd Social Studies Teacher
Massa, Karen
English Teacher
Mc Carthy, Stephen Charles
English Teacher
Mc Cluskey, Laura Ann
Science Teacher & Dept Lead
Monahan, Anne Loftus
Reading & Writing Teacher
Murray, Kevin John
English Teacher
Oshima, Heidrun Becker
Language Instructor
Pellegrini, Nancy Cicchino
Business Teacher
Pollack, Charles
Mathematics Teacher
Pratola, Elizabeth Ann
Mathematics Teacher
Rutenberg, Lynne Rauchbach
Second Grade Teacher
Sabella, Robert Michael
Mathematics Lead Teacher
Schwartz, Harriet M. (Cohen)
8th Grade Global Studies Tchr
Tocci, Marlene Perscheid
Child Development Teacher

Traver, Heidi Hacknauer
Biology Teacher
Wells, Alberta Susan
English Teacher
Westphal, Mark L.
Biology & Science Teacher
Zaleski, David George
Lead Physical Ed Teacher
PASSAIC
Briones, Ma. PUrificacion Mendoza
5th-8th Grade English Teacher
Cannata, Kathleen
Teacher of Gifted & Talented
Cisar, Joseph P.
Special Ed Dept Chairman
DeVita, John Vincent
Math, Physics & Soc Stud Tchr
Hammer, Phyllis Elaine
Mathematics Teacher
Joyce, Teresa Pellegrino
Fifth Grade Teacher
Pitts, Denise
HS Bus Ed Tchr & Peer Ldr Trnr
Schmidt, Paul Joseph
Biology Instructor
Schroder, Valerie Katherine
Chemistry Teacher
Schuman, Emily Goodman
Multicultural Education Tchr
Sponder, Harry
Naval Science Instructor
Walker, Marvin Leon
History Teacher
Wittenberg, Barbara Souther
Ldrshp Trainer & Reading Tchr
PATERSON
Adams, Anna J.
Physical Ed & Health Instr
Bria, Amy
Guidance Counselor
Cartaina, John Joseph
Social Studies Teacher
Chapman, Patricia
Eighth Grd Mathematics Tchr
Cooper, Gary Owen
Fourth Grade Teacher
Dearani, George
Drama Director
De Negri, Alexander G.
Eighth Grade Teacher
Garofalo, Donna D'Amico
Fifth Grade Teacher
Gayden, Carol J. Hickman
Hlth, PE & Drivers Ed Teacher
Hemingway, Denise Bowie
Fourth Grade Teacher
Henry, Hyden Harold
Mathematics Teacher
Hubert, Robert John
Sci Dept Chair & Physics Tchr
Hurling, Gwenyth Hill
HS Guidance Counselor
Hyman, Vivian Maria (Silverio)
6th-8th Grd Soc Stud Tchr
Jones, Sylvia De Stefano
6th Grade Teacher
Leskovics, Joseph W.
8th Grade Mathematics Teacher
Liguori, Patricia Blauvelt
Third Grade Teacher
Lyons, Daniel L.
Sociology Professor
Mamakos-Werner, Cynthia Ann Lash
English Tchr & Admin Asst
Miele, Bonnie Mc Partland
Science & Health Teacher
Pabst, Karen Marie
6th Grade Teacher
Pardine, Joseph, Jr.
Mathematics Teacher
Petrow, Evelyn Mae
First Grade Teacher
Quince, Cora Bridges
Vice Principal
Salhany, Bernadette
First Grade Teacher
Scharfspitz, Marjorie Wallen
Sixth Grade Teacher
Schuyler, Ray C.
Psychology Teacher
Simon, Joan Dineen
Student Activities Dean
Timmons, Margaret Sims
Third Grade Teacher of GATE
Vannatta, Anna Marie DelVecchio
English Teacher
Voronka, Zirka
Associate Professor of ESL
Walker, Selena Wilson
6th Grade Math Teacher
Warren, Barbara Beth
Mathematics Teacher
Wiliams, Sarah Jean
English Teacher
Younge, Denise
Kindergarten Teacher
PAULSBORO
Kirschling, William N.
Soc Stud Tchr & Dept Chprsn
Neal, Jannie M.
Teacher of Gifted & Talented
PEMBERTON
Brown, Jeffrey Sean
Mathematics Teacher
Gavin, Carole O'Connor
Prof of Language & Literature
Hammill, Charles P.
Assoc Professor of Psychology
Rife, Connie Varsaci
Fifth Grade Enrichment Teacher

Schoening, Carole Elizabeth
Professor of Chemistry
Veit, Walter Charles
Professor of Sociology
Wiener, Lisa Golden
Fifth Grade Teacher
PENNINGTON
Ashcraft, William L.
Mathematics Teacher
Burns, Terrence Patrick
English Dept Chair & Tchr
Johnson, Ervin John
Industrial Arts Teacher
Lo Riccco, Michael P.
Business Educator
PENNS GROVE
Brander, Diane Green
Fourth Grade Inclusion Teacher
Casella, Mary JoAnn
5th Grade Teacher
Cummings, Sondra Louise (Germanio)
Kindergarten Teacher
Dickey, Irene Sicoutris
English Teacher
Fratz, Carl E.
English Teacher
Harris, Linda Jacqueline (Gay)
English Teacher
Kiple, Judith Cline
Sixth Grade Teacher
Lake, Donna Houchin
Kindergarten Teacher
Maurer, Frank Hayes, III
Bus Tchr & Vice Prin for Discp
Maurer, Mary D'Urso
Frgn Lang Dept Chr & Span Tchr
Mc Coy, Daniel
Spanish Teacher
Monroe, Betty Minor
Lit, Eng & Soc Studies Teacher
PENNSAUKEN
Edmondson, Michael
History Instructor
Eyler, Suzy Rita
Theology Teacher & Dept Coord
Fligier, Lisa Ann
Secondary English Teacher
Ford, Mary Pat
Art Teacher
Gainer, Larry
Physical Education Teacher
Heath, Linda Susan
9th-12th Grade Math Teacher
Knowlton, Regina Pustie
Science Department Coordinator
Marquart, Joseph Matthew
English Teacher
Mc Carthy, Lisa Mitchell
Secondary History Teacher
Moke, Martin C.
Health, PE & Math Teacher
Sawicki, Stephanie
8th Grd Language Arts Teacher
Silvia, Mary Jane
Youth Minister
Stashis, Suzanne Bell
Counselor
Stick, Lois Marie
Music Teacher & Choral Dir
Webster, Thomas Jones
Band Director
Wiggins, Raymond F.
Music Teacher
Williams, Marylou Lazzaro
English Teacher & Admin
PENNSVILLE
Becknell, Mary Ball
Kindergarten Teacher
Davis, Howard Keasbey, Jr.
6th Grd Math Tchr & Team Ldr
Hahn, Ellen K.
Third Grade Teacher
Nuzzi, Elizabeth Rose
Third Grade Teacher
Raine, Judith Bowen
6th-12th Grade English Tchr
Rieger, Edward W.
Social Studies Teacher
Stepler, Patricia Finegan
Second Grade Teacher
PERTH AMBOY
Argemil, Vivian
Bilingual & ESL Resource Tchr
Brodbeck, Carl Axel
Instrumental Music Teacher
Doherty, Mary Gibney
Sixth Grade Teacher
Dunbar, Lynne Summer
ESL Teacher
Fiore, Carol Ann Drury
Second Grade Teacher
Giambattista, Lisa A.
Sixth Grade Teacher
Hernandez, Wilson Rafael
7th Grd Bilingual Ed Teacher
Kmiec, Andrew
Sixth Grade Teacher
Kurz, Daniel M.
Instrumental Music Teacher
Martucci, Rayna Weingart
7th-8th Grd Language Arts Tchr
Murphy, Barbara Fielek
Third Grade Teacher
Nemergut, Dolly E.
Bilingual Science Teacher
Otero, Victor R.
Bilingual & Science Teacher
Piatek, Rebecca Mary
Building Principal

Rivera, Susan Kolczynski
Eng as Second Lang & Rdng Tchr
Santamaria, William
Science Teacher
Szeliga, Christine Ann
Special Education Teacher
Zmigrodski, Thomas Bernard
5th Grade Teacher
PHILLIPSBURG
Beck, Douglas Alan
English Teacher
Eksaa, Glenn T.
Math & Science Teacher
Getsko, Anthony J.
Biology Teacher
Murphy, Laurie Johnson
History & German Teacher
Snyder, Linda Clymer
5th Grade Teacher
PINE BEACH
Savino, Jill Scharer
Technology Teacher
PINE HILL
Dunbar, Marilyn Nurse
Teacher of Handicapped
PISCATAWAY
Brahm, Walter Richard
High School Counselor
Bubnis, Joyce Ann
Jr High Teacher
Campanella, Neale
Mathematics Teacher
Carey, Anne
Science & Religion Teacher
Cirafesi, Jo-Anne K.
Chemistry Teacher
Collins, Patricia A. (Wornom)
Choral Director
Dibling, Christina M.
Spanish Teacher
Halsted, Natalie Kowalski
8th Grade Civics Teacher
Impagliatelli, Leonard M.
Sixth Grade Teacher
Kielblock, Henry Francis
History Teacher
Magulak, Mary Jane
Third Grade Teacher
Mc Kay, Donald Edward
Chemistry & Physics Teacher
Myers, Lenon Page
High School Mathematics Tchr
Nagele, Dorothy C.
Third Grade Teacher
Peterson, Joan Aszuk
Fifth Grade Teacher
Russell, Peggy, RSM
Principal
Scriba, Toby Marcus
Art Teacher
Selander, Mary Ann Copley
Science Teacher
Stepien, Carol Flesher
Second Grade Teacher
Stio, Perry Dominick
Whole Language Teacher
Storsberg, Nancy J.
Guidance Director
PITMAN
Burd, Barbara King
Math & Computer Science Tchr
Fox, Carol Kimball
7th Grd Communications Teacher
Goldschmidt, Robert H.
Assistant Principal
Hausmann, Howard Stratton
Retired Elementary Teacher
PLAINFIELD
Bernard, Sylvia Parker
Reading Teacher
Cavaliere, Robert Joseph
High School English Teacher
Coyle, Mary Louise A.
Jr High Teacher
Donnelly, Louise (Fiumara)
Guidance Director
Haklik, Sherry S.
English & Journalism Teacher
Howell, Barbara Brown
Retired Elementary Teacher
Mc Kenna, Richard E.
Advanced Biology Teacher
Middleton, Gloria Jean
Fifth Grade Teacher
Mitchell, Violet Loretta
Elem Schl Guidance Counselor
Montford, Claudian Hammond
5th Grade Teacher
Torres, Lillian
High School Math Teacher
Wiley, Helen Rolley
Eighth Grade Math Teacher
Wollman, Barbara Jean (Chase)
Secondary English Teacher
Yarborough, Phyllis (Keys-Davis)
Tchr of the Gifted & Talented
Zimmerman, Barbara Reitmeyer
Kindergarten Teacher
PLAINSBORO
Johnson, Lynn Jefferson-Webb
Sixth Grade Teacher
Sullivan, Carl G.
President of Consulting
Vroom, Peter V.
8th Grd Earth Science Teacher
PLEASANTVILLE
Benjamin, Leni Kruger
Career Awareness Teacher
Colman, Marcia Jannarone
8th Grade Teacher

PLEASANTVILLE (cont)
Hitzel, Susan Herbert
3rd Grade Teacher
Kearney, Doris Marie
Eighth Grade Teacher
Marsden, Carl L.
9th-11th Grd History Teacher
Mattern, Bonnie Storm
3rd Grade Teacher
Miller, Jacqueline I.
Counselor
Thomas, Lynda d'Elia
First Grade Teacher
POINT PLEASANT
Fedak, Madeline Stamato
Teacher
Lattimer, Sandy Cox
Fifth Grade Teacher
Ruben, Nancy Stephenson
Sixth Grade Teacher
POINT PLEASANT BEACH
Alfonse, Robert H.
High School Science Teacher
Bertolami, Lorraine Maier
High School Mathematics Tchr
Brennan, Corinne Lucier
English Teacher & Supervisor
De Fonce, Richard Paul
Guidance Supervisor
Donley, Loren D.
Performing Arts Supervisor
Ferullo, Stevan M.
Physical Education Teacher
Kostenko, Michael David
Social Studies Dept Coord
Moore, Jacquelyn Zamarra
Biology Teacher
Moore, William N., Jr.
High School Soc Stud Tchr
Smith, William Thomas
English Teacher
Weatherall, Carol Anne
Mathematics Teacher
Youngster, Carol A.
English Teacher & Adj Eng Prof
Zupko, Deborah A.
English Teacher
POMONA
Davis, Mary Beth Kain
Third Grade Teacher
Schultheis, Priscilla W.
Sixth Grade Teacher
Tapper, Jill M.
1st Grade Teacher
POMPTON LAKES
Bernstock, Maureen Ann Scagnelli
Reading Specialist
Fox, Lynn Denise
Social Studies & Lit Teacher
Gervolino, Colleen Sullivan
High School Chemistry Teacher
Porada, Carol Tereski
English Teacher
Schafer, Anna Marie Gaudio
Fourth Grade Teacher
POMPTON PLAINS
Hettinger, Gillian R.
High School English Teacher
Hoogmoed, Janyce Marie
Eng, Art & HS Foods Teacher
Moloughney, Vincent F.
Math Teacher & Dept Chair
Praschak, Diane Gibello
Teacher of Gifted & Talented
Rose, Anita Ruth (Hoogerheide)
Kindergarten Teacher
Ruby, Shawn Leon
History Teacher
PORT ELIZABETH
Trucano, John William
7th-8th Grade English Teacher
PORT MONMOUTH
Jannuzzelli, Gerald Joseph
Band Director
Pfennig, Jacqueline Frisco
Eighth Grade Science Teacher
Pflug, Barbara Siravo
8th Grd Physical Science Tchr
PORT READING
Morris, Arlene Kolesarich
Fifth Grade Teacher
PRINCETON
Adair, Nancy Victoria
Asst Head & Dean of Academics
Arnold, Carol Foster
English Teacher
Belgrave, Mario Gerardo
Educl Consultant
Brittain, Janet Ann Wilma Benkendorf
Chemistry Teacher
Falconer, Raymond Geoffrey
English Teacher & Choral Dir
Gingo, Stephen Paul
Computer Coordinator & Coach
Huchet, Mary Lou Murphy
Lang Art Tchr-Media Lit Spclst
Jacobson, Franklin Paul
Music Department Chair
Johnson, Nancy Ogles
Second Grade Teacher
Kiefer, Katharin L.
Science Department Chair
Kuenne, Janet B.
Eng Tchr & Learning Specialist
Linden-Burns, Marjorie
Biology Teacher
Mc Carthy, Mary C.
Middle School Math Teacher
Niederer, Joan Annechini
Sixth Grade Teacher
Page, Lyman Alexander
Associate Professor
Saperstein, Herbert
7th-8th Grade Teacher
Shaffer, Connie Harrison
French Teacher
Storie, Sina Procaccini
4th Grade Teacher
Vivens, Robert Edward
7th Grd Social Studies Teacher
PRINCETON JUNCTION
Black, Nadine S. (Kouba)
Gftd & Tlntd Pgms Tchr & Coord
Bruno, Gail Susan
High School Guidance Counselor
Chen, Chuen-Chin Hsu
Science Teacher
Christensen, David Alan
Vocal Activities Director
Glover, Robert S.
American History Teacher
Mauro, Jean Cranstoun
Orchestra Director
Werner, B. Lee
Mathematics Teacher
PRINCETON TOWNSHIP
Gougoutas, Linda Hattman
Fourth Grade Teacher
Marinnie, Frances Broadway
3rd Grade Teacher
QUAKERTOWN
Yates, Bernice-Marie
Social Studies Teacher
RAHWAY
Lagattuta, Diane
English Second Language Tchr
Nazzaro, JoAnn M.
English & Journalism Teacher
Nazzarro, Jo Ann M.
English Teacher
Pennell, Donald Kenneth
Music Teacher & Choral Dir
Salcito, Christine Urbank
Program Dir of Math Education
Saliola, Deborah Ann
High School Science Teacher
Tator, Adrienne Maria
French & English Teacher
Torres, Shelby C.
English Teacher
RAMSEY
Arone, Kathryn Ann
Retired Italian & French Tchr
Bednar, Kathyann (Zanelli)
Guidance Counselor
Bersano, Judy Elizabeth
Biology Teacher
DeLillo, Richard Joseph
Mathematics Teacher & Chair
Fatuzzo, John Justin
Life Science Teacher
Ferrara, Robert Gerard
US His, Latin Tchr & Dept Head
Gallagher, Mary Lou Walsh
2nd Grade Teacher
LaMotta, Vince J.
Senior English Teacher
Rohrs, Heidi
German & Social Studies Instr
Young, Noel Christian
Instrumental Music Teacher
Zawacki, Richard G.
HS Social Studies Teacher
RANDOLPH
Arcidiacono, Patricia Kelly
Nursing Professor
DeRosa, Marlyce Pedersen
Vocal Music Teacher
Gradone, Richard Anthony
Professor of Music
Krufka, Joseph J.
Retired Teacher
Leogrande, Dennis Martin
String Instrument Teacher
Mc Coach, Roger Frederick
Mathematics Professor
Pfaffenroth, Sara Beekey
Professor of English
Rachalis, Christine Frances
Mathematics Teacher
Russo, Maryann Jerbasi
American History Teacher
Seitz, Grayce Rosso
Guidance Counselor
Tobias, Ann Greenawalt
5th Grade Teacher
Tobias, Charles John
Band Director
Voorhees, Martha Cespedes
Spanish Teacher
Zulauf, Sander
English Professor
RARITAN
Galida, Michael John
Physical Education Teacher
READINGTON
D'Alonzo, Robert F.
Physical Education Teacher
Triolo, James Jack
Sixth Grade Teacher
RED BANK
Brown, Patricia Laine
First Grade Teacher
DeVito, Tina Marie
Scripture Teacher
Falco, Karen McGaheran
Math Teacher
Fayad, Salim H.
Math & Physics Instructor
Geran, Patricia Vicari
Math Department Chairperson
Oneil, Gayle Lynn
Kindergarten Teacher
Singleton, Dorothy
Fifth Grade Teacher
Sommers, Beverly Meryl
Fourth Grade Teacher
Starkman, Phyllis
Spanish Teacher
RIDGEFIELD
Carlucci, Michael
Mathematics Teacher
Crusius, Theresa D'Arminio
English Teacher
Miller, Lilyan Zaccaria
English & Theatre Arts Teacher
Voorhis, Thomas Charles
Music Teacher
RIDGEFIELD PARK
Barber, Eileen Miller
Second Grade Teacher
Battaglia, Debra Garry
Mathematics Teacher
Boylan, Sheila
PE & Health Teacher
Curtis, Patricia Trevelise
Mathematics Supervisor
Dryer, William J.
Teacher & Administrative Asst
Ippolito, Joseph Anthony
History & Economics Teacher
Mc Donough, Theresa Candleoro
Fifth Grade Teacher
RIDGEWOOD
Johnson, Patricia Anne
Biology Teacher
Onorato, Robert Anthony
US History & Law Teacher
Staub, Michael J.
Mathematics Teacher
Yearing, Jeffrey Lee
PE Teacher & Coach
RINGOES
Hibbs, Jean
First Grade Teacher
RINGWOOD
Mc Namara, Catherine Virginia (Huddy)
Reading & Language Arts Tchr
Pohl, Doris Neill
Junior High Science Teacher
Spinavaria, JoAnne Marino
Eighth Grade Teacher
RIVER EDGE
Griek, Lynda Galoardi
Special Education Teacher
Mackintosh, Kathy Kesper
4th Grade Teacher
Wexler, Robin Gold
5th Grade Teacher
RIVERDALE
Pricone, Steven John
Science & Chemistry Teacher
RIVERSIDE
Gregory, John Edward
English Teacher
Maderia, Thomas Joseph, Sr.
Guidance Cnslr & Ftbl Coach
Peters, Denise Wright
English Teacher
Schuenemann, Carol A. (Nasife)
Art Teacher
Seaman, Mary C. (Menalis)
Lit & Social Studies Teacher
Vahey, Regina Grant
Teacher & Chairperson
Wright Peters, Denise
English Teacher
RIVERTON
Guidotti, Jennifer Lynne
Biology Teacher
Krastek, Robert A.
Soc Stud Dept Chair
Mogensen, Carol ONeil
6th Grade Teacher
OMalley, E. Eileen
High School Math Teacher
Steinfort, Faith Sanderson
Language Arts Teacher
Weidner, James H.
Educator & Publisher
ROBBINSVILLE
Manning, Jacqueline Jean
General & Vocal Music Teacher
ROCKAWAY
Arnheiter, Priscilla Rose Alaburda
AP Biology I & II Instructor
Carboy, Beverly
English Teacher
Clifford, Dayle Marchesani
High School AP Art Teacher
DiPoce, Doris Lee
Assistant Principal
Elbin, Gregory Blair
High School German Teacher
Knoll, Susan Marie
Psychology & History Teacher
Melon, Ruth Bernadette
English & Social Studies Tchr
Nixon, George E.
Math Teacher
Paddock, Sherri M.
Mathematics Teacher
Rudder, Marlene Judith
Chemistry Teacher
Russoniello, Pat
High School Math Teacher
ROEBLING
Borbi, Louis
Fifth Grade Teacher
ROSELAND
Smith, Jay Mac Arthur
Eng, Rdng & Soc Stud Tchr
ROSELLE
Carter, Renee L.
Computer & Reading Teacher
DeVestern, Harold
Fourth Grade Teacher
Grayson, Carole Hammer
Principal
Greco, Vita Gallicchio
Business Ed Dept Chairperson
Konawal, Norma Napoliello
Business Education Teacher
Lightcap, Patricia Tappe
Fourth Grade Teacher
Lobozzo, Diana Andreopoulos
Hlth Occupations Tchr & Coord
Ludwig, Mark Andrew
Special Education Teacher
Manno, Barbara Chepey
Second Grade Classroom Teacher
Mayner, Edith
Teacher of Gifted & Talented
Mc Laughlin, Brian
High School History Teacher
Riley, Carol Sawicki
English Teacher
Rung-Sliwiak, Meredith
Vocal Music Director
Smith, Michael Walter, Sr.
Physical Education & Hlth Tchr
Thompson, Linda Dunston
High School Principal
Ward, Karen Ann
Business Teacher
ROSELLE PARK
Smith, Alexander John
Teacher
ROSENHAYN
Darmstadter, Leo J., Jr.
Junior High Math Chairperson
Watts, Beverly E.
Computer Lab Teacher
RUMSON
Fallon, Daniel J.
History Teacher
Galante, Robert Frederick
Social Studies Instructor
Pettigano, Dawn-Marie
Music Director
Whitehead, Le Roy Guilbert, Jr.
Vice Principal
Willett, Carol Jean
3rd Grade Teacher
RUNNEMEDE
Benson, Thomas William
HS Social Studies Instructor
Connors, Carole Sulzer
Guidance Counselor
Constantino, Adele Marie
K-2nd Grade Teacher
Damico, John Patrick
Social Studies Teacher
Eastman, Elizabeth Campbell
Vocal Music Director
Gismonde, Pasquale F., Jr.
English Teacher
Scott, Nathan C.
Social Studies Dept Supervisor
Stephens, Brian D.
Science Teacher
RUTHERFORD
Cassidy, Catherine
History Teacher
Cassidy, Michael Owen
History Teacher
Cleary, Mary Elizabeth
Sixth Grade Teacher
Corbran, Eileen DeWan
6th Grade Reading & Math Tchr
Di Bonaventura, Ines Marie, OP
Asst Prin & HS Music Teacher
Gilbert, Tracy
Mathematics Teacher
Hagar, Teresa Lynn
English Teacher
Slezak, Sophie Lukowski
English & Reading Teacher
Volpone, Ronald Anthony
English Teacher
SADDLE BROOK
Alfieri, Theresa Meskis
Early Training Program Teacher
Cahayla, Gregory
HS Guidance Counselor
Filipek, Dorothy Steffens
Business Education Teacher
Fuchs, Richard Walter
Art Teacher
Luteran, Ida Cerullo
English Teacher
Sheridan, Michael J.
English Instructor
Sommer, Susan Wolf
8th Grade Amer His & Eng Tchr
Stauss, Carol Wohltman
Photography & Art Teacher
Yarosz, Barbara Emr
Chemistry Teacher
SADDLE RIVER
Frost, Carlton P.
8th Grade English Teacher
Hubler, Freda-Lee
English Department Chairperson
Moraski, Helena Hunt
Resource Center Teacher
Tebesceff, Sergio F.
Spanish Teacher
SALEM
Bowden, Manda Lee
Tchr of the Gifted & Talented
Cossaboon, Judith Renne
Health & PE Teacher
Costabile, James Nicholas
5th-8th Grade Teacher
Cummings, Mary Mc Gowan
Agriculture Teacher
Dare, Delise K.
7th & 8th Grade Math Teacher
Hanford, Allen Frederick
Industrial Arts Teacher
Hudock, Anne Lawrence
Mathematics Teacher & Dept Ch
Nelson, Joanne M.
Fourth Grade Teacher
Racer, Patricia Dougherty
Second Grade Teacher
SCOTCH PLAINS
Agnostak, Laura Munsie
First Grade Teacher
Bernstein, Laura
Athletic Trainer
Carolan, Maryann Carroll
High School English Teacher
Hooper, Douglas L.
Broadcast Journalism Tchr
Jennings, Julia Mc Cullough
Fifth Grade Teacher
Sargent, Laura Whiting
Mathematics Teacher
Zehnle, Bruce E.
Spanish Teacher
SEA GIRT
Basiak, Gerald Joseph
5th Grade Teacher
SECAUCUS
Arnhols, Marilyn A.
Mathematics Teacher
Bartletta, Frank X., Jr.
Guidance Counselor
Cali, Joan
Mathematics Teacher
Carlson, Donna
English Teacher
Costello, Frank T.
Director of Community Ed
DePice, Douglas Joseph
Art Teacher
Ertle, Deidre A.
High School Guidance Counselor
Farley, Maryann Claudio
Elementary Teacher
Fryczynski, Stan
4th-6th Grd Basic Skills Tchr
Fryscinski, Stan
Athletic Director & Coach
Germann, Michael
High School Math Teacher
McEnroe, Maryann
English as a Second Lang Tchr
Serino, Veronica Izbicki
High School English Teacher
Wilhelm, Linda Scalzo
Teacher of Gifted & Talented
SEWELL
Bailey, William A.
Professor of Law Enforcement
Barnshaw, Robert Gary
History Teacher
Bellace, Anita D.
English Teacher
Bouchard, Martin Alonzo
Communications Technology Tch
De Felice, Linda
Assoc Prof of Lib Media Svcs
Detofsky, Louis Bennett
Biology & Earth Science Tchr
Farnum, Audrey Keefe
Instructor of English
Feild, Beverley Seward
Fifth Grade Teacher
Francis, Margaret (Kirkbride)
Third Grade Teacher
Gainer, Jere Allen
Aerospace Science Instructor
Gajderowicz, Dee Mooney
Spanish Teacher
George, Ronald A.
Art Teacher
Hart, Robert Lee
Professor of English
Hayden, Daryl J.
Math Teacher
Lawler, Christopher
English Teacher
McFadden, Deborah Witt
Special Education Teacher
Melroy, Debra Petsko
Kindergarten Teacher
Meyer, Norma Weintraub
Music Teacher & Orch Director
Moncrief, Cathy Peterka
Spanish Teacher
Murtha, Carole Tremlett
Asst Professor of Nursing
Nelson, Judith Carvelli
Guidance Counselor
Osborne, Karen S.
HS Math Teacher
Peters, Margaret Louise
English Teacher
Shaw, Jay M.
7th Grade Math Teacher
Smith, Lynn Montgomery
Associate Professor of Math
Solem, Berminna White
Hum Dev & Spec Ed Assoc Prof

L (cont)
andra Lynn
natics Teacher
Kathy L.
natics Teacher
David Brian
Teacher
HILLS
, Sally
th Grd Math & Sci Tchr
enter, Josephine Meade
Fourth Grade Teacher
SBURY
Margaret Hemberger
Education Teacher
RVILLE
oshua Lee
r of Gftd & Tlntd Pgm
oanne
Grade Teacher
MAN
n, Sara Mathews
n Teacher
Frank J.
n Teacher
, Diane M. (Bublitz)
ss Technology Teacher
, William Joseph, Jr.
chool Science Teacher
Richard
n Teacher
, Barbara (Laurenzi)
th Teacher
, John T.
c Arts & Drafting Tchr
rand, Bernice Crawford
ade Teacher
DALE
nda Ann
ced Placement Bio Teacher
Elizabeth Jane (Blackburne)
Teacher
Emanuel J.
s Tchr & Dept Asst
SET
Anne Dolores
Grade French Teacher
Phyllis Grodin
ade Social Studies Tchr
ic, Betty L.
Teacher
atherine Cahill
n & Journalism Teacher
Kendra Chordas
Grade Teacher
Marilyn
matics Teacher
Christopher D.
& Space Sci Hnrs Tchr
elvin J.
ade Science Teacher
ger, Anton J.
Grade Teacher
n, Rose Ann Borichewski
pal
, Wilton H., Jr.
s Chemistry Teacher
heryl L. (Pugh)
nce Counselor
even A.
master & English Teacher
Charles Edward
acher
, Lora F.
School Math Teacher
Joseph D.
matics Teacher
inwe Iloabachie
h Teacher
age, William Frederich
gy & Chemistry Teacher
z, Sandra Dolores
sh Teacher
art, Robert Alan
onmental Science Teacher
Henry Ross
lus Teacher
Sandra Troy
ess Education Teacher
v, Catherine Schvetz
ce Teacher
RVILLE
ola, Albert Joseph
Grade Teacher
Ravi K.
ssor of Business Admin
v, Lance Edward
ematics Instructor
, Christine
Teacher
Lynne F. Murphy
ergarten Teacher
Ty Leonard
cs & Computer Teacher
, Judith Klein
rade Teacher
nna, Greer K.
sh Teacher
Cheryl Silletti
sh Teacher
y, Raymond Scott, Sr.
sh Teacher
ds, Sandra Laurie
h Instructor
J. Anthony
stant Professor
s, Brian Alan
essor & Prgm Coordinator
son, William
umental Band Director

Thornber, Nora S.
Assistant Prof of Math Dept
Wilk, Frances Cornely
HS Math Teacher
Wright, Luevina
Cnslr & Freshman Seminar Instr
Zliceski, Walter T.
Physical Education Instructor
SOUTH AMBOY
Donnelly, Joseph Francis
Assistant Principal
Freeman, Eve
Speech Language Pathologist
Henry, Frederick Andrew
US History Teacher
Kemmerer, Barbara Ann
Principal
Klein, Richard H.
English & History Teacher
LaVigne, Joy Tarallo
Third Grade Teacher
Malhame, Eugene G., Jr.
Asst Prin & Soc Studies Tchr
O'Connor, Carolynn Flohr
Science Teacher
Panigrosso, Diana Baumlin
Dept Chprsn & English Teacher
Rosato, Helena Rodrigues
French & Spanish Teacher
SOUTH BOUND BROOK
Barber, Carole J.
Second Grade Teacher
Carfora, Annmarie Mazzacco
First Grade Teacher
Gordon, Patricia Kuhlthau
7th-8th Grade English Teacher
SOUTH HACKENSACK
Maat, Carol Dorothy
Social Studies Teacher
Truncali, Constance Henchenski
Departmental Lang Arts Tchr
SOUTH ORANGE
Bivins-Hudson, Phyllis
Language Arts Teacher
Epstein, Sanford Mark
5th Grade Math & Science Tchr
Filippello, Lara L.
Bio & Human Physiology Tchr
Holmes, Paul A.
Asst Prof of Religious Studies
Huchital, Daniel H.
Chemistry Professor
Judd, Dorothy Corson
Second Grade Teacher
Rennie, Kathleen Donohue
Pub Relation & Advrtsng Prof
Ruscingno, Gerald
Faculty Associate
Russo, Phyllis Carol
Professor of Nursing
Ryan, Ann Marie Shipman
English Teacher
San Jose, Benilda M.
Science Teacher
Wiggins, Karla Ridley
Mathematics Teacher
SOUTH PLAINFIELD
Allen, Dolores Rothbard
Kindergarten Teacher
Dixon, Constance Rebecca (Valentine)
Fifth Grade Teacher
Evegan, Elizabeth Pepe
Retired First Grade Teacher
Fech, Ralph John
High School Math Teacher
Frederickson, Ellen Decker
5th Grade Teacher
Goode, Bobby Claude
Advanced Physics Teacher
Kielblock, Lenore Farley
Mathematics Teacher
LoConte, Michael Anthony
Industrial Technology Teacher
Massey, Patricia Farry
Librarian
Murray, Tracy Glenn
Choral Director
Novak, Steve
Government Teacher
Olvany, Tara Ann
Social Studies Teacher
Pastula, Gale P.
English Teacher
Saul, Robert W.
Science Dept Team Ldr & Instr
Sausville, Linda Hambacher
7th Grade Language Arts Tchr
Senkowsky, Lorraine Jean
Third Grade Teacher
Sicola, Pierina Capetola
French Teacher
Timko, Donna Zelehoski
English Teacher
SOUTH RIVER
Chiara, Janine Longstreet
Fourth Grade Teacher
Clays, Michele LaSala
Art Teacher
Hutchison, Janice Lund
English Teacher
Irish, Nancy Hatter
Ret Lang Arts & Lit Teacher
Koziatek, Walter
Athletic Dir & Graphics Instr
Nole, Ruth A.
Fifth Grade Teacher
Seadeek, Carolyn
8th Grade Mathematics Teacher

SOUTH TOMS RIVER
Rush, J. Michael
Building Principal
SPARTA
Ferrara, Lina Andree
French Teacher
Racioppi, Maureen M.
6th-8th Grade English Teacher
SPOTSWOOD
Feldman, Steven Jay
5th Grade Teacher
Pachman, Arleen Rosen
Fifth Grade Teacher
SPRING LAKE
Mac Kenthun, Carole, RSM.
Jr HS Lang Arts Teacher
Muhlenbruck, Richard O.
Science & History Teacher
Prew, Mary Rosalie, OP
Fourth Grade Teacher
Russell, Judith, OP
Sixth Grade Teacher
SPRINGFIELD
Anderson, Ottawana Saunders
Second Grade Teacher
Damato, Bernadette (Danilewicz)
4th Grd Tchr & Asst Principal
De Corte, Annette Acquaviva
Kindergarten Teacher
Einhorn, Sandy Manes
Teacher of Gifted & Talented
Ferrara, Leonard
High School Science Teacher
Metzger, Janice Komarek
Art Teacher
Shanahan, Mary Griffin
Chemistry & Physics Teacher
STANHOPE
Buser, Catherine Hering
Second Grade Teacher
Frank, Valerie Cerciello
Business Teacher
Klesh, David
8th Grade Science Teacher
Mullen, Sharon Griffin
Spanish Teacher
Nesnay, Elisa Sakosits
Fifth Grade Teacher
Potters, Jean Sheredos
English Teacher
Ruf, Mitchell Charles
English & Theater Arts Teacher
Scala, John Charles
Planetarium Director
Soccio, Mary Frances
Guidance Cnslr & Psych Teacher
STEWARTSVILLE
Jinks, Kathleen Casey
Language Arts Teacher
Jones, Colleen O'Brien
Fourth Grade Teacher
Nenow, William Edward
7th-8th Grade Science Teacher
STILLWATER
Carovillano, Linda Paladini
Fourth Grade Teacher
STIRLING
Lissner, Ellen Soprano
8th Grd Math & Computer Tchr
STRATFORD
Citino-Fusco, Sandra
English Teacher
Colangelo, Peter Joseph
Music Director
SUCCASUNNA
Buro, William Michael
6th Grade Eng & Soc Stud Tchr
Cooper, Doris Sue
Fifth Grade Teacher
Freimauer, Jacqueline Linda
English Teacher
Geyer, Elaine T.
Advanced Placement Bio Teacher
Guernerie, Frank Walter
Science Teacher
Hagan, Cheryl Lynn
Fourth Grade Teacher
Jegge, Thomas C.
Social Studies Teacher
Mc Guire, Charles Robert
7th Grade Social Studies Tchr
Michelson, Rosellen Berlin
French & Spanish Teacher
Nasto, Dolores Polyniak
Mathematics Teacher
Remick, Thomas B.
Industrial Arts & Tech Instr
Riley, Cheryl Leonard
Span & Frgn Lang Dept Ld Tchr
Robbins, Carol Coultas
Sixth Grade Teacher
Ruggiero, Renee Evelyn
Mathematics Teacher
Smith, Maureen Anne
Second Grade Teacher
Tinquist, Denise Harrington
English Teacher
Upton, Linda Pulido
Chemistry Teacher
Warnasch, Suzanne Weill
Eng as a Second Language Tchr
SUMMIT
Bilash, Borislaw Nicholas, II
Chem, Physics & Phys Sci Tchr
Bradley, Sallie Peace
Basic Skills Teacher
Dunne, Sheila A.
Health & PE Teacher
Fava, Steven Raymond
Asst Hdmstr, Eng & Math Tchr

Flesch, Frances
Social Studies Teacher
Hopkins, Stephen Edward
History Teacher
Horan, John Thomas
Social Studies Dept Chair
Knapp, Robert S.
English Teacher
Knecht, Kathy
Third Grade Teacher
Kostal, Carolyn Z.
Mathematics Teacher
Murray, Joyce Smythe
Fifth Grade Math & Sci Tchr
Neonakis, Irene Kivlen
French Teacher
Paster, Joan Hobbs
High School History Teacher
Rozan, Paula Markowitz
Mathematics Teacher
Schnedeker, John
Director of Guidance
Walker, Robert B.
Studio Art Teacher
SURF CITY
Pirie, Barbara Springman
Special Ed Tchr & Adj Instr
SUSSEX
Beaver, Barbara Lais
Jr HS Math & Science Teacher
Dolce, Richard G.
Language Arts Instructor
Dykshoorn, Elizabeth Joyce
5th Grade Teacher
Elder, Joan Westwood
Social Studies Teacher
Hassenplug, Mary P.
English Teacher
Henry, Christine Decker
Social Studies Teacher
Konzelman, Harold
English Supervisor
Kooima, Sebert E.
Admin, History & Religion Tchr
Monat, Steven M.
Mathematics Teacher
Piereth, Mary
English Teacher
Ryan, Thomas
Social Studies Teacher
Terwilliger, Allen Ward
5th Grade Team Teacher
Toedtmann, Lore Susan
German Teacher
Zieger, Judith Gay
First Grade Teacher
SWEDESBORO
Gaglione, Rosemary S.
Social Studies Teacher
Tighe, Pauline Martha
5th Grade Teacher
Tunnat, Linda Davis
English Teacher
TEANECK
Benevento, Eva Schuck
Fifth Grade Teacher
Bogan, Leonard
English Teacher
Brown, David Lauren
Instrumental Music Teacher
Dowd, Janice Lee
ESL & Foreign Lang Tchr
Fried, Harvey S.
English Teacher
Gallo, Patrick Joseph
11th-12th Grd Amer His Tchr
Goldstein, Carol Roberta
English Teacher
Green, Sheree Slifman
Business Teacher
Hali, Henry Hiama
Science Teacher
Hankle, Robert Glenn
Band Director
Hanna, John E.
Mathematics & Computer Teacher
Heck, Dennis Michael
Physical Education Teacher
Lacey, Theodora Smiley
Eighth Grade Science Teacher
Otis, Carol D. Falleni
Family & Consumer Sci Teacher
Ottochian, Frank John
Visual Art Teacher
Sosland, David N.
Secondary English Teacher
Suppelsa, Suzanne Marie
Biology Teacher
Twombly, Alice Jacobs
AP & Honors English Teacher
Walker, Lucy Doris
Dance Teacher
Warren, Maredia D. Lewis
Vocal Music Director
White, Joseph O.
Principal
Wolff, Lawrence Alan
Psychology Teacher
TENAFLY
Danis, Dione L.
English Teacher
Strife, David
Biology Teacher
THREE BRIDGES
Munk, Janet T. Klimchak
Third Grade Teacher
Trimmer, Mary Jane
Fourth Grade Teacher

TINTON FALLS
Caldwell, Peter R.
Social Studies Teacher
Calvert, James Allen
Art & Special Ed Teacher
Gabriel, Carol A.
Home Economics Teacher
Lenk, Thomas Frederick
Mathematics Supervisor
Liebenberg, Robin Brown
English Teacher
Schneider, Cecelia Ann (Petrzilka)
Mathematics Teacher
TOMS RIVER
Acevedo, Gus A.
Spanish Teacher
Albrecht, Marjorie Green
Spanish Teacher
Altizio, Mauro
Social Studies Teacher
Bischoff, Bonnie Philo
Adjunct Instructor of English
Brackett, Kristine Kosenski
Health, Phys Educator & Coach
Bradley, Marcia Daley
Associate Professor of Science
Burke, Jorene F.
Learning Disability Specialist
Ciani, Thomas Frederic
History Instructor
Coyle, Marilyn Alice
Math Dept Coord & Teacher
Culpepper, Judith A.
Fifth Grade Teacher
Currie, Walter Erich
Math Teacher
D'Esposito, Rita A.
Fifth Grade Teacher
Ferrara, Kathleen Lindsay
Sixth Grade Science Teacher
Fitzgerald, Suzanne DeLuca
Second Grade Teacher
Fox, Raymond Peter
High School Mathematics Instr
Gonzalez, Johanna Puma
English Teacher
Goss, StacyAnn
Mathematics Teacher
Griffiths, Robert Michael
History Teacher
Harker, Kenneth H.
Computer Graphics Teacher
Herkert, Michelle Stueber
Chemistry Teacher
Hibbard, Susan Clayton
Biology Teacher
Holmquist, Donald W.
Advanced Placement Bio Teacher
Hosler, Gail E.
9th-12th Grd Bus & Tech Tchr
Husth, Geraldine Weiss
Mathematics Teacher
Isaacson, Elaine Schulman
String Instrumental Music Tchr
Jordan, Michael William
Mathematics Teacher
Kiel, Alice
English Teacher
Koehler, Barbara Jean
Teacher of Gifted & Talented
Kushner, Michael
Economics Prof
Laurie, Judith Ann
Professor of Spanish
Maccaroni, Gary
Curriculum Coord & Rel Teacher
Mackle, Elizabeth
Mathematics Teacher
Maguire, James P.
Guidance Counselor
Mc Cue, Lois Wilmott
Second Grade Teacher
Mitchell, John C.
Sixth Grade Teacher
Monti, Joseph Frank
History Teacher
Mulrane, Donna Abbato
5th Grade & Basic Skills Tchr
Mulvaney, Donna Moran
English Teacher
Opdyke, Kristen Marie
Biology Teacher
Orkfitz, Janet Elaine
K-6th Grade Vocal Music Tchr
Papetti, Linda Lopez
Fourth Grade Teacher
Peterson, Ellen F.
4th Grade Teacher
Petruski, Robert M.
Peer Education Coordinator
Quinlan, Cheryll Gudgeon
Instruction Supervisor
Quinn, Susan
English & Drama Teacher
Rankin, Neil F.
Fifth Grade Teacher
Rice, John M.
Sixth Grade Teacher
Riviere, Rosemary
3rd Grade Teacher
Robertson, Andrew John
8th Grade Soc Stud Teacher
Roselli, Elise S.
Resource Center Teacher
Roth, Robert Charles
Economics & American His Tchr
Rush-Sloan, Cheryl Lee
Biology Teacher
Santomauro, Lizabeth Mary (Toth)
9th Grd Earth Science Teacher

TOMS RIVER (cont)
Schwartz, Deborah Ann (Dietrich)
Physical Education Teacher
Senger, George J., Jr.
8th Grade Social Studies Tchr
Sermarini, Lynne T.
6th Grade Teacher
Singer, Kathleen Marie
English & Reading Tchr
Skurka, Kathleen Marie
Spanish Teacher
Taylor, Gladys Cooley
9th Grade History Teacher
Tormey-Miller, Jill D.
First Grade Teacher
Vanellis, John B., Jr.
Biology Teacher
Vescovi, James C.
Architecture & Design Teacher
TRANQUILITY
Abbott, Lori Adams
Business Teacher
Fisher, Robin DuBosque
Third & Fourth Grade Teacher
Fisher, Timothy Hyland
5th-8th Grade Teacher
TRENTON
Albright, Marjory Helfrey
Fourth Grade Teacher
Alfare, Carlo
Chemistry Professor & Coord
Alves, Carlos Serra
Mathematics Professor
Balestrieri, Gaytana Pino
Science Teacher
Banks Campbell, L. Diane
Asst Prof of Psychology
Bedard, Mary Mc Laughlin
Facilitating Teacher
Benson, Hope M. (Lajeunesse)
Chemistry Teacher
Bernoski, Daniel M.
Spanish Teacher
Boyer, Angie DiGiorgio
Fourth Grade Teacher
Buttich, Frank
World History Teacher
Capone, Peter Charles
PE, Hlth & Drivers Ed Tchr
Chalifour, Linda Polinsky
English Teacher
Charlesworth, Christine
German Teacher
Citron, Merle
12th Grade English Teacher
Coyne, Gary
Art Teacher
DAngelo, William Nicholas
English Dept Chair
De Jesus, Christopher
Bilingual Mathematics Teacher
Dempster, David Allan
Amer Govt & Economics Teacher
Everitt, Mary Ellen Kraus
Kindergarten Teacher
Faraglia, Kathleen A.
English Teacher & Librarian
Fouse, Gail Dickerson
Fourth Grade Teacher
Fysz, Joseph John
Mathematics Teacher
Gater, Jean Szymborski
Teacher
Giberson, M. Linda Morse
Business Teacher
Gilbert, Neil Robert
Biology & Marine Biology Tchr
Greb, E. Barry B.
Mathematics Teacher
Greene, Earline Evans
First & Second Grade Teacher
Hilker, Diane Nurko
Assistant Professor of Biology
Holmes, Sammie L.
Social Studies Teacher
Indrikovic, Marina Votta
Dance Coordinator
Innocenzi, David Richard
History Teacher
Innocenzi, Kathleen Wszolek
Social Studies & Psych Tchr
Kish, Christine Martin
Mathematics Teacher
Kramer, Margaret Kane
Third Grade Teacher
Langdon, William H.
Social Studies Teacher
Leonard, Florence Courtney
Assistant Principal
Lowe, Marta Nestor
Resource Center Teacher
Maack, Nancy (Pape)
French Teacher
Maguire, Kathleen Theresa
Assistant Pastor
Martin, Douglas Peter
Social Studies Teacher
May, Joanne
Resource Room Teacher
Minelli, Regina Pursell
Third Grade Teacher
Murphy, Tyler L.
Science Teacher
Musselman, Suzanne
Mathematics Dept Chairperson
Muzyk, Barbara R.
Sci, Chem Tchr & Dept Chprsn
Myers, Christy Kathleen
First Grade Teacher
Nagy, Robert Stephen
History Teacher
Parris, David Christian
Curator of Natural History
Perkins, Tyrone Alonzo
Bible Tchr & Dean of Students
Quinton, Alfred P.
Marketing Professor
Ray, James Elliott, Jr.
High School Mathematics Tchr
Reed, Theresa Skrip
English Teacher
Repko, Susan Marie
Social Studies Teacher
Rhoads, Suzanne Henderson
Fourth Grade Teacher
Robotin, Barbara Zielinski
Manager
Rowley, Dennis
English Teacher
Schmitt, Dorothy Ann
Resource Room Teacher
Silver, Edith Tickner
Professor of Mathematics
Steinmetz, Donna Hubsch
Counselor
Thompson, Robert Luther
History Mentor
Van Hise, Patricia Pingitore
Math Dept Chairperson
Walker, Barbara J.
Teacher of GATE
Walker, Phil Karl
Math Teacher & Coach
Watro, Marsha Aleksa
7th Grade History Teacher
Webber, Nathan
Social Studies Teacher
Weiner, Fred
Counseling Professor
Whalen, Elizabeth Walsh
Art Teacher
Wilder-Wokoun, Constance
HS English Teacher
TUCKAHOE
Darcy, Janet Lutz
Social Studies Teacher
Skiscim, Stephen J.
Instrumental Music Teacher
TUCKERTON
Boone, Marie Taylor
8th Grade Social Studies Tchr
Bruno, William John
Social Studies Teacher
Deyo, Stephen Allen
Sixth Grade Teacher
Lee, Alan
Social Studies Supervisor
Lee, Diane Donahue
English Teacher
Moore, Marsha J.
Home Economics Teacher
Neuroth, Joan Ferrigno
Sixth Grade Teacher
Olbrys, Donna Maria
Spanish Teacher
Penn, Carlton A.
Supvr of Media Services
Senko, William
High School & Jr HS Teacher
Wallace, Audrey Schroeck
Kindergarten Teacher
UNION
Arminio, David A.
English Teacher
Baugh, Verneda Hamm
Asst Prof of Psychology
Beach, Kathleen Segale
Mathematics Teacher
Blum, Linda Steiner
Third Grade Teacher
Cortese, Richard Philip
Social Studies Teacher
DeLaurier, Doreen Giacona
Third Grade Teacher
Disporto, Emanuel J.
Middle School Teacher
Dominic, Ann
Teacher
Glowacki, Doris Hentrich
German Teacher
Greenspan, Wendy Jill
Elementary Resource Cntr Tchr
Gross, George Ross
Chemistry Teacher
Harwin, Marie L. Jablonski
Art Teacher
Hughes, Peggy Riley
English Teacher
Jochnowitz, Johann Michael
Prof of Fine Arts
Keimach, Brad M.
Instr of His, Western Culture
Kilberg, Esta Lazarus
4th Grd Teacher
Lorenzo, Susan M.
Health & Physical Ed Teacher
Mango, Michael, Jr.
Spanish Teacher
Ndoma-Ogar, Peter Odok
Professor
Ornovitz, Irene M.
Biology Teacher
Pagano, Joan Romano
Fourth Grade Teacher
Rever, Ellen Hammer
English as a Second Lang Tchr
Rosania, Theresa Marie
Assoc Professor of Marketing
Schmitt, Karen Ellen
10th Grade English Teacher
Signorella, Mickey
5th Grade Teacher
Teufel, Jean Douglas
Retired Fourth Grade Teacher
Williams, David Michael
History Teacher
Zeh, Evelyn Fischer
Retired Third Grade Teacher
UNION BEACH
Dunham, Susan Sandra
Fifth Grade Teacher
Grabowski, Carole Frantz
2nd Grade Teacher
Toohey, Matthew Joseph
6th Grade Teacher
UNION CITY
Aprile, Henrietta V., MPF
Eighth Grade Teacher
Colaneri, Agnes
9th Grd English Teacher
Conti, Alexandria Rodriguez
ESL Head Teacher
de la Puente, Maria
8th Grd Bilingual Teacher
Enriquez, Leon Lazaro
Science Teacher
Franco, Mary Ann Ciardi
Nursery School Teacher
Lovrich-Gil, Patricia
ESL Teacher
Makar, Nadia Eissa
College Industry Liaison
Marecki, Loretta Joan
Accounting & Computer Teacher
Mayo, Angela Rodriguez
Math Tchr
Molinari, Linda Violone
4th Grade Teacher
Neye, Lucille Lorena
Social Studies Teacher
Quinto, Johanna Eleanor
Pre-School Teacher
Russo, Josephine R.
Art Teacher
Sullivan, Kathleen
Vice Prin & Jr HS Math Teacher
Zaccagna, Marjorie Censullo
English Teacher
VAUXHALL
Lynn, Billy R.
Dramatic Productions Promoter
VERNON
Accavallo, Anthony F., III
HS Guidance Counselor
Arnold, Felicia Atria
Third Grade Teacher
Batchelor, Irene Rumpf
Math Dept Coord & Teacher
Beaver, Barrie C.
Teacher
Boltz, Frances Spell
6th Grd Language Arts Teacher
Bricklin, Lois
English Teacher
Cafarelli, Mary Elizabeth
Teacher of the Handicapped
Cannavale, Michael Anthony
English Instructor
Cassidy, Terry Lawrence
High School Math Teacher
Castellana, Douglas Frank
Indstrl Ed, Tech Tchr & Coord
Coughlan, Barbara Ann Jung
German Teacher
Doran, Nancy Fontana
Basic Skills Lang Arts Tchr
Gantz, Ann Harding
Science Teacher
Gastadello, Stefanie
Guidance Counselor
Hoffmann, Kathryn Vincent
5th Grade Teacher
Kuzicki, Paula Schillaci
8th Grade Language Arts Tchr
Lightcap, George Allen, Jr.
English Teacher
Maggio, Joseph Paul
Mathematics Teacher
Malinowski, Jean L.
Math Teacher
Martin, Arlene Patricia (Lucas)
Home Economics Teacher
Mc Kay, Charles O.
High School English Teacher
Stracquatanio, Vincent
Physics Teacher
Walsh, James Michael
English Coordinator
Ziegler, Dana Robert
4th Grade Teacher, Coordinator
VERONA
Abramson, Janet
1st Grd Tchr & Lang Art Coord
Kadet, Geraldine
Retired Primary Teacher
Luks, Kenneth Robert
Secondary School English Tchr
Meares, Lorraine Poliseo
Mathematics & Computer Teacher
Nadler, Sheila Orlinsky
English Teacher
Tomeo, Claire A.
8th Grade Teacher & Advisor
VINCENTOWN
Jenkins, Ronald Lee
Geography & History Teacher
Lynd, Ann Frances
Basic Skill Reading & Art Tchr
Wolf, Janet Katherine
Teacher of Gifted Students
VINELAND
Agostini, Joyce
History & Humanities Teacher
Amadei, Lillian Lloyd
6th-8th Grade English Teacher
Baldissero, Kathleen S.
Art Teacher
Brooks, Carmi M.
Accounting & Business Teacher
Burke, Dorothy R.
High School English Teacher
Callinan, Chris
Mathematics & Physics Teacher
Dagostino, Peggy Smith
Basic Skills Teacher
Dorofee, Mary Anne
Mathematics Instructor
Dutta, Lorraine
Art Teacher
Fagan, Lisa Keim
11th & 12th Grade Science Tchr
Fay, Mary Herlihy
Director & Professor
Feinstein, Judith S.
9th Grd World His & Geog Tchr
Gardenhire, Marilyn Atlee
Nursing Professor
Gartner, Gad
Guidance Counselor
Gordillo, Hilda
English Teacher
Grussenmeyer, Mark Leo
Mathematics Teacher
Hodge-Banner, Lilliam
Counselor of Stu Support Svcs
Johnson, Katherine May
Special Education Teacher
Kapple, Nancy A.
Sixth Grade Teacher
Kaspar, Elizabeth Weathers
Fourth Grade Teacher
Lafferty, Drusilla Kerr
Social Studies & English Tchr
Lamade, Margaret Sylvia
First Grade Teacher
Langley, Carmella Mary
Psychology Teacher
Miller, Dennis Eugene
6th Grade Teacher
Monahan, Tammy Sue
Math Teacher
Mulligan, Maxine Rogers
Ninth Grade English Teacher
Napier, Kevin John
Social Studies Teacher
Oria, Maria Cristina (Gonzalez)
Third Grade Bilingual Teacher
Parks, Carol (Davenport)
Mathematics Department Chprsn
Pasquale, Charlotte Mc Dade
Resource Teacher
Ragone, Paul
PE & Health Teacher
Rhone, Darlene Banks
Biology & Anatomy Teacher
Rib, Patricia Lynn (Schenck)
IPS, Physical Science Tchr
Schneider, Christine (Ottinger)
English Teacher
Sheftall, Barbara J.
English Teacher
Smith, Patricia Ann
Science Teacher
Taylor, Laura Gassler
Fourth Grade Teacher
Touchstone, Donna Albrecht
Guidance Counselor
Volpe, Vicki Johnson
Chem Tchr & Science Dept Chm
Vorndran, David N.
Mathematics Teacher
Weintraub, Henry
Soc Stud Tchr & Dept Chprsn
Williams, Diane DeTullio
8th Grade Social Science Tchr
VOORHEES
Allen, Susan M.
Spanish Teacher
Barberio, Deborah Lynn
Math Teacher
Batchelor, Jon David
Math Teacher
Bauer, Barbara Ann (Coluzzi)
Fifth Grade Teacher
Bell, Carol Kellner
Fifth Grade Teacher
Bolden, Pamela L.
Vice Principal
Burt, Dennis Michael
History Teacher
Cser, Audry J.
Marketing Ed Teacher & Coord
DeFeo, Peter John
Mathematics Teacher
Donato, Donna Volpe
World History Teacher
Englesbe, Marilyn Marston
Classroom Teacher
Fuller, Louis Joseph
A P History & Economics Tchr
Garwood, James A.
English Teacher
Howard, Lillian D. Wheeler
Reading Specialist
Karsner, Nancy Jane
Enrichment Teacher
Koch, Barbara Borge
High School English Teacher
Musser, Robert M., II
Instrumental Music Teacher
Pointer, Linda Marie
English Teacher
Rickansrud, Kirk Martin
Social Science Teacher
Shull, Laurel A.
Reading & English Teacher
Siderio, Vincent Joseph
English Teacher
Snyder, Nancy Ann Olewinski
Spanish Teacher
Spice, Pamela Ann (Mitchell)
Eng & Creative Writing Tchr
Spittal, Dan Scott
Ftbl Coach & Weight Trng Instr
WALDWICK
Blauvelt, Mary E.
Science Teacher
DiPetrillo, Diane C.
Science Teacher
Heidloff, Frederick C.
K-6th Grade Art Teacher
Murray, Edward Joseph
English Teacher
Perkins, Christine Marie
Social Studies Teacher
Pumphrey, Eugene R.
Math & Computer Science Tchr
Reynolds, Richard R.
Chemistry Teacher
WALL
Banik, Alexis R.
8th Grade Language Arts Tchr
Bast, James Richard
Music Teacher
Jewusiak, John A.
Physical Science Teacher
Nardino, Anthony Gary
Latin & Bus Education Teacher
Scelfo, Tonia Profita
Guidance Counselor
WALLINGTON
Hnat, Joseph Michael, Jr.
Social Studies Teacher
Jordan, Steve
Resource Center Teacher
Kicinski, Gary
Math Instructor & Ath Dir
Mc Andrews, Sue Swier
Business Education Teacher
Rendzio, Emil J.
Physical Education Teacher
Tkacz, Joyce (Kolodziej)
Retired Mathematics Teacher
WANAQUE
Chevenak, Kathleen Helen
AP Biology Teacher
Di Mezza, Linda Susan
8th Grd Language Arts Teacher
Duin, Pamela
English & Social Studies Tchr
Gratale, Rocco Joseph
High School English Teacher
Hartley, Stephanie
First Grade Teacher
Kohmuench, Mary Theoharis
Computer Multimedia Teacher
Konechy, Joan
Spanish Teacher
Milos, Fred L.
Latin & French Teacher
Monica, Fredric
Guidance Counselor & Coach
Ollo, Michael Anthony
Social Studies Teacher
Rommel, Patricia Cari
Spanish & French Teacher
WARREN
Bagan, Betty Ann Boulden
First Grade Teacher
Battiato, Joseph Anthony
English Tchr & AP Coord
Benn, Gale Mauriello
French Teacher
Cebula, Mary Lou Theresa
Dean of Students
Chiselko, Bernadette Panza
Math Teacher
Filoramo, J. Robert
English Teacher
Gatens, Patricia Post
Art Teacher
Gillen, Michael Eugene
Mathematics Teacher
Halpern, Janet Simon
7th Grd Language Arts Teacher
Holmes, William H.
Choral Director
Hosp, J. Russell
Science Teacher
Muoio, Dominic
Italian Teacher
Ruff, Patricia K.
Chemistry Teacher
Schmeisser, William Richard
Social Studies Teacher
Utne, Priscilla Miller
Retired First Grade Teacher
WASHINGTON
Bowen, Alfred Richard
CIE Coordinator
Della Penta, Patricia Cipuzak
Assistant Professor of Science
Fallen, James Craig
Fifth Grade Teacher
Frank, Ann Patricia
English & Math Instructor
Kimmer, Beatrice Ayres
German Teacher

NGTON (cont)
, Christina Susan Chekan
chool English Teacher
Linda Opdyke
ade Teacher
-Jane Gerhard
ute Teacher
avid Carroll
ny & Physiology Teacher
UNG
Donna Smith
acher & Dept Chairperson
Joanne
Teacher
aren L.
n & Religion Teacher
Margaret
s Teacher
Barbara J. Bielefeld
hairwomen & Teacher
, Marlene Mazzetta
hr of Gifted & Talented
, Walter M.
eacher
arolyn
chool English Teacher
Mary Jo
on Dept Chprsn & Teacher
an, Kathryn Ann (Radke)
n Teacher
FORD
Sharon Leib
ter Literacy Teacher

therine Buda
Grade English Teacher
Tobias Joseph
str & Head Ath Trainer
Eugene Charles
of of Voice & Speech
Audrey Maria Picone
Science Teacher
-hsing S.
sor of Computer Science
William J.
Studies Teacher
nes, Danielle
ate Professor of Biology
Gerard Joseph
Studies Teacher
Oresta Mary
e Teacher
Suzanne
Prfrmng Arts Dept Chair
Tracey Lynn
a Teacher
, Wilford
nce Counselor
Roberta Gene
matics Teacher
James
sor of English
Suzanne Law
f Community Health Dept
-Wen
uter Science Dept Chprsn
Daniel
ophy Prof & Dept Chm
, Walter Edward
udies Chairperson & Tchr
one, Judith Pierce
gical Sciences Teacher
Marcelo
ssor of Math
g, James Michael
Prof Exercise Physiology
John Grouard
Prof of Pol Sci
a, Anthony John
ssor of English
cott, Virginia Ramey
ssor of English
Eleanor Costello
Studies Teacher
, Gilbert
uter Science Professor
or, John M.
ssor of Philosophy
Gloria Beers
2th Grd Math Teacher
, Matthew John
mental Music Director
I, James Anthony
Studies Teacher
acques Anthony
iate Prof of His & Hum
Robert Philip
l Studies Teacher
Christine Richer
sh Teacher
Taghi
omics Professor
, Eleanor Cooney
nct Prof Finance & Math
er, Harriett Scerbak
ed Business Teacher
agel, Robert A.
sh Teacher
ky, Doris Hanssen
ed Teacher
Carl Anton
nct Professor of History
Beverly J.
eacher
tten, Joseph P.
Professor of Fine Art
re, Bernadette
ematics Dept Chprsn & Tchr
Lois Weiser
ical Science Professor

Zellner, Jack Karl
Eighth Grd Social Studies Tchr
WEEHAWKEN
DeNicola, Anne Calate
Social Studies Teacher
Mancuso, Ann Kicey
Retired Teacher
WEST BERLIN
Szabo, Carol Ann
Second Grade Teacher
WEST CALDWELL
Kapner, W. Marvin
Retired History Teacher
WEST LONG BRANCH
Bass, Mary Lee Attarian
Director of the Reading Center
Da Silva, Mimi
Adjunct Instructor of Psych
Fell, Gilbert Samuel
Professor of Philosophy
Hershkowitz, Robert Philip
Biology Instructor
Holmes, Robyn Michele
Psychology Professor
Mahajan, Y. Lal
Assoc Prof of Econ & Fin
Miller, Edward John
Science & Mathematics Teacher
Morano, John David
Professor of Journalism
Nersesian, Roy L.
Associate Prof of Management
Nye, Judith L.
Psychology Professor
Portuondo, Alicia E.
Span Prof, Frgn Lang Dpt Coord
Rich, Everett
Assoc Prof of Communication
Sarsar, Saliba
Associate Professor of Pol Sci
Simonelli, Pasquale J.
History Professor
Smith, William David
Education Professor
Voitko, Stephen Andrew
Lecturer
Williams, Nancy Welch
Drivers & Physical Ed Tchr
WEST MILFORD
Bravante, Lorraine Pfizenmayer
Sixth Grade Teacher
Cooke, Ralph Charles
Comm, Eng & TV Production Tchr
Donegan, Mary Gibson
English Teacher
Hyland, Thomas
Math Teacher
Liapes, Peter Charles
HS History Teacher
Mc Dermott, Kathleen
US History Teacher
Mc Niff, Rosemary Linden
English & Media Arts Teacher
Sheremeta, Gregory
History, Law & Economics Tchr
Stehle, Norma Calderon
Gifted & Talented Teacher
WEST NEW YORK
Bernal, Mercedes
ESL Head Teacher
Brown, Dennis Michael
7th Grade Teacher
Cinque, Joseph John
Biology Teacher
Cinque, Mary Ann Del Duca
Sci Dept Supervisor
Goldman-Brodie, Erica Simone
Third Grade Teacher
Gologorsky, Edythe E.
Second Grade Teacher
Grabowski, Susan McDermott
Secondary Math Teacher
Hempel, Steven Paul
Science Teacher
Iacovelli, Raymond Joseph
English Teacher
Marchesani, Louis F.
Science Tchr & Asst Ath Dir
Mc Donough, JoAnn M.
Teacher of Gifted & Talented
Olivero, Ron
7th & 8th Grd Soc Studies Tchr
Passenti, Robert John
Music Department Coordinator
Rainone, Robert Paul
7th & 8th Grade Science Tchr
Rome, Glenn Owen
7th & 8th Grd Reading Teacher
Rotella, Marty John
Seventh Grade Teacher
Sosa, Albert Anthony
Career & Vocational Guid Cnslr
Tavano, Lourdes Viviana
HS ESL Teacher
Valdes, Mary H.
Eighth Grade Bilingual Teacher
Wengerter, John Michael
Physical Education Teacher
Wurzel, Belquis
Second Grade Teacher
WEST ORANGE
Barta, Nancy Laub
First Grade Teacher
Boland, Joseph Thomas
10th-12th Grd Math Teacher
Clissold, John Richardson, II
HS Chem, Bio & Physics Tchr
David, Gerald Alvin
English Teacher

Dellanno, Ralph Anthony
Dean of Men
Dodds, Deborah Joyce
HS History Teacher
Greene, Norma Herman
6th Grade Math Teacher
Hausler, J. William
High School Language Arts Tchr
Kalemba, Joyce Ann Passante
Spanish Teacher
Lawrence, Michael John
Physics Teacher
Lemaldi, Jo Ann R.
5th Grade Teacher
Lupica, Anthony
Italian Teacher
Middleton, Robert Carey
Chemistry Teacher
Mora, Robert T.
AP Biology Instructor
O'Connor, Carolyn Woods
Rdng Specialist & US His Tchr
ONeill, Christine P.
Eighth Grade Math Teacher
Piegaro, Kathleen Brannigan
Mathematics Teacher
Warnick, Susan Farrell
Kindergarten Teacher
WEST PATERSON
Hunt, Irene Walmsley
Tchr of Gifted & Talented
Ritt, Sharon Shatsky
Chairperson Information Tech
St John, Catherine
Instr of Studio Arts & Hum
WEST TRENTON
Bender, Rose Marie
7th-12th Grade History Teacher
WESTFIELD
Coe, Helen M.
Math Teacher
Dix, Kathleen M.
Mathematics Teacher
Gange, Richard Edward
Science Teacher
Hornish, Donald Thomas, Jr.
Social Studies Teacher
Kapner, George H.
Mathematics Teacher
Mathews, William Robert
Choral Director
Mazzarese, Maureen Ann
Health Educator
Miller, Karen Walsh
Special Education Teacher
Muller, Elizabeth Coreill
High School English Teacher
Nolde, Frank E.
Social Studies Teacher
Pastir, Linda Ruff
Biology Teacher
Schmidt, Maria E.
Social Studies Teacher
Seiler, Michael
Science Teacher
Torre, Marianne Buberl
German & Mathematics Teacher
WESTMONT
Lewis, Brian Salvatore
French Teacher
WESTVILLE
Munning, Mary Anne
Second Grade Teacher
Tartaglione, Nancy V.
Basic Skills Teacher
WESTWOOD
Barbour-Panico, Betsy
English Teacher
Clancy, Thomas Gerald
Business Education Teacher
Connelly, Angela Marie
Third Grade Teacher
Falk, Stephen
English Teacher
Foley, Kathleen Neilson
Chemistry Teacher
Grotto, Douglas
8th Grade Music Teacher
Guardino, Carol-Jane Piltz
Eng & Creative Writing Tchr
Hahn, Nicholas T.
English Teacher
Hanson-Harding, Brian
English & Journalism Teacher
Margolis, Judith Marcus
Guidance Counselor
McGuire, James William
Social Studies Teacher
Nicolaysen, Lucile Martinez
Spanish Teacher
Niutta, Maria Soluri
Mathematics Teacher
Pilarcek, Barbara A.
Spanish Teacher
Radoslovich, Susan Mary
Math & Computer Teacher
Romano, Ronald
World History & Cultures Tchr
Rudin, Sherwood
Teacher
Schneberger, William
Fine Arts & Art History Tchr
Wren, Mary Plummer
Math Teacher
WHARTON
Altman, Jan
Third Grade Teacher
Bocchino, Alan John
6th Grade Science Teacher

WHIPPANY
Altenderfer, Stephen H.
Science Tchr & Dept Coord
Hogan, Judith Ann
Business Education Teacher
WHITE HOUSE STATION
Johnson, Susan Ann
Second Grade Teacher
Schiff, Debra Gardner
Unified Mathematics Teacher
WHITING
Coyle, Nancy Tomasso
7th Grade Teacher
WILDWOOD
Raker, Jill O'Hara
Teacher of Gifted & Talented
WILLIAMSTOWN
Bey, Patricia A.
English, Lang Arts & Math Tchr
Brewer, Mark Richard
7th-8th Grd Soc Stud Teacher
Grant, Glenn
History Teacher
Mc Cleary, Cheryl Marie
Second Grade Teacher
Mericle, Dana R. (Friess)
Sixth Grade Teacher
Parham, Betsey L.
Fourth Grade Teacher
Straub, Donna Jean
Science Teacher
Vogelsong, Norma Munoz
Spanish Teacher
WILLINGBORO
Anderson, Rainy
Creative Thinking Teacher
Closson, Chester Robert, Jr.
World His & Geog Teacher
Eppolite, Annette Varsaci
Latin & English Teacher
Garant, Joseph A.
United States History Teacher
Hopkins, Byron J.
Mathematics Teacher
Latini, Gloria Deanna
Spanish Tchr & Japanese Fac
Lubeck, Anne Lindenbaum
Third Grade Teacher
Mc Carthy-Pascuzzo, Loretta Marie
Math, History Teacher & Coach
Pitzer, Joanne E.
First Grade Teacher
Taylor, Daryl L.
Physics Teacher
WINFIELD PARK
Groeller, Mary Damiano
Fifth Grade Teacher
WOOD RIDGE
Pruden, Bernadette Joann
English Teacher
WOODBRIDGE
Adamcewicz, Gina Marie D'Allessio
8th Grade Homeroom Teacher
Almonte, Nereida Ramos
Spanish Teacher
Brunello, Laura A.
Art Teacher
Bruno, Rose Marie
Second Grade Teacher
Ciuffreda, Lillian Christine
Teacher of Gifted & Talented
Dlugos, Joanna J.
6th Grade Teacher
Drogan, Lisa Mokatello
Vocal Music Teacher
Fisco, Mary Susan
Biology & Chemistry Teacher
Fredericks, Douglas L.
Calculus Teacher
Grasso, Norma Arnesen
Physical Education Teacher
Halas, Linda Holcomb
Fourth Grade Teacher
Horvath, Joyanne Hodges
Guidance Counselor
Kowalski, Robert Joseph
English & History Teacher
Kowalsky, Geraldine Rinaldo
9th-12th Grade English Teacher
Kuenne, Linda Haasis
Elementary Helping Teacher
Mc Guire, William James
Social Studies Teacher
Peitz, Timothy Charles
Chemistry Teacher
Pernini, Glenn V.
Science Staff Leader & Teacher
Petersen, Laurel Spina
Tchr of the Gifted & Talented
Samich, Jacqueline Catalano
French Teacher
Stankewicz, Mary Christine
Seventh Grade Geography Tchr
Trent, Edward
Earth Science Teacher
Yackinous, Frank Robert
9th-12th Grd Math Teacher
WOODBURY
DuBeau, Dolores Magazu
Fifth Grade Teacher
Klein, Jeffrey Allen
Social Studies Department Chm
Riley, Virginia Keyler
6th Grade Teacher
Sabo, Mary Rak
French Teacher
Trabosh, Carolyn Cella
High School Art Teacher

WOODBURY HEIGHTS
Christ, Robert B.
English Teacher
Matalucci, Kipp Ralph
German & Russian Teacher
WOODSTOWN
Bundens, Kathleen E.
Teacher
Du Bois, Eileen Star
AP Calculus Teacher
Frassenei, Joseph Rogers
Health & Physical Ed Teacher
Mortimer, Marilyn Welch
Math & English Teacher
WRIGHTSTOWN
McTamney, Aase Marie
English Teacher
Meyer, Daniel Luther
High School Science Teacher
WYCKOFF
Byma, Carol Ann Ten Kate
7th & 8th Grade Teacher
Gardner, Elaine Hanclich
Seventh Grade Math Teacher
Toal, Gregory C.
Former Alt Spec Ed Prgm Tchr
ZAREPHATH
Arrieta, Celina M.
Spanish Teacher
Slack, Marjorie A.
English Teacher & Guid Cnslr
Turton, Robert S., III
Minister, Bible Tchr, Chaplain

NEW MEXICO

ALAMOGORDO
Alarcon, Sylvia M.
7th & 8th Grade Band Director
Baca, Ernestine
Physical Education Teacher
Bagwell, Grace Curtis
Instruction Director
Bertolino, Vicki Maxine
Eng Jrnlsm, Tech Writing Instr
Brock, Annetta M.
Science Teacher
Cherry, Sharron Marie (Hill)
High School English Teacher
Cogill, Deanie Gaye
Sixth Grade Teacher
Cushingberry, Suzanne Hudson
Secondary Director & Teacher
Darnold, Teresa Gigante
Biology Tchr & Chrldng Coach
Dingman, Steven K.
Math Teacher
Fisk, Lois L.
Choral Teacher
Geary, Bryan A.
Physical Education Teacher
Gonzalez, Lesia Bryant
College Instructor
Johnson, Dava Winsett
Math Teacher
Kasehagen, Roxanne Pietro
English Teacher
Kelly, Steve Gregg
5th Grade Teacher
Keyes, Kurt Anthony
English Teacher
Kosinski, Joy Lee
Physical Education Teacher
Kullman, Cheryl Dryer
Principal
Lombrana, Vicente, Jr.
Instructor of Biology
Lundy, Suzanne Elizabeth
Business Education Teacher
Moore, Cay Beard
Teacher of the Gifted
Offley, Ronald Dean
Assoc Prof of Chemistry
Powell, JoLyn L.
1st Grade Teacher
Rexrode, Marla Caswell
4th Grade Teacher
Simon, Albert Matthew, Jr.
Computer Science Teacher
Skaar, Marcia (McCormack)
Biology Instructor
Smith, Cecilia Spoleti
Fifth Grade Teacher
Soistman, Gregory Allen
HS Mathematics Teacher
Sterling, Pat Patterson
English Professor
Watson, A. Christine McArthur
Fifth Grade Teacher
Whetstone, Sonya K.
English Teacher
Willis, Sunny Lynch
Foreign Lang Dept Chair & Tchr
ALBUQUERQUE
Alderman, James Othell
Math Department Chairman
Alexander, Lesia
Dev, Adult Ed Math & GED Tchr
Allen, Patricia Anaya
Second Grade Teacher
Arrowsmith, Mary M.
8th Grade US History Teacher
Arthur, Midge Yoshimoto
Family & Consumer Science Tchr
Ashby, Janna M. Barstow
Dean of Students
Ashe, Juliette Michelle
Retired Elementary Teacher

ALBUQUERQUE (cont)
Atkins, Margaret Hayner
Retired Lit & Lang Arts Tchr
Atler, LaVerne
Physical Education Teacher
Baklini, Edward, Jr.
Seventh Grd Soc Studies Tchr
Baldwin, Lewis Gilbert
8th Grade US History Teacher
Balzis, Uwe M.
German & Commnctn Skills Tchr
Bedeaux, Martha Dike
English Teacher
Biedermann, Peggy Kinkel
Fourth Grade Teacher
Blake, Eli Whitney
Mathematics & Chemistry Instr
Blottner, Myra Ann Manton
5th Grade Teacher
Blue, Connie Jane
Journalism & Comm Tchr
Brewer, Patty Durrie
5th Grade Teacher
Bucher, Isabel Bearman
5th Grd Tchr, Freelance Writer
Buckelew, Mary Bellucci
9th-12th Grade English Teacher
Buckner, Debi Kay
Drama Director
Busch, Robert Douglas
Nuclear Engineering Lab Dir
Cameron, Susan Chavez
Asst Prof of Counselor Ed
Campbell, Charlene Janet
Business Technologies Instr
Carmignani, Jeanetta Arndell
Special Education Teacher
Carpenter, Susan Lander
Fine Art Instructor
Chalmers, Catherine Faye
English Instructor
Chase, Christopher Lockwood
English & French Teacher
Chase, Kimberly Kay
English Teacher
Chavez, Carlos G.
Spanish & Bilingual Teacher
Chrusciel, Irene
Middle School Teacher
Clements, Joyce Anita Mims
7th Grade Mathematics Teacher
Coash, Monica Ann
Teacher of the Gifted
Cole, Donna Lynn
6th Grade Social Studies Tchr
Comstock, Jeannine Ljungdahl
Third Grade Teacher
Cook, Dianne Boutelle
Teacher
Cordova, Roger S.
Physical Education Teacher
Couch, Lee
Biology Instructor
Cummings, Ellen Curtin
Theology & Psychology Teacher
Cutler, Susan Jean
Instructor
Daniels, Mark
Mathematics Teacher
Danielson, Leslie Buffo
Lecturer of Clinical Chemistry
D'Anza, Larry M.
Marketing Teacher & Coord
Daughtrey, Terrell Clay
Instructor of Anthropology
Davidson, Joline Schwatken
Retired Kindergarten Teacher
Dean, Patricia A.
Dist Resource Tchr Gifted Pgm
Deck, Lorraine Marie
Chemistry Professor
Dewitt, Emmit D.
Math Dept Chairperson & Tchr
Dixon, David Brent
Science Teacher
Donovan, Leslie A.
Instr of English & Women Stud
Douglas, Nanci
English Teacher
Douglass, Dena
Teacher
Dreier, Gaylia Garrett
Eighth Grd Humanities Teacher
Duckworth, Jeanniene Cranford
Fifth Grade Teacher
Edmister, Richard E.
First Grade Teacher
Edmund, Robert Scott
English Teacher
Edwards, Gary Edwin
Social Studies Teacher
Edwards, James R., II
Special Education Tchr & Coach
Eiler-Ordonez, Alicia Ann
Spanish Teacher
Elkins, Hollis
English & Economics Teacher
Evans, Kathryn Miller
Visual Arts Teacher
Fernandez, Cristina
Spanish Teacher
Fresch, Cheryl H.
Eng Prof & Undergraduate Dir
Frey, Glenn M.
Administrator & HS Principal
Gatlin, Karen Christensen
English Teacher
Glauner, Cheryl Martin
Jrnlsm, Newspaper & Eng Tchr
Gloria, Amelia Cecilia
Fourth Grade Teacher
Goodrum, Mark Harris
Band Teacher
Gordon, Frederick
Accounting Instructor
Gracey, Kristine Perry
Health Educator
Graff, Pat Stuever
Journalism Teacher
Grice, Lola
Retired Elementary School Tchr
Gruette, Frances Mary
Mathematics Teacher
Gunckel, Susanne Egan
Accounting Professor
Gutierrez, Estella Atencio
Bilingual Language Arts Tchr
Gutierrez, Gary R.
Special Education Teacher
Hall, Sue Foster
Kindergarten Teacher
Harris, John Iliff
Retired Mathematics Teacher
Haskin, Eric
Rsrch Prof of Chem-Nuclear Eng
Heard, Martha E.
Spanish Teacher & Dept Head
Henner, David G.
Spanish Teacher
Hennigan, Rosemarie Nalda
Fr, Span & Commnctn Teacher
Higgins, Leah Kim
English Teacher
Hill, Ralph W.
Language Arts Teacher
Holder, Linda Susan
English Teacher
Holmberg, Mary Curfman
Academy Director
Hornsby, Debbie L. (Schauer)
Physical Ed Teacher & Coach
Huchmala, Julia Morrow
Eng & Creative Writing Tchr
Hunt, Susan F.
Math Department Chair & Tchr
Huntsman, Julie Ann (Nesbitt)
Bio, Anatomy & Physiology Tchr
Huston, Michael Victor
Physical Education Teacher
Jacobvitz, Robin Smith
Psychology Professor
Jones, Patricia Wheeler
Choral Director
Jordan, Laurence Clifford
English Teacher
Karni, Shlomo
Gardner-Zemke Prof
Kauffman, Victoria Clark
Math Teacher
King, Debbie E. Mc Afee
First Grade Teacher
Kissinger, Theron Anthony
Mathematics Teacher
Knauber, Tom Gregory
Business Education Teacher
Knittle, Katherine Saiers
English Teacher & Dept Chair
Koblinski, Carol L.
Mathematics Teacher
Kolosseus, Sharon Trujillo
Director of Bands
Lambie, Gary John
4th Grade Teacher
Lethem, Sandy Duke
Facilitator of The Gifted
Lindberg, Ann Emley
Fourth Grade Teacher
Lioce, Barbara LaGruth
English Teacher
Lyo, Nahmyoung Jane
Instructor of Math Dept
Mac Karon, Mel
English Teacher
Maestas, Catherine P.
Retired Spanish Teacher
Maher, Michael G.
HS Mathematics Teacher
Maji, Arup Kanti
Associate Professor
Martinez, Joseph G.R.
Mathematics Education Prof
Martinez, Maria Consuelo
First Grade Teacher
Martinez, Sofia L.
Soc Studies & Bilingual Tchr
Mc Adoo, Layne Lowrance
Instructor of Sociology
Mc Broom, Ann Marie
Third Grade Teacher
McCorkle, Timothy Clausell
Athletic Dir & Dean of Stdnts
McCormick, Tonia Ann (Wells)
Education Assistant
McDougall, Lauren Morrow
High School English Teacher
McEachran, Kelly Brian
Vice Prin, Ath Dir & His Tchr
Mc Govern, Nancy Dunbar
English Teacher
Mc Namara, Mary Colleen
Discipline Coord of Biology
Mc Nett, John
Fourth Grade Teacher
Medernach, Frances Ann E. Krier
Tchr of Gftd & High Potential
Meharg, Carrie Noland
Chemistry I-II, Physics I Tchr
Mersereau, Judith Arlene
Art Tchr & Fine Arts Dept Chr
Michaud, Richard Louis
Science Teacher
Miller, Kay Clauve
Marketing Teacher & Coord
Miller, Nan Neidel
Social Studies Teacher
Miller, William Lee
Pre-Law & Economics Teacher
Mills, Susan W.
English & Psychology Teacher
Mitschler, Paul A.
Teacher of the Gifted SPED
Mohler, Vivian Bell
Fifth Grade Teacher
Moore, Cynthia Marie
English & Humanities Teacher
Moreno, Julie Miller
English & Health Teacher
Morris, Thomas E.
Math Teacher & Dept Chair
Napper-Owen, Gloria E.
Assistant Professor of PE
Neal, B. Scott
Physical Education Teacher
Nenno, Linda D.
Multi-Age Classroom Teacher
Nenno, William Charles
Biology Teacher
Nichelason, Margery Grant
Teacher of the Gifted
Nunez, Simon, Jr.
Instructor
Orzen, William Bernard
Social Science Teacher
Osborn, James Mike
Teacher of the Gifted
Paco, Martin T.
Math Teacher
Padilla, Anastacio
Physical Education Teacher
Padilla, James Robert
English Teacher
Palmer, Jane Hipsher
English Teacher
Pariente Ahmed, Esther
Spanish Department Coordinator
Penn, James E.
Advanced Math Teacher
Pino, Linda Hansteen
ESL Teacher
Prentice, John Wayne
4th Grade Teacher
Putman, William H.
Professor
Raymond, Bruce Austin
Mathematics Teacher
Reeback, Barbara B.
French Teacher
Rescigna, Suzanne K.
English Dept Co-Chair
Reynders, Mary Neven
Orchestra Dir
Reynolds, Lorrayne Frances
Language Arts Teacher
Rhodes, Geri Marlane
English Instructor
Roberts, Susan Tedlock
Social Studies Dept Chair
Romero, Dolores Maldanado
Third Grade Teacher
Rose, Charlene Ann
English Teacher
Sacco, Louis John
9th Grd Govt & Amer His Tchr
Salazar-Jaynes, Barbara
English Teacher
Sanchez, Debra A. Reid
High School Mathematics Tchr
Sanchez, Lourdes L.
Kindergarten Teacher
Schoepke, Karen Kohlman
Teacher of the Gifted
Scorsone, Vicki L.
Eng Communication Skills Tchr
Shoemaker, William Phillips
Social Science Teacher
Siegel, Thomas Weil
Latin & World History Teacher
Simpson, M. Scott
ESL Teacher
Smith, David Alan
8th Grade Teacher
Smith-Pierce, Susan B.
English & Communications Tchr
Stratmoen, Kathleen
Middle School Math Teacher
Suchland, E. Janet Owings
Piano Teacher
Teare, Ronald Cameron
Orchestra Instructor
Tippit, Marcia Elizabeth
Drama Teacher
Tristani, Jorge E., Jr.
Ath Dir & AP Art History Tchr
Tuttoilmondo, Joseph G.
Third Grade Teacher
Tyson, Sherrie Lambert
2nd Grade Teacher
Vail, Anna de Jesus Sandoval
French & Spanish Teacher
Valigura, Mary L.
Marketing Ed Tchr & DECA Adv
Venegas, Nelinda Zuniga
Principal
Watkins, Karen H.
Journalism Teacher
Watts, Patricia Ann-Bobbs
Student Services Director
Webb, Ruth Nickelson
6th Grade Teacher
Webster, Jane Barcak
Fifth Grade Teacher
Wehrli, Bryan
High School English Teacher
Wentworth, Mary S.
Language Arts Teacher
Williams, Helen (Rouse)
English Teacher
Wilson, David Aram
Spanish & English Teacher
Wirth, Elaine Dacey
Head Teacher & Administrator
Wong, Stanley
Mathematics Teacher
Wright, Odies Lee, Jr.
Director of Student Services
Wyman, Wendy Reddy
Lead Teacher
Young, Anne Nesbitt
Teacher of the Gifted
Zawadzkas, Katharina Poppe
Russian Teacher
Zinnert, Elke
Counselor

ANTHONY
Aber, Tomasine Dawn
Special Ed Teacher
Bennett, Fern Rader
7th Grade Reading Teacher
Berry, Ginger Lynn
Kindergarten Teacher
Coles, Charlene Givens
Reading & English Teacher
Dominguez, Maria Elisa
Guidance Counselor
Donaldson, Pamela Lunt
High School Biology Teacher
Duran, Joe Paul
6th Grade Bilingual Teacher
Fuller, Fran Ellen
Teacher
Gage, Stella Chavarria
English Teacher
Galt, Melanie (Menaugh)
8th Grade Earth Sci Teacher
Gressitt, Carolyn
English Teacher
Haynes, William Johnson, III
Naval Science Instructor
Houston-Romer, Terrie
Sixth Grade Inclusion Teacher
Huntsberger, Jennifer J.
Biology Teacher
Jimenez, Arturo Segobia
6th Grade Teacher
Lara, Roseanne Baca
English Teacher
Lerma, Virginia Silva
Family & Consumer Science Tchr
Masse, Teena Matthews
Secondary Math Teacher
Moreno, Camerina Saenz
ESL Teacher
Orrantia, Azucena Dominguez
Algebra Teacher
Pickett, Linda M.
English & Math Teacher
Ramos, Raul Herrera
Biology Teacher
Russell, Alan Edward
Head Athletic Trainer
See, James Robert
Math Teacher
Selwyn, David C.
Social Studies Teacher

ANTON CHICO
Perea, Mary Ann Bernardy
Third Grade Teacher

ARROYO HONDO
Jaramillo, Marilyn
First & Second Grade Teacher

ARTESIA
Bowden, Kenneth Ridge
Math Teacher
Chambers, Michele Holt
English & Journalism Teacher
Dickerson, Randy Lee
HS World History Teacher
Gallegos, Jose E.
Former Chapter I Math Teacher
Gunderson, Anita Coffman
English Teacher
Jackson, Robin Ann (Tolle)
8th & 9th Grade English Tchr
Johnston, Tammy Winters
Third Grade Teacher
Jones, Gary Clinton
Social Studies Tchr & Dept Chm
Kizer, Sue Karnosky
7th Grade Language Arts Tchr
Moreno, Cheto
US & Street Law Teacher
Osborne, Peggy Eden
6th Grade Lang Arts Teacher
Perez, Maria Ledzma
Title I Math Teacher
Petterson, Sandra Kay
Math Teacher
Schiel, Joseph Bernard, Jr.
Biology Teacher
Trujillo, Lorena Jean Betancur
First Grade Teacher
Worley, Mike E.
English Teacher

AZTEC
Hill, Dean
Science Teacher
Seymour, Linda White
Business Tchr & Dean of Stdnts
Stinson, Herb Howard
PE Teacher & Coach
Wingate, Lonna E.
Mathematics Teacher

BAYARD
Brandt, David Roger
English Teacher
Hendrickson, Antoinette
English & Drama Director
Montoya, Susan Bennett
Social Studies EXCEL Teacher
Pena, Edward Steven
Science Teacher
Quinones, Luis Ignacio
Eng & Creative Writing Teacher
Worthington deNeenez, Helen V. B
English Department Chair

BELEN
Ashcraft, Barbara W.
Drama, Jrnlsm & Lang Arts Tchr
Benivedz, Patricia
High School Coach
Cordova, Roselyn A.
6th Grade Teacher
Davey, Linda K.
Humanities & English Teacher
Garcia, Casey Mark
Computer & Mathematic Teacher
Hayes, Phyllis L. (Sanchez)
Teacher
Jaramillo, Marilyn Pauline (Monta
Sixth Grade Math Teacher
Malitz, Richard E.
Math & Soc Studies Teacher
Rivera, Becky Shores
Teacher & Day Care Dir
Romero, Joanne Gurule
Assistant Principal
Smrt, Marie D.
Chorus & Guitar Teacher
Syers, Peggy
Hum, Drama & English Teacher
Tucker, Aubrey Edward
Fine Arts Dept Chm
Turley, Beverly B.
Asst Principal

BERNALILLO
Davis, Melba Ann
English Teacher
Mc Ilhaney, Sam Carl
History Teacher
Mondragon, Teresa I.
Mathematics Instructor

BLOOMFIELD
Anderson, Colleen
4th Grade Inclusion Teacher
Burkholder, Chad Alan
Social Studies Teacher
Carmichael, Ken F.
Principal
Gutierrez, John
Teacher & Coach
Hansen, Danny J.
Choir Director
Schneider, Diana Lynne (Oster)
Physical Education & Hlth Tchr
Stanley, Glenace Frey
Third Grade Teacher

CAPITAN
Rice, Jerry Dale
Art Teacher

CARLSBAD
Angell, Carye Benge
Science Department Head
Becker, Johnnie Lee Cole
Retired Asst Prin & Eng Tchr
Boyer, Mary Sue
Earth Science Teacher
Calvani, Josephine Eckert
5th Grade Teacher
Click, M. Paulette Rhodes
Counselor
Forni, Thomas Earl
Physical Education Teacher
Gallesgos, William Andrew
Assistant Professor of Math
Garcia, Lorina
Fourth Grade Teacher
Gossett, Janine Lee
7th Grd Lang Arts & Comm Tchr
Heaton, Julia V.
Second Grade Teacher
Lewis, Thomas Royal
Fifth Grade Teacher
Lovelace, Margaret Laurine
Behavioral Science Teacher
Marrs, MaryAnn Miletich
English Teacher
Mattson, Rich J.
HS Arts & Crafts Teacher
Netherlin, Patricia Cook
Business Teacher
Perkowski, Gary L.
Assistant Principal
Pierce, Joe Keith
English Teacher
Pitcaithley, Lynne
5th Grade Teacher
Platten, Tara Richerson
Famility Resource Mngmt Spec
Rodgers, Thomas H.
Economics & Accounting Prof
St John, Janet Harding
8th Grade Mathematics Teacher
Throneberry, Jeannette Pierce
11th-12th Grd English Teacher
Tracy, Jane Gidak
Fifth Grade Teacher
Trefren, Jane M.
Fifth Grade Teacher

AD (cont)
Claudia J. Tabor
ade Teacher
l, Rita Grabbe
te Prof of Business

Richard R.
Studies & PE Teacher
RON
renda Kay (Grafe)
Teacher
N
, Robert M.
Grd Sci & Cmptr Tchr

Eloy H.
& Communications Tchr
CROFT
, Glena Brown
rd School Admin
olie Burt
ng, Govt & Ec Teacher

ohn Wilton
Instructor
, Wayne Dennis
hool Choir Director
Leslie DeAnn
nications Instructor
yce Ford
Teacher
Carol Lillian (Tanck)
& Consumer Science Tchr
Donna Kirk
de Teacher
tzi Jennings
Teacher
vonne Anglada
mm & Theatre Teacher
, Annie R.
4th Grade Teacher
Marshall, Ruthie
havioral Sci Dept Chair
Peggy Weiss
Department Chairman
Jeannie
Radio Tech Pgm Dir
ohn E.
Instructor
n Warren
or of Graphic Arts
y
nt Principal
, Nancy Claire (Shaffer)
de Science Teacher
arri Carter
de Teacher
y Leon
American History Tchr
Kathy J. (Thomas)
ss Teacher
Sylvia Sparks
Math Teacher
y, Carol Nesbitt
& Yearbook Teacher
aye Jean (Estes)
Elementary Teacher
athy Annette Freeman
& Pre AP Teacher
helly Kay
ss & Soc Studies Teacher
ey, Doris J. Ballard
& Theory Teacher
Vestana Bilbrey
garten Teacher
Donald Gene
irector
ELOR
M. Elaine
al & 7th-8th Grade Tchr
E
, Geraldine Valdez
& First Grade Teacher
POINT
-Vesely, Rebecca Ann
ading Teacher & Dept Head
rie K.
& Comm Skills Teacher
Dennis
or of Counseling
, Renee Louise
Director
shoff, Robert Dale
Teacher

uez, Lilly Madrid
ual & Intermediate Tchr
Kenneth Walter
Teacher
G
ndra Aylaine
Economics Teacher
Sandra J.
Arts Tchr
ary C.
Training Instructor
az, Diana Marie
d Math & Soc Stud Tchr
Rose Marie Cardenas
d Grade Teacher
Charlsie Elizabeth
Grade Teacher
Shirley Baker
Grade Teacher
n, Elsie Bullington
y & Media Specialist
Elvira Zamora
d Grade Teacher
erry Lorraine
rts Teacher

DES MOINES
King, Dennis Wade
Math Teacher
DEXTER
Hobson, Judy Ross
English & Commnctn Teacher
DORA
Kibbe, Karen E.
Business, History, Eng Teacher
DULCE
Salazar, Stanford Louis
PE & Health Teacher
EDGEWOOD
Nunneley, Theresa Marie (Beliveau)
Fifth Grade Teacher
ELIDA
Holmes, Carolyn (Mc Donald)
4th Grade Teacher
Powell, Lana Wade
Science Teacher
ESPANOLA
Atencio, Eduardo P.
Frgn Lang Dept Chprsn
Border, Gena Marie
High School Math Teacher
Costello, Michael L.
Dean of Student Services
Dannenberg, William John
Lang Arts Dept Chair & Instr
Heffner, Dee Dee Krumm
Director of Church Relations
Kaiper, Ellen Zmeskal
Speech Communications Teacher
Lopez, Maria Cournoyer
English & Journalism Teacher
Lopez, Patricia Marie
Freshman High School Teacher
Miera-Martinez, Joseph D.
Principal
Money, Richard Kenneth
Math Teacher
Naranjo, Lawrence B.
Academics Teacher
Pompeo, Marie Rodriguez
Social Studies Teacher
Roybal, Ymelda Gurule
Counselor
ESTANCIA
Rawlojohn, Virginia R.
Language Arts Instructor
EUNICE
Hathorn, Perri Ann
Kindergarten Teacher
Hodges, Jill Chaffin
1st Grade Teacher
Robertson, Belinda Kay
English & Drama Teacher
FARMINGTON
Becenti, Andrew
Navajo Studies Teacher
Bergtholdt, Eloise Lambert
Kindergarten Teacher
Braswell, Betty
Mathematics Educator
Canales, Judith Wilson
Mathematics Teacher
Charles, Fran
6th Grade Teacher
Collins, Jalene A.
6th Grade Teacher
Conaway, Larry Keith
9th Grd Civics & Hnrs Ec Tchr
Conover, Rodney Russell, Sr.
Comm Skills & Civics Teacher
DeKay, Christopher William
US History & Wrestling Teacher
Dixon-Willden, Gail
English & Drama Teacher
Eide, Linda Kay
Sixth Grade Teacher
Gattis, Ann Fayad
Biology Teacher
Golden, Julie Koss
Mathematics Teacher
Graham, Nancy H.
Family & Consumer Science Tchr
Graham, Ron W.
High School Teacher
Heil, Kenneth Del
Professor
Hircock, Virginia Nickels
Coral Director
Hoskins, Karen Boesel
Social Studies Teacher
Howe, Laura W.
Science Teacher
Huntsman, Jack
English Teacher
Keller, Barbara Frances Palmer
4th Grade Classroom Teacher
Lehnus, Jeff
HS History Teacher
Lorett, Don R.
Health Education Teacher
Mc Andrews, Linda Lee
Retired Business Ed Teacher
McGuire, Richard Wilson, Jr.
Associate Professor of Biology
Mc Neal, Brenda Lea
Language Arts Teacher
Miller, Jimmy Hilbert
Prof of His & Political Sci
Munson, Nels Kevin
Sixth Grade Teacher
Scaggari, Fred J.
Biology Teacher
Stanford, Deanna H.
History & Pol Sci Asst Prof
Thomas, I. Lee
Spanish & ESL Teacher

Turner, Ed Lee
Spanish & ESL Teacher
Weems, Jann Bennett
Social Studies Department Chm
Whitaker, Vicki
Language Arts Teacher
Wooderson, Judith Lerch
Assoc Professor of Drafting
FORT SUMNER
Clark, Patricia A.
4th Grade Teacher
Cortese, Mary Ann
High School English Teacher
McMath, Lisa Props
Mathematics Teacher
Sparks, Laura Ann
Business Education Teacher
FORT WINGATE
Eustice, Michelle
Math Teacher
Helgeson, Suzanne K.
English Teacher
Hockensmith, Christine Jo
World & US History Teacher
Holtsoi, Raymond R.
Mathematics Teacher
Kingdon, William K.
Music Teacher
Marianito, Lucie
4th Grade Teacher
Mason, Verdie June
6th & 8th Grade Teacher
Sykes, Erica Rae
English IV Teacher
GALLINA
Vigil, Danny R.
Social Studies Teacher
GALLUP
Argo, L. Voncille
Family & Consumer Science Tchr
Barnard, Johnny Lee
5th Grade Teacher
Bourdage, Sherry Fuhs
Mathematics Teacher
Burt, Sandra Irene-Hill
8th Grade Science Teacher
Burt, Tommy Lee
New Mexico History Teacher
Carpenter, Patrice Joan
Kindergarten Teacher
Davidson, David Scott
Biology Teacher
Detorie, Judith Tamasi
Teacher of Gifted & Talented
Di Paolo, M. Diane
Guidance Counselor
Fortney, Curtis
HS Architect & Drafting Instr
Grigsby, Michael Scott
English Teacher
Henry, Vesta Hasler
Social Studies Teacher
Lafferty, Carol Ann Phillips
Mathematics Teacher
Langer, Robin Sue
Social Studies Teacher
Larrabee, James Mark
Marketing Teacher
Romero, Bethsheba LaVera
4th & 5th Grade Teacher
Russell, Shirley LePlatt
Calm Lab Teacher
Salazar, Judith Abernathy
Biology Teacher
Seslar, Mary Ann Nieberding
Sixth Grade Science Teacher
Smith, Tammy L.
Assistant Principal
Snell, Patricia Lange
Mathematics Teacher
Stowe, Janet M.
Second Grade Teacher
Strickland, Linda Z.
English Teacher
Wade, David D.
Science Teacher
GRADY
Lindsey, Brenda Pulliam
Business Teacher
GRANTS
Boynton, Donna Jean
Former Elementary Teacher
Cerniway, Marie Dominiano
Accounting & Business Law Tchr
Holliday, Lee Olla (Wright)
English Teacher
Lewis, Kathy Pauline
Family & Consumer Sci Tchr
Lopez, Henry Julian
Spanish Teacher
MacKendrick, Sharon Hawkins
Mathematics Professor
Meehan, Teresa Marie
Linguistics & Psychology Instr
Murdoch, Bob B.
History Instr & Dept Chprsn
Murrietta, Janet R.
Hlth & Defensive Driving Tchr
Perrow, Cecelia Roton
Associate Campus Dir & Prof
Rowley, Clayton
English Teacher
Sanchez, Rosemary
High School Counselor
Savacheck, Mary Gates
Sixth Grade Teacher
Waters, Brian John
Sixth Grade Teacher

HAGERMAN
Denning, Dink
Span, Soc Sci & Spec Ed Tchr
HATCH
Brewer, James E.
Fourth Grade Teacher
Gorman, Ernestine Dearborn
Business Department Instructor
Halsell, Patricia Gary
Biology & Chemistry Teacher
O'Brien, Edward Eugene
Bilingual Resource Teacher
Sheram, Florence Turner
Retired 5th & 6th Grd Teacher
HOBBS
Allen, David G.
Band Director
Bennett, Sue Burgamy
English Professor
Black, Ronald R.
Professor of History & Coach
Blevins, Clayton D.
Science & Mathematics Tchr
Bowman, Patricia Dooley
Professor of English
Cearley, Marie Lloyd
English Teacher & Dept Chair
Craig, Calvin
Drafting Instructor
Davis, Steven Mark
Dir of Allied Health Fields
Ford, L. Joe
Bio, Ecology & Earth Sci Tchr
Forman, F. LaRue
Sixth Grade Teacher
Fox, Sue (Smith)
Asst Prof of Math Ed
Gage, Maryna Morris
6th Grade Teacher
Hardy, Russell F.
Automotive Professor
Harper, Wilma Faye Craig
4th Grade Teacher
Jones, Judy A. (Hamilton)
Math Teacher
Knight, Pam
English Tchr & Bsktbl Coach
Mann, Jimmie Lea
Business Education Teacher
Martin, Gerald Ray
Mathematics Professor
McMurray, Becky Smith
Third Grade Teacher
Megert, Diann A.
Computer Science & Math Prof
Murphy, Melinda L.
Debate Coach
Newell, Sandra Walsh
Asst Superintendent for Instr
Roberson, Mary Grace
Band Director
Romine, Lisa
Fifth Grade Teacher
Sagerty, Kenneth Timothy
Assistant Prof of Education
Smith, Marilyn Ann
Dean of Education
Soper, Vicki Marie
Assistant Professor of English
Villegas, Ruby Garza
Third Grade Teacher
Wieser, Joan
English Teacher
HOLLOMAN AFB
Oliver, Rebecca L.
Earth Science & HEC Teacher
Stoltenberg, William Glenn
Social Studies & Science Tchr
HONDO
Yaksich, Jess D.
Vocational Agriculture Teacher
HURLEY
Morales, Deborah V.
1st & 2nd Grade Teacher
JEMEZ PUEBLO
Aguilar, Edward L.
Office Technology Instructor
Barbour, Daniel Paul
Mathematics Teacher
Barton, Richard T.
Fourth & Fifth Grade Teacher
Perkins, Matthew W.
Science Teacher
Smith, Jeanette Cook
Special Ed Teacher
KIRTLAND
Adair, Thomas Stephen
Head of Physical Ed Department
Anderson, Rich
Biology Teacher & Coach
Beasey, Nancy L. Swearingen
Special Education Teacher
Boognl, Mary Hoar
Math Teacher
Brown, Sharon C.
English Teacher
Cawood, William Joseph
Govt & SW Navajo History Tchr
Georginia, Norman H., Jr.
Math Department Chairperson
Gilbertson, Jeffrey Lynn
Mathematics Teacher
Hume, Ann A.
Soc Studies Tchr & Dept Head
Stephenson, Lori L.
Special Education Teacher
Study, Kathryn Mullins
6th & 7th Grade Math Teacher

LAGUNA
Jopek, Matthew Peter
Sixth Grade Teacher
LAKE ARTHUR
Hernandez, Susan Jill
Science Teacher & Coach
Langford, Gynn Ancell
Art & Home Ec Head Teacher
Skariah, Susie
Mathematics Teacher
LAS CRUCES
Acklin, Timothy Eugene
Science Tchr & Ath Trainer
Aguirre, Tawny Lynn
Professor
Armstrong, Joe B.
Professor of Animal Science
Baptiste, Nancy E.
Coll Asst Prof & Prgm Coord
Bellows, Ann Feddersen
Coord & Asst Prof EMS Pgm
Benson, Joseph Elliott
Professor of Management
Bickel, Douglas L.
Business Dept Chair & Instr
Brown, Irene Neumann
Coll Asst Prof of English
Brown, Susan Wightman
7th-8th Grade Science Teacher
Bullock, James Harvey
Acctng Prof & Department Head
Castaneda, Emma L.
Fifth Grade Teacher
Coburn, Horace Hunter
Science Advisor
Comer, Alice Teresa Ramirez
English Teacher
Cort, Pamela Mc Clutchey
HS French Teacher
Cothrun, Thomas Keith
German Teacher
Deblassie, Roland
8th Grade US History Teacher
De La Pena, Julio
5th Grade Teacher
Del Valle, Francisco Rafael
Chemical Engineering Professor
Dennis, Christine Anaya
English Teacher
Enomoto, Carl Edward
Economics Professor
Foster, Taylor William, III
Professor of Accounting
Franzak, Mark David
Mathematics Teacher
Gavin, Patrick Michael, Jr.
Dir of Prof Golf Mgmt Prgm
Gilpin, Susan Schuster
Mathematics Teacher
Granados, Kristi Lee
Accounting Instructor
Greene, James Michael
Mathematics & Cmptr Sci Tchr
Greenwood, Glenda E.
English Tchr & Dept Co-Chair
Greer, S. Roger
Math Department Chair & Tchr
Guevara, Yolanda R.
Fifth Grade Teacher
Hampton, Leon
8th Grade US History Teacher
Harrell, Susan Cannon
Assistant Professor of Nursing
Headrick, Roy Wayne
Assoc Prof of Bus Cmptr System
Heiden, Elden W.
College Assistant Professor
Houdek, Liz
English Teacher
Howard, Linda Turpen
5th Grade Teacher
Howard, Volney Ward, Jr.
Wildlife Science Professor
Johnson, Michael Dennis
Chemistry Professor
Juarez, Jon Edward
Assistant Professor
Kearny, Teddy L. Snow
English Teacher
Kientz, Juanita M.
Language Arts Teacher
Kirby, Rosemary Estrada
English Teacher
Leyva, Hope Holguin
3rd Grade Teacher
Lopez, Stanley Roland
Dir, Tchr Cooperative Ed Pgm
Luchini, Ingrid Trustorff
German Teacher
Lucky, George William
Prof Emer Elec, Comp Engr Dept
Lujan, Bertha Cantu
Spanish Teacher
Magoffe, Georgia Vallejos
Global His & Geography Tchr
Maya, George Reyes
Spanish Teacher
Mays, G. Larry
Criminal Justice Professor
McKenzie, Judi E.
Advanced Ed Prgm Facilitator
Miller, Kaye S.
Facilitator of Advanced Ed Pgm
Newberry, R. Bruce
Drafting & Industrial Tech
Nowotny, Kenneth Ray
Prof of Ec, Intnl Bus, Dept Hd
Pagel, Karen L.
Developmental Math Asst Prof

LAS CRUCES (cont)
Parish, Donna Joyce (Price)
7th Grade Math Teacher
Paulson, Jo Anne
8th-9th Grade Teacher
Peach, James Thomas
Economics Professor
Peerman, Stephen Sidney
Computer Science & Math Tchr
Pelking, Marian Virginia
Retired First Grade Teacher
Pincomb, Cissy Lujan
Multi-Age Teacher
Plummer, Simmie Gibson
Retired History Teacher
Ramirez, Paula (Wilmes)
Math Tchr & Academy Career Adv
Ramsey, Newell Robert
Mathematics Teacher
Ramsey, Renee Susan
Math Teacher
Ranels, Linden Fisher
English Teacher
Rumann, Susan Marie
College Instructor
Salas, Dolores Avila
Educational Biling Asst
Sandoval, Dolores Marie
Sixth Grade Team Teacher
Schutz, Diane Davenport
Choral Dir & Music Dept Chair
Seipel, Cindy
Assistant Professor
Shearer, James Edward
Associate Prof of Music
Solano, Joseph Aemilio
Business Education Teacher
Somppi, Stacey J.
8th Grade English Teacher
Soules, William Peter
Cnslng & Educl Psych Asst Prof
Staffeldt, Mary Anne Maher
Assoc Prof of Indstrl Engrng
Stapleton, Andrew Hubert Melendrez
Marketing Professor
Taylor, Javin Morse
Electrical & Cmptr Engrng Prof
Thayer, Michael Joseph
High School History Teacher
Turner, Jeffrey O.
Orchestra Teacher
Vigerust, Jeannine (Houle)
Asst Prof of Math & Sci
Volpi, Ingeborg Franz
Instr of German & Economics
Willis, Karen Perkins
Asst Professor of English
Wofford, Robert Charles
English Department Head
Woods, Emily Smith
College Asst Prof of Math
Worski, Phyllis S. (Wright)
English Teacher
Zamora, Debra Shepard
Advanced Ed Pgm Facilitator
LAS VEGAS
Abreu, Arthur L.
Bio Tchr,Head,Trk & Ftbl Coach
Bodner, Virginia Richardson
Special Education Teacher
Garcia-Briggs, Elizabeth Diane
8th Grade Science Teacher
Gonzales, James
Economics Teacher
Griego, Mary Lou Nelson
Library Media Specialist
Guenther, Trisha J. Maestas
High School English Instructor
Harrington, Julius Lee
Associate Professor
Lopez, Rosalie Baker
Title I Reading Teacher
Lucero, Jose Manuel
Social Studies Teacher
Maestas, Ronald W.
Dean, School of Business
Manafy, Abass
Assoc Prof of Political Sci
Martinez, Lorraine
Principal
Mascarenas, Isabel Urioste
Computer Teacher
Mc Elroy, Stephen Charles
8th Grade US History Teacher
Mertz, Margaret Stover
Assistant Professor of Music
Montoya, Emily Brenda
Social Studies Teacher
Rodriguez, Christine Marie
Science Tchr & Dept Chprsn
Romero, Ouidio
Retired Drafting Instructor
Salazar, Loretta Catherine
Assistant Professor
Seay, Margie Crespin
Social Studies Teacher
Tafoya, Darlene Jeanette
Computer Instructor
Tapia, Linda T.
English Teacher
Torres, Elizabeth Hern
Choir Dir & Vocal Music Tchr
Torres, Joseph L.
Math Teacher
LOGAN
Perez, Connie Lynn (Kuper)
1st Grade Teacher
LORDSBURG
Farris, Gloria Noce
5th Grade Teacher
Giedd, Gerald W.
English & Spanish Teacher
Woodard, John Thurman
US His & Cmptr Kybrdng Tchr
LOS ALAMOS
Anderson-Acosta, Barbara Jean
Spanish Teacher
Baca, Larry S.
English Teacher
Cocking, Roberta Geoffrion
Health Instructor
Farman, Bonnie (Gindlesperger)
Sixth Grade Teacher
Giesler, Maryjane Ulk
English Professor
Goetzinger, James
HS Social Studies Teacher
Hahn, Thelma Moore
Elementary Art Teacher
Handsberry, Joy Lynn
High School Math Teacher
Hipwood, Kathleen Louise
Mathematics Teacher
Hipwood, Robert M.J.
Business Education Teacher
Hopkins, Granville John
Naval Science Instructor
Love, Sean David
Soc Studies & Humanities Tchr
Mac Farlane, Jackie W.
8th Grd Math & Algebra Teacher
Malone, Joan Carol
Clinical Supvr for Tchr Intern
Marcotte, Christy Ann
Latin & History Teacher
McKenzie, Judith Allason
Second Grade Teacher
Moss, Ronalie A.
English Teacher
Parsons, Sheryl Olness
6th Grade Teacher
Patterson, Laura Dorius
5th & 6th Grade Teacher
Sanchez, Rita Sandoval
Middle School Spanish Teacher
Seidel, Tammy Miller
Marketing Teacher
Shankland, Rebecca H.
English Teacher
Trujillo, Janice Pietrowski
Tchr Gifted & Talented Child
Trujillo, Noel
Speech & English Teacher
Wangler, Julie Offen
Physics & Math Teacher
Warnock, Sandra Lynn
Special Education Teacher
LOS LUNAS
Berry, Pamela Susan
English Teacher
Carson, Judy Henderickson
First Grade Teacher
Chavez, Mildred Hernandez
Assistant Principal
Conescu, Jon D.
Associate Professor of Ed
Crippen-Chavez, Christine Elizabeth
Teacher of Gifted
Flores, Antonio Aristeo
Photography, Art & Eng Tchr
Jenrette, Michael Joseph
Mathematics Teacher
Loveless, Claudia (Ambrose)
English Teacher
Lowe, Karen S.
Economics Teacher
McMahon, William Andrew, III
Tchr of Gfted & High Potential
Meyers, Eileen (Haslett)
Third Grade Teacher
Padilla, Barbara Sanchez
Business Education Teacher
Padilla-Harris, Dianna L.
Site Specialist
Robinson, Mary Reid
Assistant Professor of Math
Sanchez, Steven Allen
Associate Program Director
Simmons, Nan Kathryn
English Teacher
Storey, Johnna (Vaughan)
Lang Arts, Spch & Drama Tchr
LOVING
Cosand, Paul Neal, Jr.
Band Director & Math Teacher
LOVINGTON
Bridgforth, Stephen T.
8th Grade History Teacher
Caudle, Joyce R.
9th Grd Social Studies Teacher
DeAnda, Patti Swinton
Second Grade Teacher
Faith, John T.
Government, Ec & US His Tchr
Franklin, Terry Jean
High School Librarian
Harris, Sandra Stiles
First Grade Teacher
Manes, Darin M.
Biology Teacher
Rutledge, Linda Rickman
1st Grade Teacher
MAGDALENA
James, M. Kelly
Agricultural Education Teacher
MAXWELL
Galli, Richard Stephen
Math Teacher
MELROSE
Bostwick, Joanna Fay
Counselor
Wade, Twyla Biggers
World History & Music Teacher
MIMBRES
Mc Cargish, Joan Topmiller
Retired Elementary Teacher
MORA
Chavez, Danny G.
Science Teacher
Olivas, Doris Griego
School Counselor
Rael, Myrtelina Tirado
Span, Lang Arts & Home Ec Tchr
MORIARTY
Alvarez, Raul F.
Special Education Teacher
Carpenter, Amy Saunders
Comm Skills, Basic Eng II Tchr
Dolce, Robbie Kuehler
High School Mathematics Instr
Johnson, Delores Jean (Williams)
High School English Teacher
Lowder, Barbara A. (Vigil)
Business & Computer Teacher
Ruben, John Porter
History Teacher
Sandoval, Manuel
8th Grade History Teacher
Smith, Reva Kay Alderman
Retired Fifth Grade Teacher
Trujillo, Yolanda Sandoval
Kindergarten Teacher
NAVAJO
Wesolowski, Eleanor Louise
Sixth Grade Teacher
NEW LAGUNA
Matte, A. Thomas, Jr.
Social Studies Instructor
Stephenson, Paul Elton
Mathematics Teacher
Timothy, Gene L.
English Teacher
NEWCOMB
McKenzie, Lynda Ashbrook
Math & Computer Sci Tchr
Wilson, Larry Eugene
Fifth Grade Teacher
PECOS
Drabanski, John Daniel
Science & Computer Teacher
Gonzales, LeRoy J.
Mathematics Teacher
Leffler, Candace Elizabeth
5th Grade Teacher
Sanchez, Dorothy E.
Middle School Counselor
Winkel, Carol Groening
English Teacher
PENASCO
Chavez, Bernadette Esquibel
Jr High & HS Science Teacher
Kline, Caroline C.
History Teacher & Coach
PORTALES
Adkins, Laura Ann
Publications & Home Ec Tchr
Ashmore, Timothy Mitchell
Professor of Communication
Austin, Elizabeth Hope
Instructor of the Gifted
Coplen, Ola Mae
Retired First Grade Teacher
Eisler, Patricia Johnson
Sixth Grade Teacher
Erdmann, Linda Jeffries
English Teacher & Coach
Gomez, Brenda Worley
US History & PE Teacher
Greathouse, Betty Toliver
Fifth Grade Teacher
Hunton, Jane Thompson
AP Jr & Sr English Teacher
Kenney, John William, III
Assoc Prof of Chemistry
Loehr, Hazel Delores
English & French Teacher
Maguire, Trish (James)
Stu Support Svcs Dir & Prof
Olmsted, Merlene Loretta
Family & Consumer Science Prof
Parker, Scott
Physical Education Teacher
Willis, Jack Kim
Science Department Chair
PUEBLO OF ACOMA
James, Rachel White
Former Teacher
QUESTA
Durbin, Dianna Porter
6th Grade Teacher
Valdez, Janice Annabel
Spcl Ed & Life Skills Teacher
RAMAH
Adams, Pamela Callaway
Language Arts Teacher
RATON
Boyle, Marilyn Dianne
Asst Prin & Spec Ed Teacher
Walton, Warren Gary
Social Studies Teacher
RESERVE
Shellhorn, Cindy C.
English & Language Arts Tchr
ROSWELL
Allen, Ann R.
Chemistry & Physics Teacher
Alsup, Nancy Storey
4th Grade Teacher
Bailey, Sharon
English Teacher
Bartl, David F.
Adjunct Professor of English
Boling, Jamie (Ward)
Math Teacher
Boswell, Lana Littell
Eighth Grade English Teacher
Butler, Keith Kevin
History, Geography & Math Tchr
Castillo, M. Lucinda Simmons
Third Grade Teacher
Castillo, Roger Kent
Science & Math Teacher
Cavin, Nancy Anne
7th-8th Grade Math Teacher
Cooper, Barbara Tallcott
4th Grade Teacher
Cooper, Britt
World History Teacher
Cutrell, Leonard Earl
Math & Computer Teacher
De Los Santos, Rudy Martinez
Counselor
Eaton, Elizabeth Hope
High School English Teacher
Edmonson, Alan
Assoc Prof of Social Science
Enox, Lonna Wenella
English Teacher
Evans, Sue Bounds
Second Grade Teacher
Ford, Pierce T.
His, Eng & Geography Teacher
Fuller, Bryan
Agriculture Education Tchr
Gottlieb, Brenda Mallory
Second Grade Teacher
Greer, Annie Craven
4th Grade Teacher
Hanson, Betty Husemoller
English Instructor
Harvey, Felecia Lee
Instructor of Life Sciences
Henry, Debbie Cheryl
Science Teacher
Herrera, Patsy Gustamantes
Dir Occupational Therapy Asst
Hill, Hayden Lee
US History Teacher & Coach
Hitchcock, Walter Theodore
Assoc Professor of History
Huckabee, Heidi
8th Grade English Teacher
Hughes, MeLinda DeAnn
Instructor of Language & Lit
Ibrahim, Abdel K.
Accounting & Business Instr
Jones, Vicki
Math Teacher
Kilness, Cherryl Kay
Instr of Study Skills & Math
Klassen, Diane June
Bus Instr & Media Specialist
Mac Callum, Joanne E.
Soc Stud Tchr & Dept Head
Maples, Robert Emerson
Chaplain & Dir of Counseling
Martin, Susan Ann
Second Grade Teacher
Massey, Gail
Algebra Teacher
Massey, Norman
Athro, Soc & World His Tchr
May, Susan Ensenat
Physical Science Instructor
Mc Nallen, Barbara J.
Business Department Chair
Monteith, Henry Clarence
Instr of Math & Science
Nelson, Norma Sue
Mathematics Instructor
Nokes, Linda Watson
Special Education Teacher
Perri, Janet E.
Math Instructor
Perri, Janet Stevens
Dev Studies English Instructor
Posuniak, Barbara Schmidt
Ceramics Department Head
Posz, Joseph Daniel
Criminal Justice Instructor
Priest, Elizabeth Schabacker
Assistant Professor of English
Reyes, Bertha Alicia Martinez
1st Grade Bilingual Teacher
Rivera, Cristina
6th Grade Teacher
Rupe, Jarrold Craig
CIS Instructor
Satterlee, Carolyn Andrecht
Reading Director
Seale, Jerry Nelle (Ward)
8th Grd English Teacher
Selmon, Janet L.
High School Mathematics Tchr
Smith, Clara Mae (Blocksom)
Communication & Theatre Instr
Taylor, Frances Evelyn
Retired AP Eng & Jrnlsm Tchr
Valdez, Flo R.
Physical Education Teacher
Valdez, Laura Wilkerson
3rd Grade Bilingual Teacher
Waldrip, Suzie
Third Grade Teacher
Watson, Barbara Jeanne
Science Teacher
Weathers, Linda Lepard
Special Education Teacher
Whalen, Stephen Patrick
Physical Fitness Tchr & Coach
ROWE
Melone, Helena Warbasse
English Teacher & Dept Head
ROY
Mayer, Loren Roe
Science Department Chair
RUIDOSO
Ames, Gerald M.
Teacher & Coach
Burns, Carla D.
8th Grade Science Teacher
Clarke, Eva Wray
Kindergarten Teacher
Durham, Rebecca L.
HS Home Economics Teacher
Keeton, Mary Ellen (Ellie)
Library-Media Specialist
Reeder, Karen Emerald
Art Teacher
Stierwalt, Diorly Jean
Language Arts Teacher
Willard, Donna J.
Eng Comm & Journalism Teache
SAN JON
Dowell, Sue York
English & History Teacher
SANTA FE
Abrahamson, Seth M.
Mathematics & Physics Teacher
Aguilar-Eoff, Sylvia Marie
Director of Guidance
Allen, Don R.
Math Instructor
Argueta Allocca, Ramona F.
Bilingual Ed & Span Teacher
Armendariz, GeorgeAnn Ashley
Sixth Grade Teacher
Baca, Michael Anthony
Mathematics Teacher
Bates, Jane Elizabeth
American History Instructor
Bush, Barney
Professor of English
Cammarata, John P.
Academic Counselor
Carroll, Arthur Paul
Prof of Biology & Dept Chair
Carroll, Michael J.
Math Department Chairman
Chapin, Carolyn Wendy
Assistant Professor
Charbonneau, Manon Pettit
Education Professor
Cook, Richard L.
Professor of Art & Dept Chair
Cozzens, Alan Charles
8th Grd Mathematics Teacher
Dailey, Charles Andrew
Prof & Dept Chm of Museum Stu
DePolo, David Michael
History Instructor
Dobson, Lisa M. Tronset
Business Teacher
Gerlach, Anita Nugent
Phys Tchr & Sci Math Curr Coor
Goldfarb, Barry E.
Tutor
Hagman, Ernestine B. Gallegos
Language Arts Teacher
Hardaway, Bonnie (Beardsworth)
US History Teacher
Johnson, David William
Professor of Biology
Lee, Davis H.
HS Teacher & Curriculum Coord
Lujan, Michael
Physical Education Teacher
Madrid, William
Industrial Education Teacher
Martza, Carlotta M.
Commnctn & Drama Teacher
Mier, Therese Bouschard
4th & 5th Grade Tutor
Mora, Victoria J.
Tutor
Pantano, John Michael
Division Head of Arts & Sci
Read, Susan Webster
English Teacher & Dept Chair
Reese, Dane Gregory
Director
Reid, Barbara Elaine
Ed Dept Chprsn & Assoc Prof
Ross, Annie Grace
Prof of Native Amer Art His
Rudolph, Susan Marie
Cmptr Specialist & US His Tchr
Sandoval, Patricia Thomas
Physics, Chem & Phys Sci Tchr
Shelton, Jay W.
Science Dept Chair & Teacher
Snider, Richard D.
Music Dept Chair & Band Dir
Weber, Dorothy M.
Third Grade Teacher
White, Marie Vasaturo
Head of Middle School
Yazzie, Melanie A.
Professor of Printmaking
Zoernig, Kevin Allen
Assistant Professor of Music
SANTA TERESA
Asbell, H. Elaine
English Teacher
Hernandez, Rudy O.
Counselor
Hinojosa, Jose Frederico
Social Studies & Art Teacher

TERESA (cont)
Brenda H.
e & Broadcst Jrnlsm Tchr
s, Robert Anthony
Director
Richard
ade Mathematics Teacher
elipe A.
Instructor
ski, Mark J.
e Teacher
OCK
Garrison, Martha A.
f Navajo Lang & History
elvin Hardy
al Ed Teacher
n, Rhetta Huff
y & Consumer Sci Tchr
ce, Donald
& Foundation Stud Instr
Lisa A.
ess Teacher
n, Kenneth LeRoy
rgarten Teacher
e, James Alfred
Sci Division Chair
Martha R. McCaw
d Earth Science Teacher
hristopher James
matics Teacher
R CITY
ez, Roberto M.
d US History Teacher
Wendy Colby
h Teacher
d, Richard Earl
sor of Sociology
Joseph Thomas
Studies Teacher
Michael J.
Crafts Teacher
Catherine Walz
h Teacher
David
Dept Chair
June I.
f Movement Sci
ack Kerr
Theatre & Drama Dscpln
nam, Joan Hodson
age Arts Teacher
William George
Grade Teacher
ich, Catherine Durrett
sh Teacher
ez de Killough, Pilar
er Science Tchr & Admin
, James Bub
ducation Instructor
n, Thomas Peter
Prof of Math
Terry Charles
tment Chair
Elizabeth Barnes
sh Teacher & Dept Chm
k, Frank Saint
ant Professor of English
Peggy Sue
uter Teacher
ez, Arthur D.
ssor of Political Science
, Annette Dominguez
ture Teacher
Christy T.
al Education Teacher
Dennis Steven
ssor
l, Linda Crutcher
ematics Teacher
Mary R.
rade Teacher
Monica C.
al Education Teacher
Robert Earl
ssor of Counseling
s, Emily Smith
& Home Ecnomics Teacher
Bonni Jo
rgarten Teacher
i, Donald Anthony
rade Science Teacher
Lydia Yvonne
chr & Head Vllybl Coach
er, John Davey
Prof of Criminal Justice
Irma Saenz
Grade Teacher
o, Nadine A.
ce Dept Chair & Teacher
-Ortiz, Janet
ng Asst Prof & Dept Chair
RRO
in, Laurel Bernice
tant Professor of Geology
, W. Greg
leum Engrng Professor
ernard R.
ipal
ker, Patrick Wynn
gn Lang Tchr & Dept Chair
IGER
va, Sherie Martinez
nglish & History Tchr
o, Elizabeth J.
ematics & Spanish Teacher

s, Nancy Mayson
sh Department Chair
o, Paul N.
s & Government Teacher

THOREAU
Heward, T. Dick
Biology Teacher
VanAlstine, Rick G.
8th Grade Social Studies Tchr
Ward, Laddie Jayne (Stanec)
English Teacher
TOHATCHI
Beverage, Fred D.
Agriculture Education Teacher
Jones, Irvinn Lonson
Social Studies & Spec Ed Tchr
Lerkins, Robert
Math Teacher
TRUTH OR CONSEQUENCES
Morrow, Tommy
Mathematics Teacher
Schnyder, Raybella Verdue
Mathematics Instructor
TUCUMCARI
Baca, Lonnie J.
US, World His & Geog Tchr
Hudson, Lynn Parker
Math Teacher & Dept Chair
TULAROSA
Burns, Elizabeth Suzanne
Chem & Environmental Sci Instr
Coleman, Terri Murphy
9th-10th Grade Lang Arts Tchr
Reid, Michael Jac
HS English Teacher
Vigil, Brenda Kay (Singleton)
Principal
VAUGHN
Gallegos, Peggy Scheihagen
Math Teacher
Maes, Pat J.
Lang Arts Tchr, Cnslr & Coach
VELARDE
Gallegos, Pauline Martinez
ESL Teacher
WAGON MOUND
Lujan, Eddie
Business Education Instructor
ZUNI
Spencer, Lisa Sandoval
Special Education Teacher

NEW YORK

ACCORD
Arra, Catherine Mary
Eng & Creative Writing Teacher
Catalfomo, Joseph Rocco
Social Studies Teacher
Constantinou, Gus
7th & 8th Grd Soc Stud Teacher
DeLuca, Linda (Benna)
Computer Coordinater
Doran, Edward G.
Science Teacher
Haber, Catherine M.
First Grade Teacher
Meoli, Patricia Ann Setariano
English Teacher
Rockmuller, Clifford N.
Spanish & French Teacher
ADAMS
Babcock, John Winford
Mathematics Teacher
Blanding, Jade Marie
7th-9th Grade English Teacher
Burnash, Peter Thomas
Social Studies Tchr & Dept Chm
Campany, Patrick Michael
5th Grade Teacher
Crast, Julie Gordinier
Sixth Grade Teacher
Lowe, Nancy L. (Gordinier)
High School Math Teacher
Ranger-Darby, Rose Nicotra
7th-12th Grd Rdng Specialist
Rudari, David Joseph
Vocal Music Dir & Spanish Tchr
Rudd, Sharon B.
Math Teacher
Shevalier, Mary Ellen Kalil
Art & Dance Teacher
Smith, Marcia Zahn
English Teacher
Spinelli, Georgette F.
Fourth Grade Teacher
Stevens, Heather Crapser
Chemistry Teacher
Stowell, William Charles
Agriculture Teacher
Wasilenko, Bruce Joseph
Earth Science & Chemistry Tchr
ADDISON
Bahantka, Scott
Physical Education Instructor
Flynn, Sheila Aldrich
Second Grade Teacher
Green, Jean M.
Chemistry Teacher
Kerwan, Debra Lee
English Teacher
Rankin, Harry Lee
Social Studies Teacher
AKRON
Drayer, Jerry K.
Social Studies Teacher
Palmeri, Kandy Beane
2nd Grade Teacher
Rosic, Jeannette Lilly
1st Grade Teacher
Serapiglia, Karla Krull
English Teacher

ALBANY
Amodeo, David Patrick
French Teacher
Andes, Barbara Marie, SNJM
Math Teacher
Bullock, Teddi Callaghan
Administrative Analyst
Bulson, Lucretia Scardillo
Mathematics Teacher
Catena, Christine Lynne
Guidance Counselor
Clancy, Pamela Jane
Sci & Soc Stud Tchr
Cole, Debbie Goliber
Biology Teacher
Conte, Nick
Guidance Counselor
Conway, Kathryn Marie
Science Teacher
Currier, Jill Anne
English Teacher
Dahlgren, Jean Garvey
Associate Professor
Dollard, William E.
Asst Principal for Stu Affairs
Dorn, Robert Adam
Physical Education Instructor
Drischell, Desmond Brady
Fourth Grade Teacher
Durocher, Robert Joseph
Biology & Health Teacher
Farley, Mary R.
Fourth Grade Teacher
Felson, Richard Barnet
Professor of Sociology
Flannery, Judith White
7th-8th Grd Soc Studies Tchr
Gansle, Paul B.
PE Teacher & Coach
Gunther, Philip
Art & Architecture Teacher
Gustin, Sandra L.
English Teacher
Hodgkinson, Patricia Mc Guire
Middle School English Teacher
Johnston, Barbara A.
Band Director
Jones, Roger A.
Retired Elementary School Tchr
Kapp, Judith A., RSM
Mathematics Teacher
Lawson, Judith Day
Secondary Mathematics Teacher
Leahey, Christopher Thomas
Health & Physical Ed Teacher
Leicht-Bowers, Barbara A.
Physical Education Teacher
Long, Patricia Burke
French & Spanish Teacher
Mc Graw, Kelly
Guidance Counselor
Mehleisen, Patricia Ann (Relihan)
Fifth Grade Teacher
Millis, Joanne M.
Art Teacher
Moore-Palumbo, Susan T.
Biology Teacher
Nimmer, Tim
Social Studies Teacher
Outman, Kenneth Ronald
Mathematics Teacher
Paone, Thomas Joseph
Hlth Educator Coord & Teacher
Ponkos-Merola, Barbara Joan
Health Teacher
Powell, Mary Jane Siegling
Junior HS Language Arts Tchr
Priest, Ronald Edward
Science Teacher
Rea, Mary Schaufert
Assistant Professor of Biology
Reynolds, Judith Malone
Music Teacher
Robelotto, Richard A.
American History Teacher
Schatz, Joan Currier
Mathematics Teacher
Seward, Jay
Social Studies Teacher
Smircich, Janice Montalbano
Eng, Lit & Rel Tchr
Smith, Lawrence M.
Chemistry & Physics Teacher
Smith, Mary Donohue
Special Education Teacher
Testo, Patricia Loonan
Art Teacher
Warde, Diane Rose
Spanish Teacher
Watkins, Marilyn Orzelek
Social Science Teacher
Wright, Wilbur L.
English Teacher
Wysolmerski, Theresa B.
Professor of Biology
Zeeh, Ann
Assistant Professor of Biology
Zentz, Robert L.
Adj Professor of Science Ed
ALBERTSON
Babbit, Barbara A.
6th Grade Teacher
Bucher, Denise Drescher
Social Studies Teacher
Fauvell, Thomas Carmine
Social Studies Teacher
Mare, Rosette Jacqueline
French & Spanish Teacher
Sollano, Rosemarie
Spanish & Italian Teacher

Tear, Howard H.
Science Teacher
ALBION
Burgio, Linda D.
Kindergarten Teacher
Grammatico, Michael P.
Music Teacher
Hellert, Patricia L.
4th Grade Teacher
Kerr, Linda Smith
Second Grade Teacher
Kingsbury, Gary A.
8th Grade Math Teacher
Kish, John B.
6th Grd Inclusion Tchr & Coord
Klatt, Roger J.
Alternative Education Teacher
Knaak, Randy Scott
Physical Education Teacher
Neal, Tammorah Mae
Aide & Coach
Nickerson, Bradford Drew, Jr.
Spanish Teacher
Ostrowski, Debra W.
Mathematics Teacher
Pierce, Maura B.
English Teacher
Sanford, Jonathan Malcolm
Third Grade Teacher
Simboli, Gary J.
Special Education Teacher
Smith, Irene Tuttle
Latin Teacher
Sodoma, Karen Goodwin
Math Teacher
Thompson, Judy A.
6th Grade Teacher
Turpyn, Susan Engle
High School Art Teacher
Wells, Suzanne DiLaura
Art Teacher
Wood, Debra Ann
Physical Education Teacher
ALDEN
Cowan, Thomas L.
Health & Physical Ed Instr
Domino, Deborah A.
9th Grade Math & Business Tchr
Garber, Georgia I.
English Teacher
Kaczmarek, Marianne (LoTempio)
Earth Science Teacher
Miller, Dolores Osterman
Chem Teacher & Sci Chairperson
Papagni, Nick
Middle School Science Teacher
Starr, Robyn J.
Social Studies Teacher
Vandenbergh, Peter
5th Grade Elementary Teacher
ALEX BAY
Hammond, Donna Hogeland
Art Teacher
Martin, Robin Marie
High School Mathematics Tchr
Sayyeau, Paul A.
French Teacher
ALEXANDER
Adrian, George M.
4th Grade Teacher
Emborsky, Eugene F.
Science Teacher
Neider, Mary Ann (Bartholf)
Sixth Grade Teacher
Nelli, Gail Becker
English, Theatre & Speech Tchr
Rupert, Anne Elm
Retired Third Grade Teacher
Schauer-Webster, Lynn
High School Art Teacher
ALFRED
Acton, Daniel D.
Professor of Accountancy
Amarakoon, Vasantha R.
Prof of Ceramic Eng
Bentz, Wesley Earl
Professor of Chemistry
Boyd, Gina Mary
PE & Health Instructor
Buckwalter, John David
Professor of Biology
Burdick, Carol
Assistant Professor of English
Caligaris, Susan Roebuck
Dance Professor
Carlo, Richard Thomas
Assoc Prof of Architecture
Fong, Jerry David
Chemistry Professor
Geiling-Yelle, Sondra Sue G.
Associate Professor
Grillo, James J.
Prof & Bus Admin Dept Chm
Heineman, Robert Allen
Professor of Political Science
Hoover, Sharon
Asst Professor of English
Jacobson, Wendee Elizabeth
English Professor
Jakobi, Steven Richard
Assistant Prof of Biology
Jeck, Doug Alan
Art Professor
Johnston, Jeffrey Francis
Associate Professor of Arch
Law, David Lawrence
Asst Prof of Computer Science
Luehman, Cynthie Bryant
Nursing Professor

Mead, Morris C.
Assoc Prof & Curr Coordinator
Mitchell, Richard Anthony
English Professor
Perrigo, Karen (Leonard)
Associate Prof of Accounting
Porter, Karen L.
Sociology Professor
Rummel, Amy Beth Powell
Assoc Professor of Marketing
Shelby, James Elbert
Prof of Ceramic Engineering
Sorochin, Ronald F.
Associate Professor
Stewart, Carol Wendt
Mathematics Instructor
Thomas, Janette Bucki
Health Information Tech Prof
Troller, Fred
Professor of Design
Vance, Gerald Alan
Laboratory Instructor
Viggiani, Frances Anne
Prof of Mgmt, Orgnl Behavior
Walker, Gail C.
Professor of Psychology
Wang, Xingwu
Assoc Prof Electrical Engrng
Wissert, Joan Kennedy
Asst Prof of Ornamental Hort
ALLEGANY
Bergan, Lois Dascomb
Fourth Grade Teacher
Fancher, William W.
Instrumental Music Teacher
Kerner, John E.
Mathematics Teacher
Quattrone, Kenneth Leo
Math Chair
Renaud, Yvonne M.
Science & Mathematics Teacher
Trainor, Helen A.
Kindergarten Teacher
Wahl, Ruth Turner
Science Teacher
Zwald, James M.
Spanish Teacher
ALMOND
Curl, Kathryn Chatham
English Teacher
Fernandez, Lori Greene
Business Education Teacher
Hackett, Harold B., Jr.
Retired Adj Professor of Math
Shultz, Ellen L.
English & Theater Teacher
ALTMAR
Harrington, Vicky Iocco
Third Grade Teacher
AMAGANSETT
Hallisey, Jeremiah Joseph
Retired Dean of Stud, Lecturer
AMENIA
Benken, Cheryl M.
French Teacher
Brizzie, Margaret Traudt
Sixth Grade Teacher
Edwards, Charles Dennis
Blackbelt Master Instructor
Gower, Lisa Chase
Foreign Language Teacher
Kelly, Thomas Michael
Biology Teacher
Laufer, Lorraine
English Teacher
Reagon, David B.
Earth Science & Driver Ed Tchr
Reagon, Janet Meade
Social Studies Teacher
Trachtenberg, Craig L.
Science Teacher
Vozab, John B.
English Teacher
AMHERST
Allen, Sue Fay
Music Teacher & Coordinator
Appler, Steven Andrew
Art Teacher
Bailey, Thomas John
History & Drama Teacher
Brogan, Michael Spencer
Asst Prof of Phys Therapy Dept
D'Agostino, R. Alfredo
9th-12th Grade Science Teacher
Griffo, Joseph J.
Social Studies Teacher
Hartwick, Patrick James
Assoc Prof of Spec Education
Hubert, Marianne Gerilyn
Junior High Teacher
Ismail, Zafar A.
Professor of Physics
Jablonski, Carol Wawrzynek
Mathematics Tchr & Dept Chprsn
Kalinowski, Douglas P.
Assistant Professor of Biology
Kehoe, Judith A. Opiela
First Grade Teacher
Kotlarz, Virginia
Dept Chair & Prgm Dir Med Tech
Kuechler, Linda Eckert
Accounting Professor
Maloney, Eileen Kathryn
Eng Teacher & Department Chair
Marvin, John D.
Retired Teacher
Mc Govern, Terry E.
Fourth Grade Teacher
Mills, Denise Gianadda
Associate Professor of Spanish

AMHERST (cont)
Passarelli, Henry David
Fifth Grade Teacher
Ram, Russell James
Art Teacher
Scharnweber, Lisa Marie
Mathematics Teacher
Sleeper, Mark David
Physical Therapy Asst Prof
Suhalla, Virginia C.
Asst Professor of Education
Viscardo, Gertrude Rieker
Accelerated Math Teacher
AMITYVILLE
Alves, Bennie Ruth
Kindergarten Teacher
Christian, James Robert
Chemistry Teacher
Deitz, Allan
High School Band Director
Doran, Kerry Parker
History Teacher & Ath Director
Gainey, Linda Perry
Science & English Teacher
Keller, Paula
Third Grade Teacher
Rickenbacker, Patricia Marshall
Guidance Counselor
Schecter, Barbara
Acctg & HS Bus Law Teacher
Thomas, Evelyn Thompkins
English Teacher
Wassmer, Agnes, OP
Retired Mentor
AMSTERDAM
Bancroft, Edward Palmer
Social Studies Teacher
Bartsch, Nancy J.
Mathematics, Computer Sci Tchr
Brooks, Raechelle Lynne
History & Typing Teacher
DeAngelis, Guy R.
Retired Third Grade Teacher
De Lilli, Michael N.
6th Grade Math Teacher
Hand, Maureen
English Teacher
Hills, Michael A.
Mathematics Teacher
Jacobs, Rose Mary
8th Grade Teacher
Kaufman, Douglas Jerome
Social Studies Teacher
Lynch, Debra Maczynski
Science Teacher
Mc Gillin, William Patrick
Social Studies Teacher
McKnight, Timothy Lee
Social Studies Teacher
Morse, Raymond Frank
Fifth & Sixth Grade Elem Tchr
Nelson, William T.
Eng, Drama & Television Tchr
Palczak, Stuart John
Social Studies Teacher
Pfeiffer, Kathleen Witek
Family & Consumer Sci Teacher
Pfeiffer, Kenneth Robert
Tech Drafting Teacher
Quatrini, Marilyn Scheckton
English Teacher
Rzeznik, Joseph J.
Chemistry Teacher
Smrtic, Sharon Palombi
Spanish Teacher
ANDOVER
Baker, Cindy Preston
High School Mathematics Tchr
Close, Joseph Manley
Jr & Sr HS History Teacher
Patrick, Kathleen A.
Science Teacher
Shoales, Michael Alan
Instrumental Music Teacher
Witherow, Catherine Saslawsky
English Teacher
ANGOLA
Bartolotti, Michael Joseph
MS Physical Education Tchr
Cislo, Tina Zdrojewski
Mid & HS Home Economics Tchr
Cristofaro, Corrinne Elizabeth
Business Education Teacher
Donovan, Thomas Paul
Sixth Grade Teacher
Harrison, Lance Edward
PE Teacher & Coach
Herlihy, Thomas Michael
Music Teacher
Hornberger, Paul M.
Fifth Grade Teacher
Lambrix, Patricia M.
9th Grade English Teacher
Mahany, Robert James
Business Education Teacher
Mc Bride, James A.
Mathematics Teacher
Swyers, Susan Lehning
Social Studies Teacher
Walter, Sharon Garthwaite
Fifth Grade Teacher
APALACHIN
Ellis, Janet Langdon
Fourth Grade Teacher
Remza, Fredricka J.
3rd-5th Grd Enrichment Prgm
Seward, Robin Dukerich
Fourth Grade Teacher
Wiggins, Mary Jean (Algar)
Fourth Grade Teacher

AQUEBOGUE
Niebergall, Joanne
2nd Grade Teacher
ARDSLEY
Chason, David Ben
Physics Teacher
Corten, Sylvie Martina
French & Spanish Teacher
Furci, Maria A.
Biology Teacher & Curr Leader
Parsons, Margaret Loconto
Physical Education Teacher
Tatlow, Patricia Whiskeman
Fourth Grade Teacher
Thurtell, Craig Martin
US History Teacher
ARGYLE
Depew, Margo Crawford
2nd Grade Teacher
Galough, Jamie Pereau
Family & Consumer Science Tchr
LaGoy, Dennis Mark
High School Math Instructor
Lane, Linda D.
English Teacher
Myott, Richard Stewart
Science Teacher
ARKPORT
Deres, Alice Sereghy
Art Teacher
Guenther, Theresa A.
Librarian
Wood, Harold Maurice, III
Mathematics Teacher
ARMONK
Cohen, Jacqueline G.
Mathematics Chairperson
Ruyack, Robert David
Spanish Teacher
Varley, Joy A.
Choir & Theatre Director
ASHVILLE
Saletta, Richard Joseph
Criminal Justice Teacher
ASTORIA
Burke, Mary Clare
Mathematics Teacher
Raspante, Patrick
Youth Family Minister
ATHOL SPRINGS
Benicewicz, Joseph
Assistant Principal
Hess, Norma M.
Spanish Teacher
Nease, David George
Fine Arts Department Chair
ATTICA
Burnside, Warren LaVerne
7th Grade Social Studies Tchr
Conway, Constance J.
High School English Teacher
Henry, Richard F.
Sixth Grade Teacher
Kriner, Holly Freeman
Second Grade Teacher
Sadlon, Kathleen E.
High School Earth Science Tchr
Skinner, Debra
Instrumental Music Teacher
AUBURN
Barnes, Scott D.
Professor of Bus & Soc Science
Blair, Thomas C.
8th Grd Health Teacher
Brunell, Robert Henry
Professor of English
Carnicelli, Anne Marie
Middle School Reading Teacher
Cresco, Carolyn Catto
English Teacher
Fama, Donald F.
Prof of Math & Computer Sci
Farnell, Alfred William
Technology Teacher
Gero, Anthony Francis
HS Social Studies Teacher
Harris, Ernest C.
Social Studies Teacher
Honcharski, Barbara A.
Math & Computer Science Tchr
Keeler, Steven Robert
Telecommunications Professor
Lawton, Bonnie Williams
Music & Strings Teacher
Leary, Donna Namisniak
Math Teacher
Locastro, William A.
7th Grade Science Teacher
Ozog, Richard Peter
Spanish Teacher
Panek, Dorothy Ryan
Literature & Composition Tchr
Patterson, John E.
English Teacher
Pearsall, Kenneth Gordon
Science Teacher
Quigley, Kevin James
Social Studies Teacher
Rizzieri, William Richard
Technology Education Teacher
Robinson, Alfred Wesley
6th Grade Teacher
Seamans, Lois Fronczek
Nursing Instructor
Seward, Mary Ann Ranalli
Foreign Language Teacher
Shinal, Paul J.
Certified Public Accountant
Smith, Gerald Michael
Mathematics Professor

Stomps, Stephen A.
Director of Choirs
Valdina, Diana Lo Castro
Associate Prof of English Dept
Weber, Lauren J.
English Teacher
Welch, Kathy Ann
Fifth Grade Teacher
AURORA
Blair, Bonny J.
1st Grade Teacher
Engram, Pamela Sue
Psych Visiting Asst Professor
AVERILL PARK
Cassella, Joseph L.
Business Education Teacher
Costello, Amelia Fusco
English & Theater Teacher
Fairchild, Daniel Jon
English Teacher
Joslin, Melissa Ann
Biology Teacher
Keith, Diane Marie
Mathematics Teacher
Ladd, Thomas Paul
Math & Science Teacher
Mac Gilfrey, June Denise
Physical Education Teacher
Monahan, Martin J.
AP History Teacher
Smith, Denise Darrow
High Schl Mathematics Teacher
Thanopoulos, Anthony Nicholas
Chemistry Teacher
Zaffuts, Gerald
Director of Bands
AVOCA
Anderson, Victoria Gledhill
Title I Reading Teacher
Tears, Elaine Kaye
Latin Teacher
AVON
Leone, Peter B.
HS Social Studies Teacher
Roberts, John A.
Social Studies Teacher
BABYLON
Bergen, Michael L.
Math Teacher
Brown, Barbara Ann
PE & Special Ed Teacher
Burns, Richard Craig
6th Grade Teacher
Castine, Patricia Dooley
Third Grade Teacher
Cuty, James Michael
Business Education Teacher
DePaola, Dominic Philip
High School Music Teacher
Dlouhy, Barry Richard
English Teacher & Dept Chair
Drake, Andrea Nina
English Teacher
Drance, Daniel A.
Mathematics Curriculum Coord
Faraone, Nicholas Frank
Social Studies Teacher
Hartz, Janet Morrow
English Teacher
Kennedy, Diane
Math Teacher
Long, Bruce John
Retired Guidance Counselor
Lynch, James R.
American History Teacher
Malaszczyk, Mark Scott
HS Social Studies Teacher
Moran, Joyce Leonardo
High School Italian Teacher
Morisie, Rosalie Valenti
Mathematics Teacher
Mountcastle, Deirdre DeGarmo
First Grade Teacher
Paris, Anita
Sixth Grade Team Leader
Procaccini, Frank Joseph
Social Studies Director
Prohaske, Donna Diane
Social Studies Teacher
Reiners, Dianne
First Grade Teacher
Scottaline, Michael E.
Asst Prin & European His Tchr
Stone Martin, Jacqueline Eileen
Orchestra Teacher
Topazio, Celeste
High School Art Teacher
Vaswani, Sheila Ann
Global Studies I Teacher
Woronowich, Nancy Arpaia
Elementary Education Teacher
BAINBRIDGE
Halsey, Kevin Edward
Mathematics Teacher
Hughes, Gordon D., Jr.
Health Teacher
Kohler, Jean Steehler
Secondary Math Teacher
BALDWIN
Bauer, Helen P.
Band Director
Belikis, Patricia
English Teacher
Bohbot, Joan Ellen
English Teacher
Bythewood, Lorraine M. Gomillion
6th Grade Teacher
Carnevale, Patricia A.
Foreign Language Teacher

Carroll, James Joseph
7th-8th Grade Science Teacher
Connolly, Eileen M.
Guidance Counselor
Dallari, Elaine Danner
Resource Room Teacher
Donohue, Patricia Ann
English Teacher
Edwards, Melinda
HS Music Teacher
Fletcher, Ina C.
Physical Education Teacher
Hart, Marian Janice
American History Teacher
Kellner, Linda Zuckerman
Spanish Teacher
Lynch, Dorothy L.
Guidance Counselor
Notto, Robert Vincent
Music Teacher & Band Director
Riess, Barbara Ann
Physics Teacher
Russo, Alisa
High School Science Teacher
Schleith, Helmut John
Science Teacher
Shenkman, Susan Fischer
Mathematics Teacher
Vineberg, Carol
6th Grade Teacher
BALDWINSVILLE
Alger, Ann Marie
Third Grade Teacher
Ast, Marlene Marty
Spcl Ed Inclusion Tchng Asst
Bader, Nancy Squire
English Teacher
Bender, David W.
Chemistry Teacher
Bick, Jon Eric
8th Grd Social Studies Tchr
Bowen, Jonathan
Band Director
Coulter, Gertrud Peukert
German Teacher
Cross, Christine Anne
Social Studies Teacher
Eassa, Rebecca Bechard
Mathematics Teacher
Guillet, Abbe Nathanson
French Teacher
Halligan, John Alfred
Fifth Grade Teacher
Lepine, Maurice Joseph
Technology Education Teacher
Malecki, Annette Hagy
High School Science Teacher
Miller, Robert Wayne
High School Art Teacher
Mincolla, Michele Marano
French Teacher
Mitchell, Joseph
Retired Fourth Grade Teacher
O'Toole, Joanne Rindenello
Spanish Teacher
Powell, Jeffrey W.
Physics Teacher
Romano, Barbara Bucci
English Teacher
Ryan, Elaine Tosh
First Grade Teacher
Tucker, Sheila S.
Earth Science Teacher
Wanzer, Norman
Instrumental Music Teacher
Ward, Shawn Michael
Math Teacher
BALLSTON LAKE
Fielding, Patricia Margaret
Fourth Grade Teacher
BALLSTON SPA
Akey, Wayne James
Math Teacher
Bertrand, Wayne Charles
Health Educator
Hall, Georgiann Maud
Science Teacher
Messing, Patrica
Spanish Teacher
Staulters, Harold Jay
Soc Stud & Global Studies Tchr
Theilemann, Ruth Morris
K-5th Grd Music Teacher
True, Pamela W.
Fifth Grade Teacher
BARKER
Few, Gary W.
Retired Jr & Sr HS Music Tchr
Haak, Kenneth J.
Global Studies Teacher
Haley, Jane Matthews
English Teacher
Mc Murray, Peggy Harrison
2nd Grade Teacher
Otto, Judith Coleman
HS Physical Ed Tchr & Coach
Roth, Robert Edward
6th Grade Science Teacher
Schian, Karen Sue (Price)
Home Economics Teacher
BASOM
Childs, Alice Meiser
Retired Kindergarten Teacher
Pillo, Angelo J.
Retired Band Director
BATAVIA
Barnes, Larry Dana
Psychology Professor
Borawski, Suzanne Mary (Drumsta)
8th Grade Social Studies Tchr

Boyd, Charles A.
Asst Prof of Eng Intermdt Stud
Brian, Marilyn S.
Mathematics Teacher
Brown, William Morgan
Professor of Commercial Art
Buresch, Pamela J.
English Teacher & Dept Chair
Cayea, Lance W.
Dean of Students
Culling, Nancy L.
Earth Science Teacher
Degenhardt, Anne Palmer
Kindergarten Teacher
DePalma, Judy Ann (Lazzaro)
Prof of Business Office Tech
Ethington, Marirose Torcello
Biology Instructor
Gayford, Norman Rodney
Assistant Professor of English
Hawkins, Donald A.
Special Education Teacher
Howell, Burton Clark
Science Teacher
Iglesias-Cardinale, Vincent Paul
English Instructor
Juliano, Mary Ellen Giordano
Business & Computer Instructor
Marcus, Joan Isabel (Cushing)
Adj Instr of French & English
Schulte, Ellen Gesser
7th Grade Social Studies Tchr
Smielecki, Kelly J.
Spanish Teacher
Starkweather, Paul Douglas
Social Studies Teacher
Starowitz, Anne Marie Peca
Fourth Grade Teacher
Tomczak, Timothy Peter
Assistant Professor of Psych
Volpe, Margaret Doyle
English Teacher
Weston, Jane A.
Biology Instructor
Whitcombe, David R.
Science Teacher
Zummo, Joan E.
Assistant Prof of Biology
BATH
Congdon, Sherry Dunlap
Second Grade Teacher
Hagadorn, Thomas W.
Secondary Math Teacher
Herter, Betty Lou K.
Computer Instructor
Howell, Dorothy VanDusen
Retired Elementary Teacher
Hy, Philip J.
Spanish Teacher
Ridley, Olivia P.
English Teacher
Updyke, Lori L.
French Teacher
Watson, Samuel P.
Instrumental Music Teacher
BAY SHORE
Boudreau, Susan Marie
Fifth Grade Teacher
Caputo, Nancy Barton
Math Teacher
Carpenter, Philip M., Jr.
MS Social Studies Chairperson
Cody, John J.
Earth Science Teacher
Damore, Richard
HS Physical Education Teacher
DiMento, Peter R.
Principal
Doyle, Donna Marie
Amer His & Humanities Tchr
Erhartic, Geraldine Mc Glinchey
Sixth Grade Teacher
Gerken, Anne
5th Grade Teacher
Kavanagh, Rosanne Lenore
English Teacher
Mincio, Ronald A.
Sixth Grade Teacher
Schaefer, Edward Anthony
Middle School Band Director
Smith, Diane B. (Vinci)
Second Grade Teacher
BAYPORT
Dolce, Anthony
AP Chemistry Teacher
Eiermann, Louisa Verde
Vocal Music Tchr & Dept Chprsn
Maggi, Karen Carmick
Amer History & Government Tchr
Petre, Rochelle Murphy
Sixth Grade Teacher
BAYSIDE
Fahrer, Linda M.
Social Studies & Spanish Tchr
Franklin, Vivian Natbony
Spanish Teacher
Matzner, Barbara J.
English Teacher
Paraskevopoulos, Anthony Andrew
High School Music Teacher
Pullman, Phyllis L.
Math Teacher
Rattien, Diane
Math Teacher
Schwartz, Sharon
HS English Teacher
Schwortz, Benyonne Joy Lee
Eng Tchr & Core Writing Coord
Spero, Ann Shaloum
Retired Elem Computer Teacher

DE (cont)
Madeline Beth
Teacher
n, Pablo Heriberto
aming, Phys & Hlth Ed Tchr
, Rona Temple
al Studies Teacher
ON
, Darlene Ten Eyck
gy Teacher
Charles Raymond
sh Instructor
y, Margo Salese
sh Teacher
ns, Bruce F.
horal Music Teacher
Catherine Ann Coffey
rade Teacher
ni, Patricia Cashin
rade Science Teacher
Mary Cramer
rade Teacher
ER FALLS
Mary Boshart
rd English Teacher
Loretta Schumacher
rade Teacher
ki, Cyndee Booras
ndary English Teacher
e, Kristine Marie
ch Teacher
chlager, Kathleen Picciano
umental Music Teacher
ORD
Margaret M. (King)
sh Teacher
a, Jon Laurence
nce Teacher
ald, Kathleen E.
h Grade Teacher
no, Richard
ical Education Teacher
an, Dale Andrew
eacher
Anthony
gy & Chemistry Teacher
Marion Caldara
sh Teacher
Elizabeth N.
sh Teacher
ORD HILLS
man, Joan Estes
sh Teacher & Director
William Ross
ical Education Teacher
AST
n, Richard J.
etic Dir & PE Teacher
EROSE
Michele Achtsam
nd Grade Teacher
EVILLE
gton, George Emile
ematics Teacher
MORE
n, Corinne L.
ipal
Thomas Daniel
nce Teacher
y, Anita Glacy
sh Teacher
, Richard Joseph
al Studies Teacher
an, Barbara Bachner
alus Teacher
one, Peter Joseph
ish Teacher
y, Anne M.
Grade Teacher
ck, William Andrew
ics Teacher
oy, Kevin P.
ocial Studies Teacher
ff, Sandra G.
Grade Teacher
Lewis
School Spanish Teacher
e, Daniel Anthony
al Studies Teacher
r, Harvey
nce Teacher
PORT
a, Joseph M.
ish Teacher
, Lillian Mannino
Grade Teacher
Gwendolyn Olivia (Steele)
rade Teacher
d, Brian Francis
th Grade Teacher
h, Valerie Volpi
ematics Teacher
Howard John
al Studies Teacher
nce, Barbara R.
ch Teacher
Guy Joseph
n Teacher
ughlin, William Francis
th Grade Tech Teacher
n, Sally Scofield
ed 6th Grd Lang Arts Tchr
, Francis
ing Teacher
Mary Louise
rade School Teacher
e, Rosemary E.
ish Teacher
Myrna
rade Teacher

BELMONT
Bliven, Judyl (Winterhalter)
Physical Education Teacher
Tenney, Cynthia A.
Spanish Teacher
BEMUS POINT
Burnett, Bernice
4th Grade Teacher
Hale, Doris M.
Spanish Teacher
Holmes, Samuel Louis
Art Teacher
Isaacson, Matthew Oke
Sixth Grade Teacher
Lewellen, Scott J.
Earth & Environmental Sci Tchr
Oste, Marla Johnson
Womens Physical Education Tchr
Pihlblad, Nancy Henderson
Reading Teacher
Plyler, Robert W.
Social Studies & English Tchr
Ventura, Julianne Pyatte
English Teacher
BERGEN
Barone, Samuel M.
Biology Teacher
Bishop, Edward F.
High School Principal
Lesslie, Dennis
Earth Science Teacher
Loughridge, Robert Leland
English & Computer Sci Teacher
Mayer, Wendy Rowland
High School Math Teacher
BERLIN
Bradley, Janet L.
Earth Science Teacher
Cary, Thomas David
Mathematics Teacher
Caywood, Melissa Rose Mary
Instrumental Music Teacher
Fairs, William R.
Math Teacher
Hoffman, Susan Lindemann
8th Grade Soc Stud Teacher
Klein, Sharon Burdick
Business Teacher
Nicholson, Thomas Charles
Health & PE Teacher
Vanderhoef, Audrey Hall
MS Science & Health Teacher
BERNE
Durr, Bonnie Saine
10th-12th Grd Biology Instr
BETHPAGE
Bennardo, Jill C.
Science Teacher
Casella, Ann Janet Wark
Kindergarten Teacher
DiPrima, Anne
Physical Ed & Health Teacher
Director, Maria Giannetta
Math Teacher
Ecker, John
5th Grade Teacher
Farbman, Paula Greenbaum
Choral Director
Iasevoli, Paul
Spanish Teacher
Licht, Steve Leonard
Physical Education Teacher
Melone, Frank Talbot
Middle School Teacher
Sarli, Robert Salvatore
English Instructor
BIG FLATS
Cortese, Krystal Kay
2nd Grade Teacher
Wipfler, William Michael
5th Grade Teacher
BINGHAMTON
Attleson, Eric Edson
7th-12th Grd Technology Tchr
Bachman, Susan Marie (Moore)
Choral Director
Bowker, Robert D.
English Department Chair
Busch, Steven Daniel
PE, Aquatics Tchr & Coach
Campoli, William A., Sr.
Adjunct Instructor of Psych
Chmielenski, Angela La Neve
Social Studies Teacher
Churchward, Richard A.
Social Studies Teacher
Cizenski, Richard Anthony
6th Grade Teacher
Cotten, Anne Boyer
Associate Prof of Art & Design
Denning, Nancy H.
Home & Career Skills Teacher
De Vita, Carmen V.
Learning Assistance Chprsn
Eagan, Mary Ann
Sixth Grade Teacher
Fenty, Martha Lamkin
Assoc Prof of Humanities
Fisher, Howard B.
AP Bio, Anatomy, Physio Tchr
Flynn, Michael James
Social Studies Teacher
Foster, Barbara R.
ESL Professor
Freedman, Martin
Professor of Accounting
Gorton, Rhonwen N.
French Teacher
Hlopko, Jane A.
Assoc Prof of Hlth Tech Pgm

Koons, Frances Jean
English Teacher
Kruppa, Kristal Maria
French & German Teacher
LaBrutto, Matthew Anthony
6th Grade Teacher
LaForce, Shirley Eddy
Retired Kindergarten Teacher
Lane Pierce, Dorothy K.
6th Grade Teacher
LoGalbo, Margaret Theresa (King)
English Instructor
Maier, Suzanne Cahoon
Professor of Dental Hygiene
Maughan, Joseph A.
French & Spanish Teacher
McGowan, William Ellis
Mathematics Teacher
Mc Kedy, John William
Mathematics Dept Chm & Tchr
McKenna, Kathleen Marie
Assistant Professor
Miller, Alberto
Dir of Contracted Intnl Ed
Myers, Brenda Wilkinson
Ed Pgms Supvr & Prof Dev Tchr
Oldfield, Bruce K.
Assoc Professor of Phys Sci
Olnowich, Larraine Barnes
Drama & English Teacher
O'Neil, Patrick Michael
Humanities & Soc Sci Asst Prof
Panko, Cheryl Sloma
Spanish Teacher
Perkins, Richard Paul
PE Teacher & Athletic Dir
Phelps, Susan Williams
Social Studies Teacher
Porter, Steven Clark
Director of Fine Arts
Reitz, Elliott D.
Professor of Biology
Rosenberg, Maxine H. (Epstein)
Elementary Art Teacher
Rosko, Keith Allan
Art Teacher
Ross, Hilary Kristen
Lecturer in English
Rozen, Hersh S.
Guidance Counselor
Shear, Jim
Physics Teacher
Shepard, Suzanne Victoria
Assistant Professor of English
Slechta, Henry M.
Music Dept Chair & Band Dir
Slifer, Mary Kathryn
English Teacher
Swenson, Ida B.
Life Science Teacher
Terwilliger, Connie Ann
Music Director
Tierno, Angela M.
First Grade Teacher
Turshman, Alfred H.
Secondary Mathematics Teacher
VanNess, Raymond Kenneth, Jr.
Professor
Younker, Adam B.
Business Law Professor
BLASDELL
O'Connell, Christine A.
8th Grade Teacher
BLAUVELT
Dougherty, Elizabeth Kirn
Curr Coord, Art & Music Tchr
Kean, Monica M. P.
Spanish Teacher
BLOOMFIELD
Orlando, Samuel Joseph
Retired Teacher
BLOSSVALE
Messmer, Rise Marie
Fifth Grade Teacher
BLUE POINT
Mc Laughlin, Virginia L.
Kindergarten Teacher
Metzendorf, Virginia Mellon
5th Grade Teacher
BOHEMIA
Dilg, Judith Solberg
Fifth Grade Teacher
Eden, Ann Bishop
Resource Teacher
Fuller, Drusilla Overwyk
Art Teacher
Jordan, Irene Ann
Elementary Art Teacher
Leddy, John Joseph
HS Band Director
Mc Mahon, Kenneth J.
Fourth Grade Teacher
Prett, Leonora A.
High School Business Teacher
Schiappa, Susan (Zalewski)
Mathematics Teacher
Welcome, Angela Anzalone
English Teacher
BOICEVILLE
Barthel, Richard Lawrence
Mathematics Teacher
Boms, Michael
Bio, Chem & Biochemistry Tchr
Cayea, Krista B.
Choral & Music Director
DeFina, George A.
Fourth Grade Teacher
Francello, Erma Jeanne
Fourth Grade Teacher

Hoeft, Mary Cooke
Advanced Placement Eng Teacher
Iannotti, John David
Social Studies Teacher
Kaindl-Richer, Margit
8th-12th Grade German Teacher
Kosarek, Cheryl L.
Home Ec Tchr & Cabinet Member
Rosato, Phyllis P.
Math Teacher
Sutherland, Linda
Art Teacher
Wolfield, Dale
Art Instructor
BOLIVAR
Jaques, Clark Robert
Computer Coordinator
Whitcher, Joel Michael
Sixth Grade Soc Studies Tchr
BOLTON LANDING
Simpson, Kenyon Ray
6th Grade Teacher
BOONVILLE
Davis, Diane Rogers
Art Teacher
Deshaies, James J.
Retired Social Studies Teacher
Mihalko, Audrey Murphy
Physical Education Teacher
Ross, Juliette Marie (Jeneault)
Mathematics Teacher
Thomas, Patricia Ann
Health Teacher
BRADFORD
Allard, Timothy R.
Secondary Mathematics Teacher
Hallberg, Douglas James
PE & Hlth Ed Tchr
Hurley, Richard Kevin
Science Teacher
Millan, Mariann Senna
English Teacher
Rutledge, Jeffery L.
Social Studies Teacher
Sorensen, Kelly Bonzo
English Teacher
BRASHER FALLS
Austin, Judy Danforth
Kindergarten Teacher
Bronchetti, Rosemary Isabel
Physical Education Teacher
Castle, Sondra Sullivan
Kindergarten Teacher
Kilcoyne, Laura L. (Patten)
Chemistry & Biology Teacher
Pickard, Robert Houghton
Science Teacher
Straight, Donald Charles
High School Math Teacher
BREESPORT
Forrest, Bonita Jean
English & Spanish Teacher
May, Todd Whitlow
PE & Science Teacher
Oldroyd, Carolyn A.
Math & Spanish Teacher
BRENTWOOD
Amideo, Ann M.
Health Teacher
Bannon, Sara Manion
Science Chprsn & Chem Tchr
Benjamin, Kathryn
Asst Professor of Mathematics
Boyle, Connell J.
Mathematics Professor
Campanile, Michael
Mathematics Teacher
Crosley, Mary Anne
Professor of Nursing
Davis, Adrienne
Science Teacher
Ferruzzi, Donald Rocco
Professor of Biology
Goodman, Marilyn
Theatre & Communications Prof
Gould, Caroline Adams
Professor of Psychology
Hearst-Weissman, Judi
English Teacher
Horan, Virginia Elizabeth
Asst Prof of Communications
Howard, James
Science Teacher & Coach
Infante, Paul R.
Instrumental Music Teacher
Jerome, John Luckner
Assistant Professor
Kelsch, Sharon G.
Asst Professor of Nursing
LaFauci, Frances Ferrante
Professor of Nursing
Mancuso, Elisa Alvarez
Nursing Professor
Mannino, Grace Zummo
Foreign Language Teacher
Marinelli, Philip Joseph
Religious Studies Teacher
Merenda, Merilyn Wensley
Communications Professor
Monte, Anthony John
Science Teacher
Moran, James Patrick
Oceanography Instructor
Mundy, Richard
High School Biology Teacher
Parker, Jan
Professor of Economics
Robinson, John James
Junior Varsity Ftbl Coach

Sano, Michaelene Barbara
Social Studies Teacher
Schultheiss, Lorraine Titolo
8th Grade Math Teacher
Vercillo, Peter Paul
5th Grade Teacher
BREWERTON
Haller, Tom
Middle School Teacher
BREWSTER
Darensod, Melanie Burns
Fifth Grade Teacher
DeVito, James John
7th Grade Soc Studies Teacher
Gross, Roger Sullivan
Social Studies Teacher
Immohr, Phillip Henry
Teacher
Koestner, Keith Allan
Math Teacher
Matra, Susan Fleischhauer
Spanish Teacher
Phillips, Annie Noyes
Science & English Teacher
Vockins, Jere Rice
Social Studies Teacher
Waszmer, Paula Spatafore
Mathematics Teacher
BRIARWOOD
Levine, Michele Kaufman
6th Grade Teacher
BRIDGEPORT
Gates, Freida Frances
4th Grade Teacher
BROADALBIN
Aery, Roxanne Reiniger
Kindergarten Teacher
Dietrich, Anne Carley
Earth Science Teacher
Fallis, Nancy Kuhne
Social Studies Curr Coord
Goodemote, Barbara Holmberg
Retired 6th Grade Teacher
Gritsavage, Lauren Miller
HS Math Teacher
Hugo, Danielle Bialobok
US History & Government Tchr
Ingersoll, Jed Samuel
English Teacher
Majewski, Cheryl S.
Business Education Teacher
Orloff, Diane A.
Second Grade Teacher
Reals, Regina Kilgallen
Chemistry Teacher
Ripchik, Paul James, Jr.
HS Business Teacher
Swatling, Jan DeLilli
French Teacher
BROCKPORT
Balling, Frank B.
Elementary Principal
Banner, Elizabeth Schlugeter
HS Music Teacher
Dumas, Robert Frank
Social Studies Teacher
Esler, Marcella Hart
Coord of Developmental Math
Farnholz, Kimberly Kaiser
Mathematics Teacher
Giese, Maryellen Zimmermann
Chorus Teacher
Groves, Patricia Hahn
Art Teacher & Department Chair
Hickerson, Dianne
3rd Grade Teacher
Hickey, Marsha Stazie
Kindergarten Teacher
Jungbluth, Eileen Obernesser
Kindergarten Teacher
Kayser, Judy
Science Teacher
Pietrzak, Joseph T.
7th Grade Life Science Teacher
Reddinger, Robert Lewis
English Teacher
Rosecrants, Mary Kathryn
English Teacher
Steffen, Rhonda Butler
5th Grade Teacher
Sutton, James R.
Retired Mathematics Teacher
Voorheis, Donald Mark
Fourth Grade Teacher
Wolff, Ward L.
Adjunct Professor
BROCTON
Boyd, Karen Angel
Instrumental Music Teacher
Huddy, Lynette Lukehart
First Grade Teacher
Sedota, G. Elizabeth
English Teacher
Smith, Harold H.
Scndry Math & Physics Teacher
Stone, Michael Charles
Earth Science Teacher
BRONX
Abend, Robert James
Physical Education Teacher
Alberty, Miguel Antonio
Fifth Grade Teacher
Aliotta, Phillip Vincent
Spanish Teacher
Angelis, Genia Marie
English Teacher
Anibal, Galiana S.
Mathematics Professor
Antinore, David
Mathematics Teacher

BRONX (cont)
Asare, Karen Gilliam
5th-6th Grade Teacher
Ashley, Muriel Tannenbaum
Social Studies Teacher
Bambrick, Catherine E.
English Teacher
Barrett, Ethlyn
Social Studies Teacher
Batts, Sharon Denise
6th-8th Grade Reading Instr
Bell, Harris Mitchell
US & Global History Teacher
Bellamy, Charlotte
Adjunct Lecturer
Bennett, Paul I.
Biology Instructor
Benson, Eric William
Earth Science Teacher
Bernal-Carlo, Amanda
Assistant Professor
Biagiotti, Sandy
Fourth Grade Teacher
Birdi, Ashwi
Biology Teacher
Blanco, America Sainz
HS Spanish Teacher
Blanding, Vermell
Instructor of Writing & Rdng
Blot, David Robert
Associate Professor of ESL
Bonasera, Linda J.
Assistant Principal
Bonilla, Aida L.
7th & 8th Grade Teacher
Bowler, Margaret
Co-Director of Guidance
Brennan, Mark Etienne
Dean of Special Education
Bridgetts, Mary Lucille
French Teacher
Broughton, Johnnie Lee
Seventh & Eighth Grade Teacher
Brown, Paul Gerald, III
7th & 8th Grade Teacher
Brown, Stephen C.
Science Teacher
Bub, Warren
Football Coach
Buensalida, Victoria Balitaan
Fourth Grade Teacher
Bulis, Maria Gerosa
Science Teacher & Chairperson
Burke, Sarah Ryan
Sociology & Religion Teacher
Byrne, John James
Dir of Evening & Weekend Coll
Campana, Theresa (Fiorino)
Science Teacher
Campbell, Shirley A.
Teacher
Canales, Joanne Christine
5th Grade Teacher
Cancro, Susan McCafferty
Assistant Principal
Caparelli, Frank Peter
Secondary Math Teacher
Carozza, Nicholas Anthony
Sixth Grade Teacher
Casaccio, Frank M.
Sixth Grade Teacher
Castillo, Constantino Alexander
Auto Body Repair Teacher
Cavalli, Christine Marie
English Teacher
Chadwick, Samantha P.
Social Studies Teacher
Chernick, Jonathan
Mathematics Teacher
Childs, Michael
Economics Teacher & Dean
Cirillo, Louis
Advanced Placement Bio Tchr
Clayton, Julie Pendergast
Social Studies Teacher
Clemente, Carmen
ESL & Modern Langs Lab Dir
Clifford, Victoria Chieco
American Literature Teacher
Cluney, Thomas Edward
12th Grade English Teacher
Cohen, Ruth Lynn (Goldberg)
Chemistry Teacher
Colavito, Arlene Dahl
English & Social Studies Tchr
Connolly, Michaela
Dean of Students
Curran, Lawrence William
Eng Tchr & Asst Advancmnt Dir
D'Andrea, Ellen DeMarco
Science Teacher
Daniel, Sabrina Russell
Science Teacher
Davaransky, Fanny Papa
Retired 8th Grade Tchr
Davis, John Wandel
Professor of Biology
Davis, Mary Beth Hurley
Mathematics Teacher
DeCesare, Gary Thomas
Administrator
DePalma, Maria Cernaro
5th-8th Grd English Teacher
DiNardo, Robert A.
Social Studies Teacher
Dippolito, Lillian Russell
Dean of Junior High
Dolan, Kim Elise
Phys Ed & Health Teacher
Dolle, Peter
Soc Stud & Woodworking Teacher
Downes, Patrick Henry
Social Studies Teacher
Du Bose, David
Jr HS English Teacher
Duggan, Kenneth J.
Asst Prin & Supv of Math Dept
Dukes, Delores Suitt
Kindergarten Teacher
Echezabal, Michelle Marie
Third Grade Teacher
Eidenberg, Karen
Guidance Counselor
Elenko, Stuart S.
Dir of Holocaust Studies Ctr
Engel, Judith S.
Mathematics Teacher
Enriquez, Anastacio Lazaro
Latin, Religion, Soc Stud Tchr
Feld, Steve
Computer Graphics Instructor
Fernan, Matthew F.
11th-12th Grade Religion Tchr
Fernandez, Damaris
English Teacher
Ferraro, Theresa Lucchi
Chapter I Math Specialist
Figueredo, Sophia Pantages
Sixth Grade English Teacher
Finder, Barbara
Dance Teacher & Counselor
Fine, Sheldon J.
Math & Science Acad Director
Fitzpatrick, Kevin Peter
Second Grade Teacher
Fitzpatrick, Mary Morales
Kindergarten Teacher
Flam, Bernard Vincent
Math Teacher
Foster, Verda Elaine
Assistant Professor of Nrsng
Fox, Mitchell
Geosciences Teacher
Foy, Joe Anthony, II
Guid Cnslr & Dir of Diversity
France, Patricia A. (mallaney)
Math Teacher
Frangella, Louise Cancro
Dean of Students
Frasene, Stephen James
Business Teacher
Fuchs, Robert Alan
Math Teacher
Futrell, Michelle Tobin
Nutrition Professor
Galdi-Weissman, Natalie Ann
Teacher
Gallo, Ann M.
Guidance Director
Garcia, Gabriel
Vocational Instructor
Garguilo, Maria Theresa
Social Studies Dept Chair
Ghafoor, Imran
Associate Professor
Gibbons, Dennis Dave
Assistant Professor
Gilberg, Margot DeRuvo
Chair Foreign Language Dept
Gillespie, Michael C.
Assoc Prof & Dir of Tchr Ed
Gloskin, Elliott Richard
Mathematics Teacher
Gloskin, Yvonne Lorenzo
Science Teacher
Goodman, Joan Goodwin
Teacher
Grate, Daivd Robert
Jrnlsm Adv & English Teacher
Green, Phyllis Goldstein
Resource Room Teacher
Greene, Gregory Ian
Mathematics Teacher
Greene, William Joseph
Asst Prof
Gresko, Michael A.
Chemistry Teacher
Gruber, Irene Lombardi
High School Chemistry Teacher
Harwell, Lynne Carol
English Teacher
Hedgepeth, Joyce Yates
English Teacher
Hilliard, Carol
Asst Prof of Nrsng, Med & Surg
Hirschfield, Jane E.
Biology Teacher
Holiday, Isaac S.
Jr HS Dance Teacher
Hourani, Moujalli C.
Civil Engineering Professor
Huie, Carol Patricia
Lecturer
Hyman, Murray
Biology Teacher
Jackson, Vivian Butler
Developmental Rdng & Ed Prof
Jakymiw, Nicole J.
English Teacher
Johnson, Pelagia Dotillos
Kindergarten Teacher
Jordan, Lillie M. (Richardson)
1st Grade Teacher
Kaen, Julie Mulry
Director of Development & Tchr
Karig, Rita Reichman
English Teacher & Coordinator
Karr, Edythe Naomi
Math, English & Bible Teacher
Kavanagh, Thomas J.
Social Studies Chair & Teacher
Keeney, Carol Gartner
First Grade Teacher
Kelley, Gloria Jean Smith
Music Teacher
Kirk, William V.
Administrative Assistant
Kramer, Lawrence
Professor of English & Music
Krumper, Claire Levine
Mathematics Teacher
Kutner, Jacqueline R.
Art Teacher
Leggio, Nancy
Early Childhood Instructor
Lester, Jo Suzanne Greenberg
Tchr of Substance Abuse Prvntn
Levine, Lewis
ESL Intensive Program Coord
Lewin, Debra Ann
HS Mathematics Teacher
Lewis, Allison
Group Teacher
Lewis, Hope Gershen
5th Grade GATE Pgm Teacher
Lovett, Cyril
Interim Principal
Lugano, Michael Raymond
4th Grade Teacher
Lynch, Stephen M.
Architectural Drafting Teacher
Made, Viena Ceballos
Spanish Teacher
Maher, Antina Stornelli
Homeroom & Science Teacher
Maisel, Harvey Michael
Fifth Grade Teacher
Maloney, Meloney
Rel, Global & Soc Stud Teacher
Manfredi, Joan M.
Third Grade Teacher
Manganello, Dennis Carmine
Social Studies, Lang Arts Tchr
Marsicano, Madeline
6th Grade Teacher
Martz, Rocco Anthony
Eighth Grade Teacher
Mathews, Kenneth Joseph
Assistant Principal
Mazen, Toby
Mathematics Teacher
Mazzola, Sal
Instrumental Music Teacher
Mc Carthy, Glenn Anthony
8th Grd Teacher & Asst Prin
Mc Carthy, Theresa M.
6th Grade Teacher
Mc Donough, Lynette Cafaro
History & Women's Studies Tchr
Mc Govern, Helen
Guidance Counselor
Mc Gowan, Brendan John
English Teacher & Band Dir
Mc Grane, Bridget Elizabeth
Third Grade Teacher
Mc Kiernan, Peggy Ann
Mathematics Teacher
Meyers, Nadine
Kindergarten Teacher
Michiels, Leo Paul
Chemistry Professor
Miller, Leonisa Floresca
Science Teacher
Moccia, Madeline Mary
Seventh Grade Teacher
Mondesire, Linda Marie
2nd Grade Teacher
Mooney, Donald Francis
Religion Teacher
Morey, Mark V.
Physical Education Teacher
Morris, Deborah Cabiness
Assistant Professor of Nursing
Mueller, Ingrid Waltraud
Lecturer in Nursing
Mueser, John Alan
Sixth Grade Teacher
Murphy, John J., Jr.
Religious Educator
Nagai, Therese Midori
Math Teacher
Naveira, Debra L.
Substance Abuse Prevention
Netti, Patricia Ann
English & Journalism Teacher
Nowak, Denise O'Gorman
Biology Teacher
Ohren, Judy Bearman
Kindergarten Teacher
O'Keefe, Elizabeth
High School Librarian
Olivieri, Martin John
Science & ESL Teacher
O'Neill, Stephen Paul
Prof of Reading & Study Skills
Orzo, Anthony J.
Assistant Principal
O'Sullivan, Bridget Teresa
Religion Teacher
Otis, Douglas B.
Music Director
O'Toole, Bernard John
English Teacher
Palmiotto, Susan Levy
Stained Glass Teacher & Dean
Papas-Kavalis, Helen
Pediatrics Nursing Instructor
Pastoriza-Crespo, Nelida
Registrar & Adjunct Lecturer
Paul, Ronald M.
Academy of Health Director
Petrillo, Thomas Francis
Director of Campus Ministry
Peyros, Mikhail
Physics Teacher
Piantieri, Anthony Thomas, III
Philosophy & Religion Teacher
Piergentile, Dolores Attinello
HS Health & Biology Teacher
Pietarinen, George
English Teacher & College Adv
Pine, Harriet Nancy
Teacher
Pollack, Sharon Selman
Third Grade Teacher
Power, Gerard J.
PE Teacher
Preston, Phyllis R.
Perfrmng Arts Coord & Eng Tchr
Puller, Laurel J.
Kindergarten Teacher
Purnell, James Preston
Mathematics Instructor
Rabino, Linda
Law & Social Studies Teacher
Rachbach, Howard L.
Chemistry Teacher
Ramirez, Jason Anthony
Fine Arts Dept Chairperson
Rector, Madelynne T.
Adjunct Associate Professor
Reilly, Thomas Patrick
Russian & Gen Language Teacher
Reynolds, Joseph Patrick
Professor of Chemical Engrng
Rhem-Tittle, Yvonne S.
Vice Principal
Rhett, Curtis Lee
6th Grade Lead Teacher
Rivera, Albert Michael
Spanish & Business Teacher
Rivlin, Timothy Bennett
Social Studies Teacher
Robinson, Lillie Mae Guest
Retired Teacher
Ronconi, Maria Lucia
Religious Studies Teacher
Rosner, Merrily
English Teacher
Rowan, Gloria Aline
English Teacher
Rubic, Glenn K.
Sr Sci Tchr & Tech Specialist
Ruiz, Sonia
Bilingual 3rd Grade Teacher
Ryan, Joseph G.
Math Chair
Safran, Hal
Teacher
Salgado, Ramona Matos
Prof Emeritus of Health Ed
Sanacore, Vicki R.
Pupil Personnel Services Coord
Santiago-Alvarez, Diana Jade
Crisis Intervention Teacher
Santiago-Dunlop, Judith
7th-8th Grd Math Teacher
Sauro, Ann Rossi
8th Grade Mathematics Teacher
Schurgin, Audrey Grishman
Dean of Students
Schwartz, Annette Fried
High School English Teacher
Schweidel, Richard Stanley
Social Studies Teacher
Sclafani, Lorraine Anne Torti
Reading Teacher
Scullion, Dennis Michael
8th Grade English Teacher
Segal, Jeffrey Barry
High School Biology Teacher
Segura, Jose D.
Spanish & Literature Teacher
Sereika, Mercedes
1st Grade Bilingual Teacher
Serrano, Ramonita
Computer Science Teacher
Shapiro, Craig Scott
High School ESL Teacher
Sharpe, Audrey Sessoms
Multicultural Writing Teacher
Shepherd, Gloria Ann
Guidance Counselor
Sheridan, Marianne
Religion Teacher
Silverson, Merrily Alberti
Kindergarten Teacher
Simmons, Deborah Yvette
Grade Coordinator & Teacher
Sklar, Livia Edith
Guidance Counselor
Slattery, Marilyn Murray
Mathematics Dept Chair & Tchr
Soave, I.
HS Mathematics Teacher
Sodikow, Richard B.
Dir of Forensics & Debate Tchr
Somary, Johannes Felix
Arts & Music Dept Chairman
Spataro, Olimpia
Chemistry & Phys Sci Teacher
Sperling, Elisabeth Esther
History Teacher
Stauber, John Michael
High School Math Teacher
Straus, Joseph
Social Studies Teacher
Strauss, M. Joanne
Mathematics Teacher
Sullivan, Sean Joseph
Calculus Teacher
Suriel, Regina L.
Earth Science Teacher
Swift, Patrick Michael
Dean
Taddesse, Mellesse Amossa
Assistant Professor
Thoman, Anthony C.
Social Studies Teacher
Thomas, Alfredo Correa
Principal
Thompson, Patricia Terry
Fifth Grade Teacher
Todaro, Joseph N.
Professor
Todd, Thomas Alexander
English Teacher
Tomasetti, Annette Della Cava
English Teacher
Torney, Peggy Cain
Asst Principal & 8th Grd Tchr
Torres, Maggie Marrero
Bilingual Teacher
Turbin, Jonathan Edward
Librarian, Eng & Cmptr Tchr
Tyler, Jane B.
Cmptr Stud & Bus Dept Chair
Varela, Ana M.
Spanish Teacher
Velez, Azalia
Spanish Teacher
Villani, Mary
Tchr, Biological Sciences Dept
Walker, Marilyn Thelma (Bailey)
Fourth Grade Teacher
Ward, Lisa
English Teacher & Dept Chprsn
Weinberg, Barbara Sloman
Social Studies Teacher
Weiss, Elaine Iris
Science Department Head
Welch, Richard James
Amer His Tchr & Dept Chprsn
Wells, Jennifer
English & ESL Teacher
Werden, Beatrice Goldschmidt
Physics & Chemistry Teacher
Werner, Madeleine
4th Grade Teacher
West, Walter Scott
Science Teacher
White, Joyce M.
Fourth Grade Teacher
Wilbekin, Theresa Mack
English Teacher
Williams, Patricia Ann (Kinney)
Accounting Professor
Wilson, Constance Teresa
Third Grade Teacher
Wing, Debbie
Assistant Librarian
Zimmerman, Cliff Blake
Earth Science Regents Teacher
Zimmerman, Nicolina Lamanna
Regents & Gen Earth Sci Tchr
Zullo, Lucy Fiorenza
Italian Teacher

BROOKFIELD
Green, Constance Rogers
First Grade Teacher

BROOKHAVEN
Bergel, Steven P.
Science Teacher
Bragoli, Patricia Carnicelli
Third Grade Teacher
Cooper, Charles C.
English Teacher
Decatur, Phyllis
Mathematics Teacher
Dinowitz, Michael
Biology Teacher
Feddern, Matthew Sean
Physics Teacher
Gill, Frank J.
English Teacher
Loewen, Marvin E.
Chemistry Teacher
Mc Gowan, James P.
Chemistry Teacher
Paradise, Nancy A.
Pre-K Teacher
Parry, Cynthia E.
English Teacher
Quinones, Diana Crane
Foreign Lang & Spanish Teacher
Robins, Faye E.
Health Educator
Rock, Patricia Lynch
Mathematics Teacher
Roeske, Eric Charles
Music Teacher & Band Director
Schlessinger, Frances Schulman
Mathematics Teacher
Schoppman, Susan G.
Mathematics Teacher
Uzzi, James Christopher
Secondary Orchestra Director
Westhoff, Colette Girard
French Teacher

BROOKLYN
Abato, Barbara
Jr High Teacher
Abergas, Olwen Gines
Math & Science Teacher
Aboud, Judith Hatem
Language Arts & Math Teacher
Acevedo, Aileen
Spanish Teacher

KLYN (cont)
:, Gloria
School Math Teacher
, Rosalie (Scaglione)
'eacher
, Jessica
gual Teacher
id, Guy
ory Teacher
olou, Argyri
ESL & Greek Teacher
ein, Lori
ogy Teacher
v, Stuart L.
sh & Humanities Teacher
ach, Curt
al Studies Teacher
e, Gabriel J.
ematics Teacher
Barracato, Kathleen
of Academic Affairs
Herminzul, Jr.
g Math & Science Teacher
Van
ty Principal & 8th Grd Tch
in, Stephen James
r School Spanish Teacher
llo, Charlaine
sh Teacher
, Thomas Paul
ian Professor
a, Maria Jimenez
irade Teacher
n, Clare L.
sh Teacher
Joanne
h Grade Teacher
man, Marlene Ann
Kindergarten Teacher
Sally Ruth
Teacher
, Alan H.
puter Coordinator
), Fortunato Joseph
al Studies II Teacher
Nancy
ance Counselor
n, Jay D.
ipal
ein, Gail Eiseman
urce Teacher
Gail Meredith
ogy Teacher
y, Anne Veronica, CSJ
ematics Teacher
, Jeff
Prin, Hlth & PE Dept
ad, Joel
ish & ESL Teacher
Raymond C.
al Studies Teacher
s, Joyce A.
ocial Studies Teacher
er, Jacob Alfred
ematics Teacher
Aaron
Appreciation Teacher
, Kristen Marie
ish & ESL Teacher
, Debra Ursula
ish Teacher
, Gloria Murph
iculture Ed Tchr
, Michelle Darlene (Wallace)
th Grade Teacher
baum, Alva Jones
nth Grade English Teacher
mo, Joan E.
ness & Computer Teacher
, Lori Chase Caiazzo
K Teacher
tro, Dominick Joseph
Stud, Cybertech Prgm Coord
agna, Alva Sobel
ergarten Teacher of Gifted
otti, Orrin
ematics Teacher
lo, Giuliana G.
ance & Athletic Director
iale, Louise Marie
nce Teacher
a, Robert F.
h & Social Studies Teacher
Amelia Panzica
School Biology Teacher
ano, Sandra
vention Specialist
no, Francesca Diane
n Teacher
lle, Eric R.
c Pastor of Secondary Ed
nan, Dorothy
ness Teacher
elli, Charles John
th, PE Teacher & Coach
:, Karen-Christine Felicity
d Grade Teacher
, Kenneth
h & Science Teacher
es, Ellen Marie
Teacher
n, Patricia M.
puter Teacher
, Elizabeth Patricia
ness Teacher
r, Ira J.
ematics Teacher
an, Edward Robert
h Grade Teacher

Cucciniello, Dawn Grace
Teacher
Cummings, Sheila L.
Biology Teacher
Curtin, Teresa Mary
Social Studies Teacher
D'Ambrosio, Michael Anthony
English Teacher
Daniels, Carmen
English Teacher
DeGennaro, Steven David
Physical Education & Hlth Tchr
Delaney, Patricia Morris
Mathematics Teacher
Dewey, Thomas Michael
High School English Teacher
Diaconescu, Ileana
French Teacher
DiPrima, Geraldine Gaudiosi
Kindergarten Teacher
Doctor, Ivin Stuart
Chemistry Teacher
Drayer, Gerald Richard
Social Studies Teacher
Drew, Anne Cregan
English Teacher
Dunn, Jenny Barrett
Chemistry Teacher
Edelstein, Dorothy Isenberg
Fine Arts Teacher
Edwards, Elwood Gene
Math Dept Chairperson & Tchr
Edwards, Michelle Stinvil
Biology & Health Careers Tchr
Ehrlich, Elizabeth Kornecki
Associate Professor
Emeh, Michelle Applewhaite
Math & Religion Teacher
Enriquez, Sergio Agusto
Spanish Teacher
Epstein, Harriet M.
Guidance Cnslr & Health Tchr
Fabietti, Louise Caputo
High School Mathematics Tchr
Fabiszak, Rose E. Monaco
Spanish Teacher
Farrell, Susan Anne
Sociology Professor
Fattorusso, Julie-Ann
High School Mathematics Tchr
Feinberg, Charles
Fifth Grade Teacher & Dean
Feldshuh, Muriel
Library Media Specialist
Ferarra, Lee
Religion Department Chprsn
Fernandez, Magali
Spanish Teacher
Fescoe, Melanie Butschere
Guidance Director
Fiori, Carolann
Early Childhood Science Tchr
Fischer, Rae-Ann
ESL Tchr & Foreign Stu Coord
Flickstein, Dan
English, Speech Tchr & Dean
Forde, Seon James
Math Dept Chairperson & Tchr
Forsyth, Louise J.
History Teacher
Friday, Marjorie Angela
Mathematics Teacher
Frost, Sandra Renaye
Fourth Grade Teacher
Fuller, Pamela Ann
High School English Teacher
Funaro, Michael Joseph
5th-8th Grade Math Teacher
Fusco, Frank L.
Community Service Director
Gallis, Dimitrios P.
Social Studies Teacher
Gamba, Maria Negron
Third Grade Bilingual Teacher
Gangi, Vincent John
Jr HS Social Studies Tchr
Gathers, Barbara Brown
Fifth Grade Teacher
Germain, Stuart H.
8th Grd Dean & Behavior Cnslr
Gershansky, Libby T.
English as a Second Lang Tchr
Gindi, Elaine
Resource Room Teacher
Giordano, Denise Marie
K-5th Grd Language Arts Tchr
Goldberg, Eileen
Biology Teacher
Goldberg, Gary M.
Math Teacher
Goodman, Marilyn
Kindergarten Teacher
Goodman, Michelle Carol
Physical Education Teacher
Gorse, Lynn Gail
Physical Education Teacher
Green, Lorraine Eileen
Eng as a Second Lang Teacher
Gregory, Lawrence
English Teacher
Hall, Anna Louise
Third Grade Teacher
Hamilton, Kay Frances
8th Grd Language Arts Teacher
Harper, Leslie
Reading Recovery Teacher
Harris, Bryant Androcles
Social Studies Teacher
Heiles, Nancy Santoro
Global Education Director

Herman, Josephine Nancy
Foreign Language Teacher
Hero, George Astor
Dir of Social Science Research
Hill, Kathleen L.
Dance Teacher & Support Cnslr
Hinds, Agnes Veronica
Mathematics Teacher
Hoeberlein, Teresa Marie
Assistant Professor
Hogan, Elizabeth Ann
Pre-Kindergarten Teacher
Holgate, Keith Silvera
English Teacher
Hoppmann, Peter C.
English Teacher & Coach
Horwitz, Phyllis
Math Resource Teacher
Hughes, Edna Cunningham
Fourth Grade Teacher
Hunt, Christine Hantzopulos
Span, Biling & Soc Stud Tchr
Husband, Daltia
Speech Improvement Teacher
Hutchinson, Ruby Nerissa
Ec & Global Studies Tchr
Hyland, Marybeth
Fifth Grade Teacher
Ingino, Elaine Berkowitz
5th Grade Teacher
Jackson, Elaine Sandra
Fourth Grade Teacher
Jacobs, Beverly Sue
Spanish Teacher
Jameson, Ella C.
Language Arts Teacher
Jeannis, Ingrid
Counselor
Jenner, Eileen Kapica
Spanish Teacher
Jennings, Barbara Jean
Cooperative Ed Coord & Teacher
Johnson, Joan Abellonio
Teacher of Visually Impaired
Johnson-Foster, Hyacinth Carmen
Upper Schl Sci Tchr & Chprsn
Joseph, Kathleen Eames
Former Teacher
Joseph, Kenneth Wycliffe
Mathematics Teacher
Kalmus, Mitchel Eli
Biology Teacher
Kamenshine, Mel
Teacher
Kapitansky, Barbara N.
Business Education Teacher
Kaplan, Chester Frank
Band Director
Karras, Foula Kontonicolas
Spanish Teacher
Kartaginer, Marilyn Wermuth
High School Math Teacher
Katsoulis, Rosina A. (Panetta)
5th-8th Grade Science Teacher
Katz, Joanne Seffens
Asst Prof of Physical Therapy
Katz, Robert Nathan
Chemistry Teacher
Kay, Alan A.
English Professor
Kelly, Kenneth
Social Studies Teacher
Kelly, Laura
Eng as Second Language Teacher
Kerr, Priscilla Wiggins
Fifth Grade Teacher
King, Linda Diane
Guidance Counselor
King, Margaret L.
Professor of History
Kirstein, Rhea S.
Literature & Writing Teacher
Klugmann, Sarah Jaroslawicz
Science Teacher
Knittel, Mary Jo, OP
Pastoral Associate
Koblick, Sandra Pomerantz
Fifth Grade Teacher
Korbeogo, Ditta Williams
Chemistry & Science Teacher
Koshy, Annamma
Science Teacher
Kotkin, Judith Samuels
Math & Computer Science Tchr
Kreinberg, Penny
Staff Developer & Rdng Tchr
Kushner, Joel
Guidance Counselor
Kwapich, Debra Corney
Math Teacher
Labianca, Domincik Anthony
Chemical Professor
Lane, Michele J.
French Teacher
Langan, Martin Joseph
Asst Prin & Physics Teacher
LaRosa, Frances Daniela LoBasso
5th Grade Teacher
Lavalas, Silvia Yolanda
Coordinator
Legros, Lionel
Science Teacher
Leiterman, Kenneth Jay
6th Grade Teacher
Letkovsky, Andreas F.
Architectural Instructor
Lew, Max
English Teacher
Lippo, Felice Didia
Kindergarten Teacher

Lloyd, Miriam
Eighth Grade Teacher
Lo, Simon
Chinese Teacher
Logan, Eileen Egert
Nursing Teacher
Losi, Carolann Sloane
Jr HS Mathematics Teacher
Lulay, Donna Patrice
Language Arts & Soc Stud Tchr
Lytle, Jane
English Teacher
Malafronte, Raffaele Joseph
English Teacher
Mandiberg, Judith Susan
Eng & Creative Writing Teacher
Manisero, Robert Michael
English Teacher
Marder, Lori Rand
Fourth Grade Teacher
Mark, Ann Mariea
Mathematics Teacher
Martinez, Inez
Professor of English
Mason, Adriana Ferdman
Bilingual Mathematics Teacher
Mathison, Dorothy Elaine
Adj Prof of Liberal Arts & Ed
Mauro, Anthony F.
Chemistry Teacher
Maxy, Leonora B.
Social Studies Teacher
Mazzarisi, Lisa Jo
Assistant Principal
McAlister, Horace Bernard
High School Mathematics Tchr
Mc Curdy, India H.
English Teacher
Mc Grath, Joseph Thomas
Social Studies Teacher
McHugh, Philip George
5th-8th Grd Mathematics Tchr
Mc Intosh-Moore, Violet Henrietta
Principal
Mc Intyre, Valerie Lumpkin
Fifth Grade Teacher
Mc Neill, Anne H.
Mathematics Teacher
Mc Shane, Helen Ramsey
Sixth Grade Teacher
Mendelson, Roberta Klein
English Teacher
Mendez, Gloria Elaine
Math Teacher
Menkes, Marsha Ann
Fourth Grade Teacher
Merced, Jose
Medical Tech & Biology Teacher
Milkman, Paul Alan
English Teacher
Miller, Angela
English Teacher
Miller, Bruce
Math Teacher
Mills, Zipporiah Portis
Sixth Grade Teacher
Mineo, Jeanne Parlato
Upper Grade Elem Schl Tchr
Mingrone, Joseph A.
English Teacher & Drama Dir
Mollo-Holmes, Linda Steo
Jr HS Mathematics Teacher
Morgan, Rhonda
9th & 12th Grade Science Tchr
Moses, Lorette
Kindergarten Teacher
Moses, Noel
Engineering & Mathematics Tchr
Mulligan, Anne
English Teacher & Dept Chprsn
Mungalsingh, Michael
Engineering & Math Teacher
Nadjar, Esther Vickie
History & Judaic Studies Tchr
Nagler, Michael P.
Assistant Principal
Narine, Keshaw
Science Teacher
Nelson, Judith
First Grade Teacher
Nelson, Sadie Yvonne
Teacher
Nero, Michele
5th Grade Teacher
Nestor, Mary Maxwell
Art Teacher
Norstrand, Thomas Fletcher
Social Studies Teacher
Noto, Caroline DeGennaro
Kindergarten Teacher
Nurse, Oral
Math Teacher
Okonkwo, Valerie Maureen (Brown)
Social Studies Teacher
Oley, Nancy Hurwich
Prof of Psychology
Olivera, Maria Mercedes
Spanish Teacher
Opinante, Philip N.
School Social Worker
Ostrin, Steve H.
History & Social Science Tchr
Ottey, Hypha Ann
Chemistry & Biology Teacher
Pace, Ellen S.
Physical Education Teacher
Palmaccio, Mary L.
Intermediate Teacher
Palmer, Raymond Tyrone
Teacher

Palmieri, Susan Laura
Speech Teacher
Parker, Delorise W.
Elementary Teacher
Parrott, Boyd Dennis
Librarian
Perl, Gary L.
Movies & Media Teacher
Peters, Joann Taura
US His, Govt & Ec Teacher
Petrie, Catherine S. Kramer
English Teacher
Phillps, Dilcia R.
Professional Development Coord
Pilchman, Peter
Prof of Biological Sciences
Pizzi, Peter M.
Dental Laboratory Teacher
Plaut, Jane M. Rifenberg
Art Teacher
Plunkett, Edward J.
Jr HS Social Stud Tchr
Podkrash-Vega, Carol Ann
Social Studies, Lang Arts Tchr
Pollack, Karen
4th Grade Teacher
Popkoff, Lauren Korn
History & Economics Teacher
Pratt, Isaiah Bami Jason
Social Studies, US His Teacher
Price, Rene T.
Physical Education Teacher
Protano, Ralph David
History Teacher
Quattrocchi, Ciro Anthony
Foreign Language Teacher
Radlow, Steven
Span Tchr & Debate Team Coach
Rajswasser, Bruce Farrel
Teacher & FBLA Advisor
Razukas, John M.
Electromechanical Engrng Prof
Reid, Sheila
High School English Teacher
Reilly, Catherine M.
Physical Education Teacher
Reilly, Donna Denise Douglas
Gifted Program Coordinator
Reiss, Jessie D. L.
English Teacher
Renguul, Thomas
Seventh & Eighth Grade Teacher
Riccio, Jessica
1st Grade Teacher
Richman, Aaron
High School Math Teacher
Rivera, Elia Iris
Elementary School Teacher
Rodriguez, Ramona Montanez
Third Grade Teacher
Romano, Elizabeth M.
8th Grade Teacher
Rosen, Diane L.
7th & 8th Grd Social Stud Tchr
Ross, Barbara
AP Government Instructor
Rourke, Frank Xavier
7th & 8th Grade Teacher
Ruddy, Margaret
Academic Guidance Counselor
Rufo, Gloria Frances
Math, Science & Religion Tchr
Rumpolo, Christopher J.
Biology Teacher
Russell, Patricia Jean
Dance Teacher
Ryklin, Ella Hadassah
French & Russian Teacher
Sabari, Joyce Shapero
Occupational Therapy Professor
Sabol, Susan
Biology Teacher
Saggese, Bettyann
English Teacher
Salemi, Joseph Salvatore
Classics Professor
Schneider, Edward A.
Vocal Music Teacher
Schneider, Estelle
Asst Professor of Phys Therapy
Schneider, Marvin A.
Assistant Principal
Schwartz, Helaine Sacks
Telecommunications & Art Tchr
Schwartz, Judith B.
HS Mathematics Teacher
Schwartz, Kenneth S.
American History Teacher
Schwarz, Eliakim Leonard Yosef
Judaic Studies Tchr
Scott, Anne Hiller
Clinical Assistant Professor
Sebekos, Peter J.
Mathematics Instructor
Seltzer, Felice Ellen (Simon)
Early Childhood Specialist
Shannon, Hilma Williams
Bilingual Guidance Counselor
Shultz, Stephen A.
Asst Prin & Soc Stud Teacher
Siler-Flowers, Joyce B.
Chairperson of Management
Silvis, Susan A.
5th Grade Teacher & Mentor
Simon, Marcia Shedrofsky
Retired Third Grade Teacher
Simon, Shirley Cohen
Resource Teacher of the Blind
Singleton, Joanne K.
Associate Professor

BROOKLYN (cont)
Smith, Claire F.
Fourth Grade Teacher
Smith, Delores Jane Hadden
Special Education Teacher
Smith, Duella
Substance Abuse Counselor
Solimando, John M.
Intermediate Schl English Tchr
Solomon, Stephanie Gail
Biology & Gen Science Teacher
Solowey, Stephen Miles
Global History Teacher
Sosa, Arlene
St Certfd Biling Guid Cnslr
Spalter, Sheila
Retired French & ESL Teacher
Spriner, Esther
Guidance Counselor & Coll Adv
Stack, Elizabeth Anne
English Teacher
Stalonas, Geraldine Gruson
English Teacher
Stanisci, Tina Bottalico
Second Language Eng Teacher
Stanislaus, Yolanda
HS Earth Science Teacher
Steele, Frank
Alternative Program Director
Stein, Charles Robert
American History Teacher
Stewart-Barrett, Dianne M.
Chemistry Instructor
Stone, Philip D.
English, History Tchr & Chair
Straker, Lynda V. Taitt
Mathematics Tchr & Vice Prin
Suberi, Naomi
6th-8th Grades Bible Teacher
Sullivan-Carr, Kathleen Mary
Social Studies Teacher
Sultanik, Helen Menche
Science Coordinator & Teacher
Talero, Eduardo
Science Teacher
Tanner, Lynne R.
Social Studies Teacher
Tarlo, David
Mathematics Teacher
Terzino, Juei-Ni Sung
Bilingual Social Studies Tchr
Thompson, Valerie M.
Elementary School Teacher
Timmins, Theodore
High School Guidance Counselor
Tirone, Lawrence D.
Science Teacher
Tizio, Cheryl
Computer Teacher & Coordinator
Tochterman, Mark Stephen
Physics & Biology Teacher
Tom, John
Chemistry Teacher
Trano, Michael Anthony
English Teacher
Trossman, Patricia Burks
Associate Professor
Trout, Gary Joel
Speech, Drama Tchr & Cnslr
Turnbull, Diane Lucas
English Teacher
Ugelow, Carol Meisels
Math Teacher & Advisor
Vagt, Francis Regis
Jr High Lang Arts Teacher
Vargas, Martha Lucia
Spanish Teacher
Vitale, James Leo
Guidance Dept Chairperson
Walker, Edna B.
Mathematics Teacher
Warshower, Ruth M.
Guidance Counselor
Watson, Brent Duane
Fifth Grade Teacher
Weekes, Dorothy
4th Grade Teacher
Weekes, Louise Scriven
11th Grade Cosmetology Teacher
Weiner, Madeline Joy
Social Studies Teacher
Weinstock, Lenore
Cluster Teacher
Whitaker, Teresa Rene
Fourth Grade Teacher
Widom, David
Teacher
Williams, Christopher R.
Adjunct Assist Prof
Wilson, Doris Edwards
Social Studies Teacher
Witte, Phyllis F.
English Teacher
Wo Lee, Chun
Mathematics Teacher
Wolf, Helen
Religion Teacher
Wong, Elliott
Social Studies Teacher
Woods, Evelyn Hargrove
Teacher
Wright, Catherine R.
History Teacher
Wu, David
Bilingual Teacher
Wurzel, Nelson
Science Teacher
Wynkoop, Robert Thomas, Jr.
Sr Instr of Architectural Tech
Young, Joseph
Assistant Principal
Zarba, Joseph Angelo
Photography Teacher
Zarrow, Alan S.
Teacher & Athletic Director
Zaza, Joseph F.
Senior Advisor
Zimmerman-Aptekar, Ronni Ilene
High School English Teacher
Zipper, Elaine Rhoda
Music & Theater Teacher
Zipper, Shelley G.
English Teacher
Zodda, Philip J.
PE Tchr & Cross Cntry Coach
BRUSHTON
Bright, Marcy
High School Resource Teacher
Dana, Janet Noreault
High School English Teacher
Dunning, Valerie Pike
English Teacher
Prairie, Charles G.
HS Social Studies Teacher
South, Gary Paul
Global Studies Teacher
BUFFALO
Abbarno, John Mark
Professor of Philosophy
Abbott, Patricia Lynn
Instructor of Psychology
Alderdice, Douglas A.
Microcomputer Coordinator
Aljuwani, Khaledah
Secondary English Teacher
Allan, Timothy Richard
Assoc Professor of History
Ampadu, Alex B.
Accounting & Law Asst Prof
Appleby, Linda Rose Lombardo
5th-8th Grade Music Teacher
Azzarelli, Lisa Marie
Former English Teacher
Barone, Marian
Eighth Grade Teacher
Bavaro, Deborah Ann
Second Grade Teacher
Baxter, Brenda S.
5th Grade Teacher
Beigel, Andrew Richard
Asst Professor of Education
Bentley, Diane Marie
History Teacher
Bernal, Maria Bova
School Counselor
Berst, Frank J.
HS Soc Studies & Soc Sci Tchr
Biggs, Edmund Logan
Business Professor
Bijak, Thomas Michael
Electrical & Electronics Instr
Boudreau, Kenneth R.
Science Teacher
Bourke, Laetitia C.
Secondary Social Studies Tchr
Bowers, Douglas Arthur
Science Chairperson
Brinson, Colin Meagher
Social Studies Teacher
Butler, Patricia A.
English Teacher
Cercone, Joseph Michael
Secondary Mathematics Teacher
Chimera, Charles C.
Religion Teacher
Choi, Namkee Gang
Assoc Prof of Schl Soc Work
Christopher, Carol Marie
Sixth Grade Teacher
Church, Keith Wayne
Math Teacher
Clark, Gregory L.
4th Grade Teacher
Colleran, Andra M. Jaremka
Fr Tchr & Frgn Lang Dept Chair
Corallo, Nicholas Warren
Music Teacher
Cordero, Alicia
Sixth Grade Bilingual Teacher
Craig, Mary A.
English Teacher
Cylar, William J.
Mathematics Teacher
Davis, Beth Ann
Religion Teacher
DelleBovi, Betsy Mary
Associate English Professor
Dietrich, Dennis Edward
Social Studies Teacher
Dishaw, Ernest John, Jr.
Associate Professor
DiSibio, Robert A.
Acting VP for Academic Affairs
Dolce, Karen Mack
5th Grade Teacher
Downey, Mary Jo
English Instructor
Drajem, Linda
Supervisor of Student Teachers
Dubois, Wilfrid
Asst Professor of Biology
Falkenstein, Jacqueline Welch
Art Teacher
Fish, James E.
Mathematics Teacher
Freda, John Michael
Third Grade Teacher
Frey-Mason, Patricia
Math Dept Chairperson & Tchr
Gamble, Robert John
Dir Tchr Cert & Asst Prof
Gleason, Rosalie Grammar
Retired 3rd Grade Teacher
Glynn, Joseph Graham
Associate Professor of Mngmt
Gondree, Lillian Lewandowski
Science Teacher & Chairperson
Goodheart, Kathleen Frances
English Teacher
Goodloe, Yvette Cecelia
Science & Zoology Teacher
Green, Deirdre Monique
Counselor & Acad Instructor
Greer, Edith Leverne
Fourth Grade Teacher
Harlos, Carol Ann Brunner
Mathematics Teacher
Harris, Robert H.
Social Studies Teacher
Hart, D. Edward
Professor of Biology
Harting, Arnold R.
English & TV Comm Teacher
Heaney, Margaret D.
Sixth Grade Teacher
Henderson, Cecelia Brown
Prevention Ed Specialist
Hibschweiler, Jane Barone
Literature & Lang Arts Tchr
Jadd, Marsha J.
School Counselor
Kellogg, Stephen
Asst Professor of Business Law
Kelly, David Harvey
Professor of History
Kelschenbach, Angela Marie
Consultant Teacher
Kent, Valarie Ann
Math Teacher
Kershner, Bruce S.
Science Teacher
Kimp, Annie Counts
Retired Teacher
Kost, Kathleen Ann
Social Work Asst Professor
Kowalczyk, Georgianna C.
Chemistry & Physics Teacher
Kuehlewind, Clara Kraus
Radiologic Sciences Professor
Kulczyk, Kimberly Ann
Math Teacher
LaHood, Marvin J.
Distngd Tchng Prof of English
Langford, Louise Watts
Biology Teacher
Le Blanc, Glorira Jean (Eichorn)
Latin Teacher
Leuchner, Linda Denise (Gaide)
Advanced Placement Bio Tchr
Little, Barbara Brown
Psych & Education Assoc Prof
Lopez, Marianne O'Keefe
Sixth Grade Teacher
Maciejewski, James John
Social Studies Teacher
Maggio, William Charles
Retired HS Art Teacher
Mandell, Olga Karman
Spanish Professor
Marschall, Claudia Ann
English & Theater Arts Teacher
Maxwell, Cynthia
Sixth Grade Teacher
Mayer, George Martin
Chemistry Teacher
Mc Kee, Elaine Lang
Prof of Foreign Ed & French
Menshel, Denny
Professor of Business Admin
Mittelsteadt, Vivian Lee
Spanish Teacher
Montante, Joseph R.
Mathematics Teacher
Mungo-Morton, Ruth Yvonne
English Teacher
Murak, Richard James
Soc Stud Tchr & Chprsn
Nasca, Linda Ann
Social Studies Teacher
O'Brien, Michael J.
Principal
Obstarczyk, Michael Francis
Science Teacher
Oliver, Dominick Michael
Acctng, Bus & Cmptrs Instr
Paxton, Douglas John
History Teacher
Perkins, Richard
6th-8th Grade Soc Stud Tchr
Platt, Jeffrey H.
Asst Vice-Pres of Stu Affairs
Pressley, Tommy L., Jr.
Electronics I Instructor
Quinn, Anita Saia
Principal
Rafael, Adeline Falk
Nursing Professor
Reimers, Catherine Kunz
German Teacher
Rittner, Barbara
Asst Prof of Social Work
Rivers, Lynn Salzmann
Physical Therapy Professor
Robbins, George Walter
Social Science Instructor
Roberts, Sharon Ann LeFauve
Spanish Teacher
Robinson, Carolyn Marie
MS Mathematics Teacher
Robson, Ruth Debo
English Teacher
Saltarelli, George Xavier
Mathematics Teacher & Dept Chm
Saracki, Irving J.
Economics Teacher
Schreiber, Paul G.
Language Arts Teacher
Shapiro, Caren Knight
Professor of Biology
Sheedy, Patricia Cwynar
Second Grade Teacher
Sheehan, Kristina K. (Krafft)
French Teacher
Sherk, Dean E.
Mathematics Teacher
Sherwin, Alice
Third Grade Teacher
Shriber, Linda Dudek
Occupational Therapy Asst Prof
Simonetta, Stefanie Gasbarre
French Teacher
Siracusa, Phyllis Freeman
Learning Specialist
Smith, Arthur J.
Retired Biology Teacher
Smith, W. Barry
Registrar
Smyth, Nancy Jean
Social Work Asst Professor
Snell, Linda Harner
Nursing Professor
Soffin, Barry Ronald
HS Mathematics Teacher
Spriegel, Shirley (Bommer)
Lecturer
Stephenson, E. Roger
Professor of English
Strachan, David Gorham
Mathematics Teacher
Stratton, Richard G.
English Teacher
Strzyz, Ronald Edward
English Instructor
Toomey, Susan Mendolia
Guidance Counselor
Townsend, Carol A.
Lecturer in Design Department
Turansky, Jeanne A.
Prof of Eng & Fac Developer
Walsh, Nancy
Resource & Consultant Tchr
Watson, William Worden
Science Teacher
Williams, Ann John
Dir of Surgical Tech & Instr
Williams, Stephen Elliot
Professor of Special Education
Wyngaarde, Jeanne Evans
Biology & Earth Sci Teacher
BURNT HILLS
Chirico, Anthony J.
Guidance Counselor
Corrigan, Wendy (Ott)
Art Teacher
Eldridge, John William
Chemistry Teacher
Ferrante, Jeanne W.
Retired Elementary Teacher
Ferris-Fearnside, Karen F.
Social Studies Teacher
Gangemi, Christine Laiacona
English Teacher
Jones, Gary Robert
English Teacher
Kosky, Mary Boeker
Mathematics Teacher
Montesano, Rocco Anthony, Jr.
Social Studies Teacher
Reynolds, Carol F.
English Teacher & Dept Rep
CAIRO
Lawrence, William B.
Science Department Chairman
Miner, Lorraine E.
Spanish Teacher
Mylott, Gary David
Mathematics Teacher
CALEDONIA
Hurley, Joseph Patrick
Math Teacher
Kelly, Sylvia Neahr
Tchr of the Gifted & Talented
True, Stephen Edward
Chemistry & Physics Teacher
CALLICOON
Schatz, John R.
Soc Studies Tchr & Dept Chair
CAMBRIDGE
Bischoff, Douglas
Choral Music & Theatre Teacher
Butkus, Christine Stephens
Rdng & Social Studies Teacher
Lacasse, Kenneth Michael
Math & Reading Teacher
Mc Elroy, Cathy
English Teacher
Morton, Robert S.
Chemistry & Physics Teacher
Oakley, Molly S.
Fifth Grade Teacher
Paprocki, Wallace Coates
Latin Teacher
CAMDEN
Baker, Steven J.
High School Mathematics Tchr
Dunn, Joan Marie
Physical Education Teacher
Edkin, Wayne Scott
English Department Chairperson
LaGatta, David
Technology Education Teacher
Mc Kenna, Richard Thomas
High School English Teacher
Mellon, Vincent G.
Physics Teacher
Montgomery, Stephen R.
11th & 12th Grd Soc Stud Tchr
Pawloski, William Anthony
Physical Education Instructor
Rodgers, Joyce
Spanish Teacher
Troyer, Ronald Edward
Health & Physical Ed Teacher
Wdowin, Jeanne Whitney
6th Grade Science Teacher
CAMILLUS
Armstrong, Carol Elaine
High School Art Teacher
Bayus, Karen A.
Social Studies Teacher
Bedy, Lorraine Anne
High School English Teacher
Capria, John Hugo
High School Art Teacher
Carr, Susan L.
Guidance Counselor
Cashier, Barbara R.
Resource Room Teacher
Christian, Johnathon Anthony
Mathematics Tchr & Dept Chair
Evans, Patricia Ann Furgal
Soc Stud Dept Chair & Tchr
Lazarski, John B.
Soc Studies & Psychology Tchr
Mannara, Joseph Frederick
Science Teacher
Mc Call, H. Gale (Brinn)
French & Latin Teacher
Mercer, William James, Jr.
Orchestra Director
Moynihan, Betsy
Business Teacher
Norman, David Alan
Vocal Music Tchr & Interim Dir
Potrikus, Leo John
Middle School Math Teacher
Schiltz, Mary Beth
Fourth Grade Teacher
Sierotnik, Anne Gaffney
English Teacher
Smithson, David G.
Fifth Grade Teacher
Williams, Janet Bean
Reading Specialist
CAMPBELL
Herron, Muriel L. (Wood)
Math Teacher
Horning, Robert C., II
High School Band Director
Miller, David Thomas
Math Teacher
Peffley, Bruce Elvert
Sci Chm, Chem & Physics Tchr
Rosko, Kevin Francis
PE Teacher & Coach
Walker, Debra K.
HS Resource Room Teacher
Wood, Elaine M. (Rogozinski)
Business Teacher
CAMPBELL HALL
Heinzelman, Geraldine Miletich
Adj Professor of Math & Psych
CANAJOHARIE
Carey, James M.
Earth Science Teacher
Schrade, Sherry Egan
Mathematics Teacher
CANANDAIGUA
Benedict, Suzanna Engman
Instructor of English
Dunham, Darrow G.
Professor of Mathematics
Fischette, Carol M.
Health & PE Instr
Freeman, Carol L.
Math Dept Chair
Gilman, Bruce Alan
Conservation Professor
Mulvaney, Louise M.
Associate Professor of English
Nettnin, Patricia Keckley
Professor of Computer Science
O'Donnell, Karen Luciano
Assoc Prof Developmental Stud
Phillips, Paul T.
Criminal Justice Assoc Prof
Plyter, Charles C.
6th Grade Teacher
Razavi, Frank
Electrical & Cmptr Tech Instr
Schultz, Frederick V.
Fifth Grade Teacher
Segbers, Dena L.
Cheerleading Coach
Snoddy, Charles William
Accounting Professor
Valvano, Dee R.
Retired Kindergarten Teacher
Wilcox, Dianne Grosser
Substitute Teacher
Zamperetti, Donald James
Prof of Business Admin
CANASERAGA
Macomber, Kathleen G.
Business Teacher
CANASTOTA
Laidlaw, Marcia Jean
Physical Education Teacher

STOTA (cont)
:, Marijane J.
rd Social Studies Teacher
son, Richard A., Sr.
ness Teacher
se, Mary Jo
h Teacher
Barbara Simpson
sh Teacher
er, Ellen Douglass
h Grade English Teacher
, Douglas C.
nistry & Physics Teacher
, Mary Sue Williams
ness Teacher
OR
Richard Edwin
School History Teacher
STEO
, Audrey K.
sh Teacher
Paula Tarquinio
selor
ON
Melanie S.
& Sixth Grade Teacher
, Arthur Glenn
ssor
Sheldon
anical Engrng Tech Prof
ns, Faye W.
: Professor of CIS
urn, Brian
ssor of Chemistry
Russell Frederick
ciate Professor
Thomas J.
ssor of English
E PLACE
Suzanne P.
ry & Media Specialist
uist, Mona Elizabeth
ance Counselor
, Richard Francis, Jr.
ematics Teacher & Supvr
Henry George
gy Teacher
EL
lorso, Patricia Pendleton
French & Homeroom Tchr
ia, Rosemary Nye
nd Grade Teacher
, James A.
ce Teacher
, Alan Stephen
: Teacher
way, John A.
Grade Teacher
, Glenn Michael
ness Education Teacher
, Nancy
h & Spanish Teacher
Gail Steinberg
ness Education Teacher
dt, Paul
ematics Department Chm
n, Linda Rodman
oreign Lang Tchr
runo, Neil G.
l Studies Teacher
erg, Jonathan B.
ner & Prof Growth Coord
on, Richard
eacher
rian
gy & Chemistry Teacher
Maureen Kingsley
sh Teacher
Susan F.
cal Education Teacher
, Carol S.
Arts Chprsn & Teacher
ro, Raymond
iology Teacher
calvo, Albert M.
: Director
an, Joan Smithwick
ergarten Teacher
Ann Johnson
ish Teacher
Louis Thomas, Jr.
ndary Social Studies Tchr
William Preston, III
: & Drama Teacher
n, Diane M.
al Studies Teacher
er, Paul D.
estra Director
HAGE
Patricia Bullock
ance Counselor
Cheryl Lynn
Science Teacher
s, Patrick M.
ech Ed Teacher
en, Ruth Bowles
ish Teacher
on, Karen Toper
School Math Teacher
f, Elaine Kraushaar
ish Teacher
n, David Edward
Grade Social Studies Tchr
Alma
ematics Teacher
an, Sarah Marie
ch Teacher
ILE
ood, Anne Mc Grath
ed Elem Teacher

MacDavitt, Charlotte Ann
1st-2nd Grade Teacher
CASTLETON
Frese, Americo Peter
US History Teacher
Maher, Paul L.
Chemistry & Earth Science Tchr
Seplavy, Stephanie
Speech Pathologist
CATO
Cancro, James Richard
Social Studies Teacher
Cappellano, Donna M.
Health Teacher
Donnelly, Kathryn R.
Guidance Counselor
Duke, Amy Lawyer
5th Grade Teacher
Gilfus, Jonna Kerst
English Teacher
Meccariello, Gerald P.
11th Grade Chemistry Teacher
Shuler, Herbert F.
Social Studies Teacher
Wood, Allan Hicks
Social Studies Teacher
CATSKILL
Headley, Janice Marie
Home Economics Teacher
Holland, James R.
Science Teacher
Melo, Chelsa A.
Third Grade Teacher
Notarnicola, Joyce Barclay
French Teacher
Patterson, Jane K.
10th Grade Biology Teacher
Szakmary, Linda E.
2nd Grade Teacher
Wolven, Barry D.
Physical Education Teacher
CAZENOVIA
Greene, John Robert
History & Comm Professor
Kasold, Stephen Joseph
High School English Teacher
CEDARHURST
Aronowitz, Barbara L.
High School English Teacher
Caraccio, Alana Gene Reiner
English Teacher
CELORON
Clark, Barbara Turkett
1st Grade Teacher
CENTER MORICHES
Kellner, Veronica Marie
English Teacher
Kispert, Maureen C.
Retired Fifth Grade Teacher
LoVece, Monica Kump
Spanish Teacher
Ripple, Kevin
Science Teacher
Rogers, David B.
Social Studies Dept Chprsn
Szymanski, Ellen M.
Social Studies Teacher
CENTEREACH
Austin, Lyle P.
Business Teacher
Beirne, Bernard Joseph
English Teacher
Brisson, Donald Paul
English Teacher
Cain, Barbara Krieger
6th Grade Math & Rdng Teacher
Cole, Nancy J.
Physical Education Teacher
Ferry, Kevin
English Teacher
Fiore, Carolyn Lee Krause
Elementary Music Teacher
Hauman, Eugene
Social Studies Teacher
Hickey, William Lawrence
Social Studies Teacher
Kirschner, Carol Ann Mc Kinney
Family & Consumer Sci Teacher
Luciano, Guy E.
Social Studies Teacher
Nystedt, Clifford P.
Art Teacher
Perreca, James N.
Sixth Grade Teacher
Pesek, John Rudolph
Science Teacher
Reed, Elena
6th Grade Teacher
Restaino-Merola, Linda
Basic Skills Teacher
Rowland, William S.
English Teacher
Schumacher, William Robert
Mathematics Teacher
Singer, Helene
4th Grade Teacher
Yenick Moir, Jean-Marie
Choral Director
CENTRAL ISLIP
Knights, Christine Wolf
English Teacher
Kurtz, Mary Curtin
Fifth Grade Teacher
Rockett, David J.
Technology Teacher
Schiavo, William Alan
12th Grade English Teacher
Seidel, Bonita Marie
Second Grade Teacher

Solaski, Paul
English Teacher
Terrana, Susan
Choral Director
Volpe, Pamela Dawn
Reading Teacher
Winograd, Helene
Art Teacher
CENTRAL SQUARE
Costello, Carolyn
Curr & Spcl Project Acting Dir
D'Amico, Kathleen Susan
Social Studies Teacher
Elwood, Craig R.
Music Teacher & Band Director
Fowler, William Arthur
6th Grade Teacher
Fries, David Mark
Elem Physical Education Tchr
Garry, Kathleen Anne
Kindergarten Teacher
Irion, John V.
Physical Ed Teacher & Coach
Miedaner, Cheryl Palucci
Social Studies Teacher
Pettit, Cindy Hollis
Second Grade Teacher
Robson, Richard
Guidance Counselor
Talley, Martha Lynn
English Teacher
Wilk, Agnes Mary
French Teacher
CENTRAL VALLEY
Arlt, Ingrid
Math & Computer Sci Tchr
DiDonato, Michele Pennisi
School Librarian & Dept Coord
Duffy, Eileen M. (Sailer)
Business Ed Instr & Chrpsn
Hintze, Stacey (Burke)
HS Art Teacher
Hodges, Raymond Philip
High School Mathematics Tchr
Neely, Mary Beth
Social Studies Teacher
Pocklembo, Ann Marie Elizabeth
Orchestra Director
Terlecky, Dolores Andres
Language Arts Teacher
Zucker, Robert W.
Mathematics Teacher
CHAMPLAIN
Kokes, Kathleen Donnelly
K-12th Grd Music Teacher
McFetridge, Janet S.
French Teacher
Power, Brian Patrick
English Teacher
CHAPPAQUA
Schlenger, Gail Susan
Resource Room Teacher
CHATEAUGAY
Helm, Anne
5th Grade Teacher
CHATHAM
Borgen, Thomas John
7th & 8th Grd Science Teacher
Giordano, Mark
Band Director & Music Educator
King, Denise Wendell
Fifth Grade Teacher
Mackowski, Greg John
HS Social Studies Teacher
Roosevelt, Barbara Veino
English Teacher
Tomaso, Patrice Lisa
High School Art Teacher
Wetherbee, Laurie A.
Biology Teacher
CHAUMONT
Davis, Barry K.
Social Studies Teacher
O'Donnell, Joseph Regan
Social Studies Teacher
Oliver, Edward Alan
Secondary Science Teacher
CHAUTAUQUA
Jantzi, Mary Holthouse
Science Teacher
Meissner, Leonard Robert
Vocal Music Director
CHEEKTOWAGA
Baiocco, Maureen Elizabeth
English Teacher
Bifano, Anthony J.
HS Mathematics Teacher
Conti, Joan Noel
School Social Worker
Dobinski, Patricia Peters
Living Skills Teacher
Durka, Chester S.
Economics & Government Tchr
Glanville, Susan Kime
Health Occupations Teacher
Graham, H. Glen, Jr.
Biology Teacher
Groszkowski, Jacqueline Wajtkus
Kindergarten Teacher
Hageman, Thomas
Junior High Teacher
Heffern, Robert James
Social Studies Teacher & Coord
Jacques, Kathleen Cleary
HS Social Studies Teacher
Kajdasz, Bonnie Marie (Peruzzini)
Fourth Grade Teacher
Krzesinski, Patricia Sullivan
Dean of Students

Leonardi, Susan Cinotti
Kindergarten Teacher
Mihelbergel, Robert Charles
English Teacher
Napier, Andrew R.
Technology Ed Tchr & Dept Chm
Noworyta, Victoria Swisher
Math Teacher
Pearce, Donald N.
Physics & Physical Sci Teacher
Place, Holly Lynn
Home Economics Teacher
Plewinski, Ronald B.
4th Grade Teacher
Ronald, Thomas J.
Third Grade Teacher
Ryan, Elizabeth Frick
2nd Grade Tchr, Asst Principal
Salisbury, Gordon Thomas
English Teacher
Shane, Nancy Lee Peruzzini
Remedial Specialist
Shaw, Scott P.
11th Grade Math Teacher
Wood, Thomas Edwards
High School Mathematics Tchr
Yanno, Jack Anthony
11th-12th Grade Soc Stud Tchr
Zichittella, Gail Eberhardt
Chemistry Teacher
Zielinski, Stephen Francis
High School Math Teacher
CHERRY VALLEY
Fazio, Ronald Walter
Art Teacher
Jaquay, Jordan Eric
Social Studies Teacher
Ruggiriello, Margaret Bouck
High School English Teacher
Shaul, William Robert
HS Math Teacher & Bsktbl Coach
Whiteman, Fern Vargo
5th Grade Teacher
CHESTER
Ravert, E. Carol Hopkins
Fourth Grade Teacher
Saddlemire, David Charles
Social Studies Teacher
Solomon, Debra Aimis
5th Grade Teacher
CHESTERTOWN
Humiston, Jean Desidoro
Guidance Counselor & Director
Robertson, Scott Raymond
High School Science Teacher
CHITTENANGO
Conklin, James C.
Science Teacher & Coordinator
Hodel, Margaret M.
English Teacher
O'Keefe, Brian David
Biology & AP Biology Instr
Smolnycki, Daniel Harry
Guid Cnslr & District Coord
CHURCHVILLE
Beardsley, Micheleann (Dravec)
Math Teacher
Blake-Wilcox, Kim Renee
Secondary English Teacher
Cerbone, Dwayne Joseph
HS Mathematics Teacher
D'Arpino, Lenore M.
Spanish Teacher
Davis, Chris Francis
Seventh Grade Science Teacher
Goodling, Rob W.
Vocal Music Director
Mead, Kevin R.
Music Teacher
Moran, Cynthia Ann Wehle
Mathematics Teacher
Parnell, Francis James
8th Grade Science Teacher
Prouty, John Mark
Chemistry Teacher
Smith, Daniel J.
6th Grd Soc Stud & Rdng Tchr
Talbott, Linda Mullens
US His & AP Tchr
Thornton, Nancy Blakely
Hlth & Physical Education Tchr
Truesdale, Carol Ann
5th Grade Teacher
Turkett, Carol Woolver
Mathematics Teacher
Vacchetto, Bernadette Bauer
Math Teacher
Wheaton, Mark G.
Instrumental Music Teacher
Wood, William Randall
Health & PE Teacher
Wormley, Teresa Renee Suozzi
Spanish Teacher
CICERO
Baker, Sandra Acker
Library Media Specialist
Bradley, William H.
English Teacher
Brown, William
Health Instructor
Chapin, Paul Robeert
Science Teacher
Chermak, Mark Allen
HS History & Government Tchr
Conner, Nancy Swartzlander
English Teacher
D'Agostino, Lorraine Ann
Third Grade Teacher
DiGesare, John
Art Teacher

Goehner, Carol J.
Social Studies Teacher
Hartwell, Andrea S.
High School Resource Teacher
Kovac, Donna Suits
Business Teacher
McCaffery, Michael Sean
Elementary Teacher
Mc Connell, Thomas Steven
7th-12th Grade Science Teacher
Mouton, Stephen Edward
HS English Teacher
Niemczura, M. A.
German Teacher
Panka, Jeanne Brostek
Bio & Environmental Sci Tchr
Papalia, Frank R.
Spanish & English Teacher
Randall, Susan Jane Countryman
2nd Grade Teacher
Rice, Theresa Riccardi
Math Teacher
Riter, Connie
Mathematics Teacher
Sammon, Scott Joseph
High School Biology Teacher
Schatzel, Patricia Audrey
Span Tchr & Fac Adv Amnesty
Van Hoven, James B., Jr.
Art Teacher
Watson, Judith
Sixth Grade Teacher
Wetmore, Cynthia Lorraine
Physical Education Teacher
CINCINNATUS
Koch, Lynn Arthur
Vocal Music Teacher
White, Lolita Loomis
High School Art Teacher
CIRCLEVILLE
Butryn, Jean Crispell
6th Grade Teacher
CLARENCE
Chandler, Scott Gordon
Technology Education Teacher
Hammerton-Morris, Linda Kay
Spanish Teacher
Ihlefeld, Sandra Lucille
Frosh English & Jrnlsm Tchr
Johnson, Kevin Joseph
English & Journalism Teacher
Light, Nancy G.
High School English Teacher
Marshall, James Alan
Biology & Wilderness Teacher
Mirand, John Paul
8th Grade Social Studies Tchr
O'Brien, Jeanne Faliero
Second Grade Teacher
Patterson, Karen O. (King)
Latin Teacher
Routt, Douglas Byrum
Substitute Teacher
Shipengrover, William L.
Business Education Chair
Starr, Kevin J.
High School Teacher
Walleshauser, Barbara Mary Bergler
Math Department Chairman
Webber, Sharon Coyle
English Teacher
CLAYTON
Babcock, Maxine Kathryn (Button)
Social Studies Teacher
Brown, Suzanne Hyde
English Teacher
LeBlanc, Stephen Wallace
Language Arts & Soc Stud Tchr
CLIFTON PARK
Bianchi, Tina
Spanish & French Teacher
Brown, Claire Tobison
English Teacher
Butler, Cynthia Houglan
Fourth Grade Teacher
Chambers, Joanne Perkins
English Teacher
Clements, Glen G.
High School Mathematics Tchr
Dallara, Ralph Anthony
HS Mathematics Teacher
De Lucco, Gary
Global Studies Teacher
Golden, David Michael
Social Studies Teacher
Grastorf, Penny A.
Ninth Grade Math Teacher
Green, Albert Thomas
Seventh Grade Art Teacher
Houlton, Carol Ann Pratt
Physical Education Teacher
Hughes, Edward Thomas
English Department Chairperson
Jones, Matthew Richard
Physical Education Teacher
Kelleher, Katherine Mary
Global Studies Teacher
Kelly, Richard B.
Amer His & Pub Affairs Teacher
Klein, Stephen D.
Biology Teacher
Kopchick, Patricia P.
Social Studies Teacher
Long, Andrew
Business Education Teacher
Lynch, Donna Rimmer
Social Studies Teacher
Mangini, John Joseph
Sixth Grade Teacher

CLIFTON PARK (cont)
Mc Tighe, Janet Nickerson
School Counselor
Miller, Alison Ann (Campbell)
Biology Teacher
Myers, Dora P.
Secondary English Teacher
Neiswender, Patricia Hughes
English Teacher
Nelson, Daniel A.
Technology Instructor
O'Connell, Christine Biss
Eighth Grade English Teacher
Peluso, Patrick Anthony
5th Grade Teacher
Pintuff, Linda Cook
High School Math Teacher
Ratzer, Mary Boyd
Senior High School Librarian
Redmond, Mary Jo Ruggiero
English Teacher
Richard, Janet
Mathematics Teacher
Rinella, Vincent John
Biology Teacher
St Clair, Helaine Collins
Spanish Teacher
Solenski, Bruce Mitchell
6th Grade Teacher
Vaccaro, Charles John
Social Studies Teacher
Van Buren, Beverly Wall
6th Grade Teacher
Weiner, Harry S.
English Teacher
White, Thomas Michael
Technology Teacher
Wichtowski, Mary C.
English Teacher
Wink, Emily M. (Bohnet)
Librarian
Zusman, Linda Waters
Spanish Teacher
CLIFTON SPRINGS
Cyphert, Henry, Jr.
Earth Science Teacher
CLINTON
Greene, Linda M.
Adjunct & Flute Instructor
Hepburn, Deborah Hatch
English Teacher
Lee, Mary Ann Hamlin
Fr Tchr & Lang Dept Chair
Mc Donnell, Mary Eastman
Lang Arts & Soc Stud Tchr
CLYMER
Benjamin, Susan Nordstrom
Home & Careers Teacher
Carlton, Laurie Sullivan
English Teacher
Harte Dmitriev, Sheila H.
Social Studies & Russian Tchr
Heslink, Dennis William
Science Teacher
Hinsdale, Dennis Minford
Girls JV Basketball Coach
Joles, Lisa
Business Teacher
Malyuk, Anne Myers
5th & 6th Grade Teacher
Roche, Nancy Marie (Bracken)
Health & Physical Ed Teacher
Sweet, Larry F.
HS Social Studies Teacher
COBLESKILL
Agoglia, Paul
Technology Education Teacher
Baron, Christopher John
Seventh Grade Soc Studies Tchr
Colvard, Mary Page
Biology & Research Teacher
Fletcher, Deborah A.
Agriculture Teacher
Herrick, Richard E.
Professor of Physical Sciences
COHOCTON
Hayward, Ruth Ann
Fourth Grade Teacher
COHOES
Drennen, Pamela Susan
French Teacher
Isles, Cheryl A.
Biology Teacher
Lombardi, Donna Ball
Third Grade Teacher
Marios, Gertrude A.
Language Arts Teacher
COLD SPRING
D'Amato, Philip
Modern Languages Dept Chprsn
LeDioyt, Sally Schaeffer
Sixth Grade Teacher
Miller, Michael
Mathematics Teacher
Peterson, Deb
Vocal Music Director
Post, William L.
5th Grade Teacher
COLD SPRING HARBOR
Umstatter, Jack David
High School English Teacher
COLDEN
Paradowski, Natalie Lamb
Fourth & Fifth Grd Tchr
COLTON
Doyle, Sandra Pryor
Kindergarten Teacher
COMMACK
Austin, Myrna Bogner
First Grade Teacher
Bamberger, Marnette
5th & 6th Grade Teacher
Brasch, Peter
Band Director
Cohn, Arlene Manginelli
Spanish Teacher
Ettinger, Marcia Miller
Special Education Teacher
Friia, L. John
English Instructor
Jorch, Nancy Sue
English Teacher
Kilthau, Jane F. (Thomas)
Social Studies & Japanese Tchr
Leiner, Evelyn Joan
4th Grade Teacher
Pautaleo, Giacomo
History & Math Teacher
Pomponio, Alan R.
Science Teacher
Roberts, Paul D.
Music Teacher & Choral Dir
Rusden, Joan Zacker
Third Grade Teacher
Sheehan, Susan Mc Gilloway
6th Grade Teacher
Sherrow, Douglas Barnes
AP Economics & Business Instr
Weitman, Joan K.
Learning Disabilities Teacher
CONGERS
Boehr, Judith Herring
Fourth Grade Teacher
Just, Robert John
Music Teacher
CONKLIN
Burke, Michael J.
Mathematics Teacher
Golden, Joyce A.
Math Dept Chairperson
Hattala, Katherine Jane
English Teacher
Keegan, Christine Shaw
French Teacher
Ludwig, Ann O.
Ninth Grade English Teacher
Lynch, Patricia O'Neal
7th Grade Social Studies Tchr
Malloy, Thomas Paul
English Teacher
Mansfield, Carol Paulie
Special Education Teacher
Northwood, William Campbell
Retired Fifth Grade Teacher
Schuster, George Henry
8th Grade Teacher & Dept Chair
Staiger, Brian Edward
Science Teacher
CONSTANTIA
Appleton, Sharon Goodale
Second Grade Teacher
COOPERSTOWN
Howard, Donald Evers, Jr.
8th Grd American History Tchr
Iversen, Nancy A. (Gorman)
Former HS Biology Teacher
Schleining, Marjorie A.
French Teacher
COPIAGUE
Borzello, Kathleen Mack
Special Education Teacher
Cesare, Melody Ann Eiermann
7th-12th Grade Math Teacher
Goldenberg, Eliot
Guidance Counselor
Lipkin, Rosemary A.
4th-5th Grade Math & Sci Tchr
Nagelberg, Marc Morris
Learning Center Teacher
Thomas, Jinu Daniel
Seventh Grade English Teacher
Turner, Maxine
Music Teacher
CORAM
Girardi, Theresa A.
Second Grade Teacher
Gitters, Susan
4th Grade Teacher
McNally, Edward James
5th Grade Teacher
Smosky, Donna Fingar
Third Grade Teacher
CORFU
Taylor, Skip
Band Director
Will, John W.
Chemistry & Physics Teacher
CORINTH
Ahern, Daniel P.
6th Grade Teacher
Farr, Rose Anne Durkin
Third Grade Teacher
Hayes, Ronald Joseph, Jr.
Mathematics & Computer Teacher
Jones, Karen
Reading Specialist
Kuntz, Maureen Elizabeth
5th Grade Teacher
Palmero, Judith Ann
French & Spanish Teacher
Wells, Lisa A. H.
Spanish Teacher
White, Ronald I.
Guidance Counselor
CORNING
Clark, Dale J.
Assoc Prof of Business Div
Deleone, Joseph John
Physics Professor
Gearhart, Kim Russell
College Field Advisor & Instr
Holden, Randall O., III
Math Teacher
Holleran, Mary Anne Quatrano
Fifth Grade Teacher
Josbeno, Larry Joseph
Professor of Physics
Kobbe, Nancy Bolt
Sixth Grade Teacher
Meckley, James William, III
Band Director
Newton, James L.
Teacher
Powell, Barbara Nelson
Computer Information Sci Prof
Strauser, Ned C.
Counselor
Thomas, William J.
Eighth Grade Social Stud Tchr
Titlow, Peter G.
High School Math & Sci Teacher
Tobia, Joseph Anthony
Special Ed Tchr & Athletic Mgr
CORNWALL
Fried, Andrew
Secondary English Teacher
Maisonet, Tito Manuel
Physical Education Teacher
Mc Lennan, Helen M.
Dance Teacher & Owner
Nichols, Denise Vallet
Frgn Lang Dept Chair & Fr Tchr
CORNWALL ON HUDSON
Burgarelli, Celina Jordan
Spanish Teacher
Fitzsimmons, Diana
Science & Mathematics Teacher
Igo, Margaret Cullen
Third Grade Teacher
Lynch, Mary Diane
Seventh & Eighth Grade Teacher
CORONA
Merker, Gail Emilia Esquivel
Parent Dev-Congruence Teacher
Vitiello, Jo Ann DiGangi
Principal
CORTLAND
Aldrich, Shirley M. (Smith)
Second & Third Grade Teacher
Burrell, Richard Starr
7th Grd Social Studies Teacher
Dippo, Jeanette Potter
Health Education Teacher
Fadale, Carl
Sixth Grade Teacher
Matos, Wilfredo
EOP Counselor
COXSACKIE
Brennan, Kathryn Keeping
High Schl Mathematics Teacher
Cornell, Janet Burch
French Teacher
Gunderman, Therun E.
Chem Tchr & Sci Dept Chm
Halley, Martha Williams
Fourth Grade Teacher
Laveroni, Bryana Hancock
Elem Physical Education Tchr
Leonardo, Jennie (Walsh)
1st Grade Teacher
Potts, Frederick Richard, III
Fifth Grade Teacher
CROSS RIVER
Kandel, Linda Beck
Math Teacher
CROTON ON HUDSON
Coons, Karin Hoerup
6th Grade Resource Room Tchr
Fetchick, Carol Anne
Former MS Math Teacher
Sarver, Barbara (Cambetes)
Math Tchr & Curriculum Coord
CUBA
Burdick, Sandra Reitzell
English Teacher & Dept Chair
Conner, David James
Social Science Instructor
Daisley, Ellie Glassmire
Biology Teacher
Johnson, Michael Dennis
Technical Education Teacher
Kunz, Michael W.
Elementary Principal
Miller, Kirk Edward
Instrumental Music Teacher
Rawson, Patricia Ann
Teacher & Coach
Tucker, William J.
4th Grade Tchr
Yatzkanic, Steven Joseph
6th Grade Teacher
CUTCHOGUE
Mc Goey, Rosemary Ann
Fifth Grd Teacher & Asst Prin
Moeller Foster, Doris Price
HS Math Tutor
DALTON
Privitera, Joanne Urtz
Kindergarten Teacher
DANSVILLE
Haywood, Barry O.
Instrumental Music Teacher
Lewis, Evelyn Elliott
Art Teacher
DAVENPORT
Lawrence, Elaine M.
HS Social Studies Teacher
Mac Cracken, Cynthia Dimon
Instrumental Music Teacher
Meschutt, Lisa Bump
Secondary Science Teacher
Trelease, Laurie A.
Mathematics Teacher
DE KALB JUNCTION
Bray, John N.
Secondary Science Teacher
Mattraw, Gail E.
Director & PE Teacher
Nee, Edward J.
Mathematics Teacher
Peters, Katherine Hayden
Secondary English Teacher
Wilson, Christy Bartholomew
Eng, Speech & Drama Teacher
DE RUYTER
Cleveland, Maxine Lehrman
Fifth Grade Teacher
Drake, Joseph Robert
7th-12th Grd Art Teacher
Fostveit, Tamara S.
First Grade Teacher
Ludwig, Edmund Bruce
Biology & Physics Teacher
DEER PARK
Bellis, William W.
Phys Ed Teacher
Bense, Roger Steven
Assistant Principal
Byrnes, Thomas James
Physics Teacher
Colletti, Peter T.
Fourth Grade Teacher
Corrao, Diana
Math Teacher
Langenthal, Suzanne A.
3rd Grade Teacher
Perry, Jill P.
Business Education Teacher
White, Patricia Ann
Social Studies & Religion Tchr
DELANSON
Buthe, Betty Ann Hess
Business Education Teacher
Rem, Marie
Spanish Teacher
Walls, Kathleen Stevens
Physical Education Teacher
DELHI
Gamble, Robert Martin
Carpentry & Psychology Prof
Gariepy, John J.
Social Studies Teacher & Coach
Grust, Patricia L.
Nursing Instructor
Harrington, Richard E.
Prof of Building Technologies
Kurz, Linda Ann
Professor of Mathematics
Mc Mullen, Douglas D.
Automotive Mechanics Instr
Van Brunt, Arthur (Peter)
Associate Professor of Bus
DELMAR
Cappiello, Jane Zameroski
Science Teacher
Fish, Peter James
Technology Education Teacher
Peters, Robert J.
Technology Teacher
Piechnik, John Stephen
Social Studies Supervisor
Quackenbush, Cathy Seaman
Biology Teacher
Quackenbush, Roger Eugene
High School Biology Teacher
Rightmyer, Jack Kevin
6th Grade English Teacher
Seaton, Kathleen Marie
Retired 5th Grade Teacher
Symula, David Stanley
Mathematics Teacher
Zornow, Kimberly Lynn
Mathematics Teacher
DEPEW
Boltz, Jean Beaumont
Secondary Mathematics Teacher
Burch, Regina L.
Kindergarten Teacher
Caruana, Anthony Francis
Jr High English Teacher
Chambers, Jacqueline Marie
High School Math Teacher
Clausen, Anglea Cometto-Bartram
Spanish Teacher
Connelly, Neil
Math Teacher
Gaynor, Bonnie Mc Kinney
Seventh Grade Math Teacher
Gorczynski, Carolyn A.
Math & Computer Sci Teacher
Hutchinson, Denis Durward
Biology & Chemistry Teacher
Kidd, Teresa Marie
First Grade Teacher
Lawniczak, James Henry
Technology Teacher
Lewandowski, Amy Kosnik
Sixth Grade Teacher
Mc Williams, Paul H.
Third Grade Teacher
Odien, Richard L.
5th Grade Teacher
O'Neill, Robert Martin
High School English Teacher
Pieniazek, Nancy
Science Teacher
Roberts, Thomas Gerard
9th-10th Grade English Teacher
Schmidt, Patricia Allen
Fifth Grade Teacher
Troutman, Barbara Jane Rothenberg
2nd Grade Teacher
DEPOSIT
Cable, Kathleen M.
Language Arts & Math Rdng Tchr
Plunkett, Eileen
Earth Science Teacher
Stever, Deborah J.
Supvr & Assistant Principal
DERBY
Schmitt, Barbara Ann (Sieg)
Fourth Grade Teacher
DEXTER
Haller, Willis Floyd
Earth Science Teacher
Harding, Treasure Kingan
PE Instructor & Key Club Adv
St Croix, Jeffrey James
8th Grd Mathematics Teacher
Wood, Francis Joseph
Chem & Earth Science Teacher
DIX HILLS
Eigen, Elliot
HS English Teacher
Martin, Carolyn Williamson
Retired Teacher
Pastoressa, Marianne Pugliese
Biology & Chemistry Teacher
Shaver, Harold D.
Physics Teacher
DOBBS FERRY
Burke, Thomus Francis
History & Religion Dept Chair
Clanton, Barbara Lynn
Mathematics Teacher
Gatti, Patricia Fitzsimmons
Religious Teacher
Rosenzweig, Jennifer Leslie
English Teacher & Dept Chair
Singer, Mary Theresa
School Administrator
Stanton, Ann Fogarty
Chem & Environmental Sci Tchr
DOLGEVILLE
Ceglia, Glenn A.
Instrumental Music Teacher
Foster, Bruce Michael
Global Studies Teacher
Huddleston, John Roland
American History & Ec Teacher
Neely, Sandra Helmer
5th Grade Teacher
Phillips, Cheryl Ann
Second Grade Teacher
Reynolds, Christine M.
High School English Teacher
Roberts, Elizabeth M.
1st Grade Teacher
Stewart, Carol Maria
German Teacher
Wagar, Diane M.
English Teacher
Williams, Richard F.
Social Studies Teacher
DOUGLASTON
Umlas, Loretta Galvin
EMT Instructor
DOVER PLAINS
Kelly, James Michael
Retired Business Teacher
Lawson, David A.
Social Studies Teacher
Webb, Judith Gautreaux
Earth Science Teacher & Chair
Wright, Thomas R.
Social Studies Teacher
DOWNSVILLE
Astor, Mark John
Special Education Teacher
Hollenbaugh, David K.
PE & Drivers Ed Teacher
Kromer, William Annesley
English & Spanish Teacher
Merrill, Arthur M.
Secondary English Teacher
Robinson, Joan Veronica
First Grade Teacher
DRYDEN
Bence, Patricia Jean Schulak
Professor
Devan, Robert James
Guidance Coordinator
Lang, Paul
Social Studies Teacher
Lattimore, Kathy Lamoreaux
Adjunct English Instructor
Lauria, Margaret Munro
English Teacher
Lauria, Peter F.
US History, Govt & Ec Tchr
Lowery, Nancy D.
Spanish Teacher & Dept Chprsn
Ochs, Scott Armin
Sociology Instructor
Rosato, Florence Genson
Asst Professor of Accounting
DUNDEE
Allen, Rhonda K.
School Counselor
Bower, Jennifer Seymour
Fourth Grade Teacher
Corey, Debra
Spanish Teacher
Keefer, Dawn E.
Business Ed & Math Teacher
Larmouth, W. David
Chemistry Teacher

EE (cont)
nd, William P.
h Grade Teacher
, Tina Sochia
umental Music Teacher
s, Thomas E.
ary Media Specialist
IRK
sley, Coby L.
ish Teacher
Carol Carlson
ocial Studies Teacher
Karen Tauffener
ness Education Teacher
korn, Lenore Catalano
nd Grade Teacher
ziej, Edward Joseph
h Teacher & Frgn Lang Chm
elli-Pendl, Jean
nce Teacher
an, Pauline
Grade Teacher
ller, William
ed Art History Professor
ori, Michael Anthony
ical Education Teacher
y, Joseph E.
al Studies Teacher
rd, Brent Mason
ogy & Anatomy Teacher
AMHERST
eborah Jean
eacher & Coach
rthy, Gloria Anna
Grade Teacher
Bernadette M.
ish & Journalism Teacher
land, Catherine Elizabeth
l Music Teacher
AURORA
lizabeth Anne
Grade Teacher
er, Dennis John
al Studies Teacher
cht, Susan Marie (Felser)
nd Grade Teacher
, James Michael
pecial Education Teacher
ELMHURST
, Ruth Alice
stant Principal
Debbie Palmieri
n Grade Teacher
, Charles
nth Grade Teacher
thal, Nancy
ish Teacher
GREENBUS
aw, Phyllis Gale
Grade Teacher
styne, Ruth Beattie
Grade Teacher
GREENBUSH
Diane Irving
mistry Teacher
r, Fred E.
ance Counselor
, Timothy P.
ish Teacher
ch, Ilona Manor
ish Teacher
Douglas Dean
ral Director
Lynda Bearup
dle & High School Math Tchr
ton, Thomas E.
ish Teacher
HAMPTON
di-Mensch, Linda
ish Teacher
Barry A.
ical Education Teacher
ISLIP
us, Sharon
a Grade Teacher
ton, R. Lois
Dean, Soc Stud & His Tchr
affrey, Margaret Costin
rth Grade Teacher
re, Francis James
a Grade Teacher
ston, Elizabeth Rose
al Studies Teacher
MEADOW
Robert
Grade Teacher
un, Antoinette Cervino
nish Teacher
eva, Laureann
h Teacher
n, Cari Silverman
ner Teacher
merle, Santina Aspromonte
Grade Teacher
, John William
8th Grade Art Teacher
an, David Henry
red Orchestra Director
na, Carol Ann
ond Grade Teacher
e, Michael Joseph
Guidance Counselor & Coach
, Marie Teresa Valent
& 8th Grd Math Tchr
, Madeline Ferrara
ond Grade Teacher
k, Peter Matthew
sical Education Teacher
, Sheila Rosenthal
Grade Teacher

Paola, Evelyn Joan
Fourth Grade Teacher
Strand, Carl Kevin
High School Art Teacher
Syden, Jeffrey
Earth Science Teacher
Vacchio, George Francis
PE Teacher & Bsbl Coach
Varricchio, Karen A.
Foreign Language Teacher
Woods, Virginia Pynn
Second Grade Teacher
EAST NORTHPORT
Angione, Dale Ann
Chemistry Teacher
Conn, Valerie Ann
Fifth Grade Teacher
Duffy, Mary Driscoll
Math Teacher
Foley, Peter Paul
Social Studies Teacher
Marino, Michael Gerard
Art Teacher
Porciello, Kerri Ellyn
English Teacher
Robey, Ronald R.
Dean & Accounting Teacher
Schioppa, Ralph Anthony
High School Coach
Schmidt, Joy Nelson
Kindergarten Teacher
Sclafani, Elisabeth Belle
English Teacher
Szokoli, Darren Robert
Health & Phys Education Tchr
Vitek, Susan Perkins
6th Grade Teacher
EAST NORWICH
Moore, Arlene Greiner
Social Studies Teacher
EAST PATCHOGUE
Dunton, Thomas Joseph
Biology Teacher
EAST PEMBROKE
Flynn, Patty Jurewicz
1st Grade Teacher
EAST QUOGUE
Brophy, James A.
Third & Sixth Grade Teacher
EAST ROCHESTER
Vercolen, Beth Lanni
High School Art Teacher
EAST ROCKAWAY
Allen, Virginia
Third Grade Teacher
Levin, Gail Susan
Fifth Grade Teacher
Liberti, Lorraine Nancy
Sixth Grade Teacher
Sanders, Carol
Social Studies Teacher
EAST SETAUKET
Cairns, Suzan Siekmann
Biology Teacher
Columbia, Michael Matthew
Foreign Language Dept Chairman
Contino, Linda Gatti
Coral Director
Daly, Jean M.
Fifth Grade Teacher
Eggers, Charles Gary
Mathematics Dept Chairperson
Fisher, Vivian M. Viloria
Spanish Teacher
Francis, Nancy D.
Fifth Grade Teacher
Goldfarb, Vicki Krasner
Health & Physical Ed Teacher
Grant, Adrienne Wilson
Elem Theatre Arts Option Tchr
Gustavsen, Laura Ann
Symphonic Band Director
Hameroff, Glenn L.
HS Social Studies Teacher
Heath, Kristin Hartford
Math, Computer & Science Tchr
Klodt, Roberta DiCarlo
Choral Director & Music Tchr
Leverich, William Francis
HS English Teacher
Massaro, Catherine Jeanne
Spanish Teacher
Rocklein, Kathleen Fusco
Chemistry Teacher
Singer, Joan
Spanish Teacher
Turano, Frank Joseph
Biology Teacher
Waszmer, Jack
Biology Teacher & Coach
EAST SYRACUSE
Arnone, Mary Ann
6th Grade Teacher
Berry, John Walter
Instrumental Music Teacher
Canestrare, Kimberley Anne
Art Teacher
Early, Joyce P.
Third Grade Teacher
Flock, Gilbert C.
Instrumental Music Teacher
Goldberg, Irwin S.
Music Teacher
Kashmann, Beth L.
Counselor
Marsh, Theresa Patricia Greek
7th Grd Language Arts Teacher
Mc Glynn, Sean E.
Science Teacher

Meltzer, Michael Robert
Physics & AP Physics Teacher
Musolino, Joseph
Business Teacher
Natali, Maureen Gilligan (Biolk)
English Teacher & Drama Dir
Oja, Linda Palumbo
Sixth Grade Teacher
Schwab, Richard A.
Mathematics Teacher
Tully, James Richard
English Teacher
Vasiliades, Martha Wert
8th Grade Science Teacher
Walcott, Carmen Lynn
Fourth Grade Teacher
Yanno, Thomas A.
Guidance Director
EAST WILLIAMSVILLE
Gruszka, Donald Leonard
Third Grade Teacher
EASTCHESTER
Amato, Marianne
English Teacher
Koscinski, Michael John
Mathematics Teacher
Sanders, Louis Edward
Social Studies Teacher
Zantay, Douglas William
Band Director
EASTPORT
Crennan, Lindsay Ann
Kindergarten Teacher
Giacolone, Steven Richard
Business Chairman
Hancock, Nancy H.
Special Education Teacher
Skala, Todd James
Social Studies Teacher
EDEN
Farace, Dennis Allen
Global Studies & Ec Tchr
EDMESTON
Lewis, Carol Cynthia Curtis
Jr High English Teacher
ELBA
Carnevale, Daniel K.
Art Teacher
Kepler, Melanie Hunt
Mathematics Teacher
Kujawski, Luanne Salvador
Business & Computer Teacher
Sands, Lenora Tyler
Secondary Mathematics Teacher
Sonne, Kenneth J.
7th-12th Grade Technology Tchr
ELDRED
Kane, Nancy Duncan
English Teacher
Moritz, Michael Nickolas
History Teacher
ELIZABETHTOWN
Haseltine, Sharon OConnor
Second Grade Teacher
ELLENBURG DEPOT
Dimick, Melody Dean
English Teacher
ELLENVILLE
Beukelman, Ann S.
Mathematics Teacher
Healy, Jane E. Newell
Home Ec & Home Careers Teacher
Kapela, Sandy
Second Grade Teacher
Phelan, Madlyn Barringer
English & French Teacher
Rahaman, Cheryl Brinson
ESL Teacher
Steinhoff, Patricia Craft
Fifth Grade Teacher
ELLICOTTVILLE
Gemerek, Gail Marie
Business & Home Economics Tchr
ELMA
Baranowski, Nance L.
Retired Social Studies Teacher
Barszcz, Edward L.
Mathematics Teacher
Davison, Mark Warren
Social Studies Teacher
Durham, Thomas Fisher
English Teacher
Jacobs, Andrew
PE Tchr & Coach
Roma, Jeanne Dunne
High School English Teacher
ELMHURST
Bonilla, Felix Carlos
Bilingual Social Studies Tchr
Cadena, Aida Delgado
Spanish Teacher
Ferreira, Anna Muntzenberger
English Teacher
Grabher, Mary Joan (Traynor)
English Teacher
Kim, Hesun
Korean Language Arts Teacher
Li, Victoria Blanca
Spanish Teacher
Marino, Salvatore Anthony
Mathematics Teacher
O'Keefe, Daniel Patrick
Asst Prin, Eng & French Tchr
O'Keeffe, Kathleen F.
Social Studies, AP US His Tchr
Russo, Lorraine Joan
English & ESL Teacher
Straczynski, Thomas S.
Sixth Grd & Foreign Lang Tchr

Terranova, Rose Antoinette
Eighth Grade Math Teacher
Votava, Mari Anne
English & Comm Arts Tchr
ELMIRA
Baker, Brenda Kay
Seventh-Eighth Grd Eng Tchr
Cain, Susan C.
Math Teacher
Caroscio, Mary Ann
First Grade Teacher
Caroscio, William J.
Mathematics Teacher
Cleary, Edward Dellon
English Teacher
Cleary-Todd, Debra L.
Secondary Social Studies Tchr
Coene, Mary Carmella
Sci & Team Physics Teacher
Cunningham, Lois Crawford
Human Ecology Teacher
Dean, Margaret Mullen
Spanish Teacher
Gordon, June Sacavage
HS Art Teacher
Hall, Thomas J.
English Teacher
Hughes, Betty Querqui
Second Grade Teacher
Keeler, Mary Driscoll
Sixth Grade Teacher
Koenig, Ann Christine
Biology & Chemistry Teacher
Ladley, Patricia Powers
Theology Teacher
LeTourneau, Carlton K.
Biology Teacher
Limes, Terri L.
Vocal Music & String Teacher
Litchfield, Beth Johnson
Kindergarten Teacher
Maitland, William D.
English Teacher
Olisky, John Joseph
Theology & Psychology Teacher
Pfleegor, Gwenda Lynn
Graduate Adjunct Professor
Pucci, Anthony J.
English Department Chairman
Ransey, Theresa Marie
Sixth Grade Teacher
Raplee, William John
Sixth Grade Math Teacher
Reagan, Christine M.
School Counselor
Romeo, Bernadette Rossi
English Teacher
Rudgers, Gregory Bruce
Music Teacher
Schnippert, Dori Glenn
Art Dept Chairperson & Teacher
Smith, Robert Elliott
Mathematics Teacher
Sullivan, Mary Marinan
2nd Grade Teacher
Tokarski, Felecia Hoodak
9th-11th Grd English Teacher
Winston, Maria T.
French, German Tchr & Dept Hd
ELMIRA HEIGHTS
Batterson, Dolores Kupres
6th Grade Teacher
Mc Nulty, Eugene P.
Biology & Health Teacher
Speciale, Laurie
English Teacher
Valicenti, Josephine Vivona
School Counselor
ELMONT
Benowitz, Corinne Joan
Mathematics Teacher
Bonich, Maria A.
Sixth Grade Teacher
Castillo, Ibis Nadal
Business Education Teacher
Crimmins, Thomas F.
Guidance Counselor
Cupelli, Lillian DeSanctis
Child Development Teacher
DiSclafani, Beverly
Third Grade Teacher
Drew, Diane Inserra
Fourth Grade Teacher
Esrick, Jo Ann GianFagna
French & Spanish Teacher
Going, Denise (Bianculli)
English Teacher
Goldstein, Jack Leon
High School Art Teacher
Gombert, Barbara
ESL Teacher
Greenan, James Patrick
Mathematics Chairman
Haigh, Rosemary Passannante
French Teacher
Helfenstein, Deborah Reis
Guidance Counselor
Hetterick, Kenneth
Health & Physical Ed Teacher
Hill, John F.
Sixth Grade Teacher
Ianniello, Teresa M.
PE & Health Teacher
Indovino, Michael
Social Studies Teacher
Kerdavid, Gisele
Fifth Grade Teacher
Mackey, Joelle Enrico
Social Studies Teacher

McDonough, Joseph Peter
Mathematics Teacher
Nielsen, Thomas Joseph
Mathematics Teacher
O'Leary, Patricia
English Teacher
Pignataro, Barbara Troiano
Sixth Grade Teacher
Seely, Steven Alan
English Teacher
Tyler, Carolyn Jeanette Vance
Second Grade Teacher
ELMSFORD
Abbate-Ryan, Laurie
HS Math Teacher
Keogan, Margaret E., RDC
8th Grade Teacher
ENDICOTT
Angeline, Fran
Retired Latin & German Teacher
Benjamin, Marsha Kay
Social Studies Teacher
Betza, Barbara Carlucci
Science Teacher
Bradley, Lynne Sweetland
Mathematics Teacher
Brafman, Kenneth Abraham
Assistant Principal
Brewer, Edward Allan
7th Grade Soc Studies Teacher
Carpenter, Carl Emerson
Mathematics Teacher
Childs, Philip Michael
8th Grade Science Educator
Cicco-Kuper, Mary A.
Retired Art Teacher
Closser, Elaine Barno
Music Teacher
Consol, Daniel A.
7th Grade Social Studies Tchr
DeLuca, Lynda Ann
Sixth Grade Teacher
Dinaburg, Robert
Teacher
Fitch, Diane Pilgrim
High School English Teacher
Goodwin, Charles Hugh
Tech & Mngmt Sciences Chair
Guccia, Bart George
Chemistry Teacher
Herceg, Robert Anthony
Earth Science Teacher
Honnick, Dorothy M. (Reynolds)
Retired PE Teacher & Coach
Hynes, Lawrence Robert
English Teacher
Iacovazzi, Dominick C.
Science Teacher
Johnson, Mitchell David
Physics Teacher
Linaberry, Robin Lee
Music Teacher
Mangialetti, Nancy E.
Third Grade Teacher
Marr, Elizabeth Timmerman
1st Grade Teacher
Mc Culloch, Carole Olkowski
Soc Stud & Economics Teacher
Musa, Beverly (Stevens)
Math Teacher
Parsons, Donald Russell
4th & 5th Grade Teacher
Peters, Barry George
Band Director
Piester, John B.
Math Teacher
Rinker, Natalie Ann (Trpik)
6th Grade Teacher
Salati, Orazio Joseph
Art Teacher
Schmidt, Rene Ann
Elementary Orchestra Teacher
Smith, William Stephen
Language Arts Teacher
Stewart, Fitzroy Anthony
Director of Choral Activities
Testa, Jim
6th Grd Teacher
Yaw, Amy Seaburg
Seventh Grade English Teacher
ENDWELL
White, Jeffrey Alan
Gymnastics Teacher
FABIUS
Sharpe, Kevin E.
High School Math Teacher
FAIRPORT
Aparo, Diane Marie
First Grade Teacher
Balzano, John G.
Math Teacher & Consultant
Baxendell, Robin Jean Burger
Art Teacher
Brown, Kenneth Lee
Orchestra Dir & Music Teacher
Carney, J. E.
History Instructor
Cooper, Stephanie Barton
9th Grade English Teacher
Daly, James Joseph
Fourth Grade Teacher
Drury, Kay P.
Biology Teacher
Gaudio, Christine L.
6th Grade Teacher
Gillan, Sally Wheaton
Retired Nursery School Teacher
Glicksman, Janet Lifschitz
Second Grade Teacher

FAIRPORT (cont)
Green, Kathleen Ann (Hayward)
Former Elementary Teacher
Hanna, Michiko Sharon
8th Grade English Teacher
Hild, Elizabeth Mc Millan
Second Grade Teacher
Horner, Donald H.
Chemistry & Physics Teacher
Kennel, Beth Mattson
French & German Teacher
Kent, Marnie Jayne
Physical Education Teacher
Kistler, Heidi E.
Fourth Grade Teacher
Laemlein, Jean Waganka
Mathematics Teacher
Lanning, David E.
History Teacher
Lynam, Jolene M.
Teacher & Facilitator of GATE
Mac Millan, Donald Hugh
Fifth Grade Teacher
Mahan, Patricia Horvath
Sixth Grade Teacher
Mancuso, Theresa A.
Fourth Grade Teacher
Mc Carthy, Molly
Physical Education Teacher
Mons, Joan Dixon
Chemistry Teacher
Northrup, Janet M.
English Teacher
Obenauf, Gregg L.
Assistant Principal
Ognibene, Richard Thomas
Chemisty & Physics Teacher
Pedersen, Anne Greer
Senior Riding Instructor
Perez, Catherine Herzog
Chemistry Teacher
Pirrello, Linda Estes
4th Grade Teacher
Pope, Rebecca K.
English Teacher
Radack, D. Michael
Elem Mathematics Tchr
Robinson, Sandra Fogg
English Teacher
Schofield, Mary Alice A.
Health Teacher
Senges, Marsha Webb
5th Grade Teacher
Sheldon, Penn
Math Teacher
Taber, David Wm
Retired 7th Grd Soc Sci Tchr
Tiberio, William S.
Instrumental Music Teacher
Whyte, William F.
Criminal Justice Instructor
Wierzbicki, Pamela Morris
High School Physical Ed Tchr
Winn, Patricia Baker
9th Grade Earth Science Tchr
FALCONER
Johnston, Steven Eric
Regents Earth Science Teacher
Mc Elheny, Michael F.
6th Grade Science Teacher
Richetti, Duane
English Teacher & Dept Chm
FALLSBURG
Cohen, Blanche Rubin
Science Teacher & Dept Chprsn
Duncan, William J.
Challenge Coordinator
Kalter, Ieleen
French & Spanish Teacher
LaBrake, Deborah Marie
English Teacher
Mayo, Kathleen Anne
8th Grade English Teacher
Park, Edward Duane
Bio Chem Teacher
Sheard, Lou Ann Somes
Guidance Counselor
FAR ROCKAWAY
Adler, Linda Blum
7th Grade Lang Arts Teacher
Black, Barbara H.
Social Studies Dept Chair
Butcher, Juanita James
Coop Coordinator
Campopiano, Thomas
Mathematics Asst Principal
Edobor-Osula, Valentine O.
Science Teacher
Goldberg, Mark B.
Soc Stud Tchr & Project Coord
Johnson, John K.
7th Grade Math & Science Tchr
Koppinger, Mary Howley
Social Studies Teacher
Levine, Marjorie Damashek
English Teacher
Mackiewicz, Barbara B.
Religious Studies Teacher
Murphy, Bridget Gorman
8th Grade Teacher
Nadler, Gail (Wirth)
First Grade Teacher
Sommers, Ann Margaret
Special Education Teacher
Sooppersand, Samnarain
6th Grade Teacher
Spence, Ann
High School English Teacher
Weiss, Carol Z.
6th Grade Teacher

Williams-Jackson, Brenda L.
Assistant Principal
Yearwood, Inez Lucina (Walters)
Ret Communication Arts Teacher
FARMINGDALE
Brown, Gary Allen
Professor of Biology
Chaskes, Stuart Jay
Assoc Prof of Med Lab Tech
Danzi, Angela D.
Assistant Professor
Fiorillo, John Anthony
Prof of Electrical Eng Tech
Friel, James P.
Professor
Gaab, Jeffrey S.
Assistant Professor of History
Hartford, Flora Marino
Humanities Teacher
Joseph, Laura Mueller
Assistant Professor
Lovizio, Paul William
Dept of His, Eco, Pol Prof
Marrone, Daniel Scott
Business Administration Prof
Menna, Larry K.
Assistant Professor of History
Reganse, Robert J.
Chair of Coll Preparation Dept
Schneider, Susan D.
High School English Teacher
Stedman, Mary Fitzgerald
Associate Professor of Nursing
Tiedemann, John E.
Chprsn & Prof Mech Engr Tech
FARMINGVILLE
Cole, Caroline
7th Grade Teacher
DiFazio, Susan E.
Third Grade Teacher
Lopez, Lynn Brilli
Kindergarten Teacher
FAYETTEVILLE
Baker, Diane Mawhinney
Vocal Music Teacher
Bracker, Christine Florence
Fourth Grade Teacher
Broadbent, Peggy Mc Creevy
First & Second Grade Teacher
Buckingham, Margo L.
6th Grade Teacher
Farrell, William Robert
Ret Latin & History Teacher
Macaulay, William Andrew
Science Teacher
Wallace, Larry
5th Grade Teacher
FILLMORE
Faulkner, Kyle L.
Social Studies Teacher
Mullen, James Laurence
Secondary English Teacher
Nolan, William H., III
Social Stud Dept Chair & Tchr
FISHERS ISLAND
Giles, Carol Spadora
Science Teacher
FISHKILL
Bretsch, Susan C.
Fourth Grade Teacher
Post, Gary Allan
Fifth Grade Teacher
FLORAL PARK
Brandt, Marie Pinello
4th Grade Teacher
Brzozowski, Marion Saloky
American History & Govt Tchr
Cirolia, Dennis T.
Occupational Ed Teacher
Condon, Phyllis Sticco
Fourth Grade Teacher
Dolan, Kristina Louise
Biology Teacher
Epstein, Rachelle Janet
6th Grade Teacher
Klieger, Alan Bruce
Technology Teacher
Kwozko, Zenon
Math Teacher
Leighton, Alison Jean Celona
12th Grade English Teacher
Lomagistro, Kathleen Crowley
Science Teacher
O Connor, Bernard
Sci Supvr & Physics Tchr
Opyr, Linda Elena
English Dept Chairperson
Palladino, Anthony
Third Grade Teacher
Werbitsky, SarahJane Taylor
Science Teacher
FLORIDA
Scheibling, Barbara Brosi
Business Education Teacher
Wynn, Ronald
HS Social Studies Teacher
FLUSHING
Altomarino, Gabriela Ferschtman
Spanish Teacher
Appel, Susan Leonore (Granek)
Assistant Principal & Sci Tchr
Arroyo, Florence D.
Chemistry Teacher
Atkins, Richard J.
English Teacher
Aufieri, Stanley Vincent
Health & Physical Ed Chairman
Belcher, John Joseph
Science Teacher

Blanc, Thelma Rosenblum
Sixth Grade Teacher
Blau, Rivkah Teitz
Principal
Brady, Brigette
Science Teacher
Burger, Ronald Mark
Math Teacher
Butler, Ana Maria (Cespedes)
Biology Teacher
Canavan, Mary Anne
Fifth Grade Teacher
Cannon, Lenore Richardson
English Teacher
Cardone, Patricia Brennan
Chrstn Ethics & Psych Teacher
Catapano, Frank Anthony
Eighth Grade Teacher
Ceraulo, Larry
Physical Education Teacher
Chresomales, Harriet
Computer Teacher
Ciano, Jack E.
Health Teacher
Clark, James Edward
Guidance Cnslr & US Govt Tchr
Cohen, Miriam Kristein
Capping & Art Cluster Teacher
DeVore, Carolyn Vance
Dean & Dance Teacher
Di Bari, Dennis Philip
Dean of Stdnts, Soc Stud Edctr
Dick, Roseanne Vitale
Fifth Grade Teacher
Doyle, Walter
Science Dept Chairman
Dwyer, Gail Gavigan
High School Science Teacher
Ehrhardt, Barbara A.
Seventh & Eighth Grade Teacher
Ehrlich, Debbie Jacobs
Fifth Grade Teacher
Featherstone, Joseph
Physical Education Teacher
Feldman, Irma Arlene
Science Teacher
Ferguson, Thaddeus Julius
Latin & French Teacher
Flori, Katherine A.
Business Education Teacher
Garcia, Odile
Science Teacher
Giannone, Marie M.
European His & Psych Tchr
Goldberg, Ira Allen
Music Coordinator
Goodman, Robert S.
Assistant Principal
Greenberg, Geraldine Gerver
Educl Enrichment Specialist
Grgas, Alice Louise
Math Teacher
Guthrie, Elaine
Mathematics Teacher
Guzowski, Jane Isabelle
Language Arts, Eng & Rdng Tchr
Hallman, Richard Douglas
Assistant Principal & Sci Tchr
Harris, Doreen Theresa
Fourth Grade Teacher
Hart, Toby Shapiro
Fourth Grade Music Teacher
Harts, Miriam V.
Student Activities Coordinator
Haser, Dana
Social Studies Teacher
Hayle, Margaret G., OP
Second Grade Teacher
Hechtman, Sylvia Schmer
Social Studies Teacher
Hobdy, Robert G.
Dept Chair & Spanish Teacher
Hock, Sheila Joan
Math & Religion Teacher
Hoffman, Karl William
Coord of Medical Biology Pgm
Hoffmann, Elizabeth Mary (Cronin)
7th & 8th Grade Teacher
Horowitz, Ruth
Sixth Grade Teacher
Joseph, Richard E.
Dean of Students
Kadamani, Adel Jamil
Chemistry Teacher
Katz, Roberta Karpf
Third Grade Teacher
Kerrigan, Michael Andrew
English Teacher
Kirsh, Roslyn M.
Guidance Counselor & Math Tchr
Kreizman, Jerry
French Teacher
Lavacek, Joseph James
Language Arts Teacher
Leeds, Michael J.
Language Arts Coordinator
Lessey, Roslyn
English Teacher
Lipkin-Weeks, Marla
Architectural Specialist
Loeffler, Julia Cowan
HS Social Studies Teacher
Lohnes, Magaly Lopez
Social Studies Teacher
Main, Dale Carbone
Health & Physical Ed Teacher
Mallozzi, Mary Ann Hoffman
Third Grade Teacher
Mann, Susan Lynn
Sixth Grade Teacher

Manos, Michele Bonini
Second Grade Teacher
Mansfield, Ellen K.
9th Grade English Teacher
Marchese, Fred V.
Fine Arts Teacher
Massucci-Ferrante, Carol A.
9th-11th Grd Italian Teacher
Mc Cue, Jeremy T.
Soc Stud, Sci & Religion Tchr
Mc Guinness, John Edward
Music & Math Teacher
Mollica, Fernando
Italian Tchr
Moscowitz, Dennis
High School Math Teacher
Muehlbauer, Eric Mark
Biology Teacher
Nash, Fern
Music Teacher
Nodiff, Ruth Abrin
Vocal Music Teacher
Nugent, Julia T.
7th Grade Life Science Teacher
Perez, Nora Elena
Bilingual Kindergarten Teacher
Perpetua, Mary
Piano Teacher
Peskowitz, Sandra
Kindergarten Teacher
Pessah, Nathan Victor
Science & Health Teacher
Pigman, James Frederic
English Dept Chair
Potter, Douglas Joseph
Fine Arts Teacher
Purus, Daniel Joseph
Computer Coordinator
Rinaldi, Karen Holda
8th Grd Math & Earth Sci Tchr
Rizzo, Andrea (Boniecki)
Mathematics Teacher
Rosa, Marie Theresa
Hlth & Physical Education Tchr
Ryan, Theresa M., SC
Jr High Teacher
Sachs, Burton Ira
Band Director & Music Teacher
Sachs, Ned
Assistant Principal
Samaroo, Amar
Math Teacher
Sapoznik, Norman
Film & Video Shop Tech Tchr
Scheer, Mary C.
Homeroom, Social Studies Tchr
Scher, Mary Guskin
Movement Ed & Enrichment Tchr
Schneider, Delores Crystal
Resource Room Teacher
Schor, Gail S.
Grade Advisor & Guidance Cnslr
Schwartz, Ellen M.
Health & Physical Ed Teacher
Scotti, Andrew P.
Mathematics Teacher
Silverman, Linda Gerhardt
HS Mathematics Teacher
Simon, Rose Temkin
Retired Teacher
Sirico, Rosetta Austin
English Teacher
Solomonic, Suzanne Orlow
Art Teacher
Son, Sook Hee
Bilingual Ed Teacher
Sprance, Robert M.
Teacher & Dean
Stampfel, Walter F.
Math Teacher
Stavola, Stephen Peter
History Teacher
Stern, Sheila B.
Sixth Grade Teacher
Sternlieb, Roslyn Phyllis
College Counselor
Strait, Peggy Tang
Professor Emerita
Talamo, Laura Ann
Eighth Grade Teacher
Tashjian, Matilda Donabedian
Mathematics Teacher
Tashman, Barbara Ann
Principal
Testa, Lauren Tung
English Teacher
Tomeo, Vincent J.
Social Studies Teacher
Tue, Philip James
Fifth Grade Teacher
Tzallas, Mary Papadopoulos
English Teacher
Vega, Adriana Ines
Spanish Teacher
Ventola, Ronald
Language Arts Teacher
Volpicella, Barbara Parillo
Language & Literature Teacher
Vorchheimer, Judith N.
Mathematics Teacher
Wainer, Susan Ploscowe
Engish Teacher
Watts, Karen Alexia
Physics & Chemistry Teacher
Weinberg, Francine Arrow
English Teacher
Weiss, Joan
Math & Cmptr Sci Tchr, Chprsn
Whalley, Christopher
High School Latin Teacher

Wilkins, Marsha R.
Kindergarten Teacher
Witt, Judith M.
Mathematics Teacher
Wrobel, Anna Miriam
Social Studies Teacher
FONDA
Bacchia, Jack A.
9th Grade Earth Science Tchr
Bellinger, Laura Jean
High School Business Ed Tchr
Burbine, MaryLou Sundilson
High School English Teacher
Butler, Lynn Grandy
Kindergarten Teacher
Cassidy, Anne V.
General Music Teacher & Dir
Petersen, David A.
PE Teacher & Coach
Purcell, Christine E.
High School English Teacher
Roberts, Martel Zarg
Business Education Teacher
Simonds, Rodney Gene
Social Studies Teacher
Stead, Donna Lynn
Mathematics Teacher
Thompson, Jon Stephen
Social Studies Teacher
Valachovic, John W.
Mathematics Department Chprsn
Widdis, Mary Elizabeth
French Teacher
FORESTVILLE
Geblein, Jeffrey P.
Instrumental Music Teacher
FORT COVINGTON
French, Lenny Sue Mayne
Jr-Sr HS Music Teacher
FORT EDWARD
Mulcahy, Noranne
Biology & Chemistry Teacher
FORT PLAIN
De Kalb, Kathleen Wright
Business Education Teacher
Karker, Charles M.
Health & Athletics Coordinator
FRANKFORT
Ceglia, Shelley (Wolcott)
Chorus Teacher
DeSarro, Jennifer Tangorra
5th Grade Teacher
Gizowski, Patricia Ann
Biology Teacher
Goodale, Elizabeth Horigan
Social Studies Teacher
FRANKLIN
Burgin, Georgianna Ransom
5th Grade Teacher
Swears, Stanley B.
Science Teacher
FRANKLIN SQUARE
Bergbom, Joanne Piccarella
English Tchr & Stu Act Dir
Bodenlos, Gail Patricia
Social Studies Teacher
Botti, Carl John
Math Teacher & Department Head
Fern, Tami Lynne
Teacher of the Gifted
Giorsos, Louis
Earth Science Teacher
Gold, Jill A.
Guidance Counselor
Goldberg, Steven A.
Guidance Counselor
Gruber, Edward J.
Chemistry Teacher
Iconis, Lucille F.
Reading Specialist
Itzkowitz, Leonard M.
Science Teacher
Kornbluth, Jane Berman
English Teacher
Laoria, Gail Hentz
Business Chairperson
Lenett, Lois Harriot
English Teacher
Loria, Marie Grilli
Frgn Lang Teacher & Dept Head
Monaghan, Maureen
6th-8th Grade Teacher
Natalie, Joan Marilyn
Art Teacher
Panse, Peter Charles
Third Grade Teacher
Polikoff, Michael
Fifth Grade Teacher
Rinaudo, Theone M.
Science Teacher
Russo, Thomas Joseph
Chemistry Teacher
Stanco, Regina Fitzgerald
5th Grade Teacher
Suzzi Valli, Sophia Braccioforte
Italian Teacher
Taverna, Anthony
Mathematics & Cmptr Sci Tchr
Tillman, Susan Sverd
Alternative Educator
Tuthill, Paul C.
Band Director
Weber, Jeanette Greco
School Social Worker
FRANKLINVILLE
Gena, David C.
History Teacher
Kayes, Lisa A.
Spanish Teacher

KLINVILLE (cont)
Stephen D.
nology Teacher
Rebecca Harris
Grade Tchr
Royce A.
Grade Teacher
l, William M.
al Studies Teacher
ONIA
s, Julius Gregg
c Professor of Education
n, Minda Rae
ish Prof & Dept Chprsn
tti, Raymond Angelo
essor of Philosophy
on, Nancy J.
stant Professor of Math
, Candice Ann
stant Professor
, Joan A.
ish Professor
wsky, Mitchell Roy
ch Pathlgy, Audiology Prof
, Alexander Michael
nct Professor of Education
Phyllis Orr
essor of Piano
, David F.
essor of Music
irn, Janet Alison
essor of Art
Efrain Jose
stant Professor
, Michael
ritus Professor of Physics
a, Andrea O'Reilly
Professor of Literature
Daniel L.
Professor of Voice
, Konrad Grzegorz
nistry Assistant Professor
en, Rose Rye
Prof of Comm Dept
ky, Bruce G.
hology Professor
, Jon P.
essor of Political Science
, Franklin Bernard
essor of Marketing
n, Holly Jon
ciate Professor of Chem
lin, Thomas William
ciate Professor of Acting
, Myron
sics Professor
ady, Lawrence Joseph
essor Dept of Education
cker, Jeanette
ish Professor
ner, Janet Anderson
ematics Lecturer
n, Malcolm A.
nguished Professor of Eng
sky, John
Professor of Accounting
, Roger L.
School Technology Teacher
k, Thomas Andrew
stant Professor of Finance
owski, James Paul
ciate Professor of Music
one, Elizabeth Giatas
ITT & PLANET Prgms Coord
r, Harold H.
g Methods & Microcomp Prof
s, Robert Roy
c Prof of Mathematics
rin, Morton Louis
osophy Professor
erg, Theodore Louis
lish Professor
ek, Mary Ann
Prof of Psychology
nson, Bruce Lloyd
c Prof Dev, Bio & Dept Chr
, James D.
d Track Coach
llo, Mario
essor
r, Stephen Douglas
lish Professor
, Deborah
Prof of History
ford, Constance E. Irwin
c Prof & Music Therapy Dir
EPORT
inacchio, Nicholas
dance Counselor
o, Peter
hematics Chairman
on, Denise L.
ngual Guidance Counselor
, John William
al Studies Teacher
, Diane Mc Laughlin
h Grade Teacher
ano, Mark M.
Grade Teacher
rickson, Linda Lee
bal Stud & Government Tchr
ney, Judith Arlene (Carroll)
nish Teacher
hbaum, Harold
th Grd Social Stud Tchr
, Glenn Lawrence
rumental Music Teacher
an, Patricia
ial Studies Teacher

Martorana, Barbara Joan
English Teacher
Spanier, Mark Richard
English Teacher
Wills, Odette Renee
Math Specialist
FRESH MEADOWS
Barricelli, Jane Ellen Lynch
English Teacher
Janjigian, Anahid
Fine Artist & Art Instr
Manniello, Andrew Francis
Mathematics Teacher
Smith, Lorraine (Kutz)
Mathematics Teacher
FREWSBURG
Anderson, Kathleen G.
English Teacher
Basile, Joseph John
English Department Chairman
Benson, Diane L.
9th & 11th Grd English Tchr
Edwards, Mary Lou
English Teacher
Rich, Cynthia Gable
Third Grade Teacher
Suchar, Evelyn Rowley
English Teacher
FRIENDSHIP
Raiff, Sheryl Jablonski
English Teacher
Stanton, Beverly Say
Spanish & Computer Teacher
Zacher, Mary Ellen Morgan
First Grade Teacher
FULTON
Bailer, Thomas William
8th Grade English Teacher
Brunson, Jane Casner
French Teacher
Cramer, Christopher Michael
7th Grade Science Teacher
Curtis, Rhonda Lee
7th-8th Grade Math Teacher
Farden, Debra Cipra
Instrumental Music Teacher
Fox, Carol Hampston
Instrumental Teacher
Gillard, Martin P.
Biology Teacher
Nami, Thomas Anthony
Music Teacher
Occhino, Rosemary Andreana
First Grade Teacher
Paparella, Francis Charles
Middle School Math Teacher
Rossi, Kathleen Carey
Physical Education Teacher
Senecal, Len Dean
English & Journalism Teacher
GAINESVILLE
Dedoszak, Steven John
5th Grade Teacher
Hadley, Stephen Philip
Social Studies Teacher
Hurlburt, Lauren McGee
French Teacher
Link, Lois E.
1st Grade Teacher
McLaughlin, Deborah Bell
K-4th Grade Reading Teacher
Mc Mullen, Timothy Daniel
Elem Physical Ed Teacher
Robinson, Martha Kay
English Teacher
Standera, Stan
Social Studies Teacher
Van Vessem, Lisa Ann
Music Teacher
GALWAY
Schakel-Troost, Carol Marie
English Teacher
GARDEN CITY
Avosso, Louis John
Professor of Biology
Cangelosi, Anthony, Jr.
Professor
De Fina, Gerard Lewis
6th Grd Math & Lang Arts Tchr
Earl, Paul F.
Professor of Biology
Eickelberg, W. Warren Barbour
Professor of Biology
Emmerson, Anne Massimo
Asst Prof & Office Tech Chrpsn
Harrington, Ivy
Sixth Grade Teacher
Kitaeff, Michael
Biology Teacher
Labiento, Aleta
Community Health Prof
Lieber, R. Okuaki
English Professor
Locopo, Maria Grazia Giugno
First Grade Teacher
Mac Burney, Andrea Eomme
French & Spanish Teacher
Mazarese, Carlo
Italian & Literature Teacher
Mc Cavitt, Carol A.
Social Studies Teacher
Mooney, Christopher P.
Philosophy Professor
Noone, Lana Mae
Music Teacher
Nuzzi, Marie Grace
Spanish & ESL Teacher
Piervincenzi, William Arthur
Professor of Biology

Resnick, Jeanette
Music & Piano Teacher
Slater, Nancy Lynne
Special Education Teacher
Teachey, Winifred Yvonne
Kindergarten Teacher
Weber, Susan Elisabeth
German & English Teacher
Weinlandt, Drew Russell
English Professor
Wertis, Sandra Karaus
Math Teacher
GARDEN CITY SOUTH
Cocoman, Kathleen
First Grade Teacher
GARDINER
Richards, Linda Tierney
Singer, Sngwrtr, Envir Ed Tchr
GARNERVILLE
Caley, Ruth P.
Teacher of the Gifted
GASPORT
Beedon, John W.
6th Grade Teacher
Craig, Joan E.
5th & 6th Grade Teacher
GENESEO
Congdon, Susan Bligh
Fifth Grade Teacher
DeBell, Bettina Pollard
Special Education Teacher
Drachman, Edward Ralph
Assoc Prof of Political Sci
Hayes, Timothy Collins
Biology Teacher
Judkins, Russell A.
Assoc Prof of Anthropology
Mauw, Stephen David
7th-12th Grd Fr & Span Tchr
Miller, Kathleen Ellen
Asst Professor of Sociology
Stone, Jo
Assistant Professor of Art
GENEVA
Harris, Victor A.
History Department Chairman
Johnson, Philip Roy
History Teacher
Mc Dougal, Alison Lane
Spanish Teacher
Mitchell, Kevin John
Professor of Mathematics
Mulvey, William, Jr.
Technology Ed Tchr & Dept Chm
Russell, Nancy Van Eenwyk
English Teacher
GERMANTOWN
Bartolotta, Bruce Benjamin
Social Studies Teacher
Doyle, Denis Alan
Math & Earth Science Teacher
Hanson, L. Dean
Secondary Science Teacher
Mossman, Richard Phillip
Social Studies Tchr & Ath Dir
GILBERTSVILLE
Stanton, Alexa Tweedie
Fourth Grade Teacher
Stoy, Sandra Keene
Health, Home & Careers Teacher
GILBOA
Henry, Sara Wallace
1st Grade Teacher
Kliza, Susan Bowie
Second Grade Teacher
GLEN COVE
Bloom, Michael Alan
Special Education Teacher
Cuomo, Mary Ellen M.
Learning Disabilities Teacher
Dutchen, Laurie
Computer & Math Teacher
Pascuzzi, Edward
Physics Teacher
Scarl, Donald
Retired Professor of Physics
Silvestri, Antoinette Grace
HS Business Education Teacher
Zwiebach, Sally Bever
English Teacher
GLEN HEAD
Beers, Susan Marie
English Teacher
Gerver, Robert K.
Math Teacher
Ketcham, Russell Alan
Humanities Teacher & Coach
Lohrius, Linda (Rosenzweig)
English Teacher
Pollatz, Brian Mark
Music Teacher
Walk, Eileen Field
Art Teacher
GLENDALE
Freese, Mathias Balogh
Retired English Teacher
Kaiser, Martin
Language Arts Teacher
GLENFIELD
Boice, Wendy Jane
Nursing Instructor
GLENS FALLS
Connolly, Gerald Francis
Reading Teacher
Fibiger, Joanne Robinson
1st Grade Teacher
Geyer, Tom F.
Art Education Coord & Instr
Hurst, W. Sheldon
Visual Arts Gallery Director

Hussa, Rick
HS Math Teacher
Merrill, Mary Murray
Education Consultant
Schulze, Holly Osborn
Kindergarten Tchr
Strader, Elizabeth Saunders
Social Studies Teacher
Wilshere, Jane Baran
English Teacher
GLOVERSVILLE
Boardway, Marion Fox
Mathematics Teacher
DeLilli, Charles N.
Soc Stud Teacher & Dept Chm
Malaqisi, Andrew P.
Guidance Counselor
Riley, Karen A.
2nd Grade Teacher
Thaisz, Lesia Prime
Physics & Chemistry Teacher
Were, Margaret Carswell
Vocal Music Director
GOLDENS BRIDGE
Kahn, Jeff
English Teacher
GOSHEN
Blaine, John M.
Culinary Foods Instructor
Cantwell, Eleanor Marianne
Culinary Arts Teacher
Chapman, Jacklyn Marie
French Teacher
DiPasquale, Mary Lee
Eng, Mythology & Writing Tchr
Gantter, Carol Stricker
Fifth Grade Teacher
Holst, Edward C.
Religion Teacher
Huldie, John Jude
7th-8th Grd English Teacher
Knieriemen, Eleanor Mary
Social Studies Teacher
Lamison, Helen Elizabeth
Spanish Teacher
Megello, Brenda J.
Earth Science Teacher
Sharp, Melvin James
Soc Stud Tchr & Stu Senate Adv
Tierney, Simonee Akstin
5th Grd Teacher & Coordinator
Trapp, Michele Staats
Remedial Ed & Stud Skills Tchr
Wengenroth, Louis F., IV
Mathematics & Physics Teacher
Wtulich, Rita F.
Mathematics Tchr & Dept Chair
GOUVERNEUR
Day, Victoria Lynn
Music Teacher & Orchestra Dir
Putman, Stephen M.
Mathematics Teacher
Wilson, Heather Ellen
Health Teacher
GOWANDA
Dye, Diane Stevens
Senior High Art Teacher
Dye, Quentin L.
Language Arts Chairperson
Jarzynski, John S.
English Teacher
Perdue, Sharon M.
Fifth Grade Teacher
Trybus-Dubiel, Tammy Lynn
Social & Iroquois Studies Tchr
Wiens, David F.
Chemistry Teacher & Dept Chm
GRAHAMSVILLE
Bright, Neil H.
District Curriculum Coord
Elberth, Constance H.
High School English Teacher
Hartman, Joyce Stapleton
7th Grd Life Science Teacher
Hendrickson, Cheryl (Barner)
HS Math Tchr & Computer Coord
TerBush, Maribel
Spanish Teacher
GRAND ISLAND
Boron, Beth Walker
Kindergarten Teacher
French, Gileen Widmer
Fifth Grade Teacher
Frisoni, Roberta Diane
Business Education Teacher
Guzzetta, Jan
Third Grade Teacher
Holmes, Dorea B.
Social Stud & Humanites Tchr
King, Robert A.
English Teacher
Lokken, Carolyn Fiegl
Vocal Music Teacher
Lyke, Sherman E., Jr.
Music Department Program Coord
Pray, Donald Walter
Social Studies Teacher
Stark, Michael D.
Fifth Grade Teacher
Stuckwisch, William Eldo
Chemistry Teacher
Swartz, Terry Howard
Mathematics Teacher
GRANVILLE
Barnes, Sandra Knipes
Mathematics Teacher
Fenton, Teresa B.
First Grade Teacher
Goodman, Les H.
4th Grade Teacher

Gray, Bonnie Lee (Mills)
Foreign Language Teacher
Macura, Michael Peter
PE Teacher & Ath & PE Dir
Owens, Susanne Kelley
Social Studies Teacher
Smith, Herbert James
Fifth Grade Teacher
Smith, Michele McLoughlin
Spanish Teacher
GREAT NECK
Bua, Frank A.
Social Studies Teacher
Burstein, Shmueal L.
Judaic Studies Teacher
DeKoff, Robert S.
Tech Ed Teacher & Dept Head
Golden, Michael S.
6th Grade Teacher
Greif, Marion
5th Grade Teacher
Hugo, Patricia Mc Nichol
Math Teacher & Dept Chprsn
Intersimone, Nancy S.
Sixth Grade Teacher
Keith, David M.
PE & Earth Sci Teacher
Lehman, Ann Marie Nazzaro
Art Department Chair & Teacher
Lewit, Phoebe Platt
Resource Room Teacher
Mendelson, Sherry Marlene
First Grade Teacher
Postiglione, Ralph Anthony
Biology Teacher
Sulinski, Dennis John
Health Ed Dept Chm & Ath Dir
Volpe, Rita Rizzello
Science Consultant
Ziring, Paul Elder
Health Education Teacher
GREEN ISLAND
Normile, Nicholas John
Guidance Counselor
GREENE
Daniels, Gordon
Principal
Martin, Mary G.
Social Studies Chair & Teacher
Mouillesseaux, Karen Lynn
Secondary English Teacher
Philippone, Rebecca G.
French Teacher
Place, Timothy
Guidance Counselor
GREENFIELD CENTER
Alexander, Joseph P.
Third Grade Teacher
GREENLAWN
DePirro, Jo-Ann Louise
English Teacher
Luna, Barbara Jabour
Fourth Grade Teacher
GREENPORT
Claire, Dennis Daniel, Jr.
English Teacher
Petrucci, Barbara J.
Fourth Grade Teacher
Wallace, Katherine Heaney
Second Grade Teacher
GREENVALE
Dwyer, Patricia A.
Adj Prof of Curr & Instruction
GREENVILLE
Davies, Linda Pilhofer
Teacher of Gifted & Talented
Eskelund, Erik David
School Chaplain
Ward, Wendy L.
Mathematics Teacher
GREENWICH
Hawks, Carol Mc Conchie
Vocal & Instrumental Teacher
Humiston, Gerard E.
Teacher
Simpson, Howard T.
6th Grade Teacher
Whiteford, Eileen M.
7th-12th Grd Home Ec Teacher
GROTON
Davis, Everett Drew
Technology Teacher
Geiger, Roma Rae
Teacher & Science Coord
LaFrance, Margaret A.
Mathematics Coordinator
Overhiser, James Lewis
8th Grd Physical Science Tchr
GUILDERLAND CENTER
Arnold, Richard D.
Physics Teacher
Catlin, Kathy
School Social Worker
Corigliano, James Vincent
High School Band Director
Gnirrep, Gary Richard
English Teacher
Grimsted, Eric F.
Mathematics Teacher
Maier, Joanne Lucille
Biology & Physiology Teacher
Parmenter, Robert Maurice
AP Social Studies Teacher
Sebuyira, Annette N.
Chemistry Teacher
Shea, Maria Anna
Biology Teacher
Wingate, James L.
Social Studies Teacher

HAMBURG
Albert, Larry John
Music Department Chairman
Baldwin, Annette M.
Chemistry Teacher
Barrett, Robert Thomas
Health Teacher
Beatty, James S.
Fourth Grade Teacher
Boland, M. Patricia Rohan
Kindergarten Teacher
Bollinger, Ellen Rushnok
5th Grade Teacher
Burns, Laura
9th-12th Grd Soc Stud Teacher
Cannan, Patricia Jean
High School Counselor
Cichocki, Sharon Ann
Scndry Math Coord & Teacher
Coffey, Melissa Ann
English Teacher
Dickinson, Karlyn (Eberhardt)
German & Spanish Teacher
Dunbar, Carol L. (Tesi)
Earth Science Teacher
Feyl, Andrew Wesley
Ninth Grade Math Teacher
Gates, Lynda
High School English Teacher
Glawatz, Marion Moeller
French Teacher
Goodremote, Cecil J., Jr.
Jr HS Science Teacher
Gorline, Gary Gene
PE Teacher & Dist Coordinator
Grace, Kay Williamson
First Grade Teacher
Greenwood, Susan Jean
Third Grade Teacher
Hanitz, Diane Marie
Spanish Teacher
Henry, Ellen E.
Social Studies Teacher
Hogan, Bonita L.
Spanish Teacher
Infante, Neil Dominic
Human Anatomy, Physiology Tchr
James, Peter C.
8th Grade Social Studies Tchr
Johnson, Judith Ann
2nd Grade Teacher
Kabza, Mary E.
High School Art Teacher
Ketchum-Colletta, Donna J.
Health Teacher
Kluckhohn, Carmen Villarini
Third Grade Teacher
Kohan, Kyle Stamer
Instrumental Music Teacher
Korthals, William H.
English Teacher
Krajewski, Karen Jones
Mathematics Teacher
Kyser, Robert E.
Technology CADD Coordinator
Lemke, Wendy (DaBolt)
French Teacher
Malican, William V.
Teacher & Coach
Mc Clintock, Mary E.
Mathematics Teacher
Mc Limans, Jeffrey Paul
English Teacher
Muncuso, Anne Marie DiMillo
2nd Grade Teacher
Nelson, Carol A.
Spanish Teacher
Ostrander, Terrance Francis
Physical Ed Teacher & Coach
Rawski, Margaret A.
Kindergarten Teacher
Rich, Kerry Ann
Mathematics Teacher
Ritz, Ann Girard
Math Teacher & Dept Chprsn
Santoro, George F.
Business Teacher
Scott, Raymond L.
9th Grade History Teacher
Skinner, Robert George
Physics Teacher
Staruch, Jeffrey Nicholas
Math & Computer Science Tchr
Szczesny, Anne T.
Foreign Language Dept Chprsn
Tobin, Susan Baverlein
Art Teacher
Tutuska, Dennis M.
English Teacher
Ward, Beverly A.
Secondary Mathematics Teacher
Wilcox, Maria Berrizbeitia
Spanish Teacher
Wyzykowski, Nancy
English Teacher
HAMILTON
Campo, David Frank
History Department Chairperson
Haskins, Marion Bader
Physics & Earth Science Tchr
Howes, Mary Wheeler
Retired Teacher
McCaslin, Elaine Neidlinger
Elementary Teacher
HAMMOND
Bush, Samuel Steward
Social Studies Teacher
Simons, Penny Pascale
7th-12th Grd Tech & Sci Tchr
HAMMONDSPORT
Boutwell, Elenor Miller
Music Teacher
Cole, Lisa Sable
First Grade Teacher
Kressly, Thomas C.
Science Teacher
Remchuk, Nancy A.
English Teacher
HAMPTON BAYS
Brosnan, Margaret Ceslack
Kindergarten Teacher
Dossiano, Antionette
Eighth Grade Science Teacher
Doty, Vincent Allan
Mathematics Teacher
Griffin, Maryalice (Finnerty)
English Teacher
Levy, Richard Andrew
Spanish & ESL Teacher
Parker, Gale J. Kemp
First Grade Teacher
HANCOCK
Turner, Douglas G.
Biology & Chemistry Teacher
Zawatsky, John Joseph
Physical Education Teacher
HANNIBAL
Bosch, Francine Aungier
Home & Careers Teacher
DiFabio, Michael Joseph
Mathematics Teacher
Rogers, Esther Rawson
High School Math Teacher
HARPURSVILLE
Bassler, Lida Mac Aulay
English Teacher & Dept Chm
Hennessey, Radcliffe William
Global Studies Teacher
HARRISON
Congi, Anthony J.
Math Teacher
Florkowski, Carolanne Fisher
Teacher
Gardner, Alan M.
Biology Instructor
Johnson, Keith W.
Secondary English Teacher
Leaf, Richard A.
Soc Stuid Dept Chprsn & Tchr
Swartz, June Ann Frattarola
English Teacher
HARRISVILLE
Visconti, Patricia E. (Small)
Sixth Grade Teacher
HARTFORD
Cutler, Carol Smith
Band Director
Farley, Sean Michael
Social Studies & Govt Teacher
Friday, Susan G.
English Teacher
North, Kevin W.
Third Grade Teacher
HARTSDALE
Claps, Maria
7th-12th Grade Math Teacher
Gamzon, Gloriane Klein
Mathematics Teacher
Gluberman, Frank Martin
Business Education Teacher
Haydel, C. C., III
English & Literature Teacher
Mac Lean, John V.
English Teacher
Morgan-Fisher, Naomi R.
Science Teacher
Pappas, Marie
Theology Teacher
Perry, Maria Romano
Business Teacher
Robinson, Marian Carter
Third Grade Teacher
Saunders, Emily E.
Health Coordinator
HASTINGS
Gillett, Daniel William
5th Grade Teacher
HASTINGS ON HUDSON
Henshaw, Paul J.
Soc Stud Tchr & Chairperson
HAUPPAUGE
Clancy, Brian Paul
High School Band Director
Hunt, Carole Elizabeth
Math Teacher
Panariello, Rosemary Pascone
Mathematics Teacher
HAVERSTRAW
Beardsley, Diane Coppola
French & Language Arts Teacher
Freda, Ellen Schwartz
Eighth Grade Teacher
Graham, Patricia Joan Hoeltzel
Middle School Teacher
Hadden, George Steven
8th Grade Soc Stud & Sci Tchr
McDermott, Kate Glass
Life Sci Teacher & Team Ldr
Toronto, Anthony Philip
Physical Education Teacher
HEMPSTEAD
Adams, Richele Brooks
5th Grade Math & Reading Tchr
Barrett, Rosemary Therese
Retired Teacher
Bent, Mary Arthur
French Teacher
Broderick, Clarice Miller
Fourth Grade Teacher
Bullock, Paulette Gladys (Brown)
Elementary Educator
Carroll, Barbara Ann
Math, Cmptr Tchr & Dept Head
Chekow, Mary Tanza-Lupo
Dance Teacher, Artistic Dir
Dyer, Ann M.
Secondary School French Tutor
Fiore, Christine Richter
Spanish Teacher
Frisenda, Attilio Arthur
Social Studies Teacher
Geldart, Leticia Cara
English Teacher
Horne, Patricia Clemmons
Second Grade Teacher
Kleemann, Nancy Becker
Music Teacher
Lafferty, Linda
Biology Teacher & Sci Chprsn
Levano, Rosemary Riendeau
English Dept Chairperson
Mc Curty, Bruce Kevin
Science Teacher
Mc Intyre, Diana Mc Intyr
English Teacher
Mullen, Elisabeth Mancusi
Chemistry Teacher
Neyland, Diana Lynne (Forte)
English Teacher
O'Neill, Kathleen Quinlan
Guidance Counselor
Prehoda, Carol Marie
Art Teacher & Department Chair
Rosen, Efrem
Professor of Biology
Salamon, George Joseph
Spanish Teacher
Snow, Marion R.
English Teacher
Truitt, Brett J.
English Teacher
White, Mary Elizabeth
Music Dept Teacher & Chair
HENRIETTA
D'Imperio, Charles James
Assistant Principal
Hilton, Kenneth H.
District Social Studies Dir
Leary, Edward William
Science Teacher
Loeffler, Cynthia Gale Robinson
Biology Teacher
Rogan, Roslyn Brisk
Reading & Mathematics Teacher
HERKIMER
Curry, Ellen Anne Marie
English & Writing Specialist
Getman, Janet M.
PE Teacher & Coach
Kapfer, Mary Ethna
Math Teacher
Marrotta, Catherine Aiello
Business Professor
Noyes, Debra Sutton
Asst Prof of Trvl & Tourism
Pannes, Helen A.
Assoc Prof of Travel & Tourism
Siniscarco, Lorraine Bono
Asst Prof of Occup Therapy
Smith, Leon R.
4th Grade Teacher
Steele, Alan Carl
Physical Education Teacher
Stone, Edward George
Assoc Prof Information Systems
Stulmaker, Richard M.
Social Science Teacher
Webster, Laura Joyce
Associate Professor
West, Susan R.
First Grade Teacher
HEUVELTON
Bertrand, Linda J.
High School English Teacher
Geddis, Marilyn Crowe
4th Grade Teacher
Kennedy, Robert William
Science Teacher
Montroy, Becky Duprey
7th-8th Grade Math Teacher
Poulton, David John
Retired Instrumental Music Dir
Timmerman, Gregory William
HS Social Studies Teacher
Wilson Mashaw, Nancy
Kindergarten Teacher
HEWLETT
Babush, Sydney Maris
Social Studies Teacher
Berman, Marlene Rachel
Eng Teacher & Coord of Stu Act
Kashman, Margery Krane
English & Journalism Teacher
Kelly, Barbara Pond
Business Education Chairperson
Kilkenny, Martin J.
Science Teacher
Machosky, Claire Johnson
Supervisor & Soc Studies Tchr
Maxwell, Marilyn
English Teacher
Pesca, Joseph G.
Social Studies Teacher
Savoy, Sara
Sixth Grd Eng & Rdng Tchr
Stahl, Sharon Ann
English Teacher
Stark, Frederic L.
Chemistry & Physics Teacher
HICKSVILLE
Anderson, Nancy Barthel
English Teacher
Bell, James M.
Eighth Grade English Teacher
Brendel, Jane Anne
Social Studies & Lit Tchr
Colucci, Colleen Jennie
Art Teacher
Conti, Linda DeTullio
Social Studies Teacher
Coughlin, Patricia Lambert
7th-8th Grd Soc Studies Tchr
Dunbar, Marylou
8th Grade Social Studies Tchr
Foscolo, Mary M.
Third Grade Teacher
Fox, Mary Consuela, RSM
French Teacher
Gentile, Richard B.
French & Spanish Teacher
Glasberg, Ruth
6th Grd Tchr & MS Coordinator
Grady, Kathy Cerda
5th Grade Teacher
Graiser, Kenneth Saul
Language Arts Teacher
Gregory, Stephanie R. Sasso
Dept Chprsn & Spanish Teacher
Grib, Evelyn Sposato
Substitute Teacher
Griffith, Carol
Science Teacher
Hantzidiamantis, Patricia Ann
Special Educator
Higginson, George G.
Honors English Teacher
Kanawada, Leo Vincent, Jr.
Fifth Grade Teacher
Kumpikas-Stravinskas, Giedre
French & German Teacher
Lapidus, K. Ninon
Resource Room Teacher
Lemmey, William
Social Studies Teacher
Loeschner, Richard Joseph
HS Math Teacher
Maggio, Jo-Ann
Religion Teacher
Mancuso, Constance Joan (Barone)
Fifth Grade Teacher
McEntee, Marylin M.
11th-12th Grades Math Teacher
Moran, Kathleen A.
Social Studies Dept Chprsn
Murphy, Catherine E.
Dance Teacher & Choreographer
Noll, Amy Marie
9th-12th Grade Orchestra Tchr
Owens, William Jude
Social Studies Teacher
Ryan, Joseph P.
Chemistry Teacher
Sadetsky, Laurie Behrman
Sixth Grade Special Ed Teacher
Salvato, Scott Vincent
10th-11th Grade Theology Tchr
Scalia, Joseph E.
Eng & Creative Writing Teacher
Schreck, Mary Scudieri
First Grade Teacher
Schweyer, Paul B.
Science Teacher
Siegel, Jan Rosenthal
8th Grade Mathematics Teacher
Sparaccio, Kathleen Malone
English Teacher
Stea, Mary Lucille (DeFelice)
Visual Art Teacher
Weinberg, Paula
ESL Teacher
Weinfeld, Linda Rutter
Spanish Tchr & Adjunct Instr
Yannone, Denise Linda
Elem Special Ed Teacher
HIGHLAND
Butterfield, Carol M.
3rd Grade Teacher
Chaisson, Maureen
Biology Teacher
Saso, Mary Beth
Kindergarten Teacher
Watkins, Charles Pete
Sixth Grade Mathematics Tchr
HIGHLAND FALLS
Baker, David W.
Science Teacher
Bardua, Wayne J.
5th Grade Science Teacher
Dapra, Elaine Marie (Burley)
7th & 8th Grd English Teacher
Dinsmore, David Raymond
Physics Teacher
Levy, Mary Fitzgerald
Social Studies Teacher
Ponchak, Gerard
Soc Stud Tchr & Dept Chair
Shapiro, Joan Aronson
Spanish Teacher
HILTON
Demo, Carl Francis, Jr.
High School English Teacher
Partridge, Charles A.
Social Studies Teacher
Surash, Barbara Celentano
High School English Teacher
Westbrook, Jack Rogers
Mathematics Teacher
Williams, Nicholas M.
Vocal Music Teacher
HINSDALE
Ramarge, Mahlon L.
HS Math Teacher & Dept Chair
HOLBROOK
Auth, William F.
Fifth Grade Teacher
Brancaccio, Vincent Christian, Jr.
Fifth Grade Teacher
Brisson, Matthew Bernard
Health Teacher
Cafferty, Anita Biondolillo
Music Tchr & Choral Conductor
Farnum, Bill
6th Grade Teacher
Finneran, Marilyn Harrison
Fifth Grade Teacher
Gatto, William Joseph
Band & General Music Teacher
Smith, Julie Grun
Mathematics Teacher
Walsh, F. George, III
Modified Curriculum Dept Chm
HOLLAND
Grieco, Leonard, Jr.
7th-12th Grd Hlth & Sci Tchr
Mc Isaac, James Joseph, Jr.
Science Teacher
Meader, Barbara Tower
Math Teacher
Morris, Margaret A.
Mathematics Teacher
Perini, Marie Hill
Vocal Music Teacher
Timmel, Cynthia Evelyn
Home Economics Teacher
Weaver, John Edward
English Teacher
HOLLAND PATENT
Bond, Holly Chappell
English & Journalism Teacher
Burt, Kenneth W.
Social Studies Teacher
Celecki, Mark Albert
Physical Education Teacher
Hosp, Rose Fuoco
Spanish Teacher
Kiggins, Donna McCurdy
Eng, Pub Speakng & Psych Tchr
O'Meara, H. Selma Hokanson
Spanish Teacher
HOLLEY
Carpenter, Carol Marie
Second Grade Teacher
Orbaker, Daniel Lee
Physics & Chemistry Teacher
HOLTSVILLE
Gilmore, Virginia Culver
2nd Grd Tchr & Prin Aide
Harney, Shaun M.
Chemistry & Physics Teacher
Knapp, John P.
Fourth Grade Teacher
La Grega, Nicholas
Third Grade Teacher
Lutz, Jeanne
Second Grade Teacher
Masciangelo, Stephen Vincent
Social Studies Teacher
Sacco, Richard N.
Sixth Grade Teacher
Strazza, Brian Anthony
Science Teacher & Dept Chprsn
Strazza, Joan M.
Math Teacher
HOMER
Agate, Carol Whitney
French Teacher
Allen, William Arthur
Eng Teacher & Dir of Dramatics
Latten, James Everett
HS Instrumental Music Teacher
Steedle, John
Architectural Design Teacher
HONEOYE
Blackmer, Sally V.
Global Studies Teacher
Dodge, Margaret A.
Foreign Language Dept Chair
Greacen, Kathleen Karle
English Teacher
Helling, Grace Marie
School Instrumental Music Tchr
Kepner, Joanne Golder
2nd Grade Teacher
Leitten, Michelle Pritchard
Mathematics Teacher
Miller-Collins, Deborah Albra
English Teacher
Pavio, A. Nicholas
Soc Stud Tchr & Dept Chm
Saxby, William E.
Middle School Soc Studies Tchr
HONEOYE FALLS
Borden, Mark Stephen
HS Instrumental Music Director
Hayes, Eileen Hawkes
English Teacher
Kosboth, Angelina Valianos
Retired Kindergarten Teacher
Mermagen, George T.
HS English Teacher
Pound, Richard James
Guidance Counselor
Zoesch, Janice Orford
Music Teacher
HOOSICK FALLS
Baratto, Michael Anthony
6th Grade Teacher
Davendonis, Mary Haviland
Sixth Grade Teacher

ICK FALLS (cont)
, Michael Timothy
rade Teacher
on, Jo B.
l Studies Teacher
WELL JUNCTION
, James R.
ematics Teacher
Anne C.
ematics Teacher
gham, Terence Richard
Science Teacher
ssunta
sh Teacher
ann, Diana Opperman
h Grade Teacher
ck, Patricia Mc Dermott
uage Arts Coordinator
, Diane Marie
6th Grd Science Teacher
ney, Eileen Mc Keon
8th Grade Math Teacher
e, William F.
sh Teacher
, Beverly
gy Teacher
Virginia Vanderwarker
Science Teacher
, William E.
istory & Government Tchr
Barbara Allen
sh Teacher
juk, Victor George
ce Teacher
, Mary Alice Toolan
l Studies Teacher
ELL
, Joan Canan
Grade Teacher
th, Denise Filipponi
sh Teacher
John Joseph
Grade Teacher
, John
motive Technology Instr
i, Francis Andrew
His & Govt Teacher
Stephen
h Teacher
Douglas B.
eacher
enbush, Ann Nelson
l Studies Teacher
d, Lisa Stephens
l Studies Teacher
rtz, Deanne Mangold
sh Teacher
, Vernon S., Jr.
School Math Teacher
an, Gail A.
ish Teacher
EHEADS
ce, Nancy C.
& Greek Teacher
ws, Barbara Whitson
h Grade Teacher
, Susan MacEwen
Home Economics Teacher
n, Warren George
Criminal Justice Teacher
Donald M.
sh Dept Chairperson, Tchr
me, Daniel E.
ics Teacher
tti, Mia Rae
e Instructor
Pamela J.
nd Grade Teacher
n, Dorothy Y.
al Studies Teacher
ich, Joseph Craig
ish & Language Arts Tchr
n, James Clinton
History & Economics Tchr
erney, Kevin James
nistry Teacher
Christopher York
sh Educator
ker, Joann Pastrick
Stud & Soc Sci Teacher
r, Fred S.
hysical Education Teacher
, Debra Maloney
al Studies Teacher
, Michael Anthony
School Science Teacher
ey, Ann M.
al Studies Teacher
on, Joan Essick
h Grade Teacher
GHTON
on, Judy Ann
essor of Organ
ans, Jayne Ellen
c Prof of Sociology
k, Elizabeth Jane Goodwin
red Elementary Teacher
ARD BEACH
nte, Grace Mantone
her Teacher
lly, Breeda Walsh
th Grade Teacher
er, Laura
3rd Teacher & Asst Prin
SON
, Keith A.
Prof of Business Admin
ue, Nancy Wolff
ciate Professor of Nursing

Gizara, Jeanne M.
Chemistry Professor
Mathews, William Philip
Associate Prof of Counselor
Perillo, Umberta
Italian Teacher
Symansky, Leonard L.
Professor of Foreign Languages
HUDSON FALLS
Dingman, Robert A.
Social Studies Teacher
Perkins, David J.
Sixth Grade Teacher
HUNTINGTON
Asaro, Ignatius
History Teacher
Colligan, Margaret M.
English Teacher
Cusumano, Christopher R.
English & Humanities Teacher
Killelea, John M.
Art & Video Production Tchr
Klein, Marc
Retired Mathematics Teacher
Kurtz, Richard M.
HS Science Teacher
Peacock, Wray Pash
English Teacher
Shoemaker, Linda L.
Director of Bands
Taylor, Sylvia Pauloo
Photography Teacher
Toomey, Joann Mary
Fifth Grade Teacher
HUNTINGTON STATION
Borowicz, Robert Joseph
Economics Teacher
Cardea-Weissmann, Barbara Ann
French Teacher
Carman, Lina T.
Biology Teacher
Carro, Ann Soranno
Law Instructor
Catalano, Thea
Social Studies Teacher
Citrano, Robert Mitchell
Guidance Counselor
Desmond, Elizabeth M.
English Teacher
Dickson, Stephen W.
Earth Science Teacher
Donat, Patricia Ann
First Grade Teacher
Dressler, Ira
Orchestra Director
Gestri, Jack
Language Arts Teacher
Hanlon, Valerie L.
Social Studies & Business Tchr
Hechler, Sandra Sherman
French Teacher
Hewlett, John A.
Social Studies Teacher
Hodum, Robert A.
Spanish Teacher
Lasky, Marsha
Social Studies Chairperson
Mason-Grell, Barbara
Business Teacher
Nunziente, Peter
Pastor
O'Hanlon, Joan Marie Casabona
Eng & Language Arts Instructor
Pappo, Stanley
Mathematics Teacher
Roberts, Elizabeth Stephens
Latin Teacher
Roemer, Harold E., Jr.
5th Grade Teacher
Rottino, Alfred A.
Teacher
Sarazen, Dennis M.
MS Math & Science Chair
Simonsen, Janette Magenheimer
4th Grade Teacher
Sterber, Joann H.
3rd Grade Teacher
Virostko, Joan
Elementary Specialty Educator
Weinberg, Helen Nosel
Fourth Grade Teacher
Wood, Leonard A.
Social Studies Teacher
HURLEY
Dini-Adams, Elissa A.
Second Grade Teacher
Griffin, Christine Arcarola
Eng Tchr & Guidance Counselor
HYDE PARK
Areno, James Leslie
HS Mathematics Teacher
Boyce, Susan Mc Clelland
Third Grade Teacher
Fitchett, Sharman Oram
Art Teacher
Gardner, Margaret Hammer
Fourth Grade Teacher
Nameth, Vicki J.
Sixth Grade Teacher
Nichol, James J.
6th Grade Teacher
Nihoff, Joseph John
Instr of Hospitality Mngmt
Scherer-Goldpaugh, Kathryn
7th Grade English Teacher
Shannahan, Kathleen Winifred
English Teacher
ILION
Vail, Joseph Thomas
Social Science Teacher

INDIAN LAKE
Hoover, Stephen J.
Retired Science Teacher
IRVINGTON
Fruci, David Joseph
Eighth Grd Social Studies Tchr
ISLAND PARK
Carrion, Kathleen Patricia
Sixth Grade Teacher
Corrado, Donald L.
Dean of Students
Iannucci, Jeanette Rose
7th-8th Grd Math Teacher
ISLIP
Ambrosio, Joseph Michael
Music Teacher
Argenziano, Michael R.
MS Social Studies Teacher
Gale, Mary Ethel
2nd Grade Teacher
Lippman, Linda Verrico
Sixth Grade Teacher
Meagher, Susan Livingston
English Teacher
Ruggiero, Donna Elizabeth
Social Worker
ISLIP TERRACE
Dlouhy, Joan Cecelia
English Teacher
Drossos, Theresa Gresalfi
Business Education Teacher
Friedman, Ira Alvin
Mathematics Teacher
McCoy, Robert A.
Government & Amer His Teacher
Rapiejko, Lisa
Spanish Teacher
Sari, Kathleen
10th-12th Grade English Tchr
ITHACA
Breckheimer, Charles Thomas
Chemistry Teacher
Cooper, Grant
Music Professor
Craig, Lana Robb
Spanish Teacher
Duncan, Thomas Michael
Assoc Prof of Chem Engrng
Egan, Hugh Mc Keever
Dir & Assoc Prof of English
Gelberg, Denise Susan
1st Grade Teacher
Habecker, Terry William
Physical Education Teacher
Perkins, Judith Robbins
Home School Teacher
Smail, Ian E. V.
English Teacher
Ternasky, Nancy
School Nurse
Teukolsky, Roselyn
Math & Cmptr Sci Teacher
Wheelock, Marjorie Mc Namara
Religion Teacher
Wirt, Steven James
Physics Teacher
JAMAICA
Adman, Marlyne
Art & Architecture Teacher
Allocca, Donna Barbarotto
Librn, Clerical & Sub Teacher
Angerville, Edwin Duyanel
Accounting Professor
Arieh, Toby Samuels
Judaic Studies Teacher
Augustin, Yvonne Williams
Vocal Music Teacher
Berdine, Janice
English Teacher & Dept Chprsn
Berg, Lennie Howard
Social Studies Teacher
Bharosay, Boadnarine
Assistant Professor
Blake, Dolores A.
Math & Computer Teacher
Bockstein, Sherry Mae
Second Grade Teacher
Borruso, Annette
English Chairperson & Teacher
Brough, Linda Ann
Eight Grade Science Teacher
Bruen, Kathryn A.
Soc Studies Dept Chprsn & Tchr
Cacciola, Angela N.
Math Teacher & Dept Chprsn
Camera, William J.
Reading Teacher
Caniglia, Rose A.
Gifted & Talented Prgm Coord
Caplan, Judith Langer
English Teacher
Carrasco, Michael A.
Span, Eng & Soc Studies Tchr
Consigli, Ben L.
Asst Principal for Academics
Cordero, Thomas, Jr.
High School English Teacher
Dim, Isaac
History Teacher
DiPietra, Helen Walker
Second Grade Teacher
Drysdale, David Vincent
8th Grade Dean
Edwin, Edward M.
Bus, Mngmt & Mrktg Professor
Ellis, Alfred G.
Assistant Principal
Emmett, Camille A.
9th-12th Grd Soc Stud Teacher

Eterno, James Nicholas
Social Studies Teacher
Ezzo, Michelle Eraclio
Hlth Chprsn & PE Teacher
Fee, Ellen Marie
Art Department Chairperson
Ferguson, William G.
Math Teacher & Asst Principal
Ferraro, Camille Maria
Second Grade Teacher
Fiore, John James
English & Literature Teacher
Fisher, Michael L.
Spanish Teacher
Fishwick, John Joseph
Advanced Life Science Teacher
Fox, James M.
Asst Prof of Criminal Justice
Frangas, Harriet
Social Studies Teacher
Getchell, Donna Giordano
Mathematics Teacher
Goldstein, Stephen Craig
Eighth Grade Math Teacher
Guadagno-Akartuna, Rosemary
Biling Spanish & Math Teacher
Gujral, Mahinderpal Singh
Adj Lecturer of English Lit
Hamlet, Rosa Janette
English as Second Lang Teacher
Heaney-Hunter, Joann Catherine
Assoc Professor of Theology
Iler, Elisabeth
Program Director
Johnson, David Martin
Lecturer in Ec, Acctng & Bus
Joyce, Thomas
Pastor & Theology Teacher
Kalan, Sharon (Winiarz)
High School English Teacher
Keegan, Beatrice Cox
First Grade Teacher
Kellier, Shirley Gloria
Physical Education Teacher
Kim, Chang-Soo S.
Finance Professor
Kinnier, James Anthony
11th Grd AP Amer History Tchr
Leichtner, Jack
Dean
Lynch, Jean M.
Religion Teacher
Malkevitch, Joseph
Mathematics Professor
Maratos, Niki
English Teacher
Marino, Diane
Second Grade Teacher
Mason, Agatha Johnson
Nursing Teacher & Counselor
McCauley, Robert James
Mathematics & Music Teacher
Michaels, Catherine Ann
Religious Studies Teacher
Nearon, Laurie A.
Mathematics Teacher
Niklaus, William Michael
Psychology Teacher
Nolan, Patricia
English Teacher
O'Brien, Joyce Brady
Math & Religion Teacher
Pearlman, Jeffrey Lawrence
Earth Science Teacher
Pero, Linda Anne
Mathematics Teacher
Perrin, Barbara
Second Grade Teacher
Pollack, Barbara R.
2nd Grade Teacher
Rainford, Evangelina Thompson
High School Spanish Teacher
Redd, Ferdie
Library Teacher
Reisman, Sandra (Neugeboren)
Mathematics Teacher
Reznick, Patricia Ann (Phelan)
7th-8th Grade Teacher
Richardson, Deborah Ann
Social Studies Teacher
Sagiani, Frederica
Principal
Santangelo, Edward William
Physical Education Tchr & Dean
Scannell, Patrick E.
Principal
Schlein, Jack M.
Professor of Biology
Schuyler, Jane
Full Professor of Fine Arts
Serfaty, Judith Chester
English Teacher
Sganga, Theresa Josephine
Social Studies & Business Tchr
Sheldon, James Edmund
Biology & Chemistry Teacher
Sirignano, Jennifer
Art Teacher
Snell, Gertrude Pannell
Fourth Grade Teacher
Spellman, Kathleen Ann
Social Stud Dept Chairperson
Spergel, Martin
Physics Professor
Stalter, Richard
Professor of Biology
Tannenbaum, Chana Goldstein
HS Judaic Studies Teacher
Tendler Fried, Ruth
Sci Dept Chprsn & Bio Tchr

Valente, Rita Quintas
Art Therapist
Wright, Herman W.
Cnslr & Cooperative Ed Instr
JAMESTOWN
Baer, James Wilson
Retired Teacher
Berkley, Mira Tetkowski
Asst Prof of Early Chldhd Ed
Bess, Joyce
Second Grade Teacher
Borstorff, Robin Lynn
Physical Education Teacher
Bush, Stephen M.
Instrumental Music Teacher
Calalesina, Sanara Larson
Math Teacher
Carlson, Franni Lee
5th-8th Grd PE Tchr
Cimo, Angelo
Fourth Grade Teacher
Collins, John James
Prof of Anthropology & Rel
Condella, James Frank
American History Teacher
DeFrancisco, Michael Anthony
Guidance Counselor
DeJoy, Maria Christine
Secondary Social Studies Tchr
Di Maio, Joseph Robert
Health Educator
Dix, David J., Jr.
Health Teacher
Enserro, Ethel G.
High School Math Teacher
Fairbanks, David Joel
AP Amer History & Ec Teacher
Fashano, GraceAnn D'Angelo
Fourth Grade Teacher
Foust, William D.
Global Studies Teacher
Frey, Frances Anne
Earth Science Teacher
Greco, Daniel Thomas
Math & Soc Stud Teacher
Gudeman, Earl G.
Jr HS Math & Science Teacher
Haugner, Pamela Hutley
Spanish Teacher
Holmes, Gerald T.
3rd Grade Teacher
Huckno, Wally Joseph, Sr.
Athletic Director
Huston, Joan Bonfiglio
HS Psychology & History Tchr
Kibler, Andrew Perry
Professor of Biology
Limberg, Patricia Baideme
Math Teacher
Lingenfelter, Thomas Payne
Science Student Tchng Supvr
Luce, Anne Crandall
Psychology Professor
Marcum, Mary Seekins
Fourth Grade Teacher
Mazzie, Rebecca Ross
English Teacher
Miceli, Carol Jean J.
Business Teacher
Miekina, Carol Branstrom
6th Grade Teacher
Miekina, Gilbert Anthony
Social Studies Teacher
Muirhead, Brian William
Earth Science & Health Teacher
Munsee, Sandra Nupp
Math Teacher
Newton, Roslin Dickinson
Assistant Professor of Nursing
Newton, Trina Smith
8th Grade Science Teacher
Peterson, Cynthia C. Carlson
Art Teacher
Priester, Thomas C.
Dir of Physical Education
Samuelson, Kristen Marie
Spanish Teacher
Sember, John Michael
Social Studies Teacher
Sember, Shirley Scott
Third Grade Teacher
Smith, Anne Tenney
Senior HS English Teacher
Stafford, Marcia Jones
Kindergarten Teacher
Stauffer, Sally Anne
English Teacher
Storms, Patricia A. Sandbloom
Comp Ed & Math Tchr
Talley, Dan R.
Art His Instr & Dir of Ctr
Thompson, Clifton C.
Math Department Chairman
Whitehead, Carolyn Taft
Eng Tchr & Stu Org Advisor
Widen, Bruce Gregory
Social Studies Teacher
JAMESVILLE
Caldwell, Kelley M.
8th Grade Math Teacher
JEFFERSON
Wexler, Joel Alan
HS Mathematics Teacher
JERICHO
Anderson, Lawrence Arthur
Science Teacher
Andres, Richard J.
Mathematics Teacher
Bott, Kathryn Morrelly
Biology Teacher

JERICHO (cont)
Fishman, Bonnie Corrine
English Teacher
Kramer, Thomas Henry
Fifth Grade Teacher
JOHNSON CITY
Brigham, Glenn
4th Grade Teacher
Brunetti, Al
Assistant Principal
Dellacorino, Benny
7th Grd Social Studies Teacher
Gal, Julie B.
Mathematics Teacher
Halladay, Jane Eastman
Home Ec Teacher & FHA Advisor
LaBrutto, Rosalyn Magistro
Spanish Teacher
Lurenz, Michael Leibert
Middle School Teacher
Munley, Elizabeth Ann
Latin, Spanish & French Tchr
Shields, Betsy A. Mc Cormick
4th Grade Teacher
Syryca, Susan W.
First Grade Teacher
Valentine, Penelope Lisy (Koval)
8th Grade English Teacher
Vaughn, Nancy Wolcott
Reading Recovery Teacher
Walter, Cora Van Ord
Science Teacher
Watson, Robert E.
Mathematics Teacher
Zahora, Wendy Straw
Special Education Collaborator
JOHNSTOWN
Chambers, Sharon Smith
Office Technology Asst Prof
D'Amore, Carmelo V.
Guidance Counselor
Martin, Robert A., Jr.
Assoc Prof Criminal Justice
Precopio, Foster Peter
High School Math Teacher
Prestopnik, Richard John
Prof of Electrical Engineering
Warschawski, Paul
Professor of Humanities
JORDAN
Baner, Mary Ann (Walter)
Retired Chemistry Teacher
Forshee, Sharon
French & Spanish Teacher
Horyl, Jane (Nelligan)
Physical Education Teacher
Mead, Pamela Ann
Earth Sci & Biology Teacher
Rury, Rebecca D.
Mathematics Teacher
Smith, Karen M.
Business Education Teacher
KATONAH
Mann, George Wyatt
Guidance Counselor
Miller, Christian O.
6th Grade Math Teacher
Van Erk, Nina
Phys Ed & Athletics Director
KEESEVILLE
Bedard, Patricia L. (Martin)
10th-11th Grd Eng Teacher
Brown, George Gibson
Teacher, Coach & Meteorologist
Driscoll, Roderick Martin
US History & Govt Teacher
Hardy, Jeanne Carey
Math Teacher & Dept Head
Longware, Alta Jo
Technology Teacher
Maningo, Sheryl L.
Social Studies Teacher
Trombley, Virginia Haskin
High School Science Teacher
Waterhouse, John David
English Teacher
KENDALL
Henschel, Sandi
English Teacher
Pollock, Gary John
Mathematics Teacher
KENMORE
Ellis, Maureen Maloney
Math Teacher & Dept Chr
Golanka, Christine Steffens
Secondary Math Teacher
Illuzi, James V.
7th Grade Social Studies Tchr
Illuzzi, James Victor
Social Studies Teacher
Keleher, James Michael
Science Teacher
Malamas, Kimberly Allgrim
Former Teacher's Aide
Monaco-Hannon, Kelli Ann
English Teacher
Russell, Deborah Wahler
Global Studies Teacher
Swarts, Evelyn Miller
Science Teacher & Dept Chm
Thompson, Mary
Eng Lit & Composition Teacher
KEUKA PARK
Sherman, Mary E.
Retired Mathematics Teacher
KINDERHOOK
Fingar, Janice M.
3rd-4th Grade Teacher

KINGS PARK
Albinder, Eric R.
Band Director
Decker-Lombardi, Carole
English & Pub Speaking Teacher
Gallagher, John Patrick
Retired Elementary Teacher
Guasp, Susan Guihan
Art Teacher
Nelson, Margaret
English Director
Palm, Jeanne S.
English Teacher
Pappas, James Peter
Mathematics Teacher
Polin, Patricia Young
Spanish Teacher
Rocco, Richard F.
English Teacher
Sackett, Jeffrey Allyn
Social Studies & English Tchr
Shanks, Richard Edwin
High School Mathematics Tchr
Tavella, Loretta Strube
Eng & Social Studies Teacher
KINGSTON
Bayewitz, Howard S.
Social Studies Teacher
Getman, John Douglas
Chemistry Teacher
Gregory, James Thomas
Math Tchr & Building Liaison
Keehn, G. Thomas
Bands Director
Lawrence, Katherine A. (Manley)
Eighth Grade Science Teacher
Lopez, Sandy Mancuso
HS Physical Education Teacher
Miressi, Ruth Scherer
Kindergarten Teacher
Monfette, Linda Pope
Third Grade Teacher
Moore, Emelia Amendola
Fifth Grade Teacher
Myer, Debra Lee
High School Math Teacher
Natoli, Thomas Aurelius, Jr.
Chemistry Teacher
Onderdonk, Richardson Dixon
Biology Teacher
Scatenato, Paul
Choir Director
Scherer, Wendell Aloysius
English Teacher
Solomon, Myrah Smith
Global Studies Teacher
Voerg, Vincent
Writing Instructor
Welsek, Carol Ann
7th-8th Grd Sci & Math Tchr
Yaun, Harriet Pendergast
Second Grade Teacher
KIRKWOOD
Coon, Nancy Rauschmeier
4th Grade Teacher
Farina, Anne Breslin
Second Grade Teacher
Harding, Catherine M.
Music Teacher
Zandt, Dorothy Ann D.
Fourth Grade Teacher
LA FARGEVILLE
Compeau, John David
Mathematics & Computer Teacher
Plank, Louis William
US History Teacher & Dept Chm
LA FAYETTE
Besten, John Joseph
Instrumental Music Teacher
Coufal, Carol Ann (Root)
English Teacher
Markoff, Karen Louise (Aungler)
Asst Prin & Special Ed Dir
Templar, Judith Ellen
Second Grade Teacher
LAGRANGEVILLE
Beahan, Judith Arkell
Business Teacher
Blanchette, Cheryl Prendergast
French Tchr & Frgn Lang Coord
Buergers, Eric H.
English Teacher
Cerniglia, Roberta Krombar
English & Public Speaking Tchr
Cross, Sally Baright
Biology Teacher
Danchenko, Halina
Russian Teacher
Di Pompei, Geraldine C.
Soc Stud Teacher & Dept Coord
Gambino, Salvatore Vincent
Mathematics Teacher
Lalli, Barbara
Biology & Chemistry Teacher
Lombardi, Margaret Rizzuti
Chemistry Teacher
Mansfield, Elyse DeNat
Second Grade Teacher
Mooney, Vincent James
English Teacher
Safford, Richard Wright
Retired Sixth Grade Teacher
Sulsky, Judy
Mathematics Teacher
Suter, Valerie Jackson
Physics & Chemistry Teacher
Usifer, Peter J.
Science Teacher
Villano, Joseph Anthony
History Teacher

LAKE GEORGE
Fair-Sears, Heather M.
Sequential Math I & II Teacher
Stanilka, Cathy M.
Physical Education Teacher
Thorne, Ruthellyn Murphy
3rd-4th Grade Teacher
LAKE GROVE
Karpf-Fritts, Charlotte
Fourth Grade Teacher
Koch, Deborah Dalessio
Fifth Grade Teacher
Markham, MaryAlice Bridget
Third Grade Teacher
Mc Cormack, Sandra J.
Special Education Teacher
Perry, Mary Jane Daly
6th Grade Teacher
LAKE KATRINE
DeLeo, John L.
Science Teacher
Franklin, Jane K.
Earth Science Teacher
LAKE LUZERNE
Noakes, Mary Claire Watson
Third Grade Teacher
LAKE PLACID
Johns, Frank Robert
Biology Teacher & Sci Chair
LAKEWOOD
Pillittieri, Betty Lou Faulk
Fifth Grade Teacher
LANCASTER
Basher, Kathleen
Retired French Teacher
Carriero, Kevin J.
Physical Education
Connelly, Patricia Kelleher
Social Studies & English Tchr
Doster, Diane LaFleur
Sixth Grade Teacher
Fay, Thomas William
Mathematics & Religion Teacher
Grahnert, Lisa Ann
German & Spanish Teacher
Guest, Leonard George
Industrial Arts Teacher
Hager, Claudette P.
Science Teacher
Krieger, William F.
Physical Ed Teacher & Coach
Marts, Diane Marie
Fifth Grade Inclusion Teacher
Maxwell, Irene
English Teacher & Chairperson
Mc Cartan, Patricia Peters
Mathematics Teacher
Meyers, Maureen Mc Donnell
English Teacher
Pierce, Ricahrd G.
History Teacher
Priebe-Marchioli, Shannon
Science Teacher
Rosenthal, Marsha Vyner
Mathematics Teacher
Sansone, Virginia VanDuzer
Third Grade Teacher
Smith, Paul R.
Health Ed Tchr & Dept Chprsn
Taylor, Raymond L.
Sixth Grade Science Teacher
Taylor, Wilma P.
English & Drama Teacher
Tokasz, Marie D. Schleining
Music Teacher & Orchestra Dir
LARCHMONT
Rubicco, John Anthony
8th Grade English Teacher
Winter, Anne Kelly
First Grade Teacher
LATHAM
Berggren, John Wilson
Third Grade Teacher
Bradshaw, Aileen O'Brien
Mathematics Teacher
Burke, Elizabeth
HS Special Education Teacher
Chamberland, Rose Marie M., CSJ
5th Grade Teacher
Donohue, Martha Cassidy
8th Grade Social Studies Tchr
Flewelling, Karen A.
HS Physical Education Teacher
Gansle, Marbry Pulver
Secondary PE Teacher & Coach
Posillico, Rosemarie Zaffuts
Family & Consumer Sci Teacher
Springstead, Edwin A.
Retired PE Teacher
Stendardo, Jeanne M.
English Teacher
Warren, MaryGrace Crispo
Retired Teacher
LAUREL
Williams, Ray Stanley
Retired Instrmntl Music Tchr
LAURENS
Back, Kim L.
English Teacher
Brunson, Timothy Michael
Social Studies Teacher
Martin, Daniel G.
Instrumental Music Teacher
Ruff, Cheree Lynne
First Grade Teacher
Sider, Heidi Anne
School Counselor
Sorrentino, Joseph Carman, Jr.
Athletic Coach

Wenck, Romona Nellis
K-12th Grade Phys Ed Teacher
LAWRENCE
Mjaanes, Holly (Walker)
8th Grade English Teacher
Seyfert, Wayne G.
Science Teacher & Rsrch Coord
LE ROY
Di Franco, Timothy S.
5th Grade Teacher
Furr, Sheila Frost
First Grade Teacher
Gugino, Elizabeth Termer
Science Teacher
Hooker, Beth Ann Lambein
Vocal Music Edctr
Lathan, Deborrah Rouse
4th Grade Teacher
LEBANON SPRINGS
Marsh, Donald H.
Jr High Science Tchr
LEVITTOWN
Abraham, Emilyann
Math Teacher
Callis, John Andrew
Bio & Environmental Stud Tchr
Condy, Dawn E.
Science & Biology Teacher
Costello, Steven
Soc Stud Tchr & Var Bsbl Coach
Cullinan, Patricia A. (Martin)
Social Studies Teacher
D'Auria, Joseph P.
Social Studies Teacher
Ditchik, Donna R.
Seventh Grade English Teacher
Fairhead, Donald E.
Health Teacher
Ferris, Patricia Anne
Sixth Grade Teacher
Grande, Nicolas
Social Studies Teacher
Greenberg, Sheila I.
Sixth Grade Teacher
Hatzfeld, Jill Anne
Biology & Chemistry Teacher
Jones, Joan Oakes
HS Social Studies Teacher
Lanfear, Dewain T.
English Teacher
Martin, Martha Smith
Enrichment Teacher
Maynard, Leslie Beebe
Eighth Grade Science Teacher
Monteleone, John
5th Grd Teacher & Bldg Chprsn
Morrison, Brian Vincent
Mathematics Teacher
Morsette, Gale Marie
11th Grade English Teacher
O'Byrne, Bruce Raymond
Phys Ed & Co-Ath Director
Pennisi, Annette Bonventre
Chairperson & Spanish Teacher
Portolano, Charles Joseph
Physical Ed & Health Teacher
Rice, James F.
Social Studies Teacher
Roemer, Elizabeth Farrand
English Teacher
Sass, Andrew Raymond
Physics Teacher
Siegel, Carol Nici
Special Education Teacher
Vulpis, Robert Alan
Social Studies Teacher
Wexler, Deborah
Home Economics Teacher
Williams, Sandra M. (Sweller)
HS Physics & Earth Sci Teacher
Wolf, Elaine
K-12th Grd Lang Arts Chprsn
LEWISTON
Reedy, John Joseph
Emeritus Prof of Biology
Weinholtz, Joanne Rickard
Culture Teacher
LIBERTY
Fleck, William Joseph
Middle School English Teacher
Gatta, Margaret Vaughan
Health Academy Teacher
LINCOLNDALE
Cuk, John C.
Director of Choirs
DiFabbio, Anthony B.
English Teacher
Hirschhorn, Ronnie Riback
HS Social Studies Teacher
O'Brien, James Daniel
Technology Education Teacher
Phethean, Nancy Morris
First Grade Teacher
Reynolds, Terry
Instrumental Music Teacher
Rosvally, Harry E., Jr.
High School Sci Teacher
Saia, Paul Anthony
AP Biology & Regents Bio Tchr
Strauss, Andrew M.
Chemistry Teacher
Ullman, Claire Ticker
Mathematics Teacher
LINDENHURST
Albano, Michael A.
English & Theater Arts Tchr
Atkinson, Daniel William
Math Teacher
Bilello, Jack
Soc Stud Teacher & Dept Chm

Bjerke, Maureen Elaina
English Teacher
Brodmerkel, Betty Jane Maduca
Spanish Teacher
Calabrese, Savino Italo Benito
English Teacher
Costa, Elizabeth Barrett
Vocal Music Teacher
DeRiggi, Jean Skinder
Home Economics Teacher
DiRusso, Annette Cesone
6th Grade Teacher
Dopkins, Suzette Fratti
Art Teacher
Giorgini, Florence Loscalzo
Art & Music Coordinator
Jakowicki, Violetta Anna
ESL Teacher
Kloberdanz, Maryann Mirante
8th Grade Social Studies Tchr
Koza, Burt T.
Social Studies Teacher
Kubik, Ann
Fourth Grade Teacher
Kubik, Elaine Marie
Senior HS Vocal Music Teacher
Lankau, Albert John
Mathematics Teacher
Logue, Robert Emmet
Science Teacher
Meyer, Harolyn
English Teacher
Montefusco, Yolanda Biancaniello
English & Journalism Teacher
Paseltiner, Lee
AP Biology Teacher
Ryan, Richard George
Science Teacher & Swim Coach
Scruggs, Roxanne Kane
Art Teacher
Sureau, James P.
Leadership Education Teacher
Wolters, Jeanette Marie
Social Studies Teacher
Zingraf, Lorraine A.
Third Grade Teacher
LISBON
Buckingham, Rebecca Shelmidine
Biology & Life Science Teacher
Masters, Elizabeth Mc Martin
Secondary English Teacher
Russell, John David
Band Director
Smith, Helen Geary
Kindergarten Teacher
Stromgren, Diane Compeau
Third Grade Teacher
LITTLE FALLS
Morotti, Joseph
7th Grade Social Studies Tchr
Murdock, Beverly A.
English Teacher
Roche, Patrick George
Secondary Math Teacher
Smith, Jean Babinec
Fifth Grade Teacher
LITTLE NECK
Altman, Carole Ronnie
French Teacher
Cazes, Arline Herz
ESL Teacher
Johnson, Remelle L. Richmond
Spanish Teacher
Kramer, Arline Singer
Third Grade Teacher
Neufeld, Valerie Thalrose
English Teacher
Smerling, Rochelle
8th Grade Social Studies Tchr
Williams, Michael L.
Adaptive Physical Ed Teacher
LITTLE VALLEY
Ferrara, Anne Quattrone
English Teacher
Troskosky, Marie Carol
Secondary English Teacher
Wahl, Glenn G.
7th-12th Grade Science Teacher
LIVERPOOL
Babcock, Michael Carter
Biology & Chemistry Teacher
Balcewicz, Susan A.
Math Teacher
Bero, Stephen James
Environmental Studies Teacher
Brooks, Janet Pfohl
Social Studies Teacher
Bumpus, Laurie Culver
Mathematics Teacher
Burrer, Daryl A.
Social Studies Teacher
Carrow, Victoria A.
Spanish Teacher
Chartrand, David Joseph
Computers & Engineering Tchr
Conklin, Alan W.
Science Teacher
De Long, Robert J., Jr.
Guidance Counselor
Ferron, Gale Hodorowski
Social Studies Teacher
Fitzgerald, Richard Daniel
Social Studies Teacher
Garfinkel, Susan Heyman
Second Grade Teacher
Garraffo, Steven Joseph
Global Stud & Economics Tchr
Gordon, Barbara
French Teacher

POOL (cont)
Peggy (Lippmann)
Grade Teacher
ı, Nancy Alden
ng Teacher
, Patricia Pennington
athematics Teacher
Thomas David
l Studies Teacher
Sandra Jean
ı Grade Teacher
Kathleen M.
ematics Teacher
aney, Michael C.
sh Teacher
ne, Robert Martin
sh Teacher
, Robert Eugene
ematics Teacher
Victoria Wilson
l Studies Teacher
i, Thomas R.
sh Teacher & Dir of Drama
ı, Patricia P.
sh Teacher
, Charlotte Faella
sh Teacher
on, Jeffry Edward
ce Teacher
, Carol R.
gy Teacher
, Gary Ross
School Mathematics Tchr
s, Susan Frances
School Math Teacher
p, Jamie S.
rade English Teacher
rtz, Cheryl Prowda
Ed & Resource Room Tchr
r, James Gervais
l Studies Teacher
Melody Louise
al Studies Teacher
n, Joseph Francis
al Studies Teacher
Priscilla E.
Grade Teacher
, Christine LeValley
Arts Dept Chair & Teacher
ore, Kathleen Giacchi
Grade Inclusion Teacher
ski, Patricia Haberer
Studies Tchr & Dept Chprsn
ski, Steven Paul
athematics Teacher
NIA
o, Stephen D.
School Physical Ed Tchr
Tracie L.
ness Education Teacher
r, Martha Maloney
ematics Teacher
, Douglas John
& 8th Grade Math Teacher
SHELDRAKE
rt, Thomas J.
essor of Sociology
William Harry
essor of Biology
PORT
athy, Diane Washbon
Grade Teacher
m, Kirk Thomas
ematics Teacher
lia, Frank Louis
al Studies Teacher
, John R.
al Studies Teacher
, Charles F.
ı & Greek Teacher
Janice M. (Hall)
stian Education Director
, Patrick Michael
of Physical Ed & Athletics
llo, Deborah Ann
nish Teacher & Dept Chprsn
Molly Elizabeth
ding & Science Teacher
am, Kathleen Marie (Reynolds)
nish Teacher
, James M.
al Studies Dept Chairman
Donna J. (Pringle)
Grade Teacher
ly, Karen Tracy
Grade Math Teacher
er, Michael Todd
nematics Teacher
t, Renee Gumins
lish Teacher
r, Bruce Robert
al Studies Teacher
, Anthony C.
lish Teacher
ay, Mary A.
al Studies Teacher
ato, Loretta Cataldo
rth Grade Teacher
lly, Barbara Steinkuhler
lish Teacher
ite, Francis J.
red 7th Grd Soc Stud Tchr
, Marsha M.
ti-Age Teacher
ourgondien, Julie Shanley
dance Counselor
r, Joseph Raymond
nish Teacher
er, Theodore J., II
cipal

LOCUST VALLEY
Axman, Douglas N.
Director
Dee, Clare
Art Teacher
Dick, Alexander C., Jr.
Mathematics Teacher
Goldmeer, Susan Ann
HS Spanish & Italian Teacher
Gray, Steven Allan
Spanish Teacher
Parsons, Ivor Richard
Social Studies Chairman
Schwan, Madeline Grunet
High School English Teacher
Smith, Frederick C. J.
Dir of PE & Athletics Coach
LONG BEACH
Duque, Guillermo
Bilingual Social Studies Tchr
Hirschbein-Bodnar, Susan B.
Home Economics Teacher
Kaplan, Bruce Jay
Music Teacher
Katz, Jill
Math Teacher
Malinconico, Rose G.
Chem & Forensic Sci Teacher
Mc Elroy, Ellen M.
High School Math Teacher
Pickus, Ellen Gordon
English Teacher
Raber, Sheila Edelstein
English Teacher
Saginario, Francine Garofalo
High School Reading Specialist
Van Dyke, William John
Foreign Language Teacher
LONG ISLAND CITY
Asregadoo, Vernon Edward
Social Studies & English Tchr
Befumo, Debra Joy
English Teacher
Behringer, Mary Alice A.
First Grade Teacher
Benson, James Patrick, Jr.
English Teacher
Bozoyan, Mary Victoria
Mathematics Teacher
Bustio, Daisy
Sr Lab Technician & Span Instr
Cattoggio, Geraldine
8th Grade Teacher
Chow, Carol
Assistant Principal
Collins, Michael
Mathematics Teacher
Connor, Timothy J.
Mathematics Tchr & Comp Coord
Constain, Sally Wahl
Staff Developer
D'Angio, Mary Ann
Physical Education Teacher
Davidson, Robert L.
Social Studies Teacher
DeMaio, Barbara Kolenovsky
Jr High Math Teacher
Dromm, Daniel Patrick
Fourth Grade Teacher
Feibel, Ann E.
Asst Prof & Academic Coord
Fitzmaurice, Jeanne M.
Mathematics Teacher
Garramone, Mario
Social Studies Teacher
Gilbert, Lainey
High School English Teacher
Graffeo, Gussie Victoria
Business Teacher & Treasurer
Graves, Randy L.
Adj Prof of Cmptr Info System
Graydon, Elizabeth Gannon
6th-8th Grade Social Stud Tchr
Hadjiminas, Elias E.
HS Chemistry Teacher
Karaiskos, Maria
English Teacher
Kenney, Mary
Art Teacher & Chairperson
Klein, Bernard S.
Physics Teacher
Klein, Harold Steven
Biology Teacher
Lawlor, Ellen Morrissey
Substitute Teacher
Leddy-Sokol, Maria Natalie
Dean & History Teacher
Noone, Mary Ellen
Learning Center Teacher
Occaso, Maria M.
Language Teacher
O'Donoghue, Mary JoAnn
Religious Educator
Pender, Karen Franz
Language Arts & Reading Tchr
Peterson, Violet
Arts & Crafts Teacher
Petr, John A.
Aviation Mechanics Teacher
Queija, Jorge
Spanish Teacher
Ray, Elizabeth Glover
English & Language Arts Tchr
Rodriguez, Fernando
Shop Teacher & Grade Advisor
Rodriguez, Max
Professor of Modern Languages
Rothenhaus, Robert C.
Mathematics Teacher

Sawyer, Jacqueline Ann
Dance Educator
Schroedel-Ugur, Huberta Wolf
Coord for Deaf & Hard Hearing
Serrano, Raymond
Social Studies Teacher
Stevens, Mary Brown
Teacher & Staff Developer
Stoller, Rita Linda
Title I Mathematics Teacher
Syntilas, Rita Koletti
Jr High & HS Greek Teacher
Tanalski, Adam John
Earth Science & Biology Tchr
Thompson, Stephanie Lynn
Computer Technology Teacher
Tillman, Ernestine Porter
Science Teacher & Dean
VanCooten, Ronald Anthony
Science & Computer Sci Teacher
Voroba, Susalea
Asst Prin for Acad Subjects
Weinstein, Lynn
Drama Teacher
Wu, Clara C.
Professor
Zuniga, Charlotte Daszewski
Chemistry & Earth Science Tchr
LOUDONVILLE
Bachman, Betty Anne
Asst Professor of Psychology
Brady, Thomas J.
Assistant Professor of Biology
Brookins, Gilbert M.
Prof of Mgmt & Org Studies
Cutler, Leonard M.
Public Law Professor
Feldstein, Bernard
Prof of Marketing & Management
Fitzgerald-Hoyt, Mary
Professor of English
Marko, Dale F.
Assistant Professor of Chem
Matcha, Duane Allan
Sociology Professor
Mc Leod, Joanne Sliwinski
4th Grade Teacher
Raux, Donald James
Asst Professor of Accounting
Repicky, George Joseph
Sci, Comp Sci & Rel Teacher
LOWVILLE
Allen, Pamela J.
7th Grade Math Teacher
Brooker, Mark William
Instrumental Music Teacher
Cole, Richard L.
PE, Ec Tchr & Var Ftbl Coach
Keenan, Ellen M.
Sixth Grade Teacher
Parker, Susan Robinson
Tchr of Gifted & Talented Prgm
Trick, Carolyn Kelly
Art Teacher
LYNBROOK
Barrett, Kenneth P.
Social Studies Teacher
Ganley, Theresa Mc Donnell
Fourth Grade Teacher
Hupe, Richard Carter
Regents Biology Teacher
Muzio, Kimberly Ann
High School Guidance Counselor
Vaeth, Mary Teresa
Fourth Grade Teacher
LYNDONVILLE
DiMiero, Phyllis Ann
Fourth Grade Teacher
Gawne, Brian John
Health Educator
Hogan, Catherine J.
Business Education Teacher
Hogan, Louise A. (Louanne)
Third Grade Teacher
Kent, Lisa R.
7th-12th Grd PE Teacher
Smith, Joanne M. Austin
English Teacher
LYONS
Clark, Roger W.
Elementary PE Teacher
Dann, John M.
English Teacher
DeCook, Harold Jacob
Math Teacher & Department Chm
Goldammer, Barbara Harford
Secondary Mathematics Teacher
Marsteiner, Carol O'Brien
Mathematics Teacher
Verkey, Rodney E.
Physical Education Teacher
MACEDON
Douglas, Kathleen Tracie
Social Studies Teacher
Klingler, Patricia Ann
Elementary School Teacher
MADISON
Ford, Jim
Junior High History Teacher
Manchester, Linda Godfrey
First Grade Teacher
Troyer, Dale Shields
Health & Phys Education Tchr
MADRID
Hildreth, Sandra Jean
Jr-Sr High School Art Tchr
Hubbard, Kathleen Boyd
Vocal Music Teacher
Moulton, Claudia Jean
Kindergarten Teacher

MAHOPAC
Burton, Martha L.
Teacher
Caltagirone, Silke Lorenzen
HS German Teacher
Castronovo, Bernadine Marro
Music Teacher
Corace, Joseph
Technology Teacher
Crawford, June Maciorowski
Second Grade Teacher
Davis, Richard
Physical Education Teacher
DiCioccio, Joseph Nicholas
Mathematics Teacher
Frese, Donald L.
Health Teacher
Mahoney, Joseph Francis
Math Teacher
Markoe, Donald John
Teacher
Paczkoski, Richard
Fifth Grade Teacher
Perry, Stuart
Business Education Teacher
Peterson, Bruce Robert
Earth Science Teacher
Racco, Luciano
Italian Teacher
Rzeznik, Lawrence David
Biology Teacher
Talbot, Deborah Johnstone
Spanish Teacher
Veglia, Daniel R.
Math Chairperson & Teacher
Zimmerman, Robert Earl, II
High Schl Mathematics Teacher
MALONE
Boyea, Margaret Perry
First Grade Teacher
Chatland, Bradley J.
Social Studies Teacher
Demers, Bonnie Smith
First Grade Teacher
Dievendorf, Jane Welch
School Counselor
DuMont, Maureen Murphy
English Teacher
Factor, Ellen Lester
Choral Director
Lewis, Donna Chatland
9th-12th Grd English Teacher
Macomber, Sandra L.
Physical Education Teacher
Matlock, Herman Bradley
Secondary Music Teacher
Monette, Nancy Ann
Spanish Teacher
Peets, Barbara Powers
7th-10th Grade English Teacher
Poupore, Lisa A. (Bigness)
Spanish Teacher
Rider, Jon Allen
Fifth Grade Teacher
Shea, Jeff A.
Math Teacher
Soper, Cynthia Cheeseman
Third Grade Teacher
Wemette, Angela Towle
French Teacher
West, Daniel E.
Physical Education Teacher
MALVERNE
DeLeo, Virginia Ann
Biology Teacher
Klingbeil, Carolyn Liberti
High School Spanish Teacher
Macher, Richard Alan
Social Studies Teacher
Moreira, Donna Marie
High School Art Teacher
O'Donohue, Susan M.
Third Grade Teacher
Trotman, Sarita Walker
6th Grade Teacher
MAMARONECK
Ehrenksanz, Eleanor Mangel
English Teacher
Horn, Pamela Vivian
Foreign Language Teacher
Kaplan, Enid Fern
English Teacher
Mahony, Elizabeth
High School Mathematics Tchr
Minor, Lorna H.
High School History Teacher
Perlman, John N.
English & Poetry Teacher
Restaino, Phillip A.
High School English Teacher
Rinello, Patricia
Teacher
Sherwood, Linda Holland
English Teacher
Zappala, John
Science Teacher
MANHASSET
Aaron, Karen M.
Elementary Teacher
Barron, Carole Jane
English Dept Chprsn & Tchr
Costello, Monica
Principal
Eng, Anna Wong
Health Teacher
Gorin, Robert Murray, Jr.
Social Studies Teacher
Prunty, Mary Mahoney
High School Mathematics Tchr

MANLIUS
Bell, Melinda Donovan
ILEX Alternative Teacher
Burns, Timothy D.
English Teacher
Chandler, Clifton Edison, Jr.
Technology Instrl Specialist
Eicholzer, Andrew Paul
Varsity Swim Coach
Fay, Brian G.
English Instr
Hall, Thomas W.
US History & Global Stud Tchr
Hebert, Ronald A.
Orch Director & District Coord
Kenneally, Christopher
Chemistry & Physics Teacher
Maier, Brenda Switzer
Art Teacher
Ring, Evelyn B.
HS Counselor
Rothman, Tovah G.
Resource Teacher
Searle, Ronald O.
Honors Biology Teacher
Skelly, Michael John
Biology Teacher
Steenberg, Matthew Alan
PE Teacher & Ftbl Coach
MANORVILLE
Conlon, Nancy Mary Kelley
English Teacher
Mishkin, Hal Richard
Social Studies Tchr & Coord
MARATHON
Niggli, Carol Appleby
Sixth Grade Teacher
Treadwell, Susan N.
French Teacher
MARCELLUS
Busa, Heidi Wilson
Science Teacher
Hunter, Andrew John
Social Studies Teacher
Madonia, Anthony Joseph
Spanish Teacher
Mc Nally, Margaret Clarke
Second Grade Teacher
Perry, Darlene Terry
4th Grade Teacher
Winnicki, Cherie Kline
Mathematics Teacher
MARCY
Beckwith, E. Kenneth
Regents Chemistry Teacher
Breckel, Jill
US History & Government Tchr
Gaetano, Richard Francis
HS Teacher
Kinney, Gary M.
Science Teacher
Maliani, Diane Guadagnino
English Teacher
Matt, Lucille Inserra
French Teacher
Pezdek, Jacqueline MacFarland
English & Social Studies Tchr
Pugh, Dale S.
Global Studies Teacher
Rumbutis, Jan Mercurio
Art Teacher
Stronach, Mary Saporetti
Spanish Teacher
Widrick, Lynn S.
English Teacher
MARGARETVILLE
Atkin, Barbara Ann
English Teacher
Fiedler, William G., Jr.
7th-9th Grade Teacher
LeServiget, Elizabeth Anne
French Teacher
Taylor, Barbara Potts
Sixth Grade Teacher
MARION
Snyder, Sarah Jane
Special Education Teacher
Stoker, Kenneth R.
German Teacher
White, Richard B.
Physical Education Teacher
MARLBORO
Antalek, Diane Carol
Reading Teacher & Consultant
Billesimo, Jo-Anne
7th-8th Grade Spanish Teacher
Detz, Joseph Anthony
Mathematics Teacher
Domanski, Ronald Richard
Art Coordinator
Forster, Anna Kathryn
Science Teacher
Giacoia, Ann Marie Volpe
Home Economics Teacher
Kroh, Penny Jean
High School English Teacher
Meyer, Glenn William
Science Teacher
Schmitz, Genevieve Recla
Business Education Teacher
Virga, Michael Gandolfo
Spanish Teacher
Waugh, John C.
Computer Teacher & Programmer
Winters, Barbara Keeping
English Teacher
Zamperlin, Frank U.
Asst Principal

MASPETH
Flori, Monica G.
6th Grade Reading Teacher
Tarasko, Basil Paul
Mathematics Teacher
MASSAPEQUA
Abrams, Douglas J.
Social Studies Teacher
Applestone, Celia Goldman
Retired Elementary School Tchr
Barra, James Richard
English Teacher
Berger, Lorraine Martin
Spanish Teacher
Casano, Salvatore
High School Chemistry Teacher
Gale, Richard G.
English Teacher
Giordano, Stephen A.
Spanish & French Teacher
Guillet, Marie Miranda
French, Italian & Latin Tchr
Hess, Diane M.
Secondary Science Teacher
Levin, Jennifer Lynne
Remedial Math Teacher
Mc Millan, Susan Alexander
Math Teacher
Prudente, Ciro R.
Assistant Principal
Rizzi, Robert B.
Spanish Teacher
Ross, Susan Chasin
High School Physical Educator
MASSAPEQUA PARK
Bambino, Jacqueline Marie
Retired Spanish Teacher
MASSENA
Bellor, Susan J. (Spadafore)
Spanish Teacher
Billington, Darryl Manley
High School Art Teacher
Bogosian, Nancy Dobies
7th-8th Grd Soc Stud Teacher
Bombard, Michele
Fifth Grade Teacher
Clark, Walter T.
English Teacher
Dyke, William Francis
PE Tchr & Athletic Coach
Hance, Cathy Kyer
Art Teacher
Taylor, Joan Ida
Retired Fourth Grade Teacher
Thibault, Stephanie Carbone
English Teacher
MASTIC BEACH
Felicetta, Mary Elena
General Music & Choral Teacher
Gilchrist, Kathleen
Social Studies Teacher
Iversen, Doris Marie
Choral Director
Merolla, Michael Bernard
High School Music Teacher
Peponakis-Matzner, Andrea Ruth
Spanish Teacher
Rhodes, Carmela Sabatiele
Chemistry Teacher
MATTITUCK
Grattan, Joyce Osborne
College Counselor & Eng Tchr
Massa, Frank
Math Teacher
MAYFIELD
Brumaghim, Merry Ellen E.
English Teacher
Capuano, Jeffrey A.
Biology Teacher
DeLilli, Faye Stanton
Multi-Age Classroom Teacher
Kline, Jane Lacy
High School Art Teacher
LoBalbo, Gina M.
Business Teacher
Yager, Tara Flanger
4th-5th Grd Multi-Age Teacher
MC CONNELLSVILLE
Marullo, Annette
Fourth Grade Teacher
MC GRAW
Kanalley, Elizabeth Mahaney
Second Grade Teacher
Mooney, Jennie Lynn
6th Grade Teacher
MECHANICVILLE
D'Alberto, Adele Daloia
Retired Teacher
Day, Elizabeth Ponzillo
Sixth Grade Teacher
Hodgson, Lynda Gayle
English Teacher
MEDFORD
Albertelli, Joseph Louis
Science Teacher
Montenare, Kathryn Prin
Secondary English Teacher
Pentola, Catherine A.
English & Philosophy Teacher
Sconone, Robert Lawrence
PE Teacher
Segelski, Anthony James
Social Studies Teacher
Silverman, Myron
A P American Government Tchr
Thoden, Michelle Ellen
Science Teacher
Tice, Lyndia Ann
English Teacher
MEDINA
Hogan Mac Evoy, Lisa Anne
Health Occupations Instructor
Hrycik, Pauline Emily
8th Grd English Teacher
March, Cathleen C.
Reading Specialist
Robinson, Robert D.
Agriculture Teacher
Roeseler, Lisa Ann
6th-12th Grade Music Teacher
Southworth, Wilson Main
Fourth Grade Teacher
Thurston, Mary Jane Murtaugh
Sixth Grade Teacher
MELROSE
Thompson, Francis A.
Retired Science Teacher
MELVILLE
Becker, Lorraine Beebe
Mathematics Teacher
Calvo, Maritza Acosta
Spanish Teacher
Clement, Philomena Ward
Eng Instr & Dept Chprsn
Crocetti, Catherine Fusillo
Science Teacher
Fabricatore, Annmarie
English Teacher
Gabriel, Robert F.
Theology Chm & Teacher
Gillespie, Linda
English Teacher
Grottano, Agatha Tina
Social Studies Teacher
Jurich, Peter Michael
High School Theology Teacher
Kelly, Robert P.
Theology Teacher
Kennedy, Nancy Macri
High School English Teacher
Kiernan, Theresa Grilli
Mathematics Teacher
O'Neill, Daniel Joseph
Social Studies Teacher
Peters, Ann Julie, SND
Sr Theology Teacher
Pfriender, Marilyn Margaret, OP
Math Tchr & Chorus Accompanist
Stern, Mel Alan
Sixth Grade Teacher
Veglia, Marilyn Rose
7th-8th Grd Soc Stud Teacher
MERRICK
Baier, Barbara
High School Mathematics Tchr
Griggs, Arlene
8th Grade English Teacher
Johnson, Denise Rondez
Teacher of the Gifted
Padalino, Leo P.
Retired HS Social Studies Tchr
Sardo, Sanford
Choral Music Teacher
Wisla, Sharon Rothstein
Social Studies Teacher
MEXICO
Battles, Jamie Himes
Math Teacher
Baum, Terry Galvin
6th Grade Social Stud Tchr
Carranti, Thomas Andrew
Band Director
Colvin, Mark Thomas
Fifth Grade Teacher
Dadey, Margaret R.
American History Teacher
DeLine, Alan Charles
Criminal Justice Teacher
Deloff, Dola Coughenour
English Teacher
Johnson, Virginia Hilton
Chemistry Teacher
Kays, William John
Scndry Sci Tchr & Dept Chprsn
LaTulip, David Arthur
Sixth Grade Math Teacher
Rehrl-Ruggio, Carmen Antoinette
German Teacher
Ryan, Kathleen Marie
8th Grade English Teacher
Santore, Sandra L. (Fox)
English Teacher
Scott, Sandra Howley
7th Grade Soc Stud Teacher
Shaw, Joseph T.
High School English Teacher
Soto, Rita
Spanish Teacher
Stickles, Peter L.
Regents Earth Science Teacher
Sturtz, Martha Searles
Fifth Grade Teacher
Thayer, Marilyn M.
German Teacher
Weaver, Alicia Ruth
7th Grade Science Teacher
Youmans, Barbara Jean
Assistant Nurse Instructor
MIDDLE ISLAND
Alfieri, Ralph, Jr.
Science Teacher
Buckman, John Francis
HS Phys Ed Teacher
Cauchi, Patrick Joseph
High School English Teacher
Colon, Ricardo
Span Tchr & Girls Track Coach
Corr, John F.
English Teacher
Darson, Donna Jean
7th Grade Social Studies Tchr
Di Martino, Robert, Jr.
Reading & Learning Specialist
Fassett, Marilyn Carol
Social Studies Teacher
Feeney, Roberta
English Teacher
Fortunoff, David
English Teacher
Gallo, Louis John
Social Studies Teacher
Graham, Beverly Nicolis
Science Teacher
Hession, Julia Cheetham
6th Grade Teacher
Kennedy-Smith, Susan M.
Secondary English Teacher
Kenzig, William Joseph
English Teacher
Lang, Deborah A.
Technology Teacher
Masone, Marleen Daddio
Jr High Math Teacher
Mc Carthy, Kevin Michael
Special Ed & Head Ftbl Coach
Militscher, Joan F.
Foreign Language Dept Chprsn
Newton, Carol Smith
Special Education Teacher
Nickerson, Penny J.
Social Science Teacher
Zakar, Gail Marie
Physical Education Teacher
MIDDLEBURGH
Bender, Matthew Patrick
Science Teacher
Clements, Patricia Bowers
English Teacher
Derby, Paul Harris
Art Teacher
Hooper, Leslie Barber
High School Math Teacher
Leith, Valorie Ann (Scott)
5th Grade Teacher
Misenhimer, Deborah McManama
HS English Teacher
MIDDLEPORT
Arnold, Robert Wayne
Chem Tchr & Sci Dept Chm
Busch, Cynthia Vogt
First Grade Teacher
Connelly, Mary Ann
Spanish Teacher
Coppola, Elaine M.
English Teacher
Morris, Karen Lea
Spanish Teacher
Wagner, Richard C.
Earth & Physical Sciences Tchr
Woodruff, Mary Brennan
5th Grade Teacher
MIDDLETOWN
Berg, Harvey Allen
Technology Professor
Bloomfield, Derek Ivan
Professor of Mathematics
Clark, Ann Frances
Health Teacher
Day, Gary Alan
Math Teacher
Freer, Roni Jo
Professional Office Technology
Geiger, Robin S.
High School English Teacher
Gilson, Michelle A.
Third Grade Teacher
Hach, Leland J., Sr.
Math & Comp Programming Tchr
Hannes, Florence Blueglass
Assoc Prof of Occuptnl Thrpy
Hindley, Leah Rometo
Mathematics Teacher
Isseks, Fred
English Teacher
Lasek, Leslie Sue (Cohen)
Spanish Teacher
Mac Mahon, Timothy
Instructor of Chemistry
Massar, Barbara Caroline
Asst Prof of Bus Management
Nappo, Anthony Joseph
Social Studies Instructor
Nappo, Janice Tarallo
HS English Teacher & Director
Orsley, Lori Bocek
High School Counselor
Quinn, Donald Anthony
NJROTC Naval Science Instr
Runnalls, Elizabeth Denmark
Frgn Lang Coord & Spanish Tchr
Sauter, Cindy Elissa (Berg)
Spanish Teacher
Scarzfava, Lawrence Dominick
Admin & World Lit Teacher
Scotto-Pdadvano, Elvira
Math Dept Chprsn & Teacher
Siers, Richard Arthur
Math Teacher
Teabo-Sandoe, Glenda Patterson
Retired Teacher
Thompson, Shirley D.
Sci Chprsn & Chemistry Tchr
Wanser, Diane L.
Physical Education Teacher
Weisberg, Patricia Anne
4th Grade Teacher
MILFORD
Ballantine, James Arthur
Social Studies Teacher
MILLBROOK
Michetti, Jean Ann
Science Teacher
Spross, Michael Dillard
9th-12th Grade Art Teacher
MILLER PLACE
Borsetti, Elizabeth M.
Physical Ed Teacher & Coach
Bray, Lisa Marie
Sixth Grade Teacher
Brindley, Grace Julia
Admin for Curr & Personnel
Budd, Robert Marshall
English Teacher
Callahan, Gerald Francis
Social Studies Chairperson
Castiglie, Joseph Paul
Chemistry Instructor
Castiglie, Mary Therese (Buckley)
Mathematics Educator
Chirch, Frances Ross
Spanish Teacher
Clark, Matt Charles
Social Studies Teacher
Danowski, Catherine Kos
English Teacher
Foley, Michael P.
Science Teacher
Kramer, David Marshall
K-3 Music Teacher
Lally, Lisa M.
Health & Physical Ed Teacher
Leary, Lawrence Vincent
Fifth Grade Teacher
Lowry, Joan Heaney
Kindergarten Teacher
Mc Caffrey, Joan Maguire
Social Studies Teacher
Neill, Stephanie Lynn
English Teacher
Parry, Cynthia
4th Grade Teacher
Robin, Elaine Dombeck
Business Education Coordinator
Scheidet, Robert August
Science Chairman
Vallone, John Richard
English Teacher
MILLERTON
DesChamps, Janet Ellen
Second Grade Teacher
MINEOLA
Bombara, Bruce John
Social Studies Teacher
Cotter, James Patrick
Science Teacher
Matthaei, Joan Ann Mc Cullough
Kindergarten Teacher
Messina, Albert Lawrence
8th Grade English Teacher
MINETTO
Bartholomew, Debora Klock
Elem Music Tchr & Choir Dir
Knight, Janet Lynn
Reading Teacher
Malone, Marjorie Ann
5th Grade Elementary Teacher
MINOA
Bay, Janet G.
Fifth Grade Teacher
MOHAWK
Domenico, Orin Philip
English Teacher
Nolan, Mariann Gardinier
Study Skills Teacher
Phippen, Monica Lynn
Secondary Mathematics Teacher
MOHEGAN LAKE
Ryan-Hsu, Monika Elisabeth
Second Grade Teacher
MONROE
Goetz, Sarah Lubka
Second Grade Teacher
Horner, Ann Petrak
Sixth Grade Teacher
MONSEY
Epstein, Diane Engelberg
English Teacher
Reiner, Sharyn
Sixth Grade Teacher
MONTGOMERY
Bonacic-Marker, Melissa
10th Grade English Teacher
Boyd, Rosa Marberio
High School Resource Teacher
Crisci, Dominick James
Social Studies Teacher
Fracalossi, Joseph R.
Biology Teacher
Gridley, Gayle M.
English Teacher
Hebbard, Ronald Walter
9th Grd Physical Science Tchr
Love, Wesley Alan
Physics Teacher
Palmer, Barbara Ann
Special Education Teacher
Ruggles, Diane (Vacirca)
Business Education Dept Chprsn
Tomann, Kimberly
Choir Director
Voegelin, June Edwards
Spanish Teacher
MONTICELLO
Belgiovene, JoAnn Penza
Kindergarten Teacher
Brooks, Jay Stevens
Art Teacher
Manz, Sheryl Lynn
Guidance Counselor
MONTROSE
Cappabianca, Silvana Petrizzelli
French & Italian Teacher
O'Connell, Constance Spanarelli
French & Italian Teacher
Ryan, Joseph Jerome
Social Studies Teacher
Savastano, Anthony F.
Middle School Guidance Cnslr
Wilkie, Grace A.
Mathematics Teacher
Williams, Annemarie Hauber
History Teacher
MORICHES
Lallos, Ann M.
First Grade Teacher
Riotto, Mary Diane
Second Grade Teacher
Sabbeth, Margery J.
Fourth Grade Teacher
MORRISONVILLE
Parrotte, Keith Eric
Jr High Math & Sci Teacher
MORRISVILLE
Baker, Rosemary L.
Assistant Professor of Eng
Cohen, Norman E.
Asst Prof of Cmptr Science
Cuney, George Charles
Assoc Prof of Automotive Tech
Fry, Victoria Tomcho
Assoc Dean of Spec Acad Prgms
Haber, Arthur
Chemistry Professor
Homer, Douglas Martin
Associate Professor of Eng
Kalicicki, Majorie Greene
Office Technology & Asst Prof
Kelly, Brian Joseph, Jr.
Assistant Professor
Manchester, Mark Allison
Professor of Mathematics
Powers, Roger W.
Prof of Automotive Technology
Sherwood, Bruce Arthur
Social Studies Teacher
Snyder, Kenneth R.
Physics Dept Chair & Prof
MOUNT MORRIS
Mlyniec, Richard Alexander
Business Teacher
Patenaude, Cynthia Ruth
Secondary English Teacher
MOUNT SINAI
Armstrong, Virginia Bartol
English Teacher
Bautz, William F.
Science Teacher
Kaskoun, Ellen Jean
High School Art Teacher
Kissel, Andrea Marie
HS Social Studies Teacher
Kulik, Gary
Mathematics Teacher
Nelson, Robert Scott
English Teacher
Robinson, Melissa L.
Social Studies Teacher
Salvia, Carolee Kapner
Spanish Teacher
Samuels, Bonnie Ettinger
Fourth Grade Teacher
Scott, Sarah Cassidy
Secondary Science Teacher
Williams, Patricia Davis
Third Grade Teacher
MOUNT VERNON
Ambert, Anita
6th Grade Teacher
Blackman, Barbara (Lee)
Counselor
Blackman, Elise Bernadette
5th Grade Teacher
Coppola, Annette M.
High School Spanish Teacher
Costantini, Frank John
Horticulture & Lndscp Teacher
Cote, Patricia C.
ESL Teacher
Jones, Melo E.
6th Grade Teacher
Moschetti, Angela Ann
First Grade Teacher
Patnett, Earnestene Enocencia
Seventh & Eighth Grade Teacher
Rajczewski, Stan Charles, Jr.
HS English Teacher
Thomas, Lynette Harris
Reading Specialist
Thompson, Patricia
Fifth Grade Teacher
Walters, Carolyn Maria
High School Math Teacher
MUNNSVILLE
Mappes, Gordon H.
Social Studies Teacher
Rehm, Carol T.
Business Education Teacher
Stepanski, Alexander Roy
Mathematics Teacher
NANUET
Ackerson, Ann Hogan
4th Grade Teacher
Fastiggi, JoAnn Maiello
Resource Room Teacher
Gremli, Jack L.
Performing Arts Dir & Teacher
Mascoll, Shirley E.
Science Instructor

JET (cont)
ell, John Patrick
lish Teacher
Joseph Vincent
hematics Teacher
tello, Maureen Gallagher
ch & Spanish Teacher
ES
rke, Aaron D.
h Grade Science Teacher
ROWSBURG
combe, Thomas Hopkins
Grade Teacher
ROW
Ronalee A.
lish Teacher
ng, Patricia Wiegand
dance Counselor
, Janet Carpenter
lish & Public Speaking Tchr
Timothy Charles
History & Government Tchr
ey, Sharon Waltz
hematics Teacher
, Nancy Bass
d Grade Teacher
u, Donna A.
ial Studies Teacher
hy, Carolyn Roye
Teacher
lla, Linda Marie
rumental Music Teacher
CONSET
a, Lucy Mennona
red Elementary Teacher
BERLIN
on, John A.
ence Teacher
r, Lucinda Bellows
lth & Physical Ed Teacher
non, Robin Millar
lish Teacher
CITY
, Robert T., Jr.
sical Education Teacher
ley, Gerald F.
iness Education Teacher
ond, Paul R.
ial Studies Teacher
nenko, Theodore R.
hematics Teacher
ser, Stuart
logy Teacher
, Eugene Martin
red English Teacher
ony, Susan Mirsky
hematics Teacher
s, Jane Francavilla
e I Coordinator & Teacher
skoff, John H.
lish Teacher
s, Jane (Ingram)
Studies Teacher
ino, Jean N.
Grade Homeroom Teacher
no, Philip A.
Grade Teacher
ham, Christine L.
glish Dept Chairperson
arthy, Kathleen Ann
ence Teacher
r, Mary Rice
Grade Teacher
olland, Kimberly Ann
emistry Teacher
kin, Sandra Armel
cial Education Teacher
y, James R.
Studies Dept Chairperson
HARTFORD
y, John C.
& Chemistry Teacher
dson, James Harry
Grade Teacher
rba, Stephen Guy
rth Grade Teacher
nerson, Jill Brodock
Teacher
s, Robert A.
cial Studies Teacher
tesano, Marilyn Cardinale
glish Teacher
gan, Marilyn Anne (Houghton)
glish Teacher
phy, David John
vernment & Psychology Tchr
Douglas R.
ology & Biology Teacher
acki, Eleanor
vertising Design Instructor
man, Ann Allen
glish Teacher & Dept Chair
ers, Jeffrey Frank
obal Studies Teacher
owski, Nancy (Shupp)
glish Teacher
V HYDE PARK
er, Jean Salerno
ology Teacher
nardo, David P.
cial Studies Teacher
son, Rhoda Frank
alth Teacher
, Michael R.
ysics Teacher
a, Frank Anthony
ence Teacher
Maio, Ron
rector of STAC

Fischer, Mary Albert, OP
Learning Center Director
Forte, Wendy L.
Spanish Teacher
Gilmartin, Helen Penczak
Substitute Teacher
Goldstein, Jan J.
Director of Guidance
Hillery, Rose Michael
Third Grade Teacher
Hoffman, Barbara Nestler
English Teacher
Hordiner, Linda Zimmerman
Biology Teacher
Hughes, Karen J.
Chemistry Teacher
Lynch, Diane F.
Biology Teacher
McKinnon, Robert John
Vocal Music Director
Murray, Edward Richard
English & Drama Teacher
Perulli, Lillian
Math Teacher
Russo, Vincent John
Social Studies Teacher
Salemson, Betsy Ann
Foreign Lang Dept Head
Scott, Vincent Arthur
Science Teacher
Solosky, Donna Marie
Chemistry Teacher
Throne, Robin M.
Spanish Teacher
Tinnelly, Pamela Jeanne
Third Grade Teacher
Waiksnis, Emalyn Lopiparo
Reading Teacher
Wilson, Dolores Margaret
English & TAG Teacher
NEW PALTZ
Collins, Kathleen Adams
English Teacher
DiPippo, Elizabeth Anne
Math Instr & Algebra Coord
Fall, Marcella McNally
4th Grade Teacher
Nadareski, Marisa Pertelesi
Former Science Tutor
Robinson, Stuart
English Instr & Ath Asst Dir
NEW ROCHELLE
Bradoc, Sonya K.
Reading Specialist
Chianese, Merigo Carroll
Language Arts Teacher
Conte, Susan Anne
Counseling Department Chair
Donovan, Edmund John
Science Department Chairman
Ferri, Lisa M.
Elementary Principal
Gramaglia, Jo-Anne Vitucci
High School English Teacher
Guiney, Patricia Ellen
English Teacher
Gunther, Virginia F.
Social Studies Teacher
Heiss, Laura Stainkamp
Visual Art Teacher
Marro, Judith
10th Grade Social Studies Tchr
Miller, Eugenia Hodge
Magnet Facilitator
O'Brien, Margaret Mary
Chemistry Teacher
Prendergast, Thomas Wilder
Science Department Chairperson
Rudell, Fredrica
Associate Prof of Mrktg
Scarella, Mary Nickens
Soc Stud Tchr & Cnslr
Schifini, Patricia Marie, OSU
Religion Teacher
Steinbaum, Martin Jay
Physics & Natural Sci Teacher
Teasdale, George F.
History & Italian Teacher
Torres, Olga Castellanos
Spanish Teacher
Veteri, Frank
Social Studies Dept Chairman
Williams, Joseph Henry
5th Grade Teacher
NEW YORK
Aberer, Bill John
Chm Bus Dept & Ath Director
Ahern, Skaidrite Varkalis
English Teacher
Amuso, Joseph Gerard
Religious Education Teacher
Anstey, Alan David Collinwood
Mathematics Dept Chairman
Archie, Eleanor Alice (Blake)
Guidance Counselor
Armfield, Carolyn Devonne Stinson
Director
Barnes, William Warren
Supervise Academy '98 Coord
Baron, Beth
Associate Professor of History
Bartilucci, Robert
Physical Education Teacher
Basden, Lois R.
Social Studies & History Tchr
Becker, Carmen Prince
Professor
Bell, Cathie L.
Middle School Teacher

Bellsey, Janet Lynn
Social Worker
Berger, Selman A.
Prof of Chem & Sci Dept Chair
Berson, James Henry
Professor of Management
Borkhuis, Charles
Creative Writing & Eng Prof
Borkon, Jeffrey Alan
Illustration & Cartooning Tchr
Bronfman, Eben Michael
Adj Professor of Govt Dept
Browne, Olivene Friday
Math & Humanities Teacher
Budhos, Shirley
Retired HS English Teacher
Bulgaris, Dalia Regina
Chemistry Teacher
Caddeau, Meg M.
English & History Teacher
Caesar, Franklin Nicholas
Assistant Headmaster
Cahn, Geoffrey Stephen
History Dept Chairperson
Callahan, Eileen M.
Social Studies Dept Chprsn
Calo, Dorothy
Guidance Counselor
Camhi, Paul J.
Prof of Eng as a Second Lang
Caputo, Caryn Patrice
Social Studies Teacher
Carvell, Peter Edward
Former Arts Dept Head
Chan, M. Donalyn
Third & Fourth Grade Teacher
Chang, Ping-Han
Mathematics & Science Teacher
Cheung, Shirley Mui
Bilingual Teacher
Clancy, Ellen M.
English Teacher & Chairperson
Clare, Ellen J.
Fourth Grade Teacher
Clement, John Thomas
Mathematics Teacher
Cobb, Milagros Maria
Second Grade Teacher
Collazo, Paula Pisarski
High School Math Teacher
Coller, Barry S.
Prof of Medicine & Dept Chm
Collins, Peter
Social Studies Teacher
Conan, Joelle
HS Biology & Geology Teacher
Contos, Carol DeMetro
Speech, Eng & Parenting Tchr
Cortes, Julio
Computer Science Teacher
Craig, Marva Migol
Speech & Communications Prof
Culvert, Edward Ross
Prof of Soc Science & History
Dadourian, Melissa Holly
Art Teacher
D'Amico, Frances Clare
Hlth & Physical Education Prof
Darmento, Ralph J., FSC
Mathematics Department Head
Dei, Kojo A.
Assistant Professor
DelCastillo, Vincent
Prof of Law & Police Sci Dept
Demetriou, Diantha Kathryn
Teacher & Arts Dept Chair
Diaz, Liza Cruz
Spanish Teacher
Dillah, Kenrick L.
HS Mathematics Teacher
Di Meglio, Daniel
Dean of Discipline
Diveki, Tivadar
Science Department Head
Donin, Warren Elliot
History & Economics Teacher
Eggers, Philip
English Professor & Dept Chair
Eichler, Sue Leung
Social Studies Teacher
Encarnacion, Nancy Bonilla
Pre-Kndgtn & Bilingual Teacher
Engle, Eugenie Hamilton
History Teacher & Tutor
Enright, Mary Rose
English & Reading Teacher
Epstein, Renee
Adjunct Lecturer
Esmilla, Barbara Angela
Phys Ed Tchr & Coach
Estreicher, Aleta Glaseroff
Law Professor
Fahey, Maria Franzisker
Instr of Eng & Anthropology
Falk, Madeline Varon
Peer Helper Pgm Facilitator
Feggins, Eric R.
Eng & Creative Writing Tchr
Feig, Werner M.
AP American History Teacher
Finando, Donna June
Oriental Medicine Teacher
Finkel, Natalie Horowitz
HS Mathematics Teacher
Fitzgerald, Doris B.
Accounting Professor
Frank, Jeffrey
Social Studies Teacher
Frank, Penny
Senior Modern Dance Teacher

Friedland, Neil M.
Coordinator of Writing
Gagliardi, Joseph Lawrence
History Dept Chairman
Gapper, Karin Freas
Assistant Professor of Nursing
Garely, Elinor
Travel Tourism Bus Mngmt Prof
Geffen, Peter A.
Founder
Gerson, Kathleen
Sociology Professor
Gibson, Lovie Henry
Reading Lab Teacher
Gilleaudeau, Marina
Biology & Russian Teacher
Ginsberg, Kari M.
Science Teacher
Goodman, Bonnie Worthman
Art Teacher
Gordet, Joan Leslie
Math Tchr & Specialist
Grabler, Roberta Kaplan
6th Grade Teacher
Grant-Nelson, Ana Loraine
6th Grade Teacher
Griffin, Keith Douglas
Physical Education Teacher
Grigorescu, Violeta Tanase
Physics Teacher
Hall, Melvin Raymond
Adjunct Professor
Hankerson, Hope Nadine
Instructor of Writing
Harris, Duriel Estelle
High School English Teacher
Harrison, Bobbie Maniece
Health Education Professor
Headley, Jacqueline Jackman
Fifth Grade Teacher
Henderson, Emily King
6th Grade Teacher
Henriques, Zelma Weston
Professor
Herbert, Rembert B.
English Teacher
Hernandez, Jose
Prof & Coord Puerto Rican Stud
Hernando, Bella
Math Dept Chairperson
Heymsfeld, Daniel
Studies & English Teacher
Higgins, Thomas Daniel
Religion Department Chairman
Hill, Linda Valerie
Director & Teacher
Hoffman, Joan
Economics Professor
Huie, Quentin John
Administrative Assistant
Iacovone, Denise Fusco
Art Teacher
Jaffe, Marvin R.
Professor
Jenkins, Odessa
Title I Comm Arts Teacher
Johnson, Ann Snowden
His Tchr & 8th Grd Class Dean
Johnson, Carl Awolowo
Lecturer in Sociology
Johnson, Fred H., Jr.
Chaplain & Teacher
Johnson, Patricia
Assistant Professor of Law
Jones, Delores Direse
Professor of Law
Jones, Reginald Bernard
Social Science Teacher & Coach
Kanganis, George E.
French & Spanish Teacher
Karmen, Andrew A.
Dept of Sociology Professor
Kashimawo, Tunde
Dir of College Discovery Pgm
Katz, Livia
English Teacher
Khan, Mansurul A.
Mathematics Teacher
Kitson, Roseann
Social Studies Teacher
Klass, Judith Alexandra
Adjunct Lecturer in English
Klebaner, Benjamin Joseph
Professor of Economics
Kling, Tatiana
Performing Arts Teacher
Knight, David Holman
Asst Professor of Accounting
Kodjo, Albert K.
Chemistry & Physics Teacher
Koehler, Michael
Adjunct Professor & Asst Dir
Kondopirakis, Emmanuel
Professor of Mathematics
Kotkin, Morton I.
Biology Teacher
Kraimeche, Belkacem
Electrical Engineering Prof
Krueger, Susan Heidi
Literature Professor
Kummer, Ida
French Teacher
Kupersmith, Abraham
English Professor
Kutner, Richard F.
Fourth Grade Teacher
Kvint, Vladimir L.
Professor of Management System
Lamour, Grace Baxter
Science Dept Chairman

Lang, Jonathan
Psychology Professor
Laurato, Vincent I.
Religious Ed Dept Chair & Tchr
Lawrence, Kathleen Rockwell
English Teacher
LeGrand, Henri
Math, Sci & Computer Teacher
Levitz, Paul
Professor
Levy, Shirley Yadgaroff
Library Teacher
Levy, Steven Elliot
Social Science Teacher
Lewis, Pamela Anne
French Teacher
Lewis, Valerie Mae
Principal & Kindergarten Tchr
Liao, Alexander
Science & Psychology Teacher
Licklider, Patricia M.
English Professor
Lieberman, Arlene
Vocal Music Tchr & Chorus Dir
Lolo, Circe M.
Spanish Teacher
Loonam, John P.
English & Humanities Teacher
Lubin, Cheryl Beth
Adj Prof of Speech & Theater
Lubinsky, Hiudy Deborah
Prof & Chair of Speech Dept
Lucas, Louis Ralph
Adjunct Asst Prof
Lugo, Emil J.
Foreign Language Teacher
Maloff, Richard M.
Science Teacher
Mandel, Veronica H.
Adjunct Professor of Law
Maniscalco, Anthony Joseph
Political Science Lecturer
Mantharam, Mythili
Assistant Professor of Math
Marcano, Ana M.
Social Studies Teacher
Marco, Sanders M.
Fifth Grade Teacher
Marino, Pamela
Prof of Office Info Systems
Marino, Vincent L.
Mathematics Teacher
Matlin, Stephen
English Teacher
Maxon, Jennifer Page
English Teacher
Maynard, John Rogers
Professor of English
McBroom, Marcia Leanne
Soc Stud Scndry Tchr & Coord
Mc Callum Peters, Yvonne Veronica
Adjunct Professor
Mc Cullough, Marsha Mc Crae
Business Education Teacher
Mc Dougle, Sharon
7th-8th Grd Math Teacher
Mc Gauran, Kathleen
Fifth Grade Teacher
Mendez, Kenneth Bernardo
Music Teacher
Mendez-Catlin, Lois Marie
Dev Skills, Stu Life Asst Prof
Meyer, Carlin
Professor of Law
Miller, Linda Aziza
Vocal Music Teacher
Millette, Robert E.
Grenadais Ambassador
Milon, Ronald Anthony
Instr of Political Science
Mincieli, Michael Vincent
Guidance Counselor
Monk, Melcher I.
Principal
Montanez, John M.
Dir of Grants & Adj Instructor
Morgan-Bell, Pearl Thomazena
English Professor
Muller, Mary D'Aquila
High School Math Teacher
Mulnick, Linda
First Grade Teacher
Murray, Fernley A.
Eng & Contemporary Issues Tchr
Myrick, Terry Darnell
Performing Arts Teacher
Napper, Shirley M.
Second Grade Teacher
Naughton, John Patrick
Lang Arts, Soc Stud, Rdng Tchr
Nayer, Sofya
Asst Professor
Nelson, Hylton Richard
Honors Chemistry Teacher
Nelson, Jeffrey Alan
Eighth Grade Math Teacher
Nemet, Rima Rossin
First Grade Teacher
Ng, Mary Gee
ESL Kindergarten Teacher
Nollez, Kerwin R.
Reading Teacher
Obey, Erica Frances
Speech World Hums Adj Lecturer
O'Connell, Charles F.
Social Studies Teacher
O'Donnell, Eugene J.
Adjunct Assistant Professor
Okonkwo, Emeka C. J.
Prof of English & Linguistics

NEW YORK (cont)
O Leary, Teresita Dwyer
English Teacher
Ostorga, Alcione
Educational Facilitator
Paolozzi, Anthony S.
English Dept Chairman & Tchr
Pappas, Nicholas
Spanish Teacher
Perez, Eileen
Administrative Assistant
Perrone, Nancy
High School History Teacher
Pichardo, Gladys
Bilingual Second Grade Tchr
Plummer, Eduoard E.
Mathematics & Soc Studies Tchr
Polishook, Sheila Stern
Associate Professor of History
Pouncie, Barbara Elaine
Artistic Dir & Dance Instr
Powell, Kelly Susan
Former Substitute Teacher
Price-Reavis, Charles Anthony
Adjunct Instructor
Pritchard, Adam Roger
Physics & Computer Sci Teacher
Pruitt, Virginia Ann
Social Studies Teacher
Purcell, Edward A., Jr.
Professor of Law
Rapisarda, Gregory Francis
French, Span & Italian Teacher
Refkin, Lois E.
English Teacher
Remland, Neil Michael
Mathematics Teacher
Resnick, Judith Polenberg
Assoc Professor of Reading
Reynolds, John Anthony
Fine Arts Teacher
Rhodes, Robert Harlan
Hum Teacher & Team Leader
Rind, Ellin Salit
Eng Prof & Commnctn Arts Prof
Rivers, Robert D.
Assistant Professor
Robbins, Patricia Moran
English Teacher
Robinson, Joyce Guinta (Mc Peake)
Director, Quest Program
Rock, Florence Cecilia
Asst Prof of Psych & Acad Cnsl
Roebuck, Sharon Jeffrey
Third Grade Teacher
Roldan, Francisco Jose
Guitar Professor
Roque-Bergonzi, Delia
Bilingual Kindergarten Teacher
Rosenberg, John David
WM Peterfield Trent Eng Prof
Ross, Ronald Opheres
Principal
Ross, Susan
Art Teacher
Rozin, Muriel Ann Lieberfarb
Consultant & Resource Rm Tchr
Rozzelle, Vanessa K.
Instructor
Rubin, Robert Marc
Asst Prin for Mrktg
Sacerdote, Marc
Teacher & Animation Prgm Dir
Saltz, Simon E.
Professor of Accounting
Samad, Abdool
Math Teacher
Sandler, Melvin
Dept of Electrical Engrng Chm
Sandomir, Larry Philip
General Studies Head Teacher
Saplin, Elizabeth J.
Sixth Grade Teacher
Sarna, Shirley F.
Adjunct Professor of Law
Scacalossi, James Joseph
Theology Teacher
Schaller, C. Sue
Humanities Teacher
Schonfeld, Bella
Assistant Professor
Schuster, Carmen
Professor
Seeley, Valerie A.
Dept of Biological Sci Prof
Seltun, Elizabeth Maddicks
Social Studies Coord & Teacher
Sepinski-Ricci, Bonnie
English Teacher
Shanack, Sheldon Marvin
Physics Teacher
Siegel, Jerome
Professor of Psych Dept
Silver, Jeffrey Yehuda
Instructor
Simon, Michael C.
Government Professor
Simpson, Peggy Ann
English & Language Arts Tchr
Sit, William Y.
Mathematics Professor
Sleigh, Burnetta
Professor
Small, James
Black Studies Adjunct Lecturer
Sobel, Kenneth Mark
Electrical Engineering Prof
Sonsky, Sidney Nathan
Elec & Cmptr Engrng Tech Prof
Sostre, Olga Iris
Exercise Physiology, Hlth Tchr
Stauffer, Marie Caruso
Music Teacher
Steinman, David Warren
Professor of Psychology
Stevens, Christopher Denver
History Department Chair
Stoney, George Cashel
Goddard Professor of Cinema
Storch, Jerome Elliott
Deputy Chair
Sullivan, Harold Joseph
Associate Prof of Govt Dept
Svoronos, Paris
Professor of Chemistry
Sygar, Janet E.
Enrichment Resource Teacher
Szereg, Sonia
English Teacher
Taylor, Lucinda Elevena Hodges
Fifth Grade Teacher
Tischler, Barbara L.
History Professor
Tobin, Douglas William
Latin & Greek Teacher
Toliver, Kay Francis
Teacher of Challenger Program
Toonkel, Manny Joseph
Health Teacher & Coach
Topper, Robert Quinn
Asst Professor of Chemistry
Trano, Jennifer Marlene
English & Social Studies Tchr
Treglia, Maria Ornella
Adj Lecturer of ESL
Tricarico, Donald Thomas
Professor of Sociology
Troutt, Bobbye Vary
Asst Prof of Cnslng & Afr-Am
Tully, Kathleen Ann
Religion Teacher
Tumin, Judtih
MS Director & English Tchr
Ubieta-Mendez, Arlene
Spanish Teacher
Vachiraprapun, Surapee
Sixth Grade Teacher
Valiente, Irving Manuel
Social Studies Teacher
Villani, Kathleen
Professor of Accounting
Vodounon, Maurice A.
Mathematics & Cmptr Sci Prof
Vogt, Tom Duncan
English & History Teacher
Volpe, Maria R.
Professor of Sociology
Vrettos, James S.
Sociology Professor
Waldman, Carol Langemass
Math Teacher & Program Chprsn
Walker, Carla Richburg
Business Teacher
Walsh, Diane
Science Teacher
Wasserman, Carol
Asst Prof of Modern Languages
Webb, John Badgley
Foreign Lang Dept Chairperson
Wenk, Theresa Ann
Earth Science Teacher
Williams, Dianne
Merchandising Teacher
Williams, Ellwood Elijah
Speech & Theatre Arts Prof
Williams, Lydia Harry
Fourth & Fifth Grade Teacher
Williams, Terri Denise
7th Grade Teacher
Wilson, Audrey
Media Specialist
Winkle, James P.
7th-8th Grd Eng & Rdng Teacher
Witherspoon, Roger
VP of Student Development
Wittner, Peter S.
Health & Physical Ed Teacher
Wolfson, Josh
Accounting Professor
Wu, Loretta
ESL Teacher
Wyatt, Paul A.
Dir of Academic Advisement
Wylegala, Amy Patrice
ESL Teacher & Grade Advisor
Yamamoto, Pamela McDonough
English & ESL Teacher
Yang, Kathleen
AP Biology & Chemistry Teacher
Yee, Mary Wing
Second Grade Teacher
Yusim, Marat
Drama Teacher
Zaid, Latifah
Global Studies & Science Tchr
Zamfirescu, Christina M. D.
Computer Science Professor
Zucaro, Michael A.
Adj Lecturer in Eng & ESL

NEW YORK MILLS
Elacqua, Peter Joseph
French & Spanish Teacher
Panebianco, Colleen T.
US History & Govt Teacher

NEWARK
Fisher, Jack
Teacher & Coach
Schwind, David C.
Music Supvr & Band Dir

NEWARK VALLEY
D'Arcy, Eric Winston
Global Studies I Teacher
Greene, Robert Deward
Tech Teacher & Dept Chair
Griffith, Jewel Ann
K-8th-12th Grd Voc Music Tchr
Romeo, Bonita A.
English Teacher
Saunders, Sandra Grant
Spanish Teacher
Ward, Sherrill Reigle
Soc Stud Tchr & Dept Chprsn
Ward, W. Jeffery
PE Teacher & Coach

NEWBURGH
Adler, Morton
Criminal Justice Teacher
Atsunyo, Mattson Kudjo
Asst Prof of Mngmt & Intnl Bus
Barker, Joel C.
Sixth Grade Teacher
Bonagura, John I.
5th Grade Teacher
Campion, Richard Peter
Assistant Professor of English
Cantor, Sadell Furman
Earth Science Teacher
Carnes, Mary Elin Korchinsky
Global Studies Teacher
Clarke, Linda J.
Adjunct Prof of Philosophy
Coogan, Mary Ellen
2nd Grade Teacher
Corsetti, Sandra Espejo
Social Studies Teacher
Cotter, James
Professor of English
Cuilty, Jeffrey L.
Business Ed Teacher & Coach
D'Alessandro, Dennis Anthony
Math Teacher
Eitel, John Charles, Jr.
Math Teacher
Fallon, Rae M.
Asst Prof of Psychology
Howard, Charles Anthony, Sr.
Program Specialist
Licata, Ann Manzo
Education Professor
Maelia, Lynn Jones
Chemistry Professor
Mauro, Nicole Marie
Psychology Professor
Monahan, Emily J.
Sixth Grade Teacher
Perry, Portia Perry
5th Grade Teacher
Rapalje, Charles H.
6th Grade Teacher
Saldivar, Toni J. Wells
Assistant Professor of English
Sarro, Thomas John
Professor
Smith, Lenore
Social Studies Teacher
Tillar, Elizabeth Kennedy
Asst Prof of Religious Studies
Treacy-Rubin, Susan E.
Third Grade Teacher
Wesneski, Olga Frankos
Sixth Grade Teacher
Wurster, Jeffrey D.
Music Teacher

NEWFANE
Ames, Charles G.
Mathematics Teacher
Barrows, Doris Jean
Middle School Teacher
Erbacher, Herman H.
HS Instrumental Music Teacher
Fare, Thomas Paul
Technology Teacher
Kogutek, Sharon
Second Grade Teacher
Tripp, George D.
Guidance Counselor
Vona, Caroline Lehmann
Mathematics Teacher

NEWFIELD
Hansen, Richard Neil
Eighth Grade Math Teacher
Kasper, Diane Carr (Dickerson)
Second Grade Teacher
Smith, Donald F.
Science Teacher
Tallman, Terry Ann (Randall)
Fifth Grade Teacher

NEWPORT
DeKalb, Francis L., III
Health & Physical Ed Teacher
Kasai, Joyce L.
Business Teacher
Van Patten, Katherine Graulich
3rd Grade Teacher

NEWTONVILLE
Sail, Michael Robert
Fifth Grade Teacher

NIAGARA FALLS
Bevilacqua, Miquel Marie
Spanish Teacher
Boyce, Jacqueline Elizabeth
Elementary Physical Ed Tchr
DelZoppo, Gerald Paul
6th Grade Teacher
Fay, William Joseph
Music Teacher
Fortin-Nossavage, Andrea S.
Social Studies Teacher
Galvano, David Mark
Chef Instructor
Laub, Robert Lewis
Guidance Counselor
MacKrell, Kevin Francis
Social Studies Teacher
Maynard, E. Paul
8th Grd Hlth Tchr & Swim Coach
Monti, Patrick A.
Accounting Teacher
Muldoon, Katherine Kerswell
High School Art Teacher
Rose, Peggy M.
English Teacher
Sheeran, Maureen Flynn
Guidance Counselor
Sturtevant, Jaye W.
Mathematics Teacher
Teller, Suzanne Dodd
Elementary Vocal Music Teacher
Tucker, Charles Edward
5th Grade Teacher

NIAGARA UNIV
Albanese, Jay S.
Professor
Bernard, Kenneth James
Assoc Prof & Math Dept Chrmn
Bonnette, Dennis
Prof of Philosophy & Dept Chm
Butera, Peter C.
Professor of Psychology
Freischlag, John Michael
Military Science Instructor
Gould, Dorothy Lunken
Assoc Prof of Speech & English
Greene, Robert Stickney
Professor of Biology
Mc Glen, Nancy E.
Professor of Political Science
Spitzmesser, Ana Maria
Assistant Professor of Spanish
Sullivan, Louise Frances
Chair Dept of Foreign Language
Whitney, Stewart Bowman
Professor & Chair of Sociology

NICHOLS
Kovall, Elizabeth Reinhardt
Third Grade Teacher

NISKAYUNA
Blom, Kenneth G.
K-12th Grd Science Director
Shipp, Russell E.
8th Grade English Teacher

NORTH BABYLON
Hirshson, Janet
Third Grade Teacher
Norton, Thomas Emmett
Retired 5th Grade Teacher
Steck, Peter Charles
Principal

NORTH BELLMORE
Potucek, Josephine Serrano
Sixth Grade Teacher

NORTH CREEK
Hill, Michael E.
Social Studies Teacher
LaRock, Robert Allen, Jr.
Mathematics Teacher

NORTH MERRICK
Howard, Joyce Sattler
Second Grade Teacher
Pfeifer, Myra Plovnick
Kindergarten Teacher
Platt, Regina J. Hegenbart
Social Studies Tchr & Chairman

NORTH ROSE
Paice, Bette S.
Fifth Grade Teacher

NORTH SALEM
Gordon, Robert Quinland
Fifth Grade Teacher
Kowgios, Nick
10th Grade English Teacher
Sagan, Catherine Meehan
Lang Arts Tchr & Dept Chprsn
Scallero, Julia Annette
9th-12th Grd Soc Stud Teacher
Vassak, Regina Burke
Foreign Language Teacher

NORTH TONAWANDA
Alexander, Norman Frederick
Instrumental Music Teacher
Cerone, Robert Alexander
Sociology, Govt & Psych Tchr
Craig, Kenneth L.
Teacher & Math Dept Chprsn
Davis, Rosemary Bodkin
Fifth Grade Teacher
Fleming, Sandra Lee
Mathematics Teacher
Frank, Timothy James
Science Teacher
Galas, Mary Michaelane, CSSF
6th-8th Grd Soc Studies Tchr
Gerlach, Paul Charles
7th & 8th Grade Teacher & Prin
Holesko, Joan Kantor
Third Grade Teacher
Kearly, Susan Noto
First Grade Teacher
Leffler, Laure Jeanne
Fourth Grade Teacher
Livingston, David G.
Fifth Grade Teacher
Mahady, Patricia Anne
Fifth Grade Teacher
Mazzi, Joan M. Lotz
Senior High English Teacher
Nagel, Kathleen Peters
Kindergarten & Music Teacher
O'Connor, David
Health & Physical Ed Teacher
O'Neill, Julie K.
3rd-4th Grade Tchr & Asst Prin
Oravec, Ronald David
Pastor & Catechism Instructor
Richner, Nancy K.
ECE Director
Sawyer, William Frederick
6th Grd Science & Health Tchr
Sinaguglia, Josephine Anne
Music Teacher
Swisher, Paul Leo
HS Science Teacher
Townsend, Duane A., Jr.
Third Grade Teacher
Wilson, Lucia Fronczak
French & Spanish Teacher

NORTHPORT
Bonell, Frances Foran
4th Grade Teacher
Colabella, Thomas Charles
Music Teacher
Eder, James Matthew
Social Studies Teacher
Fazio, Thomas Michael
Student Assistance Counselor
Leonard, Joan F.
English Teacher
Millmann, Louise M.
Photography Teacher
O'Donnell, Mary E. Corcoran
English Teacher
Sloggatt Wolf, Constance
Art Educator
Tietjen, Russell
Physical Education Teacher

NORTHVILLE
Fisher, Kimberly A.
Business Teacher
Spaeth, Barbara J.
Second Grade Teacher

NORWICH
Abbott, Mark D.
Sixth Grade Teacher & Coach
Allaire, Nancy H.
Sixth Grade Teacher
Benton, Robert Hugh, Jr.
Criminal Justice Instructor
Brooks, Joan Beltz
Mathematics Teacher & Chprsn
Burke, Donald Robert
Director of Bands
Callahan, Earl L.
8th Grade English Teacher
DeMellier, Mary Ann Tucker
3rd Grade Teacher
Fertig, Susan Shabus
Global Studies Teacher
Katen, Sheila Blaine
Math Teacher
Lawson, Joyce Mummery
Rdng Rcvry & Early Intrvn Tchr
Meek, Kathy L.
Math Teacher
Nassar, Elizabeth Fox
Resource & Consultant Teacher
Pelosi, Evelyn Tyminski
Science Dept Chairman & Tchr
Pluta, John William
US History & Government Tchr
Robinson, Beverly Anne
Remedial Reading Teacher
Thompson, Kelly Lorraine
Mathematics Teacher
Ward, Gilda P. Huntington
Science Teacher & Yrbk Adv
Whitney, Sandra M.
Speech Pathologist
Williams, David LeRoy
Technology Teacher

NORWOOD
Grant, Mary Taro
3rd-4th Grd Team Teacher
Hamrick, Christina Ann
English Teacher
Tiernan, Terry A.
12th Grade English Teacher

NUNDA
Schwegler, Robert Patrick
Science Teacher

NYACK
Alter, Deborah
Art Teacher
Antonietti, Louis
Lead English Teacher
Beck, Patricia
Science Teacher
Brady, Arthur D.
French & Spanish Teacher
Burns, Thomas James
English Teacher
Castellano, John J.
Physical Education Teacher
Coffinet, Maria Paz
French & Spanish Teacher
Cozzi, Dianne
Middle School Math Teacher
Dillon, P. Matthew
Soccer Coach & Kndgtn Teacher
Heiser, Richard R.
History Professor
Makower, Esther Rothman
9th-12th Grade Biology Teacher
McArthur, John G. M.
Associate Professor of Music
Montanez, Marie-Josee Berotte
ESL Coord & Lang Dept Chprsn
Perry, Thomas Alan
Earth Science Teacher

K (cont)
, Larry A.
ssor of Religion
William R.
ology Professor
d, Darren Leroy
Teacher & Coach
, K. Brad
Prof of Economics & Bus
son, Paul
ocial Studies Teacher
David F.
of English & Dept Head
ALE
, Joseph V.
c Prof, School of Ed
R. Bent C.
or Army Instructor
Theresa Livatino
Grade English Teacher
Christopher Leigh
Science Teacher
Geraldine Marotta
Grade Teacher
, Linda Janaro
of Learning Disabilities
ovich, Tatyana Ivanovna
Assoc Prof of Philosophy
R. Douglas
al Studies Teacher
IELD
, Darlene Marie
e Economics Teacher
tt, Kay K.
sh Teacher
a, Carol F.
ial Education Teacher
ner, Wayne Norman
Grade Teacher
g, David James
al Studies Teacher
n, Marcia L.
Lang Tchr & Dept Chair
ski, John Michael, Jr.
umental Music Teacher
uff, Thomas H.
al Studies Teacher
NSIDE
nette, Patricia Napoli
ish Teacher
er, Donald P.
mistry Teacher
, Sondra E.
Grade Teacher
o, Anita Bennett
Grade Teacher
SSA
ara, James J.
al Stud Tchr & His Chm
ENSBURG
Stephen Richard
ness Education Teacher
Edmund Joseph
mistry Instructor
, Diane Buth
cial Education Teacher
s, Susan Shambo
nentary Teacher
uire, William F.
Social Studies Teacher
, Bruce C.
Prof of Secretarial Stud
, Jennifer R.
Prof of Alchl & Chem Stud
er, Ellen Smith
metology Instructor
FORGE
Loretta Bandych
h School Math Teacher
WESTBURY
tein, Robert J.
nin & Soc Science Teacher
n, Joy Siebler
dance Counselor
, David P.
lth & PE Teacher
cci, John
eer Programs Coordinator
an, Kathleen Sheerin
lish Teacher
Carol A.
tory Teacher
AN
aus, Karlet J.
rd Grade Teacher
oan, Edward Elliot
istant Principal
tt, Esther Mae (Scott)
cial Education Teacher
mole, Carmella Colangelo
eavement Coordinator
e, J. Paige
Grade Teacher
ey, Gary M.
h Grade Teacher
, Terrance W.
glish Teacher
, Michael Dean
tory Teacher
nski, A. Jean (Hughes)
source Room Teacher
ines-Cappellini, Charlotte
sociate Professor of English
roe, Suzanne Abdo
h Grade Teacher
er, Thomas Mark
ology Teacher
ips, Robert James
thematics Teacher

Shane, Mary Kathleen
8th Grade Social Studies Tchr
Simpson, Deborah M.
Assoc Prof & Learning Ctr Coor
ONEIDA
Benedict, Mary Gerbig
Kindergarten Teacher
ONEONTA
Birdsall, Robert Perry
4th Grade Teacher
Dabulewicz, John R.
Secondary English Instructor
Drago, Mary
5th-6th Grd Teacher
Kiehn Kirkey, Carol
Math Teacher & Dept Chair
Kreck, Susan Dana
Third Grade Teacher
Malone, Laurence Joseph
Associate Prof of Economics
Nassau, Carol Dean
French Teacher
Phillips, Robert R.
Professor of Biology
Titus, Robert Charles
Geology Professor
ONTARIO CENTER
Doyle, Margaret Patricia
English Teacher
Fletcher, Judith Metz
English Teacher
Goetzmann, Katherine Wallis
Elementary Challenge Teacher
Golubjatnikov, Lisa Salerno
English Teacher
Heimberger, Roland L.
Dept Chair & Economics Teacher
Hutton, Deale A.
Librarian
Warner, Andrea Susan
High School English Teacher
ORANGEBURG
Butler, Robert Peter
Spcl Resource Education Tchr
Dries, James Henry
Social Studies Teacher
Lawton, Peter A.
Psychology & Math Teacher
Marshall, Johnnie B.
Band Conductor
Murray, John Joseph
Social Studies Teacher
Rossi, Margaret A.
High School English Teacher
VanHouten, Edward B.
Social Studies Teacher
Wright, Carl
Social Studies Teacher
ORCHARD PARK
Abel, Bonnie Lou (Ellis)
3rd Grade Teacher
Barrows, Robert Thomas
Amer His & Govt Tchr & Coach
Behm, Michael Joseph
Physical Education Teacher
Behrend, Carl W.
Guidance Counselor
Benson, Gary Richard
Fourth Grade Teacher
Braunscheidel, Daniel William
Physical Science Teacher
Bruning, Vicki R. (Swenson)
French Teacher
Carducci, Donald Joseph
Band Director
Edholm, Carl E.
Fourth Grade Teacher
Feldman, Tami Zefers
Former Music Teacher
Ferguson, F. Allan
History & Social Sciences Tchr
Ferraro, Barbara Folts
5th Grade Teacher
Frederick, Bertram Frank
History Teacher
Fritz, Barbara Jezioro
Fourth Grade Teacher
Gavin, Maurice Daniel, Jr.
Math Instructor
Grabon, Kathleen Ann
English Teacher
Hanes, Deborah Fry
Eighth Grade English Teacher
Haslinger, Patricia A.
English Teacher
Infante, Neil Joseph
5th Grade Teacher
Ingersoll, Renee Theresa
Music Teacher
Justicia-Linde, Patricia Ann Adams
Spanish Teacher
Kaul, Kim Patricia
Physical Educator & Coach
Kerwin, Michael Thomas
Social Studies Teacher
Mc Mahon, Terence Thomas
Social Studies Teacher
Nowah, Geraldine
Religion Teacher & Coord
Nowak, Ruth Ann Pifer
6th & 8th Grade Art Teacher
Peterson-Streit, Jo Ann Ruth
Guidance Counselor
Rominger, Stacy Briggs
Science Teacher
Rooney, Joseph E.
Math Teacher
Rosati, Helen Djordjevich
English Teacher

Schmitt, Donald Eugene
Math Tchr & Instrl Ldr
Schott, Kevin John
High School Technology Teacher
Shiffner, Scott Lawrence
Social Studies Teacher
Sullivan, Margaret B.
Counselor
Thiel, Carolyn
Fourth Grade Teacher
Violanti, Anne Mary
Band Director
Wahlenmayer, Carol Williams
English Teacher
Wilson, Jean Neutz
Chemistry Teacher
Worth, Jane Curley
First Grade Teacher
Zawierucha, Christina F. M.
High School English Teacher
ORIENT
Garren, Corinne Brown
Fifth Grade Teacher
ORISKANY
Stoltz, Thomas Paul
Soc Stud & Economics Tchr
OSSINING
Davis, Bruce
Technology Education Teacher
Dittelman, Faye Altshuler
7th Grd Eng & Lang Arts Tchr
Lagan, Cheryl Marie
Business Teacher
Rowe, Roger Peter
5th Grade Teacher
Totilo, Carol
Social Studies Teacher
Variano, Nancy D'Uva
Health & PE Teacher
Whatley, Ronald Gene
Special Education Teacher
OSWEGO
Allen, Nancy Lee
Secondary Soc Studies Teacher
Altman, Thomas C.
Physics Teacher
Arnold, C. William
Humanities & Anthropology Tchr
Bernreuther, Janet M.
French Teacher
Bonacorsi, Sharon Bond
7th Grade Life Science Teacher
LeFevre, Joseph William
Associate Prof of Chemistry
Mac Leod, Leah Minemier
Mathematics Teacher
Nix, Ronald James
6th Grade Teacher
Rotolo, Joseph Peter
Technology & Drivers Ed Tchr
Silveira, Augustine, Jr.
Prof & Chemistry Dept Chprsn
Von Holtz, Barbara Schmitt
Fifth Grade Teacher
OTEGO
Brown, Roger Scott
Asst Principal & Athletic Dir
DiBartolomeo, Kevin Michael
US History & Psych Teacher
Mummenthey, Carl J.
English Teacher
Richardson, Sophie Koken
Biology Tchr & Sci Dept Chprsn
OTISVILLE
Cunningham, Sean Thomas
Physical Education Teacher
OWEGO
Bertoni, Sheila Scanlon
Specialist & Recovery Teacher
Davis, Joan Mc Inerney
English Dept Chprsn & Teacher
Dean, Janice Kimmich
Science Teacher
Fabricius, Daniel
Director of Bands
Finnessey, Timothy J.
French Teacher
Frisbie, Linda Burgerhoff
English Teacher
Gretz, Linda Sue (Houghton)
Biology Teacher
Hizny, Kimberly Ann Kubisa
HS Mathematics Teacher
Howe, Ann Marie
Third Grade Teacher
Kisloski, Jeffrey J.
Environmental & Earth Sci Tchr
Morrissey, Sonja Ruth
English Teacher
Motell, Phil
High School English Teacher
Parker ca, Janet Elaine
Vocal Music Director
Pasto, Ronald J.
Science Teacher
Purtell, Karen Brion
Social Studies Teacher
Russell, David Gerald
Science Teacher
Shorten, Wiliam M.
French Teacher
Solomon, James
Guidance Counselor
Strauss, Janice Little
Spanish Teacher
White, Margaret Keene
Fourth Grade Teacher
Zandy, Patricia Worley
Elementary Principal

OXFORD
Constantine, Kathryn A.
High School Math Teacher
OYSTER BAY
Deegan, Nancy O'Connell
Music Director
Guido, Gregory J.
Physics & Math Teacher
Huneke, Wayne
History Teacher & Coach
Leone, Michele Castaldo
Math Teacher & Dept Chprsn
Nicolai, Maureen Mc Partland
Social Studies Teacher
Roche, Christopher John
Social Studies Teacher
Santoro, Karen L.
Business Teacher
OZONE PARK
Camberdella, Kristen Leigh
Health Education Teacher
Endzull, Susan
Mathematics Teacher
Greco, Ruth Anne
Math, Science Instr & Coord
Henry, Maureen P.
Asst Principal & Math Teacher
Hlawaty, Heide
Chemistry Teacher
Marinaro, Robert Joseph
7th-8th Grd Lang Arts Teacher
Marsh, Tom
History Teacher
O'Connor, Ilett Kereen
Social Studies Tchr & Grd Adv
Pryke, Elizabeth
History Teacher
Stein, Hannah Koplowitz
English Teacher
Wax, Fredene
Math Teacher
Williams, Noel Desmond
English Teacher
Winters, Raphaela Ellen
English Teacher
PAINTED POST
Bosseler, Kathryn Amey
Social Studies Teacher
Falkenberg, Kim Steven
Tchng Prin & Eng, His Teacher
Frawley, Timothy J.
Mathematics Chair
Klokus, Marcia Gongol
4th Grade Teacher
Plerhoples, Judith Steinmann
Bio, Chem & Life Skills Tchr
Scullin, Laurie E.
English Teacher
PALMYRA
Davison, Sandra (Prutzman)
Fourth Grade Teacher
Lester, Kristine Uetz
Social Studies Teacher
Ruliffson, Mary Patricia
Spanish Teacher
Russell, Gregory Dean
American History Teacher
Sams, Patricia A.
Mathematics Teacher
Vivirito, Joseph John
Technology & Driver Ed Teacher
Vrubel, Kathleen Glanton
Fourth Grade Teacher
PANAMA
Cenni, Deborah Preiss
Business Teacher
Rodgers, Janet E.
MS Social Studies Teacher
Skoog, Bonnie Luan
English Teacher
PARISH
Glickstein, Barry Neal
High School Science Teacher
Lighty, Michelle Mc Cowan
Spanish Teacher
Misenko, Nancy Beck
English Teacher
Myers, Rose Ann Burnham
Fifth Grade Teacher
Parmley, Starr Raymond
Health Sci & PE Instructor
Sherman, Richard Lewis
8th Grade Language Arts Tchr
Sortman, Frances Helen Fernan
Elementary Teacher
PARISHVILLE
Bowles, Joy E.
High School Business Teacher
Clark, Cheryl Lynne
K-12 Grd Art & Technology Tchr
Harmer, Bryan R.
Social Studies Teacher
Harper, Evan S., Jr.
Physical Education Teacher
Manley, Sara Janine
Spanish Teacher
PATCHOGUE
Alevas, Renee K.
Ret Compensatory Writing Tchr
Chance, Mary A.
Asst Professor of Accounting
Fosdick, William Charles
4th Grade Teacher
Hyllestad, Susan Janet Olivieri
Fifth Grade Teacher
Mooney, Ellen Patricia (Devaney)
Social Studies Teacher
Mulhern, Dorothy
Language Arts Teacher

Nichols, David Miller
Physical Education Teacher
Stein, Marilyn Hopmann
7th & 8th Grd Mathematics Tchr
Welch, Patricia D. (Curtin)
Third Grade Teacher
PAUL SMITHS
Chapin, Breckinridge
Volunteer Services Coordinator
Mc Allister, Francis Theodore
Professor of Forestry
McLaughlin, William John, Jr.
Associate Professor
Pillis, Patricia Kotzebue
Assistant Prof of Accounting
PAVILION
Abdella, Marilyn Tufts
5th Grade Teacher
Barone, Joanne Frank
Secondary Science Teacher
Bemont, Patricia Haines
5th Grade Teacher
Callan, Sharon Mairs
Reading Specialist
Clary, Rhonda Owens
Sixth Grade Teacher
Dickson, David Paul
Social Studies Teacher
Hollinger, Douglas Davis
Chemistry & Physics Teacher
May, Marianne Lyons
Spanish Teacher
Pembrook, Linda A.
Math Teacher
Perkins, Elizabeth N.
Kindergarten Teacher
Snyder, Jayne Silfies
Substitute Teacher
PAWLING
Bortle, Barbara Coon
Third Grade Teacher
Collette, Judith Doe
First Grade Teacher
Giannetto, Mary Grezzo
Math Department Chairperson
Godsoe, Gerald Benson
4th Grade Teacher
Polikoff, Cal
Sixth Grade Language Arts Tchr
Shannon, Anne Mc Connell
English Teacher
Smith, Mabel Anne
Soc Studies & English Teacher
Zoltan, Christine Perretta
HS Counselor
PEARL RIVER
Binkunski, Denise O'Leary
Fourth Grade Teacher
Carlacci, Michael
Math Teacher
Hanlon, Joseph P.
Guidance Counselor
Klenk-Branch, Cornelia
Fourth Grade Teacher
Maher, Judith Keenan
Science Teacher
Mangini, Rosanne Campanella
Retired Teacher
Peabody, Timothy John
Physical Education Teacher
Rothenberg, Ron S.
Mathematics Teacher
PEEKSKILL
Carroll, Thomas John
Math Teacher
Chiara, Liesl Mundorff
Mathematics Teacher
Filippelli, James Anthony
English Teacher
Johnson, Diane
6th Grade Teacher
Mahoney, Michael Edward
English Teacher
Morales, Iris Delia
Spanish Teacher
Richter, Amy Franklin
Band Director
Risoli, Allison Lee
History Teacher
Sansevere, Mary Xavier, FMSC
Retirement Club Director
PELHAM
Gunn, Evelyn Jenkins
English Teacher
Moriarty, Mildred De Lugo
Middle School Math Teacher
Nardone, Claudine Pistone
First Grd Tchr & Curr Mentor
O'Regan, Maureen Mc Auley
Retired Sixth Grade Teacher
Orfei, Frank J.
Secondary History Teacher
Sullivan, Lola Blank
English Teacher
Teitelbaum, Catalina Marie (Cinelli)
Second Grade Teacher
Vicino, Paul Alanson
Dir of Guidance
PENFIELD
Anderson, Elizabeth A.
Retired Elementary Teacher
Concannon, Mary T.
5th Grade Teacher
Costello, Susan Marie
English Teacher
Giles, Philip Laurence
History Department Chairman
Holzschuh, Donna Ross
Second Grade Teacher

PENFIELD (cont)
Krull, Steven R.
Science Dept Chair
Langerak, Jack
English & Theater Teacher
Mc Donald, Stuart Cameron
Earth Science Teacher
Platek, Gary Theodore
Mathematics Teacher
Quigley, Michael
Fifth Grade Teacher
Rogers, K. Kelly
High School Mathematics Tchr
Sparnecht, Charles Arthur
History Teacher
Starr, Richard
Physics Teacher
Strelau, Nancy Pettersen
Orchestra Director
Van Kouwenberg, Patricia Cullen
HS GT Program Coord & Teacher
Whittington, Lorraine White
Co-Chprsn Foreign Lang Dept
Zicari, Doris June McKinsey
Third Grade Teacher
PENN YAN
Beach, Donald L.
Fifth Grade Teacher
Breuer, Stephen
Mathematics Instructor
Carroll, Gloria Craugh
Superintendent
Church, Bob J.
Physical Education Teacher
Gibbon, Sherry Smith
Soc Stud Dept Chair & Teacher
Gleason, Elaine Champlin
Third Grade Teacher
Johnson, Timothy
Social Studies Teacher
Meyer, Donald Paul
Hlth, Physical Education Tchr
Minor, Brian Richard
5th Grade Teacher
Rickman, Mary L.
6th-12th Grd Art Teacher
Smart, Thomas John
Physics Teacher
Vorce, Elliot
HS Social Studies Teacher
PERRY
Bastedo, Sandra Fancher
Fine Arts Chprsn & Vocal Tchr
Carter, George Ann Flaitz
8th Grd Social Studies Teacher
Devitt, William Patrick
Physical Education Teacher
Heller, Willard Allen
Spanish Teacher
Hughes, Dawnne Byroads
English Teacher
Oltz, Margaret D.
Fifth Grade Teacher
Sylvester, David John
10th Grd Social Studies Tchr
PERU
Close, Bruce Allan
PE, Cmptr Literacy & Hlth Tchr
Evans, Donald G.
Spanish Teacher
Hermann, Helen
Principal & 6th Grade Teacher
Hurd, Philip L.
4th Grade Teacher
Monette, Mitchell
Sixth Grade Teacher
Palkovic, Carol Lee
English Teacher
Phillips, Cathy Lorraine
Physical Education Teacher
Roach, Kathleen Elizabeth
Global Studies & French Tchr
Rumph, Robert Roy
Driver Education Teacher
Wilson, Marilyn Buckley
6th Grade Teacher
PHELPS
Durso, Renee Day
2nd Grade Classroom Teacher
Holdridge, Carol G.
2nd Grade Teacher
Wright, Gay Beckner
Fifth Grade Teacher
PHILADELPHIA
Coolidge, Clinton A.
Mathematics Teacher
Dorman, Mark R.
Health Education Teacher
Fabrizio, Patricia A.
8th Grade Humanities Teacher
Kiechle, Dawn Murphy
Latin & German Teacher
Landas, Nancyann Hocking
English Dept Chair & Teacher
Mabry, Myra Cummings
Biology Teacher
Nicholas, Leonard H.
Technology Teacher
Papin, Deborah Shippee
11th-12th Grd English Tchr
Reed, Herbert Charles
Fourth Grade Teacher
PHILMONT
Peacock, Jama Lorynn
Biology & Chemistry Teacher
PHOENIX
Cutro, Francis Joseph
Biology Teacher
Goodwin, Anna Dunlap
Mathematics Teacher

Libertone, Carl Anthony
English Teacher
PINE BUSH
Bemont, Thomas David
History Teacher
Cartisano, Mark Carmen
History Teacher
Mc Laud, Carla A.
Mathematics Teacher
Natoli, Tamara Christine
Spanish Teacher
Prokopchak, Peter Andrew
HS Instrumental Music Teacher
Silverberg, Mitchel Aaron
American History Teacher
Slesinski, Richard E.
Physics Teacher
Tuthill, Annette Masaryk
Math Teacher
Zimmer, William F.
English Teacher
PINE CITY
Bennett, Cheryl Louise
Fourth Grade Teacher
Reddington, Cecily Adams
Retired English & Latin Tchr
PINE PLAINS
Cook, Jean Thomann
English Teacher
PITTSFORD
Booden, Donald S.
Retired 4th-8th Grade Teacher
Bramley, Georgie Megas
Third Grade Teacher
Cole, Thomas A.
Physical Education Teacher
Denison, John Francis
English Teacher & Drama Dir
Di Gaetano, F. Thomas
Chemistry Teacher
Elliott, Claudia Jane
Math Teacher
Genthner, Frederic
Fifth Grade Teacher
Hahn, W. Todd
4th Grade Teacher
Hamilton, Susan Clark
Physical Education Teacher
Humphrey, Laura Masotti
French, Span Tchr & Dept Head
Johnson, Bayne F.
Social Studies Dept Chair
Kawka, Lenore C.
5th Grade Teacher
Kessler, Sandra Schoeneck
5th Grade Teacher
OBrien, Thomas John
District Art Director
Oertel, Virginia Ann Perley
Secondary Social Studies Tchr
Shears, Gail M.
6th Grade Teacher
VanBuskirk, Dolores D.
Third Grade Teacher
PLAINVIEW
Blouin, George Robert
English Teacher
Cohen, Myra Wasserman
6th Grade Teacher
Hazan, Marvin Eric
Law Teacher
Isaacs, Melvin A.
Principal
Kriaris, Loretta G.
History Teacher
O'Brien, Emily S.
Sixth Grade Teacher
PLATTEKILL
Mackey, Sunni Auerhahn
Fifth Grade Teacher
PLATTSBURGH
Baroody, Frances deGrandpre
Mathematics Teacher
Bougill, James Winthrop
Assoc Professor of Business
Brooks, Ronald R.
Asst Prof & Dept Coord
Cavanaugh, Judith A.
Assistant Prof of Humanities
Demarse, Joy A.
English Teacher
Frechette, Garth Joseph
Chemistry Teacher
Latourelle, Sandra M. (Rankin)
Adjunct Professor of Biology
Mandeville, Thomas Robert
Assoc Professor of Social Sci
Onofrio, Marshall Paul
Associate Professor of Music
Queguiner, Margaret Leone
French Teacher
Rice, Elaine Davey
English Teacher & Dept Chair
Robertson, Carol (Sharron)
4th Grade Teacher
Sherman, George W.
Economics & Government Teacher
Ward, Leo J.
Adjunct Psychology Instructor
PLEASANTVILLE
Franco, Joseph Richard
Adj Assoc Prof of Sociology
Hall, Donald Richard
Physical Education Teacher
Napolitano, Ralph Anthony
High School Principal
Royal, Patricia Lawson
Home Economics Teacher
Schnitzel, Frederick Richard
Industrial Technology Teacher

POLAND
Briand, Ella E.
8th & 10th Grade English Tchr
Eramo, Peter W.
Computer Teacher
Gala, John
High School Technology Teacher
Heaton, Sheila Hayes
Middle School Science Teacher
Henry, Carolyn Lehman
Math Teacher
Hinotsky, George Philip
6th Grade Teacher
Miller, Julie
Instrumental Music Teacher
Wallace, Mary Hudak
Teacher
POMONA
Nash, Delores Anne
Retired Social Studies Teacher
PORT BYRON
Foreman, Robert George, IV
Instrumental Music Instructor
Murinka, Nancy Yura
4th Grade Teacher
Rathbun, Angelee Hitchcock
Physical Education Teacher
Triant, Richard Paul
Secondary Science Teacher
Waltos, Rosemary A.
Kindergarten Teacher
PORT CHESTER
Cascio, Judith A.
6th Grd Teacher & Team Leader
Cowle, Donna Ann LaGrande
English Teacher
Dessereau-Koch, April
Art, Photography Tchr & Chrmn
Giacopelli, Deborah Rose
English Teacher
Granville-Mc Keown, Marion (Adelaar)
MS Mathematics Teacher
Nagle, Linda (Fortuna)
Spanish Teacher
Nostro, Neil R.
8th Grd Social Studies Teacher
Obuch, Dolores Grady
Principal
Penney, Linda Helen
Music Teacher & Drama Instr
Santora, Mark Daniel
Guidance Counselor
Vitti, Robert C.
High School Tchr & Band Dir
PORT EWEN
Harnden, Laura Dauenheimer
Cosmetology Instructor
PORT HENRY
Finnessey, Thomas John, Sr.
Retired Sixth Grade Teacher
Fitzgerald, Ronald J.
English Teacher
Gilbo, Mary Mc Nulty
Second Grade Teacher
Heald, Mary Brown
Eng, Philosophy & Lit Teacher
PORT JEFFERSON
Barning, Beth Magoolaghan
Jr High Math & Science Teacher
Dayton, Constance Ellen
English Teacher
Leon, Blanche Altchiler
Retired Teacher
Padwa, Linda Baum
Science Teacher
Watkins, Allen Richard
Technology Education Teacher
PORT JEFFERSON STATION
Brodsky, Richard
Retired English Teacher
Homburger, Gail D.
Algebra Teacher
Tamberino, Philip
Fifth Grade Teacher
PORT JERVIS
Lenahan, Alice Jean
Spanish Teacher
Manfredo, Christine A.
English Teacher & Dept Chprsn
Michalenicz, Catherine M.
Fourth Grade Teacher
Woolley, Judith Ann
8th Grd Language Arts Teacher
PORT WASHINGTON
Aikman, Marie Osterman
Literature Teacher
Anthony, Anne C.
Retired Teacher
Burklund, Virginia Bedell
Retired Elementary Teacher
Cohn, Sheryl A.
4th Grade Teacher
Grady, Mary Lou Magee
Teacher of Gifted & Talented
Jones, James Patrick
Bio, Zoology & Genetics Tchr
Kosiba, Patricia Ann
Secondary Health Ed Teacher
O'Connor, David L.
History Teacher
PORTVILLE
Haley, Richard John
Band Director
Lang, Kathy Weinaug
4th Grade Teacher
Larder, Linda M.
Physical Ed Instr & Coach
Mc Cann, Michael R.
Social Studies Teacher

Molyneaux, James LeVan
6th Grade Teacher
Wood, Mary Lou Donovan
High School English Teacher
POTSDAM
Caruso, Rena Tardelli
Fourth Grade Teacher
Centofanti, Cynthia L.
Business Teacher
DeGhett, Victor John
Professor of Psychology
Donahue, Timothy S.
Mathematics Instructor
Faub, Robert Alan
Assistant Professor of Music
Heinick, David G.
Prof of Composition & Music
Iogha, Ruth Henry
Professor of Music
Reynolds, Jon Lee
Professor of Chemistry
Rudiger, Lance Wade
Chemistry Tchr & Sci Dpt Chair
Stephan, Richard A.
Professor of Music
Waters, Rolf Albert
History Teacher
Wilson, Tina Michele
5th Grade Teacher
Woy, Alan Bruce
Prof of Clarinet & Conducting
POUGHKEEPSIE
Alptekin, Omer Kemal
Social Studies Teacher
Bettencourt, Joseph Sousa, Jr.
Professor of Biology
Butler, Julett
Instructor
Chaput, Jacques Andre
3rd-4th Grd Multi-Age Tchr
Chisamore, Donald Raymond
Fifth Grade Teacher
Christie, Madeleine B.
Second Grade Teacher
Cicala, Kathleen M. Blank
7th-8th Grade Spanish Teacher
Desilets, Brian Henry
Professor
Dietz, Karen S.
Retail & Fashion Teacher
Dolan, John J.
Sr Guidance Counselor
Fiumarello, Sheila Nancy
Vocal Music Teacher
Fletcher, Julia Almeida
English Teacher
Flood, Marilyn R.
Kindergarten Teacher
Forsythe, Ralph Thomas
Fifth Grade Teacher
Gaw, Martin Joseph
Social Studies Teacher
Geddes, Suzanne Devins
Family & Consumer Sci Tchr
Herman, Tad
Physics Instructor
Hostetter, Timothy J.
Scndry Soc Stud Tchr & Prin
Kime, Sue-Ann Mc Carthy
Supervisor of Student Teachers
Kirtland, Joseph
Asst Professor of Mathematics
Loza, Leonard Antony
Physical Science Teacher
Maher, Judith Adams
AP Coll Engl Tchr & Dept Chrmn
Maset, Elisabeth Bethel
Lecturer
Mc Aulay, Robert Ernest
Associate Prof of Sociology
Menapace, Lawrence William
Assoc Professor of Chemistry
Murray, David F.
Fifth Grade Teacher
Nijhuis, Margaret Johns
Mathematics Teacher
O'Connor, Elizabeth Hesten
French & Literature Teacher
Olsen, Linda Elizabeth
Fifth Grade Teacher
Peter-Raoul, Mar
Rel Studies Asst Professor
Pritchard, Arthur H.
Prof of Biological Science
Quinn, Carol Reynolds
Kindergarten Teacher
Robinson, Cary Scott
Band Director
Santiago, Ann Marie
Sixth Grade English Teacher
Schmersal, Susan A.
Fifth Grade Teacher
Scileppi, John A.
Dir & Prof of MA Psych Prgm
Snyder-Leiby, Teresa Eileen
Assistant Professor of Biology
Stammer, Christine L.
English Teacher
Urbin, Jeffrey S.
Instructor of Government
Van Voorhis, Mareve Elizabeth (Hughes)
Instructor of Human Svcs Pgm
Wright, Wendy Lyon
Third Grade Teacher
Zito, Anthony J.
Assistant Professor of Physics
POUGHQUAG
Whittemore, Janet Brady
Second Grade Teacher

PRATTSBURGH
Bedient, Kim Lori
Kindergarten Teacher
Thaine, Michael J.
Instrumental Music Teacher
PULASKI
Cook, Anne (Durante)
Second Grade Teacher
Galliher, Kelly Marie
Speech Therapist
Johnson, Frank E.
6th Grade Teacher
Lawrence, Kim Chontosh
7th-12th Grd Math Tchr & Chair
Riley, Peter Keven
Business Teacher
PURCHASE
Hutchins, Thomasenia Myers
Asst Prof of Literature
Jones, James Edwards
Rel Prof & African Stud Chair
Morehouse, Sheila M.
Professor of Chemistry
Ryan, Edward William
Professor of Economics
Wickert, Gabriele Maria
Dean of Studies & German Prof
Williams, Randolph Andrew
Professor & Chairman
QUEENS VILLAGE
Gold, Debra Lynn
Physical Education & Hlth Tchr
Hobbs, Diane Rossi
First Grade Teacher
Weisberg, Mark H.
English Tchr & Admin Assistant
QUEENSBURY
Beadle, Susan Singer
Global Studies Teacher
Cottrell, Daniel A.
5th Grade Teacher
Hague, Bradford Barber
Science Teacher
Hummel, Robert A.
HS Social Studies Teacher
Jones, Robert H.
American History Teacher
Laroche, Helen Wirmusky
Curriculum Coordinator
Merrill, Suzanne Pesez
English Teacher & Dept Chair
Miller, Teresa Celadon
Second Grade Teacher
Notari, Robert John
Music Teacher
O'Neil, D. Michael
Assistant Prinicpal
Sawyer, Carol Robelen
French Teacher
QUOGUE
Heatley, Katherine Eileen
Kindergarten Teacher
RANDOLPH
Congdon, Cathy Carr
1st Grade Teacher
Klee, Kathleen McDermott
Math & Computer Science Tchr
Patterson, Carol King
Kindergarten Teacher
Serure, Dana Faye
Social Studies Teacher
RAVENA
DeRose, Jennifer Rausch
Eighth Grade Physical Sci Tchr
Prozik, Josephine
Spanish Teacher
RED HOOK
Ascienzo, Nicholas Joseph
Mathematics Teacher
Bollella, Dominick
Biology Teacher
Dederick, Wayne F.
Chemistry Teacher
Haines, Robert E.
High School English Teacher
Keefe, Perri Tolkoff
HS Physical Education Teacher
Nero, Joseph Michael
Business Teacher
Rafferty, Gregory Francis
Physical Education Teacher
Sheehan, Jeremiah F.
Social Studies Teacher
Sober, Sally Wilson
8th Grade Math Teacher
Tipple, Ann Beatty
Science Teacher
RENSSELAER
Grill, John Joseph
Social Studies & Science Tchr
Gustafson, Cynthia
Science Teacher
Hoffman, Robert s.
Social Studies Teacher
Keegan, MIchael
Fourth Grade Teacher
Kennedy, Linda Louise
Mathematics Teacher
RETSOF
Barie, Elizabeth J.
Social Studies Teacher
Fusco, Andy Anthony
10th Grade Mathematics Tchr
Grant, Karen Weckerle
Sr HS Resource Room Teacher
Harris, Todd Ellsworth
Middle School Science Teacher
Kelley, Karen M.
6th Grade Teacher

F (cont)
ı, Jacqueline Arrigenna
ltant Teacher
Barbara J.
entary Vocal Teacher
, David Michael
sh Teacher
BECK
gham, Maureen Brey
dary English Teacher
nn, Patricia Paulick
Grade Teacher
Sandra L.
Music Teacher & Choral Dir
m, Carol Szacik
Grade Teacher
Vincent William
sh Teacher & Dept Chm
Anthony Joseph
sh Teacher
and, Linda Armstrong
ematics Teacher
, Doreen Ostrowski
Economics Teacher
FIELD SPRINGS
, Cynthia Jean
sh Tchr & Professor
iff, Diane Gifford
ry Social Studies Teacher
MOND HILL
Rene Michele
ry & Economics Teacher
, Benita Maria
nth & Eighth Grade Teacher
o-Kuhner, Mary Cecilia
rian
e, Lola Kiser
nd Grade Teacher
n, Deborah Marie
sh Teacher
Catherine
Grade Teacher
an, Phyllis
Principal
, Vandana Dolly
nce Teacher
ane Elizabeth
sh Teacher
, Marlene
h Grade Teacher of GATE
eva, Sarita
Teacher
MONDVILLE
, Susan B.
Grade Science Teacher
grass, John R.
Grade Teacher
E
an, Jill Anastasi
Grade Teacher
ta, Roy Edward
Grade Teacher
, Sandra Smolowitz
Grade Teacher
y, Lois D. (Mitchell)
Grade Teacher
EWOOD
r, Joel Raymond
her
Anton
ner Teacher
EY
on, Deborah Bowen
n Grade Teacher
ge, Doris Heeter
dergarten Teacher
RHEAD
el, Donna Marie
nish Teacher
r, Karen M.
al Studies Teacher
, Meryl
mistry Teacher
s, Maureen
th Grade Teacher
Thomas Edwin, III
n Grade Teacher
ntino-James, Gina
al Studies Teacher
Antonieta
guage Chairperson & Tchr
nso, Faye
Prof of Graphic Design
field, Mary Ellen E.
lish Chair
illop, David J.
Stud Teacher & Adj Instr
s, Barbara Stumpt
h Grade English Teacher
Patricia Walz
Math Department Chprsn
n, Marion Budny
mistry & Physics Teacher
coy, Barbara Wainwright
lish Teacher
HESTER
as, Robin Brooks
mistry Teacher
iak, Kathy Tadio
nch Teacher
ena, Robert Lewis
h Grade Teacher
rosi-Lepore, Ersilia
ired Teacher
acida, Robert Carl
e Principal & Athletic Dir
nan, M. Garrett
fessor of English
, Carol Fields
hematics Teacher

Bell, Jonathan
6th Grade Science Teacher
Best, Allan William
Psych, Ec & Soc Stud Teacher
Blanchard, Mary Ellen L.
English Teacher
Bluntzer, Otto, Jr.
Continuing Education Teacher
Boddery, Sara Coleman
Science Teacher
Boesl, Linda Lee
9th-12th Grade English Tchr
Bond, Jennifer Ann
National Figure Skating Coach
Bougere-Harris, Gale
Home Economics Teacher
Boughton, Kathleen Ann
PE Teacher & Coach
Bowers, James
Assoc Prof of Pol Science
Brayman, Glenda K.
Adj Prof Criminal Justice Dept
Broeniman, Clifford Scott
Assistant Prof of Classics
Bromley, Kathleen Kayson
Economics Professor
Bruce, Eugene William
Social Studies Tchr & Coord
Bryant, Karen Strenzwilk
Business & Computer Teacher
Buckert, Gary Richard
Biology & Chemistry Teacher
Calvin, Mathis Anthony, III
Special Education Teacher
Cantore-Green, Jean Marie
English Teacher
Carapella, David A., Jr.
HS Media Communications Tchr
Cardillo, Karen Adack
Associate Professor
Carlson, Brita K.
First Grade Teacher
Champagne-Myers, Mary Dziuba
German Teacher
Corman, Ned W.
Commission Project Director
Costanza, John Thomas
Mission Commander
Crane, David William
Chemistry Teacher
Cummings, Glen A.
Social Studies Teacher
D'Angelo, Larem Keam
School Counselor
Defendis, David William
Sixth Grade Teacher
DeJoy, Nancy C.
Asst Prof of Eng & Prgms Dir
Denigris, Peter Richard
Fourth Grade Teacher
Dickson, Christopher Scott
Music Teacher & Dept Chair
Dollinger, Marilyn Longo
Asst Professor of Nursing
Donahue, Sally R.
Business Teacher
Doyle, Eileen M.
Assoc Prof of Radiologic Tech
Ebenhack, Ben Wright
Instructor & Research Assoc
Ehmann, Clare
Teacher
Eiselen, Claire Hirsch
Teacher & Coord of Gifted Ed
Ellis, Bonnie Besch
Special Education Teacher
Ellman, Carolyn (Wagner)
Middle School Mathematics Tchr
Evans, Sheila Jean
High School Counselor
Farber-Soule, Cynthia L.
Latin Teacher
Ferger, Kathy Schrenk
Science Teacher
Finlan, Autumn Patricia
Retired English Teacher
Finley, Mary D.
English & Business Professor
Finn, John Joseph
English & Latin Teacher
Flick, Lesley Susan
Mathematics Teacher
Fogarty, Robin A.
AP History Teacher
Forward, Terry Boling
Eng as a Second Lang Tchr
Francione, Mary Faith
Bus Ed & Cmptr Tech Teacher
Francis, John Edward
Chemistry Teacher
Frank, Ann Louise (Zeznick)
Program Director of Bus Div
Fulton, Laura Littner
Chemistry Teacher
Geer, Kimberly Dirkx
Secondary English Teacher
Gianforte, Carl Joseph
English Teacher
Gillan, Kay Dorward
Social Studies Teacher
Gladey, Mary Gibbons
Vice Principal
Glossner, Richard Augustine
Professor of Psychology
Goffredo, SSJ, Damian
Sci & Jr HS Homeroom Tchr
Gonzalez-Habes, Dolores
English & Biling Ed Teacher
Goodwin, Patricia V.
English Teacher

Goonan, Constance Sgroi
French Teacher
Grabb, Wilma C.
Freelance Artist in Residence
Graham, W. Joseph
Professor of Biology
Granville, Robert T.
6th Grade Math Teacher
Greene, Jeffrey Del
Band Director
Grossi, Raoul P.
US History Teacher
Grosso, Dawn Seibert
Business & Law Professor
Gruhn, Christine Mae
Assistant Professor of Biology
Guido, Lisa Maria
French & Italian Teacher
Hahn, Jeffrey William
English Teacher
Hanna, Kevin Paul
Math Teacher & Counselor
Hanover, Margaret Kellner
Social Studies Teacher
Harrison, Daniel
Associate Professor of Music
Hazlett, Alec E.
Head of Ceramics Dept
Heaney, Karen Carone
Middle School Counselor
Hengelsberg, Raymond C.
History & Pol Sci Assoc Prof
Holleran, Joseph Paul
Principal
Hopkins, Thomas Duvall
Professor of Economics
Ingram, Linda Foglia
Chemistry Teacher
Inya, Christopher Nwachi, Sr.
Assoc Professor of Economics
Ives, Karen Spang
Sixth Grade Teacher
Johnson, Donnell S.
Life Science Teacher
Johnson, Randall Lamar
Asst Prof of Interior Design
Jorgensen, Beth Ellen
Spanish Professor
Julian, David A.
Microcomputer Instructor
Juneau, Janet Wandersee
Kindergarten Teacher
Keach, Terrance John
Music Teacher
Keck, Jonathan Alden
English Teacher
Kimmet, Pamela B.
Head of Lower School
Kincaid, Gregory Robert
Elem Phys Ed Teacher & Coach
Kostecke, Ronald D.
Counselor & Professor
Krysa, Oleh
Professor of Violin
Landis, JoAnn Clark
Teacher
Larrabee, Deborah
6th Grade Math Teacher
Linsley, Christine Louise
Assoc Prof of Sociology
Lobell, Katy Wolitzky
Spanish Teacher
Lunt, Dawn Weidman
HS Math Teacher
Lynd, John C.
Retired Social Studies Teacher
Macpherson, Daniel Craig
Elementary Band Director
Maier, Anne Cecilia
HS English Tchr & Dept Chprsn
Mains, Tim O.
Teacher & Center Director
Mc Bride, Darrin Gerard
High School Science Teacher
Mc Farland, Bruce Edward
Band Director
Mc Lean, James Douglas
High School Mathematics Tchr
McLenon, Vonda Lynn (Keelere)
Science Teacher
Mc Naney, Patricia Barbara
Teacher
Milan, Godfrey
Biling Program English Teacher
Moore, Jennifer Cecile (Ledbetter)
English Teacher
Morales, Richard
Associate Professor
Morris, Elene S.
Third Grade Teacher
Mrva, Kimberly Ann
HS Mathematics Teacher
Murano, Donna Hemphill
9th-11th Grd English Teacher
Nielander, Barbara Benjamin
4th Grade Teacher
Nightingale, Bonnie Magar
Social Studies Teacher
Noto, Michael James
Social Studies Teacher
Ogden, Philip Myron
Natural Science & Math Chprsn
Oliveri, Judith M.
Secretarial Instructor
Oyer, W. Brian
Secondary Earth Science Tchr
Palmer, Harvey John
Professor of Chemical Engrng
Parisi, Gilda Haluska
German Teacher

Pelletier-Myers, Lisa Jean
Art Dept Chair & Teacher
Pete, Stephen J.
Amer History & Govt Teacher
Peters, Barbara Loomis
Mathematics Teacher
Pettite, Chet A.
Business Education Teacher
Pilliter, Richard John
Secondary Social Studies Tchr
Preston, Mary Jane Johnson
4th Grade Teacher
Principino, Oreshia Hyk
Second Grade Teacher
Priola, Joseph J.
Technology Education Teacher
Raines, Paul R., Jr.
Self Employed Agri-Business
Ranalli, Edward F., Jr.
Global Studies Teacher
Rand, Craig Martin
Asst Professor of Phys Ed
Redlo, Mitchell Howard
Economics Professor
Reiniger, Meredith Elizabeth (Horning)
English Teacher
Remley, William Moorhead
Social Studies Teacher
Rhoades, John D.
Assoc Prof of Anthropology
Richards, Lucinda Beard
Honors, AP Biology & Sci Tchr
Roberts, Irene L.
Retired 5th-6th Grade Teacher
Rogers, Gloria Benson
School Counselor
Ruggieri, Anthony Gerald
Secondary English Teacher
Ruggieri, Christopher Lane
8th Grd Social Studies Teacher
Samulski, Gary Joseph
Director of Bands
Sarra, Mario
Spanish Teacher
Scarfia, James M.
European & Bio-Ethics Instr
Schalge, Donna Rockcastle
Mathematics Teacher
Schauffele, Susan Ann
GED Teacher
Schirtz, Jodi Frances
Owner & Instructor
Schlegel, Robert Edward
Mathematics Teacher
Schneider, Edith Louise
Instrumental Music Teacher
Schneider, Jane Russell
Math Teacher
Schulz, Lawrence H.
Business & Economics Teacher
Schwalb, Mary L.
Secondary Social Studies Tchr
Shabaz, Caterina Petrolito
French & Italian Assoc Prof
Shakes, Gaya Robinson
English Teacher
Shoemaker, Ellen Rivers
HS Mathematics Teacher
Sizer, Clara Robinson
Business Teacher
Skelly, Marylee
English Teacher
Soule, Gardner Northup, Jr.
Air Transportation Teacher
Spriggs, Gloria Cappon
Middle School French Teacher
Starke, Richard Carl
Fifth Grade Tchr
Stendardi, Edward John
Assoc Professor of Management
Sturm, Frederick Ivan
Jazz Stud & Contemp Media Prof
Sullivan, William Joseph
Assoc Prof of Religious Stud
Swanson, Nancy E. (Povlock)
High School Art Teacher
Swingle, Herbert Hyatt, Jr.
History Teacher
Tadal, Packeta Gayle
English Teacher
Tatakis, Timothy A.
Assistant Professor of Biology
Territo, Charles Jaems
Math Teacher
Territo, Lesley Hylas
Math Teacher
Thomas, James Lee
French & Spanish Teacher
Thompson, Elaine Carter
Retired Elementary Principal
Tisa, Sheryl Smith
Fourth Grade Teacher
Trama, Anthony Gerard
Social Studies Teacher & Coach
Tufano, Harry J., Jr.
6th Grade Teacher
Turk, Charles K.
APE TV & English Teacher
Turri, Louis A.
Fourth Grade Teacher
VanderBilt, Deborah Lynn
Associate Professor of English
Vargas, Bolgen
School Counselor
Wadach, John B.
Associate Professor of Physics
Westbay, Theresa Datz
Asst Professor of Biology
Wheaton, Gail L.
Kindergarten Tchr & Admin Asst

Whiting, Kathleen M.
Elementary French Teacher
Wiecorek, Kathleen Hurley
Instructional Support Coord
Wiener, Gary Alan
English Dept Coord & Teacher
Williams, Oliver Spencer, III
Eighth Grade Science Teacher
Winship, Michelle Marie
Third Grade Teacher
Woodard, Donald L.
Social Studies Teacher
Wunder, Nancy E.
Hlth & Phys Education Instr
Yost, Carol Spies
Social Studies Teacher
Zwick, Michael A.
Associate Prof of Mathematics
ROCKAWAY PARK
Katcher, Mitchell Scott
Language Arts Teacher
ROCKVILLE CENTRE
Carter, Mary Kennedy
Social Studies Teacher
Panatier, Carolyn Cronin
Former Teacher
Pisani, Maria Curella
Secondary Level Biology Tchr
Plesnitzer, Robert
Chemistry Teacher
Resch, Audrey Lapina
5th Grade Math & Religion Tchr
Salvato, John A.
8th Grade Social Studies Tchr
Schiffman, Audrey
Retired Teacher
ROCKY POINT
Hall, Daniel
Math Dept Chairman
Hertling, Peter A.
Music & Band Director
Kjaerbye, Barbara Ann Rubenbauer
1st Grade Teacher
Molloy, Barry M.
7th-12th Grd English Teacher
Moran, Ann Kaelin
5th Grade Teacher
Russo, Richard Paul
English & Drama Teacher
ROME
Augenstein, Ruth Pritchard
First Grade Teacher
Boardman, Linda S.
Mathematics Teacher
Calogero, Christine King
Biology & Science Teacher
Carlson, David Arthur
PE Teacher & Swimming Coach
Cataldo, Linda Romano
High School Math Teacher
Colby, Elisabeth
Volunteer Latin Teacher
Debany, Beth M.
Science Teacher
Dykens, Marylin Carol
Eng Tchr & Dept Coord
Grasso, Letizia
Italian Teacher
Guarneiri, Anthony Charles
High School Guidance Counselor
Herring, Carol Wolfgang
Third Grade Teacher
Mazzaferro, John Jack
Biology Teacher
McCune, Marion Evans
Soc Stud Dept Chair & Tchr
Murphy, Raymond Joseph
Retired Teacher
Newman, Gary Gordon
Social Studies Teacher
Nickerson, Edward A.
Math & Computer Sci Teacher
Renzi, Emilio Gerald
History Teacher
Salerno, Letitia
6th Grade Teacher
Varanese, Philip Michael
Guidance Counselor
ROMULUS
Bauder, Nancy Pangburn
English Teacher
Delia, James Nicholas
Global Studies Teacher
Goloski, Peter Gregory
Instrumental Music Teacher
Nelson, Roberta Budd
Art Teacher
Prave, Karen Fairchild
Science Teacher
RONKONKOMA
Ambrosini, Catherine
Life Science Teacher
Broderick, Patricia Begley
HS Health Education Teacher
Capolino, Paul Joseph
Earth Science Teacher
Coderre, Francis John
Band Director
Conlon, Barbara A.
Math Teacher
Demas, Sandra (Nider)
Fifth Grade Teacher
Earley, Donna
Foreign Language Teacher
Flinn, Robert Peter
Social Studies Chairperson
Gerstenberg, Robert W.
Vocal Music Teacher
Gottsch, Brewster C.
Biology Teacher

RONKONKOMA (cont)
Gross, Linda Ann
Reading & English Teacher
Higgins, Eugene Thomas
Social Studies Teacher
Leogrande, Vincent
English Teacher
Maniaci, Joseph David
Social Studies Instructor
Mc Groarty, Cynthia Marion
Vocal Music Teacher
Monfett, Christine Ann
Science Teacher
Moskowitz, Andrea Harrow
Sixth Grade Teacher
Ohmela, Janet M.
Social Studies Teacher
Payne, Andrea J.
Health Teacher
Posner, Richard
English Teacher
Reulbach, Rosanne Cangemi
Eng Tchr & Adj Prof of Jrnlsm
Rowe, Eleanor Turner
Third Grade Teacher
Spelman, Kevin Lane
Advanced Placement Ec Tchr
Stanek, Sharon Moynihan
English Teacher
Thomas, Richard J.
Sixth Grade Teacher
Visco, Christopher
Earth Science Teacher
ROOSEVELT
Indelicato, Mary Valera
Special Education Teacher
ROSCOE
Cerullo, Michael Peter
7th-12th Grade Technology Tchr
Hartling, Renee Johnson
Title I Math Teacher
Katz, Regina Mary
Social Studies Teacher
Simcoe, Alison Leigh
First Grade Teacher
ROSLYN
Goudreau, Marianne
Assistant Headmaster
ROSLYN HEIGHTS
Ambrosino, Joan
Counselor
Barone, Marguerite Curreri
Spanish & Latin Teacher
Kay, Ian
Instrumental Director
Mc Elroy, Hugh J.
Ceramics & Photography Prof
Shubin, Joanna Spampanato
6th Grade Science Teacher
Wasilchuk, Stephen G.
MS Mathematics Teacher
ROTTERDAM
Schaefer, Linda Thompson
Biology Teacher
ROTTERDAM JUNCTION
Cox, Paulyn
Retired Third Grade Teacher
Rohloff, Andrea Fedeli
3rd Grade Teacher
RUSHVILLE
Arnold, Gail Anne
School Counselor
Edwards, Larry Lee
Business Teacher
Hickman, Susan Janice
French & Spanish Teacher
Kennedy, Elaine Kahler
Home Economics Teacher
Mac Kenzie, Malcolm Ian
English Teacher
Neufang, Richard
Mathematics Teacher
Pitcher, Beth Ann
Chemistry Teacher
RUSSELL
Buckley, James Michael
Secondary Science Teacher
Dalbec, Danielle Christine
French Teacher
Mc Bath, Suzanne Burke
Health & Home Economics Tchr
Mc Kinnon, Lennelle Dougherty
English Teacher
RYE
Alexander, Robert Paul
Fourth Grade Teacher
Burdick, Ross Matthew
Teacher & Coach
Conant, Judith N.
Mathematics Teacher
Day, Christopher Daniel
Humanities Teacher
Johnson, Jane B.
English Teacher
Mazza, John Michael
Spcl Education & History Tchr
Ricci, Annalea
Science Department Chair
Tuttle, Douglas
Math Teacher
RYE BROOK
Bertisch, Carolee Ackerson
Retired English Teacher
SACKETS HARBOR
Berger, Teri Lynn
Sixth Grade Teacher
Berie, Jennifer L.
Spanish Teacher
Cerow, Jacques Antoine
Business Tchr & Computer Coord

Filas, Gail Ann
Resource Room & Spec Ed Tchr
Hand, Robert Donald
English Teacher
Hochmuth, Susanne M.
Spanish Teacher
Knight, Mary Brown
Kindergarten Teacher
Thornber, Sharon Louise
English Teacher & Dept Chprsn
Weaver, Lyle M.
Health Teacher & Coach
SAINT ALBANS
Ballenas, Carl E.
Sixth Grade Teacher
Betz, Anne Louise
Mathematics Teacher
Mc Pherson, Ionie M.
Jr High Mathematics Teacher
Schor, Toby
Administrative Assistant
SAINT BONAVENTURE
Burns, Mary Klee
Supervisor of Student Teachers
Cellini, Alva Victoria
Assoc Prof of Modern Languages
SAINT JAMES
Daffner, Beverly A.
History Teacher
Daniels, Edgar Roth
8th Grade English Teacher
SAINT JOHNSVILLE
Burkhart, Carol A.
Science Teacher
Mott, DiAnne Illsley
Instrumental Music Teacher
Orlando, Lisa Marie Sommella
Vocal Director
Schoff, Marcia Wendell
Kndgtn Tchr & Colorguard Dir
Vavra, Susan
English & Remedial Wrtng Tchr
SAINT REGIS FALLS
Blais, Lynn Ann (Cameron)
English Teacher
SALAMANCA
Anderson, Carol Mongillo
Spanish Teacher
Dietrich, Geoffrey Arthur
Chemistry Teacher
Ferrara, Michael L.
Advanced Placement Eng Tchr
Jimerson, Sandra E.
Seneca Language & Culture Tchr
Lafferty-John, Laurie Sue
6th-12th Grd PE Teacher
Skudlarek, Chad Edward
8th Grade Science Teacher
Toner, Judith Anne Carter
Social Studies Teacher
Wiedman, Colleen O'Neil
Physical Education Teacher
Yehl, Ronda Kramer
Language Arts Teacher
SALEM
Harrison, Gina Heintz
3rd Grade Teacher
SANBORN
Bishara, Ann Diana
English Teacher & Co-Curr Dir
Bonacci, Mark A.
Asst Prof of Human Services
Cianciosa, Carolyn Lucy
Asst Prof of Radiologic Tech
Dewey, Paul H.
Natural Resources Teacher
Farallo, Livio
Assistant Professor of Biology
Gerlach, Betty Krolick
English Teacher
Gornicki, Henry A.
HS History & Law Teacher
Greenberg, Alex
Prof of Criminal Justice & Law
Hahn, Susan Mary
Business Teacher
Haseley, Phillip A.
Professor of Anthropology
Joseph, Deborah Hilty
Mathematics Tech Assistant
Kankolenski, Paul Frank
Psychology Prof
Knechtel, Nancy
Art History Professor
Lamb, Wallace
7th Grade Social Studies Tchr
Maglietto, Tina Marie
Asst Prof of Criminal Justice
Mittelstaedt, James Robert
Associate Professor
Moore, Ann Oppedisano
Social Studies Teacher
Nemi, David Michael
Asst Professor of Business
Pachla, James David
Mathematics Teacher
Passanese, Salvatore Michael
Professor of Biology
Pogel, Alan F.
Economics & Soc Problems Tchr
Young, Elizabeth Arnone
Spanish Teacher
SANDY CREEK
Bush, Charles A.
English Teacher
SARANAC
Morgan, Anne Marie M.
School-to-Career Coordinator
Norcross, Darry R.
US History & Government Tchr

SARANAC LAKE
Bell, Charles J.
Soc Studies Dept Chair & Instr
Durkin, Sharon Cromie
Third Grade Teacher
Farmer, Mark E.
Social Studies Teacher
Fisch, Thomas Michael
Social Studies Teacher
Fletcher, Eugene Howard
Mathematics Teacher
Schneider, Emil J.
Social Studies Teacher
Treska, Meredith I.
English Instructor
Ward, John Thomas
Art Teacher
SARATOGA SPRINGS
Alexander, Donna M.
Business Teacher & Dept Head
Armer, Donna Lee
Sixth Grade Teacher
Atherton-Ely, H. Dale
English Teacher
Atherton-Ely, Karen P.
English Teacher
Bianchi, Lucia V.
French Teacher
Cantiello, Thomas Joseph
Business Teacher
Champagne, Grahame
Automotive Instructor
Cionek, Debi Mc Laughlin
Computer Literacy Teacher
Conklin, Lee B.
Social Studies Tchr
Cuite, Gerry Nawrocki
Teacher of Gifted & Talented
DeLancey, Michael P.
Social Studies Teacher
DelGrosso, Priscilla Ann
Health Educator
DeMagistris, Cheryl Gurga
Mathematics Teacher
Foster, Louise Heaton
Retired Elementary Teacher
Gately, Daniel Edward
High School Biology Teacher
Hotaling, Eric J.
High School Art Teacher
Huckel, Jack R.
PE Instructor & Soccer Coach
Johns, Richard A.
Fourth Grade Teacher
Kuenzel, Charles A.
9th Grade Science Teacher
Lawton, Harolyn C.
Sixth Grade Teacher
Limoli, Denise Warner
Assistant Prof of Dance
Lynaugh, Barbara J.
French Teacher
McGraw, Michael Leo
8th Grd Social Studies Tchr
Rabine, Brenda-Lee Tyler
English Teacher
Sadlon, Elthea Wood
Latin Teacher
Scarano, Anthony F.
Social Studies Teacher
Schechtman, Kathryn Turone
English Teacher
Sova, Joyce Sprague
5th Grade Teacher
Strader, Arlene M.
Physics Teacher
Twyman, Ann Lynn
Sixth Grade Teacher
Zimmer, Lawrence Alton, Jr.
Sociology Professor
SAUGERTIES
Fyhr, Gordon Philip, Jr.
English Teacher
Gallagher, Louise Gardecki
English Teacher
Giacomini, Toni
Fifth Grade Teacher
Rubenstein, David M.
English Teacher
Silberg, Dorothy Draper
Science Teacher
Smith, Hank E.
Scndry Physical Ed Instr
Young, Marisa Tigue
Vocal & Instrmntl Music Tchr
SAUQUOIT
Bean, Judith Wittman
Fifth Grade Teacher
Cahill, Patrick William
Physical Education Instructor
Cannistra, Ronnie Danella
Kindergarten Teacher
Comstock, Barbara Lynn (Fitch)
Fourth Grade Teacher
Edwards, Bethann Hecox
Secondary Social Studies Tchr
Kuta, Maryann Nicolia
Home & Career Skills Teacher
Miller, Sharon Labuz
1st Grade Teacher
Nicotera, Cathy Monescalchi
English Teacher
Payne, Deborah Schepsis
4th Grade Teacher
Petrie, Gloria Ann
8th Grd Soc Stud Teacher
Smith, Suzanne Chomka
Eight Grade English Teacher
Talbot, Thomas E.
Choral Music Director

Tuccillo, Jean Pell
2nd Grade Teacher
Zak, Edward Lee
HS Technology Teacher
SAVONA
Evarts, Rhodes H.
4th Grade Teacher
Schwartz, Karleen Trant
3rd Grade Teacher
SAYVILLE
Dunham, Kathleen
6th Grade Math & Science Tchr
Gist, Donna Sabatino
Business Teacher
Guendel, Camilia A.
Russian & French Teacher
Guglielmone, Virginia Buddenhagen
Math Teacher
Kaufman, Mary Ann Burke
Second Grade Teacher
Lawlor, James W.
HS Orchestra Dir & String Tchr
Schaefer, Kenneth W.
Fifth Grade Teacher
Taber, Jane C.
English Teacher
Wittman, Jennifer R.
High School English Teacher
SCARSDALE
Five, Cora Lee
Fifth Grade Teacher
Gast, Richard H.
Mathematics Teacher
Jacobs, Jayne C.
Special Education Teacher
McBrien, Alan F.
Spanish Teacher
Renino, Christopher D.
English Teacher
Sloan, Irving Joseph
Social Studies Teacher
SCHAGHTICOKE
Kelly, Christina Shaver
Spanish Teacher
SCHENECTADY
Allen, Patrick
Assoc Professor of English
Anderson, Lynda Greeson
Materials Sci & Math Instr
Baker, William R.
English Teacher
Bianchi, Vincent
Spanish Teacher
Burger, Linda Rice
HS Math Teacher
Carter, Alan R.
Professor of Pol Sci & History
Castanzo, Barbara Therese
Fifth Grade Teacher
Cerne, Gerald John
Adjunct Biology Professor
Chank, Christopher David
Social Studies Teacher
Chiarella, Carol L.
Chprsn & Assoc Prof of Acctng
Decker, Michael George
Coll Prep Tech Dept Instr
Duxbury, Jean M.
Fifth Grade Teacher
Evans, Diane J.
Mathematics Teacher
Evans, Gerald J.
Paralegal Professor
Ewing, Bette Shelton
School Counselor
Hoff, Robert J.
Professor of Criminal Justice
Hornick, Marie Funicello
HS English Teacher
Jackson, Frances Long
Math Teacher
Karbowski, John Paul, Jr.
Physical Education Teacher
Kuntz, Nan Decker
Second Grade Teacher
Ladopoulos, Marilyn D.
Spanish Teacher
Lanahan, Rosemary Bak
Accounting Professor
Lent, Lindette Irene
Asst Psychology Professor
Lockyer, George Edmond
Professor Emeritus
Loucks, Judy Allen
1st-2nd Grades Multiage Tchr
Lynch, Karen Lawrensen
Spanish Teacher
Maki, Bruce Lawrence
Retired Teacher
Mc Kee, Patricia Girgenti
High School Counselor
Meachem, Kevin J.
Social Studies Teacher
Mogro, Patricia
Assoc Prof of Spanish & Psych
Monahan, Chris
Math Teacher
Moore, Jerry E.
Associate Professor
Novak, Patricia E.
Teacher of Enrichment Programs
O'Brien, Paul James
English Teacher
Osinski, Ronald C.
HS Physical Education Teacher
Parent, James Thomas
Math & Computer Science Prof
Patka, Joyce Casino
Business Education Teacher

Patterson, Thomas M.
Technology & Technical Teacher
Peters, Karen Lee (Marshall)
French Teacher
Petraccione, Nicola
Social Studies Teacher
Pinkham, Day
Art Teacher
Potter, George H.
Chemistry Professor
Rickert, John
HS Social Studies Teacher
Rose, Rick
Administrator & Football Coach
Sano, Anthony M.
Assistant Professor
Sargent, Craig Deward
Social Studies & Math Teacher
Schauer, Ralf Wilhelm
Associate Professor
Schill, L. Jane J.
Art Educator
Sheehan, Cheryl Darrah
7th Grade Science Teacher
Stahl, Michael E.
High School Counselor
Stopera, Michelle Steele
Business Education Teacher
Strianese, Anthony John
Culinary Arts Chprsn & Prof
Szczepanski, Carol Lee Kozak
Science Teacher
Treanor, Mark Andrew
Special Education Teacher
Treis, Alina Mildred
English College Instructor
Van Ness, Richard J.
Professor of Management
Verrigni, Rocco Gerald
Prof of Hotel Mgmt Dept
Wood, Deborah Borovsky
MS Guidance Counselor
SCHENEVUS
Ackerson, Robert Charles
Social Studies Teacher
Green, Margaret Mildred
English Teacher
Parmerter, Robert Knapp
MS Social Studies Teacher
Woods, Sally Taylor
Art Teacher
SCHOHARIE
Clayton, Thomas Francis
AP English Teacher
Cummings, Marjorie B.
Fifth Grade Teacher
Dixon, Jody J.
English Teacher
Gargiula, Jude-Ann Esposito
Music Teacher
Law, Gerald H.
Music Teacher
Mackie, J. Alexander, III
Earth Science Teacher
Marbot, David S.
Agriculture Teacher
Pracher, Mark Stephen
High School Band Director
Reinhart, Harvey J.
6th Grade Teacher
Ruland, Donna Wheeler
Third Grade Teacher
Schweigard, Susan Bray
6th Grade Reading Teacher
Wagner, Janet Tarrant
Chemistry Teacher & Sci Coord
Wissenbach, Donna Elaine
Jr Sr High Mathematics Teacher
SCHUYLERVILLE
De Lucco, Deborah Cortese
French Teacher
SCIO
Estabrook, Karen June
English Teacher
Fuller, Darcy M.
Spanish & German Teacher
Hallett, James W.
SS Dept Chm & Admin Asst
Wood, Sandra Lee
Third Grade Teacher
SCOTIA
Chant, Nancy A.
Honors English Teacher
Cooley, Ann Kelly
Fifth Grade Teacher
George, John W.
Fifth Grade Teacher
Giammattei, James L.
Math Teacher
Ketchum, Joseph F.
Law & Economics Teacher
Mc Kenney, Karen A.
High School Counselor
Miner, Carol C.
Biology Teacher
Rose, Jean Baltz
Pyramid & Horizons Pgm Dir
Vernon, Joyce L.
English Teacher
Waligora, Lori Diane Powell
Third Grade Teacher
Walsh, Patricia A.
Religious Education Director
SCOTTSVILLE
Savage, Valerie Hark
Art Teacher
Skivington, Lynne Ann
Sixth Grade Teacher
VerSteeg, Peter J.
Biology Teacher

TSVILLE (cont)
Mary Kathryn
ish Teacher
, Christopher J.
n Sci Tchr & Adult Ed Adm
ORD
r, Kathleen
ness Teacher
an, Ronald John
School Guidance Counselor
EN
ein, Stuart
al Studies Tchr & Dept Ldr
, Happy
Instructor of Philosophy
ney, Judith E.
ish Teacher
o, Steven Joseph
ish Teacher
eau, Mark William
ish Assistant Professor
Craig Earl
ic Department Head
es, Fred W.
essor of Biology
, Helene Rainis
lance Counselor
no, Beatrice Irmiere
ondary English Teacher
e, Marc Elliot
al Music Teacher
off, Alan Lawrence
al Studies Teacher
, Samuel W.
stant Professor of English
Richard Cole
essor of Mechanical Tech
er, Christine Camandona
oc Professor of Nursing
, David
hematics Professor
Carol A.
ociate Professor of Biology
si, Ronald Anthony
ogy Teacher
Evelyn Roedel
t Grade Teacher
nan, Paul
essor of Music
lyshyn, Yvonne Broere
dergarten Teacher
KIRK
enter, Cathy F.
rd Grade Teacher
ECA FALLS
niak, Marie Donofrio
Grade Teacher
o, Barbara Hawkins
ond Grade Teacher
g, Richard A.
lish Teacher
ger, Angela DeSantis
h School English Teacher
, Michael David
cher
no, Suzanne Marie
thematics Teacher
fione, Edward
th Grade Teacher
, Nancy Milner
Grade Teacher
ener, John Andreas, Jr.
th Science Teacher
RON SPRINGS
r, Conrad F.
ired Soc Stud & Math Tchr
on, Sally JoAnne
ence Teacher & Dept Chprsn
LTER ISLAND
nam, Walter Cole, III
mputer & Math Teacher
RBURNE
niarski, James Mayfred
sistant Principal
oth, Scott Richard
gh School Art Teacher
ks, Anne Marie De Prospo
ence Teacher
RMAN
erson, John Robert
emistry & Mathematics Tchr
la, Mary Park
athematics Teacher
RLEY
az, Brian James
Grade Science Teacher
man, Nina Simon
Grade Teacher
REHAM
, Ian R.
nd Dir & Elctrnc Music Tchr
guato, Barbara Terlecki
ecial Education Teacher
RTSVILLE
op, Cathryn Brown
d Grade Teacher
ward, Laurie
Special Education Teacher
ris, Leo
tired Teacher
er, Mary Lou Clark
urth Grade Teacher
tel, Susan Ternisky
ath Teacher
, Lori Jeanne
hool Counselor
r, Linda Lea (Yarger)
urth Grade Teacher

SHRUB OAK
Coles, Franklin
English Teacher
Hauser, Debra Shukin
Business Education Teacher
O'Toole, Christopher John
AP Mathematics Teacher
Piermarini, Ernest Joseph
Superintendent Assistant
Vellone-Painten, MaryAnn
Spanish Teacher
SIDNEY
Finnegan, Robert Eugene
Third Grade Teacher
SILVER CREEK
Bilas, James M.
English Teacher
Norton, Richard Walker
Multi-Age Teacher
Privitera, Anthony J.
Earth Science Teacher
Raymond, Michlena P.
Mathematics Teacher
Wright, William F.
Fifth Grade Teacher
SINCLAIRVILLE
Currah, Joey A.
Business Teacher
Ognibene, John Robert
Sixth Grade Teacher
Pecuch, Robert D.
Guidance Counselor
SKANEATELES
Armstrong, Douglas C.
Fifth Grade Teacher
Grajko, Christine Roscoe
Second Grade Teacher
Griffin, Jennifer Smith
Earth Science Teacher
Kringer, Micheal Dale
HS Vocal Music & Drama Teacher
Rivenburg, Gary Alan
Instructional Tech Specialist
Sturiale, George I.
English Teacher
Taylor, Nancy Kelly
Secondary Math Teacher
Tidd, Michael Alan, FSC
Former Rel & Soc Studies Tchr
SLATE HILL
Bailo, Lynda Morris
Honors English II Teacher
Carrozza, Frank Paul
Physical Ed & Athletics Dir
Davis, Jeffry Dennet
8th Grade Science Teacher
DeMarco, Peter George
Mathematics Teacher
Hutchings, Antoinette Jannotti
Business Education Teacher
Jarosz, Larri Vreeland
Span Tchr, Frgn Lang Dpt Chair
Jarosz, Ray
7th Grade Math Teacher
Simmons, Timothy John
Sixth Grade Science Teacher
SMITHTOWN
Backfish, Charles G.
Social Studies Instructor
Brew, Stacie Joy
Secondary English Teacher
Caffaro, Phyllis J.
Fifth Grade Teacher
Carey, Lillian Torkelsen
Spanish & French Teacher
Castellano, Marie Catherine
2nd Grade Teacher
Faust, Carl H.
Biological Science Teacher
Hyder, Thomas L.
US His & Economics Teacher
Jaye, Irwin
5th Grade Teacher
Krebs, Robert Karl
High School German Teacher
Magram, Elyse Caren (Madnick)
Mathematics Teacher
Nicosia, Salvatore Charles
Dir of Counseling Svcs
Pergolizzi, Grace Genovesi
Italian & Spanish Teacher
Renke, Joan Monks
Chemistry Teacher
Shelley, Michael Arthur
High School English Teacher
Stock, Robert E.
Physics Teacher
Stouter, Maura Olga
Physical Education Teacher
Wagner, Mary Massaro
Kindergarten Teacher
SODUS
Campbell, Nancy P.
Kindergarten Teacher
Hooper, Ann Simmons
First Grade Teacher
Palmer, Nancy H.
Retired Fourth Grade Teacher
Sullivan, Linda D.
Social Studies Teacher
Taber, Sharon Fowler
Sixth Grade Teacher
SODUS POINT
Potter, Cory O.
Retired English Teacher
SOMERS
Lockshiss, Dolores E.
English & Art History Tchr
Martin, Robert Andrew
Business Education Teacher

Mc Sweeney, Brian Thomas
Theology Teacher
Meehan, Janet Louise
Art Dept Chprsn & Teacher
Mullaney, Edward L.
7th-8th Grd Social Stud Tchr
Mungan, Mary Jane
Developmental Reading Teacher
Platow, Barry Paul
5th Grade Teacher
Trinkle, Therese Kaiven
Fifth Grade Teacher
Ziccardi, Josephine
English Teacher & Chairperson
SOUTH DAYTON
Brown, Jodi Wade
5th Grade Teacher
Kye, Terry Lee
Mathematics Teacher
Moritz, Kimberly Mormur
Spanish & Business Teacher
Ormsby, Debra
Principal
Pucciarelli, Donna Jean
Business Education Teacher
Zanghi, Douglas C.
Chemistry & Biology Tchr
SOUTH GLENS FALLS
Quigley, Loretta A.
English Department Chair
Read, Ellen Heath
Business Teacher
Riley, Robert C.
Global Studies Teacher
Roberts, Barbara J.
Resource Room Teacher
Stonebridge, Robert
Technology Teacher
Yurkewicz, William
Physics Teacher
SOUTH KORTRIGHT
Glas, J. Robert
Art Teacher
Joedicke, Joan M.
Library Media Specialist
LaVigne, Kathleen Dowd
Social Studies Dept Chprsn
Many, Ruth Rose
Kindergarten Teacher
SOUTH NEW BERLIN
Borden, Frances E.
English Teacher
SOUTH OTSELIC
Mahunik, Peter William
Business Teacher & Chair
SOUTHAMPTON
Iaccio, Frank Louis
American Government Teacher
Lengyel, Therese M.
Science Teacher
Mangano, Vincent
HS Mathematics Teacher
SOUTHOLD
Bigall, Edmond John
2nd Grade Teacher
Ferretti, Jean
Elementary Science Teacher
Sadowski, Andrew John
Social Studies Teacher
Schade, Christine Elizabeth
High School Math Teacher
Westgate, Victor R.
History Teacher
SPENCER
Potter, Dale S.
Mathematics Tchr & Cmptr Coord
SPENCERPORT
Burkey, Marilyn Elaine
Second Grade Teacher
Campanaro, Marie Juliet
Spanish Teacher
Cardella, Francis Paul
Third Grade Teacher
Clarke, Mary Hawley
Social Studies Teacher
Clarke, Stephan Paul
High School English Teacher
Coll, Lea (Hock)
Physics Teacher
Dentinger, James Anthony
Reading Specialist
Farnsworth, Jeffrey Scott
HS Social Studies Teacher
Jones, Alan David
Choral Music Director
Linhart, Thomas M., Sr.
Social Studies Teacher
Ruch, Janice Smith
English Teacher
Schneider, Douglas Richard
Physical Education Teacher
Snyder, Wayne
Physics Teacher & Dept Chair
Stewart, Judith Cholewa
Teacher
Wilcox, Gerard E.
Heavy Equip & Hydraulics Tchr
Wilcox, Sally Root
Fifth Grade Teacher
Wolf, Donna Navarra
French Teacher
SPRING BROOK
Loyst, Beverly Woods
Social Studies Teacher
SPRING VALLEY
Collazo, Janet
8th Grade Teacher
Fialkoff, Iris F.
Speech & Theater Teacher

Glick, Sylvia Perlo
Reading Teacher
Kamen, Rhonda R.
Spanish Teacher
Mason, Rebecca S.
Instrumental Music Teacher
Mc Cormack, John A.
English & Writing Skills Tchr
Pelletier, Rae Harmon
Choral Director
Schwartz, Larry
Social Studies Teacher
Whiffen, Mary Borden
English Teacher
Widmer, Walter H.
10th Grade Biology Teacher
SPRINGVILLE
Benning, Karen Ann
Fifth Grade Teacher
Claus, Michelle Rovner
Math Teacher
Clayton, Matthew W.
Chemistry Teacher
Cocca, William P.
Music Teacher & Band Director
Frank, Patricia A. Jaromin
High School Math Teacher
Metz, Robert J.
Business Department Chairman
Morse, Brenda Hendricks
English Teacher
Schlageter, Robert Leo
Retired Math Tchr & Dept Chair
Sopko, John Anthony
Social Studies Teacher
Sorensen, Robert G.
Science Chm & Physics Tchr
White, Nancy Guhl
Spanish Teacher
STAMFORD
Smith, Elaine Sprague
Home Ec, Fam & Cnsumr Sci Tchr
STANFORDVILLE
King, Virginia Ann Rolli
Elementary Teacher
Swinton, Jill Elizabeth
3rd Grade Teacher
STANLEY
De Flyer, Edward W.
Criminal Justice Instructor
High, Stephen J.
Business Marketing Mgmt Instr
STAR LAKE
Frank, Ronald James
Biology, Health & PE Teacher
Hitchman, Kelly Patraw
Guidance Counselor
Nielsen-Percy, Anni
French Teacher
Rice, Sandra McKenney
Special Education Tchrs Aide
Woods, Susan Dolores
Kindergarten Teacher & Coach
STATEN ISLAND
Acquista, Nicholas Raymond
Social Studies Teacher
Adams, Henry Morris
Fifth Grade Teacher
Anderson, Lawrence George
Social Studies Teacher
Aronson, Marilyn Ruth (Rubcich)
English Teacher
Avena, Linda Leotta
Library Teacher
Axel, Nathan Steven
Band Director & Music Teacher
Bash, Deborah Fischer
High School Mathematics Tchr
Bass, Carol Palevsky
Library Teacher
Bauer, Ilene
Language Arts English Teacher
Berger, Diane Thomas
Chemistry Director
Bernstein, Alan
8th Grade Social Studies Tchr
Bilotti, Helen Rofrano
2nd Grade Teacher
Boresta, Colleen Berry
Social Studies Teacher
Campbell, Kathleen Kiener
English Teacher
Ciulla, Karin Castelli
History Teacher
Cohen, Maxine Alice
Nursing Teacher
Costagliola, Thomas William
Italian & Spanish Teacher
Cumming, Mary K.
Fourth Grade Teacher
Cummings, Timothy
Global Studies II Teacher
Curry, Janice Schiavi
English Teacher
Dahl, Laney
Retired Mathematics Teacher
D'Angelo, Tina M.
Kindergarten Teacher
DeMeo, Kathleen Agnes
Retired Teacher
DeStefano, Elena Barbieri
Kindergarten Teacher
Dhamoon, Manmohan Singh
Chemistry Teacher
Donahue, Stephen Jeffrey
English Teacher
Donohue, Maureen Therese
Chemistry Teacher
Drew, Laura Alice
English Teacher

Fahey, Rosemary
Kindergarten Teacher
Falconett, Barbara Joan
Librarian
Faughnan, Lorraine Desiano
Mathematics Tchr
Ficara, Eileen P.
English & Keyboarding Teacher
Ford-Vitollo, Ellen Jayne
2nd Grade Teacher
Freese, Michael Edward
Math & Computer Teacher
Freifeld, Howard George
Chemistry Teacher
Fulciniti, Nicole C.
Biology Teacher
Gallagher, David
Mathematics Teacher
Gannon, Timothy Michael
Dean of Students & Math Tchr
Gianoulis, Gloria (Massa)
Jr High English Teacher
Godeski, Joan
Youth Minister
Gueli, John George
Administrator
Hamerschlag, Patricia Myers
Fifth Grade Teacher
Hamerschlag, Wain
Science Teacher
Hanover, Roy
Science Teacher
Harris, Florence Ann
Computer Tchr & Coop Coord
Hartje, Alvin Carl
Science Teacher
Horowitz, Martin L.
Social Studies Teacher
Jamiel, John
Theatre Dept Visiting Instr
Joris, Irene (Georges)
Teacher
Katz, Janice Feinzeig
English Teacher
Keenan, Nancy
Title I Teacher
Kenel, Sally A.
Theology Professor
Klein, Rosemary Diane
Art Teacher
Kornbluth, Aharon
7th Grd Religious Studies Tchr
Kovacic, Robert William
Senior Army & JROTC Instr
Krumm, Eleanor A.
English Dept Chprsn & Teacher
Kuck, F. J. M.
5th Grade Classroom Teacher
Lacagnino, Evelyn Molinary
Eighth Grade Teacher
LaMorte, David S.
Theater Arts Chairman
Lanza, Rosaria Salamone
Spanish Teacher
Lazaris, Nicole Ellen
English Tchr & Guidance Cnslr
Lerner, Lois E. (Labowitz)
Spanish Teacher
Lichtenstein, Judith Arkin
Dental Health Teacher
Liozzi, Bruce Nicholas
5th Grade Teacher
Loeb, Nina (Ben)
Mathematics Teacher
Ludwig, Marjorie
HS Mathematics Teacher
Maffei, Stephanie
Mathematics Teacher
Manske, Brian Kenneth
Mathematics Department Chm
Marino, Linda Carol
Math Teacher
Mazella, Michael A., Jr.
Principal
Mazella, Pamela Smith
Mathematics Teacher
Mc Carthy, Irene Newstad
Prof of Accounting & Taxation
McDonald, Diane Murphy
Tchr of Gifted & Talented
McMillen, Loretta Ryan
Communications Arts Teacher
Mc Quilkin, Rita Noel
Spanish Teacher & Grd Advisor
Melucci, Carol A.
Business Education Teacher
Mercaldo, David
Teacher
Mezzacappa, Rose Ann Montalbano
4th Grade Teacher
Milza, Peter Joseph
Social Studies Teacher
Mohlenhoff, Bruce R.
8th Grade Teacher
Mohr, Wilson Dawsey
Math Chairman
Mulligan, Patricia J.
Eng Tchr & Newspaper Adv
Nelson, Barbara Cackowski
Kindergarten Teacher
Panfilo, Francesca
French Teacher
Pedersen, Arne A.
Physics Teacher
Pero, Louise
Eighth Grade Teacher
Pezzuti, Vincent G., Jr.
English Teacher
Portu, Caridad
Pre-Kndgtn Teacher & Director

STATEN ISLAND (cont)
Potter, Richard Michael
Math Teacher
Rivas, Mary Mangiero
Computer Teacher
Robilotti, Jhn Joseph
Social Studies Teacher
Robinson, Sigmund
Electrical Engineering Teacher
Robitzski, Nancy Jean
7th-8th Grade Teacher
Rogg, Eleanor Meyer
Professor of Sociology
Roseman, Steven
Marketing Teacher
Rosenberg, Tracy Lebowitz
Performing Arts Teacher
Ross, Allan F.
High School Technology Teacher
Rubcich, Nicholas George
Fourth Grade Teacher
Scalisi, Paul A.
Bio, Cmptrs Tchr & Grd Adv
Schlefstein, Muriel S.
Science Teacher
Scotto Carannante, Angela
Coordinator Foreign Lang Dept
Sfayer, James Stephen
Senior Marine Instructor
Sheehy, Kevin L.
Science Institute Program Tchr
Shimony, Robert Joseph
Biology Teacher
Smith, Claire D.
Religion Dept Chairperson
Spector, Joyce Ann
4th Grade Teacher
Stern, Isabel
Russian & Art Teacher
Touhey, Julie Ann Mazella
English Teacher
Trerotola, Leonard Michael
Music Department Chair
Tulino, Ernest Anthony
Business Dept Chairperson
Ursillo, Rosalie L.
Kindergarten Teacher
Verticchio, Phillip
History Teacher
Vinal, Corrine
English Teacher
Vinet, George Ellsworth, Jr.
Hlth & Physical Education Coor
Walters, Eric A.
Science Dept Chm & Teacher
Weber, Alan J.
5th Grade Teacher
Wexler, Richard
Language Arts Teacher
Wilson, Alice Mc Ateer
Math Teacher
Wright, Henry S.
French Teacher
STILLWATER
Kinowski, Kathryn Lee
English Teacher
O'Connor, Gregory John
High School Math Teacher
STONE RIDGE
Cooke, Diane O'Brien
Instructor of Nursing
STONY BROOK
Comerford, Daniel J., III
Social Studies Teacher
DeSimone, Marie Stabile
First Grade Teacher
Ewan, Christina Anne
HS Spanish Teacher & Coach
Fonseca, Donald R.
Director of Counseling
Hall, Gemma Mahoney
1st Grade Teacher
Heischmann, Theodora DiFranco
English Teacher
Kaye, Deborah
Mathematics Teacher
Kenney, John Michael
Athletic Dir & Faculty Instr
Lannigan, Gerard Stephen
Social Studies Teacher
O'Hare, Michael James
Social Studies Teacher
Williams, Reda Ezell
Third Grade Teacher
STONY POINT
Freda, Roger Louis
Secondary School Administrator
Friedrich, Barbara Kohler
Sixth Grd Soc Studies Teacher
Murphy, Katharine Phillips
Principal
SUFFERN
Ackerson, Wallace
4th Grade Teacher
Austin, Douglas Scott
English, Comm & Drama Teacher
Coronel, Victor Felipe
Physics Professor
DePalma, Ginny Barone
8th Grade English Teacher
Edmunds, Margy
Guidance Counselor
Giles, Margaret Ellen
English Teacher
Lum, Stacy B.
Fifth Grade Teacher
Lyon, Cheryl D.
English Teacher
Miller, Joseph Michael
Secondary Level Sci Teacher
Miller, Sandra Shulinoff
Music Teacher
Moseley, Thomas Robert
Professor
Olson, Karen A.
Hnrs Science Research Teacher
Partridge, Deborah
Art Teacher
Quadagno, Ronald Thomas
Physical Science Teacher
Schneider, William Arthur
Student Support Teacher
Thelen, James M.
Mathematics Professor
Wilson, Robert J.
English Teacher
SYOSSET
Andreone, Karen Maria
PE Teacher & Athletic Director
Asaph, Philip
Creative Writing Teacher
Barry, Ronald
Assistant Principal
Berg, Sheila Blumenthal
Earth Science Teacher
Board, Nathan Samuel
English Teacher
Capolongo, Andrea Teresa
Secondary School Art Teacher
Conlin, Mary
Theology Teacher
De Stefano, Patrice Nevitt
English Teacher
Donahue, Elizabeth C.
HS Math Teacher & Dept Chprsn
Fuchs, Asenath J.
Science Teacher
Gladstone, Joseph Paul
Math Teacher
Gordon, Joan Grillo
Social Studies Chair & Teacher
Inglis, Christine Cherie
High School Guidance Chprsn
Koppeis, Patricia Stephenson
Orchestra Director
Leeds, Barbara Weisburst
English Teacher
Lukaszewski, Angela Cigna
Physics Teacher
Mallen, Janet Greene
7th-8th Grade English Teacher
Michaels, Herbert
Musical Theatre Dept Chair
Michaels, Patricia G.
Musical Theatre Teacher
Simons, Kenneth J.
English Teacher
Stoltz, Shelley H.
Dance & Drama Director
SYRACUSE
Abate, Charles Joseph
Electrical & Cmptr Tech Prof
Agonito, Joseph
History Professor
Argus, Maryann
Math Teacher
Avellino, Grenardo L.
Vice Principal
Bacon, Ernest Allen
Earth Science Teacher
Black, William Jeffrey
High School Vocal Instructor
Bonzi, Susan Monica
Assoc Prof & Dir Undgrd Pgrm
Breindel, Renee Pollack
Spanish Teacher
Brick, Francine Artin
5th Grade Teacher
Brown, Anthony L.
Program Coordinator of Tutors
Brown, Richard Earl
Technology Teacher
Browne, Joseph Bradley
Mathematics Professor
Burton, Sharon DelSignore
Fourth Grade Teacher
Caezza, Joseph Richard
Biology Teacher
Canorro, Robert D.
Tchr Asst of Culinary Arts
Carlin, Patricia Myers
Global Studies Teacher
Carr, Enzo Anthony
High School English Teacher
Catalano, Concetta Barbagallo
4th Grade Teacher
Cericola, Sharon Harrison
Third Grade Teacher
Czarniewicz, Margaret C.
6th Grade Teacher
Deegan, James W.
Mathematics Teacher
De Mott, Bernadette
Secondary English Teacher
Eager, Kevin
Physics & Earth Science Tchr
Fisher, Nellie R.
Sixth Grade Teacher
Fiutak, Erika Anne
Art Teacher & Dept Chairman
Flower, Terry
Humanities Teacher
Flynn, Margaret Hennessey
Spelling Teacher
Fox, Joanne Mary
Fourth Grade Teacher
Francis, John E.
English Teacher
Giuliano, Gerard
Graphic Comm Instructor
Goodhart, Thomas Scott
Health Educator
Harth, Dorothy Feldmann
Professor of Spanish
Hartnett, Maureen Ann
First Grade Teacher
Herron, Patrick Richard
Social Studies Teacher
Hintz, Catherine Cook
3rd Grade Teacher
Hughes, Hugh Joseph
8th Grade Soc Studies Teacher
Jordan, Mattie Joyce
4th & 5th Grade Teacher
Keefe, Michael Leonard
Chemistry Teacher
Killian, Kyle David
Instr of Human Services Dept
Klossner, Diane Reese
Fourth Grade Teacher
Leskoske, Joseph Anthony
Science Teacher
Levett, Colleen Ann (Costello)
Speech & Language Pathologist
Lindemann, Thomas
Music Teacher & Band Director
Lynch Killoran, Susan
5th Grade Teacher
Margrey, Ronald F.
Secondary Mathematics Teacher
Mariani, Melody Andriello
English Teacher
Marsh, James H.
Health Education Teacher
Mc Jilton, Thomas Steven
Eighth Grade Science Teacher
McMann, Mary Elizabeth
Assoc Prof of Counseling Dept
Merluzzi, Deborah Josephine
First & Second Grade Teacher
Miori-Merola, Doreen M.
English Teacher & Yearbook Adv
Moore, Kevin Morris
Professor of Music & Bus Law
Moore-Wleklinski, Patricia M.
English Teacher
Naumann, Paul Schiller, SJ
English Instructor
Norton, Donna Marie
Vice Principal
O'Hara, Elizabeth Ann
Fr Tchr & Frgn Lang Dept Ldr
Pallotta, Lucille Izzo
Asst Professor of Fr & Italian
Paratore, Anthony John
Advanced English Teacher
Pedrotti, Michele Ellen
Social Studies Teacher
Peterson, Patricia Hernandez
English Teacher
Petta, Katharine G.
Former Science Teacher
Phipps, Dianne Lapenta
Spanish Teacher
Pickard, Susan Boryc
Fourth Grade Teacher
Reinke, Julie M.
Math & Computer Teacher
Ridlon, James A.
Professor of Art
Ringwood, David C.
History Teacher
Risser, Barbara Gail
Assoc Prof of English & Rdng
Romano, Joseph A.
Physical Education Teacher
Saba, Vivianne A.
Span Tchr & Frgn Lang Chair
Sage, Cathy DeLair
6th Grade Teacher
Schenk, Edward A.
Fourth Grade Teacher
Short, Doris Dale
Third Grade Teacher
Simko, Joseph Michael
Tech Dept Chairman & Teacher
Spadafora, Vincent Louis, Jr.
Assistant Professor
Spillane, Kathleen Kelly
English Teacher
Starkweather, John Earl
English Professor
Staruch, Korina
Option I Teacher
Thomas, Laurence M.
Professor
Thomas, Loretha Langham
Business Teacher
Turner, Lee James
Instrumental Music Teacher
Venner, Carol Ann Hooper
6th Grade Teacher
Walker, Deborah Anne (Spina)
Secondary Math Teacher
White, Reginald Richard
7th Grd Social Studies Teacher
Williams, James G.
Professor of Religion
Wolf, Steven Anthony
Vice Principal
Youmell, Paula Marie
Health Education Teacher
TANNERSVILLE
Dearing, Susan Hoffman
French & German Teacher
Mudge, Randy Albert
Athletic Dir & PE Teacher
TARRYTOWN
Coleman, Julie Pelkan
English Tutor & Teacher
Colton, Thomas Allen
Latin & English Teacher
Conklin, Henry A.
Chemistry & Physics Teacher
Fenstermacher, Rowena Summers
Latin Teacher
Fitzgerald, Elizabeth Langle
Second Grade Teacher
Giordano, James V.
Social Studies Teacher
Hampsey, Maureen Horan
High School English Teacher
Hardy, Deborah
Bilingual School Counselor
Johnson, Robert, Jr.
English Teacher
Kaplan, Diana
Mathematics Teacher
King, Julie Dean
Counseling Co-Dir & His Tchr
Masters, Maureen Mc Greal
Remedial Mathematics Teacher
Peters, Clifford Simpson
Eighth Grade English Teacher
Reich, Rita S. (Evenson)
ESL Teacher
Siviglia, Anne Klotz
Eng & Creative Writing Teacher
Wenzel, James S.
MS Social Studies Teacher
THIELLS
Bassani, Deborah Gray
English Teacher
Chaiet, Carl K.
Art Teacher
Dillon, Mary Lou L.
US History & Pub Policy Tchr
Drinane, Janice Drunstadter
ESL-BL Coordinator & Teacher
Holmes, Laura Marie
Art Teacher
Johnsmeyer, Ellen Gilmartin
English Teacher
Korn, Richard
10th Grade Global Studies Tchr
Levy, Mary Margaret
Physical Education Teacher
Palmero, Leo John
Tenth Grade Biology Teacher
Parrillo, Matthew Anthony
Science Teacher
Singer, Larry D.
Mathematics Teacher
Tracey, Diane Peyton
Social Studies Teacher
White, Dolores Levy
Reading Specialist
Wilson, Margaret Clark
Spanish Teacher
THORNWOOD
Barber, Laura L.
Guidance Counselor
Garr, Donna Farneti
Guidance Director
Massimi, Maria G.
Foreign Lang Teacher & Liaison
Messemer, John Francis
6th Grade Teacher
TICONDEROGA
Breitenbach, Deborah Jones
English Teacher
Dolbeck, Keith Allen
7th-12th Grd Science Teacher
Smith, Richard Stephen
Special Education Teacher
Thompson, Nancy L.
Adjunct Instructor in Art
TIOGA CENTER
Boyer, Wayne M.
Business Teacher
Brougham, Mary Thompson
Fifth Grade Teacher
Maassen, Denise E.
His, Eng, Span & Ger Teacher
Pascuzzo, Joan Audrey
Retired Sixth Grade Teacher
Tulsey, Richard Lee
Social Studies Teacher
TONAWANDA
Allen, Joseph Carr
Science Teacher
Critelli, Ralph Joseph
Science Teacher
Eaton, Ronald A.
English Teacher
Golden, Catherine Harriet
2nd Grade Teacher
Marino, Janet Zidow
Spanish Teacher
McKay, David William
6th Grade Teacher
O'Connor, Robert Charles
Biology Teacher
Paterson, William M.
English Teacher
Petrinec, Kathryn Ann
Global Studies & Psych Tchr
Pudhorodsky, Kathleen Maddigan
Social Studies Teacher
Roberts, Joan Smith
High School English Teacher
Steck, Calvin Kingsley
Senior Spanish Teacher
Vine, Janet Diane
English Teacher
TRIBES HILL
Di Caprio, Elizabeth Anne (Gargiulo)
Retired 5th Grade Teacher
TROUPSBURG
Dreher, Denise Dempsey
Fourth Grade Teacher
TROY
Adamchak, Linda A.
Instructor
Allen, Marcia
Lang Dept Chair & French Tchr
Athanasiou, Robert
Medical Director
Backhaus, George R.
Science Dept Chair
Betterly, John Andrew
His Independence Fndtn Chair
Bitley, Charles Warren
8th Grade Mathematics Teacher
Bochette, David E.
Health, First Aid & PE Teacher
Boylen, Charles William
Professor of Biology
Callahan, Lisa A.
Associate Prof of Sociology
Carlson, Lorraine E.
Mathematics Teacher
Caruso, Madeline Theresa
Teacher & Admin
Cassella, Barbara A. (Heeran)
Social Studies Teacher
Clesceri, Lenore Stanke
Professor of Biochemistry
Corr, Cherie Anne Pash
Assoc Prof of Mathematics
Craney, Joan Boomhower
Fifth Grade Teacher
Cupolo, Nancy T.
Assistant Professor
Curran, Bernadette Foley
Journalism Teacher
Dagenais, Daniel G.
History Teacher
Danner, Carol A.
Assistant Prof of Biology
Darling, William Webb
Assoc Prof of Mechanical Engr
Deighan, Mary Ellen Dugan
Assoc Professor
Dennis, Timothy David
Professor & Construction Tech
DeSalvo, Darienne Anne
Student Assistance Counselor
DiBari, Joseph Vincent
Science Teacher
Drebitko, Judianne M.
Social Studies Teacher
Dunleavy, Paul D.
Life Science Teacher
Eckert, William John
Business Instructor
Ehrlich-Johnson, Dorleen
Kindergarten Teacher
Elling, Bob
Director of EMS Institute
Fiore, Susan E.
4th Grade Teacher
Fitzpatrick, John Edward
Physical Education Teacher
Flass, Barbara Uline
English Teacher
Gallagher, Joanne Kittell
Sixth Grade Science Teacher
Geuther, Ronald Charles
Chemistry & Biology Teacher
Gillespie, Mary M.
Asst Prof of Human Svcs Dept
Glaros, George Raymond
Professor of Chemistry
Hart, Mary Kay
Assistant Professor
Hartshorn, Theresa Maria
Occupational Therapy Professor
Heckelman, Donald David, Jr.
Asst Prof of Engineering Sci
Hull, Maria-Catherine (Daly)
Assoc Prof Indstrl Technology
Ingraham, Chrys M.
Asst Professor of Sociology
Irish, Joy Hanson
Director
Jacobson, Dorothy Troup
English Teacher
Jennings, Sybillyn H.
Psychology Professor
Jensen, Michael Keith
Professor of Mechanical Engrng
Jones, Richard L.
Edith Mc Crea Prof of Theatre
Joscelyn, Warren Henry
Mathematics Professor
Karpien, Carol M.
Associate Professor
Karpien, Ronald J.
Physics Professor
Kaufman, Howard
Prof of Elec, Comp & Engrng
Kolakoski, Dawn Laymond
Early Childhood Education Prof
Kowalski, Debra
Coordinator of Pace Program
Kramer, Francis J.
Retired English Professor
Lansing, Warren Donald
Fifth Grade Teacher
Leathem, Mary Tonita Armao
Fourth Grade Teacher
Levi, Mark
Mathematics Professor
List, George
Department Chair
Loomis, Jeffrey Paul
Vice Principal & Math Teacher

(cont)
ohn Richard, Jr.
ssor
rland, Frances C.
istry Teacher
urg, Charles Joseph
eering Professor
is, Bruce E.
nt Assistance Counselor
, Kathleen Millet
urce Room Teacher
, Mary Harknett
ng Instructor
son, Rosemary Austin
th Grade Soc Stud Teacher
ngelo, Laura M.
gy Instructor
oe, Brian J.
ssor of Human Services
osh, Donna D.
an Services Instructor
d, Maureen C.
: Prof Criminal Justice
Linda Guthrie
e Economics Teacher
ek, Wojciech Zbigniew
rials Engrng Assoc Prof
ll, Anne Marie
School Mathematics Tchr
n, Morris Herbert, III
: Prof of Chemical Engrng
ford, Roxanne D.
sh Professor
William George
ssor of Visual Arts
o, Leik Norwald
c Prof of Engrng & Physics
wiec, Michael Joseph
ematics & Theology Teacher
s, John Henry
nistry Professor
ier, Barbara J.
Grade English Teacher
, Mark A.
Asst Prof of Materials
Eileen Marie
ematics Teacher
n, Patricia O'Reilly
ch & Spanish Teacher
i, Terri LaReau
of Business Admin
ck, Holly A.
essor of Psychology
vcien, Todd Michael
nical Engineering Asst Prof
, Robert Joseph
stant Professor
Anne Tucker
stant Professor of Nursing
Kenneth
of Electrical Engineering
Richard
essor of Social Sciences
n, William C.
ounting Professor
n, Peter Lance
essor of Criminal Justice
oi, Joseph Thomas
Constr & Maint Assoc Prof
ck, Thomas Joseph
nan Services Instr
n, Steven I.
Grd Social Studies Teacher
arz, Gwendolyn Anne
lish Teacher
n, Nancy Olmsted
lia Specialist
our, Linda Jandreau
eer Pathways, Hlth Svc Tchr
, Joan Elizabeth
ociate Professor
ahan, Michael
r of Anatomy & Pathology
ghnessy, Franceen Lanzillo
lish Teacher
Susan Mc Morrow
h Grade Teacher
an, Joan Garner
eign Languages Teacher
, David Arthur
logy Teacher
n, Karen Reichel
ructor of Nursing
er, Curtis W.
Grade Earth Science Tchr
rscales, Euan Francis Cuthbert
oc Prof of Mech Engrng
ker, Eugenia Marie
partment Chairperson
bach, Richard Adam
Studies Tchr & Ath Coach
ff, Helen Arcuri
fessor
, Michael
t Prof of Criminal Justice
, Gordon D.
gh School History Teacher
sey, Burt L.
nior Lecturer
nzio, Marion Ann
sociate Professor
, Joseph Briggs
th Grade Teacher
zer, Robert W.
rketing Professor
er, Frederick Henry
soc Prof & Bus Admin
raub, Dawn Stuart
ssian & French Teacher

Whelden, Virginia Gostanian
English Instructor
Wisniewski, Jeanine Gabriella
English Teacher
Wnek, Gary Edmund
Chemistry Professor
Zubrick, James W.
Chemistry Professor

TRUMANSBURG

Bonnet, Gordon Paul
Biology Teacher
Kotun, Martha Essex
Kindergarten Teacher
Ploss, Robert W.
8th Grade Science Teacher
Somerville, Wesley David
Physical Education Teacher

TRUXTON

Arnold, John J.
6th Grade Teacher

TUCKAHOE

Muenzen, Marie
Second Grade Teacher

TUPPER LAKE

Skiff, Steven Douglas
11th Grade History Teacher

TURIN

Bradish, Michael James
Fifth Grade Teacher
Cook, Elizabeth Bruce
Ninth Grade English Teacher
DiBenedetto, Robert Thomas
US His & Government Teacher

TUXEDO PARK

Meekins, Olga Jean Zitman
Former Teacher
Stover, Ronald Howard
Secondary Teacher

UNADILLA

Gallo, John William
Fifth Grade Teacher

UNION SPRINGS

Delaney, Helen Elizabeth
Sixth Grade Science Teacher
Gunnip, James P.
Phys Education Teacher & Coach
Roche, Patricia Abbruzzese
7th Grd Social Studies Teacher
Sandlas, Valerie Deppa
English Teacher

UNIONDALE

Adams, Velma Jones
Vocal, Choral & Music Teacher
Eason, Brenda A.
5th Grade Teacher, Chairperson
Esposito, Robert L.
High School Chemistry Teacher
Frankel, Yitzchok David
Teacher
Friedman, Muriel Scarabino
ESL & Spanish Teacher
Graves, Lisa Denton
Third Grade Teacher
Hangen, Marilyn Ann Edgar
Assistant Principal
Jones, Evelyn I.
Guidance Counselor
Jorisch, Mara Goldman
Mathematics Teacher
Leichtman, Sue
Math Teacher
Lemmie, James
Music Teacher
Marseille, Carolyn G.
Math Teacher
Mazzarella, Mimi Fetta
English Teacher
Peterson, Ann Marie
Spcl Education Resource Tchr
Poupko-Reichman, Sara Malka
High School Teacher
Tufano, Neil Joseph
Spcl Ed & Resource Room Tchr
Wangerin, Paula Baptista
Spanish Teacher
Wright, Colleen Andrea
Secondary Ed Science Teacher

UTICA

Anibarro, Justine Santiago
ESL Teacher
Barker, Mary L.
Social Studies Teacher
Barone, Robert G.
Eng & Creative Writing Tchr
Boyle, Sharon Denise
Assistant Professor of English
Brooks, Angela Camardo
Mathematics Teacher & Team Ldr
Byington, Darlene Johnson
Third Grade Teacher
Carroll, Kathleen Mary
English Teacher
Chainey, Dolores Mancuso
Biology Teacher
Czepiel, Diane Morelle
English Teacher
Elinskas, Amy Barney
Nursing Instructor
Ferris, Carolyn Marie
Bus & Cmptr Ed Dept Chair
Fredsell, Rochelle Mary
English Teacher
Friedberg, Arthur Lincoln
Professor of Economics
Gigliorri, Linda I.
Accounting Professor
Henderson, Donald H.
Science Department Chairman
Katz, David Raymond, III
Pol Science & History Prof

Kempf, John J.
Soc Stud Tchr & Dept Chairman
Krupa, Thomas Andrew
11th Grade US His & Govt Tchr
Labuz, Ronald Matthew
Dept Head & Graphic Comm Prof
LaLonde, Jerome V.
Professor of Photography
Love, Susan Smyth
Nurse Educator
Mancini, Michelle LaQuay
Social Studies Teacher
Marcus, Peter
English Teacher
Nowak, Adela G.
Mathematics Teacher
Pace, Carolyn West
Asst Professor of Humanities
Powell, James S.
Physics Teacher
Pristera, Salvatore Joseph
Physics & Chemistry Teacher
Pulitzer, Virginia Kukowski
Teacher of Gifted & Talented
Sessler, Harriet McNamara
ESL Teacher
Steppello, Eleanor Stamboly
Retired Kindergarten Teacher
Valentini, Alfred John
Italian Teacher
Wagner, Jean VanAlstyne
Assoc Prof of Life Science
Wright, Sandra E.
4th Grade Teacher
Wronka, Alexius Michael
Vocal Music, Music Theory Tchr

VALATIE

Cain, Christine Manti
Middle Schl Soc Stud Teacher
Ferlito, Alissa Marie
Earth Science Teacher
Krumpus, Judith Ann
Second Grade Teacher
Mayer, Barbara Sutcliffe
Mathematics Teacher
Powhida, Elizabeth Coogan
Spanish & Latin Teacher
Wall, Sharon Barber
English Teacher & Dept Chair

VALHALLA

Blake, Lydia Smyth
6th Grade Teacher
Galgano, Louis John
Fifth Grade Teacher
LeGendre, Renee Denise
6th Grd Social Studies Teacher
Lloyd, Thomas Howard
Asst Professor of Marketing
Metz, Carol Ann
Mathematics Asst Professor
Orfanella, Lou
7th-8th Grade English Teacher
Priano, Michael, Jr.
Associate Professor of Biology
Silano, Paul Edward
6th Grade English Teacher
Vent, Maryanne Ciardullo
Professor of English
Widulski, William F.
Math & Comp Sci Asst Professor

VALLEY COTTAGE

Ramundo, Donna DeRico
Third Grade Teacher

VALLEY STREAM

Adams, Lyndaa Huebsch
Science Department Head
Barbone, Patricia R.
6th Grade Teacher
Beaton, Deloris Jordan
Third Grade Teacher
Dillon, Susan Breslow
6th Grade Teacher
Eisenberg, Esther
English Teacher
Franklin, Paula Hornreich
1st Grd Tchr & Math Consultant
Herrmann, Richard Edward
English Teacher
Leshefsky, Amy
Mathematics Teacher
Mellace, Edith Slovshek
Mathematics Teacher & Tutor
Pandaliano, Donna Jean
Science Teacher
Quinn, Kathleen Dougherty
8th Grade Teacher
Rosenberg, William
Math Teacher
Ruschin, Mary A.
Second Grade Teacher
Schaefer, Carol M.
Earth Science Teacher
Tenaglia, Robert C.
Spanish Teacher
Vaccaro, Susan Haner
First Grade Teacher
Vogel, Maxine D. (Marcus)
Mathematics Teacher
Wasserman, Susan Harris
5th Grade Teacher
Yelland, Edith May
Fifth Grade Teacher

VERONA

Bennati, Gene Anthony
Business Dept Chairperson
Burton, James J.
Math Teacher
Kekis, Regina Sbaraglia
Spanish Teacher

Lally, Deborah Picolla
Middle School Counselor
Merrell, Sis Sullivan
Third Grade Teacher
Tuttle, Evelyn Di Pastina
Middle School English Teacher
Wartella, Ellen Hart
Diversified Health Instructor
Zurek, Melanie Alexandra
English & Language Arts Tchr

VESTAL

Albee, Mary Jo Zemek
English Teacher & Chair
Bartos, Joanna H.
Russian Teacher
Bossong, Elizabeth Moreland
Spanish Teacher & Dept Chm
Cihiwsky, Angela Lockett
English Teacher
Corgel, Nikki
District Art Dept Chairperson
Davis, Laurie Ann
Fourth Grade Teacher
Guilfoyle, Roseanne Kaminsky
Secondary Mathematics Teacher
Harrigan, John Coleman
5th Grade Teacher
Herrick, George Frank
Bio, Anatomy & Physiology Tchr
McCoy, Debra Ann
Fifth Grade Teacher
Mee, Michael Francis
English Teacher
Merkel, Matthew Stephen
Rel & Philosophy Tchr & Chprsn
Miller, Jacqueline Marie
6th Grd Teacher
Olson, Christine A.
Kindergarten Teacher
Persley, Kristin
Vocal Music Teacher
Philipson, Wayne Ian
Biology Teacher
Pollard, Gordon Charles
Elementary PE Teacher
Seeger, Robert Paul
US History & Government Tchr
Showalter, Christine Luberto
Forensic Science & Bio Tchr
Steenstrup, Melanie Zimmer
High School Math Teacher
Surowitz, Bonita Rose
6th Grd Sci & Lang Arts Tchr
Williams, Gary Robert
Psychology Instructor
Winterstein, Christine Ann (Pierson)
Sixth Grade Teacher

VICTOR

Brion, Karen Smith
Biology Teacher
Coleman, William W.
Sixth Grade Teacher
Dix, Colleen Schrouder
Spanish Teacher
Falkman, Eric
Math Teacher
Gacioch, Francis Joseph
High School Mathematics Tchr
Goodman, Michael
American History & Psych Tchr
Martin, Carol Towne
Physical Education Teacher
Olson, Daniel Anthony
Soc Studies Dept Chm & Tchr
Pierce, Preston Eugene
Social Studies Teacher
Simpson, Glenn Thomas
Biology Teacher
Thomas, Beth Hall
English Teacher

VOORHEESVILLE

Freyer, Richard Albert
Physics & Chemistry Teacher
Mastro, Christopher Paul
Senior High English Teacher

WADDINGTON

Martin, Harlan S.
Retired Math Teacher

WADING RIVER

Benanti, Fred William
Retired Teacher

WALDEN

Winchell, Barbara Keery
5th Grade Teacher

WALLKILL

Brennan, Linda J.
Physical Education Teacher
DeSol, Paul P.
7th Grade Math Teacher
Fulton, Curt Sven
6th Grd Math, Hlth & Dare Tchr
LeBlanc, Mary Hoyt
Second Grade Teacher
Strauser, George J.
General Music Teacher
Witham, Dean
Fifth Grade Teacher

WALTON

Allen, Gretchen Marie
Biology Teacher
Budine, Alan L.
English Teacher
Little, JoAnn Buck
HS Eng & Creative Writing Tchr
Meredith, Diane Avenia
HS English Teacher, Dept Chair
Nabinger, Patricia Wemple
Vocal Music Teacher
Shackelton, George William
Business Education Teacher

VanLoan, Nanci Lynn
Economics & Government Teacher

WALWORTH

Hamilton, Sandra K.
9th-12th Grade English Teacher
Ludington, Jim
High School Math Teacher
Morabito, Anthony Richard
Coach
Pellegrino, Mark Barrett
Biology & Physics Teacher

WAMPSVILLE

Ossont, David Robin
Science Teacher

WANTAGH

Bogatz, William R.
Teacher & Coach
Dragovich, Mindy Stark
High School Band Director
Muscorfiti, Jeanne T.
Spanish Teacher
Ross, Madeline (Lemberg)
Fifth Grade Teacher
Ruane, Thomas F.
History Teacher
Skolnik, Sherry Zuckman
English Teacher

WAPPINGERS FALLS

Abrahamson, Michael
Biology Teacher
Barone, Giosafatto Antonio
Italian Teacher
Bischoff, Beverly Ann (Furnari)
4th Grade Teacher
Bloom, David S.
Special Education Teacher
DeMers, David P.
Teacher in Charge
Deppe, Charles Thomas
Social Studies Teacher
DeRosa, Reno F.
Art Teacher
Dixon, Donald T.
English Teacher
Dunda, Stephen Charles
Instrumental Music Teacher
Ghezzi, Bernard
Chemistry Teacher
Ghezzi, Judy Clarke
Fifth Grade Teacher
Lewis, John Edward
Mathematics Teacher
Lynch, Harry Edward
Band Director & Music Teacher
Lyons, Michael P.
5th Grade Teacher
Marchell, Carol Anne (Rodenbach)
Science Dept Head Teacher
Markowitz, Marjorie Dannen
7th Grade English Teacher
Markowitz, Mark J.
English Teacher
Martin, Gene Michael
Fourth Grade Teacher
Martin, R. Russell
Photography & Art Teacher
Phillips, Peter Douglas
American His & Government Tchr
Post, Rhoda Babcock
Sixth Grade Teacher
Price, Lucy Chicco
4th Grade Teacher
Rein, Stewart
Social Studies Teacher
Rohwer, Marla Fay
Arts Instructor
Skora, Dennis John
8th Grd Social Studies Tchr
Solomon, Elizabeth Kraus
Fifth Grade Teacher
Stewart, Jane Hildner
Business Educator
Watson, Barbara Reich
Social Studies Teacher

WARRENSBURG

Brown, James M.
HS English Teacher
Marquardt, Katharine Turley
Advanced Placement Bio Instr
Taibe, Sally Anne
Home Economics Teacher
Van Dusen, Karen Hudson
7th & 8th Grd Writing Teacher

WARSAW

Rowley, Lynne Johnson
Second Grade Teacher

WARWICK

Hoffman, Marilyn Meyer
K-1 Transition Teacher
Leporati, Debra Ann
English Teacher
Lorgan, Thomas Patrick
Secondary English Teacher
Loverso, Pamela Olsen
Mathematics Teacher

WASHINGTONVILLE

Brooks, Michael M.
Science Teacher
Burgos, Peter J.
Spanish, French Teacher & Adv
Cahill, Warren
English Teacher
Davis, Jodi S.
Guidance Counselor
Gaspard, Catherine
Home Economics Teacher
Mehrhof, Edward J.
US History AP & Regents Tchr
Newton, David Alan
Band Dir & Woodwind Instructor

WASHINGTONVILLE (cont)
Rosegarten, Mark Howard
Chemistry Teacher
Rosengarten, Mark Howard
Chemistry Teacher
Savini, Michael Angelo
Technology Teacher
WATERFORD
Boyd, Daniel S.
Physical Education Teacher
Calabrese, Alfred J.
US His, Govt & Economics Tchr
Mitchell, Barbara Champagne
English Teacher
WATERLOO
Bissonette, Thomas E.
Science Teacher
Boehnke, Charles R.
Math Teacher
DeMatties, Mary Mc Kone
4th Grade Teacher
Grela, Catherine
Social Studies Teacher
Johnson, Kathie (Evans)
Sr HS English Teacher
Pitifer, Mark Salvatore
Elementary School Counselor
Qualtieri, Ellen S.
Spanish Teacher & Dept Chprsn
Schwarze, Harry Thomas
PE Teacher & Coach
Smith, Stephen Charles
Reading Workshop Teacher
WATERTOWN
Armstrong, David W.
Technology Teacher
Bibbins, Donna Barney
Third Grade Teacher
Boulton, William L.
Social Studies Teacher
Burgess, Terence Daniel
Health & Science Teacher
Burns, Thomas
Social Studies Teacher
Collins, Annunciata
History & Religion Teacher
Coryea, Ann Marie (Grable)
Lang Arts Tchr & Jr HS Coord
Dietemann, Chantal M.
Mathematics Instructor
Doe, William J.
Professor of Engineering
Faunce, Russell J.
Lead Music Teacher
Jones, Jeffrey A.
Physics & Chemistry Teacher
Pearson, Patrick J.
Prof of Accounting
Phillips, Eileen M. (Carlson)
Assistant Professor of Math
Prugar, John Michael
5th Grade Teacher
Scee, Joseph E.
Third Grade Teacher
Sims, Thomas Ray
Psychology Professor
Thompson, Edwin G.
Assoc Prof of Bus, Office Tech
Wahl, Heinz Wolfgang
Electronics Instructor
Walton, David J.
Professor of Economics
Wichelns, Jerome B.
Assoc Prof of Philsphy & Eng
Widrick, Kyle W.
Math Tchr & Guidance Cnslr
Wright, Connie Sprague
3rd & 4th Grade Teacher
Zentner, Jeffery J.
Instrumental Music & Band Dir
WATERVILLE
Byrd, Robert Edward
Global Studies, Ec & Govt Tchr
Cooke, Susan Livermore
Computer & Technology Teacher
Gavett, James W.
Science Teacher
WATERVLIET
Bonville, Joseph R.
Music Teacher
Linendoll, Stewart Dana
Mathematics Teacher
Rings, Marianne Haite
English Teacher
Watson, Donna Drescher
High School English Teacher
WATKINS GLEN
LaMoreaux, Kathleen Warner
English Teacher
Mc Intyre, Richard Earl
High School English Teacher
Smith, Emma L.
Global Studies Teacher
Warren, David F.
Math Teacher & Dept Chair
WAVERLY
Eichorn, Harold
Economics & Global Stud Tchr
Harden, Henry
Earth Science Teacher
Moore, Jeanne Ackley
Resource Room Teacher
Perkins, Elaine Frances
Mathematics Teacher
Phinney-Foreman, Ann M.
Chemistry Teacher
Rockwell, Ann Mulhall
5th Grade Teacher
Shaw, Michaelle Holman
English Teacher

Watkins, Celine Saxe
Math Teacher
WAYLAND
Ferris, Linda T.
French Teacher
Griffing, Doris Beman
Kindergarten Teacher
Lewis, Robert David
Science Dept Chprsn & Tchr
Robinson, Stephen E.
Eng, His & Psychology Teacher
WEBSTER
Anne, Cathleen Sutherland
Regents Earth Science Teacher
Armstrong, James David
Fourth Grade Teacher
Bartolotti, Margaret Beuerlein
Social Studies Teacher
Berry, Robert H.
Global Studies I Teacher
Bianchi, Anthony Alan
Social Studies Teacher
Brenna, Judy Haefner
English Teacher
Brincka, Matthew P.
Chemistry Teacher
Considine, Mary Ann
Third Grade Teacher
DeMatteis, Robert Joseph
Secondary Math Teacher
Gross, Barbara E.
Band Director
Gumina, Carmen F.
Biology Teacher
Hamm, Joann Ellis
English Teacher
Herman, Richard Charles
High School Math Teacher
Iamaio, John Joseph
Bible, Psych Tchr & Fam Cnslr
Laniok, Marguerite Panepinto
Substitute Teacher
Linder, Raymond A.
Math Teacher
O'Rourke, William Joseph, Jr.
Helping Tchr & Suite Admin
Peck, Nancy Cregan
Pre Kindgergarten Teacher
Pellicano, Barbara
Spanish Teacher
Proctor, Peggy Kukla
Physical Education Teacher
Small, Wylie Jameson
English Teacher
Tacy, Stephen A.
Vocal & General Music Tchr
White, Kirke J.
Social Studies Teacher
Yokel, Ellen Morse
9th Grd Global Studies Tchr
WEEDSPORT
Fedi, Jennifer Elmer
English Teacher
Lawler, John R., Jr.
Science Teacher
Leonardi, Theresa M.
High School Soc Stud Teacher
Tall, Gordon F.
Physics & Physical Sci Teacher
WELLS
McCaffrey, Loraine Hospod
Fourth Grade Teacher
WELLSVILLE
Brocci, Ann Spencer
Fourth Grade Teacher
Bundy, Joan Hoehne
Third Grade Teacher
OConnell, Mary Ellen
Physical Education Teacher
Roby, Pamela Curd
English Teacher
Tyson, Beth Milner
Mathematics Teacher
Zacher, William Frederick
Associate Professor
WEST HAMPTON BEACH
Bass, Paul Dennis
Social Studies Teacher
Clemenz, Kathleen M.
English Teacher
Costelloe, Paul Kevin
Ec, Govt & His Insight Tchr
Goldstein, Donald Robert
Mathematics Teacher & Coord
Kommer, Joseph O.
Science Teacher
Richford, Catherine Ann
English Teacher
Troyan, Virginia Andes
Social Studies Teacher
Veeck, Robert Edward
Math Teacher
WEST HAVERSTRAW
Chapman, Margaret Elizabeth
Elementary Education Teacher
Malson, Mary Anne Lee
Fourth Grade Teacher
WEST HEMPSTEAD
Asheroff, Joan Schuler
Principal & Gen Stud Teacher
Bonasia, Joseph
High School English Teacher
Ferrigno, Robert Steven
English Teacher
Gottlieb, Elimelech
Principal
Hoyecki, Marie Cahill
Retired Teacher
Kemnitzer, Thomas Joseph
Social Studies Teacher

Sununu, Alexandra E.
Foreign Language Teacher
Wilson, Andrew Joseph
8th Grade Mathematics Teacher
WEST HENRIETTA
Vitale, Ronald L.
English Teacher
WEST ISLIP
Albert, James G.
High School Biology Teacher
Angelos, June Druian
Business Education Teacher
Born, Athena Theodoreu
Spanish Teacher
Butler, Jane Ticho
Math Teacher
Carpenter, Jean M.
Math Teacher
Devine, Elizabeth Lane
Soc Studies Tchr & Dept Chair
Farley, William Henry
Mathematics Teacher
Felix, John William
English, Drama & Speech Tchr
Freeman, Jean Perrott
Global Stud & Psychology Tchr
Griffith, James Richard
Mathematics Teacher
Happ, Marie K.
Biology Teacher
Holwell, Jean Ann Bernhard
Social Studies Teacher
Kennedy, Melissa Gregory
Mathematics Teacher
Kindberg, Janet Kathleen
5th Grade Teacher
Krebs, Leonard Carl
Chemistry Teacher
LaPinta, Lenny
Music Teacher
Lenowicz, Stephen
Social Studies Teacher
Mangels, Rosalie DiGiovanna
English Teacher
Mc Guire, Carol Brown
Mathematics Teacher
Mc Nally, Ardeth D.
Third Grade Teacher
Murphy, Julia Mary
Social Studies & Science Tchr
Murphy, Kevin Owen
Social Studies Teacher
O'Connor, Jacquelyn
Special Education Teacher
Pisani, Joseph Anthony, Jr.
Social Studies Teacher
Pitagno, Robert Louis
Science Teacher
Rossi, Virginia F.
6th-8th Grd Sci & Math Tchr
Sanna, Mary Tonra
Theology Teacher
Schlaikjer, Mary O'Leary
Social Studies Teacher
Waldman, Stephen Richard
Social Studies Teacher
WEST LEBANON
Kochenour, Lee W.
First Grade Teacher
WEST NYACK
Amster, Patricia Gatti
Social Studies Teacher
Bennett, Elizabeth Faye
Mathematics Teacher
Bladel, Rita Donaldson
High School Mathematics Tchr
Braia, Thomas Joseph
Business Education Teacher
Conroy, Patrick Joseph
Social Studies Teacher
Davies, Kathleen
Chemistry Teacher
DiBella, Vincent Bruno
Chemistry Teacher
Ginetto, Charles
Foreign Language Teacher
Hoeneveld, Diane Marie (Pappas)
Sixth Grade Teacher
Horowitz, Alan George
Technology Chairman
Laurenzi, John M.
Varsity Wrestling Coach
Schwartz, Rose Bokser
Mathematics Department Chm
Shine, Mary Quin
Practical Nursing Teacher
Shuster, Hy
Television Studio Coordinator
WEST POINT
Lomperis, Timothy John
Associate Prof of Pol Science
Mills, Carol Lynn
7th & 8th Grade Math Teacher
WEST SAND LAKE
Rogers, James Edwin
Retired Chemistry Teacher
WEST SAYVILLE
Duggan, Christine
5th Grade Teacher
Tresham, Patricia Ann
Kindergarten Teacher
WEST SENECA
Ball, Raymond Bernard
Lang Arts & Soc Stud Tchr
Baumann, Michael J.
School Counselor
Behrns, Gary M.
French Teacher
Berkman, Duane Mac Leay
Retired Fourth Grade Teacher

Boggan, Cheryl Ann
Fifth Grade Teacher
Braunscheidel, Patrick Phillip
Social Studies Teacher
Burton, Bernadette Napoli
5th Grade Teacher
Caprio, Judith Ann (Cyna)
9th-10th Grade Math Teacher
Chesley, Kathryn
English & Theater Arts Teacher
Connolly, Gerard J.
Sixth Grade Teacher
Cooper, Earl Howard
Health Educator
Craig, Maureen
Art Teacher
Danieu, Michael Joseph
English Teacher
Deering, Nancy Ann
German Teacher
Dening, Niles K.
Instrumental Music Teacher
Dudek, Mary Jo Pawlik
7th-8th Grd Math Teacher
Everett, David J.
Social Studies Teacher
Gates, Grace Ruth
Kindergarten Teacher
Getman, Harold Joseph
Mathematics Teacher
Giambrone, Marcia A.
Music Teacher
Grabenstatter, David
9th-12th Grade Math Teacher
Griffin, Kenneth Garry
Business Educator
Jacobs, Mary Jurewicz
Tchr Aide & Learning Lab Coord
Kemmerer, Leslie H.
History, Bible Tchr & Ath Dir
Kirk, Kenneth H.
Mathematics Teacher
Kosanovich, Peter
Seventh Grade Math Teacher
Krebs, William J.
English Teacher
Lady, Charles Spurgeon
Retired Music Teacher
Lapi, Jane Anzalone
Cosmetology Teacher
Masterson, Sandra Kreuter
High School English Teacher
Mc Keating, Thomas Francis
Ec, Govt & Global Stud Tchr
Militello, Frank C.
Middle School Math Teacher
Newberry, Deana Caputy
Spanish Teacher
Palumbo, Raffaele
Technology Teacher
Riforgiato, Rosalie
4th Grade Teacher
Rozbicki, Ellen A. Lates
7th-8th Grade English Teacher
Schleifer, Gerrie Schleifer
Physical Education Teacher
Schneider, Sandra Parker
Sixth Grade Teacher
Scott, John T.
Assistant Principal
Scott, Rita Kopra
Spanish Teacher
Seeger, Linda J.
Second Grade Teacher
Seel, Nancy Koubik
Choral & Voice Director
Sheehan, Carol Janicki
2nd Grade Teacher
Stotz, Judith Esther (Spencer)
Seventh Grade English Teacher
Tebo, Gary Robert
Science Teacher & Dept Chm
Toomey, Michael Patrick
American Studies Teacher
Whieldon, Thomas John
Elementary Physical Ed Teacher
Willard, Marie M.
Social Studies Teacher
Williams, Donald G., II
Math Teacher & Dept Chair
Wrzesinski, Mary (Maciejewski)
Practical Nursing Teacher
Wurstner, Laura Lee
English Teacher
Wyeth, Frances Kennedy
6th-8th Grade English Teacher
Yelich, Michael Joseph
Guidance Counselor
WEST VALLEY
Smith, Bonnie Geralyn
4th Grd Teacher & Elem Coord
WEST WINFIELD
Kirkpatrick, Thomas
English Teacher
Lattimer, Roger
High School Guidance Counselor
WESTBURY
Anderson, Norma Laurel
Elementary School Teacher
Beauchamp, Malcolm E.
Band Dir & Department Chrmn
Boyle, John Richard
Global Studies Teacher
Castoro, Norah Schwartz
Mathematics Teacher
Liguori, Richard
Fifth Grade Teacher
Neal, Eugene E.
Middle School Band Director

Sideri, Evelyn Acevedo
English Teacher
Wendel, Patricia R.
Practical Nursing Teacher
WESTFIELD
Anderson, Daniel Norris
Biology Instructor
Dowling, Audrey Kay
Teacher of Gifted & Talented
Emilson, Pauline R.
Instrumental Music Teacher
Green, Gary M.
Retired Teacher
Maher, R. William
6th Grade Math Teacher
Mansfield, Marci Williams
Elem Phy Ed Teacher & Coach
Morrison, Richard L.
Mathematics Teacher
North, Robert D.
Physical Ed Teacher & Coach
Payne, Jeffery M.
8th Grade Language Arts Tchr
Seymour, Steven Paul
Third Grade Teacher
VandeVelde, Susan Owens
High School Math Teacher
WESTMORELAND
Bianco, Joseph Anthony
High School Math Teacher
Bottini, Robin Marchese
Science & Computer Teacher
Fedor, Celia Majka
Fourth Grade Teacher
Gates, Evangeline Senior
Eng Dept Head & Tchr
Iles, Mary Lou
English & Social Stud Teacher
Jones, Elizabeth McGee
Kindergarten Teacher
Manfredo, Patrick J.
Business Education Teacher
Surace, Michele Marie
Business Education Teacher
Yager, Sharon Elizabeth
Fourth Grade Teacher
WESTPORT
Anson, Brenda
Biology Teacher
Kroeplin, Claire
Third Grade Teacher
WHITE PLAINS
Allen, Ronald Sibie
Mngmt & Mrktg Dept Chprsn
August, Arlene Brand
Prof Emerita of Office Info
Bayuk, Jo-Ann Lorraine
Business Education Teacher
Bhagoji, Shamtanu A.
Computer Teacher
Carpentieri, Pamela A.
9th-12th Grade English Teacher
Cirillo, Christine Tulotta
Science Department Chairperson
Craig, Douglas
Business Management Instructor
Cutaia, Tony J.
Physics Instructor
Danaher, James P.
Head of Philosophy
Erriera, Luisa
English Professor
Greenberg, Julie Elizabeth
Mathematics Teacher
Greene-Dansby, Sharon
Vocal Music Teacher
Hamilton, Joan T.
6th Grade Social Studies Tchr
Marcarelli, Gregory Nicholas
Mgmt & Mrktg Dept Chairman
Marinaccio, Michael Anthony
Adjunct Instr & Paralegal Pgm
McCall, Jennifer Ann
Instructor of Office Tech Dept
Norelli, Elaine
Mathematics Teacher
O'Connell, Ellen
English Teacher
Pungello, Johanna Moran
Fifth Grade Teacher
Quealy, Philip James
Guidance Counselor
Rikelman, Patricia
Computer Dept Chairperson
Schwartz, Elaine M.
Student Advisor
Strange, John Sebastian
Accounting Chprsn & Instructor
Tolchin, Gail Lynn
8th Grade Reading Teacher
Tuck, Lonnette Riley
Social Studies Teacher
Tutnauer, Karen
Chemistry & Mathematics Tchr
Zemmel, Edwin Leon
History Teacher
WHITE SULPHUR SPRINGS
Heinle, Mary Elise Scheibe
Retired 4th Grade Teacher
WHITEHALL
Monaco, Susan Oberkirch
First Grade Teacher
WHITESBORO
Blake, Ed
Social Studies Teacher
Pillsbury, Carolyn B.
Teacher of Gifted & Talented
Reppel, Joanne Carole
English Teacher

STONE
ail Rosen
Grade Teacher
SVILLE
, Judy Buchholz
garten Teacher
EY POINT
, Stephen Grant
12th Grd Soc Stud Tchr
Kathryn D'Imperio
Grade Teacher
Charles Albert, Jr.
Coach
o-Anne Catherine (Welsh)
& General Music Teacher
homas W.
ade Teacher
Margaret Duckett
d Grade Teacher
eronica Anne
n Teacher
, Sharon E.
Grade Teacher
Mary Sue
ade Teacher
Kathleen
Grade Teacher
Donald Joseph
Teacher
s, Nancy Joan
Music Instr
William
ology Teacher
AMSON
gt, Michelle Kristen
h Teacher
Michele Beauregard
h Teacher
rol Scott
Grade Teacher
AMSVILLE
o, John Arturo
sh Teacher
Mary Tepas
h Teacher
Thomas John
Prof of Medical Assisting
haron Lee
sor of Nursing
, Kathleen A.
Grade Teacher
Allison Beinert
ssor of Mathematics
, Fran E.
Grade Teacher
, Thomas Joseph
rade English Teacher
ean Haas
of Hlth Information Tech
wiwu, Azubike
ssor
ek, Catherine A. (Beardsell)
eting Teacher
ay Sylor
rpn & Global Stud Tchr
, Richard Jay
sh Professor
, Marianne L.
tant Principal
y, Kathleen
ocial Studies Teacher
in, Sharon Elizabeth
her of Gifted & Talented
r, Donald John
l Studies & Religion Tchr
, Susan Elizabeth
& Computer Sci Teacher
Nancy J.
eacher & Coach
Santo D.
of Occupational Therapy
on, Zan Dale
sh Professor
ld, Lynn R.
Grade Teacher
n, Linda Marie
ch & Language Pathologist
emann, Paul Joseph
al Studies Teacher
, Louis R.
Music Teacher
r, Michael Mark
ematics Teacher
r, Paulette R.
essor
an, Susan S.
& Computer Literacy Instr
Bonnie Bitner
ish Teacher
owski, Jack Alan
al Studies Teacher
ell, Doris
d Grade Teacher
Thomas J.
ish Teacher
ISTON PARK
o, Evelyn Israel
th Grade Teacher
, Rose Annina
nd Grade Teacher
ON
, Thomas C.
ogy Teacher
ani, Ettore, III
sical Education Teacher
night, Edith Howe
h Science Teacher
y-Palacios, Mary
lish Teacher

Mollosky, Carolyn (Karns)
Health Teacher
Russo, Joseph Philip
9th Grade English Teacher
Scherer, Suzanne Kronenberger
Senior High Schl Math Tchr
Schessl, Keith Richard
Instrumental Music Teacher
Welch, Karen S.
6th Grade Teacher
WINDHAM
Chimato, Dolores E.
Spanish Teacher
Dearing, David Richard
English Teacher
Leri, Ronald Lawrence
Eng, Soc Stud & Jrnlsm Teacher
Valenti, Joyce G.
Life Sci, Bio, & Peer Tchr
Zwoboda, Josephine
Second Grade Teacher
WINDSOR
Bednorchik, Sonia
First Grade Teacher
Bevelacqua, Donna Rae Cacciatore
Biology Teacher & Sci Coord
Gormley, Janet Susan
Second Grade Teacher
Hoyt, Debra Jean (Knapp)
Second Grade Teacher
Kniskern, Donald Eugene
Mathematics Teacher
La Mack-Lupo, Rebecca
School Counselor
Neal, Gina M.
Social Studies Teacher
Shear, Jane Wise
French Teacher
Soden, Irving W.
Earth Science Instructor
WOLCOTT
Antinore, Donna L.
Special Ed & Resource Teacher
Briscese, Barbara Bauer
English Teacher
Johnson, Nancy Bower
Social Studies Teacher
La Fountain, Mark
Second Grade Teacher
Wilber, Sharon Louise
High School English Teacher
WOODHAVEN
Kramer, Myrna Klosk
Fourth Grade Teacher
WOODMERE
Myles, Tracey A.
High School Math Teacher
WOODSIDE
Goeller, Patricia Wolf
Assistant Principal
WOODSTOCK
Hancock, Frank Fox
Retired Teacher
Okoren, Carol A.
Retired PE Teacher & Coach
WORCESTER
Kenyon, James A.
Social Studies Teacher
WURTSBORO
Rubin, Phyllis Levine
Fourth Grade Teacher
WYANDANCH
Carruthers, Stephanie
Science & Health Teacher
Morris, Walter
Social Studies Teacher
WYNANTSKILL
Papa, Christopher M.
Jr HS Language Arts Teacher
YAPHANK
Stevens, John Allen
3rd Grade Teacher
YONKERS
Assumpte Rossi, Rose
7th & 8th Grd Science Teacher
Braverman, William Paul
Social Studies Teacher
Chin, Deborah Lau
Computer Teacher
Colaio, Gerard J.
Guidance Department Chairman
Curry, Jean Ann
Guidance Counselor & Art Tchr
DePalma, Fredric Raymond
Science Dept Chair & Teacher
Dharm, Ben
Science Teacher
DiLello, Antoinette Marie
Vice Principal & 5th Grd Tchr
Dolgetta, John B.
Criminal Justice Teacher
Duffy, Bridget M.
Hlth, PE Chprsn & Science Tchr
Engel, Kate Queally
Math Dept Teacher & Chairman
Fagon, Adele C.
Enrichment Teacher
Fasulo, Rina Crespo
Bilingual Teacher
Flammia, Lougenia T.
5th Grade Teacher
Forand, Roger Kenneth
Global Studies Teacher
Frutkin, Larry
Social Studies Teacher
Gallagher, Denise O'Brien
Math, Lang Arts & Reading Tchr
Gallagher, Marilyn Flanagan
Regents Earth Science Teacher

Ginsberg, Ilse Meer
Fine Arts Teacher
Gorman, Teresa Pluntino
First Grade Teacher
Halpern, Jean Kammen
English Teacher
Houston, Carla Jean (Foreman)
Fifth & Sixth Grd Science Tchr
Iarossi, Frank E.
HS Math Teacher
Juliano, John Charles
Mathematics Teacher
Larkin, Joan Mary
7th Grade Teacher
Leonard, Richard
English Teacher
Lindia, Francesco M.
Italian Teacher
Marazita, Geraldine Gartig
English Teacher & Dept Chair
Martin, Ursula Marino
Mathematics Teacher & Dept Rep
Mc Kinney, William Samuel
English Teacher
Mc Mahon, Joe
8th Grade Teacher
Meehan, Dennis Joseph
Social Studies Teacher
Morris, George Joseph
ESL Teacher
Morschauser, Richard A.
Math Teacher & Coach
Murphy, Daniel Barker
Emeritus Prof of Chemistry
O'Rourke, Gail Ann
Computer Science Dept Chprsn
Palya, Joseph John
Social Studies Teacher
Parandelis, Rosemary Santiago
HS Religion Studies Teacher
Prol, Victoria
Spanish Teacher
Roberts, Jeffrey C.
Social Studies Teacher
Ruane, Noel A.
Business Education Teacher
Sajdak, Carole Cotter
Spanish & English Instructor
Sandberg, Karen S.
HS Social Studies Teacher
Sepi, Thomas Joseph
Soc Studies, Sci & Rel Tchr
Stenzler, William Mark
Computer Science Magnet Tchr
Sutton, Jacquelyn Fagouri
Teacher
Terracciano, Barbara Clarke
Social Studies Teacher
Thomas, Janice Marie White
Jr HS Christian Educator
Valk, Richard H.
12th Grade English Teacher
Weitmann, Roseann Viteretti
6th Grade Teacher
Zegarelli, Joy E.
Kindergarten Teacher
YORKSHIRE
Genaway, Mary-Lou Tourtellotte
Agriculture Teacher
Haun, Diane Pixley
Mathematics Teacher
Renner, Michelle
Art Teacher
YORKTOWN HEIGHTS
Basher, Maureen Ellen
Chemistry & Earth Science Tchr
Dwyer, Veronica Kelly
Health Teacher
Friedman, Marcia Kramer
Choral Music Teacher
Lavino, Richard Gary
Social Studies Teacher
Lebwohl, Eugene I.
Co-Founding Dir & Sci Teacher
Mathews, Kathryn Meyerson
3rd-5th Grd Choral Music Tchr
Mc Adams, Thomas Robert, Sr.
Third Grade Teacher
Micchelle, Patricia Ann Guider
6th-8th Grade Reading Teacher
Poznick, Jeffrey Peter
Social Studies Teacher
Santulli, Annmarie
Floriculture Teacher
Swenson, Barbara
5th Grade Teacher
Verneau, Suzanne
English Teacher
YORKVILLE
Jastrab, Sandra Lee (Kain)
School Social Worker
YOUNGSTOWN
Armstrong, Mary Lou
Language Arts Teacher
Bollinger, Michael S.
8th Grade Social Studies Tchr
Destino, Alice L.
2nd Grade Elementary Teacher
Dietz, Raymond Jon
English Teacher
Hannah, Mary Joan Alice
Retired Mathematics Teacher
Hino, Lynn (Paquin)
Fifth Grade Teacher
Mathews, Janette Adams
Mathematics Teacher
Mc Calister, Watson C.
Ret Dist Curriculum Coord
Panetski, Stanley Frank
Art Dept Tchr & Chair

Powell, Richard Anthony, Jr.
5th Grade Teacher
Ryan, Donna Carol
Elem Special Education Tchr
Sankes, Heidi Belling
5th Grade Teacher
Southwood, Nancy E.
Senior High English Teacher
Strong, Raymond William
Biology Teacher
Townsend, Michael L.
Photography Teacher
Wanamaker, James Robert
Science Teacher
Wanamaker, Jennifer Thiele
Math Teacher
Yots, Thomas Joseph
Chemistry Teacher

NORTH CAROLINA

ABERDEEN
Burns, Karen
8th Grd Lit Composition Tchr
AHOSKIE
Davis, Essie Whitaker
Chm of Early Chldhd & Spec Ed
Dickens, Jesse Julius
Social Studies Teacher
Freeman, Charles W.
Marketing Teacher
Martin, Cheryl Elaine
English Dept Chairperson
Miales, Carolyn Mitchell
Counselor
Mitchell, Carolyn Brett
English Instructor
Moore, Calvin Ray
Biology Teacher
Rawls, Katy Peele
Pre Kindergarten Director
Storie, Eric Duane
Biology Instructor
Swain, Carol LaVerne
English Teacher
ALBEMARLE
Cupples, Sharon Blumenshine
English & Dev Reading Instr
Gakis-Day, Ellen L.
Phys Therapist & Asst Pgm Dir
Gresham-Shelton, Claudia L.
Dept Head of English
Hedrick, Joseph Timothy
Band Director
Rigsbee, Audrey Hartsell
First Grade Teacher
Rogers, Melissa Ritchie
Media Specialist
ALBERTSON
Bielby, Bobbie Howard
Second Grade Teacher
Faison, Pearlene M.
4th Grade Teacher
Taylor, Pam Wages
Fourth & Fifth Grade Teacher
ANDREWS
Hardin, Jeana Conley
English Teacher
Warlick, Pamela Owenby
Third Grade Teacher
ANGIER
Bain, Kelly Smith
English Teacher
Hines, Sonia Raynor
Mathematics Teacher
Lee, Vicky Ann
Biology Teacher
Pate, Hazel Belche
Retired Third Grade Teacher
Tew, Betty Mc Lamb
Math & Science Teacher
Ward, Kimberly Bellamy
English Teacher
ANSONVILLE
Ammons, Elizabeth Harrington
Principal
Truman, Diane Hanna
Kindergarten Teacher
APEX
Adcock, Phyliss Grady
5th Grade Teacher
Armfield, Judith Mc Manus
English & Paideia Teacher
Baker, Brenda Murray
Third Grade Teacher
Baker, John Haywood
PE & Health Teacher
Bennett, Frances Tharp
Fourth Grade Teacher
Campbell, Scott Douglas
Health & Phys Education Tchr
Cochrane, Martha Ruth
Assistant Principal
Cooper, Roy Alan
Social Studies Teacher
Goolsby, Carolyn Foster
7th Grd Sci, Math & PE Tchr
Heckert, Glenna L.
German Teacher
Holcombe, Jacquelyn Kugel
Choral Director
Johnson, T. Earle, Jr.
Cmptr Programming, Bus Ed Tchr
Johnston, Mame Lutz
Soc Stud Tchr & Team Ldr
Koechling, Kristopher H.
Drama & Speech Teacher

Mata, Elizabeth A.
Spanish Teacher
Norton, Margaret Hedgepeth
Biology Teacher
Pattison, Linda
Spanish Teacher
Ramey, Jane Singleton
Social Studies Teacher
Rose, Karen Suzanne
English Teacher
Roth, Gray Maynard
Reading Recovery Teacher
Umstead, Sandra Ray
English Teacher
Whitaker, Jill Greene
English Teacher & Yearbook Adv
ARCHDALE
Lamb, Deborah McRae
Third Grade Teacher
Marley, Helen Walker
Sixth Grade Teacher
Mc Pheron, Caroline Kay
Kindergarten & Music Instr
ARDEN
Bryson, Ramona Henderson
8th Grade History Teacher
Gwennap, Marjorie K.
Music Teacher
ASH
Evans, Judy T.
7th-8th Grd Comm Skill Tchr
ASHEBORO
Abbott, Sandra Dickerson
Vocational Home Economics Tchr
Calkin, Jamie Blake
Environmental Sci & Bio Tchr
Carroll, Aileene Caviness
Mathematics Teacher
Cox, Anne Vestal
3rd Grade Teacher
Edwards, Patricia Austin
Kindergarten Teacher
Farlow, Sue F.
English & Jrnlsm Teacher
Fields, Amanda June
High School English Teacher
Fogleman, Peggy Wilson
8th Grade Teacher
Freeman, Patricia Snead
7th Grd Math & Sci Teacher
Graham, Pamela Caveness
Second Grade Teacher
Haga, Pamela Beavers
Eng Teacher & Dept Chairperson
Hampton, Peggy Carter
4th & 5th Grade Teacher
Henry, Rebecca Parks
Mathematics Dept Chm & Teacher
Hughes, Deborah Dunn
Special Education Teacher
Hulin, Nancy Cashatt
2nd Grade Teacher
Ingram, Michael J.
TV, Video & Commnctn Tchr
Kemp, Nan Teachey
Sixth Grade Teacher
Kercheval, Sarah Abernethy
Mathematics Teacher
Kiser, Mitchell Lynn
Machinist Instructor
Lanier, Max Ray
Reading & History Teacher
Ledwell, Victoria Lee
Biology & Mentor Teacher
Lucas, Doris Talley
Government & Economics Teacher
Mackie, Angela Keith
Kindergarten Teacher
Moffitt, Judi Lynn (Craven)
8th Grade Teacher
Murray, Kathy A.
Language Arts & Reading Tchr
Pulley, Sarah Jane
High School Mathematics Tchr
Ritter, Kevin James
Science Teacher
Sheffield, Julie Dunn
Business Teacher
Sherrill, Lorraine Buchanan
8th Grd Pre-Algebra Teacher
Tysinger, Sally Osborne
6th Grd Math & Science Teacher
Walters, Charles Vincent
Senior Army Instructor
Ward, Barbara O.
Business Education Teacher
Winiski, Michael Paul
Physics & Chemistry Teacher
Woodruff, Peggy Brittain
3rd Grade Teacher
ASHEVILLE
Allen, Marcia Kyzer
Chemistry Teacher
Blackburn, Barbara Cantor
Geometry Teacher
Blackwelder, Claire Lipinsky
Mathematics Coordinator
Bonner, Jack W., IV
Asst Head & Dean of Faculty
Briggs, Sara Hunt
K-12 Art Teacher
Brinkerhoff, Norman Scott
Teacher
Bryant, William D.
Fine Arts Dept Chair
Burrell, Joyce Gilley
Second Grade Teacher
Carver, Mitchell Kyle, Sr.
Eighth Grade Science Teacher

ASHEVILLE (cont)
Cathey, Connie Warf
Kindergarten Teacher
Crawford, Spencer Douglas
Director of Walker Arts Center
Dixon, Pamela Greene
Mathematics Teacher
Ferrell, Marilyn Martin
French Teacher
Floyd, Eleanor Fullilove
Special Education Teacher
Freeman, Michelle Dawn
Chemistry Teacher
Gilson, Donna Marie
Sixth Grade Teacher
Goffin, Jo Lynn
HS English Teacher
Goforth, Craig Davidson
Instr of Law Enforcement Tech
Goodstadt, Randee Brenner
History Instructor
Gurney, Ramsdell, Jr.
European History Teacher
Hagan, James Albert
Real Estate Pgm Coordinator
Hall, Calvin L.
English & Journalism Advisor
Hillyer, Martha Flynn
Science Teacher
Johnson, Louise Sanborn
English & History Teacher
Kendrick, Paul Edward
Vocational Teacher
Latimer, Nita Johnson
English Teacher
Locke, Julia Ann
5th Grade Teacher
Merolla, Robert S.
Science Teacher
Morris, Judith Payne
Social Studies & Lit Teacher
Osby, Mary Ann Mazur
High School Dance Educator
Park, Fred Luther
Math Tchr & Athletic Dir
Payne, Joyce Rymer
Retired Third Grade Teacher
Pollock, Cathy Butler
Early Childhood Dept Chprsn
Ponder, Delmar Harold
Operations Mgmt Tech Coord
Ray, Harriet Felder
Fifth Grade Teacher
Rutledge, Diane Coleman
English Teacher
Sanderson, William Edward
Biology Teacher
Sessions, Lisa Anderson
Eng & Lit Mag Teacher
Short, Debra H.
Med & Allied Hlth Science Tchr
Sizemore, Ann Weir
Retired 1st Grade Teacher
Stamatiades, Effie Hanzas
Kindergarten Teacher
Stepp, Cindy M.
Agricultural Education Teacher
Sugg, Ray Douglas, Jr.
Bible & Physical Ed Teacher
Townsend, Gregory William
English Teacher
Williamson, Beverly Dea
High School English Teacher
Wykle, Charles Wesley
History Teacher
Wykle, Eleanor Rippey
Seventh Grade Teacher
Young, Laurel Hoynoski
Adjunct Biology Instructor
ASHVILLE
Williams, Sarah
6th Grade Language Arts Tchr
AURORA
Glick, Julie Ann
English Teacher
Jakub, Rima Cohen
High School Resource Teacher
AUTRYVILLE
Matthews, Sue Jackson
Fifth Grade Teacher
Williams, Karen Mc Phail
5th Grade Teacher
AYDEN
Grimsley, Shirley Warren
Science & Soc Studies Teacher
Lawrence, Melva Tyer
Family & Consumer Sci Tchr
Matthews, Sandra Lee
Math & Social Studies Teacher
Ross, Charles Christian
History Teacher & Coach
Skinner, Catherine Barnes
Chemistry Teacher
Tyer, Edward Junior
Social Studies Dept Chairman
Williams, John Eldridge, Jr.
Physical Education Teacher
Winchell, Terrie Leggette
HS Dance Educator
BADIN
Lisk, Linda Sue Poplin
7th-8th Grade Science Teacher
Peck, Terry Almond
7th & 8th Grd Mathematics Tchr
BAILEY
Bass, Thomas Perry
Engineering Graphics Teacher
Gentile, Tracy Tarleton
French Teacher

Little, James Edwin
Aerospace Science Instructor
Taylor, Dolly Barron
Spanish Teacher
BAKERSVILLE
Barnett, Russel
High School Math Teacher
Bishop, Elaine McKinney
HS Counselor
Britt, Deborah Betthauser
High School Math Teacher
Foxx, Lana Biddix
Third Grade Teacher
Miller, Kathy B.
Chorus & Music Teacher
Potter, Robbie Ernest
GATE Teacher
Woody, Jeffery Mark
Math Department Chairman
BARCO
Ackerman, Mary Tooker
Family & Consumer Sci Teacher
Guard, James C., Sr.
Agriculture Education Teacher
Saunders, Nellie Stowe
English Teacher
Tatro, Adrienne Cochran
Math Teacher
BATH
Beddard, Linda Johnston
6th Grade Math & Science Tchr
Dickerson, Carla Fancher
Fourth Grade Teacher
Hill, Brenda Toler
Kindergarten Teacher
West, Rebecca Turner
7th-8th Grade Math Teacher
BATTLEBORO
Davis, Susan Hinton
Third Grade Teacher
Leonard, Bonnie Farmer
Lang Arts & Soc Stud Tchr
Waters, Molly Jeanine
Third Grade Teacher
BAYBORO
Caldwell, Chip
Drama Instructor
Davis, Catherine Harris
6th Grade Lang Arts Teacher
Hill, Linda Lee
7th & 8th Grade Lang Arts Tchr
Moye, Lois Gumbrecht
Secondary Mathematics Teacher
BEAR CREEK
Benton, Bennie Lee
Spanish Teacher
Heilman, Karen Sbrollini
English Teacher
Key, Lori Elberson
Choral Director
BEAUFORT
Basden, Staci Davis
English Teacher
Ellison, Victoria Eloise
English Teacher
Gaskill, Wanda Morris
English Teacher
Sawyer, Thomas W.
Agriculture Teacher
Thompson, Carol Sue
Exceptional Education Teacher
BELHAVEN
Bunn, Peggy Gurganus
8th Grade Language Arts Tchr
BELMONT
Brandon, Melissa Jane
Teacher & Coach
Caldwell, Jacqueline Hanna
Fifth Grade Teacher
Cauble, Betty Bost
Seventh Grade Math Teacher
Conover, Virginia Harrison
Asst Prin & US History Teacher
Deaton, Debra Mc Neil
8th Grade Science Teacher
Fox, Mary Steele
Mathematics Teacher
Lineberger, Michael Allen
PE Tchr & Athletic Dir
Mc Millan, Jenny Hill
Fifth Grade Teacher
Richardson, Jan White
Physical Science Teacher
Sautner, Charlotte Braswell
North Carolina History Tchr
Traywick, Howard Franklin
Drafting Teacher
Traywick, Sharon Cline
Math Teacher
VanLear, William M.
Assoc Professor of Economics
BENSON
Banks, Cecelia Godwin
8th Grade Language Arts Tchr
Denning, Elaine Barbour
Science & Math Teacher
Rogers, Bethany Denning
4th Grade Teacher
Williams, Sherry Marie
7th-8th Grd Language Arts Tchr
BESSEMER CITY
Carpenter, Diane K.
Eighth Grade Math Teacher
Leazer, Nancy Dianne
9th Grade English Teacher
Mahaffey, Michael Scott
Teacher, Coach & Athletic Dir
Matsik, John Thomas
Physics & Calculus Teacher

Pence, Robert Truette, Jr.
Teacher & Coach
Rikard, Jeri Melissa
7th Grd Social Studies Teacher
BETHEL
Moore, Denise Rountree
Third Grade Teacher
BEULAVILLE
Frederick, William H., Sr.
Biology & Physical Sci Tchr
Lanier, Linda Kennedy
Sixth Grade Teacher
Mc Coy, Valorie Chesson
3rd-12th Grade Music Teacher
Raynor, Betty Garner
7th Grd Rdng & Lang Arts Tchr
Smith, June
Eighth Grd Math & Science Tchr
BISCOE
Poole, Earle Stanley
Teacher
BLACK CREEK
Barnes, Janice Taylor
Second Grade Teacher
BLACK MOUNTAIN
Blackwell, Anna Potts
Bio, Anatomy & Physiology Tchr
Covington, Carol Davis
HS English Tchr & Jrnlsm Adv
Davis, Frances Joanne Fisher
Health & Physical Ed Teacher
Fisher, William Marsh
Director of Bands
Hawkins, Joyce M.
First Grade Teacher
Hinson, John David
Driver Education Teacher
Julian, Mary Creath
Social Studies Dept Chprsn
Murdock, Sarah Leigh
Mathematics Teacher
Pate, Donna Lynn
English Teacher
Pate-Fuller, Denise
Former Teacher
Showalter, Catherine Brutsch
HS French & Spanish Teacher
Whittington, Lorin Dale
Choral Director
BLADENBORO
Helms, Paul Wayne
Bio, Science & Driver Ed Instr
Pait, Barbara Ann
Teacher
BOILING SPRINGS
Binfield, Kevin S.
English Professor
Blackburn, Martha Burke
Kindergarten Teacher
Cabaniss, Jennifer Rhymes
Music Teacher
Witherspoon, Cynthia Hord
Third Grade Teacher
BOONE
Clifford, Mary
Criminal Justice Professor
Goddard, Robert DeForest, III
Professor of Management
Goodman, Jeffrey M.
Adjunct Instr of Media Studies
Hollar, Linda Cooke
Mathematics Teacher
James, Douglas Goff
Guitar, Music Theory Asst Prof
Jones, John Baxter
Social Studies Teacher
Nance, Nanci Tolbert
English Teacher
Stanbery, Ollie Jackson
Asst Principal
BOONVILLE
Haire, Charles Harding
Lifeskills Teacher & Coach
Hobson, Freddie Catherine
English Teacher
Hollar, Kathy Combs
Kindergarten & 1st Grd Tchr
Meeks, Gary Clark
Social Studies Teacher
BOSTIC
Helton, Judith Sansing
Eighth Grade Teacher
Porter, Sharon Callahan
8th Grade Teacher
Smith, Teresa Hunt
8th Grade Teacher
Washburn, Wanda Blanton
Seventh Grade Teacher
BREVARD
Brockman, Tammy Teresa
Head Athletic Trainer & Instr
Farrar, Susan Chambers
English Teacher
Glesener, Robert Richard
Associate Professor of Biology
Houck, Amelia Ann
Teacher
Leatherwood, Delphia Maria
HS English & Theater Arts Tchr
Lineberger, Jean McCurry
Business Education Teacher
Lytle, Randy Coyle
Student Advocate
Mackey, David Neal
Career Technology Teacher
Mosser, Daniel Vernon
Sr Teens Sunday Schl Teacher
Patane, Angela Grace
Drafting Teacher

Peeples, Paul Brannen
Mathematics Teacher
Pumphrey, Jo
Assistant Professor of Art
Sheffield, Roy Scott
Assistant Professor of History
Siniard, David Hale
Physical Education Teacher
Steuerwald, Mark Richard
Principal & Jr HS Teacher
Teague, Charles Porter
Prof of Rel & Chm of Hum Div
Weber, Linda Love
Fourth Grade Teacher
White, Robert Allwyn
Instr of Theatre Arts & Speech
Witherspoon, Jacqueline Buckbee
Eng & Creative Writing Tchr
BROADWAY
Billings, Judy P.
Third Grade Teacher
BRYSON CITY
O'Dell, Linda McConnell
English Teacher
Pattillo, Robert Samuel
7th Grd Social Studies Teacher
BUIES CREEK
Johnson, George Lloyd, Jr.
Asst Professor of History
Martin, James Ingram, Sr.
Director of Historical Studies
BUNN
Duquette, Julie Long
Mathematics Teacher
Frisbie, Robert Nelson
Vocational Agriculture Tchr
Jones, Charles Henry
PE & Earth Science Teacher
Mac Cormack, Mary K.
Chemistry & AP Biology Teacher
Massenburg, Maxine
Social Studies Teacher
Reavis, Cindy Oakley
Business Teacher
BURGAW
Best, Jack Lyyon
Biology Teacher
Byers, Heather Ludwick
Phys Ed & Aerobics Teacher
Cockrum, Linda Sue Tuttle
Science Teacher
Dorm, Alfredia Lewis
6th Grade Communications Tchr
Graham, Celestine Moore
Third Grade Teacher
Hardee, Barbara Bunn
Fourth Grade Teacher
LaFon, Darren Lee
His Tchr & Dept Co-Chair
Odom, Cynthia Kennedy
Business Teacher
Williamson, Deborah Maria
Algebra Teacher
Wooddell, William Waugh
5th Grade Teacher
BURLINGTON
Baumgarner, Glenda Squites
English Teacher
Manning, Christina Smith
English as a Second Lang Tchr
Pyles, Susan A.
AG Tchr
Raap, Kevin Matthew
Sci Dept Chair & Science Tchr
Stewart, Martha T.
English & Lang Arts Teacher
Walton, Susan Leath
Rdng Recovery & Literacy Tchr
BURNSVILLE
Adams, Kimberly Aldridge
Drama Teacher
Johnson, Dwight Harvey
Spcl Education Teacher & Coach
Koch, Thomas Bryant
Director & Teacher
McCort, Angelia Anglin
7th Grade Comm Skills Teacher
Shaw, Nancy Sexton
Health Occupations Ed Tchr
BUTNER
Perrin, Patricia Gose
Family & Consumer Science Tchr
BUXTON
Gray, Ray Dale, Jr.
Assistant Principal for Curr
Hall, Braxton B.
Social Studies Teacher
CAMDEN
Sawyer, Linda Barnes
Language Arts Tchr
CAMERON
Aldridge, Loretta Sharpe
Advanced Placement Eng Teacher
Apple, Michael Lee
Mathematics Teacher & Coach
Ray, Debra McMurray
Home Economics Teacher
Ward, Sally Anger
English Teacher
CAMP LEJEUNE
Bryan, Shirley Campbell
Science Teacher
DeFant, Liliane Anacreon
French Teacher
Kichefski, Tammie Marie
Dance Educator
Steimel, Jennifer Ruddell
Science Teacher

CANDLER
Bagwell, Sharon Diane
Seventh Grade Math Teacher
Cook, Joyce Abbott
Kindergarten Teacher
Keyes, Karen Johnson
Eighth Grade Math Teacher
Mc Alister, Lisa Wayne
Social Studies & English Tchr
Phillips, Katha Louise
Eighth Grade Teacher
Waldrup, Mary Peters
Pre-First Grade Teacher
CANDOR
Sutphin, Dianne Williams
Success for All Facilitator
CANTON
Fountain, E. Juanita Douglas
Family & Consumer Science Tch
Hill, Walter Robert
Business Teacher
Medford, Kendra Ashe
Choral Director
CARRBORO
Morris, Deborah D.
Third Grade Teacher
CARTHAGE
Alpenfels, Anita Waters
Arts Ed Coord
CARY
Allen, Barbara Blanchard
Art Teacher & Yearbook Advisor
Bates, Natalie Boaz
Fourth & Fifth Grade Teacher
Blackley, Susan Moore
Family & Consumer Science Tch
Cox, Susan Baker
Health & Physical Ed Teacher
Creech, Barbara Barnes
Teacher
Hall, Leigh Flowers
5th Grade Teacher
Hamilton, Geraldine Simmons
Fifth Grade Language Arts Tchr
Kirk, Bonnie Longest
Kindergarten Teacher
Lowe, Karen Labig
Language Arts Teacher
Norkus, Charley
History Teacher
Robinson, Tony Keivan
Band Director
Schafer, Mark Warren
Social Studies Teacher
Scott, Marguerite Harper
Social Studies Teacher
Speri, Joyce Rasnak
Latin & English Teacher
Zenick, Sally Ann Schumer
Language Arts Tchr
CATAWBA
Bolick, Gregory Neil
Spanish Teacher
Harbinson, Charles Samuel
High School Bands Director
Rutterman, Eva White
HS Social Studies Teacher
CERRO GORDO
Baysden, Julia Sumner
Math Teacher
Williamson, Mary Louise Church
Retired Teacher
CHADBOURN
Bass, Lola Garrell
Communication Skills Teacher
Lovett, Norman Kent
8th Grade Math Teacher
Thomas, Ethel Parks
Retired First Grade Teacher
CHAPEL HILL
Andrews, Katherine Caudle
Sixth Grade Science Teacher
Battle, Jacqueline Marie
Executive Director
Benavie, Arthur
Economics Professor
Brookhart, Maurice S.
Professor of Chemistry
Bursey, Maurice Moyer
Chemistry Professor
Eberlein, Patrick Barry
Professor of Mathematics
Ferguson, Paul
Performance Studies Professor
Fraser, Mark W.
Professor
Frazier, Linda Seamon
Spanish Teacher
Hinkle, Russell Wesley
Mathematics Teacher
Hunter, Cheryl Lea
Language Arts Teacher
Jones, Judith Decherd
Biology & Chemistry Teacher
Keech, William R.
Professor of Political Science
Kiger, Fred Waggoner
History Teacher
Martin, Rebecca Burke
Eighth Grd Exceptional Ed Tchr
Morrow, Valarie Clayborn
Bible Instructor in Healing
Munley, Leigh Booth
History Teacher
Newbury, Catharine
Assoc Prof of Political Sci
Nicholson, Phyllis
AP Biology & Physics Teacher
Peck, William Jay
Assoc Prof of Religious Stud

, HILL (cont)
an, John G.
& Fifth Grade Teacher
Robert P., Jr.
ogy Specialist
Albert Crane
Teacher
Elizabeth J.
of Academically Gifted
OTTE
r, Barbara A.
Music Teacher
out, Brenda Borror
Communications Instr
Catherine Anne
ial Studies Teacher
Byron A.
tography Teacher
oan Gill
re Owner
arryl Lamont
& Journalism Teacher
Myrtle Mc Clain
lor
ll, Jacqueline Rushin
nt Principal
Steve Fred
Teacher
hristine Sirface
a Department Chairperson
Robin Woods
chool Math Teacher
Erin Hennessey
Teacher
Beverly Ann
hool Teacher
, Dale A.
Prof of Architecture
Pedro Antonio
nish Teacher
Michael
ter Science Tchr & Coord
Karen Ann
al Health Issues Teacher
Christie Lynne
stry Teacher
Robert Reed
Teacher
imberly K.
Prof of Industrial Psych
l, Rhea Kuhn
Teacher & Dept Chprsn
Carmen Maria
h Teacher
ll, Calvin Raymond
Grade Teacher
ll, James William
h Teacher
ll, Paul D., Jr.
Teacher
atricia Johnson
ant Principal
er, Carol Jean
h Teacher
Mary Frances Mc Dermott
Lecturer in Spanish
n, Madelyn Lilly
acher
Timothy H.
Teacher
avid Wayne
cs Teacher
, William Roy
Hnrs Prgm & Eng Instr
Cynthia Culbreth
cal Science Professor
, Kenneth Wesley
y Teacher
, Brian Olin
& PE Teacher
ck, Stanley Wayne
Algebra & Phys Sci Tchr
er, Carolyn Mc Lellan
rade Language Arts Tchr
ebra A.
re Arts Teacher
Ronald Gilbert
cs Teacher
Sherrill Dion
oc Stud Chair & Tchr
, Susan Jackson
eacher
Wayne Phillip
l Studies Teacher
an-Merkert, Bernadette T.
istry Professor
, Patricia A.
selor & Chairperson
, Ludell Simpson
3rd Grade Tchr Assistant
nond, Thomasena Trapp
sh Teacher
Kimberly Dunn
l Studies Teacher
n, John Thomas
gy Teacher
H. Preston
inal Justice Professor
oh, Amos Hanson
stant Professor of French
Sondra Joanne
Ed Director & Asst Prof
Patricia Keifer
Department Head
Vernetta Conley
& Computer Teacher
rburk, Ellen L.
ed 6th Grade Teacher
rances Robicsek
Teacher

Garrison, Betty S.
Retired Hlth & Med Sci Tchr
Gaura, Jeffrey W.
Physics Teacher
Gilliam, D'Andrea Brevard
7th Grd Soc Stud Teacher
Givens, Vivian Williams
Elementary Music Teacher
Govan, Sandra Y.
Associate Professor of English
Graves, Frances Harmon
Industry & Education Coord
Gray, Debra Hyatt
Foods & Nutrition Teacher
Grimsley, Douglas Lee
Psychology Professor
Grossek, Henry Anthony, Jr.
High School Band Director
Hailey, Paul Hastle, Sr.
Assistant Professor of English
Hall, T. Melaine
Science Educator & Team Leader
Hardy, Allison L.
Aquatics Dir & Sports Med Tchr
Harkins, Lea Mc Laughlin
Teacher of Program for Gifted
Harris, Peggy Little
Retired Teacher
Hiltilidal, Michael Lawrence
Headmaster
Hodges, Rubye H.
Retired Elementary Teacher
Hopper, Edward Warren
Associate Professor of Spanish
Horvath, Linda Ransom
German Teacher
Howard, Linda Hilker
High School Choral Director
Howell, Jerry Dean
Graphic Arts Prgm Dir & Instr
Hughes, Marybeth Garst
English Teacher
Huntley, Geoffrey Mc Kinley
Ornamental Horticulture Tchr
Jackan, Rose Marie
US History Teacher
Jaynes, Joyce Hartis
Retired Third Grade Teacher
Johnson, David F.
Calculus Tchr & Athletic Dir
Johnson, Karen Sue
English & US History Tchr
Jones, Michael Ray
Spanish Teacher
Kalahar, Patrick Richard
Athletic Academic Counselor
Kelly, Edward Eugene
History Master Instructor
King, Connie
Health Sciences Teacher
Kreiling, Albert
Assoc Prof of Comm Arts
Kutner, Ian Jon
English Teacher
Lane, Larry Scott
Physical Science Teacher
Latham, Judith Langbehn
German & French Teacher
Ledbetter, Bessie Hardin
English Professor
Lemons, Richard Wallace, Jr.
Teacher
Long, Mildred Smith
Instr of Medical Assisting
MacKenzie, Norma N.
Chemistry & Forensic Sci Tchr
Maisto, Albert Anthony
Professor of Psychology
Martin, Christopher Bruce
English Department Chair
Matthews, James F.
Biology Chairman & Professor
Mc Afee, Larry
Chemistry Teacher
Mc Clain, Marilyn Caldwell
Fourth Grade Teacher
Mc Coy, Shari Lynn
Biology Teacher
Mc Cutcheon, Beverly C.
Social Studies Teacher
Mc Guinness, Vernessa Woodrow
French Teacher
Mc Lay, William Sinclair, III
Physics Teacher
Mee, Mary Ann A.
Modern Dance Instructor
Meehan, J. Daniel
IB Biology Teacher
Michaels, Elaine Matalas
Language Arts Teacher
Milbank Halvorson, Maren Ann
Bible Teacher
Miller, Barbara Jones
Eng Tchr & Dir of Forensics
Mitcham, Monique Crabtree
Ninth Grade English Teacher
Monroe, Vickie Starnes
First Grade Teacher
Montross, Kay Perry
5th Grade Teacher
Moore, Renee Anthony
Cities in Schools Site Coord
Moore, Sara Fields
Biology Teacher
Mozingo, Cora Leonard
Bus Ed & Computer Teacher
Ndoh, Sunday Jimmy
Assoc Professor of Business
Neil, Dolores Simril
Second Grade Teacher

Nelson, Sheila N.
English Teacher
Otterbourg, Edna Mae
Retired Human Anatomy Lb Prsn
Pallo, Venus
Jr High Science Teacher
Payne, Ronald Dean
Director of Bands
Pearson, Robynn Anne
First Grade Teacher
Perkins, Wendy Wohler
Spanish Teacher
Petty, Carolyn Granger
Math Teacher & Dept Chprsn
Phillips, Harry Robert
English Instructor
Phillips, Robert Ronder
Adj Asst Prof of Lbrl Stud
Pierce, Monica Yvonne
Biology Teacher
Pittard, Michael Larry
Choral Music Director
Plyler, Joy Ross
Chemistry Teacher
Poole, Amanda Williams
Psychology Teacher
Porter DeWitt, Brenda Anne
French Teacher
Randall, Carroll Ray
Automotive Technology Instr
Redfern, Cyphese Ramseur
Peace Builder Counselor
Reeves, Sims H.
Business Education Teacher
Reisterer, John N., Jr.
Health, PE Teacher & Coach
Rhoden, J. Lyn
Asst Prof of Chld & Fam Dev
Rhone, Aretha L.
Chemistry & Physics Teacher
Rice, Debora Schroeder
Asst Professor of Soc Work
Richardson, Allison Neill
Lang Arts & Journalism Tchr
Roads, Constance Carveth
Middle School Science Teacher
Roddey, Dorthea Robinson
Third Grade Teacher
Rose, Natalie Robinson
Language Arts Teacher
Royal, Cassandra Elaine
High School English Teacher
Ruppenthal, Jeffrey Weir
Ninth Grade Social Stud Tchr
Rutherford, James H.
Economics & Amer His Tchr
St Clair, James Alan
Auto Mechanics Teacher
Schnakenberg, James Gibson
English Teacher
Scott, Wesley Perry
Adjunct Prof of Cmptr Science
Shaw, Gregory Louis
Social Studies Teacher
Sienkowski, Randall Richard
MS Math Teacher & Coach
Sigmon, Sherry G.
Assistant Principal
Sigmon, Wayne Bernard
HS Electronics Teacher
Similton, Dale Eugene
Seventh Grade His Tchr & Coach
Simmons, Jamie Munday
English & History Teacher
Simmons, Jeanette Jones
English Teacher
Simmons, Sharon Penninger
Social Studies Teacher
Slipenczuk, Urszula Anna
German Teacher
Smith, Donna Hale
Business Education Teacher
Smith, Leigh Ann
HS English & Theatre Teacher
Smith, Susan J.
English Teacher
Smith, Todd Andrew
Social Studies Teacher
Springs, Erwin
Vocational Education Teacher
Stack, J. Richard
Mathematics Teacher
Stanley, Robin Hawkins
World History Teacher
Stanley-Hagan, Margaret Mary
Associate Prof of Psychology
Stathakis, Debbie Chonis
Spanish Teacher
Tally, Donna Mecham
Health Occupations Ed Teacher
Taylor, Jacquelyn Smith
English Teacher
Taylor, Nancy Cooke
Instructional Assistant
Thomas, Percial Moses
Associate Professor of History
Thompson, Marilyn Rose
Mathematics Teacher
Timson, Tim
Mathematics Teacher
Todd, Mary A.
Advanced Placement Eng Teacher
Toll, Christine Doebler
Latin Teacher
Tomanchek, Jeanne Emily
Marketing Ed Teacher & Coord
Totherow, Diane MacLean
Kindergarten Teacher
Turner, Ellen Lechowich
Marketing Education Teacher

Ulrich, Richard C.
MS Science Dept Head
Van Wallendael, Lori Robinson
Assoc Professor of Psychology
Visco, Elice Marie
First Grade Teacher
Wade, Jeffrey Van
History Teacher
Weart, Gary Reynolds
Violent Prevention Specialist
Weaver, Clyde Lee
US History Teacher & Coach
Whetsel, Gary Gordon
English Teacher
White, Linda Jones
Speech Communications Instr
Wilcher, Scott Reynolds
Director of Youth Ministries
Wilder, Stephanie Felder
English Teacher
Williams, Beth Ann
Sports Med Tchr & Ath Trainer
Williams, Regina Donald
Biology Teacher
Wilson, Anne Hartsell
9th & 11th Grd English Teacher

CHEROKEE
Caldwell, Penny Lynn
Health Education Coordinator

CHERRYVILLE
Barrier, Barbara Crouse
Lang Arts & Rem Math Teacher
Peak, Janie Parks
Eng Dept Chm & Tchr
Quattlebaum, Robert Timothy
Hlth, Physical Education Instr

CHINA GROVE
Campbell, Lyndall Wood
Spanish Teacher
Childers, Jennifer Helms
English Teacher
Daniel, Steven Carter
Latin Teacher
Holt, Terry Lee
Social Studies Teacher
Hord, Bonnie Patterson
8th Grade Mathematics Teacher
Knox, Donald Allen, Jr.
Science Teacher
Nixon, Wanda Fesperman
6th Grade Teacher
Vanhoy, Rick L.
Social Studies Teacher
Walker, Norma Freeze
11th Grade English Teacher

CHINQUAPIN
Gray, Laurie Brinkley
Sixth Grade Teacher

CHOCOWINITY
Bartik, Thomas Frank
Physics & Chemistry Teacher
Phillips, Everett John
Retired Dept Chairperson

CLAREMONT
Dagenhart, Diana Beaver
Sixth Grade Teacher
Harrison, Sheila Britt
Spanish Teacher
Spruill, Glenda McIntyre
Art Teacher & Department Head

CLARKTON
Thompson, Louella Peacock
6th Grade Teacher

CLAYTON
Byrd, Denise Benson
5th Grade Teacher
Garvey, Barbara Casey
7th Grade Social Studies Tchr
Glover, Timothy Scott
Biology Teacher
Heard, Brenda Chitty
Vocational Home Economics Tchr
Kennedy, Jonnie Flowers
English, Lang Arts & Ag Tchr
Marshburn, Joan Hill
6th-8th Grade Writing Teacher
Toler, Glenda Edwards
Family & Consumer Sci Tchr
Williams, Vickie Faircloth
Mathematics & Science Teacher

CLEMMONS
Beatty, Charles Lewis
Curr Coord, Assist Ath Dir
Boyer, Ann Ward
Second Grade Teacher
Cook, Rebecca K.
High School Mathematics Tchr
Gray, Barbara Rollins
Mathematics Teacher
Pope, Randy Keith
HS Anatomy & Biology Tchr
Presson, Marie Stimpson
Kindergarten Teacher
Spainhour, Patricia Anderson
Art Teacher
Williard, Judith Pilcher
Media Coordinator & Teacher

CLINTON
Barker, Thomas Garland
Media Specialist
Carlton, Joyce Honeycutt
Fourth Grade Teacher
Cooper, Shirley Brown
Business Education Teacher
Freeman, Christal Weaver
TMH Teacher
Hines, Shirley Williams
English Enrichment Teacher
Hunter, Julie Ann
Civics, World Geog & PE Tchr

Johnson, Sebrinia Grace
Math & Science Teacher
Mc Lamb, Meredith Hutchinson
Kindergarten Teacher
Sanderson, Lynn Thornton
Media & Technology Coordinator
Williams, Shirley Melinda
English Teacher

CLYDE
Boydston, Kathy Abbott
Fifth Grade Math & Sci Tchr
Powell, Gail K.
Third Grade Teacher

COATS
Chance-Morrison, Sheila
8th Grade Science Teacher
Salmon, Marie Bryant
Media Coordinator

COLLETTSVILLE
Swanson, Dianne Sharon
Physical Education Teacher

COLUMBUS
Mc Callister, Elizabeth Hooker
French Teacher
Smith, J. Richard
Vocational Agriculture Tchr

COMFORT
Houston, Elizabeth Ann
5th Grade Teacher

CONCORD
Atwell, Natalie Troutman
Math Teacher & Coach
Brawley, Pam A.
English Teacher
Campbell, Willis Alexander
English Teacher & Yrbk Advisor
Fisher, Lisa Carol
Mathematics Teacher
Fleming, Wanda White
Eighth Grade English Teacher
Hagler, Bill Gray
ICT Teacher
Hamilton, Elizabeth Hooker
Technology Specialist
Johnsen, Robert Harry, Jr.
Fourth Grade Teacher
Kiper, Laura Berry
Marketing Teacher
Maletta, Keigh Joseph
English Teacher
Martin, Phyllis A.
Math Teacher
Nance, Larry Eugene
Sixth Grade Teacher
Page, Marcella Anderson
5th Grade Teacher
Petrea, Kelly Hoyle
HS Theatre Arts Teacher
Pinto, Elizabeth
Health Teacher
Rassler, Andy A. A.
English & Drama Teacher
Smith, Sandra Early
AP Eng & Latin I Teacher
Stallings, Lane Query
Old & New Testament & Ger Tchr
Todd, Brenda Thomas
6th-8th Grade PE Instructor
White, Dodie McSherry
English Teacher
Yates, Kay Brewer
Elementary Music Specialist

CONNELLYS SPRING
Seitz, Diane Huffman
Fourth Grade Teacher

CONOVER
Cline, Catherine Yount
Second Grade Teacher

CONWAY
Harris, Larry
Hlth & Physical Education Tchr
Ryan, Eric Alan
Science, Electric Vehicle Tchr

COVE CITY
Myers, Diane Moore
Fifth Grade Teacher

CRAMERTON
Blackwell, Sharon Smith
8th Grade Language Arts Tchr
Dillard, Jo Lynn
Jr High Mathematics Tchr
Dillard, Kenneth Rowe
History Teacher
Forbes, Loretta Spirlin
9th Grade English Teacher

CREEDMOOR
Carver, Harold Ray
Principal
Cash, Donna Rogers
HS Science Tchr & Asst Prin
Ferrell, Kevin Claude
Social Studies Teacher

CRESWELL
Styons, Kitty Brown
Guidance Counselor
Upson, Stuart G.
Senior Army Instructor

CULLOWHEE
Davis, E. Duane
Professor of Criminal Justice
DePaolo, Rosemary
Dean Coll of Arts & Science
Hale, Daryl Lynn
Asst Prof, Dept of Philosophy
Hayes, Allison L.
Political Science Professor
Jacobs, Bonita C.
Assistant Vice Chancellor
Johnson, Ann Putnam
Associate Professor of Nursing

CULLOWHEE (cont)
Kowalski, Robin Marie
Psychology Professor
Luoma, Barbara Bauer
Asst Professor of Social Work
Mwaniki, Nyaga
Anthropology Professor
Pearson, Patricia Gail
Assoc Prof of Social Work Prgm
Stevens, Charles J.
Prof of Pol Sci & Pub Affairs
Wink, Kenneth Alan
Asst Prof of Pol Sci & Pub Aff
Wright, Clarence Paul
Associate Professor of Biology
DALLAS
Chiarelli, Phillip Anthony
High School Science Teacher
Lawrence, Donald L.
Dept Chair of Criminal Justice
Mc Cullough, Alicia
English Professor
Ramere, Carmen James
Vice Principal
Ratchford, Patricia Dixon
7th Grade Language Arts Tchr
Wash, Allen Gardner
Accounting Professor
DANA
Beddingfield, Dorothy B.
Third Grade Teacher
Capell, Miriam Ann
First Grade Teacher
Marshall, Peggy King
2nd Grade Teacher
Morgan, Lou Ann
Physical Education Teacher
DANBURY
Norris, Randy Ellen
High School Counselor
DAVIDSON
Baldwin, Phyllis K.
Assistant Principal
Beasley, Sara Anita
Visiting Instructor
Toumazou, Michael Kyriacou
Associate Prof & Dept Chair
Wike, Gregory Lee
Fourth Grade Teacher
DEEP GAP
Carson, Laura Lackey
Former Math Teacher
DEEP RUN
Braxton, Pamela Hardison
English Dept Chair
Harris, Laurie Leigh
Pre-Algebra Teacher
Rouse, Elizabeth B.
Chemistry Teacher
Sheppard, Danita Whaley
Health Occupations Ed Teacher
Yarbrough, Brian Geoffrey
History Teacher
DENTON
Crowell, Michael Eugene
Physical Education Teacher
Hanselman, Jill Wilson
English Teacher
Hinkle, Rosemary Sink
High School Math Teacher
Quesenberry, Navahlia Hanners
Industrial Education Coord
DENVER
Brown, Kay S.
8th Grade Teacher
Jones, Lisa Tolbert
Mathematics Teacher
Pollak, Susan Hite
Second Grade Teacher
Sherrill, Sue White
Counselor
DOBSON
Badgett, Carolyne Hamlin
First Grade Teacher
Bledsoe, Pamela Ring
English & Journalism Instr
Bolick, Katie Frances
Science Teacher
Brame, Patti Thomas
Seventh Grade Teacher
Carter, Judy Burleson
Home Economics Teacher
Dockery, Amy Rebecca
School Counselor
Hanes, Johnny Grover
6th Grd Social Studies Teacher
Knott, Nancy Bradley
English Teacher
Mitchell, Rex Phipps
Social Studies Teacher
Simpson, Andy
8th Grade Teacher
Simpson, Ann Taylor
Language Arts & Math Teacher
Wells, Michael E.
Psychology Professor
White, Sandy Altizer
Social Studies Teacher
Wolfe, Kathy Lynn
Preschool Coordinator
DREXEL
Buchanan, Bernice
Certified Nursing Assistant
DUBLIN
Jones, Rebecca Williams
Office Systems Tech Instructor
DUDLEY
Grant, Lucinda Johnson
6th-12th Band Director
Hinson, Teresa Hoff
8th Grade Science Teacher
Jackson, Carol Kirby
English Teacher
Jenkins, Elaine Parker
9th-10th Grade English Teacher
Kornegay, Lorraine Ivey
United States Teacher
Mach, James Alfonse
Social Studies Teacher
Quinn, Robbie Kirby
7th Grd Sci, Hlth Tchr & Coach
Taylor, Nancy Dail
Mathematics Teacher
Ward, Mary Lain
HS Exceptional Children Tchr
Warren, Rebecca Smith
Family & Consumer Sci Teacher
West, Julie Truesdale
Science Teacher
DUNN
Branch, Peggy Dowell
7th-8th Grd Comm Skills Tchr
Chestnutt, Lynd Herring
Social Studies Teacher
Godwin, Chris
8th Grd Sci Tchr & Gftd Coord
Jackson, Suebelle Faircloth
English & Literature Teacher
Simonetti, Margaret Wilkes
First Grade Teacher
Wells, Doris Faircloth
Social Studies Teacher
DURHAM
Bell, Cynthia Williams
Fifth Grade Teacher
Berry, Rodney Stephen
Art Teacher
Bockting, Margaret
Visiting Asst Prof of English
Brown, Kenneth Floyd, Jr.
Sports Medicine Teacher
Browning, Mike Carl
Animal Science Teacher
Burdick, Mamie Galloway
Classroom Teacher
Carroo, Agatha E.
Assoc Prof of Psychology
Clayton, Beverly Arnette
High School English Teacher
Click, Doris Lodato
Spanish Teacher
Cornigan, Dorothy Perry
Second Grade Teacher
Davidson, Kathie Lynn
Secondary Social Studies Tchr
Decatur, Cassie LeGrand
English Teacher
DiRuggiero, Karen Kahira
HS Math Teacher
Dorsey, Carmen Ellison
Counselor
Doyle, Gloria Thorpe
Math Tchr & Computer Coord
El-Khouri, Barbara Ann
Seventh Grd Pre-Algebra Tchr
Elliot, Jeffrey M.
Professor of Political Science
Enberg, Dennis Peter
Professor of Geography
Fisher, Elizabeth Grant
French & History Teacher
Forte, Minnie M.
Instructor of Comm & Speech
Foster, Mary E. W.
English Teacher
Gibson, Dorothy LeGrand
Physical Science Teacher
Gilchrist, Charles Herman
Professor of Music
Halpin, Myra Johnson
Chemistry Teacher
Hamblen, Lara L.
Performing Arts Dept Chair
Harrington-Austin, Eleanor Joyce
English & Philosophy Professor
Hueckel, Pamela Jean
French Instructor
Izydore, Robert Andrew
Professor of Chemistry
Johnson, Diane Wynn
Chemistry Teacher
Kandah, Nabeel S.
German & Science Teacher
Killett, Jean Stroud
MS Healthful Living Teacher
Kitchen, Dorothy Johnson
Director, Conductor & Teacher
Luxford, Judy Heinz
English Teacher
Mann, Jesse Andre'
Assoc Prof, Parks & Recreation
Martin, Tami Annette
3rd Grade Teacher
Mathew, Mary Thundyil
Asst Prof in English
Mc Kinney, Charles Wesley, Jr.
Former Instructor
McMurray, Harvey Lee, Sr.
Assoc Professor & Grad Coord
Mellown, Muriel Jackson
Professor of English
Oakley, Barry L.
Math Teacher
O'Sullivan, Daniel William
USAF JROTC Instructor
Perkinson, Gloria Young
Science Department Chair
Perry, Patsy Brewington
Interim Provost
Piot, Charles Daniel
Anthropology Professor
Sendlinger, Shawn Crowley
Assistant Professor
Sharpe, Susan Willis
English Teacher
Sherman, Andrew Douglas
English Teacher
Sikkink, Julie Anne
History & Social Studies Instr
Spahr, Lee Ann
Mathematics Instructor
Wilder, Ann
English Teacher
Williams, George Washington
Health & Physical Ed Teacher
Winborne, Angelina Giarrusso
Physics Instructor
Womble, Brenda Lindsey
Speech Communication Instr
Young, Janet Marie
Counselor & Asst Professor
EAST BEND
Ashe, Debra Cook
Fr Tchr & Foreign Lang Chm
Couch, Tammy Sue
Spanish Teacher
Doub, Velna Hall
Algebra I Teacher
Fish, Gloria Washington
Fifth Grade Teacher
Harless, Janis Cearley
English Teacher
Holcomb, Joan Reavis
English Teacher & Dept Chm
Mc Knight, Howard
Bio Teacher & Sci Dept Chair
Moxley, David Vernon
Drafting Teacher
Penley, Carolyn Brown
Fourth Grade Teacher
Sewell, Jeffrey Martin
Bio, Earth Sci Tchr & Coach
Sheek, Doug
Math Teacher
Venable, Eddie Gary
Social Science Teacher
EAST FLAT ROCK
Dobson, Cheryl Wilson
Choral Director
Jones, Robert Dean
Health & Physical Ed Tchr
Keel, William Howard
English Teacher
Laughter, Amy Marlowe
Mathematics Teacher
EDEN
Edwards, Terri Martin
Marketing Teacher
Joyce, Carolyn Reese
Special Populations Coord
Kimmel, Joan Lindley
English Teacher
Owens, James Edward
Director of Bands
Ragan, Fern E.
English Dept Chprsn & Teacher
Reed, Joseph Irvin, Jr.
History Teacher
Simmons, Sandra Guill
English & Literature Teacher
Surber, Laura Hines
Health & PE Teacher
Turner, Rebecca Briggs
5th Grade Teacher
Wright, Rachel Ray
10th Grade English Teacher
EDENTON
Bass, Ruth Overman
Assistant Principal
Bass, Thomas Carroll
Teacher & Athletic Director
Bryant, Gloria Davis
English Teacher
Dale, Philip Lynn
Director of Bands
Jones, Evainia Hunt
Business Teacher
Pierce, Cynthia Ann
Math Teacher & Dept Chair
Woodley, Robert Harrell
Physical Ed Teacher & Coach
Wright, David Saunders
Principal
EFLAND
Henderson, Kathleen Hoecker
Kindergarten Teacher
ELIZABETH CITY
Adams, Bobby Keith
Assoc Professor of Chemistry
Andrews, Alton Eugene
Prof of Theology & Ministry
Barefoot, Kay Butler
Business & Computer Tech Tchr
BonDurant, Sarah Elizabeth
Academic Affairs VP
Bright, Caroline Wood
Kindergarten Teacher
Brown, Susan Horton
Family & Consumer Science Tchr
Cahill, Maureen Anne
Lead Instructor of Reading
Dunlow, Dorothy Jackson
Assoc Professor of Business Ed
Gregory, Patricia Berry
6th Grade Tech Teacher
Griffin, Patricia S.
Christian Education Teacher
Hewitt, Rebecca Cartwright
Mathematics Teacher
Hodges, David Thomas
Lead Prof of Computer Science
Jennings, Carolyn Waller
Science Department Chairman
Joyner, Alexis Roosevelt
Art Professor
Omeb, Mary Patricia
Associate Professor of Nursing
Quance, Thomas Philip
Air Force Jr ROTC Instructor
Riddick, Deborah A.
Social Work Instructor
Roach, Ronald R.
Speech Professor
Roberson, Artha Vernon
Aerospace Science Teacher
Rosenblatt, Harry J.
Assoc Prof of Bus & Cmptr Tech
Sterritt, Patricia Fenwick
Associate Professor of Nursing
Swain, Martha Ward
Counselor
Thomas, David H., II
Adjunct Instr of Business Dept
Yager, Blair A.
Professor of New Testament
ELIZABETHTOWN
DeVane, Grace Beatty
8th Grade Reading Teacher
Haney, Debra P.
Band Director & Band Liaison
Henry, Stephanie Lacewell
English & Journalism Teacher
Sellers, Ella Jo J.
High School English Teacher
ELK PARK
Julian, Mary Gilmer
Primary Teacher
ELKIN
Anthony, Gayle Byrd
7th & 8th Grade Math Teacher
Caison, Bob G.
Fifth Grade Teacher
David, Linda Lyon
Kndgtn & First Grade Teacher
Duncan, Tony Lee
Hlth & Physical Education Tchr
Kallam, Larry Gray
Classroom Teacher
Laws, Jeanne Talbert
7th Grade Teacher
Stanley, Abigail Conrad
Kindergarten Teacher
White, Elizabeth Fletcher
Mathematics Teacher
ELLERBE
Smith, Terry Ray
Fourth Grade Teacher
ELM CITY
Clark, Annette Whaley
Fifth Grade Teacher
ELON COLLEGE
Bass, Sandra Bueschel
Dir of Learning Resource Ctr
Brooks, Sharon Morgan
8th Grd Math & Science Teacher
Digre, Brian
Associate Professor of History
Dupree, Susan Kaye
Second Grade Teacher
Elliott, Irene Patton
Social Studies Teacher
Griffin, Janice Purcell
Third Grade Teacher
Hall, Laura Peed
Third Grade Teacher
Hunter, Susan Finfrock
Private Tutor
Kernodle, Emogene E.
Math Teacher & Dept Chair
Sipe, Charlotte Wilson
Supervisor
Sparks, Jimmy Louis
Retired Eighth Grd Sci Tchr
Williams, Deborah
Art Teacher
ENKA
Ianniello, Steven Sal
Science Teacher
Weaver, Penelope R.
12th Grade English Teacher
Wright, Linda Wade
Math Teacher
ERWIN
Ashley, Jerry Dwight, Jr.
Special Education Teacher
Cannady, Susan Hawley
English Teacher
Grady, Vicky Godwin
8th Grd Communications Teacher
Moore, Kathy Jean
Algebra I Teacher
Nicholl, Barbara Oglesby
Mathematics Teacher
Peede, Kathy Strickland
Mathematics Teacher
Yates, Angela Tripp
Math Teacher
FAIRMONT
Kemp, Charles Edwin
Social Studies Teacher
McDowell, Belva Hunter
2nd-3rd Grade Teacher
FAIRVIEW
Sluder, LaDonna Penland
First Grade Teacher
FAITH
Stiller, Gloria Sexton
Fifth Grade Teacher
FALLSTON
Mc Intosh, Jeannette Haynes
1st Grade Teacher Assistant
FARMVILLE
Peele, Hettie Virginia
Instructor & Clinical Supvr
Phillips, Ka-Esbia
7th-8th Grade Teacher
Vines, Jennie Rosenboro
Secondary English Teacher
FAYETTEVILLE
Alford, Murray M., Jr.
Mathematics Instructor
Andrews, Maxine Ramseur
Assistant Professor
Bailey, Deborah Hudson
Fourth Grade Teacher
Bailey, Susan Russo
Fourth Grade Teacher
Baker, Janet Stevens
Teacher of Academically Gifted
Barnes, Linda Sue Donnelly
Professor of Biology
Bitterman, Joan
Assistant Prof of Fr & Ger
Brigman, Crystal L.
Tchr for the Hearing Impaired
Brisson, Doris Jackson
Fourth Grade Teacher
Brooks, Jeffrey David
Asst Prof of Sociology
Brown, Terri Moore
Asst Professor of Social Work
Bryant, Gregory Nathan
Physical Education Teacher
Buie, James Harold
Technical Drafting Teacher
Burrows, Evelyn Honor
Speech Teacher
Campbell, John Floyd
Assoc Prof of Psych & Dept Chr
Carson, Gloria Ellis
English Professor
Champion, Darl Hilton, Sr.
Criminal Justice Professor
Council, William Mc Allister
Bio, Anatomy & Physiology Tch
Datta, Rama Das
Assistant Prof of Philosophy
Davis, Jacqueline Hughes
Math Teacher
Dewar, John D.
Teacher & Coach
Diggs, Debraha L.
7th Grade Math Teacher
Dorman, Lisa Lynn
Associate Principal
Eddy, Robert
English Professor
Edmonds, Helena Montressia
Secondary Biology Teacher
Flemister-Bell, Carolyn Denise
Mathematics Teacher
Folsom, Margaret Davis
Professor of Biology
Ford, Maria Pierce
Biology Instructor
Foster, Margirie Wilson
Family & Consumer Sci Tchr
Fouquet, Patricia Root
Associate Professor of History
Franquet, Holly Gott
Spanish Instructor
Ganguli, Maya Guha
Chemistry Professor
Grunke, Susan Absalom
Home Economics Teacher
Hadley, Wynton Adams
Curr & Instruction Chprsn
Harrington, Shirley Monroe
Fifth Grade Teacher
Hatcher, Christine Rosenga
8th Grd Homeroom Teacher
Henry, Christine Barnes
English Teacher & Co-Chair
Higginbotham, Larell Mattie
Mathematics Teacher
Hight, Robert Kevin
World His, Leadership Dev Tchr
Holmes, Ophelia Morris
Eng Tchr, Comm Dpt Intrm Chair
Hood, Beverly Jones
6th Grade Comm Skills Teacher
Huffman, Kenneth
World Geography Teacher
Jeffries, Angelina T.
Spanish Teacher
Jenkins, Melanie Wyatt
Biology Instructor
Jernigan, Cecil Glynn
World History Teacher
Johnson, Dennis Wayne
Science Teacher
Johnson, Roland Everett
Associate Professor of Physics
Jones, Patricia Harris
Professor of Mathematics
Jonsson, Petur O.
Economics Professor
Jordan, Alfred Allan
English Teacher
Jordan, Judy Lancaster
Mathematics Teacher
Koonce, Connie Garner
Mathematics Teacher
Kushner, Lawrence Stephen
Math Teacher
Landon, Michael Glenn
Dept of Funeral Svc Education

'EVILLE (cont)
, Veronica Raeford
irade Teacher
ynne Randall
natics Teacher
eresa C.
irade Teacher
)-Leggett, Priscilla
or
n Michael
Economics
Beverly Jean Mull
ade Teacher
Soni
nt Professor
Betty Williams
nd Grade Teacher
, Jane Orders
Grade Teacher
in, Kathleen (Kentch)
Med Sci Dept Chprsn
ey, Kaye Lifsey
natics Teacher
Nancy Pate
natics Teacher
Eric Nichols
tor of Communications
Gwendolyn Settle
arts & Soc Stud Tchr
Trevor G. N.
ant Professor of Pol Sci
, Philliph Masila
ant Professor
Lechi Tran
Professor
e, John Claude, Jr.
a Department Chair
Candy Williams
ade Mathematics Teacher
Helen Moore
Grade Teacher
., Tina Marie (Silvetti)
rincipal
ay Neil
e Teacher
orraine Mc Iver
h Teacher
Beverly E.
iate Principal
Gail Appenzeller
h, Theatre Tchr & Chair
on, James Adam
ci Instr
on, Marria La-Quadia
rade Science Teacher
Saundra Newby
g Dean of Education
, Catherine Vernon
ctor of Religion
Marianne
stra Director
John Wiley
Prin & Athletic Director
on, Matthew Jeremy
Studies Teacher
, Mary Elizabeth
Teacher
Rickey Charles
h & Phys Education Tchr
Nancy J.
ematics Teacher
n, Michael Hugh
tant Professor
Ulysses
Prof of Business Law
n, Rose T.
Mkt Ed & Adm Svcs Chair
Eleanor Zezzo
sh & Journalism Teacher
e, Donna Knable
Teacher & Department Head
arn, John Lee
tor of Bands
ook, Michael Lynn
ness Teacher
, Deborah Wilson
Chldhd Ed Dept Chprsn
Jane White
School Math Teacher
ns, Marshena Mc Coy
c Prof, Dept of Elem Ed
, Ruth Dial
stant Professor
Jon M.
of Humanities
Guanghua
ematics Professor
ROCK
ds, Paul William
keting & Retailing Instr
, Zona Miller
ng & Business Admin Instr
ay, Marlene Moses
ish, Lit, His & Fr Teacher
s, Benjamin F., III
of Travel & Tourism Tech
ST CITY
Judith Melton
nd Grade Teacher
ood, Marjorie Loessi
ish Teacher
hoff, Sandra Phillips
ices Teacher
Kathy Kaade
lish Instructor
er, Jo Alice A.
rth Grade Teacher
, Shirley B.
hematics Teacher

Glover, Karen Smith
English Teacher
Harris, Lisa Toney
US History & Psychology Tchr
Hastings, Wanda James
Home Economics Teacher
Isenhour, Gregory Scott
Science Teacher
Ledford, Annis Byers
English Dept Chprsn & Tchr
Melton, Kimberly Diane
Social Studies Teacher
Murray, Debra Lee
Physical Education Teacher
Parker, Shawn Arrowood
English Teacher
Smothers, Teresa Price
English Teacher & Jrnlsm Adv
Taylor, Mary Kathryn Tomblin
Third Grade Teacher
White, Gary Thomas
Visual Arts Instructor

FORT BRAGG

Alvarez, Debra Huffman
Third Grade Teacher
Breeden, Jackie Carter
8th Grade English Teacher
Graham, Eleanor Payne
8th Grade Reading Teacher
Hollings, Nancy Knox
Second Grade Teacher
Joiner, Priscilla Graham
Ninth Grade English Teacher
Kelly, Margaretta Gross
Fourth Grade Teacher
Laney, Patricia Kane
Fourth Grade Teacher
Lange, Mary Schatz
8th Grd Social Studies Teacher
Livesay, Lynn Ann
Eighth Grade Teacher
Rickman, Sharon Bolton
Third Grade Teacher
Roe, Judith Mc Dowell
Sixth Grade Teacher
Schob, Patricia Smith
7th Grd Language Arts Teacher
Stotler, Joan Cook
Fifth Grade Teacher
Thomas, Hattie Clyburn
Sixth Grade Teacher
Vance, Nancy Rose
English & Journalism Teacher

FOUR OAKS

Avery, Michael Scott
Spanish Teacher
Ballard, Myrtle A.
Language Arts Teacher
Barefoot, Hobart Glen
Teacher
Bass, Lou Ellen
Business Education Teacher
Bell, David Kevin
Mathematics Teacher
Danger, Joan Brantley
Mathematics Teacher
Johnson, Sherry Jones
Choral Director
Lee, Frankie J. Barefoot
7th Grade Social Studies Tchr
Smith, Sondra Ennis
Third Grade Teacher
Stanley, Amy Hinson
6th Grade Teacher
Westbrook, Debra Bass
6th Grade Teacher
Wiggs, Shirley JoAnn
English & Journalism Teacher
Wynn, Traci Johnson
8th Grd Math & Algebra Teacher
Yates, Teresa V.
Science Teacher

FRANKLIN

Berger, Lee Hollingsworth
English Teacher
Fisher, James H.
Band Director
Willis, Joan Ledford
Science Teacher

FRANKLINTON

Carter, Sandra
Language Arts Teacher
Mc Cracken, Janice Roberts
Fourth & Tenth Grade Teacher
Melton, Clyde Jackson
Physical Education Teacher

FRANKLINVILLE

Burgess, Phillip M.
Lang Arts & Soc Stud Teacher
Dawes, Sharyn Jones
Fifth Grade Teacher

FREMONT

Gibbs, Nancy Boyle
Math, Science & Tech Tchr
Whaley, Connie Gail
Social Studies Teacher

FUQUAY VARINA

Barnwell, Maureen G.
Chem, Physics & Mentor Teacher
Boeh, Richard James
Biology Teacher
Byrne, Patricia Woodworth
10th Paideia English Teacher
Enloe, John Judson
Band Director
Harris, Belinda Woodard
School Counselor
Hicks, George Terry
Health & PE Teacher

Hobbs, Jill Kathleen
English Teacher
Lewis, Renee Averette
1st Grade Teacher
Maxey, Betty H.
Voc Support Svc Teacher
Senzig, Randolph John
Science Teacher

GARNER

Barritt, Susan Dresser
Mathematics Teacher
Collins, Dorothy Nixon
Family & Consumer Science Tchr
Cornell, Desmond Grant
Eng Tchr & Driver Ed Coord
Gardner, Terry Galloway
Mathematics Teacher
Miller, Karen Costello
French Teacher
Petherbridge, Donna Tucker
Eng Tchr & Acad Team Ldr
Pilgreen, Lynda Smith
Spanish Teacher
Smith, Nella Webb
Fifth Grade Teacher
Stephens, Helen Sommerville
Math Teacher
Vaughan, Betty Karen
US History Teacher
West, Daniel
Biology Teacher

GASTON

Mitchell, Charles Thomas
Sr Army Instr & JROTC Dept Chm
Smith-Vassor, Monica Bernette
Mathematics Teacher
Stine, Amanda Elizabeth
Biology Teacher
Tillery, James Edward, Jr.
Agriculture Education Teacher

GASTONIA

Adams, Gladys Loretta
Second Grade Teacher
Alexander, Jane S.
Fourth Grade Teacher
Anthony, Wanda Kay
Fourth Grade Teacher
Ball, Evelyn Love
Algebra Teacher
Barnwell, Myrtice Cook
4th Grade Teacher
Blount, Howard Alexander, Sr.
Retired Science Teacher
Brown, Broadus Don
Social Studies Teacher
Bumgarner, Dianne Campbell
US History Teacher & Dept Head
Caveny, Elizabeth Peeler
Science & Mathematics Teacher
Cox, Karen Sutton
Government & Economics Teacher
Coyle, Dorothy Hilburn
Spanish Teacher
Depew, Ellie Fuchs
Spanish Teacher
Dixon, Gilda Pope
Fourth Grade Teacher
Drennan, Sara Philpot
English Teacher
Farrell, Gretchen Raugust
6th Grade Teacher
Ferguson, Charles Franklin, Jr.
Fifth Grade Teacher
Franklin, Ric Lee
Teacher & Coach
Furr, Cynthia Jean
AP English Teacher
Garett, Rhonda Barnhill
Biology & Chemistry Teacher
Ghantt, Karen Clark
Third Grade Teacher
Glenn, Patricia Maiers
English Teacher
Grenier, Coleen Donovan
5th Grade Teacher
Grice, Susan Broome
Fourth Grade Teacher
Hamrick, Cynthia Susanna
Math Dept Chair & Teacher
Hankins, Patricia Baker
Fourth Grade Teacher
Harmon, Margaret Lois
Physical Science Teacher
Harrill Rudisill, Linda
Health Educator
Hayes, Candace Ashmore
Fifth Grade Teacher
Hedden, Ricky Lane
Physical Education & Hlth Tchr
Hewes, Brenda P.
Theatre Arts Teacher
Hoell, William Danny
Bible Teacher & Vice-Principal
Hyatt, Maxine Clark
Computer Teacher & Bus Ed Dept
Keever, Cheryl Harper
Health Occupations Instructor
Kiser, Billy Turner
Physics Instructor
McGraw, Junie Allen
Lead Teacher
Mc Kenzie, Sharon K.
Sociology & Psychology Teacher
Mc Namara, Ray Maria
Biological Science Teacher
Plowden, Amy Robinson
French Teacher
Richardson, Johnsie Mc Gill
History, Psych & Soc Tchr

Sheppard, Karen Dee
Physical Education Teacher
Spargo, William Scott
Sixth Grade Teacher
Starnes, Mary B.
Fifth Grade Teacher
Tanner, Tammie Mc Clure
4th Grade Teacher
Taylor, Edith Smith
English Teacher
Waldrop, Sarah Lockwood
Chairperson Math Dept
Ward, Diane Lyn
Math & Cmptr Science Tchr

GATES

White, Denise Bosnight
Third Grade Teacher

GATESVILLE

Ledbetter, Costellar Brown
Business & Office Ed Tchr

GIBSONVILLE

Enright, Jennifer Ann
Pol Sci, Ec & Geog Teacher
Fryar, Cathy Pike
Biology & Physical Sci Tchr
Hensley, Linda Bratton
World, AP European His Teacher
Katterman, Marcey Ruth
HS English & Journalism Tchr
Pleasant, Susan Hughes
Humanities & English Teacher
Temple, Lynne Marie
Photography Teacher

GLENVILLE

Gill, Emily G.
English Teacher

GOLDSBORO

Ballance, Sylvia Marie
Comm Skills & Soc Stud Teacher
Best, Cathy Hartley
Business & Office Teacher
Brehon, Sondra James
History Teacher
Carmichael, Yana Armstrong
Teacher Assistant
Clark, Kim Swaitney
Math Teacher
Daniels, Jerri Riche
Fourth Grade Teacher
Erwin, Emily Castelloe
Title 1 Reading Teacher
Fleetwood, Jo Ann (Williams)
Social Studies Teacher
Franks, Linda Cherry
Biology & Physics Teacher
Frazier, Sarah
Fifth Grd Math & Sci Teacher
Geiman, William Joseph
Health & Physical Ed Teacher
James, Elvin Junior
Hlth & Physical Education Tchr
Jones, Claude Byron
Visual Arts Instructor
Mainus, Amy Elizabeth
Eng & Advanced Math Teacher
McKnight, Susan Watts
Allied Health Science Teacher
Mc Lamb, Linda J.
8th Grade Teacher
Mewborn, Wilson
Technology Education Teacher
Mitchell, Carol Jordan
Hlth Occupations Ed Instructor
Mozingo, Betsy Wiggs
Exceptional Children Teacher
Mozingo, Brenda Mantooth
Fourth Grade Teacher
Nieves, Wanda Pecunia
Spanish Teacher
O'Daniel, Judy Annette Summerlin
Computer Applications Instr
Patterson, Phyllis Starling
Mathematics Professor
Pender-Bean, Donna
8th Grd Math & Phys Sci Tchr
Pittman, Denise Jones
Sixth Grade Teacher
Polack, Patricia Elizabeth
Special Education Teacher
Price, Ann Paquette
4th Grade Teacher
Raynor, Sue Rouse
Third Grade Teacher
Richardson, Susan Roberts
Sixth Grade Teacher
Riley, Anthony Warren
6th Grd Tchr & Bsktbl Coach
Rollins, Daniel Lloyd
Theatre Arts, Eng & Hum Tchr
Sanders, Kathy (Nickerson)
Jr High Math Teacher
Scott, Clifton Eric
Bands Director
Smith, Eddie Richard
HS Teacher & Athletic Director
Smith, Jessie Stevens
Tchr of Exceptional Children
Smith, Ralph Clyde
Chemistry Teacher
Smith, Robert
Instructor of Criminal Justice
Speight, Walter Bernard
Science Teacher
Spicer, Kathryn Cherry
Instr of English & Humanities
Stroud, Barbara Sykes
Science Teacher
Thompson, Terri Garner
Art Teacher

Turner, Amma M.
US History & Civics Teacher
Vinson, Barbara Fonvielle
English Teacher
Wagner, Richard Lewis
Math Teacher
Walden, Evelyn Anne
7th Grd Comm Skills Teacher
Waller, Jeffrey Scott
Drafting Teacher
Wiggins, Thomas Martin
Social Studies Teacher
Withrow, Christopher Mark
Band Director
Wright, Frederick William
US History & ELP Teacher
Yelverton, Deborah Sue
Art Teacher

GRAHAM

Beatty, Roxanne Darling
Commerical Art Instructor
Bunton, Robin Myers
Telecourse Instructor
Dalton, Susan Batten
Eng Instr & Acad Skills Lab Co
Davis, Lisa Hawkins
Tchr of Hearing Impaired
Hall, Kay Harvey
Health & PE Teacher
Hall, Milton Harris
Visual Art Teacher
Huffines, Ellen McPherson
8th Grade Language Arts Tchr
Hunt, Elizabeth Sue
Spanish Teacher
Johnson, Catherine Walker
Mathematics Instructor
Lipson, Garry Warren
Construction Technology Tchr
Lowell, Teresa Hawkins
Dance Teacher
Martin, Peter Alan
Mathematics Instructor
Meredith, Michael Harman
Criminal Justice Instructor
Reed, Susan Berdene
Nursing Instructor
Simmons, Robert Reece
Indstrl Maint Tech Dept Head
Smith, Patsy Gayle
7th Grade Math & Comm Teacher
Thacker, Troy Franklin
HS Lit Teacher & Dev Director
Williams, Michael Wayne
Biology & Physical Ed Teacher

GRANITE FALLS

Bryant, Sharon Turnmire
8th Grade Science & Math Tchr
Carpenter, Bennie Wilson
Second & Third Grade Teacher
Lawson, Shirley Fay
1st & 2nd Grade Teacher
Yount, Joanne C.
Retired 5th Grd Tchr

GRANITE QUARRY

Maynard, Jean Gaddy
Kindergarten Teacher
Monroe, Wanda Birdence
Second Grade Teacher

GREENSBORO

Allred, Teresa Williams
Choral Music Director
Armstrong, Michael W.
Drafting Teacher
Bangura, Bampia A.
Math Professor
Beasley, Linda Kay (Deaton)
Media Coordinator
Benson, Brian Joseph
Professor of English
Benton, Gwendolyn Spinks
English Teacher
Bergquist, Nancy Moreton
4th Grade Teacher
Bolden, Lucy Martin
Adj Asst Professor of English
Bryant, Tony W.
English Teacher & Dept Chm
Burgin, Anne Genet
English Teacher
Burke, E. Victoria
Assoc Professor in Social Work
Burke, Kelly J.
Associate Prof of Clarinet
Carroll, Gregory Daniel
Associate Professor of Music
Carson, Adrienne Teague
Fifth Grade Teacher
Carter, Audrey Forrest
Assistant Professor of English
Causey, Pamela Allen
Spanish Teacher
Chapman, Bernadine Sharpe
Assistant Prof of Adult Ed
Cheek, Jimmy Alexander, II
Choral Director
Clontz, James Albert
Stu Behavior Mngmt Specialist
Coleman, William L.
Linguistics Program Director
Cooper, Jewell Egerton
Assistant Professor
Cornwell, Jean Jennings
Latin Teacher
Cotton, Michael Jerome
Assistant Professor of Biology
Crenshaw, Michael Anthony
Television Production Teacher
Crump, Pamela Monroe
Speech Pathology Instructor

GREENSBORO (cont)
Derrickson, Evelyn Smith
ESL Teacher
Doyle, Sam Franklin
Cultural Arts Chairman
Eldred, Sandra Flynt
English Teacher
England, Eula Lea
Mathematics Teacher
Esterline, Albert Crawford
Asst Professor of Comp Science
Ett, Juliette Avery
8th Grade Language Arts Tchr
Evers, Vicki Knott
History Teacher
Fairley, Dawn Augustine
Instrumental Band Director
Faucette, Gloria Marie
Business Instructor
Feeney, Thomas R.
Honors Physical Science Tchr
Flowers, Linda Rich
Third Grade Teacher
Fonge, Fuabeh P.
Assoc Prof of His & Soc Sci Ed
Garrett, Cathy Kivett
Family & Consumer Sci Teacher
Gilles, Michael Austin
Paralegal Instructor
Granger, Maury Daryl
Assistant Professor
Gray, William Thomas
Science Teacher
Greene, Karen Sue
6th-8th Grd Computer Teacher
Hackett, Carolyn E.
7th Grade Language Arts Tchr
Hall, Marvin
Asst Prof of Psych & Counselor
Harrell, Rita Layton
Second Grade Teacher
Harris, Kathryn Martus
Retired 8th Grade Math Teacher
Haskins, Barbara Lee (Norris)
Mathematics Teacher
Henry, Carol Pridgen
Instructor of Nursing
Henry, Kay Frances
First Grade Teacher
Higgins, Jane Holt
Teacher of Academically Gifted
Hipsher, Robin LaJon
Chemistry Teacher
Hock, Raymond Paul, III
School Counselor & Coach
Hodge, Johnny Baxter, Jr.
Prof of Music & Band Dir
Hood, Gisela Brigitte
German Teacher
Hoover, Sheila Elaine
First Grade Teacher
Hoyle, Carolyn Tafone
English As Second Lang Tchr
Huddleston, Leisa Wright
English as a Second Lang Tchr
Hunsucker, Angie Amos
Business Education Teacher
Jackson, Susan Laird
Family, Con Sci & Eng Teacher
Johnson, Alison Blount
Social Studies Teacher
Johnson, Anna Lea Herman
Language Arts & Drama Teacher
Johnson, Mia Gordon
Spanish Teacher
Kea, Cathy Dinese
Assistant Prof of Special Ed
Kebede, Abebe Bahiru
Assistant Professor of Physics
Kennedy, Alvin Preston, Sr.
Assistant Professor of Chem
Kidd, Linda Piteo
English Teacher
King, Robert Burns
Lecturer & Organ Teacher
Kleinlein, Thomas
US History Teacher
Kurepa, Alexandra
Math Professor
Lea, Shelia Prather
High School Math Teacher
Lebby, Gary Louis
Elec Engrng Prof & Chprsn
Legrand, Patricia Evans
Chemistry Teacher
Lewallen, Lynne Porter
Assistant Professor of Nursing
Lohr, Laurance James
Science Teacher
Longuillo, Melissa Egolf
Geometry & Algebra Teacher
Lucier, Ruth Miller
Religion & Philosophy Prof
Lutz, Paul E.
Professor of Biology
Lynn, Jo Ann Evans
English & Guided Study Teacher
Malone, Charles Francis
Accounting Professor
Malphurs, Lorraine Brusdeilins
Second Grade Teacher
Massay, Lorace Learmond
Asst Prof of Indstrl Engrng
McAllister, Deborah Y.
Honors English Teacher
Mc Clendon, Erwin Lowe
Naval Science Instructor
McGinley, William Mark
Architectural Engrng Prof
McIntosh, Linda Comer
Nursing Instructor
Miller, Elise Rosita
French Teacher
Morrow, Kate Huggins
Mathematics Teacher
Morse, Lawrence B.
Assoc Professor of Economics
Moss, Ruth Anne
AP Biology Teacher
Newell, Charles Ansel, Jr.
AP US His, Speech, Debate Tchr
Pai, Devdas M.
Associate Professor
Parker, Thomas Dobson
Mathematics Teacher
Peace, Reginald E.
9th-12th Grd PE Teacher
Perkins, Rosetta Morrison
Mathematics Teacher
Pittman, Connie Rivenbark
AP Bio & Oceanography Tchr
Powell, Dorcas Kennedy
Math Teacher
Price, Gregory
Economics Professor
Price Lea, Patricia Jean
Associate Professor of Nursing
Rawls, Scott Wyatt
Viola & Chamber Music Prof
Richmond, Veronica Jordan
Lang Arts & Soc Studies Tchr
Royal, Denise Carolyn
Pre-Kindergarten Teacher
Salami, M. Reza
Associate Professor
Sarin, Sanjiv
Assoc Prof of Indstrl Engrng
Saunders, Betty Beyke
Fourth Grade Teacher
Sawyer, Vickie Overman
Language Arts & Reading Tchr
Scott, Karla Patricee
Instructor of Music
Seymour, Nancy Barnhill
Mathematics Teacher
Shelton, Esther Marie A.
Accounting Professor
Shelton, Keith Barrett
Social Studies Teacher
Simpson, Carole Wheeler
8th Grd Language Arts Teacher
Smith, Gayle Turner
Math & Pre Algebra Teacher
Smith, Glenda Engle
Kindergarten Teacher
Smith, James Reid
Business Teacher
Smith, Richard Wayne
English Teacher
Song, Yong-Duan
Assistant Professor
Stephens, Dayle Elizabeth
Social Studies Teacher
Temple, Mary Russel
Health & PE Teacher
Terrell, R. Jay, Jr.
Agriscience Teacher
Thevaos, Hedy Vurnakes
AP European History Teacher
Thomas, Annette Young
Assistant Principal
Tillery, Marcus DeQuincey
Manufacturing Professor
Tonkins, Nagatha Dixon
Comm Instr & Internship Coord
Tuck, Richard L.
Art Teacher
Tucker, Grace K.
Mathematics Adjunct Instructor
Turner, Henry Van
PE & Health Teacher
Ward, Audrey Ray
English Assistant Professor
Ware, Sueanne A.
Asst Prof of Landscape Arch
White, Gary Leon
Asst Prof of Chemical Engrng
White, Joan Cassandra
8th Grade Science Teacher
White, Katherine Inman
Foreign Language Dept Chprsn
Whiteside, Marian Davis
Education Consultant
Wiggins, Gail Boone
Acting Director of TV Studio
Williams, Cynthia Payne
Spanish Teacher
Wright, Sarah Hunter
Latin Teacher
Youmans, Christine Lynn (Tout)
Social Studies Teacher
Yow, Robert Alan
Algebra II Teacher
Zimmerman, Edgar C.
Mathematics Teacher

GREENVILLE
Allen, Elizabeth Bryant
English Teacher
Ballance, Paige Prevatte
English Teacher
Benedict, Ruth Holmes
Assistant Nursing Professor
Billingsley, Carl R.
Professor of Sculpture
Briley, Donna Blackwell
Fifth Grade Teacher
Burlington, Vickie Tart
Math Teacher
Daniels, Rosemary
Allied Health Science Instr
Filipowicz, Diane Helen
Architecture & Envrnmnt Prof
Gidley, Judy Clark
6th Grd English & Reading Tchr
Handron, Dorothea Scott
Assistant Nursing Professor
Hardee, Anne Allen
8th Grade Teacher
Hardy, Virginia Dare
Associate Director
Highsmith, Brenda Corbin
Second Grade Teacher
Hughes, R. Eugene
Professor of Management
Jester, James Jay
World History Teacher
Kirby, Ruby Stiltner
Physics & Chemistry Teacher
Kraszeski, Debbra Stancil
Biology Teacher
Lennon, Billie Royall
Soc Stud Chm & US His Teacher
LeRoux, Betty M.
7th Grade Communications Tchr
Mac Daid, James Gregory
Third Grade Teacher
McElhinney, James Lancel
Visiting Artist
Mills, Donna Northcutt
English & Journalism Teacher
Outterbridge, Lillian Tucker
History Teacher
Parker, Monica Sullivan
Asst Clinical Prof of Nursing
Ringer, Ellen Huffstetler
Latin & Journalism Tchr & Adv
Ross, Phyllis Paramore
Special Education Teacher
Rouse, William Arthur, Jr.
Social Studies Teacher
Smith, Denise Heather
Chemistry Teacher
Stevenson, Susan Y.
Business Teacher
Thomas, Sandra Stancill
Family & Consumer Sci Teacher
Thompson, Catherine Traynham
Eleventh Grade English Teacher
Topper, Paul Quinn
Music Professor & Violinist
Vutsinas, Steven George
Orchestra Director
West, Eve Mullen
English Dept Chair & Teacher
Yount, Eugenia Hall
Asst Prof & Dir of Stdnt Svcs

GRIMESLAND
Nichols, Candy Bottoms
Tchr of Learning Disabilities

HALIFAX
Bryant, Barbara D.
Math Teacher
Hux, Donald Fleming
Art Teacher
Liverman, Beatrice Sue Bishop
Health Occupations Ed Tchr
Pitchford, Flora Rook
Science Teacher
Viverette, George Sidney
Mathematics Teacher

HAMLET
Cuthrell, Doris Henry
Family & Consumer Sci Teacher
Robinson, Hazel Gales
Fifth Grade Teacher

HAMPSTEAD
Kermon, Gail Otts
Business Teacher

HAMPTONVILLE
Duty, Lynn Walker
Science Teacher

HAVELOCK
Benitez, Jorge Arnaldo
Band Director
Brogden, Lou
5th Grade Math & Science Tchr
Cox, Lynn Frazier
RE I & Title I Teacher
Eilertson, Sidney Anthony
Social Studies Teacher
Faust, Barbara Mc Clendon
Social Studies Teacher
Goddard, Betty Pat Rogers
Second Grade Teacher
Hamilton, Jeffrey Dean
World History & Govt Teacher
Mann, Linda Baugus
Fourth Grade Teacher
Pfeiffer, Parola Lorene
Teacher
Siler, David C.
Mathematics Teacher

HAW RIVER
Harrison, Carla Isley
Second Grade Teacher
Owens, June Evans
Second Grade Teacher

HAYESVILLE
Garrett, Cynthia Gribble
Business Instructor

HAYS
Peal, Jeffrey Patrick
World Geography Teacher
Pendry, Fonda Brewer
Third Grade Teacher

HENDERSON
Banks, Dale Boone
Asst Coord & Office Science
Bell, Timothy Roger
High School Mathematics Tchr
Boston, Mary Louise (Minor)
Business Education Teacher
Brady, Phyllis Grubb
Biology Instructor
Briggs, Etta Guerrant
Retired Elementary Teacher
Ellis, Carolyn Faye Wilson
Mathematics Teacher
Ferguson, Janet Crabtree
Office Science Education Instr
Freeman, Gloria Christine
Psychology Teacher
Hopper, Paula F.
English & Journalism Teacher
Huffaker, William Michael, Sr.
Coord & Instr of Hlth Sciences
Kelly, Alice W.
Business Teacher & Dept Chprsn
Manning-Smith, Vesta F.
Pgm Head of Frgn Lang & Hum
Moses, Brenda Poole
English Teacher
Murdock, Jerold Paul
Ag Teacher
Oxendine, Darlynn Pegram
Physical Education & Hlth Tchr
Patton, Judith (Wood)
Instr of Microcomputer Systems
Pearce, Dwight Wayne
English Teacher
Pernell, Betty Oakley
Math Teacher
Powell, James Roger
English Instructor
Reavis, Annie Lou Butts
Business Education Teacher
Smith, Wesley E.
Program Head & Instructor
Stevens, Jan M.
English Coll Transfer Instr
Thompson, Tomeka Carter
Cosmetology Instructor
Tunstall, Nancy Alberty
Coord & Instr of Bus Cmptr Pgm
Vass, Annie Woodward
Kindergarten Teacher
Washington, Gail Mc Laughlin
2nd Grade Teacher
Wheeler, James Henry, Jr.
Chm of Voc Ed & Instr Comm
Winston, Barbara Johnston
Accounting Professor

HENDERSONVILLE
Burgess, Britt Gerard
Counseling & Admin Dir
Cagle, Curtis Wayne
Math Teacher
Carter, Lynn Davis
8th Grd Language Arts Teacher
Copolillo, Betsy
Mathematics & Latin Teacher
Craig, Gregory Alan
Eighth Grade Science Teacher
Dickson, John M.
Band Director
Dutton, Ann Ford
Title I Reading Teacher
Garren, Deborah Frances
Math Teacher
Hill, Sherri W.
Secondary Science Teacher
Hooker, Barbara Elaine (Pannell)
Mathematics Teacher
Jarvis, Jimmy Ray
Mathematics Teacher
LaGrange, Joseph Lawrence
ELP Teacher
Linhart, Letitia Anne
Home Economics Teacher
Link, Norman Edward
Retired World & His Teacher
Medd, Charles Henry
7th Grd Math & Soc Stud Tchr
Miller, Sarah Louise
Drama Teacher
Norman, Michael Anthony
Math Teacher
Pace, Rosemary Underwood
History Teacher
Paulus, Linda Vanoli
Science Teacher
Pickett, Wendy Lynn
English Teacher
Price, Randal Gregory
Guidance Counselor & Coach
Sams, Patricia Banks
Business Teacher
Schneble, Jane Eastman
5th Grade Teacher
Smith, Stephen Del
Lang Arts & Soc Stud Tchr
Stanley, Jan Erickson
Physical Education Teacher
Stout, Julianna Duncan
Biology Teacher
Van Itallie, Frederick J.
Chemistry Tchr & Sci Dept Chm
Whitmire, Anne Gibson
Physical Education Teacher

HENRIETTA
Powell, Linda Ledford
Sixth Grade Science Teacher

HERTFORD
Dail, Brenda Layden
Industry Education Coordinator

HICKORY
Adams-Mongo, Trudi Kincaid
English Teacher
Ashman, H. Lowell
Political Sci Prof & Dept Chm
Burnside, Dale Frederick
Professor of Biology
Byers, Ann Bowman
Former Teacher of the Gifted
Deal, Glenn Edward
Mathematics Teacher
Forbes, Katherine Purvis
Eighth Grade Science Teacher
Gomot, Martha Mueller
HS French Teacher
Hildebran, Nancy S.
Eng as Second Lang Tchr
James, Virginia (Brown)
Fifth Grade Teacher
Jeffers, Suzanne Kramer
English Professor
Judkins, Bennett Mallory
Assoc Professor of Sociology
Kistler, James Daniel
History & Bible Teacher
Leatherman, Alice Faye
HS Math & German Teacher
Ludwig, Kathy Jacob
Former Elem Teacher
Mahan, Ronald Gair
Professor of English
Mazak, Richard Allan
Professor of Physics
Mc Connell, Robin Frasure
Fifth Grade Teacher
Periconi, Frances O'Connor
Associate Professor
Quilici, Augustin
Professor of French
Rennick, Forest J.
Professor of Physics
Richter, William
Asst Prof of Communication
Rink, Diana Schmidt
5th Grd Tchr & Math Dept Chair
Setser, Bryan Howard
English Teacher
Shuford, William Harris
Lang Dept Chair & Professor
Simmons, Robert Newell
Professor of Management
Sinclair, Thea Wicklin
Biology Teacher
Smyre, Joyce Smith
7th Grade Math Teacher
Summer, Gail Laubscher
Asst Professor of Education
Thompson, Kerry Coffey
Assistant Professor of Nursing
Wallace, Sarah Rink
Associate Professor
Yoder, J. Larry
Professor of Religion

HIDDENITE
Blosser, Paul F.
Music Teacher
Gilreath, Carolyn R.
Ec, Legal & Pol Systems Tchr
Sharpe, Janice Gwaltney
Science Teacher
Wiggins, Judy P.
1st Grade Teacher

HIGH POINT
Abourjilie, Charles Edward
11th Grd Soc Studies Teacher
Allman, Brian Douglas
Soc Studies & US His Tchr
Ault, Philip Howard
Mathematics Teacher
Belhassen, Marielle L.
French & Spanish Instructor
Bowman, B. Gray
Professor & Chairman
Caldwell, Donna Elaine
Eighth Grade Math Teacher
Clark, Carol Jones
High School Teacher
Clark, Doris L.
Fifth Grade Teacher
Cliff, Michael Paul
Social Studies Teacher
Coates, Sheri D.
Social Studies Teacher
Corns, Lorene Amos
Retired Third Grade Teacher
Cullis, Leslie Wilkie
Elementary Ag Teacher
Eanes, Susan Warrick
English Teacher
Fedor, W. Lynne Mezias
Business & Marketing Teacher
Grove, Jeffrey D.
8th Grade Math Teacher
Halvorsen, Faye Parson
Choral Director
Head, Carole A.
Modern Frgn Lang Dept Chair
Heintzelman, Carl Leroy
Social Studies Teacher
Hewitt, James Edward
History Teacher
Hill, Patsy Royal
4th & 5th Grade Teacher
Isaacs, Audrey Scott
Fifth Grade Teacher
Metzner, Michael Robert
High School Teacher
Owens, Cathy Ruth
English Teacher
Price, Carol Carter
6th Grade Teacher
Price, Joyce Mc Guire
3rd Grade Teacher & Asst Prin

OINT (cont)
Benilde Trevino
ı Teacher
oretta Campen
garten Teacher
Karen Petty
rade Teacher
Randy R.
ırs, Debate & Speech Tchr
, Cynthia Martin
ade Teacher
Keith
ı Teacher
ALLS
Mamie Purvis
rts & Soc Studies Tchr
oan Chalmers
Grade Teacher
BRAN
, Louise Perrou
Third Grade Teacher
OROUGH
enda Walker
ade Science Teacher
Esqurido B.
ı Teacher
Dickie Dean, II
Studies Teacher
, Shelley Rimmel
chool Math Teacher
ou L.
ology Teacher
Lee B.
World History Teacher
Elizabeth Forrest
Teacher
Patricia Ellis
Studies Teacher
ser, Beverly Ann (Sloan)
Teacher
James R.
Sr English Teacher
Michael Andre
Studies Teacher
lenn Andrew
Department Chairperson
od, Carol Caruthers
Grade Teacher
aick, Brenda Joyce
story & Black Stud Tchr
s, Frank R.
, Phys Ed Tchr & Coach
Gregory D.
School Business Teacher
mily Warren
Grade Math Teacher
atricia Mc Laughlin
School English Teacher
Denise Dawn
al Education & Coach
d, Lisa Levee
Grade Teacher
RIDGE
Susan Lewis
ra Teacher
Pamela Brown
h Teacher
ERTON
n, Barbara H.
d Grade Teacher
y, Marlene Barwick
pvr & English Teacher
MILLS
Brent Avery
my Teacher
eimer, Sandra Williamson
rgarten Teacher
Nancy Schermerhorn
al Music & Chorus Teacher
Bobby Jennings
story Teacher
, Estella Dunn
rade Teacher
Don R.
eacher
th, Julia Godbold
r Fifth Grade Teacher
Patricia Boone
Grade Teacher
, Timothy Augustus
h & Physical Ed Tchr
, Mary Kinlaw
Grade Teacher
n, Catherine Byrd
th Grade Science Teacher
Mary Jane Mc Callum
Grade Teacher
de, Cecilia Collins
h Occupations Instr
Nadine Georgette
eacher & Coach
Rhonda Lynn
h & Physical Ed Tchr
Broxie Powers
h Grade History Teacher
as, Ann W.
rade Language Arts Tchr
Sheila Thornton
Gifted Resource Tchr
ns, Steven Todd
Math & Algebra II Tchr
ON
Janis Skelton
Grade Teacher
, Kelly Kincaid
Teacher
d, Julie Kate
uctor of English
, Elizabeth S.
selor

Jetton, Janice Hutchinson
Mathematics Teacher
Johnston, Pamela Wakefield
Teacher
Jones, Barbara Hartsoe
English Teacher
Oxford, Sarah Jaynes
Lead Nursing Instructor
Prushinski, Nancy Whetstine
French Teacher
Summerlin, Sherry Langley
High School Spanish Teacher
Yount, Carol Ann Storie
HS Math, Sci Tchr & Asst Prin
HUNTERSVILLE
Barnette, Deeanne Enders
Child Care Services Teacher
Cline, Judy Blalock
Mathematics Teacher
Conniff, Timothy John
Physical Science Teacher
Flynn, Edwin Davis
History Teacher
Nichols, Ernest James
Sports Medicine Teacher
Shue, Janice Hall
English Teacher
Thornton, Christy Carpenter
Vocational Horticulture Tchr
Trieber, Lori Jean
Biology Teacher
ICARD
Berry, Judy Stephens
High School English Teacher
Brown, Horace Alexander
Biology Teacher
Colbert, Richard Michael
JROTC Instructor
Duncan, Ramona Abee
Mathematics Teacher
Garrou, Jan Underwood
6th Grade Teacher
Hefner, Rory
Mathematics Teacher
Jolley, Mark Kelly
Science Teacher
Mc Adams, Robert C.
History Teacher
Norman, Victoria Patton
Language Arts & Latin Teacher
Stacy, Angela Renee
High School Math Teacher
INDIAN TRAIL
Biggers, Carolyn Glenn
Second Grade Teacher
Hartis, Gwen Sustar
Second Grade Teacher
IRON STATION
Bowen, Michelle Lyons
Second Grade Teacher
Hallman, Ann Freeman
Second Grade Teacher
Soesbee, James Robert
English Teacher
JACKSONVILLE
Aurilio, Alice Cobb
Special Education Teacher
Batalias, Melinda Eldreth
Math Teacher
Bolinger, Nancy Virginia
English & Reading Instructor
Cameron, Cecelia Mitchell
Family & Consumer Science Tchr
Crawley, Sadie Del Shawn
2nd Grade Teacher
Donovan-Potts, Pat A.
Biology Instructor
Evans, Cynthia Haskell
Seventh Grade Teacher
Holtsford, Janice K.
Instr & Dept Head Office Tech
Kennedy, Barbara Davidson
8th Grade Mathematics Teacher
Kindt, Sally Stevenson
Public Administration Instr
Klingensmith, James Travis
English Teacher
Lewis, Mittie Iola
Teacher
Lisane, Brenda Kay
5th Grade Teacher
Maloka, Fran J.
French Instructor
Midgett, Harriet Armecia
10th Grd English II Teacher
Perry, Cynthia Lippard
5th Grade Teacher
Perry, Samuel Joseph
Communications Studies Instr
Shields, Mark Alan
Biology Instructor
Smith, Fred R., Jr.
Physics Instructor
Strong, LaVera Margaret
Kindergarten Teacher
Swinson, Jennifer Lynn
AP English Teacher
Thompson, Terry Lane
Principal
Tyrance, Judith Ann Hardison
Media Specialist
Warren, Martha Melton
Career Decisions, BioTech Tchr
Williams-Price, Bernita Alicia
Guidance Counselor
JAMESTOWN
Bassetti, Linda Heath
Seventh Grade Science Teacher
Branly, Louis Phillip
Anatomy, Physiology Adj Instr

Braswell, Brien William
HS PE & Health Teacher
Caudle, Suzanne Lasek
Bio Tchr & Chprsn of Sci Dept
Craven, Vicki Brown
English Teacher
Deltano, Keith John
6th Grd Math & Soc Stud Tchr
Drewry, Brenda Wofford
Third Grade Teacher
Goodman, E. Clarke
Fifth Grade Teacher
Herndon, Brian Keith
English Teacher
Hutson, Bryant Lindsay
History Instructor
Kenan, Bernice Holland
High School Mathematics Tchr
Martin, Aaron E.
Astronomy Instructor
Mc Gahee, Cheryl Fries
Accounting Instructor
Muller, Frances England
Dept Chair of Med Assisting
Osborne, Treva Smith
Fifth Grade Teacher
Redmond, Wanda Gantt
Second Grade Teacher
Robinson, Sherree Lynn
6th Grade Science & Math Tchr
Scandale, Elizabeth Phillips
Art Teacher
Simpson, Jerry Lee
Counseling Services Director
Stanley, Lloyd Herbert
Dept Chair of Fire Protection
Stover, Sharon Jean
English Professor
Summerell, Nancy Kuhrman
Instructor of Foreign Language
Thomas, Robert Emmett
Mathematics Instructor
Walden, Joan E.
Business Education Teacher
Wall, Cynthia Ellen
English as Second Lang Tchr
Wells, Janet Carter
7th Grade Science Teacher
JAMESVILLE
Hurst, Elizabeth Lewis
Mathematics Teacher
Tadlock, Pamela Price
Soc Studies Dept Chair & Tchr
Wilson, Gail Purvis
11th & 12th Grade English Tchr
JEFFERSON
Barden, Betsy Thomas
Sixth Grade Teacher
Davis, Betty Witherspoon
Third Grade Teacher
Elliott, Larry Edward
Math Teacher
Gamble, Marcus
AP US History Teacher
Young, Cynthia Ann
Kindergarten Teacher
JONESVILLE
Hall, Caroline Gilbert
Third Grade Teacher
KANNAPOLIS
Almond, Billie Gibbons
Algebra I Teacher
Carlson, Lance D.
8th Grade Science Teacher
Fishback, Vance Morgan
Business Education Teacher
Howard, Carol Church
8th Grd Social Studies Teacher
Johnson, Saundra Julian
Third Grade Assistant
MIddleton, Frances Jannette
Fourth Grade Teacher
Rodgers, Delinda Barrier
Mathematics Tchr & Dept Chprsn
Seabolt, Ronald W.
Teacher of Gifted Students
Stack, Janet Ann
Second Grade Teacher
Turner, Alison Stanford
Technology Specialist
Woody, Linda Reese
Fifth Grade Teacher
Zucker, Edith Bishop
Business Teacher
KENLY
Bryant, Perry
Art & Photography Teacher
Carter, Suzanne Herring
Fourth Grade Teacher
Cockrell, Cary Luper
Mathematics Teacher
Holland, Jean Baggett
Retired Teacher
Parnell, Judith Addison
10th Grade English Teacher
Peedin, Darla Parker
Choral Music Teacher
Sandifer, Kathy Creech
English Teacher
Smith, Kelly S.
English Teacher
Still, Sandra Roberts
Theatre Arts Teacher
KERNERSVILLE
Bennett, Carol Ragland
Mathematics Teacher
Bryan-Scales, Neda Montine
English & French Teacher
Carpenter, Libby Meggs
English IV & French Teacher

Coggins, Judith Marlene
English Teacher
Cooney, Sean Brian
Secondary English Teacher
Harris, Harry Bryant, Jr.
Wrld Civilizations Facilitator
Johnson, Luther, Jr.
Secondary Mathematics Teacher
Lipscomb, George Burke
Social Studies Teacher
Lowman, Linda Lum
Math Teacher
McGee, Lisa Mabe
Business Education Teacher
Paschal, Mary Ann Miller
5th Grade Teacher
Peppers, Mildred Strickland
Social Studies Teacher
Poole, Cathy Benita
Tchr of Mentally Handicapped
Powell, Rhonda Belcher
Curriculum Coordinator
Russ, Kirsten Pilcher
Teacher
Stanley, Marty
In-Schl Suspension & Ath Dir
Wheeler, Wilma Hairston
Kindergarten Teacher
KINGS MOUNTAIN
Allen, Dianna Neal
Elem Curriculum Specialist
Gibson, Judy Barnes
Algebra & Geometry Teacher
Hollifield, Dale Aubrey, II
Government & Economics Tchr
McDowell, Danny R.
Fourth Grade Teacher
Rupp, Richard Joseph
6th Grade Teacher
Scism, Ann Bridges
Second Grade Teacher
Terres, Suzanne Mc Daniel
7th Grade Math Teacher
KINSTON
Armstrong, Eleanor Gold
Early Childhood Program Head
Barnard, Gail Purcell
Music Teacher
Berg, Carla Brown
Office Technology Instructor
Bowen, Diane Harris
French & Spanish Teacher
Boyette, Glenda Pike
Fifth Grade Teacher
Britton, George Miller
Sociology Dept Head
Brooks, Jack J.
Assistant Principal
Ellis, Jackie Beaman
Kindergarten Teacher
Griffin, Patricia Smith
4th-5th Grd Music & Drama Tchr
Harrison, Mary Margaret
Teacher of Gifted
Heath, Pamela Braswell
Third Grade Teacher
Hill, Wendell Craig
Comprehensive Schl Coord
Jones, David V.
Elec Engrng Tech Dept Head
Jones, Doris Jones
Kindergarten Teacher
Kornegay, Annie Specks
8th Grd Commnctn Skills Tchr
McCray, Geraldyne Baker
English Teacher
McMillan, Patricia Wickline
Second Grade Teacher
Mercer, Marilyn Miller
Mathematics Instructor
Morris, Ruby Hunter
Data Processing Dept Head
Noble, Gale Taylor
HS Algebra Teacher
Pope, Susan Hall
First Grade Teacher
Price, Jeffrey Darden
Physical Science Teacher
Reaves, Carol
English Instructor
Rocker, Frank
Director of Criminal Justice
Rouse, Kevin Scott
Lab Coord & English Instructor
Scott, Roberta Hefley
Retired Chemistry Teacher
Smith, Mary Louise
4th Grade Teacher
Suits, Mildred Rouse
Retired AP Eng & Comp Teacher
Tunstall, Patricia Stokes
Sixth Grd Tchr of Acad Gifted
Uastin, Patsy Lee
Fifth Grade Teacher
KIPLING
Howard, Florice Rumph
First Grade Teacher
Lee, J. Glenn
Physical Education Teacher
KITTRELL
Dawson, Wanda Spencer
Fifth Grade Teacher
Moore, Anita Gore
Third Grade Teacher
Pirie, Robert Clifford, Jr.
5th Grade Math Teacher
LA GRANGE
Bryan, Betty Hodges
Third Grade Teacher

Burnett, Isaac, Jr.
Biology & Science Teacher
Hinson, Cleo Singleton
First Grade Teacher
Hodges, Joseph Milton
Band Director
Hull, Michael Quinton
Math Tchr
Humphrey, Jan Spence
English Teacher & Dept Chair
Kennedy, Marian Elizabeth
Choral Director
Melton, Carolyn Hardy
Kindergarten Teacher
Melton, Robert Forrest
Soc Stud Teacher & Coach
Palmer, Peter L.
Science Teacher
Ramsaur, Amy Thornburg
Music Teacher
Strong, Mamie Rice
Math & Science Teacher
Wynn, Gwendolyn Coad
Learning Disabled Resrc Tchr
LAKE WACCAMAW
Bass, Lori Kaye
Dance & Theate Arts Teacher
Chestnutt, Dorothy Jayroe
Mathematics Teacher
Faulk, Alan
Biology I & II Teacher
Sbardella, Kimberly Cartrette
Health Occupation Ed Teacher
LANDIS
Haywood, Marianne Linn
Physical Education Teacher
Trexler, Judy H.
Tchr of Academically Gifted
LAURINBURG
Britt, Thomas Curtis, Jr.
Teacher & Coach
Bundy, Susan
English Teacher
Byrd, Robert Lewis
Physics & Chemistry Teacher
Cross, Eleanor Wirfs
Health Occupations Ed Teacher
Dawkins, April M.
HS Social Studies Teacher
Fish, David Lee
Associate Professor of Music
Frank, Barbara Jean
Assoc Prof of Math
Hall, Robin Lynn
7th Grd Math & Science Tchr
Hancock, Shannon Raper
Math Teacher
Laurin, Sallye M.
Science Teacher & Coach
McLaurin, Sallye M.
Science Teacher & Coach
Moore, Anne Reed
12th Grade AP English Teacher
Prust, Richard Charles
Professor of Philosophy
Purcell, Angela Jackson
Secondary Math Teacher
Quick, Rosa Etta Mc Neill
Second Grade Teacher
Reichner, L. Howard
Asst Professor of Politics
Snead, Eleanor Marks
Marketing Education Teacher
Trulove, Patricia Coppedge
Communication Skills Teacher
Van Hooser, Toula Yeapanis
6th Grd Mathematics & Sci Tchr
LAWNDALE
Canipe, Glenda McEntire
Sixth Grade Math Teacher
Cooke, Janet Howard
Science & Social Stud Teacher
Davis, Albert Eugene, Jr.
Chemistry & Physics Teacher
Elmore, Phyllis Boggs
Health Occupations Teacher
Glover, Christopher Warren
Chemistry Teacher
McKee, Alisa Newton
Mathematics Teacher
Parrish, Donna Wall
7th Grd Math & Science Teacher
Spangler, Iris Keever
Eighth Grade Math Teacher
Strain, Martha Johnson
French & English Teacher
Walker, David Raymond
Driver Education Teacher
Wright, Thomas G.
HS Health & PE Teacher
LEICESTER
Sluder, Gerald Miles
Retired MS Sci Tchr
LELAND
Ruff, William Arthur
Mathematics Teacher
LENOIR
Baker, Robert Ferrell
Business Department Instructor
Barnes, Brian F.
Govt, Ec & Soc Stud Teacher
Barrier, Regina Morrison
Chemistry Teacher
Carswell, Dennis T.
Director of Bands
Church, Jeffrey Robert
Exceptional Childrens Teacher
Duncan, Paul David
Math Teacher & Department Chm

LENOIR (cont)
Hawkins, John Oliver
English Teacher
Kincaid, Mary Anderson
Computer Instructor
Kwiatkowski, Jon Stanley
Microcomputer Instructor
Lail, Janice Anderson
English & Drama Teacher
Miller, Sherry Tuttle
7th Grade Math & Science Tchr
Ramsey, Jonathan Neil
History Teacher
Spicer, John A.
Social Studies Teacher
Suddreth, Rita Dula
Second Grade Teacher
Thomas, John Edward
Mathematics Instructor
Tighe, Carol Hood
Spanish Teacher
Whitener, R. Edgar
Director of Bands
LEWISTON
Mc Glone, Coleen Peele
Retired Early Chldhd Teacher
LEWISVILLE
Linville, Justine Patrick
Visual Art Teacher & Dept Head
Peeler, Roslyn Arthur
1st Grade Teacher
LEXINGTON
Barnes, Coy Howard
Mathematics Tchr
Blackburn, Larry Gene
Chemistry Professor
Brown, Renae Talley
Social Studies Teacher
Casto, Mark J.
Drafting Teacher
Crump, Kiwana Talbert
Science Teacher
Everhart, Stephen Daniel
Math & Soc Stud Tchr
Gainor, Max Ulmer
Sixth Grade Teacher
Gobble, Tina Morgenson
Third Grade Teacher
Hendrick, Jane Elizabeth
Math Teacher
Hines, Joyce Lytle
Science Teacher & Curr Coord
Hinkle, Winifred Bristow
4th Grade Teacher
Hunt, Irma Smith
Nursing Instructor
Kesler, Barbara Campbell
Business Teacher
King, Crystal Thomason
Biology, Life Sci & PE Teacher
LaLonde, Margaret Elizabeth
Psychology Instructor
Mabe, Walter Lee
Chorus Teacher
Mercer, Amy Runkle
HS Science Teacher
Parker, Warren Cameron
Jr Sr High Math Teacher
Pickett, Londa Koonts
HS Mathematics Teacher
Presson, Russell Dean
Head of Music
Price, Valerie Elizabeth
Soc Studies Tchr & Dept Chair
Reid, Paul Randolph
Science Teacher
Reynolds, Rita Hege
Fifth Grade Teacher
Smith, Margaret Powell
Retired Primary Teacher
Swicegood, Nancy Parnell
Ninth Grade Algebra Teacher
Talbert, Dorothy R.
Teacher
Teal, Barbara Berrier
Anatomy & AP Biology Teacher
Terrell, Susan C.
English Teacher
Todd, Bonnie Sweat
5th Grade Teacher
Williams, Mischa K.
English Teacher
Worley, Roxanna Young
Language & History Teacher
LIBERTY
Cromer, Ann L.
Retired Elementary Teacher
LILESVILLE
Williams, Nancy Taylor
6th Grade Teacher
LILLINGTON
Dark, Patricia Clark
Business Teacher
Davis, Barbara Ann
Hlth & Physical Education Tchr
Elliott, Viola Lewis
Assistant Principal
Frye, Thomas Scot
Instr of Tech Specialist
Gurtis, Ruth Bain
Healthful Living Teacher
Hunter, Rebecca Collins
Science Teacher
Senter, Michael Craig
Horticulture Teacher
Shaw, Angus Thomas
United States History Teacher
LINCOLNTON
Cloninger, Jeffery Elliott
Social Studies Teacher
Dalrymple, Fred McIver
Communities Site Coordinator
Hallman, Peggy Jonas
Third Grade Teacher
Hubbard, Tammy Hoyle
Mathematics Teacher
Martin, Bobby Lee, Jr.
Anatomy & Biology Teacher
Mattox, Evelyn Inabinett
Remedial Reading Teacher
Reynolds, Lori Jean
Third Grade Teacher
Ward, Timothy Crenshaw
Band Director
Yoder, Vicki Hudson
Multi-Age Teacher
LITTLETON
Duke, William Howard
History Teacher
Thornton, Matilda Ann
Business Education Teacher
LOUISBURG
Hinton, William Jones, Jr.
Professor of Arts
Mc Ghee, Donald Rose
4th Grade Teacher
Rector, Robert E.
Assoc Prof of History & Govt
Wilder, Danny
Health & Physical Ed Teacher
LOWELL
Aldridge, Carolyn Quilliams
9th Grd Eng, Ag & Jrnlsm Tchr
Harmon, Steve
Science Teacher
LOWGAP
Collins, Jackie Sprinkle
Tchr of Exceptional Children
Gordon, Cara Dianne
First Grade Teacher
Luffman, Barbara Laster
4th Grade Teacher
Martin, Sheri M.
5th Grade Teacher
LUCAMA
Liles, Anne Boyette
Retired Third Grade Teacher
LUMBERTON
Carter, Sandra W.
Visual Arts Teacher
Freeman, Rose Oxendine
Family & Consumer Sci Teacher
Frye, Jean Waters
Foreign Lang Dept Chair & Tchr
Harvey, Laurence Alan
Band Director
Howard, Ursula Rosetta
English Teacher
Locklear, Sally Cummings
11th Grade English Teacher
Rogers, Madeline Bryant
Home School Coordinator
Strickland, Trudi Lyn (Wiggs)
Media Specialist
Taylor, Vickie Hill
Third Grade Teacher
Thompson, Marion Dorsett
French Teacher
MADISON
Adams, Clarence Lee
8th Grade Science Teacher
MAIDEN
Wilson, Kathryn Mosteller
French Teacher
MANTEO
Basnight, Elizabeth Skipsey
Fifth Grade Teacher
Osmon, Julie Workman
English Teacher
MARION
Beck, Martha Nesbitt
First Grade Teacher
Foster, Melvin Arthur
English Teacher
Goodson, Jan Hall
Sixth Grade Teacher
Greene, Robin H.
Math Teacher
Kelley, Leatha Patton
Yearbook Teacher & Advisor
Lawing, Iris Rabb
5th Grade Teacher
Mock, Ida Kaylor
Chemistry Teacher
Morris, David Wayne
7th Grade Teacher
Setzer, Sandra Sasser
Algebra & Social Studies Tchr
Styles, Keith W.
World History & Psych Teacher
MARS HILL
Meacham, Katharine Rothrock
Asst Professor of Philosophy
MARSHALL
Bowman, Michael J.
Physics Teacher
Flynn, Faye B.
Media Coordinator
Gilliam, Suzanne DuVall
6th Grade Teacher
Grigg, Judy Allen
Mathematics Teacher
Gunter, Paul Robert
Chemistry Teacher
Teague, Robert Derrick
Band Director
Thomas, Elaine Ray
HS Counselor
Waldrop, Patsy Hale
Mathematics Teacher
Wallin, Ronnie Lee
Mathematics Tchr & Dept Chair
Ward, Anita Ramsey
Health Occupations Teacher
Weaver, Henry Andrew
Head Football Coach
Wells, Diane Lee
Science Teacher
Wyatt, Barbara E.
8th Grade Math Teacher
MARSHVILLE
Collins, Cara Kirby
Marketing Ed Teacher & Coord
Gordon, Gerri Medlin
French & Spanish Teacher
Lowery, John Warren, Jr.
Hlth, Phys Ed Tchr & Ath Dir
Morgan, Patricia Deese
Chem & Physical Science Tchr
Tucker, Jane H.
5th Grade Teacher
MATTHEWS
Brock, Doris Thomas
Advanced Literature Tchr
Davis, Kathryn Ashley
8th Grd Social Studies Teacher
Fleming, Betty Bryan
History Teacher
Flowe, Lynda Dillard
Sixth Grade Teacher
King, Christine M.
HS Math Teacher
Tassy, Jean-Rene
Second Grade Teacher
MAXTON
Fairley, Annie Langston
Helping & Lead Teacher
Locklear, Kim Swett
Communication Skills Teacher
Oxendine, Linda Kay (Carter)
Second Grade Teacher
MAYODAN
Akers, Wiley Mac
Art Teacher
Eaves, Timothy Lane
Band Director
Freeman, Joseph W., Jr.
High School Science Teacher
Porter, Connie Friddle
English Teacher
Russell, Deborah Doss
English & Journalism Teacher
MC ADENVILLE
Rice, Connie Carringer
4th-5th Grade Teacher
MC LEANSVILLE
Clayton, Lois Bumpass
Exploring Life Skills Teacher
Hurley, Oscar Raymer, Jr.
Physics & Chemistry Teacher
Maxson, Reba Babb
8th Grade Language Arts Tchr
Owen, Susan V.
General Music Specialist
Owens, Robert DeWitt
Sports Medicine & History Tchr
Pursley, Howard Thomas
Weight Trng Instr & Ftbl Coach
Thompson, Catherine Sublett
Chemistry Teacher
MEBANE
Brumble, Michael R.
Vocational Teacher
Bullins, Deborah Timberlake
8th Grade Science Teacher
Clegg, Alfreda Currie
9th Grd Eng & Journalism Tchr
Grubbs, Teresa Warren
English Teacher
Henderson, Cassandra Wright
First Grade Teacher
Kirby, John Vernon
HS Exceptional Children Tchr
Moore, Karla Greeson
Biology & AP Biology Teacher
Roney, Carolyn R.
Communication Skills Teacher
Sims, Brenda Richmond
Third Grade Teacher
Thompson, Janet Lynch
7th Grade Science Teacher
Whittington, Deborah Wallace
Dance Teacher
MERRY HILL
Outten, Audrey Rich
Kindergarten Teacher
Ward, Katherine Sawyer
4th Grade Teacher
MICRO
Crocker, Pamela Foster
ALC & DOP Teacher
Evans, Richard Danny
Physical Education Teacher
MIDDLESEX
Batten, Janet Boykin
Sixth Grade Teacher
MILL SPRING
Hardin, Linda Hensley
Fifth Grade Teacher
Odel, Sarah O.
Kindergarten Teacher
MILLERS CREEK
Foster, Betty Kilby
English & French Teacher
Holbrook, Deborah Elledge
Secondary Mathematics Teacher
Little, Brenda Mc Neill
Soc Studies Tchr & Dept Chair
Parsons, Judy Foster
Fifth Grade Teacher
MISENHEIMER
Burke, Melva McCrory
Dept of Teacher Ed Head
Campbell, Karl Edward
Assistant Professor of History
Clark, Alan Randall
Assoc Prof of Communications
Heckel, David Calvin
Professor of English
Ingram, E. Jack
Sports Med & Mngmt Asst Prof
MOCKSVILLE
Carothers, William Thomas
7th Grade Social Studies Tchr
Cook, Teresa Ward
Sixth Grade Teacher
Donaldson, James William
English Instructor
Havnaer, Stephen David
10th-12th Grade Biology Tchr
Hoyle, Robert Terry
HS English & Spanish Teacher
Kokoski, Kristine Knapp
English Teacher
Lowrance, Mary M.
Literacy Classes Teacher
Ramsey, Freda Lois
High School Teacher
Scott, Gladys White
Second Grade Teacher
Stewart, Katherine Edwards
Family & Consumer Sci Teacher
Stovall, Susie Johnson
Spanish Teacher
MONCURE
Little, Freddie Wesley
Physical Education Teacher
MONROE
Baker, Marty
English Teacher
Carson, Leslie Anderson
Mathematics Teacher
Carson, Timothy Wade
Physical Education Teacher
Conrad, Peter Edward
Spanish Teacher
Conway, Mary Jo Bird
Chem & Forensic Tchr
Crook, Deborah Palmer
Kindergarten Teacher
Currington, Debbie Watwood
Choral Director
Cuthbertson, Jeffery Kevin
Secondary Science Teacher
Dolan, Nina M.
Biology & Earth Science Tchr
Faulkner, Trent Shawn
Ec, Legal & Pol Systems Tchr
Fumo, Raymond R., Jr.
Social Studies Teacher
Harris, Kathryn Pierce
Business Education Teacher
Helms, Lisa Anne
Mathematics Teacher
Helms, Susan Cox
Art Teacher
Helton, Susan Southerland
Math Teacher
Hollman, Mari Kristina
Mathematics Teacher
Huntley, Susan Denise
Math Teacher
Irwin, Allen L.
Physics & Physical Sci Teacher
Jacumin, Scott
Secondary Social Studies Tchr
Jeffries, Evelyn Massey
Fourth Grade Teacher
Jones, John Allison, Jr.
Assistant Principal
Liles, Betty Downs
MS Academically Gifted Sci Tch
Lindley, Terry Wayne
Atuo Body Repair Instructor
Menendez, Theresa Montale
Eng & Creative Writing Tchr
Moser, Cecil A.
History Teacher
Peed, Meri-Kathryn Myer
Health Occupation Ed Teacher
Price, Tracy Kennington
Art Teacher & Dept Head
Puckett, Barbara Jewel
E. C. Teacher
Salzer, Deborah Davis
8th Grade Language Arts Tchr
Schmitt, Karen Christine
Social Studies Teacher
Stevens, Joy Smith
HS Math Teacher & Dept Chprsn
Wade, Tamara Lynn
Math Teacher
MONTREAT
Daniel, Richard Bradley
Assoc Prof Environmental Stud
Forstchen, William R.
Asst Prof of His & Teacher Ed
Glassford, Darwin King
Associate Professor
Lassiter, Mark Timothy
Assoc Prof of Env Stud & Bio
Sullivan, John Jay
Business Professor
MOORESVILLE
Davidson, Katherine Denig
8th Grd Sci & Soc Studies Tchr
Gardner, Nancy Smith
Jr-Sr HS English Teacher
Hallman, Rita Landis
Spanish & ESL Teacher
Mauney, Stephen Andrew
History Teacher
Smith, Karen Brown
8th Grade Language Arts Tchr
VanderWall, Barbara Davis
Eighth Grade Teacher
Welsh, Kimberly Erin
Tenth Grade English Teacher
Witcher, Nancy Phillips
Choral Dir & Music Specialist
MOREHEAD CITY
Dominick, Betsy McCool
English Teacher
Jackson, Inez Smith
HS Mathematics Teacher
Neagle, Catherine Hewitt
Math Teacher
Springle, Jan Hanes
Biology Teacher
MORGANTON
Asbury, Sheila Yates
Nursing Instructor
Brewer, Coron Aves
Home Economics Teacher
Buchanan, Martha Boyd
Science Teacher
Bullins, John Christopher
Assistant Principal
Callaway, Cynthia Hagaman
Dean of Inst Effectiveness
Crump, Linda Branch
Math Teacher
Fitzsimmons, Jean Vincent
Social Studies Teacher
Fletcher, John James David
High School English Teacher
Garrison, Randal Scot
English Teacher
Greene, Katherine F.
Second Grade Teacher
Hardy, Tommy Jones
Criminal Justice Coord & Instr
Hartley, Rosanna Higgins
Computing Instructor
Hicks, Tracy Ollis
Physical Science Teacher
Keller, Christina Harris
First Grade Teacher
Orders, Judy Dean
Fifth Grade Teacher
Pharr, Ruby Deaton
Biology Instructor
PIttman, Timothy Michael
English & Drama Teacher
Rhoney, Kelly McDaniels
Algebra Teacher
Smith, Rick Lee
7th-12th Grade English Tchr
Watkins, Donald Lynn
US History Teacher
Williams, Elizabeth R.
Science Teacher
MOUNT AIRY
Ayers, Carole Annette
Social Studies Teacher
Basham, Dwight Cornell
Choral Director
Beamer, Louise Beasley
Third Grade Teacher
Brown-Sardler, Christine Gentry
Business Education Teacher
Bryant, Ann Barker
Spanish Teacher
Danley, Melissa Ann
8th Grade Science Teacher
Fariss, Kathryn Melton
High School Math Teacher
Fletcher, William Charles, Jr.
Fourth Grade Teacher
Grow, James Leonard
Vocational Teacher
Hambrick, Mary Essa
French Teacher
Hardy, Sharon Smith
3rd-6th Grade Teacher
Howlett, Cathy Thompson
Third Grade Teacher
King, Ronald Gray
PE Tchr & Mens Bsktbl Coach
Kirkman, Joseph Roy
Teacher of Academically Gifted
Lowe, Carol Norman
High School Mathematics Tchr
Mosley, Terri Ellswood
Health & PE Teacher
Reynolds, Vera Smith
5th Grade Teacher
Spurlin, Joan M. Parker
Kindergarten Teacher
Younger, Glenda Bullen
5th Grade Teacher
MOUNT HOLLY
Burris, Ann Manus
First Grade Teacher Assistant
Caddell, Debbie L.
Dance Teacher
Henson, Janet Andrews
Reading Teacher
Hill, Sharon Bumgardner
Mathematics Teacher
Kirby, Seth Dean
Band Director
Little, Ann Farris
Kindergarten Teacher
Luckey, Tony Eugene
Technology Education Teacher
Mallon, Joseph Lewis
Science Teacher
Mc Manus, Gary Eugene
9th Grade US Studies Teacher

' HOLLY (cont)
immy Terrell
Studies Teacher
' MOURNE
, Lucy Mc Neely
Grade Teacher
' OLIVE
Richard Rue
Prof of Bio & Dept Chair
Angelene Musgrave
unication Skills Teacher
enneth Wayne
Professor
Michael Lamont
ology Instructor
Diane Bishop
sor of Mathematics
Irene
ate Professor of Music
gton, Pepper
Professor
Penny B.
on & Speech Professor
PLEASANT
Doris Blackwelder
Teacher
ri S.
ade Teacher
, Corey William
nment & Economics Teacher
resa Isenhour
Teacher
Brenda F.
Teacher
ULLA
evonia M.
ss Teacher
Katherine Renee
h Teacher
EESBORO
or, Betty Nethercutt
h & Spanish Professor
Charles P.
er Education Dept Chair
ee, James Monroe
sor of Music
gh, Scott Haines
iate Prof of Hlth & PE
Ernest Leslie, Jr.
matics & Science Teacher
e, James Curtis
Prof of Business Mgmt
Douglas Elbert
ate Professor of Art
arth Dalmain
nan Department of Science
ck
ant Professor of English
Brenda
Professor of English
, Wallace Eugene
ud & Lang Arts Teacher
Carol Sharon
Dept Assoc Prof & Chprsn
Patsy Woodard
of Bus Asst Prof
, Dorothy Adkins
Prof of Business
Peggy Hemmann
ntary Education Instr
HY
oan R.
Teacher
Alissa G.
ath & Biology Teacher
Joanne Hedrick
Sci & Prin of Tech Tchr
onnie Joe
nist Instructor
d, Boyd Edward
of Biology & Psychology
James Matthew
Sci & Tech Resource Tchr
Barbara Bishop
Basic Skills Instructor
VILLE
Cynthia Brown
Grade Teacher
aw, James Wilson, II
Ec Tchr & Dept Chair
Mary Catherine
ra Teacher
, Wanda Stallings
Grade Teacher
thy, Joseph Patrick
rd Health & PE Teacher
, Aaron Baxter
h & Physical Ed Teacher
rd, Alvin Avey, III
rd Lang Arts Teacher

Mary Alice
rade Teacher
Joyce Jaynes
ergarten Teacher
BERN
Dianne Kinney
Teacher
, Roger King
ssor of English
Rudolph
eacher
ell, Brenda Linko
Grade Teacher
Brenda Linyear
Arts & Soc Studies Tchr
, Deona Harris
ergarten Teacher
erry David
ch Instructor

Duncan, Carlon Clavis, Jr.
High School Biology Teacher
Evancho, Philip Steve
Fine Arts Chairperson
Fuhrman, Terence William
Assistant Principal
Gardner, Gail (Rice)
Math Teacher
Gratz, Karl LeRoy
Retired 6th Grade Teacher
Hall, Pamela Mackey
8th Grade Social Studies Tchr
Hepler, Paul Rufus, II
History Professor
Hodges, Mary Ann Isles
English Instructor
Hunter, Eugene Robert
Retired 5th Grade Teacher
Joyner, Winona Stine
Mathematics Teacher
Lenderman, Victoria Scearse
Director of Financial Aid
Long, Philip Linton
Spanish Teacher
Lyles, Thomas Brooks, Sr.
Health & Physical Ed Instr
Morehead, Saundra Carlyn
Business Teacher
Morse, Marilu Murphy
Junior High Teacher
Pfautz, Chris
Counselor & Orientation Instr
Rackley, Lynda Grady
High School Math Teacher
Smith, Marge Kaczynski
Math & Science Teacher
Smith, Walter Randall
Sixth Grade Teacher
Squier, Virginia Craig
Fifth Grade Teacher
Wallace, Kenneth Wayne
Director of Business Programs
Warren, Sharon Broich
Fourth Grade Teacher
White, Barbara Ford
K-5 Grd Triad Enrichment Tchr
Whitehead, Caroline Parham
Sociology & Anthropology Instr
Wood, Susan
English Teacher
NEW LONDON
Huneycutt, Linda Speight
Business Teacher
NEWLAND
Huffman, Mitzie Mc Kinney
5th Grade Teacher
Krege, Marion Sanders
Marketing Education Teacher
Shirley, Ruth Ann
Social Studies Teacher
Tatum, Edwina Young
Title I Teacher
Tatum, Robert Laurence
Comm Skills & Science Teacher
Thompson, Glenda Rae
7th Grade Teacher
NEWPORT
Austin, Donald Lee, Jr.
Algebra Teacher
Humphrey, Lovey Deane
Music & Chorus Teacher
McClanahan, Jacqueline Lancaster
Third Grade Teacher
Ormsby, Catherine Adeimy
8th Grade English Teacher
Watkins, Matthew Robert
Eng & Soc Stud Transition Tchr
NEWTON
Awad, Sally Kathryne (Hall)
Biology Teacher
Comer, Vicki B.
English Teacher
Crowder, Diane Joyce
6th Grd Language Arts Teacher
Headrick, Martha Holsclaw
8th Grade Language Arts Tchr
Hefner, Dianne Bradshaw
8th Grade Teacher
Jarrett, Nancy Hapel
Chemistry Teacher
Jones, David Hamilton
Mathematics Teacher
Paysour, Michael Glenn
US History Teacher
Sigmon, Jane Coley
First Grade Teacher
Stockner, James Irven
Band Director
Willard, Jerry W.
Pub Spkng, US His Tchr & Coord
NEWTON GROVE
Cobb, Katherine Simon
Theatre Arts & Chorus Instr
Jackson, Margaret Hudson
Retired Teacher
NORTH WILKESBORO
Beck, Billie Scott
Elementary Educator
Blankley, Glenda Sale
Third Grade Teacher
Bumgarner, Joan Henderson
7th-8th Grade Math Teacher
Nichols, Martha Smithey
Fourth Grade Teacher
NORWOOD
Blalock, Candace Waller
Third Grade Teacher
OAK RIDGE
Hall, Joan Overby
Science Dept Chairperson

OAKBORO
Adams, Susan Thomas
Mathematics Teacher
Hunsucker, Gary Dale
Biology Teacher & Coach
Poole, Kaye
6th Grade Teacher
OLIN
Barron, Jane Sloan
English Teacher
Brown, Richard Harrison
8th Grade Math Teacher
Campbell, Elizabeth Steele
Teacher of Gftd Comm Skls
Cannan, Elizabeth Mc Elwee
Media Specialist
Hankins, Dianne Wood
High School Mathematics Tchr
Higgins, William Franklin
US History & Psych Tchr
Moore, Murphey Ann
English Teacher
Smith, Cheryl Johnson
Spanish Teacher
Walters, Elizabeth Batten
Latin & English Teacher
OXFORD
Abbott, Paula Duncan
English Teacher
Bullock, Rosa Edwina
Third Grade Teacher Assistant
Burnette, Patricia Wright
English Teacher
Capps, Amy Elizabeth
High School Science Teacher
Capps, Frank Albert
Student Assistant Counselor
Feggins, Lorraine Spencer
Second Grade Teacher
Herring, Howard Garner, Jr.
Biology Teacher
Keene, Paul L.
French Teacher
Sergent, Herve Olivier
Spanish Teacher
Swift, Bonnie Compton
Seventh Grade Lang Arts Tchr
Wilkinson, Dolores Harris
English Dept Chairperson
Williams, Johnny Otis
8th Grade Math Teacher
PANTEGO
Keyzer, Anna Myers
High School Mathematics Tchr
PATTERSON
Jenkins, Lynne P.
Second & Third Grade Teacher
PEACHLAND
Caudle, Cornelia Gaddy
Teacher
PEMBROKE
Bukowy, Stephen Joseph
Director of MBA Program
Bullard, Frances Holmes
Communication Skills Teacher
Chavis, Jane Oxendine
Kindergarten Teacher
Lowry, Fannie Dial
HS Science Teacher
Manning, Mahetta Rena
Business Education Teacher
Reese, Brenda Sue
High School Science Teacher
Watts, Dennis W.
Counselor
PIKEVILLE
Collins, Christy Crumpler
Science Teacher
Mann, Robert Wayne
Honors English Teacher
PILOT MOUNTAIN
Atkins, Sandra Pike
Business Education Teacher
Carter, Tony Oscar
English Teacher
Hauser, Richard Doub
Algebra, Math & Soc Stud Tchr
Lowe, La-Shene C.
Tchr of Excptnl Gftd Children
Marion, Dawn Johnson
HS Mathematics Teacher
PINE LEVEL
Strickland, Sandra
1st Grade Teacher
PINEHURST
Baker, Robert H.
Social Science Instructor
Biamonte, Robert Louis
Professor of Engineering Tech
Cole, Barbara Hancock
Prof of English
Davenport, Reynold S.
Engineering Technology Prof
Mc Inerney, Judy Sample
Math Professor
Swanson, Richard Everett
Physics Prof & Assoc Dean
Weaver, Terry E.
Professor of Biology
Williams, Alisa Anderson
Mathematics Professor
PINETOPS
Barnes, Linda H.
High School Science Teacher
Drake, Melissa Morgan
Physics & Chemistry Instructor
Green, Maureen Joyce
Mathematics Teacher
Newsome, Kolouia Woodring
Secondary Math Teacher

Thomas, Kathryn Parks
Mathematics Teacher
Webb, Kathy Deal
Science Teacher
PINETOWN
Adams, Beverly Meekins
Spanish Teacher
Burbage, James T.
Welding Teacher
Foster, Charles Leonard
Vocational Teacher
PINNACLE
Brady, Nancy Boles
Retired Science Dept Chair
PISGAH FOREST
Bingle, Glenda Chappell
Former Teacher
Dodson, Mildred Louise
Instructor
Hogsed, Sharon Olivia
Second Grade Teacher
Kiviniemi, Ann Harris
First Grade Teacher
Parker, Jolene Prewit
English Instructor
PITTSBORO
Broda, Martha Simpson
Social Studies Teacher
Bryant, Neasha Marvette
History & Government Teacher
Chandler, Ethel Richardson
Fifth Grade Teacher
Foust, Henry O.
Spanish Teacher
Horton, Ronald Wilson
High School PE Tchr & Coach
Lee, Becky K.
Spanish Teacher
Massei, JoAnn McDuffie
First Grade Teacher
Parks, Robin Gerringer
Industry Education Coordinator
Temple, David Brian
English Teacher
PLYMOUTH
Evans, Mary Charlene
Math Teacher
Norfleet, Natisha Earlise
Business Education Teacher
Rogerson, Christi Lilley
Mathematics Teacher
Stanfield, Kathryn Mac Kay
English Teacher
Thyng, Alan Richard
Senior Army Instructor
Walker, Katie Johnson
Business Education Teacher
West, Linda Porter
Health Occupations Ed Prgm Mgr
Whitfield, Donna Lynn
Social Studies Teacher
POLKTON
Huntley, Bettie Baker
Dev Math Teacher
Robertson, Marilyn B.
Instructor of Accounting
Stack, Connie West
Dir of Medical Assisting Prgm
Ward, Byron John
Arts & Science Chairman
Wittich, Tami Lynn
Criminal Justice Instructor
POWELLSVILLE
Simms, Andrea Sessoms
Eighth Grd Language Arts Tchr
PRINCETON
Johnson, Judy Siler
Art Teacher
PROVIDENCE
Covington, JoAnn Yancey
Fourth Grade Teacher
Shelton, Judith Atkins
Second Grade Teacher
Underwood, Julie Clayton
Second Grade Teacher
RAEFORD
Black-Flippin, Glendia
Teacher
Callender, Stanley C.
HS PE Teacher & Bsktbl Coach
Dunkley, Audrey W.
8th Grd Comm Skills Teacher
Edmonds, Iris Smith
First Grade Teacher
Faulk, Carolyn Caine
English Teacher
Hutchison, Theresa Messer
American History Teacher
Johnson, Barbara Plummer
Choral & General Music Teacher
Johnson, John Edwin
Auto Technology Instructor
King, Mary Senter
Sixth Grade Teacher
Mc Neill, Cordelia Carter
Math Teacher
Miller, Amy Black
Special Education Teacher
Mirovsky, Anthony Albert, II
Chemistry Teacher
Oxendine, Jerry Clifford
Indian & ESL Education Dir
Pilkington, Lynda Gay
Family & Consumer Sci Teacher
Sellars, Jane Morgan
Theatre Arts-Tech Theatre Tchr
Shepard, Joseph Lawrence
7th Grd Soc Stud & Sci Teacher
Stanley, Deborah Sumners
English Teacher

Villines, Dorothy Jenerette
Second Grade Teacher
Wiles Singletary, Vicki
Spanish Teacher
Wilson, Sara Lamb
Social Studies Teacher
Wrigtt, Gertie Campbell
Teacher
RALEIGH
Archer, Annette Batson
Physical Education Teacher
Asato, Cheryl Wicker
Sixth Grade Teacher
Bamforth, Mary Beth Edwards
English Instructor
Bierlein, David Randall, Jr.
Mathematics & Cmptr Sci Tchr
Bingham, Lorelie
English Teacher
Brock, Lucy Brannen
Science Department Head
Brown, Josephus Cornell
Physical Education Specialist
Brown, Marilyn Shull
Teacher, Founder & Director
Bunce, Mamie Chason
Kindergarten Teacher
Burrows, Donna Bland
7th Grade Language Arts Tchr
Carr, Judith Thompson
5th Grade Teacher
Clifford, Leslie Warren
Math Teacher & Dept Chair
Costin, Lillie H.
Third Grade Teacher
Covington, Diane Brown
Choral Director
Crowley, Nancy Kenyon
Assistant Principal
Curry, Mary Woods
Third Grade Teacher
Daniel, Bettye Works
English Teacher
Davis, Sandra Holder
Teacher
Dickens, Claudia Johnson
Music Teacher
Dolton, Joanne Wefers
7th Grd Language Arts Teacher
Downey, Toni Honey
Consultant & Teacher
Everett, Kelly Aman
English Teacher
Florin, Julie Lechnes
Choral Dir & Drama Teacher
Frazier, Doris Forney
Lang Arts Tchr & Dept Chprsn
Gills, Jonathan Royce
High School Physics Teacher
Glassmire, Eileen B.
Chemistry Teacher
Gloden, Karyn A.
Seventh Grade Teacher
Grannan, Laura Caruso
12th Grade Teacher
Greenberg, Bluma K.
Asst Prof of Art His Emeritus
Hardin, Sharon Wilson
Mathematics & Science Teacher
Hege, Kendra Layne
English Teacher
Hennessee, William Edward
8th Grd Social Studies Tchr
Henson, Cynthia Sanford
Sales & Former Teacher
Hill, Penny Middleton
Music Teacher
Johnson, Brenda Jones
First Grade Teacher
Johnston, Jan Steger
Choral Director
Jones, Frederick Claudius
Assoc Prof Eng & Dir Hnrs Pgm
Jones, Olivia Metzger
French & German Instructor
Kabis, Rebecca Sloop
Fifth Grade Teacher
Kauffman, Karen Chaney
Fourth Grade Teacher
Kay, Lynda Beville
8th Grade Math Teacher
Keck, Charles Dotson
8th Grade Science Teacher
Keith, Patricia Watson
Instr of Philosophy & Religion
Kissinger, Harry Philip
Asst Admin & Bible Teacher
Kutscheid, Gloria Jean
Photography Instructor
Lowry, Virginia Bell
English Teacher
Mallette, David Leon
Professor of Biology
Manship, Bee Wells
Ninth Grade English Teacher
Marks, Patricia Johnson
Modern Dance Teacher
Martinez, Ollie Cuddington
Business Teacher
Mc Fadden, Annie W.
Science Teacher
McGill, Steven Thomas
English Teacher & Track Coach
Miller, Bruce Grantier
Instructor of Economics
Mobley, Ronald Wayne
Instr of Biology & Mathematics
Moore, Deborah Lynn
Guidance Counselor & Math Tchr

RALEIGH (cont)
Moore, Katherine K.
Medical Lab Tech Instructor
Morley, Elizabeth King
Second Grade Teacher
Murray, Marcy Mashburn
Algebra Teacher
Noble, Ophelia Darlene (Davis)
Eng & African Amer Lit Teacher
Page, Anne Bailey
French & Latin Dept Chair
Pfeifer, Deborah Adams
Social Science Teacher
Poe, Terry Lynn
Music Teacher
Pope, Elizabeth Stephens
Dance Instructor
Prater, Cheryle Robinson
9th-12th Grd Dramatics Teacher
Pritchett Vaughn, Betty Johnson-Clark
Director Enloe Enterprises
Ramsey, Carol Chaffin
English Teacher
Ratliff, Philip S.
Social Studies Dept Chair
Rochelle, Barry Phillip
Environmental Modeler
Rogers, Janie Moore
Second Grade Teacher
Rose, Gladys Cooke
5th Grade Teacher
Rushin, William Gray
Chemistry Teacher
Santo, Donna Marie
Department Head & Instructor
Shimpi, Lalchand T.
Comp Information Systems Prof
Sifers, Thomas Leon
Biology Teacher
Smith, Deborah K.
Biology Professor & Dept Head
Somers, Joyce Ratliff
Social Studies Teacher
Stark, Lucien Hadley
8th Grade Lang Arts Teacher
Stephens, Sue Ann
Physical Ed & Health Teacher
Stinner, Michelle Lynn
English Teacher
Taylor, Louisa Todd
Professor of English
Thomas, Wendy Solomon
English Teacher
Upham, Susann Leonard
Chemistry Teacher
Vick, Laura Greer
Anthropology Professor
Walker, Kelley Leigh
History Teacher
Wall, Lawrence Edward, Jr.
Latin Teacher & Principal
Wallis, Carol Anne (Helberg)
5th Grade Teacher
Wilson, Stephanie Anne
Biology Teacher
Zagula, Karen R.
Biology Dept & Lead Instructor
RAMSEUR
Boniface, Beverly Lynn
Learning Center Director
Dry, Belinda Rebecca
8th Grade Math Teacher
Fogarty, Lynda Saunders
Eighth Grade Teacher
Goldston, Brenda Ewing
Sixth Grade Teacher
Hall, Kimberly Patterson
Counselor
Lowe, Cynthia Martin
Business & Office Teacher
Pilson, James Gregory
Chorus Teacher
Shaw, Julie Burch
Secondary English Teacher
Thompson, Jess John
JROTC Instructor
Tysinger, Clyde Edward, Jr.
Discipline Coord & PE Teacher
RANDLEMAN
Becker, Maureen Sweeney
Counselor & Industry Ed Coord
Beeson, Kim Hinshaw
Math, Sci & Soc Stud Teacher
Crutchfield, Delores Brawley
Choral Director
Hughes, Lee VanThomas
Language Arts & Reading Tchr
Jones-Townsend, Sharon Dawn
4th Grade Teacher
Lowery, Lois Ward
7th Grd Soc Stud & Lang Tchr
Morris, Lina Black
English Teacher
Parlier, Rhonda Overton
First Grade Teacher
Vaughn, Cynthia Lynn
English Teacher
Watkins, Gloria Kearns
Family & Consumer Sci Teacher
RED SPRINGS
Freeman, William Herbert, Jr.
Var Mens Bsktbl Coach
Gay, Tianda Thomas
Marketing Ed Teacher & Coord
Harris, Dell
Mathematics Teacher
Joyner, Carol Summerlin
Third Grade Teacher
Martin, Kate Scates
Choral Dir & Chm of Arts Dept

McAllister, Tomasine Browne
French & English Teacher
Mc Queen, Barbara Ivey
7th Grade Communications Tchr
Mims, Grady
JROTC Instructor
Watson, Margaret Gay
Lang Arts & Soc Stud Teacher
REIDSVILLE
Brown, Anna Bolden
Fourth Grade Teacher
Carroll, Linda Pryor
Retired English Teacher
Hines, Cheryl Marie
Science Teacher
Hodnett, Lea Ann
Principal & Geometry Teacher
Howard, Suzanne Forbes
Spanish Teacher
Kater-Walton, Judy G.
Art Ed & Photography Teacher
Morris, Robin Gerringer
Fourth Grade Teacher
RICHLANDS
Aloia, Karen Griffin
Fourth Grade Teacher
ROANOKE RAPID
Aycock, Cathy C.
Social Studies Teacher
Duke, Trudy Carawan
English Teacher
Fulkerson, Wilma Futrell
Tchr of Academically Gifted
Hammack, Jerry Wayne
Mathematics Tchr & Dept Chair
Robinson, Marie Johnson
Comm Skills & Soc Studies Tchr
ROBBINS
Beane, Jerry Franklin
PE Teacher & Coach
Brewer, Ada Cheryl
Health, PE Teacher & Coach
Caviness, Elton Theron
Chemistry & Physics Teacher
Morris, Kimberly Hussey
Technology Teacher
Muccio, James Paul
Instrumental Music Teacher
Stewart, June Mc Kenzie
Tchr of Academically Gifted
Thomas, Theresa Brady
Theatre Arts Teacher
Williams, Edwin Lee
Agricultural Education Teacher
ROBBINSVILLE
Anderson, Rhonda Orr
Business Teacher & Dept Head
Caldwell, Melissa Adams
Physical Education Teacher
Hobbs, Michael Alan
Eighth Grade English Teacher
Morphew, Bill
Spanish & Social Studies Tchr
ROBERSONVILLE
Freeman, Evangeline Modica
8th Grade Science & Math Tchr
Hawkins, Stephen N.
Media Coordinator
ROCKINGHAM
Floyd, Kimberly Peninger
Algebra & Geom Teacher
Hagler, Todd Duncan
Physical Education Teacher
Holland, Jeffrey Dean
English Teacher
Jackson, Sara Graham
Teacher of Academically Gifted
Mc Neely, Ann Dillman
Even Start Lit Project Coord
Rainey, Marjorie Greer
Spanish Teacher
Watkins, Trudy Dawkins
HS Mathematics Teacher
ROCKWELL
Fisher, Kathey Peeler
Second Grade Teacher
Lyons, Kimberly Nottingham
First Grade Teacher
Wall, Sue Lingle
Second Grade Teacher
ROCKY MOUNT
Alexander, Benny
Athletic Director & Coach
Ankers, Dale Lynn
Science Teacher
Blice, Chris David
Director of Bands
Brame, Joel Kenneth
Mathematics Teacher
Brown, Irene Silver
First Grade Teacher
Davis, Angela Parker
8th Grade Social Studies Tchr
Dickens, Dolly Clark
English & Paideia Teacher
Dunn, Charlene Griffin
Allied Health Instructor
Gainey, Michael Gerard
Health & Physical Ed Teacher
Green, Jo Kimball
First Grade Teacher
Heath, Jean Riddle
Retired Assistant Professor
Heck, Debra Sugg
Home Economics Teacher
Helms, Denise Juren
Algebra Teacher
Hill, William Dorsey
Physical Education Teacher

Holt, Margaret McLeod
School Counselor
Kincheloe, Debra Winstead
English Teacher
Kulie, Teresa Candy
High School Biology Teacher
Morton, Felix, III
Career Decision Teacher
Mullinix, Gay Snuggs
Math & Physics Teacher
Parvin, Jane Wilson
Spanish Teacher
Purvis, Irma Braswell
Third Grade Teacher
Stocks, Carolyn Johnson
Sixth Grade Teacher
Thompson, Karen Riggs
Art Teacher
Uhrin, Sylvia Lewis
4th Grade Teacher
Waters, Trudi Jaber
Science Teacher
Williams, Dawn F.
9th Grade English Teacher
RONDA
Benge, Anna-Marie Bare
Choral Director
Burcham, Mark Wayne
Physical Sci & Geology Teacher
Dobbins, Brenda Lorraine (Adams)
Business Teacher
Lowe, Mary H.
Business Education Teacher
McLean, Michael Frederick
Mathematics Teacher
McLean, Pamela Burcham
Seventh & Eighth Grade Teacher
Payne, Nancy Tilley
Math Teacher
West, Avery Lloyd
Math, Physical Ed Tchr & Coach
ROPER
Bradshaw, Mary Kay Allsbrook
Teacher of Academically Gifted
Wilkins, Gloria Williams
Sixth Grade Teacher
ROSEBORO
Pahl White, Mildred
Retired First Grade Teacher
Pope, Jennifer
English Teacher
Reeves, Margaret Keane
Language Arts Teacher
Strickland, Sue Holland
Retired Third Grade Teacher
ROSMAN
Cothran, Lillian Constance
Science Teacher
Patterson, Gaynelle Stockdale
7th-12th Grd Resource Teacher
Peeples, Linda Benson
English & Drama Teacher
Pierce, Lisa E.
Biology Teacher
ROWLAND
Deese, Gala Lowry
Principal
Ward, Peggy Wilkins
Marketing Education Teacher
ROXBORO
Anderson, Cheryl Jan
Principal
Bowes, Janet Beene
PE Teacher & Coach
Cooley, Lisa Kaye
Math Instructor
Furbish, Dean
Biology Instructor
Hubbard, Maryellen Winstead
Fifth Grade Teacher
Jeffries, Paulette Stewart
English Teacher
Kay, Norman Bruce
Instructor of Business Studies
Kincaid, Laura Tuck
Social Studies Teacher
Loflin, Michael Todd
HS Principal & Teacher
Lunsford, Sandra Featherston
Algebra & Geometry Teacher
Mangum, Marie Wilkerson
7th Grd Soc Stud & Math Tchr
Moore, Elizabeth Mc Phaul
Stu Support Svcs Cnslr
Oakley, Edna Dean
Business Teacher
Parker, Randall Vaughn
Instr of Microcomputer Systems
Pulliam, Dorothy P.
Elementary Teacher
Rivera, Rafael
Spanish Teacher
Terry, Darrell Pleasant
Agriculture Teacher
Thomas, Timothy Michael
Criminal Justice Prgm Coord
Tillman, Freda Smith
Kindergarten Teacher
Ward, Lynwood Allen
History & English Teacher
Wilkins, Sue Wooten
Mathematics Teacher
Young, O. Randolph
Dean
RUFFIN
Lovell, Mary Chandler
8th Grd His & Lit Teacher
Merritt, Cathy Pruitt
7th & 8th Grd Lang Arts Tchr

Wallace, Marjorie Jean
Fifth Grade Teacher
Walsh, Rhonda Early
Eighth Grd Math & Eng Tchr
RUTHERFORDTON
Higgins, Karen Elizabeth
HS Social Studies Teacher
Hopper, Marty Luke
Assistant Principal
Hoyle, Catherine T.
Sixth Grade Teacher
Paris, Janice R.
Teacher
Shook, Marie Shehan
Fourth Grd Tchr
SAINT PAULS
Caudell, Luanne Kennedy
Biology Teacher
Johnson, Larry B.
Counselor
Sutton, Katie E. C.
Dance & Theatre Arts Educator
SALEMBURG
Barnes, Judith Bass
Third Grade Teacher
Hall, Sharon McPhail
Fifth Grade Teacher
Wilson, Lynnette Strickland
Kindergarten Teacher
SALISBURY
Antosek, Carmelita Poole
Home Economics Teacher
Baker, Ben L.
Assoc Professor of Accounting
Ballard, Brett Charles
Band Director
Basinger, Dale Barry
US History Teacher
Cherry, Charlotte Cooper
Social Studies Teacher
Corriher, Nancy Graham
Teacher
Cotton, James Andrew
Eighth Grade Science Teacher
Cranford, Kathy A.
Biology & Anatomy Teacher
Current, Jane Sloan
7th Grade Social Studies Tchr
Durham, Louetta Mc Combs
High School Math Teacher
Halley, Theresa Hayes
English Tutor
Insley, Jeffrey Robert
Resource, DARE & GREAT Officer
Lauer, Cynthia Lee
Sports Medicine Dir & Instr
McKenzie, Denise Turner
Accounting Instructor
Merrell, Linda Lefler
Business Ed & Multimedia Tchr
Miller, Calvin Luther
Old & New Testament Instructor
Miller, Joe Van, Jr.
8th Grade Science Teacher
Moore, Marilyn Lashley
Administrative Asst & Sub Tchr
Ponder, Frederick Douglas
Prof of PE & Administrator
Poole, Phyllistine Goode
Instructor of English Dept
Rhoney, Keith Andrew
Social Studies Teacher
Rogers, John Boyce, Jr.
Language Arts Teacher
Russ, Robert A.
English Professor
Saxe, Allen B.
Asst Prof of Sociology
Shinn, Judith Deal
Third Grade Teacher
Sigmon, John Alvin
Technology Lab Instructor
Sloop, Carl Eugene, III
Physics & Chem Teacher
Turner, Patricia Cockerham
Seventh Grade Resource Teacher
SANFORD
Baucom, Debra Vernon
Sixth Grade Teacher
Caldwell, Elizabeth Pate
Honors English Teacher
Capps, Julia White
Sixth Grade Teacher
Carter, Susan Gothard
8th Grade Math & Algebra Tchr
Cashion, Jan Avery
High School English Teacher
Davis, Carol Dianne
MS Director
Dithman, Leland F., Jr.
Asst Administrator & His Tchr
Faulkner, Linda Johnston
Communications Skills Teacher
Holden, Ernest Todd
US History & Psychology Tchr
Howard, John Joseph
Senior Army Instructor
Ingram, Kathryn Durden
History Teacher
Jones, Lucinda Lee
Kindergarten Teacher
Keller, Barbara Sims
Special Education Teacher
Keller, Brenda Cole
Secondary Math & English Tchr
Leighton, Sandra G.
High School Counselor
London, Regina Martin
Secondary Math Teacher

Luck, Steven Craig
Social Studies Teacher
Mc Donald, Sherry Jalynn
Science Teacher
Parker, Mary Susan (English)
High School English Teacher
Payne, Teresa Tucker
Spanish Teacher
Slaughter, Lucille Kay
Third Grade Teacher
Stewart, Marla Cooper
Health & Physical Ed Teacher
Thomas, Patricia M.
Computer Applications Teacher
SEABOARD
Gee, Delois
Fourth Grade Teacher
SEAGROVE
King, Elda Moffitt
Third Grade Teacher Assistant
SELMA
Cox, Bobby Emmett
Rdng, Lang Arts & Comm AG Tc
SEVEN SPRINGS
McDowell, Jacqueline McCann
Title I Dir of Rdng & Math
SHALLOTTE
Bennett, Gene Allen, Jr.
Chemistry Teacher
Jolly, Sherrill Lanett
9th & 10th Grade English Tchr
Lemon, Deborah Bowman
5th-8th Grd Math Teacher
Wilmoth, Karen Russell
Second Grade Teacher
SHELBY
Brooks, Kenneth Eugene
Choral Director
Cash, Gwen Biggers
Fourth Grade Teacher
Fortenberry, Joy Wright
English Teacher
Harris, Roger Michael
Social Studies Teacher
Kiser, Frances Allen
Retired English Tchr
Newton, Claire Heasley
English Teacher & Dept Chair
Putnam, David Carson
English Teacher
Ramsey, Merry Lynn Evans
English Teacher
Scruggs, Wanda Smith
Health Occupations Ed Teacher
Sisk, Michael
AP Comp Sci Teacher
White, Joy Patrick
Mathematics Teacher
Wright, Dianne Woods
8th Grade Social Studies Tchr
SILER CITY
Boone, Norma Elizabeth
Counselor
Edwards, Thomas Shelton
Social Studies Teacher
Headen, Monica Dolores
English Teacher
Love, LeAnn Hollowell
HS Business Ed Teacher
Morris, Judith Weaver
Fifth Grade Teacher
Morse, Robert Sandy
High School Math Teacher
Snelling, George Alexander
In School Suspension Teacher
SMITHFIELD
Batten, Jenny Lou
Language Arts & Soc Stud Tchr
Carter, Jeffrey Scott
Resource Teacher
Cox, Kim Beam
Family & Consumer Science Tchr
Cox, Nicky Herring
Early Childhood Director
Dodd, Sue Lee
English Teacher
Hales, Lisa Price
Math Teacher
Holloman, Nancy Moore
Lang Arts & Social Stud Tchr
James, Vennie Bush
Social Studies Teacher
Johnson, Karen Massengill
Health & PE Teacher
Mills, Ruth Stambaugh
Drama Teacher
O'Neill, Dale Adams
English Instructor
Perkinson, Sandra Mc Leod
English Teacher
Phillips, Bobby L.
Business & Accounting Instr
Spragins, James Michael
Paralegal Instructor
Sutton, Mary Ann
US History Teacher
SMYRNA
Murray, Doris McClain
Early Childhood & Pre-K Tchr
SNOW HILL
Blizzard, Susan Moore
Earth Science Teacher
Carraway, Shelia Shingleton
5th Grade Teacher
Hamm, Denise B.
Lang Arts & Soc Stud Teacher
Heath, Christine Eubanks
Fourth Grade Remediation Tchr

A
wen Brown
rgarten Teacher
ERN PINES
ephen Frederick
ic Dir & Phy Ed Teacher
Wilbert N., Jr.
ept Chairman & Teacher
Anne Barton
& General Music Teacher
Rodney Ernest
a Teacher
, Jennifer Ellington
cs & Algebra Teacher
Lorna Campbell
rd Eng Tchr & Yrbk Adv
iams, Barbara Fox
l Social Worker & Teacher
John Joseph
Teacher
Angela Hinson
gy Teacher
ds, Vicki Taplin
ematics Teacher
Elaine Cooper
d Grade Teacher
son, Joan Gould
ess Teacher
IPORT
Mary Catherine Cabaniss
rade Math Teacher
tricia Armstrong
sh Teacher
, Beverly C. Bernard
Grade Teacher
Nikita T. Webb
selor
ld, Sandra L.
rade Tchr
, Annie Cartee
h Grd Lang Arts Teacher
ns, Mary Jones
ematics Teacher
A
trout, Judith Sellers
ess Education Teacher
Donna Jenkins
ematics Teacher
Villiams, Donna
School Art Teacher
CER
Vivian Mackey
sh Teacher
Betty Burner
er of Academically Gifted
, Kendal Hoke
h Grade Science Teacher
ALE
ar, Mohamed Galal
ronics Instructor
, Pete Joseph
istry & Physics Instructor
ames Lee
ematics Teacher & Dept Chm
G HOPE
ter, Cynthia Smith
h Grade Science Tchr
, Audrey Nanette
Grade Teacher & Chprsn
Christie Early
rade English Teacher
ad, Peggy Whitehurst
alism & Lang Arts Teacher
G LAKE
, Myra Collins
rade Teacher
, Kathleen Colbert
rade Teacher
CE PINE
ell, Renie Stewart
sh Instructor
on, Nancy Watson
h Grade Teacher
n, Chad Travis
rade Science Teacher
Jean B.
e Technology Instructor
Vicki S.
nd Grade Teacher
Terry Sanford
tional Education Teacher
y, Stephen Parker
hology Instructor
urry, Ricky Lee
rade Mathematics Teacher
Elizabeth F.
ergarten Teacher
Shelley Boone
th Grade Teacher
n, David Forb
tronics Engrng Dept Chm
nk, Jacqueline B.
Grade Social Studies Tchr
, Michael Carl
8th Grade PE & Hlth Tchr
FIELD
ock, Gregory Burl
n Grade Teacher
LEY
ll, Sandra Gaye Horton
Grade History Teacher
Shannon Beusse
Grade Math & Science Tchr
tter, Phyllis Adams
n Grade Teacher
tt, David Paul, III
h Grade Math Teacher
ers, Betty Smith
h Grade Teacher

Wingo, Sandra Gardner
3rd Grade Teacher
STATESVILLE
Allie, Janice Tutterow
7th Grade Teacher
Avery, Christine Summers
5th Grade Teacher
Broadway, Kathy Rains
7th Grade Teacher
Campbell, Tena Mc Kinney
Soc Studies, Rdng & Eng Tchr
Carter, Virginia Wood
Mathematics Teacher
Conley, Carey Sherrill
5th Grade Teacher
Cress, Paula Wade
Business & Office Ed Teacher
Daniel, Gloria Bunton
English & Drama Teacher
Dull, Laurinda Jordan
Secondary Business Ed Teacher
Foster, David Lee
Math Teacher
Fox, David Michael
Fifth Grade Teacher
Hall, Pat L.
English Teacher
Hartsoe, Sherrie D.
English & Spanish Teacher
Jordan, Carolyn Tolbert
Retired Teacher
Joyce, Brenda S.
English Teacher & Dept Chair
Lane, Stephen Eugene
History, Finance & Ec Tchr
Mc Coy, Omer Fields, III
History Teacher
Moore, Donald Everette
Art Instructor
Nicks, Kristy Rink
Spanish Teacher
O'Neal, Lynne Hartline
English Teacher
Page, Martin Duane
Automotive Technology Teacher
Pickrell, Alison Winfree
Special Ed Resource Teacher
Putnam, Christopher Lee
Biology Teacher
Raub, Joan Summers
Senior High English Teacher
Reeves, Robin Alexander
English Teacher
Sherrill, Gary Thomas
Driver's Ed Teacher & Coach
Sigmon, Doris Parker
Health Occupations Teacher
Stanley, Allein Carson
Retired Middle School Sci Tchr
Stramecky, Eric Arvid
Physics Teacher
Thompson, Sara Walker
English Teacher
Whitley, Sylvia Carson
Science Teacher
Wilson, Glynita Jadene
Business Education Teacher
Witcher, William H., Jr.
Band Director
Wooten, Joyce Christenbury
English Teacher
Workman, Elizabeth Jenkins
Family & Consumer Science Tchr
STEDMAN
Bullard, Thelma Brown
5th Grade Teacher
STOKES
Wooten, Jackie Carpenter
Fourth Grade Teacher
STONEVILLE
Knight, Joanne Stone
Third Grade Teacher
STONY POINT
Fox, Elizabeth Barnes
Sixth Grade Teacher
SUMMERFIELD
Mallard, Rosemarie Clement
Fourth Grade Teacher
Wrenn, Kathryn White
Tchr of Academically Gifted
SUPPLY
Parker, Ramona Milligan
Kindergarten Teacher
SURF CITY
Grimsley, Linda Cravotta
Freelance Editor of Books
SWANNANOA
Norman, Elizabeth Ennis
Literature Teacher
Quinlan, Melisa Lankford
High School Science Teacher
Rountree, John David
Social Studies Teacher
SWANQUARTER
Fernandez, Toni Ann
History Teacher
SWANSBORO
Davis, Dorothy Chadwick
English Teacher
Metzler, Mary Ellen
5th Grade Teacher
Moore, Deloris Fagan
Business Teacher
Prescott, Melva Hawkins
Spanish Teacher
SYLVA
Beck, Deborah Carolyn
Respiratory Care Tech Prof
Buchanan, Elizabeth Evans
Resource Teacher

Burnette, Michael Edd
Criminal Justice Professor
Chapman, Dorothy Walker
Retired Kindergarten Teacher
Corzine, Kim Phillips
Secondary Science Teacher
Cox, Chris
English Instructor
Deitz, Sandra Sue
Fourth Grade Teacher
Frye, Mary Ann Lawrence
Sixth Grade Teacher
Herren, Wanda Stephens
Mathematics Teacher
Holt, Janice H.
Sixth Grade Teacher
Monroe, Sue O.
Science Instructor
Painter, Karen Cabe
Math Teacher & Dept Chprsn
Triplette, Mary Somerville
Instructor of Social Sciences
Wooten, Kathy Goforth
Kindergarten Teacher
TABOR CITY
Barkley, Wayne David
Music Teacher & Band Director
Byrd, Pamela Young
Science Teacher
Chestnutt, Carl Wayne
Science Teacher
Haynes, Barretta Shronda
8th Grade Social Studies Tchr
Jones, Cathy Wright
Mathematics Teacher
Smith, Peggy Taylor
English & Foreign Lang Tchr
TAR HEEL
Bunn, Kathryn S.
Art Teacher
Kelly, Clarissa Burnett-Mc Dowell
Mathematics Teacher
Lewis Brooks, Suzette
English Teacher
Thompson, Susan Kinlaw
Math Teacher
TARBORO
Entzminger, Fanette Hines
Biology Teacher
Erich, Frederick Jerome
Math Professor
Fleming, Monika Sutherland
Instr & Eng, Hum Dept Chair
Hudson, Gayle Daniel
HS Mathematics Teacher
Mitchell, Mary Modlin
Former Teacher of the Gifted
Neal, Donna Vick
Respiratory Care Tech Instr
Palmer, Elizabeth Weeks
Art Teacher
Perry, Anne Williams
Third Grade Reading Teacher
Ross, Kathy Jo
Science Resource Specialist
Spain, Ragan Sutton
Science Teacher
Stensland, Mitchell
Amer Lit & Journalism Tchr
Worden, Carolyn Myers
Social Studies Teacher
TAYLORSVILLE
Bollinger, Melissa Rhyne
Seventh Grade Lang Arts Tchr
Burke, Loretta Huggins
Pre-AP English & Latin Teacher
Elder, Tony Douglas
Social Stud Dept Head & Tchr
Graham, Linda Gould
High School Counselor
Harrington, Lisa Darlene
Math & Principles of Tech Tchr
Hensley, Veronica Rabb
Acad Gifted Lang Arts Teacher
Poole, Kenny Watt
North Carolina History Tchr
Reid, Jean Pennell
School Counselor
Rudisill, Denise Austin
Math, Sci & Hlth Teacher
Sherrill, Monte Lynn
Physical Education Teacher
Spry, Aaron
Assistant Principal
Wilson, Linda Young
Second Grade Teacher
TEACHEY
Carr, Linda Collier
US & World History Teacher
Cottle, Ann S.
English Teacher
Hanchey, Sonja L.
Allied Health Science Teacher
Sanderson, David
Art & Photography Teacher
THOMASVILLE
Brown, Benjamin Allen
Science Teacher & Coach
Collett, John Pernell
World His & Comp Speech Tchr
Drye, Yvonne C.
Accounting Teacher
Huneycutt, Susan Hampton
Math Teacher
Kennedy, Mary Smith
6th Grade AG Math Teacher
Outlaw, Rosemary Mitchell
Language Arts Teacher
Torrence, John Eric
Teacher

TOBACCOVILLE
Nance, Susie Bellamy
Third Grade Teacher
TRENTON
Iazzetta, Tara Ann
Mathematics Teacher
Martin, Jon P.
English Instructor
Waters, Catherine Narron
Biology & Physical Sci Teacher
TRINITY
Blanchard, John David
Science Teacher
Carlson, Joni James
English & French Teacher
Chapman, Dedie A.
Biology Teacher
Hunsucker, Gary Van
8th Grd Sci & Pre Algebra Tchr
Johnson, Karon Hartman
Sixth Grade Teacher
McGee, Patricia Patrick
Biology Teacher
Morgan, Larry Garland
Social Studies Teacher
Phillips, Robert William, Jr.
French Teacher
Ray, Juanita Shew
Drama Teacher
Routh, Sandy Jay
Social Studies Teacher
Seltzer, Dawn Holland
Math Teacher
TROUTMAN
George, Linda Jenkins
Eighth Grade Lit & Eng Teacher
Graham, Anne Tron
First Grade Teacher
TROY
Lunday, Michael T.
Accounting Professor
Mc Intosh, Ruth Mc Leod
Fifth Grade Teacher
Miller, Judy L.
Office Technology Instructor
Morgan, Virginia D.
Mathematics Instr & Chprsn
TYNER
Fleming, Christine Bonds
Fifth Grade Teacher
King, Jill Hendrix
Art Teacher
Perry, Krista Hare
Former Teacher
UNION MILLS
Yelton, Karen (Denise)
Social Studies Teacher
VANCEBORO
Arbegast, Jeannie McGirt
Teacher of Academically Gifted
Cox, Elizabeth Marie
Science Teacher
Eriksson, Shirley Snyder
Business Education Teacher
Foster, Nancy Parker
English Teacher
Gladson, Donna Bland
English Teacher & Yearbook Adv
Nichols, Rita Thigpen
Mathematics Teacher
Nipper, Debbie Gladson
English I & III Teacher
Pearce, Susan Matthews
Social Studies Teacher
Rouse, Henry William, Jr.
Electronics Teacher
Russell, Joy Gaskins
Fifth Grade Teacher
Shepley, Lori Burkett
Art Teacher
Sledge, Linda Dillahunt
First Grade Teacher Assistant
Smith, Denise Fillingame
Math & Spanish Teacher
Stokes, Dennis Allen
Graphics Teacher
White, James E., III
Social Studies Teacher
VASS
Rice, Carol Ann
Language Arts & Soc Stud Tchr
WADE
Horne, Ann Collier
Pre-Kindergarten Teacher
WADESBORO
Beam, Rick Austin
English Teacher
Mc Queen, Patricia Arnice
Algebra Teacher
McRae, Kristin Horne
High School Math Teacher
Morse, Melanie Lockhart
Business Education Teacher
Royal, Deborah Little
9th Grade English Teacher
Sikes, Patricia Moore
High School Algebra Teacher
WAKE FOREST
Denning, John Delano
Amer Govt & US History Tchr
Fuller, Jan Taylor
8th Grade Lang Arts Teacher
Hess, Charles Evan
Special Education Teacher
Merrill, Barry Alan
History Teacher
Mitchell, Calvin Egbert, III
Healthful Living & PE Teacher
Monte, Christopher Johnston
United States History Teacher

Shepherd, Sylvia Thomas
Science Specialist
Storey, Sue Carol
8th Grade Math Teacher
WALKERTOWN
Crews, Donald R.
Social Studies Teacher
Hicks, Timothy Mark
Bible, US His, Govt & Ec Tchr
Martin, Willie Ellis
Sixth Grade Teacher
WALLACE
Fussell, Jo Ellen Wood
Third Grade Teacher
WALLBURG
Motsinger, Debra Altman
Third Grade Teacher
Myers, Carol Byerly
Fourth Grade Teacher
WALNUT COVE
Adams, Meta h.
Third Grade Teacher
Crabbe, Charles John
Band Director
Hall, Bruce Numa
Mathematics Teacher
Hawkins, Whitney Westmoreland
Health Occupations Teacher
Jessup, Tamara Smith
English Teacher
Mendenhall, Franklin Kent
Health & Physical Ed Teacher
Miller, Wayne Lloyd
Technology Education Teacher
Murphy, Doug
Biology & Physical Sci Tchr
WARRENTON
Crosson, Sandra R.
English Teacher
Henderson, Mary Alexander
Third Grade Teacher
Johnson, Jean Anthony
Fifth Grade Teacher
Jones, Diariece Williams
Pre Kindergarten Teacher
Jones, Morton Spencer
Health & PE Teacher
Long, Joyce B.
Alg I Teacher
WARSAW
Benson, Shirley Hildebrand
English, Soc Stud & Drama Tchr
Davenport, Betty Wyatt
Family & Consumer Science Tchr
Edwards, George Roland
Agricultural Education Teacher
WASHINGTON
Bova, Sherri Clark
English Teacher
Boyd, Jeannie Parker
English Teacher
Haywood, Mable Gray
Third Grade Teacher
Holloman, Judy Mumau
6th Grade Science Teacher
Jones, Doris Juanita Godley
High School Guidance Counselor
Lee, Margaret Dianne Smallwood
Kindergarten Teacher
Mc Laughlin, Lois Cutler
Fifth Grade Sci & Math Teacher
Miller, Diana Douget
8th Grd Language Arts Teacher
Parker, Carrie Sykes
7th Grade Math Teacher
Pinkham, Albert Franklin
Drafting Teacher
Reddick, Iris Lodge
Fourth Grade Teacher
Thomas, Gregory James
PE Tchr & Ftbl Head Coach
Tonra, Christopher Bourne
Social Studies Teacher & Coach
WAYNESVILLE
Atwood, Stephen James
Science Teacher & Coach
Brow, Larry Dean
Physical Ed & Health Teacher
Cochran, Heather Phillips
Hlth & Physical Education Tchr
Cooke, Nada Garber
Language Arts Teacher
Crawford, Sybil Bradshaw
Retired Sixth Grade Teacher
Davis, Leigh Brooks
English Teacher
Eleazer, William E.
Art Teacher
Fox, Larry Phillip
Spanish & French Teacher
Hart, Yvonne Monnin
7th Grade Comm Skills Teacher
Hartsell, Susan Bulloch
Health, PE Tchr & Vlybl Coach
Henke, Nikki Smith
Language Arts Teacher
Hooker, Carolyn
Eighth Grd Language Arts Tchr
Kingshill, Susan Mc Neer
English Teacher
Lancaster, Martha Crafton
Retired Third Grade Teacher
Markley, Jane Terrell
6th Grade Science Teacher
Medford, Tinga Jaynes
Math Teacher
Rochester, Joanne Mosley
7th Grade Language Arts Tchr
Smith, Rebecca Lynn Swanson
Eighth Grade Mathematics Tchr

WAYNESVILLE (cont)
Sorrells, James Allen
Fourth Grade Teacher
Wise, Timothy Lee
Director of Bands
WEAVERVILLE
Byers, Diane Cooper
Kindergarten Teacher
Cole, Sarah Higgins
8th Grade English Teacher
Hensley, Elaine Allen
English Dept Chair & Teacher
Holt, Edna Ruth
Sixth Grade Math Teacher
Landers, Judy Capps
First Grade Teacher
Morgan-Hill, Charlene M.
English & Journalism Teacher
Talbot, Carolyn Durant
Eighth Grade Science Teacher
WELDON
Farless, Betty Brickhouse
4th Grade Teacher
WENDELL
Andrews, Susan Wilder
Teacher & Mathematics Dept Ldr
Brown, Luanne Roebuck
Business Teacher
Cozart, Kimberly Marie
Choral Music Director
Hirsch, Susan (Stein)
Social Studies Tchr, Dpt Chair
Kennemur, Lois Carter
Fifth Grade Teacher
Ludwick, Mike
History Teacher
Moore, John Stephen
Visual Arts Teacher
Sasser, Sue Joyner
English Teacher
Scott, Joyce Anderson
HS Electronics Teacher
Talley, Dorothy Elaine
Advanced Chem & Bio Teacher
WENTWORTH
Butler, Lelia T. Clinard
Mathematics Instructor
Capps, Kenneth Lee
Professor of Biology
Griffin, Hal Raine
Dean of Student Services
Hines, Eric Wesley
Vocational Teacher
Keesee, Gladys Stacey
Business Teacher
Prigge, Penne Longhibler
Dean of Hum & Social Science
WHITEVILLE
Barkley, Cheri Phillips
Kindergarten Teacher
Brinson, Louise L.
Retired Math & Science Tchr
Cartrette, Sara Woodard
English & Theater Arts Teacher
Cigary, Lawrence Steven
Algebra I & II Teacher
Parris, Jeff
Agriscience Teacher
Reed, Richard Gordon, Sr.
Principal
WHITTIER
Casey Mc Donald, Victoria Arvella
Social Studies Teacher
WILKESBORO
Bentley, Ginger Welch
High School Mathematics Tchr
Foster, Judy Toliver
8th Grd History & ISS Teacher
Grayson, Tamara Amelia
Art Instructor
Johnson, Dennis Turner
Teacher of Academically Gifted
Necessary, Elizabeth Williams
8th Grade Mathematics Teacher
Stancil, Pamela Stone
Math & Science Teacher
Watts, Bernadette Draper
Choral Director
WILLIAMSTON
Ashley, Carolyn Ford
Art Teacher
Cotten, Barbara Everett
5th Grade Teacher
Roberson, Lou Ann Windley
JJPA Program Dir, Counselor
Shepherd, Anne Boyd
US History Teacher
Stephens, Karen Gurley
AP Calculus & Honors Math Tchr
WILMINGTON
Adams, Mike S.
Criminology Professor
Baker, Linda Rawlings
High School Math Teacher
Barber, Margaret Scott
English Teacher
Batchelor-Marley, Sherry Otis
Business Admin Lead Instructor
Berry, Shirley Hart
Chair of English & Other Langs
Bordwine, Carol Keane
5th Grade Teacher
Burton, Sarah Andrews
Theater Arts Teacher
Crowder, Virginia Tyson
Tchr of Mentally Handicapped
Crumpler, Ginger Gail
English Instructor
Dombroski, Richelle Bragg
Teacher & Department Head
Faison, Jimmy
Counselor
Flagler, Diane Wharton
Academically Gifted Stu Tchr
Freiberg, Susan Andrews
8th Grade Teacher
Hayes, Rhoda Holmes
Kindergarten Teacher
Hestikind, Robert Howard
Social Studies Teacher
Highsmith, Samuel James
Social Studies Teacher
Hoffman, K. Douglas
Associate Prof of Marketing
Irving, Sharon Eugenia
Business Education Teacher
Ivey, Hannah Worth
Asst Prin, His & Bible Tchr
Jacobs, Eleanor Powell
Lang Arts & Soc Stud Teacher
Jefferay, Paula F.
English Teacher
Jones, S. Bart
Associate Prof of Chemistry
Kallfelz, Marcia
Language Arts & Soc Stud Tchr
Kirkland, Ronnie Melvin
History Professor
Knape, Wesley Walter, Jr.
Theatre Teacher
Lynch, Gloria Ervin
Sixth Grade Language Arts Tchr
Mc Allister, Nancy Hardacre
Admin, Instr, Director & Owner
Merritt, Frederick Hampton, Jr.
A P Amer & World History Tchr
Metcalfe, Dale M.
Sociology Tchr, Asst Prin
Montgomery, Beverly Guy
5th Grade Teacher
Morris, Randy McBride
7th Grade Science Teacher
Morrison, Carol Ann
History Teacher
Pender, Rosalyn Foy
Science Teacher
Perry-Canoutas, Suzan Marie
6th Grade Teacher
Piner, Jean Hemby
Assessment Counselor
Puckett, Robert W.
Sociology Professor & Fac Pres
Query, Carol Dague
English Teacher & Dept Chm
Rath, Charlotte Mary
Assistant Professor
Reid, Jan Murray
English Teacher & Yearbook Adv
Rowell, Pearl Robinson
Soc & Behavioral Sci Chprsn
Schmidt, Hattie Williamson
Family & Consumer Science Tchr
Settle, Mary Alice Gibbons
Director of Student Affairs
Siguaw, Judy Ann Judice
Associate Prof of Marketing
Sloan, Donna DeVane
Tchr of Academically Gifted
Spackman, Gloria Rachau
9th Grade Counselor
StClair, Rose M.
Third Grade Teacher
Swartzlander, Sharon Pope
K-5th Grade Art Teacher
Thomas, Gaye Boren
Academically Gifted Teacher
Upton, Beth Batten
4th Grade Teacher
Upton, Robert Livious, III
History Teacher
Walters, Gordon William
Instructor & Coach
Watson Bowen, Anne
Third Grade Teacher
Whetstone, Sally Rodwell
School Counselor & Dept Chair
Whilden, Dolores R.
Instructor of Mathematics
Whitley, Helen Saparilas
Mathematics Teacher
Williams, Genia Beddoes
English Teacher
Wolfson, Susan Mulcahy
Science Teacher
Wood, Melody Jane
Sociology & Social Work Instr
Yeates, Marion Shoemaker
8th Grd Eng & Lang Arts Tchr
WILSON
Batts, Joy Fluegel
Mathematics Teacher
Blaylock, Susan West
Guidance Counselor
Collingwood, Timothy Clark
Director of Instrumental Music
Elks, Wanda Lane
8th Grade Math Teacher
Franks, Fate Turner, Jr.
8th Grd Social Studies Teacher
Gwaltney, Sally Jones
Math & Computer Teacher
Harden, Crystal Ward
Chemistry Teacher
Harris, Altise Reid
Teacher of Exceptional Child
Herring, Melanie Donna
Mathematics Teacher
Johnson, Susan Jennings
Middle School Teacher
Jones, Joe Frank, III
Philosophy Professor
Jr., D. E. Kim Watson
Paralegal Prgm Lead Instr
Lee, Carolyn Lucas
Fifth Grade Teacher
Mooring, Lynn Hooks
Science Teacher
Pace, Ronald Henry
Teacher of the Deaf
Parris, Gloria Bass Newbern
Second Grade Teacher
Peele, Angela Renea
Math Teacher
Poole, Bessie Ruffin
English Teacher & Dept Chprsn
Pope, David L.
8th Grade Teacher
Proctor, Kathy Hayes
English Teacher
Roberts, Teresa Lynne
Accounting Instructor
Sessoms, June Jones
Counselor
Simms, Preston Demetrist
English & Communications Tchr
Sutton, Sandra Sjostrom
Art Teacher
Tayloe, Hulda Miller
Tchr of Academically Gifted
Watson, B. Jean (Grubb)
Middle School Math Teacher
Watson, Robert Charles
Computer Education Teacher
Williams, Stephanie Rochelle
Science Teacher
WILSONS MILLS
Barbour, Gayle Culbreth
Fifth Grade Teacher
WINDSOR
Battle, Priscilla Mae
English Teacher
Boller, Bruce William
Science Teacher
Bond, Styron Cortis
Social Studies Teacher
Cox, David M.
Social Studies Teacher
Dunlow, Sherry Todd
High School Teacher
Parker, Barbara Jean
Eighth Grade Algebra Teacher
Ruffin, Brenda Benjamin
Eighth Grd Lang Arts Teacher
Towne, William Eugene, Jr.
Mathematics Teacher
WINFALL
Griffin, Peggy Boyce
Mathematics Teacher
Leete, Suzanne Brasher
Instructional Facilitator
WINGATE
Etters, Stephen Campbell
Music Professor
Traynham, Sue Hinson
Kindergarten Teacher
WINSTON SALEM
Abrams, Kim Clark
5th Grade Teacher
Addison, Patricia Gibson
North Carolina History Teacher
Alexander, Lowell Jackson
Professor of Church Music
Allred, Leonard P.
Chrstn Ministries Div Chairman
Alsup, Jean Enderle
Environmental Studies Teacher
Amos, Ronald David
Band Teacher
Arnold, Christine Hill
5th Grade Teacher
Bernhart, Norma Woosley
English Teacher
Bottoms, Rebecca Strebig
Lit & Soc Studies Teacher
Bowman, Hoyle Eugene
Theology Professor
Boyst, John R.
Spanish Teacher
Brown, Nancy Hauser
Secondary Mathematics Teacher
Cathey, Ida Powell
Third Grade Teacher
Cavanaugh, Tonya Diane
Chemistry Teacher
Crossley, Betsy Schubring
Science Teacher
Dail, Kathy Glover
A P Biology Teacher
Dougherty, Bernice Bracalieuo
Cataloging Librarian
Faltynski-Privette, Carol Anne
Math Teacher
Freitag, Sue Ann (Arant)
Math Teacher
Griffin, Garrett Edward
Business Technology Instructor
Hage, Ellen Elaine (Harner)
Instructor of English
Henighan, Evelyn Harris
Comp Information Systems Tchr
Howerton, Terry Gregg
Science Teacher
Hymes, Addie B.
Director of Upward Bound Prgm
Jett, Michelle Renee
Business Teacher
Jochim, Beverly Burkeen
Guidance Counselor
Johnson, Helen Delores
Fourth Grade Teacher
Kennedy, Linda Jane
Foreign Language Dept Chairman
Kirkman, Margaret Forbes
2nd Grade Teacher
Kneisel, Michael Thomas
Social Studies Teacher
Lail, Donald Ray
Curr Coord & Mathematics Tchr
Lawing, Barry Alan
History Instructor
Ljungquist, Gary R.
Spanish & Women's Studies Prof
Mac Millan, Emily Celeste Hord
Spanish Teacher
Mc Carthy, Beverly Kaye
English Teacher
Mc Daniel, Carolyn Wills
First Grade Teacher
McMillan, Felecia Piggott
English Department Head
Mc Quaig, Regeania
Teacher & Dept Chairperson
Morrison, Janet Nance
Social Studies Teacher
Mueller, Margaret Snodgrass
Piano Teacher
Muse, Andrew Brown
Marketing Teacher
Muse, Jean Brown
Guidance Counselor
Muse, Michael G.
Social Studies Teacher & Coach
Nelson, Judy L.
Assistant Principal
Parham, Gerry Craig
Latin Teacher
Patterson, Alice Conger
Dean of Continuing Studies
Patti, Maureen Kenna
3rd Grd Teacher
Powers, Amy Bittner
English Teacher
Rabe, Rebecca Moore
8th Grade Math Teacher
Reavis, Amelia Thomas
Fourth Grade Teacher
Reeves, James S.
Communication Skills Teacher
Reiner, Susan Brown
Speech & Language Specialist
Rhodes, Peggy Reid
Retired English Dept Chm
Rogers, Geri
6th Grade Teacher
Seaver, Thomas Arthur
Science Teacher
Seymour, Lynda Davis
Education Professor
Sheek, James L., Jr.
Choral Music & Drama Teacher
Sheets, Sue Hickman
Chemistry Teacher
Sigers, Johnny E.
Mathematics Teacher
Squire, Patsy O'Neal
5th Grade Teacher
Stiener, Adam
For Lang Dept Chair & Ger Prof
Street, Ernestine McLean
Home Economics Tchr & Chprsn
Tapscott, Deborah Foster
Assistant Administrator
Tyndall, Evelyn Edwards
Retired Fifth Grade Teacher
Walls, Roby Gray
Economics Teacher
Watts, Ann B.
Early Childhood Teacher
Weaver, Frances Smith
Choral Music Teacher
Westmoreland, Dorothy Douglas
Latin Teacher
Whisnant, Patricia Neal
Department Chairperson
Wilson, Stancil Wayne
Technology Teacher
Winner, Joan Kathryn
Chair of Music Division
Wood, Priscilla Gentry
French Teacher
Woody, Mary Lamberth
Math Teacher
Worley, L. Ernestine Davis
Instr of Practical Nursing Pgm
WINTERVILLE
Grant, Janet Stell
1st Grade Teacher
Melvin, June Culbreth
6th Grade Math & Sci Teacher
WINTON
Harrell, Mary Ruffin
Fifth Grade Teacher
WRIGHTSVILLE BEACH
Merritt, Margaret Long
Third Grade Teacher
YADKINVILLE
Bryant, Rebecca Parker
7th Grd Sci & Pre-Algebra Tchr
Campbell, Eddie Wallace
Principal
Shermer, Ruth Dobbins
Math & Science Teacher
Steelman, Margaret Aileen
Physical Ed Teacher & Coach
Welborn, Patricia Poteat
Special Education Teacher
YANCEYVILLE
Bradsher, Sarah Winstead
HS Mathematics Teacher
Collie, Janet Fowlkes
Sixth Grade Teacher
Dennis, Kimberly Dawn
Psychology & Sociology Teacher
Felton, Tonya Donnell
Fourth Grade Teacher
Foster, Lynn Mise
Eighth Grd Language Arts Tchr
Merchant, Gail Dix (Smith)
World Studies Teacher
Owen, David Jasper
Hlth & Physical Education Tchr
Pedigo, Sheree Atkinson
Language Arts Teacher
Richmond, Vanessa Dale
8th Grade Language Arts Tchr
Slade, Sherri Scott
HS Mathematics Teacher
Stilwell, Gail Furgurson
Math Teacher & Dept Chprsn
Vernon, Cyrus Cordell
Agriculture Education Teacher
YOUNGSVILLE
Daly, Suzin R.
Instructor, Trainer & Coach
ZEBULON
Dupree, David
Admin & Pastor
Parrish, Rochelle O'Neal
First Grade Teacher
Privette, Cynthia Sullivan
Yearbook Teacher
Wheless, Deborah Temple
Fourth Grade Teacher

NORTH DAKOTA

ARTHUR
Meyers, Carol Skogen
Music Teacher
Sinness, James A.
Social Studies & English Tchr
ASHLEY
Miller, Caroline Emma (Sayler)
Third Grade Teacher
Paulsrud, Donald Jay
Social Studies & Phys Ed Tchr
BEACH
Hardy, Jean E.
2nd Grade Teacher
Tosseth, Dean Connell
Business Tchr, Coach & Ath Dir
BELCOURT
Aalund, Renee C.
High School Science Instructor
Britton, Linda Heavin
Reading & Language Arts Instr
Hall, Kellie Thomas
World History & Psych Teacher
Laducer, Lisa Peterson
High School Humanities Teacher
Palm, Violet Elaine
Science Teacher
Waldera, Jill Suzann
4th Grade Teacher
BELFIELD
Dorval, Paulette June (Haugrud)
Family & Consumer Sci Tchr
Duttenhefer, David James
Social Studies & PE Teacher
Fischer, Roberta L.
English Teacher & Dept Chm
Pomarleau, Geri M.
Elem Music & Business Teacher
BERTHOLD
Christianson, Dennis Olaf
Social Studies Teacher
Debertin, Richard Harold
Agricultural Education Teacher
Ross, Troy H.
Mathematics Teacher
BEULAH
Bren, Joseph Allan
Physical Education & Bus Tchr
Dinkins, Gwen Pfennig
Second Grade Teacher
Erickson-Armstrong, Fran Schield
3rd Grade Teacher
Helm, Vivian A.
Family Life Science Instructor
Maize, Linda Oestreich
First Grade Teacher
Miller, Pearl Bauer
Retired Teacher
Oihus, Janice Gale
Social Studies Teacher
Olwell, Rick
Earth Science & Soc Stud Tchr
Schmidt, Connie (Morlock)
High School Math Teacher
Swegarden, Jay Edward
English Instructor
BISBEE
Keller, Michelle R.
7th-12th Grade Science Teacher
BISMARCK
Allan, Craig Bruce
Math Teacher
Anderson, Cindy Layne
Secondary English Teacher
Angell, David Irwin
Biology & Ecology Teacher
Avey, Jeanne Glasoe
Mathematics Teacher

RCK (cont)
heri Bearking
Tech Instr & Dept Chair
Bela Alexander
or of Psychology
Kathy Hindemith
tary Principal
Carole A.
of of Indian Studies
thy Jenelle
School Counselor
Carol Seiler
Grade Teacher
ay Redington
ade Teacher
Sharon A.
Ed Teacher & Coordinator
, Pamela Jo
ality Management Instr
llie Ann
& Consumer Science Tchr
Virginia Dorena
d Tchr & Asst Principal
, Catherine Michaelis
ng Disabilities Teacher
George William
Studies Teacher
, Karen McConnell
ate Professor
, Barbara Gibbons
r & State Senator
en, Grace Ellen
rade Teacher
Cindy Kay (Crabtree)
ade Teacher
ack D.
nstructor
Shannon Marie
ade US History Teacher
Susan M.
matics Teacher
, Denis Richard
ate Professor of English
ka, Krystyna G.
Professor of Chemistry
ayne Winifred
haplain
, Kass
str of Criminal Justice
eger, Randy Joe
Teacher
, Dale Wilbert
ch Coordinator
Fran Woodmansee
ade Teacher
Robin Lynne
y Teacher
an, Jean Pfliger
iate Professor
Ethel S.
chr & Spcl Projects Coord
, Vanessa Erhardt
Grd Teacher & Asst Prin
eggy L.
Grade Teacher
Kelvin J.
matics & Physics Teacher
Kevin Philip
Grade Teacher
Robert Duane
onics Technology Instr
radley Patrick
Chem Teacher
Eliazabeth Burke
Grade Teacher
on, Jon Paul
mic Dean
, Janelle
iate Professor of English
Jaime Paul
Prof of Communications
Mary Lynn (Burchill)
Grade Teacher
Jack W.
y Teacher
, Pamela Anne
Prof of Math & Cmptr Sci
Mary Beth (Schauer)
sh & Journalism Instr
oelle A.
sh Teacher
d, Daniel
Science Teacher
, Carol Parsons
Studies & Health Tchr
Olaf J.
an & Latin Teacher
Russell William
sh & Speech Teacher
on, Linda
sh Teacher
uane
rade Teacher
James R.
unting Associate Professor
Betty Anita Elizabeth
Childhood Ed Instructor
aas, Douglas P.
ciate Professor of Biology
der, Vicki L.
er
der, Loretta Egger
sh, Speech & Spanish Tchr
ert, Rose E.
rade Teacher
Sue Wong
Grade Teacher
Daniel E., Sr.
ciate Prof of Accounting

Stack, Donna J.
Assoc Prof of Communication
Thompson, Claudia Ann
Elementary School Counselor
Tomanek, Claudia Albrecht
Assistant Principal
Twedt, Don B.
Earth Science Teacher
Vadnie, Ann Logan
English Teacher
Walter, Lisa Smyle
Fourth Grade Teacher
Wilson, Jerry D.
Mathematics Teacher
Wohlsdorf, Eugene M.
English Teacher & Asst Coach
Zink, Beverly Ann (Roberts)
Second Grade Teacher
BOTTINEAU
Geiszler, Phyllis C.
4th Grade Teacher
Gilje, Lynnette
First Grade Teacher
Whiteman, Gerald
Band Dir & Music Dept Chrmn
BOWMAN
Thompson, Cordella Jean
Fourth Grade Teacher
Werth, Russ G.
Health, PE & Psychology Instr
Ziemann, Jack E.
Jr High Math Teacher
BUFFALO
Clancy, Alba Nudell
Retired Elementary Teacher
Johnson, Daniel A.
Fourth Grade Teacher
BURLINGTON
Rostad, Carol Arness
First Grade Teacher
BUTTE
Yecoshenko, Ruth Nachatelo
Retired Elementary Tchr & Prin
CARRINGTON
Frahm, Kristi A.
English Teacher
Schmitz, Jim J.
Social Science Teacher
Torgerson, Patricia K.
Fourth Grade Teacher
CARSON
Dahners, Audrey Ann Pfliiger
Family & Consumer Science Tchr
Hertz, Ann Nicolai
English & Music Teacher
CASSELTON
Garland, Russell Dennis
Math, Physics & Chemistry Tchr
CAVALIER
Fisher, Douglas Steven
Biological Science Teacher
Peterson, Sandy Darlene
Voc Family & Consumer Sci Tchr
Rusten, Jacqueline Anderson
English Teacher
CENTER
Erhardt, Timothy L.
Eng, Jrnlsm & Soc Studies Tchr
Oss, Jackie
English Teacher
Wolf, Walter W.
German & Computer Teacher
Yates, Kiley Owen
History Teacher
COOPERSTOWN
College, Wanda Tufte
Art & Math Instructor
Olson, Linda Sue
Science Instructor
Surerus, Dorthea Berg
Third Grade Teacher
CROSBY
Buck, Connie Rae
Second Grade Teacher
Hoger, Wendy Lee
Business Ed & Comp Sci Tchr
Lund, Patty J.
Mathematics Teacher
DES LACS
Medalen, Scott Alan
US & World History Teacher
DEVILS LAKE
Bosch, LaVina DeVier
Sixth Grd Teacher & Asst Prin
DeFoe, MIchael J.
Math & Computer Science Tchr
Follman, Debra Schwanke
1st Grade Teacher
Forde, Roger D.
Media Coordinator & Teacher
Johnson, Ingrid Olson
Fourth Grade Teacher
Klemetsrud, Jeanne L.
High School English Instructor
La France, Teresa Tande
7th-8th Grd Language Arts Tchr
Larson, Sally Ann
Associate Principal
Light, Delcie Danroth
Sr English Tchr & Dept Chair
Loberg, Myron P.
Mathematics Teacher
Newcomb, Marlys Kenner
Kindergarten Teacher
Samson, Jim
Biology Instructor
Warner, Keith B.
Language, Rdng & Soc Stud Tchr

DICKINSON
Barbier, John P.
Math Teacher
Ciavarella, Gloria Erhardt
Second Grade Teacher
Fields, Janice Cram
2nd Grade Teacher
Fruh, Joelle Medinger
Spanish & French Teacher
Gjermundson, Carol E.
English Teacher
Hebert, Robert Arthur
Sociology & Psychology Tchr
Heinert, Dalila
Fourth Grade Teacher
Jacobsen, Susan K.
6th Grade Instructor
Keller, Kenneth K.
English Teacher
Keogh, Priscilla Ann (Alme)
Jr & Sr HS Choral Music Instr
Kinnischtzke, Beverly Schuh
Family & Consumer Science Tchr
Lisko, Shirley Ann (Ridl)
Kindergarten Teacher
Medlar, Deborah Starkey
Social Studies Teacher
Schank, Frank
Art Teacher
Shinagle, Richard Louis
Former English Teacher
Steiner, Mary Keller
4th Grade Teacher
Stevenson, Michael Read
HS Choral Dir & Gen Music Tchr
Winter, Todd Mark M.
Art & Science Teacher
DRAKE
Holler, Valerie Beth Bruner
6th Grade Teacher
DRAYTON
Gardner, Kenneth C., Jr.
History & English Teacher
DUNSEITH
Ekern, Kimberly Faye
English Teacher & Librarian
EDGELEY
Kosel, Todd Edward
Science Teacher
Lee, Shane A.
Spanish & English Teacher
EDMORE
Blomquist, Marlys Schatzke
Title I Instructor
ELGIN
Klein, Glenda Mattis
Elem Principal & Teacher
Klein, Sharon Marie
English & German Instructor
ELLENDALE
Johnson, James Joseph
Mathematics Teacher
Jones, David Lancaster
Prof in Bible & Ministerial
Munyon, Darlene Esther (Blackburn)
General Education Dept Instr
Munyon, Timothy
Theology Biblical Studies Prof
Ulmer, Rick Ray
Social Science Teacher
EMERADO
McEwen, Feryl Jean (Larson)
First Grade Teacher
FAIRFIELD
Goldsberry, Karen
Second Grade Teacher
FARGO
Bhandary, Madhusudan
Statistics Professor
Bierwagen, Diane Fischer
High School Math Teacher
Brandt, Kristine Finney
6th Grade Reading Teacher
Coons, Linda Bakken
Life Science & Math Tchr
Cordova-Nemer, Lisa Lynn
Spanish Teacher
Danbom, David B.
Professor of History
Elliott, LaVonne Marie
Fifth Grade Teacher
Froelich, Andrew I.
Prof & Coordinator of Music
Gould, Odette N.
Psychology Professor
Grafton, Kristina Wells
Sixth Grade Teacher
Gross, Carla Jean
Assistant Professor
Hardie, Rodney Gene
4th Grade Teacher
Hendricks, Robert Dean
Journalism & English Teacher
Jellison, Terry McDonald
Social Studies Teacher
Legowski, Claire Elise (Moen)
Lecturer of Eng Composition
Lisko, Carolyn Marcusen
Sixth Grade Teacher
Lucas, William M.
Title I Coordinator
McCarthy, Denise Elizabeth
Phys Sci Teacher & Dept Chair
Mickelson, Pearl E. (Nygaard)
Second Grade Teacher
Robinson, Michael
Associate Professor
Rott, Jessica Miles
Sixth Grade Teacher

Sanders, Gregory Frank
Family Science Professor
Schwaiz, Jurgen Gerhard
Food Science Professor
Stenberg, Diane J.
8th Grade English Teacher
Terbizan, Donna J.
College Professor
Tilton, James Earl
Prof of Animal & Range Science
Uebel, Robert George
Assistant Professor of German
Wallman, Joyce D.
English Teacher
Whited, Dean A.
Genetics Teacher
Wood, Robert Allen
Assoc Prof of Political Sci
FESSENDEN
Moellenkamp, Lae Eric
Agriculture Education Teacher
FINLEY
Votava, Kenneth F.
Agricultural Education Teacher
FLASHER
Heinle, Clyde Dallas
High School Mathematics Tchr
Malm, Nancy Neumiller
Teacher
Townsend, Kerri Ann (Mahrer)
Business Education Teacher
FORDVILLE
Brodina, Karen K.
Business Education Instructor
Helland, Cathie E.
Music & French Teacher
FORMAN
Wolsky, Judy Ann (Hill)
HS Math Teacher
GARRISON
Hill, Julie A. (Scheid)
Mathematics Teacher
Miller, Deane Leland
Sixth Grade Teacher
Seidler, Theresa L. Huettl
Math, Chem, Physic, Cmptr Tchr
GLENBURN
Bierman, Marlys Limke
Math & Physical Science Tchr
Heine, Sherie Faye
6th Grade Teacher
GLENFIELD
Spickler, JoAnn D.
English Teacher
GOLDEN VALLEY
Beckwith, Maxine Huber
Scndry Principal & Counselor
Lindemann, Renee A. (Duerre)
English Teacher & Librarian
GOODRICH
Anderson, Robert L.
Science Teacher
Bender, Julie Ann
Fifth & Sixth Grade Teacher
Erdmann, LaDonna Lynn (Benge)
Math Teacher
Schneider, Vernon
Social Studies & German Tchr
Sweep, Patricia J.
English Teacher
GRAND FORKS
Antes, James R.
Psychology Professor
Beard, Victoria Knapp
Accounting Assistant Professor
Bengiamin, Nagy N.
Professor & Chairman
Bethke, Gary John
Mathematics Tchr & Dept Chair
Blumkin, David B.
Lecturer of Flight Physiology
Brewinski, John
6th Grade Teacher
Christenson, Linda S.
English Teacher
Denome, Roger Martin
Assistant Professor of Biology
Ferraro, Francis Richard
Asst Prof of Psychology
Fischer, Carolyn Miller
AP English Teacher
Guy, Mark D.
Assistant Professor of Sci Ed
Hager, Terrence Joel
Third Grade Teacher
Handy-Marchello, Barbara Claire
Assistant Professor of History
Harmeson, Phil
Assistant Professor
Hess, Carla Wulff
Prof of Comm Sci & Disorders
Hinzpeter-Rindt, LeAnn
School-to-Work Community Coord
Hume, Wendelin M.
Criminal Justice Professor
Jacobson, Daniel Christopher
Associate Professor of Music
Janes, Allen L.
10th-12th Grd Mathematics Tchr
Jones, Kathleen K.
Management Lecturer
Kalka, Yvonne Marie
Speech & English Teacher
Keck, Arnie W.
Asst Professor of Phys Therapy
Kelley, Mavis Toso
Asst Professor of Math Ed
King, Alan Russell
Associate Prof of Psychology

Kweit, Robert W.
Prof of Pol Sci & Pub Admin
Larson, Omer Richard
Professor of Biology
Leduc, Robert E.
Asst Prof of Dept of Math
Loyland, Mary Olson
Associate Prof of Accounting
Lund, Bonnie Baker
Clinical Instructor
McCleary, Vikki Blegen
Director of Undergraduate Ed
Mc Nary, Gregory Alan
US History Teacher
Medalen, Rodney E.
Assoc Professor of Accounting
Mohagen, Roberta Barta
Asst Prof of Business Ed
Mohr, Thomas M.
Physical Therapy Dept Chair
Morstad, D. P., Jr.
Senior Lecturer
Mulhern, Thomas M.
History Instructor
Munski, Douglas Charles
Professor
Nelson, Cynthia Neuharth
Mathematics Teacher
Nwoke, Ben U.
Assoc Professor & Coordinator
Olson, Jennie E.
Health Careers Teacher
Olson, Myrna Munson
Special Education Professor
Peake, Vicki Delaney
English & Literature Teacher
Plaud, Joseph Julian
Asst Professor of Psychology
Rand, Steven Mitchell
Senior Lecturer & Eng Dept Chr
Rand, Thomas Albert
Humanities Professor
Robinson, Thomas John
Prof & Assoc Chprsn of Math
Rodde, James Frederick
Music Professor
Ronkowski, Keith R.
Marketing Instructor
Schjeldahl, Dennis O.
English Instructor
Schjeldahl, Jane Eisner
Kindergarten Teacher
Skinner, Avis Brustuen
English Teacher
Stradley, Scot Arthur
Assoc Professor of Economics
Tunseth, Darryl Gene
Sixth Grd Tchr & Admin Intern
Wacker, Maureen Ravnaas
English Teacher
White, Francis Duane
Sociology Instructor
Wolf, Glen W.
Instrumental Music Instructor
GRAND FORKS AFB
Eriksmoen, Douglas Roland
Third Grade Teacher
GRANVILLE
Schwan, Patrick Boyd
Music Teacher
GRENORA
Helm, Karen Cecelia
Music Teacher
GWINNER
Almond, Bonnie K.
7th-12th Grade Math Teacher
HALLIDAY
Stedder, Dave
5th-6th Grade Tchr & Elem Prin
HANKINSON
Knodel, Kristi L.
English & History Teacher
HARVEY
Cahill, William John
HS Social Studies Teacher
Keller, Beckee Bentz
PE & Health Teacher
Lang, Brenda Cole
4th Grade Teacher
Lesmeister, Maloye (Cink)
English Teacher
Reindel, Bernie M.
Math & Science Teacher
HATTON
Berg, Emilie Ringsrud
First Grade Teacher
Omdahl, Chad Lewis
5th Grade Teacher
Strand, Donalee Ann (Domier)
4th Grade Teacher
Strand, Fredrick Paul
Mathematics Teacher
HAZELTON
Renz, Gwen
Science Teacher
HAZEN
Johnson, Randy W.
Math, Health & PE Instructor
Krein, Kirk K.
Physics & Mathematics Instr
Loney, Nancy A.
7th-12th Grade Counselor
Wood, Janice Rae (Dahl)
First Grade Teacher
HEBRON
Uttech, Bonnie Buchli
First Grade Teacher
HETTINGER
Doe, Linda L.
Business Education & Comp Tchr

HETTINGER (cont)
Smith, Bonnie M.
Upper English Elective Teacher
Wilz, Gary Allan
Secondary Science Instructor
HOPE
Roach, Karen E.
Home Ec, Sci & Health Teacher
HURDSFIELD
Nelson, Barbara Thurson
Teacher, Music Dir & Librarian
JAMESTOWN
Berg, Bruce G.
English & Speech Teacher
Exner, Carolyn Kay (Linstaedt)
Fourth Grade Teacher
Gould, Tom
Civics & Social Science Instr
Holmen, John R.
English Teacher
Larson, Leslee Deeanne
Former Jr High Math Teacher
Steinmetz, Lennie Dee
8th Grd World Geography Tchr
Tews, David Allen
US History Teacher
Torbert, David G.
Instrumental Music Instructor
KENMARE
Burkhardt, Julie Ann
English Teacher
Lindquist, Shirley Ann Benshoof
Retired 5th Grade Teacher
Munson, Alan W.
High School Math Teacher
KIEF
Donelenko, Jeanette Kanko
Retired Vocal Music Director
KILLDEER
Abrahamson, John Edwin
English Teacher
Hanson, Cynthia Jo
Soc Stud, PE & Math Tchr
KINDRED
Johnson, Kermit Axel
Social Studies & Science Tchr
Mc Cord, Terrance Robert
Social Studies & Lit Teacher
Schnabel, Nancy Louise
HS Math & Science Teacher
KULM
Schlabsz, Wilbert
Science Teacher
LAKOTA
Bahe, Susan
7th-12th Grd Science Teacher
Ferguson, Shirley Ann
1st Grade Teacher
Nelson, Faye Brosy
School Counselor
Sattler, Chad S.
Math Teacher
LAMOURE
Aas, Jeffrey Owen
Social Studies Teacher
Falter, Jean Oelke
Second Grade Teacher
Greicar, Peggy (Durkin)
Kindergarten & Title 1 Teacher
Hermes, Greg R.
Business Education Teacher
Hopman, Denise Jean
Hlth, Spelling & Math Teacher
Schimke, Dennis J.
HS Advanced Math & Sci Tchr
LANGDON
Mitchell, Guy E.
Science Teacher
LANKIN
Hejlik, Monica Fern (Fauske)
Elem Principal
LARIMORE
Gurbada, David John
6th Grade Teacher
LEEDS
Brown, Jane
Family & Consumer Sci Teacher
LEHR
Runyan, Walter W.
English & Spanish Teacher
LIGNITE
Berg, Pamela J.
Mathematics Teacher
Monson, Marsha Berg
Third Grade Teacher
LINTON
Carr, Daniel Paul
History Teacher
LISBON
Butenhoff, Peder Charles Cole
US His, Amer Govt & Art Tchr
Hanson, Diane I.
Second Grade Teacher
Himmelspach, Sherri Ann
Spanish Teacher
Howell, Joe M.
Health, PE Teacher & Track
Lyons, Tracey Ose
Tutor
Ofstedal, Larry D.
Economics, Geog & Govt Teacher
MADDOCK
Knowlen, Cindy Throlson
Math Teacher
Simon, Charlotte Ann (Heilman)
First Grade Teacher
MAKOTI
Shaw, Marty James
Math & Computer Teacher
MANDAN
Allan, Scott Edward
US & World History Teacher
Conlon, Lynn
English & PE Teacher
Franz, Kim R.
Third Grade Teacher
Hanson, Donald Christian
9th Grade Math Teacher
Kartes, Donald Francis
Technology Education Teacher
Klemisch, Bob
Elementary Principal
Landsberger, Rita Lorraine
4th Grade Teacher
Mack, Dewitt Gregory
Chemistry Teacher
Mayer, Bonita Dobbert
Language Arts Teacher
Nagel, Karen Marcotte
Fifth Grade Teacher
Nider, Michael Edward
Jr High Hlth Tchr
Schroeder, Henry Nick
Math Dept Chair & Teacher
MARION
Handt, David Dean
Mathematics Instructor
MAYVILLE
Fugleberg, Vicki S.
Mathematics Instructor
Johnson, Marlene Kaye
MS & HS English Teacher
Kruger, Robert Miller
Associate Professor of Science
MCCLUSKY
Fischer, Doris Ann
Fifth Grade Teacher
MEDORA
Johnson, Ruth Haas
Seventh & Eighth Grade Teacher
MINOT
Anderson, Howard Bucky
Biology Teacher
Austin, Joanne Obrist
First Grade Teacher
Beaumont, Geohe Alfred
Cmptr & Advanced Math Tchr
Bohlig, Corey Jerome
World Geography Teacher
Bugbee, Cordell
Band Director
Burnside, Joan
Third & Fourth Grade Teacher
Cederstrom, Theresa Phillips
Jr High Language Arts Teacher
Colby, Warren Arthur
World History Teacher
Dufner, Sharen Alta (Selvig)
Teacher
Eggl, Lisa Marie (Klein)
Science Teacher
Evanoff, Scott James
Mathematics Teacher
Feldner, Rochelle Pearl (Kulish)
Band Director
Filipek, Linda Susan Reiner
1st Grade Teacher
Goldade, Lisa Hurdelbrink
Language Arts Teacher
Groce, Hal F.
Spanish & French Teacher
Gumbert, Karma Turner
Sixth Grade Teacher
Holtz, Thomas Erik
8th Grade Language Arts Tchr
Hornecker, Janet Wahlund
1st Grade Teacher
Jensen, Theresa Alida (Black)
3rd Grade Teacher
Johnson, Jim M.
Language Arts Teacher
Johnson, Michael J.
Physical Education Instructor
Johnson, William Lee
Ecology & Geology Instructor
Jorgenson, Pat Jessen
Title I Reading Teacher
King, Ernest L.
Sixth Grade Teacher
Kjos, Tanya L.
Theatre Dir & Speech Instr
Larson, Malinda Jean (Kirbie)
Science Teacher
Larson, Michelle Kay
Business Education Instructor
Martin, Stephanie Tarrant
Associate Prof of Audiology
Mayer, De Ann Margaret
Math Teacher
Neff, Betty Ann
9th Grade Language Arts Tchr
Nelson, Jenny Pfau
HS Language Arts Teacher
Olson, Diana Whitty, III
Fourth Grade Teacher
Pfau, LaVerne Sitter
First Grade Teacher
Remmick, Betty Lou Gietzen
Second Grade Teacher
Sande, Sandra Lee (Norton)
English Teacher & Dept Chprsn
Schmidt, Kathy
HS Religion Teacher
Sovak, Ragene Ellen
8th Grade Social Studies Tchr
Stehr, Luann L.
Mathematics Teacher
Torgerson, Elaine D. (Bye)
Asst Prof of Comm Disorders
Torgerson, John Kenneth
Prof of Comm Disorders
Walz, Du Wayne Edwin
7th Grd Life Science Teacher
Wittliff, Peggy Loveland
Lang Arts Teacher & Dept Chair
Zander, Diane Marie
5th Grade Teacher & Principal
MINTO
Kasprick, Barbara Sitzer
Third Grade Teacher
Mach, Harold Allen
Supt, HS Math & Science Tchr
MOHALL
Albright, Marlys
Kindergarten Teacher
Overby, Linda L. (Gates)
Third Grade Teacher
Voigt, Robby E.
PE & Psychology Teacher
MOTT
Moore, John
English & Social Studies Tchr
Schweitzer, Myron J.
Agricultural Science Instr
MUNICH
Albrecht, Marion
Secondary English Teacher
Dawley, Deborah Rufsvold
4th Grade Teacher
DeMaine, Betty Jean
Kindergarten & Sixth Grd Cnslr
Schuler, Mercedes Ann
Mathematics Teacher
NAPOLEON
Schneider, Brian Andrew
Agriculture Education Instr
NASH
Wilebski, James Wilebski
5th-8th Grade Instructor
NEW ENGLAND
Schlenvogt, Norma Jean Aipperspach
Spanish & English Teacher
NEW LEIPZIG
Gruebele, Shirley Heim
Third & Fourth Grade Teacher
Roth, Priscilla Dohrmann
English & Social Studies Tchr
NEW ROCKFORD
Burgad, Debra Kay
Social Studies Instructor
Elkins, Renee Marie
6th Grade Teacher
Johnson, Rita Moe
Retired 1st Grade Teacher
Manly, Janice Ruth (Parker)
Fifth Grade Teacher
Nitschke, Jay Marie
Eng Dept Chair & Speech Tchr
NEW TOWN
Mackey, Mary Jo Work
Science Teacher
Odermann, Leslie Greenshields
Title I Math Teacher
Thomte, Kay
First Grade Teacher
NEWBURG
Stevenson, Lenora R. (Hoff)
Social Studies, Bus & Eng Tchr
NIAGARA
Reinholz, Diane Mc Lachlan
Former Business Teacher
OAKES
Yale, Gregory Wayne
Math Teacher
PAGE
Utke, Donna
Family & Consumer Science Tchr
PARK RIVER
Alkofer, Kay L.
Retired 5th Grade Teacher
Holand, Richard Henry
Elem Prin & 6th Grd Rdng Tchr
Kibler, Katheryn Suzanne
Second Grade Teacher
PETERSBURG
Reinholz, James M.
Business Teacher
PINGREE
Stefonek, Kathy Ann
Math & Science Teacher
POWERS LAKE
Dihle, Donna Kettel
Math & Psychology Instructor
Starr, Waylan D.
Social Studies Teacher
REGENT
Andrus, Clarice (Kuhn)
English Teacher
RICHARDTON
Jordan, Mickey Allen
Mathematics Teacher
ROCKLAKE
Knutt, Sharon Kaye
Junior High Teacher
ROLETTE
Orgaard, Marilyn Bosserman
Area Voc Counselor
ROLLA
Lagasse, Armand J.
Science Teacher
RUGBY
Froehlich, Leo Wesley, Jr.
Music Dept Chairman
Grochow, Scott J.
Math Teacher
Hagen, Jan Marie
HS Science Teacher
Mund, Curry G.
HS History & Geography Teacher
Schilke, Karen Marie
First Grade Teacher
Smith, Barbara R.
Spanish & English Teacher
SAWYER
Rauschenberger, Paula Smith
Language Arts Teacher
SELFRIDGE
Kronberg, Russell K.
High School Principal
Maxwell, Myra M.
English & German Teacher
Ova, Gregory Kent
Principal & Teacher
SHELDON
Bunn, George Dennis
High School English Teacher
SHERWOOD
Keith, Arlyn D.
Science Teacher
SHEYENNE
Lindstrom, Shirley Thiel
Elem Principal & 6th Grd Tchr
Westby, Laurel (Ploium)
First Grade Teacher
SOLEN
Kelley, Jack D., Jr.
HS History & Government Tchr
SOUTH HEART
Hoffman, Scott Virgil
Technology Education Instr
Jost, Jan (Martin)
2nd Grade Teacher
STANLEY
Enget, Lyne Dale
History Teacher
STANTON
Lamsters, Janis
Sci, German Instr & Ath Dir
Waddingham, Kelli K.
Mathematics & Science Instr
STARKWEATHER
Roller, Maria Antoinette
Science Teacher
Wright, Kenneth Richard
7th-12th Grade Math Teacher
STEELE
Lang, Sherleen Jean (Norling)
English & Science Teacher
Mc Allister, Marlene A. (Rohrich)
6th Grade Teacher
Olson, Paul D.
High Schl Business Ed Teacher
STRASBURG
Dosch, Alois
Counselor & Athletic Director
Eiseman, James
Superintendent
SURREY
Bubach, Marjory Annie
English Teacher
Magnuson, Todd James
Math & Social Studies Teacher
Walhaug, Gary W.
Business Teacher
SYKESTON
Johnson, Brenda Marie
Music & Elementary Teacher
THOMPSON
Erickson, Todd Allen
Math & Science Teacher
Knutt, Sherry Lynn
Sixth Grade Teacher
TIOGA
Johnson, Allen L.
English Teacher
TOWER CITY
Anderson, Shirley Jean
Science Teacher
TRENTON
Folkestad, Ruth L.
Math Teacher
TURTLE LAKE
Loffelmacher, Thelma Nielsen
Title I Teacher
Wolfe, Holly Jean
Science Teacher
TUTTLE
Sand, Randel
Science Teacher & Asst Prin
Wells, Mary Lou
Math Teacher & Principal
UNDERWOOD
Simenson, Shirley M.
English Teacher
Swanson, Val Rae Slagg
2nd Grade Teacher
VALLEY CITY
Cummings, Sheila DeNae (Schafer)
Secondary English & Span Tchr
Dufner, Mark S.
Jr High Math Teacher
Hanson, Tamara Alwin
Business Technology Teacher
Hooper, Ralph Edward
Business Professor
Laumb, Kathy Hannig
Media Specialist
McRoberts, Daniel Arthur
Commnctn Arts Dept Chprsn
Nathan, Theodore A.
Mathematics & Geometry Teacher
Netland, Arlys
Geography & History Teacher
Schatz, Kathleen Charlotte
Mathematics & Science Teacher
Skroch, Diana P.
Division of Fine Arts Chair
Starr, Eileen Marie
Earth Science & Geography Prof
Stickler, Joseph C.
Chemistry Professor
White, A. LuANN
HS Eng & Journalism Teacher
Winning, Eileen Lyste
5th Grade Classroom Teacher
VELVA
Hoff, Donald L.
Science Teacher & Dept Chair
Swedlund, Iris
Librarian
VERONA
Worrel, Alan Lee
7th-12th Grd History Teacher
WAHPETON
Asche, Crystal (Jones)
Guidance Counselor
Hunter, Janice Swenson
Substitute Teacher
Jacobson, Brent Allen
Agriculture Education Instr
Rittenour, Neil Edward
Asst Prof of Culinary Arts
WALHALLA
Corbit, Denise Kay (VonRuden)
High School Mathematics Tchr
Nilsson, Gary Duane
Business & PE Teacher
WASHBURN
Anderson, Daniel Leroy
Math & History Teacher
Anderson, Maureen Klein
Fifth Grade Teacher
Hanson, Randall Wade
6th Grade Teacher
Janssen, Darlene Susan
Retired Fourth Grade Teacher
Kurle, Ardythe K. (Boger)
Family & Consumer Sci Teacher
Moe, Peter C.
Social Studies Teacher
Phillips, Lesley A.
Mathematics Instructor
WATFORD CITY
Brew, Lois Marie Becker
Second Grade Teacher
Flatland, Delores Marie
Voc Bus & Office Tech Instr
Levang, Patsy L.
Admin & Counselor Designate
Peterson, Arlon Duane
Mathematics Teacher
Simpson, Charles Michael
English & Drama Teacher
Simpson, Marilynn Turner
Fourth Grade Teacher
WEST FARGO
Conant, Mary (Corrow)
English Teacher
Fahrman, Daniel L.
7th Grade Science Teacher
Liebl, Lori (Arzt)
English Instructor
Osterberg, Kristen
French Teacher
Scott, Kathlyn J.
Spanish Teacher
Speral, James S.
Eighth Grade Mathematics Tchr
Swanson, Richard Jerome
Chemistry Teacher
Thompson, Pamela Carlson
Science Teacher
Wraalstad, Shelly May
Mathematics Teacher
WESTHOPE
Saville, Mary Ann Woeste
Math Teacher
WILLISTON
Anderson, Loren Carter
10th Grade English Teacher
Emly, Eilene M.
Third Grade Teacher
Emly, George Leonard
Third & Fourth Grade Teacher
Hermes, Dean W.
Psychology & US History Tchr
Larson, Jaylene K.
8th Grade English Teacher
Mc Pherson, Scott Allan
8th Grade English Teacher
Owan, Isabell A. (Engelhardt)
Eighth Grade Teacher
Parker, Herbert Mitchell
Director of Vocal Music
Thoreson, Sue (Brown)
Fifth Grade Teacher
Vannatta, Carla Huck
Algebra & Geometry Teacher
WILTON
Kinn, Rachelle Hegg
English Teacher
Scallon, Michelle Buckeye
Teacher
Speten, Kathy Mc Callum
6th Grade Teacher
WIMBLEDON
Kvislen, Paul Joseph
Mathematics Teacher
WISHEK
Duchscherer, Brian D.
Business Teacher
Woehl, Linda Lou Ketterling
Sixth Grade Teacher
WOLFORD
Arlien, Gary Ellsworth
High School Science Teacher
Gronos, Ramona Mildred Lunde
Substitute Teacher

RD (cont)
ı, Larry Dean
Teacher
Debra Graber
Teacher & School Cnslr
WORTH
ı, Doris Jean (Miller)
Teacher
HERE
ki, Paul William
Studies Teacher

.THERN RIANAS ANDS

Bob Tex
Teacher

ward Watson
er Science & Sci Tchr

O

Myra Sue
Grade Teacher
anne C.
ofessor
Lyn
& Speech Teacher
Roseanna Lewis
ate Professor of French
Michele Gaspich
y Teacher
Richard L.
or of Law
, Charles Howard
Teacher
ı, Peter Daniel
ogy Professor
Mary Heitmeyer
Grade Teacher
E. Lynn Lanier
Music Director
J.
er & Technology Coord
Nelson Jay
or of Biology
rold Lee
or of Mathematics
Sherry
or of Law

, Donna J.
Grade Teacher

Diane M.
Biology Teacher
, Karen (Leber)
Tchr & Asst Principal
Timothy R.
nental Music Tchr
Dennis John, CSC
story Teacher
ssell A.
s Teacher
Michael Stephen
Prof of Social Science
Paula Galat
Grade Teacher
Raita
ade Teacher
Stephanie Yancey
Grade Teacher
Diane Rose (Hicks)
ade Teacher
Nikki Irene (Polites)
Music Teacher
arlene (Thomas)
Grade Teacher
Les
Training & Health Tchr
Sally Johnston
Band & Orchestra Dir
nice Deena (Jones)
Grade Teacher
arbara Wise
matics Tchr & Dept Chm
n, Harry Lee, Jr.
Prof of Music & Dir
, Shawn Mc Cary
ional Consultant
Earl Leslie
sor of Art
arksz, Mary Jo
rade Teacher
Robert Ernest
ı Grd Lang Arts Teacher
Dennis Alan
Grade Teacher
Vernon C.
ce Tchr & Pgm Manager
Kathryn M.
d Earth Science Teacher
, Rita Ann (Vargo)
ade Math Teacher
k, Pamela M.
y & English Teacher
Nancy Gentzler
ade Teacher
arl E.
h Teacher

Hammond, Susan Wojno
English & Literature Teacher
Hanna, C. Sue
Fifth Grade Teacher
Harrigal, Maureen Holleran
English Dept Chprsn & Teacher
Harris, Donald Eugene
4th Grade Sunday School Tchr
Hartman, Leonard Damon
Eng, Jrnlsm Tchr & Yrbk Adv
Jackson, Michele Yvonne
Home Economics Teacher
Jacobs, Nancy Loeb
Assistant Prof of Child Dev
Jones, Rick Van
HS Social Studies Teacher
Kammer, Lonnie D.
Social Studies Teacher
Kemp, Melanie Hawks
History Teacher & Principal
Kessler, Cynthia Lee
Biology Teacher
Kiel, William T.
Middle School Counselor
Kittelberger, Frederick William
Retired Math Tchr & Dept Head
Kyle, Jacquelyn F. Bowman
Second Grade Teacher
Laktash, Sandra Smith
Vocal Music Dir & Dept Chprsn
Laubaugh, Ronnie
Mathematics Teacher
Lewis, Julia Ann
Physical Education Teacher
Lewis, Rowena Louise
8th Grade Language Arts Tchr
Lichi, Donald Allen
VP, Dir of Ed & Professor
Lillie, Michael Wayne, II
Math & Science Coordinator
Lockhart, Cleo Simons
Third Grade Teacher
Lovell, Elizabeth Helen (Corbissero)
High School Math Teacher
Luton, Bryan
Math Teacher
Malone, George Manuel
Pastor
Marks, Karen Cecelia
7th-8th Grade Science Teacher
Marshall, Victoria L.
Third Grade Teacher
Martter, Steven Butler
Social Studies Teacher
Mayfield, Dolores Camille (King)
Social Studies Teacher
McCauley, W. Keith
Secondary School Counselor
McDonald, Cynthia Kuthan
Business Education Teacher
McGinty, Regis William
Social Studies Teacher
McMillan, Mary Donataccio
HS Home Economics Teacher
Meek, Gary Edwin
Prof of Management & Chair
Michalec, Daniel John
Retired Language Arts Teacher
Milcetich, Christine Ann
AP Physics & Chemistry Teacher
Mugler, Dale H.
Professor
Natoli, Joseph R.
School Guidance Counselor
Oberdorfer, Carmel Janota
Spanish Teacher
Oplinger, Diane Leach
Social Studies Teacher
Parenti, Robert Bernhard
Senior Parole Officer
Parks, Marilyn Jayne (Riley)
Kindergarten Teacher
Reasor-Lewis, Phyllis Marilyn
8th Grd Work & Fam Life Tchr
Redding, Thomas H., Jr.
English Teacher
Rodgers, Donzella
ESEA Title, Math Instructor
Rufus, Nancy Gentile
AP European His Teacher
Sabol, John Robert
Social Studies Tchr & Ath Dir
Salter, Carol Lynn
Fifth Grade Teacher
Schmidt, Phillip Harry
Professor of Mathematical Sci
Schreiber, Maria Desillas
High School Counselor
Seeley, Mary Beth Cavanaugh
Kindergarten Teacher
Silvidi, Alan Charles
English Teacher
Smith, Curtis Alan
Fifth Grade Teacher
Starks, Carole Bragg
8th Grd Amer History Teacher
Stevens, Rebecca A.
Sociology Professor
Stuyvesant, Mary Ann
Consumer & Family Science Tchr
Talbott-Semonin, Nancy J.
5th-8th Grade Eng, Health Tchr
Taylor, Tina M.
Admission Dir & Eng Teacher
Tolle, Stuart A.
8th Grade Science Teacher
U-Rycki, Paulette Zumpano
English & Social Studies Tchr
Wallace, Don L.
Math Teacher

Walls, Jennifer Lynn
Math Teacher
Warner, Michelle Louise
Family & Consumer Sci Teacher
White, Marilyn Johnson
Senior Guidance Counselor
Whited, Linda Lee (Davis)
English Teacher
Wilson, Dawn E.
Vocal & General Music Teacher
Zager, Betty
English Teacher
Zolyniak, Timothy A.
Band Director
Zupke, Lori Hayes
Mathematics Teacher
ALEXANDRIA
Martin, Patricia Sue
Language Arts Teacher
ALLIANCE
Beltz, Julie Dunn
Business Teacher
Bugansky, Sue A.
Spanish Teacher
Crookshank, Martha Ermlich
Art Teacher
Eibel, Albert Andrew
Biology Teacher
Frank, Carolyn Mc Kimm
Third Grade Teacher
Henning, John Edward
English Teacher
Henning, Maria Colaizzi
American Government Teacher
Hepler, Maryjo
8th Grade Social Studies Tchr
Holub, Nancy Dennis
High School Science Teacher
Lanzer, Marisa Randall
SLD Special Education Teacher
Poyser, Julie Johnson
Reading & Language Arts Tchr
Seavy, Gerald L.
US History & Amer Govt Teacher
Williams, Wendy Barrick
High School Math Teacher
Young, Raymond Albert
World History & Geography Tchr
AMANDA
Edler, Alice G.
Work & Family Life Teacher
Justice, Michael Ray
Math & Physics Teacher
Shonebarger, James Alan
Sixth Grade Teacher
Smittle, Harry E.
Coordinator of Gifted Ed
AMELIA
Carter, Lisa Brownlee
Second Grade Teacher
AMHERST
Anthony, Edward E.
6th Grade Teacher
Dorsch, Jacqueline Dickey
Health & Physical Ed Teacher
Glenn, Sally Ann Piazza
7th Grade Language Arts Tchr
Ingersoll, Judith Ann Ruminsky
Mathematics Teacher
Loboda, Catherine Nicoloff
Russian & Drama Teacher
Nossek, William L.
Seventh Grade Teacher
Obbey, Kimberly Pawlizak
K-8th Grade Guidance Counselor
Parent, Daniel Paul
Social Studies Teacher
Primm, Mary Fey
Eighth Grade Teacher
Schneider, Holly D.
6th Grade Teacher
AMSDEN
Livoti, Stephen Joseph
World Studies Teacher
ANDOVER
Groff, Kristin F.
6th Grade Teacher
Mc Caslin, Shari K.
French & English Teacher
Siembor, Anne M. Schaefer
Biology Teacher
Spellman, Marlin James
Business Ed & Soc Stud Teacher
ANNA
Bayat, Carolyn Anne Smith
French Teacher
Bergman, Janet Manuel
Third Grade Teacher
Quinter, Victoria (Maurer)
Science Teacher
ANSONIA
Custer, Harold Richard, Jr.
HS & MS Art Teacher
Hemer, Nancy Pearson
Fourth Grade Teacher
Hemmerich, Carol Jean
Retired English Teacher
Hoening, Eugene Frank
Biology Teacher
Koverman, Gerald Allen
Agri Ed Teacher
LaRoche, Barbara Hawkey
2nd Grade Teacher
Miller, Todd Allen
Social Studies Teacher
Shrock, Tamara Ann
Third Grade Teacher
Sowry, Ginger La Faye
Spanish & Reading Teacher

Spencer, Rex LeRoy
Social Studies Tchr & Dept Chm
ANTWERP
Chamberlain, Robin Renee Walk
Vocal Music Teacher
Clemens, Tim A.
Mathematics Teacher
APPLE CREEK
Fuss, Christopher C.
Mathematics & Science Teacher
Mays, Lona J.
Language Arts Teacher
Reetz, Randy L.
Instrumental Music Teacher
Shultzman, Bonnie Reeves
Third Grade Teacher
ARCADIA
Ebersole, Barbara Jane (Blake)
AP Eng, Fr & Chorus Dir
ARCANUM
Delk, Darrell D.
Retired Teacher
Hollinger, David L.
7th & 8th Grd Math Tchr
Kelly, Martha Jean
Science Teacher
Ressler, Debora Jean Besecker
2nd Grade Teacher
ARCHBOLD
Beck, Wendell Dale
Mathematics Teacher
Delay, Kathleen M.
Commercial Art Instructor
Elton, Gail Ann
Voc Computer & Acctng Tchr
Griteman, Cathy Leatherman
Nursing Instructor
Hoverman, Philip Thomas
Band Director
Jeffery, J. Elmalene
Vocational Spec Ed Coord
Plessner, Von Roderick
Professor
Richter, John David
Comp Sci Instr
Sheeks, Donna M.
Computer & Accounting Teacher
Short, Cherie Salisbury
English Teacher & Dept Chair
Wilhelm, Peter William
His & Cultural Geog Professor
ARLINGTON
Anderson, Rachel Lynn (Spracklen)
English Teacher
Augsburger, Jane Elizabeth
Art Teacher
Jolliff, Sharon Kay
Kindergarten Teacher
Rader, Rachel M. (Oman)
Mathematics Teacher
Suter, Steven Matthew
Social Studies Teacher
Wilson, Jeffrey Dean
Agricultural Education Instr
ASHLAND
Fish, James Leon
Retired Voc Power Equip Tchr
Green, Loren R.
Fourth Grade Teacher
Gross, Richard Allen
Computer Sci Tchr & Technician
Kemp, Janet Painter
Retired Teacher
Keplinger, Thomas Lowell
5th Grade Teacher
Mc Graw, Joseph Allen
Social Science Teacher
Messner, Diane L. (Straits)
Retired Third Grade Teacher
Otermat, Virginia Bok
Retired Second Grade Teacher
Rawson, Julie
English Teacher
Rinehart, Donald R.
Religion Professor
Rinehart, Janet L.
Teacher
Spore, Kay A.
Gifted & Talented Coordinator
Wade, Janice M. (Myers)
Fourth Grade Teacher
ASHLEY
Heine, Carolyn Harrison
Retired French Teacher
ASHTABULA
Buck, Lou Spurlock
6th Grade Teacher
Cain, Kenneth Robert
9th Grade English Teacher
Collins, Scott Gordon
American Government Teacher
Custead, Nancy Lou
6th Grade Teacher
Diaz, Edward L.
Art & Business Teacher
Doyle, Katherine Ann
4th Grade Teacher
Fazenbaker, R. Allen
Science Educator
Harper, Brian Douglas
Mathematics Teacher
Hedrick, Douglas Frank
Science Teacher
Heusinger, Earle Charles, Jr.
Instrumental Music Director
Hilin, Marlene N.
Math Teacher
Hornbeck, Marianne Massi
Computer Science Teacher

Horton, Lucille Marie
Business Education Teacher
Jarvi, Lois A. Perugine
Second Grade Teacher
Kiphart, Andrew Paul
Hlth & Physical Education Tchr
Lawson, Catherine Ann
French, Speech & Drama Teacher
Moroski, Encie Mossford
English Teacher
Moseley, Sandra L.
10th Grade English Teacher
Mullen, Walter H.
Language Arts Teacher
Pallo, Janet Lee
5th Grade Teacher
Petrunger, Jeffrey Louis
7th & 8th Grd Amer His Tchr
Stauffeneger, Patricia
French Teacher
ASHVILLE
Allen, Jennifer Lynn
Tchr of Devlpmntly Handicapped
ATHENS
Conaty, Donna M.
Associate Professor of Oboe
Farrar, Miriam Oman
5th Grade Teacher
Hikida, Robert Seiichi
Prof of Biological Sciences
Huntley, Reid DeBerry
English Professor
Mace, Joan Rodrian
Retired Professor of Aviation
Manning, Nancy J.
Asst Prof of Political Sci
Remonko, Guy Andrew
Professor of Percussion Music
Safran, Joan Schulman
Assoc Prof Educational Psych
Stewart, Margene A.
Piano Professor
Talley, Phyllis
Asst Prof & Prgm Chair Art Ed
Theiss, Sheila Tilbrook
County Schl Bd Mem & Sub Tchr
Wilson, Larry E.
Associate Prof of Chemistry
ATTICA
Cole, Janet Ann
HS Mathematics Teacher
Davies, Julie Lyn
Learning Disabilities Teacher
Enders, Patricia Logan
Retired Elementary Teacher
Frankart, Carol Sue
English Teacher
Hartschuh, Jean F.
High School Mathematics Tchr
Lamoreaux, Frank C.
High School English Teacher
L'Italien, Anne
HS Art Teacher
Manasco, Gary Wayne
Science & PE Teacher
Willman, Dana M. (Miller)
Band Director
ATWATER
Harcar, Raymond Andrew
5th-12th Grade Band Director
AURORA
Black, Jeffrey
Social Studies Dept Chair
Freer, Kathie J.
French Teacher
Hillyer, Sarah Costello
Second Grade Teacher
Kinnan, Sonja (Kuljko)
German Teacher
Kudley, John James, Jr.
Social Studies Teacher
Rose, George Carl, Jr.
Business Education Instructor
AUSTINBURG
Taylor, Martha Cate Middendorf
6th Grade Teacher
AUSTINTOWN
Antell, James Andrew
HS Vocal Music Teacher & Coord
Antonelli, Ronald Patrick
Sixth Grade Math Teacher
Beltempo, Jerry Alan
K-4th Grade PE Teacher
Boggs, Theodore Arthur, Jr.
Health & PE Teacher
Cervello, Alphonse Aden, Sr.
5th & 6th Grade Principal
Davis, Karen Powell
First Grade Teacher
Ford, Wally
Social Studies Teacher
Frankford, Stephanie Ann Ragozine
Health & Physical Ed Teacher
Gerrard, Ruth
English Teacher & Gifted Coord
Landy-Pearce, Judith Hetman
5th Grade Language Arts Tchr
Lynch, Billie S.
English Teacher
Marino, Joseph Anthony, Jr.
Greek Mythology & Drama Tchr
Mc Cue, Harold Lewis
Mathematics Teacher
Reedy, Gerald Charles
Earth Science Teacher
Stuber, Ann Marchionda
Spanish Teacher
Villella, Kathleen Coppola
5th-8th Grade Teacher

AUSTINTOWN (cont)
Weinberg, Karen Minkin
Art Department Chairman
Wittmann, Kathy Ann
Math & German Teacher
AVON
Ritzert, Tammy Lyn
Choir Director
AVON LAKE
Dematte, Antoinette Paro
Eighth Grade English Teacher
Dickson, Donald Scott
Industrial Tech Ed Tchr
Dlugosz, David A.
Health Teacher
Judson, Jane Thrun
Fifth Grade Teacher
Kloc, Sheila Schweitzer
Retired Second Grade Teacher
Mankis, Stacey Renee
Language Arts Teacher
Mc Laughlin Bruegger, Ruth E.
Fifth Grade Teacher
Prickett, Karen L.
Second Grade Teacher
Szegedy, Pamela Marie (Hill)
Fifth Grade Teacher
Weaver, Kenneth Ray
Mathematics Teacher
Weinert, Joanne Ruth
Kindergarten Teacher
Zurkey, William Gavin
Vocal Music Director
BAINBRIDGE
McClain, Ruth A.
English Teacher
Newsome, Gary Lee
Asst Principal & Athletic Dir
BALTIC
Johnson, Brenda Mc Queen
First Grade Teacher
BALTIMORE
Johnson-Miller, Ruth A.
English & Reading Teacher
Mc Quade, Richard John
Coordinator
Reed, Jim Neal
MS Tchr & HS Golf Coach
Shonebarger, Julie Ann
Band Director
Zellner-Zeglen, Hildegard
Spanish & German Teacher
BARBERTON
Bagwell, Billie R. Johnson
Second Grade Teacher
Graham, Roy P.
6th Grade Teacher
Hinman, Robert Guy
5th Grade Classroom Teacher
Janiga, Jeffery Allan
Govt, Econ & Hnrs History Tchr
Lair, Sandra
Retired 12th Grd English Tchr
Miller, Heather Smith
Sixth Grade Teacher
Rosnick, Robert
Vocational Graphic Arts Tchr
Wennerstrom, Jennifer Susan (Gaiser)
Vocal Music Director
Wuescher, Kim (Woodhall)
English Teacher
BARNESVILLE
Hughes, Cynthia Ann Brown
Fourth Grade Teacher
Kosanovic, Leslie Ann (Wagner)
Life Science Teacher
Pierce-Coleman, Lloren Caryl
History General Science Tchr
Reynolds, Nancy Rose
GATE & Accelerated Math Tchr
Sells, Linda Wilson
Title I Reading & Math Teacher
BARTLETT
Robinson, Terry Lynn
7th-8th Grade Teacher
BASCOM
Cramer, Ann M.
Social Studies Teacher
Rouser, Sandra Mae
Business Education Instructor
BATAVIA
Branham, Pamela Foley
Fourth Grade Teacher
Ciliberti, Vicki Holewinski
English & Drama Teacher
Conway, Teresa J.
English Teacher
Donohue, Ethel Mae
Fifth Grade Teacher
Fitzpatrick, Cathy Eileen Condon
High School Counselor
Hager, Debbie Stoll
Guidance Counselor
Harvey, Jayne Hauke
5th Grade Classroom Teacher
Hasser, Julia M.
Mathematics Teacher
Hinton, Rebecca Stingley
Lecturer in English
Johnson, Meri E.
Biology Teacher
Jones, Rochelle R.
Art & Photography Teacher
Miller, Michael Allen
Health & Language Arts Tchr
Perkins, Beth Anne
Lecturer on Philosophy
Sanders, Lois Bentley
Fifth Grade Teacher
Sebastian, Linda Ann
Teacher of Gifted & Talented
Smith, Mark Mc Callum
8th Grade US History Teacher
Smith, Terry Seldon
Occptnl Work Experience Coord
Warner, Peggy Mills
Music Teacher
Welage, Larry A.
Social Studies Teacher
Wells, Dennis Geoffrey
Biology Teacher & Athletic Dir
Williams, Bonnie B.
Dir of Developmental Education
BATH
Peters, David Allan
Study Skills Teacher
BAY VILLAGE
Assenheimer, Carl Frederick, III
9th-12th Grade English Teacher
Liberatore, Margaret Mary
Fifth Grade Teacher
Tedrick, Kathleen Ann
Biology Teacher
BEACHWOOD
Bellin, Allan
Counselor
Brewster, Gail Leila
HS Social Studies Teacher
Fried, Linda Joyce
Third Grade Teacher
Glickman, Andi
Social Studies Teacher
Haas, Robert William
Science Teacher
Kasprisin-Rus, Thea M.
Social Studies Teacher
Kucich, Karen Ann
7th-8th Grade Latin Teacher
Morse, Jamie P.
Art Photography & Art His Tchr
Queen, Joyce E.
Primary Science Coordinator
Rakow, Susan Bosnick
Language Arts Teacher
Sonnie, Wallace H.
Math Teacher
Southard, Don Mc Cormick
Science Department Head
Zatko, Frank
Physics Professor
BEALLSVILLE
Monticello, Charles E.
4th-12th Grd Musical Director
BEAVER
Bennett, Linda Ann
Home Economics Teacher
Hendricks, M. Marie Poe
Bio, Chem & Earth Sci Teacher
Leist, Neil E.
Health & Physical Ed Tchr
Mc Ginnis, Steven Christopher
High School English Teacher
Rittenour, Kimberley Harper
Social Studies & Span Teacher
Young, Patricia Morgan
First Grade Teacher
BEAVERCREEK
Arnold, Matthew Dean
Social Studies Teacher
Ferguson, Patricia Rauch
6th Grd Language Arts Teacher
Gardetto, Mary-Sue Withington
English Tchr & Dept Chair
Gribler, Lois Ann (Kruse)
Math Teacher
Group, Kimberly Howland
English & Speech Teacher
Pappas, Carole E.
Social Studies Tchr & Dept Chm
Rountree, Linda Simmons
Elementary Music Teacher
Starrett, William Grant
Eighth Grade Teacher
BEDFORD
Bindernagel, James William
6th Grade Teacher
Hilty, Paul Allen
6th Grade Math Teacher
Holloway, Barbara Chambers
Dept Chprsn Business Education
Rice, James A.
Fourth Grade Teacher
Saxton, Timothy Lawrence
Mathematics Teacher & Coach
Shy, Terri Rawls
10th Grade Science Teacher
Sullivan, Donald Dayne
Band & Orchestra Director
BELLAIRE
Ducci, Nancy Lynn Krieger
Second Grade Teacher
Dunaway, Karen Zanke
Principal
Durant, Rosemary Derry
Fifth Grade Teacher
Ferrick, Patricia S.
Mathematics Teacher
Starkey, Roxane Marie
Math & Science Teacher
Thiele, Lauren Flannery
School Psychologist
Tuttle, Catherine Boccabella
First Grade Teacher
BELLBROOK
Breese, Marlissa Marie
Social Studies Teacher
Jamison, William Edward, III
Chemistry & Physics Teacher
Rauch, Cathy Lynn
HS Social Studies Teacher
Sharpe, Charles E.
HS Tech Education Instructor
Wilson, Mary K. (Rohman)
Gifted Program Teacher
Woody, Michael E.
Government Teacher
BELLEFONTAINE
Beck, Rick L.
Law Enforcement Instructor
Cost, Dorothy Groch
Sixth Grade Teacher
Croutwater, Charles Harry
Educl Television Specialist
Harman, Mary Elizabeth (Belser)
Third Grade Teacher
Knecht, Mary Ann
American Studies Teacher
Krock, Theresa Anne (Johnson)
Lang Arts & Reading Teacher
Mc Guire, Nancy King
Third Grade Teacher
Mc Kelvey, Jill Hatcher
Social Studies Teacher
Ramsey, Kathryn A.
4th Grade Teacher
Royer, Ronald Paul
Activities Director
Spessard, Carol Sue (Andrews)
French Teacher
Stoner, John Blaine
7th Grd Language Arts Teacher
Walker, Larry Robert
Instrumental Music Teacher
Wildermuth, Ann Kyle
Mathematics Teacher
BELLEVUE
Claus, Larry E.
Science & Cmptr Sci Tchr
Howard, John William
8th Grd American History Tchr
Lilli, Nick J.
Track & Football Coach
Mitchell, Mary J.
Mathematics Teacher
Netcher, James Harland
Junior High Math Teacher
Parks, Susan Marie (Sherman)
Algebra & Pre-Algebra Teacher
Sarty, Mary Jane (Laparo)
Second Grade Teacher
BELLVILLE
Hubler, Joan Keppler
Math Teacher & Dept Chairman
Orr, Sue Moore
Second Grade Teacher
BELMONT
Bartels, Michael Stanley
Seventh & Eighth Grade Teacher
Boich, Peggy Ann
Guidance Counselor
Dimmick, Mary Ellen (LoCoco)
French & English Teacher
Doty, Sharon M.
Mathematics Teacher
Griffin, Donna DeWitt
English Teacher
Kaczor, Cheryl Hysong
Work & Family Life Teacher
Krebs, George Edward
Industrial Arts Teacher
Laposki, Stephen
American Government Teacher
Mehl, Thomas R.
Social Studies Teacher
Sketel, Amie Lynn
Mathematics Teacher
Sobel, Stanley Allen
High School Science Teacher
Vannest, Nancy Collins
Work & Family Life Teacher
BELOIT
Barnett, Robert James
Instrumental Music Director
Buckley, Kevin Dale
Chemistry & Physics Teacher
Grove, Lynn Allen
Eighth Grade Mathematics Tchr
Plano, Sandra Kay
Scndry English & Reading Tchr
Taylor, Karen
Eng & Creative Writing Tchr
Zamarelli, John Andrew
High School Choral Teacher
BELPRE
Arnold, Norma Joyce (Newell)
High School Math Teacher
Bartimus, Jo Ann
Teacher of Talented & Gifted
Cunningham, James Franklin, III
Math Teacher & Dept Chairman
Hlubb, Jacqueline Elizabeth
8th Grade Science Teacher
Holmes, Kathy Diane
7th-12th Grd PE Teacher
Klinger, Charlita Craig
English Teacher & Team Leader
Needs, David Wayne
6th Grade Teacher & Coach
Poe, Larry Wayne
World Literature Teacher
Suttle, John L.
World Cultures Teacher
BEREA
Kich, Marie Bonsutto
5th Grade Teacher
BERGHOLZ
Allen, Jayma Sue (Smith)
7th-8th Grd Lang Arts Teacher
Goddard, Sandra Kay
Sixth Grade Teacher
Neptune, Diane Mignella
Fifth Grade Teacher
Waller, Mike
Physical Science Teacher
Webber, Paula K.
9th Grade English Teacher
BERLIN
Baur, Loretta Mumaw
Second Grade Teacher
Brubacher, Robert E.
Fifth Grade Teacher
Dunn, Roger C.
Biology Teacher
Jeschke, Marlin
Ret Prof of Philosophy & Rel
Rausch, Robert Franklin, Jr.
Industrial Technology Tchr
Steiner, Virginia M.
6th Grade Teacher
BERLIN CENTER
Cramer, Lona Lee
Biology & Chemistry Teacher
Sheridan, Joan Eileen
Spanish Teacher
BERLIN HEIGHTS
Drake, Margaret Elizabeth
Fourth Grade Teacher
BETHEL
Hannah, Fred Homer
Quest Teacher
Lonaker, Linda Sue
5th Grade Math & History Tchr
BETHESDA
Thompson, Randy Jarold
7th-8th Grade Teacher
BETTSVILLE
Underwood, Carole Bahnsen
Spanish & English Teacher
BEVERLY
Bostic, John E.
Social Studies Educator
Graham, Donna Mc Carver
High School Business Ed Instr
Mace, Cathy Bonar
Vocal Music Teacher
Moegling, Lawrence Anthony
Spanish Teacher
Pierce, Brenda Kay (Biehl)
1st Grade Teacher
Sprague, Cathy L.
Senior English & Drama Teacher
BEXLEY
Schneider, Jeffrey W.
Instrumental Music Teacher
Winer, Susan Hope
6th Grade Science Teacher
BIDWELL
Stout, Patricia
Junior High History Teacher
BLACKLICK
Sammons, Karen R.
Tutor, Sub Tchr, Testing Coord
BLANCHESTER
Appleby, Gloria J. (Holt)
French & English Teacher
Tumbleson, Sue Ann
High School Art Teacher
BLOOMDALE
Ault, Diane Lynn Anderson
Mathematics Dept Chm & Teacher
BLOOMINGDALE
Abdalla, Cecilia Gruszecki
Bus Legal & Medical Instructor
Blubaugh, Robert Louis
Senior Social Studies Teacher
BLUE ASH
Cebula, James E.
Professor of History
Garnett, William B.
Professor of Biology
Goodman, Elise
Art History Professor
Hagerty, Robert E.
Associate Professor of Art
Hansen, Barbara Louise
English Professor
Walker, Michael J.
Asst Professor of English
BLUFFTON
Bollenbacher, Duane R.
Mathematics Teacher
Bumbough, Susan Moritz
Asst Prof of Education
Buroker, Dawn (Spengler)
6th Grd Math & Phys Ed Tchr
Friesen, Ronald Lee
Professor of Economics
Goodwin, Tim J.
Math Teacher
Hostetler, Elizabeth Ann
Dir of Tchr Ed & Prof of Ed
Jeffs, Jeanne L.
Intrvntn, Eng & Dev Rdng Tchr
Johns, Loren L.
Asst Professor of Religion
Schiefer, Gary Lee
Assoc Prof of Bus
BOARDMAN
Arnold, Simone G.
ESL Teacher
Burkhardt, Kathy Kendall
HS MH Teacher
Clark, Carol S.
Orchestra Conductor & Coord
Collins, Kathy Imobersteg
Elementary Counselor
Dryburgh, Susan Alice
Junior-Senior English Teacher
Gerberry, Kathryn Schrum
Biology I & Chemistry Teacher
Grabman, Pamela Garvin
Sixth Grade Teacher
Groth, Thomas A.
Dir of Bands & Dept Chair
Kennedy, James Michael
English Teacher
Mazzella, Bernice Bongiorno
Spanish & Italian Teacher
Olson, Beverly Lynn
High School Math Teacher
Pavlansky, David S.
English Teacher
Russo-Haber, Vincetta R.
English Teacher
Sampson, Sally Ann
French Teacher
Shiveley, M. Scott
Biology Teacher
Smrek, Richard MIchael
Orchestra Teacher
Sole, MariLouise Anne
English Instructor
Zitto, Richard Joseph
Physics Teacher
BOLIVAR
Taylor, Barbara Slaybaugh
First Grade Teacher
BOTKINS
Boyer, Candyce L. (Agnew)
Reading, Math & Computer Tchr
Buehler, Peg Taubken
Business Teacher
Eyink, Nancy J. Manger
Math Teacher
Niekamp, Jennifer Ritter
7th-12th Grade Science Teacher
BOWERSTON
Lada, Judson
Guidance Counselor
Pumphry, David
Math, Physics & Chemistry Tchr
BOWLING GREEN
Bennett, Joan Walters
Sixth Grade Teacher
Bosworth, Frank Maling, III
Pgm Dir & Assoc Prof of Arch
Brown, Albert Brian
Fourth Grade Teacher
Chambers, Virginia Eileen
7th Grade Life Science Teacher
Corrigan, Bruce William
Jr High Band Director
Diehl, Alta A.
Second Grade Teacher
Ensinger, Larry Ray
9th Grade Algebra Teacher
Geer, Tari Scholler
7th & 8th Grade Health Teacher
Johnston, Jeffrey M.
Fifth Grade Teacher
Kruppa, Richard Andrew
Prof of Manufacturing Tech
Luidhardt, Donna Adornetti
Second Grade Teacher
McClary, Kent Lee
Fourth Grade Teacher
Reublin, Mary Lou Klemencic
6th Grade Teacher
Ross, Thomas Tod
English & Reading Teacher
ST John, Marcy Domergue
French Teacher
Shertzer, Michael James
Agricultural Education Instr
Thiel, Pamela B.
Orchestra Director
Vannett, R. Michael
Ath Dir, Head Basketball Coach
Vogtsberger, Diane M.
English Teacher
Waggoner, Todd Charles
Technology Systems Asst Prof
BRADFORD
Besecker, Scott Joe
Math & Science Teacher
Harshbarger, Nancy Jane (Conway)
Sixth Grade Teacher
BRECKSVILLE
Benedict, Margie Preston
Retired Second Grade Teacher
Dauria, John Joseph
American History Teacher
Kan, Beverly Rehor
Eng, French Tchr & Eng Chair
Stehlik-Baker, Wendy Knight
Asst Principal & 5th Grd Tchr
BRIDGEPORT
Dailer, James M.
OWA Coordinator
Marty, George A.
Algebra & Calculus Teacher
Moore, Lynn Edward
9th-12th Grd Spanish Teacher
Wilson, Carol Connelly
Dev Handicap Specialist
BRILLIANT
Verhovec, Jodee Straus
7th & 8th Grade Science Tchr
BRISTOLVILLE
Price, Merial H.
Spanish Teacher
BROADVIEW HEIGHTS
Dinse, Debra Poppy
Classical Ballet Instructor
Papadopoulos, Eftehia Koconis
Retired Scndry Math Teacher

FIELD
Daniel Vincent
r of Bands
ri, Cheryl L.
.it & Eng Comp Tchr
LYN
yce F.
Math Tchr & Math Chair
aula Jeanne
Grade Teacher
n, Mary
Department Chairman
Rebecca Lynne
Grade Teacher
mmy (Gum)
Music Director
Beverly Danchisin
g Teacher
annette Boyd
Teacher
Marilyn Pierce
Grade Teacher
Barbara Ann
Teacher & Dist Coord
VILLE
James R.
Reading Teacher
bert Wesley
tructor
enee L.
Teacher
WICK
d, Yvette
anish & French Teacher
inda L.
Grade Teacher
Penelope Swingle
World History Teacher
Ronald William
Sci & Field Stud Tchr
z, Ursel Haffer
r
. Timothy
His, Geog & Govt Teacher
Mary Anne Gemma
rade Teacher
Donna S.
& Theatre Teacher
wicz, Rebecca Ann (Quinn)
rade Teacher
va Kay
rade Teacher
Karen Lee (Burger)
Grade Teacher
Thomas Gerald
ade Teacher
y, Robert Earl
ade Elementary Teacher
r, Julia Lynn Bresnahan
ade Teacher
Roger Benn
ade Teacher
auer, Mary Toelke
ge Arts & Lit Teacher
dith Kuhns
ade Math Teacher
Terri Lassond
Grade Teacher

der, Roger Owen
stra Director
udith L.
ath & Language Arts Tchr
Amy Beth
Studies Teacher
Ned Alan
acher
, JoNell
Language Arts Teacher
ody Berry
Music Teacher
Melene Louise
Grade Teacher
Elizabeth Martino
& History Teacher
r, Ron Eugene
ntary Principal
, Gerry Rader
Teacher
Mary Beth
Grade Social Sci Tchr
Reta Mc Lauchlin
ade Teacher
Denise Carol
ud & Lang Arts Tchr
US
Linda Saunders
erated Program Teacher
Jane Nienberg
Grade Teacher
Missi Hemm
Teacher
, Michael Anthony
lture Instructor
Peggy Laber
Grade Teacher
, Robert Le Roy, Jr.
g & Language Arts Tchr
Glen Allen
y Teacher
Glenda Kay (Louis)
Grade Teacher
N
Marillyn Bizjak
h Teacher
, Kathleen Lewis
Studies Teacher
Mary M.
, Keyboarding & Bus Tchr

Yoder, Kara Maria (Menosky)
Sixth Grade Teacher
BUTLER
Fletcher, Marcia Ann
Title I Coordinator
Stewart, Vicki Dennison
Title I Reading Teacher
BYESVILLE
Arent, Cynthia Thaxton
First Grade Teacher
Brown, Leisa Sokol
Third Grade Teacher
CADIZ
Drexler, Janet Elaine (Savage)
9th-12th Grade Math Teacher
Fristick, Susie J.
Latin & Social Studies Tchr
Moore, Linda Kay (Grimes)
9th & 10th Grade English Tchr
Swartz, Jane Lee
Spanish & English Teacher
CALDWELL
Briggs, Susan Darlene (King)
4th Grade Teacher
Brooks, Stephen Michael
Scndry Soc Studies & Dept Chm
Hill, Howard Dugan
Science & Health Teacher
Peoples, Joyce Lee (Dennis)
Fifth Grade Teacher
Powers, Franklin Harry
Science Teacher
Truax, Patsy L.
Fourth Grade Teacher
Van Scyoc, Cindy Ann
6th Grade Teacher
CALEDONIA
Cones, Joan Planson
Third Grade Teacher
CAMBRIDGE
Barber, Tom Alden
Fourth Grade Teacher
Carpenter, N. Darlene Miller
Adv English & Reading Teacher
Ford, Gene Allen
9th Grd World Studies Teacher
Marks, Robert Gale
Vocal Music Director
Pavlik, Diane Day
Special Ed Resource Tchr
Weber, Keith Allen
Social Studies Teacher
CAMDEN
Crumbaker, Debra Elliott
Primary Multi-Age Teacher
Immel, Cheryl Pendell
High School Guidance Counselor
Powell, Kipling John
HS OWA Coordinator
CAMPBELL
Capito, Robert Gregory
English Teacher
Pennanzio, Janet Fraile
School Psychologist
CANAL FULTON
Bernard, Pamela Jane
Tchr of Prmry Lrng Dsblts
Boedicker, Laurie Bellew
Former Physics & Math Teacher
CANAL WINCHESTER
Chester, Deborah L.
High School English Teacher
Gehlbach, Gretchen D.
English Teacher
Gibson, John
HS Bible & Math Teacher
CANFIELD
Albanese, Judie Marie
Pre School Teacher
Frey, Lee E.
Psychology & Amer His Teacher
George, Donald P.
Mathematics Chprsn & Tchr
Lippiatt, Nancy Miller
Teacher of Gifted & Talented
Roberts, Kathryn Gintert
Retired Fourth Grade Teacher
CANTON
Bashoor, Susan Fosselman
Math Teacher & Dept Head
Bergert, John Calvin
5th Grade Teacher
Biviano, J. Martin
Instrumental Music Director
Boerner, Tina Marie (Christie)
Math Teacher
Bowman, Lee James
Band Director
Bremer, Karen Maola
8th Grd Language Arts Teacher
Brown, Susan Douglas
Speech Teacher
Burlingame, Virginia Kay (Jones)
Mathematics Teacher
Cain, Alice Farrell
Assoc Prof & Phy Thrpst Dir
Colombo, Maria Carmela
Teacher of the Gifted
Dudra, Ted E.
Science Teacher
Fedder, Tamara A.
Mathematics Teacher
Fisher, Raymond Robert
Remedial Mathematics Teacher
Foltz, Anne Moegling
4th Grade Teacher
Forbes, Liesl Lux
English & Psychology Teacher
Fowler, Deborah Louise
Physical Ed & Health Teacher

Gallagher, Judith Leona (Franks)
Fourth Grade Teacher
Gann, Deborah Miller
Second Grade Teacher
Geib, John David
Instructor in Biblical Studies
Gross, Lou Anne DeWitt
5th Grade Teacher
Hare, Roberta M.
Social Studies Teacher
Haren, Thomas Edward
Biology Teacher & Coach
Harsh, Jeffrey Gilbert
5th Grade Teacher
Hart, Lisa Schenck
German & Reading Teacher
Holloway, Lewistine Conn
5th Grade Teacher
Johnson, Cynthia Brady
Science Teacher
Johnson, Russell A.
8th Grd Tchr & Guidance Cnslr
Jones, Donald Leonard, Jr.
Health Education Specialist
Kieffer, Dahlia Kay
Cosmetology Teacher
Leedy, Joyce Strimel
Reading Teacher
Le Pore, Mary Lucille
Primary Teacher
Long, Dolores Grayson
Retired 2nd Grade Teacher
Madden, Grace Wilson
5th Grd Lang & Soc Stud Tchr
Manard, Belinda Mc Ginnis
Language Art Curriculum Spclst
Mancini, Richard Guy
5th Grade Teacher
Marchbank, Tammy Jo
Teacher of Multihandicapped
Meunier, Carol Ann
8th Grd Math & Alegebra Tchr
Milano, Stephen Paul
Health & Physical Ed Tchr
Miller, Douglas
Health & PE Teacher
Miller, Robert Lee
Fifth Grade Teacher
Miller, Timothy I.
Retired MS & HS Teacher
Moser, Barbara Anne
French Teacher
Moser, Michael L.
Mathematics Teacher
Moss, Armentha Darleen
French Teacher
Novak, Robert James
Fourth Grade Teacher
Pappas, Susan Chirumbolo
5th Grade Teacher
Perkins, Teresa
Math Teacher
Rasile, Michael L.
Assistant Spanish Professor
Reed, Kyle Robert
Language Arts Teacher
Sammet, Claudia Corbit
English Teacher
Samoila, Frances Evelyn
Vocal Music Instructor
Scott, Phyllis Diane (Harvey)
Social Studies Teacher
Spurgeon, Larry D.
9th-12th Grd Art Instructor
Tewanger, Bonnie Lou
Third Grade Teacher
Tisci, Marilyn Ann (Stratton)
Sixth Grade Mathematics Tchr
Trbovich, Donna Sergi
Reading Teacher
Vinci, Julia Ann
Lang Arts & Soc Studies Tchr
Vitullo, Janice Marie
High School Latin Teacher
Wageley, William Harold
8th Grd Amer History Teacher
Wagner, Cynthia (Andaloro)
Fifth Grade Teacher
Wallace, Eleanore Gawlak
Retired 2nd Grade Teacher
Wilson, Thomas Lee
Sr High School Guidance Cnslr
CARDINGTON
Keil, Judith Simpson
Second Grade Teacher
Studer, Melanie West
Work & Family Life Teacher
Thompson, Vicky Southcott
8th-12th Grade French Teacher
Tocheff, Janet Poole
High School Social Stud Tchr
CAREY
Kitzler, Melinda Myers
Kindergarten & Reading Teacher
Lease, Kristine Renea Lewis
Mathematics Teacher
Mumma, Judith E.
Special Education Teacher
CARLISLE
Catron, Vickie Claude
HS Spanish I, II, III Teacher
Helsinger, James David
American History Teacher
CARROLL
Dosch, Gregory Martin
Soc Stud Tchr & Dept Chm
Freeman, Cynthia Ann
Fifth Grade Teacher
Hodge, Janice Kay
Occupational Work Coordinator

Loy, Susan Sinclair
Teacher of Gifted & Language
Norris, Parry L.
Fifth Grade Teacher
CARROLLTON
Clark, Brian S.
Humanities & US History Instr
Conley, Maria Jo (Rose)
Mathematics Teacher
Dye, Pamela Frampton
Elementary Classroom Teacher
Emerick, Karen Sue (Crawford)
Gifted & English Teacher
Furey, Florence L.
Govt Ec & Humanitites Teacher
Scarlott, Charlotte Lee Custer
7th-8th Grd Literature Teacher
Shanks, Marilyne E.
Chemistry Tchr & Sci Coord
CASSTOWN
Brown, Donna Teresa
Sixth Grade Teacher
Klepinger, William R.
Agriculture Education Teacher
CASTALIA
Drumm, Timothy S.
Business Teacher
Edwards, James A.
Social Studies Teacher
Mc Coy, Lynn Marie
Choir Director
Nestra, John E.
Teacher
Pitts, Beth Nell
Kindergarten Teacher
Schoenegge, Paul William
HS Spanish Teacher
Yantz, Michael James
Jr High Special Education Tchr
CEDARVILLE
Barber, Frances Noel
English Dept Chprsn & Tchr
Drullinger, David Wayne
Assoc Prof of Biblical Educ
Fawcett, Cheryl Lynn
Asst Prof of Chrstn Ed
Phipps, Terry Lee
Professor of Zoology
Sellers, James Allen
Mathematics Professor
CELINA
DeBrosse, Martha Helen, CPPS
Retired Teacher
Franzer, Patricia Rose (Severt)
Algebra & General Math Tchr
Grace, C. Dwane
Curriculum Director
Guingrich, Mary Ann (Wannemacher)
4th Grade Teacher
Hilty, Ann Estelle
Family & Consumer Sci Tchr
Kennedy, Timothy Murlin
Advanced Biology Teacher
Loughrige, Robert Ashley
Music Dept Chairman
Mader, Douglas Paul
Mathematics Teacher
Otten, Daniel J.
Dev Handicapped Coach
Scott, Calvin Lloyd, Jr.
Social Studies Teacher
Tobe, Margaret K. Zehringer
German Teacher & Dept Head
Weidman, Ruth Hainline
Retired First Grade Teacher
Whited, Darlene May (Simmons)
First Grade Teacher
CENTERBURG
Maurer, Cindy Davenport
First Grade Teacher
CHAGRIN FALLS
Allen, William J.
English Instructor
Biederman, Marianne Miller
Fifth Grade Teacher
Hosmer, Patricia Crain
Retired Third Grade Teacher
Hunter, Nathan Andrew
Youth Pastor
Mc Natt, Jody Lynn
English & Drama Teacher
Ray, Troy R.
High School English Teacher
Thombs, Todd Wesley
Eighth Grade Mathematics Tchr
Zeigler, Pamela Sohm
Biology Teacher
CHARDON
Carino, Donna Marie Ritter
5th Grade Teacher
Chadowski, Therese C.
Guidance Counselor
Horvath, Madelon Toft
English & Drama Teacher
Inderlied, Barbara Drinkwater
Title I Teacher
Jeric, Rick Henry
Campus Minister
Jurjans, Baiba Anna (Dabols)
First Grade Teacher
Kinser, Ann Yelverton
Language Arts & Reading Tchr
Miller, Patricia Field
English & Reading Teacher
Mills, William Andrew
7th-8th Grade Math Teacher
O'Malley, Catherine B.
Health & Religion Teacher
Stone, Annette Grodecki
Music Teacher

Winkler, Janet L.
Spanish Teacher
CHATFIELD
Omwake, Jane Ellen
First Grade Teacher
CHESAPEAKE
Brown, Ken David
Special Education Teacher
Callicoat, David Lyle
Science Department Chm & Tchr
Hardy, Fred E.
Science Teacher & Dept Head
Harris, Pamela Slaughter
Health & Physical Ed Teacher
Johnson, Tommie Templeton
High School Counselor
Kendrick, Raymond H.
Diesel Instructor
Lafon, Mark Allen
Social Science Teacher
Lang, Sharon Smith
Fourth Grade Teacher
Lemke, Sandra Costanza
K-4th Grade Music Teacher
Mayo, James Brent
Mathematics Teacher
Miller, Larry Kent
Instrumental Music Teacher
Miller, Terry Burns
Music Teacher & Choir Director
Morgan, Larry L.
Bus Ed & Cmptr Sci Instructor
Payne, Rebecca Phillips
English Speech & Drama Teacher
Pemberton, Lawrence, Jr.
Sixth Grade Math & Rdng Tchr
Rice, Charles Kevin
7th Grade Science Teacher
Sexton, Colleen Linda Moore
Jr & Sr Coll Prep Eng Teacher
Sheets, Stephen Lee
Social Studies Dept Chm & Tchr
Stollings, Leslie L.
English & Home Ec Teacher
Tillis, Beverly Barnett
Third Grade Teacher
CHESHIRE
Bahr, William Roger
Science Teacher
Bradbury, Connie Stidham
Home Economics Teacher
Mays, Pat L.
French Teacher
Moore, David Allen
Social Studies Teacher
Oiler, James William
Science Teacher
Petrie-Forgey, Sandra C.
Science Dept Head & Math Tchr
Smith, Ernestine
Teacher
CHESTERLAND
Benson, Jean Gartner
Retired Elementary Teacher
Henck, Joan E.
5th Grade Teacher
Hoffman, Elfriede Schanz
Mathematics Teacher
Houser, Jo Ann H.
English & Writing Teacher
Kirschner, Carol Merriman
7th & 8th Grade Teacher
Knuth, Diana G.
French Teacher
Mc Carthy, Michael James
High School Science Teacher
Rothlisberger, Pamela Berry
7th-8th Grd Life Skills Tchr
Schutz, Donald E.
Occupational Work Exp Coord
CHESTERVILLE
Ballard, Connie Spencer
Fourth Grade Teacher
CHILLICOTHE
Ater, Terry D.
Language Arts Teacher
Bastin, Dan Edmund
Visiting Tchr & Social Worker
Blesedell, Patricia Ross
First Grade Teacher
Brady, Barbara
Remedial Reading Teacher
Buskirk, Lorna (Cockrell)
First Grade Teacher
Christman, Sandra K.
Spanish Teacher
Comer, Cora Ann
K-1 Multi Age Teacher
Corker, Martha Stack
Third Grade Teacher
Curtis, Timothy J.
Physics & Chemistry Teacher
DeBord, Timothy A.
English & Speech Teacher
DeBord, Tina Elliott
Business Teacher
Ely, Ted C.
High School Principal
Gahm, Connie S. (Jackson)
Kindergarten Teacher
Greene, Judy
English Teacher
Harrison, Leda Hammond
Language Arts Teacher
Hill, Suzanna Leilani
Physical Education Teacher
Hixon, James Thomas
Retired Business Ed Teacher
Hoops, Judith Kay
English Teacher & Dept Head

CHILLICOTHE (cont)
Jamison, Connie Elaine
Vocal Music Teacher
Jones, Beth Chris
English Teacher
Jones, Susan Elaine
Middle School Health Teacher
Litter, Kimberly Riley
Clerical Services Instructor
Parsons, Madelyn Mattingly
Retired 1st Grade Teacher
Payne, Kathy Louise (Litter)
Reading & Language Arts Tchr
Pollock, Patricia Wolski
High School Teacher
Powell, Jolene D.
Biology Teacher
Sherman, Richard David
Instrumental Music Teacher
Stanton, Grace S.
Learning Disabilities Teacher
Stevens, Dave
Social Studies Teacher
Swan, Steven R.
Social Studies Teacher
Weaver, Muriel Mc Kibben
Instrumental Music Teacher
Woods, Tony
Earth Science Teacher
CINCINNATI
Adkins, Anzora
Sixth Grade Teacher
Al-Ubaidi, Muthar Radif
Energy Professor
Amato, Barbara Jones Brough
Senior English Teacher
Anderson, Sheila Jefferson
Business Data Processing Tchr
Avington, Carla Michelle
Biology Teacher
Backherms, Kathryn Anne
Music Director
Barger, Kathy Hall
Art Instr & Computer Liasion
Basler, Patricia Bruning
Social Studies Teacher
Bauer, Susan Eckart
Vocal Music Director
Bayliss, James Leroy
Social Studies Teacher
Behnken, Diane Eaton
English, Jrnlsm & Typing Tchr
Bell, David M.
Head Choral Director
Bell, Mary Frances
Fifth Grade Teacher
Berno, Catherine A.
Elementary Montessori Teacher
Berno, John P.
Elementary Montessori Teacher
Besse, Gerald A.
Soc Studies Teacher & Director
Bessler, Catherine Lynn
French & English Teacher
Bessler, Timothy Jospeh
English Teacher
Blakely, Kay Lacey
Kindergarten Teacher
Borman, Barry J.
Biology Teacher & Athletic Dir
Bossard, Crystal Calbert
Professor of Humanities Dept
Bowers, Mark Thomas
Assoc Prof of Civil Engrng
Bowling, Shannon Maureen
PE Teacher & Athletic Trainer
Brauer, Shelly Maffey
Art Department Chair
Braun, Dana Candace Ostholthoff
5th & 6th Grade Math Teacher
Breiman, Robyn Hope
Director
Brewer, Marilyn Sue
Spanish Teacher
Bright, Karen B.
4th Grade Language Arts Tchr
Brodbeck, Barbara
HS Math Teacher
Broerman, David W.
Physics & Biology Teacher
Brokamp, Lisa Marie
Science Teacher
Brunsman, Patricia Dowling
4th Grade Teacher
Buttelwerth, John W.
Instr of Civil Engrng Tech
Campbell, Sandra Carpenter
Chemistry Teacher
Canty, Charlotte Mary
Third Grade Teacher
Carlton, Margaret Helen
Jr High Language Arts Teacher
Castelino, Amy D'Souza
Sixth Grade Teacher
Christin, Carmela Palazzolo
Third Grade Teacher
Churchill, Susan Schutte
Fourth Grade Teacher
Closs, Janice Holman
9th Grade English Teacher
Clutter, Timothy John
English Teacher
Cohan, Sandra Lee
French Teacher
Cole, Gwendolyn
Ninth Grade English Teacher
Colussi, Donald R.
English Teacher
Combs, Landa Darlene
Home Ec, Fmly & Cnsmr Sci Tchr
Comstock, Walter C.
Biology Teacher
Copens, Carla Sue
Art Teacher
Cornett, Susan Bachus
Sixth Grade Teacher
Cramer, Gayle
Sixth Grade Math Teacher
Cross, Barbara Ann
Mathematics Teacher
Cross, Thomas Michael
Cmptr Assisted Drafting Tchr
Cummings, Janet Arnold
Language Arts Tchr of Gifted
Dasenbrock, Alice Frank
Spanish Teacher
Davidson, Evelyn C.
AP Biology Teacher
Davis, Nanci N.
Fourth Grade Teacher
Day, Michael Paul, Sr.
Mathematics Teacher
Dehnbostel, Nancy L.
4th-5th Grd Gifted Stdnts Tchr
De Jonckheere, Marcel, S.C.
Sixth Grade Teacher
DeMougin, Kathleen S.
Science Teacher
Depoe, Cynthia K.
Mathematics Teacher
Diamond, Mark A.
Ballet Instr & Choreographer
Diehl, Jan A.
Dir of Bands & Gen Music Tchr
DiGiacomo, Donald Scott
Physical Ed & Health Teacher
DiMuzio, Sally Ann (Moser)
Scndry Math Tchr & Dept Chm
Dressman, Joan Arens
Fourth Grade Teacher
Dugan, Timothy Patrick
World History Teacher
Dumas, H. Scott
Mathematics Professor
Dunn, Dwight Anthony
School Counselor
Dunn, Paula Fernandez
Spanish Teacher
Eger, James Lawrence
Mathematics Teacher
Eisenhard, Bruce E.
AP US History & Psych Tchr
Eisenhard, Ronda Grueninger
Guidance Counselor
Emery, Patricia Furlong
Fifth Grade Teacher
Emmich, Linda L.
Mathematics & Literature Tchr
Endris, Anne Beeson
Religious Studies Teacher
Engel, Kimberly S.
Spanish Teacher
English, John N.
HS Spanish Teacher
Ennis, Rosemary Kolks
History Teacher
Erdmann, Tim Alan
Bio & Environmental Sci Tchr
Everett, Minnie Bobbitt
Special Education Tchr & Coord
Faig, Carol Maybriar
Third Grade Teacher
Faris, Kay E.
Elementary Principal
Feghali, Elias
Architecture & Math Instructor
Ferris, Kenneth James
English Teacher
Fettner, Ellen Ruth
Former Ethnic Studies Tchr
Fitzsimmons, Verna M.
Research Assistant
Fluharty, Kay A.
Latin Teacher
Fogelson, Nancy J.
History Teacher
Ford, Grable Medina
English Teacher & Dept Chair
Foreman, Robert B.
Chemistry Teacher
Frey, Shirley N.
Chemistry Teacher
Frieman, Lauren Jill
9th-12th Grd Soc Stud Teacher
Friskney, Thomas E.
Prof of Greek & New Testament
Fuqua, Leniese Marie
4th Grd Self-Contained Teacher
Gardner, John Thomas
Percussion Instructor
Gardner, Lynn Ellen
Special Education Teacher
Gartner, Linda F.
Vocal Music Director
Gates, Lesli Ferrara
3rd Grade Teacher
Gee, Todd D.
Chemistry Teacher
Geiselman, Kate Bradley
English Teacher
Gentile, Jacque Anderson
Third Grade Teacher
Gibson, Diane Knox
Family & Consumer Science Tchr
Glass, Jennifer McConkey
Biology & Anatomy Teacher
Goble, Kenneth C.
Professor of Counseling
Goldstein, Vicki Lyn
Classroom Teacher
Golubieski, Mary Willard
Art Teacher
Gomez-Cortes Villalo, Maria Elena
High School Spanish Teacher
Gorey, Robert
Upper School Science Educator
Gray, Patricia Hooks
6th Grd Rdng & Soc Stud Tchr
Green, Gwendolyn Gray
Family & Consumer Sci Teacher
Green, Sharon
Sixth Grade Teacher
Gregg, Katie O'Connell
Language Arts & Religion Tchr
Gregory, Gary J.
Professor of Church Music
Groshoff, Jan K.
High School Counselor
Grunder, Scott Kenral
History Teacher
Gulino, Rosanne M.
Latin Teacher
Gutzwiller, Deborah S.
Marketing Education Coord
Haas, Al John
Business Teacher
Hafner, Bernadine Schafner
Eighth Grade Teacher
Hague, Richard
Eng Dept Chair & Writing Coord
Halloran, Vincent E.
Principal
Halsall, Mary Katarski
Science Teacher
Hanson, Jay Roger
Soc Studies Curriculum Coord
Hardesty, Joseph Robert
Business & Accounting Teacher
Hardtke, Karen Sue Peet
Mathematics Teacher
Harmeling, Gail A.
Mathematics Teacher
Harper, Edith Baer
Retired 6th Grade Teacher
Harris, Victor Leon, Jr.
Social Studies Teacher
Hart, Marla Kay
Pre-K Teacher
Hatfield, Danny L.
Sixth Grade Teacher
Haucke-Davis, Mary Helen
French Teacher
Hausman, Mary Lou Grimshaw
Eighth Grade Teacher
Haworth, Sherry Humphreys
Substitute Teacher
Haynes, Richard G.
Social Studies Teacher
Heidkamp, Teresa A. Schuermann
Elementary Position Educator
Heilmann, Diane Maureen
Mathematics Teacher
Heizman, Mike W.
7th & 8th Grade Math Teacher
Hekler, Barbara Ahlers
High School Math Teacher
Helbling, Stephen Joseph
Chemistry Teacher
Hendrick, Paul M.
English Teacher
Herring, Marilyn Parks
English IV Teacher
Hill, June Logan
Vocal & General Music Teacher
Hiller, Nancy Elberg
Retired Teacher of GATE
Hillman, Elizabeth Trent
Tchr of Acad Prgm for Talented
Hoar, Patricia Ann
English Teacher
Hodgson, Matthew
English Teacher
Holly, Kathy P.
Health Teacher
Holthouse, Jeanine Marie
Mathematics Dept Chairperson
Homan, Cindy Renee
4th Grade Teacher
Hout, Grant D.
High School French Instructor
Howell, Michele Charna
Family & Consumer Science Tchr
Hubley, Melody A.
Biology Teacher
Hurd, Patricia Mondrut
English & Speech Teacher
Hurley, Sue A. Bogenschutz
Junior High Teacher
Huseman, Brian Edward
PE & Health Teacher
Hussel, Dave W.
PE Tchr & Athletic Director
Iles, Mark Andrew
American His & Govt Teacher
Isaly, Fran Hedgpeth
Second Grade Teacher
Jaeger, Janet Lynn
Varsity Volleyball Coach
Jameson, Amy R.
Physics Teacher
Jasper, Minnie R.
Eng as a Second Lang Teacher
Johnson, Helen Goble
Third Grade Teacher
Johnson, Mary Jo Payne
English Teacher
Jones, Judy Miller
Math Tutor
Jones, Lynn A.
6th Grade Teacher
Jones, Nancy Justin
Teacher
Kearns, Robert Dean, Jr.
Phys Ed & Drafting Instructor
Kelemen, Elizabeth, CDP
7th & 8th Grade Teacher
Kelly, Anna M.
Sixth Grade Teacher
Kelsch, Robert H.
Latin Teacher
Kennedy, Gerald Joseph
History Teacher
Kesler, Edward
Elem Schl Principal
Kessinger, Thomas Anthony
Social Studies Teacher
Keuper, Cindy Archer
MS Language Arts Teacher
Kidwell, Rollin Jay
Psychology Professor
Kilgore, Jenny Shafer
English Teacher
King, Leanne Catherine
Science Teacher
Kinney, Beverly Seeman
Teacher of the Gifted
Klotz, Robert Patrick
Social Studies Teacher
Krix, Barbel
German & Russian Teacher
Kroner, Louis Richard
Teacher of Gifted & Talented
Krueger, Daniel W.
Vocal Director
Krueger, Margaret Wolf
Elementary Music Teacher
Kuranga, Abraham Akanbi
History Professor
Lafkas, Karen Skinner
HS Mathematics Teacher
Lakes-Fales, Marta
Voc Coord & Soc Stud Teacher
Lammers, Holly Biermann
Business Vocational Ed Teacher
Lammert, Penny J.
Physics Teacher
Lampe, Ann L. Flick
Chemistry Teacher
Lamping, Gregory L.
Spanish Teacher
Layne, Ellen Rose
Program Facilitator & Teacher
Lewis, Joan Carol
Chemistry Teacher
Lilly, Laura Peebles
Sixth Grade Teacher
Lindenmaier, Rachel Mary
Asst Mgr of Tele-Ministry Dept
Lipps, Raymond
Mathematics Teacher
Lisi, Richard Roland
Electronics Teacher
Loechle, Susan D.
English Teacher
Lones, Steve Alan
Physical Education Teacher
Lovelace, Juanita Faye (Murray)
LPC High School Counselor
Luehrmann, Rosa Patricia (Larrea-Perez)
Spanish Teacher
Maginn, John Patrick
Mathematics Teacher
Maher, Margaret K.
Life Science Teacher
Marchal, Michael Hubert
English Teacher
Marketos, George B.
Mathematics Professor
Marlow, Georgette Freeman
English Teacher
Maroon, David James
Band Director
May, Marnie Roether
English Teacher
Mc Collom, Burton L.
Lang Arts Tchr & Theatre Dir
Mc Cosham, Joyce L.
Counselor
Mc Coy, Ella Marie
Seventh Grade Social Stud Tchr
Mc Cullough, Mary Jo Meyer
Former 4th Grade Teacher
McHugh, Kevin Clader
English Teacher & Dept Chprsn
McLaughlin, Paul Francis
Principal
Mechley, Donna Kathman
Algebra & Geometry Teacher
Meiering, Judith Ann
Social Studies Dept Chprsn
Meinking, Terry
Athletic & Facilities Director
Merritt, Jodi Ann
Montessori Teacher
Metz, Elizabeth Ann
Third Grade Teacher
Metz, Kenneth Alan
Associate Professor of Physics
Meyer, John Robert
For Lang Chair & Span Instr
Meyer, Michelle Monica Monnin
Admission Counselor
Miller, Brian Douglas
Biology Teacher
Miller, Gretchen Maria
Math Teacher & Computer Coord
Minton, Michael Vernon
Sixth Grade Teacher
Montgomery, Patrick Lawrence
Science & PE Teacher
Mooney, D. Michael
English Teacher
Moore, Barbara Harmony
Retired Elementary Teacher
Moore, Bernice Ghee
US History Teacher
Moors-Dressing, Mary Ellen
English Teacher
Morehouse, Terry
English Composition Teacher
Morganroth, Patricia A.
Nursing Instructor
Moses, Carol Topicz
Sixth Grade Teacher
Muenchen, G. Joe
Individual Instr & Pgm Coord
Murdock, Wanda Brooks
Home Ec & Consumer Sci Tchr
Murph, Margaret Shelton
Fifth Grade Teacher
Murphy, Pamela Northcutt
High School English Teacher
Nakoff, Michael H.
Prof of Business Computer Sci
Nerl, Thomas G.
Assistant Prin & Alegbra Tchr
Nichols, Lois A.
Teacher of the Gifted Ed
North, James B.
Professor of Church History
Obasogie, Faithe Trent
Lead Teacher
O'Connor, Irene
5th Grade Teacher
Outt, Daina Ashley
Mathematics Teacher
Owens, Michael Robert
English & Latin Teacher
Parts, Catherine Marie
English Teacher
Patterson, Robert Sloane
English Teacher
Pelzel, Michael J.
Fourth Grade Teacher
Perry, Monzell
Math Teacher
Pharo, James William
Social Stud Tchr & Dept Chm
Phillips, Teri Lee
Eng Teacher & Dept Chair
Piazza, Shirley E.
Professor & Advisor
Pitts, Marjorie B.
Business Education Teacher
Powers, Walter Kenneth
US History & Civics Teacher
Pressley, Johnny Gordon
Professor of Theology & Ethics
Proctor, Jacqueline Brock
English Teacher
Rahnfeld, Vincent D.
Instrumental Music Director
Ramsey, David Craig
Graphic Arts & Phtgrphy Tchr
Ray, Jennifer Lee (Ulrey)
English Teacher
Razor, Sharon L.
English Teacher
Reger, Stephen Anthony
Social Studies Teacher
Reichle, Philip
Admissions Dir & Religion Tchr
Reyes, Gloria Desiree
Retired Teacher
Rheinecker, Thomas C.
Physics & Chemistry Teacher
Rich, Carole Wells
6th Grade Homeroom Teacher
Richardson, David L.
Eighth Grade Lang Arts Teacher
Riehle, Barry Steven
Physics Teacher
Ries, Rick Stephen
Fifth Grade Teacher
Rieselman, Paul Joseph
Religious Stud & Spanish Tchr
Roebel, Tom John
Health Teacher
Ross, Joan Heitz
Sci & Social Studies Teacher
Ross, Mary Jo
Fourth Grade Teacher
Russo, Lisa A.
9th-12th Grade English Teacher
Ryberg, Margene Roberta
Mathematics Teacher
Salerno, Adele Gombita
Science Dept Chair & Teacher
Salvato, Vincent
Social Studies Teacher
Samuels, Patricia Lynn
Cooperative Bus Ed Tchr, Coord
Sauer, Johnothon A.
Math Teacher
Scarbrough, Philip E.
Social Studies Teacher
Schaeffer, Teresa Joan
Spanish Teacher
Schiering, Jerald
Bus Teacher & Activities Coord
Schneider, Ferd Michael
Math Teacher
Schneider, James William
Social Studies Teacher
Schneider, SC, Mary Dolores
Latin & World Cultures Teacher
Schrenker, Richard Robert, Jr.
Principal
Schumacher, Christopher Clinton
Mathematics Teacher

NATI (cont)
, Mary Ling
ade Language Arts Tchr
eborah Howard (Bell)
rade Teacher
ancy Strikman
Teacher & Dept Chprsn
eonard Dean
e Teacher
Jennifer
Grade Math Teacher
s, John Audren
Tchr & Theatre Dir
Colleen Jones
Education Teacher
Mary F. (Reddy)
h Teacher
aula Sanford
acher
Denise Lynn
& Physical Ed Teacher
Joyce Ann
Grade Teacher
, Shelia Yvonne
rade Teacher
Karen H.
y Teacher
iana (Dickerson)
n & Reading Teacher
, Ronald R.
on Teacher
k, Rita Patrice
ade Language Arts Tchr
son, Mary Bradley
& Health Teacher
Douglas M.
unication Arts Teacher
Nancy Ellen
Grade Teacher
, Rebecca Ellen
stry Teacher
an, Elizabeth Zink
h Teacher
eh, George G.
sor
, Eileen Mary
rade Teacher
, James F.
sor of Physics
burg, James Kent
Studies Teacher
, Cheryl Ann
Grade Math & Sci Tchr
Ann Manuel
sor & Academic Advisor
on, John R.
Teacher
on, Mark Andrew
Grd PE Teacher
rry, Vicki Lynn
th Grd English Teacher
ary Lou P.
& Classics Teacher
Linda L.
Reading Teacher & Tutor
, Arleene M.
ade Teacher
eier, Christina Maria
Grade Teacher
Suellen Samples
h Teacher
, Milton Joe
Studies Teacher
Michael Vincent
s Teacher
ein, Sam Anthony
ade Math Teacher
harles Jeffrey
Govt & Economics Teacher
Patricia
story Teacher
lizabeth Lowe
ade Teacher
onald F.
e Teacher
Lindy Kay
ade Teacher
ly, Jon Allen
sor of Biblical Studies
Natalie Board
sh Teacher
Matthew Karl
on Teacher
r, Marilyn Mussman
er
n, Jennifer Lynn
ns Furniture Company Mgr
nn, Claudia Tredway
h Teacher
Nan E.
Studies Teacher
onstance Scoles
Education Teacher
er, Cyril W.
& Theology Teacher
Mary Benita Hageman
Teacher
ver, Frederick Paul
2th Grade Math Teacher
s, Myron David
mic Dean & Chrstn Ed Prof
s, Robert B. R.
sh & Social Studies Tchr
s, William H. A.
sor & Advisor
Bonnie A.
Tchr & Department Chair
asahn-Savage, Susan Mary
istry Teacher

Woodring, Dean
English Teacher
Wooten, Terry Sims
Special Education Teacher
Wymer, Elizabeth Fessemeyer
9th-12th Grade Teacher
Yonka, Joyce Baum
English Teacher
Zachary, Clarie Deal
High School Theatre Tchr & Dir
Zappa, Paul Joseph
Music Teacher
Zumbiel, Barbara Rehm
Guidance Counselor

CIRCLEVILLE
Conrad, Millie L.
Math Teacher
Frost, William J.
Athletic Dir & Schl Counselor
Klein, Pamela Jean
8th Grade Science Teacher
Maite, Jennifer Evans
Mathematics Teacher
Metzger, Stephanie Neff
Special Services Coordinator
Moyer, Bruce Eugene
Professor of Bible & Theology
Penn, Deborah
Assistant Professor
Saxton, Jon C.
10th Grd World History Tchr
Smith, Rodney Ray
American History Teacher

CLARKSBURG
Earich, Kristen L.
Fourth Grade Teacher
Hill, Connie D.
Fourth Grade Teacher

CLARKSVILLE
Bradshaw, Bunny Peterson
Third Grade Teacher
Moon, Bonnie Young
First Grade Teacher
Trampler, Nancy Peters
5th Grade Math & Science Tchr

CLAYTON
Beach, Alan Robert
High School Counselor
Downey, Susan Marie Wolbert
Career Development Secretary
Fraley, Marian Scarazzo
Employability Instructor
Hauschild, Patricia Snyder
Mathematics Teacher
Haws, Kelly L.
Business Education Teacher
Heinrichs, Stephen Conrad
Physical Education Teacher
Hoffman, Terry L.
Business Teacher
Long, James DeWitt
German Teacher
Parks, Terry V.
Communications & English Tchr
Sharp, Kimberlee Anne
American History Teacher
Skaroupka, Norman J.
Art Tchr & Fine Arts Dept Chm

CLEVELAND
Abernathy, Regina Ann
High School English Teacher
Akos, Dennis J.
Mathematics Teacher
Alexander, David John
Physical Ed Tchr & Asst Prin
Ali, Gail Louise (Mack)
Fifth Grade Teacher
Alicea, Gloria
Biology Teacher
Allen, Frank
Social Studies Teacher
Anderson, Larry
English Teacher
Anderson, Marcia Elaine
10th Grade Biology Teacher
Anderson, Sidney Edward
Special Education Teacher
Antwine, Stella Louise
Fifth Grade Teacher
Apana, James Leslie
English Department Chairman
Arancibia, Sandra L. S.
Spanish Teacher
Ashford, Stephanie Grair
English Teacher
August, Marilyn Burke
Third Grade Teacher
Aukerman, Marie Terlizzi
Second Grade Teacher
Austin, Felicia Williamson
Vocational Teacher
Baker, Barbara Jean (Staples)
Art Teacher
Baker, Lisa S.
Spanish Teacher
Barrick, Michael Patrick
Physics Tchr & Sci Dept Head
Bartolucci, Jean Soppelsa
Social Studies Teacher
Bates, Suzanne
Voc Consumer Homemaking Tchr
Bauer-Blazer, Karen A.
Social Studies Dept Chair
Bell, Michael Shane
8th Grade Reading Teacher
Benander, Vince A.
Math Instructor
Benedict, James A.
Social Studies Teacher

Bennett, Dorothy M. Hovorka
History Teacher
Blatnica, Dorothy Ann, VSC
Religious Studies Professor
Blum, Judith Opper
Tchr of Learning Disabilities
Boehnlein, Carolyn Joyce (Bolek)
Jr High Math Teacher
Bokausek, Frank Robert
Spanish & US History Teacher
Bonezzi, Nina Alice
Social Studies Teacher
Border, Constance Corssar
French Teacher
Borovac, Daniel Michael
Math & Soc Stud Teacher
Boyle, Barbara Eileen
History Teacher
Brazil, Era Buchanan
English Language Dev Teacher
Brenkus, Marilyn Runo
Music Teacher
Brudy, Roselyn Jenita
6th Grade Teacher
Buchko, John
Economics Teacher
Buckley, Denise
K-8th Grade Art Teacher
Buettner, Paul Elmer
Math Teacher
Burkitt, Jeff F.
Amer His & Urban Stud Tchr
Bursi, Marianne Mc Murrin
Academic Resource Specialist
Busch, Ronald J.
Professor of Political Science
Calco, Doreen R.
English Teacher
Cambareri, Margaret Stebelski
3rd-6th Grd GATE Program Tchr
Cargile, Rosie Smith
Mathematics Teacher
Carlson, Dee Ann
Vocal Music Teacher
Carney, Mary Tupta
7th Grade Teacher
Carroll, Mary Anne Kenney
Fifth Grade Teacher
Cassidy, Deborah K.
Social Studies Teacher
Chapman, Deborah L.
Guidance Counselor
Clark, Karen Hallam
Spanish Teacher
Clark, Linda Darus
7th & 8th Grd Soc Stud Tchr
Clarke, Darlene Ann
Nursing Instructor
Claytor, Wanda Jeanne
Resource Teacher
Cleggett, Lily Thomas
Fifth Grade Teacher
Clemson, Candy
Art, Gifted Ed & Hum Teacher
Coate, Charlene Dinardo
Fifth Grade Teacher
Collier, Cynthia Ann
Social Studies Teacher
Comer, Jerry Byron
Science Teacher
Connolly, Thadda Delia
8th Grade English Teacher
Cook, David A.
HS History & Bible Teacher
Cosner, Janet Ehlert
English Teacher
Culp, Madelyn Moore
5th Grade Teacher
Dare, John S.
History Teacher
Davies, Trevor Weldon
Biology Teacher
Davis, Shirley Rae (Sims)
Vocational Business Ed Tchr
Davis, Z. Harold, Jr.
French & Spanish Teacher
Dayton, Charlene Fairchild
Secondary English Teacher
DeGennaro, Alfred Joseph
Math & Computer Science Tchr
Delisle, Deborah Smith
Language Arts Specialist
Deszo, Carmen Lind
Medical Lab Assisting Teacher
Dickson, Dorothy Louise Rice
Third Grade Teacher
Didion, Susan Ann
Sixth Grade Teacher
DiGeronimo, Richard Anthony
Algebra Teacher
Disantis, Paul Anthony
Science Department Chairman
Dooner, Vincetta DiRocco
Second Grade Teacher
Douglass, Jacqueline Stratford
Third Grade Teacher
Dowdell, Timothy Michael
Math Department Chairman
Dunn, Cathy Martine
Math Teacher
Ehrbar, Joe Vincent
Social Studies Teacher
Ertle, Karl Joseph
Theology Teacher
Evans, Mary K.
Med & Biological Thematic Tchr
Ewings Travis, Willie Mae
Science Teacher
Favazzo, Dominic Michael
Chemistry Teacher

Fetko, Sally Duckwall
History Teacher
Fitzhugh, Shari Rondo
Home Economics Teacher
Forhan, Jeanna Kathleen
Administrator
Fredrick, Mark
English Dept Chprsn & Tchr
Fuchs, Hildegard Mary
English Teacher
Funtek, Karen Ann
Sixth Grade Teacher
Gabel, Patricia Rielinger
6th-8th Grade Teacher
Gannon, Barbara Bendler
Second Grade Teacher
Gentile, Patricia
Junior High Teacher
Gibbons, Margaret Ann O'Malley
Second Grade Teacher
Goosman, Charles William
Diesel & Auto Teacher
Greppin, Mary Hannan
4th-5th Grade Directress
Guiao, Raymond Paul
English Teacher
Hagen, Richard Carl
9th-12th Grade Math Teacher
Hansen, Robert Edwin, Jr.
8th Grade English Teacher
Hanson, Connie B.
8th Grade Science Teacher
Harland, Madelyn Shaffer
Second Grade Teacher
Harp, Marilyn Bryant
Honors English Teacher
Hatcher, Rayfield
Computer Sci & Math Teacher
Hefter, Lillain
3rd Grade Teacher
Heipp, Raymond Thomas
Cura Personalis Director
Herbenick, Agnes
Eighth Grade Teacher
Hill, Mark David
HS Social Studies Teacher
Hoffman, Rose Mary
Instr of Devlpmntl Handicapped
Houser, Lillian Drag
Science Teacher
Howell, Thomas C.
Mathematics Teacher
Hulin, Paul
Occptnl Work Adjustment Tchr
Hunter, Mary Williams
Medical Office Asst Teacher
Innocenzi, Darryl A.
Associate Principal
Jerdon, William H.
Photography Teacher
Jira, Rose Mari Chinigo
6th Grade Teacher
Joeright, Diane Budan
7th-8th Grade English Teacher
Jordan, Patrick Joseph
Social Studies Teacher
Jordan, Terry Lynn
A P American History Teacher
Kelly, Ann
Philosophy Professor
Kerschbaum, James
Chemistry Teacher
Kester, Linda J.
Kindergarten Teacher
Key, Helen Elaine
Assistant Principal
Kilbane, Mary Jane Manak
5th Grade Teacher
Kirk-Hull, Terri
English & Reading Teacher
Kirsch, Mary Louise
5th Grade Teacher
Knittel, Gregory J.
Latin, Greek & English Teacher
Koehl, Ruth Ann
HS Chem & Earth Science Tchr
Komar, Jonathan Daniel
Science Teacher
Konchan, Kenneth J.
History & Humanities Tchr
Kopp, Carol Allberg
English Teacher
Kovach, Gary
Social Studies Teacher
Krakowski, Richard A.
Math & Computer Teacher
Kriska, Cynthia Louise (Seskes)
English Teacher
Kunikis, Michael Anthony
Social Stud Tchr & Dept Chair
Kupchik, Marion E.
English Teacher
Laplanche, Jean-David
French Teacher
Laubaugh, Bonnie Kay
Math Teacher
Lawrence, Shawn Daniel
English Teacher
Leary, Mary Deborah Oldman
Spanish & Reading Teacher
Leek, Natalie Ann
Admns & Pub Relations Director
Le Hir, Marie-Pierre
French Professor
LePelley, Terese Lhota
Fourth Grade Teacher
Levkanich, Cyril
Reading Teacher
Lipinski, John Joseph
Junior High School Teacher

Lofton, Samuel C., Jr.
Dept Chair & Soc Stud Tchr
Long, Kenwyn Judith
Research Physicist
Lopez, Elba I.
Bilingual Spec Ed Teacher
Lubinger, Joseph David
American History Teacher
Lucht, Sonita Teise
Mathematics Teacher
MacDowell, James Wilbert
Building Construction Teacher
MacKain, Cheryl Lynn
English Teacher
Mahon, Colleen Cochrane
Chairperson & Tchr of Classics
Makee, Linda Meredith
French Teacher
Malone, Patricia Bulicek
Reading Recovery Teacher
Manningham, Cheryl A.
International Studies Teacher
Markle, David E.
High School Vocal Music Dir
Marr, William Mitchell
Fifth Grade Teacher
Martins, Paul William
Social Studies Dept Chairman
Mathews, Georgeanne
English Teacher
Mazanec, Polly Himes
Medical & Surgical Nrsng Instr
McCollum, Delores LaRheine
Secondary Social Studies Tchr
Mc Dermott, Michael Stephen
Seventh & Eighth Grade Teacher
McGregor, Pamela Rae (Waltenbaugh)
AP Chemistry Teacher
McLaughlin, Michael Patrick
Theology Teacher
Mennefee, Susan L.
Fifth Grade Teacher
Messerly, John G.
Asst Professor of Philosophy
Michney, Karen M.
Theology Teacher
Mihocik, Nancy Schmidt
French Teacher
Mikes, Lucine
Mathematics & Drafting Teacher
Mills, Fred W.
Social Studies Teacher
Milosevic, Michelle
9th-12th Grd Mathematics Tchr
Moenich, Kenneth Michael
Second Grade Teacher
Moreland, Susan K. (Ramsey)
Choral Music Director
Mortensen, Earl Miller
Chem Dept Chair & Assoc Prof
Muthersbaugh, David Howard
Mathematics Teacher
Nagy, Patricia A.
Fourth Grade Teacher
Neal, Bennie Frank
Reading & Social Studies Tchr
Nelson, Elizabeth
Math Teacher
Nelson, Ronald Harry
Bible & Science Teacher
Nemecek, Anthony Joseph
English, Speech & Debate Tchr
Newton, Juanita Williams
Business Teacher
Niese, Karla Ann
Music Dir & Dept Chm
Noble, Dana L.
English Teacher
Norman, Richard E.
Spanish Teacher
Olsen, Jeanne Brophy
Span Tchr & Frgn Lang Dpt Head
O'Mara, Eva Pozmann
Art Teacher
Overton, Paulette Cullum
Sixth Grade Science Teacher
Overton, Theretha Dariyah
HS Vocal Director
Pacsi, Fran
Computer Education Teacher
Panek, Judy
6th Grade Teacher
Pankiw, Mary
Span Tchr & Frgn Lang Chprsn
Parisi, Lori Ann
Math Teacher
Pastor, Renee S.
Jr High Lang Arts Teacher
Patrick, Thomas Richard
Mathematics Teacher
Paul, John Donald
5th Grade Teacher
Pearce, Mary Nantell
History & Literature Teacher
Peebles, Timothy L.
English & Drama Teacher
Perrigo, Janis Ruth (Houck)
Fourth Grade Teacher
Petkovsek, Sherry J.
4th Grade Teacher
Phillips, Cheryl Kleis
HS Orchestra & Asst Band Dir
Polefko, Carol Walczak
Dir of Religious Education
Poluse, Martin
High School Religion Teacher
Porter, James Earl
Physical Ed & Science Teacher
Prevost, Clarice Jackson
Principal

CLEVELAND (cont)
Primous, Rosa Ann
Third Grade Teacher
Provenzale, Anthony Joseph
7th-8th Grade Science Teacher
Przybojewski, Frank Walter
Principal
Pymn, Marcia Rable
Spanish Teacher
Rabinsky, Leatrice Bergida
English Teacher
Ravanelli, Michael Joseph
English Teacher
Ream, Lawrence Robert
Industrial Technology Teacher
Redfield, Beverly S.
Fifth Grade Teacher
Renstrom, Susan Ward
Music Teacher
Repasy, Paul Allan
Biology Teacher
Reznik, Ralph E.
Math, Reading & Religion Tchr
Roach, Joan Bucscher
Retired 4th Grade Teacher
Robertson, Timothy W.
Academic & Discipline Dean
Rodriguez, Renee Lynn
High School Math Teacher
Rohlik, Margaret Rejdak
AP His, Govt Tchr & Intern Adm
Romeo, William Joseph
English Teacher
Roseberry, Nina Loving
Seventh Grade English Teacher
Rouse, Nancy Lynn (Carnes)
Sixth Grade Teacher
Rudd, Lance Damon
Social Studies Teacher
Rush, Debra Lobaugh
Teacher & Assistant Principal
Russell, Rodney Brooks
French & Spanish Teacher
Russo, Jaquelin F.
Fourth Grade Teacher
Sainato, Diane Marie
Sixth Grade Teacher
Salzgeber, Karen A.
HS Mathematics Teacher
Scaravilli, Gayle L.
Theology Teacher
Scasny, Timothy James
Journalism & Publication Tchr
Schenkelberg, Susan Rogers
High School English Teacher
Scheufler, David Earl
Band Director
Schultz, Donna L.
English Teacher
Schweitzer, John H.
Deputy Principal
Scotton, Mark Allan
Theology Teacher
Seredick, Michael John
Choral Director
Sesso, Carol Ann
Jr HS Teacher
Sheranko, Frank
Gifted Ed Coord & Biology Tchr
Shirey, Connie Mae
English Teacher
Simmons, Bernard Dean
Social Studies Teacher
Simons, Thomas Clay
Elementary Principal
Sinnema, Jeffrey Warren
Industrial Arts Teacher
Slak, Mary Donna
English Teacher
Smith, Brian Thomas
Soc Stud, World His, Geog Tchr
Smith, Deborah Y.
Reading Specialist
Sowers, Amy Rawlins
High School English Teacher
Spagnola, Natalie Joan
Mathematics Teacher
Speed, Carolyn White
English Teacher
Spiegelberg, Kristin Jeanne
Mathematics Teacher
Spinner, Charles Michael
Social Studies Instructor
Sprafka, Maria DiNardo
English & Humanities Teacher
Stovall, Sherry Ingram
5th Grade Teacher
Svoboda, William Joesph
Computer & Business Chprsn
Sweeney, Mary Sheila
Dept Chair & Teacher
Sylak, Robert Stanley
Science Teacher
Taylor, Gretchen Celeste
Teacher & Athletic Director
Teeter, Jeffrey Paul
Science Teacher
Tesluk, Myra
Elementary Principal
Thomas, Catheree Chambers
Communications Skills Teacher
Thomas, William D.
Music Teacher
Tibbitts, Elizabeth Ann-Wirkus
English & French Teacher
Torrelli, Robert Anthony
8th Grade Math Teacher
Tyminski, Linda Glinka
Art Teacher & Dept Head
Van Jura, William J.
US & World History Teacher
Vega, Gladys Torra
Math Teacher & Dept Head
Vinci, Doris Opatrny
Second Grade Teacher
Viola-Barrett, Jennifer Jean
High School Mathematics Tchr
Wallace, James Edward
Math Dept Head & Teacher
Walter, Donna Keith
Fifth Grade Teacher
Wasowski, James Andrew
History Teacher
Watson, Georgetta Ann
Third Grade Teacher
Weber, Kimberly Cochran
Voc Commercial Art Teacher
Wilson, Dorothy Jean
English & Literature Teacher
Woods, Dennis Theodore
Health & Physical Ed Tchr
Yonosik, Sheryl Tucci
Home Economics Teacher
Zasa, Richard J.
English Department Head
Zayac, Gene
Chemistry Teacher
Zelazny, Michele Ann
High School French Teacher
Zupancic, Keith Ronald
English Teacher
CLEVES
Schmidt, Elizabeth Milne
School Nurse
CLINTON
Skidmore, Helen L.
Retired Elementary Teacher
CLYDE
Evans, Jerry
Social Studies Teacher
Gray, Glenn William
Science Teacher
Kinnear, Sharon Rae
Soc Stud & Rel Tchr
Martin, Michael James
Health & Physical Ed Teacher
Marty, David Lee
Mathematics Teacher
Monaco, Ralphael Christopher
5th Grade Teacher
Sankey, Cathie Green
Elementary Guidance Counselor
COAL GROVE
Lambert, Janet Phillips
Retired 4th Grade Teacher
Morgan, Lydia Margaret
Kindergarten Teacher
COALTON
Bateman, Cynthia Lee
Fourth Grade Science Teacher
Geiger, Peggy Chevalier
4th Grade Language Arts Tchr
COLDWATER
Lee, Larry D.
Social Studies Teacher
Riethman, Dennis Joseph
Agricultural Education Teacher
Virasith, Michele L.
Spanish Teacher
COLLINS
Kastner, Michael Paul
Vocal Music Director
Maire, Frank H.
Fifth Grade Teacher
Toney, Brenda Kay
9th-12th Grd Eng & Speech Tchr
Whanger, Dennis Wyatt
French Teacher & SERC Coord
Wilson, Rodge Floyd
Science Teacher
COLUMBIANA
Cattrell, Kathy Wilson
Biology Teacher
Cooley, Patty Lynn
5th-12th Grade Art Teacher
Mealy, Marsha Hoff
Math Teacher
Natale, Barbara Jones
5th-8th Grade Media Specialist
Olenych, Thomas Steven
Language Arts & Soc Stud Tchr
Patterson, Paula Stanyard
English & Reading Teacher
Thillberg, Charlotte J.
6th Grade Teacher
Tinlin, Shelley Rae
Spanish Teacher
Yoakam, Ronald Allen
Social Studies Teacher
COLUMBUS
Abruzzi, Marlene C.
Lang Arts Tchr
Alexander, Sandra Anderson
5th Grade Teacher
Allen, Rosalie Kay
Music & Drama Director
Alpert, Andrea L.
Specific Lrng Dis Tchr & Tutor
Amos, Ruth Norann Mueller
Grad Instructor
Aquila, Navy V.
Math Teacher
Atlas, Roberta Teal
Art Teacher & Yearbook Advisor
Ayers, Carol Peery
Foreign Language Dept Chair
Back, Yvonne Darst
Volleyball & Basketball Coach
Baker, Frederick Leslie
Legal Studies Dept Chprsn
Beane, Janice M.
Teacher
Beery, Leafee J.
1st Grade Teacher
Benett, Sharon
Instructor of Voice
Binns, Mary Ellen Straub
Home Economics Teacher
Boltz, Elaine Leslie
Health Teacher
Brewster, Ron
US History Teacher
Byrnes, Susan Kathryn
Sixth Grade Teacher
Caslin, Eugene H.
8th Grade US History Teacher
Causey, Marion, Jr.
Assistant Principal
Cave, Timothy J.
European & Global History Tchr
Cheesman, Kerry Lee
Assoc Prof & Chm of Biology
Cohen, Victor S.
Natural Science Professor
Conley, Joseph John
Communications Teacher
Cooley, Shirley Scott
Assistant Professor of Nursing
Corbin, Ivan Jeffrey
Social Studies Teacher
Corn, Alan Mitchell
Latin Teacher
Darling, Stanton Girard, II
Professor of Law
Decatur, Steven Robert
High School Art Teacher
Demos, Brenda Suzanne
Visual Arts Educator
Denton, Sandra Elizabeth
English Instructor
DeWitt, Kathy Stewart
Math Instructor
DiPofi, Kathleen Jean
French Teacher
Dodrill, Davan James
English Teacher
Dorman, Margaret A.
Marketing Education Teacher
Dosky, Douglas Allan
High School Mathematics Tchr
Dove, Timothy Mark
7th Grade Social Studies Tchr
Drugan, Barbara
Retired Kindergarten Teacher
Dudas, Julie Wander
MLT Program Director & Prof
Dunn, Jennifer S. (West)
Fifth Grade Teacher
Ebright, Jack Cain
Social Studies Teacher
Eck, Phyllis
Instructor
Eichensehr-Gordon, Doris Ellen
Elementary Teacher
Ekleberry, Lee Edward
Secondary Art Teacher
Eldridge, William D.
Assoc Position & Psych
Evans, David Charles
8th Grade Lang Arts Teacher
Evans, L'Tanya C.
Eng Tchr & Coll Counseling Dir
Fraser, David Michael
Science Teacher & Coach
Frazier, Mark Lewis
Band & Asst Director
Freece, Eric W.
Fifth Grade Teacher
Frisbey, Robert Eugene
Retired Principal
Geckeler, Douglas Lee
Mathematics Teacher
Gehres, Ann Christina
8th Grade Science Teacher
Gehres, Stanford Paul
Computer Awareness Teacher
Gerbes, Angelika Renate
Dance History Professor
Glann, Al Thomas
Associate Professor of Art
Gnezda-Smith, Nicole
Art Teacher & Dept Chairperson
Goldsmith, Kathryn Koret
Latin & English Teacher
Goodlett, Roxie Wright
Business & COE Teacher
Graves, Beverly J.
English Teacher
Griffin, Larry
Director of Choral Music
Grist, Rodney W.
HS Theatre Arts Teacher
Haas, Linda Kathryn (Candel)
Teacher, Math & Science Supvr
Hahn, Mary Lee
Fifth Grade Teacher
Harriman, Jeffrey Glenn
Band Director & Music Teacher
Hatton, Dawn Marie (Rice)
5th Grade Teacher
Hayer, Patti A.
Fourth Grade Teacher
Hayes, Christine Yvonne
Social Studies Teacher
Hermiller, John Thomas
Mathematics Teacher
Herrmann, Margaret Ellsworth
Reading Teacher
Hinrichs, Raymond D.
Latin Teacher
Hock, Seth Allen
Computer Science Professor
Hodges, Jeana Jeckell
Third & Fourth Grade Teacher
Hodskievic, Kerry P.
Teacher & GATE Coordinator
Hogue, Amanda J.
8th Grade Algebra & Math Tchr
Houchen, Charles Rick
Tchr & Dir of Christopher Pgm
Hughes, Jessica Barkasi
8th Grd Rdng & Lang Arts Tchr
Husse, Carol Ann
8th Grd Social Studies Teacher
Jackson, Aaron Cicero
Director of Bands
Jarrell, William A.
Mathematics Teacher
Johnson, Michael K.
Math & Soc Stud Tchr
Jones, Linda Millsaps
SS & Health Teacher
Kazee, Linda Sue
8th Grd Math & Algebra Teacher
Kimbell, Alice E.
PAR Consultant & Teacher
King, Rose Hitchcock
Teacher & Coordinator
King, Walter Clemens
Asst Prof of Illstrtn & Fndtns
Kraker, Leslie Wilson
Middle School Art Teacher
Krebs, Marjori Maddox
Social Studies Teacher
Krier, Timothy James
Secondary English Teacher
Kruczynski, William Joseph
Chem & Physics Tchr & Chprsn
Lampe, Philip Anthony
Biology & Chemistry Teacher
La Muth, Jo Ann
English Teacher
Larrabee, Nathaniel
Professor of Fine Arts
Lawson, Alisa Lynnette
English Teacher
Lease, Robin Mears
Early Childhd Education Tchr
Lee, Gordon Sui-Kwong
Assistant Prof of Fine Arts
Lehman, Iris Elaine
Social Studies Teacher
Lenox, Darrell E.
Language Arts Teacher
Long, James Richard
Physical Education Instructor
Lovett, Shirley J. Coston
Span & Frgn Lang Survey Tchr
Lucas, Pamela Howe
Fourth Grade Teacher
Lucas, Renee Sue
Biology Teacher
Ludlum, Daniel Spencer
Social Studies & Comm Tchr
Macioce, Catherine Ann
Math Teacher
Mannarino, Thomas A.
8th Grade History Teacher
Mark, Estelle Ida
Extended Projects Program Tchr
Marker, Rita Maxwell
Spanish Teacher
Matticola, Brian Michael
Instrumental Music Teacher
Mc Cullen, Wendy Howell
Associate Professor of Biology
Mc Ferran, Martha
Social Studies Teacher
Miller, Victorian Lee
English Instructor
Mills, Lori Ann
Government & US History Tchr
Mohler, Leonard H.
Bible & Science Teacher
Moore, Alvis James
Commnctn Theatre Arts Teacher
Morton, William Heywood
7th-8th Grd Soc Studies Tchr
Newland, Linda Marie (Weiss)
Math Teacher
Nguyen, Lori Rimar
4th Grade Teacher
Noble, Richard A.
8th Grade Health Teacher
Novotney, Virginia Disney
Sixth Grade Teacher
Oldham, Sally Nimocks
4th Grade Teacher
O Rourke, Mary Curtin
Spanish Teacher
Osborn, Randy R.
Science Teacher
Pagnanelli, Edward Victor
High School Math Teacher
Palm, Kittie A.
High School Fine Arts Teacher
Palmer, Frauke
Physics Teacher
Papp, Cynthia M.
Chem, Bio & Earth Sci Tchr
Peer, Penny May
Chemistry Teacher
Peterson, Tamara Jean
Asst Prof of Fndtn Studies
Pollock, Karen Pease
Health & Physical Ed Teacher
Powell, Diane Elliott
English Teacher
Pritchard, George H.
Rel & Comp Stud Dept Chair
Reece, Beth Elaine
Music Teacher
Richards, Denise Michael
Former 1st Grade Teacher
Rife, Jane Sweeney
Retired English Teacher
Riffee, Michael Brian
Coordinator
Rissmeyer, Karen Starkey
First Grade Teacher
Robinson, Bruce H.
Associate Professor
Robinson, Diane L.
Home Economics Teacher
Rogers, Carolyn Hunter
Principal
Rohr, Rita Marie
Science & Health Teacher
Rowlands, Kim R.
Fifth Grade Teacher
Sanders, Elizabeth Wilder
Vocational Home Economics Tchr
Schrader, Jill Ellen (George)
Surgical Technician Instructor
Seibert, Margaret Armbrust
Professor of Art History
Shaffer, Diane J.
8th Grade Teacher
Shanahan, Thomas G.
Legal Studies Instructor
Shew, Nancy Carol
English Teacher
Sidner, Anne C.
English Teacher
Smith, Richard Granville
Chemistry Teacher
Spears, Pamela Ann
4th Grade Teacher
Spencer, Ralph S.
Fifth Grade Teacher
Sprunger, Jonathan S.
Social Studies Teacher
Stebbins, Barry Steven
Biology & Physics Teacher
Stern, Martin Richard
US History Teacher
Stevenson, Beth
Physical Education Teacher
Stewart, James E.
English Teacher
Strandberg, Beth A.
Vocal Music & World Hum Tchr
Sweet, Marcia S. (Clay)
English Teacher
Taggart, Julie Anne
Fine Arts Instructor
Taylor, Gregory Spence
Band Director
Taylor, Linda O'Donnell
English Teacher
Taylor, Sheila Smithers
8th Grade Science Teacher
Thompson, Anna Fuller
Teacher of Handicapped
Tolstedt, Lowell C.
Dean of Division Fine Arts
Traini, Jackie Sue
8th Grade Science Teacher
Trombetti, Vince Michael
Science Dept Chair & Teacher
Wampler, Nan Searles
English Dept Chr & Tchr
Weed, Sylvia Yearick
German Teacher
Welch, Patrick Lewis
College Art Teacher
White, Brian N.
World History & Geography Tchr
Wiley, Johnetta Denise
Chemistry & Biology Teacher
Williams, Quentin Darrell
Science Teacher
Wolfe, Antoinette Klimkowski
4th Grade Teacher
Zidonis, Peg McGinty
English Tchr & Newspaper Adv
COLUMBUS GROVE
Edwards, Joyce A.
Second Grade Teacher
CONESVILLE
Gibbs, Linda L.
6th Grade Teacher
Pooley, Patricia Brownlee
First Grade Teacher
CONNEAUT
Dennison, Margaret Ann Mc Guire
Principal
Hazeltine, Russell Gene
Social Studies Teacher
Howell, Marsha Peaspanen
First Grade Teacher
Palmer, T. Katherine
Lang Arts & Reading Teacher
Poros, Stephen John, Jr.
Computer & Art Instructor
Rowbotham, Brenda Caldwell
First Grade Teacher
Schuster, Julie A.
6th Grd Lang Arts & Rdng Tchr
Sterling, Judyth Ocshier
2nd Grade Teacher
Tharp, Susan Dufour
Title 1 Teacher
Wheeler, Karen Perkio
Kindergarten Teacher
Young, Mary Cebasek
Third Grade Teacher

AUT (cont)
onald G.
th Grade Teacher
ENTAL
Julie Ann (Berger)
er Tchr & Network Admin
avid Allen
Studies Teacher
Doug Eugene
s Tchr & Athletic Dir
Y
eiser, Mary Jean Cordray
Studies & Math Teacher

en, Diane Marie
irector
itney A.
de Teacher
ch, Connie
& Marine Biology Tchr
Ruth Ann
de Teacher
r, Liela M.
eacher
Mary Gail
& Communications Tchr
AND
Alexis Ann (White)
Teacher
oyce E.
ade Teacher
Barbara Park
of Gifted
nnie Holquist
& World Studies Teacher
Cheryl R.
cher
ally Ann (Matthews)
Grade Teacher
, Thomas H.
Studies Teacher
san C. Winkler
ade Teacher
ebecca Durig
Teacher
ke, Karen Morris
Teacher
, Judy Brown
garten Teacher
CTON
aren Lynn (Zimmer)
ator for The Gifted
n Fredrick
Teacher & Sci Dept Chm
Lyn Freeman
ator & Tchr Gifted Svcs
ade E.
Grd Math Teacher
athy Ann (Wuyak)
ial Studies Teacher
Hilma Rehard
rade Teacher
GTON
Joan Denise
ge Arts Teacher
n, Rose Ann
eventh Grd Math Teacher
Laura Baum
chool English Teacher
avid A.
matics Teacher
arb
garten Teacher
Nadine (Denlinger)
er & Business Teacher
INE
atricia Redenbach
American History Tchr
RSVILLE
, Dave
High Science Teacher
SVILLE
abeth Ann
Director
Carol Ruth
matics & Computer Teacher
Debora Griley
Teacher
Diane Marie
tory & World Geog Tchr
athy A.
Economist
N
Mary Jo Fletcher
ade Teacher
CITY
Patricia Sadler
Studies Teacher
John Henry
Studies Teacher
R
rri A.
ade Teacher
OGA FALLS
Jane Hoose
rade Teacher
Dee Ann (Dagwell)
al Education & Art Tchr
Patricia Rae
Studies Consultant
Walter C.
al
Susan Bard
chool English Teacher
ian D.
Music Teacher
Gay
Instr Director
Alan Scott
irector & Auditorium Mgr

Greathouse, Susan E.
Reading Teacher
Haas, Paul Thomas
Social Studies Teacher
Haubert, John Ellis
7th Grade Social Studies Tchr
Henry, Patricia Ann
Fifth Grade Teacher
Hoyer, Dexter Craig
Principal
Kinaitis, Kimberly Hartman
French & English Teacher
Kreiner, Sandra Beckwith
Social Studies Teacher
Lieberman, Richard Robert
High School Government Teacher
Marousch, Orrin Wesley
Mathematics Teacher
Mc Callops, Mary Kriska
Fourth Grade Teacher
Mc Donald, Carol Conkle
Accounting & Computer Teacher
Neal, Kathy Suzann
Home Economics Teacher
Osborn, Marlene Hazlett
Science Teacher
Pollock, Margaret Arlene
Fifth Grade Teacher
Sparhawk, Helen Susanne
Second Grade Teacher
Strubbe, Jon Scott
Mathematics Teacher
White, Ruth Mann
Third Grade Teacher
Wilkins, Rebecca King
Vocal Music Tchr & Dept Chair
CYGNET
Dierksheide, Mary Ellen
7th & 8th Grade Math Teacher
DALTON
Walton, Kevin Deane
American History Teacher
DAMASCUS
Kirby, Mark S.
8th Grade History Teacher
DANVILLE
Holmes, James Robert, Jr.
Social Studies Teacher
DAYTON
Adkins, Angela Lynn
Band & Choir Director
Aldridge, Elaine Gawlik
6th Grade Teacher
Alter, E. Jane
Business Teacher
Amin, Julius A.
Associate Professor
Anderson, Janice Lyn
Biology Teacher
Bagwell, Bill L.
Mathematics Teacher
Ballauer, Andrew
Chemistry Teacher
Batra, Prem P.
Biochem & Molecular Bio Prof
Berger, Mary Butler
Soc Stud Tchr & Dept Chair
Boesel, L. Jan
English Teacher
Boggs, Charmaine M.
5th-6th Grade Science Teacher
Bonham, Michael E.
6th Grade Science Teacher
Bowman, Tammy Lynn
Business Teacher
Brademeyer, Kathryn Huelsman
Third Grade Teacher
Brown, Mary Helen (Speech)
English Teacher
Brown, Sharon K.
Fr, Span Teacher & Dept Chair
Bryner, Paula Hartmann
English & Reading Teacher
Burkard, John J.
Bible Teacher
Burks, Peggy Coleman
Kindergarten Teacher
Chadwick, Donna Mc Cowan
Assoc Professor of Accounting
Chapman, Mary Ann Srode
Sci, Hlth, Soc Stud, Math Tchr
Colbert, Lisa Garrison
Religion Tchr & Dept Chprsn
Cook, Jane Jane
Speech & English Teacher
Cooke, Cynthia Lou
High School English Teacher
Cooper, Garry
Marketing Education Coord
Corpus, Deborah P.
10th Grade English Teacher
Cottrel, William Russell
Naval Science Instructor
Craig, Toni G.
Secondary English Teacher
Creech, W. Angela
Business Teacher
Davis, Barbara Deese
9th-12th Grd ESL Teacher
Davis, Jennifer Sue
Teacher of Gifted
Decker, Judy Marsh
Fourth Grade Teacher
DeConinck, MaryBeth Schnittker
Instructor of Marketing & Mgmt
Delamer, Patricia Ann
English Instructor
Dietz, Kathleen Hurley
Math Dept Chair

Dodsworth, Annette Marie
Junior High School Teacher
Downie, Mary Jane
English Teacher
Dugan, Paul Edward
Chem & Advanced Bio Tchr
Dukes, Linda M.
Medical Assisting Program Dir
Eby, Marlene J.
Mathematics & Cmptr Sci Tchr
Emmert, Jorie (Keyser)
English Teacher
Ephraim, Elizebeth
Language Arts Teacher
Erbe, J. Michael
Associate Prof of Biology
Fett, Basil Ray
Choir Director
Fife, D. Mark
Science Teacher
Friedrichs, Virginia Ann
First Grade Teacher
Gayle, George William
Health & PE Dept Chair
Geary, K. Michael
Accounting Professor
Geniusz, Jean Ann
Biology Teacher
Gilbert, Jean H.
Retired Elementary Teacher
Gillaugh, Melanie Roberta (Smith)
Spanish Teacher
Glovka, Mary Claire Bauer
Third Grade Teacher
Godsey, Melissa Ann
Spanish Teacher
Green, Barbara Layenette
Associate Professor of History
Grimes, Roy M.
Algebra & Geometry Teacher
Grogg, Kathleen Knisely
Fourth Grade Teacher
Grothouse, Mark Anthony
4th-5th Grd SLD Teacher
Hahn, Sarah Steele
English as Second Lang Teacher
Hays, Dennis James
Health Teacher
Haywood, Gayle L.
Language Arts Teacher
Head, Lawrence V., Jr.
English Teacher
Heath, Joan Hudnell
6th Grade Teacher
Heider, Christopher G.
Social Studies Teacher
Henninger, Francis Joseph
Director of Amer Studies Prgm
Hilliard, Vicki Lynn Hall
Chemistry Teacher
Hoffman, Sue Ellen
Fifth Grade Teacher
Howell, Norma Jean Grandfield
Physics Teacher
Howland, Tammy
Math Teacher
Hurt, Krystal Anita
English Teacher
Hutchins, Ronald L.
Engineering Professor
Jenkins, Gloria Jackson
Eighth Grade Lang Arts Teacher
Jenks, Denise J. DeVer
4th Grade Teacher
Joyner, Rachelle Habig
Mathematics Teacher
Karl, Joy Ruark
Teacher
Kavouras, Peter George
Social Studies Teacher
Kay, Ellen Kemp
Span Teacher & Jr Class Adv
Keller, Kathleen Liptak
Chem Tchr & Sci Dept Chprsn
Kikenbery, Steven Kent
HS English Instructor
Kilby, Jill Ann
Social Studies Teacher
King, Deborah Lynn
Sixth Grade Teacher
Kinnear, Kelli Duchak
Religion Teacher
Knight, Molly Schehr
Univ Supvr of Student Teachers
Kochensparger, Jonathan Wayne
Social Studies Teacher
Krauskopf, Teresa Lynn
English Teacher
Laughlin, Debra J.
Marketing Education Coord
Law, Norma Prather
Language Arts Teacher
Letavec, Monica A. Maleta
First Grade Teacher
Lewis, William F.
Associate Professor of Mrktg
Loges, Brian T.
Art Teacher
Lollar-Schmidt, Julie
Art Teacher
Lonsert, Lori Mazzone
Head Girls Cross Country Coach
Macklin, Francis Anthony
English Professor
Magee, Mollie Patrick
Proficiency Skills Teacher
Manuel, Emma J.
Teacher
Markworth, Wayne
Band Director

Maxton, Wayne Charles
7th Grade Language Arts Tchr
McGriff, Bonnie Marie
Spanish & French Teacher
Mc Kenny, Diane Marie
English Teacher
Meyer, Barbara Jean
Kindergarten Teacher
Meyer, Nancy E.
Speech & English Teacher
Meyers, Ann E.
Math Teacher
Miller, Michael Edward
History Teacher
Minor, Tom W.
Chemistry & Physics Teacher
Money, Matthew Michael
Bio, Chem & Physics Teacher
Moore, Kenneth Rodney
Sixth Grade Teacher
Moore, Marva Ann (Rucker)
School Counselor
Moorman, Mary Metcalf
Math, Science & Soc Stud Tchr
Moss, Elaine Ginger
5th Grade Teacher
Murray, Ted William
Marketing Education Coord
Nealy-Clarke, Martha Patton
8th Grade Language Arts Tchr
Nims, Carol L.
Second Grade Teacher
Orme, Jessica Lynn (Burkard)
Eng Tchr & Girls Soccer Coach
Parker, Taxi John
Physical Education Teacher
Pepitone, Brenda Kolentus
English Teacher
Peters, Barry W.
English Teacher
Peterson, Betty Morgan
Art Dept Chairperson & Teacher
Pfrogner, Michele Marie
8th Grade English Teacher
Porter, Bonnie Ruth
Science Teacher
Porter, Shirley Laster
Lang Arts Teacher
Pyle, Paul William
Bible Department Head
Reese, Tanza Elois Trim
Work & Family Life Teacher
Reynolds, Linda Jane
English Teacher
Rike, Martha Rish
Foreign Lang Dept Chairperson
Robinson, Sherry Alford
Mathematics Teacher
Rodenfels, Jerome Francis
Music Coord, Bands & Orch Dir
Ruffolo, Angela Marie
Senior American Govt Teacher
Rugh, W. Dean
Psych Peer Helper & His Tchr
Rykoskey, Carol Kleber
Fifth Grade Teacher
Sableski, Thomas Lee
Pub Speaking, Comm & Eng Tchr
Saliba, Tony Elias
Chem Engineering Assoc Prof
Schmitt, Warren G.
Language Arts Teacher
Schweikart, Larry Earl
Professor of History
Seilhamer, William Buzz
Sci Instr & Athletic Coach
Seitz, Carolyn Walters
Social Studies Teacher
Shafer, Thomas Russell, Jr.
English Teacher
Sheridan, Beverly Karanovich
Gen Music Tchr & Choral Dir
Shuman, Sherry L.
Mathematics Teacher
Simons, Karen Martin
Computer Sci & Busniess Tchr
Slagel, James Gerard
Physics Instructor
Smith, Lee E.
High School Counselor
Sommer, William Frederick
English Teacher
Sparrow, James
History Teacher
Spencer, Karen Allen
5-6th Grade Elementary Teacher
Stein, Mary Alice
English & Latin Teacher
Steinlage, Ralph Cletus
Professor of Mathematics
Stimpson, Judy K.
Mathematics Teacher
Stoeckicht, Charlene Lewis
Director & Kdg Teacher
Stone, Joyce Calmeise
Seventh Grade Mathematics Tchr
Street, Eric P.
Keyboard Studies Director
Takacs, Audrey Pumilia
6th Grade Educator
Tallan, Joan Harnett
Art Teacher
Tarpey, Daniel James
Principal
Taylor, Beverly Sue
6th Grade Teacher
Tebben, Marc F.
12th Grd Psychology Teacher
Thomas, Dennis A.
English Teacher

Thornton, James Michael
Eighth Grade Science Teacher
Tibbetts, Paul E.
Professor of Philosophy
Toia, Kathleen Inez
Kindergarten Teacher
Townsley, Gerlinde Mueller
German Teacher
Trent, Tony Leon
American History Teacher
Troxell, Jean (Maxwell)
Kindergarten Teacher
Ullery, Ronnie Zorn
Mathematics Teacher
Vail, David S.
Mathematics Teacher
Waite, Darlene Rose (Walters)
VP for Academic Affairs
Walters, Paula Laurens
ESL Teacher
Warnock, Judith E.
Allied Hlth Technologies Instr
Watson, Shirley Brockman
Social Studies Teacher
Weimer, Peter
Chemistry & Physics Teacher
Whetstone, Barbara Sue
Second Grade Teacher
White, Mary E.
Prof of Hlth Information Mgmt
Wiethorn, Robert Nelson, SM
Cmptr Sci Dept Chprsn & Tchr
Wiggins, Jane L. (Price)
Principal
Wilson, Thomas H.
Professor of Mathematics
Witzmann, Pamela Jo
Physical Education Teacher
Woodgeard, Linda Van Reeth
Speech Teacher
Woods, Sharon Needles
English Teacher
Wright, Nancy Arnold
Third Grade Teacher
Young, Ronald Ulrich
American Government Teacher
Zimmerman, Kent L.
Professor of Communication Art
Zofkie, Michael Joseph
Social Studies & History Tchr
Zubeck, M. Teresa
6th Grade Teacher
DE GRAFF
Holycross, Susan Schrader
Business Teacher
Lundy, Debra Lynn (Howell)
Language Arts Teacher
Yoder, Rodney Lyn
High School Science Teacher
DEFIANCE
Bush, Deborah Ann
Fourth Grade Teacher
Dement, Martha Mallott
Mathematics Teacher
English, Randy Steven
Fifth Grade Teacher
Fisher, Patricia Jayne (Norton)
Fourth Grade Teacher
Gambler, Rae Ann Richman
Sixth Grade Teacher
Gerken, Joan Nicely
Third Grade Teacher
Hobgood, Marabeth B.
Third Grade Teacher
Karnes, Philip M.
Seventh-Eighth Grade Teacher
Martin, Emily L.
Spanish Teacher
Mc Ghee, Mike
7th Grade Teacher
Parrish, Karen King
Kindergarten Teacher
Snyder, Sally Jeanne (Rhoades)
Third Grade Teacher
Stanton, Alex William
Human Anatomy & Health Teacher
Stevens, Jerry Lynn
Mathematics & English Teacher
Tille, Mary Ann
English & Speech Teacher
DELAWARE
Beck, James Herbert
Career Graphics Teacher
Boyd, Kim Sturgeon
Music Department Chair
Brown, Gina Gayle Bair
6th Grade Teacher
Davis, Ann L.
Mathematics Teacher
Esler, Michael Vaughn
Political Science Professor
Held, Donna Schmidt
Math Teacher
Huckabee, Colleen Jenkins
Enrichment Director
Joseph, Doug
HS Health & Amer History Tchr
Melfi, Patricia S.
Early Childhood Education Dir
Nesselroad, Michael A.
Chemistry Teacher
Smith, Lois Kime
Retired Third Grade Teacher
Straits, Shelley Ann
English & Journalism Teacher
Turner, Randy Leon
Math Teacher
DELPHOS
Fischer, Judith (Weber)
Health & Religious Stud Tchr

DELPHOS (cont)
Hablitzel, Patricia Dickman
5th Grade Teacher
Roney, Kelli Ann (Schroeder)
Sixth Grade Teacher
Scherger, Miriam Young
Kindergarten Teacher
Stearns, David Allen
Instrumental Music Teacher
Suever, Sandy Stallkamp
First Grade Teacher
Talboom, Sandra Makuh
Fourth Grade Teacher
Turnwald, Blyth Marie
7th Grade Teacher
DELTA
Anderson, Keith
Social Studies Teacher
Brickner, Michael John
Mathematics Teacher
Gray, William J.
High School Biology Teacher
Lintermost, Randy Lee
Social Studies Teacher
DENNISON
Craig, Jan D.
Technology Coordinator
Haney, Kathi D. (Cady)
4th Grade Teacher
DILLONVALE
Gonot, Cathy Lynn (Franke)
4th Grade Teacher
DOLA
Dennis, Michael Lee
Physical Ed & Health Instr
Peltier, Sarah M.
Vocal Music Director
DONNELSVILLE
Harness, Evelyn Christina (Begley)
Fourth Grade Teacher
Suver, Sara L.
Principal
DOVER
Bonamico, Roseanne
Comm Arts & Religion Teacher
Harris, Amy L.
Second Grade Teacher
Mc Ilvaine, Karen Barbara
HS English Teacher
Staley, Richard Ray
5th Grade Teacher
DOYLESTOWN
Robbins, Denise Steiner
9th-12th Grade Art Teacher
Shelton, Curtis L.
Middle School Art Teacher
DRESDEN
Conrad, Beth Burris
7th Grade Language Arts Tchr
Dickson, Janet Mc Clintock
Retired First Grade Teacher
Hendershot, Douglas Lloyd
Eighth Grade Math Teacher
Welch, Larry Dean
Math Teacher
Wolfe, Elizabeth Simmons
High School Art Teacher
DUBLIN
Aquila, Toni Van Benthuysen
Mathematics Teacher
Biegler, Chad Alan
US History Teacher
Bornhorst, Tony Joe
Health & Physical Teacher
Carlson, Daniel T.
AP Chemistry Teacher
Coleman, Linda Minor
Library Media Specialist
Curts, Gary R.
Physical Science Teacher
Diniaco, GeorgiAnn
Safe & Drug Free Schls Coord
Foley, Kevin Thomas
HS Social Studies Teacher
Griffith, Jean Milner
Reading Specialist
Hall, Hollys Easterling
French Teacher & Dept Chair
Hardesty, Todd Harper
Math Tchr & Asst Ath Dir
Havlice, Ronald Anthony
Chemistry Teacher
Hodges, Gary Howard
Music Educator & Band Director
McFarland, Kathy Lynn
High School English Teacher
O'Connor, Timothy Roch
Math Teacher
Rowe, Kathleen Elizabeth
Guidance Counselor
Saunders, Tim R.
Physical Education Teacher
Stowell, Matthew H.
8th Grade Social Studies Tchr
Sulser, Jayne Rybar
English Teacher
Vornbrock, Cheryl L.
English Teacher
DUNCAN FALLS
Gatton, Susan Ryan
First Grade Teacher
Harper, Dean
Seventh Grade English Teacher
Janicki, Mary Anderson
Learning Tchr for At Risk Stud
DUNDEE
Ely, Jo Ann
First Grade Teacher
EAST CANTON
Conrad, Julie Barrick
French & Spanish Teacher
Flanigan, Victoria Lynn
Special Education Teacher
Geiger, John Raymond
Retired Second Grade Teacher
Potts, Douglas H.
6th Grade Teacher
EAST CLEVELAND
Bell, Aslean Poole
Seventh Grade Math Teacher
Rush, Jacquelyn Christina
6th Grade Teacher
Williams, Van Oliver
Spcl Ed Intervention Specialst
EAST LIVERPOOL
Dahl, Nancy VoDrey
English Teacher
Doll, Virginia Lee (Rowe)
French & Latin Teacher
Ensinger, Ronald H.
Retired Health & PE Teacher
Hlivko, Richard Paul
Math Teacher
Irons, James C.
Social Studies Teacher
Marcelt, Denise Marie
Soc Stud & History Teacher
Mc Gee, Anne Foxworth
Math Teacher
Raffa, Sandra Lee Hermand
Business Teacher
Ridgeway, Edward Leroy
Physical Education Teacher
Rollo, Robert Anthony
Band Director
Russo, Merle Arden
French & Spanish Teacher
Thayer, M. Susan
Fourth Grade Teacher
EAST PALESTINE
DiCesare, Jeffrey Ettore
Band Director
Guy, Geraldine Ruth (Wilhelm)
High School Spanish Teacher
Pupino, Marc Steven
Assistant Band Director
Silhanek, Douglas Mark
Amer His, Govt & Ecnmcs Tchr
Wright, Robert Lyndon
World Cultures Teacher
EASTLAKE
Arnold, Lois Jean
American Government Teacher
Day, Catherine Barker
Third Grade Teacher
DeSantis, John W.
Mathematics Teacher
Hace, Dennis Edward
11th & 12th Grd Soc Stud Tchr
Hostetter, Katherine Balsley
Eng, Advanced Composition Tchr
Hurtack, Stephen George
Spanish Teacher
Mormile, Gayle L.
French Teacher
Newhous, Natalie F.
Teacher of Handicapped
Rayl, Brian Lee
Physics & Chemistry Teacher
Spinner, Barbara
Mathematics Teacher
Strumbel, Barbara Ann
English Teacher & Dept Chair
Tayek, Jon Gerard
Choral & General Music Tchr
EATON
Borucki, Catherine Flamm
Fourth Grade Teacher
Brooks, Mary Ann A.
Bus Dept Chair, Tchr & Adv
Burnett, Jeffrey Scott
Science Teacher
Karn, Allen Ray
High School Mathematics Tchr
Mc Kinney, Randall Lynn
US History & Government Tchr
Moses, Karen Donahue
Title I Rdng & Lang Arts Tchr
Neanen, Ronald D.
Guidance Counselor
North, Mary Ellen Villarreal
Fourth Grade Teacher
Pollock, Arthella A. (Mote)
Retired Teacher
EDGERTON
Glore, Beverley Anne
Second Grade Teacher
Krill, Bruce C.
High School Math Teacher
Mc Pike, James I.
Chemistry Tchr
Schroeder, Carol Ann
Fourth Grade Teacher
EDON
Hall, Lanna Pendleton
Art Teacher
Murray, Timothy Wayne
Physics, Chem & Anatomy Tchr
Priest, Robert A.
OWA Coordinator
ELIDA
Clum, Allen J.
AP Calculus & Psychology Tchr
Craft, Linda Sue
Kindergarten Teacher
Desenberg, David Arthur
High Schl Social Studies Tchr
Gordon, Hazel Kiser
First Grade Teacher
Hieneman, Michelle Layne (Montague)
Fourth Grade Teacher
Kennedy, Janice Kay
Third Grade Teacher
Klaus, Michael Edward
Anatomy, Physiology & Bio Tchr
Owen, Patricia Lynne
English Teacher
Schwinnen, Dennis Anthony
Guidance Counselor
Wilson, Rita Marie (Nolan)
Third Grade Teacher
ELMORE
Haensch, Karen S.
English Teacher
Kruse, Jane Thier
Retired Third Grade Teacher
Preston, Janet Reifenstahl
Guidance Counselor
Weirich, Daniel Ray
Mathematics Teacher
Williams, Howard George
Band Director
ELYRIA
Bier, Jane Klein
HS Social Studies Teacher
Bloomfield, David Ross
6th Grade Teacher
Branzel, Donald Allan
Third Grade Teacher
Brown, Merry C.
Business Education Teacher
Brunkow, Sharon Parlock
Eighth Grade Teacher
Carson, Patricia Fay
Kindergarten Teacher
Clark, Christopher Roy
Band Director
Clark, Susan
Music Department Chair
Day, Carol Crider
Art Teacher
Dixon, Susan Gale (Weber)
HS English & Lang Arts Tchr
Ellis, Howard Charles
Associate Professor of History
Ereditario, Rebecca Koth
3rd Grade Teacher
Fritz, Carolyn Rodak
Mathematics Tchr & Dept Chprsn
Gause, Julia M.
2nd Grade Teacher
Grau, JoAnn (Molinaro)
English Teacher
Harding, Karen MacKeigan
Business Teacher
Hoover, Beverly Marie
Sixth Grade Teacher
Kilker, Barbara M.
Academic Affairs Asst Prin
Kitzler, Elizabeth Rosemary
Fourth Grade Teacher
Krueck, Suzanne Lee
Social Studies Teacher
Lyon, Darlene L.
German Teacher
Neher, Donna S.
Art Teacher
Owens, Eloise Suzanne
Professor of Arts & Humanities
Parks, Trudi James
Clinical Coord & Radiography
Perkins, Scott Howard
7th Grade Social Studies Tchr
Pollack, Pamela Roberts
7th Grade Teacher
Prusak, Patricia Ann
Reading Resource Teacher
Sawinski, Ernest P.
Technology Education Teacher
Schlegel, Diane Kay
Spanish Teacher
Schroeder, Diane Lynn
Third Grade Teacher
Simonson, Carol
4th Grade Teacher
Smith, Thomas Carl
7th Grade Science Teacher
Stall, Donald Lloyd, Jr.
5th Grade Teacher
Vinicky, Sandra (Szymczyk)
Seventh Grade Teacher
ENGLEWOOD
Harper, Teresia Ann (Hall)
Elem Physical Education Tchr
Leapley, Pamela Anne
First Grade Teacher
Litvin, Elaine Diamonstein
GATE Teacher
Weikert, Barbara Swigart
Fifth Grade Teacher
Weitz, Roberta Roshkind
Kindergarten Teacher
Zent, Sally Inez
Second Grade Teacher
ENON
Arnold, Barbara Studebaker
8th Grd Reading & Comm Teacher
Dix, Robin Harper
5th Grade Teacher
Tully, Deborah Imri
Reading, Writing & Comm Tchr
ETNA
Bradley, Carolyn Veenoy
Third Grade Teacher
EUCLID
Corrigan, Patricia Walsh
Language Arts Teacher
Gery, Karen Ann
Math Teacher
Hoffert, Frank
Social Studies Teacher
Kilroy, Maureen Anne
Eighth Grade Teacher
Kostansek, Mary Silva
Special Education Teacher
McLaughlin, Judith Sweet
English Teacher
Miller, Pauline Srsen
2nd Grade Teacher
Serra, Paul Thomas
Retired Mathematics Teacher
Smith, C. Wayne
World History Teacher
Stucki, Daniel Robert
Social Studies Teacher
Tkac, Carol M.
Eng, Spch, Creative Write Tchr
Wilson, Scott William
History Teacher
FAIRBORN
Beerbower, Susan Hnat
English Teacher
Kirk, Phillip Wayne
Chemistry Teacher
Lawson, Joe D.
High School Algebra Teacher
Levine, Kathleen Ann (Huebner)
Former English Teacher
Mays, Kristin Lee (Cook)
Mathematics Teacher
Russell-Rader, Kathleen
English Teacher
Seewer, Michael L.
AP History & Literature Tchr
Shelley, Ellen W.
Eng Tchr & Jrnlsm Pub Adv
Spiegel, Dennis D.
Training Specialist
Stephens, Beth Ann
Second Grade Teacher
Utt, Lawrence Alfred
Latin & English Teacher
Wilkinson, Gary F.
Health & Physical Ed Tchr
FAIRFIELD
Allison, James Michael, Jr.
Science Teacher
Austin, Karen F.
Mathematics Teacher
Beaver, C. Wayne
Bible, Greek & Drama Teacher
Christen, Toni Kallmeyer
5th Grade Teacher
Garshelis, Judith Maggard
6th Grd Lang Arts & Rdng Tchr
Hasseman, Brian Lee
High School Guidance Counselor
Hembree, James Robert, III
History Teacher & Coach
Jackson, Nancy Sloneker
French Teacher
Johnson, Eric A.
Language Arts Teacher
Kinnard, Michael Lane
Earth Science Teacher & Coord
Krauss, Charlotte Cheatham
3rd Grade Teacher
Lapp, Richard Gordon
Science Teacher of GATE
Nelson, Bronwyn Jones
Chemistry Teacher
New, Wendy Rose
Fourth Grade Teacher
Peters, Kathleen Ann
Latin Teacher
Rice, Gary Lynn
Scndry Math Tchr & Dept Head
Scheid, Constance A.
6th Grade Lang & Rdng Teacher
Smith, Ronald D.
Spanish Teacher & Athletic Dir
Vafides, Alexis
World & American History Tchr
FAIRVIEW PARK
Shafer, Donald Marion
Eng Tchr & Dept Chair
Westcott, Susan Gail
Fifth Grade Teacher
FARMDALE
Santell, Anthony J.
Fifth Grade Teacher
FAYETTEVILLE
Harley, Lisa Dawn
English & Psychology Teacher
Johnson, Louis Bernard
History Teacher
FELICITY
Adams, Ralph Edward
Social Studies Teacher
Aninao, Kelly Lynn (Mc Williams)
High School English Teacher
Benjamin, Leah Raye
Gifted & Reading Teacher
Wehrum, Adele DiLonardo
Spanish Teacher
FINDLAY
August, Katy Anderson
Third Grade & Chemistry Tchr
Hanson, David Alan
Music Instructor
Hooks, Nancy Carol
6th Grade Teacher
Kerns, C. Michael
Dir of Vet Svcs & Asst Prof
Laux, Albert
High School Mathematics Tchr
Mulrane, Jeanie Courtney
Fifth Grade Teacher
Stahl, Rebecca J.
First Grade Teacher
Straley, Linda Radkey
Fifth Grade Teacher
Swecker, Elizabeth Ann
Intermediate Lvl Tchr of Deaf
Wagner, Patrick Alan
Physical Education Teacher
Williman, Stephen Mark
Physical Education Teacher
Zalinski, Barbara Kay (Snell)
Math & Computer Teacher
FOREST
Huffman, Beverly Thacker
4th Grade Teacher
Taylor, Jackie Lee (Pelton)
Sixth Grade Teacher
FORT JENNINGS
Altenburger, Mary Lou
Science Teacher
Schroeder, Judith Feathers
Kindergarten Teacher
Warnecke, Rose Mary Kuzma
Music Education Teacher
Wilcox, Eileen Joan (Ernst)
Business & History Teacher
FORT LORAMIE
Bailar, Alan Lee
Biology Teacher
Sowards, Kenneth R.
Social Studies Department Chm
Stickley, Steven Alan
Chem Physics & Math Teacher
FORT RECOVERY
McAbee, Marna Wilson
First Grade Teacher
FOSTORIA
Bucher, Catherine Stalter
English Teacher
Carnicom, Connie
Media Specialist
Cousin, Kim Fant
Physical Education Teacher
Haddix, Patricia Grimm
Language Arts Teacher
Jaegle, Deborah Justen
Rel Teacher & Campus Minister
King, Sandra (Zierolf)
Mathematics Teacher
Matz, Karis Horner
Fifth Grade Teacher
Pohlman, Ben J.
Occupational Work Adj Teacher
VanCuren, Mary Lonsway
7th & 8th Grade Math Teacher
Ward, Cheryl S.
Fourth Grade Teacher
FRANKFORT
Guthrie, Rebecca Carter
English, Speech & Lit Teacher
Lusk, Tabitha Price
Art Teacher
Yates, Edward C.
Math Dept Chairman & Teacher
FRANKLIN
Allen, Geraldean
Sixth Grade Teacher
Coleman, Antoinette Knowles
Kindergarten Teacher
Gregg, Lori Hartman
HS Mathematics Teacher
Harty, Larry Duane
English Teacher
Imfeld, Kathy Scearce
Second Grade Teacher
Noland, Patti Munsey
Biology & Physiology Teacher
Ostermann, Edwin Paul
Environmental Science Teacher
Sample, Barbara F.
Second Grade Teacher
Stevens-Gleason, Helen Elizabeth
Fourth Grade Teacher
Stewart, Jennifer Kirby
Tchr & Coordinator of Gifted
Valiante, Susan K.
Music Teacher
FRANKLIN FURNACE
Duduit, Jeffrey B.
K-12 Physical Education Tchr
Royse, Dale Alvin
Social Studies Teacher
Stidham, Mary Bihl
Title I Math Teacher
FREDERICKSBURG
Richards, Kenneth Lynn
Sixth Grade Teacher
FREDERICKTOWN
Ackerman, Loretta Ann
Amer Govt & World His Teacher
Brown, Katherine Dremann
School Counselor
Miller, Patty Mc Laughlin
K & Title 1 Rdng Recovery Tchr
Weller, Betty J.
High School Business Teacher
Weller, Tracie Jo
Science Teacher
FREEPORT
Deromedi, Gary Lee
Mathematics & Cmptr Sci Tchr
FREMONT
Avery, Charlene Cornell
Office Systems Program Instr
Beckley, Jane Ellen (Aspacher)
Elementary Teacher
Brough, Kathleen Welter
Third Grade Teacher

NT (cont)
amela Joy (Kaczor)
Teacher
Melissa Mann
Teacher
, Jamie Lynn
Teacher
cie Ann
de Teacher
even L.
ocial Studies Teacher
oerg, Melissa Susan
try Teacher
Michael Jon
de American His Teacher
imothy Neff
Prof of Bus Management
re, Steve Frank
g Disabilities Teacher
Bernard John
rade Teacher
Mary Elizabeth
Science Teacher
ger, Ellen L.
ss Education Teacher
odney Lynn
Grade Teacher
Kathie L.
ss Education Teacher
ary Ellen Hughes
I & Journalism Teacher
ey, Kathleen Tansey
de Teacher
Barbara Sponseller
Dvlpmntlly Handicap
Joseph P.
gy Tchr & Dev Dir
r, Anne Dibert
garten Teacher
Richard John
atics Instructor
Kea Karu
nstructor
Kathy L. (Hill)
Dvlpmntlly Handicap
niel J.
High School Teacher
san Jennifer
Administration Instr
, Gary Allen
ce Counselor
William Alan
& Sociology Teacher
udith Decker
atics Instructor
arol Anne (Feick)
de Teacher
NA
Carole Paris
atics Dept Chair & Tchr
Mary Eve Barrett
School Science Teacher
, Penelope Susan
of Gifted & Talented
Joan Marguerite
Studies & English Tchr
Marshall Darwin
al Arts & PE Teacher
MaryAnn Schneider
& Reading Teacher
Dennis Randall
Studies Teacher
Katharine Wach
matics Teacher
, Gary Robert
matics Teacher
Michael Christopher
ade American His Teacher
Mark A.
Teacher
amer, Jeffrey Del
irector
, Lori Jo
ade Teacher
A
Susan Babula
rade Teacher
N
la Diane
ade Teacher
andra Kay
ade Teacher
POLIS
ary Alice
Eng & Lit Teacher
mes Roger
Teacher
erry D.
Grade Teacher
oan Diane Smith
Aide & Study Hall Supvr
ay Allen
Teacher
eborah
Grade Teacher
, James P.
al Ed Tchr & Coach
WAY
Sue Ellen
Instructor
ne Ann
rade Teacher
an Ackerman
garten Teacher
Evelyn Noelle
e Teacher
auer, Mary M.
h Teacher
Carol Essex
Grade Teacher

Wilcox, Sean A.
9th Grade English Teacher
GAMBIER
Brint, Michael E.
Assoc Prof & Humane Stud Dir
GARRETTSVILLE
Farthing, Carol Ellen
English Teacher & Dept Chprsn
Howell, Steven J.
English Teacher
Korode, Ed D.
Industrial Arts Teacher
Korode, Ruth E.
English Teacher
Teresi, Richard Anthony
Biology Teacher
Walker, Iva L.
Social Studies Educator
GATES MILLS
Monroe, Victor Allen
English Teacher
Rosewater, Gail Atleson
French Teacher
GENEVA
Carrel, Marion L.
Band Director
Redline, Barbara Watson
Eighth Grade Teacher
GENOA
Bundy, William N.
High School Math Teacher
Hitchen, Marrilee Van Cleve
4th Grade Teacher
Kilmer, John S.
HS Guidance Counselor
Klingbeil, Lorene Elizabeth
6th Grade Teacher
Kopena, Jolene Frances (Rombach)
Spanish Teacher
Miller, Dave K.
Composition & Philosophy Tchr
Rotondo, Cindy Kidd
First Grade Teacher
Stanley, Thomas E.
English Teacher
Tanner, Cheryl Felts
3rd Grade Teacher
GEORGETOWN
Reichardt, Beatrice Taylor
Retired Elementary Teacher
GERMANTOWN
Gabbard, Paula D.
Fourth Grade Teacher
Tanner, Charlene Rae
Fifth Grade Teacher
Williams, Dorothy Ayers
7th & 8th Grd Mathematics Tchr
GETTYSBURG
Stump, Krista Hurley
First Grade Teacher
GIBSONBURG
Fisher, Judith Wright
First Grade Teacher
Foos, Lisa Michael
English & Reading Teacher
Krotzer, Sheryl Clark
Sixth Grade Teacher
Phillips, Lois Ingalls
French Teacher
Sneider, Patricia Welter
Bio & Human Physiology Teacher
Van Tassel, Laura Leah
Band Director
Young, Raymond Arthur
Language Arts Teacher
GILBOA
Parker, Tom R.
Science Teacher
GIRARD
Chambers, Gerry Szpanka
Chem, Physics Tchr & Dept Chm
Deramo, Donald P.
American History Teacher
Gabriel, Peter James
Social Studies Teacher
Labato, Regina M.
Kindergarten Teacher
Pirlo, Frances Chomos
First Grade Teacher
Radza, Joseph Edward
Science Teacher
Reams, Lynn Ray
Retired Eng & Lang Arts Tchr
Szallai, Patricia Siranovic
Library & Media Specialist
Vaccaro, Katherine Ann
Italian Teacher
GLOUSTER
Kutscherenko, Susan Teresa
First Grade Teacher
GNADENHUTTEN
Brown, Janadean Wright
Proficiency Intervention Tchr
Mc Connell, Ronald Charles
English & Reading Teacher
Young, Scott A.
Math Dept Chairperson, Teacher
GRAFTON
Baker, Jonell Harrison
Fifth Grd Inclusion Class Tchr
Dawson, William Bruce
Chemistry & Physics Teacher
Wright, Sandra Lee Scheid
Kindergarten Teacher
GRAND RAPIDS
Cavanagh, Paul T.
Fourth Grade Teacher
Mohr, Norma Bateson
Sixth Grade Teacher

GRANVILLE
Hill, Donita Shaeffer
Latin Teacher
Hollen, Robert B.
Art Teacher
Krumm, John Henry
Band Director
Lewis, Patty L.
English & History Teacher
Nichols, Nancy Shea
French Teacher
GRAYSVILLE
Taylor, Robert Gregory
History, Math & Reading Tchr
GRAYTOWN
Bolander, Fay Schwamberger
Retired Jr HS & Elem Tchr
Fabian, Lorraine L. (Lighthall)
Second Grade Teacher
GREEN
Andrus, Faith I.
Arabic, French & Spanish Tchr
Davidson, Dale A.
Instrumental Music Director
Ohlson, Matthew Paul
Physics Teacher
Taylor, Norma Sue
Amer History & Sr Govt Teacher
GREEN SPRINGS
Baker, Helen (Wagner)
First Grade Teacher
GREENFIELD
Roe, Helen M.
Family & Consumer Science Tchr
GREENFORD
Van Pelt, Elsie
Eighth Grade English Teacher
GREENSBURG
Burch, Beth Ann Stalnaker
Third Grade Teacher
Snyder, Joan Botschner
Adult Education Teacher
GREENVILLE
Burchett, Karen Coppess
Kindergarten Teacher
Butts, Susan Leis
Cooperative Bus Ed Coord
Fries, Doug W.
High School Counselor & Coach
Hart, Brenda Lee
8th-12th Grd Math & Sci Tchr
Jones, Carlton Lee
Tech Coord
Knasinski, Frank Stanley, Jr.
Life Science Teacher
Kuhbander, Kathleen Sue
English, German & Yrbk Tchr
GREENWICH
Cotterman, M. Scott
Mathematics Teacher
Hunt, Theron L.
Bio, Ecology & Life-Sci Tchr
Sommers, Danielle d'Evegnee
Second Grade Teacher
Stoneham, Lisa Hipp
Eng, Drama, Speech & Rdng Tchr
GROVE CITY
Camp, Deborah Sue (Redman)
Tchr of the Gifted & Talented
Coss, Edward James
6th Grd Math Tchr & Team Ldr
Daily, Roswitha Burkey
German Teacher
Graham, Michael Patrick
Social Studies Teacher
Jerome, Marlene S.
6th Grade Teacher
Kennedy, Janette Kuhn
5th Grade Teacher
Kuhn, Linda C.
Sixth Grade Math Teacher
Schreiner, Lee Charles
Elementary Enrichment Teacher
Simpson-Levi, Kelley Jo
Music Teacher & Band Director
Sparks, Judith Lenze
4th Grade Teacher
Stark, Jane Brandt
Substitute Teacher
Sullivan, Wayne Harris
Amer History & Lang Arts Tchr
Vail, Chris L.
HS Mathematics Teacher
Weber, Peggy Ramsey
Choral Director & Dept Head
Wessels, Joyce Rita Lavoy
Visual Education Teacher
GROVEPORT
Coster, Elizabeth Peiss
High School Art Teacher
Hilbert, Jean Ann Brown
5th Grade Teacher
Hoskins, Sharon Hoy
Business Education Teacher
Kennedy, Brian Andrew
Voc Agrcltrl Mechanics Instr
Leffler, James Tracy
7th-8th Grd Hlth & PE Teacher
Neth, John Watson, III
Biology Teacher
Rexford, Kathryn Ann
Assistant Principal
GROVER HILL
Peck, Sharon Bennett
Fifth Grade Teacher
Priest, Janet Renn
Fourth Grade Teacher
Voirol, Sarah L.
Sixth Grade Teacher

GYPSUM
Engler, Gary Robert
Fifth Grade Teacher
Twarek, Greg L.
Sixth Grd Sci & Math Teacher
HAMDEN
Eberts, Carol Ann (Peters)
Retired Elementary Principal
Leonard, Sharilyn Anne
Third Grade Teacher
HAMERSVILLE
Pride, Celia Ann (Groves)
Fourth Grade Teacher
HAMILTON
Burkhardt, Paul Erwin
Dir of Adult & Vocational Ed
Chizek, Andrea Wagner
5th & 6th Grade Teacher
Davis, Belinda Walsh
7th Grade Math Teacher
Dunnette, J. Kevin
HS Language Arts Teacher
Franek, Martha Louise
Engineering Technology Instr
Gross, Alfred, Jr.
Sixth Grade Teacher
Horne, Lori Jo (Butz)
Third Grade Teacher
Huff, Kelly Smith
Rel Ed Coord & Yth Minister
Huff, Kristi Adkins
Third Grade Teacher
Lidman, Monica von Haefen
Sixth Grade Teacher
Lowe, Catharine M.
9th Grade Civics Teacher
Mc Cann, Carolyn L.
Fourth Grade Teacher
Mc Gowan, Teresa M.
English Teacher
Moonitz, Daniel Alexander
Band Director
Neal, Roberta L.
English Teacher
Nelson, Timothy Taft
English Teacher
Niehaus, Susan Jane
Math Teacher
Overholts, Judy L.
Third Grade Teacher
Pallo, Laurel Sexton
Language Arts & Lit Teacher
Pfirrman, Nancy Ann
French Teacher
Phillips, Paul Allen
Mathematics Teacher
Poff, Harvey Edward
Criminal Justice Instructor
Riggs, Nancy Strodtbeck
1st Grade Teacher
Ringel, Marlane Baldridge
5th Grade Teacher
Satyal, Lalita Bali
Third Grade Teacher
Schnipper, Linda Martin
Physical Science Teacher
Snyder, Anita Dye
2nd Grade & Head Teacher
Stitsinger, Joelle Munson
Spanish Teacher
Suedkamp, Lori Elizabeth Imhoff
9th Grade Math Teacher
Tilney, Joanne M.
Fourth Grd Tchr & Asst Prin
Turner, Steve
Twelfth Grade English Teacher
Utley, Beverly Nelson
Computer Lab Instructor
Vido, Fay Wagner
English Teacher & Dept Chair
Young, Beth Ann Griesinger
Physical Education Teacher
HAMLER
Bloor, Ruth Pearl (Davison)
Math Teacher
Brown, Diann Ellen (Geiser)
Jr HS Soc Stud & Eng Teacher
Kirkendall, Helen Rolf
Sixth Grade Teacher
Rohrs, Teresa Lynn (Bostelman)
Fourth Grade Teacher
HAMMONDSVILLE
Cable, William Brant
Adult Basic & Literacy Ed Dir
Potenzini, Monica L.
7th Grade Reading Teacher
Tranto, Pearl (Psaros)
Guidance Counselor
HANNIBAL
Indermuhle, Joyce Marie
Kindergarten Teacher
McGlone, Kathy Jean
Biology Teacher
HANOVERTON
Field, Robert
Secondary Soc Science Tchr
Houk, Alan Lee
Band Director
Van Kirk, Michael R.
Math Teacher
Ward, Denise Logozzo
Spanish Teacher
Warner, Rodney K.
Science Teacher
HARRISON
Bader, David Edward
World History Teacher
Bihr, Shirley Ann
Language Arts & Religion Tchr

Brown, Christopher Robin
Science Teacher
Cron, Marc C.
Secondary Science Teacher
Ernst, Marc William
Physical Education Teacher
Friermood, Pamela A.
7th Grade Language Arts Tchr
Glasscock, Ruth Knepfle
Sixth Grade Teacher
Harrison, Jennifer Boeckmann
HS Mathematics Teacher
Hershberger, Jennifer Diane
Instructional Media Coord
Karn, Eric Michael
Social Studies Teacher
Madama, Pamela Ann
English Teacher
McCarthy, Kenneth
Eighth Grade Science Teacher
Miller, Kimberly Pietsch
Language Arts Teacher
Sowders, Shawn Gregory
8th Grade History Teacher
Spurlock, Connie Kaiser
Media Specialist
Wilhelm, Leslie Ann
Family & Consumer Science Tchr
HARROD
McPheron, John W.
7th-8th Grd Language Arts Tchr
HARTVILLE
Denny, David Frank
Fifth Grade Teacher
Eady, Vikki Lynn
Jr HS Tchr & Math Dept Head
Feldman, Marilyn W.
Language Arts Teacher
Gingerich, John Edwin
Bible & English Teacher
Largent, Kathleen Kucyk
English & Spanish Teacher
Obney, Nora Cavanaugh
Social Studies Dept Chairman
Richards, Jeanette M. Mae
6th Grade Math Teacher
Semegen, Linda Coulter
Fourth Grade Teacher
HAVILAND
Allen, Mary Ann
Language Arts Teacher
HAYESVILLE
Dever, Cherie Ann (Cox)
Third Grade Teacher
HEATH
Johnson, Linda Bayliss
Social Studies Teacher
Jones, Joseph Alan
English Teacher
Pond, Robert Joseph
Retired Professor
Schramm, Patricia A.
French Teacher
HEBRON
Adkins, Nancy G.
Kindergarten Teacher & Dir
Bush, Robin T.
Science Teacher & Coach
Crozier, Scott W.
4th Grade Teacher
Keller, Traci Lynn
Assistant Band Director
King, Betty (Harness)
Economics Teacher
Millspaw, Mary Louise
Fifth Grade Teacher
Palm, Deborah Snelling
Assistant Elementary Principal
Rauch, Judith Adams
Vocal Music Teacher
Robinson, Sarah Hemstock
Spanish Teacher
HEMLOCK
Arms, Beverly Jill
Social Studies Teacher
HICKSVILLE
Baringer, Deborah Ann
Middle School Science Educator
Blue, David Allen
Social Studies Teacher
Brown, Sandra Copeland
4th Grade Teacher
Fabian, Carol Flory
First Grade Teacher
Guilford, Debra Kay
Second Grade Teacher
Hange, Ann Wendling
4th Grade Teacher
Hill, Ramona Mabe
1st Grade Teacher
McPike, Karlyn Korsgaard
German & French Teacher
Pelton, Robert Daniel
Social Studies Teacher
Peter, C. Lee
High School Math Teacher
Peverly, Susan Beasley
MS Reading & HS Jrnlsm Teacher
Rex, Virlynn Leigh
7th & 8th Grade Teacher
Sunday, Nancy Jo
Special Education Teacher
Sweet, Sharon Snyder
Health Teacher & Vlybl Coach
Zeedyk, Larry Joseph
Computer & Business Ed Teacher
HILLIARD
Clutter, Marianne
Third Grade Teacher

HILLIARD (cont)
Justice, Ray Eugene
Biology Teacher
King, Julie Morvai
American History Teacher
Linley, Marcia Guest
English Teacher
O'Shaughnessy, Jane Jackson
College Counselor
Reed, Peg Rhoades
Retired Teacher
Remy, Delores Stangel
German Teacher
Shepherd, Kim Charles
Creative Writing Teacher
Trace, Thomas E., Jr.
7th-8th Grade Science Teacher
Volbert, Kevin M.
Lang Arts Teacher & Ath Dir
HILLSBORO
Eberts, Howard Louis
Mrktg Ed Coord & DECA Adv
Garey, Jay Allen
Bands Dir & Fine Arts Dpt Head
Jolly, Peggy Shupert
First Grade Teacher
Mc Closkey, Mildred Crago
Adjunct English Teacher
Newby, Judy Ann
7th Grade Language Teacher
Porter, John Paul
Associate Prof of History
Snyder, Thomas Michael
Native Amer & World Hist Tchr
Wolfe, Terri Jean
Math Tchr & Var Chrldng Coach
HINCKLEY
Gerk, Carolyn Craig
First Grade Teacher
Nicholas, Jeffrey John
Fifth Grade Teacher
HOLGATE
Schlosser, Bruce E.
Middle School Teacher
HOLLAND
Anderson, Wanda S.
Business & Computer Teacher
Karazim, Linda Staszak
Coll Prep, AP, English Teacher
McIlwain, Elizabth Palicki
Junior English Teacher
O'Leary, Anne Swarthout
HS Social Studies Teacher
Short, Michael Patrick
English & Video Teacher
HOPEDALE
Leggett, Sandra Rebres
Kindergarten Teacher
Miser, Katharine Kovacik
First Grade Teacher
HOUSTON
Barber, Deanna Marie
Spanish & Reading Teacher
McKinney, Chester Edward
Science Teacher
HOWARD
Bell, Marlene L.
Computer & Business Teacher
Dodd, Brian Willard
Music & Chorus Teacher
Gregg, David P.
Biology Teacher
Smith, Karen Mc Donald
Family & Consumer Sci Teacher
HUBBARD
Benigas, John R.
4th Grade Reading Specialist
Forrester, William J.
Band Director
Gehring, Christine Johnson
Geometry Teacher
Gontaruk, Rita Papa
Jr High Teacher
Hamrock, Ardaith Alderman
History & English Teacher
Hart, William Henry
Eighth Grd Phys Science Tchr
Kim, Mimi T.
Tchr of Learning Disabilities
Knupp, Dorothy Castner
First Grade Teacher
Kolacz-Belanger, Vilma
HS Math & Computer Sci Teacher
Petrusko, Pam (Nutter)
Mathematics Teacher
Pinney, Carol Susanne (Albrecht)
English Teacher
Rindy, Patricia Picino
Business Teacher
Slater, Linda J.
Span Tchr & Publications Adv
Stoffer, Ross W.
American Government Teacher
Tate, Richard John
Guidance Counselor
Vukovich, Ruth Ramsey
English Teacher
Zirafi, Robert Anthony
HS Honors History Tchr
HUDSON
Banks-Burke, Betty A.
Business Ed, Computer Sci Tchr
Breuker, John, Jr.
Latin Teacher
Carnes, Ernest Russell
Physics Tchr & Sci Dept Head
Giles, Billie Moore
Art Teacher
Hallenbeck, Linda Sue
Fifth Grade Teacher

Isler, William Conrad
7th Grade Science Teacher
Koberna, Charlene
8th Grade Amer History Tchr
Lathan, Lance Emerson
History Teacher
Lustic, Therese Durkin
English Teacher
Miner, Margaret Holbrook
Special Education Teacher
Nold, James Jay
7th Grade Science Teacher
Schnellinger, Michael E.
Mathematics Teacher
Sheldon, Cinda Kay
High School Science Teacher
Suchanek, David Paul
Chemistry & Physics Instructor
Yanko, Robert Nicholas
Social Studies Teacher
Zema, Susan Guyette
Bio, Chem & Gen Sci Teacher
HUNTSVILLE
Fry, Melanie Ann (Worley)
Kindergarten Teacher
HURON
Adams, Jan Edward
Assoc Dean for Instrl Support
Berry, Edgar Allen
Instrumental Director
Horchler, Judith Beck
Social Studies Chairman
Smith, Martha Ward
Middle Schl Vocal Music Tchr
INDEPENDENCE
Stenger, James A.
8th Grade Teacher
INDIAN SPRINGS
Mc Kain, Lisa Meckstroth
Former Math Teacher
IRONTON
Burwell, Carolyn Rose (Henry)
Kindergarten Teacher
Corey, Karen Powers
Vocational Work & Family Tchr
Dutey, Gail Mc Manis
Elementary Teacher
Fisher, Bette L. Hinman
English Teacher
Harvey, Steven Craig
Biological Sciences Instructor
Kearns, James Lester
5th & 6th Grade Teacher
Kelley, Randy Lee
Fourth Grade Teacher
Kelly, Peggy Lee Dingus
Teacher & Coord of Gifted
King, William Everett
Program Manager
Lucas, David Miguel
Professor of Spanish & Speech
Massie, Annette Alban
Third Grade Teacher
Medinger, Joseph Christopher
High School Guidance Counselor
Sexton, Gina Dutey
Teacher of Learning Disabled
Sites, Kimberly Ann
English Teacher
Waller, Carol Crain
Business Education Teacher
Woodward, Martha C.
Instructor of English
Worthington, Mark
Mathematics Teacher
IRWIN
Yoder, Alvin L.
Bible Teacher
JACKSON
Armstrong, Denise Lynn Perkins
Spanish & English Teacher
Horsley, Wayne D.
Social Studies Teacher
Layton, Gene Alan
Learning Disabilities Teacher
Patton, Susan Midkiff
Third Grade Teacher
Riegal, Mary Christman
2nd Grade Teacher
Smith, Alyce M.
Spanish & Speech Teacher
JACKSON CENTER
Elchert, Scott Thomas
Social Studies Teacher
Sailor, Barbara Hart
Retired HS Art Teacher
Tenney, Catherine Williamson
Media Specialist
JACKSONTOWN
Coble, Nancy Lou (Davis)
Fourth Grade Teacher
JAMESTOWN
Aaronson, Ann Schroeder
6th-8th Grade Art Teacher
Craver, Cheryl Christina (Dennison)
Biology Teacher
Hartman, Cindy Mercer
High School English Teacher
James, Peggy Joyce
Fourth Grade Teacher
Ryan, Timothy Frank
Art Teacher
JASPER
Burkitt, Lori Vulgamore
Fourth Grade Teacher
JEFFERSON
Hannah, Ruth Ann
3rd Grade Teacher
O'Meara, Jacklyn Armour
Acctng & Computer Tech Tchr

JEROMESVILLE
Burns, Stephen Mark
Chem, Physics & AP Bio Tchr
Fair, Timothy Allen
Industrial Tech Instructor
Heyl, Linda S.
Hum, Speech & English Teacher
Selvage, Thomas Allen
Secondary Teacher
JOHNSTOWN
Bowman, Carol Marker
Chemistry & Physics Teacher
Green, Wanda Rizpah
Retired Title 1 Reading Coord
Hill, Donna Butler
Vocal Music Director
Wright, Trudy Feil
AP English Teacher
JUNCTION CITY
Paxton, Judith A.
Third Grade Teacher
KALIDA
Birkemeier, Judy Schroeder
Fifth Grade Teacher
Gasser, Janice Langhals
English Teacher
Gasser, Robert J.
Social Studies Teacher
Hellman, Carol Marie (Wiley)
4th Grade Teacher
Kahle, Janice M.
Kindergarten & EDK Teacher
Luersman, Roger John
Sixth Grade Sci & Lang Tchr
Myers, Charles Stelzig
Band & Choir Director
Schroeder, Frank Richard
Social Studies Teacher
Schumacher, Roxanne Lea
Mathematics Teacher
KANSAS
Yount, Clair L.
Social Studies Teacher
KEENE
Arney, Barbara Ann
Fifth Grade Teacher
Bell, Mary Katharine
Lang Arts & Social Stud Tchr
Mathias, Cindy
Third Grade Teacher
KENT
Albrecht, Theodore John
Music Professor
Baird, Joseph L.
Emeritus Professor
Baker, Johnnie W.
Professor of Computer Science
Barb, Cynthia M.
Mathematics Professor
Beck, Karen A.
Retired Teacher
Benjamin, Keith Ward
Accel Biology Teacher
Bissonnette, Anne Eveline
Collections Manager
Chandler, Timothy J. L.
Assoc Prof of Exercise
Commisso, Rosa
Elem Italian Lecturer & Coord
Danks, Carol Nickles
English & Journalism Teacher
Davis, JoDee
Music Professor
Delisle, James Robert
Professor
Dzeda, Bruce
Social Studies Dept Chairman
Ferritto, John Edmund
Associate Professor
Fitts, Janice Harvey
Retired Counselor
Fox-Cardamone, Lee
Asst Professor of Psychology
Guffey, Julie Anne Myers
Language Arts & Reading Tchr
Hockenberry, Nancy Carol (Haines)
Teaching Fellow
Hosta, Luann Kathleen
Math Teacher
Howard, Geoffry Stanton
Assoc Prof of Information Sys
Kerr, Dianne Lynne
Asst Professor of Health Ed
Lambert, R. Mitch
Chemistry Teacher
Mayo, Michael Allen
Marketing Professor
McCloskey, Diane L.
Professor of Flute
Moore, Edmund Timothy
Asst Prof of Pan African Stud
Pisegna, Jeanna Marie
Biology Teacher
Proudfoot, Jill Lin
Teaching Fellow
Reith, Mary Knisely
English Teacher
Rhodes, Kathleen Ann (Brown)
Teacher of Hearing Impaired
Richardson, Rhonda Anne
Associate Professor
Rippey, Sandy Schulenberg
Second Grade Teacher
Romeo, Anita Mary (Prochko)
Fourth Grade Teacher
Sargi, Terrie Anderson
Fifth Grade Teacher
Schultz, Robert Arthur
Elem Sci Methods Tchng Fellow

Sheppard, Kenneth P.
Kindergarten Teacher
Steiner, Carol J. (Erzeh)
Instr, Basic Math Concpt Coord
Swinford, Dennis D.
Critical Lang Coord, Eng Instr
Taylor, B. Jane
Fourth Grade Teacher
Theodore, Michael
Mathematics Teacher
Uhlik, Kim Stephen
Geography Instructor
Ujvari, Amy E.
Teaching Fellow
West, Robert D.
Associate Professor
KENTON
Allen, John Michael
Army JROTC Instructor
Barthlow, Cheryl Worthington
Director of Curriculum
Mc Callister, Elizabeth Renee
CP Biology Teacher
Prater, Joseph Michael
8th Grade Amer History Teacher
KETTERING
Applegate, Edith (Metzger)
Professor of Science & Math
Balent, Scott Andrew
Social Studies Teacher
Butch, James Van
HS Speech & Drama Teacher
Craig, Charles Robert
Director of Bands
Dunaway-Haney, Amy
Spanish Teacher
Gagliano, Rebecca Ann
Biology Teacher
Googash, Steven James
English Teacher
Gross, David Ian
Retired Professor
Karl, Robert Edwin
US History Teacher & Coach
Kozarec, Mark S.
Middle School Art Teacher
Kramer, William Karl
Honors Geom & Cmptr Sci Tchr
Lamb, Lawrence Robert
Guidance Counselor
Lewis, Cyndi M.
Chemistry Teacher
Martin, Margaret Russell
Biology Teacher
Mauch, Jeffrey David
9th Grade English Teacher
Mc Manus, Jeffrey Scott
Science Teacher
Mc Sherry, Susan Dee
Eng Tchr & Stu Assistance Adv
Mihalik, Michelle Renee (Brinkley)
Substitute Teacher
Moore, Mari Lou Antin
High School English Teacher
Neustein, Sondra Miriam (Lipp)
French & Spanish Teacher
Oexmann, Norval L.
Retired Math Teacher
Peters, James Ambrose, Jr.
Math & Cmptr Programming Tchr
Priser, Dennis A.
Retired Mathematics Teacher
Protos, Amy Reed
Math Teacher
Ramey, Kyle Bruce
Science Teacher
Runzo, Donna Stevenson
English & Reading Teacher
Shearer, Mary Ruth
Sci Dept Chprsn & Chem Tchr
Yux, Judith Ann
Tchr of Learning Disabilities
KILLBUCK
Underberg, Lee Henry
Principal
KINGS MILLS
Smith, Corinne Isaac
English Teacher
KINGSTON
Prickett, Kevin Vernon
Occupational Work Adjust Tchr
KINGSVILLE
Gaio, Laurel Louise (Duncan)
First Grade Teacher
KINSMAN
Boring, Elizabeth Crea
Sixth Grade Teacher
Hanselman, Jeanne Marie
High School Principal
Mitchell, Dane Edward
English Teacher
Wade, James Edward
HS Integrated Science Teacher
KIRKERSVILLE
Larson, Patricia Mackil
Speech & Language Pathologist
LA RUE
Bear, Rosella Mae (Walton)
Retired Elementary Teacher
LAFAYETTE
Downey, Marsha Lamke
High School English Teacher
LAGRANGE
Lokai, Larry P.
Agri-Business & Science Tchr
Thomas, Karen Lynn
7th Grade Language Arts Tchr
LAKESIDE MARBLEHEAD
Dayton, Audrey Hallier
Third Grade Teacher

Larson, Dennis R.
7th-9th Grd Social Stud Tchr
LAKEWOOD
Cavoli, Daniel Joseph
Latin Teacher
Dance, Anne Gabriel
Mathematics & Science Teacher
Dent, Phaidra Ann
Teacher of Hearing Impaired
Drotleff, John E.
Retired Fine Arts Dept Chr
Ebner, Dennis John
English Teacher
Edwards, Robert A.
Chemistry Teacher
Fassett, Bert Arnold
4th Grade Teacher
Gannon, David Stephen
English, Drama Tchr & Dir
Griebel, Brian R.
Instrumental Music Teacher
Jacoby, Joseph Harold
English Teacher
King, Kristine Larsen
Soc Stud & Lang Arts Tchr
Laing, Alan Rudolph
Math Tchr & Dept Facilitator
Lash, Margaret Clare
Health & Physical Ed Teacher
Leickly, Portia Elaine (Sergeant)
Science Teacher
Levindofske, Matthew Damian
Social Studies Teacher
Maskow, Brian David
Director of Bands
Maver, Robert Edward
High School Math Teacher
Mc Cutcheon, Catherine Jorgensen
Physical Education Teacher
Mescan, Mary Ann
6th-8th Grade Teacher
Muliolis, Amanda Gelazis
Math Department Chairperson
Nieberding, James Edward
Social Studies Dept Chair
Pollock, Allen Tom
Sixth Grade Teacher
Pollock, Barbara
Second Grade Teacher
Pommerening, Nancy Kondas
History Teacher
Ralls, Nancy Kavcar
Voc Family & Consumer Sci Tch
Rathge, Mark Lynn
Earth Science Teacher
Rodd, B. Diane (Matthews)
Educational Consultant & Tutor
Smerick, Jacqueline Elizabeth
First Grade Teacher
Stack, Kathleen Marie (Klubert)
Assistant Principal
Vanuch, Joseph Paul
Vocational Special Ed Coord
Wightman, Melanie Mumma
English Teacher
Wisniewski, Mark Edward
Science Teacher
Wondrak, Gerald A.
Vocal Music Teacher
Zickes, Jane M.
Science Tchr & Dept Chairman
LANCASTER
Anderson, Denissa (Whittington)
English Instructor
Bates, Rick Alan
8th Grd Language Arts Teacher
Beck, Maureen Denise (Mock)
English Teacher
Brown, Catherine Alice
Vocal Music Teacher
Casner, Brian Lance
Earth Science Teacher
Clippinger, Steven L.
Amer His, AP Govt & Ec Teache
Davenport, Anthony Wyatt
Art Instructor
Gerken, Bruce Victor
Percussion Studies Director
Grein, Marilyn Louise (Yound)
Kindergarten Teacher
Hancher, Peggy Arlene (Scott)
2nd Grade Teacher
Heidenreich, Christopher Paul
Director of Bands
Johnson, June Carvel
English Dept Chairman & Tchr
Kiger, Marcia Mae (Deeds)
Retired 6th Grade Teacher
Klein, Karen Helle
Math Teacher
Lamb, Larry Lee
Instructor of Electronics Tech
Mathias, Stephen Arthur
Social Studies Teacher
Mauller, Bette Fraser
Sixth Grade Teacher
Myers, Michael Raymond
Biology & Accelerated Bio Tchr
Packard, Teresa (Koralin)
English Teacher
Schromme, Jean Bibler
Third Grade Teacher
Smith, Jane McDaniel
School Nurse
Snively, John Thomas
Occupational Teacher
Spieth, Elizabeth Schall
3rd Grade Teacher
Tenney, Cindy Ansel
Kindergarten Teacher

ASTER (cont)
er, Cathy Sue (Miller)
Grade Teacher
ia, Robert Clifton
c Supervisor
Marci Ann
ce Teacher
indy, JoEllen Kleinschmidt
ness Teacher
erholt, Deborah Bruck
uage Arts Teacher
Sarah E. Kane
Grade Teacher
, John Louis
al Studies Teacher
SVILLE
an, Julia Ann
Reading & Math Teacher
ING
oan Lee (Trytko)
Grade Teacher
AM
Ruth Burton
ict Librarian
, Jonathan A.
School English Teacher
ITTSBURG
Linda
School Spanish Teacher
, George David
ce Teacher
NON
t, James Edward
ce & Health Teacher
, Deborah Palmer
Tchr & Department Chair
Kimberly Lynne
Grd Lang Arts Tchr
Wayne Lewis
Jrnlsm & Photography Tchr
s, Matthew Keith
ora Teacher
eski, Donald Joseph
sh Teacher
nzie, Wilma Teel
Grade Lang Arts Tchr
Constance Marie
Teacher
dinger, Gary L.
c Computer Graphics Instr
n, Anne M.
outerized Accounting Tchr
y, Martin J.
sh Teacher
r, Ann E.
Grade Teacher
ing, Ronald Eugene
rd American History Tchr
s, John Joseph
Studies & Amer His Tchr
ONIA
Michael Duffy
Director
di, Theodore
History & Govt Teacher
o, Guy W.
School Social Stud Tchr
sco, Anna Marie
Music Teacher
o, Penny Laakso
ematics Chairperson
Judith Lynn
ematics Teacher
IC
Darren Del
Grade Teacher
rink, Gary William
Language Arts Teacher
Beckie A. (Honigfort)
Art Teacher
der, Diane Marie
c Teacher
YNE
felder, Jane Frances
nd Grade Teacher
S CENTER
Cathy Lynn
Grade Science Teacher
ell, Rosemary Elaine
Grade Teacher
ld, Nancy Armstrong
sh Teacher
Bonnie Cary
ge Prep & English Teacher
enski, Liz
ce Teacher
ch, Hap
nce Teacher
Mary Seeley
ish Teacher
s, Ray A.
& Computer Science Tchr
SBURG
er, Melissa Anne
uage Arts Teacher
ski, Julie Anne
ematics Teacher
STOWN
David Shane
Teacher
Kathleen Detrick
rd Language Arts Teacher
, Russ Eugene Bobby Dan, Jr.
sh Teacher & Bsktbl Coach
c, James Richard
Teacher
, Wade Kenneth
Language Arts Instructor

LEXINGTON
Berdanier, Doris Anne
Family & Consumer Science Tchr
Heidlebaugh, Randy Lynn
Instrumental Music Director
Kapustar, Kathleen Ann
German Instructor
Korbas, Todd Andrew
Mathematics Teacher
Russell, Sharon Lynn
English Teacher
Weirich, Sue Metzger
Spanish Teacher
LIBERTY CENTER
Homan, Kerry Bostelman
Mathematics Teacher
Lingruen, Rex C.
Physical Education Teacher
LIMA
Bailey, Jane Moening
Third Grade Teacher
Barnhart, Thomas H.
Mathematics Dept Chairman
Besecker, Jay Allen
Science Teacher
Bible, Ronald Lee
8th Grade History Teacher
Bonifas, Joseph Arthur
AP Art His & Sculpture Tchr
Breitigam, Julie Ann
Health & Physical Ed Tchr
Burden, Martha Wilcox
Fifth Grade Teacher
Carver, Jon Cameron
Social Studies Tchr & Dept Chm
Christen, David Robert
Instr of Computerized Engine
Dellifield, Dennis L.
Band Conductor
Faulkner, Shawn Alan
Teacher
Fisher, James Clyde
Math Teacher
Foley, Douglas Edward
Guidance Counselor
Foley, Patricia Mary Lockemeyer
Kindergarten Teacher
Giesige, Thomas Edward
Spanish Teacher
Haidet, Trent L.
Fifth Grade Teacher
Horlander, Judith Ann
Math & Algebra Teacher
Horner, Keith William
Social Studies Teacher
Iames, Mary Steiner
Guidance Counselor
Ireland, Diana Lehmann
Jr HS Science Teacher
Jordan-Squire, Jeannine M.
English & Yearbook Teacher
Kaple, Patricia L. (Trame)
High School Science Teacher
LaGrande, Charles Norman
German Instructor
Maloney, Diane Berneburg
Associate Professor
Mc Elwee, Helen Reid
Retired Elementary Teacher
Mershman, Dorothy A. (Fisher)
Diversified Cooperative Coord
O'Brien, Caroline Samantha
6th Grade Teacher
Ozuk, Christine M.
English Teacher
Seiling, William W.
Mathematics Teacher
Stout, Thomas Michael
Accounting Instructor
Straub, MaryBob Hogenkamp
Spanish Teacher
Wierman, Kevin Carl
7th & 8th Grade History Tchr
Wolfe, Gary L.
High School Math Teacher
LINDSEY
Theller, Kimberly Kay
Elem Prin & Dist Test Coord
LISBON
Avallynn, Sherilee
Vcl Music & Theatre Arts Tchr
Forzano, Robert John
History Teacher
Henceroth, William A.
4th Grade Social Studies Tchr
Janek, Nancy Reese
English Teacher & Dept Chair
Lamoncha, Charmaine Ellen (Hawkins)
Fifth Grade Teacher
Mack, Robert D.
Senior Marine Instr
Stanfield, William Frederick
Art Teacher
Turner, Susan Zigler
Gen Ed Curriculum Consultant
LOCKLAND
Kreiner, Diane
Family & Consumer Science Tchr
Moore, Trina Denniston
Drill Team Co-Director
LODI
Filous, Audrey Cincala
Sci Dept Coord & Bio Instr
Hayas, Galye Lynn
Teacher, Advisor & Coach
Salem, George Gregory
Business Teacher
Schleich, Jeffrey Dennis
Soc Stud Tchr & Asst Coach

LOGAN
Barrell, Trina Yvette (Sparks)
8th Grd Rdng & Lang Arts Tchr
Benoy, Robert Frank
Fifth Grade Teacher
Brewster, Charlotte Burns
First Grade Teacher
Daubenmire, Jeffrey Alan
Director of Choral Activities
Dietz, Susan Ball
8th Grd Lang Arts & Grad Instr
Dotson, Pamela Jane
Sixth Grade Teacher
Fickel, R. Edward
Biology Teacher
Herrick, Patricia Mc Connell
8th Grade Math Teacher
Horsky, Al G.
Retired Band Director
Mace, Roger D.
Physical Education
Wolfe, Kelly
7th Grade Mathematics Teacher
LONDON
Kurt, Edward Paul
Dean of Students & Ath Dir
Schwartz, Jodi Knox
10th & 12th Grd Biology Tchr
LORAIN
Bakalar, Ronald A.
English & Speech Teacher
Baker, Margaret Cunningham
English Teacher
Barnes, Laura Ann (Glawe)
4th Grade Teacher
Bryant, Emily Catherine
Sixth Grade Teacher
Butcher, Sandra Jean
First Grade Teacher
Cintavey, Kathleen Otterson
High School Teacher
Colon, Carmen Maria
Spanish Teacher
Darcy, Mavis Joan
Latin & English Teacher
Ferguson, Jay W.
Math Teacher
Harizal, Susan May
Music Director
Ivancic, Karita
Vocal Music & Religion Teacher
Jackson, Germaine D.
Assistant Principal
Jones, Robert John
History Teacher
Kelly, Gina Poyle
Kindergarten & First Grd Tchr
Klein, James Allen
High School Math Teacher
Kreeger, Kathy Lynn
French Teacher
Mendak, Mirta Mendez
ESL Teacher
MIller, Alicia Jo
Math & Reading Title I Teacher
Mittler, Dianne Bentley-Burk
Gifted Resource Teacher
Parker, Richard K.
Technology Teacher
Peddie, Carol E.
Vocal Music Teacher
Petz, Susan L.
Teacher of the Deaf
Pietromica, Rudolph V.
5th Grade Teacher
Robbins, Mark Allen
Elem Physical Education Tchr
Sallay, Christine Gutzeit
Art Instructor
Schultz, Anna Marie (White)
Seventh Grd Tchr & Asst Prin
Smith, Vickey D. (Jornod)
Social Studies Teacher
Spruill, William L.
Band & Orchestra Director
Stroman, Roger Joe
8th Grade Civics Teacher
Teaman, Linda Kay
6th Grade Teacher
Vitale, Janet L.
Fifth Grade Teacher
Walther, Daniel B.
Science Teacher
Werner, Darlene Miller
Kindergarten Teacher
LORE CITY
Cunningham, Deborah (Dovicsak)
Math Teacher
LOUDONVILLE
Kick, Stephen Phillip
American History Teacher
Shrimplin, Jo
English Teacher
LOUISVILLE
Aljancic, Andrew A.
English & Speech Teacher
Ashley, David Lee
Math Teacher
Baker, Elizabeth Lee
German Teacher & Club Advisor
Eddins, William Cole
Fifth Grade Teacher
Faigley, Joseph R.
Social Studies Dept Chairman
Gresko, John James
6th Grade Teacher
Hawkins, Andrew Albert
High School Computer Teacher
Hirsch, Janet Louise
English Department Chairperson

Karasarides, Jennifer Anne
2nd Grade Teacher
Kew, Kristin Lynn
French & Spanish Teacher
Maher, Jeanne Elizabeth
Religious Education Teacher
Ray, Sue Ann
Math Dept Chairperson & Tchr
Scott, Harry G., III
Mathematics Teacher
Scott, Suzanne Glass
Math Teacher & Department Chr
Snyder, Carol Lynn
Seventh Grade English Teacher
Vagedes, Joseph Carl
Chemistry Teacher
Wolpert, Debra Ann (Betz)
Algebra & Geometry Teacher
LOVELAND
Mc Cune, Alex
Reading Recovery Teacher
Miracle, Mary Ann Havlena
Retired Fifth Grade Teacher
Monroe, Jane Hamilton
Retired Fourth Grade Teacher
LOWELLVILLE
DiMatteo, Candida
Italian Teacher
Solak, Ivan
Math Teacher
LOWER SALEM
Jiles, Kathryn Gambill
2nd Grade Teacher
LUCAS
Dickerson, Steven Edward
Industrial Technology Teacher
LUCASVILLE
Bibbey, Vaughn David
Cmptr Sci Tchr & Tech Coord
Gampp, Michael Lee
Junior Accounting Instructor
Mc Clay, Randall Elliot
Chemistry & Physics Teacher
Preston, Robyn Rae (Doss)
6th & 7th Grd English Teacher
Sayre, Connie L.
Legal Asst Program Instructor
LYNCHBURG
Louderback, Carol Fawley
English & Latin Teacher
LYNDHURST
Patrick, Bonnie Mc Kee
Second Grade Teacher
Scully, James Andrew
Sixth Grade History Teacher
LYONS
Laver, Carla (Haynes)
Fifth Grade Teacher
MACEDONIA
Dambrogio, Kimberly A.
Chemistry Teacher
Devore, Janice Fichtner
English Teacher
Gaffney, Carmella Sue
Business Education Teacher
Mc Combs, Brian Joseph
Math Teacher
MADISON
Cox, Rosemary Colegrove
5th Grade Gifted Class Tchr
Hytree, Marysue Mason
Second Grade Teacher
Jackson, Kathryn Renee
English Teacher
Loeffel, John William
Eng & Wstrn Civilization Tchr
McIntyre, Jerry L.
Mathematics Teacher
Mc Leod, Julia Marie
Third Grade Teacher
Palagyi, Lorna (Haapanen)
Fourth Grade Teacher
Staley, Linda Lucrezi
6th Grd English Teacher
MAGNOLIA
Bressi, Eugene Richard
8th Grade Mathematics Teacher
Gotchall, Glenn Joseph
Marketing Ed Coordinator
Haglock, Jill Kinsey
HS Lead Science Teacher
Johnstone, Timothy Leon
Mathematics Teacher
Leach, Robert Homer
Social Studies Teacher
Lotz, Robin Elizabeth (Palmer)
Spanish Teacher
Marcoaldi, Joseph John
Junior High School Teacher
Richards, R. Kenneth
Industrial Arts Instructor
Wigfield, Stephanie Hannan
Special Ed & 4th Grd Teacher
MALINTA
Hoover, Nancy J. (Cordes)
Third Grade Teacher
MALVERN
Anderson, Anna Prychodczenko
Music Teacher
Bille, Donna L.
Science & Math Teacher
Marshall, Robert Dale
HS Mathematics Teacher
Young, William F.
Band Dir & Music Theory Tchr
MANCHESTER
Meyers, Sandy Sue
High School Spanish & Eng Tchr

MANSFIELD
Alexander, Betsy L.
Coord of GATE & Career Prgms
Bair, Jay C.
Earth Sci Tchr & Dept Chprsn
Campbell, Bernard Marie
Science Teacher
Coon, Barbara Riggle
Second Grade Teacher
Godsil, Matthew Burton
Art Teacher
Hassmann, Joni Alexander
Kindergarten Teacher
Hock, Merrillie Sibbald
Second Grade Teacher
Holmes, Edwin M.
Mathematics Teacher
Jacobs, Judy Ruth (Anthony)
Sixth Grade Teacher
Lilly, Ellen (Motter)
Former Teacher
Majewski, Dianne Calascibetti
Social Studies & Relgion Tchr
Mapes, Thomas Carl
Occptnl Work Adjstmnt Tchr
Mathews, Georgiann Elizabeth
Spanish, French & Hlth Teacher
Mosier, Douglas Wayne
Head Wrestling Coach
Mudra, James Gregory
8th Grd American History Tchr
Smith, James R.
Asst Prin & Jr HS Math Teacher
Tarino, Janet Z.
Assoc Professor of Chemistry
White, John Ivan
Eighth Grade Science Teacher
Willhelm, Deborah A.
Counselor
Wolff, Thomas Lee
Asst Principal & Athletic Dir
Yoost, Barbara Lynn
Nursing Professor
MANTUA
Furillo, Mary Beard
English & Reading Instructor
Moore, Yvonne Pearson
6th Grade Teacher
Nichols, Edward Lee
6th Grade Teacher
Perfect, Kathy Ann
Fourth Grade Teacher
Siegenthaler, Eileen Cubon
Mathematics Teacher
Siman, John Andrew
Fifth Grade Teacher
Vanags, John Robert
Physical Education Teacher
MAPLE HEIGHTS
Bednarik, Antoinette Sospirato
Business Teacher
Clay, Susan Geitgey
Chemistry Teacher
Elias, Bridget Gallagher
English & Reading Teacher
Esposito, Lucille Riccilli
English & Drama Teacher
Guerini, Jody Lyn (Plank)
Business Teacher
Hindenlang, James Grant
7th Grade Science Teacher
Johnson, Carolyn Renita
Seventh Grade Soc Studies Tchr
Kolesar, Lynn Toth
Business Teacher
Quier, Geoffrey Douglas
5th Grade Teacher
Sejba, Donna Marie (Bastian)
Jr High Tchr & Pastoral Min
Spallone, Barbara Nolia (Soper)
Third Grade Teacher
Toth, M. Jane
Science Tchr & Dept Chprsn
Walter, Dale Allen
Government & Psychology Tchr
Weaver, Mary K.
English Teacher
MARENGO
Goodge, Joyce B.
Sixth Grade Teacher
Miller, Hazel H.
Retired 4th Grade Teacher
MARIETTA
Aebi, Imogene Mc Donough
Business Teacher
Carbone, Cindy Seehafer
English Composition & Lit Prof
Cisar, Susan Marie
Social Service Instructor
Crandell, Carolyn G.
Adjunct Instructor of Math
De Laat, Jacqueline
Assoc Prof of Political Sci
Dunaway, Michael Eugene
6th-12th Grd Vocal Music Tchr
Dunn, Billy Ray
Associate Professor of Ed
Dutton, Carol Tyminski
Acctng & Bus Mgmt Assoc Prof
Duvall, Gary Edgar
Retired Teacher
Egolf, Debra Sue
Chemistry Professor
Finley, James Bogard
7th & 8th Grd English Teacher
Foutty, Stephen Troy
Eighth Grade Science Teacher
Gilde, Hans-Georg
Retired Professor

MARIETTA (cont)
Johnson, Grace F.
Asst Prof of Mngmt & Acctng
Kimball, Marshall Coleman
Band Dir & Music Dept Chm
Kolankiewicz, Sandra J.
English & Leadership Professor
Krawczyk, Carl-Michal
Assistant Professor
Luthy, Nancy Morris
Mathematics Teacher
Mac Haffie, Barbara J.
Assoc Prof of History & Rlgn
Mahan, Nancy L.
French Teacher
McAfee, Tracy L.
Assoc Prof of Speech & Theatre
McGrew, John D.
Emeritus Professor
Meeks, Marilyn (Moffat)
Quest, Hlth & Teen Tchrs Tchr
Miller, A. Brad
Mathematics & History Teacher
Miller, Kimberlie Witzberger
7th-8th Grd Sci & Hlth Tchr
Morrow, Kathryn Board
Third Grade Teacher
O'Donnell, James Howlett, III
History Professor
O'Donnell, Mabry Miller
Prof of Speech Communication
Osborne, Edward Henry
Accounting Professor
Peery, Barbara Jones
First Grade Teacher
Pienkos, Sarah E.
Voc Work Prgm Teacher & Coord
Poling, Dewayne O.
Carpentry Teacher
Putnam, Robert Ervin
Retired Adjunct Faculty
Rett, Kelly Lynn
Developmental Psych Asst Prof
Sharpe, Peggy A.
Early Childhood Dir & Prof
Sibicky, Mark E.
Asst Professor of Psychology
Smith Wagner, Lisa Rexann
Bus Ed Instr & Tech Coord
Steckel, Tom
Assoc Professor of Chemistry
Taylor, Michael Brooks
Professor of Mgmt & Ldrshp
Thomas, Deborah Ann
Assistant Professor of Psych
Thomas, Paula N.
Mass Media & Asst Professor
Unroe, Chris Fraser
English Teacher
Wesel, Barbara J.
English Composition Instructor
Yi, Xiaoxiong
Asst Prof of Political Sci
Zhang, Ende
Associate Professor
MARION
Akers, Cathy Jo (Crum)
6th Grade Teacher
Aly, Hassan Y.
Assoc Prof of Economics
Appelfeller, Sherril Kay (Converse)
Health & Phys Ed Teacher
Bishop-Long, Beth E.
English Teacher
Buchanan, Marvin Darrell
7th Grade Math Teacher
Bucher, Carl
English Teacher
Burris, Lynette S.
Choral & General Music Dir
Evans, Sue Ann
Twelfth Grade English Teacher
Goins, Laurie Leeann
Spanish Teacher
Hawkins, Joy Carole
7th Grd Language Arts Teacher
Hill, Kathy E. (Null)
Science Teacher
Hughes, Joyce Marie Martin
Fourth Grade Teacher
Jones, Richard Alonzo, II
Social Studies Teacher
Kubbs, Chris Robert
HS Math Teacher
Mally, Nancy Gail
Language Arts Teacher
Matthews, Adam Lee
Mathematics Teacher
Mc Elroy, Betty Hougendobler
Vocal Music Teacher
Mc Guire, Mark Sean
Biology Teacher
Mensing, Teresa Marie
Geology Professor
Oyster, Betty Jean (Nightingale)
6th Grade Teacher
Parrish, Karen I.
Social Studies Dept Chair
Pettijohn, Terry Frank
Professor of Psychology
Porter, Wayne I.
Director of Student Services
Saull, Margie Diane (Sheets)
Fourth Grade Teacher
Sauselen, Elwood Larry
Visiting Asst Professor of Art
Schuette, Lisa Holden
Mathematics Teacher
Schuster, Beverly Kay Brown
Fifth Grade Teacher
Steffel, Vladimir
History Professor
Steng, John P.
Sixth Grade Teacher
Turner, Teresa A.
Vocal & Music Teacher
Vaflor, Ednita Gonzaga
Sixth Grade TAG Teacher
Vitartas, Paul
English & American His Tchr
Webb, Robert Okey
English Teacher
White, Carol Owen
Seventh Grade Teacher
MARK CENTER
Bassett, Belva Ann (Zeeolyk)
Retired 2nd Grade Teacher
MARTINS FERRY
Hoffman, Barbara S.
Fourth Grade Teacher
Hoffman, Rose Marie
Sixth Grade Teacher
Hohman, Heidi Sue
Fourth Grade Teacher
Javersak, Alice Mathieson
English & Speech Teacher
Johnson, Lisa Ann
Seventh Grade Teacher
Krupnik, Thomas Edward
6th Grd Sci & Lang Arts Tchr
Mc Farland, Anna Muntean
7th Grd Social Stud Teacher
Minder, Judith Mowry
Eight Grade Teacher
Rippey, Betty Thompson
Mathematics Teacher
Sarratore, Anthony A.
Seventh Grade Teacher
Slanchik, Joanne DeCesare
Business & History Teacher
Snodgrass, Gretchen Ann
English Teacher
Suriano, Thomas Michael
High School Guidance Counselor
Wagner, William Glenn
Chemisty & Physics Teacher
Wayne, Julia Ann (Yoho)
Band & Choral Director
Wood, Robert Russell
Eighth Grade Science Teacher
MARYSVILLE
Allen, Linda Koehler
7th Grade Language Arts Tchr
Burns, Dawn Marie
Business Teacher
Holton, Richard L.
Calculus Teacher
Honaker, J. Wayne
Mathematics Dept Chm & Teacher
Koukis, Susan Robinson
English Teacher
Ludwin, Robert A.
Math & Computers Teacher
Winters, Dolores Leis
Choral Director
MASON
Balm, Debra F.
Mathematics Teacher
Furia, Robert
Guidance Counselor
Gaskin, Paul Scott
High School Math Teacher
Griffith, Donna Margaret
American History Teacher
Hendricks, Andrew Michael
Marketing Tchr & Coordinator
Stroud, Diana Wiechman
Mathematics Teacher
MASSILLON
Beane, Patricia Jean Johnson
Second Grade Teacher
Brown, Debra Mahoney
Kindergarten Teacher
Coker, Susan
Fourth Grade Teacher
Farrah, Paul Greg
Math Teacher
Gallucci, Dale Joseph
Fifth Grade Science Teacher
Gard, Darleen Duffy
Fifth Grade Teacher
Geise, Lucille Marie Nuncia, SND
Adult Rel Ed Tchr & Principal
Hartline, Rebecca Sue (Boyd)
English & Psychology Teacher
Hedges, Sharman Kline
Music, Speech & Drama Director
Hilterbrand-Ward, Janet Louise (Pauli)
First Grade Teacher
Lautzenheiser, Bruce Allen
Chemistry Teacher
Marsh, Karen Jane (Sanford)
First Grade Teacher
Mercer, Scott Deming
History Teacher
Morey, John Charles
6th Grade Teacher
Nielsen, Karen Englehardt
English Teacher
O'Brien, Mary Niewierski
Second Grade Teacher
Pitz, Harold L.
Retired Science & Math Teacher
Plybon, John D., Jr.
Construction Trades Teacher
Rukavina, Madalana L.
Language Arts Teacher
Schubert, Chey Costello
Theatre Arts & English Teacher
Schuetz, Elmer David
Social Studies Teacher
Schwyer, Robert Glenn
History & Government Teacher
Seeds, Laurel Hines
Voice Teacher
Speicher, Judy L.
Home Economics Teacher
Van Wey, Nate J.
Physics Teacher
Wertz, James Thomas
Mathematics Teacher
Woods, Darrell Scott
Physics Tchr & Teen Inst Adv
Young, Joanne Marie
Kindergarten Teacher
Zucal, Daniele Pierrette
High School French Teacher
MASURY
Houk, Dolores Jean (Gasparec)
Fifth Grade Teacher
Reiser, Kathleen Ann
Fifth Grade Teacher
MAUMEE
Dick, Matthew Robert
Physics Teacher
DuGai, David John
Business Education Teacher
Kratzman, Eugene L.
Math & Algebra Teacher
Welch, Larry James
Biology Teacher
MAYFIELD HEIGHTS
Richardson, Jean Czyzycki
Gifted Intervention Specialist
MC ARTHUR
Foster, Bette Carol
Sixth Grade Teacher
Mullins, Kelli Oliver
Language Arts & Reading Tchr
Mundy, Connie Jarrell
First Grade Teacher
Phillips, Christie Ciano
Speech & English Teacher
Shuter, David H.
Spanish & French Teacher
Spitler, Christopher Scott
Industrial Arts Instructor
Walker, Erick C.
English Teacher
MC CONNELSVILLE
Bragg, Kim D.
Computer Business Skills Instr
Danese, Sylvia Paulette
English Teacher
Hemkes-Ross, Norvel M.
Jr Computer Accounting Teacher
Jarvis, Rebecca S. Maikranz
Guidance Counselor
Moore, Ronald Lee
Lang Arts Tchr & Bldg Coord
Morrison, Donna Haskinson
In-School Suspension Teacher
Powell, Richard O'Bryan
High School English Teacher
Quaintance, Julia Ann
Chemistry & Physics Teacher
Schubert, Blythe Gallaway
English Teacher
Thompson, Susan I.
Elementary Principal
MC CUTCHENVILLE
Goeller, Judith Ann
Third Grade Teacher
MC DONALD
Dolsak, Donna Millik
Math Teacher
Franko, Susan Marie
Seventh & Eighth Grade Teacher
Hawk, Brenda Kay
Home Economics Teacher
Hetzler, Patricia Ann
2nd Grade Teacher
Krumpak, Diane L.
Chemistry Teacher
Miles, Joan Bako
Business Education Teacher
Miller, Diane Lin
Spanish Teacher
MC GUFFEY
Dudek, Sandra Lou
English Teacher
Price, Jeffrey S.
Social Studies Teacher
Rex, Julia A.
Third Grade Teacher
MECHANICSBURG
Poland, Kimberly Kay (Jones)
Language Arts Teacher
MECHANICSTOWN
Dunlap, Ellyn Atchison
Fourth Grade Teacher
MEDINA
Barge, Albert
English Teacher
Beall-Brandes, Tamara
Music Educator
Bender, Hildegarde
English Teacher
Betz, Maryann
Vocational Business Ed Instr
Brown, Kathryn Makowski
English & Journalism Teacher
Clevidence, Richard Herbert
Instr of Learning Disabilities
Cullin, Jane Busson
Health & Physical Ed Teacher
Dodson, James Richard
Soc Studies & History Teacher
Domer, Mitchell Parker
Junior High Teacher
Fisher, Katherine A.
Eng, History & Theater Teacher
Gee, John Howard
5th Grd History & Reading Tchr
Greene, Lucia Ann
Vocational Special Ed Coord
Holmes, Joan Elizabeth
Spanish & English Teacher
Ilg, Christopher Paul
6th-12th Grd Vocal Music Tchr
Jack, Timothy James
Social Studies Teacher
Kirk, Bill, III
Teacher
Kubilus, Daryl George, Jr.
Instrumental Music Teacher
Lenk, Carol Ann
Language Arts Dept Head
Ludwig, Sheila James
Vocal Music Teacher
Magier, Thomas George
Language Arts & Amer His Tchr
Nairus, Judith (Kortsehl)
Latin & English Teacher
Palmer, Barbara Foderaro
4th-5th Grade Teacher
Phillips, Susan Bucklew
Geometry & Alg II Teacher
Richardson, Sharron Young
2nd Grade Teacher
Ruff, Donald Raymond
Literature Teacher
Rush, Linda Lee
Elementary Guidance Counselor
Sawan, Amy J.
Latin Teacher
Schmoyer, Kathryn Anderson
Substitute Teacher & Volunteer
Shepherd, Valencia Radcliff
Diversified Med Tech Instr
Stauffer, Kathy Sue
Mathematics Teacher
Ulich, Dorothy Brumm
English Teacher
Walker, Douglas L.
Biology Teacher
Wilhelm, Catherine Simpkins
8th Grade English & Rdng Tchr
MEDWAY
York, Terry E.
Third Grade Teacher
MENDON
Schwartz, Gloria Jean (Ringwald)
Fourth Grade Teacher
MENTOR
Allen, Yvonne Hobbs
English Teacher
Armstrong, William Allen
Mathematics Professor
Bassett, Sharon Burdette
7th-8th Language Arts Teacher
Begin, Paulette Marie (Mazie)
Former Jr High Teacher
Benns, Charles E.
Technology Education Teacher
Bontempo, Catherine Mary (Locker)
Mathematics Teacher
Carr, Sally Sprague
Assoc Professor of Psychology
Cline, Bruce, Ph.D
Prof & Photography Dept Chair
Enyedy, Zoe Zachlin
Chemistry Teacher
Finley, Kelly Ann
English & Art Teacher
Henrich, William Robert
Ninth Grade Earth Science Tchr
Hill, Deborah Tulley
5th Grade Teacher
Kandalec, Richard Alan
Dept Coord & Tech Ed Instr
Kapostasy, Margaret Ann
1st Grade Teacher
Keller, William Edward
6th Grade Teacher
Kindsvatter, George Jerry
Biology Teacher
Lagerstedt, Arthur P.
Retired Teacher
Litz, Claudia
Science Teacher
Luciano, Lawrence Patrick
English Teacher
Mackar, Thomas P.
Health, Phys Ed Tchr & Coach
Michels, James Robert
9th Grade English Teacher
Oleksak, Sharon Daniels
Health & Physical Educator
Roberts, Mary Jane Puleo
History Teacher
Rossi, Mary May
Sixth Grade Teacher
Skilton, Kenneth Douglas
Mathematics Teacher
Stadulis, Janet Klimasz
Assistant Professor of English
Troha, Richard Joseph
Industrial Arts Teacher
Turoczy, Robert John
English Teacher
Wardeiner, Mark Richard
6th Grade Teacher
Wood, Ron Edward
English Teacher
Woodman, Richard Dennis
Honors & AP Biology Tchr
Yowell, Timothy O.
Instrumental Music Teacher
MIAMISBURG
Berry, Craig Steven
High School Counselor
Brigati, Marilyn Drake
Lang Arts Tchr & Dept Chair
Chapman, Janet Anderson
Art Teacher
Collinsworth, Jane Fleming
Music Teacher
Davis, Vickie Rae
High School English Teacher
Fisher, Diane Schaeffer
Spanish Teacher
Hesler, Vickie Williams (Carter)
6th Grade Teacher
Houser, Roy G.
Accounting & Business Teacher
Kinner, LeeAnn Foster
Music Teacher & Entertainer
Lee, Betty A.
HS Speech & Comm Instructor
Myers, Tonya Evans
Fourth Grade Teacher
Petry, Mary K.
High School English Teacher
Richardson, Cheryl F.
First Grade Teacher
MIDDLEFIELD
Clemens, Cynthia Ferrell
American History Teacher
Kovanes, William G.
Eighth Grd Language Arts Tchr
MIDDLEPORT
Kennedy, Michael Curtis
Junior High Math Teacher
MIDDLETOWN
Brewer, Beverly Lynn
6th Grade Teacher
Chambers, Opal T.
Second Grade Teacher
Dickson, Melinda Sue (Henderson)
Spanish & Psychology Teacher
Frederick, Barbara Jo
7th-8th Grade Special Educator
Gardner, Richard Allen
Chemistry & Math Teacher
Gebhardt, Paul Louis
Theology Instr & Rel Dept Chm
Glynn, Patricia Holweger
Third Grade Teacher
Goecke, Lynda
4th Grade Teacher
Hess, Suzanne K.
L D Support Specialist
Kennedy, Pauline Danice (West)
Second Grade Teacher
Kinney, Kevin Dwayne
Fifth Grade Teacher
Kitchen, Deborah L.
Art Teacher
Kukuk, Ellen Cording
Third Grade Teacher
Lykins, Lavern Brooks
Owner & Manager
McCommons, Brenda Perkins
5th Grade Teacher
Munson, Alice Faye Owens
First Grade Teacher
Myers, Sharon Back
Sixth Grade Teacher
Neu, Brenda Greenwell
Mathematics Tchr & Asst Prin
Radcliffe, Sue Ellen Kinsey
Physics & Math Teacher
Rauter, Patricia Frost
Arts Dept Chm & Teacher
Sams, Sandra Bailey
Mathematics Teacher
Worbis, Deborah Gephart
Spanish & English Teacher
MILAN
Spitler, John Edward
Law Enforcement Coord & Instr
Wilbur, Dora Lynne
Third Grade Teacher
MILFORD
Aenis, K. James
Asst Prin, Ath Dir & Sci Tchr
Drake, Anne Melanie
Language Arts Teacher
Eckert, Daniel A.
Math & History Teacher
Hook, Larry R.
Biology Teacher
House, Nancy Catherine
English & Publications Teacher
King, Janet Wells
Cooperative Business Ed Coord
Moore, James Carl
Psychology & Economics Teacher
Morris, Della Lyn
7th Grade Life Science Teacher
Peters, Christal Wikoff
Secondary English Teacher
Priede, Laura Lynn
Math Teacher
Radloff, Jeffrey Edward
Physics & Mathematics Teacher
Williams, Pamela Kaiser
1st Grade Teacher
MILFORD CENTER
Hegenderfer, Debbie Stuart
Fourth Grade Teacher
Roesch, V. Jean
Second Grade Teacher
MILLBURY
Glaze, Vicki L.
Sixth Grade Teacher

BURY (cont)
r, Marilyn Dalling
th Grade Teacher
gomery, Jo Anne
Grade Teacher
., Robin Eugene
n Grade Teacher
ER CITY
Suzanne Theresa
Language Arts Teacher
ERSBURG
, Ty
h Grade Science Teacher
, Wilma Conkey
red Teacher
aso, Gail Baier
nd Grade Teacher
s, Lindy Brian
h & Space Science Teacher
Nina Lanning
Grade Teacher
ERSPORT
ff, Nancy Evans
ling & English Teacher
Juanita A.
ogy Teacher
RAL CITY
Susan Kohler
man & Civics Teacher
r, Jennifer Jo
ity Volleyball Coach
n, James Allen
ish Teacher
Laura Nofsinger
guage Arts Teacher
n, Michelle LaFountaine
ling Teacher
RAL RIDGE
, Virginia Lou (Briggs)
hematics Teacher
, Kimberly Tolbert
her
cante, Cal Joseph
8th Grade English Teacher
y, Patricia Coppinger
ish Teacher
RVA
l, Gerald Lynn
al Studies & US His Tchr
r, Thomas Ray
ish Instr & Newspaper Adv
ORD
Patricia Louise Turner
Grade Teacher
ls, Lana Diane Childress
Grade Math Teacher
o, Pamela Sue
al Studies Teacher
Lisa Cook
of the Talented & Gifted
er, Joyce Anne Keaton
Grade Teacher
der, Rama Lynn
ness Ed & Comp Sci Teacher
arbara Ann
Grade Teacher
wiler, Mark Alan
I Reading & Math Tchr
Michael H.
Anatomy & Physiology Tchr
t, Michelle Rene (Shover)
Grade Teacher
eter, Carroll L.
tional Agriculture Teacher
O JUNCTION
tino, Richard Vincent
nce Teacher
y, James A.
gh Math Teacher
Linda Jean
Tchr of Talented & Gifted
evich, Michael Robert
Arts & World His Tchr
e, Steven
th Grade Teacher
man, Georgia Krnich
ish Teacher
Sherri Cox
S His & Sci Teacher
TER
aus, Debra Hoehne
ness Teacher
cht, Anita Maltinsky
ily & Consumer Science Tchr
ADORE
Christian Eugene
School English Teacher
, Kathryn Marie (Kruer)
& 9th Grade Health Teacher
art, Janet (Rumbaugh)
th Grade Teacher
, Barbara Mc Curdy
of Learning Disabilities
ellan, Sylvia J.
ial Needs Teacher
son, Denise
Grade Teacher
s, Margaret Anne Battin
h Grade English Teacher
ll, Jim Gervase
Grade Lang Arts Teacher
n, Janet Nentwick
Grade Science Teacher
CLOVA
y, Vera M. Moore
l 2 Teacher
ROE
ia, Elizabeth Ann (Reichard)
al Director

Collins, Dennis Charles
PE & Health Teacher
Cotter, Carmela Marie
English Teacher
Stewart, Eleanor Yeager
English Teacher
MONROEVILLE
Deitz, Karen LaFene
First Grade Teacher
Roach, Beverly Dennis
Business & Computer Instructor
Rose, Edward Joseph
Jr High Teacher
Wearsch, Richard Michael
Biology Teacher
Wood, Kevin Richard
Fourth Grade Teacher
MONTPELIER
Belden, David
Seventh Grade Lang Arts Tchr
Blake, Joseph Daniel
Fourth Grade Teacher
Faler, Kay D.
Kindergarten Teacher
Meyers, Debbie Boetz
Lang Arts Teacher
Tippin, Lisa Irene
Lang Arts & Soc Stud Tchr
MORRAL
Cybak, Edward John
HS Social Studies Teacher
Hicks, Darla Jean
Fifth Grade Teacher
Laucher, Doug M.
Mathematics Teacher
Sheets, George William
Lang Arts Tchr & Dept Chair
MORRISTOWN
Goff, Cindy Koerber
Third Grade Teacher
Parker, Chris
Second Grade Teacher
MORROW
Allen, Raymond John
Band Director
Anness, Candance R. (Stratton)
Fifth Grade Teacher
Baughman, John Lester
Fourth Grade Teacher
Cook, Beatrice R.
Spanish Teacher
Davidson, Ronald
Sixth Grade Teacher
Elliott, Theresa Dare
Fifth Grade Teacher
Franek, Sharon Alderson
Teacher of Gifted & Talented
Levo, Roger A.
Mathematics Teacher
Melampy, Ronald F.
Vocal Music Director
Mershon, Lucretia Whitacre
Language Arts Teacher
Mershon, Robert Michael
Social Studies Teacher
Mihalik, Christopher Steven
World His & Psychology Tchr
Russell, Dorothy B.
Language Arts Teacher
West, Mary Elizabeth
High School Guidance Counselor
MOUNT BLANCHARD
Bowman, Debra (Betts)
5th Grade Teacher
Dale, Linda B.
Math Teacher
Gatien-Durenberger, Janet
HS Art Education Teacher
Hohn, Diane L.
English & Psychology Teacher
Kuch, Kathleen Marie (Filler)
Instrumental Director
Taylor, James Monroe
American History Teacher
Verhoff, Patricia
Mathematics Teacher
Whetstone, Emilee Anne
Spanish & French Teacher
MOUNT EATON
Kaderly, Peg A.
Title I Teacher
MOUNT GILEAD
Chapman, Donald Charles
Administrator
Clauss, Debra Lyn
Spanish Teacher
Graham, Judith Anne
2nd Grade Teacher
Grubb, Jill Robinson
English Teacher
Sample, Bobbi Klingel
Second Grade Teacher
West, Dennis James
Social Studies & Reading Tchr
MOUNT ORAB
Berlinger, Gary Lee
6th Grd World History Teacher
Bohrer, Mary Jones
4th Grade Teacher
Ekstedt, Paula Young
Spanish Teacher
Henderson, Dinah Coleman
Second Grade Teacher
Wisby, Quentin Ray
Mathematics Teacher
MOUNT ST JOSEPH
Abplanalp, Georgianna
Adj Tchr of Non-print Material
Schuppig, Lois Umberg
Math Instructor

MOUNT STERLING
Cottrill, Cheryl Lynn
Second Grade Teacher
Dill, Alisha Hill
First Grade Teacher
MOUNT VERNON
Behrensmeyer, Mary Jo Euvino
Latin Instructor
Bunnell, Robert
HS Mathematics Instructor
Dewald, Dan William
Geology Teacher
Dilley, Terra E.
8th Grade Teacher
Dolwick, Donald M.
Business Education Teacher
George, Jeffrey Craig
8th Grade Science Teacher
Lougheed Dessert, Kathryn Isobel
Fifth Grade Teacher
Neigel, Gladys Mae (Feltman)
Business Education Teacher
Paulson, Carol Phillips
3rd & 4th Grade Teacher
Pearson, Judith Clark
English Teacher
Portzline, JoAnne (Martin)
Third Grade Teacher
Shriver, William Russell
History Teacher
MOUNT VICTORY
Poling, Ruth Ann
Second Grade Teacher
MOWRYSTOWN
Dunnavan, Jay C., Jr.
Math Teacher
Luck, Robbin Lynn
Physical Education & Hlth Tchr
Vance, Teresa
Art & Geography Teacher
Veidt, Chris E.
Health & Physical Ed Teacher
MUNROE FALLS
Abdoo, Angela Di Lullo
Math, Algebra & Geometry Tchr
Mottice, William
7th Grade Teacher
Painter, Carolyn Wilson
Lang Arts & Gifted Teacher
Parker, Kathleen Kelly
Eng & Reading Tchr of Gifted
NAPOLEON
Benedict, Joyce Arendosh
Retired Third Grade Teacher
Borton, Linda Boyers
7th & 8th Grade English Tchr
Burke, Michael Stephen
Speech & Publications Teacher
Downey, Timothy Joseph
Mathematics Teacher
Funchion, Peggy Jo
Learning Disabilities Teacher
Kruse, Rick L.
English Teacher
Langenhop, Lori Ards
High School Visual Arts Tchr
Long, Larry Eugene
High School Principal
Nelson, Beverly Jean
English Teacher
Nichols, Mary A. (Newman)
High School Guidance Counselor
Snyder, Kathryn Ann
Sixth Grade Teacher
Spiess, Timothy L.
High School Mathematics Tchr
Stuebe, David F.
Junior HS Social Studies Tchr
Sullivan, Lenore Savelkoul
Sixth Grade Teacher
NAVARRE
Hissong, Jeffrey Keith
Spanish II, IV & Psych Tchr
Werner, Blaine Jay
HS Social Studies Teacher
NELSONVILLE
Agee, Gerald L.
Human Svcs Instr
Berry, Barbara A.
Coord & Cmptr Sci Lead Instr
Hall, Vickie Lynn
Third Grade Teacher
Kasler, Kathy Lynne (Beeler)
Applied Mathematics Teacher
Shrieves, Sandra Grubb
Computerized Accounting Tchr
VanSickle, Stephen Carl
Emergency Care Instructor
NEVADA
Anderson, Linda Brown
3rd Grade Teacher
NEW ALBANY
Darling, Mary Louise
Math Teacher & Dept Chair
Morgan, James Robert
HS Social Studies Teacher
NEW BREMEN
Clark, Randall Howard
Music Director
Overman, Howard Anthony
Phys Ed & Health Teacher
NEW CARLISLE
Brooks, Amy L.
Physical Education Teacher
DeLong, Robert Lee, Jr.
Biology Teacher & Head Coach
Herbert, Scott Alan
Adv Bio & Chemistry Teacher
Krikke, Florence
Sixth Grade Teacher

Mac Keown, Marjorie Gabriel
English Teacher & Dept Chair
Massie, Byron Kent
Teacher of Learning Disabled
Miller, Dwight
Earth Science Teacher
Nagel, Barbara Ann
Health & Physical Ed Teacher
Sharp, Kathryn Mallet
French & Spanish Teacher
Sparks, Carol Cowden
English & Theater Teacher
White, Jerry
Science Teacher & Dept Chair
Zeller, Terrence Lee
World History & Geography Tchr
NEW CONCORD
Brady, Martin A.
Accounting Professor
DeVolld, MaryAnn (Spitznagel)
Eng & Publications Teacher
Drubel, August Charles
Assoc Professor of Business
Harlan, David L.
Technology Teacher
Hudson, Paul Jeffrey
Band Director & Music Teacher
Jones, James Alan
Lecturer in Physical Education
Mazeroski, Ronald Franklin
Associate Dean of Student Life
Mc Kean, Keith Joseph
Asst Professor of Psychology
Nichols, Betsy L.
Asst Prof of Education
Nowakowski, Joseph Mark
Asst Professor of Economics
Nutt, Ricki Lee
Professor of Religion
Porter, Lorle
Professor of History
Stults, Taylor
Professor of History
Swift, Doug
English Professor
NEW LEBANON
Wharton, Kym
English & Publications Tchr
NEW LEXINGTON
Adam, Deborah Glasgow
Eighth Grade Lang Arts Teacher
Albanese, Beth Kullman
Social Studies Teacher
Black-Willison, Kay
Acctng & Computer Ed Teacher
Cushing, Judith Feil
Physics Teacher
Halaiko, J. Michael
Dist Tech Dir & Asst Principal
Mentzer, Gene Stephen
Science Teacher
NEW LONDON
Bucher, Mark Jan
First Grade Teacher
Gore, Susan Sitterly
Second Grade Teacher
Todd, Ann M. Knoll
Business Teacher
NEW MADISON
Nealeigh, Thomas T.
French & Hum Tchr
NEW MATAMORAS
Elder, Vincent K.
Mathematics Teacher
Goddard, Frances Evelyn
Sci, Health & Spelling Teacher
Lucas, Eileen
Special Education Teacher
Van Pelt, William Edward, II
Music Teacher
NEW MIDDLETOWN
Campbell, Linda S.
Third Grade Teacher
Hiznay, Jerome Joseph
Social Studies Teacher
Joseph, Keith John
LD Aide & PE Teacher
Putarek, Paula Marie (First)
English & Journalism Teacher
Smercansky, Mary Lynn
Social Studies Teacher
NEW PARIS
Alexander, Todd Elwood
HS Mathematics Teacher
Doran, Rosalie Schuler
3rd Grade Teacher
Flommersfeld, Jody L.
Guidance Counselor
Heiser, Heather (Fourman)
Math Teacher
Hoce, Joanele Vanzant
Primary Multi-Age Teacher
Norman, Sharon Lynn (Creech)
Library Media Specialist
Sizelove, Coleen M.
English Teacher
NEW PHILADELPHIA
Beitzel, Rebecca Masten
Math Dept Head & Teacher
Contini, Marie E.
Voc Info Processing Tchr
Egler, Sharon K.
Computer Programming Teacher
Goforth, Mary Davey
Retired English Teacher
Ladrach, Janet Meisner
5th Grade Teacher
Liberatore, Melody Leggett
English & Speech Teacher

Mann, Mary E.
Former English Teacher
Rowe, Frank J.
Attendance Coordinator
Sandy, Mary H.
7th Grade Math Teacher
Sweitzer, Jack Joseph
Sr HS Art Teacher
Tope, Lana Feller
Third Grade Teacher
Weber, Kathleen Fearon
Sixth Grade Teacher
Wittkop, Vickie L.
Senior English Teacher
NEW PLYMOUTH
Mc Vey, Marjorie White
Retired Business Teacher
NEW RICHMOND
Brittingham, Cindy Dennis
Business Education Teacher
Callebs, John Cecil
High School Math Teacher
Chambers, Regina Montgomery
High School English Teacher
Harrison, Diane Manning
8th Grade US History Teacher
Mc Kenney, Betty Valentine
English & Journalism Teacher
Reaker, James Dale
Social Studies Teacher
Richards, Lori Shepherd
8th Grade US History Teacher
Richardson, Cy B., Jr.
Civics Teacher
Robinson, Jim A.
Industrial Technology Teacher
NEW RIEGEL
Bouillon, Stephen Carl
History Teacher
Yount, Gale E.
English Teacher
NEW VIENNA
Hartman, Wannetta Jane
Sixth Grade Teacher
NEW WASHINGTON
Arnold, Bill
Chemistry & Physical Sci Tchr
Stump, Rosanna M.
Second Grade Teacher
NEW WATERFORD
Kershner, Susan
2nd Grade Teacher
Weber, Susan G.
Kindergarten Teacher
NEWARK
Anthony, Sharon Kay
Former 6th Grade Teacher
Bartoe, James Franklin
Electronics Teacher
Bendixen-Noe, Mary K.
Child Development Professor
Bradley, James Eugene
Geological Science Professor
Campolo, James L.
High Schl Business Ed Teacher
Carter, Carole Hanshue
Guidance Counselor
Cross, Thomas R.
Coll Prep 9th Grd Eng Tchr
Ganz, Albert Harding
History Professor
Grindrod, Jeff Allen
English & Reading Teacher
Grube, Joyce Anne
Program Director & Instructor
Hays, Thomas Eugene
Associate Prof of Mathematics
Hockenberry, James Owen
7th Grade Science Teacher
Horvath, Kathleen Mac Donald
Reading Teacher
Lamb, Randall Glen
Director of Bands
Lemasters, Karen Sue (Abbott)
Sixth Grade Teacher
Low, Sharon Ruth
First Grade Teacher
Mc Gregor, Diane Agnes
English & Writing Teacher
Nichols, Marie Joanne
Band & Orchestra Teacher
O'Dell, Kimberly Fudge
English Teacher
Philips, Connie Mc Quigg
Instructor & Cmptr Pgm Tech
Poth, Wesley Steven
Social Studies & PE Teacher
Ritzius, Doris Jean
Third Grade Teacher
Ross, Karen Swinehart
Elementary Kindergarten Tchr
St John, Fraze Lee
Assoc Prof of Zoology
Siegrist, Sandra Cameron
Mathematics Instructor
Smithinsky, Andrea Noel
Special Ed Teacher
Steinbrook, Rusetta Lynn
Fourth Grade Teacher
Stelzer, Karl Alan
Bible & Art Teacher
Unternaher, Marlene K.
Math & Algebra Teacher
VanDervort, Sharyn L.
English Teacher
Watson, Susan Scott
French Teacher
NEWBURY
Cataldo, Patrick J.
Sixth Grade Teacher

NEWBURY (cont)
Edmondson, David Len
English Instructor
Johnson, Kathy L.
Mathematics Department Chair
Nelson, Nancy Weiss
Jr HS Science Teacher
Wright, Susan Weismantel
Eighth Grade Teacher
NEWCOMERSTOWN
Addy, Sandra Parks
Soc Stud, His & Geography Tchr
Feller, John Allen
Math & Algebra 1 Teacher
NEWPORT
Fleming, Paige
Middle School Math Teacher
Leonard, Betty Lorraine
Primary Teacher
NEWTON FALLS
Baker, Don Forrest
12th Grade Government Teacher
Clay, Joyce Holmes
7th Grd Sci, 8th Grd Rdng Tchr
Gintert, Connie Jean
English Teacher
Hoffman, Gary L.
Instrumental Music Director
Liber, Marilyn Spahlinger
Fifth Grade Teacher
Robinson, Mari-Lin Schneider
English Teacher
NILES
Batson, Carol Barber
Fourth Grade Teacher
Bilovesky, Sandra Ciminero
Third Grade Teacher
Bufwack, Marlane Marie
Mathematics Teacher
Butto, Dana Giannetti
Math Teacher
Crist, DiAnne Sheldon
Computer Literacy Teacher
Eckelberger, Linda De Mare
Fifth Grade Teacher
Garbus, Cheryl Salerno
6th Grade Teacher
George, Judith Ann
Second Grade Teacher
Gregory, Christine Maria (Petak)
Sixth Grade Teacher
Ifft, William Edward
7th Grade Social Studies Tchr
Paolone, Reynald Joseph
Jr HS Soc Stud & Rdng Tchr
Papas, Fran S.
Cooperative Bus Ed Coordinator
Ries, Richard L.
Retired Eng & Speech Teacher
Shrodek, Michael Anthony
English Teacher
Walters, Christine Elizabeth Ryan
Lang Arts Tchr of Gifted
Zubyk, Alan Wayne
Health Teacher
NORTH BALTIMORE
Christman, Barbara L.
HS Mathematics Teacher
Hastings, Margaret Mc Clure
Second Grade Teacher
Lyon, Michael Eugene
HS Mathematics Teacher
NORTH BEND
Tuerscher, Daniel P.
Mathematics Teacher
NORTH BLOOMFIELD
Harrison, Thomas Francis
Principal
Pruban, David Ray
Former Elementary Teacher
NORTH CANTON
Carroll, Virginia Schaefer
Associate Professor of English
Cartechine, Kathryn Ann (Kubat)
Assistant Professor
Couch, Carol Diedrich
Mathematics Teacher
Hayward, John Charles
Vocal Music & Drama Director
Hobe, Paul G.
Chemistry Teacher
Horvath, Brooke Kenton
Associate Professor of English
Kilchenman, Willetta Embick
Retired English & Acctng Instr
Mc Elroy, Richard Lee
Social Studies Teacher
McIntyre, Paul Douglas
Biology Teacher
Moore, Richard Emil
Instrumental Music Teacher
Norton-Smith, Thomas Michael
Assoc Professor of Philosophy
Riske, Beverly Nogen
Fifth Grade Teacher
Sidoti, Mary Angela (Svik)
Coord of Dev Edctrs
Stanley, Beth A.
Social Studies Teacher
Varn, Ronald Christopher
Instrumental Music Teacher
Vulanovic, Relja
Assistant Mathematics Prof
Weeks, Philip
History Professor
NORTH FAIRFIELD
Oney, Bryan L.
6th & 7th Grade Science Tchr

NORTH JACKSON
Drevna, David Gene
General Music & Band Teacher
Tomaino, David Allen
7th-8th Grd Soc Stud Teacher
NORTH LEWISBURG
Benge, Mary E. Downey
Kindergarten Teacher
Henson, Jacqueline McKean
Biology Teacher
Instine, Nancy O'Brien
Special Education Teacher
Kitchen, Douglas Lee
English & Social Studies Tchr
Rish, Linda Bowman
High School English Teacher
Simpson, Ernest Gene
Physical Ed Teacher
Tavenner, Joy Jean Leugers
Learning Disabilities Teacher
NORTH LIMA
Baker, Susan Brandon
First Grade Teacher
Hoff, Carole Welch
3rd Grade Teacher
Mink, Sandra Phillips
Business Education Teacher
NORTH OLMSTED
Currens, Lance William
Health & PE Instructor
Elzeer, Wanda
First Grade Teacher
Mittler, David E.
Language Teacher
Savel, Beth Rose
HS Mathematics Teacher
Yambor, Elaine Margaret
Mathematics Teacher
NORTH RIDGEVILLE
Baillie, Adam J.
Mathematics Teacher
Crum, Sean Christian
Art Teacher
Dearth, Sherry Chilcote
6th Grade Teacher of Gifted
Hase, James Robert, Sr.
United States History Teacher
Malinar, Branka Marie (Frigan)
Intervention Specialist
Orange, Linda C.
Math Teacher
NORTH ROBINSON
Cauley, Michael
Industrial Technology Instr
Johnson, Joyce Yancey
English Teacher & Dept Chair
Luidhardt, Bettie Meister
6th Grade Teacher
Martin, Cynthia LaTurner
2nd Grade Teacher
Seif, Mary Joan
Fourth Grade Teacher
Thorpe, Richard Kevin
Amer, World His & Soc Teacher
NORTH ROYALTON
Arvay, Lisa B.
High School Math Teacher
Bacher, Gerald James
Mathematics Teacher
Black, Janet Marie (Honroth)
English Teacher
Boehm, Christopher Scott
Social Studies Teacher
Broadwater, Michael Robert
Mathematics Teacher
Brown, Aimee J.
Latin Teacher
Burdette, David Andrew
Sixth Grade Math Teacher
Casteel, Brenda Sue
English & Reading Tchr
Daugherty, Denise Mendenhall
HS Math Teacher & Dept Chprsn
De Luca, Denise Bernard
6th Grade English & Rdng Tchr
Evanich, Katherine Poulos
Spanish & German Teacher
First, Leslie Suzanne
HS Home Economics Teacher
Grida, Rena E.
Health & Physical Ed Teacher
Kleem, Anthony Mark
Social Studies Teacher
Namestnik, Albert John
Fifth Grade Teacher
Rudolph, Michael Scott
High School Math Teacher
Smith, Kriste DeAnna
Business Teacher
NORTHFIELD
Ashley, Ronald L.
Principal
Domokos, Larry
5th-6th Grade Teacher
Hamad, Nancy L. (FioRino)
First Grade Teacher
Storry, James Douglas
Music Teacher
NORTHWOOD
James, Kristel Shutt
English Teacher
Karrick, Mary Kay (Huffman)
8th Grd Language Arts Teacher
Laird, Tim H.
English Instructor
Orlowski, Nancy Laubenthal
Second Grade Teacher
Stroud, Judy Graves
Mathematics Teacher

NORTON
Baker, Sandra Kay
Ohio Studies & Amer His Tchr
Beddow, Linda Sue
Language Arts Teacher
Hagey, Harriet Elizabeth
8th Grade Phys Sci Teacher
Jennings, Nancy E.
Fourth Grade Teacher
Knapp, Theresa Marlene
Health & Physical Ed Teacher
Luce, Jeffrey Roger
Mathematics Teacher
Moore, Sandra (Stewart)
7th & 8th Grd Lang Arts Tchr
Robinson, Donald Franklin
Social Studies Teacher
VanDeventer, James B.
Retired Earth Science Teacher
NORWALK
Bersche, James H.
Social Studies Teacher
Broz, Kenneth Stephen
HS History Teacher & Coach
Durham, Thomas A.
Marketing Education Coord
Ford, Scott Clinton
Eighth Grade English Teacher
Genovesi, Joseph Philip
Teacher
Graham, Susan Ann (Henning)
Enrichment Teacher
Pleasnick, Alan L.
American History Teacher
Smith, C. Kendall
Elementary Social Studies Tchr
NORWOOD
Barker, Nancy Greene
English Teacher & Dept Chair
Beridon, Judith Ducote
Third Grade Teacher
Burton, Rae Lynn
8th Grade Math Teacher
Gilliam, Edra L.
Math Teacher
Hester, Patricia Jean
High School Math Teacher
Landon, Hobart Powell
5th Grade Teacher
McClorey, Mark J.
Mathematics & Science Teacher
Reynolds, Jacqueline M.
Fifth Grade Teacher
Turner, Donald Harold
HS Counselor & Coach
Westermann, Ann L.
High School French Teacher
NOVELTY
Seith, Nancy L.
4th Grade Teacher
OAK HARBOR
Bahnsen, Carolyn Good
Specific LD Teacher
Burkett, Ron L.
Band Director
Gamble, Nancy Strohscher
High School English Teacher
Hany, Susan Loeffler
His, Sociology & Psych Teacher
Hoover, Daniel Zerah
PE Teacher & Athletic Trainer
Oakley, Carey Francis
Language Arts Teacher
Pickut, Gail (Herbert)
Science Teacher
Quisno, Gary A.
Geometry Teacher
Radel, Samuel M.
Science Teacher
Siefke, Nancy Lynn (Shipan)
Science Teacher
Vreeland, James Edward, II
High Schl Mathematics Teacher
Whitman, Kent B.
6th Grade Teacher
OAK HILL
Hedden, Brian Lee
Social Studies Teacher
Lewellen, Dale Eric
Band Director
Ramsey, William Russell
Biology & Chemistry Teacher
OAKWOOD
Burnett, Ernest A.
Instrumental Music Teacher
Hornyak, Debra Louise
Third Grade Teacher
Spangler, Virginia Marie
Second Grade Teacher
OBERLIN
Beursken, Michael Robert
Chemistry & Physics Teacher
Binggeli, Sandra Schlegel
Algebra Teacher
Cruz, Yolanda Paje
Professor of Biology
Johnson, Stephen, III
Band Director
Levin, Richard Alexander
Professor of Biology
Mc Daniel, Susan Hearth
Special Education Teacher
Michitsch, Timothy M.
Chef & Instructor
Patterson, Elizabeth Hostetler
7th Grd Math & Reading Tchr
Resek, Michele Noday
Voc Spcl Ed Coordinator
Walzer, Michaelene Ann (Baker)
Sixth Grade Teacher

OHIO CITY
Johnson, John Wayne
6th Grade Teacher
OLD FORT
Deatrick, Sarah Ann
Spanish Teacher
Heiby, Lori Ann
Agricultural Education Instr
Jury, Roger Allen, II
English Teacher
Vosburgh, Dawn Lynn
Bus Teacher & Tech Coordinator
Young, Lynn Susan
Jr HS Eng Tchr & HS Librarian
OLMSTED FALLS
Bennett, Cynthia Coriell
6th Grd Lang Arts & Sci Tchr
Emigh, James Michael
Science Teacher
Gibeaut, Tom Lloyd
Social Studies Teacher
Sidun, Ann Keefer
Third Grade Teacher
Smith, Joan Botnick
Teacher
Willson, David Eugene
Mathematics Teacher
ORANGE VILLAGE
Belliveau, Gregory Kenneth
English Dept Chair & Teacher
Herston, Kevin Roy
History Teacher
Jones, Roberta Lyn (Brown)
Physical Ed & Health Teacher
Jones, William I.
Principal & Chemistry Teacher
Roop, Clifford Eugene
Health & Physical Ed Teacher
OREGON
Adkins, Sally S.
English Teacher
Angevine, Michael E.
6th Grade Teacher
Bosch, Jenifer Rose
Art & Theology Teacher
Bruns, Scott C.
English & History Teacher
Bunck, Laraine Anne (Kosco)
French Teacher
Colburn, Melissa Strayer
English Teacher
Hackathorn, Angela M.
English Teacher
Harmon, Sandra Jean
First Grade Teacher
Heuring, Amy Spaulding
English & Speech Teacher
Johnson, John Franklin
American History Teacher
Klewer, Elaine Lehman
Second Grade Teacher
Klinger, Amy L.
Gifted Education Coordinator
McCullough, George Heath
Biology Tchr & Sci Dept Chm
Reynolds, Robert Anderson, Jr.
Pre-Engineering Graphics Tchr
Schabel, Diane Burson
10th Grade Health Educator
Simon, Linda Ondrus
Work & Family Life Teacher
ORRVILLE
Billions, Karin Ferguson
Assoc Professor of Mass Media
Burnett, Kay (Egner)
Third Grade Teacher
McHenry, Linda Bupp
5th Grade Teacher
Mendenhall, Warner D.
Professor
Simpkins, Mary Ellen (Siegenthaler)
Third Grade Teacher
Smith, Forrest Joseph
Biology & Anthropology Prof
Snyder, Anne H.
Third Grade Teacher
Tohill, Mary Dietsch
English Composition Instructor
Warner, Patricia Ann
English Teacher
Webster, Cynthia Buehler
Language Arts Teacher
Weeman, Margaret Ann Crill
Second Grade Teacher
ORWELL
Carlson, Timothy A.
Director of Bands
Dingman, Donald Lee
Mathematics Teacher
Marsh, Donald A.
History Teacher
Schaub, Terry Bobsien
American His & Geography Tchr
Sulzbach, Tracy Lynn
Mathematics Teacher
OTTAWA
Dickman, Margaret L.
Sixth Grade Teacher
Leis, Donald Bradly
Senior Amer Government Teacher
Leis, Virginia Susan
English Teacher
Warman, Donald Edward
Jr High Math Teacher
OTTOVILLE
Hanneman, Darlene Culler
Second Grade Teacher
Heitz, Catherine Ruen
6th Grade Teacher

Kaufman, Linda K. (Martin)
Fifth Grade Teacher
Knott, Mark A.
Counselor & Business Teacher
Kroeger, Nancy Jane (Horstman)
English & Science Teacher
Maley, James Andrew
HS Social Studies Teacher
Notar, Michael Robert
Sixth Grade Teacher
Stokes, Nina O.
Biology & Anatomy Teacher
Thomas, Kathleen L.
French Teacher
OXFORD
Beyer, Sara LaSetta (Schutz)
Teaching Assistant
Johnson, Mary Anne (Black)
Lang Arts & Soc Stud Tchr
Pettitt, Ruth Allyn (Jenista)
8th Grade Language Arts Tchr
Vajda, Cheryl Costanzo
Fourth Grade Teacher
PAINESVILLE
Beyerle, Susan D.
Supplemental Services Teacher
Cruikshank, David Earl
Attorney, Private Practice
Denner, David Thomas
Earth Science Teacher
Haught, Margaret Tank
Fmly & Consumer Sciences Tchr
Homovec, Kathleen McKinley
2nd Grade Teacher
Jordan, Mark Edward
Health Teacher
Kleps, Cheryl Lynn
English Teacher
Miller, Greg A.
Sixth Grade Math Teacher
Miller, Sheryl Lee (Babics)
Library & Media Specialist
Pfefferle, Kathie Marie
Fourth Grade Teacher
Raczko, Terrence Michael
English Teacher
Vaidean, Sally Wilbur
Computer & Mathematics Teacher
Vidmar, Glenda Kay (Stevens)
Fifth Grade Teacher
Walter, Tanya Lynn
Vocal Music Teacher
PARMA
Apostle, Nancy Mary
Theology Teacher
Bauman, Mary Johnson
High School Math Teacher
Boynar, Shirley Chervenak
Family & Consumer Sci Teacher
Buchholz, George P.
7th Grade Science Teacher
Carroll, Thomas Richard, OFM
Acad Dean & Spanish Teacher
Cihy, Charlene F. (Kavec)
Third Grade Teacher
Frey, Kimberly Hau
5th Grade Teacher
Gathers, Lillian J.
Business & English Teacher
Gibson, Cheryle L.
Diagnostic Reading Specialist
Gressock, Joseph E.
Theology Teacher
Kortan, Joseph John
Mathematics Teacher
Kucko, Carol Zuchowski
Fourth Grade Teacher
Mazur, Daniel F.
Social Studies Educator
Mc Ginty, Linda Wagy
Retired English Teacher
McSweeney, Dina Lucarelli
Fifth Grade Teacher
Messerly, Marilou Beres
French Teacher
Miller, Karen Kay Droppers
Advanced Placement Eng Tchr
Novak, Ronald John
Government Teacher
Reffert, Mary Jane Lawler
Theology Teacher
Shaffer, James
Principal
Vince, Melvin James
Retired Teacher
PATASKALA
Fairall, Mary Lou Nichols
Retired Tchr of GATE
Funk, Patrick Eugene
Chemistry Instructor
Heidenreich, Beth A.
English & Theater Teacher
Higgins, Terry H.
8th Grd Lang Arts & Rdng Tchr
Massarelli, Gregory A.
HS Mathematics Teacher
Ratchford, Aileen Crawford
French Teacher
Smith, Peggy A.
Spanish Teacher
Starn, Nancy Geiger
Biology Teacher
Wiard, Herb
Social Studies Teacher
Yost, Jill Lemon
Art Teacher
PAULDING
Barnes, Elcena O.
Coordinator of Gifted Programs

DING (cont)
ddle, David E.
2th Grd Vocal Music Tchr
n, Betty Lee
Grade Teacher
·d, Max A., Jr.
ish Teacher
re, Phillip Gene
nce & Social Studies Tchr
Arden Ray
School Science Teacher
s, Mark Allen
epartment Head & Teacher
ier, Karen Kay
uidance Counselor
Mark Kevin
eacher & Drivers Ed Instr
LES
ield, Wayne Eric
ndary Education Teacher
ERTON
an, Jodi Kay (Watkins)
h Grade Teacher
ERVILLE
Janet E. Close
irade Teacher
Marcia Lynn
h Teacher
Norma Jean
c Specialist
eier, Patricia R.
irade English Teacher
NSULA
, Lois A.
rt Teacher
, Paul John
uage Arts Teacher
Y
Jeffrey C.
ird Social Studies Tchr
on, Lynne Latter
School Language Arts Tchr
Barry Gray
rade Teacher
YSBURG
, Theodore A.
ry Department Chairman
avid Wayne
al Studies Teacher
, Rita J.
uage Arts & Reading Tchr
YSVILLE
Ralph G.
sh Teacher & Dept Head
SVILLE
n, John F.
culture Science Teacher
David Charles
ance Cnslr & Athletic Dir
D
on, Pauline Dingey
h Grade Teacher
, Amy Jo
sh Teacher
ERINGTON
Kenneth Carroll
ipal
Carla Sikora
hemistry Teacher
, Ronald William
nan Teacher
n, Jack Allen
h & PE Teacher
-Low, Carol
or English Teacher
atricia A.
ish & French Teacher
John Sherman
c Dir & Cross Cntry Coach
, Patty Arlene
ish Teacher
Chrisopher Paul
& Social Studies Teacher
ke, Cynthia Boving
nistry Teacher
er, Lynda L.
panish Teacher
e, Kay I.
Teacher
TON
Julie Smith
nistry & Physics Teacher
r, Carole Belinda
Grade Teacher
Brian
Teacher
Cheryl Smith
tional Evaluator
ms, C. Roger
ematics & Cmptr Sci Tchr
EER
g, Larry Eugene
ematics Department Chair
ss, Dianne Midtgard
Dept Chprsn & Soc Sci Tchr
A
, Robert Joseph
ory Teacher
ugh, Joyce A.
School Mathematics Tchr
on, Lawrence Edwin, Jr.
ory Teacher
in, Elizabeth Boorse
nce Teacher
Gary Dee
r His, Psych & Ec Teacher
ard, Gail Apple
th Grd Lang Arts Teacher
Gary L.
ematics Teacher

PITSBURG
Phipps, David Eugene
School Counselor
PLAIN CITY
Carothers, Jill White
Fourth Grade Teacher
Faulk, Pamela Cole
7th-8th Grade English Teacher
Houchard, Carolee Weiss
Cooperative Business Ed Coord
McGill, Thomas A.
Industrial Arts Teacher
Stalnaker, Tammy Adams
Sixth Grade Teacher
Wright, Dana Marie
Business Teacher
PLEASANT HILL
Jenkins, Donald Eugene
Instrumental & Vocal Teacher
Wilberding, Donna Marie
Spanish Teacher
PLEASANTVILLE
Patchen, Lynn Hedges
Second Grade Teacher
PLYMOUTH
Creamer, Christina
First Grade Teacher
Cullen, Chris Frederick
Physical Education & Hlth Tchr
Daniel, Deborah K. Fryman
English Teacher
Kirkpatrick, Carole Ann (Myers)
Work & Family Life Teacher
POMEROY
Edwards, Cathy S.
Basketball Coach
PORT CLINTON
Anderson, Paul Mark
Communications Teacher
Armstrong, Douglas L.
Computer Applications Teacher
Bixler, Thomas Lorin
Band Director
Drusbacky, Jane Ellen (Biro)
Sixth Grade Teacher
George, Patricia Karlovetz
English Teacher
Greer, Victoria Lee (Burr)
8th Grade Life Science Teacher
Kohlman, M. Avolene
Mathematics Teacher
Passabet, Kimberly Ring
Reading Teacher
Phelps, Jann Campbell
Family & Consumer Science Tchr
Pope, Anna Marie Gould
Fifth Grade Teacher
Quayle, Julie Somsen
8th Grd Language Arts Teacher
Randels, David George
Instrumental Music Teacher
Schweitzer, Kathy Jo
High School English Teacher
Sherick, Philip L.
German Teacher
Walls, Robert Thomas
Mathematics Teacher
Zeitzheim, Eric
History Teacher
PORT WASHINGTON
Arnold, William James
Fifth Grade Teacher
PORTSMOUTH
Coriell, John Gerald
Mathematics Tchr & Dept Chprsn
Deal, Janet L.
Social Studies Teacher
Imm, Nancy Maxwell
Retired Elementary Teacher
Pfleger, Mary Jo
English Teacher
Riley, Rossanna V.
Spanish Teacher
Skelley, Dympna, OSF
Latin Teacher & Media Director
Skipworth, Kelly Oakes
English Teacher
Smalley, Richard Lee
Science Teacher
Spearry, Alberta
Retired Teacher
Spradlin, Pat
English & Art Teacher
Tomko, Theodore Michael
9th Grd Sci & Adult Ed Teacher
POWHATAN POINT
Johnson, Anna Ciszewski
First Grade Teacher
Montgomery, Suzanne T.
4th Grade Teacher
PROCTORVILLE
Keeney, Jaime Leigh
Title I Math & Lang Teacher
King, Ronald Lee
Science Teacher
RACINE
Phillips, Kimberly Lynn
Librarian & Media Specialist
Ritchie, Joyce A.
Title I Teacher
Sayre, Aaron Lee
Agricultural Education Teacher
RADNOR
Daniels, Robert Arthur
Math Teacher
RANDOLPH
Matthews, Jeffrey J.
Lang & Social Sciences Teacher

RAVENNA
Brunner, Beth K.
First Grade Teacher
Budd, Martha H.
Science Teacher
Claytor, David Lee
Speech & English Teacher
Ettinger, Richard S.
High School Biology Teacher
Felton, Robert Oneil, II
OWA Coord
Fesemyer, Cynthia Fitzsimmons
Primary Physical Ed Teacher
Jarrett, Cynthia Walburn
Business Teacher
Johns, Jeanne Marie
English Teacher
Kotun, Carol Ann
Mathematics Teacher
Landon, Judy Ann
General Music Teacher
McCarrell, DeAnna Trivelli
Business Teacher
Muster, Naomi L.
Retired 3rd-5th Grade Teacher
Patrick, Robyn D.
Science Teacher
Romanic, Jennifer Kennedy
Latin Teacher
Waickman, Dorothy Doerrer
English Teacher
Walchalk, Richard Keith
Guidance Counselor
RAWSON
Bauman, Joan Lou Clymer
Third Grade Teacher
RAYLAND
Basinger, Amy Milliken
Biology & Life Science Teacher
Bonnell, Kenneth Lee
Band Director
Closser, Barry Joseph
Media Specialist & Schl Librn
Cowan, Andrea Stock
Home Economics Educator
Durbin, Jeffrey Allen
Science Department Head
Ferguson, Pamela Lamone
Spanish & French Teacher
Glikes, Gladys Graham
English Teacher
Gron, Rosemary Elaine
Fourth Grade Teacher
Guy, Robert D.
English Instructor
Heaton, Dalene Jones
Mathematics Teacher
Levi, Larry J.
Am Government Teacher
Posgai, Robert Alex
Biology Teacher
Robey, Michael K.
Geography & Amer History Tchr
READING
Bernheim, Jeanne Marie
Retired Teacher of GATE
REEDSVILLE
Douthitt, Pamela Ann
Phys Ed Tchr & Ath Director
Rose, Archie Carl
History & Government Teacher
Williams, Rita Peer
French & English Teacher
REPUBLIC
Bloomberg, Linda Whitely
Math Teacher
Kiess, Lynne Kane
Third Grade Teacher
Schlick, Jerome Francis
Govt Instructor
REYNOLDSBURG
Courey, Maria Regina
Jr High Instructor
Hay, Jo Anne (Durst)
Math, Science & Health Teacher
Huth, Karen Marie
Second Grade Teacher
Lower, Jean Biggs
Retired Elementary Teacher
Murphy, Sue Jemison
Sixth Grade Teacher
South, Cynthia Kallos
French Teacher
RICHFIELD
Marko-Devore, Deborah
Choir Director
Shane, Jeffrey S.
Physics Teacher
Welch, Donald Frederick
Speech, English & Drama Tchr
RICHMOND
Ash, Marjorie Brown
English Teacher
Cline, Cheryl Ann Sutton
Third Grade Teacher
Dull, James Jeffrey
High School Band Director
Evanosky, Rebecca Milligan
Kindergarten Teacher
Kovalesky, Tony Ray
American History Teacher
Lauri, Rosann
Spanish, English & Jrnlsm Tchr
Lautzenheiser, Ray Eugene
Vocal Music Teacher
Neptune, Larry Edward
Science Teacher
Swickard, Ellen Ruth (Grafton)
Chem Tchr & Science Dept Chair

RICHMOND DALE
Brown, James Elba
Amer Lit, Speech & Drama Tchr
Easterday, Dannie Dean
History & Geography Teacher
Eycke, Diana E. (Bush)
Title I Reading & Math Tchr
RICHMOND HEIGHTS
Bezdek, James Thomas
5th Grade Teacher
Booth, Jeffrey L.
Health Teacher
Capello, Laura Anne Fondran
Art Teacher
Grant, Andrew Morton
Life Science Teacher
Hodder, Robert Kenneth
History Teacher
Lombardo, Paul Anthony
Math Teacher
McBride, Mary Therese
Jr High English Teacher
Nally, James Thomas
Health & Physical Ed Teacher
Vejdovec, Jennifer A.
Social Studies Teacher
RICHWOOD
Cooley, Cheryl Lynne
Title I Teacher
Gardner, Stewart Charles, Jr.
English & Speech Instructor
Mathey, Lee Edward
HS Math Teacher
Metzger, James D.
Industrial Technology Teacher
Stidham, Beverly Davis
Sixth Grd Rdng & Lang Teacher
RIDGEWAY
Aburto, JoAnne Allen
Spanish Teacher
Baughn, Kyle Shane
Mathematics Teacher
RIO GRANDE
Abukamail, Nasseef A.
Computer Science Professor
Bapst, Jacob Lamar
Dir of Instrl Media Center
Barton, Marcella Biro
History Professor
Bauer, Linda Lou
Assoc Prof of Professional Ed
Dean, Alan Ross
Associate Prof of Education
Hatfield, Barbara Scott
Assoc Professor of Mathematics
Perry, Michael James
Principal
Rhodes, Thomas Michael
Professor of Mathematics
Sofranko, Edward Roger
Professor of Psychology
Tribe, Ivan Mathews
Professor of History
RIPLEY
Curtis, Russell Glenn, Jr.
Social Studies Teacher
Miller, Kevin Eric
Science Teacher
Schwartz, Carolyn Colgan
Language Arts Teacher
Sroufe, Shelley H.
8th Grade Math Teacher
RITTMAN
Kitska, Susan A.
Eng, German Tchr & Dept Chair
Sabo, Judith M.
Biology Teacher
Sims, Edward Frederick
Director of Bands
ROCKFORD
Clouse, Nancy L.
Business Teacher
Clouse, Tom Lee
Mathematics & Science Teacher
Esselstein, Mark J.
PE, Driver Ed Tchr & Coach
Freck, Harrison James
Social Studies Teacher
Habegger, Martha (Kirkpatrick)
Retired Elementary Teacher
Holscher, Elizabeth Davison
Physiology & Biology Teacher
Post, Alan H.
Agriculture Teacher
Sherrick, Richard Hugh
Music Teacher
ROCKY RIVER
Chahda, Isabel Jimenez
Spanish Teacher
Dabrowski, Elizabeth Marie
Chemistry Teacher
Peterson, Camille Diane
Reading & History Teacher
Sheridan, Donna Dowling
English Department Chair
ROOTSTOWN
Hazlett, Betty Ealy
English Teacher
Mullenix, David Ray
Social Studies Teacher
Slocum, Karen Howman
High School Art Teacher
Stowers, Charlotte W.
Business Teacher
ROSEVILLE
Lucas, Cynthia Sekel
Mathematics Teacher
Taylor, Timothy Alan
5th & 6th Grade Science Tchr

ROSEWOOD
Ward, Marcia Balmut
Sub Abuse Prevention Coord
ROSSFORD
Clayton, Delbert Eugene
Social Studies Teacher
Gutierrez, Carol L.
Seventh Grade Teacher
Hiner, Donald John
7th-12th Grade Choral Director
Krieger, Michael Troy
English Teacher
Laubenthal, Nadine Rich
First Grade Teacher
Oberdorf, Nancy Demko
Seventh Grade Reading Teacher
RUSSELLVILLE
Beucler, Rob G.
7th & 8th Grade Math Teacher
RUSSIA
Dapore, Mary Naveau
Kindergarten Teacher
Schmiesing, Judy A.
Third Grade Teacher
Vietze, Stephen B.
Director of Music
SABINA
Howell, Michelle Elane (Davis)
Reading & Language Arts Tchr
SAGAMORE HILLS
Bernath, Donn L.
Retired Mathematics Teacher
SAINT CLAIRSVILLE
Barnes, Doris L.
OH His & World Geography Tchr
Biernot, James Joseph
6th-7th Grade Science Teacher
Blatnik, Michael W.
High School Science Teacher
Craig, Judith Lewis
Kindergarten Teacher
Davis, James Wayne
Machine Trades Instructor
Glasgow, Harry Kirk
Technology Education Teacher
Hawthorne, Debbie Dierkes
Certified Dental Asst Instr
Hill, Charlotte Jozwiak
Spcl Ed Inclusion Teacher
Kish, Kathi Ann
Teacher of Gifted & Talented
Kish, Robert Stephen, Sr.
Assistant Professor of HVAC
Krahel, Linda Sue Mathews
Fourth Grade Teacher
Ogilbee, Barbara Louise (Setzer)
8th Grade Teacher
Stiles, Bruce Edward
Physical Science Teacher
Teliga, Darlene Annette
English & Applied Comm Tchr
Underdonk, Leslie Gall
English Teacher
Vass, Ernest Allen
Biology Teacher
Wilhelm, Charles William
Mathematics Department Chm
Yavelak, William Michael
American History Instructor
SAINT MARYS
Smith, Page Andrew
AP His, Govt & Ec Instructor
SAINT PARIS
Duer, Kathy Kline
Bus Ed Tchr & Dept Chair
Griest, Jo Ann Louise
6th Grade Teacher
Jess, Diane Thompson
Mathematics Teacher
Knoble, Patrick Michael
Agriscience Instructor
Scott, Shirley E.
German Teacher
Wurth, Henry B.
Sixth Grade Teacher
SALEM
Esposito, Jean Kiliman
English Teacher & Dept Chair
Esposito, William M.
English Teacher
Fellenger, Janet Daniels
Third Grade Teacher
Fieldhouse, Sally Steffel
5th Grade Teacher
Hays, Christina M.
Mathematics Teacher
Henry, William Dean
Social Studies Teacher
Jackson, Lynne Berryman
Third Grade Teacher
Jeckavitch, Carol Roth
Vocal Music Director
Julian, Mary Alice
Second Grade Teacher
Lehman, Dallas Wayne
School Administrator
O'Brian, Cindy J.
Fourth Grade Teacher
Ramunno, Kerry Kowalski
Fifth Grade Teacher
Rice, Doug F.
Asst Professor of English
Soyars, Nancy
Fourth Grade Teacher
Starkey, Kay Casper
Middle Schl Lang Arts Teacher
Wasson, Karen Jo Stalma
1st Grade Teacher
Wolfgang, Susan Maher
Sixth Grade Teacher

SALINEVILLE
Adams, Linda C.
5th Grade Teacher
Francis, Gwen (Sturgeon)
English Teacher & Dept Chm
Glavan, James David
Vocational Agriculture Instr
Infanti, Ronald Anthony
Industrial Technology Teacher
Thompson, Evelyn Boyd
Second Grade Instructor
SANDUSKY
Albert, Ronald Russell
Choral Director
Brooker, Walter Ronald, Jr.
Orchestra Dir & Strings Tchr
Ceccoli, Christopher John
English Teacher
Collins, Carol Yeager
Religion Teacher
Gasteier, Chris James
Agriculture & Soc Studies Tchr
Hartmann, Holly Lynn
High Schl Mathematics Teacher
Huggins, Virginia Finnegan
First Grade Teacher
Huneke, Mary Kay (Murphy)
Third Grade Teacher
Lehrer, Lynne Holzapfel
Spanish Teacher
Mc Dowell, David W.
MS English & Soc Studies Tchr
McGory, Darlene Kay
Third Grade Teacher
Melching, Susan Bundschuh
Teacher of Gifted & Talented
Py, Susan T.
Kindergarten Teacher
Reed, Jeff L.
Adjunct Instructor
Runner, Kathleen Kahle
Secondary Teacher
Shaylor, Karen Ann
Art Dept Chair & Teacher
Smith, Carol Ann Barone
Business Education Teacher
Toney, Robert Louis
Principal
Wilber, David B.
High School English Teacher
SARAHSVILLE
Barnett, M. Jane Davis
Fourth Grade Teacher
Furry, Deborah Norquist
Second Grade Teacher
SARDINIA
Gardner, Phyllis Jean
High School Mathematics Tchr
Germann, Wanda Faulkner
Social Studies Teacher
Kaising, Karen Ann
Social Studies Teacher
Salisbury, Ronald Dean
Science & Biology Teacher
Tracy, Sandy Arn
7th & 8th Grd Sci & Rdng Tchr
SCIO
Palmer, Barbara Sue (Henson)
Art Teacher
Raymond, John Michael
Junior HS Mathematics Teacher
SCIOTOVILLE
Smith, James Howard
Student Services Facilitator
SEAMAN
Hull, Sherry R.
Second Grade Teacher
Leonard, Jane Eldridge
Special Education & LD Teacher
SEBRING
Garrity, Debbe Anne
Language Arts & Math Teacher
Lushinsky, Marie Daniels
English Teacher
Martinelli, Jeanne Ann
4th Grade Teacher
SENECAVILLE
Dailey Hylkema, Patricia A.
Applied Communications Teacher
SEVEN HILLS
Backston, Robert Phillip
Art Teacher
Falkman, Frank Martin, Jr.
Reading Instructor
SHADYSIDE
Durante, Lea R.
Social Studies Teacher
Hall, Sherri Short
English Teacher
King, Jane Louise Stidd
Fourth Grade Teacher
Snodgrass, Francis Thomas
Social Studies Teacher
SHAKER HEIGHTS
Fitzpatrick, Suzanne L.
Kindergarten Teacher
Gilbert, Stuart Marc
Physical Ed Teacher & Coach
SHARONVILLE
Stouder, William Dennis
Jr HS Lang Arts, Soc Stud Tchr
SHEFFIELD LAKE
Gallagher, Marjorie Ruth-Taylor
4th Grade Teacher
Gang, Carolyn Frances
Mathematics Teacher
Hildebrand, Dale A.
Instrumental Music Teacher
SHELBY
Costein, Ike John
Applied Physics & Chem Instr
Dahn, Gail Swank
7th & 8th Grade Teacher
Depler, Nancy Schull
Kindergarten Teacher
Dorka, Charles Anthony, Jr.
Sixth Grade Teacher
Gray, Jack F.
Director of Bands
Keib, Donna Lee
3rd Grade Teacher
Kurtzman, Susan Walker
Kindergarten Teacher
Ream, Anita J.
English & Journalism Teacher
Rinehart, Ken
Director of Guidance
Spangler, David Lee
Fifth Grade Teacher
Traven, Barbara Ann (Touby)
Spanish Teacher
Vermilya, Ray N.
Retired Vocal Music Director
Zimmerman, Mark J.
8th Grade Amer History Teacher
SHERWOOD
Penner, Betty
Chemistry & Physics Teacher
Rhodes, Marjorie L.
Sixth Grade Teacher
Trachl, Mary Loretta
French & Spanish Teacher
SHILOH
Fugate, Eliza Combs
Sixth Grade Teacher
Mc Clintock, Elizabeth Beveridge
Third Grade Teacher
McClintock, Paul N.
English Teacher
Zirkle, Barbara Jean
Science Teacher
SIDNEY
Anderson, Angie Marie
7th Grade Math Teacher
Asher, Ann Tenbosch
Art Teacher
Behr, Laura Homan
Special Education Teacher
Camp, Kristina Lynn
German Teacher
De Velvis, Linda Harp
Social Studies Teacher
Eilerman, Christina Gilmore
Fifth Grade Teacher
Fahrer, Franklin James
7th-12th Vocal Music Instr
Gilfillen, Rita E.
Science Teacher
Hall, Brenda Basinger
Second Grade Teacher
Hedberg, Lori Jean
Physical Education Teacher
Higgins, Pamela K.
Elementary Principal
Hosack, John Leroy
Mathematics Teacher
Lieber, Marla Kay Busch
Family & Consumer Sci Teacher
Luebke, Jennifer Weigandt
9th-12th Grd English Teacher
Mintchell, Beverly Moseley
Third Grade Teacher
Papenfuss, Lynne Marie
English & History Teacher
Roddy, Scott L.
Head Football Coach
Ross, Janet Grimm
Sixth Grade Teacher
Scherer, Virginia Lee
Science Teacher & Dept Chair
Schweller-Snyde, Elaine
Band Director
Schweller-Snyder, Elaine
Music Dept Chair & Band Dir
Shoemaker, Sherry Lynn Lundy
Language Arts Teacher
Stahlman, Mary Badertscher
Retired 3rd Grade Teacher
Stephan, Donald L.
English Department Chairman
Thoma, Joyce Elizabeth (Shipman)
Kindergarten Teacher
Trapp, Frances Martin
Fifth Grade Teacher
Wagner, Anthony Wayne
Mathematics Teacher
Weadock, Stephen W.
AP Amer Govt & World His Tchr
Wiford, Melanie Jane
Biological Science Teacher
SMITHVILLE
Douglas, Ronald Paul
Drafting Technology Instructor
Rowe, Leonette Sutter
6th-8th Grade Teacher
Saris, Charles J.
Biology Teacher
Smucker, Linda L. (Zimmerman)
Advocate Coordinator
SOLON
Aker, Jeffrey Charles
Social Studies Teacher
Bergen, Susan E.
11th Grd Amer History Teacher
Caroff, Carol Henikman
Math Teacher & Dept Chprsn
Christian, Dan
Science Department Chairman
Heinrich, Bruce G.
Mathematics Teacher
Iwan, Thomas Michael
Eighth Grd Math & Alg Teacher
Krouse, Camille Rosso
11th Grade American Lit Tchr
Minch, Ellen Somerville
Art Teacher
Morgan, Byron E.
Hlth & Phys Conditioning Tchr
Shoby, Susan K.
6th Grade Teacher
Stilson, Jennifer Palmer
Former Fifth Grade Teacher
SOUTH AMHERST
Nicastro-Baldwin, Gena Sue
Math & Computer Teacher
SOUTH CHARLESTON
Berkhofer, Karen Ipsen
Language Art Teacher
Blazer, Lisa Newkirk
Fourth Grade Teacher
Frantz, James Albert
Mathematics Teacher
Mc Ginnis, Sam
6th-7th Grade Mathematics Tchr
Wood, Casey Howard
HS Social Studies Teacher
SOUTH EUCLID
Alfonso, Regina Marie, SND
Education Dept Assoc Prof
Curran, Audrey Harwell
Assoc Professor of Psychology
Dolovacky, Karen
Science Dept Chair & Chem Tchr
Greene, Joseph Andrew
Govt, Ec & AP US His Tchr
Kreager, Mary
English & Enrichment Teacher
Llewellyn, A. James, III
Technology Coordinator
Mc Cafferty, Kathleen
English Teacher
Moenk, Jeanne A.
Assistant Professor of Math
Mrazek, Mark Edward, Jr.
Physics & Environmntl Sci Tchr
Tercek, Beth Anne
Assoc Prof of Economics
Winkler, Steven Robert
Spanish & English Teacher
Zupancic, Anthony J.
Assoc Prof of Eng, Comm, Thtre
SOUTH POINT
Meade, Jamie Lester
English, French & Speech Tchr
SOUTH VIENNA
Ark, Pamela Butler
Language Arts Teacher
SOUTH WEBSTER
Fannin, Elizabeth
Resource Teacher
SOUTHINGTON
Leon, Paula (Hassay)
Reading Specialist
Orleans, Michael Salvatore
Jr High Teacher
Tomasiak, Joanne C.
9th-12th Grd English Teacher
SPARTA
Dewald, Judy Kay
First Grade Teacher
Thayer, George Howard
Band Director
Ward, Cory Reed
English Teacher
SPENCER
Miley, Connie Lynn
Vocal & General Music Teacher
SPENCERVILLE
Ambroza, Nelson Larry
HS Math Teacher
SPRINGBORO
Berlean, Jacquelyn Pigan
High School Teacher
Black-Gregg, Mary Jane
7th Grd Rdng & Math Team Ldr
Metzger, Judith A.
5th Grade Teacher
Miracle, Kathy Turpin
Mathematics Teacher
Oren, James L.
Retired Elementary Teacher
Stuckey, Dave Bruce
Social Studies Teacher
Thompson, Lynn P.
6th Grade Mathematics Teacher
Wurzelbacher, Lynn Raker
French Teacher
SPRINGFIELD
Ahlm, Carl Edward
Senior English Teacher
Berkhofer, George H., IV
Latin Govt & Economics Teacher
Bingham, Dawn Lorraine
7th & 8th Grd Lang Arts Tchr
Bingman, David Bernard
Mathematics Teacher & Dept Chm
Candia, Diane Theresa
Fourth Grade Teacher
Davenport, Gloria
Second Grade Teacher
Denkewalter, Lori Kathleen
Spanish Teacher
Dolbeer, Cynthia Abbe
Third Grade Teacher
Dorn, Kathleen Moore
Second Grade Teacher
Dunstan, Donald Lee
English Department Chairman
Edwards, Manola Lee Cole
Retired Teacher
Foltz, Carrie Melissa
English & Journalism Teacher
Henschen, Larry Reuben
Math Teacher
Hoagland, Janice Honaker
Math Teacher
Holderby, Linda (Herold)
4th Grade Teacher
Horn, Sandra (Booth)
Med Lab Technician & Instr
Joyce, Anne Johnson
Fourth Grade Teacher
Killian, Lawrence Neil
Assistant Professor of Biology
Kludt, Behte Hall
Science Teacher
Krueger, Cecilia Eileen
First Grd Rdng Recovery Tchr
Kushmaul, Thomas R., Jr.
Music Teacher
Lockhart, Kimberly A.
English Teacher
Marsh, Rita Mahoney
Kindergarten Teacher
Mast, Ruby Baier
Retired Math Teacher
McClain, Theresa Howard
English Teacher
Mouser, Joyce Elaine
3rd Grade Teacher
Newland, Janet Foster
Spanish Teacher
Perosa, Richard John
Retired Eng, Sci & Math Tchr
Phillips, Beverly Ann
Second Grade Teacher
Redder, Deborah Mumpower
English Teacher
Sheridan, Elaine S.
Spanish Teacher
Short, Gregory Gordon
Sixth Grade Teacher
Smith, Julie Loe
Seventh Grade Teacher
Smith, Peter R.
Social Studies Teacher
Stevens, Ronald L.
Mathematics Teacher
Stewart, Ellen Hickman
Guidance Counselor
Tiffany, Frederick Glenn
Economics Professor
Yeazell, James Gerard
Instrumental Music Director
Young, Lori Miller
Spanish & Latin Teacher
STEUBENVILLE
Alex, Stanley Earl
4th Grade Teacher
Ardito, Donna M.
Second Grade Teacher
Biasi, Joseph Anthony
Social Studies Teacher
Chociej, Helen R.
Sixth Grade Teacher
Dixon, Betty Jo Zimmerman
Third Grade Teacher
Freedman, Matthew R.
Tech Arts Dept Chair & Tchr
Green, Robert Bruce
Orchestra Director
Hervey, Darlene Plotts
First Grade Teacher
Karabaic, Mary Jane Takach
7th Grade Science Teacher
Klisowski, Clara Grunfeld
French Teacher
Lee, James Ray
Criminal Justice Instructor
Lee, Patrick
Professor of Philosophy
Mankowski, Diana Yingst
Mathematics Teacher
Mc Million, Laura Lane
9th Grade English Teacher
Nurzyck, Victoria J.
Second Grade Teacher
Polimeni, Joanna Angela
English & Language Arts Tchr
Soly, Paul Wilhelm
Social Studies Teacher
Spanner-Morrow, Minerva
Spanish Teacher
Straka, Debra Lynn
Science Teacher
Travis, Sharon A.
Guidance Counselor & Math Tchr
Tubaugh, Marilyn Albert
Instructor of Accounting
Wells, Lloyd Arnold
Social Studies Teacher
STOCKDALE
Brown, Wanda Mae (Atkins)
First Grade Teacher
STOCKPORT
Bebout, Lori Latture
Math Teacher
STOUTSVILLE
Cordle, Nancy Archer
Earth Science & Lang Arts Tchr
Cordle, Terry Allan
Math & Industrial Arts Tchr
STOW
Adkins, Harold Dale
Business Teacher
Alpeter, Janice Skromme
French Teacher
Artz, Rebecca Sue Shank
Third Grade Teacher
Bechtel, Donald Eugene
Music Department Chairman
Beck, Audrey Marie
Sixth Grade Teacher
Bella, Norene June
Fourth Grade Teacher
Borsuk, Edward Joseph
Sci, Physics & Geology Instr
Brandon, L. Fran (Shipley)
Health Teacher
Bruns, Nancy Jayne (Perkins)
Spanish & French Teacher
Burns, Kay Marie
Fifth Grade Teacher
Colligan, Elizabeth Ann (Benson)
English Teacher
Crocker, Laurie L.
Sixth Grade Teacher
Garrison, Deborah Gardner
Spanish Teacher
Graves, Bonnie Laura Read
French & Latin Teacher
Harmon, Patricia Jeanne
Mathematics Teacher
Haslett, Ethel Mae
Senior High English Teacher
Jackman, Frances Louise
Music Teacher
Keller, Lori Henderson
6th Grade Tchr & Cheer Coach
King, Carlene Wooster
English Teacher
Leatherman, David K.
5th Grade Teacher
Mc Coy, Deborah Faye
HS Social Studies Teacher
McDivitt, Gregory Thrasher
Health & Physical Ed Teacher
McIntyre, Jane Elizabeth
Second Grade Teacher
Prather, Deborah Nichols
English Teacher
Putka, Robert Joseph
Art Tchr & Dept Chairman
Shellenberger, Richard L.
American History Teacher
Stehman, Rose Mary
Guidance Counseling Chprsn
Theisen, Suzanne Petrella
English Teacher
Zimmerman, Steven R.
Mathematics Teacher
STRASBURG
Leggett, Sheryl L. (Cox)
Sixth Grade Teacher
Quillen, Susan Harriff
9th-12th Grd Span & Fr Tchr
STREETSBORO
Mc Kee, Barbara Jo Snyder
Librarian & Media Director
Sovchik, Andy
Asst Principal
Stoner, Paula Smith
Biology Teacher
STRONGSVILLE
Chmelik, Susan M.
Music Educator
Cleveland Boyle, Janet Hawthorne
Jr High Math Teacher
Dylag, Candace Ray
Second Grade Teacher
Favorito, Lee Ann Martindale
Science & History Teacher
Jones, Carole Huey
Jr High Math Teacher
Karmilowicz, Floyd Edward
Sixth Grade Teacher
Kozma, Terry Alan
Economics Teacher
Lucas, Gay Lynn
Sixth Grade Teacher
Mack, Richard Clarence
History Teacher
Niro, Donna Heinrich
Fifth Grade Teacher
Nyrod-Dunn, Susan Kelly
Geometry & Pre-Chemistry Tchr
Parks, Keith
Spanish Teacher
Ruese, Timothy L.
Industrial Tech Teacher
Sapara, Linda Harris
Elementary Counselor
Scriven, Peter S.
Guidance Counselor & Teacher
STRUTHERS
Campbell, Carol J.
Business Instructor
Gage, Richard Charles
High School English Teacher
Grandy, John Richard
Eighth Grade History Teacher
Karis, Chrisdell Marie Watson
Third Grade Teacher
Markovich, Debra Ann
High Schl Social Studies Tchr
Martz, Beverly Dobos
English Teacher
McDanel, Joanne Emilo
Elementary Principal
Skurich, Monica Mary Sabula
Mathematics Teacher
Tarajcak, Stephanie J.
Religious Education Parish Dir
STRYKER
Friend, Tim Allen
English & Journalism Teacher

KER (cont)
Shannon Scott
ogy & General Science Tchr
, Janet Dilbone
k & Field Coach
Glenda Cooley
Prin & First Grade Tchr
Judy
ematics Teacher
R GROVE
s, Larry Alan
Grade Teacher
, Donald Lee
nce Teacher & Dept Chair
g, Phyllis D.
ish Teacher
e, Joan Marie
10th Grade PE Teacher
IVAN
r, Dale
bra II & Calculus Teacher
HUR SPRINGS
r, Maralyn Kennedy
d Grade Teacher
MIT STATION
Howard Daniel
School Business Teacher
, Jeffrey A.
ational Lab Director
Carol Byrnes
uage & Reading Teacher
y, Jacqueline Ellis
Grade Teacher
ng, Nancy Stahler
& 7th Grade Math Teacher
, Trond L.
al Studies Teacher
URY
, Verna J.
ding Specialist
Karen (Locy)
ish Teacher & Dept Chair
y, Angie
School English Teacher
anney, Terra Baker
ish Teacher
Daneen Comunale
ish & Reading Teacher
e, Ann Harkrider
Grade Teacher
NTON
d, Sharon (Sloan)
& 6th Grade Teacher
an, Nicholas Ralph, II
erplant Teacher
on, Marianne P.
School Science Teacher
Troy Allan
School Math Teacher
ski, Betty Jo
Grade Teacher
co, H. Sharon (Saunders)
Grade Teacher
ANIA
, David Andrew
nistry Teacher
Mary Jacqueline
ed Ed & 7th Grd Eng Tchr
, Bridgette Michelle (Whitaker)
Grade Teacher
ck, Susan B. Liber
her
nd, Eugene Raymond, Jr.
d Director
put, Marsha Ann
ematics Teacher
, Penny Karabedian
nce Teacher
as, Linda Pelton
Grade Teacher
, Jonathan P.
her & Athletic Trainer
man, Carol Niemeyer
nd Grade Teacher
William Frank
ory Teacher
Susan Adele
al Studies Teacher
ski, Claudia Smith
Teacher & Dept Chairman
h, Carole Hanif
ish Teacher
lough, Mary Clare Rychlewski
Teacher
, Gerald P.
PE Teacher
z, Gary L.
rature Teacher
, Kelly (Mc Adoo)
nalism Teacher
MADGE
Joyce Arbuthnot
Grade Teacher
, Jacqueline Kienzle
homore English Teacher
ers, Kimberly Renee
inistrator & Teacher
man, Brenda Joy
dle School Teacher
, Dee Ann
hematics Teacher
ko, Tony
th Edctr & PE Dept Head
Marjorie A. Cirullo
Grade Tchr & Private Tutor
PLAINS
s, Suette C.
English Teacher
Milagros Santoni
ish Teacher

Rizer, Kelly Dawn
Reading & English Teacher
Shafer, Diane Louise
Mathematics Teacher
Shevel, William Robert
English Teacher
Smith, Timothy Mack
Social Studies Teacher
Wryst, Mary Louise
English Teacher
THOMPSON
Bookbinder, Linda Olmstead
Mathematics Teacher
Johnson, Debra Lou
First Grade Teacher
Miller, Charlene Marie
8th Grd History & Reading Tchr
Nightengale, Russell E.
Counselor
Orr, Barbara Dillworth
Span Tchr & Foreign Lang Chair
THORNVILLE
Bozigar, Virginia Quillen
Sixth Grade Teacher
Cattran, David Frank
Sr Govt & Social Psych Teacher
Steen, Karen Keister
Business Education Teacher
Sturgeon, Sue Winegardner
First Grade Teacher
TIFFIN
Bartlett, H. Thomas
Biology Teacher
Cunningham, Betty Sikinow
English Tcacher
Curlis, Deborah Jean
Medical Careers Instructor
Ehrman, Nancy Wilson
Retired Third Grade Teacher
Fillman, G. Allan
Religion Teacher
Gilbert, Steven Edward
HS Social Studies Teacher
Gower, Richard Edward
Elem Instructor
Hampp, Michael Allan
Band Director
Hart, Gary Charles
Social Studies Teacher
Hillier, Cynthia Peterson
Art Teacher
Hite, Nan E.
History Teacher
Hoover, Kayleen (Kin)
Kindergarten Teacher
Kanzig, Maria F.
Spanish Teacher
Kimmel, Judith Snyder
First Grade Teacher
Kisabeth, Larry Jay
Guidance Counselor
Kish, Paul Michael
English Teacher
Kline, Emma Catherine
Math Teacher
Lawrence, Ruth A. (Sutton)
Tchr of Severely Handicapped
Margraf, Mary E. (Lutz)
Third Grade Teacher
Mass, Anthony J.
His, Psych & Sociology Tchr
Murray, Margaret Rose
Teacher of Gifted & Talented
Myers, Emily Jane (Brickner)
English Teacher
Overholt, Robert Allan
Advanced Chemistry Teacher
Pope, Charlene Whitacre
Gifted & Talented Prgm Coord
Printz, Payton Arthur
Instructor
Shreiner, Gail Fredericks
Tchr & Coord of Gifted Studies
Walters, Roger L.
Building Trades Teacher
Woodruff, Judy Marie
Computer Science Instructor
Zahner, Kimberly Ann (Pryor)
Seventh Grade Teacher
TILTONSVILLE
Closser, Blair N.
Occupational Work Adjust Coord
Signorini, Daniel Albert
US History Teacher
TIPP CITY
Ahmed, Gail Horner
General Music Teacher
Anderson, Bart G.
Asst Prin & Activities Dir
Bringman, Debra Ann
Vocal Music Teacher
Ferrell, James Frederick
Spanish Teacher
Mc Alexander, Nancy Keely
Third Grade Teacher
Pallant, Marilee Lehman
English Teacher
Rettig, Thomas William
Athletic Director
Rogers, Thomas Michael
Biology Teacher
Warner, Sara F.
Mathematics Teacher
TIRO
Gray, Susan Tellor
First Grade Teacher
TOLEDO
Alexander, Michele McClure
Spanish Teacher

Algee, John R., III
Religion Teacher
Arbinger, Richard K.
Mathematics Teacher
Augustyniak, Donna
6th Grade Language Arts Tchr
Barailloux, Carol Ann (Williams)
Sixth Grade Teacher
Barthold, Jenny R.
English Dept Chair
Beck, Charles O.
Instr of Dev Math & Tech Wrtng
Bias, Bonnie (Fulwider)
6th Grade Teacher
Blackburn, Margaret Ellen
French Teacher
Blinn, Lois Ann
Second Grade Teacher
Blochowski, Michael J.
Computer Science Teacher
Bohnett, Sally Marie
Rel Tchr & Campus Minister
Bourland, David E.
Science Teacher
Bowes, Charles Thomas
Integrated Language Arts Tchr
Buganski, Pamela
Math Tchr & Dept Co-Chair
Burgard, Mary Kent
Readiness Teacher
Burns, Lynn
Former Teacher
Carlisle, James Edward
English Teacher
Carroll, Gretchen Schwoppe
Business Management Instructor
Christiansen, Toni Isaacson
Science & Chemistry Teacher
Conrad, Joseph Patrick
Cross Country Coach
Cooper, Judith Buckner
Fifth Grade Teacher
Crowe, Barbara J.
2nd Grade Teacher
Daugherty, Karen Jane (Olmstead)
Mathematics Teacher
Dayton, Kimberly Ann
8th Grade Teacher
DeMars, Jane
Sixth Grade Teacher
Denman, Thomas Charles
Science Teacher
Denniston, Mary Ann Bonk
Fourth Grade Teacher
Denos, Gloria
Religion & Health Teacher
DeVriendt, Mary Lou Mc Intire-Welch
Choral Music Director
Dewey, Paulette Baker
English Teacher & Dept Chair
Dunnett, Cindy Jacobs
Preschool Teacher
Duwve, Larry R.
Social Studies Teacher
Dye, Ivan D.
Mathematics Teacher
Epstein, Davie Jean (Asnis)
7th-8th Grd Lang Arts Teacher
Eulberg, Lyn
Math Teacher
Evans, Betty R.
Sixth Grade Teacher
Faulkner, Sylvia Jane (Sanford)
Music Teacher
Fernandez, Kathy Miller
7th & 8th Grd Lang Arts Tchr
Fraley, Marilyn Price
Bible & Science Teacher
Gallaher, Laura Essex
English Teacher
Gargas, Kelly Reed
Spanish Teacher
Geha, William Arthur
Substance Abuse Coordinator
George, Stanley Emerson
5th-12th Grade Music Educator
Gilbert, Helen C.
Guidance Director
Gloer, Mary S.
English Teacher
Graham, Linda Marie
Second Grade Teacher
Greebe, Catherine Kaufman
Fifth Grade Teacher
Griesheimer, Cindy Lorraine
Pre-Kndgtn & 8th Grd Span Tchr
Grombacher, Raymond T.
7th & 8th Grade Art Teacher
Gucciardo, Judith Povse
Math Teacher
Gulich, Susan Carol
Business Teacher
Hackett, Majean Bowles
Fifth Grade Teacher
Hammitt, Kathy Jo McMurray
Second Grade Teacher
Hannah, Ann M.
Special Education Teacher
Hanthorn, Jeffrey W.
Elementary Principal
Hardy, Janet Jarzeboski
First Grade Teacher
Hart, Miriam Anne (Utter)
Fourth Grade Teacher
Hook, Donna Jean
English Teacher
Hrosko, Sue Gladieux
English Teacher
Hutchinson, Joseph Frederick
Geog & World History Teacher

Jamison, Norman Harvey, Sr.
7th & 8th Grd Science Teacher
Jankowski, Barbara Lou (Chambers)
Teacher
Jordan, Pamela Lee
Eighth Grade Teacher
Katzman, Lannie S.
High School Teacher
Kemp, Katherine Lee
Jr High Language Arts Teacher
Kennedy, Kathleen Patricia
Sixth Grade Teacher
Kirchhoff, Jon R.
Chemistry Professor
Knight, Linda Marie Cook
Family & Consumer Sci Tchr
Knox, Denise Schulte
Associate Prof of Life Sci
Konwinski, Jacqueline Marie Koralewski
History & Economics Tchr
Koslovsky, Sue Weidman
4th Grade Teacher
Krompak, Frances A.
Guidance Counselor
Kudzia, Renee M.
Womens Basketball Head Coach
Lambrecht, Cynthia Marie
English Teacher
Larabee, Dave M.
Physics & Mathematics Teacher
Lin, En-Bing
Professor
Loch, Janis Beaver
Sixth Grade Teacher
Long, Donna Jean
Retired English Teacher
Lowry, Chieko
Japanese Language Teacher
Luedde, Susan Knowlton
Math Teacher
Malone, Thomas Edward
Social Studies & Speech Tchr
Martin, Roy Edward
Science Teacher
Masters, Shehrever
Honors Phys & Anat Teacher
Matthes, M. Kristin
Rel & Integrated Math Teacher
Mc Clain, Patricia Marie
Intermediate Teacher
Mc Clure, Gordon Arad
Administrator
McCoy, Samuel Aaron
Department of Science Chairman
Miller, Charles Frederick
Writing Teacher
Mitchell, Elaine Marie (Estelle)
Fifth Grade Teacher
Mocek, Brenda M.
German Teacher
Molyet, Anne Mary M.
Counselor
Morton, Carmella Sye
Jr High Science Teacher
Narges, Barbara Zankl
German Teacher
O'Neal, Frances Alvey
English Teacher
Parker, Mary Junellen
Social Studies Teacher
Perlaky, Martin W.
Science Teacher
Petryk, Patricia Nietrzeba
Science Tchr & Dept Chprsn
Powell, Joyce Delores Anderson
8th Grade Language Arts Tchr
Price, Dale Lee
Mathematics Teacher
Price, Lela Vonetta
Fifth Grade Teacher
Pruden, Mary A.
English Teacher
Quigley, Mary Hall
Band & Orchestra Director
Quinn, Julie Renaux
Eng, Speech, Bible & Bus Tchr
Randolph, Brian Walter
Associate Prof of Civil Engrng
Ransey, Linda Marie
High School English Teacher
Ritter, Lois Marvin
Intermediate Teacher
Rothhaar, Twila Kay (Miller)
Fourth Grade Teacher
Rybarczyk, James Edwin
7th Grade Math Teacher
Sacks, Deborah J.
English Teacher
Saddoris, Dana J. Kyler
5th Grade Teacher
Schall, Joy K.
Math Teacher
Shaneck, Christine Tscherne
Third Grade Teacher
Shawver, Robert Lance
Mathematics Teacher
Shope, Kevin Ray
Director of Bands
Skelding, James Edward
Fifth Grade Teacher
Smith, Catherine D.
Dean of Students
Smith, David Jeffery
Social Studies Teacher
Spiesman, Sarah J.
Spanish Teacher
Standley, Denise Janowiecki
7th Grd Language Arts Teacher
Starr, Patricia Van Harken
Sixth Grade Teacher

Stine, Judy Ann
Fifth Grade Teacher
Straka, Mary Kaiser
Business Ed Tchr & Dept Head
Tober, Sandra Mollen
HS Social Studies Teacher
Topolski, Carol C.
Junior High School Teacher
Topp, Robert
Assoc Prof & Dir Clin Rsrch
Torrence, David Michael
Science Teacher
Valuck, Sandra Jean
Assistant Professor of Nursing
Wagner, Barbara Burgmaier
English & Basic Speech Teacher
Walasinski, Alice Dziewiatka
Jr HS Language Arts Teacher
Wambold, Suzanne
Associate Professor
Warnsley, Johnnye VanBuren
History Teacher
Weiss, Raymond T.
Social Studies Teacher
Windsor, Charlene
English Teacher
Winterstein, Alecia M.
8th Grd Language Arts Teacher
Wolf, Jean Lehman
Jr HS Bible, Math & PE Tchr
Yost, Jason Lynn
Music Director
Zielinski, Paul
Science Teacher
TONTOGANY
Grindstaff, James R.
Math & Cmptr Sci Teacher
Mc Cord, Jennifer Revis
English & Speech Teacher
Rosinski, Connie Louise
Mathematics Teacher
Scott, Bernard J.
Agriscience Teacher
Snyder, John Arthur
Science & Physics Teacher
TORONTO
D'Amico, Valerie Growden
Math Teacher
Dobrick, Dennis Stephen
Principal
Johnson, Linda K.
Social Studies Teacher
Meyer, Mary Alice (Goddard)
First Grade Teacher
TRENTON
Demczyk, Jill Schue
Chemistry Teacher
Mignery, Michael E.
Secondary Social Studies Tchr
TROTWOOD
Andrews, Michael Roger
Junior High Science Teacher
Ridenour, Kenneth Robert
Spanish Teacher
TROY
Bartley, Rusty
Sixth Grade Teacher
Gallagher, Rita Davis
Retired 5th Grade Teacher
Latta, Edward M., Jr.
5th Grade Teacher
Mitchell, Helena Theresa (Sekular)
Sixth Grade Teacher
Penny, Patricia Ann
Sixth Grade Teacher
Pfeffenberger, Sandy Moeller
Instrumental & Gen Music Tchr
Shiptenko, Ellen Marie Malacky
French Teacher
Young, Diana Serio
Second Grade Teacher
TWINSBURG
Brownfield, Robert Beaumont, Jr.
Fifth Grade Teacher of Gifted
Fosnight, Jennifer Trexler
5th Grade Teacher
Moldovan, Michael John
English Instructor
Murphy, Kathleen Sue
Science Teacher
Zenisek, Carol Pinter
Second Grade Teacher
UHRICHSVILLE
Arthurs, Jeffrey Alan
World History & Geography Tchr
Ribo, Marilyn Ruth (Young)
French Teacher
Sweitzer, Melody M. Foster
Fourth Grade Teacher
Whitmure, Susan M. Risher
High School English Teacher
UNION CITY
Gates, Emily Ann (Mangas)
Business Teacher
Gibson, Wauneta Marceil (Horine)
Retired Teacher
Loy, Jennifer Amole
English Teacher
Young, Wanda Kochersperger
HS Sci Teacher & Dept Chair
UNIONTOWN
Bonsky, Kathleen Ann (Becker)
1st Grade Teacher
Gooding, Marianne Ball
Fr, Span Teacher & Dept Chair
Hoffman, Marc Thomas
Senior English Teacher
Kocher, David Jerome
Teacher & Science Dept Head

UNIONTOWN (cont)
Selden, Mary Beth
Third Grade Teacher
UPPER SANDUSKY
Anderson, Audrey Halm
Soc Studies Teacher
Biro, Michael Leroy
Bus Tchr & Head Bsktbl Coach
Fadley, David Allen
Fifth Grade Teacher
Wagner, Barbara Place
Junior High Teacher
URBANA
Basinger, Karen S.
Psychology Professor
Beard, Jack
English & Reading Teacher
Beck, Richard W.
Associate Prof of Psychology
George, David F.
Professor of English
Hastings, Deborah Kay (Britton)
Consultant & Teacher of Gifted
Lear, Debra Kay
Family & Consumer Sci Tchr
Marratta, Terri Walls
History & Psychology Teacher
Parcels, Martha S.
First Grade Teacher
Puckett, James David
Jr High Health & PE Teacher
Salzgaber, Bette Young
Fourth Grade Teacher
Sanders, Mary Ann Bankston
7th Grd English & Reading Tchr
Thompson, Lucy Dawson
Language Arts Teacher
Weston, Lorie Ann
Developmentally Handicapped
Winkler, James Edward
Family Life & Sex Ed Tchr
UTICA
Baker, Ronald L.
Science Teacher
Bender, Paula Gail
English Teacher
Hatch, Susan Jane
Title I Rdng & Lang Arts Tchr
VALLEY CITY
Knittel, Betty Turner
Intermediate Special Educator
VAN BUREN
Eakin, Richard Eugene, II
Instrumental Music Teacher
Munsey, Sandra Morgan
6th Grade Teacher
Obenour, Robert B.
Social Studies Teacher
Rhoten, Linda Dutton
5th Grade Teacher
Thomas, Deb Kuhlman
1st Grade Teacher
VAN WERT
Bagley, Linda Sue Kirchenbauer
Pre-First Grade Teacher
Jamieson, Carolyn Eilene
Health Career Instructor
Jones, Bradley K.
US His & Amer Govt Teacher
Nolan, Gary L.
Physics, Chem & Algebra Instr
Parrish, Douglas D.
Secondary Mathematics Teacher
Reichard, Terry David
Fourth Grade Teacher
Rohrs, Frank Lee
Business Ed & Driver Ed Tchr
Rozevink, Linda L.
Mathematics Teacher
Thatcher, Bonnie L.
Mathematics Teacher
White, W. Quinn
6th Grade Teacher
Wilusz, Kay Marie
Art Teacher
Yohey, Michael Todd
Chemistry Teacher
VANDALIA
Bybee, Dawn Marie (Brawn)
Mathematics Teacher
Edwards, Michelle Lynn
Chemistry Teacher
Hughes, Beth A.
High School English Teacher
Maenza, Leonard Francis
History Teacher
VERMILION
Bryan, Pamela Ann
English & Humanities Teacher
VERSAILLES
Huddle, John E.
Biological Sciences Teacher
Shively, Phyllis Ann
Retired Kindergarten Teacher
Spangler, Faye S.
English Teacher
VICKERY
Kuns, Melissa Milburn
Sixth Grade Teacher
VIENNA
Abbott, Karen Stitzlein
Mathematics Teacher
Clagett, Wendy Morris
Spanish Teacher
Gall, Ann M.
Business Education Teacher
Rohm, Eddy Duane
Technology Education Teacher
Webber, Robert Bruce
Mathematics Instructor
Webber, Sandra Marie (Perry)
English Teacher
VINCENT
Alkire, Carol Courtney
Fourth Grade Teacher
Boggess, Josette Trent
7th & 8th Grd English Tchr
Bolden, Kristin Spindler
Spanish Teacher
Brant, Michael L.
Social Studies Dept & Teacher
Brooks, Andrew Wayne
Fifth Grade Teacher
Daughety, John Mark
Principal
Dye, Deana Gail
HS Math Teacher
Hammett, Linda C. (Perry)
Former Secretarial Sci Intsr
Jameson, Roy M.
HS Mathematics Teacher
Johnson, Jason R.
American His & Government Tchr
WADSWORTH
Brown, Darla Jean Williams
8th Grade Math & Algebra Tchr
Mayes, Samuel William
Instrumental Music Director
Nedoh, Sandra Wheeler
Art Teacher
Ott, Mary Lou
Sophmore English Teacher
Roher, Ann McClain
Senior Composition Instructor
Schoonover, Robert Alan
English Teacher
Shrimplin, Joyce Thompson
English Teacher
Toth, Twila S.
English Teacher & Dept Chair
WAKEMAN
Wolfe, Enid Ione
Guidance Counselor
WALDO
Parish, Mary Reed
Second Grade Teacher
WALNUT CREEK
Cleveland, C. Diane
Kindergarten Teacher
Mc Key, Dan E.
6th Grade Teacher
WAPAKONETA
Dellinger, William Earl, III
Social Studies Teacher
Fahncke, Ronald Eugene
Junior High Language Arts Tchr
Johnson, Joyce Delzeith
Jr High Teacher
Lewis, Carol Hawisher
First Grade Teacher
Meyer, Dale Anthony
Spanish & French Teacher
Niemeyer, Connie Phillips
Chemistry Teacher
Ruck, Byron James
High School Biology Teacher
Shaw, Marilyn L.
4th Grade Teacher
Short, Mark Davis
Math Teacher
WARREN
Angelo, Christine Hendrickson
5th Grade Teacher
Baran, Virginia McCabe
First Grade Teacher
Barile, Frank Patrick
Sixth Grade Teacher
Beachum, Janice L.
Eighth Grade English Teacher
Berkhouse, Sally Liphart
English & Composition Teacher
Bernard, Kathleen Louise
Third Grade Teacher
Cooper, Scott Meredith
Assistant Music Director
Creighton, Sherry Santilli
12th Grade Teacher
Doran, Carmen Burt
English & Social Studies Tchr
Franko, Marilyn
Elementary Teacher
Girton, Dennis
Choral Activities Director
Gregory, James Ronald
HS Social Studies Teacher
Grischow, A. Lynne Steffen
Sociology Teacher
Grunenwald, Michele Waples
Chemistry Teacher
Hilbun, James Robert
Language Arts Tutor
Houck, Maxine Wenzler
English Teacher
Hrobak, Mary K. Ramage
Retired Elementary Teacher
Isabella, Bobbe Whiteman
Acctng & Computing Sr Instr
Jackson, Karen Toohig
Fifth Grade Teacher
Jewell, Victoria Fiocca
Fifth Grade Teacher
Kepner, Nancy M.
Fourth Grade Teacher
Kindelberger, Sue Ann
Retired English Teacher
Krisher, Michele Le Laidier
Teacher of Gifted & Talented
Lytle, Connie Sue
Second Grade Teacher
Marino, Bernice Bogden
High School Guidance Counselor
Minor, Annette Pollard
Cosmetology Instructor
Morris, Karl A.
English Teacher
Patrone, Eileen Ciminero
American History Teacher
Porter, Linda
French & Spanish Teacher
Powell, Janet Lee (Mc Clish)
Science & Math Teacher
Rappach, Norma Jeanne
Diversified Hlth Teacher
Reinhardt, Barry L.
Health & PE Teacher
Rek, Ramonda Fitzgerald
High School Spanish Teacher
Ricciardulli, Sara Lee (Horvath)
Spanish & English Teacher
Rottenberg, Betty Mac Lellan
High School English Teacher
Ryznar, Matthew Thomas
8th Grade English Teacher
Salo, Arne Ellis
7th-8th Grd Soc Stud Teacher
Shaw, Gordon Robert
Elementary Guidance Counselor
Shilling, Thomas Lee
8th Grd Social Studies Teacher
Starcher, Lois Ague
Art Teacher
Stocz, Shirley L.
6th Grade Language Arts Tchr
Summers, Bonnita Steen
First Grade Teacher
Sweeney, Marilyn L.
Math, Sci Tchr & Dept Chr
Terlecky, Paula Sooy
English & German Teacher
Titus, Betty J.
Mathematics Teacher
Trunick, Gail Gordon
Visual Arts Teacher
Vouvounas, Roseann J. (Antonucci)
Sixth Grade Teacher
WARRENSVILLE HEIGHTS
Geiger, Marge Vitko
Assoc Prof of English
Mitchell, Janice Bell
Language Arts Teacher
Myers, John Thomas
Fifth Grade Teacher
WARSAW
Fry, Jill Baumgardner
Reading Recovery Teacher
Henderson, Charlotte A.
French & Spanish Teacher
Jones, Richard Warren
Chemistry & Physics Teacher
Knuth, Sandra Rae
Tchr of Disabilities Behavior
Moran, Karin Barrick
Business Teacher
Nelson, Beth Mikesell
Language Arts Teacher
Seas, Richard Andrew
HS Assistant Principal
Starner, Francis Eugene, Jr.
Industrial Technology Teacher
WASHINGTON COURT HOUSE
Grim, Robert E.
Soc Studies Tchr & Dept Chair
Halliday, John Carroll
Mathematics & Physics Teacher
Marinacci, Eric A.
Mathematics Teacher
Meinert, Robin Van Meter
2nd Grade Teacher
Pittser, Meda Marise
Library Media Specialist
Poe, Diane Roberson
Family & Consumer Sci Tchr
Radabaugh, William E.
HS Math & Spanish Teacher
Robinson, Pamela Jean
MS Basketball & Track Coach
Rowe, Glenna P.
Chemistry Teacher
Sagar, Jefferson William
6th Grade Teacher
Sollars, Rebecca Ellen
Adv Biology & Physiology Tchr
Spears, Jeffrey William
High School Art Teacher
Wollam, Dennis Russell
Band Director
WATERFORD
Barnett, Jerry Lynn
Fifth Grade Teacher
Darragh, Janine S.
9th & 10th Grd English Teacher
Simms, Debbie L.
Math Teacher
Sloter, Wayne
Mathematics Teacher
Smith, Joan Fusaro
Title 1 Reading Teacher
WAUSEON
Burgei, Kenneth R.
Elementary Guidance Counselor
WAVERLY
Bryant, April Desiree
Fourth Grade Teacher
Kritzwiser, Helen P.
5th-8th Grade Lang Arts Tchr
Ramsey, Mary Ann
First Grade Teacher
Roar, Danny Joe
Biology Teacher
WAYNESFIELD
Baumgardner, Lois Kay Boham
Fourth Grade Teacher
Snyder, Carol K.
Mathematics Teacher
Stauffer, Deborah Swartley
First Grade Teacher
Wical, Janice Marlene Snider
Third Grade Teacher
WAYNESVILLE
Bilbrey, Robert E., Jr.
Director of Bands
Campbell, Ellen L.
Fifth Grade Teacher
Watson, Wilma Moody
Retired Physical Ed Teacher
Wisser, Robert Clayton
9th-12th Grd Science Instr
WELLINGTON
Conklin, David Charles
Speech & English Instructor
Conley, Karen Bragg
Computer Education Teacher
Coultrip, Marsha Louise
Health & Physical Ed Teacher
Farago, Martha Willey
English Teacher
Hyde, Richard Albert
Mathematics Teacher
Kauffman, Susan Ann (Polakowski)
Art Teacher
Stevens, Douglas A.
8th Grade Science Teacher
Stoll, Matthew Edward
Life Science Teacher
WELLSTON
Barr, Dave
7th Grade Science Teacher
Blankenship, M. Diane
Business Education Teacher
Fink, Linda Turner
Reading Teacher
Hall, Garry Allen
Work Adjustment Coordinator
Nodruff, Sandra Jayne
Retired Music Teacher
Riepenhoff, Dorothy Sanger
Elementary Music Teacher
WELLSVILLE
Davis, Linda Kay
Spanish Teacher
Fantone, James Joseph
Biology Teacher
Ferguson, Lisa Corbisello
Elementary Principal
Fieger, Barbara A.
Instrumental Music Teacher
Logston, Stephen Kenneth
Title I Math Teacher
Raffa, Brenda Kay Rose
English Teacher
WEST CHESTER
Bond, Jeanne Carlson
Sixth Grade English Teacher
Carras, Betsy Britton
HS English Teacher
Chapman, Dana L.
Spanish Teacher
Cornett, Brigitte Bibiana
French Tchr & French Club Spon
Curtis, Shirley Haubner
Fourth Grade Teacher
Dahlstrom, Denise Elaine Reem
Music Teacher
Eger, Linda Lolos
Latin Teacher
Fifarek, Mary Anne (Sanoica)
8th Grade Language Arts Tchr
Frederick, Audrienne Mercure
Fifth Grade Teacher
Hall, J. Tim
Biology Teacher
Hall, Tamara Lynn (King)
Health Education Teacher
Hannah, Shari K.
High School Mathematics Tchr
Horncastle, Megan Abbott
English Teacher
Hume, Dean B.
Teacher & Advisor
Jackson, Steven K.
Science Teacher
Kamm, Karen K.
Antmy, Physlgy & Adv Bio Tchr
Keller, Robert W.
5th Grade Teacher
Kobert, Linda W.
Math Teacher
Meibers, Lawrence John
Mathematics Teacher
Miller, B. Rene
English Teacher
Nadler, Thomas Edward
Mathematics Department Chair
Noble, Linda Ann
Physics Teacher
O'Brien, Donald Gene, Jr.
English Teacher
Sansalone, Mary C.
Math Teacher
Schmidt, Mary Elizabeth
Mathematics Teacher
Schultz, Lois V.
Gifted Ed Specialist
Smardon, Carolyn Carden
History Teacher
Snyder, Gregory Lynn
Band Director
Stamp, Audrey Finnell
German Teacher
Thomas, Brian Robert
8th Grade Amer History Teacher
Totten, Jill Noella
Computer Bus Application Tchr
Watson, C. Kay Taylor
English Teacher
WEST JEFFERSON
Hoenie, Nancy E. (Tewell)
Third Grade Teacher
Hunter, Robert Randall
6th Grd Science & Math Tchr
O'Harra, Susan Looby
Mathematics & Business Teacher
Prellwitz, Nancy A.
Second Grade Teacher
Roberts, Edwin Lee
Science Teacher
Snyder, Judy Johnson
1st Grade Teacher
Stauffer, Brenda Garrett
English Teacher & Dept Head
WEST LIBERTY
Day, John T.
HS Math Teacher
Heminger, Linda Foust
First Grade Teacher
Roberts, J. Michael
Social Studies Teacher
Steider, Judith Hartzler
English, Jrnlsm & Rdng Teacher
WEST MILTON
Abbott, Richard H.
6th Grade Science Instructor
Houser, James C.
Science Teacher
Jacobs, Janet M.
English Teacher
Lee, John A.
Reading Specialist
WEST PORTSMOUTH
Newlan, Cathy Sue Tieman
Seventh Grade English Teacher
WEST SALEM
Ryder, Thomas H.
Mathematics Teacher
Wertz, Kathryn Reichert
High School Mathematics Tchr
WEST UNION
Harper, Raymond Keith
Eighth Grade Science Teacher
Kirker, Lydia Richmond
Kindergarten Teacher
Meyer, Brian Joseph
Music Teacher
Mowen, Robert Earl, Jr.
Automotive Technology Instr
WEST UNITY
Krause, Terry L.
Instrumental Music Director
Kyser, Paul Lavon
Technical Education Teacher
Sauder, Robert Jay
Spanish Teacher & Athletic Dir
Smith, Thomas Neil
Jr High Math Teacher
Stuckey, Emagene K.
Third Grade Teacher
WESTERVILLE
Bain, Bruce
Social Stud Instr & Dept Head
Benjamin, Linda Stoll
First Grade Teacher
Berrier, Monica Gogul
Spanish Teacher
Boggs, Lucy Messing
5th & 6th Grade Teacher
Brockman, William Lee
High School Mathematics Tchr
Bryant, Nancy S.
Retired Elementary Teacher
Bucey, Kathryn Ann (Kalivoda)
English & Speech Teacher
Campbell, Mary Hebert
English Teacher
Denney, Carol Margaret
English Teacher
Gillivan, Sharon L.
2nd Grade Teacher
Hacker, Gregory Charles
Science Teacher
Henman, Beth Anne
Spanish Teacher
Hines, Maryann
English & Journalism Teacher
Holford, Jane Ann
Fifth Grade Teacher
Kirchhoff, Harding
American History Teacher
Kulju, William David
Health Teacher
Love, Sherri Lee (Wright)
6th-8th Grade Teacher
Manning, Greta Sorgenfrei
Biology Teacher
McMeekin, Jane Margaret
Social Studies Teacher
Miller, Julia Ellen
High School Counselor
Neubig, Mike A.
Language Arts Teacher
Oxley, Margaret Stewart
Second Grade Teacher
Power, Marcine Baumgartner
5th-6th Grade Math Teacher
Scarberry, Barbara Hohman
7th-12th Grade Teacher
Schell, Richard C.
History Teacher
Snouffer, John I.
Social Studies Teacher

'ERVILLE (cont)
Peggy DeRosa
ıer Teacher
s, Mark B.
ırade Teacher
r, Linda Scott
ıematics Teacher
r, Debra Scott
ish Teacher
er, Sharon Clark
Grade Teacher
ey, Cynthia Baker
Grade Teacher
ore, Charles Christian
ırian & Media Specialist
ell, Jane Nichols
Grade Teacher
'FIELD CENTER
ıll, Sharon Sue (Yost)
ırade Challenge Teacher
'LAKE
ı, Jeanne Emmons
ıce Tchr & Planetarium Dir
ck, Margaret Leigh
ch & History Teacher
ıtcheon, Maureen C.
ational Consultant
v, Kay Cameron
ırade Math & Algebra Tchr
, John Thomas
ics & Physical Sci Teacher
y, Robert Edward
al Studies Tchr & Dept Chm
, Patrick Kenneth
al Studies Teacher
RTON
, Elaine Ann
ıce Teacher
rill, Elizabeth Phillips
ish & Reading Teacher
ELERSBURG
Paul Anthony
ogy Teacher
', Sharon Jenkins
vention Specialist
ore, Patricia Ann Flannery
lergarten Teacher
, Carol Jane (Hill)
ling & English Teacher
, Paul Stephen
mistry I, II & Physics Tchr
Kathy Jo
ness Teacher
ls, Rebecca Schroeder
ance Counselor
rinon, Mary Zoellner
ı Grade Teacher
ıhoff, Joyce Bradford
ish Teacher
', Patricia Sparks
her
Thomas Edwin, Jr.
Instructor
'EHOUSE
Margaret Ann
ness Teacher & Dept Chprsn
David Allan
ı Grade Teacher
an, Shirley Bistline
her
Deena Schwamberger
ıish & French Teacher
, Janet Kadowaki
Grade Teacher
ry, James Richard
h Grade Teacher
Karrie L.
Teacher
ıy, Robert James
ıematics Teacher
KLIFFE
ar, Tony
sical Education & Hlth Tchr
t, Barbara Pasqualone
d Grade Teacher
Michael James
ic Department Chair
, James Franklin
ı School Vocal Teacher
Michael John
h Teacher
', Ken R.
hematics Teacher
ky, Robyn House
ness Technology Teacher
BERFORCE
v, Lugene
arian
, Eve Lorraine
lish Instructor
, Terrence L.
'essor of English & Chair
Sam L.
'essor of Economics
e, Fatou Ndene
ıch Professor
e', Gerald Sidney, Sr.
ology Professor
ll, Katherine R.
istant Professor
LARD
Michael A.
mistry Teacher
r, Keith D.
& 6th Grade Teacher
n, Dale C.
Grade Science Teacher
k, Susan Thornton
lish Teacher

WILLIAMSBURG
Blair, Ava L. Cornett
Sixth Grade Teacher
Osborne, Ken
Assistant Principal
WILLIAMSPORT
Diltz, Linda Bayes
Sixth Grade Math Teacher
Downing, Keith
OWA Head Football Coach
Ramey, Ann L. (Posey)
8th Grd American History Tchr
Schaffnit, Mark Christopher
Middle School Band Director
WILLOUGHBY
DeFazio, Kit
Secondary Social Stud Teacher
Elias, Judith Brichford
Flute Instructor
Flamik, Judy Onysyk
Vocational Commercial Art Tchr
Frieder, Wendy Schmidt
HS Multi-Handicapped Teacher
Fynn, Carol Witwer
English & Psychology Teacher
Gay, Liela Marie (Engelhaupt)
Eng & Sci Tchr, Dept Chm
Guthrie, Helen Ross
Fourth Grade Teacher
Harman, Marilyn Soinski
English Teacher
Hobart-Kovatch, Joan
Accounting & Business Teacher
Holden, Sue Malaby
Cooperative Bus Ed Coordinator
Kapitanec, Nancy Battles
Sixth Grade Teacher
Koelling, Charles W., II
AP & General Biology Instr
Komocki, Lydia V. (Pokorny)
High Schl Spanish Instr
Laning, Theresa Kausek
English Teacher
Maine, Richard Wayne
History, Gov & Economics Tchr
Mulhern, Patricia Ann, OSU
Junior High English Teacher
Pennington, John Robert
Science & Biology Teacher
Pfeister, Ray L.
High School Guidance Counselor
Richard, Roger L.
History Department Chairman
Sanderson, Cynthia A.
French & English Teacher
Stumpf, Carl Richard
Cmptr Information System Instr
Vanderground, Ruth Dunn
Second Grade Teacher
WILLOW WOOD
Bartram, Linda Clark
Third Grade Teacher
Burcham, Diana G.
Sixth Grade Teacher
Curry, Sandra Lambert
6th Grade Teacher
Goodall, William Robert
History & Government Teacher
Wade, Brenda Faye (Brown)
Secondary Mathematics Teacher
WILMINGTON
Bustle, Rod E.
HS Social Studies Teacher
Curtis, Robert I.
6th Grd Rdng & World His Tchr
Dunn, Georgia Stilwell
English Teacher
Wiederhold, L. Jeff
Math Teacher
WINDHAM
Baum, Joseph John
Spanish & English Teacher
Cannatti, Patricia A. (Stamm)
7th Grade English Teacher
Chaffee, Michael Anthony
English & Humanities Teacher
Eakins, Roger Allen
Math Teacher & Dept Co-Head
Kobus, Steven Albert
Algebra & Geometry Teacher
Starcher, Maryanne Horack
3rd Grade Teacher
WINTERSVILLE
Boylan, Dorette Elaine
English Teacher
Hocking, Melanie E.
Chemistry & Biology Teacher
Leone, Sandra Elaine
Business & Comp Ed Teacher
Smith, Bonnie Wilson
English Teacher
WOODSFIELD
Casto, Steven Eugene
Social Studies Teacher
Indermuhle, Robert Eugene
Mathematics Teacher & Leader
Kidd, Cale A.
Sixth Grade Teacher
Peter, Sharon Kulp
Third Grade Teacher
WOODVILLE
Hoover, Rick Lane
Physical Education Instructor
Traver, Sharon Rideout
Fourth Grade Teacher
WOOSTER
Beach, Brenda L.
First Grade Teacher
Bowman, Connie Sue Simpson
Secondary English Teacher

Carmel, Randall Anthony
10th Grade Sci Teacher
Dennis, Sherrie (Bicksler)
Art Teacher
Gillentine, Linda Emerson
Sixth Grade Teacher
Hammond, Kent Douglas
Assoc Prof & Tech Coord
Headings, Mark Elmer
Associate Professor
Hibbs, Todd William
Student Assistance Coordinator
Houston, Linda S.
Assoc Prof of Comm Skills
Lunsford, Shirley Badger
Communication Skills Asst Prof
Miles, Patricia Bailey
Sixth Grade Teacher
Munn, David Alan
Associate Professor of Soils
Perley, James E.
Professor of Biology
Redick, Janet Taylor
Retired Teacher
Reed, Barbara Ann (Chirdon)
Second Grade Teacher
Wiles, Lisa J.
HS Art Teacher & Dept Chprsn
Zody, Shirley Klenk
Tchr of Learning Disabilities
WORTHINGTON
Cellar, Thomas K.
School Counselor
Ellwood, Mark W.
His Tchr & Soc Stud Chprsn
Fish, Jan S.
English Teacher
Galipault, Pamela Hecker
Soc Stud Tchr & Schlsp Cnslr
Hall, Larissa Jo
Multi-Age Classroom Teacher
Hasebrook, Christopher L.
English & Speech Teacher
Larson, Elizabeth Wellman
French Instructor
Mack, Timothy Alan
Middle School ESL Teacher
Parsons, Jerry Lee
Choir & Music Theory Teacher
Rogers, Patricia J.
Peer Assistant
Shaw, Pauline Holland
Chemistry Teacher
Sheth, Sonal B.
High School Science Teacher
Smith, Margaret Molinaro
Third Grade Teacher
Wilson, Gerald William
6th Grade Teacher
XENIA
Allen, Donald E.
Agricultural Science Teacher
Caldwell, Eugene L.
Machine Shop Teacher
Cottle, Shirley Darlene (Fodor)
Computer Office Tech Teacher
Cunningham, James Thomas
English Teacher & Dept Chair
Gayda, Jacqueline Elizabeth
7th-12th Grd Eng & Lit Teacher
Maley, Michael Benjamin
Social Studies Chairman
Onder, Kristina Manuel
English Teacher
Richards, Robert Reyburn
Art Education Teacher
Richey, William K.
Chemistry Teacher
YELLOW SPRINGS
Mullins, Shirley Strohm
Music Educator
Robey, John Samuel
7th-8th Grade Math Teacher
YOUNGSTOWN
Altinger, Joseph
Mathematics Professor
Anderson, Alicia Veremel
Music Teacher
Antenucci, Joseph William
Assoc Professor of Accounting
Armeni, Tony
Art Instructor
Ausmann, Stephen Wade
Asst Prof & Music Ed
Banks, Robert
Latin Teacher
Barber, Juanita Elaine
First Grade Teacher
Bartos, Larry Mark
Speech & English Teacher
Baun, William Robert
4th-6th Grade Citizenship Tchr
Beatrice, Jonelle Cohen
Instr of Rdng & Study Skills
Berger, Martin
History Professor
Binning, William C.
Political Science Professor
Blake, Dorothy Lipka
8th Grade Home Economics Tchr
Blue, Frederick Judd
Professor of History Dept
Bodnovich, Thomas A.
Information Systems Professor
Bosley, Cheryl Lynn (Markuten)
Assistant Professor
Bowers, Bege
Prof of English & Editor
Boyd, Joan Webster
Allied Health Associate Prof

Brown, Ifeteo J.
Honors English I & II Teacher
Brown, Steven R.
ESL Coordinator
Campbell, Robert C.
Coordinator & Assoc Professor
Catone, Joseph R.
Mathematics & Inclusion Tchr
Christofil, William Steven
Social Studies Teacher
Claypoole, Joan Louise
Fine Arts Teacher
Clinkscales, Claudette Richardson
Math Teacher of GATE Program
Coe, Maurene Ann
Lang Arts Tchr of GATE
Colella, Albert C.
High School Band Director
Conser, James Andrew
Chair of Criminal Justice Dept
Cordner, Diane Atkin
Reading Teacher
Crittenden, Jacqueline Lapaze
Math Teacher
DeToro, Jim
8th Grade Math Teacher
DeVincentis, Richard Arthur
Mathematics Teacher
DiGiulio, Joan Ferry
Chair & Prof of Social Work
Dougherty, Elaine
Seventh Grade Teacher
Duda, Karen Polahar
Professor of Computer Science
Edwards, Jane Otterman
6th-8th Grd Span & Eng Tchr
Ellyson, Steve L.
Professor of Psychology
Farina, Mary Dolores-Susinka
Mathematics Teacher
Fennessey, Bettyanne A.
Second Grade Teacher
Feurtado, Margaret Boyd
Math Department Chairman
Gage, Stephen Lawrence
Asst Prof of Music & Band Dir
Glasser, Elaine Junasz
Professor of Art
Grace, Sally Ann (Lefoer)
Kindergarten Teacher
Grassell, Duane V.
Mathematics Teacher
Hamilton-Harrison, Janine Gayle
Eleventh Grade English Teacher
Hanzely, Stephen
Prof of Physics & Astronomy
Hassell, Jean Treverton
Assoc Prof Food & Nutrition
Heinzer, Nicholas James
English Teacher
Heras, Elaine M.
Fourth Grade Teacher
Hlasta, Chester Paul
8th Grd Amer History Teacher
Hogue, Robert A.
Computer Sci Asst Prof
Hunter, Allen Dale
Associate Professor
Huzicka, Mary Ann (Reesen)
5th-6th Grade Science Teacher
Jones, Raymond F.
Spanish Teacher
Kabalan, Mary Jane Tamburino
Multi-Age Learning Ctr Teacher
Kascher, Rosemarie Anne
Teacher
Kesner, MaryJane
Head Kindergarten Teacher
Kestner, Jane E.
Professor of Psychology
King, Ellen Mc Gowan
6th Grade Language Arts Tchr
Kittle, Barrent R.
Marketing Professor
Klein, Karen Lynn
English Teacher
Kos, Anthony J.
Instructor of Management
Krispinsky, Leonard Stephen
Head Varsity Soccer Coach
Laird, Susan Diana
Sociology Instr
Law, David B.
Associate Professor
Leck, Glorianne M.
Professor of Education
Leenheer, Patricia Trell
Reading Teacher
Leonardi, Anthony Salvatore
Prof of Music & Coordinator
Maloney, Mary Theresa
English Teacher
Mamakas, Maria
High School Mathematics Tchr
McDougal, Diane Bateman
Asst Professor of Nursing
Mc Farland, S. Diane
Asst Prof of Communication
Mc Vicker, Barbara J.
Italian & Amer Lit Teacher
Milliken, Teresa Maley
Music Teacher & Choir Director
O'Brien, Robert Burke
OWE Coordinator
O'Hara, Bryan
Secondary Mathematics Teacher
Palazzo, Josephine Mele
Fourth Grade Teacher
Pallante, Martha Irene
Assistant Professor of History

Parise, Dennis William
8th Grade Science Teacher
Perry, Wayne
Math Teacher
Peters, Dolores J.
Retired Teacher
Raridon, Rosemary Jenkins
Instructor in Voice
Rodenbaugh, Karen Elizabeth
Advanced Lang Arts & Gate Tchr
Ruggieri, Thomas Michael
Band Director
Rygiel, Randy L.
Eighth Grd Language Arts Tchr
Salpietra, Nicholas Richard
Mathematics Instructor
Schaiper, Len Louis
Assoc Prof, Dept of Spec Ed
Scott, Marion Lisi
Asst Prof of Hlth & Med Sci
Sebastiani, Aurora Morelli
Assoc Prof of Biological Sci
Sekeres, Eugene A.
Prof of Adv, PR & Marketing
Sgambati, Patricia M.
College Preschool Lab Instr
Shipton, Sharon Pearl
Associate Professor of Nursing
Simington, Michael William
High School English Teacher
Skomra Kuskowsk, Ann
Executive Producer
Slanina, Donald R.
Electrical Engrng Tech Instr
Sracic, Paul Albert
Asst Prof of Political Science
Stacy, Barbara Ellen (Wire)
Voc Home Economics Tchr
Stolle, Nancy Siegel
French & English Teacher
Stone, Michelle Diane
Asst Prof of Social Grntolgy
Suchora, Daniel H.
Professor of Mechanical Engrng
Thomas, Kathleen Susan
Assistant Principal
Thompkins, Loretta Marie
Elementary Teacher
Tunanidas, Irene
Teacher of Deaf Students
Van Meter, Sue Honey
English & Journalism Teacher
Vargulich, Luke Horvath
High School Math Teacher
Vittorio, Lynn E. (Clifton)
First Grade Teacher
Vitullo, Raymond D.
Band Director
Vrabel, Kathryn Kohanov
Spanish & French Teacher
Wagner, Timothy R.
Assistant Chemistry Professor
Watts, Bonnie Yacouone
Seventh Grd English Teacher
Wilson, Dean Marlon
Elementary Music Specialist
Wood, William Alexander
Coord of Civil Engrng Tech
Zalka, Patricia Ann
Fourth Grade Teacher
Zona, Louis A.
Prof of Art His & Museology
Zyznar, Lucille Kraynak
Elementary Teacher
ZANESVILLE
Allen, Darlene Trussell
Business Teacher
Bevard, Larry Russell
9th-12th Grd Math Teacher
Downard, Thomas
English Teacher
Duncan, Joanna Louise
Sixth Grade Teacher
Edwards, Sarah Mc Donald
English & Government Teacher
Frey, Gary Michael
Chemistry Teacher
Gibson, Amy J.
English Teacher
Gillette, Susan Lynn
Chemistry Teacher
Hankinson, Susan Jane Giffen
Retired Eng & Lit Teacher
Henderson, Robert Fredrick
French & English Teacher
James, Anita Marie (Young)
Retired Teacher
Kimble, Robyn Snyder
Fourth Grade Teacher
Kolesar, Cheryl A. K.
French Teacher
Koncar, George Alan
Mathematics Teacher
Kuhn, Robert Sterling
Computer Science Professor
Mc Kirahan, Donna Browning
Cosmetology Instructor
McLaughlin, James Lee
Vocal Music Director
Miracle, Ronald Bryce, Sr.
Carpentry Instructor
Morgan, Gail A.
Vocational Business Ed Tchr
Nicholson, James Joseph
Cmptr Aided Drafting Instr
Overdorff, Marjorie Keller
Elementary Music Specialist
Peng, Grace N.
Accounting Professor

ZANESVILLE (cont)
Potts, Lisa Ann
Med, Legal & Fin II Instr
Sharrer, Ruth Walters
Language Arts Teacher
Skinner, Christopher James
Physical Education Teacher
Thompson, Marian Sharp
6th Grade Teacher
Thompson, Timothy John
Science & Mathematics Tchr
Waite, Gregory Michael
Technology Education Teacher
Ware, Ruth Porter
Eighth Grade Teacher
Watson, Kathy Ann
Spanish Teacher
Wilson, Richard Lee
Language Arts Teacher
Wolfe, Glorian Jean (Parks)
Fifth Grade Teacher
Workman, Carlotta Peterson
Guidance Counselor
Yetter, Carole Short
Business Tech Tchr & Dpt Chair
Zirke, Barbara L.
Biology Teacher

OKLAHOMA

ACHILLE
Anders, Kay
Business Education Teacher
Hearn, JoAnn (Lewis)
Language Arts Teacher
Phipps, Morene W.
Fourth Grade Teacher
ADA
Asklund, Retha Bratcher
Coop-Counselor
Brendle, Kathy Morgan
Third Grade Teacher
Brendle, Ron D.
Chemistry Teacher
Byers, Glinda Coulson
Fourth Grade Teacher
Byrd, Cindy L.
Fr Teacher & Drill Team Dir
Byrd, Connie Jean
5th Grade Teacher
Collins, Lucille Orr
Secondary English Teacher
Cornelison, Deborah Brown
Science Teacher
Crabtree, Rodney
Biology & Chemistry Teacher
Dansby, Lawana Tomlinson
Business Education Teacher
Embry, Linda Sue (Brinlee)
High School English Teacher
Euper, Tresa Coffey
Physical Education Teacher
Fleming, JaNell Thompson
Second Grade Teacher
Fortner, Dennis Scott
Physical Education Teacher
Frye, Linda Beth
Art Teacher
Gilmore, Janet Lynn
PE Teacher & Coach
Hall, Michael Van
Teacher & Coach
Hanson, Judy Timmons
First Grade Teacher
Harwell, Bryan Alan
American History Teacher
Hathcock, L. Joy Fuller
Learning Lab Teacher
Henderson, Becky Allen
Title I Reading & Math Tchr
Jessop, F. Bradley
Instructor of Art
Lillard, Glenda Hudson
First Grade Teacher
Matthews, Juanita Rae
Secondary Science Teacher
Mitchell, Betty Dorene
Mathematics Teacher
Morgan, Shelby Lynn
Jr HS Principal & Girls Coach
Murray, Carla Beth (Cole)
Fourth Grade Teacher
Neman, Robert Lynn
Prof & Chairman of Chemistry
O'Neal, Jo Ann
Math Teacher
Overturf, Marilyn Sue
Marketing Teacher
Prince, Junita Kay
Science Teacher
Pults, Carolyn Ruth (Lentz)
English Teacher
Scalf, Mary Boren
Third Grade Teacher
Scott, Rita Johnson
Secondary Art & Crafts Teacher
Turner, John Wayne
Math Teacher
Villines, Sadie Clark
Vocational Business Teacher
White, Lynne Ferrero
6th Grade Math Teacher
Young, Clay C.
Agriculture Education Instr
ADAIR
Kruse, Russell Wayne
High Schl Soc Sci Tchr & Coach
Kruse, Terri Annette
English & Journalism Teacher
AGRA
Cawlfield, Anita J.
9th-12th Grd English Teacher
Grayson, Mary Jane Criner
Voc Family & Consumer Sci Tchr
ALINE
Meyer, Karan Staerkel
Business Education Teacher
Weeks, Lary Leon
Tech Ed Instr & His Tchr
ALLEN
Spain, Linda Clift
Transitional 1st Grade Teacher
ALTUS
Allen, Betty Ann
Sixth Grade Mathematics Tchr
Coakley, Toni Parker
Anatomy & Physiology Professor
Darby, Dana DeAnn
Mathematics Instructor
Garner, Kerry Elaine
8th Grade Science Teacher
Glass, Jeanne D.
4th Grade Teacher
Haught, Carolyn Beach
Counselor
Johnson, Fannie Chapel
Dir, Bus & Information Systems
Madl, Cathy Starr
First Grade Teacher
Mc Elroy, Jim Lee
Secondary Science Teacher
Mc Lean, Norma Sue
Retired 5th Grade Teacher
Meier, Allan
Aquatic Director & PE Instr
Patton, Betty Craven
English & Spanish Instructor
Ray, Lori Wilburn
First Grade Teacher
Self, Christy Davis
Chemistry & Physics Teacher
Smith, Donna Yuvonne (Rombold)
Instructor of Teacher Cadets
Steen, Carol Claiborne
9th Grd Lang Arts Instructor
Vernon, Ilena Biggs
Fourth Grade Teacher
Wiginton, Linda Bryce
Eng III Tchr & Swimming Coach
York, Rebecca Reynolds
Advanced Placement Eng Tchr
ALVA
Gallon, Linda D.
Elem Physical Ed Teacher
Levetzow, Jeffrey Paul
Science Teacher & Coach
Tyree, Imagene M.
Retired Second Grade Teacher
Ward, Maris E.
Seventh Grade Science Teacher
AMBER
Sanders, Dickie Dee
Math Teacher
ANADARKO
Bailey, Bob James
Sixth Grade Reading Teacher
Edmiston, Donna Ross
Business Teacher
Liles, Trina J.
Business Education Teacher
Matlock, Debra Lynn (Ensminger)
Mathematics Teacher
Pulis, Sonja marie (Cobler)
Algebra & Geometry Teacher
ANTLERS
Fry, M. Lyndol
Art & Social Studies Teacher
Gardner, Amy Caraway
Chemistry & Physical Sci Tchr
Gregg, David Christopher
Band Director
Haddox, Wes
Math Tchr & Basketball Coach
Mc Cullough, Edward Eugene
Comp Lab Instructor & Tchr
APACHE
Bruce, Chris (Hickman)
Fifth Grade Teacher
Nix, Judy Stockton
Physical Education Teacher
ARAPAHO
Kirk, Hazel McClanahan
Gifted & Talented Spec Ed Tchr
ARDMORE
Bates, Tracie Welch
Math Teacher
Britt, Laura Ellen
Chemistry Teacher
Brown, Frances Wilson
Math Teacher
Collier, Bonnie Scribner
Language Arts & Speech Teacher
Collings, Martha Jean
English Teacher
Guy, Sheila Kay
6th Grade Language Arts Tchr
Lampkin, Amie Butler
High School Math Tchr & Coach
Lively, John Lee
Ret Eng, Psych & Soclgy Tchr
McCutcheon, Jenny Carmack
English Teacher
McGowen, Diane June
Fifth Grade Teacher
O'Daniel, Mary Alice
Mathematics & Physics Teacher
Richmond, Robert Steven
Health Teacher & Coach
Saner, Scott Allen
Math Teacher
Shuman, Anson P.
Debate & Drama Teacher
Stricker, Karl Andrew
Science Teacher
Thompson, Denise Herrell
Business Instructor
Wade, Angela Lester
Physical Science Teacher
Willis, Becky Jane
High School Math Teacher
ARNETT
Coram, Elaine Sawaya
Business Education Teacher
ASHER
Franklin, Anita Jackson
Language Arts Teacher
ATOKA
Baldwin, Hood
American History Teacher
Crow, Clifteen J.
Vocational Business Teacher
Lewis, Jerry Lee
Technology Education Teacher
Lytle, Virginia A.
Lang Arts & Lib Media Spec
Moore, Rick D.
Coach & Health Instructor
Rice, Sandra Kay
2nd Grade & Spanish Teacher
BALKO
Grose, Joe Burnett
6th Grade Teacher
BARNSDALL
Hurt, Joyce Terrill
Substitute Teacher
BARTLESVILLE
Anderson, Virginia Becker
Teacher
Austerman, Donna Lynne (Ogg)
Spanish Teacher
Baird, John Edward
Math Teacher
Beaulieu, Diana K.
5th Grade Teacher
Bennett, Colleen G.
Chemistry Teacher
Benton, Carolyn Frank
Math Coordinator & Teacher
Berger, Rod D.
Psychology Teacher & Coach
Brant, Teri
Business Teacher
Carter, Marilou Moffatt
Spanish Teacher
Conover, Mitsuye Hamada
Social Studies Teacher
Cross, Kenneth Leroy
Weight Training Teacher
Dixon, Diane Gaines
2nd-5th Grd GATE Tchr & Coord
Dronyk, Cynthia Walker
Math Teacher
Gardner, Keri Dawn (Morgan)
7th Grade Math Teacher
Gibson, Sandy K.
Tchr of Learning Disabilities
Helmer, Barbara Sloan
Adult Basic Education Director
Jenner, Sonja Jeanne
Study Skills Teacher
Johnston, MaryEllen Higburg
Retired Teacher
Lawson, Anita Cowan
Biology Teacher & Bldg Coord
Lovejoy, Judy Plaster
5th Grade Teacher
Mc Intosh, Beverly A. (Wortz)
Honors Biology Instructor
Miller, Larry D.
Social Studies Teacher
Moore, Terri Lyn
Science Teacher
Newson, John T.
German Teacher
Potter, Jeff Mark
Physical Science Teacher
Purvis, Barbara Ervin
Second Grade Teacher
Redmon, Robert James
English Teacher
Smith, Carol LaVon
French Teacher
Spencer, Ginny Easter
High School Counselor
Timmons, John Wyeth
Science Teacher
Tresner, Darla Jones
Journalism Teacher
Watson, Lora Wade
English & Lit Teacher
BATTIEST
Smith, Ron Gene
English & Speech Teacher
BEGGS
Colbert, Kathryn Ann (White)
Third Grade Teacher
Walker, Phyllis Carol
Health & Physical Ed Teacher
BENNINGTON
Redwine, Stephen Lee
Social Studies Teacher
BETHANY
Adkison, Sherry L.
Science Teacher & Adminstrator
Burger, Linda Wilson
Elementary Counselor
Cook, Wanda Reedy
Music Specialist
Drommond, Jamie Longacre
Eighth Grade English Teacher
Fuller, Mark Anthony
7th Grade Earth Science Tchr
Grant, Z. Flo
Social Studies Teacher
Hamilton, Kathleen Lumpkin
Fourth Grade Teacher
Hyatt, Carolyn Wagner
Second Grade Teacher
Iven, Marjorie Clayton
Teacher of Gifted & Talented
Ledbetter, Spencer Ray
Professor of Bible
Lott, Douglas Robinson, II
Bible Instructor
Reagan, Jay Robert
Mathematics Teacher
Runion, Betty J.
Third Grade Teacher
Sampson, Marion J. Talley
5th Grade Teacher
Tashjian, Jirair Samuel
Religion Professor
Thompson, Betty-Lou
Associate Prof of Elem Ed
Wiedemann, Cindy Brown
Journalism Teacher
BIXBY
Blackwell, Stephanie A.
MS Title One Math Tchr
Horn, John William
Science Department Chair
Jackson, Vivian Davis
Retired Teacher
Ledford Davis, Judy Cheatham
English & Psychology Teacher
Maxey, Eloise Evelyn
Coord of the Gifted & Talented
Nobles, Janet Hays
Drama, Speech & English Tchr
Pease, Lou Ann Longbotham
Second Grade Teacher
Schmitt, Claudia K.
English Tchr & Newspaper Adv
Shanks, Myra Gibson
Business Teacher & Dept Chprsn
Teel, Kimberly Cloud
Soph & Junior English Teacher
Vargus, Helen Etter
Tchr of the Gifted & Talented
Watkins, Tracy L.
Fourth Grade Teacher
Westerberg, Dotti Smeck
Third Grade Teacher
BLACKWELL
Chronister, Sherri Whitlock
Business Teacher
Hoose, Alberta Jean (Peters)
Second Grade Teacher
Kerr, Dennis Gene
Band Director
BLAIR
Burks, Rhonda Kim Middick
Science Teacher
McKee, Ronnie Wayne
Social Studies Teacher
BLANCHARD
Albarran, Lila Fosmo
Spanish Teacher
Armstrong, Lizabeth Jane (Lewis)
English & Lang Arts Teacher
Fogle, Kayron Martin
English I Teacher
Johnson, Sara Wood
English Teacher
McConathy, Donna K.
7th Grade Reading & Geog Tchr
Miller, Nancy Osborn
Third Grade Teacher
Moore, Pam Boutwell
Business Teacher
Munhollon, Leslie (Trent)
English & Psychology Teacher
Richey, Louise Genelle (Bayless)
English Composition Teacher
Sharp, G. Thomas
Science Coordinator & Teacher
Wood, Cassie Coggins
History Teacher
BLUEJACKET
Thomas, R. Duane
Superintendent
BOISE CITY
Jenkins, Kim Louise (Ukens)
Family & Consumer Sci Teacher
Jinkens, Mike Dean
US History Teacher & Coach
Miller, Gladys Wilson
Fifth & Sixth Grd Rdng Tchr
Prather, Melissa Woolley
5th Grade Teacher
Ramsey, Patricia J.
Language Arts Teacher
Wilson, Carla Jane (Johnson)
HS English & Business Teacher
BOKCHITO
Bowen, Billy Jack
HS Math Teacher & Coach
Dill, Cheryl Patty
Language Arts Teacher
Finch, Susan Ward
English Tchr & Acad Team Coach
Fleming, Arnold Eugene
Mathematics Teacher
Parker, Marilla Ladd
Vocal Music Director
BOKOSHE
Oliver, Jeff Warren
Coach & Spec Ed Teacher
Taylor, Darlene Marie (Dix)
Second Grade Teacher
BOSWELL
Boyd, Dorothy Miles
Retired 5th Grade Teacher
Deaton Goodwin, Linda Kay
Family & Consumer Sci Teacher
Jones, Beth Bailey
English & Humanities Teacher
Snow, Paula Yandell
Business Education Teacher
BRAGGS
Duncan, Mickey Allen
Science Teacher & Coach
BRAMAN
Cannon, Catherine Letzig
English & Speech Teacher
DeWitt, Dale R.
Agriculture Education Instr
BRAY
Gensamer, Dian Kay
English Dept Chair
BRISTOW
Holderby, Linda
English & Speech Teacher
BROKEN ARROW
Barnes, Janet N.
8th Grade English Teacher
Barnes, Karen Mead
Math Teacher & Dept Chair
Bass, Sherry S.
Fifth Grade Teacher
Burdick, Melanie Ann (Salcher)
Eng & Creative Writing Teacher
Burton, Joe Bob
Middle School Band Director
Calvert, Barbara Christensen
Biology Teacher
Cap, Allen D.
History Teacher
Carter, Judy Nilan
Elementary School Counselor
Cline, Mikel Thomas
English Teacher
Cook, John Duane, Jr.
Academic Principal
Coursen, Donald Toppin
6th Grade Teacher
Crofford, Penny Niland
Communicative Skills Teacher
Day, Kay Isbell
Mathematics Teacher
Dobbs, Glenn, III
Bio & Phys Sci Teacher
Evans, James E.
Physics & Chemistry Teacher
Fischer, Colleen Sandeen
Music & Bible Teacher
Franklin, David Samuel
Fifth Grade Teacher
Garrison, Donna Lynn
Civics Teacher
Goolsbay, Michael Linn
HS Chaplain & JH Bsktbl Coach
Hedges, Peggy Salisbury
Kindergarten Teacher
Hoffman, Carol Chenault
Learning Disabilities Teacher
Holder, Carolyn Dee
Eng Tchr & Coord of Gifted
Holmes, Christopher James
Orchestra & Music Theory Tchr
Imbo, Mary Ellen Croke
Elementary Principal
Jack, Martin Douglas
Science Teacher
Jackson, Joyce Coaly
Fourth Grade Teacher
Kinzer, Kenny Wayne
9th-10th Grade US His Teacher
Kufahl, Corlene
Secondary Teacher
Kufahl, Dale E.
Administrator
Lewis, Donna Jean (Rank)
Teacher
Long, Teri J.
Physical Education Teacher
Lybarger, Karen Kay (Buzard)
Bus, Yrbk & Newspaper Teacher
Maney, Kay (Moore)
Third Grade Teacher
McLain, Linda German
English Dept Chair & Teacher
Meeker, Jennifer Lynn
Honors Biology Teacher
Mills, Linda Sue (Mc Grath)
Fifth Grade Teacher
Nichols, Greer S.
Fifth Grade Teacher
Palmer, Lisa Cole
8th Grd Algebra & Math Teacher
Patch, Sharon H.
AP Calculus Instructor
Pollard, Rebbecca Rae (Kreisher)
Counselor
Ramler, Mary Dawn
Physical Education Teacher
Reel, JoAnn Elrod
Gftd & Talented Soc Stud Tchr
Reynolds, Susan Carol
Family & Consumer Sci Tchr
Ross, Dana L. Putt
Math Teacher
Sargent, Patricia Ann (Turner)
7th Grade Life Science Teacher

EN ARROW (cont)
b, Steven Ray
sh Teacher
ght, Lorraine Schuering
ace Teacher
rt, Pat A.
sh Teacher
ord, Jackie Garrett
Grade US History Teacher
pool, Cynthia Orene
Grade Elementary Teacher
n, Ruth Ellen (Hopkins)
te Tutor
, Michael Lynn
hysical Education Teacher
Linda Kay
Grade Teacher
Angela Graff
Teacher
Georgia Thomason
ish Teacher
EN BOW
Charles LeRoy
th Grade Teacher
, R. Wayne
Teacher
, Dennis C.
ematics Teacher
ns, Gary E.
th Grade Science Teacher
Janet Marie
th Grd Language Arts Tchr
ALO
, Tonya Roy
d Grade Teacher
EYVILLE
Virginia Bell
h Grade Teacher
S FLAT
, Roxane Leigh
l Director
an, Joe Neal
-Mechanic Instructor
son, Brenda K.
Teacher
E
Rodger Keith
mediate School Principal
, Ronald Wayne
ish Teacher
n, Penny Sue (Gaunt)
ematics Teacher
nix, Val J.
rd Soc Studies & Sci Tchr
on, C. Dale
rincipal
Darrell Lynn
Director
O
, Juanita Wells
nd Grade Teacher
ng, Marilyn Morgan
Teacher
ns, Jenna Bee Barnes
Grade Teacher
nd, Judy Joines
ish Teacher
RA
son, Vicki Lynn Collman
3rd Tchr
, Donell Collier
uage Arts & Art Teacher
all, Elizabeth (Langham)
ish & Elem Math Teacher
MET
, Arlen Lee
ed Fifth Grade Teacher
dy, Cathi Mac
Grade Teacher
y, Craig
al Studies Teacher & Coach
IN
s, Lorene Turner
nce & Spanish Teacher
ERON
, Gloria M.
ness Teacher
n, Joe F.
her
ADIAN
ern, Sheila Carol
Grade Teacher
Homer Ray
Teacher & Asst Principal
EY
, Clinta Mattingly
ily & Consumer Sci Tchr
TON
er, Nita Coffman
th Grade Teacher
NEGIE
er, Dena L.
Grade Teacher
TER
son, Bobbie Ann (Coffman)
d Grade Teacher
OSA
s, Samuel Brad
al Studies Teacher & Coach
, Andrea Janet
3rd Language Arts Teacher
, Zelma Thompson
School Counselor
son, Marion Carnes
Grade Teacher
James Mason
ory Teacher
e, Dena Keplinger
ish, Speech & Drama Tchr

Stockard, Jil Elizabeth
English Teacher
Thompson, Debra J. (Gowen)
Director of Special Services
Warma, Gayle L.
1st Grade Teacher
CEMENT
Reiss, Connie Robbins
First Grade Teacher
CHANDLER
Battershell, Eddie Ray
Mathematics Teacher
Canady, Pamela S.
English Teacher
Greenfield, Patty Bridge
4th Grade Teacher
Myers, Anna Hoover
8th Grade English Teacher
CHECOTAH
Haskett, Jim L.
9th-12th Grade English Teacher
Llewellyn, Margie Emerson
Fourth Grade Teacher
Mann, Patsy Farrimond
English Teacher
Mc Clure, Mary Neill
English Teacher & Dept Chair
Nemecek, Wyman
Agricultural Education Tchr
CHELSEA
Conine, Irene D.
High School Counselor
Moyer, Henry L.
Technology Education Teacher
Onspaugh, Paul Evan
Band Director
CHEROKEE
Smith, Elizabeth Jones
Family & Consumer Science Tchr
CHICKASHA
Allen, Randy L.
Fourth Grade Teacher
Cole, Barbara Jo
High School Mathematics Tchr
Hodges, Frankie Geraldine
Reading Specialist
Kirby, Lorene (Pulis)
Retired Teacher of the Deaf
Mather, Jeanne Ramirez Corpus
Asst Professor in Education
Risner, Wanda Holland
Speech Pathology & Class Tchr
Williams, Tammie Renee
Mathematics & Geometry Teacher
CHOCTAW
Beck, Gregory Alan
Fourth Grade Teacher
Bynum, Charlene (Seebeck)
Math Teacher & Dept Head
Cottom, Sandra G.
Fourth Grade Teacher
Farmer, Terri Grayson
Transitional First Teacher
Gaddis, Jana Adkins
Mathematics Specialist
Hayhurst, Rita Jo
2nd Grade Teacher
Holland, Linda Sue Westfall
Sixth Grade Teacher
Hudspeth, Tami S.
Counselor
Kincade, Carol Snow
History Teacher
Kline, Patricia Fletcher
Communications Specialist
Mangus, Jimmy Darrin
Spanish Teacher
Ryan, Paula Evonne
Science Teacher & Coach
Sharry, Elizabeth Wasson
Biology Teacher
Stine, Keith Arlin
Ninth Grade English Teacher
Uselton, Bill W.
Afrcn, Eurpn, & US His Tchr
Uselton, Karen Charla
Sixth Grade Teacher
Vaeth, Sharry Kaye
Elementary Principal
Zuck, Laurie Simonton
Fifth Grade Teacher
CHOUTEAU
Ashley, James Walter, Jr.
HS Language Arts Teacher
CLAREMORE
Brown, Richard Dennis
Civics Teacher
Carpenter, Farren Floyd
Coord of Ag & Horse Mgmt Pgms
Cegielski, Carolyn Nicholson
Junior High Science Teacher
Christmann, Barbara D.
Adjunct English Instructor
Damron, Kandy K.
Coach & Teacher
Dial-Driver, Emily
Professor
Fowler, Pamela Southard
Instructor of Health Sciences
Garroutte, Samuel David
Athletic Director & Math Tchr
Hedge, Jack R., Jr.
Biology & Phys Science Teacher
Hedge, Nancy S.
Teacher of Gftd & Tlntd Sci
Henzel, Joyce L.
Office Administration Coord
Jagel, Martha C.
Office Administration Instr

Kendall, Nancy Gale Pinney
Music Teacher
Kroutter, Paul Joseph, Jr.
Criminal Justice Instructor
Luscomb, Julie Ann
Computer Science Instructor
Luscomb, Thomas Ed
Computer Science Instructor
Main, Sherry Bates
Kindergarten Teacher
McGregor, Sharron Annette Hale
Director of Forensics
Moore, Sharon Mc Spadden
English Teacher
Newton, L. J. Scott
Political Science Instructor
Ohman, Clement John
Paramedic Technology Instr
Palmer, James I.
Art Teacher
Pendley, Bob Lee
Computer Science Instructor
Raasch, Susan Lucille
Junior & Senior English Tchr
Rachels, Linda
Bio, Anatomy & Physlgy Instr
Schramme, Lois M.
Sixth Grade English Teacher
Semkoff, Beverly Giles
Biology & Science Instructor
Shelton, Emilie Johnson
Biology & Zoology Teacher
Shortridge, Carol Murphy
Seventh Grade Teacher
Thomas, Charles Wayne
Behavioral Sciences Coord
Toalson, George Jeptha
Physical Education Teacher
Von Thaden, William
Jr HS Math Teacher & Coach
Wagner, Sarah Gaither
Adjunct Instructor of History
Westfall, Ronda Gail (Welch)
6th Grade Teacher
Young, M. Beth
English Teacher & Dept Chm
CLARITA
Lee, Jeana Diann
Math Teacher
CLAYTON
Huddleston, Betty A.
Business Teacher
Kirkes, Mike Stanley
Math Teacher & Coach
Sprouse, E. Ruth (Brown)
High School Math Teacher
Wright, Marcia Fuller
Voc Bus & Cmptr Tech Teacher
CLEVELAND
Berryman, Esther Clavin
5th Grade Teacher
Eason, Kimberly Kay
English Teacher
Kellert, Paul H., Jr.
Mathematics Department Head
CLINTON
Donley, Vicki Steiner
Eighth Grade English Teacher
Gemaehlich, Toni Lynn
High School Algebra Teacher
Hirschman, Dale R.
Art Teacher
Lacy, Don S.
American History Teacher
Lumpkin, Brenda Smith
High School Counselor
Rother, Donna Eischen
Teacher of Gifted & Talented
Stone, Jeanette Ruyle
Math Department Teacher
Ward, Kenneth James
Instrumental Music Teacher
COLBERT
Clark, Deborah Lea
Spanish Teacher
Hillburn, Jennifer Horn
Vocational Teacher
Mc Williams, Janet Kistler
English Teacher
Newcomb, Aaron L.
7th-12th Grd Asst Principal
Wallace, Ronnie Glenn
English & Humanities Teacher
COLCORD
Garside, Lynn Bumgardner
Art Teacher
COLEMAN
Germany, Karon Wallis
Second Grade Teacher
Hamilton, Marylin Hildebrand
English Teacher
Whitmire, Glenda O'Dell
1st Grade Teacher
COLLINSVILLE
Borthick, Michelle (Anderson)
5th Grade Teacher
Dortch, Ellen Ross
MS American History Teacher
Hewlett, Cheryl Heaton
School Counselor
Limbocker, Jennifer (Wiswell)
LD Teacher
McLaughlin, Ruth Pemberton
Sixth Grade English Teacher
COMANCHE
Ames, Billie Jo
Pre-Alegbra Teacher
Barber, Patricia Hampton
Library Media Specialist

Denslow, Keith
Debate, Speech & Drama Teacher
Gann, Sheila Kay (Wilson)
6th Grade Teacher
Garrett, Sue Lee
English I Teacher
Herrington, Kim W.
English Teacher
Phillips, Jerry H.
Business Education Teacher
Roberts, Kerry Preston
US & OK History Teacher
Smith, Mary Beth
Middle School Science Teacher
COMMERCE
Burns, John Michael
Spanish Teacher
Marshall, Kennett Don
Eng, Life Skills & Rdng Tchr
COPAN
Davis, Randy Lee
History & Drivers Ed Tchr
Martinez, Dianne K.
Math, Sci & Cmptr Tchr
CORDELL
Haas, Jeramy Scott
Band Director
Koehn, Nancy K. (Schmidt)
School Counselor
CORN
Brown, Kevin D.
Mathematics Teacher
Prindle, Eric A.
Social Studies Teacher
Regier, Charles Eugene
Music Teacher
Slagell, Reonna Richele
Science Instructor
Straub, Brenda Lynne
English Teacher
COVINGTON
Beeby, Jean Cordell
Visual Arts & English Teacher
Johnson, Waldinete Miranda
Spanish Teacher
Stovall, Bridget Ann
5th Grd & Elem Span Tchr
COWETA
Aston, Sandy Kay
Second Grade Teacher
Baker, Linda Wayne
Business Instructor
Baker, Rhonda Weaver
Business & Computer Teacher
Brown, Paula Halfast
French & Spanish Teacher
Clark, Mark Byron
Social Studies Teacher
Cochran, Stacy Stierwalt
Fifth Grade Teacher
Daniels, Jeanne Miller
English Teacher
Garrett, Sue Tharp
Eleventh Grade English Teacher
Gilbert, Elva Mae (Hembree)
Fourth Grade Teacher
Hladik, Peggy Ann
Mathematics Teacher
Howard, Steven Ray
HS & Jr Speech & Drama Teacher
Johnson, Timothy Leigh
Science Teacher
Lormer, Deena Gail
Second Grade Teacher
Merrill, Jennifer Feil
Art Teacher
Rutherford, Mary Beth
Second Grade Teacher
Wilson, Linda Sue
Math Teacher
COYLE
Rice, Melisa Ann (Rother)
Mathematics Teacher
Vick, Ella Louise (Burns)
Eng & Creative Writing Teacher
Weathers, Mark Shane
PE & Drivers Ed Teacher
CROMWELL
Bass, David Keith
Mathematics Instructor
Legg, Arthela Dooly
6th Grade Teacher
CROWDER
Duff, John Keith
Fourth Grade Teacher
Guinn, Diane (Nedbalek)
8th Grd Span Tchr & Coach
Stapp, Goldie C.
Vocational Business Teacher
Wilson, Charles Larry
Fifth Grade Teacher
CUSHING
Anderson, Linda Donahue
Elementary School Counselor
Evers, Jay Henderson
Teacher & Principal
Hawkins, Brad
Science Teacher
CYRIL
Crow, Rita Ryland
English & Spanish Teacher
Higdon, Lilla Codding
Science Teacher
Jones, Glenn Darin
Social Studies Teacher
Whitman, Dee Ann
Elem PE, His Tchr & Coach
DALE
Hampton, Donna S.
Sixth Grade Teacher

DAVENPORT
Brinson-Moser, Glenda Faye (Hunt)
7th-8th Grd Humanities Teacher
Walker, Sandra Kay
Secondary English Teacher
DAVIS
Brown, Sheila Ann (Green)
HS English Teacher
Connors, Maureen Ann
Social Studies Teacher
Raper, Jerry Don
Math Teacher & Football Coach
Schilling, Gary Lynn
Speech, English & His Teacher
DEL CITY
Bower, Cheryl Annette
Eng, Speech Tchr & Drama Chm
Bullard, Joshua Scott
Teacher & Coach
Estell, Brian Keith
High School History Teacher
Hanson, Susan Kaye
6th Grd Tchr & Elem Admin Asst
Mc Kenzie, Kay Lynne
Third Grade Teacher
Plunkett, Gil Andrew
Gen Physcial Sci Teacher
DELAWARE
Jones, Larry Gene
Secondary Science Teacher
DEPEW
Reeder, Molly M.
Retired Teacher
DEWAR
Burney, Becky Lightner
Business Teacher
Dunham, Kathy Spurlock
Vocational Home Economics Tchr
DEWEY
Head, Dianne Dowdy
English Teacher
Mingle, Linda (George)
Vocal Music Teacher
Raleigh, Don R.
Technology Teacher & Coach
Raleigh, Stacy Hall
8th Grade Soc Stud Teacher
Ruble, Troy Lee
Secondary Math Teacher
Thiessen, Linda Herbert
6th Grade Social Studies Tchr
DIBBLE
Burns, Preston Joe
High School Principal
DOVER
Robinson, Judith A.
Language Arts Instructor
DRUMMOND
Parker, Charlene Pospisil
Third Grade Teacher
DRUMRIGHT
Dock, Elaine Ruth (Smith)
Cosmetology Instructor
Leach, Delbo
Secondary Principal
Palmer, Judy Ann
English Teacher
DUNCAN
Arze, Rita Elisabeth
Spanish Teacher
Baldridge, Jessica James
Middle School Life Sci Tchr
Bechtel, Kay Hodgson
6th Grade Math & Science Tchr
Cruz, Shanon McClennen
High School Math Teacher
Davis, Carolyn Ridge
Business Instructor
Dennis, Linda Hardin
Counselor
Gray, Nancy (Herndon)
1st Grade Teacher
Jech, Lori A.
High School Band Director
Johnson, Kathy Hull
6th Grade Teacher
Labyer, Sherry Careathers
7th & 8th Grade Counselor
Mc Ghghy, Donna Sheryl
Family & Consumer Science Tchr
Parnell, Suzanne
Mrktg Mgmt Tchr & Coord
Pruett, Mary Anne Goode
6th Grade Teacher
Sellers, Janell Starcher
Biology Tchr & Bsktbl Coach
Shiffer, Deborah L.
French & English Teacher
Womack, Christine Hall
Algebra Teacher
DURANT
Adams, Shawn J.
Occupational Safety Hlth Instr
Baggs, Jo Ann
6th Grd Language Arts Teacher
Birdsong, Linda K.
Fourth Grade Teacher
Brese, David P.
Algebra & Cmptr Science Tchr
Chambers, Kathy Foster
Biology Teacher
Cherry, Karla Jan (Kelley)
Chemistry Teacher
Coats, James Edward
Social Studies Chairperson
Compton, Shana Kaye
Science Teacher
Daniel, Juanita Jo
8th Grade English Teacher

DURANT (cont)
Hartin, Haljean
English Teacher
Hendrix, Ellen (Kennedy)
Fifth Grade Teacher
Howse, Barbara Burns
Mathematics Teacher
Karn, Marilyn Kay
Sixth Grade Reading Teacher
Lilley, Melissa Dawson
English & Humanities Teacher
Lindley, Tanya Kaye Crow
8th Grade Lang Arts Teacher
Manning, Connie Sims
Second Grade Teacher
Massey, Betty Lou
Fourth Grade Teacher
McArthur, John Mark
Physics Professor
Merideth, Melanie Hughes
Chemistry Teacher
Newton, Neta (Jeffcoat)
Geometry & Algebra II Teacher
Nolan, Larry Russell
Assistant Prof of Technology
Patton, Linda Lavender
Seventh Grade Science Teacher
Pickens, James Kent
OK History Teacher & Coach
Risso, Roberta Ann
Director of Theatre
Rustin, Phyllis Ann
English & Journalism Teacher
Sawyer, Elaine
Computer Teacher
Stilwell, Terri Redden
Math & Music Teacher
Tucker, Melinda S.
8th Grade Amer History Teacher
Weiner, Kathy Carole
English Teacher
Williams, Judy Ann
Assistant Professor of Biology
EAKLY
Copus, Ernest Wayne
High School Principal
King, Melody Ann
Seventh Grade Teacher
Smith, Pamela Cusick
9th-12th Grd English Teacher
EARLSBORO
Mc Afee, Nancy Chandler
School Counselor
EDMOND
Ackerman, Judy
11th Grade English Teacher
Allen, Charity E.
6th-8th Grade Vocal Music Tchr
Altstatt, Adys Regina
Span Tchr & Foreign Lang Head
Andrus, Mark Scot
HS Assistant Principal
Arbuthnot, Jeanne Ann
Second Grade Teacher
Arrington, Tom Gene
History Teacher
Ashby, Vickie Fleming
English Teacher
Avellano, George Paul
Dean of Research & Grad Stud
Baker, Mary Jo Bondurant
AP US Gov & Politics Teacher
Barsaloux, Carole Anne
Science Teacher
Barsaloux, Robert E.
Computer Science Teacher
Bartley, Mary Jane
Drama Teacher & Drama Coord
Bauman, Nancy Ellen
Fifth Grade Teacher
Becannen, Mark S.
World History Teacher
Blake, Kathleen A.
Art Teacher
Bollenbach, Ricky Don
6th-8th Grade Physical Ed Tchr
Brown, Betty Henson
Second Grade Teacher
Brown, Duane
Driver Education Instructor
Brown, Lisa Maskus
Secondary Mathematics Teacher
Cobb, Mary Dowers
Mathematics Teacher
Coby, Malcolm W.
Professor of Education
Craig, Dana Sue (Robertson)
Mathematics Teacher
Crampton, LaDonna Meador
Third Grade Teacher
Currat, Conde Aline
Secondary Art Teacher
Dean, Dalra Lee
Substitute Teacher
Doan, Sharon
English Teacher
Eskridge, Evelyn Doray
6th-8th Grd Enrichment Teacher
Findley, Joyce Ellis
Math Dept Chairperson
Friess, Faye E. Whitman
Voc Family & Consumer Sci Tchr
Gantz, Jacci I.
English Teacher
Graham, Chris Harris
Teacher & Lang Arts Specialty
Greear, Deborah Lynn (Hinds)
Chemistry Teacher
Haralson, Millicent Mendenhall
3rd Grade Teacher
Harris, John Lee
English & History Teacher
Hayden, Tracy Lynn
Spanish Teacher
Heitz, Carole Atwood
English & Journalism Teacher
Hensley, Yvonne Deerinwater
English Teacher
Howell, Thomas Wayne
Aerospace Science Dept Chair
Judkins, Edie Ann
12th Grade English Teacher
Krakowski, Diane Mc Closkey
Fourth Grade Teacher
Leebron, Linda Winter
English Teacher
Leonard, Frances Jean
7th Grade Mathematics Teacher
Lichtenwalter, Sandra Swanson
Teacher
Linam, James Edward
Chemisty & AP Biology Teacher
Lisle, Jolyn Collins
Psychology & Cadet Teacher
Mc Curdy, Thelma Lee Mathis-Hearn
Kndgtn Tchr & Division Admin
Mc Laughlin, Michael King
AP American History Teacher
Meeks, Sherry L.
Science Teacher
Moran, Mark Allen
English Teacher
Morrow, Raelynn Marie
8th Grd History & Civics Tchr
Nordyke, Richard Lawrence
United States History Teacher
Oard, Marva Perkins
Mathematics Teacher
Oswalt, George E.
Art Instructor
Parker, Jerald Dwain
Retired Professor of Mech Engr
Pearson, William H.
Band Director
Pierce, Joseph M.
Administrator
Pulliam, Shelley Kay
8th Grd Amer His & Eng Tchr
Reichardt, M. Jeanette Marsh
Honors Geometry & Algebra Tchr
Richards, Jacki Kyle
Social Studies Tchr & Dept Hd
Rodman, Leslie James
Ec, Amer Govt & US His Tchr
Sevier, Elisabeth K.
French Teacher
Shackelford, Jennifer Lynne
Secondary Science Teacher
Snow, James David
Science Teacher
Taylor, Ronald Arthur
Algebra Teacher
Teague, Rebecca Slade
Chemistry Tchr & Sci Dept Chm
Warren, Abraham Roy
Vocational Agriculture Teacher
Woodrome, Beverly Kaye
Latin Teacher
EL RENO
Asbury, Donnie Sue
2nd Grade Teacher
Baker, Vana Moore
Grammar & Writing Teacher
Boyer, Jerry Lee
Dir & Instr Criminal Justice
Campbell, Dia Darlene
Nursing Instructor
Carter, Rocky Kenneth
HS Teacher & Coach
Crider, Janet Lee (Walker)
8th Grade English Teacher
Davis, Virginia Stults
Voc Family & Consumer Sci Tchr
Dill, Colleen Pazoureck
Health Science Tech Instructor
Duren, Brad Lee
Adjunct Prof of US History
Ellis, Ken Lee
World History & PE Teacher
Fox, Connie G.
History & Government Teacher
Gorden, William W., Jr.
Instructor
Hedgecock, Jamey Eavon (Dennis)
8th Grade Social Studies Tchr
Hoffman, Vicki L.
ICE & Comm Ldrshp Coordinator
Hooker, Bobby Lee
Director of Equine Science
Jennings, Karen J.
Chemistry & Biology Teacher
Krittenbrink, Juanita Wittrock
Eng, Speech & Hum Professor
Locke, Christopher Nathan
Sci, His, PE & Span Teacher
Loveland-Roles, Bobbi Laulette
6th-8th Grd Mathematics Tchr
Meyerhoeffer, Jane Ellen
Business Teacher
Osborn, G. Steven
Dir Student Support Services
Piper, Martha J.
Nursing Instructor
Rains, Rachel W.
HS Show Choir Director
Rickman, Louise Moore
Occupational & Tech Div Dir
Rosenckranz, Betsy J.
Second Grade Teacher
Rupp, Kelly Rogers
English Instructor
Smith, E. Norbert
Pre-Nursing Instructor
Tarver, Juanita E.
Retired Elementary Teacher
Walsh-Davis, Jennifer A.
Sixth Grade Teacher
Wilbur, Sharon Ashton
Secondary Art Teacher
ELDORADO
Batson, Penny Sharon
Secondary English Teacher
Hankins, Dwight Allen
Agricultural Education Instr
ELGIN
Butler, Ruth E.
Science Teacher
Martin, Jay A.
Band Director
Thomas, Brenda (Smith)
Psychology & English Teacher
ELK CITY
Bollinger, Judith Lookinghill
English & Art Teacher
Carpenter, Mary Fern
Literature & Composition Tchr
Fender, Kristi King
Mathematics Teacher
Heward, Sherri
English Teacher
Hobbs, Phyllis Kaye
Teacher
James, Loreta Ruth
English Teacher
Sanders, Carolyn Patten
Vocational Home Economics Tchr
Yates, Tana Smith
Second Grade Teacher
ELMORE CITY
Paul, Carmoleta (Vaughn)
Retired Teacher
ENID
Abbott, Daniel Phillips
Assoc Prof of Philosophy & Rel
Burkhart, Lisa Marin
Chemistry Teacher
Butts, Carmen Humphrey
Spanish & Home Ec Teacher
Campbell, Barbara Lyle
Title I Math & Reading Teacher
Clausing, Lois Cowan
1st Grade Teacher
Clayton, Corey Christopher
High School History Teacher
Costello, Bob J.
Supvr of Instrumental Music
Cruzan, Marsha Holloway
Math Teacher
Davis, Penny
Director of Bands
Dittmer, Gina Kay
English & Bible Teacher
Evans, Debra Brown
Tchr of the Learning Disabled
Fortson, Kay Kenney
Professor of English
Greer, Virginia G.
Language Arts Teacher
Johnston, Catherine
Speech, Drama & Debate Teacher
Kowalski, Sharon Elaine Gorton
Speech, Theatre & Debate Instr
Lowery, Richard Harlin
Old Testament Professor
Lyon, Edward L.
Social Science Teacher
Mac Donald, Paul Shafer
Headmaster
Mc Donald, Mary F.
English Teacher
McDonald, Thomas Patrick
Psychology & Neuroscience Prof
Mc Keaigg, Carolyn Specie
Elem Guidance Counselor
Price, Dee Johnson
Culinary Arts Instructor
Reed, Douglas Paul
Asst Professor of Sociology
Rider, John Allen, II
Retired Assoc Prof
Riley, Ann Frazee
Language Arts Instructor
Sloan, Julie Ann
Language Arts Instructor
Smith, Cynthia Mandrell
Social Science Teacher
Stuever, Vicki M.
English Teacher
Sturgeon, Rick L.
Science Teacher & Coach
Unruh, Susan Callison
Sixth Grade Teacher
Wright, Brenda Hughes
Sixth Grade Teacher
EUFAULA
Applegate, Gale Petersen
High School English Teacher
Kiener, Sharon June (Burns)
9th Grade English Teacher
Mc Kinney, Brenda Bolding
Special Services Director
Thompson, Roger Dale
History Teacher
FAIRFAX
Crabtree, MaryLou Martin
Life Science Teacher
Mayberry, Penny (Wright)
Mathematics Teacher
FAIRLAND
Brixey, Deborah Lea (Van Almon)
Science Teacher & Coach
Brock, Kathy Ann
Second Grade Teacher
Crockett, Glenna L.
Mathematics Teacher
Hayes, Kelly D.
Science Teacher & Coach
Mailes, Jo Glover
Business & Computer Teacher
Shaw, Carla K.
Science Teacher
FAIRVIEW
Walton, Barbara Smith
Third Grade Teacher
Welsh, Ann Woodman
English & Reading Teacher
FITTSTOWN
McGehee, Jeannie (Cooper)
High School Business Teacher
Standridge, Vicky Horton
Language Arts Teacher & Librn
FLETCHER
Morris, Susan Diann
5th & 6th Grd Science Teacher
Sanders, Craig Allen
History & PE Teacher
Sullivan, Vicki Sizemore
Spanish & English Teacher
FORT GIBSON
Dewoody, Marilyn Tignor
Mathematics Tchr & Dept Chair
Hamlin, Sherry Duncan
Speech, Dramas & Debate Tchr
Imhoff, Kim Dyer
English Teacher
Johnson, Thrissa Anne
Humanities & English III Tchr
Nations, Joe L.
English & Journalism Teacher
Smith, Randy A.
Driver Education Tchr & Coach
FORT SILL
Smith, Sharon Kay Goldsby
Sixth Grade Teacher
FORT SUPPLY
Ramey, James Dale
Science Teacher
FORT TOWSON
Adams, Ada (Ashmore)
Retired Elementary Teacher
Nowell, Annette
HS Math Teacher
FOX
Butler, Dale Charly
Football Coach & Soc Stud Tchr
Gossvener, Penny Sturgeon
2nd Grade Teacher
Jenson-Wilson, Kathy
Reading & Science Tchr
Smart, Karrollton Mc Donald
Business Teacher
FOYIL
Forsman, Linda Ann (Boyd)
Secondary Math Teacher
Hendrickson, Robert Dean
Science Teacher
Johns, Alice Faye (Vanzant)
5th & 6th Grade Math Teacher
Wilson, Michelle Ward
1st Grade Teacher
Wyche, Sue Martin
Second Grade Teacher
FREDERICK
Caldwell, Donald D.
Business & Computer Ed Tchr
Fuller, Peggy Sue (Blackburn)
HS Library Media Specialist
FREEDOM
Grice, Bill C.
Jr & Sr HS Teacher & Coach
Nixon, Kari (Nixon)
High School Science Teacher
GAGE
Pittman, Deloris (Smith)
HS English & Speech Teacher
GANS
Bullard, Charles Lynn
Spcl Ed Dir & Amer His Teacher
Miller, Lester Lynn
High School Science Teacher
Riggs, Janice Ruth (Williams)
Scndry Counselor & Bus Teacher
GERONIMO
Mallow, Paula Leveille
Social Studies Teacher
GLENCOE
Holt, Tony
Teacher & Coach
Mc Cain, Georgia Russell
Math & Computer Teacher
Nichols, Charles Lloyd
6th Grade Teacher
GLENPOOL
Bushyhead, Charles Wayne
Assistant Principal
Graves, Tammi L.
Eng & Applied Comm Instructor
Howard, Michon Wynn
Geometry, PE Teacher & Coach
Jones, Elizabeth Bradley
7th-8th Grade English Teacher
Main, Carla Sue
Fourth Grade Teacher
Olansen, Jerry Don
HS Biology Teacher
Patterson, Mary Herseth
High School English Teacher
Terronez, Linda Sanford
Sixth Grade Lang Arts Teacher
Zeiler, Shirley Jean
Eng I, Speech & Drama Tchr
GOODWELL
Brooks, James Darrell
Asst Professor of Education
Dreher, Sonja Pilar
English Teacher
Gourley, Jim A.
Director of Counseling
Guthrie, Russell Allen
Assoc Prof of Communications
Lark, Floyd J.
Dean of Education
Manning, Wayne
Head Business Department
Maxwell, Mark Matthew
Asst Prof of Mathematics
Pate, Bobbie Kohler
English, Spanish & Psych Tchr
Rose, Jane Ellen
Assistant Professor of English
GORE
Carter, Betty Fields
Retired 6th Grade Teacher
Chair, Lisa D. (Mc Lemore)
Science Teacher
Johnson, Ted William
Retired 5th Grade Teacher
Justice, Nita Ann
Mathematics Teacher
Warren, Barbara Johnston
English, Speech & Spanish Tchr
GRACEMONT
Remy, Lisa Bradley
English Teacher & Librarian
GRANDFIELD
Clemmer, Bobbye Lynn
Retired Math & Eng Teacher
GROVE
Johnston, Barbara Ann
Biology & Chemistry Teacher
Pattison Yirsa, Ruby Vera
Speech & Drama Teacher
Smith, Mary Jo Robinson
High School Counselor
Stinnett, Carol Teel
MS Mathematics & English Tchr
Trumbull, Edward J.
Science Teacher
GUTHRIE
Allen, Lori Ann
Biology Teacher
Gilliland, Mary Beth
Art & Photography Teacher
Underwood, Sheryl Jean (Stark)
Fifth Grade Teacher
Wright, Linda Lee (Ewing)
6th Grade Teacher
GUYMON
Anderson, Judy K.
Computer Teacher
Campbell, Leota Gillenwaters
Language Arts Teacher
Dale, Nancy Fajen
Sixth Grade Math Teacher
Gammon, Marla Lemmons
Seventh-Eighth Grade Teacher
Heath, David Benton
Physical Education Teacher
Ratlief, Judy Russell
Principal
Reust, Betty Charlene
Sophomore English Teacher
Richardson, Viki L.
6th Grade Teacher
Sherbon, Mary Ann Roberts
Art Teacher
Tomlinson, Wilma Marie
English Teacher
Tuttle, John Gregory
6th Grade Science Teacher
Wadley, June Fay (Rathke)
Fifth Grade Teacher
Williams, Cindy Shaffer
4th Grd Math & Soc Stud Tchr
Yancey, Marcia Ann (Dain)
Fifth Grade Teacher
Zollinger, Christina Rice
Band Director
HAILEYVILLE
Moore, Patricia Garrett
Second Grade Teacher
HAMMON
Dew, Robbi Lois
Math Teacher
Wood, Minnie Nell (Buomer)
Fifth Grade Teacher
HARDESTY
Eisenhauer, Dale Edward
Science Teacher
Mariconda, Paula Cavis
1st-2nd Grade Teacher
HARRAH
Davis, Dianna Ruth
Second Grade Teacher
Melton, Shirley Ann (Sims)
Elem Facilitator of GATE
Rothrock, Debbie Parrish
Vocal Music Instructor
HARTSHORNE
Dickenson, Sue Gibbs
Third Grade Teacher
Hadly, Stephanie
Secondary Science Ed Teacher
Henderson, Dianne Loree
English Teacher
Johnson, Sharon Ruth Waterfallen
Chapter I Reading Specialist

TSHORNE (cont)
wetter, Connie Davis
guage Arts Teacher
ski, Patricia Kay
Kindergarten Teacher
t, Vicki Janis
hematics Teacher
LDTON
r, Virginia Jane (Dunlap)
ondary English Teacher
ett, Patricia Jewell
I Reading Teacher
VENER
hern, Tery Fields
mentary Counselor
, Judy Lynn
rth Grade Teacher
Pamela Ancell
Business Education Tchr
, Janice (Bacon)
nish & French Teacher
ners, Johnna F.
& 8th Grd Rdng & His Tchr
all, Joseph Henry
hematics Teacher
ENA
Lynn Gean
er Level Science Teacher
ip, Debbie Schroeder
ness & Computer Teacher
k, Judith Kathleen
guage Arts Teacher
on, Donna Van Buskirk
ily & Consumer Svcs Tchr
NESSEY
rson, Kay Bugg
nce Teacher
Diane Milacek
Math & Computer Teacher
ney, Robin Hogsett
guage Arts Teacher
RYETTA
n, Diana Cook
d Grade Teacher
r, Sherry Cook
dergarten Teacher
Britton Lee
Math Teacher & Dept Chair
nd, Jean Storz
ish & Humanities Teacher
ade, John Charles
Algebra II Teacher
herd, Phyllis Irene (Button)
I Math Teacher
TON
way, Cleada Gabehart
red Second Grade Teacher
ART
ns, Lynda Burchfiel
ory & Geography Teacher
DENVILLE
er, Syble Kaye
ily & Consumer Sci Teacher
, Heather A.
al Music Director
LIS
amson, U'Vonna
ch & Social Studies Teacher
INY
o, Norma Kathryn
lish Teacher
dy, Jacque Sue (Barber)
VII Federal Project Dir
O
d, Richard Steven
8th Grade Mathematics Tchr
ine, Jimmy Floyd
culture Education Teacher
Carolyn Johnson
lish IV Teacher
, Cleatus Troy
ence Teacher
nbotham, Wayne R. L.
ence Teacher
s, Rhonda C.
ing Teacher
Freeland D.
ld History & Geography Tchr
ll, Lynn
erican History Teacher
Richard Morris
Grade Teacher
, Kimberly Jo (Marshall)
nputer Teacher
BERT
, Linda McNiel
lgy, Lang, Sci & Geog Tchr
, Samantha Sanders
, Yrbk, Nwspr & Choir Tchr
roon, Harley Keith
h Tchr & Cmptr Coord
roon, Murna Switzer
Grade Homeroom Teacher
Linda Jean (Schultz)
nedial Mathematics Teacher
RO
, William Jeffrey
h Department Chair
Mitzie Majors
ational Home Ec Instructor
EL
n, Billy Steve
ial Science Teacher
man, Jeffery Lamar
alth Ed Teacher
re, Janice Engler
Grade English Teacher
, Linda Meredith
Grade Reading Teacher

Eldred, Lorene G.
Fourth Grade Teacher
Harkey, Ellen Ruth
7th Grade Math Teacher
Luesada, Ruth Ann Beshear
Second Grade Teacher
Nichols, Lana Gentry
Teacher of Gifted & Talented
Wake, Diane M.
Fifth Grade Teacher
Walls, Desmond Dean
Social Studies Teacher
INOLA
Fowlkes, Judith Williams
Biology & Physiology Teacher
Kight, Janet Lee
8th Grade English Teacher
JAY
Durham, Patsy Anne (Curry)
Teacher
Hendren, Billie Lynn (Brown)
11th Grade World History Tchr
Teel, Anita Rena
English Teacher
Thornton, Mary Hardin
High School Counselor
Tugmon, Terri Sue
Math Teacher
Waterbury, Judy Stump
OK, US His & Democracy Tchr
JENKS
Abshire, George Edwin
7th Grade Math Teacher
Carlson, Tammie Lynn
Marketing Management Teacher
Gaither, Dorothy Leister
German Teacher
Hall, Donna Rogers
Language Arts Teacher
Hargis, Gene Paul
Industrial Technology Teacher
Hines, Charlotte Sload
Science Dept Chair & Teacher
Hudson, Nancy J.
French & Spanish Teacher
Meyer, Carol Pennington
Science Lab Coordinator
O'Neil, Judy Vaughan
Voc Family & Consumer Sci Tchr
Roden, Tanda Sue
Educator of Gifted & Talented
Spencer, Diana Blake
Antmy, Physiology & Bio Tchr
Sturgell, Barbara Mc Cormick
Math Teacher
Zaloudek, Jan Walters
Middle School Math Teacher
JENNINGS
James, Charles Gary, Jr.
1st-8th Grd Physical Ed Tchr
JONES
Barrington, Jannie Denise
Family & Consumer Sci Teacher
Graham, Gayela A. (Jennings)
Middle School Math Teacher
KANSAS
Spiker, Terrance Dean
Instrumental Music Director
KELLYVILLE
Allen, Jimmie David
Middle & High School Teacher
Haile, Nellie Dianne
Honors Eng & Yrbk Tchr
Hathcock, Gregory Wayne
Math Tchr
Jones, Julie Sue
Fourth Grade Teacher
Lowry, Marilyn Denham
8th Grd Eng & Speech Teacher
KEOTA
Davis, Thomas Pinkney
Mathematics Teacher
Smith, Tiffany Lu
High School Science Teacher
KEYES
Cochran, Bob G.
Science Teacher
KIEFER
Abbott, Douglas Neil
Algebra & Geometry Teacher
KINGFISHER
Barrick, Lou Ann Jones
Fifth Grade Teacher
Cameron, Christopher Michael
Algebra Teacher & Coach
Eischen, Karla Sue
High School Counselor
Hart, Larry
History Teacher & Coach
Hubbard, Karen Schwarz
9th Grade English Teacher
Jech, Vicky Lynn
5th Grade Sci & Math Tchr
Soudek, Linda Burns
Speech, Drama & Debate Tchr
KINGSTON
Martin, Shirley A.
Language Arts Teacher
Uber, Cheryl Armstrong
Second Grade Teacher
KIOWA
Self, Zelma Bowman
High School Teacher
Weaver, Deborah Elaine (Lewis)
Business Education Teacher
KREBS
Logan, Larry Dale
History & Geography Teacher
Mincher, Jerry Wayne
4th Grade Teacher

KREMLIN
Buller, Jon L.
Technology Ed Instructor
Gossen, Roger W.
Secondary Math & Comp Teacher
Watkins, Ann Tefft
Bus Ed Chm & Scndry Schl Cnslr
LAHOMA
Kuhnemund, Shannon Ewbank
First Grade Teacher
Powell, Susan Havemann
Jr HS Math & German Teacher
Sheffield, Christine Laubhan
English Teacher & Librarian
LAMONT
Davis, Robert Paul
Business Education Instructor
Leslie, Tiara Ann
Health & Physical Ed Teacher
LANGSTON
Flasch, Neva Joy (Childers)
Prof of Eng & Dir of Hnrs Pgm
Heard, Pamala Denice
Asst Prof of Math
Thurston, Flossie A. Mc Kerson
Youth Dev Program Leader
LAVERNE
Cook, Janet Terbush
Fourth Grade Teacher
Dunn, Robin Junker
3rd Grade Teacher
Hendrick, Margarette Ann
5th Grade Teacher
Johnson, Larry R.
Math & History Teacher
Miner, Linda Lee (Berry)
Business Education Instructor
Moseley, Melvin Wayne
Retired Teacher & Head Coach
Smith, Doran Eugene
Science Teacher
LAWTON
Abercombie, Don
US His & Geography Teacher
Adams, Stephen M.
Asst Prof in Broadcasting
Alexander, Ralph Jon
Associate Prof of Psychology
Argyros, Ioannis Konstantinos
Professor of Mathematics
Barker, Barbee Pelton
Acctng & Keyboarding Teacher
Benefield, Richard Glenn
Professor
Blodgett, Ralph Edward
Dept of His & Humanities Prof
Boucher, Mary Ann (Martin)
Fifth Grade Teacher
Brown, Janie B.
5th Grade Teacher
Bryan, Clinton Dave
Assistant Prof of Phys Sci
Buehne, Paula Smith
6th Grade Teacher
Burton, Mary Grant
Chem & Bio Teacher
Chenoweth, Don Wilson
Assoc Prof of Political Sci
Chenoweth, Roma Bradley
English Teacher
Courington, John Mark
Economics Professor
Davis, Bradford Dion
Mathematics Professor
Dirickson, Dianne Hoy
Speech & Drama Teacher
Dzialo, Linda Giles
Principal
Dzindolet, Mary T.
Assistant Prof of Psychology
Edwards, Claudia Huskey
English & Study Skills Teacher
Fennema, David Harold
Professor of Theatre Arts
Frost, David Lynn
Driver Education & PE Teacher
Gilbert, Patricia McMillan
Kindergarten Teacher
Givens, Kirk
8th Grd Sci Tchr & Dept Chprsn
Gooch, Roxanne
Accounting Instructor
Goos, Shirley Jean (Martin)
Math Instr & Stu Support Fac
Hatch, Larry Gene
Band Director
Hatcher, Wayne
Dean of Students
Heflin, James L.
Assoc Prof of Communciation
Hinman, Lois Thompson
Third Grade Teacher
Holland, Judy Ann (Pamplin)
Accounting Teacher
Honeycutt, Brenda R. Bench
Instr of Foreign Languages
Huckabay, Gary M.
Professor of Math Sciences
Hunt, Joan Fay
Social Studies Teacher
Jackson, Coy Steven
Math, Cmptr Sci Tchr & Chprsn
Jackson, Wanda
4th Grade Teacher
Jones, Glen
Computer Instructor
Karasz, Janice Mildeen (Karasz)
Cmptr Information Systems Prof
Kervin, Shelby LLoyd
Professor of Criminal Justice

Kitzrow, Frederick George
Chemistry Teacher
Klein, Scott Richard
Dept Chairman of Theatre Arts
Knott, Patrick Allen
Art Teacher
Kuchynka, Randal
World Studies Teacher
Logan, Brenda Rae
Secondary Science Teacher
Logan, Janice Wilkes
Coord Interdiscplnry Act Instr
Love, Inez Kay
Student Support Counselor
Mabry, Dorothy McGhee
Assistant Principal
Mager, Linda B.
Counselor
Mathis, Darcie Eyvette
8th Grade Math Teacher & Coach
May, Richard J.
Criminal Justice Professor
McKeown, Loren Ferris
English Professor
Michener, Jean W.
Accounting Professor
Nalley, Elizabeth Ann
Professor of Chemistry
Nelson, Carolyn A.
Reading Instr & Center Dir
Pazoureck, Rebecca Kieffer
Human Ecology Professor
Petty, Lucy Adair
Spanish Teacher
Price, Ronald Dean
Communication Professor
Ramey, Reginald Wayne
Counselor
Robideaux, Marilyn Perry
Bible & English Teacher
Sampson, Susan Roth
Third Grade Teacher
Schmahl, David Edward
Psychology & Biology Teacher
Simpson, Timothy James
9th Grade English Teacher
Smith, Richard Wayne
Dir Forensics-Comm & Asst Prof
Smith-Gratto, Karen
Education Professor
Snider, Beverly Annette
Mathematics Teacher
Spencer, Mark Morris
English Professor
Stevens, C. Wanda Storie
Assoc Prof of Bus Sys & Mgmt
Teed, Lorene Bendure
Fine Arts & Anthology Advisor
Thompson, Debra Brewczynski
Administrative Assistant Instr
Thompson, Stella Sessums
English Instructor
Thorne, Jerry Lee
Truant Ofcr, Stu Adj Ctr Coord
Totte, Melinda Delores
Fourth Grade Teacher
Weinstein, Lawerence
Prof of Psychology
Whiteley, Joetta M.
First Grade Teacher
Wickens, Terri Raulston
Geometry, Algebra I & II Tchr
Youngblood, Karen N.
Prof of Criminal Justice
LEEDEY
Holcomb, Danny Lee
Jr HS & HS Science Teacher
Kauk, Sarena Schomp
English Teacher
LEFLORE
Heaton, Doylene Padgett
Voc Family & Cnsmr Sci Instr
LEXINGTON
Norton, Rita Fern (Elkins)
Social Studies & Art Teacher
Quinn, Joel Douglas
Science Teacher
LINDSAY
Gibson, Vickie (Cain)
3rd Grade Teacher
Riddle-Finley, Sherri Ann
Transitional Second Teacher
LOCUST GROVE
Asbill, Juanita Tillman
Eng & Creative Writing Tchr
Back, Janet Grissom
Kindergarten Teacher
Bennett, Joan M.
Library & Media Specialist
Bowin, Beth Marie
Psychology Teacher
Couch, Joy Hatfield
Chemistry Teacher
Cowan, Frances W.
Eleventh Grade English Teacher
Hix, Bryan L.
Biology Teacher
LONE GROVE
Bloodworth, Brenda J.
Counselor & Teacher
Coley, Rebecca Steele
HS Science Teacher
Daugherty, Sue
Guidance Counselor
Daughtery, Sue
Guidance Counselor
Ellis, Emmy Weldon
4th Grade Spanish Teacher
Gavin, Deanne Dyer (Cashman)
English Teacher

Griffin, Norma Jean
Third Grade Teacher
Hallum, Derek Franklin
Agriculture Education Teacher
Hoffman, Jolene White
7th Grade English Teacher
Jackson, Debbie Lynn
English & Journalism Teacher
Kurtz, Katheryn Brooks
Eng IV, Speech & Debate Tchr
Mitchell, Patty Sue (Smith)
Third Grade Teacher
Noland, Russell Bob, III
Keyboarding & Accounting Tchr
Piatt, Kay (Fuller)
First Grade Teacher
Pyle, Brenda Renee (Grinstead)
Eighth Grade Writing Teacher
Scott, Sherri Beth (Cox)
Second Grade Teacher
Smiley, Cheryl (Bower)
Voc Family & Consumer Sci Tchr
Stinson, Kevin Harold
Asst Prin & Soc Stud Tchr
LOYAL
Garms Scott, Toni Lee
Spanish Teacher
Helgeson, Maxine Faye (Fevurly)
K-6th Grade Teacher
Sipe, LaRita Cerny
4th Grd Tchr & Rdng Specialist
LUTHER
Agan, Geoffrey X.
Science Teacher
Kever, Jackie Hubbell
Middle School Teacher
Steffens, Eddie Lee, Jr.
Ag Ed Instr & FFA Adv
Willis, Lynda Faye (Lewis)
High School Mathematics Tchr
Wrinkle, Sheri Lenora
English Tchr & Alt-Ed Eng Tchr
MACOMB
Loveless, LaDeen Faye Ervin
Family & Consumer Sci Tchr
Townes, Treisa Ann
Fifth-Seventh Grd Tchr
MADILL
Baskin, Daniel Gregory
Art Teacher
Carter, Pam Leazure
Chemistry & Biology Instructor
Earnest, Tia Juana
Retired 3rd Grade Teacher
Ellett, Darla Burnett
High School Math Teacher
Estep, Charlotte Dunivan
Lit, Composition & Speech Tchr
Haynes, Stephen Ray
Agricultural Sci Instructor
MANGUM
Bull, Ruby Jane Howell
Math Teacher
Reeves, Roger Glenn
9th & 10th Grade Science Tchr
MANNFORD
Routh, Douglas George
Science Teacher
Thomas, Lisa Schutte
Spanish Teacher
MANNSVILLE
Cothran, Susan Elaine
Third Grade Teacher
Crane, Linda Allen
1st Grade Teacher
MARBLE CITY
Miller, Charles Gaylon
Math Teacher
MARIETTA
Clampet, Cynthia Lea
Family & Consumer Sci Teacher
Donaldson, Carolyn L.
Computer Science Teacher
Dooley, Jeffery Neal
Middle School Principal
Kime, Janet Luke
First Grade Teacher
Stewart, Linda L.
Math Lab Teacher
Tow, Betty Sue (Sykora)
Chem, Bio & Phy Sci Teacher
White, J. Elaine
English Teacher
MARLOW
Bloomer, Patricia A.
Biological Science Teacher
Collins, Lisha Ann
First Grade Teacher
Cosgrove, Tommy
High School Principal
Jones, Glenda P.
Science Teacher
Nease, David Charles
Science Teacher
Pryor, Debbie Stover
Fourth Grade Teacher
MARSHALL
Foreman, Carol Ann
Elementary Music Teacher
MAUD
Jackson, Tommy Ray
HS Math Teacher & Counselor
MAYSVILLE
Allen, Zara Jane Wattenbarger
Fifth & Sixth Grade Teacher
Little, Janet Norton
Fourth Grade Teacher
Sharp, Mark Stephen
High School Mathematics Tchr

MC ALESTER
Brock, Katherine Burden
4th Grade Teacher
Brown, Linda Callahan
Eng III & Serv Learning Tchr
Burden, Sherri Lynn Erickson
English Teacher
Horne, Don Clayton
History & Government Teacher
Lewis, Ron James
High School Band Director
Miller, F. Lee
High School Math Teacher
Pearson, Yvonne Elizabeth Haught
Spanish Teacher
Scoggins, John P.
Computer Teacher & Coach
Shans, Charles Brian
Biology Teacher
Smith, Karon Frew
8th Grade Life Science Teacher
Wickham, Jimmie C.
Elem TAG & Spanish Tchr
Woodley, Robin Cline
English Teacher
MC LOUD
Burkhart, Gary Mitchell
Science Dept Chair
Caruthers, June Ray
Fifth Grade Teacher
Dilliner, Saundra Whitehead
7th & 8th Grade Math Teacher
Gokey, Val Gene
Junior High Guidance Counselor
Mennis, Constance M. (Ries)
High School Mathematics Tchr
Myers, Leta Megehee
First Grade Teacher
Nikkel, Elfridge Seals
Second Grade Teacher
Robison, Francine Roark
English & Humanities Teacher
Rooker, Sarah E.
7th-8th Grd Soc Stud Teacher
Smith, Cathy Gaye
Second Grade Teacher
MCALESTER
Allar, Kathy Jean (Crum)
5th Grade Teacher
Cantrell, Evelyn JoAnn Grant
Science Lab Teacher
Clifton, Rhonda Denise (Groves)
Art Teacher
Herzer, Glenna White
Librarian
Homer, Sharla Diane
Transitional First Grade Tchr
Kuykendall, William Douglas
6th Grd Self Contained Teacher
Mc Gee, Mary (Cathey)
Sixth Grade Teacher
Mc Phetridge, Joyce Freas
Fifth Grade Teacher
Welch, Joan Davis
Second Grade Teacher
MCCURTAIN
Shimp, Tommy Joe
3rd-12th Grade Art Teacher
MEEKER
Carpenter, Lana (Mc Lean)
Voc Family & Consumer Sci Tchr
Linville, Danny Lee
English & Reading Teacher
Purdy, Mary Rosiland
Director of Bands
MIAMI
Aldridge, Jeff
Physics & Mathematics Instr
Boehne, Gary L.
Mathematics Teacher
Grigsby, Mark E.
Biology Instructor
Maxson, Judith Buzzard
Third Grade Teacher
Riley, Darcy Jean Hale
7th-8th Grd Language Arts Tchr
Schnakenberg, Eve (Hofmann)
High School Counselor
Smith, Carol Faye
Eng Instr & Mu Chptr Advisor
Smith, Peter C.
Agriculture Instructor
Stidham, Marla Buckmaster
6th Grade Math Teacher
Vanpool, Cynthia Paula
Special Education Instructor
Whaley, Mary Susan
Instructor of Music
MIDWEST CITY
Barnett, Kris Allison
Social Studies Teacher
Bishop, Marcia Jo
Professor of Radiologic Tech
Brannon, Ursula A.
German & ESL Teacher
Carter, Carl Edward
English Professor
Effinger, Lori Anne
Counselor
Geer, Kenneth Wayne
6th Grd Social Studies Teacher
Giger, John M.
Professor of Engineering
Glaze, DeDe Bennett
Early Childhood Consultant
Greider, Roger Ellis
Mathematics Professor
Hall, Victor Mugge
Chemistry Professor
Harrell, Beverly Ellen (Davis)
Acad Advisor & Math Professor
Harrell, Gerold Lee
Adjunct Math Professor
Hibbard, Antoinette Patten
Adjunct English Professor
Holt, Karen Young
Professor
Hoover, John Robert
Chemistry Professor
Hyde, Ragenia Buckmaster
Professor of Nursing Science
Kane, Ann Maloy
Business Professor
Kaufman, Robert Allen
Fourth Grade Teacher
Lollis, Sue E.
Humanities & English Professor
McIlvoy, Michael D.
9th Grade OK History Tchr
Morgan, Michael J.
History Professor
Roe, Detia M.
Physics Professor
Rose, Sheila Marcuola
Speech & Language Pathologist
Sennhenn, Carl George Braun
Professor of English
Severson, Maurice A.
Jr HS Computer Science Teacher
Smith, Earl Lee
Accounting Professor
Smith, Stephen I.
Professor of Economics
Townsend, Henry Lee
Pgm Dir, Prof Radiologic Tech
Troth, Rebecca Gay
Life Science Professor
Wagner, Linda Hansen
Communications Teacher
Webster, JoAnn M. Hartley
ESL Instructor
Woodard, Judy McSparrin
Social Studies Teacher
MILBURN
Brantley, Brenda Kay Smith
8th Grade Teacher
Washington, Russell
Social Studies Teacher
MILL CREEK
Marquard, Billy Dean
Math & Science Teacher
MINCO
McElvany, Sam D.
Principal
MONROE
Davis, Darla Elaine
Eighth Grade Teacher
MOORE
Bedner, James
Mathematics Teacher
Brown, B. Diane
First Grade Teacher
Clark, Roma Kirby
Social Studies Teacher
Craft, Cheryl Jourdan
School Counselor
Crosbie, Chris J.
Psychology & World His Tchr
Earsom, R. Eugene
Soc Stud Teacher & Dept Chair
Ewy-Handke, Penny R.
English Teacher
Ferguson, Valerie Hill
Chem & Advanced Placement Tchr
Gorton, Stephen Andrew
Sixth Grade Teacher
Griffin, Connye Le
English Teacher
Handke, Penny R. Ewy
Secondary English Teacher
Keeley, Melinda Mc Elroy
Math & Pre-Algebra Teacher
King, Bette Anne
Latin Teacher
Martin, Darlene
English II & IV Teacher
Mays, Randell H.
Special Education Teacher
McClurg, Marilyn Clark
English Teacher
Miner, Patricia Ann
Fourth Grade Teacher
Moffatt, Kathy Jackson
Business & Cmptr Tech Instr
Mueller, Marc D.
Director of Bands
Murphey, John W., Jr.
World His & US Govt Teacher
Payne, Sharla Beth
3rd Grade Teacher
Pirpich, Lora Lynn
Mathematics Teacher
Randolph, Judy R. (Murdock)
English Teacher
Risinger, Glen
Math Teacher
Schlegel, Betina Jones-Parra
Math Teacher
Scott, Tonya Renae
7th Grd Eng Tchr & Ath Coord
Sellon, Jana Norton
English III & IV Teacher
Shobert, Sharon Kay
English Teacher
Southard, Janet Rene Freeman
Biology Teacher & Admin Intern
Wall, Vicki J.
Secondary Counselor
Whittington, Rochelle Mc Pheeters
2nd Grade Teacher
MORRIS
Evans, Kerry L.
High School Counselor
Hobbs, Craig Wynn
HS Mathematics Teacher & Coach
Stacy, Jewell Leslie (Clark)
Business Education Instructor
Todd, Sam D.
Vocational Agriculture Teacher
MOYERS
Armstrong, Brian Keith
Elementary Principal
Coffman, Marlin K.
Social Science Teacher
MULDROW
Alderson, Niki Adcock
Speech & English Teacher
Fair, Donald George
7th & 9th Grade Teacher
Jones, Joey Dale
Science Department Chairperson
Rogers, William H., Jr.
World History Teacher
Secratt, Sharon Eillene
Science Teacher
Williams, Angela Duke
Physical Science Teacher
MULHALL
Kindschi, Kelli Schwandt
Second Grade Teacher
MUSKOGEE
Allen, Dorothy Jeanne (King)
7th Grd Amer His & Civics Tchr
Bolding, Melanie Ann (Hagerdon)
First Grade Teacher
Chaffin, Susan Jane (Beall)
Fifth Grade Teacher
Davis, Kathy Joann (Benge)
Mathematics & Algebra Teacher
Duncan, Carole
Fifth Grade Teacher
Foster, June Thompson
8th Grd Literature & Rdng Tchr
Gay, Bonito Juarez
Math Teacher & Athletic Coach
Gore, Betty I.
Professor of English
Goss, John Wayne
Science Teacher & Coach
Hamilton, Cathy Dickerson
Third Grade Teacher
Hammer, Linda Charlton
First Grade Teacher
Hearn, William Charles
Vocal Music Teacher & Dept Chm
Howell, Melvin Gene
Mathematics Teacher
Humphrey, Vicki Craig
5th Grade Teacher
Jayne, Lillian P.
English Teacher
Jestice, Pamela Eller
Health Sci Technology Instr
Littlefield, Pamela Jeanne
Principal
Littlejohn, Nelda Sue
Assistant Professor of Nursing
Mc Guire, Anne Swim
Mathematics Teacher
Mc Lemore, Nancy Leeds
Spanish Teacher
Mc Millan, Susan Wright
Fifth Grade Teacher
Morrow, Mary M. (Huff)
10th & 12th Grade English Tchr
Reavis, Jack Anthony
Geography Teacher
Ryan, Darla Page
4th Grade Teacher
Standridge, Lisa L.
English Teacher
Wiles, James Steven
Band Director
Williams, Arthur R.
5th Grade Classroom Teacher
Williams, Suzette Horn
6th Grade Teacher
Wise, Ray G.
French Teacher & Coach
MUSTANG
Bush, Carol Jensen
High School Spanish Teacher
Caplan, Pam
English & Journalism Teacher
Coble, Frank L.
Fourth Grade Teacher
Dobbs, Cynthia Kay
Sixth Grade Science Teacher
Dorris, Curtis N.
American History Teacher
Hale, Jimmie
Mathematics Tchr & Dept Chair
Howell, Kathy Taylor
6th Grade Mathematics Teacher
Larios, Lisa Long
6th-8th Grd Theatre Comm Dir
Lindsay, Brenda Cox
High School Science Teacher
Miller, Craig C.
Chemistry Teacher
O'Brien, Susan Bush
Fourth Grade Teacher
Rankin, Stephanie Ann
Business Teacher
Robbins, Mary Ruth (Langston)
Guidance Counselor
Selby, Shelli Miner
Student Assistance Coordinator
Spencer, Marva Schapka
Guidance Counselor
Willett, Ann Thompson
Fifth Grade Teacher
Yates, Jennifer Ketchum
Mathematics Teacher
MUTUAL
White, Angela Pearl
English Teacher
NASH
Buller, Elfrieda R.
Third Grade Teacher
NEWCASTLE
Compton, Elisha Lynne
English Teacher
Lee, Glenda Kingsbury
Bio, Anatomy & Physiology Tchr
Wedel, Deborah Lynn (Smith)
Chemistry & Physics Teacher
NEWKIRK
Farris, Mary Helen
Science & English Teacher
Martin, Ronda Brady
Spanish & English Teacher
Ross, Laura Poole
Soc Studies & Lang Arts Tchr
Turner, Richard Lee
Spcl Ed & Elementary Teacher
NICOMA PARK
Merkel, David Lynn
Amer World His & Geog Teacher
Steffen, Jo Ann
Language Arts & Speech Teacher
NINNEKAH
Stockton, Joyce L.
Cnslr & Fmly-Cnsmr Sci Tchr
NOBLE
Baker, Melody Lynn
Teacher
Clements, Brent R.
Bus Law & Intnl Problems Edctr
Gilje, Ann Elisabeth
Mathematics Teacher
King, Karen S.
First Grade Teacher
Lewis, Kanella Gaither
7th Grd Math Teacher & Coach
Reynolds, Karen
Science Department Chairman
Rowland, Michelle (Sutton)
Jr High English Teacher
NORMAN
Askey, David Mall
Phys, Chem Tchr & Sci Dept Chm
Bahan, Sanoranel
Advanced American History Tchr
Ballard, Elizabeth Lyons
Aegis English Mentor
Barry, John Franklin
8th Grade Science Teacher
Bounds, David Alan
History Teacher
Burns, Judy Ann
8th Grade Civics Teacher
Cooper, Lyn Patterson
K-5th Grade Physical Ed Tchr
Crocker, Ann Noleta
American History Teacher
Culwell, Terri M.
Science Teacher
DeMoss, Susan Elaine Freese
Math Educator & Dept Chprsn
Ellis, Shirley Ruth
Third Grade Teacher
Estes, Nancy Pierce
Fashion Merchandising Instr
Ferguson, Kecia Massey
Business Teacher
Ford, Kristy Breitenkamp
2nd Grade Teacher
Friedrich, Gustav W.
Professor of Communication
Gibson, Jay Walton
9th & 10th Grade Math Teacher
Girdner, Karen Burke
9th-10th Grd English Teacher
Grace, April J.
Anatomy & Physiology Teacher
Griffith, Terry L.
Physical Ed Instr & Coach
Hale, Scott W.
Graduate English Teaching Asst
Harris, Carol Lynn Mc Laughlin
7th Grade Science Teacher
Harris, Gina J.
English Teacher
Hawkins, Nancy Hubbard
9th & 10th Grd Spanish Teacher
Hentz, Brian S.
Graduate Teaching Assistant
Jarvis, Reda Wilson
Sociology & Soc Stud Tchr
Lenington, Joseph Patrick
Amer History Teacher & Coach
Littlejohn, Terry Eugene
Algebra Teacher
Loflin, Margo Mc Call
American & OK History Teacher
Manis, Mischelle Christian
History Teacher
Mantione, Meryl E.
Associate Professor of Music
Medlin, Jerry L.
Fifth Grade Teacher
Meiller, Brook Ellen
English Teacher
Meiller, James R.
Band & Orchestra Teacher
O'Neal, Steven George
Chemistry Teacher
O'Rear, Edgar Allen, III
Professor of Chemical Engrng
Osborn, Cheryl Mc Math
Tchr of Emotionally Disturbed
Osisanya, Samuel Olusola
Engineering Professor
Pounds, Linda L.
Third Grade Teacher
Ringer, Karol Elaine
Biology Teacher
St John, Gayle Mullen
English Teacher
Seapy, Charles F., Jr.
Fifth Grade Teacher
Shaw, Terry Joe
Middle School Science Teacher
Shoaf, Edna M.
Span, Eng Tchr & Eng Dept Chm
Skrdla, Lana Beerhalter
Vocal Tchr, Dist Music Supervr
Steer, Alicia Matthews
Fourth Grade Teacher
Stevenson, Barbara Schuldt
Home Economics Education Tchr
Wilkins, Brenda Condren
Middle School Teacher
Winters, Marty
Latin & World History Teacher
Wright, Hallie Rae
Business Education Teacher
NOWATA
Deen, Betty Ann
English Teacher
Whitford, Rebecca Temple
Kindergarten Teacher
OCHELATA
Sydebotham, Judy Ann Slanker
Tutor
OILTON
Roberts, Donna Sue (Moore)
English, Government & Hum Tchr
OKARCHE
Black, Larry Glenn
World History Teacher
Klade, Jeffrey H.
6th-8th Grd Tchr & Principal
OKAY
Perry, Linda Boggs
Sixth Grade Teacher
OKEENE
Jones, Micheal B.
Art & English Teacher
Lamle, Sonya Ellen
Business Teacher & Counselor
OKEMAH
Cooper, Darrell L.
Science Teacher
Duncan, Darin Blaine
Social Studies Teacher
Holmes, Robert Trey
Math & Physics Teacher
Hudson, Lisa Morgan
Eng & Comm Creative Wrtng Tchr
McVeigh, Guy Leon
Elem Supt & Math Tchr
Sexton, Penny Burden
Library Media Specialist
OKLAHOMA CITY
Adkins, Paul Michael
US History & Sociology Tchr
Allred, Sandra Lynn
Fifth Grade Teacher
Allred, Vicki Gail
Biology Teacher
Anderson, Dennis Ivan
Professor of Biology
Arn, Marguerite Watts
Retired Fifth Grade Teacher
BAker, Doug W.
History Professor
Baker, Jeanne Haggard
Fourth Grade Classroom Teacher
Barker, Patricia Yvonne
Elementary School Counselor
Barr, Rebecca Jane Rutland
Special Education Teacher
Baskett, Carol Deck
Mathematics Teacher
Bates, Richenda Davis
9th Grade History Teacher
Bean, Ronda K.
Jr High Geography Teacher
Beeson, Victoria Toland
Learning Center Teacher
Behrens, Carolyn Hummel
Drama Teacher
Best, Mary Lynne
Business Teacher
Bilcik, Tricia Haggart
Interim Dean
Birch, Edwin K., Jr.
4th-5th Grd Gifted Ed Instr
Blackburn, James Andrew
Language Arts Teacher
Bodtke, Susan Hershberger
Professor of Nurse Science
Bollman, Jimmy D.
Mathematics Teacher
Botkin, Sam L.
High School Math Teacher
Bowes, Joy Leach
Sixth Grade English Teacher
Bowling, Linda Marie (Phillips)
French Teacher & NHS Spon
Boyd, Cynthia M.
Yrbk Advisor & Jr Eng Teacher
Brackenbury, Cynthia Nelson
Fourth Grade Teacher
Brafford, Sarah Andrews
Gifted Education Coordinator

AHOMA CITY (cont)
ard, David Lee
ish Teacher
on, Charles Douglas
ospace Science Instructor
ing, Brenda Gail
essor of Biology
er, Walter Eugene, Sr.
cher & Coach
n, Carole Williams
th Science Technology Tchr
n, Jason Douglas
ernment Teacher
es, J. Dianne Fields
ern Languages Professor
, Richard A.
al Studies Teacher
nan, Frances Brantley
iness Education Teacher
Sally Ann (Bucher)
nalism Teacher
r, Diane
iness & Computer Tech Tchr
Webster, Garce Marie
nish Teacher
y, Virgie L. (Beavers)
ors English II Teacher
s, Mary Jane Stark
hman English Teacher
Laura Blackburn
& Weightlifting Teacher
enpeel, Myrtle Foster
hematics Teacher
an, Leila Elaine Mallory
lish Teacher
ll, Phillip Allen
ector of Bands
n, Robin Perry
h School Spanish Teacher
ford, Lori Renee
lish Teacher
ion, David L.
Professor of Art & Design
w, Cathy Elaine (Wells)
hematics Teacher
, Debra Lunease Hudson
Grd Ec & Geography Teacher
er, Myra Wilcoxson
fessor of Accounting & Bus
ney, Frances Caddell
Grd Social Studies Teacher
on, William C.
ence Department Chairperson
g, Diane H.
nselor
son, Deanna Young
ence Teacher
, Bryan Len
lish Teacher
s, Donna Stokes
rew Bible Dept Chair
Linda Parsons
Teacher
ns, Antionette Belinda Hannah
dergarten Teacher
Dana Marie
lish Teacher & Dept Chprsn
ee, Marvin
Teacher
Robert Edward, Jr.
Stud Tchr & Alt HS Prin
, Roger M.
tory Teacher
er, Elizabeth Aubrey
ech & Drama Teacher
w, Bradley Steven
ver Ed Teacher & Coach
, Susan Gayle
glish Instructor
helm, Leonard N.
ural Sciences Dept Chair
Kelly Looper
th Teacher & Coach
er, Gayle Ann (Stout)
siness Instructor
th, Lynda Lee
logy Teacher
er, Lou Francis
fessor of Mathematics
n, Carol Anne Bowlin
glish as Second Lang Tchr
son, Mary Alley
ial Studies Teacher
la, Theresa Lynn (Weaver)
ence Teacher
ry, Lawrence Everett
neral Science Teacher
Mary Lee
air Eng Dept
le, Donald Wade
glish & Physical Ed Teacher
lman, Lisa Ann
m PE Tchr & Coach
nan, Mary Ellen Price
th & Seventh Grade Teacher
on, Mary Jane Owens
g Arts & Soc Stud Teacher
brell, Tammy Ann
thematics Teacher
n, Karen Cole
ktg Fundmntls & Mngmt Tchr
a, John Andrew
mentary Reading Lab Teacher
rie, Mary Frances (Heinen)
ndergarten Teacher
Debi Dunsworth
ama Teacher
sen, John Henry
in Teacher

Harmon, Karlie Kenyon
Mass Comm Prof & Dept Chair
Harper, Sandra Stecher
VP of Academic Affairs
Harris, Donald Gene
Psychology Teacher
Harris, Jim D.
Science Teacher & Dept Chprsn
Haught, Denise Ebert
Professor of Nursing
Hawkins, Stephanie
Seventh Grade Teacher
Haws, Tim Dean
OK History & Government Tchr
Heanue, Tommy Jay Driffill
Social Studies Dept Teacher
Henline, James H.
Science Teacher
Heppler, Michael F.
Counselor & Instructor
Hicks, Patrick
Life Science Teacher
Higgins, Veronica Therese
Fourth Grade Teacher
Hill, DeVonna Sue
Drama Teacher
Holloway, O. June (French)
5th Grade Teacher
Hopkins, Minta Anderson
Pre-Algebra, Speech & His Tchr
Horn, Jeff Taylor
Business Teacher
Hougardy, Daniel A.
Assoc Prof of Natural Sciences
Houlette, Gary Wayne
Physical Science Professor
Howe, Sandra R.
Math Teacher
Humble, Karen Gayle
Math Teacher
Hurt, Teri Lynn
Math Teacher
Infante, Manuel
Mathematics Teacher
Ivich, Betty E.
Latin & Humanities Teacher
Jay, Louise Creason
Sixth Grade Science Teacher
Jenkins, Lara D.
English Teacher & Coach
Jensen, John Robert
Biology & Health Teacher
Johnson, Dan Lynn
Assistant Professor
Johnson, Deborah Jane
1st Grade Teacher
Johnson, Heidi T. Haller
German & Business Ed Tchr
Jones, Hannelore G. Wannemacher
German, Russian & Bus Teacher
Jones, Harold Gene
HVAC/R Teacher
Jones, R. Jeffrey
Anatomy & Physiology Teacher
Keener, Sherry C.
5th Grade Classroom Teacher
Keller, Thomas H.
Social Studies Teacher
Kelley, Carolyn Sue
Kindergarten Teacher
Kelley, Willie T.
Economics Teacher & Coach
Kennedy, Virginia Ann
Social Studies Teacher
Kenney, Laurette D.
English Department Chair
Kerr, Janis Garrett
Science & Math Teacher
King, Jeannie D.
Biology & Earth Sci Teacher
Koss, Carol Patricia Davis
Eng & Creative Writing Tchr
Kutch, Kathryn M.
English & Literature Teacher
Kutch, Lloyd Kent
Jr High Soc Studies Teacher
Kyle, Nicholas Scott
Visual Art Teacher
Larsen, Susan Seglem
Vocal Music Teacher
Lesko-Bishop, Julie E.
Journalism Teacher & Advisor
Lestina, Roger Henry
Lead Frosh Composition Instr
Liston, Sharon Straka
Mathematics Tchr & Dept Chprsn
Maclin, Ruby L.
Second Grade Teacher
Maddox, Mary Alice (Reese)
5th Grade Teacher
Mallett, Michelle Marie (Carlson)
Jr & Sr HS Science Teacher
Mallory, Colleen Lewis
English Teacher
Mann, Charlotte Young
Fourth Grade Teacher
Maple, John Thomas
Professor of History
Martin, Sandra Farris
Mass Communications Professor
Massey, Kathleen C.
Journalism, Drama & Spch Tchr
Mathews, Lora Mae
English Teacher
Mayes, Elizabeth R.
Early Childhood Teacher
Mc Cornack, Karen Brewer
2nd Grade Teacher
Mc Coy, Jane E.
Business Teacher

Mc Cullough, Hortense Martin
High School English Teacher
Mc Elroy, Patricia Ann (Jones)
Third Grade Teacher
Mc Garrity, Patricia
Spanish Teacher
Mc Ginn, Barbara Beasley
Sign Lang & Vocal Music Tchr
McKinney, Sandra LaVelle
Science Teacher
Mc Neely, John B.
Assistant Band Director
Medina, Norma Travieso
Coord of Community Education
Merideth, Julie Marie (Murdoch)
Sixth Grd Math Teacher
Miller, David Brian
Physics & Chemistry Teacher
Montgomery, Deborah S.
9th Grade English Teacher
Morgan, Joanne Ruggiero
First Grade Teacher
Morris, Illona M. Burford
German Teacher
Morris, Laura Hendrickson
4th Grade Teacher
Murray, Janet Odema (Vaught)
8th Grade Reading Teacher
Murray, Sue Thomas
English Teacher
Nedbalek, Steve
Sociology Teacher
Neisent, Lawrence Franklin
Principal & Bible Teacher
Nelson, Merlynn Salathiel
English & Reading Teacher
Nida, Vivian Finley
English Teacher
Noel, Beta Thompson
English Teacher
Opichka, Romeo Lenard
Coordinator
O'Rourke, Nancy Foree
Honors Eng II & IV Teacher
Owen, Ann Scarinzi
Assoc Prof Comm Sci & Disorder
Parker Shrader, Barbara Ann Boyd
First Grade Teacher
Parks, Karen Patton
Eng, Drama & Jrnlsm Teacher
Peck, Gina Lynn
History Teacher
Piccolo, Nancy Nichols
Third Grade Teacher
Pickel, Frank Edward
English Teacher
Pitchlynn, David
Seventh Grade Life Sci Tchr
Powell, Eddie J.
Mathematics Teacher
Pratt, Robert Willaim
Instrumental Music Instructor
Rains, Mary Boatman
Retired Primary Teacher
Reames, Richard Wayne
Geography & Economics Teacher
Reynolds, Janice Gay Griffith
First Grade Teacher
Rhea, Judith Harrell
2nd Grade Teacher
Rider, Vernon L.
Classroom Teacher
Roberts, Charles Martin
Professor of Chemistry
Roberts, Jeffrey Kent
PE & World His Tchr
Roberts, Lisa Mc Kitrick
Former 3rd Grade Teacher
Rollin, Kevin Lee
Secondary English Teacher
Roy, Ruth Moore
6th Grade Teacher
Rust, Annette Hames
Mathematics Teacher
Sanders, Dale Newman
English & Communications Tchr
Schultz, Joyce Baker
Math Teacher
Scott, Rick H.
Physical Education Coordinator
Sexton, Melva J.
First Grade Teacher
Shellhammer, Alvin Joe, Jr.
Professor of Biology
Shiflett, Kathleen G.
English Teacher
Shreck, Gary L.
Professor
Shults, Cheryl Anne
Language Arts Teacher
Sikes, Mark Anthony
Advanced Placement Bio Tchr
Simmons, Mike
Math Teacher
Smalley, Candace Jones
Mathematics Teacher
Sparks, Paula Jo
Former HS Science Teacher
Spencer, Angela Marie
9th Grade English Teacher
Spillers, Deanna L.
Spanish Teacher
Spradling, Suzanne Shaw
Biology Tchr & Sci Dept Chair
Springall, Anne
Mentor Program Instructor
Springfield, Ronald Dean
12th Grade English Teacher
Stafford, Dee Dee Drisdale
Spanish Teacher

Stamm, Tammy Smith
Ethics & Psychology Teacher
Starling, Linda Ammons
Science & Social Studies Tchr
Stefanek, Rosemary Ann
Sixth Grade Teacher
Stephens, Karen Sue
Algebra Instructor
Stogsdill, Angela Darter
Third Grade Teacher
Stotler, Linda
4th Grade Teacher
Strozdas, Ruth Oordt
Lead Instructor
Stults, Ruth L.
Second Grade Teacher
Styron, Susan
Language Arts Teacher
Sullivan, Brad Stuart
Mathematics Dept Chairperson
Sullivan, Sue
Retired Amer History Teacher
Swales, Linda Rogers
Teacher, Chrldng & Yrbk Spon
Swindall, Marion Kirkpatrick
English & Reading Teacher
Tamage, Terry Michael
Gen Hon Biology Teacher
Taylor, Betty Jean (Starks)
Elementary Music Teacher
Taylor, Cheryl Lynne
Vocal Music Teacher
Taylor, Jane Rainey
High School Counselor
Taylor, Samuel O.
High School Math Teacher
Tibbitts, Thomas George
5th Grd Social Studies Teacher
Torrey, Noel Roger
Teacher
Trammell, Latricia Ruth
Antmy, Physiology & Bio Tchr
Triplett, John W.
Assistant Professor
Troelstra, Arne
Physics Professor
Tyler, Deborah L.
Social Studies Teacher
Vaverka, Brian D.
World His Tchr & Coach
Vincent, Abbi
Cosmetology Instructor
Vincent, John D.
Prof of Education & Psychology
Vollmer, Richard E.
Professor of Political Science
Walker, Kelly Warren
Math Teacher
Ward, Lola Carroll
English Teacher & Dept Chair
Watson, William Joseph
VP for Administration
Weaver, Janet L.
Sci, Math & Soc Stud Tchr
Webster, Kathy Jantzen
Honors Mathematics Teacher
Williams, Nancy Lee
Seventh Grade Reading Teacher
Willingham, Janice Darrah
Advanced Placement Chem Tchr
Wilson, Bob Wayne
Driver's Ed Tchr
Wilson, Lulla Moore
Science Teacher
Wilson, Theresa Rose Cipollone
Vocational Education Instr
Wise, Bertha Wheeler
Composition, Lit & Hum Prof
Witcher, Lisa Chare (Haller)
English Teacher
Wood, James Alvin, Sr.
Business & Computer Tech Tchr
Woodfield, Samuel Mark
Associate Director of Bands
Wooldridge, Glenda Dianne
Elem Physical Education Tchr
Wylie, M. Sue
Gifted Spec & Soc Studies Tchr
Zumwalt, John Willis
Missiology Professor

OKMULGEE
Barnett, Joe Louis
Third Grade Teacher
Brewer, Marsha Carol
HS Advanced Biology Teacher
Byrd, Lois Jean
9th Grade Science Teacher
DeWitt, Mike K.
Shoe, Boot & Saddle Supervisor
Dickson, Mary A.
Visual Communications Instr
Duncan, Rachelle Deawn
Math & Science Instructor
Gee, Estherlene
Senior High School Counselor
Hutchinson, David Randall
History & Government Teacher
Johnson, Darin Scott
History & Geography Teacher
Lewis, Mary Louise (George)
Retired Kindergarten Teacher

OKTAHA
Jones, Patricia Carol
Art Teacher

OLUSTEE
Mc Kee, Randy Curtis
History Teacher & Coach

OMEGA
Geis, Tim E.
Sci & Cmptr Application Tchr

OOLOGAH
Bradshaw, Bradley Joe
MS Asst Prin & Soc Stud Tchr
Brown, Gary E.
Math Teacher
Harrison, Mary Hammer
Chemistry & Ecology Teacher
Oakley, Jennifer
Speech & Drama Teacher
Stauffer, Patty Greene
Second Grade Teacher

ORLANDO
Dunn, Cynthia Lynn
Lang Arts & Soc Stud Tchr
Larman, Gary B.
Agriculture Education Teacher
Pfeiffer, John Henry, Jr.
High School Science Teacher
Raupe, Ruth E.
English Teacher

OWASSO
Clark, Leslie Kay
Bio, Zoology & Genetics Tchr
Hammack, Deloris Elaine
7th Grade Life Science Teacher
Holleman, Steven Ray
Creative Literature Tchr
Kirk, Heidi (Gregory)
English Teacher
Oliver, Susan Carver
8th Grade Science Teacher
Poplin, Wallace Daniel
Business Teacher
Reutlinger, Linda Sherman
Fifth Grade Teacher
Wallace, Sallyanne Lindblad
English Teacher
Wilson, David Robert
History Teacher
Wilson, Paul William
Science Teacher

PADEN
Adams, Darlene Agnes
Library Media Specialist
Cook, Darlene Davis
2nd Grade Reading Teacher
Simpson, Debby Heffington
Third Grade Teacher
Wylie, Myrtle Coy
Business Education Teacher

PANAMA
England, Chuck
Science Teacher
England, Susan Helen (Eader)
Fifth Grade Teacher
Peterson, LaVern Lee
Band Director

PANOLA
Albright, Linda Stewart
Counselor & Home Ec Tchr
Paulk, Carla Faye
English, Drama & Speech Tchr
Travis, Glenda Gayle
Mathematics Teacher

PAOLI
Benson, Greg J.
Principal, Teacher & Coach
Meisel, Veronica
Voc Home Ec Tchr & Counselor

PARK HILL
Marsh, Sherlyn Hendrix
Third Grade Teacher

PAULS VALLEY
Carter, Betty Sue Blakely
Second Grade Teacher
Chambers, Susan Terry
7th Grade Teacher
Dingler, Linda Cleaver
First Grade Teacher
Fine, Michelle Christina
English Teacher
Freeman, RexAnn Lawson
Kindergarten Teacher
Hill, Cynthia Estes
Math Teacher
Jarman, Stephen G.
8th Grade Mathematics Teacher
Johnson, FLoyd W.
Science Teacher & Head Coach
Riddle, Fawn Suzanne
Computer Teacher
Salazar, Teresa
Spanish Teacher

PAWHUSKA
DeMoss, Richard T.
Retired Spanish Teacher
Graham, Linda Manning
Mathematics Teacher
Holloway, Sharon Sossamon
Voc Business & Cmptr Tech Tchr
Martin, Kim A.
Voc Indiv Cooperative Ed Tchr
Pitts, Rod Dale
Dean of Students

PAWNEE
Harp, Ted
HS Science Teacher
Miller, Suzanne M.
Earth Science & Biology Tchr

PERKINS
Collins, Judy Ann
Elem Prin & Spec Ed Dir
Hawkins, Christie
High School Mathematics Tchr
Shelton, Mark Lynn
Science Teacher
Wilson, Jan Fickel
Spanish & French Teacher
Woods, Kathleen Edmondson
Library Media Specialist

PERRY
Hentges, Sandra L.
Band Director
Hodge, C. Lynn Winkelman
Resource Teacher
Keating, Carolyn Franey
Pre First Grade Teacher
Musshafen, Phillip Sheridan
Physical Sci & AP Bio Teacher
Nicholas, Judy K.
English Teacher
Scherman, Dana Jane (Schrick)
7th Grade Mathematics Teacher
Stevens, Rhonda L. Brinkley
9th-12th Grd Guidance Cnslr
PICHER
Patterson, Mary Ann Thomas
Social Studies Teacher
Vogler, Margo Lynn
English Teacher
Volger, Margo Lynn
English Teacher
PIEDMONT
Adams, John N.
Physical Sci & Democracy Tchr
Bargman, Cheryl Moffat
Home Economics & English Tchr
Crabtree, Cheryl Wallace
Soc Stud & Bus Teacher
Grellner, Diane Laureen
5th Grade Teacher
Jergensen, Laura Sharie
Math Teacher & Dept Chair
Lykes, Steve O'Hara
Social Studies Teacher & Coach
Phillips, Robin Hogan
Fifth Grade Teacher
POCASSET
Davidson, Joetta Mae (Garrett)
Retired Third Grade Teacher
Monroe, Tammy J.
Physical Education Teacher
POCOLA
Bugg, Delores Ann
English & Journalism Teacher
Johnston, Christina Mae (Tucker)
Math & Computer Teacher
Taylor, Lucille Cummings
Second Grade Teacher
PONCA CITY
Bovenschen, Tricia Bailey
Middle & High Schl Bands Dir
Brackett, Frances Hines
Substitute Teacher
Bright, Nancy Williamson
Sixth Grade Teacher
Brooke, Deborah S. (Boyd)
Special Education Teacher
Counter, Marianna Lehman
Retired Kindergarten Teacher
Danbom, Susan Gready
3rd Grade Teacher
Easley, Betsy Leabeth
English Teacher
Gallagher, Gary W.
Technology Coordinator
Hill, Phyllis Flora
First Grade Teacher
Hoffmeyer, Jean (Von Strohe)
Sixth Grade Teacher
Magstadt, Midge Eilene
4th Grade Teacher
McNeese, Sandra Jane
Teacher of Multihandicapped
Mueller, Gale Aulds
HS Mathematics Teacher
Munger, John Robert
HS Biology Tchr
Paynter, Janet Porter
Journalism & English Teacher
Poole, Richard William, Jr.
Social Studies & Amer His Tchr
Powers, Linda (Waltermire)
English Teacher
Purdum, Mary AnnCurrey
6th Grade Teacher
Sodowsky, Rick M.
Amer His, Geog & Govt Tchr
Stigge, Trudi Schmidt
Eighth Grade Civics Teacher
Tatum, Betty Lisby
English Teacher
Tipton, Lenora Ann (Williams)
Business Education Teacher
White, Kymberly Greenfield
Math Teacher
POND CREEK
Hendrix, Steve R.
Elementary Principal
PORUM
Dearman, Janis Rock
Mathematics Teacher
POTEAU
Caldwell, Lorraine Ives
Assistant Principal
Holton, Jerry L.
Math & Science Division Chprsn
Smith, Linda Ruth
6th Grade Math Teacher
Taylor, John Bill
Adjunct Professor of Science
PRAGUE
Bolander, John Jay
English Teacher
Quattrochi, Cherl Searcy
Language Arts Teacher
Smith, David Craig
Asst Principal & Sftbl Coach
Stefansen, Peggy Ann
Teacher of Learning Disability
PRUE
Whorton, Patricia Anne
Business Teacher
PRYOR
Burger, Leann B.
Student Activities Faculty
Dotson, Granville Barry
Fourth Grade Teacher
Dryden, Ronald L.
Art & Language Arts Teacher
Elliott, Jana Gayl
English Tchr & Dept Chprsn
Fogleman, Melinda Coker
Adult Education Teacher
Robertson, Douglas S.
Science Teacher
Wood, Wilma Joyce (Biggs)
Computer Technology Instructor
PURCELL
Bell, Teresa Burgan
Director of Bands
Cavnar, Ernestine J.
Retired Teacher
Coale, Dane S.
Math, Computer Teacher & Coach
Feroli, Debbie Benton
Spanish Teacher
Lind, Norma Jean (Morgan)
Retired Vocal Music Teacher
Swayze, Jerry W.
Middle & HS Science Teacher
QUINTON
Spears, Hester Lillian (Terrell)
English Teacher & Dept Chair
Votravis, Jan
Counselor
Wood, Michael Don
High School Teacher & Coach
RAMONA
Shklar, Mike
Social Studies Teacher & Coach
RATTAN
Bailey, Russell Ray
HS Social Studies Teacher
Watts, Tracey Marie (Smith)
Voc Family & Consumer Sci Tchr
Work, Betty A.
5th & 6th Grd Science Tchr
RAVIA
McDaniel, Susann Canada
Vocal Music Teacher
RED OAK
Mankin, Donnas (Brannon)
First Grade Teacher
Shaw, George Bernard
5th Grade Teacher
RIPLEY
Howard, Deneen A.
Social Studies Teacher
ROFF
Crawford, Paula Kay (Spurgin)
Business Education Teacher
Hisaw, Judy Patton
HS Mathematics Teacher
ROLAND
Davis, Russell Wayne
Social Studies Teacher
Lattimore, Gary Trad
History Teacher
Lawson, Janice Stephens
Math Teacher
Tibbits, Mary Anita
Spanish & English Teacher
Whitsitt, Frances Katherine
High School Counselor
RUSH SPRINGS
Pelley, Oreta
Reading Teacher
Stewart, Jana Brown
Computer & Business Teacher
RYAN
Boucher, Karen Elizabeth (Gift)
AP English Teacher & Librarian
Northrip, Arvella (Pitmon)
High School English Teacher
SALINA
Purcell, Bessie M. (Whited)
Mathematics Teacher
SALLISAW
Caughman, Nancy Lee Helm
3rd Grade Teacher
Gipson, Barbara Blackwood
3rd-5th Grd Reading Specialist
Lattimore, Annie Lucinda
Computer Science Teacher
Weddle, Patsy Mc Lemore
Retired Third Grade Teacher
SAND SPRINGS
Anderson, Jane Israel
Sixth Grade Teacher
Baker, Sheree Hart
English Teacher
Cotton, Stephen L.
Hnrs Biology & Chemistry Tchr
Lovelace, Bill L.
Science Teacher & Coach
Wentworth, Kathy Diane
Fourth Grade Teacher
SAPULPA
Aycock, D. Edward
Social Studies & Computer Tchr
Carver, Joan Roesner
7th-8th Grade Science Teacher
Dodge, Karen L. (Clark)
French Teacher
Henry, Evelyn Mae
Ninth Grade English Teacher
Johnson, Jeaneen R. Wehnes
Substitute Teacher
Mc Reynolds, Mary F. Mehlhorn
Spanish & French Teacher
Mears, Murphy George
Retired Science Teacher
Patterson, Del
Geography Teacher
Ragsdale, Norma Kinsala
8th Grade Teacher
Sharber, John E.
Agriculture Ed Teacher
Shibley, K. K.
US History & Amer Govt Tchr
Tilford, Patricia Anne
Business Teacher
Vannoy, Julie Shankle
English Teacher
Voss, Deborah Gayle
Math Instructor
SAVANNA
Frederick, Greta George
High School Art Teacher
Reeder, Iris Aline (Birdwell)
Social Studies Teacher
SAYRE
Ellison, Joan Milan
Family & Consumer Science Tchr
Ford, Terry Callahan
English & Journalism Teacher
Robinson, Fay
Retired Mathematics Teacher
SCHULTER
Hill, Barbara Torres
Early Childhood Teacher
SEILING
Grabow, Holly Joy (Hart)
First Grade Teacher
Harris, Karen Cummin
Kindergarten Teacher
SEMINOLE
Beene, Russell Dale
Ath Dir & Speech Instr
Bowles, Deborah Denice
High School Science Teacher
Gunter, Elizabeth Ruth Littlejohn
Fifth Grade Teacher
Hamm, Dawna Rea
Business Instructor
Henderson, Cindy A.
Eleventh Grade English Teacher
Hill, Robert Ratcliff
English Instructor
Johnson, Nancy Jo
First Grade Teacher
Kirk, Kelly Douglas
Art Dept, LA, & Humanities Chm
Miller, Steven L.
History Teacher
Parks, Judy Ann
Business Instructor
Richardson, Vic Roy
6th Grade Teacher & Coach
Schelb, Colleen Silva
Chemistry & Physics Teacher
Taron, Laurel Rawey
Counselor
Willis, Claudia Harp
Middle School Counselor
SENTINEL
Maddox, Carla Jo
English Teacher
Rozell, Jayne Ann (Stowers)
Math & Computer Teacher
SHARON
Burgess, Freida Hoffman
Elementary Principal
SHATTUCK
Mitchell, Karen (Corbitt)
Vocational Family Teacher
Owen, Rebecca Anne
English Teacher
SHAWNEE
Buckley, Charles J.
Instructor of Math
Clayton, Kay Marshall
First Grade Teacher
Cline, Debra Hobbs
Speech & Drama Teacher
Crossley, William Thomas, III
Spanish Teacher
Dagy, Melba Hopfer
English Teacher
Dinsmore, Carla Reese
Fifth Grade Teacher
Genn, Jessie Lynn (Cox)
7th Grade English Teacher
Hall, Joe
Professor of English
Humphrey, Cindy Hillerman
First Grade Teacher
Hunter, Ruth Owen
Jr High & HS English Teacher
Lane, Jack Duane
Secondary Mathematics Teacher
Mc Mahan, Linda S.
8th Grade Science Teacher
Miles, E. Carolyn
Second Grade Teacher
Powell, Nanette Biggs
Fifth Grade Teacher
Rich, Jane (Biles)
Science & Math Teacher
Russell, Jimmie Smith
Assoc Professor of Education
Scott, Marcia Driscoll
Fifth Grade Tchr of Gifted
Smith, Melody A.
Director of Counseling
Smith, Rosie Mae
ESL Director & PE Teacher
Sokolosky, Veronica, OSB
Transfer Cnslr & Prof of Eng
Swanson, Douglas J.
Asst Prof of Jrnlsm & PR
Totten, Jeff W.
World History Teacher
Totty, Thixe Henderson
Math & Bible Teacher
Trim, Leanna F.
Teacher
Trout, Anita Gwin
Life Science Instructor
Vincent, Robert E., III
Mathematics Teacher
Williams, Avis Anita (Neely)
Fifth Grade Teacher
SKIATOOK
Anduss, Janet Fleming
Mathematics Teacher
Francis, Betty Modgling
English & Spanish Teacher
Hill, Krisandra Owens
Vocational Business Teacher
Jech, Joyce May
Elementary Principal
SMITHVILLE
Lumpkin, Susan Rose
Business Teacher
Webb, Ron Patrick
Mathematics Teacher
SNYDER
Barker, Kent Dewayne
Band Director
Boles, R. Marc
Ag Education Teacher
Mc Phail, Carol Jackson
Elementary Principal
SOPER
Barnes, Roger Dale
HS Social Studies Teacher
Dominick, Donna Fern
Fifth Grade Teacher & Librn
SOUTH COFFEYVILLE
Hotfelt, Kenneth Alan
7th & 8th Grade English Tchr
Maxey, Donna Lynn (Straw)
First Grade Teacher
Mc Kellips, Ginny Mc Farlin
English Teacher
SPENCER
Easlick, Betty Robinson
Vocational Occupational Tchr
Gaona, JeanAnn M.
Language Arts & English Tchr
Henderson, Joyce Ann (Johnson)
High School Principal
Irons, Reginald Damon
Band Director
Vrooman, Kay
Business Technology Teacher
Woods, Cynthia Carolyn
Kindergarten Teacher
Zalabak, Allen Emmett
English Teacher
SPIRO
Branscum, James Wade
HS Bio, Chem & Algebra Tchr
Ford, Lance Mason
Vocal Music Instructor
Lovell, Kasandra Reece
Freshman English Teacher
Minner, Carolyn Kaye
Third Grade Teacher
Parker, Judy Elaine
High School Business Instr
Perrin, Linda Lee
4th Grade Social Studies Tchr
Stiles, Joyce C.
Teacher
Stoughton, Cindy Aline (Shaw)
Home Economics Instructor
Wilson, Betty Marie (Vaughan)
Mathematics Teacher
Young, William Ira
Retired Fourth Grade Teacher
STIGLER
Bailey, William G.
Math Teacher
Burnes, Betty Jane
Home Economics Education Tchr
Carlton, Nellwyn Lacey
Business & Computer Teacher
Eaton, Joe P.
Chemistry & Physics Teacher
Osborne, Gerald F.
US History Coach
Parker, Brenda A.
8th Grd English & Lit Teacher
Perryman, Judy Kay (Fowler)
First Grade Teacher
STILLWATER
Allen, Timothy Michael
Phys Sci & Teacher of Gifted
Ashbaugh, Robbi Jabara
High School Science Teacher
Ayers, Michael E.
Associate Professor
Davis, Judy Chapman
Second Grade Teacher
Defee, William Charles
Social Studies Teacher
Ehrlich, Dixie Lee (Dain)
Sixth Grade Reading Teacher
Erickson, Mahlon Gustav
Sci & Extended Studies Teacher
Groce, Carolyn McVay
6th Grade Math Teacher
Jones, Marjory Maffitt
Retired Journalism Teacher
Ketchum, Jane P.
5th Grade Teacher
Kinnick, Tommy Ray
Social Studies Teacher
Klingsick, Teresa Arlene
Vocational Business Teacher
Matthews, Megan Mc Graw
Fourth Grade Teacher
Meyer, Carolyn West
Elementary Music Specialist
Oberlender, Garold Dee
Professor of Civil Engineering
O'Hara, Steven Eugene
Architectural Engineering Prof
Pratarelli, Marc Enrique
Psychology Professor
Tipps, Sherry Schooley
High School Science Teacher
Wensell, Robert Wayne
Oklahoma History Teacher
Westbrook, Stephen Michael
Band Dir & Music Coordinator
Whaley, Jerita Southern
Prof Development Ctr Director
Zwerneman, Farrel Jon
Professor
STILWELL
Brashear, Leon
Math Teacher
Hummingbird, LaRhonda Duncan
Seventh Grade Teacher
Inman, DaLana Hudgins
High School English Teacher
Patterson, Beverly (Osborn)
English Teacher
Patterson, Julie Faith
Biology II Teacher
Sawney, John W.
History Teacher
STRATFORD
Lamb, Carol Turner
Business Instructor
Watts, Helen Peters
Media Specialist
STRINGTOWN
Potts, Tony Warren
Principal & Soc Stud Teacher
STROUD
Jones, Sherry Lynn Briggs
English & French Teacher
STUART
Reynolds, Kelly Worrell
Science Teacher
SULPHUR
Day, Clarinda Ann (Leming)
Kindergarten Teacher
Hunt, Karen Andrina
Sixth Grade Reading Teacher
TAHLEQUAH
Ballew, Margie (Ritch)
English Teacher
Bookout, David Jay
Junior High School Principal
Boren, Norma Jean
Government & History Teacher
Butler, Owen Ray, Sr.
7th-8th Grade Science Teacher
Crawford, Stephanie Ann
Language Arts Teacher
Digranes, Swen Haakon
Professor of College Education
Fisher, David Ray
Math & Science Teacher
Huntley, Willard J.
8th Grade Teacher
Ivins, Marsha Huntley
Elementary PE Teacher
Jones, Barbara A.
Retired English Tchr
Lawrence, Janet Marie
Science Teacher
Leeds, Georgia Rae
US History Professor
McClain, Leigh Ann Pruitt
Band Director
McCollum, Glenda S. Blakemore
Home Economics Teacher
Mc Intosh, Jacquelyn Mc Collough
Language Arts Teacher
Meigs, Mike
Language Arts Instructor
Morton, Johnnye Lou
Associate Professor of Reading
Nowlin, Kimberly Parks
English Teacher
Smith, Jonathan Robert
Bible & Outdoor Skills Teacher
Springwater, Linda A.
Business Teacher
Stinson, Donald Randy
English Instructor
Warren, Paul Michael
Mathematics & Music Teacher
Winton, Jacqueline Harper
Freshman English Teacher
TALALA
Buchfink, Merrillyn Intemann
Retired Second Grade Teacher
TALIHINA
Adams, Shelley (Free)
Business Teacher
Bradberry, Caren S.
4th Grade Teacher
Holt, David Wayne
Social Studies Teacher
Polk, A. Marie
Algebra & Geometry Teacher
TECUMSEH
Burrough, Lisa Read
Social Studies Teacher

MSEH (cont)
ger, Mary Ana
iology & Zoology Teacher
Steven Wade
Ed Tchr & Ftbl Coach
ight, Jennifer Sue
School History Teacher
lls, George Henry
nce Teacher
ford, Sondra VanArnam
nd Grade Teacher
Ron
ory Teacher
ns, John C.
h & Physical Ed Instr
LE
, Adrienne Grace
nce Teacher
, Nancy L.
ory & Govt Teacher
IAS
s, Dixie Ann (Harris)
Mathematics Teacher
Cindy Shelton
uage Arts Teacher
, Karen R.
entary Principal
ER AFB
ny, Annette Farley
th Grade Teacher
Craig A.
d Grade Teacher
ON
r, Brenda Partain
ish Teacher & Counselor
gton, Leslie Marie
nce Teacher
OMINGO
n, Curtis N.
nomy Instructor
r, Charles Edward
ish Instructor
r, Lisa Cressler
Prof of English & Theatre
n, Jon S.
of Botany & Microbiology
arty, Billye Loard
7th Grade Science Teacher
, Charlene Trent
al Studies & Reading Tchr
an, Jeffrey Ayala
Prof of Engl
Mary Don
Grade Teacher
aville, Eva Easley
10th Grade English Teacher
Donald Frederick
ish Professor
mmerhorn, James E.
nistry Instructor
KAWA
y, Roy Lee, Jr.
al Sci Chprsn & Instr
ell, Judy R.
ounting Instructor
Judy Kaye
se Educator
r, Kim Lee (Battles)
Instructor & Nursing Chair
, Melody J.
nce & Mathematics Instr
A
son, Nancy Pedersen
nce Teacher & Dept Chprsn
, Art A.
h Teacher
, Johnny Mac
Prof of Broadcasting
, Karen L.
al Studies Teacher
n, George M.
hematics Teacher
r, Kim Parker
dergarten Teacher
Byrd, Brenda Treadwell
ial Science Tchr & Dept Chr
e, Marvin Cornelius
h School History Teacher
ann, David C.
ineering Professor
rous, Edgar Elie
nch Teacher
rous, Judy Lee Taylor
nch Teacher
ord, Cheryl Williams
lish Teacher
hill, Donna Claver
dent Leadership Specialist
s, Laurice Nesser
mmunication Skills Teacher
Carol Sue
istian Education Professor
non, Margaret Ellen
Stud & Hnrs World His Tchr
kenridge, Lillian Vandekrol
oc Prof of Christian Ed
ner, George Marvin
rmacology Professor
ey, Peggy Ann
h Grade Teacher
ghton, Linda K.
ding Teacher
n, Roger Clark
dent Council Spon & Coach
n, Sandra Vale
rd Grade Teacher
ham, Ann Roden
siness Computer Tech Instr
ess, Pamela Brown
cational Business Teacher

Burnham, Judith Dryden
Asst Professor of English
Buto, Rachel M.
6th-8th Grade Teacher
Byford, Frankie Mitchell
Communication Skills Teacher
Calderon, Brenda Hessenaur
Assistant Professor of Spanish
Carter, Carolyn S.
Algebra Teacher
Carter, Nita Lee
Fifth Grade Teacher
Carver, Marilyn Gassei (Chapman)
Music Professor
Chaboya, Nancy Lee
Day Care Licensing Rep
Chappelle, Janice Webb
English Teacher & Dept Chair
Cheek, Diana Matousek
Business Instructor
Chew, Pamela
Asst Prof of Italian & ESL
Childers, Robert W.
Physics Professor
Clements, Cindy H.
Mathematics Teacher
Coleman, Barbara Ann Cato
Social Studies Teacher
Cornish, Karen
ESL Teacher
Cotney, James Edward
Geog Tchr & Soc Stud Dept Chm
Cressman, Sherrill J.
Jr High Math Teacher
Culp, Even Asher
Professor of Communication
Davis, Gregory Emanuel
Elementary Physical Ed Tchr
Davis, Jonathan Arthur
HS Mathematics Teacher
Davis, Linda Lytle
6th & 7th Grd Vocal Music Tchr
Davis, Nancy Poulton
First Grade Teacher
Decker, Edward E., Jr.
Professor of Christian Cnslng
Dill, Euva Williams
Fifth Grade Teacher
Dorries, David William
Assistant Prof of Church His
Dotson, Saundra Gayle
Comm Arts Dept Asst Professor
Dudley, Jeffrey Lee
US His Teacher & Asst Coach
Duncan, Patricia Goble
Vocal Music, French & Eng Tchr
Dunham, Sandra Louise
Biology Teacher
Dyer, Barbara Jean
Counselor
Dyson, David Arnold
Dean of Business
Edwards, Theresa Marie
High School English Teacher
Embry, Martha Hutchins
High School Counselor
Enos, Phyllis Bean
2nd Grade Teacher
Evett, Hollie L.
Phys Ed Teacher
Farmer, Agena Lee
Orgnl & Interpersonal Instr
Farrar, Lucian Montgomery, Jr.
History & Bible Teacher
Ferguson, Patricia Wallace
Drama Teacher
Fields, Kathy A.
US History Teacher
Fields, Starla
Marketing & Management Teacher
Foyil, Andy R.
Fourth & Fifth Grade Teacher
Foyil, Marilyn Mallette
First Grade Teacher
Freesemann, LeAnne Luikart
Secondary Vocal Music Director
French, Rondi Bailey
PE Teacher & Coach
Gamble, Karen L.
Math Dept Chairperson & Tchr
Gerardi, Beth Mary
Science Teacher
Giddens, Jason Paul
Algebra Teacher & Coach
Gillert, Kimberly L. (Farris)
Speech Arts Instructor
Glocker, Donna Darlene
Computer & Social Studies Tchr
Goodman, Sally K.
Junior English Teacher
Goodridge, Joan Vinroe
Second Grade Teacher
Green, Janet Preston
4th Grade Teacher
Gregg, James Burton
6th Grade Math Teacher
Grizzle, Trevor Lloyd
Assoc Prof of New Testament
Hall, Rowena Kay
Kindergarten Teacher
Haller, LuAnne Wortham
Eight Grade Teacher
Halsmer, Dominic Michael
Asst Professor of Engineering
Hardin, Jana Goforth
Visual Arts Instructor
Havey, E. Michael
ROTC Instructor
Hayes, Sandra Herring
Vocal Music & English Teacher

Herr, Stephen Richard
Asst Prof of Physical Science
Hesketh, Robert Paul
Chemical Engineering Professor
Heyne, Robert V.
High School Math Teacher
Hogue, Dianne McDaniel
Fifth Grade Teacher
Holbrook, Lloyd Kent
Second Grade Teacher
Holland, Laura Lee (Bird)
Associate Professor of Theatre
Hollingsworth, Patricia Lance
Kindergarten & Art Teacher
Horton, Sandra Theresa (Stromie)
Third Grade Teacher
Hunter, Barbara S.
Advanced Placement Teacher
Jackson, Antoinette Johnson
Guidance Counselor
Jones, Don L.
Advanced Biology Teacher
Jones, Rebecca Powell
Geog Dept Head & GATE Coord
Kanitz, Lori Ann
Instructor of English
King, Stephen Miles
Asst Professor of Government
Kirk, James Arthur
Instrumental Music Teacher
Knauls, Karen Michelle
Third Grade Teacher
Korstad, John Edward
Professor of Biology
Kouns, Tracy Todd
Math Teacher
Kuzminski, Bernadine
Retired Mathematics Teacher
Larson, C. Lyn
Adjunct Prof of Sociology
Lilly, Tamara
Third Grade Teacher
Lowery, Gearld H.
Title I Rdng & Lang Arts Tchr
Luiskutty, Cheriyakalathil Thomas
Prof, Chm of Engrng & Physics
Lund, Carla Thompson
Mathematics Teacher
Lytal, Bonnie Smith
US History Teacher
Maddox, June Marie
English & Psychology Teacher
Malaby, Mark R.
English Instructor
Margrave, Karen West
Math Teacher
Martin, Betty Wise
English Teacher & Dept Chair
Martin, Ellis Ray
Science Teacher
Mathew, Thomson K.
Professor of Pastoral Care
Mc Bride, David Grant
US History & Sociology Teacher
Mc Cartney, Karen Keeter
Algebra & Geometry Teacher
Mc Culley, Casey Benjamin
Adjunct Instr of Humanities
McKinnis, Suzanne Sloan
Business Teacher
Mefford, Darlene Curtis
7th & 8th Grade Counselor
Miller, Steven Jim
US World History & Psych Instr
Miller, Teresa L.
Dir of Ctr Oklahoma Writers
Minson, Maxine Peacher
Asst Prof of Speech & English
Mukasa, Joseph Balikuddembe
Assistant Prof of Comm Arts
Namavar, Bozorgmehr Reza
ETT Teacher & Trainer
Neller, Timothy Paul
Speech, Drama Tchr & Coach
Null, Peggy M.
Instructor of English
Olinske, Scott Alan
Mathematics Teacher
Page, Ann Moody
French Teacher
Pantoja, Paul Dean
Fine Arts Program Director
Parish, Ann Merritt
Middle School Teacher
Pascoe, Neal Sittel
Fourth Grade Teacher
Passmore, Eva Sponsler
Math Teacher & Department Head
Payne, Jim
Dir of Information Tech Ctr
Peterson, Earl Hanson, III
Orchestra Director
Petty, Janice Carol
4th & 5th Grade Teacher
Philipp, Douglas Roland
German & History Teacher
Pifer, Francis Marie, OSB
Social Studies Teacher
Postier, Robin Doneine
Math & Pre-Algebra Teacher
Prayson, Alex S.
Asst Prof, Drftng & Mech Dsgn
Prenger, Pamela Jean
Computer Instructor
Pringle, Richard Braden, Jr.
History & Government Teacher
Quinn, Camille M.
Professor of Psychology
Rankin, Sue Hofstetter
Mathematics Teacher

Reid, Jacqueline Hope
11th & 12th Grade French Tchr
Rhodes, Patricia Dorsey
2nd Grade Teacher
Ridgway, Lori Theresa
Life Science Teacher
Ritchey, Jamie Marie
HS Science Teacher
Roark, Thomas George
Auto Mechanics Instructor
Rogers, Keith Rodney
Speech, English & Drama Tchr
Rose, Jacquinita A.
Math Professor
Schell, Carter B.
Asst Prof of Political Science
Schmidt, Zelimir
Prof of Petroleum Eng Dept
Scoles, Stace Cody
Computer & Physics Teacher
Scott, Dennis Ray
Senior English Teacher
Scott, Douglas Kemp
Instrumntl & Vocal Music Tchr
Scott-Hall, Marinell Richardson
Adj Fac of Communication Dept
Shaw, Ginger Yardley
English Teacher
Shroff, Allison Weir
Health Science Tech Instructor
Simmons, Eileen McPherson
English Teacher
Smith, Charlene Cope
Adjunct Instructor of English
Smith, Tammy Michael
PE & Health Teacher
Snyder, Phyllis Warmack
Math Teacher
Steeley, Jill Edwards
Assoc Prof of Elem Education
Stemmons, Patricia Regan
8th Grade Teacher
Stephens, Connie L.
Spanish Teacher
Stevenson, George William
Music Professor
Stich, Marianne Gloriod
Drama Tchr & Campus Minster
Stiver, Charles Gregory
Art Instructor
Stone, Carolyn Sue
Second Grade Teacher
Strattan, Robert D.
Prof of Electrical Engineering
Sullivan, Bobbie Dale
7th Grade Science Teacher
Swails, John Washington, III
History Professor
Tennant-Mc Daniel, Cora H.
English Teacher
Thompson, Audrey Helen
Nursing Instructor
Thorpe, Robert Samuel
Theology Professor
Tocci, Rick
Jr High Social Studies Tchr
Tollett, James Caroll
Assoc Prof of Practcl Theology
Tomlin, Charles Steven
Elementary Art Teacher
Townsend, John General
Elementary Vocal Music Teacher
Treadwell, Terree Ogle
2nd Grade Teacher
Tucker, David B.
Adj Instr of Physical Sciences
Tull, Michelle Jeannine
Mathematics Teacher
Tumleson, Yolanda Martinez
Adjunct Faculty
Unruh, Terry Michael
Assistant Prof of Accounting
Vance, Brenda Kaye
Assistant Psychology Professor
Vaniadis, Denise Greene
Asst Principal & Ldrshp Tchr
Vickery, Paul S.
History Professor
Vincent, Roxianne
Fifth Grade Science Teacher
Walker, Tammy Sparks
High School Resource Teacher
Wallace, Gayle Griffin
Latin Teacher & Stu Act Coord
Wallace, Michael Paul
High School Soccer Coach
Wallace, Sharolyn
Psychology & Sociology Instr
Warris, Michele Korshet
English III Teacher
Weaver, H. Kevin
German & Philosophy Teacher
West, Edward W.
Music Faculty
Whitby, Janell D.
Music Teacher
White, Ed
Mathematics Dept Chairman
Williamson, Joyce Evelyn
Latin & World History Teacher
Wilson, Carol Maples
Assistant Professor
Wilson, Jill Lansden
Math & Science Teacher
Wolfe, Benjamin Wesley
7th Grade Health & PE Teacher
Woods, Shirley Tuttle
Eng Core Chprsn & Tchr
Worley, Barbara Thomason
Tchr of Emotionally Disturbed

Worthington, Mark Leon
Special Education Teacher
Young, Brad H.
Judaic-Chrstn Stud Assoc Prof
Zaller, Andy
Art Tchr & Fine Arts Dept Chr
Zetik, Ruth Nelson
Fifth Grade Math Teacher
Zubillaga, Helga Suzanne
Professor of French & German
TUPELO
Campbell, Janna Kaye (Palmer)
Second Grade Teacher
Crisp, William Albert
Agriculture Ed Teacher
TURPIN
Elerick, Kathy Hill
Speech & English Teacher
TUTTLE
McPherson, Deborah Standridge
English Teacher
Utley, Juliana Gail (Clemmer)
Mathematics Tchr & Dept Chair
TWIN OAKS
Strong, Mary Helen (Hix)
Kindergarten Teacher
TYRONE
Hicks, Linda Reona
Vocal Music Teacher
Manning, Debra Patton
Science Teacher
UNION CITY
Kelley, Terese Tate
Fourth Grade Teacher
Walsh, Ione Willene
Family & Consumer Sci Teacher
VALLIANT
Coffman, Linda Ann (Fischer)
HS Mathematics Teacher
Dean, Steven Craig
Government Teacher
DeLozier, Shonda Lynn
High School Counselor
Elizondo, Cynthia Hughes
English I, Speech & Drama Tchr
Gaddy, Malacha Austin
Retired Second Grade Teacher
Mc Reynolds, Pauline
HS Science Teacher
Monk, Ida Cheryl Coffey
7th & 8th Grade Math Teacher
Pittman, Nan
Retired Teacher
Scarborough, Louise Basl
English Department Head
Woolsey, Bill H.
Voc Trade Carpentry Teacher
VELMA
Brumley, Steve C.
Science Teacher
Evans, Terry D.
Tchr of Learning Disabilities
Garrett, Deanne J.
English Teacher
Linke, Donna Karlin
Library Media Specialist
Loveall, Jerry Duane
Social Studies Teacher & Coach
Pool, Freda Rhodes
MS Teacher & Dir of Gifted
Tadlock, Diana Aurora
Spanish & Vocal Music Teacher
VERDEN
Fagalde, Marcia Chaffee
Reading Specialist
VIAN
Bloomer, Bob D.
High School History Teacher
Hill, Joe R.
HS Biology & Zoology Teacher
Shelby, Peggy Ross
1st-12th Grd Vocal Music Tchr
VICI
Peoples, Leila Osborn
Retired Third Grade Teacher
VINITA
Bostwick, Donnie Lee
Amer His Tchr & Coach
Pippin, Carolyn Houghton
Third Grade Teacher
WAGONER
Cooper, Carolyn G. (Hoofard)
11th Grd Language Arts Teacher
Farris, Margaert Jane (Rule)
Social Studies Teacher
Jackson, Karen J.
HS American History Teacher
Lane, Janet (Moody)
12th Grade English Teacher
WAKITA
Bellamy, Sheryl L.
Eng Tchr, Lib Media Specialist
Turney, Oleta Darlene
Kindergarten Teacher
WARNER
Beaver, Bridget Smith
Comm & Fine Arts Chrprsn
Bullard, Barbara Sue
Third Grade Teacher
Dunn, Charlotte A. (Hurley)
Nursing Instructor
Eyres, Robert Smith
Bio, Anatomy & Physiology Tchr
Goats, Carolyn Vice
Teacher of the Gifted & Eng
Hensley, Robert Michael
Mathematics Teacher & Coach
Hilbern, Sandra Hamilton
Fine Arts Instructor

WARNER (cont)
Hornback, Cecelia Bruce
Adjunct Instructor
Howell, Karen Kay
Dir of Learning Skills Ctrs
Major, Larry D.
Math Instructor
Pulliam, Jim F.
Instructor of Humanities
Stewart, Wanda Hutson
Kindergarten Teacher
Woods, Stuart Henry
Professor
WASHINGTON
Hamilton, Randall Keith
Earth & Life Sci Teacher
Mc Cray, Dennis
HS History & Govt Teacher
WATONGA
Frey, Jamae Hobbs
High School Counselor
Lettkeman, Shirley Beadles
Second Grade Teacher
WATTS
Tiger, Lisa Dawn
English & Journalism Teacher
WAUKOMIS
Anderson, Ron
Art Instructor
Hajek, Elaine Seamans
4th Grade Teacher
Hampton, Joan Markes
HS Mathematics Teacher
Mc Cartney, Kimba Marie
Spanish Teacher
Patterson, Betty S.
Title I Instructor
WAURIKA
Hodges, Anna Waid
High School Math Teacher
WAYNOKA
Green, Mary Bentley
Eng Tchr, Lib Media Specialist
Wilson, William B.
High School Science Teacher
WEATHERFORD
Bailey, Cathie McPhetridge
Social Studies Teacher
Hamm, Kelley Moore
Middle School Math Teacher
Hull, Vickie Ann
Eng & Creative Enrchmnts Tchr
Powell, Ginger A.
HS Academic Counselor
Purdum, Laura Lewis
5th Grade Teacher
Sears, Connie Vogt
High School English Teacher
Seifried, Catherine Jean (Ratzlaff)
English Teacher
South, James Dwight
Director of Bands
Spurgeon, Debra Lea
Vocal Area Coordinator
WELCH
Callahan, Sherri Kay
Physical Education Teacher
Karnes, Mike D.
Social Studies Teacher & Coach
WELEETKA
Porter, Michelle Lynn
English Teacher
Williams, Pamela Ray
Third Grade Teacher
WELLSTON
Harriet, Donna May (Pappan)
Title I Teacher
Taylor, Glenda Sue Miller
Retired Home Economics Teacher
Throne, Denise Gail
Band, Choir & Gen Music Dir
WETUMKA
Lockhart, Millie (Phillips)
Mathematics Teacher
Osborn, Ronald W.
Guidance Counselor
Sams, Glenda Osborn
5th Grade Teacher
WEWOKA
Bennett, Linda Stewart
Business & Computer Teacher
Brooks, Janis Cossey
High School Science Teacher
Brown, Frankie C.
Language Arts Teacher
Eaves, Christi A.
Sixth Grade Teacher & Coach
Merideth, Jean A.
Spanish & English Teacher
WHITESBORO
Elrod, Johnny Wayne
Principal
Grey, June Goss
Kndgtn, PE & Rmdl Math Tchr
Phillips, Judy Russell
High School Science Teacher
WILBURTON
Couch, Katharyn Ann
Instructor & Department Chair
Duncan, Marilynn Frances
Liberal Arts Division Chprsn
Givens, Billye Kay
Eng Professor
Harp, Randy M.
Dept Head & Instructor
Morgan, Linda (Wessel)
Office, Bus, Admin & Com Instr
Ridge, Victoria Leigh
Biology Teacher
Walker, T. Leland
Agriculture Science Chairman
WOODWARD
Ansley, Karen
English Teacher
Bassett, Mary Jane
Science Teacher
Bird, Peggy Ann
Business Teacher & Dept Chair
Fisher, Tom
Mathematics Teacher
Glasgow, Verna Taylor
Sixth Grade Teacher
Johnson, Gregory Brent
Physics, Math Teacher & Coach
Selman, M. Corene Phelps
Kindergarten Teacher
Stine, Debby Ganes
Fifth Grade Teacher
Swigart, Glenda Foiles
7th Grade English Teacher
Washmon, Sandy Damon
A P English Teacher
Woodruff, Dolores Anne (Smith)
Business Teacher
WRIGHT CITY
Andoe, Mary R.
Third Grade Teacher
WYANDOTTE
Hofschulte, Phillip
Agriculture Education Teacher
Ransom, Randy Joseph
Technology Education Teacher
WYNNEWOOD
Huitt, Keith David
Director of Bands
Lynch, Kevin Mark
His Teacher & Acad Team Coach
Mc Kay, Barbara Ann
High School Counselor
Moore, Wayne Clinton
HS Language Arts Teacher
Robertson, Barbara Alexander
8th Grade English Teacher
WYNONA
Berry, Viola Kay
High Schl Language Arts Tchr
YALE
Gripe, Deborah Bingaman
Kindergarten Teacher
Jackson, Cecile Frederick
First Grade Teacher
Mann, Judy Koehn
HS Eng & Journalism Instructor
YUKON
Bunch, Su Steelman
Gifted Education Counselor
Corn, Betty Jean
Eng, Speech & Debate Teacher
Critchfield, Jimmye
Psychology Teacher
Davis, Kathy L.
6th Grd Language Arts Teacher
Estep, John R.
Algebra Teacher
Fike, Matthew Dale
Social Studies Teacher
Hawkins, Sue Ann (Barber)
6th Grade Teacher
Henley, Deidra McKenzie
7th Grade English Teacher
Holmes, Betty Gayle (Rogers)
Fourth Grade Teacher
Jackson, Justin George
Biology Teacher
Johnson, Sandra Jane Anderson
6th Grade Science Teacher
Lamb, Joe Ben
Math Teacher
Luschen, Kathy Gorshing
Fifth & Sixth Grade Teacher
McIntire, Debra Yowell
Honors & AP English Teacher
Mc Vay, Larry Joe
World History Teacher
Ommart, Linda Ann
Sixth Grade Teacher
Phares, Ardith Kaye
6th-12th Grade Science Teacher
Raab, Jerry Don
9th Grade American Govt Tchr
Rezek, Linda Ann (Martin)
Choral Music Teacher
Schweitzer, Dawna June
High School Biology Teacher
Smith, Janet Arlene
Choir Director
Tate, Sarah Jean (Hayes)
8th Grd American History Tchr
Taylor, Greg M.
Math Teacher
Tucker, Shirley Rosinski
History Teacher
Wolfe, Charles Arthur
Algebra II Teacher
Yates, Shirley Murphy
Teacher of the Gifted
Yetter, Roxanna Cline
Fifth Grade Teacher

OREGON

ALBANY
Allen, Raymond Gene
Principal
Angel, Karen R.
Business Teacher
Badger, Brian Evan
Special Education Teacher
Bechtel, Dennis A.
Program Coord of Graphics Arts
Bohles, Faye G.
Teacher & Work Exprnc Coord
Cammack, Sue Woods
Retired Fourth-Fifth Grd Tchr
Chase, Tom M.
English Instructor
Evans, Marie Saffery
Youth Transition Specialist
Fernald, Linda
Second & Third Grade Teacher
Krakauer, Karin
English Teacher & Librarian
Lindsay, Deborah Mathay
German Teacher
Lucas, Jim
Animal Science Tchr
Mason, Ron
Instructor of Mathematics Dept
Roberts, Dean E.
Social Studies & PE Teacher
Vanderplaat, Andrew Charles
Instr & Bus Dept Chprsn
Weiler, Pamela Anne
Marketing & Business Ed Tchr
ALSEA
Dvornak, Laurie Nightingale
Science & Math Teacher
AMITY
Harmon, Phoebe Trebell-Luke
Bus & Cmptr Publications Tchr
Holwett, Craig Allen
Math & Science Teacher
ASHLAND
Daniels, Rick Donald
Associate Professor of Nursing
Davidson, Laura P.
Family & Consumer Stud Tchr
Gill, Gudrun
Associate Professor of German
Hilyer, S. Barbara
Middle School Teacher
Pirasteh, Hassan
Economics Professor & Dept Chm
Rudolph, Sydney Hill
Third Grade Teacher
Schaffer, Lauren
High School French Teacher
ASTORIA
Davis, Tighe E.
6th Grade Language Arts Tchr
Deford, Jerry Allen
Dean of Students
Dominey, Carl Arthur
Health & Physical Ed Teacher
Fennerty, Augustus Michael
Fisheries Teacher
Hale, Sharon Caferro
English Teacher
Stromquist, Lee George
Band Director
Stromquist, Sandra Cushman
Orchestra Teacher
Tomlinson, Steven Scott
English & Journalism Teacher
AUMSVILLE
Pendleton, Kay Morris
Child Development Specialist
AURORA
Filonczuk, Cynthia Lou
6th Grade Teacher
Fowler, W. Kirk
Math & History Teacher
Marble, Earl Eugene
Drafting & Wood Tech Tchr
BAKER CITY
Read, Sally Manary
Business Teacher
Winegar, Leanne DeRoest
Language Arts & Speech Teacher
BANDON
DeGree, Sandy
1st-8th Grade Teacher
BANKS
Ainge, Douglas Everett
US History & US Govt Tchr
BEAVER
Marvis, Bryan
Lang Arts & Social Stud Tchr
BEAVERTON
Barrow, Yi Suan T.
Secondary Math Teacher
Bessette, Monique
Former Language Arts Tchr
Bittner, Andrew M.
Bible & Social Studies Tchr
Brock, Susan C.
2nd & 3rd Grd Multi-Age Tchr
Copelin, Ray Edward
Fifth Grade Teacher
Deal, Beth Sabrina
Bio, Zoology & Health Teacher
Dougherty, Melodie Ann
Second Grade Teacher
Elia, Catherine Ann (Roggero)
French Teacher
Ennis, Kyle
Japanese Teacher
Fagan, Kay M.
3rd Grade Teacher
Grosse, Keith P.
Chemistry & Biology Teacher
Johnson, Pam R.
German Teacher
Mandt, Martha E. (Edwards)
Fifth Grade Teacher
Mc Intyre, Mary Lee
Fifth Grade Teacher
Meyers, Brenda Gregg
English & Social Studies Tchr
Morton, Sonja Bockes
5th Grade Teacher
Moser, Mark Bayard
Social Studies Teacher
Moshofsky, Susan V.
English Teacher & Yearbook Adv
Navarro, Leonor E. (Nenita)
Foreign Language Dept Chprsn
Raney, James William
French Teacher
Ritter, Eleanor Campbell
HS Humanities Teacher
Smith, Genevieve Eileen
7th Grade Social Studies Tchr
Waibel, Pauline Rose
Religion & Calligraphy Teacher
Weber, Robert George
His, Eng Instructor & Coach
Yarnell, Kenneth Edward
Social Studies Teacher
BEND
Blaustein, Sharman Jane
Math Instructor
Booster, Doug E.
Assistant Professor of Health
Brock, Michael Van
NRROTC Instructor
Brookover, Robert Eugene
Bus Equipment Svc Tech Prof
Buck, Bill
Humanities Professor
Carvalho, Linda L.
Visual Arts Instructor
Clark, Barry S.
Criminal Justice Instructor
Early, Daniel K.
Assoc Prof of Anthropology
Ekstrom, Lynne Beguhl
2nd Grade Teacher
Emerson, Bruce L.
Associate Professor of Physics
Hawkins, Peter D. H.
Physics Teacher
Keppler, Donald John
Science Teacher
Lamberton, Lowell Harvey
Professor of Business
McDermott, Mary Katheryn (Wise)
Science Teacher
Milliron, Nancy Holmes
Music Teacher
Minor-Evans, Leslie B.
Asst Prof of Psychology & Ed
Owings, Ann H.
English Teacher
Shoop, Daniel Hahn
Supported Ed Specialist
BLACHLY
Bellingham, James E.
Science Teacher
Harrison, Paula May
Elementary Teacher
Larsen, James Edward
4th-5th Grade Art Teacher
BOARDMAN
King, Patricia Ann (Perry)
Resource Room & Spec Ed Tchr
Mc Elligott, C. Maureen
Social Studies Chm & Professor
BORING
DeWittie, Alice Ann
History & English Teacher
Gandara, Margo Giberson
Junior High Teacher
Hayley, Stephen James
Sci & Contemporary Issues Tchr
Hunter, Charles William
Government & Economics Teacher
Rasmussen, Darrell George
Sixth Grade Teacher
BROOKINGS
Burdett, Ted Leonard
Social Studies Educator
Dingle, Arthur Lee
English Teacher
Gerlach, Janet Marie
Kindergarten Teacher
Golden, Alan Peter
Science Teacher
Mc Donald, Lynda Marie
Spanish & French Teacher
Raley, Kathleen Martin
English & Journalism Teacher
Reallon, Marilyn Graham
First Grade Teacher
BURNS
Cargill, Sandy Nelson
Principal
Morris, Mary Johanna
Third Grade Teacher
Mues, Deborah (King)
1st Grade Teacher
Peckham, Kendall I.
Instrumental Music Teacher
Wassom, Ronald Evans
Science & Math Teacher
BUTTE FALLS
LeFever, Carla Alvernaz
Social Studies Teacher
CAMAS VALLEY
Bishop, Jon Loren
SS & LA Teacher
CANBY
Johnson, Linda G.
5th Grade Teacher
Jones, Bob Lloyd
Forensics Director
Milbrooke, Tom
HS Physical Education Teacher
Moore, Earlyn Kraft
High School English Teacher
Ricksger, Darrell L.
Pro-Tech Instructor
Robins, Gregory James
Fourth Grade Teacher
CANYONVILLE
Cox, Diane S. (Dukes)
7th-8th Grd English Teacher
Rich, Phillip Eugene
Science, Math & Shop Teacher
CARLTON
Dunn, Annette Burich
Teacher
CAVE JUNCTION
Crocker, Theodore Howard, Jr.
Social Studies Teacher
Fromme, Amy
Foreign Language Teacher
Morgan, Steven Ray
High School Govt & US His Tchr
Smith, Emma Hood
Business Teacher
CENTRAL POINT
Baird, Steven E.
English & Language Arts Tchr
Barlow, Sharon L.
Third Grade Tchr & Tech Coord
Carlson, Lynda Sue
Math Teacher
Kuehnert, Calie Jean
Science Teacher
Reed, Deborah Joan
Former Primary Teacher
Taylor, Christine Johnson
Family & Consumer Studies Tchr
Taylor, Gary Dean
PE & Drivers Ed Teacher
CLACKAMAS
Glauner, Katharine McKenna
English Teacher
CLATSKANIE
Wilson, Frederick Charles
5th Grade Teacher
COLTON
LaFollette, Kellie Ryan
Fourth Grade Teacher
COOS BAY
Bowden, Jim
Lang Arts & Soc Studies Tchr
Carter, Brian E.
Pol Sci, Wrld Geog & Hlth Tchr
Dinkins, Eleanor Spencer
Arts & Commnctn CAM Co Chair
Houghton, Marlis L.
German Teacher
Ingham, Zita
English Instructor
Kirkendall, Lon
Second Grade Teacher
Kotsovos, Jerry Frank
Govt, Ec & US History Teacher
Ledesma, Allan Roy
Soccer Coach
Miller, Robert Allen
Accounting Professor
Muffett, Sharon Sampsel
Science & Math Teacher
Novak, Garrett Dennis
Intermediate Teacher
Prescott, Katherine Lee
Humanities & Spanish Teacher
Schrader, Marianne (Landrith)
Library & Media Specialist
Tedder, Nancy Lathers
Humanities Teacher & Coach
COQUILLE
DeBoard, Elaine Lee
English Tchr & Schlsp Cnslr
CORBETT
Brinkman, Rosemary Gayle
Fifth Grade Teacher
Miller, Eliza Gallardo
Spanish Teacher
Smith, J. Tyler
Social Studies Teacher
CORVALLIS
Appleby, Gerry Smith
Primary Teacher
Brownell, Philip Harry
Professor of Zoology
Burke, Mary Ellen
Senior Instr in Microbiology
Carlson, Paul N.
Jr-Sr High Art Teacher
Carver, Joyce Graves
Retired Elementary Teacher
Cotton, Todd Maskel
Intnl Coordinator of Projects
Crafton, Linda Louise
Mathematics Tchr & Dept Head
Creighton, Charles Lee
Orchestra Director
De Hus, Mattie Mae
Sixth Grade Teacher
Ford, Jacquelyn Eubanks
Bible, Health Teacher & Cnslr
Frates, Dennis
4th-5th Grade Teacher
Freed-Elefant, Peggy
English & Social Studies Tchr
Gosser, Virgil V.
Mathematics Teacher
LaVietes, Anne Sherr
Spanish Teacher

ALLIS (cont)
n, Elizabeth DiCesare
sh Teacher
n, Marlene Fraley
ol-To-Career Coordinator
on, Mary L.
ssor of Plant Pathology
Susan L.
Prof of Public Health
Lloyd Walter
: Prof Molecular Biology
s, Ruth-Anne
y Resource Mgmt Spec
r, Richard
rical Engineering Prof
e, Richard Stanton
re & Speech Teacher
y, Sandra Simpson
Grade Teacher
ad, Ronald E.
of Food Science & Tech
AGE GROVE
, Heidi (Stauber)
uage Arts & Spanish Tchr
, Keith Mills
rade Teacher
Frank M.
ed Language Arts Teacher
on, Mary Jo
sh Teacher
Richard Earlan
nistry & Physics Teacher
E
t, Linda Jo White
ness & Spanish Teacher
ey, David L.
Science Teacher
WELL
, Vicki L. (Parsons)
sh Teacher
Natalie Conley
ness Education Instructor
ER
e, Roberta Garman
Grade Teacher
ning, Elizabeth Katherine
uage Arts & ESL Tchr
AS
arla Brandon
ctns Adv & Lang Arts Tchr
Carol M.
sh & US History Teacher
er, Joyce Hatcher
ness Teacher
CREEK
ux, Alfred Hermon
al Studies & Science Tchr
, Klaus Jorgen
, History, & Art Teacher
Nancy Ann (Teague)
ish Teacher
N
rent Lyle
al Studies & Math Teacher
R
n, Kelly Colleen Fay
Grade Teacher
n, Laurie Diane
Grade Teacher
EE
ach, Arnold Mark
ed Elementary Teacher
E CREEK
linor Woods
ate Tutor
E POINT
, J. Vincent
Grade Teacher
on, Robert L.
Arts & Soc Stud Tchr
Ted Allan
S Science Teacher
VILLE
y, Jerry R.
, Shop & Prsnl Fntss Tchr
N
n, Dick
ical Education Teacher
arth, Paul David
Grade Teacher
ON
uk, Mark
th Grade Teacher
RPRISE
s, Kent Charles
rnative Education Teacher
CADA
, Jim Berten
lance Counselor
y, Thomas J.
Science Teacher
n, Gary L.
hematics Teacher
n, Cynthia Diane
Grade Teacher
nacher, Conrad Robert, Jr.
ctor of Mainstreet
am, Renee Marie
& Second Grade Teacher
n, Michael Burr
n Grade Teacher
ENE
s, Kathleen
ic Teacher
rson, Edith Willis
mistry Teacher
ull, Ronald Lee
ructor & Academic Advisor
Betsy Lien
Grade Teacher & Team Ldr

Bumstead, Robert Garrison
English Teacher
Burke, Lonny Roy
Christian Ministries Professor
Di Liberto, Thomas Christopher
Spanish Immersion Teacher
Edwards, Lily Margaret
Business & Computer Teacher
Fast, Marce L.
6th Grade Teacher & Team Ldr
Garger, Jerome S.
Prof of Writing & Literature
Gaudia, Shelley
Science Instructor
Haffner, Robert Wayne
Math Teacher
Hodges, James Melvin
High School Counselor
Immonen-Boyd, Marcy K.
High School Business Teacher
Jagger, Alice Janes
10th Grade Global His Tchr
Kargel, Garry W.
Mathematics Teacher
Kempf, Constance Susan (Little)
English & Bible Teacher
Lane, LeRoy Ludeman
Communications Professor
Larson, Jody
Math Instructor
Legler, James Richard
Management Professor
Llewellyn, Grace K.
Editor
Loveland, Nancy Jean
1st-5th Grade Tchr
Mathes, Ernest Leo
Professor & Chrstn Ministries
McCauley, Kevin J.
Sci Dept Bio Tchr & Co Chair
Montgomery, Bradley Maul
Health Education Teacher
Montgomery, Sue
Associate Professor
Myers, Joseph Rutledge
Economics & Government Teacher
Nott, Nena Leann
Second & Third Grade Teacher
Nuxoll, Jon Owen
History Teacher
Oleson, Clifton Ross
Retired Mathematics Teacher
Oleson, Donald D.
7th Grade Math Teacher
Oswald, Robert C.
Professor of Biology
Pinkstaff, Bill
Fifth Grade Teacher
Rhee, Song Nai
Academic Dean & Vice President
Rodgers, Sharon L.
Science Teacher
Rohde, David L.
Math Teacher & Administrator
Rubinstein, Robert Edward
Lang & Performing Arts Teacher
Saul, Lynette Johnson
Fourth Grade Teacher
Sparks, Lance Thomas
Instructor
Strums, Charles L.
Asst Prof of Cross Cltrl Stud
Weiherman, Kimberly Anne
High Schl Mathematics Teacher
Westergaard, George Henry
Political Science & Psych Tchr
Wiard, Robert B.
Language Arts Teacher
Wilbur, Fredric Paul
Fifth Grade Teacher
FLORENCE
Bollinger-Pickell, Kimberly J.
Family & Consumer Stud Teacher
Byrd, Marcia Jean
Health & Physical Ed Tchr
Church, Mary-Jean Urgo
6th Grade Teacher
Jennings, Dorothy Jean Bass
First Grade Teacher
McCorkle, Roger W.
High School Teacher
McKibbin, Bruce Malcolm
Elementary Physical Ed Tchr
Perry, Ty
Sixth Grade Educator
Slonecker, Beverly Anne (Johnson)
Choral Director
Thenell, Carol Brown
Lang Arts & Soc Studies Tchr
Wartnik, Neil Anthony
High School English Teacher
FOREST GROVE
Czajkowski, Paul George
Self Contained Classroom Tchr
Graham, Charles L.
Fifth & Sixth Grade Teacher
Kastberg, Richard James
Math Teacher
Schubothe, Ralph
Mathematics Teacher
GARDINER
Meyer, Larry B.
6th Grade Teacher
GILCHRIST
Baker, Jeffrey A.
Physical Ed & Health Teacher
Brannan, David James
Science Teacher

GLADSTONE
Zarnekee, Mary Barland
Retired Teacher
GLENDALE
Chandler, Sammy Dan
Fifth Grade Teacher
GLIDE
Costanzo, Sharon Molinari
Physical Education Teacher
GRANTS PASS
Amos, Robert Edwin
Physics & Chemistry Teacher
Baldwin, Lisa Elaine
English & Language Arts Tchr
Campbell, Jeffrey R.
Social Studies Teacher
Chamberlain-Bickle, Julie Rae
Secondary Art Ed Teacher
Childers, James Dale
Science Instructor
Doob, Jeannette Frame
College English Instructor
Eikleberry, Burt R.
Teacher & Scholarship Coord
Gates, Gary Alan
Anatomy, Physiology & Sci Prof
Gooch, Elizabeth Summers
Psychology Instructor
Hitchko, F. Keith
Technology Teacher
Honken, Gene Le Roy
Automotive Technology Instr
Keeling, Jerry Wayne
Counselor
Kightlinger, Mary Anne Sinnott
Special Education Teacher
Knapp, Debbie
Mathematics Teacher
Mc Kinnon, Matthew Jon
AP American Govt Teacher
Meehan, Betty-Jo Campbell
Retired Teacher
Mills-Price, Philip Stephen
Teacher
Orris, Sue
Counselor
Prince, Leana Marie
Language Arts Tchr, Dept Coord
Richardson, Cristine Marie
Fifth Grade Teacher
Salinas, John T.
Chemistry Instructor
Skudstad, Katie Kelley
English & Drama Tchr
Sperbeck, Bonnie Stromme
Third Grade Teacher
Stanley, Alan Hawk
8th Grd Eng & Lang Arts Tchr
Tardieu, Greg A.
History Teacher
Wade, Randall Eugene
Bus & Office Tech Dept Chair
Wheatley, Carolyn Woodward
Eng & Composition Teacher
Worley, Phillip Mandy
Junior High School Teacher
Zottola, Martin D.
10th-12th Grade English Tchr
GRESHAM
Armstrong, Thom M.
Assoc Dean of Soc Sci Division
Barra, Gerry M.
Instr of Language & Literature
Bremer, Thomas Michael
Lang Arts Dept Chprsn & Tchr
Conrath, Michael E.
Mathematics Teacher
Cuda, Tony
Language Arts Teacher
Dawson, Susan W.
AP Coordinator & Instructor
Dials, Judy
English Teacher
Halligan, Teresa Cuba
Fifth Grade Teacher
Hilsenteger, Julie Ann
Physics Teacher
Irwin, Ursula
English Instructor
Keller, John Eugen
Athletic Director
Knudsen, Chris A.
Math, PE Instructor & Coach
Lakey, Robert Wayne
Chemistry Teacher
Lawson, James Blaine
Social Studies Teacher
Long, Sandy
Science Tchr & Division Ldr
Lovejoy, Gary Harold
Instructor of Psych & Religion
Maneval, Keith P.
PE Instructor & Coach
McCarty, Douglas James
Astronomy Instructor
Phillips, Barbara Jean
Pre-Schl & Kndgtn Admin
Pollack, David James
Global Studies Teacher
Porterfield, Mark Alan
Activites Director & Teacher
Rabe, Paul C.
Anatomy & Biology Instructor
Starr, Thomas Mark
Chem, Phys Sci & Algebra Tchr
Stewart, Julia Ellen (Burwell)
High School English Teacher
Suter, Bill H.
High School Mathematics Tchr

Thomas, Colonel Francis
7th-8th Grd Humanities Teacher
Weitzel, Gloria A.
7th-8th Grade Science Teacher
Wickham, Carole Lynn
Medical Office Coord & Instr
Young, Jeffrye Lytle
Radio Pgm Coord & Instr
HALFWAY
Kuwahara, Charles Walter
Lang Arts & Social Stud Tchr
HARRISBURG
Pluth, Donna
English Teacher
HELIX
Miller, J. Wayne
5th Grade Teacher & Coach
HEPPNER
Beck, Karen Collins
Math Teacher
HERMISTON
Bounds, Karen Bisgaard
US His & Government Teacher
Carlson, Jerald Loraine
Biology Teacher & Dept Head
Duncanson, Kathleen Hansen
Fourth Grade Teacher
Keys, Robert Taylor
Retired Elem Tchr of GATE
Parkins, Tamara Schlader
Kindergarten Teacher
Youngman, Kathryn Marie Groshong
Spanish Teacher
HILLSBORO
Allnutt, Robert Wayne
Mathematics Instructor
Coleman, Mark A.
Jr High Math Teacher
Day, Mary Carol Leavens
English Teacher
Ericksen, Donna Clodfeller
Reading & Language Arts Tchr
Farr, Jerry William
Ninth Grade Health Teacher
Gardner, Margaret Boice
TAG & Language Arts Teacher
Harris, Rocky
Social Studies Teacher
Holliger, Jeffrey Leonard
Technology Education Teacher
Johnson, Franklin G.
Science Teacher
Kuehn, Bernd Reinhard
Choral Director
Martone, Marcella
Chemistry Teacher
Pettis, Beth Krause
7th Grade Teacher
Powell, Gary Robert
English Teacher
Thompson, Christy Lichtig
Biology & Physical Sci Tchr
Tinnesand, Michael John
Science Teacher
Wunder, Mark John
English Teacher
HOOD RIVER
Bohlmann, David Dale
Math Dept Chair
Frost, Kristen Uhler
Spanish & Health Teacher
Lynch, Joan Skeen
Retired Second Grade Teacher
Mayer, Rosemarie (Pace)
Computer Teacher
Mendez-Treneman, Nancy Catherine
Biology Teacher
Yamashita, Ron Tsutomu
Third Grade Teacher
Zastrow, Paul Frederick
Science Teacher
HUNTINGTON
Hopkins, Gerald Frank
Teacher, Administrator Title I
Raley, Beverly Baxter
English & Business Teacher
IMBLER
Daugherty, Susan Cawrse
HS Science Teacher
Lehner, Jude
Professional Tech Instructor
Wilkens, Sharon Lynn (Welbes)
Fourth Grade Teacher
Wilson, Rebecca Lynne
Language Arts Teacher
IONE
Holland, Dale William, II
Science & Math Teacher
Raible, James Robert
Language Arts Teacher
IRRIGON
French, Tom Ralph
PE & Health Teacher
Houk, Benn L.
Computer Science Teacher
JACKSONVILLE
Beeler, Sherri
Literature & Drama Teacher
Crowe, Judy J. Harper
First Grade Teacher
Hartwell, Michael Robert
3rd & 4th Grade Educator
Slaughter, Kimberly Reeve
Health Science Tchr & Coach
JOHN DAY
Ivers, Kenneth R.
Fourth Grade Teacher
Kimball, Maurice Dale
Math & Science Teacher

JOSEPH
Eggers, Janet Kerns
Science & Art Teacher
JUNCTION CITY
Breese, Paul
Science Teacher & Coach
DuBrowa, Michael Thomas
Social Studies Dept Chair
KLAMATH FALLS
Bastian, Robert Lee
Biological Sciences Tchr
Campbell, Anne Simonds
Second Grade Teacher
Cox, Chubbin Spero
Business Education Teacher
Daw, Vincent Walter
Science Teacher
Hanson, Lorna Johnson
Migrant Education & ESL Coord
Holcomb, Ralph Edward
Applied Arts Teacher
Honan, Bridget Elizabeth
Fifth Grade Teacher
Keener, Dan James
Health Teacher
Kozeliski, Albert George
Art Department Chair
Lake, James Warren Edward
Spanish Teacher
LeQuieu, Carol Y.
First Grade Teacher
Patterson, Thomas G.
Math Teacher
Scanlon, Mary Harris
Retired Third Grade Teacher
Schell, Linda M.
Sixth Grade Head Teacher
Smith-Clifton, Judy Katherine
8th Grd Lang Arts Teacher
Story, Judy Crawford
Business Teacher
Swisher, Joanne Haller
Lecturer, Clinical Nrsng Instr
Vance, Valerie Jo
Assoc Prof Communications Dept
LA GRANDE
Arritola, Judie E.
Second Grade Teacher
Fetz, Billie
6th Grd Lang Arts & PE Tchr
Gregory, Michael Sean
Fourth Grade Teacher
House, Marti Morris
Fifth Grade Teacher
Marks, Anthony
Youth Orchestra Director
Miller, Verl Edward
Physical Ed Tchr & Coach
Nicholson, Larry Dean
Social Studies Teacher
LA PINE
Verboncoeur, Gary
English Teacher
LAKE OSWEGO
DeBoer, Carol J.
Third & Fourth Grade Teacher
Gates, Kristine Paulson
4th-5th Grade Classroom Tchr
Harvester, Jennifer Nadine
Chem, Physics & Gen Sci Tchr
Kayser, MaryLou Lyman
English Teacher
Korach, Rachel M.
Eng Dept Chm & Teacher
Martin, Valarie E.
6th Grade Teacher
Meeter, Robin Dale
HS PE, Health Tchr & Coach
Miller, Anni Bennett
Girls Head Tennis Coach
Nakamura, Ted R.
Fifth & Sixth Grade Teacher
Weber, Gery L.
US His & Government Teacher
LAKEVIEW
Parkinson, Jerry Lee
High School Math Teacher
Robertson, Dennis Michael
Mathematics Teacher
Sazama, David E.
Industrial Education Teacher
Steninger, Barbara J.
PE & Sports Medicine Teacher
Stratton, Lane Haught
Mathematics Teacher
LEBANON
Buglione, Joseph W.
Math Teacher
Deacon, Terence Pyne
9th-12th Grd Science Teacher
Edwards, Debbie Carlson
Humanities & Drama Teacher
Harbeck, William Loyd
Computer Teacher
Johnson-Miller, Kim
Director of Bands
Kirk-Davalt, Susan
Elementary School Teacher
Knapp, Gloria Buchfink
Health Teacher
Krebs, Tracy Alan
Dir of Bands & Soc Stud Tchr
Rose, Kirk Anthony
Health & Computer Science Tchr
Scott, Vanda A.
Second Grade Teacher
Seward, Alaine Jody (Almon)
Language Arts Teacher
Shanks, Rodney Allen
Substitute Teacher

LEBANON (cont)
Steele, Penny Jane
Science & Math Teacher
LINCOLN CITY
Ballas, Barbara Butler
Sixth Grade Teacher
Kinney, Richard Douglas
English Teacher
Phelps, David Gayton
Vice Principal
Willoughby, Caren Darlene
Fourth Grade Teacher
MADRAS
Griffith, Phyllis Knight
Middle School Counselor
Henry, Matthew Steven
Economic, Civics & Ldrshp Tchr
Rankin, Steven Clyde
Govt, Politics & Geog Tchr
MARCOLA
Joll, Thomas W.
Social Science Teacher
MARYLHURST
Haek, John B.
Music Instructor
MAUPIN
Wong, Sandra
Math Teacher & Dept Chprsn
MCMINNVILLE
Beyer, Katherine L.
English Teacher
Cahill, Michael Linn
US History & Economics Teacher
Cooper, Marilyn Louise
Elem School Music Specialist
Cooper, Steve Wayne
Science Teacher
Crafton, Daniel Joe
Global & American Studies Tchr
Karlin, Billie L.
5th Grade Teacher
Lay, Patrick Alan
High School Band Director
Libonati, Dana
Choral Director & Music Tchr
Nesland, Larry V.
Math Teacher
Schalock, Monica O'Keefe
8th Grade Language Arts Tchr
MEDFORD
Applen, Jayne P.
Third Grade Teacher
Bloomquist, Todd Paul
English Teacher
Bourne, Judith Elaine
Kindergarten Teacher
Burrelle, Ralph W.
Guid Cnslr & English Teacher
Freeman, J. Dean
Senior Economics Teacher
Gregg, Terry Dale
PE Teacher & Athletic Director
Jager, Micheal Dean
US His Instr & At Risk Coord
King, Anne Elizabeth
Sixth Grade Teacher
Porter, Gary James
Social Studies Teacher
Reed, Ronald R.
History & Geography Teacher
Reese, Robert Roy
Fifth Grade Teacher
Schulz, Lisa Lynn
Spanish Teacher
Shellem, Bernie
Biology Teacher
Steinhardt, Linda Nash
Sixth Grade Teacher
Sullivan, Rebecca Ann
Third Grade Teacher
Warren, Sean Patrick
Vocal Music Teacher
MERRILL
Dalton, Gary Lee
Soc Stud & Economics Tchr
Duncan, Dan Wayne
Reading Lab & Lifeskills Tchr
MILTON FREEWATER
Agidius, Michael Gregory
Band Director
Doherty, Nancy C.
4th Grade Teacher
Grigg, Colleen Kay (Ott)
Biology & Math Teacher
MILWAUKIE
Cole, Marjalee
4th & 5th Grade Teacher
Hazel, Teresa F.
Chemistry & Physics Teacher
Johnson, Susan D.
Counselor
O'Brien, Timothy Michael
German Teacher
Schroeder, Jeffrey Paul
Physical Ed & Leadership Tchr
Terhaar, Colleen Patricia
8th Grd Soc Stud & Eng Teacher
MOLALLA
Friesen, Timothy Charles
Choral Director
Miller-Moore, Linda Kay
Seventh Grade Teacher
MONMOUTH
Lushenko, Martha Susan
First Grade Teacher
MONROE
Henderson, Tresa
Science Teacher
MORO
Townsend, Ron E.
Health & Algebra Teacher
VanGilder, Janet Pinkerton
French, English & Spanish Tchr
MOUNT ANGEL
Jones, Andrew James
Hlth & Physical Education Tchr
Russell, Janet Eyre
Language Arts Teacher
MYRTLE CREEK
Harbaugh, Patricia Susan
Life Science Teacher
Kuk, Mary Halvorson
Health Studies Teacher
NEWBERG
Bauman, Kathy Antrim
Teacher & Asst Principal
Beebe, Ralph Kenneth
Professor of History
Halstead, Decker John Edward
World History & Geography Tchr
Halstead, Karlene Ruth
Fifth Grade Teacher
Irish, Kerry Eugene
Assistant Professor of History
Koch, Christopher
Psychology Professor
Lynott, Tom J.
Guidance Counselor
Nissen, Jacalyn Marie
7th-8th Grade Math Teacher
Orkney, George Dale
Professor of Biology
Phillips, Ken A.
HS Science Tchr & Dept Chair
Roid, Gale Harold
Psychology Professor
Sherrill, Sherie L.
English Instructor
NEWPORT
Bartlow, Jon
Counselor
Dempster, David
Math & Computer Teacher
Giuliani, Nancy
Language Arts Teacher
Hargett, Kurt Dale
Anatomy & Physiology Teacher
Harrington, John Patrick
English Teacher
Montgomery, Brian John
Chem, Physics & Astronomy Tchr
Stater, Susan Kennedy
English & Speech Teacher
Werner, Trisha Ann
Teacher
NORTH BEND
Crueger, Jeffrey Richard
Choral Director
Kent, Therese Reilly
Bus & Alternative Lrnng Tchr
Olson, John Fjelde
Mathematics Teacher
Younker, Diana Allado
Jr HS Math & English Teacher
Younker, Thomas Henry
HS PE Teacher & Coach
NYSSA
Ball, Kenneth R.
HS Health Education Instr
Bullock, Barbara Stafford
Language Arts Teacher
Pankey, Wendy Sue (Randolph)
English & Drama Teacher
OAKLAND
Clark, Jeffrey Edward
US His, Prsnl Fin & Govt Tchr
OAKRIDGE
Gardner, Regina A.
History, Personal Finance Tchr
Hampton, Judith Bramhall
Vice Principal
ONTARIO
Berry, Gregory Wayne
English & Drama Instructor
Gaskill, John W.
Social Studies Teacher
Linegar, Les Lawrance
Agriculture Teacher
Moss, Meg
Mathematics Instructor
Parsons, Dave C.
Health & Physical Ed Teacher
Robertson, Marliss Paine
Second Grade Teacher
Seward, Dean
3rd Grade Teacher
Stringer, William Mark
Soc Sci & Lang Arts Teacher
Susuki, Larry S.
Math Teacher
Trenkel, Patricia M.
Head Counselor
Willison-Boyd, Tobi Marie
6th Grade Teacher
OREGON CITY
Darris, Dean M.
Political Science Professor
Espino, Richard
Anatomy & Physiology Instr
Fullerton, Cheryl Hattan
Third Grade Teacher
Hobart, Roxie Ellen
Business Instr & Controller
Hockett, Eloise Withrow
Music Teacher
John, Leland Louis
Art Instructor
McCorkle, Garry Dean
Math Teacher
Peck, Kathleen E.
Substitute Teacher
Salisbury, John E.
7th-8th Grd Soc Stud Teacher
Saqueton, Medy Cajulis
Mathematics Instructor
PACIFIC CITY
Rissel, Sally Anne (Higgins)
Consultant
PENDLETON
Charlton, Marla Maria Phelps
9th Grade English Teacher
Gundlach, Janis Fassler
5th Grade Teacher
Jones, Sam D.
Career Teacher
Peterson, Jon Arthur
Guidance Counselor
West, Charles Timothy
Math Teacher
Zoske, Natalie
Secondary Teacher
PHILOMATH
Kinman, Gary W.
Marketing Teacher
Rybel, Theresa
4th Grade Teacher
PHOENIX
Frey, Ralph
Teacher
Hagler, Joseph Dee
9th-12th Grd Health & PE Tchr
Murakami, Atsuko
Japanese Teacher
Walker, Kyle Kenneth
Math & Advanced PE Teacher
Wolfe, Mark Abraham
Social Studies Teacher
PILOT ROCK
Braniff, William J.
Mathematics Teacher
Sherman, Edward Joseph
High School Principal
PLEASANT HILL
Kennedy, Thomas Carl
5th & 6th Grade Teacher
King, April Cummings
Computer & Home Ec Teacher
Roberts, Marcia D. Fellows
Language Arts & Religion Tchr
Wiggins, Michael Glynn
Music & Psychology Teacher
PORTLAND
Adams, Nadene Elizabeth
Home Ec & Language Arts Tchr
Aleckson, Sharon Ann
Third Grade Teacher
Allen, Alice S.
French Teacher & Lang Dept Chm
Arend, Thomas Fredrick
Social Studies Teacher
Arwood, Ellyn Lucas
Education Professor
Barnes, Deborah Claudia
Telecommunications Instructor
Barr, Pat Ann (Walker)
Language Arts & Jrnlsm Tchr
Barton, Sharon Kaiser
Retired Elem Teacher
Battles, Stephen Thayer
5th Grade Teacher
Beck, Gary Howard
Engrng, Drafting Instr & Chm
Berdahl, Angela Arnoldi
English Professor
Berlureau, Ann Linder
Mathematics Teacher
Betts, Jeffrey C.
Band Director
Bevington, Marisa Baragli
Spanish Teacher
Bingenheimer, Virginia Liebertz
Third Grade Teacher
Bock, Peter Lindley
English Teacher
Bolduan, Michael
Mathematics Teacher
Bond, Wendy L.
School Age Coordinator
Brace, B. Fred
Science & Physics Teacher
Bradburn-Ruster, Michael John
Visiting Prof of Span & Hum
Brandel, Judith A.
Art & Photography Teacher
Brenner, Joan Lamb
English & Humanities Teacher
Brooks, Joe B.
Junior High Teacher
Browning, Andrew Holt
Humanities, American Stud Tchr
Button, Jerry E.
Professor of Biology
Campbell, Kimberly Hill
High School Principal
Cardinalli, Michael Anthony
Bible, Eng Teacher & Vice Prin
Casurella, Anthony
New Testament Prof & Minister
Chamberlain, Michael Len
Assistant Principal
Chizum, Susan Reese
5th Grade Teacher
Cole, Elizabeth Betsy
Curriculum Vice Principal
Coleman, Joy F.
Latin, Eng & His Teacher
Coles, Francis Robert
Social Studies Teacher
Conine, David Arvyn
Chemistry Teacher
Culbertson, David Mark
ESL Teacher
Davis, Randolph Faller
English Teacher
DeKlotz, Erin Willis
Spanish & English Teacher
Dellerba, David
Activities Director
De Shaw, Michele
Honors American Studies Tchr
Dowd, Carolyn Sellers
English Teacher & Dept Chair
Dukart-Sherwood, Lynette
Middle School Teacher
Dumas, Michelle Annette
High School Science Teacher
Dyal, James G.
Law, Pub Svc & Soc Stud Tchr
Eames, Jean Sang
Science Instructor
Elliott, Anna Louie
Art Tchr & Apparel Desgn Instr
Fazio, John A.
Prof of Developmental Pysch
Fong, Bruce William
Assoc Prof of Bible
Ford, MaryLynn Ramstad
Elem Schl Teacher
Francis, Frank John
6th Grade Teacher
Gebron, Julie
Freelance Sign Lang Interprtr
Geddis, Cheryl Ann
3rd & 4th Grade Teacher
Gould, Arthur Wayne
8th Grade Mathematics Teacher
Hampton, Margaret Hesse
6th Grade Teacher
Hansen, Karin Elizabeth
FSA Business Teacher
Hart, Harold Canfield
Civics & Law-Related Ed Tchr
Hartness-Reichle, Alice
6th Grd Classroom Tchr
Heppner, Gregg
Biology Teacher
Hinds, Gary Everett
High School Science Teacher
Hoddick, Jill Peterson
Assoc Prof of Theatre
Hong, Lisa J.
Language Arts & Jrnlsm Tchr
Honl, Rosemary Phillips
PE Teacher & Volleyball Coach
Johnson, Dawn Schnibbe
PE, Hlth & Global Stud Teacher
Johnson, Gordon Merle
Industrial Ed Teacher
Johnson, Jeanne Marie
Middle School Educator
Karaman, Kimberly A.
Mathematics Educator
Kashuba, Barbara
ESL Teacher
Keating, Paul B.
English Teacher & Dept Chair
Kelly, Rick C.
Marketing Teacher
Kimsey, Christian
Former School Counselor
Koby, Frank Mark
Social Studies Teacher
Kohlmeier, Kamala Lynn
HS Health, PE Tchr & Coach
Kottkamp, Carrie Joan
Lang Arts & Soc Studies Tchr
LaFayette, Clara Watson
Lang Arts & Soc Stud Teacher
Landsdorf, Vaughn Guthrie
Math Teacher
Lawson, Larry George
History Teacher
Lesch, Jerry I.
Drama Teacher
Lockwood, Daniel Ralph
VP, Dean & Prof of Theology
Looney, Susan Fancher
Third Grade Teacher
Looney, Walter Gilbert
Mathematics Teacher
Lorenz, Carol
Middle School Teacher
Maloney, Katherine Elaine
Fifth Grade Teacher
Mandis, Bill G.
Language Arts Teacher
Martin, Janet L.
English Teacher
Martin, Nancy Prestwood
Mathematics Teacher
McCarthy, Annie Cuddington
Fifth Grade Teacher
McCusker, Patrick J.
Global Stud, His & Ed Tchr
McDonald, Connie Mae
Interdisciplinary Teacher
Mc Dowell, Michael J.
Instructor
Mc Kinney, Lawrence Frederick
English Teacher
Melton, Rob
English & Journalism Teacher
Messina-Azekri, Mario Andres
Parole Investigator & Cnslr
Meyer, Karen Ann
Media Specialist
Monheimer, Paul W.
Computer Teacher
Morgansen, Gregory Glenn
Fifth Grade Teacher
Morten, Douglas L.
Fine Arts & Photograph Teacher
Morton, Frederick Allan
High School Teacher
Muncie, Martha Jo
Spanish Teacher
Navi, Pardis
Mathematics Teacher
Nelson, Leonard M., Jr.
History Instructor
Nicola, Karen E.
2nd Grade Teacher
Nielsen, Charles Emmet
Sociology Professor
Nuttall, Drayton G.
English as a Second Lang Tchr
Paradis, Ann, SNJM
Junior High School Teacher
Pedersen, Joyce (Williams)
English, Math & Basic Ed Tchr
Perkins, A. Wesley
Biology Teacher
Perry, Judith Ann (Roake)
Art Instructor
Powell, Joan Edwards
Jr-Sr Lit & Comp Teacher
Proffitt, Monette K.
Retired 7th Grade Sci Teacher
Ramsey, Melanie
Science Electives Teacher
Reisig, Ray David
7th Grade Teacher
Relampagos, Ismael
Science Teacher
Robbins, David G.
English Teacher
Rogers, Donald H.
PE Teacher & Football Coach
Romanos, Vickie Veltman
High School Spanish Teacher
St Clair-Thomas, Melissa Jo
Dance Teacher
Sauer, Bob
Science Teacher
Schattenberg, Herman F.
Frosh & Jr HS English Tchr
Scheffler, Larry James
Chemistry Teacher
Scott, Stanley
Health Teacher
Setterholm, Suzanne Lee
PE & Hlth Tchr & Yrbk Adv
Shaw, Susan M.
Director of HIV Center
Sheedy, Maureen Mellda
Night School Teacher
Sibley, Stacey Sutherland
Special Education Teacher
Siebold, Kent Donald
English Teacher
Siegel, Allan Michael
Eighth Grade Teacher
Sindmack, Katheryne SChodrof
Assistant Professor
Smith, Judith Ann
8th Grade Teacher
Smythe, Ray M.
History Teacher
Sollars, Sherri Marie
Marketing & Accounting Teacher
Solomon, Gene Barry
Social Science Teacher
Staatz, Ann D.
Professor of Journalism
Straw, Mike
8th Grd Lang Arts & His Tchr
Stross, Barbara
High School Teacher
Swanson, Muriel Breyer
Special Education Assistant
Taiby, Laura Diane
Kindergarten Teacher
Takamura, Ted Jiro
Business & Accounting Prof
Thompson, George Murray
High School Counselor
Thurman, Richard Scott
English Teacher
Tidwell, Richard K.
Fifth Grade Teacher
VanHatcher, Karen Annette
Fifth Grade Teacher
Verlo, Terrence Allen
Biology & Chemistry Teacher
Vogel, Michael C.
Physical Education Specialist
Wald, Roberta Rygh
Microbiology Professor
Wallulis, G. Paul
German Tchr & Math Dept Head
Warner, Marlin Robert
Mathematics Teacher
Wells, Kelly Thor
English Teacher
Wood, Maryann Gilbaugh
5th Grade Teacher
PRAIRIE CITY
Isley, Irene Nadine
Language Arts Teacher
PRINEVILLE
Phay, Richard V.
Social Studies Teacher
RAINIER
Davies, Pamela Dee Siestreem
Third Grade Teacher

IER (cont)
an, Jean Vanover
ish Teacher
gan, David Bruce
al Studies Teacher
on, Len Warren
nology Education Teacher
IOND
el, Mary Damson
3rd Grade Teacher
teven H.
d Grade Teacher
ren, Nanaline J.
red 6th Grade Teacher
heim, Marc Douglas
Grade Teacher
, Linda Kliewer
ner Teacher
nter, Terry J.
d Grade Teacher
e, Patricia Clabaugh
ily & Consumer Stud Tchr
e, William Clark
al Studies Teacher
, Michael L.
nce Teacher
ni, Ted F.
cultural Science Teacher
nblast, Gail L. (Bieker)
& 8th Grade English Tchr
SPORT
Karol (Hodge)
d Grade Teacher
Linda Dailey
& 2nd Grade Teacher
, Harvard Steve
n Grade Teacher
LE
, Ralph Michael
nce Teacher
son, Karyn D.
n School Substitute Tchr
KAWAY BEACH
hy, Richard James
Language Arts Instructor
m, G. Todd
nish & German Teacher
UE RIVER
s, Floyd Wayne
& Drivers Ed Teacher
s, James Roy
US History Teacher
EBURG
, Leonard Thomas
sics, Chem & Gen Sci Tchr
, Barbara Johnson
Career Ed & Psych Tchr
David Roald
h Grade Teacher
illa, John Anthony
d Director
, R. Dale
mistry Dept Chairman & Prof
er, Kelly Cooper
ructor
r, Richard A.
ir, Speech & Drama Teacher
ams, Diane Stevens
ting & Journalism Professor
, Kelly Pat
hematics Instructor
g, Jeffrey Dean
d Director
s, Nita V.
lish Tchr & Bell Choir Dir
T HELENS
, David Allen
Grade Teacher
ger, Rebecca L.
ired Math & German Tchr
EM
ns, Dale E.
emistry & Biology Teacher
rson, Holly Mann
nmunity College Instructor
Merrily Daniels
arth Grade Teacher
nen, Jeffrey Leonard
ence & Math Teacher
hy, John C.
d Counselor
s, Raymond
fessor
en, Randy Craig
nguage Arts & Math Teacher
les, Charles Joseph
ck & Cross Country Coach
ks, Gail L.
anish Teacher
l, Gregory Lowell
glish & Writing Professor
n, Gary Lee
tivities Dir & Teacher
hart, Ronald Lee
st Principal & English Tchr
eel, Pam Corinne (Pillette)
glish & SS Teacher
rio, Gary W.
cial Studies Teacher
rio, Joni Linn
sistant Principal
ey, James S.
ology Teacher
cker, Kasey Lynn
glish & Drama Teacher
ter, Joan Elizabeth
glish Teacher & Dept Coord
er, Lynn Charles
Teacher

Gann, Jeaneen L.
Instructional Ldr, Math Chprsn
Goldstein, Andrew F.
Environmental Issues Teacher
Hawkins, Dan Clarence
Head Football Coach
Heer, Robert D.
Science Teacher
Herinckx, Karen Wilmes
Eighth Grade English Teacher
Hill, Nancy Atkins
5th Grade Teacher
Hire, Douglas J.
PE & Math Teacher
House, Shirley Ricks
Retired Teacher
Hughes, Wesley Eugene
Social Studies Teacher
Hull, Gary Dean
PE, Health & Careers Ed Tchr
Johnson, Lesley Lynn
2nd Grade Teacher
Kawmura, Jon Kojiro
Math Teacher
Klein, Virginia Gray
Kindergarten Teacher
Lampert, Michael S.
Physics Teacher
Lang, Lynnette J.
4th Grade Teacher
Lindersmith, Lara C.
Language Arts & ESL Teacher
Long, Wallace Harris, Jr.
Music Dept Chair & Choral Dir
Mc Intosh, Valerie Meacham
Assistant Professor of Music
Moss, Patricia Graves
Spanish Teacher
Nowlen, Nancianne
3rd Grade Teacher
Olson, Darrol K.
Computer Teacher
Owens, Mary Ellen Byford
Fourth Grade Teacher
Perez, Laura Lynette
Math Teacher
Phillips, Sally Adams
6th-8th Grade Teacher
Read, Russell A.
Life Science Instructor
Rodin, Philip Craig
Math Teacher
Sage, Cynthia Lynn
Band Director
Slack, Kenneth Alan
American Government Teacher
Steiner, Jon A.
French Teacher
Terhes, John Stephen
Instructor
Terry, Mark E.
Art Teacher
Thex, Alberta Hughes
Substitute Teacher
Vellutini, Jerry Ernest
Strength & Conditioning Coach
Vohland, Janet Miniaci
College Student Health Nurse
Vohland, Wallace Ross
Principal
Vollmar, Valerie
Professor of Law
Walsh, Michael John
Elementary Teacher
Walsh, Patrick Allen
Health Occupations Instructor
Wetle, Victoria Lee
Pgm Chair of Hlth Svcs Mngmt
Worral-Poole, Linda Farr
Art History & Art Teacher
Zacharias, Patricia Ann
Health Svcs Mgmt Instr & Adv
Zolkoske, Gary
Manufacturing Engrg Tech Instr
SANDY
Anderson, LeRoy Hartley
Band Director
Ball, Byron Wilbert
Biology Teacher
Brisbin, Daniel L.
Anatomy & Physiology Teacher
Drew, Kress Gregg
Mathematics Teacher
Harris, Chris G.
Drama Instructor
Heflin, Gloria Jeanne
Fourth Grade Teacher
Mc Queen, Doris Norman
Retired First Grade Teacher
Moffitt, Lila Marie
Composition & Voc Eng Teacher
Olson, Donald Berdean, Jr.
Computer Literacy Instructor
Scarth, Bruce Worden
Choral Music Director
Schuhl, Jonathan Michael
Language Arts Teacher
SCAPPOOSE
Kimes, Mark Loren
Choir & Band Teacher
Phillips, Myrna L.
English Teacher
Rees, Ed C.
HS Counselor & Asst Coach
SCIO
Harms, James Albert
MS Social Studies Teacher
Priest, Corinne Sue
5th Grade Teacher

SEASIDE
Dickson, Richard Joel
Bands Director
Knutson, Carol Elizabeth
English Teacher
SILETZ
Ross, Joanne Gorman
Second Grade Teacher
SILVER LAKE
Mead, Darla
Music Teacher
Short, Walter Wayne
Social Studies Teacher
SILVERTON
Bruns, Wilfried H. J.
Retired Teacher
Fox, Pamela
French, English & Spanish Tchr
Hachler, Eloise Deanne
3rd Grade Teacher
Hazekamp, Patricia Costello
Art & Drama Teacher
Jenkins, Douglas Paul
Third Grade Teacher
Lowery, Judith Johnson
4th Grade Teacher
Mc Cartney, Chadwick Gerald
Physics & Physical Sci Teacher
Rasmussen, Cheri Hoppes
Math & Computers Teacher
Robinson, Robby L.
College Writing Instructor
Rogers, Robert Lucky
Math Teacher
Scott, Patrick Mc Callie
Physical Education Teacher
Teeney, Jill Turner
English Teacher
Todd, Larry Leonard
Earth Studies Teacher
Zade, Doug
Science Teacher
SISTERS
Lindahl, Dennis Leroy
Music Teacher
SPRAY
Sherman, Steven Edward
Soc Stud & Cmptr Sci Tchr
SPRINGFIELD
Baker, Edith Madean
Counselor
Case, Robert Stewart, Jr.
Industrial Technology Teacher
Caulley, Kathleen Bullock
Second & Third Grade Teacher
Dixon, Ronald Dean
Fourth Grade Teacher
Elkington, Grant C.
Fine Arts Chair & Band Dir
Fountain, Ronald William
High School Counselor
Gerhardt, Suzanne Lesley
Social Stud & Lang Arts Tchr
Gienger, Connie Hales
Kindergarten Teacher
Gray, Roy C.
Health Teacher
Halupa, Paul Robert
Language Arts Teacher
Lively, Tresa Brotherton
Fifth Grade Teacher
Mann, Joanne Louise
Fourth Grade Teacher
Mason, Terri Fries
4th-5th Grade Teacher
Moore, Carol Marie Smith
3rd Grade Teacher
O'Donnell, Diane Rae
Teacher
Perkins, Karen Irene
Art & Ceramics Teacher
Roberts, Barbara Jensen
2nd Grade Teacher
Roderick, Roma Durfey
Fifth Grade Teacher
Saunders, Pamela
English Teacher
Smith, William Alan
Social Studies Teacher
Sundahl, Sheila J.
Language Arts Teacher
Tubbs, Jerome Perry
5th Grade Teacher
Wenger, Diane Berry
Sixth Grade Teacher
Willis, Linda Shoemaker
High School English Instructor
STAYTON
Conley, Brunk Wesley
Physics & Chemistry Teacher
Heli, Steven
Science Teacher
SUBLIMITY
Lulay, John Douglas
Lang Arts & Social Stud Tchr
Smith, Trycia Lynn
7th-8th Grade Teacher
SUNRIVER
Miller, Lois Millicent Moss
Retired Headmistress & Teacher
SUTHERLIN
Croft, Saralee Bosacci
Family & Consumer Studies Tchr
TALENT
Bishop-Stratton, Erin
Computer Specialist
Bursk, Cynthia Ann (Ryerson)
1st & 2nd Grade Teacher
Finkbiner, John Lee
Fifth Grade Teacher

Hudson, Janet M.
First Grade Teacher
Morkert, Stanley E.
Fourth Grade Teacher
Vann, C. Larry
Core Teacher
THE DALLES
Brockman, Robert A.
Math Teacher
Buchanan, Joseph Donald
Industrial Arts Teacher
Heath, Joanne Huffmon
Fourth Grade Teacher
Jenks, Colleen L.
English Teacher
Keller, Cherri Adams
Kindergarten Teacher
Orr, Susan K.
Art Teacher
Ressa, Mary
Mathematics & Spanish Tchr
Schoer, Denise
High School Guidance Counselor
Sutherland, Ronald Jay
Health & Physical Ed Instr
TIGARD
Baker, Susan
Activities Dir & Lead Tchr
Chasko, David W.
Social Studies Teacher
Daw, Lawrence Daniel
Theatre Arts Director
Hanson, Richard D.
High School Science Teacher
Lamb, William G.
Winningstad Chair in Phys Sci
Lutes, Nadine Ann
High School Science Teacher
McKemey, Suzanne Marie
3rd Grade Teacher
Moore, Terry Lee
Math Teacher
Mosher-Lewis, Dana
Spanish Teacher
Tolon, Michael Oded
Director of Bands
Wolf, Wendy
High School English Teacher
TILLAMOOK
Crowston, John Gordon
Retired Teacher
Gross, Joyce Thompson
Retired Teacher
Nash, Donna Kay
Business Education Teacher
Rouse, Shannon Lee
6th Grade Teacher
Varner, Linda S.
8th Grd Language Arts Teacher
TOLEDO
Gilmont, Rose Marie (Sinsel)
Retired 1st Grade Teacher
TRAIL
Birdseye, Sheri Dawn
Second Grade Teacher
TROUTDALE
Beaman, Tom
Social Studies Teacher
Klotter, Kristin Schleich
Social Studies Teacher
Osborne, Teresa Squires
Social Studies Teacher
Stites, Ed
English Teacher
TUALATIN
Brinkman, Sandi Marie
High School English Teacher
Darr, Byron Craig
Art Teacher
Finigan, Jack F.
Career Education Teacher
Fox, Lisa Twietmeyer
Fifth Grade Teacher
Langer, Pamela Ann
4th-5th Grade Teacher
Spencer, Margaret Kent
English Teacher
Weber, Donald G.
Science Teacher
TURNER
Colby, Suzanne Aileen
Health Teacher
Deedon, Darrel Marvin
Amer Govt & US His Teacher
Jenkins, Jay
Economics & Leadership Teacher
Polacek, Matthew Francis
Instrumental Music Teacher
Reinhardt, Robert Norman
Marketing & Business Educator
UKIAH
Barber, Norma Jensen
Language Arts Teacher
UMATILLA
Fedde, Steven A.
Math Teacher
Tracy, Raymond E.
Language Arts & Civics Tchr
VALE
Standage, Mary Ann Lindley
Health Education Teacher
WALLOWA
Emmons, Dawn Crow
Counselor & Business Teacher
WARREN
Pillar, Donald Ray
Retired Jr HS Counselor
WARRENTON
Hill, Lesa Noel
4th-5th Grade Multi-Age Tchr

Wolfe, Lennie Steven
English Teacher
WASCO
Durnin, Charles Lewis
Asst Superintendent & Prin
Smith, Susan Rae
First Grade Teacher
WELCHES
Well, Tom
Physical Education Teacher
WEST LINN
Couturier, Stacey
3rd Grade Teacher
Dearborn, Tana Marie Sparks
Chemistry Instructor
Druse, Anna Baiocco
English Teacher
Eby, Arden L.
AP European History Teacher
Mitchell, Marybeth Merwin
5th Grade Teacher
Mussell, Alan Edward
Former Math Teacher
Samarron, Douglas Lee
Science Teacher
Sherman, Paul Evan
Biology Teacher
Swearingen, Thomas L.
High School Counselor
Weaver, Cheri Pickens
Fourth & Fifth Grade Teacher
WESTON
Clark, Barbara Bainbridge
Special Education Coordinator
Cummings, Dave Lou
7th-8th Grd Soc Stud Teacher
WHITE CITY
Sparks, Jay Arlon
First & Second Grade Teacher
WILLAMINA
Peters, Julie Anne
Math & Science Teacher
WILSONVILLE
Woods, Daniel Lee
Eighth Grade Civics Teacher
WINSTON
Brown, Lawrence Walton
Choir Teacher
Chandler, Stephanie Thomas
Media Specialist
Lapp, Madaline Dee
Math Teacher & Dept Chairman
Lapp, William K.
English Teacher
Warren, William Kenneth
Cmptr Drftng, Engrng Tech Tchr
WOLF CREEK
Volenski, Mary Rae Slater
K-2nd Grade Teacher
WOODBURN
Browder, Patricia Jo
Teacher
Cooper, Laurie Zauner
HS English & Speech Teacher
Dunning, Dennis Michael
Science & Math Teacher
Fox, Maureen A.
7th-8th Grd Math Teacher
Jackson, Tracy W.
Teacher & Head Football Coach
YAMHILL
Harris, R. Ann
Kindergarten Teacher
Johnston, James
Language Arts & Drama Tchr
Petrovich, Olga Kachin
English Teacher
YONCALLA
Derbyshire, Thomas R.
Sixth Grade Teacher
Inouye, David John
Social Studies Teacher
Ruzicka-Simons, Cheryl Lynn
Math Teacher
Simons, Cheryl Ruzicka
Math Teacher

PENNSYLVANIA

ABINGTON
Baxter, Shirley Nelson
Former Teacher
Cross, Dee Fichter
LaCrosse Coach
Emely-Roach, Jane Kathryn
English Chairperson
Garcia-Esteban, Fernando
Spanish Teacher
Hanlon, Teresa Vetrulli
Sixth Grade Teacher
Maltese, Ralph
High School Teacher
Marmon, Jeffrey D.
Guidance Counselor
Petersen, Julianne Elizabeth
Social Studies Teacher
Ryan, Marlena Catherine
Seventh Grade English Teacher
Shapiro, Sheila Aronson
Spanish Teacher
Shovlin, Gerald
English Teacher
ACME
Boggs, Brenda Lee (Kaiser)
His, Bio & Accounting Teacher
Johns, Doris E.
Math Teacher

ACME (cont)
Johnston, Joy Buterbaugh
Music Teacher
ALBION
Evanoff, Mark L.
Visual Communications Teacher
McCalmon, Donald A.
English & Drama Teacher
Sampson, Virginia Jane
Counselor & French Teacher
ALDAN
Johnson, Francine Porter
Second Grade Teacher
ALEXANDRIA
Espy, Barbara McCloskey
English & Speech Teacher
ALIQUIPPA
Alaica, Joanne Bufalini
9th-10th Grade English Teacher
Aquino, Christine Aloi
Sixth Grade Teacher
Castagna, Robert Charles
Math Tchr & Athletic Dir
Cramer, David James
Biology Teacher
Dattilo, Monica K.
English Teacher
Davie, Lois Lemmon
K-Jr HS Substitute Teacher
Demko, Joseph Andrew
Science Teacher
Dran, Kathleen Anderson
English Teacher
Dreshman-Chiodo, Janice
Prevention Specialist
Drevna, Dennis John
Industrial Arts & Tech Ed Tchr
Dufalla, Rosetta Volpe
English Teacher & Dept Chm
Falloretta, Charles A.
Fourth Grade Teacher
Faulkner, Sandra
Title I Coordinator
Fuller, Hope Toliver
Mathematics Teacher
Galasso, Nancy Hankins
Jr High Art Tchr & Dept Chprsn
Haushalter, Susan M.
First Grade Teacher
Longo, Vito Anthony
French Teacher
Masley, Sue Veri
Sr HS Art Teacher
Mason, Garry R., II
Physics & Chemistry Teacher
Mendenhall, Jack Leonardo, Jr.
Biology Teacher
Messner, Carol
Sixth Grade Teacher
Miller, Nancy S.
Music Teacher
Morris, Sonya Krainin
Fifth Grade Teacher
Pierce, Richard James
Honors English Teacher
Schuller, Linda K.
German Teacher
Scursatone, Joyce Maravich
Business Teacher
Shevchik, Stephanie S.
Drama Teacher
Turkovich, Donald H.
Physical Education Teacher
Weatherholt, Rose Marie (Hryhorchok)
Former Sci Tchr
Welsh, Sharon Steiner
Mathematics Teacher
Wojtkowski, Robert S.
Social Studies Dept Chm & Tchr
Zaccari, Judith Mc Farland
Fourth Grade Teacher
ALLENTOWN
Ackley, James Rittew
Social Studies Teacher
Bachman, Sandra J.
2nd Grade Teacher
Barrett, Yvonne Atiyeh
Fourth Grade Teacher
Borland, Stephen Arthur
Naval Science Teacher
Brady, Patrick Martin
General Music Teacher
Brommer, Wanda Marshall
French Teacher
Brunner, Regina Baron
Assoc Prof Math & Comp Sci
Bryant, Thomas Mark
Jr High Science Teacher
Cary, Paul Francis
Electronics Technology Teacher
Crouthamel, Jane Maria
3rd Grade Teacher
Crush, Henry Kenneth
Mathematics Teacher
Davidson-Roth, Judith Ann
Spanish & ESOL Teacher
Egolf, Robert H.
English Teacher & Curr Coord
Englund, Gail Buttler
Social Studies Teacher
Ernst, Joanne
Reading Consultant
Finizzi, Marguerite Martin
English Teacher
Firestone, David Frederic
AP Studio Art Teacher
Gasdaska, William George
Biology Teacher
Gebey, Jane Wilson
6th Grade Teacher
Gessler, Christopher L.
Accounting Teacher
Glazier, Rhoda Raab
English Teacher
Groller, Richard J.
Band Director & Asst Principal
Hartman, Bryan G.
Chemistry Teacher
Hathaway, Sandra Deppen
Math Teacher
Heidrich-Strohl, Charlene Williams
9th Grade English Teacher
Howe, Judith Yoder
English Teacher & Dept Chprsn
Hunter, Colleen F.
English Department Chair
Kachmar, Stephen, Jr.
Fourth Grade Teacher
Kelly, Nadia S.
English Teacher
Kidd-Jenny, Elizabeth Coblentz
Language Arts & History Tchr
Klotz, Patricia Ann
8th Grade Teacher
Krause, Mike John
Administrative Intern
Kurcz, Mary Ann Herbal
Science Teacher
Kurtz, Anne Babin
7th Grd Social Studies Teacher
Lakatosh, Debra
Spanish Teacher
Mc Gouldrick, Francis Joseph
Mathematics Tchr & Dept Chair
McGurrin, Sandra Hrapsky
Mathematics Teacher
Mikovich, Theodore
Sixth Grade Teacher
Miller, Susan E.
Cnslr & Stu Assistance Coord
Monahan, Rita Dolores, OV
Secondary Theology Teacher
Muniz, Raymond C.
English Teacher
Neuman, Jerald
Mathematics Teacher
Newkirk-Squire, Sheila D.
Secondary Special Ed Teacher
O'Neill, Jane Scharle
Chemistry Teacher
Porter, Peter
Chemistry & Physics Instructor
Psathas, Barbara (Bennett)
English Teacher
Reeder, Patricia Ann
First Grade Teacher
Reigel, Russell H.
Science Teacher
Rosenberger, Scott Edward
Science Teacher
Roth, Richard C.
Ninth Grade Math Tchr
Siegle, Mary Ann
Fifth Grade Teacher
Simpson, Rosemary
English & Journalism Teacher
Sproul, Maureen S.
Spanish Teacher
Stevens, Anita Altieri
5th Grade Teacher
Stewart, Paul Michael
Health & PE Teacher
Stimmel, Kathleen McFadden
Bus Ed Dept Chprsn & Teacher
Stinebaugh, Marilyn Madison
9th Grade English Teacher
Tannery, Charles N., Jr.
7th Grade English Teacher
Valent, Paul M.
Chemistry Teacher
Walker, Larry Ernest
Science Teacher
Wetherhold, Renee Cruckenmiller
6th Grade Teacher
Wildonger, David Martin
Physical Education Teacher
Wotring, Timothy J.
Social Studies Teacher
Young, Bruce Alan
Mathematics Teacher
ALLENWOOD
Riddell, Harry W.
Teacher
ALLISON PARK
Adams, M. Diane
French & Spanish Teacher
Beckwith, Susanne Evelyn
Second Grade Teacher
Bumbernick, Benigna, CDP
Retired Teacher
Durrant, Sally Hoffman
Honors Political Sci Teacher
Ellena-Wygonik, Mary Louise
English Teacher
Konig, Janet Ann
French Teacher
Torchia, Thomas Anthony
Mathematics Teacher
Werger, Bridget Susan
Second Grade Teacher
ALTOONA
Ansman, Marjorie Ellen (Bare)
Retired Teacher
Appleman, Mary Lou (Tomlinson)
German Teacher
Bartek, Timothy Allen
Industrial Electricity Instr
Berardinelli, Barbara Kepner
Chemistry Teacher
Bohn, Vida Goodman
Retired Teacher
Brown, Alan D.
Third Grade Teacher
Brown, Katrina Seidel
English Teacher
Conners, Betty A.
English Teacher
Cooper, Gerald Lee
Math Teacher
Crocker, Stuart
Chemistry & Computer Teacher
Frank, Stephen Eugene
Mathematics Teacher
Green, Doris Jean
Academic Chemistry Teacher
Helsel, Melanie Collins
Social Studies Teacher
Hoyer, Kristina Krstulich
English & Writing Teacher
Hugg, C. Frances Berman
Secondary Social Studies Tchr
Huschak, Irene Timura
Technologies-Software Dev Tchr
Johnston, Christine
Business Education Teacher
Jones, Evelyn (Shea)
Dept Chairperson & Eng Tchr
Kipp, Samuel James
Fifth Grade Teacher
Kopac, Paul Lewis
Gifted Program Specialist
Lanier, Robert Glenn
Biology Teacher
Long, Randall David
Eighth Grade Reading Teacher
Lowe, James Scott
History Teacher
Martin, Kent Adam
Instrumental Music Teacher
Miller, Irma Jean
Teacher
Neely, Edna Loraine
English & Journalism Teacher
Stere, Athleen Jacobs
Associate Professor of Biology
Swartz, Beverly J. (Wray)
Child Care Specialist
Wilson, Steven Lynn
Soc Studies & English Teacher
Wolfe, Kristie (Beck)
English Teacher
Woomer, Muriel Faye
Fourth Grade Teacher
ALVERTON
Bowser, Harry Paul
Scndry World Cultures Teacher
Detore, Philip G.
Jr HS American History Teacher
Vance, Dolores Fricano
Spanish Teacher
Zamperini, Richard Louis
Band Director
AMBLER
Johnston, Christian Thomas
Mathematics Teacher
Kline, Richard Charles
District Supervisor
Marsh, Catherine Regan
Lit Tchr & Rdng Specialist
Romeu, Alicia H.
High School Spanish Teacher
Sabia, Michael G.
Mathematics Teacher
AMBRIDGE
Finnegan, Dawn Turney
Sixth Grade Teacher
Gilmore, Robert H.
HS American History Teacher
Hladio, Paul R.
Physics & Math Teacher
Kalervo, Angela DeFilippi
5th-8th Grd Teacher
Leonardo, Kristine K.
English Teacher
Sheffield, Charlotte Anne
English Social Studies Teacher
Thompson, Nancy Marie
Psychology Teacher
Yurfick, Joyce Szedny
Instruction Support Teacher
ANNVILLE
Dieffenbach, Jodie Walmer
Second Grade Teacher
Dimick, Mark S.
English Teacher
Enders, Mark Eugene
High School Spanish Teacher
Helock, James Kevin
Biology Teacher
Stocker, Bradley Dennis
Teacher of the Gifted
APOLLO
Mazanek, Patrick
Sixth Grade Teacher
Romito, Pamela Joanne
Third Grade Teacher
Rupert, Larry Joseph
Sixth Grade Teacher
ARCHBALD
Burns, Joyce A.
Sixth Grade Teacher
Grigalunas, Ann
English Teacher
Krempasky, Thomas Francis
Soc Studies Educator & Chprsn
Lacotta, Jerome Paul
Chemistry Teacher
Petorak, Janice M.
Sixth Grade Teacher
Pettigrew, Christopher Ross
Spanish & English Teacher
Wasilchak, Ann Cavagnard
Health & Phys Ed Teacher
ARDMORE
Betegh, Maryflor Sandra
Spanish Teacher
Brown, Mary Rita
Latin Teacher
Elliott, Thomas Henry
Instrumental Music Director
Erickson, Carrie Shuman
Spanish Teacher
Frey, Cecile Parris
Supvr of Gifted Support Prgm
Miller, Cynthia Mooney
English Teacher
Nelson, Judith Binner
French Teacher
Smith, LeVan Pretzman
Art Teacher & Coordinator
Stauffer, Robert J.
Mathematics Teacher
Wilk, Leon J.
English Teacher
ARMAGH
Cavanagh, Jacqueline Weltner
Eng, World Lit & Adv Comp Tchr
Colgan, Linda L.
7th Grd Language Arts Teacher
Dixon, Billie B.
Business Teacher
Gilbert, Timothy Paul
Senior Army Instructor
Horner, Barbara L.
Third Grade Teacher
Huston, Kathryn L.
Fifth Grade Teacher
Johnson, Carol Ann (Miller)
Fourth Grade Math Teacher
Mack, Sharon Leslie
First Grade Teacher
Meyer, Donna Bowser
Third Grade Teacher
Ofman, Ronald Joseph
Second Grade Teacher
Sexton, Patricia Strohmaier
Learning Support Teacher
Stumpf, Richard Dawson
Agriculture Teacher
Szelong, Richard Joseph
English Teacher & Yrbk Advisor
Verba, Rita K. (Zanaglio)
Learning Support Teacher
Whitcomb, Thomas W.
Chemistry Teacher
ASHLAND
Brown, Margaret Mary
English Teacher
Chesney, Robert Vincent
Social Studies Teacher
Cuff, Edward Thomas
Fourth Grade Teacher
Edwards, Richard L.
Social Studies Teacher & Coach
Hackenberg, Barry Miller
11th & 12th Grd Soc Stud Tchr
Koshuta, Anne Dougherty
Science Dept Chairperson
Lucas, Harry D.
English Teacher
Mitchell, Jacquelyn A.
Chem, Math & Phys Sci Tchr
Paul, Rodney George
Science Teacher
Yanuskiewicz, Bonnie Kaplan
English Instructor
ASTON
Boston, Martha Bibee
Psychologist & Adjunct Prof
Corso, Gail Shanley
Asst Prof Of Commnctn Arts
Given, Mac Fadden
Associate Professor of Biology
Grassano, Charles A.
Language Arts Teacher
Huke, Theresa Albany
Junior High English Teacher
Keegan, Julia M.
Associate Professor of Nursing
Kerezsi, Patricia Ann
Fourth Grade Teacher
Kovach, Claudia Marie
Professor of English & French
Kozlowski, Edward T.
Mathematics Teacher
Lumley, Jayne Peffer
Third Grade Teacher
Massey, Janet F.
Assistant Professor
Mc Coy, Mary Grove
Chemistry Associate Professor
Mc Henry, Nadine K.
Education Professor
Pesotski, Ronald Robert Peter
Social Studies Teacher
Sanchez, Ana Cristina
Spanish Teacher
Savitz, Fred Robert
Professor of Education
Weiss, Sandra Marano
Clinical Lab Sci Asst Prof
White, Karen Lee
Fifth Grade Teacher
ATGLEN
Beaton, Nancy Guercia
Science Teacher
Butcher, Nancy Jane
High School Language Teacher
Curiel, Judith
Spanish Teacher
Dull, Stanley Lynn
HS English Teacher
Fraker, Max T.
Mathematics Teacher
Fridy, Jere Wayne
Director of Music
Lapp, Wanda D. King
7th Grade Math Teacher
Mundy, Michael Francis
American History Teacher
ATHENS
Gabb, Philip Lawrence
Sixth Grade Teacher
Grego, Nicholas V.
Sixth Grade Teacher
Soprano, Kathleen Coombs
Math, Reading & Soc Stud Tchr
Tubbs, Stephen Walter
HS Soc Stud Tchr & Chprsn
Walters, Vicki Jordan
4th Grade Teacher
ATLANTIC
Murray, Thomas M.
Retired Music Teacher
ATLASBURG
Snyder, Carol Stanek
5th Grade Teacher
AUDUBON
Vermuth, Jeffrey Wayne
Fifth Grade Teacher
AUSTIN
Hurt, Roger A.
Social Studies Teacher
Shields, Sandra G.
English Teacher
AVELLA
Baur, Cheryl Ann
Secondary Mathematics Teacher
Blose, Ruth Elayne
Spanish & French Teacher
Dudas, Joseph J.
English & Language Arts Tchr
Kushner, William Alan
English Teacher
Repole, Sheila Katherine (Neate)
Social Studies Teacher
AVOCA
Puscavage, Deborah A. Scatena
Fifth Grade Reading Teacher
AVONDALE
Harriz, Margaret D.
Retired Adjunct Instructor
BADEN
Biskup, Susan Lynn
Chemistry & Physical Sci Tchr
Litzinger, Mary Jude, CSJ
Retired Teacher
Mc Kenna, Christine Ann
Secondary Mathematics Teacher
Mc Lane, Robert T.
Mathematics & Science Teacher
Van De Car, Nancy Shane
Third Grade Teacher
BALA CYNWYD
Cappalli, Paula Garganese
Eng & Creative Dramatics Tchr
Coyne, Mary
2nd Grade Teacher
Friedman, Susan Barbara (Ross)
6th Grade Teacher
BANGOR
Capone, Sandra P.
English Teacher
Cope, Lynn E.
7th Grd His & 8th Grd Geo Tchr
Curtolo, Robert Leonard
Mathematics Teacher
De Nicola, Desiree Diane
College Prep & AP Eng Teacher
Heiney, Debra Ann
Band Director & Music Teacher
Legath, John George, Jr.
Jr High Guidance Cnslr
Marozzi, Sandy Loretta Falcone
Kndgtn & Reading Recovery Tchr
Ruggiero, Robert F.
Spanish & Latin Teacher
Schiavone, Colleen Kells
Physical Science Teacher
Steele, Kathleen Patricia
Science Teacher
Taylor, Mary Anne
English Teacher
BARNESBORO
Bisko, Roslyn Jean (Formeck)
7th Grade Pre-Algebra Teacher
Bowman, Karen Barkhymer
Secondary Soc Studies Teacher
Eckenrode, Paul Anthony
Chemistry Teacher
Hogan, Michael C.
Mathematics Teacher
Litavish, Frank T.
Science Teacher
Resinski, Bonnie M. Lucas
English & Drama Teacher
Sibert, John
Third Grade Teacher
Suwinski, William S.
Fifth Grade Teacher
Zatorsky, Nancy Shackelford
First Grade Teacher
BARTONSVILLE
Mikloiche, Anthony Michael
Vocational Agriculture Teacher
Piccini, Leonard A.
Cosmetology Instructor

c, Helen Duh
entary School Educator
on, Richard J.
Grade Teacher
Joseph J.
Grade Teacher
ER
, Melanie Graham
ch Teacher
Lucille Graham
ical Education Teacher
Gregory E.
ory Teacher
wski, Corinne Marko
ematics Teacher
ey, Gail Mc Vay
ish Teacher
rt, Julia Reed
guage Arts Teacher
er, Willard L.
ogy Teacher
ER FALLS
Gerri Arbutina
Grade Teacher
er, Roland Edward
th Grade Teacher
ach, Edward Charles
ndary Math Teacher
on, Harvey
Prof of Theater & Speech
Alice L.
d Grade Teacher
nbom, Sue Anne Knowles
d of Gifted Support
sky, Nancy Melani
n, Cmptr Tchr & Coord
vits, Kenneth William
al Studies Teacher
ne, Samuel Alex
nish Teacher
, Mary Beth B.
n Tchr & Dept Chair
ack, Annie Farrell
enth Grade Teacher
, Paul Edgar
ish Prof & Dept Chprsn
r, Erich Detlef
nan Teacher
ER SPRINGS
, Thomas Gary
rumental Music Director
th, Brian Keith
hematics Teacher
tt, Sonya DeShong
guage Arts Teacher
, Elsie L.
lish Teacher
FORD
, Gina Ciambotti
ogy Teacher
, John Thomas, Jr.
ial Studies Teacher & Coach
, Tracy Koshko
ondary Math Teacher
nan, Carol Lee
n, French & English Tchr
et, Glenn Arthur, II
nputer Science Teacher
nd, Mahlon U.
sic Teacher
myer, Gretta M.
lish Teacher
etler, James Dwight
tory Teacher
, Susan Clemson
tory & Psychology Tchr
, David Emory
Grade Teacher
, Sharon Sciranko
lish Teacher
ams, Vicky Blattenberger
ence Teacher
MINSTER
ger, David Lamar
th Grade Teacher
CH CREEK
r, Richard E.
th Grade Teacher
LE VERNON
si, Henry Anthony
nd & Chorus Teacher
, Timothy C.
ddle School Reading Teacher
, Betty Ann
urth Grade Teacher
uhar, Robert A.
emistry & Psychology Teacher
ar, John Kent, Jr.
h Grd Amer Cultures Tchr
s, Christine
anish Teacher
ston, Janetta Overand
urth Grade Teacher
s, Cheryl Lynn
-6th Grd Gftd Support Tchr
esky, George Andrew
-8th Grade Math Teacher
dy, Judith Ceccarelli
ndergarten Teacher
rson, Linda (DiVirgilio)
Grade Teacher
ffer, Mary Ann Kristoff
thematics & Physics Teacher
sh, Henrietta Christine
Grade Teacher
ta, Denise Rose
glish Teacher
relli, Patricia Ann Guzzie
me Economics Teacher

Williams, Donald G.
Retired Social Studies Teacher
Yuschak, Gloria
School Counselor
BELLEFONTE
Achuff, Elizabeth H.
Fifth Grade Teacher
Acker, Lawrence Arthur
Instrumental Music Instructor
Anderson, Guy Edward
Chemistry Teacher
Bolin, Douglas S.
Math Teacher
Brungart, Ann Ash
Math Teacher
Crock, Donna E.
French Teacher
Eckenroth, Patty Yarnell
First Grade Teacher
Feldman, Mark Jeffrey
Mathematics Teacher
Gentzel, Mark Joseph
Fifth Grade Teacher
Gephart, Raymond G.
9th Grd Team English Teacher
Hale, Susan Andrews
2nd Grade Teacher
Hildebrand, John Carroll
German & Latin Teacher
Hoffman, Barbara Ellen
Mathematics Teacher
Johnson, Fran
Biology Teacher
Orwick, Lane Nestlerode
Fourth Grade Teacher
Probst, Robert Ernest
8th Grade REAL Teacher
Shively, Terry William
Fourth Grade Teacher
Sillman, Kathleen Anderson
REAL Teacher
Spicher, Kathleen Louise
World Cultures Tchr
Steckel, Tricia R.
Math, Computer Science Teacher
Stone, Michael
6th Grade Teacher
Wetzler, John Lewis
Guidance Cnslr & Ftbl Coach
Whitman, Mary Lou Mc Ilroy
Fifth Grade Teacher
Williams, Scott Alan
Chemistry Teacher
BELLEVILLE
French, Robin Jon
Fourth Grade Teacher
BELLWOOD
Johnson, Diane Irene (Scaglione)
10th Grade English Teacher
Renney, Linda Schucker
1st Grd Tchr, Math Curr Chprsn
Stewart, Constance Corso
8th Grade Reading Teacher
Tate, Richard Robert
Senior English Teacher
BENDERSVILLE
Kennedy, Larry Keith
6th Grade Teacher
BENSALEM
Dickinson, Robert Paul
Principal
Fanning, Joseph Patrick
8th Grd Social Studies Teacher
Gordon, Eric Tyler
6th & 7th Grade Science Tchr
Gramlich, Elaine Marie
High School Biology Teacher
Gutknecht, Maryanne
First Grade Teacher
Jaquette, Florence Evelyn
6th Grd Communications Teacher
Kline, Sharon Myers
5th Grade Teacher
Koszowski, Lillyan Introzzi
Art Teacher
Kovolisky, Antoinette L.
First Grade Teacher
Lapergola, Denise Maureen
Third Grade Teacher
Lynn, Anne Marie Agnes
Sixth Grade Teacher
McCullough, James Joseph
Social Studies Teacher
Rakowsky, Ademar
Physics Teacher
Saybolt, Adrienne, IHM
Eighth Grade Teacher
Schoenstadt, Barbara L.
Teacher of Gifted Education
Tozzi, Anne Frances Pascucci
2nd Grade Teacher
Wargo, Robert Joseph
Social Studies Teacher
Weiner, Jerry
11th-12th Grd Physics Teacher
Wellington, Jonnakoty
AP Calculus Teacher
BENTLEYVILLE
Fields, Howard Russell
Math & Computer Sci Teacher
Johnson, Ronald G.
American History Teacher
Ryan, Melissa O'Dell
French & Russian Teacher
Strang, Marilyn Hughes
English & Journalism Teacher
Strangis, Daniel Anthony
Band Director

BENTON
Bates, Jennifer Dammer
English Teacher
DiRado, Linda Marie (Williams)
Mathematics Teacher
Grozier, Gary W.
Social Studies Instructor
Martin, Richard Emory
Music Teacher & Band Director
Mc Cullough, Joseph
Third Grade Teacher
McHenry, Jay Robert
Earth, Life Sci & Cmptr Tchr
Musitano, Charles A.
Biology Teacher
Powlus, Gary Ray
School Counselor
Turner, Allen B.
Mathematics Teacher
Yost, Shirley Schuyler
French Teacher
BERLIN
Boyer, Anne E.
Varsity Head Softball Coach
Czekaj, Robert
Health & PE Instructor
Deaner, Marjorie Vaughan
First Grade Teacher
Eutsey, James Edward
Secondary Math Teacher
Friedline, Karen Ann
First Grade Teacher
Menhorn, Norman W.
Fifth Grade Teacher
Orendorf, Debra D.
French, English & Jrnlsm Tchr
Sarver, Phyllis Ann
Kindergarten Teacher
Shark, Diane Marie
Spanish Teacher
Shealer, Michael L.
Health Teacher
BERNVILLE
Althouse, Linda Haag
Amer History & Civic Teacher
Boltz, Michael Gene
Sixth Grade Teacher
Clay, Scott Lee
7th & 8th Grd Science Teacher
Frantz, Richard Earl
English Teacher
Leininger, Carol (Levan)
Math Teacher
Voigt, David J.
Social Studies Instructor
Wentling, Eric Paul
Social Studies Teacher
BERWICK
Allen, John Robert
Chemistry Teacher
Bulkley, Robert H.
7th Grade Social Studies Tchr
Ermish, Gloria Mazzitti
Fourth Grade Teacher
Isenberg, Annette Janice Bieber
Spanish Teacher
Kile, Debbie Stevens
Fifth Grade Teacher
Learn, Nelson R.
HS Math Teacher
Malatesta, Betsy A.
Health & Physical Ed Teacher
Mc Clintock, Edna Sprung
Mathematics Teacher
Mc Clure, Nancy Scott
Seventh Grade Reading Teacher
Mc Donnell, Thomas Allen
History Teacher
Ross, James Anthony
Math Teacher
Scott, Clyde Eugene
Retired Band Director
Spencer, Allison Blair
Science Teacher
Voveris, Joan Marie
Music Teacher & Dept Chprsn
Wasser, Ronald E.
Music Teacher
Yeager, Robert Lee
8th Grd Crrnt Wrld Prblms Tchr
BERWYN
Brennan, Charles
Sixth Grade Teacher
Mancuso, Barbara Rice
Physics Teacher
Rosenberger, Nancy Harting
Eng Dept Chprsn & Teacher
BESSEMER
Bredl, David M.
Jr High Science Teacher
Donfrio, Archie Joseph
Jr Sr High Math Teacher
Robb, Carol E.
Retired Math & Cmptr Sci Tchr
Turner, Robin Lynn
Seventh Grade Reading Teacher
BETHEL
Brightbill, Judy K.
Math Teacher
Smith, Evelyn M.
Fourth Grade Teacher
BETHEL PARK
Beltz, Joel L.
Geometry & Trigonometry Tchr
Buetzow, David Bennett
Band & Orchestra Director
Conrad, Ellen Critchfield
Latin Teacher
Culbertson-Stark, Mary
High School Art Teacher

Deal, John C.
8th Grade Mathematics Teacher
Delsandro, Betty Barle
French Teacher
Fisher, Linda Diane
English Teacher
Georgiana, Sam
Chemistry Instructor
Henderson, Sally Krams
English & Theater Teacher
Keeling, Agnes Curran
Fourth Grade Teacher
Kennedy, Janice Pascoe
Secondary Counselor
Knapp, James P.
Guidance Counselor
Knauff, George Oakland
Retired Social Studies Teacher
Kochinski, Gerald J.
Reading Specialist
Liberatore, Anthony A.
Science Teacher
Mannion, Frances Chase
English Teacher
Meyer, George R.
Leadership Teacher
Nagel, Christopher Andrew
English Teacher
Palombo, Christen M.
Art Teacher
Reynolds, John E.
6th Grd Social Studies Teacher
Ridge, Lewis O., Jr.
4th Grade Teacher
Roberts, Janet H.
3rd Grade Teacher
Ryan, Lorri Lynne
Biology Teacher
Siverts, Rodney D.
Math Teacher
Vieceli, Samuel John
Physical Education Teacher
Wargo, Eugene M.
Physics Teacher
Weise, Billie Dee Mc Ilroy
Retired Spanish Teacher
BETHLEHEM
Acerra, Donna Shipman
Adj Prof of Comm & Theatre
Achenbach, Charles M.
Anatomy & Physiology Professor
Ahmadizadeh, Ebrahim
Math Professor
Ardoline, Mary Ann Elisabeth
Asst Prof of Writing & Reading
Bigatel, Christina
5th Grade Teacher
Bogusky, Joyce Livingston
English & Drama Teacher
Boykas, Linda
HS Social Studies Teacher
Cole, JoAnn Sherman
Eng Dept Chairperson & Tchr
Cullin, Michael Joseph
Physics Teacher
Cyr, Traci Jane
8th Grade Mathematics Teacher
Dean, Rebecca Kay
Assoc Prof of Spch, Prgm Coord
DePaola, Georgene Helen
Seventh Grade Teacher
DiStravolo, Loredana Margaret
Spanish Teacher
Dolan, Karen Deirdre
English Teacher
Durante, JoAnn Sennetti
Assistant Principal
Egan, Kathleen A. Grossman
English Teacher
Evitts, Eric Allen
High School Mathematics Tchr
Favinger, Anthony William
8th Grd Earth & Space Sci Tchr
Fertal, Carol Cooke
Fifth Grade Teacher
Fielding, Patricia M.
Kindergarten Teacher
Frangicetto, Thomas Joseph
Professor of Psychology
Freeh, John
Secondary Computer Specialist
Gorman, Barbara Jo Amato
Spanish & French Teacher
Harmanos, George
Mathematics Teacher
Heath, Douglas Edwin
Geography & Geology Professor
Heine, Margaret Edmund
Theology Teacher
Hudak, Roger John
Teacher
Iannelli, Barbara Diane
1st Grade Teacher
Jordan, Diane M.
Business Teacher & Dept Chm
Jordan, John J., Jr.
Lang Arts Dept Supvr & Tchr
Karam, Jody F.
Health & Physical Ed Teacher
Keenan, Marjorie
Vice Principal
Kennedy, James Edward
Social Studies Teacher
Kleist, David A.
English Teacher
Kondikoff, Linda Anne
Art Teacher
Krug, Edward William, Jr.
Criminal Justice Prgm Coord

Long, Peter Gregory
Third Grade Teacher
Lynn, Nancy Chamberlain
Chemistry Teacher
Mack, Janet Shaffer
Music Teacher
Matheson, Susan E.
Tchr of Elem Gifted Students
Mc Carty, Margaret Marie
English Teacher
Mc Cauley, Michael Robert
Admin Assistant & Band Dir
Meek, Susan Hudock
Sixth Grade Teacher
Miller, Bruce Wayne
Math Teacher
Mirabella, Thomas Patrick
Theology Teacher
Moukoulis, Mary Pitsilos
Third Grade Teacher
Nolf, Gail H.
Business Dept Chair
Orsi, Martha D.
Adjunct Professor of English
Osborne, Mary Jean
Assistant Professor of Nursing
Pinto, Lois Blaser
Health & Phys Ed Teacher
Reed, Corliss A.
Seventh Grade Teacher
Reese, Judith Rodgers
Eighth Grade Teacher
Roberts, Eric Lee
Guidance Counselor
Rodriguez, Samuel, Jr.
Social Studies Teacher
Rosati, Joy (Felker)
5th Grade Teacher
Rowan, Gerald J.
Professor of Art
Schaffer, Theodore
Biology Teacher
Schneider, Calvin William
Industrial Arts Teacher
Segatti, Laura Kratzer
Adj Instr of Early Chldhd Ed
Seifert, William Norman
Director of Spiritual Act
Smullen, Judith Eisenhart
English Teacher
Snovitch, Elaine
Mathematics & Cmptr Sci Tchr
Stone, Colleen Mc Nevin
Guidance Counselor
Temlin, Dennis L.
English Teacher
Tilli, Susan
French & Spanish Teacher
Traupman-Carr, Carol A.
Asst Prof of Music
Tully, Angela Ripp
Eighth Grade Teacher
Vanya, Mary Kathleen
Seventh & Eighth Grade Teacher
Vazquez, Elizabeth Rivera
Guidance Counselor
Viehman, Lidia L.
Social Studies Teacher
Volk, Nancy Wroblewski
Language Arts Teacher
Wetcher, Neil Steven
Math Teacher & Department Chm
Whildin, AnneMarie Linkert
Assoc Prof of Early Chldhd Ed
Whirl, Robert J.
Mathematics Teacher
Wiedl, Evelyn J.
5th & 6th Grd Math & Sci Tchr
BIG RUN
Neal, Jerry D.
Sixth Grade Teacher
BIGLER
Seprish, Mary Jo (Spagnolo)
5th Grade Teacher
BIGLERVILLE
Bushman, Daniel McClain
Latin Teacher
Young, Laura Anne
8th Grade English Teacher
BIRDSBORO
Bossler, Bryan Kent
Social Studies Teacher
Grim, Patricia Ann
Fifth Grade Teacher
Grow, Ann Gutekunst
Art Teacher
Jacobs, Michael D.
Business Dept Chairperson
Klinger, Judith Ann
French Dept Chair & Teacher
Lenhart, Janice Kintz
Biology Teacher
Long, Daniel M.
Music Teacher & Band Director
Marshall, James Jay
Chemistry Teacher
McComsey, Oliver James, Jr.
7th Grade Geography Teacher
Miller, G. Dane
10th Grade Health & Ath Dir
Piazza, Raymond L.
Asst to the Superintendent
Shannon, Elizabeth J.
English Teacher
BLAIRSVILLE
Cravotta, Nicolene Faye
Language Arts Tchr & Dept Chr
Dettorre, Albert Joseph
Health & PE Teacher

BLAIRSVILLE (cont)
Lanza, Joseph John
Math & Computer Tchr
Popp, William Frederick
Fifth Grade Teacher
Rippel, Patricia Black
Fifth Grade Teacher
Valerio, Denise Walker
A P Eng & Journalism Teacher
Yenchik, Carol Ann Hrabcsak
Second Grade Teacher
BLANCHARD
Kinley, Barbara Herbert
Third Grade Teacher
Young, Movias Eisenhower
Third Grade Teacher
BLOOMSBURG
Archey, Laurel Mowery
Health Occupations Instructor
Bolinsky, Joseph John, Jr.
Carpentry Instructor
Burrows, Velma Avery
Language Arts Teacher
Fisk, Frank Edward
Retired Teacher
Gaughenbaugh, Kathleen Williams
Fifth Grade Teacher
Kakaley, Michael James, Jr.
Math Teacher
Latsha, Timothy
High School Choral Director
Osborne, Jeffrey Duane
Mathematics Teacher
Rothermel, Victoria Anne (Snyder)
HS Math Teacher
Strine, Harry Cornelius, III
Communication Professor
Weaver, Emily I. (Link)
German Teacher
BLOSSBURG
Barton, Jay S.
Instrumental Music Instructor
Bogaczyk, James Joseph
Math Tchr & Dean of Students
Fry, Karen Ann (Swinsick)
Acad Learning Support Teacher
Koernig, Barbara Rarrick
8th-12th Grade French Teacher
Prough, Sherri Lynn
Health & Physical Ed Teacher
BLUE BELL
Andren, Richard Johnson
Prof of Biological Sciences
Baccari, Albert A., Jr.
Assistant Prof of Biol Sci
Baron, Steven Howard
Social Science Instructor
Brobst, Duane James
Economics Professor
Cairns, Roger A.
Professor of Fine Arts
Carfagno, Ursula
Assoc Prof of English
Connell, Walter Glen
Professor & Coordinator
DeGrendele, Julia Walton
Prof of Reading & Study Skills
Eckhardt, Joseph Paul
Associate Professor of History
Essig, Carl E.
Associate Professor of Bus
Farrington, Ronald J.
Prof of Business
Freiwald, Joseph A.
Professor of Mathematics
Goldberg, Aleck
Physics Professor
Horan, Diane Whitehead
Associate Professor of English
Hunt, Debra Buckwalter
Hotel & Restaurant Mgt Coord
James, Eleanor D.
English Coordinator
Johnson, Marty
Professor of Mathematics
Lacy, Ann Walker
Speech Communication Prof
Levin, Debbie Gantman
Professor of Education
Morrone, Michael Joseph
Associate Prof of Cmptr Sci
Nestler, Patricia Cundiff
Associate Professor of English
Richman, Wendy Dresner
Nutrition Instructor
Rizzo, Gary E.
Assoc Dean of Academic Affairs
Sewell, Fay Barbara
Mathematics Professor
Short, Frank J.
Professor of Fine Arts
Ukazim, Emenike
Math Professor
Ullman, Wendy Collier
Adjunct Instructor of English
Willig, Roger P.
Mathematics Professor
Winston, Patrick Henry
Art Professor
BOALSBURG
Kibelbek, Mary Boyle
Elementary School Teacher
BOBTOWN
Powelko, Annette Magdalene
Third Grade Teacher
BOILING SPRINGS
Akin, Dennis Peter
Prof of Fine Arts Emeritus
Boggs, Ronald Bruce
Health & First Aid Teacher
Crum, James Robert
Math Teacher
Grove, Nila F.
Fifth Grade Lang Arts Tchr
Ramirez, Gloria J. (Finkenbinder)
Third Grade Instructor
Schwartz, Jeffrey Wayne
Secondary Math Teacher
Stallings, Susan F.
Coordinator of the Gifted
BOOTHWYN
Mathews, Edward William, Jr.
Special Education Teacher
BOSWELL
Aikey, Patricia Ann (Boback)
Math Teacher & Dept Chprsn
Bissett, Susan
Secondary Librarian
Coughenour, Sallie Eileen
Chemistry & Math Teacher
Croft, Daniel Thomas
Band Director
Ely, Lynette Friedline
Art Teacher
Ewing, Robert E., Jr.
Social Studies Chairman
Kohler, Mary Ann
6th Grade Teacher
Koontz, Donald F.
English Teacher
Lohr, Anne Margaret
Math & Computer Teacher
Naugle, Gloria Andolina
4th Grd & Instrl Support Tchr
Shifflett, Marie Geisweidt
Physics & Math Teacher
Vatavuk, John Paul
Fifth Grade Teacher
BOYERTOWN
Brumbach, Marcia A.
Supvr of Wellness & Fitness
Christ, Arline Sand
Visual Arts Teacher
Colangelo, Patricia Jo (Barns)
Senior High Chemistry Teacher
Colasanti, James Nicholas
Teacher & Dept Chairperson
Dietz, Elizabeth Ann
Music Teacher
Fries, Daniel Thomas
American Cultures Teacher
Hendricks, Donald L.
Chemistry & AP Chemistry Tchr
Howey, William Calvin
Soc Stud, His & Ec Teacher
Jameson, Ronald E.
Social Studies Teacher
Jorgensen, Donna W.
English Teacher & Dept Leader
Kershetsky, Daniel F.
Music Educator
Kirk, Kathryn A.
Biology Tchr & Sci Dept Chm
Leinbach, Leslie Ann
Telecommunications Teacher
Mauger, Cynthia Carroll
English Teacher
Merkley, Robert B.
Math Teacher
Repko, Philip E.
English Teacher
Seifarth, Linda Ritchie
Art Teacher
Staats, Frank Dayton
Biology Teacher
Suarez, Carmen Maria
Spanish Teacher
Updegrove, Bruce Howard
11th Grd American History Tchr
Vishio, Susan A.
Spanish & French Teacher
Wilkins, Patricia Short
Biology & Chemistry Teacher
Windish, Roberta M. (Reinert)
Mathematics Teacher
Yorgey, Barbara J.
Second Grade Teacher
BRACKENRIDGE
Keryeski, Michael Paul
Fifth Grade Teacher
BRADDOCK
Dillahunt, Herbert A.
Music Teacher
BRADFORD
Ambuske, Gregory Charles
Chemistry Teacher
Chandler, John S.
Professor of Biology
Dzirkalis, Elga Gutmanis
Studio & Fine Arts Asst Prof
Freda, August Robert
Prof of Engineering & Dept Dir
Lutz, Richard J.
Gifted Support Teacher
Mattis, Ronald Eugene
Associate Professor of Engrng
Picklo, Janelle Little
Mrktg & Distributive Ed Tchr
Pletcher, Duane K.
English Department Supervisor
BRIDGEVILLE
Bacha, Connie A.
Business Ed Instructor
Blunkosky, James A.
Chem Tchr & Sci Dept Chprsn
Fleming, Mary Margaret Day
Math, Computer & Sci Teacher
Gerlach, JoAnne Elizabeth
Eight Grade Teacher
Holliday, Diane F.
Secondary Math Teacher
Janoss, Frank S.
8th Grade Math Teacher
Keil, Renee Ann Giovane
Dance & Acting Instructor
Kirker, Robert H.
Physical & Gen Science Tchr
Marusak, Robert
Math & Reading Teacher
Mc Connell, Timothy John
Head Basketball Coach
Orr, Joseph H.
Industrial Technology Instr
Petrucci, Earl R.
Guidance Counselor
Rodrigues, Robert M.
9th-12th Grade History Teacher
Timbario, Phyllis Dato
8th Grade Teacher
BRISTOL
Cimochowski, Eileen Marie
Third Grade Teacher
Donnelly, Daniel Edward
English Teacher
Joiner, Dennis F.
English Dept Head & Teacher
Kopcho, Denise Jermyn
Math Support Tchr & Coord
Suter, Grace
Physical Science Teacher
Trendler, Elaine Babboni
English Teacher
BROCKWAY
Bittner, Bran Alan
Vocational Agriculture Teacher
Hynes, Sheila Gegogeine
Reading Specialist
Mooney, M. Patricia Duffy
HS Business Instructor
Preston, Denise De Larme
Biology Teacher
Sprague, Charlotte Himes
English Teacher
BRODHEADSVILLE
Beers, Marsha J.
7th-12th Grd Span & Ger Tchr
Edmiston, Robert Beverly, Jr.
English Teacher
Frey, Ro Mc Govern
Instructional Support Teacher
Godshall, Gail Elyse
5th Grade Teacher
Greggo, Thersa S.
First Grade Teacher
Martin, Richard Neal
Sixth Grade Teacher
Miller, Gerald H.
Guidance Counselor
Nicholas, Todd
6th Grade Social Studies Tchr
Pappalardo, Peter E.
Teacher
Percey, James W.
9th Grade Earth Science Tchr
Rabenold-Norwood, Georgine
English Teacher
Rodriguez, Ada I.
Spanish Teacher
Young, Janice Besecker
High School German Teacher
BROGUE
Fuller, Kay Ann (Markel)
Second Grade Teacher
Keller, Sandra
Third Grade Teacher
Landis, Craig Steven
Fourth Grade Teacher
Pettyjohn, Priscilla Hopkins
Sixth Grade Teacher
BROOKHAVEN
DiRosa, Steven Joseph
Math Instructor
Gray, Anita Gambone
Principal
Haseltine, Rodman Dan
Junior High School Teacher
Johnson, Wayne
7th & 8th Grade Science Tchr
Riney, Daniel Edward
Amer History & Geography Tchr
Weaver, Sandra Jean
Fifth Grade Teacher
BROOKVILLE
Coughlin, Heidi Schifferli
English Teacher
Dillman, Peggy Lou Limley
Fourth Grade Teacher
Ferko, Thomas J.
Sixth Grade Teacher
Johnson, John David
Social Studies Teacher
Kitko, Anthony Stephen
Industrial Arts Teacher
Mccleary, Jean Wagner
HS Physical Ed & Health Tchr
McLaughlin, James A.
Fourth Grade Teacher
Piper, Dixie Canon
Secondary English Teacher
Smith, Trina Luann
Mathematics Teacher
Smith, Wiliam
Biology Teacher
Watson, Amy (Stewart)
Sixth Grade Teacher
BROOMALL
Crooks, Annelouise Peterson
5th Grade Teacher
Lambert, Jayne Panetta
Soc Stud & Sci Teacher
Zimmerman, Sandra Turner
Integrated Language Arts Tchr
BROWNSVILLE
Angelo, Gregory Phillip
English Teacher
Conte, Donna
English Teacher
Franko, Wilma A.
Latin, French & English Tchr
Haddad, Diane Lynn
English Teacher
Harasty, Kenneth James
Teacher of Gifted
Novotney, Frank A., Jr.
Science Dept Chair & Teacher
BRUIN
Vensel, Janet L.
Reading Specialist
BRYN ATHYN
Bergman, Mary Elizabeth
Guidance Counselor & Fr Tchr
Boyce, Cory Britton
Mathematics Teacher
Hodgell, Bonnie Colleen
English Teacher
Schadegg, Kira Runion
Science Teacher
Stevens, Louise Doering
Math Teacher & Dept Chair
Walker, Margaret M.
His, Spanish & English Teacher
BRYN MAWR
Barnett, George R., III
History Teacher & Dept Chm
Bednarcik, Kerri A.
PTA Program Co-Director
Betz, Antoinette Conte
Eighth Grade Teacher
Dougherty, Mary Ann C.
Director & French Teacher
Gold, Victoria J.
Art & Pottery Teacher
Holt, Helen H.
Reading Consultant & Eng Tchr
Lovejoy, Dawn De Wolf
Biology Teacher
Potter, Kristin
Occptnl Therapy Asst Pgm Dir
Smith, Anne Reidell
Eighth Grade Latin Teacher
Toland, Heather E.S.
Program Director
BUCKINGHAM
Bolton, Mary Catherine
Mathematics Teacher
Book, Maureen Hutchinson
4th Grade Teacher
Burkett, Richard W.
Social Studies Coordinator
Christoff, Ellen Balnis
Mathematics Teacher
Curtis, Jane Ann (Kane)
Tchr of Deaf & Hard of Hearing
Gueiros, Joas C. B.
Spanish Teacher
Hagan, Maryalice
8th-9th Grade English Teacher
Kulick, Barbara May
Social Studies Instructor
McKelvey, Marie Nuyianes
Math Teacher
Nissly, Joseph A.
Frgn Lang Coord & Span Tchr
Perry, Marjorie Bartleson
Sixth Grade Teacher
Strohm, Jane Pennybaker
Mathematics Teacher
Tannery, Gail Holmes
Mathematics Tchr & Dept Coord
BURGETTSTOWN
Calabro, Susan Leigh
Spanish & French Teacher
Cooper, Barbara Ann (Yonek)
Fifth Grade Teacher
Enos, Theodora Seder
Third Grade Teacher
Gillen, Vince J.
4th Grade Self Contained Tchr
Hanna, Marshall W.
Business & Social Studies Tchr
Latella, James J.
English Teacher
Marler, Ann-Frances Testa
English & Publications Teacher
Mastrangelo, Dean Ross
Choral Music Director
Mc Wreath, Cynthia Louise
Eighth Grade English Teacher
Price, Susan (Randolph)
Home Economics Teacher
Stokum, Sondra Lynnette
Learning Support Teacher
Zollars, Katherine Durinzi
Retired Lang Arts Teacher
BUTLER
Angert, Mary C.
Mathematics Teacher
Ayers, Deborah A.
Economics Instructor
Brown, William Paul
Phys & Learning Support Instr
Calhoun, Chris A.
Park & Recreation Program Mgmt
Campbell, Charles R.
Cmptr Information Systems Prof
Cavaliero, Cheryl Fuhrer
Mathematics Teacher
Champ, Valjean Jeffreys
Third Grade Classroom Teacher
Cherry, Kenneth James
Fifth Grade Teacher
Cooper, Larry L.
Third Grade Teacher
Crawford, Frederick L.
2nd Grade Teacher
Goettler, Christine Young
Science Teacher
Hinchberger, Terry Dale
Soc Studies Dept Head & Tchr
Jeffries, Bessie Weyand
Mathematics Instructor
Kamerer, Barbara Jo
English Teacher
Kovacik, Geoffrey John
Soc Stud Dept Chm, AP His Tchr
Kuehn, Drew W.
French Teacher
Lane, Rodger Lee
Life Science Teacher
Logan, Clifford Robinson
American History Teacher
Loomis, Donald Austin
Business Professor
McElhaney, Barbara Gangone
Physical Education Teacher
Mc Kinney, Nancy Lobaugh
Social Studies Teacher
Meissner, James J., Sr.
Mathematics Asst Professor
Meute, Dana Rae
English Teacher
Morrison, Karen Johnston
9th & 10th Grade Business Tchr
Moser, David Dean
Communications Instructor
Motko, Jo Renee
Second Grade Teacher
Musko, Karen Waslo
Learning Support Teacher
Natili, Armand Louis, Jr.
Asst Professor of Psych
Nicodemus, James Ray, Jr.
Carpentry Teacher
Oswald, Ronald R.
Equipment Repair Instructor
Pedersen, Eric Randall
Associate Professor of English
Peterson, Orvan B.
Professor of Humanities & Eng
Ram, Shunila Naomi
Kindergarten Teacher
Rau, Melinda Susanne
Chemistry Instructor
Schmidt, Jeannette Colonna
7th-10th Grd HS Band Director
Shiring, Stephen Boyd
Hospitality Mgmt Program Dir
Spang, Debra Reeping
Chemistry Teacher
Tremba, Roger Lee
Physics Teacher
Weisensee, Tina
Chemistry Teacher
West, Dorothy H.
Social Studies Teacher
Williams, Leah Ann (Rieg)
High School Biology Teacher
Woods, Douglas Elliot
English Teacher
CABOT
Maier, Cynthia Follsteadt
Third Grade Teacher
Pfeiffer, Jacqueline Carol
Third Grade Teacher
CALIFORNIA
Bennett, Bill
English Professor
Nass, John Phillip, Jr.
Asst Prof of Anthropology
Ribar, Margarita
Associate Professor of Spanish
Yahner, William A.
Associate Professor of English
CAMBRIDGE SPRINGS
Mc Kissock, Scott Hardy
Bio & Adv Physiology Tchr
CAMP HILL
Ahrens, Sara Ann
French Teacher
Boyer, Kenneth Carl
Math Department Chairman
Casey, Robert A.
English Teacher
Colestock, Julie Conrad
Hlth & PE Instructor
Girondi, Alfred Joseph
Chemistry Teacher
Haubrich, Nancy
Mathematics Teacher
Hessmiller, Joanne M.
Former Director
Kiker, Janice A.
Mathematics & Computer Teacher
King, Kim Yvonne Bulmer
French Teacher
King, Stephen Alan
English Teacher
Kunkle, Craig Ross
Social Studies Teacher
Markowski, Patricia Allwein
Mathematics Teacher
Miller, Shirley Huber
Retired String Tchr & Orch Dir
Perkey, Susan Walker
First Grade Teacher
Scotto, Joseph Nicholas
Science & German Teacher

HILL (cont)
Scott Joseph
rd World Cultures Tchr
, Russell T., Jr.
n Teacher
Harry S., III
y Teacher
ISBURG
chards S.
Studies Teacher
ohn A.
ng Support Teacher
, Thomas J.
Teacher
ames Louis
Music Teacher
n, Ellen Fonner
Teacher & Facilitator
nna Stark
stra Teacher
n, Cheryl Lynn
h & Theater Teacher
ore, Teressa Ann
tute Teacher
Lawrence Arthur
School Music Teacher
son, Susan Coen
elor
, Andrea Coleman
Grade Teacher
Gary
uter Programming Teacher
er, Susan Ellen
athematics Teacher
Dennis Buzz
Studies Teacher
ski, John Vincent
School English Teacher
n, Robert L.
ematics Teacher
John
dary English Teacher
efsky, Albert
ical Occupations Teacher
Barbara Steri
ess Data Processing Tchr
ON
Nancy Coons
sh Teacher
ki, Susan J.
sh & Journalism Teacher
Sherry Ann
Grade Teacher
June Franklin
h Teacher
ONDALE
Marie Benovitch
ematics Teacher
, Joseph Frank
ctivities, Dev & Adv Dir
Alicia Maria
rade Teacher
Rose Marie Leitza
ing Support, Spec Ed Tchr
vich, Mary Ann
h, PE Tchr & Dept Chair
Kathryn Farrell
Grade Teacher
, Jean Marie
ergarten Teacher
arcik, Marcella Ziemba
sh Department Chm & Tchr
Mary Diane (Bruno)
ndary Math Teacher
, Josephine Levite
Grade Teacher
le, Thomasina T.
Grade Teacher
aro, John Joseph
al Studies Teacher
Martin John
sh Teacher
, Frank J.
ch, Eng Tchr & Dept Chair
ISLE
sser, Connie Clevenger
d Grade Teacher
son, Sylvie G.
c Prof, Romance Lang & Lit
Kenneth Lee
Teacher & Dept Chm
alma Christine
mistry Teacher
art, Oliver C.
red English Teacher
ugh, Denise Lynne Martin
Grade Teacher
Vicki Gerhard
nce Dept Teacher
ael, Susan Ridgway
ti-Age Teacher
inger, G. William
lish Teacher
, Debra Rhen
al Studies Teacher
ns, Cathie S.
Grade English & Lead Tchr
zer, Marsha Lee (Rhodes)
lish Teacher
ic, Sandy A.
nth Grade Teacher
er, David A.
d Dir & Music Dept Chm
pp, Janice Finkey
Grade Teacher
, James Arthur, II
logy Teacher
s, Harold L.
Tchr & Cross Cntry Coach

CARMICHAELS
Batis, Deborah S.
Biology & Adv Biology Teacher
O'Hara, David Alvin
Computer Teacher
Relovsky, John M., Jr.
Title I Reading Specialist
CARNEGIE
Bevan, Cynthia Susan
First Grade Teacher
Carroll, Zeffie Lucas
7th-10th Grade English Teacher
Esterburg, Arlene Catherine
5th Grade Teacher
Jesek, Charles Jerry
Fifth Grade Teacher
Martin, Nancy Joseph
French Teacher
Petronsky, Rebecca Dixon
English & AP Teacher
Saunders, Donald E.
9th-12th Grd Earth Sci Tchr
Smith, Grover, III
Social Studies Teacher
Torchia, John F.
6th Grade Teacher
Valalik, William A.
Biology Teacher
Wood, William Kenneth
Instructional Support Teacher
CARROLLTOWN
Horne, Rita Litzinger
2nd Grade Teacher
Kepshire, Cheryl Ann (Wilshire)
Second Grade Teacher
CASHTOWN
Prevoznik, Therse
Sixth Grade Teacher
CASTLE SHANNON
Binek, Joann
Ret Elem & Intermediate Tchr
CATASAUQUA
Abraham, Joseph Robert
Fourth Grade Teacher
Cadden, Tim Francis
English Teacher
Pantella, Janet Marie
Biology Teacher
CATAWISSA
Atherton, Rae Smith
Retired Teacher
Derr, Penny Motto
Second Grade Teacher
Thomas, Mark Phillip
Senior High Band & Chorus Dir
Yocum, Mary Ann P.
Algebra II & Geometry Teacher
CENTER VALLEY
Bradley, Beverly Donchez
Business Educator
Dailey, Thomas
Assoc Professor of Theology
Kane, Brian M.
Asst Prof of Moral Theology
Mahala, Michael J., Jr.
US Cultures Teacher
O'Neill, Brian F.
Assistant Professor
Vas Dias, Richard Andre
English & Journalism Teacher
Walker, James C.
Physics Teacher
CHALFONT
Rissinger, William Hoffman
Science Coordinator & Teacher
CHAMBERSBURG
Austin, Deborah S.
Associate Professor of Chem
Branham, Anne Kinney
Eng & Creative Writing Tchr
Brough, Cynthia L.
Veterinary Medical Tech Prof
Burnett, Freya Berglund
VMT Instructor
Byers, Rita Myers
Fourth Grade Teacher
Dickinson, Donald C.
Eng Tchr & Dir of Forensics
Ebersole, Jean Etter
English Teacher
Etter, Louisa Slaybaugh
Art Teacher
Gaugler, Franklin Norwood
Business Data Processing Tchr
Goetz, Sharon Fortna
Chem, Physics & Phys Sci Tchr
Grove, M. Louise Smith
Biology Tchr & Sci Dept Chm
Henn, Christine J.
English Teacher
Hocker, Gary Lynn
Amer History & Economics Tchr
Jiles, Savilla Weaver
Civics Teacher
Kessler, Kate
English Teacher
Killinger, Mary Margaret (Cowan)
Kindergarten Teacher
Knisely, George Arthur
Agricultural Science Teacher
Kochert, Theresa A.
French & Spanish Teacher
Lundy, Renwick P.
HS Math & Science Teacher
Peeling, Michelle L.
English Teacher
Rabinowitz, Sheldon Mark
Fifth Grade Teacher
Rountree, Leitha Byers
Second Grade Teacher

Thieme, Vicki Lynn
High School German Teacher
Walker, Robert James
Chemistry Teacher
Westberry, Bonnie Lee (Billings)
Accounting Teacher
CHARLEROI
Medved, Bernard
Social Studies Teacher
Primm, David Edward
Drafting Teacher
Protin, Eileen Dolan
Math Teacher
Ritacco, Joseph S.
Middle School Principal
Shearson, Nancy (Waters)
Sixth Grade Teacher
CHESTER
Apple, Thomas Turley
Asst Eng Prof & Theatre Dir
Cates, Joyce M. Dent
First Grade Teacher
Daniels, Joseph R.
Second Grade Teacher
Daniels, Marlene Alexis
Guidance Counselor
DiAngelo, Joseph A., Jr.
Dean & Professor of Management
Doran, Renata Theresa
Spanish Teacher
Edgette, J. Joseph
Associate Professor of Ed
Faldeti, Kathryn T.
Social Studies Dept Chprsn
Glover, Shirley Robinson
Guidance Counselor
Godsall-Myers, Jean E.
Assistant Professor of German
Hargadon, Joseph M.
Associate Prof of Accounting
Kegler, Carolyn W.
English & Journalism Tchr
King, Mabel A.
Business Education Teacher
Maffia, Gennaro Joseph
Assoc Prof & Chem Eng Dept Chm
Mc Closkey, Donna Weaver
Management Professor
Reigner, Thomas E.
Civics & World Cultures Tchr
Rigik, Elnora
Prof of Hum & Dir of Hnrs Prgm
Scurry, Lenora R.
Science Teacher
Serembus, John Herman
Philosophy Professor
Sheikh, Sohail
Associate Professor
Wood, Catherine S.
Mathematics Teacher
Zahka, William Joseph
Professor of Economics
CHESTER SPRINGS
Ayotte, Marilynn Olds
Sixth Grade Teacher
CHESWICK
Holliday, Joseph William
Ret Chem Tchr & Sci Dept Chm
Thompson, Henry B., Jr.
5th & 6th Grade Teacher
CHEYNEY
Brantley, Wanda L.
Assoc Prof, Guid & Cnslng Dept
Flemming, James E.
Assoc Professor of Education
Jones, Eugene, Jr.
Professor of Biology
Livezey, Marlen Dodszuweit
Communication Arts Professor
Manspeaker, Janet Bechtel
Asst Prof of Political Science
Royster, Eugene Canfield
Assoc Professor of Sociology
Sheldon, Joseph Francis
Professor
Smith, J. Otis
Professor of Psychology
Songster, Charles E.
Associate Professor of Ed
Williams, Edward Emanuel
Prof of Mgmt & Orgl Studies
CHURCHVILLE
Weber, Sandie Melnikoff
First Grade Teacher
CLAIRTON
Emmerling, Keith
Soc Stud Coord & His Teacher
Fleet, Diane Marie (Smith)
Fourth-Fifth Grade Teacher
Jaskulski, Judith Cathcart
Accounting Instructor
Marcinowski, Jane Stuart
Fourth Grade Teacher
Mercalde, Amy L.
English Teacher
Tobin, Linda L.
Math Tchr & Stu Asst Pgm Coord
Wiggins, Bloneva Flowers
Kindergarten Teacher
CLARIDGE
Barron, Carol N.
5th Grade Teacher
DeVincentis, Nicholas Albert
Science Teacher
Stock, Rosemary Dilling
Math & Social Studies Teacher
CLARION
Arendas, David William
Math & Cmptr Programming Tchr

Arth, Alex J., Jr.
Biology Tchr & Sci Dept Chair
Bowersox, Robert E.
World Cultures & Soc Stud Tchr
Brown, Lisabeth J.
Education Professor
Bruner, Judy Venturella
Kindergarten Teacher
DeLuca, Richard S.
Dir Cntr for Educl Leadership
Felicetti, Linda Roscoe
Professor of Marketing
Gent, Pamela Joyce
Asst Professor of Special Ed
Gregg, Gary Lee, II
Professor of Political Science
Grejda, Gail Fulton
Associate Professor
Grugel, Barbara Chesler
Asst Prof of Ed Department
Gurecka, Lou
Associate Professor of Spec Ed
Hall, Jack Shelburn
Professor of Music
Harry, Vickie D. Smith
Assistant Professor
Hilton, Susan M.
Department of Comm Asst Prof
Holden, James E.
Computer Information Sci Prof
Huber, Joan Raphael
Assoc Prof of English
Johnson, Stephen R.
Coll of Arts & Scis Assoc Dean
Kavoosi, Jehan Gir
Assistant Professor of Busines
Kole, James Patrick
Assoc Prof of Acad Support Svc
Kuehn, Myrna Foster
Speech Communication Professor
Leavy, Thomas A.
Earth Science Prof Emeritus
Lewis, Richard A.
Mathematics Teacher
Mac Daniel, Elizabeth Jo
Assistant Professor of English
Mc Cord, Donald Eugene
Soc Stud & Photography Tchr
Mc Cullough, John Robert
Elementary Education Instr
Mc Elhattan, Glenn Richard
Chemistry Professor
Mechling, Kenneth R.
Prof of Bio & Science Ed
Miller, Mary Jane
English Teacher
Otte, Randon C.
Accounting Professor
Pesek, James Gregory
Prof of Mgmt & Dept Chair
Quesenberry, Legene
Assoc Prof of Bus
Raehsler, Rod D.
Economics Professor
Sabousky, Richard Anthony
Spcl Ed & Rehabilitation Prof
Sayre, Nancy Ressler
Professor
Schumaker, Ronald C.
Professor of English
Smaby, Beverly Prior
Assoc Professor of History
Smith, Kathleen Ann
Professor of Education
Spina, Vincent
Associate Professor of Spanish
Stuhldreher, Thomas John
Professor of Finance
VanLandingham, Marguerite H.
Professor of Finance
Weckerly, Gary L.
Industrial & Technology Tchr
Zielinski, Edward J.
Science Education Professor
CLARKS SUMMIT
Bailey, Jacklyn Evans
2nd Grade Teacher
Bartz, Mary Alice
Kindergarten Teacher
Chase, Barry A.
Dept Chairperson & Teacher
Daniels, Robert G.
Physical Education Teacher
Eynon, William L.
Health & Physical Ed Teacher
Firmin, Michael
Assoc Prof & Psych Dept Chrmn
Foster, Jean Zenke
Mathematics Teacher
Frutchey, James A.
Soc Stud Coord Tchr
Healey, Patricia Anne
Spanish Teacher
Holdridge, Donald Wesley, Sr.
Bible & Greek Professor
Kauffman, Larry Dale
Professor of Music
Kieffer, Donald H.
Physics Teacher
Lefchak, Arlene Harris
High School Math Teacher
Long, Jay Edwards
Professor of English
Mamana, Lisa Ann
English Teacher
Maxwell, Brian
Assistant Professor
McNamee, Joyce Marie
Prof & Dept Chair of Chrstn Ed

Palmer, Vincent Louis, Jr.
Professor of Education
Petty, Dena
Art Teacher
Reidenbach, Robert David
Social Studies Teacher
Rhodes, Mary Belin
Mathematics Teacher
Schrecengost, Laurie Ann
Music Professor
Searfoss, Denise DeStefano
Orchestra Director
Steier, Gary L.
4th Grade Teacher
Steinberg, Sandra Lebowitz
Learning Support Teacher
Urnoski, Barbara Keating
Third Grade Teacher
Welcome, Claude
Weight Training Supervisor
CLAYSBURG
Crist, Daniel Thomas
Sixth Grade Teacher
Harella, Shelda J.
First Grade Teacher
Hauck, Candace Ann
Business Education Teacher
Lantz, Thomas H.
Admin Asst & English Instr
Markel, Donald L.
Instrumental Music Teacher
Slick, Nancy Corle
Remedial Math Teacher
CLAYSVILLE
Buckholt, Paul Allan
Chemistry Teacher
Clutter, Barbara Mary
7th-8th Grade Teacher
Farabee, Darlene F. H.
Fifth Grade Teacher
Flanigan, James Robert
English Teacher
Harris, Kathleen Kline
Teacher of Gifted Support
Leshor, Alan Wayne
Mathematics Teacher
Little, Janet Marie
French Teacher
Manni, Karen Bertolotti
Business Teacher & Dept Chprsn
Marasco, Floyd C., Jr.
Instr of Math & Computer Sci
Mc Elhaney, Gayle Grim
5th Grade Elementary Teacher
Shingle, Zonie S.
English Teacher
Smiley, Billie Jo (Ferrari)
Kindergarten Teacher
Stewart, Pamela Widdup
Middle School Counselor
CLEARFIELD
Carr, Robert Lance
Chemistry Teacher
Gilliland, Judy Witherow
8th Grade Science Teacher
Haag, Harvey Eugene
Physics Instructor
Hoover, Nancy Royer
High School Business Teacher
Love, Betsy Jay
2nd Grade Teacher
Mandel, John Paul
Vocational Welding Teacher
Mandell, Raymond Andrew
Band & Orchestra Director
Marsh, Kimberly Ann Heller
Nursing Instructor
Marshall, Barbara Undercofler
Second Grade Teacher
Martin, James Edwin
Driver Education Teacher
Meckey, Marylynne Learish
English Teacher
Moore, Jerry Lee
5th & 6th Grade Teacher
Myers, Sandra Ellen
Eighth Grade English Teacher
Williams, Barbara Lee
Social Studies Teacher
Young, Susan Fleming
Fourth Grade Teacher
Zelenky, Susan Smith
Biology Teacher
CLEARVILLE
Border, Richard Allen
Head Teacher
Hedrick, Andrew Roy
Third Grade Teacher
COAL CENTER
Antal, Linda M.
Teaching Assistant
Dillon, Richard Lawrence
Biology & Adv Biology Tchr
Dillon, Susan
English Teacher
Pietrzak, James Kevan
English Teacher
Scrip, Diane Webb
Fifth Grade Teacher
Ulrich, Sandra Anne
Speech & Language Pathologist
COAL TOWNSHIP
Davis, Chet John
Art Teacher
Dobeck, JoAnn Naroleski
4th Grade Teacher
Fegley, Denise Kissel
Business Teacher
Korbich, Lee Edward
Accounting Teacher

COAL TOWNSHIP (cont)
Losiewicz, Debra Reed
2nd Grade Teacher
Roman, Janet Marie
Art Instructor & Dept Chprsn
COATESVILLE
Arvay, Camie Marie
Elementary School Principal
Buckwash, Anthony Joseph
Physics Teacher
Campayo, Karin Poole
Spanish Teacher
Churchill, Deborah Jean
Music Teacher
Clees, Pamela Cressman
Art Teacher
Coates, David B.
Social Studies Teacher
Davis, Donald Lee
Math Tchr & Interim Dept Chair
Di Felice, Christy Anne
Biology Teacher
Dunleavy, Patricia M.
Third Grade Teacher
Fogell, Heather E.
Biology Teacher
Ford, John W.
7th Grd Soc Stud Tchr & Coach
Grady, Verona Marjorie
4th Grade Teacher
Hager, Peggy Mc Adam
6th Grd Math & Reading Teacher
Holley-Sheppard, Camille J.
8th Grd Lang Arts & Rdng Tchr
Johnson, Crystal Perry
African Amer, Global Stud Tchr
Keech, Thomas N.
Seventh Grade Science Teacher
Kimes, Kaye M.
Mathematics Teacher
Lacey, Patricia Verdieck
Substitute Teacher
Lucerne, Mary Joyce Davidson
Second Grade Teacher
Mendenhall, William L., III
Chemistry Teacher
Osterberg, Kristen Caloun
Middle School Science Teacher
Riley, Mary C.
7th-8th Grd Science Teacher
Stubinski, Julia A.
Science Teacher & Dept Chair
COCHRANTON
Aleksiewicz, William
Geog, Psych & Sociology Tchr
Bradshaw, Annette M.
Art Teacher
Buckeye, Carole Lynn (Osborne)
Health & PE Teacher
Niebauer, Bernard Andrew
Mathematics & Computer Teacher
Wilcox, Emma Elizabeth
Eng Instructor & Dept Coord
COCOLAMUS
Hart, Delmar Ray
Biology Teacher
Weaver, Ray Edward
English Teacher
COGAN STATION
Rost, Michele L.
Substitute Teacher
COLLEGEVILLE
Buckwalter, Lydia Taxis
First Grade Teacher
Cochran, Frederick Hayden
Technology Education Teacher
Dugan, Natalie M.
English & Computers Teacher
Economopoulos, Andrew James
Economics Professor
England, Eileen M.
Assoc Professor of Psychology
Evan, Andrew J.
Technology Education Teacher
Farrell, Susan Janet
7th Grade Social Studies Tchr
Fortmann, Nancy Merrion
11th Grade English Teacher
Hersh, Lynn Casselberry
Librarian
Joseph, Laurie B.
Visiting Professor of Biology
Klinger, Susan Smith
Art Teacher
Krieger, Ford
History Teacher
Mc Connell, Lois Naylor
Retired First Grade Teacher
Rembisz, James Theodore
Eighth Grade English Teacher
Schofield, Timothy L.
Instructor of Statistics
Shinehouse, E. Jane
Prof of Biology
COLLINGDALE
Kearney, Paula F.
Owner & Instructor
COLUMBIA
Martin, Jolene Hohenadel
Math Teacher & Dept Chair
Morgan, Debra Hilbert
Math Teacher
Phiel, Jean Elizabeth
English Teacher
Roat, Randy Scott
Visual Communications Teacher
Swarr, Frederick Dean
Designer & Graphic Coord

COMMODORE
Cicon, Melanie Ann
Chemistry Teacher
Hess, Joy Morgan
Choral Music Teacher
Keith, Raymond J.
Business Education Teacher
Lenzi, Sandra (Henry)
Learning Support Teacher
Marsh, Mary Frances
Family & Consumer Sci Teacher
Price, James Ray
POD & Economics Teacher
Raymond, James F.
Mathematics Teacher
Rescinito, Nancy R. Snyder
12th Grade English Teacher
CONFLUENCE
Hall, Glen
Social Science Teacher
CONNEAUT LAKE
Rea, Ruth Wilson
Music Teacher & Band Director
CONNEAUTVILLE
Baker, Donna M.
English Teacher
Bizjak, Frank A.
7th-12th Grd Ag Ed Teacher
Cameron, Glenn Richard
Music Teacher
Willmarth, Jacquelin Louise Tillack
First Grade Teacher
CONNELLSVILLE
Coles, Natalie Moon
Reading Specialist
Colvin, William Dolquest
English & Theater Teacher
Egan, Richard A.
Rel Studies Tchr & Dept Chm
Fedorko, Robert J.
Social Studies Teacher
Hanna, Toni Cocciardo
Learning Disabilities Instr
Hornick, Chris C.
Band Director
Karp, Barbara Molinaro
9th Grade English Teacher
Karwatsky, Donna J.
Mathematics Teacher
Kirk, Carol Rebecca
Day Care Dir & Child Dev Instr
Krasonic, Barbara L.
Cosmetology Supervisor
Lloyd, Barbara Shirey
7th Grade English Teacher
Lynn, Donald R., Jr.
Health & Physical Ed Teacher
Lynn, Sara Horton
Fifth Grade Teacher
Mascia, Cheryl A.
5th-8th Grade Teacher
Mc Garrity, Michael Patrick
English Teacher
Poindexter, James Allen
Chemistry Teacher
Ritch, Gregory Allen
Sixth Grade Teacher
Ritenour, Lynne E. (White)
English & Rdng Enrichment Tchr
Shultz, Edward Dane
Band Director
Simonsen, Mary Gartner
French Teacher
Swan, Andrea Speshock
Second Grade Teacher
Thompson, Eugenia Gay
Art Teacher
Wandel, Gary Lewis
Mathematics Teacher
Witt, Donald
Band Director
Work-Nardone, Judy Swan
2nd Grade Teacher
CONSHOHOCKEN
Bazela, Mary Theresa Ann
Fourth Grade Teacher
Kelly, William Joseph
Teacher
White, Beverly Spangler
3rd Grade Teacher
CONWAY
Giannette, Helen
Retired Elementary Ed Teacher
COPLAY
Mertz, Mary Beth Danko
Seventh Grade Teacher
CORAOPOLIS
Bellotti Puppo, Janet Marie
French & Religion Teacher
Boni, Jimmy Julian
6th Grade Social Studies Tchr
Brasko, Robert James
Social Studies Teacher
Brenneisen, Claudia (Grogan)
High School English Teacher
Corwin, Norma Baum
Band & Choral Director
End, Albert W.
8th Grade Social Studies Tchr
Gibson, Pamela H.
5th Grade Teacher
Griffith, William Grady
8th Grade Math Teacher
Guiler, Jeffery Kent
Asst Prof of Management
Keller, Karen Jean (Wilson)
Family & Consumer Sci Teacher
Keller, Robert Eugene
Physics Teacher

Kirk, George William, III
Fifth Grade Math Teacher
Laverty, J. Patrick
Assistant Professor
Meacci, Kathy Zajackowski
Science Dept Chair & Teacher
Miller, Jacqueline Wilson
First Grade Teacher
Morelli, Richard
Span Tchr & Frgn Lang Dept Chm
Munger, Sarah Virginia (Quarles)
Retired Teacher of GATE
Pander, Betty J.
Marketing Tchr & Coordinator
Robinson-Dryja, Diane M.
First Grade Teacher
Skovira, Robert Joseph
Computer & Systems Professor
Vogler, Bernard J.
Chemistry Teacher & Dept Head
Walters, Laura Plesluska
Learning Support, Spec Ed Tchr
CORRY
Baressi, Terri Moore
Second Grade Teacher
Hixson, Heather A.
Fifth Grade Teacher
Johnston, Christine Lynne
Personal Care Teacher
Laird, H. A. Skip
Business Teacher
Machek, Kimberly Fernberg
Business Education Teacher
Maynard, Dean Clark
Elementary Principal
Potocki, Edmond James
Sci Dept Chair & Physics Tchr
Yovich, James Eli
5th Grd Math, Sci & Rdng Tchr
COUDERSPORT
Harpst, Thomas A.
Counselor & Athletic Director
Kirby, Barbara B.
Jr High English Teacher
Todd, Linda Stohr
Third Grade Teacher
Wilkinson, James W.
English Teacher
CRESCO
Jabaro, Judith Nixon
Fourth Grade Teacher
Kielceski, Thomas Aquinas
Junior High School Teacher
Romspert, Ralph Carl, Sr.
Fourth Grade Teacher
CRESSON
Anderson, Albert F.
Legal Asst Pgm of Studies Dir
Baacke, Nancy L.
English Teacher
Baacke, Timothy A.
Director of Bands
Bittner, Rosemary Cherban
Assistant Professor of Nursing
Grafton, Dirk S.
Asst Prof of Criminology
Hoffman, Anne Shields
School Counselor
Hoover, Mark Francis
Natural Science Instructor
Inman, John G.
English Teacher
Kopanic, Michael J., Jr.
Asst Prof of Social Sciences
Lawlor, Dana Rose
Senior English Teacher
Mc Cool, Deborah (Butler)
Science Teacher
Myers, Kenneth James
Mathematics & Science Teacher
Rodgers, Ramona Thraese
Spanish Teacher
Smith, Janice Koshak
Med Lab Tech Instr & Ed Coord
Weyant, Lee E.
Adjunct Instructor Bus Admin
CROYDON
Hansell, Eleanor Williams
Retired Elementary Teacher
CROYDON MANOR
Bobst, Cynthia Wojcik
Third Grade Teacher
CRUM LYNNE
Ludman, Karen Lee
Second Grade Teacher
CURWENSVILLE
Buhler, Jay Warren
Music Teacher
Decker, George R.
English Teacher
Irwin, Elmo
English Teacher & Dept Chm
Linsenbigler, David Allen
Math Teacher
Mc Cracken, Dorothy Knepp
Fourth Grade Teacher
Wetzel, Sally
Spanish Teacher
Witherow, Wendy Lee (Bloom)
Swimming Instructor
DALLAS
Amesbury, Norine Mary
English Teacher
Calderone, Antoinette Battista
Asst Prof of Nursing Dept
Calderone, James Michael
Assoc Prof of Soc Work
Campbell, Abby Ann
Bio & Human Physiology Tchr

Cipriani, Joseph Anthony
Assistant Professor
Crabtree, Glenda Wilson
Fifth Grade Teacher
DiPino, Frank
Professor of Biology
Fries, Donald O.
Professor of History
Halesey, Elaine DiRisio
Radiography Prof & Dept Chair
Howanitz, Eugene J.
Staff Dev Dir & English Instr
Hunter, Todd Lee
Music Dept Chprsn & Band Dir
Jenkins, Georgia Ann (Bershee)
High School Math Teacher
LaJeunesse, Charles Allen
Director Dept of Psychology
LoRusso, Stephen Michael
Assistant Prof of Biology
McCann, Patricia Marie, RSM
Associate Professor
Moran, Michael Lee
Assistant Prof of Phys Therapy
Morris, Claire Palchanis
Art Teacher
Nolan, Kathleen M.
Professor of Teacher Education
Patrick, David George
Assistant Professor
Payne, David Minton
Associate Professor of English
Pedersen, Larry David
Chemistry Associate Professor
Rakowski, Joan Levandowski
6th & 8th Grade Teacher
Rybak, Ronald Edward
Physical Sci Teacher & Chair
Shah, Lalit Jamnadas
Asst Prof of Occup Therapy
Silfies, Sheri Paulette
Asst Prof of Phys Therapy
Simon, Abraham Joseph
Mathematics Teacher
Sprau, Sandra Gordon
Mathematics Teacher
Sunday-Lefkowitz, Lisa
Asst Prof of Occuptnl Therapy
Walker, Karen Elizabeth
Asst Professor of Biology
DALLASTOWN
DeLancey, Donald E.
7th Grade Social Studies Tchr
Gable, David Joseph
Biology Teacher
Geesey, Kathy Louise (Zimmerman)
Math Teacher
Ilyes, Mark Allen
Physics Teacher
Miller, Beth Reichard
English Teacher
Miller, Nadine C.
Social Science Teacher
Noll, Mark Vincent
Social Studies Teacher
Raver, Debra Ellen (Eshelman)
English Teacher
Reese, James E.
Early American History Teacher
Shultz, Carolyn L.
10th Grade World Cultures Tchr
Stauffer, Jud Fix
English Teacher
Stock, Sandy
Science Teacher
Taylor, Nancy K.
Book Store Owner
DANBORO
Mulholland, Susan Steele
Teacher of the Gifted
Reese, June Bucciarelli
Fourth Grade Teacher
DANVILLE
Ackerman, Patricia Driscoll
English & Speech Teacher
Albertson, Harold Joseph
Math Teacher & Athletic Dir
Berkey, Charles C.
Art Teacher & GED Instructor
Bower, Jack R.
Band Director
Brandt, Jeffrey Earl
8th Grade Math Teacher
Callahan, Thomas J.
English Teacher
Gaugler, Penny L.
Seventh Grade Reading Teacher
Gilmore, Sandra Buchanan
Latin & Spanish Teacher
Harter, Mollie
English Teacher
Kettlewell, Jane
4th Grade Teacher
Mc Donnell, Darby Unger
8th Grade Science Teacher
Moser, Steve William
Mathematics Teacher
Nied, John A.
Librarian
Pongratz, Elaine M.
Title I Reading Specialist
Romanski, Carl Vincent
Spanish Teacher
Woll, Bernard D.
Elementary Teacher
DARBY
Dingle, Donna Victoria
Elementary Teacher

DARLINGTON
Benetti, Marsha Burns
Second Grade Teacher
DAVIDSVILLE
Bowman, Jan Albright
English Teacher
Drusak, Linda C.
Guidance Counselor
Grisin, Suzette Aline
Band Director
Haddle, Deanna Chirillo
Chemistry Teacher
Kory, Mary Moore
Reading Teacher
Pepoy, Marya Alexandra
HS PE Teacher & Ath Trainer
Ricotta, Santo Joseph
Math & Computer Teacher
DEFIANCE
Feight, Carolyn Conley
Second Grade Teacher
DENVER
Brubaker-Shober, Gloria A.
First Grade Teacher
DERRY
Baltzer, Cindy Eisenhauer
Vocal Music Teacher
Basciano, Anthony Norman
HS Guidance Counselor
Egner, Karen I.
Tchr & Frgn Lang Dept Chair
Mc Wherter, Kimberly Rupert
Chemistry Teacher
Werner, Robert
English Dept Chairman & Tchr
Yourish, Kenneth Paul
Social Studies Teacher
Zahuranic, Debra Louise
Business Education Teacher
DEVAULT
Wilkey, Robert W.
Fifth Grade Teacher
DEVON
Reilly, Jean Francis
Instrl Aide for Emtnl Sprt Cls
DILLSBURG
Parry, David G.
Driver Education Instructor
Rehmeyer, Terry Louis
Health Education Teacher
Rudisiu, Clair Michael
Physical Education Teacher
Smith, Linda Springer
Learning Support Teacher
Thuma, Kathy Knaub
Home Economics Teacher
Young, Anne Bennighoff
Third Grade Teacher
DIMOCK
Cimino, James Louis
Automotive Teacher
Denkenberger, Charles Dean
Math Teacher & Dept Chair
Dymond, Kimberly Ann
Chemistry & Physics Teacher
Falkowski, Edward Albert
School Psychologist
Ferguson, Robert W., Jr.
Sixth Grade Teacher
Holbert, Barbara Ellen
Vocal Music Tchr & Dept Head
Host, Kathleen E. Flanagan
French & English Teacher
Jones, Donna Marlene
German & English Teacher
Montross, H. Chris
Guidance Counselor
Morahan, John Kelly
HS Soc Stud & Drivers Ed Tchr
Thornton, Michael Francis
Dean of Students
Zurn, Vickie C.
Fourth Grade Teacher
DOUGLASSVILLE
Smith, Leonard C.
Fifth Grade Teacher
DOVER
Apgar, Andrew Russell
Vocal & Choral Music Teacher
Arendt, Donald M.
Social Studies Chair
Bailey, Gary Dean
8th Grade English & LA Tchr
Bishard, Lois Burd
Fifth Grade Teacher
George, Danielle Ruth (Barone)
Spanish Teacher
Gise, Nancy Jeannette (Reed)
Retired 4th Grade Teacher
Hamilton, Robert M.
Principal
Hoover, Douglas E., II
History & Government Teacher
Kaltreider, Carolyn A.
8th Grade English Teacher
Lipschutz, Betty Lowe
Second Grade Teacher
Long, Susan J.
Transitional First Grd Tchr
Ney, Cassi E.
English Teacher
Shuman, Susan Evancho
French Teacher
Snyder, Jeffrey Lynn
Fine Arts Dept Chr, Music Tchr
Snyder, Lisa Kay
Family & Consumer Sci Tchr
Spahr, Bertha E.
Chemistry Teacher

(cont)
, Linda R.
rade Teacher
, James M.
logy Education Teacher
Ann M.
Teacher
ieila Van Pelt
Teacher
NGTOWN
ren Lynne
Teacher
Kelly J.
Teacher
ichard J.
r
l. Michele
ade Teacher
Louis Eugene
rade US History Teacher
Rebecca Backstetter
Teacher
erri-Lee Morris
acher
June Mc Lorie
Grade Teacher
, William G.
nce Counselor
Darryl Frank
d Physical Ed Teacher
inda J.
ade Teacher
d, Rebecca C.
acher & Dept Chair
Mary Penketh
n Department Chair
homas Allen
h Teacher
Karen Lynne
ss Education Teacher
Margaret J.
h Teacher
Michael John
n & English Teacher
ie A.
Grade Teacher
Hayden
matics Teacher
, Kathy Morgan
s Teacher
Pamela Ann
matics Teacher
a, Jacquelyn Lee
Grade Teacher
den, Yvone
n Teacher
Francis J.
ss Education Teacher
harles Stanley
Music Teacher
Martha Dilworth
ng Support Teacher
eborah T.
Teacher
George Winston
Studies Teacher
, Ronald James
acher
, Maryanne Ford
rade English Teacher
David John
& Physical Science Tchr
on, David Emanual
rade Teacher
on, Nancy Wessels
sh Teacher
r, Cynthia Knisley
an Teacher
t, Virginia Alison
Grade Teacher
hirley Palmer
chr & Sci Dept Chair
a, Cindy Nelson
y & Consumer Sci Teacher
no, Nita Harris
istry Instructor
ino-Sutton, Erica
sh Teacher
, Gerald Louis
sh Teacher
son, Barbara Pitts
rade Teacher
Mary Sue
nd Grade Teacher
son, Terry Allen
gy & Earth Science Tchr
n, Joan Marie (Hess)
r High Mathematics Tchr
ben, Lynore Heinzelmann
& Environmental Sci Tchr
awsky, Nancy Tighe
al Studies Teacher
Sandra M.
nd Grade Teacher
ESTOWN
Ann M.
stant Professor of English
John Herbert
Business Dept Chair
ler, Merry Lee
h Grade Teacher
nan, Pamela Geisert
School Librarian
Sarah R.
ematics Teacher
Howard L.
scape Contracting Prof
, Gerry
ish Teacher

Gilbert, Rodney
Asst Prof of Animal Science
Hofsaess, Fredrick Roger
Professor of Animal Science
Holowathy, AnnMarie
Science Teacher
Kane, Douglas Henry
Environmental Design Asst Prof
Kane, Marie Reddington
English Teacher
Kolman, Matthew Howard
English Department Chairman
Kuntzmann, Ann Lewine
Guidance Counselor
Lomas, Jeremy Richard
Elem Gifted Education Teacher
Marino, Paul M.
Asst Professor of Education
Mishler, John Milton
Professor of Biology
Morris, Larry D.
Animal & Diary Science Prof
Novelli, Robert John
Adjunct Prof of Liberal Arts
Ohrt, Joseph Glen
Director of Choral Activities
Perry, John R.
Math Teacher
Rusiloski, Benjamin Edward
Asst Professor of Chemistry
Shenberger, Gerald R.
HS Industrial Technology Tchr
Sinnamon, Robert Hume, Jr.
Chemistry Teacher
Tabachnick, Michael Neil
Associate Professor of Physics
Walty, Margaret
English Teacher
Willoughby, Lynne Eve
Equine Science Instructor
Yetto, Lynette M.
Teacher of the Gifted & Eng
Ziemer, Richard Carl
Professor of Liberal Arts
DRESHER
Bernstein, Patricia Lange
Health & Physical Ed Teacher
Bishop, Susan Mason
First Grade Teacher
Long, John Tees, Jr.
Sixth Grade Math & Sci Tchr
Lower, Conrad H., III
English Teacher & Admin Asst
Parsons, Craig Lloyd
Fifth Grade Teacher
DREXEL HILL
Buckley, Paul A.
English Teacher
Carpenter, Loraine Kelly
Art Teacher
Celidonio, Ralph Joseph
Asst Principal & Math Tchr
Citro, Patricia H.
Science Teacher
Cullerton, Carol L., SSJ
Secondary Mathematics Teacher
Curran, Mary Denise D.
Mathematics Teacher
Dickerson, Maxine Morris
English Teacher
Ferrence, John Joseph, OSA
Chemistry Teacher
Frick, Robert George
5th Grade Teacher
Lotka, Edwina Rose
Retired Teacher
McDonald, Amy E.
High School Science Teacher
Moore, Linda Dawson
Science & Lang Arts Teacher
Plagge, Maureen Anne
Language Arts Teacher
Rishel, Craig David
Fourth Grade Teacher
Shaw, Florence L.
Third Grade Teacher
Smith, Aniece Odelia
Business Teacher
Spotwood, Joseph Benson
Spanish Teacher
Streibig, Jean C., RSM
Math Teacher
Taylor, Elizabeth Mary
Second Grade Teacher
Yost, Michael Joseph
Seventh Grade Science Teacher
DRUMS
Stiller, Connie Kreider
Pastor
DU BOIS
Bonomo, Daniel
Music Educator & Dir of Bands
Bundy, Samuel Lewis
English & Mass Media Tchr
Chollock, Donna Reed
Biology Teacher & Dept Chmn
Crooks, Kathleen Myers
1st Grade Teacher
Gallagher, Barry Lee
Eco, World & European His Tchr
Haser, Barbara Lundberg
2nd Grade Teacher
Mounts, Dorothy L.
Math Teacher
Pasternak, Charles John
Social Studies Teacher
Rensel, Aileen Mc Elhattan
Senior High English Teacher
Shade, Thomas Earl
9th Grade History Teacher

Shindledecker, Elizabeth Morris
Fourth Grade Teacher
Stellabuto, David L.
Mathematics & Reading Teacher
Swoger, Mark Stephen
Language & Theology Teacher
Vallone, Antonio
Associate Professor of English
DUNBAR
Culver, Susan Jane
Second Grade Teacher
DUNCANNON
Becker, Kathleen A.
Secondary Biology Teacher
Gunderman, Rick Allen
HS Learning Support Teacher
Kerstetter, Jeffrey Allen
Seventh Grade Science Teacher
Lesh, Mary Hagstrom
Third Grade Teacher
Wiehe, James Michael
History Teacher
DUNCANSVILLE
Bundy, Robert Bryon
5th Grade Teacher
Ross, Patricia May (Durkin)
Emergency Med Tech Instr
Vella, Diane Elaine
6th Grade Teacher
DUNMORE
Ferguson, James Joseph
Sixth Grade Teacher
Revta, Joyce
Fourth Grade Teacher
DUQUESNE
Geric, James W.
Sr High School Guidance Cnslr
Kavish, Linda L.
English & Gifted Ed Teacher
EAST BERLIN
Smith, Richard C.
Retired Teacher
EAST FREEDOM
Heuston, Linda Dutrow
2nd Grade Teacher
EAST GREENVILLE
Farkas, Richard David
Sixth Grade Teacher
Horn, Marti Meyer
Teacher of the Gifted
Johnson, Roger William
Guidance Counselor
Krum, Carol Ann (La Bar)
Seventh Grade Math Teacher
Wehr, M. Scott
Sixth Grade Teacher
EAST LANSDOWNE
Cashwell, Jeanne Willert
Eighth Grade Teacher
Kurley, Dolores Therese
Administrative Assistant
EAST STROUDSBURG
Catrillo, Michael
Assistant Principal
Christian, Edward Henry
English Tchr & Head Ftbl Coach
Fritz, Nancy Jane
French Teacher
Gilliland, Linda Frace
German Teacher & Dept Head
Hahn, Elizabeth R.
English Teacher
Hickey, Deborah Peeney
Latin & English Teacher
Huffman, Barbara J.
English Teacher & Dept Chprsn
Johnson, Frank E.
HPE Teacher & Dept Chprsn
Kreiter, Dee Andress
Title I Reading Specialist
Lantz, David J., III
Vocal Music Director
Lubrecht, Karen Emley
Math & Computer Science Tchr
Marcial, Laurence Gabriel
Sociology & US History Teacher
Martini, James A.
Instrumental Music Teacher
Molin, Maurice John
Social Studies Teacher
Nace, Kevin D.
Social Studies Teacher
Nauman, Deborah Fredrick
Eighth Grade Reading Teacher
Nye, John Boland
Mathematics Teacher
Rine, Jerome T.
Retired 5th Grade Teacher
Rogers, Denise S.
Business Teacher
Seely, Brian L.
Mathematics Teacher
Steere, Daniel Edwards
Assistant Professor
Stem, Clark A.
World Cultures Instructor
Stem, Darla
3rd Grade Teacher
Ullo, Carol Michaels
French Teacher
Yarnall, Lois Groff
Social Studies Teacher
EASTON
Bath, Richard John
Mathematics Teacher
Brown, Jacquelyn C.
9th Grade English Teacher
Bruen, Thurza
Second Grade Teacher

Chisesi, Cheri Sweeney
Math Teacher
Cimino, Maryann Dietrich
High School Art Teacher
Corpora, Jeffrey Allen
Social Studies Teacher & Coord
DeGrandis, Ronald Wayne
Instrumental Music Teacher
Di Candia, Anthony
Italian Teacher
Dolan, Deborah Jo
English & Writing Teacher
Erhardt, Wendy Charles
English Teacher
Ernst, Beverly Kay (Repsher)
Principal & HS Supervisor
Galie, Doreen J.
Theology & Pub Speaking Tchr
Halley, Lewis Edward
History Teacher
Irish, Linda Hogerhuis
HS Family & Consumer Sci Tchr
Kaye, Daniel B.
English Dept Chairperson
Kellow, Glenda Phillips
Hlth & Physical Education Tchr
Leyshon, Deborah L.
Vocal Music Teacher
Loch, Dale Ann A.
Instructional Support Teacher
Lutte, Carole Anne
Instrumental Teacher
Matus, Bernard T.
Director of Science & Tech
Nagy, Christopher Joseph
Assistant Principal
Orlemann, Karen Sergi
Private Tutoring
Persichini, Carl Joseph
Math Teacher
Pfeffer, Nancy Louise
Vocal Music Teacher
Phillips, Fred Cleveland, III
Senior Accounting Instructor
Pulli, Michael Charles
Fifth Grade Teacher
Sayago, Teresa Borio
English Teacher
Shriver, Norma Pratt
English Teacher
Shupp, Richard C., Jr.
Spanish Teacher
Siegfried, Christine L.
Business Education Teacher
Silhanek, Anda M.
Latin Teacher
Sullivan, Rosemarie Trinchere
First Grade Teacher
Thomas, John Joseph
Mathematics Teacher
Trimble, Eleanor Seeley
11th-12th Grade English Tchr
Vernarr, Susan Bray
First Grade Teacher
Warman, Linda K.
English Dept Chair & AP Instr
Wendell, Meryl Tarlow
English Tchr & Rdng Specialist
EBENSBURG
Bixel, Allen P.
Music Director
Burda, Diana
English Teacher
Corrente, William F.
Social Studies & English Tchr
Furnari, Kimberly A.
7th-8th Grade Science Teacher
George, Deborah Dee
Cosmetology Teacher
Hertzog, M. Judine
Fifth Grade Teacher
Hostetler, Sharon Poeta
English Teacher
Kakabar, Carole M. (Leonard)
Science Teacher
Karwoski, Joseph P.
Mathematics & Computer Teacher
Klezek, Stanley Joseph, Jr.
Social Studies Teacher
Koren, Charles J.
High School Principal
Mazzarella, Fred A.
7th Grade Math & Science Tchr
Mazzarella, Michael Lynn
Eighth Grade Science Tchr
Solomon, Allen D.
Mathematics Teacher
Thomas, Alan Edward
Chaplain & Religion Teacher
Thompson, Leslie Roberts
Eighth Grade Teacher
Vaughn, Carolyn Schrader
Art Teacher
Yewcic, John Paul
Health & Physical Ed Teacher
EDINBORO
Alward, Wanda Sandy
Chemistry Teacher
Brickner, Patrick David
Remedial, Enrichment Math Tchr
Donche, Louis
Physical Science Teacher
Gibson, Ben
Professor of Art
Giltinan, David A.
Prof & Physics Dept Chprsn
Gramley, Harold Dean
Professor
Grant, Gary Samuel
Band Director

Kozuchowsky, Michael Edward
Technology Education Teacher
Manchester, Sidney Ronald
Health & PE Teacher
Mc Laren, Harriet Kaye
Chemistry Teacher
Rogers, Nancy Jenkins
Business Teacher
Sababu, Umeme
History Professor
Scaletta, Judith Palmer
Secondary Mathematics Teacher
Solberg, Roger Lee
Assistant Professor of English
Stauffer, Roy Allen
Social Studies Teacher
Warner, D. P.
Art Professor
Weinkauf, David
Assistant Professor
White, Loren F.
Sixth Grade Teacher
ELDERTON
Foust, Susan E.
Business Teacher
Przybysz, Christie Minor
Science Teacher
SeCaur, Robert Michael
Chem, Gen Sci & Math Teacher
ELIZABETH
Bricker, Alan Keith
MS Band & French Teacher
Caranese, Ellen E.
Teacher of Bus Ed & Gifted
Dumm, James F.
Science Teacher
Dykstra, Janet Dzvricsko
Mathematics Teacher
Hartle, Sallie E.
Eng II & American Lit Teacher
Heimlich, Judy Nicholas
Fourth Grade Teacher
Holder, Margaret C.
English & Spanish Teacher
Kroskie, Karen A.
English Teacher
Macik, Patricia Ann
English Teacher
Martin, George A.
Fifth Grade Teacher
Mazurek, Malena Marie
Biology Teacher
Mc Keever, Gary W.
Instrumental Music & Band Dir
Menzies, Thomas James
Math Teacher
Semchak, Janet L.
6th Grade English Teacher
Thuransky, Sally Simon
Speech & English Teacher
Vitori, William Scott
Chemistry Teacher
Yarosh, John Keith
Gen & Accelerated Chem Tchr
ELIZABETHTOWN
Barnada, Kurt
Assoc Prof of Modern Languages
Baylor, Scott A.
Chemistry Teacher
Biddle, Kevin Lee
Social Studies & Reading Tchr
Brandt, Karen Wolfe
9th & 11th Grd English Tchr
Cairns, Colette D.
Business Teacher
Cox, Carol W.
Former English Teacher
Ellsworth, Delbert Warren
Professor of Psychology
Ficca, Tammy Knerr
English Teacher
Gattens, Gary Hugh
Technology Education Teacher
Koman, Marcy Firestone
Third Grade Teacher
Martzall, Deborah Weaver
Art Teacher
Miller, Beth Longwell
Seventh Grd Language Arts Tchr
Miller, Donald James
German Teacher
Shahid, Lisa Gross
Global Studies Teacher
Truitt, Margaret Lockerman
Fourth Grade Teacher
Ulrich, Beverly Gish
Third Grade Teacher
Whitmore, Joseph Armstrong, Jr.
PE & Head Ath Trainer
Wollaston, Diane
American History Teacher
ELIZABETHVILLE
Hamme, Ronald Edward
Fine Arts & Humanities Teacher
Lentz, Eileen H.
Substitute Teacher
Smeltz, Todd Brian
Chemistry & Mathematics Tchr
ELKINS PARK
Pasceri, Cynthia Esmark
Instructional Support Teacher
Poindexter, David Emory
6th Grade Teacher
Tuckman, Lyn Anne
Curriculum Associate
ELKLAND
Bontempo, Mary Jones
Learning Support Teacher

ELLIOTTSBURG
Elmes, Celia M. Haflett
English Teacher
Hege, Stephen K.
6th Grd Math, Sci & Hlth Tchr
Kennedy, Nada Trout
Third Grade Teacher
Morrison, Jennifer E.
English Teacher
Neely, Fred Eugene
Biology Teacher
Richelderfer, Julie Rigby
Social Studies Teacher
Riter, Betsy Henderson
Teacher of the Gifted
Smith, Carl D.
Math Instr & Department Chair
Wagner, Samuel Robert
Agricultural Teacher
Weishaar, Carol
English Tchr & Lang Arts Chair
ELLSWORTH
Mazza, Donald
Instrumental Music Teacher
Medve, Joseph E.
Science Teacher
Nevin, Richard L.
Elem Gen Music & Chorus Tchr
ELLWOOD CITY
Atkins, Marjorie Ann
Mathematics Dept Chairperson
Bowers, Kenneth R.
English Teacher
Cavett, Philip A.
Mathematics Teacher
Craig, Richard Franklin
Sixth Grade Teacher
Finney, Daniela Buccilli
9th Grade English Teacher
Geniviva, Frank J.
Biology Teacher
Ialongo, Vic
High School English Teacher
Lewis, Robert Alan
Industrial Language Teacher
Nathan, Robert
Mrktg Tchr & DECA Advisor
Ottaviani, Virginia Ottobre
Business Ed Tchr & Dept Chprsn
Panico, Samuel John
8th-12th Grade Art Instructor
Rak, Robert Stanley
World Cultures, Sociology Tchr
ELVERSON
Gehret, Jane Henry
Elementary Life Skills Teacher
Koch, Christine Pfennig
Third Grade Teacher
Murphy, Alice Hughes
English Dept Chair & Teacher
Newpher, Nancy A.
6th Grade Teacher
Paull, Susanne Kay
Mathematics Teacher
Peters, Susan A.
Mathematics Teacher
Regener, Dale Kay
Earth Sci Chemistry Teacher
Rodgers, Lana Lusch
Third Grade Teacher
Swart, Marilyn Long
Fifth Grade Teacher
EMLENTON
Joy, Susan Christy
Fourth Grade Teacher
Wilkins, Beth Bishop
Sixth Grade Science Teacher
EMMAUS
Anger, Timothy Alan
Math, Sci Tchr & Asst Prin
Baluh, Marilyn Young
Fourth Grade Teacher
Beidelman, Rebecca Ellen
Social Studies Teacher
Blackstone, Carlen L.
HS Math & Comp Sci Teacher
Butler, Keith D.
Biology & Computer Teacher
Hersperger, Susan Lynn
7th Grade Language Arts Tchr
Kohl, Anthony Thomas
American Literature Teacher
Moll, Suzanne Huber
Mathematics Teacher
Moundschein, Richard Joseph
Mathematics Teacher
Peiffer, Derek William
Social Studies Teacher
Smartschan, Carl Ernest
Biology Teacher
Smith, Paul Michael
Biology Teacher
Souders, Bud
General Science Teacher
EMPORIUM
Brody, Rosemarie (Wolfel)
English Teacher
Murray, Erwin L.
Technology Education Teacher
Perkins, Rose M.
First Grade Teacher
Purcell, M. Lea Kennedy
Kindergarten Teacher
Schwer, Patricia Sedor
Home Economics Teacher
Zoschg, Nancy Clark
4th Grade Teacher
ENOLA
Donovan, Michael E.
Fourth Grade Teacher

Gainor, Barry
Amer His & Legal System Tchr
Gardner, Alice Rundell
Fourth Grade Teacher
Seibert, Lee Martin
Social Studies Teacher
Shields, Kimberly
Scndry Learning Support Tchr
EPHRATA
Kurz, Nancy Patterson
Third Grade Teacher
Long, Katharine Mae (Harteustine)
Math Teacher & Supervisor
Miller, Michael Charles
8th Grade English Teacher
Murr, Paul William
Frgn Lang Dept Chair & Tchr
Wee, Patricia Hachten
Biology Teacher
ERDENHEIM
Bierema, Ronald William
Mathematics Teacher
ERIE
Adams, Ann Marie (DeFazio)
Fourth Grd Tchr & Psychologist
Aiello, John Frances
Receptionist
Alexa, Michael Kurty
Math Teacher
Alexander, Sheran Jones
Secondary English Instructor
Amicucci, Frank Vincent
Social Studies Dept Chair
Arnold, John Charles
5th-6th Grd Science Teacher
Astemborski, Yvonne Marie (Hayes)
Third Grade Teacher
Barney, Paul Edward, Jr.
Assistant Professor of Biology
Barthelmes, Ronald Alan
Math & Hnrs Geometry Tchr
Bekic, Leila Esper
Math Teacher
Benedict, Judith Weaver
Spanish Teacher
Benekos, Peter J.
Professor of Admin of Justice
Bennett, Ray
4th Grade Teacher
Best-Proctor, Yvonne Denise
Business Education Teacher
Blakeslee, Clare Eugene
English Teacher
Blinzler, Kay Kingston
Second Grade Teacher
Callaghan, Christopher John
7th & 8th Grd Soc Stud Teacher
Chojnacki, Daniel
Eng as Second Lang Teacher
Christensen, Mitch
Athletic Trainer
Cunningham, H. Wayne
Crafts Teacher
Cunningham, Karen Guyton
Fine Arts Teacher
Daeschner, Rolf Emil
Frgn Langs Dept Chr & Ger Tchr
Davis, Norman Eugene
Coach
Del Rio, Antonio Francisco
Director of Religious Affairs
DeSantis, Nick Charles
6th-8th Grade Science Teacher
Dodsworth, Marjorie VanScoyoc
English Teacher
Drew, Barbara L.
9th & 10th Grade Eng Teacher
Dunn, Emmarae English
Language Arts Teacher
Dworakowski, Karen Cooper
3rd Grade Teacher
English, Patricia Suppa
Teacher
Evans, Joan Pauline
Third Grade Teacher
Fetzner, Katherine Coletta
8th Grade Physical Sci Teacher
Filley, Cheryl Ann
Family & Consumer Sci Educator
Fox, Betty Lou (Corbin)
Second Grade Teacher
Gandolfo, James M.
Instructor in Theatre & Speech
Gehrlein, William Joseph
Reading Specialist
Gourley, Roy James
8th Grd Physical Science Tchr
Grode, Marcia Nelson
French & Spanish Teacher
Grzelak, Diane Zimmerman
Family & Consumer Sci Tchr
Hall, Patricia Nowakowski
Earth Space Science Teacher
Halquist, Shawn Allen
Instrumental Music Teacher
Hanesy, Michael John
Physical Education Teacher
Hanlon, Paige Pulice
Third Grade Teacher
Hansen, John Bryan
7th Grade Science Teacher
Hansen, Thomas Joseph
English Teacher
Haven, Mary Pat
Art Teacher
Henninger, Robert H.
Ec & World Cultures II Tchr
Holland, Gregory Matthew
Social Studies Teacher

Holliday, Melinda Barthelson
English Dept Chprsn & Tchr
Huegel, Darlene M.
German Teacher
Johnson, Johnny C.
Health Teacher
Keough, Margaret Mc Gaughey
Second Grade Teacher
Kirkwold, Korissa Ann
Music Director
Kurre, James A.
Assoc Professor of Economics
Laughlin, Deborah A.
Spanish Teacher
Lee, Clarence A.
Principal
Lego, Pamela Morton
Instructional Support Teacher
Lowrey, Joyce Ann
Education Professor
Lucht, Cheryl Adams
Reading & English Teacher
Lute, Charles Edward
Music Teacher & Dept Chairman
Mac Gregor, Catherine Louise
MS Science & Math Teacher
Maraden, David E.
English Teacher
Margraf, David Jon
Social Studies Teacher
Mastrog, Rosemarie Brindle
Fifth Grade Teacher
Mc Intire, Jack Louis, Jr.
US History & Government Tchr
Merriott, Charles Ronald
ROTC Aerospace Science Instr
Miller, Wendy Dibble
Chemistry Teacher
Morgan, Susan Lorraine
Admin Director of Enrichment
Morosky, Frederick Harry
Science Teacher
Moyer, John Thayer
Language Arts Teacher
Mulligan, David F.
Health & Physical Ed Teacher
Mulligan, James Francis, SSJ
Fac, Eng & Writing Lab Coord
Nawrocki, Daniel A.
Guidance Counselor
Niebauer, Martin Anthony
Mathematics & Computer Chm
Norton, Lisa Ann Holl
First Grade Teacher
Parker, Randy Paul
Science & Computer Teacher
Patton, Shannon Shephard
World Cultures & Ec Teacher
Perrotto, Carol F. (Moser)
5th Grade Teacher
Petrianni, Paul Dana
Social Studies Teacher
Pfisterer, James Richard
Mathematics Teacher
Plavcan, John C.
Physics, Math & Cmptrs Teacher
Pora, Patricia Ann
Second Grade Teacher
Przepierski, Marie Stankavich
Eighth Grd Tchr & Asst Prin
Pulice, Michele Dawn
Second Grade Teacher
Pulice-Loomis, Traci
2nd Grade Teacher
Roddy, Robert Conlin, Jr.
Honors English III Teacher
Ropski, Steven Joseph
Associate Professor in Biology
Rounsley, Susan Loucks
Mathematics Teacher
Sala, Tracy Leigh
Applied Biology & Chem Teacher
Sandusky, Candyce Stebbins
6th Grade Science Teacher
Schmitt, John M.
AP Psychology Teacher
Schroeck, John Thomas
Computer Teacher
Seifert, Marilyn F.
English Teacher
Shesman, Matthew Mark
Mathematics Teacher
Skrypzak, Stanley Robert
English Teacher
Sluga, Craig Charles
Sixth Grade Teacher
Smit, Nancy Jean
Science Teacher
Soliwoda, Pamela Jane (Tonty)
Spanish Teacher
Spinelli, Jack
Earth Science Teacher
Stadtmiller, Marilynn Burdick
English Teacher
Stemmler, Catherine Considine
Fourth Grade Teacher
Stiles, Ruth Hull
Kindergarten Teacher
Tann, Carrie Marie
Fine Arts Dept Chprsn & Tchr
Thayer, Allan Richard
Drafting & Design Tech Tchr
Tracy, Patricia Streich
Health Teacher
Tysiachney, Darlene Nelson
Scndry Schl Reading & Eng Tchr
Vahey, Ellen O'Hara
2nd Grade Teacher
Walsh, Ardis
6th Grade Language Arts Tchr

Wieczorek, Corrine Bush
Business Education Teacher
Williams, Kathy J.
Business Education Teacher
Williams, Stephanie Marie
Family & Consumer Sci Tchr
Williamson, Kent
6th-8th Grd Social Stud Tchr
Yacobozzi, Barbara Lendick
French & English Teacher
Zeisloft, Ruth Bovaird
AP & Hnrs Eng Tchr
ESSINGTON
Braun, Norman F.
8th Grade Algebra Teacher
Mobley, Nancy Hrimnak
Language Arts Teacher
Said, Jane Ann Warburton
Instructional Support Teacher
Schiff, Murray
K-8th Grd Health & PE Teacher
EVANS CITY
Bischak, Kathleen (Huff)
Art Teacher
Edwards, Herbert John
5th Grade Teacher
Griffin, John William
6th Grade Teacher
Simmons, Katherine Smith
Sixth Grade Teacher
Thiebaud, Sandra Robinson
4th Grade Teacher
EVERETT
Ault, Brenda Giffin
Business Teacher
Baca, Fred A.
Spanish Teacher & Dept Head
Dodson, Linda Mae
Math Teacher
Engle, Elizabeth DeVore
Lang Arts Dept Chpsn, Eng Tchr
Karns, Mary B.
English Teacher
Kline, Genie M.
Chemistry & Physics Teacher
Krauss, Laurie Sue
6th Grade Teacher
Snow, Linda Cooper
Family & Consumer Science Chm
Whetstone, Joni Lee
Vocal Music Instructor
EXETER
Gfeller, Marc Andre
Mathematics Teacher
Harmanos, Stephen A.
AP American History Teacher
Kuffa, Elaine Smiles
First Grade Teacher
Lawler, Gloria Ann
Second Grade Teacher
Madrack, Deborah Fialko
Third Grade Teacher
Pizano, David Michael
Mathematics & Physics Teacher
Russo, Philip Thomas
Social Studies Teacher
Wall, Anne Maria
Secondary Biology Teacher
EXTON
Filiaci, Camillo
Track Coach
Garrett, Robert L.
Third Grade Teacher
Knight, Dolores Elaine
Fifth Grade Teacher
Maglio, Mary Beth Hetherington (Evans)
Second Grade Teacher
Maguire, Margaret Bransfield
Second Grade Teacher
FACTORYVILLE
Brown, Nancy Krakosky
English Teacher
Hlavaty, Nancy
Math Teacher
Lengel, Gena
Secondary English Teacher
Malia, Mary
Fourth Grade Teacher
Pencek, Diane R.
First Grade Teacher
Richter, John Louis
Biology Teacher
Smith, James Richard
Instrumental Music Teacher
FAIRFIELD
Riley, Peter H.
Music & Chorus Director
Santay, Roslyn Caiazzo
9th & 10th Grade English Tchr
FAIRLESS HILLS
Abbott, Bruce R.
Social Studies Teacher & Coord
Arndt, Karen Susan
English Teacher
Barto, David Monroe
English Teacher
Bowen, Richard Allen
Chemistry Teacher
Carocci, Gertrude, OSF
Math Teacher
Cellini, Dorothy B.
Chemistry Teacher
Cherill, Anthony F.
Global Studies Teacher
Crosby, Anne Cordell
High School English Teacher
Dampman, Dianne I.
First Grade Teacher
Devlin, Edward John
United States History Teacher

Falconello, Patricia L.
Business Education Teacher
Fogarty, Rosemary A.
Math & Computer Science Tchr
Golden, Darcy Sender
Spanish & French Teacher
Griffiths, Linda Liedke
School Counselor
Grothman, Michael Richard
Band Dir, Instrumental Music
Hendrickson, Howard Ray
Computer Science Teacher
Hileman, Robert L., Jr.
Math Teacher
Hohwieler, Elizabeth Voss
Vocal Music Teacher
Krier, Norman John
Environmental Science Teacher
Lawrence, Susan Hughes
HS Mathematics Teacher
Magyar, Vincent J.
History & Sociology Teacher
Majikas, Vincent J.
9th Grade Phys Science Tchr
Mankowski, Daniel Christopher
English Teacher & Drama Dir
Metzger, Marylou Schoppe
Math Teacher
Milner, Donna A.
Medical Assistant Instructor
Myers, Keith Joseph
American History Teacher
Myers, Stephen Grove
Science Teacher
Nadig, John Clymer
Mathematics & Cmptr Sci Tchr
Pitonyak, Frank
Math Teacher
Puchino, Richard Anthony
Social Studies Teacher
Reichenbach, Allan J.
Mathematics Teacher
Shea, Sandra Barnes
Soc Stud Tchr & Dept Chair
Templeton, Anne L.
Mathematics Teacher
Waskie, Anthony J.
Language Teacher & Curr Coord
FAIRVIEW
Balest, Ricard James
Science Teacher
Bencivenga, Dominic Michael
Technology Teacher
Coleman, Lori Ann
Biology Teacher
Henry, Cindy Floyd
HS Teacher & Chairperson
Julio, Pamela Sisson
English Teacher
Kessler, Larry Douglas
Principal & Chair
Layman, Douglas Dinsmore
English Teacher
Lewis, Dale J.
Secondary Social Studies Tchr
Luce, Amy E.
11th & 12th Grade English Tchr
Olson, Linda (Wallin)
Mathematics Teacher
Park, David Glenn
Spanish Teacher
Sydow, Holly Nelson
Music Teacher
Taylor Chevalier, Faythe M.
Third Grade Teacher
Toy, Tamara Rastatter
High School Math Teacher
FALLSINGTON
Basanavage, Sandra Starr
Elementary Math Teacher
Whitley, Richard A.
Secondary English Teacher
FARMINGTON
Hershberger, Maureen H.
Seventh & Eighth Grade Teacher
Wiser, Stephen
Youth Counselor
FARRELL
Bobish, Debra McDonald
Reading & English Teacher
Fanone, Pamela Vellente
French Teacher
Muntean, Jane Peel
First Grade Teacher
Padobrick, Gary W.
7th Grade Math Teacher
Wachter, Cheryl Ann (Vasko)
8th Grd Math & 5th Grd Teacher
FAWN GROVE
Cregan, Brendan Patrick
World Cultures Teacher
Hinton, Keith Milton Duane
7th & 8th Grd English Teacher
Korb, Suzanne B.
Music Educator
Long, Carole Kulpon
Business Teacher
Markey, Diane Louise
8th Grd Science Teacher
Rill, Doris Stiles
Business Education Teacher
Scott, Diane E.
6th Grade Teacher
Snyder, Karen Stein
Spanish Teacher
FEASTERVILLE TREVOSE
Quigley, Annemarie Fliegel
Fifth Grade Teacher

ON
aundra Marie
de Teacher
VILLE
ur, Linda Feick
English & Reading Tchr
li, Joseph A.
th Grade Math Teacher
li, Kathleen Elizabeth
rade Teacher
Richard P.
irector
Sara Huhra
r of Gifted Education
onstance M.
ade Teacher
TOWN
effery K.
rade Teacher
Thomas Louis
Grade English Teacher
WOOD
, Charles M.
irector
, Sandra Kemp
Grade Teacher
n, Bill Michael
American History Tchr
ennifer Camberg
Teacher
Thomas M.
& Space Science Teacher
ill Schaeffer
h Teacher
arm A.
atin Tchr & Dept Chair
Alton Ray
al
NG
, Ethel Brace
Elem Teacher
N
ter, Richard
s & Chemistry Teacher
Theo Ann (Fogan)
garten Teacher
Richard Wilson, II
h Grade Art Teacher
TOWN
a, Mary VanDyke
Teacher
ein, Jean Frances, SSJ
ous Studies Instructor
, John Joseph
of Modern & Clscl Langs
ey, Mary Carroll C.
hr & Sci Dept Chprsn
, Marguerite Mulligan
11th Grade English Tchr
iams, Marie Charlotte
h Teacher
osina Mc Avoy
h Teacher
OFT
o, Elizabeth
Gifted Support Teacher
Carol A.
Grade Teacher
M
LuAnn S.
matics Teacher
y, Leslie Mc Coy
Grade Teacher
o, Dennis Stephen
matics Teacher
v, Richard Kenneth, Jr.
ntary Music Dept Supvr
ELL
, Myrna Ordway
d Sixth Grade Teacher
CITY
Guy Kenneth, Jr.
istry Teacher
Karen L.
& 12th Grd Med Tech Tchr
Barbara Klear
sh Teacher
y, Georgia Catherine
cs & Mathematics Teacher
y, Robert W.
Teacher
l, Richard Gallentine
ematics Teacher of Gifted
Sandra Lee
sh & Social Studies Tchr
lo, Anthony J.
sh Teacher
, Mary Jo
eacher
ST CITY
Patrick Michael
& Computer Science Tchr
ano, Helen Wysocki
Teacher
Annette
h Grade Teacher
, Catherine McAndrew
sh Teacher
LOUDON
an, Betty Mc Laughlin
ed Third Grade Teacher
WASHINGTON
, Frederick Albert
Teacher
er, Janice Decker
Tchr & Frgn Lang Dept Chr
, Debra A.
selor
sky, Adria
sh Teacher

Reydel, John J.
History Department Chairman
Russomagno, Gabrielle
Barness Endowed Chair in Art
Skoug, Reed Stevens
Spanish Language Teacher
Spatz, Robert Alan
Mathematics Teacher
Stephens, Mark W.
Tchr & Lower Schl Wrtng Coord
Traver, Sharon Ruth
English Teacher
Vischer, Linda Breckenridge
Chemistry Teacher
Wilhelm, Richard Kirkhoff
Choral Music Teacher
FORTY FORT
Thomas, Cindy Harlan
First Grade Teacher
FOXBURG
Hanby, Judith Mc Laine
5th Grade Teacher
Kinman, David J.
Spanish & French Teacher
Stormer, Kimberlee Malah
Chemistry Teacher
Williams, Michael Parrish
High School History Teacher
FRACKVILLE
Jones, Jeanne Sarra
Retired Elementary Teacher
Kamarousky, Irene Petock
Sixth Grade Teacher
Kraft, Kathryn M.
Fourth Grade Teacher
Yanuskiewicz, Michael Matthew
Third Grade Teacher
FRANKLIN
Bliss, Sara Gadsby
Third Grade Teacher
Engles, Christina Sue
Social Studies Teacher
Green, Susan Bell
English Teacher
Hancox, Richard Andrew
Math Teacher
Homer, Sandra Wass
English Teacher
Miller, Rosalyn Ann (Walker)
French & German Tchr
Phillips, William Kenneth
Fourth Grade Teacher
Rexford, Priscilla Ann (Green)
Teacher of the Gifted
Sanner, Roy Eugene
Supervisor of Transportation
Slautterback, Lou M.
Elementary PE Teacher
FREDERICKSBURG
Brewer, Ronald E.
Industrial Technology Teacher
Burkholder, Jon R.
Math Teacher
Fischer, Barbara Ann (Brown)
Resource Room Teacher
Guldin, Maryann L.
Family & Consumer Science Tchr
Neuhard, Todd Anthony
Asst to Prin & HS Math Tchr
Weaver, James Wilbur
English Teacher
FREDERICKTOWN
Adreon, Nancy C.
Math Teacher
Dreucci, William M.
Public Relations Coordinator
Finley, Earlene E.
K-12th Grd Gifted Support Tchr
Hess, Dolores Jean
Sixth Grade Language Arts Tchr
Maloy, James W.
Physics Teacher
Pryor, Frank Anthony
Health & Physical Ed Instr
VanSickle, Ray L.
Spanish Teacher
Yuratovich, Amalia Marie
English & Spanish Teacher
FREEDOM
Byrnes, William Andrew
English Teacher
Chinn, Teresa L.
Physical Science Teacher
Piccinini, Mary Jane Mc Caw
English Teacher
Pickard, Bert Kenneth, III
Secondary Teacher
Saludis, William Christerphor
Chemistry Teacher
Schweinsberg, Sally Mc Kay
English Teacher
Vild, Rose M.
Fourth Grade Teacher
Williams, James Stoddart
Sixth Grade Teacher
Ziegler, James Robert
English Teacher
FREELAND
Korol, Stephen George
Science Teacher
Ruggiero, Lynn Marie
Kindergarten Teacher
Seyler, Scott Alan
German Teacher
Stiller, David W.
Teacher & Science Dept Chprsn
Titus, Donna Panckeri
English Teacher

FREEPORT
Amy, Barbara Blair
Business Teacher & Dept Chprsn
Davies, Garrie Lynn
English & Speech Teacher
Dillen, William C., Jr.
Biology Teacher
Grasha, Philip John
Chemistry & Physics Teacher
Hutchison, Susan K.
First Grade Teacher
Livrone, Robert G.
Chemistry Teacher
Nolen, Howard Earl
Social Studies Teacher
Orlowski, Donald Lou
Science Teacher
Skradski, Ellen M.
Mathematics Teacher
Spagnola, Sandra Debernardi
High School Art Teacher
Szuch, Annette E.
Vocal Music Teacher
Verbena, Albert
Director of Bands
FRENCHVILLE
Moyer, Patricia Marino
2nd Grade Teacher
GALETON
Lantzer, Jeffrey D.
Music Teacher
Moses, Karen Perrotto
Jr High Math Teacher
Yilek, Ruth S.
Third Grade Teacher
GALLITZIN
Elko, Wendy Swank
Instrumental Music Teacher
Tranquillo, Valarie Ann
Seventh Grade Teacher
GEIGERTOWN
Fosbenner, Kenneth Lee
Mathematics Teacher
Krystowiak, Randy Jay
Science & PE Teacher
Takamori, Craig K.
5th Grade Teacher
GEORGETOWN
Watts, Marcia Rae
Former Riffed Spanish Teacher
GERMANSVILLE
Burnhauser, Romaine Bollinger
Retired Fourth Grade Teacher
GETTYSBURG
Arrison, Jerry L.
7th Grade Life Science Teacher
Bonebrake, Robert C., Jr.
Sixth Grade Teacher
Boyd, Nancy Bosher
Home Economics Teacher
D'Agostino, Nancy Fadel
Fifth Grade Teacher
Dayhoff, Glenda Hess
Second Grade Teacher
Forstater, Mathew Bram
Asst Professor of Economics
Guerrieri, David Alan
Technology Education Teacher
Hazuda, Juliana
Math Seminar Leader & Sub Tchr
Jennings, Vaughn M., III
Teacher & Principal
Leslie, William Thomas
Biology & Computer Sci Tchr
Marks, Nora Maralea
Dir of Vocal Music
McLaren, Martha Goode
Eighth Grade Science Teacher
Miller, Beth Ann
Guidance Counselor
Novotny, Debra A.
American History Teacher
Orner, Carol Lynne (Payne)
English Teacher & Dept Chair
Stafford, Joseph John
Teacher & Coord of Gifted
GIBSONIA
Drop, Ronald J.
Biology & Earth Science Tchr
Erb, Lisa M.
HS English Department Chair
Franchak, MaryAnn Bilich
Algebra Teacher
Joyce, Thomas C.
French Teacher
Plat, Robert R.
Earth Science & Astronomy Tchr
Reetz, Janet Carol
Third Grade Teacher
Seftas, John
Speech & Theatre Teacher
Stepp, Barbara Malis
Retired First Grade Teacher
Swift, Melissa Mc Kay
English Teacher
Vojtko, Deborah Jean (Finniss)
Chemistry Teacher
White, Patricia Fogarty
Biology Teacher
GILBERTSVILLE
Loeben, Priscilla Suzanne
Physical Sci & Honors Bio Tchr
GIRARD
Chizmar, Stephen John
Senior English Teacher
Double, Barbara Harney
Learning Support, Spec Ed Tchr
Johnson, Aaron S.
Health, PE Tchr & Ath Dir

Konkel, Mark Raymond
English Teacher
Mc Laren, John R.
Health Teacher
Nichols, Karolyn Kreider
High School English Teacher
Shaffer, Dan M.
Development Dir & Teacher
GIRARDVILLE
Eiche, Barbara Ann V.
Fifth Grade Teacher
GLASSPORT
Sowerby, James A.
Instructional Support Teacher
GLEN MILLS
Gatchell, Susan Cook
Business Teacher
Mc Groerty, Phyllis Murray
First Grade Teacher
Wenner, George L.
Senior High English Teacher
GLEN ROCK
Hortman, David Jones
Technology Education Teacher
Nicholson, David Allen
Choral Dir & Music Theory Tchr
Shank, Tracy Suzanne
6th-12th Grd Dir of Bands
Yeater, Kathleen Wecker
Dir of Orch & String Instr
GLENOLDEN
Flynn, Joseph M.
MS Social Studies Teacher
GLENSHAW
Hogan, Rosemary
Teacher of Gifted
Keller, Jennifer A.
5th Grade Teacher
Merritt, Judith Pschirer
Fifth Grade Teacher
Truman, Dale W.
Sixth Grade Teacher
GLENSIDE
Bomzer, Jo Ann Weiner
English Associate Professor
Burke, Mary Anne Mc Connell
Second Grade Teacher
Cook, Kenneth E.
Religion & Social Studies Tchr
Donohoe, Francis Xavier
Retired English Teacher
Drescher, Arthur J.
Fourth Grade Teacher
Goldstone, Bette Perilstein
Professor
Leahy, William Lawrence
Intro to Business Teacher
Mascavage, Linda Marie
Asst Prof of Organic Chemistry
Mersky, Martin
Assistant Principal
Molush, Edward Nicholas, Jr.
English Teacher
Moore, Trudy E.
Coordinator of English
Peters, Norah Dugan
Sociology Professor
Rawlins, W. Scott
Assistant Prof of Fine Arts
Roche, James W.
Mathematics Teacher
Rohrbach, Carol Hood
English Teacher
Springer, Josephine Franzone
Third Grade Teacher
Thompson, Joan Hulse
Assoc Prof of Political Sci
Tippin, Susan Palmer
Third Grade Teacher
GLENVILLE
Koontz, Beth M.
Third Grade Teacher
GRANTHAM
McDermond, Jay E.
Asst Prof of Chrstn Ministries
GRANTVILLE
Lutz, William Harry
Fourth Grade Teacher
GREENCASTLE
Beegle, Judith Frey
Business Teacher
Black, Keith Donald
5th Grade Teacher
Clemmer, Paul M.
Fifth Grade Teacher
Dracz, Susan Busovsky
Reading Specialist & Teacher
Esquer, Patricia Ann
Second Grade Teacher
Everetts, Russell L.
Sixth Grd Mathematics Teacher
Herman, Mark Wesley
Asst HS Principal
Leedy, Kathleen B.
10th Grade Health Instructor
Marks, Penny Eckstine
Spanish Teacher
Morrow, Kimberly Jo
MS Mathematics Teacher
Olson, Clifford Arthur, Jr.
Language Arts Teacher
Pike, Jill Avery
English Teacher
Rine, Ruth Kilpatrick
Varsity Field Hockey Coach
GREENSBORO
Teagarden, Vonnie Marie
Community Service Coordinator

GREENSBURG
Albright, Richard C.
Math Department Chairman
Beitel, Donice Cheryl
Chemistry Tchr & Asst Band Dir
Bills, Beverly Sokosky
Instructional Support Teacher
Brisbane, Gene Dennis
Soc Stud, Math & Eng Teacher
Colland, Ronald D.
History Teacher
Collins, John Edward
High School Math Teacher
Cook, Adren M.
English Teacher
Debich, Natalie Long
Teacher of Gifted Students
Dillon, Alexis
Visual Arts Instructor
Eicher, Donna Alexovich
Eighth Grd Social Studies Tchr
Fields, Dennis Allen
Mathematics Teacher
Gaiardo, Albert John
Social Studies Teacher
Galvanek, Joy B.
Second Grade Teacher
George, John Keith
Biology Teacher
Gillott, Marianne J.
Physics & Mathematics Teacher
Hammill, Timothy Sean
Music Teacher
Hersh, Vicki Dobbs
English Teacher
Hervol, Joanne (Dusza)
Chemistry Teacher
Hilty, Susan L. Shick
Math & Computer Science Tchr
Jones, Lori Ann
Spanish Teacher
Jones, Patricia Diane
HS Health & Phys Ed Tchr
Kalp, Robert D., Jr.
Chemistry Teacher
Katarski, Joseph M.
English Teacher
Kniha, Charles Martin
English Teacher
Kudrick, Benjamin L.
Science Teacher
Lackey, Nancy Simeral
Retired Elementary Teacher
Law, Mary Wilhelm
Second Grade Teacher
Leshock, Carol Sargent
Learning Support Teacher
Lynn, Peggy Lee (Skibo)
Kindergarten Teacher
Majcher, Patricia Ann
Art Teacher
Mc Ardle, Maureen (Mc Cauley)
Spanish & French Teacher
Mc Cormick, Amy D.
Math & Science Teacher
Mc Cormick, Edward
English & Social Studies Tchr
Miller, Duane R.
Biology Teacher
Rankin, Catherine Pearce
Music Teacher
Schildkamp, R. Joseph
HS Visual Arts Teacher
Smith, Delver B.
English Teacher
Smith, Stephen D.
Chemistry & Biology Teacher
Sullenberger, Roger W.
Mathematics Teacher
Tucci, Maria
English Teacher
Welch, Debra Wilkins
English Instructor
Wilson, LaRoyal
Social Studies Teacher
Zolock, Sarah Rugh
Mathematics Teacher
GREENVILLE
Arkilander, Patricia Mc Dougall
Social Studies Teacher
Bost, Diann Eckley
9th-12th Grd Art Teacher
Bottorff, Merrily S.
Secondary Art Teacher
Davis, Annette T.
Latin & Reading Teacher
Fisher, Robin (Fry)
Physics & Mathematics Teacher
Gay, Thomas Scott
Science Teacher
Griffin, Jennifer S.
Psychology Professor
Herrick, Brian Douglas
Math Teacher
Hinderliter, Carl M.
Instructional Support Teacher
Kollar, Karen Marks
English & Journalism Teacher
Korcinsky, Terri Ann
Math & Science Teacher
Legters, James R.
Sixth Grade Teacher
Luciani, Lia Anne (Azzato)
Fourth Grade Teacher
McParland, Mary Patricia
4th Grade Teacher
Patterson, Sandra Clark
Kindergarten Teacher
Ramsdell, Gregory A.
Vocal Music Teacher

GREENVILLE (cont)
Rickert, Richard Edward
Librarian
Smith, Alva N.
Retired Professor of Education
Tofani, MaryAnn Joy
Science & Biology Teacher
Ward, Jay A.
Honors Eng Prof & Dept Chair
Weikal, James E.
Senior High English Teacher
White, Arthur A.
Professor of Philosophy
Worley, Barbara Lynn (Weber)
Spanish Teacher
Zilla, Rick Kenneth
Technology Teacher
GRINDSTONE
Katko, Charlotte Martell
Elementary Teacher
GROVE CITY
Browne, Douglas Alan
Prof of Music & Dir of Choirs
Cardille, Kathleen Reeher
History Teacher
Craig, Betsy J.
Asst Prof of Communications
Desue, Ernie
Industrial Arts Tech Teacher
Fleming, Larry D.
Professor of Accounting
Groves, Edgar S.
Adjunct Lecturer
Johncar, Derek Kent
Mathematics Teacher
Longnecker, James Edward
Physical Education Professor
Lyle, Donald Lee
Chairman of PE Department
Mateer, G. Dirk
Associate Prof of Bus & Ec
Mc Clelland, Terry
Visual Communications Teacher
Mc Intire, Gerald Allen
Associate Professor of Finance
Miller, Carole Foti
French Teacher
Mills, Judith Zilla
English Teacher
Mohr, Timothy A.
Asst Prof of Electrical Engrg
Mueller, Robert K.
Assoc Prof & Acting Chm
Nan, Kelly Samuel
10th Grade US History Teacher
Roberts, Susan Kay
Asst Prof of PE & Head Coach
Samsa, Richard Anton
Chemistry Teacher
Smith, Gary Scott
Professor of Sociology
Sparks, John A.
Bus Adm, Ec & Intnl Mngmt Chm
Spradley, Garey Britton
Philosophy Professor
Struble, Terry W.
Physics Teacher
Taliani, Craig Louis
Global Studies Teacher
Taylor, Gordon S.
Math & Science Teacher
Tomasello, Christine Dianne
8th Grade English Teacher
Trammell, Richard Louis
Assoc Professor of Philosophy
Walters, Cynthia Ann
Assoc Athletic Dir for Women
Wise, William Charles
Guidance Counselor
GUYS MILLS
Achenbach, Tina (Pheil)
French Teacher
Eriksen, Ted D., II
English Department Chairman
Levens, Barbara Lynn
English Teacher
Morris, Neil Ward
Social Studies Instructor
Murphy, James Edward
English & Social Studies Tchr
Rhodes, Caroline (Passage)
US History & Psych Teacher
GWYNED VALLEY
Fontana, Janet Marie
Spanish Teacher
HADLEY
Cook, Linda G.
Second Grade Teacher
Schrader, Eric Byron
Band Director
HALIFAX
Batzel, Charles William
High School Math Teacher
Boyer, Gay Karen
7th & 8th Grd Reading Teacher
Campbell, William Harry
Retired English Teacher
Fasnacht, Judy Ann
Science Teacher
Hills, Suzanne Robson
Mathematics Teacher
Klinger, James R.
Coord of Gifted & Talented Ed
Lazar, Bernice Mary (Obzut)
Secondary Mathematics Teacher
Nace, Sharon Kay
Fourth Grade Teacher
Osenbach, Robert John
7th-8th Grd Math Teacher

Rummel, Cathy Marie (Flyte)
Family & Consumer Sci Teacher
Skelly, Susan J.
Fifth Grade Teacher
Suhr, Lois Ella (Walters)
Supervisor & Teacher
HAMBURG
Althouse, Robert L.
Social Studies Dept Chair
Behm, Margaret VanDriel
English Teacher
Bickelman, John Carl
Secondary American His Tchr
Corbin, Cary Douglas
Math & Physics Teacher
Edison, John D.
Math & Computer Teacher
Edison, Nancy Sharpe
Music Department Chairperson
Eisenhuth, Nanette Litwin
Biology Teacher
Ferguson, Duane Francis
Guidance Dir & Amer His Tchr
Gabriel, Judith A. (Tobias)
English Teacher
Groff, Jim
Secondary Lifeskills Teacher
Heffner, Lee Stanley
Assistant Principal
Kowker, Donna
Home Ec & Computer Tech Tchr
Miller, Titus Alfred, III
5th Grade Teacher
Mriss, Paul E.
Guidance Services Coordinator
Nobile, William Michael
Linguistics & Spanish Teacher
Roth, Christine Bobek
Tech Specialist & Cmptr Tchr
Sakusky, William A.
Social Studies Teacher
Schenck, Susan Reibie
Foreign Language Dept Supvr
Snyder, Stanley Robert
Biology Teacher
Stambaugh, David Allen
English Teacher
Stender, Carol J.
English Teacher
Sweigart, Jean Rebecca (Horning)
Sixth Grade Teacher
Turner, Thomas Gary
High School Art Teacher
Weiss, Gerald Francis, Jr.
Physics Teacher
Werley, Leslie A.
Third Grade Teacher
Wolfe, Jeffrey Lee
Chemistry Teacher
Zerr, Cindy Shollenberger
Spcl Ed Learning Support Tchr
Zweizig, Timothy John
4th Grade Teacher
HANOVER
Biesecker, Charles Calvin
7th Grade Life Science Teacher
Boehne, Gregg W.
Gifted & English Teacher
Bowersox, Mark Alan
World Geography Teacher
Brilhart, Christine M.
Fourth Grade Teacher
Conover, Terry L.
9th-12th Grd Hlth & PE Tchr
DeWitt, Pamelia Metcalf
4th Grade Teacher
Hovan, James M.
Science Teacher
Lippy, Martha J.
Kindergarten Teacher
Martin, Judith Ann
Business Teacher
Mc Kee, Erika L.
Vocal Music Teacher
Smith, Gregory Lee
8th Grade Math Teacher
Stover, Kellie Boozer
Biology Teacher
HARBORCREEK
Hess, David Scott
Mathematics Teacher
Sturdevant, Sandra L.
Reading Specialist
Wagner, Linda Mitchell
Intervention Counselor
HARLEYSVILLE
Close, Richard A.
Science Teacher & Coord
Frankenfield, Jeanette
Second Grade Teacher
McCue, Anne E.
English & Language Arts Tchr
Roberts, Jane E.
First Grade Teacher
Ruth, Nanette Easter
English Teacher
HARMONY
Cuffia, James A., Jr.
French Teacher
De Polo, Robert John
Chemistry Teacher
Hune, Theresa (Gambon)
Introduction to Theater Tchr
Lisica, Gary Charles
Science Teacher
Matchett, Robert Kenneth
Director of Bands
Peaco, Ray F.
Senior High Business Teacher

Ruzga, Patricia Ann
Latin I-III Secondary Tchr
Sample, Daniel Edward
AP American History Teacher
Stewart, Lynn Alouise
English & Drama Teacher
Weimer, Stewart G.
Mathematics Teacher
Wilhelm, Jeffrey H.
Biology Teacher
Zuccala, Bruno Domenick
Third Grade Teacher
HARRISBURG
Bokma, Grace Elizabeth
Social Studies & English Tchr
Boswell, James Aurthur, Jr.
Eng Prof & Writing Tutor Coord
Braucher, Elaine Culton
Third Grade Teacher
Britton, Tricia Sarappo
7th Grade Life Science Teacher
Burkepile, Gerald Eugene, Jr.
Math, Sci Tchr & Dept Head
Caffier, Jamie A.
English & Public Speaking Tchr
Cavanaugh, Patricia Ann
Adjunct Instructor of English
Chow, Oiyin Pauline
Associate Professor of Math
Chronister, James Bradley
Technology Education Teacher
Crewsaw, Charles L.
Social Studies Teacher
DiClemente, Lorie Cvijic
Eighth Grade Math Teacher
Dunson, Clenistine Norvell
Bus & Industry Prep Teacher
Engle, Karen Elaine
Sixth Grade Teacher
Fahnestock, Charles R.
Mathematics Professor
Farver, Barbara May
Second Grade Teacher
Flicker, Mark A.
7th Grade Social Studies Tchr
Foltz, Peter Christian
Professor of Mathematics
Fosselman, Linda Eileen
French Teacher
Gehret, Melissa Dolchin
Science Instructor
Gewirtz, Joseph M.
3rd & 8th Grade Teacher
Herigan, Patricia R.
English Teacher & Dept Chair
Hoepfer, Donald Charles
Professor of Philosophy
Hoffman, Mary Hills
English Teacher
Howley, Kathleen M.
Asst Professor of Counseling
Kearns, Richard L.
Poetry Tchr, Writer & Musician
Kluz, Beth Hill
Mathematics Teacher
Kroh, Ann C.
Kindergarten Teacher
Laubach, Gerald T.
Adjunct Instructor
Lauver, Joanne Pickell
1st Grade Teacher
Lee, Donna L. (Dugan)
Fourth Grade Teacher
Leuschner, Frederick Graham
Chemistry Teacher
Lipsett, Kathleen E.
French Teacher
Mc Closkey, Robert Jay
United States Government Tchr
Mc Dowell, Stephen A.
In School Suspension Supvr
Miller, William C.
Anatomy & Physiology Teacher
Milspaw, Yvonne Jean
Eng & Humanities Assoc Prof
Moyer, David Roy
Math Teacher
O'Brien, Susan D.
Advanced Placement Eng Tchr
O'Donnell, Patricia
8th Grade Teacher
Patrick, Eva E.
Biology Teacher
Potteiger, Carol Jordan
Jr HS Health & PE Teacher
Potter, Christopher G.
Prof of Psych & Counseling
Potter, Elizabeth A.
Mathematics Teacher
Rempe, Robert H.
English Teacher & Dept Chair
Robertson, Gerald William
Senior Prof of Music & Hum
Romberger, Mary J.
Mathematics Teacher
Sanderson, Colleen McLaughlin
English Teacher
Shipley, Jane A.
Secondary English Teacher
Shires, Judith Redclift
English Teacher & Dept Rep
Slaughter, Earlette Earnestine
English Dept Rep Teacher
Smith-Talbott, Monica Alice
Art Professor
Stahl, Barbara DeVita
Senior High English Teacher
Stahler, Jerald W.
Bible Teacher & Counselor

Stohler, Thomas Clyde
8th Grade American His Teacher
Summers, Nancy
Coord of Hum Svc Pgm
Vishnesky, Carmen Lorraine
Fr Tchr & Frgn Lang Dept Chm
Wagner, Edward Demmy
6th Grade Teacher
Winger, Joanne B.
Third Grade Teacher
HARRISON CITY
Akers, Harold William, Jr.
English Instructor
Caruso, Carolyn V.
Health & Physical Ed Teacher
Cooper, Glen Lawrence
Health & Physical Ed Teacher
Crovak, Mark Eric
Social Studies Teacher
Cunningham, Patty Lynn (Rotta)
Spanish & English Teacher
Frescura, F. Daniel
English, German & Video Tchr
Hood, Cristy
French Teacher
Laughlin, Sandra Elaine
Mathematics Teacher & Dept Chm
Loughner, Helen L.
Chemistry Teacher
Popovich, Faith M.
Spanish Teacher
Rizzardi, Andrew J.
High School Math Teacher
Sawayda, Marlene Lanzi
Spanish & Social Studies Tchr
Smith, Karen Jean
Child Dev Coordinator & Tchr
HARRISON VALLEY
Warriner, Ruth Ann
7th-12th Grade Teacher
HARRISVILLE
Amon, Cheryl Ann
6th Grade Teacher
Lewis, Joanne
Fifth Grade Teacher
HARVEYS LAKE
Mc Laughlin-Smith, Dave
Intermediate Math Teacher
HASTINGS
Bassaro, Rose R.
Math & Computer Teacher
Weakland, Bonnie Lou
Kindergarten Teacher
HATBORO
Thompson, Maria Regina, IHM
Eighth Grade Teacher
HATFIELD
Buck, Richard Leslie
Fourth Grade Teacher
White, Michael Francis
6th Grade Teacher
HAVERFORD
Duffany, Richard Arnold
Fifth Grade English Teacher
Macbeth, Danielle Monique
Philosophy Professor
HAVERTOWN
Arcidiacono, Steven John
Director of Drama Program
Belcher, Catherine Lee
Social Studies Teacher
Bobnak, Marsha Core
Choral Music Teacher
Booth, William P.
Math Teacher
Brockman, Frank
Science Teacher
Corcoran, William C., Jr.
American History Teacher
Demos, Roger D.
Physics Teacher
Gallagher, Joseph James
Physical Education & Hlth Tchr
Gardner, Seth F.
Music Teacher
Hostetler, Robert Jay
English Teacher
Irons, Faith Eisenhuth
Lead & Home Economics Teacher
Judice, Joan Kane
Spanish & English Teacher
Kennedy, Janet Carol
Biology & Gen Science Teacher
Kime, Carol A.
3rd Grade Teacher
McGlade, Carol Powell
Second Grade Teacher
McIntire, Jean Morse
Vocal Music Teacher
Over, Renee MacFadyen
Second Grade Teacher
Perlish, Joel S.
Retired Elementary Teacher
Rice, Judith S.
Mathematics Teacher
Rudolph, Thomas E.
Music Director
Sabatini, Smeraldo Joseph, Jr.
Lang Arts & Soc Stud Tchr
Sanborn, Paul Joseph
Dean of Social Studies
Shively, Laird D.
German Teacher
Siegerman, Brad Allen
Social Studies Teacher
Taylor, Carol McGuire
Gifted Program Seminar Teacher
Weiss, Edward Paul
French Teacher

Whitney, Starr
English Teacher
Yusem, Debbi Ellen
Special Education Teacher
HAWLEY
Genello, Denise Maria Ann
Instructional Support Teacher
Kieff, Dorothy M.
Third Grade Teacher
Kolcun, Lorraine M.
Co-Op Work Coordinator
Lucier, Edward Gerard
English Teacher
Maza, Norman John
Instrumental Music Teacher
McGinnis, Robert J.
Social Studies Teacher
Rishko, Stephen George
Art Teacher
HAZLETON
Barletta, Frederick A., Jr.
Social Studies Teacher
Beam, Janet A.
Third Grade Teacher
Bohrman, Kristine
Biology Teacher
Cannella, Richard Anthony
TV Commnctn & English Teacher
Conahan, Jeanne Shober
Home Economics Teacher
Cusatis, Lorraine A.
Family & Consumer Sci Educator
Edmondson, Adam Russel, Sr.
AP Chemistry & Physics Teacher
Eichorn, Elena Maria DeRojas
Spanish Teacher
Franzosa, Samuel C.
Resource Room Science Teacher
Garramone, Rosemarie Janine
English Teacher
Gibson, Eileen Myra
Fourth Grade Teacher
Gibson-Gallagher, Kathleen
1st Grade Teacher
Hauze, Catherine Anne
Secondary English Teacher
Hedesh, Lynn Powell
Teacher of the Gifted
Jackson, Karen Toslosky
Eng & Creative Writing Tchr
Kaschak, Karen Marie (Mehalko)
Fifth Grade Teacher
Kelshaw, Delmar
Math Teacher
Kennedy, Thelma Mary
Spanish & English Teacher
Lazur, Carole Gennaro
English Teacher
Leib, Bruce J.
Amer Government & History Tchr
Marchetti, Rick
Guidance Counselor
Martini, Judith A.
Theology & English Teacher
Mc Afee, Diane Elaine (Stoudt)
Eng & Creative Writing Teacher
Miller, Robert Thomas
Math Dept Chm & Teacher
Pauline, Anna Marie
Spanish Teacher
Pavlick, Judith E. North
Physical Education & Swim Tchr
Samoyedny, John Michael
High School English Teacher
Scalleat, Samuel A.
Supervisor Guidance
Sharp, Sharon Ann (Washko)
Second Grade Teacher
Spence, Linda Samuelson
7th Grd Health & PE Ed Teacher
Steber, Ronald John
Power Technology Instructor
Stefanik, Charlotte Kathleen
6th Grd Rdng & Lang Arts Tchr
Thompson, Margaret A. (Franks)
Music Teacher
Tkatch, Nancy P.
Culinary Arts Teacher
Turri, John Joseph
Earth, Phys Sci & Bio Teacher
VanEeden, Cecilia F.
French, Spanish Tchr & Chprsn
Veet, Mary (Walton)
English Teacher
Warg, Margaret Boyle
French Teacher
Wood, Dorothy C.
Seventh Grade English Teacher
Yacina, George
Technical Writing Teacher
Yamulla, Judith Sipple
Secondary English Teacher
Young, Bruce E.
Mathematics & Science Teacher
HEGINS
Luckenbill, Barbara Miller
Family & Consumer Sci Tchr
Otto, Nora Kathryn
Retired Elementary School Tchr
Palmer, Barry Keith
Tech Coord & Math Teacher
Readinger, Mary Lou
English Teacher
Rodichok, John D.
Reading Teacher
HELLERTOWN
Bartolet, Charles Elsworth, Jr.
8th Grade History Teacher
Irvin, E. Diane
Health & PE Teacher

RTOWN (cont)
, John Leonard
Studies Teacher, Chprsn
nry M.
ade Math & Algebra Tchr
, Robert J.
Teacher
ra Willemet
ge Arts Teacher
Dale A.
ism & English Teacher
Gwendolyn K.
Grade Teacher
ennis Greyling
Teacher
ORD
n, Bruce
Grade Teacher
NIE
, Joan Kushnir
ss Education Teacher
onna Marie
Teacher
aniel Andrew
y Teacher
r, Erna L.
Teacher
, Gloria Novak
n Teacher
ohn S.
ology Teacher
, Patricia DerMotta
rts Tchr & Dept Chprsn
er, F. Keith
Studies Instructor
eborah Balentine
English Teacher
k, Jeffrey Charles
matics Teacher
, Donald F.
, Govt Tchr & Dept Chm
ky, Kathleen Mc Cann
Grade Teacher
andra L.
matics Teacher
k, Betti Ann (Dedo)
an
TAGE
ko, William David
Teacher
Susan
h Teacher
Stephen Richard
Teacher & Band Director
Ann Irene
Soc Stud Dept Chprsn
Gary R.
stry Teacher
, Elizabeth Gierhart
h Teacher
n, Anthony P.
y Teacher
Rhonda Thompson
ade Teacher
d, Harold
School Science Teacher
William Rice, II
ud Dept Chprsn & Teacher
ad, Jeanette Odem
dary Guidance Counselor
ON
Donna Marie
School English Teacher
ay Marie
n & Spanish Teacher
Karen Machtley
sh, Hum & Gifted Tchr
Tina M.
my, PE & Tchr of Gifted
EY
, William G.
h Teacher
Barbara Anneliese
an & Speech Teacher
, Russell p.
matics Tchr & Pgm Ldr
ell, Ethel M.
Arts Tchr & Dept Coord
ames H.
Residential Administrator
, Wallace R.
matics Teacher
sen, Clifford Allen
Parent of Sr Div Boys
, Deborah A.
Music Teacher
, Sarah Staples
School English Teacher
ay, Leroy Michael
n Grade English Teacher
Deborah Mc Garry
d Grade Teacher
Sharon Louise
Mathematics Teacher
, Allen M.
ematics Teacher
er, Ronald E.
ess Teacher
chick, Cristal S.
Music Teacher
berger, Timothy Harry
Grade Biology Teacher
n, Richard R., Jr.
l Studies Tchr & Dept Chm
o-Govelovich, Teresa M.
rvisor of Student Teachers
ynthia Rogers
al & General Music Teacher
, Carol Ruth
sh & Journalism Teacher

Patrick, Donna C.
Principal
Reitnouer, Gary Lee
Mathematics Tchr & Dept Chprsn
Rockland, Edward
8th Grade English Teacher
Rosenberg, Scott Douglas
Learning Assistance Coord
Ryan, Angela Udovich
Spanish & French Teacher
Sanger, Joseph M.
Span Tchr & Foreign Lang Chm
Sheaffer, Joel C.
English Teacher
Shearer, Leslie Wian
French & Spanish Teacher
Squaresky, Martha Slater
Spanish & French Teacher
Webster, Lewis Kenneth
Secondary Education Teacher
Zapata-Morales, William
Spanish Teacher
Zimmerman, Thomas Warren
High School English Teacher
HILLTOWN
Borusiewicz, Terri Burke
Language Arts Teacher
HOLLAND
Koopman, Diana Bonazza
Mathematics Tchr & Dept Chair
Mc Brinn, Laurie Mary
AP English Tchr & Dept Chprsn
Michel, Mary T.
Guidance Director
HOLLIDAYSBURG
Adams, Elaine Marie
Computer Programming Teacher
Bridges, Dale Eugene
Fourth Grade Teacher
Clewell-Parker, Sharon Leigh
Teacher of the Gifted
Deremer, Renetta Folk
Mathematics Teacher
Deremer, William Jay
Orchestra Director
Ellis, Stephen Charles
Social Studies Dept Chair
Hoffman, Beth M.
Math & Computer Science Tchr
Kachur, Thomas Michael
Sr HS Math Teacher
Kunkle, Thomas Joseph
Music Teacher
Kutz, John Thomas
Health & PE Teacher
Long, Craig Sheridan
English Teacher
Mc Donald, John William
Dean of Students
Miller, Milton Maxwell
Sixth Grade Teacher
Murphy, James Michael
8th-9th Grade English Teacher
Rhodes, Gary R.
Chemistry Teacher
Rossi, Judith Labriola
Mathematics Teacher
Schreyer, Mary Benamati
Home Ec & Food Service Instr
Stern, Veronique Shultz
French Teacher
Stevens, Glenn L.
Biology & Physical Sci Teacher
Stevens, Linda
7th Grd Language Arts Teacher
Treese, Deborah
First Grade Teacher
Wimer, Martin B.
English Teacher
HOLLSOPPLE
Bantly, Barbara Lynn
English Teacher
HOMER CITY
DeVivo, Sarah
Fr, Bus & Social Studies Tchr
Finotti, Roger C.
Fifth Grade Teacher
Iandiorio, Edward A., Jr.
Tchr of the Hearing Impaired
Yurky, Christine Bewley
Social Studies Teacher
HOMESTEAD
Firestone, Russell George
Social Studies Teacher
Hunt, Hazel
Chapter I Math Teacher
Sweeney, Gretchen Bruce
English Teacher
HONESDALE
Connor, Barbara
3rd-6th Grd Title I Math Tchr
Crosby, Deborah Kawalko
Mathematics Teacher
Gaylets, Raymond T.
Social Studies Teacher
Longenecker, Dennis Lee
HS Mathematics Teacher
Murtaugh, Cynthia Ann
Language Arts Teacher
Simons, Robert Lawrence
English Teacher
HONEY BROOK
Urbine, Mary Brice
Fifth Grade Teacher
HOOKSTOWN
Churovia, Robert M.
History Teacher
Cusato, Daren
Biology Teacher

Deep, Annora R.
4th Grade Teacher
Gayhart, David Keith
Math Teacher, Basketball Coach
Gifford, Gara L.
English Teacher
Hauner, Tammy S.
Emotional Support Teacher
Hornick, Norma Murdock
Elementary Music Teacher
Ledbetter, Ronald Edward
Mathematics Teacher
Robbins, Carson Susan
Social Studies Chair
Schultz, Dana Richell
English Teacher
HORSHAM
Ayton, Robert Ward
History Teacher & Coach
Castor, Karl Fredrick
Track & Conditioning Coach
Flieder, Karen W.
English Teacher & Dept Chprsn
Heywood, Gary Douglas
High School Math Teacher
John, Dan Wayne
Gifted Support Teacher
Judd, Thomas E., Jr.
Mathematics Dept Chairman
Naydan, William Joseph
Music Teacher & Choral Dir
Pancoe, Craig Albin
6th Grade Teacher
Puglia, Joanne Z.
Support Tchr of the Gifted
Reynolds, Carol Barbara
Business & Comptr Sci Teacher
HOUSTON
Block, Stan A.
Biology Teacher
Carter, Glenna Carole
English Teacher
Forquer, Ray Warren
Art Teacher
Henderson, Richard L.
Language Arts Instructor
Popiolkowski, Gary
MS Science & Dept Chairperson
Solobay, Amelia Fantini
World Cultures Teacher
Stultz, Larry Thomas
Teacher
Zeremenko, Stephanie Pankas
Spanish Teacher
HOUTZDALE
Hawkins, Kathleen
4th Grade Teacher
Hopkins, Thomas Clayton
Guidance Department Chair
Larson, Einar Evert
Chemistry Teacher
Marcinko, Thomas John
Science Teacher & Dept Chair
HUGHESVILLE
Arnone, Samuel Frank
Band Director & Music Chrprsn
De Santo, Susan West
English & French Teacher
Hancock, H. Stephen
Social Studies Teacher
Murray, Susan Dawn
Sixth Grade Elementary Teacher
Storm, Bruce James
Art Department Head
Stover, Michael R.
American Civics Teacher
HUMMELSTOWN
Allwine, Constance Marsh
Calculus Teacher
Barton, Scott A.
Business Education Teacher
Conway, Phyllis Audrey Netterblade
Stu Assistance Coord, Bus Tchr
Etter, Charles R.
10th Grade World Cultures Tchr
Kreiser, Linda L.
Seventh Grade Science Teacher
Marshall, Sheron Evans
Mathematics Teacher
McGarvey, Barbara Gaffney
Third Grade Teacher
Sharpe, Rudolph, Jr.
English Teacher
Smith, David C., Jr.
Sci Dept Chair & Biology Tchr
Stroman, Clyde Bradley
Art Teacher
Yerger, Ronald Lee
Sci & Environmental Ed Teacher
HUNKER
Black, Clyntell Y.
His, Eng Lit & Bio Teacher
HUNTINGDON
Pile, Jean A.
Third Grade Teacher
Swigart, Martha Hunter
English Teacher
Tomlinson, Michael Steven
High School Spanish Teacher
Walker, Christine Tataliba
English & Spanish Teacher
HUNTINGDON VALLEY
Brown, Mark Patrick
Fifth Grade Teacher
Howett, Richard A.
Soc Studies Tchr & Asst Prin
Leong, Lawrence
Social Studies Teacher
Mc Kee, Frank Xavier
English & Humanities Teacher

Parry, Ritchard George
Chemistry Teacher
Reilly, Timothy Edward
English Teacher
Schur, Judith P.
Eng Teacher & Curr Coordinator
Shoff, Virginia Sutton
English Teacher
Shuster, Sandra Garber
Spanish Teacher
Trumbore, Barbara Davis
History & Bible Teacher
IMMACULATA
Clark, Kathleen Mulhern
Prof of Foreign Lang & Lit
Gallagher, Barbara Muzio
Physical Education Dept Chm
Galligan, John Sheila
Theology Professor
Hughes, Agnes T.
Professor of Psychology
Isselmann, M. Carroll, IHM
Undergraduate Academic Dean
Mayer, Suzanne M.
Adjunct Prof of Psychology
Sparks, Maria Consuelo
Professor of History
IMPERIAL
Boustead, Diane Behnke
Chemistry Teacher
Cain, Harold C.
Eng Comms & Videography Tchr
Fox, Jennifer L.
Ninth & Tenth Grd English Tchr
Henkel, Kathy M.
Mathematics Teacher
Hoover, James Patrick
Assistant Principal
Kramer, Barbara Jean (Lottes)
First Grade Teacher
Melnick, Richard Andrew
French & English Teacher
Snyder, Thomas James
Instrumental Music Teacher
Zanella, Katie
German Teacher
INDIANA
Amendt, Susan Purdy
Junior English Teacher
Angelo, Joseph Samuel
Mathematics Professor
Begres, Sherrill Jean
Associate Professor
Bell, Barbara J. Barry
Fourth Grade Teacher
Berg, Jill
Assoc Prof Nursing & Health
Chow, Sung Gay
English Professor
Cunningham, Josephine A.
Civics & Economics Teacher
Dietrich, William Edward, Jr.
Professor of Biology
Duffy, Harold F.
Assistant Principal
Fairman, Robert C.
Sixth Grade Teacher
Fennimore, Beatrice Schneller
Professor
Ferrence, Gary M.
Professor of Biology
Feulmer, Judith A. (Dotts)
First Grade Teacher
Gaggini, Norman Wayne
Physics Professor
Henderson, Joyce Herod
Principal
Irwin, James Robert
Elem PE Teacher
Kachur, Georgann Jerko
Senior English Teacher
Katana, John Joseph
Geography Teacher
Kealey, Walter G.
Principal
Kraszewski, Barbara King
Associate Professor of English
Matolyak, John
Physics Professor
Mc Caffrey, Susan Warrington
English Teacher
Mc Elheny, Wade L.
Secondary Social Studies Tchr
Mehus, Helen Ann (Bencic)
Family & Consumer Sci Teacher
Miller, Susan Lepley
Spanish Teacher
Orchard, Robyn Bailey
Former Eng Tchr & Drmtcs Dir
Roffman, Rosaly DeMaios
Associate Prof of English Dept
Salser, Scott Alan
Choral Director
Snyder, Patrick Sherdell
Health & PE Teacher
Stokes, Gary Lee
Biology Teacher
Stonebraker, Robert J.
Professor of Economics
Weber, Denise Dusza
AP European History Teacher
Werner, Kathleen
Instructor
INDUSTRY
Bizzarri, Ellen Barrett
English Teacher
DeMarco, Jill Esther
Music Teacher
Haas, Richard Alan
Math Teacher

Kuntz, Debbie
Special Populations Guid Cnslr
Militello, Brenda S.
Business Education Teacher
Nelson, Paula Perkins
Business Education Teacher
Podolak, Joseph J.
Math & Physics Teacher
Steffanina, Ron
Band Director
IRWIN
Abrams, Elaine cheran
Fourth Grade Teacher
Anselmino, Lori Arnold
Biology Teacher
Bluhm, John M.
Chemistry Teacher
Breeger, Chris Ann A.
Adv Chemistry Teacher
Clark, Marsha Musick
English Teacher
Frasca, Grace Ballenger
First Grade Teacher
Grkman, Louis
Sixth Grade Teacher
Hancock, Louis J.
Dir of Bands & Music Dept Chm
Harvath, Leslie Mark
History & World Cultures Tchr
Hoak, Thomas C.
7th Grd World History Teacher
Hunter, Wilda Faison
Fifth Grade Teacher
Huszar, Carl George
Amer His & US Geog Tchr
Kotch, Timothy John, Sr.
Middle School Math Teacher
Macuga, Nadine Leavy
Music Teacher
Martin, Terry Michael
Principal
Mc Corkle, Robert
Algebra & Calculus Teacher
Occhuizzo, John
Science Teacher & Dept Chm
Parry, W. David
Health & Physical Ed Teacher
Patrick, Irene Joyce
High School Art Teacher
Peer, Larry E.
Science Teacher
Peters, James Floyd
Physics Teacher
Redden, Alona Hope Jesson
Mathematics Teacher
Serafin, James T.
High School English Teacher
Shrump, Barbara Ann
English Teacher
Thompson, Renny Millen
High School English Teacher
Walter, Cheryl Brabender
Choral Director
Watt, Vivian Perotti
AP Lang & Composition Tchr
JAMESTOWN
Donner, Patricia Ann (Martin)
Health & Life 101 Teacher
Miller, James L.
Music Tchr, Band & Choral Dir
JEANNETTE
Kotok, Linda D.
Kindergarten Teacher
Mazurek, Kathleen Hartz
Business Education Teacher
Sakowski, Catherine A.
Second Grade Teacher
JEFFERSON
Caputo, Janet E.
Reading Teacher
Legal, Barbara L.
Secondary Librarian
Perri, Laura Ague
Librarian
Skirchak, Carol Janine
Spanish & English Teacher
Tracanna, Suzanna Estvanic
Sixth Grade Teacher
Willis, Karen Reynolds
English & Journalism Teacher
Zetty, Nina
Math & Cmptr Programming Tchr
JENKINTOWN
Burke, Barbara A.
Soc Studies Tchr & Act Coord
Cappella, Joseph Albert
Mathematics Teacher
Ceranic, Nancy A.
Program Director
DiGiesi, John V.
Eighth Grade Teacher
Ellis, John Sidney
Veterinary Technology Prof
Hanto, Helen Mary
English, Jrnlsm Tchr & Chair
Lill, Kathleen Gargano
First Grade Teacher
Mc Veigh-Schultz, Jane
Third Grade Teacher
Ratner, Elaine Taxin
Sr Assoc Prof of Psychology
Stremba, M. Rita, OSBM
Religious Studies Teacher
Viggiano, Christine Mc Bride
Spanish Teacher I-VI
Yacovino, Anne Frances
7th & 8th Grade Teacher
Zegestowsky, Jane Habina
Mathematics Instructor

JENNERSTOWN
Kowalczyk, Kathleen Kerry
Fourth-Fifth Grade Teacher
Risch, Theodore Thomas
Second Grade Teacher
JERMYN
Barrett, Edward James
Science Teacher
Bryla, Thomas R.
English Teacher
Case, Daniel Harold
Health & Physical Ed Teacher
Edwards, Joanne Morava
Elementary Art Teacher
Hameza, Nicholas
Industrial Arts Teacher
Kucharski, Ann Brieden
Chemistry & Pre-Algebra Tchr
Sawka, Paul
Math Department Chairman
Tochelli, Philip August, Jr.
Scndry Ed & Math Teacher
JEROME
Liska, Cynthia
Second Grade Teacher
JERSEY SHORE
Brown, Jeanne Crist
Third Grade Teacher
Cropf, Thomas Irwin
French Teacher
Decker, Daniel Edward
Civics & PA History Teacher
Fox, Robert Harry, Jr.
Mathematics Teacher
Griswold, Rock Lowell
Business Education Teacher
Hawkins, Gary L.
Fourth Grade Teacher
Herman, Joann May
Retired Teacher
Hopple, Mary Weaver
Science Educator
Maines, Donna Jeanne
English Teacher
Parks, Elsie B.
Fourth Grade Teacher
Rhinehart, Shelby Breon
English Teacher
Sundberg, Arnold Peter
Amer History & Govt Educator
Terry, Maureen Yvonne
Mathematics Teacher
Thatcher, Carolee Mary
Developmental Reading Teacher
Zimmerman, Karen Berg
Business Teacher
JESSUP
Skierski, Linda Susan
Assistant Principal & Teacher
Tone, Maureen A.
Third Grade Teacher
JIM THORPE
Hawk, Mary Ellen Watto
Kindergarten Teacher
Mc Fadden, Kathryn Susko
Fifth Grade Language Arts Tchr
Morgan, James T.
English Teacher
Romanisko, Judith W.
ESL Teacher
Steber, Jack
Bio, Sci Dept Instrl Rsch Tchr
Tite, Sara J.
9th-12th Grade Math Teacher
JOHNSONBURG
Allegretto, Judith Caribardi
Secondary Mathematics Teacher
Bigley, Lynn M.
8th Grade Teacher
Britten, Richard Lane
Business Education Chairperson
Cox, John W.
English & Social Studies Tchr
Crawford, Joanne, SSJ
First Grade Teacher
Crozier, Lois Stahl
Science Teacher
Dunworth, Donna Costanzo
Eng, Sci & Cmptr Tchr
Eckert, Natalie Allenbaugh
Mathematics & Chem Teacher
JOHNSTOWN
Alwine, Judith S. Weigle
Third Grade Teacher
Barnhart, Debra L.
Third Grade Teacher
Bell, Joseph, Jr.
Algebra & Mathematics Tchr
Bosworth, Richard
6th Grade Teacher
Boyle, Frederick John
Religious Studies Teacher
Brett, Jocelyn (Maslo)
German & English Teacher
Claar, Lori L.
Math Teacher
Clifton, Charles H.
English Professor
Colbert, David Charles
Fourth Grade Classroom Teacher
Corle, Trisha A.
Asst Girls Vars Bsktbl Coach
Csehoski, Helen Trimble
Math & Cmptr Programming Tchr
Cyburt, Marian (Hostensky)
Jr High Science Teacher
Davis, Mary Ann Yokitis
Fourth Grade Teacher
Davis-Geist, Rita Marie
4th Grade Teacher
DeFazio, John M.
Mathematics Teacher
Ditchcreek, Glenna M.
First Grade Teacher
Dodrill, Jill Suzanne
K-12th Grade Music Teacher
Dudukovich, Darlene
Social Science Teacher
Dupnock, Lori Anne
English Teacher
Ed, Norman
Art Teacher
Engleka, V. Lynne
Cosmetology Teacher
Ewing, Sharon Wilt
Secondary Math Teacher
Fetchko, John D.
Physics Instructor
Fulton, Gary Roy
6th Grade Teacher
Furman, Ann Marie
Third Grade Teacher
Gardenhour, Richard Earl
Instrumental Music Tchr
Garland, Winsome W.
Orchestra & Music Dept Dir
Geiser, Linda Wise
Fourth Grade Teacher
Golish, Larry G.
Mathematics Teacher
Green, Mary Carroll
Third Grade Teacher
Gridley, Patti Lynn (Hutcheson)
English Teacher
Gritzer, Patricia Ann
Second Grade Teacher
Grove, Carol Mc Daniel
Math Teacher & Dept Chprsn
Harrigan, Timothy James
Social Studies Teacher
Harshbarger, Laurene Fether
Elem Teacher & Administrator
Hillard, Samuel Marc
Soc Stud, Civics & Geog Tchr
Ickes, Leslie J.
History & Physical Ed Tchr
Joswick, Donald Vincent
Sixth Grade Teacher
Keller, Wanda Diane
Mathematics Teacher
Klonicke, Mary Elizabeth Mulcahy
Sr HS Guidance Counselor
Kopco, Marilyn Kimmel
Art Teacher
Kotzan, Janice Meier
Spanish & English Teacher
Kush, David J.
Fourth Grade Teacher
Leap, Barbara Golian
Computer Coordinator
Leffler, Linda L.
French Instructor
Lopresti, Catherine
Allied Health Instructor
Lunko, Ginny Weir
5th Grade Teacher
Madison, Christine M.
Biology & General Science Tchr
Malfer, Thomas Wayne
HS Mathematics Teacher
Mauk, Patricia Furlong
Fifth & Sixth Grade Teacher
Mc Cloud, Scott G.
Journalism Teacher
Meyers, Gary Phillip
Biology Teacher
Napolitan, Richard A.
Choral Director
Oliver, Linda Newhouse
Eng, Bus Law, Para-Legal Instr
Olsen, Kristine E.
Mathematics Tchr & Dept Chprsn
Pekala, Dorothy A.
Third Grade Teacher
Pessolano, Christine Kowal
First Grade Teacher
Piatak, Mary Clare
French Teacher & NHS Adv
Picklo, Mary Jo Borecky
8th Grade English Teacher
Poole, Bernard John
Assoc Prof Ed & Instrl Tech
Potasnik, Patricia Ann (Boratko)
Business Teacher
Pozun, Edward S.
Art Teacher
Preuss, James Francis, Jr.
2nd Grade Teacher
Raich, Michael J.
Sci Dept Chairperson & Teacher
Reighard, Kimberly Jane
Health & PE Teacher
Rita, Jane Robinson
English Teacher
Roccio, James Joseph
Mathematics Department Chair
Roccio, Mary Agnes Aust
Third Grade Teacher
Rok, John Joseph
Mathematics Teacher
Ryan, Vicki L.
Math, Science & History Tchr
Sabol, Michael C.
9th Grd Earth & Space Sci Tchr
Sarosi, Bridget
English Teacher & Dept Head
Scarton, Dino W.
Assistant Principal
Seftic, Eva Yanzetich
First Grade Teacher
Shever, Doris V.
English Teacher
Shroyer, Virginia C.
Third Grade Teacher
Sigmund, Mary Joan
Fourth Grade Teacher
Slifko, Joseph G., Jr.
Instructor
Stoicovy, Christopher George
Social Science Teacher
Tanchick, Susan E.
French Teacher
Tomak, Daniel E.
Sixth Grade Teacher
Trotz, Donald William
English Teacher
Wechtenhiser, Bruce A.
Mathematics Teacher
Yanity, Lynne Patterson
Elementary Teacher
JONES MILLS
Zimmerman, Jane M.
Third Grade Teacher
JONESTOWN
Clemens, Tracie Lee-Moyer
5th-6th Grd Classroom Tchr
KANE
Casey, Timothy Frank
Librarian
Odonish, John Michael
Sixth Grade Teacher
Perry, Christine Allison
HS French & German Teacher
Sheppard, Charlene Ann
Fifth Grade Teacher
Smith, Lois Shroyer
Sixth Grade Teacher
Wismar, Donald E.
Mathematics Teacher
KARNS CITY
Austin, Carol Appelt
Scndry Learning Support Tchr
Fleeger, Connie L.
English Teacher
Hillis, Lucille Gibson
Kindergarten Teacher
Whitmer, Marie Carnesale
Substitute Teacher
KEMPTON
Hamm, Rose Marie (Hafer)
Second Grade Teacher
KENNET SQUARE
Caputo, Kathleen Ann
Elementary Art Teacher
Cipollini, Daniel Joseph
Teacher
Fulginiti, James Kevin
Assistant Principal
Kello, Roseann Marie
Elementary Vocal Music Teacher
Leathers, Stan
High School Mathematics Tchr
O'Donnell, Vincent Patrick
12th Grade Biology Teacher
KERSEY
Johnson, Marion Ohlin
Instructional Support Teacher
Mullaney, Katherine Dippold
Fourth Grade Teacher
KIMBERTON
Mac Leod, Heidi Highmark
Third Grade Teacher
KING OF PRUSSIA
Balukas, Janet V.
Lang Arts & Soc Stud Teacher
Bamford, Rebecca (Sheftman)
MS Home Economics Teacher
Coull, Penny Pruett
High School Art Teacher
Daniels, Charles R.
Biology Teacher
DeMarro, Angela E.
Music Teacher & Choral Dir
Fox, James A.
History & Government Teacher
Kondrath, Martin Edward
Teacher & Coord of Marketing
Kozol, Stephen Michael
Social Studies Teacher
Manser, Richard L.
History Teacher
Mazzerle, Robert S.
Biology Teacher
Moser, Charles W.
Mathematics Teacher
Nodecker, John Raymond
Behavioral Management Teacher
Patton, Scott Gardner
Technology Education Teacher
Symonds, David Marshall
Seventh Grade Math Teacher
KINGSLEY
Albeck, Rae Belle
Third Grade Teacher
Edwards, Teri Lynne
Mathematics Teacher
Fisher, Robert R.
Fourth Grade Teacher
Fisher, Scott J.
Sixth Grade Teacher
Garm, Fred Gerard
High School English Teacher
Jackson, Gail Pompey
Developmental Reading Teacher
Ketterer, Mary Atherton
Eng Tchr, Lang Arts Dept Chair
Lake, Christopher John
Language Arts Teacher
Rehn, Brian L.
Music Teacher & Band Director
Reynolds, Cindy G.
Instructional Support Teacher
Schulte, David H., Jr.
Science Teacher
Slocum, Stuart W.
Biology & Anatomy Instructor
Tracy, Linda Elliff
Third Grade Teacher
Tully, Judy Krewson
Business Education Teacher
KINGSTON
Carr, Joyce (Lutson)
Fourth Grade Teacher
Smith, Vern J.
Fifth Grade Teacher
KINTNERSVILLE
Beck, David Scott
Technology Chairperson
Holtmeier, Joanna Tharp
12th Grade English Teacher
KINZERS
Amspacher, Dale Paul
Spanish Teacher
Bassett, David E.
Business Education Instructor
Celli, John Robert
Biology & Environment Sci Tchr
Edwards, Dana James
Health & Physical Ed Teacher
Herr, Cassie Rene
Health & Physical Ed Teacher
Spodnik, Jason Kent
American History Teacher
Yuninger, Dianne M.
English Teacher
KITTANNING
Bower, Edwin Charles
English & Communications Tchr
Formaini, Guido
Sociology, World Cultures Tchr
Hall, Candace Joan (Cogley)
Business Teacher
Hawk, Laura Kathryn
Tax Collector
Kovalchick, Joseph J.
Technology Education Teacher
Smith, Charles Richard
Advanced Biology Teacher
Turco, Angelo D.
Algebra I Teacher
KNOX
Henry, Gary Richard
Fifth Grade Teacher
Himes, Kenneth Franklin
High School Math Teacher
Schwab, Joyce Bryant
Algebra Teacher
Sheatz, Frances Eileen
French Teacher
Whisner, Mark Andrew
Health & Phys Education Instr
Williams, Daniel Kenneth
Elementary Counselor
Witkowski, Barbara B.
Coordinator of Gifted
KUTZTOWN
Bien, Peggy Cherrington
Third Grade Teacher
Bonhage, Laurel Rowlette
Prof of Communication Design
Cirulli, Eileen Mary
10th Grade Language Arts Tchr
Clair, Kate
Assoc Prof in Comm Design
Cunfer, Elaine B.
Graphic Design Professor
Grim, Linda Sue (Roth)
Third Grade Teacher
Johnson, Dennis Einar
Professor of Art
Landis, John K.
Assoc Prof of Comm Design
Snyder, Sally Ann
Retired 5th Grade Teacher
Walker, David C.
Mathematics Teacher
Youse, Ruth E.
9th-12th Grade German Teacher
LA PLUME
Davis, Patricia Charney
Assoc Professor of Acctng
Ravaioli, Charlotte McIlwee
Associate Dean of Support Svc
Strain, Sherry Shylene
Associate Professor of Comm
LAIRDSVILLE
Robbins, Donna Reece
First Grade Teacher
LAKE ARIEL
Blaum, Joseph Paul
12th Grade US Government Tchr
Christopher, Donna L.
12th Grade Music Teacher
Finlon, Jane Hirsch
8th Grd Language Arts Teacher
Reed, Dana J.
English Teacher
Rocht, EvAnn Cox
Earth Science Teacher
Shaffer, Jeffrey D.
Spanish Teacher
Weiss, Pamela June
Math & Science Teacher
LAKE CITY
Beisel, Patricia Ann
Third Grade Teacher
LANCASTER
Armstrong, Sally Smith
Music Teacher
Austin, Neville P.
Assistant Principal
Ayers, James Ray
Assoc Prof in Pastoral Studies
Banks, Janet Fitzroy
English Teacher
Bentz, Christopher T.
Social Studies Teacher
Bliss, Brian Andrew
HS English Teacher
Bohan, James F.
K-12th Grd Math Program Coord
Bomberger, Donald C.
Health & PE Teacher
Borden, Robert F.
English & Journalism Teacher
Bostock, Paul Timothy
Latin Teacher
Bower, Carol Langley
Lead Teacher
Bowlby, Judy Ann
Family & Consumer Sci Teacher
Brown, Sandra King
7th Grade Reading Teacher
Brunner, Steven Neal
US History & Bible Teacher
Buss, Dale
Art Teacher
Butt, Beverly L.
Mathematics Teacher
Ciprich, Cynthia P.
Mathematics Teacher
Clouser, Anne Frances
English Teacher
Cooper, John Arthur, Jr.
9th Grade Science Teacher
Dreibelbis, Neil R.
Art Teacher
Dreyer, Jeff S.
Math Teacher & Network Supvr
Duffy, Patrick Michael
High School Business Teacher
Fahs, Berit Margareta
Adjunct Professor of Psych
Flick, Douglas Yarnall
Communication Arts Teacher
Forte, Stephen J.
English Teacher & Dept Chm
Gallagher, James Rodgers
Art Teacher
Garman, Thomas Lamar
History & Science Teacher
Gernert, Lee Henry
World Cultures Teacher
Godbois, Cathy Ann
Instructor of Mathematics
Harter, Jean Ann
Sixth Grade Teacher
Hollenbach, Steven Glenn
Music Teacher
Husler, Kenneth Michael
Music Teacher
Jenson, Mary Shuletsky
Business Instructor & Chprsn
Johnson, James Robert
Science Teacher
Kauffman, Crawford
Biology Teacher
Kinsey, Neil R.
Career Education Teacher
Koser, Donald Eugene
Business English Teacher
Lau, Pamela Havey
Assistant Professor of English
Lefavic, Wendy Smith
7th Grd Eng Tchr & Team Ldr
Longenecker, Charles Brubaker
High School Biology Teacher
Martin, Daniel Robert
His & Soc Stud Dept Chprsn
Martin, Susan M.
Librarian
McCracken, Bruce R.
Chrstn Ed Chm & Yth Ministry
Mc Cullough, Diane Susan (Stoner)
Latin Teacher
Mc Gary, Jeffrey O.
Communication Arts Teacher
Mercier, Linda
Frgn Lang Dept Chair & Fr Tchr
Miller, Erika Vittur
German & French Teacher
Morrow, Farra McCartney
Communication Arts Teacher
Nichols, Ted R.
Chemistry Teacher
Price, Mary Ann Bolenius
Math, Sci, Spelling & Art Tchr
Pugh, Lucia Ann (DeLutis)
Spanish Teacher
Puschak, Beth (Horvath)
Reading Specialist
Reinford, Merle R.
Mathematics Teacher
Rice, Vernon Dale
Health & Physical Ed Teacher
Risser, Pasqualina Campopiano
Spanish Teacher
Rossell, Joan Miller
7th Grade Reading Specialist
Schall, Robert B.
Math & Cmptr Applications Tchr
Scott, Irvin Leon
English Teacher
Sedlak, Ronald Frank
Campus Minister & Sr Rel Tchr
Siegrist, David Harnish
Former Administrator
Sohonyay, Anna Marie Hussar
Social Studies Teacher

STER (cont)
arroll Joseph
nt Principal
ohn Paul
Studies Teacher
onald Robert
nication Arts Teacher
Beth Cardello
rade Teacher
aryl Edward
& Philosophy Teacher
Linda Louise
nication Arts Teacher
Mark S.
ental Music Teacher
Carl Allen
Studies & History Tchr
Virginia P.
& Physical Ed Teacher
s, Zaferula Valudes
Grade Teacher
chael Lee
Grade Teacher
SVILLE
William E.
stry Teacher
Jeffrey R.
ade Mathematics Teacher
Cynthia L.
pervisor & Teacher
on, Amy Jane (Herman)
stry Teacher
Joseph James
chool English Teacher
ORNE
aniel Stephen
Professor
, Judith Murphy
Teacher
, Jane
e Dept Chprsn & Tchr
Paul Dennis
Teacher
Robert
& Phys Ed Teacher
Judith Ramp
s Teacher
ger, Harold H.
PE Dept Chair
n, Sheila Armstrong
& PE Teacher
chael J.
stry & Physics Teacher
Samuel
sor of Music
aul S.
ant Professor of Music
use, Daniel E.
Grade Teacher
Jill Waterson
h Teacher
, Sharon Sophie
ss Teacher
, Presentation Mary
Assistant
Ronald Charles
ss Teacher
, David Matthew
iate Professor of Voice
William E.
mics & Sociology Teacher
, Clayton
etry Teacher
ALE
lli, William Randal
Studies Teacher
J. Eric Eric
h Instr & Dept Chair
ner, Robin Lee
d Grade Teacher
Douglas Craig
s Instructor
anice Altemose
Tchr & Gifted Adv
James Francis
s Teacher
, Paul Edward
School Math Teacher
an, S. Duane
Studies Teacher
Barbara E.
ant Principal
aureen Connelly
rd Tchr & Sci Curr Coord
Patti Ann
sh Teacher
, Gregory
Grade Teacher
Dean K.
Teacher & Pastor
, Marsha Reynolds
eacher
Joanna Kett
gh Science Teacher
, Patricia Anne
rade Teacher
ty, Barbara V.
ol Counselor
Sue Ellen
dary Social Studies Tchr
, Carolyn Correll
an Teacher
eter Scott
Director
, Josephine Sklanka
Teacher
ngton, William Scott
ology Education Teacher
rg, Brian Luther
Director

LANSDOWNE
Barrett, Kathleen Theresa
Fourth Grade Teacher
Byars, Denise A. Stewart
Mathematics Teacher
Devenney, Anne Connellee
Spanish Tchr & Director of Act
Gilbert, Robert Craig
Fourth Grade Teacher
Guy, Richard Lee
High School Guidance Counselor
Haines, Harry J.
Biology Teacher
Krueger, Barry A.
Mathematics Teacher
LaMar, Ronald William
Band Director
Realer, Wendy
Teacher
LANSFORD
DeAngelo, Joseph
Social Studies Teacher
LAPORTE
Fahrenbach, Melinda Wood
Third Grade Teacher
Moyer, Mary Laubach
Business Education Teacher
LATROBE
Banker, Linda C.
Kindergarten Teacher
Bronder, Joseph
Department of Music Chair
Bucheit, Kristine Ann
9th Grd PE & Hlth Teacher
De Bacco, Jane Oliver
German Teacher
Dillon, Carolyn Henderson
English Teacher
Ferguson, Loretta Mensch
Social Studies Teacher
Gosser, Richard Allen
Mathematics Professor
Gravelle, Steven John
Asst Professor of Chemistry
Grobe, Daniel
Physical Education Teacher
Herrod, Catherine I.
Bio, Anatomy & Physiology Tchr
Hill, Webster C.
Social Studies Coordinator
Holtz, Vernon Andrew, OSB
Chairperson of Psychology Dept
Lipecky, Marilyn
Physics Teacher
LoCascio, Steven Andrew
Mathematics Teacher
Maggiore, Mary Istanish
Family & Consumer Sci Tchr
Maloney, Elliott Charles, OSB
Religious Studies Dept Chair
McGuire, Scott Allen
Biology Teacher
Mikula, James E.
English, Theater & Film Tchr
Mismas, Larry J.
Mathematics Lecturer
Pescatore, Gloria Sproch
Sixth Grade Teacher
Quinlivan, Gary Martin
Chairperson & Prof of Economic
Rand, Shirley Gallagher
Business Admin Professor
Rossi, Dominic Savio Richard
Director of Choral Activities
Ruffner, Robert D.
US His, Psych & Sociology Tchr
Svidron, Kevin Joseph
8th Grd American Cultures Tchr
Tourre, Marc Louis
Music Teacher
Tranquilla, Ronald E.
English Professor & Chair
Wnek, Andrew Paul
Science Teacher
Zahuranic, Mary Louise Korzak
Business Education Teacher
LAURELDALE
Goeltz, Heather Wertley
Spanish Teacher
LE RAYSVILLE
Whitehead, Carl A.
Retired Fifth Grade Teacher
LEBANON
Albright, Larry Richard
12th Grd Culinary Arts Chef
Ambrosia, Michele (LePage)
Sixth Grade Teacher
Bare, Robert Todd
Elementary Hlth & PE Teacher
Bensing, Claire McCall
History Teacher
Bernhard, Debra LeVan
Secondary Mathematics Teacher
Brandt, Rosalie B.
Adjunct Professor
Brown, Kathy Shiffer
English Teacher
Campbell, Christopher Douglas
Director of Bands
Clemens, Deborah Sherman
French Teacher
Derr, Amy S. (Moore)
8th Grade American His Teacher
Detwiler, Patricia Aurentz
Fourth Grade Teacher
Elliott, Deborah Smith
Assessment & Spec Ed Aide
Erb, Susal Patches
Fourth Grade Teacher

Grove, Timothy Shawn
World Cultures Teacher
Han, Yong
High School Teacher
Hetrick, Frank William
Physical Education Instructor
Hibshman, Clinton Benjamin
English Teacher & Coach
Keesey, Maurice James
Fifth Grade Teacher
Lausch, Ronald Robert
Latin & English Teacher
Leisawitz, Ann Golden
Humanities & Music Professor
Marks, Randall J.
Vocal Director
Messersmith, Elaine Cooper
Family & Consumer Science Tchr
Meyer, Sylvia Adey
Soc Stud Tchr & Honors Coord
Minor, Mary L. (Myer)
Math, Art & Music Teacher
Peiffer, Susan Marie
Middle School Math Teacher
Petry, Jean Walmsley (Healy)
English Teacher
Rothermel, Alan Richard
Chemistry Teacher & Curr Ldr
Salter, Keith Theiss
Fourth Grade Teacher
Scipioni, Luke
Biology Tchr & Sci Dept Chm
Shay, Susan Marie
Third Grade Teacher & Coach
Snyder, Yolanda K.
English & Speech Teacher
Stoddard, Beryl Boeshore
Science Teacher
Stoudt, Michael Douie
6th Grade Teacher
Stover, Gerald I.
Biology & Env Biology Teacher
Strait, Gene Martin
Biology Teacher
Templin, Stanton A., Jr.
Earth Science & Astronomy Tchr
Toews, Bette
Ger & Eng as Second Lang Tchr
Vojtko, Gail F.
German & Latin Teacher
Wentzel, Richard William
Director of Religious Ed
LEECHBURG
Ferretti, Carol N.
School Nurse
Liberato, Pamela Diane Howard
Spanish Teacher
Reighard, Donna Scalzott
Fifth Grade Teacher
Ritzel, David J.
Band & Choral Director
LEESPORT
Davis, Lewis N.
Automotive Technology Teacher
Hornberger, Daniel Luke
English Teacher
Rudy, Stacey Colleen
Cosmetology Teacher
Smith, David Allen
Chemistry Tchr & Sci Dept Chm
LEETSDALE
Fredericks, John Robert
Chemistry Teacher
Hoepp, Rita D.
English & Journalism Teacher
Panucci, Kelly Deep
10th-12th Grade English Tchr
Stevens, Shirley S.
English Coordinator
LEHIGHTON
Bennett, Richard Robert, Jr.
Mathematics Teacher
Bisbing, Richard G.
Anatomy & Physiology Teacher
Gardiner, RuthAnn Audrey
English Teacher
LEHMAN
Agustini, Mary Anne C. Shabelski
Kindergarten Teacher
Kerkowski, Scott Paul
Chemistry Teacher
Koch, Madelyn Ann
HS Math & Computer Teacher
Kopcho, Christine
Biology Teacher
Langan, Robert Michael
Social Studies Teacher
Lipski, Jean Johnson
Secondary English Teacher
Reinert, Paul Michael
School Counselor
Smith, Jane Coyle
11th Grd Eng & Amer Stud Tchr
Sorber, Walter
HS Social Studies Teacher
Toole, Marietta
Third Grade Teacher
Toole, Michael Patrick
America Cultures Teacher
Wilk, Theresa Ann
Business Education Dept Chair
Yoniski, Thomas Joseph, III
8th Grade Social Studies Tchr
LEMOYNE
Frederick, Elizabeth Bilderback
English Teacher
Hamme, Marta Nelson
US History Teacher
March, Leslie Susan
Acad Dean & English Teacher

Roller, Susan Schug
English Teacher
Sanders, Pamela Fleet
Math Tchr & Asst Dir
Stewart, Steven Brian
History Teacher
LENHARTSVILLE
Laub, Mary L.
Third Grade Teacher
Schwalm, Rita Adam
Kindergarten Teacher
LEOLA
Gigl, Ronald William
Industrial Technology Teacher
LEVITTOWN
Barker, Hellen Elizabeth
Social Studies Teacher
Birkbeck, Cheryl Morris
5th Grade Teacher
Campbell, Doris
English Teacher
Campbell, Ruth J.
Fifth Grade Teacher
Cox, Grady L.
First Grade Teacher
Gross, Carol L.
Health & Physical Ed Teacher
Haws, William Patrick
Chemistry Teacher
Jones, Diane Crimmins
Third Grade Teacher
Kramarenko, George
Spanish & Italian Teacher
Kreshover, Linda (Mayover)
Sixth Grade Teacher
Lavelle, James J.
Teacher
Manes, Elizabeth Joan
Math Teacher
McGee, Robert M.
9th Grd Math Tchr & Dept Chair
Silverman, Francine Dianne
English Teacher
Tatman, Michael Jon
Instrumental Music Teacher
Trendler, William A.
Art & Photography Teacher
Viola, Florence Szokoli
7th-8th Grd Soc Studies Tchr
LEWISBERRY
Beck, Phyllis Elaine
Aquatics Instructor & Coach
Butler, Karen Rowley
7th-8th Grd Social Stud Tchr
Gordon, Bruce Lee
Social Studies Teacher
Landis, Jon Charles
Chemistry Teacher
Offutt, Shelly Wylie
Teacher of Gifted
Schubauer-Hartman, Marjorie Ann
Science Teacher
Ulsh, Mark Stephen
Health Teacher
LEWISBURG
Mac Williams, Mark Wheeler
Visiting Professor
Mike, Valerie W.
Spanish Teacher
Nuttall, Linda Lawrence
Secondary English Teacher
Orris, Dale Alvin
Instrumental Music Dir
LEWISTOWN
Belfiore, Arthur Francis
Band Director
Dybach, Theresa Maria
English Teacher
Hartley, Nancy Norton
Social Studies Teacher
Hoover, Duane Paul
Scndry Art Education Teacher
Rhodes, Duane Allen
English Teacher
Trgovac, Sherry D.
Choir Director
Wilson, Sharon M.
Spanish & English Teacher
LIBERTY
Bower, Steven Allen
Art Teacher
Goodyear, Michael John
Business Education Teacher
Krotzer, Mary Horner
English Teacher
Pequignot, Jane Kreger
Reading Specialist
Reed, Ellen Kay
Learning Support Teacher
LIBRARY
Collins, Maureen Kennedy
English Teacher
DePuy, Kathy N.
Business Education Teacher
Eirtle, Karen S.
Fr Tchr & Frgn Lang Dept Fac
Golia, Michael Anthony
English Teacher
Nester, Carol Baird
4th Grade Teacher
Spalla, Thomas William
Biology Teacher
Stellute, Daniel J.
Social Studies Teacher
Thomas, William Benjamin
High School Art Teacher
Trader, Lonnie Kay Dahm
Biology Teacher
Wengryn, Linda S.
5th Grade Teacher

LIGONIER
Hutzell, Larry William
American History Teacher
Leu, Michael R.
Music Teacher
Sydeski, Randal T.
Social Studies Teacher
Vallino, Kenneth John
Art Teacher
LINCOLN UNIVERSITY
Aleong, Chandra
Business Professor
Asaithambi, N. S.
Associate Professor
Barimani, Ali
Computer Science Instructor
Dadson, William Kwame
Economics, Bus Dept Chm & Prof
Maazaoui, Abbes
French & Arabic Professor
Milovanovich, Zoran M.
Law & Criminal Justice Prof
Nagase, Goro
Professor of Mathematics
Pollard, James Alfred, Sr.
Professor of Religion
Polychroniou, Chronis
Chair & Assoc Prof of Pol Sci
Thomas, Judith Ann Waugh
Professor of Education & Chair
Troy, Roberta Maxine
Professor of Biology
Walden, Denise E.
Asst Dir & Upward Bound Prgm
Willis, Gladys January
Prof of English & Dept Chair
LINESVILLE
Bossard, Herbert Paul
Mathematics Teacher
Chesko, Richard Lee
History Tchr & Bsktbl Coach
Krankota, Richard A.
Health & Physical Ed Teacher
Peters, Gregory G.
Music Teacher
Watt, Christine A. Dudenhaver
Third Grade Teacher
LINWOOD
Hughes, Kathleen
Fourth Grade Teacher
LITITZ
Aichele, Wendy Anderson
Science Teacher
Boyer, Guy H.
Amer Political Behavior Tchr
Clair, Anne Lantz
Second Grade Teacher
Droms, Paul Alan
Teacher & Educl Tech Coord
Fuhrman, Elisabeth P.
Fine Arts & Art History Tchr
Hess, Mark A.
High School Spanish Teacher
Huntsinger, Donald Ross
American Cultures Tchr & Adv
Jones, William Michael
Social Studies Teacher
McGrath, Susan J.
English, Science & Math Tchr
Prosack, Claudia Mary
Spanish Teacher
Shull, Michael
Fifth Grade Teacher
Snyder, Mark
High School Guidance Counselor
Sukenik, John K.
Teacher & Coach
LITTLESTOWN
Bitting, Greta Frantz
Mathematics Teacher
Delzingaro, Anthony Robert
American Studies Teacher
Hevner, Kathy Ann
Social Studies Teacher
Karas, John Richard
Science Teacher
Mauck, Susan Reider
English Teacher
O'Connor, Linda Naugle
Mathematics Tchr & Dept Head
Purnell, Janis Groft
Fifth Grade Teacher
Rule, Vernon Charles
12th Grd English Teacher
Smith, Patrice
Eighth Grade English Teacher
LOCK HAVEN
Arrigonie, Jean Marie
4th Grade Teacher
Bailey, John H.
English Teacher & Dept Chm
Baker, Scott Martin
Social Studies Teacher
Banfill, Carmen Brown
Fourth Grade Teacher
Banfill, Maynard
Fourth Grade Teacher
Berry, Nancy W.
Accounting Professor
Bohart, Edythe Pauline
Quantity Foods Voc Instr
Bowers, Gloria Mills
Art Teacher
Bowes, Jane Louise
Special Education Professor
Chatterton, Raymond Edward
Economics Professor
Cooper, Dale E.
Physics Professor

LOCK HAVEN (cont)
Cox, Kenneth Mervin
Prof of Hlth, PE & Recreation
Dolan, James Laurence
Assoc Professor of Health Sci
Dwyer, Chris B.
Fifth Grade Teacher
Egleston, Patricia G.
English Teacher
Eisenhower, Doreen Mc Carthy
Health Assistant Instructor
Emanuel, Linda J.
Assistant Professor of French
Forbes, Edward John, III
Associate Professor of Psych
Frederick, Erla Mae (Kreider)
Math Dept Chm & Tchr
Glace, Joanne Konkle
Second Grade Teacher
Greninger, Richard D.
Math Teacher
Grissinger, Arthur David
Asst Professor of Mathematics
Hanna, Joseph Patrick
Amer Gov & Economic Tchr
Hanson, Colleen Ann
6th Grade Teacher
Karichner, Joyce Shelly
6th Grade Teacher
Kleinman, Roberta W.
Professor of Chemistry
Liddick, David E.
Math Teacher
Lima, Sally Murphy
Elem & Scndry Ed Professor
Long, Leonard Karl
Asst Prof & Head Soccer Coach
Long, Maribeth Hanna
Assistant Professor
Maddox-Hafer, Marjorie
Associate Professor of English
Malin, Sue A. Mc Carthy
Professor of Music
Metzger, Ronald John
Mathematics Instructor
Michener, Lori Ann
Assistant Professor
Moore, Marta L.
Assistant Professor
Neff, Rose Ann
Associate Professor
Oakley, Donald L.
Professor of Science
Packer, Paula Grubb
Associate Professor
Podol, Peter L.
Professor of Spanish
Robbins, Suzanne Marie
Asst Prof, Dept Educl Techs
Rockwell, John E.
Professor of Education
Rose-Colley, Mary I.
Associate Professor
Rudella, Mary Ann (Rodosky)
Nursing Instructor
Sayers, Therese Marie Rudella
Asst Prof of Nrsng & Dept Chmn
Seyfarth, Robert Ernst
Professor of Management
Shaw, Daniel Charles
Assoc Prof of Philosophy
Shepard, Leonard Douglas
Asst Professor of Education
Wardell, Patrick Joseph
Professor of Social Work
Welch, Marie M.
Physical Education Teacher
Whitman Hoff, Joan
Assoc Prof of Philosophy
Witman, Jeffrey Paul
Instructor
Yorks, Kathy (Fleisher)
Science Teacher
LOGANTON
Adams, Carrie L.
Social Studies Teacher
Mc Caleb, June Nicholas
Second Grade Teacher
Owens, Scott T.
Agricultural Education Instr
Wunder, William Lloyd
Principal
LORETTO
Bertocci, Rosemary Juel
Associate Professor
Cook-Huffman, Daniel Jay
Adj Instr, Sociology & Pol Sci
Cope, Victoria Wardzwski
English Instructor
Cuppett, Jeanne J.
Asst Prof of Nursing
Deskevich, Paul
Associate Professor of Math
Frye, Randy Lynn
Chairman of Business Dept
Harris, John Aaron
Physics Prof & Chair
Islam, M. Mahabub-Ul
Assoc Professor of Economics
Langer, Marian Gongola
Assistant Professor of Biology
Leap, Susan K.
8th Grade Science Teacher
Logue, James W.
Accounting Professor
Lynch, Mark Thomas
Asst Professor of Social Work
Melusky, Joseph
Prof & Chair of His & Pol Sci
Monborne, Edward H.
Associate Prof of Accounting
Neeley, G. Steven
Asst Professor of Philosolphy
Olson, Charles Richard
Associate Professor of Art
Putnick, Mary Elizabeth
Asst Professor of Psychology
Remillard, Vincent Leonard
Professor of French
Resconich, Samuel
Chemistry Professor
Wallace, Dee Ann
Prof of Education
Woznak, John Francis
Assoc Prof of English
Zovinka, Edward Paul
Chemistry Professor
LOWER BURRELL
Buzzard, Louise Annthonette
Second Grade Teacher
De Felice, Hugo
Retired Social Studies Tchr
Genito, Deborah Johnson
Art Teacher
Gruseck, Gary F.
Civics Teacher
Legters, Christopher James
7th-8th Grd Math Teacher
Rogalla, Julie A.
French Teacher
LOYALHANNA
Owens, Darlene J.
Owner & Teacher
LOYSBURG
Adams, David Joseph
Anatomy, Physiology & Bio Tchr
Bowser, Melanie Dodson
Health & Physical Ed Teacher
Browell, Marilyn Jean
First Grade Teacher
Drenning, Alan Ross
Social Science Teacher
Housman, Jan Lurie
Teacher
Potchak, C. David
Junior High Science Teacher
MACUNGIE
Ebert, Jeffrey C.
Sixth Grade Teacher
Schmoyer, Jean C.
6th Grade Teacher
Wells, Douglas Ray
Elementary School Principal
Ziegenfuss, Randy Michael
Music Teacher
MAHAFFEY
Baughman, Sandra Elbel
Elementary Teacher
MAHANOY CITY
Ambrulavage, Janice Ann
Seventh Grade Teacher
Brutto, Paul Anthony
Eighth Grade Teacher
MALVERN
Bauer, Laura A.
Mathematics Teacher
Becker, Francis David
Math Teacher & Dept Chairman
Coghlan, Rosemarie Mammele
Dean of Students & Eng Tchr
Eaton, Lisa C.
English & Theater Arts Teacher
Flynn, James R., OSA
Mathematics & Theology Teacher
Grove, Bernadette Joanne
Business Education Teacher
Ledieu, Susan Day
French Teacher
Leeper, Jacqueline Elliott
GATE Teacher
Mc Carrick, Timothy
Music Director
Mc Dermott, Maureen Lawrence
English Teacher
Mc Grath, Gerald
HS Social Studies Teacher
Mc Laughlin, Charles John
Social Studies Tchr & Attorney
Morabito, Donald Vincent
Social Studies Teacher
Morgan, Linda Moore
Health & Physical Ed Tchr
Rhoads, William Lee
Physics Teacher
Rohlfing-Napoli, Mary Kay
English Teacher & Drama Instr
Treisbach, Jean Elizabeth
Mathematics Tchr & Dept Chprsn
Vecchiolli, Joyce A.
Second Grade Teacher
Verno, John Anthony
History & Health Teacher
Walsh, Joanne Elizabeth
English Teacher
MANCHESTER
Firestone, David Allen
Mathematics Teacher
Gibb, William Martin
Mathematics Teacher
Haag, Alana Z. (Forry)
French Teacher
Kowalewski, Hope Carter
Aquatics Teacher & Coach
Schedin, Steven William
7th Grd Social Studies Teacher
Shank, Charlene Ryder
Health, PE Tchr & Ath Trainer
MANHEIM
Bower, Kathleen Yinger
Fourth Grade Teacher
Bright, Carol
Third Grade Teacher
Hartman, Michelle Marie
Health & Phys Ed Teacher
Hoover, Ann Louise
Spanish Teacher
Jennings, Carole Behrens
English Teacher
Metzler, Marion Gish
Fourth Grade Teacher
Shaw, Douglas Arden
Sixth Grade Teacher
Soltys, Stephen Robert
Mathematics Teacher
Travitz, Royal C.
6th Grade Classroom Teacher
Winters, Valerie A.
Third Grade Teacher
MANSFIELD
Detweiler, Karen Holleran
English Teacher
Dunkleberger, Linda Straw
Secondary Mathematics Teacher
Horning, John Byron
English Teacher
Moshier, Melinda Muto
Physical Education Teacher
Mudge, Jane Bennighoff
2nd Grade Teacher
Putnam, Thomas Wells
Seventh Grade Teacher
Wilson, Jane Hughey
First Grade Teacher
MARCUS HOOK
Cloud, Elizabeth Williams
Spanish Teacher
Cole, John David
Mathematics Dept Chairman
Collins, Marc Steven
High School Science Teacher
Davis, Robert Arthur
Eighth Grade Teacher
Donnelly, James Charles, III
9th & 10th Grade Biology Tchr
Gill, James Edward
American History Teacher
Konigsberg, Noah Judah
Art Department Moderator
LaBranche, Donald R.
Fifth Grade Teacher
Milligan, Colleen Loughran
Sixth Grade Teacher
Mortimer, Georgianne R.
Second Grade Teacher
O'Hanlon, Cynthia Marie
Kindergarten Teacher
Perekupka, Walter
Mathematics Teacher
Peterman, Mark S.
High School Chemistry Teacher
Pierro, Linda Pfau
Mathematics Teacher
Pitts, David Lawrence
Third Grade Teacher
Reath, Harvey D.
Computer Sci & Math Teacher
Viotti, Stephen Michael
Honors Math & Algebra Teacher
Wendeler, Elva Virginia
Second Grade Teacher
MARIENVILLE
Quinn, Duane L.
Music Teacher
MARIETTA
Enck, Kurt E.
American Cultures Teacher
Powell, D. Hunter
Sixth Grade Health & PE Tchr
MARION CENTER
Betts, Cynthia Tucker
English Teacher
Coffman, John Dodson
Social Studies Tchr & Dept Chm
Pearce, Michele Deegan
Secondary Guidance Counselor
MARS
Greb, Linda S.
Mathematics Teacher
Harding, Margaret Trainor
Sixth Grade Soc Stud Teacher
Johnson, Rita T.
Art Teacher
LaPorte, Daniel B.
Soc Stud Tchr & Dept Chprsn
Olszewski, Suzanne Summerville
English Teacher
Prijatelj, Charles Anthony
Band Director
MARTINSBURG
Adamson, Charles Ralph
Bio, Anatomy & Zoology Tchr
Biddle, Karen Norton
Mathematics Teacher
Ebersole, Jane M.
4th Grade Teacher
Gahagan, Patricia Hill
Mathematics Teacher
Lightner, Linda Lingenfelter
Communications Teacher
Pannebaker, Frank Allen
Assistant Principal
MASONTOWN
Rossini, Arleen
8th Grade Teacher
MAYFIELD
Buratti, Carmel Ann
Itinerant Teacher of the Deaf
MC CONNELLSBURG
Christophel, Paul William
Science Teacher
Reeder, Leona
4th Grade Teacher
Wooldridge, Gaye J.
English Teacher
Younker, Nancy Bivens
Fifth Grade Teacher
MC DONALD
Aguayo-Gielata, Emelina
Spanish Teacher
Brentin, Linda Kristine
Fifth Grade Teacher
Cain, Judith Ann
5th Grade Teacher
Carter, Sheila M.
Sixth Grd Social Studies Tchr
Carter, T. Lee
Agriscience Teacher
Chambon, Mary Tweedlie
7th Grade Social Studies Tchr
Chome, Rebecca Snyder
Elementary Computer Specialist
Craig, Trisha Ann Varish
English Teacher
Deichler, James K.
Math Teacher
Denti, Sandra M.
Mathematics Teacher
Einwag, Kathleen Falce
Mathematics Department Chprsn
Gavazzi, Karen Hisiro
7th Grade Reading Specialist
Goddard, Jeffrey K.
Sixth Grade Teacher
Hainaut, Jerilynn
English Teacher
Johannes, Paula Marie
Elem Teacher of Gifted Stdnts
Korchnak, Karen H.
Business Teacher
Kosik, Christine Zill
Eng Tchr & Lang Arts Chprsn
Lazzini, Denise Laval
Kindergarten Teacher
Matty, Jeffrey Alan
Japanese Teacher
Maurer, Kevin Michael
Music Teacher
McCalmont, Veronica J.
Mathematics Tchr & Dept Chair
Mc Vicker, Richard John
Fifth Grade Teacher
Monaghan, Kevin Matthew
Science Teacher
Nichols, Kent L.
Biology Teacher
Noll, Richard Gregory
English Department Head
Petersavage, John Richard
Comprehensive English Teacher
Rodkey, Charles
Secondary Gifted Coordinator
Rush, Karen Mc Conaghy
Physical Education Teacher
Spada, Toni Diane
Geometry Teacher
Vosnick, Carolyn Lee
Math Teacher
Zeno, Carl Louis
7th Grade Math Teacher
MC KEAN
Stuyvesant, Katherine Fennell
Kindergarten Teacher
MC KEES ROCKS
Angelo, Carmen
Guidance Counselor
Arch, Stephen Paul
English Instructor
Deceder, Kimberly Folino
Business Education Teacher
Galiyas, Mitchell Edwin
History Teacher
Gregg, LuAnn M.
German Teacher
Hufnagel, William Thomas
Technical Drawing Teacher
Lucas, Constance Santariello
HS French & Spanish Teacher
Mc Kenzie, Thomas William
GATE Teacher
O'Shea, Terry V.
Honors English & Psych Teacher
Partridge, Darlene Smigiel
9th Grade US History Teacher
Pecori, Susan Horvath
English Teacher
Rots, Charla Catania
German Teacher
Rynn, Joseph C.
Social Studies Teacher
Urbani, Paul Joseph
Coordinator of Gifted Ed
Wasco, John
Teacher of the Gifted
Wilson, Audra Ewonce
Math Teacher
MC KEESPORT
Andrews, Jacquelyn Gault
8th Grd American History Tchr
Antoszyk, Charles D.
Earth & Space Sci Teacher
Butcher, Ralph Edward, Jr.
Social Studies Teacher
Cadman, Charles Robert
Science Department Chairman
Cleary, William Joseph
Health, PE & Business Teacher
DeGregorio, David Jon
Health & Physical Ed Teacher
Elko, Donald J.
Hlth & Physical Education Tchr
Gordon, Pamela C.
Sixth Grade Teacher
Kudla, Virginia Wawrzeniak
Upper Elementary Science Tchr
Kwasny, Carl
9th Grade Government Teacher
Lawrence, Victoria Hencz
Biology Instructor
Lepsch, George W.
Band Director & Music Coord
Luft, Michael
Dean of Students
Mc Pherson, Sandra S.
English Teacher & Dept Chprsn
Moran-Harr, Nancy Ochs
Fifth Grade Teacher
Nemchick, Mark Allan
Physics Teacher
O'Neil, Vida Jean
History & German Teacher
Ratesic, Dorothy
English Teacher
Sarber, Carole Breuer
Academic Director
Schmidt, Ruth L.
Choral Teacher
Shaw, Frank David, Jr.
English Teacher
Skraly, Janice Kuzak
Chemistry & Computer Sci Tchr
Squeglia, Bernadette Wasko
French Teacher
Taylor, Joyce V.
4th Grade Teacher
Thuransky, George J.
8th Grd American History Tchr
Vargo, Mark Edward
Secondary Math Teacher
MC MURRAY
Brown, Bettina Belefonte
Literature Teacher
Hull, Mary Ella
Retired Teacher
MC SHERRYSTOWN
Lecrone, Virginia Sternbergh
Spanish Teacher
MC VEYTOWN
Aurand, Dale K.
Retired Teacher
Knepp, M. Elizabeth French
5th Grade Teacher
MCADOO
Minor, Mary Angela
3rd-4th Grd Teacher
Riley, Frances McFadden
Language Arts Teacher
MEADVILLE
Achenbach, Kenneth Robert
Social Studies Teacher
Amato, John Mark
Social Studies Teacher
Bowser, Marilyn Hartman
Fourth Grade Teacher
Daddio, Marlene Bergamasco
Second Grade Teacher
DiAngi, Dick Angelo
Amer His & World Culture Tchr
Fait, William Lance
Mathematics Teacher
Fleischer, Jon Henri
Chemistry Teacher
Frazier, Roderick John
Electrical Instructor
Gettys, Darrell Lee
Fine Arts Teacher
Grzegorzewski, Barbara Hagen
English & Reading Teacher
Hootman, Dan Winfield
Biology & Ecology Teacher
Kennedy, David W.
Social Studies Teacher
Kilburn, Susan Cannon
Health Assistant Instructor
Morfenski, Mary Patricia Mariskar
Business Education Teacher
Roe, Suzanne Mary Milliron
Fifth Grade Teacher
Ruoff, Elaine Neubrand
Third Grade Teacher
Smith, Diana Masson
English Teacher
Turnbull, Carolyn Yoest
Sixth Grade Teacher
VanZandt, James G.
6th Grade Teacher
Zurovchak, Paul J.
Retired Business Ed Teacher
Zylak, Richard E., Jr.
Physics & Astronomy Teacher
MECHANICSBURG
Andrews, Brenda J.
School Counselor
Barrick, Margaret
English Teacher
Billman, Matthew Lewis
10th Grade Biology Teacher
Chilton, Susan Strohmenger
6th Grade Reading Teacher
Church, Judith Fox
English Teacher
Conrad, Michael D.
Earth & Space Science Teacher
Doughty, Selby M.
Fine Arts Educator
Gates, Kathryn Burgeson
Sixth Grade Math Teacher

ANICSBURG (cont)
Geoffrey William
ctional Technology Tchr
enneth C.
& Computer Teacher
Constance H.
ade Teacher
Douglas A.
e Teacher
, Sharon Dinsmore
ade Teacher
ale E.
nental Music Teacher
ohn C.
ic Arts Teacher
Susanne Kahn
nce Counselor
, Leslie Marie
& Physical Ed Teacher
chard Allen
matics Teacher
d, Kay Barker
ade Teacher
, Thomas J.
ade Teacher
on, John M.
rade Biology Teacher
, Barbara Jordan
nce Counselor
r, Lloyd E.
h Teacher
Shelby Lynn
Teacher
Donald R.
h Teacher
Thomas J.
cial Studies Teacher
Colleen Quinn
& PE Teacher
, Louis S.
Humanities Teacher
Joseph A.
matics Teacher
r, Janice Bubernack
ce Teacher
Carol Elaine (Mover)
sh Teacher

Dean C. T.
ssor of Biology
ick, Sharon
Grade Teacher
James E.
Teacher
hn Anthony
h & Physical Ed Teacher
er, Terrence
ssor of Criminal Justice
Randall L.
age Arts Teacher
alton B.
ent Asst & Math Coord
Richard Morrison
nce Director
oann Zaiko
dj Instr of Surg Nrsng
Carol A.
Professor of Nursing
Madeleine Schmidt
eader & Speech Therapist
nna, Maryann Veronica
Prof of Nursing
ston, Joseph E.
Newtworking Tech Instr
Paul A.
tant Professor of English
John S.
l Studies Teacher
Roberta K.
er & Counselor
r, Maureen Wilkinson
h, PE Tchr & Coach
t, Carol DeSilva
uage Arts & Reading Tchr
Susan Nealy
sh Teacher
, Robert Charles
Department Chrmn
OPANY
Beverly Holton
Grade Teacher
ER
Arthur William
l Studies Teacher
ell, Denise Bryant
Grade Teacher
, Richard R.
l Studies Teacher
Tina Kusch
f Secondary Vocal Music
Barbara Squeglia
rd Learning Support Tchr
Elaine B.
ocal Music Tchr, Dept Chm
rd, Alice J.
sh Teacher
son, Nancy Lee
Grade Teacher
Linda Philson
Grade Teacher
ms, Lawrence Alan
er English Teacher
, Deborah (Kurtz)
sh Teacher
ERSBURG
Allen Dale
gy Teacher
ro, Lydia Marie
ish Teacher

Boyd, Christopher William
English Teacher
Burbank, Bouldin Gaylord, Jr.
Mathematics Teacher
Chace, Joel Edward
English Teacher
Decker, Delores Krouse
First Grade Teacher
Fetterman, Catherine Obreza
French Teacher
Galey, Paul Wayne
Schl Minister & Rel Dept Head
Gift, Gerald Brenton
Biology Teacher
Harry, Steve R.
Environmental Sci & Bio Tchr
Haugh, Donna Arendt
8th Grade Reading Teacher
Horohoe, Martha Mary
French & Spanish Teacher
Jansen, Sheree Byers
11th & 12th Grd English Tchr
King, Betsy Ingram
First Grade Teacher
Lucas, Theodore Alan
Chemistry Teacher
Rahauser, Tom Edwin
Spanish Teacher
Rutherford, Frank A.
Registrar & Chemistry Tchr
Stoner, Mary Krauss
World Cultures Teacher
Swailes, Alice Leger
Sixth Grade Science Teacher
Swailes, James Edward
8th Grd Social Studies Teacher
Toms, Susan Barton
Gifted Support Teacher
Wagner, Frederick Lloyd
Band Director
Winebrenner, Wirt Shriver, Jr.
English Teacher
Wootton, Suzanne Dawson Thomas
English Teacher & Dept Head
MERION STATION
Davis, Marlene Sokol
2nd Grade Teacher & Trainer
Ferrari, Rosalie
Spanish Teacher
Herron, Mary Anne
Admissions Dir & Geometry Tchr
Johnson, Catherine Graham
Campus Minister & Rel Tchr
Mc Clennen, Karen Fern
Science Teacher
Small, Rita
Latin Teacher
Ueland, Elizabeth Pritchard
English Teacher
Wattles, George V.
5th Grade Teacher & Coach
Weinstein, Linda S.
Fourth Grade Teacher
MEYERSDALE
Cober, Kay Ann Lichvar
English Teacher
Deakins, Jessica Stahl
English Teacher
Spoerlein, Roger Lee
6th Grade Teacher
MIDDLEBURG
Boyer, Marikaye S.
Business Education Teacher
Conrads, Ursula Margarethe
German Teacher
Kerstetter, Barbara Reindollar
Second Grade Teacher
Mohapp, Les Steven
High School English Teacher
Reitz, Tedd A.
6th Grade Teacher
Troup, Mary Lee Thomas
5th Grade Teacher
MIDDLEBURY CENTER
Weil, Julien B.
High School Mathematics Tchr
MIDDLETOWN
Baer, Roger Alan
7th Grade Geography Teacher
Bell, Marlin Norman, Jr.
4th Grade Teacher
Duncan, David Vincent
8th Grd Phys Science Teacher
Farmer, David L.
Language Arts Teacher
Fasnacht, Lloyd J., Jr.
Economics & Government Teacher
Hess, Lori Barkle
Spanish Teacher
Heusser, Robert Ernest
Biology Teacher
Kulha, Dorothy J.
French Teacher
Martin, Samuel Raymond
Band Dir & Dist Dept Crair
Pettis, Scott Tracy
Social Studies Teacher
Schlicher, Erich William
Music Teacher
Schmidt, Rebecca Hammond
Second Grade Teacher
Stitt, Robert Keith
Woodworking & Drafting Teacher
Stoffer, William E.
Earth & Space Science Teacher
Woodward, Dorothy
5th Grd Sci & Reading Teacher
MIDLAND
Petties, S. Estelle Johnson
First Grade Teacher

MIFFLINBURG
Bollinger, Ronald R.
Fourth Grade Teacher
Bordner, Debra Clifford
Family & Child Specialist
Eddowes, Wayne Arnold
Business Education Teacher
Edwards, John Alison
English, Science & Math Tchr
Fickes, Elizabeth James
Elementary Art Teacher
Gerst, Linda Wallace
First Grade Teacher
Hessert, Gary Lee
Science Teacher
Hoy, Eldon Wayne
Secondary Math Teacher
Latchford, Wayne H.
Physics Teacher
Minium, Linda Laird
Communication Teacher
Musser, Karen Weaver
Biology Teacher
Runton, Keith L.
Middle School Librarian
Sauers, Jamie L.
Health & PE Teacher
Southerton, James Patrick
7th-8th Grade English Teacher
Spangler, Glenn Lewis
Agriculture Education Teacher
MIFFLINTOWN
Brubaker, Roy Lester
Former Administrator & Teacher
Cunningham, J. Kevin
Band & Chorus Director
Gantz, Scott M.
4th & 5th Grade Teacher
Kramer, Nancy Davis
English Teacher
Smith, Janet M.
Physical Education Teacher
MILFORD
Alderfer, Mark Richard
Science Teacher
Briggs, Susan June
Health Occupations Teacher
Ericson, Roger John
Music Instructor
Merow, Craig Banks
Math Coord & Physics Teacher
Thorsen, Carl F.
Social Studies Teacher
Wilson Jones, Mollie
Instrumental Director
MILL HALL
Agostini, John Charles
Special Education Teacher
Haagen, Benjamin F.
Mathematics Teacher
Rogers, Lois Courter
Retired 5th Grade Teacher
Temons, Pamela
Science & Technology Teacher
Wilt, Roseanne (Hamer)
Art Education Teacher
Winslow, Douglas Lee
World Cultures Teacher
MILLERSBURG
Adrian, Scott Steven
Spanish Teacher
Baker, June Witmer
Health & Physical Ed Teacher
Bowman, Deborah Lee
7th & 8th Grd Pre-Algebra Tchr
Boyer, Terry N.
Physics & Chemistry Teacher
Burtnett, James Edward
English Teacher
Frank, Hara Simmons
Computer Coordinator
Higgins, Alice Fisher
Ret 6th Grd Sci & Rdng Tchr
Klinefelter, Kay Smeal
Business Teacher, Curr Planner
Laudenslager, Kevin Wade
French Teacher
Magyar, Sally Faber
Fifth Grade Teacher
Price, Myron Charles
Mathematics Teacher
Rudy, Pamela Menges
Third Grade Teacher
Sheaffer, John Clarence
Middle School Science Teacher
MILLERSTOWN
Dubaich, Michele Mekis
Biology Teacher
Graybill, Donna Marilu (Robb)
Music Teacher & Choral Dir
Hults, Deborah Ann
Spanish & French Teacher
Patton, David Richard
Third Grade Teacher
Troutman, James Barry
7th Grd English & Math Teacher
MILLERSVILLE
Allen, Judith Mann
Spanish Teacher
Briola, Richard D.
English Teacher
Elder, H. William
Soc Stud & US Cultures Tchr
Grenier, Kathleen
Math Teacher
Gutshall, Mary Kathryn
High School Counselor
Leinberger, Gary
Associate Professor of Finance

Lewis, Karen Jean
Sixth Grade Teacher
Luft, Gary Lee
Math Teacher
Oatman, Jon P.
Drafting Teacher
Rager, Amy Jordan
Business Teacher
Tomlinson, Ronda Kaye
Second Grade Teacher
MILLVILLE
Acor, Allen F.
Substitute Teacher
Koschoff, Joann Marie
Hlth, PE & Drivers Ed Tchr
Kramer, Shirley A.
6th Grade Teacher
Shade, Jon L.
6th Grd Science & Health Tchr
Sherlinski, Mark
Fifth Grade Science Teacher
Shultz, Chris Ann (Case)
Secondary Mathematics Teacher
MILTON
Amos, Beverly Jean
Fifth Grade Teacher
Fannick, Anthony Joseph
Sixth Grade Teacher
Gingrich, Cindy Lane
Mathematics Teacher
Hort, Vickie Park
Eng & Advncd Composition Tchr
Izer, Anastasia TeHansky
Retired Teacher
Mc Bryan, Brian Anthony
Hlth & Physical Education Tchr
Shearer, Nancy Yocum
Sixth Grade Teacher
Smeltzer, Deborah Rhoads
Chemistry Teacher
MINERSVILLE
Eisenhuth, Edward George
Social Studies Teacher
Ferrence, Suzanne Louise (Snyder)
Secondary English Teacher
Piccioni, Patricia Brennan
Kindergarten Teacher
Sabaday, Gail Yost
6th Grade Language Arts Tchr
Sabaday, Joseph Andrew
Math, Science & Reading Tchr
Stablum, Robert J.
Political Sci & Economics Tchr
MONACA
Bau, Peter John
Assoc Professor of Business
Biebuyck, Lizabeth Hogsett
Math Tutor
Cairns, Theresa Ann
Health Occupations Instructor
Camp, Vernon Paul, Jr.
Professor of Eng & Fine Arts
Campbell, Russell G.
Mathematics Teacher
Carney, Suellen
Computer Science Teacher
Dean, Shirley Ruth
Mathematics Teacher
Dran, James A.
English Teacher
Flasco, Anita Salloum
Spanish Teacher & Dept Chprsn
Jozefov, Kathy M.
Sub Commercial Art Instructor
Lesko, Valerie Juran
Associate Professor of Nursing
Marshall, Cynthia L.
Associate Professor
Morelli, Paula Savanovich
High School English Teacher
Mulilis, John-Paul
Psychology Professor
Pitt, C. Leon
Associate Prof of Sociology
Policastro, Ellen
9th-12th Grd German Teacher
Scott, James E.
Air Traffic Control Instructor
Takahashi, Leo H.
Assistant Professor of Physics
MONONGAHELA
Amato, Anthony Michael
Chemistry Teacher
Barrett, Judy Topetcher
English Department Chairperson
Bewick, Dorothy VanVoorhis
Teacher of Gifted Students
Carson, Frank
World Cultures Teacher
Fetchen, Linda J. (James)
Tchr of Gifted Support Stdnts
Frederick, L. Scott
American Cultures Teacher
Pergola, Phillip R.
HS English Teacher & Coach
Reda, Donna Balogh
1st Grade Teacher
Roscoe, Mary Lou L.
Chemistry Teacher
Sapko, Nancy Y.
Mathematics Teacher
Suchy, Robert L.
6th-7th Grade Math Teacher
Suchy, Saundra Trona
Guidance Counselor
Vigliotti, Patricia Myor
Home Economics Teacher
MONROEVILLE
Aiken, Kathryn Cauley
English Teacher

Barilla, Jack George
Retired Teacher
Bevan, Ronald Verle
Choral Dir & Music Dept Chm
Blaker, Louise A.
Professor of Biology
Cohen, Debby Moyer
Spanish Teacher
Conrad, Margaret Stringer
Literature Teacher
Des Lauriers, Eileen Robertson
English Teacher
Dull, Jacqueline Ann (Mc Guire)
Kindergarten Teacher
Jeffcoat, Joanne Theresa
Assoc Prof & Fieldwork Coord
Johnson, Norman Lee
Phys Therapist Asst Pgm & Prof
Kravits, Barbara A.
Sixth Grade Teacher
Lorinchak, Marianne Schmid
Latin Teacher
Lubanovic, Thomas Francis
Professor of Civil Engineering
Mastorovich, Melissa Lynne
Nursing Instructor
Mukungurutse, Manomano Maraini Moyo
Prof of Philosophy & Sociology
Murray, Daniel Kevin
English Teacher
Nowicki, Jill Gercken
Child Care Teacher
Peters, Larry E.
Professor of Physics
Quashie, Leroy Andrew
Assoc Professor of Sociology
Read, Robert Allen
Band Director
Roche, Peggy Keaton
Adjunct Professor of English
Rosko, John A.
Computer Technology Instructor
Salicce, Linda Ann (Borowski)
Associate Professor of Biology
Shaffo, Joseph L.
Physical Therapist Assoc Prof
Stephens, Kimberly Sherwood
Nursing Instructor
Sutliff, William Francis, III
English Professor
Turchetta, Bruce A.
Health & PE Professor
Weaver, Raymond E. F.
Math Professor
Wilson, Christine Ann Mazurek
Professor of Biology
Wisniewski, Michele A.
Physical Education Teacher
Zwirn, Gail Sandra
Adjunct Instructor Eng Dept
MONT ALTO
Zemyan, Stephen Michael
Professor of Mathematics
MONTANDON
Murray, Catherine Hoffman
Fourth Grade Teacher
MONTGOMERY
Barbus, Georgia Ann (Kinley)
French Teacher
Keefer, Kristin M.
English Teacher
Poeth, Mark B.
5th Grade Teacher
Stola, Alfred J., Jr.
Art Teacher
Zalonis, John Joseph
Biology Teacher
MONTOURSVILLE
Bergen, James Lyman
High Schl Mathematics Teacher
Bogart, Maynard William
Secondary Mathematics Teacher
Bower, Christopher Michael
English Teacher
Boyer, Harry Starr
Industrial Arts & Tech Ed Tchr
Friant, G. David
English Teacher
Gilvary, Margaret Laggan
Second Grade Teacher
High, Edward William
Biology Teacher
Huff, Carl Raymond
English Teacher
Kaskey, Richard R.
High School Social Stud Tchr
King, Donald S.
Social Studies Teacher
Nowicki, Christine Curry
Middle School Librarian
Peifer, Laurel Denise
Spanish Teacher
Raymond, Lana Lippoli
Sixth Grade Teacher
Shearer, Steven Edward
Math Teacher
Sherman, Doris Edith Weaver
Retired Third Grade Teacher
Shoemaker, Susan Milroy
Mathematics Teacher
MONTROSE
Brown, Jerry R.
5th Grade Teacher
Cherundolo, John Joseph
6th Grade Math Teacher
Cornell, Jeffrey L.
Business Department Chair
Elias, Susan S.
English Teacher

MONTROSE (cont)
Galati, Joseph A.
Biology Teacher
George, Thomas C.
Geography Teacher
Henning, Judith Van Flett
Family & Consumer Sci Tchr
Houck, Dean R.
Music Teacher & Band Director
Roman, Ruth M.
Mathematics & Physics Teacher
MOON TOWNSHIP
Hosselkus, Sandra Beitsinger
Fifth Grade Teacher
Kraus, Larry Matthew
PE & Bible Teacher & Ath Dir
Lupinacci, S. Claire (Newell)
Third Grade Teacher
MOOSIC
Donovan, Marie Roche
6th Grade Teacher
Gogas, Carol A.
5th & 6th Grd Homeroom Teacher
Khalife-Mc Cracken, Rosa
Principal & Teacher
Praschak, Diane Griffith
Fourth Grade Teacher
MORRISDALE
Beahan, Joseph Sheridan
English Teacher
Houston, Carlene Pearce
American History Teacher
Hubler, Madalyn White
4th Grade Teacher
Johnson, Van Allen
Fourth Grade Teacher
Kelley, Patricia L.
Health & Physical Ed Teacher
Klees, Janet Potter
4th Grade Teacher
Lingenfelter, Caroline F.
Fifth Grade Teacher
Miller, Gary Lee
Title I Math Teacher
Penvose, Cindy Mc Kee
Instrumental Instructor
Shugarts, William Blake, Jr.
High School Math Teacher
MORRISVILLE
Hills, David Richard
Sixth Grade Teacher
McGarry, Michael F.
Band Director
Picciotti, Robert Anthony
Eighth Grade Science Teacher
Rubin, Phyllis M.
Mathematics Teacher
Sheaffer, Kimberly Phillips
Advanced Mathematics Teacher
Stempien, Sharon Kay
5th Grade Teacher
Strickberger, Frances Evans
English Teacher
MORTON
Edmiston, Rosemary
Sixth Grade Teacher
Rossi, Donna T.
First Grade Teacher
MOSCOW
Barrett, Robert T.
Assistant Principal
Bewick, Geri Rispoli
Drama Director
Ciuferri, Richard David
Music Teacher & Band Director
Collins, Sandra Petrucci
Third Grade Teacher
Davis, Angela Lentini
Retired First Grade Teacher
Del Prete, Michele Pierre
High School Choral Director
Fesolovich, Deborah Wilde
Second Grade Teacher
Hennigan, Alexandria
Sixth Grade Teacher
Kakareka, Arlene
Latin & Gifted Teacher
Kraus, Carol Winn
Sixth Grade Lang Arts Tchr
Lisandrelli, Elaine Slivinski
English Teacher
Moore, Joseph
Chemistry Teacher
Rickard, Virginia Scoblick
Secondary English & Drama Tchr
Rozdilski, Peter William
7th Grade Math Teacher
Thomas, Stewart P.
Biology & Hum Physiology Tchr
White, Sandra Hrywnak
Third Grade Teacher
Zingermann, Karen
Health & Physical Ed Teacher
MOUNT CARMEL
Bartko, Paul A.
Business Education Teacher
Deromedi, Chris M.
Business Education Teacher
Fedock, Mary Justine
4th Grade Teacher
Leshinski, Trina Vernon
Sixth Grade Science Teacher
Litchko, Joseph Michael
7th & 8th Grade Teacher
Procopio, Rene, CSSF
Principal
MOUNT JOY
Aston, Carolyn Ann
Fourth Grade Teacher
Kline, Marilyn L.
Computer Science Teacher
Lauderman, Sharon Green
English Teacher
Smith, Mary Jane
Fourth Grade Teacher
MOUNT MORRIS
Lemley, Bruce B.
Kindergarten Teacher
MOUNT PLEASANT
DiVecchio, Frances
High School Computer Teacher
Ficco, Michelle Annette
Athletic Trainer
Grubich, Samuel
History Teacher
Hall, Cassandra West
Jr HS Reading & Tchr of Gftd
Holiday, James E.
Teacher of Handicapped
Karfelt, Frank James
Sixth Grade Teacher
Pyda, Dianne Terhorst
Art Teacher
Schroll, Beverly Lohr
English Instructor
MOUNT UNION
Corson, Nancy Lynn
8th Grade Literature Teacher
Crosson, Mark Allen
Civics, Geography, PA His Tchr
Danish, Gasper Joseph
Social Studies Teacher
Funk, Dana Shearer
Secondary Health & PE Teacher
Kuehl, John Thomas
Instrumental Music Teacher
Mowery, Charles G.
High School Business Teacher
Mykut, Teresa A. (Los)
Mathematics Teacher
Shugarts, E. Dayton
Math Teacher
Smith, Ronald L.
Sixth Grade Teacher
MOUNTAIN TOP
Barretts, H. Daniel
Secondary Business Teacher
Bosevich, Antoinette Coroniti
6th Grade Teacher
Bradshaw, Barbara Ann
7th Grade Literature Teacher
Burginia, Noreen Sack
4th Grade Teacher
Gallagher, Thomas F.
Elementary Education Teacher
Gola, Howard R.
Third Grade Teacher
Jarolen, Mark John
Soc Studies Dept Chair & Tchr
Kovaleski, Paula Heckman
Third Grade Teacher
Licata, Frank M.
English Teacher
Lukas, Edward Michael
Sociology & Psych Teacher
Myers, Clare Draper
Kindergarten Teacher
Pendziwiatr, William J.
Band Director & Music Teacher
Ronan, Joan Lillian
Retired Elementary Teacher
Roskowski, Sandra Lee
French & Spanish Teacher
Rozitski, Lorilee
Secondary Mathematics Teacher
Savitski, John William
English Teacher
Uram, Jerome F.
Fifth Grade Teacher
Wincek, Patricia Denault
HPE Teacher
Yatsko, Jerome William
Science Teacher & Dept Chprsn
Zimmerman, Richard Thomas
Fifth Grade Teacher
MOUNTVILLE
Levy, Susan Gail
Sixth Grade Teacher
MUNCY
Auten, Carla Overhiser
Instructional Support Teacher
Bixler, Daryl Elizabeth
Secondary English Teacher
Buckle, Peter Alexander
Science Teacher
Enterline, Susan Picton
Fourth Grade Teacher
Fry, Woodrow Warren
Sixth Grade Teacher
Heincelman, Dorothy Corson
Retired Second Grade Teacher
Temons, Mark J.
Science Teacher
MUNHALL
Altman, Michael E.
English Teacher & Drama Instr
Clair, Regina A.
Guidance Counselor
Frollini, Dominick, Jr.
Chemistry Teacher
Irwin, Adrienne Toth
Teacher of Gifted & Talented
Meade, Scott A.
History Teacher
Unites, Imelda McDermott
English Teacher
Vautier, Drew John
Social Studies Teacher
Vincent, Thomas
5th Grade Teacher
Wolf, Regis Joseph
Physical Science Teacher
Wright, Mary Ann Konecheck
7th-8th Grd Math, Algebra Tchr
MURRYSVILLE
Blank, John K.
8th Grd Physical Sci Teacher
Brecht, Linda Jean
Fourth Grade Teacher
Cicco, Audrey Womersley
Second Grade Teacher
James, Jeffrey R.
Communication Arts Teacher
Jarzynka, Barbara Mercer
Fifth Grade Teacher
Kalanja, Robert A.
Fifth Grade Teacher
Lazzaro, Linda Bernacchi
8th Grade Mathematics Teacher
Makrides, Mary Angela Pope
First Grade Teacher
McLaughlin, James Martin
Amer & European His Teacher
Pollock, Kevin Michael
HS Instrumental Music Teacher
Rice, Peter Edmund
Social Studies Teacher
Shaneyfelt, Samuel R.
Elementary Principal
Shank, Julie
10th Grade Biology Teacher
Shawley, Harold Lee
7th Grade Social Studies Tchr
Sheahan, Patricia Ann Pennett
Principal
Sinning, Karen M.
8th Grade English Teacher
MUSE
Rutkowski, Mary Pauleck
4th-5th Grade Science Teacher
Sweton, Eva J.
Fourth Grade Teacher
MYERSTOWN
Aponick, Lynn J.
Science Teacher
Becker, Donna Rothermel
Second Grade Teacher
Boehler, Cynthia Lou
Chem & Applied Science Instr
Bucher, Nancy Hottenstein
Family & Consumer Sci Teacher
Heiser, Janet D.
Health, PE Tchr & Dept Chrprsn
Hirshland, Judy L.
Spanish Teacher
Kline, Paul H.
Mathematics Teacher
Oliver, Judy Lynne
High School English Teacher
Sitler, Roberta Caroline
Language Arts Teacher
Slike, William W., Jr.
Spanish Teacher
Stick, Richard Claude, Sr.
High School Math Teacher
Troil, Linda Innes
5th Grade Teacher
Trout, Robert Jay
Fifth Grade Teacher
Weik, Betty L.
3rd Grade Teacher
Zimmerman, Laura Henry
English Teacher
NANTICOKE
Bau, Ronald David
Fifth Grade Teacher
Guzofsky, David P.
Earth & Environmental Sci Tchr
Kashatus, Mary M.
Spanish Teacher
Lach, Barbara Repotski
First Grade Teacher
Machinchick, Joan W.
Kindergarten Teacher
Makowski, Elaine Roman
First Grade Teacher
NANTY GLO
Ardini, Roxann
Sixth Grade Teacher
Conzo, Rosemary McDonald
Second Grade Teacher
Gibson, Brian Scott
Secondary Math & Science Tchr
Hurtack, James Thomas
Fourth Grade Teacher
NARBERTH
Smith, Jacquelyn Smith
First Grade Teacher
NARVON
Martin, Kathrine Overly
Music Teacher
Read, Maureen (Hay)
English Teacher
NATRONA HEIGHTS
Bruni, Angelo G.
Writing & Journalism Teacher
Burton, Kathleen Bonner
Second Grade Teacher
Derbaum, Mercedes A.
Librarian
Doelfel, Evelyn Katherine
Fourth Grade Teacher
Doelfel, Paula M.
US History Teacher
Eck, Tracy J.
Civics & World Cultures Tchr
Foster, William Chet
Health & Physical Ed Teacher
Hanna, Margaret Voltz
French & Spanish Teacher
Heid, Alice Wilson
English & Latin Teacher
Kossick, Sherry Lynn
Mathematics Teacher
Mc Aninch, Joseph W.
Guidance Counselor
Mc Curdy, Janet L. (Bibza)
Speech & Language Therapist
McQuaid, Barbara Moline
PE & Aquatics Teacher
Mravintz, Anne Marie Divelbiss
Kindergarten Teacher
Nalitz, Janice A.
Religion Teacher
Pisani, Louis Anthony
Band Dir & General Music Tchr
Rocchi, Linda L. Keller
First Grade Teacher
Ross, Sandra L.
Family & Consumer Science Tchr
Sabow, Richard Michael
Retired Fifth Grade Teacher
Schiebel, Wayne R.
English & Latin Teacher
Summers, Barbara Levett
Family & Consumer Science Tchr
NAZARETH
Achenbach, Linda Gay
First Grade Teacher
Frey, Karen Trimmer
Learning Support Teacher
Hallman, Robert Richard
Ninth Grade English Teacher
Hontz, Krista Hoch
Second Grade Teacher
Israel, Richard William
7th Grade Social Studies Tchr
Johnson, Robert S.
5th Grade Teacher
Knecht, Brad Kevin
9th Grade Biology Teacher
Kulicki, Steven M.
7th-8th Grd Graphic Arts Tchr
Mayorak, Mary Ann Wukovitx
Fifth Grade Teacher
Morman, Marie S.
Reading Specialist
Newman, Peter Henry
English Dept Head & Teacher
Podwika, John Edward
4th Grade Teacher
Rakos, Gina Maria
9th Grade Biology Teacher
Remo, Gail Sensenbach
Sixth Grade Teacher
Schleifer, Margenett Roth
Fourth Grade Teacher
Schuster, Fred J.
8th Grade Government Teacher
NEW ALBANY
Lutz, William D., Jr.
Fourth Grade Teacher
NEW BERLIN
Boonie, Terry Lee
Electronics Instructor
NEW BETHLEHEM
Brown, Michael G.
Hlth, PE & Driver Theory Tchr
Fedak, John George
Science Teacher
Kammerdiener, Helen Virginia
Sixth Grade Teacher
London, David Edwin
Mathematics Teacher
Moore, David R.
History Teacher
Moore, Morna Ruth W.
Retired 3rd Grade Teacher
Moore, Nancy Stewart
English Teacher
Serene, Janet Yeany
Kindergarten Teacher
Weber, Edward Earl
Chemistry & General Sci Tchr
NEW BLOOMFIELD
Comolli, David Michael
Junior Schl Dir & English Tchr
Kaseman, Jane Lankford
Retired Language Arts Teacher
Moyer, Mary Jane Clark
7th Grd Social Studies Teacher
Stuart, Kenneth Pelham
Dept of History Head
NEW BRIGHTON
Birchler, Robert Samuel
HS Mathematics Teacher
Byers, Lynn Miller
8th Grade Language Arts Tchr
Crespo, Stella Pournaras
Spanish Teacher
Davies, Nancy Ann
First Grade Teacher
Fazio, Gregory Grant
Soc Stud Tchr & Dept Head
Harris, David L.
Social Studies Teacher
Hart, Jody Macioge
Alternative Education Teacher
Mac Arthur, Linda S.
Learning Support Teacher
Mahosky, Henry J., Jr.
Science Teacher
Obrist, Ledea M. (Quattrone)
Chemistry & Physics Teacher
Piroli, Patricia Rhoads
Fifth Grade Teacher
Romeo, Ronald E.
High School Band Director
Santangelo, Meredyth J.
English Teacher
Seese, Donanne Parkhurst
Spanish Teacher
Sega, Denise Anne
High School English Teacher
Tomayko, Yvonne
Art Teacher
NEW BRITAIN
Casey, Richard Michael
Sixth Grade Teacher
NEW CASTLE
Anderson, Tim Wilbur
Dir Training & Development
Baker, Robert K.
Coord of Gifted & Tech Coord
Book, David G.
Social Studies Teacher
Bryan, Catherine Ann
Chapter I & Title I Teacher
Carando, Peter Michael
Biology Teacher
Cavalier, Michael Jeffrey
12th Grade Eng Tchr
Cole, Todd Scott
First Grade Teacher
Colella, Rosemary Lynn (Moscipan
3rd Grade Teacher
Curry, Robert A.
English Teacher
Deal, Edwin E.
English Instructor
DeMatteo, Lori (Frank)
Second Grade Teacher
De Prille, Michele Anne
Tchr of Multi-Hndcppd Support
Desch, Eugene Michael
World Cultures Teacher
DeVincentis, Brenda Kordish
Earth & Space Science Teacher
Eade, Ronald E.
Administrator & Principal
Fulena, Stephanie Lee
Coordinator of Gifted
Galiano, Maryann Melcer
Language Arts Teacher
Graham, Sandra Kendra
Kindergarten Teacher
Grimm, Donna Lea
English & French Teacher
Hilton, Rebecca (Smith)
Reading & English Teacher
Krouse, Janice Zawacki
Mathematics Teacher
Kustra, Joella Zingaro
First Grade Teacher
Mackey, Jamie Cryan
Fourth Grade Teacher
Manifrang, Mark Andrew
Social Studies Teacher
Martone, Ralph Anthony
Physics Teacher
Micsky, Gregg Patrick
Industrial Arts & Tech Ed Tchr
Miller, Carol Ann
Spanish & Reading Teacher
Mort, Lori Lee (Trimble)
7th-12th Grd Lrng Support Tchr
Nerti, David Michael
Senior Soc Studies Head Tchr
Novak, Nancy Mlakar
Consumer, Family Life Sci Tchr
O'Neill, Linda Sylvester
First Grade Teacher
Palumbo, Jeri
World Cultures Instructor
Patrick, Patricia Kinkela
6th Grade Social Studies Tchr
Pontius, Beverly Jo
Fourth Grade Teacher
Santini, Annmarie Pratt
Business Education Teacher
Trimble, Gerald
Chem Tchr & Sci Dept Chprsn
Yahn, Edwin L.
Art Instructor
Young, Stephanie G.
Biology Teacher
NEW CUMBERLAND
Holmes, Laura Reimer
Reading & Science Teacher
Maldet, Mark William
Chemistry Teacher
Pepoli, Anthony Gerard
6th-8th Grade Science Teacher
Peters, Karen Nelson
First Grade Teacher
Slayton, Jeanette Vivian
Instructor of the Gifted
Zimmerman, John William
Sixth Grade Teacher
NEW EAGLE
Artis, Arthur
Retired Mathematics Teacher
NEW FLORENCE
Bennett, Donna West
Business Education Teacher
Mitchell, Sandra Mundorff
2nd Grade Teacher
Ritenour, Jay Kenneth
Fifth Grade Teacher
Schwartzel, Romayne Rohaly
Spanish & English Teacher
Shaffer, Cynthia N.
Elementary Reading Specialist
Stillwagon, Joanna Pietropaoli
Sr HS Art Teacher
NEW FREEDOM
Wentz, Barbara Jean
Elem Supvr & 1st Grade Teacher

REEPORT
, John Douglas
d Grade Teacher
OLLAND
Carol Landes
& Consumer Sci Tchr
Daniel J.
Teacher
Stephen Robert
acher
Deborah J.
matics Teacher
Linda
d Grade Teacher
elanie Beck
Grd Teacher of Gifted
OPE
Tom C.
Learning Skills Prgm
ENSINGTON
K. Robert
rofessor of Psychology
off, Tracie Blaskovich
gy Laboratory Instructor
ll, Robert Lewis
nmental & Earth Sci Tchr
ck, Edith Ann
matics Teacher
Robbie L.
tion Coordinator
a, Gregory A.
matics Teacher
Dennis Peter
Science & Astronomy Tchr
Janet E.
ess Teacher
Beverly Marzullo
Grade Teacher
Carol Thomas
n Language Instructor
Lawrence Wayne
hr, Chairman & Golf Coach
Jeanne Smith
l Counselor
Robert Kenneth
Studies Chairman
, Cheryl Glaister
Grade Teacher
Lorraine Ozimek
matics & Science Teacher
Lucille Ferraccio
dary Med Assist Teacher
Robert Joseph
anical Engineering Instr
, Theresa Bruno
gy Teacher
k, Andy
h & Speech Teacher
Robert B.
ic Arts & Arch Instr
no, James Allen
ce Instructor & Director
imberly Sharer
ctor of Education & Dir
Joseph Michael, Jr.
th Grd Band Director
Evelyn Clare
8th Grade Science Tchr
Paul H.
Tchr & Sci Dept Chairman
nd, Frank A.
can Cultures Teacher
, Kathleen (Kelly)
d Grade Teacher
Jennifer Tafi
School Social Stud Tchr
Ronald Eugene
Science Teacher
Keith Samuel
l Dir & Music Dept Chm
Julia R. Pataki
Lab Tech Pgm Dir & Instr
us, Theodore T.
iate Professor of Biology
MILFORD
Lori Koons
y & Consumer Sci Teacher
, Jeffrey O'Hara
mental Music Teacher
, Holly Stempien
entary Music Teacher
OXFORD
chik, William Edward
sh Teacher
ugh, Nathan John
rade Language Arts Tchr
, Ann Louise
sh Teacher
r, Stanley Guy
rd Social Studies Teacher
a, Deborah Kay
gy Teacher
PARIS
rode, Prudence D.
ess Education Teacher
Francis Raymond
S History & POD Teacher
oy, James Edward, Jr.
gy & Chemistry Teacher
PROVIDENCE
, Jay Richard
Grade Teacher
RINGGOLD
Nancy Markwordt
h Grade Teacher
Joseph Dominic
Grade Teacher
STANTON
n, Alan
ricity Teacher

Broker, James Fred
Electronic Tech Instructor
Conko, Colleen Staines
Mathematics Teacher
Howell, John Scott
Business Education Teacher
Johnston, M. Pamela
Elementary Librarian
Shoaf, Ruth Ann
Vocational Instructor
NEW TRIPOLI
Babb, Freda Crissinger
Business Education Teacher
D'Argenio, Ron Anthony
English & Journalism Teacher
Gekoskie, Andrew R.
Director of Bands
Melicharek, Milan Paul
High School Art Teacher
Metrick, Katherine Dunton
Biology Teacher
Ruch, Carolyn Mary
Sixth Grade Teacher
Weiss, Steven Douglas
Science Teacher
Williams, Gary Dennis
Chemistry Teacher
NEW WILMINGTON
Bender, Caryn R.
Mathematics Teacher
Canon, Mary Ellen Snyder
Business Ed Tchr & Dept Chprsn
Castner, Priscilla Cooper
English Department Chairperson
Cebula, Raymond J.
7th Grd Math Teacher
Corrado, Marilyn S.
Instructor of Finance
Earl, Sandra Hall
7th Grade Life Science Teacher
Elder, Katherine McDowell
Home Economics Teacher
Faires, Barbara Trader
Professor of Mathematics
Grunewald, James Paul
Biology Teacher
Imbornone, Janet S.
English Teacher
Kelliher, Thomas P.
Computer Science Professor
Marshall, Gregory James
Pastor
McCormick, Kimberly Ann
Sixth Grade Teacher
McFarland, James Russell
Physical Education Teacher
Nichols, Gail Brenneman
Retired Teacher
Perrotta, Robert D., Jr.
Elementary Teacher
Santillo, Jacqueline Bakuhn
Fourth Grade Teacher
Smolko, Marie Breznai
Spanish Teacher
Walker, John Chalmers
Adjunct Prof of Music
White, Connie Aiken
Tenth Grade Biology Teacher
Wise, Martha Ann (Zuzich)
5th-8th Grade Hlth & PE Tchr
NEWFOUNDLAND
Box, Anita
Fifth Grade Teacher
NEWRY
Lanzendorfer, Linda Ann Yingling
First Grade Teacher
NEWTOWN
Armillei, Patricia Carver
Physics Teacher
Buck, Josephine Celano
Mathematics Teacher
Bursk, Christopher
Professor
Conyne, Sally B.
High School English Teacher
Cooper-Frotrik, Julie
Writing Instructor
Corwell, George V.
Adjunct Instr Language & Lit
Detwiler, Dorothy Wynn
Mathematics Teacher
Drechsel, Joanne Jeitner
Professor of Lang & Lit
El-Naggar, Leticia Jimenez
Chemistry Prof & Area Coord
Fischer, Claudie Deschaseaux
Lang Dept Head & French Tchr
Hentz, Dean Thomas
HS Social Studies Teacher
Kluck, Terry C.
French & Spanish Teacher
Lamberth, Andrea M.
AP English Teacher
Lanfrey, Judith Lee (Winters)
Literacy Specialist & Coord
Lee, Michaeleen Peipon
Chemistry Professor
Longo, Derek Daniel
American Studies Teacher
Machemer, Paul Aubrey
Mathematics Teacher
Mc Arthur, Kaye Ives
English Teacher
Mc Nutt, Helen Elizabeth
4th-6th Grade Math Teacher
Milliken, Marian D.
Health & Physical Ed Teacher
Pianoforte, Donna Ream
Mathematics Teacher

Rabberman, Anna Maria Lehner
Social Studies Teacher
Rosenberger, Lyle L.
Prof of History
Rusnak, Matthew Francis
Professor
Saldan, Darlyne Young
5th Grade Teacher
Tiso, Mary M. (Petrecco)
English Teacher
Vick, Gerald Keith
Sci Lrng Ctr Adj Instr & Dir
Warg, Astrida K.
German Teacher
Whitebread, Gail K.
HS Mathematics Teacher
NEWTOWN SQUARE
Andrews, Dennis
Physics & Mathematics Teacher
Erickson, Richard E.
HS Social Studies Teacher
Estis, Dorothy Montagnolo
Retired First Grade Teacher
Innaurato, Lawrence D.
Mathematics Teacher
Keyser, Keith Allen
Modern European History Tchr
Leach, James Grant
HS Chemistry Teacher
McDevitt, Jane F.
3rd Grade Teacher
Mc Hale, Barbara Majewski
English Teacher
Patterson, Charles William
High School Teacher
Ricks, Janice D.
Math Teacher
Schwenk, Ernest
Chemistry & Physics Teacher
Stirneman, Dawn Kidd
Kindergarten Teacher
Witwer, Mark Turin
High School Science Dept Chair
NEWVILLE
Crusey, Beth Hockley
Developmental Reading Teacher
Ellingsworth, Rebecca Anne Rolar
Second Grade Teacher
McClure, Robert Lee
Physics Teacher
O'Neil, Thom
Coordinator of Gifted
Shaker, Kathleen N.
Spanish Teacher
Sponenberg, Carl G.
High School Band Director
NICKTOWN
Burba, Theresa Catherine
8th Grade Teacher
Farabaugh, Sally Ann (Parrish)
Math Teacher
NORMALVILLE
Van Sickle, Christine Lizza
Kindergarten Teacher
NORRISTOWN
Ames, Kelly Ann
Health & Physical Ed Teacher
Barnshaw, Thomas J.
Algebra Teacher
Basalik, Susan Esposito
Elementary Music Teacher
Baumgartner, Sherill
Biology Teacher
Bigham, Susan Hughes
8th Grd Phys Science Teacher
Boehner, Eleanor A.
Mathematics Dept Chprsn & Tchr
Britt, Denise Eizzo
Former Eighth Grade Teacher
Dowd, Mary Ann
7th Grade Math Teacher
Druckenmiller, Ronald Lee
Kindergarten Teacher
Emery, David R.
Mathematics Teacher
Flynn, James Walter
Sixth Grade Teacher
Frangiosa, Jesse V.
Middle School Reading Teacher
Fryling, George E.
Art Teacher
Hangey, Jon Dean
Geography Teacher
Hoskins, Maryanne Foulke
K-3rd Grade Facilitator
Kapp, Lehman E., Jr.
Mathematics Teacher
Kenney, Michael William
Fourth Grade Teacher
Kerrane, Leona Giordano
7th Grade English Teacher
Kramer, Charles Miller, Jr.
PE & Aquatics Instructor
Kunka, Joseph J.
Mathematics Teacher
Leaf, Joseph Edward
Eng as a Second Lang Teacher
Leahan, Charles J.
Spanish Teacher
Mainhart, David Alan
Teacher of the Gifted
Mascaro, Bret L.
Band Director & Music Teacher
Mc Aliley, Frances Wright
8th Grd Comm & Lit Teacher
Meissner, John Charles, III
Teacher of the Gifted
Menichiello, John
English Teacher

Moono, Steady Hatukali
Upper School Administrator
Nickerson, Jill Ann
French Teacher & Yrbk Advisor
O'Donovan, Richard A.
AP Amer His Tch & Soc Stud Chm
Paul, John
School Minister, Theology Tchr
Pflug-Felder, Karen N.
Science Dept Chair & Teacher
Pucell, Janet M., IHM
Asst Principal of Stu Services
Reilly, Linda Pritchard
8th Grade Math Teacher
Schopp, David L.
Music Teacher
Silverman, Phyllis Weitz
Coordinator of the Gifted Pgm
Stevenson, Jim
Fifth Grade Teacher
Subers, Richard C.
Social Studies Teacher
Trumbore, Judith Ann, IHM
Theology Teacher
Weaver, Jane Howson
Biology Teacher
Welsh, Rosemary Corrado
English & Theater Teacher
Winkel, Patricia Murphy
English Teacher
NORTH EAST
Blystone, Jane Marie
English Teacher
Bowers, Nancy Marshall
Chorus & General Music Teacher
Christensen, Heidi S.
Fourth Grade Teacher
DeNardo, Richard Ray
Business Teacher
Fetcko, Beverly Larson
2nd Grade Teacher
Hoyt, Christina Hess
Language Arts & Math Teacher
Koster, Edward H., Jr.
Chemistry Teacher
Lamb, Jeanne Cucuzza
Family & Consumer Sci Teacher
Moore, Anita Crowe
English Teacher
Rider, Barbara Jane
Bus Dept Chairman & Teacher
Rodgers, Lucinda Mac Taggart
6th Grade Teacher
NORTH HUNTINGDON
Barr, Monica Grazan
Music Teacher & Chorus Dir
Boby, Charles Anthony
8th Grd Earth Science Teacher
Milne, Sandra Carpenter
Second Grade Teacher
Pittavino, MaryAlyce Frick
3rd Grade Teacher
Stone, Carole Kowallis
Social Studies Teacher
NORTH VERSAILLES
Frost, Fred N.
Anatomy & Physiology Chem Tchr
Gaydos, Richard C.
Trigonometry & Geometry Tchr
Kahl, James E.
Mathematics Teacher
Rizzo, Robert William
Band Director
NORTH WALES
Armstrong, Richard W.
Fifth Grade Teacher
Carroll, Ann Louise L.
8th Grade English Teacher
Mc Nerney, Michael Kenneth
Sixth Grade Teacher
Sherlock-Robson, Nancy
Mathematics Teacher
Van Tryon, Patricia Jean
Life Science Teacher
NORTHAMPTON
Bilheimer, Margaret I.
Span Tchr & Rdng Specialist
Bryant, Robert John
Scndry Ed & Soc Stud Teacher
Pany, Edward A.
Teacher
Petro, Thomas Michael
Secondary Social Studies Tchr
Transue, Susan B.
Science Educator
Vulcano, Pat, Jr.
Marketing, Bus Tchr & Coord
NORTHUMBERLAND
DiRicco, Carol Garvine
Communication Arts Teacher
Fetterolf, Scott J.
Guid Counselor & Bible Tchr
Landau, Sharon Altha
Kindergarten Teacher
Olson, Joyce Fogel
MS Mathematics Teacher
Ritchie, Elizabeth Ann
Retired 4th Grade Teacher
Tuomisto, Gale Moore
Science Teacher
Williams, James R.
Fifth Grade Teacher
NORWOOD
Kane, Grace Mullen
Teacher
Paris, Francis Joseph
Assistant Principal
NUANGOLA
Stanek, Michael Francis
Math & Science Teacher

OAKDALE
Speranza, Eugene A.
Drafting Teacher
OAKMONT
Dolan, Rita B.
Sixth Grade Teacher
Frederick, Donald A.
Fifth Grade Teacher
Hepner, Barbara E.
Music Instructor
Panian, Mary Frances F.
Principal
Semper, Frank Victor
5th Grade Science Teacher
Sullivan, F. Patrick
Lang Arts & TeleComm Teacher
OAKS
Herczeg, Marilyn Smith
2nd Grade Teacher
OIL CITY
Adelson, Louis David
Asst Prof of Computer Science
Curran, Melodie Whitling
Math Teacher
Dixon, Roswitha B.
Math Instructor
Forden, Carie L.
Professor of Psychology
Grenci, John Louis
Mathematics Instructor
Heckathorne, Deborah Kathryn
(Garmong)
Mathematics Teacher
McBride, Kathy (Andres)
7th Grd Social Studies Teacher
Scott, Margaret Clay
Second Grade Teacher
Wenner, Douglas Keith
English Teacher
Winger, Terri Sue
Music Classroom Teacher
Yarnell, Rebecca Grau
Reading Specialist
OLD FORGE
Brutico, Roseann Pikulski
Learning Support Teacher
Cummings, Wendy Elizabeth
Mathematics Teacher
Giacomini, Patricia Bernardi
Second Grade Teacher
Gilotti, Barbara Elizabeth
Spanish Teacher & Librarian
McLane, Daria Marie (Muzi)
6th Grade Teacher
Notari, Richard Paul, Sr.
Mathematics Teacher
Pawlik, W. Timothy
Band Director & Music Teacher
Tumavitch, Martha Conon
First Grade Teacher
Vender, Cynthia Maciborski
Fifth Grade Teacher
OLEY
Wildermuth, Larry Guy
Social Science Teacher
Wingert, Anna Louise (Williams)
Health Occupations Instructor
OREFIELD
Bleam, Christopher Allen
Health & PE Teacher
Boyer, Cary R.
AP Biology Tchr, Sci Dept Chm
Buss, Edward Wilson
History, Geography & Govt Tchr
Cortazzo, Diane (Dreisbach)
German Teacher
Farnsworth, Gerald M.
Senior High Math Teacher
Heckman, Rosanne Flamisch
Mathematics Tchr & Dept Chair
Heist, Michelle (Sharga)
Secondary Biology Teacher
Kester, James Marvin
Technology Education Teacher
Lerew, Jason D.
Instrumental Music Teacher
Marcante, John Paul
Reading Specialist & Coach
Mondschein, John F.
Business Teacher
Posegay, Linda Ann Staib
German Teacher
Ritter, John R.
English Teacher
Schwarz, Timothy Sean
English Teacher
Verenna, Charles Anthony, Jr.
Chemistry Teacher
Zosky, Deborah Ann
History Teacher & Dept Head
ORELAND
Carson, Dianne Bupp
Fifth Grade Teacher
ORWIGSBURG
Herb, Mark Ray
Life Science Teacher
Rauenzahn, John O.
Fifth Grade Teacher
Shuttlesworth, Lynn Ellen
Second Grade Teacher
OTTSVILLE
Romberger, Norma Mc Elhaney
Soc Studies, Reading, Rel Tchr
OXFORD
Bender, Norma Jean
6th-8th Grade Music Teacher
Connelly, Denise Lorraine
Fifth Grade Teacher
Day, Sandra Fulton
Family & Consumer Sci Tchr

OXFORD (cont)
Fritsch, Joseph Edward, III
Math Teacher
Geesey, L. Kathleen
Language Arts Teacher
Keiths, Lisa K.
HS Physical Education Teacher
McCardell, Kimberly Kilby
Health & Physical Ed Teacher
Orner, Donald James
HS Art Teacher
Shuda, Lynne Garver
Seventh Grade Lang Arts Tchr
Stapleton, Leanne Peticca
Mathematics Teacher
PALMERTON
Chmiel, Rhoann Jones
Fourth Grade Teacher
Heinick, Thomas Karl
Instrumental Music Teacher
Larvey, Audrey Lois (Sheffer)
Social Studies Teacher
Little, Dennis Robert
Adjunct Faculty
O'Donnell, Leo Edward
5th Grade Teacher
Olivia, Susan (Rehrig)
Sixth Grade Teacher
Plessl, Maria Angelisanti
German Teacher
Smelas, Thomas William
Business Education Teacher
Tavella, Bonnie Barno
High School English Teacher
Yeager, Ronald Alfred
English Teacher
PALMYRA
Baum, Katherine Seitz
Geometry Teacher
Bucks, Susan Goodman
Gifted Facilitator
Harbaugh, Kelly Denise
Spanish Teacher
Hill, Aura M.
English & Journalism Teacher
Snyder, William Birch
9th Grade Language Arts Tchr
Willis, Richard Craig
Biology Teacher
PAOLI
Craigie, Carter Walker
Retired Professor
PARADISE
Lehman, Mary-Alice Eaby
First Grade Teacher
PATTON
Bem, John Eugene
Physics & AP Chem Teacher
Bishop, Richard Allen
Science Teacher
Bradley, Mimi F.
Health & Physical Ed Teacher
Kolonay, Louise Anne Schrenkel
French Teacher
Kuskoski, John W.
Cross Country Coach
PECKVILLE
Delonti, James Joseph
4th Grade Teacher
Kotcho, Nancy Bushta
Kindergarten Teacher
Racowski, Paula Branning
Reading Specialist
PEN ARGYL
Angelita, Maria
Sixth Grade Teacher
Fiorot, Rose Mary Valletta
Spanish Teacher
Ronca, Joan (Peron)
Spanish Teacher
Zavacky, Patricia A.
First Grade Teacher
PENN HILLS
Bauman, B. Lee
Implementation Specialist
PENNS CREEK
Fellencer, David Eugene
Education Professor
Wilson, Robert Wesley
Mathematics & Physics Teacher
PENNSBURG
Baker, Suzanne Eames
Mathematics Teacher
Bieler, Edward K.
United States History Teacher
Gallagher, Michael
AP Biology Teacher & Coach
Jacobs, William David
Biology Teacher
Lampe, Richard F.
Vocal Music Director
Leskusky, Vincent Edward
English Teacher
Morris, Larry Bernard
Economics Tchr & Athletic Dir
Piza, Roberta Watkins
English Teacher
Quatrani, Ernest Joseph
English Teacher
Rushatz, Tasha Jo
10th Grade English Teacher
Sheppard, Thomas Whittier
Asst Soc Stud Dept Chrmn
Thren, Vicki L. (King)
Phys Ed Teacher & Dept Chprsn
Walsh, Barbara A.
Former Kindergarten Teacher
PEQUEA
Baumbach, Walter David
School Counselor
PERKASIE
Androkites, Allen David
Technology Education Coord
Bachtell, David Larry
Music Coordinator
Dunning, Donna M.
Psychology & Sociology Teacher
Ehst, Kenneth M.
Biology Teacher
Graney, Colleen H.
American History Teacher
Graver, James Brian
Elementary Teacher
Greeley, Doris
German Teacher & Dept Coord
Knipe, Frank Stephen
Spanish Teacher
Knott, Patricia C.
Art Teacher
Moyer, R. Bruce
Secondary Mathematics Teacher
Redmond, Garrett G.
Seventh & Eighth Grd Eng Tchr
Robinson, Deborah Cotner
Physics Teacher
Saari, Karen Cecilia
Social Studies Teacher
Snyder, Jean Fister
9th-12th Grade Math Teacher
Wasser, David A.
High School Mathematics Tchr
Weierbach, Judith Houseworth
Jr & Sr English Teacher
White, Michael R.
Math Teacher & Stu Cncl Adv
Yoder, Richard D.
Social Studies Teacher
PERRYOPOLIS
Britvich, Joetta L.
Chemistry Teacher
Clark, Donna Marie Savona
Science Teacher
Mc Vey, Marilyn
Sr High School English Teacher
PHILADELPHIA
Abboud, Bechara Elias
Associate Prof of Civil Engrng
Adams, David H.
Math & Science Teacher
Amoroso, Gaetano Nichols
Meat Science Teacher
App, Thelma E.
Kndgtn Tchr & Preschool Dir
Appel, Sheila Cooperstein
7th-8th Grade Science Teacher
Avakame, Edem Frank
Criminal Justice Professor
Baren, Robert
Mechanical Engineering Prof
Barilla, James S.
English Teacher
Beauchemin, Philip Ernest
Social Studies Teacher
Begley, Ursula C.
6th Grade Teacher
Belcher, Cherrie Fuller
First Grade Teacher
Bentley, John
Science Teacher
Benton, Gloria Leggett
Art Teacher
Berk, Patricia A.
Art & Mechanical Engineer Tchr
Bivins, Barbara Perry
Teacher & Coordinator
Bliss, Harry F.
Teacher
Blume, Wendy Malkoff
Assoc Prof in Med Lab Tech
Bobroff, Sandra Rahl
English Teacher & Dean
Bolton, Marion Grant
Fourth Grade Teacher
Bonner, Jane A.
8th Grade Teacher
Boylan, Elizabeth A.
Pre-First Grade Teacher
Braithwaite, Antony Xavier
Theology Teacher
Braithwaite, Brenda Evelyn
Fifth Grade Teacher
Brangman, Dorothy Speight
House Director & Teacher
Branigan, Mary Grace
Resource Room Teacher
Brehmer, Carl R.
Science Teacher
Bright, Daniel A.
Guidance Counselor
Bright, Patricia Dowell
Coordinator of Student Svcs
Broder, Linda H.
Librarian
Brown, Camille Lewis
Principal
Brown, Dudley Cowan
4th Grade Teacher
Brown, William
TV Production Teacher
Brown, Willie Cannon
Asst Professor
Bryan, Henry C.
Mathematics Teacher
Bryant, Eleanor Spurlock
Program Support Teacher
Burghart, Margaret D.
Theology Teacher
Burke, Carlos Alvino
Mathematics Teacher
Burnett, Mariam Robinson
Retired Teacher
Burney, Skip
HS Mathematics Teacher
Burns, James Edward, Jr.
5th Grade Teacher
Bush, Elaine Hopkins
Fifth Grade Teacher
Caputo, Mary Theresa Gallagher
5th Grade Teacher
Capuzzi, Judy
Accounting & Finance Professor
Carazo, Janine Snyder
English & German Teacher
Carlin, Mary O'Neill
2nd Grade Teacher
Carolan, Joseph Patrick
5th Grade Teacher
Carroll, Joseph Aloysius
Seventh Grade Teacher
Carroll-Parker, Margaret Ann
Second Grade Teacher
Carter, Marvin L., Jr.
Director
Caruso, Joseph Peter
Mathematics Tchr & Dept Chprsn
Casey, Walter J.
English Instructor
Cattell, David F.
Physics & Math Asst Professor
Charnock, James Talbert
Eighth Grade Teacher
Chirlin, Larry E.
High School Math Teacher
Ciarroco, Ralph Anthony
8th Grade Teacher
Cipparone, Frank C.
Social Studies & Lit Teacher
Cody, Patricia Ann
Eighth Grade Teacher
Colavechio, Maryellen E.
Eighth Grade Teacher
Condello, John A.
Mathematics Teacher
Cooper, Arvela Odd
Art Education Teacher
Costello, Jeanne Russ
Integrated Language Arts Tchr
Coyle, Sandra
Kindergarten Teacher
Culp, Judith Williams
Educational Technology Teacher
Datz, Alan
Government & Soc Sci Teacher
Davidson, Barbara Tana
Spanish Teacher
Davis, La Deva Maureen
Dance Teacher
Derricotte, Mark Lamont
Teacher & Coordinator
Dessner, Linda Eckhardt
Adjunct Professor of ESL
DiCicco, Rosemarie Petrocik
8th Grade English Teacher
Dillon, Sandra Bowden
Instrumental Music Director
DiVirgilio, Barbara Ann
Vice Principal & 6th Grd Tchr
Dixon, Shirley Ann
Elementary School Principal
Drelich, Robert Joseph, OSFS
School Minister
Duffy, Mary Martin, CSFN
Principal
Dugan, Joan M.
Math Teacher
Dunlap, Dwight Patrick
High School Science Teacher
Dunn, Mary M.
Theology Teacher
Dunne, Anne Marie
Eighth Grade Teacher
Easley, April
Special Education Teacher
Edwards, Ruth Sykes
Elementary Teacher
Ehrlich, Shirley Lewine
3rd Grade Teacher
Endy-O'Kane, Genevieve Elizabeth
First Grade Teacher
Epstein, Marcia Goldschlager
Psych Assoc Prof & Ed Coord
Farrell, Charles
Social Studies Teacher
Federman, Deanna
Eighth Grade Teacher
Feeley, William A.
English Chairperson & Teacher
Feighan, Regina Ann
Seventh Grade Teacher
Ferere, Gerard Alphonse
Prof of Fr, Span & Linquistics
Filoon, Raymond George
8th Grade Teacher
Fischer, John Edward
Art, Drafting & Business Tchr
Fisher, Mary Lou Pollick
Sixth Grade Teacher
Fisher, Robert W.
Mathematics Teacher
Fitzgerald, Kelly Anne
Fifth Grade Teacher
Ford, Ronald Harrison
Learning Support Teacher
Forrester-Frye, Lois G.
English, Soc Stud & Sci Tchr
Forster, Dieter
Professor of Physics
Fox, Francine Trani
1st Grade Teacher
Freed-Fagan, Elise
Assistant Professor
Freedman, Michael Paul
Science Department Head
Fulton, Rhonda Beverly
Fifth Grade Teacher
Gagliardi, Josepha
Social Studies Teacher
Gallagher, Linda Marie
6th Grd Language Arts Teacher
Gallagher, Robert J.
College Instructor
Gard, Claudia Trout
High School Guidance Cnslr
Garrett, Isabel T., OSF
Teacher & Asst Dean of Stdnts
Garrinato, Frank
Mathematics Teacher
Garris, Alander Wilson, III
Eighth Grade Teacher
Gaul, Gerald Martin
7th-8th Grd Sci & Math Teacher
Gibson, Joseph Thomas, Jr.
Business Education Teacher
Gilbert, Harry James
High School Math Teacher
Gladstone, John Joseph
Science Teacher
Goldentyer, Patricia Young
Visiting Lecturer of Psych
Goldman, Myron W.
Math Teacher
Gonzalez, Lydia Lizzette
Spanish Teacher
Graham, Wanda D.
Tchng, Lrng Network Faciliator
Greene, Jean Hill
Elementary Guidance Counselor
Gustafson, Sandra Lynne
Spanish Teacher
Haggerty, Eileen Marie, SSJ
Kindergarten Teacher
Hamilton, Katie Hill
English Teacher
Haub, Charles L.
Eng & Pre-College Writing Tchr
Heidorn, Kenneth A.
Athletic Dir & Bible Teacher
Hess, Megan
2nd & 3rd Grd Classroom Tchr
Hill, Jeanne
8th Grade Teacher
Hill, Thelma L.
English Teacher
Hoffman, Barry L.
5th Grade Teacher
Holland, Joan Marie
Secondary Mathematics Teacher
Hooten, Roseanne
1st Grade Teacher
House, Gale (Fellenser)
High School Teacher & Coach
Hoye, Gwendolyn Sanders
7th Grade Teacher
Hurvitz, Randee Krone
English Teacher
Huszcza, Celeste Mary
Latin & Italian Teacher
Jackson, Robert A., Jr.
Social Studies Teacher
Jackson-Baytops, Lorraine Mallory
First Grade Teacher
Jacobs, Mary Joan, CSFN
English Teacher
Joftis, Frank Jay
Eighth Grade Teacher
Johnson, June Thurston
First Grade Teacher
Johnson, Walter J.
German & English Teacher
Jones, Alan Robert
Health & Physical Ed Teacher
Kane, Eileen Marie
Kindergarten Teacher
Kaporch, Moya Regina
Asst Prin & Eng Lecturer
Keiser, Patricia Elrena
Seventh Grade Teacher
Keller, John Charles
Senior High English Teacher
Kervick, Irene T.
8th Grade Teacher
Kilbride, Patricia Kiesa
Eighth Grade Teacher
Kilty, Cornelius Francis, OSFS
French & English Teacher
Kirk, Richard J.
History Teacher
Konell, Susan L.
Seventh Grade Teacher
Kosinski, Christine (Gorzoch)
Second Grade Teacher
Kosola, Charles Erik
Technology Teacher
Kost, Deborah Rose
Upper School Biology Teacher
Kruvcuk, Sandra C.
Reading & English Teacher
Kubach, Patricia J.
Biology Teacher
Laurich, Jean
Principal
Lee, Alfred W., Sr.
Social Science Teacher
Lee, Carla Antoinette
4th Grade Teacher
Leek, Richard D.
Social Studies Teacher
Lekic, Anita Marie
Elementary Education Teacher
Lesley, Mellinee K.
Adjunct Professor
Levy, Lynn
6th Grd Rdng & Soc Stud Tchr
Liebchen, Rosarita Loretta
History Teacher
Lim, Teck-Kah
Physics Professor
Lobron, John Richard
Spanish & Social Studies Tchr
Lodanosky, Francis Anthony
Math Teacher
Lomis, Lois M.
Business Teacher
Lucey, Jeannette, IHM
Eighth Grade Teacher
Lynch, Joseph Francis
English Teacher
Maglione, Mary
Pre K Teacher
Malseed, Zoriana Kawka
Associate Prof of Physiology
Marques, Alice Jeanne
Math Teacher
Marshall, Cheryl Wright
First Grade Teacher
Martino, John James
Mathematics Instructor
Mason, Jose
Associate Prof of Mathematics
Mastrangelo, Angela M.
Former Music Educator
Matthews, James M.
Asst Prof of Civil Engineering
Mayo, Patricia A.
Teacher
McCarrick, Marybeth Duffy
Music Teacher
McClurken, Sandra Lea
Teacher of ESL & Comp Tech
McCormick, Mark
Law Professor
Mc Creery, Barbara Lypka
Small Bus Learning Comm Coord
Mc Entee, Marcille, IHM
English Teacher
McGinn, Ronald Brian
Social Studies Teacher
Mc Gorry, Marian Elizabeth
Assoc Prof of Office Admin
Mc Hale, James F.
8th Grade Teacher
Mc Inerney, Patricia Coyne
Reading & English Teacher
McKay, James J.
Foreign Language Teacher
Mc Keown, Sandra L. (Rowley)
Sixth Grade Teacher
McMackin, William J.
Economics Teacher
Mecherly, George Joseph
Eng Dept Chair & Tchr
Meehan, Duane
Biology Teacher
Merriweather, Barbara Christine
Sixth Grade Teacher
Michaelson, Barry Leonard
5th Grade Teacher
Michelone, Roger A.
Agriculture Coordinator
Miles, Lillian E.
Fifth Grade Teacher
Miller, Ernest John, FSC
History & Religion Teacher
Miller, Joyce Ann
Religion & Art Teacher
Miller, Nancy Hill
Sixth Grade Teacher
Minehan, Paul Richard
Contract Law Teacher
Mockus, Carol
Chemistry Teacher
Montgomery, Michelle Lolli
Science Teacher
Moon, Richard E.
Science Teacher
Moore, Zenola Hubbard
Third Grade Teacher
Mudrick, Susan Ellen
Assistant Dean
Mulherin, Roseanne Cavallaro
French Teacher
Nayowith, Nancy M.
Health & PE Teacher
Newman, Ina M.
PE & Health Dept Chairperson
Oberholzer, Cecilia Garvin
Chem Tchr & Sci Dept Chairman
OConnell, Daniel Timothy
Foreign Languages Department
Oddou, William E.
Professor of Kinesiology
Odum, Lori Lyn
Eighth Grade Teacher
O'Grady, Cloe Gissinger
8th Grade Math & Science Tchr
Organsky, Florence Dayton
5th Grade Teacher
Pallozza, Frances Bernadette
Music Teacher
Parisi, Robert V.
Instrumental Music Director
Parker-Capolingua, Joan Marie
First Grade Teacher
Passas, Nikos
Criminology Professor
Patzelt, Karen E.
Seventh Grade Teacher
Pelta, Maureen
History of Art Assoc Prof

ELPHIA (cont)
Joseph Charles
ry Teacher
frey D.
Arts Department Chair
atricia Ann Mc Kenty
Grade Teacher
ning, Denise Lacelle
Teacher & 6th Grd Dean
arie McCullough
ry Teacher
san
th Grade Teacher
aryellen Menna
rade Teacher
ioseh Michael
te Professor of Hum
a M.
ntionist Teacher
Roslyn Gundy
Grade Teacher
pez, Linda
Teacher
dward William
Grade Teacher
Frances J., Jr.
rama Teacher
dira
Teacher
Anne Cellucci
Fac Med Practice Mgmt
wrence Grant, Jr.
& Government Teacher
elen Francis, SSJ
Office Assistant
Peter H.
Teacher
ny J.
ctn & English Teacher
rbara Rose
Grade Teacher
on, Cal
Physics & Phys Sci Tchr
on, Teresa
Grade Teacher
gela Johnson
natics Department Head
Lois Elliott
Grade Teacher
Robert L.
ter Education Teacher
, Bernard Jerome
oordinator & Teacher
Arnold David
Teacher
, Joyce Ann
garten Teacher
Stephanie M.
n Support Teacher
arol Renee
g Instructor
, Mayra C.
Prof of Physi & Kinesio
la, Albert Joseph
gy Teacher
David William
Studies Teacher
Joan A.
Grade Teacher
ohn Newman
ate Professor
ean Labriola
dical Editor
John R.
Studies Teacher
Pascal E.
Health Associate Prof
Margaret Mary Fowler
Environmental Sci Tchr
, William J.
r
ohn J.
Studies Dept Chprsn
Paul Allen, Jr.
ade Mathematics Teacher
, Michael Francis
glish Teacher
a, Madeline
m Coordinator & Teacher
Eleanor Mirarchi
e Professor
Barbara Gitlin
Teacher
ein, Ronald M.
1th Grade Chemistry Tchr
ichael Ralph
ate Professor
Michael D.
h Grade Teacher
ohn H., Jr.
sor & Director
Richard Robert
& Mathematics Teacher
David Lee
Animal Tech Teacher
William Joseph
Stud Dept Chair & Tchr
Doss
s Teacher
, Rose Anthony
stry Teacher
e, Frances Evelyn
Grade Teacher
o, William James
ade Teacher
Deena Label
ade Elementary Teacher
Margaret Mary
matics Teacher

Stegmaier, Anne Marie
7th Grd Tchr & Pastoral Cnslr
Stella, James Michael
Art Teacher
Stewart, Rickie Lynn
English Teacher
Sticco, Patricia Caraccio
English & Theology Teacher
Stokes, Jannie Myrick
Keyboarding Teacher
Subramanian, E. V.
12th Grade Teacher
Swayne, Janet M.
Math Teacher
Taylor, Anne Thomas
High School Music Teacher
Taylor, Jeffrey Matthew
HS Mathematics Teacher
Tedesco, Joan Black
English Teacher
Texter, Lynne A.
Assoc Prof Comm, Asst Dept Chm
Toczylowski, Mary Breen
Kindergarten Teacher
Topely, Charles John
English Teacher
Tori, Irene M.
Math Chairperson & Teacher
Toub, Eleanor Goman
Kindergarten Teacher
Trasken, Josef M.
Physics Teacher
Tregnan, Nancy L.
Health & Physical Ed Chrprsn
Tschopp, Charles
Fifth Grade Teacher
Turner, Frances Williams
Fifth Grade Teacher
Vanderpool, Rosemary Scanlon
General Education Professor
Vasey, Wendy Snyder
Eighth Grade Teacher
Vaughn, Darlene Frances
Fifth Grade Teacher
Venditti, Thomas S.
Theology Teacher
Vilsmeier, Beth Bedford
Music Director
Voron-Bultena, Sharyn R.
First Grade Teacher
Walton, Yvonne Lelia
Health & Physical Ed Teacher
Ward, Rosemary
English Teacher
Washington, Margie Goodwin
Family & Consumer Sci Teacher
Washington, Rochelle Elois
5th Grade Teacher
Watson, Pampalena C.
Life & Earth Science Teacher
Wesolowski, Wanda Eleanor
Prof & Radiologic Tech Chprsn
West, Eve Adelman
ASL & Eng Interpretation Prof
Wible, Mary C.
6th Grd Reading & English Tchr
Wilkinson, Maureen C.
Psychology Teacher
Williams, James F.
Freshman World History Teacher
Williams, Monique Rochelle
Electronics Instructor
Winterbottom, Michele E.
Science Teacher
Woehr, Eugene Walter
Social Studies Teacher
Wolf, Wanda Gang
School Counselor
Wooden, Adrienne Hearst
8th Grade Teacher
Wyzykowski, Carmela
8th Grade Teacher
Yarmus, Reuben L.
Foreign Language Dept Head
Yelder, Joyce Dyson
Fifth Grade Teacher
Young, Marilyn S.
Science Teacher & Dept Chm
Zion, Vilma
Eighth Grade Science Tchr

PHILIPSBURG
Henchbarger, Burton Lee
In School Suspension Teacher
Henry, Donald Scott
Band Director
Shealer, Brenda Norman
Eng, Jrnlsm Tchr & Dept Chprsn
Shetrom, Richard David
Amer History & US Govt Teacher
Shore, Shirley Walther
English Teacher
Wagner, Linda Long
Social Studies Teacher

PHOENIXVILLE
Barron, Gary Edward
Science Teacher
Bertone, John Anthony
Asst Prof of New Testament
Bilodeau, Ida Barto
Sixth Grade Teacher
Bogus, Joseph P., Jr.
Director of Guid & Psych Tchr
Brethauer, Alma Stoelting
10th Grade Health Educator
Bretzius, David Charles
Music Specialist
Coyne, Henry Francis, Jr.
History Teacher
Dore, Lynne Marie
French Teacher

Everett, Cheryl Gilbert
Biology Teacher
Ford, Richard J.
Math Teacher
Francis, David Franklin
Electronics Instructor
Good, Vivian D.(Ye)
English & Theater Teacher
Grubbs, Thomas Gene
Economics & Government Teacher
Harrington, Richard Alexander
English Teacher
Hartwick, A. Reuben
Adjunct Professor
Hutchinson, Elaine Frances
Soc Stud & Gifted Hum Teacher
Kalnins, Dace
German & English Teacher
Keehn, Rudolph W.
English Teacher
Keenan, James N.
English & Writing Wrkshp Tchr
Kelley, William David, Jr.
Seventh Grade Soc Studies Tchr
Kennedy, James Michael
Former Swimming Coach
Mandlowitz, Linda D.
6th Grade Teacher
Mc Mullin, Marcia Turtzo
Biology Teacher
Messick, Linda Lopes
6th Grade English Teacher
Mitchell, Megan J.
History, AP Government Teacher
Moore, Lonny Russell
PE Teacher & Chm
Myers, Mary Daher
Math & Reading Teacher
Peterson, Regina Liscio
Sixth Grade Teacher
Ridgeway, Kenneth E.
7th Grd Language Arts Teacher
Schnabel, Susan Jane
Social Studies Teacher
Uliano, Nicholas J.
Spanish Instructor

PICTURE ROCKS
Mordan, Carol Ritter
Third Grade Teacher

PINE FORGE
Brown, Milton Irvin
Principal

PINE GROVE
Fennelly, Jane Kozura
Math & Physics Teacher
Heller, James R. X.
Art Teacher
Herber, Laurence Lee
4th Grade Teacher
Horst, Linda Quietmeyer
Physical Education Teacher
Hughes, Renee L.
Business Teacher
Manbeck, Sandra Potts
Mathematics Teacher
Reilly, Donna Marie(Lehman)
12th Grade English Teacher
Smith, Terri Leffler
Soc Studies Teacher
Stolarick, Catherine Ruth
IST Support Teacher
Wagner, Susan Marie
English, German & ESL Tchr
Wilgus, William David
Senior Army & JROTC Instr
Williams, Thomas C.
Industrial Arts Teacher
Zwiebel, Jeffrey Scott
High School Band Director

PITTSBURGH
Abram, George C.
Sociology & Psych Teacher
Adam, Donald G.
Professor of English
Adams, Patricia E.
High School Teacher
Affleck, Silvia
Latin Teacher
Albert, Eugene N.
HS Instructional Team Teacher
Andrews, Barbara Jacob
German & English Teacher
Antisdel, MaryEllen O'Toole
Retired Teacher
Baier, Thomas C.
AP Eng Lit & Comp Teacher
Baird, Deanna Morrison
German Tchr & Foreign Lang Ldr
Baldasare, Anthony
Pupil Affairs Dept Chprsn
Balmert, Michael E.
Assoc Prof of Commnctn Stud
Banks, John David
Math & Computer Science Tchr
Barbus, Arlene M.
Mathematics Teacher
Barnea, Ravid (Oron)
Hebrew Teacher
Batson, Susan Kurtz
Chem Teacher & Planetarium Dir
Bazala, Michelle Monahan
French Teacher
Beckwith, Sandra K.
MS Computer & English Tchr
Belles, Suzanne Lee
Latin Teacher
Bender, Christine Kristich
Chemistry Teacher
Bercini, MaryAnn LeDonne
Teacher & Asst Administrator

Betts, Patricia Taliaferro
Guidance Counselor
Bjorhovde, Reidar
Prof of Civil & Envrnmntl Engr
Bond, E. Denton
Stu Asst Coord & Math Instr
Bordell, Patricia A.
Chemistry Teacher
Borecky, Catherine Mary
Science Teacher
Borecky, Stephen R.
Associate Professor of Biology
Botta, Gregory John
Health & Physical Ed Teacher
Boules, Theodore Louis, III
Math Teacher
Bowen, Charles P., Jr.
English Teacher
Boyer, Jean Groves
Kindergarten Teacher
Boyer, Linda Jean
Spanish Teacher & Dept Chprsn
Braden, John B.
School Counselor
Bradley, George E., II
Biology Teacher
Brandtonies, William H.
Secondary Guidance Counselor
Bricker, Lillian (Fazi)
7th & 8th Grade Math Teacher
Brink, David M.
English Teacher
Brozick, James R.
English Dept Chair
Brucker, Elizabeth Gleba
Upper Elem Lang Arts Tchr
Brumberg, John Carl
Science Teacher
Bruno, Audrei Mataya
Professor of Nursing
Bubbina, Vincent S.
English & Religion Teacher
Bunardzya, Vance Richard
American Cultures Teacher
Burack, Carolee Mirsky
Eng as Second Lang Tchr
Bykowski, Marie
Latin Teacher
Calgaro, Louis A.
Spanish Teacher
California, John Marshall
Physics Teacher
Carney, Bruce N.
Physics Teacher
Carper, Jeffrey Rhodes
Asst Professor of Accounting
Carter, Oliver Thomas
Science Teacher
Carter, Rebecca D.
Facilitator & Teacher
Cassandro, James Anthony
Drafting Teacher
Caughey, Barbara Hodge
Second Grade Teacher
Cawley, Lori Awenowicz
7th Grade Language Arts Tchr
Chapman, Phyllis
3rd Grade Teacher
Charny, Kris Vecchio
Third Grade Teacher
Chase, Helenann
9th Grade English Teacher
Clarke, Ilene Idell
English Teacher
Coll, Kathy Ann Knitter
English & Leadership Dev Tchr
Collage, Patricia Karavas
Social Studies Teacher
Collins, Laurel L.
English Teacher
Colvin, Susan Pugliese
Asst Prof of Pediatric Nursing
Connelly, Bruce R.
English Teacher
Cook, Marianne
4th-5th Grade Teacher
Copeland, Camille Carpenter
Asst Prof, Dept of Counseling
Copich, Robert A.
Mathematics Teacher
Cothran, Mary Mc Caa
Nursing Instructor
Cronauer, Donna
Language Arts & Religion Tchr
Crone, Thomas G.
Band & Orchestra Director
Croyle, Allysen Toddsen
English Professor
Cunningham, Deborah May
Kindergarten Teacher
Davis, Delia Myers
7th Grade Reading Teacher
Davis, James Richard
Reading Teacher
Davis, Louanne Burg
5th Grade Elementary Teacher
DeFilippo, Dennis Anthony
Ec & American Government Tchr
DeJulio, Patricia Diamond
Intermediate & Jr HS Sci Tchr
Delaney, Jacqueline Harms
Kindergarten & Spanish Teacher
DePalma, Joseph William
English Teacher
De Riggi, Catherine Iannotta
Senior Academic Counselor
Detzel, Carl W.
Mathematics Teacher
Dillon, Kimberly M.
Title I & Reading Specialist

DiPietro, Thomas G.
6th Grade Math Teacher
Doerr, Veronica Magdalena
English Professor
Dolgos, David C.
Social Studies Teacher
Donaldson, Leonard Ross
Social Studies Dept Chprsn
Donnelly, Kathleen V.
Assistant Prof of Advertising
Donohue, Patricia M.
Voice Teacher
Doyle, Margaret G.
Science Teacher
Drotar, Cherie Aber
Mathematics Teacher
Duda, Judith Jamitis
Elementary Guidance Counselor
Dunlop, Sandra Lahet
Retired High School Hlth Tchr
Eckman, Mark A.
Religion Teacher
Edner, Robert Griffith
Biology Teacher
Egan, Marilyn M.
Assistant Prof of Eurhythmics
Ellis, John Michael
High School Chemistry Teacher
Ellison, William Charles
Mathematics Teacher & Coach
Evans, Lynnae Richter
History Department Chair
Evans, Margaret A.
Chemistry Teacher
Evans, Timothy E.
Sociology Professor
Facaros, Sophia Calaboyias
Health, PE Tchr & Dept Chprsn
Farrell, Mark O.
Chemistry Professor & Chprsn
Faub, Patricia A.
English Teacher
Fazio, Dolores Ann (Danko)
Eighth Grade English Teacher
Ferguson, Victoria Runac
9th Grade Business Teacher
Finnegan, Diane DeFilippo
English Teacher & Dept Chm
Fiori, Sandra Turlik
Language Arts Teacher
Fish, Ruth Siedle
Music Instructor
Flavin, Jack
Intermediate Grade Teacher
Fleming, Susan J.
English Teacher
Floyd, Muriel Hefflin
Main Stream Teacher
Flynn, Ida Moretti
Information Science Professor
Foley, Deana Schoch
Chemistry Teacher
Forgrave, Susan Monroe
Intl Baccalaureate Eng Teacher
Forman, Honey Davidson
Instructional Teacher Leader
Fortun, David R.
English Teacher
Foster, Jane Wallis
First Grade Teacher
Frank, Ronald Patrick
Art Teacher
Fry, MaryBeth B.
English Tchr & College Cnslr
Galardini, Maureen L.
Cmptr Ed Tchr & Coord
Galuska, Michael R.
6th-8th Grade Teacher
Gargani, Mary Ann (Winjerson)
Mathematics Teacher
Garrubba-Castelli, Mary Rose
English Professor
Gibson, Janet Mahaney
First Grade Teacher
Ginder-Delventhal, Tracy L.
Teacher of Acting
Gist, Karen Wingfield
High School English Teacher
Glencer, Suzanne Thomson
Science Teacher
Gleser, Marilyn Beth (Zolotor)
Developmental Studies Instr
Goetz, Gary R.
Language Arts Teacher & Coach
Goldberg, P. David
Fourth Grade Teacher
Golden, Terrance
Science Teacher
Golla, William J.
Biology Teacher
Goodman, Karen Sidehamer
6th Grade Teacher
Graff, Hal
English Teacher
Grode, Linda Downing
MS Math & Social Studies Tchr
Grove, William Allen
High School Tech Ed Teacher
Gruseck, David John
History Teacher
Guerra, James E.
Adjunct Professor of Saxophone
Gula, John A.
Director of Bands
Gustafson, Nancy Ann
Secondary English Teacher
Haines, James Barr
Professor of English & Spanish
Hamel, Dorothy
Third Grade Teacher

PITTSBURGH (cont)
Hancock, Judy Pfile
Music Professor
Haney, Edward F.
Civics & Leadership Teacher
Hart, Randall Lee
Engineering Technology Teacher
Hartlep, Dorothy Kosmach
MS Language Arts Teacher
Hawbaker, David George
Art Teacher
Hawkins, Clinton Matthew
History & Social Work Prof
Heath, Elisabeth Laura
Music Tchr & Dir
Heberle, Janet Miller
Business Education Teacher
Hefflin, Patrick
Physics & Calculus Teacher
Helon, David Joseph
HS Visual Communcations Tchr
Herrmann, William Anton
Secondary Soc Studies Teacher
Hill, Judith Rhodes
Social Studies Teacher
Hindes, Paul D.
Civics Tchr, Coach & Act Spon
Hobson, Mary Ann
Instructional Teacher Leader
Holdan, Gregory
Math & Computer Science Tchr
Holman, Richard F.
Professor of Physics
Holste, Benjamin E.
Music Director
Holzen, Janice Raymont
Math Tchr & Gifted Facilitator
Holzer, Ralph Adam
English Teacher
Hornick, Stephanie Balta
Kindergarten Teacher
Horowitz, Pamela Sue
Spanish Teacher
Hunter, Marilyn K.
11th & 12th Grade English Tchr
Hutson, Ronald Lee
Associate Prof of Fine Arts
Iacchetti, Raffalina Frances
Middle School Science Teacher
Iezzi, Carl Thomas
Instrumental Music Dir
Ilov, Laura Ann
Reading & History Teacher
Irlbacher, David E.
Principal
Irwin, John Jay
Physics Teacher
Iyengar, Maria Hrebenak
Fifth Grade Teacher
Jackson, Anne Martin
Early Learning Skills Teacher
Jameson, Patricia Galley
Psychology Instructor
Janecek, Karen Kearney
Second Grade Teacher
Jessy, Carl William
Social Studies Teacher
Johnson, Mary Beth Habas
Professor of Court Reporting
Johnson, Sheila LaBlanche
Assoc Prof of Counseling
Jones, David Meredith
Journalism Professor
Jordanoff, Christine (Kunko)
Music Education Chair & Prof
Joseph, Patricia Tallerico
8th Grade Reading Teacher
Kalogeras, Areta
Music, Band & Orch Teacher
Kaminski, Joan M. Jankowski
5th & 6th Grade Teacher
Kapron, Cecelia Fleckenstein
Dance Teacher
Kasunic, Mary Claire
French Teacher
Katz, Thelma Ackerman
Full-Day Kindergarten Teacher
King, Mark E.
Assoc Prof Dept of Child Dev
Klein, Terry Mueller
Latin Teacher
Kling, David D.
Sociology & Psychology Teacher
Kocur, Edward Alan
German Teacher & Coach
Koger, Dorothy DeSchon
Former Teacher
Koontz, Mary Beth Ann
Music Teacher
Kozusko, Genevieve Mary
Physical Education & Hlth Tchr
Krotec, Mark Charles
Biology Teacher
Kuhns, Martha
Nursing Professor
Kuntz, Raymond L.
Computer Science Teacher
Kurke, Lance Brownson
Assoc Professor of Management
Kustron, Thomas P.
Mathematics Instructor
Lackman, Conway Lee
Schl of Business Professor
Laine, Raymond Alan
Voice & Speech Prgm Coord
Larko, Michael J.
Math Teacher
Lawson, Annamae
English Teacher
Laychak, Lawrence Joseph
Physics & Chemistry Teacher
Lear, James P.
Sci Dept Chm & Physics Tchr
Leibach, Charlotte Lee
Science Teacher
Leicht, Lynn M.
Physical Education Teacher
Leonard, Stanley S.
Adjunct Prof of Percussion
Lester, Richard Reese
Math Dept Chair
Levenson, Mina Terry (Altshuler)
Health, PE & Spanish Teacher
Levine, Evie A.
11th-12th Grade English Tchr
Lewis, Robert Anthony, Jr.
Civics & US History Tchr
Liebowitz, S. Jay
Assoc Prof of Org Behavior
Ligons, Frank Joseph
Music Teacher & Chorus Dir
Lijewski, Dori Jean
Science Teacher
Lipchek, John Joseph
Social Studies Teacher
Lishack, John H.
Math Teacher
Lishack, Nancy DiClemente
Business Teacher
Lobaugh, Donna Pascarella
6th Grade Teacher
Logsdon, Marge
English Teacher
Long, David M.
Health & Phys Ed Teacher
Long, Veryl Dewey, Sr.
Health & Phys Ed Teacher
Lowe, Carol Mc Burney
HS Humanities & Bible Teacher
Lowe, James Lawrence
Business Teacher
Lucarelli, John A.
Assoc Professor of English
Lucot, Mary Alice A.
6th-8th Grade Teacher
Lynch, MaryAnn Yannotty
English Tchr & Dept Chair
Madaras, Paul Michael
Gifted Program Coordinator
Mantella, Rose M.
English & Spanish Teacher
Marchlewski, Joseph Harold
Life Science Instructor
Martin, Douglas G.
Television Production Teacher
Marvin, Angela (Mead)
Third Grade Teacher
Marziale, Henry William, Jr.
Psych & World Cultures Tchr
Maser, Margaret Frace
French Teacher
Matesic, Charles Thomas, Jr.
Eighth Grade Math Teacher
Matone, Virginia Elaine
Art Instructor
Matthews, David Gerald
High School Band Director
Matthews, Donald Frank
History Teacher
Matuszewski, Anne Cunningham
Language Arts Teacher
McAleer, Frances D.
Supervisor of Gifted Programs
Mc Cabe, Shannon Marie
English Teacher
Mc Call, Marlene
Biology & Chemistry Professor
McCalley, Barbara Vaglia
Honors Eng & Speed Rdng Tchr
Mc Closkey, Mary Ann
English Teacher
Mc Conville, Melissa Ann
Middle School Math Teacher
Mc Coy, Ray Arthur
Senior High Biology Teacher
Mc Donald, Jacqueline Ann
French Teacher
McGrath, Michael Bernard
English Teacher
McLaughlin, Rosemary Katrryn
English Teacher
Mc Nulty, Cindy
English & History Teacher
Meehan, Terence P.
Business Education Instructor
Megahan, Larry E.
Physics & Astronomy Instructor
Meigs, Helen Yablonski
Russian Teacher
Mertz, Larry A.
Art Teacher
Michalowsky, Donna Marie (Donahue)
Seventh & Eighth Grade Teacher
Miller, Evan Kimball
English Teacher
Miller, Joyce Susan
English Teacher
Miller, Philip Carl
Algebra II Teacher
Milliken, Patricia Koppenhauer
Biology Teacher
Modic, Eugene Leigh
Biology Teacher & Dept Liaison
Mohney, Thomas Lee
High School Supervisor Teacher
Monteleone, Vincent Joseph
Instrumental Music Teacher
Mooney, Mark Patrick
Anatomy & Physiology Asst Prof
Moore, Nancy J.
Associate Professor of English
Moreland, Muriel Reynolds
Retired Classroom Teacher
Morelli, Phil Anthony
Director
Morgan, James M.
English Teacher
Mueller, Jacqueline Gasior
English Teacher
Muffley, James Daniel
Chemistry Teacher
Muha, Arla H.
English Teacher
Mullen, Geraldine
6th Grade Teacher
Munns, Joyce Ann
English Teacher
Mushrush, David E.
Algebra & Geometry Teacher
Nagle, Brian M.
Accounting Professor
Nelson, Ellen Valentine
Language Arts Teacher
Nettrour, Elizabeth Lynn
English Graduate Tchng Fellow
Nicklos, Richard Woody
Principal
Nowack, George P.
Language Arts Teacher
Oakley, Harriett Hutchinson
Professor of Nursing
O'Connell, James Patrick
Business Education Teacher
O'Donnell, Joseph N.
7th Grade Mathematics Teacher
Ogren, S. Robert
Retired Mathematics Teacher
O'Neill, Cynthia Benanti
Biology Teacher
Oriss, James J.
Guidance Counselor
Orr, Darlene Cole
Music Teacher
Orr, Marian Andrea
Counselor
Palka, Janet Wight
Assoc Professor of Biology
Partridge, Richard
9th Grade Mathematics Teacher
Patterson, Patricia Fordyce
Professor of English
Patton, R. Scott
Technology Education Teacher
Perpetua, Kathleen G.
Emotional Supprt, Spec Ed Tchr
Peters, Bruce E.
Mathematics Teacher
Petracchi, Helen E.
Asst Prof of Social Work
Phillis, Roy Andrew
Mathematics Teacher
Pierallini, Maryann Husovitz
Instructional Support Teacher
Pierce, Dan
Science Teacher
Pipak, Michael John
HS Social Studies Teacher
Pisaneschi, Katherine Marchetti
Former Third Grade Teacher
Platt, Linda Sue
Professor in Athletic Training
Ploskunak, J. Robert
Architectural Drafting Instr
Poetain, Charles A.
Assistant Professor of Math
Pogue, Linda Khouri
Teacher
Pollock, Arthur Jerome
Guidance Counselor
Post, Kay D. (Howells)
Professor of Computer Science
Posteraro, Carolyn Avolio
Fifth Grade Teacher
Posteraro, Gino
Elementary Band Director
Powers, Mary Victor
Principal
Pozar, Kathleen Louise
Speech Arts Teacher
Pratt, Richard P., Sr.
HS Assistant Principal
Pryor, Paul R.
Soc Stud & Pol Sci Teacher
Radocay, Connie Mc Claren
Math Instructor & Dept Chair
Rehm, MaryAnn
Eng Tchr & Acting Instrl Ldr
Reich, Donna Anania
English Teacher
Reilly, Judith Howard
English Teacher
Richard, Linda R.
Teacher
Rocco, Marilyn K.
Home Economics Teacher
Rockwell, Diane Marie
Biology, Chemistry & Sci Tchr
Rodgers, Vincent Paul
Frgn Lang & Speech Arts Chprsn
Romano, Teresa
Guidance Counselor
Rose, Patricia Colangelo
Rdng, Lang Arts & Math Tchr
Rosen, Sandra Platt
Kindergarten Teacher
Rosnick, Kathy Conrad
Mathematics Teacher
Ross, Carl Anthony
Assistant Professor
Ross, Charles Daniel
6th Grade Teacher
Rowland, Stephen C.
Mathematics Teacher
Rucki, Debra Stephanie
Dean of Students
Russman, David Wayne
Science Dept Chair & Teacher
Rutter, Charles Edward
Soc Stud, PE Tchr & Ath Dir
Samko, Paul George
Chemistry Teacher
Sands, Frank James
Head Crew Coach
Santee, William L.
A P English Teacher
Santo, Dorothy E. Wiatrak
Elem & Jr High Teacher
Schachter, Dorothy Seidel
Business Education Teacher
Schafer, William Patrick
Demonstration Teacher
Scheller, Jeff James
Fourth Grade Teacher
Schlachter, Paul A.
History Teacher
Schwarzel, John C.
Auto Body Teacher
Scott, Jeanne A.
Dir of Campus Ministry, Cnslr
Scrima, James V.
Language Arts Teacher
Seelhorst, Wayne John
Mathematics Teacher
Sekinger, Roxan Henk
English Teacher
Selinger, Adele Corrin
Biology & Ecology Teacher
Seward, David B.
Latin Teacher
Shearer-Bicanovsky, Deborah Jean
Art Teacher
Shipley, Janet Elaine
Fourth Grade Teacher
Sikora, Gloria DiMarco
Social Studies Teacher
Silianoff, Michael
Mathematics Teacher
Sillup, Ann Walsh
Mathematics Teacher
Simmons, Del
Mathematics Teacher
Siska, Peter Emil
Chemistry Professor
Skowronek, Patricia Ann
Math, Cmptr & Sci Teacher
Slabe, Ronald S.
4th & 5th Grd, Geog & His Tchr
Sloan, James Alan
World Cultures Teacher
Smeaton, William Andrew
Fourth Grade Teacher
Smerdel, Jo DeSimone
Zoology Teacher & Sci Chair
Smith, John S.
Mechanical Engrng Tech Instr
Smith, Joyce Emily
Fourth Grade Teacher
Smutko, Patricia Lee Weber
Asst Prof of Nursing
Snider, Nancy S.
US History Teacher
Soberg, Cynthia Ann
Counselor
Sobolewski, Ronald
Ceramics Instr & Fine Arts Chm
Spagnolo, Shirley Ballard
English Teacher
Stagger, Anita E.
Geography Teacher & Admin Asst
Stancil, Daniel Dean
Prof of Electrical & Comp Engr
Stanko, Dianne Danka
Biology Teacher
Stearns, Peter N.
Dean of Humanities & Soc Sci
Stein, Sandra McKean
Special Education Master Tchr
Stephens, Harry
Science Teacher
Stiffler, Robert Bland
Retired Middle Schl Math Tchr
Stone, Lawrence Harvey
Social Studies Teacher
Strasser Rush, Mona Diane
English Teacher
Streiff, Jean Ann Capizzi
English Teacher & Dept Chair
Stutz, Paul Lawrence
English Teacher & Dept Chprsn
Stypula, Amy Lynn
Spanish Teacher
Sweitzer, Richard
Social Studies Teacher
Tarasovic, George M.
Social Studies Teacher
Tardio, Rosemary Matarazzo
Family & Consumer Sci Tchr
Taylor, Ellie (Schobel)
Kndgtn & Instrl Support Tchr
Then, Arlene M.
Honors Biology Teacher
Thomas, Richard N.
Fifth Grade Teacher
Thompson, Julia A.
Professor of Physics
Tima, Dianne Luther
Lang Arts Tchr & Dept Coord
Tippett, Bryan Keith
Professor of Biology
Totin, David William
Fourth Grade Teacher
Trubic, Mary Rita
Social Stud & Lang Arts Tchr
Vasser, Beatrice Wright
Health, PE Dept Head & Ath Dir
Vida, Shirley Moody
Fourth Grade Teacher
Vitenas, Diana
9th Grade English Teacher
Vizza, William A.
English Teacher
Vukela, Robert John
Business Ed Teacher
Vuono, Richard Gerald
Mathematics Teacher
Walker, Janet Lois
Professor of French & Dept Chm
Warner, DAvid Richard
AP Amer His & Psych Teacher
Waronsky, Frank T., Jr.
Art Teacher
Weaver, Earl D.
Asst Prof of Musical Theatre
Weber, Patricia G.
English Teacher
Weiss, Bernard J.
Professor of History
Williams, Kenneth Alan
German Teacher
Williams-Giuliani, Joan M.
Prof of Jrnlsm & Communication
Winn, Laura L.
French Teacher
Wisker, Lisa Spanziani
Fifth Grade Elementary Teacher
Wolstoncroft, Howard Steven
US History & Amer Govt Tchr
Woodburn, Morrow
6th Grade English Teacher
Woodward, Lynne Hess
German Teacher
Zbozny, Frank T.
Professor of English
Zegar, Janet Moricz
Choral & Dance Teacher
Zerebnick, Michele
Associate Professor
Zinger, Patricia Miscimarra
Second Grd, Instrl Tchr Leader
Zivic, Donna Marie
Mathematics Teacher
Zollner, Patricia Fedishen
Gifted Program Coordinator

PITTSFIELD
Savko, Janet Lynn
First Grade Teacher

PITTSTON
Biga, Victoria Phyllis
Teacher of Gifted
Caprio, Joseph James, Jr.
Science Teacher
Charney, Sandra Lee Ann (Beglion
4th-5th Grd Math & Sci Tchr
Curry, Joseph L.
English & Journalism Teacher
Dowd, Joan Baker
2nd Grade Teacher
Egan, Joan Morrow
Math Tchr & Dept Chairperson
Feeney, Jane McGarry
Business & Soc Studies Teacher
Glennon, Beverly Ann Sabbatini
Art Instructor & Dept Chprsn
Granteed, Donna DeAngelo
English & Applied Comm Teache
Langman, Jacqueline Capozucca
Literature Teacher
Lonergan, Santina Palmeri
Social Studies Teacher
Minella, Ann Barrette
Sixth Grade Reading Teacher
Murphy, E.J. Joseph
7th Grade Reading Teacher
Myers, Mary Kathryn Toole
Second Grade Teacher
Ostrowski, Lois Baker
Mathematics Teacher
Pavlick, Joyce M.
Fifth Grade Teacher
Sarnowski, Helen Ann
Business Teacher & Dept Chair
Sassi, John J.
Advanced Placement Lit Tchr
Schillaci, Patricia Ann
Mathematics & Spanish Teacher
Tetlak, John Charles
Science Teacher
Timchak, Robert M.
Dir of Religious Formation
Timlin, James T.
Chemistry Teacher
Turner, Cathie Azaravich
English Teacher
Walsh, Ann Marie
8th Grd Soc Stud & Lit Teacher
Williams, Ann Marie Kuplinski
7th Grd Social Studies Teacher

PLEASANTVILLE
Johnson, Carol Boddorf
Fifth Grade Teacher

PLUMSTEADVLLE
Bauer, Edward William
Chemistry & Physics Teacher
Kitabjian, Mary S.
High School Biology Teacher
Reif, Stephen Bruce
Vocal Music Teacher
Wolfskill, Heidi A.
Music Department Head & Tchr

UTH
aine A. Watson
· & Director
ski, Robert Owen
y & General Science Tchr
Deborah O'Malley
rade Teacher
Joseph L.
n Teacher
bert Paul, II
: Science Teacher
Thomas Robert
Teacher
Catherine Cannon
nt Principal
h, Joseph Edward
Studies Teacher
, Leslie James
Teacher
arol Pajor
Teacher
, Mary Jean DeLycure
Studies Teacher
uth Sharkus
n Teacher
nowski, Diane Hodgson
chool Orchestra Teacher
UTH MEETING
Patricia Leighton
matics Teacher
E. Scott
: Computer Science Tchr
, Judy B.
Teacher
, Elsa M.
rade Teacher
Barbara Elaine
ss Education Teacher
John Charles
Studies Teacher
ams, Christopher J.
Production Teacher
omas Robert
stry Teacher
David William
tion Pgm Supvr & Coach
ski, Edward Joseph
can Government Teacher
Bernard
n Teacher
even R.
n Dept Chair & Teacher
LLEGANY
Hazel F.
ter & Accounting Teacher
IATILDA
, Dianne M.
ade Teacher
UE
Katherine Kolanko
Grade Teacher
GE
Trudy Grose
th Grade French Teacher
Deborah M.
y & Geography Teacher
rman E.
stry & Physics Teacher
Cynthia Lee
d Grade Teacher
Martha Bacon
garten Teacher
Kathleen L.
ade Teacher
Freya Weister
matics Teacher
eva Scaromizzino
garten Teacher
Fred A.
h Teacher
RSVILLE
Betty J. (Fulton)
d Grade Teacher
Edward Donald
th Grade Teacher
TOWN
Donald William
h Teacher
, Karen H.
d Social Studies Tchr
Richard H.
Grade Geography Teacher
, Charles Louis
Studies Teacher
W. Christopher
str & Alumni Pblctns Dir
Philip Wilson
Grade Mathematics Tchr
Carole Ann Dee
Grade Teacher
Robert James
cs Instructor
. Todd
h Teacher
Joan Yocum
h Teacher
Shelby Coy
Grade Teacher
, Barbara Joan (Pierson)
elor
, David E.
n & PE Teacher
, Ray W.
Grade Teacher
, Michele
Teacher
Robert Plewes, II
matics Teacher
Willis John
matics Teacher

Smith, Theresa Clair
Former Prof of Intnl Relations
Taylor, Elwood Albert
Seventh Grade Social Stud Tchr
Troutman, Gregory Gene
High School Math Teacher
Wentzel, Rosemary Koury
Fourth Grade Teacher
POTTSVILLE
Bertsch, Hal F.
Accounting Teacher
Bodenberg, Lynn Alan
English Teacher
Fedoriska, Richard Paul
History, Psych, Sociology Tchr
Flanagan, Bernard A.
Director of Spiritual Act
Fries, Richard Donald
Band Director
Jones, Georjean Russlyn
Bio Tchr & Science Dept Chm
Norton, William
Social Studies Teacher
Ray, Ellen Everett
English Teacher
Rennick, Robert Dennis
Mathematics Teacher
Schwenk, Sandra Mates
French Teacher
Ward, Thomas John
9th-10th Grade English Teacher
West, Harlan R.
Science Teacher
PROSPECT
Shidemantle, Donna Price
First Grade Teacher
PROSPECT PARK
Acker, Kenneth L.
Science Teacher
Blackburn, Brian Keith
Media Technician
Duggan, Bonnie June
3rd Grade Teacher
Englander-Kraut, Denise L.
European History Teacher
Gaston, Gail Haydon
Latin Teacher
Gefrorer, Charles A.
German Teacher
Gerspach, Virginia A.
Second Grade Teacher
Hostetter, Allyn E.
Business Education Teacher
Livingston, Jean Marie
Math Teacher
Livingston, John William
Amer History & Govt Tchr
Mc Grotty, Kirk Thomas
Chemistry Teacher
Ohlson, Helen
English Teacher
Renzetti, Theresa Ann
English Teacher
Schalleur, Maryann C.
English Teacher
Venturini, Marian T.
Physics Teacher
PUNXSUTAWNEY
Bowser, Anita Quinlisk
Substitute Teacher
Brazier, William B. J.
Band Director
Conti, Neil Alvin
English Teacher
Giavedoni, Barbara Cuba
Math Teacher & Yearbook Adv
Harrold, Janis McMillen
English Teacher
Kallas, Cynthia Gresock
Kindergarten Teacher
Meneely, James Clyde
9th-11th Grd Biology Teacher
Rotolo, LuAnn
Spanish Teacher
Shields, Gale Lewis
Health & PE Teacher
Smith, John F.
Scndry Physical Education Tchr
QUAKERTOWN
Friel, Martin Joseph
Fifth Grade Teacher
Guise, Judith L.
World Geography Teacher
Jacoby, Terry Pennell
Kindergarten Teacher
Jarrett, Peter J.
7th Grade Life Science Teacher
Kenney, LInda Ann (Freefield)
Second Grade Teacher
Mc Carty, Rosanne M.
Eng, Rdng & Study Skills Tchr
Reitz, Carol Tellip
Sixth Grade Teacher
Ruhl, Robert K.
Physics Tchr & Sci Dept Coord
Rusin, John J.
Instrumental Music Teacher
Sabol, Jack Jospeh
Algebra Teacher
QUARRYVILLE
Althoff, Ronald James
Agriculture Teacher
DeBerdine, Faye B.
Retired Teacher
Gleason, Lisa Franchi
Learning Support Teacher
Griffiths, Diane Arlene
Spanish Teacher
Griffiths, Frederick John
Chemistry Teacher

Hammer, Cathy E.
6th Grade Block Teacher
Henry, Arba L.
Agricultural Ed Dept Chm
Hess, John Marvin
Social Studies Teacher
Kopf, Linda Lorenzon
5th Grade Teacher
Kreider, Dawn DeLong
Health & Physical Ed Teacher
Lloyd, Brenda S. (Willing)
Mathematics Teacher
Miller, Brett R.
Environmental & Life Sci Tchr
Pasko, Jennifer Ann
Dept Chairperson & Eng Tchr
Pasquino, William A.
8th Grade Social Studies Tchr
Sangrey, Cynthia Elaine
Soc Studies Tchr & Dept Chprsn
Vasco, Betty Joan
8th Grade Communications Tchr
Wenger, Carolyn M.
Business Department Teacher
QUINCY
Glenn, Jane Benchoff
2nd Grade Teacher
Shadler, Donald I.
Sixth Grade Teacher
Sullivan, Cynthia Pelger
Instructional Support Teacher
RADNOR
Benson, Barbara J.
Art Chairperson & Teacher
Falini, Dominick Joseph
HS Social Studies Teacher
Fisher, Dennis Joseph
Theology Teacher
Hekker, Rita Frances
Senior Theology Teacher
Howard, Ralph J.
English & History Teacher
Mc Geehan, Paul T.
English Teacher
Sicoli, M. L. Corbin
Professor of Psychology
Whiteman, Carol Szmurlo
Biology & Physical Sci Tchr
RANKIN
Leith, Ronald Edward
Sixth Grade Teacher
READING
Achenbach, Rita Maria
English Teacher & Dept Chair
Achenbach, Sara Sharadin
English Teacher
Albright, Eleanor Zarinsky
7th & 8th Grade Math Teacher
Ashcraft, Richard Waitman
Mathematics Teacher
Attili, Mary L.
Instr of Eng Composition Lit
Backenstoss, Stanley
Bio & Environmental Sci Tchr
Ballantyne, Robert L.
Adj Instr of Environmental Sci
Bellettiere, Marc Philip
Social Studies Teacher
Buckendorff, Rosemary Hauseman
Eng Dept Co-Chair & Teacher
Colon, Edwina
Instructional Support Teacher
DiStravolo, Pietro
Assoc Prof of Italian & Span
Eshbach, Valetta Painter
Mathematics Teacher
Fehnel, Barry James
Business Ed & Computer Teacher
Fleck, Robert K.
Social Studies Teacher
Fletcher, Barbara (Arters)
2nd Grade Teacher
Fluharty, Charles Robert
Chemistry Teacher
Fries, Gregory Thomas
History Teacher
Gable, Marian E.
Laboratory Facilitator
Hall, Kathleen Susan
English Teacher
Hartline, Stephanie Kane
Language Arts Teacher
Hartranft, Karen Rohrbach
Phys Ed & Health Teacher
Hatt, Michele Elaine
English Teacher
Hetrick, Dennis R.
Computer Technology Instructor
Hines, Avon Adams
First Grade Teacher
Homan, Dolores R.
Health Occupations Ed Tchr
Kase, Suzanne LaManna
Fifth Grade Teacher
Kitsock, Michael John
Latin Teacher
LoFrumento, Debra Elaine
Kindergarten Teacher
Lorchak, John Joseph
AP American Government Teacher
MacAusland, Mary Bardsley
Asst Professor of Accounting
Marmarou, Stephanie
Spanish Teacher
Mc Crae, Linda R.
German & Latin Teacher
Mc Elhattan, John T.
Mathematics Teacher
Murphy, Patricia
Mathematics Department Chm

Naffin, Charlotte Oursler
Latin & French Teacher
Pondo, Julliann Virginia
First Grade Teacher
Randazzo, Charles Michael
Sixth Grade Science Teacher
Rathman, Denise Renee
Science Teacher
Reinstein-Polins, Anna T.
Art Teacher
Ruch, Margaret Minnich
Music Teacher
Rutt, David Earl
Vocal Music Teacher
Sallade, Kathleen
Title I Reading Specialist
Sechrist, Sara Jane
Third Grade Teacher
Shollenberger, Cherylene Trace
Fr Teacher & Foreign Lang Chm
Sullivan, Mary Dolan
Third Grade Teacher
Sychterz, Teresa A.
First Grade Teacher
Thren, Joanne Marie
5th Grade Teacher
Vaughan, Hallie Anne (Freebourn)
4th Grade Teacher
Vroman, Patricia Lynn
English Teacher
Weaver-Coleman, Karen
Composition, Lit & Rdng Prof
Westley, Sharon Louise
US History Teacher
REAMSTOWN
Englert, Thomas G.
Fifth Grade Teacher
RED LION
Beshore, Sharon Fitz
Instructional Support Teacher
Cooley, Sandra Elizabeth
General Science & Geology Tchr
Durchin, Steven Andrew
Technology Education Teacher
Fitzkee, Carla Waelde
Elementary School Librarian
Gamber, Donna Lee
Learning Support Tchr
Herbst, Cora Sue Hedges
Second Grade Teacher
Jefferis, James B.
Social Studies Teacher
Kowalik, Michael S.
English Teacher
Murphy, Gwendolyn Bolton
7th Grade English Teacher
O'Shell, Martha Louise
First Grade Teacher
Schmuck, Joan Marie
Math & French Teacher
Smith, Ben
Physics Teacher
Willson, C. Wesley
Math Teacher
Wise, Thomas Scott
Vocal Music Teacher
Yeckley, Linda Bender
Business Education Teacher
RENOVO
Williams, Mary Ruth Goetz
Business Education Teacher
Young, Cathy (Dietz)
4th Grade Teacher
REPUBLIC
Giel, Corrine, VSC
Elementary School Principal
RICHBORO
Benson, John W.
5th Grade Teacher
Carroll, Frances M.
French Teacher
Iampietro, Loraine Arlyn
Humanities Teacher
RICHFIELD
Lebo, Robin Snyder
4th, 5th & 6th Grade Teacher
RIDGWAY
Aiello, Cynthia Kathryn
English Teacher
Allenbaugh, Richard E.
Math Teacher
Buhite, William Russel, Jr.
Biology Teacher
Grandinetti, Francis
Superintendent
Kemick, Joseph Edward
Math Teacher
Kielbowick, Frederick Joseph
Guidance Counselor
Koos, Ernest John
Physics Teacher
Kosakowski, Richard Joseph
Art Teacher
Lenze, Herbert Brent
Fifth Grade Teacher
O'Neil, Kelley Sue
Social Studies & French Instr
Ryan, Joseph Dennis
Learning Support Teacher
Skinner, Phillip R.
Business Education Teacher
RIDLEY PARK
Bleacher, Darthi Ann
Special Education Teacher
Carney, Mary O'Leary
Fifth Grade Teacher
Klisch, Denea Laurelli
Guidance Counselor
Mc Intyre, Elizabeth J.
Math & Computer Teacher

Salvati, Diana Maria
Junior High Teacher
Schoeninger, William F.
Sixth Grade Teacher
ROARING SPRING
Loth, Bonnie Jean
Math & Science Teacher
Nevins, Reginald Alan
Mathematics & Science Teacher
ROBESONIA
Fisher, Natalie Ann
8th Grade Mathematics Teacher
Gerhart, Rose Wolf
English & German Teacher
Hampson, Roberta Budura
Junior HS Reading Teacher
Hays, Phillip George
World Geography Teacher
Karlson, Conrad Charles
Television Production Teacher
Lutz, Ronald L.
Mathematics Teacher
Manbeck, Margaret A. (Spittier)
Biology Teacher
Miller, Michael Lee
Art Teacher
Moyer, Charles N.
Teacher of the Gifted
Royer, Richard R.
Science & Ag Dept Chair
Weber, Wallburga Mank
Chemistry Teacher & NHS Adv
Wissinger, Elizabeth M.
Business Instructor
Wolfe, Susette (Brown)
Fifth Grade Teacher
ROCHESTER
Acon, Marian R.
English Teacher & Dept Chair
Di Sante, Angelo
7th-12th Grade Art Teacher
Furgiuele, Janis
Spanish & English Teacher
Grabner-Sinclair, Evonne
2nd Grade Teacher
Hopkins, Barbara Mc Farland
Bible, Soc Stud & Span Tchr
Noble, Jo Ann
Secondary Science Teacher
Orsag, James O.
Social Studies Teacher
Palakovich, Frank Emil
Fifth Grade Teacher
Reed, Debra L.
Fourth Grade Teacher
Taylor, Keith David
English, Speech & Jrnlsm Tchr
Wolbert, Kristine Batto
Coordinator of Gifted Ed
ROCKWOOD
Emert, Joyce Diane
English Teacher
Metz, Mary Lou Dietrick
Mathematics Teacher
Puffenberger, Judith Burley
Third Grade Teacher
Sowerbrower, Shirley J.
5th Grade Teacher
ROME
Devine, Gerard Paul
Fourth Grade Teacher
Eastman, J. Edwin
Math Teacher
Lacey, Marian Hopewell
Kindergarten Teacher
Moore, Robert James, Jr.
Social Studies Teacher
Obert, Kathryn F.
English Teacher
Roof, Joyce Ann
Home Economics Teacher
ROSEMONT
Bradley, Ronald John
Chemistry Tchr & Sci Dept Chm
Eisenstaedt, Lynne Ellen
Mathematics Teacher
Liberi, Richard
Math Department Chairperson
Mc Closkey, Margaret R.
Math Teacher
Walters, Meg
Assistant Head & English Tchr
ROSETO
Dentith, Diane Barleib
Mathematics Teacher
Trott, Linwood Roger
7th-12th Grade Bible Teacher
ROYERSFORD
Brotzman, James W.
Biology Tchr & Sci Dept Chm
Coates, Patricia Walsh
Social Studies Teacher
Hiles, Helen Adele
6th Grade Reading Teacher
Marquette, David Wayne
Math Teacher
Michewicz, Nancy Carol
Mathematics Teacher
Moran, Michael Paul
Music Teacher & Band Director
Moyer, Joy Charmaine
Physical Education & Hlth Tchr
Palladino, Mary Sweet
Mathematics Teacher
Petrillo, Miranda L.
Social Studies Teacher
Ruppert, Andrew C.
Social Studies Teacher
Wambold, Judith Z.
French Teacher & Dept Chprsn

ROYERSFORD (cont)
Webb, Tamara Boureier
7th-8th Grd Language Arts Tchr
Weidenbaugh, Theresa Gentili
Sixth & Seventh Grd Eng Tchr
RUFFS DALE
Lawson, Terrence Bruce
Fourth Grade Teacher
Smith, Pamela S.
6th Grade Social Studies Tchr
RURAL VALLEY
Blake, Mandy Shreckengost
Earth & Space Science Teacher
RUSSELL
Graziano, Barbara Lynne (Johnston)
3rd & 4th Grade Teacher
Lanzel, Harris J.
Instrumental Music Teacher
Larson, Patricia M.
English Teacher
Ritter, R. Richard
Environmental Science Teacher
Stanton, Bradley John
Reading & Cmptr Applctns Tchr
Yovich, Suzann Shield
Second Grade Teacher
RUSSELLTON
Burk, John H.
Mathematics Teacher
Farster, James Ray
Mathematics Teacher
Gross, Phyllis Jean
Sixth Grade Teacher
Kubicko, Stephen J.
Social Studies Teacher
McCormack, Michael David
8th Grade Earth Science Tchr
Mc Cutcheon, Jeannine E.
Chemistry Teacher
Taliani, Lisa Dean
English Teacher
SAEGERTOWN
Clark, Robert Donald
Biology Teacher
Duncan, Susan Marie (Flood)
General Music Teacher
Manuel, Andrea DeJohn
French Teacher
Marvin, James A.
Mathematics Tchr & Dept Chair
SAINT DAVIDS
Corbitt, J. Nathan
Assoc Prof of Music Comm
SAINT MARYS
Bordick, John Daniel
Science Teacher
Bullers, Joseph
Instrctnl Support Pgm Tchr
Burfield, Rosemary Halloran
Mathematics Teacher
Cheatle, James Michael
Elementary Art Teacher
Chiappelli, Donald Francis
Health, PE Tchr & Dept Coord
Damon, Michael Scott
Spanish Teacher
Donahue, Brian Frank
Social Studies Tchr & Dept Chm
Fedorko, John Charles
Mathematics Department Chm
Finger, Marilyn Engstrom
Spanish Teacher
Gahr, Craig Joseph
Drafting Teacher
Granche, William J.
9th-12th Grade English Teacher
Herbstritt, Eleanor Rupprecht
Chemistry Teacher
Kearney, Anna M.
HS Librn & Media Specialist
Knight, Ray S.
Instrumental Music Teacher
Kurtz, Barbara A.
Tchr of Mentally Gifted Stud
Lallman, James Richard
Physics & Mathematics Teacher
Lazore, Mary Ann
Junior High School Teacher
Lucanik, Karen M.
Pub Speaking, Drama & Eng Tchr
Lyle, Kristine Kreckel
Middle School Teacher
Marconi, Victoria
Store Mgr & Retired Teacher
Massaglia, Gary John
Biology & Earth Science Tchr
Moyer, Karen Lynn
Health Related Tech Tchr
Nekuza, Kathleen M. Breindel
6th Grade Teacher
Ogg, Carol Ruth
Special Education Teacher
Reuscher, Melissa Rose
English Teacher
Sekeres, Mark William
Instr of Engineering Tech
Sidelinger, Debra Day
English Teacher
Steele, Mary Kopp
English & Computers Teacher
Taylor, Benita Espinoza
Special Education Teacher
Troberg, Beverly Jo Ann
Substitute Teacher
SAINT THOMAS
Ramsey, Coetta Poe
Second Grade Teacher
SALISBURY
Cutter, Donna Joe
Business Education Teacher
Houser, Scotti Blackmon
Third Grade Teacher
SALTSBURG
Buran, David S.
Chemistry & Computer Teacher
Hamp, John Harry
Mathematics & Science Teacher
Murphy, Janet Compton
Sixth Grade Teacher
Shaffer, Richard Allen
Sixth Grade Teacher
Shuey, Lorraine J.
4th Grade Teacher
Szilagyi, Tamas
History Teacher
Vlahos, Zachary J.
History Department Chairman
SARVER
Harrison, Karin Claypool
Fourth Grade Teacher
Hileman, Linda L.
4th Grade Teacher
Mc Means, Jan
Gifted Support Tchr & Consult
Thimons, Jim F.
World Cultures Teacher
SAXONBURG
Atkinson, Edith Frola
English Teacher
Bauman, Deborah Jane
Health & PE Teacher
Dawson, Perry J. E.
Business Ed Dept Chair
Elder, Carolyn Kay
Elementary Teacher of Gifted
Finney, Pamela Lynne
Art Teacher & Dept Head
Hutchison, James H.
Sixth Grade Teacher
Johnston, Kip Anne Mc Claury
Elem Instrumental & Vocal Tchr
Malobicky, John Joseph
Computer Science Teacher
Negley, Heston Rachal (Musko)
Mathematics Teacher
Rupert, Kelley Estadt
Second Grade Teacher
Sendry, Andrea Elizabeth
Mathematics Teacher
Sharick, Brian Adam
Secondary Mathematics Teacher
Shoop, Leslie James
American History Teacher
Sontum, Lynn O.
Physics Teacher
Stumpf, Joseph R.
Technology Education Instr
SAXTON
Ash, Beth Lynn
Spanish Teacher
Fagan, Trudy Brown
Family & Consumer Science Tchr
Mowchan, Linda Marie
Russian Teacher
Russell, John G.
Business Education Teacher
SAYRE
Calomino, Gail Ann
Fourth Grade Teacher
Cleary, Beryl Boardman
Retired Instructor
Cole, Mary Collins
Business Education Teacher
Davison, Thomas Edward
AP & Precalculus Teacher
Gross, John C.
6th Grade Math Teacher
Halton, Susan Higley
First Grade Teacher
Hickey, Sarah Ann (Torrance)
English Teacher
Quigley, Anastasia Marie
First Grade Teacher
Zimmerman, David Matthew
Music Instructor
SCHAEFFERSTOWN
Reedy, Susan Reppert
2nd Grade Teacher
SCHNECKSVILLE
Barthlow, Robert Lee
Adj Professor of Psych & Ed
Blue, Ronald Calvin
Asst Professor of Psychology
Boehmer, Linda M.
Teacher of the Hearing Imprd
Karch, Peter B.
Professor of Biological Sci
Lepre, Anthony
Professor of Mathematics
Mc Menamin, Margaret Mary
Assoc Professor & Prgm Coord
Ragosta, Stephen W.
Horticulture Teacher
Smith, Lynette Cuthbertson
Reading Specialist
Tallarita, Diane T.
Adj Instr of Paralegal Studies
Villard, Walter L., III
Anatomy & Physiology Teacher
Warner, Richard Charles
Assoc Prof of Bus
SCHUYLKILL HAVEN
Bacz, Richard Alan
Bands & Instrmntl Music Dir
Evert, Gloria Pochekailo
Elementary Guidance Counselor
Fligge, Herman R.
High School Math Dept Chair
Gelting, Karen A.
Spanish Teacher
Hupka, Joseph Michael
High School Art Instructor
Imschweiler, Anita Frances
High School Business Teacher
Kristoff, Joan M.
Business & Computer Teacher
Lenick, Mary Ann Anderson
High School Mathematics Tchr
Orff, Thomas Martin
Music Director
Sarno, Patricia A.
Science Dept Chair & Bio Tchr
Ulsh, E. Jane McGoey
5th-8th Grd Soc Stud Teacher
SCIOTA
Mc Cool, Connie Mc Afee
Second Grade Teacher
SCOTLAND
Chontos, John Albert
American History Teacher
Kroepil, Kathy Ellen (Spangler)
2nd Grade Teacher
Rosenberry, Susan Hartzell
Fifth Grade Head Teacher
Shelly, Ruth Ann Byers
Home Economics Teacher
Stewart, Jerry Edwin
Admissions Director
SCOTTDALE
King, Robert Lee
6th Grade Teacher
Sember, J. Elizabeth Shoemaker
Retired First Grade Teacher
SCRANTON
Adamsky, Grace Fiorenza
Spanish Teacher
Barrett, John W.
Social Science Professor
Berendes, M. Benedicta, IHM
College Professor
Borja, Marianne E.
Assoc Professor
Brassard, Deborah Ellen
English Professor
Burke, Carol Connolly
Fourth Grade Teacher
Burkhouse, Ellen M.
5th Grade Teacher
Cantafio, Anthony L.
10th Grade Geometry Teacher
Carpenter, Brian Wells
Acctng Assoc Prof & Dept Chair
Cerra, Linda Strasburger
Spanish Teacher
Chapla, William Mark
12th Grd Language Arts Teacher
Colley, Stephen John
Art Instructor
Concilio, M. Alphonsa, IHM
Assistant Professor of Voice
Corcoran, Virginia Mc Dermott
Asst Prof of Nutrtn & Diet
Czachor, Thomas Anthony
Computer Maintenance Tech Tchr
Davis, Bryan Scott
Protective Services Instructor
Dawson, Geraldine Yarnal
Assistant Professor
De Freitas, Robert Joseph
Biological Science Teacher
Donath-Graham, Leslie C.
Science Teacher
Dreater, Lois Ann
Art & Photography Teacher
Dumdum, Uldarico Rex, Jr.
Associate Professor
Durkan, Ann A.
Third Grade Teacher
Fein, Denise Burne
Sociology & Criminology Instr
Feudo, Peter
Professor & Chair
Fitzsimmons, Suzanne N.
Science Dept Chair & Teacher
Foley, Mary Anne A.
Asst Professor of Theology
Frantz, Cheryl Dettenmayer
Sixth Grade Teacher
Galante, Joseph James
Asst Professor of Business
Gedrich, Kathleen Holmes
Art & Photography Teacher
Gorman, Thomas Joseph
Mathematics Teacher
Grecco, David A.
Social Studies Teacher
Gruen, Judy Ann
Mathematics Teacher
Heffernan, Cor Immaculatum
Assoc Prof of Art
Hewitt, Henry Charles
Religious Educator Teacher
Hildebrand, Lloyd Burton
English Lecturer
Hoffman, Barbara A.
English Professor
Hudzina, Patricia E.
Latin Teacher
Jaeger, Gale A.
Assistant Professor
Katusak, Edward Richard
French & English Teacher
Kellar, Cheryl
Instructor
Kilker, James Frederick
Theology Teacher
Killiany, Eugene Francis
Mathematics Teacher
Langan, Ann Klimaitis
Senior English Teacher
Lemoncelli, John Joseph
Assoc Prof of Psych & Cnslng
Lobo, Francis X.
Prof of Biological Science
Lukasik, John Peter
School Psychologist
Marino, Rosarie Semenza
English Teacher & Dept Chprsn
Martinetti, Raymond F.
Professor of Psychology
Mc Connell, Leon Mary, IHM
Tutoring Program Teacher
McDonald, Nancy E.
AP Amer & European His Tchr
McDonald, Victoria Corine
Latin Teacher
Mc Goldrick, Ellen Terese
Sixth Grade Teacher
Mecca, Joseph Matthew
Mathematics Teacher
Melnick, Michael J.
High School Business Teacher
Mowrey, James
Graphic Design Program Coord
Munley, Kathleen Purcell
Assoc Professor of History
Muracco, Linda Louise
Science Teacher
Murrin, Kathleen Anne
AP US History & Govt Teacher
Nagy, Nancy Mammarella
Asst Prof of Graduate Ed
Nemotko, Anitra Dougherty
Chrpsn & Instr of Sci Dept
Nervegna, Mary H.
Mathematics Teacher
Norcross, John C.
Psychology Professor
O'Brien, Edward Joseph
Professor & Chair of Grad Dept
Phillips, James Walter
Electromechanical Tech Instr
Pugh, Gladys Helen (Burnison)
Math Teacher
Quinn, Thomas Joseph
Computer Science Teacher
Rainey, Ann Marie Kane
Music Tchr & Choral Director
Reinhardt, Miriam Joseph J.
Assistant Professor of Music
Ruddy, Thomas A.
Math Teacher
Russell, Frances Eleanor, IHM
Assoc Professor of Education
Schwartz, Richard Joseph
Band Director
Sherman, Larry Ray
Chemistry Professor
Shuta, Barbara Spellman
Speech & Drama Teacher
Siska, Kathylene Frances
Social Work Assoc Professor
Sloan, Annette Marie
English Instructor
Smith, Thomas John
Social Studies Teacher
Sykes, Todd Philip
Art Educator
Witiak, Donna M.
Mathematics Tchr & Dept Chprsn
Zanghi, Judith Ceccacci
Fifth Grade Teacher
SELINSGROVE
Fisch, Walter H.
Social Studies Teacher
Grove, John G.
Assistant Principal
Gruenberg, Alex T.
English Teacher
Hooper, Fred Grant
Choral & Classroom Music Tchr
Kalcich, Norma Jean
HS Mathematics Teacher
Miller, Ellen M.
Health & PE Tchr
Switala, William J., Jr.
Social Studies Teacher
Wilhour, Donald Eugene
Mathematics Department Chair
SELLERSVILLE
Detweiler, Carl Wright
Student Act Dir & Math Teacher
Harris, Richard Dwight
History Teacher & Coach
Johnson, Mark Anton
Eng, Speech & Drama Teacher
Lausch, Ronald Eugene
Fifth Grade Teacher
Winton, Debra L.
Reading Specialist
SENECA
Allaman, Paul W.
9th Grd Social Studies Teacher
Fesenmyer, Diana Kalamajka
7th Grade Teacher
Greenlee, Kimberly Beighley
Business Teacher
Holquist, Beverly Smith
Mathematics Teacher
L'Huillier, Lorraine Deane
French Teacher
Thomas, Sherry Lee
Business Teacher
SEWICKLEY
Baumann, Candice Jeanne
6th Grade Literature Teacher
Getsy, Jennifer L.
Learning Support Teacher
Gray, M. Kathleen
Second Grade Teacher
Hague, Robert Graham
8th-9th Grd Soc Stud Teacher
Martin, John David
Director of Admissions
Robatisin, Charles C.
English & Social Studies Tchr
Sadd, Thomas E.
History Teacher
Wardrop, James Richmond
Photography Teacher
SHAMOKIN
Lahr, Dale Edward
8th Grade Mathematics Teacher
Losiewiczs, Paul B.
Middle School Teacher
Miller, J. Richard
Learning Support Teacher
SHANKSVILLE
Rhea, Joyce Custer
Vocal Music Teacher
Tiffany, Diane Roberta
English Teacher
Walsh, Patrick Charles
Guidance Counselor
SHARON
Akins, James E.
Gifted Support Teacher
Atwell, Carole Ann (Terchila)
Fifth Grade Teacher
Black, Stephanie Eileen
Business Teacher
Ciafre, David A.
Guidance Counselor
Clary, William Arthur
Art & Theatre Teacher
DeBonis, Donna Marie
Supvr of Curr & Instruction
Hric, Anne Joan
Retired Elementary Teacher
Kovac, Shirley Antos
Second Grade Teacher
Shaffer, Stanley John
Art Teacher
Staul, Dennis Richard
Assistant Principal
Wenger, Eric P.
Math, Science & Computer Tchr
Woge, Gasperina Morocco
Spanish Teacher
SHARON HILL
Davis, Doris Releford
Social Studies Teacher
Iannone, Vincent Joseph
Music Teacher
Poynton, John T.
US History Teacher
Schellinger, Thomas
5th Grade Teacher
Seaman, Michael J.
Eng Tchr & Lang Arts Dept Head
SHARPSVILLE
Brown, James Mark
Mathematics Teacher
Fauceglia, Marion Lynn
Teacher
Patton, Barbara Yoest
Math Teacher
SHEFFIELD
Carlson, Robert Pratt
Industrial Arts Teacher
Crozier, Nancy Stotz
Science, Health, Spelling Tchr
Dunn, Thomas J.
Math Teacher & Dept Head
Haberberger, Nancy J.
English & Reading Teacher
Hutchins, Susan Elizabeth
Chemistry & Physics Teacher
Olson, Sandra Irene (Ryan)
English Teacher
Patterson, Marilyn
English Teacher
Pitlock, Robert Neal
Science & History Teacher
SHELOCTA
Meyerhuber, Lisa Walker
Teacher of Gifted
SHENANDOAH
Ashford, Judi Anne
English & Latin Teacher
Ciszek, Leonard R.
Social Studies Teacher
Hoy, Margaret Troyanoski
7th & 8th Grade Gen Sci Tchr
Marchetti, Eileen Marie
Spanish Teacher
Roncek, Robert P.
Math & Calculus Teacher
SHICKSHINNY
Barchik, Raymond Henry
History Teacher
Cragle, Wyanita M.
Biology Teacher
Gardner, Judith Rodda
High School English Teacher
Gardner, Robert S.
Social Studies Teacher
Sorber, Barbara
Computer Coordinator & Teacher
Stillman, Dyane Alaine
Sub Teacher & Drama Ensmbl Ad
Uter, John Anthony
Language Arts Instructor
SHILLINGTON
Argentati, David Mark
Business Education Teacher
Bausher, Richard Scott
7th Grade Geography Teacher
Cameron, Judy Reddy
Sixth Grade Teacher

NGTON (cont)
ough, Cathleen Marie
h Teacher
Joanne M. (Althouse)
dv Bio & Genetics Tchr
LEHOUSE
n, Teresa Aiken
ng Teacher
, Jacqueline D.
Grade Teacher
esse Daniel
acher
ary Edward
uter & Mathematics Teacher
Jane Hurd
Economics Teacher
Ayers, Nancy Harris
h & Journalism Teacher
ard, Deborah Jean
d Grade Teacher
ENSBURG
t, Cheryl Kohli
Grade Teacher & Chprsn
n, David F.
ored Research Director
d, John Richard
aphy Teacher
, Margaret Bailey
Grade Teacher
William R.
gy Teacher
Nitham Mohammad
rofessor of Accounting
John R.
stry Teacher
Winifred Catherine
d Math Teacher
James Edward
Teacher
Frank Paul
Stud & Sociology Tchr
n, Janet Smith
h Teacher
Huberta Shanholtz
d Elem Tchr
Robert Arthur
& Orchestra Director
Richard Hugh
Physics Teacher
Jeanne M.
d Language Arts Teacher
Jayne
Grade Teacher
AKERSVILLE
Nancy Kauffman
d English Teacher
N
Martha Ellen
2th Grade English Tchr
Lawrence Peter
Grade Reading Teacher
r, Christine Hutzell
Grade Teacher
, Patrice Marie (Yonish)
gy Tchr & Sci Dept Chprsn
a, Geraldine Ann
y Teacher
on, John Paul
s Teacher
Carol Ann
acher
Marjorie Gates
rgarten Teacher
ak, Steve J.
nce Counselor
Thomas C.
d Grade Teacher
, Anthony Raymond
ce Teacher
k, Michael Dominic
matics Instr & Dept Chm
, Henry
ian & Speech Teacher
, Ricky Charles
Studies Instructor
oseph
sh & Music Teacher
Debora Zigerell
ocial Studies Teacher
Wayne D.
matics Teacher
, Linda Barnett
ess Education Teacher
Helen
rgarten Teacher
Douglas William
ce Teacher
Susan Noon
rade Math Teacher
Mary Lou
ra Teacher
ugh, Melissa Lee
sh Teacher
Diane (Lamar)
Studies & Reading Tchr
t, Cloe Stinebiser
d Grade Teacher
ng, Myra (Dibert)
ra Teacher
NG SPRING
, William L.
Grade Teacher
NGTON
usan Stover
sh Teacher
Susan Jane
Grade Teacher
Alan Michael
Grade Teacher

Schell, Brian Duane
Social Studies Teacher
SLIPPERY ROCK
Burns, Kirby L.
Science & Physical Sci Tchr
Burtch, Christopher John
Economics & Amer History Tchr
Ellis, Janet DeCorte
Mathematics & Tchr of Gifted
Hannam, Susan Elizabeth
Assoc Prof of Allied Health
Herman, Susan Leigh
Assistant Professor
Kowalski, Janet L.
High School Guidance Counselor
Laux, James Lawrence
Assoc Prof of Communication
Meier, Janine John
Physics & Computer Sci Teacher
Pagni, Elizabeth M.
6th & 8th Grd Math Teacher
Selinger, Erik L.
Chemistry Teacher
Starz, Kenneth J.
Social Studies & Reading Tchr
SMETHPORT
Condon, Earl Arthur
Teacher of Learning Support
Digel, Seth Richard
Fourth Grade Teacher
Miller, Diane Marie
Teacher of Gifted Students
Newcome, Connie Larson
Fifth Grade Teacher
Rosenswie, Carl William
Fifth Grade Teacher
Stephen, William H.
Biology Teacher
Young, Brenda McGavisk
Secondary Mathematics Teacher
SMOKETOWN
Burkholder, Susan Ranae
Health & Physical Ed Tchr
SOMERSET
Barta, Margaret Bender
Occupational Child Care Instr
Coulter, Christine Wilson
Business Teacher
Gould, Linda Harkcom
Sixth Grade Teacher
Hardwig, Michael James
Instructional Support Teacher
Hartman, Gwen Tataleba
Family & Consumer Science Tchr
Hay, Nancy Landis
Physical Education Teacher
Maurer, Alice Ann
Kindergarten Teacher
McCall, David Nelson
Counselor
Schimpf, Jerry Alan
Machine Shop Instructor
SOUDERTON
Cicacci, Fred Carl
Social Studies Teacher
Colonna, Elizabeth A. (Motto)
High School Mathematics Tchr
Gill, Patricia Derstine
Third Grade Teacher
Hartzel, Norman D.
Math Teacher
Hundley, Pamela Ems
Fifth Grade Teacher
Italiano, Dona
Language Arts Teacher & Coord
Landes, Philip B.
Science Teacher
Leight, Jon
Vocal Music Teacher
Rentschler, Thomas C.
Social Studies Teacher
Russell, Christine Marie
Physics Teacher
Sell, Bonnie J.
Business Teacher
Siggins, Michael John
Mathematics Teacher
Silva, Jack P.
Social Studies Teacher
Smith, Darryl J.
English Teacher
Smith, Stanley
HS Social Studies Teacher
Westcott, Jan Harris
Third Grade Teacher
Williams, Iyabo Ogunnaike
Chemistry Teacher
Wood, Robert John
Social Studies Teacher
SOUTH WILLIAM
Ackerman, Charles Larue
American History Teacher
Allison, Michael Edward
Seventh Grade Science Teacher
Lepley, Bonnie Elizabeth (Rapp)
English Teacher
Manning, Scott Edward
Biology & Science Teacher
Robbins, James M.
Physics Teacher
Smith, Cheryl Canfield
Science & Photography Teacher
Ward, Linda M.
General & Vocal Music Teacher
SOUTH WILLIAMSPORT
Bastian, Douglas Porter
Retired 8th Grade Science Tchr
Churba, Mary Ann White
Elem Cnslr & Computer Coord

Hetner, Robert F.
Social Studies Instructor
SOUTHAMPTON
Conrad, Stephen Edward
Social Studies Teacher
Keen, Carol Nancy Munyon
Second Grade Teacher
Kenny, James F.
Social Studies Teacher
Maugle, Randy S.
History Teacher
Moore, Richard Edward, Jr.
Humanities Teacher
Nordbye, Mark Steven
6th Grade Teacher
Raab, Gretchen
English Teacher
Rubin, Judith Herman
Math Teacher
Schade, Jere Allen
8th-9th Grade Science Teacher
Traum, Carol Franceschi
7th-8th Grd Math Teacher
SPARTANSBURG
Clark, Daniel R.
5th Grade Teacher
Dorman, Dale L.
2nd Grade Teacher
Hopkins, Gary A.
6th Grade Teacher
SPRING CHURCH
Lees, Dolores R.
1st Grade Teacher
Opalka, Julianne T. Kupchik
9th-12th Grd Chem & Bio Tchr
SPRING GROVE
Annable, Richard Lee
Retired MS Guidance Counselor
Black, Barry Diehl
Math & Computer Science Tchr
Buckovich, Marjorie Brands
Teacher for At-Risk Students
Crawford, Rodney Gene
Social Studies Teacher & Chair
Dietz, David L.
Band Director
Downie, Mark
7th & 8th Grade Math Teacher
Gault, G. Gary
World Cultures Teacher
Inners, Daniel J.
Sixth Grade Teacher
Jennerjohn, Marilyn Rinker
English Teacher
Johnston, Dwight Davis
Physics I & II Instructor
Kelly, Barry Niel
Science Teacher
Mosser, Sylvia Eckenrode
Language Arts Teacher
Ormond, Terri Crumrine
French Teacher
Sabaka, Judith Loehr
Second Grade Teacher
Scheivert, Rebecca E. (Maloney)
9th-10th Grade English Teacher
Singer, Mickie Ruth
English Teacher
Wingerd, Kathy L.
Biology Teacher
Yonker, Martha Miller
Communication Arts Teacher
SPRING MILLS
Benfer, Bonnie Hall
Health & Physical Ed Teacher
Harpster, Franklin Scott
Math Teacher
Ott, Barbara Barkman
Family & Consumer Science Tchr
Patten, Susan Shirey
English Teacher
Thompsen, John
Physics Teacher
Wagner, Jacquelyn Spaide
Biology I & II Teacher
SPRINGDALE
Dunmyre, Kathleen Halwa
Mathematics Teacher
Engles, Deborah Spinelli
Learning Support Teacher
Herrington, Leonard Dudley
Social Studies Teacher
SPRINGFIELD
Adams, Edward Thomas, Jr.
High School Math Teacher
Ames, John Joseph
Theology Dept Teacher & Chair
Ancone, Kenneth Joseph
Math Teacher
Bakey, Ann T.
6th Grade Teacher
Bohner, Harvey Clifford
8th Grade Science Teacher
Brennan, James Joseph
Theology Teacher
Budiwsky, Anna
Spanish Teacher
Caffey, Kimberly Ann
Secondary Education Teacher
Carocci, Albert E.
Seventh Grade Science Teacher
Dannaker, Cynthia Armitage
Eng Teacher & Activity Adv
Dugan, Alice Bernice Farris
Math Chair
Eley, Robert L.
Mathematics Teacher
Fulcomer, William E.
Psychology & History Teacher

Funk, Constance Ann
8th Grade Amer History Teacher
Gardler, Bud
English Teacher & Bsktbl Coach
Keller, Sandra Mellor
Kindergarten Teacher
Lattari, Nicholas B.
9th & 12th Grd Soc Stud Tchr
Maloney, Phyllis A. Miraglia
Social Studies Teacher
Mc Devitt, Meg Callahan
Mathematics Teacher
Miller, Susan Steggert
Math Teacher & Dept Chprsn
Moral, Aurora Emelina
Spanish Teacher
Obdyke, Phoebe Stambaugh
Director & Curator of Museum
Purvis, Susan C.
Hlth, Physical Education Tchr
Rooney, Dorothy
7th & 8th Grade Teacher
Schmidt, Gloria Rook
Fourth Grade Teacher
Shaw, Rosalie P.
Chem Tchr & Sci Dept Chprsn
Torrence, William T., Jr.
Theology Teacher
Vandenberg, Daniel Kase
Chemistry Teacher
Wallin, Daniel J.
Math Teacher
STATE COLLEGE
Andrews, Linda Kaye
Fourth Grade Teacher
Gittings, Julie Anne
Enrichment Teacher
Given, Scott W.
Reading Teacher
Gold-Toulson, Diane Wehner
Music Teacher
Holt, Carolyn Ann (Falck)
Biology Teacher
Latta, Debra Lee
Asst Principal
Long, Ryan Jon
Social Studies Teacher
Marshall, Charles Donald
Science Teacher
Moyer, Peter Clayton
Soc Studies Tchr & Swim Coach
Noll, Mary Keefe
Retired First Grade Teacher
Oyler, Diane Williams
6th Grade Teacher
Royse, Lynn Volle
5th Grade Teacher
Seamans, Jeffrey Dean
Technology Education Instr
Shapiro, Michael Charles
Health Education Teacher
Vernon, Robert Pat
Architectural & Comp Instr
Willenbrock, Marsha F.
First Grade Teacher
STEELTON
Pilkerton, William John
Social Studies Teacher
STEVENS
Horst, Blanche Mohler
Retired Third Grade Teacher
STONEBORO
Cotton, Taylor H.
Librarian
Davis, Bernard Byron
Biology Teacher
Engstrom, Jeffrey DuWaine
Eighth Grade Reading Teacher
Hoye, David C.
Social Studies Teacher
Marstellar, Jay Edward
8th Grade Math Teacher
Miller, Keith Robert
Sixth Grade Teacher
Persch, Martin Orin
Fourth Grade Teacher
Reynolds, Sherry M.
High School English Teacher
STORY CREEK MILLS
Fegely, Kathy Muller
German Tchr & Frgn Lang Chprsn
STRATTANVILLE
Clark, Deborah Best
French Teacher
Dulavitch, Edward Joseph
Social Studies Teacher
Feldman, Judith L.
English & Journalism Teacher
Louder, David Edward
English Teacher
Zahoran, John Michael
English Teacher
STROUDSBURG
Bickart, Mary F.
Fifth Grade Teacher
Cooney, Charlene D'Agostino
Former English Dept Chair
Kohlmann, Judy Fleming
Mathematics Teacher
Miller, William H., III
Span Tchr & Frgn Lang Dept Chm
Nesley, Maureen Lee
French Teacher
Newman, Jacqualyn James
Social Studies Teacher
Scarsella, Theresa Tyanne
6th Grade Teacher
Scerbo, Gail L.
Spanish Teacher

Steen, Michael Alan
English Teacher
Wentzel, Lynn N.
Mathematics Teacher
White, William J.
Senior Social Studies Teacher
SUGARLOAF
Meyers, William Angove
5th Grade Science Teacher
Pawlowski, Stella Marie
First Grade Teacher
SUMMERDALE
Brillinger, Ruth W.
Academic Chair
DeLeo, John Daniel
Professor
Elias, Janilyn
Tchr of Deaf & Hard of Hearing
Hepner, Kathryn Ella
Accounting & Mathematics Prof
Logan, Cathy D.
Professor
Lowe, Gregory Mark
Professor of Comp ACC Division
SUMMERHILL
Gramling, Donna Gallardy
Former Spanish Teacher
SUNBURY
Cafiso, Bonna Zuch
Fr Tchr & Foreign Lang Supvr
Campbell, George Robert
Fifth Grade Teacher
Donkochik, Winifred Jane
Economics & AP US History Tchr
Duke, David Allen
4th Grade Teacher
Felix, Carol W.
Business Education Teacher
Haupt, Samuel W.
Supervisor of Guid & Counselor
Menges, Robert Lee
Business Teacher
Reaser, James Robert
Vocal Music Tchr & Dept Chm
Renn, Vicki Lee
Art Teacher
Tonzetich, Susan Rhodes
Spanish Teacher
SUSQUEHANNA
Escandel, Rose Ann
Family & Consumer Sci Tchr
Escandel, Thomas Raymond
6th Grade Teacher
Fuller, Charles Lincoln
Science Teacher
Fuller, Kathryn Dean
Fourth Grade Teacher
Gerchman, Mark Robert
Mathematics Teacher
Homer, Carolyn Frederick
Fourth Grade Teacher
Lee, David J.
Sr HS Studies Teacher
Wolfe, Daniel Edward
Chemistry Physics Teacher
SWARTHMORE
Metzidakis, Philip
Spanish Professor
SWIFTWATER
Ayers, Marianne Kozak
Sixth Grade Teacher
Barbush, Thomas Donald
6th Grade Teacher
Blair, Charles E.
Teacher
Bras-Danges, Maria
Social Studies Teacher
Carroll, Kenneth Allen
Studies Teacher
Catalano, Richard L.
Guidance Director
Coco, Nancy (Nawrocki)
8th Grd Language Arts Teacher
Demarest, Robert A.
Earth Science Teacher
DiBilio, Michael Patrick
Spanish Teacher
Fisher, Bonnie Boyle
Art Department Head
Hall, Rick Lee
Health & Physical Ed Teacher
Hannon, Joseph James
7th Grade Reading Teacher
Hershey, Jeffrey B.
Language Arts Instructor
Lathrop, Robert D.
Choral Director
Lengel, Traci Lavon
Health & Physical Ed Teacher
Lynch, Edward Joseph
Hlth & Alternative Prgm Supvr
Marvin, Daniel
American Cultures Teacher
Mc Gorry, Eugene Coleman
Social Studies Teacher
Nish, Geraldine Valonis
Language Arts Teacher
Ragonese, James A.
English Teacher
Sparrow, Sally Wilson
English Teacher
Tomedi, James Francis
Language Arts Teacher
SYKESVILLE
Fye, Jerry E.
5th Grade Teacher
TAMAQUA
Bonner, Thomas Patrick
3rd Grade Teacher

TAMAQUA (cont)
Confer, Leslie Anne (Kulha)
Fifth Grade Teacher
Forgotch, Bernard M.
Social Studies Tchr & Dept Chm
Hunt, Eloise J.
Language Arts Teacher
Hunt, Robert J.
Instrumental Music Teacher
Kinder, Joanne Pangonis
LA Dept Head & Teacher
Kline, Dale D.
World Cultures & GATE Teacher
Laughman, Drusilla Belle
Lang Arts & AP Eng Tchr
Leitzel, William Earl
4th Grade Teacher
Mateyak, John Aaron
Earth & Space Science Teacher
Mc Cormick, Marjorie Lynn
10th Grade English Teacher
Ryan, Karen Lynn
8th Grade Writing Teacher
Stianche, Robert Michael
Science Teacher
Waidell, George
8th Grade Social Studies Tchr
Zerbe, Eric S.
Health & Physical Ed Teacher
Zerbe, Susan McHenry
Health & Phys Education Tchr
TANNERSVILLE
Canale, Lorraine Dougherty
Fifth Grade Teacher
Martinell, Judith Seber
Kindergarten Classroom Teacher
TARENTUM
Wray, Dennis Clark
Third Grade Teacher
TAYLOR
Helcoski, Jack E.
Supervisor of Pupil Services
Migal, Lewis
Social Studies Dept Chairman
TERRE HILL
Miller, Eldo James
Music Director
THOMASVILLE
Karlitskie, Lynn Dee
First Grade Teacher
THORNDALE
Stuber, Kristina Jane
First Grade Teacher
THREE SPRINGS
Hicks, Regina Alesi
English & Journalism Teacher
Hummel, Cheryl Ann (Coons)
Business Education Teacher
Loewen, Philip Jon
Band Director
THROOP
Adams, JoAnn Calvario
French & Spanish Teacher
Fitzgerald, Gary M.
Geometry Teacher
TIDIOUTE
Wright, Stacy Rae
Span, Practical Computing Tchr
TIOGA
Nelson, Thomas John
Band Teacher
Sottolano, Matthew Joseph
Driver & Physical Ed Tchr
Swerdloff, Margaret Taub
English Teacher
TIONESTA
Kuhn, Jackie Humphrey
2nd Grade Teacher
TITUSVILLE
Anderson, Cathy L.
Asst Prin & Math Dept Chprsn
Cope, David James
High School Teacher
Cressman, Lynn Johnson
English Teacher
Dellemonache, Carlene
Business Teacher
Hall, Mary
Assistant Professor of English
Hirsch, Mary Edith
Pastoral Minister
Hughes, Diana Cornell
Sixth Grade Teacher
Joyce, Ron
Career Counselor
Kitson, Herbert William
Associate Professor of English
Millar, Judy Lynn
English Teacher
Miller, Sharon Wiatrowski
Spanish Teacher
Ritke, Mark E.
Professor of Biology
Winkler, Linda A.
Bio & Anthropology Assoc Prof
TOPTON
Lovello, Samuel Joseph
Social Studies Teacher & Coach
Rhode, Karen B.
Teacher of the Gifted
Slick, Kim Joel
Chemistry & Computer Sci Tchr
TOWANDA
Beardslee, Donna Marie
English Teacher
Cartwright, M. Jean
Health & Physical Ed Teacher
Davenport, Stephen F.
Fourth Grade Teacher
Dunn, Ann Stalford
English Teacher
Henery, Glenn M.
Biology Teacher & Ath Dir
Hettich, Donna M.
Business Teacher
Ryan, Carolyn Royer
7th Grd English Teacher
TOWER CITY
Blackwell, Scott C.
Math Department Chairperson
Cickavage, William John
Mathematics Teacher
Hart, Sheryl McNoldy
Transitional First Grade Tchr
Koch, Carrie Kimmel
Teacher of the Gifted
Laskowski, Allan L., Jr.
Teacher & Coach
Mosteller, Gwen Theresa
Life Science & Biology Teacher
Potlunas, John Francis
Instrumental Music Director
Russelavage, Randall Lee
Reading Teacher & Athletic Dir
Schach, Claude Henry
Retired Earth & Space Sci Tchr
Smith, Jolene DeLeath
Admin Asst & Choral Director
Underkoffler, Philip Eugene
Science Teacher
TOWNVILLE
Maas, Linda Jean
Teacher of the Gifted
TRAFFORD
Cush, Barbara Jo
Fifth Grade Teacher
Testa, Vincent Samuel
Health & Phys Ed Teacher
TREMONT
Wiscount, Brenda Atkins
Second Grade Teacher
TROUT RUN
Mitstifer, Arwood E.
Retired Teacher
TROY
Butters, Glen Edward
Computer Teacher
Gestwicki, Ralph Allen
Social Stud Tchr & Dept Chair
McNeal, Kay D.
Elementary Librarian
Myfelt, Carol J.
Fourth Grade Teacher
Sliwinski, Steven T.
Art Teacher
TUNKHANNOCK
Adonizio, Sara G.
First & Second Grade Teacher
Brogan, Frances Crowley
Third Grade Teacher
Casterline, Jean M.
English Teacher
Cobb, Gary R.
Physical Science Teacher
DAgata, Hollie Williams
Instructional Support Teacher
Daniels, Nancy Loch
English Teacher
Davidson, Nancy Delinsky
Spanish & Latin Teacher
DeLeo, Louis
Developmental Rdng & Lit Tchr
Evans, Robin Stevens
Spanish Teacher
Gaylord, Carol Ann
4th Grade Teacher
Griggs, Howard G., Jr.
Business Education Dept Chm
Haas, Judie Sullivan
English Teacher
Harding, Fred A.
9th-12th Grd Electronics Instr
Kaufer, Larinda Dyson
First Grade Teacher
Montross, Carol Story
Mathematics Teacher
O'Boyle, Maria Rodeghiero
Biology Teacher
Poder, Frank
8th Grade Social Studies Tchr
Renoll, David H.
German Teacher
Rhinard, Edwin W.
Social Science Teacher
Ross, John Joseph
Fourth Grade Teacher
Stevens, Jay G.
Science Teacher
Tinner, John Joseph
History Department Chairman
Walker, Elaine Post
High School Math Teacher
Walker, Kenneth Thomas
Soccer Coach
West, Carol Vaiana
Applied Comm & Speech Teacher
Wisser, Denise L.
Health & Physical Ed Tchr
TURBOTVILLE
Holtzman, Nancy Bangs
Business Education Teacher
TURTLE CREEK
Connors, Jean Hohman
5th Grade Teacher
Price, Patricia Katana
Language Arts & Preschool Tchr
TYRONE
Barlett, John Rexford
Industrial Education Teacher
Bloom, Francis A.
Math Teacher & Dept Chairman
Harris, Laura Marie
Jr High & Elem Choral Teacher
Harrison, Carol Sharon
Second Grade Teacher
Marasco, Michele Renee (Malone)
Mathematics Teacher
Wilbur, George Everett
Latin & World Cultures Teacher
ULSTER
Kraus, Sheila Peters
Third Grade Teacher
Mc Cauley, John A.
Fourth Grade Teacher
ULYSSES
Eckenrode, Kimberly Redding
Elementary School Counselor
Garner, Judith Lynn
English & Computer Teacher
Sherman, Nancy Carol
First Grade Teacher
Shirk, Wanda (Gehret)
English Teacher
Valentine, Susan Amy
Secondary Principal
VanDusen, Susan Mildred
Fourth Grade Teacher
White, Benny Joe
Sixth Grade Teacher
UNIONTOWN
Abbott, Anita Halfhill
Secondary Spanish Teacher
Ables, Gloria Jean
Business Education Teacher
Bubonovich, Carol Hines
Sixth Grade Teacher
Capozzi, Ann M.
7th Grade Teacher
Cuppett, Patricia Oldland
3rd Grade Teacher
Dzurisin, M. Philip, OSBM
Religion Teacher
Fullem, Linda DeCarlucci
Eighth Grade English Teacher
Garbart, Marilyn J.
Teacher of Gifted
Goldberg, Jacqueline Fredricka
Second Grade Teacher
Hahn, Ewaldine M.
Second Grade Teacher
Klimko, Cecelia Skovira
Second Grade Teacher
Mattiucci, Chris Meucci
Kindergarten Teacher
Mazurek, John Michael
American History Teacher
Morgan, Laura Ansel
Retired 4th Grade Teacher
Morich, Vincent A.
Social Studies Teacher
Nutting, Thomas K.
Spanish Teacher
Page, B. Louise Davis
4th Grade Teacher
Ptak, Bernadette Marie
Second Grade Teacher
Radcliffe, Jenny Robinson
Sixth Grade Teacher
Saluga, Mary Ann (Vaccaro)
Drama & English Teacher
Savini, Joanne
Teacher & Business Dept Chair
Shutok, Cynthia Marie
First Grade Teacher
Zack, Daniel F.
Social Studies Teacher
UNIVERSITY PARK
Tikalsky, Paul J.
Civil & Envrnmntl Engrng Tchr
Worrell, Frank
Education Professor
UPPER DARBY
Blair, Kathleen M.
Seventh Grade Science Teacher
Bosch, Karin Patricia
Health & Physical Ed Teacher
Byrne, Kelly Ann
HS Mathematics Teacher
Cannella, Joseph James, Jr.
Physics Teacher
Citarelli, Vincent E.
Mathematics Teacher
Clossick, James J.
Social Studies Teacher
DeAngelis, Joseph F.
Fifth Grade Teacher
Harendza, Elizabeth Garabedian
Art Teacher
Higgins, Mary McFadden
Eighth Grade Teacher
Klugh, Kristen M.
English Teacher
Lynch, Robert Vincent
Sixth Grade Teacher
Maguire, Jack
English & Humanities Teacher
Maguire, Kim G.
English Teacher
Marinelli, Elizabeth A. O'Neill
8th Grade Teacher
McGovern, Terrence Michael
High School English Teacher
Moffett, Sharon Mc Closkey
Seventh Grade Lang Arts Tchr
Over, Philip R.
Mathematics Teacher & Ath Dir
Scaramuzza, Theresa M.
6th Grade Teacher
Smith, Jean V.
English Teacher
Smith, Richard C.
Social Studies Teacher
UTICA
Bailey, Dorothy Power
First Grade Teacher
Caldwell, Deanna Muldoon
Second Grade Teacher
Hamilton, Patricia Ann
Fourth Grade Teacher
VALLEY VIEW
Snyder, Gary Frederick
6th Grade Teacher
VANDERGRIFT
Balla, Gregory Joseph
Secondary Social Studies Tchr
Ceraso, John W.
Guidance Counselor
Duppstadt, Margaret Louise
4th Grade Teacher
Held, Kathleen (Varano)
Spanish Teacher
Kettering, Nancy Louise
Geometry Teacher
Mc Clarnon, William Francis
Social Studies Teacher
Musselman, Susan Edens
English & Speech Teacher
Pipman, Millie Haas
English Teacher
Poleski, Kimberly Luisi
Math Teacher
Rossi, Sylvia Mitchell
Health & Phys Ed Teacher
Rupert, Ellen Fenton
Vocal Music Director
Troilo, Anthony r.
5th Grade Teacher
Wozniak, George Nelson
Director of Bands
Zito, Andrea J. (Guzzo)
4th-5th Grade Teacher
VENETIA
Sherwin, Rene DiBartola
Former 3rd Grade Teacher
VENUS
Jackson, Diane Louise
4th Grade Teacher
VERONA
Hughes, Regis William
First Grade Teacher
Neale, Jo-Ann
Third Grade Teacher
Zaremski, Sharon L.
2nd Grade Teacher
VILLANOVA
Emig, James Matthew
Associate Prof of Accounting
Falcone, Frank E.
Adj Assoc Prof of Engineering
Holinger, Dorothy B.
Mathematics Teacher
Mc Govern, Marycarol W.
Nursing Professor
Stansbury, Lorraine S.
School Counselor
Suppa, Veronica Petrusky
Music Dept Chair & Eng Tchr
WALLACETON
Reiter, Daisy Zimmerman
Fifth Grade Teacher
WALLINGFORD
Babish, Dorothy Oliva
6th Grade Reading Teacher
Bansbach, Diane Cormany
Mathematics Teacher
Comey, James Hugh
Academic Services Director
Ellis, Carol Dominick
English Teacher
Farrell, Emily C.
English Teacher
Gabel, Nancy J.
Frgn Lang Chair & Fr Teacher
Hameka, Charlotte Procacci
Chemistry Teacher
Jolles, Mitchell I.
Physics & Mathematics Teacher
Lower, Conrad H., IV
French Teacher
Styer, Timothy L.
Biology Teacher
Van Koski, James
9th Grade Social Studies Tchr
Yarnall, Wendy Coltman
Special Education Teacher
WALNUTPORT
Fehnel, Louise Keppel
1st Grade Teacher
WAPWALLOPEN
Andreas, Caroline Strunk
Retired Teacher
WARFORDSBURG
Butts, Kenneth Edward
Industrial Arts Teacher
Souders, Carol Ann (Mauer)
Fourth Grade Teacher
WARMINSTER
Abel, Theodore
English Teacher
Adamsky, Richard Allen
7th Grade Teacher
Bernheisel, Marilyn Henry
Fifth Grade Teacher
Boyle, Frank J.
Accounting Teacher
Di Chiara, Frederick John
Health & Physical Ed Teacher
Heil, David C.
Mathematics Teacher
Koch, Nancy Joy
Vocal Music Tchr & Choral Dir
Kruvczuk, Robert Joseph
Earth & Space Science Teacher
Lovecchio, Joseph Anthony
Instrumental Music Director
Masterson, William, Jr.
Director of Dev & English Tchr
Puettner, Rosemarie Elizabeth, SSJ
Ger Tchr & Frgn Lang Dept Chr
Pukowski, John Patrick
Social Studies Teacher
Riddle, Ira Lee
HS Mathematics Teacher
Rooney, Kathleen, SSJ
Theology Teacher
Taylor, Albert J., Jr.
English Teacher
WARREN
Albaugh, F. Darlene
Business Education Teacher
Anderson, Joanne Marie (Graziano
Second Grade Teacher
Angove, Douglas L.
Physics Tchr & Sci Dept Chair
Barney, Diane Bartimoccia
Spanish & French Teacher
Bonavita, John F.
Social Studies Teacher
Burroughs, Linda Saporito
Learning Support Teacher
Bussoletti, Susann Riggi
Gifted Support Teacher
Daubenspeck, Nora J.
Third Grade Teacher
Finzel, Cheryl Harrison
8th Grade Science Teacher
Hibner, Constance Woolslayer
English & Study Skills Teacher
Johnson, Dennis A.
Health & Phys Ed Instructor
Lopez, Bonnie J.
Fourth Grade Teacher
Lyle, Pamela Bonace
Fifth Grade Teacher
Marti, Caroline Lindell
Third Grade Teacher
Mead, Ann Turowski
Music Specialist
Mesing, Margaret L.
English Teacher
Morgan, Margaret Reilly
AP US History Teacher
Norris, Steven Joseph
5th Grade Teacher
Shaffer, Robert John
Spanish Teacher
Tridico, Anthony James
Former Teachers Coach
Van Gilder, Sharie Husted
Fourth Grade Teacher
Wellek, Eugene Louis
Secondary Social Studies Tchr
WARREN CENTER
Darling, Jill Ann
Home School Teacher
WARRINGTON
Fuller, Gary David
Social Studies Teacher
Harrington, James S.
English Teacher
Johnston, Joanne Santarone
7th Grade Teacher
Loughran, Patricia Ann
Spanish Teacher
Schimpf, Shirley J.
Algebra Teacher
Sinn, Keith Michael
8th Grade Science Teacher
WARRIORS MARK
Stoner, Steven Reynolds
Sixth Grade Teacher
WASHINGTON
Booher, Rebecca Rea
English Teacher
Bullotta, Dominick Mark
Fifth Grade Teacher
Camden, Kathleen A.
MS Mathematics Teacher
Drakeley, Thomas Edward
Social Studies Teacher
Fuselier, Cynthia Maranich
English Teacher
Gilbert, Lori Shea
Prevention Specialist
Haines, G. W., Jr.
Social Studies Teacher
Heastings, Barbara Miller
Choral Music Director
Jones, Mary Livi
Special Education Teacher
Lacock, Lynn A.
5th Grade Teacher
Lawrence, Vinnedge Moore
Professor of Biology
Lee, Thomas Allen
Social Studies Teacher
Masciola, Douglas Anthony
Administrative Assistant
McMurtry, Emma Lee Elizabeth
Social Studies Teacher
Meldrum, Joan Leslie (Matthews)
K-12th Grd Tchr of Gifted Ed
Miller, Judith W.
Second Grade Teacher
Myers, Larry Robert
Psychology Teacher

IGTON (cont)
Rebecca Jo
Teacher
Elizabeth A.
Teacher & Dept Rep
awrence Anthony
Studies Instructor
lith Pasqua
English & Theatre Tchr
IGTON BORO
ristina Wolf
astrl Support Teacher
FALL
Craig C.
& PE Teacher
aeAnna Willauer
rade Teacher
borah Kay
chool English Teacher
FORD
David John
& Physical Ed Teacher
arlene Ann
h Grade Music Teacher
an K.
Stud & Driver Ed Tchr
Margaret Lee
rade Language Teacher
n, Andrew E., II
logy Coordinator
Deborah Swanson
natics Teacher
, Dan G.
Teacher
obert William
& Theater Teacher
onald Stephen
Stud & Drivers Ed Tchr
Robert Louis
natics Teacher
NTOWN
Laura Louise
Grade Teacher
BURG
bert Kohler
Dir, Instrumental Music
LY
athleen Marie
ade Teacher
RT
ynthia Wallace
rade Teacher

Sheila Starr
a Teacher
no, Mary Ann Mathauer
4th Grade Teacher
Jane Swift
acher
Danny
aster, Dir Instrmntl Mus
ames Edward
nt Prof of Mathematics
a, Laurence Mark
Teacher
Murray Neil
Studies Teacher
nneth Alan
f HS Gifted Program
SBORO
Dennis P.
y Teacher
axine Sheeley
a Teacher
Camille Finney
ss Education Teacher
rley Cooper
a Teacher
ly Ann (Gorndt)
r of the Gifted
ker, Randy Lewis
Studies Teacher
, John A.
s Instructor
ft, Sherry L.
ade Teacher
g, Jane Sneddon
Grade Teacher
se, Kimberly Jean
l American Cultures Tchr
Phillip Arthur
nental Music Teacher
Linda Louise
rade Teacher
SBURG
Merri Lu
School Guidance Cnslr
, Patricia Krajnak
l Lang Arts Teacher
John Charles
n Teacher
Brenda Kay
rade Teacher
John Joseph
c Dir & Spec Ed Teacher
Lori E.
rade Teacher
Carol Engle
ade Social Studies Tchr
Janice Ford
n Teacher
Lynn Ann
Teacher
Morgan A.
& Geography Teacher
mes William
Trig & Pre-Calculus Tchr
th, Debora Carol
n Teacher

Matthews, Sarah C.
Fourth Grade Teacher
Montgomery, Bridget Wade
High School Choral Director
Smereczniak, Jerilyn M.
Vocational & Tech School Tchr
Trump, Carl William
6th Grade Science Teacher
Winters, Bill
Social Studies Teacher
WEATHERLY
Antinozzi, Anthony James
Teacher & Coach
Jemo, David Nicholas
Social Studies Chairman
Kelshaw, Ronald H.
Guidance Counselor
Knight, Janice A.
Third Grade Teacher
McClafferty, James Joseph
Math Department Chair & Tchr
Spallone, Sharon Lee
Eng, Comm Instr & Dept Chr
WELLSBORO
Briggs, Joan Stratton
French & Gifted Support Tchr
Hafer, Sonya Jane
Fifth Grade Teacher
Schwab, John Alan
Math Teacher
Warner, Sherman Ammon
Math Teacher
West, Eileen O'Brien
Sixth Grade Teacher
Wise, Jeanne Harvey
Second Grade Teacher
WELLSVILLE
Weber, Judy S.
First Grade Teacher
WEST BROWNSVILLE
Cross, Ervin
Retired History & Science Tchr
WEST CHESTER
Banks, Linda Diane
English Teacher
Behan, Linda Heuvel
Spanish & English Teacher
Bernardi, Grace C.
Prevention Specialist
Best, Harry M., III
Technology Education Teacher
Bott, Jeffrey Thomas
Health & PE Teacher
Brunner, Steven L.
8th Grade Language Arts Tchr
Casals Diaz, Zaida E.
ESL Teacher
Cass, Sarah Mumford
8th Grd Amer His Teacher
Epstein, Richard Gary
Professor
Everhart, John Mark
Fine Arts Teacher
Fagan, Margaret M.
Eighth Grade Teacher
Feldman, Sallie Allman
Frgn Lang Tchr & Dept Chprsn
Finsel, Sandra L.
High School Math Teacher
Fitzmier, C. Dianne
Physics Teacher
Galitsky, Darleen Yeager
Family & Consumer Science Tchr
Gibson, Geraldine D.
6th Grd Tchr & Asst Principal
Gilland, Mary Matsko
Third Grade Teacher
Hall, David Ashworth
Supervisor of Student Tchrs
Heim, Jeffery Paxson
Teacher
Herley, Bettyann Murphy
4th Grade Teacher
Hester, Jeffrey M.
5th Grade Teacher
Hetherington, James Joseph
History Teacher
Hibberd, Josiah
Retired Social Studies Teacher
Hill, Jeanne Delia Sciubba
Chemistry Teacher
James, Donald L.
Math & Bible Teacher
Kamin, Gary David
Chemistry & Physics Teacher
Kerstetter, Harold William
Geography Teacher
Komar, Mary Ann JaFolla
High School Mathematics Tchr
Lion, Rita Gleason
Retired Teacher
Mc Dermott, George J.
AP American History Teacher
McKenna, Barbara Kosiba
Mathematics Teacher
McQuiston, David M.
High School History Teacher
Monaghan, John Michael
Western World Soc Stud Teacher
Mulligan, Eugene Dennis
Science Teacher & Dept Head
O'Toole, Susan Renner
Chemistry Teacher
Radle, Wendy Burry
High School English Teacher
Rafetto, J. Scott
Health Teacher
Sawyer-Hudson, Sheila Lorraine
High School English Teacher

Stevens, Walton Craig
Asst Professor of Kinesiology
Timmins, Peter Riehm
Former Bible Teacher
White, Helen Catherine
Eng Teacher & Rdng Specialist
WEST GROVE
Garvin, Megan Elizabeth
Seventh Grade Teacher
Hoffman, Ann Denkin
English Teacher
King, Mary Bilek
Biology Teacher
Przywitowski, Marie B.
Sixth Grade Teacher
Rossi, Stephen H.
Social Studies Teacher
Schenker, Shirley Anne (Blatzheim)
Social Studies Teacher
Thomas, Anne S.
English Teacher
Vanderkraats, Barbara-Jo (Friese)
Choral Music Teacher
Vogt, Christine Cucore
7th-8th Grade Teacher
WEST LAWN
Brok, Stephanie Sue
English & Writing Process Tchr
Debiec, David Anthony
6th Grade Teacher
Heckard, Ida Rose (Doenng)
School Psychologist
Kane, Dorothy Brinjak
Third Grade Teacher
Kovary, Loraine Brita
Spanish Teacher
Pyle, Deborah Yatron
Spanish Teacher
Ruth, Thomas
Asst Prin & Phys Ed Teacher
Schmoyer, Bruce Carl
Instrumental Music Tchr & Chm
Seagreaves, Peter
Principal
Voguit, Steve George
Social Studies Teacher
Wanner, Ann-Louise Focht
English Teacher
Weirich, Robert J.
English Supervisor
Weiss, Reggie
Business Ed Teacher & Coach
Wisniewski, Mark Stephen
Language Arts Teacher
Wonder, Jamie Lynn
French Teacher
WEST MIDDLESEX
Burke, Mary L.
2nd Grade Teacher
Emmett, Karen Campman
Vocal Music Educator
Geroni, Claudia
Social Studies Teacher
Hutchison, Thomas C.
Biology Teacher
Lynam, James Richard
Computer Science Teacher
McCaslin, Gary Ray
Sixth Grade Teacher
Messett, Dennis Martin
Principal
Morris, Robert A.
Bus Ed Instructor & Ath Dir
Partridge, Vicki Vee
English Teacher
Pinch, Paula Marie (Yonchak)
Business Teacher
WEST MIFFLIN
Anater, Paul F.
Science & Technology Dept Chm
Barley, Charles F.
Teacher
Chiponis, Michael Anthony
4th Grade Classroom Teacher
Cole, Fred J.
Business Education Dept Chm
Di Cioccio, Gary F.
Chemistry Teacher
Edwards, Keith David
Learning Support Teacher
Eley, Adele Winters
Reading Teacher
Galya, Betty Jakubovics
English & Theme Writing Tchr
Geis, George Edward
French Teacher
Hall, William Roy
Professor
Hayden, Alice B.
Kindergarten Teacher
Karas, Patricia A.
Business Teacher
Kern, Robert William
High School Math Teacher
Krisantz, Cheryl Knapp
Fifth-Eight Grade Teacher
Lawrence, Sharon Lee
Home Economics Teacher
Lax, Barbara K.
Professor of Biology
Leith, Robert Allan
Retired Elementary Teacher
Licata, Marcia L.
Spanish Teacher
Mattson, Veronica Wharton
Science Teacher
Maydak, Dawna M.
High School English Teacher
Montgomery, Larry C.
Guidance Counselor

Needle, Donna Vogt
Fam & Consumer Sci Tchr
Neshoff, Darlene
Business Education Teacher
Proksa, Anita M.
English Teacher
Rozgonyi, Gregory Alan
9th Grade Health Teacher
Schuchert, Robert J.
Counselor
Thayer, Joan Stewart
Retired Third Grade Teacher
Walendziewicz, Walter Cyril
Spanish Teacher
Watson, Donald Lloyd
7th Grade Life Science Teacher
Weber, Haddie Frey
Elementary Music Teacher
Welch, Charlene Genes
Biology Teacher
Woolf, David Wilson
Assoc Prof of Art
Zimmerman, George Albert
Math Teacher & Dept Chair
WEST MILTON
Hoffman, Marilyn-Lee Holley
Elementary Teacher
WEST PITTSTON
Curley, Mary Dwyer
8th Grade Science Teacher
Mahalsky, Bradley P.
Environmental Teacher
Prescavage, Eileen
Chemistry Teacher
Tarone, Marion
Principal
WEST SUNBURY
Garner, Emily McNickle
12th Grade English Teacher
Metz, James David
8th Grade Social Studies Tchr
Morton, Thomas Richard
5th Grade Teacher
Swank, Charles F.
Science Teacher
Travaglio, E. Gay
Elementary Education Teacher
Wetzel, Cindy L.
English Teacher
WESTCHESTER
Sabatino, Debra O'Brien
Chemistry & Physics Teacher
WESTFIELD
Andrews, Linda J.
Fourth Grade Teacher
Heyler, Martin C.
Agri & Industrial Arts Tchr
Krysiak, Doris Parks
Fifth Grade Teacher
Little, Marcy Hall
Jr High & Elem Title I Tchr
Mc Cawley, William Peter
Biology Teacher
VanEtten, Carolyn P. (Tomb)
Librarian
Zerby, Clair W.
Agriculture Teacher
WESTTOWN
Newton, Evans Kendrick, III
Spanish Teacher
Vogel, Ken J.
Private Drum Instructor
WEXFORD
Aresto, Helen Jean Hutchison
Science Teacher
Bergman, Ronald Clair
Mathematics Teacher
Caldwell, Robert J.
Social Science Teacher
Dattilo, Jerry M.
7th Grade Social Studies Tchr
Mull, Marianne J.
Senior High Math Teacher
Novak, Jean Finnegan
Eighth Grade Teacher
Peel, Carol Berberich
Amer History & Govt Teacher
Pielin, Gilbert Martin
Chemistry & Biology Instructor
Poluszejko, Maureen Strauss
Senior HS Guidance Counselor
Smolter, Mary Catherine Cynkar
5th Grade Teacher
Thomas, Jay J.
Latin Tchr & Frgn Lang Chprsn
Wienand, Robert Allen
Chemistry Teacher
Will, Robert I.
12th Grd Psychology Teacher
Zaun, Barbara Klueber
French Teacher
WHITEHALL
Berner, Nancy Kratzer
Third Grade Teacher
Bower, Kelly Ann
English Teacher
Brosky, Jeffrey J.
Health & PE Teacher
Buschta, Mary Schimpf
Sixth Grade Teacher
Confer, Carol Simon
Third Grade Teacher
Ehrig, David Alan
Sixth Grade Science Specialist
Fried, Patricia Helen (Smith)
Science Teacher
Fries, Marika H. Prosak
Fourth Grade Teacher
Gober, Steven
Fourth Grade Teacher

Hale, Annette J.
English Teacher
Hettinger, Joanne Schreiner
Kindergarten Teacher
Hilborn, L. Rick
Band Director & Music Teacher
Kolb, Robert H.
Soc Stud & Geography Teacher
Luckenbill, Stanley M.
MS Physical Education Teacher
Makary, Frank J.
Social Studies Teacher
Marsteller, Jean N. W.
Spanish Teacher
Panny, Robert J.
Social Studies Teacher
Rabenold, Laura C.
Fine Arts & Vocal Music Tchr
Ryan, Margaret R.
Kindergarten Teacher
Sobrinski, Joseph William
Third Grade Teacher
Toth, John Paul
Fourth Grade Teacher
WILKES BARRE
Alexander, Christopher Scott
Asst Prof of Mrktg
Banik, David Richard
Social Studies Teacher
Baranoski, Karen Metzger
Life Science & Biology Teacher
Berard, Anthony D., Jr.
Math & Computer Sci Professor
Biniek, Matthew James
Chemistry Teacher
Blizman, Joseph J.
Eighth Grade Teacher
Booth, Michael Dennis
Academy Dean & English Teacher
Burns, Richard J.
Social Studies Teacher
Cardoni, Agnes Toloczko
English Instructor
Chappell, Judy A.
Biology Teacher
Chernesky, Edward Joseph
5th Grade Teacher
Costello, Marsha Sims
Latin Teacher
Craig, Corinne Ann
Mathematics Teacher
Drahus, Suzanne Ciliberto
Spanish Teacher
Elias, Michael Donald, Jr.
Science Teacher
Evans, Ned John
6th Grade Teacher
Fischer, Brian J.
Music Educator
Germak, George A.
English & Latin Teacher
Gfeller, Nicole Louise
Swim Coach
Gildea, Judy A.
Health & Physical Ed Tchr
Glod, Andrea Anne
English & Speech Teacher
Grasso, Frank James
Sixth Grade Teacher
Gregg, Jayne Roderick
Support Rdng Teacher of Gifted
Griffiths, Kit
Business Education Teacher
Griseto, Toni Harzinski
Fifth Grade Teacher
Guesto, Marie Frances
World & Amer Literature Tchr
Gula, James Robert
Language Arts Teacher
Hogan, Barbara E.
Cmptr Sci Dept Chm & Math Tchr
Houck, Dale Charles
Music Teacher & Orchestra Dir
Houseknecht, Mary Jean
Fifth-Sixth Grade Teacher
Hromisin, Jerome Thomas
English Teacher
Huntzinger, Janice Ziegler
Education Director
Jabers, Priscilla Salome
Second Grade Teacher
Jacobs, Ronald J.
Mathematics Teacher
Johnson, Linda Makowski
Art Teacher
Johnson, Thomas M.
English Teacher
Jones, Dale Richard
Fourth Grade Teacher
Jones, Diane M.
Biology Teacher
Kane, Kathryn Straub
Instructional Support Teacher
Kellar, Tina Ann
Instrumental Music Teacher
Klemow, Kenneth M.
Associate Professor of Biology
Kotchick, Michele R.
Cmptr Tchr & Rdng Specialist
Kravitz, Jeanne
Health Related Technology Tchr
Krehely, Robert John
Spanish & World History Tchr
Kurilla, Michael Andrew
Social Studies Teacher
Lapinski, David J.
Mathematics Teacher
LaScala, Philip Michael
Special Education Teacher

WILKES BARRE (cont)
Makalusky, Maripat MacDonald
English Teacher
Makravitz, Carol
Vice Prin & Advanced Bio Tchr
Manganiello, Ann M.
Music Teacher & Dept Chprsn
Mc Ginley, Mary Maloney
Jr Sr HS English Teacher
Mc Nulty, Carol Danowski
Fourth Grade Teacher
Meehan, David
Social Studies Teacher
Michaels, Frank J.
Physics Teacher
Milz, Michael Andrew
History Teacher
Monico, SueAnn Leandri
6th Grade Social Studies Tchr
Moore, Thomas Edward
Sixth Grade Teacher
O'Konski, Barbara A.
French Teacher
Palfey, Thomas Joseph
Sixth Grade Teacher
Pieck, Michael
Fourth Grade Teacher
Podczasy, Anthony Peter, Jr.
Science Teacher
Porzucek, Donna
Math Teacher
Rollins-Ruffin, Taj-Teresa A.
Social Studies Teacher
Sartin, Jean Kobowski
English & French Teacher
Schaefer, Myrna L.
Senior English Teacher
Smith, Mark John
Sixth Grade Teacher
Smith, Robert Donald
Mathematics Teacher
Sorchik, Scott William
Industrial Arts Teacher
Spagnuolo, John Ralph
Biology Teacher
Stanski, Sharon Rowny
Math & Computer Teacher
Sulcoski, Michael Stephen
Science Teacher
Thomas, Thomas James, Jr.
Program Counselor
Vasile, Mary Ann Rochelle
First Grade Teacher
Volpetti, Barbara A.
Kindergarten Teacher
Wallace, James Michael
Assistant Professor of English
Woloski, John J., Jr.
Music Teacher & Orchestra Dir
Wozniak, Ninaleigh Stratton
7th-8th Grd Special Ed Teacher
Zaledonis, Mary Ann Daru
6th Grade Teacher
Zaleta, Lex
Secondary English Teacher
Zdanowicz, Virginia M. (Berti)
French Teacher
Zola, Judith Ann
Music Teacher
WILKES BARRE TOWNSHIP
Mihalos, Marie S. Denessi
Gifted Support Teacher
WILLIAMSPORT
Coffman, Billie A.
Early Childhood Ed Asst Prof
Elion, Sandra (Hainline)
3rd-6th Grade Teacher
Fedorko, Mary Weis
Fifth Grade Teacher
Fisher, Carol Best
Retired Second Grade Teacher
Hartzel, Paul Franklin, Jr.
High School Drafting Teacher
Henneman-Bartlett, Denise
7th-12th Grd Girls PE Teacher
Judd, Jeffrey R.
Orchestra Teacher
Matter, David LeRoy
Practical Arts Curr Coord
Miller, Linda Kaufman
Third Grade Teacher
Puller, Jodi Stuck
Fifth Grade Teacher
Whitehill, Leslie
Health Educator
Zimmerman, Karen Ancarana
Business Teacher
WILLOW GROVE
Barron, Robert Reid, Jr.
Band Director
Brewer, Wm. Terry
Fifth Grade Teacher
Cassady, Linda E.
10th-12th Grades Soc Stud Tchr
Cohen, Richard L.
AP Eng, Gifted Education Tchr
Hamilton, Joyce Elaine
Social Studies Teacher
WILMERDING
Polski, Bernard Joseph
Fourth Grade Teacher
WINDBER
Daniel, Paul Edward, Jr.
English Teacher
Durst, Gail Stasko
4th Grade Teacher
Lambert, Arthur R.
Teacher & Department Chairman
Morrison, William Francis
Business Education Teacher
Ripple, Lee Allen
English Teacher & Dept Chprsn
Soohy, David
Middle School Science Teacher
Vatavuk, Michael John
General Music Teacher
WINDSOR
Snyder, Jeannette S.
Kindergarten Teacher
WINGATE
Erb, Melanie Chapman
Mathematics Teacher
Herold, Bruce Walter
Spanish Teacher
WOMELSDORF
Elliott, Christy L.
Guidance Counselor
Snyder, Mary Jane Missmer
Third Grade Teacher
WORTHINGTON
Blakney, Steven Dwight
Principal & HS Teacher
WRIGHTSVILLE
Bloom, Gary L.
English & Drama Teacher
Herr, James R.
Retired Teacher
Sonneborn, Sylvia Hott
English Teacher & Dept Chm
Trofatter, Susan G.
English Teacher
White, Kerry Allen
American History Teacher
Wolf, Michael Allen
Music Dept Chair & Band Dir
WYALUSING
Astare, Edward J.
Math Teacher
Bovine, Kathi Turturro
Art Teacher
Chase, Mary Hammond
Strings Tchr & Orch Conductor
Conrad, Paulette Ashcraft
Fifth Grade Teacher
Fisk, Walter C., Jr.
7th Grade Life Science Teacher
Flood, Joyce A.
English Teacher of Disabled
Kipp, Rose Wells
English Teacher
Long, Anne Williams
Fourth Grade Teacher
Manney, Laurie Williams
Third Grade Teacher
McNeal, Phyllis Elaine
English Teacher
Meteer, Marvin G.
English Teacher
Minetola, Albert J., Jr.
Head Teacher
Minetola, Janice R.
First Grade Teacher
Murphy, Glenn Ellsworth
Mathematics Teacher
Schulze, Jonathan Bruce
English Teacher
Shumway, Robert Lane
Band Director
Welles, Lynn Koch
Instructional Support Teacher
Wilson, Diane F.
Economics & Psychology Teacher
Yadlosky, Richard D.
Social Studies Teacher
WYNCOTE
Achuff, Albert C.
Asst Prin & Soc Studies Instr
Agster, Kathleen Mary (Mc Carthy)
Theology Teacher
Ambler, Charles Henry
English Teacher
Brandley, Joseph S.
English Teacher
Ciao, Frederick J.
President
Coyne, Cecelia Eble
Biology Teacher
Dandridge, Valarie Cooper
Guidance Counselor
Dominello, Carole Anne Mc Geehan
AP Biology Teacher
Fisher, Thomas Jay
Amer His & Behavioral Sci Tchr
Graham, Robert Thomas
Math Teacher
Hanselmann, Maria
Mathematics Teacher
Harper, Maria Champagne
8th Grade Earth Science Tchr
Horn, David Thomas
12th Grade AP English Teacher
Lemke, Marilyn B.
3rd Grade Teacher
Leven, Ray
Spanish Teacher
Maloney, Miriam Gary
Eng Dept Chprsn & Teacher
Mazen, Rebecca Ann
Science Teacher
Mc Kenna, Shannon M.
French & Spanish Teacher
McNutt, Thomas Ignatius
English Teacher
Minieri, James John
Social Studies Chairman
Pancione, Loretta Harrill
Honors & Academic Bio Teacher
Poiesz, Paul Joseph
Math Teacher & Track Coach
Redican, J. Stacey
English Teacher
Rogalski, John T.
Middle School Teacher
Sack, Patricia Frances
7th-8th Grade English Teacher
Spohn, Susan Shields
High School Math Teacher
Traynor, Lucille Burns
Mathematics Chairperson
WYNDMOOR
Taggart, Nancy
Former Teacher
WYNNEWOOD
Arnold, Jeanne Carol
Second Grade Teacher
Crauderueff, Michael L.
Spanish Teacher
Mc Collum, John Hatcher
English Teacher & Dean
WYOMISSING
Dowling, William C.
Chemistry Teacher
Evans, Roger J.
Mathematics Teacher
Kozloff, Jeraldine D.
Social Studies Teacher
Luyben, Sharon Patricia (Love)
Choral Dir & Music Dept Chair
Martin, David Irvin
Eng Tchr & Dept Chprsn
Palcho, Karen D.
Art Teacher
Quinlan, Sharon Guerro
Math Teacher
WYSOX
Silverstrim, C. Elaine
3rd Grade Elementary Teacher
YARDLEY
Bitner, Rita C.
Retired 6th Grade Teacher
Magg, Robert
Head Coach
O'Connell, Richard M.
Teacher
Tickel, Nancy Boyd
Fourth Grade Teacher
YATESVILLE
Devlin, Robert W.
HS Tchr of Special Education
Draus, Anthony Joseph
Guidance Department Supervisor
Roberts, Anne Marie Latona
Chemistry Teacher
YORK
Adams, Karen M.
First Grade Teacher
Adams, Paul Edwin
Science Teacher
Akins, Julie (Brallier)
Language Arts Teacher
Bedard, Kathleen Dunnington
HS Chemistry & Biology Teacher
Bowman, Richard Edward
History Teacher
Buckingham, Kathy Ruby
Fourth Grade Teacher
Bulinski, Daniel Gregory
Senior Army Instructor
Carnahan, Peggy Stenken
Fourth Grade Teacher
Clark, Thomas C.
History Teacher
Cleary, Barbara Kessler
English Teacher
Cleaver, Ann Elizabeth
Second Grade Teacher
Crone, Aleta Kay
Vocal Music Teacher
DeStephano, John Anthony
Junior High Math Teacher
Dietz, Rochelle Erb
Kindergarten Teacher
Dorf, Lawrence Peter
Mathematics Teacher
Ehrhart, David S.
Soc Stud Teacher & Dept Chm
Elder, Beverly Jill
Choral Music Teacher
Fahringer, James Nolan
4th Grade Teacher
Fero, Mary Jo Tressler
High School Art Teacher
Gable, Kent Eric
Math Teacher
Gangloff, Gail Margaret
HS Mathematics Teacher
Godine, Heather Lynn
High School Mathematics Tchr
Grimm, Dona Burhans
English Teacher
Hartenstein, Alice L.
English Teacher
Harvey, Torance Neil
Guidance Counselor
Haynes, Julia Ann
Spcl Educ & Lrngn Supprt Tchr
Hertzog, Diane Lee
Mathematics Teacher
Hollinger, Janet Zortman
Business Education Teacher
Hopkinson, Constance Mc Kinney
Learning Support Teacher
Kollmar, Gail E.
Family & Consumer Science Tchr
Krepps, Kathleen Marie
Third Grade Teacher
Krout, Noah Eugene
Sixth Grade Teacher
Love, Mary Joyce
Retired Elementary Schl Tchr
Matthews, Kenneth Harry
Music & Band Director
Meckley, Rod L.
Music Teacher
Mentzer, Patricia Gable
6th-8th Grade Reading Teacher
Missildine, Kathryn Long
English Professor
Morales, Manuel Joseph
Spanish Teacher
Mueller, Janyce Morte
Health Occupations Teacher
Murphy, Daria Fedorovich
Library & Media Specialist
Murphy, Wendy Lorraine
Social Studies Teacher
Myers, Connie Rose (Barley)
Former Teacher
Overmiller, Laurie (Weinfurtner)
Art Teacher & Dept Head
Patterson, Charles E.
5th Grade Teacher
Polites, Doris Morrette
First Grade Teacher
Reihart, Stephany Bettermann
World Cultures Teacher
Savidge, Thomas K.
7th Grade Mathematics Teacher
Schenck, Jane Louise
English Teacher
Sciortino, Angela Renee
Math Teacher
Shearer, John W.
Mathematics Teacher & Ath Dir
Siddiqui, Abdul Majeed
Assoc Professor of Mathematics
Snyder, Donna Gieselman
Third Grade Teacher
Stahlman, Mary Butler
Softball Coach
Stayer, Jane Frey
Substitute Teacher
Swartz, Rodney Eugene, Jr.
Retired English Teacher
Teague, Peter Wesley
Superintendent
Thomas, Lulu L.
Language Arts & Reading Tchr
Thompson, Ernest Francis, Jr.
Reading Specialist
Wagner, Lenore M.
HS Music Teacher
Warner, Michelle Butler
English Dept Chairman, Teacher
Weitkamp, Jan Leiphart
First Grade Teacher
Wert, Timothy Dale
Physics Teacher
Willoughby, Earl Orr
Business Education Instructor
Wolfgang, Greg Robert
English Teacher
YORK HAVEN
Himes, Linda A.
Second Grade Teacher
YORK SPRINGS
Coleman, Craig Wayne
High School Math Teacher
Paxson, Alice Boyd
Elementary Gifted Ed Tchr
Reinecker, Cheryl Collins
Secondary Social Studies Tchr
YOUNGSVILLE
Coleman, Joyce Jefferson
2nd Grade Teacher
Gerardi, Josephine A.
Family & Consumer Science Tchr
Hendrickson, Scott D.
Sec Math Teacher
Montgomery, Christina Lynn
Vocal Music Teacher
Petrush, Barbara Jean
Math Teacher
Scheid, Cynthia Louise
Band Director
YOUNGWOOD
Cecchetti, Mario Eugene
Computer Technology Professor
Hersh, Mortimer Bennett, Jr.
Social Science Asst Prof
Hoden, Beth A.
Asst Prof of Early Chldhd Ed
Lewis, Carol (Rupp)
Kindergarten Teacher
Walters, Cheryl Ann
Mathematics Instructor

PUERTO RICO

AGUADILLA
Acevedo, Nancy
Business Professor
Gonzalez, Aura Galarza
Home Economics Teacher
Gonzalez, Violeta
Associate Professor
Hernandez, Myrna
Chemistry Teacher
Solorzano, Jose R.
Electronics Teacher
Torres, Myrna E.
English Professor
AIBONITO
Colon, Emilio Colon
Health Teacher
ARECIBO
Aguilar, Vilma E.
Criminal Justice Professor
Bravo-Nunez, Arnaldo R.
Chemistry Professor
Dommenech, Michael
Religion & Philosophy Prof
Gines, Maria del Rosario Marin
Spanish Teacher
Quinones, Weyna M.
Business Education Professor
Velez, Myrna
Founder, Director & Teacher
Vissepo, Hector E.
Soc Sci, His & Pub Admin Prof
ARROYO
de Romero, Myrtha Joubert
Social Studies Teacher
Diaz, Jose Eduardo
Band Teacher
Flores, Elia Nazario
Spanish Teacher
Pagan, Migdalia
English Teacher
Rodriguez, Carmen M.
HS Mathematics Teacher
Valentin, Lucila Rafaelina
Kindergarten Teacher
Vazquez, Francisco C.
School Registrar
BARRANQUITAS
DeJesus, Juan Bautista
Spanish Professor
Ramos-de-Diaz, Marfa H.
Business Administration Dir
BAYAMON
Agrinzoni, Maria Mercedes
Math Teacher & Team Leader
Alicea, Luz N.
Spanish Teacher
Aponte, Rafael
Lecturer of History & Soc Sci
Aviles, Wanda
Biology & Earth Science Tchr
Cabezudo, Maria Del C.
Math Teacher
Colon, Gladys M.
Ninth Grade History Teacher
Cotto-Gonzalez, Felix
Sociology Teacher
De Diaz, Lillian Bras
Computer Science Professor
DeJesus, Rebecca Ivette
Chemistry Teacher
Delgado Quiles, Virgilio
Accounting Professor
Del Valle, Mildred Annettee
Biology Teacher
Gonzalez, Celida
Professor of Education
Lamboy, Eleazar Daniel
Director
Miranda, Monsita Barbosa
All Class Teacher
Murray, Carola Lehmacher
6th Grade Teacher
Paleo, Lazara Elsa
11th Grade Chemistry Teacher
Pico, Lara Maria
French & Spanish Teacher
Rivera, Yolanda
Religion Teacher
Rodriguez Pinero, Juana M.
Spanish Teacher
Rosado-Figueras, Gladys
Dir of Adult Higher Ed Prgm
Rosario de Gonzalez, Nivia E.
School Director & Owner
Tolentino, Dinorah Jimenez
Professor of Biology
Vazquez, Jaime
Athletic Director
Vega-Santiago, Mayda
Business Admin Dept Chair
CABO ROJO
Seda, Heldie M. Zapata
Superior Spanish Teacher
CAGUAS
Carrion Martinez, Gloria M.
English Professor
Figueroa-Luciano, Francisco
Music Teacher
Jimenez, Pedro Luis
Band Director
Munoz, Vilma Socorro
Kindergarten Teacher
Ortiz-Gallio, Carmen V.
Chemistry Teacher
Pabon, Milena Lucia Gomez
Mathematics Teacher
Pauneto, Rebecca
Spanish Teacher
Ramirez, Jose
Spanish Coordinator & Tchr
Ramos, Luz Maria
Science Teacher
CAMUY
Cardec, Magali
Health Teacher
CANOVANAS
Figueroa, Haydee
Spanish Teacher
CANOVANILLAS
Rivera, Helga Ivonne
Elementary School Teacher
CAPARRA HEIGHTS
Merced, Elba Luz
Spanish & Bible Teacher
Santini, Jaqueline
English Teacher

NA
:arlos Ivan
stration & Computer Prof
onia Mercedes
hr & Dept Chprsn
, Yanira
try Teacher
z, Maribel
an
Maria de Los Angeles
n Teacher
Delia
Teacher
NA ALTA
India C.
n Teacher

Merlin B.
try & Physics Teacher

Zaida Enid
n Teacher

Eva Lourdes
Teacher
, Ana
n Teacher
IO
Ramon A. Baez
natics Teacher
DO
odriguez, Hector Jose
n Teacher & Dept Dir
AL
Rafael Marrero
n Teacher
Nydia
Teacher
adio Rivera
natics Teacher
Carmen L.
stry Teacher
AUREL
in, Berta Silvia Sanchez
Studies Teacher
O
esbia S.
nt Professor
ulie J.
stics & ESL Professor
Wanda Ortiz
nt Professor of Biology
, Elba Nydia Santiago
n Teacher
Reyes, Arlene
nt Professor
z, Angel M.
or
Arroyo, Willie A.
ss Administration Prof
errero, Ismael
f Academic Affairs
UCHANAN
olanda
School Teacher
MA
Gloria Maria
Teacher
, Luis Alberto
ating Teacher
Acevedo, Elba I.
n Teacher
rgio B.
natics Teacher
ABO
elda F.
ath Tchr & Dept Chprsn
Edith N.
Teacher & Coord
Noris
eacher
ose L.
natics Teacher
do, Maria Martinez
h Teacher
, Rosa M.
Fndtn Dissertation Fllw
osamelia
y Teacher
la, Ana Victoria Recurt
al Education Teacher
ler, Wanda Joselyn
e Teacher
ez, Evelyn Diane
h Teacher
-Caraballo, Josefa
y Teacher
ez, Ana Doris
natics Teacher
O
ernadette
n Department Head
, Maria Magdalena Cruz
d Grade Teacher
Mildred
e Teacher
Migdalia
e Teacher
REY
Conchita Diaz de Cerio
h Teacher
Cintron, Alvaro
sor
a, Arnaldo H.
stry Professor
uis A.
ate Professor
, Manuel
nical Engrng Dept Dir

Borras, Julio I.
Physical Education Coll Prof
Borras-Osorio, Belma A.
Accounting Department Director
Buhring, Dagmar A.
Eng, ESL & Linguistics Tchr
Collazos, Omaira M.
Asst Prof of Civil Engineering
Cruz, Rafael Nicole
Assoc Prof of Indstrl Engrng
de Munoz, Laura Pando
Associate Prof of Eng Dept
Dumois, Martha R.
Physics & Math Instructor
Faria, Rafael
Prof of Industrial Engrng
Garcia, Maribel
Prof of Guidance & Counselor
Gaya-Gonzalez, Lillian
Professor of Biology
Gomez, Nelida
Associate Professor
Jimenez, Clarivel Velez
English Teacher
Lamba, Ram S.
Professor
Lopez, Thalia Sacarello
Principal
Lugo-Lugo, Herminio
Professor of Biology
Maldonado, Jenny Ivette
Human Resources Professor
Martinez, Daphne Marie
English Professor
Martinez-Gamez, Jose A.
Civil Engrng Asst Prof & Coord
Ortiz-Vetez, Lizette
Assistant Prof of Marketing
Pacheco, Gustavo Emilio
Civil Engrng Dept Asst Prof
Padro, Jose Rafael
Professor of Mathematics
Perez-Lloveras, T. Rafael E.
Ed & Criminal Justice Prof
Pique, Armand L.S.
Economics Professor
Pomales, Eliezer Cotto
Mathematics Professor
Rivera, Nilda Rosa
Assistant Professor
Roman, Alvin
Electrical Engineering Prof
Tobin, Beatrice
Assoc Prof of English
Vazquez, Jose Enrique
Finance Professor
Vazquez, Juan H.
Associate Professor
Veras-Jorge, Eduardo Jose
Engineering Professor
HORMIGUEROS
Rodriguez, Sylvia M.
Spanish Teacher
HUMACAO
Ceide, Gloria
Dept of Span Professor
Cruz, Diana L.
Special Education Professor
DeLeon, Luis Sanchez-Longo Pio
Professor of History
Gierbolini-Rodriguez, Angel M., Sr.
Prof of Spec Ed & Dept Head
Hodges, Elizabeth J.
English Professor
Ortiz, Wanda
Assistant Professor
Roman-Garcia, Lourdes S.
History Teacher
ISABELA
Ramos, Lourdes Milagros
Science & Health Teacher
JAYUYA
Morales, Daisy
Art Teacher
JUANA DIAZ
Castaner, Norma
Spanish Teacher
Rodriguez Vega, Francisco J.
Spanish Teacher
JUNCOS
Rivera Pabellon, Jose O.
Music Teacher
LAJAS
Portela, Ana Rosario Mulero
High School Science Teacher
LARES
Figueroa, David
Science Teacher
Gonzalez, Blanca L.
Science Teacher
Perez, Ibeth Yolanda
Sixth Grade Soc Studies Tchr
Velez, Beatriz
Math Teacher
LEVITTOWN
Soto, Nayda Ivette
Physics Teacher
Vega de DeJesus, Carmen Gloria
Spanish Teacher
MANATI
Fernandez-Repollet, Carmen
Bio, Chem & Physics Teacher
Velez, Jose Luis
Mathematics Teacher
MAUNABO
Lebron, Aurea Rodriguez
Mathematics Teacher
Ramos, Marina Rosado
English Teacher

MAYAGUEZ
Acosta, Migdonia
Fourth Year English Teacher
Anglada, Ramon
Theology Professor
Arde, Jose C.
Asst Professor of Biology
Baumgardt, Paulette A.
Professor of German
Berrocal-Lopez, Ramon
Professor
Bruno, Jorge Mauncio
Psychology Teacher
Buxeda, Rosa J.
Assistant Professor
Centeno, Ingrid Marianne
Music Education Professor
Colon, Marisol
Chemistry Teacher
Colucci, Benjamin
Engineering Professor
Colucci, Jose Antonio
Chemical Engineering Professor
Cruz Marti, Carmen M.
Spanish Teacher
Davoodi, Hamid
University Professor
DePinedo, Judith Garcia
Counselor, Adviser & Span Tchr
Fortuna Vazquez, Jose Manuel
Spanish Teacher
Garcia, Abda
Kindergarten Teacher
Godoy, Luis Augusto
Professor of Civil Engineering
Goyal, Megh R.
Engineering Professor
Hunt, Susan Conway
High School English Teacher
Liciaga, Virgilio
High School History Teacher
Lizardo, Benjamin Arturo
Computer Science Professor
Miura, Zulma V.
Humanities Professor
Morales, Delma
Science & Religion Teacher
Munoz-Sola, Yldefonso
Assoc Professor of Chemistry
Navas, Vivian
Assoc Professor
Ortiz-Seda, Darnyd W.
Assoc Prof of English
Perez, Carmen Mercedes
English Professor
Quinones, David L.
Spanish Teacher
Quintana, Sephora C.
Lang Coord & HS Eng Tchr
Ramgolam, Roopchand
Economics Professor
Ramirez, Carlos A.
Professor of Chemical Engrng
Rivera-Acosta, Zwinda L.
Chemistry Professor
Santana-Nieves, Carmen S.
Assistant Professor
Santos, David Anthony
Math Professor
Soto, Nancy Tirado
Spanish Teacher
Suarez, Luis E.
Engineering Professor
Velez Figueroa, Abda Rebecca
Kindergarten Teacher
Velez-Morales, Myriam
Psychologist
Velez-Sepulveda, David
Assoc Prof Span, Hum Dept Chm
Villanueva, Raul G.
Professor of Biology
MERCEDITA
Clampitt, Sharon
Eng as Second Lang Instr
Moura, Jose' Emmanuel
Accounting Professor
Teissonniere-Ortiz, Arnaldo J.
Business Instructor
Vazquez, Hector Luis
Business, Accounting Professor
MIRAMAR
de Chinea, Carmen Amadeo
History Teacher
MOCA
Hernandez, Brunilda
Second Grade Teacher
OROCOVIS
Aviles, John
Science Teacher
Gomez, Jose L.
Catholic School Director
PENUELAS
Gelpi, Luis M.
Secondary Biology Teacher
PONCE
Asencio, Carmen I.
Associate Professor of Biology
Baez, Arvin Manuel
Cnslr & Asst Dean Stu Affairs
Carrasco-Serrano, Clara E.
Genetics Professor
Carrasquillo, Arnaldo
Chemistry Professor
Carta, Candida Gerardino
Spanish & Social Studies Tchr
Esacbi-Perez, Jose R.
Professor of Chemistry
Gotay, Edda Vivian
Elementary English Teacher

Hupka, Arthur L.
Pharmacology & Toxicology Prof
Lopez, Marisol del S.
Marketing Instructor
Mayoral, Julie M.
Director, Owner & Producer
Mendez, Hilarion
Accounting Professor
Montero, Marta I.
Science Teacher
Munera, Jose Juan
Guidance Counselor
Orengo, Lydia Ortiz
Science Teacher
Ortiz, Cedia Ramos
Professor of Criminal Justice
Quinones, Luzaray
Study Skills Professor
Ramos, Sandra
Criminology Professor
Rodriguez, Velma E.
Kindergarten Teacher
Silva, Walter I.
Assoc Dean, Grad Stud & Rsrch
Soler-Bonnin, Olga
Law Professor
Toro-Hernandez, Isabel
Library Information Technician
Torres, Melba Fortuno
English Professor
Vera, Hernan A.
Associate Professor of Pol Sci
Zayas, Victor Manuel
Mathematics Professor
QUEBRADILLAS
Vives, Miguel A.
Retired High School Teacher
RAMEY
Reece, Mary Nell
Elementary Principal
RINCON
Morales, Luz M.
First Grade Teacher
RIO GRANDE
Perez, Antonio
Teacher
RIO PIEDRAS
Alvarez, Rafael H.
College Humanities Professor
Alvarez-Gonzalez, Jose Julian
Law Professor
Bernacet, Acenet
Science Program Director
Betancourt, Rosa
Chemistry Professor
Cao, Ramon J.
Economics Professor
Caro, Doris A.
Chemistry Professor
Davila, Norma
Assistant Psychology Professor
DAvila-Beltran, Norberto
Structures Professor
de Azor, Gladys Rodriquez
Math Teacher
Delmestre, Marie-Helene H.
Pre-Med Advisor
Duckett, Catherine Natalia
Professor of Biology
Dufrasne-Gonzalez, J. Emanuel
Assoc Prof of Music & Hum
Febres-Santiago, Manuel
Social Science Professor
Fernandez, Leticia M.
Accounting Professor
Ferrer, Silvia
Science & Home Economics Tchr
Figueroa, Efren Benitez
Associate Professor
Frontado, Matilde Waleska
English Teacher
Garcia, Mercedes I.
Bus Communication in Eng Prof
Garcia-Ochoa, Maria Asuncion A.
Humanities Professor
Gonzalez-Perez, Jorge Luis
Biological Sciences Professor
Hernandez, Gladys Davila
Biology & Human Ecology Tchr
Jimenez, Maria Teresa
Information Systems Professor
Lopez, Sandra
Business Educator
Medina, Francisco
Mathematics Professor
Narvaez, Maria Teresa
Assoc Professor of Span Lit
Navarro, Silgia M.
Assoc Professor of Ed Dept
Nazario, Gladys Margarita
Assistant Professor
Otero Marrero, Jose F.
Disease Project Coordinator
Ramos, Luz M. Herrera
Spanish Teacher
Ramos-Alamo, Sylvia A.
Professor in Architecture
Romero Garcia, Luz Virginia
Catedraitica Full Professor
Rosado Almedina, Maria G.
Spanish Teacher
Ruiz, Belinda
Honors Program Director
Torres Rivera, Francisco
Professor
Turull, Carmen
Spanish Professor
Vazquez, John
Education Professor

Vicente, Jose C.
Prof of Phys Education
Villafane-Cepeda, Wanda
Mathematics Professor
ROSARIO
Munoz, Carmen
History Teacher
SABANA SECA
Del Valle, Norma
Science Teacher
SALINAS
Aponte, Jesse
English Teacher
SAN GERMAN
Alameda, Zaida Oshmara
Math & Science Teacher
Alvarez-Pons, Francisco A., Jr.
Associate Professor
Antommarchi, Dolly
Counselor
Aponte, Juan Anibal
Dean of Studies
Aponte-Colon, Anibal Jose
Assoc Prof of Political Sci
Arcelay, Angel R.
Assoc Professor of Chemistry
Arroyo, Gilberto
Assoc Prof of Political Sci
Boateng, Peter Alex
Prof of Accounting & Finance
Borges-Arroyo, Vanessa C.
Public Administration Prof
Cardona, Arelis
Social Science Professor
Davila, Samuel
Botany Teacher
DelValle, Pedro
Professor of Theology & Logics
Deschler, Ralph Joseph
Professor of Languages
Echevarria, Luis A.
Associate Professor
Enriquez, Nitza M.
Microbiology Professor
Jimenez-Garrastazu, Diana L.
Dir Intnl Stud Prgm Asst Prof
Landry, Jacques Serge
Guitar Professor
Lecompte, Alvaro
Physics Professor
Llantin, Irma Sofia
Spanish Teacher
Lugo-Negron, Carmen
Secretarial Sciences Professor
Medina, Marcos E. Acosta
Mathematics & Electronics Prof
Millan, Abel
Laboratory Technician
Morales, Carmen J.
Professor of Biology
Nigaglioni, Madeline
Spanish Teacher
Pagan, Silma I.
English as Second Lang Prof
Quintero, Hector E.
Associate Professor of Biology
Roman, Felix Roberto
Chemistry Department Chairman
Saciuk, Olena H.
Professor of English
Smith, Delia Gimenez-Cuervo
Assoc Prof of Education Dept
Stephens, William Powell
Chemistry Professor
Uzdavinis, George C.
Assoc Professor of Sociology
Velez, Axel
Chemistry Professor
Velez-Tomassini, Yolanda
Professional Counselor
Zapata, Evelyn
Human Resources & Mrktg Prof
SAN JUAN
Angueira, Elena Andraca
Business Education Teacher
Aviles, Aurea M.
Elementary Teacher
Bush, Gregory G.
Chemistry & Physics Teacher
Calonge, Nancy
English Teacher
Concepcion, Ebelmar
Spanish Teacher & Dept Coord
Correa-Luna, Adolfo
Associate Professor
Crespo, Hildelisa
Math Teacher
Davis, John Vincent
American Studies Teacher
de Morales, Dora Vazquez
English Teacher
Fernandez, Rafael
Math Teacher
Font, Sara
Math Teacher
Gandara, Hortensia
Assistant Professor
Garcia, Ana Elba De Jesus
Professor
Garcia, Aurelio A.
Adj Fac in Church History
Gomez, Adele Mouakad
Science Teacher
Gonzalez Keelan, Carmen I.
Assoc Professor of Medicine
Huggins, Julia E. Sanchez
Alphabetization Teacher
Janoson, Nancy Jane
Music Teacher

SAN JUAN (cont)
Kirkham, Sharon Kay
English Teacher
Lopez, Victor Manuel
Physical Education & Hlth Tchr
Maldonado, Wanda T.
Associate Professor
Manon, Ralph
Secondary Social Stud Teacher
Mongil, Elisa Calderon
HS Spanish & French Teacher
Nigaglioni, Dana Brewer
Principal
Norberto, Barreto
History Teacher
Perez, Wanda Iris
High School Science Teacher
Ramos, Myriam C.
Art Teacher
Rivera, Jorge
Mathematics Department Chair
Rivera-Rodriguez, Irene
Economics Associate Professor
Robles, Hector Rene
PE Teacher
Santiago-Merlo, Antonio S.
Spanish Teacher & Dept Head
Santos, Belkis
Mathematics Teacher
Sierra, Iliada
Biology Teacher
Solis, Leticia
AP English Teacher
Tamayo, Blanca Ortiz
High School English Teacher
Trittschuh, Paul L.
Math & Cmptr Programming Tchr
Yoder, Pearl Renae
HS Mathematics Teacher
Zurkowsky, Milagros Cruz
Counselor
SAN LORENZO
Delgado, Lydia M.
History Teacher
Pantoja, MariA Julia
Home Economics Teacher
SAN SEBASTIAN
Gonzalez-Laboy, Agustin
Minister & Chaplain
SANTURCE
Abruna, Ruben E.
Communications Professor
Alonso-San Roman, Mayra
Mathematics Professor
Beauchamp-Sierra, Awilda Milagros
Conference Professor
Caro-Perez, Ariel O.
Law School Professor
Cordova, Jose F.
Full Professor
Cruz, Zuckie Sola
Communications Professor
Garcia, Carmen Sara
Journalism Professor
Gorrin-Peralta, Carlos I.
Professor of Law
Pierce-Beall, Tamara A.
Guidance Counselor
Rivera, Alex Javier
Athletic Director
Rodriguez, Luciano
Computer Science Teacher
Ruiz, Rosa Raquel
Professor
Velez, Luz M.
Psychology Professor
TOA BAJA
Figueroa, Maria S.
Third Grade Teacher
TRUJILLO ALTO
Rivera, Maria De Los Angeles
English Teacher
Rivera, Myrta I.
11th & 12th Grade English Tchr
VABUCOA
Tirado, Carmen Lydia
Mathematics & Science Teacher
VEGA ALTA
Hernandez, Luis Angel Diaz
Biology & Scientfic Rsrch Tchr
VEGA BAJA
Negron, Madeline
English Teacher
Rios, Luis E.
Spanish Teacher
YABUCOA
Buitrago, Merecedes
Counselor
Sanchez Gomez, Maria I.
Spanish Teacher
YAUCO
Gonzalez, Luis
Mathematics Teacher

RHODE ISLAND

BARRINGTON
Geraghty, James Joseph
Social Studies Teacher
Pezzullo, Jane Dickson
2nd Grade Teacher
Rotondo, Steven William
School Psychologist
Telford, Althea Adams
Eighth Grade Lang Arts Teacher
BRISTOL
Brito, Elizabeth
English Dept Chair
Crowell, Dianne E.
Director of Musical Theatre
DeLeo, Michael G.
Social Studies Teacher
DeMeo, Michael
Social Studies Teacher
Ferrara, Emile Joseph
Art Instructor
Hardie, Thomas Austin
English Teacher
Kalafarski, John Michael
English Teacher
Lehrer, Stephen L.
Mathematics Teacher
Parisi, Patricia Andrews
Fourth Grade Teacher
Pelletier, Valerie Mae
Music Dir & Teacher
Schattle, Arthur G.
Technology Ed Department Head
Weinberg, Elliot George
Social Studies Teacher
Wruck, Linda A.
English Teacher
CENTRAL FALLS
Akers, Paula Jean (Wnuk)
Teacher of Gifted
Anderson, Rennie Loudon
Art Teacher & Dept Head
Chevrette, Helen, SSA
Religion & Math Teacher
Jacob, Monique
French Teacher
Labossiere, Donald G.
HS Social Studies Teacher
CHARLESTOWN
Heines, Mary Gardner
First Grade Teacher
COVENTRY
Erinakes, James H., II
High School Mathematics Tchr
Feinberg, Robert Charles
American History Teacher
Kelley, Mary Elizabeth
English Teacher
Larocque, Kathleen Campbell
Business Teacher
Richardson, Katherine L.
Biology & Anatomy Teacher
Richtarik, Denise
Resource Teacher
Spaziano, Carol Ann
Math Teacher
Woodard, Kathleen Thompson
Business Teacher
CRANSTON
Abosamra, Charles
Guidance Counselor
Arbor, Elaine Frances
Family & Consumer Sci Tchr
DiNunzio-Hall, Barbara Ann
Third Grade Teacher
Egan, Jerome P.
Asst Uniserv Director
Garceau, Mark C.
Director of Instrumental Music
May, Joseph Anthony
Social Studies Teacher
Maynard, Scott David
History Teacher
Mellor, Colleen Kelly
HS English Teacher
Miller, Winifred E.
MS Math Teacher
Townsend, Muriel (Burbank)
Art Teacher
White, Stephanie A.
Resource Teacher
Zolli, Mary Yates
Kindergarten Teacher
CUMBERLAND
Aragao, Victor John
Retired Band Director
Browning, Glenn C.
Social Studies Teacher
Clark, Emma L.
Fifth Grade Teacher
Dombrowski, Frances Nolette
First Grade Teacher
Ethier, Gerard Wilfred
High School Math Teacher
Hoyle, Carol A.
English Teacher
Labonte, Celeste A. (Rocheleau)
Music Teacher & Choral Dir
Lancaster, Merla Sozek
English Teacher
Lourenco, Dolores Nobrega
English Teacher
Murphy, Carolyn Mancini
Mathematics Teacher
Noble, Ronald Ernest
10th-12th Grd Social Stud Tchr
Young, Kirk J.
Instrumental Music Director
EAST GREENWICH
Alfano, Raymond Louis
English Teacher
Allard, Paula Minnucci
Art Teacher
Bessette, Normand H.
Spanish Teacher
Carlson, Patricia Belden
English Teacher
D'Amario, Ursula A.
Mathematics Teacher
Gravelin, George David
French Teacher & Dept Chprsn
Hincks, Patricia Sue
Fifth Grade Teacher
Kostyla, Dennis J.
Mathematics Teacher
Mc Nulty, Mary (McLaren)
Mathematics Dept Chairman
Mehlman, Lesley Lunin
Latin Teacher
Parent, Marilyn Jean (D'Amore)
Spanish Teacher
Rath, Erin Kiernan
Guidance Counselor
Roderick, Doris Catanio
English Teacher & Dept Chair
Witham, Marie E.
English Teacher
Young, Patricia Lee
Guidance Counselor
EAST PROVIDENCE
Armstrong, Patricia Colella
English Teacher
Barber, Constance Ann
Social Studies Teacher
Cashman, David H.
English Teacher
Cavallaro, Robert A.
Guidance Counselor
Cronan, Edward L., Jr.
Guidance Department Head
Floor, Frank Richard
Human Development Teacher
Holmes, Peter John
US History & Soc Studies Tchr
Laderer, Anne F.
French Teacher
Long, Rae Holland
2nd Grade Teacher
Lowery, Clark C.
English Teacher
Martin, Richard John George
Civics Teacher
Mc Bride, Sandra Marie
Business Department Chprsn
Quirk, Janafe Osmanski
Computer & Business Ed Tchr
Quirk, John P.
Economics Teacher
Shadrick, David G., Sr.
Social Studies Dept Head
Silvestri, John E.
Math Teacher
Tsonos, Peter Themis
Mathematics Teacher
Upole, Paula M.
French Teacher
EXETER
Mc Guckin, Deborah Anne
Sixth Grade Teacher
GREENVILLE
Lachapelle, Tracie Ann
Fourth Grade Teacher
HARRISVILLE
Ballou, Dennis Rawson
Fifth Grade Teacher
Boucher, Charles Louis
Technology Ed Dept Chair
Cameron, Moira
French & Spanish Teacher
Favali, Dalen Nawrocki
Music Dept Chair
Hughes, Priscilla Polly
Second Grade Teacher
Martin, Richard Thomas
English Department Chair
Menard, Barbara Chandler
Mathematics Teacher
Mospaw, Kathan Judith
Eighth Grade Soc Stud Tchr
Murphy, James William
Sixth Grade Teacher
Sandstrom, Ellen S.
Family & Consumer Science Tchr
Short, Lois E.
Mathematics Teacher
Villatico, Nancy Jane
History & Sociology Teacher
HOPE
Beattie, Jean Thurber
Fifth Grade Teacher
HOPE VALLEY
Macksoud, Richard Charles
4th Grade Teacher
JAMESTOWN
Fletcher, Janice Whitehead
Fourth Grade Teacher
JOHNSTON
Donovan, Stephen
Social Studies Teacher
Henseler, Suzanne Mc Goldrick
Social Studies Teacher
Luongo, Linda
English Teacher
Madonna, William A.
Horticulture & Biology Teacher
Marandola, David C.
Social Studies Teacher
Mc Crave, Linda
English Teacher
Natale, Lorraine Marcia
Guidance Counselor
Ratcliffe, Helen (Mazza)
5th Grade Teacher
Ryan, Linda Morin
English & ESL Teacher
Skitt, Kenneth A.
Principal
Taylor, Christine Tillinghast
Seventh Grade English Teacher
Zarrella, Julie-Anne
Foreign Language Teacher
Zarrella, Mark Joseph
Physical Education Teacher
KINGSTON
Ladas, Gerasimos
Professor of Mathematics
Mc Kinney, Wm. Lynn
Professor of Ed & Human Svc
Sink, Clay V.
Management Professor & Chair
Vangermeersch, Richard
Accounting Professor
LINCOLN
Bramley, Doreen Ann Lambert
Professor & Director of Drama
Buck, Joyce Davis
Professor of Ed & Spec Ed
Butler, Janet Julia
Science Teacher
Champagne, David John
English Department Chairperson
Cheney, Leren William
Professor of Psychology
Conti, Joyce A.
Hum & Social Studies Teacher
De Riso, Theresa Patterson
High School English Teacher
Gagne, Robert Leonard
English Teacher
Hunnibell, Sherrill Edwards
Professor of Visual Arts
LaPorte, Vicky Gordon
Teacher Assistant
Lyle, John W., Jr.
Assistant Principal
Moreau, Peter L.
Mathematics Teacher
Verde, James J.
Professor of Biology
Viruleg, Mary Kathleen
Math Department Chairperson
LITTLE COMPTON
Kirchner, Christine F.
Sixth Grd Language Arts Tchr
Ouellette, Roger J.
Fifth Grade Teacher
Updegrove, Kathleen Flack
Third Grade Teacher
MIDDLETOWN
DeAngelis, Leonard A.
Scndry Eng Tchr & Dept Chair
Hines, Samantha Lee
English Teacher
NARRAGANSETT
Ashley, Thomas T.
5th Grd Teacher & Program Ldr
Brown, Lynne J.
English Teacher
Hilley, William Allen, III
Social Studies Teacher
Petro, Robert Anthony
Chemistry Teacher
Robinson, Andy
Social Studies Teacher
NEWPORT
Bernstein, Alan Lloyd
Music Teacher & Orchestra Dir
Caswell, Caroline Johnson
Mathematics Teacher
Hennessey, Marilyn Joan
Biology Teacher
NORTH KINGSTOWN
Ferrario, Edward John
Fourth Grade Teacher
Hall, Pendleton
German & English Teacher
Koulet, Cassandra
Tech Prep Coord & Guid Cnslr
Leonard, Julie Ann
Physical Education Teacher
McGovern, Lynn Archambault
Chemistry Teacher
Resch, Cynthia Fortes
Spanish Teacher
Tarbox, Susan Joyce
First Grade Teacher
NORTH PROVIDENCE
Bussiere, Joyce Gentile
7th-8th Grade English Teacher
D'Aloisio, Tracey Jean
2nd Grade Teacher
Kane, Brenda Carole
Fourth Grade Teacher
Manning, Elizabeth A.
4th Grade Teacher
Whipple, Ruth B. (Erb)
Retired Teacher
NORTH SCITUATE
Crowley, Sheryl E.
Secondary Guidance Counselor
Di Masi, Frank S.
Social Studies Teacher
Duhamel, Paul G.
Art Teacher
Kane, Kevin E.
Music Teacher
Maruszczak, Joseph Peter
Chemistry Teacher
Neves, David
Band Dir & Music Supervisor
Nobrega, Otilia M.
French & Spanish Teacher
Papineau, Margaret Sabetti
Spanish Teacher
Rhodes, Charles Timothy
Biology Teacher
Tvenstrup, Lisa M.
Social Studies Teacher
PAWTUCKET
Altonian, Charles Vincent
Assistant Principal
Asermely, Thomas A.
Biology Teacher
Benoit, Nancy Louise
High School Spanish Teacher
Burke, Mary Kathleen
Social Studies Dept Chair
Gordon, Barbara June
Former Social Studies Teacher
Laramee, Paula Webber
4th Grade Teacher
Rolland, Sheila Lucas
Chemistry Teacher
Sienko, John W.
Retired Principal
PEACE DALE
Englander, Carol Marcus
7th-8th Grade Science Teacher
Poirier, Lauren Rose
Language Arts Teacher
PORTSMOUTH
Alfano, Frank John
Mathematics Teacher
Arruda, Joao Pereira
Portuguese & Spanish Teacher
Bisbano, Julie A.
English Teacher
Burrows, John W.
Art Department Chairman
Conners, Lisa Jane (Mellen)
Spanish Teacher
Farias, Terry De Francesco
Third Grade Teacher
Ferri, Eleanor Hardy
Math Teacher
Fullerton, Ila R.
Fourth Grade Teacher
Hathaway, Vicky Grout
English & Theater Arts Teacher
Marra, Michael H.
History Teacher
O'Keefe, Mary Kate McGoldrick
English Teacher
Travers, Marie P.
Mathematics Teacher
Ustick, Patricia F.
English Department Chair
PROVIDENCE
Alexion, John C.
Social Studies Teacher
Anderson, James Arthur
Assistant Dean
Ashby, Mary Curry
Spanish Teacher
Bianco, Donald Robert
Guidance Counselor
Carlone, Joanna Insana
History Teacher
Chorba, Carrie C.
Spanish Instructor
Cohen, Jay Victor
Mathematics Teacher
David, Jenn
Middle School English Teacher
Day, Elaine M.
Assistant Professor
Deutsch, Richard Alan
Social Studies Department Head
Erlenmeyer, Edith C.
Retired French Teacher
Evans, David R.
Science Teacher
Fields, William A.
Eng Tchr & 9th Grd Prgm Coord
Fish, Diana Staab
English Second Lang Tchr
Fontaine, Pamela E.
10th-11th Grade Chemistry Tchr
Giordano, Mary D.
Principal
James, Michael D.
Math Teacher
Krajewski, Junean Gourley
Education Professor
Laffey, Judith Sheridan
Spanish, French & Italian Tchr
Lenon, MaryJane
Economics Instructor
Lucciola, Patricia Ann
Secondary School Art Teacher
Manning, James Michael
Middle School Mathematics Tchr
Martin, Robert J.
Social Studies Teacher
Mc Cabe, Marion Louise
English Teacher
Morgan, John Donald
Photography Teacher
O'Connell, Catherine, OP
Religion & Reading Teacher
O'Neill, John William
Hotel & Restaurant Mgmt Prof
Paolozzi, Linda Ann
Fourth Grade Teacher
Quinterno, Marianne Rao
Chapter I Reading Specialist
Ragano, William John
History Teacher
Ruscito, Steven Silva
Social Science Teacher
Russell, Teresa Lupoli
Art Specialist
Santoro, Maria Hallas
Home Economics Teacher
Schnacky, Celia
Chemistry Teacher
Simas, Joseph C.
Latin & French Teacher
Simonson, Trudy B.
Lower School Principal
Spoehr, Luther William
History Teacher

IDENCE (cont)
oung
ory Teacher
ker, C. Martha Hackett
ish Teacher
Sandria L. (Brown)
ondary Health Teacher
, Joseph A.
nematics Instructor
RSIDE
da, Sandra S. (Alessandro)
ond Grade Teacher
do, Paul Stephen
ogy Teacher
agh, Elizabeth
ish Teacher
on, Rebekah John
nology Education Teacher
ton, Mary Michaeleen, RSM
n & Religion Teacher
ous, Marion Koutnik
ond Grade Teacher
a, Michelle-Anne
nce & Social Studies Tchr
, Lloydanne Ellen
ed Program Teacher
ansky, Lynn
nematics Teacher
an, Pauline F.
ological Tchr & Dept Chair
Marion
ish Teacher
FORD
pio, Ronald J.
ic Teacher
DERSTOWN
er, Ruth E.
red Teacher
HFIELD
, Adelio A.
nematics Teacher
in, Pauline M.
lance Counselor
ey, Lori Ann
Prof of Management
aro, Catherine Barbariu
n Tchr & Stu Act Dir
bile, Cynthia A.
enth Grade English Teacher
ert, Andrea Axile
ne Economics Teacher
, William F.
ish & Pub Speaking Teacher
urst, Leoda Giroux
lish Department Chairperson
, George William
ish Teacher
Ann Roslyn (Stifano)
red 6th Grade Teacher
a, James Joseph
d Director
, Judith Integlia
Grade Teacher
RTON
Kathleen Furnas
Resource Teacher
ette, Gerald Paul
al Studies Teacher
ieu, Conrad
ch & Portuguese Teacher
n, Mary Ferreira
her of GATE & Coordinator
n, Linda Daum
ily & Consumer Science Tchr
pagne, Norman Edward
dle School Teacher
, Elizabeth Dagrosa
lish Teacher
Edward P., Jr.
uguese & Spanish Teacher
EFIELD
s, Judith Whitford
red 7th Grd English Tchr
da, John M.
nce Teacher
o, Susan G.
nce Teacher & Dept Chair
n, James Michael
al Studies Teacher
pion, John S.
red PE Teacher
Elizabeth Anne (Bowley)
Social Studies Teacher
lo, David S.
Art Dept Chr & Drama Dir
ck, Crandall W.
sics Teacher
, Joan Robbins
al Studies Teacher
le, Donald Louis
hematics Teacher
, Patricia A.
istant Principal
field, Robert E.
istant Principal
ley, Catherine DiToro
Grade Teacher
Pacheco, Cynthia Lynn
Grade Teacher
enson, Holly Winslow
lish Teacher
ley, Karen C.
nish Teacher
REN
sque, Maria Rodrigues
lish Teacher & Dept Head
nha, Mary
Class Adv & Amer His Tchr
er, Roberta Ann
h Tchr & Technology Mentor

WARWICK
Agnew, Maureen Brennan
English Teacher
Atturio, Andrea Jean (Viele)
Social Studies Teacher
Boyer, David Michael
Physics & Chemistry Teacher
Capaldi, David A.
Mathematics Department Head
Cousineau, Gerald E.
Social Studies Dept Chairman
Crudale, Alfred Robert
Italian & Spanish Teacher
DiGiando, Julio Joseph
Resource Teacher
Dombrowski, John Wayne
History Teacher
Fucci, Richard M.
English Dept Chairman
Higgins, Sue Nunnally
Asst Prof of Cmptr Stud & Info
Holtzman, Samuel Mark
High School Science Teacher
Johnson, William Carter, II
Assoc Professor of Biology
Judge, Robert Anthony
Professor of Fine Art
Keefe, Thomas J.
Professor of Physics
Klanian, Lillian Berberian
4th Grade Teacher
Lytle, Patricia A.
Mathematics Teacher
Mc Namara, Dennis Bowen
High School Mathematics Tchr
Mercurio, Victor Donald
English Teacher
Miner, Jeffrey T.
English Teacher
Paquin, Joseph V.
Geology & Science Teacher
Patterson, Lillian Cooper
Dept of Human Services Prof
Pellegrino, Carol Barto
Music Teacher
Price, Richard Douglas
Fine Arts & Music Chairperson
Prisco, Rosemary Winifred
Professor of English
Richards, Paul J.
English Dept Chairperson
Sharlin, Jonathan
Photography Adj Prof
Terezakis, Emanuel George
Professor of Chemistry
Toevs, Elaine F.
1st Grade Teacher
Ventura, Louis
Biology Teacher
Villeneuve, Grace Linda
6th Grade Teacher
WEST GREENWICH
Anderson, Stephen James
8th Grade Geography Teacher
Brown, Celia D.
Seventh Grade English Teacher
Oliveira, Louise A.
Social Studies Dept Chprsn
Rounds, Ronald John
English Teacher
Shannon, Tracy Jane
Mathematics Teacher
WEST WARWICK
Kowalczyk, Theresa Zapp
English Teacher
Layden, Marcia Arlene
Fifth Grade Teacher
Machado, Joan Marie
Spanish & French Teacher
Moniz, Karen Marie
Mathematics Teacher
WESTERLY
Angelo, Alan Lee
Social Studies Teacher
Chaffee, Linda Jane
Science Department Head
Corah, Lori Gingerella
Reading Specialist
Fusco, Paula G.
Social Studies Teacher
Gecawich, Michael
Business & Computer Teacher
Gradilone, Edward Anthony
Guidance Counselor
Moon, Stephen R.
English Teacher & Coach
Purtill, Joseph James
Mathematics Teacher
Spargo, Robert Brook
Ret Instrumental Music Teacher
Visgilio, Gail Thelin
High Schl English & Rdng Tchr
WOOD RIVER JUNCTION
Belden, Patricia Anne
Sixth Grade Teacher
Dipollino, Patricia Anne
High School Business Teacher
Hall, Laurence Pennell
Mathematics Teacher
Kaschuluk, Ann B. C.
Guidance Counselor
LaFrance, Paul R.
Business Teacher
Miller, Kathleen Kenyon
Instrumental Music Teacher
Musch, Linda Lapiene
Culinary Arts Instructor
Willis, Eleanor Reichstetter
Computer Literacy Teacher

WOONSOCKET
Alves, Lisa Cynthia
Music Teacher
Arees, George A.
English Teacher
Branchaud, C. Andre
Foreign Lang Dept Chairperson
Briggs, George E.
High School Soc Stud Teacher
Calascibetta, Robert Angelo
In School Suspension Coord
Comire, Gary Charles-Joseph
Soc Stud Tchr & Dept Chm
DeCubellis, Kenneth
HS Guidance Counselor
Dominique, Charlotte Rose
English Teacher
Dubois, Patricia A.
Assistant Principal
Gauvin, Ann Marie
English Teacher
Gentili, Rita Klimasewski
Elementary Counselor
Hogue, Donald Robert
English Teacher
Huart, Eileen
MS English & Reading Teacher
Jzyk, Linda Zonfrillo
Biology Teacher
Kafalas, Dennis J.
8th Grade Language Arts Tchr
King, Clifford Michael
Principal & Spanish Teacher
Lamarre, Leo E.
Mathematics Teacher
Marchetti, Vivian Annette (Froment)
Second Grade Teacher
Morelle, Beryl Gail (Mack)
Second Grade Teacher
Paige, Pamela Archambault
Spcl Education & English Tchr
Paquette, Eveline Gail
Visual Arts Teacher
Roy, Samuel Normand
8th Grade Religion & Sci Tchr
Scott, Alfred Robert
Health Teacher
Tanfani, Robert R.
8th Grade Social Studies Tchr
Tenczar, Margaret Mary
Sixth Grade Teacher
Thornton, Louise M.
Mathematics Teacher
Vaillancourt, Alice Paquin
Third Grade Teacher
Walker, Suzanne Ross
High School Mathematics Tchr
Weymouth, Lorraine M. Turner
Special Education Teacher
Woodman Laquerre, Claire Rosina
High School Biology Teacher

SOUTH CAROLINA

ABBEVILLE
Bibb, Donna Grant
8th Grade Language Arts Tchr
Bridgers, Linda Brothers
Retired English Teacher
Bush, Joyce Milligan
7th & 8th Grd English Teacher
Campbell, Hilbert Miles
8th Grd Language Arts Teacher
Gaulden, Susan Miles
English Teacher
Gilliam, Samuel Grady, Jr.
Agricultural Mechanics Teacher
Jameson, Margaret Johnson
Language Arts Tchr & Dept Chm
Raines, Fred L.
Natural & Environmental Tchr
Sherard, Sara Cartledge
8th Grade Mathematics Teacher
Smith, Cherri Williams
Health Teacher
Smith, Mark Linwood
PE & Science Teacher
Tyner, Linda Zorn
Social Studies Teacher
Wright, Willie Bell
Fifth Grade Teacher
AIKEN
Bailey, Belva Bronson
Mathematics Teacher
Barton, Rosalyn Weigle
Chemistry Teacher
Beckham, Elizabeth B.
Science Teacher & Dept Head
Bolton, Cynthia Ann
Asst Prof of Educl Psych
Bowman, Elizabeth Cole
Guidance Counselor
Brockington, Celeste Williams
Mathematics Teacher
Brown, Katherine Hogan
English Teacher & Dept Chm
Chou, Mary Bell
Associate Professor
Culbertson, Bonnie Rapp
Second Grade Teacher
Davidson, Phebe Clynes
Assistant Professor of English
Delionbach, Leroy J.
Pgm Coord of Criminal Justice
Dunker, Ginger Sanders
Eng & Creative Writing Teacher
Felkel, Charlene Campbell
Assistant Professor

Fenstermacher, Barbara Schwarze
6th Grd Sci Tchr & Dept Coord
Garrett, Carol U.
English Teacher
Goidell, Pamela Joyce
Math Teacher & Dept Chm
Hamilton, Sharon Harley
English Teacher & Jrnlsm Adv
Hammett, Priscilla Hoover
Math Teacher & Department Head
Hanlin, Hugh Grady
Associate Professor of Biology
Harrington, Robert Jeffries
Latin Teacher
Hawley, Kimberly Cope
Teacher of Gifted & Talented
Henson, Trudy Knicely
Professor of Sociology
Hickson, Eavon Holloway
Fifth Grade Teacher
House, William J.
Professor of Psych & Music
Huffman, Carl Haller
History Teacher
Jaspers, David G.
Senior Mathematics Instructor
Johnson, Barbara E.
Assoc Professor of Sociology
Kelly, Myra O'Shields
8th Grade English Teacher
Kitchings, Gaylon Brodie
Language Arts & Lit Teacher
Kuck, Douglas L.
Department of Sociology Chair
Lader, Lisa Taylor
9th-12th Grd Ger & Fr Teacher
Martin, Nancy Sofge
Fifth Grade Teacher
McDaniel, Patricia Abney
US History Teacher
Miller, Collette Rosso
Eng, Lit & Religion Teacher
Morgan, Betty J. W.
Mathematics Teacher
Morris, Michael Pate
Visiting History Professor
Nashatker, Janice Weimer
Spanish Teacher
Poplin, Anne Summerall
English Teacher
Rhoden, Susanne Bodie
Algebra Teacher
Rice, Diana C.
Assistant Professor of Ed
Rich, John Stanley
Professor of English
Roczok, Harry Alex
Biology Teacher
Rutland, Sara Fulmer
5th Grade Teacher
Salter, David Wyatt
Biology Teacher & Sci Chprsn
Saunders, Laura Sylvia
Assistant Professor
Sykes, Richard Nesbit
His Instr & Coord of Soc Sci
Timmerman, Patsy Smith
Guidance Counselor & Director
Urich, Michael Lynn
High School Algebra Teacher
Vadasz, Carl
Mrktg Ed Teacher & Coordinator
Valiquette, Richard Jospeh
Phys Sci, Applied Physics Tchr
Wates, Kathleen Wooley
Accounting Instructor
Willing, Patricia Thomas
English Teacher
Wilson, Charmaine E.
Assoc Prof of Speech Comm
Woods, Deborah Powell
Biology Teacher
Yates, James Richard
Associate Professor of Biology
ALLENDALE
Lamprecht, William Otto, Jr.
Professor of Biology
Runnebaum, William Marcus
Assoc Tchr of Rel & Chaplain
Zeidan, Hussein Saleh
Associate Prof of Chemistry
ANDERSON
Batten, Linda Poole
Third Grade Teacher
Browning, Kathy Jennings
1st Grade Teacher
Chambers, Carolyn Gordon
Art Teacher
Crittendon, Trudy Hall
English I Teacher
Darnell, Jeffery Reese
English Teacher
Durkee, Frank Michaels, Jr.
Chemistry Teacher
Gilbert, Kay Kauffman
Orchestra Director
Haynie, Lynn Kay
Mathematics Tchr & Dept Chair
Hicks, Ann Morehead
English & Language Arts Tchr
Jennings, Janis Melton
French Teacher
Johnson, Michael Edward
Navy JROTC Instructor
Kinert, Gary Charles
Building Trades Teacher
Longo, Wendy Martin
English IV Teacher
Mack, Margaret Adger
English Teacher

Milner, Anita Beasley
English & Latin Teacher
O'Neal, Lelsie Whitehead
Retired 2nd Grade Teacher
Orcutt, Jerry Earl
History Teacher
Pearson, Betty Fowler
Bus Ed Tchr & Voc Dept Head
Rankin, George David
Industrial Engineering Teacher
Reinert, Susan Morton
Science Teacher & Dept Head
Roberts, Janet Lynn
Assistant Professor of Music
Shotwell, Marilyn Stovall
Fourth Grade Teacher
Sparrow, Margaret Dunlap
Multi-Age Classroom Teacher
Vickery, Jo Ann Howard
Counselor & Guidance Director
Wilson, Larry Keith, Sr.
Bible, Span, Govt & Ec Tchr
Wilson, Vanette Jones
Third Grade Teacher
ANDREWS
Haselden, Kimberly Moss
English Teacher
Haselden, Tennyson Kenneth
His Tchr & Basketball Coach
Knowlin, Doris Greene
Social Studies Teacher
Lambert, Pennie Hinson
French & English Teacher
McCants, Tracy Wildes
HS Social Studies Teacher
Pittman, Joey Jay
Band Director
Roller, James Albert
English Teacher
Scott, Veronica Louise
MS Music Teacher
Tucker, Pearl Howard
3rd & 4th Grade Span I Teacher
AYNOR
Avant, Silvester Lee
JROTC Instructor
Dawsey, Sheryl Vaught
Soc Studies Dept Chprsn
Fox, Kenneth E.
Biology & Anatomy Teacher
Hall, James Stephen
Guidance Counselor
Jamison, Tamria
Language Arts Teacher
Lewis, Trina Stanley
English & Journalism Teacher
Thomas, Carolyn Skipper
9th Grd English Teacher
BAMBERG
Deibel, Melissa Ramsey
English & Cadet Teacher
BARNWELL
Anderson, Rosemary Fender
Mathematics Teacher
Dodge, John Mc Neal
Industrial Technology Instr
Hunter, Jane Gray
4th Grade Teacher
Kirkland, Dorothy Naomi
Family & Consumer Science Tchr
Maddox, Anne DuRant
Second Grade Teacher
Mayfield, Frank Hunt
Social Studies Teacher
Mc Kay, Sam
Assistant Principal
Mew, Mary Baxley
6th Grade Math Teacher
Morris, Tessie Jenkins
SC & US History Teacher
Price, Melinda Hill
Business Education Teacher
Priester, Franciner Elaine
Bus Ed Tchr & Career Cnslr
Robinson, Sammie L.
9th Grade Physical Sci Teacher
Shealy, Kelly
Mathematics Teacher & Coord
Smith, Billie Gilley
High School Spec Ed Teacher
Wier, Sara S.
7th-8th Grade Math Teacher
Zidlick, Pauline Perrow
English Teacher
BATESBURG
Burton, Sara Weathers
Health Occupations Ed Teacher
Derrick, Matilda Smalls
Second Grade Teacher
Ellison, Darlene
Business Education Teacher
Hall, Betty Jean Cooper
Teacher of Gifted
Hall, Dorothy Long
Math Dept Chairperson & Tchr
Hayden, Janet Marie
7th Grade Life Science Teacher
Moody-Still, Melodie Ann
Sci & Cmptr Applications Tchr
Rimer, David Nickles
Modern Lang Dept Chair & Tchr
Smallen, Lynda Kneece
Fourth Grade Teacher
Willis, Barbara Watkins
Secondary Math Teacher
BATH
Cooke, Lorraine Clak
First Grade Teacher

BEAUFORT
Abel, Joyce A.
Science Teacher
Bates, Arlene L.
12th Grade English Teacher
Bischoff, Jeff
English Teacher
Buckner, Brenda Kay (Poore)
Math Teacher
Callahan, Christine Voellger
US History Teacher
Dickson, Mona Lise (Lewis)
Mathematics Teacher
Dowling, Patricia Atwater
Guidance Counselor
Drake, Nathaniel Lanier
Band Director
Jackson, Peggy Nelson
Kindergarten Teacher
Mack, Kinsler Boyd
Chemistry Teacher
Moss, Daisy Rogers
Third Grade Teacher
Murphy, Julie
Psychotherapist
Murphy, Pamela McNabb
Visual Arts Teacher
Norris, Jean Gurley
Fourth Grade Teacher
O'Neill, Elizabeth Rader
English & History Teacher
Radest, Howard B.
Adjunct Prof of Philosophy
Roberson, Felicia Riggs
Eleventh Grade English Teacher
Rowland, Lawrence Sanders
History Professor
Sbuscio, Raymond Joseph, Jr.
World Geog & Sociology Teacher
Scheper, Melissa Parrish
US History & Psychology Tchr
Sherman, Joseph Benjamin
Chem, Physics Tchr & Lead Tchr
Simmons, Margaret Marie
Mathematics Teacher
Sproul, Gordon Duane
Chem Educator & Consultant
Stahle, Cheryl Diane (French)
Professor
Steman, Pamela Wheeler
Mathematics Teacher
Stewart, Vernell Speaks
7th Grd Lang Arts & Rdng Tchr
Taylor, Joan Stoddard
Associate Professor of English
Tombe, Sheila Joan
Assistant Professor of English
Tompkins, Sallie Dudley Pendleton
History Dept Chair
Upshaw, Jane Thomas
Associate Prof of Mathematics
Villena-Alvarez, Juanita
French & Spanish Asst Prof
Walker, Gladys Black
7th Grade World Geography Tchr

BELTON
Berry, Charles A.
6th Grd World History Teacher
Campbell, Barbara Ashley
First Grade Teacher
Florence, Lori Yvette
Physical Education Teacher
Johnson, Tauna Redus
8th Grd English & Lit Teacher
Jones, Jean Ashley
First Grade Teacher
Mayberry, Sandra Lancaster
Sci, His & Tchr of GATE
Olson, Natalie Ann
English & Literature Teacher
Sain, Vicki Culbreth
Fourth Grade Teacher
Wright, Pamela Gilmer
Fifth Grade Teacher
Young, Judith Allen
8th Grade Lang Arts Teacher

BENNETTSVILLE
Austin, Lillian Cynthia
Mathematics Teacher
Bedenbaugh, Cynthia Brown
AP US History Teacher
Chavis, Cheryl Brock
Science Teacher
Craddock, Bonnie Lambeth
Third Grade Teacher
Douglas, Marilyn Bridges
Social Studies Teacher
Hilliard, Annie Newton
Social Studies Teacher
Humbert, Calvert Hale, Jr.
Sci Dept Chprsn & Physics Tchr
Prince, Carolyn A.
Horticulture Instructor
Rogers, Anne M.
Bus Tech Tchr & Support Coord
Wafer, Joan Carol
Science Teacher

BISHOPVILLE
Collins, Minnie Robinson
Biology Teacher
Edwards, Thomas Lawton, Jr.
Social Studies & English Tchr
Heriot, Elizabeth Manning
Third Grade Teacher
Nowlin, Otis, Jr.
9th-12th Grade Voc Teacher
Scott, Lenora
Math Teacher & Dept Chprsn
Wallace, George Otis
PE, Hlth & Drivers Ed Tchr

BLACKSBURG
Harris, James Franklyn
History, Geog Tchr & Dept Head
Hughes, Pamela Martin
Advanced Placement Eng Teacher
Phillips, Helen Gregory
Business Education Instructor
Ramsey, Earlene Burgess
Home Economics Teacher
Reynolds, Shirley Hannon
7th Grade Mathematics Teacher

BLACKVILLE
Dawson, Leslie Tracy
French, English & Span Tchr
Gaines, Dinah Flint
English Teacher
Orr, Frederick Burt
Mathematics Teacher
Rivers, Bentley
Computer Teacher
Taylor, Thomas H.
Science & Soc Studies Teacher
Ussery, Amy C.
Third Grade Teacher

BLYTHEWOOD
Watson, Curtis Ronald
Elementary Principal

BOWMAN
Dupuis, Glenn Allen
Social Studies Teacher
Mc Carty, Kevin
Earth Science Teacher

BRANCHVILLE
Pruett, Katherine Bonnette
Third Grade Teacher
Young, Velma Felder
Seventh Grade Teacher

BUFFALO
Anthony, Donna Langley
Second Grade Teacher

CALHOUN FALLS
Carroll, Michael Eugene
Science Teacher
Cochran, Bonita J.
English Teacher
Evans, Elza H.
Mathematics Teacher
Evans, Llewellyn Yon
Mathematics Teacher
Mc Connell, Robin Chrisley
8th Grd Rdng & Eng Teacher
Rapley, Alice Jackson
Business Education Teacher
Towe, James Randall
Special Education Teacher

CAMDEN
Mickle, Roetta Dean
Elem Schl Guidance Counselor
Young, Ardell
Wld History & Economics Instr

CAMPOBELLO
Greene, Melinda Dill
Science Teacher

CAYCE
Davis, Julia Jackson
Secondary Math Teacher
Easley, David Patrick
Math & German Teacher
Ebener, Elizabeth Dickerson
English Teacher
Fisher-Mercer, Carolyn Inman
Science Department Head
Hammond, Beth Bridges
High School English Teacher
Hammond, Ruth Riley
Business Teacher
Jones, Flora Gilfillan
Third Grade Teacher
Lee, Cheri Anderson
Special Education Teacher
Nye, Sibela Pinochet
Spanish Teacher
Sims, J. Ronald
Teacher
Swittenberg, Linda Adams
Second Grade Teacher
Whetstone, Angela Rainey
Social Studies Teacher

CENTRAL
Boggs, Donald Gregory
Social Studies Teacher
Holstead, Charles
AP US History & Psych Teacher
Newton, Helen G.
French & English Teacher
Price, Grace Earle
4th Grade Teacher
Raines, Marilyn Elizabeth
8th Grade Language Arts Tchr

CHAPIN
Anderson, Carol Stanislawski
Cmptrs & Career Awareness Tchr
Anderson, Helen Anne
Government & Economics Teacher
Crabtree, Susan Jones
First Grade Teacher
Painter, Thomas Michael
Social Studies Teacher
Talbert, Martha Elmgren
Third Grade Teacher
Waldrop, Marie R.
Director of Alternative School

CHARLESTON
Ahrens, Jon Peter
Band Director
Alley, Raymond Steven
Soc Stud & Life Sci Teacher
Barans, Allene Claire
Biology Teacher
Bates, Stephanie Wiggins
Mathematics Teacher
Beam, Kathlee Toole
First Grade Teacher
Benson, Debra Smith
Choral Director
Blake, Barbara Bradley
English Teacher
Blanchard, Sheldon Gardner
Mathematics Teacher
Boucher, Philippe David
Chef Instructor
Bridges, Sheree Lea
Assistant Principal
Brown, Cora Myers
Sixth Grade Teacher
Burn, Beverly Baker
Chemistry Teacher
Carder, Vicki Wilkerson
English Tchr & Co-Dept Chrpsn
Coaxum, Elinor Holmes
Language, Reading & Sci Tchr
Counts, Donna Abee
Second Grade Teacher
Dawson, Eva M.
Fifth Grade Teacher
Dearhart, Virginia Middleton
Math Instructor
Doig, Marion Tilton, III
Professor
Frankis, Robert Charles, Jr.
Professor of Biology
Frayer, Linda G.
Guidance Director
Gadsden, Edwina Nannette
High School English Teacher
Gasdek, Erika Lynn
French Teacher
Gazes, Catherine
8th & 9th Grd Eng & Fr Tchr
Goff, Judith Clark
Kindergarten Teacher
Green, April Flowers
Business Education Teacher
Hacker, Gail Pritcher
English Teacher
Hardee, Bridget Ann (Mc Guire)
High School Math Teacher
Hatchell, Annette Chandler
8th Grd Language Arts Teacher
Hazel, Marvette Colson
Retired 5th Grade Teacher
Heath, Nancy McNurlin
Soc Stud Tchr & Dept Chair
Hernandez, Sebastian
Spanish Teacher
Hills, Rhonda Reames
Sixth Grade Teacher
Hucks, Irene P.
1st & 2nd Grade Teacher
Jarman, JoAnn Tumbleston
7th Grade Geography Teacher
Jones, Timothy J.
Mathematics Teacher
Jordan, Judy Clark
Math Department Chairperson
Knight, Josephine Sedivy
American Government Teacher
Knotts, Michael Lawrence
High School English Teacher
Lavely, Anne Boggs
Theatre & English Teacher
Lavely, Louis E., Jr.
Chemistry & Physics Teacher
Le Noir, Astrid G.
German & Psychology Teacher
Lenz, Sheila Jones
Secondary Guidance Counselor
Long, Judith Lubs
Math Teacher
Mackey, Gerald
Associate Dean & Prof of Eng
Mallard, Ruth Hills
First Grade Teacher
Maney, Janet Pero
US History Teacher
Massey, Frederick Thomas
Naval Science Instructor
Maynard, Carol Ferrara
Literature & Drama Teacher
Mc Kevlin, Brenda Gamble
2nd Grade Teacher
Moller, Robert Francis
Middle School Teacher
Moore, Wesley Lee-Edward, III
English Instructor
Moore, William Vincent
Prof of Pol Sci & Dir MPA Pgm
Morrison, Nan
Professor of English
Murphy, Hope Norment
High School English Teacher
Newton, Caroline Mc Elwee
High School Math Teacher
Norton, Susan Barnett
Assoc Dean of Arts & Sciences
O'Neill, Luanne Parks
Science Teacher
Parker, Minnie D.
First Grade Teacher
Pfaehler, Edward C., Jr.
Math Teacher
Rashford, John Harvey
Assoc Prof of Anthropology
Robinson, Delphine Buckner
Social Studies Teacher
Ruch, Louise D.
Language Arts & History Tchr
Ruff, Dean Edward
3rd Grade Teacher
Seabrook, Paula Milton
4th Grade Teacher
Shaw, Twila Sue
Science Teacher
Slan, Alice Singleton
Science Teacher
Slay, Franny Rivers
Athletic Dir & Health Teacher
Smalls, Betty Ann
Third Grade Teacher
Smalls, Essie Renee
2nd Grade Teacher
Smith, Michelle Stacy
Commercial Graphics Dept Instr
Southard, Robin Anne
Social Studies Teacher
Spainhour, Marcia S. Boykin
8th Grade Lang Arts Teacher
Squires, Patrick Charles
AP Macroeconomics & Govt Tchr
Stewart, Karen Weaver
Ninth Grade English Teacher
Strobel, Candy Jan
Biology Teacher
Suggs, Pamela Sears
English Teacher
Townsend, Judy Mosley
Math Teacher
Trapalis, Sylvia
World & Amer History Teacher
Verdugo, Robin Robbie
Science Teacher
Vogt, Kathleen Cunningham
Teacher & Band Director
Wadsworth, Ben Awbrey
Science Teacher
Waring, Darline Cellier
7th Grade Mathematics Teacher
Williams, Mary Anne Riding
MS Choral Music Teacher
Williams, Sylvia Horlbeck
4th Grade Teacher
Wilson, Barbara S.
Fourth Grade Teacher
Wilson, Catherine Ann
Spanish Teacher
Woodhall, Janet Coker
English Teacher
Zenauskas, Thomas L.
Teacher

CHERAW
Burgess, Christia Lyons
French Teacher
Erby, Ken W.
Business Division Chair
Gaskins, Jacqueline Eddins
Mathematics Instructor
Hicks, Susan Hornsby
Kindergarten Teacher
Mackey, Marie
Science Instructor
Meland, Tammy W.
5th Grade Teacher
Milligan, J. Heath
Computer Programming Instr
Sumter, Michael Herbert
High School Band Director
Weaver, Marvin Samuel
Accounting Professor
White, Hayne Liles
Business Instructor

CHESNEE
Conner, Joan W. (Wright)
Fifth Grade Teacher
Davis, Carol C.
Math & Cadet Teacher
Hollifield, Rene Humphries
3rd Grade Teacher
Mason, Terrie Horton
9th-12th Grade Science Teacher
Scruggs, Louise Petty
English & Journalism Teacher

CHESTER
Bell, Mary Robbins
Algebra Teacher
Ezell, Doris Amurr
7th Grd Language Arts Teacher
Gardner, Leonard Jeffers
Building Construction Instr
Jordan, Sandra Wilson
Senior High School Counselor
Sellers, April Tillman
High School English Teacher
Wisert, Jo Ann Chappell
Choral Director

CHESTERFIELD
Studebaker, Joseph Elizan, III
English & Applied Comm Teacher

CLEMSON
Carter, George E., Jr.
Dir of Undergraduate Acad Svcs
Wallace, Mae Frances Kay
Retired Fourth Grade Teacher

CLINTON
Brehmer, Donna Undari
Mathematics Teacher
Mc Leod, Anita Reynolds
Asst Professor of Education
Norris, Lynn Nabors
Fifth Grade Teacher

CLIO
Phillips, Doris Wright
Language Arts & Math Teacher

CLOVER
Adams, Anne Stanton
Latin & English Teacher
Campbell, David Brent
HS Math Teacher
Campbell, Mary Allison
Kindergarten Teacher
Cauble, Marilyn Brown
7th Grade Life Science Teacher
Edge, Christopher D.
Agriculture Teacher
Garver, Brenda Laughlin
English Teacher
Gilfillan, Jane Comer
American Government Teacher
Lollis, Sheila Stewart
Physical Education Teacher
Simpkins, R. Scott
Mechanical Drawing Teacher
Surrett, Melody Hines
English Teacher
Turner, Patricia Willis
Mathematics Teacher
Yandle, David Alan
Instrumental Music Teacher

COLUMBIA
Adams, Doris Mc Bride
AAP Teacher
Akhavi, Shahrough
Govt & Intnl Stud Professor
Alexander, Marion Maurice
Guidance Counselor
Amstutz, A. Keith
Professor of Trumpet
Anderson, Faye Mills
First Grade Teacher
Atkinson, Ronald R.
History Professor
Barrineau, JoAnne Sulak
English Teacher
Blair, Ruby
English Instructor
Blocker, Miranda Nixon
Fashion Merchandise Teacher
Bolin, Patricia Pearce
Psychology & Economics Teacher
Bonner, Thomas Cameron
English Instructor
Bouknight, Fran Schoolbred
Science Dept Chprsn & Teacher
Bouknight, Mary Worrell
Life Science Teacher
Brasington, Caroll Rush
Mathematics Professor
Breneman, Anne Rowley
Social Studies Dept Chprsn
Bridgett, Effie Gray
Business Teacher
Brock, Nancy-Lee
World History Teacher
Broome, Kathleen Indihar
Retired Acad Advanced Teacher
Brown, Suzann Lindquist
First Grade Teacher
Cafferty, Thomas P.
Assoc Prof of Psychology
Campbell, Thomas Cramer
Campus Life Dir
Carter, Becky Batchelor
Family & Consumer Sci Tchr
Charlebois, Lucile C.
Span Assoc Prof & Graduate Dir
Chen, Grace Chien Ching
Professor of Biology
Clark, Mary G.
Micro Computers Teacher
Clavon, Thelma
Physics Tchr & Sci Dept Chm
Clodfelter, Richard Guy
Assoc Professor of Retailing
Coller, Maribeth Schlictman
Asst Professor of Accounting
Coon, Edward H., III
Associate Professor
Cottingham, Fran Burgess
Third Grade Teacher
Crediford, Gene Joseph
Assoc Professor of Photography
Currier, Tonya Leigh
Assistant Professor of Music
Davidson, Patricia Kay
Chemistry Teacher
Dawson, Wallace D.
Professor of Biology
Day, James Todd
French Professor
Dean, John Mark
Professor of Marine Science
DeBure, Olivier C.
French Instructor
DeCoursey, Patricia J.
Professor of Biology
Dickson, Charles LeGrande, Jr.
Social Studies Dept Chprsn
Dillon, Susan Wienefeld
Social Studies Dept Chair
Doerpoinghaus, Helen I.
Assoc Prof of Fin & Insurance
Dolin, David Franklin
World History Teacher
Edens, Kellah Mauldin
Educational Psychology Prof
Edgar, Walter Bellingrath
History Professor
Fleak, Ken
Associate Professor of Spanish
Francis, Annette West
Music Teacher
Frape, Rosalee Draffin
First Grd Tchr & Rdng Tutor
Gabbard, Anita Norrell
Reading & Drama Teacher
Garmany, Gloria Smalls
Fifth Grade Teacher
Gasque, Audrey L.
Mathematics Teacher

JMBIA (cont)
Michial Anthony
rd of Opportunity Scholars
r, Darlynn Cheryl
al Science Instructor
n, Andrew D.
stant Dean
, Louise Harrell
ish Teacher
on, Teressa Teague
th Science Teacher
e, Gwenda Richburg
Instr & Svc Learning Coord
, Edward
ociate Professor of History
ng, Robert, IV
d Director
, Susan K.
piratory Care Instructor
Christine M.
Prof of Information Mgmt
ghi, Aliakbar Montazer
hematics Professor
er, Pooly Cameron
ical Assistant Professor
ck, Lorine H.
ish Teacher
ll, Genovia Lavon
n Teacher
, Beverly Young
uid Cnslr & Dept Chair
ins, Sonja Merriwether
her
y, Cynthia Sebrell
n Dept Chairperson
, Loretta Rasberry
stant Professor of Health
er Kaufman, Natalie
of Gov & Intnl Studies
ir, Frances (Bangwa)
Science Teacher
nan, R. Scot
al Arts Teacher
es, Arthur
her
rd, Gail Diane
al Studies Teacher
ston, Joyce
n Teacher
Margaret Holmes
& Asst Dir of Fin Aid
son, Robert
essor
Martha Weeks
red Mathematics Teacher
Rebecca A.
ounting Instructor
c, K. C.
ociate Professor of Psych
igh, Mark Allen
ing, Air Conditioning Tchr
, Betty Caldwell
e Economics Teacher
ten, Ashlyn Kay
unct Professor
icka, John R.
ngs Teacher
Joyce Bellamy
anced Acad Program Teacher
zec, Patrick G.
ogy Teacher
er, Walter
inguished Lecturer
ncott, Susan Kathleen
ond Grade Teacher
gston, James William
ory Teacher & Dept Chair
Robin Barnett
nentary PE Teacher
, Oscar Armando
ting Assistant Professor
, Maria
Grade Teacher
Willie E.
d Director
, Brenda Gean
h Teacher
ood, Barbara Stokes
ructor
otra, Manoj Kumar
oc Prof of Management Sci
y, Millie Tyler
iologic Sciences Instructor
pin, Carol Joan
n School English Teacher
rnett, Mac L.
sian & English Teacher
ie, Harriet Davis
ish Teacher
od, Dawne DeLozier
ector of Sci & Math Prgms
niak-Mikolajczak, Bozena
oc Prof Basic Pharm Science
r, Yvonne Britt
ily & Con Sci Specialist
e, Carroll Michael
sical Education Instructor
enroth, William Mason
keting Professor
s, Wendy Rauch
enth Grd Life Science Tchr
d, Lucille P.
ior Instructor of French
ay, Carrie Richardson
lish Teacher
e, Jeanie Sharp
ner Teacher
, Linda Kay
Teacher

Ness, Jane Hoover
Grad Student & Assistant
Nussbaum, Janet Selecman
Assistant Professor
Parker, Geraldine Stroman
Mathematics Teacher
Paulovic, Amari Roland
Exit Exam Rdng & Speech Tchr
Pauluzzi, Faust F.
Director of Italian
Perkins, Russell Theodore
Social Studies Teacher
Pernell, Julian Janatus, Jr.
Chef, Instr & Food Svc Supvr
Peterson, Barbara Jimas
Kindergarten Teacher
Peterson, Donna Price
Math Teacher
Pittenger, Ann Cunningham
Secondary English Instr Prof
Pouncey, Sandra Cavin
Art Teacher
Preacher, John E.
Assistant Professor of English
Preedom, Barry Mason
Professor of Physics
Pride, Lewis D., Jr.
History Teacher
Prouse, Nora Anne
First Grade Teacher
Quarles, Angela Wash
5th Grade Teacher
Reed, Hope Wilder
Math Teacher
Regan, Tom H.
Prof of Sport Administration
Reger, Daniel L.
Chemistry Professor
Reibold, Peter G.
Dept of Religious Stud Chair
Reisman, David
Professor of Biology
Rembert, David Hopkins, Jr.
Prof of Botany & Assoc Dean
Richstad, Barbara Helkoff
Montessori Tchr & Admin
Riddick, Lynne Russell
Fifth Grade Teacher
Ritter, James Anthony
Assistant Professor
Robinson, Daniel Armstrong
Graduate Teaching Asst Instr
Robinson, Sarah Richardson
Language Arts Teacher
Roof, Walter Dean
English Teacher
Ross, Kathleen Murchison
Senior Instructor of Latin
Roys, Gerald R.
Political Science Professor
Sadik, Farid
Professor & Associate Dean
Sasiene, Sidney Martin
Industrial Technology Teacher
Schultz, Loretta Young
Second Grade Teacher
Scott, Patrick Greig
English Professor
Sears, James T.
Professor of Curr & Higher Ed
Sellers, Julie Winn
English Teacher & Yrbk Advisor
Sims, Patricia Davis
Sixth Grade Mathematics Tchr
Sligh, Gardenia Smiling
Business Education Teacher
Smith, Thomas Ewin
Professor of Sociology
Stephenson, Robert M., Jr.
Prof & Chair
Stine, John Edward
Associate Professor of History
Stowe, Donald E.
Professor
Sutton, Michael Albert
Distinguished Carolina Prof
Swafford, Ann J.
Assoc Prof & Admin Info Mgmt
Swinton, Patricia Lewis
9th-12th Grd Science Teacher
Thaxton, Jessie Jordan
Fifth Grade Teacher
Thompson, Eric Fontelle, Jr.
Assoc Prof of Biological Sci
Timmons, Judy Herring
English Teacher
Tucker, Kelly Hennessee
Director of Bands
Walker, Emma Plair
Reading, Science & Math Tutor
Wehman, Karen K.
English & SAT Prep Teacher
Whisnant, Charles Steven
Associate Professor of Physics
White, Clifford Martin, III
Mathematics Teacher
Wilbanks, Charles Lionel
Speech Communication Professor
Williams, Jesse
Gospel Choir Director
Williams, Valeria Prince
Social Studies Teacher
Wills, Pamela Shealy
Instructor of Elem Education
Wilson, Juanita Hill
English Teacher
Windham, Mark M.
Art Teacher
Woody, Lauren Cox
Language Arts Teacher

Woollen-Hanna, Linda M.
English Professor
CONWAY
Arrington, John Mitch
Hospitality Mgmt Dept Head
Beard, John Paul
Associate Professor of English
Berry, David C.
History Instructor
Bowman, Denvy Allen
Associate Professor of History
Byrd, Alice Wilson
Kindergarten Teacher
Carpenter, Karen Dallis
Associate Professor
Case, Alan John
Asst Professor of Rec & Parks
Causey, Phyllis Bradham
Fifth Grade Teacher
Clark, Brian Joseph
Dept Head & Forestry Mngmt
Dame, Richard F.
Professor of Marine Science
Dirienzo, Charles L.
Dept Chair of Criminal Justice
Eason, James Franklin
Accounting & Mgmt Assoc Prof
Fleming, John Kelly, Jr.
US History Teacher
Freeman, Jane Taylor
First Grade Teacher
Galbraith, Arthur Rand
Radiologic Tech Dept Head
Gilbert, Michael John Tyler
Assistant Professor of German
Haas, John Carl
His Instr & Dept Chair
Hall, Eleanor Dina
Instructor of Art Ed & History
Hollandsworth, Linda Padgett
Associate Professor of English
Johnson, Martha Ann Hardwick
English Teacher
Kenny, Maura Hannon
Art Professor
Lavado, Kimberly Russell
Spanish Teacher
Mc Collough, Claudia Jowitt
Asst Professor of Philosophy
McKever-Floyd, Preston L.
Philosophy & Religion Prof
Moye, Roy Ray
Assistant Professor
Olsen, Paul Anton
Art Professor
Palm, Linda J.
Assoc Professor of Psychology
Parker, Joyce Bennett
Professor
Peterson, Paul Carson
Political Science Professor
Pierce, David Donald
Hotel & Restaurant Mgmt Instr
Piroch, Joan F.
Prof of Psych & Dept Chair
Purcell, Sarah Cameron
Adjunct English Instructor
Rudolph, Karlene Gochenour
Lecturer
Spjut, Ronald Walter
7th Grade Social Studies Tchr
Thompson, Sharon Howell
Assistant Professor of Health
Todd, Belinda C.
Fifth Grd Language Arts Tchr
Townsend, Kenneth William
Assistant Prof of US History
Twigg, Ann Morris
English Teacher
Veas, Nina
Assoc Professor of Chemistry
Weldon, Richard N.
Business Law & Politics Prof
White, Mark Edward
Fifth Grade Teacher
Whitley, Lester Stanley
Associate Professor of Biology
CORDOVA
Cooper, Nancy Hutchins
AP English Teacher
Jenkins, Shirlan Mosley
Asst Principal & Math Tchr
Peterson, Brenda Charles
Social Studies Teacher
Wolfe, Larry Wayne
Transportation Director
COWPENS
Cook, Pamela Lucas
6th Grade Teacher
Kirby, Tamanda S.
Kindergarten Teacher
CROSS
Clemons, Shelia Ravenell
Business Teacher
DALZELL
Beard, Rita Kay
Business Education Teacher
Hathaway, Jospeh Michael
English Teacher
Rowe, Edward George
Eng, Anatomy & Physiology Tchr
Wilson, Dale Donnell
Math Teacher
DARLINGTON
Bacote, Eugene Charlie, Jr.
Mathematics Teacher
Bryant, Ina Claire
English Department Chairperson
Dargan, Eugene Edward
Sixth Grade Teacher

Ehlman, Demetria Atkins
Physics & Chemistry Teacher
Hayes, Gail S.
English Teacher
Heitsman, Susan Hoffman
Mathematics Teacher
Hopkins, Virginia Anderson
Science Teacher
Middleton, Margaret Ann
Ninth Grade English Teacher
Mims, Judith Powell
Third Grade Teacher
Reeder, Andrea Ellis
Biology Teacher
Robbins, Claudia Wilson
English Teacher & Dept Chair
Robinson, Audrey Franklin
Fourth Grade Teacher
Wallace, Sherry
Mathematics Teacher
White, Sandra Hudson
Business Education Teacher
Williams, Fletcher
Chemistry & Physics Teacher
Wingate, Kathryn E.
5th Grade Teacher
DENMARK
Dowling-Ferguson, Constance Marie
Dean, Arts, Sci & Eng Tchr
Islar, Idella Shelliedean
Coord Cnslng Recruiter
McCord, Betty Smith
Instr of Developmental Reading
Reed, Theodocia Kennedy
Adjunct Professor of Eng
Wilson, Betty Wright
Mathematics Teacher
DILLON
Carlson, Randolph Jay
Social Studies Teacher
Elvington, Myra Massey
English Teacher
Ledford, Donald Crawford, II
PE Teacher, Ath Dir & Coach
Proctor, Teresa Matthews
Math Teacher
DONALDS
Farner, Margaret Uldrick
Middle School Science Teacher
Greer, Martha Clark
Fourth Grade Teacher
Seawright, Jenny Padgett
Middle School Math Teacher
DORCHESTER
Hooks, Darlene Thomas
English Teacher
Hughes, Melanie Baucom
Science Teacher
Irvin, Elaine Wilson
Rdng, Eng, Jrnlsm & Comp Tchr
DUE WEST
Beck, Michael Jerome
Science Teacher
DUNCAN
Edwards, Zenobia Collins
Biology Teacher
Klim, Paula Smith
English Teacher
Miller, Cindy Bomar
Chairperson of Math Department
Mussman, Bonnie Merritt
Social Studies Teacher
Spieker, Matthew Howard
Orchestra Director
EASLEY
Anthony, Glenda G.
Fourth Grade Teacher
Beitz, Stephen Walter Arthur
History Teacher
Chang, Patricia Yung-Hwa
Math Teacher
Clardy, Marilyn Jones
Seventh Grd Life Science Tchr
Deland, Douglas Eugene
Mathematics Teacher
Dorsey, Janice Craft
Former Teacher
Hunnicutt, Julia Bates
Retired 3rd Grade Teacher
Layman, Virginia Rogers
Social Studies & Spanish Tchr
Liskey, Linda M.
Elementary Prin & English Tchr
Little, Cheri Wharton
High School Teacher
Manigault, Terry L.
Band, Choral & Music Tchr
Miller, Beth Freeman
English Teacher & Yrbk Advisor
Shealy, Wilma Bonham
Math Teacher
Snider, Patricia Stapleton
Choral Director
Stegall, Susan L.
Fifth Grade Teacher
Turner, Judy Miller
7th Grade Math Teacher
Welborn, Lisa Kim
English & French Teacher
White, Cynthia Floyd
5th Grd Language Arts Teacher
EASTOVER
Smith, Tonya Faulkner
Science Teacher
EFFINGHAM
Smith, Teresa Renee
Third Grade Teacher
EHRHARDT
Kirkland, Paula Ann
High School English Teacher

ELLIOTT
Caesar, May Rogers
Mathematics Teacher
Ellen, John H.
English Teacher
Johnson, Alfreda
English & Drama Teacher
ELLOREE
Banks, Michael Lathal
Junior ROTC Senior Instr
Frederick, James, Jr.
Administrative Asst & Teacher
Johnson, Ruby Mae
Math Teacher
EMERY
VanLeur, Jeffrey James
Industrial Arts & PE Teacher
ESTILL
Altman, Michelle M.
HS Social Studies Teacher
Blain, Janie Mae
Parent Educator
Johnson, John W., Jr.
Advanced Math Teacher
Pollins, Vicky P.
Rdng, Lang Arts, Soc Stud Tchr
FAIR PLAY
Hodges, Jean Gleason
First Grade Teacher
FAIRFAX
Armstrong, Walter Davis
Algebra & Geometry Teacher
Capehart, Willie R.
Agriculture Teacher
Holmes, Viola Price
7th-8th Grade Lang Arts Tchr
Jarrell, Nancy Clifton
Kindergarten Teacher
Jenkins, Everett Ray
Senior Army Instructor
Priester, Pam Main
Math Teacher
Rhodes, Thomasena Tyler
Second Grade Teacher
FAIRFOREST
Raney, Bonnie Smith
Fifth Grade Teacher
FLORENCE
Alexander, Scott L.
First Grade Teacher
Allen, Kevin Lynn
Physical Ed Teacher & Coach
Auls, Stephanie Vanessa
Science Teacher
Bailey, Sandra Du Bose
Business Education Teacher
Baxley, Janet Alleida
Treasurer
Brandis, Phyllis Scaturro
Asst Prin & 5th Grd Tchr
Briggs, Ann Holder
Special Education Teacher
Brown, L. Winfield, Jr.
Psychology Instructor
Burkett, Betty Berry
US History Teacher
Carter, Christopher R.
Dean of the Upper School
Caudill, Rachel Ann
High School Math Teacher
Chapman, Marilyn Kay
Secondary English Teacher
Cox, Arla Mann
Special Education Teacher
Crawford, Elizabeth Ann
4th Grade Elementary Educator
Crawford, Lennette Surlene
English Teacher
Eagleton, LaMaris Hammonds
Secondary English Teacher
English, Lena Cokley
7th Grade Science Teacher
Fraley, Patricia Evans
Resource Teacher
Gerald, Dorothy Wilson
Home Economics Teacher
Gilbert, Ella Lois
Fifth Grade Teacher
Hanrahan, Kathleen Lamerand
Medical Lab Technology Instr
Hawkins, Kevin R.
Physical Education Teacher
Hawkins, Lisa Gordon
LD Resource Teacher
Hill, Carol Current
English Teacher
Hitchings, Brad Harter
7th Grade Life Science Teacher
Hodges, Betsy Lee
Fourth Grade Teacher
Holliday, Carol Johnson
Elementary Curriculum Coord
Jenkins, B. Joy
Spanish Teacher
Jones, Michael Stuart
Band Director
Junkins, Mia Cribb
Chemistry Teacher
King, Deborah Lynn
Sixth Grade Teacher
LaCross, Randall Martin
Teacher-In-Residence
Lamont, Robin Olsen
Mathematics Teacher
Lane, Rebecca Gibbons
Math Teacher
Maron, Christopher William
Mathematics Teacher
McCandrew, Debra Ann
Math Instructor

FLORENCE (cont)
McCutcheon-Cooper, Rebecca
Social Studies Teacher
Mc Dowell, Gail Edgerton
Reading Teacher
McFadden, Vivian Edwards
Sixth Grade Teacher
Montrose, Rebecca McMillan
7th Grade Life Science Teacher
Neely, Anne Ellis
Biology Teacher
Nelson, Charles Arthur
Psych, Sociology & Hlth Tchr
Page, Darryl Christopher
English Teacher & Coach
Parker, Robert Corbett
Mathematics Teacher
Perkins, Lynn Cox
Chorus Teacher
Redfearn, Thomas William
Science Teacher
Register, Vicky Ballard
French Teacher
Rhodes, Yvonne Pope
Social Studies Teacher
Sanders, LaRosa Narcissus
Business Education Teacher
Sell, Andrew George
American Government Teacher
Sills, Doris Alsmeyer
Fifth Grade Teacher
Skoko, Paul Ivan
English Teacher
Smith, Kevin William
History Teacher
Strickland, Anna-Marie Tolson
Math Teacher
Turnage, Maxine McLaughlin
English & Spanish Teacher
Volk, Maria Ramos
Spanish Teacher
Ward, Diann S.
German Teacher
Zuppa, Evon Rhoden
Prog Coord of Cmptr & Off Sys
FORT MILL
Ayers, Christopher Earl
Latin Teacher
Bennett, Peggy Busby
8th Grade Science Teacher
Griffin, Edith I.
Math Teacher
Hannon, Sandra Furr
English & Journalism Teacher
Helms, Mattie Mc Lean
Kindergarten Teacher
Huggins, Lucinda
Spanish Teacher
Keitzer, Carole Uber
Fifth Grade Teacher
Kosanke, Scott William
High School Teacher
Mc Dow, Carolyn J.
Business Teacher
Pittman, Donald Keith
Biology & Physical Ed Tchr
Quinn, Lydia Dawn
8th Grade Math Teacher
FOUNTAIN INN
Chapman, Brenda Cates
Third Grade Teacher
GAFFNEY
Alexander, Debra Wylie
7th Grade Math Teacher
Bell, Joyce Davis
Resource Teacher
Berry, Scott Donald
Director of Academic Computing
Blackwell, Sherry Carter
First Grade Teacher
Blackwood, Martha Lou
Assistant Principal
Blanton, Pamela Gunter
Math Teacher
Boheler, Ronald N.
Algebra Teacher
Broome, Lennie Crosby
K-6th Grade Music Teacher
Burgess, Karen Alley
First Grade Teacher
Cabaniss, Nanette Allen
Teacher of Gifted & Talented
Childers, Joyce Harrill
4th Grade Teacher
Crenshaw, Pamela Stowell
Biology Teacher
Dedmon, Susan Brown
Sixth Grade Teacher
Elmore, Patricia Hannon
Fifth Grade Teacher
Hames, Kay Horton
12th Grade English Teacher
Hirschy, Gail R.
Industrial Technology Teacher
Jollay, Holly Parris
Sixth Grade Teacher
Kennington, Nancy Elizabeth
9th & 10th Grade English Instr
Marett, Paula Barnhill
9th Grd Physical Science Tchr
Mc Craw, Martha Stroup
11th Grade US History Teacher
Miller, Louise Quilliam
French & Typing Teacher
OConnor, Jan Huckaby
Social Science Teacher
Pack, Frances M.
French Teacher
Robbins, Judy Lee
3rd Grade Teacher
Roberson, Julia C.
Fifth Grade Teacher
Smith, Eleanor Burns
Spanish Teacher
Sullivan, John Michael
Soc Work, Sociology Assoc Prof
Turner, Vivian Ann
Second Grade Teacher
Wilkins, Richard D.
Fifth Grade Teacher
Wylie, Kay Ramsey
5th Grade Teacher
GALIVANTS FERRY
Jenerette, Brenda A.
Math Teacher
GARNETT
Green, Irene Addison
Retired Teacher
GASTON
Campbell, Joy Potts
Fifth Grade Teacher
GEORGETOWN
Atkinson, Arneitta Keitt
Elementary Teacher
Balthis, Sandra Huggins
11th Grade US History Teacher
Beach, Lila
Fourth Grade Teacher
Bessellieu, Louise Nelson
English & Lang Arts Teacher
Bull, Margaret Thomas
2nd Grade Teacher
Gordon, Sharon Young
English Department Chairperson
Greene, Lena Mc Donald
Sixth Grade Language Arts Tchr
Hooks, Sara Chandler
Tchr of Gifted
Jones, Tammy S.
Physical Education Teacher
Kennedy, Sarah Fleming
World History & Geography Tchr
Killmer, JoAnne S.
Fifth Grade Teacher
Meyer, Laura Jones
HS Social Studies Teacher
Moore, Tamera Lambert
7th Grade Science & Math Tchr
Nelson, Leola Wineglass
Second Grade Teacher
Perkins, Cherri Russell
Second Grade Teacher
Pyatt, Comeletia Cox
Seventh Grd Life Science Tchr
Scott, Laurietta Marie
Accounting & Keyboarding Tchr
Sutton, Caffie
5th Grade Teacher
Thompson, Teressa Ann
Guidance Counselor
Waddell, Yvonne Taylor
Mathematics & Science Teacher
GILBERT
Jones, Alicia Camille
Choral Director
Mathis, Johnnie Smith
Life Science & Math Tchr
GOOSE CREEK
Auld, Gail Davis
Computer Education Teacher
Brown, Deidre M.
Hnrs English & Literature Tchr
Buchman, Mark D.
Physical Education Teacher
Fesler, Holly Stilley
Psychology Tchr & Bsktbl Coach
Gaddy, Valerie Caroline
8th Grd Math & Algebra Teacher
Gilbert, Richard Lee
Industrial Tech Ed Teacher
Graham, Deborah Wilborn
Math & Science Teacher
Guice, Mack, II
Music Teacher
Haskell, Karen Altamese
Business Education Teacher
Hensley, Christy Price
English & Journalism Teacher
Howard, Carolyn Alston
Accounting Teacher
Hoyle, Tena Bostrom
Project Director
Kelly, Rose M.
Business Teacher
Lloyd, Raymond Eugene
French Teacher & Coach
Loftis, Darius
His Tchr, Coach & Admin Asst
Mauney, Caroline Bagby
7th Grade Mathematics Teacher
McDavid, Pamela Garris
Third Grade Teacher
Pitcher, Brandon Tisdale
Biology Teacher
Plowden, Claudia M.
Choral Director
Pridgeon, C. John
World Geography Teacher
Schaible, Linda B.
English Teacher
Schultz, Pamela Simons
English Teacher
Scott, Jeffrey Ryan
Band Director
Stoudenmire, John David, II
Choral Speech & Drama Teacher
Summer, Melinda Jo
HS Social Studies Teacher
Tuten, Donna Atkins
Math Teacher
Ware, Linda Wilson
First Grade Teacher
Watterworth, Rosemarie Eads
Mathematics Teacher
Wenz, Clarice J.
Chemistry & Physics Teacher
Wieters, Pamela Shields
English Teacher
Wood, Cathy Huxford
Third Grade Teacher
Young, Debra Gussler
Mathematics Teacher
GRANITEVILLE
Powers, Kay Ward
Math Teacher
Williamson, Deborah Greene
First Grade Teacher
GRAY COURT
Collins, Linda Aldridge
7th Grade Math Teacher
Ivie, Terri Emerson
Second Grade Teacher
Loper, Linda Burns
Fifth Grade Teacher
Quinton, Myrna Camp
Language Arts Teacher
Strickland, Celita Thomas
Preschl & Elem Guidance Cnslr
GREAT FALLS
Ellison, Amelia Patrick
Science Dept Chairperson
Nichols, Josianna F.
English Teacher
Whitaker, Darlene Smith
Spanish Teacher
GREELEYVILLE
Anderson, Alvarez L.
French Teacher
Darby, Alfred Leonard
Social Studies Teacher
Gamble, Janice Murray
Science Instructor
Taylor, Earnest Clifton, Jr.
JROTC Instructor
GREEN SEA
Lovett, Judy S.
Social Studies Teacher
Stevens, Natasha T.
Spanish Teacher
GREENVILLE
Adamee, Kathy Carter
English Instructor
Bagwell, John Ronald
Assistant Principal
Bagwell, Sherry Davis
Biology Teacher
Bartlett, Linda Boone
Assistant Professor of Spanish
Bell, Rose Mary Fellers
French Teacher
Blackhurst, Dana K.
Headmaster
Bowling, Nancy Helton
Schl Clerk & Cheerldng Coach
Britt, Kenneth G.
Field Consultant Textbk Pblshr
Carriger, Charles Roy
Jr High Phys Education Tchr
Casey, Donna Harrison
1st Grade Teacher
Christie, James E.
Building Construction Teacher
Cochran, Kathy Holcombe
Choral Director
Cook, Darryl Allen
HS World History Teacher
Davis, Rose Curry
Third Grade Teacher
Day, Sandra Diehl
Mathematics Teacher
Duncan, Jefferson Mitchell
Soc Stud Tchr & Stu Cncl Adv
Edwards, Ann Corbin
Computer Technology Teacher
Eshelman, Ellis Edwin
Teacher
Essex, Robert Lee
HS Science Teacher
Ferguson, Kristi Boroff
Soc Studies Dept Chair & Tchr
Fletcher, Madeline Chandler
English & Latin Teacher
Florence, Susan Antrim
Fourth Grade Teacher
Gadberry, Donna Martin
Lang Arts & Soc Stud Tchr
Grier, Jon Jeffrey
Instr & Composer in Residence
Hall, Elizabeth DeWitt
8th Grd Math & Algebra I Tchr
Harmon, Corinne Crockett
Instructor of Nursing School
Howard, W. Lynn
Math Teacher & Athletic Dir
Karns, Sara Brandeberry
Fourth Grade Teacher
Kuykendall, Ronald Anthony
Instructor of Political Sci
Kwok, Lynda Bird
5th Grade Teacher
Long, Mary Fogle
Sixth Grade Math Teacher
Marsh, Richard A.
Marketing Instructor
Martin, Juanita Moses
Fifth Grade Teacher
McGee, Charles Edward
High School Mathematics Tchr
Merck, Sharon Krill
8th Grade Algebra & Math Tchr
Metz, Sara B.
Instructor in Dental Hygiene
Mullaney, Mary Ann Jones
Nurse Educator
Neely, Christine Alford
Business Education Teacher
Nelsen, Brent Franklin
Assoc Prof of Political Sci
Nolen, Kenneth Wayne
Math Teacher
Nunes, Erica Wilson
Science Teacher
Otengho, Sunday-Joseph J.
Social Studies & Swahili Tchr
Parker, Pamela Heyward
6th Grd Language Arts Teacher
Pearson, Deborah Payne
7th Grade Science Teacher
Poeta, Elane Triebels
7th Grade Math & Science Tchr
Poster, Mary (Lee)
English Teacher
Ramler, Kent Benjamin
Bible Teacher
Reid, Mamie Mills
Student Development Specialist
Riddle, Charles Daniel
Anatomy & Physiology Instr
Schall, Judy Hartley
Reading & Soc Studies Teacher
Seibert, Lesa Marie
Ninth Grade English Teacher
Shirley, Peggy Crowder
Spanish Teacher
Sloop, Vicki Kirkpatrick
5th Grade Teacher
Stroud, Beverly Cally
Writing & Literature Instr
Treffinger, Thomas F.
English Professor
Tuculescu, Razvan Anton
Anatomy & Physiology Teacher
Utsey, William H., Jr.
Director of Athletics
Waters, Yvonne Dillard
Lead Science Teacher
Whisenhunt, James Eric, III
Chemistry & Physics Teacher
White, Nora Davis
Retired 2nd Grade Teacher
Williams, Bryan Crawford
Social Studies Teacher
Willis, Sharon Phillips
Eighth Grade Math Teacher
Wilson, Carolyn Sue
12th Grade English Teacher
Wynn, Gaye Moss
Span, World His & Eng Tchr
GREENWOOD
Adams, Irene Campbell
Student Services Counselor
Banks, F. Ann Southern
Third Grade Teacher
Bartley, Josephine Cooner
Math Tchr & Dept Head
Beck, Evelyn Regina
English Instructor
Black, Kevin J.
High School Asst Principal
Burton, Beverly Elaine
Instructor of Human Services
Burton, Franklin Delano, Jr.
Director of Bands
Cooper, Angela Davenport
Job Training Coord & Counselor
Cothran, Janice Curran
Honors Bio Teacher & Chrprsn
Cox, Linda Tharpe
Latin Teacher
Crawford, Jerry Williams
6th Grd Lang Arts & Math Tchr
Crawford, Lisa Mc Kinney
Developmental Math Teacher
Daulton, Judy Tucker
Accounting Instructor
Dickey, Alice Jo
Comp Prgrmng & Geom Tchr
Ebo, John Allen
School Counselor
Edwards, James Lewis
Instructor of Criminal Justice
Epps, Susie (Smith)
Social Studies Teacher
Figueira, Robert Charles
Professor of History
Lutz, Laura Bruce
Chemistry Teacher
Matsko, Beth Brown
Honors English Teacher
Mc Adams, Alice Jewell
Retired Math Teacher
Mc Daniel, Audrey Fender
Science Instructor
Nash, Zelda LaVern
Fourth Grade Teacher
Rasmussen, Howard Loton
History Teacher
Schulze, Sarah Tinsley
Social Studies Teacher
Scotland, Barbara Legree
Home Economics Education Tchr
Simpson, Thomas Wheeler
Mathematics Instructor
Smith, Sara Cushing
Instr of English & Writer
Smoak, Kerney Dale
Science Coordinator
Stark, Jean J.
Choral Music Teacher
Stephens, Wynita
Business Education Teacher
Sumerel, Delora Jarvis
Co-Head, English & Hum Instr
Taylor, Robert Russell
Professor of Education
Urquhart, Ann Brooks
9th Grade English Teacher
Walton, Susan Chapman
Choral Director
Wilkerson, Betty Grice
3rd Grade Teacher
Williams, Kay Cochran
HS Chemistry Teacher
Witt, John Andrew
Head Cmptr Dept & Instructor
GREER
Crain, George Robert
Soc Stud Tchr & Dept Chair
Dalby, David Kent
Advanced Placement Chem Tchr
Eggleston, Susan P.
Social Studies Teacher
Faulk, Julie Ligon
High School Psychology Teacher
Franzen, Judith Clardy
English Teacher
Frazier, Peggy Cann
Assistant Principal
Freeman, John Thomas
Psychology Teacher
Gillespie, Kenneth Webb, Jr.
English Teacher
Hunter, Laura Speed Simmons
9th Grd Eng & AP Eng Teacher
Knight, Cynthia Bishop
Teacher
Kutz, Elizabeth Kennedy
Spanish Teacher
Smith, Gwyn W. (Williams)
Language Arts & Lit Teacher
Sterling, Lorraine Doherty
US History Teacher
Thompson, Joan Ann (Murphy)
High School Math Teacher
Way, Katrina Murphy
Math Teacher & Dept Chairman
Wooden, Willie Lewis
High School Math Teacher
GRESHAM
Richardson, Janice Marie
Language Arts Teacher
HAMPTON
Beth, Daniel Richard
Sci Dept Chm & District Coord
Bonnet, Thomas Gregory
World Geography Teacher
Burch, William Albert, IV
Social Studies Teacher
Causey, Judith Armstrong
6th Grd Rdng & Spelling Tchr
French, Mary Elizabeth
English Teacher
Houck, Margaret Lyerly
Mathematics Teacher
Lawton, Daisy Harley
Guidance Counselor
Miller, Betty Jane
English Teacher
Phillips Holstein, Ellen Deery
Science Teacher & Dept Chair
Schofield, Tammy Topley
Social Studies Teacher & Coach
Woods, Ruth Anne Guerry
Fourth Grade Math & Sci Tchr
HANAHAN
Beers, Angel Urban
8th Grade Math Teacher
Fisher, Merrie Smith
Tchr of the Gifted & Talented
Gallagher, M. Loretta
Seventh Grade Teacher
HARDEEVILLE
Pinckney, Sarah L.
7th-8th Grade Lang Arts Tchr
Singleton, Rachel M.
Science Teacher
HARTSVILLE
Alexander, William C.
Professor of Biology
Bolden, Nancy Thornhill (Zupp)
Prof of Dance & Dept Chair
Chalmers, James K.
Art Dept Chair & Prof of Art
Crocker, Donna Turnage
Rdng Recovery & 1st Grade Tchr
Culyer, Richard C., III
Professor of Education
Eykyn, Lollie Barbare
French Professor
Fisher, Teresa Haywood
Eng, His Tchr & Guidance Cnslr
Fitzpatrick, Casey Goldston
Director of Student Services
Gaskins, Sandra Tweed
Earth Science Teacher
Harter, Ronald Glenn
English Teacher
Hewitt, Pat A.
Physical Education Teacher
Holliday, Darrell T., Jr.
Professor
Hulsey, Alice Brenneman
Fourth Grade Teacher
Mc Clam, Norma A.
Spanish Teacher
Montgomery, Linda Endicott
Lrnng Disabled & Spec Ed Tchr
Mzoughi, Taha
Physics Instructor

SVILLE (cont)
ffe, Ronald Wayne
h & English Teacher
, Lois L.
ce Teacher
tein, Joseph H.
ssor & Department Chair
, Alice Hedges
eting Teacher & DECA Adv
, Tamara Burnette
Grd Hnrs Eng & Wrtng Tchr
Dorothy Mote
, Computer Science Teacher
mar, Venkataraman
c Prof of Intnl Bus-Mrktg
Marjorie Gill
Grade Teacher
Vickie S.
ematics Teacher
Martin VanKley
Prof of Modern Languages
, Dan Lewis
Prof of Bus Admin
H SPRINGS
, Deborah Driggers
Grade Teacher
, Sheri Mc Kinney
Grade Teacher & Asst Prin
NGWAY
n, Kyle Stephen
nce Teacher
, James H.
al Studies Teacher
ns, Lynn Edwards
h Grade Teacher
Patricia C.
her of Gifted & Talented
, W. Fred, Jr.
s & World Geography Tchr
Susan Gordon
sh Teacher & Dept Chm
ON HEAD ISLAND
ove, Joe J.
School Math Dept Chm
ello, Mary Ann
ish Teacher
oars, Julias Terese
mistry Teacher
ngham, Bobby G.
ematics Teacher
George Nasey
stling Coach
ano, Ralph Peter
n & Phys Sci Tchr
ied, Steve John
Grade Teacher
Christine Anne
ematics Teacher
ton, Peg Griebel
ish Teacher & Dept Chm
ames Patrick
d Director
d, Nora Kathryn W.
nce Teacher
, Sandra A.
etic Dir, PE & Hlth Tchr
ne, Nicholas A.
ish Teacher
on, William T.
red Ed Prof & Dept Head
an, Thomas C.
& Health Teacher
Cesar A.
nish Teacher
rs, Sandra Watts
her of Gifted & Talented
LY HILL
ord, Jane Elizabeth
ish Teacher & Yearbook Adv
Julian Quayle, Jr.
ctor of Bands
, Pansy
nary Arts Teacher
, Sharon Lourice
h Teacher
n, Incentlee Bookard
lish Instructor
, Linda Riley
ness Ed Tchr & Dept Chprsn
eyer, Sandra Remley
lish Teacher
e-Jones, Jerelene
, Jrnlsm Tchr & Staff Adv
, Mary Berry
lish Teacher
EA PATH
rson, Roger Neal
Force Jr ROTC Instructor
, Nancy Ramey
ond Grade Teacher
, Gloria Thornton
mistry Teacher
James Michael
istant Principal
Judy Shaw
ond Grade Teacher
ll, Kay Patterson
ne Economics & Elem Ed Tchr
John Randolph
& Soc Stud Tchr
KINS
orth, Robert Don
pentry Tech Teacher
, Nathan Jerry
ial Studies Teacher
, Eleanor M.
Grd Language Arts Teacher
son, Bryan Scott
tory Teacher

Masdonati, Jean OHara
Math Teacher
Mills, Hayley M.
Biology Teacher
Robertson, Lora Faye
English Teacher
Smelser, Elke Kunz
8th Grd Lang Arts & Rdng Tchr
Stringer, Eunice Leilani
Teacher & Site Consultant
Woodard, Sandra R.
Accounting Teacher
INMAN
Banks, Connie Marie (Davis)
Fourth Grade Teacher
Brady, Barbara Ballenger
Sixth Grade Teacher
Camp, Delores Snelgrove
Guidance Counselor
Clark, Marsha Bishop
Psychology Teacher
Deahl, Linda McCuiston
Fourth Grade Teacher
Lyles, Karen Darby
Kindergarten Teacher
Poteat, Shirley Page
Fourth Grade Teacher
Waldrop, Pat A.
Kndgtn & Rdng Recovery Teacher
Wyatt, Susan M.
First Grade Teacher
IRMO
Batson, Debbi Wilhelm
6th Grade English Teacher
Burkett, Christopher Joseph
History Teacher
Bussell, Mary Beth M.
English Teacher
Dixon, Noah Lavern
HS Physical Education Teacher
Hanley, Shelia Franklin
Fourth Grade Teacher
Hogan, Kathy O'Neill
US History & Govt Teacher
Hyatt, Julie Marie
Social Studies Teacher
Jamison, Judy Shelley
9th-12th Grd Eng & Hum Teacher
Jones, Patrice Zimmerman
Fourth Grade Teacher
Lumpkin, Arthur Hirst
English Teacher
Peters, Ellen Mc Afee
Coord of Gifted Pgms, Eng Tchr
Pritz, Teresa Mc Allister
First Grade Teacher
Sommers, Cindy Lee
Second Grade Teacher
Spruill, Marion Humes
History Teacher
Warren, Amy W.
Math Teacher
Younginer, Kathleen Sharpe
Fifth Grade Teacher
IVA
Charlesworth, Jean Ann Donnald
Second Grade Teacher
Holbrook, Sherry Mc Junkin
English Teacher
Mc Mullan, Rita Fields
Biology Teacher
Mize, Anna Walters
Fifth Grade Teacher
JEFFERSON
Baker, Fidelia Linker
Second Grade Teacher
Knight, Barbara Cato
Reading & English Teacher
JOHNS ISLAND
Limehouse, Retha Hodge
Fourth Grade Teacher
Nelson, Linda Booker
English Teacher & Librarian
JOHNSONVILLE
Askins, Donna Wofford
6th Grade Teacher
Silvernail, Linda Watts
English Teacher
JOHNSTON
Hare, Helen Padgett
Second Grade Teacher
Jackson, Denise
Government, Ec & History Tchr
JONESVILLE
Byrd, Brenda Wright
Business Ed Tchr & Dept Chprsn
Camby, Donna Burns
English Teacher
Haynes, Roy E.
Chemistry & Physics Teacher
Sanders, Rita Belue
First Grade Teacher
Wooten, Sandra Denise
Math Teacher
KERSHAW
Barton, Merrio Neal
Advanced Placement Eng Teacher
Demby, Anne Sill
First Grade Teacher
Faulkenberry, Roslynn Glosson
Fifth Grade Teacher
Ferguson, William Franklin, Sr.
Drafting Teacher
Horton, Chet Reed
8th Grade Math Teacher
Jarvis, Phyllis D.
French & English Teacher
Parker, Mary W.
Third Grade Teacher

Phillips, Scott Lee
Math Teacher
Thompson, Frances M.
Social Studies Teacher
Wall, Ronnie Lee
Science Teacher
KINGSTREE
Campbell, Margaret C.
Cosmetology Instructor
Chambliss, Carolyn D. S.
Business Education Teacher
Easterling, Louise Marshall
Former Lit & Pub Speaking Tchr
Elliott, Clifton Russell
Business Instructor
McElveen, Martha M.
Lower School Coordinator
Moore, Maureen Patricia
Chemistry Teacher
Murphy, Mae Hazel Anderson
1st Grade Teacher
O'Quinn, Sara T.
Business Instructor
Tisdale, Katherene A. (Warren)
Science Lab Teacher
KLINE
Stewart, Anne Reynolds
Retired Teacher
LADSON
Ashley, Cynthia Kay
Sixth Grade Sci & Math Tchr
Branyon, Sandra Buckner
6th Grade Mathematics Teacher
Fowler, Pamela Boatwright
8th Grade Science Teacher
Jenkins, Doris Boland
7th Grade Social Studies Tchr
Knowles, Sherrolyn Phillips
Seventh Grade Reading Teacher
Miller, Joanne Conroy
Language Arts & Reading Tchr
Smith, Diane Fogle
Teacher
Stafford, Ellen Jayne
Fifth Grade Teacher
LAKE CITY
Andrew, Susan Powell
PE Teacher & Coach
Daniels, Thomas Kent
US History Teacher
Floyd, Anna Jackson
Guid Cnslr & Asst Headmaster
Mc Allister, Debbie W.
Third Grade Teacher
LAMAR
McJunkin, Portia Myers
High School English Teacher
Weiland, Sally Norris
French Teacher
LANCASTER
Bowers, Linda Baker
HS AP Bio & Coll Prep Tchr
Carnes, Nannette
5th Grade Teacher
Clements, Ruth L.
English Prof & Dir of Hnrs Pgm
Cooper, Susan Hogan
First Grade Teacher
Crawford, Mae Frances
Assistant Principal
Crenshaw, Gregory Paul
Mechanical Drawing Teacher
Eddins, Sara Jernigan
Algebra Teacher
Evans, Dianne Threatt
Assoc Prof of Psych & Cnslr
Gardner, Barbara Bennett
Mathematics & Algebra I Tchr
Garris, William Ralph
Professor of Criminal Justice
Hickel, Debra Joyce
Third Grade Teacher
Hough, Francis Madison, Jr.
Eighth Grade English Teacher
Langston, Judy Patricia
Spanish Teacher
Mc Manus, Darlene Hinson
Business Professor
Moore, Thomas George
US History Teacher
Pitts, Cheryl Lynn
Junior High Teacher
Rutledge, John Edward
Adj Lecturer Criminal Justice
Smith, Elizabeth Cooke
US His Tchr & Stu Act Dir
Starnes, Vivian Couick
English Teacher
Walton, Nancy Lee (Felici)
First Grade Teacher
Williams, George, Jr.
Biology Teacher
Williams, Kelley Lynn
Science Teacher
LANDRUM
Smith, Joyce B.
Biology Teacher & Lab Coord
Strother, Patricia C.
HS French & English Teacher
LANGLEY
Armstrong, Carol Foster
English Teacher
Durham, Tina Lee
Marketing Tchr & Coordinator
Golden, Kelly L.
History Teacher
Kent, Theresa Bratek
MS Math, PE Tchr & Coach
Sartori, Mary Ellen Burris
English & Drama Teacher

Sawyer, Robert F.
Biology I Teacher
Schrade, Larry Leonard
Naval Science Instructor
Snyder, Sherri Byrd
Chemistry Teacher
Soyars, Linda Russell
French Teacher
Swindell, Traci D.
US History & Amer Govt Tchr
Toepke, Patricia Ellen
Mathematics Teacher
Webb, Helen Hatley
English Teacher
LATTA
Ellis, James Herbert
Sci Dept Chm & Physics Tchr
Haselden, Denise Michelle
Sixth Grade Teacher
LAURENS
Arrington, Barbara Joyce
8th Grade English Teacher
Belangia, Elaine Funk
9th Grade English Teacher
Black, Stephanie Rene
Pub Speaking & Drama Teacher
Blakely, Jean Lesslie
First Grade Teacher
Cheek, Sonia Cunningham
English Teacher
Coggins, Sherry Estes
Assistant Principal
Humphries, Judy Strickland
Guidance Counselor
Kennedy, Janice Pressley
Tchr of the Learning Disabled
Mathis, Edna S.
Fourth Grade Teacher
Moss, Paula Allen
Bands Director
Mullikin, Timothy Steven
Biology Teacher & Coach
Owens, Kathy Mc Elhannon
English Teacher
Pittman, Alwin Glenn
Technical & Career Ed Director
Prince, Janice Jenkins
Journalism & English Teacher
Smith, Kelly Simmons
Business Education Instructor
Stone, Kathryn Gill
Mathematics Teacher
Taylor, Drenda Hanley
Tchr of Hearing Handicapped
Wallace, C. Ann Reedy
Home Economics Teacher
West, George Edward
Health & PE Teacher
Wilson, Anita Wilson
Math Teacher & Admin Intern
Wilson, Sherry Parker
Business Education Teacher
LEXINGTON
Croxton, Karen A.
Chemistry Teacher
Darnell, Barbara Ayers
Third Grade Teacher
Ellsworth, Mary-Dozier (Lee)
Amer Govt, Ec & Geog Tchr
Garner, H. Wayne
South Carolina History Teacher
Glenn, Constance Patricia
9th Grd Civics & Geog Teacher
Hamby, Emily Harmon
Teacher of Gifted
Johnson, Martha Hobson
German Teacher
Lorick, Betty Gardner
Mathematics Teacher
Maguire, Linda Wallace
8th Grd Reading & English Tchr
McKnight, Timothy Kemp
Physics & Biology Teacher
Morrison, Sherrie Crawford
English, Journalism Tchr & Adv
Polk, Charles K.
Director of Bands
Pumphrey, Carolyn Goodale
English Teacher
Sease, Peggy Price
Business Education Teacher
Sharpe, Ella Elizabeth
English Teacher
Suber, Ethel Wylie
Tenth Grade English Teacher
Warren, Pandra D.
Marketing Teacher
Williams, Gloria Dillard
Chemistry Teacher
Wise, Susan
Second Grade Teacher
LIBERTY
Hamilton, Maria Gay
First Grade Teacher
Henderson, Larry Taylor
US His Tchr & Soc Stud Chm
Kirby, Sandra H.
Mathematics Teacher
Sims, Richard C., Jr.
6th Grade Teacher
Voiselle, Michael Lucky
Retired Physics & Chem Instr
LITTLE MOUNTAIN
Moon, Loretta Bowers
Third Grade Teacher
LITTLE RIVER
Allen, Francis Raymond
Naval Sci & JROTC Instr
Lamson, Roberta Taniser
7th Grade Math Teacher

Marvin, Elizabeth Glenn
8th Grade Lang Arts Teacher
O'Brien, Thomas James
Technology Teacher
Wilson, Edward Earl
Assistant Principal & Teacher
LORIS
Fowler, Ronald M.
Assistant Principal
France-Kelly, Wanda Sarvis
Retired Kindergarten Teacher
Isom, Frank
Science Teacher
Mixer, Thomas David
Technology Teacher
Richardson Jones, Melissa
Social Science Teacher
LUGOFF
Hicks, William L.
Visual Arts & Photography Tchr
Maltby, Sarah Walker
Mathematics Dept Chairman
Maples, Rebecca Anderson
AP Calculus Teacher
LYMAN
Coan, Teresa Humphries
Fifth Grade Teacher
Mc Makin, Nancy Fleming
First Grade Teacher
LYNCHBURG
McFadden, Legatha Montgomery
Fifth Grade Teacher
Richardson, Ruth
4th Grade Teacher
MANNING
Benton, Jane Baker
7th Grade Science Teacher
Brooke, Barry Raiford
Asst Instr & Air Force JROTC
Corbett, Jacqueline Schmit
French Teacher
Diller, Ann Cloninger
English Teacher
Epps, Natasha Rene
Fourth Grade Teacher
Grant, Linda King
Guidance Counselor
Jackson, Thomas Jehu, Jr.
9th Grd Eng Tchr & Yrbk Adv
Johnson Aycock, Jenny
English Tchr & Newspaper Adv
Krise, Leora J.
Elementary Guidance Counselor
Lewis, Kimberly Elizabeth
Math Teacher
McCaskill, Tina Watts
7th Grade Math Teacher
Weigle, John McMaster
7th & 8th Grade Lang Arts Tchr
Younts, Linda Trotter
English Teacher
MARION
Pogue, Deborah Altman
Biology Teacher & Dept Chrprsn
Tanner, Helen Roberts
8th Grade Language Arts Tchr
Ward, Rebecca Elizabeth
Science Teacher
MAULDIN
Riopelle, Barbara Buckley
Mathematics Teacher
MAYESVILLE
Payne, Eva Givens
1st Grade Teacher
MC CLELLANVILLE
Buscemi, Cynthia Cauthen
Middle School Science Teacher
Carico, Deborah Harley
Lang Arts, Eng Tchr & Coach
Gibbs, Carrie Nesbitt
Language Arts Tchr & Asst Prin
Kablick, Jean Mercer
Fifth Grade Teacher
MC CORMICK
Childress, Charles Edward, Jr.
Social Studies Teacher
Cozart, Carla Arnold
English Teacher
MONCKS CORNER
Brown, Jerry
Athletic Director & Coach
Caddell, Marilyn Bunch
First Grade Teacher
Cameron, Richard D.
Mathematics Teacher
Durkee, Michelle Bird
Math Teacher
Gaskins, Elizabeth Rogers
Child Development Teacher
Gehlmann, Susan Gunter
6th Grade Math Teacher
Jones, Robert J.
JROTC Instructor
Mc Bride, Judith Lewis
Music Coordinator
Meyer, Cinda Stambough
American Government Teacher
Morris, Trudy
K-12 Itinerant ESL Teacher
Polk, Patricia R.
Health Occupations Instructor
Taylor, Michelle B.
Business Teacher
Thacker, Judy Kitchen
Coll Prep & Gen Bio Tchr
Thomas, Sharon Sue (Veraguth)
First Grade Teacher
Trivett, Robert Lee
Welding Instructor

MOORE
Weaver, Robert Malone
7th Grade Science Teacher
MOUNT PLEASANT
Agrest, Marina Yefimovna
Piano Teacher
Allred, Claudia Russell
7th Grade Math Teacher
Bartels, Richard Louis
Aerospace Science Instructor
Berkhan, Drucilla
Social Studies Teacher
Blackford, Sheryl Allen
HS Social Studies Teacher
Burns, Courtney Patrick
Teacher of Gifted & Talented
Douty, Ann Spurlock
Mathematics Teacher
Germain, Nancy Browne
Mathematics Dept Chair & Tchr
Hopkins, Robert Randolph
Fourth Grade Teacher
Kerr, Basil Joseph, Jr.
Band Dir & Music Theory Tchr
Moore, Jan Mc Pherson
Third Grade Teacher
Owen-Early, Pamela Hendrix
7th Grd Language Arts Teacher
Pinckney, Lou Ester Wright
8th Grade Social Studies Tchr
Schlachter, Michelle Smith
Algebra Teacher
See, Millie Willis
Seventh Grade English Teacher
Thomas, H. Franklin, Jr.
Economics, Govt & Mrktg Tchr
MULLINS
Blake, Karen Eileen
3rd Grade Teacher
Fowler, Cynthia M.
4th Grade Teacher
Gause, Carolyn Donnelly
Preschool Child Dev Tchr
Hinson, Mary Lynn Rogers
5th Grade Teacher
Martin, Teresa Stanton
Math Teacher
Smith, Elaine Echerd
Chemistry Educator
MYRTLE BEACH
Bannon, Rebecca S.
Lang Arts, Drama & Jrnlsm Tchr
Barron, Brenda Moore
Spanish Teacher
Baxley, James Ronald
Teacher
Bradford, Beverly Howell
3rd Grade Teacher
Cartrette, Sandra Joyce
Third Grade Teacher
Cooler, Norma F.
7th Grd Language Arts Teacher
Crooks, Gail M.
Retired 3rd Grade Teacher
Durfey, Barbara J.
Third Grade Teacher
Eastin, Deborah Murphy
Math Teacher
Floyd, Deborah Cave
English, Drama & German Tchr
Ham, Joyce Johnson
8th Grade Language Arts Tchr
Helton, Debra T.
Mathematics Teacher
Kidd, Brenda Natale
6th-8th Grd Social Skills Tchr
Lang, Harriett E.
Fourth Grade Teacher
Lee, Paula Angell
Physical Education Teacher
May, Margaret Carrington
Chemistry & Physics Teacher
Mc Intyre, Annabel Ray
Language Arts Teacher
McQueen, David Norman, Jr.
Choral Music Teacher
Nadeau, Angela L.
9th Grade Mathematics Teacher
Oskin, Sherri Brunty
5th Grade Teacher
Pace, Debby L.
English Teacher
Powell, Michele E.
Biology Teacher
Purcell, Deborah O.
Assistant Principal
Sanders, Cleveland Bernard
Teacher
Sery, Diane Christine
Science Teacher
Skews, Emily Ann Bennett
Third Grade Teacher
Smith, Rhonda Ward
Sr & AP English Teacher
Swan, Sinclair Ottis, Sr.
Biology Teacher
Yorke, Jewell Ann
5th Grade Teacher
NESMITH
Allen, Carol Louise
7th-8th Grd Social Stud Tchr
NEW ELLENTON
Hayes, Patricia Johnson
Science & Social Studies Tchr
Holloway, Veronie M.
Fifth Grade Teacher
NEW ZION
Coaxum, Jo Ann
Fifth Grade Teacher

Floyd, Cheryl Buddin
Fourth Grade Teacher
NEWBERRY
Carley, Robert K.
Professor of Political Science
Cockrell, Philip Carlton
Assistant Professor of History
Fritz, Kathlyn Ann
Assoc Prof of Sociology
Horn, Charles N.
Associate Professor
Johnson, Mamie Lynn
Consumer & Family Sci Tchr
Kleckley, Russell C.
Asst Professor of Religion
Lee, Chee Aun
Adj Professor of Physical Ed
Moseley, Merritt, III
History & Social Studies Tchr
Obermeyer, Dennis Herman
Prof of Physical Education
Riddle, Paula Matthews
Art Teacher
Scott, Jesse Lee
History Professor
Sommerville, William Robert
Social Studies Teacher
Wise, William Darr
Associate Prof of Music
NINETY SIX
Bishop, Alan Douglas
Band Director
Bradley, Terrance Henry
Chemistry & Dr Ed Teacher
Browning, Cheryl Almeria
Physical Education Teacher
Price, Cynthia Anderson
Reading & Literature Teacher
Vines, Glenda Fortner
First Grade Teacher
Yeargin, Debra Lynn
Fifth Grade Language Arts Tchr
NORTH
Colter, Oneida Williams
1st-6th Grd Title I Rdng Tchr
Geiger, Naomi Hills
Social Studies Teacher
Scurry, Shirley F.
Music, Art & Exploratory Tchr
Valois, Thomas Ralph
Social Studies Teacher
Wright, Deedra O.
Band Director
NORTH AUGUSTA
Anderson, Sara Jones
English Teacher
Belger, Teresa Posey
Math Teacher
Butts, Martha H.
English & Spanish Teacher
Creamer, Carol McColl
7th & 8th Grd Lang Arts Tchr
Hall, Gloria Washburn
Biology Teacher
Hammond, Jeanette Walton
Fourth Grade Teacher
Head, Barry Nathan
Interim Principal
Head, Mary Margaret
Guidance Counselor
Hernandez, Gwen Videtto
Sixth Grade Teacher
Hill, David Lee
Bands Director
Jenkins, Mary Seel
Retired 7th Grade Teacher
Koonts, Sharon K.
Mathematics Instructor
Luquire, Elizabeth Crouch
Chemistry Teacher
Lusk, Laura Davis
English Teacher
Montgomery, Evelina Staggs
Retired 8th Grade Science Tchr
Palmore, Georgia Prince
Math Teacher
Quarles, Rosemary
Second Grade Teacher
Richardson, Margaret O'Brien
Retired Kindergarten Teacher
Shelton, Jennifer L.
Eighth Grade English Teacher
Williams, Jon Robert
History & Business Law Teacher
NORTH MYRTLE BEACH
Thompson, Karen Ann Dengler
Retired English & Speech Tchr
NORWAY
Jones, Mary Jamison
Language Arts Teacher
Mc Kinnon, Gladys Bolar
Business Education Teacher
ORANGEBURG
Amos, Mary Walker
English Teacher
Anderson, Sharon K.
Gifted Ed Social Studies Tchr
Anoruo, Ambrose Okechukwu
Professor of Biology
Benton, Lisa Birchmore
Math & Algebra Teacher
Bradley, Robert Holmes
PE Teacher & Dept Chairman
Bradley-Gass, Carolyn
English I Teacher
Buckner, Izetta P.
Mentally Disabled Rsrce Tchr
Cantley, Marjorie Hunter
Spanish Teacher & Dept Chair

Charley, Priscilla Elaine (Little)
Math, Science & Health Teacher
Coleman, Linda Calhoun
Social Studies Teacher
Collier, Rosa W.
English Teacher
Ekpono, Bassey Edetebok
Assoc Prof of Human Svcs Dept
Fersner, Angelia Zimmerman
Guidance Counselor
Fields, Joslyn Sanders
Child Care Services Teacher
Gadson, Caroline Elaine
Science Teacher
Gamble, Jacquelyn Valdena
Second Grade Teacher
Grimes, Tresmaine Rubain
Psychology Professor
Haigler, Ann Felkel
Guidance Counselor
Heggins, Martha Jean Adams
Early Chldhd Prof & Coord
Hill, Elizabeth Lee (Lowe)
Chemistry Teacher
Hugine, Abbiegail Hamilton
Social Studies Teacher
Hugine, Andrew, Jr.
Mathematics Professor
Hutson, Calvin Delano
Professor of English
Ihekweazu, Stanley N.
Mechncl Engrng Tech Chm
Inabinet, Georgie Ann Dukes
Music Teacher
James, Jean Ulmer
Assistant Professor of English
Johnson, Yvonne Gooden
Third Grade Extension Teacher
Massoudi, Ruhullah
Assoc Professor of Chemistry
Palmer, Chester Delacy
Social Studies Teacher
Resseau, Annette Joyce
Reading Lab Teacher
Scott, Jutta Katharina
Assistant Professor of History
Staley, Alvin
Artist & Teacher
Swami, Umesh M.
Associate Prof of Mathematics
White, Giselle LaMarr
Criminal Justice Professor
Whiting, Sylvia Anderson
Professor of Nursing
Wilson, Gwendolyn Dianne
Professor & Administrator
PACOLET
Bryant, Jolene W.
8th Grade Social Studies Tchr
Corbin, Ronald E.
Math & Science Teacher
PAGELAND
Gay, Janie R.
Kindergarten Teacher
Godfrey, Belinda Gilmore
Home & School Coordinator
Helm, Robin Mills
English & Spanish Teacher
Stroud, Helen Adams
Chorus Teacher
Wright, Kimerla Denise
Business Education Teacher
PAMPLICO
Allison, Orger Weaver
Science Teacher
PAULINE
Hough, Teresa Stuart
First Grade Teacher
PAWLEYS ISLAND
Brown, Patricia M.
Business Ed Teacher
Cook, Cara Heginbotham
Special Education Teacher
Floyd, Margaret Louise
Science Teacher
Janes, Robert Glenn, Jr.
English Teacher
Mc Cray, Loretta Cox
Fourth Grade Teacher
Streiffert, Scott D.
Social Studies Teacher & Coach
PELION
Barwick, Ann Ritter
Fourth Grade Teacher
Bennett, Timothy Dale
Orchestra Director
Black, William Lee
Social Studies Teacher & Coach
Kleckley, Nancy Amelia
Phys Science & Biology Teacher
Price, Deborah Doles
Third Grade Teacher
PELZER
Gilliam, Susan Hammond
Third Grade Teacher
PENDLETON
Allen, Douglas Ray
Instr of Ind & Engrng Tech Div
Belcher, D. Ray
History Instructor
Byrd, Richard R.
Science Teacher & Coach
Campbell, Rosco
Government & Economics Teacher
Cokley, Sabrina B.
English Instructor
Gray, Rupert Algernon
Vocational Agriculture Teacher
Jones, Dallas F.
Med Lab Tech Program Director

Jordan, Charles Henry
Broadcasting Department Head
Kirschman, Jill Spelina
Mathematics Teacher
Mc Clure, Susan W.
Accounting Department Head
McFall, Robin Bunton
English Instructor
Nelms, Mike O.
Biology Teacher
Reeves, Sandra Ann
Psychology Instructor
Spragins, Catherine Rogers
Instructor in Nursing
Stazer, Linda Strub
Adjunct Economics Instructor
Taylor, L. Marianne
English Professor & Dept Chair
Wood, Louise S.
Developmental Eng Dept Head
PICKENS
Adkins, William Edward
Math Teacher
Blackwell, John Lemuel
Math & Science Instructor
Bowie, Pamela Earle
Rdng, Lit Tchr & Stu Cncl Adv
Chastain, Jane Fields
Kindergarten Teacher
Crowe, Catherine Hinnant
Orchestra Instructor
Hicks, Virginia Buchholz
Art & History Teacher
Morrison, Russell Byers
Science Teacher
Newman, Kathy Mc Donald
Cnslr & Civic Rspnsblty Tchr
O'Shields, Debra Tarlton
Third Grade Teacher
Sullivan, Francis L., III
Science Teacher
Wamsley, Kermit Howard, Jr.
Band & Chorus Director
Weekes, Alan Frank
Science Teacher
PIEDMONT
Benjamin, Ann
7th Grade Lang Arts & Lit Tchr
Case, Edward Leo
Chemistry Teacher
Coyne, David Patrick
Math Teacher & Coach
Culbertson, Virginia Hayes
8th Grade Lang Arts Teacher
Geisler, Frances Schneider
Elementary Art Teacher
Kaminska, Kathy Morris
Eng, Jrnlsm & Frosh Focus Tchr
Norris, Jennifer Rae
Health & Physical Ed Teacher
Tate, Jeffrey F.
Physical Education Instructor
Tippett, Bill Lloyd
Marketing & Business Teacher
Waits, Peggy Slaton
6th Grade Language Arts Tchr
POMARIA
Doolittle, Charlsie Counts
Fourth Grade Teacher
Yarborough, Bonnelle Graham
Second Grade Teacher
PROSPERITY
Collins, Sandra Smith
Biology Teacher
Elswick, Rebecca Parrish
English Teacher
Griffin, Helen M.
English Dept Chair & Instr
Harmon, Jeanette Dominick
Algebra Teacher
Holland, Sherrie Jones
Math & Algebra Teacher
Johnson, Vincent
8th Grade Social Studies Tchr
Kinard, Harriette Hedgepath
Second Grade Teacher
Miller, Terrilee Brune
Kindergarten Teacher
RICHBURG
Hemphill, Mildred G.
Geography & Reading Teacher
Mc Murray, Bennie E.
Athletic Director & Coach
Nelson, Carolyn Lawson
English Teacher
Sherrill, Joan Catoe
Science Teacher & Dept Head
Stringfellow, Wanda Yvette
Parent Educator
RIDGELAND
Batten, Brenda
Mathematics Teacher
Ellison, Kier Abraham
Mathematics Teacher
Fazzino, Paul J.
High School Math Teacher
Goodman, Yvonne
African American History Tchr
Ladson, Evalina White
Classroom Teacher
Maye, John W., Jr.
Assistant Principal
Riley, Malden G.
Kindergarten Teacher
Small, Doris Kenney
Hlth Occupations & Teacher
RIDGEWAY
Hanna, Doretha Prioleau
Child Development Teacher

ROCK HILL
Ahl, Arthur William
Aerospace Science Instructor
Alt, Patricia Worsham
Educational Therapist
Bagwell, Jack Norman
Instructor of Biology
Carrigan, Lisa Mullis
Health Occupations Instructor
Dye, Linda Ash
Business Education Instructor
Fern, Peggy Baker
English Teacher
Fitzpatrick, James Ward, Jr.
Instr of Civil Engrng Tech
Freeman, Susan Miller
Art Education Teacher
Gaskins, Joanne Smith
English Teacher
Griffin, Cathy Ligon
Social Studies Teacher
Grogan, Claire Traxler
Government & Economics Teacher
Hallman, Paulette Sherer
Second Grade Teacher
Hayes, Charles Evans
English Teacher
Jackson, Ruth Ann Mauney
Art Dept Chair & Teacher
Johnson, Elizabeth Lee
Fifth Grade Teacher
Lang, Betty Lou Jackson
Professor of Reading Education
Mayo, Sharon Kelly
5th Grd Teacher of GATE
Moore, Mildred Althora
Language Arts & English Tchr
Muckenfuss, Danielle Touchberry
Mathematics Teacher
Nicholson, Brenda Polk
Counselor
Nielsen, Robert Andrew
Math Teacher
Nies, Cheryle Dillon
Journalism Teacher
Plair, Bobby S., Jr.
Cnslr of Student Support Svcs
Reeves, Carrie May Love
Retired 9th Grd Science Tchr
Reeves, John C.
Assoc Prof of Rel Studies
Renwick, Sylvia Heath
English Teacher
Rogers, William
Professor of Biology
Sanford, Susan Dusek
Horticulture Teacher
Sherlock, Susan Vinson
Engr Graphics Tech Instructor
Stout, Cree Whitaker
Electronics Engrng Tech Instr
Sturgis, Laura Ross
Instructor of Economics
Sturgis, Robert Kenneth
Instructor
Sumwalt, Gail Sigmon
Biology Teacher
Swiger, Kay I.
Nursing Instructor
Templeton, Leslie Smoak
Art Teacher
Thomas, Linda Hamilton
Second Grade Teacher
Turner, Elaine McHargue
English Teacher
Wells, Ella James
Life Science Teacher
Whisonant, Richard D.
History & Political Sci Prof
Williams, Delbert Lincoln
Retired Teacher
Wilson, James Edward
History Tchr & Dept Chairman
Winders, Pamela Burch
AP Economics Instructor
Wingate, Debbie Ingraham
2nd Grade Teacher
Wyatt, Elizabeth Love
Biology Instructor
Yost, Mark Steven
Director of Bands
ROEBUCK
Smith, Sherry Lowery
Physical Education Teacher
RUFFIN
Murdaugh, Phyllis Walker
Kindergarten Teacher
Ryant, Jackie
Teacher
SAINT GEORGE
Brown, Rhetta M.
8th Grade Science Teacher
Doty, Christine Horvath
English Teacher
Giordano, Toniann
French Teacher
Kinnon, Elizabeth Evans
French Teacher
SAINT HELENA ISLAND
Ladd, Rosie Marie
Fourth Grade Teacher
SAINT MATTHEWS
Spiers, Mary Jo Herlong
5th Grade Teacher
Walker, Yvonne S.
Typing Teacher
Weeks, George Xennie
Gifted & Talented Teacher

T STEPHEN
:, Emily G.
lish Teacher
eton, Eartha Lee
h Teacher
:M
an, Mark Alden
ematics Teacher
DA
Marion Scott
Arts & Reading Teacher
Martha Bradley
Teacher
aumer, Melany Hamilton
nce Tchr, Curriculum Coord
kins, Jennie S.
Mathematics Teacher
CA
chael, Felicia Young
her
, Suan Buchanan
Grade Teacher
ton, Angela Blackston
ege Prep & AP History Tchr
, Nancy Norbeck
History Teacher
t, Robert O'Bryan
lish Teacher
Cathy Jones
Grade Teacher
Carolyn J.
metology Teacher
, Ann D.
ed & Talented Pgm Teacher
SONVILLE
l, Cynthia Marie (Avery)
hematics Teacher
rong, Sarah Limehouse
sical Education Teacher
, James Anthony
dle School Teacher
er, Valarie Howard
al Studies Teacher
mond, Julia Elaine Butler
Grd Soc Stud & Drama Tchr
, Carolyn Malphrus
th Grade Reading Teacher
n, Sandra Jones
Math & Science Teacher
, Clarinda Carter
nd Grade Teacher
Valerie Elaine
hematics Teacher
edy, LeRoy D.
ral Director
, Barbara Geressy
h Science Teacher
, Annie Nelson
Grd Language Arts Teacher
e, Polly Ann Petherbridge
d Grade Teacher
n, Sandra Taylor
d Grade Teacher
er, Susan Cook
iness Education Teacher
, Martha A.
cipal & Guidance Counselor
MILE
nder, R. Clifton
h Grade Teacher
n, Deborah Whitee
h Grade Teacher
AKS
es, Susan Cannon
lish & Lang Arts Teacher
RTANBURG
nder, Phyllis Huneycutt
ial Studies Teacher
ugh, Faith Youmans
guage Arts Teacher
Charles Gibson
oc Professor of Chemistry
p, Brenda Richards
ld His & Western Civ Tchr
, Carla Trovato
ogy Teacher
on, Peggy L.
h Teacher
rs, Michael Esley
igion Professor
n, Elizabeth Ann
h & Computer Science Tchr
n, James Wilson
tory Professor
t, R. Elizabeth
chology Teacher
, Daniel Ray
erican Government Teacher
on, Andrew Hugh
lish Teacher
ners, Alan Douglas
lish Professor
man, Anne Mosier
h Grade Teacher
, Susan Thackston
th Grade Resource Teacher
, Diana Hunter
oc Prof of Accounting
oor, Karen Fowler
h School Math Teacher
spoti, Daniel J.
f of Computer Science
olly, John Patrick
ver Education Teacher
e, Linda Kocher
ructor of Mathematics
James R., Jr.
fessor of Communication
Richard Ward
Teacher & Varsity Coach

Crosland, Andrew Tate
English Professor
Davis, Christine J.
Art Teacher
Dempsey, Nan Neumeyer
6th Grade Teacher
Dickson, Roy Edgar
World History & Pol Sci Tchr
Dinsmore, Donna J.
Choral Director
Donovan, Edward Peter
Professor of Science Education
Drucker, Meyer
Tax & Law Business Prof
Dunn, Bernard H.
11th Grade US History Teacher
Earle, Dianne Hughes
Chemistry Teacher
Edmonds, Billie O'Shields
AP French Teacher
Edwards, Donna Fortenberry
AP American History Teacher
Ellis, Trudy Black
First Grade Teacher
Everhart, Duane Darrell
Prof & Dir of Criminal Justice
Farr, Virginia Allgood
Spanish Teacher
Fischer, Mark Edward
Band Director
Garrett, Janet Richards
Tchr of Acad Gifted & Talented
Garrick, James Wesley, Jr.
English Teacher
Genoble, Janet Cash
English Teacher
Goode, Linda Pearson
9th Grade Social Studies Tchr
Gordy, Laurie L.
Asst Professor of Sociology
Green, Edythe Radford
English Teacher
Green, Julian Wiley
Geology Professor
Gregory, Randy Timothy
Math Teacher
Griffin, Janet L.
Psychology Professor
Hamilton, Traci Patterson
Tenth Grade English Teacher
Hardy, Frances Lee
English Teacher
Haynes, Judy Henson
English Professor
Henderson, Conway Wilson
Professor of Political Science
Hill, Jeanie "Velma" P.
Phys Sci, Coll Prep, Chem Tchr
Hill, Suzy Monaghan
Adjunct Professor of Geography
Hilton, Pamela Fowler
English Teacher
Hipp, Harriette Jolley
Biology & Anatomy Teacher
Hosley, Broncher Wells
Sixth Grade Teacher
Jeffords, John Stephen
Chemistry Teacher
Johnson, Danny James
Algebra Teacher
Johnston, Caroline Brown
Latin & English Teacher
Jones, Cheryl Jeter
Fourth Grade Teacher
Jones, Kimberley Kirsch
Drama & Public Speaking Tchr
Jones, Ronald David
Math Teacher
Kimbrell, Billie Bethea
English & Honors Rdng Teacher
King, Jeri DeBois
Professor of French
Knight, Barry Allen, Jr.
Science Instructor
Latham, Barbara Ann
9th Grade Language Arts Tchr
LeFrancois, Janet Reames
Assoc Prof of Psychology
Lofton, Paul S., Jr.
History Professor
Marin, Patricia Margaret (Mendez)
Assoc Prof of Elementary Ed
Mc Cravy, Susan Mackenzie
Second Grade Teacher
Mc Dougal, Yancy Beach
Psychology Assistant Professor
Mc Kittrick, Hilda Reynolds
Mathematics Teacher
Meeks, Patsy Player
Soc Stud Teacher & Dept Head
MItchell, Patricia Thomas
Business Education Teacher
Moore, Larry Edward
Asst Prin & Activities Dir
Page, Robert Kenneth
8th Grd Algebra & Math Teacher
Pell, William Herman
Advanced Placement Eng Teacher
Prioleau, Rachelle Charisse
Speech Communication Instr
Prosser, Harold Bascom
Retired Elementary PE Teacher
Rampey, Janet Elizabeth
Physical Ed Teacher & Coach
Redmond, Charles Edward
Assistant Principal
Remaley, Timothy Alpha
US History & Sociology Tchr
Revan, David Randall
9th Grd Eng & Odyssey III Tchr

Robinson, Sandra Satterfield
Biology Instructor
Roper, Aurelia Burns
4th Grade Teacher
Schiltz, Teresa Ray
Biology Teacher
Scott, Aileen Bennett
Sixth Grade Teacher
Settle, Dennis Ralph
Math Tchr & Beta Club Advisor
Smith, Steven Griffith
English Teacher & Dept Chm
Soderlund, Myra Greene
Math Dept Chairperson & Tchr
Taylor, Suzy Goodson
Creative Writing Teacher
Ward, Barry Dean
Hlth, PE Instr & Dept Chair
Worthy, Caroline Henderson
Controller
STARR
Thrasher, Debbie Bagwell
Language Arts Department Chair
STARTEX
Turner, Debra Mason
Science Lab Teacher
SUMMERTON
Fleming, Lottie Henry
Mathematics Teacher
Gould, Katherine Elizabeth
Art Instructor
Konitzer, James Clifford
High School Math Teacher
Oliver, Ernestine Dennis
Seventh Grade Reading Teacher
SUMMERVILLE
Asbury, Mittie I.
Physical Education Teacher
Bilotta, Marie A.
Mathematics Teacher
Boller, Yolanda Hutchinson
Third Grade Teacher
Dearing, John Allard, Jr.
Math Teacher & Dept Chprsn
Dixon, Shirley Mae
Business Education Teacher
Linder, Lillian Little
5th Grade Teacher
Ramon, Toni Sumersett
Fourth Grade Teacher
Robinson, Kelly Dufford
Reading & Language Arts Tchr
Shillabeer, Joyce Maher
Social Studies Teacher
Townsend, Frances Wilder
History & Broadcasting Teacher
SUMTER
Alexander, Martha Mae
Remedial Reading Teacher
Allen, Eva Swisher
Professor
Anderson, Dale Lesley
8th Grade Math Teacher
Betchman, M. Wynn
English Teacher
Bochette, Deidre Tuffelmire
Latin Teacher
Brock, Nate
Ninth Grade English Teacher
Brunson, Sylvia Morris
Third Grade Teacher
Bullard, R. Dale
Asst Dean for Student Affairs
Burns, Regina Barwick
Mathematics Teacher
Cook, Diana L.
French & Speech Teacher
Cousar, Tarah Faith
English Department Chairperson
Dallery, Mary Lee
4th Grade Teacher
Davis, Irene Wells
Teacher
Davis, Jacquelyn Foster
English Teacher
Davis, Stephanie Atkinson
Media Specialist
Decker, David F.
Assistant Professor of History
Disney, Vernon J.
Asst Professor of Business
Dunlap, Jeannette Sims
Soc Stud & Lang Arts Tchr
Freed-Levenson, Andrea
Owner
Frierson, Agnes Pringle
Fifth Grade Teacher
Geddings, Billy Ray
7th Grade Science Teacher
Hatcher, Jean Adams
Associate Professor
Hendley, Susan Goldstein
Asst Professor of Education
Jackson, Deborah Gettys
LA & Reading Teacher
Jackson, James Michael
Jr High History & Bible Tchr
Jones, Ethel N.
Family & Consumer Sci Tchr
Keels, Bernice L.
Math Teacher
Knight, Jacqueline Robin
HS Spanish & English Teacher
Larkin, Ernestine Dickson
Title One Teacher
Lewis, Janice F.
English & Drama Teacher
Locklear, James Grady
English Department Chairman

Lovell, Margaret Welch
First Grade Teacher
Macias, Salvador, III
Psychology Professor
McCrea, Johnnie Boone
Business Education Teacher
Mc Ginnis, Lizabeth Ogburn
Chem, Bio & Anatomy Teacher
Mitchell, Betty Ann Goodman
Soc Stud & Character Ed Tchr
Newman, Terry Fletcher
Science Teacher & Dept Chprsn
Pantuosco, Louis Joseph
Economics Professor
Powers, Thomas Lynwood
History Professor
Ragin, Viola Durant
Preschool Teacher
Richardson, Irene Anderson
Fourth Grade Teacher
Rogers, Marietta Elaine (Peeples)
7th & 8th Grd Reading Teacher
Safford, John L.
Professor of Govt & Philosophy
Sanders, Marilyn S.
Mathematics Teacher
Sepulveda, Sonja Atkinson
Choral Studies Director
Sims, Deborah Gibson
Reading & Language Arts Tchr
Stockbridge, Kay Meadows
Instructor of His & Pol Sci
Veatch, Ann Alexander
US History & Psychology Tchr
Weston, Debra Howard
Keyboarding Teacher
White, Donise Broughton
English Teacher
Wilder, Dorothy A.
Business Education Teacher
Williams, Drefus
Agriculture Teacher
Wilson, Kathleen H.
6th Grade Reading Teacher
Wilson, Mary Ruth
Career Education Teacher
SURFSIDE BEACH
Smoak, Sharon Staursky
Computer & Career Ed Teacher
Stout, Mary Gordon
Tchr of 3 & 4 Year Olds
SWANSEA
Andrews, Emily Suzanne
English Teacher
Ott, Linda Fleming
English Teacher
Powell, Michael Arthur
Band Director
TAYLORS
Barnebee, Rhonda Sims
Spanish Teacher
Brown, Charles Alfred, III
Social Studies Teacher
Carroll, Robin Cordts
Former Teacher
Everette, Kirby Lee
Science Teacher
Garrett, Steve L.
French Teacher
Hardin, Jane Lewis
Choral Music & Drama Teacher
Horton, Rene Spires
English Teacher
Peake, Doris B.
5th Grade Teacher
Sinclair, Lynne Gregory
First Grade Teacher
TIGERVILLE
Bielecki, Dee Riles
English Professor
Hamilton, David Leonard
Assistant Professor of Music
Watson, J. Stephen
Adjunct Professor
TRAVELERS REST
Alexander, Susan Allena
Director of Bands
Bailey, Angela Kay
Math Teacher
Blackwell, Ann S.
Science Teacher
Buchanan, James Clelle
Health & Physical Ed Teacher
Gaines, William H., Sr.
History Teacher
Smith, Betsy Wren
Spanish Teacher
TURBEVILLE
Gibbons, Sherrilyn G.
Math Teacher
Kemp, Penny Phillips
Media Specialist
McElveen, Norman Leon
High Schl Social Studies Tchr
Moore, John Curtis, Jr.
Spanish Teacher
Sowell, Rebecca Early
English Teacher
Taylor, Teresa Fenters
Teacher
UNION
Crocker, Melinda Culbertson
Mathematics Teacher
Gunter, Susanne Floyd
Art Teacher
Inman, James Hayfant, Jr.
High School Electronics Tchr
Jeter, George Davidson
Art & Language Arts Teacher

Knox, Janelle Peay
Job Placement Coordinator
Melton, Reva Faile
Biology Teacher
Moorman, Hattie Loretta
First Grade Teacher
O'Dell, Peggy Farr
Retired Elementary Teacher
Pitt, Joseph Burton, Jr.
Biology Teacher
VARNVILLE
Crawford, Linda Carter
Literature & Lang Arts Tchr
Jacobson, Val Don
Earth Science Teacher
Kemmerlin, Stephen Kearse
Counselor & Driver Ed Teacher
Platts, Martha Price
First Grade Teacher
Rogers, Ann Montgomery
English Teacher
Tuten, Annette Bridges
Choral Music Teacher
WAGENER
Gantt, Phyllis C.
Social Studies Teacher
Pippen, Rhonda Faucette
Fourth Grade Teacher
WALHALLA
Addis, Connie Derrick
1st Grade Teacher
Arisman, Kathleen Mary
Head Supervisor & Teacher
Bearden, Greg Edward
English Teacher
Dyar, Martha Ann
American History Teacher
Johnson, Rebecca Stuart
English Teacher
Layne, Margaret Sprinkle
Fifth Grade Teacher
Scarborough, Joni W.
English Teacher
Shealy, John Player
Social Studies Teacher
WALLACE
Pence, Kimberly Howard
Fourth Grade Teacher
WALTERBORO
Armentrout, Charles Edward
Naval Science Instructor
Bowen, Mary Lewis
Health Occupation Instructor
Bowling, Julie Ann
English Teacher
Carmical, Eleanor Meckley
Language Arts Teacher
Fields, Donna
Guidance Counselor
Jackson, Jenny Loadholt
English & Applied Comm Tchr
Johnson, Pat Spell
7th Grd Tchr of Gifted Stdnts
Martin, Susan Tilley
Teacher & Choral Director
Murdaugh, Cheryl Crapse
Math Teacher
Pawlak, Patricia Rebecca (Burke)
World History Teacher
WELLFORD
Bruce, Tracey Pruitt
Fifth Grade Teacher
Mace, Toni Lynn Berry
Third Grade Teacher
Starnes, Melanie Beiers
K-4th Grade Teacher
WEST COLUMBIA
Allen, Rhonda Elizabeth
Third Grade Teacher
Breland, Angela R.
Math Teacher
Butler, Carolyn
Third Grade Teacher
Covert, Carol Carnley
Third Grade Teacher
Darnell, Erin Aiello
Substitute Teacher
Davis, Michelle Platt
Eighth Grade SC His Tchr
Gordon, Judy Roof
7th Grade Language Arts Tchr
James, William Buryl, Jr.
Principal
Mc Gowan, Brenda Bowers
Choral Director
Meggs, Laura Bradford
8th Grade Pre-Algebra Teacher
Moore, Ellen Clark
Fourth Grade Teacher
Morrison, Venning
Teacher
Pappas, John Larry
Driver Education Teacher
Pennington, Mary (Boylston)
Eighth Grade Reading Teacher
Price, Brenda Rawls
First Grade Teacher
Quickel, Jennifer LaRussa
Spanish Teacher
Rawl, Melissa Caughman
Lang Arts Dept Chm & Teacher
Richbourg, Lola White
Eng Tchr & Stu Act Adv
Seigler, Tammy Long
8th Grade Science Teacher
Sightler, Jerome Charles, Jr.
Retired Instructor
Simmons, Sue Scaife
Marine Science & Bio Teacher

WEST COLUMBIA (cont)
Starkey, Doda R.
Eng I, Creative Dramatics Tchr
Stevens, Rose Galloway
Second Grade Teacher
Strother, Sonya LaPrince
Computer Technology Teacher
Taylor, Amy Chapman
Mathematics Teacher
Thompson, Elizabeth Nichols
Math Teacher & Dept Chprsn
White, Darlene Peterman
Kindergarten Teacher
Wilkerson, Jacob Roy
PE Teacher & Department Head
Young, Jodie Skipper
Fourth Grade Teacher
WESTMINSTER
Corley, Glenn Nixon
Language Arts Teacher
Cothran, Angie Fickling
Home Economics Teacher
Fanning, Kimberly Joy
Spanish Teacher
Holleman, Kelly Norton
Health & Physical Ed Tchr
Joplin, Lisa Powell
English Teacher
Marcengill, Timothy A.
Agricultural Education Instr
Martin, Lisa Hood
English Teacher
McManamay, Randy A.
Biology Instructor
Porter, James Andrew
Business Education Teacher
Smith, Virginia Edwards
Business Teacher & Chprsn
Thorsland, David Campbell
Biology Teacher
WHITMIRE
Oswald, Ann King
Fifth Grade Teacher
Statz, William Lee
LD Resource Teacher
WILLIAMSTON
Albert, Linda Wolff
Second Grade Teacher
Davis, Monica Dee
PE Teacher & Coach
Foster, Parniece Allen
Math Teacher
Hudson, Charlene Coleman
Language Arts Teacher
Pethel, Jean McCown
8th Grade Mathematics Teacher
WILLISTON
Yelton, Buff Morrow
History Teacher & Dept Head
WINNSBORO
Chiles, Sarah James
Soc Studies Tchr & Dept Chair
Gibson, Priscilla Hunter
Alternative Teacher
Mazyck, Raymond Edward
Band Director
Robinson, Vickie Boulware
HS English & French Teacher
WOODRUFF
Brady, Mary Ann Hutto
Mathematics Teacher
Dempsey, Phillip Mark
Social Studies Teacher
Foster, Betsy Edwards
Fifth Grade Teacher
Hughes, Peggy Hall
6th Grade Language Arts Tchr
Lanford, Ginger Switzer
5th Grade Teacher
Lanford, Wanda Crooke
First Grade Teacher
Mc Ferrin, Jane
Third Grade Teacher
Richards, Jan Poston
3rd Grade Teacher
Walker-Merrell, Twedis C.
Home Economics Teacher
Welchel, Ed
Social Studies Teacher & Chm
YEMASSEE
Braswell, Virginia Bowers
4th Grade Teacher
Lester, Johnnie Mae Badger
3rd Grade Teacher
YORK
Brown, Matt
Band Director
Hamilton, William F. (Lin)
World Geography Teacher
Jordan, Lee Boyd
Fine Arts Teacher
Love, Catherine Irene
Soc Stud Dept Head & Tchr
Moore, James G.
Science Teacher
Thomason, William Bonner
Art Teacher

SOUTH DAKOTA

ABERDEEN
Bacon, Richard
Sixth Grade Teacher
Bratland, Cyndi Allmendinger
First Grade Teacher
Chapman, Corene Kay
7th & 9th Grd Lang Arts Tchr
Deibert, Connie Rae Mischke
7th Grade Health Teacher
Everson, Paul O.
Accounting Professor
Garry, Elaine Joyce
Asst Prof of Religious Studies
Haigh, William E.
Professor of Mathematics
Hinds, Kelly Ann
5th Grade Teacher
Kamen, Dennis L.
Anatomy & Physiology Asst Prof
Kraft, Rose Marie (Kline)
7th-8th Grade Math Teacher
LaFave, Linda Christine
Instrumental Music Teacher
Link, Lisa Marie (Braun)
Language Arts Teacher
Mallow, Gail Hollerbach
Assistant Professor of Nursing
Marmorstein, Arthur Robert
Assoc Prof of History
Martens, Bill W.
Business & Physical Ed Teacher
McGregor, Ralph E.
Chemistry Dept Chairperson
Omland, Jacqueline Leigh-Knute
Physics Teacher
Sheehan, Joseph
English Professor
Shekore, Mary Konrath
Title I Reading Teacher
Stone, Mark L.
Social Studies Teacher
Svendsen, Steve Marc
Phys Ed, Hlth Teacher & Coach
Wein, Susan Jane
Social Work Professor
Weins-Kersten, Sandra L.
Business Educator
White, Linda Marie
Sixth Grade Teacher
Wieland, William John
Music Professor
Wuertz, Carol Krueger
Language Arts Instructor
ALCESTER
Clark, Roxanne Marie
High School Business Teacher
ALEXANDRIA
Bell, Deb Lynn
5th Grade Teacher
Gross, Cynthia June (Wagner)
4th Grade Teacher
Pociask, Jill Suzanne Ingemansen
English & Speech Teacher
ALPENA
Gohring, Mary Sievers
Mathematics & Physics Teacher
ARTESIAN
Bowman, Donald Keith
Band & Vocal Teacher
Goldammer, Diana Shelstad
English Teacher
Guericke, Janelle Diane
Business Teacher
Sutera, Don J.
Vocational Ag Teacher
Whitney, Linda K.
K-12th Grade School Counselor
AVON
Kuhlman, Paul R.
Science & Math Teacher
Mikkonen, Patrick Lee
Secondary Social Studies Tchr
Poppe, Bradley Allen
Business & Computer Teacher
BALTIC
Schmitz-Stadem, Marilyn Fae
K-12th Grade Counselor
Sittig, Robert Alan
Secondary Prin & Athletic Dir
BELLE FOURCHE
Ballenger, Gayleene A.
English Teacher
Bryan, Denise Stover
Elementary Teacher
Colling, Jane Alice Hammerquist
Chemistry & Physics Teacher
Custis, Douglas Alan
Biology Teacher
Frink, Joan H.
2nd Grade Teacher
Gusso, Clark
8th Grd American History Tchr
Massie, Margaret Louise
Second Grade Teacher
Ternes, Denise Toevs
Wellness Teacher
BIG STONE CITY
Hansen, Patricia Rae
Fifth Grade Teacher
BISON
Blosmo, John M.
Industrial Ed & Art Teacher
BLACK HAWK
Nemecek, Jane Ryan
Reading Recovery Teacher
BOWDLE
Knecht, Victoria Lynn
Guidance Counselor & Teacher
BOX ELDER
Freeman, Rosetter Mc Knight
High School Teacher
Purcell, Michael James
HS Science Teacher & Coach
Rathe, Michelle Marie
HS AP English Teacher
Richter, Sherry Lou
2nd Grade Teacher
Vogel, Vicke
Pottery Teacher
Williams, Melinda J.
8th Grd Language Arts Teacher
BRANDON
Cool, Pamela Kay
Secondary English Teacher
Foss, Eric
HS Math Instr & Dept Chm
Goheen, Robert Russell
Band Director
Moss, Julie
High School English Teacher
Stadem, Mark
Chemistry Teacher
BRIDGEWATER
Brost, Linda Sue
Math Teacher
Konda, Steve William
Science Teacher
BRITTON
DeVine, Karen Nale
English, Economics & His Tchr
Schultz, Gloria Honrud
Fifth Grade Teacher
Thompson, John H.
Science & Computer Sci Instr
BROOKINGS
Brown, Lewis F.
Assoc Prof of Elec Engrng
Caldwell, Chad Alan
HS Biology & Chemistry Tchr
Cong, Bin
Computer Science Professor
Cumber, Carol J.
Economics Professor
Froehlich, Donell P.
Mechanical Engrng Dept Head
Hatch, Sherwood
Mathematics Teacher & Coach
Hauge, Chad Michael
Intermediate Block Teacher
Johnson, Winnie Krier
1st & 2nd Grade Teacher
Klein, Marsha Case
Spanish & German Teacher
Mc Daniel, Joyce E. Nollmann
Spanish Teacher
Roybal, Desiderio E.
Theatre & Film Instructor
Ryder, Mary Ruth
Associate Professor of English
BUFFALO
Fowler, Maurine Brengle
Substitute Teacher
CANISTOTA
Wicks, Sherry Lane
HS English & French Teacher
CARTHAGE
Walter, Bonita R. (Wipf)
4th-6th Grade Teacher
CASTLEWOOD
Bach, Anita K. (Roe)
9th-12th Grade English Tchr
CENTERVILLE
Anderson, Janice Paulsen
Third Grade Teacher
Ellison, Marilyn Dahl
Language Arts & Science Tchr
Kraning, Lisa Marie
Business Teacher
CHAMBERLAIN
Carlson, Dennis Ray
HS Instrumental Music Teacher
Clark, Karen Elaine
HS English & Speech Teacher
Klein, Bill
Math Teacher
Skinner, Suzanne Jaspers
Family & Consumer Science Tchr
CHANCELLOR
Westbrock, Laura AnnErin
Junior High English Teacher
CLARK
Isaak, DeLane W.
Business & English Teacher
Warren, Luanne E. (Remund)
Sixth Grade Teacher
CLEAR LAKE
Lundberg, Gale Gordon
9th-12th Grade Math Teacher
COLMAN
Albers, Craig J.
Business Teacher & FBLA Adv
COLOME
Bertram, Kimberly London
Sixth Grade Teacher
COLTON
Breitkreutz, Jeffrey Allen
Science Teacher
Leuning, Dean F.
Voc, Ag Teacher & Coach
CORSICA
Brandt, Kelly David
Science Teacher & Bsktbl Coach
De Boer, Susan Gronlund
Fifth Grade Teacher
Moege, Anne M.
High School English Teacher
CUSTER
Cook, Karen Froiland
English Teacher
Grablander, Constance Lorraine
3rd Grade Teacher
Peters, Deanna Olivia
Former Teacher
Shuck, Larry Dean
Eighth Grade Soc Stud Teacher
DE SMET
Geyer, Connie Marie (Steen)
Math & Physics Teacher
Knock, Sharry Lee
Consumer Home Economics Tchr
Strasser, Steven James
9th-10th & 12th Grd Eng Tchr
DELL RAPIDS
Kumerfield, Craig Eldon
Fifth Grade Teacher
Nelson, Randy Lee
English & German Teacher
Schwebach, Robin Rene
Computer & Business Teacher
Stanford, Rodney Lee
Third Grade Teacher
DOLAND
Greenfield, Lana Jean
English Teacher & Chairperson
Nielson, Sally Schulz
Agricultural Ed Instr, FFA Adv
DUPREE
Kissack, Marcella
Second Grade Teacher
Lenk, Quinn Patrick
High School Principal
Wall, Michelle Gill
Third Grade Teacher
EAGLE BUTTE
Eisenbraun, Monica Kinney
English & Journalism Teacher
Keckler, Jessie Tibbs
6th Grade Teacher
Mann, Barry L.
Secondary Teacher & Coach
Peacock, Jerry D.
HS Bus Ed & Computer Tchr
Tays, Glenny Trimble
Upper Elem Media Center Supvr
EDGEMONT
Hendricks, Susan Kay
Secondary Level Math Teacher
Watland, Michelle R.
Guidance Counselor
ELK POINT
Vanderlinde, Robert Carl
Science Teacher
ELKTON
Lundgren, Deanna Renae (Steen)
Kindergarten Teacher
EMERY
Robinson, Sandra Nelson
Science & Chapter I Teacher
ENNING
Baker, Marilyn Elise (Gerdts)
3rd-5th Grade Teacher
ESTELLINE
Schroeder, Michael Lawrence
Science Teacher
Taylor, Gwen Juntunen
High School Mathematics Tchr
EUREKA
Delzer, Sharel (Lorenz)
English Teacher
Greco, Richard V.
Bio, Science & Spanish Teacher
Hermansen, Randy Ray
High School Math Teacher
FAITH
Carmichael, Bryan Lee
8th Grade Teacher
Peterson, Joel Marie
7th Grade Teacher
Vance, Toni Sue
School Counselor
FAULKTON
Bode, Gloria A.
Science Teacher
Witte, Beth Bellack
Third Grade Teacher
FLANDREAU
Benson, Leroy Charles
Mathematics Teacher
Leraas, Dorothy Smallfield
8th Grade Language Arts Tchr
Relf, Brian Richard
6th Grade Teacher
Sutton, Clifton L.
Business Education Teacher
FLORENCE
Black, Mary Kay Young
Business & Computer Instructor
GARRETSON
Schultz, Sandra Kay Merkle
Second Grade Teacher
GAYVILLE
Simons, Elizabeth Kleeman
English Teacher
Steckelberg, Ronald Dean
High School Teacher
GEDDES
Gant, Sandra M.
Bus & Computer Science Instr
GETTYSBURG
Permann, Shirley Ann (Kramer)
English, History & Drama Tchr
Stoner, Patricia Anderson
Sixth Grade Lang Arts Teacher
Torbert, Barton Douglas
Choral & General Music Teacher
GROTON
Nelson, Dorene Sager
English Teacher
Schuring, Brian Joseph
PE & Health Teacher
HARRISBURG
Rebnord, Renee Sue
Secondary English Teacher
Stoebner, Jim H.
Jr HS Science Teacher
HARTFORD
Borgen, Verla Jean (Howe)
HS Mathematics & Physics Tchr
Knutson, Sheryl L.
English & Journalism Teacher
Matheson, Mary Kay (Ireland)
8th Grd Lang Arts & Span Tchr
Mielke, Dawn Rachelle
Kndgtn Tchr & Cmptr Coord
Rist, Linda Anne
Agriculture Teacher
Strom, David James
Science Teacher
Voss, Brian John
Cmptr & Industrial Tech Tchr
HECLA
Nelson, Terry M.
PE, Hlth & Soc Stud Tchr
HENRY
Petrik, Mary Freidel
7th-12th Science Instructor
Weigel, Theresa Malsam
3rd & 4th Grade Teacher
HERMOSA
Hammer, Karen Ann
Second Grade Teacher
Vickers, Larry Arthur
Middle School Math Teacher
HILL CITY
Freeland, Patricia M.
English & Science Teacher
Jobman, Carol A. (Best)
3rd Grade Teacher
Prautzsch, Connie Joan (Roach)
Counselor & Coord of Gifted
Prautzsch, Detlev Klaus
Middle School Principal
Prelle, Margaret Maria
Middle School Instructor
Rudolph, Penny Pike
K-4th Grade ESL Teacher
Sampson, Darwin (Sam) A.
Math Instructor
Shuck, Donna A.
Second Grade Teacher
Weber, Angela Marie
Vocal Music Teacher
HITCHCOCK
Podraza, Frank Joseph
Principal & Mathematics Instr
HOT SPRINGS
Bergen, Ronald Joseph
District Tutorial Prgm Dir
Blair, Patricia Dahlberg
English, Rdng & Writing Tchr
Brost, Sheryl Marshall
Business Teacher
Harris, Beverly Ann Jonas
Teacher for Gifted Education
Snow, DeVonne Condon
Retired Vocal Music Teacher
HOVEN
Coyne, Linda L.
Soc Stud & Frgn Lang Teacher
VonWald, Sheila Lee (Roark)
Sixth Grade Teacher
HOWARD
Eggert, Vernon Ronald
Mathematics & Science Teacher
Foster, Todd Curtis
Business Teacher
HURON
Kleinsasser, Paula Hofer
4th & 5th Grade Teacher
Knight, Mark Lee
Project Coordinator
McLaury, Jane Schallenkamp
Language Arts Instructor
Mueller, Karen Ann
Spanish Teacher
Oleson, Ruth Edna
Assoc Prof & Dean of English
Poore, Margaret Melissa
High School Art Teacher
Reimer, Gertrude A. (King)
Retired Elementary Teacher
Rich, Gretchen Speece
Eng & Speech Comm Instructor
Tate, Vern Aubrey
Professor of History
Tschetter, Edwin John
Professor of Education
IRENE
Kjellsen, Leon D.
Social Studies Teacher
Morrison, Susan Scoblic
Third Grade Teacher
Satter, Barbara Kay
Family & Consumer Sci Teacher
Wohlleber, Arlyn E.
Business Education Teacher
Wohlleber, Connie Hemingway
Band Director
ISABEL
Brenner, Jean Ann
Social Science Teacher
JEFFERSON
Booth, Christina Lynn
Biology Teacher
Riley, David Arthur
Math & Physics Teacher
KADOKA
Fugate, Kathleen A. Schneider
Mathematics & English Instr
Jensen, Kay Norton
Lang Arts, Math & English Tchr
Lund, Arnold
Science & Math Instructor

NEBEC
, Sandra A.
nce Teacher
E
oraun, Cloreta Riggins
dergarten Teacher
E ANDES
ux, Connie Fiscus
lish & Journalism Teacher
GFORD
l, George Alan
al Science & Health Tchr
n, Arthur Everett
nce Teacher
, Ernie
hematics Teacher
:, Barbara Bohle
graphy & Government Teacher
as, Mary Lee (Vehe)
1 Grade Teacher
)
im, Barbara E.
lish Teacher
, Pat
ctor of Bands
Kandace Kay (Mac Kaben)
iness Education Instructor
os, James Thomas
th & Phys Ed Teacher
r, Edith Louise Phillips
d Grade Teacher
MON
n, Ellen M.
al Sci & Bus Ed Teacher
ies, Mary Kathryn James
lish & Spanish Instructor
y, Dorothy Jean
ily & Consumer Sci Teacher
Ronald A.
nce Teacher
, Rebecca Lynn
sic Educator
NOX
tz, Linda Gloe
Teacher
ies, Dan Lee
hematics Teacher
ra, Margaret Joffer
red Elementary Teacher
d, Rick Allen
ory & Geography Teacher
n, Timothy Eston
icultural Ed Instructor
n, Trisha L.
h School Math Teacher
nga, Sandra Gaede
rth Grade Teacher
, Lois Kay
lish Teacher
CHER
ly, V. Jean (Cross)
red Teacher
ISON
an, Jeff Leonard
amural Sports Dir & Coach
ll, Thomas Lee
istant Professor of Busines
ammer, Carolyn Marie
ne Ec Instr & FHA Adv
m, Dorothy D.
red English Teacher
, Barbara Johnson
al Music Teacher
, Dennis James
ector of Bands
erson, Cheryl Lynn
chers Aide
n, Iva May (Gugel)
f of Bus Ed & Office Mgmt
er, Jeffrey Scott
t Professor of Mathematics
nons, Rick
t Professor of Mathematics
, Rhondora Villarta
mistry Assistant Professor
mann, Dorothy M.
istant Professor of Ed
ng, Vicki Woodard
istant Professor
e, Bruce
f of Information Systems
lin-Jansen, Eva
h, PE Instr & Vlybl Coach
RTIN
ofe, Nancy Preszler
glish & Journalism Teacher
n, Michael Vernon
thematics Teacher
hardson, Lisa Sorensen
Grade Teacher & Coach
Overshelde, Tony James
cational Teacher
RTY
hn, Brenda Boughey
glish Teacher
INTOSH
s, Patricia Ann
urth Grade Teacher
h, Robert N.
th Teacher
LAUGHLIN
t, Roy Adam
ostitute Teacher
y, Darlene
Resource Room Teacher
her, Everette Eugene, Jr.
mputer, US His & Ec Tchr
wsma, Wade Allen
-12th Grade Science Teacher

Schmeichel, Georgia M.
English Teacher
MELLETTE
Graves, Kathryn Mary
English & Math Instructor
Larson, Dennis Durand
High School English Teacher
MENNO
Bruckner, Ken D.
Social Science Teacher
Buechler, Jeffrey Karl
Agricultural Science Teacher
Hasz, Joi Ellen (Loudenslager)
7th-12th Grade Math Teacher
Schmitz, Robert Douglas
Math & Science Teacher
MIDLAND
Beck, Bo August
Secondary Principal
Hunt, Effie L.
Coord for Gifted Education
MILBANK
Sussex, Boyd G.
American History Instructor
MILLER
Dannenbring, Lana
Speech & English Teacher
MISSION
Chauncey, Kathy Kary
Psychological Evaluator
Delander, Greg John
Communications Teacher
Dillon, Sandra K. (Figert)
7th Grd Language Arts Teacher
Medhaug, Cal Joe
8th Grade Social Studies Tchr
MITCHELL
Fisher, Donna Schmidt
English & Journalism Teacher
Graber, Diane Adkins
Asst Professor of Human Svcs
Harrington, Karen Scherschligt
Language Arts Teacher
Jorgensen, Mary Kay
Resource Coord of Gifted Ed
Krier, Daniel Lee
General Biology Teacher
Lemon, Robert Harold
HS Science & Elem PE Teacher
Leonard, Gloria G.
Assistant Prof of Ed & Psych
Mitchell, David
Prof of Business & Economics
Olson, Maylin Kevin
Social Studies Dept & Teacher
Padrnos, Diane E.
English Instructor
Sprang, Robert M.
Biology Tchr
Sprung, Randall Lee
Asst Prof of Behavioral Sci
Tatina, Robert Edward
Professor of Biology
Thompson, Gloria Solberg
Assistant Professor of Nursing
Twedt, Patricia Becker
Assistant Professor of Nursing
Weg, Alfred
7th-8th Grade Teacher
Widman, Elizabeth Ann Healy
Family & Consumer Science Tchr
MOBRIDGE
Paulson, Donald G.
Math & Physics Teacher
Utter, Byron D.
Health, PE & Drivers Ed Tchr
MONTROSE
Erickson, Denise Jaspers
Substitute Teacher
MOUNT VERNON
Case, Linda Ward
English, French & Drama Tchr
Fouberg, Jeffrey Thomas
Mathematics Teacher
Giedd, Patricia Ann (Lodman)
First Grade Teacher
Koepke, Carol DeSmet
High School Science Teacher
MURDO
Peters, Margie E.
Language Arts Instructor
Willard, Steven Alan
Tech Ed Instructor
NEW HOLLAND
Koetje, Rick Alan
High School English Teacher
Veurink, Donna J.
Guidance Counselor
NEWELL
Johnston, Delores Wilcox
High School Math Teacher
Parker, Laurie Losch
Title I Teacher
Vissia, Larry Dean
Span, Eng & Soc Stud Teacher
NORTH SIOUX CITY
Hansen, Lisa Karstens
Language Arts Instructor
Young, Gregory Kent
Junior High Science Teacher
ONIDA
Anderson, Darrel Craig
Math & Computer Science Tchr
Schuett, Dale O.
Social Science Instructor
PARKER
Hascall, Barb Soukup
Math Teacher
Huber, James Charles
Sixth Grade Teacher

PARKSTON
Globke, Coleen Albrecht
Family & Consumer Science Tchr
Malloy, Robert Joseph
Math Teacher
Schmiedt, Donna May
Biology Teacher
Schnabel, Melissa A.
High School Math Teacher
Scott, Mike Lee
Soc Stud & Amer Civics Tchr
PIERRE
Armstrong, Hope H.
Sixth Grade Science Teacher
Asher, Lynell DeBoer
Sixth Grade Teacher
Eisnach, Shirley M. (Salmonson)
Retired English Teacher
James, Dennis Ray
Fourth Grade Teacher
King, Carla (Hiemstra)
Lang Arts & Social Stud Instr
Kurth, Harvey Louis, Jr.
American Government Teacher
Mickelson, E. Jay
Latin & German Teacher
Rose, Margaret Ann (Wilcox)
Senior English Teacher
Schlekeway, Gerald R.
Secondary Math Teacher
Smith, Gloria Lind
State Equity Supervisor
Thelen, G. Cleo
K-8th Grade Teacher
Wanner, Troy E.
Sixth Grade Teacher
Williams, Roberta A.
First Grade Teacher
PINE RIDGE
Stands, Janet Schaffter
Jr High Science Teacher
Summers, Steven Wayne
HS Math & Weight Lifting Tchr
Zuver, Judith Gowan
Title I Head Teacher
PLANKINTON
Bartscher, Bonnie Rae
Third Grade Teacher
Harris, Jill Sacks
English & Spanish Teacher
Hoffman, Gail Lynn
Elem Prin & 5th Grd Math Tchr
PLATTE
Peterson, Christa Van Zee
High School Business Teacher
POLLOCK
Borr, Julie Osterloh
K-12th Grade Music Teacher
PORCUPINE
Lessert, Jerry E.
8th Grade Teacher
RAPID CITY
Blackhurst, Shari L.
Business Teacher
Brandt, Gloria J.
Music Specialist & Choir Dir
Braun, Stefani Smith
French Teacher
Bray, Katherine Weaver
English Teacher
Brewick, Dorothy Rees
Soc Stud, World Geog, His Tchr
Bryson, Dean A.
Psychology Professor
Bryson, Janet L. Peterson
Second Grade Teacher
Burnette, Earl
Teacher & Counselor
Cabrera, Pete J., Jr.
Spanish Instructor
Callies, Barbara Ann
Third Grade Teacher
Carpenter, Mary Lynn (Jenks)
English Teacher
Dickschat, Marlene Moss
Third Grade Teacher
Eberle, Julie Platt
English Teacher
Edwards, Susan Madden
Language Arts Teacher
Farrar, Beth Sterner
Biology & Chemistry Teacher
Gill, JoLynn Mc Dougall
7th Grade Science Teacher
Goebel, Mary J.
Science Teacher
Griggs, Robert J.
Paralegal Instructor
Gross, Gary James
8th Grade Social Studies Tchr
Grundstrom, David H.
Social Studies Teacher
Gulbransen, Jeffrey Lee
Art Teacher & Dept Chr
Hime, Alesa Hain
Art Teacher
Houska, Mary Kay (Kelley)
Language Arts Teacher
Hudyma, Irving Ronald
Math Teacher
Johnson, Jami
Spanish Teacher
Johnson, Sheila Ann
Fifth Grade Teacher
Kendall, Carol Jean
8th Grade Amer History Teacher
Kinzer, Joni Rae
5th Grade Teacher
Larson, Linda Marie
English Teacher

Mahoney, Daniel James
World History Teacher
Martin, James
Prof of Geology & Engineering
Mc Lain, Sandra K.
Counselor
Miller, Steve Michael
PE Tchr & Athletic Dir
Minkel, Daniel Goodwin
6th Grade Science Teacher
Mulder, Douglas W.
HS Social Studies Teacher
Muth, Barbara Jeanne
Fifth Grade Teacher
Olsen, Mary Helen
MS Religion Tchr & Liturgy Dir
Powell, Teri Veon
Spanish Teacher
Prosser, Laura Jorgensen
Business Instructor
Ramakrishnan, Vijayalakshmi Unnava
Chemistry Teacher & Dept Chair
Rich, Debra Lynn
Computer Teacher
Richardson, John C.
Computer Coordinator & Teacher
Richardson, Kim A.
HS Mathematics Teacher
Riherd, Ron
Computer & Physical Ed Teacher
Robinson, Arthur Willam
Social Science Teacher
Roper, Carlene Grace
6th Grade Teacher
Rounds, Sybil K.
Foreign Language Teacher
Saunders, Carol Evan
Dean of Students
Scheiber, Eva Ittzes
German Teacher
Schroeder, Kara Strong
5th Grade Teacher
Schroeder, Sabrina Giacometto
Language Arts Teacher
Sneller, Judy Ellen
Asst Professor of English
Southwick, Anella M.
High School Choral Director
Southwick, Clayton Lowell
HS Vocal Music Teacher
Stapert, Rebecca Ann (Harris)
Photography Teacher
Steinken, Ken
Journalism & Spanish Teacher
Tubbs, Scott Sears
American History Teacher
Vetch, Kristina Eichler
First Grade Teacher
Wallace, Jerrianne Hantz
Sixth Grade Teacher
Welsh, Judith Colleen (Anderson)
Fourth Grade Instructor
West, Dana L.
Mathematics Teacher
Whitehead, Karen Louise
Prof of Math & Computer Sci
Wold, Kathleen Kirschenmann
7th Grade English Teacher
REDFIELD
Brace, Cindy Lea (Hauge)
Home Economics Teacher
REVILLO
Boerger, Esther H.
English Teacher
Gussor, Chad Delane
Social Studies Teacher
Pickner, Barry D.
Social Studies Teacher
ROSCOE
Carlson, Mitch C.
Computer & Physical Ed Teacher
ROSLYN
Dunn, Mary Jensen
6th Grade Teacher
Gaikowski, Carol (Carston)
English & Government Teacher
Walker, Joan L.
4th Grade Teacher
SALEM
Norberg, LaVonne A.
First Grade Teacher
SCOTLAND
Busker, Stacy Lynn
Math & Science Teacher
Nicolaus, Stan
Mathematics Teacher
SIOUX FALLS
Anderberg, Ricky Louise (Bryant)
Vocal Teacher
Anderson, Kent Douglas
Soc Stud, World, Amer His Tchr
Bartling, Kimberly Schetnan
Drama & English Teacher
Belfrage, Marta Simon
8th Grade Soc Stud & Hum Tchr
Blunk, Rosella Norma
Speech & Theatre Teacher
Britton, Cathleen Clark
Choral Director
Brown, Sandra Kay (Martinson)
Foreign Language Teacher
Cosby, Michael Ray
Associate Prof of Religion
Coyne, Mary Frances
Mathematics Teacher
Dummermuth, Chris E.
Language Arts Teacher
Dyer, Lynn E.
Accounting Instr & Dept Chm

Eidsness, Jean Sorteberg
Mathematics Teacher
Elverud, Larry C.
7th Grade Math Teacher
Erickson, Eugene Merle
Chemistry Teacher
Fopma, Bryce Dean
English Teacher
Fopma, Phyllis Dragstra
Language Arts Teacher
Gibson, Beverly Hird
Assistant Professor of Music
Handel, Greg Alan
Instrumental Music Educator
Hart, Dale Reed
Speech, Eng & Theatre Teacher
Herman, Charles Wendell
History Professor
Hewlett, Carol Ann
Second Grade Teacher
Hoiland, Pamela J.
K-5th Grade Elem PE Teacher
Jasper, Judy Ann
Elem Physical Education Tchr
Jennings, Jeannette Koch
English Teacher
Jeske, Mary Jane
Middle School Science Teacher
Johnson, Michele Myers
Asst Prof of Accounting
Leitheiser, Carol Danielsen
First Grade Teacher
Leitheiser, Scott Dennis
Biology Instructor
Lubeck, Thomas A.
American History Teacher
Lukens, Jeffrey D.
Biology Teacher
Martell, Shirley Fox
6th Grade Teacher
Miller, Gloria Hofer
Adult Education Instructor
Pickard, Stanely Ray
Physics & Physical Sci Teacher
Pope, Elizabeth Grant
Language Arts & Reading Tchr
Pope, Frank Michael
Drama Teacher & Director
Quam, Joel Eric
Asst Professor of Geography
Rames, Victor Allen
Science Teacher
Rokusek, Charles Raymond
Physical Science Teacher
Schnell, Jane K.
Advanced Chem & Physics Tchr
Schwint, Karyl Heckelsmiller
English & Journalism Teacher
Severson, Mary K.
Spanish Teacher
Skiles, Beverly Hendricks
3rd Grade Teacher
Smith, James F.
Band Director
Streeter, Leonora (Johnson)
Retired Teacher
Streff, Francine K.
Fifth Grade Teacher
Sudbeck, Lois Lawless
Elementary Classroom Teacher
Sylliaason, Alice Helene (Bak)
5th Grade Teacher
Thoreson, Kris James
Biology Teacher
Timm, Jayne Sample
French Teacher
Tucker, Kathleen Grace
First Grade Teacher
Uecker, Eric William
Gifted & Talented Coordinator
VanDenTop, Deonne Renae
Lit, Civics & Social Stud Tchr
Weflen, Gerald G.
8th Grade Math Teacher
Wentzlaff, Maribeth Faye
Campus Minister
SISSETON
Ellingson, Carol Bonnema
Vocal Music Teacher
SPEARFISH
Ahmad, Ahrar
Asst Prof of Political Science
Childs, Jerry L.
Middle School Science Teacher
Gabriel, Stephen Richard
Physics & Physical Sci Teacher
Grant, Teresa Marie
English Teacher
Hansen, Janet J.
5th Grade Teacher
Haux, Robert Harold
Chemistry & Physics Instructor
Syman, Douglas Joseph
Instrumental Music Teacher
Wolff, Roger Dennis
Asst Professor of Education
STICKNEY
Casavan, Duane Lowell
Social Studies Tchr & PE Coach
Punt, Kandy Beesley
Lang Arts Dept Chair & Tchr
STURGIS
Bates, Marilyn L.
Eng Tchr & Adjunct Coll Instr
Benne, Robert Kim
Biology Teacher
Cunningham, Duane Mark
Agriculture Mechanics Instr
Flagstad, Kathie Carlson
French & German Teacher

STURGIS (cont)
Hartmann, Josephine Prior
Curriculum Director
Javersak, Judith K. (Young)
English Teacher & Debate Coach
Kissinger, Michael Keith
Agricultural Education Instr
Maples, Bev Cromwell
Counselor
Martinson, David LeRoy
Director of Bands
Paris, Michael Ray
Physics & Bio Chem Teacher
Rhoden, Sandy Murphy
Elementary Teacher
Schmunk, Virginia Eneboe
6th Grd Math & English Teacher
Williams, Sharon K.
8th Grade Reading Teacher
SUMMIT
Gerriets, Ann M.
English & German Teacher
Kane, Autumn Lee
Health & Physical Ed Instr
TEA
Nelson, Sue M.
Science Teacher
Peterson, Shannon D. (Nelson)
Language Arts Teacher
TIMBER LAKE
Dahl, Shirley Hofmann
Sixth Grade Teacher
Holzer, Diana K. L.
English, Math & Speech Teacher
Maher, Bobbi Woodbury
Spanish & English Teacher
Pecenka, Michael Robert
Physical Education Teacher
TRIPP
Dempster, Wayne Kent
Instrumental Music Director
Hansen, Ray J.
Math & Science Teacher
Wagner, Janet M.
Science Teacher
TYNDALL
Haar, Linda Marie
Language Arts & English Tchr
VALLEY SPRINGS
Hansen, Diana M.
Third Grade Teacher
VERMILLION
Alpers, John Charles
Director of Bands
Baron, Roger M.
Professor of Law
Breed, Philip G.
German Instructor
Green, Roberta Jane
4th Grade Teacher
Kephart, Helen Orr
Mathematics Teacher
Mc Cahren, Nancy Blythe
Director of Alumni & Professor
Olson, Curtis J.
Mathematics Professor
Roegiers, Charles L.
Professor of Management
VIBORG
Snow, Laura M.
Instrumental Music Teacher
VOLGA
Bennett, LeEtta Warren
7th-12th Grd Vocal Music Tchr
Bonde, Machelle L. (Whaley)
Family & Consumer Sci Teacher
Holderby, Sam Scott
Jr High & HS Principal
Livingston, John Herman
Art Educator
Winter, Jeanne Rae
Third Grade Teacher
VOLIN
Jensen, Connie Miller
Third Grade Teacher
WAGNER
Bich, Howard
High School Science Teacher
Kennedy, Shawn Patrick
4th Grade Teacher, Track Coach
Schoepf, Glen L.
Mathematics Instructor
WAKONDA
Olson, Callie Ann
English Teacher & Librarian
WALL
Smith, Guy Clark
Social Science Instructor
Walker, Lori Lenette
MS Language Arts Teacher
Wolford, Amy Marie
Country School Teacher
WARNER
Martens, Gayla Dawn (Hise)
English, Spanish Tchr & Librn
WATERTOWN
Dagel, Carol Zirbel
5th Grade Teacher
Ewald, Scott Joseph
Sixth Grade Teacher
Fischer, Wayne Lee
Administrator
Holm, Jeff Michael
Math Teacher
Meyer, Todd K.
Amer Studies & History Teacher
Ripperger, Dan D.
Psych & Speech Comm Teacher
Roberts, Donus D.
English & Forensics Teacher

WAUBAY
Crawford, Russ E., Jr.
Soc Stud & Span Tchr
Elsinger, Gary L.
Agriculture Teacher
Hanson, Georgia Rae
English, Math & Reading Tchr
Wagner, Lori Tompkins
Mathematics Teacher
WAVERLY
Owen, Nancie L.
Business Education Teacher
WEBSTER
Breske, Cathy Murphy
Nurse
Pirner, Randy A.
Govt Teacher & Coach
Torrence, Gail M.
First Grade Teacher
WESSINGTON
Carda, Charlotte J.
Science Teacher
Larsen, Ann Wendland
Spcl Educ Coord & 6th Grd Tchr
WESSINGTON SPRINGS
Christopherson, Karen Marie
Vocal Music Director
Fonder, Craig Anthony
Junior High English Teacher
Mikkelsen, Mike S.
High School Anatomy Teacher
WESTPORT
Hemen, Elizabeth Ann
Retired 1st Grade Teacher
WHITE
Greenbaum, Lillian Harriet
Foreign Language Teacher
Hofer, Mark Charles
Science & PE Teacher
WHITE LAKE
Krohmer, Jan Sletten
Band Director
WHITE RIVER
Sharp, Lisa A.
Secondary Language Arts Tchr
WHITEWOOD
Kling, Ann Gallagher
Kindergarten Teacher
WILLOW LAKE
Folkestad, Judy Kay
Sixth Grade Instructor
WINNER
Carlson, Glenn Merle
Math Teacher
Johnson, Betty Lloyd
Retired History & English Tchr
Naasz, Brian Patrick
History & Health Teacher
Witte, Gerald Le Roy
Industrial Technology Teacher
WOLSEY
Scheel, Charnelle Lynn
Social Science & Spanish Tchr
WOONSOCKET
Olinger, Kaye E.
5th Grade Teacher
Whitepipe, Carrie Ann
English & Spanish Teacher
YANKTON
Anderson, Richard C.
English Teacher
Gravholt, Loy Eugene
English & Speech Teacher
Haar, Douglas Alan
8th Grd Social Studies Teacher
Johnson, Earl Gilbert
HS Visual Arts Instructor
Lofthus, Richard Robert
History Professor
Merrill, Dorothea Helga
German Teacher
Merrill, Thomas O.
8th Grd Life & Earth Sci Tchr
Messler, Linda Long
Elementary Teacher
Miner, James A.
Math & Astronomy Teacher
Neeman, Patricia F.
Spanish Instructor
O'Connell, Kristi Lee
English Teacher
Petrik, Virgil Dennis
Associate Professor
Tessier, Todd E.
Physical Science Teacher

TENNESSEE

ADAMSVILLE
Campbell, Patricia Leach
Mathematics Teacher
Hovater, Lesia
English & Journalism Teacher
Sims, Joyce Mitchell
Third Grade Teacher
AFTON
Babcock, Linda Lewis
English I Teacher
ALAMO
Bingham, Doris Allen
7th Grade Math Teacher
Jaquess, Virgie E.
GED Instructor
Sherrod, Reida Greenway Hall
5th-6th Grade Soc Studies Tchr
Speer, Lindia Williams
English Teacher

ALCOA
Boone, Robert Allen
Sophomore English Instructor
Brown, Michael
Mathematics Teacher
Clark, Patricia DuBose
English & Theater Teacher
DeYoung, Harry R.
Biology Teacher
Fugate, Paul Stephen
History, Ec & Govt Tchr
ALTAMONT
Myers, Lisa Ann
7th & 8th Grade English Tchr
ANTIOCH
Barbee, Mary Jane
Mathematics Teacher
Cotham, Miles Stanley
French & Biblical History Tchr
Crowder, Janice Beth
Fourth Grade Teacher
Cruze, Chaney L.
English Teacher
Groom, Pamela Jones
French, English Tchr & Mentor
Harville, Gary D.
Social Studies Teacher
Head, Anita Nix
Seventh Grade Teacher
Henson, Linda Keller
Third Grade Teacher
Hunt, Paul G.
AP US & European His Tchr
Lowe, Charles Timothy
Maintenance & Coach
Meadows, Elaine Roberts
Chemistry & Math Teacher
Plummer, Elaine S.
Lifetime Wellness Teacher
Rigsby, Kenneth W.
Biology Teacher
Sanderlin, Alice James
English Teacher
Shreeve, Kristi Sinor
Junior HS English Teacher
Smith, Patricia A.
Visual Arts Specialist
Swor, Charlotte Sooter
Choral Music Teacher
Wilson, Mark Alan
US History Teacher
ARLINGTON
Chipman, David E.
Instrumental Music Teacher
Finley, William H.
American History Teacher
Riggs, Diane Hurst
Kindergarten Teacher
Shriver, William Garrett
AP US History Teacher
Spillers, Teresa Tonette
English Teacher
ASHLAND CITY
Angevine, Philip Dale
Foreign Language Tchr & Chair
Brashears, Jo Murphy
HS Counselor
Darrow, Thomas Wayne
Soc Stud Dept Chm & AP Tchr
McElhaney, Delores R.
Spanish Teacher
McGlasson, Kate Chiles
Geometry Teacher
Redfern, Lori Olds
French Teacher
ATHENS
Anderson, Sharon Griffin
Home Economics Teacher
Blevins, Scotty L.
6th-8th Grd Soc Stud Teacher
Coppinger, Lynn Peterson
Chemistry & Physics Teacher
Godsey, Sherry Buckner
English Teacher
Hall, Reita J.
12th Grade English Teacher
Lockmiller, Mark Douglas
Teacher & Coach
Maynor, Leslie Keith
Drafting Instructor
Monroe, Francis Starr
Retired Eng & Reading Teacher
Pierce, Jonathan Ray
Vocational Agriculture Leader
Reece, Judy Norwood
Kindergarten Teacher
Stevenson, Jean Myers
Education Department Chair
Webb, Ashley
Mathematics Teacher
ATWOOD
Nelson, Ramona L.
Science Teacher
Williams, Rutha C.
Mathematics Teacher
BARTLETT
Tarallo, Connie, SCN
First Grade Teacher
BAXTER
Dillehay, Vickie Gann
Second Grade Teacher
Fletcher, Barbara Ann
Sixth Grade Teacher
McCaleb, Joy
Rdng, Journalism & Speech Tchr
Shanks, Doris Gillen
Third Grade Teacher
Tucker, Linda Gail
English Teacher

BEAN STATION
Day, William Douglas
Assistant Principal
Hagan, Linda McDaniel
1st Grade Teacher
Scheick, Martha Eyvonne (Livesay)
First Grade Teacher
BEECH BLUFF
Coyne, Pamela Belch
Fifth Grade Teacher
BELL BUCKLE
Smith, Ronald Martin
English Teacher
BENTON
Davis, Ronald T.
Teacher & Coach
Dunn, Connie Fay
12th Grade English Teacher
Mason, Bobbie Loren
Business Education Teacher
Pippenger, Wilma Jean
United States History Teacher
BETHPAGE
Anderson, Judith Simpson
Fifth Grade Teacher
BLOUNTVILLE
Adams, Rosemary Uccello
Instructor
Bloomer, Charles Edward
Welding Instructor
Davidson, Robert Church
Instrumentation Professor
Davis, Linda Dennise
Assistant Professor
Foerster, Kathy Diann
Language Arts Teacher
Hall, William Alexander
Assoc Prof Drafting & Design
Hamilton, Allana Rose
Biology Instructor
Irick, Jeffrey Allen
Asst Prof of Math & Physics
Landers, Jerry Franklin
Athletic Director & Coach
Larkins, Jan H.
Counselor
Lyon, Yvonne Fisher
4th Grade Teacher
Mc Kinnie, James Allen
Assoc Professor of Accounting
O'Dell, Sue Ella
Chemistry Teacher
Palmer, Gary Lester
Machine State Technology Instr
Poe, Sandra Meade
English Teacher
Smith, Janice Greene
6th Grade Teacher
Smith, Lanny D.
History Teacher
Stephens, John F.
Teacher
Street, Anita Jan
Mathematics Teacher
Walters, Gregory Norman
Asst Dir of Public Information
Weatherly, Martha Cox
Fourth-Fifth Grade Teacher
BLUFF CITY
Burleson, Christopher Rae
Biology Teacher
Combs, Betty Hardin
Fifth Grade Teacher
Dyer, John Lyndon
American History Teacher
Lawrence, Rebecca Ann Holly
First Grade Teacher
Morton, Mary Littrell
Mathematics Teacher
O'Dell, Patsy Griffith
11th-12th Grade English Tchr
Simerly, Betty Jo Nidiffer
Guidance Counselor
Stitt, Deborah Sartain
English Teacher
BOLIVAR
Beaver, Gregory Todd
9th-12th Grd Mathematics Tchr
Harris, Fredell
Wellness & PE Teacher
Harrison, Anthony R.
Band Director
Kessler, Gail Heinzen
6th Grade Teacher
Kirk, Teresa Houston
Kindergarten Teacher
Powell, Dorrie Johnson
English & Journalism Teacher
BRADFORD
Essary, Nancy Poston
Guidance Counselor
Matheson, Carolyn Sue
Third Grade Teacher
BRENTWOOD
Ash, John E.
Chem Teacher
Box, Randal Wade
Band Director
Burton, Glyn Allen
Calculus & Physics Teacher
Capehart, Vicki Haselip
Math Teacher
Medlin, Harriet L.
English Tchr & Forensic Coach
Pate, Dennis Franklin
Social Studies Teacher
Stockton, Judith Beeler
Rdng, Eng & Math Teacher
Vorbusch, Irene Margarete
Fifth Grade Teacher

BRICEVILLE
Barnes, Betty Moberley
Third Grade Teacher
BRIGHTON
Seagrave, Marlyn Wright
Fourth Grade Teacher
BRISTOL
Ahlseen, Mark Jason
Associate Prof of Economics
Ashburn, Sheila Andrews
Child Care & Guidance Teacher
Beth, Susan H.
Computer Science Teacher
Booher, Anna L. Carr
Govt, Ec Tchr & Dept Chprsn
Brown, Jacalyn Stigall
Third Grade Teacher
Chandler, James William
Teacher & Principal
Collier, Marsha Golden
Mathematics Teacher
Daugherty, Anita Ann
English Teacher
Davis, Patsy Leonard
Office Technology Teacher
Dickerson, Nancy Leonard
Honors Biology Teacher
Dirlam, David Kirk
Professor of Psychology
Dodson, Brenda Lou
2nd Grade Teacher
Gatanis, Harry Stephen
Clinic Director
Grindstaff, Mark Dean
Social Studies Teacher
Hale, Dianna Lynn
7th Grd Soc Stud & Rdng Tchr
Jennings, Debbie Crawford
Math Teacher
Loudermilk, Rebecca Anderson
First Grade Teacher
Loveday, Melinda Maynard
Seventh Grade Teacher
Macione, Beatriz Huarte
Assistant Professor of Spanish
Mc Clanahan, James Samuel, Jr.
Asst Prof of Bible & Religion
Messer, Stacey J.
Spanish Teacher
Peake, Thomas Rhea
History Prof & Soc Sci Div Chm
Peters, Doris C.
English Teacher & Coordinator
Pickard, Simeon Taylor
Assistant Prof of Chemistry
Schartung, Joan Riney
AP Chemistry Teacher
Sochalski, Steve D.
Physics & Biology Teacher
Weeden, Debbie Arrants
Kindergarten Teacher
Woolsey, Linda Mills
English Professor
BROWNSVILLE
Angotti, Sandra S.
Fourth Grade Teacher
Bond, Dorothy Jean Mann
5th Grade Math Teacher
Clark, Ray W.
Computer Teacher
Jackson, Susan Denise
Choral Teacher
Sain, Adrienne Johnson
Biology & Physical Sci Teacher
Thompson, Rhonda Irvin
HS Consumer & Family Sci Tchr
Watts, Ruth Schaefer
Retired Kindergarten Teacher
BRUCETON
Blackwell, J. Dennis
Science Teacher
Norval, Joe Robert
Special Education Tchr & Coach
Scott, Theresa Diane
Math & Science Teacher
BUFFALO VALLEY
Stout, Dorothy Denny
Retired Teacher
BULLS GAP
Jones, Brenda Burris
6th-8th Grd Advanced Math Tchr
Snelson, Martha Harrison
Fifth Grade Teacher
BURNS
Fisher, Leverne Woods
Second Grade Teacher
Madden, Rhonda Jean
Fourth Grade Teacher
BUTLER
Calhoun, Jerry Fred
5th-8th Grade Teacher
CAMDEN
Allen, Wanda Waller
Adv Amer His & US Govt Teacher
Florence, Linda Wages
American History Teacher
Garrett, Jerianne
Resource Teacher & Coach
Hawkins, Paula Covington
Spanish Teacher
Leonard, Michelle Marie
Biology I & II Teacher
Liebergesell, Anita L.
Retired Eng & Span Teacher
Lumpkin, Cynthia Rawls
7th & 8th Grade English Tchr
McDowell, Shawn Carter
Geography Teacher
Meise, Kathy Latham
Kindergarten Teacher

EN (cont)
, Linda Barrett
nistry Teacher
Phyllis Park
h Science & Tech Teacher
Judy Christopher
Grade Teacher
HAGE
nt, Martha C.
ocal Ed & Earth Sci Tchr
, Janet Sanderson
omics & Business Teacher
s, Katherine Beech
entary Teacher
, Debbie Agnew
or English Teacher
ee, Lisa Saxton
ial Education Teacher
es, Pamela Elaine
nth Grade Lang Arts Tchr
l, Wendolyn Kemp
d Geog & Economics Tchr
Dorris Taylor
l Grade Teacher
ll, Cynthia Heim
culture Extension Agent
y, Larry Dean
th Grade Math Teacher
, Eudelle Wilburn
or High Guidance Counselor
n, Diana Brooks
Grade Teacher
re, Jill High
ergarten Teacher
Marie Roberts
n Grade English Teacher
R HILL
t, Louis Eugene
n Teacher
s, Elizabeth B.
al Studies & Spelling Tchr
NA
e, Diana Faye
n Teacher
, Jerry L.
culture Teacher
ERVILLE
y, James Wilson
t Education Supervisor
Marlon Jay
His, Ec, Psych Tchr & Coach
pasture, Ridonna Horner
Grade Teacher
l, Mary Jane
atre Teacher
ey, Betty Thomas
ner 1st Grade Teacher
s, Mike DeWayne
ers Education Tchr & Coach
son, Elizabeth Leigh
ource Teacher
n, Linda Morrell
netology Teacher
Janice Spencer
ors English I & II Teacher
Billie Herndon
Grade Math Teacher
n, Juanita Nell
nish, French & English Tchr
PEL HILL
Rebecca Scott
Grade Teacher
an, Peggy Dugger
e Economics Teacher
, Nancy Allen
n & English Teacher
RLESTON
, Bonnie R.
His, Govt & Ec Tchr, Chprsn
n, Sharon Watson
ebra Teacher
ard, Cynthia Lynne
nce Teacher
RLOTTE
s, Ernestina Mc Elrath
Principal
TTANOOGA
nson, Rebecca S.
Grade Teacher
rson, Kemmer
ish Teacher
rson, W. Frankie Taylor
h Teacher
eby, Judy Madron
Grade Teacher
r, Catherine Elton
ors Jr & Sr English Teacher
ss, Dorothy Hale
ond Grade Teacher
l, Karen H.
e I Teacher
ing, Beverly June
Grade Teacher
son, Anne Hanshaw
nish Teacher & Dept Head
lnax, Sarah Edwards
dance Director
n, Carolyn Tinker
eral & Choral Music Teacher
n, Charles Addison
iness Admin Dept Chair
ll, Carolyn P.
Grade Teacher
on, R. Foster
fessor of Sociology
ard, Nina Stephens
ector of Counseling
nan, Helen Thorton
ond Grade Teacher

Craft, David R.
Fine Arts Teacher
Craw, Roxanna Edwards
Music Teacher
Crawford, David Hale
Economics Teacher
Dammann, Ruth Smith
English Teacher
Dance, Noble S.
Math & Social Studies Teacher
Deering, Raymond P.
English Teacher
Downer, Rita Heard
Kindergarten Teacher
Edmundson, Louie
Professor of English
Elder, Natalie Scott
7th Grade Science Teacher
Erhart, Michael David
Mathematics Teacher
Fischer, Sharen F.
5th Grade Math Teacher
Foster, Edwin Powell
Prof & Dir of Civil Engrng
Gawrys, Sue S.
English Department Chair
George, C. Steven
English Teacher
Gibson, Elaine Wilson
French & English Teacher
Gwaltney, Edward Parks
Music Director
Hain, John David
Associate Professor of English
Hall, Linda Shepard
Flight Dir & Hamilton Co-Tchr
Harris, David Mc Clain
History Teacher
Harvey, Jamie Fairbanks
Exercise Science Instructor
Henry, Kenneth H.
English Teacher & Bsktbl Coach
Hill, Michael Gene, Sr.
History & Geography Teacher
Hixson, Madeleine Davis
Lang Arts & Soc Stud Tchr
Hood, Tassi Renee
Soc Studies & AP His Tchr
Howie, Ronald Wyman
JROTC Instructor
Huddleston, Mary Barnes
Fourth Grade Teacher
Hysinger, Frances A.
Algebra I & Math IV Teacher
Jarrett, Linda Young
Early Childhood Ed Director
Kasch, Cathie Ault
Director of Dance
Kaye, Brenda
Third Grade Teacher
Kennedy, Daniel
Mathematics Teacher
Kerr, Jan Jones
English, Speech & Theater Tchr
Key, Perry Connor
Experiential Education Dir
Krabbendam, Lubertha J.
HS German Teacher
Lane, Billie Slatten
Assistant Professor of Biology
Lanza, Robert M.
English Teacher
Ledford, Allan Aubrey
Choral & Musical Theaters Dir
Leffew, Penny Ingle
Fourth Grade Teacher
Lyons, Beatrice Rutledge
Assoc Prof Amer Sign Lang Stud
Marlowe, Robert Lloyd
Associate Professor of Physics
May, Mary Knott
Chemistry Teacher
Mcafee, Janice Shipley
English Teacher
Mc Call, Isabel Bryan
Art Teacher
McCance, Carol McDevitt
Student Court Teacher & Adv
Meagher, Eileen Mary
English Professor
Monroe, Timothy Wayne
Fourth Grade Teacher
Morgan, V. Lynne
English Instructor
Mynatt, Cheryl Logue
Mathematics & Bible Teacher
Neely, Catherine M.
Physical Education Teacher
Nevins, Gail Louise
Math Dept Chm & Teacher
Olson, Robert Bernard
History Teacher & Dept Chm
Parker, Jim Edward
Math Teacher
Parks, Terrie Jean
Wellness & Physical Ed Teacher
Pearson, Constance Purtee
Academic Services Vice Pres
Penny, James Warren
Senior Army Instructor
Perry, Wilma White
Language Arts Teacher
Roland, Paul Todd
Science Teacher & Coach
Rushing, S. Kittrell
Communication Dept Head
Sholl, Kenneth A.
Dean of Students & Math Tchr
Smith, Andrew
Fine Arts Faculty

Smith, Frank Wilson
Electrical Engineering Instr
Smith, Karen Morse
Dance Instr & Schl Dir
Smith, Melissa Amburn
Social Studies Teacher
Sneller, Calvin Dean
High School Mathematics Tchr
Sparks, Linda Raulston
Eng & Broadcast Jrnlsm Teacher
Sparn, Mary Margaret
Math Teacher
Starling, Harriet G. C.
Social Studies Teacher
Stephenson, Mark Lee
World History & Economics Tchr
Strang, John Sharp
7th Grade Bible Teacher
Sturtevant, Thomas B.
Assistant Professor
Swygart, Glenn Lavon
History Professor
Trayer, David Mc Guire
Industrial Hygiene Professor
Underwood, Jeanette Dysart
Co-Director & Instructor
Walton, William Lee
Mathematics Teacher
Ward, Allene Taylor
English Teacher
Ware, Robert Allen
Biology & Chemistry Teacher
Watson, Thomas Edward
Mathematics Teacher & Coach
Weiss, Debra Steranko
Algebra & Pre-Algebra Teacher
Welsh, David M.
Spanish Teacher
Wood, Grant Jay
Dean of Residential Life
Woodward, Michael Vaughan
American History Dept Chair
Wooley, Stephen Bruce
Bible & Religion Teacher
Young, Annette Toles
French Teacher
Young, Michael Jacob, Sr.
Social Studies Teacher
CHUCKEY
Tarlton, Richard Lee
5th & 6th Grade Teacher
Wright, Nancy Barkley
7th Grade Teacher
CHURCH HILL
Cloud, Danny Scott
Social Studies Teacher
Dougherty, Jimmie Winegar
8th Grade English Teacher
Grigsby, JoAnn Jenkins
Spanish & Math Teacher
Osborne, Terry Johnson
Art Teacher
Wines, Bobby L., Jr.
6th Grade Science Teacher
CLAIRFIELD
Cobb, Evelyn
Second Grade Teacher
CLARKRANGE
Burnett, Wanda Gail (Bassett)
Third Grade Teacher
Hendricks, Debra Reagan
Math Department Chairman
CLARKSBURG
Baker, Teresa Thomas
Mathematics Teacher
Scott, Olivia Ann (Lewis)
Social Studies Teacher
CLARKSVILLE
Armstrong, Juna Lee
Third & Fourth Grade Teacher
Ashcraft, Carole Reed
3rd Grade Teacher
Batie, Lynne
Guidance Counselor
Berard, Beverly Ann
Biology & Physiology Teacher
Brengel, JoAnne Ruth
Fifth Grade Teacher
Brunet, Martha Kimbrough
Biology Teacher
Celusta, Teresa Jean
Chemistry Teacher
Cobb, Gail H.
Assistant Principal
Conner, Lynda Wilkerson
Seventh Grade Science Teacher
Cook, Beverly Noel
Title I Math Teacher
Cooper, Sarah Ditmore
English Teacher
Damron, Dorothy H.
7th Grade Math Teacher
Daniel, Nancy Jones
5th Grade Teacher
Eaves, Arthur Joseph
English Professor
Ervin, Phyllis Boyer
First Grade Teacher
Ferrell, Carolyn Stier
Biology I Teacher
Genz, David Martin
Anatomy, Physiology & PE Tchr
Gibson, Gloria Jean
Business Education Teacher
Gildrie, Richard Peter
Professor of History
Haddock, Marilyn Cowan
Fourth Grade Teacher
Hix, Sharon Floyd
Biology, Phys & Earth Sci Tchr

Irwin, Edward
Professor of Language & Lit
James, Betty Sykes
Science & Social Studies Tchr
Jarrett, Pamela Deneen
Biology & Chemistry Teacher
Jones, Karen Sue
Mathematics Teacher
Kennedy, Kerri Dougherty
Former 5th Grade Teacher
Kirby, Anita S.
Mathematics Teacher
Lange, Kathleen Golla
5th Grade Teacher
Littleton, Jackie F.
6th Grade Teacher
Long, Ann Young
Assistant Principal
Meacham, Karen Vickrey
Vocational Office Ed Teacher
Monaghan, Patrick Charles
HS Physical Science Teacher
Parker, Pamela Herring
Science Department Chairman
Parker, Pollyanna Norman
Theatre Arts Teacher
Petty, Cathy Byrn
Chemistry Teacher
Phillips, Betty Beaumont
Eighth Grade Science Teacher
Ramsey, Gordon Edward
7th Grade Social Studies Tchr
Rice, Janet Welch
6th Grade Social Studies Tchr
Riggins, Carolyn Frances
Dir of Choral Music & Chair
Rye, Patricia Combs
Science, Jrnlsm & PE Teacher
Scapellato, Sean Adam
English Teacher
Schoonover, Lynne Potter
English Teacher
Slight, Kimberley Lynn
Mathematics Teacher
Spiceland, Janet H.
Guidance Counselor
Taylor, David Michael
Senior Army Instructor
Taylor, Pamela Bartholomew
High School English Teacher
Tharpe, Michael Lynn
Assistant Principal
Tidwell, Brittie Cunniff (Cole)
German Teacher
Tucker, Elaine Hammond
Spanish Teacher
Wanstrath, Gay Arnold
Physical Ed & Health Teacher
Williams, Iona Milburn
Kindergarten Teacher
CLEVELAND
Adams, Jerry Kenneth
Asst Prof of Mathematics
Bagwell, Ann C.
Kindergarten Teacher
Bailey, R. Mark
Music Asst Prof & Bands Dir
Bayles, Bob R.
Christian Education Professor
Bishop, Patricia Smith
Asst Professor & Hnr Prgm Dir
Blankenship, Gary Steven
English Teacher
Bowdle, Donald Nelson
Prof of History & Religion
Burns, Charles Alan
Assistant Professor of Bus
Burns, Jim W.
Professor of Music
Coulter, Christopher Allen
Assistant Professor of English
Donegan, Ricky Wilson
Instrumental Music Teacher
Echols, Evaline
Professor of Business & Chair
Eledge, Jean Dorothy
Fr & Foreign Lang Methods Prof
Fair, Frances Dianne
Fifth Grade Teacher
Felton, Rudy Jay
Social Studies Teacher
Flowers, Jerry Everette
Instructor of Bus & Computer
Frazier, Martha Montgomery
World Geography Teacher
Gibson, Janice Ann
Science Teacher
Goff, Doyle Roger
Associate Professor of Psych
Golledge, Cynthia Philippa
Coord of Freshman Studies
Goodman, Cathy B.
Math Teacher
Grant, Raymond A.
Teacher & Coach
Green, Angela Creech
Instructor of English
Griffith, Robert V., Sr.
Associate Professor of Math
Harris, Ronald Lee, Sr.
Professor
Herron, Robert
Vice President & Exec Asst
Hill, Mitzi Ann
Spanish Teacher
Hixson, Doris K.
Advanced Placement Eng Tchr
Hoffman, Daniel Lee
Assistant Professor of History

Jasso, Hermilo, Jr.
Asst Professor of Business
Johnson, Dianna Lovelace
8th Grd Language Arts Teacher
Kidwell, Martha Allen
Art Teacher
Lackey, Carol King
Office Education Teacher
Lindsey, Ruth Crawford
Associate Professor of English
Lofgren, Janet Kruse
8th Grade Language Arts Tchr
Mauldin, Penny L.
Chemistry Professor
Mauldin, Walt
Dir of Grad Studies in Music
Mc Amis, Steven Earl
8th Grd American History Tchr
Mc Clanahan, Kaye White
Algebra Teacher
Mc Cormack, Vivian Richards
Third Grade Teacher
Morris, Randy T.
Algebra I & II Teacher
Mundy, Karen Carroll
Professor of Sociology
Murphy, Adelia Goodrum
Kindergarten Teacher
Nolte, Molly Mulligan
English Teacher
Norman, Phyllis Jones
Biology Teacher
Pace, Shirley Barnett
Choral & Musical Director
Payne, Daina Teague
Trade Industrial Instructor
Reno, Martha Hooper
Elementary Librarian
Riggins, Gary Lee
Assoc Prof of Psych & Ed
Sheeks, Eleanor S.
Former Instructor
Sines, Richard Ray
His & Ed College Instructor
Smith, Dani Allred
Asst Prof of Sociology
Smith, Haden
Exploring Techology Teacher
Smith, Lynda Word
First Grade Teacher
Snell, William Robert
Professor of History
Snider, Sandra Evon
Health Science Instructor
Suits, Daina Christine
Fifth Grade Teacher
Suttles, David C.
Mass Communications Professor
Swearingen, Mary Reed
Fifth Grade Teacher
Thompson, Dewayne G.
Assoc Professor of Business
Tillman, Joel Robert
Band Director
Veenstra, Jeri Jones
Adjunct Professor of Biology
Walkins, Mary Belinda
Assistant Professor of Math
West, Robert Paul
Assistant Professor of Biology
White, Charles A.
Asst Professor of Biology
Wood, Lyman Richard
Social Studies & History Tchr
Wood, Martha H.
Fifth Grade Teacher
Wright, Phyllis Nichols
Latin & Bible Teacher
CLIFTON
Franks, Carolyn Dicus
Reading & Social Studies Tchr
Lay, Peggy Selph
Third Grade Teacher
CLINTON
Caldwell, Mary M.
First Grade Teacher
Davis, Jim D.
Teacher
Eggers, Elaine S.
Bus & Off Technology Teacher
Fellers, Diane S.
Biology Teacher
Foulds, Elizabeth Pennell
Home Economics Teacher
Ingle, Michael Edgar
Honors Science Teacher
Ingle, Paula Medlin
Choral Music Teacher
Jones, Gail Hutchison
Kindergarten Teacher
Jones, Jo Ruth
Third Grade Teacher
Kile, Jeffrey Alan
Band Director
Leach, Janice Jernigan
Health Science Tech Instr
Muncy, Estle P., II
Drafting Instructor
Norris, Kaye Vandagriff
8th Grd English & Reading Tchr
Oliver, Linda Ritchie
8th Grade US History Teacher
Ousley, Ralph Lea
6th Grade Teacher
Pickel, Randall Leon
Choral Music Teacher
Rains, Virginia Patrick
Retired Fifth Grade Teacher
Shelton, Brenda K.
Scndry Office Technology Instr

CLINTON (cont)
Smith, Joy Alley
Marketing Teacher
Stansberry-Nolen, Teresa
English Teacher
Usry, Mary Anne
Office Technology Coop Coord
Williams, Leslie Arthur
Choral Music Dir, Fine Art Chm
COALFIELD
Jackson, Betty Wilson
Fourth Grade Teacher
Justice, Mona Anne
English & Journalism Teacher
COLLEGEDALE
Anders, Pamela K.
Business Education Teacher
Benge, Robert Cameron
Physical Education Specialist
Bolton, Robert Mack
Director of Bands
Leeper, Jeffrey Charles
Assoc Professor of Accounting
Mc Clarty, Wilma K.
Professor of English & Speech
Morford, Alvin Melvin
Math, Physics & Chemistry Tchr
Nyirady, Laura Fae
Associate Professor of Nursing
Ries, Mary Jayne Davis
First Grade Teacher
Swafford, Carleton Lee
Science & Outdoor Ed Tchr
Winters, Judy Brodersen
Associate Prof of Nursing
COLLIERVILLE
Bennett, Valerie Michaud
High School French Teacher
Brasher, Shelli C.
Mathematics Teacher
Comella, Carolyn Hastings
Guidance Counselor
Fiveash, Peggy Scott
8th Grade Science Teacher
Fuller, Brian Keith
Social Studies Teacher
Kaiser, Dolores Huffington
Second Grade Teacher
Kenley, Becky June
Biology Teacher
Kerns, Cheryl A.
Algebra, Business & Mrktg Tchr
Lebo, Julie Ann Barker
English Teacher
Martin, Judith Tipton
English Teacher
May, Lee Etta
Retired Teacher
Medling, Pat Widner
3rd Grade Teacher
Ryan, Robbie
Physical Science Teacher
COLLINWOOD
Morris, Leslie Stegall
Third Grade Teacher
COLUMBIA
Bone, Rosemary Cook
Fourth Grade Teacher
Bridges, Mark Thomas
History Teacher
Burns, Phillip Wade
Drafting Teacher
Byrn, William Womack, Jr.
History & Geography Teacher
Cathey, Jo Hasty
Coord of Developmental Math
Curry, Jim
Sixth Grade Math Teacher
Duncan, Dorothy Pardue
7th & 8th Grade Math Teacher
Farris, Barry Lain
Science Department Chm & Tchr
Flanigan, Nadine Faye
Science Teacher
Franklin, Tracy Norman
Mathematics Teacher
Fulton, Lou Banks
Math & History Teacher
Gidcomb, Debra Martin
Home Economics Teacher
Hargrove, Terry Clay
Eighth Grade Reading Teacher
Hulen, Molly C.
Math Teacher
Jessop, Sharon Griggs
Algebra Teacher
Lester, Linda Shepard
Drug-Free & Safe Schls Facltr
Lewis, Cynthia Bales
Math Teacher
Matlock, Constance Marks
Latin Teacher
Moore, Betty Jane Graham
Family & Consumer Sci Teacher
Pruett, Pamela G.
English Teacher
Richardson, Charlene G.
Third Grade Teacher
Roberson, Judy Pitts
English Teacher
Speed, Karen Johnson
Spanish Teacher
Vaughan, Hilda King
Second Grade Teacher
Vick, Gregory Harris
Speech & Bible Teacher
Walker, David J.
English Teacher
Williams, Anita O'Rear
7th Grade Science Teacher
Williams, Victoria Lynn
General Business Teacher
COOKEVILLE
Amaral, Brian Robert
Instrumental Music Teacher
Anderson, Bruce Martin
Drama Teacher
Anderson, Teri Sloan
Instructional Supervisor
Bailey, Sue Dodson
Home Economics Professor
Cunningham, Cathy Hix
Professor
Durm, Angeli Buck
Asst Professor, Schl of Nrsng
Gunter, Michael Martin
Professor of Political Science
Hawkins, Carolyn C.
Senior Guidance Counselor
Jared, Barbara Slatten
Instructor
Phillips, Hugh L.
6th Grade Math Teacher
Schrader, William Christian
Professor of History
Shanks, Kathy Sutton
Chemistry Teacher
Stanton, Beverly Bruce
5th Grade Teacher
Stearman, Gail Wehrmann
Assistant Prof of Nursing
Talbert, David Lowell
Band Dir & Fine Arts Comm Chm
Watson, Tara Denise
Assistant Professor
Winfree, Sam K.
Professor of Animal Sciences
CORDOVA
Baker, Dee
Algebra Teacher
Best, Joan Frances
English, French Tchr & Chair
Cheatham, Wanda Marie
High School Choral Director
Fee, Wanda Beaver
6th Grade Teacher
Gemeinhardt, Carol Boutwell
Retired Band Director
Higley, Jean Irene
Physics & IPS Teacher
Meadows, Bonnie Cox
Sixth Grade Reading Teacher
Nixon Rhoads, Jan
Third Grade Teacher
CORRYTON
Cooper, Sheila Ray
English Teacher
COSBY
Whaley, Kathy O.
7th-8th Grade Classroom Tchr
COVINGTON
Barger, Grace L.
Span & World History Teacher
Claybrooks, Rhonda Vonnette
7th Grd Math & Lang Arts Tchr
Fleming, Betty Ervin
Music Teacher
Frego, George Richard
Spcl Ed, Gifted & Spanish Tchr
Hadley, Marshall Ray
Principal
Jacobs, James Robin
Teacher & Coach
Jenkins, Daphne Dianne Parr
Science & Language Arts Tchr
King, Beverly Flinn
Elementary School Counselor
Miller, Douglas H.
Algebra Teacher
Rone, Theta Kelley
8th Grade Math & Algebra Tchr
Somerville, Katie Frances
Fourth Grade Teacher
Spray, Martha Jane
6th Grade Math Teacher
Thompson, Lois W.
English Teacher
Turner, William Ted
Agriculture Education Instr
Wortham, Avonne
English Teacher
Young, Sharon Ann
8th Grade Language Arts Tchr
COWAN
Brewer, Randall E.
Math Teacher
Carter, Kimberly Danley
Math Teacher
McCaleb, Glenda W.
Fifth Grade Teacher
Smith, Debbie Robertson
8th Grade English Teacher
Watson, Gail H.
Librarian
CRAB ORCHARD
Johnson, Elizabeth Kaye
7th & 8th Grd Mathematics Tchr
CROSS PLAINS
Hooper, Renee Fisher
4th Grade Teacher
Weeks, Danny L.
Assistant Principal
Whitlow, Daniel P.
Asst Prin & Agriculture Tchr
CROSSVILLE
Allen, Patricia Winters
7th Grd Eng, His & Comp Tchr
Atkinson, Elmer J. D., Jr.
Marketing Teacher
Coffey, Sherrie Bonita
Second Grade Teacher
Davis, J.C.
American History Teacher
Eberhart, Janice S.
Keyboarding & Typing Teacher
Hedgecoth, Ruby Loretta
Third Grade Teacher
Kidwell, Evangeline Connelly
Adjunct Prof & Instr of JTPA
Kidwell, Murray Dean
History Teacher & Band Dir
Lay, Jill Caroline
Bio, Anatomy, & Physlgy Tchr
Mayfield, Barbara H.
Chem, Bio Tchr & Sci Dept Chr
McDuffee, Linda Thompson
Phys Science & Chemistry Tchr
Robinson, Susan Horne
Kindergarten Teacher
Smith, Charles Timothy
7th Grade Science Teacher
Tatum, Mary Londa
First Grade Teacher
Wallace, Jeff E.
Social Studies Teacher
Webb, Cynthia Pippin
Third Grade Teacher
Zimmerman, Jo Ann (Kern)
Fifth Grade Teacher
CULLEOKA
Harris, Ken
Phys Ed, Hlth & His Teacher
McMasters, Joy Parker
Science Teacher
Peery, Hugh E.
Agricultural Education Teacher
Sweeney, Beth S.
Math & Science Teacher
CUNNINGHAM
Davis, Mary Nina Gibson
High School Guidance Counselor
Gray, Brenda Lawson
Science Teacher
Horsey, Philip Carter
PE & Industrial Tech Tchr
Hunt, Deborah Slayden
Health & Physical Ed Teacher
Kendrick, Sandra Walker
Third Grade Teacher
Nunn, Ruth Russell
Eng & US His Resource Tchr
DANDRIDGE
Cagle, John B.
Marketing Ed Teacher & Coord
Franklin, Teresa Ann
Mathematics Teacher
Jones, Kenny Earl
6th Grd Social Studies Tchr
Leonard, Betty Jo Lindsay
7th Grade Science Teacher
Price, Jeffrey Reese
English Tchr & Newspaper Adv
Stallings, Dorothy Richey
Biology Teacher
DAYTON
Ardelean, Jane Brown
Fourth Grade Teacher
Bauer, Amy Lynn
4th Grade Teacher
Crook, Debra Roddy
Eighth Grade Science Teacher
Dorsey, Chloe Baker
Third Grade Teacher
Ketchersid, William L.
Professor of History
Linn, Cecile Kerley
1st Grade Teacher
Luther, Sigrid Skogstad
Professor of Music
Marler, Brenda Kelly
7th-8th Grd Lang Arts Teacher
Poole, Kimberly Lee
Sixth Grade Teacher
Roddy, James Grant
World Geography & TN His Tchr
Tallent, Bobby C.
Sixth Grade Teacher
Tallent, Susan Anderson
Fourth Grade Teacher
Vincent, Elizabeth Maxine Brown
Kindergarten Teacher
DECATUR
Harris, Patricia Simpson
Third Grade Teacher
Hunt, Patricia A.
Biology & Chemistry Teacher
Simpson, Joyce R.
English Teacher
DECATURVILLE
Pratt, Rita Jeanene
Science & History Teacher
DEL RIO
Woodson, Evelyn Hedwig
Sixth Grade Teacher
DICKSON
Bone, Jimmy
10th Grd Language Arts Tchr
Brown, David Page
History Teacher
Buhler, Barbara Ellen
Fourth Grade Teacher
Chandler, Johnny
Assistant Principal & Coach
Hall, Teresa Jackson
Mathematics Teacher
Hamilton, Eve K.
Physical Education Teacher
Hammer, Mary Evelyn
English Teacher
Hayes, Linda Peeler
Guidance Counselor
Pettes, Carl Wayne
US History Teacher
Sullivan, Glenda Lee
Latin & English Teacher
DOVER
Baggett, Connie Edlin
Business & Technology Instr
Hargis, Rita Gray
10th Grd English Teacher
Hicklen, Jimmy Dale
Geography Teacher & Coach
Tanner, Joe Eddie
Special Education Teacher
DRESDEN
Myrick, Mary Dunn
4th Grade Teacher
Pentecost, Sarah Holman
7th Grd English & History Tchr
Powers, LouAnn Anderson
First Grade Teacher
Simmons, Marjorie Hearn
First Grade Teacher
Stooksberry, Mary Ellen Nielsen
English & Theater Arts Teacher
DUCKTOWN
Cheatham, Johnnie Sue
Math Teacher
DUFF
Leffew, Larry Ronald
Science Teacher
Prim, Linda Miller
Language Arts Teacher
DUNLAP
Land, Lola Myers
Retired Social Studies Teacher
Roberts, Robert Eldon
Spanish Head Teacher
DYER
Fortner, Jane Hill
Third Grade Teacher
Jackson, Carolyn Stewart
Consumer Homemaking Teacher
Nicholson, Mary Nelle Thomas
Second Grade Teacher
Rollins, Gil Shane
Supervisor of Voc Education
Thompson, Rebecca P.
English Teacher
Warren, Dennis Ray
Special Education Supervisor
DYERSBURG
Burks, Judy Hall
Fifth Grade Teacher
Campbell, Connie
Social Studies Teacher
Cashdollar, Sophie Huie
English Professor
Cobb, James Thomas
7th & 8th Grade Soc Stud Tchr
Cutler, Gary
Associate Professor of Mngmt
Edwards, Suzanne Styron
English & Journalism Teacher
Flatt, James L.
Professor of Biology
Godwin, Charlotte Stockton
Chemistry & Physics Teacher
Goldsby, George Earl, Jr.
Science & TN History Teacher
Goodwin, Marion B.
Eighth Grade Science Teacher
Grossner, Linda Lloyd
Nursing Instructor
Hook, Cynthia Black
Fourth Grade Teacher
Kellar, Paul Jae
World Geography Teacher
Mc Atee, Mindi Lynn
Math Teacher
Moore, Debbie Duffel
Family & Consumer Sci Tchr
Reynolds, Emma Mays
Assoc Prof, Office & Info Syst
Robertson, Wanda Bailey
Math Instructor
Theiling, Jane Heckert
Mathematics Asst Professor
Watson, Emily R. Clay
Retired Third Grade Teacher
Young, Janice Ann
Biology Teacher
EAGLEVILLE
Hill, Theresa Clark
3rd Grade Teacher
Wilson, Carlos Wayne
Social Studies Teacher
ELIZABETHTON
Barker, Marilynn Pless
First Grade Teacher
Buck, Nancy Slagle
Science Dept Chair & Bio Tchr
Campbell, Zelma Radford
English & Keyboarding Teacher
Church, William E.
6th Grade Science Teacher
Dobes, Patricia Thomen
4-H Volunteer Leader
Gouge, Deborah Karen Bowers
Choral Director & English Tchr
Greene, Margaret Murphy
English & French Teacher
Hardin, John H.
Vocational Agriculture Teacher
Hardin, Nyoka Lee
Computer Teacher
Hart, Brenda Morton
English & Computer Teacher
Holt, Amanda McKeehan
Typing Teacher
Jenkins, Thomas Nathaniel
5th Grade Teacher
Roberts, Carol
Language Arts Teacher
Salyer, Roy Wesley
Mathematics Teacher
ELKTON
Newton, Ernest Brent
Math Teacher
ELMWOOD
Owen, Bobby Lee
Principal & Teacher
Radke, Patricia
Sixth Grade Teacher
ENGLEWOOD
Catron, Anne G.
Senior English Teacher
Dingess, Janice H.
Kindergarten Teacher
Ealy, Sally DeWitt
History Teacher
Galloway, Ronald L.
Biology Teacher
Jones, Vivian Givens
English Teacher
ERIN
Moore, Marilee M.
Span, Eng & Theater Arts Tchr
ERWIN
Brewer, Connie Ford
Social Studies Teacher
Mc Inturff, Joyce Holloway
6th Grade Language Arts Tchr
Rutter, Patricia Hardin
Fifth Grade Teacher
ESTILL SPRINGS
Casey, Mollye Ann Cook
6th Grade Classroom Teacher
Stewart, Rachel Temple
Fifth Grade Teacher
ETOWAH
Jones, Ralph Russell
Physical Education Teacher
Partain, Tracey L.
Fifth Grade Teacher
EVENSVILLE
Allred, Kenneth Lee, Jr.
Senior Army Instructor
Bowman, Sandra Norton
Math Teacher
Byles, James Charles
English Teacher
Cannon, Valerie Thurm
English Teacher
Clarke, Janet Hina
Home Economics Teacher
Cooper, Judy Bailey
Special Education Teacher
Finch, Teresa Ann
Honors Eng II & Span I Tchr
Gravitt, Christopher Scott
Special Education Teacher
Holder, Steffan Edward
United States History Teacher
Ludwig, James E.
Math Teacher
O'Neal, Janet Fitzgerald
Biology Teacher
Rankin, Marquetia Fisher
English Teacher
Riggs, Kari Ballentine
Ninth Grade English Teacher
Sheddan, Frank Robert
Band Director
FAIRVIEW
Blakeney, Mary Elizabeth (Shaw)
Seventh Grade Reading Teacher
Bradley, Robert R.
English Teacher
Dowland, Myrta Teresa (Reyna)
Spanish Teacher
Mc Bryde, Shannon Woodward
English Teacher
Satoloe, Ralph Eli
Eighth Grade Mathematics Tchr
FALL BRANCH
Stevens, Brenda Tomlinson
Fourth Grade Teacher
FAYETTEVILLE
Belcher, Glen
Band Director
Eakin, William Dennis
Agriculture Education Teacher
Hatcher, Flavil Ragan
6th-7th Grade Science Teacher
Humphrey, Arden Smith
European History Teacher
Jenkins, William Edward
Third Grade Teacher
Mc Alister, Fredna Womack
Fifth Grade Teacher
Parks, Julia Motlow
Hlth & Physical Education Tchr
Shelton, Lynda J.
Spanish Teacher
Silvey, Debra Hill
Third Grade Teacher
Washburn, Lisa D.
6th Grade Teacher
FINLEY
Littlejohn, Jeannie Daniels
Second Grade Teacher
FLINTVILLE
Currin, Paul Clayton
Science Teacher
FRANKLIN
Allen, Claude Wayne
Senior Army & JROTC Instr

KLIN (cont)
vall, Danielle D.
ish Teacher
Mark Alan
r Lit & Amer Studies Tchr
, Gail C.
Teacher & Dept Chair
an, Lori Katherine
ish & Psychology Teacher
on, Ted Marvin
Math Teacher & Coach
Charlotte Booker
ory Teacher
, Diane
Grade Teacher
s, Teri Hannum
Grd English & Drama Tchr
, Kathie J.
ness Teacher & Coach
roy, Emma Jean
nematics Teacher
erman, Walker Harold, Sr.
TC Teacher
er, Timothy Michael
nology Education Teacher
ons, Rachel Waggoner
of the Gifted Education
on, Paul Wayne
d Director
, Marla Jeffers
ish Teacher
da, Judy Pinson
Chemistry Teacher
Mitzi Hanback
Stud Tchr & Dept Chprsn
, Artie Louise
or Honors English Teacher
Jennifer Joy
lish & Spanish Teacher
t, Janet Mott
School Counselor
NDSHIP
Helen Cherry
red Professor of Chemistry
ESBORO
, Cheryl Judd
lish Department Head
rson, Carole
ial Studies Teacher
n, Barbara Gipson
h Teacher
ette, Judy Sue
Grade English Teacher
cre, Joan Anderson
boarding & Computers Tchr
Patsy Spurlock
ondary School Counselor
vich, Herbert Lynn
tory & Economics Tchr
ney, Patsy Ann
nedial Reading & Math Tchr
, Jimmie Denton
Grade Social Studies Tchr
LATIN
nette, Alice Alexander
f of Health & Physical Ed
el, Ralph Conrad
h & Pre-Algebra Teacher
ella, Nancy Rushing
ructor of Biology
er, Richard Allen
ergency Med Svcs Assoc Prof
ad, Charles Richard
ructor of Mathematics
ison, Mary Davis
glish Teacher
lon, Carol J.
ding Manager
yway, Sidney E.
chology Instructor
ison, Judith W.
soc Prof of Dental Asst Ed
re, Teresa Tidwell
mputer Science Teacher
is, Nancy Garnett
ence Dept Chair & Professor
el, Pat
sociate Professor of English
Robert Monroe
f of His & Political Sci
man, Robert E.
urth Grade Teacher
or, Christine
st Professor
or, Lance David
nerican History Teacher
ster, Linda Scott
ience Teacher
ted, Donna Joan
st Grade Teacher
TLINBURG
ner, Rob
vner
ss, Richard Allen
acher
drick, Joseph L.
glish Teacher
ks, Ronald A.
nd Director
ldox, Marie M.
nglish & Latin Teacher
randt, Perry Charles
story Teacher
son, Elaine Johnson
ology Teacher
RMANTOWN
hop, Leslie Seymour
h Grade Language Arts Tchr
ir, Arletha Murdock
h Grade Science Teacher

Hudson, Lou J.
8th Grade Mathematics Teacher
Lewis, Linda Roberts
Kindergarten Teacher
Prescott, Patricia Baker
Assistant Principal
Rich, Janet L.
Language Arts Teacher
Thompson, Jo Ann Luton
Third Grade Teacher
Whitaker, Edna P.
Fifth Grade Teacher
Williams, Elissa Marlene
8th Grd English Classroom Tchr
GLADEVILLE
Bradford-Head, Shirley
6th Grade Teacher
Mercer, Sherry Wright
Fifth Grade Teacher
GOODLETTSVILLE
Forehand, Linda Mallory
Kindergarten Teacher
Moore, Rentonia Jenice
Fourth Grade Teacher
GORDONSVILLE
Agee, Virginia Lester
Guidance Counselor
Carr, David Matthew
Agriculture & Science Teacher
Driver, Frances Rose
First Grade Teacher
Habersberger, Patricia Ann
Spanish & Social Studies Tchr
Tisdale, Dana Renee
Third Grade Teacher
GRAY
Barr, Larry Thomas
Biology Teacher & Sftbl Coach
Burleson, Susan Raines
Second Grade Teacher
Congdon, Teresa Ann (Barnett)
Middle School Band Director
Davis, Deanna Holley
English Dept Chm & Teacher
Ford, Sandra Light
Vocal Music Teacher
Garrett, Jewell Johnson
Amer History Teacher
Harrison-Wagner, Deborah
7th & 8th Grade Math Teacher
Harvey, J. Helen
Physical Science Teacher
Howell, Harvey Eugene
Art & Photography Teacher
Jarrett, Dale
Teacher
Johnson, Corilla June
Home Ec & Cmptr Sci Tchr
Nelson, Mary Ann Bacon
Lifetime Wellness I Teacher
Roller, Bobby Ray
5th-8th Grd Physical Ed Tchr
Rose, Dorothy Carter
English Teacher
Stafford, Gary Michael
HS Mathematics Teacher
Street, Bebe H.
Science & Language Arts Tchr
Swartz, Robert E.
Tech Ed, Sci & Math Teacher
GREENBACK
Cooper, Thelma Hammontree
English & French Teacher
Hudson, Ronald George
Math & Drivers Ed Teacher
GREENBRIER
Allen, Laurie Ann
Sixth Grade Special Ed Tchr
Bunch, Roger Dale
Band Director
Crutcher, Thomas Brooks
Physical Education Teacher
Dickerson, Melanie Williams
Sixth Grade Teacher
Fentress, Judy Haggard
Home Economics Teacher
Hatfield, Andrea Barnes
Resource Teacher
Heilman, Nita Rae
8th Grade Science Teacher
Lassiter, Barbara Crain
Librarian
Owsley, Patricia Rae
5th Grade Teacher
Palmiter, Peggy Scruggs
8th Grd Math & Pre Alg Teacher
Robinson, Carolyn Crowe
Principal
Walling, Lewis G.
Choral Director
Zimmerle, Susan Polen
Language Arts Teacher
GREENEVILLE
Barilovits, Karlyn Ammons
Pgm Coord, Cmptr Info Systems
Barkdoll, Sharon Lanceford
Psychology Professor
Botta, Pamela Howe
Sixth Grade Lang Arts Tchr
Brickell, Danna Fannon
8th Grade Language Arts Tchr
Clanton, Barbara Bewley
Math Dept Chairman & Teacher
Conley, Ronald Albert
Associate Professor of Math
Dennis, Dorothy Germano
Early Childhood Assoc Prof
DuBrisk, Marilyn
Artist in Residence & Instr

Dunn, Mary Glennis
Business Teacher
Ellis, Lisa Johnson
Special Education Teacher
Franklin, Mike S.
English & Social Studies Tchr
Haun, Eddie L.
Fourth Grade Teacher
Hendricksen, David Alan
Music Prof & Acad Stu Svc Admn
Hodges, Peter Michael
Band Director
Humphreys, Eddie
5th Grade Teacher
Jones, Heather S.
Art Teacher
Loftin, Alice Cornelia
Associate Professor of English
Mc Inturff, Rebecca Mills
Librarian
Morrell, Bart Dwight
7th Grade Science Teacher
Neas, Susan Catherine
Latin Teacher
Pierce, Robert Eugene
Psychology Teacher
Ramsay, Lindsay Homer
Home Room Teacher
Scheel, Leanna Bible
Fifth Grade Teacher
Southerland, Sue DeLozier
Office Technology Teacher
GREENFIELD
Hearn, Linda M.
English & Drama Teacher
Kendall, Tara D.
Span, Eng & Psychology Teacher
GRUETLI LAAGER
Bowen, Edward H.
History Teacher
HALLS
Baker, Kay
High School Teacher
Roberts, Shirley P.
French & English Teacher
HAMPSHIRE
Farlow, Melissa Lovell
Office Technology Teacher
HAMPTON
Anderson, William H.
History Teacher & Soc Stud Chm
Arwood, Melinda E.
Librarian
Graham, Hilda Renae
Mathematics Teacher
Lyons, Lloyd Allen
Physical Ed & Health Teacher
Thomas, Sharon Williams
Eng, Sociology & Jrnlsm Tchr
HARRIMAN
Andrews, Rebecca Lucas
Assoc Professor of Accounting
Asbury, Cathy L.
Clinical Dir Radiology Program
Bailey, Patricia Gibson
Assoc Prof of Dev Mathematics
Barnes, Delorise Creecy
Professor of Business
Bouldin, Charles Larry
Professor of Mathematics
Byrne, Janet Owens
Professor of Education
Childs, Vickie Hensley
Clinical Coor, Radiologic Tech
Crowe, Margaret Wilkinson
Assoc Professor of Nursing
Denison, Betty Nan
Assoc Prof of Acad Dev Math
De Wick, Roberta Louise
Adjunct Psychology Professor
Eiselstein, Mary Sue
Associate Professor of English
Ferguson, Roy R.
Pgm Director of Opticianry
Foltz, Richard William
Associate Professor
Galloway, Pamela J.
Assistant Professor of Biology
Garner, Susan Adams
Assoc Prof of Health & PE
Goodwin, Julia Field
Associate Professor of English
Gowan, Joye Elaine
Assoc Prof of Academic Dev
Heidinger, Gary
Assoc Prof of Sociology
Howard, Rebecca Miller
Associate Professor of Math
Kring, James Byron
Associate Prof of Biology
LeMire, Leslie Manthorp
Mathematics Teacher
Livingston, Lona G.
Associate Professor
Malveaux, Ken R.
Associate Professor
Marsh, Linda Sue
Medical Transcription Instr
Mc Nutt, Alison Mason
Assoc Prof of Acad Dev Math
Miller, Donald Eugene
Anthropology Prof & Assoc Dean
Pack, David Lacy, Jr.
Math & Adult Basic Ed Teacher
Sain, Susan (Bell)
Prof of Occuptnl Therapy
Sellin, Helen Gill
Asst Professor of Chemistry
Smith, Billy L.
Associate Professor of Math

Strunk, John Thomas
Spanish Teacher
Waddle, Joette Tarpley
Assistant Professor of English
Williams, Hilda Jordan
Adj Instr of AD Rdng & Writing
Windham, Donald Lindsey
Assoc Professor of Psychology
Wright, Gary Lee
Associate Professor of Math
HARRISON
Belva, Sharon Rachel
Accounting & Typing Teacher
Crawford, John S.
Drafting Teacher
Hill, Kathie L.
Teacher of the Gifted
Lane, Patty Sue
Health, PE Teacher & Coach
Lee, Betty B.
Math Tchr & Department Chair
Mc Connell, Thomas Craig
JROTC Teacher
Moore, Ora Neal
English Teacher
Robbs, Cathy Gross
English Teacher
Sanchez, Jose Antonio
Spanish & Bible History Tchr
Sellers, Donna Northcutt
Science Teacher
Taylor, Deborah Waller
World His & Cultures Tchr
Womble, Diana L. (Liner)
English Teacher
HARROGATE
Cornelius, Georgette
Science & Health Teacher
Fultz, Mary Sandefur
Business Teacher
Howard, William James
Sociology Professor
Jones, Nancy Dillman
Literature & Drama Instructor
Meade, Donald R.
US History Instructor
Pava, Mary Burrell
Assistant Professor of Nursing
Snyder, Gregory A.
Mathematics & Science Dept Chm
Vann, Dolores Poore
Seventh Grade Teacher
Wilhoit, Charles David, Jr.
Math Instructor
Wright, Connie Delores (Smith)
Teacher Education Asst Prof
HARTSVILLE
Martin, John Kenneth
Economics Teacher
Moreland, Grace Mc Donald
Second Grade Teacher
Moreland, Ronald Kent
Asst Prin & Phy Ed Teacher
HEISKELL
Cummings, Carolyn Jo
5th Grade Teacher
HENDERSON
Anderson, Gloria Culver
6th Grade Teacher
Carroll, Barbara Christine
Third Grade Teacher
Cooper, Janice Annette (Terry)
7th-8th Grd PE Teacher
Cravens, Gayle Michael
Prof of Family Stud & Cnslng
Davis, Frances Wilcoxson
United States History Teacher
Gilmore, D. Ralph
Prof of Interdisciplinary Stud
Hibbett, Eugene P.
Chemistry Professor
Massey, Gregory De Van
Assistant Professor of History
Moore, Kevin Loren
Missionary-in-Residence
Oliver, Michael H.
Asst Prof in Accounting
Rogers, Judith K.
Mathematics Teacher
Sorrell, Tamie DePriest
Marketing Instructor
Trice, Teresa Mae
Dir of Curr & Instruction
HENDERSONVILLE
Anderson, Marie Massey
Voc & Business Education Tchr
Barnard, Julie Scott
Mathematics Teacher
Callis, J. T.
English Teacher
Clark, Martha Frances
Latin Teacher
Clifford, Verna Hoffer
French Teacher
Crook, Arthur James
World Geog Tchr & Dept Head
Cundiff, Carolyn Vorgang
6th Grd Math & Science Tchr
Edgin, Beverly Winn
Mathematics Tchr & Dept Chair
Edmonds, Venice Porter
Science Teacher
Hasty, Judy
English Teacher
Helton, Ronnie Cornel
PE Teacher & Coach
Hodges, Leslie Steenbergen
Business Teacher
Jung, William Louis
Chemistry Teacher

Kandros, Sandra Louise
Art Teacher
LeMarbre, Patricia Strickland
Data Processing Teacher
Lind, James Steven
US History Teacher
Marks, Karen Beasley
Business Education Teacher
Mc Ghee, Jewell Lasley
Elementary Principal
Meadows, Scott E.
Physical Education Teacher
Medlin, Terry Diane
Kindergarten Teacher
Miller, Creighton Herbert
Band Director
Morris, Melanie
5th Grade Teacher
Peterson, Bonnie L.
Mathematics Teacher
Phillips, Jeffrey Taylor
Director of Bands
Pitts, Nancy Hickerson
2nd Grade Teacher
Rappuhn, William Scott
English Teacher
Reed, Rebecca Coffman
Second Grade Teacher
Reynolds, William Stephen
English Teacher
Rizor, Margaret
Third Grade Teacher
Roach, Ralph Ann Eblen
Third Grade Teacher
Rucker, Jeanie League
Spanish Teacher
Stein, Sue Terrill
Business Teacher
Stubblefield, Sandra Chester
Business Education Teacher
Towe, Linda M.
Choral Director
Whited, Roxanne Fink
First Grade Teacher
Withrow, Glema Schreiner
Theatre Arts Teacher
Wright, Dianne Donnell
Transition 1st Grd Tchr
HERMITAGE
Hooper, Mary Donna
Sixth Grade Teacher
Smith, Laurie L.
5th Grade Teacher
Wheeler, Ricky Darrell
Seventh Grade Teacher
HILHAM
Parsons, C. C.
Science Teacher
HILLSBORO
Clay, Rebecca Ann (Jenkins)
Kindergarten Teacher
HIXSON
Becker, Charlene E.
Teacher
Burkhart, Doug Eugene
Residential Construction Tech
Callahan, Mary Anne Rutledge
Fifth Grade Teacher
Calvert, Carol Lee
Math Teacher
Delbrugge, Bill
Band Director
Ellis, Diane Marie (Ebert)
Tchr of Spcl Ed for Gftd Stu
Gill, Gary Thomas
Dean of Students
Gooden, Thomas W.
Teacher
McClintock, Dixie D.
HS Mathematics Teacher
Mc Govern, Linda Rodrigues
Spanish Teacher
O'Brien, Kathryn Veller
Fifth Grade Mathematics Tchr
Smith, Regina Bowen
Bible History Teacher
Swafford, Lynn Hunt
First Grade Teacher
Swope, Cynthia Louise (Chase)
Second Grade Teacher
Thompson, James Robert
History Teacher
Windham, Kathy Andrews
English Teacher
HOHENWALD
Jackson, Sherry Stubblefield
Librarian
Kavara, Catherine Rose Ford
English, Math & Resource Tchr
Mitchell, Frankie Jean
Kindergarten Teacher
HUMBOLDT
Barker, Martha Carol
Retired Mathematics Teacher
Flowers, William Steven
Applied Communications Teacher
Hawks, Linda Luster
English & Speech Teacher
Myatt, Scott Bradley
Art Teacher
Shelton, Lillian B.
Algebra & Geometry Teacher
Walker, Ann Johnson
Health Science & Tech Instr
HUNTINGDON
Byars, Betty Boyd
Business Teacher
Cole, Cindy Hutcherson
English I & III Teacher

HUNTINGTON (cont)
Dickens, Larry Rudolph
Band Director
Garrett, Jean
English Teacher
Tedford, Wayne John
Mathematics & Physics Teacher
HUNTLAND
Partin, Randall J.
Vocational Agriculture Teacher
Robinson, Pamela Houck
Part Store Owner & Manager
Welch, Brenda Barnes
Seventh & Eighth Grd Eng Tchr
HUNTSVILLE
Banks, Lisa Mae
Spanish Teacher
Chambers, Nita Marie
Health Sci & Tech Instructor
Cross, Anna Sue
Freshman English Teacher
Hamilton, Lisa Burress
Eighth Grade Math Teacher
Lay, Thomas L.
Director
Thompson, Cara Sue (Phillips)
Family Resource Tchr & Coord
Vann, Imogene Burress
Jr High Reading Teacher
HURON
Amis, Tommy Wayne
5th & 6th Grade Math Teacher
Powell, Lisa Ann
7th & 8th Grd Lang Arts Tchr
JACKSBORO
Brantley, Vanessa Pierce
Fourth Grade Teacher
Claiborne, Richard Wayne
6th Grade Teacher
Grieve, William George, Jr.
Agriculture Teacher
Hatmaker, Julie Newport
Math Teacher
Hickey, Rex Ervin
7th Grade Science Teacher
Jones, William Arnold
Performing Arts Dept Head
Kenik, Mary Ann Scherer
Fifth Grade Teacher
Lynch, Jack Allan
Economics Teacher
Owens, Kenneth W.
Guidance Counselor
Rutherford, Nancy J.
Occupational Food Serv Tchr
Rutherford, Steve Edward
Driver's Ed, Hlth Tchr & Coach
Stout, Jerry Lynn
Assistant Principal
Tackett, Connie Overbey
Typing & Chorus Teacher
Wood, Louise Wilson
Fourth Grade Teacher
JACKSON
Austin, Linda Shoe
9th Grade Honors English Tchr
Baldwin, Janice Ann
Mathematics Teacher
Bird, Julie Cash
English Teacher
Black, Karee Scott
K-5th Grd Teacher
Boatright, Patricia Bond
Mathematics Teacher
Boehms, Mary Jo
Associate Prof of Business
Boone, Louise May
9th Grade English Teacher
Bradford, Sophira Walker
Business Education Teacher
Brantley, Wayne Devon
History Tchr & Head Var Coach
Brown, Linda Brogden
Music Specialist
Bryant, Deborah Duffey
Math Teacher & Chairperson
Bush, Randall Bruce
Assoc Prof of Rel & Philosophy
Carls, Stephen Douglas
Prof of His & Dept Chair
Chambers, Rilla Morrison
Algebra Teacher
Clark, Bridget Glover
Dept Chair & English Teacher
Clifford, Anna Crews
Assistant Professor of Ed
Cole, Janice Neil
Fifth Grade Teacher
Coltharp, Martha Terry
8th Grade Language Arts Tchr
Cox, Marsha Lynn
Spanish Teacher
Davis, Pamela Newbill
10th-12th Grd English Teacher
Day, Wayne Allan
Assoc Prof of Chrstn Studies
Dayton, Nancy E.
Assoc Professor & Assoc Dean
Debnath, Nirmalendu
Prof of Economics & Chair
Derryberry, Betty
Assistant Principal
Dougan, Eddie
Chemistry & Physics Tchr
Dyer, Florence Hughes
Assistant Prof & Theatre Dir
Eddleman, Joan
Algebra & Pre-Algebra Teacher
Everhart, Rodney Duane
Education Professor
Flowers, Chuck
Agriculture Education Teacher
Frye, Jonathan David
Science Teacher & Coach
Goforth, Beth Nanney
Resource English Teacher
Gott, William Gene
Art Teacher
Grant, M. Thomas, II
Fine Arts Chm & Gen Music Tchr
Greene, Susan Gillmann
Accounting & Keyboarding Tchr
Guthrie, George Howard
Religion Professor
Hardegree, Adair Duncan
Amer History & English Teacher
Hardegree, Jim F.
PE & Drivers Ed Teacher
Hardin, Beverly Byron
Associate Prof of Geography
Hardin, Faye R.
English Teacher
Harris, John Robert
Associate Professor of English
Hearn, Beverly Jean
Eng as a Second Lang Tchr
Hedspeth, William C.
Professor of Education
Henley, Brenda M.
High School Guidance Counselor
Henning, James Donaldson
6th-8th Grade Band Director
Hornbuckle, Donald R.
Assistant Professor of History
Hornsby, Wanda Jernigan
First Grade Teacher
Hubbard, Mary K.
Coordinator & Teacher
Jackson, Paul Norman
Asst Prof of Christian Studies
Jones, Marian C.
Spanish Teacher
Lindley, W. Terry
Associate Professor of History
Logan Sheppard, Shirley
7th Grd Social Studies Teacher
Maddox, Teri Thomson
Associate Professor of English
Mallard, Kina S.
Communications Arts Dept Chair
Mallard, Michael Charles
Assoc Prof of Art & Chair
Mc Call, Martha
1st-3rd Grade Teacher
Mc Kinney, Chester
Band Director
Mc Mahan, Michael L.
Professor of Biology
McNatt, Richard Craig
Algebra & Math Teacher
Mercer, E. M.
Language Arts Teacher
Moore, R. Kelvin
Asst Professor of Chrstn Stud
Newell, Debbie Hughes
Instructor of Accounting
Page, Linda Mc Natt
Special Education Teacher
Patterson, Patrick O'Brian
Professor of Criminal Justice
Pettit, Nancy Kemp
Honors English II Teacher
Pinson, Ernest R.
Prof of English
Pinson, Patricia T.
Art & Music Professor
Ramer, Jane Terrell
Science Department Head
Reynolds, Sue Pritchett
Third Grade Teacher
Rickman, Janet Prather
Fourth Grade Teacher
Rose, Judy Carr
5th Grade Teacher
Roth, Georgia Middlebrooks
Associate Prof of Accounting
Russell, Judith Alley
English Teacher
Seltzer, Mary Beth
Spanish Teacher
Simpson, Debra B.
English Teacher
Singleton, Ann Haltom
Special Education Professor
Smith, Elsie Young
Professor of Biology
Springfield, Minnie Pearl
8th Grd Amer History Teacher
Thompson, Myriam Borges
Spanish Teacher
Warren, Kimberly Jo
Speech & Communication Prof
Warren, Molly Williams
Asst Prof of Chem & Nutrition
White, Thomas Bedford
Principal of Technology Instr
Wyatt, Robert Lane
Assistant Prof of Accounting
Yenawine, Theresa Ann
Fifth Grade Teacher
JAMESTOWN
Atkinson, Rachel Marie
Retired Teacher
Cobb, Barbara Ann
Fifth Grade Teacher
Peavyhouse, James Wendel
Band & Vocal Director
Voiles, Valeria Lynn
Drama & English II Teacher
Winningham, Mark Lee
Economics Teacher
JASPER
Brown, Barbara Stanton
Chemistry & Physics Teacher
Elliott, Golda P.
Vocational Office Ed Teacher
Koger, Deborah Pollard
Special Education Teacher
Long, Richard Kelly
Wellness Instructor
Quarles, Kathy Lowrey
Special Education Teacher
Sartain, Judith Harrington
Owner, Director & Teacher
JEFFERSON CITY
Ball, Mary Charlotte Swann
Emeritus Assoc Prof of Music
Barker, Sheridan Clinton
Communication Arts Asst Prof
Biddle, Mark Edward
Religion Prof & Hnrs Pgm Dir
Bull, Bernard F.
Professor of Education
Carroll, Diana D.
Professor of Home Economics
Clark, Donald Wayne
Assoc Prof of Bus & Economics
Driver, Phyllis Nelke
Assoc Prof of Accounting
Ferrell, Brenda Young
Assistant Professor of French
Good, Donald Wayne
Chair of Teacher Education
Hazucha, Andrew W.
Assistant Professor of English
Hodges, Mary Bozeman
English Instructor
Millsaps, Ellen McNutt
Professor of English
Norris, Catherine
Assoc Prof of Home Economics
Page, Michael Richard
Associate Professor of Biology
Peck, Arlene Bell
Instr of Special Education
Swilley, W. Sue
Professor of Music
Wadlington, Laura Robinson
Asst Professor of Psychology
Welton, John Lee
Prof of Comm Art & Drama Dir
Whitlow, Jay P.
Asst Professor of Special Ed
Wood, Angela F.
Asst Prof in Nursing
JELLICO
Archer, Eddie
5th Grade Teacher
Clifton, Irma Petrey
Second Grade Teacher
Cummins, Donna Elizabeth
English, Spanish & His Tchr
Halcomb, Betty Eileen Spitzer
Special Education Teacher
Maiden, June R.
Keyboarding & English Teacher
JOELTON
Bryson, Gloria Vaughn
Third Grade Teacher
Finch, Timothy Wayne
8th Grade Science Teacher
Taylor, Patti Midgett
Third Grade Teacher
JOHNSON CITY
Bowman, James Dale
Reading Education Professor
Broeder, Craig Elliot
Professor
Buck, John Bell David Lee
8th Grade Teacher
Buck, Kathy Jo Hughes
7th Grade Teacher
Crawford, Kathleen Ann
7th Grade Science Teacher
Crawford, Thomas Franklin
Instructor of Woodwinds
Daniel, Eleanor A.
Dean, Prof of Christian Ed
Davis, Betty Crawford
Biology Teacher
Duty, Clyde Roger
6th Grade Math Tchr
Faust, Melody C.
Elementary School Teacher
Hardin, Sherri Hodge
Math Assistant Professor
Harris, Melissa Litton
Mathematics Teacher
Hendricks, Joan Kinkead
English Teacher
Hostetler, Susie Johnson
Fifth Grade Math Teacher
Keyt, John Charles
Associate Professor of Mrktg
Marable, Henry Douglas
Asst Principal
Mc Donald, Nancy Rinehart
English & Physical Ed Teacher
McInturf, Kathleen Reed
Resource Teacher
Parris, Cathy Counts
1st Grade Teacher
Rapp, Carl Steven
Physics Astronomy Chem Instr
Robertson, C. Warren
Professor & Dir of Theatre
Simmerman, David Howard
Upward Bound Ed Specialist
Stanton, William J.
History Teacher
Stone, William L.
Professor of Pediatrics
Swingle, Joan Lincoln
Kindergarten Teacher
Swor, Lisa Robbin
8th Grade English Teacher
Treece, Joaquiha Michelle
Science Teacher
JONESBOROUGH
Beene, Virginia Dunbar
Amer Govt & World His Tchr
Bishop, Sharon Taylor
Cosmetology Instructor
Cook, Anne Poston
Director of Choruses
Davis, Janet Evelyn Breeden
Biology Teacher
Grogg, Kay Hess
Art & Photography Teacher
Moore, Connie Rose
Fourth Grade Teacher
Oliver, Judy Lewis
Fifth Grade Teacher
Ruetz, Juanita Potter
Retired Choral & Music Tchr
Russell, Dava Lee Broyles
Span Tchr & Foreign Lang Dept
Sisk, Zenobia Ann
Chemistry, Physics & Bio Tchr
Turpin, David Grant
Resource Teacher & Coach
West, Anne Marie Wood
7th & 8th Grd Lang Arts Tchr
KINGSPORT
Adams, Jerry Lynn
Social Studies Teacher & Coach
Anderson, Pat H.
Fifth Grade Teacher
Austin, Richard Lyon
Social Studies & Language Tchr
Bloomer, Phyllis Shipley
Fifth Grade Teacher
Bogart, Gayle Matherly
English Tchr & Dept Co-Chair
Bowden, Kathryn Davis
Fifth Grade Teacher
Bratton, Lisa Dingus
7th Grade Mathematics Teacher
Butler, William George, Jr.
Physics Teacher
Carroll, Kathy Fine
Fifth Grade Teacher
Clark, Annas Thompson
7th-8th Grd Classroom Teacher
Clark, Graham
9th-12th Grd PE Teacher
Clevinger, Vicki Ann Bissett
Eighth Grade English Teacher
Coates, Vicki Diana
First-Third Grd Tchr
Davis, Valerie Johnson
First Grade Teacher
Diamond, Terry Lee
7th Grd Social Studies Teacher
Edmonds, Melanie R.
Office Technology Teacher
Eggleston, Stan P.
English Teacher
Eiklor, Devonda Robinette
Biology Teacher
Fischer, Elizabeth C.
Seventh Grade Math Teacher
Fulkerson, Joseph Michael
Special Education Teacher
Galloway, Darwin Anthony
Social Studies Teacher
Herron, Charlie Kyle, Jr.
Band Director
Hobbs, Deanna Jeter
Fifth Grade Teacher
Hoover, David Allen
AP American History Teacher
Hull, William E.
English & Journalism Teacher
Humphreys, William Collins, Jr.
Business, Acctng & Law Teacher
Johns, Sandra Peal
Health Sci & Tech Teacher
Knaff, Sheila Rhaan
Assistant Principal
Lambert, Frankie Sage
Classroom Teacher
Martin, Martha Overbey
Third Grade Teacher
Mc Lellan, Wanda Gulley
Fourth Grade Teacher
Mc New, Dinah Dean
Multi-Age Intermediate Tchr
Meade-Lewis, Susan Salyer
Primary Teacher
Peterson, Norma Jo
Third Grade Teacher
Rochelle, Peggy Goodson
Advanced Studies Teacher
Rose, Constance Hill
Intermediate Teacher
St Clair, Gerri Gilbert
Chemistry Teacher
Tharp, Philip L.
Principal
Tipton, Dennis Ray
Interim English Teacher
Turner, Fay P.
Retired Teacher
Weaver, John Robert
Principal
White, Angela Kathleen
History Teacher
Wing, Frank Maurice, Jr.
Classroom Teacher
Wright, Sylvia Hope
Third Grade Teacher
KINGSTON
Burnett, Dianne Breeden
Science Teacher
Hagy, Sylvia P.
Sixth Grade Teacher
Hayes, James Michael
Social Studies Teacher
Hirt, Shawn Wilson
Chem, Bio & Earth Sci Tchr
Lannom, Julie Hudson
Math Teacher
Snow, Michael Eugene
8th Grd Health & PE Teacher
KINGSTON SPRINGS
Dorris, Priscilla Beard
Third Grade Teacher
KNOXVILLE
Akins, Rheba Gould
Second Grade Teacher
Ammons, Rachel Pilkinton
First Grade Teacher
Anders, Bonnie Fawcett
8th Grade Language Arts Tchr
Anderson, James Archie
Math Teacher
Angelini, Suzanne Black
English as Second Lang Teacher
Baah, Richard
Political Science Professor
Baker, Sara Spearing
English Department Head
Baldwin, Edward
Mathematics Teacher
Banker, Mark Tollie
History Teacher
Banks, Elven K.
Instrumental Music Tchr
Bible, Alvah Boyce
Lifetime Wellness & PE Tchr
Bible, Cheryl Barger
Spanish Teacher
Booker, Bob
Prof of Environmental Laws
Brentz, Charles Everett
HS Ecology & Biology Teacher
Broom, Rebecca A.
French Teacher
Brown, Carla Bradshaw
Chemistry Teacher
Bryant, Gay Davis
Assoc Prof of Office Systems
Buckner, Mary Catherine Lawhorn
Mathematics Teacher
Burkey, Johnnie Mathis
French Teacher
Burleson, Marilyn Elaine
French Teacher
Burnett, Kathy Gilstrap
Fourth Grade Teacher
Cathey, Richard Allen
Teacher & Coach
Cave, Lois Louise
Third Grade Teacher
Clark, Stephanie Darrell
French Teacher
Clear, Kimberly Halsey
Spanish Teacher
Cleveland, Arlene Austin
Instructor of Legal Asst Tech
Cofield, Judy Bartlett
Fifth Grade Teacher
Coker, Carolyn Sue
2nd Grade Teacher
Colbert, Janet Guthe
Latin Teacher
Corum, Cynthia Stevens
Fr Tchr & For Lang Dept Chm
Cox, George M.
Program Head
Davenport, Shirley Kennedy
Fourth Grade Teacher
Davis, Barbara Wise
1st Grade Teacher
Doak, Rita Methvin
English Teacher
Dunne, Thomas William
German Teacher
Edmonds, Kelley Hall
Speech & Theatre Teacher
Eubanks, Kori Collins
English Teacher
Fethe, Judith Hanks
Assoc Professor of Mathematics
Finley, Jane Carroll
English Teacher
Fisher, Bruce Dwight
Professor of Business Law
Garner, Farris Sharon
Teacher & History Dept Head
Garrison, Kim
English Teacher
Garst, Thomas Parkinson
Former Teacher
Gillespie, Ralph D.
Remedial & Dev Rdng Asst Prof
Gravitt, Randy Lee
Head of Bible Dept & Instr
Grogan, Bobbi Dill
Chemistry Teacher
Hall, George Dalton
8th Grade Teacher
Handley, S. Michele
English Teacher
Hardy, Donna Mara
English Teacher

KVILLE (cont)
d, Carol Poston
d Grade Teacher
son, Pamela Marie
lish Teacher
ns, E. Lorna Browne
Grade Teacher
han, Cheryl Moore
lish Tchr & Department Chm
er, Mary Guinn
red 4th Grade Teacher
hreys, W. Lee
essor of Religious Studies
on, Deborah Suits
nputer Applications Teacher
, Delores
d Grade Teacher
e, Nancy K.
istant Professor
atrick, Paul Silas
lth Teacher
el, Walter Emerson
essor of Anthropology
nt, John Geoffrey
rnational Student Advisor
rumpf, Carroll
hematics Teacher
m, Renata C.
glish Teacher
Gloria Fife
glish Teacher
en, Martha W.
ence Chprsn & Biology Tchr
eur, Terri Prince
ence Teacher
s, Helen Diane Johnson
t Prof of Soc Wrk & Hum Svc
, Jeannine Wolfe
ebra Teacher
e, Stephen Edward
glish Teacher
dox, Robert Casey
sociate Professor of Mgmt
uire, John H.A.
sociate History Professor
um, Betsy L. Rule
nch Teacher
Mahon, Susan Henderson
sistant Professor of Biology
hell, Dudley Dwayne
mmercial Foods Instructor
ley, Robert E.
sociate Professor
gan, Sandra Welch
tired Teacher
ins, Susan Turner
l Education Resource Tchr
rs, Lisa S.
cial Studies Teacher
er, Douglas Brown
sistant Principal
dorff, Diana Carter
ird Grade Teacher
r, Rick Stanton
counting Instructor
ons, Darrell John
ble & Chemistry Teacher
, Sor-Bee Leow
Mathematics Teacher
, Philip Dale
ecial Education Teacher
makoff, Bill
ath Teacher
at, Robert Nicholas
sistant Professor
o, Gary Alan
gh School Mathematics Tchr
le, Donna Rae
uidance Counselor
ogios, Diane Apostolou
anish Teacher & Dept Chair
cliffe, Linda Sturgis
ology Teacher
erts, James Ernest
ath Teacher
er, Teresa Downey
anish Teacher
h, Catherine Lowe
urth Grade Teacher
, Gordon Mc Bride, III
S History & Geography Teacher
, Natalie Leach
hysical Science Teacher
nner, Jane Johnson
hemistry & Geology Teacher
ith, Sarah Trewhitt
ology Teacher
ith-Staton, Linda Diane
sst Prof of Bio, Prgm Coord
nsberry, Kenneth L.
nglish Teacher
vens, Barbara Brown
chr of Careers with Children
ann, Jeanna Carol
lementary School Principal
sendorf, Roger Willis
rincipal
omas, Deborah Gibson
atin Teacher
omas, Kathy Vasa
djunct Professor of Chemistry
nDeGriff, Vicki Bolding
th Grade Math & Science Tchr
gner, Caroline Margaret
thletic Director
lters, Debbie C.
hysical Education Teacher
rd, June Staples
IS Language Arts Teacher

Webber, Sheri Fellin
English Teacher
Weed, Debbie Blackwell
Former Teacher
White, Rela Anderson
Science Teacher
Wilson, James Gregory
Band Choir Director
LA FOLLETTE
Childress, Ruby V. (Claiborne)
Kindergarten Teacher
Clotfelter, Starla G. (Bowman)
Kindergarten Teacher
Kilgore, Mamie Marie
Third Grade Teacher
King, Shelley B.
Sixth Grade English Teacher
Leach, Nancy Rogers
Third Grade Teacher
Vestal, Janice Wolfe
Science Teacher
LA VERGNE
Calahan, Paula Tabor
Marketing Education Teacher
Johns, Nancye Ann
Multi-Age Tchr
McCreery, John Thomas, IV
Radio & TV Broadcasting Instr
McCulloch, Carole A.
Counselor
Shelton, William A.
Assistant Principal
Smith, Rhonda Cowan
Mathematics Teacher
Woods, Sarah Dickerson
History Teacher
LAFAYETTE
Brawner, Tammy Shrum
Math Teacher
Carter, Janice Dell
1st Grade Teacher
Cochran, Sheila Peterman
Fourth Grade Teacher
Trent, Robbie West
Kindergarten Teacher
Walrond, Pamela Crabtree
Language Teacher
LAKE CITY
Amos, James Howard
Eighth Grade English Teacher
Ezell, Andrea Joyce (Mc Daniel)
Fourth Grade Teacher
Jones, Judy Lynn
Second Grade Teacher
McGrew, Kathleen G.
K-5th Grd Art & History Tchr
LASCASSAS
Hopkins, Martha Caffy
6th-8th Grade Reading Teacher
LAWRENCEBURG
Bonner, Ronald
Classroom Teacher
Freeman, James Hollis
American & World History Tchr
Hill, Joan Gieske
6th Grade Teacher
Hill, Rosa Marie
Fifth & Sixth Grade Teacher
Joiner, Marion Fowler
English Teacher
Marston, Jamie Brown
Reading & Math Teacher
McCroskey, Aaron, Jr.
Health Teacher
Mc Masters, David Rex
Reading, Math & Algebra Tchr
Perry, Shirley Daughtry
German & English Teacher
Pettus, Rose Mary
English & Drama Teacher
Pinckley, Frances Ann (Mitchell)
8th Grd Language Arts Teacher
Roberts, Cindy Webb
7th-8th Grd Language Arts Tchr
Thigpen, Bonnie Elizabeth Hardison
Teacher & Assistant Principal
Thomas, Jerry Dale
Mathematics & Physics Teacher
Tinin, Stanley Aaron
Horticulture Teacher
Trapp, Mary Chapman
Third Grade Teacher
LEBANON
Ashby, Mary Buehler
9th & 12th Grd English Teacher
Calvin, Debbie Parks
University Teacher
Coggins, William Earl
Criminal Justice Teacher
Cozart, Dianne Goodall
6th Grade Teacher
Dillard, Robert Hugh
Hd Football Coach & Math Tchr
Edwards, Terry Thomas
Soc Stud, Drama & Jrnlsm Tchr
Eskew, Sherry M.
2nd Grade Teacher
Fakes, Bonnie DeHoff
English Teacher
Grandstaff, Juanita Williams
7th-8th Grd Language Arts Tchr
Harris, Terry Atkinson
Language Arts Teacher
Murphy, Stanley Douglas
Dir of Cnslng & Residence Life
Neal, Delene Fortmeyer
Science Teacher
Patton, James William
History, Psych, Geography Tchr

Walker, Sue Carol Sparrow
Fourth Grade Teacher
LENOIR CITY
Allen, Brenda Ellis
4th Grade Reading Teacher
Berdal, Darla Kaye
Math & Science Teacher
Dunlap, Kenneth Melton
Biology Teacher
Jones, Reta Morton
Fifth Grade English Teacher
Proder, Sedonna Warren
English & Japanese Teacher
Russell, Julie Williams
Fifth Grade Science Teacher
Salata, Brenda (Smith)
Science Teacher
Schwall, Robin Lee
Secondary English Teacher
Wielfaert, Marcia Norris
Speech, Drama & Chorus Teacher
LEOMA
Glass, Jamie Lynn
7th Grd Language Arts Teacher
LEWISBURG
Burton, Deborah Taylor
4th Grade Teacher
Clark Park, Sherry
Supervisor of Instruction
Ewing, Cheryl Smith
Third Grade Teacher
Gordon, Emily Lawrence
Seventh Grade Science Teacher
Hill, Nona DuVall
Health Sci Tech Instr
Hinds, Lucy-Fay Morgan
Math & Reading Teacher
Jent, Patricia Harris
4th Grade Teacher
McCullough, Rose Ann
Vocational Home Economics Tchr
Reese, Bonnie Adcox
Assistant Principal
Smith, Beth Phillips
English Teacher
Smith, Love Cathey
Kindergarten Teacher
Steely, Donald Ray, II
Algebra I & II Teacher
Wells, Brenda Burgett
Art Teacher
Wells, Gary Traughber
Guidance Counselor
Wiles, Jeanne Phillips
Math Teacher
LEXINGTON
Casselberry, John Thomas
Math, Sci & Soc Studies Tchr
Fesmire, Anita Gail
Spcl Ed & Resource Teacher
Fiddler, Katherine Ann
Language Arts Teacher
Frizzell, Danny Lynn
Guidance Counselor
Harris, Dinah Bowman
9th-12th Grade Teacher
Harris, Louise Wilson
8th Grd Language Arts Teacher
Hehe, Jim Edward
Physical Education Teacher
Holmes, Elizabeth Walker
Business Teacher
Lewis, Lisa A.
Data Proc, Keybd & Cmptr Instr
Maness, Ann Peddy
Mathematics Teacher
Melton, Julia Patterson
Child Care & Guidance Teacher
Pierce, Donna Kaye
5th-6th Grd Language Arts Tchr
Walker, Susan Scott
Typing, Mrktng & Jrnlsm Tchr
Williams, Lonnie Lynn
Art Teacher & Director
Youngerman, Gail Neisler
English & Theater Arts Tchr
LIMESTONE
Hale, Joyce L.
6th-8th Grd Lang Arts Teacher
Lachman, Donna Hartsell
Science Teacher
Nanney, Jeannie Mitchell
4th Grade Teacher
LINDEN
Alley, Judy Trull
7th-8th Grd Special Ed Teacher
Mercer, Cindy Warren
English & Psychology Teacher
Rawdon, Maria Matthews
Spanish Teacher
Tucker, Donna DePriest
8th Grd Lit & Eng Teacher
LIVINGSTON
Byers, Janie S.
Fourth Grade Teacher
Dingwall, Gregory Scot
Band & Choir Music Director
Howard, Karen A.
Instructor of English
Maynard, Elizabeth Sue
Psychology & English Teacher
Ogletree, Teresa Maynord
Dir of Family Resource Ctr
Rios, Marjorie Evans
Span Tchr & Foreign Lang Chm
Upton, Susan Hollis
German Teacher
LOOKOUT MOUNTAIN
Bullard, Ellen Pospisil
Writing Lab Teacher

MacDougall, Daniel W.
Assoc Prof of Biblical Studies
LORETTO
Davis, Larry Andrew
7th-8th Grade English Teacher
Jones, Ricky Elwin
Science Teacher
Smith, Helen Bryan
English Teacher
LOUDON
Daniels, Timothy Scott
Psychology & Sociology Teacher
Foster, Dian Fisher
Librarian
Foster, Jerry Lynn
AP American History Teacher
Garland, Gail Boone
Home Economics Teacher
Holton, Susan Dorrans
Speech & Language Pathologist
Laing, Leneda Jo
7th Grd Math Teacher
Peters, Sandra Fiechter
Fourth Grade Teacher
Stamey, Carl Clayton
Phys Ed Teacher
Thomas, Pamela Boone
Eighth Grade Science Teacher
LUTTRELL
Mc Bee, Elizabeth T.
First Grade Teacher
LYLES
Hobbs, Frances Luther
Fourth Grade Teacher
LYNCHBURG
Beavers, Thomas G.
Agricultural Education Teacher
Fletcher, Karen Bobo
Business Education Teacher
LYNNVILLE
Boring, Connie Uselton
Eighth Grade Teacher
Hollis, Bobby Allen, Jr.
Librarian
Lovell, Gloria Hellon
4th Grade Teacher
McMasters, Bobbi B.
English & French Teacher
Sisk, Elizabeth Mc Anally
Second Grade Teacher
Watson, Linda Rose
Second Grade Teacher
MADISON
Boyle-Parsley, Jeannie Marie
Sixth Grade Teacher
Clark, Deloras Jeanette
English Teacher
Dorris, Amy Lorene
Retired Director & Owner
DuBose, Katherine C.
Third Grade Teacher
Griggs, Carol Elizabeth
Second Grade Teacher
Hagan, Donna Smith
Biology Teacher
Hewlett, Ted
7th Grade Teacher
Hickman, Lana (Barske)
Math, Physics & Geography Tchr
Postal, Gordon August
Mathematics Teacher
Spear, Bobette Bonds
Sixth Grade Teacher
Stanford, Charles L.
Counselor & Bible Teacher
Thomas, Shirley Tisdale
Second Grade Teacher
Weeks, Frances A.
Fourth Grade Teacher
MADISONVILLE
Daugherty, Carolyn Carter
Assistant Prof of Sociology
Evans, Dave Malcolm
Wellness Instructor
Howard, Beth Rapking
Prof of Family & Consumer Sci
Mc Clendon, Nancy Marlene
Kindergarten Teacher
Miller, Ann Lawson
Psychology Instructor
Moser, Floyd maurice
History US & Geography Teacher
Pennington, Kimberly Peery
Science Teacher
Peterman, Shari Hatcher
Business Teacher
Shoopman, Patricia Ann
Seventh Grade Teacher
Wade, Elizabeth
Mathematics Professor
Wright, Debbie Sue
Math Teacher
MANCHESTER
Allen, Joyce Payne
English Teacher
Banks, Sheila Williamson
Spanish & English Teacher
Breeden, Jeffrey Kirk
Physical Science Teacher
Clark, Richie Dale
Eighth Grade English Teacher
Daniel, Carolyn Mc Clure
8th Grade Lang Arts Teacher
Elrod, Bobbie Gail
First Grade Teacher
Foster, Mickey Guess
English Teacher
Greene, Douglas Hall, Jr.
World History Teacher

Hickerson, Cathy Hatcher
English & Journalism Teacher
Hickerson, Charles Franklin
Advanced Sr Eng & Jrnlsm Tchr
Keel, Margia Henegar
Math Teacher
Long, Carolyn Duke
5th Grade Teacher
Mc Cullough, Joyce Ann
English Teacher
Vaughn, Joey Wayne
8th Grade Social Studies Tchr
Weaver, Dennis Robert
Mathematics Teacher
Young, Robert Encil
Retired Teacher & Counselor
MARTIN
Ahlschwede, Margrethe P.
Assistant Professor
Bernard, John Kyle
Former Assoc Prof of Anim Sci
Boyte, Cheryl James
French & AP English Teacher
Brundige, Julia White
Adjunct Professor
Bruning, Merribeth Davis
Asst Prof of Early Chldhd Ed
Carls, Alice-Catherine Maire
Asst Professor of History
Carroll, Sherrill Ross
Fifth Grade Teacher
Cashdollar, Parker
Professor of Economics
Clark, Anna Hackward
College Professor of English
Collard, Teresa Y.
Professor of Communications
Conner, Florence Bell
Retired 2nd Grade Teacher
Cook, Douglas J.
Associate Professor of Theatre
Cooley, Sharon Renee
American History Teacher
Durden, Kay Akin
Professor
Eskew, Thomas Eugene
College Mathematics Teacher
French, Samuel Earl
Prof of Engineering Tech
Gale, Paula Michelle
Assistant Prof of Soil Sci
Gathers, Emery George
Math & Computer Science Prof
Gibson, Michael Allen
Associate Prof of Geology
Glover, Polly Stone
Eng Prof & Learning Ctr Coord
Hathcock, Bob R.
Professor of Agronomy
Hewitt, Patricia Anne
Asst Professor of Science Ed
Irwin, Rebecca Emily
Assistant Professor of Biology
Jolly, Robert Morrison
Professor of Art
Jones, Lucia Earlene
Professor of PE & Health
Keene, Beuford Wayne
English Professor
Kiesling, LeeRoy W.
Professor Emeritus of Ag Ed
Kolitsch, Stephanie Tyler
Assistant Prof of Mathematics
Maness, Lonnie Edward
History Professor
Mathesen, Nancy Adams
Associate Professor of Music
Nanney, Robert
Communications Professor
Ogg, Elton Jerald
Communications Professor
Overby, John David
Assoc Professor of Management
Parker, Henry H.
Professor of Philosophy
Poore, Michael T.
Instructor
Pritchett, Ann Stanford
Eighth Grd Language Arts Tchr
Ray, David L.
Mathematics Instructor
Rayburn, John Michael
Assoc Professor of Marketing
Rushing, Theresa Collins
Instructor of Mathematics
Shadden, Richard Carl
Assoc Prof Agricultural Engrng
Timmerman, John Edwin
Marketing Professor
Welden, Alicia Galaz
Assoc Prof of Span Lit & Lang
West, Cynthia Hurley
Social Work Instructor
Whitt, Martha Ann
English Professor
Wright, Jenna Stoker
English Teacher
MARYVILLE
Barnes, Louise Rymer
Math Teacher
Barto, Mary Ann (Nichols)
6th-8th Grade Math Teacher
Best, Linda Delaney
Mathematics Dept Chairman
Blackburn, Patricia Ann (Hopp)
Math Teacher
Blevens, Anne Whitehead
8th Grade Language Arts Tchr
Bradshaw, Terri Hall
Composition, Lit & Hlth Tchr

MARYVILLE (cont)
Britt, Robert Eugene
Student Affairs Principal
Carnes, Timothy T.
8th Grd Pre-Algebra Teacher
Carpenter, Stephen DeWayne
English Teacher
Clark, Linda Yoder
English Dept Instructor
Crowe, Dodd Bruce
Social Studies Teacher
Dunlap, Rebecca Mize
7th & 8th Grd Lang Arts Tchr
Franklin, S. Kelly
Intnl Services Dir & ESL Tchr
Garner, Douglas Allen
9th Grd Physical Science Tchr
Heckert, Sharon Odom
Fifth Grade Teacher
Lane, Patricia B.
English & Drama Teacher
McCarter, Rita Maddox
First Grade Teacher
McClure, James Woody
Third Grade Teacher
Petrowski, Sherry Lockwood
HS English & Drama Teacher
Robinson, William Nathaniel, Jr.
Orchestra Director
Rosevear, Burt Lewis
Adjunct Professor of Music
Simpson, Terry L.
Assistant Prof of Scndry Ed
Talley, Penny
3rd Grade Teacher
Tipps, Vivian D.
Retired 1st Grade Teacher
Webb, Sharon Grubb
Second Grade Teacher
Williamson, Mark Anthony
Government & Economics Teacher
Wolfe, Charlotte L.
English Teacher
MASCOT
Greene, Kathy Morell
Fifth Grade Teacher
MAYNARDVILLE
Edds, Carrie Shoffner
Business Teacher
Parks, Willie Keene
Seventh Grd Rdng & Art Tchr
Roberts, Mark Anthony
Supervisor of Attendance
Smith, Deborah Ann
Sixth Grade Teacher
Williams, Tommy Lynn
Seventh Grade Science Teacher
MC KENZIE
Hendricks, Harlan Judson
Assistant Professor of Biology
Hendricks, Mary Beth
Asst Professor of Education
Nelson, John Peter, Jr.
Assistant Professor of Biology
Scruton, Sharon Styck
English Instructor
MC LEMORESVILLE
Pirtle, Karen Gowan
Second Grade Teacher
MC MINNVILLE
Clark, Melba Dean
7th Grd Reading & History Tchr
Drake, Bonnie C.
Bio & Chem Teacher
Fisher, Joseph Franklin
World History Teacher
Gillespie, Paula Pierce
Math & Tech I Teacher
Hendrix, Jana Kristin
8th Grade Teacher
Jacobs, David Michael
Math & Geometry Teacher
King, Linda Womack
AP Calculus Teacher
Mc Neal, Nancy Mullins
Physics Teacher
Reep, Melissa Loring
Fourth Grade Teacher
Sanderson, James W.
Principal & Teacher
Walker, Jimmy Doyle
Physical Science Teacher
Williams, James C.
Guidance Counselor
MEDON
Arnold, Mary L. Delashmit
Retired HS English Teacher
MEMPHIS
Abel, Zena Bailey
English & Latin Teacher
Adesipe, Oluwatoyin Adeniyi
Asst Professor of Acctng Tech
Akins, Sandra Kay
Senior English Teacher
Alden, E. Linda
Biology Teacher
Aldrich, Johnnie Ruth
Assistant Prof of Span & Eng
Aldridge, Patricia Roebuck
6th Grd Language Arts Teacher
Anderson, Theodore
Amer History Tchr & Ath Dir
Bacon, Juana Jones
Home Economics Teacher
Bafford, Charlene Person
Honors Government Teacher
Battaly, David Eugene
Latin, Ger & Russian Lang Tchr
Baumgartner, Ann Gregory
Language Arts Teacher
Beasley, Daphne P.
Geometry Teacher
Beck, Michelle Lynne (Call)
6th Grade Teacher
Begley, Leontine Marie
Retired Teacher
Bentley, Janice Amanda
Science Teacher
Berlin, Charles Roger
Art Teacher
Betton-Glenn, June Renee
Choral Director
Black, Beverly Jeanne
10th & 12th Grade English Tchr
Blakney, Mableleen Mabry
Office Technology Teacher
Blanchard, Mary S.
Early Childhood Teacher
Bland, Dave Lawrence
Associate Prof of Preaching
Bond, Beverly Greene
American History Teacher
Boone, Wanda Sipole
Art Teacher
Boskey, Freda Diann
Health Science Teacher
Boyd, Adelene Brown
Kindergarten Teacher
Bradford, Patti
Home Furnishings Asst Prof
Brandon, Sharon Alice
First-Third Grade Teacher
Brangenberg, Carla M.
Physical Education Teacher
Brooks, Angela Thomas
Mathematics Teacher
Brooks, Hayley Corn
11th Grade English Teacher
Brown, Linda Joyce (Horn)
Latin Teacher
Brown, Patsy Tooles
Geometry Teacher
Brown, Sandra E. Harris
5th Grade Teacher
Bullard, Shirley Bennett
Microcomputer Instr
Burke, Tracie L.
Asst Prof of Social Sciences
Bush, Charlotte Romell
English Teacher
Cacy, James Kyle
World Geography Teacher
Calhoun, Mary E.
Spanish Teacher
Callicoat, Elizabeth Ann
Biology & Health Teacher
Callicoat, Libby Ann
Biology Teacher & Coach
Callis, T. Keith
Associate Professor of English
Carpenter, Christine Boyd
Kindergarten Teacher
Carr, Betty Kay Davis
6th Grade Teacher
Carruthers, Alice Myracle
Calculus & Honors Adv Mth Tchr
Carter, Kathlyn Ann
First Grade Teacher
Casteel, Robert Blake, II
Science Teacher
Caviness, Telitha
Instructional Facilitator
Chaney, William L.
Professor of Psychology
Chappel, Patricia Dugger
First Grade Teacher
Chester, James A.
Director of Choral Activities
Childress, Debra Ann
Sixth Grade Teacher
Christian, Georgine
Teacher
Claybon, Curtis Anthony
6th Grade Teacher
Coleman, Juanita Johnson
7th Grd Soc Studies Teacher
Coleman, Marcia Doyle
Pre-Algebra & Geometry Teacher
Coleman-Terry, Aretha
Honors Algebra Teacher
Collier, Kim F. Crump
Asst Professor of Dev Math
Collins, Louise Hall
Resource Teacher
Cook, Cynthia L.
Asst Dir of Distance Education
Cook, Vava Finch
Human Services Professor
Cooper, Elizabeth A.
Honors Geometry Teacher
Cooper, Lala Ball
Honors English, AP US His Tchr
Copeland, Gloria Jean
Kindergarten Teacher
Crawford, Danny Louis
Social Science Teacher
Crawford, Sherrye Elizabeth
History & Mathematics Teacher
Creasman, Sharon Louise
Third Grade Teacher
Crosthwait, Lisa Holiman
Teacher
Crout, Pamela Jones
Early Childhood Teacher
Cummings, Minnie Harris
6th Grade Teacher
Curlin, Rebecca Goodwin
Art Teacher
Dacus, Janice Morton
Spanish Teacher
Dahlberg, Christopher Hoffman
Mathematics & Physics Teacher
Dahlman, Gloria Spadini
French Teacher
Daniels, Mary Polk
Fifth Grade Teacher
Darlington, Andrea B.
Ninth Grade English Teacher
Davis, Esther O. Wilkerson
Dev Studies Math Instructor
Davis, Henrene Cannon
9th & 10th Grade English Tchr
Dean, Karen Ann
Communication Arts Teacher
Dezell, Eunice Watt
Second Grade Teacher
Ditto, Florence Jean
Middle School Teacher
Dixon, Mildred E. Thomas
Classroom Network Admin
Donald, Edmond
Assistant Prof, Dept of Ed
Donaldson, Cathy Green
English Teacher
Douglas, Lindsay
English Teacher
Duff, Wayne E.
Latin Teacher
Eastham, Constance Walker
6th Grd Language Arts Teacher
Ellis, Paulette
Kindergarten Teacher
Enriquez, Richard Nicholas
Religion & Ethics Teacher
Entzminger, Mary Lou
English Teacher
Erskine, Helen Charcalis
Eng Tchr of Gifted Students
Espinosa, Carlos
Spanish Teacher
Field, Elizabeth Jacobsen
Home School Art Teacher
Finnern, Susan Avery
Spanish Teacher
Finney, Jane Scott
Kindergarten Teacher
Fitch, Chris Reagh
English & Religion Teacher
Flannagan, Ella Ingram
Intermediate Teacher of Gifted
Fletcher, Carol Odom
Data Processing Teacher
Flowers, Doris Davis
Vocational Instructor
Forman, Ellen Kaplan
Second Grade Teacher
Foster, Clabourne B.
Associate Professor
Foster, Patricia Applewhite
Third Grade Teacher
Frey, Sara Ackerman
Principal
Gaines, Marily Humphreys
English Teacher
Gilland, Angela Poindexter
English Teacher
Gilliland, Burl E.
Professor of Counseling Psych
Goddard, Paul Edward
Dean of Stu & Amer His Tchr
Gooden, Rosalind Renee
Second Grade Teacher
Gorman, Reita Katherine
9th & 11th Grd English Teacher
Gosnell, Deborah Lynn
10th-12th Grd Computer Teacher
Green, Mildred Denby
Music Professor
Greene, Irma Humphrey
Speech Pathologist
Greenhill, Elizabeth Dianne
Professor of Nursing
Greer, Irene
Third Grade Teacher
Greer, James M.
Guidance Coordinator
Griffin, Dorothy Anita
Instructional Facilitator
Griffin, Lorraine Simmons
Math, Sci & Cmptr Skills Tchr
Hagemann, Bob
Math & Computer Teacher
Haghtalab, Mary Ann
3rd Grade Teacher
Halfacre, Sandra L.
Mathematics Teacher
Hammond, Josephine
Bus, Office Ed Teacher & Chmn
Hammond, LouVenia Holmes
English Teacher
Hammons, Charlene Heywood
First Grade Teacher
Hankins, Elizabeth Porter
English Department Chairman
Hanson, Linda Kaeding
Retired Teacher
Hardin, Barbara Anne
Latin Teacher
Harman, Sandra M.
Mathematics Teacher
Harmon, Barbara Tucker
Accounting Teacher
Harrell, Goldie Parks
Educl Resource Specialist
Harrington, John L.
World History Teacher
Harris, Dorothy Jean
Marketing Teacher
Harris, John Hollister
Assoc Prof of Math & Cmptr Sci
Haseltine, Deborah Ward
Assoc Prof of Information Tech
Hathcock, Angela Peak
Second Grade Teacher
Hatley, Linda Phillips
Seventh Grade Math Teacher
Hatsell, Mary Suzanne
Biology & Honors Biology Tchr
Haughton, JoAnn Gardner
Latin & Humanities Teacher
Hawkins, Sandra J.
English Teacher
Henderson, Doris Elcenia
Mathematics Teacher
Hendrix, Barbara
10th & 11th Grd English Tchr
Hess, Dorothy Rice
English Teacher
Hester, John Robert
Vocal Music Teacher
Hight, Lisa J.
Assistant Professor of Biology
Hopkins, Joan Holder
Instr of Critical Care Nrsng
Huggins, James Anthony
Prof of Anatomy & Physiology
Hugo, Nancy Eddins
Second Grade Teacher
Hull, Patricia McCullough
1st Grade Teacher
Hunt, Terri Jackson
Kindergarten Teacher
Indingaro, Margaret Ann (Utterback)
Mathematics Supervisor
Ingram, Minnie Alston
World History & Geography Tchr
Irving, Karen E.
Chemistry Teacher
Ivins, Ann E.
Science Teacher
Jackson, Addie Beatrice
Retired Soc Stud Dept Chair
Jackson, David Hamilton, Jr.
Social Studies Tchr & Dept Chm
Jackson, Linda Wiley
English Teacher
Jackson, Nancy Wells
2nd Grade Teacher
Jackson, Pamela Hall
Elem Schl Asst Principal
Jamerson, Bonnie Joy
1st Grade Teacher
James, Dorothy
Fifth Grade Teacher
James, June Griffin
Third Grade Teacher
Jarrett, Linda Key
Computer Teacher
Jefferson, Chirelle Yvette
Speech & Drama Teacher
Jennings, Theresa Browning
Mathematics Teacher
Johnson, Sonia Leigh
History & English Teacher
Jonakin, Bebe Burford
Ninth Grade Guidance Counselor
Jones, Kathryn Snell
English Teacher
Jones, Samynna Laster
Tenth Grade English Teacher
Jones, Sue Lansford
Curriculum Coordinator
Jones-Peppers, Linda
Third Grade Teacher
Jones-Wallace, Nichole N.
10th Grade English Teacher
Joy, Deborah Williams
World Geography Teacher
Keller, Melinda Kay
Advanced Placement Bio Teacher
King, Camille Kendall
Office Technology Teacher
Kitts, Judith Pate
English Teacher
Knowlton, Mildred
Business & Office Tech Teacher
Kolheim, Constance Mitchell
6th Grade Teacher
Kyles, Betty Tyson
Biology Teacher
Kyles, Mary Ann (Winfield)
Vocal Music Tchr & Choir Dir
Lane, Carol Shannon
5th Grd Reading & Science Tchr
Langston, Andrea Gilliam
Resource English Teacher
Lanois, Johnie L.
English Teacher
Lard, Amelia Sullivan
Business & Economics Teacher
Laster, Ada Collins
Fourth Grade Teacher
Lavecchia, John Vincent
English Instructor & Dept Chm
Lavenue, Harriette Joan
Professor
Layton, Sarah Evenda (Nettle)
AP English & English Teacher
Lee, Katheryn
Second Grade Teacher
Logan, Minnie E. W.
Guidance Counselor
Love, Frank Michael
Science Chairman
Lucas, Beth
English Teacher
Lurie, Jennifer Okeon
AP & Honors English Teacher
Luther, Jane Longmire
HS Geography Teacher
Lynn, Bettye Claire
Mathematics Instructor
Malone, Kay Ray
First Grade Teacher
Malone, Willie Ann
Classroom Teacher
Matthews, James Albert
Health & Physcial Ed Teacher
Maxwell, Robyn Fuller
Math & Social Studies Teacher
Mc Carthy, David Patterson
Assistant Professor of Art His
McClelland, Trudie Hostettler
Secondary Business Ed Teacher
Mc Dade, Barbara Bennett
English & Art Teacher
McDonald, Zella Carothers
Professor of Education
Mc Elwee, Mildred Vallery
Homebound Teacher
Mc Gruder, Ruth Drake
Biology Teacher
Mc Hugh, Nancy Clark
Sixth Grade Teacher
Mc Lin, Mollie Mae (Jenkins)
Business Teacher
McWilliams, Mary Hubbard
Mathematics Teacher
Mears, Lesa Carol
Athletic Director & Coach
Milam, Betty Haun
English Teacher
Millen, Rhendle Michael
Instrumental Music Director
Mitchell, Sue Powers
English Teacher
Moody, Dennis L.
Exemplary Teacher
Moore, Jossie A.
Reading & Study Skills Prof
Moore, Judie Jones
Senior Guidance Counselor
Moore, Sherron Ledbetter
First Grade Teacher
Morris, Kay Hobbs
Kindergarten Teacher
Muizers, Lois Jean (Earner)
English Teacher
Mullins, Carolyn Hopkins
Algebra & Math Teacher
Mullis, Betty Ann
Geography & Economics Teacher
Myers, Deborah Miller
Seventh Grade Teacher
Myers, Sally Wilson
Fifth Grade Teacher
Nelson, Elizabeth Mc Ghee
Psychology Professor
Nickelberry, Ellen Wells
Third Grade Teacher
Noeth, George J.
Honors Chemistry Teacher
O'Daniel, Marion M.
Assoc Prof of Telecomm Engrng
Olson, John Dennis
Physics Teacher
Overton, Johnnie Mae (Coleman)
Microcmptr Info Systems Tchr
Padgett, Robert James
Lead Science Teacher
Paris, Anna M.
Kindergarten Teacher
Parker, Natalie Neely
Theatre Arts & Eng Teacher
Parrott, Monika Irene
Mathematics Teacher
Pate, Eddie
Assistant Professor of History
Patterson, Mary Brown
5th Grade Teacher
Peebles, Dianne
English Teacher
Penn, Pamela Williams
Home Economics Teacher
Pensak, Karl J.
Science Teacher
Pentecost, Donna Peacher
German Teacher
Perkins, John Dudley
Physical Ed Teacher & Coach
Pernell, William, III
Night School Principal & Tchr
Peterson, Mary Nance
Sixth Grade Teacher
Pettit, Barbara Sacks
8th Grade Math & Religion Tchr
Pfeiffer, Carl Logan
English Teacher
Phillips, David Alan
Russian Lang & Lit Teacher
Phillips, Mary Thompson
Instructional Facilitator
Pierson, Eddie, III
Teacher & Coach
Pittman, Charlotte Young
Pre-Kndgtn Tchr & Math Coord
Polk, Patricia Ann
First Grade Teacher
Pool, David Louis
Secondary School Teacher
Poole, Clementhia Parker
English Teacher
Poole, Martha Gunn
Advanced Placement Bio Teacher
Prendergast, Patricia Collins
Fifth Grade Teacher
Prewitt, James A., IV
Guidance Counselor
Price, Carl
Mathematics Teacher

PHIS (cont)
›r, Cindy Strawn
ch Teacher
, Billy M.
atre Arts Teacher
y, Maurice Taylor
›nd Grade Teacher
opalan, Meenakshi
Prof of Math
Metra Muskelley Baker
Grade Teacher
›lds, Jo Alexander
Grade Teacher
›s, Opanell
›th Grade Teacher
rdson, John Jay
Grade Math Teacher
, Jerry Albert
hematics Teacher
›ts, Robert H.
sics Teacher
Dianne D.
Tchr & Sci Dept Chprsn
ering, Patricia
Grade Teacher
, Bryan George
hematics Instructor
Barbara Williams
ne Economics Teacher
ng, Ann H.
›d Grade Teacher
Lisa Broussard
ntessori Teacher
wski, Theresa Turner
›metry & Math Tech Teacher
by, Dolores
dergarten Teacher
fer, Leslie Ozbirn
logy Teacher
, Sonja Hall
fessional School Counselor
ent, Lula Harris
History Teacher
fer, John Edgar
sistant Professor of Biology
, David
logy & Chemistry Teacher
, Gwendolyn Roberts
st Grade Teacher
, Wanda Deloise
anish Teacher
, Yeu-Sheng
st Prof of Engineering
, Dorie Doss
ence Instructor
well, Ada Christena
an of General Studies
, Lisa Hayes
rketing Education Teacher
, Ernelle Wright
nch Instructor
nons, Deborah Kay
m Science Teacher
, Loretta Mc Kay
h Grade Teacher
n, Rebecca Matlock
ndergarten Teacher
h, Amy McCullen
emistry Teacher
h, Blount Devlin
tin Teacher
h, Vinnie Johnson
tired Math Teacher
l, Glora Taylor
ath Dept Chprsn & Teacher
alding, Lisa Mansfield
emistry Teacher
ncer, Annie L. Drake
Grade Teacher
ford, Melanie McWilliams
glish Teacher
henson, Michael Randolph
& World History Teacher
atenburgh, Charles Ignatious
etals Technology Teacher
obs, Linda Kershaw
ench Teacher
or, Lynette Elaine
ology & Chemistry Teacher
, Jacquelyn S.
eneral & Vocal Music Teacher
lor, Mae Goodman
uidance Counselor
y, Willie Ray, Sr.
S History Teacher
mson, Judith A.
h-6th Grade Teacher
man, Glover Jean
uidance Counselor
s-Boccia, Kathleen
nglish Teacher of the Gifted
n, Pamela Kay
ssociate Professor of Math
gle, Melvin
rofessor of Philosophy
ner, Roger Dennis
structor of Criminal Justice
ner, Ronald Steven
irector of Bands
derwood, Sherri Lynn
cience Lab Teacher
Velsor, Sandra Barron
panish Teacher
de, James S.
ssistant Professor
de, Lottie Nash
etired 1st Grade Teacher
lker, Sherrie
lgebra I Teacher

Ward, Gloria M.
Retired Teacher
Ward, Joyce Stidumn
Third Grade Teacher
Warner, Janie Marie
Eighth Grd Language Arts Tchr
Warren, Judith Ann
English Teacher
Washington, Pearl Ivy
English & Journalism Teacher
Weatherly, Marsha Agar
Fifth Grade Reading Teacher
Weathers, Linda Tatum
4th Grade Teacher
Webb, David Ray
Spanish Teacher
Webber, Jo Ann Wells
Teacher & Computer Curr Coord
Weir, John Thos
Spanish Teacher
Werner, Charlotte Faye
12th Grade English Teacher
Wexler, Jeri Kahn
Science & Social Studies Tchr
White, Gaynell Reeves
Fifth Grade Teacher
Wicks, Mona Newsome
Assistant Professor of Nursing
Wiggins, Ventress Jackson
Sixth Grade Teacher
Wigginton, Brenda Dyer
Sixth Grade Teacher
Wilkins, Lisa Carter
Teacher
Willcox, Robin Posner
French & English Teacher
Williams, Betty D.
Mathematics Teacher
Williams, Dorothy Ewing
Vocational Home Economics Tchr
Williams, Gary Howell
Math Teacher & Coach
Williams, George W.
Prof of Bio & Dept Chrmn
Williams, Gloria Darlene
Math, Voc & Home Ec Teacher
Wilson, Arlene Durham
5th Grade Science Teacher
Wilson, Beverly Kaye
Kindergarten Teacher
Winfield, Barbara Griffin
Instructional Facilitator
Wolfe, Henry Austin
Spanish Teacher
Wood, Joyce Thorne
English Teacher
Woods, Constance Weddle
Guidance Counselor
Woods, Tonjua Beal
First Grade Teacher
Wooten, Jacqueline
Pre-Calculus Teacher
Word, Donnell, Jr.
English Teacher
Wranovix, Ann Marie
Assoc Prof of Lit & Languages
Yarwood, Teresa Elaine
Kindergarten Teacher

MICHIE

Bowers, Anne Qualls
7th & 8th Grd Lang Arts Tchr
Forsythe, Steven Craig
Jr High Teacher

MIDDLETON

Jobe, Glindan Gale
Bus Ed & English Teacher
Shelly, Sue V.
Vice Prin & Media Specialist

MILAN

Branson, Linda Arnold
Third Grade Teacher
Collins, Mary Moore
Science & Social Studies Tchr
Jackson, Timothy William
Math Teacher
Maness, Mary Moore
8th Grade Language Arts Tchr
Priddy, Bobbie Pratt
Kindergarten Teacher
Sering, Cynthia Boehler
2nd Grade Teacher

MILLINGTON

Barger, David Lee
High School Spanish Teacher
Barron, Pamela Dawn
High School Science Teacher
Clark, Jo Etta Sixsmith
Biology Teacher
Dickenson, James Edward
Accounting Teacher
Donnelly, Jane Moore
Kindergarten Teacher
Gillespie, Kenneth Lee
Dean of Curriculum
McLaughlin, Rose Dathelyn
Computer Teacher
Miller, Regina Marie
Math Teacher
Schmall, Linda Reding
English Tchr & Dept Chprsn
Thomas, Nelba J.
Choral Music Director
Tolbert, Vera Dean (Wright)
Office Technology Teacher
Whitehead, Susan R.
Biology Teacher

MINOR HILL

Kennedy, Linda Bonita
Second Grade Teacher

Murphy, Crista Cornelison
Third Grade Teacher

MONTEREY

Clift, Martha Upton
English Teacher
Garrison, Elaine Blake
Mathematics Teacher
Sells, Retta Cross
Title I Teacher

MORRISTOWN

Claborn, Jim W.
Social Studies Teacher
Cole, Kimberly Harrison
Speech & Language Pathologist
Eichelman, Sarah Moreman
Assoc Professor of English
Evans, John
Asst Prof of Public Safety Div
Farmer, Raymond Mack, Jr.
Wellness & Fitness Teacher
Fleming, Laurence E.
Professor of Biology
Fowler, Angel Cureton
Marketing Education Teacher
Hagan, Frankie Hendrixon
English Professor
Helm, Carroll Manford
Director of Greeneville Campus
Jenkins, Cary E.
Assoc Prof of Health, Phys Ed
Justice, Susie Fishman
First Grade Teacher
Kell, Josephine Ann Wooden
Assoc Prof of English
LaBreck, Robert Michael
Asst Prof of Criminal Justice
Lamar, Doris Linda
English Teacher
Newman, Lynn Patterson
7th Grd Rdng Teacher & Coach
Noe, Donna Chapman
Fifth Grade Teacher
Nutter, Teressa Jo Ann
Special Education Consultant
Seals, Wanda Cross
3rd Grade Teacher
Tilson, Kathryn Walli
German Teacher
Vance, Donna Mott
Business Education Teacher
Williams, Ruth Brock
Second Grade Teacher
Woodroffe, Marcia Frederico
Biology Teacher

MOSHEIM

Duryea, Jeanette S.
English I Teacher
Swanay, Donald Eugene
Agricultural Education Teacher
West, Peggy Davis
Kindergarten Teacher

MOUNT JULIET

Ash, Nancy Williams
US History & Psychology Tchr
Barnes, Patricia Stines
Honors Biology Teacher
Bates, Angela Blackburn
Senior English Teacher
Baunefeind, James Charles
Criminal Justice Teacher
Brooks, Teresa Griffin
Social Studies Teacher
Bucy, Deanie M.
Business Teacher
Custer, Arlene H.
Fourth Grade Teacher
Ghee-Messick, Carol C.
Fifth Grade Teacher
Gibbs, Sandy F.
English Teacher
Gilbert, Jill R.
Geometry Teacher
Hall, Betty Jean
English Teacher
Harrod, Russell D.
9th Grd Pre Alg & Math Tchr
Jenkins, Christie Condra
Science Teacher
Johnson, Edward V.
French Teacher
Lewis, Bridgette Henslee
Science Teacher
Sharpe, Beverly J.
Math Teacher
Smith, Geneva A.
Third Grade Teacher
Tate, Dina Frye
Spanish Teacher
Thompson, Barbara Jean
Mathematics Teacher
Unland, Fran Watkins
6th Grade Teacher
Willoughby, Don O'Neal
Agricultural Education Teacher
Wright, Theresa Belcher
General & Physical Sci Teacher

MOUNT PLEASANT

Anderson, Judy Peery
Home Economics Teacher
Cannon, Charles E.
Math Teacher
Lacy, Berthaleen Webster
English & Reading Teacher

MOUNTAIN CITY

Brown, Marilyn Vannoy
Fifth Grade Teacher
Davis, Nancy Farris
Music Educator
Dobbins, Patricia Anne
First Grade Teacher

Manuel, Ron E.
Teacher
McGuire, Tina Renee
English Teacher
Pratt, Pamela Rene
Spanish Teacher
Tilley, Patricia Humphrey
General Science Teacher
Triplett, Gay Mast
Assistant Principal

MUNFORD

Acree, Nancy Luther
Geometry Tchr & Math Chprsn
Combs, John David
English Teacher
Corcoran, Virgina Thompson
Third Grade Teacher
Davison, Lynda Matthews
Physical Education Instructor
Fayne, Martha Rodgers
Guidance Counselor
Haywood, Mary Murphy
2nd Grade Teacher
Jenkins, Vannessa
Special Education Teacher
Laxton, Joseph Wayne
Biology & Chemistry Teacher
Mohon, Elizabeth Aycock
English & Journalism Teacher
Roaldson, Claudia Arthur Wiley
Eighth Grade Teacher
Starnes, Eddie Clyde
Technology & Science Teacher
Stitt, Susan G.
Counselor

MURFREESBORO

Ace, Judith Davis
Third Grade Teacher
Alsup, Beverly Carol Vaughan
American History Teacher
Anthony, Andrea Fayeth
Mathematics Teacher
Bader, Lawrence Edward
Fifth Grade Teacher
Berning, Carol Norville
Teacher of the Gifted
Boyd, Cynthia Donnell
Business Teacher
Boyd, M. Lance
Physical Science Teacher
Bradshaw, Nancy Waters
Second Grade Teacher
Brangenberg, David James
American History & Bible Tchr
Bryant, Joe Houston
Social Science Teacher
Cates, Steve D.
Ecology, Govt & Folklore Tchr
Cheatham, Thomas J.
Chair & Professor of Comp Sci
Cole, Carolyn Johnson
English Teacher
Couey, Ronald A.
7th Grade Science Teacher
Crowder, Deane Fuson
Fifth Grade Teacher
Daniel, Katherine Emery
Physics & Physical Sci Teacher
Davis, Glenn B.
Band Director
DeHoff, Valerie Stone
Music Teacher & Choral Dir
Dent-Gregory, Brenda Kay
Choral Director
Dollins, Ida Panko
Spanish Teacher
East, Pamela Cagle
5th Grade Teacher
Eichas, Toby
English & Journalism Teacher
Fiveash, Betsy Buchanan
2nd Grade Teacher
Foster, Marylee Emler
Math & Supercomputing Teacher
Frazer, Freda King
French Teacher
Gaither, J. Maxine
Art Teacher
Gould, Richard Henry
Professor Emeritus
Greene, Christopher Lee
Guidance Counselor
Hatfield, Joye Elrod
Vocational Business Teacher
Hayes, Rhonda Lynne
English Teacher
Hebden, Susanne St Clair
Spanish Teacher
Hedrick, Betty Guermonprez
4th Grade Teacher
Hudgens, Patricia Haile
7th & 8th Grade English Tchr
Jakes, Sheryl Anne
World History Teacher
Jenne, Nollie Sharp
Human Sciences Teacher, Chprsn
Jennings, Elizabeth Holden
Fifth Grade Teacher
Johnson, Sharon L.
Art Teacher
Jones, Marcia Eaton
1st Grade Teacher
Lancaster, Jason Warren
English Teacher
Lee, Terrence Allan
Asst Professor of Chemistry
Leyhew, Debra Wyatt
1st Grade Teacher
Little, Raymond, Sr.
Sixth Grade Teacher

Little, Ruby Woods
5th Grade Teacher
Loucky, David L.
Associate Professor in Music
Lyons, Pierre Lee
Physical Ed Teacher & Coach
Marks, Judy Holt
English Teacher
Matthews, Kristy Robertson
Sixth Grade Teacher
Mc Cord, Martha Bass
Fifth Grade Teacher
Meers, Ronald S.
Band Director
Miller, James Arthur
Pre-Calculus Teacher
Murchison, Janet Barber
4th Grade Teacher
Nance, Douglas Nathan
Fifth Grade Teacher
Peak, Virginia M.
Latin Teacher
Pittard, Janice Underwood
8th Grade English Teacher
Rogers, Joy Phifer
Fourth Grade Teacher
Sanford, Beverly Schmidt
7th Grade Teacher
Sherman, Theodore James
Assistant Professor of English
Sides, Judy Taylor
Social Studies Teacher
Smith, Betty Campbell
First Grade Teacher
Staley, Bobbie Allen
Principal
Stanczak, Allan Michael
Science Teacher
Stanczak, Barbara Kay
Spanish Teacher
Stanczak, David John
Math Teacher
Wallace, Karen Rene
Language Arts Teacher
White, Patrick L.
English Teacher
Williams, Jernita Hite
Third Grade Teacher

NASHVILLE

Adebanjo, Jennifer Warden
Assistant Prof & Pol Sci Chrmn
Adkins, Rutherford Hamlet
Natural Sci & Math Director
Allen, Frank Smotherman
Retired Teacher
Alsup, Julia Owen
Second Grade Teacher
Archer, Lisa Ferguson
Eighth Grade English Teacher
Armstrong, Shirley Talley
Kindergarten Teacher
Arndt, Andrea Dickson
Middle School History Teacher
Askew, Barbara Ellen (Dixon)
Third Grade Teacher
Atkinson, Ronald
Professor of Mathematics
Baker, Bonnie Bruce
Spanish Teacher
Bandy, Beverly Sue
Third Grade Teacher
Bearman, Amy L.
Exec Admin Asst & Former Tchr
Bell, Marty Gail
Associate Prof of Religion
Bisson, Douglas Ronald
Associate Professor of History
Boden, Marlene
Elementary School Teacher
Bourg, Carroll J.
Professor of Sociology
Boyd, Rena Anderson
English Teacher
Bradshaw, Mary Catherine
American Studies Teacher
Brewer, Carol Coaker
9th Grade English Teacher
Britt, Steve
High School Bible Teacher
Broad, David Benjamin
Professor of Sociology
Burgess, Bettye Patrick
English Teacher
Burgess, Nicole
Math Tchr & Girls Bsktbl Coach
Burrow, Teresa Bean
Algebra Teacher
Callaway, Rebecca Wade
5th Grade Language Arts Tchr
Callis, Norman Crawford
8th Grade US History Teacher
Carr, Jeffrey
Dean of Stu & Anatomy Tchr
Carter, James McCord
Adjunct Prof of Music Business
Chaney, Sharon Henderson
AP English IV Teacher
Cleveland, Barbara Hansen
Social Studies Chair
Cornelius, Hilke Maria Oepping
German Teacher
Cox, Lula Leach
Mathematics Teacher
Crawford, Sharon Lynett
Assistant Professor
Dammann, Daniel L.
Latin Teacher
Davis, Mary Lou Hysinger
2nd Grade Teacher

NASHVILLE (cont)
Davis, Michael Eugene
Wellness & Phys Ed Tchr, Coach
Davis, Paul J.
English Teacher
Delvaux, William Preston
High School Bible Teacher
Dhindsa, Gurjeet K.
Fifth Grade Teacher
Dickerson, Connie Raye
French & Latin Teacher
Dunn, Mary Virginia
Mathematics Professor
Easterly, Daniel A.
Theater Teacher
Ensminger, Linda Joyce
Career Ladder Evaluator
Entsminger, Deen Edward
Associate Professor of Music
Ertelt, Jonathan Bradley
Former Bio Lecturer
Faulk, Gregory Kenneth
Assistant Professor of Finance
Felch, Barbara Anne
French Teacher
Feltner, William F.
Social Studies Teacher
Fenton, Susan Marie
French Teacher
Foreman, John Charles
Theology, Human Sexuality Tchr
Forrister, Cathy S.
English & Speech Teacher
Freeman-Junior, Phyllis
Assistant Professor of Biology
Frensley, Tommy Patrick
Social Studies Teacher & Coach
Fry, Shannon S.
Guidance Counselor
Gallagher, Amy Ralston
Director of Teacher Licensing
Gibson, Rebecca L.
Spanish Teacher
Gilley, Donna G.
Business & Economics Teacher
Gilmore, Sue Chaney
Latin & European History Tchr
Glasper, Zeta Moore
5th Grade Teacher
Godwin, Paul Milton
Professor of Music
Goodwin, Cora Russell
Assoc Prof of English
Granberry, Dorothy
Interim Associate Dean of Ed
Gray, Mary Ann
World History Teacher
Gray, Sandra Ruth
Family & Consumer Science Tchr
Gregg, Robert Baxter
Music Professor
Griffin, Philip Wayne
Team Leader & Lead Teacher
Grimes, Charlene Smith
Mathematics Teacher
Gross, Karen Benton
5th Grade Teacher
Gundlach, Teddie Duke
Sixth Grade Teacher
Hagewood, William Lowell
History & Government Teacher
Hall, Deborah Jean
Math Tchr & Dept Chprsn
Harrington, E. Michael
Assoc Prof of Music Compostion
Hayes, Robert D.
Professor of Accounting
Hayslett, William F.
Associate Prof of Horticulture
Held, David Francis
Academic Dean
Henley, Thomas Stephen
History & Economics Teacher
Henry, Romelle Points
Foreign Lang & English Tchr
Hill Kelly, Sherry
Associate Professor of Music
Hodge, Harmon E.
Amer His Tchr & Dept Chairman
Hodge, Phyllis Goodman
English Teacher
Holland, Rosie Lee
Third Grade Teacher
Holt, Sandra W.
Assoc Prof of Communications
Hooper, William H.
Assoc Prof of Computer Science
Hoots, Nancy Connelly
Theology Teacher & Dept Chm
Horton, Carrell Peterson
Professor & Psychology Chair
Hughes, William Hunter
Math Teacher
Hunter, Wendy A.
Asst Prof of Political Science
Hurst, Arthur Brent
Mathematics Teacher
Hyde, Bonnie Forehand
Sixth Grade Teacher
Jackson, Jeanetta Williams
Asst Prof of Mathematics
Jenq, Jingfu
Computer Science Professor
Johnson, Cheryl Shanks
Science & Health Teacher
Johnson, Terrance Lewyne
Assoc Prof of Chem & Biol Sci
Jolley, Terry D.
Band Director
Keckley, Andrea Boyce
6th Grade Teacher
Kunnu, Elizabeth Idowu
Health Information Mngmt Prof
Lange, Donna Rash
English Teacher
Langley, Lawrence Leon
8th Grade Teacher
Lawrence, J. David
History & Political Sci Prof
Lee, Terry A.
8th Grd Teacher & Vice Prin
Longhauser, Patrice Norris
English Teacher
Lovett, Bobby L.
Dean Coll of Arts & Science
Mandela, Mayibuye
Africana Studies Professor
Marpaka, Dhananjaya Rao
Asst Prof of Elec & Cmptr Engr
Martin, Julie Skalka
Algebra II Teacher
Martinez, Veronica Fannin
6th Grade Reading & Lang Tchr
Maxwell, Otis
Dental Professor
Mc Caleb, Glenda Queen
English Teacher
Mc Kinney, Jane-Allen
Sculpture & Ceramics Instr
McNeil, Albertine Denise
4th Grade Teacher
Meiere, Paul Lumpkin, III
Mathematics Teacher
Middleton, Suzanne Swann
Math Teacher
Millson, David Sidney
Bible & Life Science Teacher
Monteverde, Margaret Pyne
Associate Professor of English
Moon, Patricia Minton
Sixth Grade Teacher
Morrow, Jane Sharp
Algebra & Psychology Teacher
Mosely, Marcella M.
Asst Prof & Tchr Ed Coord
Moxley, Haywood Dudley
English Teacher
Mulder, Robert G.
Bible Dept Chrmn
Mullins, Nancy H.
6th Grade Language Arts Tchr
Neal, Thelma Jane
Academic Director
Nimley, Anthony Jlanyene
Political Science Professor
Olaleye, Gideon A.
Assistant Professor
Orman, Ann Isenberg
General Science Teacher
Osborn, Patricia Dianne Rucker
Kindergarten Teacher
Ownby, Cindy
2nd Grade Teacher
Pell, John Nicholas
Instructor of Music
Pettus, Carole G.
English Teacher
Phister, Joan Mendes
Third Grade Teacher
Pinter, Michael
Assoc Prof of Mathematics
Posey, Susie J.
Science Teacher
Pulliam, Quenton
Business Management Professor
Ramage, Donald R.
Dean, Schl of Sci & Bio Prof
Reid, Garnett H.
Old Testament Professor
Reynolds, Ellen Clarissa
Development Director
Roberts, Beverly Graham
Fourth Grade Teacher
Roberts, Wesley Hayes
High School Ecology Teacher
Robertson, Joy Boone
Speech, English & Drama Tchr
Roche, Richard Wade
American History Teacher
Rolston, Clyde Philip
Assistant Professor
Rose, Michael Alec
Associate Prof of Composition
Ross, Michael Lewis
Social Studies Teacher
Royal, Brenda Campbell
Chemistry & Biology Teacher
Ryan, Katherine Hendrick
Kindergarten Teacher
Sanderfur, Emily Smith
Family Living & Home Ec Tchr
Schipani, Susan B.
Language Arts Teacher
Schwarzmeier, Regine
Adjunct Instructor of German
Scott, Wanda J. Banks
Language Arts Teacher
Seay, Richard H., Jr.
History & Latin Teacher
Shaw, Lynda K.
Counselor
Shoaf, Diann Blakely
Amer Lit & Creative Wrtng Tchr
Shores, Lynne Simpson
Asst Professor of Nursing
Smith, Judy Ledford
Guidance Counselor
Smith, Ronnie H.
Sci Tchr & Boys Track Coach
Smotherman, Debbie Lynn
Math & Algebra Teacher
Springer, John Mervin
Physics Professor
Spry, Richard Wayne
Assistant Principal
Stewart, Elizabeth Suzanne
MS English & Drama Teacher
Sturgill, Lowell Vernon
Business Department Chairman
Tarkington, Linda Pruett
Kindergarten Teacher
Taylor, LaVada U.
World Geography Teacher
Tays, Dwight L.
Political Science Professor
Thach, Sharon V.
Professor
Thorn, Charlotte Ruth
English Teacher
Tune, Elizabeth Brown
English Department Chairperson
Turner, Cathy J.
Dance Instr & Choreographer
Underhill, George L.
7th Grade Geography Teacher
Vaughan, Christina Lonzo
French Teacher
Vo, Kieu Van
Professor of Animal Science
Wade, Paul Frederick
Coach & Teacher
Wade, Peter William
Mathematics Teacher
Waller, Joyce Richardson
Psychology Teacher
Waller, Melissa Leah
English Instr & Dean of Acads
Wallis, Linda Gady
Biology Teacher & Acad Dean
Ward, Patricia S.
English & Theater Arts Teacher
Washington, Arthur Clover
Prof of Biology & Biochemistry
Washington, Theresa B. Higgins
Fourth Grade Teacher
Weathers, Cyndi Kay
Bus, Computer Tchr & Coach
White, Katie Kinnard
Prof of Biological Sciences
Wilbert, Lillian Taylor
English Teacher
Wilkinson, Melissa Kelly
French Teacher
Williams, Jerry S.
Soc Stud Chair & His Tchr
Williams, Marsha Rhea
Professor of Computer Science
Wollaber, Debra (Bond)
Assoc Prof of Family Nursing
Wonders, Kim
Choral Dir & Music Dept Chair
Yates, Faye Eubank
Seventh Grade Teacher
York, Andrea Joy
World & Amer His Teacher

NEW JOHNSONVILLE
Rehrig, Barbara Twelkemeier
Sixth Grade Sci & Reading Tchr

NEW MARKET
Noyes, Katherine Hallowell
4th Grade Teacher

NEW TAZEWELL
Russell, Diana Lynn
Fourth Grade Teacher
Williams, Walter Tipton
Fifth Grade Teacher

NEWBERN
Campbell, Glynda Bricker
Inclusion Coordinator
Dickerson, Shawn Craig
7th & 8th Grd Science Teacher
Fowlkes, Janet Studard
Art, Phys Sci & Bio Tchr
Fulwood, Richard Keith
History Teacher
McDonald, Steffany Carol
7th Grade Math & Reading Tchr
Reeves, Joyce Bomar
Business Teacher
Sanders, Stephanie Carson
Mathematics Teacher
Schlabach, Robert Ellis
High School Band Director
Smith, Dan L.
Agriculture Instructor
Stark, Carolyn McLean
English Teacher
Turner, Vernita
Home Economics Teacher
Young, Betty Myatt
English Teacher & Dept Head

NEWPORT
Brown, Janie Mc Mahan
Fourth Grade Teacher
Burchette, R. Gail
English Teacher
Burchette, Sandra White
Kindergarten Teacher
Clark, Mary Ann (M.)
First Grade Teacher
Crosby, Jane Sluder
Soc Studies Tchr & Dept Chair
Ellison, Wesley Eric
Agricultural Education Teacher
Hurley, Brenda
Second Grade Teacher
Jones, N. Carlene
8th Grd Language Arts Teacher
Messer, Pamela Rene Click
Sixth Grade Teacher
Parks, Trena LaShea
Earth Science & Geog Teacher
Parris, Stephen J.
Director of Bands
Roberts, Shirley Smith
Fifth Grade Teacher
Runnion, Cindie J.
Third Grade Teacher
Suggs, Tamra Brown
6th Grd Tchr & Tech Coord
Wilson, Charles Clay
Building Trades Instructor

NIOTA
Kyker, Frank
History Teacher

NORRIS
Crouch, Linda Hayes
Kindergarten Teacher

OAK RIDGE
Alexander, Kathleen Delaney
Spanish Teacher
Bowers, Helen Hopkins
Math Teacher
Carter, Delora Shubert
Third Grade Teacher
Ewing, Juanita Marlow
Kindergarten Teacher
Fillauer, William Keys, II
US Govt & Civics Teacher
Finane, Naida Louise
English Teacher
Monday, Marilyn Layman
Asst Prof of English
Ribble, John Phillip
Choral Music Teacher
Short, Katrina Anne
Library Media Specialist
Watson, James Rule, III
Physics & Chemistry Teacher

OAKDALE
Rogers, Tammy Redmon
Mathematics Teacher
Young, Susan H.
1st Grade Teacher

OLD HICKORY
Bullion, Benita Jane
Third Grade Teacher
Jackson, Belinda Gooch
Sixth Grade Teacher

OLDFORT
Hamby, Willard
5th Grade Teacher
Vilanova, Jane Stevenson
Second Grade Teacher

OLIVER SPRINGS
Forman, Marc Gary
Economics & Computer Teacher
Rayborn, Rebecca Martin
Principal
Whedbee, Donna Harvey
Title I Math Teacher

ONEIDA
Anderson, Lisa Beaty
Kindergarten Teacher
Bridges, Michelle Wright
8th Grade Math & Algebra Tchr
Delk, Lisa Anne
Biology Tchr & Sftbl Coach
Laxton, Rhonda Dean
Family & Life Sciences Teacher
Lay, Bertha Lou Terry
Business Teacher
Shoemaker, Barbara Quillen
Science & Math Teacher

OOLTEWAH
Bean, Mark Russell, Jr.
Physical Science Tchr & Coach
Brown, Sharon Cary
US His Tchr & Soc Stud Chm
Chastain, Joan Walker
5th Grade Teacher
Cook, Teresa Gail
Mathematics Teacher
Gass, Debbie Wilson
Math Tchr & Dept Chair
Hopkins, David Ray
US History Teacher
Howell, Joyce Melvin
Former Fifth Grade Teacher
Hughes, Sandra Hicks
Latin & Exploratory Lang Tchr
Jones, Sarah Frances Brown
Music Teacher
Lewis, Paul T.
7th Grade Science Teacher
Mc Kinney, Brenda Mc Nabb
Math Teacher
Parks, Gayle Mc Rae
English Teacher
Ramage, Judith Bixler
First Grade Teacher
Rogers, Robert Lee
Physics Tchr & Sci Dept Chair
Rogers, Suzanne Carlson
6th Grd English & Reading Tchr
Selvidge, Charlotte Thomason
4th Grade Teacher
Stafford, Nancy Rogers
Sixth Grade Math Teacher
Stewart, Robert Lee
Computer Science & Math Tchr
Ware, Rhonda Daniel
Science Teacher
Williams, Gerald
Seventh Grade Science Teacher
Wilson, Rebecca Lovell
Eng Dept Co-Chprsn & Tchr

PALMERSVILLE
Dunning, Rachel Lee
Mathematics Teacher
Gifford, Ronald Lynn
Former Guid Cnslr & Eng Tchr
Hale, Ewing
Fifth & Sixth Grade Teacher
Perkins, Kathy Dale
Librarian & Guidance Counselor

PARIS
Brashear, Joy Ramona
Mathematics Teacher
Buford, James Rex
Physical Science Teacher
Collins, Cynthia Parker
7th Grd Tchr, Chm & Team Ldr
Frazier, Carol Tabers
Fifth Grade Teacher
French, John Dale
Social Studies Teacher
Howard, Amber Jean
Chemistry & Physics Teacher
Howard, Gerald Dwayne
8th Grade Science Teacher
Hudson, Rebecca Turner
Social Science Teacher
Humphreys, Kenneth Edwin
Choral Director
Jones, Shelly Lee
Wellness Teacher
Moon, Deborah Morgan
8th Grade Alg & Math Teacher
Neese, Susan Ingergard
Spanish & English Teacher
Nesbitt, James Edward, Jr.
High School Math Teacher
Wilson, Linda Paschall
Speech & Theater Teacher
Wilson, Sonja Greenfield
Business Teacher

PARROTTSVILLE
Wilds, Sandra Proffitt
Kindergarten Teacher

PARSONS
Boggan, Angela D.
Marketing Teacher
Scott, Michael Lee
12th Grd English & French Tchr
Swift, Renee T.
Ninth Grade VOE Instructor
Wright, Wayne Daniel
Band Director

PHILADELPHIA
Dutton, Johann Beall
Math, Lang Arts, Art & Music
Roberts, Ronald Eugene
7th-8th Grade Teacher

PIGEON FORGE
Harmon, Mary Frances Turner
Math Teacher
Henson, Tanya Shea
Math Teacher

PIKEVILLE
Brock, Norma Jean
7th-8th Grade Teacher
Harding, Mary Ellen
Spanish Teacher
Loyd, Judy Apgar
Teacher of the Gifted
Pickett, Linda Cagle
Algebra Teacher
Reagan, Michael Allan
English & Sociology Teacher
Reed, Treva Gann
Kindergarten Teacher

PLEASANT HILL
Griffith, Gail Hannah
7th Grd Language Arts Teacher

PLEASANT VIEW
Borum, Caroline Allen
Sixth Grade Teacher
Harris, Linda Richardson
8th Grade Math Teacher
Patton, Wayne
Social Studies Teacher

PORTLAND
Brown, Brenda Fay
Title I Reading & Math Teacher
Cothron, Patsy Johnson
Retired Elementary Teacher
Draper, Kelly Renae
English Teacher
Driver, Stephen C.
Social Studies Department Head
Mathis, June Powell
Girls Dean & PE Teacher
Wortham, Emma Louise
5th-6th Grade Teacher
Wright, Robin Roxane
English Teacher

POWELL
Bryant, Kathy Merriman
1st Grade Teacher
Peccolo-Taylor, Saralee
French Teacher
Weber, Gregory Lynn
Chemistry & Physics Teacher

PULASKI
Abernathy, Mary Peters
English & Drama Teacher
Harwell, Albert Brantley, Jr.
Professor of English
Heon, Virginia Linscott
Mathematics & Cmptr Sci Tchr
Higginbotham, Mabry R.
Spanish Teacher
Long, Johnny Allyson
Ninth Grade Teacher & Coach
Mc Ree, Betty Price
5th Grade Classroom Teacher

SKI (cont)
Randall Gwyn
ing Instructor
, Deborah Davis
sified Technology Instr
Elizabeth Bass
h Science & Tech Teacher
rd, Carole Walls
Grade Teacher
BANK
, Sharon L.
r History Teacher
n, Robert J.
rade American His Teacher
dy, Evelyn Swanson
Teacher
Walter George
Grade Social Studies Tchr
BOILING SPRINGS
Timothy Allen
ed States History Teacher
VILLE
t, Penny Lingerfelt
th Grade Teacher
Carolyn Swafford
nd Grade Teacher
, Sandra L.
Grade Teacher
Patti C.
Grade Teacher
MAN
nan, Sharon Qualls
d Grade Teacher
Betty Little
dergarten Teacher
ELY
ey, Penny Attaway
Grade Teacher
, Judy Roberson
nmar Teacher
EY
eld, Ellen Pitt
d & US History Teacher
d, Tamara Young
rth Grade Teacher
owski, Lory Balos
Grade Teacher
N MOUNTAIN
n, Kenny Lou
Home Economics Teacher
ers, Daniel Keith
ence Teacher
KVALE
, Carol Anderson
Grade Teacher
KWOOD
, Donna Marie
t Grade Teacher
kawa, Paul Y.
His Tchr & Bsktbl Coach
, David Rufus
graphy & Computer Teacher
ullough, Shirlie Smith
rth Grade Teacher
ERSVILLE
my, Barry Dwight
t Principal
ers, Norma Cope
siness Education Teacher
ens, Larry Gene
ial Studies Teacher
, Carol Forbes
Grade Teacher
s, Harriet
st Grade Teacher
hild, Dorcas Sexton
glish Teacher
lson, Carolyn Harris
th Grade Reading Teacher
ns, James C.
ial Studies Teacher
mond, Pamela Owens
glish Teacher
nson, Bonnie Walker
ndergarten Teacher
erfield, Jim
Education Instr & FFA Adv
mpson, Wanda Russell
me School Teacher
er, Maxie Steadman
sistant Director
SSVILLE
well, Julie Wilson
idance Counselor
an, Melissa Anne
ccounting & Economics Teacher
SSELLVILLE
ms, Nancy Wilson
n Grade Math Teacher
d, Mark
ysical Education Teacher
THERFORD
cade, Mary Camilla
nguage Arts Teacher
TLEDGE
bage, Ronald Carson
incipal
fey, Virginia Needham
ffice Technology Teacher
more, Mary Lynn Stiner
ellness & Human Anatomy Tchr
ford, Gwen Green
igh School Guidance Counselor
rgan, Barbara Mc Curry
ome Economics Instructor
th, Barbara W.
etired 4th Grade Teacher
eyard, Christopher Glenn
ath Teacher

Wynn, Kate Austin
Fifth Grade Teacher
SALE CREEK
Lewis, Stephen Charles
JROTC Army Instructor
SANTA FE
Farmer, Pamela Alderson
Vocational Office Teacher
Lyons, Michael R.
Chemistry & Algebra Teacher
Walters, Wayne
Social Studies Teacher
Warf, Eddie
Science Teacher
SAVANNAH
Cantrell, Dannette Maxham
Biology Teacher
Carothers, Teresa Dillinger
Mathematics Teacher
Hardin, Rana Perry
Eng & Creative Writing Tchr
Sharp, Kim Taylor
8th Grd Language Arts Teacher
Smith, Tim E.
Math, Lit & Soc Stud Teacher
Watson, Jackolyn Pugh
Consumer Homemaking Teacher
Whitlow, Janice Graham
Voc-Occupational Home Ec Tchr
Williams, Ann Marie
12th Grade English Teacher
Williams, James Edward, Jr.
History & Government Teacher
Yeiser, Lee Davenport
8th Grade Lang Arts Teacher
SCOTTS HILL
Dyer, Margaret Goff
English & Psychology Teacher
Grissom, Mae Nelle
Retired 1st Grd Teacher
Long, Paula Karen
Kindergarten Teacher
SELMER
Brooks, Patricia Thaxton
Resource Teacher
Brooks, Ronnie Lynn
Director of Bands
Browder, Suzanne Beckham
Assistant Principal
Day, Gail Armstrong
7th & 8th Grd Lang Arts Tchr
Faulkner, Jill Webb
Algebra II & AP Calculus Tchr
Forsythe, Lisa C.
Computer Teacher
Harbin, Debbie Ross
English Teacher
Kiestler, Katherine Jolley
Fifth Grade English Teacher
Maness, Melissa Ann
Social Studies Teacher
Moore, Patsy D.
7th-8th Grd Sci & Math Teacher
Powers, Scott
Ec & Criminal Justice Teacher
Sanderson, Leigh Anne
Geometry & Basic Prgmng Tchr
Sweat, Pat Lee
Spanish Teacher
Thomas, Janet Maness
Algebra & Math Technology Tchr
Ward, Dennis Edwin
Fifth Grade Reading Teacher
SEVIERVILLE
Baxter, Jerry Ray, Jr.
Student Management Specialist
Blair, Shirley Hatcher
American History Teacher
Cardiel, Kimberly Dixon
Honors English Teacher
Catlett, Paula Condra
Biology & Geology Teacher
Chambers, Dennis Earnest
8th Grd US History & Rdng Tchr
Fuller, Patricia L. Davenport
Eighth Grade Math Teacher
Gibson, Barbara Ann
Kindergarten Teacher
Hodges, Nancy Gardner
Health Science Tech Instr
Maples, Jack Edwin
Science Teacher
Rose, Sheley Darby
English & Theater Arts Teacher
Schrandt, Marcie Seagle
Children Liaison
Smith, Nellie H.
English as a Second Lang Tchr
Walters, Tammy Hurst
Guidance Teacher
SEWANEE
Robinson, Rowena G.
6th Grade Teacher
Warne, William Thomas, III
Episcopal Seminary Student
SEYMOUR
Ailey, Robert Kent
8th Grade History Teacher
Burkhart, Jean E.
Eng, Pub Speaking & Drama Tchr
Carpenter, Alice S.
Business Teacher
Dunlap, Sue A.
English Teacher
Johnson, Janet Lynn
Special Education Teacher
Summerford, Gera L.
Math Dept Chairperson
Whaley, Sherry Hensley
Mathematics Teacher

SHADY VALLEY
Honaker, Patricia Callahan
4th & 5th Grade Teacher
SHARON
Brigance, Rebecca Compton
HS Math & Jr HS Arts Teacher
Carroll, Catherine Lee (Pearson)
Fifth Grade Teacher
High, Betty Viar
Jr High Math Tchr & Asst Prin
Seymour, Elaine Roberts
School Counselor
SHARPS CHAPEL
Bledsoe, Jerry Lynn
7th & 8th Grade Tchr
Sharp, Allena H.
Retired Teacher
SHELBYVILLE
Attig, Mark Richard
Music Teacher
Brock, Donna K. (Massengale)
Sixth Grd Social Studies Tchr
Casson, Melanie Lane
Fifth Grade Teacher
Esslinger, David Thomas
Sci Tchr & Girls Bsktbl Coach
Landers, Connie Gordon
Mathematics Teacher
Rittenberry, Ardis Hunter
Mathematics Teacher
Saylor, Virginia S.
Fifth Grade Teacher
Smith, Estel H., Jr.
Biology Teacher
Wix, Doris Mae (Walker)
Third Grade Teacher
Yoes, Jeff W.
Title I Rdng Tchr & Asst Prin
SIGNAL MOUNTAIN
Burton, Marcena Horton
Fifth Grade Teacher
Thomas, Carole Cooper
7th Grade Social Studies Tchr
SMITHVILLE
Adamson, Linda Gillem
Spanish Teacher
Foster, Jerry Wayne
Drivers Ed Tchr & Bsktbl Coach
Franklin, Linda Early
Biology Teacher
Hendrix, Gayla Colvert
Home Economics Teacher
Hendrix, Kathy Keyt
Math Teacher
Howard, Virginia Erlene
First Grade Teacher
Johnson, Joe Norman
Residential Construction Tech
SMYRNA
Barnickle, Larry J.
CP & AP Chemistry Teacher
Brown, Tommy S.
Wellness & Phys Sci Teacher
Messick, Sue Spivey
Office Tech & Business Teacher
Millsaps, Martha Cartwright
Latin & Visual Arts Teacher
Moore Tolbert, Karen Smith
Science & Health Teacher
Newberry, Patsy Price
7th & 8th Grd Lit Tchr
Newman, Lynda Y.
7th Grade Soc Studies Teacher
Nolan, Gloria Moseley
Sixth Grade Teacher
Paschal, James Daniel
Band Director
Rowlett, Joel Everett
Calculus & Geometry Teacher
Royal, Michael Terry
Band Director
Womack, Dana Cowan
French & English Teacher
SNEEDVILLE
Fannon, Debra Reed
Art, Drama & Music Teacher
Greene, Dennis D.
Principal
Horton, Katharine Jane
Biology Teacher
Shockley, Michael L.
World Geog & Math Tchr
SODDY DAISY
Barnes, Edward Robert
JROTC Instructor
Bird, Seldon W.
Science Teacher & Coach
Boydston, Lucy Tullos
Speech & Drama Teacher
Chambers, Richard Lamont
Band Director
Cole, Shannon Smith
Physical Science Teacher
Collett, Sandra Newton
English Teacher
Daniels, Carolyn Stooksbury
History Teacher
Levi, Judy Stewart
Fourth Grade Teacher
Preston, Linda Blackwelder
Math Teacher
Renfro, Tracy Moody
Sixth Grade Reading Teacher
Temples, Lonnie O.
Classroom Teacher
Woodall, Melissa Faye
French & Pre-Algebra Teacher
SOMERVILLE
Bailey, James D.
Teacher

Cross, RoseMarie Barrasso
English Dept Chprsn & Teacher
Crowe, Euretta Kee
Supervisor of Special Services
Day, Sarah Belle
Teacher & Guidance Counselor
Redding, Paula Winter
History & English Teacher
Thomas, Eleanor Johnson
Office Technology Teacher
SOUTH FULTON
Lohaus, Peggy Reams
Mathematics Teacher
Seratt, Charles B.
Physics & Chemistry Teacher
Wood, Gwin L.
Wellness & Fitness Teacher
SOUTH PITTSBURG
Johnson, Mary Hill
English Teacher
Tuck, Lynn Lewis
Title I Math Teacher
SPARTA
Anderson, Ruth Gribble
Sixth Grade Teacher
Carter, Willa Dean Lowery
Sixth Grade Teacher
Harding, R. Fredrick
Physics & Chemistry Teacher
Orr, Linda Luna
Sixth Grade Teacher
Sparkman, Gary Joseph
Principal
Taylor, Linda Lowery
US Government & His Teacher
SPEEDWELL
Cheatham, Cathie G.
Spanish Teacher
SPENCER
O'Neal, Mary Virginia Brymer
Retired Eng & Journalism Tchr
SPRINGFIELD
Bain, Patricia H.
High School Teacher
Beirne, Richard Alan
Mathematics Teacher
Carter, Caroline Mc Mahan
First Grade Teacher
Colvin, Mary Lynne
Drama, Speech & English Tchr
Goostree, Cynthia Lynn Gregory
Mathematics Teacher
Gregory, Patti Cohea
Fourth Grade Teacher
Holman, Kathy J.
Kindergarten Teacher
Jernigan, Lisa M.
Choral Director
Powell, Charles Thomas
Band Director
Smith, Nora Lee Gardner
Retired Second Grade Teacher
Walker, Diane Black
Math Teacher
Webb, Cynthia Womack
Teacher & Guidance Counselor
SPRINGVILLE
Owen, Rita Weber
6th-8th Grd Language Arts Tchr
STRAW PLAINS
Burnett, Suzan Rhea
Special Education Teacher
Charles, Melissa Welch
Language Arts Teacher
Chollman, Jani Sellers
Biology & Physical Sci Teacher
Grandstaff, William Eugene
Business Teacher
Henderson, Linda M.
6th Grd Language Arts Teacher
McGill, J. Walter
Drafting Instructor
Sanders, Danny K.
Biology Teacher
White, John Robert
US History Tchr & Soc Stud Chm
Whitney, Carole Tudor
Third Grade Teacher
Wyatt, Brenda L.
Fourth Grade Teacher
Wyatt, George Michael
7th Grd Geog & TN His Teacher
SUMMERTOWN
Doerflinger, Shay G.
Tech Prep Counselor
Perry, Linda Shaffer
His, Govt & Economics Teacher
SUNBRIGHT
Carroll, Kathy Scott
Third Grade Teacher
Douglas, Rebecca L.
Eighth Grade Teacher
Galloway, Janett Freels
Library & Media Specialist
Henderson, Linda Stanford
English Teacher
Sexton, Lisa Chapman
Sixth Grade Teacher
SWEETWATER
Allen, Kathryn Ann
English Tchr & Dept Chprsn
Hitson, Julie Trail
7th Grade Reading Teacher
Howard, Diana Evans
Third Grade Teacher
Littreal, Wanda Jones
Math Teacher
Sadikoff, Karen Kyker
Multi-Age Teacher

Tucker, Rebecca Fitzgerald
Third Grade Teacher
Tyler, James Clyde, Jr.
Chemistry Teacher
TAZEWELL
Banks, Mata J.G.
Science & Mathematics Teacher
Beeler, Richard D.
Biology, History & Sci Tchr
Chumley, Katherine Harber
Second Grade Teacher
Coffey, Linda Vannoy
Fifth Grade Teacher
England, Carolyn Mc Cray
Math Teacher
Epperson, Lisa England
English Teacher
Hawkins, Jeffrey M.
Social Studies Teacher
Overton, Annette Shockley
7th Grade Teacher
Parkey, Dayton
Wellness & Applied Math Tchr
Russell, Janet S.
Eighth Grade Teacher
TELLICO PLAINS
Anderson, Karen Suzanne (Burt)
Junior High Science Teacher
Best, Carolyn Jeanette
7th & 8th Grd Soc Stud Tchr
TENNESSEE RIDGE
Miller, Janet D.
First Grade Teacher
TOONE
Shaw, Carolyn Perry
5th-7th Grd Lang Arts Teacher
TRACY CITY
Clay, Frank Emmett
Agriculture Education Teacher
Dickerson, Karen Elizabeth
English Teacher
Geary, Michael
Math & Computer Science Tchr
Jones, Dennis Alan
US His & World Geography Tchr
Masters, Brian Alexander
Physical Science Teacher
Nixon, Martha K.
Principal
Price, Christine Meeks
Mathematics Teacher
TRENTON
Davis, Fred W.
Chem, Phys & Earth Sci Tchr
Doaks, Charlotte LaVonne
Job Specialist
Love, Anne Berton
First Grade Teacher
Price, Sharline R.
Special Education Teacher
Scott, Mary Jane (Hill)
Language Arts & Reading Tchr
TREZEVANT
Carter, Travis Lee, Jr.
Pre-Algebra Tchr & Asst Prin
Joyner, Pamela Diann (Hall)
Language Arts Teacher
TROY
Austin, Dianne Miller
Chemistry & Science Teacher
TULLAHOMA
Arman, Sandra Ann (Durkee)
Mathematics Instructor
Baldwin, Ann Sanders
Choral Director
Carter, James Gregory
Social Studies Teacher
Cox, Jan McNutt
Reading Specialist & Teacher
Giltner, Linda Butler
Science Teacher
Hendrickson, Betty Pierce
Vice Principal
Hix, Billy Reagor
Associate Professor
Horton, Jeanne (Cloer)
Fifth Grade Teacher
Kelly, Larry L.
Dir Dev Stud & Asst Prof Eng
Lanham, Carol Coffey
Algebra Teacher
Liechty, Sara LeMay
Language Arts Teacher
Mathis, Jerry Rad
Teacher & Coach
Maxey, Susan Danette
Mathematics Teacher
Olive, John Howard
PE Teacher & Football Coach
Palmer, Jeannette B.
Assistant Professor of English
Pockrus, Joan Marie
Social Studies Teacher
Price, Tommye Thompson
English & Journalism Teacher
Pyron, William Thomas
Biology Teacher
Reeder, Robert E.
Assistant Professor of Biology
Robbins, Minnie Lucille
Second Grade Teacher
Roberts, Charlotte Boles
English Teacher
Sawyer, Dianne Marie
English Teacher
Thomas, Dan Charles
Sixth Grade Teacher
Tucker, Jeannie M.
Instructor of Communications

TULLAHOMA (cont)
Werlein, Halsey Ewing
Asst Prof of French & English
Zimmerman, Debbie
Assoc Prof of Communications
UNION CITY
Dew, Olga Adell
Spanish & English Teacher
Dunavant, Beverly Butler
Second Grade Teacher
Hardy, Cindy Hall
Biology & Physical Sci Teacher
Hitt, Connie Coggin
Sixth Grade Language Arts Tchr
White, Elizabeth Tillman
Second Grade Teacher
UNIONVILLE
Williams, Keith Rogers
Math & Economics Teacher
VONORE
Rollins, Betty Leslie
Third Grade Teacher
WALLAND
Norville, Richard Gerow, Jr.
Computer & Gen Science Teacher
WARTBURG
Goodman, Donna Daugherty
8th Grade Teacher
Headden, Regina
US History Teacher
Headen, Regina
Social Studies Teacher
Roark, Barbara Peake
High Schl Mathematics Teacher
Sweat, Lucy Louellen
Third Grade Teacher
WASHBURN
Daugherty, Joyce Carter
Home Economics Teacher
Dorton, Barbara Roszell
Title I Math & Reading Teacher
Mc Elhaney, Ginny Ann
Soc Stud Tchr & Asst Prin
Meadows, Donna Beeler
Kindergarten Teacher
Merrifield, Emma Daniels
Second Grade Teacher
Snead, Sabra Farmer
Third Grade Teacher
WATAUGA
Curde, Debra Dean
Resource Teacher
WATERTOWN
Alexander, William Lewellyn
Science Teacher
Johnson, Dolores Hemontolor
9th-10th Grade English Teacher
Steward, Nancy Hailey
Mathematics Teacher
Wade, John Thomas
Fine Arts Teacher & Band Dir
WAVERLY
Bostian, Debra Hutchison
Spanish Teacher
Haxton, Betty Pollard
3rd Grade Teacher
Hickerson, William Bruce
Eighth Grade Soc Stud Tchr
Jared, Sue Sherman
Technology Supervisor
Morgan, Cheryl Mitchum
Third Grade Teacher
Rye, Linda Brake
Chemistry Teacher
WAYNESBORO
Barnett, Vada Copous
Business Education Teacher
Kershaw, Cynthia Beth
English & Drama Teacher
WESTMORELAND
Creasy, John Franklin
Soc Stud Tchr & Team Leader
Paladino, April Cecelia
Art Teacher
WHITE BLUFF
Hale, Donna R.
Asst Prin & 4th Grade Teacher
Martin, Beverly Brazzell
4th Grade Teacher
WHITE HOUSE
Brugman, Claire R. (Fantow)
Mathematics Dept Chprsn & Tchr
Edson, Sandra Sechrist
Mathematics Teacher
Faires, Mary Wood
Guidance Counselor
Gilley, Nancy Dowell
Teacher
Graves, Vicky Howell
7th Grade Social Studies Tchr
King, George Robert
Math & Computer Teacher
Lamberth, Mark Aaron
World Geography, Bus, His Tchr
McCandless, Shirley Crawford
Jr High Chm & Math Teacher
Mc Minn, William Warren
Band Director
Searcy, Anita Wade
Chemistry & Physics Teacher
Tomkins, Susan Gail
English Teacher
WHITES CREEK
Bruce, John Frank
Founder & President
Eldridge, Sarah Kyle
11th Grade Guidance Counselor
Hutchinson, Ann
Mathematics Teacher
Nash, Tammy Ruth
Psychology & Sociology Teacher
Rector, David Curry
Geography Teacher
WHITWELL
Grooms, Katherine Jeanette
4th-6th Grade Teacher
Terry, Roy Lynn
English & US History Teacher
Wells, Vicki Bailey
Sixth Grade Language Arts Tchr
WINCHESTER
Bandy, Margaret Harryman
Biology Teacher
Boyd, Phyllis Norwood
Gifted Education Teacher
Edens, Deborah Brown
Marketing & Advertising Tchr
Fernander, William Robert
English Teacher
Hopkins, Terri Mandzak
Mathematics Teacher
Howton, Bryan Allen
Mathematics Teacher
Majors, Frank Larry
American History Teacher
Rabb, Mary Comeaux
Business & Computer Teacher
Simmons, Caroline Holder
First Grade Teacher
Smith, Mary Ann M.
Mathematics Teacher
Tankersley, Penny Wilson
4th Grade Teacher
WINFIELD
Ivey, Marilyn F.
Kindergarten Teacher
WOODBURY
Barker, Kay L.
Business Education Teacher
Duggin, Peggy R.
Teacher
Parker, Barbara Nichols
English Teacher
Parsley, Kimberly Hale
Principal & Title I Teacher
WOODLAWN
Muir, Carol Thornton
Title I Reading Specialist

TEXAS

ABBOTT
Beseda, D. J.
K-12th Special Ed Tchr & Coach
Thomas, Betty Bowles
Fifth Grade Teacher
ABERNATHY
Anderson, Lowell Harvey
4th Grade Teacher
Hardin, Bettie Shipman
Mathematics Teacher
Rieken, Margaret Wages
Junior High Math Teacher
ABILENE
Adams, Rae Banks
Professor of Sociology
Anderson, Jana Wall
Dept of English Instructor
Armstrong, Virginia Crounse
Professor of Political Science
Arnic, Sabrina Kelley
5th Grade Teacher
Bacon, Cheryl Mann
Jrnlsm & Mass Comm Assoc Prof
Ball, Beverly Ann
Physical Education Teacher
Beauchamp Jones, Priscilla Lea
Fifth Grade Teacher
Berryman, Jeffrey William
Asst Prof of Dept of Theare
Best, Mark Preston
Orchestra Director
Blackburn, Betty Ann Mc Call
Staff Accompanist
Blue, Patricia Beaty
Mathematics Teacher
Bonney, Rosey Lorain Burdette
Third Grade Teacher
Boyd, Cindy Huskin
High School Mathematics Tchr
Brister, Jozell
Economics Professor
Brown, Gail Leggett
Fifth Grade Teacher
Brown, Lee McCain
Elementary Counselor
Brunner, Larry G.
Department Head of English
Bryant, Donna S.
Business Teacher
Burton, Lavon Duncan
Academic Advance Program Coord
Bush, David Frederic
PE & K-5th Grd Tchr
Calvert, Linda Darnell (Nell)
Asst Prof & Jr Level Coord
Churchman, Travis B.
Biology Teacher & Coach
Clayton, Lawrence Ray
Dean & Professor of English
Coco, Malcolm P., Jr.
Asst Professor & Assoc Dean
Collins, Betty Renee
Fifth Grade Teacher
Cowart, Edgar Miles
Football Coach & Science Tchr
Crousen, Barbara Davis
Dept Chm & PE Tchr
Dawson, Dan Paul
Mathematics Professor
Dowell, Janna Conner
Elementary Gifted Ed Tchr
Drake, Sharon Freeman
7th & 8th Grd Skills Dev Tchr
Drennan, Jerry Dale
Professor of Industrial Tech
Dubose, Leo Edwin
Professor Emeritus
Elston, Ron Stephen
Mens & Womens Tennis Coach
Etheridge, Charles Larimore, Jr.
Associate Professor of English
Flournoy, Lynn Chasteen
10th Grade English Teacher
Flynt, Louan Cox
3rd Grade Teacher
Follis, Ned L.
Industrial Technology Teacher
Foster, Douglas Allen
Assoc Prof of Church History
Fowler, William Eugene
Accounting Professor
Frazier, Donald Shaw
Assistant Professor of History
Fry, Tommy Joe
Associate Professor of Music
Gardner, Anna M.
Retired Teacher
Gillette, Lynn G.
Dean, School of Business
Godfrey, Terri Wilson
Choral Director
Goodrich, Jack H.
6th Grade Social Studies Tchr
Green, Ina Lynch
Professor of Psychology
Hager, Lawson James
Asst Prof of Brass & Mus Thry
Haire, Carol D.
Professor & Director of Speech
Haley, Perry Kay
Dept Chair & Asst Prof Curr
Hall, Moses Clinton, Jr.
English Teacher
Hallmark, Barbara Cox
Sixth Grade Reading Teacher
Hanks, Sherilyn Carter
Counselor
Harper, Preston Frank
English Professor
Hatch, Lee Thomas
Special Education Teacher
Haynes, Kathy Wells
Elementary Principal
Hennig, Charles William
Professor of Psychology
Hernandez, Patricia B.
Assistant Professor
Hood, Bonnie Sykes
First Grade Teacher
Howland, Deborah Kay
History Teacher
Hukill, Charles E.
Prof of Theatre & Dept Chair
Hundley, Patricia Goetsch
Advanced Placement Eng Tchr
Ince, Leigh Ann
Business Teacher
Jones, Margaret Brinell
Fourth Grade Teacher
Jordan, Candice Taylor
Professor
Kane, Gwenette Jackson
English Teacher
Kingore, Bertie Wilhelm
Shelton Professor & Chprsn
Lakey, Paul N.
Communication Professor
Lapoint, Patricia A.
Assistant Professor
Lee, Sharon Mc Creary
7th Grade Science Teacher
Little, John Clifton
Professor of Biology
Lynn, Monty LaFon
Assoc Professor of Management
Lytle, Richard S.
Marketing Professor
Madden, J. Paul
Prof & History Dept Head
Mankin, Jimmie Moore
Asst Prof of Bible & Ministry
Martin, Terry Lee
2nd Grade Teacher
Maxwell, Jill Thompson
4th Grd Tchr & Art Curr Coord
Mc Crum, Michael Ross
Math Teacher
Mc Donald, Kay Condron
Kindergarten Teacher
Miller, Doris Anne
English Professor
Miller, Michael Scot
Philosophy Instr & Dept Head
Mills, Foy Dan, Jr.
Associate Prof of Agribusiness
Morgan, Diane Lee
All Levels PE Teacher
Moritz, Thomas Edward
Assistant Prof of Marketing
Nease, Nathan David
AP Physics & Physics Tchr
Nichols, James Ross
Professor of Biology
Nichols, Jeanenne Yadon
Kindergarten Teacher
Osburn, Carroll Duane
Professor of Greek
Parker, Linda Sue
Third Grade Teacher
Parr, Sonja Casey Jeanne
Second Grade Teacher
Patrick, Nancy Smith
High School English Teacher
Penton, Robert W.
Asst Prof of Sociology
Petty, Carole Ann (Felts)
6th Grade Language Arts Tchr
Pickens, Jimmy Burton
Science Dept Chair & Teacher
Pierson, J. Kregg
English Teacher
Pigott, Susan Day
Asst Prof of Old Testament
Pogue, James M.
English Teacher
Popelka, LaVerne D.
English III Instructor
Pruett, Julie Sikes
Assistant Prof of Voice
Rains, Jacqueline Carol
Eng & Creative Writing Teacher
Raney, Jennifer Johnson
Principal
Rausch, Cammie Walrath
Physical Education Instructor
Risse, John Thomas
Adjunct Professor of Bible
Robbins, Kay A.
Eng & Social Studies Teacher
Roberts, Paula Noline (Strond)
Fifth Grade Teacher
Schonberg, Jeffrey Brett
Associate Professor of English
Shake, Roy E.
Associate Professor of Biology
Sharp, A. C.
Professor of Physics
Shaw, Jeana Vassar
Biology Teacher
Shields, James L.
Senior Professor of Theology
Shuler, Philip L.
Professor of Rel & Dept Chair
Singleton, Lymeda Hoover
Mathematics Coord & Instructor
Sloan, Derrell N.
Industrl Cooperative Trng Tchr
Sorrels, J. Paul
Grad Stud Dean & Psych Prof
Speck, Henry E., III
Professor of History
Spragg, Arthur William
World Geography Teacher
Stanfield, Charles Irvan
Algebra Teacher
Starr, Suzanne L.
Math Teacher
Straus, Bob
Theater Arts Teacher
Thaxton, Eric Warren
English Teacher
Thomas, Beth Elene
Bio II & AP Teacher
Trussell, David Michael
Government & History Instr
Villa, Toby Anthony
US History Teacher & Coach
Villarreal, Adelaido Luvin
Assoc Band Director
Wallace, Robert W.
Assoc Prof of Sociology
Watkins, Daya Christian
His, Pysch & Soc Teacher
Weinstein, Mark
Asst Prof of Pol Sci
Wheeler, F. Larry
Assistant Prof of Theatre
Whitmill, Sarah Baker
High School Algebra Teacher
Willerton, Christian William
Prof of Eng & Hnrs Pgm Dir
Williams, Curtis Lee
Mathematics Teacher
Williams, Maxine S.
5th Grade Reading Teacher
Williford, Pamela Torrance
Asst Prof of Education
Wilson, Gary Roy
Associate Professor of Biology
Winter, Thomas L.
Director, Social Work Program
Wood, Karen Womack
Math Teacher
Wray, David William
Assoc Professor
Young, Janel Mayhall
Secondary Science Teacher
ACKERLY
Scott, Chandra Suzanne
Ag Science Teacher
AGUA DULCE
Doramus, Sharon Mihalko
High School Math Teacher
Harris, Denise Willis
Home Economics Teacher
ALAMO
Cantu, Nelda Zepeda
Program Administrator
Forina, Maria Elena (Chaves)
6th Grd Gifted Talented Tchr
Garcia, Maria Hilda
Fifth Grade Teacher
Rydl, Mary Berny
Kindergarten & Bible Teacher
Weideman, Margarethe Sundstrom
Computer Lab Teacher
ALBA
Allen, Joyce Wortham
Kindergarten Lead Teacher
Ballard, Sara Beth
5th & 6th Grade Math Teacher
Houghton, Diane Riddle
Elem Special Education Teacher
ALBANY
Barker, Edward DeWayne
Chemistry & Biology Teacher
Terrell, Thomas Wyatt
HS Counselor
Viertel, Sherry Spurgin
Kindergarten Teacher
ALEDO
VanDuzee, Ann Werner
5th Grade Teacher
ALICE
Barrett, Graciela Garcia
Fourth Grade Teacher
Garcia, Teresa Longoria
Fourth Grade Teacher
Gotcher, Joel C.
World History Teacher
Lerma, Fidencio Pena
Sixth Grade Math Teacher
Lopez, Sandra DeLeon
5th Grade Teacher
Martinez, Jose S.
3rd Grade Teacher
Murphey, Sharron Dennis
Third Grade Teacher
Richardson, Debra Wylie
Business Teacher
Rodriguez, Janie Chapa
Second Grade Teacher
Rushing, Judith Richter
7th Grade TX History Teacher
Trevino, Nelma Lopez
8th Grade Math Teacher
Vela, Carol Annelise
Journalism Teacher
Weinberger, Melissa Jane
Reading Specialist
ALIEF
Armstrong, Denise Carreathers
English Teacher
Blalock, Melanie J.
English Teacher
English, Wayne Howard
Orch Dir & Music Theory Tchr
Ferron, Caroline Ellen
High School Mathematics Tchr
Hebert, Martha S.
AP Teacher
Hurst, Kevin David
Theatre Director
Jackson, Joyce Guyer
Teacher
Koehn, Connie Lee
Math Teacher
Koran, Dale
Band Director
Laauwe, Beth Hawkins
English Teacher
Shivers, Susan Victoria
7th Grade Math Teacher
Startzman, Martha Lisa
AP Amer History & Govt Tchr
ALLEN
Belzer, Harriet Gail
Teacher of Gifted & Talented
Biggs, Alton L.
Biology Educator
Box, Ronald Marvin
Sixth Grade Teacher
Breedlove, Alton E.
Principal
Burdette, Linda S.
Assoc Director of Tex Prep
Dodgen, Felicia Lestage
Science Instructor
Green, William Alan
Government & US History Tchr
Kirkpatrick-Lundy, Lisa
German Teacher
Lawson, Donald Larry
Math & Cmptr Programming Tchr
LeClair, Joyce Skloss
Biology Teacher
Loftin, Jacqueline Young
7th Grade Mathematics Teacher
Long, Jo Leffler
Fourth Grade Teacher
Martin, Pamela Sue
Gifted & Talented English Tchr
McGhee, Nancy Lynn (Wilmeth)
Sixth Grade Teacher
Mitterer, Gayle
Science Teacher
Pierson, Carole Celio
1st-2nd Grade Teacher
Portman, Laura Zeigler
Middle School Counselor
Puckett, Jim Bob B.
Economics Tchr & Coach
Sayer, Suzanne Vicchrilli
English Teacher
Scalf, Wendie Ellen
High School Math Teacher
Souan, Carol Irvin
English Teacher
Specht, Steven Gregory
English Teacher & Coach
Young, Todd P.
Assistant Principal

NE
pion, Laurie
stant Professor of English
ls, Roberta Fordham
her of the GATE & Coord
r, Dan E.
, Ec & Photo Teacher
), Rosario R.
ness Teacher
a, Martin
urer, Equine Podiatry
, William C.
& Chm of Business Admin
wood, Kathy Lynn
urer in Lang & Literature
Charles Robert
essor of Art
er, Raymond G.
of Criminal Justice Chair
ame, Jimmy T.
oc Prof of Ag Economics
lith, Bennye Sims
ish Teacher
n, Barbara DeGear
lish Professor
ng, Ernest O.
of Range Animal Science
David M.
essor of Geology
Brenda Laney
Instructor
est, Larry James
nomics Professor
sberry, Barbara Ann
h Science Teacher
ey, William Steven
turer in Criminal Justice
James Craig
istant Professor
AIR
nings, Debra Janelle
tent Mastery Teacher
er, Claudine Brooks
stitute Teacher
ner, Mary Jeanette
h Teacher
g, Jerry Allen, II
alth & Physical Ed Teacher
O
en, Jamie Denise
ne Economics & Rdng Tchr
man, Jennifer Marie Griffith
th & Cmptr Literacy Teacher
ener, Charisse Meyers
thematics Teacher
, Dianne Holcomb
rarian
ARADO
ston, David Bruce
Grade US History Teacher
on, Linda Driver
glish Teacher
Jan R.
thematics Teacher
, Jonni Koonce
glish Teacher
ey, Becky Sue
eech & Drama Teacher
nen, Terri Kay (Hall)
ench Teacher
w, Haven Heffner
acher of Gifted & Talented
w, James Aubrey
alth & Drivers Ed Teacher
burrow, Dennis Keith
th Teacher & Department Head
IN
ow, Jean Rater
acher of Gifted & Talented
, Janice Smyth
anish Teacher
quist, Mary Lee (Kelm)
ng, Lang, Wrtng, Spllng Tchr
n, Perry Keely
rector of Respiratory Care
ey, Jackie Doucet
TE Resource Tchr
is, Mark A.
ych & Sociology Teacher
ahn, Julie Goodman
emistry Teacher
ks, Beverly Hargrove
athematics Teacher
ne, Johanna M.
overnment & History Instr
n, Wallace Norwood
eography Teacher
pp, Patsy (Miller)
nglish Instructor
b, Nancey G.
sychology Instructor
h, Lisa Haws
nglish Teacher
der, Sandra Susan
thletic Coordinator
Reaken, Katherine Anne
ndgtn-Second Grd Teacher
ntgomery, Margaret Cartnell
nglish Instructor
son, Sylvia A.
st Grd Teacher of Gifted
ter, Martha Sue
irst Grade Teacher
berts, Julia
nglish Teacher
dmore, Gerald D.
ivision Chair of Math & Sci
ith, W. Alvin, Jr.
cience Chm & Athletic Trainer

Yancey, Pennie Joy
Vocational Home Economics Tchr
Yeats, Kippling Vaughn
Math Teacher
AMARILLO
Abramson, Jay Paul
Mathematics Instructor
Anderson, Marie
2nd Grade Teacher
Barker, Sheila Kae
Chemistry Teacher
Bauman, Robert Warren, Jr.
Professor of Biology
Baumgardner, Paulette
Computer Science Teacher
Bentley, Kimberlee S.
English Teacher
Brasell, Letha Fedric
English Teacher
Bratcher, Rudy E.
CIS Instructor
Bridenbaugh, Debra Sava
3rd Grade Teacher
Brown, Carrie Dippel
Third Grade Teacher
Brunson, Tena Wynell
5th Grade Teacher
Carver, Jana Lea
Business Teacher
Cash, Curt
Teacher & Principal
Cates, Brenda D.
Microcmptr Applications Tchr
Clark, Becky
Business Teacher
Collins, Terry Glenn
Fourth Grade Teacher
Combs, David E.
Social Studies Teacher
Cost, Steven
Lead Instr of Graphic Design
Cowley, Brenda Gwen
US History & Texas His Tchr
Crockett-Heath, Donna Marie
French & German Teacher
Crump, Mary L. (Bevers)
Home Economics Teacher
Dale, Sandra H.
Mathematics Teacher
Daugherty, Brenda Lee
Fifth Grade Teacher
Felton, Melinda Houdashell
Fifth Grade Teacher
Ferguson, Terry Vaughn
World History Teacher & Coach
Frazer, Jeff Clark
Govt & American His Teacher
George, Donna Fife
7th & 8th Grd Rdng Lab Teacher
Gill, Dee G.
Science Teacher & Dept Chm
Gitchell, Aloha J. Terrell
Elementary String Specialist
Glenn, Ronnie Lynn
Coach & Teacher
Godfrey, Susan Gayle
History Teacher
Grantham, Jacqueline Jessup
Second Grade Teacher
Haraden, Mary Capps
AP & IV English Teacher
Harrison, Pattian
English as Second Lang Tchr
Henderson, Sammye Mardis
Physics & Anatomy Teacher
Hernandez, Lorraine Cynthia (Gomez)
Librarian & Cmptr Teacher
Hilleary, Becki J.
Seventh Grade English Teacher
Hock, Wendy Susan
Journalism Teacher
Horner, Karen Sue
First Grade Teacher
Howle, Melissa Craig
Science Teacher
Hutson, Jimmy W.
Director of Bands
Jackson, Lana Fulton
Journalism Teacher
Jacob, Lynae Latham
9th-12th Grd Theatre Arts Tchr
Jenkins, Ann Snodgrass
Fourth Grade Teacher
Jennings, Mavis Coleman
8th-9th Grd Algebra I Teacher
Jones, Charles Thomas
Elementary Principal
Kinnan, Pamela Baber
Pregnancy & Parenting Coord
Ledwig, Roxanne
Science Teacher
Lehnick, Emmarie Turner
7th Grd Communicative Art Tchr
Litherland, Denise Dixon
Math Teacher & Dept Chair
Littrell, Molly Orr
ESL Teacher
Loan, Lisa Middleton
World Geography Teacher
Logan, Craig Donald
Chemistry & Physical Sci Tchr
Logan, Denise Marie (Fix)
Office Education Teacher
Louis, Mary Day
Chemistry & Physics Teacher
Lowery, Glenda Miller
6th Grd Language Arts Tchr
McCall, Melinda Kay (Ivey)
High School Math Teacher

McCarter, Luella Irwin
4th Grd Rdng & Soc Stud Tchr
Mc Connell, John T.
Math Teacher
McDaniel, Clarence Earl
8th Grd His Tchr & Head Coach
McIntyre, Susan Gentry
Algebra & Geometry Teacher
McKee, Connie DeNiel
Speech & Debate Coach
Mc Kinley, Nancy Ann (Samuels)
Counselor
Mc Mahan, Carolyn Burp
Pre-Kndgtn & Home Ec Teacher
Meador, Robert Kent
His Tchr & Bsbl Head Coach
Meaker, Jo Dell
Marine Science Teacher
Miller, Jeane
Reading, Soc Stud & Art Tchr
Morehead, Donna Sue
English Dept Chair & Teacher
Needham, Mary L.
4th Grade Teacher
Neusch, Nancy Ann
Principal & Day Care Director
O'Hair, Rennaye Chapman
Volleyball Coach & PE Teacher
Olson, Betty Anita
Spanish Teacher
Ostrowski, Pamela
Amer His Tchr & Dept Chair
Parsons, Suzella Bursey
Retired Student Teachers Supv
Patel, Nagarbhai Govindji
Senior Machine Instructor
Patterson, Rosemary
Span Tchr & Frgn Lang Chair
Person, Ruby Jean
4th Grade Teacher
Peterson, Sandy Jo
Counselor
Phillips, Andrea Shepic
Business Education Teacher
Phillips, Suzanne Davis
Home Economics Teacher
Pirtle, Tarrie Straube
Chemistry Teacher
Powers, Diane Fox
Fifth Grade Teacher
Rhodes, Robyn Baker
HOSTS Teacher
Rickstrew, Judy Lee
Cosmetology Teacher
Rosson, Penny Briant
World History Teacher
Scott, Mona Carol Rucker
Communicative Arts Teacher
Segura, Gene
Assistant Principal
Sewell, Phyliss Goodwin
English Teacher
Smith, Deborah Lynn
Soph English Teacher & Coach
Smith, Preston R.
Head Football Coach
Smith, Renae
Physical Ed Teacher & Coach
Stennis, Gail Thomas
History & Government Teacher
Stribling, Lee Ellen
English Teacher
Townsend, Mary Jean
English Teacher
Trader, Marilyn Calloway
Business Teacher
Tschirhart, Janis Lynn
English Teacher
Urton, Ronetta Ruse
English Teacher
Webb, Maelynn Cator
4th Grade Teacher
Weiss, Craig Edward
Journalism Teacher
West, Steve Wayne
Principal
White, Gail Baxter
6th Grade History Teacher
White, Peggy Winfree
Mathematics Teacher
Whitney, Linda Word
Second Grade Teacher
Williams, Don E.
Biology Teacher & Coach
Williams, John David
Assistant Director of Bands
Williams, Shelly Marie
Health Tchr & Volleyball Coach
Wise, Oleta LaNell
Third Grade Teacher
Wrinkle, Kris Suellen
High School Science Teacher
Zanchettin, Laura Fuller
Bio, Anatomy & Physiology Tchr
AMHERST
Roberts, John Lyndon
English & Reading Teacher
Royston, Cassie
Home Economics & Science Tchr
ANAHUAC
Willcox, Ben Thomas
Life Science Teacher
ANDERSON
Rankin, Lizabeth Bryant
English Teacher
ANDREWS
Boyd, Angela Jackson
English Teacher & Dept Chm
Bright, P. Jeff
8th Grd Math Teacher & Coach

Dittberner, Tommy Lee
Math Dept Chairman
Gross, Teresa Bruce
Third Grade Teacher
Hogan, John Felder
US History Teacher
Jefcoats, Shanon Martin
Physical Science Teacher
Overman, Jerry Cliff
Math Teacher
Scarbrough, Judy Blocker
Title I Reading Teacher
ANGLETON
Amos, Betty Morriss
Third Grade Teacher
Baccus, Gerrie Boggs
2nd Grade Teacher
Casey, Beth Baldwin
Director of Choirs
Chalmers, Frances M.
English Teacher & Dept Head
Cheever, Karla Jean
4th Grade Teacher
Clegg, Kathryn Jacobson
Third Grade Teacher
Dearman, Teresa Ann
Content Mastery Center Teacher
Eby, Paul Alan
High School Biology Teacher
Edge, B. Alan
Band Director
Fry, Mary Scudi
English Teacher
Gaddy, William Edward
Latin & English Teacher
Hoffpauir, Laura Espinosa
Office Education Teacher
Jones, Darcelle Ann
First Grade Teacher
Kibodeaux, Katherine Maria
First Grade Teacher
Kruk, Brian Kenneth
US History Teacher & Coach
Lucus, Mark Aian
Assistant Band Director
Mc Dougal, Ann (Ferguson)
3rd Grade GATE Teacher
Sheppard, Deana Patterson
High School Business Teacher
Valenta, Joyce Shiflet
Second Grade Teacher
VanHorn, Donald Lee
Mathematics Teacher
Wilson, Rebecca Easley
Algebra II Teacher
ANNA
Hillman, Penny Comb
Business Ed Teacher
McMahon, Curren William
English Tchr & Defensive Coord
ANSON
Baccus, Jay Michael
Mathematics Teacher
Huber, Eva Beth
English Teacher
Richmond, Jimmie Mayfield
Teacher
Simpson, Geneva Ward
Eng, Jrnlsm & Title I Teacher
Stalder, Ann Hawkins
Title 1 Teacher
Welch, Marolyn Talley
English & Reading Teacher
ANTHONY
Mahar, Phyllis DiPofi
Business & Computer Teacher
ANTON
Chenault, Sandy Bilberry
English Teacher
James, Harla Stone
HS English & History Teacher
APPLE SPRINGS
Schaade, George Edward
History Teacher
Tipton, Doris Spurlock
Fifth Grade Teacher
ARANSAS PASS
Everett, Sylvia Runte
American His & Theatre Teacher
Grover, Guy Matthew
World History Teacher
Hayes, Charles Glen
Biology Teacher
Johnson, Janet Lynn
English Teacher
Kitchens, Jimmie Faye Mc Mahan
HS Mathematics Teacher
Mc New, Stephanie Dotson
Science Teacher
Turnage, Eleonora Doucette
Second Grade Teacher
ARGYLE
Erwin, Joye B.
Kindergarten Teacher
Quaid, Evelyn Egbert
7th & 8th Grade Science Tchr
Willis, Elizabeth Atchison
7th-8th Grade English Teacher
ARLINGTON
Aaron, Janean Chanler
District Attendance Officer
Adams, Barbara Watson
Sixth Grade Teacher
Adams, James E.
Principal
Allen, Carol E.
Band Director
Allred, Joe Edwin
History Teacher

Apilado, Vincent Paul
Professor of Finance
Atkinson, Kathy Cherry
Speech & Drama Teacher
Baker, Julie Ann
Marketing Professor
Baldridge, James H.
Education Professor
Barron, Jane Spence
English Teacher
Bartlett, Mary Jeanice
First Grade Lead Teacher
Bassett, David Vincent
Math & Sci Dept Head
Bearden, Carolyn Scrivner
English Teacher
Beehler, John Michael
Accounting Professor
Bell, Jill A.
Math Dept Chairman & Teacher
Beyer, Al R.
Religion, Biology & Hlth Tchr
Boyd, Willie Jean
English Teacher
Bronson, Maryhelen
6th Grade Teacher
Brooks, Scott Andrew
History & World Geography Tchr
Brown, Barbara Beck
Physics Teacher
Broyles, Marilyn Joy
9th Grade Algebra Teacher
Byrne, Eric Joseph
Asst Prof of Computer Science
Campbell, Sandra Shew
American Government Teacher
Carpenter, Galen Darrell
Accounting Lecturer & Grad Adv
Cline, Jeanneane Lewis
Nursing Instructor
Cornelius, Billie Jean (Sellman)
Economics Tchr & Soc Stud Chm
Cox, Sandra Louise
Special Education Teacher
Critzer, Marilyn Padgett
11th-12th Grade English Tchr
Crowther, Jeanne Burton
Sixth Grade Teacher
Darr, Dian M.
English Tchr & Stu Cncl Spon
Davidson, Kay Shivelbine
Sixth Grade Teacher
Davis, Jonni Bradford
English Teacher
Detrick, Danny
Choir Director
Dewey, Terresa Lynn
Sixth Grade Teacher
Dickinson, Roger Allyn
Marketing Professor
Diltz, John David
Professor & Dept Chair
Dowdy, John V., Jr.
Business Law Senior Lecturer
Downing, Carol L.
Sixth Grade Teacher
Draper, Paul Avery
Physics Assistant Professor
Edgemon, Kyle Lee
Mathematics Department Head
Elrod, Peggy Martin
Fourth Grade Teacher
Estes, Emory Dolphous
Professor
Fischer, Abbie Jo
Business Education Teacher
Floyd, Gina Lambert
English I Teacher
Foster, Cindy Rosellini
8th Grd Math Teacher
Fratto, Brian David
Texas History Teacher
Fratto, Michelle
Speech Teacher
Garner, Ouida Wright
Speech Teacher
Goolsby, Hannah E.
English Teacher
Grabowski, April Tucker
Ninth Grd Physical Sci Teacher
Griffin, Robbie Parr
Jrnlsm Tchr & Publications Adv
Grooms, Doris Elizabeth (Wilson)
US Government & Health Teacher
Hamilton, Merideth Ruth (Snider)
Seventh Grd Mathematics Tchr
Heard, Chinta Ann
Assistant Professor
Henry, Craig A.
High School Physics Teacher
Hodge, Mary Lee Rorex
Asst Dean & Acctng Lecturer
Hohulin, Steven Kent
Ath Dir, Coach & Physics Tchr
Holland, Connie Jo
Business Education Teacher
Homan, Tina Logue
Fourth Grade Teacher
Howard, Gail Collins
High School Teacher
Howell, Ann Mc Auley
Retired 4th-5th Grd Teacher
Howell, Jennifri Machelle
Second Grade Teacher
Jackson, Vicki Kline
Mathematics Teacher
Katsikas, Suzanne Jolicoeur
Political Science Professor
Keefer, Linda Huff
Orchestra Director

ARLINGTON (cont)
Kellam, Jonathan Martin
English Teacher
Kinnaird, Trish
Eng I & II Hnrs Teacher
Kitchin, Electra Magdalene
Guidance Counselor
Largent, Susan Elaine
English Teacher
Layton, Margaret Ann
Spanish Teacher
Lovett, Steven Russell
Instructor
Lowe, Ronald Edward
Teacher & Coach
Malone, Susan Michelle
Music Teacher
Marshall, Mary Kay Dawson
English Teacher
Martin, Michael Jean'
Social Studies Tchr & Coach
Mc Conine, Allan Jay
Texas History Teacher
Mc Dermott, S. Margaret
English Teacher & Dept Chair
Meyer, Kathy Herchman
Chemistry Teacher
Michener, Elaine Collins
Kindergarten Teacher
Miller, Claire Anne Rockwell
Home Economics Teacher
Miller, Diane
English Teacher
Miller, Pamela Kay (Williams)
Fifth Grade Teacher
Moffett, Mike M.
Health & PE Teacher
Moore, Barbara Williams
Assistant Head
Moore, Maxie Garner
Teacher & Coach
Musser, Steven T.
Director of Bands
Myers, Tiffany Thomas
Sociology Teacher
Naughton, Chris M.
World Geography Tchr & Coach
Peacock, Klata R.
HS French Teacher
Pickett, Chris Lynn Brouse
World History Teacher
Putnam, Judith Kay
English Teacher
Reber, Carrie R. (Schriefer)
4th Grd Tchr & Choir Dir
Rector, Darlene Laursen
A P Biology Teacher
Reeder, Larry Craig
7th Grd TX History Teacher
Richeson, Heidi K.
Fifth Grade Teacher
Riley-Mc Crary, Sherry D.
Reading Teacher
Rogers, Donald Wayne
World His, Soc Stud Tchr & Chm
Rose, Bob W.
Biology Tchr & Football Coach
Schkade, Lawrence L.
Ashbel Smith Professor
Scott, Judith Ross
Chemistry Teacher
Seipel, Scott J.
Instructor & PHD Student
Sessions, Wanda Madding
Dir of Theatre Arts Dept
Singleton, Sandy Campbell
Math Tchr & Cheerleader Spon
Sircar, Sumit
Dir, Ctr for Info Techs Mngmt
Small, Dana Lynn
8th Grade History Teacher
Smith, Diane Halbert
Latin Teacher
Smits, Allan W.
Associate Professor of Biology
Solomon, Lanny Michael
Accounting Professor
Spencer, Hoy Max
9th Grd Physical Science Tchr
Steinhibel, Teresa Potts
English & Reading Teacher
Strybosch, Marguerite VanSant
Science I Teacher
Stucker, Barbara Pontius
Math Teacher
Sutter, Gail Layne
Fifth Grade Elementary Teacher
Sutton, Margaret Zink
7th Grade Science Teacher
Swanson, Peggy Eubanks
Professor of Finance
Thomas, Ann Hardy
English Teacher & Level Leader
Waldman, Matthew John
Geometry Teacher & Coach
Webb, Kathy D'Lynn
Third Grade Teacher
Wehr, Roger Edward
Economics Professor
Whittington, James L.
Dept of Management Instr
Wilhelm, Martha Keller
Social Studies Teacher
Williams, Suzanne J.
Science Teacher
Wilson, Linda Morris
Economics Instructor
Wolfe, Bobbie Boyd
Third Grade Teacher
Woodul, Carolyn Volpato
Business Education Teacher
York, David Anthony
Health Teacher & Coach
Young, Charles William
Lecturer & Instructor

ARP
Dwire, Betty Terry
Home Economics Teacher
Froman, Paul Anthony
High School Biology Teacher
Jackson, Viola Simmons
Kindergarten Teacher
Rooks, Alice Pettey
Art Teacher
Rousseau, Joy (Webb)
Curriculum Director

ASHERTON
Fernandez, Agustin
Mathematics Teacher

ASPERMONT
Coats, Larry D. Hamilton
English Teacher
Hagle, Mary Jenell
Vocational Home Ec Teacher
Kupatt, Leslie Moore
Guidance Counselor

ATASCOCITA
Turegano, Rita Mc Clure
Third Grade Teacher

ATHENS
Allen, Denise Dianne
Business Instructor
Baker, Paige Parker
Bus & Mrktg Division Chprsn
Bracken, Mary Parker
Anatomy, Psych & Microbio Inst
DeHart, Margaret LaVonne
English Instructor
Dossett, Vicki Preston
Psychology Instructor
Griffin, Thelma Roberts
High School English Teacher
Hargrove-Huttel, Ray Ann
Soph Team Ldr & Nrsng Instr
Jordan, Cecil Ray
Speech & Debate Teacher
Moseley, Cindy Pearson
Coll Cnslr & Psych Instructor
Moses, David Eugene
Instructor of Government
Pulley, Glenna Kay
History Teacher
Seabourne, Janelle L.
Second Grade Teacher
Welborn, Patsy Sealy
Retired Elementary Teacher
Woodard, Angela Maffitt
Business & English Instructor

ATLANTA
Dickerson, Bobbie
Vocational Home Economics Tchr
Hagan, Larry
Math Teacher
Lester, Deanna Futrell
Special Education Teacher
Nichols, Martha Morris
Third Grade Teacher
Tomberlain, Marvin Patrick
World History Teacher

AUBREY
Fuller, Jackie Balthrop
Retired Social Studies Teacher
Harms, Susan (Wood)
HS Guidance Counselor
Herrera, Sherri Gay
Third Grade Teacher
Jameson, Garry Wayne
Secondary Mathematics Teacher
Lock, Craig J.
HS Content Mastery Teacher
McNabb, Terrie Cable
High School Teacher
Owens, Sharlotte Hampton
Art Specialist
Purcell, Sharon Earley
Kindergarten Teacher
Stensgard, Craig Lynn
7th Grade Math Teacher
Stensgard, Kay
High School Math Teacher

AUSTIN
Adair, Gloria Greene
Science Teacher
Adame, Arabella Gonzalez
Math Teacher & Chairperson
Alcorn, Bob J.
Lecturer
Allen, Dianna Meriwether
Spanish Teacher
Allen, D'Maris Anne
Biology Instructor
Ammons, Sheila K.
Accounting Department Head
Arnold, Daniel E.
Psychology Teacher
Austin, Mary L. (Collum)
Secondary Math Teacher
Autrey, Robert Lee
Computer Literacy Teacher
Barker, David Brian
Communication Professor
Bibbs-Terry, Cheryl Jean
2nd Grade Teacher
Billingsley, Mark
Journalism Teacher
Bingham, Sheila Gail
Mathematics Teacher
Blair, Patrick Gerard
Athletic Trainer
Bledsoe, Renette Sauls
7th Grade Soc Stud Teacher
Bogan, Robert Clay
Latin & Spanish Teacher
Brack, Erin Roberson
7th-8th Grade Math Teacher
Brewer, Diane Mc Curley
Theatre Teacher
Brown, Valenda Hemphill
Fifth Grade Teacher
Browning, Becky Beck
Fifth Grade Teacher
Bryant, Michael John
Athletic Trainer
Bryant, Steven Lawrence
Associate Professor of Music
Burke, Marilyn Clampitt
Reading & Study Skills Instr
Butts, Nina
Instructor of English
Buxkemper, Harriet Ewing
PE Dept Head & Assoc Prof
Campbell, Wendy Joyce
Curriculum Specialist
Carter, Mia Elizabeth
Assistant Professor of English
Ceder, Dennis Keith
Delta Program Teacher
Chiu, Charles B.
Professor of Physics
Cloud, Dana Lee
Asst Prof & Speech Comm Dept
Collier, Robert Thomas, Jr.
Industrial Technology Teacher
Conn, Pamela Ann
History Professor
Conquest, Patricia Lamb
English Teacher
Cooley, Kathleen Marie
Math Teacher
Craig, Jane Ann
Government & Law Teacher
Crawford, Lynn West
Business Teacher
Crayton, Minnie Bazy
4th Grd Teacher
Crider, Paula Ann
Director of Longhorn Bands
Crooks, Belinda Gail
K-5, High Schl Spanish Teacher
Darrow, Melinda Lee
English Teacher
Davis, Martha Susan
5th Grade Teacher
Delbar, Christiane Marie
Science Teacher
del Castillo, Jeffrey Arlen
Industrial Technology Teacher
Dick, William Joe
Youth Symphony Teacher
Dickson, Warren Edward
Vocal & Choral Music Director
Dingley, Hurshal Mike
US Government Teacher
Dismukes, Cinderella Mason
Fshn Merchandising Dept Head
Donaho, Diane M.
Spanish Teacher
Donegan, Jacquelyn King
MS History & Math Teacher
Duffy, Brian Jay
Martial Arts Instructor
Duran, Bonifacio Cruz
Principal
Dusek, Carol Miles
Kndgtn Tchr
Dyer, Robbie
Chemistry Teacher
Ellis, David Walter
Superintendency Fellow
Estes, Yvonne B.
Biology Instructor
Fernandez, Richard
Tech Coordinator
Fisher, Lefty
Hlth & Cmptr Application Tchr
Flatau, Susie Kelly
English Teacher
Fleming, John Patrick
Grad Instructor in Theatre
Fleming, Kathryn Rae
Advanced Placement Eng Teacher
Franzen, Lynn Mitchell
World & AP European His Tchr
Frizzi, Adria
Italian Lecturer
Furtado, Robert A.
Science Dept Chair
Fushille, Marisa I.
Russian Teacher
Garza, Jose Cruz
6th & 8th Grade PE Teacher
Gerlach, Rob
Teacher
Giles, Connie Guinn
Middle School Counselor
Glidden, Elizabeth Marie
Spanish Teacher
Glowka, Keith Rayford
Third Grade Teacher
Grace, Craig Thomas
Social Studies Teacher
Greulich, Dale Farley
Tchr of the Gifted & Talented
Grosskopf, Lisa Anna
Biology Teacher
Guthrie, Tammie Jill Craigie
Dance Tchr & Cheerleading Dir
Haddock, Drenda Neese
Third Grade Teacher
Hailey, Pamela Nadene
Science Teacher
Hall, T. Bruce
Marine Science Teacher
Hancock, Joyce Ann
Home Economics Teacher
Hawkes, JoAnn Curry
Contnt Mstry Ctr & Reg Ed Tchr
Heikkinen, Taimi Louise
Elementary School Art Teacher
Hensen, Mindy
Math Department Chair & Tchr
Hewlett, Carol W.
5th Grade Teacher
Hinojosa, Elsa
Honors US Government Teacher
Hobbs, Nancy Elaine
Kindergarten Teacher
Houston, Alice Allen
Executive Director
Hunger, Bobbi Faye
English & Journalism Teacher
Hurley, Ginny Fields
Fourth Grade Teacher
Jackson, Addie Novosad
Honors Biology Teacher
Jackson, Suzanne Hickman
Seventh Grade Lang Arts Tchr
James, Michelle Lea (Jones)
Health Sci Tech Instr & Coord
Jannuzi, F. Tomasson
Economics Professor
Jeffery, Janene Council
Nursing & Thanatology Instr
Johnson, Bonnie C. Edwards
AP US History Teacher
Johnson, Cynthia Rhea
8th Grd Soc Studies Teacher
Johnson, Lynne Renee
High School Art Teacher
Jones, Doris Marie
Fourth Grade Teacher
Jones Beavers, Doris Anne
Special Education Teacher
Jost, Norma Lillian
Mathematics Teacher
Kahn, Pat Singer
Spanish Teacher
Karrer, Kenneth M.
HS Teacher & Coach
Keel, Kathy Ashby
Sixth Grade Science Teacher
Kelley, Suzanne A.
English Dept Chairperson
Kendall, David Laurence
Dean, School of Bus Admin
Kenney, Susan Harrison
Math Teacher
Killough, Joy Haas
Science Department Chairman
King, Cheryl J.
English Teacher
Kirschner, Steve
Professor of Chemistry
Klau, Robert Scott
Tech Comm Lab Manager
Knudsen, Jane Elizabeth
Spanish Teacher
Lantelme, Bobby J.
Geometry Teacher
Lardon, Ellie
English Teacher
Lariviere, Janis Worcester
Science Teacher
Lasby, Clarence George
History Professor
Lehmann-Carssow, Nancy B.
Geog Tchr & Var Tennis Coach
Lickteig, Melissa Blair
Language Arts Teacher
Lindberg, Jo Burroughs
Mathematics Teacher
Lockwood, Vickie Jane
8th Grd Language Arts Teacher
Long, Nancy Quillin
6th Grade Language Arts Tchr
Lopez-Cox, Guadalupe
Spanish Teacher
Lotfalian, Ardavan
Health & Physical Ed Prof
Maddox, Steven Paul
Fifth Grade Teacher
Madrigal, Armando
Mathematics Teacher
Mariner, Jean Anne Miller
Mathematics Department Chair
Martin, Frederick Noel
Professor of Audiology
Martin, Linda Butler
Fourth Grade Teacher
Masch, Kristen Fasolino
Third Grade Teacher
Mc Call, Vicki Lynn
English Teacher
Mc Connell, Kim
Former Senior Bible Teacher
Mc Gorty, Kimberly Heeley
Former Biology Teacher
Mc Kinley, Doris M.
Content Mastery Teacher
Mc Pherson, John Cook
Middle School Teacher & Coach
Mertz, H. Beth Horton
Fourth Grade Teacher
Meyer, Kimberly Lynn
Mathematics Teacher
Miller, Catherine Becker
8th Grd American History Tchr
Miller, Ron
Band Director
Minter, Katherine Prehn
AP Psy & AP Eng Tchr
Misage, Mark Alan
Science Teacher
Moore, Lydia Hayden
Mathematics Teacher
Muhoberac, Buena Haecker
7th Grade Math Teacher
Mullen, Michael S.
Mathematics Teacher
Munguia, Gloria Ramirez
Spanish Teacher
Munn, Carole Lewandoski
Theatre Arts Director
Munn, Evwella
Physical Education Teacher
Munoz, Celia J.
Spanish & ESL Teacher
Munoz, Norma Cortez
10th Grade Math Teacher
Murphy, Lois Crain
6th Grd Tchr & Elem Schl Cnslr
Nabona, Kathy Graybill
Chemistry Dept Head & Prof
Nauert, Ronald G.
Agriculture Teacher
Neff, Susan Niels
Middle School Choir Director
Nelson, Malcolm George
Choir Director
Nolly, Glenn L.
Principal
Nyberg, Linda G.
Marketing Coordinator
Odom, Beverley Jones
Sixth Grade Teacher
Palermo, Janet Autreg
8th Grade Math Teacher
Paredes-Holt, Bill
Asst Instructor of English
Parker, Donna Owen
5th Grade Teacher
Parris, Miriam Erickson
German & Spanish Teacher
Parsons, Faynell Connally
American History Teacher
Patterson, Philip
Mathematics Teacher
Peoples, Reed
Department Head of Accounting
Phillips, Daisy Scott
English Professor
Pike, Mark Alan
American History Tchr & Coach
Polhill, Mildred Ann Gormel
3rd Grade Teacher
Poliakoff, Laura E.
Language Arts & Soc Stud Tchr
Powers-Martinez, Tina Lynn
Physical Ed Teacher & Coach
Preston, Vera Alma
Mathematics Teacher
Priem, Beth Seward
Junior English Teacher
Ramirez, Joe M.
8th Grade Social Studies Tchr
Reed, Jack M.
Senior Lecturer School of Adv
Reese, Carol Berman
Coord of Gifted & Talented Pgm
Rodi, Sue
Senior Lecturer
Rodriguez, Merlinda Zamora
Third Grade Teacher
Russell, Marsha K.
Humanities & Art History Tchr
Rutkowski, Kenneth Mathew
High School Math Teacher
Sanders, Allen
Asst Band Director
Scallon, Michael Patrick
Language Arts Teacher
Schmidt, Marita Drake
Algebra II & Pre-Calculus Tchr
Schmitt, Marvin R.
Counselor
Scott, Jenny Lind Porter
Chairman & Prof of English
Seitz, Ernest Ray, Jr.
8th Grade Science Teacher
Shanley, Jack Thomas
Fourth Grade Teacher
Shapiro, Paul Robert
Astronomy Professor
Sheehan, Aimee Kane
Fifth Grade Teacher
Smith, Frances J. Lee
Department Head
Smith, Melanie Maxted
Retired Teacher
Somerholter, Kerstin Evelyn
Assistant Instructor of German
Speck, Lawrence Wayne
School of Architecture Dean
Stallones, Jared Revel
Social Studies Dept Chairman
Steen, M. Elizabeth Lowther
High School Math Teacher
Stein, Suzanne Forester
2nd Grade Teacher
Stewart, Landon
Ath Dir, PE & English Teacher
Strand, Deirdre Mary
Tapestry Dance Company Co-Dir
Sulcer, Robert Phillips, Jr.
Asst Instructor of English
Sussman, Harvey M.
Professor
Swinton, Marilyn (Johns)
Speech Comm, Theatre Arts Prof

IN (cont)
Vicky Lynn (Froh)
ır Drftng, Comm Grphcs Tchr
J. Carole
ing Instructor
, Barbara Elaine
ıce & Multiculture Teacher
ı, Margaret Jane
ch Instr & Debate Coach
ult, Gerald Raymond
12th Grd Soc Stud Tchr
ıs, Georgia Robinson
ness Education Teacher
pson, Sheryl Freeze
ish Teacher
ton, Thomas Raymond
World Geography Teacher
erman, Gayle M.
stant Professor of Nursing
, Alice Branton
ıe Economics Teacher
r, Johnny B.
ı School Math Teacher
rs, John Carter
ıestra Teacher
n, Stephen Avery
ish Teacher & Coach
, Jerry Lynn
avior Specialist
, Michael Kevin
ector of Bands
Lynda Smith
lish Teacher
:, Stephanie Chanda
turer
ıns, Martin Lee
Stud & Cmptr Literacy Tchr
ams, John L.
gram Manager
on, Susan Maxine
atic Sci & Chem Tchr
ən, William DeCal
ospace Science Studies Dir
lett, Brenda J.
fessor of Business Law
ra, Roberto Garza
ınish & Science Teacher
ov, Alexander F.
:hematics Teacher
c, Nereida Samuda
ınish Teacher
LON
osque, David
ıcher
RY
nan, Robert Floyd
glish & Spanish Teacher
NGER
eda, Tonia Stroman
: Stud, Hlth & PE Tchr
'ELL
brick, Jeannine Lynn (Ingraham)
glish Teacher
ens, Dwan F.
anish & Math Teacher
y, Lisa Dyer
glish Teacher
E
nisch, Keith Wayne
ı Grade Earth Science Tchr
əertson, Mary Ann Page
mputer Science Teacher
hter, Jean Clark
S Mathematics Teacher
tley, Rita Young
glish Teacher
ks, Sharon Harris
glish Teacher & Dept Chair
, Judy Wilburn
dvanced English & Rdng Tchr
ston, Robert Warren
ath Teacher
oe, Mark
orld History Teacher
Neill, Jamie J.
ology Teacher
llins, Stormy Lee
gricultural Science Teacher
rce, Cheryl Parks
ourth Grade Teacher
e, Carol L.
horal Director
ffin, David Aliston
heatre Art Teacher
vino, Lynne Marie
istory & Reading Teacher
ston, Carolyn Brown
S His & World Geography Tchr
ight, Johnnie M.
areer, Tech & Office Ed Tchr
ung, Kim Ray
ourth Grade Lead Teacher
CLIFF
ngenberg, Lynn (Lesco)
nd Grade Teacher
IRD
own, Carla Dillard
Mathematics Teacher
artin, Gordon Lee
Health & Science Teacher
LCH SPRINGS
ugere, Pamela Routon
English Teacher & Tennis Coach
ALLINGER
lis, Dale E.
Elem Music & Choral Act Dir
anke, Virginia J. (Jost)
2nd Grade Teacher
y, Marsha Amyett
Home Economics Teacher

Geistmann, Sherran Rowe
English Teacher & UIL Coord
Reeder, Margo Brunson
HS English & Journalism Tchr
Sykes, Deborah Douglas
7th & 8th Grade Reading Tchr
Travis, Dana R. (Collins)
Sixth Grade Sci & PE Teacher
Tyree, Brenda Jan
1st-5th Grd Tchr of the Gifted
BALMORHEA
Hernandez, Yolanda Muniz
Business Teacher
BANDERA
Castillo, Janda Aleese
8th Grade English Teacher
Fleming, Alicia Valadez
Retired Teacher
Kline, Andy Steven
Teacher & Principal
Robbins, Telvy Fronsford
Ag Science Teacher
Rogers, Darcy D.
World Geography Tchr & Coach
Shearhart, Robert H.
Sr English Teacher & Coach
Zickler, Karen K. King
English Teacher
BANGS
Garner, Patricia Burleson
Science Teacher
Huggins, Maurice Dale
Math Teacher & Coach
Ornelas, Brenda
Resource Math Teacher
Page, Debbie Denise
Kindergarten Teacher
Porter, Lyn L.
Resource English Teacher
Willey, Rebecca Slayton
Second Grade Teacher
BARKSDALE
Lloyd, Wanna Lou (Dean)
Junior High English Teacher
Whatley, Tom J.
6th-8th Grade History Teacher
BARTLETT
Kneten, Garland J.
Band Director
Mc Cutchen, Sallie Chambers
Teacher
BASTROP
Cauley, Chris Michael
11th Grade US History Teacher
Choiniere, Robert Alan
9th-12th Grd Agriscience Tchr
Clemons, Barbara Gail
Fifth Grade Teacher
Dobie, Cindy Cox
Fifth Grade Teacher
Hamm, Teresa Terrell
Counselor
Jenkins, Mary Jo Mercer
First Grade Teacher
Thielen, Michael Louis
Band Director
Visage, Kristi Hess
Business Technology Teacher
BAY CITY
Allison, Linda Smith
Mrktg Ed Teacher & Coord
Anderson, Sandra Mae
Algebra Teacher
Brown, Jan Short
French & English III AP Tchr
Cook, Melissa Sawyer (Hill)
Algebra Teacher
Crain, Karen Muskiet
Pre AP Math Teacher
Fant, Sylvia Fisher
8th Grade Math & Algebra Tchr
Hall, Beverly Elaine
Band Director
Howard, Elizabeth Atthowe
Librarian
Kinsey, Barbara Lee
Art Teacher
Lyle, Patricia Ann
Principal
O'Briant, Lynette Marie
Kindergarten Teacher
Reed, Debbie J.
Science & Math Teacher
Thames, Beverly Breaux
Teacher of Gifted & Talented
Woolsey, Patricia Andel
Teacher
BAYTOWN
Barry, Marianne J.
Instr of Emergency Med Tech
Black, Sally Bryan
Mathematics Teacher
Bobbitt, Kitty Sue
Science Teacher & Acad Coord
Borah, William Bryan
Eng Dept Chair & AP Teacher
Britt, Donna Montgomery
US History & 8th Grd Teacher
Capps, Steffani Strickland
6th Grade Reading Teacher
Cook, Bettye Alexander
Honors & AP Eng Teacher
Cox, Christina Putnam
Spanish Teacher
Harris, Karen Mitchell
Eleventh Grade Teacher
Hartman, Michele Diane
Biology Teacher
Hill, Kay
Fr Tchr & Frgn Lang Dpt Chm

Kellner, Laura Ward
Algebra Teacher
Kunz, Dianne Manley
Title I Peer Facilitator
Lewis, Elizabeth Ussery
Eng Tchr & Tech Writing Coord
Manley, Michael Paul
Head Football Coach
Puchot, Raymond Charles
Speech Professor
Scheffler, Kenneth A.
Accounting Instructor
Sheley, Susan Cummings
Visual Performing Art Div Chm
Shoemaker, Lindsey K.
Sci Dept Chm, Bio & Sci Tchr
Tadlock, Paul Wesley
Biology II Honors Teacher
Turner, Ronney Edward
Electronics Teacher
Woods, Elizabeth Buntin
High School Math Teacher
BEAUMONT
Aldrich, Candice Ann Brittain
Theatre Arts Teacher
Bailey, Beverly Rairigh
Biology & Phys Sci Teacher
Barrett, Chad Dwight
Head Athletic Trainer
Barton, Sheila Breaux
Teacher
Blewett, Sally Williams
Principal
Bryant, Daria Maria (Orbro)
Spanish Teacher
Buchwald, Lynne Strong
Teacher of Gifted & Talented
Buscher, Henry N.
Department of Science Chair
Caffery, Susan Mc Larin
Chemistry Teacher
Christ, Earline
Fourth Grade Teacher
Clark, Marcia Galvan B.
Spanish Teacher
Coco-Cobb, Paulette Devillier
Manager's Assistant
Cohen, Mary Ann (Aldridge)
Teacher of Gifted & Talented
Cronin, Susannah Mc Neill
US & World History Teacher
Darby, Delores (Bob)
4th Grade Teacher
DeHart, James Thomas
Physics & Physical Sci Teacher
Dixon, Enoch Noble, Jr.
Physical Education Teacher
Drake, Rillie Jefferson
English Teacher
Dreyer, Julie Hawkins
English & Social Studies Tchr
Ellis, Cecilia Jo
Theology Teacher
Englander, Mary Oxford
9th-10th Grd English Teacher
Falk, Andrew Justin
History Teacher
Fisher, Elizabeth Oldham
First Grade Teacher
Gay, Elizabeth Gainey
Multi-Age Group Teacher
Graves, Belinda Jordan
Librarian & Media Specialist
Guadagno, Anne Maria
Rel Teacher & Yth Minister
Harrington, Dorothy Jean
Sixth Grade English Teacher
Hudson, Lonnie Clark
Economics Teacher
Jones, Ivan Paul
Assistant Principal
Keath, Celia Josephine
8th Grade Math Teacher
Kilbane, Angelina
4th & 5th Grade Teacher
King, Carole Krepper
Fourth Grade Teacher
Koehn, Carol Butcher
Geography & History Teacher
Latta, Karen Kimrough
Cmptr Keyboarding Teacher
Lee, Elizabeth Gardner
His, Eng, Yrbk & Bible Instr
Lehner, Judy Lynn
Counselor
Lester, Annie L.
High School Reading Teacher
Long, Rose Mary
Counselor & Administration stf
Martin, Carol Ann (Parker)
AP & Senior English Teacher
Minyard, Deborah Collins
Algebra & Geometry Teacher
Paduch, Frank Joseph
Chaplain & Teacher
Pitre, Josephina, OP
First Grade Teacher
Powell, Vicki Peveto
Math, Hlth & Phys Sci Teacher
Reeves, Bonnie Bounds
Chemistry Teacher
Roy, Kathryn
Algebra Teacher
Schroeder, Ronald Eugene
Texas History Teacher
Shaw, Willie M. (Sinegal)
First Grade Teacher
Sherman, Paula Malain
Fifth Grd Language Arts Tchr

Smith, Chanda Farnsworth
Bio I, Anatomy Physiology Tchr
Snyder, Patricia Ann
Math Department Chairman
Stevens, Carole L.
Geometry & Calculus Teacher
Stone, Nettie Gayle
8th Grd Language Arts Teacher
Theriot, Jan Hudnall
Cmptr Lit & Life Mngmt Tchr
Trousdale, John Miller
Fine Arts Dept Chm & Band Dir
Verde, John Michael
English Lecturer
Welch Morris, Helen Mc Coy
Remedial Reading Teacher
Wheaton, Dorothy DeJean
Counselor
Young, Rudi Beth
English Teacher
BECKVILLE
Tuttle, Ann Martin
Fifth Grade Teacher
BEDFORD
Blair, David Mathew
Science I Teacher
Browning, Barbara K.
6th Grade Teacher
DeHaven, Nancy Underwood
Speech & Theatre Arts Teacher
Fargo, Susan Dianne
ESL Teacher
Franklin, Nancy Kay
8th Grade English Teacher
Kercho, Alene Zubb
Third Grade Teacher
Laywell, Vernon Paul
Science Teacher
Lufcy, Wanda Waller
Kindergarten Teacher
Moore, Kenneth Ray
Science Department Chair
Peterson, Susan Pannell
7th Grade TX History Teacher
Pruitt, Michele Rowan
PE Tchr & Dist PE Coord
Swink, Deanna (True)
Fourth Grade Teacher
Thrash, Eileen Raney
9th Grd World Geography Tchr
BEEVILLE
Belew, Bennie C.
Bio Tchr & Head of Sci Dept
Duryea, Jayne
Art Dept Prof & Chprsn
Elizalde, Velma C.
Upward Bound Asst Director
Horton, Marion Barnhart
English Teacher
McClintock, Cherry Dee
Math Teacher & Math Dept Chm
Medina, Pennie A.
Instructor of Psychology Dept
Past, Kay Cude
Spanish Teacher & Dept Chair
Whitten, Robert Alex
American History Teacher
BELLAIRE
Axelrod, Lawryn
Director of Media Arts
Bagley, Carole Anita
English Teacher
Borik, Devora P.
Hebrew Teacher
Janes-Kowalski, Catherine John
Mathematics Teacher
McLendon, Elizabeth Lee
Professor of Russian Language
Rogers, Mary Katherine
Art Teacher
Tsay, Susan Shu-Yuan
Mandarin Chinese Teacher
Watts, Sandra Ann
United States History Teacher
Wright, Thomas Hugh
Math Teacher
BELLS
Carnes, La Zetta
Spanish & English Teacher
Gray, Raylene Craft
5th Grade Teacher
Johnson, Mary Lou (Parker)
Retired Elementary Teacher
Kremer, Annie Matthews
Vocational Home Economics Tchr
Mc Neil, Carolyn Blankenship
Retired Elem Teacher
Mitchusson, Martha Cobble
Retired Fifth Grade Teacher
Reeves, Gary Lynn
Athletic Director & Coach
Rutledge, Frances Russell
4th Grade Teacher
Threadgill, Barbara Sue
English & Government Teacher
Wilson, Stacey Ann
High School Business Teacher
BELLVILLE
Beckendorff Pinson, Vera Cowart
English Teacher
Kana, Scott Henry
HS English Teacher & Coach
Schmitt, John William
Auto Technology Teacher
BELTON
Atmar, Robert Nelms
US His Tchr & Dept Chair
Baugh, Robert Frank
American History Teacher

Boney, Darlyn Goetz
Kindergarten Teacher
Boren, Mary H.
Speech & English Teacher
Brandon, Milayna L.
High School Biology Teacher
Davis, Sharon A.
English Teacher
Fabritius, Michael M.
Economics Professor
Haywood, Jane Ferguson
Asst Professor of English
Horton, Howard Lee
Assoc Professor of Management
Kenas, Alice Chambers
Spanish Teacher
Lorenz, Sandra Sayre
Theater Teacher & UIL Coord
Ludlow, Wanda Anne (Poole)
Spanish Teacher
May, Dennis Keith
World History Tchr & Coach
May, Rozanna San Miguel
Science Teacher & Team Leader
Meriwether, Elizabeth Stieferman
Hnrs Bio II, Hlth Careers Tchr
Smith, John Wm
Art Teacher
Valenta, Debbie Lee (Corsentino)
PE & Tennis Coach
Wurster, Carol Deviney
Mathematics Teacher
Wyrick, Stephen Von
Professor of Hebrew Bible
Yarbrough, Martha A.
English Teacher
BEN WHEELER
Martin, Randall H.
History, Health & Math Teacher
Sides, Peggy Chandler
Elementary Counselor
BENAVIDES
Hinojosa, Efa Iris
English Teacher & UIL Coord
Ramos, Reymundo
Geometry Teacher
BENJAMIN
Koepf, Carolyn Scott
English Teacher
BIG BEND NATIONAL PARK
Forsythe, Melissa McCann
6th-8th Grade Teacher
BIG LAKE
Brown, E. Ray
Biology Teacher & Coach
Champion, LaNell Hibdon
Speech & Theatre Teacher
Hall, Brenda Boyd
Vocational Junior English Tchr
Terrell, James A.
HS Ind Technology Teacher
BIG SANDY
Allen, Stephen John
Biological Sciences Instructor
Barr, Todd R.
History & Speech Teacher
Brenner, Sandra Jo
Professor of Nutrition
Bruhn, Albert
Assistant Professor & Director
Burnett, Andy Glen
Physical Education Instructor
Clemmons, Ricky Bob
Soccer Coach Men's NAIA Div I
Dean, Aaron Keith
Asst Prof of Business Admin
DeKoster, Renate Rohweder
German Instructor
Good, Johnny Lee
Director of Teacher Education
Griffin, Byron Leslie
Math Instructor
Holcomb, Curtis Dwight
Asst Professor of Mathematics
Kirkpatrick, Thomas Lee
Business Admin Dept Chair
Maas, David Frank
Professor of English
Matkin, Harvey Neil
Chair of CIS Department
Mc Lemore, Joy Ellis
Adjunct Professor of English
Mohr, Eric Simpson
English Professor
Patton, Timothy John
Asst Professor of Business
Pruett, James Ralph
Science Teacher
Randolph, E. Dale A.
Spanish Professor
Roberts, Patti Lee
Home Economics Teacher
Rogers, Nina Yulanda
Instructor in Speech
Schattel, Joan M.
Media Specialist
Sherrod, Ricky Lee
History Department Chair
Smith, Danny L.
Associate Professor of English
Steep, Estelle M.
Associate Librarian
Urwiller, Randal R.
Instructor of English
Wainwright, David P.
Foreign Lang Chair & Fr Prof
Worthen, James Thomas
Lecturer in Business Admin

BIG SPRING
Baker, Kimberly Jo
Spanish Teacher
Becerra, Javier V.
School Resource Officer
Bell, Shirley White
4th Grade Teacher
Bowerman, Kathie McDaniel
Government Teacher
Carlile Lindell, Linda Cheryl
Choral Director
Conley, Janie Wooten
4th & 5th Grade Reading Tchr
Cunningham, Wilbur Paul
Mathematics Teacher
DePauw, Tammy Newsom
Social Studies Teacher
Gibson, Tommy
HS Mathematics Tchr & Coach
Gladden, Lyndon K.
8th Grade Math Teacher
Hamby, Sharon Lynette
English Teacher
Hendrickson, Glenda Ann
Second Grade Teacher
Locke, Doris Marie
Second Grade Teacher
Miller, Virginia Ruth
Soc Studies Tchr & Dept Head
Parks, Patricia Conway
English Teacher
Pierce, Traci Cravey
English Teacher & Coach
Piercefield, Lana Lanell
Microcomputer Teacher
Reese, Larry Eugene
Professor of Ec & History
Richardson, Sharion Bernaud
Mathematics Teacher
Sincleair, Mary Baker
Math Teacher
Smith, Rhonda Raquel
Sign Language Teacher
Terrazas, Kathy Howle
English Teacher
Willbanks, Jill Ann
Home Economics Teacher
BISHOP
Marcotte, Clara Mae (Vonn)
English & Journalism Teacher
BLACKWELL
Anderson, Randy
Assistant Principal & Bus Tchr
Smith, J. Keven
Agri Science Teacher
BLANKET
Helm, Nancy Nicholes
Second Grade Teacher
Rodgers, Barbara Black
6th Grade Teacher
BLOOMBURG
Shofner, Steve Keith
Science Instructor
Timmons, Jo Booth
Social Studies Teacher
BLOOMING GROVE
Holmsley, Rickey Dale
History Teacher & Bsktbl Coach
Tipping, William David
High School Math Teacher
BLOOMINGTON
Olivarez, Raela Johnson
History Department Chair
Parenica, Gayle Lynn (Mikulenka)
English & Social Studies Tchr
Rain, Norma Davis
Freshman English Teacher
Sauer, Sabra Hosek
Science Teacher
Schaefer Taylor, Carol
English & Speech Teacher
Westfahl, Debra A.
English Teacher
BLOSSOM
Sugg, Katherine Malone
Fifth Grade Teacher
BLUE RIDGE
Butler, Lisa Matthews
Science Teacher
Clay, Angela Yvette
English Teacher & Coach
Crawford, Pamelia Dewiece
Language Arts Teacher
BLUFF DALE
Eldredge, Ann Ray
Fifth & Sixth Grade Teacher
BLUM
Gant, Gloria Ann
Fourth Grade Teacher
Higgins, Kathi
English Chair
BOERNE
Arnold, Roger Dale
Industrial Technology Teacher
Arnott, Kevin Dale
Director of Bands
Champion, Samuel Vernon
Principal
Davis, Richard Stephen
US & World History Teacher
Greenlees, Susan Dore
HS Math Teacher & Dept Chair
Jones, Le Lan Jefery
Choir, Debate & Theatre Tchr
Kilfoy, Sue STurges
Reading Teacher
Kyle, Kathryn Anne
High School English Teacher
Schmid, Jack Paul
Retired Mathematics Teacher

BOGATA
Gunter, Brenda Kay
English Teacher
Russell, Barbara Jean (Mankins)
Eng III & Acad IV Tchr
BOLING
Shaw, Sandra Jean (Mc Kim)
Third Grade Teacher
BONHAM
Ashcraft, Roger Neal
Band Director
Beauford, Latayne Swinney
HS Special Education Teacher
Caylor, Donna Gilbert
English & Journalism Teacher
Clark, Debbie Goss
HS Counselor
Hale, Glenda R.
History & Language Arts Tchr
Knight, Rebecca Jean (Williams)
English Teacher
Manhart, Billie Campbell
Substitute Teacher
Richardson, Stanley Wayne
Drafting Teacher
Youree, Cheryl Ann
Theatre, Speech & English Tchr
BOOKER
Wynn, Susie Seaney
English Teacher
BORGER
Brink, David Ernest
Sci Dept Chair & Physics Tchr
Close, Jenny Lynn
7th Grade Reading Teacher
Davis, Arthur Keith
Chemistry Professor
DeLoe, Susan Grimsley
Biology & Physical Sci Tchr
Gould, Linda Watson
Vocational Nursing Instructor
Hart, Judy Morgan
Instructor of English & Rdng
Haygood, Mary O'Rear
Retired Business Dept Chprsn
Johnston, Marsha Gregg
2nd Grade Teacher
Lozier, Mary Lou Simmons
Biology Teacher
Moore, Jan Park
Institutional Advancement Dir
Morris, Gina Marie James
Biology Instructor
Myers, James Michael
Instructor
Rhoton, Fletta Mae (Stephens)
Instr of Voc Nursing Dept
Robinson, Glenn Arthur
Speech Instructor & Dept Chair
Schneider, Jill Rankin
Algebra II Teacher & Coach
Strecker, Judy E.
Chair of the Music Department
Thomas, Gayelynn L.
Engish, Speech & Ed Instr
Unruh, Judy Hamilton
Licensed Voc Nursing Instr
Webb, E. J.
Cross Country & Track Head
Werhan, Lanetta Diann
2nd Grade Teacher
Wheeler, Susie Jackson
French Teacher
Wood, Brandon Keith
US Government Teacher
Worsham, Sharon Montgomery
4th Grade Teacher
BOWIE
Clayton, Louis W.
Microcomputer Instructor
Fitzner, Linda White
Speech & Theatre Arts Teacher
Haralson, Trudy Jo Hendrickson
Ninth Grade English Teacher
Hood, Joel W.
Science Teacher & Coach
BOYD
Lowry, Kathleen Jo
Chemistry & Physics Teacher
Martin, Brenda Adams
5th Grade Math & Science Tchr
Wilson, Ladean Holland
Business Teacher
BOYS RANCH
Brown, Kenneth Alan
Science Teacher
BRACKETTVILLE
Crumley, Karen D.
High School Science Teacher
Curry, Delia Kay
English I & II Teacher
BRADY
Andrews, Karen F.
English II & Journalism Tchr
Bailey, Charles V.
Teacher & Coach
Bauer, Zane Randell
Earth Science Teacher
Day, Betzy Williams
Third Grade Teacher
Edmiston, Peggy June (Scott)
First Grade Teacher
Friar, Sherry
English & GATE Teacher
Futrell, Brent Kevin
High School Teacher & Coach
Graves, William Lamar
History & Soc Stud Dept Chprsn
Land, Liesa Lemke
Mathematics Teacher

Lewis, Lynon Royce
Technology Teacher
Munden, Lynn K.
High School Counselor
Peel, Polly Hibdon
Retired 4th Grade Teacher
Popnoe, Matt
High School Science Teacher
Sessom, Cecelia Claburn
Reading Teacher
Siler, Avanell Oliver
English Teacher
Underwood, Ruby F. Matthews
Sixth Grade Teacher
Williams, Tanya Powell
English, PAL & GATE Tchr
BRAZORIA
Hatch, Susan Marie
Third Grade Teacher
BRECKENRIDGE
Broyles, Dana Michele
Math Teacher & Dept Chprsn
Ridgeway, Linda Bradford
Sixth Grade Teacher
Sims, Linda J.
6th Grade Mathematics Teacher
White, Guyla June
ESL Teacher
BREMOND
Barnhart, Carol Parr
English, Science & Art Teacher
Briles, Mark Wayne
Science Teacher
West, Kelvin Wayne
Agricultural Sci & Tech Instr
Williams, Lisa F.
Home Economics Teacher
BRENHAM
Bosse, Robert Dale
Math Teacher
Campbell, Tracy Marie
English Teacher
Dietrich, Wilfred Oscar
Division Chm of Humanities
Doherty, William Gary
Instrumental Music Coordinator
Klemm, Doris M.
History Instructor
Kossie, Mary Strozier
Home Economics Teacher
Kovar, Debra
4th-5th Grd Computer Lab Tchr
Kremmer, Jennifer Jones
English Teacher
Mc Gaugh, Cozette Brakebill
Social Studies Teacher
Mueller, Janis May
Business Teacher & Golf Coach
Pollock, George Willard
Instructor of English
Sapenter, Bettye Harris
High School Counselor
Schroeder, Johnnie W.
Agriculture & Engnrng Instr
Scott, Jeffrey Keith
English Instructor
Taylor, Pat G.
Biology Instructor
Thaler, Linda Lehrmann
Home Economics Teacher
Wahrmund, Barbara Haby
English Teacher
Wied, Jesse Lee
Botany Instructor
Wilkening, Mark Allen
Bus Admin & Economics Prof
BRIDGE CITY
Ballard, Charlotte
Tenth Grade English Teacher
Briggs, Richard James
US History Instructor & Coach
Dorman, Kathie Harrison
Spanish Teacher
Fontenot, Maria Richard
Business Education Teacher
George, Michele Anne
English Teacher
Gottschalk, William H.
Assistant Band Director
Guidry, David Andrew
World History Teacher
Hodgkinson, Lyndell Kittrell
English Teacher
Hollier, Amelia Votti
English Teacher & Coach
Johansson, Leah R.
Economics & Business Ed Tchr
Miller, Clarice Clark
Fifth Grade Reading Teacher
Nichols, Rebecca Ann
Kindergarten Teacher
Parish, Elizabeth Faye
Math Department Chair
Pittman, Kenneth Preston, Jr.
Sixth Grade Science Teacher
Sanders, Wanda Scales
4th Grade Teacher
Schwalm, Cynthia Gentry
Journalism & Art Instructor
Stout, Richard H.
Math Teacher
Tarter, Phyllis Smith
English IV Tchr & Dept Chair
Todd, Robert Carroll, III
5th Grd Social Studies Teacher
Wiegreffe, Frank Wayne
Chem Tchr & Sci Dept Chairman
Woodall, Samuel Troy
Assistant Principal

BRIDGEPORT
Campbell, Karen Englerth
Tchr of Eng Gifted & Talented
BRISCOE
Meadows, Rolonda Annette
Secondary Science Teacher
Smith, Curtis
Principal & Coach
Tatyrek, Janet Lea
Elementary Principal
BROADDUS
Huggins, John E., II
Mathematics Teacher
Lane, Deborah Collins
Counselor
BROOKELAND
Carter, Mary Taylor
7th & 8th Grd Lang Arts Tchr
BROOKESMITH
Schoen, Melody Fedora
Social Studies & Lang Art Tchr
BROWNFIELD
Barnett, Keri Shults
English Teacher
Barnett, Timothy Shaun
US History & PE Teacher
Evans, Tera Sims
High School English Teacher
Foshee, Linda Harrell
Former Second Grade Teacher
Fulton, Patricia Lary
Fifth Grade Teacher
Herrera, Loretta F.
Chemistry & Human Anatomy Tchr
Jackson, Mary Jane
English Teacher
Jones, Karen Kainer
Fourth Grade Teacher
Mc Whorter, Donald Wayne
Speech & Media Teacher
Phillips, Jane Ann Glover
Content Mastery Teacher
Pittman, Kevin Lynn
American History Teacher
Pope, R. Leon
HS Biology Teacher
Rutledge, Michelle
Algebra II Teacher
Shipp, Billy Gordon
Band Director
Sparks, Nancy
Texas History Teacher
Wood, Sharron Marie
Fifth Grade Teacher
BROWNSBORO
Debenport, Maggi Hood
High School Teacher
English, Kathlene Johnson
Fifth Grade Teacher
Howard, Jeffrey Dewayne
Anatomy & Physiology Teacher
Innerarity, Wayne Wayne
Theater Arts Teacher
Parker, Charlotte Tompkins
7th Grade Math Teacher
BROWNSVILLE
Arrese, Maria Aurora
Student Director & Instructor
Ayala, Alberto
World & US History Teacher
Balboa, Ruben R.
English & Reading Teacher
Barrera-Perez, Monica
Career & Technology Teacher
Berry, Walter Evans
World History Teacher
Betancourt, Marsha L.
Art Teacher
Bryan, Diane (Klepfer)
Fifth Grade Teacher
Bryant, Mary Lou (Jones)
English Teacher
Caballero, Bertha Lucio
English Dept Chair & Tchr
Cantu, Oscar, Jr.
11th Grade English Teacher
Cardona, Rosario
Spanish Teacher
Chesley, James Michael
Mathematics Teacher
Coyne, Judy
High School Counselor
De Leon, Sergio
Bilingual Elem Teacher
de Saenz, Elisa Morales
French & Spanish Teacher
Diaz, Gabriela M.
8th Grade Reading Teacher
Domene, Fernando J.
High School Counselor
Fisher, Robert William
Voc Micro Computer Instr
Garcia, Claudia Patricia
English Teacher
Garcia, Rosemary G.
4th Grade Teacher
Gavito, Manuel
Dir of Radiologic Tech Prgm
Gomez, Carlos Guillermo
Assoc Professor of Fine Arts
Gonzalez, Alma L.
Spanish Teacher
Gonzalez, David
HS Head Choir Director
Gonzalez, Paula Garza
HS Physical Education Teacher
Gonzalez, Susana Robledo
Title I Math Teacher
Griffin, James H.
Health & Physical Ed Dept Chm

Griffin, Shirley Mangum
Tchr of Biling Gftd & Tlntd
Handelman, David Irwin
High School English Teacher
Harlan, Kathrine Ann
High School Counselor
Harris, William Herbert
Eng Instr, Dir of Honors Stud
Haught, Michael A.
Art Instructor
Hendricks, Patti Staggs
Journalism Teacher
Hernandez, Francisco
Physical Science Teacher
Hopwood, Debra Lynn
Amer His, Lit & Eng Teacher
Horn, Gale J.
High School English Teacher
Hotcaveg, Sandra Elizabeth
Fifth Grade Teacher
Hughes, John C., Sr.
Senior Lecturer in Government
Johnson, Dianne Kaye
Reading Professor
Kearney, Milo
History Professor
Knopp, Anthony Keith
Professor of History
Lawrence, Ellener Wagner
Fourth Grade Teacher
Lewis, Ronda Maria
7th Grade Reading Teacher
Leyendecker, Billie Yarbrough
Business Teacher
Longoria, Marcos
FL Dept Chairman
Loop, D'Ann Funkhouser
English Teacher
Lopez, Christina
At-Risk Teacher
Lopez, Genaro
Professor of Biology
Lutsinger, Carolee Andrews
Science Teacher
Marquez, Jose T.
Geography Teacher
Martinez, Sergio N.
Fourth Grade Teacher
Mc Call, Robert Cameron
6th Grade ESL Teacher
Medrano, Manuel F.
History Professor
Menard, Leticia delBosque
Art Teacher
Miller, Andy F.
Eighth Grade Science Teacher
Morales, Celeste Canant
Assistant Band Director
Moreno, Estela Rivera
High School Counselor
Nanze-Davis, Deloria Jean
Math Professor & Chairperson
Neeley, Alan L.
Mathematics Teacher
Novelo, Myriam Elizabeth
General Ed Diploma Instructor
Ortega, Luis Roman
Physical Education Teacher
Perez, Terri
Secondary Counselor
Phillipp, Paul Urban
Physics Teacher
Putegnat, Sharon Stevens
Director
Quintanilla, Alberto Perez
History Teacher
Ramirez, Timmy
Social Studies Teacher
Rausch, Sara Lucia
High School Biology Teacher
Reik, Douglas Allen
Third Grade Teacher
Rocha, Olivia
Second Grade Teacher
Rodriguez, Maria Esmeralda Torres
Reading Teacher
Rowan, Chris
Fifth Grade Teacher
Salazar, Tom
Health Teacher & Coach
Sarmiento, Tessie Fernandez
Science Teacher
Schmidt, Robert John
Campus Ministry Coordinator
Schovley, Janet Ruth
Montessori Teacher
Silguero, Jorge Antonio
Mathematics Teacher
Solitaire, Gloria
Resource Instructor of GATE
Stephenson, Mimosa Summers
English Professor
Stone, Robert Jude
Physics Teacher
Suarez, Gabriel
English as A Second Lang Instr
Tamayo, Edna
Educational Consultant
Thomas, Catherine Ann
Mathematics Teacher
Torres, John
HS Algebra Teacher & Coach
Uresti, Robert
ESL Teacher
Vega, Estanislao Solana
Fifth Grade Bilingual Teacher
Villarreal, Minerva Medrano
English Teacher
Villela, Gracie
Reading Teacher

NSVILLE (cont)
Iarry O., Jr.
ate Professor
Janice I.
ced Placement Eng Tchr
eth Ann (Martinek)
Grd Tchr of the Gifted
., Jeanne Williams
Mathematics Specialist
Martha Kate
h Teacher
Sessia, III
ant Professor of Math
ng Ling
Professor of Mathematics
Julia Rocha
2nd Grd Biling Ed Tchr
NWOOD
Roger Carlisle
matics Teacher
ay, Brian Layne
School Technology Teacher
Olga D.
Prof Bus Admin & Soc
Sherry Gilbert
pal
n, Gerry Wane
Prof of Physical Science
gton, Sammie Rees
& Tennis Teacher
nne Lee
Work Program Director
Darwin Dwayne
ry Teacher & Coach
Gretchen Williams
istry & Biology Teacher
Robert Randall
tor of Bands
d, Nancy Jo
ssor of Musical Theatre
Ian F.
of Sociology & Dept Chair
, Glenda Cox
Grade Reading Teacher
, Betty Boedeker
Counselor
than, Dora Jean (Smith)
h Grade Teacher
Kristin Denise
Lang Arts, PE Tchr & Coach
y, Justin Duane
ry Professor
s, John M.
ry & Political Sci Instr
, Doris Evans
ipal
, Ann Hice
rade English Teacher
, Evelyn Matthews
essor of English
Laura Jenkins
d Geography & PE Teacher
rd, Jack Wayne
& Bio Dept Head
r, Brenda Gayle
nish Teacher
ce, Elizabeth Ellis
ociate Professor of Music
n, Karen Mae Pinkerton
K, Kndgtn & ESL Teacher
n, Marvin Rick
ld History Teacher
ery, Doris Everts
ness Computer Teacher
NI
, Anthony A.
ory Teacher & Coach
y, Phil W.
al Studies Chprsn & Tchr
AN
ng, Kathleen Shirley
cial Education Teacher
d, Mary E.
ector of VOCN Program
Shari Zwernemann
h Teacher
t, Sue Churchman
Grade Biology Teacher
r, Martha Youngs
t Grade Teacher
vin, Judy Kay
t Grade Teacher
es, Jackie Dee
sical Education Teacher
beck, John H.
oir Director
ghton, Dana Sue
smetology Instructor
Gaye Sanders
urth Grade Teacher
mierski, James Daniel
alth Ed & Teen Ldrshp Tchr
en, Diana Essary
rd Grade Teacher
bardi, Maryam Jalali
th Department Chairman
k, Melinda Studer
nguage Arts Teacher
Irvin Marion, Jr.
story Instructor
ller, Eleanor Allen
athematics Teacher
phy, Martha Gibson
st & Second Grade Teacher
n, Beverly C.
glish IV Tchr & Dept Head
ardo, Mary Sue (Renick)
History Teacher
ser, Terry Nelson
ass Communications Instructor

Samuelson, M. Scott
9th-12th Grd Math Teacher
Trant, Robert M.
Accounting Instructor
Vetters, Imogene Stanley
11th Grd US History Teacher
White, G. Ray
Psychology Instructor
Williams, Betty Hinkle
Second Grade Teacher
Zeig, Nanette Sepolio
Language Arts Teacher
BUCKHOLTS
Aycock, Kenneth Donald
Vocational Agriculture Teacher
BUDA
Bray, Chas. Bruce
Band Director
Carlson, Donald G.
Earth Science Teacher
Gartzke, Hilda L.
Counselor
Herrington, Renee Ramey
Business Teacher
Johnson, Paula Herrel
Ninth Grade World Geog Tchr
Kirkpatrick, Phyllis Ann
Physical Sci & AP Bio Teacher
Leach, Victoria Lynn
GATE Facilitator & Tchr
Moeller, Paula J.
English Dept Chairperson
Schriever, Lesley Lenihan
6th Grade Math Teacher
BUFFALO
Leach, Tony Melvin
HS Mathematics Teacher
Van Nostrand, Terry Lynne
Science Teacher & Chairperson
BULLARD
Barron, Glenda Stanley
5th Grade Social Studies Tchr
Bossley, James Albern
High School Art Teacher
Godfrey, Cynthia Sue
Spanish & Dept Chprsn Teacher
Hippler, Tabitha Leanne
English Teacher
Lester, Virginia Masters
Fifth Grade Reading Teacher
Wood, Margie Elizabeth (Gee)
Second Grade Teacher
BULVERDE
Walker, Linda Kay
HS Math & Science Teacher
BUNA
Hunger, Timothy Ellwin
Band Director
Simmons, Kay Cobb
English & Journalism Teacher
BURKBURNETT
Barrick, LaVelda Rose
English Teacher
Bohuslav, Diana Awtrey
Writing Lab Teacher
Flory, Judy Marie
Third Grade Teacher
Fonville, Jeannie Hayes
English Teacher
McNeil, Curtis Alan
Secondary Biology Teacher
Moody, Camille Rose (Robey)
Spanish Teacher
Novak, Tim
Fifth Grade Teacher
Seman, Lee
Mathematics Teacher
West, Rebecca Rine
8th Grade English Teacher
BURKEVILLE
White, Cynthia LeDoux
Business & Computer Teacher
BURLESON
Bankston, Regina Lynn
Physical Education Teacher
Black, Barbara Nelson
Fifth Grade Teacher
Brock, Ann Williams
Teacher of the Gifted
Bruner, Charles Robert
English Teacher
Castillo, Doralee Garcia
Kindergarten Teacher
Daenzer, Valerie Truly
6th Grade Language Arts Tchr
Davis, Tracey Lane
Third Grade Teacher
Dublin, Rebecca Conly
8th Grade Mathematics Teacher
Eaton, John R.
Math Teacher
Shaha, W. Scott
World History Teacher & Coach
Smith, Mary Pritchett
Third Grade Teacher
Whisenant, Martha Ann (Smith)
Mathematics Tchr & Dept Chair
Willcoxon, Martha Jackson
Second & Third Grade Teacher
BURNET
Middlebrooks, Nancy Pattillo
5th Grade Teacher
Munsell, Melissa Hallmark
Social Studies Teacher
Neal, Gerald Robert
English Teacher
BURTON
Harmel, Charles D.
Social Stud Tchr & Head Coach

Stelter, Sharon Cook
World His, Govt & Ec Teacher
CADDO MILLS
Kirkpatrick, Kathy Grimes
Kindergarten Teacher
Partin, Rennda Raylene
English Teacher & Dept Chair
Smith, Bennie R.
Texas History Teacher & Coach
Stephenson, Betty Stuart
4th Grade Teacher
Walker, Carole Johnson
Third Grade Teacher
CALDWELL
Hiney, Robert Edward
8th Grade US History Teacher
Novosad, Vickie Jo (Malazzo)
7th Grade Reading Teacher
Oates, Sharon Walding
High School Art Teacher
Sellers, Cynthia Lynn
Elementary Counselor
Stefka, Deborah Ann
HS Mathematics Teacher
CAMERON
Lance, Kay Burney
HS Math Teacher
Liles, Linda Aaron
History Teacher
Tergerson, Jon Craig
Computer Science Teacher
CAMPBELL
Morgan, Sherri Cordell
English Teacher
Short, Marsha A.
4th-6th Grade Math Teacher
CANADIAN
Amerson, Phyllis Blanscet
Fifth Grade Teacher
Podzemny, Marea Lea
School Counselor
Stippel, Nova Smith
Reading Teacher
CANTON
Bailey, Susie Walden
Kindergarten Teacher
Chambless, Michael M.
Science Dept Chair & Teacher
Haldeman, Peggy Woolverton
Fourth Grade Teacher
Hilliard, Sue Caviness
Second Grade Teacher
Jordan, Mary Reese
English Teacher
Mitchell, Patti McLachlan
Office Education Teacher
Neely, Kimberly Soza
Spanish Teacher
Nixon, Jimmie Jones
English Teacher
Toups, Robley Louis
Band Director
Waters, Betty Tyer
High School Counselor
CANUTILLO
Estrada, Gloria
English Teacher & Coach
Lunceford, Lisa Elizabeth
Bus Ed, Trades & Industry Tchr
McMahan, Jerry L.
High School Math Teacher
White, Barbara S.
1st Grade Teacher
Zweber, Laura Jou (Welch)
Dance Teacher
CANYON
Bigham, Marsha Ellis
Government & World His Teacher
McCarter, Patricia Ann
Business Teacher
Munsell, Jane Kliewer
English Department Chairperson
Rickles, Shauna Blankenship
Home Economics Teacher
Skow, Leland Wayne
Mathematics Teacher
Teweleit, Russell Dean
Assistant Director of Bands
CANYON LAKE
Lindley, Nancy Richie
Science & Social Studies Tchr
CARRIZO SPRINGS
Adams, Ruby Jimenez
Speech, Theatre Tchr & Coach
Baker, Bonnie Moore
Math & Science Teacher
Escamilla, Hector Zaragoza
Teacher & English Dept Chm
Escamilla, Marcela M.
English Teacher
Escamilla, Ruben Zaragoza
English Teacher
Hartung, Harold Jack, Jr.
Health Teacher & Coach
Horton, Louise Wilkins
Assistant Librarian
Jackson, Doris Jean
Reading Teacher
Pacheco, Jose Nieves
Computer Literacy Teacher
Riha, Mary Price
Second Grade Teacher
Risinger, Gail J. Phillips
High School English Teacher
Salazar, Sandra Sauceda
High School Counselor
Ward, Lou Ella
Teacher's Asst & PE Dept Coach

CARROLLTON
Azzi, Zoe Ellen
AP European History Teacher
Bean, Martha Powel
Science Teacher
Bensend, Kari Lee
Health Teacher
Byrne, Erica Caroll
English Teacher
Cagle, James Lee
Math Teacher
Chiever, Carolyn Evans
English Teacher
Clark, Mary Baker
First Grade Teacher
Crandall, Caren Hollingsworth
German Teacher
DelSignore, Janet Lee
Sixth Grade Teacher
Doderer, Mark Sterling
HS Computer Science Teacher
Donaldson, Christine Gates
8th Grd Language Arts Teacher
Flynn, Ellenore Kordick
English Teacher
Fowler, Sheryl Stalcup
Health Teacher
Fried, Rhonda Faye
English Teacher
German, Patsy Byfield
Amer History & Hum Teacher
Giesey, Robert G.
Physical Education Teacher
Gilchrist, Paul Don
Orchestra Teacher
Hanus, Deborah A.
High School Mathematics Tchr
Keith, Gerald E.
World Geography Tchr & Coach
Kenney, Melody Lynn
Social Studies Teacher
Li, Michelle Aimee
English Teacher
Mancini, Joseph Ray
Spanish Teacher
Mannering, Dan Lester
Science Teacher & Head Coach
Mannering, Monique Frances
6th Grade Reading Teacher
Mayeur, Betty J.
English Teacher
Mc Comas, Jean
Art Teacher
McCreary, Barbara Hillebrenner
Algebra Teacher
Meade, Glenna Burns
Sixth Grade Teacher
Moore, Kelli Parker
Sixth Grade Teacher
Morris, Sandra Doughty
Creative Writing & Gifted Tchr
Myers, Christy Lurene
Orchestra Director
Newton, Bradley Robert
Education Specialist
Newton, Janet Jordy
Art Teacher
Palmer, Douglas Earl
Building Trades Teacher
Peters, Patrycia Atkinson
English Teacher
Pino, Susan Lynn
English Teacher
Post, Bedie J.
Astronomy & Science Teacher
Prytor, James Truett
Mathematics Teacher
Quinn, Doris E.
Secondary Teacher
Rachel, Richard W.
Math Teacher
Reese, Suzanne Meadows
Social Stud & Gifted Ed Tchr
Singer, Bonnie Whitmire
Fifth Grade Teacher
Smith, Kerry Lynn
Psychology Teacher
Stafford, Patricia Cunningham
Mathematics Teacher
Stallings, Bettye Ridgway
Counselor
Stell, Cynthia Critz
4th Grade Teacher
Tindel, Jacque Torbert
Teacher & Coordinator
Umbach, Keith Andrew
Jazz & Asst Bands Director
Wallace, Michael Alec
Tenth Grade English Teacher
CARTHAGE
Anderson, Shirley (Broadway)
Journalism Teacher
Ashby O Neal, Karon
Mathematics Instr & Dept Chair
Baushke, Judith Ann
Sixth Grade Science Teacher
Baysinger, Michael Scott
Biology Teacher
Bishop, Paul Wayne
History Teacher & Coach
Boland, John William
Social Studies Teacher
Bond, Rhonda Fullen
Special Education Teacher
Boone, Penny Smith
Home Economics Teacher
Cheshire, Carla Wallace
Third Grade Teacher
Cockrell, Lisa Brooks
Kindergarten Teacher

Gamble, Eva L.
Chemistry Tchr & Sci Dept Head
Jesurun, Elizabeth Boyer
Honors World History Teacher
Johns, Eva Holland
Vocational Adjustment Coord
Jones, Kaylan Mc Fadden
Second Grade Teacher
Marshall, Kimberley Wright
Art Teacher
Pyle, Celia Conwell
Biology Teacher
Sargent, Donald Charles
Spanish Department Chairman
Scott, Katherine Brady
Language Arts & Speech Teacher
Sims, Gerry Lynn
7th Grade Eng & Reading Tchr
CASTROVILLE
Arnold, Linda Nelson
Third Grade Teacher
Butler, John Gordon, Jr.
English Teacher
Chacon, Jo Seibert
8th Grd Eng & Spanish Teacher
Darter, Carl Gene
Special Ed Resource Teacher
Hagen, Carol Ewald
Computer Literacy Teacher
Huerta, David Curiel
Social Studies Teacher
Jackson, Susan Randle
Span & French Teacher
Jacobs, Jean J.
English Teacher
Thompson, Kimberly Ann
Spanish Teacher
Wurn, Kathleen DeCock
English Dept Coordinator
CAYUGA
Giles, Maurica Howell
Voc Home Ec & Art Teacher
Harper, Karen Sue
Chemistry Teacher
Kelley, Xan Sellers
Kindergarten Teacher
Link, Charla Ann
Reading Recovery Teacher
Moseley, Eric Stratton
Band Dir & Elem Music Teacher
CEDAR HILL
Bonner, Kelly Dane
PE & English Teacher
Brinkmeyer, Connie Burry
High School Teacher & Coach
Brown, Carol Neely
Honors & AP English Teacher
Cox, Rebecca Christine (Bland)
English Teacher
Emerson, Keri L.
High School Counselor
Farmer, Gina Kay
English I Pre AP Tchr & Coach
Garner, Michael James
Teacher
Grimes, Cynthia Cox
First Grade Teacher
Helfenbein, Kimberly Ann
World & AP European His Tchr
Hill, Michelle Denise
Physical Ed Teacher & Coach
Hough, Billy Mack
Office Admin Cooperative Tchr
Kirk, Joan Karen
Math Teacher
Maddox, Moshae Lynette
Career & Technology Teacher
Martin, Karen Walters
Foreign Language Dept Chprsn
Martin, Linda Holland
Art & Journalism Teacher
McMullen, Stacey Knight
Math Teacher
Megill, Marc John
Head Athletic Trainer
Miller, Lyn
Spanish Teacher
Walker, Joan B.
HS Mathematics Teacher
Wood, Barbara Starling
Business Education Teacher
CEDAR PARK
Hoeft, David A.
Principal & Music Teacher
Hoeft, Nathan Paul
Music Director
McKeever, Mary Alice
Science Teacher & Dept Head
Rodriguez, Elias P.
8th Grade Math Teacher
Sisler, Karen Jo
Principal
CELESTE
Sorrells, Suzanne
English & French Teacher
CENTER
Payne, Robert Rex
Math Teacher
CENTER POINT
Amster, Mary Anne Anderwald
Journalism & English Teacher
CENTERVILLE
Dunn, Lynn
Biology & Chemistry Teacher
Easterling, Connie
Health Teacher & Coach
Hammock, Patricia Lynn
Counselor & Kindergarten Tchr
Heil, Theresa Rodell
High School English Teacher

CENTERVILLE (cont)
Jackson, Vickie Box
Theater Arts & Speech Teacher
Pierce, Kathy Morgan
Sixth Grade Teacher
Stanford, Donnie W.
7th-11th Grade Science Teacher
CHANNELVIEW
Campbell, Sue Hopper
Fourth Grade Teacher
Carsey, Kathleen Cotter
HS English & French Teacher
Clark, Cindy Lou
Principal
Coats, Kelly
World Geography Teacher
Cory, Tamala Broadway
First Grade Teacher
Hyman, Patsy Jane
5th-6th Grd Choir & Elem Supvr
Lau, Georgia Graeter
Chemistry Tchr & Sci Dept Chm
Maybin, Charles Marvin
Agricultural Science Teacher
Moresco, Annette Edmundson
Teacher of Gifted & Talented
Sandel, Tony
Math Teacher
Seghers, Vanessa A.
Biology Teacher
Turner, Leigh Ann
Choral Director
VanDerKarr, Katlin Elizabeth
Eng, Sociology & Psych Teacher
Whitcomb, Rebecca Rose (Rodgers)
Retired HS Mathematics Teacher
CHANNING
Carey, Barbara Beadles
Career & Technology Teacher
CHARLOTTE
Collazo, Steve
High School Spanish Teacher
CHICO
Actkinson, Bobby Royace
Economics Teacher
CHILDRESS
Anders, Ronald Paul
Texas History Teacher
Davidson, Susan Mc Queen
Spanish Teacher
Jenkins, Zeldon
Chemistry & Physics Teacher
Long, Donna Eddins
Third Grade Teacher
Parker, Billye Cecelia (Weatherbee)
Classroom Teacher
CHILLICOTHE
Whitaker, Wanda
Retired Teacher
CHILTON
Little, Lisa Engelke
HS Math Teacher
Phelps, Ann Jones
High School Math Teacher
CHINA
Campbell, Ann Gaby
Third Grade Teacher
Martin, Candye Patricia
8th Grd Earth Science Teacher
Ridley, Molly Sue Kolander
First Grade Teacher
CHINA SPRING
Brenner, Herb
Band Director
Carruth, Christienne Lilly
English & Special Ed Teacher
Carruth, Richard V.
English I Teacher
Harris, Edna Oehlke
Science Teacher
Nelson, Linda Hughes
Computer, Math & Business Tchr
CHIRENO
Powers, Rita Hodge
Secondary Business Teacher
Sewell, Reagan L.
English & Biology Teacher
Wilson, Warner Percy, Jr.
Agricultural Science Teacher
CISCO
Muller, Katherine Fricke
Accounting & Mathematics Instr
Rains, Jeanne Bryant
Third Grade Teacher
White, William Wayne
Band Teacher
CLARENDON
Anglin, James William
Math Instr & Off Campus Coord
CLARKSVILLE
Bryant, Pamela Powell
Teacher of Gifted & Talented
Harris, Madge A.
7th Grade Teacher
Storey, Diane Robertson
Kindergarten Teacher
Whitney, Marc Aaron
Mathematics Teacher
CLAUDE
Minkley, Sally Loudder
English II, III & IV Tchr
CLEBURNE
Beatty, Kay Hindman
Second Grade Teacher
Bundock, Gene Bostick
High School Science Teacher
Ganong, Joyce Gilliam
Third Grade Teacher
Gonzalez, Estelita Rene
Spanish Teacher
Hadley, Norma Jean
Fourth Grade Teacher
Jones, JoNell Bailey
4th Grade Teacher
Mariott, Bernadine Conner
Math Teacher
Mc Clure, Barney Mike
Agriculture Science Teacher
Miles, Rebecca Lynn (Mc Gown)
English Teacher
Moser, Ann Bradley
Kindergarten Teacher
Sewell, Eddie N.
Social Studies Dept Head
Sloan, Marcia Rauch
Science Teacher
Smith, Lorna Crouch
Home Economics Teacher
Wall, C. Earl
Government & Economics Teacher
Weddel, Shelley Y.
Adult GED Teacher
Wollenschlager, Jean Giesler
Principal
CLEVELAND
Adams, Joyce O'Neill
Fifth Grade Math & Rdng Tchr
Ainsworth, Doyle Eugene
Computer Drafting Instructor
Chaney, Rennie Marshall
Physical Ed Teacher & Coach
David, Davy Lee
Biology Teacher & Coach
Haley, Janet Bay
Third Grade Teacher
CLIFTON
Evans, Dan Jerome
Retired High School Teacher
Evans, Nancy Carol
8th Grade Math Teacher
Sheppard, John D.
Retired Teacher
Thoede, Donald R.
Director of Bands
Thoede, Joan Kaska
English Teacher
Wise, Jo Carrol
7th-8th Grade History Teacher
Zuehlke, Lawrence David
Science Teacher
CLINT
Alvarez, Rudy C.
Math Tchr
Hoffmann, Leonard Richard
Math Teacher
Laffler, Cookie S.
HS Speech & Journalism Teacher
Laird, Alan Douglas
Science Dept Chair & Teacher
Ramirez, Luis Pineda
Spanish Teacher
CLUTE
Anderson, Mary Jane
Art Teacher
Blankenship, Mary Beth
French & English Teacher
Bryan, Anna Maise
Health Occupations Ed Teacher
Casey, Brian D.
Assistant Band Director
Hunt, Deason L.
Teacher & Publications Advisor
Lorms, David P.
Teacher & Coach
Mc Cutchan, R. David
Orchestra Director
Mitchell, Mary Hernandez
English Teacher
Quock, Lai Sid
Mathematics Teacher
Simpson, Brian Chandler
Mathematics Tchr & Vlybl Coach
Vallone, George John
Assistant Principal
White, Ronald Lynn
Fine Arts Dept Chairperson
CLYDE
Black, Nora Jordan
Dyslexia Teacher
Broadfoot, Charlene Lenker
Third Grade Teacher
Brown, Carla
Computer Science Teacher
Law, Kenon, Jr.
History Teacher
Mantooth, Janice White
Fifth Grade Teacher
Steph, Barbara Thomas
Third Grade Teacher
COAHOMA
Mc Lean, Mark Kenneth
Industrial Technology Teacher
COLDSPRING
Creech, Royce Lynn
Band Dir & Fine Arts Dept Chr
COLEMAN
Brown, Bonnie Jean (Kennedy)
Home Economics Teacher
Cardinas, Vicki Maedgen
Science Teacher
Cox, Barbara Mae
Biology Teacher & Coach
Steele, Shanna Lee
Family Nurse Practitioner
COLLEGE STATION
Angel, Travis L.
Fine Arts Chair & Choral Dir
Averitt, Dennis Ross
Sixth Grade Reading Teacher
Bevans, Jami Foy
High School Art Teacher
Boles, Walter Wesley
Asst Prof of Civil Engineering
Brereton, Todd Richard
Lecturer
Briaud, Jean-Louis
Professor of Civil Engineering
Caton, Jerald A.
Professor of Mechanical Engrng
Ernst, Mary Anne Olsen
Second Grade Teacher
Frenkel, Michael
Adjunct Professor of Chemistry
Ganze, Jane Thomason
Fourth Grade Teacher
Henry, James Lee
High School Guidance Counselor
Hoelscher, Anita Clark
7th-8th Grade Speech Teacher
Holtzapple, Mark Thomas
Chemical Engrng Assoc Prof
Klein, Gregory Stephen
Lecturer
Kohutek, Terry Lee
Senior Lecturer
Kosztolnyik, Zoltan J.
Professor of History
Lalk, Thomas Robert
Assoc Prof of Mechanical Engrn
Larson, David Royal
Mathematics Professor
Lowery, Lee Leon, Jr.
Professor of Research Engineer
Lowy, Susan Wagner
Sr Lecturer of Kinesiology
Miner, David Sean
Chemistry Teacher
Morrow, Eva M. Garrett
Assistant Lecturer Stu Tchrs
Pineda-De-Gyvez, Jose J.
Electrical Engrng Asst Prof
Riley, Cindy Sparkman
Eighth Grade English Teacher
Rizzo, Dorothy Borski
Mathematics Teacher
Robertson, Deborah Daws
6th Grade Social Studies Tchr
Roschke, Paul N.
Associate Professor
Ruoff, Lynn Marie
Lecturer of Veterinary Anatomy
Sanders, Rex M.
US History Teacher & Coach
Scott, Timothy Patton
Lecturer & Undergraduate Adv
Shellenberger, Melina M.
Eng III Tchr & Stu Cncl Spon
Wellborn, Lindy Jackson
High School Mathematics Tchr
Wellmann, Courtney Haggard
English & Journalism Teacher
White, Christy Smithwick
PE Teacher & Coach
White, Ron W.
Orchestra Director
Williams, Linda Valigura
Sixth Grade Math Teacher
Wolfenden, Alan
Prof of Mechanical Engineering
Womack, Raby Beakley
Second Grade Teacher
Woodfin, Robin Stacy
Spanish Teacher
COLLEYVILLE
Allen, Julie Ann
Choral Music Teacher
Brunson, Harold Elliott, Jr.
History & English Teacher
Culberson, James Kevin
HS Social Studies & Math Tchr
Duncan, Nancy Jane
8th Grade English Teacher
Goodwin, Caroline Morgan
Gifted & Talented Reading Tchr
Haley, Kimberly Kay
6th Grade Physical Educator
Jones, Pamela Susan
Language Arts GATE Teacher
Kirby, Martha Elise
8th Grade Math Teacher
Mc Cord, Kathryn Stevenson
Spanish Teacher
Peretti, Beth Bryant
Campus Technologist
Sanders, Ronny Othel
Social Studies Teacher
Sass, Mignon Louise
English & History Teacher
Votto, Jan Alyne Welsh
English & Reading Teacher
Wrenn, Ruthanne Bloyd
Middle School Teacher
COLLINSVILLE
Bedford, David Ray
Mathematics Teacher & Coach
Latham, Norman Dale, Jr.
Agricultural Science Teacher
Mc Horse, Patty Webb
Eng, Health, Theater Arts Tchr
COLMESNEIL
Butler, Steven Ray
High School Math Teacher
COLORADO CITY
Claxton, Marcy Allene
Mathematics Teacher
Lemonds, Teresa Ann
Kindergarten Teacher
Lemons, Joan Gover
Business Computer Teacher
Mathis, Linda J.
Physical Education & Art Tchr
Reeves, Fern
Former Substitute Teacher
COLUMBUS
Davis, Kecia
HS PE & Athletics Teacher
Hayward, Deborah L.
Secondary Special Ed Teacher
Leopold, Gary Joe
8th Grade Math Teacher
Sunderman, Cynthia Spanihel
Mathematics & Religion Teacher
Teltschik, Sophie Rouse
Home Economics Teacher
Zimmerhanzel, Wayne Harlan
High School Teacher & Coach
COMANCHE
Kasberg, Patricia A.
Kindergarten Teacher
Lively, Mary Hanson
Math Teacher
McDougal, James Francis
Agricultural Science Teacher
COMBES
DeLaGarza, Joel Santiago, Sr.
Assistant Principal
Hudnall, Elizabeth Hunter
HOSTS Teacher
COMFORT
Davis, Mark Bradley
Fourth Grade Teacher
Schneider, Rose-Marie Bartel
Computer Applications Teacher
Smith, Bob
US History Teacher & Coach
COMMERCE
Hendrix, Mary White
Dir of Educational Partnership
Overduin, Henry
Acting Department Head
Rudoff, Judith Kidd
Spanish Teacher
Wyse, Mary Dishongh
Sophomore English Teacher
COMO
Elmore, Jan Lile
HS Science & Math Instructor
Evans, Patsy Matthews
Counselor
Mc Elroy, Jacquelyn Mercedes Wise
Art & Drama Teacher
CONROE
Allen, Lewis DeWayne
Social Studies Teacher & Coach
Balusek, Dennis A.
Exploring Technology Teacher
Barber, Craig Alan
Technology Education Teacher
Bonner, Judy Ann
4th Grade Language Arts Tchr
Brooks, Wanda Bergen
Span Tchr & Frgn Lang Team Ldr
Bruce, Cherlynn Kay
1st Grade Teacher
Counts, Belynda Mc Mullan
Kindergarten Teacher
Crawford, Jayne Cutsinger
Kindergarten Teacher
Dias, Peter Franklin
Drama Director
Dinkins, Jean Waller
Business, Computer & Voc Tchr
Gibson, Elizabeth Brown
5th-6th Grade Math & Sci Tchr
Greer, Cheri Emanis
Artistic Director & Owner
Gregory, Denise Mc Coy
Mathematics Teacher
Harrington, Twyla A.
English Teacher
Harwood, Bonnie Humphrey
High School Fine Arts Tchr
Herndon, Norma Meyer
Speech Comm & Jrnlsm Teacher
Keller, Susan Kay
6th Grade Teacher
Knott, Karen P.
HS Mathematics Teacher
Larza, Garnett M.
7th Grd Texas History Teacher
Lockwood, Bob
Economics Teacher
Mc Cutcheon, Alice Cangemi
Math Teacher
Milliff, Karen Champagne
Social Studies Teacher
Oberthier, Cynthia Bodemann
Mathematics Teacher
Peoples, Frances Knight
Social Studies Teacher
Pliler, Virginia P.
English Teacher
Pratt, Wesley Alan
Mathematics Teacher & Coach
Preble, Joy Brown
English Teacher
Rapp, Danielle Brasher
Dance Tchr & Drill Team Dir
Reid, Cynthia K.
Art Teacher
Rippetoe, Scott
Physics Tchr & Sci Dept Chair
Robertson, Clay Randall
US History Teacher
Salak, Kathy Ann
4th Grade Teacher
Simmers, Patrick H.
Athletic Director & Coach
Smith, Deanna Marie
8th Grade US History Teacher
Spell, Ava Bargmann
Biology Teacher
Stinson, Janie (Kieke)
Speech Pathologist
Suchma, David Alan
Business Teacher & Coach
Tamborello, Virginia Slade
Biology Teacher & Chairperson
Thrasher, Nancy Robertson
Fourth Grade Teacher
Tingle, Janet Kay
PE & Health Care Science Tchr
Tyler, Gail Thompson
3rd Grade Teacher
Vogel, Dolly Sutton
Eighth Grade Math Teacher
Wilkerson, Karen Michele
8th Grade History Teacher
Wilson, Barry Leonard
Social Studies Teacher & Coach
CONVERSE
Anderson, George Emery
Asst Aerospace Science Instr
Arteaga, Kathleen Marie
Spanish Teacher
Bading, Barbara Mc Gonagil
School-Age Parenting Coord
Baumann, Larry Wayne
Secondary Math Teacher
Booker, Marcus A.
Health & PE Teacher
Bushala, Jeraldine Louise
HS Social Studies Teacher
Carlton, Sharon Fike
High School Counselor
Castaneda, Tony
Soccer Coach & PE Teacher
Chambers, William Richard
Third Grade Teacher
Hamilton, Gus
Mathematics Teacher
Harris, Scott Kellam
Honors World His Tchr & Coach
Hartmann, David W.
Language Arts Teacher
Housing, Raymond Charles
Physical Science Teacher
Johnson, Karen Cahill
Psychology Teacher
Lamothe, Richard Roland
Bus Cmptr Prgramming Tchr
Mc Mahon, Peter John
Career Studies Teacher
Medford, Tandy Otekia
Sophomore English Teacher
Moreno, Victoria Robinson
Home Economics Teacher
Oliveros, Rosa Vital
Spanish Teacher
Pope, Jacob V., Jr.
High School Art Teacher
Richmond, Mary Ann Mc Kenzie
Biology Teacher
Robinson, Rebecca M.
Classroom Teacher
Rutledge, Dudley William
Athletic Coordinator
Seale, Rose Ann Lozano
Health Science Tech Instructor
Selman, Jeanette W.
German & English Teacher
Slatton, Brenda Kay Johnson
Journalism Teacher & Yrbk Spon
Stanson, Kay Rasmussen
6th Grade Science Teacher
Vahek, Brenda Kay
Mathematics Teacher
Weishaar, James Arthur
Physics Teacher
Woodlief, Ellamae S.
Child Care Guid & Mgmt Teacher
Woodrome, Michael Randy
Assistant Choral Director
COOPER
Ingram, Debra Rose
Teacher & Technology Coord
Mc Fadden, Deborah A.
8th Grade Teacher
Rainey, Tina Johnson
Second Grade Teacher
COPPELL
Ackerman, Molly Board
Spanish Teacher
Armes, Lori Gene
Spanish Teacher
Bloomer, Sid
Geometry & Algebra I Teacher
Bratton, Shona Lea
Director of Speech & Debate
Cook, Linda Austin
Science Tchr & Dept Head
Curliss, David W.
Geometry Tchr & Baseball Coach
Green, Sandra Miller
Home Economics Teacher
Griffin, Jim
History, Govt Teacher & Coach
Howard, Carla Burt
2nd Grade Teacher
Jackson, Jane Ellen
Phys Educator & Tennis Coach
Jensen, Daniel E.
Math Teacher
Jones, Eric Leslie
AP Biology Teacher
Kass, Kimberly Drda
Chemistry Teacher

LL (cont)
aren Ann
& Talented Teacher
nice Ferris
/ Teacher
, Joan Deckinger
a & Pre-Algebra Teacher
illian Kolar
rade Teacher
ken, Jenny Jones
, Content Mastery Tchr
, Jolene Webster
Director
renda Railsback
er
Brenda L.
ade Teacher
Diana Marie
stry & Physics Teacher
Ron-Marie Ann
ting Coordinator
RAS COVE
, Katherine Taylor
Science Teacher
Elva Carreon
h Teacher
Michael William
Geography Teacher
lt, Judy R. (Vise)
uter Literacy Teacher
, Donita Jean
Ed Coord & DECA Advisor
, John David
s English III Teacher
, Virginia Louise
n Grade Teacher
venyth R.
h Grade Reading Teacher
, Dawn M.
School Home Ec Teacher
, Frederick Mark
rade Math Teacher
, Suzanne Welch
er Teacher
ki, Francis Craig
n Grade History Teacher
Jesse Paul
ology & Sociology Teacher
ff, Vicki Dianne
tant Principal
el, Mary L.
Teacher & Dept Chair
s, Robert Clark
outer Science Teacher
Mary Kay (Weghorst)
& Teen Involvement Teacher
end, Sammye Lynn
outer Literacy Teacher
, Vicki Perryman
Teacher
US CHRISTI
Goldie Bowles
ergarten & Bilingual Tchr
illo, Juan Antonio (Tony)
School Art Teacher
illo, Linda Rodriguez
h Grade Teacher
a, Laura Nelly
ish Teacher
Eugene Patrick
Teacher
ow, Betty Jean
Grade Elementary Teacher
Diane Dyer
ish Teacher
n, Renie Washburn
mediate School Principal
off, Whitney Rogers
Prof of Nrsng & Hlth Sci
nard, Rosario Munoz
Grade Teacher
, Aaron Sank
ial Education Teacher
er, Martha C.
ral Director
bell, Nancy Getz
or English & AP Teacher
Barbara Arleen Silberman
ogy Teacher
a, Raymond, Jr.
n School Band Director
Mary Ann Castilla
Grade Teacher
s, Jeff
ch & Teacher
, Cliff
ch & Physical Ed Teacher
, Sherri Lynn
ech & Theatre Arts Tchr
a Pena, Roy
Teacher & Coach
oss, Pennie Clements
t Grade Teacher
e, Richard Leon
Grade History Teacher
erson, Janet Hoskins
rld History Teacher
ich, Charlene
eatre Director
r, Kathryn Arkwright
enth Grade Math Teacher
n, Kenneth
fessor of English
, Beverly Crawford
nors & AP US History Teacher
es, Anna Maria
th Grade Teacher
, Richard Kirby
ricultural Science Teacher

Frank, Carolyn Bowren
English Teacher
Freeman, Marlo Tarice
English & Theater Arts Teacher
Gaddis, Joye L.
Home Economics Teacher
Gadell, Michael Lee
Assoc Professor of Kinesiology
Garcia, Maria Eureste
Teacher of Gifted & Talented
Garza, Roland C.
Social Studies Teacher
Germany, Joyce Mikulencak
Science Teacher
Glenn, Laura Gaye
Math Dept Chairman & Teacher
Godoy, Ricardo Alonzo
English Department Chairperson
Gonzales, Elizabeth Aldape
6th Grade Language Arts Tchr
Guerra, Annette Stein
6th-8th Grd Language Arts Tchr
Gutierrez, Lupe
Teacher & Coach
Hamilton, Mary Jane
Undergrad Coord Dept of Nrsng
Hammond, Christine A.
English Teacher
Harris, Valerie J.
5th Grade Teacher
Hart, Brian
Asst Prof of History
Harwell, Nancy C. (Matlock)
Teacher of Gifted & Talented
Hatch, Sherri J.
Anatomy Teacher
Hite, James Harvill
Ath Coord & Head Ftbl Coach
Hodges, Leticia Paniagua
Mathematics & Science Teacher
Holt-Henderson, Brenda
Theatre Arts Teacher
Huntsman, Louann
Business Teacher
Isaacs, Ronald R.
Economics Teacher & Coach
Jensen, Valda Maeckel
First Grade Teacher
Johnson, Linda Anne (Shaughnessy)
English Teacher
Johnson, Mary L.
Social Studies & Psych Teacher
Johnston, Diana Hanshaw
Mathematics Teacher
Jones, Bobby Gene
High School History Teacher
Jones, Lynda A. J.
Art Teacher & Fine Arts Chprsn
LaPointe, Nancy Marie
English Teacher
Laudadio, Peggy Osborne
Assoc Prof of Court Reporting
Laursen, Pamela Anne
Kndgtn & 1st Grd Principal
Livengood, Kimberly Kay
Chemistry Teacher
Lopez, Oralia Escobar
French Teacher
Lupo, Tom
Physical Education Teacher
Martin, Bonnie Collins
Chemistry Teacher
Martinez, Melva Lopez
Spanish Teacher
Mata, Maria G. (Lupita)
Sixth Grade Teacher
Mc Cormick, John Rickert
French & Math Teacher
Medina, Patricia Ann Gonzalez
World Geography Teacher
Milnar, Courtney Ann
Intinerant Band Director
Moore, Diane Elaine (May)
Fourth Grade Teacher
Moore, Mary Winklmann
Directress
Morrow, Daniel Thomas
World History & Geography Tchr
Moss, Camilla
Math Teacher
Mott, Gary Stephen
Theatre Teacher
Nelson, Sheryl Lynn
Marketing Teacher
North, Judy L.
Kindergarten Teacher
Oliveira, Denise D.
Speech Pathologist
Oliveira, Olga Hinojosa
Texas History Teacher
Pailes-Krause, Pamela S.
Young Peoples Theater Director
Pickett, J. Michael
AP Govt Teacher & Dept Chrmn
Picozzi, Kimberly Winburn
English Teacher
Piercefield, Lois Wafer
English Teacher
Primozic, Daniel Thomas
Asst Professor of Philosophy
Ragsdale, Freda Geary
English Teacher
Ransleben, Suzanne DeMouche
Honors English Teacher
Reyna, Frank, III
Engrng, Arch & CAD Tchr
Rezarch, Robert Carl
Sci Tchr of Gifted & Talented
Robeau, Sally Garwood
History Teacher

Rodriguez, Cleto E.
Algebra Teacher
Russell, Jimmie Daniel
Band Director
Schroeder, Kay (Howell)
8th Grade Science Teacher
Seaberry, Judy D.
School Counselor
Shufelt, Patricia McQuaid
Assistant Professor
Simms, Selia Garcia
Third Grade Teacher
Skinner, Robert Eugene
French Teacher
Smith, Nancy Creel
Associate Professor
Stalmach, Linda Cover
Fourth Grade Teacher
Tajchman, Susie Nemec
First Grade Teacher
Taylor, Ruth A.
Lang Arts & Soc Stud Teacher
Thomas, Leston Michael
Biology & Health Teacher
Thornton, Shirley Nowlin
English Teacher
Trees, Jay Franklin
Agricultural Science Teacher
Trevino, Elizabeth Martinez
Fifth Grade Teacher
Vasquez, Melinda
8th Grade Math & Algebra Tchr
Veech, Anne
History Teacher
Vegh, Linda Libasci
English & Humanities Teacher
Walston, Beverly Smith
Computer Tchr & Tech Coord
Wester, Sandra Brenneman
Science Teacher
Whiteley, Michael Austin
Mathematics Teacher
Wilkins, Barbara Jean
Kindergarten Teacher
Wood, Cheri Johnson
Biology Teacher
Wood, Michael Gray
Associate Professor of Biology
Young, Carl Travis, Jr.
Mathematics Teacher
Zonick, Veronica Counihan
Biology Teacher
CORRIGAN
Austin, Diana Mickel-Monroe
English Teacher
Bates, Susan Heron
Mathematics Tchr & Dept Chprsn
Bostick, Ray
Jr High Principal
Harvey, Kathleen Ruth
8th Grade English Teacher
Powell, Ann O'Quinn
English Teacher
Scarborough, Marty E'Lisa
Second Grade Teacher
Stephens, Sonja Havard
Biology & Business Ed Tchr
Vance, Dena Alfred
Math Teacher & Dept Chm
CORSICANA
Batchelor, Carolyn Reynolds
Math Teacher
Curington, Mona D.
Biology Teacher & Sci Dept Chm
Dillman, Lisa Caye (Lowe)
Biology Instructor
Duncan, Stephen L.
Accounting Instructor
Dunlap, Martha Grady
Home Economics Teacher
Edens, Rita Jane
Social Science Dept Chprsn
Ellis, Jo Beth
Dyslexia Therapist
Garner, John Joel, Jr.
Management & Business Instr
Goodman, Sharon Stubbs
Literature & Speech Teacher
Green, Randy Lee
World History Teacher & Coach
Herrington, Linda LaRue
6th Grade Science Teacher
Hill, Bobbie Jo
Math & Science Teacher
Miller, Richard E.
Professor of Psychology
Newton, Joanne Barron
Math Teacher
Newton, Rick Lee
Coach & US History Teacher
O'Dell, Betty Perkins
English Second Language Tchr
Piel, Deborah (Luther)
English Teacher
Robinson, Sharon Lassiter
6th Grade History Teacher
Rushing, Maude A.
English Teacher
Stringer, Tommy W.
Div of Humanities Director
Timmerman, Linda Davis
English Instructor
Williams, Patricia Martin
7th Grade Language Arts Tchr
COTTON CENTER
Buffa, Robert Matthew
US History & PE Teacher
COTULLA
Canales, Rita Beck
History Teacher & Dept Chprsn

Daughtrey, Judy Germer
Home Economics Teacher
Patterson, Linda Maria
High School Science Teacher
CRANDALL
Bailey, Gwen Goodwin
Language Arts & Health Teacher
Dowlearn, Janice Walton
Library Media Specialist
Thompson, Norman Allan
Science Teacher
Waits, Mea-Joy King
Retired Teacher
Williams, Todd
Assistant Principal
CRANE
Beverly, Diana Chubb
Physical Education Teacher
Cass, Paula Davidson
Second Grade Teacher
Crumrine, Judy Butler
Algebra Teacher
Ford, Benni Anne (McDaniel)
4th Grade Teacher
Harrelson, Laurie D'Lynn Cheatham
Fifth Grade Teacher
Heath, Jimmy Ray, Jr.
Math & Physics Teacher
Ifera, Raymond Philip
World Geography & US His Tchr
Vasquez, Mary Dolores
Spanish Teacher
Weis, Leslie Homer, Jr.
Physical Sci Teacher & Coach
CRANFILLS GAP
Cox, Larry Cornelious
Soc Stud, Bus & Aviation Tchr
Dickey, Kenneth Edward
English & Language Arts Tchr
CRAWFORD
Kelm, Delbert Kenneth
Math Teacher & Coach
CROCKETT
Mize, Beverly Moses
English IV Teacher
Petty, Melissa Mc Kinney
Chemistry Teacher
Piland, Jo Adams
5th Grade Science Teacher
CROSBY
Aiken, Martha Estes
Second Grade Teacher
Bench, Carolyn Mc Swain
World History Teacher
Clevinger, Terry L.
AP Calculus & Honors Geom Tchr
Dusek, Madelyn Rod
Science Dept Chair & Teacher
Green, Robert Wayman
Earth Science Teacher
Greene, Melinda Martin
Pre-AP English Teacher
Heaslet, Don L.
Middle School Band Director
Hurst, Ettie Scantlen
Librarian
Jackson, Ann Simpson
English Teacher & Dept Chair
La Fear, Sherry Mouton
School Counselor
Neuman, Deborah Jean (Rock)
Spanish Teacher & Dept Chair
Owen, Paula Wray
Mathematics Teacher
Ramon, Mary Jeanine
English Teacher
Waihman, Lisa G.
Mathematics Teacher
Walsingham, Mary Ann
6th Grade Reading Tchr, Chprsn
Worthen, Phyllis E. Lisa
HS & MS Music Teacher
CROSBYTON
Morris, Bessie Smith
English Teacher
CROSS PLAINS
Barclay, Thomas Adison
Math Teacher
Coppinger, Joe Kenneth
High School English Teacher
Fullen, Robbye S.
Spanish & English Teacher
CROWELL
Bowman, Sharon Linker
Business & Computer Teacher
Gidney, Billye Jeanette (Bell)
English & Spelling Teacher
Mayes, Darren Kent
History Tchr & Athletic Dir
Scarbrough, Susan Peters
Teacher
CROWLEY
Arnold, Linda F.
Health & Phys Education Tchr
Crowley, Barbara Elaine
Counselor
Hardisty, Linda Castle
Mathematics Teacher
Holley, Kerry Kathleen
Science Teacher
Krueger, Robert T.
Eighth Grade English Teacher
Leach, Michael Norman
Student Activities Admin Asst
Manning, Danny E.
Lead Assistant Principal
Martin, Patricia Denis
Spanish Teacher
McGuire, Joe Newton
Special Ed & English Teacher

Mc Lean, Sara C.
US History & Sociology Teacher
Mitchell, Jim
Secondary Art Teacher
Munford, Julia Alzine
German Teacher
Pokluda, Diane Miller
4th Grade Teacher
Ptacek, Cher Leach
English Teacher
Richardson, Georgia Ann Jordan
American History Teacher
Rue, Joye Blackmon
Government Teacher
Rueter, Christy A.
Secondary Art Teacher
Stevens, Steve
US Government Teacher
Tomlinson, Becky Durham
Junior English Teacher
Williams, David Odell
Economics & Government Teacher
Wilson, Kay Kyle
History & English Teacher
Woods, Ellisann Burt
Volleyball Coach & Teacher
Wynne, Paul Tannahill
Chemistry Teacher
Yount, Barbara Parish
American Sign Language Teacher
CRYSTAL CITY
Gomez, Dora Elva
6th & 7th Grade English Tchr
Moreno, Rebecca Ciprian
High School English Teacher
CUERO
Benner, Terry D.
Coach
Carlson-Henion, Wendy J.
Senior English Teacher
Colman, Linda Kuester
Chemistry Teacher
Duff, Mary Beth
Voc Ed & Bus Computer Teacher
Janssen, Lyn
Sophomore English Teacher
Kirk, Ada Koenig
English Tchr
Post, Sara Armstrong
Government & Economics Teacher
Pullin, Clay Wilson
Probation Officer
Roark, Ryan Douglas
World Geography Teacher
CYPRESS
Burke, Lisa Cooper
Math Teacher
Harms, Janice L. Huhmann
Math Teacher
Kessler, Donald Paul
Vocational Auto Tech Teacher
Little, Susan Elizabeth Carter
Physical Education Teacher
Mc Aneny, Pamela Murray
6th Grade Language Arts Tchr
Pekkanen, Cindy Dearth
US History Teacher
Thomas, Arnold Lee
Head Athletic Trainer
Waldrop, Linda Joan Lopeman
Reading Teacher
Walters, Gwendolynn Van Dusen
Sixth Grade Language Arts Tchr
D HANIS
Tschirhart, Glynn W.
Business Teacher
DAINGERFIELD
Gauntt, Anthony Adam
Government & Economics Teacher
Leppert, Stephanie A.
Math Teacher
Loyd, Nancy J.
Junior English Teacher
Walker, Judy Grace
4th Grade Teacher
DAISETTA
Little, Grace B.
2nd Grade Teacher
Ringer, Paula Hollenshead
Mathematics Teacher
Saucier, Walton E.
AG Science Instr & Voc Dir
Spivey, Candace Read
English Teacher
Walker, Addie Stewart
Biology & Chemistry Teacher
DALHART
Green, Jon J.
Mathematics Department Chair
Hand, M. Scott
Math Tchr & Technology Coord
Methvin, Carroline Mc Gee
Science Tchr & Department Head
Przilas, Kay Clara Koch
5th-6th Grade Teacher
Smith, James
Teacher, Coach & Admin Asst
DALLAS
Abbe, John A.
Mathematics Teacher
Adams, James C.
Graphic Arts Instructor
Adams, Thomas S.
History Teacher
Adkisson, Sandra Jean
Second Grade Teacher
Aguirre, Penny Milynda
Debate Coach
Alexander, Doris Hunter
Retired Spanish Teacher

DALLAS (cont)
Alfers, Kenneth Gerald
History Professor
Allen, Wilma Turner
Teacher of Talented & Gifted
Anzaldua, Cynthia Veronica
Visual Arts Department Chair
Arnold, Cecelia Henson
2nd Grade Teacher
Arnswald, Barbara Anne
6th Grade Lang Arts Teacher
Ashmore, Marion Kathryn Tracy
Fifth Grade Math Teacher
Atlee, Linda Kathryn
Office Careers Instructor
Babb, Judy Killen
Journalism Teacher
Baker, Lori Anne
English & History Teacher
Balden, Anne Simmons
English Teacher & Dept Chprsn
Baldor, Juan Antonio
Spanish Professor
Ball, Jennie
Journalism Program Director
Balthrop, Sandra Stover
Counselor & Psychology Teacher
Barber, Luke Eugene
Professor of Philosophy
Barkley, Susan Ellen Ragsdale
Fr, Travel & Tourism Instr
Barley, Kathy Jane
Physical Education Teacher
Baskin, Douglas Averill
Band Director
Baty, Nedra Ann (Thompson)
5th Grade Lang Arts Teacher
Bausch, Barb Rausch
6th Grade Teacher
Baxter, Jerry Dean
Choral Director
Beadles, Carmen Lide
Science Teacher
Beasley, Stacy Ann
Spanish Teacher
Beeler, Barbara G.
Principal
Behreud, Elisabeth Kugel
6th Grade Homeroom Tchr
Beidel, Mary Kristen
Hlth, Anatomy, Physiology Tchr
Bell, Esther Price
Fourth Grade Math Teacher
Bell, William Everett, Jr.
Dean Coll of Rel & Philosophy
Bendy, G. T.
ESOL Teacher
Benson, Paul Francis
Professor of Humanities
Berbarie, Dulce Maria
Spanish Teacher
Bishop, Leonard Eugene
Physical Education Teacher
Blagburn, Curtis Wayne
Science Teacher
Blanton Glorioso, Barbara
Bio & Environmental Sci Tchr
Blaydes, Rod P.
Drama Director
Bob, Mary Easley
Keyboarding Teacher
Bolton, Lynn Thompson
French Teacher
Boone, Julie Hunter
Reading Teacher
Bostick, Autry Jerome
English & Social Studies Tchr
Boykins, Earlene Whittenberg
Media Specialist
Brew, Eleita Williams
Physical Education Teacher
Bristol-White, Anne
Theater & Journalism Teacher
Britt, Rebecca Ann
3rd Grade ESL Teacher
Brooks, Patricia Lohman
Second Grade Teacher
Brosette, Camille Marlene
5th Grade Self-Contained Tchr
Brown, Evelyn Sheffield
Language Arts & Reading Tchr
Brown, James Edward
Physical Education Teacher
Brown, Joan Leslie
Math Teacher
Brown-Bell, Karen Teresa
World Geography Tchr
Bryan, Delna Lorenza
Spanish Teacher
Burns, Barbara A.
Professor of Communications
Burns, John Lanier, Sr.
Professor & Chprsn of Theology
Burr, Bryan Scott
History, Bible & Art Teacher
Butler, Karla Renee (Key)
Lang Arts & Foreign Lang Tchr
Byrd, Patricia Green
Fifth Grade Teacher
Calden, Karl Kevin
Science Teacher
Caldwell, Lynn W.
Director of Guidance
Calhoun, Barbara Jean
Third Grade Teacher
Callahan, Clara R.
Math Teacher
Campers, Gloria Leonard
Lang Arts & Soc Stud Teacher
Cannon, Donna Lynn
Third Grade Teacher
Carlson, Catherine Kossan
Sci Teacher & Dept Chairperson
Carmichael, John Craig, Jr.
Career Academic Counselor
Carol, Barbara Marie
4th Grade Teacher
Carter, Celeste Peyton
Mathematics Instructor
Carter, Melinda T.
Mathematics Teacher
Cates, Martha Ann DeCharles
World Geography Teacher
Chambliss, Charlotte M.
Instructor of Visual Arts
Chambliss, Ginny Ricci
Ec, Sociology & Psych Teacher
Cherry, Patricia Washington
Reading Teacher
Chester, Demetria LaRae
Chemistry Teacher
Churchman, Mary Hearn
Jewelry Teacher
Clark, Sylvia Jefferson
Office Education Tchr & Coord
Cockrell, Margaret Peggy
Counselor & Teacher
Coder, Kay
Sociology Professor
Cogdill, Karon Leigh
Theatre Teacher
Coggan, Patricia Conner
Fourth Grade Teacher
Cole, Leta Denning
ESOL Teacher
Cole, Sheri Dale
Guidance Counselor
Cole-Geason, Debra Faye
Second Grade Teacher
Collett, Penne Booras
English Teacher & Dept Chair
Colson, Terry Lee
MS Mathematics Teacher
Conaway, O'Lysia Bowden
Second Grade Teacher
Conner, Carolyn Scott
First Grade Teacher
Cox, Pamela Welsh
2nd-6th Grade Teacher
Crawford, Doris Greer
GATE, Computer Technology Tchr
Criswell, Rosi L.
Third Grade ESL Teacher
Crotty, Mark Joseph
English Tchr & Writing Ctr Dir
Crouse, Susan Brown
Biology & Physics Teacher
Cummings, Vanessa Johnson
Special Education Teacher
Cummins, Cindy Faulkner
Language Arts Teacher
Cundiff, Janet Barnes
Kindergarten Teacher
Custer, Mary Johnson
4th Grade Teacher
Daniels, Vivian Bernice
Business Teacher
Davenport, Alice Martinez
Physical Education Teacher
Davis, Alice (Thompson)
First & Second Grade Teacher
Davis, Willis Ray
Math Teacher
Dean, Sherry Lynn
French & Speech Comm Instr
Deeves, John Francis
Physics & Theology Teacher
Degen, Michael E.
English Teacher
DeJesus, Teresa E.
Bilingual Kindergarten Teacher
Delabano, Martin Foley
Art Teacher & Student Cncl Adv
Delafield Frazier, Mary Ann
8th Grade Lang Arts Teacher
Delaney, Michael D.
Mathematics Teacher
Dickinson, Sharon Rose
Business Dept Chair
Dillard, Mary Harris
AP English Tchr & Dept Chrmn
Donnell, Carolyn Roberts
Fine Arts Teacher
Dorn, Sally A.
Elementary Coordinator
Dorsey, Joyce
Librarian
Douglas, Bertha
Fifth Grade Teacher
Draper, Sherry Chwerchak
1st Grade Teacher
Dubsky, Richard Leslie
Mathematics Dept Chairman
Duckworth, Paula Oliver
English Teacher & Art Sponsor
Dunk, Timothy Carl
Board of Education Chairman
Dunn, Colleen D.
Math Teacher
Durrett, Jo Ruth Jordan
Eng Dept Head & Jrnlsm Spon
Eades, Thelma Lee
English Teacher
Ehrich, Lisa Michele
Art Professor
Ellis, Susan Louise
PE & Soccer Coach
English, Lewis Donald
Sophomore English Teacher
Ennis, Linda Larche
Sixth Grade Math Teacher
Ensley, Richard Lawrence
Algebra & Geometry Teacher
Eubanks, Marsha G.
Chemistry Teacher
Evans, Erma Jean
Mathematics Teacher
Farish, Michael Anthony
Student Leadership Coordinator
Felice, Linda Smith
English Teacher
Ferguson, Carol E.
Teacher
Ferguson, Jim C.
8th Grade US History Teacher
Ferguson, Judy Ann Hill
Life Management Teacher
Fields, Jacqueline Elaine
6th Grade Teacher
Finney, W. Howard
Administrator & Prof of Bus
Fleisher, Gregg F.
Calculus Teacher
Fletcher, Ann M.
Instructor & Counselor
Flowers, Terry James
Principal
Francingues, Kenneth Raymond
Geometry Teacher
Franklin, Rufus Thirl
Mathematics Teacher
Frie, Kim Cornell
Music Teacher
Froelich, Jon H.
HS Counselor, Teacher & Coach
Funnell, Marcia R.
Mathematics Professor
Gallo, Joseph Frederick, Jr.
AP Research Bio Teacher
Gambrell, Jean Ann (Black)
English Teacher
Garcia, Edward Harold
Professor of English
Gardner, Holly Weaver
English Teacher
Garza, Miguel Enrique
Span Tchr, Frgn Lang Dept Head
Gee, Gracie Dewberry
Art Teacher
Geffen, Joani Solomon
English Teacher
Gerard, Janet Kathryn
English & Theater Arts Tchr
Gifford, Peter B.
Wellness Director
Giles, Robert Anthony
7th-8th Grade Teacher
Glover, Betty Hunnicutt
Teacher of Gifted & Talented
Gonzalez, Maria R. Garcia
Bilingual Kindergarten Teacher
Gordon, Larry John
Humanities Associate Professor
Graham, James L.
Geometry Teacher
Grant, Norma Jean (Bork)
Science & Computer Teacher
Gray, Linda G.
Fundamental Nrsng Coord
Greer, Rheamond Douglas, Jr.
Choral Music Instructor
Gregory, Gwendolyn Anita
Science I & Biology Teacher
Grinage, Jennifer Jolly
Science Teacher
Groggs, Excell Gatson
English Teacher
Grossman, Suzan
English & French Teacher
Gump, Linda Ann
Foreign Language Dept Chair
Gussis, Jerri Dee
Political Science Professor
Guthrie, Philip Todd
Honors Biology Teacher
Hague, George Russell, Jr.
Chemistry Teacher
Hail, Amy Line
Junior High Special Ed Teacher
Hall, Marcus H.
Secondary Social Studies Tchr
Hall, Zane Bruce
Eighth Grade History Teacher
Hall-Chiles, Sandy
Jrnlsm & Photography Instr
Halperin, Rick
Professor of Human Rights
Hammert, Marian Dieckman
Kindergarten Teacher
Hannah, John David
Dpt Chm & Prof of Hstrcl Thlgy
Hardee, Ruthie Aucoin
Sixth Grade Teacher
Hardeman, Felecia Diann
English Teacher
Hare, Samuel
Computer Lab Teacher
Harp, Barbara Krueger
1st-2nd Grade Teacher
Harper, Diana Mc Gruder
7th Grade Science Teacher
Harris, Carolyn Rogers
Group Piano Instructor
Harris, Deanna Lee
Physical Educator & Coach
Harris, Debbie S.
Speech & Drama Teacher
Haskins, Barbara Reed
Elementary Teacher
Hay, Ronda Lee (Pullar)
7th-8th Grade Reading Teacher
Hays, Karen Anita
Reading Teacher
Henderson, Jim R.
Choral Activities Dir
Henley, Judith MacKenzie
Assistant Prof of Nursing
Henry, Carl Alan
English Teacher
Henslee, Jimmie J.
Accounting & Co-op Coordinator
Hepburn, Jacelyn Wallace
Mathematics Tchr & Dept Chprsn
Herschkowitsch, Cynthia Deaton
English & German Teacher
Higgins, Maureen A.
Jr High Language Arts Teacher
Hilton, Gene
Management Professor
Hinchen, Willie Frank
High School English Teacher
Hines, Mark Robert
Counselor
Hobbs, Kevin Jason
6th Grd Science & Bible Tchr
Hodge, Darla Winstel
Math Teacher
Holton, William Edward
Senior Army Instructor
Horace, Bettye Rose
Computer Teacher
Horne, Linda Kay
Reading Teacher
Host, Timothy R.
English Teacher
Howard, Rhonda Yvette
5th Grade Mathematics Teacher
Hudson, Debrit Jean
Sixth Grade Math Teacher
Humphrey, Cheryl Davis
HS Counselor
Hutchins, Mary I. Mc Cray
Fourth Grade Teacher
Hynson, Diann
Eng as a Second Lang Tchr
Ippolito, Dennis Stephen
Professor of Political Science
Irby, Robert Hudson
Mathematics Department Chair
Irvin, Ceclia Aguilar
Fifth Grade Teacher
Jackson, Irene Haynes
6th Grade Teacher
Jacoby, Charline
2nd Grade Teacher
James, Freddie
Tchr, Ath Dir, Head Ftbl Coach
Jelks-Saulter, Mattie
English I Teacher
Johnson, Angela Renee
English Teacher
Johnson, Cleo LoRaine
Reading Teacher
Johnson, Herbert Ray
Social Studies Teacher
Johnson, Lauretta Thompson
Fifth Grade Teacher
Johnson, Mary McKnight
Mathematics Teacher
Johnson, Sara Yowell
9th Grade ESOL Teacher
Johnson, Sue Depwe
Vocal Music Teacher
Johnson-Gallo, Christine Kaye
Eng Tchr, Acad Decathlon Coach
Jolly, Robert C.
Assistant Principal
Jones, Regina Smith
Orchestra Teacher
Jordan, Nellie L. Howard
Teacher of Talented & Gifted
Jordan, Thomas Andrew
AP Physics Teacher
Justice, Theodora Y'Barbara
Vocational Education Teacher
Kaloki, Philip K.
Economics & Management Prof
Kane, Marietta A.
Life Transitions Coordinator
Kasten, Daniel B.
English Teacher
Keever, Mary Louise
Upper School English Teacher
Kelley, Kathy Ann
Adjunct Professor
Kelton, Shari Tipps
Health Occupations Ed Teacher
Keyes, Laura Weaver
English Teacher
Kidd, Patricia Binkley
Medical Careers Cluster Coord
Kieschnick, Leslie Millender
Economics Teacher
Kilgore, Deborah Jean
9th-12th Grade English Teacher
Kilman, Carol Kay
5th Grade Social Studies Tchr
Kimball, Scott Paul
Asst Head of MS & History Tchr
Kindred, Donna Michelle
Honors Science & Biology Tchr
Kindt, Karl Martin
Chemistry & Physics Teacher
Kingston, Denice
Music & Drama Teacher
Kleinneiur, Marjorie M.
English Teacher
Knight, Elizabeth Gerbetz
Coll Learning Skills Teacher
Knighton, Jayne Gulley
Adjunct Professor
Koch, David P.
Physics Teacher
Kohler, Jennifer Fran
Agriculture Teacher
Koop, Karen Chadderdon
Former 5th Grade Teacher
Kores, Becky S.
Advertising Design Teacher
Krueger, Kathi Donahue
Spanish & French Teacher
Lacey, Jerry Edward
Humanities Teacher
Laman, Patricia Turner
Basic Skills Core-Strings Tchr
Landre, Sharon Chapman
Language Arts Teacher
Lanier, Robert G.
Science Chairman
Lau, David Leung
Science Teacher
Lavery, Jean
History & English Teacher
Lawe, Gwendolyn McMillan
Off Ed, Travel & Tourism Tchr
Leachman, Mariah Louise
8th Grade Science II Teacher
Leeds, Joseph Christopher
Soc Studies & Journalism Tchr
Leeman, Peggy Moore
English Department Chair
Lehman, Glen Alvin, Jr.
Govt, Ec Tchr & His Chair
Leslie, Gary Allen
Sixth Grade Teacher
Limuel, Bruce Edward
English Teacher & Dept Chprsn
Linamen, Larry Harold
Provost
Lindstrom, Sue Briscoe
English Instructor
Lipman, William Mc Cullem, Jr.
Middle School Sci Dept Head
Lipton, Carolyn R. Lewis
Mathematics & PSAT Teacher
Lockhart, John H.
US Government Prof & Principal
Locks, Patricia Black
Guidance Counselor
Lynch, Eileen M.
Professor of Political Science
Magurie, John A., II
Professor of Chemistry
Mairs, Barbara L.
Computer Teacher
Makar, Michael Allan
Biology Teacher
Malick, David Eugene
Asst Prof of Bible Expostion
Malone, Camille Shields
Secondary Mathematics Teacher
Maness, Marie Yost
Nutrition Professor
Martin, Bette McCall
German & World History Teacher
Martin, Peggy Ann
K-6th Grade Art Teacher
Martinez, Marcelino Aquirre
Third Grade Bilingual Teacher
Marzuola, Tim D.
TAG Govt & Economics Teacher
Masters, J. E.
Oral Interpretation Teacher
Matsumura, Donna Shigeko
Eng I Tchr & Drill Team Dir
Matthew, Amy Axtell
Coordinator & Instructor
Maurokordatos, Loucia
Mathematics Teacher
Mayberry, Lois Frederick
Business Teacher
Mc Collister, Deborah Hart
Associate Professor of Eng
Mc Cormick, Lauren Kelley
Special Education Teacher
Mc Cray, Peggy (Gibson)
Language Arts Teacher & Chprsn
Mc Cray, Roosevelt N.
Teacher
Mc Curdy, Jane Grillot
Spanish Teacher
Mc Daniel, Anna Maurer
HS ESOL & Russian Tchr
Mc Dermott, Carol Keck
Math Teacher & Dept Chprsn
Mc Elveen, Jerry Donald
English Teacher
Mc Gee, Brenda Holt
Curriculum Coordinator
Mc Gowan, David John
English Department Chair
Mc Laughlin, S. Gail Fowler
Theatre Arts & Speech Teacher
Mc Spadden, Amy Anderton
German Teacher
Mead, Susan Bonner
Math Teacher
Mendez, Tina
Spanish Teacher
Mendoza, Paula Smith
Marketing Education Coord
Meredith, Michael
Economics Teacher
Metzger, Sally Glockner
Theology Teacher
Mewhinney, Christina E.
Chemistry Professor
Meyer, Robert Reinhart
Instructor of Marketing & Mgmt

AS (cont)
ls, Betsy Benthall
h Grade Teacher
, Nilda E.
sh Teacher
adorf, Barbara Ann
ogy Teacher
, Lee Anne Smalley
er Teacher
Mary
rade Teacher
Daniel Paul
Dept Chairperson
Lana Burkhart
uage Arts & English Tchr
Marsha (Tandy)
Grade ESL Teacher
, Glenda Sheryl Cox
Grade Teacher
la, Janet Betten
selor
ll, Virginia Ruth Carraway
sh Teacher
y, Frank
essor of Education
Garry J.
etic Director & Coach
, Larry Donnell
Dept Head
, Amy L.
d Geography Teacher
on, Diane B.
rade English Teacher
on, Faith Ann
her
y, Hattye Louise Bell
th Grade Reading Teacher
y, Fred Ray
th Grade Teacher
, H. Wayne
essor of Biology
s, Marion Hall
ish Teacher
Charles Anthony
stant Principal
el, James Robert
n Teacher
n, Angela C.
n Tchr & Attendance Coord
n, Frederick Carl
e & Industrial Teacher
Billie Good
d Director
s, Early M.
n Grade Teacher
an, Jack Russell
or Development Director
nd, Martha Ford
Grade Science Teacher
en, Minh Ngoc
hematics Teacher
, Connie Lee
hematics Teacher
s, Gail Streater
h Teacher
s, Sandra Speegle
t Grade Teacher
s, George D.
ogy Teacher
n, Spencer Lee
lish Professor
sky, Barbara Welch
& Creative Writing Tchr
esa, Maleli
cher
rne, Donna DeHart
ondary Mathematics Teacher
owski, Mary Jean (Noble)
ech Communication Professor
er, Michael Reid
t Principal
er, Dianne
ial Studies Teacher
nal, Paula Smith
glish & Literature Teacher
, Kanti D.
fessor of Mathematics
rson, Nelson
unselor
rson, Tolly Smith
glish Teacher
e, John William
fessor of Aviation
leton, Kent Lund
th Dept Chair
, Marilyn Jean (Dad)
gh School English Teacher
son, Doris Archambault
cond Grade Teacher
son, Robert Ward
story Teacher & Coach
to, Joe S.
s, Govt & Geog Teacher
e, Constance Smith
ird Grade Teacher
ce Stiffel, Francine Bloom
ng Arts & Soc Stud Teacher
, Cecil Larry
ofessor of History & Pol Sci
e, Melva Greer
a & 8th Grd Math Teacher
e, Timothy Paul
anish & Theology Teacher
icary, Ann L. (Nordin)
ath Dept Chairperson & Tchr
ger, Linda M.
glish Teacher
t, Kevin
overnment & Economics Teacher

Proctor, Wanda Cox
Retired 7th Grade Sci Tchr
Pruitt, Allie E.
English as Second Lang Teacher
Puckett, Lawrence Verner
Chemistry Teacher
Pyle, Kevin Lewis
Adjunct Professor of History
Quisenberry, Martha Jones
Resource Teacher
Randolph, Cubie Allison
Medical Lab Teacher
Randolph, Laverda Kay
Speech & English Teacher
Rawlins, Patricia L.
Foreign Language Dept Chair
Raya, Linda Brown
Coordinator of Fine Arts
Redmond, Verette Wynne
Science Teacher
Reece, Randi S.
Counselor
Reese, Paul Keith
Counselor
Robbins, Scott Alan
PGA Professional & Instructor
Rodriguez, M. Alejandra Hernandez
First Grade Bilingual Teacher
Roe, John Thomason
Horticulture Instructor
Rosen, Jo-An
Language Arts & Soc Stud Tchr
Rufus, Leonard Thomas
Spanish Teacher
Ruhly, Karin I.
Alternative Education Teacher
Rumbley, Rose Mary
Professor of Fine Arts
Russell, Melissa
Anatomy & Physiology Teacher
Ryals, Sherry Saijee
Library Media Specialist
Ryan, Linda Kay
History Teacher
Saltzman, Suzann Steele
English Teacher
Samuels, Eloys Guinn
Biology Teacher
Sargent, Gwendolyn Byrd
Language Arts Teacher
Sauls, Linda Austin
6th Grade Teacher
Schmidt, Stephanie
Choir Teacher
Schmoeckel, Margaret Fisher
Reading Teacher
Schneider, Michael Jay
Physical Education Dept Chm
Segura, Richard Torres
Career & Technology Ed Teacher
Sehr, Cecilia, OP
Chem & Adjunct Physics Teacher
Shelton, Donna Skeen
Professor of English
Sherman, VeroniKa Mancuso
MS Home Economics Teacher
Simon, Sharon Trombello
Sixth Grade Teacher
Sims, Dale Benjamin
Asst Prof of Computer Sci, Bus
Smiles, Ronald
Professor of Management
Smith, Adell Baker
Third Grade Teacher
Snell, Charlotte Hernblom
Secondary Mathematics Teacher
Sparks, Nita Jan
Lang Arts, Soc Stud & ESL Tchr
Spencer, Shauretta La-Kay
Elem Schl Guidance Cnslr
Springer, Rachel Adler
Anthropology & Sociology Instr
Stanley, Jacqueline Beatrice
HS Mathematics Teacher
Stark, Denise Mosley
MS Social Studies Teacher
Sterling, Joyce Cheatham
Math Teacher & Dept Chprsn
Stetler, Elizabeth
2nd Grade Bilingual Teacher
Stewart, Geoffrey Cope
Bio Tchr & Wilderness Co-Dir
Stone, Beverly Bennett
Eng as Second Lang Tchr
Stout, Stacy M.
Sixth Grade Teacher
Strickland, Doris Washington
Science Teacher & Dept Chprsn
Sutterfield, Jerry Don
Technology Teacher
Swedlund, Trudi Jean
College Professor
Szeljack, Peggy Ann
Principal
Taulbee, Thomas L.
Prof of Psychology & History
Taylor, Claudette Jones
Licensed Professional Cnslr
Temme, James Joseph
World Geography Teacher
Theriault, Mary Shehan
English Teacher
Thigpen, Esther Johnson
Lang Arts & Soc Stud Tchr
Thomas, Barbara Overton
Instrl Specialist & Math TAAS
Thomas, Lou B.
4th Grade Teacher
Thomas, Richard Phillimore
Drafting & CAD Teacher

Thomas, S. Elaine Collins
Music Teacher
Timmons, Cherise Wilson
HS Business Education Teacher
Trevino, Margarita Christela
Adjunct Professor
Tucker, Allison C.
Instrumental Music Director
Tyler, Toby J.
Contect Mastery Teacher
Varnell, John Nelson
Algebra Teacher & Coach
Vaughn, Rebecca Gina
ESL Teacher
Venable, Gigi Brown
Science Teacher
Vice, Doris Hebert
2nd Grade Teacher
Wakefield, Charles William
Director of AEGD Residency
Walker, Gracie Conner
Counselor
Walker, Mariannette Parker
7th Grade Reading Teacher
Walker, Marty Huddleston
English Teacher
Walsh, Dawna Hamm
Dept of Art Professor & Chprsn
Walther, James Robert
Social Studies Teacher & Coach
Ward, Patricia Hurley
Science Teacher
Warren, Rodger E.
Electronics & Mathematics Tchr
Washington, Victor
Mathematics Teacher
Watts, Edwina Carribia
English Teacher
Weadon, Paul Ashford, III
German Teacher
Weithers, Joseph Oliver
Chem, Phys Sci & Physics Tchr
Wenthe, William Dean, Jr.
8th Grade Athletic Director
West, Dorthery Gean
Instructional Specialist
Weston, Joan Laveson
Sociology Professor
Wetherington, Sandra Lee
Choral Director
Wheeler, Jerry Thomas
Physical & Life Science Tchr
Wilson, Verna Elaine
Sixth Grade Teacher
Winkley, Sandra Bryant
Special Education Teacher
Wortley, Beth Peabody
Dance Department Director
Wright, Barbara Burch
6th Grade ESL Teacher
Yenne, Elaine Roach
Reading & Thinking Teacher
Young, Jerry Paul
Instructor
Zimmerman, Mike Paul
Math, Computer & Physics Tchr
Zyglewyz, Maryanne Bridget
Kindergarten & ESL Teacher

DANBURY

Bullock, Carol Zschiesche
Science Department Head
Delcambre, Carol Canady
High School Math Teacher
Welsch, Laura Lynn
Math, Rdng & Lang Arts Tchr

DAWSON

Tallant, Louise
5th Grade Teacher

DAYTON

Dyer, Michael James
World History Teacher
Gassiott, John Timothy
Career & Technology Admin
Harbour, Catherine Glass
Seventh Grade History Teacher
Johnson, Jessica Ford
Pre-Algebra Teacher
Johnson, Linda Andrews
First Grade Teacher
Lewis, Susie Sackett
Mathematics Teacher
McClaugherty, Donna Kenneally
Bio I & Physical Science Tchr
Meacham, Jeff Oran
Sixth Grade Math Teacher
Merritt, Robin Lee
Industrial Vocational Teacher
Miller, Kathy Spann
Kindergarten Teacher
Mullins, Candace Roberson
Home Economics Teacher
Murphy, Nancy Farnsworth
5th Grade Teacher
Skewes, Ellen K.
Spanish Teacher

DE KALB

Addington, Donna Atchley
Counselor
Crawford, Wallie Mc Graw
Chem, Physics & Phys Sci Tchr
Germany, James La Forest
5th-6th Grd Soc Studies Tchr
Meadows, Michael Douglas
Ag-Science Instructor
Reeves, Samuel Eugene
Texas History Teacher

DE LEON

Hare, Dotty Kay
Business & Office Ed Teacher

Howard, Frances Louise
Fourth Grade Teacher

DE SOTO

Bentley, Vicki Buckley
HS English Teacher
Cross, Dennis Dale
ROTC Department Head
Daniel, Karen June
English Teacher
DeBorde, Pamela S.
Athletic Coord & Instructor
Dial, Ben F.
Taas Math & Head Ftbl Coach
Fowler, Keven S.
English Teacher
Hancock, Brenda Kaye
Math Tchr, Chrldng Dir & Coach
Herrod, James Steven
Physics Teacher
Hunter, Mary Jean
AP Biology Teacher
Hydes, Ray Arden
World History Teacher & Coach
Larson, Kenneth Ray
Headmaster
Mc Cormes, Roy
Jr Rsrv Trng Corp Army Instr
Meyers, Lynda Mc Gowen
Third Grade Teacher
Milligan, Mida Figliulo
High School English Teacher
Murphree, Linda Faye
High School Counselor
Ray, Jerene Elseman
Teacher
Robinson, Deborah Pogue
Fourth Grade Teacher
Singleton, Chuc M.
High School Art Teacher
Strange, Rebecca Page
English Teacher
Suson, Andy C.
English II Teacher
Wilson, Lynn Barton
US History Teacher
Witherspoon, Danise Newton
HS Home Economics Teacher
Young, Linda Kay Washington
6th Grade Mathematics Teacher

DECATUR

Adams, Tami Cohen
Fine Arts Director
Clark, Lori Verner
Second Grade Teacher
Griffin, Janna J.
History Dept Head
Long, Lavaga R.
Fourth Grade Teacher
Overton, Leisa Gettys
English Teacher
Whiddon, Linda Comeaux
Dyslexia Coord & Rdng Spclst
Woodruff, Joy
Sci Dept Chair & Teacher

DEER PARK

Blaylock, Cindy L.
Computer Science Teacher
Bowen, Nina De Los Santos
German Teacher
Boykin, Thomas Bennett
Physical Science Teacher
Buchelli, Dawn Grams
Spanish Teacher
Carden, Constance Collier
6th Grade Social Studies Tchr
Carter, J. B.
High School Math Teacher
Davidson, James Edward
Athletic Trainer
Deutsch, Denise Priest
Photography Teacher
Fuchs, Gerald R.
Assistant Principal & Teacher
Garcia, Penny Ann (Hambrick)
English IV Teacher
Gordon, Diane Murphy
First Grade Teacher
Hayman, Terry Meza
Reading & English Teacher
Hazard, Vern Paul, II
Theatre Production & Arts Tchr
Hillail, Carolina Torres
High School Spanish Teacher
Hines, Denise Marie
Health Occupations Coordinator
Hughes, Billy Boyd
US History Teacher
Kirk, Robert L.
Health Teacher & Ftbl Coach
Kouba, Ronda Gardner
8th Grd Language Arts Teacher
Means, Louie E.
Algebra Teacher
Mills, Adelia Jan
French Teacher
Moore, Margaret Mount
Mathematics Chair
Passmore, Susan Holland
English III Teacher
Patterson, Peggy Lucas
Itinerant Specialist of GATE
Polk, Linda
English Dept Chair
Richard, Micki Lane
Math Teacher
Stubbs, Bruce B.
Biology Teacher
Talley, Barry
Fine Arts Coord & Choral Dir

Taylor, Donna R.
Theatre Productions Teacher
Thomas, Richard H.
Librarian & Media Specialist

DEL RIO

Aberle, Judeen Louise
English Teacher
Anderson, Julia Ann
English Teacher
Avalos, Irma Elda
4th Grade Teacher
Banks, Paul Randall
Instructor of Biology
Barrera, Yolanda Magdaleno
High School Spanish Teacher
Benavides, Nilda M.
English IV & Pre AP Teacher
Clavira, Gustavo R.
American History Teacher
Gerringer, Mildred Sue
Mathematics Teacher
Gonzalez, Roger
Business Education Dept Head
Hanson, Edward Allan
Aerospace Science Instructor
Hill, Rebecca Brien
Kindergarten Bilingual Teacher
Lehnert, Lillian Miller
2nd Grade Bilingual Teacher
Love, Jodonne Donreath (Potts)
Latin Teacher
Martin, Dudley Graham
Texas History Teacher
Martinez, Ernesto Santellanes
School Teacher
Mc Crary, Gerald
American History Teacher
McCulloch, Robert Charles
Government & Economics Teacher
Mireles, Carol Lynn
PE Teacher & Track Coach
New, Pamela Kim
Govt, Politics, Economics Tchr
Nunley, Barbara June (Crain)
HS Mathematics Teacher
Perez, JoAnn Robles
5th Grade Teacher
Sagan, Ralph William
American History Teacher
Salazar, Rose Reyes
Second Grade Teacher
Salazar, Virginia Villarreal
First Grade Bilingual Teacher
Sanchez, Richard B.
High School Educator
Sotelo, Carmen Cecilia
1st Grade Teacher
Sutton, Carmen Abascal
Journalism & English Teacher
Turner, Earl H.
Life Science Teacher
Villarreal, Maria Rosario
First Grade Bilingual Teacher

DEL VALLE

Adkins, Lisa McNabb
Fifth Grade Teacher
Armstrong, Robert Virgil
Language Arts Teacher & Coach
Everett, Leigh Casselberry
8th Grade Amer History Teacher
Miller, Karen Sue
HS Health & PE Teacher
Morgan, Debra Sonntag
Teen Pregnancy Program Coord
Vera, Daniel Reil
Counselor

DENISON

Barlow, John David
Coordinator & Instructor
Barrett, Mary Nell
Ninth Grade English Teacher
Bowers, Paul David
Psychology Professor & Chprsn
Brock, Billy W.
Womens Basketball Head Coach
Brown, Barbara Runk
English & Humanities Instr
Butler, Jackie Love
Instructor
Cannon, Shonda Annyce
Span Tchr & Head Vllybl Coach
Donowho, David Calvin
History Professor
Johnson, Janice Carole Warwick
Fifth Grade Teacher
Kirch, Anne Marie
Coll Instr of Devlpmtl Writing
Massey, Dena Burrows
Dance Teacher & Drill Team Dir
Romanski, Fred F.
Coordinator & Instructor
Russell, James Saunders
7th Grade Science Teacher
Smith, Virginia Ann Williams
Nursing Professor
Sulser, Janice Cox
Kindergarten Teacher
Warren, Kevin Rex
Teacher & Coach

DENTON

Ackerson, Mark I.
Dept Chair & Math Teacher
Adler, Kathleen S.
Visiting Asst Prof of Ec
Andrews, Marsha Miller
Fourth Grade Teacher
Arnold, Carol Michelle (Green)
Assistant Clinical Professor
Austin, Zan L.
Science II Teacher

DENTON (cont)
Bean, Judith Mattson
Asst Professor of English
Beck, Patricia Jane
5th Grade Teacher
Bednar, Carolyn Johnson
Dept of Nutrition Asst Prof
Bernstein, Tonnette L.
English Teacher
Bershell, Cynthia Walker
Speech & Language Pathologist
Bolin, Janet Smith
8th Grd American History Tchr
Bowers, Jean
7th Grade Teacher
Bowles, Patrice Noga
Mathematics Teacher
Bowman, Kent Adam
American History Teacher
Braune, Veriena M. (Hutchins)
Visiting Professor of Reading
Bray, Nancy Crockett
English Teacher
Broussard, Jeanne L.
Assoc Prof of Graphic Design
Burns, Barbara Nickell
Social Studies Teacher
Calabrese, John Anthony
Associate Professor of Art
Campbell, Randolph B.
Regents Professor of History
Capps, Helen Simpson
Seventh Grade History Teacher
Carrell, Lisa Ann
Third Grade Teacher
Chan, Josephine Suk-Kuen
Occupational Therapy Professor
Cherri, Mona Abo-Chedid
Associate Professor
Code, Rebecca Banasiak
Professor of Biology
Cowan, Anita
Social Work Professor
Cross, Shelley Creagh
First Grade Teacher
Davis, Linda Weiss
4th Grade Teacher
Davis, Roderick M.
HS Health Teacher & Coach
Denney, Susan Jones
French Teacher
DiMarco, Nancy M.
Associate Professor
Doyle, Eva I.
Asst Prof of Health Educ
Drain Allen, Johnnie Lee
Kindergarten Teacher
Ellis, Cheryl Dreher
English Teacher
Emerson, Gaile
ESL Teacher
Emmott, Victoria
Clinical Instructor of Nursing
Ephraim, Norma Louise (Howerton)
Teacher
Estes, Jenny Lynn
Music Teacher
Everett, Elaine Triche
Fifth Grade Teacher
Fedric, Tara Cain
Asst Clinical Prof of Nursing
Fischer, Gary
US His Tchr & Head Ftbl Coach
Fleming, Nely Saraoz
Adjunct Spanish Professor
Foreman, Reta Smiddy
Bio & Microbiology Lab Coord
Gailey, Dana Burke
Fifth Grade & Drivers Ed Tchr
Ganzer, Barbara K.
Second Grade Teacher
Garner, Dean Evans
Institute Director
Garrison, Deborah Ruth
Assistant Clinical Professor
Garza, Christine Seftchick
Assistant Professor of Nursing
Gates, Claire Caton
Mathematics Teacher
Gerdes, Melissa
Second Grade Teacher
Glick, Nancy Parsons
Dept Dental Hygiene Chair-Prof
Gossett, John Sartain
Communications Stud Dept Chair
Gross, Carolyn Smith
6th Grade Mathematics Teacher
Haag, Claudia Christensen
Language Arts Instructor
Hadsell, Nancy Ann
Prof & Coord of Music Therapy
Hajek, Eloise
Reading & Biling Ed Lecturer
Harn, Annabelle Allen (Latham)
English & Language Arts Tchr
Harris, Cynthia Holley
Mathematics Teacher
Henderson, Betty Sampson
Asst Prof & Coord RN-BS Prgm
Hipple, Lee B.
Assistant Professor
Hoemeke, Diane Kasich
Mathematics Teacher
Iaia, Joseph Anthony
Mathematics Professor
Ingram, Jan M.
Fifth Grade Teacher
Ingram, Vanna Briscoe
Math Teacher
Istook, Cynthia Saylor
Marketing Professor
Jano, Issam I.
General Chemistry Professor
Jeffers, Jolyne Antista
Singer, Conductor & Teacher
Jez, Terri Adair
Content Mastery Teacher
Juren, Donna Darrow
Social Studies Teacher
Killian, Janice Nelson
Music Education Professor
King, Kimi Lynn
Asst Prof of Political Science
Kinnison, Lloyd R.
Assoc Prof of Special Ed
LeForce, Leroy Spencer
Fourth Grade Teacher
Lippe, Sarah Gulledge
English Teacher
Mallam, Winifred Ann
Assistant Professor of Math Ed
Martin, Rita Nixon
Clinical Instr of Nursing
Martinez, Dorothy Argumaniz
ESL Teacher
Matteson, Carolyn (Rhodes)
English Teacher
May, Ann Newton
Math Coordinator
McDaniel, Floyd Del
Professor of Physics
Mc Sween, Roger Brett
Industrial Technology Teacher
Merchant, Michael Louis
Asst Prof of Chem & Physics
Mott, Kenneth Lee
Assoc Prof of History & Govt
Murphy, Sharon Marr
Business Education Teacher
Naxon, Elya Edna
Asst Prof of Occup Therapy
Neville-Smith, Marsha Ann
Instr of Occupational Therapy
Nickum-Marshall, Linda L.
Asst Professor
Nik, Ninfa Verdin
Assistant Professor
Norman, Kay Treadway
Government Teacher
Northam, Sally Engelbrecht
Assistant Professor
Nunez, Mario Leoncio
Orchestra Director
Orbison, Charley E.
Broadcast Coordinator
Palmer, Joyce Cornette
English Professor
Palmer, Leslie Howard
English Professor
Parmentier, Joyce Carole
Academic Advisor
Perry, Susan P.
Frosh & Soph Eng Instructor
Peteet, William E.
Math Teacher
Phillips, Brenda D.
Sociology Assistant Professor
Pulattie, Mike W.
Bio Tchr & Cross Cntry Coach
Raffen, Eleanor Anne
Clinical Instr Fieldwork Coord
Ragland, Ruth Ann Vaughan
Journalism Professor
Reeves, Vernon Lloyd, Jr.
7th Grade Texas History Tchr
Rektorik-Sprinkle, Patricia Jean
Latin Teacher
Rezac, Reginald Nolan
Accounting Professor
Roach, George C.
Retired Math Teacher
Rubin, Linda J.
Counseling Psychology Prof
Sadri, Mahmoud
Sociology Professor
Sain, Reggi Harris
Math Tchr & Coach
Schoen, Janice (Kvam)
Dental Hygiene Instructor
Schorg, Chandra A.
Lecturer in Accounting
Schropp, Anissa Breaux
Graduate Teaching Fellow
Scott, Gail Hestbeck
High School Math Teacher
Scott, John Curran
US History Teacher
Scott, Paula Louise
Associate Professor Ed of Deaf
Scroggs, Charlotte I.
Mathematics Teacher
Shoffit, Richard Calvin
Professional Teacher
Simmons, Gloria Annette
English Teacher
Simmons, Judy Carol
Library Media Specialist
Sitterly, Connie S.
Adjunct Prof
Sluder, Linda Carson
Assoc Professor of Education
Smith, Elizabeth Edwards
English Teacher
Souris, Stephen
Asst Prof of Eng
Swain, Colleen R.
Lecturer
Sweatmon, Robert Bruce
History Teacher
Taylor, Sherrie (Ingalls)
Lecturer in Management
Terrell, Paul L.
6th Grade Teacher
Thompson, Frances McBroom
Mathematics Professor
Wainscott, Michael Dale
Eng & Stu Cncl Leadership Tchr
Waldo, Nancy (Allen)
Biology Teacher
Wallace, Milton DeNard
Principal
Ward, Sandra June
Assistant Professor of Physics
Watts, Karen Mc Donald
4th Grade Tchr & Coord
Weatherford, Jennifer Tonge
HS Dance Tchr & Drill Team Dir
Welborn, Jane Stoffels
English Teacher
Weldon, Rhonda Haigler
Mathematics Teacher
Wesson, Gail J.
Honors Physical Science Tchr
Willis, Kraig L.
Former Fifth Grade Teacher
Wilson, Vickie Clarkson
Math Teacher
Woods, Lana Kay Jenkins
Asst Professor of Phys Therapy
Wootten, Steven Alan
Graduate Teaching Assistant
Yeatts, Ronnie Alan
Algebra & Geometry Teacher
Young, Deborah Dee
Assistant Professor
Zinn, Margaret Spies
Principal

DENVER CITY
Bruton, Shirley Bowen
Teacher of Gifted & Talented
Cargill, Karen Ruth (Gibson)
First Grade Teacher
Carrillo, Mary Margaret
8th Grade Algebra Teacher
Duzan, Darrin Ray
Industrial Technology Teacher
Ham, Paula Blount
Elementary PE Teacher
Harris, Linda Sanders
Language Arts & English Tchr
Jividen, Michelle Huckleberry
7th Grade Science I Teacher
Reves, David E., Jr.
HS Social Studies Teacher
Riker, David Lawrence
6th-12th Grd Band Director
Suttle, Mary Lisa (Risinger)
8th Grd Phys Ed & Health Tchr
Taylor, Steve
Coach, Ath Dir & HS His Tchr
Tucker, Betty Jewell
Second Grade Teacher

DETROIT
Brown, Leisa Johnson
5th Grade Teacher
Mc Coin, Albert P.
Agriculture Science Teacher

DEVINE
Cowan, Jessie Wayne
Science Teacher
Darnell, Kandi Ascencio
Eng & Gifted Talented Teacher
Lorraine, William V.
HS Science Teacher & Dept Chm
Mc Anelly, Linda Burleson
English Teacher & Dept Chair
Poerner, Amy Mitchell
Third Grade Teacher
Schneider, Jill Jackson
Reading & Theatre Arts Teacher
Schwab, Diane Haby
Algebra & Geometry Teacher
Thames, Sylvia Marlene
Assistant Principal

DEWEYVILLE
Carter, Linda Harris
4th Grade Teacher
Coffman, Tonya Edwards
First Grade Teacher
Waldrum, Joe Boyd, Jr.
Agricultural Science Teacher

DIANA
Boney, Janie Owens
5th Grade Teacher
Mc Luckie, Gloria Lindsey
Theatre & Speech Teacher
Norman, Roger Allan
Calculus & Pre-Calculus Tchr
Shaw, Nancy Blakeley
Elementary Reading Teacher
Witt, Shirley Graves
Third Grade Teacher

DIBOLL
Martel, Gary Lee
9th Grd Phys Sci Tchr & Coach
Mc Elroy, Ellen Kaye
Jr HS Counselor
Musick, JoAnne S.
8th Grade Language Arts Tchr
Vanover, Sharon Tilley
Pre Algebra Teacher

DICKINSON
Boldrighini, Susan Layton
Assistant Band Director
Denman, Marchelle Ann
Third Grade Teacher
Derrick, Peter Marshall
Mathematics & Physics Teacher
Fant, Pat Rutledge
Algebra & Geometry Teacher
Hinojosa, John Robert
Band Dir & Percussion Instr
Laird, Ruth Abendroth
Third Grade Teacher
Mc David, Andrew
Former Teacher
Terrell, Elaine Reffitt
9th Grd American History Tchr

DILLEY
Hutchison, Shanda Hines
English & Writing Teacher
Mc Millian, Marilyn Lindsey
Kindergarten Teacher
Thetford, Carolyn S.
Business Ed Teacher

DIME BOX
Mikulin, John David
Fourth Grade Teacher

DIMMITT
Ball, Rose Duesterhaus
7th Grade Life Science Teacher
Beck, Danna Odom
US History Teacher
Book, Becky Sue (Hand)
Math & Business Teacher
Bradley, Cinnamon Cox
Biology Teacher
Goolsby, Dawn Endebrock
5th Grade Science Teacher
Ivey, Katie Barclay
History Teacher
Miller, Carla
8th Grd American History Tchr
Odom, Jacqueline Louise
Career & Technology Teacher

DONNA
Ayala, Arturo, Jr.
Building Trades Teacher
Batungbacal, Cecilia Tiongson
Accelerated Lang Arts Tchr
Castillo, Nancy Lopez
HS Math Teacher
De La Garza, Josefina
Teacher & Librarian
Mc Caffity, Sonia Melendez
Math Teacher
Mims, James Henry
Senior Marine Instructor
Navarro, Elvia Lopez
Kindergarten Teacher
Neal, Robert DeWitt
Math, Sci & German Instr
Ramirez, Maricela
High School Science Teacher
Rodriguez, Francisco R.
Teacher
Rodriguez, Robert
10th Grade Social Studies Tchr
Ruiz, Araceli Ruiz
Biology Teacher
Schlaefer, Dan Allen
Math Chairperson & Teacher
Tovar, Roel
6th Grd Spec Ed Resource Tchr

DOUGLASS
Allen, Mary Grace
English & Journalism Teacher
Kelly, Marie Thies
Math & Business Teacher
Serpas, Deborah Bowers
Physical Education Teacher

DRIPPING SPRINGS
Botkin, Janie L.
English Department Chairperson
Smith, Ellis Carlton
Teacher & Gifted Coordinator

DUBLIN
Stone, Vicky Turley
English Teacher

DUMAS
Benson, Mary Hutton
Social Studies Teacher
Burrus, Holly Brooke
Eighth Grade English Teacher
Coyle, Cheryl Abrahamson
5th & 6th Grade Reading Tchr
Fox, Pamela Lynne
English Teacher
Heaton, Sally D. (Hill)
Biology Teacher
Holland, Patricia A.
English Dept Chairperson
Hood, Martha Marte
English as Second Lang Teacher
Lynn, Nadyne Faulkenberry
Kindergarten Teacher
Murry, James Randall
Biology Teacher & Bsktbl Coach
Quintana, Michael Louis
Instructor & Coach
Rawlins, Douglas Andrew
7th Grade Science I Teacher
Rodman, Jack Leonard
US History & World Geog Tchr
Rush, Ted Jay
Biology Tchr & Science Coord
Vessels, Ruth Ogden
ESL Teacher & Coach
Welch, Pam Hanes
Speech Comm & Home Ec Teacher
Williams, Trevor Dean
Agriculture Science Instructor

DUNCANVILLE
Adamson, Sally Clark
Government & Economics Teacher
Barr, Kathleen Moser
Second Grade Teacher
Berryman, Evelyn Clark
8th Grade Honors English Tchr
Cothren, Kennith Dell
Physical Ed Teacher & Coach
Darden, Debra Lynn
Fourth Grade Teacher
Hale, Connie Watson
Office Careers Chm & Instr
Harris, Paula Pascoe
Spanish Teacher
Harrod, Kelly Martha
Head Tennis Coach
Jackson, Mary Alice Humes
Second Grade Teacher
Kastrop, Kye Middleton
Chemistry & Physics Teacher
Ketron, Carrie Ogden
Vocational Teacher
Martin, Lee A.
Advanced Placement Bio Teacher
Mc Farling, Carol Gowen
English Teacher
Peters, Vicki Cobern
Hnrs Alg II & Pre-Cal Teacher
Register, Deborah Rose
HS Mathematics Teacher
Shafer, Elizabeth Terry
3rd Grade Teacher
Smith, Robert (Scott)
Athletic Director
Villarreal, Abby Gullett
Middle School Band Director

DYESS AFB
Mouser, Bennie Ruth (George)
Fourth Grade Teacher

EAGLE LAKE
Sykowski, Raymond J.
7th & 8th Grd History Teacher

EAGLE PASS
Castillon, Maria R.
8th Grade Math Teacher
Duewall, Virginia Valdez
English Teacher
Garza, Ana Maria Mack
Principal
Gonzalez, Rosalinda Barrera
High School Guidance Counselor
Hernandez, Osvaldo, Jr.
Math Teacher
Lozano, Ruben Anthony
Health Teacher
Lugo, Eleanor H.
Counselor
Mayer, Charles
History Teacher
Mc Beath, Debra Sparks
English Teacher
Mello, Daniel
Business Teacher
Mello, Dawn Valdez
Science Teacher
Olivares, Rosa Trevino
English Teacher
Opperman, Charles E.
English Teacher
Ramos, Irma Frausto
English IV Teacher
Yebra, Sofia Gonzalez
High School Counselor

EARLY
Chapman, Dan G.
High School Principal
George, Charles Edward
Social Studies Dept Chair
Powell, Lennell Claunch
Second Grade Teacher

EARTH
Conkin, Janet Shutes
Business & Computer Teacher
Williams, Sharon L'Heureux
Junior & Senior English Tchr

EAST BERNARD
Grahmann, Donna
Jr High Social Studies Teacher
Hlavinka, Patsy A.
5th & 6th Grd English Teacher

EASTLAND
Gregory, Diana Kay Maynard
Third Grade Teacher
Hughes, Karen (Krai)
5th Grade English Teacher
Miears, Judy Brown
Math Dept Chairperson
Vermillion, Marsha Treadwell
Senior English Teacher

EDCOUCH
Barrera, Amelia
Fifth Grade Lang Arts Teacher
Ramirez, Hector
6th Grade Teacher

EDDY
Martin, Hazel Lynn
Counselor
Rainer, Christifer L.
Jr High Science Teacher

EDEN
Green, Marlyn Kay
Fifth Grade Teacher

EDGEWOOD
Bunce, Katherine Cawley
7th-8th Grade Science Teacher
Stewart, Mary Hooks
Second Grade Teacher
Tavis, Wendy Pettycrew
Biology Teacher

EDINBURG
Alamia, Yolanda I.
ESL Teacher
Alvarado, Jose Francisco
Math Lecturer

URG (cont)
Nadav
g Assistant Professor
Jorge Alberto
y Teacher
, Norman Alfred
f Art & Biological Illus
n, Kenneth L.
rofessor of Philosophy
eld, R. E.
er
rma Marmolejo
Geography Teacher
as, Norma Alicia
stra Director
s, Max M.
ce Dept Head
na, Dalia Guerra
rd Content Mastery Tchr
David Blaine
n & PE Teacher
, Norma Ann
rade Teacher
James L.
sh Professor
dez, Horacio
d English Teacher
a, Elva Salazar
th Grade English Teacher
Yolanda
n Grade Reading Teacher
n, Robert A.
anical Engineering Prof
i, Gouranga
of Acctng, Bus Law & Chm
Daisy Parrao
dary Mathematics Teacher
Sarita
ational Diagnostician
n, Salma I.
rer
es, Barbara Barrera
Ed Teacher & Vlybl Coach
es, Enirique, Jr.
Grade Math Teacher
, Walter Earl
of Strategic Management
, Ramon Santiago
ology Professor
ro, Herlinda Gomez
ng & Comp Literacy Tchr
n, Josefina Perez
ch & Language Pathologist
Bahram
unting Professor
Michael R.
r of Natural Sci & Lrning
eler, Paul Robert
ciate Professor of History
ndez, Jennie
ogy Teacher
ndez, Maggie V.
ish Teacher
Michael Allan
School English Teacher
osa, Jose Rolando
essor of Political Science
d, Naida Salazar
d Choral Director
wen
stant Prof of Psychology
ma, Irene
stant History Professor
, Crispin
th Teacher
, Janie Johnston
d Grade Teacher
nez, Jose A.
nce Teacher
emore, Donna Regina
Grade English Teacher
ell, Paul L.
oc Professor of English
, Albert Christopher
ociate Professor of Music
, Vivian Carole
sic Professor
, Ercan G.
agement Professor & Chm
nan, Jane Ann
t Professor in Rehabltn
an, Theresa J. C.
turer in Philosophy
ott, Isabel Rodriguez
nish Teacher
rez, Leo
Enforcement Instructor
rez, Mary
nselor
os, Francis
ld Care & Guid Voc Teacher
mel, Dorothy Lillian
h Grade Classroom Teacher
hez, M. Sandra
sing Professor
hez, Maria Luisa
siness & Economics Teacher
oval, Abigail Villanueva
Grade Math Teacher
z, Graciela
anish Adv Placement Teacher
kley, William Carl, Jr.
ysics Professor
ey, Jack R.
soc Prof Theatre, & Dept Chr
e, Stacie Lynn
emistry Lecturer
g, Cindy Martinez
ogram Coordinator

Wiener, Bella
Senior Lecturer
Wilken, Dorothy J.
Science Teacher
Zuniga, Marta Elisa
Former Lecturer
EDNA
Gann, Sheila O'Briant
English Teacher
Granberry, Estelle Timme
Mathematics Teacher
Kallus, Eugene James
Ag Science Teacher
Kozelsky, Joycelyn Klimitchek
Kindergarten Teacher
EL CAMPO
Moore, James Marion
Math Teacher & Coach
Mueller, Alton A.
Middle School Counselor
Rainbolt, Kelley Scheel
4th Grade Teacher
Rice, Mike O.
Pre Calculus Teacher
Rod, Marie Naiser
Fourth Grade Teacher
Sanchez, Manuela Gomez
ESL Teacher
EL PASO
Acosta, Irma Esparza
Dance Teacher
Adame, Hector
5th Grade Teacher
Aguilar, Barbara Aliaga
Science Teacher
Alden, Martha Leigh
Reading Recovery Teacher
Alderete, Teresa
Reading Teacher
Alvarez, Maria Elizabeth
Biology Instructor
Anderson, Holly
English I Teacher
Anderson, Terri Lyn
Physical Education Specialist
Andrade, Timothy Bryan
Band Director
Anthony, Edwin Dell
Social Studies Teacher
Armendariz, Patricia
Fourth Grade Bilingual Teacher
Arriola, Rosemary Terrazas
Dance Teacher
Arroyos, Alicia Acosta
7th & 8th Grade ESOL Teacher
Asprion, Georgi
Kindergarten Teacher
Avila, Patricia Alarcon
4th Grd Bilingual Ed Teacher
Baguera, Rosetta Marie
History & Art Teacher
Bailey, Beverly Spillman
8th-9th Grd History & Eng Tchr
Ballard, James Mark
Drafting Instructor
Baltazar, Jose Moncada
Counselor & Dev Ed Instr
Baray, Diane Madalene
Business Teacher
Barnes, Joe S.
Broadcasting & Geography Tchr
Barreras, Rene Burgueno
Wghts, Cndtng & Wellness Tchr
Barron, Ruben Jesus
Journalism Teacher
Barton, Zuilma Dehesa
School Librarian
Bath, Caledonia Payne
7th & 8th Grd Gftd & Hum Tchr
Bauer, Carole Ann Zinter
Elem Teacher & Asst Principal
Baxter, Lura Virginia
Home Ec Cooperation Ed Tchr
Bechtel, Rose Marie DeLa Cruz
4th-5th Grd Gftd & Tlntd Tchr
Becknell-Bower, Sue Carol
2nd Grade Teacher
Beeman, Leslie Kay
Wellness Teacher & Ath Trainer
Bell, Catherine Clark
Humanities Teacher
Beltran, Jesus
Assistant Principal
Benson, Mary Anne Borden
4th Grade Teacher
Bigham, Annette Marye
Occupational Ed Div & Lecturer
Blanco, Viola Carrasco
Second Grade Teacher
Blevins, Leon Wilford
Political Science Instructor
Boaz, Linda Kaiser
Fifth Grade Teacher
Boddy, Mark Joseph
PE Tchr & Var Tennis Coach
Bode, Elroy
Eng & Creative Writing Teacher
Bode, Phoebe Ordonez
English Teacher & Dept Chair
Boon, Suzanne Wright
Mathematics Teacher
Booth, Johnny Dean
Teacher of Gifted & Talented
Borrelli, Anthony James
Mathematics Teacher
Bruce, Ella Inez
Fourth Grade Teacher
Bruns, Richard Dean
English Teacher

Bunn, Fred R.
Receivables & Accounting Instr
Byrd, Cornelius, Jr.
Army JROTC Instructor
Caldwell, Chiao Ai
9th-12th Grd Math Teacher
Cannon, Michael W.
Teacher of Gifted & Talented
Card, Mitchell R.
8th Grd Earth Science Teacher
Carpenter, Gloria Ann
Retired Assistant Professor
Carpio, Cecilia
At Risk Coordinator
Cavazos, Karen Jensen
Chemistry Teacher
Chacon, Elza Candelaria
9th-12th Grade Math Teacher
Condra, Rebecca Mc Vay
Comms Teacher & Speech Coach
Cornell-Stufflebeam, Dawn Marie
Counselor
Correa, Sandra Gonzales
Sixth Grade Teacher
Cotham, Faye
AT-Risk Coordinator
Crofford, Geary Don
Honors Biology Teacher
Culler, Richard Thomas
Health Ed & Sports Med Instr
Curless, Irving Charles
English Teacher
Daniel, Kenneth Lee, II
English Teacher
DeLacretaz, Cheryl Hollingsworth
English Teacher & Dept Chprsn
Delgado, Rito
Math Professor & Sr Programmer
DeLisser, Lori Ann
English Teacher
Del Valle, Lynda Anderson
Lecturer of Eng Composition
Dickinson, Sharon Temple
Instructional Coord & Instr
Dominguez, Joseph George
Secondary English Teacher
Dominguez, Vicente Leyva
5th Grd & Adult Basic Ed Tchr
Dozal, Leonor Macias
Bilingual Education Teacher
Duarte, Ysela
Community College Instructor
Duemling, Ellen K.
English Teacher
Dunbar, Henry Wright
7th Grade Texas History Tchr
Dunlap, Karen L.
Assistant Principal
Earley, Carlton Blaine, Jr.
World History Teacher
Earnest, Candace Cook
Dance Teacher
Edgar, Don Wayne
Agricultural Sciences Instr
Edmisten, L. Leo
8th Grade Science Teacher
Edwards, John Steven
Social Studies Teacher
Eickhoff, Randy Lee
English Instructor
Endlich, Brenda Delaney
Reading Teacher
Enger, Thomas Franklin
Theater Arts & English Teacher
Escamilla, Alberto
Fine Arts Teacher
Escobar, Veronica
English Instructor
Esparza, Sylvia Renee Villa
Biology Teacher
Evans, Nancy L.
Secondary Social Studies Tchr
Faunda, Terry John
Political Science Instructor
Ferland, Cynthia Ann
Chemistry Teacher
Ferland, Norman George
Science Instructor
Fernandez, John Anthony
Math Tchr & Dept Coord
Fischer, Lucy Casavantes
GATE Program Facilitator
Flato, Steven David
Physical Education Teacher
Fleet, Randell David
1st Grade Teacher
Flores, Georgia Alice
Teacher of Gifted & Talented
Foged, Leslie Owen
Mathematics Professor
Fountain, Marcia Taylor
Professor of Music
Fourzan, Elizabeth Ann
English Teacher
Fowler, Karen (Bowers)
Nursing Instructor
Frady, Tonda Murr
8th Grade US History Teacher
Fresquez, Teresa Armendariz
High School Spanish Teacher
Friedlander, Mitchell Jay
ESL Eng Instr
Galindo, Cynthia Irene
English Teacher
Garcia, Denise Jay
English Teacher
Garvin, Eva Lee
Retired Fourth Grade Teacher
Garza, Jesus C.
Chemistry Teacher

Gawell, Francis J.
Science Teacher & Dept Chm
Geary, Ofelia Rojo
8th Grd Language Arts Teacher
Geery, Betsy Ann
Student Activities Director
Getzlaff, Kathleen Jean
English Teacher
Gillis, Joanne Siranovich
Mathematics Teacher
Golding, Frances Jean
Math Teacher
Gonzales, Bobbi Mc Conaughey
English Instructor
Gonzales, Olga Zambrano
Fourth Grade Bilingual Teacher
Gonzales, Yolanda
Secondary Mathematics Teacher
Gonzalez, Cristina
Chemistry Teacher
Gonzalez, Joe Luis
English Teacher
Gonzalez, Rosa Maria Villalobos
Spanish Teacher
Gonzalez, Yolanda
Secondary Mathematics Teacher
Gonzalez, Yvonne Aragon
English Teacher
Gonzalez-Ash, Otilia
Special Education Teacher
Goon, Walter Eugene
Teacher of Behavior Adjustment
Gragg, Diane Garman
6th Grade Teacher
Graham, Chantel Renee
English & Theater Arts Teacher
Greenberg, Luanne J.
7th Grade Language Arts Tchr
Groh, Jacklyn Lee
8th Grade Reading Teacher
Guerrero, Antonio Moreno
Photography Instructor
Guerrero, Betty Garcia
Spanish Teacher
Gutierrez, Richard
Government Ec & US His Teacher
Hafner, Donald F.
His Tchr & Soc Stud Dept Chair
Hagan, Kathy Ann
Language Arts Teacher
Hale-Hobby, Janice
Tchr of Gifted Humanities
Hall, Marilyn Miller
Science & Technology Teacher
Haney, Owen Brian
Amer Govt, Ec & World His Tchr
Hansen, Tod A.
6th Grade Teacher
Hartley, Lorry Goldfarb
Band Director
Hauser, Carolyn Steward
High School Math Teacher
Hayden, Else
High School English Teacher
Head, Kathleen Culligan
Anatomy & Physiology Teacher
Henry, Teresa M., CSJ
Math Teacher
Herman, Mark N.
Social Studies Teacher
Hernandez, Armando Raul
Social Studies Teacher
Hernandez, Susana Gomez
MS Teacher & Math Coordinator
Hill, Cheron Lee
Third Grade Teacher
Hitter, Gerald Scott
Physical Education Teacher
Hodge, Cynthia K.
HS English & Literature Tchr
Holder, Peter Cornelis
Teacher of ESL & English
Holguin, Emma H.
Foundations of Wellness Instr
Howard, Jeanne M.
Instructor & Coordinator
Hundley, Deborah Perrin
English Teacher
Hussien, Gamal Mosleh
Mathematics Instructor
Hutchins, Donald Louis
Mathematics Teacher
Hutman, Patricia Mc Gill
Social Studies Teacher
Jabalie, Carol Herron
Sixth Grade Teacher of GATE
Jimerson, Kimberli Gubis
4th Grade Teacher
John, Jurate Andrulis
First Grade Teacher
John, Sarah Elizabeth
Instructor of History
Jones, Leslie Steinmann
Social Studies Dept Chair
Juarez, Antonio
Psychology Instructor
Jubera, Christine Carol (Gazzola)
Choir Director
Kahoe, Stephen Ray
Human Services Instructor
Keller, Judith Thorsen
Sixth Grade Teacher
Kelly, Mary C.
Math Teacher
Kewley, Lona Waddel
Assistant Principal
Kiefer, Todd Cameron
Educator & Athletic Trainer
King, Steven J.
Math Teacher

Kitchens, Shirley Morgan
Science Teacher
Kolster, Mary Jane (Putschler)
Mathematics Teacher
Korri, Susan Dawn
Health & PE Teacher
Kotarski, Sharon Bridges
Mathematics & Cmptr Sci Tchr
Lamb, James Warner
Dean of Instruction
Lambrecht, Barbara Sperberg
Band Director
La Velle, Christopher Justin
Social Studies Teacher
Leonard, Christine France
Fourth Grade Teacher
Lockhart, Gerrianne
Freshman English Teacher
Long, Andrew John
Math Teacher
Look, Carolyn Eisenwine
Sixth Grade Teacher
Lopez, Patricia Arlette
Mathematics Teacher
Love, Gail Mit
TV & Radio Broadcasting Tchr
Love, Gretchen Green
Admissions & Development Dir
Lowenberg, Georgina Orellana
3rd Grade Teacher
Lundeen, Hazel Streetman
5th Grade Teacher
Lunow-Wagner, Deborah Lynn
Eighth Grade Math Teacher
Maas, Peter Edward
English Instructor
Macias, Tammy Whitt
Fifth Grade Teacher
Mackay, Emma E.
Mathematics Teacher
Marin, Alma Yvonne
Spanish Teacher
Marquez, Blanca H.
Third Grade Teacher
Martin, Sherita Steger
Mathematics Teacher
Martinez, Argelia Carmen (Gomez)
Third Grade Bilingual Teacher
Mayr, Janet Simon
Math Teacher
Mc Burrows, Bernadette Jeanne
Mathematics Teacher
Mearns, Gerri Marie
4th Grade Teacher
Mena, Criselda M.
Social Studies Teacher
Mena, Maria Socorro (Sukie)
8th Grade Humanities Teacher
Mende, Carol Durham
4th & 5th Grade Teacher
Mendez, Mary Ellen (Jorgenson)
Orchestra Director
Mendoza, Pablo, Jr.
Coordinator & Instr of Biology
Michal, Emil J., Jr.
College Instructor
Michal, Lucy Hernandez
Mathematics Instructor
Milbourn, Lawrence E.
Professor of English
Miller, Richard Scott
English Tchr & Head Bsbl Coach
Minjarez, David Joseph
6th Grade Art Teacher & Coach
Molinar, Dian O'Brien
English Teacher & Dept Chair
Molloy, Carol W.
Speech & Debate Teacher
Morales, Cristina Espinoza
5th Grade Monolingual Teacher
Morales, Norma
English Teacher
Mortensen, Carolynn Hooper
Math & Algebra Teacher
Mosier, Joel G.
World His & Journalism Teacher
Muizers, Steven Dennis
English Teacher
Neiman, Lucy A.
Math Tchr, Dept Chprsn & Coach
Ng, Alister Ying-Kau
Math & Band Teacher
Nichols, Wilton C.
American History Teacher
Olsakovsky, Elaine Japhet
Med Discipline Coord & Instr
Ornelas, Joe
Bus, Office Ed Tchr & Coord
Orona, Laura E.
4th Grd Gifted & Talented Tchr
Orrantia, Alicia Cristina
High School Special Educator
Orrantia, Juan Francisco
Instructional Tech Specialist
Ortega, Yolanda Isela Rivera
Fourth Grade Teacher
Oswald, Philip Joseph
Religion Teacher
Oth, Virginia Licon
Fifth Grade Teacher
Otto, Carlene Mario
Fourth Grade Teacher
Padilla, Josefina Legarreta
ESL Teacher
Page-Edwards, Mary
English Teacher
Parker, Marvin Leroy
Math & Science Department Head
Parrish, Valorie W.
4th Grade Teacher

EL PASO (cont)
Paselk, Nina Hon
Music Director
Pate, James Eugene
Interior Design Instr & Coord
Paton, James N.
Chemistry & Biology Teacher
Pearson, Kathryn Born
English Teacher
Pearson, Paul William
English Teacher & Coach
Peeples, Joanne V. (Larson)
Instructor of Mathematics
Penn, Barbara J.
First Grade Teacher
Perdue, Jane Cocke
Social Studies Teacher
Perez, Brenda Burke
Nursing Instructor
Phillips, Kimberly Ann
Science Teacher
Pippen, Gary
Government Teacher
Pippen, Pamela Seitz
Social Studies Teacher
Polhamus, Sylvia Garcia
English Teacher
Pool, Pat
Social Studies Teacher
Porter, Kathy Knickerbocker
7th Grd Social Studies Teacher
Portillo, Ines Fernandez
Upper Elementary Teacher
Powell, Gary
Visual Media & English Teacher
Prats, Victor Jaime
Teacher & Coach
Prim, Brent Thomas
Physics Teacher
Ramirez, Estela Isidra
Spanish Teacher
Rankin, Rebecca Partridge
Modern Dance Teacher
Ratcliffe, Barbara R.
Third Grade Teacher
Rayon, Maria Vera
6th Grade BiLingual Teacher
Reedy, Michael Eugene
Eighth Grade Reading Teacher
Resari, Felix, Jr.
Computer Literacy Teacher
Reyes, Ruben Gomez
Ind Tech & Crr Invstgtn Tchr
Richards, Jeffrey Kingman
Physical Education Teacher
Richardson, Jennifer Leslie
Publications Teacher
Rodela, George Art
History & Science Teacher
Rodriguez, Consuelo Esperanza (Castro)
Bilingual Kindergarten Teacher
Rodriguez, Margaret
Child Development Professor
Ruhl, Kenneth C.
Instructor of US History
Russell, Keith Alan
English Teacher
Saenz, Roswitha Korger
Biology Instructor
Schildt, John Mark
PE Teacher & Tennis Coach
Schwartz, C. C.
Broadcast Insructor
Schwartz, Michelle
Eighth Grade English Teacher
Seanez, Fred
Sixth Grade Teacher
Sells, Deborah Bartlett
Dept Head & Career Counselors
Shelton, Kay Frances (Ziegler)
Special Ed Resource Teacher
Shoop, Cathy D.
High School Science Teacher
Siewert, Patricia Franklin
Writing Center Director
Silva, Linda Elizabeth
Office Info Systems Instr
Skidmore, Roberta Heilhecker
English Teacher
Smith, Brenda A.
Assoc Prof of Health Science
Smith, Danny Charles
Physical Education Teacher
Smith, Jeanene Sandra Krause
Health Science Tech Instr
Snoddy, Sammy Lee
8th Grade Computer Lit Teacher
Sobey, David Lawrence
English & Pre Algebra Teacher
Soto, Fred
A P Chemistry Teacher
Souers, Sally Rutledge
Business Education Teacher
Spangler, Amy Elizabeth
English Teacher
Spott, Ronald T.
World Geography Teacher
Steadman, Ida Capshaw
Orchestra Director
Steagall, Stella Ruth
Speech Professor
Stephens, Pamela Denise
German, Spanish & Algebra Tchr
Stevenson, Arne Russell
Social Studies Teacher
Strikland, Nancy
Computer Science Professor
Swafford, Sue Cass
Honors English Teacher
Tansey, Charles Walter, II
Activities Advisor
Tapia, Armando
Physical Education Coach
Tarango, Mary Acosta
Career & Technology Teacher
Taylor, Byron Richard
English Teacher
Tess, Charlene Bourland
Eng & Creative Writing Tchr
Thompson, Barbara Barrett
English Teacher
Thompson, Barbara J. Tipps
Instr of Coll Frosh Compstn
Thompson, Ivonne Urueta
Second Grade Teacher
Thorp, Janet Feezel
1st-4th Grd Teacher of GATE
Todar, JoAnn
Drama Teacher
Townsley, Marjorie Marie
Sixth Grade Teacher
Tredway, Curtis Brook
Asst Prof of Music Education
Trominski, Gretchen Hill
Math Teacher
Trussell, Cecil Oliver
8th Grade Mathematics Teacher
Tucker, C. Yolanda Santillan
Bilingual 1st Grade Teacher
Tucker, Loralee
Counselor & Instructor
Tyler, Donna Carroll
6th Grade Reading Teacher
Valencia, Carmen D.
Third Grade Teacher
Valenica, Arlinda Mesa
Reading & Video Prdctn Teacher
Valenzuela, Joel E.
7th Grade Math Teacher
Valenzuela, Maria Yolanda
First Grade Bilingual Teacher
Valls, Minerva Ramon
2nd Grade Teacher
Vargas, Marta Lechuga
Librarian
Vasquez, Frank A.
Elementary Teacher
Vaughan, Susan Greene
Reading Specialist
Vega, Henry R.
Band Director
Velez, Patricia Ann
Reading Teacher
Vera, Veronica G.
Math Teacher
Villarreal, Armando G.
Biology Instructor
Vincent, James Thomas
AP Chemistry & Physics Teacher
Vogel, Charlene Sue
Retired Elem Tchr of GATE
Wade, Eileen Gray
Support Team Member
Wall, Gregory Wayne
High Schl PE & Health Teacher
Ward, Mattie White
Retired Elementary Teacher
Watkins, Roger A.
Vocational Business Teacher
Webb, John E., III
Student Activities Manager
Weber-Watts, Dennese
Frgn Lang Dept Chair & Teacher
Weir, Robert Paul
Elementary School Teacher
Wells, Dorothy Stewart
High School Dance Teacher
Werfelli, Mohamed E.
Math Instructor
White, Estelle Hill
Elem Physical Education Tchr
Wiederkehr, Marie Weigant
Science Teacher
Wieland, Laura Macmanus
Social Studies Teacher
Williams, Jennifer (Curbo)
English Teacher
Williams, Ruth Ybarra
Spanish Teacher
Williams, William Boyd
History Teacher
Wofford, Gordon R.
English Teacher
Wood, Leah Michele
High Resource Teacher
Worlton, Pamela Vandermark
Mathematics Teacher
Young, Nathan
Eng, His & Theater Teacher
Zubia, Raquel
Legal Admin Systems Teacher
ELECTRA
Felts, Virginia Jones
Retired Teacher
Goodwin, Janet Karen
2nd Grade Teacher
Gray, Andrea Bryant
Computer Technician
Patton, Barbara G.
Secondary Math Teacher
Pitts, Phillip Gary
Soc Stud Instr & Head Coach
Swenson, Rhonda Gay
Psych & Sociology Teacher
Wolf, Steven D.
Agriculture Science Teacher
ELGIN
Davis, Mary Jane Mundine
Elementary Teacher
Hardcastle, Ron V.
Science Teacher
Henry, Van A.
Head Band Director
Snow, Brenda Pickens
Business Teacher
Vague, Melinda G.
High School Biology Teacher
ELKHART
Bruton, Linda Thomas
High School Math Teacher
Collins, Robert Wayne
Biology Teacher
Harrod, Ted Maurice
8th Grade Earth Science Tchr
Link, Bonnie Haught
5th Grade Teacher
Lintelman, Hazel Akin
English Teacher
Mays, Alison April
Second Grade Teacher
Trim, Susan Dianne
Pre-Kindergarten Teacher
ELMATON
Pierce, Mike E.
Athl Dir & History Teacher
ELYSIAN FIELDS
Goyne, Debbie Jorstad
English Teacher & Coach
Miller, Dana Flanagan
Art Teacher
EMORY
Fisher, Lela Maxton
Business Teacher
Flagg, Denise G.
6th Grade Science Tchr & Coach
Griffin, Gigi G.
Math Teacher
Harper, Deena Brock
Science Teacher
Holden, Sandi Watts
Teacher & Cheerleader Sponsor
Peacock, J. Richard
US & World History Teacher
Rabe, Charlotte Shoemaker
Third Grade Teacher
Steinsiek, Liz A.
Business Ed Teacher
ENNIS
Cooper, Margaret S.
Mathematics Teacher
Freeman, Kay Branton
5th Grade Teacher
Hyde, Harryett Burden
Teacher of Gifted & Talented
Ivie Webb, Andrea
Teacher of Gifted & Talented
Keener, Thomas Franklin
Science Teacher
Martin, RaeAnn
Math Teacher & Dept Chprsn
Mc Burnett, Mary Barron
6th Grd Social Studies Tchr
Morgan, Tony R.
History Teacher
Mraz, Carol Nesuda
Home Economics Teacher
Muirhead, JoAnn Cribbs
Sixth Grade Reading Teacher
Muirhead, Sarah Luddecke
Special Education Teacher
Phillips, I. Virginia
English Teacher
Scott, Beverly Ann
Mathematics Teacher
Smith, Janet Eileen
Second Grade Teacher
Strunc, Ruth Carrell
History & Economics Instructor
Wastoskie, Jana Lee
Hlth, Drivers Ed Tchr & Coach
EULESS
Anderson, Jill Lynn
English & Reading Teacher
Berry, Nell Largent
Math Teacher
Coffey, Sharon Thornton
Biology & Chemistry Teacher
Fajardo, Susan Hall
English Teacher
Hayes, Patricia Anne
Biology Teacher
Hickman, Ed W.
Ath Dir & Head Ftbl Coach
Horton, Anne Gaston
Sixth Grade Teacher
Hyden, Patricia J.
GATE Teacher
Jones, Jedda
Asst Choral Director
Kallas, Karen Marie
Home Economics Teacher
Norris, Jerry David
Chemistry Teacher
Oujesky, Joy Ray
5th Grade Social Studies Tchr
Patterson, Regina Wiese
Third Grade Teacher
Shardy, Mary Murray
Mathematics Teacher
Slease, Paula Louise
Health & PE Teacher
Summy, Millicent Duncan
Office Ed Tchr & Coordinator
Travers, Joann Neil
Honors Chemistry Teacher
Woods, Gerry Geistman
Biology Teacher
EUSTACE
Beasley, Janice Mills
Principal
Hart, Robert Dennis
Assistant Superintendent
Keeling, Sandy Harris
First Grade Teacher
Large, William Norman
Director of Bands
Mizell, Maggie Boatwright
Theatre Arts, Speech, Eng Tchr
Myers, R. Gene
Chemistry Teacher
Powers, Charles Lee
Science & Biology Teacher
Slaton, Joanna Duke
English Teacher
Turnbo, Bonnie Cobb
Home Economics Teacher
EVADALE
Byrd, James M.
Vocational Agriscience Teacher
Terry, Joycelyn Harris
English Teacher
Wilson, Evelyn Dolores
Art Teacher
EVANT
Lee, Linda Roberson
4th-6th Grd Sci, Soc Stud Tchr
Tanner, Donna Hightower
Math Teacher
FABENS
Giner, Gabriel, Jr.
Secondary English Teacher
Jones, Penny Vera
English II & US History Tchr
Mangold, James Jay
Science Instructor
Russell, Lorene Katherine
Career & Technology Ed Tchr
FAIRFIELD
Wilbourn, Lynna McGuire
PE & Biology Teacher
FALLS CITY
Newberry, James Alton
Jr HS & HS Math Teacher
FARMERSVILLE
Jacobsen, Carolyn King
6th Grade Teacher
Morgan, David Andrew
Spanish & English Teacher
Tedford, Kailyn Turner
6th Grade Language Arts Tchr
FARWELL
Cole, Marcia Johnson
Middle School Teacher
Ray, Kay Struve
7th & 8th Grd Lang Arts Tchr
Stephens, Eva Dean
Jr High Teacher
FAYETTEVILLE
Mahlmann, Clarence Edward, Jr.
Science Teacher
Martinek, Sharon Malota
HS Business & Computer Teacher
FERRIS
Clark, Harold Clonce, Jr.
Physical Science Teacher
Knowles, Bobbie Vaughan
Math Teacher & Coach
FLATONIA
Orsak, Kathy Anders
Algebra I Teacher
FLORENCE
Bush, Nanci Banks
Texas & American History Tchr
Guthneck, Patricia Webster
English Dept Head
Hasbrook, Stacey
8th Grade English Teacher
Hedges, Debra S.
Health & TAAS Remediation Tchr
Killian, William Adair, Jr.
English Teacher & Coach
Melton, Claudia Dedear
Fourth Grade Teacher
Owen, Beverly Lisby
Bus Ed & Computer Instr
Roberson, Elizabeth Len
Home Economics Teacher
Smith, Patricia Laubach
Spanish & Art Teacher
FLORESVILLE
Armstrong, Katherine Ann (Gutz)
Reading Teacher
Barber, Mary Anne (Woolsey)
Teacher
Bennett, Neal Scott
Algebra & Geometry Teacher
Byrd, Virginia Rohr
Language Arts Teacher
Flieller, Linda Stuebben
Fifth Grade Teacher
Harrison, Robert Joseph
World History Teacher
Ingram, Camille Rider
English Teacher
Ingram, Walter Edward
English Teacher & Coach
Koenig, Leila (Bailey)
Home Economics Teacher
Laskowski, Barbara McFadden
English Dept Teacher & Chprsn
Reed, Bonna Jackson
Theater Arts Teacher
Robinson, Charlotte Jane
MS Physical Education Teacher
Schulz, Linda Freeman
Business Teacher
Witten, Sue K.
English Teacher
Young, Ernest D.
Sci Chair, Math & Physics Tchr
FLOWER MOUND
Atkinson, Kevin G.
Health Teacher & Coach
Brown, Diana L.
AP Caluclus Teacher
Cochran, Susan Kay
English Teacher
Cooley, Marcie F.
English II & IV Teacher
Crawford, Cheryl L.
English Teacher & Dept Chm
Feaster, Henri Lynn
Mathematics Tchr & Dept Chair
George, Rose Kathrine
Social Studies Teacher
Godbey, Rhonda Layne
Eng & Creative Writing Tchr
Kemper, Lou Ann McClatchey
Eng & AP European His Tchr
Kuecker, Cerelle Brinson
4th Grade Teacher
Leech, Bonnie Coulter
Secondary Mathematics Tchr
Maddox, Melisande
Latin Teacher
Martin, Peggy Morrison
Assistant Principal
Milam, Frank Byron
A P Biology Teacher
O'Leary, Daniel George
Principal
Pearson, Jeanne Frazier
English Teacher
Rooker, Paige
Spanish & Honors Teacher
Sutcliffe, Gail Baker
French Teacher
Telaneus, Steven Edward
Biology Teacher
Van Vooren, Marilyn Barnes
Fourth Grade Teacher
Woodard, Ami Elizabeth (Lipscomb
Dance Teacher & Drill Team Dir
FLOYDADA
Chadwick, Jackie
Language Arts Teacher
FORNEY
Johnson, Grace E.
Assistant Principal
Kreder, Lori Renee
Soc Stud & Jrnlsm Tchr
Rogers, Virginia Krause
Fifth Grade Teacher
Watts, Sandy S.
7th Grade English Tchr & Coach
FORSAN
Light, Linda Ritter
Jr High Reading Teacher
FORT DAVIS
Davidson, Terence Donald
Director of Music
Medley, Oscar L.
HS Principal
Seipp, Pamela Peiser
7th-12th Grade Science Teacher
FORT HANCOCK
Garcia, Rick
Health Teacher & Vlybl Coach
Robles, Luis Antonio
9th-12th Grd Eng Tchr & Coach
FORT HOOD
Mullen, Candace Hubin
English Teacher
FORT SAM HOUSTON
Hudson, James Patrick, Sr.
Social Studies Teacher
Jolivette, Angela Stokes
Sixth Grade Teacher
Rowland, Nancy Sue
Math Teacher
FORT STOCKTON
Card, Tracy Lee
High School Math Teacher
Cordero, Rosalinda Celaya
7th Grade English Teacher
Franco, Janice Sutton
Fifth Grade Teacher
Hammond, Charles Thomas
In Schl Suspension Dir & Coach
Houston, Belva Hebison
Third Grade Teacher
Huelster, Dorthea L.
English Teacher
Lopez, Philip J.
Athletic Director
Mc Masters, David Lee
Social Studies Teacher
Newton, Janet Link
AP Math & AP Cmptr Sci Teacher
Tavarez, Rachel R.
High School Math Teacher
Yeager, Molly L.
Facilitator of the Gifted
FORT WORTH
Adams, Leann Cox
Humanities Teacher
Aikman, Phillip Leroy
Band Director
Anagnostis, Anthe
Lang Arts & US History Teacher
Anderson, Jeanett May
Associate Prof of Nursing
Arredondo, Alice M.
Business Education Teacher
Bach, Pamela (Hodges)
Mathematics Teacher

VORTH (cont)
na, Wayne Joseph
ate Professor
Kathy L.
ant Professor in Nursing
Jerry Duane, II
tor of Biology
Shelly A.
y Teacher
tha M.
Science Tchr & Dept Chm
Paul
rof of Pol Sci & His
Dana D.
d Eng & Soc Stud Tchr
Kathy S.
Band Director
atsy Burks
n Language Pathologist
Betsy Jan
y Teacher
l, Bettie Munn
h Teacher
Rita Collins
School Teacher
Cindy Adams
Grade Teacher
onald Lynn
y Teacher
Mildred Elizabeth Bailey
& Physical Ed Tchr
arol Anne
English Teacher
k, Tonya Brock
Geography Instructor
Margaret Mogg
er & Coach
, Julie
h Teacher
Iris Ann
e Teacher & Coordinator
an, Michelle Greenlee
h Teacher
, Arnel A.
on Teacher
Martha Lee
rade English Teacher
anice Jones
Grade Teacher
Barbara Dyson
matics Teacher
ell, Sherry Martin
y & Government Teacher
ell, Valerie Denise
Grade Music Teacher
Stephen Scott
h Teacher
David Clark
d Tchr, Coach & Ed Prof
ers, Georgia T.
ade Teacher
Lisa Michelle
History Teacher
Cynthia Ann
sh, French & ESL Teacher
, Tina Remualdo
rade Language Arts Tchr
Pamela Denise
d States History Teacher
ale, David Jay
Prof of History & Govt
n, Janet Morton
ng Teacher
, L. Mark
nced Placement Eng Tchr
Block, Cathy
ssor of Education
on, Barbara Ann
entary Music Teacher
on, Joanna Hooker
2th Grade Health Teacher
ly, Sharron S.
eacher
y, Brian Arthur
rd Language Arts Teacher
s, Jerry Lynn
orce Jr ROTC Instructor
Joyce Evelyn
Cmptr Applications Teacher
Wilma Brown
rade Teacher
Loita (Oldham)
h Teacher
ck, Lela Brown
rade Language Arts Tchr
l, Elaine
rade Teacher
el, Susan Stevens
School Math Teacher
son, Kathy Tatum
ance Counselor
t, Angela Sneed
ipal
, Penny Keating
nistry Teacher
, Catherine
Teacher
, Twyla Thomas
of Reading & Dept Chair
s, Gloria Gail
nd Grade Teacher
Darrell Logan
Grade Teacher
Janet E.
Grade Teacher
Mildred Delois
ish Teacher
Pamela Washington
sh Teacher

Day, Allison Womack
Sr English Teacher
Dickey, Linda
Kindergarten Teacher
Dixon, Donna Karalyn
English Teacher & Dept Chair
Dollar, David Lynn
Chemistry Teacher
Donaldson, Elizabeth Cardiff
Kindergarten & First Grd Tchr
Downs, Jarrett Dalton
Former Sci Instructor
Drisdale, Vivian Alpha
Retired First Grade Teacher
Dudek, Katherine Perry
10th Grade English Teacher
Edwards, Joseph, Jr.
Technology Systems Instructor
Eikenberry, Linda Poremba
Social Studies Teacher
Ellis, David W.
Assistant Principal
Ellison, Steven Fletcher
World Culture & Thought Tchr
Emerson, Donna Marie
Academic Counselor
English, Richard Paul
Teacher & Coach
English, Teresa Smart
Director
Epstein, Marcia Dawn
Reading Teacher
Espinosa, Miriam Tankersley
Dept of Languages & Lit Chair
Fellers, Lynne Herthum
High School Teacher
Felts, Lee A.
English Teacher
Ferguson, Vivian McClanahan
Second Grade Teacher
Fisher, Susan Denise
Assistant Principal
Force, Catherine Alden
English Teacher
Ford, Janice Lynn (Coopwood)
English Teacher
Ford, Kevin Andrew
Mathematics Teacher
Franklin, Chris
Elementary School Counselor
Franklin, Ron Dale
Choral Director
Fredette, Robert Michael
Sixth Grade Social Stud Tchr
Frost, Laura Reaka
Anatomy, Physiology & Bio Tchr
Frye, Bob J.
Professor of English
Gaos-Cornehls, Paloma
Spanish & Literature Teacher
Gavras, Sally Schwierzke
Freshman Teacher
Gavrel, Beverly Bass
Kindergarten Teacher
Gehrmann, William H.
Professor of Biology
Gilbert, Timothy Dwain
Assoc Prof of Philosophy
Glenn, Lexie Renfro
Theatre Arts & Comp Lit Tchr
Grissom, Vicki Terry
Title 1 Teacher
Guyon, Keith
Life Science Teacher
Haber, Marian Wynne Feit
Coll Nwspr Adv & Jrnlsm Tchr
Halbach, Melodee
Theatre Arts Instructor
Hammond, Gayle C.
HS Am Govt, Ec, & AP His Instr
Hammond, James Michael
French Teacher
Hardgrove, Molly Kate
English Teacher
Harding, Beverly Pyles
English Teacher
Harrison, Susie Kathrine
Lead Teacher of Art Department
Haynie, Janette Mc Kithan
Business Ed Teacher
Hedin, Norma Sanders
Foundations of Ed Asst Prof
Hemminger, Clyde Clayton
Texas History & Science Tchr
Hill, Marsha Cooper
Owner & Director
Holder, Elizabeth Barrett
Choir Director
Hollerich, Laura Koni
5th Grade Teacher
Horn, Bruce Gavin
Social Studies & German Tchr
House, Linda Jones
7th Grade Mathematics Teacher
Howton, Lucille Bremner
Latin & Spanish Teacher
Hudkins, Linda Taylor
English Teacher
Huff, David V.
Fine Arts Chairman & Bands Dir
Ingram, James A.
Fifth Grade Teacher
Ivie, Tonya Lynn
American History Teacher
James, Luanne Riggs
Social Studies Teacher
Johnson, Lou Vetrice Kennard
4th-5th Grade Music Teacher
Johnson, Marilyn A.
World Georgraphy Teacher

Jones, Charles Alan
Economics & US Government Tchr
Jordan, Nancy Nunn
Child Care & PAL Teacher
Joy, Rebecca Jett
Teacher
Joyce, Katie M.
English Teacher
Kanaga, Cynthia Scott
English & Art Teacher
Kenny, Sean Joseph
Amer Govt & Hist Tchr
Kerr, MaryBeth
Journalism Teacher
Kimberling, Cheryl Gray
Professor of Sociology
King, Marge E.
Spanish Teacher
Kliewer, Stacia Findley
Math Teacher
Kramer, Suzanne Bir
Foreign Lang Coord & Span Chr
Krause, Frederick William
ESL, Algebra & Geometry Tchr
Kuban, Joseph Frank, Jr.
Biology & Ecology Teacher
Langston, Lisa Lynne
Intramural Athletics Director
Le Doux, Angela Erin
Ninth Grade English Teacher
Leonard, Sara Botello
Fourth Grade Bilingual Teacher
Levy, Elisabeth Livingstone
Director & Teacher
Light, Triesha M.
Associate Professor of Psych
Lindsey, Lori Wallace
Math & Business Teacher
Lott, R. Allen
Music History Professor
Love, Donna Bostick
Second Grade Teacher
Lowrance, Hazel Monnette (Cantrell)
Retired Teacher
Lunday, Kristi Jean Willis
Drug Prevention Pgm Specialist
Maas, Nancy Mc Neill
Retired Tchr of the Gifted
Maddux, Deborah Taylor
Seventh Grade Science Teacher
Malunowe, LaShan Benson
PE & Dance Teacher
Martin, Patricia Richmond
English Dept Chprsn & Teacher
Martinez, Irma Flores
Spanish Teacher
Marut, Janice Beverley
8th Grade Teacher & Asst Prin
Massey, Connie
8th Grade Science Teacher
Massie, Eddie
PE Teacher & Coach
Master, Lesa Daffern
Freshman English Teacher
Matthews, Cynthia Ann
High School English Teacher
May, Patsy Jean
Fifth Grade Teacher
Mc Combs, Linda Clark
English Teacher
Mc Keean, Stephen D.
HS Principal & Teacher
McLelland, Terry K. Hart
Vice Principal
Mercer, Jan Stanford
Associate Prof of Biology
Michael, Cynthia Kennedy
Social Studies Teacher
Miller, Danna Lewisa
English Teacher
Milligan, Kay Lynn
Speech & Theatre Arts Teacher
Mitchell, Robert Clinton, III
Physical Education Teacher
Moddrell, Cheryl M.
Mathematics Instructor
Moeller, Michael Lynn
Physics & Biology Teacher
Moerbe, Beverly Murray
Theatre Director
Moore, Sara Bolen
Clinical Instructor
Moreaux, Pamela J. Sanders
Social Studies Coord & Chprsn
Morgan, Lorraine Jones
5th Grade Teacher
Morris, Regena Blasdel
Business & Vocational Teacher
Morrow, Stephen Twain
Assistant Principal
Mowry, Janice Litton
Math & Bible Teacher
Murray-Zinn, Martha
Eighth Grade English Teacher
Nabors, Robert Edward
Professor of Biology
Neisius, Jean Gano
English Teacher
Nichols, Glenda Wilkes
Asst Prof of Social Sciences
Pace, Frank
Educational Consultant
Paulose, Painadath Ettoop
Mathematics Dept Chairman
Pemberton, Debra Moses
Teacher & HECE Coordinator
Penland, Cheryl Ann
Speech & Theatre Arts Teacher
Philp, Marjory Kay
AP US His Teacher & Chrmn

Pittard, Pamela Berry
First Grade Teacher
Polito, Kenneth Lee
English & French Teacher
Poteet, Pamela Joy
8th Grade Math Teacher
Powell, Jodie E.
Physical Education Teacher
Preston, Robin Louise
5th & 7th Grade Teacher
Price, Jenny Bolt
Magnet English Teacher
Price, Joel David
Mathematics Professor
Pridemore, Ann Morrison
Home Ec Cooperative Ed Teacher
Prince, David Glenn
4th Grade Teacher
Proctor, Candace Bates
History Teacher
Rainwater, Joyce Kelley
Educational Consultant
Rankin, Loris Jean
Fifth Grade Teacher
Reirdon, Suzanne R.
Professor of English
Reyelts, Beatriz
First Grade Teacher
Reynolds, William Jensen
Distngd Prof of Church Music
Richmond, Annemarie Strobl
Associate Professor & Coord
Riggs, Melba Woolsey
Sci Teacher & Dept Chairperson
Rist, Mark Joseph
Theology Teacher
Rittby, C. Magnus L.
Assistant Professor
Roberts, Cheryl W.
English Instructor
Robertson, Charlene Kerns
Coach
Robinson, James David
Associate Professor of Voice
Rogers, Patti Maberry
Fifth Grade Teacher
Rolfe, Teresa L.
Band, Orchestra Dir & Coach
Rowe, Rachel Escobar
Assistant Principal
Rueda-Garcia, Ana Isabel
Assistant Professor of Spanish
Russell, Rebecca Ritchie
American History Teacher
Sabin, Patricia Dianne (Penn)
Fifth Grade Teacher
Sawyer, Chris Roberts
Associate Professor of Speech
Schrantz, Theresa Lee
Asst Prof of Soclgy & Psych
Schulte, Elizabeth Barbara
Assistant Professor of Nursing
Schuricht, Joann Scaparra
2nd-3rd Grd Montessori Tchr
Scott, Judith Higgins
US History & English Teacher
Self, Mary Jane
Choir Director
Shelton, William Allen
History Dept Chairman
Shults, Linda Marshall
PE Teacher & Coach
Sims, Deborah C.
Second Grade Teacher
Slaughter, Arthur, Jr.
Government Professor
Smith, Janice Yoder
Professor of Biology
Somerville-Holland, Saundra L.
English Teacher
Spellmon, Regina Griffin
Vice Principal & Bible Instr
Stafford, Claudia Jones
5th Grade Teacher
Steinberger, Jacque
High School Business Teacher
Stephenson, Carol A.
Assoc Prof of Nursing
Stewart, G. Bryan
Math, Physics & Engrng Tchr
Stewart, Stan Mark
Hlth, CPR Instr & Golf Coach
Stone, Jana Townsend
Spanish Teacher
Stone, Patti Lynn
Third Grade Teacher
Stringer, Bobbi Rhe
Assistant Professor of Speech
Sunkel, Cathryn Cunyus
Health Science & Tech Teacher
Szedeli, Brenda Blair
Assistant Principal
Talbert, Jerre Suddath
Reading & English Teacher
Tatum, Margaret A.
Pre-K Teacher
Taylor, Brenda Jeanette
Assistant Professor of History
Taylor, Martha Roberson
Science Teacher
Taylor, Shirley Williams
Multi-Age Teacher
Templeton, Candace Resener
English II Teacher
Tepfer, Judith Jo
English Teacher
Thomas, Rexanne Bower
Curriculum Director
Thorn, Charles Leon
Assoc Prof of Criminal Justice

Thornton, Lue Ann Renfro
Eighth Grade English Teacher
Thrasher, Christy Allison
Biology Teacher
Thurman, Kathy Gene
Gifted & Talented Specialist
Tinsley, Robert James
Spanish & Science Teacher
Townsend, John Eric
Industrial Technology Teacher
Trawick, Gene Sossamon
First Grade Teacher
Treat, Barbara Ann
Foreign Lang Tchr & Dept Chm
Tunstle, Bennie Ruth
Social Studies Teacher
Tutton, Kimberly Anne
Kindergarten Teacher
Tweed, Marsha C.
Teacher & AP Coordinator
Vandewalker, Eddie
Vocal Music Teacher
Vann, Elton G.
Vocational Drafting Teacher
Vann, Laura Clark
Math & Physics Teacher
Vera, Adan P.
7th-8th Grd Soc Studies Tchr
Vissotzky, Dawn Andress
Business Computer Teacher
Walker, Dawn Barnard
Art Teacher
Wamsley, John
Mathematics Teacher
Ware, Sherry Moore
French Teacher
Watkins, Regina Peck
Business Teacher
Weatherholt, Pauline Shipp
Mathematics Teacher
Welden, Melinda Merrill
5th Grade Teacher
West, Etalia Elaine
Physical Education Teacher
West, Michael Patrick
High School Science Teacher
Westfall, Richard E., Jr.
Mathematics Teacher
White, Betty Jackson
Theatre Art Teacher
Wilson, Evelyn M. Funderburk
Professor of Eng
Winslow, John Lynn
Band Director
Wolanski, Barbara Bryant
Reading Teacher
Wood, Barbara Hedgecock
Dance Teacher
Wood, Laura Matysek
Assoc Prof of History & Govt
Wooley, Kent Richard
Social Studies Teacher
Wright, Nancy D.
Spanish & English Teacher
Wright, Theda Martin
Lead Math Teacher
Yokely, Danny Eugene
Athletic Coordinator
Young, Sharon Townsend
Computer Applications Tchr
Zamora, Margarita Christina
Office System Tech, Assoc Prof
Zamora, Pauline Zarate
Pre-Kndgtn & Bilingual Teacher
Zobal, Julie Miller
8th Grade English Teacher
Zuege, Pamella DeBord
World Geography Teacher
Zurawski, Janice Berry
Mathematics Teacher

FRANKSTON
Bacon, Billie Horn
English Teacher
Beard, Dianne Harris
MS Science & English Teacher
Horton, Carol
Amer History, Govt & Yrbk Tchr
Merritt, Susan K.
Computer & Business Teacher
Phillips, Mary Mc Lane
English, Reading & Cmptr Tchr
Smith, Jim
Middle School Teacher

FRED
Fountain, Karen Smith
First Grade Teacher

FREDERICKSBURG
Bonn, Terry Walter
Mathematics Teacher
Childers, Jim L.
Band Director
Fields, Scott
Agricultural Sciences Teacher
Grona, Karen Kozusko
Journalism Teacher
Hickman, Paul
Computer Teacher
Iden, Catherine Reindel
Coord of Mentoring Program
Pruessner, Hal
Math & Science Teacher
Smith, Natalie D.
English Teacher & Dept Chm

FREEPORT
Comeaux, Bryan P.
Marine Science Teacher & Coach
Darby, Garth Mark
History Teacher & Coach
Flores, Paula G.
Title I Reading Teacher

FREEPORT (cont)
Garcia, Rita Rene
Physical Science Teacher
Harrison, Cynthia L.
Reading Teacher
Johnson, Susan Lloyd
4th Grade Teacher
Martin, Laura Coleman
8th Grade Lang Arts Teacher
Mc Fadden, Marjorie (Rezabek)
Retired 5th Grade Teacher
Robinson, Karen Wycliff
Ninth Grade English Teacher
Schulte, Ken
Physics Teacher & Coach
FREER
Ford, Robert Todd
Physical Science Teacher
Guajardo, Carol E.
Fifth Grade Teacher
Radske, Frederick Walter
History Teacher
FRIENDSWOOD
Cornelius, Viki F.
Honors Algebra II Teacher
Daniels, Gary D.
Social Studies Teacher
Fernandez, Norma D.
School Counselor
Flagg, Helen Morrissette
English Teacher
Foulk, Richard David
Chemistry & Physiology Teacher
Freytag, Vicki Lynn
English & Journalism Teacher
Fried, Aaron Arnold
Chemistry Teacher
Galli, Marni
4th Grade Teacher
Graham, Barbara R.
Spcl Ed Teacher & Team Leader
Graham, Joe
Yearbook & Newspaper Advisor
Hannemann, Joel F.
Head Athletic Trainer
Harvey, Larry D.
Biology Teacher
Kyle, Carol Tindall
Chemistry Teacher
Lane, Janet (Rose)
Third Grade Teacher
LeBlanc, J. Eric
Geometry & Health Teacher
Martin, Diane Liggio
Assistant Principal
Mc Gown, Douglas Lamar
HS Physical Science Teacher
Payne, Mary Kathryn
Computer Reading Teacher
Pieniazek, Gail P.
Agricultural Science Teacher
Scharff, Gayle Fogarty
Fourth Grade Teacher
Schultz, Sven Eric
Bus Computer Tchr & Coach
Scott, Marian Elizabeth
Counselor
Shanks, Carol Mills
French Teacher
Simsarian, Karen Ann
6th Grade Mathematics Teacher
Stuckey, John Raymond
Band Director
Swalin, Diane A.
English Teacher
True, Judy Keenum
5th Grade Teacher
Tyler, Linda Hutchens
First & Second Grd Rdng Tchr
FRIONA
Mc Lellan, Loy Christian
Elementary School Counselor
FRISCO
Burnett, Rick Allan
Principal
Hill, DiAnn Carroll
English Teacher
Hodge, Gary Bruce
Sociology Professor
Jackson, Rhonda Gail Furr
English & Sociology Teacher
Mills, Stacy Winton
Reading Recovery Teacher
Oldham, Sharon L.
Math Teacher
Watson, David A.
Seventh Grade TX History Tchr
Williams, Karen Jean Cordell
French & History Teacher
FRITCH
Jackson, Mitzi Scoggins
Choral Director
Jameson, Dusti Whatley
Spanish Teacher
Johnson, Carolyn Haverkorn
English Teacher
McFerrin, Janice Bruce
English & Journalism Teacher
Mooring, Sarah Schroeder
Secondary Mathematics Teacher
Thomas, Paul Edward
Phys Sci, Chem & Physics Tchr
Youngblood, Patti Martin
English Teacher
FROST
Griste, Charles R.
Computer Teacher
FRUITVALE
Beatty, Mark
Director of Bands
Lambright, Carol Hampton
Kindergarten Teacher
Murphy, Samantha F.
First Grade Teacher
Sutton, Mischeal Steinert
Composite Science Teacher
GAIL
Lewis, Carol Patterson
English Teacher
GAINESVILLE
Bowden, Patricia Keil
English Teacher
Carter, Louis H., Jr.
Art Teacher
Dozier, Mary J.
Retired Teacher
Evans, Melissa S.
English Teacher
Fleitman, Debbie Interwicz
English I Teacher
Foster, Mary Ann Williams
Teacher for Visually Impaired
Gibson, Gail F.
College Accounting Instructor
Henry, Eddy
Texas History Teacher
King-Stark, Margaret Jo
Retired Kindergarten Teacher
Lacey, Kathryn Aronson
Science Teacher
LaFlamme, Rebecca A.
English Teacher
Schalk, Joybell
Algebra Teacher
Spillers, Douglas Clinton
High School Computer Teacher
Van Pelt, Mary Frances (Evans)
Art Professor
Zangoei, Candace Vincent
English III Teacher
GALENA PARK
Breaux, Edwina Lilly
Mathematics Teacher
Brinkley, Roland
Band Dir & Arts Dept Head
Calderon, Gloria R.
Spanish Teacher
Fantini, Julie Ann
English Teacher
Goodwin, Traci Sanders
Curr Ldr & Lang Art Tchr
Googins, Julie Barrett
4th Grade Teacher
Grantham, Terri L.
French Teacher
Huffman, Nancy Eileen
Language Arts Teacher
Leslie, Roger James
Creative Writing & Eng Tchr
Lewis, Earline Breed
7th Grade Math Teacher
Mc Comb, Jilldeana Koehler
Coord of Gifted & Talented
Newcomb, Martha Jane
Social Studies Dept Chair
Reyes, Camilla Anne
Bilingual ESL Teacher
Sivil, Valerie Landry
Second Grade Teacher for GATE
Smolka, Kimberley Fielder
High School Math Teacher
Trawick, Sharon Spencer
Science Teacher & Dept Chprsn
GALVESTON
Daniels, Barbara LaDean (Ray)
English Teacher
Elias, Juanita White
Physical Education Teacher
Eriksson, Erika Victoria
Math, PE & Hlth Tchr
Evans, Jeffery D.
Morality & Ethics Teacher
High, Jeffrey James
Assistant Principal
Iliffe, Thomas M.
Asst Prof of Marine Biology
John, Brock Beckham
Physics Teacher
Kleinecke, Barbara L.
English Teacher
Leyva, Simon
Spanish Teacher
Meng, Anne L.
Assistant Professor
Merchant, Diane Bowers
6th Grd Language Arts Teacher
Mignerey, Linda
Math Teacher
Morgan, Beverly Bentley
World History Teacher
Rappaport, Bethany A.
Asst Professor of Nursing
Weatherton, Jerry Linn
English Teacher
Worthy, Graham Anthony James
Assoc Prof of Marine Mammalogy
GANADO
Kruse, Georgie Kovar
Fourth Grade Teacher
Marquardt, Rhonda Brauchle
Social Studies Teacher & Chm
Prochaska, Timmy James
Agriculture Science Teacher
GARDEN CITY
Kinnibrugh, Misty Clay
Sixth Grade Teacher
GARLAND
Abronowitz, Todd Jason
AP Chemistry Teacher
Arnold, Debbie
Student Services Specialist
Axe, Charles David
HS Gifted World His Teacher
Baker, David M.
Health Ed Tchr & Ath Trainer
Banks, Katrina Linder
Third Grade Teacher
Barnes, Ricky Joe
Teacher
Baugher, Gail A.
6th Grade English Teacher
Beam, Gay Osburn
English Teacher
Beene, Silvia Gutierrez
Home Economics Teacher
Bell, Betty J.
Journalism Teacher
Bell, Ronald Thomas
Vocational Drafting Instructor
Berwald, Denise Marie
Fr Tchr & Frgn Lang Dept Chair
Beshears, Robert Earl
6th-12th Grade Band Director
Boring, Jeri Rollins
First Grade Teacher
Bost, Jennifer Ann
Intl Baccaulaureate Psych Tchr
Briggs, Alanna Jorja
Theatre Arts Dir & Speech Tchr
Brock, Shirley Rosemarie
PE & History Teacher
Brown, Beverly Diane
Reading Recovery Teacher
Burns, Margaret Ann
First Grade Teacher
Clare, Robert John
Industrial Technology Teacher
Coalson, Virginia Ann (Jordan)
5th Grade Teacher
Collins, Joyce Ball
Third Grade Teacher
Collins, Susan Adler
First Grade Teacher
Crumpley, Paula L.
English Teacher
Dewees, Vernon Ross
Physics Teacher
Driver, Derek Brian
World Geography Tchr & Coach
Driver, Elizabeth M.
AP English & British Lit Tchr
Dveirin, Janice Lynn
7th Grade English Teacher
Gordon, Mary Ellen
Fifth Grade Teacher
Graham, Garry Dwain
American History Teacher
Hager, Terry Alan
Band Director
Hammerle, Stephen Helms
High School Asst Principal
Harris, Rosalyn Bartol
Mathematics Teacher
Harter, Val Jean (Pinkner)
Fourth Grade Teacher
Haskell, Loretta Carolyn
High School Media Specialist
Helton, Gail Buzbee
Counselor
Herrington, Stewart Clay
Math Tchr & Stu Cncl Spon
Heslink, Sue Ann
Math Department Chair
Hicks, Barry Reid
AP & Reg Economics Teacher
Hollenkamp, Linda Feldman
First Grade Teacher
Holmes, Marimozelle
Stu Svcs Specialist & PAL Tchr
Hooper, Randy L.
Choir Director
Hunter, Evelyn Love
Assistant Principal
Jones, George W.
Band Director
Kersh, David
Director of Theatre Arts
Kinsey, Tari Smith
Mathematics Teacher
LeMaster, Mark E.
Assistant Principal
Lewis, Karen Mabry
Choral Director
Like, Susan Mary
Math Teacher
Littleton, Ronnie Charles
English Teacher & Athletic Dir
Lowen, Elaine Jackson
Mathematics Teacher
Luecht, Craig Michael
Stu Act Dir & Soc Stud Tchr
Maher, Daniel L.
English Teacher
Mairs, Judi Ferry
Fourth Grade Teacher
Matteson, Jennifer Leigh
Spanish Teacher
Maveety, Claudia Storminger
French Teacher
Mayfield, Jana Lynn
English Reading Teacher
Mc Coy, Johnny Ray
Girls Athletics Coach
Mc Elmon, Barbara Eades
Career & Technology Teacher
Mc Kinney, Linda B.
Biology I, II, AP Teacher
Mills, Cynthia Sue
Spanish Teacher
Millsap, Mary Lou
Career Tech Tchr & Dept Chair
Motl, Kevin Conrad
Social Studies Teacher
Murray, Julie Trolinger
Spanish Teacher
Olschwanger, Lisa Joy
HS Mathematics Teacher
Parker, Stephen Wayne
Business Teacher
Philp, Paul William
World His, AP European Teacher
Pierce, Barnard
Reassignment Room Teacher
Potter, Linda Sue
6th-8th Grade Reading Teacher
Reyna, Paul Vincent
Sixth Grade Science Teacher
Richard, Geoffrey William
Retired Math & Cmptr Sci Tchr
Ridley, Sharme Sparrow
English Teacher
Robertson, Rick
Social Studies Teacher & Coach
Roden, Linda Presley
Fourth Grade Teacher
Roger, James Philip
Art Teacher
Rogers, Sharon Ann Lowe
Fine Arts Dept Head & Teacher
Schaefer, Bobbi Lea
Psychology & History Teacher
Scheu, Michael Dale
Agricultural Sci & Tech Tchr
Schnitzer, Larry
Band Director
Schoch, Patricia Johnson
English as Second Lang Teacher
Schrap, Wanda Marie
Mathematics Teacher
Scott, Sue J.
Third Grade Teacher
Seidel, Harry Samuel, Jr.
Anatomy & Physiology Teacher
Shanks, Dawn Ely
8th Grade Algebra Teacher
Smith, Frances Gooch
Fourth Grade Teacher
Smith, Linda Leanse
Rdng, His & Cultural Stud Tchr
Spain, Phyllis Ann
HS English II Honors Teacher
Speer, David John
HS Science Teacher
Spurgin, Kevin Scott
Science Teacher
Stone, Billie Dee
Senior Honors English Teacher
Svensson, Peggy Jackson
Honors English III Teacher
Swor, Judy Long
Spanish Teacher
Terry, Charles Richard
Science Teacher
Terry, Marilyn Adams
Art Teacher
Timpa, Gerald Lee
Student Activities Director
Toney, James Todd
Band Director
Treadway, Patricia Dawn Williams
World Geog & Economics Tchr
Vonderheid, Randy
Journalism Teacher
White, Patricia Ainsworth
5th Grade Teacher
White, Patricia Pearcy
Lead Counselor
Williams, Diana Bryant
2nd Grade Teacher
GARRISON
Caldwell, Nellie Ruth Bryant
First Grade Teacher
Hubbard, Donald R.
AD, Head Coach & History Tchr
Kimbrough, Sheron Rushing
7th & 8th Grade English Tchr
Prince, Wayne Allen
Chemistry, Anatomy & Phys Tchr
GARY
Boone, Timothy Kiel
Ag Science Teacher
GATESVILLE
Ament, Deborah Lynn (Hosek)
6th Grade Reading Teacher
Evans, Paul
Indstrl Cooperative Trng Tchr
Graham, Linda Dorsey
6th Grade Language Arts Tchr
Kerr, Reba Janelle Richardson
Retired Teacher
Payne, Carol Ann (Woodlock)
Math Teacher
GEORGETOWN
Cavender, Theresa Marie
English Teacher
Chamier, Suzanne
French Professor
Davidson, Pamela Griffeth
Teacher of Multihandicapped
Giddings, Janice Minger
8th Grade Language Arts Tchr
Green, Moya Jan (Wilkinson)
English Teacher
Hewlett, Janet Busby
High Schl Business Teacher
Hill, Clayton Louis
Health Teacher
Hindelang, Judy Wolf
English Teacher
Hudspeth, Paul Emmett
11th & 12th Grade Physics Tchr
Krenek, Terri Cole
Chemistry Teacher
Reese, Lana Krueger
Language Arts Teacher
Reierson, Sherry Ann Lipham
Seventh Grade Lang Arts Tchr
Sansom, Anna Jane Jones
First Grade Teacher
Spruill, Butch
High School History Teacher
Treuhardt, D. Beverly Huie
Third Grade Teacher
Warren, Ryder Forrest
Administrative Assistant
Washington, Rebecca Nan
Principal
Williams, Janiece Marie
6th Grade Language Arts Tchr
Wright, Lisa Dunson
7th Grade English Teacher
Zenner, Nancy Mc Millan
Health Science Tech Coord
GERONIMO
Coulston, Benny Carl
Guidance Counselor
Haberle, Cathy Lynn
First Grade Teacher
Morris, Paul Ray
Teacher
Mueck, Martin James
Agricultural Science Teacher
Sagebiel, Mary Alice Hardy
Sixth Grade Teacher
GIDDINGS
Berger, Debra Cowsert
Second Grade Teacher
Boatman, Zack W.
English & Theater Arts Tchr
Dock, L'Anna Howard
Biology Teacher
Horne, Leslie
Third Grade Teacher
Sheffield, Rhea Slaughter
Keyboarding Teacher
Smith, Helen Fox
Retired Teacher
Varnado, Jerry Evans
Business Manager
GILMER
Adkinson, Carla Joyce Rowe
English Teacher
Cannon, Debbie O.
Math Teacher
Clifton, Beth Ferguson
Music Teacher
Davidson, Vicki Lynn
Physical Education Teacher
Gaddis, Donna Kaye
Health, History & PE Teacher
Griffin, Sally Beth
Business Teacher
Gunn, Karen K.
Kindergarten Teacher
Holmes, Tammy Gray
6th-8th Grades Art Teacher
Johnson, Charles M.
Social Studies Teacher
Marshall, Judy Carroll
Third Grade Teacher
Metzel, Robert Alan
World History Teacher
Rancilio, Guy J.
Social Studies Dept Chairman
Shipp, Carla G. England
Kindergarten Teacher
Smith, Lisa McPeek
Pre-School Teacher
Walker, James W.
Secondary Science Teacher
Webb, Darren Lomax
Health Teacher & Coach
Whitaker, Jed E.
Athletic Director & Coach
GLADEWATER
Boyd, Betty Jane
4th Grade Teacher
Chitwood, Ray Allen
Retired Principal
Crews, Brian Lee
Graphic Arts & Printing Tchr
Freeman, Frances DeLois
Physical Education Teacher
Haggard, Carol Young
Home Economics Teacher
Harrison, Gay Owens
Jr HS Language Arts Teacher
Hudson, Betty Jo (Magness)
Mathematics Teacher
Lambert, Suzanne M.
English Teacher
Mathews, Gloria Langford
6th Grade Language Arts Tchr
McChristian, Dawn Michelle
High School Counselor
Mitchell, Stelvin
Agricultural Science Teacher
Montgomery, Jeanene Ford
First Grade Teacher
Rappazzo, John B., Jr.
US, World His, Govt & Ec Tchr
Smith, Melinda Clare
Biology Teacher & Coach
Sutton, Gailyn Harris
Business Teacher
Woodruff, Barry Kevin
Health & Physical Ed Tchr

ROSE
·, Susan Ferguson
sh, History & Dance Tchr
EY
gham, Jackie-Jo Adair
iative Education Tchr
SMITH
lo, Mary (Anaya)
entary School Principal
THWAITE
, Edward Dalton
rade Math Teacher
D
Glenda Diane
er of Gifted & Talented
Larry
sh & Journalism Teacher
ann, John W.
Studies Dept Chm & Tchr
, Yvonne Arnecke
d Grade Teacher
Edward Arnez
School Art Tchr & Coach
James Kent
ematics Chairperson
Shannon Elizabeth
sh Teacher
ALES
Claudeane Bird
ctional Specialist
, Geraldine Mc Glothlin
Grade Teacher
Kathryn Marks
& Second Multi-Age Tchr
Edith Neuse
ergarten Teacher
Lori L. Fullilove
sh & Theatre Arts Teacher
, Imogene Burnett
ed Teacher
RICH
Lester Lewis
her & Athletic Director
vey, Billie Brasher
School Vocational Teacher
ON
, Mary Ringo
ed Teacher
, Cynthia Stoner
School Science Teacher
, Bradley S.
cal Education Teacher
MAN
, Vicki Vineyard
Span, Jrnlsm & Art Tchr
ORD
on, Bonnie Newton
nglish & History Teacher
Ruth Oleta
Grade Teacher
Betty Turner
nd Grade Teacher
er, Marguerite M.
ed Elementary Schl Tchr
, Coni Berg
ipal
AM
rd, Randy Herbert
selor
, Bronwen Webb
& History Teacher
, Louise
ory Instructor
Jack
Dept Chair & Drama Dir
, Greg Alan
stant Principal
Tanys Gene
nce Teacher & Dept Chm
Stacy Hancock
Grade English Teacher
cken, Renoka Hooker
Grade Teacher
, Ellen Pitcock
sh Teacher
, Rita Mc Alister
Grade Math Teacher
BURY
d, Tammy Juanita
atre Arts Teacher
un, Beth Cain
Grade Teacher
, Ann Oglesby
Grade Teacher
Suzanne Randolph
nematics Teacher
Craig Carter
metry Teacher
Joy Powell
stant Choir Director
Jeffrey Allan
ernment Teacher
ely, Judi Lee
Grade Teacher
r, Rhonda
Grade Teacher
on, Henry Alexander, Jr.
h Teacher
Cynthia Stroud
Science Tchr & Dept Chair
Donna Kathleen
ne Economics Teacher
er, Margaret Ann Schmeling
h & Language Arts Teacher
nake, Sharon Dyer
Grade Teacher
, Barbara Brady
& Spanish Teacher

GRAND PRAIRIE
Blackstock, Cindy Zadwick
Ninth Grade English Teacher
Borders, Jacqueline Denise Saunders
Speech, Debate & Govt Teacher
Brown, Michael Gene
Youth Pastor
Carrol, Patricia
Elementary Physical Ed Tchr
Clarke, Barbara Jacquelyn
Kindergarten Teacher
Cobbs, Connie L.
History Teacher & Coach
Coggins, Dan Lee
8th Grade Science Teacher
Cunningham, Margaret Anne
English Teacher
DeArment, Katrina Kay
English Teacher
DeBerry, Deena Kay
Fifth Grade Teacher
Drake, Mary H. (Wieland)
Special Education Dept Chprsn
Dudley, Gwen
Marketing Education Coord
Fischer, Al
Biology Tchr & Football Coach
Fulkerson, Wanda Taylor
Social Studies Tchr & Dept Chm
Fuller, Cindy M.
Spanish Teacher
Garcia, Jesse M.
Teacher
Gilmore, Benjamin Brookes, Jr.
4th Grade Teacher
Graham, Bill R.
Computer Science Teacher
Heisig, Randall C.
Dept Chairman & Health Teacher
Hollas, Patricia Ann
Third Grade Teacher
Jefferson, Ruby Lee
Fourth Grade Teacher
Kendrick, Freddie Diane (Hoff)
Sixth Grade Lead Teacher
Lorenz, Ann Biagioli
History & Government Teacher
Mallery, Kathleen Phillips
Fifth Grade Teacher
Manor, Eric James
English Teacher & Tennis Coach
Mattox, Sheila Dawn
9th Grd PE & Eng Teacher
McGill, Judith Elaine
US His Tchr & Vlybl Coach
Mc Gilvray, Christine Jill Whitsitt
High School Counselor
McGinn, Kathy
Teacher of Gifted & Talented
Murry, Vicky Lynn
A P English Teacher
Oertel, Cheryl Wiley
Computer Literacy Teacher
Pederson, Irene
Government, His, Law Stud Tchr
Perkins, Kathleen Wallace
Special Education Teacher
Randolph, Madeline Kay
English Teacher
Roberson, Sam
Physical Education Teacher
Roetzel, Pat Smart
Spcl Ed & Resource Eng Tchr
Rogers, Lynn Willner
Biology & Psychology Teacher
Russell, Virginia Ann
Drama Director
Sanders, Pam L.
Eng Tchr & Cheerleader Coach
Scattergood, Robert Alan
English Dept Chair & Teacher
Seider, LeAnn Alspaugh
4th Grade Teacher
Sisco, Patty
Counselor
Smith, Kim Ross
Chemistry & Physics Teacher
Summers, Herbert Rolland, Jr.
AP US Politics & Govt Teacher
Thompson, Juanita Elizabeth
Mathematics Teacher
Wallace, Ruth Page
Science Dept Chair & Tchr
White, Mary Kay Schmoeller
Lang Arts Dept Chm & Team Ldr
Williamson, Lucretia Burney
Second Grade Teacher
GRANDVIEW
Bentz, William Dyar
Bio Tchr & Head Bsktbl Coach
Neff, Alan Lane
Math Teacher & Coach
GRANGER
Campbell, Patsy Henderson
Social Studies & Art Teacher
Carpenter, Janet Taylor
High School Science Teacher
Duke, Virginia C.
Mathematics Tchr & Tech Coord
Killpatrick, Kay Bowden
Home Economics Teacher
Thornton, Johnnie Douglas, Jr.
Special Education Teacher
GRAPELAND
Franklin, Carrie Ann Haltom
Kindergarten Teacher
Hobson, Kathy Kight
English Teacher
Vaden, Melissa Maria
Spanish Teacher & Coach

GRAPEVINE
Andre, Steven Christopher
Director of Bands
Annis, Angela Barnes
Computer Sci Tchr & Dept Chprs
Boyd, Jane Gail
Co-Dir of Forensics & Debate
Brown, Judy Solomon
Pre-K Teacher
Browne, Patricia Garrett
English Teacher
Calvert, Sue Oldham
AP English Teacher
Carter, Terri Manns
High School Latin Teacher
Chew, Joella M.
Theatre Teacher
Coffee, Larry Glenn
Science Teacher
Cook, Janice J.
Eng Tchr & Department Chair
Cullum, Debbie Madeley
Spanish & French Teacher
Cunningham, Christopher Brian
HS Coach & Math Teacher
Ebersole, Billie Hurst
1st Grade Teacher
Evans, Cynthia Leigh
Biology Teacher
Evans, Mary Catherine Light
Soc Stud & Future Edctrs Tchr
Fox, Patrecia Schlegel
Honors English Teacher
Galbraith, Terry Lynn
Math Teacher & Coach
Goodwin, Scott Michael
Law Studies & Psychology Tchr
Hamilton, DeLaine Terrell
Teacher of Gifted & Talented
Hayes, Katherine Eriksson
English Teacher
Horak, Dayna Farmer
PE Teacher & Volleyball Coach
Horton, Linda Luellen
Eng, Lit & Lang Arts Teacher
Hudson, Valerie Garris
Algebra II Teacher
Iovinelli, Bob
Mathematics Teacher
Kohn, Gail A.
Social Studies Teacher
Leondar, Brandt Samuel
Assistant Band Director
Melton, Linda Wingfield
Fourth Grade Teacher
Middleton, Freda Breed
Director of Choral Music
Morris, Catherine Crichton
Sociology Teacher
Pittman, Susan Waits
English Teacher
Price, Glenda Anne Revis
Mathematics Teacher
Renfro, Kay Lynn Coulson
Dance Tchr & Drill Team Dir
Schneider, Joyce J.
Mathematics Teacher
Sharp, Nadine Martin
Sixth Grade Language Arts Tchr
Showalter, Deanna J.
Science & Math Teacher
Street, Patricia Miller
English Teacher
Symon, William Harold
Chem Teacher & Coach
Tallant, Sharon Ann
Ninth Grade Inclusion Teacher
Telford, Margaret Agnew
Soc Stud Dept Chprsn, His Tchr
Tillery, Ronald J.
Retired Mathematics Teacher
Tipton, L. Kathleen
High School Math Teacher
Weber, Marilyn Ann (Orsucci)
AP Amer His Tchr
Wilson, Nancy Morris
English Teacher
Wyatt, Marty L.
Chem Tchr & Sci Dept Chair
GREENVILLE
Brown, Sally Johnson
Reading & Lang Arts Teacher
Davenport, Judith Scott
K-12 Gifted & Talented Coord
Fincher, Marsha Kidd
High School Counselor
Goodson, Jo Brown
Eng Tchr & UIL Acad Coord
Harris, Linda Ann
8th Grade American His Teacher
Lee, Edward Dale
Theatre Teacher
Sanders, Ralph Lee
Intermediate School Principal
Vaughn, Janis Carpenter
English & Business Teacher
Wensel, Linda Zeman
English Teacher
Wimberley, Alan Dale
Secondary Administrator
GREGORY
Matocha, Barbara Scott
Third Grade Teacher
GROESBECK
Barnes, Sharon Kilgore
Consumer Home Economics Tchr
Meadows, Leona Kopecki
7th Grade Lang Arts Teacher
Phillips, Gloredia O. Tipps
Math, Social Stud & Sci Tchr

Ross, Gwendolyn Ruth
English Teacher
GROVES
Anabtawi, Dana Ann
Language Arts Teacher
Hamilton, Kristin Mc Clure
Eighth Grd Math & Algebra Tchr
GROVETON
Dominey, Mary Barkley
Fourth Grade Teacher
Johnson, Kerri Centilli
High School Business Teacher
GRUVER
Blassingame, Laura Lee
Principal
Brown, Diane Gailey
2nd Grade Teacher
Burnam, Lonnie Merle
Phys Science & Physics Tchr
Logsdon, Julie Pollard
Senior English Teacher
Montgomery, William Clay
Agricultural Science Teacher
Renner, Glenda V.
Jr High Librarian & Rdng Tchr
TeBeest, Amy Stavlo
Science Teacher
GUNTER
Davis, Marilyn Scoggins
Home Ec, Speech & English Tchr
GUSTINE
Cummings, Annette Priddy
Special Education Teacher
Thedford, Valrie Stephens
HS Lang Arts & Jrnlsm Teacher
GUTHRIE
Williams, Debbie Gragg
HS Math Teacher & Counselor
HALE CENTER
Bice, Alicia Uptergrove
HS Mathematics Teacher
Klatt, Kathy Haussler
Former Teacher
HALLETTSVILLE
Bludau, Elizabeth Parks
English Teacher
Bludau, Ida Hrncir
HS English & Art Teacher
Fenner, Doris Dworsky
Elementary Teacher
Hale, Sherry Hoffer
Third Grade Teacher
Little, Linda Smith
Social Studies Teacher
Matula, Irene Loredo
Span Tchr & Frgn Lang Dept Chm
Rabke, Suzanne Boedeker
Computer Teacher
Skelton, Carol Wendler
Special Education Teacher
HALLSVILLE
Beadles, Harold Dean
Science Dept Chairperson
Carter, Donna DeStena
Reading Teacher
Clark, Annette Collier
Mathematics Teacher & Coach
Conway, Bret Kevin
Math & Computer Science Tchr
Jones, Kay Middlebrook
Chemistry & Physical Sci Tchr
McGuire, Donna Wilson
Choral Music Director
McLemore, Ida Stansell
English Teacher
Moon, Nanette Lasater
Business Education Teacher
Morgan, Sherri Fechner
Director of Bands
Porter, Ava Steele
Math Teacher
Simmons, Dave Michael
11th Grade US History Teacher
Tutt, Gayle Potter
Seventh Grd Mathematics Tchr
Walenta, Belinda Pustejovsky
High School Counselor
Walker, Pamela Ogle
Mathematics Teacher
Wright, Sheila Foster
9th Grade World Geography Tchr
HAMILTON
Edins, Timothy Dale
Director of Bands
Gardner, Mary K. Caldwell
Counselor & Testing Director
Glasscock, Bena Leanne
Home Economics Teacher
Johnson, Melissa Benson
Junior High Science Teacher
Jones, Pamela Thompson
Math & Computer Literacy Tchr
Massingill, Faith B. Ballard
CEA-FCS Hamilton County
Sharp, Susan Warren
Teacher & Coach
HAMLIN
Lytle, Latrese Williams
Government Teacher
HAMSHIRE
Chesson, Janice Ann
Business & Computer Teacher
Mott, Linda Gill
English Dept Chair & Tchr
Peltier, Debra Ann (Royer)
Kinesiology Teacher & Coach
Sachitano, Sheila Louviere
English & French Teacher
Williams, Ginger White
English Teacher

HAPPY
Mc Broom, Casey Carl
History & Health Teacher
Smith, Ilona Tanner
Eng, Spanish & Reading Tchr
HARDIN
English, Carrie Buford
Math Teacher
Tidwell, Nancy Barrett
Social Studies Teacher
HARKER HEIGHTS
Askins, Gary Don
Math Teacher
Dahl, Merleann Ziemer
Librarian
Dodson, Virginia Brown
Fourth Grade Teacher
Huckaby, Deborah Angus
World History Teacher
Webb, Erma Horne
5th Grade Teacher
HARLETON
Mock, Lyndoll Hamby
Science Teacher
Moore, Kelly Westbrook
First Grade Teacher
HARLINGEN
Araiza, Daniel L.
Cmptr, Tech Tchr & Chprsn
Bazan, Dolores
World History Teacher
Casares, Sylvia Pena
Third Grade Teacher
Cavazos, R. Carlos
Sociology Instructor
Diaz, Susan S.
Assistant Band Director
Dolph, Darrel Allen
Instructor
Duncan, Jane Cohen
Mathematics Dept Chairman
Duran, Gracie
First Grade Teacher
Esparza, Aracely
Spanish Teacher
Fisher, Janet Michel
Retired Teacher
Fitting, Deborah Brown
Assistant Principal
Forstner, Marilyn Tillman
Language Arts Teacher
Garcia, Edward Y.
Spanish Teacher & Coach
Garcia, Juan Manuel
7th Grade History Teacher
Gomez, Alberto
Instrumentation Tech Instr
Jaramillo, Dora Yzaguirre
Nursing Instructor
Lauritzen, Louis Dee
Comp Drafting & Design Tech
Leggett, Margaret Ann Malone
English Teacher
Lunsford, Linda Jo
8th Grade English Teacher
Martin, Leland M.
Adjunct Professor of History
Monsevalles, Rodolfo
Mathematics Teacher
Pezeshki, Hossein
Math & Science Dept Chair
Ramirez, Maggie Martinez
3rd Grade Teacher
Ransom, Beatrice
Spanish Teacher
Rasch, Richard J.
Choral Music Director
Reyes, Carlos
Electronics Instructor
Reyes, Velma Cardenas
3rd Grade Teacher
Ritt, Michael David
Science Teacher
Salinas, Rosario Quintanilla
English Teacher
Smith, Michael Alan
Mathematics Teacher
Smith, Thomas Eugene
Agricultural Science Teacher
Sonnier, Mervin Joseph
Instrumentation Tech Instr
Theriot, Jane Harrington
2nd Grd Tchr of Gifted
Vassberg, Paul Edward
Developmental Eng Instructor
Vaughn, Deborah Struby
Language Arts Teacher
Vermaas, John
Biology Teacher
HARPER
Hawkins, Ronald Scott
English Teacher & Coach
Jones, Joy Caffey
Counselor
Masser, Katherine Goforth
Elementary School Teacher
HART
Birkenfeld, Jeanie Marie
Mathematics Teacher
Castillo, Marcos
Spanish Teacher
Henry, P. Lanette Allison
Business & Commercial Art Tchr
Wilcox, Rachelle
English Teacher & Coach
HASKELL
Doerschuk, John Wade
Secondary Mathematics Teacher
Foster, John Charles
Bio, Anatomy & Physiology Tchr

HASKELL (cont)
Larned, Gerre Colbert
Counselor & English Teacher
HASLET
Green, Patricia Johnson
Retired Kindergarten Teacher
HAWKINS
Boyce, R. Sheldon
Drama & English Teacher
Craft, Michael R.
Health, PE Teacher & Coach
Easterling, William Don
Retired Head Swimming Coach
HAWLEY
Caffey, Evynne Clark
Jr & High School Art Teacher
Doyle, Jimmy Dale
English Teacher & Coach
Thompson, Terry Floyd
Industrial Technology Teacher
HEARNE
Galloway, Nelda Miller
Mathematics Tchr & Dept Chprsn
Roese, Kimberly Ilene
Science Teacher
HEBBRONVILLE
Morales, Eliseo, Jr.
Band Director
Myers, Annette P.
Secondary Mathematics Teacher
Pena, Jorge A.
5th Grade Social Studies Tchr
Saenz, Manuel, Jr.
High School Art Teacher
HEDLEY
Adams, Lon Ray
Agricultural Science Teacher
HELOTES
Nichols, Anna Mae Moore
Retired Fourth Grade Teacher
Welkener, JoAnn Rosas
Second Grade Teacher
HEMPHILL
Mc Naughten, Montez Corbell
Math Coordinator & Teacher
HEMPSTEAD
Arnold, Leonard Jay
Band Director
Connor, Donald F.
Sixth Grade Science Teacher
Connor, Mary Fritzsching
Sixth Grade Teacher
Ford, Theresa Lee
Health Teacher & Coach
Malcom, Carl Ray
English Teacher
Wooldridge, David Glenn, II
Health & Phys Ed Teacher
HENDERSON
Adams, Deedy Lynn
French Teacher & Drill Tm Dir
Bailey, Donna Hamburg
Mathematics & Title 1 Teacher
Gardner, Carol Clegg
Biology Teacher
Melton, Martha Husband
Teacher of Gifted
Melton, Michael Ray
United States History Teacher
Moseley, Margaret Spear
English Teacher
HENRIETTA
Brown, Deborah Jeanne
Junior High Science Teacher
HEREFORD
Brown, Nina Buckner
English & Journalism Teacher
Buckley, Myrna J.
English & Speech Teacher
Cole, Amy G.
Business Co-Op Teacher
Conlee, James R.
Economics & Govt Teacher
Dean, Randy Lynn
Algebra I Teacher
Gerlich, Becky Jo
Mathematics Teacher
Gregoris, Julia Elizabeth
English Teacher
Paetzold, Martha J.
Health Science Tech Teacher
Summersgill, Tammy L.
Band Director
Szydloski, Dorothy Cecilia
Physical Science Teacher
Vincent, David Ross
Science Teacher
Waters, Carolyn Briscoe
Texas History Teacher
Wright, Heather Hendrix
Tenth Grade English Teacher
HERMLEIGH
Finley, Judith Mc Elyea
Math Teacher
HEWITT
Back, Sandy Dennis
Kindergarten Teacher
Baughman, James Edwin
Marketing Education Teacher
Billeaud, Thomas Dale
Head Athletic Trainer
Broadway, Mary A.
HECE Teacher & Coordinator
Edminster, Laurie Malpass
English Teacher
Hahn, Katherine Eliabeth
English & GATE Teacher
Hall, Mary Fleming
French & Spanish Teacher
Hulke, Billie R.
Spanish Teacher
Judd, Lonnie Lee
English Teacher & Coach
McAnelly, Elizabeth Smith
9th Grade English Teacher
North, Martha H.
Kindergarten Teacher
Powers, Fredna Horn
Algebra & Pre AP Calculus Tchr
Scott, Pat Foytik
3rd Grade Teacher
Spooner, Stephen Earl
Band Director
Tucker, Audrey Janda
Geometry Teacher
Walsh, Holley Jackson
Fourth Grade Teacher
Wiethorn, Rikki Paschall
English Teacher
HIDALGO
Acevedo, Alfredo
Physical Sci & Chem I Tchr
Brandt, William S.
Teacher & Coach
Castilleja, Cynthia Ann
7th & 8th Grd Science Teacher
Derrada, Edith Salandanan
Chemistry Teacher
HIGGINS
Meller, Paula Detrixhe
English, Span & Theatre Tchr
HIGHLAND VILLAGE
Fite, Kate Bennett
Language Arts Department Chair
HIGHLANDS
Simmons, Douglas Livezey
Amer His Tchr & Dept Chprsn
Wells, Karen Bultzo
Second Grade Teacher
HILLSBORO
Edwards, Veneta Bond
Div Dir of Hum & Fine Arts
Fitch, Sharon Lee
Pre-K & Kindergarten Teacher
Hillyard, Richard Allen
Instructor of Auto Body Repair
Porter, William Howard, Jr.
Math & Physics Instructor
Smith, James DWayne
High School Math Teacher
Woody, William Thomas, Jr.
Agriscience Teacher
HITCHCOCK
Cokins, Edrea Chambers
Fifth Grade Teacher
Kearns, Linda Deily
Eng, Dance & Speech Teacher
Maxwell, Brenda McManus
Business Tchr & Stu Cncl Spon
HOLLAND
Owens, Don Alan
English & Spanish Teacher
HOLLIDAY
Eakins, David Wayne
Band Director
Leeth, James David
Assistant Principal & Teacher
HONDO
Ainsley, Melissa Walden
GED Coord
Arcos, Vicente
Principal
Bergmann, Margaret Koch
High School English Teacher
Cowan, Renean Balke
Algebra II & Cmptr Math Tchr
Haley, Carolyn Vasbinder
Tchr of Spec Ed & Inclusion
Howard, Dorothy Arnim
Kindergarten Teacher
Muennink, Karen Howard
HS Home Economics Teacher
Rochat, Patricia Sparks
Reading Resource Teacher
Vance, Rita Gianotti
High School Math Dept Chair
Wooten, Bette Bullard
Frosh Eng & Tech Writing Tchr
HONEY GROVE
Dobbs, Frances Warren
Home Economics Teacher
Newhouse, Kathryn Magnani
Second Grade Teacher
HOOKS
Bell, Suzanne Lundberg
HS Chem & Physics Teacher
Knight, Carrel W., Jr.
7th Grade Life Science Teacher
Ramage, Cindy Marlane
Theatre, Speech & Debate Tchr
Sackett, Carolyn J.
Business Teacher
HOUSTON
Absher, Danne M.
English Teacher
Acosta, Lynette Borgyon
English & French Teacher
Addison, Renee Nelson
Skills Specialist
Adolph, Randy
5th Grade Teacher
Albers, Margaret Irene
Instructor of ESL
Albright, Dana Lindsay
Mathematics Teacher
Albright, Mark Alan
Social Studies Teacher
Aldstadt, David Philip
History Professor
Allen, Olivia Kokko
Math Dept Chair & Teacher
Alsup, Linda Sue
English Teacher
Alva, Joseph Michael
7th Grd ESL Teacher
Anderson, Charlotte Faye
2nd Grade Teacher
Angelo, Tina C.
English Teacher
Anglin, Connie Noble
Health Educator
Arceneaux, Denise
English Teacher
Archibeque, Laura Henry
6th Grd Tchr of Gftd & Tlntd
Arehart, Marilyn Rider
Sr AP English Tchr & Dept Chm
Armstrong, Alice Claudia (Smark)
Reading Teacher
Arya, Sharda
Associate Prof of Physics
Attisha, Khalid Paulus
Professor of Biology
Baacke, Deborah Jean (Snyder)
Pre-K, Kndgtn Tchr & Asst Prin
Baacke, Mark L.
Biology & Astronomy Teacher
Baggett, Joyce Y.
Parental Involvement Spec
Bahl, Saroj Mehta
Assoc Prof of Nutrition, Diet
Bai, Yiyan
Chemistry & Physics Professor
Bailer, Jill
Science Teacher
Bailey, Margaret Elizabeth
English Teacher
Baker, Mary Teresa
Fourth Grade Teacher
Baker, Ronald Lee
Aerospace Teacher & Coach
Balderas, Stela Raquel
Social Studies Teacher
Balis, Sandra Schiffman
Mathematics Teacher
Banks, Beth Anne
Fifth Grade Teacher
Baranowski, Colette Ann
Teacher
Barber, Jane Gardiner
Physical Education Teacher
Barker, Ethel Mitchell
Math Teacher
Barnes, Mary Jean
Math Teacher
Barrera, Maria E.
Business Teacher
Bartel, Carolyn Crow
Restaurant Owner
Bartel, Mimi Casey
Dept Head & Instr Resp Care
Barth, Stephen C.
Prof of Hotel & Rest Law Mgmt
Bartlett, Coleen Speidel
Secondary Math Teacher
Bartlett, Sandra Jewett
4th Grade Teacher
Bartling, Kandi K.
English Teacher
Bashinski, Beth Marie
English Department Chairperson
Batsche, Julie Fuerstenau
English Teacher
Batten-Bishop, Ann
Speech & Theatre Arts Teacher
Beaty, Ruth Brigham
Fourth Grade Teacher
Becker, Richard Randolph
Professor of Criminal Justice
Bediko, Barbara Harris
Pre-School & Kindergarten Tchr
Belk, Joan Pardue
Advanced Placement Eng Tchr
Benedict, Joann O'Reilly
Mathematics Teacher
Benner, Rebecca Lee
Biology Teacher
Bennett, H. Dixon
Division Chairman of Fine Arts
Bettis, Glenda Domingue
Speech & Drama Teacher
Bigner, Martha Elin
High School Algebra Teacher
Biles, Gloria C.
Assoc Professor of History
Black, Ira J.
Fine Arts & Humanities Faculty
Black, Judith Booher
Teacher of GATE & English
Blackman, Lesli Susan
Dance & Drill Team Director
Blind, MaryAnn
Dir of Applied Learning Ctr
Blodgett, Dorothy Wilson
Soc Stud Tchr of the Gifted
Bloom, Rachel Sonnie
High School Dance Teacher
Blume, Polly Whiddon
Skills for Adolescence Teacher
Bolen, John Harold
Government Instructor
Bolzman, David Howard
Elem Lang Arts teacher
Bonds, Sylvia Christopher
8th Grade Math & Science Tchr
Bonner, Howard Ray
Fifth Grade Teacher
Bosque, Vivian A.
Spanish Teacher
Boswell, Jackie (Reece)
First Grade Teacher
Boutwell, Sharon Marie (Woods)
Instrl Fac Pgm for Evaluation
Bowie, Adriane
Dev Instr of Reading II
Boyd, Jeffrey Robert
Accelerated Algebra Teacher
Boyd, Linda Crockett
Second Grade Teacher
Boyd, Saundra Yvonne
Instructor
Boyer, Beverly Bell
Fifth Grade Vanguard Teacher
Bradford, Cheryl Rene
Theatre Arts Tchr & Director
Bradford, Eunice Jones
Retired Resource Teacher
Bradford, Mary Lou Kendall
Third Grade Teacher
Brawner, Donna
Yrbk & Photojournalism Teacher
Breaux-Healy, Julia F.
English & Journalism Teacher
Breedveld, Linda Bayer
Art Teacher
Brelsford, Carolyn Nash
6th-8th Grd Mathematics Tchr
Brewton, Rebecca Jane
Eng & Creative Writing Teacher
Bridges, Carolyn Elane
Fourth Grade Teacher
Bridges, Glenn
Fifth Grade Teacher
Brinkley, Charlotte Lister
Mathematics Teacher
Brooner, Michelle Magdanz
Mathematics Teacher
Brown, Danny Marshall
Drafting Instructor
Brown, Larry Eugene
Instructor of Biology
Brown, Naomi Davis
First Grade Teacher
Brown, Ronnie B.
Ninth Grade English Teacher
Brownlee, Avin Scott
Dept of Bio Prof & Chairman
Brownlee, Steven Albert
Assistant Principal
Bryson, Ernest Ervin, Jr.
Soc Stud Tchr & Debate Coach
Buelow, Judith Salisbury
English Department Chairperson
Buettner, Sharon Donohue
English IV Teacher
Burch, Linda Kana
Professor of ESOL
Burch, William E.
Accounting & Bus Professor
Burge, Annette L.
8th Grd Math Tchr & Dept Chm
Burnley, Ruth Tolbert
8th Grade Language Arts Tchr
Burns, Kathleen Elizabeth
Principal
Burns, Kaylynn
Biology Teacher
Burr, Bean Lamberson
Science Teacher & Dept Head
Busby, John Overton
Industrial Technology Teacher
Butt, Debra Lynne
ESL Dept Chairperson
Byrne, David Jerome
Science Teacher & Bio Team Ldr
Bywaters, Emilia Mpwo
Mathematics Teacher
Calhoun, Karen Firmin
Fourth Grade Teacher
Caligur, Matthew William
Asst Prof in Communications
Callicutt, Johnathan Dean
History & Economics Teacher
Cameron, Joanna Mac Donald
Adjunct Instructor in English
Cantrell, Marybeth Johnson
Pre-Kindergarten Teacher
Carey, Pamela Kaye
Home Economics Teacher
Carpenter, Bettye Harrison
Teacher & Team Leader
Carrier, Charlotte Wright
Teacher
Carroll, Lecia Bess (Malone)
6th Grade Eng & Rndg Teacher
Carter, Lillian Jones
Science I Teacher
Case, Carol Ann
Honors English Tchr & Dept Chr
Cason, William E.
Business Law Instructor
Catanese, Michele .
Theology Teacher
Catchings, Victoria Coby
Science Teacher
Caylor, F. Martin
Eighth Grade Algebra Teacher
Champagne, Lonnie Dean
Soc Stud & Cultural Stud Tchr
Chandler, Kathy Ann
High School Counselor
Chapman, Mark Alan
Soc Studies Dept Chair & Tchr
Chappel, Daphne Hightower
Bands Director
Cher, Judith Silber
Chemistry & Biology Teacher
Chesnutt, Charles Marshall
7th Grade Social Studies Tchr
Churchill, Craig William
8th Grade US History Teacher
Cirio, Celia
Teacher of the Deaf
Clack, Joe Ann
Teacher
Clark, Patrick William
Soc Stud Tchr & Dean of Stdnts
Clark, Richard Rual
Asst Prof, Dept of Pathology
Clark, Yvonne Boykin
Texas History Teacher
Clarke, Janet Pokorski
English Teacher
Coan, Lois Westerman
Math & Language Arts Teacher
Coffey, Sharon Ann
Radiography Program Instr
Coit, Karen Sue
3rd & 4th Grade Teacher
Cole, Mildred Joan
4th Grade Teacher
Coleman, Brenda Lovett
Health Sci Technology Teacher
Collins, Charlie Keith
Director of Choirs
Collum, Ann M.
Fifth Grd ESL Teacher
Comello, Harold Raymond
Government Instructor
Conner, Ellen Haskins
English Teacher
Constantine, Heather Catherine
Counselor
Coogan, Genevieve B.
English Instructor & Dept Head
Cooksey, Beverly Harris
5th Grade Teacher
Cotterell, Alaye
Biology Teacher
Cox, Vinola Loyce Nelson
Choral Music Teacher
Coyle, Claudette Eley
Chemistry Teacher
Craft, D'Anne Parker
Guidance Counselor
Crandall, George Jeffrey
Theology Teacher & Dept Dean
Criner, Nancy Carol
Marketing Coordinator
Crocker, Elizabeth Ann
Technical Theatre & Drama Tchr
Crook, Jack Marvin
Humanities & History Teacher
Cuneo, Philip Anthony
HS Biology & Astronomy Teacher
Cypert, Suzi
ESL Teacher
Dabbs, Deborah Denise
English Teacher
Dahlgren, Duane A.
Chemistry Teacher
Dale, Ruth Mayes
AP English IV Teacher
Dang, Cam Dac
CAD Instructor
Dao, Immaculate Thuy
10th Grade Teacher
Darke, Lillie Marie Allen
Science Teacher
Darling, Mary C.
First Grade Teacher
Davis, Gail A.
Math Teacher
Davis, Sylvia Annette
English Teacher
Davis, Wanda Jeannette (Koontz)
Choir Teacher
Day Trigg, Sally
English Instructor
Deese, Agnes Boudoin
Home Economics Teacher
Defibaugh, Ginger
Honors English Teacher
DeForke, Josephine Palasota
Chemistry & Mathematics Tchr
DeFranco, Agnes Lee
Asst Prof of Hotel Mgmt
De Los Santos, Yolanda Mejia
Assistant Principal
Demarchos, Donna Steinbrenner
Reading Skills Specialist
Denmon, Alvin Louis
Dean of Instruction
DeVault, Jan Logan
Secondary French Teacher
Diaz, Manuel Angel
Human Anatomy Professor
Dibrell, Sam Clark
Counselor
Dick, Gregory William
Band Director
Dietrich, Sandra K. (Fath)
Instr of Med Lab Tech Pgm
Dilworth, Tish R.
Latin Teacher
Dinkins, Bertha Maxine
Soc Studies Tchr & Dept Chprsn
Dixon, Kaleen Keithcart
Mathematics Instructor
Dixon, Linda Kay LaMance
Math Teacher
Dodson, Daton A.
Professor of Languages
Dominguez, Patricia Brown
Nursing Assistant Professor
Dominy, Melinda Glenn
English Teacher
Donato, Linda Diann Wells
Fifth Grade Teacher

TON (cont)
y, Clarence Wills
d Social Studies Teacher
Terrance
ssor of English
Lisa Marie
Grade Teacher
, John Stanley
ant Principal
an, Martha M.
sh Teacher
s, B. J.
School Choir Teacher
y, Robert Lloyd
age Arts, Literature Tchr
Mary Nell Mc Cauley
tor of Extended Day Pgrm
Lynne Drew
& Creative Writing Tchr
Melody Scott
ce Teacher
Holly Lizabeth
School Geography Teacher
, J. Fred
ry Teacher
Mary E.
ce Professor
Linda Louise
8th Grade French Teacher
n, Debra Romas
Grade Teacher
, Rose Whittington
selor
, Carrie Leigh
sh Teacher
rd, Jeffrey Lawrence
lathematics Teacher
Thomas Charles
cal Education Teacher
Yvonne M.
l Studies Teacher
Patricia Elizabeth
School French Teacher
n, Jack
sh Teacher
ray, Katherine Wirges
ndary Math Instructor
ls, Darrell Alan
of Gifted & Talented
ls, Frances Lee
h Grade Teacher
ls, Marilyn S.
Professor of Nutrition
ls, Sheila Renae (Calhoun)
h Grade Teacher
Rose Soapes
sh & Theater Arts Tchr
nn, Jane
rian
rances Green
r School Spanish Teacher
b, Mohamad Moussa
Dept Chprsn & Chem Tchr
Mary Charlotte Beeson
ing Teacher
, Larry
sh Teacher
, Mildred Michelle
sh Instructor
Charlene Taylor
sh Prof & Dept Chprsn
, Johnny Levern
puter Teacher
, Sunday O.
& Chm of Biology Dept
Brenda Hetrick
book Advisor & Sub Tchr
ally Boon
History Teacher
tt, Paulette Toporowski
nth Grade English Teacher
zi, Mariann
te, Speech Teacher & Coach
o, Katie M.
o, TV & Film Teacher
, Michael Denis
ish Teacher
, Linda Page
ch Teacher
Vincent J.
nematics Teacher
, Jon Kent
l Director
Sylvia Mooney
l Coordinator & Teacher
rald, Karen Fellows
dinator for GATE Programs
nan, Sandy Wiggins
, Ec Teacher & Dept Chair
le, Jean Holland
Span I & World Geog Tchr
Terry Wayne
sical Science Teacher
s, Sarah Walden
nematics Teacher
r, Ruth G.
ish Teacher
es, Brenda Brown
Teacher & Coach
Deborah Harrison
ness Education Teacher
lin, Mary Gouvea
nish Teacher
, Diane Allison
lish & Psychology Teacher
er, Wendy Michelle
ogy & Physical Sci Tchr
Jammie Michele
ors English Teacher

Friery, Mary Louise
Career & Technology Teacher
Fuentes, Barbara Gail
8th Grade Spanish Teacher
Fuqua, Toni Fowler
Kindergarten Teacher
Furlong, Norman Burr, Jr.
Upper School Science Teacher
Gajkowski, Lara Hackney
Head of Middle School
Gale, Donna Howell
Mathematics Teacher
Galiette, Joyce L.
Network Administration
GAlloway, Irma N.
Assistant Principal
Gant, Debra Watson
8th Grd Reading Teacher
Gaona, Gil
Spanish Teacher
Gardley, Vincent Edward
Speech, Debate & Psych Tchr
Garrett, Carmen Elaine
Dean of Students
Garrett, Jimmy F.
JROTC Instructor
Garris, Charles H.
Teacher & Professor
Garrison, Candida Raycraft
11th Grade English Teacher
Gartner, Kristen Kay
Business Teacher
George, Christine Steele
English Teacher
Gerecci, Patricia S.
HS Teacher
Geringer, Tomye Ray
Dept Head Medical Asst Prgm
Gex, Robert William Daniel
Asst Principal
Giacchetti, Claudine A.
Associate Professor of French
Giacona, Lisa R.
Music Teacher
Gilbreth, Joe Wayne
Colorguard Director
Gillespie, Virginia Carpenter
Retired Teacher
Glenn, Susan Tippit
Psychology Instructor
Goad, Candice Shelby
Philosophy Professor
Goforth, Cathleen Hanlon
Theatre Arts Teacher
Goldsmith, Marissa Pollak
Spanish Teacher
Golliday, Isiah
Physical Education Teacher
Golub, Gary D.
Math Dept Chairperson
Gomez-Cano, Gricelle Elena
Coord & Dev Studies Instructor
Gonzalez, Larry Justin
Political Science Professor
Gosdin, Robin Mc Coy
Hlth Occupations Tchr & Coord
Grabstald, Kathie Jernigan
11th Grade English Teacher
Grau, Marina Romero
Department Head
Graves, Nancy Shelver
Asst Prof of Food Svc Mngmt
Gray, Gennella Taylor
Social Studies Teacher
Gray, Patsy R.
Professor of English
Greco, Janice Teresa
Psychology Instructor
Green, Bonnie Johnson
English III Team Leader
Green, Craig Anthony
Bands Director
Green, Donald R.
Psychology Instructor
Green, Ella Baldwin
Exceptional Education Teacher
Green, Helen Lois
Mathematics Teacher
Green, John Lucious
Professor of Accounting
Greenfield, Myron Serle
English Teacher
Gregory, Don Peter
Eng Hnrs Tchr & Soccer Coach
Gregory, Lawrence Newman
6th Grade Social Studies Tchr
Griffin, LaVerne Johnson
Lang Arts & Gifted Teacher
Griffin, Linda Coleman
English Instructor
Guillory, Dolores Winfield
Asst Prin & MS Science Tchr
Guillot, Janet Walters Jacobs
High School Art Teacher
Haas, Susan Young
7th Grd Life Science Teacher
Haglund, Jane Alice
ESOL Teacher
Halbert, Lola Loftin
Second Grade Teacher
Hall, Gary Wayne
Anatomy & Physiology Teacher
Hallmark, David G.
Mathematics Teacher
Ham, Robert Michael
Social Studies Teacher
Hamid, Tariq Usman
Biology Teacher
Hamilton, Stephanie Ann
Pgm Dir, Cytotechnology Supvr

Hamling, Linda Lee (Benz)
Health Occupations Teacher
Hammons, Jane Grace
US History Teacher
Hancock, Glennette Goodwill
English Teacher
Handlin, William George
Mathematics & Astronomy Tchr
Hann, Shirley Meester
Second Grade GATE Teacher
Hardwick, Jacqualine Sullivan
Spanish Teacher
Hardy, Nelwyn Ann
Home Economics Teacher & Coord
Harger, Kimberly Michelle (Daniel)
Ninth Grade Geography Teacher
Harness, Celia Woods
Tenth Grade English Teacher
Harris, Carmita Edmond
Sixth Grade Teacher
Harris, Lykethia Renee
Home Economics Teacher
Harris-Bell, Julie Maryanne
Sociology Teacher
Harrison, Calvert W.
Biology Teacher
Harrison, Charles E.
Lang Arts Division Chairman
Hartgrove-Freile, Janice Lynn
Psychology Professor
Haynes, Sandy Nicks
Early Childhood Teacher
Hemphill, Boyd Edward
Math Teacher
Henderson, Nellie Evans
Middle School Math Teacher
Hernandez, Karen Jackson
ESL Teacher
Hill, Deborah James
Amer His Tchr & Dept Chprsn
Hines, Peggy Plough
Swim Coach & PE Teacher
Hobbs, Thomas Marland
Geology Pgm Coord & Instructor
Hodges, Anna Cowley
Jrnlsm Tchr & Publications Adv
Hodges, Carolyn King
US History & Citizenship Tchr
Hoke, Ruth Pederson
English Teacher
Holden, Sue Rolf
Media Specialist & Librarian
Hollis, Bill C.
English Teacher
Horton, Whitney Tipton
Journalism Advisor & Eng Tchr
Howard, Cynthia L.
Assistant Professor of Biology
Howe, Harlan George, III
Physics Teacher
Hsu, Chiehwen Lai
Psychology Instructor
Hulse, Lois Carole (Kullenberg)
5th Grade Bilingual Teacher
Hult, Susan Freda
History & Geography Dept Head
Hunter, Deirdre Lynn
Mathematics Teacher
Hunter, Gwendolyn A.
Title I Coordinator
Hurwitz, Marsha Gail
Math Teacher
Huse, Kathleen Sue (Shipley)
US History Teacher & Team Ldr
Hussain, Rehana Ahmad
Instructor of English
Hutchison, Collin James
English Instructor
Hyare, Paramjit Bains
Math Teacher
Iacoponelli, Mark Edward
US History Teacher & Coach
Ibarra, Benjamin
Psychology Teacher
Improta, Ann Marie
Fourth Grade Teacher
Irizarry, Janet
ESL Teacher
Isaac, David P.
Language Arts Teacher
Jackson, Debbie Walsh
Physical Ed Tchr & Dept Chprsn
Jackson, James H.
9th Grade English Teacher
Jackson, Muriel Batiste
Physical Ed & Health Teacher
Jackson, Ralph
History Teacher
Jackson, Susan Stilwell
Assistant Principal
Jackson, Vivian
6th-8th Grd Lang Arts Teacher
Jacobs, David L.
Professor
Jahnke, Thomas Paul
Third Grade Teacher
James, Jacquelyn O.
Exceptional Education Teacher
Johnson, Doris White
8th Grade Counselor
Johnson, Jana S.
English Teacher
Johnson, Rita J.
Soc Stud Dept Chair & Teacher
Johnson, Roy Wayne
Health Education Coach
Johnson, Shelia Baker
Freshman English Teacher
Johnson Van Ness, Wilma Dolores
Math Teacher

Johnston, Marilyn Miciotto
English Teacher
Johnston-Blair, Donna Catherine
Accounting Instructor
Jolley, Cassandra Ann
Fifth Grade Teacher
Jolliff, Gloria Tucker
Second Grade Teacher
Jolly, William Gregory
Agricultural Science Teacher
Jones, Charles L.
Physical Science Teacher
Jones, Danny M.
Physical Ed Teacher & Coach
Jones, LaRayne Warren
Family & Consumer Science Tchr
Joseph, Natalie Griffin
Dance & Drill Team Director
Kabnick, Karen Stephanie
Biology Instructor
Kanzig, Ray F.
High School Spanish Teacher
Kasper, Ann Corboy
Honors Biology Teacher
Kay, Michael D.
Choral Director
Kaylor, John Paul
Span Tchr, Frgn Lng Dpt Co-Chm
Kearns, Michael Patrick
Sophomore English Teacher
Keating, Robert J.
Professor of Biology
Keener, Joan Hogan
Senior Guidance Counselor
Keig, Michael Scott
Assistant Band Director
Kelley, Kimberly Lynne
Third Grade Teacher
Kemble, Kary D.
World History Teacher
Kestenbaum, Miriam
Algebra Tchr & Math Dept Chair
Kettler, Jean
English Teacher
Keys, Denise Simon
9th & 10th Grd Science Teacher
Khym, Georgia June
Spanish Teacher
Kikta, Frank James
6th-8th Grade Counselor
Kilgore-Elizalde, Cynthia Lassiter
Mathematics Teacher
Kimble, Marylyn Wills
Economics & Government Teacher
Kingsley, Charles E.
Director of Bands
Kirkwood, Shirley Adams
7th & 8th Grd Mathematics Tchr
Klein, Charles Andrew
High School Physics Teacher
Kloh, Edmund Nah
English Teacher
Kluge, Cheryle Jobe
English Teacher
Kocian, Michael Stephen
Agriculture Science Teacher
Koop, Karla Jean
Art Teacher & Department Chair
Kral, Nancy Bolin
Political Science Professor
Kravetz, Ruth A.
Mathematics & Chemistry Tchr
Kretzer, Marilyn
Soc Stud Teacher & Dept Chprsn
Kruse, Sammy Ray
Social Studies Dept Chair
Laine, Sharon Tillman
Second Grade Teacher
Lamb, Lloyd Vernon
Mathematics Teacher
Landgraf, Tom
Psychology Teacher
Landgrebe, Charles Michael
Theatre Arts Teacher
Lane, Carol Ann
5th Grade Math & Sci Teacher
Lane, Joanne Eaker
History Teacher
Langille, Sharon Marie
Geometry Teacher
Langlois, Beneva Miller
Substitute Teacher
Larson, Dan Philip
Orchestra Director
Laukaitus, Karen Hagstrom
Seventh Grade Math Teacher
Lawson, Beverley Sheppard
Mrktg Ed & Travel Arts Teacher
Lee, Daisy D.
English Teacher
Lee, Mary B.
English Teacher
Leibfried, Theodore Frederich, Jr.
Instructor in Computer Science
Leisenring, Margaret
Fifth Grade Teacher
Lemm, Deborah Davies
Spanish Teacher
Lemons, Penelope Miskel
Middle School Math Teacher
Levendoski, Lori A.
Fourth Grade Teacher
Levine, Cheryl Driver
Assoc Prof & Dept Chrmn
Lewellyn, Jennifer Louise
Third Grade Teacher
Lewis, Elaine Thibodeaux
Mathematics Tchr & Chairperson
Linsley, Joan VanHorn
Geography & Social Stud Tchr

Lloyd, Lillie Gilford
HS Mathematics Teacher
LoBue, Laura Lea
Teacher
Loh, Kathleen Schaak
Social Studies Teacher
Long, David R.
French & Spanish Teacher
Lopez, Elda
Mathematics Teacher
Lopez, Matthew John
Spanish Teacher
Lorio, Angela M.
Chemistry Teacher
Lovinggood, David Charles
Biology & Geology Teacher
Loyde, Delic Emanuel
Assistant Principal
Lyle, Kenneth Stuart, III
Chemistry Teacher
Mack, Bettye Lyons
English & Lang Arts Teacher
Mackey, Fletcher R.
Asst Professor of Fine Arts
Madden, Nan Soulette
Third Grade Teacher
Magill, Cheryl Kaye
Speech, Debate Tchr & Coach
Manby, Valerie Todd
Fourth Grade Teacher
Marcantel, Helen K.
Third Grade Teacher
Marczak, Julie Smith
Elementary Music Teacher
Markos, Louis A.
Assistant Prof of English
Marmaduke, Linda Otto
Fifth Grade Teacher
Marquez, Judith Martinez
Asst Prof of Biling Ed
Martin, Ferryn
History Teacher
Martin, Judy Tiller
Bus Info Processing Co-op Tchr
Martinez, Amy Walker
Sixth Grade English Teacher
Marzouk, Darlene Lynn
Teacher of Gifted & Talented
Mathews, Will Ed
Physics Teacher
Mauldin, Patricia Spencer
Government & Economics Teacher
McAdams, Benjamin
Air Force Junior ROTC Instr
Mc Andrews, Barbara Bownds
Biology Teacher
Mc Cauley, Michael Dean
Physical Sci & Physics Teacher
Mc Charen, Michelle Henson
Counselor
Mc Clendon, Pamela Kay
History & Economics Teacher
McCrindle, Lisa Bennett
Art & Photography Teacher
Mc Curdy, Heidi Dawn
Calculus & Computer Sci Tchr
Mc David, Teddy Allen
Retired School Administrator
Mc Donald, Amy E.
Business Education Teacher
Mc Donald, Johnny Morgan
Administrator
Mc Donald, Lynn
Teacher & Coach
Mc Donald, Ronald Gene
Counselor
Mc Fadden, Zelma Lois Haywood
7th-8th Grade Math Teacher
Mc Ginley, Theresa Kurk
History Professor
Mc Kelroy, Ann Cross
8th Grd Social Studies Teacher
Mc Kinney, Jerry Blake
Math Teacher
McLelland, Sally Bartlett
English Teacher
Mcmahon, John Thomas
Social Studies Teacher
Mc Neil, Janice Feistel
AP Amer History & Govt Tchr
McSweeney, Joe A.
6th Grade Language Arts Tchr
Meacham, Karen Johnson
Special Education Teacher
Meconi, Honey
Musicology Professor
Medlen, Robert Byron
Biology Teacher
Meine, Bonnie Williford
Fourth Grade Teacher
Mendez, Michele Liebhafsky
4th Grade Teacher
Miller, Gabrielle Hunter
Day Camp Director
Miller, Karen Sowaen
High Schl Mathematics Teacher
Miller, Kathy Wright
Computer Math & Geometry Tchr
Miller, Mary Slocomb
Child Development Instructor
Miller, Sally Kelly
English Teacher
Mitchell, Diane (Roe)
Mathematics Teacher
Mitchell, Dwight
History Teacher
Mitchell, Portia Ward
English Teacher
Mitchell, Susan Smith
School Administrator

HOUSTON (cont)
Mize, Jimmie Michael
Counselor
Mladenka, Dorothy Tucker
Communication Graphics Teacher
Modest-Ashley, Dorothy Mignon
Former Dept of Math Instructor
Moncrief, Judy M.
English Teacher
Mondy, Sandra Phelps
High School Mathematics Tchr
Montgomery, Lara (Carbajal)
High School Choral Director
Moore, Bill Earl, II
English Teacher & Coach
Moore, Fanita Rose
5th Grade Teacher
Moore, Janice Gorka
Third Grade Teacher
Moore, Meg O'Brien
World History Teacher
Moore-Davis, Feleccia
Psychology Professor
Moran, Teresa S.
Health Teacher
Morgan, Robin Goodwin
Spanish Teacher
Morrell, Steve L.
Math Teacher
Morris, Jan Taylor
Lecturer in Accounting
Morton, Karen S.
Management Professor
Moseley, Marcus
American History Teacher
Mouton, Robin Elaine
Art Team Leader
Musick, Mickey Lynn
Team Ldr & Phys Science Tchr
Myers, Anne
Special Education Teacher
Nah, Blecho Wokleh
US History & AP Rdng Instr
Napierala, Sara Jo
History & Sociology Teacher
Nelson, Georgia Moore
Math Dept Chprsn, Coord & Tchr
Nelson, Ricky Alan
Athletic Trainer
Nettles, Kathryn Myers
Physics Tchr & Sci Dept Chair
Neumann, Tommy A.
Band Director
Newsome, BEverly A. Mc Washington
Sixth Grade Teacher
Nguyen, Lauren Matalamaki
6th-8th Grade ESL Teacher
Nichols, Linda H.
English Teacher
Nicklow, Lisa Lawrence
Instructor
Nielsen, Niels Albrecht
German Teacher & Dept Chprsn
Nix, Shirley A.
Bus Info Processng Teacher
Nong, Truong Duy
Mathematics Teacher
Norman, Carol Ann
Nursing Professor
Nottebart, Robert Edward
History Teacher
Novak, Catherine Elizabeth
History & Dance Teacher
Nsonamoah, Deloris M.
Department Head & Instructor
Olavesen, Kristine Marie
Computer Science Teacher
O'Leary, Carol Ann
Spanish Teacher
Oliver, Peggy Fish
College English Instructor
Opp, David E.
9th Grade Honors Biology Tchr
Orphe, Annie Harris
Kindergarten Teacher
Orr, Wendy Hamilton
Fifth Grade Teacher
Overton, Karen E.
Instructor of Business Admin
Owen, Ann English
Asst Prof of Psych & Sociology
Owens, Beth Ernst
English Teacher
Owens, Laura Lee
Counseling & Guidance
Padmore, Vashti Mc Clain
English Instructor
Pae, Alice E.
ESL Instructor
Pare, Denise Brown
Instruction Director
Parish, Delia Cummns
English Teacher
Parker, Betty Lee
Teacher & String Specialist
Parker, Jennifer Lyn
Government & Economics Teacher
Parmeter, Nancy Cyrus
Career & Technology Teacher
Parrott, Richard Thomas
Human Services Professor
Patterson, Jennifer Streeter
History Teacher
Pavlas, Patricia Lynne
Social Studies Teacher
Pearson, Janet Myers
High School Counselor
Peccio, Sharon
Eng & Theory of Knowledge Tchr
Peel, Shirlene Phillips
Biology Teacher
Peri, Robert Gasper, Jr.
Dir of Music, Chm of Fine Arts
Perkins, Sharon
Associate Professor
Perridon, Charles H.
Social Studies Teacher
Perry, Anne Marie (Litchfield)
Teacher of At-Risk Students
Peterson, Glen Stuart
High School Math Teacher
Peterson, Verna Martin
Professor
Phillips, Brenda Irby
English Teacher
Pickens, Willie Tennyson
Physical Education Teacher
Picus, Mark Alan
English as a Second Lang Instr
Pikus, Donna Marie
English Teacher
Pinsky, Lawrence Steven
Professor & Physics Dept Chair
Plunkett, Mark Alan
Technology Specialist
Poinsett, Janice Hanel
3rd Grade Teacher
Porter, Valerie Hill
Science III Teacher
Potter, Lee Ann Uppendahl
Social Studies Teacher
Potts, Eric Sherard
Computer Science Teacher
Poxon, Ellen Maxwell
Health Occupations Teacher
Price, Johnnie Andrew, II
Hlth & Physical Education Tchr
Prince, Lacy Young
Third Grade Teacher
Pruzan, Beverly Sovitsky
Vocational Office Ed Instr
Pummill, Jane Mc Guirt
Fourth Grade Teacher
Pumphrey, Cynthia Ann Bailey
Seventh Grade Science Teacher
Pyle, Ouida J.
Second Grade Teacher
Quiroz, Mona Lisa
History Teacher & Dept Chair
Rabb, Corliss A.
Coordinator of Advisement
Radtke, Robin R.
Asst Prof of Accounting
Rainey, Clota Gamble
Third Grade Teacher
Randle, Olevia Booker
Second Grade Teacher
Randle, Robert Wesley
Algebra Teacher
Randon, Mary Walker
Lead Teacher
Rawls, Millie Norton
Business Education Teacher
Redman, Malinda Louise
Librarian
Reece, Brendel Elaine
6th & 7th Grade English Tchr
Reece, Lana Cavitt
Eighth Grade Reading Teacher
Reed, Josolynne Marie
World History Teacher
Reed, Julius A.
Chemistry Teacher
Reed, Kennard Wendell, Jr.
Mathematics Instructor
Reynolds, Elise Melanie
Former Counselor
Reynolds, Melissa E.
Phys Ed Dept Chprsn & Coach
Rhea, Kay Crossley
Middle School Sci & Hlth Tchr
Rice, Judy Margaret
Mathematics Teacher
Rice, Linda Perry
Teacher of Gifted & Talented
Rich, Melinde
Secondary Soc Studies Teacher
Rickard, Gayle Murff
American History Teacher
Roberts, Sharon
Fine Arts Dance Teacher
Robertson, Pat R.
Fourth Grade Teacher
Robinson, Esther Martin
History Teacher
Robinson, Terrie Ann
High School Art & Photo Tchr
Rodriguez, Alma Garza
Pre-K Teacher
Rogers, Myrtle Dillon
Mathematics Teacher
Rogers, Robert David
Geology & Science Teacher
Ross, Doris L.
Professor & Dean Protem
Ruby, Ami Leigh
English Teacher
Rucker, Pauline Grigg
Asst Prin & Lang Arts Coord
Ruckman, Elizabeth Aufderheide
Spanish Teacher
Ruggiero, Paula Canessa
Math Teacher
Runnels, Aretta Carden
Asst Principal
Ruppert, Julieta Melo
ESL Teacher
Russell, Jan L.
History Teacher & Dept Chprsn
Russo, Colleen
Physical Ed Tchr & Coach
Ruthstrom, Laura
7th-8th Grd GATE Teacher
Ruthstrom, Mark Sigmund
8th Grade Science Teacher
Sabom, Gay Morrison
Marketing Education Coord
St Denis, Amy Winston
Eng, French Tchr & Counselor
Salter, Rita Beach
9th Grd Algebra, Geometry Tchr
Sample, Hugh Workman
English Teacher
Sampson, Joan Smith
Fifth Grade Teacher
Sanders, Russell J.
English Teacher
Savage, Debra Jeanne
Social Studies Teacher
Savage, Wanda Drew
Math Teacher
Saxton, Lori Michelle
Theatre Arts Teacher
Schmidt, Karen Lee
Eng as Second Lang Instructor
Schmidt, Luz Maria
Teacher & Coach
Schneider, Cynthia Ann
English Teacher
Schow, Carl Emil, III
English Resource Teacher
Schwalbach, Marshall Ray
6th Grade Teacher
Scott, Cynthia Schenck
Math Teacher
Semler, Ann Lorraine
Economics & World Geog Teacher
Sessum, Virginia L.
Magnet Coordinator
Sharp, Jan Taylor
ESL Social Studies Teacher
Sheehan, Laura Marie
Eng as a Second Language Instr
Shepard, Lewis Montross, Jr.
Music Teacher
Shields, Susan Bush
Sixth Grade Science Teacher
Shipp, Carol Ann Toups
English Teacher
Shiu, Bingiee Overton
Orchestra Conductor
Simon, Henry Louis
Instructor & Safety Officer
Simpson, James N.
Assistant Principal
Sinclair, Rose Pharr
School Librarian
Sitton, Robert Alan
Business Education Teacher
Small, Andrew
Asst Professor of French
Smith, Darryl Mattheu
Biology Instructor
Smith, Frank
English Teacher
Smith, Joellen (Piskura)
Dean of Students
Smith, Sennie Goines
ESL Teacher
Smith, Susan Huhndorff
8th Grd Math & Algebra Teacher
Smith, Vickie Moore
Advanced & GT English Teacher
Smith, William Michael
Journalism Teacher
Snooks, Margaret Konz
Fitness & Hum Performance Prof
Sparacino, Jo Ann
Honors English Teacher
Spiers, Barry Lee
Science Teacher
Stanley, Belinda Beall
Science Dept Head
Steach, Delsi Joy
Spanish Teacher
Steinway, Roger F.
9th Grade US History Teacher
Stevens, Genevieve Dee
Psychology Professor
Stevens, Larry Lamar
Choir Dir & Music Dept Coord
Stevens, Linda G. Charles
High School Business Teacher
Stewart, Barbara Ann
Chemistry & Biology Teacher
Stewart, Wilfred Thomas
HS Drafting Teacher
Stimson, Zita
Jr High Teacher & Asst Prin
Stoner, Mary Winters
English Teacher
Stowe, Rhonda Goode
Second Grade Teacher
Strader, Janie Lee
English Teacher
Strahan, Geraldlyn Watts
Third Grade Teacher
Streetman, Gale T.
Government & Economics Teacher
Strother, Julie Carter
His Tchr & Yrbk Adv
Strout, Dan A.
Accounting & Economics Prof
Summers, Susan Carrie
Principal
Sutter, J. Ramsey
Government Professor
Swanson, Steve David
Health Teacher
Swiantek, Carolyn Ann (Pengely)
English Teacher
Swords, Judy
3rd Grade Teacher
Sykes, Karen Owen
Computer Literacy Teacher
Tarrant, Judith Rollins
Computer Science Teacher
Tate, Mildred Cecelia
English Professor
Tatum, Charles Edward
History & Geography Professor
Taylor, Elizabeth Coleman
Social Studies Teacher
Taylor, James Sheppard
Prof & Comm Dept Chair
Taylor, Patricia Popham
English Instructor
Taylor-Thompson, Betty
Professor of English
Teaster, Patricia Lee
Home Ec Cooperative Ed Tchr
Temkin, Larry Scott
Philosophy Professor
Thibaut, Amy Nelson
World His Teacher & Dept Chair
Thomas, Molly
Biology Instructor
Thomason, Patrick Miller
Chemistry I Teacher
Thompson, Burnette, Jr.
Mathematics Instructor
Thompson, Kathi
Mathematics Teacher
Thornton, Ronald Bernard
Band Director
Thornton, Shauna Maher
Elem Schl Spanish Teacher
Thuman, Alice Fisher
Latin Teacher
Tidwell, Deborah Lynn
Choral Director
Tillman, B. Lynn
Asst Prof of Human Psychology
Timm, Cheryl A. (O'Cain)
Didactic & Clinical Instr
Todd, Suzanne W.
Principal
Truscott, Donna Marie
7th Grd Life Science Educator
Tuckwiller, Tony
Choir Teacher
Tulich, Eugene Nicholas
Political Science Adjunct Fac
Tumy, Kelly Eileen
English II & Lead Teacher
Turnbull, Chris A.
English & Reading Teacher
Turner, Pam
Science Teacher
Turner, Polly
Health Care Admin Asst Prof
Ulmer, James Kenneth
Assoc Prof & Writer-in-Res
Van Cleave, Kay Vivian
Safe & Drug Free School Cnslr
Veletsos, Anestis S.
Brown & Root Professor
Vera, Al
Teacher
Verraires, Dora Ana Gonzalez
Spanish Teacher
Victery, John Bailey
Second Langs Chair & Teacher
Viladevall, Ana Mitchel
ESL Teacher
Vogan, Jodi Miller
US History Teacher
Vogel, Debra Whitworth
ESL Teacher
Vogt, Allen Roy
American History Professor
Vories, Priscilla A.
Assoc Degree Nrsng Prgm Instr
Vu, Nho Huu
Drafting & Design Tech Head
Wagle, Jyoti Ravindra
Biology Department Chprsn
Wagner, Michele Rabbitt
High School Art Educator
Walke, Mary Blackman
English Teacher
Walker, Nancy Robertson
Science Dept Head & Bio Tchr
Wallace, Susan Elaine
Art Teacher
Waller, Brenda R. Guillory
English Teacher
Waller, Edward Roland
Finance Professor
Walters, William E.
Developmental Studies Instr
Walters, William Robert (Jake)
Dean of Secondary Education
Wang, Wei Li
Sculpture Teacher
Ward, Kimberly Ann
Ninth Grade English Teacher
Warden, Mary Therese, OP
Mathematics Teacher
Warner, Eleanor Curtis
First Grade Teacher
Washington, Peggy Mallow
English Teacher
Washington, Wanda Faye
Second Grade Teacher
Watkins, Priscilla D.
Social Studies Teacher
Weaver, Teresa Anne
Math, Algebra & Geometry Tchr
Webber, Mark Joseph
Debate & Public Speaking Tchr
Weiman, Barbara Lynn
Biology & Psychology Teacher
Weisinger, Eloise Acree
Debate Teacher
Weisinger, Robert Julian
History Teacher
Welch, Lisa Autry
US History Teacher
Weller, Eddie E., Jr.
History Professor
Wells, Julie M.
11th Grade US History Teacher
Wentland, Stephen Henry
Professor & Chair of Chemistry
Wheeler, Kevin Marshall
US History Teacher
White, Bobbie L. (Dale)
English Teacher
Whitehurst, Charlene Todd
Fifth Grade Teacher
Whyle, Jeffrey Alan
Math Teacher
Wichmann, Russell Kenneth
Teacher & Coach
Wieck, K. Lynn
Assistant Professor of Nursing
Wiederhold, Dorathea Elizabeth
Lang Arts & Gifted Prgm Tchr
Wiersema, Donna Sanders
Instructor of Math & Science
Wilbratte, Barry
Prof of Ec & Dept Chair
Wilkins, Lenita D.
Science Teacher
Wilkson, William Roger
English Teacher
Williams, Audrey Jordan
Biology Teacher
Williams, Cathy Ann
Fifth Grade Teacher
Williams, Debra Delores
American History Teacher
Williams, Marjorie Cobbs
Second Grade Teacher
Williamson, Ruth Ann
Professor
Williams-Rausin, La Donna Jean
8th Grd Social Studies Teacher
Willis, Allye Butts
Counselor & Instructor
Willis, Irene Leslie
Librarian
Wills, Mary Alice
History & Geography Dept Head
Wilson, Ann Johnston
Mathematics Teacher
Wilson, John-Douglas
Dept Head & Instr
Wilson, Mary Maull
Second Grade Teacher
Wilson, Ruth Scott
Retired Third Grade Teacher
Wilson Meyer, Dianne Scott
English Teacher
Winfree, Veda L.
English Teacher
Winkelmann, Kelly Marie
World Geography Tchr & Coach
Wissen, William Theodore
Athletic Teacher
Witt, Donald A.
Computer Sci & Physics Instr
Wofford, Milton Gene
Professor
Wolff, Mary Ida
English Chairperson & Teacher
Wolfgang, Dorothy Marianne
Science Teacher
Wood, Curtis L.
Geometry Teacher
Wood, Kat
Speech Instructor
Woodbury, Wan-Ling
Calculus & Alg II Teacher
Woods, Anne Richardson
Fifth Grade Teacher
Woods, Iva Jewel
English Professor
Woods, Treacy Lynn
Assoc Professor of Chemistry
Woodson, Charlie Elbert
Admissions Counselor
Wooten, Helen Goffney
Director & Owner
Wooten, Theresa Else
Nursing Instructor
Wright, Cynthia Kay (Barton)
Reading & Writing Wkshp Tchr
Wright, Lynda Rene
Publications Advisor
Wright, Priscilla Ann
ESL Teacher
Wright, Stephanie D.
Principal
Wurst, Tom
World His & Geography Tchr
Wylie, Helen Lee
Mathematics Professor
Young, Bobbie Austin
Mathematics Teacher
Young, Mercie B. Sandling
Special Education Teacher
Zech-Stephenson, Becky L.
Elementary Counselor
Zibilski, Nathan C.
Administrative Principal
Zimmer, Lana Mae
Mathematics Teacher

ON (cont)
na Stansel
rincipal
Kevin Paul
Geography Teacher
Rina Miskind
Grade Teacher

Donna Marie
h & Spanish Teacher
s, George Stephen
PE Tchr & HS Coach
Patricia Ann (Sims)
iter & Technology Instr
ina Lynn
l Education Teacher
RD
Sheryl A.
School English Teacher
acquelyn Jarvis
Teacher & Coordinator
AN
Nancy Meley
e Teacher & Director
Marilyn Buxhemper
gy Teacher
Cynthia Louise
ra, Calculus Tchr & Coach
George A.
onal Coordinator & Coach
ES SPRINGS
Richard Wayne
e Teacher & Coach
n, Darlene Amelia
& Computer Literacy Tchr
LE
Toni Rae (Mensing)
s Teacher
Brenda Lott
th Grd TX History Tchr
Clare Marie
8th Grade Math Teacher
Carl Vincent
e School Choir Director
an, Kirk Howard
elist
n, Babett Schneider
istry Teacher
re, Jeffrey Joseph
ult Sci & Tech Teacher
rd, Sheryl T.
story Tchr & Dept Chprsn
Felicia Jackson
sh Teacher
r, Bernetta Harris
sh & Psychology Teacher
, Ida Kristine
nunity Class Teacher
son, David Franklin
Science Educator
s, Beverly King
er & Dept Chairperson
s, Shawn Wilson
School Latin Teacher
, Marlys Melicher
ded Learning Teacher
Janice Marie Morris
e School Choir Director
o, Louis Michael
istry Lead Teacher
, E. Kathleen
istry & Physical Sci Tchr
eanne K.
rade Teacher
rews, Robert Jules, Sr.
eting Ed Tchr & Coord
Kimberly Herr
Grd Soc Stud Teacher
Linda Ann (Shy)
ctor & Education Coord
Evelyn Aiken
rd Language Arts Teacher
n, Patricia Bush
His & Economics Teacher
t, Patricia Ann
Teacher
, Deitra Fleetwood
ess & Computer Teacher
Mona M.
ra I & Math Teacher
our, Wanda Faye
d Geography Teacher
son, Annette Covin
nth Grade Math Teacher
er, Louise Riley
re Arts & Speech Teacher
Nelson, Kathleen
gy Teacher
Pamela Christian
cal Ed Instructor & Coach
, Katy Satterwhite
ing Teacher
Linda Gallagher
munity Class Teacher
Dena Beth
Director
son, Theresa Schmidt
Grade Science Teacher
hill, Janet Clair
nd Grade Teacher
nan, Hallie Diane
n Grade English Teacher
Joseph Lloyd
r Director
Keith Wayne
sh Teacher & Dept Chm
INGTON
Tracie Marshall
ematics Teacher

Nesbit, Michael Wesley
Principal & History Instructor
HUNTSVILLE
Ameen, Elsie Coker
Instructor of Accounting
Barnosky, John David
Assistant Professor
Barrett, Wayne
Asst Director of Choral Act
Brashears, Robert Eugene
Director of Bands
Cammarata, Katherine Ferguson
Instr in Health & Kinesiology
Casey, James E., Jr.
Professor
Chasteen, Thomas Girard
Professor of Chemistry
Child, Paul William, III
English Professor
Coers, Donald Vernon
Professor of English
Davis, Sophia Willis
Eng & Creative Writing Tchr
Davis, Thomas Franklin
Professor of Mathematics
Donnelly, David William
Physics Professor
Fair, Janet B.
English Teacher
Fuller, John David
Art I Teacher
Gratz, Cindy Carpenter
Assistant Professor of Dance
Gutermuth, Mary Elizabeth
French Prof & Languages Coord
Hail, Darol Wayne
Senior English Teacher
Hayes, Donald M.
Sociology Professor
Hyman, Bill
Assoc Prof & Coord of Hlth Ed
Kelley, Stanley F.
Asst Professor of Animal Sci
Ketchand, Alice Adams
Accounting Professor
Kirmani, Zaheer Ali
Assistant Professor
Krienke, Marion D.
Professor of English
Krystyniak, Franklin D.
Adjunct Instructor
Lesesne, Teri Stewart
Assistant Professor
Louis, Cathy Winfrey
Language Arts Teacher
Mallory, Rexann (Outland)
Science Teacher
Marshall, Linda Drabek
Marketing Ed Tchr & Coord
Mitchell, Eleanor Rettig
Retired Prof of Eng & Lingstcs
Muns, Nedom Conway
Professor of Tech & Tchr Ed
Nash, Patricia Kay
Mathematics Teacher
Nash, Paul Douglas
Geometry Teacher
Nestroy, Jerry Ann
Prof of Hlth & Kinesiology
Netoff, Dennis Ivan
Asst Prof of Geog & Geology
Neunuebel, Paul Michael
Psychology Professor
Nolteriek, Mary Ann
Music Therapy Associate Prof
Odon, Gary Lynn
Assoc Professor of Kinesiology
Olson, James Stuart
Distinguished Prof of History
Parotti, Phillip Elliott
Professor of English
Phelps, Deborah Lynne
English Professor
Sangster, Carol Lee Burley
Professor of Accounting
Schroeder, Phillip John
Asst Prof, Music Theory & Comp
Shelly, Randy Lynn
Physical Science Tchr & Coach
Sikes, Letcher Nathaniel
Professor of Animal Science
Sousa, Gary D.
Director of Bands
Sower, Victor Edmund
Asst Prof of Management
Sparks, Elaine Whitten
Phase III Teacher
Thibodeaux, Terry Mark
Speech Communication Professor
Tucker, Shirley Hatcher
Assistant Professor
Ward, Barbara Jean (Hostetter)
Asst Professor of Animal Sci
Warner, Laverne
Prof of Early Childhood Ed
Williams, Patricia Ann
Prof of Education & Director
Williamson, Michelle Andrea
Mathematics Teacher
Williamson, Randal Guy
Substitute Teacher
Young, Eugene Owen
Chair & Professor of English
Zalaquett, Carlos P.
Asst Dir of Counseling Center
HURST
Barber, Shelley Small
English Teacher & Coach
Bolen, James Cordell
Mathematics Professor

Brock, Mary Stribling
English Teacher
Bruhn, Christopher Jon
Physics Teacher
Carruthers, William Spencer
Algebra Teacher
Crow, DeAnne
Math Teacher
Dunn, Julie Diane
8th Grade English Teacher
Gibson, Dianne Jordan
Teacher
Hamilton, Janet V.
Chemistry Professor
Helverson, Janice Martin
Eighth Grade Teacher
Jackson, Andrew Hudson
Coord & Prof of Legal Asst Pgm
James, Michelle Harris
Fifth Grade Teacher
Jones, Doris J.
Department Chair
Kahlig, Cathy Halencak
English Teacher
Latimer, Billie L.
Kindergarten Teacher
Lee, Mary Ann A.
Assoc Prof of History
Matthai, William C.
Assoc Prof of Natural Sciences
Miller, Cindy Hanking
Journalism & English Teacher
Monks, Julia Whitinger
Instructor of Political Sci
Neal, C. P.
Video Instructor
Pate, J'Nell Rogers
History & Government Instr
Rosse, Sherri Hejtmancik
Business & Computer Teacher
Russell, Gary L.
High School Counselor
Spann, Carolyn Holland
Second Grade Teacher
Warren, Kimberly Smith
Business Teacher
Washmon, Dan
Social Studies Instructor
HUTTO
Duren, Kyle F.
Chemistry & Physics Teacher
Everett, Sandy Plummer
English Teacher
Womack, Jennifer Lynn
Math Teacher
IDALOU
Fugate, Sondra Ward
Language Arts Teacher
Pruitt, Rhonda Simpson
Teacher
INDUSTRY
Barlow, Carolyn Elaine
Kindergarten Teacher
INEZ
Kalina, Deidra Garbade
5th Grade Teacher
INGRAM
Livingston, Deborah Jean
English & Journalism Teacher
McCarty, Larry W.
Soc Stud Chm & Dir Forensics
IOLA
Morris, Becky Elaine
Business Education Teacher
IOWA PARK
Dillard, Vicki Jane
English & Business Teacher
Hodges, Brenda
History Teacher & Coach
Perkins, Joyce Hodges
Retired Teacher
IRA
Gardner, Sandra Jo
Second Grade Teacher
Northcott, Gale White
Third Grade Teacher
IREDELL
Dowell, Brenda Hale
Secondary Teacher
Lindsey, Linda C.
Kindergarten Home Ec Teacher
Proffitt, Janis L.
Business & Computer Teacher
IRVING
Adelmann, Louis Francis
Social Studies Teacher
Baer, Cinda K.
Physical Ed & Health Teacher
Baker, Carolyn Knight
Biology Teacher
Barr, Alvin Francis
Mathematics Instructor
Barrett, Donald Decatur, Jr.
Professor of Electronics
Brahinsky, Phyllis Lee
7th Grade Sci Tchr & Dept Head
Branson, Arsetta Spieker
Spcl Ed Teacher & Dept Chprsn
Bravo, Lou A.
Accounting Professor
Childress, Waldene Pike
Health Sci Tech Tchr & Coord
Connatser, Rebecca Ann
History Teacher
Connolly, J. Doug, Jr.
Social Studies Instructor
Connolly, Melinda Kay
Professor of Dance
D'Ambrosio, Marcellino G.
Assistant Prof of Theology

Davis, Dana Dianne (Moore)
English & Humanities Teacher
Dickson, Jan Wood
English Teacher
Dobbs, Betty Jane
Retired 1st Grade Teacher
Fields, Carole Beth
Eng Dept Head & Tchr
Foster, Stephen Preston
Biology Teacher
Fuller, Kelly D'Ann
1st Grade Teacher
Gallemore, Marla Mathena
Mathematics Teacher
Garnier, Valerie Barnes
Social Studies Dept Chair
Goss, Mary Lou (Pritchard)
Pre-First Grade Teacher
Greenfield, Jaclyn Lancaster
English Teacher
Hahn, Janis Stephens
Honors World History Teacher
Herrera-Omar, Olga Sue
Lead Resource Teacher
Hertwig, Jim
Math Teacher
Horak, Patricia Devers
5th Grade Teacher
Ironside, Robert Albert
Professor of Business
James, Will E.
Head Band Director
Johnson, Judy
Elementary Music Teacher
Kemper, Frederick William
Economics Teacher
King, Mary Johnigan
5th Grade Teacher
Lee, Sue
Asst to the President
Lewis, Janie Martin
Third Grade Teacher
Lilly, S. Diane
4th Grade Teacher
Long, Linda J.
Professor of Speech
Marcellus, Monica M.
Tchr of Eng, Gifted & Talented
Marchell, Jeanne Hight
Fourth Grade Teacher
Martin, Jennifer Lynne (Fawcos)
Biology Teacher
Mc Donald, Margie Carr
Third Grade Teacher
McVay, Barbara Jean (Chaves)
Mathematics Teacher
Mendrek, Joan Ayer
Biology Teacher
Mpinga, Derek A.
Professor of Mathematics
Myers, Madeleine Becan
English Teacher
Oliver, Glen Ivan
Director of Bands
Parrish, Patsy Charlene
Home Economics Teacher
Perkins, Mary Lynn
Fifth Grade Teacher
Postlewate, Maria-Luisa Herrera
Foreign Language Dept Chair
Rahn, Russell A.
Jr High Science Teacher
Rambo, Dotty Ann
Secondary Mathematics Coord
Reagan, Susan Walker
Reading Teacher
Romero, Yolanda Garcia
Professor of History
Scattergood, Florence Gassler
Choral Director
Schrantz, David Marshall
US History & Phy Ed Teacher
Shields, Lisa Turnbull
5th Grade Teacher
Sommerfeldt, John Robert
Professor of History
Stephens, Annette Craze
10th Grd Honors Eng Teacher
Stephens, Staci Ann
Dance Teacher & Drill Team Dir
Strain, Charles Edward
Accelerated Program Teacher
Sullivan, Charles Robert
Assistant Professor of History
Vickrey, Peggy Church
English Teacher
Walker, Pat Pringle
Kindergarten Teacher
Weldon, Timothy Jules
Adjunct Instructor
White, Margaret Sewell
6th Grd World Cultures Teacher
White, Michael Dean
US History Tchr
Wilhoit, Ruth Ann
Second Grade Teacher
Wilson, Carolyn Burris
2nd Grade Teacher
Wilson, Janice Beal
Math Teacher
Wilson, Kay Beredezen
Real Estate Professor
Wootton, Kim E.
Biology Teacher
Wyatt, Robert Edwin
Biology Teacher
Young, Nancy Duncan
Math Teacher

ITALY
Bridge, Marjorie Ann
Science Teacher
White, Joe Arthur, Jr.
Music Teacher & Band Director
ITASCA
Walters, Janet Elaine
English Teacher
IVANHOE
Morris, Tammy Adian
History & Government Teacher
Smith, Mary Frank
English Teacher
JACINTO CITY
Puett, Sarah Jane
Second Grade Teacher
JACKSBORO
Burnett, William Bradley
Agriculture Sci & Tech Teacher
Kuhn, Thomas Neil
Bands Director
Smith, Linda Marie
Fourth Grade Teacher
Spears, Liz
Mathematics Teacher
JACKSONVILLE
Beasley, Gail Harrington
English & Speech Comm Instr
Brooks, Jack Evans
Music Instructor
Hoheisel, Peter F.
Assistant Professor of English
Jackson, Lee
History & Geography Teacher
Knous, Melissa Mechling
Eighth Grade English Teacher
McCullough, John Lemuel
Physical Science Tchr & Coach
Moore, Cindy Pryor
English Professor
Norvell, Bradley Fred
Biology Teacher & Coach
Rich, Mary Tidwell
Music Instructor & Dept Chair
Ross, Johnnie Hutson
Professor of Mathematics
Ross, Madeleine Traill
Assoc Prof of His & Philosophy
Sanford, Lisa Knous
Biology Teacher
Sheppard, Jon LeRoy
High School Math Teacher
Slawson, Richard
Marketing Ed Teacher & Coord
Terry, Glen C.
Chem Professor & Golf Coach
Waller, Philip Ray
US Politics & US History Instr
Wilson, Douglas Allen
Religion Department Chairman
Wise, Donna Marie (Edwards)
Science Teacher
JARRELL
Holladay, James Gregory
English Teacher
Hughes, Anna Faye
Span, Govt & World Geog Tchr
Woodley, Martha McCullough
7th & 8th Grd Lang Arts Tchr
JASPER
Dickerson, Judy Foley
First Grade Teacher
Dougharty, Rebecca Lynn
Third Grade Teacher
Morgan, Sammye Daniels
Home Economics Teacher
JAYTON
Hall, Nancy Hinds
Sixth Grade Teacher
Owen, Katherine Harper
Home Ec Teacher & Counselor
JEFFERSON
Cerliano, Rebecca Ann
Spanish Teacher
Evans, Sheryl Anderson
High School Math Teacher
Flowers, Maxine Larthridge
English Teacher
Robeson, V. Martin
Principal
Strickland, Bobby
High School Math Tchr & Coach
Taylor, Colleen H.
Educational Diagnostician
Teacher, Pauline Phillips
4th Grade Math Teacher
JEWETT
Baldwin, Richard Phillip
Agricultural Sci & Tech Tchr
Jones, David Ray
Principal
Stone, Patty Coker
Fourth Grade Teacher
JOAQUIN
Barlow, Ronald Earl
High School Principal
Pate, Patricia Carroll
Business Education Teacher
Smith, Danielle Carroll
Home Economics & Yearbook Tchr
JOHNSON CITY
Birck, Susan Bruce
Social Studies Teacher
Marek, Felice Pfeiffer
Agricultural Science Instr
Milner, Douglas Bailey
Social Studies Teacher
Rust, Cicero Alexander, III
Spanish & English Teacher

JOHNSON CITY (cont)
Starr, Pamela Foster
Business Education Teacher
Sultemeier, Cindy Beale
Math Teacher
Voron, William David
English, Speech & Drama Tchr
JONESBORO
Kinney, Darla Simmons
4th Grade Teacher
Stephenson, Ida Ellis
Special Education Teacher
Young, Dorothy M.
Business & Computer Teacher
JOSHUA
Ammons, LeeAnn Cantrell
Teacher
Cade, Phyllis Kay (Askew)
Fifth Grade Teacher
Cameron, Kevin L.
HS Counselor
Crysup, Cinda Philbrick
Seventh Grade Math Teacher
Kretzschmar, Wileta Dickey
Home Ec & Cooperative Ed Tchr
Medford, Kay Lynn
Choir Director
Miller, Glenda Denise
Biology Teacher
Weaver, Dale Allen
Lang Arts Tchr & Asst Prin
Wood, Gary Michael
Health Dept Head
Worn, Carol Ann (Jackson)
Fifth Grade Teacher
JOURDANTON
Andrus, Jane Steinle
4th Grade Teacher
Below, Kathryn Lumpkin
Eng & Gifted Ed Tchr
Clary, Pamela A.
High School Algebra Teacher
English, Sandra Baccus
Elementary Special Ed Teacher
Johnson, Judy Lynn
7th Grade Texas History Tchr
Maddox, Cecilia Beszborn
English Teacher
Schultz, Susan Schaefer
Title 1 Teacher & Coordinator
SoRelle, Norma Jo
Fourth Grade Teacher
Strauss, Erin Hermes
Fifth Grade Teacher
JUNCTION
Baugh, Jimmy
Biology Teacher
Bierschwale, Sheryl Cassens
English I Yrbk & Jrnlsm Tchr
Hepburn, Joycelyn Kothmann
Business Education Teacher
JUSTIN
Bell, Donna Day
French Teacher
Chadwell, Jim F.
Psychology Teacher & Coach
Diaz, Lynnita Humphries
Spanish Teacher
Doughty, Michael Todd
Government & Economics Teacher
Fielder, Catherine Graves
History Teacher
Holbrook, Eldene
Eng, Gifted & Talented Tchr
Maulding, Wanda Smith
Biology Teacher
Spann, Patti Salerno
Honors English II Teacher
Sparks, Jody Lobaugh
English Teacher & Dept Chprsn
Stevens, Marilyn
Jrnlsm & Photo Teacher
Whittenberg, Mary J.
Indstrl Tech & Stu Ldrshp Tchr
Wood, Susan D.
Science Dept Chair & Teacher
KARNACK
Crump, Gloria Joyce Washington
Special Education Teacher
Jones, Gloria A.
Business Education Teacher
Rice, Ernestine Thompson
Curriculum & Spec Programs Dir
KARNES CITY
Johnson, Melanie Gotthardt
Physical Science Teacher
Wheat, Dixell H.
4th Grade Teacher
KATY
Allendorf, Penny Strickland
Chemistry Teacher
Brown, Jill Followell
Art & Publications Teacher
Chandlee, Linda Jean Appleby
Guidance Counselor
Cochran, Debby Huebner
Third Grade Teacher
Cunningham, Bradley D.
Computer Science Honors Tchr
Fields, Ben C.
Marketing Ed Corp Teacher
George, Rebecca Gisbon
Mathematics & Cmptr Sci Tchr
Gifford, Micheal Van
Science, Math & Bible Teacher
Gunn, Meredith Ann (Miller)
Lang Arts Instrl Specialist
Harris, Sharon Masterson
Spanish Teacher
King, Pat Ricketts
Microcmptr Applications Tchr
Kirby, Kerry Murphy
Soc Stu Elem Inst Specialist
Mccormick, Linda Jones
Third Grade Teacher
Mc Donald, Sondra Ebeling
Honors Biology Teacher
Mc Stravic, Paul
Soc Stud & Texas His Tchr
Mc Stravick, Paul Richard
US History Teacher
Owens, Betty Edwards
Fourth Grade Teacher
Papaioannou, Sage Rudd
3rd Grade Teacher
Phillips, Barbara Ann (Smith)
First Grade Teacher
Read, Jinx Allen
English Teacher
Reynolds, Nancy Lockhart
Chemistry & Physics Teacher
Scearce, Judy A.
Counselor
Spaulding, Patricia Hitt
Spanish Teacher
Thornton, Cynthia Ann
AP US Govt & Economics Teacher
Tynes, Gladys Wall
English Teacher
Vos, Gary A.
Agriscience Instructor
Waldrep, Suzanne Olson
Honors World His & Psych Tchr
KAUFMAN
Becker, Linda Gay Ryan
Sixth Grade Teacher
Liska, Theresa Pollinzi
8th Grade History Teacher
Rodgers, Becky Jo
PE & Tennis Class Tchr & Coach
KEENE
Anderson, Robert William
Fine Arts Chm & Band Director
Jones, Barbara Crutch
Professor of Chemistry
Larkin, Harley Paul
Math & Cmptr Programming Tchr
Mosley, Frances S.
History & Education Professor
Pitts, Darla Davis
Art Teacher
Sheffield, Marcus Lee
Associate Professor of Eng
Sicher, Erwin
Social Science Dept Chprsn
Willis, Edith Bradbury
Director of ESL Program
Willis, Lloyd Allan
Religion Professor
KELLER
Blevins, Kaye Jarvis
Teacher & Soc Stud Dept Chm
Burchfield, Janie Crane
Eng & Journalism Teacher
Burge, Kim Tomlin
Home Economics Teacher
Collins, Karen Kuykendall
7th Grd Eng & Lit Teacher
Collins, Wesley Barham
High School Mathematics Tchr
Daniels, Beverly Buchanan
English Teacher
Doverspike, Roselyn Van Orden
6th Grade Math Teacher
Evans, Jill Hetrick
HS Math Teacher
Ferguson, Marie Poland
Journalism Teacher
Harrell, Susan L.
Spanish & French Teacher
Harvey, Margaret Lucas
English Department Chair
Holliday, Paul Douglas
Assistant Principal
Hyde, Anette Lamb
Mathematics Teacher
Kimbrough, Stephen Scott
HS History Teacher & Coach
Lewis, Helen Rodgers
Theatre Arts Director
Mercer, Cindi Tyma
Spanish Teacher
Newkirk, Rhonda Renee
Mathematics Teacher
Pino, Kimberly Brumfield
English Teacher
Price, John Richard
7th Grade Texas History Tchr
Rodges, Melanie Griffith
Business Education Teacher
Self, Catherine Thurmond
High School Art Teacher
Shaw, Debra Currie
Business & Vocational Teacher
Styron, Scott
World Geography Teacher
Tidmore, Maynard Earl
Hnrs US His Tchr & Dept Head
KEMAH
Larrabee, Barbara Squibb
Librarian
KEMP
Carney, Michaelle Renee
History Tchr & Drill Team Dir
Dally, Woody W. C.
Retired Social Studies Teacher
Ewers, Randy Lloyd
Social Studies Teacher & Coach
Klecka, Trina Brunson
Eng, Photojrnlsm & Jrnlsm Tchr
Oehrlein, Timothy Joe
Geometry & Algebra Teacher
Rogers, Mandy F.
English Teacher & Coach
Stephenson, Jeanan York
Assistant Band Director
KENEDY
Cassler, Luther Scott, Jr.
Bio, Anatomy & Physiology Tchr
Goad, Brenda Kay
Business Teacher
Harris, John R.
Chem, Physics Tchr & Sci Chair
Pogue, Dorothy McClane
5th Grade Teacher
KENNEDALE
Boenig, Glenda Schumann
Vocational Adjustment Coord
Campbell, Rita Elrod
Eng Tchr, Yrbk Spon & Coach
Dannheim, Wayne Gilbert
Band Director
Ellsworth, Betsy Jayne
High School Counselor
Ford, Theresa Gilliland
Hlth & Life Mgmt Teacher
Greenfield, Kara Lynn
Third Grade Teacher
Johnson, Kelly Joe
Social Studies Teacher & Coach
Piske, Darrell Wayne
Resource Teacher
Rodenkirk, Carla Schneider
Fourth Grade Teacher
Taff, Ann Marshall
Business Education Teacher
Tidwell, Philip Harrison
Honors Algebra Teacher
Wallis, Melissa Benton
Theatre Director & Speech Tchr
KERENS
Latta, Barbara D.
English Teacher
KERMIT
Oglesby, Gordon Everett
US & World History Teacher
Parker, Dorothy Jean (Williams)
2nd Grade Teacher
Richardson, Menet Mays
Fourth Grade Teacher
KERRVILLE
Blanton, Daryl Glen
Biology Teacher & Coach
Bracken, Susan Fry
Secondary Math Teacher
Bradley, Chris Boultinghouse
English Teacher
Coldwell, Cynthia Brehmer
Second Grade Teacher
de la Pena, Daniel Jose
HS Mathematics Teacher
Eisaman, Helen Loree (Dew)
English Teacher
Guerrero, Kathryn Lovelady
English Teacher
Laurence, Donnie Ray
Athletic Director
Marquardt, Gregory Lewis
German, US His & Geog Teacher
Olson, Mike
Band Director
KILGORE
Baggett, Gloria Lozaine
US His & Citizenship Teacher
Baxter, Gayla Bowne
Fourth Grade Teacher
Booker, J. Terry
History Instructor & Governor
Calhoun, Deborah Daniels
Sci Tchr of Gifted & Talented
Crutcher, Richard Lee
Instr of Business Admin
Haden, Melissa Anyse Dickson
Computer Instructor
Hanshaw, Emilee O.
Eighth Grade English Teacher
Melton, Martha Lawrence
Fifth Grade Teacher & Chprsn
Mobley, Laney Talmage
Instructor of Biology
Osborne, Dorothy Butler
Retired Elementary Teacher
Reif, Steven Jay
Dept of Soc & Behavioral Sci
Sitton, Lynn Wylie
Instr of Early Chldhd Profssns
Smythe, Jack Bradley
Career Guidance Teacher
Still-Smith, Joan
Instr of Office Admin Dept
Stroud, David Vernon
History Instructor
Stroud, Karen Caig
English Instructor
Verheyden, Nina Leah
Mathematics Instructor
Weaver, Samuel Ross
Lead Instructor of Engineering
White, Sarah Shelton
Legal Assisting Instructor
Williams, Frank R.
Psychology & Sociology Instr
KILLEEN
Adams, Renata Yolanda
Guidance Counselor
Ainsworth, David Riley
Director of Theatre Arts
Barnett, Kenneth Glenn
Agricultural Science Teacher
Bohn, Rita Lynn
English Teacher
Brown, Kay Wiggins
Tenth Grade English Teacher
Brown, Ruby Lee Henderson
Nursing Instructor
Coachman, Kaye Steelman
Dance Teacher
Coen, Ken B.
Mathematics Teacher
Darnell, Patricia
10th Grade Eng & Bus Teacher
Davis, Melissa Ann
Advanced Accounting Teacher
De Vault, Susie Moore
Jr Regular & Hnrs Eng Teacher
Donahue, Sheila Edmonds
Choral Director
Dutton, Kent Owen
Physics Teacher
Einspahr, Michaelene Dawn
PE Teacher & Coach
English, Ronald Wain
Economics Instructor
Evans, Stephanie Freitag
Social Studies & German Tchr
Fisher, Sharon Walden
Biology Teacher
Fix, Robert Joseph, Jr.
American History Teacher
Glover, Laurene Mc Bride
TAG Coord & English Teacher
Hardin, Jennifer Michele
Alternative School Coordinator
Herrmann, Katrina Liesel
Mathematics Teacher
Hills, Johnnie Reed
Physical Science Teacher
Hollan, Melinda Bartlett
Math Teacher
Holmes, Anita Schulze
Instrl Resource Consultant
Ingram, Don
Physics & Anatomy Teacher
Keller, Jerry W.
Facilitator of GATE
Knightes, Peter Witbeck
Geology, Geog & Astronomy Prof
Laney, Billie Johnson
Instr of Sociology & Psych
Lunt, Linda Green
English Teacher
Maston, Malinda Barnes
Teacher
McNutt, Marjorie Elizabet
Math Teacher
Mc Pherson, Katharyn Ann (Ross)
Fifth Grade Teacher
Montgomery, Marietta H.
Senior English Teacher
Neault, Patrick Martin
Band Director
Noteboom, Sarah Cummings
Agriscience Teacher
Reid, Thomas Michael
7th Grd Lang Arts & TAG Tchr
Roberts, Nancy Cecil
Counselor
Schilhab, Joann Elkins
Professor of Psychology
Scott, Anne Seigman
Advanced Placement Bio Teacher
Seigman, Deborah Werst
Facilitator of Tlntd & Gftd
Shepard, Aubrey, Jr.
Industrial Technology Teacher
Sherman, Norman Joseph
Auto Repair & Refnshng Instr
Smith, Deb D.
8th Grade History & Coach
Smith, Sarah Sue
Government & Economics Teacher
Talbot, Frances Galbraith
US History Teacher
Teer, Barbara Alice
Eng Tchr & GATE Facilitator
Turchiano, Nicholas J.
Government & Economics Teacher
Turner, Mary Lee
Geography & Sociology Teacher
Vitucci, S. Stephen
Assistant Professor
Warner, Connie Garlic
Journalism Teacher
Weissenburger, David Allen
Psychology Professor
Wells, Carolynne Ruth (Moffatt)
Office Admin Coop Instr, Coord
Yeilding, Thomas David
Soc, Behavioral Sci Dept Chair
KINGSVILLE
Alvarado, Maria Lopez
Chemistry Teacher
Beck, Ellen R.
Phys Ed Teacher & Var Coach
Bruno, Kent
PE & Health Ed Teacher
Coker, Ann Jankowski
11th Grade English Teacher
Culp, Sidney Thomas
English & Humanities Teacher
Eardley, Beth Ann
English Teacher
Garcia, Manny
Math Teacher & Coach
Green, Sondra Frew
Psychology & Humanities Tchr
Hackenberg, Gail Hanner
Biology Teacher
Hall, Sheryl Lee
English Teacher
Hardman, Rodney Blaine
Biology Teacher
Huebel, Harry Russell
Professor of History
Hunsucker, Carla Allen
Health Care Science Teacher
Isassi, Norma Cantu
Career & Technology Teacher
Lyon, Jane Marie
Art Teacher
O'Brien, Loretta Mercuri
Physics Teacher
Perez, Lupita Gonzalez
Computer Applications Teacher
Pollard, Laura Case
Business Education Teacher
Rogers, Carol Thies
Biology II Teacher & Dept Chm
Saenz, William Paul
Math Teacher
Sanchez, Arnold Perez
Junior ROTC Teacher
Smith, Linda Catherine
Spanish Teacher
Wiley, Judith Mann
Retired 1st & 5th Grd Teacher
Willett, Peggie O'Neal
Orchestra Director
Zapalac, Terry Trombley
Tchr of the Gifted & Talented
KINGWOOD
Blackburn, Laura Vann
AP Biology Teacher
Bodus, Theresa Marie
Geology Professor
Braine, Alice Judkins
Librarian
Busceme, Lynette Cochran
Biology Teacher
Conley, Spencer Frazer
Mathematics Teacher
Davis, Judith McCracken
Assistant Principal
Eddins, Phyliss
Jrnlsm Dept Chprsn & Instr
Feierabend, Diana Parker
1st Grade Teacher
Fenley, Philip L.
History Teacher
Fortinberry, Betty White
7th Grade TX History Teacher
Frank, Deborah Richard
Marine & Physical Sci Tchr
Garcia, Louis D.
Counselor
Hackett, Kathy L.
Choral Director
Hayden, Linda Felton
Third Grade Teacher
Helmke, Nancy McGill
Math Teacher
Jernigan, Wanda S.
Fifth Grade Teacher
Jordan, Connie Renee
Life, Earth Sci Tchr & Coach
Ketcher, David Ross
Teacher & Coach
Ketcher, Mary McDaniel
Physical Education Teacher
Landtroop, Sandra Bledsoe
English Teacher
LeGrand, Wanda Vann
Chemistry Teacher
Lewis, Nancy Louise
Earth Science Teacher
Lobrecht, Merry Pohl
World Geography Teacher
Lowry, Sharon Lanier
Art Teacher
Madson, Marilyn Marie (driver)
American History Teacher
Martin, Mary VanderMeulen
Spanish Teacher
Massey, Elena Patterson
Physical Education Dept Head
New, Valerie Ruth
7th Grd Texas History Teacher
Pearson, Patsy Rivers
Art Teacher
Pedraza, Yvonne
English Department Teacher
Peniche, Eduardo Alberto
Associate Professor of Spanish
Pruitt, Malea Adams
Audio Visual Specialist & Spon
Robinson, Robin G.
High School Theater Arts Tchr
Shepeard, Anna Palm
History Teacher
Sherrer, Onnie Simons
Math Teacher
Spiegel, Karyn
8th Grade Math & Algebra Tchr
Swartz, M. Melvin
US History & Psychology Tchr
Sydow, Christie
Eighth Grade US History Tchr
Tarte, Edward Cartwright
Math Teacher
Vladyka, Barbara Ann
Guidance Counselor
Zindler, Linda Mc Fadden
Fifth Grade Teacher
KIRBYVILLE
Jones, Randy
US History Chairperson & Coach

VILLE (cont)
d, Larry Scott
Director

ler, Sheila Bertram
alism Advisor & Teacher
sa Cook
matics Teacher & Coach
ater, Todd
ant Band Director
a, Marilyn M.
Teacher
, Cheryl Wassmundt
matics Teacher
Eldon D.
acher
erome Victor
s Chemistry Teacher
Jo L.
School English Teacher
Tony
istry Teacher
M. Marie Apel
gy II Teacher
Evelyn Forester
sh Teacher
ally Ann
sh Teacher
, Cindy A.
y Volleyball Coach
Kathryn Marie (Brown)
Teacher
Sandra Riley
h Teacher
on, Merlin
iate Director of Bands
al, Charlotte Lynn
sh Teacher
, Marjorie Mitchell
sh Teacher
Stephen Walter
istry Teacher
., Laura Leigh
Team Director
Sandy Lynne
l Geography Teacher
son, Patricia Rather
sh Tchr & Dept Chprsn
Barbara Toler
rs English Teacher
an, Maria Victoria
rs & Regular Span Tchr
A
g, Hal S.
ce Teacher
CITY
e, David Kent
Anatomy & Physiology Tchr
n, Wayne Hubert
ematics Teacher
er, Patrick Lee
sh Teacher
a, Renella Mansfield
School Teacher
r, Ray Lavelle
Director
ERL
le, Tony
ry Teacher
TZE
vay, Patti Lynn Drew
bra Teacher
a, Sandra Heath
Grade Teacher
S
nan, Tom
cultural Science Teacher
an, Randell Gene
d & US His Tchr
r, Leah Jackson
nce Teacher
OSTE
hart, Sherry Kay
Grade Teacher
ERIA
Hilda M.
nd Grade Bilingual Ed Tchr
William Hammond
ogy Teacher & Coach
RANGE
n, Carolyn Wessels
ish III & Speech Teacher
ndez, Irma Linda Villarreal
Grade Teacher
efeld, Audrey A.
cipal & Teacher
Melanie Kay
er & Technology Ed Tchr
uhn, Carolyn Ann Pavlu
n Grade Teacher
OYA
e, Jose Ruben
stant Band Director
, Alba Faye
Choir Director
Mickey
History Teacher
ar, Oscar
Mariachi Music Director
s, Jose Roel
hematics Teacher
z, Ruben
iness Education Teacher
MARQUE
m, Jeanette I.
nth Grade English Teacher
, Kathleen Heffernan
lish Teacher & Dept Chair
lle, Karen Sue
Art Instructor

Harris, Krystal Ann (Curtis)
Reading Teacher
Lawrence, Emilee Inez
Home Economics Teacher
Mendonsa, Julie Harris
Mathematics Dept Chprsn
Payne, Linda Winn
French Teacher
Phelps, Paula Ritter
Second Grade Teacher
Randall, William Lloyd
7th Grd Math Teacher
Roberts, David Curtis
Anatomy & Physiology Teacher
Smith, Beverly Faye
Mathematics Teacher
Smith, Susan Cording
Instructional Specialist
Stingley, Fred (Ray)
Teacher
Tepera, Raymond David
High School Science Teacher
LA PORTE
Funda, Bari Eugenia Watson-Wright
High School Science Teacher
Glasco, Christie Wilson
Fourth Grade Teacher
Lebanowski, Patricia Lucas
High School Math Teacher
McKinzie, Marty B.
Agricultural Science Teacher
Moe, Rebecca Anne
Tchr of GATE, Eng & Journalism
Moore, Ricky Dan
Special Education Tchr & Coach
Nixon, Lisa Marie
HS Math Dept Chair & Teacher
Powell, Kay Reeves
8th Grd Language Arts Teacher
Turnquist, David Walter
Geography Teacher
Wacey, Mary Theresa
Psychology Teacher
Waligora, Lisa Marie
World History Teacher
LA PRYOR
Ayers, Shirley Smith
4th Grade Teacher
Salazar, Irma Teresa Teran
Elementary & MS Counselor
LA VERNIA
Griner, Linda Faubion
Business Teacher
LA VILLA
Castillo, Santos B.
Gifted & Talented Teacher
Mendoza, Veronica
4th Grade Teacher
LADONIA
Snell, Mary Yarbrough
Business Education Teacher
LAGO VISTA
Bussart-Walker, Denise Aileen
Eng & Creative Writing Tchr
Green, Karen Marie
High School Science Teacher
Ray, Darla Dunlap
Drama & English Teacher
LAKE DALLAS
Angove, Dawn Annyce
Assistant Superintendent
Huggins, Charles William
8th Grd US History Teacher
Spencer, Jan M.
Physical Education Teacher
LAKE JACKSON
Davies, John T.
Spanish Teacher
James, Jerry Lynn
Human Anatomy & Physlgy Prof
Johnson, Camie Churchill
Life Skills & PALS Teacher
Loveless, Marian Jackie
Counselor & Teacher
Nicholson, Carolyn Carter
English Teacher & Librarian
Patton, Wilda Gentry
Algebra Teacher
Perez, Annie Cantu
Third Grade Teacher
Rehms, Dixie M.
4th Grade Teacher
Shaw, William Edward
Professor of English
Simmons, Diane Johnston
Second Grade Teacher
Way, Jim Dwain
Bible Teacher
Woodard, Cynthia Brown
Physical Educator
Yarborough, Harvey Louis
Professor of Mathematics
LAKE WORTH
Pace, Roger C.
Band Director
LAMESA
Aldridge, Ronny Carrol
Algebra Teacher
Chapman, Suzanne Batson
Center Manager
Duran, Ann Morris
8th Grd GATE & Rdng Teacher
Franklin, Rob A.
Choral Music Dir
Griego, Tony M.
Health Teacher
Hamrick, Marsha L.
Art Teacher
Hess, Pam Stephens
Social Studies Teacher

Hester, Cornelia Wyatt
Second Grade Teacher
Larson, Trish L.
5th Grade Math Teacher
Leonard, Virginia Bray
Chemistry Teacher
Lindsay, Ashley
Junior-Senior English Teacher
Mc Collum, Nancy Mc Clure
Theatre & Speech Teacher
Telchik, Lisa Gayle
Business Teacher
Wade, Debbie Dendle
First Grade Teacher
LAMPASAS
Barlow, Kevin Lynn
Math Teacher
Fellows, Paul D., III
Band Director
Henniger, Pamela Lively
Third Grade Teacher
Smith, Robbie Prater
Home Economics Teacher & Coord
Thorp, Alice Smith
5th Grade Math Teacher
Volpe, Paul Joseph
Physics & Chemistry Teacher
LANCASTER
Balthrop, Dickson Wade
Biology Teacher
Beesley, Cathy Marie
7th & 8th Grd PE Tchr & Coach
Bozeman, Hugh P.
Science Department Chairman
Christman, Calvin L.
History Professor
Coston, Sandra Hahn
Spanish Instructor
Faulkner, Susan Kohler
English Professor
Gray, Brucy Clothus
Professor of Mathematics
Kosydar, Peter John, Jr.
Guidance Counselor
Mc Kee, Donna Jayne
English III Tchr
Meachum, Bettie M.
Psychology Professor
Slone, Jane Dar
Professor of Biology
Smith, Patricia M.
Spanish Teacher
Stanglin, Gerald M.
Division Dean & Instr of Govt
Swanson, Janet Middleton
10th Grade English Teacher
Wascom, Joyce Martin
English, Speech & Rdng Teacher
LAREDO
Alvarez del Castillo, Sandra
Assistant Prin & English Tchr
Appling, Sarah Lynn
Fourth Grade Teacher
Arambula, Gerardo Odie
Math Teacher & Vllybl Coach
Averill, Arleen M.
Physical Education Teacher
Barrera, Glenda Campos
Aerobics Tchr & Bsktbl Coach
Barron, Nora Davila
Reading Instructor
Benavides, Guadalupe Perez
Business Teacher & UIL Coord
Bergstrom, Anna R.
Chemistry & Computer Sci Instr
Bosnic, Anthony Martin
Chemistry Teacher
Botello, Graciela Cantu
Accounting Teacher
Canales, Estella J.
HS His & Sociology Instr
Cardenas, Gerardo Pena
HS Mathematics Teacher
Castillo, Carmen Lozano
High School Counselor
Centilli, Jeroladette
History Teacher
Cerda, Manuel Jr.
Career & Applied Tech Teacher
Chavez, Graciela Gonzalez
Third Grade Teacher
Chekuri-Rao, Rajkumari M. P.
English Instructor
Claes, Dolores L.
7th-8th Grade Science Teacher
Cortez, Sylvia Farias
Elementary Principal
Cuellar, Omar Leonel
English Teacher
De Hoyos, Julio, Jr.
Assistant Principal
De Hoyos, Sandra Jean
Fourth Grade Teacher
de La Garza, Edna Richardson
Health & Science Tech Instr
De La Garza, Vivian R.
French Teacher
DeLaTorre, Ramon C.
Human Anatomy, Physiology Prof
Farrokh, Lucinda Anderson
English Professor
Flores, Berta Delapass
Math Teacher
Foster, Paul Milburn, Jr.
Choir Director
Gallegos, Esperanza DLS
9th Grade English Teacher
Garcia, Dinora
Math Teacher

Garcia, Laura Guzman
Counselor
Garcia, Marco Armando
Physics Teacher & Bsktbl Coach
Garcia, Yolanda P.
Spanish Teacher
Garza, Mary Lou
Math Teacher
Gilpin, Vita Rehm
Math Teacher of GATE
Gonzalez, David Homar
English & Sociology Teacher
Gonzalez, Higinio
Honors & AP Chemistry Teacher
Gonzalez, Santiago
Fourth Grade Teacher
Guajardo, Cesiah
First Grade Teacher
Harewood, Patrick O.
Teacher
Haslam, Martha Freytag
Psychology Instructor
Jimenez, Humberto
Career & Technology Counselor
Juarez, Graciela C.
Keyboarding & Computer Teacher
Kurczyn, Elizabeth
Nrsng Prof of Adv Med & Surg
Lara, Pedro, Jr.
English Teacher
Lee, Daisy Hsu
Chemistry Instructor
Lerma, Antonio, Jr.
Texas History Master Teacher
Maldonado, Laura Ortiz
Mathematics Master Teacher
Martinez, Arabella
Soph & JR AP English Teacher
Martinez, Elsa Hinojosa
Senior English Teacher
Martinez, Gilbert
Var Ftbl & Baseball Asst Coach
Martinez, Nora Moreno
Fifth Grade Teacher
Martinez, Olivia Obregon
Third Grade Teacher
Mayers, Anthony
Agriculture Science Teacher
Mendiola, Genoveva Cantu
Business Teacher
Mendoza, Nelda Alicia
Business Education Teacher
Meza, Sylvia Zapata
Art Tchr & Fine Arts Dept Chr
Mitchell, Linda Marie
English Teacher
Moctezuma, Olga Leticia
Junior Class Counselor
Montemayor, Sara D.
High Schl Mathematics Teacher
Moore, Polly Sue Garrett
Home Economics Teacher
Mora, Laura R.
Business Education Teacher
Moreno, Maria G.
Fifth Grade Teacher
Moreno-Dally, Maria Antonieta
11th Grade English Teacher
Munoz, Norma Montoya
Art Teacher
Nguyen, Quoc Dinh Minh
Mathematics Instructor
Ornelas, Melba Nydia
English Teacher
Perez, Alejandro
Mathematics Instructor
Perez, Amanda Gutierrez
Fourth Grade Teacher
Praska, John F.
Mathematics Teacher
Quintanilla, Maria Estela
Gifted & Talented Teacher
Ramirez, Blanca DeLaPena
Early Childhood Teacher
Ramirez, Elsa Tijerina
2nd Grade Teacher
Ramon, Luciano
Community College Instructor
Rodriguez, Alejandra Garza
Choral Director
Rodriguez, Melita Ann
Gifted & Talented Science Tchr
Rollin, Marie Farias
ESL & Spanish Instructor
Rosales, Mario
Science Dept Head & Chem Tchr
Salinas, Alicia Veronica Garcia
AP English & College Prep Tchr
Salinas, Ana Laura Rangel
High School English Teacher
Salinas, Cynthia Garza
High School Counselor
Urrabazo, Yolanda Urby
English Teacher
Valadez, Jorge
Reading Teacher
Vera, Javier Ricardo
District Music Coodinator
Villa, Lizette Marie
Fifth Grade Teacher
Villarreal, Maria Guadalupe Zamarripa
8th Grade English Teacher
Whitehawk, Ann Shirlee
Speech & Debate Teacher
Wilkins, Walter Leslie, Sr.
Chemistry Teacher
Wilson, Beth-Ellen
World Geography Teacher

LARUE
Traugott, John W.
Social Studies Teacher
LASARA
Castaneda, Ninfa Alicia
Eng, Sci & Composition Teacher
LEAGUE CITY
Bauch, Birgit Roesler
German Teacher
Bearden, Elizabeth E.
English IV Teacher
Berner, Donna
English I Pre-AP Teacher
Campbell, Linda Rudolph
English Teacher
Cash, Gwendolyn Wilson
AP & Reg US His Teacher
Crowell, MaryAnn Ewers
12th Grade English Teacher
Cullen, M. Maureen
Math Teacher
Estopinal, JoAnne Wenglar
Science & Physical Ed Tchr
Eubanks, Bruce Joseph
US Government Teacher & Coach
Gardner, Nancy June
Pre-AP World & US His Teacher
Givens, Rosanne
Counselor
Glenn, Mariglyn Frazier
Fifth Grade Teacher
Hatfield, Laurie
US History Teacher
Holtman, Patricia Ann (Knight)
Fourth Grade Teacher
Hooper, Arthur Duane
Bible & History Teacher
Jameson, P. Wynette
Journalism Teacher
Jantzi, Collena Lynette
5th Grade Teacher
Johnson, Jerry Wayne
Ag Science Teacher
Jordan, Ruben C.
Sociology Teacher
Lofland, Karen Sue
Bio II & AP Honors Teacher
McKinnis, George D.
Grade Level Principal
Michael, Linda Lewis
Fifth Grade Teacher
Mire, Vincent Edwin
Biology Teacher
Morrell, Janine Dacus
Social Science Teacher
Owens, Anne Paine
Retired 4th Grade Teacher
Pate, James Orville
Social Studies & PE Teacher
Peterson, John William
Director of Bands
Peterson, Roycelyn Barfield
8th Grd Math & Algebra Teacher
Raymond, Katherine Matson
2nd Grade Teacher
Whitley, Peggy Lane
Physical Education Teacher
LEAKEY
Beaty, Betty Lou Allison
Kindergarten Teacher
Bradley, William J.
English Tchr
Williams, Ronald C.
Ag Sci & Phys Science Teacher
LEANDER
Brymer, Elizabeth Marie
Second Grade Teacher
Reed, Carol Summerlin
English Teacher
LEFORS
Barnes, Sheila Fancher
Third & Fourth Grade Teacher
Daugherty, Laurie Salmon
English & History Teacher
Hill, Pamela Dianne
Scndry Math & Science Teacher
Vincent, Carol Lou
Elementary & HS Girls PE Tchr
LEGGETT
Jones, Vicki Galloway
Title I Teacher
Willson, Carolyn JoAn
His, Theater Arts, Jrnlsm Tchr
LENORAH
Workman, Ann Koerting
History, English, Spanish Tchr
LEONARD
Blackerby, Jane Stapp
Math Teacher
Boyer, Gwendolyn Miller
3rd Grade Teacher
Cruit, Darryl Wayne
Band Director
Middleton, Allen Michael
Math Teacher
Morman, JoLynn Sullivan
Business Computer Ed Teacher
LEVELLAND
Baldwin, Reva Lynn Hefner
Assistant Professor
Beck, Robert Earl
Professor of Chemistry
Bryant, Natalie Berryhill
Asst Prof of Speech Comm
Bunye, Daniel A.
Asst Professor of Government
Carr, Joseph Allen
Asst Professor of Music
Cleavinger, Dave Alan
Asst Professor of Agriculture

LEVELLAND (cont)
Dinkins, Paul H.
Physical Education Teacher
Felker, Michael David
English Department Chair
Fesperman, Randall Lee
Criminal Justice Instructor
Garner, Stephen Clark
Music Instructor
Gomez, Drake Robert
Assistant Professor of Art
Hill, Les Lee Reed
Jr Honors English Teacher
Himango, Melissa Ann
History Teacher & Coach
Hope, John Derwood, Jr.
Art Teacher
Hutchinson, Kathy
Home Economics Teacher
Keeling, Iris W.
Assistant Professor of Biology
Mc Cook, Mollie Mirth
Asst Prof & Coord Human Svcs
McLean, Shirley Stroh
Kindergarten Teacher
McLure, Victoria Elizabeth
Assistant Professor of English
Modawell, Rita Avery
Cosmetology Teacher
Moody, Stuart M.
Sound Technology Instructor
Morris, Beverly Brown
Library Media Specialist
Nichols, Larry D.
Coord & Prof of Law Technology
Norris, Larry Frank
Government Asst Professor
Parker, Rodney Lee
Band Director
Patton, Linda Embick
11th Grade English Teacher
Payne, Deborah A.
Music Teacher
Pearce, Robert Morrow
Mathematics & Engineering Prof
Platt, Gail Malone
Prof of Human Development
Price, Monica Enloe
Algebra & Cmptr Literacy Tchr
Pugh, Donna Peters
Home Ec Cooperative Ed Instr
Redford, Vickie Sue (Barnes)
Fifth Grade Teacher
Robinson, Rick Joe
World History Teacher
Rombokas, Scott Andrew
Junior High School Teacher
Skinner, Peggy June
Professor of Psychology
Slaughter, Robert Edward
Professor of English
Stansifer, JoEllen Harrison
Computer Teacher
Trevathan, Teresa Norris
Assistant Professor of English
Winders, Mara Panzarella
Instructor of Chemistry
Womble, Donna Mae (Ruder)
Pgm Coord & Asst Prof Nursing
Zamora, Rebecca Kennedy
Assistant Professor of Biology
LEWISVILLE
Bason, Carolyn Morriss
Librarian
Blaser, Reginna Carole
High School English Teacher
Chadwell, Maria Galindo
Band Director
Church, Jo Hall
English Instructor
Coleman, Alice Tracy
1st Grd Rdng Recovery Teacher
Cook, Margaret Jean
Special Education Teacher
Davis, Sherill Ann
Special Education Counselor
Domer, Cynthia Gipson
6th Grade Science Teacher
Faulkner, Darene Mitchell
Health Science Tech Ed Coord
Ferris, Ruth Mc Clellan
Second Grade Teacher
Goldsmith, Peggy Elaine (Massey)
First Grade Teacher
Gregg, Vernell Trice
Reading Teacher
Harper, Karen Kearns
Fourth Grade Teacher
Henea, Ronny Clayton
English Teacher
Johnson, Chris Binggeli
Mathematics Teacher
Johnston, Ruby Y.
K-12th Grd Academic Advisor
Kuhn, Suzanne Welch
Fifth Grade Teacher
Mc Connell, Cheryl Lanham
US History Teacher
Rankin Collins, Mary Katherine
ESL Teacher
Wallace, Paula Rae
Eng, Charm & Home Ec Tchr
White, Karen Tetrick
Math Teacher
Young, Troy Allen
Social Studies Teacher
LEXINGTON
Guthrie, Iris Smith
Retired Teacher
Hanson, Linda Kay
Computer Science Teacher
Schoener, Marcella
Language Arts Teacher
LIBERTY
Berry, D-Ann Davis
Career Technology Teacher
Burrell, Gloria Jean (Rynes)
Special Education Teacher
Cain, Stacey Collier
Math Teacher & Team Coach
Little, Lisa O'Banion
Second Grade Teacher
Ming, Charles Keith
Agricultural Teacher
Munson, Robert Anthony
Biology Tchr & Sci Dept Chm
Stroud, Arleen Ronette Land
Physical Ed Teacher & Coach
Watson, Pamela Sulak
Librarian
LIBERTY HILL
Gersch, Denise G.
Business Teacher
Robinson, Agnes Pelachik
Retired English Teacher
Truex, Stephanie Lee
English & Social Studies Tchr
LINDALE
Burdette, Penny Thompson
Theatre Arts Teacher
Florence, Laurie Williams
5th Grade Teacher
Johnson, J. Denese
4th Grade Teacher
Klein, Robert Garth
Human Anatomy, Physiology Tchr
Moss, Erma Hartsfield
Fourth Grade Teacher
Myers, Cassandra Perdue
Math Teacher
Owens, Gregory Lynn
US History Teacher & Coach
Payne, Valerie Ann
Secondary Span & Fr Teacher
Purl, Jack Clark
US History Teacher & Coach
Ragsdale, Walter B., Jr.
Math Teacher
Simmons, Stefanie Elaine
Marketing Education Teacher
Turner, Kathleen Mary
6th Grade Teacher
Watson, Kim S.
HS Teacher & Coach
Williford, Mary Ann Weiss
Mathematics Teacher & Dept Chm
LINDEN
Mc Caskill, Morris
Mathematics Teacher & Coach
Woolfolk, Mavis Byrd
Fifth Grade Math & Sci Tchr
LINDSAY
Fleitman, Elizabeth Ann (Reed)
HS Math & English Teacher
Schumacher, Denise Tredenick
Kindergarten Teacher
LITTLE ELM
Griffin, William G.
Marketing Coordinator
Schindler, Keith W.
Industrial Technology Teacher
LITTLE RIVER
Comp, Jeff
High School Band Director
Donley, Linda Jo
Social Studies Teacher
Ehrig, Nila Poe
Home Ec Teacher & Coordinator
Henson, Rhonda Harden
Math Teacher & Dept Head
Jones, Susan Denise
English Teacher
Whitis, Katy Andres
5th-12th Grade Counselor
LITTLEFIELD
Anderson, Bonnie Faye
Bands Director
Brice, Juannah Woods
Science Dept Head & Bio Tchr
Demel, Tammy Boomer
Computer Teacher
Ingram, Rick Lynn
Industrial Technology Teacher
Muller, Janice Elaine
English III & AP Teacher
Sokora, Janice Arlene (Arnett)
5th Grade Elementary Teacher
LIVINGSTON
Galloway, Alvene Tabor
Fifth Grade Language Arts Tchr
Helm, Gregory Kent
Amer His Tchr & World His Tchr
Maze, Delores J. (Jones)
English Teacher
Moore, Elna Stanford
9th Grade English Teacher
Oliver, Lawrence A.
Agriculture Science Teacher
Sharum, Neil D.
Teacher & Coach
Snook, Tommy Ray
Agriculture Science Teacher
Tipton, Diane Truett
Phys Education Teacher & Coach
LLANO
Ball, Lillie Ratliff
Sixth Grade Soc Stud Tchr
Croker, Jimmie Griffin
Special Education Teacher
Lancet, J. Nicole
Eng, Theater Arts, Speech Tchr
Langley, Evelyn Diane
Home Economics Teacher
Park, Brenda Ann
English Teacher
Parson, Gale Herridge
Third Grade Teacher
Swope, Donna Lynn
High School Science Teacher
Walter, Virginia Lee
Special Education Teacher
LOCKHART
Brooks, Susan K.
US His & Theatre Arts Teacher
Johnson, Linda D.
Director of Bands
Sneed, Earline D.
HS & Jr HS Choir Director
LOCKNEY
Fulton, Pam Cathey
Algebra I & Geometry Teacher
Norwood, Holly Vaughn
English Teacher
LOLITA
Crisp, Norman Glenn
Science & Health Teacher
LOMETA
Potts, Janie Glimp
4th Grade Teacher
LONE OAK
Davies, Leanette Cherry
Business Teacher
Graves, Gregg T.
History & Government Teacher
Haley, Lisa Lynn
English Teacher
Smith, Jeffrey Arlen
Health, World Geog & PE Tchr
LONE STAR
Hughes, Billie Dove Tyler
Retired Teacher
LONGVIEW
Anthony, Pamela Lynne Willis
8th Grade Language Arts Tchr
Bates, Melanie Amy
Eng I & Pub Speaking Teacher
Bitikofer, Kathleen Mowers
History Teacher
Bitikofer, Lauren Gail
Chairman of Aviation Div
Bruski, Beth Hales
Math Teacher
Chaffin, Barbara Wood
8th Grd GATE & Lang Arts Tchr
Crawford, Ivy Tucker
Biology Teacher
Davis, Bonnie Hauk
Math Dept Chair & Teacher
Donner, Martin Walter
Asst Prof, Aviation Maint Tech
Dunbar, Vicki Walker
Math Teacher
Dunlap, Mary Ruth Gallaspy
Student Activities Coordinator
Dunnovant, Betsy R.
Sixth Grade Teacher
Enger, Linda Wilbanks
Mathematics Teacher
Gilson, Jeanne Benedict
Theater Teacher & Director
Griffin, William David
Social Studies & Jrnlsm Tchr
Hayes, Paula Sutton
Physics Teacher
Heflin, Lynn Alan
World His Tchr & Bstkbl Coach
Hemmen, Janene Withers
10th Grade English Teacher
Herbert, Ellen Carlton
Art Teacher
Jackson, Debbie H.
GED Coordinator
Jones, Jackie
Safe & Drug Free Schls Coord
Kasper, Brian Scott
Agricultural Science Teacher
Kendrick, James Lee
Athletic Trainer
Kindle, Angela Gray
6th & 7th Grd Lang Arts Tchr
Kreider, Donald Lester
Social Studies Teacher
Law-Cason, Kimberly Jean
His & Creative Writing Tchr
Manning, William Partrick
HS Health Teacher & Head Coach
Mc Farland, Donna Holland
8th-9th Grade Choir Director
Mc Garvey, Linda Kulak
Eng I Tchr & Leaders Core Dir
Mc Kinney, Brenda Cabbiness
Mathematics Teacher
Minter, MiKeanne
Biology Teacher
Moore, Brenda Ann
Second Grade Teacher
Morrow, Tessie Portley
Parent Coordinator
Neely, Mitzi Rowland
Home Economics Teacher
Newsom, Sue Williamson
Third Grade Teacher
Nylund, Carol Lynn (Wesatzke)
Librarian
Olson, Ann Marie
English, Drama & Bible Tchr
Palsha, Charyl Ann
PE Instr, Coach & Dept Head
Petty, Shirley A.
Second Grade Teacher
Preston, Jenny L.
Instruction Asst Supt
Puckett, Barbara Vanderslice
Mathematics Teacher
Ray, Gloria Kay (Helvenston)
Facilitator of Gifted & Tlntd
Reagans, Angela L.
7th-8th Grade Teacher
Rhodes, Margaret Brady
English IV & Lead Tchr
Roberts, Jessie Sue
Lead Biology Teacher
Scott, Madolyn Clark
Fifth Grade Teacher
Shepherd, Annamaria
Fifth Grade Teacher
Simcox, Linda (Maedke)
His Tchr & Soc Stud Dept Head
Snowden, James Wyn
Band Director
Snowden, Shirley Ann
Fourth Grade Teacher
Thompson, Debbie Johnson
Math Teacher
Thompson, Helen Butler
Fourth Grade Teacher
Thompson, Jeanne Matheny
High School Mathematics Tchr
Wilson, Janis Freeman
English I Teacher
Wilson, Oscar Allan
HS Social Studies Teacher
Windham, Nita Hunter
Fifth Grade Teacher
Yates, Sigrid Rawlings
English Teacher
LORENA
Allen, Rebecca Farson
Director of Bands
Coker, Kimberley Stovall
Sophomore English Teacher
Fehler, Kathleen Pick
Third Grade Teacher
Furl, Linda Vann
Reading Teacher & Dept Chair
Mc Clain, Judith Elaine (Watson)
Counselor
Penoli, Carol Harwell
Band Director
Wolfe, Sharon Teague
Fifth Grade Teacher
LORENZO
Dunn, Barbara Shepard
Retired 5th Grade Teacher
Mason, Gloria Robinson
English, Theatre & Speech Tchr
LOS FRESNOS
Boisen, Mary Elizabeth
Physical Education Teacher
Chacon, Concepcion
Anatomy, Physiology & Bio Tchr
Cox, Wayde Preson
Sixth Grade Math Teacher
Degasperi, Ana
Kindergarten Teacher
Dominguez, Diana V.
English Teacher
Leal, Tony
HS Mathematics Teacher
Lucio, Lynda Anne
World History Teacher
Markley, Clement R.
English Teacher
McWherter, Pamela Jo Jeffries
Reading Teacher & Coach
Miller, Virginia Garza
HS Eng, PE & Dance Tchr
Neeley, Kathleen Pepin-Zeoli
Second Grade Teacher
Ramirez, Maria del Rosario
Spanish Teacher
Robertson, Janette Helen
US History Teacher
Thomson, Stacy Jo
Math Teacher
Trevino, Gilbert
Math Teacher
Vela, Gloria Jean
High School Math Teacher
Woods, Rebecca Sue
Health & PE Teacher
Ybarra, Juan M.
High School Science Teacher
LOTT
Ritenour, Keith Paul
Asst Prin, Teacher & Coach
LOUISE
Cosby, Darren Gayle
Agriscience Instructor
Peikert, Rose (Marusik)
Business Teacher
LOVELADY
Messer, Evelyn Whitmire
Kindergarten Teacher
Yarbrough, Jane Wood
Computer Literacy Tchr & Coord
LUBBOCK
Allen, Laurie Patterson
Literature & World His Tchr
Ammons, Julie White
Math Teacher
Anders, Carol Craft
Journalism Advisor
Armstrong, Billy Dean
Geom & Pre Calculus Teacher
Barnes, Jane Jennings
Second Grade Teacher
Barr, Nancy Dement
Mathematics Teacher
Beyer, Jim L.
Psychology I Instr
Black, Catherine Rutherford
Assistant Professor
Brink, James Eastgate
Associate Professor of History
Burcham, Carroll F.
Associate Professor of English
Burk, Michael Wynn
Industrial Technology Teacher
Button, Kathryn
Asst Prof of Lang & Literacy
Caddel, Melanie Kay
Fourth Grade Teacher
Caffrey, Roberta S.
Asst Prof of Clinical Nursing
Caplinger, Carolyn Kendrick
Eighth Grade English Teacher
Casarez, Kenneth
Social Studies Teacher
Chavarria, Dana Bickford
6th Grade Science Teacher
Claybrook, Bettye Books
English Teacher
Coburn, Vanessa (Goza)
Home Economics Teacher
Cochrane, Michael Jon
Naval Science Instructor
Cole, William Lowell
Mathematics Teacher
Cooper, Susan Joiner
Special Education Teacher
Copeland, Janet Graham
Health Sci Technology Instr
Copeland, Suzanne Samson
Art Teacher
Cowell, Robbie Lee
Earth & Physical Science Tchr
Cox, Ronda Lummus
Spanish Teacher & Coach
Crooks, Paul Gene
Sixth Grade Teacher
Cross, Melissa Wafer
MS Humanities Prgm Teacher
Cundiff, Linda Lewis
Kindergarten Teacher
Cunningham, Resa Elaine
Title I Teacher
Deahl, Lora Ching
Associate Professor of Music
Dean, William F.
Assoc Professor of Mass Comm
Dobbs, Christa Blue
Business Professor
Ducote, D'Ann
Associate Professor
Dunn, Darla Henderson
K-5th Grade GATE Teacher
Dunn, Joanna
6th Grade Teacher
Elbow, Gary S.
Professor of Geography
Elliott, Stacy Jeter
Vocational Counselor
Ervin, Robin Terry
Assoc Prof of Ag Economics
Esquivel, Lydia Guzman
Third Grade Teacher
Ewan, Starla Ann
Pathology & AP Biology Teacher
Farr, Brett Conan
Choral Activities Director
Flusche, Daryl Glen
Principal
Fortenberry, Gary Douglas
Science Dept Chair & Teacher
Fraze, Steve Dee
Asst Prof of Agricultural Ed
Galindo, Henry Louis
Principal
Gallegos, Matthew Edward
Instructor
Galvan, Toni Jane (Bennett)
Asst Prof of Clincial Nursing
Gammill, Tamara B.
Fifth Grade Reading Teacher
Garrett, Marilyn Langley
Vice Principal
Gary, Sally A.
Former Forensics Director
Geiger, Kay
Social Studies Teacher
Giboney, Keith Eric
High School Teacher
Granberg, Stanley Earl
Bible Professor
Gregory, James Marling
Undergrad Studies Assoc Dean
Griffin, Cornelius LaCosta
Dir of Minority Engrng Prgms
Grimes, Corinne
Assistant Professor of Nursing
Hale, Fred Gray
Retired Teacher
Handa, Rumiko
Assistant Professor
Hardin, Joyce F.
Dean College of Education
Harland, Jaclyn Hawkins
Elem Title I Teacher
Hay, Anita Hampton
First Grade Teacher
Headley, Allan Dave
Associate Professor of Chem
Hernandez, Lori
PE Teacher & Coach
Hill, Valerie Komkov
Dance Teacher

CK (cont)
Deborah Ann
sh & Physical Ed Tchr
, Jerry Charles
of Advertising & Grad Dir
, Debbie Hoffman
Grade Teacher
, Margaret Brown
stra Director
, Rita Gail
d Grade Teacher
, Kyra Wagner
al Education Teacher
Jay Glenn
Teacher
oAnn Denny
ctor of Nursing
Rosendo
Teacher
Karl A.
ciate Professor of Ed
g-Hill, Carale
re Arts Professor
, Joetta Sailors
ra II Teacher
lion, Janis Wall
h Grade Teacher
Jill Relf
Professor of Mathematics
Cynthia Louise (Allen)
ess Education Teacher
Paul Allen
Prof of Classics & Lit
ll, Sherry Coleman
Ec & Career Teacher
-Lubowicz, Barbara Elizabeth
sh Teacher
, Gabriel
Director
Linda Jean
sh Professor
Stephanie Schreiner
nglish Tchr & Dept Chrmn
, Dorothy Kelly
rade Science Teacher
, Connie
LA Teacher
, Carolyn Watkins
ctional Coordinator
Stacy L.
ous Studies Assoc Prof
Floyd
ematics Teacher
Kathryn Johnson
handising Instructor
, Ellen B. (Stallbaum)
Prof of Horticulture
s, Anthony Craig
h Tchr & Athletic Trainer
n, Carol Clohset
outer Coordinator
on Paul
Instr of Surgical Tech
Robert Wendall
Teacher
, Gregory Allen
Grade AP English Teacher
, Vikki Cheryl
Teacher & Tennis Coach
ds, Stacy Rene
sh I Teacher
on, Gena Beth
tant Prof, Dept of Psych
on, Hedy Coffman
cal Science Teacher
s, Sue Y.
tant Headmaster
Joyce Price
unting I & II Teacher
ford, Dee Wayne
gy Teacher & Trainer
Barbara Mc Coy
ed Teacher
, Deborah Lansford
c Specialist
l, Tony D.
ctor of Theatre Department
go, Huy
itecture Adjunct Professor
Phillip Spelman, Jr.
Prof of Physical Therapy
Donna Reynolds
culum Specialist
MaryJo Guynes
ch Teacher
Chris Clements
sh Teacher
e, Anna Jo J.
g Teacher & Band Dir
Cara Gilbert
al Work Professor
Charles Wheeler
Instructor
er, Sherry Lynn
School Mathematics Tchr
Susan Houle
ing Instructor
, Shirley Gensler
ematics Teacher
Ginger Lee-Roy
rican Sign Language Tchr
James Lee
Govt & Economics Teacher
tt, Susan Green
ogy II Teacher
oson, Debbie Hobgood
ish Teacher
ons, Brenda Kay
gh Math Teacher

Valentine, Charles Owen
Art Teacher
Vann, William Pennington
Civil Engineering Assoc Prof
Vierra, Steven Eric
PE & Wellness Teacher
Vines, Darrell L.
Professor
Wanjura, Sue Oats
Fourth Grade Teacher
Waters, Tommy Dale
US History Tchr & Ath Coach
Weathers, Donna Kisner
Soc Stud & Jrnlsm Tchr
White, John Poston
Architectural Professor
Wilson, Scott Matthew
9th Grade World Geography Tchr
Wolfe, Carol Foerster
World History Teacher
Wood, Debra Griffith
4th Grade Teacher
Worth, Michael James
History Teacher

LUFKIN
Alexander, Melinda Lee
Second Grade Teacher
Arnold, Marilyn Louise
5th Grade Teacher
Baker, Kevin Scott
US History & Basketball Coach
Baldwin, Debbie Duke
Sixth Grade Teacher
Ballenger, Virginia Whittley
Retired Elementary Teacher
Bassinger, Angelyn Witte
Reading Recovery Teacher
Bolt, Marilyn Deerman
Business Education Teacher
Bradford, Suzanne Rowin
Business & Accounting Instr
Bruce, Sharon Smith
English & Language Arts Tchr
Deaton, Olivia Taylor
Second Grade Teacher
Dudley, Tom
Biology Instructor
Evans, Vickie Anders
5th Grade Teacher
Grisham, Sharon
Health & Phys Ed Teacher
Harris, Tracy C.
History Teacher & Coach
Hinson, Nancy Gail
Spanish Teacher
Jeffrey, Lisa Diana
Art Instructor
Jones, Billy Joe
8th Grade Science Teacher
Jones, Cindy Christie
Home School Educator
Keeley, Susan Dawn Thompson
Coach & Teacher
Killingsworth, Jo Ann Grant
Math & Honors Algebra Teacher
Kuykendall, Viola Patricia Timms
Choir Director
Langford, Suzanne Burkhalter
Second Grade Teacher
Moore, Carroll L.
Mathematics Instructor
Palmer, Robin Casey
Kenisiology & Health Sci Prof
Ragland, Joan Davis
7th Grade Science I Teacher
Rawcliffe, Janet Tisdale
Spanish Teacher
Ray, Cheryl Alison
Physical Science Tchr & Coach
Shaw, Richard Russell
Biology Teacher
Smart, Fant A.
Language Arts Teacher
Steed, Karen Kimmey
Tchr of the Gifted & Talented
Vaughn, Patrick Clay
Instructor of Theatre
White, Patricia Johnson
Frosh Coach & Phys Educator
Wilkerson, William David
Paramedic Instructor
Williams, Terri Little
Third Grade Teacher
Wilson, Mary Twohig
Professor of English
Wright, Kimberly Bain
English Teacher
Wright, Pascuel Gaylon
Business Instructor
Zayler, Jamie Kidwell
Director

LULING
Barnett, Larry Dean
Band Director
De Laney, Barbara Ann
Fourth Grade Teacher
Jones, William Darrell
7th Grd Sci I Tchr & Ath Coach
Metz, Ronald E.
Math Teacher
Moore, Susan Lynn
Mathematics & Government Tchr

LUMBERTON
Baldwin, Margaret Elizabeth (Bridger)
Teacher of GATE Program
Chandler, Cynthia Cox
English IV Tchr & Theatre Dir
Goodman, Diane D.
Math Teacher

Hayes, Mary Schrimsher
Art Teacher
Hurtado, Jerry Joseph, Jr.
History Teacher & Soccer Coach
Phelps, James Ray
HS Vocational Teacher
Smart, Joe Darrell
His, Drivers Ed Tchr & Coach
Spears, Sharon Jeffcoat
Kindergarten Teacher
Tomplait, Douglas Gerald
8th Grd American History Tchr
Wolford, Lydia Yentzen
Communications Teacher

LYFORD
Correa, Armando J., Jr.
Agriculture Science Teacher
Garcia, Tammie Lee
Former 8th Grade English Tchr
Hunter, Melissa Gayle
Resource Teacher
Reynolds, Millicent Camille
World History Teacher

LYTLE
Carter, Susan Burk
7th Grade Texas History Tchr
Emley, Brenda S.
English & Speech Teacher
Grothues, Julie A.
Soc Stud & Theatre Arts Tchr
Pagonis, Wanda Roe
Physics & Chemistry Teacher
Shirtum, Joe Lynn
Math Dept Chairperson & Tchr

MABANK
Clamon, Judy Bernard
English Teacher & Dept Head
Conner, Patrick James
Voc Building Trades Teacher
Horton, Elizabeth G.
Assistant Principal
Lindsley, Catherine Trimble
Choral Music Teacher
Mize, John Clay
Director of Bands
Smith, Patricia J.
French, Latin & AP His Tchr
Sweet, Brian Scott
US History Teacher
Taylor, Sandra Gayle
Marketing Teacher & Coord
Whatley, Melba Reese
Mathematics Teacher

MADISONVILLE
Cermin, Corey Heldridge
Bio & Physical Education Tchr
Swinney, William Ray
Band Director
Ward, Larry Don
Assistant Band Director

MAGNOLIA
Halekakis, Roxy
High School Counselor
Howard, Tanya
2nd Grade Teacher
Klaus, Marilyn F.
Sixth Grade Math Teacher
Koebelen, Christine
PE Teacher & Coach
Korpita, Lynette Kelly
Substitute Teacher
Luedecke, Lois Oualline
5th Grade Teacher
Mc Nulty, Nita A.
6th-8th Grd PE Tchr & Coach
Miles, Sue Robertson
Social Studies Teacher
Payne, Rebecca Baker
6th Grade Mathematics Teacher
Pendland, Kathy Elaine
English Teacher
Smith, Buddy
Agriculture Science Teacher

MANOR
Eubank, Teri Ann
HS Math Teacher & Var Coach

MANSFIELD
Andress, Patsy S. (Greenway)
Speech & Debate Coach
Bellows, Lena Inez
Physical Science Teacher
Benbarka, Mohamed Halim
Mathematics Teacher
Britton, Cathy Fetters
HS Health, PE Teacher & Coach
Brown, Kathy Pressley
English Teacher
Cawood, Richard Alan
High School Geometry Teacher
Curtis, Deborah Lapping
English Teacher
Gray, Cynthia Wayne
Biology Teacher
Grimes, Wayne T.
Teacher
Harris, Robert Blake
Marine Science Teacher
Johnson, Martha Clampitt
Math Teacher
Muldner, Kimi Kathryn
Secondary English Teacher
Scott, Marsha Howse
Math Teacher
Williams, Mary Anne
Biology Teacher

MANVEL
Jacobus, Robert Donald
Social Studies Chairman
Kenny, Sheryl McKee
Gifted & Talented Resrce Tchr

Rogers, Paul D.
Band & Choir Instructor

MARBLE FALLS
Abercrombie, Rita Weber
German & English Teacher
Davis, Ron E.
Director of Bands
Herrington, Nancy Mattiza
8th Grd American History Tchr
Jette, Debra Mc Kinney
English & Journalism Teacher
Montgomery, Frances Lee
Second Grade Teacher
Neely, Wayne Douglas
High School Teacher
Nesrsta, Rhonda Thomas
English Teacher
Pace, Dorothy Fay
Third Grade Teacher
Pack, Kami McSpadden
Spanish Teacher
Taylor, Guy Wayne
Criminal Justice Teacher
Woods, Charles Robert
American Sign Lang Instr

MARFA
Flanagan, Timothy M.
Agricultural Sci Tchr, FFA Adv
Foster, Jay
Science Teacher
Mendoza, Marta Cortez
Title I Rdng, Cntnt Mstry Tchr
Sanchez, Jose A.
Special Education Teacher
Wood, Felicia Brailas
Teacher of Gifted & Talented

MARION
Pemberton, Katherine
2nd Grade Teacher

MARSHALL
Alonzo, Jose Alfredo
Span Tchr & Head Soccer Coach
Banks, Vicki Gail
English Teacher
Benton, Julia Matthews
Algebra Teacher
Cox, Allan
Assistant Professor of Music
Dahl, Shirley A. (Wise)
Professor
Dierksen, Carolyn Nelson
Education Professor
Fisher, Bettye Guice
Counselor
Ford, Jeffrey Edward
World History Teacher
Garcia, Robert Charles
Earth Science Teacher
Gibson, Nancy Holland
First Grade Teacher
Hambright, Barbara Davis
Mathematics Teacher
Harrison, Suzan Cook
Social Studies Chrpsn & Tchr
Hess, Hollie Jean
Health & PE Teacher
Hollis, Raylean Carter
US History & Chrldng Tchr
Huesing, Alan Martin
Director of International Ed
King, David Warren
Retired Adjunct Prof of Rel
Mc Coy, Gloria Hamilton
English Teacher
Mc Daniel, Beverly Mc Millian
Elementary School Counselor
Mc Keever, Janet Ruddick
Home Economics Teacher
Myers, Melanie Renee
Health Teacher
Newman, Anne T.
Social Studies Teacher
Simpson, Suellen Ogden
First Grade Classroom Teacher
Sparks, Theresa (Segovia)
Math Department Chairperson
Stuart, John G.
Assoc Prof & Division Chrmn
Summers, Jerry Lynn
Assistant Professor of History
Taylor, Mary Moore
Fourth Grade Teacher
Weidman, Mary Meisenheimer
2nd Grade Teacher
Wiley, Karen Powell
Assistant Prof of Computer Sci
Wilson, Peggy Kilpatrick
Business & Career Tech Teacher

MART
Havenhill, Timothy Glen
Science Teacher
Mann, Mary G. Muhl
English & Lang Arts Teacher
Rothrock, Laura Elizabeth
5th-8th Grd Tchr of Spec Ed

MARTINSVILLE
Holloway, Penny Williams
Business Teacher

MASON
Ash, Corey Don
Band Director
Graham, Linnda H.
Home Economics & Health Tchr
Ince, Mary Beth
Special Ed Teacher
Mahnken, Ann Mc Millan
1st Grade Teacher
Schmidt, Bonnie Kay
Science Teacher

MATADOR
Alexander, Kimberly Hand
Science & Math Teacher
Gillespie, Kathryn Knadle
Math & Science Teacher

MATHIS
Elliott, Carol B.
Business Education Teacher
Hicks, Sue House
High School English Teacher
Mc Craw, Jenie Eugenia
Lang Arts Dept Chm & Eng Tchr

MAUD
Foster, Lora Ann Blanks
Secondary Mathematics Teacher

MAY
McInnis, Jessica Gearhart
Spanish & English Teacher
Pallette, Vella Henry
First Grade Teacher
Thornhill, Jeanne Hounsel
Business Teacher

MC CAMEY
Collett, James Lee
Curriculum & Staff Dev Dir
Folger, Iris Rowena (Mc Campbell)
7th & 8th Grade Math Teacher
Folger, Raymond Michael
5th & 6th Grade Math Teacher
Holik, Fraron Emil
Math Chairman

MC GREGOR
Douglas, David Doyle
Agriculture Science Teacher
Lindemann, Catherine Ashworth
Algebra II Teacher
Pulattie, JoAnn Boyd
AP Eng IV & Journalism Teacher

MC KINNEY
Bruck, Mike
AP History & German Teacher
Gerber, Jody Marie
AP & Pre-AP Biology Teacher
Hill, Nana Boyd
Facilitator
Hoffmann, Barbara Ann
Academic Specialist
Johnson, Peggy Black
Sr HS English & Writing Tchr
Lowe, Brian Mack
Ag Sci Tchr & FFA Advisor
Murff, Ernie
Science Teacher
Palmer, David Alan
4th Grade Teacher
Rivera, Grace Carreno
Spanish & English Teacher
White, Cecil Don
Science Teacher

MCALLEN
Arias, Joseph Giorgio
French Teacher
Benjamin, Howard William
Social Studies Chair
Billings, Jackie E.
Teacher
Canales, Elizabeth
Folklorico Instructor
Carriere, Sheryl Dianne
Third Grade Teacher
Cole, Sharon
Social Studies Teacher
Copold, Linda Kay Ashcroft
English IV Teacher
De Leon, Juan Manuel
Spanish Teacher
Garcia, Miroslava Cano
Business & Math Teacher
Gindler-Bishop, Paulette
German Teacher
Gomez, Elizabeth Ann
Head Band Director
Guerra, Maria Del Rosario Trevino
5th Grade Teacher
Guzman, Dora Maria
Language Arts Teacher
Haule, Margaret Ann
Reading Recovery Teacher
Johnson, Barbara Fisher
Fifth Grade Teacher
Kostenko, Walentin
6th Grade Teacher
Kowalski, Nellie Lamas
English Teacher & Dept Chair
Liljedahl, Curt Leon
Aquatics Dir & Chemistry Tchr
Linkenboger, Garland S.
High School Math Teacher
Martinez, Lynda Farias
High School Algebra Teacher
Menchaca, Joe M.
Bands Director
Mills, Cynthia Alpers
Mathematics Department Chair
Plummer, Anthony George
Mathematics Tchr & Swim Coach
Reyna-Zapata, Patricia
English Teacher
Rios, Melissa Ann
High School Biology Teacher
Saenz, Melinda Castillo
Language Arts Teacher
Santiago, Helen Marie
Business Teacher
Sarabando, Lou
English & Debate Teacher
Schmidt, Maureen (Hilbrands)
8th Grd Math Tchr & Dept Head
Schnase, Esther Washington
English Teacher

MCALLEN (cont)
Spees, Eric A.
English Teacher
Stanley, MaryLee (Hodde)
Teacher of Gifted & Talented
Stendahl, Janice Irene (Curbo)
Eng Composition & Lit Teacher
Todd, Kenneth Webb
Head Orchestra Director
Trevino, Daniel David
Agriculture Science Teacher
Weber, Matthew Joseph
Assistant Dir of Fine Arts
Whittaker, Phyllis L.
Physics Teacher
Winston, Teresa Woodson
PE Tchr & Volleyball Coach
Zenz, Cornelia Risatti
Lang Arts Teacher & Dept Head
MCLEAN
Buckhaults, Texas D.
Mathematics Teacher
Eldredge, Cherry Raymond
Teacher & Coach
Glass, Janet Braden
1st Grade Teacher
Hauck, Cynthia Price
Junior High Language Arts Tchr
Reeser, Richard C.
Counselor & Math Teacher
Riley, Jacqulyn Gillispie
English & Spanish Teacher
Watkins, Judith Michele
Science & Music Ed Teacher
MEDINA
Harbour, Greg John
Earth & Life Science Teacher
Lumpkins, Gina Redden
PE Teacher & Coach
MEGARGEL
Carson, Darren Scott
Ag Sci Tchr & Head Ftbl Coach
MEMPHIS
Berry, Attie Baker
Retired Teacher
Stewart, Judith Edelmon
Business & Math Teacher
MENARD
Lyckman, Susan Kothmann
Language Arts Teacher
Russell, Madeline Elaine Smith
9th-12th Grd Home Ec Teacher
MERCEDES
Badillo, Rodolfo
Texas History Teacher
Coalson, Dale Adam
Technology Teacher
DiGennaro, John Julian
Social Studies Teacher
Fulmer, Kristen S.
Social Studies Teacher
Gentry, Karen Elizabeth
English Teacher
Guerrero, Sophia Dumford
Mathematics Teacher
Hoehn, David Thomas
Government Teacher
Hoehn, Rona Mae
9th & 10th Grd English Tchr
Irby, Lisa Kay
Fifth Grade Teacher
McVeigh, Dianne Louise
Health Science Technology Tchr
Medrano, Rosa Maria (Vela)
Business Education Teacher
Miller, Terrence Gene
World Geography Teacher
Mink, Chet
Art Teacher
Pena, Ubaldo F.
English & Writing Teacher
Ross, Patti Ruth
5th Grade Teacher
Salas, Mary Rangel
8th Grade History Teacher
Saldana, Helen Rhodes
8th Grade Reading Teacher
Sanborn, Sandi Lucas
Science Teacher
Schroll, Mark
Technology Teacher
Wood, David G.
Computer Science Teacher
MERIDIAN
Avance, Pamela (Swindle)
Scndry Social Studies Teacher
Henderson, Dana Lechler
Physical Education Teacher
MERIT
Morrison, Cherie Porter
English, History & Drama Tchr
MERKEL
Neff, Patricia M.
Art Teacher
Snow, Veronica Dickerson
Teacher
Stegemoller, Laura Davis
Third Grade Teacher
MERTZON
Moseley, Ann Warnock
Language Arts Teacher
Rosson, Jeanette Holland
Bus, Computer & Drafting Tchr
Rowley, Nita Fields
English Department Chair
MESQUITE
Alexander, Arlene Louise (Mara)
Bio AP & Chemistry Teacher
Allen, Brenda Miller
English Teacher
Ankrum, Patricia Hollingsworth
Fifth Grade Teacher
Barrington, W. Doug
Health Teacher & Coach
Blackmon, Anne Elyse
Speech & Debate Coach
Bolsterli, Jane Mercedes
World History Teacher
Bonner, Linda Kay
4th Grade Teacher
Bradley, Cathy
Art Teacher
Bragg, Steven Wade
World His Tchr & Ftbl Coach
Brewer, Helen Robledo
Eighth Grade US History Tchr
Brown, Denise Theriot
Math Teacher, Athletic Trainer
Browning, Terri Elizabeth
English Teacher
Bruce, Barbara White
First Grade Teacher
Brumbach, Virginia Whitcomb
Commnctn & English Prof
Campbell, Robert Eugene
Teacher & Coach
Coulson, S. Scott
Head Band Director
Crooks, Patricia K.
French Teacher & HS Counselor
Danaher, Beverly Brown
8th Grade Earth Science Tchr
Daniels, J. M.
Teacher
Davis, Rick F.
Associate Band Director
DeVoll, Ruth Saunders
1st Grade Teacher
Dodd, Amy Lucille
5th Grade Teacher
Dunlap, Laurie (Johnson)
Math Teacher
Edwards, Cathy Sue Campbell
Math Teacher
Felker, Tony
Amer His & Govt Ed Teacher
Frazer, Marilyn Kay
Math Teacher
Halliday, Gary Lloyd
Teacher & Coach
Hardin, Madelyn Hill
AP English Teacher
Heaps, Judy Rawson
English Teacher
Henson, Jerry C.
Prof of History & Religion
Holland, Jo Jeaine
Spanish Teacher
Ivie, Ruth Mc Cool
Sixth Grade Teacher
Johnson, Linda Ellison
Fourth Grade Teacher
Johnson, Tommy Ben
Indstrl Arts & Drafting Tchr
Jones, Susan Mary (Prusha)
Third Grade Teacher
Kemp, Regina Sims
Elementary School Counselor
Kline, John Victor
Band Director
Kotrany, Anne M.
7th Grd Language Arts Teacher
Kuykendall, Sonja Matthews
First Grade Teacher
Latham, Mary Rollins
Sixth Grade Teacher
Lisewsky, Lisa Lynn
Math & Physical Education Tchr
Main, Suzanna LeVelle
Mathematics Teacher
Mann, Gina Michelle
8th Grade US History Teacher
Massey, Deborah Marion
History Teacher
McFaul, Ray C.
Mathematics Dept Head
Miller, Lana Lawson
Tchr of Gifted Hum & Eng IV
Minx, Johnny
PE Teacher
Mitchell, Wanda R.
First Grade Teacher
Mowrer, Paul Dean
Band Director
Muhl, Linda Thompson
Language Arts Teacher
Myers, Arlene Holman
Second Grade Teacher
Myers, Mike
Assistant Band Director
Nelson, Linda Carolyn
Fifth Grade Teacher
Owen, Thomas Clinton
Adjunct English Instructor
Pleasant, Leon
Accounting Professor
Porter, Belle Morgan
Title I Reading Teacher
Ramos, Sulema Riojas
Academic Counselor
Reynolds, Kandy Kiker
Senior English Teacher
Rideout, Deryl Blaine
Dir of Career & Technology
Robertson, Norma Bibb
Chem, Anatomy, Physiology Tchr
Sanders, Beverly R.
English & American His Tchr
Scheu, Sandra Kay
Agriculture Science Teacher
Sharp, Bob G.
Professor of History
Shepherd, Leslee Haltom
Spanish Teacher
Shiflet, Sarah Phinney
English Teacher & Dept Head
Skaggs, Rick
Algebra II Teacher
Stone, Jeannie Milligan
12th Grade English Teacher
Swindling, James Allan
Prof of Developmental Reading
Taylor, Gary Wayne
Head Boys Bsktbl & Eng Tchr
Taylor, Janis May
Title I & Rdng Recovery Tchr
Transon, Janet Kaye
Sophomore English Teacher
Trapp, Judy Stark
3rd-4th Grade Looping Teacher
Trower, Dorothy Clark
First Grade Teacher
Tupperadagelesen, David Paul
Psychology & English Teacher
Turner, Charlotte Karlen
English Teacher
VanSickle, Jane Denise
Orchestra Teacher
Vaughn, Sheila Lorraine
First Grade Teacher
Wasson, Rhonda Crump
Reading & Theater Arts Teacher
Weaver, Gayle M.
Professor of Biology
Wendel, Mark
Coach & Teacher
Whitaker, Susan R.
Lang Arts & Latin Teacher
Whitmore, Wayne
Math Teacher
Witherspoon, Marjorie Banaugh
Phys, Art & Jr High Sci Tchr
Yium, Susie Joe
Spanish Teacher
York, Cindy Malone
English Teacher
MEXIA
Clark, Patricia Louise (Almquist)
Physical Education Teacher
Turpin, Teresa Wiedemann
Geometry Teacher
MEYERSVILLE
Slovacek, Cindy Konczewski
History & PE Teacher
MIAMI
Blasingame, Joel Dean
Science Teacher
Neighbors, Larry Wayne
Principal
Tucker, Misty Files
Science Teacher
MIDLAND
Arrell, Kay Bowers
Math Teacher & Dept Chairman
Arthur, Jill Feldhousen
Writing Specialist
Baesa, Felicitas Heredia
Third Grade Bilingual Teacher
Bartel, Robin L.
Geology Teacher
Battle, Jane Lynn
Secondary Mathematics Teacher
Bell, Rebecca Caroline
Office Systems Tech Instr
Benavides, Charles Robert
Science Teacher
Blair, Cyndye Camarillo
Second Grade Teacher
Blase, W. Sherrilyn Odom
Bio, Anatomy & Physiology Tchr
Boen, Ricky Darrell
Math Teacher
Burton, Rosalind Veronica
Eighth Grade Reading Teacher
Bybee, Michael Shane
English Teacher
Carlisle, Janet Van Houten
Reading Specialist
Cason, Ben Sanford
Latin I & II & Etymology Tchr
Catania, Richard J.
Foreign Lang Dept Chair & Tchr
Conner, Virginia Spencer
7th & 8th Grade ESL Teacher
Cooke, Sally Brown
Kindergarten Teacher
Crockett, Jack David
Computer & Science Teacher
Cropper, Carolyn B.
Teacher of Gifted Education
Daugherty, Diana Lynn
English Teacher
Depew, Betty Moore
Spanish Teacher
Dobbs, Carrie L.
Biology Instructor
Dominguez, Linda Sanchez
Reading Specialist
Edwards, Dwight Phillip
Math Teacher & Department Chm
Edwards, Shirley Grimes
Business Teacher
Ellison, Linda Sue
English Teacher
Evans, Una Merle
Counselor
Favor, Kathy E.
English Teacher
Feeler, William Glenn
Instructor
Felio, Genelle (Hamilton)
Home Economics Teacher
Fishman, Lyn Lamkin
Lang Arts Chprsn & Eng Tchr
Flores, Tracey Renee
Counselor
Fly, Naghmeh Samandari
High School Mathematics Tchr
Freeman, Pat L.
Primary Teacher
Garcia, Gilberto Martinez
Instructional Services Dir
Garton, Cary Winifred
Third Grade Teacher
Givhan, R. Joyce Curnutt
Office Education Coord & Tchr
Goodin, Lily Koesjan
Honors English Teacher
Goodyear, Russell H.
English, Spanish & Latin Instr
Hall, Carol Ann
Assistant Choral Director
Ham, John Stuart
Algebra Teacher
Harbison, Claudia Jackson
English Teacher
Harrington, Charles B.
Athletic Trainer
Hart, Nancy L.
Coord of Legal Asst Program
Hayes, Doris Ann
1st-4th Grade German Teacher
Heredia, Gloria Anna
Bilingual Teacher Assistant
Hicks, Tacy Lee
7th Grade English Teacher
Hightower, Jeane (Smith)
Soc Sci, Govt & Geography Tchr
House, Jon E.
Teacher & Coach
Howell, Connie Truesdell
Jr English Teacher
Howell, Pamela Rene
Instructor of English
Huckabay, Paula
Journalism Teacher
Jones, Frankie Jo Saunders
Second Grade Teacher
Kauffman, Jane S.
Government Teacher
Keel, Debra Ann
English Teacher
King, Nancy Lee
Math Teacher
Krueger, Patricia Campbell
First Grade Teacher
Lacy, Rhonda J.
Kindergarten Teacher
Langley, Chandler
Bio Tchr, Vllybl, Bsktbl Coach
Lorenz, James D.
English Teacher
Manning, Linda Mc Kenna
Sophomore English Teacher
Martin, Loyce Volcik
English Teacher
Mc Clendon, Gregory Neal
History Teacher
McColloch, Terri Lynn
Health Tchr & Var Vllybl Coach
Mc Fadden, Mary Laws
Lower School Head
Merritt, Betty Henry
9th Grade English Teacher
Moore, Wanda Harp
First Grade Teacher
Morett, Justin
Business Teacher & Coach
Mullins, Donald Lee
Professor
Negri, Connie Hanvey
Bus Info Processing Teacher
Neimeyer, Marcia Velette
Science Department Head
Nelson, E. Gail
Spanish Teacher
Newton, Julie
Pre-Calculus Teacher
Oliver, Debbie Kay
Spanish Teacher
Pallanez, Tony Richard
Amer His Tchr & Bsbl Coach
Peetz, Robert William
Criminal Justice Coordinator
Peterson, Chad Michael
Teachers Aide & Soccer Coach
Ralston, Rene Elizabeth
Executive Director
Rodgers, Sabrina Kay
Chemistry & Physical Sci Tchr
Rulla, Mary Mc Donald
High School Math Teacher
Salas, Pablo Ortega
5th Grd Tchr of Gftd & Tlntd
Sawyer, Rhonda Wallace
English & Theater Teacher
Schneider, William Edgar
Head Athletic Trainer
Sever, Dennis W.
Dir of Information Systems
Shirley, Lucinda Vroman
Drawing Teacher
Sipko, Jo Ann Ljungdahl
4th Grd Language Arts Teacher
Smith, Cheree Luther
Senior English Teacher
Stricklin, Darlene Warren
Social Studies Teacher
Stumbaugh, Monty George
Biology Teacher & Coach
Sweet, Daniel Eric
Bio I, Environmental Sci Tchr
Templeton, Robert Dudley
Allison Chair of Journalism
Tervooren, Linda Harris
Latin & Spanish Teacher
Wade, Margaret Gaston
Biology Instructor
Walker, Geoffrey Paul
AP English Teacher & MOAS Adv
Wallum, Kevin Dwight
HS Christian Life-Bible Tchr
Walters, Scott
Life Science Teacher & Coach
Weant, Pamela Clinard
Chemistry Teacher
Whiles, Donna Kay
Spanish Teacher
Wilson, Ed Calvin
7th-8th Grd Soc Studies Chprsn
Winkley, Russell
Speech & Drama Teacher
Woodruff, Barbara Brown
First Grade Teacher
Yarbrough, Barbara Bolden
Sixth Grade Teacher
MIDLOTHIAN
Arroyo, Laurencio Perez, Jr.
Band Director
Beard, Nancy Ann Hall
1st Grade Teacher
Bergvall, Nancy Stiles
Gifted & Talented Teacher
Bolgiano, Susan Elaine
Math Teacher
Burnett, Patricia Gayle
Fifth Grade Teacher
Dieterich, Marthalu Baker
Spanish Teacher
Doherty, Vicki Lynn (Dillard)
Sixth Grade Reading Teacher
Ellis, Saundra Kay
First Grade Teacher
Gilreath, Janet Turner
Biology Teacher
Jones, Suzann Holland
English & Dance Teacher
Lynch, Marilyn Wallace
High School Mathematics Tchr
Malke, Beverly S.
Mathematics Teacher
Miller, LaRue Kilgore
Retired Elementary Teacher
Nance, Janice Rhea (Amyx)
English & PAL Teacher
Pilchiek, Jeffrey Allen
Counselor
Treibly, Linda Hill
Science Dept Chair & Chem Tchr
Vincent, Cathy Payne
Math Teacher & Dept Chair
Wagoner, Cherie Taliaferro
Middle School Counselor
MILES
Brandon, Merl Wayne
Math, Computer & Bus Tchr
Harris, Becky Ann
Secondary Science Teacher
Mc Laurin, Joan Rohmfeld
Second Grade Teacher
Pelzel, Marla Gaye (Lacy)
Fourth Grade Teacher
Snowden, Kathy Jackson
6th Grade Teacher
MILLSAP
Adkins, Lori Beth Littlefield
English Teacher
Jessup, Judy Burch
Home Economics Teacher
Stults, Maria Gloria
Kindergarten Teacher
Whitling, Sherri Brumbalow
6th & 9th Grd Eng Tchr, Coach
MINEOLA
Blaylock, Lori Snyder
Counselor
Castillo, Claudia Wilson
High School Spanish Teacher
Emerson, La Vica Ann
Counselor
Lamb, Kay Haley
8th Grade English Teacher
Phillips, Donald A.
HS Math Teacher
Smith, Theresa Dianne
World Geography Teacher
MINERAL WELLS
Anderson-Logan, Sandy Lynn
Spcl Ed Teacher & Var Coach
Brazil, Lambertine Fritz
Spanish Teacher
Cleveland, Frances Adkins
Teacher
Deaver, Billie Pearson
Business Education Teacher
Ferguson, Margue R.
4th Grade Teacher
Ford, Joyce Eaves
English Teacher
Fouts, Teresa Knouse
Math Teacher
Gomez, Berdonna Witt
6th Grade Langauge Arts Tchr
Gonzales, Delone Witt
First Grade Teacher
Jackson, Bata Parisa
2nd & 3rd Grade Title I Tchr
Locke, Juanita Rinkle
Reading Pgm Paraprofessional

:AL WELLS (cont)
-Prejean, Janet
Grade Teacher
, Leah Janess
h & Journalism Teacher
, James Edward
ent
Cathy
h Teacher
ON
, Norma Rodriguez
ure Teacher
Carolyn Tippen
Grade Teacher
es, Esther Marie
School Counselor
Dina Barrera
alism Advisor
Ruth M.
Grade English Teacher
Brian A.
Grade Teacher
, Delia F.
gy Teacher
son, Linda Reinold
dary Eng & Rdng Teacher
, Norma Lee
Teacher
oft, Kitty Lynn
n Teacher
, Randy Allen
cs Teacher
smith, Larry Lee
overnment & Economics Tchr
ras, Aaron G.
th Grade Science Teacher
April Moss
ce, Hlth & English Tchr
, Irma Guerra
rade Math Teacher
bi, Yosef Mohammad
Teacher
Neil Christian
Director
smina Coral
ess Teacher
Sandra Marie
rade Language Arts Tchr
Shirley Childs Hayward
Economics Teacher
rs, Gregory K.
intendent
Joanna Maria Hunt
er of Gifted & Talented
a, Cecilia Ybarra
Grade Elementary Teacher
Leslie Law
8th Grade Choir Director
John Patrick
rade Teacher
Patricia Glenn (Bush)
S Teacher
URI CITY
, Michael C.
ican History Tchr & Coach
Nancy Schindel
Band Director
Pang-Chieh
cs Teacher
Maurisa Dee
rade Teacher
in, Larry Marc
nal Justice Instructor
Elizabeth Johnson
rade Math Teacher
Clyta Foster
sh Teacher
Ray Peter
Director
ala S.
sh Teacher & Dept Chair
Laren Poach
ess Teacher & Dept Head
Diane De Leon
ng Dept Chair
s, John William
ematics Teacher
Ashly Shadwick
ry Teacher
mily
th Grade TX History Tchr
Jacqueline Denise
tant Principal
, Mary Lydia
rade Social Studies Tchr
, Ruthie Jean (Williams)
rade Reading Teacher
Johnnie Calhoun
rade Teacher
HANS
d, Judy Atkins
rade Teacher
Jane Anne Winborn
ier of Gifted & Talented
, Lisa Langford
ing Teacher
Lynda Heck
ess Teacher
on, Lisa Ward
al Ed Resource Educator
, Jeppie S.
ematics Teacher
, Tommy Earl
rade Amer History Teacher
, Mary Jane
itute Teacher
BELVIEU
rom, Jim R.
mediate School Principal

Bordelon, Mary Touchstone
Math & Social Studies Teacher
Griffith, Kathy Lea
Multi-Age Teacher
Harvey, Gina Benedict
Journalism Teacher
Mc Manus, Charles C.
Math Teacher & Coach
Skidmore, Kenneth Ray
Mathematics Teacher
MONTGOMERY
Grubbs, Tommy Jay
Art Teacher
Johnson, Johnny D.
AP Honors English IV Teacher
Russ, Judy Beth
English & Journalism Teacher
Wienecke, Keith R.
Teacher & Math Dept Chprsn
MOODY
Rothermel, Karren (Vaughn)
English Teacher
MORAN
Pittard, Linda
English Teacher
MORGAN
Miller, Pam (Cox)
Principal
Williams, Cathy R.
6th Grade Teacher
MOULTON
Chaloupka, Helen Matus
Language Arts & Speech Tchr
Dornak, Jamie Owens
English & Journalism Teacher
Price, Lezlie Cooper
Acctng, Keyboarding & Bus Tchr
MOUNT PLEASANT
Blount, Linda Gail Holcomb
Business Teacher
Brown, Cathryn Blalock
6th Grade Science Teacher
Buchanan, Phyllis Lynn
Biology I Advanced Teacher
Caskey, Judy White
Field Service Facilitator
Craven, Janette Marie
Fifth Grade Teacher
Dowdy, Jess T.
Physics, Engrng & Chem Instr
Hammonds, Marsha Kerbow
1st Grade Teacher
Hill, Sue Simms
English Teacher
Ivery, Sharon Hayes
6th Grade Math Teacher
Mc Cowan, Winston Clay
Professor of Biology
Means, Mollie Walker
Seventh Grade Math Teacher
Nash, Nathan Wayne
Texas History & Geography Tchr
Norris-Sears, Krisan Hope
Business Education Teacher
Quary, Rick L.
8th Grade Science Teacher
Richey, James Douglas
Mathematics Instructor
Rios, Lori Smith
Govt & Ec Teacher
Sanford, Martha Griffin
Fourth Grade Teacher
Stratton, Diane E.
Special Education Tchr & Coach
Thomas, Suzi Wall
First Grade Teacher
Turbyfill, Jana Julian
8th Grd English Teacher
Wallace, Carol June
Jr High Band Director
Wells, Steven P.
Director of Fine Arts
Whiting, George David
Math Teacher & Coach
MOUNT VERNON
Kent, Cindy Rutherford
Art Teacher
Stoker, Ronnie Earl
Seventh-Eighth Grade Teacher
Talley, Linda Sue
Kindergarten Teacher
Taylor, Clayton Leyden
Music Educator
Wood, Lynda
8th Grade English Teacher
MUENSTER
Arami, Cabrini
Math Teacher
Nasche, Gary John
Comp Sci, Rel & PE Tchr
MULESHOE
Bandy, Todd Reed
World Geography Teacher
Boutell, Thomas Charles
Junior High Teacher
Langen, Jacinda Stockett
US History Teacher
Smith, April Shiplett
Secondary Business Teacher
MUNDAY
Longan, Karen L.
Spanish Tchr & Theatre Dir
MURCHISON
Daniel, Nancy Glover
Jr High Teacher
NACOGDOCHES
Brightwell, Carol Roebuck
Fourth Grade Teacher
Clifton, Linnea Henderson
Science Teacher

Darville, Ray L.
Sociology Professor
Dixon, Leigh Ann
Woodwind Teacher
Grimland, Mary Neal Huff
8th Grade English Teacher
Holbert, Robin Wyman
English II Teacher
Jones, Wilma Dunivin
4th Grade Teacher
Justus, Judy Griswold
PE Teacher & Coach
Mc Grath, Sylvia Wallace
Professor of History
Pierce, M. E.
English Instructor
Skipper, Cheryl Martin
7th Grade Math Teacher
Tarrant, Brian Duane
American History Teacher
NATALIA
Denison, Robert Joseph
Science Teacher
Francies, Fred A.
Classroom Teacher
Frankenberry, Tanya Souddress
Band Director & English Tchr
Loza, Gloria Ann
Spanish, English & ESL Tchr
Taylor, Norma Gaile
Kindergarten Teacher
Tope, Diane Barden
Jr High Self Contained Teacher
NAVASOTA
Anders, Gail Graff
English Teacher
Condrey, Lee Roy, Jr.
US History Teacher & Coach
Dorsey, Loraine
English Teacher
Joswiak, Cheryl L.
Vocational Office Ed Teacher
Morgan, David Nelson
Director of Bands
Rohsner, Norma DeLaFuente
Home Economics Teacher
Walton, James L.
High School Biology Teacher
NAZARETH
Makeever, Mark L.
Health, PE Teacher & Coach
Myers, Roger Zirl
Band Director
Schulte, Brenda Durrett
English & Journalism Teacher
Waldo, Joel Richard
Elementary Principal
NEDERLAND
Bordelon, Cindi Karol
Biology & Marine Science Tchr
Broussard, Shirley M.
Science Teacher
Cobb, Linda Eastis
US History Teacher
Davis, Rose Holland
Third Grade Teacher
Dial, Dale Winston
Elem PE Teacher & HS Coach
Distefano, Norma Whigham
Lang Arts & Reading Teacher
Fisher, Annette Parigi
Math Teacher
Hill, JoAnne Gerace
French, Span Tchr & Dept Chair
Johnson, Julie Ann
English Teacher & Soccer Coach
O Connor, Betty Aline Breaux
Math Teacher
Reynolds, Helen Pate
English Teacher
Viterbo, Patricia Moreau
Second Grade Teacher
NEEDVILLE
Briscoe, Beth
Elementary Principal
Graham, Kim Burgin
Third Grade Teacher
Marek, Karla Austin
6th & 7th Grd Soc Stud Teacher
Mc Minn, Jo Ann
English Teacher
Newton, Brenda B.
Technology Coordinator
Zatopek, Sandra
Math Teacher
Zwahr, Tammy Rene
Counselor
NEVADA
NeSmith, Phyliss Eubank
Substitute Teacher
Pool, Marsha Morehead
English Teacher
Todd, Margaret A.
English III Teacher
NEW BOSTON
Hensley, Charles Rodney
World & Amer His Teacher
Martin, Larry Oliver
Health Teacher & Coach
NEW BRAUNFELS
Adams, Charles Wilfred, Jr.
Assistant Principal
Anderson, Larry Mark
Science Teacher & Dept Chair
Bartos, Susan Johnson
Choir Director
Bingham, Nancy Nelson
5th Grade Teacher
Brooks, Georgia Reese
Language Arts Teacher

Engler, Gail Weyel
Algebra Teacher
Flores, Joanne Marie
Scndry PE, Hlth Tchr & Coach
Garza, Joannie Kloc
Home Economics Teacher
Green, Connie Grant
Former Teacher
Hendricks, Rebecca (Averyt)
Asst HS Director
Holden, Barbara Haskell
8th Grade Language Arts Tchr
Jaroszewski, Lisa Winter
English Teacher
Johnson, La Verne Bodemann
Former English Teacher
Rychel, Ronald Drew
Teacher
Simmons, David Lynn
AP Government & Economics Tchr
Spears, Charles Bill
Mathematics Teacher
Vernon, Elivia Layne
Bus Tchr & Dept Chairman
Webb, Shirley Frankenfeld
Substitute Teacher
NEW CANEY
Barton, Jean K.
Teacher
King, Janet Canty
World History Teacher
Koen, Craig A.
Debate & Broadcasting Teacher
Mc Clure, Susan Kennedy
High School Teacher
Moore, Carol Mott
6th Grd Lang Arts & Rdng Tchr
Moore, James Alan
Marine Science & Biology Tchr
Walton, Mary Alice Saul
Spanish Teacher
NEW DEAL
Hockenberry, Julie Hill
English & Journalism Teacher
NEW HOME
Goodloe, Julie Michelle
High School English Teacher
Young, Allen Wayne
Science Teacher
NEW LONDON
Jarvis, Russell Alvin
Earth Science Teacher & Coach
Luton, Tony Glenn
Geography Teacher
NEW SUMMERFIELD
Cumbee, Rebecca Ann
Vocational Home Economics Tchr
Lorio, Rita R.
Director of Guidance
Murphy, Kimberly Owens
Business Teacher
NEW WAVERLY
Klawinski, Vergie Decker
Instruction Director
Lively, James Ray
Math Teacher
Mc Cutcheon, John David
School Counselor
Roark, Beverly Frenzel
Marketing Teacher, Coordinator
Ross, Carolyn Klodzinski
4th Grade Teacher
Sims, Eric
Secondary Teacher
NEWCASTLE
Bates, Bobby Jack, Jr.
Head Girls Basketball Coach
NEWTON
Brooks, Sue Smith
English Teacher
Snell, Carzetta
Retired Teacher
NIXON
Paul, John Edward
English Teacher & Ath Coord
Schmoekel, Jerry Lee
Science Teacher
Sikes, Lester E.
Senior English Teacher
NOCONA
Fenoglio, Paulette Szot
Secondary Mathematics Teacher
Haralson, Laura Jordan
Science Dept Chair & Teacher
Walker, Janet E. O'Mealey
Fourth Grade Math & Sci Tchr
NOLANVILLE
Ward, Marvin D.
Campus Technologist
NORDHEIM
Foster, Myrna Ahlhorn
Math & Language Arts Teacher
Garcia, Rene Mario, Sr.
History & Government Teacher
Warwas, Joyce Ann Schuenemann
4th Grade Teacher
NORMANGEE
Stevens, Betty Jo
English Teacher
NORTH ZULCH
Fitzgerald, Laura Ann
High School English Teacher
NURSERY
Harryman, Kathy Lynn
Second Grade Teacher
OAKWOOD
Barnett, Loyce Grant
Campus Supervisor
Roach, Samuel V.
School Counselor

ODEM
Salazar, Cirilda Ramon
ESL Teacher
ODESSA
Acuff, JoAnn Floyd
Teacher of Hearing Impaired
Armenta, Peggy Pepper
Fourth Grade Teacher
Baber, Stephen Douglas
Industrial Technology Teacher
Barth, Corlyce
Math Teacher
Bedford, Yvonne Deal
Special Education Teacher
Bolen, Sheri Sander
Eng II Tchr & Chrldng Coach
Briscoe, Mary Jane (Willis)
Vocational Adjustment Coord
Brown, Julie Kay (Goode)
Specialist of Gftd & Tlntd
Brumelle, Sharon Suther
First Grade Teacher
Callarman, Gary D.
G & T Physical Science Teacher
Camacho, Ana Marie
Fifth Grade Teacher
Campbell, Bonnie Ragland
7th Grade Reading Teacher
Carroll, Jeanette Southern
Kindergarten Tchr
Cherry, Leella Hall
Special Education Teacher
Cole, Kathleen Marie
Physical Science Teacher
Cone, Joanna Ruth
Speech, Debate Teacher & Coach
Cowan, Teri Lyn
Eighth Grade English Tchr
Crumley, Grace Allen
Third Grade Teacher
Dannheim, Paula Deann
Head Coach & Health Teacher
Davis, Lillie Newton
English Teacher
Drake, Jalynn Cay
World History Teacher
Dutko, Thomas Michael
GED & Economics Teacher
Ervin, Johnette Darlyne
Chairman of Speech Department
Estensen, Dawn Elise
Head Athletic Trainer
Ferguson, Sue
Counselor
Fishburn, Kathy Lyn
Orchestra Director
Fisher, Christine Lynn (Wilks)
English Teacher
Fowler, Dorothy Nell
Government & Economics Teacher
Fry, Traci Renee
Journalism Teacher
Gray, Pamela L.
English II Teacher
Gray, Rhonda Miles
Elementary Music Specialist
Heezen, Pam D.
Mathematics Teacher
Hitt, Lou Ann Kirk
Professor of Cosmetology
Humphries, Gary Lynn
6th Grade Teacher
Humphries, JoAnn Waddell
Sixth Grade Teacher
Jackson, Dorothy Greene
Assistant Professor of Nursing
Jacobs, Don E.
Dept Chair of Psych, Sociology
Jewell, Nancy Lynn (Bradshaw)
Teacher of Gifted & Talented
Johnson, Thresa Moshier
Health Sci Tech & Ed Coord
Jones, Paul Allen
Reading Teacher
Karr, Janet Hodgkiss
AP Eng Teacher & Acad Coach
Kirksey, Sherry Luedecke
English Teacher
Langham, Edward Lee
8th Grd Math Tchr & Dept Chair
Lawler, Sydney Kent
Science Teacher & Dept Chair
Leach, Ron
Assistant Principal
Lewis, Trudy Butschek
AP History Teacher
Love, David Wayne
Mathematics Teacher
Lozano, Erlinda Talamantez
Kindergarten Teacher
Mann, Mary Kay Sudbury
Physical Education Instructor
Manning, Peggy James
Assoc Prof & Acad Coord
Marshall, Amy Jo Fox
Accounting & Keyboarding Tchr
Mata, Pano
Band Dir & Orch Interim Dir
Mays, Mende Carole
Algebra I & Geometry Teacher
Mc Dowell, G. J.
Biology Teacher
Medlen, Suzanne Isabelle
High School Choral Director
Miller, Jill Caswell
Advanced Placement Eng Teacher
Monacelli, Kym LeBlanc
6th Grd Math & Science Teacher
Moseley, Ellouí Harwood
Asst Professor of Reading

ODESSA (cont)
Myers, Jerry Lynn
Teacher
Neill, Nathalie Ann
Home Economics Teacher
Newman, Marjy Ferrell
English Tchr & Yearbook Adv
Palmer, Sherry Hallford
Educ for Tomorrow Lead Tchr
Prescott, Billy R.
Orchestra Director
Rasor, Doris Lee DuBose
Bus Info Processing Coord
Roberts, Katherine Ann Gray
English Teacher
Russell, Jeanne Vine
Lecturer
Rutherford, William Mark
Government Professor
Sadler, Helen Kimbrough
PE & Sociology Teacher & Coach
Sample, Jimmy Dale
Biology I Teacher & Coach
Slater, Tommy R.
Teacher
Smith, Carolyn June
K-6th Grade Music Teacher
Smith, Dayna King
Second Grade Teacher
Sofge, Steve Wayne
Instructor of Biology
Speck, G. Michael
Biology Instructor & Coach
Taylor, Edward Donald
Professor of Chemistry
Thompson, Milton Blair, III
Biology Teacher
Thornton, Jan Shadowens
Kindergarten Teacher
Villegas, Elsa
Personnel Administrator
Waddell, William Franklin
Industrial Technology Teacher
Walker, Janet Lea
Associate Choir Director
Weathersby, Carla Hue
Ninth Grade Algebra Teacher
Whirley, Gingi Vaughn
11th Grd English & AP Teacher
Whytlaw, Penny Schroeter
Eng Dept Chprsn & Tchr of GT
Wilson, Karen Kelleher
Bio, Anatomy & Physiology Tchr
Woods, Beverly Dawn (Miller)
Third Grade Teacher
Young, Patsy Preslar
Third Grade Teacher
ODONNELL
James, Byron Kevin
HS Boys Basketball Coach
OLNEY
Richardson, Marsha L. Rexroat
Third Grade Teacher
OLTON
Couch, Cindy Rankin
Secondary & AP English Teacher
Jefferies, Karolyn Kay Murray
Elementary Counselor
Pruitt, Belinda Gaither
Business Teacher
Smith, Deborah Lackey
High School English Teacher
OMAHA
Frost, Neesa Neal
Math Teacher
Jones, Samuel Perry
Speech & Theatre Teacher
Young, Helen Mc Cormack
Health Teacher
ORANGE
Aleman, David George
History, Art & PE Teacher
Brown, Linda Mae
HS Counselor
Cochran, Florence Jeanelle
Home Economics Teacher
Copelin, Ann Chancelor
4th Grd Gifted & Talented Tchr
Curtis, Bettie J.
Business Education Teacher
Grooters, Diane Skillman
Eng, Soc, Psych & Art Teacher
Havens, Tom S.
Biology Teacher
Kyle, Jacqueline H.
Anatomy, Physiology & Bio Tchr
Leyendecker, Sandra Wicker
Math Teacher
Mathews, Betty Arrington
Gifted & Talented Teacher
Peebles, Robert H.
Professor of History
Preslar, Andrew Basil
Composition & Rhetoric Instr
Priest, Karen Miller
Eng Prof & Lbrl Arts Div Chair
Reeves, Katherine Miller
Biology Teacher
Shannon, Neva Lorraine
Journalism Teacher
Steglich, Sharon
First Grade & Religion Teacher
Womack, Betty Lou
Fourth Grade Teacher
ORANGE GROVE
Salinas, Rachel Naomi
Algebra Teacher
Winterbottom, James Eric
Band Director
ORANGEFIELD
Reeves, Louise Albers
Journalism & English Teacher
Rice, Deborah Gunn
English IV Teacher
Thomen, Janice (Steed)
Math Teacher
Wood, Connie Rush
Fourth Grade Teacher
ORE CITY
Barton, Debra Machen
1st Grade Teacher
Buckner, Traci Turner
Business Teacher
Johnson, Ethel Watkins
Eng & Rdng Improvement Tchr
Rogers, Patricia Middleton
Fifth Grade Lang Arts Teacher
Whatley, Hertha Stahl
Social Studies Teacher
OVERTON
Gonzalez, Barre Lee
English, Speech Tchr & Coach
OZONA
Jones, Fred B.
Jr High Earth Science Teacher
McWilliams, David Norris
K-12th Grade Counselor
Pena-Alfaro, Ruben
High School History Teacher
PADUCAH
Trent, Jane Wilson
English & Journalism Teacher
Trent, Kenneth Eugene
Math Teacher
Truelock, Vicky Jan (Crupper)
2nd Grade Teacher
Utley, John L.
Agriculture Science Teacher
Wilson, Ernestine Boothe
2nd Grade Teacher
Yarbrough, Jacquelyne Kaye
English & Theater Arts Teacher
PALACIOS
Elliott, Cynthia F.
Theatre, Speech & English Tchr
Hester, Fredia Rice
Fourth Grade Teacher
Hutto, E. H.
AP Calculus & Physics Teacher
Matusek, Deborah (Schulte)
Language Arts Teacher
Petrisky, Michael Ennis
Choral Music Director
Porter, Mary Kay Dyson
AP Eng Teacher & Dept Chrmn
Schuetz, Lydia Virginia
Eight Grade English Teacher
Wassel, Jean
Sixth Grade English Teacher
PALESTINE
Anleu, Rafael E.
Spanish Teacher
Barber, Brenda Wilson
7th Grade English Teacher
Bradly, Louis
Teacher & Coach
Cooksey, Becky Lincoln
GATE 2nd Grade Teacher
Eiben, Suzanne Stanaland
Principal
Estep, William Merl
History & Government Instr
Guthrie, Keith Edwin
Health Teacher & Coach
Haney, Bill F.
7th Grd Lang Arts & Eng Tchr
Harris, Jill Herod
Business Computer Teacher
Hessong, William A.
Teacher
Jones, Bobby
Junior & Senior English Tchr
Kelly, Kathleen Warren
Science Dept Chair & Chem Tchr
Maple, Claudia Martin
Kindergarten Teacher
McWhorter, Maria Cristina (Molina)
Physical Ed Teacher & Coach
Rhodes, William Don
Science Department Chairperson
Rister, Lana Jo
Resource Mathematics Teacher
Shokrian, Rebecca Ramirez
Kindergarten Teacher
Taylor, Stephanie Camille
Biology I & II Teacher
Whitehead, Edith K.
English Resource Teacher
PAMPA
Barker, Daniel Ross
HS English Dept Chairman
Bromlow, Susan E.
Business Teacher
Diller, Marcella M.
Sixth Grade English Teacher
Kibbe, Kay Kerbow
English Teacher
Kuhn, Steven Ray
Chemistry Teacher
Lane, Jerry Ross
Counselor & Humanities Prof
Mc Cullough, Frank
Mathematics Teacher
Nava, Mary Margaret (Preston)
Geometry & AP Calculus Teacher
Osborne, Sandra Lynn
High School Business Teacher
Porter, Stephen Duane
Government & Psychology Tchr
Shannon, Beth Gibson
Chemistry Teacher
Wheeler, Sherrell Rasco
Business Teacher
Wilbon, Tammy Denise
Language Arts Teacher
Wilson, Susie Johnston
Assistant Choir Director
PANHANDLE
Garner, Ronda Roberts
Art Teacher & Coordinator
Land, Steve Edward
High School Math Teacher
Robinson, Mary Wade
Tchr of Learning Disabilities
Roselius, Peggy L.
Second Grade Teacher
Spalding, Warren D.
Mathematics Teacher
PARADISE
Myers, Laura Elaine
English Teacher
PARIS
Bankhead, Gerrie Dale
Business & Office Ed Tchr
Davis, Jason Lee
Electronic Tech Coord & Instr
Denison, John Robert
Drafting Technology Instructor
Eatherly, Barbara Owen
Mathematics Teacher
Felty, Tommy Albert
History Teacher
Floyd, Karon Oakes
Math Teacher
Hancock, Emory Charles
Division Chm Math & Science
Harris, Marlia Bettes
7th Grade Math Teacher
Jackson, Dolores Scott
Computer Teacher
Jarrell, Jerry Thomas
7th Grade Language Arts Tchr
Jones, Randy Martin
Director of Bands
Kasper-Chaney, Rita LaRue
Chemistry, Bio & Anatomy Tchr
Keywood, Kay Hill
Eighth Grade Math Teacher
Kutzer, Marla O'Quinn
7th & 8th Grade Art Teacher
Lewis, Monta Lee (Powers)
Retired Vocational Ed Tchr
Lippiatt, Shanna Kay Hudgeons
World Geography Teacher
McDowell, Diane LaFerney
Social Studies Teacher
McVay, Paula Boyd
Reading Recovery Teacher
Rooks, Carol Ann
US History & English Teacher
Sanders, Agnes Anne
Eighth Grade Math Teacher
Shelton, Beth Bell
English Instructor
Shiver, Diane Jean
Deaf Education Teacher
Smith, Kim Walker
Science Teacher
Tyler, Cathie A.
Instructor of Art
PASADENA
Alexander, Doyle B.
Assistant Principal
Askine, Ruth Parse
Economics Teacher
Bagwill, Cynthia Martinez
7th Grd Life Science Teacher
Besch, Dawn Mc Crory
PE Teacher & Coach
Blalock, Susan Eileen
Assistant Principal
Blasingame, Grace I.
Physics Teacher
Blocker, Mary DeLaCruz
Fifth Grade Teacher
Boren, Jamie Carol
Special Education Teacher
Boyd, John Mark
English Teacher & Golf Coach
Boyd, Rachel Sigur
8th Grade English Teacher
Bretke, Steven Ray
Band Director
Buckley, Michelle A.
Mathematics Teacher
Burrell, Carroll F.
Professor of Business Law
Cadwalder, Maurice H.
Professor of Psychology
Cartwright, Ann
Dept of Chemistry Chairman
Chambers, Jo Sellers
English Teacher
Chamblee, Donna Watts
Counselor
Christopherson, Steven Douglas
Teacher
Coe-Killian, Christine Lynn
Art & Photography Teacher
Doley, Rebecca Kelly
Kindergarten Teacher
Duggan, Laura Finger
Theatre Arts & Dance Teacher
Duvall, Brenda S.
Theatre & Televison Dir
Falls, Barbara Sheaper
Fifth Grade Teacher
Finch, Doretta Richardson
Sixth Grade English Teacher
Fleming, Steven G.
Chemistry Teacher
Flores, Domingo, Jr.
Third Grade Bilingual Teacher
Flynt, Jim
Physical Education Teacher
Forshee, John R.
Government Instructor
Garcia, Barbara Matthews
English Department Chair
Griffin, Richard S.
Music Educator
Guillory, Jennifer Tempel
Soc Stud Dept Chair
Harris, Patricia Anne (Haywood)
Nursing Instructor
Helmle, Carole Donelson
Health Occupations Teacher
Hext, Gary
Asst Principal
Hill, Constance Cunningham
Pre-Calculus & Algebra Teacher
Hooper, Lynne Whitehurst
Peer Facilitator & Hosts Coord
Hurt, Linda Lee
Instructor
Jackson, James Clark
Automotive Instructor
Jurek, Kenneth J.
English Teacher
Kelly, Robert Harold
Head Aquatics Coach
Koch, Jean Parnell
Senior English Teacher
Latimer, S. Darleen (Gentry)
Geometry Teacher
Marshall, Ginger
Math Teacher
Martin, Debbie Ann
Geometry Teacher
Martin, Glynda F.
American History Teacher
Mc Kinney, Mark Lynn
Basketball Coach & PE Teacher
Mikulencak, Marsha Overton
8th Grd Eng & Journalism Tchr
Mills, Jean
English Teacher
Moore, Paulette L.
ACE Learning Center Supervisor
Morgan, Michael Cary
History Teacher
Norman, David R.
Toyota Tech Ed Network Instr
Pancheri, Alex
Orchestra Director & Teacher
Pearce, Denise M.
Biology Teacher & Coach
Poole, Carolyn Gibson
Instructor
Purdy, Debra Finn
HS Science Teacher
Rice, Debbie D.
Math Teacher
Rios, Hilda Cabrera
English Teacher
Ritthaler, Michael David
Math, Science Teacher & Coach
Robbins, Janice Belcher
Voice Instructor
Robinson, Norman D.
Mathematics Teacher
Roesler, Debbie Veatch
Social Studies Teacher
Sells, James Chat
Instructor
Skyles, Darren Stanton
English & Philosophy Teacher
Spigner, Rufus Edward
US Marine Corps JROTC Instr
Stahl, Beth Goehring
Dept Chm & Med Lab Tech Instr
Steele, Greg Bruce
Math Professor
Stocco, Karen Ellen
Science Teacher
Stoddard, Debbie D.
Fifth Grade Teacher
Sword, Paula Kay
Soc Stud Teacher & Dept Chm
Sydnor, Granville Lassiter
Psychology Instructor
Watts, Peggy Stoeckle
7th Grade Science Teacher
Webster, Ken D.
Sociology & World Geog Teacher
Weiss, Jutta A.
Department Head of Anatomy
West, Ruth Marie
High School Math Teacher
PATTONVILLE
Ballard, Jeffery Lynn
Agriculture Sciences Teacher
Moseley, Bill Richard
Spanish & Journalism Teacher
Richey, Dorothy S.
Typing & Accounting Teacher
Winters, Bobby G.
Agri Science Teacher
PAWNEE
Pogue, Jimmie Lacy
Jr HS Social Studies Teacher
PEARLAND
Atkins, Judith
Math Teacher
Belan, Levenia Fitzgerald
Teacher
Bishop, Lue
Assistant Principal
Caletka, Brenda Schaefer
High School Math Teacher
Dawson, Glenda Miles
Career & Tech Chairman
Ellis, Barbara Huseman
6th Grd Language & Rdng Tchr
Gruener, Barbara Natzke
Counselor
Hollis, Kimberly DeHart
Teacher
Lowe, Annette Dominy
AP Govt & Economics Teacher
Nuber, Holly B.
Health Education Teacher
Pare, Sherry Cade
6th Grd Lang Arts Teacher
Posern, Elsie Holdiness
English Teacher & Dept Chair
Stephens, Sara (Floyd)
Teacher of Gifted & Talented
Wood, Barbara Hahn
Spanish Tchr & Stu Cncl Spon
PEARSALL
Aleman, Eduardo
Assistant Band Director
Carpenter, Allene Loessberg
First Grade Teacher
House, Cheryl Lynn
8th Grade Language Arts Tchr
Knox, Sharon Brettell
English Teacher
Kurtz, Darrell W.
Vocational Agriculture Teacher
Neal, Nina Nelson
High School Geometry Teacher
Ozuna, Neftali G.
Amer His, Psych, Sociolgy Tchr
Urban, Lynda Kohlenberg
Mathematics Teacher
Zirkel, Jeannie Carlson
Special Education Director
PECOS
Boutwell, Mary Lynn
English Tchr & Chrldr Spon
Fowlkes, Carol Mills
Spcl Education & 2nd Grd Tchr
Green, Jane Jones
First Grade Teacher
Overcash, Sandra Eileen (Corson)
Math Teacher
Rankin, Carolyn Abernethy
Retired Math Dept Chairperson
Urias, Crissy Tersero
Principal
Urias, Felix Venegas, Jr.
Spanish Tchr & Head Ftbl Coach
PERRYTON
Barclay, Danny K.
Auto Tech Teacher
Cummings, Sharon Lamberson
First Grade Teacher
Diedrich, Dana Lynn
Mathematics Teacher
Doerrie, Bobette Belinda
Physical Science Teacher
Hayden, Carol Jan
Health Dept Coordinator
Langston, Cindy Steele
6th-8th Grade Resource Teacher
Nall, Linda Miller
Physical Education Teacher
Rutherford, Kenneth Alvin
Coach & Teacher
Schiffelbein, Layne (Sinclair)
Literature & English Teacher
Towner, Debra Hill
Second Grade Teacher
Wilson, Minta Lue (Mc Aninch)
Librarian & Media Director
PETERSBURG
Marr, Carolyn Janette Willingham
Fifth Grade Teacher
Robertson, Wayne
Vocational Agriculture Teacher
PETROLIA
Russell, Doris Jane
English Teacher
PFLUGERVILLE
Anderson, Carroll Greer White
8th Grd Amer History Teacher
Anderson, Gary Lee
Photography & Graphics Teacher
Artz, Susan Whaley
English Teacher
Blair, Penny Franson
Lang & Rdng Tchr of GATE
Cox, Rebecca Joanne
Social Science Teacher
Eary, Carolyn Lee
American History Teacher
Faulkner, Steven Howard
Technology Specialist
Friday, Maria Angela
World Geography Teacher
Garcia, Jesus Torres
8th Grade Earth Science Tchr
Gibson, Rebecca Neale
Spanish Teacher
Hamilton, Rebecca Williams
English Teacher
Kohler, Micala Mc Cullough
Language Arts & History Tchr
Lake, Audrey Elaine (Dietz)
English Teacher
Laurence, Georgette Lowes
Mathematics Teacher
Maresch, Claire Williams
Home Economics Teacher
Meister, Elena Meza
ESL & Reading Teacher

ERVILLE (cont)
James W., Jr.
an & History Teacher
rian C.
gy Teacher
nnie Gross
's World History Teacher
, Nancy Lou
sktbl Coach & Hlth Tchr
R
, Olga
Grade Teacher
, Anita (Mc Broom)
athematics Teacher
n, Karen Theresa
sh Teacher
Beatrice Laurel
tud Tchr & Dept Chprsn
Susana Loza
athematics Teacher
, Jeffrey L.
ng Teacher
e Patrick, Jr.
Teacher & Department Head
Surry G.
l Director
ez, Rolando Noel
ce Teacher & Dept Head
ez, Noelia Munoz
rd Language Arts Teacher
dez, Angie
Grade English Teacher
dez, Maria Yolanda
er of Gifted & Talented
Gary Robert
ed Content Mastery Tchr
Margaret Elizabeth
ng Improvement Teacher
, Juanita
Grade Teacher
ez, Diane R.
icrocmptr Application Tchr
z, Celia Suarez
Grade Teacher
lson, Timothy Charles
r Army Instructor
Mana
ess Teacher
Monica
acher & Coach
POINT
e, Barbara Berend
ematics Teacher
Gary Edward
tor of Bands
BURG
, Carolyn Gibson
earning, PALS, Dance Tchr
, Susan Rhoades
sh Teacher
Gregory Eric
Director
, Jimmy W.
ry Teacher
VIEW
, Benjamin Ola
on of Business Chairman
, Nancy Wilson
h Grade Science Teacher
, Susan Reichle
ce Teacher
honda G. (Meadows)
Grade Teacher
arbara S.
Education Teacher
ck, Darin Patrick
overnment Teacher
dez, Fermin
rade Art Teacher
Jane Richards
Science Technology Instr
Nancy Terrill
Teacher
ng, Paulette Cunningham
ematics Teacher
, Janie Gordon
Grade Teacher
, Estelle
ry Professor
dson, Jamie Lynn
gy Teacher
Renvy Evans
Tchr & Ath Coach
ns, Sue Landreth
ematics Teacher
O
, Elizabeth Carsten
ematics Teacher
Beverly Moeller
nd Grade Teacher
on, Karen Brooks
pan Tchr & Frgn Lang Chm
, Arlene Siegman
Math Instructional Assoc
cott Patrick John
nd Grade Teacher
d, Sandra (Flesner)
ical Education Teacher
y, Linda Kay (Heimsath)
netry Teacher & Team Leader
s, Regina Elena
School Spanish Teacher
acher, Donna Gail
or English Teacher & Coach
om, Terrance Howard
nth Grade Science Teacher
, Martin R.
nce Department Chair
, Patsy Bennett
nce Department Teacher

Burch, Daniel K.
Physical Education Teacher
Buteyn, Linda Rae
Hum of the Gifted & Eng Tchr
Cawthon, Marsha A.
English Teacher
Childress, Laura Ann
Business Teacher & Team Leader
Clark, Nancy Morris
Fifth Grade Teacher
Corley, Alton Lee
Band Director
Davey, Diane F.
Womens Athletic Coordinator
Davis, Jeffrey Alan
Biology Tchr & Ath Trainer
Deaton, David William
Science Teacher & Coach
Delgado, Bernadette
Spanish Teacher
Duke-Ruhd, Betty
Latin Teacher
Everett, Dianne
Eng, Dance & Drill Team Tchr
Ezell, Judy Roach
Assistant Principal
Fabre, Rodney
World History Teacher
Farquhar, David
Mathematics Teacher
Farrell, Mary Beth B.
English Teacher
Ferrara, Vanessa Morris
French & Spanish Teacher
Ferrell, Elizabeth Bailey
Mathematics Teacher
Freeman, Sara Ann
Math Teacher
Garrison, Glenn David
Professor of Political Science
Gerick, Jan L.
Team Leader & Teacher
Gibbs, Diann Summers
English III Teacher
Gideon, Sharon Lee Dever
Latin & English II Teacher
Gleason, Sherry Burton
Freshman Honors English Tchr
Goodwin, Cynthia Shergalis
English Teacher
Griffin, Deedra Jo
Business Tchr & Soccer Coach
Griffith, Rebecca Runyan
English Teacher
Grimes, Robert Wesley
HS Coach & History Teacher
Hanafy, Billie Jean Hadley
English & Humanities Teacher
Hargreaves, Cynthia Lynn
6th Grade Social Studies Tchr
Harpole, Carole Burdon
Second Grade Teacher
Hassell, Carol Dickinson
Bilingual Teacher
Havins, Linda J.
High School US History Teacher
Henderson, Carolyn Owens
ESOL Teacher & Tennis Coach
Henry, Patricia Joanne
Math Teacher & Team Leader
Herrmann, Carl Gerard
Band Director
Hester, Margaret Tanner
Counselor
Hitt, David R.
Band Teacher
Hoffmann, Karleen Hightower
Science Teacher
Howard, Michael Stephen
8th Grade Science Teacher
Hunt, Tim
Advanced Placement Art Teacher
Inman, Thomas W.
Computer Literacy Tchr & Coach
Jakus, Betsy Barrett
Reading Teacher
Johnson, Laura Aurelia
Sci, Chem & Phys Sci Teacher
Karr, Rosemary Mc Croskey
Professor & Coord of Math
Klier, Barbara Harden
English Teacher
Kollmann, Angela Bentley
Biology Teacher
Kottwitz, Doris (Miller)
Mathematics Teacher
Kruse, Stanley E.
8th Grd Teacher & Athletic Dir
Kukal, Mary Bartle
Fifth Grade Teacher
Landers, Cindy Sue
German & English Teacher
Landingham, Mary Jo
HS Coach
Lawrence, Marsha A.
AP Government Teacher
Lilley, Marte Maxwell
Humanities Tchr & Eng Dept Chr
McCrary, Patricia
11th Grade English Teacher
Mc Kenzie, Karen Dooley
English II Team Ldr & Teacher
Meger, David Michael
Science Teacher & Coach
Michael, Elizabeth Baly
English Teacher
Michael, Karen Sue (Poole)
2nd Grade Teacher
Miller, Joyce Marie Penny
English Professor

Moon, Mary Ann
Chemistry Teacher
Morris, Donna R.
Home Economics Teacher
Morse, James D.
9th-10th Grade JROTC Instr
Newman, Kent Drew
8th Grade Earth Science Tchr
Nieb, Karen Jensen
English & Latin Teacher
Nitcholas, Gay Walker
Retired 3rd Grade Teacher
Palmer, Linda Moser
Math Teacher
Parker, Kathleen Ugolini
Fifth Grade Teacher
Parker, Sandra Marie
Theatre Teacher
Pelley, Gwen Marie
Third Grade Teacher
Penix, Bill
World History Teacher
Pyle, Nell B.
Counselor
Reban, LaJuana Jean
AP American History Teacher
Resnik, Susan Ellen
Dean of Students
Robinson, Pam Ricci
Art Teacher & Dept Team Leader
Saigling, Rick
Journalism Teacher
Salamone, Gene Michael
Retired Teacher
Schieck, Katherine Burns
First Grade Teacher
Selznick, Victoria Maximciuc
8th Grade Science Teacher
Shepherd, Karen Schiller
Honors Biology Teacher
Shields, Samuel A., Jr.
World History Teacher
Silva, Lori Dean
Former Algebra I Teacher
Sinnamon, Pauline Nancy
French & Spanish Teacher
Skinner, Wana Viator
Int Design & Ind Living Tchr
Smith, Beverly Lynn
Subject & Acad Team Leader
Smith, Travis Reginald
High School Band Director
Stanton, Mary E.
English Teacher
Staton, Duane
History Dept Chairman, Teacher
Sterling, Carolyn Campbell
Third Grade Teacher
Steward, Edith Carolyn (Carr)
Mathematics Teacher
Stinson, Susan Kennedy
English Teacher
Sweany, Susan Joy
Physical Education Teacher
Tenzer, Karen France
4th Grade Teacher
Thomas, Jerry Neal
Director of Bands
Timme, Jennifer Stearman
11th Grade English Teacher
Toney, Bibs Chadwick
1st Grade Teacher
Ward, Cyndie Stevenson
Physical Ed Teacher & Asst
Washington, Jackie Chereese
Theatre Director
Watkins, Donna Faulk
Business Teacher
Wheeler, Patricia Feeney
Eighth Grade English Teacher
White, Susan Siebert
Math Teacher & Dept Head
Williams, David Paul
Counselor
Wilson, Julia Gayla
Mathematics Teacher
Young, Estelita Calderon
Prof & Coord of Spanish
PLEASANTON
Akin, Charlin Susan
English Teacher
Anderson, Gary Michael
Chemistry Instr & Acad Coord
Beeter, Neva Ray
Teacher & Coach
Bryan, Rick Thomas
6th Grade Math Teacher
Greene, Anna Holmes
Math Dept Chair & Teacher
Stutts, Sharon Mc Murry
Biology Teacher
Terry, Chester Don
Accounting & Economics Teacher
POINT COMFORT
Thonsgard, Florence Elisabeth
Kindergarten Teacher
POLLOK
Davis, Paula Ralaford
Chorus & Theater Director
Norris, William O.
Assistant Principal
Simms, Tammy Brooks
Third Grade Teacher
Sloan, Mary Hudgins
Vocational Home Economics Tchr
Tucker, Janis (Sifford)
Lead Tchr of Career & Voc Dept
PONDER
Henry, Amanda Long
7th-8th Grd Lang Arts Teacher

Phelps, Earnie F., III
Elem PE & Health Teacher
Routh, Lorri Belle
Guidance Cnslr & English Tchr
Wallum, Debbi Butler
Mathematics & Business Teacher
PORT ARANSAS
Byrd, Robert Stephen
Govt, Ec, His & Eng Tchr
Freeman, Suzette Hash
Physical Education Teacher
PORT ARTHUR
Blanton, Linnis Edward
Art Teacher
Bradford, Sandra M.
PE Teacher & Track Coach
Branson, Alice Marlow
Developmental Math Lecturer
Charlie, Francine
Fourth Grade Teacher
Cole, Bobbie Watkins
School Nurse
Collins, Barbara Ann
6th-8th Grd Social Stud Tchr
Cox, Frances Strauss
Fourth Grade Teacher
Creed, Patricia Ann (Parent)
Librarian & Media Specialist
Gibbs, Cheryl Renee
English & French Teacher
Glaze, Robin Tielke
Kindergarten Teacher
Gloston, Jerry Fontenot
9th Grade Counselor
Goza, Trudy (Loyd)
First Grade Teacher
Gregory, Susan Gail
Mathematics Instructor
Hardee, Charlenee Renee
Geography Teacher
Hill, Sandra Jones
Elementary Supervisor
Holstead, Katie Cecile
Chemistry Teacher
Huval, Barbara Jane Bobbitt
Assoc Professor of English
Jackson, Donnetta Eulian
First Grade Teacher
Kiel, Elizabeth Marie
Title I Teacher
Landry, Faith Broadway
8th Grade Science Teacher
Lee, Kenneth Reeves
Computer Science Teacher
Lucas, Rebecca Moore
Biology Teacher
Neal, Harold Dean
8th Grade Mathematics Teacher
Newton, Kathleen Adams
High School Supervisor
Owens, Joyce H.
Business Education Teacher
Powers, Mary Ellen
Fifth Grade Teacher
Presley, Kathryn Thompson
English Instructor
Redd, Jo Carol
Teacher of Gifted & Talented
Roden, Sherrie San Angelo
Health Teacher
Rose, George M.
Math Department Leader
Sewell, Carolyn Hughes
Math Teacher
Smith, Joseph Michael
Spcl Ed Teacher & Coach
Sonnier, Alvine Gradley
Mathematics Teacher
Spears, LeRoy Carl
Speech, Drama & History Tchr
Vanatta, Joan Kinlaw
Kindergarten Teacher
VanZandt, Delores Mari
Director of Computer Services
Vurlicer, Maureen Hawkins
HS English Tchr & Dept Ldr
Wallace, Linda Gail (Palombo)
Elementary School Counselor
Wheat, Mary Wimberley
High School Reading Teacher
Williams, Barbara Lynn (Carron)
First Grade Teacher
Worthington, Donna
Eng & Physical Education Tchr
Wukosch, Loyce Fehl
Sixth Grade Reading Teacher
PORT LAVACA
Adkison, George Robert
Teacher
Allgaier, Benny H.
Mathematics Teacher
Bland, Rosemary Wenona
Resource English Teacher
Crow, Shelly Lynn
Science Teacher
Jurica, Linda Horecka
Teacher
Ratliff, Kim Killingswortth
Teacher & Coach
Roberts, Susan
Biology Teacher
Thorn, Margo Leinneweber
Art Teacher
Ueckert, Keith
World History Teacher
PORT NECHES
Anthony, Donna Kay
Texas History Teacher
Bryant, Debbie Lynn
Second Grade Teacher

Carson, Sandra Montondon
Kindergarten Tchr
Comer, Stephen Louis
Mathematics Teacher
Davis, Jan Adams
Business Teacher
Fournet, Jean
English Instructor
Kemble, Jackie Henderson
Ret 6th & 7th Grd Math Tchr
Mendoza, Catherine Mary
Texas History & PE Teacher
Moore, Mary Jane
Biology Teacher
Nelson, Donna Jordan
8th Grade Teacher
Spiegel, Vanessa Ann
8th Grade Algebra & Math Tchr
Thompson, Kimberly Rene
Math Teacher
PORTLAND
Butler, Deborah Carson
High School Math Teacher
Jennings, Sylvia Beyer
Educational Diagnostician
Loeckle, Judy Walker
Second Grade Teacher
Matula, George, Jr.
7th Grade TX History Teacher
Quintanilla, Bernice Alvarez
5th Grade Language Arts Tchr
Vance, Jerry Odell
Math Teacher
Yowell, William Mercer
History & Radio-TV Teacher
POST
Pool, Joy Scott
English Teacher
POTEET
Czarza, Frances
Business Teacher
Powell, Gayle Lorraine
Eleventh Grade English Teacher
Stewart, John Raymond, Jr.
Science Teacher & Coach
Strickland, Sandra Torres
English Teacher
POTH
Seidenberger, Michael Max
Agricultural Science Teacher
POTTSBORO
Day, Mary Westman
Business Teacher
Dutton, Janie Brown
Computer Application Teacher
Moore, John W.
Math & Science Teacher
Stewart, Jan Talley
Theatre Art Teacher
Williams, Ann Mast
Mathematics Teacher
PRAIRIE VIEW
Engedayehu, Walle
Political Science Professor
Freeman, Bee Jay
Professor of Eng Composition
Haley, Kenneth Layne
Asst Professor of English
Jones, Howard James
History Professor
Muoneke, N'Ekwunife Nick
Associate Professor of Math
Obadele, Imari Abubakari
Assoc Prof of Pol Sci Pgm
PRICE
Rhame, Scott
Band Director
PRINCETON
Alagna, Mary Ellen Gerrity
Tchr of Eng Gifted & Talented
Bliss, Frances Camille (Windle)
Sophomore English Teacher
Buckley, Terresa Ann
HS Special Education Coord
Trout, Una Jean
Eng, Gifted & Talented Tchr
Witt, Jay Ross
Scndry Amer History Teacher
PROGRESO
Alvarado, Viviano, Jr.
Spanish Teacher
Palacios, Jose Margil
Criminal Justice Teacher
Torres, Raul, Jr.
ESL, US His & Jrnlsm Tchr
PROSPER
Barker, Michael Ray
Spanish Teacher
Brown, Janet W.
7th-8th Grd Rdng & Eng Teacher
PYOTE
Lowry, Lee Hargis
Counselor of Drug & Alcohol
QUANAH
Holt, Timothy Tab
HS Social Studies Tchr & Coach
Hutchison, Pequita Jackson
Language Arts Teacher
Melear, Robert Edwin
HS Cmptr Sci & Math Teacher
Wade, James Earl
Biology Teacher
QUEEN CITY
Goodson, MaryLou Harper
Math & Computer Sci Teacher
Sewell, Donna Gail Young
5th Grade Social Studies Tchr
Smith, Linda Harp
Spanish Teacher

QUEMADO
Dickerson, Mirtha Ibanez
Second Grade Teacher
QUINLAN
Breazeale, Rodney E.
Psychology & Phys Sci Tchr
Keck, Tammie Giddens
HS Dance & Drill Team Dir
Murray, Darlena Marie
Business Teacher
Rowe, Heather Renee
6th Grade English Teacher
Smith, Patricia Ann
Choir Teacher
QUITMAN
Attaway, Sally Sheffield
Transitional First Grade Tchr
Carney, Carolyn Shaw
6th Grade Teacher
Grider, Janet Sue
7th-8th Grade Teacher & Coach
Hathaway, Lana Dee
Spanish Teacher
Keith, Frances Noble
Home Economics Teacher
Mc Entire, Kay Murley
Computer Science Teacher
Morrow, Micheal Dale
Speech & Debate Instructor
Nichols-Milner, Mary Ann
Specialist & French Teacher
Shackelford, Paula Lynn (Mc Faul)
Business Teacher
Shackelford, Todd Wayne
HS American History Teacher
Wilson, Karla Jan
Honors English & Gifted Tchr
RALLS
Brandt, Nan Leigh
High School Counselor
Rude, Stacie Heil
Chemistry & Biology Teacher
Wilson, Jeanette Wheeler
Home Economics Teacher
RANGER
Marlow, Herb
Sociology Instructor
RANKIN
Corder, Paula Gay
English, Speech & Theatre Tchr
RAYMONDVILLE
Arevalo, Elizabeth
Health & Spanish Teacher
Austin, Robert Ray
Agriscience & Tech Instructor
Brackhahn, Angela Satterwhite
Kindergarten Teacher
Brown, Bonnie (Shirley)
English I & II Teacher
Garcia, Belia Sanchez
7th Grade Science Teacher
Martinez, Josie Vasquez
2nd Grade Teacher
Niemeier, Stephanie Ellis
Chemistry Teacher
Scarborough, James S.
Counselor
Scarborough, Jane M.
PAL & HOSTS Teacher
RED OAK
Cheshier, Carolyn H.
English IV Teacher
Colvin, Kathy Kvale
High School Teacher
Deal, Etha Lorraine
English III Tchr & Coach
Fry, Leah Renee (Bolton)
English Teacher
Goodman, Suzann Tepe
Fifth Grade Teacher
La Borde, Bobby L.
Economics Teacher
Little-Lee, Charla Fay
Theatre Teacher
Ray, Judi L.
Art Teacher
Stuart, Kimberly Libby
Reading & Social Studies Tchr
Tuma, Gayle Thomas
District Technology Coord
Wooton-Bitting, Melissa Ann
Bio, Anatomy & Psychology Tchr
REDWATER
James, Debbie Brock
Eng, Sociology & Psych Teacher
Scales, Linda Kay
Fourth Grade Reading Teacher
REFUGIO
Blaschke, James Patrick
Govt, Economics & Geog Tchr
RHOME
Koch, Gretchen Theis
3rd Grade Teacher
RICHARDSON
Abrams, Steven S.
Biology Teacher
Andrlik, Mary K. Burnett
Spanish & French Teacher
Attaway, Linda Sides
Third Grade Teacher
Baggese, Judy Hull
Spanish Teacher
Bambach, Charles R.
History & Philosophy Professor
Benson, Gaye Miller
9th Grade Math Teacher
Biedenhahn, Letitia M.
Third Grade Teacher
Black, Nancy Dix
Eng & Knowledge Theory Tchr
Bootman, Barbara Grover
Mathematics Teacher
Boyer, Joyce Foltz
Secondary Mathematics Teacher
Bynum, Susan Lea
Art Teacher
Campbell, Bill D.
Physical Science Tchr & Coach
Casaday, Cheryl Gilmore
Gifted Programs Specialist
Casey, Audeen M.
Teacher of Hearing Impaired
Caudill, Kaye Maples
Second Grade Teacher
Cook, Julie
9th Grade Algebra I Teacher
Copeland, Myrna Bea
Latin Teacher
Cotten, Virginia Reeder
Reading Tchr & Instrl Assoc
Cottingame, Karen Ekstrand
English Teacher
Coward, Karen Ford
English IV Teacher
Cunningham, Wesley Scott
Health Education Chairperson
Darling, Jill Ann
German Teacher
Darrough, Monta Hitt
Economics & Art History Tchr
Davenport, Mark Joseph
Orchestra & Strings Teacher
Davenport, Philip
Art & Photography Teacher
Davis, Judi Mc Auley
Fourth Grade Teacher
Dempster, Lynn Clayton
Fifth Grade Teacher
Eisenmann, Mary
Chemistry Teacher
Farrar, Karen S.
Sixth Grade Teacher
Fisher, Nancy Gail
Fifth Grade Teacher
Gee, Janet Baird
4th Grade Teacher
George, Linda Lee (Burke)
Math Teacher, Dept Chair & Dir
Gerard, Donna Jo
High School Latin Teacher
Goff, Christina Field
Counselor
Halada, Richard Stephen
Physics Teacher
Hames, Gregory Alan
Band Director
Hanna, Bettie Fairey
4th Grade Teacher
Heider, Kim D.
Senior Guidance Counselor
Hewitt, Carol Rodgers
Eng Tchr, Acad Decathlon Coach
Ingalls, Dana
8th Grade Science Teacher
Jackson, Lynne Ann
Band Director
James, Linda Janan
High School Eng & Fr Teacher
Johnson, Janet Chatfield
Third Grade Teacher
Keenan, Deborah LeFevre
Resource Teacher
Kinard, Jerrett Scott
Asst Director & Music Teacher
LaReau, Pamela Nausley
History Teacher
Larimer, Gregg
PE Teacher & Coach
Love, Claudia Meier
English Teacher
Lucht, Lynn Elliott
Second Grade Teacher
Martin, Andrea Jarrell
English Teacher
Martin, Caroline Page
Math Teacher
Mc Cormick, Jeffrey Lee
Teacher, Ath Director & Coach
McFarland, Marsha L.
Foreign Language Dept Chprsn
Muncy, Darrell Gene
Theatre Arts Teacher
Murray, Lynn McDonald
High School Math Teacher
Nevill, Dana Carol
Math Teacher
O Neill, Jacqueline Mae
Secondary Mathematics Teacher
Owens, Wanda Louise
Third Grade Teacher
Pearson, Karen Buss
Fourth Grade Teacher
Peters, Deanna Rucker
English Teacher
Prater, Zita G.
English Teacher
Seawright, Gaye Lynn Henry
Education Consultant
Sheff, Honey Mendelson
Clinical Psychologist
Sidweber, Ellen Ann
First Grade Teacher
Staffin, Ellen Beth
English Teacher
Sutton, Jeri Kingcaid
Mathematics Teacher
Swanson, Janice Haney
Math Teacher
Terwey, Kenneth Lee
Health & Physical Ed Teacher
Thompson, John Mark
HS Bible, Art Tchr & Coach
Ubl, Nicole Lieb
Math Teacher
Warshaw, Peter J.
Bands Dir & Music Dept Chrmn
Watkins, Wanda Follie
Spanish Teacher
Weigel, Catherine Gilmore
Journalism Teacher
Wood, Roberta Woodbury
Social Studies & Health Tchr
Wylie, Peggy Pomroy
Math, Science & Health Tchr
Zednick, Lynn Jeanette
Theatre Arts Teacher
RICHMOND
Calloway, Michele Rapp
Third Grade Teacher
Guinn, Kim Howell
Third Grade Teacher
RIESEL
Sellman, Elisabeth Anne
English Teacher
RIO HONDO
Harms, Mary Adele
English Teacher
Kutscher-Waters, Karen Naomi
Agriscience Instructor
Lopez, Teresa
Algebra Teacher
RIO VISTA
Dagley, Robert Houston
Anatomy, Physiology & Bio Tchr
Davis, Debra Alice
8th Grade Teacher & Coach
RISING STAR
Chambers, Patricia Joanne Lennington
Home Economics Teacher
Ezzell, Anna Paulette
Special Education Teacher
Wood, Cynthia Pallette
Business Teacher
RIVIERA
Garcia, Anita Escobar
Mathematics Teacher
Myers, Sharron R.
Eng, Journalism & Spanish Tchr
Scott, Will Braxton
Ret Soc Work & Sociology Prof
Wheeler, Tina Cochran
MS Mathematics Teacher
ROANOKE
Brown, Fran Lindsey
Principal
Foster, Pam DeEtte
Fifth Grade Teacher
Outlaw, Nina Stephenson
Retired Sci Dept Chair & Tchr
ROBERT LEE
Roe, Tammy Haines
Secondary Math Teacher
Wilson, Melba Jameson
5th Grade Teacher
ROBSTOWN
Carr, Robert Paige
Athletic Director & Coach
Edge, Carla Ehlers
Music Teacher
Knauff, Larry Grant
Chemistry, Physics & Bio Tchr
Loera, Cecilia A.
Gifted & Talented Pgm Teacher
Medrano, Irma
5th Grade Math Lab Teacher
Mireles, Dawn Valerie
Math Teacher & Supervisor
Sandate, Sofia
English & Spanish Teacher
ROBY
Fenton, John Sherman
Mathematics Teacher
ROCKDALE
Boyer, Laura Jean
English & History Teacher
Gaeke, Lisa Brown
Business & Computer Teacher
Gest, Marie Eiland
Retired Second Grade Teacher
Goeppinger, Patricia Coates
Fifth Grade Teacher
Grindle, Sandra Schmidt
Teacher
ROCKPORT
Jaggard, Yvonne O'Bryant
Associate Choir Director
Luigi, Martha Voges
HS Choral Dir, Fine Arts Chair
McGuire, Janice Hardy
Art Teacher
Miller, Heather Johnson
Cnslr & Drug prevention Coord
Morgan, Ann Kleypas
Title I Teacher
Nicolau, Donna Boyd
Curriculum Facilitator
ROCKWALL
Coburn, Claudia Johnson
Earth Science Teacher
Cordell, Kita Pickrell
English Teacher
Dryden, David Vernon
Secondary Principal, Math Tchr
Eldredge, Carolyn Jacobus
Algebra Teacher
Greenwalt, Joy Bounds
High School English Teacher
Hanson, Wendi Kay (Riveland)
Geometry & Algebra I Teacher
Harris, Gloria Anne
Eighth Grade Teacher
Holland, Jan Ives
Bio & Environmental Sci Tchr
Hughes, Suzanne Rutland
Visual Fine Arts Teacher
Johnston, Douglas Riley
Bio II & Human Anatomy Teacher
Jones, Connie Young
English & Soc Studies Teacher
Kelley, Teresa Wright
Chemistry Teacher
Kelly, Lisa K.
HS Math Teacher & Girls Coach
Kessler, Mark Manning
German Teacher
Kostas, Karen Jean
Geometry & Algebra Teacher
Kretchmar, Patricia Lea
Third Grade Teacher
Lamb, Patsy Hopkins
Retired Teacher of GATE
Lyon, Linda E. Winston
Elementary School Counselor
Merritt, Sarah Granstaff
Business Education Teacher
Muscanere, Marilyn Beth
Mathematics Teacher
Nevill, April Paige
Spanish Teacher
Nix, Beverly Boyce
5th Grade Teacher
Plagens, Leigh Putman
French Teacher
Shannon, Stan
Lang Arts Teacher & Ath Dir
Shoquist, Shirley Smith
Public Speaking & English Tchr
Smothermon, Deborah Kay
Elementary Principal
Stanert, Sue Sanders
Fourth Grade Teacher
Stodghill, Patsy Hall
Literature Specialist
Stout, Tomi Led
First Grade Teacher
Stovall, Russ A.
Success Teacher & Coach
Talley, Randy L., Jr.
Baseball Coach & Energy Mgr
Williams, Jan Koret
English Teacher
Wooldridge, Jeraldine Bass
Sixth Grade Soc Studies Tchr
ROGERS
Dohnalik, Diane
Spanish Teacher
Gantenbein, Marie T.
Language Arts Teacher
Marsh, Robin Elaine
HS Sci Head, Chem & Bio Tchr
Schneider, Kenneth Alan
Agriscience Teacher
ROMA
Alaniz, Cynthia Arratia
Chemistry Teacher
Aleman, Servando
Band Director
Benitez, Norma Hinojosa
Third Grade Teacher
Canales, Lamar
English Teacher
Escobar, Magda Molina
PE Teacher & Coach
Martin, Janice Marie
English Teacher
Springer, Krista Lynn
High School English Teacher
Villarreal, Juvenal, Jr.
Computer Science Teacher
ROSCOE
Edmiston, Ernestine Parrott
Computer Teacher & Librarian
Owens, Karry Dewayne
History Teacher
ROSEBUD
Barkemeyer, Alan Roy
Commercial Business Ed Teacher
Borden, Billy Dave
Jr High Science Teacher
Koslosky, Karen Schneider
Reading Teacher
Sammon, Michael Daniel
Agricultural Science Instr
Stock, Carol Lucko
Cmptr Literacy & Math Teacher
Whitlow, Carla Tate
English Teacher
Wright, Heidi Ann
Science Teacher & Dept Chair
ROSENBERG
Alford, Sheri Y.
Career & Technology Teacher
Benge, Sandra Russell
Fine Arts Chairman & Art Tchr
Biesiada, MaryAnn
Spanish Teacher
Butler, Stephen Paul
HS World Geography Teacher
Buzek, Veta Ann (Williams)
Career & Tech Dept Chairperson
Cox, Dorothy Moore
French Teacher
Durham, Nancy Lyles
Computer Lab Manager
Elizondo, Lupita Ibarra
Licensed Professional Cnslr
Gilbert, Bruce
Math Teacher
Grant, Doris Lingnau
Second Grade Teacher
Head, Janie Shelton
Physics, Bio Tchr & Dept Chair
Hill, Linda Lou
History Instructor
Jones, Melody
English Teacher
Joseph, Scott Anthony
Coach & Teacher
Kelly, James Ian
Science Teacher
Lindsey, Terry Pruetz
Voc Homemaking Teacher
Matthys, James W.
7th Grade TX His Tchr & Coach
Mc Daniel, Richard Fred
Social Studies Teacher
McNair, Iris Minieta
English Teacher
Melasky, Jeanette Beth
8th Grade Algebra Teacher
Myers, Shirley Brodecky
8th Grade English Teacher
Perales, Amalie Beaver
English Teacher
Raley, Sharon Williams
English Teacher
Richard, Beverly Ann (Ryan)
Kindergarten Teacher
Smith, Dietra K.
English Department Chairman
Steffey, Susan Lee
High School Counselor
Sulak, Nita Sliva
Third Grade & ESL Teacher
Vader, Shareen (Allen)
Choral Director
Wiesner, Mary Wallace
Mathematics Teacher
Wingfield, Elizabeth Hassel
English Teacher
ROSHARON
Fike, Doris Bullington
Special Education Teacher
ROTAN
Burnes, Debby Fay
4th Grade Teacher
Fryar, Cynthia Jane
Second Grade Teacher
Nowlin, Aurora Price
Kindergarten & GATE Teacher
Pittman, Verna Mae
Fifth-Sixth Grade Math Teacher
ROUND ROCK
Cotter, Sue
Fr Tchr & Frgn Lang Dept Chm
Crowell, Lyn Denise
Math & Algebra Teacher
DeLavan, Philip Duane
Teacher & Coach
Duncan, Sue Matson
8th Grd Language Arts Teacher
Edgar, Kenneth Lynn
Agriculture Teacher
Frasier, James
French Teacher
Furman, Debora Ley
Biology Teacher
Harthcock, Donna Garrison
6th Grade Language Arts Tchr
Hendrix, Susan Bissett
Fifth Grade Teacher
Hirt, Janet Mumford
Health & PE Teacher
Holmstrom, Lane
5th Grade Teacher
Koym, Zala Cox
2nd Grade Teacher
Kwallek, Vollne Floyd
High School Art Teacher
Mc Cready, Kristan Alvord
Art Teacher
Mica, Peggy Ann
Cmptr Sci Tchr & Tech Coord
Moldenhauer, Andrew Lee
Math Teacher
Readyhough, Cynthia Kogel
Secretary
Sams, Christine Mary
Pre Kindergarten Teacher
Sikes, Gary Haltom
Math Teacher
Tidwell, Tommy Noel
Science Teacher
Watson, Steve G.
Physics Teacher
Wrinkle, Shirley Buenger
7th Grade Mathematics Teacher
ROWLETT
Bolton, Judy Janeece Hyden
Kindergarten Teacher
Burris, Dretha J.
Lead Counselor
Isabell, Rodney Andre
Assistant Principal
Lutz, Terri Eades
Eighth Grade Science Teacher
Malinowsky, Karen
Fifth Grade Teacher
Mulkey, Jeff
Computer Teacher
Rymer, Patricia Gathard
7th Grade Science Teacher
Swafford, LaVenda Bogue
Fourth Grade Teacher
ROXTON
Foster, Jennifer Sherwood
Business & Journalism Teacher

SE CITY
Sheila Veronica
hematics Teacher
ardson, Sandra Graham
istant Principal
GE
n, Janice Ladner
ory & Government Teacher
en, Patricia Ann
t & Second Grade Teacher
ing, Ronnie Lee
iculture Science Teacher
K
erson, Kenneth York
er Grade Elementary Tchr
, Carolyn West
& 2nd Grade Teacher
on, Harold
lish Teacher
ons-Poteet, Sylvia Ann
as History Teacher
, Donna Bothwell
lish Teacher
Pamela Cleveland
sical Education Teacher
y, Bettye Earle
logy Teacher
NAL
, Joe M.
History & Geography Teacher
, George F., Jr.
Math Teacher & Dept Chm
LER
Sue Trigg
ior Honors English Teacher
NAW
erson, Paige Corley
lish Teacher
T JO
opa, Nancy Davis
ater Arts Teacher
r, Donna Gayle
ool Counselor
NORWOOD
er, Judy A.
ational Homemaking Teacher
, Bonita Tate
nselor & Kindergarten Tchr
ANGELO
ns, Anita Armstrong
lish Teacher & Dept Chair
, Sue Craig
ond Grade Teacher
ony, Terri Lyne (Randle)
f of Anatomy & Physiology
y, Cathy Komadina
h Teacher
n, Richard Jaquez
Grade Teacher
ens, Laura Pool
lish Teacher
ers, Nancy Cunningham
cher of Gifted & Talented
well, Todd
le History Teacher
n, Jimmy Dean
sical Education Teacher
n, Pamela Parsons
, Psy Professor & Div Chm
ly, Sandra Lee
iness Computer Teacher
ova, Rene S.
ld History Teacher
ir, Kay Denman
th Grade History Teacher
tsch, Jillian Transki
hematics Teacher
n, Elizabeth Anne (Files)
hematics Teacher
y, Barby Glassett
rd Grade Teacher
ngton, Jay A.
ociate Professor of English
sh, Peggy Green
istant Principal
klin, Katy England
rnalism & TX History Tchr
nan, Deborah Pounds
-Kindergarten & Kndgtn Tchr
nan, Mitchell Glen
ory Teacher & HS Coach
y, Dan
letic Director
, Cecilia Sotelo
rd Grade & ESL Teacher
ne, Laura Townes
ssroom Teacher
in, Carolyn Kidd
nebound Teacher
ley, Frederick Neal
rumental Music Dir
ley, Lori Lenore
hestra Teacher
andez, Jehu
oral Music Teacher
smith, Jamie Jenes
ad Counselor
s, Baynes Mac Lea
Cmptr Applications Teacher
omb, Phillip A.
fessor of English
ard, Sharron S.
glish Teacher
, Anna Fishel
rd Grade Teacher
el, Dorothy Kent
hestra Teacher
Cynthia Young
& 8th Grade Science Tchr

Lopez, Raul F.
Aerospace Science Instructor
Lowe, Kathryn M.
Mathematics Teacher
Martinez, Aurora Trevino
Bilingual & ESL Teacher
Martinez, Linda Perez
Sixth Grade Teacher
McCullough, Deborah Phillips
Chemistry Teacher
Muzquiz, Margie Torres
Math Teacher
Phillips, Cynthia Ann
Teacher
Phillips, Theresa Schlaudt
History Teacher
Ramirez, Zeke
Jr High Counselor
Ransbarger, Judy Stanford
HS Mathematics Teacher
Roe, Grady C.
Mathematics Teacher
Sanford, Shelly Speck
Algebra Teacher
Savoie, Terry Allen
Aero Space Science Instructor
Sefcik, Sherry Stinnett
Third Grade Teacher
Sheldon, Darylene
Chemistry Teacher & Dept Chair
Shelton, Joyce Belmont
Social Studies Teacher
Smith, Brenda Tilton
HS Math & Science Teacher
Smith, P. Kent, Jr.
Coach & Physical Science Tchr
Smith, Willie Beth
Speech Language Pathologist
Snodgrass, Sybil Durham
Former Kindergarten Teacher
Srader, Jane Ann Burt
Latin Teacher
Stewart, Homer Charles
Band Director
Terrill, Vicki Schkade
Government & Economics Teacher
Tinney, Ed R.
English Teacher
Trimier-Jones, Ruth Johnson
Earth & Life Science Teacher
Varela, George Luis
US & World History Teacher
Vaughan, Nancy Tartt
Art Teacher
Waters, William W.
Math Teacher
West, Carol Lane
Bilogy Teacher
Wheaton, Wendell Travis
Fourth Grade Teacher
SAN ANTONIO
Abbott, Beverly Najera
Mathematics & Science Teacher
Abrego-Sanchez, Minerva
8th Grade English Teacher
Adams, Harold S., Jr.
Economics Teacher
Adkisson, Donald Carl
Secondary Principal
Alanis, Dana Carole
Reading Specialist
Alexander, Lloyd Stuart
Teacher & Coach
Allbright, Karen Lee
Algebra & Geometry Teacher
Almeida, Michael James
Philosophy Professor
Alvares, Frederick Lucian
Associate Prof of Biochemistry
Amezquita, N. Telly
Fifth Grade Teacher
Anderson, Misty Anne
Choir Director
Anderson, Vicki Dawn
8th Grd American History Tchr
Arizola, Wanda Klemcke
Second Grade Teacher
Armstrong, Rita Crudup
High School English Teacher
Armstrong, Sarah Christian
World History Teacher
Arnold, James Vernon
Physical Education Teacher
Badillo, Diana C.
Fifth Grade Teacher
Baer, Howard L.
Coach & Special Education Tchr
Bailey, Wanda Smith
At Risk Students Teacher
Baker, Barbara Trost
3rd Grade Teacher
Baker, Carolyn Williams
English Professor
Baldwin, Roy A.
Science Teacher
Balentine, James Scott
Music Professor
Bales, Judy
Third Grade Teacher
Barham, Patricia Blanks
Middle School Coord & Teacher
Barker, Wendy Bean
Professor of English
Barnett Gibson, Kimberly Denise
Asst Prof of Comm Stud
Barton-Rivera, Martha Jane
Biling Math & Sci Teacher
Baucum, Beverly Gutelius
World History Teacher

Beechinor, Diane B.
Chairperson of Sciences & PE
Beedle, Bill T.
Industrial Arts Teacher
Bell, Linda Ann
Retired French Teacher
Benson, Carlee Gladwin
Dir of Field Based Ed Prgms
Bernal, Mary Anne B.
Assistant Professor of English
Berry, Rubina Rodriguez
Counselor
Bewley, Sandra Sue
Fifth Grade Teacher
Bibb, Michele Kay
1st Grade Teacher
Bittner, Debora Frances
World Geography Teacher
Bitzkie, Gary Lee
English Teacher & Coach
Blankenhorn, Daniel Roy
Eighth Grade Science Teacher
Boles, Bennie Carroll
Army Instructor
Bomba, Darohl Mark
Physical Education Teacher
Bondurant, William Thomas, Jr.
Executive Director
Borchers, Lawrence Clark
Social Science Teacher
Bowe, Mary Blanchard
Bilingual Kindergarten Teacher
Bradley, Lee Vaughan
First Grade Teacher
Brinson, Clara Hudson
Mathematics Instructor
Brischetto, Barbara Palmieri
Math Teacher
Brooks, Catherine Alling
Fourth Grade Teacher
Brooks, Richard Paul, Jr.
Art Teacher
Brown, Carol Bentley
Chemistry Teacher
Brown, James Willis
Electrnc & Bio-Med Tech Instr
Brown, John, Jr.
8th Grd American History Tchr
Bryan, Edward Ransome, III
Senior Army Instructor
Bubul, Marchie Knittle
Reading Teacher
Bucher, David Michael
Fourth Grade Teacher
Buell, William Collins
Dean of Academics & Vice-Prin
Bukala, Susan Katerine
Principal
Bunce, Nancy Ann
Fifth Grade Teacher
Bunnell, Phyllis Ann
Assistant Professor of English
Burton, Gilliam Maxwell
Assoc Prof of English
Buske, Gail Jackson
Sixth Grade Reading Teacher
Bussineau-King, Deborah
Music Dept Chm & Assoc Prof
Buttles, Sunny
Professor of Biology
Byrd, Don Wayne
Math Teacher & Coach
Calder, James Douglas
Assoc Prof Criminal Justice
Calentine, Jack Edward
Asst Prof of Analytical Chem
Calvert, Maria Stumpf
US History Teacher
Candia, Ruben Araiza
Prof & Chair of Languages
Cano, Beatriz
English Teacher
Cantu, Bernice De Leon
Instructional Guide
Caponi, Gena Dagel
American Studies Asst Prof
Carr, Phyllis Lynn
Instructional Guide
Carruba, Richard Wayne
Science Dept Chm & Teacher
Carty, Margaret Lore
Counselor
Castano, Teresa
Pre College Advisor
Chamberlain, Carol Miller
5th Grade Teacher
Chamberlain, Emma R.
Fourth Grade Teacher
Chambers, Mark John
Band Director
Charles, Rita Ramirez
Spanish Teacher
Chicoine, Donald Mark
Geometry & Algebra Teacher
Chouinard, Helen Veazey
Govt, Ec Teacher & Dept Chair
Christianson, Joseph Marion
Philosophy Professor
Cisneros, Lorenzo
Physical Education Teacher
Clark, Ellen Riojas
Asst Prof of Bicultural Stud
Clark, James Richard
Health Teaching Associate II
Clayton, Sharon L.
Math Dept Chairperson
Coates, Sue Schoeneck
Mathematics Teacher
Collenback, Loyce Lee
Retired Math Tchr & Dept Chm

Collins, James Alexander, II
9th-12th Grade Science Teacher
Connor, Carolyn Ann Kerr
Social Studies Teacher
Connor, Paul Robert
Head Band Director
Cook, Gillian E.
Assoc Professor of Education
Cooper, Fredric M.
Lecturer of Finance
Corbo, Linda Stevenson
12th Grade English Teacher
Coy, Alfredo Ricardo
6th Grd Social Studies Teacher
Craighead, Randal Keith
English Teacher
Crowl, Norma Santullo
Fifth Grade Teacher
Cuellar, Emeterio Rick
Science Teacher
Culpepper, Joy Oehler
HS Mathematics Teacher
Cummings, Charles Howard
Bible Teacher
Cunningham, Graciela Virjan
Fifth Grade Teacher
Daise, Betty Stover
Computer Math Teacher
Danelo, Kathleen Thompson
College & Career Counselor
Daniels, Wayne Eugene
Computer Manufacturing Teacher
Davila, Jose Carrizales
Spanish Teacher
Davis, Gina Gail
English IV Teacher
Davis, Quinton Dale
Teaching Associate
Dawson, Brad Roderick
Math Teacher
Dean-Olsen, Meredith Hilmes
Lecturer
Dear, Kellye S.
Geography Teacher
Degutis, Renee Christine Barowski
English Teacher
DeHoyos, Jose J., Jr.
Theatre Arts Teacher
De La Garza, David Fernando
Fourth Grade Teacher
DeLeon, Marcella A.
English Teacher
Delgado, Martha Laura
8th Grade Homeroom Teacher
Diaz, Gwendolyn
Assoc Professor of Literature
Dierolf, Wallace Charles
High School Band Director
DiGuardi, Mary Goodwin
Social Studies Teacher
Dimler, Lisa Destefano
Orchestra Director
Doby, Gary Paul
Associate Band Director
Doby, Terri Carr
World Geography Teacher
Doom, Sharon D.
4th Grd Teacher of GATE
Douglass, Laura McCaffrey
7th & 8th Grd Lang Arts Tchr
Duda, Cynthia A.
8th Grade Teacher
Duda, Timothy Edward
Soc Studies & Government Tchr
Dukes, Thomas H.
Eighth Grade Science Teacher
Dunlap, Marge Dirksen
Industrial Technology Teacher
Duren, LaFaye Carpenter
Third Grade Teacher
Ebben, Maureen Majella
Asst Prof of Speech Comm
Edmiston, Ninette Alsop
US History & Economics Teacher
Edson, Jeanine Clare
Latin Teacher
Eichenholz, Sally Burke
Social Studies Teacher
Eisenhauer, Pat Castoria
Elem Schl Co-Ordinator
Elmer, Trudie Ann
Mathematics & English Teacher
Embry, Mary Lee Blackmore
Second Grade Teacher
Enriquez, Tanya M.
Biology Teacher & Coach
Erickson, Margaret Barnett
Social Studies Dept Head
Escobedo, Sonia Yvonne
Texas History Teacher
Espinoza, Myrtha I.
5th Grade Teacher
Esquivel, Alfred
Band Director
Evans, Alfred W.
Social Studies Tchr & Dpt Head
Evans, Lee Paul
Bible & Phys Education Teacher
Everhart, Robert J.
Clinical Professor
Fain, Catherine Lieck
PAL Eng I Teacher
Fairchild, Keith Wm
Associate Professor of Finance
Feola, Pat Deering
English Teacher
Fernandez, Lily
English Teacher
Fernandez, Patricia Janet, FMA
Former Kndgtn & 8th Grd Tchr

Fey, Mary Ann
Math Teacher
Fiedler, Alice Green
Chemistry Teacher
Fielding, Kathy Hofner
Computer Literacy Teacher
Fierros, Lucille Duarte
Special Education Teacher
Firestone, Juanita M.
Assoc Professor of Sociology
Fisher, Deborah Nell
Interactive Math Program Tchr
Flaig, Catherine Marie
Fourth Grade Teacher
Flannagan, Dorothy Anne
Psychology Professor
Fleming, George Beckwith
Social & Religious Stud Chair
Flora, Dorothy Polson
HS English & Math Teacher
Flora, Richard Arlen
Athletic Dir & Bible Teacher
Flores, Belinda Bustos
Title VII Coordinator
Focht, Donna Williams
Teacher of Gifted & Talented
Foerster, Paul A.
Math Tchr & Textbook Author
Ford, Tommy Ellis
High School English Teacher
Forrester, Norma W.
8th Grade Language Arts Tchr
French, Lucy S.
Kindergarten Teacher
Frost, Carolyn Cunningham
Spanish Teacher
Fryburger, Ann Plankey
First Grade Teacher
Frye, Larry
Third Grade Teacher
Fullen, Kennon Neal
English Teacher
Galindo, Karla Holmes
Social Studies Dept Chairman
Galvan, Joanne Eloise
Social Studies Teacher
Gambino, Ruth Ann Johnson
English Instructor
Gambitta, Richard Anthony
Pol Sci & Pub Admin Assoc Prof
Garcia, Daniel Alfredo, Jr.
English Teacher
Garcia, Josefina Lujan
Fifth Grade Teacher
Garcia, Maricela
Spanish Teacher
Garcia-Wukovits, Flor de Maria
Math & Computer Sci Teacher
Gardner, Judith Gorman
English Instructor
Gary, Susan Krackhardt
Math Teacher & Dept Chprsn
Gately, Jeanne
Special Education Supervisor
Geer, Linda Arnn
Math Teacher & NHS Sponsor
Geimer, Eugene Edward
Band Director
Gelo, Daniel J.
Anthropology Professor
George, Amiso Margaret
Asst Prof of Communication
George, Carol Marie
Mathematics Teacher
Gherman, Lynn Pack
Teacher & Cheerleader Dir
Ghinaudo, Penny Alicia
Dir of Studies & Science Tchr
Gilbert, Michael John
Asst Prof of Criminal Justice
Gilliland, Irene Chodan
Nursing Instructor
Gingrass, June Nissalke
Third Grade Teacher
Giordanelli, Vincent Douglas
Mathematics Teacher
Gittinger, Dennis Joseph
Professor of Mathematics
Glaspy, Phillip Eugene
Assistant Prof of Chemistry
Goff, Lawrence William
Band Director
Goldsberry, Sally Mc Murry
Third Grade Teacher
Gomez, Maria Teresa
Counselor & Coordinator
Gomez Kelley, Sally T.
Dir Theological Field Ed Prgm
Gonzales, Joe Luis, Sr.
Engineering CAD Teacher
Gonzales, Juan Jose
Teacher & Administrator
Goodman, Dorothy Dobler
English Teacher & Librarian
Gordon, Gary Howard
Professor of History
Gorton, Everett D.
Retired Teacher
Gottstine, Shannon Rae (Mc Pherson)
Former Bio & Gen Sci Teacher
Graham, Eleanore Davis
Teacher of Gifted & Talented
Graham, Gina Goldsberry
2nd Grade Teacher
Graham, Marie Henry
Retired Math Teacher
Grant, Johnnie Mae (Hamilton)
Fourth Grade Teacher
Gray, Patricia Sue Armstrong
Trainer Emeritus, Educl Consul

SAN ANTONIO (cont)
Green, Christopher John
Architectural Drafting Teacher
Greenwood, Betty Mc Clure
Retired 2nd Grade Teacher
Greer, Carolyn Cloud
First Grade Teacher
Gregorash, Lawrence Anthony
Eighth Grade History Teacher
Grimley, Karen R.
English Teacher
Grinkemeyer, Susan Kirk
Chemistry Teacher
Groesch, Julie E.
English Teacher
Grokhovski, Valeri A.
Assistant Professor
Groos, April Cox
English Teacher
Groves, Michael Lynn
Biology I Teacher
Guerra, Milton E.
Mathematics Teacher
Guerra, Velma E.
K-5 Grd Extended Learning Tchr
Guerrero, Virginia A.
English Teacher & Dept Chprsn
Guthrie, Julia Frances (Ragsdale)
Office Education Instructor
Gutierrez, Guadalupe Salvador
5th Grade Bilingual Teacher
Guzman, Agustin L.
Asst Prin for Stu Activities
Hager, Joseph Robert
JROTC Instructor
Haggard, Victoria Marie
Lang Arts Dept Chr & Eng Tchr
Hairgrove, Kenneth D.
History Professor
Hall, Beverly Ann
Senior English Teacher
Halwe, Fred, SM
Asst Principal & Eng Tchr
Hamblin, Katie Elaine
English & Latin Teacher
Hancock, Sandra Kay
High School Counselor
Hankins, Roger Charles
Soc Stud Tchr & Dept Chair
Harkreader, Robert Allen
English Teacher
Harris, Carolyn Besser
Accounting Teacher
Harris, Delphia Francine
Associate Prof of Chemistry
Harris, Patricia Mary
Assoc Prof of Criminal Justice
Harris, Sarah Sears
Band Director & French Teacher
Harrison, Beatrice Johnson
Third Grade Teacher
Harrison, Jennifer Jordan
Mrktg Tchr & Red Jacket Dir
Hartman, Margaret A.
Fourth Grade Teacher
Harvey, Sherrie Franklin
Science II Teacher
Haskins, Janet E.
4th Grade Teacher
Haufler, August Otto
Band Director
Hawkinson, David Alan
Mathematics Teacher
Hawkinson, Susan Carol
Honors Government Teacher
Hayes, Peggy Walker
Second Grade Teacher
Haynes, Titus
Assoc Professor of Social Work
Hendrick, Leighton S.
Coach & Physical Ed Teacher
Hengst, Donna Nicol
MS Theater & Speech Teacher
Hermosa, Thelma Garcia
Fourth Grade Teacher
Hernandez, Mary J.
Instrl Specialist & Teacher
Hernandez, Miriam
Spanish Teacher
Herrera, Fernando
Eighth Grade Math Teacher
Herring, John Miller
Earth Science Teacher
Heye, Mary Louise
Assistant Professor
Hickman, Robert Kaser
Physics Teacher & Tech Coord
Hildebrand, Byron Wade
Math Teacher & Soccer Coach
Hill, Kay Lynn
Phys Ed Tchr & Dept Coord
Hines, Donna Taylor
Office Systems Tech Assoc Prof
Hinojosa, Yvonne (Hernandez)
Math Teacher
Hoag, Rebecca Ebner
English Teacher
Hoberg, Jorgen Ernest, Jr.
Soc Stud & Cmptr Literacy Tchr
Hodge, Hattie Bryant
Retired Elementary Teacher
Hoke, Philip Wilder
Communication & Theatre Instr
Hooper, Judy Barefield
Ind Study Mentorship Teacher
Hoover, Karen Stelly
Fourth Grade Teacher
Hopkins, Jean Burrell
Life Science Tchr & Dept Chair
Hudspeth, Armeania
English & Speech Teacher
Huerta, Yolanda Moya
Spanish Teacher
Irwin, Meg L.
Social Studies Teacher
Jackson, Darcy Ann (Haxton)
Phys Education Teacher & Coach
Jacobson, Grant Hunter
Soc Science Teacher & Coach
Jeanes, Cecil B.
Chemistry Teacher
Jeffery, Clinton Lewis
Assistant Prof of Comp Sci
Jennings, Cynthia Ann
English Teacher
Jensen, Tracie Leanne
Physical Education Teacher
Jerrell, Jesse Earl
Teacher of Gifted & Talented
Jimenez, M. Carolina Hernandez
8th Grade Math Teacher
Johnson-Hodge, Noel Lynn
English Teacher
Jones, Brenda Yarbrough
English Teacher
Jones, James Ogden
Geology Professor
Jones, Richard Crouch
Professor of Geography
Jones, Robert Cooper
Math Teacher
Jose, Ginger Hillert
Vice Principal
Jowers, Sherrie Lee
English Teacher
Judson, Phoebe Thompson
Assoc Professor of Mathematics
Kaiser, Louise Stach
Second Grade Teacher
Kaiser, Tracy Lynn
Math Teacher
Kanning, Jimmie McGraw
AP English Tchr & Dept Coord
Kappmeyer, Patricia Whitworth
Journalism Teacher
Karimi, Amir
Assoc Prof Mechanical Engrng
Karpienski, Kirk K.
Business Education Teacher
Kay, Aman Bekheirnia
English Teacher
Keaveney, Ailbe M.
US History Teacher
Kellogg, Miriam G.
World, Amer History & Ec Tchr
Kemble, Marcia Kay
Science Department Chairman
Kimura, Raymond Yoshito
Foreign Language Dept Chprsn
Kirkland, Sandra M.
Teacher of Gifted & Talented
Kleiman, John Reeve
English Dept Head & Teacher
Knight, Cecile Collins
Instructional Guide
Koch, Marilyn Buck
Chemistry Teacher
Koehler, Linda Gregory
Fifth Grade Teacher
Kramer, Roger Hart
High School Science Teacher
Krause, Mary Ellen Egan
Texas History Teacher
Kunkel, Mary Kathryn
Language Arts Teacher
Kurek, Darrell Jay
US History Teacher
Lansford Coulter, Jayne
English Teacher
Larocca, Joseph Peter
Senior Naval Science Instr
LaRocca, Michael John
Instructor of Economics
Laxson, Barbara Greer
8th Grade English Honors Tchr
Leal, Ray
Public Justic Professor
Leies, John Alex
Professor of Theology
Leissner, Renee Griffin
Life Science Teacher
Libbers, Edward W.
11th Grade Chemistry Teacher
Lingo, Lesley L.
First & Second Grade Teacher
Littlefield, Arlene Wright
Middle School Teacher
Lloyd, Shelia Brown
Math Teacher
Loew, Marcia
Counselor
Lolatte, John Louis
Fifth Grade Teacher
Lopez, Debbie L.
Assistant Professor of English
Lora, Maria Luisa
Business Teacher
Lott, Lisa Hahn
PE Teacher & Coach
Lowak, Christine Mc Cormick
Government Teacher
Lucchelli, Mary Beth
Theatre Arts & Fine Arts Tchr
Ludwikowski, William John
Social Studies Teacher
Lundy, Eileen T.
English Professor
MacDougal, Jill O'Brien
English Teacher
Machu, Teresa Ann
Teacher
Macias, Armando Ramirez
Math & Science Teacher
Mac Kinnon, Christy Anne
Associate Professor of Biology
Mahoney, Sherry Graves
Fifth Grade Teacher
Maley, John Francis
Prof of Exercise & Sports Sci
Maloof, Edmund K.
Teaching Associate
Mammarella, Jim
Prof of Theatre & Commnctn
Manchester, Lucien Caleb
Assoc Professor of Biology
Mann, Randall C.
Special Education Teacher
Marechal, Linda Stanick
Seventh Grade Science Teacher
Marin, Michele P.
Fr Tchr & Intnl Lang Dept Chm
Marques, Steven Joseph
Religion Teacher
Marron-Lindsay, Mikki R.
Psychology & Geography Teacher
Marsh, Joe Donald
Driver Education Instructor
Marso, Lori
Asst Prof of Political Science
Martin, Irvin Earl
Science Teacher
Martinez, Rudy James
Amer Govt Honors & His Teacher
Martinez-Lopez, Gloria
Second Grade Teacher
Marty, Mark Stephen
Music Director
Marx, Lee Ellen
Kindergarten Teacher
Mauricio, Marguerite Munoz
Child Dev Teacher
Maynard, Hugh Bardeen
Associate Prof of Cmptr Sci
Mc Anally, Devin Dean
High School English Teacher
McCarthy, Beverly Ward
Mathematics Teacher
Mc Carty, Marla F.
Health Teacher & Coach
Mc Clellan, Marjorie York
Eng & Rel Tchr & MS Coord
Mc Clure, Carolyn James
Administrative Assistant
Mc Cormick, Marguerite B.
Choir Director
Mc Coy, Helen Marie
First Grade Teacher
Mc Curdy, M. W., Jr.
History & Latin Teacher
Mc Daniel, Matthew Patrick
Anatomy & Physiology Teacher
Mc Donald, Lori Denise
1st & 2nd Grade Teacher
Mc Donald, Ruby Hobbs
Third Grade Teacher
Mc Gee, Heather Clark
English Teacher
McLeod, Mark S.
Philosophy Professor
Mc Queen, Blanche Demartra
Elementary Teacher
McQuien, Tillman Paul
Prof of English
Medlock, Desiree
Third Grade Teacher
Mendoza, Josie Gamez
Spanish Teacher
Meuth, Stephen Anthony
Seventh Grd Texas History Tchr
Meyer, Ann Jones
French Teacher
Meyer, Virginia Namias
University Instructor
Meza, Ray
Director of Bands
Mikesell, James Gregory
Sr Army Instr & ROTC Chair
Miller, Bosco D.
Junior Religion Teacher
Miller, Daniel L.
English Teacher
Miller, Rebecca Anne
English Teacher
Mireles, Adelina
Spanish Teacher
Mitchell, Margaret Ann
Asst Professor of Theatre Arts
Molloy, Marilyn
Professor of Mathematics
Monk, Cheryl Williams
5th Grade Teacher
Montejano, Nelda
Fourth Grade Teacher
Montgomery, Mary Dove
Math Teacher
Mooneyham, Mitchell Eugene
English Teacher
Moreno, Rosemary G.
Fifth Grade Bilingual Teacher
Morgenroth, Gerry Rohan
Business Teacher & Dept Chair
Morin, Gregorio P.
Mathematics Teacher
Morris, Mary Ella King
Pre-School Teacher
Morton, Jeanne Butler
Math Teacher
Mueller, Cynthia (Williams)
Orchestra Director
Mumbower, Kelly A.
Asst Professor of Mathematics
Munoz, Ciprano
Physics Teacher
Murphy, Bettye Jean (Dismuke)
Sixth Grade Math Teacher
Murphy, Julia Ann
Instructor
Musselman, Judy Lynn
High School Math Teacher
Myers, Ellen Howell
Professor of History
Myler, Ross H.
Ath Dir, Science & His Teacher
Narvaez, Rose Contreras
Teacher & Instrl Specialist
Negrete, George Raymond
Chemistry Professor
Neuman, Douglas Charles
Math Teacher & Coach
Neville, Linda Pilon
First Grade Teacher
Ng, Wing Chung
History Professor
Nickson, Dalena
Science Teacher
Nordstrom, David P.
Science Tchr & Swimming Coach
Norris, Peggy Ann
Teacher
Nowlin, Sue Minton
English Teacher
O'Connor, Robert Benson
Professor of Theology
O'Connor, William John
Mathematics Teacher
Olivares, Nora Mahon
Assistant Professor of English
Orange, Carolyn Montgomery
Asst Prof of Educational Psych
Ortega, Jose Hilario
Spanish Lecturer
Osborn, Jerry Wayne
History Instructor
Ottmers, Sandra Baumgart
High School Health Teacher
Overby, Lisa G.
Geography, Texas & US His Tchr
Ozuna, George Flores
Communications Tchr
Paddock, Susan Blair
Math & Computer Sci Instructor
Page, Nancy Cavoli
Art Teacher
Palacios, Therese Hamilton
Office Systems Tech Asst Prof
Palmer, Pamela Peters
Mathematics Teacher
Parker, Phyllis Alexander
US History Teacher
Parr, Eugenia Suzanne
Mathematics Teacher
Pasterchick, George A.
Athletic Director & Coach
Pasterchick, Julie Laud
English Teacher
Patterson, JUdith Galindo
7th Grade English Teacher
Patterson, Maxine (Barlow)
High School Business Teacher
Pearish, Alice Schirmer
1st Grade Reading Teacher
Peoples, Kaye Jones
Fifth Grade Teacher
Pepin, Madeleine
Philosophy Professor
Perez, Eyra Alicia
Special Programs Coordinator
Perrenot, Valerie Troilo
Sixth Grade Science Teacher
Petersen, Karen S. (Fuller)
Vice Principal
Poetschke, Linda Catt
Associate Professor of Music
Polak, Doris Winn
English Teacher
Pool, Mary Chambless
Pre-Kindergarten Teacher
Powell, Betty Slater
1st Grade Teacher
Preston, Paul
Associate Professor
Prieto, Bertha Zuniga
Teacher & Instrl Specialist
Priewe, Mark Ewart
Tchng Assoc of Pol Sci
Prince, John Edward
5th-6th Grd Science Teacher
Purnell, Eula Justice
7th Grade Science Teacher
Quillo, Julie A. (Farnsley)
Religious Studies Teacher
Rainwater, Celia Green
Secondary Science Teacher
Rambo, Carole Jean
5th Grade Teacher
Ramon, Elizabeth Debra
Fourth Grade Bilingual Teacher
Ramos, Jodi Hafermann
Music Teacher
Randell, Richard
English & Psychology Teacher
Rechtien, John G.
Professor of English
Redmon, Demetra Derdeyn
English Teacher
Rehfeld, Vaughn R.
Teacher & Coach
Reifschneider, Thomas J.
Mathematics Teacher
Reposa, Carol Coffee
Associate Professor of English
Resendez, Isabel Elizalde
Retired Elementary Teacher
Reyna, Stella Leal
English Teacher
Rhodes, Milton Lane, Jr.
Professor of Sociology
Ribble, Ronald G.
Lecturer in Psychology
Rich, Shirley Jean
Mathematics Teacher
Richard, Dinah Lynn Daniel
Teacher
Richno, Renee' Marie
Biology Teacher
Rickabaugh, Charlotte Marie
Science Teacher
Ricketts, C. H.
Art Dept Chair
Rico, Edie Burk
Police Officer
Riley, James Bryan
Assoc Professor
Rinaldini, Dante Joseph
Spanish Teacher
Rinehart, Ann Strong
First Grade Teacher
Robb, Ruby Kuhlmann
Computer Lab Teacher
Robeau, Barbara Snyder
English Teacher
Roberts, Cynthia Clarke
Middle School Science Teacher
Robinette, Ross Alan
Eighth Grade Earth Sci Teacher
Robinson, Sylvia Martinez
Mariachi & Choir Director
Rodgers, Elizabeth CAstleberry
French Teacher
Rodriguez, Carol Schuetz
Jrnlsm Tchr & Pub Advisor
Rodriguez, Leonor A.
English Teacher
Rodriguez, Sharon Lynn (Moon)
6th Grade Reading Teacher
Rojas, Dahlia Zuniga
Associate Professor
Roland, Karen Kay
Athletics & PE Coordinator
Roolf, Marjorie Hall
Fifth Grade Teacher
Rosenauer, Johnnie L.
Professor of Real Estate
Ross, Jan Calabro
Gifted & Talented Eng Teacher
Rothen, Robert R.
English Teacher
Royal, Elizabeth Beckham
High School Counselor
Rudi, Bruce David
Administrator
Russell, Janice Neuse
English Teacher
Russell, Steve
Asst Prof of Criminal Justice
Rutland, Rick
Science Teacher & Chair
Ryan, Mary Schram
Mathematics Teacher
Saenz, Lucia C.
Biling Kndgtn Tchr & Adm Asst
Salas, Emma Trono
High School Spanish Teacher
Sanchez, Candelario, Jr.
High School Counselor
Sandoval, Cordelia
High School Counselor
Sandoval, Xavier
JROTC Army Instructor
Santos, Albert DeLeon
Third Grade Teacher
Savage, Helen Gilland
Teaching Associate
Schmidt, Larry Lee
Band Director
Schott, Linda Kay
Assoc Prof of His & Amer Stud
Schraub, Michelle Belto
Fine Arts Teacher
Schubert, Anne Orrison
Lecturer II
Schulz, Ulrike Mack
German Teacher
Schulze, Dorothy Ozan
Social Studies Teacher
Scott, Carolyn Waldrop
Honors English Teacher
Scrivano-Kelmstein, Phyllis
Special Ed Science & Math Tchr
Segvin, Ilena
Retired Spanish Teacher
Seidenberger, Sidney Carl
English Teacher
Senseman, David Michael
Associate Professor
Severyns, Kathleen Meeker
8th Grade US History Teacher
Shaffer, David Emanuel
Social Studies Teacher
Sheldon, Karen Stolle
Reading Specialist & Dept Head
Shires, Susan Schulte
Asst Principal & History Tchr
Shumaker, Warren Burdette
History, Geog & Psych Teacher
Silva, Aurelia Davila de
Education Researcher
Simmang, Cynthia Janet
Math Teacher

ANTONIO (cont)
on, George Ann
Prof of Kinesiology
Charles Estes
dergarten Teacher
ston, Martha McMullan
nalism Teacher
l, Ted Dawson
ociate Prof of Accounting
, Sharon Murphy
h Teacher & Specialist
, Teresa Ruiz
I Supervisor
, Veda Eiland
lish Composition Instructor
, Willa Dunlap
h Teacher
Daniel, Jr.
d Director
s, Christine Michelle Rodriguez
ding Specialist
Melanie Covganka
hestra Director
s, Teanna Melinda
robiology Professor
ridge, Katheryn Anne
Principal
ey, John Mark
hematics Teacher
ey, Janet Vaska
hematics Teacher
t, Denise Spencer
cation Professor
t, Susan Matjeka
cher
lein, Mina Smith
ech, Debate & English Tchr
art, Karen Sittre
ding Specialist
ners, Jeannie
lish Teacher
son, John C.
h School Mathematics Tchr
, Robert T.
Teacher
tt, Susan Joy
lish Teacher
r, Debra Dibble
ond Grade Teacher
r-Mitchell, Laurie
Professor of Art
, Mickey (Quinn)
lish Teacher
as, Carita Chapman
ironmental Science Instr
as, Maria J. Jesus
nish Teacher
pson, Jon Hunter
ociate Professor
son, Thomas A.
ance Assistant Professor
, Tracy Davenport
Science Teacher
man, Tammy Jo Olson
nalism & English Teacher
l, Paul
hematics Teacher
, Elsie Emma
h School Biology Teacher
e, Phyllis M.
hematics & Computer Teacher
no, Marie A.
ond Grade Teacher
io, Robert Joseph
lish Teacher
Andrew T. C.
fessor of Biology
er, Roy Nelson
hematics Professor
, Cindy L.
atomy & Physiology Teacher
ert, Terry N.
istant Principal
ades, Katherine Dakie
l Instructor of Chemistry
ez, Molly Burke
glish Teacher
a, Frank Phillip, Jr.
Dir,Coach & Math Dept Chrm
ey, Kenneth J.
ondary Math Teacher
Arturo
st Prof of Political Science
-Rosenthal, Edilia
nth Grade Reading Teacher
na, Janet Ballew
h Grade Teacher
escusa, F. Warren
emistry Professor
lobos, Rosa Teresa
ired Spanish Teacher
rreal, Criselda Urive
Grd Rdng & Lang Arts Tchr
gas, Clifton A.
ondary Graphic Arts Teacher
nak, Edward Paul
thematics Teacher
, Adah Gaylon
glish Teacher
oner, Patricia Ann
me Economics Teacher
lrop, Kathy Hyatt
vt Teacher
er, Donald Michael
uatics Director
ter, Lester Eugene
ence Teacher
ace, Mary Jeanette (Baity)
st Grade Teacher

Waller, Geraldine L.
6th Grade Science Teacher
Wallis, Patty
Middle School Teacher
Wantzloeben, Kenneth L.
Math Teacher
Wartell, Sandra G.
English Teacher
Watkins, John Philip
HS Science Teacher
Watson, Sylvia Ann
Science Department Chairperson
Way, David M.
Latin Teacher
Wayne, Robert N.
Mathematics Teacher
Weeaks, Thomas Ray
Head Womens Basketball Coach
Weed, Roger Martin
Assoc Professor of Dentistry
Welch, John R.
Seventh Grade English Teacher
Welch, Marilyn Jean (Walker)
Kindergarten Teacher
Wetherell, Melanie Green
English Dept Chair & Teacher
Whitaker, Daniel Roy
US History & Teen Law Teacher
White, Deanna McCrary
English Professor
White, Patricia Jean Benagh
Home Ec Tchr & Stu Cncl Spon
Whited, Donnie Windham
Special Education Teacher
Wiatrek, Lorene
4K Teacher
Wiatrek, Tara Alison
First Grade Teacher
Wilkerson, Jim
4th Grade Teacher
Wilkinson, Laura Anne Walker
5th Grade Teacher
Wilkinson, Sandra Rubrecht
Third Grade Teacher
Williams, Deborah Allen
Rdng, Gifted & Talented Tchr
Williams, Edmond Carroll
Geography Teacher
Williams, W. Wayne
Physical Education Dept Coord
Willstrop, Beth Ann
Rdng Specialist & English Tchr
Winter, Suzanne M.
Assistant Prof, Div of Educ
Woodfill, Rita J.
Computer Technololgy Coord
Worrell, Linda Shaddox
Teacher of Gifted & Talented
Wray, Robert Sanford
Math Teacher
Wright, Carla Potter
Supervisor of Strings
Wright, Judy L.
Mathematics Teacher
Wroten, Terri Jeffrey
Spanish Teacher
Young, Charles Wahlfred, Jr.
Band Director
Yzaguirre, Homer
Band Director
Zajicek, Faith Springer
Art Teacher
Zaleski, Mary Hardie
Office Admin Systems Coord
Zamora, Jimmy
Principal
Zamora, Vick G.
French & Spanish Teacher
Zeeman, Mary Lou L.
Mathematics Professor
Zepeda, Rachel A.
Science Teacher
Zoller, Lawrence Anthony
Band Director
Zolzer, David G.
Associate Professor of CIS
SAN AUGUSTINE
Caston, Cindi Woods
Kindergarten Teacher
Evett, Gene D.
Biology Teacher
Michalec, Randy Joe
Agriculture Science Teacher
SAN BENITO
Carmona, Sylvia Tamez
6th Grade Reading Teacher
Cortez, Rene Perez
High School Band Director
Guzman, Arminda Mata
Fifth Grade Bilingual Teacher
Moreno, Debbie Crisler
Math Teacher
Robinson, Sylvia Michelle
HS Language Arts Teacher
SAN DIEGO
Alaniz, Caridad Leonor
Business Teacher
De Los Santos, Humberto
Social Studies Teacher
Perez, Sylvia Bazan
Second Grade Teacher
Saenz, Rebecca Ann
English Teacher
Upchurch, Renee Joyaline
Math Teacher & Dept Head
Valdez, Ana Maria Briones
English II Teacher
SAN ISIDRO
Munoz, David Daniel
High School Science Teacher

Saenz, Teresa Gonzalez
Eng, Amer His Tchr & Librn
SAN JUAN
Acosta, Francisco Xavier
Algebra & TAAS Math Tchr
Delgado, Homero Narciso
2nd Grade Oral Language Tchr
Dimas, Delia Navarro
Kindergarten Teacher
Farias, Romelia
English Tchr & Dept Chprsn
Gamboa, Cayetano
Math Teacher
Gomez, Rosalinda Gomez
Elementary Music Teacher
Guerrero, Salvador, Jr.
Spanish Teacher
Hoornaert, Dwight Douglas
9th Grade English Honors Tchr
Johnson, Marilyn
Business Teacher
Luna, Rebecca Anna
Math Teacher
Martinez, Juan Manuel
HS English Teacher
Mata, Rogelio
History Dept Chair & Teacher
Puente, Albert
PE Teacher & Coach
Quiroz, Jesus
Mathematics Teacher
Salinas, Raul, Jr.
JROTC Senior Army Instructor
Solis, Juanita
English Teacher
SAN MARCOS
Augustin, Byron D.
Dept of Geography & Plng Prof
Barragan, Celia Silguero
Fifth Grade Reading Specialist
Bueno, Jeanette Clymer
Computer Teacher
Clark, Susan Benzinger
English Teacher
Coulson, J. Peter
Grad Stud Theatre Dir & Prof
Fluker, Laurie Hayes
Asst Prof of Mass Comm
Flynt, Jack Winston, II
Jr ROTC Aerospace Sci Instr
Ford, Judy T.
Ath Dir Asst & PE Dept Head
Garcia, John L.
Assistant Prof of Counseling
Grubb, Christiana
Biology Teacher
Herron, Stacey Dawn
French Teacher
Kernion, Charles Allen
High School Spec Ed Teacher
Kyle, Brenda Gary
8th Grade Language Arts Tchr
Lutz, Karen Ann
Mathematics Teacher
Martinez, Eloy John
Instrumental Music Director
Mc Leod, W. Angus, III
Director of Choral Music
Norman, Jacquelynn S.
Social Studies Teacher
O'Dell, Delores Eggemeyer
Home Economics Teacher
Partin, Joe Ann Hopper
Retired English & Reading Tchr
Perkins, Annie Russell
Facilitator of GATE
Pino, Carol Willett
English Teacher
Pratt, Fred V.
Spanish Teacher
Renfro, Robert Bruce
Mass Communication Professor
Riepe, Russell Casper
Music Professor & Composer
Ryser, Judith L.
9th-12th Grade French Teacher
Schiflett, Peggy Kucera
English Teacher
Smith, Jacqueline Weakley
Dance Teacher
Terry, Danal Wayne
Asst Prof of Mass Commnctn
Thompson, David Lee
Supvr of Stu Tchrs, Asst Instr
Weeks, Patricia Kay (Fillippa)
8th Grade Math Teacher
Welch, Laura Katherine Posey
Sixth Grade Math Teacher
Wood, Melanie Erin
Teaching Assistant
SAN SABA
Ellis, Patsy Tripp
Senior English & Theatre Tchr
Gary, Harley Joe
High School Mathematics Tchr
Schulze, Ronnie C.
8th Grd Soc Stud Tchr & Coach
SANGER
Davis, Sallyann A.
US History & English Teacher
Higgs, Elizabeth Gillum
Home Economics Teacher
Hughes, Sally Beams
Health Science Tech Teacher
McCarroll, Bradley Thomas
Science Teacher
Osburn, Martha Ann (Kemper)
Algebra Teacher
Schwartz, Joanne Michelle
Art Teacher

Swindle, Molly Ply
Home Economics Teacher
Waston, Lee Ann Blalock
School Counselor
SANTA ANNA
Guthrie, Montie L., III
School Counselor
Guthrie, Sandra Davis
English Teacher
Huffman, Cindy Mash
7th-8th Grd Lang Arts Tchr
Markham, Shayna Renea
Science Teacher
SANTA FE
Baker, Cynthia June
Language Arts Instructor
Meier, Sheila Oberg
Math & Computer Science Tchr
Orsak, Barbara Dankert
English Teacher
Rowden, Boyd E.
High School Band Director
Wilson, Nancy Donahoe
Health Teacher & Coach
SANTA ROSA
Guilliams, Frank C.
11th & 12th Grade English Tchr
Hernandez, Jaime
Social Studies Teacher
Hinojosa, Eduardo
Government Teacher
Lawrence, Larry Wayne
English Teacher
Totora, Juanita G.
ESL Teacher
SANTO
Beckham, Judy Lynn (Baxter)
Third Grade Teacher
Young, Gary Douglas
Coach & HS English Teacher
SCHERTZ
Bellesen, David Anthony
Life Science Teacher
Black, Avis Lynelle (Nell)
Art Teacher
Carson, James Daniel
Fourth Grade Teacher
Donahue, Patricia Eileen
Eng Tchr & Coord of GATE
Hutchinson, Lara Moore
Eng Dept Chair & Teacher
Kincaid, Dana Hood
Chemistry Teacher
Muenster, Donnie Carlene
Language Arts Teacher
Nunley, Joanne K.
Librarian & Latin Teacher
Routon, Ted M.
Language & Theatre Arts Tchr
Stadtmueller, Julie Kay
Art & English Teacher
Teter, Kelly Jean
English Teacher
SCHULENBURG
Balcar, Patricia Zapalac
Teacher of Gifted & Talented
Beltran, J. D.
Art Teacher & Coach
Bonner, Miranda (Machac)
5th & 6th Grade Lang Arts Tchr
Brown, Conley H., Jr.
Health & PE Teacher
De Smet, Elizabeth Cummings
Business Teacher
Martin, Rumaldo L.
Head of Frgn Lang & Instructor
Mathis, Ronald Gene
MOCT & Biology Teacher
Pohl, Robert J.
History, Govt & Economics Tchr
Venghaus, Phyllis Langhamer
Science Teacher
SCURRY
Crabill, Melissa Anne
Biology & Chemistry Teacher
Medlin, Robert Livingston
History Teacher
SEABROOK
Boyle, Dorothy (Shaw)
Retired 4th Grd Teacher
Eichenauer, Connie Rhoades
Kindergarten Teacher
Milligan, June Moore
Retired HS English Teacher
SEADRIFT
Finster, Dwana Braun
Second Grade Teacher
SEAGOVILLE
Garrett, Linda F.
Fourth Grade Teacher
Gattis, Robin Arneson
Kindergarten Teacher
Golston, Doris Rosser
First Grade Teacher
SEAGRAVES
Calfee, Dan E.
Business Education Teacher
Hamilton, Jerry Xan Hudson
Third Grade Teacher
Hamilton, Jimmie L.
US His Tchr & Ath Dir
SEALY
Adams, Jean Olsovsky
Speech, Theatre Arts Tchr, Dir
Ashorn, Patricia Ann Dzierzanowski
5th Grade Teacher
Barrett, Patricia Bodenman
Lang Arts & History Teacher
Kaminski, Allen Wayne
Agriculture Teacher

Kendrick, Terri Hagan
5th Grd Math & Sci Teacher
Klecka, Rudy N.
History Teacher & Dept Head
Machala, Wendy Wright
US History Teacher
Reinbeck, Betty P.
Career & Technology Ed Coord
Rivers, Sharon Allred
Honors English II Teacher
SEGUIN
Beicker, Cathy Erxleben
Technology Leader & Counselor
Berry, George Sawtelle
Science Teacher
Chambliss, Terry Jay
Sixth Grade Teacher
Dyess, Susan Zipp
Fourth Grade Teacher
Keddal, Mark Joseph
Teacher
Krippner, Pamela Lynne
Lang Arts Teacher of GATE
Lippe, Cathy Ehlers
World Geography Teacher
Marsh, Rebecca Wells
Journalism & Theatre Arts Tchr
Petrisky, Robert Franklin
Band Director
Reyna, Gloria T.
US History Teacher
Rodriguez, Juan
Eng & Modern Langs Assoc Prof
Smetzer, Gerald Dale
Mathematics Teacher
Smith, Joan Ellis
Third Grade Teacher
Wilke, Dorothy Vordenbaum
Fifth Grade Teacher
Woerndel, Mildred
Business & Office Ed Teacher
SEMINOLE
Campbell, Deanna Cathey
Mathematics Teacher
Cates, Steven Clark
Mathematics Teacher
Chappell, Robert Black
Eng, Debate Tchr & Acad Coord
Lanier, Joel Denton
Agriculture Science Teacher
Linthicum, Betty Lois
Second Grade Teacher
Ryan, J'Lyn Mc Donald
Business Education Teacher
Touchstone, Shelly Everett
Cosmetology Instructor
Turner, Gaynette Edwards
High School Math Teacher
SEYMOUR
Browning, Enoch Doyle
Biology Teacher & Coach
Carver, Donna Holman
Span & Eng Teacher & Dept Chm
McClung, Carol Richardson
3rd Grade Teacher
SHALLOWATER
Austin, Barbi Traeder
7th-8th Grd Math & Span Tchr
Janssen, Teresa L.
High School Biology Teacher
Kerr, Melinda Sue
Reading & Speech Teacher
Pointer, Jo Ann
Counselor
Tarter, James Donald
Assistant Principal & Coach
Warren, Mary Glass
Reading Teacher
SHAMROCK
Greene, Laurie S.
Spanish & English Teacher
SHELBYVILLE
Ellis, Winola Williams
HS English Teacher & Librarian
Gurley, Claudann McClellan
Home Economics Teacher
Morrison, Tommie Greer
Business Education Teacher
SHEPHERD
Williams, Clara Granberry
Science Teacher
SHERMAN
Allen, Linda Honts
3rd Grade Teacher
Andrews, Marilyn Tuttle
8th Grade English Teacher
Baldwin, Shirley Mozingo
Cosmetology Teacher
Berghauser, Bill
Electronics Instructor
Cape, Robert Wayne, Jr.
Assistant Prof of Classics
Cullum, Rick E.
Geometry Teacher
Cullum, Stormy Magee
Business Teacher
Erger, Robert J., II
Physics Teacher
Estes, Bill W.
Science Chair & Hnrs Bio Tchr
Farrington, Mark Steven
American History Teacher
Graham, Karla Snipes
Teacher
Hudgeons, Dorothy R.
History Teacher
Loper, Laura Kathleen
Orchestra Director
Majors, Charles E.
Journalism Advisor & Tech Adv

SHERMAN (cont)
Meadows, Anita Y-nay (Lyons)
Assistant Principal
Owens, Mickey Calvin
Band Teacher
Roy, Janet Mc Gruder
Third Grade Teacher
Sharer, Verna Freese
Home Ec Tchr & Stu Cncl Spon
Southerland, Robert Bruce
US History Teacher
Spraberry, Beth S.
Teacher of Gifted
SHINER
Britsch, Betty Jones
First Grade Teacher
Mraz, Marilyn Welfl
Reading & Am History Teacher
SIDNEY
Cummings, Robert Kent
Science Teacher
SILSBEE
Atmar, Carol Stokesbury
Advanced Placement Eng Tchr
Bodle, Mona Harrell
12th Grade Government Teacher
Calloway, Alice L.
5th-6th Grd Fine Arts Teacher
Donalson, Alyson Derkits
Science Teacher
Edwards, Ouida Mc Cullough
Retired Teacher
Hart, Darlene David
High School Math Teacher
Irvin, Addie Mae (Davis)
Fourth Grade Teacher
Johnson, Shirley Ann
Social Studies Teacher
McDonald, Gregory Todd
English Teacher
Mc Lain, Lynn Bond
Math Teacher
Van Pelt, Judy Forse
10th Grd English & PAL Teacher
Wharton, Kevin F.
High School Mathematics Tchr
Woodard, Charlie
Head Football Coach
SILVERTON
Francis, Michelle Mc Donough
Math & Tchr of Gifted-Talented
Weaver, Sheryl Worrall
Business Ed & Cmptr Tchr
SINTON
Alaniz, Norma Linda
Fifth Grade Teacher
Allen, Rita F. Herd
Speech & Lang Arts Teacher
Henicke, Orlean Imelda
Lead Counselor
Houser, Lynn G.
Fourth Grade Teacher
Janysek, Lisa Skrobarcek
7th & 8th Grade Math Teacher
Kopetsky, Greg P.
HS Mathematics Teacher
SKELLYTOWN
Stuart, Paulene Mc Kinney
Kindergarten Teacher
SKIDMORE
DuBose, Mavournee Dominy
HS Eng Hnrs, Theatre Prod Tchr
Valentine, Jeffrey Harold
High School Math Teacher
Wallace, Donna Wendel
Home Economics Teacher
SLATON
Alexander, Karla Gayle (Weaver)
Theatre Arts & Algebra I Tchr
Bain, Gayla Maria
Elementary Counselor
Berry, Steve Frank
Student Services Director
Cole, Mickey Ann
HS Math Teacher
Cross, Charles Edward
Band Director
Evans, Judy Sells
English Teacher
Heathington, Linda S.
Spanish Teacher
Hernandez, Gregory Lujano
Chemistry Teacher
Inmon, Shalan Jan
Home Economics Teacher
Moore, Jeanette Burrell
4th Grade Teacher
Pruitt, Jim Ray
High School Math Teacher
Waller, Jay Earl
Ag Science Teacher
Witt, Jane R.
Kindergarten Teacher
SMITHVILLE
Boyd, Sharyn Rey
Jr & Sr English Teacher
Enis, Troy Alonzo, Jr.
Science Teacher
Fleck, Helen Tietjen
English & German Teacher
Hamm, Lexie Gaye
Multi-Age Teacher
SMYER
Propst, SueBell Brister
English Teacher
SNOOK
Bedford, Theresa Louise (Landry)
High School Science Teacher
Sears, Vikki Bert (Cunningham)
HS English Teacher

SNYDER
Arnold, Diane W.
Journalism Teacher
Cozart, Linda Spence
1st Grade Teacher
Gressett, Sue Cook
Fourth Grade Teacher
Jarrell, Sammie Davis
6th Grade English Teacher
Vest, Theresa Kaye (Abbott)
8th Grd Math Tchr & Dept Chair
SOMERSET
Bartos, Sharon Jo
GATE Language Arts Teacher
de la Cruz, Wilda Deane
2nd Grd Span & Eng Teacher
Geyer, Jeanette Metzger
Math Teacher
Purkey, Larry Keith
English Teacher
Voigt, Bernice Ann
Computer & Keyboarding Teacher
Wiley, Bernice Henry
Language Arts Teacher
SONORA
Love, Carol Davis
Science Teacher
Snodgrass, Bob G.
Math & Science Teacher
SOUR LAKE
Beavers, Susan Nicholson
Second Grade Teacher
Cooper, Brenda Tarver
Sixth Grade Reading Teacher
Davis, Jeanette Owen
Title I Reading Teacher
Huckabay, Brian Scott
US History Teacher & Coach
Mc Keller, Claudia Joyce (Ferrell)
Eng Advanced Placement Tchr
Parish, Teresa Ann (Guedry)
Teacher of Gifted & Talented
Park, Kathleen Ann (Burtscher)
Health Sci Technology Teacher
Peveto, Cynthia Holecek
English Teacher
Turner, Cheryl Anita (Billings)
First Grade Teacher
Van Noord, Ruth
Physical Ed Teacher & Coach
White, Elizabeth Ann
Chemistry Teacher
SOUTH HOUSTON
Beal, Carol L.
Bio, Hum Antmy & Physlgy Tchr
Blanton, Shirley Watts
English Teacher
Cartmell, Shannon Lyn
HS ESL Teacher & Coach
Dickson, Gene Carroll
English Teacher
Goode, John Paul
Asst Band Director
Howlett, Jeffrey Bruce
Health Teacher
Livesay, Bonnye Ann
Fourth Grade Teacher
Oliver, Ron Brian
Math Teacher
Smith, Vicki Cooper
Elementary Music Teacher
Stringer, Jo Ann Harper
Honors Biology Teacher
Ward, Marjorie Marsalis
Retired English Teacher
White, John Mark
World History & Sociology Tchr
SOUTHLAKE
Held, Kaye Ashby
Social Studies Teacher
Moody, Beverly (Dempsey)
Teacher
Oglesby, Gregory Alan
Teacher & Coach
Ondrasek, Robert Lee
Environmental Sci & Bio Tchr
Rapp, Thomas Craig
Economics Teacher
Rutzen, Amy Elizabeth
English Teacher
SOUTHLAND
Jones, Marilyn Ellis
Secondary Mathematics Teacher
Mc Lendon, Rebecca Kennady
AP Eng, Span & Art Teacher
SOUTHMAYD
Morris, Paula Young
US History & Reading Teacher
Sanna, Pamela Blurton
Lang Arts & Reading Tchr
SPEARMAN
Jarvis, Wesley Woodville
Science Teacher
Lozano, Kim
Math Teacher
Neff, Wendell Dale
Math Teacher & Coach
SPLENDORA
Calhoun, Ray Arnold
Music Teacher & Supervisor
Findeisen, Ben Henry
Science Teacher & Dept Chair
Hurley, Pamela Diane
Fourth Grade Teacher
SPRING
Adkins, Susan Calhoun
Honors English Teacher
Applegate, Todd Edward
Sixth Grd Social Studies Tchr

Arellano, Cathy Martini
Drill Team & Dance Instructor
Aries, Shari M.
Math Teacher
Baratti, Catherine Nell
Government Teacher
Beago, Karen Cadle
Speech & Theater Teacher
Brown, Deanna Galyean
Second Grade Teacher
Cambron, Virginia L.
Advanced Placement Eng IV Tchr
Cavanaugh, James Michael
English Teacher
Coffey, Janet Gourley
Pre-First Grade Teacher
Courtney, Linley Gail
Secondary Math Teacher
Crosby, Billy Scott
Health, TX History & PE Tchr
Dillard, Cathy Hunley
Second Grade Teacher
Ditta, Frances Mary
Government Teacher
Duesing, Bonnie Bull
English Teacher
Dunnagan, William Rush
World History Teacher
Eaton, Denise Renee
Choral Director
Fairbanks, R. Eileen
Mathematics Teacher
Foster, Dorothy Mc Guire
Mathematics Teacher
Fowler, Rhonda I.
Eng, Speech & Debate Tchr
Fulmer, Patricia Ann
Reading & English Teacher
Grayson, Thomas David
Chemistry Teacher
Guillory, Julie Joubert
Biology & Physical Sci Tchr
Harwood, Thomas Folson
Health Teacher & Coach
Hebert, Jennifer Breaux
American History Teacher
Kreml, Mary Beth Kuczkowski
Fourth Grade Teacher
Loveless, Sandra K.
Social Studies Teacher
Martin, Patricia
7th Grade English Teacher
Massie, Linda Burke
Teacher of Gifted & Talented
Mattair, Judy Moore
Mathematics Tchr & Dept Chair
Mc Clure, Michael Craig
Science Dept Chair & Teacher
Mc Donald, Linda S.
7th Grade Math Teacher
McDonald, Michael Worden
Physical Ed Teacher & Coach
Mc Elroy, Kelly Elaine
Counselor
Meissner, Barbara Graham
English Teacher
Mendieta, Pamela Joy (Schramm)
Homerm, Sci, Health & PE Tchr
Metzger, William Allen
Teacher
Mosley, Kenneth Paul
Physics Teacher
Neumeyer, Randy A.
History Teacher
Nuckols, San Scifres
7th-8th Grd Theatre Arts Tchr
Patterson, Tina Marie
Mathematics Teacher
Pichini, Cecelia Desjardins
Art Dept Chairperson & Teacher
Rankel, Richard Charles
Vocational Drafting Instructor
Richardson, Judith Lynn
Fifth Grade Math & Sci Tchr
Robertson, Debbie Holt
Accelerated Language Arts Tchr
Rodriguez, Cheryl Matassa
8th Grd Eng Tchr & Team Leader
Schweiger, Peggy E.
Physics I & II Teacher
Sheffield, Kimberly Kay
High School Math Teacher
Sheridan, Melissa Collier
Eng & Creative Writing Teacher
Sneed, Laurel Rose
Kindergarten Teacher
Snook, Donald Ray, Jr.
Honors Chemistry Teacher
Sprunk, Edna M.
Mathematics Teacher
Stalder, DeAnne Thompson
US History Teacher
Stockton, Carolyn Crowther
Math Teacher
Thornton, Paul Timothy
Math Dept Chairman
Travis, Danielle Ferguson
Choir Director
Veach, Charles Edward
Science Department Chair
Welch, Robin E.
Theatre Arts & Speech Chair
White, Irene Ault
Math Teacher
Wilson, Betty Corie
6th Grade Language Arts Tchr
SPRING BRANCH
Dierksen, Kathryn Z.
History Teacher

Kolbe, Timothy Paul
Tchr of Criminal Justice Pgm
McDonald, Ruth Ann (Robb)
Math Teacher
Palos, Fernando
HS Assistant Principal
Rawlinson, Bobbye Burnam
Algebra & Geometry Teacher
Rider, Ann Wofford
Business Teacher
Saunders, Shawn Brown
Theatre Arts Teacher
Shepard, Joseph Edward
History & Psychology Teacher
Stoore, Philip Scott
Industrial Technology Tchr
Taylor, Teri Kimball
Science Dept Chair & Teacher
Williams, Nancy Dubuisson
Counselor
SPRINGTOWN
Carter, Curtis
Science Teacher
Dills, Donna Brosig
Office Education Teacher
Fisher, Nanette Stavenhagen
Teacher of Gifted & Talented
Fox, Shara Bryan
English Teacher
Huddleston, Sharon Teeters
Eng, Gifted & Talented Tchr
Lindsey, Melanie Bass
Eighth Grade English Teacher
Lowery, Cari L.
Head Vllybl Coach & Ath Dir
Luebke, Monica Thomas
English, Speech & Drama Tchr
Perry, J. B.
Band Director
Peterson, Elaine Rone
TAAS Coordinator
Schniebs, Pamela Cort Brassey
6th & 7th Grd English Teacher
Simmons, Joyce Reynolds
6th Grd Soc Stud Tchr
SPUR
Arney, Shawn D'Wayne
Science Teacher
Marion, Mila
Kindergarten Teacher
Scott, Crystal King
Bank Director
Sexton, Harold Dewayne
Social Studies Instructor
Watson, Merla Foreman
Kindergarten Teacher
STAFFORD
Bannister, Beverly Moore
Math, Sci & Soc Studies Tchr
Brown, Penny Powell
2nd Grade Teacher
Lippert, John Ernest
Mathematics Teacher
Moody, Paul Scott
Teacher & Coach
Newkirk, Mark Steven
Chemistry Teacher
Orman, Helen Belton
English Instructor
Ray, Valerie Williamson
8th Grade Math Teacher
Soliz, Yolanda R.
Spanish Instructor
Stabler, Scott Lawrence
US History Teacher
Sullivan, Sondra Jean
High School Counselor
Turner, Laurie Kay
Algebra I & II Teacher
STAMFORD
Burnett, Jean Treadwell
First Grade Teacher
Pritchard, Betty JoAnn
Retired Math & Comp Lit Tchr
STANTON
Baker, Albert Harvey
Computer Teacher
Bird, Robert Ray, Jr.
Social Studies Teacher
STEPHENVILLE
Adcock, Darlene Curtis
Kindergarten Teacher
Anderson, Joyce Mitchell
Director of Guidance
Burks, Brenda K.
English II Teacher
Crouch, Nancy Lee
7th Grade History Teacher
Freed, Rusty
Asst Professor of Management
Gibson, Judd Kyle
Secondary Math Teacher
Jeffus, Hugh Milton
Dir of Hydrology & Engineering
Muncey, Jennifer Godair
12th Grade English Teacher
Ratliff, Addie Olson
Spanish Teacher
Sims, Larry Kyle
Marketing Ed & Tech Prep Coord
Snodgrass, Susan E.
English Teacher
Walton, Sandra Casper
English Teacher & Dept Chair
STINNETT
Amaro, Elaine B.
Third Grade Teacher
Blankenship, Treasure Thaggard
English Teacher & Girls Coach

Knobloch, Dawn Rae
Spanish Teacher
Maxwell, Stanley Dean
Advanced Mathematics Teacher
Parks, Rosemary O'Brennan
English Teacher
Williams, Deborah Bruce
3rd-5th Grd Title I Math Tchr
STOCKDALE
Maierhofer, Marie Theiss
Business Teacher
STOWELL
Kahla, Bobbie Platt
Retired Elementary Teacher
STRATFORD
Kautz, Viola Cordova
School Counselor
Kendrick, Cagle Kenneth
Mathematics Teacher
Pulliam, Annie Hodge
Retired 1st Grade Teacher
Ragsdale, Sonja Guffee
Third Grade Teacher
Russell, Cindy Patterson
Art Teacher
Young, Linda Sue
Library Media Specialist
STRAWN
Windham, Bonnie Alice
HS Mathematics & Sci Teacher
SUGAR LAND
Anderson, Valerie
Mathematics Teacher
Aschenbeck, Sandra Meischen
Eighth Grade US History Tchr
Batek, Kathryn Alford
English Teacher
Berliner, Suzanne Marie (Fowler)
World Geography Teacher
Blunt, Linda Lee
Algebra Teacher
Brown, Brenda George
3rd Grade Teacher
Carrell, Debbie A.
8th Grade Reading Teacher
Casasent, Audrey Malinowski
Latin & English Teacher
Clark, Marjorie Trulan
US History Teacher
Clay, Patricia A.
Chemistry Teacher
Cornelius, Cindi DeLaro
Dance Tchr & Dance Team Dir
Cox, Janet Dumay
Physical Ed Teacher & Coach
Cummons, Bradly Joseph
Theatre Arts Teacher
Duggan, William Don
Band Director
Dunn, Bobette Chapman
Span Tchr, Frgn Lang Dept Head
Fleming, Michael Roy
Orchestra Director
Green, Patricia Wilson
English Teacher
Grist, Cathy Davis
Third Grade Teacher
Guerrero, Arnold Eduardo
7th Grd Science Tchr & Coach
Hitt, Rankin Virgle, III
Teacher & Athletic Trainer
Holcombe, Joe Thomas
Social Studies Teacher
Johnson, Don Edward
Fifth Grade Teacher
Kilgore, Timothy E.
Choral Dir & Music His Teacher
Kleinschmidt, Ulrich Karl
Government & Economics Teacher
Klemstein, Jimmy Justin
Ag Science Teacher
Knox, Janice Kaye (Bonds)
English Teacher
Mack, Jenny B.
English Teacher
Madison, Yvette N.
English Teacher
Maly, Ed
English Dept Chairman & Tchr
Maresca, Joan McDonald
4th Grd Teacher & Team Leader
Maresh, Joan
Art Educator
Matney, Judy Mc Caleb
Physics Tchr & Sci Dept Head
Neuendorff, Kim Wagner
Art Teacher
Ordeneaux, Paula Ann
Mathematics Teacher
Prater, Roberta Louise (Cooke)
Industrial Technology Teacher
Pratt, Mary Jean J.
High School Spanish Teacher
Puerto, Dania Isabel
Math Teacher
Rogers, Benita Michelle
Geometry Teacher
Royal, Tere J.
English & Reading Teacher
Seward, Angela Jean
Computer Science Teacher
Slack, Kay Lane
Dept Chairman, Teacher & Coach
Stanford, Britton Lloyd
Latin & English Teacher
Strader, Charlotte Manoushagian
Fifth Grd Lang Arts Tchr
Stuart, Thomas Lee
Head Ftbl Coach & Campus Coord

R LAND (cont)
g, James Scott
ish & Speech Teacher
son, Robyn Lynn
3rd Language Arts Teacher
pson, Colleen Dany
d Grade Teacher
n, Tracy M.
Grade English Teacher
ek, Yvette Arguello
ness Education Teacher
nan, Kitty Lynn Ervin
3rd Eng & Rdng Teacher
, David Scott
stant Principal
HUR BLUFF
1, Phyllis Williams
arian & Math Teacher
n, Montie Whisenhunt
Grade Teacher
ill, John Thomas
culture Teacher
HUR SPRINGS
n, Deborah Ailes
ond Grade Teacher
rong, Renee Shelton
lish Teacher
v, Karen Jackson
lish Dept Chair & Teacher
Berry, Rebecca Jean
Grade Teacher
Rickey D.
tg Ed Tchr & Coordinator
am, Mary Lou (Owens)
nselor
rtson, Mary M.
h Dept Chairperson & Tchr
, Sandra K.
cher
r, Bob
nputer Aided Drafting Tchr
Annada Elliott
lish & Honors Teacher
, Frances Ann (Whitlock)
t Grade Teacher
ley, Johnnie Clint
ence Teacher
, Patricia Henegar
h Grade Math Teacher
air, David Shawn
ory Teacher & Coach
Vleet, Lana Jeanne
t, Ec & Law Related Ed Tchr
NYVALE
, Michael Todd
ence Teacher & Coach
nd, Karen
erican History Teacher
, Laura Andersen
glish Teacher
es Davis, Cynthia Jane
ding Coordinator
ourn, Tammy Pruitt
h & Algebra Teacher
RAY
ett, Bud Addison
ool Guidance Counselor
ENY
ado, Margaret Annette Trost
Teacher
er, Rebecca K.
rld History Teacher & Coach
ay, Diane R.
cher
ETWATER
ns, Dale Boyd
tructor
r, Jan (Richard)
rth Grade Teacher
Donna Merrick
rth Grade Teacher
am, Vicki Carlene
Grade Teacher
eu, Treva Pettit
Grade Math Teacher
dox, Peggy Barnes
acher of Gifted & Talented
Marjorie Beth (Hastings)
v Placement English Tchr
ir, Marina Harrison
cl Education Inclusion Tchr
T
hardt, Merle G.
odworking Instructor
er, Wendy Bernadette
ath, Sci & Soc Studies Tchr
ey, Diana Lynn Hajek
Grade Science Teacher
Ninch, Elisabeth A.
phomore English Teacher
, Joyce R.
ndergarten Teacher
IOKA
ess, Barbara Jean (Kitchens)
mputer & Business Teacher
brough, Julie K.
vt, Ec & Hlth Ed Tchr
CO
erts, Ann Seay
tired Business Teacher
PA
ter, Sarah Rocquelle
glish Teacher
erick, Raeann Mae
ience Teacher
ce, Vicki Ramona
glish & Speech Teacher
UM
n, Scot Riley
dustrial Tech Teacher

Green, Susan Temple
Fifth Grade Teacher
Hillin, Charlotte Jameson
5th Grade Teacher
Jones, Marilyn Williams
Librarian & Media Specialist
McGowan, Karen Jeannine
Eng Tchr & Drill Team Dir
Mize, Terri L.
MS Special Education Teacher
Worthy, Donald Gene
Physics & Chemistry Teacher
TAYLOR
Bell, Jeffrey Foy
Health & PE Teacher
Grimm, Debbie Kubala
Second Grade Teacher
Hall, Vicki Lynn (Simcik)
Quest & Health Teacher
Hendriex, Carolyn Eddings
High School Art Teacher
Hill, Jeannie
Business Computer Teacher
Kalbaugh, Mary Still
Pre-Calculus & Algebra I Tchr
Kerlin, Shalene Boland
5th Grade Lang Arts Tchr
Leschber, Barbara Menning
Office Ed Cooperative Coord
Lindell, Carol Hoerig
Eighth Grade Mathematics Tchr
Magers, Raymond B.
Social Studies & Speech Tchr
Parsons, Priscilla Zimerhanzel
English Teacher & Dept Head
Rogers, Pat Busby
Business & Vocational Teacher
TEAGUE
Casey, Herbert R., Jr.
Ag Science Teacher
Hancock, Amanda Landgrebe
Home Economics Teacher
King, Linda Torno
English IV & Journalism Tchr
Monson, Joel Mark
High School Band Director
TEMPLE
Bartek, Pam Cawthon
Second Grade Teacher
Bourland, Paula Kay K.
Adult Ed & Business Teacher
Buchhorn, La Nell (Carlson)
Science Department Chair
Burgess, Mary Vinnie Mitchell
Retired Elementary Teacher
Carter, Bettye Batterton
Math & Science Teacher
Etheridge, Rhonda Stephen
9th Grade English Teacher
Faulk, Odie B.
Professor & Chair Dept of His
Floyd, Viola Frances Johnson
8th Grd Lang Arts & Rdng Tchr
Greco, Janice Friemel
Honors World History Teacher
Henry, Bobby Lee
Agricultural Science Teacher
Hobbs, Annelle Haddock
Physical Education Teacher
Hoskins, Janet Elvira
8th Grd Language Arts Teacher
Mattern, Margarette Dominich
Physical Science Teacher
Murray, Linda Jo (Rumbel)
AP Regular Govt & Ec Tchr
Newman, Talma Haile
Computer Professor
Post, Linda Williams
Honors English Teacher
Remoy, Amanda Miller
English Department Teacher
Sanders, Cheryl Redwine
Office Admin Systems Tchr
Schofield, Dominique Jimenez
Fourth Grade Teacher
Shipes Alexander, Pamela Lucille
US History Teacher
Smart, Rebecca Foust
Mathematics Teacher
Smith, Carol Clark
Honors & IB Anatomy Teacher
Thigpen, Marcia Tepe
Algebra II Teacher
TENAHA
Reimer, Karen M.
Science Teacher
TERLINGUA
Mc Entire, Dennis Ray
Science Teacher
TERRELL
Abbott, Michael E.
Computer Science Instructor
Blanton, Molly
Home Economics Teacher
Butler, Dennis Ray
Assoc Prof of English
Eason, Terry James
Principal
Fineout, Virginia Sims
Am His Tchr, Soc Stud Dept Chm
Hogan, Lela Wilson
8th Grd Math Tchr & Dept Chair
Lantrip, John Mark
8th Grd American History Tchr
Nolen, Judy Truett
Assistant Principal
Ratzlaff, Randy Lee
Band Director
Steadham, Stacey Renee
Biology Teacher

Stevens, Pamela Messimer
Bus Comp Applications Tchr
Stokes, Kathy Huffman
English Teacher & Choral Dir
Tample, Charles W.
Science Teacher
Thompson, Becky Owens
Third Grade Teacher
Thompson, Nancy Collins
Marketing Teacher & Coord
Williamson, Gary Howard
Administrator & Teacher
TEXARKANA
Ables, Lori Lyndon
English Teacher
Allard, David Wayne
Professor of Biology
Bartley, Criss Pearson
Science Teacher
Beasley, Tommy Anthony
Physical Education Teacher
Belonie, Norma Jeanne (Sorsby)
Third Grade Teacher
Blackwell, Marilyn Dianne
5th Grade Language Arts Tchr
Boyce, Roderick Duane
High School Band Director
Bratton, Jean Harrison
Chemistry I & II AP Teacher
Bridges, Carolyn Brown
Third Grade Teacher
Cheatham, Chester Lee
Mathematics Teacher
Coe, Deloris Stephens
Asst Principal
Dale, James Michael
High School Science Teacher
Davis, Susan Oates
Home Economics Teacher
Day, Jo Ann (Rucks)
6th Grd Eng, Rdng & GATE Tchr
Deese, John Byron
Band Director
Deese, Phyllis Anne
Algebra Teacher
Delk, Mary Mc Guire
English & Language Arts Tchr
Dunn, Annette Thompson
Instruction Director
Elrod, Jane Measel
English Teacher
Gilbert, Barbara Murray
Fine Arts Music Director
Griffie, Nathanael
HS Social Studies Teacher
Gunn, Bonnie L. Talent
Eng II, Speech & Drama Tchr
Harris, Charla Knowles
Journalism & English Teacher
Harrison, Lela Coe
Business Teacher & Dept Head
Hawkins, Paula R.
Assistant Principal
Helton, David L.
8th Grade Science Teacher
Hobson, Peggy Messimer
English Teacher
Holick, James Kenney
US History Teacher
Holland, Sylvia Walker
8th Grade Algebra Teacher
Houff, Marion Albert
Spanish Teacher
Howard, Martha Richey
English Teacher
Huckabee, Vicki Stearn
First Grade Teacher
Iverson, Lorene Stuart
Asst Professor of Nursing
Kimbro, Sue DeLoach
High School French Teacher
Laird, Robert Dean
Assistant Professor of Biology
Lansdell, Pamela Runge
History Teacher
Lipscomb, William Ernest
7th Grade TX History Teacher
Logan, Alice Powers
Kindergarten Teacher
Lollies, Olston William, Jr.
Bio, Anatomy & Sci Dept Chprsn
Mc Cright, Delores
Professor of Biology
Mc Lain, Keitha
Biology Teacher
Miller-Greer, Dee Houins
Technology Specialist
Moore, Carolyn C.
Senior Counselor
Moore, Patricia Anderson
Assoc Prof of Business Div
Mueller, Martha M.
Fourth Grade Teacher
Owen, Kathy McNeil
Middle School Counselor
Pace, Dorothy King
English & Reading Teacher
Randall, Wanda Louise Roberson
5th Grade Teacher
Rice, Jo Ann (Lester)
HOSTS Coordinator
Shimanek, Gloria Mary DeJardin
Marketing Coordinator & Instr
Smith, Sharon Wyatt
English & Speech Teacher
Tate, Nancy J.
English Teacher
Thornton, Mary Lou Adkins
Senior English Teacher

Tolleson, Sheila Mc Elhannon
Social Studies Teacher
Womack, Sharon Stuckey
English Teacher
TEXAS CITY
Aldrich, Sharon Tweito
Kindergarten Teacher
Anderson, Frank B.
Band Director
Bludworth, Glenda Gail
English & Dance Teacher
Buffa, John J.
Associate Professor
Byrd, Lynda Joyce (Berryhill)
Mathematics Teacher
Calhoun, Patricia Kay
Tenth Grade English Teacher
Clubb, Candace Kay (Mylon)
French Teacher
Dodd, Emmeline I.
Professor of Biology
Eames, Sherri Lewis
6th Grd Sci & Soc Stud Tchr
Earl, Cathleen Twardowski
Mathematics Tchr & Dept Chprsn
Lee, Judy A.
Science II Teacher
Luna, Mary Alice
Instructor & Hlth Sci Coord
Luster, Randall Earl
Asst Band Director
Olive, Jess H.
Instr of Math, Physics & Ec
Prouty, Thomas M.
Assistant Principal
Ravandi, Mohammad Ali
Mathematics Professor
Rock, Joanne Lopez
Teacher of Gifted & Talented
Savage, Kristi Lynn
10th Grd English Teacher
Selman, Olivia Ernestine Blythe
Teacher of Gifted & Talented
True, Renate Schlenz
Professor of Biology
Walker, Jane (Vacker)
Third Grade Teacher
Waugh, Judith Lloyd
Business Dept Chairperson
TEXLINE
Bass, Brande Moseley
Agriculture Science Teacher
THE COLONY
Adams, Janet Doyle
English Teacher
Beckel, Ann Marie
Gifted & Talented Teacher
Chilcoat, Phyllis Walker
English Teacher
Cruz, Roque Oscar
Army Instructor JROTC
Davis, Steve C.
9th & 12th Grd Hlth & Ath Tchr
Denton, DeLynn Biggs
French Teacher
English, Billy R.
Algebra Teacher & Coach
Hildebrand, Mrs. Lou Ann
Middle School Mathematics Tchr
Lafferty, Carol Ann
Math Teacher
Mitchell, Melvin Clifford
Vocal Music Director
Thomas, Tommy
Teacher & Coach
Vincent, Melissa Ann
Drill Team, Dance & His Tchr
Yoder, Steven T.
HS Social Studies Teacher
THE WOODLANDS
Brown, Wanda Spencer
7th-8th Grade Teacher & Coach
Cammarata, Nelda Nolen
Math & Algebra Teacher
Charley, Georgia Williams
History Teacher
Cox, Virginia Alice
Fourth Grade Teacher
Cronan, Jenise Toudouze
Assistant Principal
Fowler, Janene Pulley
8th Grade Science Teacher
Hickingbottom, DAnn Marie
4th Grd Teacher & Team Leader
Hime, Sheryl Stout
Advanced Placement Bio Teacher
Hoffland, Carol Rudolph
Senior English Teacher
Howard, Madeline J.
Physical Science Teacher
Joscelyne, Charles Paul
Mathematics Dept Chairperson
Knott, Carol Cantrell
Mathematics Teacher
Kovach, Linda Smithson
Speech Teacher
Mc Adams, Elizabeth Caldwell
3rd Grade Teacher
Rafferty, Mary Stevens
English Teacher & Dept Head
Russell, Janet North
Geometry Teacher
Sandiford, Lynne Ann
Third Grade Teacher
Savir, Etan
Mathematics Teacher
Seamans, Kathleen Hull
Health Science Tech Teacher
Thomas, Alice Stone
Business & English Teacher

Venier, Lynn Finell
Chemistry Teacher
Webb, Clabe Franklin
Physical Science Teacher
Wiley, Shannon Terry
English Teacher
Wojtczak, Kathy Kavene (Jackson)
Elementary Teacher
Woods, Linda Wannamaker
Advanced Placement Eng IV Tchr
THORNDALE
Brown, Elaine Vines
English Teacher
Hoines, Donald E.
Mathematics Teacher
Summers, Judy Westlake
High School Teacher
THRALL
Baker, Dean Carroll
High School Science Teacher
Erwin, John Wesley, Jr.
Government & Economics Teacher
Grace, Beverley Michalik
Math & Computer Sci Teacher
Johnson, Harvey Duane
Agricultural Science Teacher
Morrison, Elizabeth Powell
Band Director
THREE RIVERS
Elliott, Dorene Nehr
Home Economics Teacher
Porter, William Ross
Athletic Dir & Head Ftbl Coach
THROCKMORTON
Redwine, Sandra Nees
Counselor & Chapter Math Tchr
Walker, Sheryl Swaim
High School Business Teacher
TILDEN
Lansford, Abigail Stroud
Science Teacher
TIMPSON
Simon, Gladys Hooper
Kindergarten Teacher
TOM BEAN
Bumpus, Roberta (Henninger)
Curriculum Director
Hatch, Edward Eldon
Secondary History Teacher
Jackson, Janet Lee
English Teacher
Porter, Connie Lea
Secondary English Teacher
Reynolds, Teresa Hamilton
English & Biology Teacher
Robison, Marilyn Denise Gateley
Science Teacher
Taylor, Bobbi D.
English Teacher & Asst Librn
Thornton, Janet Underwood
Special Education Teacher
TOMBALL
Bentley, Julie Davis
5th Grade Teacher
Bozic, William Joseph, Jr.
US History & ESL Math Tchr
Chapman, Andrea Lynn (Douglas)
Third Grade Teacher
Evans, Ann Hall
Math Teacher
Greco, Karen Grotlisch
Language Arts Instructor
Hartman, Brenda C.
Accounting Professor
Hill, James W.
Music Teacher
Huff, Connie Spoor
Biology Teacher
Kilzer, Dinah Lee
Mathematics Teacher
Melton, Debbie H.
Dance & Drill Team Educator
Oswald, Andrew Arthur
Mathematics Instructor
Planje, Christina Elizabeth
Biology Teacher
Pollard, Michelle Cook
Mathematics Teacher
Pope, Derryk Douglas
Speech & Debate Coach
Stackhouse, Janet Lynn
English Teacher
Vaculin, Jimmy E.
Agriculture Science Teacher
Whitmire, Dora Lee
World Geography Teacher
TRENT
Hammond, Linda J.
English, Speech Tchr & Coord
TRINIDAD
Airheart, Julie Tackitt
History & Government Teacher
Kent, Amy Manning
English & History Teacher
TROUP
Duncan, Carol Shrode
Business Teacher
Evans, Glen
Counselor
Hunt, Janey
Government & Economics Teacher
McSwain, Stacy Gamble
Spanish Teacher
Stanley, Kevin Glen
Science Teacher & Coach
TROY
Ashlock, Rodney Olen
Former Associate Professor
Jolliff, Michelle Myers
Social Studies Teacher & Coach

TROY (cont)
Klement, Janet Maedgen
Kindergarten Teacher
Morgan, Mary Ann
Physical Ed Tchr & Coach
TURKEY
Brannon, Peggy Walker
HS History & Government Tchr
TUSCOLA
Pearce, Janet Gail
High School Art Teacher
Wells, Charlotte Petroski
Speech & Fine Arts Teacher
TYLER
Adams, Mary Boggs (Wright)
Instructor of English
Adams, Sandra Crawley
Government Teacher & Dept Chr
Alden, Dennis J.
Junior High Math Teacher
Andrews, Mildred Kay Gean
English Teacher
Anthony, Gerald Allen
Biology Teacher & Coach
Baker, Sheila Beach
Bus Computer Applications Tchr
Beaton, Gigi Richardson
Computer Science Instructor
Bledsoe, Nick Kelly
Drafting Teacher
Bohn, Pamela Dunn
12th Grd Eng Tchr
Brach, Jane Kristoff
Biology Instructor
Brown, Larry D.
Band Director
Byerly, Sandy (Smith)
Algebra Teacher & Coach
Byrum, Noamie R.
Instructor of English
Cade, Kay Montgomery
Comp Sci & Applications Tchr
Caldwell, Sandra
4th Grade Teacher
Calloway, Ethel Warren
Soc Stud, His Tchr & Dept Head
Campbell, Sharon Milligan
Mathematics Teacher
Cates, Cathryn Patterson
Instructor of Biology
Champion, Willie C.
Associate Professor
Childs, Brenda Tompkins
American History Teacher
Clark, Susan Elizabeth
Business Ed Tchr & Dept Chprsn
Cobb, Kristy Williams
Gifted & Talented English Tchr
Collins, Tom R.
HS Math Teacher & Coach
Cooke, Tillman Timotheus
Government Teacher & Coach
Coyne, Lorraine
History Teacher
Craddock, Katie Knight
Eng II Honors Teacher
Cross, Linda J.
Instructor of History
Cummings, Carole Odom
English Teacher
Davis, Virginia Ann (Bivens)
Assistant Principal
Diamond, Richard Major, II
Former Instructor of English
Edwards, Mildrene Anderson
Fourth Grade Tchr
Ellis, Susan
Mathematics Teacher
Erickson, Christel Theresa
Physical Ed Teacher & Coach
Girard, Charlotte M.
Pre-Calculus & Geometry Tchr
Goode, Leron Kenward
English & US History Teacher
Goodsell, Belinda Williams
Photography & Newspaper Tchr
Goss Williams, Ivonda Reshell
Chldrn With Disabilities Tchr
Haley, Julie Kay
7th Grd Language Arts Teacher
Haley, Kathy Lynn
Fifth Grade Teacher
Hall, Jennifer Lee
Second Grade Teacher
Hall, Stephen Craig
HS Agricultural Science Tchr
Harris, Carol Keeton
5th Grade Teacher
Hart, Barbara Lane
Assoc Prof of Criminal Justice
Hitt, Deborrah Wood
English Teacher
Holston, John Thomas
Health Science Tech Pgm Coord
Hooper, Callie Phipps
Home Economics Teacher
Irwin, David Ray
Horticulture & Agrisci Tchr
Johansson, John E.
Photography Instructor
Johns, Mary Patricia
Sr Composition Teacher
Johnson, Barbara Jean (Jackson)
English & Spanish Teacher
Johnson, Debbie Cooper
Pre-Calculus Teacher
Jones, Jan Elinor
Theatre Teacher
Jones, Peter E.
His Instr & Head Soccer Coach
Kersh, Marshella Johnson
Computer Science Instructor
Kirkpatrick, I. E. (Gene)
Instructor of US History
Koerner, Robert Duane
Bio, Anatomy & Physiology Tchr
Kuster, Deborah A.
Secondary Art Teacher
Lee, Michael Lynn
HS Algebra Tchr & Coach
Lisner, Pamela Moore
Drama & Debate Team Coach
Mahaffy, Arlena Cross
Elem Teacher & Preschool Dir
Malone, Glenn R.
5th Grade Science Teacher
Marta, Larry Weldon
Music Instructor
Maxwell, Milly
Lecturer in Nursing
Mc Croskey, Vista Kay
Assistant Professor of History
Mc Gowen, Janice White
English Teacher
Mc Keller, Pennie Gene
English Teacher
Mercer, Rebecca Morgan
Life Skills Teacher
Milling, Judy Elizabeth
English Teacher
Muller, Joan Shaver
English Instructor
Newman, Judy Gayle
Office Technology Instructor
O'Bannon, Richard Neil
English & Russian Teacher
Peggram, Gloria Dickson
English Instructor
Preast, Katie Baldwin
Math Instructor
Reid, Tobin L.
Health Teacher
Rossman, Cynthia Nelson
Math Teacher & Softball Coach
Samples, John Charles
High School Band Director
Sanders, Edward
Spanish Teacher
Sansom, Paula Lanney
Dance Teacher
Schaefer, Candace Hastings
English Instructor
Scheidler, Karen M.
French Teacher
Sebring, Linda Baldwin
Third Grade Teacher
Shackelford, Jacque Atchley
Instructor of Speech & Theater
Shannon, William W.
8th Grd American History Tchr
Sherrouse, Janice Goss
Instr & Dir of Office Admin
Shumate, Alan H.
Speech Teacher
Smith, Angel Fay Whitmill
Third Grade Teacher
Smith, Rebecca Wise
Honors English Teacher
Smith, Sue Barlow
Broadcast Jrnlsm & Eng Teacher
Smith, Travis Neil
Band Director
Sparks, Lisa Johnston
English & Geography Teacher
Spellman, Penny Lynn (Cepak)
Biology Teacher
Sturrock, Teresa Priest
6th Grade Reading Teacher
Sulser, Nan Brewer
Home Economics, Education Tchr
Tankersley, Shawna Hellman
Algebra Teacher
Turman, Judith Jenkins
English Instructor
Turman, Laurie Simpson
10th Grade English Teacher
Watson, Patricia Adcock
Reading Recovery Teacher
Webster, Bennie Burks
Instructor
Willbanks, Patricia Whitley
American History Teacher
Wilson, Ellen Hughes
Algebra Teacher
Wilson, Robin Denise
Business Teacher
UNIVERSAL CITY
Baughman, Mark Anderson
8th Grade History Teacher
Davidson, Robin Gray
Language Arts Teacher
Lain, Kathy Seay
8th Grade Algebra I Teacher
Nichols, Bea Kramer
Kindergarten Teacher
Ramsey, Sara Criss (Sargent)
6th Grade Teacher
Schulze, Shirley Gail
Business Teacher
Schuster, Randy Joseph
Bio Tchr & Head Bsktbl Coach
UVALDE
Baker, Cheryl Bealsey
HS Science Teacher
Baum, Barbara Ingram
English Teacher
Blair, Barbara Atkins
History Instructor
Box, Wilford Winston
Bus Dept Mngmt Instr & Coord
Bozovich, George Michael
Univ Service Dir & Consultant
Coe, Jill
Instructor of English & Rdng
Collier, LeeAnn
English Teacher
Fowler, Sharon Bagley
Social Studies & Science Tchr
Hilderbran, Betty Frantzen
Math Teacher
Ireton, Melanie Marie
Latin Teacher
Kerbow, Stephen M.
Professor of History & Govt
Kothmann, Marilyn Kallus
Math Teacher & Dept Chprsn
Lesosky, Mark Steven
US History Teacher
Mortensen, Jeffrey Charles
Band Director
Pena, Valerie Lois
Physics & Biology Teacher
Rhodes, Virginia Webb
Business Education Teacher
Rodriguez, Rebecca Saiz
English Teacher
Stewart, Mary Lou
Theater & English Teacher
Stocks, Maria Raquel
Span Tchr & Drill Team Spon
Swink, James A.
Chairman of Sci & Math Dept
Weisinger, Vickie Greathouse
English Teacher
VALERA
Priddy, Debbie R.
Reading & Fine Arts Teacher
VALLEY MILLS
Bruton, John Ray
Science Department Chairman
Word, Diane Waller
Home Economics Teacher
VAN
Currin, Bruce L.
Earth Science Teacher
Griffin, Kenneth L.
Band Director
Kellam, Brenda Parham
Debate & Theatre Arts Teacher
Nations, Rhea Lene (Stinson)
Math & Peer Helpers Teacher
Praytor, Beth
Business Teacher
Wallace, Donna Lynn
12th Grade English Teacher
Waters, Terry D.
Advanced Math Teacher & Coach
Wilson, Betty Page
6th Grade Social Studies Tchr
VAN ALSTYNE
Boyd, David Warren
Secondary Teacher & Coach
Denton, Gwen Lay
ESL & Title I Teacher
Howard, Elizabeth Turner
Spanish Teacher
Martin, Larry Parker
English & Latin Teacher
Wade, Mary King
Fourth Grade Teacher
VAN HORN
Luna, Heradio G.
Spanish Teacher
Solis, Lynn C.
Mathematics Teacher
VAN VLECK
Llanes, Susan Horstmann
English Coordinator & Teacher
McBee, Leonard Wayne, Jr.
6th-12th Grade Band Director
Osina, Martha A.
English Teacher
Peabody, Patrick Timothy, Sr.
History Teacher
Peabody, Wanda Bell
Math Coordinator & Teacher
VANDERBILT
Griffith, Carol Sappington
High School Mathematics Tchr
VEGA
DeMasters, Rick Dale
Social Studies Teacher
VENUS
Baker, Estelle A.
English Teacher
Smith, Pamela Sue
Assistant Principal
VERNON
Adams, Mary Tabor
First Grade Teacher
Harkey, Gary Don
Ag, Farm & Ranch Mgmt Instr
Mayer, Tony O'Keith
Fifth Grade Teacher
Morrissey, Evelyn (Wight)
Seventh Grade Art Teacher
Parmer, Sandy Slye
Fifth Grade Reading Teacher
Ramsey, Patsy Hainline
Soc Stud Tchr & Dept Chprsn
Rogers, Rebecca B.
English Teacher
Vargas, Deanna Hughes
English Teacher
Waskiw, Daria Maria
Nurse Educator
Winn, Sharon Lewis
Bus & Tech Dept Chair & Instr
Wofford, Kay (Writer)
English & Speech Teacher
VICTORIA
Ahmed, Sharon Rose
Biotechnology Science Teacher
Barboza, Olga
7th-8th Grade Spanish Teacher
Brooks, Brenda Carville
Director of Development
Campbell, Jo Dunnica
Assistant Professor of Psych
Carroll, Susanne Ryan
Algebra Teacher
Coons, William J.
Biology Instructor
Darilek, Faith Chumchal
Director of Education
DeLosSantos, Estella Palacios
Assistant Professor
Etzler, Gwendolyn Joan
Computer & Math Teacher
Ford, Marilyn Claire
Instructor of English
Garrett, Caroline Creel
Accounting & Bus Admin Prof
Grunewald, Laura Mangold
Mathematics Teacher
Hahn, Judith Anne
High School English Teacher
Hardin, Stephen L.
History Professor
Harrington, Rick
Assoc Prof of Psychology
Harris, Ken
5th Grade Teacher
Heinold, Sandra Garrett
English Teacher
Horton, Debbie Dismuke
Biology Teacher
Janda, Paul L.
History & Political Sci Instr
Kallus, Chris Edward
Director of Respiratory Care
Laurence, Allan Hardee
Dean of Students
Laurence, Bo
Latin Teacher
Lewis, Ruth Middendorf
Retired Med & Srgcl Nrsng Tchr
Lovejoy, Tom
Math Teacher & Bsktbl Coach
Martin, Sylvia Jurena
Mathematics Teacher
Mc Cord, Nancy Lynn
6th Grade Math Teacher
Mc Crury, James Earl
Director of Bands
Moeller, Barbara Breed
English Instructor
Moritz, Joan Hobbs
High School Teacher
Muschalek, Jody
Drafting Technology Dept Head
Parks, Joanne Torres
Pre-Primary Montessori Teacher
Pawlik, James Stanley
Agriculture Science Teacher
Peters, Nancy J.
English Teacher
Plemons, Marie Stern
Assistant Professor
Pozzi, David Charles
Mathematics Teacher
Ramirez, Elizabeth Garcia
Spanish & Bible Teacher
Rosser, Andrea Lynn
Latin Teacher
Sager, Ray S.
Chemistry Instructor
Salley, Kaydeene Stubblefield
Mathematics Teacher
Sanchez, Blanca Lopez
Art Teacher
Sarna, Dawn Wayne
Chemistry Tchr
Scott, Judith Hedrick
Second Grade Teacher
Scull, Alberta Christine
Math Teacher
Shafer, Patricia Rene
Assistant Principal
Soliz, Thomas J.
High School Math Teacher
Stokes, Harold Tad
Electronics Instructor
Totah, Jeanette T.
Language Arts Teacher
Urbanovsky, Tresa Maxwell
Social Studies Teacher
Venegas, Raphael
Instructor of Span & Eng
Weber, Michael James
Music Prof & Dir of Choirs
White, Bertha Littles
Secondary Counselor
Zavesky, Robert Jerry
Div of Bus & Pub Svcs Chm
VIDOR
Bates, Vicki Jean
PE, Health & Girls Ath Coach
Busceme, Terry Sue Sheffield
English Teacher
Giarratano, Belinda Marie
Speech Communications Teacher
Guidry, Paige Lormand
English III Teacher
Hester, Linda Dillahunty
Choir Teacher
Holman, Krista Lauren
High School English Teacher
Hoosier, Linda Roeder
Social Studies Teacher
Lanier, Wendy Hinote
4th Grade Science Teacher
Leslie, Bettye Edwards
Teacher & Department Chairman
Morris, Margie Mc Gahey
Third Grade Teacher
Painter, Sherri Kay
PE & Health Education Teacher
Parks, Beverly Landry
Choir & Music Specialist
Portie, Lyndia Johnson
Teacher
Rice, Loren Melvin, Jr.
Assistant Principal
Salisbury, Joan L. Smith
Third Grade Teacher
Spiers, Carolyn D.
English Teacher & Dept Head
Strange, June Monic
Drafting Teacher
Thomas, Linda F.
Assistant Principal
Todd, Donald Linn
Band Director
Trahan, Jo Ann Rice
Second Grade Teacher
Wilkinson, Carolyn Fuller
Mathematics Teacher
WACO
Achor, Sharon L. (Slack)
English Teacher
Alexander, Jeanette Pick
Biology Teacher
Amyett, Paddy Westergard
Program Director & Instructor
Austin, Linda Mason
English Instructor
Baird, Robert M.
Philosophy Professor
Balmos, Donald Clyde
Fine Arts Chairman
Battles, Mary Helen
Science & Amer History Teacher
Beck, Rosalie
Assoc Professor of Religion
Bishop, Joe Howard
Physical Science Teacher
Bohde, Cheryl D.
Instructor of English
Bringol, Laura Anita
Physics & Chemistry Teacher
Brooks, Robbie Alberta
Elementary School Counselor
Brown, Jacki Stanley
Sixth Grade Lang Arts Tchr
Bunting, Helen Mc Cance
Reading Teacher
Burnette, Hoyt Jackson
Prof of Anatomy & Physiology
Calhoun, Christin C.
Secondary Mathematics Teacher
Capers, Cathy Cawood
K-5th Grd Tchr of G & T
Casarez, Irene Guajardo
Educational Consultant
Comer, Lori Lewis
French & English Teacher
Concilio, Paul A.
Instr of Business & Accounting
Cummings, Rhonda Carol (Willard)
English Teacher
Davis, Carol Smith
3rd, 5th & 8th Grade Teacher
Davis, Elaine
High School Art Teacher
Detlefsen, Nancy Roberts
Middle School Counselor
Doherty, Marilyn (Garner)
Home Economics Teacher
Dominik, Pam Mann
1st Grade Teacher
Dunham, David F.
Band Director
Flentge, Clark
German Teacher
Flowers, Jamelle
Theatre Fac & Costume Designer
Frosch, Mary Lynn
8th Grade English Teacher
Gawloski, Anne
Retired 2nd Grade Teacher
Glomb, Debbie Marie (Kramolis)
7th-8th Grade Math Instructor
Hahn, James Edward
Bible Teacher
Hahn, Jan Smithey
Director
Hall, Juliet Metcalf
Retired Third Grade Teacher
Hall, Mamie Bragg
Title One Teacher
Hankins, Barry G.
Assoc Dir of Church-State Inst
Hassell, Patricia Berryhill
Teacher
Hibbitts, Max Comelle
Coach & Biology Teacher
Hopkins, Kathryn Harmon
Science Department Chair
Houser, Sheila Ann
Lrng Disabilities Specialist
Hughes, H. Dale
Professor of Religion
Jackson, Janis (Odom)
Instructor of Biology Dept
Johnson, Janice Murray
Earth Science Teacher
Johnson, Mildred Martin
Third Grade Teacher

O (cont)
on, Walter Edward
ructor of Collision
ow, Debbie Golden
lish Teacher
Karen Ann
t Grade Teacher
, Teresa Sims
logy Teacher
, Carol Ann
lish Instructor
, Charlotte Vrba
glish Teacher
, Ricky Lynn
atre Dir & Fine Arts Chm
nay, Susan Milligan
Grade Teacher
hall, Paula Teague
sics & Chemistry Instructor
n, Ronnie Earl
rumentation Tech Asst
lain, Johnnie Gaston
eer & Technology Teacher
r, Sue Nell (Graham)
t Grade Teacher
emayor, Gilbert
d Coord of Upward Bound Pgm
, Bobbie Nell
ired 3rd Grade Teacher
nes, Manuel
rld History Teacher
ck, Mary Howell
glish Department Chairman
s, Branda Preston
glish Teacher
cek, Debra Rudolph
glish Teacher
rd, Nadine
ired 5th Grade Teacher
oy, James Richard
ds Dir & Percussion Stud
Mary Levan
oir Dir & English IV Teacher
Mitchell, Nancy Denise
nagement Instructor
ovich, Marcia D.
Grade Language Teacher
, Linda Senior
dergarten Teacher
olds, Karen Blackwell
ial Studies Teacher
rs, Kathleen M.
me Economics Teacher
ifer, Ann Maxwell
hth Grade English Teacher
oeder, Martha L.
cher & Coach
on, Kelly J.
logy Instructor
ers, Yvonne Reed
unselor
lwood, Roy Clinton, III
ence Dept Chairman
, Carol Hanna
glish Teacher
enson, Charles Milton
gh School Band Director
az, Sara
igion Teacher
her, Phyllis Mondell (Helms)
acher
blefield, Anita Jean
st Grade Teacher
ek, Debbie M.
& 8th Grade English Tchr
, Patricia Ann
& 8th Grade Spanish Tchr
or, Elva Jo
urth Grade Teacher
or, Mary Katherine
junct English Instructor
nson, Margaret Shepard
rector & Principal
tow, Gretchen Marie
cial Studies Teacher
, Rhonda Ashley
glish Teacher
er, Brian Allen
th & Computer Sci Teacher
eman, David A.
glish Teacher
en, Denny Smith
vernment & Economics Teacher
ey, Archie, Sr.
nior Instructor
s, Lori Kathleen
glish Instructor
iams, Maxine Barham
reign Lang Chm & Span Tchr
ELDER
ner, Roy Wayne
gh School English Teacher
LL
pbell, Elsie Gustafson
ath Teacher
rod Goff, Susan Harting
alth Occupations Faculty
ren, Coral Jean (Mc Nutt)
mputer Applications Teacher
elis, Noni (Stalnaker)
orld Geography Teacher
man, Jay D.
mputer Literaacy Teacher
LLER
nett, Sabrina Roberts
gh School Counselor
ell, Dianne Hundley
glish Teacher
g, Verna Petry
ome Economics Teacher

Ellis, Angie
Teacher & Dept Chairperson
Faigle, Lois Elaine
Elementary Couselor
Garrett, Mary Freeman
Business & Vocational Ed Tchr
Johnson, Chandra
7th-8th Grd Drama & ESL Tchr
Juby, Suzanna C. M.
French Teacher
Lowden, Jonathan Lee
Mathematics Teacher
Nickleberry, Teresa Kemp
Consumer & Tech Ed Teacher
Powell, Linda Stermer
Mathematics Teacher
Turlington, Mary Evelyn Cliver
Fourth Grade Teacher

WALLIS

Kreitz, Denise Muegge
Algebra, Trig & Calculus Tchr
Mize, Shirley Arlene
Administrator & Teacher

WARREN

Thompson, Sharon Booth
4th Grade Teacher

WATER VALLEY

Thornton, Pamela Lewis
Eng Dept Chair & Teacher
Williams, Sharon Helsley
Science Dept Chair & Teacher

WAXAHACHIE

Adams, Donna Nelson
World History Teacher
Centera, Linda Spencer
Third Grade Teacher
Centera, William A.
Director of Bands
Christmas, Jan
Spanish Teacher
Edwards, Nancy Price
ESOL & English Teacher
Fenton, Jan Lewis
Fifth Grade Teacher
Gilbert, Larry D.
Director
Hughes, Vance Tarice
Content Mastery Tchr & Coach
Jenkins, Karen Navarro
English Teacher
Loveland, Candace Anne
US History Teacher
Matteson, Elizabeth Herrington
Asst Principal & Math Teacher
Smith, Jacqueline Annette
Kindergarten Teacher
Yowell, David Robert
World Geography Tchr & Coach

WEATHERFORD

Anderson, Patricia Fleming
Chemistry Teacher
Ash, Kala Carlisle
Office Adm Coop Coordinator
Baker, Elizabeth
Music Teacher & Choir Dir
Baker, Elmo C.
Business Management Instr
Bourland, Cleo Patterson
Eighth Grade Teacher
Boyles, Mary Ann
Cosmetology Dir & Instructor
Broughton, Eloise Lawson
Vocational Nursing Instructor
Brown, Deborah Mallette
Biology & Algebra Teacher
Brown, Michael Leland
Division Dir of Agriculture
Cantrell, Jay
English Teacher & Coach
Carroll, Charles Thomas
11th-12th Grd AP English Instr
Carter, Nika Orm
Dance Team Director & Teacher
Church, Twyla K.
English Teacher
Clark, Paula Jane
Spanish, GATE & PAL Teacher
Ferguson, Laura Robinson
Mathematics Instructor
Goben, Steven Douglas
History Teacher
Harrison, Sheila Starr
6th-8th Grd Sci & Hlth Tchr
Hudgens, John R.
Criminal Justice Professor
King, Shirley Fowler (Morris)
AP English Teacher
Littlefield, G. Duane
Psychology Professor
Mc Cleery, Will Cody
Agriculture Science Teacher
Poston, Timothy F.
Criminal Justice Division Dir
Ribble, Orville Wayne
Retired Teacher
Schmidtzinsky, Barbara Ann
Math Teacher
Spivey, Theresa Mc Mahon
Reading Improvement Teacher
Tate, Anita L.
Div Dir of Speech & Fine Arts
Walden, David Brian
Coach & World History Teacher
Wright, Elizabeth Susan
Bus & Ofc Systems Tech Instr
Young, Mary Kay
Office Systems Tech Instr

WEBSTER

Mc Glothlin, Tanya Hurst
1st Grade Teacher

Stitsinger, Martha Arthur
1st Grade Teacher

WEIMAR

Jurecka, Nancy Wyatt
Bio, Chem & Physics Teacher

WELLINGTON

Ford, Rocky Kyle
English Teacher
Spillman, Norma Beseda
Second Grade Teacher

WELLMAN

Vann, Leslie Lee
Principal

WESLACO

Aguirre, Maria Evangelina (Alonso)
3rd Grade Bilingual Teacher
Bovee, Jean A.
11th Grade English Teacher
Casas, Fidel Oscar
American History Teacher
Cavazos, Juan J.
Social Studies Teacher & Coach
Gering, Steven James
Biology Teacher
Gonzalez, Mary A. Ansiso
Business Education Teacher
Hendrick, Mary Esther Hudgins
French Teacher
Hicks, Diana Tovar
Business Education Teacher
Huff, Ronald Eugene
His, Ec, Govt & Bio Teacher
Miller, Marion Hellman
Home Economics Tchr & Coord
Rodriguez, Mariya Coleman
English Teacher
Whitney, J. Marvin
Guidance Dir & Bible Teacher

WEST

Byers, Michelle Renee
Theatre Arts, Speech Comm Tchr
Farmer, Sandra Phillips
English Teacher
Janek, Debbie Gerik
Third Grade Teacher
Sandifer, Carol S.
Retired 3rd Grade Teacher
Sansom, Janet Lea
High School Math Teacher
Smith, Kimberly Natt
Social Studies Teacher

WEST COLUMBIA

Brasseux, Patricia A.
Fifth Grade Teacher
Fenley, Anice Edwards
First Grade Teacher
Heble, Anita Schmidt
6th Grade Teacher
Nordt, Paula Powell
Speech Teacher
Sauer, Gay Sizemore
English & Publications Instr
Schmid, Ise Carla
French & German Teacher
Taylor, Nancy Boring
High School Mathematics Tchr
Tosch, Cheryl Ward
American Government Teacher
Willoughby, Joyce Payne
6th Grade Teacher

WHARTON

Billings, Mary Ann White
Fifth Grade Teacher
Davis, Joe Tom
History Instructor
Jones, Marcus Owen
Teacher & Coach
Luttrell, William Douglas
Economics & Graphic Arts Tchr
Scheller, Margaret Frankum
Retired Social Studies Tchr
Wilkinson, Sharon Roberson
6th Grade English Teacher

WHITE DEER

Bolling, Pace Walker
HS Spanish & English Teacher
Bradshaw, Alayne Slover
Bsktbl Coach & Biology Teacher
Coffey, Susan Lorraine
Biology I & Art Teacher
Crain, Jonetta Reynolds
Computer Teacher
Haiduk, Renae
Science Teacher
Nusser, Kelly Coker
Language Arts Teacher
Petty, Wade
Math Teacher
Rapstine, Carolyn A.
Home Economics Teacher

WHITE OAK

Bardwell, Suzanne Brown
Jrnlsm, Sociology & Psych Tchr
Barrow, Norma Thomas
Fifth Grade Teacher
Breitenberg, Norman Eugene
Sixth Grade Social Stud Tchr
Earnhardt, Carolyn Arnold
Second Grade Teacher
Harrison, Karen Willbanks
3rd Grade Teacher
Honea, Travis L.
7th Grd Life Sci & Hlth Tchr
Kennedy, Linda Turner
Fifth Grade Teacher
Mason, Melissa
8th Grade US History Teacher
Snoddy, Linda Diane
Kindergarten Teacher

Stagner, Donna Sue
First Grade Teacher

WHITEFACE

Roulain, Sally McAteer
Special Education Teacher
Stockman, Durward Travis
Teacher

WHITEHOUSE

Albright, Jeanne Wood
Eighth Grade English Teacher
Brazeal, Frances Post
Cmptr Sci Dept Head & Teacher
Brown, Tammy Wynn
HS Math Teacher & Coach
Burch, Jim D.
Athletic Director
Carruth, Carolyn Edwards
Sixth Grade Math Teacher
Deike, Terri Roberts
Biology Instr & Bsktbl Coach
Dews, Sharon DeLois (Ford)
Fourth Grade Teacher
Etheredge, Shelta R.
4th Grade Teacher
Falls, Patricia Freeman
HS English Teacher
Gaddis, Cynthia Cagle
8th Grade Math Teacher
Hays, Deanna Lytle
Life Management Skills Teacher
Jackson, Lisa Irwin
7th & 8th Grd Science Teacher
Johnson, Tina Miller
High School Teacher
Klueppel, Brenda Reagan
HS English Teacher
Littrell, Karen Brandenburg
Computer Teacher
Perry, Vickie Marie Smith
Spanish Teacher
Randall, Sherri Meyer
Counselor
Rawlings, Charles Wesley
History Teacher & Coach
Sadler, Amanda Cordelia
Dance Tchr & Drill Team Dir
Smith, Craig Johnson
Biology I Teacher
Thompson, Tony C.
Social Studies Teacher
Walker, Ann B.
World History Teacher

WHITESBORO

Amos, Donna Bloomer
Middle School Counselor
Bateman, Susan Mary
8th Grade Earth Science Tchr
Davenport, Laurie Mackey
Fourth Grade Teacher
Denton, D. Rebecca
7th Grade English Teacher
Hayes, Janette Sandridge
Spanish Teacher
Raley, Brenda Fulenchek
Math, Cmptr Sci, Physics Tchr
Sissney, Nanette
Government, Ec & US His Tchr
Underwood, Nelma Sissney
Retired 5th Grade Teacher

WHITEWRIGHT

Watkins, Regina Threet
Fifth Grade Teacher

WHITHARRAL

Albus, Karol Steffens
8th-11th Grd Math & Eng Tchr
Baker, Micky Kent
Government Teacher
Snell, Benjamin Franklin
Science Teacher

WHITNEY

Haley, Curtis Lynn
Science Teacher
Watson, Melaney O'Neil
Fourth Grade Teacher

WICHITA FALLS

Aldridge, Margaret Curwen
6th Grade Homeroom Teacher
Arnold, Rhonda Pistole
10th Grd Eng & PAL Tchr
Arp, Kay Lynn
Lang Arts Tchr, Rdng Specialst
Babbitt, Barbara Ann (Jones)
Math Teacher
Beshear, Kennetta Slagle
Math Dept Chairman & Teacher
Burnett, Lavere
Electronics Instructor
Callahan, Mary Ahern
Fifth Grade Teacher
Carroll, Wendell Gene
Coach & Health Teacher
Cecil, Carol Hulsey
4th Grade Teacher
Chancellor, Thomas Franklin
Campus Athletic Coordinator
Cline, Jack C., Jr.
Mathematics Teacher
Cook, Kathi
Mathematics Teacher
Davis, Toi Cara
Spanish Teacher
Farris, Patricia Lile
2nd Grade Teacher
Faulkner, Patricia Diane (Howard)
5th-6th Grade Reading Teacher
Fleming, Richard G.
Associate Professor of Physics
Forsythe, Ute Reinig
German & French Teacher

Gilbert, Katherine A. Snyder
Spanish II & III Teacher
Gillette, Soni
English Teacher
Gilley, Cheryl Kaye
Eng Tchr & Dept Chprsn
Goodman, Deborah Kay Chapman
Govt & Honors Economics Tchr
Henderson, Steven Brent
Honors Biology Teacher
Himstedt, Tillie
Math Department Chair
Hoggard, James Martin
English Professor
Hutson, Carol Sandefur
7th Grade Literature Teacher
Isbell, Billie Ross
English Teacher
Jackson, Alice M. (Piggee)
Fifth Grade Teacher
Keeter, Georgia London
Second Grade Teacher
LaBeff, Emily Elizabeth
Professor of Sociology
Malone, Judith Kathryn
7th Grade Math Teacher
Martin, Gwen Moore
English & Psychology Teacher
Maxwell, Nancy Breneman
High School Business Teacher
Mayo, Susan Edwards
Third Grade Teacher
McGalliard, Jana Lynn
Business & Computer Teacher
McKee, Dorothy Candice
Spanish Teacher
Menefee, Larry Donnell
American Culture Teacher
Merder, Kathy A.
Yearbook, Photo & Art Teacher
Merrill, Linda L.
Teacher
Mikalunas, Robin Dawn
Choral Music Director
Moser, Tanya Jones
Math & Science Teacher
Newsom, Hal E.
Debate & Communication Teacher
Patrick, Daniel Burch
Biology Teacher
Pearson, John Joseph
AP US History & Honors Teacher
Ray, Betty Marak
Instructor of Office Tech
Riordan, JoCarol Dowd
8th Grd Eng Tchr & Dept Head
Roberts, James Wayne
Reading, Health & PE Teacher
Roberts, Olga Davis
Fifth-Sixth Grd Eng Teacher
Robertson, Linda Ripper
High School Math Teacher
Savell, James William
JROTC Teacher & Ftbl Coach
Smith, JoBeth Lambert
6th Grade Science & Music Tchr
Stone, Tammy G.
1st Grade Teacher
Studer, Joe Henry
Soc Stud & Amer His Dept Head
Tate, Jody Vassar
English Teacher & Coach
Travis, Tracy Lynn
Second Grade Teacher
Urban, Barbara Ranallo
Science Teacher of GATE
Vantrease, Mary Sue Gay
Science Teacher & Dept Chm
Warren, LeeAnne Clink
Biology Teacher
Wearth, Patricia Beuselinck
Math Teacher
Webber, Mary Watson
Mathematics Teacher
Wilkinson, Kelly Oden
6th Grade Teacher
Wiseman, Margaret Johnson
Teacher of English & GATE

WILLIS

Bennett, Minnie Sams
7th Grade Reading Teacher
Chenault, Debra Jackson
US His Tchr & Soc Studies Chm
Kendrick, Leigh-Anne
History Teacher
Marquart, Wendy Elaine
Director of Bands
Morrow, Kate Ketner
Math, Sci & Soc Stud Teacher
Piskura, Irene Kraith
Retired Elementary School Tchr
Vela, David G.
Drama Department Chair
West, Pam
Spanish Teacher
Wilson, Nancy Rabuck
French & Spanish Teacher

WILLS POINT

Gibson, Cynthia R.
Mathematics & Algebra Teacher
Margan, Bettie Savannah
Third Grade Teacher
Ragland, Othela James, Jr.
Agricultural Science Teacher

WIMBERLEY

Flatt, Danna C.
Eng I Pre AP Tchr & Coach
Richards, Ronald Russell
HS Science Teacher & Dept Chm

WINDTHORST
Coppage, Delberta Frances
English & AP English Teacher
Haile, Donna Bullock
Soc Stud & Lang Arts Teacher
Schreiber, Carolyn Ashbrook
English & Reading Teacher
Schroeder, Scotta Lea
Fifth Grade Mathematics Tchr
Scott, Nancy R.
Kindergarten Teacher
WINK
Horner, Lillian
Retired Math Teacher
Martin, Roger E.
History, PE Teacher & Coach
Thomas, Daniel Scott
I T Teacher
WINNIE
Devillier, Dianne
Chapter I Teacher
Franzen, Steven Wayne
Science Teacher
Gilfillian, Tammie LeBlanc
5th Grade Mathematics Teacher
Hope, Elena Watts
Advanced Biology Teacher
LaPointe, Georgia Louise
English Instructor
Mc Donald, Beverly Pyka
Algebra Teacher
WINNSBORO
Morrison, Mirtie (Lee)
Second Grade Teacher
Warren, Kristie Lynn
English Teacher & Dept Chair
WINONA
Denson, Debbie Hickson
2nd Grade Teacher
West, Syntha Traughber
Secondary Counselor
WINTERS
Davis, Cindy Johnson
English Teacher
Magee, Brilla Jane
Kndgtn-6th Grd Teacher of GATE
Ramariz, Antonio
High School Spanish Teacher
Rice, Sharon Steen
Jr High Reading Teacher
WODEN
Allen, Angela Kaye Gammill
Pre Kindergarten Teacher
Gleghorn, Darrin
PE & Computer Literacy Tchr
Prause, Charles
Agri-Science Teacher
WOLFFORTH
Arendell, Russell W.
Math Teacher
Dallas, Fern I.
8th Grade English Teacher
Dodson, Teresa Tindell
Mathematics Teacher
Donini, Susan Kay (DeBord)
Teacher of Gifted & Talented
Fletcher, Cathy
Computer Specialist
French, Kari Lyn
Speech & Theatre Teacher
Garcia, Ana Flores
Spanish Teacher
Gary, Rhonne Elaine
5th Grade Teacher
Graves, Tina Gossett
Math Teacher
Guajardo, Barbara A.
8th Grade Reading Teacher
Hall, Susan Murray
Title I Parent Invlvmnt Coord
Hamilton, Kathryn Jay
English IV Teacher
Hartsfield, Iva Simpkins
Seventh Grd Soc Studies Tchr
Jerabek, Jerry D.
HS Math Teacher & Coach
Meadows, Carolyn Marie
Algebra Teacher
Morris, Susan Grigsby
Economics Teacher
Parrish, Carol Graham
5th Grade Teacher
Scarborough, Donna Snyder
Math Teacher
Shelfer, Stephen A.
Computer Science Teacher
Vardy, Mary Lou
5th Grade Teacher
Weese, Tiffany A.
English & Reading Teacher
West, Robin Reeves
Art Teacher
Willis, Priscilla Rothwell
HS & Scndry Level Eng Teacher
WOODLANDS
Stover, Jill Vittrup
English Teacher
WOODSBORO
Sweet, Tim Eugene
History Teacher
WOODVILLE
Borel, Jan Vinson
Fifth Grade Language Arts Tchr
Cooley, John Allen, Jr.
Biology Teacher & Coach
Santos, Rebecca Basil
English Teacher
WORTHAM
Sheffield, Connie Adkisson
Science Teacher
WYLIE
Barefoot, Lexie Cantrell
Dyslexia Coord & Therapist
Black, Julie Jordan
English Teacher
Cherry, Claudia Smith
Special Education Teacher
Dale, Carolyn Cross
Business Ed Teacher
David, Kimberley Michelle Carter
English & GATE Teacher
Dodd, Norma Beard
Eighth Grade History Teacher
Doyle, Margaret Minto
First Grade Teacher & Team Ldr
Eavenson, Marica Whitten
4th Grade Teacher
Green, Nancy Germany
English Instructor
Hartley, John Michael
Agriscience Teacher
Hudson, Robert Allen
Economics Teacher & Coach
Robinson, Perry D.
Counselor
Shirey, V. Timothy
Choir Director
Stone, Joe Carroll
English Teacher & Coach
Wilbanks, Philip D.
CAD Teacher & Baseball Coach
YANTIS
Allison, Sandra Broyles
5th Grade Teacher
McKeever, Carol Harmon
Social Studies Teacher
YOAKUM
Kurtz, Johanna Helen
Seventh Grade Teacher
Parr, Patricia Dian
High School Business Teacher
YORKTOWN
Wolf, Joyce Ann
English Dept Head & Teacher
ZAPATA
Araiza, Antonia
Mathematics Teacher
Benavides, Jose Santana
Special Education Teacher
Bingham, Belinda V.
English Teacher
Garcia, Cesar Eduardo
Band Director
Garcia, Homero
Self Employed
Garza, Amada Villarreal
Science Teacher
Goodwin, Sharon Needham
American History Teacher
Legaspi, Rogie B.
Dept Chprsn & Science Tchr
Lujan, Federico
Health Occupations Ed Teacher
Martinez, Leticia V.
Counselor
Uribe, Omar David
Teacher & Art Instructor
ZAVALLA
Gulley, Phyllis Eugenia (Powell)
Science Teacher
ZEPHYR
Yantis, Lorenna Bird
Secondary Science Teacher

UTAH

ALPINE
Pope, Nancy Ann
Third Grade Teacher
Searle, Ann Christensen
Fourth Grd Tchr & Intern Coord
Wiser, Analee Carlin
Fifth Grade Teacher
ALTAMONT
Brotherson, Virginia Wardle
4th Grade Teacher
AMERICAN FORK
Allen, Robin Jacobsen
English Teacher
Barr, Merrilee Judd
Music Specialist & Math Tchr
Bennion, Karen B.
Gifted & Talented Teacher
Brown, Diane Batmale
US History Teacher
Durrant, Ross Duane
Fifth Grade Teacher
Johnson, Carolyn Walters
Fifth Grade Teacher
Keetch, Suzanne Smith
Family & Consumer Science Tchr
Mc Bride, Kristine
Reading Recovery Teacher
Miller, John Lewis
Director of Bands
Mower, Michael Don
9th Grd World Studies Teacher
Rawlings, Elaine Ahlstrom
A P English Teacher
Richards, Audrey Ann
HS Biology & PE Teacher
Shelley, Laurel T.
English & Latin Teacher
Thomas, Vallen Lee
English & Social Science Tchr
Wilson, Gary Richard
Spanish Teacher
Woodward, Sherry Murphy
HS Teacher & Dir of Forensics
Zaugg, Melanie Gamble
Russian Teacher
BINGHAM CANYON
Mitchell, Cindy Pier
Geography Teacher
BLANDING
Gutke, Lurlene Palmer
2nd Grade Teacher
Wilcox, Janet Keeler
Journalism & English Teacher
BLUFFDALE
King, Sandra Dee
5th Grade Teacher
BOUNTIFUL
Allred, Anne Wilson
English Teacher
Andersen, Marilyn Clay
Math Teacher & Dept Chair
Bigler, Mary Kay
First Grade Teacher
Birdsall, Paulette C.
Spanish Teacher
Bonner, Marion
Third Grade Teacher
Busk, David John
Art History & Music Teacher
Coe, Janis A.
English Teacher
Decker, David Stephens
French & English Teacher
Drake, LeAnn Cutler
AP English Lit & Lang Teacher
Dubois, Lynn L.
Social Studies Teacher
Fager, Trudena
Library Media Teacher
Gill, David Robert
Math Teacher
Goldberg, William
Mathematics Dept Chairman
Harris, Ross Long
Sociology & Spanish Teacher
Kirkland, Theda Crook
4th Grade Teacher
Klein, Rebecca T.
First Grade Teacher
Knight, Kimberly Ann
AP Calculus Teacher
Layton, Kathy L.
A P European His Tchr
Nielsen, Jennifer A.
Speech & Debate Teacher
Porter, Barbara J.
English Teacher
Stewart, Dyan Holbrook
Ninth Grade English Teacher
Wall, Larry J.
Head Football Coach & PE Tchr
Ward, Robyn Tolman
Mathematics Teacher
Watts, Lynette Flake
Teacher
Winter, Paula Panarello
5th Grade Teacher
Zeeman, Kenneth L.
English Teacher
BRIGHAM CITY
Barney, Wendy Mertlich
Health Educator
Batzel, Joseph Anthony
Speech & Drama Chairman
Burningham, Lee
Pottery & Sculpture Teacher
Cefalo, Ronald
Physics Instructor
Checketts, Preston J.
Cnslr, Regnl Schl to Wrk Coord
De Monja, Marko
History & English Teacher
Findley, Thomas Glenn
High School Seminary Teacher
Fuller, James D.
Psychology Teacher
Goldsberry, A. Reid
English Teacher
Graham, Cheryl Walker
Third Grade Teacher
McDonald, William Eric
Spanish Teacher
Merrill, Wendy Hawkes
Fourth Grade Teacher
Nielsen, Douglas Lawrence
Fourth Grade Teacher
Wankier, Bruce M.
Sixth Grade Teacher
Wiberg, Delos P.
German Teacher
Wight, Richard F.
English Teacher
CASTLE DALE
Kofford, Lana Leonard
5th Grade Teacher
CEDAR CITY
Ault, John Thomas
Professor of Psychology
Bowns, James E.
Professor of Biology
Duerson, Bradley Keith
Asst Prof of International Bus
Hinton, Wayne K.
Chair of Social Science Dept
Lee, Wm David
Language & Lit Dept Chair
Modesitt, Carol Ann Janes (Hill)
Asst Prof of Choral & Music
Overson, Rae
Home Economics Teacher
Shirts, Steve
Director of Bands
Silber, Linda Diane
Asst Prof of Sociology
Walker, Thomas W.
Elementary School Principal
CENTERVILLE
Hanson, Davie Lonis
Mathematics Teacher
Memmott, Mary Ellen Russell
TAP Teacher & Asst Principal
Prinster, Shelly Lynn Dunroe
Math Teacher
Remington, Norma Jean Skidmore
Geography & Civics Teacher
Roy, Barbara Freestone
Sixth Grade Teacher
CLEARFIELD
Anderson, Steven R.
Band Director
Chandler, Lori
Student Activities Director
Dumas, Connie S.
History Teacher
Godfrey, Kirk B.
Religion Instructor
Hansen, Craig Keith
History & Current Issues Tchr
Heninger, Michelle Hansen
First Grade Teacher
Johnson, Randy T.
World His & Conditioning Tchr
Manning, JaNae
Fifth Grade Teacher
Nelson, Wendy Moore
Marketing & Advertising Tchr
Polad, Daniel Ross, Sr.
History Teacher
Sanders, Julie Musgrave
4th Grade Teacher
Smith, Brenda Kaye
Physical Science Teacher
Sommerkorn, Susan Julian
Mathematics Teacher
Sparks, Susan Lloyd
Sixth Grade Teacher
Stander, Max L., Sr.
Art Teacher
Van Dyke, Rebecca L.
Advanced Placement Eng Teacher
Vaterlaus, Launa Bennett
5th Grade Teacher
Welty, Jaynee Adair
Dance Teacher
Whitesides, Boyd
Business Law & Accounting Tchr
Yorgason, Stephanie Thompson
Math Teacher
Zurbuchen, John Frederic
Jr High Eng & Soc Stud Tchr
CLEVELAND
Bingham, Christy Emmett
Fourth Grade Teacher
Rasmussen, Vicki Lynn
Second Grade Teacher
COALVILLE
Garfield, Douglas Kent
Science Teacher
Richins, Brett Normon
Middle School Teacher
Roemmich, Barbara Willoughby
Business Teacher
DELTA
Nickle, Sherry Lee Payne
Family & Consumer Science Tchr
Schena, Patricia Probert
Kindergarten Teacher
DUGWAY
Nielson, LeeRoy
Music Director
Swynenburg, Betsy Lynn
Biology Tchr & Sci Dept Chprsn
EAST CARBON
Doporto, David, Jr.
High School Art Teacher
EDEN
Arnell, Stuart Gaylen
History Teacher
EPHRAIM
Baker, Roger G.
Prof of English & Education
Gardner, Paul Allen
Assoc Prof of Biology
Spencer, Diana Major
Associate Professor of English
EUREKA
Taylor, Thomas Mark
Drivers Ed, His & Hlth Tchr
FARMINGTON
Bunderson, Richard J.
Social Studies Teacher
Cressall, Don
Electronic Instruction Spclst
Hutcheson, Carol Manning
English & Drama Teacher
Page Flygare, Kathleen
Second Grade Teacher
FERRON
Card, Rose Marie
Language Arts Teacher
Clement, Collette Powell
Sixth Grade Teacher
Larson, Lynn B.
History Teacher
Wareham, Maribelle Brown
Fourth Grade Teacher
FIELDING
Warren, Richard Fredrick
4th Grade Teacher
FILLMORE
Baugh, Linda Wright
English Teacher
Keel, Tracy Shane
Social Studies Teacher
Myers, Ralph J.
English Teacher
GARLAND
Hawkes, Leonard Morgan
German Teacher & Stu Cncl Adv
Johnsen, D. Brent
AP Mathematics Teacher
Leyva, Charles B.
Spanish Teacher
Mazaros, Claudia Ann
Chemistry Department Head
Payne, Shauna Adams
4th Grade Teacher
GROUSE CREEK
Roybal, Christine L. Luedtke
Head Teacher
HEBER CITY
Carlile, Marjorie
Ec, Acctng & Japanese Instr
Felsch, Brian Hanks
High School Biology Teacher
Gale, Stephen Leon
Art & Computer Teacher
Hendry, Shanna Burbidge Fenton
Second Grade Teacher
Patterson, Marie Hansen
1st Grade Teacher
Sulser, Allan R.
Agriculture Instructor
Turner, Gary Bruce
Math & Science Teacher
White, Kris Wayne
Religion Teacher
HIGHLAND
Ericksen, Boyd K.
7th-9th Grade Teacher
Feland, Cheryl Crook
Geography Teacher
Gosar, Michael Scott
Biology Tchr & Sci Dept Chair
HOOPER
Dowd, Norma A.
Third Grade Teacher
Hansen, Heidi K. Adams
Mathematics Teacher
Leak, Sheri Nelson
Third Grade Teacher
Rogers, Scott Cannon
Mathematics Teacher
Sharp, Lanette Lloyd
Third Grade Teacher
Sly, Denise
Jr High Social Studies Teacher
Tanner, Donald R.
Science Teacher
HUNTINGTON
Callahan, Gwen B.
Principal
Mc Elprang, Teri L.
Second Grade Teacher
HUNTSVILLE
Evans, Michelle Nowak
6th Grade Teacher
HURRICANE
Candland, Edwin James
Music Director
Christensen, Steven J.
Spanish & English Teacher
Goulding, Robert Lynn
High School Principal
Johnson, Tral D.
Technology Education Teacher
Wilson, Stewart D.
Religious Education Teacher
HYDE PARK
Austin, Leslie Kofoed
Seventh Grade Lang Arts Tchr
HYRUM
Andreasen, Patricia A. C.
English & Art Teacher
Culbertson, Jean
Math Teacher & Team Leader
Hansen, Sheri Perrett
World Geography Teacher
Hunsaker, Stephen K.
Religious Instructor
Lamb, Richard Grant
German Tchr
Pettis, Margaret L.
English Teacher
KAMAS
Embry, Sandy S.
Family & Consumer Science Tchr
KAYSVILLE
Boss, Paula Killpack
Assistant Administrator
Clark, Jan Bishop
3rd Grade Teacher
Comiskey, Gloria Eileen
French Teacher
Hendricks, Steven R.
Music Teacher
Houtz, Randy Lee
Director of Bands
Leo, C. David
Math Teacher
Lochhead, Louise Keiser
Business Teacher
Palmer, Lola H.
9th Grade English Teacher
Robbins, Jennifer Singer
German & Ancient History Tchr
Spencer, Mark Jenson
English & Journalism Teacher

SVILLE (cont)
pson, Michael R.
lish Teacher
RNS
es, Terry Blake
al Studies Teacher
e, Jolene
Grade Teacher
g, Lewis William
n of Stdnts, GATE Geog Tchr
ERKIN
n, David Dale
d Grade Teacher
TON
d, John Hooker
ory & Government Teacher
r, John Kent
Grade Teacher
nan, Jamie Alex
culus Teacher
ng, Brian Keith
Stud & World Cvlztns Tchr
nan, Robert K.
ial Studies Dept Chair
n, Patricia Mehl
ily & Consumer Sci Teacher
tensen, LeAnn
dergarten Teacher
on, Corrine Burningham
& Health Teacher
, Janet Renee
-12th Grd Special Ed Tchr
en, Vicki B.
lish Teacher
n, Suzi Miya
ce Teacher
nt, Steven B.
ative Writing & Eng Teacher
, Preston Warren
amics Teacher
land, Reed C.
Teacher
, Tamara Heaps
Grade Teacher
son, Jolene Clegg
red Third Grade Teacher
, Kevin F.
lish Teacher
ins, Jan
ily & Consumer Sci Educator
ins, Debora Jean
lish Teacher
nette, Kurt Max
inary Instructor
r, Claudia Collier
ial Studies Dept Chair
nons, Stacie Campbell
lish & Journalism Teacher
, Rebecca Tullis
ne Ec Tchr & Stu Cncl Adv
ners, Kathleen Timothy
rth Grade Teacher
, Heidi
h Teacher
ure, Nancy Yoak
emistry & Mathematics Tchr
ht, Nathan Todd
of Choirs & Music Dept Chm
g, Vicki Maureen
og & Creative Writing Tchr
I
ey, Sandra Thalman
glish Teacher
hwaite, Mari Lee
Grade English Teacher
Kent Roundy
em & Physics Tchr, Sci Chm
ois, Marianne D.
-6th Grade Tchr of Gifted
ield, Linda Adamson
Grade Teacher
son, Mary Ann Judd
Chairman & Teacher
rson, Brenda Tanner
& Honors English Teacher
ell, Reva Beth Loveridge
Bio & Physical Earth Tchr
ng, Shauna Hansen
st Grade Teacher
DON
u, Maren Kovacich
ior High Science Teacher
AN
n, Janet Jorgensen
urth Grade Teacher
ood, Scot M.
st Prof of Fam & Hum Dev
no, Gary
ector of Piano Studies
erson, D. Andy
ncipal & Lecturer
erson, Janet B.
trition Professor
erson, Luella F.
sistant Professor
one, Deborah Brown
iversity Lecturer
e, James E.
n Lecturer
na, Dale Jeffrey
soc Prof of Forest Resources
d, Dee R.
ad Adv, Instr & Cont Ed Dir
e, William Bruce
story & Sociology Teacher
er, D. Richard
soc Prof & Asst Dept Head
, Steven Lynn
ncipal

Ehrhart, Jean Abel
Home Ec, Human Grwth, Dev Tchr
Eldredge, Garth M.
Special Education Prof & Coord
Elliott, Cathy Heyrend
Dance & Aerobics Teacher
Hendricks, Deloy G.
Professor of Nutrition
Huerta, Grace C.
Asst Professor of Secondary Ed
Jeppson, Roland W.
Professor
Krebs, Cynthia Olsen
Assoc Prof of Office Tech
Lilieholm, Robert John
Natural Resources Mgmt Tchr
Merrell, Kenneth Winston
Associate Prof of Psychology
Openshaw, D. Kim
Assoc Prof of Fam & Human Dev
Peterson, F. Ross
History Professor
Phillips, Dallin James
Philosophy Instructor
Provenza, Frederick D.
Professor
Rhees, Kaye
Multi-Aged Teacher
Riggs, Lynette Andersen
English Teacher
Rogers, Elizabeth A.
Assoc Prof of Interior Design
Simms, Steven R.
Anthropology Professor
Stephens, Alan A.
Associate Prof of Finance
Strong, Carol Joan
Assoc Prof Commnctv Disorders
Tarnutzer, Shari R.
Mgmt & Human Resources Prof
Turner, Denice H.
English Teacher
Walker, Homer Franklin
Professor of Mathematics
MAGNA
Allen, Ben Roger
Marketing Teacher
Bachman, Lark Spencer
Fourth Grade Teacher
Behling, Kathy Cottle
Fourth Grade Teacher
Child, Warren G.
Drafting Instr & Tech Coord
Crookston, Douglas
Fourth Grade Teacher
Hand, Marcia Majors
5th Grade Teacher
Jones, Robert Allen
Advanced Placement His Teacher
Loch, Starling D.
Title I Specialist
Quigley, Lisa Shafer
7th-9th Grade English Teacher
Roach, Kathy Richins
High School English Teacher
Turner, Elane
English Teacher
Woodring, Angie Jo
French Teacher
MANTI
Miller, Marilyn
Third Grade Teacher
Schiffman, Karen Ashdown
Concurrent Coll English Tchr
MAPLETON
Bennett, Sylvia Storey
Retired Teacher
Christensen, Darlene Jensen
Fifth Grade Teacher
MIDVALE
Brinton, Victoria Ruth
European, Art, & World Tchr
Ekberg, Arlen Fredrik
Biology Teacher
Hose, Gregory Martin
Mathematics Teacher
Kerns, Sharon L.
AP US History Teacher
Leydsman, Thomasania Montgomery
Fifth Grade Teacher
Luker, Steven Thomas
Former Tchr of Hearing Imprd
MILLVILLE
Maughan, Rocky Kellett
5th Grade Teacher
MINERSVILLE
Hollingshead, Chad Steven
Fourth Grade Teacher
MOAB
Calkins, James Ray
English Teacher
Force, Gary Steven
Principal & Teacher
Roy, Philip Lane
Second Grade Teacher
MONROE
Barnson, Jay
5th Grade Teacher
Roberts, Paula B.
Business Teacher
MONTEZUMA CREEK
Lopez, Cecelia B.
Kindergarten Teacher
MONUMENT VALLEY
Dee, Antoinette Smith
Family & Consumer Science Tchr
Silversmith, Boyd
Industrial Arts & Tech Teacher

MORGAN
Bowers, Jill Hoffman
Instrumental Music Teacher
Compton, Annie Rosella
Retired Elementary Teacher
Jensen, Eldon C.
Geology, Chem & Physics Tchr
MOUNT PLEASANT
Boyle, Shannon Leigh
Mathematics Teacher
MURRAY
McConnell, John Tyler
Science Teacher
MYTON
Jones, Gloria Uresk
2nd-3rd Grade Split Teacher
NEOLA
Manning, Dennis Charles
5th Grade Teacher
NEPHI
Carter, Kristy Lynne
Art Teacher
Squire, Everd L.
Mathematics Teacher
Wallace, Lorraine Davis
English Teacher & Choral Dir
NORTH SALT LAKE
Fisher, Karen
6th Grade Teacher
Unger, Daniel L.
6th Grade Teacher
OGDEN
Aiken, Barbara ann
Fifth Grade Teacher of GATE
Armstrong, Deborah Yasenko
Counselor
Atkinson, Richard Paul
Psychology Professor
Ballif, Bryce Dixon
High School Biology Teacher
Barker, Holly
Science & POT Teacher
Barker, Steven W.
Chemistry & Earth Science Tchr
Benson, Carol R.
Home Economics Teacher
Booker, Larry Michael
US History & Geography Teacher
Borup, Byron Lee
World Civilizations Teacher
Boyce, Kay Webster
French Teacher
Cale, Crystal Heslop
English Teacher
Checketts, Glen E.
Fifth Grade Teacher
Christensen, Douglas A.
Technology Instructor
Clausse, Orlou V.
4th Grade Teacher
Coleman, Robert D.
Band Teacher
Courney, Mary K.
9th-12th Grd Math Teacher
Curtis, Elden Marven
Music Dept Head & Vocal Instr
Dame, Sherrie Tucker
5th Grade Teacher
Davis, Andrew Albert
English Teacher
Duncan, Douglas J.
Math Dept Chairperson
Eaton, Linda B.
Assoc Prof of Anthropology
Egbert, Richard Scott
World Geography Teacher
Farnsworth, Rosalyn L.
US & Utah History Teacher
Fink, Nancy Eileen
Third Grade Teacher
Ford, William Emmett
World Geography Teacher
Garner, John Lynn
English & Humanities Teacher
George, June Reynolds
Social Science Teacher & Coord
Green, Diana Jensen
Assoc Prof of Telecmntns
Green, Earl E.
Social Studies Teacher
Griggs, Kevin D.
Band Director & Japanese Tchr
Gruis, Kay Fox
Third Grade Teacher
Hall, Larry R.
5th Grade Teacher
Hart, Jay H.
English History & Hum Teacher
Heiter, Sheri W.
AP Calculus Teacher
Henley, Kay A.
English Teacher
Hirschi, Joan P.
High School English Teacher
Holmes, Margo L.
English Teacher
Isaacs, Nancy Cottrell
English Teacher
Johnson, Helen C.
First Grade Teacher
Johnson, John Marshall
Design Drafting & Arch Instr
Larson, Nadine Fullmer
Fourth Grade Teacher
Leatham, Janet Hatch
Business Teacher
Mc Cullogh, Terri
Assistant Principal
McGregor, Ilene P.
Art & Language Arts Teacher

Miller, Terry Wallace
5th Grd Tchr & Music Director
Miner, Karen Preece
European History Teacher
Miya, Mildred N.
English Professor
Mortenson, Jane Salisbury
Math Teacher
Mortimer, Greg A.
Math & Computer Teacher
Muir, Ferril Ray
Band, Orchestra & Math Instr
Newey, Reid P.
Health Teacher & Coach
Ottley, Merlin Kirk
English Teacher
Palmer, Rita Marie (Mori)
7th-8th Grade English Teacher
Parish, Ralph Aaron
Educator & Baseball Coach
Parry, Michele Thomas
Sr English & Journalism Tchr
Raymond, Lynn Owen
Human Physiology, Anatomy Tchr
Reed, Nancy K.
AP Lit & Composition Teacher
Rogowski, Teresa Jordan
Second Grade Teacher
Rostkowski, Margaret I.
English & Composition Teacher
Salvo, Alexis Eduardo
Spanish Teacher
Searle, Paula Brixius
First Grade Teacher
Sepulveda, Judith Dudley
US History Teacher
Spencer, Mark Rogers
Religion Teacher
Stettler, Krista Henley
Drama Teacher
Stevenson, Alan
Hearing Specialist
Tams, Ken
Fourth & Fifth Grade Teacher
Taylor, Lewis R.
Mathematics Teacher
Taylor, Mary Ann Edwards
Fr & Metalsmithing Design Tchr
Thompson, Suzanne Blake
Biology Teacher
Thurgood, Brent K.
Science Dept Chair
Turner, Gary Ward
Spanish Teacher
Vause, L. Mikel
Professor
Wayment, William Thomas
AP & Coll Prep US History Tchr
Weiss, Annette Johnson
Mathematics Teacher
White, Warren Sevy
Geography & US His Teacher
Wilding, Daren
Art Instructor
Wilson, Charlean S.
Fifth Grade Teacher
Yang, Yu-Jane
Assistant Professor of Piano
OREM
Asay, E. Doyle
Teacher
Borup, David K.
9th Grade English Teacher
Buchman, Joseph Geddes
Prof of Multimedia Marketing
Buck, Lynette Riding
Special Ed & Life Skills Tchr
Burns, Barclay F.
Community Bound Teacher
Bybee, Paul Joseph
Asst Professor of Science
Capell, Rosilene Swenson
HS Teacher, Coord at Risk Prgm
Carpenter, David S.
US History Teacher
Chruma, Jack L.
Human Biology Teacher
Clark, Eugene Edward
Physics & Geology Teacher
Clark, Richard D.
Assistant Principal
Crittenden, Jim F.
Instructor of Physical Ed
Darais, Karin Edmondson
Assistant Professor of Acctng
Davies, Lynn Joyce
Administrative Asst & Teacher
Davis, Bonnie Ottney
Adjunct Faculty
Davis, Suzanne
Physiology & Anatomy Teacher
De Vries, Pia Marjatta (Kirsi)
German Teacher
Evans, Daniel D.
Religion Teacher
Fitzgarrald, Garlan D.
English Teacher
Gillespie, William Bus
History Teacher
Hammond, Ron J.
Sociology Professor
Hemond, Diane Robitaille
History & Journalism Teacher
Hill, Terry S.
Director of Orchestras
Hodson, Terry
6th Grade Teacher
Holt, Julie Rae
Mathematics Teacher

Hwang, Jong S.
Math Professor
Johanson, William Carl
English Teacher & Dept Chm
Kelley, Jeri
Social Studies Teacher
Lamb, James Henry
Science Teacher
Madsen, Vanessa Syphus
French & Japanese Teacher
Manning, David Eugene
Drafting & Design Tech Instr
Mc Allister, Stephanie Walker
Dance Teacher
Mc Clintock Kent, Brenda G.
English Teacher
Mecham, Harvey D.
Chemistry Professor
Melville, James Weller
Elementary Principal
Merrin, Christine Rossi
Asst Professor of Mathematics
Miller, Janice Youngstrom
English & Japanese Teacher
Minor, Beverly Denos
Title I Teacher
Mortenson, Margaret L.
English Teacher & Dept Chair
Muntzing, Elsa P.
5th & 6th Grade Spanish Tchr
Musto, Anita Fabrizio
Business Communication Prof
Nelson, Jean Marie
Fourth Grade Teacher
Olsen, Grant Melvin
Third Grade Teacher
Ormond, Pat Reed
Assoc Prof, Comp Sci Dept
Ostler, Brian H.
Math Teacher
Pella, Rita Harris
Family & Consumer Science Tchr
Phippen, Jillian Preston
English Teacher
Ramstedt, Gregory John
Social Studies & History Tchr
Rice-Macfarlane, Elizabeth Ann
US History Educator
Richardson, Karen
Sixth Grade Teacher
Rogerson, William Kenneth
Sixth Grade Teacher
Sartori, Elizabeth Ann
Second Grade Teacher
Shepherd, Michelle
Art Teacher
Shumway, Linda J.
3rd Grade Teacher
Steele, Robert M.
Bio Tchr, Ftbl & Wrstlng Coach
Stubbs, Marilyn R.
Computer Science Instructor
Tanner, Paul A.
English Professor
Teh, Swee Hor
Asst Prof of Computer Science
Thomas, Cecile Jackson
Art & Photography Teacher
Thomas, Rex L.
Instructor of History
Titemore, Kari Wardrop
Third Grade Teacher
Walker, Christine Ingles
Professor of Mathematics
Weiler, Spencer Charles
History Teacher
PANGUITCH
Houston, James Frank
Science & Math Teacher
PARK CITY
Daly, James Patrick
Social Studies Teacher
PAROWAN
Zaleski, Tom W.
Third & Fourth Grade Teacher
PAYSON
Barber, Paul D.
US History & Geography Tchr
Chynoweth, Elizabeth Legh Neal
English & Spanish Teacher
Deuel, Geneve Cornell
Retired 5th Grade Teacher
Ericksen, Connie Madson
Band Teacher
Osborn, Sunya F.
8th-9th Grade English Teacher
Tanner, Lauren Janice
5th Grade Teacher
PLEASANT GROVE
Gann, Daniel Duane
Fourth Grade Teacher
Gowans, Michael Dan
Agricultural Education Instr
Gurr, RosaMae Finch
Second Grade Teacher
Harper, Daniel Ray
English Teacher
Hrynyshyn, Alec E.
Earth Systems Teacher
Lewis, Laura
Foreign Language Teacher
Nicoll, Diana VanWagenen
Dance Teacher
Thompson, Charlaine Woolfenden
AP Scndry Social Studies Tchr
Thompson, Rachel Joy
English, PE Tchr & Coach
PRICE
Carrillo, Alayne Young
Biology Teacher

PRICE (cont)
Cha, Joe F.
Journalism & US History Tchr
Cox, Phyllis O.
9th Grd Resource Teacher
PROVIDENCE
Kerr, Linda Roskelley
Fifth Grade Teacher
Whoolery, Kristen Cederwall
MS Mathematics Teacher
PROVO
Adams, Michele Arrowsmith
English Teacher
Andrus, Gwendolyn
Dir of Sci Simulation Lab
Ashton, Alan
Electronics Technology Instr
Barker, Michael T.
Sci Chair, Bio & Hlth Teacher
Barker, Sharon McBride
Facilitator
Benson, Alvin K.
Geophysics Professor
Betts, Kristen Carter
History Dept Chair & Teacher
Billings, Todd
Instructional Facilitator
Bohn, Ursula Merz
French Teacher
Bolli, Damon Gerhard
LDS Seminary Prin & Instructor
Brown, Karen Thomas
English Teacher
Burch, Robert John
School Psychologist
Cherry, Scott Clair
Vocational Cabinetmaking Tchr
Clearwater, Tracy Lyneane
11th & 12th Grd Soc Stud Tchr
Crowe, Christopher E.
Associate Professor of English
Day, J. Rodney
Mathematics Teacher
Deichman, Laura Hunt
5th Grade Teacher
Drussel, Patricia Rollins
English Teacher & Dept Chprsn
Durrant, George D.
Senior Consultant
Earle, Rodney Stan
Professor of Teacher Education
Evensen, Nancy Child
University Instructor
Fishler, Jeanette
Health Teacher
Franz, Reinhard O. W.
Visiting Associate Professor
Fullmer, David Charles
Director of Bands
Gibbs, Gaye Lynne
5th-6th Grade Teacher
Goldston, Linda Carol
History & Health Teacher
Hampton, Shannon Snyder
English Teacher
Hudnall, Gregory Allen
Principal
Johnson, Ruth Butcherite
English Teacher
Judd, Allan M.
Assistant Professor of Zoology
Linebarger, Joyce J.
HS English & Math Teacher
Madsen, Joyce H.
5th Grade Teacher
Maenner, Thomas James
Math Instructor
Mitchell, Richard Lynn
Eng Tchr & Boys Bsktbl Coach
Monroe, Eula Ewing
Professor & Mathematics Ed
Murphy, Philip Edward
World His, Global Stud Teacher
Myrup, Alan Ray
AP Biology Teacher
Olson, Barry Wayne
German Teacher & Coach
Parsons, Connie Cloward
First Grade Teacher
Peery, Irene Weiss
Piano Teacher
Perkins, Jerome Marvin
Asst Prof of Church History
Pierce, Kristin Lee
English Teacher
Rasmussen, Keith Farrel
Instructor
Rasmussen, Kristie Jensen
Kindergarten Teacher
Rees, James M.
High School Art Instructor
Rowley, Maxine Lewis
Home Ec & Family Sciences Prof
Schulthies, Shane Sly
Physical Education Professor
Shively, Ann Pye
Dir of Behavior, Medicine Unit
Sloat, Taunia Folkman
Career Center Coordinator
Smith, Kevin L.
Head Ath Trainer & Sports Med
Soerensen, Karen Moake
United States History Teacher
Swenson, Janet Lorraine
Assoc Prof of Theatre & Film
Thurgood, Karen Pendleton
Business Teacher
Twitchell, Gary D.
Science Teacher
Walker, Steven Charles
Professor of English
Walter, Janet Guymon
Mathematics Teacher
RANDOLPH
Batty, Cynthia Fujimoto
Business Education Teacher
Weston, Paula Sue
Kindergarten & 4th Grade Tchr
RICHFIELD
Call, Ronald Glenn
Biology Teacher
Jenson, Mc Kay
Agriculture Education Teacher
Jones, Troy B.
Mathematics Teacher
Morrison, Corey E.
PE & Science Teacher
Stokes, Linda Sistrunk
Family & Consumer Sci Teacher
Wall, Sharon Elaine
Dance & PE Teacher
RICHMOND
Hall, Jennifer Nyman
9th Grade Physical Ed Teacher
Larson, Larry Lee
9th Grade Science Teacher
Petersen, Larry
Home Bound Teacher
Rock, Larry
Fourth Grade Teacher
Sorenson, Stephanie B.
Health Teacher
RIVERTON
Lambdin, Patricia Ann
Science Teacher
Shaddick, Danielle Pratt
Second Grade Teacher
Shirley, Sharon E.
Math Dept Chairman & Teacher
Springer, Barbara K.
English Teacher & Dept Chair
ROOSEVELT
Ebright, Carole Ann
First Grade Teacher
King, Alan Lloyd
School Social Worker
Richmond, Myra Lynne
Family & Consumer Sci Tchr
Scholes, Melody Martin
Upward Bound Academic Advisor
Stradinger, Kirk
English Tchr & Wrestling Coach
Van Wagoner, John Lyndon
Choral & Guitar Instructor
Wood, Rona S.
Former 3rd Grade Teacher
Yack, Lane
Business Education Teacher
ROY
Boyson, Steven R.
English Teacher
Bradshaw, Penn M.
English Teacher
Carper, Donald James
8th Grade English Teacher
Dixon, David Ray
Religious Educator
Dursteler, Linda (Monk)
English Teacher & Dept Chair
Harrop, John C.
Spanish Teacher
Maass, Teresa
Physical Education Teacher
Marcheschi, Thomas D.
Jr High Math Teacher
McAllen, Linda Sue (Price)
Art Teacher
Nelson, Sherrie Rackley
Physics & Chemistry Teacher
Ochsenbein, Kathleen Phipps
Sci & Earth Systems Teacher
Pace, Betty L.
Counselor
Peterson, Gwendlyn F.
6th Grade Teacher
Randall, R. Gordon
Business Dept Chairman & Tchr
Smith, Mark Stephen
History Teacher
Walker, Pamela
Mathematics Teacher
SAINT GEORGE
Abernathy, J.J. (Joyce Marie Jensen)
Eng Dept Chairperson & Teacher
Basile, Don J.
Sociology Instructor
Beck, Lana Metcalf
Third Grade Teacher
Brooks, Warren Paul
HS Mathematics Teacher
Comeford, Robert John
Secondary Mathematics Teacher
Coppinger, Christine Elizabeth
Fifth Grade Teacher
Esmeier, Virginia Clark
English & Journalism Teacher
Everett, Robbie
Science Academy Director
Ford, Catherine
Art Teacher
Iverson, Harley Pratt
Math Instructor
Johnson, William Evan
Fifth Grade Teacher
Kreyling, Paul Richard
Mathematics Teacher
McArthur, Richard C.
Business Ed & Voc Dept Chair
Mulford, Tammy Snell
Family & Consumer Science Tchr
Myers, Burton G.
Spanish Teacher
Prince, Brent Pace
Fourth Grade Teacher
Smyly, Pauline Harper
Teacher
SALINA
Christensen, Judy Cloward
English & Business Teacher
Demille, Denise Terry
Spcl Prgms Coord & Drama Tchr
Holt, Eva Lynn Huntsman
Drama & Talent Search Advisor
Thompson, Chad Gary
Social Studies Teacher & Coach
Torgerson, Jim L.
Science Educator
SALT LAKE CITY
Adams, Julie J.
English Teacher
Adler, Dianne Bott
English Teacher
Anderegg, Cathy P.
English Teacher & Yearbook Adv
Anderson, Carol Day
English Teacher
Anderson, Kathryn Jensen
9th Grd English & Geog Tchr
Applegate, Anne Ely
Choral Director & Music Tchr
Austin, Diane Steele
2nd Grade Teacher
Barton, Quinn Bott
Vocational Technology Teacher
Battle, Frances Phelps
Assistant Principal
Beeman, Caren Greger
Teacher & Adjunct Professor
Begue, Christopher Paul
5th Grade Teacher
Bernini, Linda Gardner
Third Grade Teacher
Bettin, E. Thomas
Art Teacher & Coach
Blood, Helen
Fourth Grade Teacher
Bona, Vickie Plott
8th Grd Physical Science Tchr
Boyce, Valerie Ann
Fifth Grade Teacher
Bragg, Laurie E.
History & English Teacher
Breznick, Carol N.
First Grade Teacher
Brimmer, Patrick Edward
Mathematics Instructor
Brodhead, Warren H.
Social Studies Teacher
Brough, Julie Defriez
Theatre Teacher
Brown, Helen Louise G.
Fifth Grade Teacher
Brown, Jeffery J.
Individualized Study Teacher
Bullock, Richard M.
Mathematics Teacher
Burningham, Mary-Lynn Fairbanks
Retired Kindergarten Teacher
Busath, Gerry Romney
Coordinator & Teacher
Bushnell, Scott
Science Teacher
Callahan, Michele R.
Spanish Teacher
Camlott, Doris J.
Fifth Grade Teacher
Cannon, Gayle Mc Pherson
English Teacher
Carey, Doreen Jo
Middle School Counselor
Chabries, Michael Paul
Instructor
Chapman, Richard Green
Economics Professor
Christensen, Connie Shipp
AP English Teacher
Christensen, Jan Blackmer
US History & Elem Fr Teacher
Christensen, Kathy-Lee
Dept Chair of Resource Dept
Church, Dolph
Physical Science Teacher
Clark, Myrna Finau
Paraprofessional & Coach
Compton, Tamara Lynn
Assistant Professor
Corsi, Roy
Math Department Chairman
Crawford, Lori A.
Mathematics Instructor
Cunningham, Linda M.
Assoc Prof of Business Comm
Curry, Robert A.
Instrumental Music Teacher
Decker Wamsley, Holly K.
Mathematics Teacher
Demal, Katherine N.
Teacher
Dietering, David Walter
Math & Computer Science Tchr
Ekberg, Terry N.
AP Biology Teacher
Engar, Ann Willardson
Instructor of Liberal Ed
Fallon, Carol S.
French & Spanish Teacher
Ficks, Larry Norman
Psychology & Culture Teacher
Fielder, Dorothy Robison
Education Professor
Fink, Kristin Danielson
Character Education Specialist
Francis, Todd C.
2nd Grade Teacher
Frese-Berges, Mirtha Esther
Art Teacher
Fulmer, Steven Kenneth
Vocal & Instrumntl Music Tchr
Gadd, John D. C.
AP American History Teacher
Gilchrist, Donald Bruce
Area Admin Asst & Rel Instr
Glazier, Linda Hatch
Math Teacher
Gledhill, Becky Wilde
Eng & Skills for Success Tchr
Gonzales, Eileen R.
Mathematics Teacher
Gray, Edward C.
Social Studies Teacher
Gygi, Alah T.
Social Studies Teacher
Habel, Shana Lee
Dance Teacher
Hagen, Jean Louise
Drama, Speech & Math Teacher
Haldorson, Lorna R.
Math Teacher
Hale, Jill Crandall
Fourth Grade Teacher
Haluska, Michael J.
5th Grade Teacher
Hamelin, Edith Garrett
Pgm Dir of Health Svcs Dept
Hansen, Marene Rae
English Teacher
Hardy, Robert Douglas
German Teacher
Harsh, Lemuel, III
Theater Arts Teacher
Hart, Donna Peterson
First Grade Teacher
Hartney, Emmilia S.
Middle School Teacher
Hemmert, Tamara Baker
Sixth Grade Teacher
Henriod, Kathleen S.
Geography Teacher
Higbee, Keller A.
English Teacher
Hoar, Christie
Third Grade Teacher
Hogensen, Ann Beveridge
Registered Nurse & Teacher
Holtry, Donald Gene
Physical Education Teacher
Hopkins, Walda
First Grade Teacher
Horton, Rod Scott
Swim Coach & Spanish Teacher
Hughes, Mitchell Scott
Physical & Earth Science Tchr
Jardine, Sherry Dalling
Health Education Teacher
Jarratt, Karrie Adair
Counselor
Jensen, Lucille Rae
English Tchr
Johnson, Brenda Ashman
Third Grade Teacher
Johnston, Gregory Leon
Sixth Grade Teacher
Jones, Wendy Homer
Sixth Grade Teacher
Karlson, Monica Irene
Sixth Grade Teacher
Kasparian, Audra Ann
Spanish Teacher
Kawa, Glen S.
Health & Sports Medicine Tchr
Kinnison, Karen Bunij
High School Math Teacher
Kranes, Carol J.
English Teacher & Dept Chair
Lago, Adeena C.
HS Dance Teacher
Larson, Carol
Second Grade Teacher
Larson, Jane L.
Elementary School Principal
Laursen, William Kenneth
Art Dept Chair & Teacher
Lee, Morris Franklin
Music Department Chairman
Lerdahl, Dianne Weston
English & Reading Teacher
Liddle, Jacqueline Sonne
English & Latin Teacher
Liechty, Victor Jay
Professor of Accounting & Ec
Liston, Nancy Reilly
Third Grade Teacher
Lowe, Rick A.
Psychology Professor
Mackie, Kathy Westra
6th Grade Teacher
Madsen, Ross Martin
His, Govt & Politics Teacher
Mariotti, Linda D.
Language Arts & Frgn Lang Tchr
Martinez, Michelle
6th Grade Teacher
Mc Kee, Thomas Edmond
Naval Science Instructor
Mc Spadden, Toni Lise
Sixth Grade Teacher
Middleton, Becky Clark
6th Grd Tchr, Sci Specialist
Mollerup, LeeAnn Jones
Science Teacher
Moore, Christine May
Home Economics Teacher
Moray, Geraldine
6th Grade Teacher
Morgan, Claudia Tuft
First Grade Teacher
Morgan, Kay Wight
Family & Consumer Sci Teacher
Murrell, Edward J.
Amer History Honors Teacher
Nagata, Sharon N.
US His & Comp Literacy Tchr
Neeley, Ira Jonathon
History Teacher
Norman, Kim Ann
Physical Education Teacher
Oakeson, David W.
Mathematics Teacher
Olsen, B. Christine
Health & Physical Ed Teacher
Olsen, Christy D.
Social Studies Teacher
Olsen, Suzanne Miltner
Latin Teacher
Ostermiller, Judy Yorgason
Sixth Grade Teacher
Page, Alfene Meyer
English Teacher
Pardon, Douglas Jay
Reading Professor
Partner, Shauna Clayton
First Grade Teacher
Payne, Deborah Sue
English Teacher
Peacock, Julie Kirkham
History Teacher
Pedersen, Gilbert
8th Grade US History Teacher
Pehrson, Karen J.
2nd Grade Teacher
Pitts, Kristie Tolman
AP American History Teacher
Poffenberger, Lachell Simmons
Business Teacher
Richards, Paul Chad
Instructor of Physical Science
Ricketts, Dana K.
English Teacher
Riley, Michael L.
Physical Ed & History Teacher
Rittel, Keith Charles
Assistant Principal
Robinson, Yvonne Kim
Kndgtn, Gftd & Tlntd Teacher
Rogers, Carla Sevy
Pgm Dir & Interior Design
Rosen, Wendy L.
4th-6th Grade Teacher
Rosvall, Patricia
Biology Teacher
Roundy, Heidi L.
Chem & Phys Earth Sci Tchr
Rush, A. Tracy
Spanish & English Teacher
Rushton, Sharrie Charlene
First Grade Teacher
Scott, Lorri Naegle
High School Counselor
Searle, Kristy Whitworth
English Teacher
Seehusen, Linda Field
3rd Grade Teacher
Shaw, Deanne
Spanish & English Teacher
Sheffer, Dean Bert
Mathematics Teacher
Shepherd, Paul H.
Teacher Leader
Shepherd, Raymond L.
Accounting Teacher
Sheya, Sharon Patricia
English Teacher
Short, Calli W.
English Teacher
Simpson, Linda Newman
English Teacher
Smedberg, Keith
Science Teacher
Smith, Gary R.
History Teacher
Smyth, Jennifer Holbrook
Former Teacher
Sonzini, Dianne Hinich
Media Specialist
Sorben, Geraldine
English & Latin Teacher
Sorensen, Carolyn Johnson
Ninth Grade English Teacher
Southam, Susan Chausow
English Teacher
Spencer, B. Claire
Tchr of Gftd & Tlntd Pgm
Springer, Debra C.
5th Grade Teacher
Staley, Larry Esmond
Geology, Physiology & Bio Tchr
Starks, Charlotte
Adjunct Instr Comm & Sociology
Story, Anne P.
AP & Cell Biology Teacher
Strassburg, Jennifer Audentia
Music Educator
Summerhays, Todd S.
Physics Teacher
Sundell, D. Carl
Art Department Chairman
Tanner, Donna House
Second Grade Teacher

LAKE CITY (cont)
ert, Dalene
cher of Gifted & Talented
rson, Richard Christen
al Music Dir
, Ronald L.
ege Accounting Instructor
r, Paula Welling
ily & Consumer Science Tchr
Patricia Gareau
cation Specialist
nis, Carolyn Goodman
& 6th Grade Teacher
r, Teresa Frampton
lth & Swim Teacher
y, Noray Riggs
obics Tchr
, Deborah Nielsen
h Grade Teacher
hell, Ronald A.
hematics Teacher
, Clayton Kevin
ensics Director
ne, Mary Ann
lish Teacher
, Michael J.
fting & Technology Teacher
, Pauline Vaughn
Grade Teacher
Lezlie Mc Kenzie
Sci & Technology Teacher
n, Denise Wilson
cher of Hearing Impaired
, Mary A.
h Teacher
el, Norman Richter
al Music & Dept Chair
, Ann Price
h Grade Teacher
man, Dennis Hale
tical Science Instructor
gman, Curtis William
fessor of Marketing
DY
, Dan William
anced Placement Bio Tchr
ey, Cathy Card
dle School Dance Teacher
n, Cheryl
Grade Teacher
igh, Jacqueline Newman
English Teacher & Yrbk Adv
, Arna L.
lish & Journalism Teacher
, George Kay
d Grade Teacher
s, Jacalyn Falck
Grade Teacher
s, Willemina E. (Mieneke)
enth & Eighth Grade Teacher
non, Donald Robert
inary Teacher
er, Raylene Maxfield
graphy & History Teacher
on, Jean L. (Wallace)
th Grade Teacher
Tiffany K.
alth Science Teacher
on, Kelley Page
er History & English Tchr
er, Marc Riches
h Teacher & Athletics Dir
ns, David Craig
Religion Teacher
field, Linda Johnson
Honors History Teacher
rs, Brad Alan
ence Teacher
ello, Dominic Edward
etic Dir, Coach & PE Tchr
rd, JoEllen Dugan
obyist
e, William Larkin
cher
, Carolyn Mc Arthur
h Grade English Teacher
art, Shelby Mikkelsen
glish Teacher
enski, Mary Mc Shane
Grade Teacher
mon, Wendy Ann (Jakins)
th Department Chair
, Mark Monty
ial Studies Teacher
yk, Diana Ice
thematics Teacher
, Charles E.
emistry Teacher
e, Joseph Malcolm
th Teacher
ey, Gregory G.
rman Teacher
sley, James Georg
thematics Teacher
THFIELD
es, Michael
thematics Teacher
, Darlee Pitchford
rman & English Teacher
Evan B.
siness Teacher & Act Advisor
h, Susan
siness & Marketing Teacher
am, Louise Butler
glish Teacher
rton, Nanette Perry
ama & Communication Teacher
, David Frederick
rector of Bands

SOUTH JORDAN
Allen, Jennifer Dorius
Dance Comp Advisor & Teacher
Asay, Dale A.
His, Hlth & Psychology Tchr
Bickmore, John Robert
6th Grade Teacher
Brinton, Jana K.
French Teacher
Crump, Scott
Social Studies Teacher
Ernsten, Traci K.
Eng Dept Chprsn & Tchr
Hageman, Colette Van Wagenen
Sixth Grade Teacher
Hart, Nancy Villella
Secondary French, Math Teacher
Herret, Thomas Roger
Physics Teacher
Kinsel, Gregory John
High School Mathematics Tchr
Kolstad, Lisa Parkinson
Lang Arts Tchr & Dept Chair
Rideout, Jane A.
English, Speech & Health Tchr
Willmore, LeAnna Read
Choir Teacher
Wylie, James Michael
Psychology Teacher
SPANISH FORK
Ballard, Jeffrey Craig
3rd-5th Grade Teacher
McKell, RaShel Anderson
Mathematics Teacher
Moses, Susan Elizabeth
English & Speech Teacher
Roach, Kristee A.
English Dept Chm & Teacher
Robinson, Ty Scott
8th & 9th Grd Science Teacher
Snell, Douglas William
Mathematics & PE Teacher
SPRINGVILLE
Bohling, Troy Dean
Soph World Civilizations Tchr
Burdett, Beverly Jean
Soc Sci & Foreign Lang Teacher
Clements, Kelly Reed
US Studies Teacher
Fox, David Reed
Fifth Grade Teacher
Leek, Priscilla F.
Psych, Intnl Rltns & His Tchr
Rosenlof, Rebecca Turner
English Teacher
Streeper, Carolee
French Teacher
Wickes, Bonnie
Fifth Grade Teacher
Winegar, Shauna
German Teacher
SUNNYSIDE
Clark, Carol Lynn Ockey
6th Grade Teacher
SUNSET
Hupp, Carla Ruth
English Teacher & Dept Chair
Mathews, Aimee Anderson
9th Grade Geography Teacher
SYRACUSE
Barnes, Steven B.
9th Grade English Teacher
Behling, Karol Kinney
Math Teacher
Calvin, John R.
Geography Teacher
Holbrook, Jacqueline Jackson
Geography & English Teacher
Roderick, Gaylene Rapp
1st Grade Teacher
Sill, Douglas Mc Entire
7th Grade Life Science Teacher
Stephens, Leann Wayment
5th Grade Teacher
TABIONA
Burton, Jeffrey Lloyd
Math & Science Department Head
TOOELE
Cummings, Marilyn O'Neill
Third Grade Teacher
Ferrin, C. Roy
Band Director
Hammond, Bryan John
Biology Teacher & Dept Head
Mestas, Lillian Ann
Secondary Language Arts Edctr
Olsen, Dennis J.
Math Teacher
Olsen, Ervin C.
English Teacher
Powell, Karen Nielsen
Third Grade Teacher
Stanley, Judy French
6th Grade Teacher
Trotter, Louette Olsen
Business Education Teacher
Valdez, Richard C.
Guidance Counselor
TREMONTON
Johnson, Maizie Matsuda
English Teacher
VERNAL
Allen, Gregory Keith
Chemistry Teacher
Anderson, Larrie Cal
6th Grade Social Studies Tchr
Baker, Kay
Mathematics Teacher
Bullock, Karen H.
English & Novels Teacher

Dittmore, Wayne B.
Marketing Instructor
Galley, Gary D.
Graphic Arts Teacher
Harrison, Carmen Ramirez
Second Grade Teacher
Harrison, Teresa Seamons
Family & Consumer Sci Tchr
Kurtenbach, Linda Kay
Humanities Teacher
Merkley, Patrice Ensign
Fifth Grade Teacher
Olsen, Wade L.
Library Media Specialist
WASHINGTON
Gillies, Phil M.
Retired Elementary Principal
Smith, Lucille Dean
First Grade Teacher
WEST BOUNTIFUL
Mills, Michael L.
Sixth Grade Teacher
WEST JORDAN
Berg, Shauna Lauritzen
Fourth Grade Teacher
Bojak, Rick Keith
Psychology & PE Teacher
Brown, Marshall I.
Business Teacher
Courrier, Susan Colby
Art Teacher & Dept Chairperson
Daugherty, Sheryn Lee
3rd Grade Teacher
Densley, Don William
Science Teacher & Dept Chm
Fletcher, Kevin Arthur
Spanish Teacher & Coach
Flygare, Lauren Roblez
Music Teacher
Glaittli, Kathy Rockwood
10th Grade English Teacher
Hennick, Loren D.
Fourth Grade Teacher
Henrie, Patricia Ann (Olds)
3rd Grd Gifted & Talented Tchr
Houlihan, Sandra D.
English Teacher
Jenson, Linda Thorn
Title 1 Teacher
Kemp, Kristi Lynn Jorgensen
Family & Consumer Sci Tchr
Leyva, Chelle Hansen
Instrumental Music Director
Madsen, Shirley Johnson
7th Grade G & T CORE Teacher
O'Hara, Kathleen James
Sixth Grade Teacher
Price, Terry Lee
Teacher & Department Chairman
Roberts, Pat Jeanne
Sixth Grade Teacher
Sweat, Carol
1st Grade Teacher
Wasden, Bruce LaMar
Retired Elem School Principal
Westerman, Lanny Jay
American History Teacher
Young, Gerry Wright
Interior Design Teacher
WEST VALLEY CITY
Brockbank, Lynette
6th Grade Teacher
Garrard, Diane Criddle
Bus, Cmptr & Skill Tchr
WOODS CROSS
Anderson, Kayloa L.
Math & Cmptr Programming Tchr
Carlson, Carolyn
Third Grade Teacher
Riley, Virginia E.
Advanced Placement Eng Tchr
Sorensen, John W.
Drafting & Woodshop Teacher
Walker, Robert R.
Fourth Grade Teacher

VERMONT

BARRE
Acebo, Philip Steven
8th Grade History Teacher
Adamski, Gary Matthew
French & Spanish Teacher
Allen, Stephen Jackson
Fourth Grade Teacher
Bison-Rossi, Annette
First Grade Teacher
Blouin, Bonnie Blanchet
4th Grade Teacher
Cary, Doreen Kay
Language Arts Teacher
Chickering, Susan Herndon
Guidance Counselor
Clark, Stephen Lynn
7th Grd Lang Arts Teacher
Desmarais, Gerald
High School History Teacher
Klinefelter, Suzanne Mills
Third Grade Teacher
Lawson, Peggy Licht
4th Grade Teacher
Macy, Drusilla
English Teacher
Morris, Martha I.
English Teacher
Romeo, Frances P.
2nd Grade Teacher

Sedore, Tom
9th-12th Grd English Teacher
Shadroui, Janet Theresa
English & Social Studies Tchr
Wilgoren, Richard Allen
History Teacher
BELLOWS FALLS
Blacketor, Jean Fitch
Social Studies Teacher
Johnson, David B.
Chemistry Teacher
Lockerby, Robert William
8th Grade Social Studies Tchr
Zachary, Nicholas
Math Teacher
BENNINGTON
Berman, Constance Hartofil-Milliken
English Professor & Dept Coord
Bolesky, Stephen Anthony
Social Studies Teacher
Caswell, Richard H., II
History Tchr & Faculty Advsr
Cleveland, Stephen
Sixth Grade Teacher
Cormier, Anne
English Teacher
Engle, Katherine Lesher
High School English Teacher
Gray, William Suttie
Dir of Hospitality
Guerino, Vincent James
6th Grade Teacher
Kochenour, Chris
High School Chemistry Teacher
Kovage, Carmela
Spanish Teacher
LaFage, Wendy L.
Director of Nursing Programs
Nuvallie, Anthony Joseph
Business Management Professor
Rollson, Robert Warren
Social Science Dept Prof
Souza, Donna L.
Mathematics Specialist
Waldo, Kimberly Farra
7th Grade Math Teacher
BETHEL
Griffith, Richard R.
9th-12th Grd Soc Stud Teacher
Monts, Eileen Mc Manus
English Teacher
Parker, Carolynn Stockwell
School Counselor
BRADFORD
Clough, Karin Elisabeth
English Teacher
Mac Lean, Bruce Edward
Social Studies Teacher
BRANDON
Breen, David Christopher
Third Grade Teacher
Cillo, Richard Joseph
Mathematics Teacher
Dardeck, Judy Simpson
Social Studies Teacher
Israel, Donald Kirk
Head Wrestling Coach
Kelley, Michael John
Language Arts Teacher
Pelletier, Mark Charles
Fifth & Sixth Grade Teacher
Sarno, Jane Elizabeth
English Teacher
Wright, Joan Simpson
6th Grade Teacher
BRATTLEBORO
Cornell, Maribeth
Business Teacher
Hecker, Zeke
English Teacher
Hilding, Rebecca Guth
Coordinator of Career Services
Holiday, William
HS Social Studies Teacher
Lacy-Limoges, Elizabeth Jean
Career, Hlth & Home Ec Tchr
Miller, William Thomas
Assistant Dean of Students
Quay, Linda S.
Medical & Human Svcs Teacher
BRISTOL
Perlee, Nancy Solomon
1st Grade Teacher
Snyder, Shelley F.
Science Teacher
Steggerda, Richard John
HS English Teacher
Tailer, Thomas Lorillard
Physics Teacher
Thelen, Karl E.
English Tchr & Yearbook Co-Adv
BURLINGTON
Allen, Christopher W.
Chemistry Professor
Bosworth, Kirk
English Teacher
Boutsikaris, Barbara
Psychology Instructor
Copp, Jacqueline D.
6th Grade Teacher
Daigle, Melody Anne
Sixth Grade Teacher
Dates, Elaine Zak
Latin Teacher
Flanagan, Joyce Bippes
Piano Teacher & Pianist
Francis, Gerald Peter
Mechanical Engineering Prof
Keller, Tony S.
Mechanical Engrng Assoc Prof

O'Keefe, Lawrence
Middle School Teacher
Sabourin, Edgar G.
Accounting & Bus Mgmt Tchr
Simko, John Joseph
Alternative Educator
Terrien, Gertrude Schwab
Computer Coordinator
CANAAN
Lienau, Mark W.
Science Teacher
CASTLETON
Bourgeois, Ernest Joseph, Jr.
Professor of Business Admin
Gillen, John Michael
Professor of English
Kimmel, Peter Blair
Asst Prof of Natural Sciences
Ryerson, Marjorie Gilmour
Journalism Professor
Scott, Jonathan F.
Associate Professor of Art
Thomas, Joyce A.
Professor of English
Waara, Carrie Lynne
Assistant Professor
CHESTER
Harned, Joseph E.
Biology & Anatomy Teacher
Morton, Linda Lovett
4th Grade Teacher
CHITTENDEN
Courcelle, Wanda Harwood
Sixth Grade Teacher
COLCHESTER
Blanchette, Bradley N.
English & Social Studies Tchr
Bozzone, Donna M.
Associate Professor of Biology
Dameron, George Williamson
Assoc Professor of History
Gillard, Gregory Albert
Former Teacher
Hier, Lynn DelBianco
Mathematics Teacher
LeClair, Paul Joseph
Professor of Fine Arts
Waldron, Donna Cioffi
Spanish Teacher
Zeno, Carl Arthur
Assoc Professor of Philosophy
CONCORD
Croteau, Nancy Roberts
Eng, Art Instr & Asst Prin
Hill, William Francis, III
Science & Mathematics Teacher
DANVILLE
Lewis, Joanne
Business Education Teacher
Rapoza, Christine O'Connell
1st-2nd Grade Teacher
DORSET
MacDonald, Debra J.
English Teacher
Wright, Kathleen O'Brien
Second Grade Teacher
EAST MONTPELIER
Christy, Kathryn Mangan
Fifth & Sixth Grade Teacher
ENOSBURG FALLS
Garrow, J. Brent
4th Grade Teacher
Lovelette, Roxanne Picton
10th Grade English Teacher
Nilsson, Christopher Nils
Science Teacher
Vaillancourt, Sandra F. W.
7th-12th Grade Art Teacher
ESSEX JUNCTION
Earley, Clare Lepore
Mathematics Teacher
Ferreira, Steve
Ec, Law & Finance Teacher
Jiamachello, Thomas A.
French Teacher
MacIntyre, Ruby L.
English & Latin Teacher
Rich, Karen St Pierre
Math Teacher & Dept Chair
Taft, Marilee Bobian
Social Studies Teacher
FAIR HAVEN
Kruml, Gary William
Social Studies Teacher
Lynch, Peter
Math, Sci Instr & Dept Chprsn
Pierce, Raymond Charles, Jr.
Music Teacher
Ruby, Nancy Dunlap
Social Studies Teacher
FAIRFAX
Griswold, Lisa M.
7th-8th Grade Science Teacher
Schnell, Joan E.
Language Arts Instructor
Stewart, Judith E.
HS Social Studies Teacher
Walford, Deborah W.
HS Art & K-12 Enrichment Tchr
HARDWICK
Harrington, Steven J.
English Teacher
Metcalf, Mike
HS Social Studies Teacher
HARTLAND
Staples, Paula Howe
3rd Grade Teacher
Warren, Jack
Fifth Grade Teacher

HIGHGATE CENTER
Tarr, Wayne S.
Sixth Grade Teacher
HINESBURG
Cluff, Greg Bruce
US History Teacher
Costello, William John
Science Teacher
Ely, David S.
Science Teacher
Greenwald, Joseph Gilston
Eng, His & Greek Teacher
La Chance, Andre
English Teacher
London, Susanne Abrams
English & Alternative Ed Tchr
Martellaro, Matthew Joseph
7th-8th Grade Math & Sci Tchr
Metz, Constance B.
French Teacher
Miller, Pamela Blevins
Music Teacher
Morrison, Judith Peitscher
Language Arts & Soc Stud Tchr
Recchia, Carl
Vocal Music Teacher
Richman, Carol Ann Koerner
6th-8th Grade Teacher
HYDE PARK
Anderson, Karen Brett
2nd Grade Teacher
Baker, William E.
Math Teacher & Department Head
Bedard, Todd Brent
Automotive Technology Instr
Buttolph, Patricia Mc Carthy
Mathematics Teacher
Damon, Gretchen F.
Biology Teacher
Kaseoru, Dianne Joy
High School Special Educator
Merriam, Donna Bridges
Latin Teacher
Messier, Timothy Jay
Mid Level Soc Stud Tchr
Oxnam, Philip Linton
Theatre Director
JACKSONVILLE
Molina, Karen Kinzer
Spanish & French Teacher
JERICHO
Capone, Adrienne M.
English & Humanities Teacher
Citro, Anthony Ralph
Social Studies Teacher
Slayton, Robert Gary
Latin Teacher
Streeter, Linda Eleanore
High School English Teacher
JOHNSON
Brighton, Kenneth Lyle
Assistant Prof of Education
Marlowe, Bruce Alan
Education Professor
LUDLOW
McKaig, Colin Piersol
High School English Teacher
Salmon, Margery M.
Biology & Chemistry Teacher
LYNDON CENTER
Raymond, Christopher Curtis
His Teacher & Media Specialist
LYNDONVILLE
Daley, Daniel David, III
Acad Counselor & Math Instr
MARLBORO
Holzapfel, David James
5th & 6th Grade Teacher
MIDDLEBURY
Bates, Tony
7th Grade Teacher
Corey, Diane Geary
Learning Specialist & Educator
Nessen, Richard Stephen
Principal & Teacher
MILTON
Eckerson, John David
Social Studies Teacher
Gilbert, David Wayne
Science Teacher
LaFromboise, Marie B.
3rd Grade Teacher
Mc Clellan, Wesley Russell
Social Studies Teacher
Olson-Holmes, Deborah
Fourth Grade Teacher
MONTGOMERY
Ward, Jeffrey Phillip
SS, PE Teacher & Asst Prin
MONTPELIER
Arsenault, Daniel Mark
ESL & English Teacher
Beebe, Larry Francis
Math Teacher
Blakeman, Alan E.
Social Studies Teacher
Edwards, Nerissa Michele
Career Counselor
McGraw, David C.
Science Teacher
Skea, Edmund G.
French Teacher
MORETOWN
Maynard, Barbara Burns
Physical Education Teacher
Ververs, Judith Ellen
Translator
MORRISVILLE
Nordquist, Stacy Sturmer
French Teacher

Stevens, Patricia A.
Sixth Grade Teacher
Tripp, Deanna Alice
Second Grade Teacher
NEW HAVEN
Cross, Debra Dugan
Multi-Age Classroom Teacher
NORTH CLARENDON
Brownell, Mark Griffen
History Teacher
Lind, Joan K.
Third Grade Teacher
Maniery, Nick Angelo
Head Football Coach
Mc Shane, John Bernard, Jr.
English Department Chairman
NORTHFIELD
Evans, Peter M.
Fine & Applied Arts Teacher
Gonneville, Michael Andre
PE Tchr & Girls Soccer Coach
Morvan, Hannah Rikert
Teacher
Richards, Edward Lambert, Jr.
English Professor
NORWICH
Kelly, Lorraine Tompkins
French Teacher
ORWELL
Dunne, John Benham
Fifth Grd Teacher & Asst Prin
PITTSFORD
Kaufman, Paige Scott
Music Teacher
POULTNEY
Hannum, Kraig B.
8th Grd Social Studies Teacher
Nichol, Sandra Mary
Math Teacher
Paquette, Linda Parsons
7th-12th Grd Lang Arts Teacher
Parsons, Mark Lane
Assistant Professor of Music
Thivierge, Amy Seago
English Teacher
POWNAL
Strange, Bonnie L.
6th Grade Teacher
PROCTOR
Nichols, Donna Eileen
Music Teacher
Sherman, Madeline Schnabel
Librarian & History Teacher
PROCTORSVILLE
Firkey, Ann Cleminson
Retired 6th Grade Teacher
PUTNEY
Kerr, Linda
Assistant Professor
RANDOLPH
Ennis, Roger D.
Social Studies Teacher
RANDOLPH CENTER
Hughes, G. Gregory
Associate Professor
RICHFORD
Baker, Nancy Buzzell
High School Science Teacher
Little, John Albert
High School Science Teacher
RICHMOND
Collom, Mary Irene Palmer
Foreign Language Teacher
RUTLAND
Costello, Brian Patrick
English Teacher
Coughenour, Reeta Colton
Instrumental Music Teacher
Fregosi, Mary Helen
History Teacher
Lopes, Kathleen M.
Mathematics Teacher
Lopes, Raymond Edward
Science Teacher
Peterson, Dana Andrew
French Teacher
Peterson, John E.
Social Studies Teacher
Pilcher, Paul Gordon
Tech Instr & Adj Prof of Math
Schaft, Theodore E., Jr.
Math & Physics Teacher
Wilson, Donna Jean
Special Educator
SAINT ALBANS
Chase, Joseph Duane
Physics Teacher
Patenaude, Diana L.
Multi-Age Teacher
Trombley, Larry Lee
HS Soc Stud Tchr & Bsbl Coach
Zakrzewski, Frank Joseph
Social Studies Teacher
SAINT JOHNSBURY
Driscoll, John Thomas
High School Science Instructor
Haskins, Merle Lowell
English Teacher
Knox, Ann Mansfield
Special Education Teacher
Newell, Graham Stiles
Latin Instructor
Prevost, Gerard Armand
Culinary Arts Instructor
Richardson, Edward C.
Sci, Math & Soc Stud Instr
Wright, Peter J.
High School Math Teacher
Wright, Sandra J.
Health Education Teacher

Zuccaro, Carol Bessette
High School English Teacher
SAXTONS RIVER
Farrell, Sean Michael
Assistant Dean of Students
Hibler, Alfred William
History Teacher & Dept Chair
Ormiston, Todd Graham
Math Teacher
SHELBURNE
Shedd, Cynthia Collom
Fourth & Fifth Grade Teacher
SOUTH BURLINGTON
Byrnes, Anne Elizabeth
Director
Comolli, Timothy Doyle
Imaging Lab Director
Kaye, Kathleen Page
Lang Arts & Soc Stud Teacher
Pearo, Michael Charles
Social Studies Dept Chprsn
SOUTH ROYALTON
Wheatley, Ann Mercer
Chapter One Teacher
Whitney, Carol Elizabeth
Mathematics Teacher
SPRINGFIELD
Barrett, Elizabeth Nancy Allen
Graphic Arts Instructor
Carbonetti, Larry S.
English Teacher
Fog, Susan Fairbanks
History & Psychology Teacher
La Bonte, Linda
Fifth Grade Teacher
Mac Gillivray, Sandra J.
Bus Ed Office Admin & Instr
Malinowski, Charles John
Science Teacher
Matush, Stephen J.
Title I Reading Teacher
Metcalf, Rosamond Smith
Retired Fifth Grade Teacher
Plas, Alayne Marquard
French & German Teacher
STOWE
Austin, Betsy Jean
French Teacher
Bouffard, Jane Denise
Band Director
Pinckney, Elaine Fauteux
Middle School Principal
SUTTON
Nugent, Edward Roy
Fifth Grade Teacher
SWANTON
Jette, Beth Hunter
Middle Schl Mathematics Tchr
THETFORD
Deffner, Joseph John
English Tchr & Guidance Cnslr
Finn, John Francis
Visual Arts Instr
Heinzmann, Karen L.
French & Mathematics Teacher
TOWNSHEND
Bennett, Mary Ann E.
Computer & Science Teacher
VERGENNES
Brown, Pamela Taylor
10th-12th Grd Soc Stud Tchr
O'Daniel, Susan Philputt
Instrumental Music Teacher
Potter, Carol Gale
4th Grade Teacher
WAITSFIELD
Lewis, Carla Kotas
Third & Fourth Grade Teacher
Mitchell, Grant Joseph
Director
WARREN
Phillips, Nancy
Fifth & Sixth Grade Teacher
WEBSTERVILLE
Fritjofson, Kenneth Herbert
HS Science Teacher
WELLS RIVER
Foley, Paul Patrick
Guidance Counselor
WEST BURKE
Bangs, Lawrence Bailey
Headmaster
WEST DOVER
Olmstead, Doris Edna
Administrative Assistant
WEST RUTLAND
Cray, Dana L.
English Teacher
Malette, John
Special Education Teacher
Tyrrell, Dawn Hudgings
General Music & Band Teacher
WEST TOPSHAM
Chase, Hazel Valliant
Retired Elementary Teacher
WHITE RIVER JUNCTION
Bouthillier, Philippe Henri
Chemistry Tchr & Sci Dept Head
Carsley, James Frederick
History & Humanities Teacher
Cooke, Edward James
Mathematics Dept Chairman
Esdon, Lynette Grace
Retired Teacher
Kobe, Alexander William
Biology Teacher
Lovering, Judith Hollie (Whittemore)
Sixth Grade Teacher
Wheeler, Herbert Ellis
Cmptr Office Tech, Mngmt Instr

Wolfe, Norman William
Instrumental Music Teacher
WILLIAMSTOWN
Bergeron, Roland J.
French & Spanish Teacher
Carson, Melissa Ann
4th-5th Grade Teacher
WILLISTON
Munt, Margaret Staples
1st & 2nd Grade Teacher
WILMINGTON
Wax, Ilene L.
Learning Specialist
WINDSOR
Carr, Jayne Meier
Kindergarten Teacher
WINOOSKI
Atkins, Kenneth W.
Fourth Grade Teacher
Chiott, Judith Woodard
6th Grd Math & Science Teacher
Libuda, Linda Johnson
Fourth-Fifth Grade Teacher
WOLCOTT
Lilley, Arthur H.
Math, Science & PE Teacher
WOODSTOCK
Burroughs, Richard Philo
5th-6th Grade Teacher
Chiefsky, Susan J.
English & Amer Stud Teacher
Schulte, Lynne C.
Fine Arts Chair & Art Teacher
Tremblay, Louis Joseph
MS Mathematics Teacher
Young, Louis Alonzo
Mathematics Teacher

VIRGIN ISLANDS

CHRISTIANSTED
Cobrall, Heather J.
Business Mgr & Dept Chair
Golphin, Charles, Jr.
Athletic Director
Gonzalez, Carmen Ada
Spanish Teacher & Dept Chprsn
Gordon, Anna Marie
12th Grade English Teacher
Henry, Elizabeth George
English Teacher & Dept Chprsn
Rodgers, Deborah Martin
Principal
Ryan, Avonelle Thomas
Vice Principal
Schmidt, Demetrius A.X.
Biology Teacher
Trotman, Gloria Lindsay
Counselor
FREDERIKSTED
Henry, Beverly C.
Elementary Alt Ed Teacher
Provost, Mary Jane
Director of Upper School
Renee, Luther F.
MS Director & Math Teacher
KINGSHILL
Alexander, Otis Douglas
Music Teacher & Chorus Dir
Belle, Claudia Merlin
Language Arts Resource Teacher
Keylin, Margaret Mc Manus
Lang Arts & World Geog Teacher
Perez, Gail Harris
Special Education Teacher
Roebuck, Chesley S.
Math Teacher, Dept Chairperson
Ross, Marilyne Pascal
11th Grade English Teacher
Smith, Verona Henry
Mathematics Teacher
Walcott, Olive May
Math Teacher
Williams, Eddie
Agricultural Education Teacher
Woods, Allen M.
Chemistry Teacher
SAINT THOMAS
Beauvais, John Edward
English Teacher
Blyden, Sheila I.
Scndry Business Education Tchr
Bowry, Audrey A.
English Teacher
Bushnell, Jon L.
Associate Professor
Cooper, Vincent O.
Prof of English & Linguistics
Depusoir, Francisco
Assoc Professor of Accounting
Govindan, Meledath
Prof of Chem & Phys Sci Coord
Gupta, Ram Prakash
Associate Prof of Mathematics
Henry, Gertrude Catharine
Retired Teacher
Hermann, Marie Janig Raoul
Lecturer in Marketing
Hill, Valdemar A., Jr.
Professor of Bus Admin
Iannucci, Douglas E.
Professor of Mathematics
Iniama, Ededet Akpan
Assoc Prof of Geography
Kean, Renee Maria
Intergenerational Volunteer
Kelley, James Robert
Assoc Prof Cmptr Info Systems

Lamkin, Martin Jacob
Assistant Professor of Music
Lyon, Robert Harold
Accounting Professor
Mihalek, J. P., Jr.
Asst Prof of Math Dept
Murray, Marcia Berta
Instructor of Mathematics
Nelson, Agatha Powell
Asst Professor of Psychology
Nicholls, Myron Everton
Secondary Mathematics Teacher
Phillips, Dion Ernest
Full Professor of Sociology
Ramsay-Johnson, Edith M.
Professor & Chair of Nursing
Turner, Teresa
Division of Sci & Math Chprsn
Washington, Aubrey Dexter
Assistant Prof of Accounting
Wells, Alecia M. Frett
Secondary Deputy Supt
Williams, Gordon Llewllyn
Vice Principal
Wrensford, Granville Elisha
Asst Professor of Chemistry

VIRGINIA

ABINGDON
Blesi, Emily Ellen
English Professor
Buchanan, Robert Franklin, Jr.
Math Teacher
Case, Ruth Hope
Second Grade Teacher
Chafin, Howard Dwayne
Physical Education Teacher
Colangelo, Thomas C., Jr.
Police Science Professor
Cook, Renna Smith
Lang Arts & Soc Stud Teacher
Jonas, Eddie B.
Soc Stud Teacher & Dept Chm
Jonas, Sandra Blair
English Teacher & Dept Chair
Mc Elroy, Heidi Hansen
Art Teacher
Musgrove, Jack
Professor of Design Drafting
Ogle, Douglas W.
Associate Professor of Biology
Peaks, Kerisha L.
Music Dept Chprsn & Choral Dir
Rowland, Alma
Counselor
Sironko, Margaret Friel
Fifth Grade Teacher
Vernon, Brenda Lee (Wilburn)
English Teacher
Vestal, Brenda Lloyd
Social Studies Teacher
Williams, Barbara Kitty
Med & Surgical Nrsng Asst Prof
Witherspoon, Martha Miller
Chemistry Teacher
ALBERTA
Adams, Mary-Robyn R.
English Instructor
Baldwin, Thomas L.
Assoc Professor of Electronics
Hightower, William H.
Biology Instructor
Thompson, Myrna Rivers
Associate Professor
ALEXANDRIA
Allison, Bonnie Buice
Counselor
Amer, Usama Al-Muhamady
Mathematics Teacher
Anderson, Ronald Westley
Technology Teacher
Barnwell, Jimmi Summers
Guidance Director
Beeby, Donald Mc Lallen
Social Studies Teacher
Beeckman, Luc
AP French Instructor
Berry, Jerry
Math & Computer Science Tchr
Bigger, James A.
Latin Teacher
Bogger, Pauline Dennis
Mathematics Teacher
Bolland, Roger Allan
AP Chemistry & Chem Tchr
Boone, Monica Lynn
English Teacher
Bowie, Marie Elizabeth
Health Occupation Teacher
Brown, F. Eugene, Jr.
Math Prof & Division Sci Chair
Bryant, Inez I.
Health & PE Teacher
Cain, Devon Waynick
Middle School Art Teacher
Carl, Jane L. Mellott
Government Teacher
Christensen-Fox, Carol
Science Resource Teacher
Cooper, Jarene Cornithia
Choral Director
Corner, Cynthia Moore
Second Grade Teacher
Corro, Peter Francis
Earth Science & English Tchr
Dell, John C.
Physics Teacher

KANDRIA (cont)
Barbara Brant
nish Teacher
ap, Patricia Riley
unct Instructor
, Jack
ector of Bands
, Michael Duane
Grd Social Studies Teacher
s, Victor Allen
hematics Teacher
y, Barbara Purdie
chool Alternative Coord
, James N.
anese Teacher
er, Marilyn Jean
h Teacher
nd, Gina Keemer
h Teacher
reault, Laurent Albert
logy Teacher
oa, Victor Lawrence
omotive Tech Dept Head
on, Hilda Montemayor
n Tchr & Hispanic Liaison
ckson, Jane Aarnes
manities Teacher
, Emma Coleman
h Grade Teacher
oh, Pamela Kay
manities & Psychology Tchr
s, Zelma Leandrew
ial Studies Teacher
y, Horace Clinton
ad of Criminal Justice Prgm
ard, Kevin B.
glish Teacher
es, Lawanda Sharon
h School Mathematics Tchr
, Samuella Merchant
st Grade Teacher
on, Michael David
alth, PE & Drivers Ed Tchr
son, Ernest L.
cal Music Teacher
son, Thomas
thematics Teacher
ston, Therese Clasen
ence Teacher
s, Sheila Hammond
h Grade Teacher
edy, Karen Kozlowski
emistry & Physics Teacher
, Beverly Hope
siness Teacher
, Kevin P.
h-12th Grd Religion Teacher
grabe, Eleanor Anne (Jones)
nch Teacher
ley, Charles Joseph
glish Teacher
, Paul G.
cial Studies Teacher
s, Carolyn B.
sistant Principal
o, Garfield Lenworth
cial Studies Teacher
ey, Ronald Wayne
story Teacher
g, Rosita Kerr
dependent Music Teacher
sett, Margaret Anne
Grade Teacher
sh-Ardoline, Natalie S.
Acad Ofcr & Business Admin
ers, Patricia Judson
cond Grade Teacher
elle, Janice Jones
glish Teacher
rone, Camille Gigliotti
gh School Guidance Counselor
kolls, Suzanne Griffin
ath Coordinator
na, James David
soc Director of Athletics
as, Roberto Andrew
sistant Principal
ne, Mary Whiting
glish Teacher
ez-Reyes, Emily Evans
gh School Spanish Teacher
eault, Albert L.
orld Studies Teacher
ine, Charlotte C.
h Grade Math & Science Tchr
nnig, Dennis Joseph
ocial Studies Dept Chair
or, Susan Marie
ology Teacher
mmer, Michelle
panish Teacher
thress, James Shannon
ociology, Psych & Govt Tchr
ner, Patricia Lunceford
usiness Education Teacher
kel, Bradley Robert
heatre Arts & Film Stud Tchr
sser, Alvin L.
usiness Instructor
snak, Sonya Y.
rt Teacher
ssell, Paul
reative Writing & Eng Teacher
o, John Eugene
athematics Teacher
eer, Sandra Foster
istory Teacher
tt, Loretta C.
ntermediate Math Lab Teacher

Scully, David John
French & Spanish Teacher
Selby, Christopher Roland
Orchestra Teacher
Soulier, Betty Mayes
Fifth Grade Teacher
Sparks, Ann Walker
Math Teacher
Stallings, William Thomas
Mathematics Teacher
Steinhauer, Dolores M. (Dorsey)
American Civilization Teacher
Struck, John Roger
American History Teacher
Thompson, Lori R. W.
Art Teacher
Umbeck, Ronald Lester
Mathematics Teacher
Vathing, Gale S.
Associate Prof of English
Wagner, Sarah Lilly
Math Teacher & Dept Chairman
Wahl, Bruce Nolan
Assistant Prof of Mathmetics
Wampler, Steven C.
Band Director
Wellington, Stanley
9th-12th Grade Spanish Teacher
Wenzel, Tricia Marie
Fashion Marketing Teacher
Whaley, Garwood Paul
Fine Arts Director
Wilburn, Rebecca S.
Theatre Arts Teacher
Williams, Joan Webber
High School Counselor

ALTAVISTA
Goldsmith, Helen Carter
Life Science Teacher
Mason, Deborah June
Latin Teacher
Powell, Audrey C.
English Teacher
Roderique, Tess Wojcik
English Teacher

AMELIA COURT HOUSE
Ford, Deborah Wilkinson
French & Art Teacher
Lewis, Dallas deKrafft
Headmaster, Law Economics Tchr
Pearson, Linwood Earl
Alternative Ed & GED Teacher
Weigand, James Moorman
His Tchr & Soc Stud Dept Chair

AMHERST
Camden, David Gayland
Health & Physical Ed Tchr
Ferrell, Helen Anne Bryant
AP Govt & Law Ed Teacher
Hartless, Rita Rice
8th Grade Language Arts Tchr
Irvin, Kevin Charles
Principal Tech & Physics Tchr
Kelley, Cynthia Jane
English Teacher
Madigan, Janna Nesitz
ED Teacher
Nuckols, Deloris Frazier
Teen Living & Fmly Mgmt Instr
Pitsenbarger, Wendell Sherwin
Art Teacher & Dept Chairman
Stokes, Mary Soles
Eleventh Grade English Tchr
Swift, Robert Stephen
Culinary Arts Instructor
Taylor, Kimberly Arthur
Health Occupations Teacher
Tracy, Elizabeth Susan
English Teacher

ANNANDALE
Beene, Joe F.
Professor
Booth, Fred N.
Associate Professor of Math
Campbell, Wendy U.
Teacher of Gifted & Talented
Conroy, David Edward, Sr.
Professor of Mathematics
Corbett, Bobbie D. Davenport
Instr of Mgmt & Bus Classes
Daron, Patricia Read
Professor of Biology
Feil, Pamela Cherry
English Teacher
French, Velma Faulcon
English Teacher
Goral, Donald Robert
Associate Professor of Math
Hook, Cindy Regina
Math Teacher & Coach
Howard, Barbara Corbett
Bus Mngmt Prof & Dept Head
Hutcheon, Wallace S.
Prof of History & Soc Sci Asst
Leinwohl, Malcolm F.
Science Teacher
Lenert, Mark Edward
Math Teacher
Linville, Larry J.
Professor of Admin of Justice
Martin, Alfred A.
Computer Science & Math Tchr
Molter, Konrad Earl
English Teacher
Pellerin, Richard O.
Assoc Professor of Mathematics
Piscitelli, Emil James
Professor of Philosophy
Rice, William L. R.
Physics Teacher

Savkar, Reva Anil
Assoc Prof of Chem & Cmptr Sci
Sherry, Susan Carroll
Assistant Professor of Math
Smith, Lawrence Melvin, Jr.
Program Head of PE
Stair, Nola G.
Soc Studies & Technology Tchr
Vaganos, Kimlyn R.
Teacher
VanderMaten, Mary Ann
Associate Professor of Biology
Visco, Nick
Computer Science Instructor
Woodke, Robert Scott
Asst Professor of Drafting

APPALACHIA
Buckles, MaryFaye Fowler
Business Department Teacher
Jervis, Patton Lee
World Geography & History Tchr
Monahan, Margaret Thompson
Kindergarten Teacher

APPOMATTOX
Burcher, James Leon
Agricultural Education Instr
Fisher, Susan Grady
English & Journalism Teacher
Herndon, Melvin Willie
Latin Teacher
Jones, Marcie Shinholser
Work & Family Studies Teacher
Kane, Rodney Douglas
Health & Physical Ed Teacher
Pettyjohn, John Kemp
World & US History Teacher

ARARAT
Smith, Maxine Fox
5th & 6th Grade Teacher

ARLINGTON
Allen, Cecilia Pakos
French & Spanish Teacher
Allen, Michael B.
Social Studies Teacher
Anfinson, Lawrene Nixon
US History & Government Tchr
Atkins, Julie
English Professor
Beaston, Dona S.
Fr Tchr & Chprsn Foreign Lang
Borges, Annette S.
Spanish Teacher
Buster, Patricia Hayes
Second Grade Teacher
Callaway, Carol Sue
PE & Health Teacher
Clark, Ellen Mc Chesney
Third Grade Teacher
Clark, Josette F.
French Teacher
Connolly, Joseph William
Math Teacher
Dilworth, Ruth Ann Hoffman
History & Sociology Teacher
Englishman, John Wostbrock
Social Studies Teacher
Funari, Tracey Anne
Mathematics Teacher
Groves, Anne Kerlin
English Teacher
Guiffre, Tonya Ann Saupp
Scndry Soc Studies Teacher
Hicks, Ann Marie
Biology Tchr & Sci Dept Chair
Jeens, Peggy Duncan
Social Studies Teacher
Kerns, Brian Lewis
Chemistry Teacher
Klevins, Judy
Arts Education Specialist
Klontz, Mary-Hannah Mc Cray
Choral Director
Kluge, Elly Gardner
Social Studies Teacher
Lane, Margaret Susan (Hoskins)
Theology Teacher
Lopez, Carole H.
Guidance Counselor
Ludwick, Betty Lou Takacs
English Tchr & Rdng Specialist
Marrinucci, Nancy Anne
Spanish Teacher
Massengill, Anna Herring
English Tchr
Matthews, Susan Jeanne
Social Studies Teacher
McNamara, Richard John
Physics Teacher
Mc Nulty, Catherine E.
US, Virginia His & Govt Tchr
Meyer, Michele Moyer
HS Mathematics Teacher
Mon, James T.
Mathematics Teacher
Morales, Ramona Edwards
Special Education Teacher
Morris, Barbara J.
English Teacher
Murphy, Emily Cassano
Fr Tchr & Frgn Lang Dept Chair
Oxenrider, Stephen Paul
English as a Second Lang Tchr
Randolph, Judith Howard
Science & Business Teacher
Russell, Diana Rogers
AP English Teacher
Settle, Patricia Thorne
12th Grd US Govt & Ec Tchr
Shenk, Belinda A.
High School Science Teacher

Siebenaler, Sharon Louise
Social Studies Teacher
Spicer, Gary Wayne
Art Teacher
Torrenzano, James Paul
Adjunct Faculty
Welsford, James J.
High School Religion Teacher
Whitten, Elizabeth Anne
Fifth Grade Educator
Williams, Susan D. Alford
English Second Language Instr
Wolla, Karen Lawrimore
Second Grade Teacher

ASHBURN
Berry, Sonia C.
French & US Government Tchr
Blair, Rosanna R.
Art Teacher
Bornarth, Norma L.
English & Reading Teacher
Grant, Judith Elaine
Adjunct Professor of Bus Dept
Mc Lean, Roger Dale
Mathematics Instructor
Virgo, Diana L.
Mathematics Teacher

ASHLAND
Bush, Carolyn Wyatt
Business Education Teacher
Davis, Howard E.
Professor of Political Science
DeBernardo, Jane Ann
Tenth Grd Advanced Eng Tchr
Ellithorpe, Robert Wayne
Band Director
Hansbrough, Frances Pierson
Lead Teacher Specialist
Malloy, Lisa Ann
English & Spanish Teacher
Mc Coy, Dawn Marie
US History & Sociology Teacher
Moores, Constance A. (Harrell)
Second Grade Teacher
Rife, Dianne Eck
Government Teacher
Rives, Nancy Jawish
AP US History Teacher
Vessels, Regenia Ross
Counselor
Wright, Randolph Stewart
Eighth Grade Civics Teacher

ATKINS
Mc Ghee, Theresa Keesee
4th-5th Grade Teacher

BASSETT
Byrd, Gerald Lee
Eng Dept Chm & His Tchr
Collins, Pamela Wilson
Reading Specialist
Morris, Sallie Millner
English Teacher
Plaster, Carolyn De Barr
Seventh Grade Teacher

BEALETON
Burgwyn, Eileen Roth
English Teacher & Dept Chair
Madden, Evelyn L.
English Teacher
McDonald, Virginia Joseph
US Govt Tchr & Stu Cncl Advr
Woodward, Pamela Bayne
Agriculture Teacher

BEAUMONT
Mebrahtu, Aurora Cruz
Language Arts Instructor

BEAVERDAM
Wright, Anita Cary
4th Grade Teacher

BEDFORD
Bennington, Teresa Kibler
Biology Teacher
Davis, Thomas A.
World History Tchr
De Berry, Ernestine Foy
English Dept Chair
Dow, Carole Lynn
Latin & Mythology Teacher
Ebersbach, Ellen Chapman
PE & Health Teacher
Fowler, Beatrice Canady
Fourth Grade Teacher
Harmony, Michelle O'Connor
Science Teacher
Hopkins, Elizabeth Davis
Tenth Grade Biology Teacheer
Lee, Robert Terrell, Jr.
Chemistry & Physics Teacher
Martin, Julie Lyn
French Teacher
Nelms, Douglas Wayne
Collision Repair Tech Instr
Raines, James Brian
Business Education Teacher
Rappaport, Gregory Scott
German Teacher
Saunders, Karen P.
English Teacher
Shupp, Ray C., III
Social Studies Teacher
Wingfield, Marcia Kristin
English Teacher

BEN HUR
Cridlin, James Nelson
Math & Accounting Teacher
Grabeel, Edward Shannon
Technology Teacher
Murphree, Patricia Graham
Asst Prin & Guidance Counselor

BERRYVILLE
Burkholder, James G.
Algebra Teacher
Childs, Jeannine Gruber
6th Grade Social Studies Tchr
Doerwaldt, Werner Franz
English Teacher
Harper, Philip Edwards
Latin & Classical Studies Tchr
Parker, Christopher Peyton
Social Studies Teacher & Coach

BIG ISLAND
Ellison, Estella Bushaw
Sixth Grade Teacher

BIG ROCK
Elswick, Helen Ratliff
Retired Teacher
Lester, Sharon Fraley
6th-7th Grade Teacher
Prater, Dorothy Sullivan
English Teacher

BIG STONE GAP
Bates, James Edward
Assistant Professor of Acctng
Belcher, Deborah Shuler
Second Grade Teacher
Brooks, Wilma Brewer
Retired Mathematics Teacher
Collinsworth, Judy Carol
Second Grade Teacher
Freeman, Diana Baker
Math & V-Quest Lead Teacher
Ogbonnaya, Chuks Alfred
Professor of Environmental Sci
Reynolds, Carolyn Hamilton
Assistant Professor of English
Sydow, Debbie L.
Dean of Academic Services
Tucker, Kendall Wayne
Sociology Assistant Professor
Vandergriff, Susie Stone
Sixth Grade Teacher
Wells, Shirley Miller
Assoc Prof of Office Systems

BIRCHLEAF
Compton, Judy Carolyn
7th Grade Science Teacher
Owens, Marta Diana
Title I Reading Teacher

BLACKSBURG
Carr, Jane W.
English Teacher
Collins, Belva Lee
Principal
Glanville, Jim
General Chemistry Director
Johnston, Carolyn Chafin
Retired Teacher
Loganathan, Vasudevan G.
Associate Professor
Maddy, Teresa Helms
Secondary Mathematics Teacher
Mauney, Suzan Watts
Physical Science Teacher
Mc Guigan, Michael Scott
Math & Science Teacher
Okie, Sharon Margaret
Former Teacher
Olin, Linda King
Art Teacher
Reynolds, Daina Trimble, II
ESL Instructor
Shrader, Margaret Shaw
Fifth Grade Teacher
Sinha, Barbara Ann
Fourth Grade Teacher

BLAIRS
Alexander, Angie W.
Seventh Grade Lang Arts Tchr

BLAND
Faulkner, Janet Breedlove
English Teacher & Dept Chair
Nelson, Rachelle C.,
Sixth Grade Teacher
Pruett, Iris Lynn Crabtree
Kindergarten Teacher
Whitt, Deborah Belcher
Social Studies Teacher

BLUEFIELD
Bryan, Scott C., II
Associate Prof of Hlth & PE
Byrd, Terry Sherwood
SS Dept Ch & Teacher
Campbell, Morgan C.
PE, Drivers Ed & Hlth Tchr
Crawford, Timothy Gray
Assoc Prof, Old Test & Hebrew
Cyrus, Kimberly Pruett
Assoc Prof of Criminal Justice
French, Gloria Crockett
First Grade Teacher
Gillespie, Rodney Dewitt, Jr.
Computer Literacy Teacher
Grabeel, Deborah Burton
Assistant Professor of Music
Hale, James E.
Biology, Phys Sci & Cmptr Tchr
Hash, Linda Osborne
Kindergarten Teacher
Lane, Wilma C.
Mathematics Teacher
Levine, Niki Dombrower
Spanish Teacher
Marrs, Richard W.
World & American Hist Teacher
Mc Daniel, Charity Young
Teacher
Merritt, Robert Charles, Jr.
Assistant Professor of English

BLUEFIELD (cont)
Porter, Barbara Kidd
6th Grd Middle School Teacher
Steenken, John Parker
Asst Prof of Eng & Comm Arts
BOWLING GREEN
Jordan, Lynn Blatt
Learning Disabilities Teacher
BOYCE
Hardesty, Linda Russell
Fifth Grade Teacher
Myer, Paula Marvin
Director of Athletics
Robb, Laura
Curr Coord & Rdng Wkshp Tchr
BOYDTON
Hester, Patricia Morse
Title I Teacher
BRIDGEWATER
Brumbaugh, Erich E.
Professor of Chemistry
Gardner, Doris Elizabeth (George)
Business Teacher
Grant, Wayne Paxton
English Professor
Grove, Carole Copeland
Associate Professor of Ed
Hill, L. Michael
Prof & Biology Dept Chm
Kline, Paul Miller
Art Professor & Sculptor
Mc Quilkin, David Karl
His, Pol Sci Prof & Dept Chair
O'Mara, Philip Francis
Assoc Prof of Eng
Piepke, Susan L.
Frgn Lang Prof of Ger & Span
Roller, Ann W.
English Teacher
Swank, Sarah Elizabeth
Professor of Biology
BRISTOL
Blankenship, Diana Sue (Conrad)
Sixth Grade Teacher
Booher, Larry D.
Biology Tchr
Booher, Ralph Garnett, Jr.
Soc Stud Dept Chair & Tchr
Brittle, Linda Vaughan
First Grade Teacher
Browning, Kim Rizzico
Asst Prof
Connolly, Carole Palmer
Math, Reading & English Tchr
Crockett, Sally Allen
English Teacher
Dillard, Geneva Hammond
Fourth & Fifth Grade Teacher
Ferrell, Robin Bundy
Instructor
Gallagher, John Stephen
Adjunct Faculty Management
Johnson, Sharon Denton
French & Spanish Teacher
Lotito, Tony, Jr.
Adj Prof of Rsrch & Statistics
Marler, Joseph William
Teacher of Gifted & Talented
Marshall, Bobbi Porter
Spanish Teacher
Mullins, Belinda Gauntt
Math & Science Teacher
Murthy, Julie Long
Pgm Coord of Paralegal Stud
Norwood, Melissa Bryant
9th Grd Health & PE Teacher
Parker, Nancy Puckett
Mathematics Teacher
Rederwisch, Eddie R.
Dir of Equine Studies Dept
Sams, Maxine Clark
Chemistry Teacher
Schultz, Roger Daniel
History Professor
Shumaker, Anne Wolfe
Social Work Professor
Smith, Judy Kennedy
Learning Disabilities Tchr
Stribling, Herman Albert, II
Finance Professor
Westerman, Janyce Raye (Winter)
Director of Adult Degree Stud
Whitehead, Edgar Wade
5th Grade Teacher
Wilson, Judy Buchanan
Assistant Principal
BROADWAY
Bange, Steven Patrick
Science Teacher & Coach
Bass, Tricia Rae
Mathematics Teacher
Burket, Adam Leslie
Teacher & GATE Coordinator
Fawley, Kim Leigh
Eighth Grade Civics Tchr
Keyser, Lynn Randolph, II
Vocational Agriculture Teacher
Ornstein, Michelle
English Teacher
Smith, Scott Zane
Choral Dir & Musical Producer
Suter, Angela K.
English Teacher
BUCHANAN
Miller, John Newton
Fr, Latin & Spanish Teacher
Ross, Douglas Alan
Hlth & Physical Education Tchr
BUCKINGHAM
Cope, Wendy Patrick
English Teacher & Dept Chair
Lewis, Katherine Potter
Latin Teacher
BUENA VISTA
Mc Clung, Anne Drake
Sociology Professor
Stearns, Laura Moore
Professor of History
BURKE
Cummings, Elaine Perchuck
Tchr of Gifted & Talented Chem
Daski, Maria Canizares
Spanish Teacher
Deppe, Sharon Morris
French Teacher
Ehrenberger, Donald S.
Earth Science Teacher
Filson, Maureen Hannam
Sixth Grade Teacher
Fry, Kathleen Perotta
Mathematics Teacher
Holder, Roy Cecil
Director of Bands
Mariani, Michael John
English Teacher
Mc Gann, Christine Galvydis
Senior English Teacher
Pablo, Kathleen Fenwick
French Teacher
Townley, Linda M.
Chemistry Teacher
Troia, Daniel Joseph
Mathematics Teacher
Vance, Anne Holderby
English Teacher
Wilhelm, Rosemary Romeo
Fourth Grade Classroom Teacher
BURKEVILLE
Jones, Linda Oliver
Fourth Grade Teacher
CANA
Reavis, Douglas Park
Social Studies Teacher
CARROLLTON
Day, Patricia Clarke
5th Grade Teacher
Mason, Sharon F.
Fifth Grade Teacher
CASTLEWOOD
Dingus, Linda Taylor
Third Grade Teacher
Hodges, Herman William
Math & Physics Teacher
Marshall, Mary Elizabeth Griffith
Sixth Grade Teacher
Roberson, Michael Ray
History Teacher
Shortt, Larry Amos
Mathematics Teacher
CEDAR BLUFF
Jessee, Martha Kersey
Elementary Guidance Counselor
CENTREVILLE
Cooley, Cheryl Lynn
Music Teacher & Orchestra Dir
Deal, Elizabeth Meyer
7th Grade History Teacher
Pangman, Todd M.
Fifth Grade Teacher
Payne, Martha Rowland
Fifth Grade Teacher
Wayne, Jennifer Brennan
8th Grade English Teacher
CHANTILLY
Arena, Paul John
HS Concepts Sci Teacher
Bhojwani, Roger R.
Chemistry & Physics Teacher
Dowdy, Dorothy Williams
AP Goverment Teacher
Gallagher, Mondania B.
Jr High Science Teacher
Hood, Theresa G.
English, Writing & Jrnlsm Tchr
McCunney, Anne Sodwith
7th Grade English Teacher
McMillie, Pamela Gail Lilly
Social Studies Teacher
Myers, John R.
Computer Science & Math Tchr
Patey, Marian Beirne
Education Teacher
Schieffer, Katherine C.
8th Grd & Jr HS Soc Stud Tchr
Seeley, Ginger Wright
Guidance Counselor
Wayne, Mark Hampton
Government Teacher
CHARLOTTE COURT HOUSE
Blount, Marcus Gerald
Carpentry & Cabinetmaking Tchr
Catron, William Eugene
Biology Teacher
Cox, Shirley Fleming
English Teacher
Garris, Claudia Barrett
Jrnlsm, Publication Design Dir
Graves, James Patrick, Jr.
US World History Teacher
Jackson, Deborah Martin
English & Social Studies Tchr
Lucado, Kaye Bolton
Govt, Ec & Sociology Teacher
Morris, Winifred Walker
High School Art Teacher
Mowery, Davis Gilbert
Band Director
Prophett, Andrew L.
Soc Stud Tchr & Adjunct Prof
Schuler, Elizabeth Chase
Spanish Teacher
Wilmouth, Brenda Harris
Math Teacher, Dept Chairperson
CHARLOTTESVILLE
Baber, Dina James
Spcl Education & Resource Tchr
Baylor, Kathryn Lane
US History Teacher
Block, Martin Edmund
Asst Professor of Physical Ed
Bradley, Pamela Lorene
Health & Physical Ed Teacher
Brashers, Valentina Louise
Assistant Professor of Nursing
Burke, Lois Brown
Mathematics Teacher
Catlin, Beverly Lewis
Gifted Education Coordinator
Clutter, Martha Taylor
Associate Professor of Math
Crescimanno, Russ E.
Sociology Professor
Dixon, Susan Holden
Kindergarten Teacher
Eddy, Deleanna Faye
Algebra Teacher
Edwards, Alvin
Mathematics Teacher
Ely, Michael Gary
Guidance Counselor
Finley, Peggy Shell
English Teacher
Frankel, Marie Kovach
Social Studies Teacher
Frazier, Chapman Hood
Secondary English Teacher
Gilkey, Susan Nicodemus
Mathematics Teacher
Gobble, Marsha Cann
LD Resource Teacher
Graham, Ann Gray
Former His, Eng & Span Tchr
Henerberry, James
English Teacher
Hickerson, Robert Alan
English Teacher
Hughes, Sue Critzer
English Teacher
Hull, Susan Haney
English Teacher
Hutchinson, William Joseph, III
Asst Headmaster & Athletic Dir
Johnstone, Ann L.
Fifth Grade Teacher
Kelley, Joseph P.
Yearbook Editor & Photographer
Krag, Linda Bourque
English as Second Lang Teacher
Larrick, Rollin David
Latin, Linguistic & Hmnts Tchr
Layman, Jennifer Leah
Choral Director
Lendermon, Susan Carey
Tchr of Gifted & Indp Stu Spon
Love, Patricia Haney
First Grade Teacher
Massie, Carolyn S.
Drama Teacher
McElwee, Robin G.
7th Grd Language Arts Teacher
Overstreet, Gretchen VanSickler
Fifth Grade Teacher
Owen, William Davisam
Professor of English & Speech
Parton, Jewell-Ann
Professor of English
Pemberton, Barbara Ann (Sauer)
Sixth Grade Teacher
Pilgrim, E. Denise Zeigler
Reading Specialist
Ridenour, David L.
Physcs, Astrnmy & Enrgy Tchr
Shiflett, Janet B.
French Teacher
Spivey, Jonathan Keith
Choral Director
Steinbach, Bernhard Z.
English Teacher
Surdukowski, Leigh Jones
Science Teacher
Thomas, Laura Mulligan
Orchestra Director
Thomas, Leta Enoch
Third Grade Teacher
Tornello, Vincent J.
Band Director
Wainwright, Lester Leon
Math & Computer Science Tchr
Watson, Kenneth Lee
AP Government Teacher
Williams, Lois Gasparro
K-12th Grade Math Specialist
Willis, Lloyd L.
Associate Professor of Biology
CHATHAM
Bradley-Miller, Deborah
6th Grd Language Arts Teacher
Braun, Geoffrey David
History Department Chairman
Brown, Barbara Harris
Special Ed Teacher
Burke, Carl Whitt, Jr.
Physics & Chemistry Instructor
Cooke, Brenda Newcomb
First Grade Teacher
Crews, Sandra Dee
Fourth Grade Teacher
Dance, Iris Flinchum
Social Studies Teacher
Harper, Diane Boy
ESL Instr & Foreign Stu Adv
Inge, Annie Rogers
Business Teacher
Lee, Joseph Charles
Govt, His & Sociology Teacher
Lumpkins, Nathan Wayne
8th-12th Grade Math Teacher
Lyle, David Lee
Mathematics Teacher
Reiss, Randall Joseph
Band Director & Tennis Coach
Taylor, Sharon Jane
Second Grade Teacher
Thacker, Tonie Womack
Sixth Grade Teacher
Vaden, Sandra Townes
Social Studies Teacher
Wilkes, Roger L., Jr.
Teacher & Counselor
Wood, Bill
Spanish Instructor
CHESAPEAKE
Albertson, Teresa Hawkins
Fourth Grade Teacher
Bailey, Hyden Edward, Jr.
Athletic Director
Barnes, Karen Painter
Marketing Teacher
Bodnar, Brenda Peele
Fine Arts & Choral Director
Bowen, Shirley Holmes
English Teacher & Dept Chair
Brandriff, Ginny
Health & Physical Ed Teacher
Brazil, Maxine Mc Glothlin
Reading & Language Teacher
Brennan, Patricia Sigmon
K-5th Grade Music Educator
Brennan, Robert Daniel
Principal
Brox, Loula Parsons
High School English Teacher
Carroll, Vince Corey
Fifth Grade Teacher
Carter, Penelope Rogers
English Teacher
Chenery, Barbara Lavalette
High School Guidance Counselor
Clark, Randle Dennis
English Teacher
Colaiacovo, Kimberly Lynn (Martz)
Math Teacher
Cole, Susan Cheryll Leidig
Fifth Grade Teacher
Coleman, Patricia Smith
Kindergarten Teacher
Condon, Virginia Clark
English & Journalism Teacher
Connor, Gloria Hines
6th Grade Teacher
Cuffee, Catherine Lawson
Art Teacher
Curtis, Rosemary Vassar
Mathematics Teacher
Doyle, Linda Foskey
Reading Resource Teacher
Duda, Brenda Cerza
French Teacher
Duvall, Frank William
European History Teacher
Eike, Theresa Harrell
8th Grade English Teacher
Floyd, Carol Little
Kindergarten Teacher
Garnett, George Muscoe
Technology Education Tchr
Grady, David Philip
English Teacher
Gregg, Carole R.
Spanish Teacher
Grigg, Judie Anne
7th Grade Mathematics Teacher
Hagen, Marcelle (Smart)
Frgn Lang Dept Chm & Span Tchr
Holliday, Christina Oliva
Spanish Tchr & Frgn Lang Chair
Ivey, Sharon Dee (Everton)
Physical Ed & Hlth Teacher
Jennings, Gregory Worth
Technology Education Teacher
Jennings, Rosalind Battle
Earth Science Teacher
Johnson, Thomas E.
7th Grade Life Science Teacher
Kimmerle, Nancy Sharp
English & SAT Prep Teacher
Kubo, Judith Tucker
Science Teacher & Dept Chair
Lambert, Samantha B.
US History Teacher
League, Caren Davis
German Teacher
Lindblad, Arnold
6th Grade Teacher
Losee-Hoehlein, Jill
Biology Teacher
Mac Donald, William Robert
American History Teacher
Mannolini, Carol Ann
Philosophy Professor
Mattos, Ann Zwoyer
Biology Teacher
Mayhue, Bruce Allen, Jr.
Math & Chemistry Teacher
Mc Guire, Ronald W.
Teacher & Coach
Mc Kee, Betty Davis
English Teacher
Meissel, William Howard
Soc Stud & Art History Tchr
Montanez, Shelly Blankenship
Latin Teacher
Moore, Ro Criscoe
Hlth, PE & Drivers Ed Tchr
Mowery, Chirs
High School Principal
Mowery, Jacqueline Butler
History & Psychology Teacher
Myers, Carolyn Greene
Choral Director
Naylor, Mary Henry
History Teacher
Oliver, Truman
English Teacher
Owens, John Skinner
Technology Ed Department Head
Owle, Janet Jacobs
Lang Arts Teacher & Dept Head
Parker, Dwight M.
Social Studies Instructor
Parker, Patricia McKenney
9th-12th Grd Mathematics Tchr
Patillo, Constance Thomas
Fourth Grade Teacher
Pearce, Judith Mc Duffie
5th Grade Teacher
Perdew, Terrence Lee
10th Grade Hlth & PE Teacher
Phillips, Michael Thomas
Mathematics & Bible Teacher
Pitt, Anne Trent
Health & Physical Ed Teacher
Revelle, Daniel Young
Physics Teacher
Richardson, James Kenneth
English Teacher
Sabbato, Phillip Christian
Spanish Teacher
Savage, Susan Smith
Substitute Spanish Teacher
Schuler, Jeannette Wiese
Theatre Arts Director
Scott, Peggy Joyce
Business Education Teacher
Smith, Susan Lorraine
Spanish Teacher
Speralakis-Babb, Christine Marie
Biology & Chemistry Teacher
Stanley, Grant Richardson
Technology Education Teacher
Still, Stephen Patrick
Chemistry Teacher
Stribling, Lenore Love
French & Spanish Teacher
Tate, Claudia Diane
Mathematics Teacher
Teachey, Diane Schmid
8th Grade Physical Sci Teacher
Transeau, Cindy Lee
English Teacher
Troia, Patrick John
Health & Physical Ed Teacher
Valentine, Valery Evans
Sixth Grade Teacher
Vaughan, Thomas L.
Asst Principal for Instruction
Venters, Richard, Jr.
Social Studies Teacher
Vernon, Rodman H.
US History Teacher
Vinson, Erma Thornton
Eng & Creative Writing Tchr
Waddell, Margaret Cowling
Mathematics Teacher
Waggen, Linda L.
Fifth & Sixth Grade Teacher
Whitehurst, Audrey Marriner
First Grade Teacher
Whitfield, Sherri-Lyn Myers
Mathematics Teacher
Wieck, Ryan Logan
Biology Teacher
Williams-Mosher, Judith Eileen
Chemistry & Biology Teacher
Wilson, Sandra Garrett
English Teacher
Woodford, Susan Adine
Physical Ed & Bible Teacher
Youmans, Elizabeth Leety
Consultant, Writer & Teacher
CHESTER
Alcarez, Christine Todd
Math Teacher
Armstrong, James O., II
Professor of Business Mgmt
Fadika, Gibril Owereh
Associate Professor of Anatomy
Gholson, Joan Cuthbertson
Second Grade Teacher
Koch, John Charles
Adjunct Instructor of Biology
Parrish, Nancy Clyde
Eng & Creative Writing Tchr
Schlesman, Susan Jane
Former Teacher
Singleton, Huey Andrew
Asst Prof of Police Science
Storino, Donne Matthew
English Teacher
Tompkins, Patrick
Assistant Professor of English
Waters, Cindy Anderson
English Teacher
CHESTERFIELD
Brown, Lawrence M., Jr.
English Teacher

STERFIELD (cont)
, Marilyn Patterson
h Grade Teacher
ier, Steven Arn
ial Studies Teacher
ey, Bernice Lewis
hematics Teacher
, Margaret Monahan
f Development Specialist
arlane, Judith Copenhaver
lish Teacher & Dept Chm
eil, Ann Lovelace
f & Hearing Impaired Tchr
, Catherine Thorburn
nish Teacher
rac, Laura Keller
h School Math Teacher
e, Lillian White
lish Teacher
ds, Albert Maury, Jr.
hematics Teacher
HOWIE
Mary Bowman
iness Education Teacher
h, Peggy Bowers
Grd Social Studies Teacher
Beverley Clear
rk & Family Relations Tchr
ry, Sandra Peake
h Grade Teacher
er, Joleen Bryant
th Grade Teacher
NCOTEAGUE
and, Melissa Johnston
ial Studies Teacher
es, Joseph Wesley
ence Teacher
rs, Thelma Chase
ondary Math Teacher
ISTIANSBURG
op, Joyce Henderson
ir & Coord of Hlth Occup Ed
Norma E.
-10th Grd Hlth & PE Tchr
erick, Colleen Berg
Grade Teacher
ner, Olen Wade
afting Instructor
e, Martha Morgan
assroom Teacher
e, Betti Carson
athematics Teacher
uz, Charlena Wright
ama & Film Studies Teacher
, Patricia Galea
source Teacher of Gifted
or, Pamela Goode
Teacher
, Robert Thompson
trumental Music Teacher
JRCH ROAD
dwyn, Dora Shelton
ired 5th Grade Teacher
ARKSVILLE
ison, Shirley Weston
urth Grade Teacher
h, Joyce Ewing
th Grade Teacher
EAR BROOK
pbell, Jean Carson
urth Grade Teacher
FTON
don, Mary Frances
glish Teacher
wford, Nancy A.
emistry Teacher
kin, Elizabeth G.
nth Grade English Teacher
Hartog, Deanna Jean
rth Science Teacher
rmann, Tim
zz Lab Band Director
dner, Lynn
athematics Dept Chair
san, Taalibah Sakeena
ology Teacher
ndon, Peggy Alderman
hemistry Teacher
song, Gloria E.
eading Teacher
za, Jim
athematics Teacher
ller, Virginia Anne (Coffman)
usiness Teacher
ry, Margaret Moir
uidance Counselor
te, Caryl R. M.
2th Grade English Teacher
omas, Timothy Jerome
panish Teacher
en, John W.
omputer Science Teacher
ight, George Mason
erman Teacher
ing, Pamela Smith
rt Teacher & Dept Chair
IFTON FORGE
tocci, Charles August
ulp & Paper Tech Pgm Head
unch, Jon Edward
gm Head of Mechanical Design
ntington, Lucille Mullins
ourth Grade Teacher
oez, Linda Jo Arrington
th Grade Teacher
cely, Howard Kenneth
ighth Grade Teacher
ffsinger, Pam Hepler
eacher of Gifted

Turner, Robin Duncan
Asst Prof of Acctng & Prgm Hd
CLINCHCO
Moore, Ronnie Lee
Auto Mechanics Instructor
CLINTWOOD
Baker, Brenda Dolinger
High School English Teacher
Baker, Johnny Preston
Fourth Grade Teacher
Baldwin, Joyce Ann
Fifth Grade Teacher
Barnett, Debra Lynn
Spanish Teacher
Bise, Janie Baker
Second Grade Teacher
Bragg, Richard, Jr.
Health & Physical Ed Teacher
Castle, Billy R.
6th Grade Teacher & Coach
Crabtree, Ella Jean
Math Teacher
Estep, Cheryl Puckett
Government Teacher
Fleming, Teresa Lynn
Band Director
Fulks, Karen Leigh
Third Grade Teacher
Large, Pat (Strouth)
6th Grade Teacher
Mullins, Elizabeth Dotson
Seventh Grade Teacher
Skeen, John Winston
English & Psychology Teacher
CLOVER
Humbles, Sharon Moore
Second Grade Teacher
COEBURN
Brown, J. Michael
Sixth Grade Teacher
Hill, Judy Blackburn
English Teacher
Meade, Letha Burke
4th Grade Teacher
Peters, Karen Horne
English Teacher
COLLINSVILLE
Cannoy, James C.
Teacher
Goodman, Thomas Ralph, Jr.
Social Studies Teacher
McGriff, Dyna Freda
Choral Music Director
Smith, Gail Robertson
French Teacher
Stegall, Elizabeth Russell
Biology Teacher
Stone, Linda Spencer
Speech, Drama & Eng Teacher
COLONIAL BEACH
Chatham, Kenneth Wayne
Sci Dept Chair & Biology Tchr
Greenlaw, Katherine Rynders
Elem Reading Resource Teacher
Hunter, Robert Stuart
Secondary Art Ed Instructor
Ware, Fran G.
Business Teacher
COLONIAL HEIGHTS
Belcher, Elizabeth Heartwell
Kindergarten Teacher
Burton, Tina Marie
English Teacher
Dunton, Jim C., III
Marketing Teacher
Form, Mark Doran
Mathematics Tchr & Ath Dir
Hamman, Ronald Rodgers, Sr.
Sci, Soc Stud & Bible Teacher
Kennedy, Sherie Ragsdale
English Teacher
Perkinson, Marion Curtis
Kindergarten Teacher
COURTLAND
Gyoker, Deborah Shanaberger
Chemistry Teacher
Jessee, Randy Ray
PE & Math Teacher
Jones, Dorothy Maxine
Social Studies Teacher
Magette, Eleanor Bagley
Mathematics Teacher
Peele, Linda Sessoms
Math Teacher
Vernon, Carolyn Elaine
Science Teacher
Woodley, Ella Person
Program Director
Wyatt, Thelma Winston
English Teacher
COVINGTON
Barron, Deena Clark
English Teacher
Bartley, Dorothy Showalter
Mathematics Teacher
Burks, Vivian Poston
5th Grade Teacher
Buzzard, Donald Dean
US History & Humanities Tchr
Carter, Mildred
4th-7th Grade Computer Teacher
Cook, Kellyson
Math Teacher
Dean, Anne Moersh
Learning Disabilities Tchr
Dixon, Mary Agnes
Eng & Pub Speaking Tchr
Farmer, Deborah Locks
Title I Teacher & Coordinator

Keyser, Kenneth Kyle
Fine Arts Chmn & Art Instr
Proffitt, Anita Driscoll
English Teacher
Rice, Anita Noel
Work & Family Studies Teacher
Scott, Rebecca Woodrum
English Teacher
Strang, Nancy Wilkin
Biology Teacher
Wing, Mary L.
Mathematics Teacher
Worley, Wesley Franklin
Technology Education Teacher
CROZET
Abell, Scott Parrish
Physical Ed & Health Teacher
CULPEPER
Allen, Peggy Milam
Health, Drivers Ed & PE Tchr
Brooks, Bessie Burrus
Science Dept Chm & Bio Teacher
Byrd, Amy Connor
English Teacher
Davis, B. J.
English Department Chairman
Davis, Kathryn Dix
Biology Teacher
Earles, Thomas Thornton
Chemistry Teacher
Frazier-Petty, Esther Irene
Practical Nursing Teacher
Jenkins, Robert Lee, III
History Teacher
Knewstep, Nancy Coleman
Science Teacher
Kotheimer, Lucila Camargo
HS Spanish Teacher
Lassiter, Richard Hilary
Leadership Training Specialist
Montgomery, Eleanor Smith
English Teacher
Onderdonk, Michele Thomson
5th Grade Teacher
Rose, Patricia Bates
Sixth Grade Teacher
Sawyer, Evelyn Ingram
Kindergarten Teacher
Seward, Thomas Frederick, Jr.
Social Studies Dept Chair
Smith, Eilene Lillard
5th Grade Teacher
Sorrentino, Louis Michael
US History Teacher
Southard, Margery Gardner
English Teacher
Taylor, Gwen J.
English Teacher
Thomas, Susan Blake
Latin Teacher
Underhill, Deborah Harris
Fourth Grade Teacher
Walters, Jo Ann Ellis
Elem Assistant Principal
Williams, Kim A.
Visual Arts Teacher
Yates, Pamela Denise
History Teacher
CUMBERLAND
Anderson, Judith Ruth
French & History Teacher
Nowlin, Carolyn Mason
English Teacher
Robinson, Ruby Robertson
Librarian
Tillerson, Kempy Mercell
Health & PE Instructor
DAHLGREN
Flemer, Darlene Warren
4th Grade Teacher
DALE CITY
Dolan, Kathleen Anne
Math Teacher
Sakshaug, Cynthia B.
Language Arts & French Teacher
DALEVILLE
Jargowsky, Louise Shick
Chemistry Tchr & Dept Chairman
Kohler, William Fredrick
Technology Education Teacher
Roberts, Michelle Huffman
Math Teacher
DAMASCUS
Daniels, Uley Scott, Jr.
Band Director
Matney, Kimberly Dawn
8th Grd Social Studies Tchr
Puckett, Trilla DeFriece
Art Teacher
DANVILLE
Aaron, Larry Gene
High School Science Teacher
Bass, Barbara Day
Mathematics Teacher
Black, Mary Lee
French Teacher
Clark, Rebecca Leigh
Assoc Professor of Sociology
Compton, Elizabeth
Dean of Arts & Sciences
Creasy, Leo Steven
Third Grade Teacher
Duff, Partricia Ratledg
Fifth Grade Teacher
Ferguson, Richard M.
Asst Prof of Physical Ed
Fesperman, Janet Ducharme
Health Teacher
Fleming, Merrill Morehead
Fifth Grade Teacher

Foster, James Thomson
Assoc Prof & Dept Chm of PE
Garmon, Virginia M.
Instructor
Gould, Treva Carter
Mathematics Teacher
Graham, Cynthia Johnson
Kindergarten Teacher
Graves, April Dawn
Algebra & Economics Teacher
Gurley, Margaret Elizabeth
History Teacher
Hairston, Delores Sanford
Seventh Grade Lang Arts Tchr
Harris, Thomas Coleman
Social Studies Teacher
Helm, Kenneth Darrell
Counselor & Student Dev Prof
King, Lola Jean
First Grade Teacher
Laughlin, Janet Trogdon
Office Systems Tech Asst Prof
Marlowe, Jean Statzer
Third Grade Teacher
Mc Call, Carolyn W.
HS Business Dept Teacher
Millner, Gwendolyn Dalton
Mathematics Teacher
Otersen, Jennie Beck
High School Math Teacher
Price, Daisy Jeffers
Fifth Grade Teacher
Robertson, Carol Clark
First Grade Teacher
Slack, Maclyn M.
Spanish Teacher
Walker, Martha Allgood
Assoc Prof, Office System Tech
Walton, Richard Allen
Art Teacher
DAYTON
Smiley, Sandra Staten
8th Grade Math Teacher
DENDRON
Bailey, Geraldine Virginia
Second Grade Teacher
Bailey, Marsha A.
Business Education Teacher
Bain, William Heath
English Teacher
Fauntleroy, George Linwood, Sr.
Assistant Principal
Hopper, Barbara G.
English Teacher
Lunsford, June Ellis
Eighth Grade Civics Teacher
Pike, James Justin
PE & Health Teacher
DILLWYN
Elliott, Betty Dunnavant
Civics Teacher
DINWIDDIE
Bailey, Elizabeth Hayman
4th Grade Teacher
Cox, Magalene Boyd
Business Teacher
Creath, William F., Jr.
Mathematics Tchr & Dept Head
Glass, Elizabeth Sneade
English & Language Arts Tchr
Gunnels, Janet Hoon
French & English Teacher
Harris, Trenia Winbush
Science Teacher
Johnson, Sharranne Ellis
Business Teacher
Madison, Deborah Stone
Health, PE Teacher & Coach
Perry, Bettie Claiborne
Business Teacher
Sturdivant, Rose Jackson
English Teacher
DRY FORK
Kent, MaryJo Connor
Second Grade Teacher
DRYDEN
Harvel, Nancy Curtis (Tubesing)
Kindergarten Teacher
DUBLIN
Hallstead, Carla Barnett
Chemistry Teacher
Harris, Angela Jeanette
Choir Director
Hylton, Brenda Slusher
Business Education Instructor
Kanipe, Barbara Clark
Third Grade Teacher
Lineberry, Sharon Clark
Tchr of Resource Lrng Dsblty
Lockard, Gary P.
7th Grade Math Teacher
Meyer, William Richard
Social Studies Instructor
Priest, Robert Ernest
Band Director
Waller, Brenda Elaine
English Teacher
Wurzburger, Ray
Asst Professor of Accounting
DUFFIELD
Pendleton, Paul Edward
Calculus, Chem & Algebra Tchr
Quillen, Charles Case
Math Teacher
DUMFRIES
Caricofe, Brenda Quick
Second Grade Teacher
Higgins, Frank
Technology Ed Dept Chairman

Hijar, Maureen Boyd
Mathematics Teacher
Jones, Rodger Logan
Business Teacher
Jones, Shirley Tolbert
Chemistry Teacher
Kubiak, Virginia Mc Ewan
Family Studies Tchr & Chprsn
Mc Vay, Cynthia L.
Kindergarten Teacher
Miller, Gloria Cash
Fr Tchr & Foreign Lang Chm
Ragland, Leon Clifton
Chemistry & Physics Teacher
Stevens, Dianne Farria
Dept Chrpsn & Bus Ed Teacher
EAGLE ROCK
Lowe, Doris Wilson
Kindergarten Teacher
EASTVILLE
Fuller, Connie M.
English & Journalism Teacher
Mc Carter, William Sanford
English Teacher
Smith, Angela Irene
Business Education Teacher
ELLISTON
Jakubowski, Mary H.
Media Specialist
EMORY
Davis, Diedre Brantley
Adjunct Professor in Piano
Kellogg, Frederic Richard
Religion Professor
EMPORIA
Bell, Willie James, Jr.
Math Teacher
Bottoms, Brenda Pinchbeck
Lang Arts & Soc Studies Tchr
Deloatch, Juanda Goode
Guidance Director
Gray, Ruby Brown
Math & Lang Arts Teacher
Judkins, Sandra Jones
English Teacher
Kern, Janet Ruth
Earth Science Teacher
Powell, Martha Starke
Business Teacher
Presson, Cassandra Rinehart
English & Drama Teacher
Raymond, Wilcox Audley
English Teacher & Coach
Roach, Debra Mitchell
Mathematics Teacher
Sasser, Ray
English Teacher
EWING
Beaty, Kathryn Sergent
Civics & Government Teacher
Clouse, Brenda Graham
School Counselor
Richmond, Judy L.
Seventh Grade Teacher
Skeen, Carol Penn
Eng, Jrnlsm & Keyboarding Tchr
Smith, Betty Yeary
Third Grade Teacher
EXMORE
Bott, Brigitte Hurtt
French Teacher & Dept Chair
Goffigon, Sara Nottingham
Teacher & Soc Stud Chair
Milburn, Debra Gianniny
Bio Teacher & Sci Dept Chprsn
FAIRFAX
Belton, Toni Ward
6th Grade Teacher
Brilliant, Akiko
Japanese Language Teacher
Byrd, Philip Bradley
Math Department Chairman
Cannon, Isaac James, Jr.
6th Grade Teacher
Carson, Margaret Kress
Journalism Teacher
Casipit, Anthony David
Electrnes, Engrng & Tech Tchr
Dirner, George W.
Assistant Principal
Donelson, Darlene Jennifer
AP Chemistry Educator
Dower, Janet Bosworth
Eng & Creative Writing Tchr
Ehrlich, Michael Lewis
Choral Director
Elder, Carlyn Lang
HS American History Teacher
Elder, Ruth Goulding
Health, Math & Science Teacher
Franklin, Linda Lee
Kindergarten Teacher
Gates, Clifford C.
History Teacher
Gee, Samuel Y.
World Studies & Economics Tchr
Goldin, Mark G.
Spanish Professor
Henry-Gross, C. Anne
High School Teacher
Hudgins, Elizabeth Lee
AP English Teacher
Ibbotson, Harry Owen
Sixth Grade Teacher
Johnson, Joann Patricia Reed
English Teacher
Jonhston, Nancy Schrum
Business Teacher
Kronz, Annetta Keys
Sixth Grade Teacher

FAIRFAX (cont)
Lane, Wanda Duncan
Assistant Principal
Lopez, Sarah Palmer
Spanish Teacher
Louis, Susan Kisinger
Marketing Teacher, Coordinator
Martin, Jam A., II
His & Civilizations Teacher
Martin, Monika Darragh
Mathematics Teacher
Mc Niff, Sheila Hendershott
Social Studies Teacher
Mouzavires, Crosby Elias
English Teacher
Ott, Lindsey Charles
Chemistry Teacher & Coach
Patten, Elizabeth Rice
Orientation Assoc & Acad Adv
Place, Sherri Vance
Sixth Grade Teacher
Pratt, Riva Dopler
Psychology Teacher
Recasner, Ann Oberlitner
Teacher & Generalist
Riley, Corina Lyn
PE Teacher & Coach
Rismiller, Jeannette Davis
Spanish Teacher
Salewski, Robert Joseph
Mathematics Teacher
Sayers, Nancy Miller
Sixth Grade Teacher
Schneider, Patricia Kilgore
1st Grade Teacher
Starnes, Mary Adele Phipps
4th Grade Teacher
Stevens, Jeffrey Warren
Biology Teacher
Treubert, Doris Bowden
Advanced Placement Bio Tchr
Ulrey, Mary E.
Band Director
Walker, Jay C.
Marketing Coordinator
Wallace, Teressa Schimkus
High School Science Teacher
Wardinski, Paul Anthony
Marketing Teacher
Welch, Marilyn Kay
Latin Teacher
West, Donna Lutkus
Chemistry Teacher
White, Patricia C.
English Teacher
Williams, David R.
Adjunct Professor of English
FAIRFIELD
Teague, Lori Staton
Seventh Grade Science Teacher
FALLS CHURCH
Alnwick, Judith Jones
French Teacher
Barretto, Deborah Susan
Psychology & Sociology Teacher
Berard, Ulric Claiborne
Social Studies Teacher
Berg, Stephanie Jones
Asst Principal & Teacher
Cavanaugh, John Joseph
Span & Social Studies Teacher
Coling, Shirley Cogdell
Eighth Grd Algebra & Math Tchr
Cook, Pamela Margaret
Var Cheerleading Coach & Spon
Dabney, Dana Trice
Math Teacher & Program Manager
Daggett, Marilyn Pettinicchi
Orchestra Director
Davis, Carolyn Susie Inscoe
Retired Teacher
Diaz, Sara Thomasin
Japanese Teacher
Fall, Marsha Wolfe
English & Journalism Teacher
Ferentinos, Paul A.
Social Studies Teacher
Gillum, Myra Hull
English Teacher
Gray, Lillian Hadjis
Biology & Chemistry Teacher
Hamilton, Gail Gregory
Learning Disabilities Teacher
Hawkesworth, Eleanor Marie
Social Studies Teacher
King, Sue Addison
Work & Family Studies Teacher
Klass, Steven Jeffrey
English Teacher & Dept Chair
La Violette, Helen Gilligan
Work & Family Studies Teacher
Oglesby, Judy Ailes
Business Teacher
O'Hara, Margaret Mary
Biology & Earth Science Tchr
Ponton, John V.
Social Studies Teacher
Rogers, Mark David
Social Studies Teacher
Rose, Peter D.
Fifth Grade Teacher
Ruff, Barbara Cohen
AP US History Teacher
Schepps, Madison Clinton
Spanish Teacher
Shenk, Sylvia Lynn
French Teacher
Singer, Stuart Alan
Math Dept Chm & Yrbk Adv

Thompson, Marlena Carol
Judaic Studies Coordinator
Valentine, Jane Harriet
English Teacher
Whitney, John William
Math Teacher & Dept Chairman
FARMVILLE
Adusei, Edward Opoku
Asst Professor of Economics
Barber, Patrick G.
Chemistry Professor & Co-Dir
Bidwell, Lee Millar
Asst Professor of Sociology
Blauvelt, Joseph Charles
Associate Professor
Charleston, Kathy Elizabeth Knies
Assistant Registrar
Couture, Richard Thomas
Assoc Prof of History
Douglas, Otis Whitfield, III
English Professor
Dukes, Thomas Arthur
Associate Professor of Mrktg
Green, Faye P.
Guidance Director
Herring, John Joseph, Jr.
Instructor of HPER
Howe, Frank
Associate Professor
Jordan, James William
Professor of Anthropology
Koesler, Rena A.
Outdoor Education Professor
Marks, Melanie Beth
Asst Prof of Ec & Dspln Coord
Meese, Ruth Lyn
Assoc Professor of Special Ed
Oliver, Amie
Associate Professor of Art
Palmer, G. Dean
Business Administration Prof
Palmer, Kristine Nelson
Asst Prof of Accounting
Reich, Eike
Asst Professor of Chemistry
Ross, Charles Dolan
Assistant Prof of Physics
Rowland, Rhonda Stockton
Mathematics Teacher
Sams, Judith P.
Depart Chair & Business Tchr
Scott, Marvin Wade
Professor of Biology
Simmons, Betty Jo Whitaker
Education Professor
Somers, Philip Edward
Mathematics & Physics Teacher
Stinson, Massie C., Jr.
Associate Professor of English
Whitfield, Patricia Ann Rainwater
Asst Prof of Spec Education
Williams, Rodney Lee
Theater & Dance Instructor
Williams, Thomas A.
Assoc Prof of Music
Wood, Cynthia Nunnally
Acting Assistant Dean
Woodburn, Mary Stuart
Professor of Education
Wright, J. Patrick
Latin Teacher
Yarborough, Allie Chaffin
English Teacher
FERRUM
Young, Thomas Michael
Fifth Grade Teacher
FIELDALE
Lintecum, Gale Easterbrook
Third Grade Teacher
FINCASTLE
Eubank, Emily Gale
Algebra I Teacher
Johnson, Linda Smith
7th Grd Eng & Humanities Tchr
FISHERSVILLE
Kiser, Elsa Negron
Spanish Teacher
Meade, William Everard, III
Head Soccer Coach
Ravn, Deborah Sondrol
Mathematics Teacher
FLOYD
Blackburn, Karen Roberts
Sixth Grade Teacher
Johnson, Nanette Macknick
English & Drama Teacher
Keith, David Joel
Math Teacher
Keith, Janet Slusher
English Tchr & Forensics Coach
Pratt, Joel Wayne
Art Teacher
Profitt, Peggy Morris
Second Grade Teacher
Shelor, Robert Neal, Jr.
Technology Education Teacher
Wells, Dayne Hankinson
Business Education Teacher
FOREST
Cardwell, Virginia Langel
5th Grade Teacher
Folger, Kathy Wilson
Mathematics Teacher
Herring, Sandra Stewart
Fourth Grade Teacher
Hunt, Nancy Rodden
Computer Science Teacher
Hunter, Doris Anita
English & Drama Teacher

Loy, Jerome Harper
Health & Phys Ed Teacher
Mulligan, Patricia G.
Fifth Grade Teacher
Murphy, John Calvin, Jr.
Science Teacher
Nosenzo, Maryann Elizabeth
English Teacher
Rodman, Carole Link
Earth Science Teacher
Schowe, Jean Longnecker
7th Grd Language Arts Teacher
Stanley, Susan Marie
Kindergarten Teacher
Stutzman, Ruth Gerlach
Algebra Teacher
Thornton, Roberta H.
Third Grade Teacher
Toms, Donald A.
American Government Teacher
Turner, Jody Hopwood
Library Media Specialist
Williams, Charles A., Jr.
PE Teacher & Athletic Director
Woconish, Vincent M.
Mathematics Teacher
Zaring, Jedd Alan
American Studies Teacher
FORK UNION
Feathers, Karen Hough
Hum, Lang Arts & Drama Teacher
Hardy, Joan Jerrell
Language Arts & Novel Tchr
Ritchie, Robert Francis, IV
Social Studies Teacher
FORT BELVOIR
Bartus, Carol Speciale
Learning Disabilities Teacher
FORT DEFIANCE
Ball, Bonnie McDonald
Spanish & French Teacher
Berg, Cornelia Grace
Mathematics Instructor
Bowers, Robert S.
7th Grade Social Studies Tchr
Coffman, Terry Susan
First Grade Teacher
Conca, Lorraine Frances
English Teacher
Dunsmore, Wade Gaston
Soc Stud & Rdng Tchr
Fauerbach, Cheryl Elrod
Fourth Grade Teacher
Hawkins, Deborah Diehl
Fourth Grade Classroom Teacher
Lilly, Gene Philip
Driver Education Instructor
Metcalfe, Mark Cameron
Chemistry Teacher
Myers, Beverley Simmons
Geometry Teacher
Petras, Carrington Hannah
Latin Teacher
Raab, Christine Colbert
7th Grade Language Arts Tchr
Saufley, Royal N.
Sixth Grade Math Teacher
Smith, George Robert, Jr.
Special Education Teacher
Spitzer, Dale Allen
Health & Physical Ed Teacher
Vass, Susan Lewis
English, Drama & Speech Tchr
FORT LEE
Crossley, Pamela Jean
Course Director & Instructor
FRANKLIN
Atkinson, Sandy Miller
Marketing Teacher
Blunt, Mechelle Savedge
Science Teacher
Bretikreutz, Melissa M.
French & Spanish Teacher
Brown, Sandra Elaine
Fourth Grade Teacher
Carter, Michael Andrew
Applied Biology & Chem Teacher
Denton, Eric Matthew
High School English Teacher
Morlino, Vito J.
Chemistry Teacher
Porter, Mazina Scott
Mathematics Instructor
Soucek, Linda Pitts
English Teacher
Stewart, Richard Kenneth
Science Teacher
FREDERICKSBURG
Armstrong, David Gray
Math Teacher
Berggren, Marcia Field
Sr HS Academic Supervisor
Bevan, Sharon Ann
Language Arts & History Tchr
Brown, E. Gerald
Sociology & History Teacher
Carter, Mayo
6th Grade Teacher
Cash, Eileen Suiter
Mathematics Teacher
Casserly, Carolyn Carter
Mathematics Tchr & Dept Chprsn
Cordell-Robinson, Shirley Jean
English Teacher
Crooks, Rod W.
Athletic Director
Davis, Larry Donnell
Director of Upward Bound Pgm
DeBell, Michele
Science & Social Studies Tchr

DeMarco, Joseph Anthony
Mathematics Teacher
DeVall, Gloria F.
English Teacher
Dixon, Barbara Williams
Second Grade Teacher
Farnsworth, Stephen J.
Senior Lecturer
Feducia, Gregory Allen
English Teacher
Ford, R. Denise Roberts
Math Teacher
Geary, Eileen Moore
7th-8th Grade English Teacher
Gordon, Teresa Davis
English Teacher
Hall, Rusty Wayne
Agricultural Business Teacher
Humphrey, Bernard Douglas, III
Mathematics Teacher
Jett, Robert Earl
Drafting Teacher
Johnson, Mary Lewis
Fourth Grade Teacher
Long, David Jeffrey
Music Professor
Mc Grady, William Oscar
Sixth Grade Teacher
Mears, Suzanne Almirall
Talent Development Coordinator
Newcomb, Sharon R.
English Teacher
Payne, Wendy Howell
Health, PE Tchr & Dept Chair
Racheau, Judith Diann
Fr, Span Tchr & Dept Chair
Serbay, Richard Michael
PE Instructor & Athletic Dir
Shinberger, John Barclay
Teacher & Coach
Shinberger, Molly Blanton
English Teacher
Shrum, Linda Newland
Counselor
Siegmund, Winona Schlam
AP & 10th Grd English Teacher
Sloan, Heidi Montague
Former Teacher
Snyder, Gerald Warner
HS Mathematics & Physics Tchr
Stello, Patricia Smith
Work & Family Studies Teacher
Watson, Helen M.
Retired Second Grade Teacher
Wray, Wayne Wilson
Latin Teacher
FRONT ROYAL
Barr, Eric F.
Mathematics Dept Chairman
Barrs, Michael Alan
English Teacher
Biggs, Jane Clarke
Psych & Social Studies Teacher
Clark, Bruce Thomas
Historian & Dir of Soc Stud
Corker, Marilyn Jean
Language Arts & English Tchr
Crouch, Robert Jackson
History & German Teacher
Culbertson, Robert Wayne
Assistant Aerospace Sci Instr
Dashiell, Sarah Elizabeth Gibbs
Third Grade Teacher
Fristoe, Linda Beth Shaffer
Creative Writing Teacher
George, Rose Jacobs
12th Grd US Government Teacher
Hartsell, Barbara F.
Business Teacher
Harvey, Althea Diller
First Grade Teacher
Haywood, Lucy P.
6th Grade Teacher
Henry, Dennis Lyle
5th Grade Teacher
Knight, Eunice Karnes
Art Teacher
Lamb, Roy Albert, Jr.
Social Studies Dept Chairman
Megeath, Ann Rector
Business Teacher
Michaels, Elizabeth Gander
Social Studies Teacher
Moffa, Marcus John
English Teacher
Nelson, Frank William
Health & PE Tchr
Newcomer, Richard Dean
Earth & Environmental Sci Tchr
Noel, Janet Michaely
Latin Teacher
Rathman, Julie Kress
English Teacher
Rauscher, Janet Longwell
Retired 3rd Grade Teacher
Rewis, Richard Smart
Chemistry Teacher
Sowell, Rayford Michael
Fr Tchr & Frgn Lang Dept Chm
Thompson, Nancy Woodward
Fourth Grade Teacher
Thomson, Paul Jones, III
Electricity Instructor
Trott, Margaret Akers
History Teacher
Vance, Muriel Saunders
Spanish Teacher
Wiesner, Robert Mark
Academic Counseling Director

Wright, Harold David
Assistant Principal
GAINESVILLE
Spellman, Linda Tolley
Fourth Grade Teacher
GALAX
Burnette, Linda Kay
Retired Sci Dept Chm & Tchr
Key, Rita K.
Biology & Physics Teacher
Meador, Marie Ashlock
High School Business Teacher
Robinson, Mark Edward
5th Grade Teacher
GATE CITY
Blalock, Marjorie Gilliam
Mathematics Teacher
Coleman, Geoffrey Mc Comb
Science Teacher
Coleman, Margaret Mc Connell
English Teacher
Dye, James Bernard
Chemistry Teacher
Hobbs, Linda Mc David
Business Teacher
Jackson, Pauline Collinsworth
English Teacher
Jennings, Betsy Thornton
Business Teacher
Keene, Joyce Wallace
Drafting Teacher
Kilgore, Rhonda Alleena Oakes
Marketing Education Teacher
King, Judith Ernst
French Teacher
Lockhart, Regina Annette (Kilgore)
Algebra Teacher
Mason, David Dwight
Bio, Math & Cnsmr Chem Tchr
Osborne, Maggie T.
Spanish Teacher
Spicer, Joanna Argoe
Special Education Teacher
Wininger, David Paul
7th & 8th Grd Pre Algebra Tchr
GLADE SPRING
Fulwider, Teresa Price
Spanish Teacher
Shockley, Harold Guy
Horticulture & Earth Sci Tchr
Wright, Elizabeth Ann
Science Teacher
GLADEHILL
Thompson, Shirley Ann
Kindergarten Teacher
GLEN ALLEN
Melton, Joyce Hayes
Retired Elementary Teacher
GLENNS
Alston, James Lindsey
Assoc Prof of Bus Mgmt
Bolden, Reba Burnette
Administrative Officer
GLOUCESTER
Ailsworth, Alfred Ellyson, Jr.
History Teacher
Brown, Elizabeth Knight
World His & Lang Arts Teacher
Bryant, Laurel Denise
Spanish Teacher
Byrne, Terryl Mc Millan
Seventh Grade English Teacher
Earley, Della Roselle
Guidance Counselor
Goodhart, Sally S.
German Teacher
Gosselin, Claudette Jean
Health Occupations Instructor
Hedrick, Camille Holmes
Latin Teacher & SCA Sponsor
Lowery, M. Audrey
7th Grd Lit & Writing Tchr
Mushinsky, Pamela Owens
Spanish Teacher
Reffo, Patricia Ball
7th Grade Language Arts Tchr
Ringstaff, Martin
Biology Teacher
Robertson, Andrew C.
Mathematics Teacher
Teagle, Margaret Cushman
First Grade Teacher
Waravdekar, Michelle Patrice Mc Kinn
Reading Specialist & Eng Tchr
GOOCHLAND
Beauchamp, Lucie
French Teacher & Dept Head
Budryk, Douglas Paul
High School Elective PE Tchr
Gall, Kent Russel
Band Director
Pinner, Victoria Webster
English, Speech & Drama Tchr
Trice, Linda Kalen
Mathematics Tchr & Dept Head
GREAT FALLS
Baltimore, Janice Bodrick
Third Grade Teacher
Horan, John E.
Former Teacher
GRETNA
Angell, Jane Williams
Fourth Grade Teacher
Clark, Sheila Sheff
Language Arts Teacher
Craig, Martha Elizabeth
Chemistry & Biology Teacher
Herndon, Sallie Pannell
6th Grade Language Arts Tchr

TNA (cont)
., Linda Munkus
th Grade Teacher
st, DeLois Lassiter
rth Grade Teacher
, John B., III
keting Teacher & Coord
er, Ann Staples
dance Department Chair
ggs, Patricia Wyatt
Grade Teacher
e, Deborah Hardy
thematics Teacher
a, Brenna Hagiwara
ond Grade Teacher
a, Calvin Tokushi
alth & Physical Ed Teacher
, Lonnie Thomas, Jr.
History Teacher
NDY
dwine, Jeffrey
ited States History Teacher
s, Sheila Sue
enth Grade Teacher
on, Barbara Mitchell
th Teacher
er, Virginia Ratliff
rk & Family Studies Teacher
lanahan, Betty O.
gh School Business Ed Tchr
ns, Susan Belcher
glish Teacher
h, Kenneth Edward, II
ial Studies Teacher
y, Vicki Justus
siness Education Teacher
ey, James Marvin
sident & Sacred Lit Teacher
e, Deborah Childress
thematics Teacher
s, Sherry Raines
siness Teacher
IFAX
er, Brenda Tune
urth Grade Teacher
MPDEN SYDNEY
e, David J.
st Prof & Dir of Theatre
on, Dianne Marie (O'Donnell)
etoric Instructor
sler, Daniel C.
ychology Professor
MPTON
kley, Priscilla B.
Grade Language Arts Tchr
ard, Ann Vantrease
sociate Professor
es, Mary Grambling
cond Grade Teacher
, C. Thomas
athematics Teacher
, Margaret Shearin
ssistant Professor of English
zard, Diane Manley
ird Grade Teacher
die, Timothy Tee
glish Professor
th, Susan Parsons
ience Teacher Specialist
wn, Virginia Tadlock
ghth Grade Math Teacher
ion, Michael Lee
ocial Studies Teacher
ke, Lynda D.
ath Specialist
nham, Pamela J.
edical Lab Tech Instructor
penter, Johanna Grosley
th Grade US History Teacher
ter, Garry Wayne, Jr.
gebra Teacher
wthorn, Janice Dodson
sst Professor in Education
ambers, Catherine Miller
usiness Teacher
wson, Barbara Shockley
h Grade Math Teacher
oley, Julia C.
erman Teacher
oper, Wendy Simmons
etired Kndgtn Tchr & Supvr
riere, Joyce Harlow
cience Teacher
llieslager, Richard A.
ng Prof & Dir of Dev Writing
ver, Kathryn Mitchell
rench Teacher
ckworth, Melissa Huffman
nglish Teacher
guson, Barbara H.
nglish Teacher
zier, Teresa Stafford
ssoc Prof Early Childhood Ed
dge, Sammy
ocial Studies Teacher
lerton, Marly M.
panish Teacher
ntry, Gerald Gladstone, Jr.
th & 10th Grd Hlth & PE Tchr
dsey, Edward K., Jr.
etired Teacher
ant, Dave
rofessional Counselor
ggard, Lynn Stieffen
hird Grade Teacher
hn, Norman P.
mptr Information Systems Prof
atwole, Deborah Fairfield
Adjunct English Professor

Heatwole, Samuel R., Jr.
English Teacher
Heldreth, Cynthia Holt
Mathematics Department Chair
Hellberg, Dianna Stephenson
Middle School Teacher
Henney, Frederic Allison
English Professor & Pgm Head
Holloman, Ronald A.
Cooperative Education Teacher
Hopson, Ruth Whitaker
Mathematics Teacher
Howard, Felicia Joy Jones
Third Grade Teacher
Hurst, Mary White
Computer Lab Teacher
Hurwitz, Sharon Hodges
English Teacher
Johnston, Donald H.
Physics Teacher
Johnston, Olive Macdonald
LD Resource Teacher
Kaneko, Debbie Carole
Lecturer of Computer Science
Kaplan, Kenneth
Government & Geography Teacher
Kessel, Isidorore
Foreign Language Dept Chm
Knewstep, Nancy Gay
English Teacher
Knipple, Dan L.
Band Director
Kuhn, Florence Smith
English Teacher
Langford, Antoinette Davis
Assistant Professor of Nursing
Lewis, Charlie Bland
PE & Drivers Ed Teacher
Lewis, Larry Wayne
Assoc Prof of Math & Cmptr Sci
Limerick, Dianne Audrey
Math Teacher
Lindsey, Elizabeth O'Donnell
Professional Counselor
Long, Betty Hutchinson
Chemistry Teacher
Mac Donald, Richard Emerson
Science Teacher & Dept Chm
Mars, Richard Allen
Biology Teacher
Mauney, Brenda Cunningham
Language Arts & Math Teacher
McClanahan, Alice Jane
French Instructor
Mc Cracken, Barbara Wiletta
Fifth Grade Teacher
McLaurin, Janet Gallaher
Third Grade Teacher
Mc Queen, Alfred Percell, Sr.
Bio Assoc Prof, Hlth Sci Coord
Megginson, Ernestine White
Algebra Teacher
Metus, Paul Andrew
Science Teacher
Motoanga, Gabriella
Math & Science Teacher
Ouellette, Claire Buckley
Mathematics Teacher
Overton, Lucy Taylor
Fourth Grade Teacher
Parrish, Sandra Grigg
Second Grade Teacher
Petersen, Anne Redner
10th-12th Grd Bio & Chem Tchr
Putnam, Darlene Capps
Asst Prof of Office Systems
Rambeau, M. Ansley
English Teacher
Richardson, Catherine Jane
Adminstrative Intern
Riddick, Charlotte Ann
Guidance Counselor
Rittenhouse, Edward Franklin
Assoc Prof Cmptr Information
Rothstein, Albert J.
Drama Director
Rowe, Kent Seabury
Math Specialist
Shriver, Louis M.
Mathematics & Soc Stud Tchr
Sigrist, Charles Alfred
Associate Professor of Math
Sillah, Mohammed Bassiru
Political Science Professor
Smith, Donald Damien
Math Teacher
Smith, Gloria Andrews
Art Teacher
Smith, Nan Giles Mills
Vision Specialist
Snead, Lillie Frances
5th Grade Teacher
Sommer, Deborah Kelly
9th-12th Grd Spanish Teacher
Spratley, Teresa Ann
6th Grade Lang Arts & Sci Tchr
Stanton, Cathy Berman
English Instructor
Szynal, Pamala Ann
Marketing Education Coord
Thompson, Melanie Stetson
French Teacher
Vick, Mary Postell
Lecturer & Instructor
Vishneski, John Stanley
Accounting Dept Chairman
Waters, Mary G.
Teacher & Sponsor
Waters, Regina Jones
Elementary Principal

Willis, Robert Alexandre, Jr.
Asst Prof of Computer Science
Willoughby, Kenneth Lee
Social Studies Teacher
Wray, Beverley Atkins
Fifth Grade Teacher
Wright, Bobbie Jean
Professor of Sociology
Zagursky, Meredith Christine
English & Yearbook Teacher
HARRISONBURG
Abrahamson, Craig Eilert
Professor
Buhl, Henry Franklin
Soc Stud Chm, Gov & His Instr
Dalton, Jean
Kinesiology Professor
Hawthorne, Mark Douglas
Professor
Hershberger, Ann Graber
Nursing Instructor
Hillyard, Helen Layman
Substitute Teacher
Holmes, Stephanie Eleanor
Asst Orchestra Director & Mgr
Holt, Judith K.
Associate Professor of Nursing
Horn, Robert Neil
Professor of Economics
Huber, Vida Swartzentruber
Prof & Nursing Dept Head
LaSala, Kathleen Bradshaw
Assistant Professor of Nursing
Linn, Reid Jeffrey
Professor of Special Education
Liskey, Rebecca Marie (Zinn)
French Teacher
Livingston, Virginia Cline
Assoc Professor of Nursing
Long, Dolores Whitten
5th Grade Teacher
Morris, Marie Schuessler
Nursing Department Head
Mumaw, David K.
Science Dept Chairman & Tchr
Rhea, Deborah C.
College of Business Instructor
Schoenfeld, Gerald A.
Assistant Prof of Management
Stoltzfus, Ronald L.
Associate Professor
Sullivan, Kathleen Donovan
Fifth Grade Teacher
Welter, Cole H.
Director & Professor of Art
Wszalek, H. Steve
Mathematics Teacher
HAYES
Encrapera, Kathleen Rossi
3rd & 4th Grd Multi-Age Tchr
HAYSI
Barton, Vickie Lynn
English Teacher
Colley, Stewart Alexander
Instr of Biology & Chemistry
Delaney, Lisa June
Hlth, PE & Drivers Ed Teacher
Minion, Kevin D.
Math & Computer Science Tchr
Rush, Ernest J.
Science Teacher
HEATHSVILLE
Phillips, Dennis Ray
English Teacher
HENRY
Clifton, Karen Meador
Kindergarten Teacher
Nunn, Peggy Jamison
Second Grade Teacher
HERNDON
Bobzien, Catherine Hardy
Mathematics Teacher
Chern, Ronni Singer
English Teacher
DeMaria, JoAnn E.
5th & 6th Grade Teacher
Gepford, Gary B.
Spanish Teacher
Graney, Douglas Robert
History & Political Sci Tchr
Griffith, Elvira Settler
German Teacher
Hines, Ardeth Keller
English Teacher
Peroutseas, Melissa Daniels
High School French Teacher
Thoms, Gretchen Harris
6th Grade Math & Science Tchr
Tuller-Brooke, Claudia Sue
Teacher of Learning Disabled
Webster, Beth A. French
Spanish Teacher
HIGHLAND SPRINGS
Guthrie, Clyde James
High School Mathematics Tchr
Hancock Henley, Barbara
Work & Family Studies Teacher
Patterson, Christine Carniotis
History Teacher
Scoggin, Jeffrey J.
Dept Chprsn & Soc Stud Teacher
Williams, Michelle Mc Queen
English Teacher
HILLSVILLE
Chitwood, Edmond Webb, II
Biology Teacher
Davidson, Leonard Alvin
World History & Geography Tchr
Goad, Lois C.
English Teacher

Goad, Yvonne Lea
Mathematics Teacher
Goldwasser, Marion McAdoo
Drama & English Teacher
Newman, Dave C.
Electronics Technology Teacher
Shockley, Jo Lynne
Art Teacher
Stanbery, Byron Gene
Guidance Counselor
Sutherland, Liza Bravo
Spanish Teacher
HILTONS
Adams, Deborah Osborne
Kindergarten Teacher
Wampler, Paula Hagler
Second Grade Teacher
Williams, Donna Hillman
4th-6th Grade Math Dept Tchr
HIWASSEE
Buckland, Rebecca Howe
Elementary Guidance Counselor
HONAKER
Altizer, Angela Tutka
Seventh Grade Teacher
Garrett, Randall H.
Special Ed & PE Teacher
Hopkins, Donrita Davis
School Librarian
Mutter, Suzette Dean (Owens)
Title I Aide
Rasnake, David Dwayne
Math Teacher
Stilwell, Kevin Lee
Chemistry Tchr & Sci Dept Chm
Vance, Barbara Ann
Mathematics Teacher & Chprsn
HOPEWELL
Barnes, Barbara Dutton
Lang Arts & US History Tchr
Beaty, Sue Ann
Reading Resource Teacher
Bell, Christine Marie (Stroh)
Social Studies Teacher
Bortner, Carlotta Nesbitt
Second Grade Teacher
Bouck, Julia Brown
World Geography Teacher
Covington, Janet Clara
Elementary Principal
Edgerton, Pamela Comer
Biology Teacher
Kirksey, Kelly Lynn
Algebra & Biology Teacher
Lee, Brenda Baker
English Teacher
Noble, Kinta O.
History Teacher
Shewmake, Sandra Williams
Spcl Education Resource Tchr
Slachter, Phyllis Kunkler
Marketing Education Instructor
Taylor, Carolyn Cooper
Vocal Music Teacher
HOT SPRINGS
Groseclose, Mary Grace
Language Arts Teacher
Isaacs, Steve
Mathematics Teacher
Petrosky, Tony
Math, Soc Stud & Spanish Tchr
Tenny, Rodney Eugene
Physics, Chem, & Phys Sci Tchr
HURLEY
Blankenship, Ruby H.
Third Grade Teacher
Cooper, Patricia Lynn Tester
Third Grade Teacher
Dotson, Pamela Tester
Physical Education Teacher
Stacy, Curtis Alan
Chemistry & Earth Science Tchr
HURT
Croucher, Laura Densford
Middle School History Teacher
INDEPENDENCE
Calhoun, Jane Burnette
Special Education Teacher
Cole, James Alex
Agriculture Education Instr
Cunningham, Brenda P.
Mathematics Teacher
Diamond, Brenda Alderman
Work & Family Studies Teacher
Lawson, L. Alan
Social Studies Teacher & Coach
Nuckolls, Babette Holder
Bio, Anatomy & Physiology Tchr
Reece, Dina Cruise
Spanish Teacher
Reeves, Sharon Sawyers
Business Teacher
Upchurch, Mike Joseph
English Teacher
Werth, Patricia Guy
Home Economics Teacher
Young, Mary Osborne
Mathematics Teacher
JONESVILLE
Adams, Wandaleen
Library Media Specialist
Bales, Sue Ann
Secondary Science Teacher
Bishop, Dorothy Fowler
English Teacher
Brewer, Lisa Ann
Mathematics Teacher
DeFore, Judy Scott
Sociology & Philosophy Teacher

Garrett, Debbie (Wolfenbarger)
English Teacher
Kirk, Gina Cox
Eighth Grade Teacher
Mc David, Robert
Math Teacher
Porterfield, Lila Byers
Visual Arts Teacher
Rasnic, Margaret Marie
Honors US Goverment Teacher
Sandel, Jane Coffey
English Teacher
Scott, Tammy Charlene
Social Studies Teacher
KENBRIDGE
Floyd, Anthony Wayne
5th Grade Teacher
KEYSVILLE
Chernault, Edward Neal
Assoc Prof of Engrng Tech
Nipper, Patricia Diane Henderson
Professor of Accounting & Ec
Stokes, Judy L.
English Professor
KING & QUEEN COURT HOUSE
Freit, Raymond Edward
Army Instructor
Harrison, Andrew Charles
English Teacher
Holmes, Fred Douglas, Jr.
Mathematics Dept Chairman
Palmer, Ramona Yvette (Shears)
Business Education Instructor
KING GEORGE
Bladel, Michael Paul
German Teacher
Burke, Valerie Allison
Fifth Grade Teacher
Cockey, Sheila Wands
Spanish Teacher
Graves, Viola Marie
English & AP English Teacher
Greenberg, Eileen Stein
Fourth Grade Teacher
Hall, Francine M.
English Teacher
Hill, Kristine Lucyna
Social Studies Teacher
Meka, Robert Alan
Math Teacher & Dept Chair
Miller, Karen Marshall
7th & 8th Grade English Tchr
Milne, Robert William
Chemistry Teacher
Pekarek, Rudolph Eric
World & US History Teacher
Picariello, John Joseph
History, Law & Economics Tchr
Sydnor, Katherine Gail
English Teacher
KING WILLIAM
Cline, Vicky Callison
English Teacher
Hall, Richard Allen
Mathematics & Algebra Teacher
Miller, Catherine Anne Bennie
Business Teacher
LA CROSSE
Lambert, Cassandra Tisdale
Fifth Grade Teacher
LANCASTER
Blake, Robin Bell
First Grade Teacher
Casto, Nell King
English II Teacher
Forrester, Mary Frances Keith
Third Grade Teacher
LAWRENCEVILLE
Allgood, Mary Starling
Business & Math Teacher
Daniel, Ann Hill
Mathematics Teacher
Gill, Gretchen Moore
Phys Ed & World Geog Teacher
Grizzard, Nancy Owen
6th-7th Grade Math Teacher
Hardy, Maurice Hall
Second Grade Teacher
Haws, Shawn J.
Primary Extension Teacher
Hicks, Nancy Harris
Mathematics Tchr & Dept Head
Jones, Gloria Womack
Language Arts Ext Teacher
Manning, Sharon L.
8th Grade Civics Teacher
Meredith, Carolyn Hendricks
Sixth Grade Teacher
Nanney, Barbara Greeson
10th Grade Biology Teacher
Nelson, Audrey Jarrett
Fourth Grade Teacher
Owen, Evelyn Bernadette
English Teacher
Piercy, Elaine B.
Business Teacher
Propst, Sharon Newcomb
English & Public Speaking Tchr
Rainey, Bessye Coleman
Education Professor
Randolph, Ruth Woodley
English Teacher
Robinson, Marveen Webb
Pre-K Teacher
Russell, Virginia H.
Retired Chairman & Professor
Satcher, Robert Lee, Sr.
Professor of Chemistry
Shiel, James Michael
Health & Physical Ed Teacher

LEBANON
Cox, Loretta Cunningham
English Teacher
Dickenson, Joan Karen Cox
Fourth Grade Teacher
Gilmer, Ava Yates
Seventh Grade Teacher
Gray, William Giles, Jr.
7th Grade Teacher
Johnson-Lowdermilk, Kathy
Mathematics Teacher
Lester, Judy Jessee
Third Grade Teacher
McClanahan, Karen Willis
Fourth Grade Teacher
Rainbolt, Leisa W.
Social Studies Teacher
Shortt, Kathy Blevins
World History & Civics Teacher
Thompson, Brenda Hamilton
Teacher
Wallace, Cheryl Smith
Art Teacher
Wright, Jo Ann Fleenor
English & Journalism Teacher
LEESBURG
Baird, Laura Zimmerman
8th-12th Grade English Teacher
Bell, Barbara Ferguson
HS Social Studies Teacher
Blakeney, Martha Ridgely
Mathematics Teacher
Cooper, Karen Shustack
Learning Disabilities Teacher
Dahlinger, Thomas Ray
Physical Science Teacher
Doerken, Elizabeth Ross
Music Supervisor & Teacher
Francis, Felicity Shepherd
Earth Science Teacher
Kent, Lee Daniel
Social Studies Teacher
Mc Guire, Babe
First Grade Teacher
Rader, Toni Christine
English Teacher
Ricci, Richard Thomas, Jr.
High School Math Teacher
Sheffield, Linda Payne
English Tchr & Department Chm
Walls, Jetta Lynne (Hall)
7th Grd Social Studies Teacher
LEXINGTON
Balazs, Mary Webber
Associate Professor of English
Davis, Thomas Webster
Professor of History
Gines, D. Scott
Head Baseball Coach
Jamison, Donald Kinzle
Professor
Leadbetter, Wanda Johnson
English Teacher
Monsour, Mike Ellis
Professor of Modern Languages
Ramsey, Elizabeth Courtenay
US History II & Ec Tchr
Trandel, Richard Samuel
Division Dir of Engineering
Vandervort, Bruce Charles
Associate Professor
Williams, Paul Wayne
History & World Geog Teacher
LOCUST GROVE
Barber, Elaine (Haught)
Asst Professor of Mathematics
Crane, Suzanne Gennrich
Assistant Professor of English
Ford, Bruce Douglas
Comp Information Systems Instr
Howard, Franklin Leeman
Electronics Instructor
MacKenzie, John Strong
Assoc Prof of English & Hum
Martin, Carla Nicole
History & Humanities Instr
McCormick, Delois Rodda
Mathematics Instructor
Mix, Linda Foster
English Teacher
Neidigh-Arnold, Carol Jean
Assistant Professor of Nursing
Reid, Robert David
Assoc Professor of Accounting
Stein, Richard Louis
Professor of Chemistry
Tate, Joel C.
Professor of Social Studies
Wilson, Philicia Jefferson
Counseling & Dev Asst Prof
LOCUST HILL
Thornton, Mary Jordan
6th Grade Soc Stu Tchr
LOUISA
Jurlando, Linda Eisenstadt
Fifth Grade Teacher
LOVINGSTON
Apperson, Debra Morris
Business Teacher
Ponton, Marsha H.
English Teacher
Racich, Leo P., III
Former Science Dept Chair
Wozniak, Phyllys Bare
Spanish Teacher
LOW MOOR
Hayslett, Rebecca Anderson
Social Studies Teacher
Underwood, Judith C.
6th & 7th Grd Reading Teacher

LURAY
Baldwin, Jodi Lynn
US History Teacher
Cawthorn, George Terrence
Fourth Grade Teacher
Chrisman, Kathy Thomason
Business Teacher & Dept Chair
Chrisman, Michael Vernon
Earth Sci, Hlth & PE Tchr
DeMeritt, Linda Benner
English Teacher & Librarian
Dickson, William Thomas
10th & 11th Grd English Tchr
Funkhouser, Lisa Michele
Business Teacher
Getz, Sarah Ellen
Civics & Geography Teacher
Harden, Karen Entsminger
Teacher & Curr Coord
Hinegardner, David Alan
Physical Education Teacher
Johnson, Carolyn Sue
8th-9th Grd English Teacher
Lancaster, Rita F.
Math Teacher
Ponn, David Edward
Government Teacher
Stombock, Barbara L.
Business Teacher
LYNCHBURG
Adkins, ElizabethA. (Dibbie)
Fourth Grade Teacher
Adkins, Robert T.
Schl of Business & Govt Dean
Armstrong, Cheryl Lindower
English Teacher
Arrington, Betty Hawkins
Span Tchr & Frgn Lang Dept Chm
Bell, Karen West
Spanish Teacher
Bell, William John
Coach
Berry, Charlotte Michal
Dir of Studies & Math Teacher
Breen, Nadine Smith
Music Teacher
Bridgett, Britta Leigh
Eng Tchr & SCA Spon
Caldwell, Marie Emore
Fourth Grade Teacher
Calvert, Lee Ann
Chemistry Teacher
Campbell, Julia S.
French Teacher
Capps, Janet Foster
Math, Science & Bible Teacher
Carson, Dwayne E.
Campus Pastor
Chadbourne, Alison Burton
8th Grade Pre-Algebra Teacher
Chamberlin, Ruth Louise
English Professor
Chase, Katharine Barnhardt
Soc Stud & Literature Teacher
Corell, Martha Peery
Mathematics Teacher
Crie, Mollie Rauh
Kindergarten Teacher
Culbertson, Stephen B.
French Teacher
Currence, Carol Jean (Smith)
Public Speaking & English Tchr
Currie, Suzanne Zeigler
English Teacher
Dellinger, Charles Edward
Career Technical Teacher
Diemer, Carl J., Jr.
Church His & New Tstmnt Prof
Dudley, Jerry Marshall
Building Trades Teacher
Farver, Linda L.
Full Professor of Physical Ed
Fink, Paul Richard
Chm & Prof Biblical Stud Dept
Foster, Randy Thomas
Scndry Physics & Math Teacher
Freerksen, James Albert
Professor of Biblical Studies
Fulcher, Brenn Phelps
German & English Teacher
Gedicks, Herbert D., Jr.
Assoc Professor of Marketing
George, Michael Lynn
Government & Sociology Teacher
Gibson, Judy D.
Social Studies Teacher
Gillispie, Kate Wallace
Kindergarten Teacher
Gladden, Joseph Rhea, III
Physics & Computer Sci Tchr
Greenhalgh, Patricia
Asst Professor of Education
Haynes, Eddie Wayne
Radiologic Technology Instr
Holloway, Rebecca Brandt
English Teacher
Horter, Glenn Gideon
Performing Arts Music Tchr
Howard, Nancy Wellons
Biology Teacher
Hughes, Ella Brown
Latin Teacher
Jamerson, Beth Campbell
Fourth Grade Teacher
Kitts, Charles Walter
Physics Teacher
Kramer, Cecil Vernon, Jr.
Communications Professor
Lindeman, Cheryl Ann
Instructor & Partnership Coord

Longo, Kenneth Frank
Spanish Teacher
Loos, Karl Wesley
6th Grd Adv Lang Arts Tchr
Lovett, Danny
Director of Pastoral Training
Lowry, Beverly Davis
Professor of Psychology
Marston, David Lee
Assistant Prof of Religion
Martin, Vicki Clinedinst
Assistant Professor of Nursing
Mateer, Robert N.
Prof of Finance & Dept Chair
Matthes, Lloyd Jacob
Mathematics Professor
Matthes, Sandra Schmickl
Music Theory Assoc Professor
Mc Cain, Carolyn Jackson
Math Teacher
Mickles, Muriel Brown
Student Services Specialist
Morrison, John Douglas
Assoc Prof Theolgy & Philosphy
Muller, Paul David
Asst Prof of Eng & Linguistics
Nelson, Larry Fay
Psychology Dept Chair
Nutter, Laurie J.
Communications Professor
Parker, Laura Anne
Fifth Grade Teacher
Pastors, David A.
Assistant Baseball Coach
Patterson, Richard Duane
Professor of Biblical Studies
Pickering, James Joseph
Assistant Professor
Pierce, JoAnne Green
Science Teacher
Poggemiller, Esther L.
English Teacher
Poggemiller, Helmuth Carl
Professor of English
Queen, Scott M.
Assistant Track Coach
Quel, Robert Samuel
English Teacher
Randlett, Douglas H.
Assoc Prof of Youth Ministries
Rist, Boyd Clifton
Dean of Faculty & History Prof
Roberts, Jody Bennington
Librarian
Ross, Jeffrey Clay
Math Teacher
Rowlette, Elizabeth Ann
Bus Tech Teacher & Dept Chm
Rumore, Sandra Vee
Assoc Prof of Mathematics
Sale, Nancy Whitmire
Library Media Specialist
Sanders, Linda Ballard
Social Studies Teacher
Schmitt, Frank Joseph
Prof of Educational Ministries
Schwartz-Kenney, Beth M.
Psychology Professor
Smith, Kimberly Sue
Mathematics Teacher
Smith, Stephen Claude
Mathematics Teacher
Spencer, Mary Reed
Womens Life Dir & Span Tchr
Stone, Carole Poff
Horticulture Teacher
Storey, Karen Fink-Owens
Chemistry & Biology Teacher
Stroud, Lisa May
Instructor of English
Sudduth, Janice Hatton
Soc Stud Tchr & Dept Chprsn
Sullivan, Gene R.
Assoc Professor of Accounting
Swain, Dorothy Mae
Computer Applications Teacher
Templeton, David Earl
Physics Teacher
Thompson, Sandra Mc Ivor
English Teacher
Thurman, Julia McCrory
English Instructor
Towns, Elmer L.
Dean, School of Religion
Travis, Mildred Lindsay
Mathematics Teacher
Troxel, Steven Richard
Assoc Prof Communication Stud
Waller, Jettie Marie
AP US His, Govt US & Comp Tchr
Weigand, Claudia Gayle Harrison
Cosmetology Teacher
Whalen, Sarah Thompson
Math & Computer Sci Tchr
Wharton, Carolyn Ann (Teel)
Professor of Journalism
Whitehead, Catherine Cecile (Goewey)
Mathematics Teacher
Wilkerson, Deborah Reynolds
Biology Teacher
Willmington, Matthew L.
Asst Prof of Youth Ministry
Willoughby, Jenipher RAuh
Earth Science Teacher & Leader
Wood, Jane Martin
Biology Teacher
Woodard, Branson Lee, Jr.
English Professor
Woodford, Kim Howard
English & Latin Teacher

Worsham, Patricia Stokes
English Teacher & Dept Chm
Wright, Benjamin Ward, Jr.
Professor Emeritus of History
Wright, Susan Burnett
Law & Business Teacher
Zappulla, Nancy Wade
English Teacher
MADISON
Huso, Dianne Rae
English Teacher & Dept Chair
Tanner, William Dawson
Biology Teacher
Utz, Virginia P.
4th Grade Teacher
MADISON HEIGHTS
Burk, Kathy R.
Seventh Grade Teacher
Glasser, Donald William
Social Studies & Civics Tchr
Jones, Beverly Campbell
Math, Rdng & US His Teacher
Martin, Judith Bing
Fifth Grade Teacher
Moore, Anita Taylor
6th Grd Tchr & Coord of Gifted
MANASSAS
Avalos, Ellen Raisner
Mathematics Teacher
Barth, M. Jane
IB History Teacher
Beauchamp, Glen Thomas
Math Teacher
Blackwell, Lillian Peterson
Second Grade Teacher
Boley, Wandalyn Gaye
Choral Director
Bowles, Susan Ann
High School Math Teacher
Cadogan, Florence Moses
Math Teacher
Cannon, Martha Ann
Math Teacher
Constantino, Steven Mark
High School Principal
Cottrell, Scott S.
Mathematics Teacher
Donley, Yvonne Elizabeth
English Teacher
Engman, Gilta Casanova
Spanish Teacher
Fair, Barbara Colvin
Fourth Grade Teacher
Faul, Michael James
English Teacher
Finch, Jo W.
Mathematics Instructor
Flakowicz, Cheryl Ann
Business & Marketing Teacher
Gaydos, Catherine Sherwin
Mathematics Teacher
Germann, George Edward
French Teacher
Goins, Donna Gail
Science Teacher
Harrah, Thomas E.
Math Teacher
Janes, Paula Niswander
English Teacher
Jardin, Bronwyn Best
Language Arts Teacher
Kaminsky, Margaret Offterdinger
English Teacher
Kenney, Barbara Boyle
6th Grade Teacher
Kent, Marilyn Flynt
Guidance Counselor
Lawson, Deborah Bissett
Marketing Education Dept Head
Lobstein, Marion Blois (Coble)
Assoc Professor of Biology
Lowry, Charles Wesley, III
Latin & Alternative Ed Teacher
Lynch, Nora Miller
Eighth Grade Civics Teacher
Martin, Anna M.
Orchestra Director
Matty, Maureen Elizabeth (Morsey)
First Grade Teacher
Mc Elfish, Joseph B.
Health & PE Teacher
Mc Farland, Jeff James
Vocational Dept Head
McMahon, Maureen Hannigan
English Teacher
Navangul, Himanshoo V. B.
Science Teacher
Nemerow, Larry Glen
Bio II & Gen Biology Tchr
Pennefather, Robert Michael
Religion, Geography & His Tchr
Poindexter, Karen Stowers
Middle School Principal
Porter, James Robert
Naval Science Instructor
Powell, Nancy W.
English Teacher
Ross, Brenda Flory
Librarian
Schlatter, Rose Golden
English Teacher
Soderberg, Charles Ramsey
Fifth Grade Teacher
Thompson, Gregory Scott
6th-8th Grade Tchr & Principal
Yankey, Jack
8th Grade Civics Teacher
MARION
Adams, Larry Edward
Electrical Instructor

Burger, Denise Hoots
Art Teacher
Edmiston, Joyce Ann
Sixth Grade Teacher
Evans, Sara Sue Hankins
Sixth Grade Teacher
Goodman, Nancy Fisher
Chemistry & Physics Teacher
Harris, Sondra Adele Eastridge
Earth Science & Biology Tchr
Henson, Vicki Ellen
Family Studies Teacher
Mellinger, Mariann Berry
Mathematics Teacher
Pennington, Deborah Parsons
Third Grade Teacher
Rigely, Robert E.
Sixth Grade Teacher
Robertson, Cynthia Jo
History Teacher
Rotenberry, Mary Russell
Retired Teacher
Thomas, Deborah Yvonne
English Teacher
Wright, Richard Steven
Physical Ed Teacher & Coach
MARSHALL
Doyle, Margaret Ormstedt
History & Social Science Tchr
Fraser, Susan Leslie
History Dept Teacher
Genther, Gary Alan
Fine Arts Department Chairman
LaMonica, Clelia McGowan
Science Teacher
Pegues, Kathleen Garcia
Lang Arts Tchr of the Gifted
Stapp-Harris, Tutt
English & Psychology Teacher
Stevens, Deborah Lynn
Chemistry & Science Teacher
Thompson, Robyn Walker
Fourth Grade Teacher
MARTINSVILLE
Armstrong, Jo Ann
Assoc Prof of Sociology
Bannan, Gerald Paul
Fine Arts Instructor
Bourne, Aileen Burnette
Biology Teacher
Britton, Diana Feather
English Teacher
Brown, Timothy Elijah
Social Studies Teacher & Coach
Brunson, David Ronald
Engrng & Furniture Tech Instr
Cox, Jimmy Dale
Junior ROTC Instructor
Epperly, Barbara Thomas
English Teacher
Epperly, Herbert Dailey, Jr.
Director of Alternative Ed
Gale, Linda Hudson
Prof of Office Systems Tech
Garrett, Marie M.
English Associate Professor
Holland, R. Darryl
Agriculture Instructor
Imgram, Willie Douglas, Jr.
Teacher
Ivey, Betsy Davis
Teacher of Gifted
Jamison, William
Program Director
McCary, Mark Henry
High School Instructor
Mc Craw, Carolyn Mason
English Teacher
Overby, Bronte Allen
Developmental Math Instructor
Pritchett, Louis Henry
Accounting & Computer Teacher
Pulliam, Linda Bowman
English Department Chairperson
Sawyers, Thomas Ronald
Principal
Simington, Paulette Rodgers
Principal
Simpson, Deborah Sue
Mathematics Teacher
Turner, Carolyn Davis
Coordinator for Gifted Stdnts
Waddy, Connie Witcher
First Grade Teacher
Wade, Gayle Panagos
Assistant Professor
Walmsley, Pat Brown
English & Publications Tchr
Wray, Joyce Hutson
Art Instructor
Wreden, Carol Keister
Adj Instr of Art, Pntng, Drwng
Zollars, Michelle Wood
Assistant Professor of English
MATHEWS
Anthony, David Bertram
History Teacher
Deputy, John William, Jr.
English Teacher
Hatch, Jean Lawter
Art Teacher
Jackson, Alvertis Taliferro
Business Education Teacher
Mc Daniel, Virginia Handy
English & Dramatic Lit Tchr
Rowe, Judy Moore
Math & French Teacher
MAX MEADOWS
Anders, Gena Boyer
Fourth Grade Teacher

MEADOWS (cont)
Margaret Shockley
hematics Teacher
on, Marion Dyer, Jr.
nnology Teacher
, Constance (Medlock)
lish, Drama & Jrnlsm Tchr
, Tammy Curtis
s Ed & Health Teacher
enberry, Linda Woodward
hematics Teacher
, Jack L.
rumental Music Director
LEAN
r, B. Philip
ory Teacher
n, Jason Charles
ner Science Physics Teacher
Melby S.
h Teacher & Dept Chair
ee, Karen G.
ence Teacher
Henry Nelson
ence Dept Head & Teacher
ott, Sara L.
logy Tchr & Sci Dept Head
, Trinket
& Photography Teacher
ey, Anne Hassink
dergarten Teacher
, Jean Butler
Teacher & Department Chair
el, Connie (Olson)
nce Teacher
nbach, Elizabeth
in Teacher
anek, Mary Minarik
g & Journalism Teacher
yk-Chao, Susie
glish Teacher
n, Arthur Warren
glish Teacher
son, Sharon Walworth
English Teacher
onnor, John Desmond
em, Bio & Earth Sci Tchr
ps, Patricia Wilcox
reemnts Documentation Drftr
es, David Charles
vt, Sociology & Ec Tchr
cich, Matthew William
rector of Vocal Music
a, Rebecca
ology Teacher
yer, Mary Ellen Keeffe
cial Studies Teacher
rett, David
glish Teacher
flett, Susan Svensen
orts Medicine Teacher
u, Ghislaine A.
ench Teacher
erfall, Mildred Moye
S World & American Lit Tchr
ADOWS DAN
ntgomery, Sandra Jane
incipal
ADOWVIEW
hran, Jenny Maness
rst Grade Teacher
cher, Victoria Ann
h Grade Teacher
ly, Ruth Caldwell
h Grd Language Arts Teacher
se, Rhonda Duncan
indergarten Teacher
mmler, Shirley Sullivan
indergarten Teacher
CHANICSVILLE
rd, Debra K.
nglish Teacher
lard, Jean Bragg
lath Teacher
Ville, Sheilah Murdock
rt Teacher
lling, Michael F.
Mathematics Teacher
wles, Betty Jones
usiness Education Teacher
wles, Phyllis Payne
orticulture, Floricultre Tchr
nser, Sherry Lynn
panish Teacher
tler, Donna Farmer
anguage Arts & Civics Teacher
rter, Alicia Hawkes
enior & English Teacher
llins, Karen Hill
Mathematics Tchr & Dept Chm
oley, Carolyn Van Ness
ocial Studies Teacher
monson, Deborah Davidson
panish Teacher
rrell, Kimberly Jewell
Citizenship Teacher
bbs, Mary Cutting
Chemistry Teacher
enberry, Steven Ferris
Social Studies Teacher
nnings, Carole E.
Health & Physical Ed Teacher
tchen, Will Rogers
History Teacher & Coach
ambert, James Edward
Social Studies Teacher
c Aleer, Karen Virginia
Fifth Grade Teacher
cFaden, Daniel Caldwell
History Teacher

Munchel, Deborah King
High School Psychology Teacher
Polifka, Judith Jones
French Teacher
Simon, Alice Richards
Art & Crafts Teacher
Triemplar, James Elvyn
Computer Lab Manager
Tucker, Virginia C.
Counselor
Valentine, James H.
Fine Arts Chairman
Vest, Nancy Daniel
Second Grade Teacher
Webb, Kimberly Carter
Third Grade Teacher
Weiglein, Janice Leslie (Kerr)
Eighth Grade Science Teacher
Whitehurst, Ann Sloan
Home Economics Teacher
Williams, Sara Todd
Guidance Counseling Director
Witherow, E. C., III
Health & PE Teacher
Woodson, Stephany Hagan
French & World History Tchr
MIDDLEBURG
Bergan, Celeste Porter
Science Teacher
Bergan, Paul Kenneth
9th-11th Grade English Teacher
Bryan, Mary Leora
Mathematics & Computer Teacher
Roscoe, Yvonne, SND
Math Dept Chairperson & Tchr
MIDDLETOWN
Cogan, Felicia Henderson
Assoc Prof of English & Hum
Garrand, Michael L.
Mathematics Assoc Professor
Mc Mullen, Harold Gene
Prof of Philosophy & Education
MIDLOTHIAN
Averill, Christopher Armand
American History Teacher
Beachy, Alice Schreiner
Algebra & Earth Science Tchr
Bowman, Anna Mae
English Teacher
Bray, William Joseph, Jr.
US History Teacher
Brooks, Marjorie Lynn
Hlth & Physical Education Tchr
Childress, Garland Wesley
Mathematics Instructor
Clements, Karen Randle
English Teacher
Coffey, Eloise G.
French & English Teacher
Cooke, Mary Deisher
Sci Dept Chm & Biology Tchr
DeCicco, Karen Moschler
English Teacher
Dollings, Donna Justice
Latin Teacher
Dunkum, Joan Cashion
Bus Teacher & COE Coordinator
Ellis, Theresa Torregrossa
Math & Computer Sci Teacher
Geary, Daniel Joseph
Counselor & Dir of Career Ctr
Harris, Diane Bosher
English Teacher
Hayes, William C., III
Mathematics Teacher
Henry, James Slater
Chemistry Teacher
Herting, Robert Michael
US & Virginia History Teacher
Hopkins, Amelia Nespoli
Guidance Counselor
Hubbard, Jamie A.
Hlth & Physical Education Tchr
Jenkins, Terry Dryer
American Studies & Eng Teacher
Jennings, Pamela Ferguson
Mathematics Teacher
Kirtley, Victoria Chapman
High School Art Teacher
Lasswell, Juanita Glaspie
Mathematics Teacher
Legard, Annette Paul
10th Grade Biology Teacher
Liesfeld, Robin Belcher
Social Studies Tchr & Dpt Head
LLoyd, Jeremy Michael
Science Teacher
Lowery, James Timothy
Health, Drivers Ed & PE Tchr
Lukens, Deborah Baird
Marketing Teacher
Malarky, Fredia Plyler
Guidance Counselor
Melillo, James Patrick
History Teacher
Moore-Raful, Robin Celeste
Fine Arts Dept Chair
Morgan, Stan
Health, PE Instructor & Coach
Murray, Elizabeth Booth
English Teacher
Newman, Patti Melissa
Band Director
Perry, Donna Lynne
French Teacher
Pierson, James Frederic
Honors Govt & US His Teacher
Pillar, Kristie K.
Mathematics Teacher

Pritchett, Billy
Practical Law & Govt Teacher
Riggs, Dale Robinson
Spanish Teacher
Rinehart, Karen Snopkowski
Elementary Guidance Counselor
Robertson, Katherine Toney
Latin Teacher
Robertson, Tracy Fair
English Teacher
Seal, Cynthia Lynn
English & Journalism Teacher
Seay Young, Ellen A.
English & Communications Tchr
Shelton, Warren Michael
Science Teacher
Sours, Charles Kevin
Math Teacher
Vaughan, Joan Stengel
10th Grade English Teacher
Vipperman, Carla Lacy
US His & Practical Law Teacher
Whitlow, Kathryn Abernathy
Biology Teacher
Wilborn, Kathryn Tanner
English Teacher
Wilkinson, Cynthia Gayle
Biology Teacher & Admin Asst
Woodle, Gregory Douglas
Social Studies Teacher
MILFORD
Adkins, Mary Young
English Teacher
Griffis, Diane White
Reading & Language Arts Tchr
Hinders, Lawrence Frank
English Teacher
Otero, Lourdes P.
Spanish Teacher
Raynes, Michael Steven
American History Teacher
Robinson, Shirley Brown
Sixth Grade Teacher
Stanley, Lillian Chadwick
High School Biology Teacher
Thompson, Geneva Johnson
Admin Asst & Acting Voc Dir
MILLBORO
Gilchrest, Betty Mill
First Grade Teacher
Jenkins, Bonnie Weaver
Second Grade Teacher
MINERAL
Buhrer, Edward Frederick
Eng, Writing Tchr & Dept Chm
Chaney, Walter G.
Biology Teacher
Massie, Rebecca Rigsby
Art Teacher
Morris, Lillian J.
English Teacher
Onesty, Rachel Mc Coy
French Teacher
Quarles, Gracie Brooks
Work & Family Studies Teacher
MONETA
Hedrick, Larry Steven
Band Director
MONTEREY
Hodges, Kenny W.
Carpentry Teacher
Moats, Melody Terry
Fifth Grade Teacher
Neil, Virginia Edvards
Coordinator of Gifted Programs
Ralston, Joyce H.
Social Studies Teacher
MONTPELIER
Harlan, Betty Satterwhite
Fifth Grade Teacher
MONTROSS
Austin, Nancy Straughan
Social Studies & Rdng Teacher
Pannell, Vonda Diana Coleman
Tchr of Learning Disabilities
Ransone, Holly Scates
9th-12th Grade Art Instructor
Wagstaff, Rita Mae
Eng & African Amer Stud Tchr
MOUNT JACKSON
Fansler, Margaret Robinson
9th Grade English Teacher
Fifer, Ruth A.
7th Grd Language Arts Teacher
Grandle, Cynthia Myers
L D Specialist
McInturff, Adina Swartz
Math Teacher
Rosenberg, Trish Diachenko
English & Theater Arts Teacher
MOUNT SOLON
Reeves, Jessie Ware
Second Grade Tchr & Asst Prin
NARROWS
Dillow, Cindy Lynn
English Teacher
Franklin, Richard Ray
Biology Teacher
Meadows, Rhonda Sue Thomas
2nd Grade Teacher
Stafford Wood, Betsy
English Teacher
Waselchalk, Charles Gregory
Social Studies Teacher
NARUNA
Dunn, Winifred Ellington
Art Teacher
Flowers, DeAna Holsinger
Business Teacher

Jones, Beverly Ann
English & Drama Teacher
Phillips, Cecil Clinton, III
US, VA Govt & World Geography
NATHALIE
Trice, Anita Danna
Second Grade Teacher
NEW CASTLE
Barnes, Julian Glen
Science Dept Teacher & Chm
St Leger, Mark F.
Vocational Instructor
NEW KENT
Cox, Jack Ronald, Jr.
US His & World Geography Tchr
Gulick, Patti Hughes
Social Studies Teacher
Pinelli, Jayne Thomas
Gifted Resource Teacher
NEW MARKET
Decker, Edward Thomas, Sr.
Bible Teacher
Graves, Randall Keith
Science Teacher
Osborne, Susan Harris
English & Drama Teacher
Wensell, Waldemar Orlando
Choral Teacher
NEWPORT NEWS
Anby, Betty Rave
Fifth Grade Teacher
Anderson, Maxie Kendall
Security & Truancy Officer
Ashburn, Dorothy Drudge
Fifth Grade Teacher
Ballard, Joyce Davis
English Teacher
Bell, Mary Fish
Science Teacher & Dept Chm
Blood, Lorrie
High School Mathematics Tchr
Booker, Henry Marshall
Program Dir of Intnl Business
Bowers, Leslie Nickerson
9th & 11th Grd English Teacher
Brown, William Scott
Director of Jazz Studies
Brunson, Ethel Dean
Tenth Grade English Teacher
Crisp, Betsy Patterson
Second Grade Teacher
Curtis, T. Howard, III
Percussion Specialist
Davidson, Bruce E.
Physics & Biology Teacher
Dempsey, Tom Gene
Dir Criminal Justice Admin
Dixon, Betty B.
Social Studies Teacher
Ferrell, Julie H.
English & Journalism Teacher
Fichter, Ann Bowles
Upper School Math Teacher
Fletcher, Stephen Lynn
Bible & Physical Ed Teacher
Forestier, Elizabeth Aldrich
English & Journalism Teacher
Frazier, Anthony Keith
8th Grade Teacher
Gesualdi, Patricia Stevenson
English Teacher
Gordon, Douglas Kirke
Professor of English
Grau, Harold James
Assistant Professor of Biology
Gunter, Gail S.
Mathematics Teacher
Hankins, Jane Hunsucker
Mathematics Teacher
Hayden, James D.
Eighth Grd Mathematics Tchr
Herrick, Julie Anne Warriner
Latin Teacher
Holder, Randolph C.
Marketing Teacher & Dept Chair
Hopson, Barbara Barham
Biology & Zoology Teacher
Horne, Belinda Scholl
Sixth Grd Math & Science Tchr
Howard, Ann Simons
Music & Drama Teacher
Jones, Nancy Hiebert
Psychology & Biology Teacher
Jones, Sheila Driggs
4th Grade Teacher
Ketchum, Sherri Spencer
Fourth Grade Teacher
Kitchen, Annou Karavias
Psychology Teacher
Lee, Ivy Daniel
English Teacher
Lilley, David Lawrence
English Teacher
Lowe, Bonnie Ould
Mathematics Teacher
Ludy, Claretha Wallace
Elementary School Counselor
Lusk, Richard Vernon
Secondary English Teacher
Makepeace, Michael Dennis
7th Grade Mathematics Teacher
Mitchell-Robbins, Letitia Hayne
German Teacher
Paul, Jay Snyder
Prof & English Chair
Pesolinski, Paul D.
High School Health Teacher
Pierce, Anne Lynne
US & World History Teacher

Raines, Barbara Gaskins
English Teacher
Roberts, Page Willey
English Teacher
Roe, Dale E.
Marketing & Ed Coordinator
Satchell, Frank Fletcher, Jr.
Academic Instructor
Schmidt, Cynthia Morrissette
Math Teacher
Shepherd, Lesa Hanlin
AP Bio Tchr & Intl Bac Coord
Spady, Frances Kelley
Elementary Assistant Principal
Troy, Kathy Anasovich
6th & 7th Grade Teacher
Tumminello, Sandra Folse
Guidance Counselor
Tutunjian, Yvonne Ortega
Spanish Teacher
Wagner, Lauren Hamilton Beamer
6th Grade Teacher
Waller, G. Darryl
Choral Dir, Fine Arts Dept Chm
Watkins, Marilyn Hortense
Health & Phys Ed Teacher
Webster, Falesia Delfine
Guidance Counselor
White, James Harold, II
Art Teacher & Department Head
NICKELSVILLE
Dishner, Teresa O.
HS Math & Chemistry Teacher
Lockhart, Christopher Thomas
Band Director
NOKESVILLE
Harris, Athena
Fifth Grade Teacher
Poteat, Steven Blain
6th Grade Science Teacher
Thiele, Katherine M.
Orchestra Dir & Music Tchr
NORA
Delaney, Mona Rasnick
English Teacher
Herndon, Arthur Ray
English Teacher
Kirk, Rosa C.
Mathematics Teacher
Patton, Ginger Paige
VA, US His & Government Tchr
Stanley, Denise Rose
English, Speech & Drama Tchr
NORFOLK
Anderson, Belinda Childress
Dean, Schl Gen & Continuing Ed
Anderson, Joseph Donald
Social Work Professor
Ayres, Charles Craig
Social Studies & History Tchr
Bagby, Janet Forbes
English Teacher
Baird, Michele Nowicki
7th Grade Science Teacher
Baker, Hollie
Assoc Professor of Mathematics
Baldwin, William Barton, Jr.
Headmaster
Banatte, Jean-Marie M.
Prof of Accounting & Taxation
Barnes, Gail Van Aernum
Orchestra Director
Baylor, Ellen Cundiff
Counselor
Best, Lydia
Assistant Professor of Nursing
Bethea, Joycelyn S.
Mathematics Teacher
Blair, Rose Ellen Julian
Science Teacher
Bly, Donald Andrea, Sr.
5th Grade Teacher
Bridgeforth, Carolyn McKinley
Comm Skills Tchr & Rdng Spec
Broadbent, Arthur, III
Choral Director
Brown, Del M. Mauhrino
Assistant Professor
Byrne, William Andrew
History Professor
Caja, Stephen Francisco
Physics Teacher
Calebro, Joanne Mueck
First Grade Teacher
Carlisle, A. Mischelle
English Teacher
Charitos, Stephane Andre
Assistant Professor of French
Chasten, Muriel Holmes
Associate Professor in History
Chavoustie, Suzanne Santucci
English Teacher
Cotter, Michael James
English Instructor
Cox, Tommy
Doctoral Student
Crawford, Sharon Paige
Eng, Speech Tchr & Asst Cnslr
Crump, Carathene W.
Teacher & Math Dept Chairman
Curtis, Anne Park
7th & 8th Grade Math Teacher
Davenport, Juliana Maccubbin
French Teacher
Deadrick, Diana Lyn
Asst Professor of Mngmt
Dewberry, Jane Clifford
Third Grade Teacher
DiRosa, Rebecca Snyder
Social Studies Teacher

NORFOLK (cont)
Easley, Vickie Donnelly
Latin Teacher
Feincis, Diane Hollenbock
Guidance Department Chair
Feser, David Henry
Government Teacher
Fitzgerald, Debbie Thomas
Practical Nursing Teacher
Foreman, Belinda Susan
Span Tchr & Fine Arts Dept Chr
Frederick, Christy Holloman
University Instructor
Gallagher, Chip
Performing Arts Dept Director
Gebler, Michael Paul
Math Teacher
Hackworth, John Richard
Professor
Harris, Carl Gordon, Jr.
Prof & Music Dept Chairman
Harris, Keith D.
Art Teacher & Yearbook Spon
Harris, Patricia Parrish
English Teacher
Hart, Joan Bourbeau
4th Grade Teacher
Hayes, R. David
Student Resource Coordinator
Henry, Louis H.
Professor of Economics
Hester, Vivian Monroe
Learning Disabled Scndry Tchr
Honeycutt, Earl D., Jr.
Assoc Professor of Marketing
Howard, Betty Spears
Kindergarten Teacher
Hubbard, Harold Douglas
Asst Prof of Pol Sci & Urbn Pl
Igareda, Susan Maria
History Teacher
Jenkins, Danny Taylor
Naval Science Department Head
Johnson, David Earl
Associate Prof of Visual Arts
Johnson-Vaughn, Emogene F.
Health Education Professor
Jordan, Ruth G.
Professional Counselor
Josephsen, Steven A.
Extended Learning Program Dir
Joshi, Ravindra Prabhakar
Associate Professor
Kern, Kristen Tulloch
Professor of Physics
Lee, Cloteen Yarbrough
Fifth Grade Teacher
Leidy, Herbert Wayne
Fourth Grade Teacher
Lupton, Rita Jackson
Spanish Teacher
Mapp, Johnnie Albert
Accounting Dept Head
Mc Coy, Elizabeth Mills
French Teacher
Mc Kinney, Sueanne Elizabeth
6th Grade Math & Science Tchr
Mc Neil, Phillip Eugene
Math Prof & Department Chair
Miller, Sheila Dinetta
Prof of Grad & Undr Grad Prgms
Moran, Sharon Hamrick
7th Grade Soc Studies Teacher
Myles, Vernetta Hall
Social Studies Teacher
Nelson, Laura J.
Chemistry Teacher
Newman, Ronald Wayne
Drama & Speech Director
Newman, Tracy Maria
Biology Teacher
Oberdorfer, Richard Wallace
History Teacher & Dept Chm
Opfer, Steven E.
Broadcast Journalism Professor
Payne, Robert L., III
Eng & Creative Writing Tchr
Peeples, Theresa Blunt
6th Grade Math & Reading Tchr
Penn, Celethia Darlene
Music Teacher
Pickett, Yvonne Gudemard
French Teacher
Pierce, Milton Elbert
Third Grade Teacher
Pope, Stephanie Marie
Latin Teacher
Randall, L. Jane
Distance Learning Pgm Site Dir
Rayford, Orren L.
Dir, Prof Cnslng & Career Dev
Razzaq, Zia
Professor of Civil Engineering
Ritz, John Michael
Tech Ed Professor & Dept Chair
Royster, Sue Scarborough
AP General Biology Teacher
Rushing, Bonnie Lucille
Comm Skills & Reading Teacher
Russell, Susan Webb
6th Grade Reading Teacher
Self, Lynda Hall
English Teacher & Chair
Sergeant, Robert Stewart
English Teacher
Shepherd, Brenda Patterson
Multicultural Ed Specialist
Sigler, Susan M.
Guidance Counselor
Sorrell, Patricia Pepper
Faculty & Master Teacher
Strauss, Richard Theodore
Science Chprsn & Biology Tchr
Sweeney, Claudia Tripp
Guidance Counselor
Tatem, Nancy McAllister
MS Teacher of Gifted Program
Thiele, Douglas M.
High School & College Instr
Thorpe, Deborah Levitan
Department Chairperson
Threlfall, K. Denise
Marketing Educl Pgm Leader
Ward-Petroske, Sarah
Biology Teacher
Warner, Jennifer Cecile
Learning Disabilities Teacher
Weis, Patricia Oglesby
Educational Therapist
Weiss, Morisa Bendett
Eighth Grade English Teacher
Wells, Steven Curtis
Engineering Professor
Wiggs, John Frederick
Mathematics Professor
Williams, Edgar L., Jr.
Assistant Dean
Williams, Maria Powell
High School English Teacher
Williams, Paula Wayno-Morris
Social Studies & Civics Tchr
Womick, George Palmer, Jr.
Student Assistance Counselor
Yochum, Gilbert R.
Dept of Economics Chairman
Zaleski, Lucy Minchen
Sixth Grade Teacher
NORTH TAZEWELL
Barrett, Claire Fields
4th Grade Teacher
Black, Sheree Deskins
Second Grade Teacher
Crawley, Evelyn Anderson
Retired School Teacher
Duncan, Katherine Lee
Title I Reading & Math Teacher
Hagy, Lynn Hawks
Third Grade Teacher
Mc Call, Connie Necessary
Primary Department Supervisor
Ross, Mary Kathryn
Teacher
NORTON
Fore, Susan Lawson
6th Grade Math Teacher
Scott, Terri R.
Fifth Grade Math Teacher
Wade, Elizabeth Ann
Science Teacher
NOTTOWAY
Britt, Mitchell Lance
Director of Bands and Ensemble
Conley, Matilda Powell
English & Photojournalism Tchr
Greene, Madelene Leath
US Govt, Wrld Geog Tchr
Mumford, Lawrence Edward
Civics, US & VA History Tchr
Smith, Beverley Randolph
English Teacher
Teillon, Lance William
Associate Naval Science Instr
Tucker, Mae Alexander
Math & Pre-Algebra Teacher
Wilson, Marilyn Elizabeth
Health, PE & Drivers Ed Tchr
OAK HALL
Killmon, Donna Chapman
Math Teacher & Dept Chair
Van Dyck, Carolyn See
Biology Teacher
Wood-Blake, Judith Gaye
Mathematics Teacher
OAKWOOD
Boyd, Martha Mitchell
6th-7th Grade Math Teacher
Burton, Wayne Talbert, Sr.
Senior Army Instructor
Clevinger, Ola Gay (Brown)
Kindergarten Teacher
Crumpton, Deborah Jackson
Home Economics Teacher
Dailey, Diana Rowe
French, Health & PE Teacher
Epling, Ronald Jack
Mathematics Teacher
Gillespie, Cathy Frye
Kindergarten Teacher
Jackson, Mary Fisher
6th & 7th Grade Science Tchr
Jones, Raymond Lee
History Teacher
Matney, Julia Deel
Secondary Mathematics Teacher
Mitchell, Wanda E.
English Teacher
Mullins, Lenville, Jr.
Secondary English Teacher
Owens, Janie Layne
Principal
West, Betty Jane (Crigger)
Science & Math Teacher
ONLEY
Defosse, Patricia Ann (Barbera)
Chemistry & Physics Teacher
Holmes, Harold Francis
Earth Science Teacher
Linton, Glenn
Middle & High School Art Tchr
ORANGE
Arbogast, Larry Cameron
Physics & AP Biology Teacher
Brasted, Janice Waymack
Language Arts Teacher
Carraway, J. Marcus
Social Studies Teacher
Duncan, Douglas Allen
Seventh Grade Teacher
Goodwin, Lillian Wright
Kindergarten Teacher
Hawkins, Patricia Ann
Health Occupations Teacher
Hogan, Charmaine Twist
Language Arts Teacher
Lee, Shirley Treadwell
Third Grade Teacher
Mc Clellan, Wendy Bradshaw
4th Grade Teacher
Mc Leod, George Roderick, III
US History Teacher
Vitez, Michael Andrew
Dean & Drama Director
Yurasits, Leigh Goddin
Home Economics Teacher
PALMYRA
Black, Barbara Kitchen
HS Special Education Teacher
Brennan, Lisa Frances
Chemistry Teacher
Broad, K. Peace M.
English Teacher
Daly, William P.
Math Teacher
Evans, J. Michael
English & Humanities Teacher
Ford, Jane Snead
History & Law Teacher
Lucas, Lisa A.
Resource Teacher
Muir, J. Thomas
History & Government Teacher
Nail, Kenneth Edward
Band Director
PEARISBURG
Bayless, Patricia Norton
Mathematics Teacher
Coulter, Alicia Young
Mathematics Teacher
Kelley, Russell M., Jr.
Physical Education Teacher
Mann, Judy Jackson
Health & PE Teacher
Schmidt, Neil Robert
Biology Teacher & Coach
Wilburn, Bobby Dent
Biology Teacher
PEMBROKE
Farmer, Kimberly Kessinger
6th & 7th Grade Science Tchr
PENN LAIRD
Failes, James Robert, Jr.
Research & Biology Teacher
Floyd, Kelly Daniele
Business Teacher
Larosa, Margaret Monger
Art Teacher
Ryder, Deborah Averette
Choral Director
Smith, Judith R.
Business Teacher
Suter, Marian Brown
English Teacher
Trobaugh, Gregory Stephen
Technology Ed Tchr
PENNINGTN GAP
Chester, Renee Lamb
Eighth Grade English Teacher
Ely, Thomas H.
Fifth Grade Teacher
Hathaway, Robert William
Sixth Grade Teacher
Laningham, Connie Daugherty
Sixth Grade Teacher
Sayers, Mary Hines
Technology Education Teacher
PETERSBURG
Alexander, Gail Patricia
Assistant Principal
Amaram, Donatus Theukwumere
Professor of Management
Amobi, Emmanuel N.
Accounting Professor
Askew, Sharon W.
Communication Instructor
Blount, Catherine Irene Joyce
Band Dir & Fine Arts Dept Chm
Branch-Torrence, Michelle
Teacher
Burbank, Kenneth
Engrng Technology Assoc Prof
Cain, Arletha Wood
9th Grade English Teacher
Eseonu, Maxwell Obioma
Assoc Professor of Economics
Ford, Bruce Lassiter
Social Studies Teacher
Franklin, Joan Cabler
Business Teacher
Gilchrist, Alvin Reginald
English & Drama Teacher
Gilliam, Conrad M.
Plant & Soil Science Professor
Gore, Pauline Jones
Fourth Grade Teacher
Gray, Kerry Lorenzo
Health & Physical Educator
Gregory, Sadie Raines
Dean, School of Business
Hale, Vicki Jan
AP Government Teacher
Hall, John Thomas
Social Stud Chm & Track Coach
Harper, Starria France
Business Teacher
Hatchett, Susan Waller
Latin Teacher
Janto, Andrew Stephen
English Teacher
January, Imogene B.
Biology Teacher
Jefferson, Linda Eanes
Assistant Professor of English
Jones, Sylvia Ethylene
Kindergarten Teacher
Kent, Michelle Astwood
Hlth & Physical Education Tchr
Loving, Madeline Peebles
8th Grade English Teacher
Lundy, Bernard Joseph, Jr.
Special Education Teacher
Lundy, Donna Roberts
Choral Director
Miles, Ruby Williams
English Teacher
Mitchem, Cheryl Drake
Dept of Acctng Chr & Asst Prof
Montgomery, Sandra Dowlin
Spanish Teacher
Moore, John William
Accounting Professor
Orange, Charlotte L.
Special Education Professor
Park, Carla Adkins
Art Teacher
Phillips, Ellen Butterfield
English Teacher
Price, Charles Landon
Spanish Teacher
Pritchard, Chalmer Lee, Jr.
Physical Education Professor
Rhodes, Charlotte Hall
Assoc Prof of Health & PE
Richards, Clark David
JROTC Dept Chairman
Scott, Margaret Regina
7th Grd Language Arts Teacher
Sims, Yvonne Bethea
Earth Science Teacher
Weiland, Elizabeth M.
Associate Professor of Biology
Williams, Janie Cherry
Business Tchr & Dept Chprsn
Williamson, Tracy Bubier
Kindergarten Teacher
Wood, Elizabeth Kinch
Health & Physical Ed Teacher
PILGRIMS KNOB
Compton, Ronald Thomas
Earth Science & Geography Tchr
Pritchard, Linda (Stiltner)
Art Dept Chairperson
POCAHONTAS
Orr, Myra Elizabeth
Science Teacher
POQUOSON
Baker, Robert Eugene
Social Studies Dept Chair
Griffin, Candis Smith
Coll & Dev Reading Teacher
Knight, Janet Girardi
Math Teacher
Van Dervort, Mark K.
English & Journalism Teacher
Walsh, Rosalie Yates
High School Guidance Counselor
PORTSMOUTH
Campbell, LaVerne Darden
Biology Teacher
Carlucci, Jeffery Van
Principal
Cody, Ann Freeman
Second Grade Teacher
Daniels, Annette V.
Eighth Grade Math Teacher
Diggs, Carol Bemory
French Teacher
Drake, Lorenz N. C.
Prof of Engineering Division
Dugan, Joyce Ellen Doud
Secondary Science Teacher
Edmonds, Evelyn Lewis
English Teacher
Ferry, Margaret Mixon
Second Grade Teacher
Grau, Michelle Horner
Spanish Teacher
Griffin, Nancy Gilbert
English Teacher
Harrison, Cynthia Rawls
Sixth Grade Teacher
Hinton, Vanessa Burton
Fourth Grade Teacher
Jones, Frances Hoffler
Mathematics Teacher
Lee, Elizabeth Keel
Spanish Teacher
Leonard, Thomas Edwards
Associate Prof of Business
Linyear, Jessie Bell
Business Education Teacher
Mapp, Ramona Hartley
Professor of English
Matthews, Marsha Wine
5th Grade Teacher
McGlothlin, Aaron Lee
Theater & English Director
Myers, Debra Marlene Horeis
Marketing Education Coord
Paquette, William Arthur
Professor of History
Peacock, Marilyn Lawson
Asst Professor of Mathematics
Prather, Susan Smith
Associate Professor
Shepard, Anna Richardson
7th Grd Mathematics Teacher
Smart, Audrey Corbitt
Teacher of Gifted & Talented
Smith, Larry Eugene, Jr.
History Teacher & Athletic Dir
Smithwick, Thomas Myers, Jr.
Arts & Technology Dept Chrmn
Snellinger, Diane Benton
Marketing Teacher
Spencer, Renee Nelson
Eng & Creative Writing Tchr
Stewart, Jeffrey B.
Science Teacher & Dept Chair
Taber, Barbara Robinson
Science Teacher
Vance, Verna Mills
Fourth Grade Teacher
Vick, Heather Noel
English Teacher
Wall, Anna Morris
English Department Chair
Williams, Leroy Stephen
English & Public Speaking Tchr
Wilson, V. Bene
Art Professor
Yearby, Susan Benton
Teacher
Young, Edna Compton
Business Education Teacher
POUND
Hall, Lockwood Taylor
English & Reading Teacher
Hamilton, Glenna Boggs
Language Arts Teacher
Hubbard, Nancy Green
Kindergarten Teacher
Leach, Barbara Gail
Band Director
Sturgill, Donna Mullins
First Grade Teacher
Wallace, Joyce Childers
6th Grade Math Teacher
Whittaker, Carolyn Mullins
English Teacher
POUNDING MILL
Gillespie, Lucy Campbell
Retired Health & PE Teacher
POWHATAN
Briesmaster, Mark Alan
Spanish Teacher
Brock, Gary McKenzie
Soc Stud, His & Psych Tchr
Harrison, Mary Midgett
Coord of Talented & Gifted Pgm
Hoffman, Louise Norman
History Tchr & Dean of Stdnts
Kyte, Teresa Jane
Physics, Math & Chemistry Tchr
Myrick, Bonnie Cullom
MS & HS English Teacher
Noechel, J. David
Eng, Humanities & Jrnlsm Tchr
Thomas, Christy Lynn
Chemistry Teacher
PRINCE GEORGE
Bradley, Jessica Marie
English Teacher
Chiarky, Marcia Barlow
High School Art Teacher
Coker, Kenneth Wayne
World History Teacher
England, Jeannie Lynn
English Teacher
Fischer, Peter A.
Social Studies Teacher
Hill, June Ryles
Eng Tchr & Dept Chprsn
Merrix, Cynthia Pollock
English II Teacher
Nall, Barbara Anne
Earth Science Teacher
Pettigrew, Sandra Fitz
Principal
Rivera, Rick
9th Grd Health & Phys Ed Tchr
Walker, Terry Alexander
Technology Education Teacher
Wendt, Sarah Melissa
French Teacher
Zaborsky, Ellen Garrett
Earth Science Teacher
PULASKI
Anderson, Robert B.
Band Director
Gardner, Diann Strauser
8th Grade Language Arts Tchr
Thompson, Alice Beke
GATE Resource Teacher
PURCELLVILLE
Akers, Martha L.
English & Journalism Instr
Dorsey, Vicki Jo
Dean of Students
Gillespie, Richard Trent
Social Studies Tchr
Johnson, LeeAnne F.
Guidance Counselor
Keilty, Carmel Marie
Driver's & Physical Ed Teacher
Lincicome, Kristi Lusk
US History & Philosphy Tchr
Livesay, Douglas Reid
Social Studies Teacher

CELLVILLE (cont)
inski, Elizabeth Sampson
Biology Tchr & Dept Chrmn
NTICO
n, Nancy
ish Dept Teacher & Chm
r, Jeanette G.
ich Teacher
, Candra McCoy
ial Studies & Psych Tchr
:, Edgar M.
sic Dept Head
John James
ence Teacher
shune, Robert
Grd Language Arts Teacher
ers, H. Charles
h School Principal
CKSBURG
ole, Pamela Sue
Govt & World History Tchr
FORD
rson, Katherine Schneider
erior Design Professor
r, Moira Phyllis
glish Professor
r, Paula Tabarini
r of Human Development
chi, Terri Lynn G.
rsing Professor
ng, James E.
of Music Therapy
er, Kimberly Ferren
st Prof of School of Nursing
sley, Barbara Mc.
soc Prof & Dept Hlth Svc Chm
, Elaine Ross
cond Grade Teacher
rt, J. Dana
soc Prof of Computer Science
ck, Matthew J.
soc Prof & Chm of Pol Sci
-Nunn, Pamela G.
ech & Lang Pathologist Prof
ns, Karolyn Whittlesey
sociate Professor of Nursing
gory, Russell Inman
ilosophy & Rel Stud Prof
sell, Barbara Franklin
Grade English Teacher
onsmith, Robert Warren
soc Professor of Psychology
y, Susan Collins
glish Professor
os, Jerry A.
soc Professor, Dept of Art
bert, Rogers F.
emistry Professor
d, Sylvia Miller
glish Teacher
:, F. Gordon
structor & Lab Coordinator
esell, Patrick Bruce
ofessor of Biology
, Gloria Lee Dragolovich
ursing Professor
vhouse, Janette Kaplan
ofessor
ely, Sonya Jones
brary Media Specialist
haus, Judy Harms
ology Department Chrmn
ak, Roxie
sst Prof of Math
orne, Jerry Johnson
ursing Instructor
sh, George David
of of Music
lgen, R. Wayne
P Govt & Geography Tchr
reef, Reginald A.T.
ssoc Prof of Pol Sci & Pub Ad
th, Albert Clinton, Jr.
anagement Professor
chler, Chloe Ann
sst Prof of Criminal Justice
rick, Annabelle (Henry)
nglish Instructor
i, William Bruce
rof of Physical & Health Ed
STON
lin, Rena J.
h Grade History Teacher
wns, Judith Haas
heatre Arts Teacher
scio, Charles E.
igh School English Teacher
scio, Faye Gottlieb
iology Teacher
ew, Cheryll Paula
st & 2nd Grade Multiage Tchr
ans, Ada Miller
ixth Grd Teacher & Vice Prin
rris, Maria Pinson
heatre Arts Dir & Dept Chair
mfeld, Diana L.
Math Teacher
:, Sue Ellen E.
merican Sign Language Teacher
ndy, Mary Arrington (Lynch)
GATE & Mathematics Teacher
acdonald, Lydia Irvine
Retired Sixth Grade Teacher
chardson, Eric Adam
High School English Teacher
llenberger, Judith Edwards
String Instrument Instructor
CHLANDS
shbrook, Craig Monday
Assoc Prof Environmental Mgmt

Bise, Polly Maloyed
PE, Health & Drivers Ed Tchr
Blevins, Rhonda Hess
Health & Physical Ed Tchr
Calo, Rhonda Bennett
8th Grade Pre-Alegebra Tchr
Cassell, Bobbie Miller
Writing Teacher
Dale, Elizabeth Ann
Asst Prof of French & Spanish
Davis, Hester Hagy
Latin Teacher
DiPietro, Joseph Samuel
Prof & Dir of Resp Care Pgms
Fiess, William Berry
Asst Prof of Mathematics
Fletcher, Jereial Byron
Associate Professor of English
Gibson, Anne Gillespie
Art Teacher
Hall, Terry Lynn
Choral Director
Hart, Christina
10th & 12th Grade English Tchr
Hayden, Judith Hillman
Fifth Grade Teacher
Hibson, James H., Jr.
Business & Industry Asst Prof
Householder, Georgia T.
Biology Instructor
Hughes, Jane
Kindergarten Teacher
Jackson, Kimberly Martin
Art Teacher
Lawson, Mary T.
Art & Reading Literacy Teacher
Lester, Paris, Jr.
Assoc Professor of Management
Little, Lavonne Mc Glothlin
Seventh Grade Life Sci Tchr
Lockhart, James Thomas
Business Teacher
Lyons, Ann Marie
Kindergarten Teacher
Marrs, Peggie Wingo
Associate Prof of Human Svc
Mc Peak, Kay Jewell
Algebra Teacher
Mullins, James Allison
Civics & Global Ed Instructor
Persin, Brenda McDonel
Asst Prof of Office Syst Tech
Phillips, Fred Arver
Physical Education Teacher
Proffitt, Ron E.
Program Dir of Radiography
Ramer, Faith Ellen
French & Psychology Teacher
Ramsey, Cheryl B.
English & Journalism Teacher
Reynolds, Anita VanDyke
Chemistry Teacher
Robinson, Donna Rose
Physics & Algebra II Teacher
Smith, Elizabeth Dye
9th Grade English Teacher
Stamper, Judy Lynn
Lang Arts & Rdng Tchr
Stevenson, Diane R. (Altizer)
5th Grade Teacher
Taylor, Jan Turner
Language Arts Teacher
Templin, Lemuel Ray
Asst Professor of Mathematics
Templin, Patty Taylor
Seventh Grd Lang Arts Teacher
Tolbert, James Homer
Director of Clinical Education
Vance, Cassandra Tackett
US History & Government Tchr
Warner, Amibeth Davis
History Teacher
Wymer, Carolyn King
Business Teacher
Young, Judy Caldwell
Mathematics Teacher
RICHMOND
Adams, Edwin David
Magnet Program History Teacher
Aiken, Peter H.
Asst Professor of Info Systems
Anderson, Della G.
English & Writing Teacher
Anderson, Paige Townsend
French Teacher
Appiah, Joseph Y.
History Professor
Atkins, Henry, III
Health, PE & Admin Aide
Austin, Terry L.
Bands Dir & Music Assoc Prof
Balducci, Paula Maria
First Grade Teacher
Ballinger, Franklin Fretz
Mathematics & Flying Teacher
Bassett, Louise Leland
Business Teacher
Baul, William H.
Automotive Teacher
Beaton, Mac Raiford
Technology Education Teacher
Bernstein, Stuart A.
Biology Teacher
Binns, Earl
Choral Music Director
Blackwell, Joyce Pearson
Fifth Grade Teacher
Bladen, Phillip Nelson
Health & Physical Ed Teacher

Blake, William Ernest
Retired Professor
Blem, Charles R.
Professor of Biology
Bolling, Andrew Jackson, III
Health Teacher & Advisor
Bowen, Carol Lynne (Kofahl)
High School Guidance Counselor
Bradshaw, Weldon A.
Teacher, Coach & Administrator
Brickley, Brenda Bullock
Asst Prin & Mathematics Tchr
Brilliant, Susan Stark
Assoc Professor of Comp Sci
Brown, Carolyn Walker
Kindergarten Teacher
Brown, Ozzie W.
Technology Education Teacher
Buhl, Nancy James
8th Grd Physical Science Tchr
Burke, Henri-Etta Crump
Academic Advisor for Athletics
Bynum, Gayle Chandler
Mathematics Teacher
Caldwell, Pamela Peters
HS Bus Tchr & Dept Chm
Cambisios, Stephen Andrew
Economics Education Coord
Carlton, Paul Helmick
Assistant Professor of English
Chance, Patricia Hewitt
High School German Teacher
Coleman, Julie Savage
Science Teacher
Collie, Johnnie Lee, Jr.
Computer-Aided Drafting Instr
Conway, Carolyn Mohler
Professor of Biology
Cooke, Rodney Quentin
Mathematics Teacher
Costanzo, Linda S.
Professor of Physiology
Crenshaw, Maria Fatima (Casado)
Multi-Age Teacher
Damizon, Conley Mac
Drama Teacher
Day, Ben Randolph, II
Visual Communication Professor
Dean, Barbara Jackson
Seventh Grade English Teacher
Donovan, Gregory E.
Associate Professor of English
Dooley, Tunie
Health & Physical Ed Teacher
Edelstein, Robin Kim
Upper School Math Teacher
Ellis, Robert Wayne
Math & Computer Science Tchr
Evans, Betty J.
English Instructor
Felice, Don Michael
Social Studies Teacher
Foldenauer, Dan L.
Fifth Grade Teacher
Fout, Donna Crites
Elem Gifted Students Teacher
Franks, David Denton
Professor of Sociology
Frauenfelder, Caroline Pirtle
Horticulture Teacher
Fry, Curtis Irving
Social Studies Teacher & Coach
Gainous, Donna Dixon
Marketing & Business Ed Tchr
Gallier, Carolyn Gowen
7th Grd Social Studies Teacher
Geisler, Margot Lynn
Earth Science Teacher
Giacobbe, George A.
Assoc Prof of Special Ed
Glancy, Donna Kennedy
Tchr of Emotionally Disturbed
Gould, Ann Stuart
Fifth Grade Math Teacher
Graham, Rose Beech
Fifth Grade Teacher
Grainger, Ellen Kiser
Orchestra Director
Gulick, Michelle Harman
Private Voice Instructor
Gutowski, Judy B.
Third Grade Teacher
Hall, Mary Frances
8th Grd Physical Science Tchr
Hall, Pamela Adams
Latin Teacher
Hall, Ronald Edward
12th Grade Social Studies Tchr
Hammel, Bruce Ray
Associate Professor of Music
Hammond, Daniel J.
Fifth Grade Teacher
Haug, Elaine Prasck
Spanish Teacher
Hawkins, L. Paige
Health & Physical Ed Teacher
Hawkins, Sterling Liebert
Drafting Instructor
Hicks, Marcelle Armstrong
Third Grade Teacher
High, Steven S.
Director Anderson Gallery
Holmes, Judy Lambeth
English Teacher
Horton, Sandra Kiser
English Teacher
Howells, Jane C.
History Dept Chair
Jameison, Robert Charles
7th Grade Amer Stud Teacher

Jeannette, Catherine Harrison
COE Coordinator & Teacher
Jones, Susan Blount
Social Studies Teacher
Kenyear, Frances Butler
History Teacher
Khanna, Shiv Narain
Chairman & Professor of Physic
King, Louise Orr
Life Science Teacher
Kirkpatrick, Peter Steven
Professor of French
Kliewer, Wendy
Asst Prof of Psych
Kramb, Lois Szyper
His, Geography & Govt Teacher
LaBelle, Deanna Bryson
Guidance Director
Lacy, Cynthia Tucker
First Grade Teacher
LaFratta, Mary Anna A.
Assoc Prof of Visual Comm
Lewis, Howard Benjamin, Jr.
Teacher of Special Needs
Llewellyn, Donna N.
Mathematics Teacher
Lyman, Gaynell Jepson
Physics Teacher
Mack, Sandra Lee
History Teacher
Madison, Elizabeth Ames
10th Grade Biology Teacher
Marshall, Karen Laslie
Russian & French Teacher
Martin, Deborah Kaye
Earth Science Teacher
Matthews, Sherri Anne
Choral & Orchestra Director
Mc Callum, Gregory Louis
Instrumental Music Teacher
Mc Donald, Kathleen Sweeney
English Teacher
Meggs, Philip B.
Communication Arts Design Prof
Meloney, Laura E.
Spanish & French Teacher
Melvin, Brenda Howlett
Elementary Guidance Cnslr
Mercer, Beth Duke
Choral Director
Metcalf, Elizabeth Salmon
AP Biology Teacher
Metcalf, Gregory R.
Earth Science Teacher
Meyer, Norva Lintecum
History Department Chm & Tchr
Middleton, Delores Daniel
Mathematics Teacher
Moore, James Tice
History Professor
Moran, Mary Thomas
Fifth Grade Teacher
Morgan, Anne Gilbert
Fifth Grade Teacher
Morris, Sheila Mc Michael
Life Science Teacher
Munoz, Eugenia
Assistant Professor
Mustafa, Nancy C.
Spanish Instructor
Myers, Barbara J.
Assoc Prof of Psychology
Noel, Mary Alice
Math Department Chairman
Pasquantino, Dennis James
Guid Dir & Girls Bsktbl Coach
Payne, Dorothy Myers
Honors English Tchr & Dept Chm
Pennington, Nancy Reed
Special Education Teacher
Perozzi, Rhoda Edens
Biology Instructor
Perry, Patricia Harris
Asst Professor of English
Piven, Faina
Russian & German Teacher
Pollard, Margaret Watkins
Fifth Grade Teacher
Puryear, John Carlyle
French Teacher
Ragland, Ines Colom
Assistant Prin & Spanish Tchr
Ragland, Piper Whitney
Seventh Grade Reading Teacher
Randolph, Rebecca Fountain
Kindergarten Teacher
Rao, Bijan Kumar
Physics Professor
Redford, Andrew C.
Associate Prof & Counselor
Rexroad, Dennis H.
Visual Communications Prof
Robert, Doris Anne
LD Resource Teacher
Schiltz, Jack H.
Assoc Prof & Division Chrmn
Scott, Frederick Webster, Jr.
Seventh Grade Math Teacher
Search, Philip Warner
Retired Science Teacher
Sears, Robert E.
9th-10th Grd Soc Studies Tchr
Selden, Jane Tibbs
Biology Teacher
Shear, Jonathan
Philosophy Professor
Shults, Margaret Louise
Third Grade Teacher
Smith, Courtney Soling
Social Studies Teacher

Smith, Darlene Morris
Business Teacher
Smith, James Ronald
Writer in Residence
Smith, Robin Mc Collough
Asst Professor of Recreation
Staton, Ellen Mc Daniel
7th Grd English Teacher
Stauffer, Gary Bruce
American History & Govt Tchr
Sutter, Kevin Lee
8th Grd Social Studies Teacher
Thomas, Mary Ellen
Mathematics Teacher
Thomas, Valencia Glasper
Kindergarten Teacher
Thompson, Carolyn Williams
Retired Business Teacher
Thornburg, Irene Bacas
Fourth Grade Teacher
Trumbo, Richard L.
History & Latin Teacher
Turnage, Jean Williams
Fifth Grade Teacher
Turner, Lelia Aldora
Coordinating Teacher
Upton, David Edward
Associate Professor of Finance
Urban, David James
Associate Prof of Marketing
Urena, Julie Baroody
French Teacher
Urofsky, Melvin Irving
Prof of Constitutional History
Vallentyne, Peter L.
Philosophy Professor
Vaughan, Judith Hillers
HS Guidance Counselor
Vick, William Dalton
HS Technology Ed Teacher
Wallace, Keith Chesterton
Social Studies & Math Teacher
Warren, Jacqueline Bennett
7th Grade Social Studies Tchr
Weiser, Neil Eugene
AP History Tchr & Dept Chair
Weston, Tracie Amos
Health & Physical Ed Teacher
Whitehead, W. Camden
Assoc Professor
Williams, Connie Elaine
Business Education Teacher
Wilson, Linda Ann
Kindergarten Teacher
Wilton, Barbara Adele
2nd-3rd Grade Classroom Tchr
RIDGEWAY
Bodkin, Barbara W.
Eng Teacher & Dept Chair
Chaney, Ann Frazier
Work & Family Studies Teacher
Davis, Beverly Williams
Speech, Theatre & Jrnlsm Tchr
Farmer, Bonnie Schlueter
Reading Specialist
Hardie, Champ C.
Agricultural Education Teacher
Hullett, Jerry Wayne
Sixth Grade Math Teacher
McGhee, Martha Clifton
Seventh Grade Mathematics Tchr
Perry, Pelzetta H.
Spanish Teacher
Reynolds, Linda Marshall
English Teacher
Wilson, Linda Rorrer
Sixth Grade Team Leader
RILEYVILLE
Hernley, Daniel James
Science Teacher
RINER
Brennan, Kathryn Altizer
Retired 6th Grd Science Tchr
Bull, Stephen William
Social Studies Dept Chair
Dodson, Patricia Quesenberry
Choral Director
Jervis, Charles K.
Science Teacher & Dept Head
Sauter, Jerry Anthony
English Teacher
RINGGOLD
Bauguess, Sherri Mericks
Science Dept Chm & Bio Teacher
Coles, Elizabeth Salle
Work & Family Studies Teacher
Hutcherson, Frances Diane
Drama & English Teacher
Keen, Audra Jayne
Spanish Teacher
Kidd, Gale R.
Chemistry Teacher
Seay, Judy Scott
Math Teacher
Vess, Susan Jarvis
4th Grade Teacher
ROANOKE
Austin, Ellen Bowen
Teacher & Coordinator
Bazak, Benjamin Fredrick
Mathematics Instr & Chprsn
Bersch, Martha Ratledge
AP American History Teacher
Bonds, Ethel Littlejohn
Associate Professor of English
Brown, Jeanne Marie
9th Grade Earth Science Tchr
Capps, John Spencer
Professor & Eng Dept Head

ROANOKE (cont)
Carr, Patricia Taylor
Art Teacher
Cartner, Kathleen (Stoller)
English Teacher
Casey, Deborah Edwards
4th-5th Grade Teacher
Chubb-Hale, Virginia Mignon
7th-8th Grade Soc Stud Teacher
Ciappina, Thomas J.
Mental Health Instructor
Clay, Hazel Yvonne
5th Grade Teacher
Crites, Richard Wayne
Assoc Prof of Biology
D'Alessandro, Sandra Taylor
Art Teacher
De Berry, Mollie Colston
9th Grade World Geography Tchr
DeHart, Gabriel Gates, III
English Teacher & Drama Coach
Dolan, Sheri Beane
Physical Science Teacher
Elliott, Helen Yvonne
English Professor
Eubank, Gerald Thomas
World History & Geography Tchr
Farmer, James C., Jr.
PE, Health & Algebra Teacher
Fishwick, Ann Chandler
Hum, Ethics, Eng & Rel Tchr
Fuller, Frederick Lee
Theatre Teacher & Director
Hackley-Hale, Rose
Third Grade Teacher
Hammes, Marilyn Timberlake
Intro & Advanced Psych Teacher
Harpold, Donna Janeczek
Microbiology & Bio Assoc Prof
Harrison, John Todd
History & Government Teacher
Humphreys, Patrick Arnold
Health & Physical Ed Teacher
Hunley, William Johnson
MS Science Teacher
Isaacs, H. Timothy
Ctr for Humanities Director
Johnson, Ernest Edward, Jr.
Mathematics Teacher
Johnson, Sharon Brabson
Band Director
Jones, Cynthia Louise
Art Teacher
Kenna, Kathleen Marie
Assistant Professor
Lamanca, Shirl Duke
Radiography Program Director
Lanning, Dana Vaughn
Mathematics Teacher
Livengood, Linda Clarke
Business Teacher
Lonker, JoAnn Short
English Teacher
Mc Michael, Edward John
High School Biology Teacher
Miller, George Curtis
Asst Prin & Head Ftbl Coach
Miller, Sally Liples
English Teacher
Osborne, Carol Hawks
High School Math Teacher
Patterson, Nancy Ruth
CITY School Director
Rosenbaum, Nancy R.
English Teacher
Ross, Cecilia Gayle Ford
Advncd & Coll Bound Chem Tchr
Russell, Mary Hehn
Govt, Psych & Sociology Tchr
Saunders, Thomas Bricen
Fourth Grade Teacher
Schilling, Barbara Renick
Kindergarten Teacher
Sheedy, Patricia H.
Tchr of the Learning Disabled
Shepherd, Betty T.
Professor
Smith, Erica
US History & Psychology Tchr
Smith, Paul Thomas
Social Studies Teacher
Speidel, Donna Mountford
Fourth Grade Teacher
Taibbi, Julie Drewry
Mathematics Teacher
Tillery, Reba Blevins
Kindergarten Teacher
Trostle, Patricia Clark
Spanish Teacher
Weddle, Douglas Kenneth
Mathematics Teacher
Wert, Vicki Board
American Studies Teacher
West, Jenny Lynn
Chemistry Teacher
Whorley, Shirley Quarles
Biology Teacher
Wright, John David
Director of Bands
ROCKY GAP
Powers, Wanda McKinney
6th Grade Teacher
White, Dorcas Slaughter
First Grade Teacher
ROCKY MOUNT
Anderson, Gloria Vickers
First Grade Teacher
Chaney, Wileina Fisher
Math Teacher
Collins, Dorothy Haddon
7th Grade Life Science Teacher
Gring, Judy Dickinson
Physics Teacher
Guthrie, Donna Morter
English & Journalism Teacher
Hawkins, Elaine C.
English Teacher
Jamison, Serena Whitlow
Work & Family Studies Teacher
Poff, Phillip Lynnwood
Assistant Principal
Roach, Jesse Neal, Jr.
Math Teacher & Coach
Ross, Martha Cleland
Latin Teacher
Sledd, Kathy Zimmerman
6th Grade General Sci Teacher
Taylor, John Allen
8th Grade Social Studies Tchr
Temple, Susan Vass
French Teacher
Traynham, Darryl Jerome
Spanish Teacher
Tyree, Carla D.
English Teacher
Washington, George F.
Associate Principal
Wimmer, Rebecca Kitzmiller
Art Teacher
ROSE HILL
Ayers, Verda Katherine
Fourth Grade Teacher
Hall, Noel
Seventh Grade Teacher
ROSEDALE
Vencill, Judy Sproles
Kindergarten Teacher
RURAL RETREAT
Dalton, Melissa Medley
Mathematics Teacher
Hensley, Quinton Anthony
Marketing Education Teacher
Holmes, LeAnna Snead
Biology & Physics Teacher
Lester, Rose Mills
Soc Stud & Rdng Teacher
Wilkerson, Debra Corns
Social Studies Teacher
RUSTBURG
Culbreth, Patricia Riviere
English Teacher
Davis, Annie McDaniel
Teacher
Dodgion, Jerry William
High School Math Teacher
Finch, Nelly Watson
Retired English Teacher
Holt, William Kenneth
Counselor
Hurtt, Mary F.
Kindergarten Teacher
Jennings, Ann L.
English Teacher & Dept Chair
Johnson, Gwen Keesee
Eighth Grade Civics Teacher
Morton, June May
First Grade Teacher
Olah, Susan May
Biology Teacher
Richardson, Brenda Whitt
Tchr of Spec Ed LD & ED
SAINT CHARLES
Bowman, Dottie Rhea
6th Grade Teacher
Martin, Margaret Gibson
Third Grade Teacher
SAINT PAUL
Cassell, John D.
Social Studies Teacher
Lawson, Lucille S.
Retired Teacher
SAINT STEPHANS CHURCH
Atkinson, Wanda Williams
Kindergarten Teacher
SALEM
Au, Bobbye Green
English & Dir Hnrs Pgm Prof
Bolton, Laura Duncan
French Teacher
Bruce, Mary Lou Bredlow
Math Teacher
Carter, Deborah Waldron
English II Teacher
Combs, Brenda Alice
Fifth Grade Teacher
Deegan, Eve A.
7th Grade Social Studies Tchr
Emmerson, Bryan Alston
English Teacher
Franco, Steve R.
Theatre Arts Instructor
Gibson, Michael Darden
Art Teacher
Goodwin, Judy Seay
Sixth Grade Teacher
Graham, Linda Pagans
Anatomy, Bio & Physly Tchr
Hagen, L. Bolling
Math, Cmptr Sci Tchr & Coord
Hall, Elizabeth Ellen
Physical Ed & Health Teacher
Hoffman, Donna Meredith
English Teacher
Humphrey, Margaret Tillman
K-12th Eng & Lang Arts Coord
Johnson, Martha Warren
English Teacher
Jones, Barbara Kirby
Math Teacher
Jorgensen, Darwin D.
Chair & Assoc Prof of Biology
Lubbs, Gresilda Anne Tilley
Span Tchr & Frgn Lang Dept Chm
Marshall, Darlene Crowder
First Grade Teacher
Mc Clearn, Betsy Blizzard
Intnl Baccaluareate Coord
Montgomery, Karen Nichols
First Grade Teacher
Noell, Joyce F.
Business Teacher
Robison, Nancy Lou
Guidance Cnslr & Soc Stud Tchr
Sailer, Rachel Pinkham
Drama Teacher
Sarver, Melinda Phillips
Music Specialist
Scholand, Stefanie E.
Ger Tchr & Frgn Lang Dept Chr
Secor, Garry Philippe
World Geog & Civics Teacher
Secor, Margaret J. (Stofko)
Bio Teacher & Sci Dept Chair
Seibert, Alan
Science Teacher
Selby, John Gregory
History Professor
Shrader, Mary Ellen Mewborn
Spcl Proj Asst & Visiting Tchr
Simmons, Nancy Compton
English Teacher
Taylor, Susan Caligan
Learning Disability Teacher
Tingler, Debbie Orange
Former Teacher
Tucker, Chris S.
Science Teacher
Ward, Charles Randolph
Guidance Director
White, Willis Howard
Algebra Tchr & Football Coach
SALTVILLE
Buchanan, David Cox, Jr.
World Geography Teacher
Roberts, Randall Scott
Marketing Education Teacher
SALUDA
Farina, Deborah Overacre
English Teacher
Luttrell, Diane Sampson
Mathematics Teacher
Rothery, Patricia Hand
Bio, Chem Tchr & Sci Dept Chm
Scanlan, Hugh Norman, Jr.
English Teacher
White, Helen Wright
Business Dept Chairperson
SAXE
Brogdon, Ruth Elam
Retired Fifth Grade Teacher
SCOTTSVILLE
Conrad, Anne Dandridge
5th Grade Teacher
SEAFORD
Estes, Elizabeth Copley
Reading Specialist
SHANGHAI
Foster, Brenda Michelle
Kindergarten Teacher
SHAWSVILLE
Davidson, Denise Girard
Mathematics Teacher
Downs, Melissa Brooks
Art Teacher
Hurt, Carol Mc Lawhorn
8th Grd Language Arts Teacher
Jenkins, Tracy Ann
Mathematics Teacher
Poff, Tracy Alan
6th-12th Grd Hlth & PE Teacher
SHENANDOAH
Dickerson, Darlene Wayland
English Teacher
Dickerson, Larry Franklin
English & Journalism Teacher
Hight, Nancy C.
Algebra Teacher
Trumbo, Kristee Rosenow
Tchr of Severe & Prfndly Dsbld
Weatherholtz, Patricia Sandra
Government Teacher
SKIPWITH
Blanks, Eleanor Crowder
7th Grade Teacher
Coghill, Tanya Lynn
Eng & Creative Writing Tchr
Dyne, Carolyn Elizabeth
Marketing Teacher
Hamilton, Deborah A. Jennings
Science Department Chairperson
McInturf, Donald Lee
Mathematics Teacher
Price, Ronald L.
Agricultural Education Teacher
Whitten, Stephen G.
6th Grade Teacher
Wolven, Winifred Ann Reed
Photojournalism Teacher
SMITHFIELD
Jackson, William Henry
6th Grade Teacher
SOUTH BOSTON
Coles, Deborah Gail
Math, Pre-Algebra & Hlth Tchr
Day, Kenneth Edward
Geog, Sociology & Psych Tchr
Edmonds, Allan R.
8th Grd Social Studies Tchr
Hughes, James Allen
Junior ROTC Teacher
Jackson, Mabel Walker
Lead Teacher
Kilpatrick, Alicia Ballard
Ninth Grade English Teacher
McAdams, Annette Wright
8th Grade Social Studies Tchr
Mercer, Linda Marie
English & Journalism Teacher
Newbern, Michael Edward
Bio, Anatomy & Physiology Tchr
Owen, Carol Bane
Seventh Grade Lang Arts Tchr
Poole, Vickie Tillotson
Health Occupations Teacher
Richardson, Essie James
Math Teacher & Dept Chairman
Saunders, Melanie Dawn
Health, PE & Drivers Ed Tchr
Smith, Karen Shelton
English & Theater Arts Teacher
Trickey, Lydia Reaves
Fourth Grade Teacher
Wallace, Sandra Nunn
Science Teacher
Watson, Margaret Farley
Government Teacher
SOUTH HILL
Bradshaw, James Robert
Music Chair & Band Director
Conner, Ernest Calvin, Jr.
Agricultural Education Teacher
Crowder, Rebecca Lennon
Former Music Teacher
Goldenberg, Barbara
French Teacher
Greene, John Michael
Math Teacher
Merritt, John Marshall
Eng Tchr
Piercy, Nancy Beane
Math Teacher
Puryear, Louise Bigger
Business Education Teacher
Smith, Lucinda
Social Studies Teacher
Snead, Elizabeth Rose Perry
Librarian
Talley, Deborah Karnes
Work & Family Studies Teacher
Taylor, Jean Mull
Work & Family Studies Teacher
Walker, Arlene Mc Intyre
Business Education Teacher
Wheeler, Mary S.
Retired Teacher
SPEEDWELL
Hamm, Norma Hutton
4th Grade Teacher
SPENCER
Hill, Cecelia Dianne Richmond
5th Grade Teacher
SPOTSYLVANIA
Brittain, Judi Barber
Physical Education Teacher
Driest, Gloria P.
English Teacher
Gratzick, Gail Lentz
Math Teacher
Hallett, Barbara Potts
Science Department Chm & Tchr
Holcomb, Rick
Mathematics Teacher & Dept Chm
Jordan, Jill Beckmann
7th Grd Lang Arts & Rdng Tchr
Jordan, Sally Spindler
Math Curr Coord
Jusino, Martha Powell
Latin & ESL Teacher
Kemp, Kimberly Peck
Theatre Arts Teacher
Mc Donald, Joyce Ann Martin
Admin Assistant & Teacher
Penn, Elizabeth Ann
English Teacher
Whitehead, Randal Kevin
Drafting Teacher
SPRINGFIELD
Adjapon-Yamoah, Francesca Ama
Span, Fr & English Lit Teacher
Benton, Robert Spurgeon
HS Mathematics Teacher
Bloodworth, Peggie G.
Sixth Grade Teacher
Borden, Gloria Winslow
English Teacher
Brinckman, Joy Alice
HS Resource Teacher
Brown, Lillie Deloris
Teacher
Carpenter, Alice Clare
Second Grade Teacher
Cecere, Michael Anthony
12th Grade Government Teacher
Copeland, Mary Jo
Third Grade Tchr & Dept Head
Foronda, Carolyn Kreiter
Eng & Creative Writing Tchr
Geleta, Gayle Shelton
2nd Grade Teacher
Harris, Sue Chandler
Business Teacher
Holmes, JoAnn Mac Lean
Second Grade Teacher
Hylton, Joyce M.
Psychology & Soc Stud Teacher
Jarvis, Kathryn DiSciullo
Latin Dept Chair & Teacher
Kossoy, Shirley
8th Grade Math Teacher
Landrum, Kathleen Clisham
7th Grade Social Studies Tchr
Lind, Sandra Lou (Glidden)
English, Speech & Debate Tchr
Lobred, Clydette Griffith
English as a Second Lang Tchr
Lundahl, Elaine Rupnik
Teacher & Administrator
McMenamin, John Patrick
US & VA Government Teacher
Noun, Judith A.
Science Teacher
Pappas, Eva
7th Grd Environmental Sci Tchr
Paprocki, Margaret Urbas
Math Teacher
Peduzzi, Constance (Hurd)
Government Teacher
Percoco, James A.
Social Studies Teacher
Pincus, Esther Zuckerman
Guidance Counselor
Pompei, Ronald E.
Spanish Teacher
Popovich, Jeanne Marie
Guidance Counselor
Roop, Beth Ann
Math Teacher
Russell, Mary Kathryn
AP English Teacher
Saffron, Merceda Biordi
Fine Arts Dept Chprsn
Sierzant, Bobbie Smith
Fifth Grade Teacher
Vance, Helen Higgins
English Gifted & Talented Tchr
Ward, Elizabeth A.
Mathematics Teacher
Welch, Sandra Kreger
Theatre Arts Teacher & Dir
Wright, Nancy E.
Guidance Counselor
Yardumian, Michele Louise
Math, Science & Art Teacher
STAFFORD
Arthur, David William
Math Teacher
Breede, Walter John
Mathematics Teacher
Carr, Stephen L.
Drama & Video Production Tchr
Coates, Alice Carolyn
Math Teacher
Davis, Jane White
7th Grade Social Studies Tchr
Dow, June Mace
Health Occupations Instructor
Eshelman, David Stephan
Technology Education Teacher
Garrison, AnneMarie Dickinson
Math Teacher
Getgood, Jacqueline Faillace
8th Grade Math Teacher
Givens, Rhonda Hubble
Middle School Educator
Gottschalk, Gary Ward
Adv Plcmnt Govt & His Tchr
Green, Patricia Bishop
English Teacher
Harris, Thomas
Elementary Art Teacher
Harrison, Victoria Calamos
Fourth Grade Teacher
Hegland, Glenda May
English Tchr & Dept Chprsn
King, Jewell H.
English Teacher
Lawson, Marlene Tyler
Mathematics Teacher
Marshall, David G.
Orchestra Teacher
Mc Elfish, Bobbie Andrews
English Teacher
Miller, Lynn W.
English & Photojournalism Tchr
Moore, Caldonia Ward
Biology Teacher
Munoz, Mary A.
Fifth Grade Teacher
Newton, Karen Hunt
Hlth & Physical Education Tchr
Nichols, Adela Rivero
Spanish Teacher
Parker, Marian Edwards
English Teacher
Reagan, Betty Parmer
Second Grade Teacher
Reilly, Carol Taylor
7th Grade Language Arts Tchr
Schelzo, Joseph E.
Social Studies Teacher
Schwartz, Helen Lacell
Mathematics Teacher
Scott, Alana Tyndall
Seventh Grade Teacher
Shea, Nancy M.
Spanish & French Teacher
Smith, Kim W.
Marketing Coordinator
Steele, Joyce Snead
Social Studies Teacher
Stone, Helen Christine
8th Grade Phys Sci Teacher
Trant, Cynthia Guy
Bio & Human Physiology Tchr
Vanderberg, Michael John
Latin Teacher

FORD (cont)
›rn, Mary Peterson
ıish Teacher
ın, Gary Lee
›hic Communications Tchr
›r, Judith Knapp
man Teacher
ARDSVILLE
t, Kirsten Ingrid
ıish Teacher
ins, Linda Dixon
Grd Tchr & GATE Coord
, Jonathan Mark
iness Teacher
on, Carolyn Marie
h Grade Teacher
, Linda Brown
hematics Teacher
ard, Philip Dale
, Chemistry & Math Teacher
ssell, Patricia Moon
cl Sign Lang Interpreter
NLEY
, Karen Moore
Resource Teacher
JNTON
, Martha Phillippe
rd Grade Teacher
anan, Kathleen Cook
rk & Family Studies Teacher
mer, Betty Jo Lunsford
Grade Teacher
n, Martha Bruin
er Arts Instructor & Artist
n, William Henry
glish Teacher
mock, Gordon Lee
siness Professor
er, Kenneth Wayne
fessor of History
, Carol Hill
anish Teacher
, Marilyn Hall
cond Grade Teacher
on, Sue Ann Robinson
& Education Instructor
on, Mary Thompson
Grade Teacher
y, James K.
-8th Grd Tchr & Vice Prin
ay, Constance Pair
story & Government Teacher
well, Christopher Dewitt
eative Writing & Eng Tchr
or, Cherie Gray
glish & Journalism Teacher
, Steven Bruce
schological Svcs Supvr, GATE
d, Marion Anne
r of First Year Experience
PHENS CITY
, Walter A.
idance Counselor
k, Kimberly Lineborg
Instr & FFA Adv
r, Dee Campbell
acher
ard, Elaine Resta
anish Teacher
ker, Sallie Clarke
glish Teacher
ins, Beverley Massey
ioral Music Teacher
Garmo, Robin Ann
anish & Journalism Teacher
aola, Louis George
ology Teacher
ers, Barbara Woore
eventh Grade English Teacher
nings, Alfred Stephen
ioral Director
ner, Steven Jay
ysics Teacher
g, Marguerite V.
ocial Studies Teacher
neth-Barath, Anne Collins
h Grade English Teacher
nter, Arch W.
nglish Teacher
nn, Robert Chester
ci, Drama, & Theology Tchr
dolph, Jacob Taylor, Jr.
ife Science Teacher
vatori, Angela Renee
Mathematics, Life Science Tchr
erry, Arthur H.
atin Teacher
wart, Bill
High School Math Teacher
nestreet, Patsy P.
nglish Teacher
out, Jeffrey Thomas
gricultural Education Teacher
livan, Phyllis H.
r Tchr & Frgn Lang Dpt Chprsn
n Metre, Holly Morgan
JS History Teacher
lliams, Garland Turner, Jr.
E & Health Teacher
ERLING
rns, Pamela Rountree
Choral Department Director
rton, Amy Douglas
English Department Chair
rter, Sue
Lecturer in Eng & Legal Stud
embach, Dave
Athletic Director
hnson, Bobbie June
Social Studies Teacher

Johnson, Bruce Michael
Latin Teacher
Korte, Elizabeth Nickel
Mathematics Teacher
Krowe, Judith Ellen (Gill)
Spanish Teacher
Mitchell, Gregory Keith
Technology Education Teacher
O'Quinn, Anita
Fourth Grade Teacher
Pratt, Elaine Kaminski
English Second Language Tchr
Reaves, Richard Bruce
Director of Bands
Spencer, Janet Carr
Former Teacher
Thompson, Kathleen NaQuin
English & Public Speaking Tchr
STRASBURG
Currie, Duncan Edmund
Guidance Director
Hall, Bruce Lane
English Teacher
Hobbs, Patricia Hockman
5th Grade Teacher
Smoot, Judith Jones
Health & Physical Ed Teacher
STUART
Blackburn, Norman Glenn
Assistant Principal
Eastridge, Phyllis Newman
English Dept Chair & Tchr
Fain, Patricia Ann
Mathematics Teacher
Hill, Billie Beamer
Kindergarten Teacher
Mitchell, Mary Lee (Whitten)
Spanish Teacher
Nowlin, Rebecca Williams
Math Teacher
Pendleton, Barbara Byers
Health & PE Teacher
Pons, William Francis, Jr.
SCA & Elementary Band Dir
Rigney, George Daniel
Senior English Teacher
Short, James Kevin
American History Teacher
STUARTS DRAFT
Howell, Teresa Harner
Second Grade Teacher
Sheets, James E.
7th Grade Lang Arts Teacher
Taylor, James A., Jr.
Instrumental Director
Wade, Frank
Social Studies Teacher
SUFFOLK
Babb, Sandra Joyner
Social Studies Teacher
Bowles, Deborah Beuth
Chemistry Teacher
Bull, Charles Lee, Jr.
Spanish Teacher
Byrum, Phyllis Collier
HS Social Studies Teacher
Carson, Michael
Band Director
Cooper, Alease Spruill
Employment Ed Coop Coord
Copeland, Mary Wilson
Work & Family Studies Teacher
Creekmur, Deborah Carter
Work & Family Studies Teacher
Dailey, Jane-Marie Benton
English Teacher
Daughtrey, Ronald Carr
Agriculture Teacher
Dohey, Douglas Brian
Junior Counselor
Draper, Jean Acey
Marketing Coordinator
Driggins, Elaine Eure
Fourth Grade Teacher
Duncan, S. Michele
Marketing Ed Teacher & Coord
Edwards, Jo Anne Thomas
English & Drama Teacher
Emmons, Ruth Snowden
4th Grade Instructor
Furlough, Richard Melton
Chemistry Teacher
Goodrich, Eva Page
Latin Teacher
Harrell, Esther Layton
Guidance Counselor
Herrmann, Amy Smith
Earth Science & Biology Instr
Holcombe, Emily Jane
Biology Teacher
Hurst, Lucille Rountree
7th Grade Teacher
Kittle, Dale Alan
Instrumental Music Director
Martin, Mary Braford
English Teacher
Montgomery, Patricia Fuller
Principal
Roberts, Maryland Knight
Algebra Teacher
Sherard, Mary Stallings
English Teacher & Chairperson
Snow, Martha Mc Farland
9th-12th Grd Guidance Cnslr
Varacallo, Jerome Michael
PE Teacher & Coach
SUGAR GROVE
Noble, Nancy Eames
Fourth Grade Teacher

Sword, Hugh Taylor
Teacher
SUSSEX
Lundy, Gary Leroy
Art Instructor
Mason, Hazel Sheppard
Business Educator
Mudrick, Donald B.
English Teacher
SWEET BRIAR
Armstrong, Gregory Timon
Professor of Religion
SWORDS CREEK
Osborne, Terry Boyd
6th & 7th Grade Teacher
TAPPAHANNOCK
Garrett, Betty Anne Rennolds
English Teacher
Hewitt, Clark Stanley
9th Grade Earth Science Tchr
Lipscomb, Valerie Dieter
8th Grade English Teacher
Mc Dowell, George Ellis
English History & Ldrshp Tchr
Rittenhouse, Michelle Lynn
Math & Computer Science Tchr
Ruffa, JoAnne
Guidance Counselor
Thompson, Nancy Hicks
Eng & Creative Writing Tchr
TAZEWELL
Billips, Lou B.
Business Education Teacher
Dye, Dada Thompson
Civics Teacher
Harman, Raejean Ann
Choral & Assistant Band Dir
Hill, Deidra Gaye
Physical Ed & Health Teacher
Hutchinson, Gail Chapman
Tchr of Learning Disabilities
Johnson, Linda Hand
Title 1 Reading Teacher
Jones, Brenda Kay Duty
Fifth Grade Teacher
Kallander, Margaret Roberts
English Teacher
Keene, Thomas Arthur, III
Special Education Teacher
Martin, Pat Tatum
Fifth Grade Teacher
Mullins, Terry W.
Advanced Placement Govt Tchr
Peery, Lucian Harold
Teacher & Coach
Poskas, Rose Brewster
Mathematics Teacher
Sizemore, Bruce Stephen
Math Teacher
Thompson, Darrell
Fourth Grade Teacher
TIMBERVILLE
Anderson, Susan Dove
Third Grade Teacher
UNIONVILLE
Hughes, Lillian Yancey
First Grade Teacher
VERONA
Dixon, Donald F.
Retired Seventh Grd Math Tchr
VICTORIA
Abernathy, James Marvin, Jr.
Bus Cmptr Applications Tchr
Clary, Jean Yancey
8th Grade Algebra Teacher
Cousins, Joan Lea
Retired Third Grade Teacher
Hawkes, April Brame
English Teacher
Hawthorne, Mary Lou Howe
English Teacher & Language Dev
Jones, Asia Roche'
Special Education Teacher
Palmore, Phyllis Corker
Spanish Teacher & Dept Head
Wilkins, Anthony Edward
American Civics Teacher
Wright, Rose Abernathy
6th Grade Mathematics Teacher
VIENNA
Askounis, Anna C.
Counselor
Audley, Eileen Collins
Fourth Grade Teacher
Clagg, Linda Jenkins
Speech & Theatre Arts Teacher
Lewis-Green, Denise W.
First Grade Teacher
Lisagor, Trude Talpis
Sixth Grade Teacher
Losada, Ximena
Spanish Teacher
Muldoon, Rosemary Rita
English Teacher & Dept Chprsn
Odrick, Rosemary Mason
Science Teacher
Oliver, Michael C.
History Teacher
Rupert, Anne Mascaro
Orchestra Director
Scholla, Stephen R.
Physics Teacher
Shapiro, Ronald H.
High School English Teacher
Sheridan, Frank
Former HS English Teacher
Stanford, Elaine Parsons
Choral Director
Stockenberg, Julie Tetley
Gen & AP Biology Teacher

Worek, Dennis Michael
Math Tchr & Asst Athletic Dir
VINTON
Bullington, Laura Carroll
Spanish Teacher
Cecil, Regina Rakes
French Teacher
Covington, Julia D.
Band Director
Culicerto, David Anthony
9th Grade Geography Teacher
Holbrook, Gail
Fifth Grade Teacher
Morris, Jill Tracey
Marketing Coordinator
Riggs, Richard Gene
Secondary LD Teacher
Travisano, Phyllis
Health Teacher
Williams, Debra Smith
German Teacher & Dept Chair
Wise, Alicia Purdy
Mathematics Teacher
Woods, Ernestine Cook
English Dept Chair & Teacher
Wymer, Janice Dube
First Grade Teacher
VIRGINIA BEACH
Allen, Grace Miller
Retired 2nd Grade Teacher
Alley, Marguerite Cole
Director of Orchestras
Antley, Lenora Garrison
AP English Teacher
Artrip, Paul Douglas
Anatomy, Bio Tchr & Ath Trnr
Bailey, Herbert T., Jr.
English Teacher
Baker, Noreen Nugent
English Teacher
Bandy, Judy H.
English Teacher
Bonner, Judith A.
Business Teacher
Bowden, David Michael
Elementary PE Teacher
Bowman, Alfred Virginius
US History Teacher
Bright, Anne Fentress
English Teacher
Broglie, Marion F.
AP European & World His Tchr
Bryant, Joy Yost
English & Speech Teacher
Buchanan, Susan Henry
English & Journalism Teacher
Buffington, Claire Wilson
English Teacher
Bulleit, James Randolph
English Teacher
Butler, H. Christine
Director
Butler, Phyllis Ann (Wilson)
Science Teacher
Butts, Eleanora Doane
VA & US Government Teacher
Butts, Mark Elvis
Art Teacher
Byers, Jack L.
Oceanography Teacher
Carrow, Donald Hubert
World Geography Teacher
Chin, Linda LeRoy
Kindergarten Teacher
Churray, Rose Theresa
Scndry Earth Science Teacher
Clarke, Linda Ressani
8th Grade Pre-Algebra Teacher
Clements, Michele P.
Fourth Grade Teacher
Coefield, Margie Wilson
English Teacher
Cook, Annette Maceikis
English Teacher
Craig, Mary Alice (Brown)
School Counselor
Crawley-Jordan, Suzanne Robinson
French Teacher
Creamer, Kim Lewis
Marketing Ed Tchr & Coord
Cromwell, Mitzy O'neal
Business Teacher & COE Coord
Cunningham, William Linwood, Jr.
Associate Prof of Psychology
Dailey, Julie Calongne
Asst Prof of Accounting
Danielson, Jody Perkins
Math Teacher
Davis Wynn, Gaye
Third Grade Teacher
Deloglos, Christopher Stephen
HS Chemistry Teacher
Denis, Cheri Ruby
Second Grade Teacher
de Trevino, Estela (Jimenez Reyna)
Spanish Teacher
Dickens, Lena Pittman
Computer Typing Teacher
Dinsmore, Georgia Carroll
Guidance Counselor
Dorrance, Kristie Siverts
Spanish Teacher
Downs, Susan Harrington
Eighth Grade English Teacher
Dugan, Jill Franken
Spanish Teacher
Dunbar, Nancy McKinley
Kindergarten Teacher
Dunn, Talmage Linwood
7th Grade Mathematics Teacher

Eason, Jo-Ann Morse
English & Public Speaking Tchr
Eitel, Kathleen O'Toole
Third Grade Language Arts Tchr
Eldredge, Laura Cameron
Earth Science Tchr
Eldredge, Timothy Robert
In School Suspension Coord
Ellerbee, Lisa Elaine
Director of Choral Activities
Emmick, Lori Ann
Spanish Teacher
Fausel, George Edward
Electronics, Cmptr Repair Tchr
Fentress, Susan K.
Student Assistance Pgm Dir
Ferrell, Catherine West
English Teacher
Fincher, Diane
AP English Teacher
Fletcher, Talmage Russell
Health & Phys Ed Teacher
Fortune, Leslie Allen
English Teacher
Fowler, Elizabeth White
English Teacher
Frank, Gregory Paul
Division Chair & Asst Prof Bio
French, Joanne C.
Lang Arts & Soc Stud Tchr
Friedman, Penny Michelle
Third Grade Teacher
Fritz, Todd H.
School Counselor
Frost, Sue Loudon
Art Teacher
Fruit, Grace Tucker
Art Teacher
Gardner, Faye Smith
Social Studies Teacher
Garrison, Diane White
English Teacher
Giordano, Randall Patrick
English Teacher
Gladden, Nancy Parker
4th Grade Teacher
Goldstein, Linda Ann
8th Grade Science Teacher
Goodboy, Richard Lawrence
Biology Teacher
Gowin, Terry Kent
English Teacher
Graves, Michael Phillip
Schl of Comm Studies Chair
Green, Deborah Day
Reading Resource Teacher
Griffin, Claudia Greene
Choral Director
Guarnieri, Nancy Stuart-Maxwell
Prof & Asst Division Chair
Hackworth, Darlene Elaine
Fifth Grade Teacher
Hallberg, Julie Elizabeth
Fourth Grade Teacher
Hammond, Gussie Koriath
Assistant Prof & Program Dir
Hansen, Susan Pediso
English Teacher & Dept Head
Hass, Sheri Blessing
English Teacher
Hatzopoulos, Frances Love
3rd Grade Teacher
Heins, Jacquelyn Rivenbark
Fourth Grade Teacher
Helke, Eric Robert
4th Grade Self-Contained Tchr
Hofferbert, Jane Averette
Third Grade Teacher
Hofler, Kay Robertson
Art Teacher
Holmes, Kenneth Wilson
Mathematics Teacher
Hucks, Virginia Gehrmann
First Grade Teacher
Hunn, Jane L.
English Teacher
Hunt, Maureen Anne
Spanish Teacher
Hyman, Mary Virginia
English Teacher
Jacobs, Chris Randall
US History Teacher
Jacobson, Frances Morris
History Professor
Janz, Wanda Witt
Spanish Teacher
Kamakaris, David George
Science Teacher
Kaminski, Ben
English Teacher
Karl, Robert John
Art Instructor
Keener, Arlene Ramicone
Chemistry Teacher
Kessel, Arlene Soroko
German Teacher
Kight, Bettye Teague
Math & Computer Teacher
Kinsler, John L.
Biology & Earth Science Tchr
Knapp, Holly Forman
Social Studies Teacher
Koon, Albert V.
Assistant Division Chrmn
Kreider, Janet Simmons
Business Teacher
Krudop, Donald W.
Sr HS Choral Director
Labahn, Dorothy Ann
Art Teacher

VIRGINIA BEACH (cont)
Lambert, Nancy H.
7th Grade English Teacher
Leonard, Dwight Edward
Band Director
Loudermilk, Judith Harbour
Second Grade Teacher
Mac Donald, Douglas Alexander
AP Europ Hist & Wrld Geog Tchr
Mather, James Phillip
Spanish Teacher
Matney, Kathryn Campbell
Advanced Placement Chem Tchr
Maull, Willie David
Health & Physical Ed Teacher
Mc Chesney, Jean Jinnett
Retired Teacher
Mc Ginnis, Sheila Kester
High School English Teacher
Mc Gloine, Patricia Hynes
History Teacher
McLaughlin, Carol Ann
World History Teacher
Mc Laurin, Imelda B.
Life Science Teacher
McNicholas, Mary Amelia
Seventh Grade English Teacher
Melton, Joan Marie Van Horn
Teacher Assistant
Meyer, Mary Jane Kittler
Chemistry Teacher
Midkiff, Cindy K.
Anatomy & Sports Medicine Tchr
Miller, Monica Maria
English Teacher
Moskway, Nancy Sykes
English Teacher
Motley, Susan Anne
English Teacher
Nagel, Donna Van Kleeck
Kindergarten Teacher
Newswanger, Elizabeth Boykin
7th Grade Amer History Teacher
Noll, Jeannie
Math Tchr & Softball Coach
Norris, Stacy Lee
History Teacher
O'Hara, James Michael
History Teacher
O'Hara, John Joseph
Government & World His Tchr
O'Hara, Michael
Mathematics Teacher
Ohmes, Doris E.
Chemistry Teacher
Pascua, Angelina Maria
Religion Teacher
Pearl, Andrea Elizabeth
VA, US His & World Geog Tchr
Pearson, William Tabb
US History Teacher
Perrenot, Hal Franklin, III
Bio & Environmental Sci Tchr
Peter, Paul Burton
Mathematics Teacher
Phelps, Lynne Reilly
Spanish Teacher
Pindur, Nancy Herring
German Teacher
Pravecek, Judith Lee
Social Studies & Math Teacher
Prince, James F.
Physical Education Teacher
Puckett, Susan Turbyfill
Gifted Education Resource Tchr
Reddish, Kimberly Allison
8th Grd English Teacher
Ridill, Winifred Meyers
Eng Tchr & Dept Chairperson
Rinehart, Cindy Lou
Mathematics Teacher
Roupas, Eva Kay
Theatre Arts Tchr & Dept Chair
Rowan, Bruce A.
United States History Teacher
Rutherford, Leslie Marie
Theatre Arts Teacher
Salzler, Teresa Vanini
Middle School Math Teacher
Sanders, Sonja L.
Choral Director
Saulsberry, Barbara Yates
Assistant Principal
Schmitter, Stephen Paul
Computer Science & Math Tchr
Seaford, Gail Lynch
Elementary School Counselor
Seltzer, Lynn S.
Fourth Grade Teacher
Shearin, Dianne Corinne
English Teacher
Singleton, Jacqueline Mann
Mathematics Teacher
Smith, Arlene Rhoda
English Teacher
Smith, Harriett Brownson
Second Grade Teacher
Snyder, Kim Alan
Government Professor
Solheim, Constance Marie
7th Grade Language Arts Tchr
Speckhart, Eva Marie
Chemistry Teacher
Stamm, Carolyn C.
Tchr of Gifted Ed Resource
Steele, George McIver
English Teacher
Surace, Richard Carter
Mathematics Teacher
Swinson, Lanier
Biology Teacher
Tassone, Craig R.
Social Studies Tchr & Team Ldr
Tata, Kendall T.
Tenth Grd PE & Health Teacher
Thompson, Douglas Edward
11th Grd VA & US History Tchr
Vincent, Rabiah
Upper School Art Instructor
Wales, Mary Watson
10th Grade English Teacher
Warhola, Kenneth James
Earth Science Teacher
Webb, A. Collier
Biology Teacher
Weiss, David Andrew
Psychology Teacher
Wells, Lillian Wimmer
Retired Fourth Grade Teacher
White, Cynthia Boutte
Lang Arts & Soc Stud Teacher
White, Helen Mary
Fifth-Sixth Grade Teacher
White, Hubert Wendell
Science Teacher
White, Jeffrey Alan
Prof of Sociology & Philosophy
Williams, Gayle Gresham
6th-7th Grade Soc Stud Teacher
Wilson, DeLynda Wood
7th Grade Math Teacher
Wong, Susana Lee (Wong)
Mathematics Teacher
Worthington, Mary Jenkins
English Teacher
Wright, Joan Byrnes
Earth Science Teacher
Yano, James M.
English Teacher
Young, Donna Hamilton
First Grade Teacher
Zirkle, Luisa Ladaga
AP Biology Teacher
WAKEFIELD
Justice, Brian Christopher
History Department Chairman
WARRENTON
Bailey, Phyllis R.
US History Teacher
Brinson, Anita Palmer
Special Education Teacher
Hasie-Daniels, Marcia
Guidance Counselor
Helkowski, Douglas Alan
PE & Health Teacher & Coach
Kelican, Kraig Kirk
Agriculture Instructor
Kreh, Amee Hodges
English Teacher
Pennington, Phoebe Tufts
7th & 8th Grd Lang Arts Tchr
Sachs, Maxine M.
Kindergarten Teacher
Sims, George Lester
Orchestra Teacher
Staiko, Joan Cormack
Sixth Grade Teacher
Wilson, Carolyn Wiltshire
Business Ed Tchr & Dept Chair
WARSAW
Holbrook, Jim
Instructor
Johnson, Judy Weaver
Sixth Grade Reading Teacher
Johnson, Wade S.
Professor of Health & Wellness
Marsden, Marie Perrine
Professional Cnslr, Assoc Prof
Newtzie, Karen Cowart
Assistant Professor
Sebren, Elizabeth Brown
Mathematics & Geometry Teacher
Swonk, Joseph Leo
Associate Professor of English
Tidwell, Betty Young
Language Arts Teacher
WASHINGTON
Grimes, Jeanne Griffin
Social Studies Teacher
Lamma, Candace McDaniel
Elementary School Counselor
WAYNESBORO
Clatterbuck, J. David
7th-12th Vocal Music Teacher
Coffey, Yvonne Wiley
Science & History Teacher
Doyle, Kathleen Meeteer
Physical Education Teacher
Hamp, Michael Gerard
English Teacher & Asst Coach
Mc Callum, Beverly Joan
Retired Teacher of GATE
Wade, Dianne Elizabeth
Secondary Drama Teacher
Wood, Carol Critzer
Bus Tchr & Career Dev Chprsn
Wright, Irene Ottaway
5th Grade Teacher
WEST POINT
Dorsey, Mark A.
Coordinator & Teacher
Hodge, Martha L. House
Retired Teacher
Hoppe, Patricia Ann
English Teacher
Metzger, Ronald Edward
Mathematics & Physics Teacher
Moncure, Janet Croswell
Math Dept Chairperson
Wilson, Cathy Lipscomb
English Teacher
WEYERS CAVE
Lynch, Edward Houston
Associate Professor of Physics
Shank, Wendy Kidd
Adjunct Instructor of English
WHITEWOOD
Rife, Mary Ward
First Grade Teacher
WILLIAMSBURG
Boyd, Edward Thomas
Social Studies Dept Chairman
Dunnigan, Lynda Kern
Secondary G & T Resource Tchr
Fields, Jonathan Daniel
Assistant Principal
Gaston, David William
Social Studies Teacher
Hadley, Kathy Schneider
7th Grd His & Lang Arts Tchr
Hermance, Fran Rucker
Retired Teacher
Kerr, Carole Boren
Science Teacher
Mills, Joan Elizabeth
English Dept Chair
Perger, Donna Spagnoli
Secondary Mathematics Instr
Sanderson, S. Laurie
Asst Prof of Biology
Steffey, Ron Squire
Sociology & Government Teacher
Vermeulen, Carl William
Professor of Biology
Wade, Bonnie Kirkwood
Kindergarten Teacher
Wiseman, Lawrence L.
Professor of Biology
Young, Mallory Haskins
English Teacher
Zaki, Ahmed Soliman
Information Technology Prof
WILLIS
Hylton, Pauline Rutrough
Retired Teacher
Miller, Cora Gardner
5th-7th Grade Math Tchr
WINCHESTER
Beard, Carolyn Shier
Counselor
Beitzel, Marlin C.
High School Chemistry Teacher
Bolyard, Gene William
Mathematics Teacher
Chrisman, Martha Brewer
Health & Physical Ed Teacher
Cox, Cynthia Young
Math & Science Teacher
Funkhouser, Reba Karen
US History Teacher
Greathouse, Judith Pugh
Sixth Grade Teacher
Hager, Sherry Reid
Choral Music Teacher
Harmon, Melvin Shelan, Jr.
Choral Director
Hartle, Pat Ellen
Coord of In Schl Suspension
Helmick, Audrey Swanson
Retired Teacher
Hill, Todd
Health & Physical Ed Teacher
Kane, Robert Joseph
Mathematics Teacher
Kerns, Kathy S.
HS Mathematics Teacher
Laster, Madlon Travis
Soc Stud & English Teacher
Lee, Marvin William
Associate Professor of Psych
Longsworth, George Lull
Special Education English Tchr
Lowe, James T.
Mathematics Teacher
Lucas, Gail L.
English Teacher
Magee, Elaine Faye
Mathematics Teacher
Mankins, Scott Daniel
Accounting Tchr & COE Coord
Mc Cormick, Betty Gibbs
Fifth Grade Teacher
Medeiros, Martha Blossom
English Teacher
Nicholas, George Stephen
6th Grade Teacher
Pitcock, Victoria Armacost
English Teacher
Pleacher, David Henry
Mathematics Teacher
Root, Dale Allen
Art Teacher
Schachel, Steven M.
Physics & Mathematics Teacher
Sheppard, Bruce Allen
Health & PE Teacher
Shrum, Richard Irvin
Fifth Grade Teacher
Snyder, Donna Helms
7th Grade Social Studies Tchr
Thomas, Beverly Ann
Elementary Teacher
Thomas, Marsha L.
Math Teacher
Tillmann, Richard Craig
English Teacher
Wever, Robert B., Jr.
Bio Teacher & Sci Dept Chair
WINDSOR
Richardson, Carita Jones
Algebra & Spanish Teacher
WIRTZ
Bowman, Karen Sue
Third Grade Teacher
WISE
Baird, J. Rex
Professor of Biology
Bickers, Phyllis Muse
Psych Adj Prof, Dir Career Dev
Bott, Gwyneth Roeger
First Grade Teacher
Brewer, Janet Edwards
Biology Teacher
Briggs, Guy Vinton
Bus Admin & Musical Art Prof
Carter, Willie Charles
Physical Education Teacher
Dye, Roderick Dean
Band Director
Frank, Mary Lou Bryant
Psychology Assoc Professor
Freeman, Linda Amburgey
Cosmetology Instructor
Garrison, W. Fay Stidham
English Teacher
Giles, Edward Dwight
Computer Lab Teacher
Mangan, Peter Anthony
Asst Professor of Psychology
O'Quinn, Mary Darcy
Asst Professor of Psychology
Prater, Lana Meade
Health & PE Teacher
Reynolds, Jeff
6th Grade Teacher
Richardson, Sandra Clark
Assistant Professor of Ed
Rose, Kenneth William
Retired Seventh Grade Sci Tchr
Short, Bobby Joe
US Govt & World Geography Tchr
Silcox, Roncie G.
4th Grade Teacher
Swindall, Ron Edward
Biology & Chemistry Teacher
Whittaker, Kathryn Chantale
6th Grade Math Teacher
Yun, Peter Subueng
Professor of Economics
WOODBERRY FOREST
Cirves, Brent Allen
English Instructor
WOODBRIDGE
Beauregard, Janet Anne
Chemistry Teacher
Bindra, Surinder Kaur
Science Teacher
Bona-Bonacquisti, Susan Ann
Health, PE & Drivers Ed Tchr
Borkowski, Thomas Vern
Adjunct Professor
Branch, Reba C.
Guidance Counselor
Centola, Mary Jane Judith
Mathematics & Dept Chairman
Cherry, Michele Mc Kenney
First Grade Teacher
Christie, Linda Bassford
Sixth Grade Teacher
Cornwell, Carolyn Huddleston
5th Grade Teacher
De Jesus-Brent, Diana
Guidance Counselor
Derrickson, Denise Torie
Social Studies Teacher
Dew, Gene Thomas, Jr.
Technology Teacher
Dillon, Kathleen Johel
Fifth Grade Teacher
Dorsey, Linda Parker
Chemistry Teacher
Drake, Edwina Cheatwood
English Teacher
Early, Norma West
Business Teacher & Coordinator
Eaton, Alfred Francis
Technology Education Teacher
Elk, D. T.
Lang Arts & ESOL Teacher
Erickson, Kathleen Noble
Civics Teacher
Ferrara, Patricia O'Neil
4th Grade Teacher
Grodsky, Alicia
Assoc Professor of Psychology
Harrelson, Debra Jeanne
Ath Trainer, Hlth & PE Tchr
Hart, Angela Buczek
8th Grade Language Arts Tchr
Hicks, Kenneth Warren
Earth & Space Science Teacher
Higgins, Phillip James
History & Civics Teacher
Jackson, Barbara O.
English Teacher
Jones, Paulette Prattis
Language Arts Teacher
Jones, Wesley James, Jr.
Latin Teacher
Lane, Cathy Anne
Physics Teacher
Lorson, Cheryl Branighan
Language Arts Teacher
Luther, Carmen M.
Realtor
Lyall, Nancy A.
Social Studies Teacher
Maat, Virginia Ortt
Language Arts Teacher
Madorma, Jeffrey Vincent
High School Math Teacher
Martin-Rivers, Kelly E.
English Teacher
Mc Laurin, Mary Porter
Instructional Support
Moss, Enola Ryan
Music Teacher
Moulen, Dawn Sundberg
English & Photojournalism Tchr
O'Connor, James Acker
Administration of Justice Prof
Pennline, Richard John
Physics Instructor
Phillips, Laura Rae Smith
Kindergarten Teacher
Piepke, Walter Joachim
Art Teacher
Pollock, Scott David
Sixth Grd Social Studies Tchr
Polly, Richard Taylor
Biology Teacher
Powers, Judith Daughtry
English Teacher
Rodgers, Arthur James
Driver Education Teacher
Schenkelberg, Connie Eggart
Language Arts & Soc Stud Tchr
Schwarz, Robert Joseph
Science & Math Teacher
Smith, Albert Len
Speech & Drama Teacher
Teets, Shirlee K.
Language Arts Teacher
Warner, Jeanne H.
English Teacher
Weiler, Amy Trout
English Teacher
White, Nancy Philips
Mathematics Teacher
Wynne, Mary Love Duplain
English & Humanities Teacher
WOODLAWN
Bobbitt, Rubye C.
Fifth Grade Teacher
Whittington, Shirley Morris
Retired Chem & Physics Tchr
WOODSTOCK
Babcock, Donna Marie
Language Arts & Math Teacher
Dysart, Judy Ann (Reed)
7th Grade Language Arts Tchr
Good, JoAnn Nixon
Special Education Teacher
Good, Steven Wayne
Biology & Chemistry Teacher
Hammond, Rachael Warfield
English Teacher
Helsley, Martin Jacob, Jr.
Eighth Grade Mathematics Tchr
Johnson, Gary Lane
Mathematics Teacher
Lytton, Rick Ferrell
US History Teacher
Maggiolo, Paulette Blanche
French, Span & Coll Eng Tchr
Overton, Carole DeVoe
Latin Teacher
Sperry, Pamela Stewart
Middle School Counselor
WYTHEVILLE
Beauchamp, Sherry Hyde
Spanish Teacher
BeCraft, Patricia Arnold
Basic Skills Supervisor
Campbell, Jacqueline Hubble
Kindergarten Teacher
Coeburn, Ann Wolfenden
Second Grade Teacher
Compton, Patricia Williams
Art Teacher & Coach
Copenhaver, Larry Randall
Science Teacher & Tech Coord
Craft, Donald David
Assoc Professor of Psychology
Jessee, Linda Gochenour
Second Grade Teacher
Linzey, Donald Wayne
Professor of Biology
May, Alva Dixon
Reading Recovery Teacher & Ldr
Midkiff, Connie Crews
Third Grade Teacher
Moore, Lillian Hall
PE Teacher & Coach
Morgan, Joseph Wilmer, Jr.
Assoc Prof Civil Engrng Tech
Murray, Jean Mc Kay
Assistant Professor of Biology
Nester, Michael B.
Instructor of English
Rudolph, Anthony Johnson
Agriculture Teacher
Stanley, Sue Worley
Business Teacher
Wilson, Joanne Baldwin
Special Education Program Dir
YORKTOWN
Abrahams, Shaheem
Science Teacher
Bengtson, Edwin Glenn
Band Director
Blalock, Jane Aldridge
French Teacher
Burns, Cynthia Sue (Wilsted)
Third Grade Teacher
Callaway, Kathryn Nash
Kindergarten Teacher

TOWN (cont)
Melinda G.
sh Teacher
Cynthia Gresham
Tchr & Voc Dept Chair
, Lilinau Yvette
ematics & Physics Teacher
m, Reba C.
rican Studies Teacher
w, Patricia Elaine
bra & Chemistry Teacher
ld, Amy Taylor
al Studies Teacher
ood, Sharyn Powell
Grade Teacher
onger, Percy Edward
d Director
on, Marilyn M.
lance Director
, Jan Edward
3rd Life Science Teacher
wski, James Michael
al Science Teacher
kkan, Melinda Bursch
lish Teacher & Yearbook Adv
sky, Gerry Baltes
ish Teacher

SHINGTON

RDEEN
ett, Anne Gavareski
French, Honors English Tchr
r, Korinda Ebenhack
of Counseling, Psych Instr
, William Carroll
lish Teacher
an, Carolyn Mathison
2 Resource Tchr
, William Thomas
nselor
Christine Marie
plied Music & Voice Prof
, Russell Curtis
emistry & Biology Instructor
ghan, Evan Lewis
h School Librarian
os, James B.
ructor
nelson, Donald Fred
nber, Fish, & Wildlife Instr
mpson, Jeff Alan
alth & PE Teacher
elms, Patricia (Parrott)
cal Music Teacher
A
gan, Shawn
thematics Teacher
, Rankin T.
Grade Teacher
in, Gary Alvin
His & Sr Economics Teacher
CORTES
klund, Ruth Ann
gh School French Teacher
erworth, Scott Allan
Grade Teacher
s, Joanne (Cicchetti)
s Ed Dept Chprsn & Tchr
stner, John Robert
cational Instructor
ke, Larry K.
hletic Director & PE Teacher
er, John Carl
h Grade Teacher
EL
fman, John D.
d-5th Grade Teacher
LINGTON
esworth, Edgar Alan
ounselor
em, Jann Robertson
ome & Family Life Teacher
istine, Jerry D.
h Grade Teacher
Gross, Tiffany Lynelle
nglish Teacher
s, Katherine J.
terature & Drama Teacher
Torre, Bob
panish Teacher
ys, Thomas Glenn
athematics Teacher
ver, Brett Allen
usiness Education Teacher
atz, Beverly Karen
rt Teacher
effer, John Dale
S Social Studies Teacher
oots, James David
hysical Education Teacher
ylor, Ginger Lynn
h Grade Teacher
nchell, Julia Hemmer
h Grade Math Teacher
OTIN
ack, Robert Arthur
nglish & Math Teacher
emner, Kathy J.
cience & PE Teacher
ace, Kay Mc Dowell
th-6th Grade Science Teacher
BURN
hnsen, Morna Golke
English Teacher
ck, KarrLayn Gruesbeck
quatics Instructor

Beck, William Brandon
Band Dir & Music Dept Chrmn
Bittner, Sandra Tarie
Biology Teacher
Butz, Gloria Kathryn (Mann)
Sixth Grade Teacher
Calhoun, Steven Isaac
Human Anatomy, Physiology Tchr
Carson, Ron
High School Art Teacher
Cunningham, Brent K.
Math Teacher
DeFrancesco, Denis
School Counselor
Diehl, Bruce David
Global Issues & AP US His Tchr
Fackenthall, Peter John Anton
Speech & History Teacher
Falkenhagen, Lisa Diane
Spanish Teacher
Farrell, James E.
Coach & Soc Stud Teacher
Filson, Robert Harold
Geology Instr & Sci Div Chair
Frederick, Michael John
Marketing Coordinator
Hill, Kathy Kohlmeier
Peer Ministry Advisor
Isham, Gregory Scott
French Teacher
Jacobs, Marianne Scherer
Prof of Anthrplgy, Ethnic Stud
Johnson, Douglas S.
English Instructor
Johnson, Larry R.
Physical Science & Chem Tchr
Jones, Jeffrey A.
Mathematics Teacher
Jones, Marlene Helen
German Teacher
Kemp, Cynthia Ann
Attendance Officer
Leerar, Pam
College Instructor
Mardon, Jan Vooge
Accounting Instructor
Martin, Patrick Walter
History Instructor
Mc Cauley, Jeffrey Francis
Technology Division Chair
Mc Key, JoAnne Riley
Librarian & English Teacher
Mc Pherson, Ruthie Emily (Glenn)
First Grade Teacher
Miles, James Matthew
Counselor
Moores, Margaret Lois
Fourth Grade Teacher
Nilsen, Kay Ann
Elementary School Principal
Nyman, Toni G.
English & Yearbook Instructor
Rohlff, Geri Gustafson
English Dept Chprsn & Tchr
Rosevear, Sheryll Fredekind
Classroom Teacher
Rupert, Robert Douglas
Philosophy Instructor
Sanborn, Linda Kay Gibbons
Dean of Girls
Spalding, Beverly Jo
Ath Director & Phys Ed Teacher
Sprague, Bradley L.
HS Social Studies Teacher
Sprouse, Sherry Thibeau
Act Dir & World History Tchr
Strain, Joyce Marie
Business Instructor
Taylor, Marie Koury
English Teacher
Teague, Darcy Marie
Sixth Grade Teacher
Thornton, Laird Michael
Vocal Music Instructor
Tooley, Janet Elizabeth
4th Grade Teacher
VanAmburg, Ruthann Holden
Director of Bands
Watts, Vivian Marie
Social Studies Teacher
Wigle, Linda M.
Vocal Music Teacher
Wilder, Linda Courtwright
6th Grade Teacher
Withrow, Carolyn Rockwell
Mathematics Dept Chairman
Zeiger, Ernie E.
High School Math Teacher
BAINBRIDGE ISLAND
Gilbert, Marilyn Smith
Retired Teacher
Koch, Susan Irene
Spanish Teacher
Mauk, Scott Frederick
Alternative High School Tchr
Peterson, Theresa Joy
Fourth Grade Teacher
BATTLE GROUND
Baty, Robert Mitchell
Third Grade Teacher
Groeber, Emily Hanisko
English Teacher
Hallman, Rod O.
8th Grade Science Teacher
Hodgins, Kathleen Nicholson
Marketing Teacher
Lamoreaux, Kathryn
English & Debate Teacher
Nelson, David Duane
Math & Physics Teacher

BELFAIR
Andringa, Allen Greg
Vocal & Instrumental Music Dir
Rose, Ken L.
Art Teacher
BELLEVUE
Baldwin, Don Merlyn
Math Teacher
Becker, Enid Smith
French Teacher
Belcher, Richard Vern
English Teacher & Head Coach
Benson, Glenda Lea (Fain)
Kindergarten Teacher
Burke, Robert Adams
Speech Instr & Dept Chprsn
Collins, Sharon M.
Math Teacher
Darling, Pamela M.
Career Specialist
Ellis, Robert Lee
PE, Fr & Intnl Stud Tchr
George, Roger Allen
Eng Instr & Comm Chair
Haines, Eric Gordon
History Department Chair
Hobbs, Robert Dale
Physics Instructor
Hogan, Emmet Patrick
His Tchr, Crs Cntry Trck Coach
Husby, Lars Peter
Ceramics & Art Instructor
Lang, Eleanor
Chemistry & I. B. Teacher
Lockerbie, James G.
Social Studies Teacher
McDowell, Eric Thomas
Mathematics Teacher
Mc Glasson, Ruthmary
Counselor & Instructor
Neal, William Patterson
Science Teacher
Norton, Kim Bakalyar
English & Fine Arts Teacher
O'Dea, Marcia Aileen
English Teacher
Olver, G. John
Drafting & Math Teacher
Oman, Linda Schultz
Middle School Teacher
Postma, Kimberley Ann
English Teacher
Potter, Nancy Schultz
English Teacher
Rose, Douglas Lee
Geography Department Chair
Steffen, Ann Louise
7th & 8th Grade Bible Teacher
Storey, Mark Christopher
Philosophy Instructor
Tarbox, Chuck
Athletic Director
Taylor, Helen K.
Psychology Department Chprsn
Terry, Kathee Gerde
Chemistry Tchr & Educl Coord
Vall-Spinosa, Pete A.
Social Studies Dept Chair
Warren, Don LeRoy
Lang Arts & Soc Stud Tchr
Wright, Joyce D.
Fourth & Fifth Grade Teacher
Yerabek, Gene A.
Math Teacher
BELLINGHAM
Allen, Carolyn N.
Primary Teacher
Allen, Craig Karl
Instructor
Ayres, Nola Mc Cauley
Physical Education Teacher
Bjork, Barry Lee
History Professor
Carmean, Clara Jean
English & Humanities Instr
Donahue, Andy Lloyd
High School Mathematics Tchr
Dougherty, Debbi Beremand
4th Grade Teacher
Grube, Valerie White
Spanish Teacher
Hageman, David P.
History Instructor
Jack, Dana Crowley
Professor of Psychology
Jacklin, Marquita Olson
Seventh Grade Teacher
James, Susanne Marie
Professor of Biology
Johnson, Millie J.
Mathematics Professor
Kennedy, Kathleen
Asst Professor of History
Lynch, Patty J.
Medical Assisting Instructor
Lynch, Signee
English Instructor
Michel, Christopher Alan
Integrated Studies Teacher
Mooers, Douglas Francis
Coord of Math, Hlth & Sci
Newman, Gregory L.
Social Studies Teacher
Patterson, Mark E.
Director of Bands
Pittis, Charles C. S.
Library Media Specialist
Priddy, Coralie Anne Balch
Retired Elementary Teacher

Riggins, Ronald D.
Professor
Rutschman, Edward Raymond
Music Professor
Sellereit, Eric L.
5th Grade Teacher
Small, Gary A.
Prin, Eng, Ec & Bible Tchr
Smith, Eunice J.
Retired Teacher
BENTON CITY
VanderMaas, Amy Elizabeth
Spanish Teacher
BLAINE
Foster, Andrea Marie
8th Grade Language Arts Tchr
Worthy, Jeffrey
English Teacher
BOTHELL
Anderson, Andrea Ann (Crain)
4th Grade Teacher
Atkins, Lydia Myles
Social Studies & US His Tchr
Chaney, Judy Lynn (Hartvigson)
Math Teacher
Cudmore, Bud
Library Media Specialist
Du Bois, Bruce Dean
Activities Director
Dwyer, David William
Math Teacher
Elefson, Caroline A.
Humanities Teacher
Files, Steven Thomas
English Teacher
Filibeck, Judy Marie
Choral Director
Gilbert, Kathryn Irene (Robinson)
Spanish Teacher
Halazon, Donald Guy
English & Social Studies Tchr
James, Marge Cannon
Junior High English Teacher
Lenseigne, Kert Benedict
Science & Health Teacher
Lusier, Laurel Mc Guinn
Business Education Teacher
Lyons, Joyce DalSanto
HS Family & Consumer Sci Tchr
Matalon-Munro, Irene
French & Spanish Teacher
McCarty, Bryan John
Biology & Science Teacher
Mead, Kimberlee Ann
Industrial Technology Teacher
O'Connor, Tessa Janae
Language Arts & Spanish Tchr
O'Rourke Hartman, Fran Doyle
4th-5th Grade Multi-Age Tchr
Stewart, Mary Ann
Teacher of Gifted & Talented
BOW
Costanti, Dan James
4th Grade Teacher
McGuire, Teresa K.
Math, Sci, Hlth & Rdng Teacher
BREMERTON
Botkin, Barbara Freund
Elem School Counselor
Gillis, Cassie J.
8th & 9th Grade Choir Teacher
Jacobson, Bobbie Jo
Physical Science Teacher
Kieburtz, Robert D.
Chemistry Professor
Loeber, Kathy Mosteller
Spanish Teacher & Chairperson
Martin, Mary J.
First Grade Teacher
Norton, Richard H.
Professor of Philosophy
Pargman, Susan Rae
6th Grade Tchr & Drama Tchr
Sheline, Sue Mandler
Mathematics Teacher
Surette, Linda Bonnema
2nd Grade Teacher
Thacher, Gregory Lee
US History Teacher
BREWSTER
Brown, Stella J.
Family & Consumer Science Tchr
Finkbiner, Robert G.
Principal & Teacher
Frey, Jim B.
Counselor
Swanberg, Dennis Robert
Agriculture Education Instr
BRIDGEPORT
Stark, Calvin Scott
Science Teacher & Dept Chair
Turner, B. Paul
Mathematics Teacher
BRUSH PRAIRIE
Patton, Carol Lorraine
Choral Director
BUCKLEY
Brunt, Bonnie Glantz
Spanish Teacher
Rawlings, Kristin Ann
Spanish Teacher
Renz, Connie (Hertzog)
4th Grade Teacher
BURIEN
Dillman, Rose Marie F.
Retired Religion Tchr & Cnslr
BURLINGTON
Adeline, Robert Paul
Sixth Grade Teacher

Johnson, Linda (Wilson)
Full Time Substitute Teacher
Mc Cauley, Michele (Horngren)
8th Grade Teacher
Place, Tim
Technology Systems Manager
Powers, Jay B.
Mathematics Teacher
Tallquist, Kenneth Michael
English Teacher
CAMAS
Albert, Les Thomas
Phys Sci & Pre-Algebra Teacher
Bruni, Estrella Marie (Tamayo)
English, Hum & Jrnlsm Teacher
Condon, John Thomas
7th Grade Science Teacher
Hyde, Herbert W.
Drama & Leadership Teacher
Mc Graw, Gerald Dean
Retired Chem & Bio Teacher
CARNATION
Cruz, Ruth Mead
8th Grade Science Teacher
Loudenback, Judy Bond
6th-12th Grd Choir Teacher
CASHMERE
Hamilton, Suzan Gail
English Teacher
Kenoyer, Louise Peterson
Fourth Grade Teacher
Morrison, Shawn R.
English Teacher
Sturtz, Amy Rae
6th Grade Teacher
CASTLE ROCK
Stuart, John Charles
US History & Social Stud Tchr
CATHLAMET
Hedman, Audrey Jean (Sly)
Second & Third Grade Teacher
Landroche, Tina Michele
Social Studies Teacher
Uthmann, Richard W.
K-12th Grd Music Instructor
CENTRALIA
Benedetto, Margo Traber
English & Drama Teacher
Calvert, Douglas J.
English Teacher & Chair
Chaney, Ronald DeVearle
Newsletters & Special Projects
Floth, Nathan Harold
6th-8th Grade Tchr & Chaplain
Jett, Dorothy Anne Hemphill
Physics, Science & Math Tchr
Jun, Heesoon
Tenured Psychology Faculty
Rash, Lynn Turner
Fifth Grade Teacher
VonRotz, Elizabeth O'Neill
Eighth Grade Mathematics Tchr
CHATTAROY
Friedman, Scott M.
Physical Science Teacher
Martin, Allen Lloyd
High School Teacher
Taylor, Julie Smith
Eighth Grade Earth Sci Tchr
Wolfe, John Thomas
English Teacher & Coach
CHEHALIS
Cope, Dawn McCann
Science Teacher
Fay, Lawrence C.
Science Teacher
Gilmore, Jerrilyn Magley
4th Grade Teacher
Hunter, Glen H.
Math Teacher & Dept Chair
Ogden, Carol Jean
English Teacher
Sanchez, Tino
Educl Assistant & Soccer Coach
CHENEY
Alvy, Bonnie Elizabeth
Former Teacher
Appleton, Valerie Edith
Professor of Counseling
Beal, Bruce Douglas
Professor of Art
Britt, Beth Davey
Computer Science Professor
Buchanan, John P.
Geology Professor
Carr, Robert L.
Professor of Biology
Davis, Maxine Mary Maxwell
Professor of Health & PE
Klyukanov, Igor E.
Communications Professor
Megaard, Susan Brennan
Taxation & Accounting Prof
Morgan, Joanne Holling
2nd Grade Teacher
Mullin, Thomas
Television & Film Professor
Pratt, Mary Margaret
Chemistry Teacher
Puckett, Thomas F. N.
Asst Prof of Rhetoric & Film
Radebaugh, Muriel Rogie
Education Professor
Rahn, Jeffrey A.
Professor
Seedorf, Martin F.
Professor of History
Zyskowski, Martin James
Director & Professor of Music

CHEWELAH
May, John P.
High School Teacher
CHIMACUM
Schmitt, Joanne (Barker)
Mathematics Teacher
CLARKSTON
Havens, Charles Eldon
5th Grade Teacher
Hill, Bonnie J.
US History Teacher
Peltonen, Philip Carl
Sixth Grade Teacher
COLBERT
Kibbey, Susan
Second Grade Teacher
Marchant, Karin Lynn
Second Grade Teacher
COLFAX
Brannan, Tenny Jean (Cluckey)
Jr HS Language Arts Teacher
Madole, James Eugene
English Teacher
COLLEGE PLACE
Bailey, Cindee Melissa
Social Work Associate Prof
Bennett, Frederick Roland
Civil Engineering Professor
Bursey, Ernest James
Professor of Biblical Studies
Clark, Douglas R.
Dean, School of Theology
Cross, Carlton E.
Professor of Engineering
Haenni, Viviane Francoise
Visiting Guest Lecturer
Morton, Todd Leroy
Assistant Professor of Psych
Mowat, Ryan Glen
Instructor of Engineering
Rouse, William Leon
Technology Professor
Saturno, Malinda Mc Kee
Biology Instructor
Schafer, Don W. E.
Math, Spanish & German Teacher
Schafer, Scott Greyson
Physical Education Teacher
Semotiuk, Nancy L. D.
Asst Prof of Communications
Staab, Janice M.
Asst Professor of Philosophy
Ward, Verlie Yvonne Florence
Professor of Education
Wiggins, Kenneth Leroy
Mathematics Dept Chair
COLVILLE
Hopkins, Mary L.
Head Teacher
Lovett, Linda Lou Blount
US History Teacher
Noble, Ronald Garlen
Electronics Instructor
Paccerelli, George Anthony
Instr of History & Pol Science
Rudd, Cheryl Kai
World Cultures & Japanese Tchr
Smith, Richard A.
3rd Grade Teacher
Stalp, Sheila Kay
Contemp World Problems Tchr
CONCRETE
Janda, Mary DeWees
Seventh-Eighth Grade Teacher
Schweigert, Michael Clay
Business Teacher
COSMOPOLIS
Farnell, David Charles
Math & Science Teacher
COULEE DAM
Darnold, Gary Allen
Math & Science Teacher
McDowell, Sally Arbon
11th & 12th Grade English Tchr
COWICHE
Glenn, Janet K.
Business Teacher
CURLEW
Almquist, Donald Paul
Sixth Grade Teacher
CUSICK
Fulp, Ralph Edwin, Jr.
Social Studies & English Tchr
Longly, Douglas S.
Counselor & Teacher
DAVENPORT
Edwards, Benjamin Dale
Math & Physics Teacher
Fisk, Rawleigh Dean
Science & Physical Ed Teacher
Lyle, Karen L.
Fourth Grade Teacher
Mielke, Kristy Ann
Kindergarten Teacher
Patterson, Harold Freeman, Jr.
Principal
Pauls, Skip
Elementary Principal
DEER PARK
Anderson, Lance M.
Social Studies Teacher
Heydet, Sharon Ford
English Teacher
DEMING
Rightmire, Todd Edward
Agriculture Instructor
DUVALL
Beyer, Theodore John
PE & Health Teacher

Carlson, Dea Johnson
English Teacher
Drake, Charles Nathan
Graphic Arts Instructor
Greer-Merkel, Karen Diane
History Teacher
Hauser, Christine Sifferman
1st Grade Teacher
King, Karen Sue (Buff)
Speech & Dramatics Teacher
Ridgewell, Jill K. M.
Drill Team Advisor
EAST WENATCHEE
Anderson, Joe Turner
English Teacher
Davisson, Jeanne Myer
High School Spanish Teacher
Davisson, John Willard
9th Grade Biology Teacher
Grubb, Tamara Anne
Junior High English Teacher
Huylar, Paula Monette Better
Mathematics Teacher
Huylar, Steven R.
Social Studies Teacher
Kane, Sheila McGregor
Kindergarten Teacher
Olson, Monte R.
9th Grade Geography & Eng Tchr
Schreck, Sherry Lee Chastain
English & Drama Teacher
Smith, Lloyd Franklin
English Teacher
EDMONDS
Beem, Marilyn Petrie
Third Grade Teacher
Borden, Patricia Wolny
Kindergarten Teacher
Dezell, Margaret Claire
Instrumental Music Teacher
Hayes, Kelly Roger
Science Teacher
Richardson, Joyce E.
Fifth & Sixth Grade Teacher
ELLENSBURG
Marjerrison, Mary Kathryn
Teacher of Gifted & Talented
Mayberry, Larry Dean
7th Grd Social Studies Teacher
Ott, Gay
Choral Director
ELMA
Fielding, Crystal
6th Grd Sci & Lang Teacher
Locatis, Daniel Ray
6th Grade Teacher
Peltier, Douglas Alan
Math Teacher
Wolverton, Kathryn Dowling
English Teacher
ENTIAT
Edwardson, Bill Stewart, Jr.
History & Physical Ed Teacher
Gibbs, LeeAnn F.
6th Grade Teacher
ENUMCLAW
Adams, Jenny Sue Spaulding
Kindergarten Teacher
Gulsvig, Julie Somers
Drama & Video Productions Tchr
Rogers, Judi Wallich
Instrumental Director
EPHRATA
Boland, Megan A.
Mathematics Teacher
Bremner, Donna May
Art Teacher
Parker, Laurel Ann
Art Dept Instructor
Tinnell, Leslie Ann (Fluegge)
Physical Education Teacher
EVERETT
Aaby, Sue Jensen
Art Teacher
Barrett, Patrick J.
Biology Teacher
Bean, Raymond Thomas, Jr.
Para Educator
Bergevin, Christina Lynn
Choral Music Teacher
Burns, Bruce Wayne
Social Studies Teacher
Callaghan, Mary Anne
English Teacher
Carey, Elaine Jester
German Teacher
Chamberlin, Ruth
Mathematics Tchr & Dept Head
Corbett, Kevin Allan
Science Teacher
Davis, Susan S.
Math Teacher
Figurelli, Theresa B.
Fifth Grade Teacher
Gipson, Laurie Feldman
Math Teacher
Haase, Donald A.
Retired Math Teacher
Hansen, Kris A.
Fourth Grade Teacher
Haueter, Gordon R.
Mathematics Teacher
Henry, Carol Kay
5th Grade Teacher
Irons, Michael
Band Instructor
Johnson, Jane Mc Kee
Mathematics Teacher
Kuper, Gregory P.
World His & Philosophy Tchr

Lang, Ronald M.
Criminal Justice Dir & Instr
Lewis, Chadwick Terry
General Business Instructor
Lockman, James George
Spanish & ESL Teacher
Lucas, Twyla Wiechmann
Health Sciences Educator
Metzger-Levin, Jo
PE Tchr & Coach
Murphy, Mark Steven
Speech Comm Instructor
Nesting, Tami Mills
English Teacher & Debate Coach
Nuessle, Karen Paulik
Associate Supt of Schools
Olson, Sue Udman
First Grade Teacher
Ralston, Charles Philip
Junior High History Teacher
Robinson, Richard Lee
7th Grade Teacher
Romerdahl, Nancy Sue Cantrell
History Teacher
Smith, Matthew James
German, English & Jrnlsm Tchr
Stohl, Maureen Dougherty
Sci Tchr & Jr High Dept Head
EVERSON
Digerness, Joan Garber
Sixth Grade Teacher
Elsner, Mike W.
Eng, Soc Stud & Rdng Tchr
Heutink, Joni Beth
5th Grade Teacher
Maier, Terry C.
Comp Coord & Math Instructor
Walsh, Ann Dingle
Third Grade Teacher
FALL CITY
Kirby, Richard Lee
Teacher & Coach
Neyland, Marti Jenner
Fourth Grade Teacher
FEDERAL WAY
Beck, Terry
Elementary School Principal
Benoit, Michael Robert
5th & 6th Grade Teacher
Cantwell, Dennis M.
Headmaster
Dean, Molly Jean
High School Science Teacher
Dickerson, David Clifford
Director of Choral Activities
Ditlefsen, David Edward
Math Teacher
Fankhauser, Francine Oishi
8th & 9th Grade English Tchr
Ford, Patricia Sue
Business Education Teacher
France, Robert C.
Tchr & Certified Ath Trainer
Harris-Phipps, Rebecca S.
Senior High English Teacher
Hensley, Dan N.
Alg, Geometry & Pre-Calc Tchr
Libadia, Larry C.
Third Grade Teacher
Luttinen, Wendy E. Simmons
6th Grade Teacher
Packard, Teri A.
5th Grade Teacher
Puu, Charles Kersting
Second Grade Teacher
Records, Valerie O.
ESL Specialist
Reintsma, Mary Jo Whitley
Eng, Reading & US His Teacher
Spencer, Laura J.
Chemistry Teacher
Victor, Eugene William
Science Teacher
FERNDALE
Andres, Beth Youngquist
Math Teacher
Smedley, Gail
7th & 8th Grd Humanities Tchr
Sobjack, Eileen Barker
Home School & English Teacher
FORKS
Jensen, Terry A.
Physical Education Teacher
Lyons, Stanley Curtis
Physical Education Teacher
FORT LEWIS
Duguay, Richard Crawford
Elementary School Counselor
Luther, Chris Burne
3rd Grade Teacher
FOUR LAKES
Walter, C. Ralph, Jr.
Principal & Teacher
FRIDAY HARBOR
Anderson, David Bruce
Physical Ed & Health Teacher
GIG HARBOR
Belcher, Morgia Jane
Retired Teacher
Broten, Hilda Gean
English & Reading Teacher
Halsan, Lisa M.
Soc Stud Dept Head & Tchr
Hara, Toni Bremer
Second Grade Teacher
Hughes, Susie Dittmann
First Grade Teacher
Johnson, Dale Hunter
Counselor, Teacher & Coach

Kinkead, Shele Windt
Assistant Principal
Lackman, Wayne Douglas
Choral Music Teacher
Lieruance, Ben J.
HS Math & Leadership Teacher
Miller, Lyle W.
Psychology & Geography Teacher
Ozier, David James
Spcl Education Resource Tchr
Pollard, Gloria Meyer
English & Social Science Tchr
Tart, Vicki M.
7th Grd Source Stud Eng Tchr
Wiley, Jay C.
Chemistry Teacher & Sci Chair
GOLDENDALE
Olson, W. Jay
Social Studies Teacher
Young, Daniel Wayne
Technology & Math Teacher
GORST
Newell, Clinton Harrison
Teacher
Struble, Robert C., Jr.
Junior High School Teacher
GRANDVIEW
Brownlee, Roy
Business Education Teacher
Durado, Frank A.
HS Marketing Teacher
Ferguson, Bettie Jackson
Retired HS History Teacher
Leas, Loyal Stapleton
English Teacher
Manship, Melanie Renee(Charvet)
Middle School Teacher
Maxwell, Susan Mowry
LAP Reading Teacher
Newberry, Curtis L.
Algebra Teacher
Roberts, Rodney Guinn
Mathematics Chairman
GRANGER
Ely, Gary Joe
Soc Sci & Hlth Teacher & Coach
Hubert, Brenda Joyce
Junior High Teacher
GRANITE FALLS
Howell, Debra Schireman
Multi-Age Teacher
GREENACRES
Dunham, Joan Marie
Able Learner Teacher
Klassen, Gary Lee
Jr HS & Driver Ed Teacher
HARRINGTON
Frank, Elizabeth A.
Science Teacher
Peterson, Niels H.
English & French Teacher
HARTLINE
Higginbotham, William Everett
HS Girls Basketball Coach
HOQUIAM
Allin, Therese Pope
High School Math Teacher
Bruun, Allen James
Special Education Teacher
Descher, John Daniel
Technology Coordinator
Kogin, Diane Yaste
Kindergarten Teacher
Root, Michael Gayne
5th Grade Teacher
Root, N. Diane
First Grade Teacher
Sexton, Alta Stamper
Business Education Teacher
White, Roger Allen
Director of Bands
ILWACO
Bono, Jan
Sixth Grade Teacher
Hickman, Russell H.
Social Studies Teacher
Holland, Laurence Raymond
Physics, Chem & Math Teacher
Johnson, Glenn Erick
Administrative Assistant
Williams, Joe G.
PE Teacher & Coach
INCHELIUM
Berg, Debra Renae
Science Teacher
Heath, Robert Lee
PE & Voc Shop Teacher
Johnson, Don E.
Mathematics Teacher
Vanderholm, Don W.
History Teacher
ISSAQUAH
Budzius, Patricia Sherman
8th Grd Lang Arts Teacher
Drew, Jody Lyhne
HS Coll Prep Eng Tchr
Ginger, JoAnne
7th Grd Math & Special Ed Tchr
Kananen, Marvin
Professor
Lutzenhiser, Mark Andrew
Physics Teacher
Miller, James Paul
English & Theater Teacher
Moore, Mary Lou Pripp
Third Grade Teacher
Peterson, Joe H.
Soc Stud Dept Chm & AP Teacher
Precht, Charisse Elizabeth Evelyn
Fourth Grade Teacher

Watson, Lavonne Cook
HS Choral Music Teacher
KALAMA
Buchanan, Mark Andrew
7th & 8th Grade Math Teacher
Young, Lee
Assistant Principal
KELSO
Collins, Lisa (Hoffman)
6th Grade Teacher
Doebele, Patricia Gassner
Third Grade Teacher
Ingram, Patricia Martin
Retired Elementary Teacher
Simonsen, George Albert Milton, Jr.
Orchestra Instructor
Skillingstead, Jeff David
Junior High School Art Teacher
Solbrack, Craig Noreen
Band Director
Wingate, Carl Edmond
Latin Tchr & Foreign Lang Chr
Woods, David R.
5th & 6th Grade Teacher
KENNEWICK
Andrews, Evelin Janis
Second Grade Teacher
Bissell, Eric Steven
English Teacher
Butler, Alan Dale
Physical Education Teacher
Clark, Joyce Gunwall
Fourth & Fifth Grade Teacher
Clemmens, Kurt Dean
English & Literature Teacher
Collins, Dennis Clinton
Physics & Geology Teacher
Dron, Phillip A.
HS Social Sciences Teacher
DuBois, Kay Fenster
German Teacher
Eisenbarth, Brian Douglas
Math Teacher
Flora, Patti Lynn (Malloy)
Math Teacher
Fontana, Sharon Simarro
Early Childhood Ed Instructor
Galloway, Clint E.
High School Teacher
Garvey, John
Social Studies Teacher
Kirsch, Richard Allen
Special Education Teacher
Locke, Gary N.
Physical Education Specialist
McReynolds, Sara Lindsey
ESL Teacher
Paye, Patricia McGill
English Teacher
Regan, Rick
PE, Health Teacher & Dept Chm
Schenter, Marlene Kravetz
Teacher
Schlekewey, Jeffery Dean
Math Teacher
Shaw, Janna (Roetcisoender)
English Dept Chair & Teacher
Smith, Patricia Skinner
Business Education Teacher
Sonderland, Roger Lee
Social Studies Teacher
Stanton, Connie Koran
Social Studies Teacher
Traver, Dennis D.
Social Studies Teacher
Young, Jeffrey Lynn
Mathematics Teacher
KENT
Albrecht, Michael R.
Educational Assistant & Coach
Bento, Michael James
General Music Teacher
Black, Joel D.
Private School Director
Bohrmann, Gunter B.
Phys Ed, ESL & German Tchr
Durand, Sandra Karine Hall
First Grade Teacher
Edgerton, Kathryn Hocson
Lang Arts Tchr & Span Tchr
Ewer, Ann Babbitt
Fifth Grade Teacher
Foyston, Frederick Lynn
English & Lang Arts Instructor
Grimstad, Ronald Edward
Math Teacher & Ath Dir
Howe, Daniel L.
Science Teacher
Howell, John J.
Retired English Teacher
Iseri, Doug
Junior HS Mathematics Teacher
Johnson, Kristina Gurnsey
English & Humanities Teacher
Kedward, Richard Ian
History & English Teacher
Kever, Michael V.
Social Studies & English Tchr
King, Molly
French Teacher
Kirkland, Mary Ann Kestler
First Grade Teacher
Lewandowski, Patricia K.
Fifth Grade Teacher
Marafino, Stephen
Mathematics Tchr & Dept Chm
Martin, Richard Earl, Jr.
Art & Mathematics Teacher
O'Brien, Sylvia Buzzard
7th-8th Grade Block Teacher

' (cont)
·dson, Steve C.
al Studies Teacher
ki, Matthew Edward
.anguage Arts Teacher
t, David A.
Math Teacher
'LE FALLS
ckson, Mike J.
PE Teacher & Coach
STON
., Ann Marie
Grade Teacher
LAND
rd, Jeremey Lee (Higgins)
hematics Teacher
man, Ward Scott
d Director
an, Steve
ory Teacher & Computer Adv
lin, Joleen Pitman
cial Education Teacher
on, Robert Lawrence
gion & History Teacher
, Karin Linn (Newman)
f Dev Spec Assignment Tchr
Susanne Cocklin
ily & Consumer Science Tchr
son, Robert D.
sics Teacher
, Scott Allen
lth, Religion & PE Tchr
as, James Richard
h Grade Teacher
'ENTER
and, Pam Rinta
& 8th Grd Math Teacher
sen, Roseann Tyler
rd Grade Teacher
CONNER
p, Kathy A.
glish & Drama Teacher
EY
man, Don James
lti-Age Classroom Teacher
itz, Marcella C.
g Arts & Music Teacher
swell, George E.
ired Weight Lifting Coach
ROSSE
in, Glenn Allyn
-12th Grd Soc Studies Tchr
E STEVENS
man, Shannon Riley
Grade Teacher
vley, John David
gh School English Teacher
ey, Kristi Stermetz
her Stud & Lang Arts Teacher
en, Karen Lynn
glish Instr & Yearbook Adv
, Elisha Jeffrey
story Teacher
ke, James Howard
cial Studies Teacher
er, Harold
nguage Arts Instructor
KEBAY
bochia, David W.
ath Teacher
KEWOOD
ows, Mike H.
ology Tchr & Sci Dept Chair
n, Ronald Wayne
ath Instructor
ney, Genese
story Teacher
ster, Chris Ray
t Teacher
AVENWORTH
hoff, James Martin
acher & Coordinator
man, James Douglas
S Mathematics & Spanish Tchr
Millan, John Saunders
hysical Education Teacher
dlington, William Jewell
cientist & Coach
ND
leberg, Oscar Marion
eacher & Counselor
TTLEROCK
te, Janis (Bade)
rst Grade Teacher
NG BEACH
anitger, Ron
etired Biology Teacher
NGVIEW
own, Dana C.
heatre Dept Director & Tchr
vey, Kenneth M.
and Teacher
unch, Loren E.
Math Instructor
rrell, Donald Albert
heatre Director
wan, Betty Parker
Vice Principal & 7th Grd Tchr
hnert, Paul Duane
Administrator & Principal
ewig, Elizabeth Jane
French Teacher
che, Julia Harmon
Ceramics Teacher
rrell, Aileen Frances
English & Social Studies Tchr
sch, Timothy Paul
Vice Principal & Athletic Dir
busch, Shelly Ann
Sixth Grade Teacher

Johnson, Amy Armstrong
8th Grade English Teacher
Kearcher, Karen Lynne (Schroeder)
Nurse Educator
Lawson, Ellen Nickenzie
Instructor of History
LeMonds, Jim
English Teacher
Maldonado, Cynthia Ogren
Math Tchr & Asst Admin
Mallory, Allyn F.
Chemistry & Physics Teacher
Mc Elliott, Michael W.
English & Social Studies Tchr
Meharg, J. Howard
Freshstart Program Coordinator
Meyer, Gary B.
Eng & Tech Writing Instructor
Noah, Robert Michael
Secondary Counselor
Robbins, Quentin Noel
Art Instructor
Sims, Scott Richard
Elementary Schl PE Specialist
Stone, Mary Ellen
Counselor & Faculty
Suek, Philip J.
English Teacher
VonDracek, Tami K.
Intervention Specialist
Woodriff, Larry L.
Automotive Mech Tech Instr
LYMAN
Tobiason, Marianne Swapp
4th Grade Teacher
LYNDEN
Hanaway, Carole Charlene
AP Eng & Lang Arts Instr
Maberry, Christine Louise
Eng Tchr, Yrbk & Nwspapr Adv
Nymeyer, Elmer Roy
Retired Fifth & Sixth Grd Tchr
Wark, Sandra Poulsen
7th-8th English & Spanish Tchr
Williams, Thom
Language Arts Teacher
LYNNWOOD
Arnold, Clorinda Rodriguez-Waters
Spanish Teacher
Ballinger, Sandra Harker
English Instructor
Berg, Daniel F.
Economics Instructor
Botley, Paulette Elizabeth (Harrell)
Mathematics Instructor
Hart, Patricia Anne
Instructor
Henning, MaryAnn Robblee
Spanish Teacher
Hoff, Kathy Swanson
4th-5th Grade Teacher
Ireland, Rita Rae
Library Media Specialist
Kozelisky, Debra Lynnwood
French Teacher
Lee, Ronald Harrison
Teacher
Moffat, Lesley Caldwell
Bands & Orchestra Director
Oakley, Barbara Schrader
Music Teacher
Rogers, Adam Jon
Intermediate Multi-Age Teacher
Shaw, Henry
History Teacher
Silliman, Clark Dwight
Instr of Legal Assistance Pgm
Tissot, Gary Pierre
Elementary Teacher
MABTON
Affholter, Andrew Albert
Vice Principal & Bus Tchr
Hurn, Greg S.
Mathematics & Sci Dept Chair
Jaquish, Karen Stiltner
English & Physical Ed Teacher
MANSON
Bennett, Rachelle Marie
Special Education Teacher
Garrett, Wayne R.
Band & Choir Director
Pepple, Bonnie (Weekes)
Reading Specialist
MAPLE VALLEY
Clift, Kathleen D.
Sixth Grade Teacher
Oglesby, Mark Nolan
Social Studies Teacher
Simmons, Debra Nadine
Quest & Acad Support Instr
Welch, Corinne D.
Elem PE Specialist & Coach
MARYSVILLE
Andersen, Michelle Ross
English & History Teacher
Barker, Greg P.
History Teacher & ASB Adv
Davidson, Kari Mc Cracken
6th Grade Homeroom Teacher
Frisk, Julie P.
English & Art Teacher
Hodgins, Patrick John
Business Education Teacher
Jensen, Susan Hopkins
Mathematics Teacher
Mandich, Rosalie
English Teacher & Dept Head
Nilson, Barbara Smith
Physical Education Teacher

Pankiewicz, James Frank
Marketing Teacher
Pierce, Deborah Moen
PE & Aerobics Teacher
Rockhill, Lynn Barnhouse
Language Arts & History Tchr
Roop, Carla Marlene
First Grade Teacher
Rowley, Lynn Enquist
Social Studies Teacher
Scrimgeour, Lee Robert
Math Teacher
Shultz, Gary Eugene
Social Studies Teacher
Swenson, Gary Lee
9th Grade English Teacher
Wilson, RuthAnn Nielsen
Teacher of Highly Capable
Wright, William R.
Third Grade Teacher
MATTAWA
Parkison, Marion Olga
HS Science Teacher
MC CLEARY
Geer, Sharon Hodges
First Grade Teacher
MEAD
Hare, Michael D.
Physical Education Teacher
Larsen, Dennis Eugene
Choir Director
Petty, Karen Ellis
English Tchr & Yearbook Adv
MEDICAL LAKE
Brown, Kathie Tenneson
Special Education Teacher
Earl, Athlyn G.
Span, Business & English Tchr
Hartman, Sheila M.
Rdng Specialist & Scndry Tchr
Huffman, Sharon Mesmer
Fifth Grade Teacher
Nelson, JoAnne Webb
PE Teacher & Librarian
Von Lehe, Valerie L.
Biology & Physical Ed Tchr
MENLO
Friese, Rob Lewis
English Teacher
Green, Pam J. Bullard
Kindergarten Teacher
Peterson, John R.
Coach, Athletic Dir & Tchr
MERCER ISLAND
Call, Frances B.
Ret Soc Stud & Lang Arts Tchr
Ceteznik, Gloria J.
English Teacher
Lindquist, Mary
Social Studies Teacher
Monahan, Cathleen Caley
English & Drama Teacher
Montstream, Nancy Stark
HS Spcl Ed & English Teacher
Pullen, Jane Ann Arnold
Retired Dir of Human Svcs Prgm
Sayers, Janet L.
English & Business Teacher
Spickard, Nelsen Beim
Librarian
MIDWAY
Harrison, Fred
Hlth Instr, PE Coord & Ath Dir
Henshaw, Christine M.
Nursing Program Coordinator
Hirnle, Robert Wayne
Resp Care Pgm Dir & Instr
James, Sibyl
English Teacher
Pawula, Hellyn Moore
Jewelry Design & Tech Prof
Ross, Geraldine Yvonne
Professor of Biology
Stegall, Sydney Wallace
Music Professor
Stowe, Lorain
Philosophy & Humanities Prof
Wilson, Donna Mae
Span Prof, Arts & Hum Div Chr
MILTON
Nelson, Jeffrey Thomas
Middle School Teacher
MONROE
Adams, Brenda Byrne
English & Drama Instructor
Lowe, Anne M.
Agricultural Education Teacher
Mann, Rhonda Louise
Health & Physical Ed Teacher
Rose, Dave Shawn
Math Teacher
MONTESANO
Furnia, Geraldine Reid
Retired Third Grade Teacher
Holliday, Judy Mears
Mathematics Teacher
Rota, Louise Ann
Elementary Phy Ed Teacher
MORTON
Jones, Carleen Viola
1st-8th Grd Teacher
MOSES LAKE
Andress, Cathy
Psychology Instructor
Bailey, Lora Lee Mathews
4th Grade Teacher
Burton, Ramon
Assessment Coordinator
Doumit, Peter George
Social Studies Teacher

Iverson, Patricia Brown
Office Information Mgmt Prof
Koester, Larry Christian
Science Teacher
Lindholm, Steven Blaine
English Teacher
Lowther, Theresa Wolfe
High School Math Teacher
Lynch, Michael Joseph
Social Studies Teacher
Mac Donald, Linda R.
Drama & English Teacher
Masterson, Billie West
Retired Fourth Grade Teacher
Paris, Helen Samuel
High School English Teacher
Swanson, Ann Davis
English Professor
Warkentin, Hans R.
Biology Teacher
Wilks, Rex G.
Retired Instructor
MOUNT VERNON
Best, Joe
8th Grade Math Teacher
Bogensberger, Joan Hess
Founder & Administrator
Hoare, Robert Donald
Fifth Grade Teacher
Johnson, Michael Richard
Mathematics Teacher
Lange, Brett Steven
Physical Education & Hlth Tchr
Lopez, Jovita A.
Writing, Literature Instructor
Marion, Marc
Principal
Moore, Arlene Sylvia
Kndgtn-First Grade Teacher
Moore, Gary Edward
Eighth Grade Science Teacher
Muga, David A.
Professor of Sociology
Olpin, Bonnie LeBlanc
Librarian
Roy, Jack Levi
Social Studies Instructor
Smith, Kristina A.
Choir Director
Wisen, John P.
Retired Teacher
Zappone, Peggy I.
HS American Govt & His Tchr
MOUNTLAKE TERRACE
Aardsma, Carl A.
History Chair & Bible Tchr
Breysse, Peter Vincent
English Teacher
Dremousis, George Athan
Social Studies Teacher
Gidner, Colleen Wendt
Teacher of Gifted Students
Matheson, Fred Ray
Scndry Math & Science Teacher
Moynihan, Timothy J.
English Teacher
Reeder, Eeva Liisa Keranen
Math Teacher
Schindler, Debbie Ann
Principal & Teacher
Schlaman, Robert Otto
Mathematics Teacher
Traxler, John Andrew
Science Teacher & Swim Coach
Ummel, Jon David
English Teacher
Zink de Diaz, Laura Suzanne
World Languages Dept Chair
MOXEE
Walter, James Patrick
5th Grade Teacher
MUKILTEO
Bull, Wayne E., Sr.
Business Technology Teacher
Nickerson, Frank Michael
High School English Teacher
Russell, Julie Aldrich
English Teacher
Wolfe, Bill G.
Social Studies Teacher
NACHES
Cooper, Kerry Taylor
8th Grd Social Studies Teacher
Jetton, Sanford Paul
English Teacher
Stauffer, Brett A.
Educator
NAPAVINE
Stone, Michael James
High School Math Teacher
NASELLE
Wise, Bruce D.
English Teacher
NEAH BAY
Hellwig, Gary Wayne
Junior High School Teacher
NEWPORT
Anselmo, Harold Thomas
Teacher
Sauer, Lawrence P.
6th Grade Teacher
NINE MILE FALLS
Anderson, Barbara Kay (Smart)
High School Math Teacher
Sullivan, Matthew G.
Classroom Teacher
NOOKSACK
Dallas, Bradford Lee
Math & Science Teacher

NORTHPORT
Goodwin, James Michael
Math & Science Teacher
Goodwin, Karma Arlt
Mathematics & Science Teacher
Nesse, Kristine G.
Jrnlsm, Arts & Kybrdng Tchr
OAK HARBOR
Boyer, Kevin Stroncek
Business Education Teacher
Des Voigne, Katy Campbell
High School Math Teacher
Des Voigne, Mark E.
Mathematics Teacher
Harbour, Kathy A.
Title I Reading & Math Tchr
LaBombard, Louis Wendell
Sociology & Anthropology Prof
Schiele, Leann Marie
HS Health & PE Teacher
Zylstra, Marianne Eisses
6th-8th Grd Math & Sci Tchr
OAKVILLE
Bishop, Susan Stow
Resource Room Teacher
OCEAN CITY
Lundstrom, Shirley Zitka
Retired Office Tech Instructor
OCEAN SHORES
Loomis, Kenneth Michael
Science Teacher
ODESSA
Pitts, Michael Duane
8th-12th Grd English Teacher
OKANOGAN
Figlenski, Rita (Eder)
Business Education Teacher
Patrick, Pamela Paige
Home & Family Life Teacher
OLALLA
Banks, Janet L. Hansen
Third Grade Teacher
OLYMPIA
Anderson, Michelle Ann
9th-12th Grd Japanese Teacher
Arth, Leslie Chamberlain
English Teacher & Program Ldr
Backman, Lhonda Shaw
Spanish Teacher
Bein, Kathleen Leoma (Fauquier)
Enrichment Teacher
Brand, Tom E.
Science Teacher
Colbeck, Connie Marie
Spanish Teacher
Creighton, Laurie Wescott
PE Teacher & Coach
Day, Myrna Sonja (Ware)
7th-8th Grd Soc Stud Teacher
Dittrich, Barbara Thompson
Activity Coord & History Tchr
Drennon, Julie Marie
Business & Technology Teacher
Finkel, Donald L.
Professor
Fischer, Celia Lynn
Sixth Grade Teacher
Gibbons, Michael Lennis
Mathematics Teacher
Holland, William Dale
6th-8th Grd Soc Studies Tchr
Hoonan, Brian Robert
Lang Arts & Soc Studies Tchr
Karanson, Ted
Teacher of Deaf & Blind
Layton, David Allan
English Instructor
Livesay, Elizabeth Dick
Bus Tech Pgm Ldr & Tchr
Long, Charles E.
Math Teacher
Loring, Ann J.
Kindergarten Teacher
Mauer, Charles Michael
Teacher of the Highly Capable
Miller, Patricia Timm
Sixth Grade Teacher
Nettleton, John Graham
Counselor
Palmer, Janet Lynn
Science Teacher
Parks, Deborah Green
French Teacher
Racus, Ronald James
Sixth Grade Teacher
Ramm, Renate
German Teacher & Dept Chair
Rich, Denise Elizabeth
Language Arts Teacher
Riffe, Linda Rawlinson
Business Teacher & Dept Chair
Rood, Stephen Paul
Social Stud Tchr & Act Coord
Rosen, Michael L.
Sensei
Schooler, Charles Oakley
Orchestra Teacher
Sparks, Robert Chapman
English Teacher
Stone, Stuart Allen
Band Director
Thompson, Kathleen Zelasko
5th Grade Teacher
Thorson, Laury Lee
Gifted Ed & Foreign Lang Tchr
Uhrich, Jacob Ernest
Mathematics Faculty
VanTroba, Albert Bruce
Art Teacher

OLYMPIA (cont)
Vernoy, David Richard
Teacher
Villeneuve, Phyllis E.
Instructor
Wells, Colleen McKay
8th Grade Humanities Teacher
Wood, Bonnie Cooper
History Teacher
Yelenich, Richard Franklin
English Teacher
OMAK
Balthazor, Stacy James
Elementary Teacher
Hilts, John David
Soc Stud, Eng Tchr & Counselor
Hoover, R. C.
Instructor of Eng & Humanities
Mastey, James Anthony
Vocational Automotive Instr
Steffen, Peggy Jean (Kestie)
Teacher of Enrichment & Gifted
OROVILLE
Hughes, Grace Wilson
Retired Teacher
Ricevuto, Charles John
Bus Ed Teacher
OTHELLO
Beus, Glenn W.
7th Grd Soc Stud & Hum Teacher
Collett, Merrill Murray
Currnt Wrld Prblm & Psych Tchr
Dickey, Charlie Bates
US History Teacher
Martinez, Ruben
Span Tchr, Head Wrstling Coach
Stewart, Kristy Ann
Sixth Grade Teacher
OTIS ORCHARDS
Allison, Mary Lou Menegas
Fourth Grade Teacher
OUTLOOK
Quigley, Barbara Michaelsen
First Grade Teacher
PASCO
Brouns, Donna T.
Counselor
Durand-Batres, Melody Ann
English as a Second Lang Tchr
Foster, James Ronald
8th Grade Math Teacher
Greenwell, Janice Thomas
Eighth Grd American His Tchr
Hille, Karen Eugenia
5th Grade Teacher
Kimmel, Susan Steinhaus
College Art Instructor
Mc Clelland, Thomas A.
Instr of Sculpture & Art His
Rampy, Mona Y. Pearson
Chemistry Teacher
Rickenbach, Karen Middleton
Attendance Clerk
Riojas, Marie Louise
Bilingual Kindergarten Teacher
Sandbeck, Michael Keith
Substitute Teacher
Staten, Moody Ross
Instructor of Speech
Steach, Misti L.
Spanish Teacher
Templeton, William Ryan
ESL Teacher
Walker, M. Carol
Instructor of Geology
Williamson, James Joseph
Mathematics Teacher
Wright, Donald J.
English Teacher
Zhang, Limin
Mathematics Instructor
PATEROS
Hagenbuch, Betty Johnson
Junior High Math & Sci Tchr
PATERSON
Craig, Betty
First & Second Grade Teacher
POMEROY
Kucklick-McGreevy, Toddette L.
English Teacher & Dept Head
Manring, Jim Darrell
Math Teacher
PORT ANGELES
Blake, Paul
Fifth Grade Teacher
Clausen, Donald John
Choral Music Teacher
Durr, Patrick
8th Grade English Teacher
Ellefson, Julie Judd
2nd Grade Teacher
Elliott, Phillis Louise
English Teacher
Hickerson, Lloyd L.
5th Grade Teacher
Hirst, Christine Kay
High School Math Teacher
Johnson, Keith G.
English Teacher
Kilmer, Joseph Charles
Curr & Instr Consultant
Leinart, Tom Robert
Science & Mathematics Teacher
O'Malley, John Damian
English Teacher
Pena, Maria J.
Counselor
Reavey, Kate
English Instructor

Uranich, David Edward
Social Studies Teacher
PORT ORCHARD
Christman, E. Christie
English & Spanish Teacher
Conley, Mark Joseph
Vice Principal
Emans, Deborah Helm
Theatre Instructor
Gerrish, Karen Stich
Social Studies Tchr
Giantvalley, Ann Meredith
Fourth Grade Classroom Teacher
Hatch, Mary Anne
Language Arts Tchr & Cnslr
Houge, Alice M. (Renn)
Fourth Grade Teacher
Kaio-Maddox, Stephen Knute
Multi-Age Teacher
Kimball, Bonnie Ann
Sixth Grade Teacher
Kuchera, Cynthia Suzanne
4th Grade Teacher
Lobe, Randy Lowell
Math Department Chairperson
Luginbill, Leila Retherford
Bio, Anatomy Physiology Tchr
Matheny, C. David
Multi-Age Classroom Teacher
Moser, Melissa Anne
Language Arts & Drama Teacher
Murphy, Shanna Marie
Marketing Instructor
Olson, Carl Anders
Drama & Technical Theater Tchr
Parker, Robb Gregory
English Lit & Writing Teacher
Pfeiffer, James Johnathon
History, Language & PE Teacher
Smith, Mary Celeste C.
Reading Recovery Teacher
Thoraldson, Patricia Clark
First Grade Teacher
Wilkin, Jennifer E. Lee
Secondary Art Teacher
PORT TOWNSEND
Jackson, Jim
1st-3rd Grade Teacher
Jackson, Sue Anne
Art & Theatre Arts Teacher
Ornelas, Robin Groshelle
Retired Kindergarten Teacher
Simpson, Steven Warren
English & Journalism Teacher
Thielk, E. David
Science & Math Teacher
POULSBO
Acton, Elizabeth Ann
7th Grade Language Arts Tchr
Johnson, Don Lee
Counselor
Konopaski, Ellen Smith
Spanish & German Teacher
Lisle, Rande
Art Teacher
Miranda, Marshall Stephen
Lang Arts & Soc Science Tchr
Owens, C. Anna
Math Teacher
Strayer, Pat Keim
English Teacher
PROSSER
Bell, John Allen
5th Grade Teacher
Boyle, Steven Leonard
Music Teacher
Lemke, Deborah A.
First Grade Teacher
Lobos, Carlina
ESL & Sheltered Eng Teacher
Motsenbocker, Bill L.
Asst Principal
Newhouse, Patricia Louise Noteboom
Spanish Teacher
Padelford, Stewart
Agriscience Teacher
Pillers, James E.
PE & Drivers Ed Teacher
Talbot, Janice Rae
Third Grade Teacher
Warriner, Barbara Barrett
11th-12th Grd English Teacher
Wierenga, Susan K.
Biology Teacher
Yetter, Larry A.
Mathematics Teacher
PULLMAN
Cooke, Linda Bradley
Seventh Grade Mathematics Tchr
Leigh, Joan Brill
Fifth Grade Teacher
McCormick, Craig Rodger
English Teacher & Dept Chair
Mc Michael, Kirk Dugald
Assoc Professor of Chemistry
Wells, Carl Vincent
Electrical Engineering Prof
Wiest, Lori J.
Assistant Professor of Music
PUYALLUP
Ahre, Ronald G.
5th-6th Grade Teacher
Armstrong, Susannah Dee
6th Grade Teacher
Barager, Paul Anthony
Spanish Teacher
Barber, Dave Jerred
High School Biology Teacher
Bates, Jay Alan
Eng, Yrbk & Jrnlsm Teacher

Brown, Denise Kay
Fifth Grade Teacher
Burrough, Peggy Kim
Choral Director
Cimino, Michael L.
Science Teacher
Gilbertson, William Jerome
Biology Teacher
Graham, Julie Jamieson
French, German & English Tchr
Grieve-Fent, Margaret Louise
French Teacher
Hadley, Lori Kissick
English Teacher
Harris, Mark S.
Science Teacher
Hendrickson, Jerry E.
HS Math Teacher
Henzler, Jannette M.
Chemistry Teacher
Hibbs, Gary Lee
Agri Science Teacher
Hodous, Phillip Charles
Social Studies Teacher
Horne, LeAnne Marie
Jr High Health Tchr
Iverson, Rod Wayne
Social Studies Teacher
Jasinski, Mark H.
Orchestra Teacher
Lee, Gary George
Social Studies & Math Teacher
May, Margo Crowell
Director of Education
Mundy, Don Edwin
7th & 8th Grade Teacher
Murray, Jane Eyrich
Fifth Grade Teacher
Nelson, Thomas Howard
English Teacher & Soccer Coach
O'Hanlon, Kathleen Nutt
Fifth Grade Teacher
Orton, Frederick Lee
HS History Teacher
Parker, John Glidden
Chemistry Instructor
Pisetzner, Jeffrey
Rdng, Stud Skills Instr & Adv
Rosdahl, David Carl
English Teacher & Coach
Siqueland, Sonya Marie
Secondary Social Studies Tchr
Stein, David Glenn
Mathematics Teacher
Thomas, Anne Maureen
Family & Consumer Science Tchr
Vanneson, Christopher Theodore
Assoc Prof His, Geog, Pol Sci
Volland, Larry Stephen
Social Studies Teacher
Wilson, Mark
Social Studies Teacher
QUILCENE
French, Timothy L.
PE, English Teacher & Coach
Pendleton, Christopher Charles
Business Teacher
QUINCY
Bryant, Judith Urey
English Teacher
Mc Kenzie, Wayne E.
Science Teacher
Palelek, Joyce Stockdale
High School English Teacher
Wachtel, Franklin Eugene
Industrial Technology Instr
RAINIER
Kenney, Mary Jo Kaufer
Special Education Teacher
Rossmaier, Sandra Moberg
Vocational Dir & Business Tchr
Willmarth, Cris Eric
English & Geography Teacher
REDMOND
Baker, Stephanie Jane
Humanities Teacher
Bennett, David A.
Social Studies Teacher
Crickmore, Kelly Leonard
Fourth Grade Teacher
Foster, Brian Vernon
English Teacher
Gehring, William B.
6th Grade Teacher
Gutheil, Suzanne Carol
5th-6th Grade Teacher
Hansen, Petra Koldewey
Spanish Teacher
Hoffman, Susan Christy
First Grade Teacher
Klube, Starr (Angell)
5th Grade Teacher
Matsushita, Jon
Advisor, Teacher & Coach
Mc Allister, Katie Sarver
High School Special Ed Tchr
Miller, Linda J.
Humanities Teacher
Morris, Blanche Ellen
First Grade Teacher
Pape, Sharon Wilkins
Drama Teacher
Robertson, Andrew David
Band Director
Sinclair, Heather
Staff Dev & Humanities Tchr
Sypher, Beverley Anne
Fourth Grade Teacher
Wadsack, Diana M.
Art Teacher

Wood, Robert Edwin
Middle School Administrator
RENTON
Alvey, Nanete Gillespe
Advanced English Teacher
Annerl, Annemarie Schneider
French Teacher
Becker, Debra Dixon
Spanish Teacher
Carlson, Robert William
History & English Teacher
Inkpen, Robert J.
Teacher
Ito, Richard B.
Principal
Jasper, Thomas W.
Fourth Grade Teacher
Kusumoto, Jean Sumida
First Grade Teacher
Longman, Jann K.
Psych, Film & Site-Based Chm
Mitsui, James Masao
English Teacher
Orsborn, Edward E.
Dept Chair, Educl Tech Teacher
Santos, Thomas Alfred
Teacher
Simpson, Michael George
Instrumental Music Teacher
Wood, Jeffrey Bruce
Social Studies Teacher
RICHLAND
Boatman, Doyle C.
PE Teacher
Boatman, Kimberley Moore
8th Grade Language Arts Tchr
Bowden, Annette (Gilbertson)
Office Technology Instructor
Castleberry, Jim
Sixth Grade Teacher
Castleberry, Pamela Lee
US & WA St History Teacher
Commeree, Claire Druffel
Librarian
Cranford, Evonne Meyers
Math Teacher
DeBuigne, Renee Philleo
Math, Computer Science Teacher
Gonzalez, Delia C.
Spanish Teacher
Kelly, Vickie Lynn
Mathematics Tchr & Dept Chprsn
Larrabee, Edward P.
Mathematics Teacher
Larson, John William
4th Grade Teacher
Leggett, Marjy Wessels
Third Grade Teacher
Maki, Rebecca Lee (Kenney)
Business Education Teacher
McDonald, Richard William
US Govt & Geography Teacher
Mohatt, Maureen Ann
Art Department Head
Moore, Mary Bennett
Inclusion & Sci Specialist
Morris, Robin Clark
Jrnlsm, Eng & Speech Teacher
Neitzel-Cleavenger, Lynn
German Teacher
Olivares, Juan Carlos
Spanish Teacher
Orr, James Lowry
Mathematics Teacher
Piippo, Steven William
Materials Science Tech Tchr
Sevigny, Gregory Leonard
Mathematics Teacher & Coach
Staley, Paul Norman
Biology Teacher
True, David W.
Math Teacher
Vigneron, Sylvia Ann
Fourth Grade Teacher
Westphal, Russell Von
Assoc Prof Mechanical Engrng
Wilson, James C.
AP History Teacher
RIDGEFIELD
Bochart, Judith Mary
Sixth Grade Teacher
Norton, Bill
Math Teacher
Potter, Deborah Kent
High School Art Teacher
Yates, Robert R.
English Teacher
ROCHESTER
Heinz, Larry E.
Social Studies Teacher
Hess, Jeri S.
Language Arts & History Tchr
Poths, Helen Jane
Retired High School Teacher
ROCKFORD
Hatch, Kristi Cleveland
Math Teacher
Hays, John Michael
Physics, AP Bio & Chem Teacher
Jeremiah, Peggy
Mathematics Teacher
ROSALIA
Goldsworthy, Eugenia Lynn (Ellis)
K-12th Grd Sub Teacher
Wolf, Susan Maria
Family & Consumer Sci Teacher
ROYAL CITY
Brown, Wayne C.
Third Grade Teacher

Miller, Judy
English Teacher
SAINT JOHN
Gfeller, Marianne Blackwell
Kindergarten Teacher
Hubble, Eugene Max
Retired Sixth Grade Teacher
Wagner, Jean Judd
First Grade Teacher
Watson, Frank Clarence
Math, Physics & English Tchr
SEATTLE
Adams, William Nolan
Spcl Ed Teacher & Team Leader
Amble-Snyder, Debbie May
Bible Teacher
Angersbach, Jeanie Hunter
Intnl Baccalaureate His Tchr
Bachelor, Judy Mary
Second Grade Teacher
Ball, Lawrence E.
7th Grade US History Teacher
Ballou, Gary Wayne
Vocal Music Teacher
Beaumonte, Phyllis Ilene
High School Teacher
Bhat, Clarita Csaky
Chemistry Professor
Boon, Rebecca Ann
English Second Language Tchr
Bottelli, Suzanne
Humanities Teacher
Bowton-Meade, Amy Helen
Social Studies Teacher
Braun, Glenda
Choral Music & Lang Art Tchr
Brink, Dean Clifford
History Department Chairman
Cabot, Nick
Physics Teacher
Cannon, John M.
Mathematics Professor
Carroll, Gerardine Patricia
MS Language Arts Teacher
Carver, Victoria Joan
English Teacher
Chesak, Cynthia Jane
Drama & English Teacher
Clymer, Margaret Livingston
Social Studies Teacher
Cobb, Linda Bunce
Family & Consumer Science Tchr
Cobbs, Paul-Elliott
Conductor & Music Director
Cogley, Connie Jean
ESL Teacher
Dailey, Diana (Shreve)
HS Math Teacher & Dept Chair
Deguchi, Jean Fujii
Retired Third Grade Teacher
Del Rosario, Virginia Adelle
Employment Counselor
del Valle, Roberto Esteban
Spanish Teacher
Denckla, Carol Ann
Instructor & Coordinator
Devine, Joanne Johnson
Eng Tchr & Basic Skills Dir
Doig, Carol Dean
Humanities Professor
Dominguez, Gloria Ann Oman
Spanish & Honors Teacher
Drost, Mark Alan
Mathematics Teacher
DuPen, Carolyn Ritchie
Science Teacher & Dept Chair
Durbin, Yarrow Rosamond
Math Teacher
Dyck, Philip Henry
US History & Bible Teacher
Echols, John David
MS History & Geography Tchr
Ellingson, Shirley Haustveit
Bus Ed Dept Head & Teacher
Eng, Richard Kaiso
Secondary Mathematics Teacher
Enquist, Nels
Activity Coordinator
Evans, Gail Gunderson
English Teacher
Garnand, Don S.
English, His & Forensics Tchr
Hein, Teri M.
Teacher
Helfgott, Jacqueline B.
Asst Prof of Criminal Justice
Henderson, Eulene Reed
Retired English Teacher
Hendricks, Andrew Joseph
Social Studies Teacher
Hibbard, Randall Ernest
Family Living & Bible Tchr
Higgins, Loraine D.
Teacher of the Gifted
Hikida, Allan M.
English Instructor
Hodge, Janae LeAnn
Spanish Teacher
Holsinger, Donald C.
Prof of History & Dept Chair
Homann, Theodore Richard
PE Teacher
Hopkins, Hoover L.
World History Teacher
Hovis, Susan Elizabeth
Fourth Grade Teacher
Hutchins, Web
High School History Teacher
Imanaka, Cynthia Chan
Instructor of Sociology

TLE (cont)
ı, Robert O.
eacher
n, Sandra Harbour
ch Teacher
Kathryn Marie
nd Grade Teacher
Annabelle Lee
selor
Robert Earl
c Tchr, Band Dir & Chprsn
Carlton David, Jr.
ance Counselor
tz, Barbara Jean
Grade Humanities Teacher
Suellen Marie
ish Teacher
pelle, Nancy Lee
Skills Teacher
ı, Patricia C.
ial Education Teacher
Kay
5th Grd Tchr Gifted Stdnts
ns, Ileana Rebozo
History Instructor
enora L.
Pgm Head Teacher
anna
Instructor
lad, Christina A.
ndary English Teacher
, Roberta Runyan
Teacher
y, Janet Cuppage
al Studies Teacher
, Katherine Parks
Teacher
ess, Christine Bryan
Relations Dir & Yrbk Adv
ell, Antony Edward
d Rowing Coach
lister, Donald Robert
ructor
luskey, Brian Joseph
gion Teacher
uskey, Faith
hematics Tchr & Dept Chair
lone, Sherry Sawe L. Garner
endance Specialist III
amey, Frances Helene
mentary Band Program Dir
illen, Paul
h School Mathematics Tchr
ll, Thomas Charles
PE & Health Teacher
r, Artice M.
hematics Teacher
r, Ralph H.
Grade Mathematics Teacher
ette, Richard Warren
ial Studies Teacher
e, Susan Bement
glish Teacher
son, Maureen Kay
lti-Age Classroom Teacher
on, Annette Wadiyah E.
unselor & Instructor
on, Robin O.
Social Psychology Teacher
en, John Eric
ence Teacher
ng, Maureen Murphy
story Instructor
ey, Nada Illeen
glish Instructor
n, Meredith B.
ddle Schl Sci Specialist
Michelle Lynn
Grd Social Studies Teacher
ker, Edward Stephen
cial Studies Instr & Coach
brooke, Janice Ujhelyi
Grade Teacher
rson, Brian Dean
acher, Coach & Athletic Dir
rson, Linda Chase
rsing Instructor
, Philip Rens
mputer Science Professor
Mary Louise
ird Grade Teacher
hle, Margaret Elizabeth
ndergarten Teacher
inson, Lucretia Metz
Eng, Hum & Sr Proj Teacher
man, Kim Lian
glish as Second Lang Instr
sendaal, Lavonne
adgtn Tchr & Elem Curr Coord
sso, Jack N.
overnment, Law & Soc Tchr
wedel, Helen Irene
etired Kindergarten Teacher
p, Andrew Paul
glish Teacher & Dept Head
, Mitzi A.
h Grade Teacher
neider, Jennifer Brainard
12 Grd His & Law Tchr
reef, Na'eem
h Grade Boys Bsktbl Coach
rman, David Kevin
ocial Studies Teacher
onsen, Ann-Mari
hemistry Professor
ith, Cora Fay
h & 5th Grade Teacher
ith, Randall D.
arsity Lightweight Mens Coach

Snow, Barbara Nedrud
Professor
Stevens, Timothy Dean
Assoc Principal & Athletic Dir
Stewart, Barbara Ann
Coord of Spec Acad Svcs & Tchr
Stover, Joan Christine
Instr of Chemistry & Science
Stowers, Allen Don
Instructor & Counselor
Summers, Robert Wesley
Biology & Physiology Teacher
Sweeney, Michael Patrick
History & Literature Teacher
Swisher, Gloria Wilson
Professor of Music
Temple, Larry Robert
Health & Drama Teacher
Thenell, Patricia Dennehy
Rel Studies Tchr & Dept Chair
Thomas, Carol Guggenheim
Ancient Greek History Prof
Valerio-Buford, Lenore de Leon
Senior Instructor
Van Kempen, Ruben
Teacher & Theatre Director
Vannoy, Gertrude H. (Knuettel)
6th Grade Team Teacher
Vannoy, Ronald W.
6th Grade Teacher
VanReeuwyk, Jo-Ann Patricia
Art Teacher
Voeller, Judy A. (McGillivray)
Preschool Teacher
Waggoner, Dawn Richelle
Health, PE Tchr & Dept Chair
Wall, Carla Mierendorff
English Teacher
Willems, Malcolm Edward
Intnl Baccalaureate Coord
Wraspir, Jeanette Olive
Language Arts Teacher
SEDRO WOOLLEY
Dillard, Janet VanDaveer
Occupations & English Teacher
Hadwin, Brenda Lee
Physical Education Teacher
Rawson, Bennie Wayne
Music Teacher
Reynolds, David Wayne
Psych & Human Behavior Tchr
Schmidt, Laura Wendland
Eng & World History Teacher
Semrau, Julie A.
HS Biology Teacher
Stewart, Michael Keith
Vocational Woodworking Teacher
Thomas, David Henry
Science & Math Teacher
Willmoth, Jack Fitz-Randolph
English & World Travel Teacher
SELAH
Cook, Joy (Kelly)
Freshman & Sophomore Eng Tchr
Elliott, DeLynn Slocumb
Fifth Grade Teacher
Furstenau, Joyce Hovde
6th Grade Classroom Teacher
Johnson, Thomas Allen
Fifth Grade Teacher
North, Carl V.
Music Teacher
SEQUIM
Anderson, Shirley
Biology Teacher
Cross, David Paul
Choral Director
Garwood, Elizabeth Baxter Morrison
Retired 4th-6th Grade Teacher
Hall-Link, Jaye Alison
High School Art Teacher
Hooper, Gary
6th-9th Grade Teacher
Woolley, John Vernon
Soc Studies Tchr & Dept Chair
SHELTON
Baugh, Randy David
English Teacher
Hinkle, Matt Jay
HS Math Teacher & Coach
Keith, Chambliss
5th Grade Teacher
Korte, Richard Kenneth
Science Teacher
Mc Gee-Furrer, Jenny Lynn
Counselor
Mogolis, Joani M.
4th-8th Grd PE & Hlth Tchr
Nelson, Gary D.
7th Grade Biology Teacher
Otto, Ronald Paul
8th Grade Math Teacher
Pegg, Judith Shapiro
4th-5th Grd Teacher of Gifted
Perry, John Joseph
Sixth Grade Math Teacher
SILVERDALE
Duenow, Christopher Todd
Director of Bands
Green, Constance Fields
Business Education Teacher
Kornas, Barbara Ellen
Science Teacher
Manchion, Roberta Jean (Eddy)
3rd-4th Grade Teacher
Murphy, Marcella Eileen
English Teacher
Shaw, Annita Louise
Visual Arts Teacher

Weymiller, Kathryn Kaminoff
Choir Teacher
SNOHOMISH
Albertine, Mark Randy
Health & Physical Ed Tchr
Chamberlain, Paddy L.
HS English Teacher
Charvet, James
Photography Instructor
Dahl, Clifton Philip
Sixth Grade Teacher
Heckman, Lynne Elise
8th Grd Eng & His Teacher
Perry, Mark Darrell
Math Teacher & Coach
Peterson-Moens, Zan Marie
Teacher of Gifted & Talented
Pierce, Patricia Gabrielsen
Third Grade Teacher
Salvadalena, Gerry Allen
Biology Teacher
SNOQUALMIE
Kinnune, Charles Henry
Social Studies Instructor
SOAP LAKE
Nickel, Cheri Weigandt
Eng, Soc Stud & Jrnlsm Tchr
SOUTH BEND
Huber, Mark Emmett
History & Spanish Teacher
Lazelle, Steven Harold
Science & Aquacultar Teacher
Marte, Michael Alan
7th Grd Eng, Geog & PE Tchr
Schroeder, Michael Harlan
Eighth Grade Teacher
SPANAWAY
Adler, Bruce H.
History Teacher
Burnett, C. Glenn
Choir Teacher
Caramandi, Debbi
Family & Consumer Sci Tchr
Franklin, Donald Loren
HS Mathematics Teacher
Gunnarson, Judy Ann (Lovstrom)
Sixth Grade Teacher
Knelleken, Kathy Malcom
French Teacher
Loose, W. A. Robert, III
Science Teacher & Ftbl Coach
Lorenz, Ghita C.
8th Grade English Teacher
McFarland, Kathryn Ann
Fifth Grade Teacher
Paris, Kathy J.
Advanced Placement Bio Teacher
Riggen, Jennifer Lynn
Band Director
Stone, Teresa M.
Family & Consumer Sci Teacher
Wasterbarth-Brown, Sandra A.
Communication Arts Teacher
Wilson, Dennis E.
Mathematics Teacher
SPANGLE
Aldrich, Mary Beth
Business Teacher
Coulter, Norman James
Teacher
Fletcher, Rodney Lee
Math Teacher
Jydstrup, Michael Robert
Instrumental Director
Lacey, Florence M.
Biology & Mathematics Teacher
Lacey, Stephen M.
English Teacher
Martling, Michael Britton
History Teacher
Perry, Donna Rhea
Span Tchr & Library Specialist
Stevens, Charles Aaron
Guidance Counselor
SPOKANE
Allen, Carole Elaine
English Teacher
Aller, Angeles G.
Span Tchr & Frng Lang Dept Chm
Anderson, Calvert H.
Director of Bands
Banks, Douglas Paul
8th Grd Teacher & Vice Prin
Barnes, Steve James
Facilitator
Barnum, Stephen Earl
Fourth Grd Tchr & Sci Chm
Baye, Diane L.
Horticulture Teacher
Bonin, Laureen Legrand
Former English Teacher
Bonin, Michael Richard
English Prof & Dept Chairman
Brezinski, Millie L.
7th Grade PE Teacher
Bridges, William Theodore
Sixth Grade Teacher
Cadagan, Diane Volosing
First Grade Teacher
Carroll, Michael Joseph
High School English Teacher
Chaney, Helen Mc Connaughey
English Teacher
Christianson, Bill
Business Instructor
Cleary, David A.
Chemistry Professor
Cline, Tom Grear
Math Teacher

Cooper, Penny
Interactive Satellite Teacher
Corley, Ivan Wendell
9th-12th Grade English Teacher
Courchaine, Marie Hendrickson
Third Grade Teacher
Crain, Robin Kent
LOC Teacher
Cullen, Richard Rice
Math Tchr & Head Soccer Coach
Davis, Kristeen L.
Spanish & English Teacher
Davis, Stanley John
8th Grd Eng, His & Drama Tchr
Dreis, Margaret Makini
Choral Director
Elsom, Larry Mark
Physics Teacher
Feist, Joseph A.
Business Education Instructor
Freeland, Roed Enrique
Earth Science Teacher
Frey, Patrick Keith
5th & 6th Grade Teacher
Fries, Donald Dean
US History Teacher
Fronk, Cheryl Lynn
Drama Teacher
Garofano, Marilyn K.
8th Grade Language Arts Tchr
Gunning, Patricia Ann Baker
MS Choir & Orchestra Director
Halseth, Claudia Loraine
Fine Arts Teacher & Dept Head
Halstead, Jeffrey S.
English Teacher
Hartse, Kevin E.
Instrumental Music Director
Henry, TAmi Jo
Family & Consumer Science Tchr
Hensely, Jim Michael
Mathematics Teacher
Herbert, Peggy
Spanish Teacher
Huston, William P.
Middle School Teacher
Jayne, Mary B. Hofseth
Orchestra Teacher
Johnsen, Peggy Mac Gown
Multi Age Teacher
Jones, James Richard
5th Grade Teacher
Jones, Jeffrey Robert
Japanese & Mathematics Teacher
Kaldahl, Timothy B.
Math & Science Teacher
Karim, Tanya Kara-Sokol
3rd & 4th Grade Teacher
Kerfoot, Louis M.
Administrator
Knight, Irene Kay
First Grade Teacher
Knight, Lynda R.
2nd Grade Teacher
Kobe-Smith, Daniel Houston
8th Grade Earth Science Instr
Kozeliski, Glenda L.
First Grade Teacher
Kukuk, Ann Helen Fogelquist
Hnrs Eng III & Lang Arts Tchr
Kyle, Deborah S.
Journalism & English Instr
Lenhart, Janice A.
3rd & 4th Grd Multi-Age Tchr
Lentz, Richard H., Jr.
Business & Computer Teacher
Linahan, Jerry Wesley
4th Grade Teacher
Lobdell, Michael W.
Sixth Grade Teacher
Martin, Josette Comets
French & English Teacher
Martin-Shaw, Cindy
Special Education Teacher
Mattoon, Susan Carney
First Grade Teacher
Mc Carty, Dave Tom
Math Teacher
McIvor, Merrie Wallace
Russian & Spanish Teacher
Migliazzo, Arlin Charles
Professor of History
Mohrlang, Roger Lloyd
Professor of Biblical Studies
Moran, Matthew Charles
Scndry Eng as Second Lang Tchr
Mullins, Bill Edward
Bible & Outdoor Education Tchr
Munoz-Flores, Katherine Ann
High School Math Teacher
Nauditt, Laurene Harrison
3rd Grade Teacher
Nees, Susan Coleen
Spanish Teacher
Nemri, Kamilia Sulieman
Mathematics Instructor
Osborne, Donelle Lynn
Spanish & English Teacher
Peterson, Terri Lee
Fifth Grade Teacher
Pfeifer, Sally Plummer
English Dept Chair & Teacher
Phillips, Janice J.
Fourth Grade Teacher
Posten, Sharron Bradley
9th Grade English Teacher
Procunier, Rosemary Horey
Kindergarten Tchr & Director
Ratliff, Garry Lee
Soc Studies & Geography Tchr

Ray, Jerry Dale
Administrator & Teacher
Rendon, Marie Egbert
Interpreter Trng Prgm Instr
Riggs, Patricia N.
5th & 6th Grade Teacher
Riggs, Susan G.
Third Grade Teacher
Roth, James Edward
College Instructor
Sanders, Marilyn Anderson
Sixth Grade Teacher
Schmerer, Dana Wayne
His & Physical Education Tchr
Schmitz, Carolyn
Art Teacher
Schroeder, Barbara Jean (Brooks)
1st Grade Teacher
Shawen, Robert Joe
Arts, Wood & Metal Teacher
Simmons, David Mabry
ESL Teacher
Skeman, Kathleen Ann
Spanish & Lang Arts Teacher
Skeman, Toni Rae (Destefano)
Third Grade Teacher
Smith, Tricia Hensel
English Teacher & Advisor
Snyder-Currier, Kathleen D.
Sixth Grade Teacher
Stohs, Phillip Wayne
Honors World History Teacher
Straub, Sharon Marie
Eng Dept Head & Focus Coord
Swisher, Clay B.
Eng Dept Head & Teacher
Taylor, Steven D.
Sixth Grade Teacher
Thomas, F. Conrad
Retired Teacher
Toppe, Georgia Tiffany
Humanities & English Teacher
VandeVeer, Philip Joel
Instr of Legal Resrch & Wrtng
Vianney, Marie
Teacher, Dean & Guid Counselor
West, Lynn Spellman
English & Humanities Professor
Wilson, Peggy Edwards
Dir of Bands & Music Dept Chm
SPRAGUE
Swanger, Lorrie Meserve
Eng, Ger, Speech & Jrnlsm Tchr
STANWOOD
Buse, Penny Hutchison
Seventh Grade Block Teacher
Estvold, Dan Lynn
Librarian & Principal Intern
Johnson, Paul Emanuel
Spanish Teacher
Love, Jack Douglas
Pacific NW & World His Tchr
Main, Darryl Kenneth
High School Agriculture Tchr
Schiessl, Fred
Physics & Physical Sci Teacher
Sedy, Duane J.
Sixth Grd Mathematics Teacher
Taylor, Brenda Donine
World History Teacher
STEILACOOM
Barnett, Molly M.V.
Director of Guidance & Cnslng
Palmanteer, La-Rae J.
Administrator & 5th Grade Tchr
Vann, Marvin Carl
Choir & Band Teacher
Wusterbarth, Gary
History Teacher
STEVENSON
Stump, Cindy Gae
Third Grade Teacher
SULTAN
Otteson, Shannon Kulle
Physical Education Teacher
Sifferman, Scott Thomas
Language Arts, US History Tchr
Woolley, William Kenneth, Jr.
Mathematics Teacher
SUMNER
Anderson, Stephen Gregory
Senior High School Art Tchr
Dean-Erlander, Todd
Math Teacher
Ellis, Michelle Renae
Physical Education & Math Tchr
Nybo, Nancy Kathleen
Lang Arts, Comms & Drama Tchr
Orcutt, Moe
Girls Varsity Soccer Coach
Percival, Dennis Lee
Academic Assistance Coord
Stockslager, Michael Scott
PE & Alternative Ed Teacher
Thompson, Scott Gerber
Drafting Teacher
Urling, Scott P.
Social Studies Teacher
Weberg, Kevin P.
Social Studies & English Tchr
SUNNYSIDE
Ahrenholz, Steven Jay
Math Teacher
De Groot, Tim
Sixth Grade Teacher
Glanzer, Tyrone Wayne
Social Studies Teacher
Gonzalez, Mary Alice
Second Grade Teacher

SUNNYSIDE (cont)
Hellner, Heidi Ann
English Teacher
Partch, Joanne Smalla
Music Teacher
Vermeer, Daniel Robert
History Teacher
SUQUAMISH
Bell, Mary C.
First Grade Teacher
TACOMA
Aboubakr, Karim Dessoukie
Algebra & Pre-Algebra Teacher
Algeo, J. Richard
Fifth Grade Teacher
Anderson, Brian T.
Retired Science & Math Teacher
Anderson, Dana DeWitt
Professor of Psychology
Anderson, Ruth Fulkerson
Language Arts & History Tchr
Baldassin, Michael Robert
Social Studies Teacher
Bannister, Ursula Regina
German Teacher
Bath-Balogh, Mary
Biological & Health Sci Instr
Beckwith, Ruth Lawrence-Berrey
Science Teacher
Benham, Steven R.
Professor of Geosciences
Boburka, Carl Michael
Eighth Grade Teacher
Bod, Ryliss Jeanna
Clothing Construction Instr
Bohna, Judith Meyer
8th Grade US History Teacher
Broeckel, June Sather
Kindergarten Teacher
Bronstad, Christopher H.
Science & Math Teacher
Brown, Cameron Clay
Computer Science Dept Chairman
Catalmich, James Mark
Teacher & Athletic Director
Cherbas, Chris Andrew
8th-9th Grd US History Teacher
Clark, Dexter Wayne
Math & English Teacher
Clark, Susan Patrick
English Teacher
Clayton, P. Marc
Teacher & Administrator
Close, Suzanne Marion
Substitute Teacher
Dale, Dennis John H.
Teacher
Demas, Mavourneen Fitzpatrick
English & US History Teacher
Densley, Kathleen Rose
HS English Tchr & Dept Chair
DiJoseph, Michael
Automotive Technology Tchr
Dykman, Bernie Jay
Art Teacher
Ellickson, Esther Miriam
Language Arts Chairperson
Erwin, Patrick Joseph
History Teacher
Federico, Domenick
6th Grade Teacher
Gamas, Richard Alfred
Bio, Astronomy & Geology Tchr
Gardner, Jeff E.
Social Studies & PE Teacher
Gormly, Brenda Ann (Rice)
Physical Education Teacher
Hanselman, Wendell Franklin
Asst Aerospace Science Instr
Harkness, John Robert
Naval Sci & JROTC Instructor
Harris, Todd S.
Science Department Head
Hatten, Jamie K.
6th Grd Core Teacher
Hayne, Malinda Morgan
Social Studies Teacher
Hicks, Heather Ann
Math, Bible & Drama Tchr
Jander, Mark
Physics Teacher
Johnson, Ardis Geyer
Retired Elementary Teacher
Johnson, Cynthia Christine Haslett
English Teacher
Judd, Kevin Douglas
Math Teacher
Kemp, Alan R.
Instr & Dir of Social Service
Kemp, Connie
Intermediate Multi-Age Teacher
Kennedy, Leanne Goss
Counselor
King, La Roy William
Theatre, Soc Stud & Rdng Tchr
Kirby, Ruth Allison
High School Math Teacher
Langford, Sonya M.
7th Grade Teacher
Lawler, Michael Joseph
English & Lang Arts Teacher
Leitzinger, John D.
Science Teacher
Lewis, Sandra Schlotzhauer
Coordinator Bio,Hlth Sci Dept
Lim, Brian S.
Mathematics Teacher
Loose, Deward Warren
History Teacher & Coach
Maloof, Vivian R.
Biology Teacher & Dept Chair
Markham, Marie C.
Counselor & Instructor
Mc Intosh, Robert Lester
Math & Cmptr Programming Tchr
Mc Neal, Evelyn Boyk
Supervisor
Merrill, Rebecca Cox
Language Arts Teacher
Mikels, Ruth Ann
Instructor of Biology
Miner, Kathleen (Rockway)
Math & Computer Teacher
Morrow, Kevin Christopher
9th Grade English Teacher
Mosupyoe, Boatamo Yvonne
Professor of Anthropology
Navarro, Mon-Nel Steven-Lastimosa
Computer Maintenance Instr
Neighbors, Patricia Rustwick
Math Teacher & Curr Writer
Neunherz, Richard E.
History & Ethnics Bayne Chair
Nino, Ronald Frank
Third Grade Teacher
Olson, Marty (Adams)
High School Art Teacher
Paillette, Beverly Irene
Math Teacher & Dept Chair
Pierson, James Allen
4th Grade Teacher
Rose, Donald S.
Band Director
Ross, Bryan Mitchell
Math, Eng & Journalism Tchr
Rupert, Barbara Smith
Spanish & Intl Bus Teacher
Sager, Robert J.
Professor & Chair of Earth Sci
Sarmiento, Pepita Porras
Spanish Teacher
Schimke, Dale Gordon
Counselor
Schlosser, Lynda Ann Spencer
Business Teacher
Schneider, Mila E.
Career Dev-Multicultural Tchr
Seistrup, Linda Purcell
Choir, Drama & English Tchr
Sepic, F. Thomas
Professor of Schl of Business
Shelton, John A.
Social Studies Teacher
Slater, Lonnie Wayne
AP US History Teacher
Stevens, Dawn L.
X-Ray Technologist & Instr
Throssell, William Thomas
Physical Education Teacher
Tongish, Mark Anthony
High School History Teacher
Tyson, Susan M.
Language Arts Teacher
Urschel, F. Mel
Human Anatomy, Physiology Prof
Van De Putte, Stacie Lee
HS Mathematics Teacher
Walker, Katherine Ann
Hnrs Lit Comp & Amer Lit Tchr
Wallis, Karen E.
Science Teacher
White, Rick Alan
Band Director
Whited, Diana Griffith
Horticulture & Science Teacher
Williams, Leslie J.
Chapter I Reading Teacher
Woodard, Mary Anne
3rd Grade Teacher
Wouters, Howard Lee
Mathematics Teacher
Zarling, Judy Sage
Teacher of Highly Capable
TENINO
Downey, Theresa Greiner
Math & Leadership Teacher
Johnson, Duane Lee
Woodshop & Drafting Teacher
Kitterman, Nancy Jean
6th Grade Teacher
Sisk, Oscar K.
Math & Science Methods Teacher
TOLEDO
Waag, William D.
7th & 8th Grd PE & Math Tchr
TONASKET
Babcock, Darrell DeWayne
Phys Ed & Behavior Mgr Tchr
Johnson, Jerry L.
English Teacher
Mitchell, David Arthur
Social Studies & English Tchr
Smith, Montie Matlick
English Teacher & Librarian
White, Harry D.
Science Instructor & Dept Head
TOPPENISH
Arango, Roger J.
Asst Prof of Pub Adminstration
Bonfield, Dale David
Athletic Dir & PE Tchr
Deters, Carol L. (Deraita)
Spanish & English Teacher
Dorr, Doris Fae (Fuller)
PE, Health & Ldrshp Teacher
Ellis-Lopez, Susan
Acting Chair
Keenan, Michel
Prof of Philosophy
Massey, Wm. Richard
Assoc Instr of Mntl Hlth Prof
TOUCHET
Gary, Marge Franjola
Math & Spanish Teacher
VANCOUVER
Abbott, Ramona Harby
First Grade Teacher
Baus, Philip B.
Instr of Diesel Technology
Brands, Bob James
Mathematics Teacher
Bruce, Randy J.
Biology Teacher
Cate, Randolph Armistead
8th Grade Language Arts Tchr
Clegg, David Harding
English Teacher
Daltoso, Mike Joseph
9th Grade Health Teacher
Dane, Joni
1st Grade Teacher
Davidson, Joy Bushnell
Language Arts Teacher
Dawson, Stephen R.
ASB Advisor & Leadership Tchr
Deckard, Lois A.
5th-6th Grade Excel Teacher
Delaney, William Alexander, Jr.
Art Teacher
Duncan, Frances Dring
Social Studies Teacher
Epton, Charles L.
Professor of Philosophy
Estrada, Kim
5th Grade Teacher
Fitzgerald, Jean Ketcham
Coordinator of Adult Basic Ed
Friehauf, Norman Ford
Math & Physics Teacher
Fryer, Rosemary
English Teacher & Dept Chair
Gaffrey, Frank Michael
Teacher & Coach
Gillingham, Janet A.
English Teacher
Hall, Betty Ann
Mathematics Teacher
Hegedus, Timothy James
US History Teacher
Hibbs, Heather Jeannine
Former Pub Speaking Instr
Hill, Karen Louise
PE Teacher
Hoffman, Mick A.
Social Studies & English Tchr
Jameson, Terrill Ann
Fourth Grade Teacher
Johnson, Kristen Eileen
8th-9th Grd Language Arts Tchr
Johnson, Robyn Louise
Science Teacher
Jones, Bob
Elementary Teacher
Jones, Kay
Mathematics Teacher
Lambert, David A.
Horticulture Teacher
Le Coq, Lindy Low
Counselor
Lehrman, Pamela Abo
Chemistry Teacher
Leonard, Betsy Stauffer
Former Language Arts Teacher
Lindeman, Carolynn Vassar
Physical Ed & Aerobics Teacher
Lueth, Carole S.
Multi-Age Teacher
Lynch, Joseph H.
Biotechnology Teacher
Maxwell, Edward Charles
Biology Teacher
Morrow, Gloria Chapman
7th Grade CORE Teacher
Mortek, Valerie Cave
Social Studies Teacher
Moyers, Anne A.
Fifth Grade Teacher
Muhich, Mary B.
US History Teacher
Neshyba, Mark
Band Director
Perry, Carolyn Jo
4th Grade Teacher
Rastovski, David Edward
Physical Education Teacher
Robson, Gilda Hutchinson
Soc Studies, Eng, Reading Tchr
Sanders, Michael William
9th Grade English & Drama Tchr
Smith, Janet Burr
Sales Representative
Spear, George G.
Language Arts Instructor
Stanek, Pamela Deane
Secondary Language Arts Tchr
Streur, Cindy K.
6th Grade Teacher
Sullivan, Kimberly Anne
Professor of English
Summers, Stan W.
Chemistry Teacher
Williams, Debby Totsy
Third Grade Teacher
Wright-Perez, Susan
Spanish Teacher
VASHON
Fuller, Deena Louise
Japanese & World History Tchr
VAUGHN
Donehower, Ernest John
Cultural Enrichment Specialist
VERADALE
Clowe, Theresa Hagerman
Health Educator
Cox, Charlie Louis
Science & Career Teacher
Hubble, Eunie Reynolds
2nd Grade Teacher
Kerns, Maxine Mordhorst
1st-2nd Grade Teacher
Stolp, Janelle Martin
Kindergarten Teacher
Sullivan, Thomas C.
English Teacher
Ulrich, Mary Lou Aebly
Second Grade Teacher
Zachrison, Lynda Fletcher
Fourth Grade Teacher
WALLA WALLA
Barber, Joel Arthur
Science Teacher
Burseth, Gwen Reoch
Former Teacher
Cox, Kim Thomas
Sci, PE & Traffic Safety Tchr
Geidl, Mary Jo
English Teacher & Dept Head
Kiefel, Michael Joseph
English, Speech & Jrnlsm Instr
Mc Corkle, William Harold
Biology Teacher
Parrish, Sue Lovezzola
Science Teacher
Phillips, Carmella Daniel
History Teacher
Poole, Richard Andrew
English Instructor
Ramsey, Marleen Berry
Psychology Instructor
Roberson, Lynn
Language Arts & Drama Teacher
Schulz, Eric
Mathematics Instructor
Schumacher, Robert K.
7th Grade Math & Science Tchr
Sutlick, Cheryl Ann (Fitch)
Middle & High School Teacher
Thorne, Linda Rose
US History & Amer Govt Tchr
Westergard, Sue Benzel
Learning Specialist
WAPATO
Beaudry, Larry William
Fifth Grade Teacher
Daniels, JoAnne Parker
Retired 3rd Grade Teacher
Dunston, Lowell Glenn
Principal
Eaton, Bob Lee
6th Grade Teacher
Grosso, Robert W.
High School Math Teacher
Parker, Lisa Schmuhl
Intermediate Music Teacher
Rigdon, Sue R.
Indian Education Counselor
Snell, Sean Joseph
Biology & Physical Ed Teacher
WARDEN
Brown, Michael L.
Social Science Instructor
Trammell, Hershel Robert
Physical Education Teacher
WASHOUGAL
Carver, Donna
Retired Third Grade Teacher
Ross, Scott Lee
High School Soc Stud Tchr
Washburn, Gordon Bennett
Instrumental Music Teacher
WATERVILLE
Hamon, Kay N.
Third Grade Teacher
Padden, Douglas D.
Jr High Science Teacher
WELLPINIT
Dennigan, Dennis
English Teacher
WENATCHEE
Baker, Maryjo
Language Arts Teacher
Block, Joyce Carol
Biological Science Teacher
Eagle, Bill David
Math Teacher
Evans, Donna June
Spanish Teacher
Fitch, Rob S.
Biology Instructor
Flannagan, Cynthia Denise
Spanish Teacher
Goveia, Mark Evan
Science Teacher
Hall-Thur, Celia
Prof of History & Pol Science
Johnson, Jack Alan
English Teacher
Logan, Richard Michael
Chemistry Instructor
Love, Lynn Jeglum
Music Teacher
Madis, Clinton F.
History Teacher
Stephens, Daniel Amos
Professor of Biology
Van Bronkhorst, Ted
Math Teacher
WEST LYNNWOOD
Forsberg, Nancy B.
Tchr of Deaf & Hard of Hearing
WESTPORT
King, Michael Joseph
Social Studies Teacher
Watkins, Donald Mark
Art Teacher
WHITE SWAN
DeVon, Don G.
High School Counselor
WILBUR
Sherwood, S. Joanne Largent
6th Grade Teacher
WILSON CREEK
Trepanier, Philip H.
Math, PE Teacher & Dept Chprsn
WINLOCK
Moses, C. David
Fourth Grade Teacher
WOODINVILLE
Clifton, Linda J.
English Teacher
Criscione, Kurt Samuel
Business Education Teacher
Goff-Kalinski, Patti
Sixth Grade Teacher
Gulberg, E. Lawrence
Chemistry Teacher
Hallenbeck, Jennifer
French & Spanish Teacher
WOODLAND
Cline, Paul Douglas
High School Music Instructor
YAKIMA
Adamson, Robert William
5th Grade Teacher
Altshuler, Bob A.
HS Industrial Arts Teacher
Anderson, Eric Andrew
Anthropology Instructor
Bernazzani, Renee
Business Teacher
Bischoff, Kenneth L.
History Teacher
Caldwell, Jeff M.
7th-9th Grd Math Teacher
Campbell, Mike
Instructor of English & Speech
Chama, Ricardo David
Spanish Instructor
Donaldson, Ronald Dale
Band Dir & Soc Stud Teacher
Duerre, Michael Sean
Social Studies & Spanish Tchr
Gregory, Carolyn McCallum
Math Dept Chair & Instructor
Grimshaw, Sue C.
High School Art Instructor
Groenic, Jerry Lorin
HS Var Bsktbl Coach
Gunvaldson, Jeffery Colin
Sixth Grade Teacher
Halfmoon, Thomas William
US His, Lang Arts & Geo Tchr
Harlan-Ivy, Marie Christine
Nursing Instructor
Heinemann, Wilton Walter
Animal Science Teacher
Lange, Karen Crosby
2nd Grade Teacher
Leadon, Betty
English Teacher
Leadon, Twila Dawn (Marsh)
English Teacher
Meshke, George Lewis
Drama Department Chairman
Mir, Qui-Chee Ayesha
Chemistry Teacher
Nehl, Robert Dean
Language Arts & Reading Tchr
Noll, Daniel R.
HS Chemistry Teacher
Repp, John Jay
Shop Teacher
Rice, Christine Marie
Instructor
Ringhouse, Ardelle Joan
Biology Teacher
Rogers, Paul W.
US History & Psychology Tchr
Shaw, Alice Mc Ilree
Coord & Intnl Students Program
Sorensen, Lance James
5th Grade Teacher
Steiner, Peter Dowd
Counselor
Stenehjem, Mildred Hegrenes
Retired Speech & Drama Teacher
Terk, I. Cecil
Accounting Instructor
YELM
Craig, Kristine Hemion
4th Grade Teacher
Henderson, Ann Michelle (Grant)
French & Spanish Teacher
Wheeler, Nancy Lee
Math Teacher & Dept Chairman
ZILLAH
Brant, Lynn K.
Eng, Drama & Yrbk Teacher
Gabriel, Kekoa Kelly
Social Studies Teacher

ST VIRGINIA

RSON
Richard Emil, Jr.
Grade Teacher
ORD
, Nancy L. Shamblin
Grade Teacher
ON
, Sharon Adkins
Grade Teacher
er, Abra Burris
sh Teacher
Danita Moats
l Studies Teacher
NS
ns, Linda C.
nct Music Professor
R
man, Arthur W.
th Grade Science Teacher
Elizabeth Moyer
sh Teacher
erman, Joyce Kisamore
& Home Economics Teacher
ER
r, Susan Sparks
selor
Linda Lou
her of Gifted Students
ell, Judy K.
Grade Teacher
, Teresa Ann (Bolton)
Grade General Science Tchr
ay, Angela Meadows
School Teacher
ond, Linda Cadle
Grade Educator
LEY
nder, Garnette Nowlin
& World History Teacher
r, Ernestyne Woods
& 6th Grade Math Teacher
in, Alice Callaway
Eng & Lang Arts Teacher
Leslie Eugene
ROTC Instructor
eal, Jewell Hartsog
Grade Teacher
hrey, Jimmy Edward
Grd Self-Contained Teacher
, Claudine Blavier
ch Teacher
ows, Barry Clifford
nce Teacher
ows, Patricia Emonds
Grade Teacher
in, Candace Henderson
d Director
on, Janet Kesler
lish Teacher
omb, Phyllis Lyall
ogy & Anatomy Teacher
las, Ronald Brent
sic Teacher
old, Richard Craig
lish & Health Teacher
Susan Torrico
keting Instructor
ett, Revonda Rene'
tal Assistant Instructor
art, Laura Rose Mills
dergarten Teacher
, Alexandria G.
gram Director & Professor
NGTON
Judith Bowles
sical Education Teacher
Anita Renee (Poling)
-8th Grd Health & PE Tchr
dfoot, Dana Evans
g Arts, Rdng & Jrnlsm Tchr
LE
ett, Susan Faye
th & Social Studies Teacher
comb, John E., Jr.
cial Studies Teacher
MONT
Dowell, David Samuel
ence Teacher
WOOD
ey, Robert H.
Teacher
KELEY SPRINGS
er, Angela M. (Ganoe)
sic Teacher
chart, Kathryn L.
Grade Collaborative Tchr
nd, Eleanor H.
g & Creative Writing Tchr
, Melanie Ann
ence Teacher
nan, Allan Eugene
th Grade Teacher
er, Louise Bushman
tired Kindergarten Teacher
er, Shirley Clark
xth Grade Language Arts Tchr
, Kathy Cain
mily & Consumer Science Tchr
THANY
am, Katherine Shelek
ssociate Prof of Sociology
on, Billie Jo (Hart)
urth Grade Teacher
man, Frank Harrison, Jr.
ligious Studies Tchr
nes, Larry Edward
nglish Professor

Hoff, Jeanne Brandt
Asst Professor of Accounting
Komorowski, Mary Ellen
Professor of Mathematics
Morgan, Kenneth Lee
Asst Professor of Fine Arts
BEVERLY
Stemple, Cynthia Walker
Title I Math Teacher
BIG SANDY
Lacy, Gwendolyn
Sixth Grade Teacher
BIRCH RIVER
Seabolt, Karen Bragg
Second Grade Teacher
BLACKSVILLE
Delaney, Deborah Ann
Third Grade Teacher
Elliott, Wilma C.
Sixth Grade Teacher
Layton, Andrea Lynn
English Language Arts Teacher
Mc Cabe, Twyla (Tennant)
Business Education Teacher
Wilson, Ryan Scott
Driver Education Instructor
BLUEFIELD
Addington, Duard G.
Math & Computer Ed Teacher
Bailey, James Thomas
Sixth Grade Science Teacher
Cromer, Frances Alba
Third Grade Teacher
Jessee, Robert G.
Soc Studies Teacher & Dept Chm
Kersey, Bobbi Hunter
Fourth & Fifth Grade Teacher
Long, Carolyn Wilson
Fifth Grd Self-Contained Tchr
Martin, Barbara Gillispie
Middle School Special Teacher
Morton, Blanche Cook
Mathematics Teacher & Team Ldr
Peacock, Virginia Addington
World History Teacher
Williams, Carolyn Cawthorne
Family & Consumer Science Tchr
BRADLEY
Chesley, Eddie Arnold
Librn & General Studies Prof
BRADSHAW
Shelton, Janet F.
Second Grade Teacher
Wimmer, Doris L.
Science & Health Teacher
BRANCHLAND
Davidson, Colleen (Colby)
Sixth Grade Teacher
Davis, Richard Scott
Health & Kinesiology Teacher
Forth, Deborah Stewart
Fourth Grade Teacher
Mabe, Judith Damron
9th Grade English Teacher
Mc Comas, Mark Anthony
WV His & American Civics Tchr
Porter, Karen Lucas
Fifth Grade Teacher
Prichard, Myrtle Mae
Retired Teacher
BRENTON
Boggs, Kelly
Computer Lab Teacher
Hall, Deborah Morgan
Library & Media Specialist
BRIDGEPORT
Booth, Kay Baker
AP & Honors English Teacher
Brown, Josette Madia
First Grade Teacher
Brown, Shirley Urtso
6th Grade Math & Reading Tchr
Byrd, Anita Broslawsky
Human Anatomy & Bio Tchr
Cathell, Charlotte H.
Algebra II & Cmptr Sci Teacher
Griffith, Jonathan Alan
Chemistry Teacher & Coach
Haught, Ceferina Maditz
First Grade Teacher
Kinard, Carole Wright
Fourth Grade Teacher
Lutz, Sandra Garrett
Life Management Teacher
Marshall, David Alan
9th-12th Grd Math Teacher
Pfunder, Eniko Thoma
French & Spanish Teacher
Ramsburg, Patricia Jay
Library Media Specialist
Rexroad, Jackie Lee
Second Grade Teacher
Wunderlich, Carl Michael
Fifth Grade Teacher
BRUCETON MILLS
Rice, Patricia Ann
Language Arts Teacher
BUCKHANNON
Bulka, E. Jeanie
At-Risk Intervention Specialst
Cupp, Melissa Jo
English Teacher
Green, Daniel R.
Fourth Grade Teacher
Hasbrouck, Thomas Wayne
Elem Physical Education Tchr
Hite, Linda Hidalgo
Spanish Teacher
Hurst, Hallie S. Davidson
6th Grade English Teacher

Lemley, Michael Lee
Science Teacher
Mc Vaney, Barbara Louise
7th Grade Teacher
Michel, Donna Gail Plymale
High School English Teacher
Newman, Fred D.
Science Teacher
Oldaker, Lois L.
HS English Teacher
Post, Bethany Cupp
Reading Teacher
Raffety, Cynthia Kirby
Math Teacher
Ralston, Carole Burkhead
Voc Home Economics Teacher
Sharpolisky, James Michael
AP English Instructor
BUNKER HILL
Ash, Karen J.
Science Teacher
Cline, Judith Lintz
7th-8th Grade Math Teacher
Fine, Marianne Schick
English & PE Teacher
Guesford, Linda Frances
Math Tchr & Dept Chprsn
Pettersen, Eileen King
Unified Arts Teacher
Shore, Daniel Barton
Social Studies Teacher
Webster, Jeneane Sagle
9th-12th Grade Math Teacher
CABIN CREEK
Wilson, George William
Fifth Grade Teacher
CAMERON
Bayza, Samuel Paul
Sixth Grade Teacher
Hartley, Bradford W.
Biology Teacher
Perkins, Marilyn Kay
Fourth Grade Teacher
Turk, Doris Locke
Librarian & Yearbook Advisor
Weaver, Shawn Wright
Chemistry & Physics Teacher
CAPON SPRINGS
Metz, Cheryl L.
Supervisor
CEDAR GROVE
Mc Cune, Rose M.
English & Drama Teacher
Myers, Mary Lou Maloney
Jr High Social Studies Teacher
Price, Phyllis Jean
Fourth Grade Teacher
Tackett, Sallie Pat (Belcher)
Math, Physical Ed & Hlth Tchr
CEREDO
Brewster, Linda Hatten
First Grade Teacher
CHAPMANVILLE
Bell, Cynthia Anne
Business Teacher
Chambers, Patricia Gail
English & Lang Arts Teacher
Christian, Linda Browning
American History Teacher
Elkins, Karan Hall
First Grade Teacher
Hager, Johnny F.
Coordinated Science Teacher
Mc Cann, Donald R.
Math & College Prep Teacher
Triplett, Joseph Patton
Math & Science Teacher
CHARLES TOWN
Richmond, Laura Vance
Library Media Specialist
Sherman, Gail Barr
Instructional Specialist
CHARLESTON
Asay, Charles Edgar
Sr Counselor
Beckett, Joseph Alan
Sports Medicine Dept Chair
Bookhout, Thomas Nathan
Director of Choral Activities
Bowen, Amanda Sheets
Sixth Grade Teacher
Bowles, Sandra Sulsberger
Division of Hlth & Sci Dean
Casey, Florence Walker
1st Grade Teacher
Clem, Phillip Dee
Assistant Professor of Biology
Cox, Lisa Dawn
Fifth Level Teacher
DeMark, Tony Samuel
Safety Ed, Hlth & PE Teacher
Estes, Deborah Reeves
Mathematics Teacher
Ferrell, Terry Wayne
Mathematics Teacher
Fisher, Glenda Jean
Dir of Clinical Education
Frostick, Robert M.
Junior High Science Teacher
Harris, Celestial H.
Third Grade Teacher
Harrison, Susan J.
Vocational Home Economics Tchr
Hess, Blaine C.
Director of Bands
Howard, Elizabeth Souleyret
History & Geography Dept Head
Jacobs, Kathleen M.
11th Grade English Teacher

Jones, Nanetta
7th Grd Mathematics Teacher
Kerner, Paula
Social Studies Teacher
Loper, Joy Mc Cutcheon
Former Math Teacher
Matheny, Sharon Martin
English Teacher
Meadors, Merewyn Davis
Assoc Professor of Biology
Perry, Catherine Greenwald
Elementary School Counselor
Persily, Cynthia Armstrong
Nursing Professor
Peters, Carma J.
8th Grade Social Studies Tchr
Phelps, Constance Humphrey
Science Teacher
Ritenour, Diana Simmons
Special Education Teacher
Rogers, Pamela Dulin
English Teacher
Shaver, Donna J.
Business Education Teacher
Teufel, Judith Ann, SSJ
Principal
Woo, Lisa J.
Civics Teacher
Young, Carolyn S.
Voc Family & Consumer Sci Tchr
CHARMCO
Boone, Daniel O.
High School English Teacher
Mc Clung, Martha Elizabeth
HS Business & Cmptr Sci Tchr
Mc Million, Harold Wayne
Fr Instr & Frgn Lang Dept Head
CHESTER
Casini, Louis A.
Director of Instrumental Music
Di Biase, Warren James
Former AP Chem II Tchr
Horstemeyer, Ruth A.
Math Teacher
La Neve, Edward Bernard
Science Teacher
Popovich, Donna Kaye
Math & Algebra Teacher
CLARKSBURG
Alvaro, Rebecca Wick
Seventh Grade Science Teacher
Coffman, Katereni Canfield
Fifth Grade Teacher
Davis, Karen Kelley
Business Education Teacher
Douglas, Sandra Auvil
Teacher
House, Roger A.
Electronics Technology Teacher
Koreski, Jennifer Hood
4th Grade Teacher
Lachapelle, James F.
Social Studies Teacher
Ritter, Larry P.
PE & Hlth Tchr & Asst Coach
Stanley, Karen Andersen
French Teacher
Staton, Paige Browne
Guidance Counselor
Todd, Michele P.
Secondary Teacher
Tonkery, Nancy Karen
English & Language Arts Tchr
Westfall, Joyce T.
Anatomy & Biology Teacher
Wilt, Pamela L.
Business Education Teacher
CLAY
Kleman, Frank William, Jr.
World History Teacher
Meyer, Karen Drewery
Librarian
Woods, David Lee
8th Grd His & Civics Teacher
CLENDENIN
Harper, Edward
Science Teacher
Kee, Bettie Ann
3rd Grade Teacher
Loyd, Karen Saundra
History & Civics Teacher
Mc Clung, Christopher Woodrow
French Teacher
COAL CITY
Adkins, Marcella A. Cullop
11th Grade English Teacher
COMFORT
King, Kirk Lewis
K-6th Grade Music Teacher
Weikle, Eddie
Physical Education Teacher
Williams, Betty Ann (Stine)
Spelling & Reading Teacher
Williams, Vonna Lee
First Grade Teacher
CRAB ORCHARD
Lee, Alma Rema (Meadows)
Fifth Grade Teacher
CRAIGSVILLE
Hamrick, Jerry Allen, Jr.
Forest Technology Instructor
CROSS LANES
Hardin, Judith Lanham
English Teacher
Keefer, Brett Vernon
History Teacher
Ray, Thomas Boyd
Mathematics Teacher

CRUM
McCoy, Shirley Ratliff
Second Grade Teacher
DAILEY
Plauger, Patricia (Hayes)
Third Grade Teacher
DANVILLE
Davis, Sue Ann
Teacher
Startzel, David Grant
Elementary Teacher
DAVISVILLE
Wells, Robert Mark
5th Grade Teacher
DELBARTON
Chafin, James L.
PE & Health Teacher
Picklesimer, Stephen Paul
Chemistry & Physics Teacher
Picklesimer, Victoria White
English & Journalism Teacher
Preston, Vonda Mae (Messer)
Family & Consumer Science Tchr
DIAMOND
White, Anna Denise
6th Grade Teacher
DIANA
Glendenning, Donald Ray, Jr.
First Grade Teacher
Gregory, Trisha Lynn (McCourt)
Seventh Grade Teacher
DUNLOW
Varney, Julian
5th Grade Teacher
EAST BANK
Cavendish, Brenda Harrick
Counselor
Hamilton, Deborah Sue
Ninth Grade Science Teacher
Milam, Mark E.
Social Studies Teacher
ELEANOR
Erwin, Michael A.
Science Teacher
ELIZABETH
Calebaugh, Michael Paul
WV History & Amer Govt Tchr
Lipps, Deloris J.
Mathematics Dept Chair & Tchr
Lydon, Patricia Walcutt
Social Studies Teacher
Morgan, David B.
7th-8th Grade Science Teacher
Pierotti, David Lee
Fifth Grade Teacher
Prince, Beverly S.
Family & Consumer Sci Teacher
ELK GARDEN
Long, Polly Bean
Guidance Counselor
ELKINS
Beckwith, Robert Nicholas
Biology,Botany & Zoology Tchr
Brewster, Marty
Eng & Creative Writing Tchr
Casey, Richard L.
Driver Education Teacher
Channell, Timothy Lee
Band Director
Goddin, Margaret Purdum
Eng Prof & Non-Trad Prgms Dir
Hall, Karen Doll
Kindergarten Teacher
Hott, Gregory W.
Biology Teacher
Jones, Ann Rainey
Music Teacher
Lewis-Lambert, Nancy L.
Mathematics Teacher
Long, Helen Sala
Fifth Grade Teacher
Metheny, Martha Ratliff
Spanish Teacher
Mullennex, Victoria Thompson
Assoc Prof Dept of Bus Admin
Payne, Gloria Marquette
Prof of Bus & Dept Chair
Seibert, Machelle Moore
First Grade Teacher
Super, Deborah Harvey
English Teacher & Yearbook Adv
Wells, Gregory Scott
Coordinator William James Ctr
ELKVIEW
Bender, Glenadine Carolyn
Bible Teacher
Hooper, Susan Hoskinson
Itinerant Teacher of Gifted
Morris, Edwina Susan
English Teacher
Sampson, Betty Copenhaver
Third Grade Teacher
ELLENBORO
Andrews, Katrina M.
Eighth Grade Science Teacher
Goff, Roberta D.
English Teacher
Jameson, Sheryll Nichols
English Department Chair
Kaufman, Steven Neal
Mathematics Teacher
Newland, Cynthia Ann
7th Grade Literature Teacher
FAIRDALE
Archie, Wilda Mae Bowyer
4th Grade Teacher
Campbell, Meliessa Rae
Fourth Grade Teacher

FAIRMONT
Beafore, Jennifer Little
French Teacher
Bombardiere, Dennis J.
Social Studies Teacher
Bonasso, John Gerard
Former Inter-Disciplinary Tchr
Brake, Mary Frances Piscitelli
Second Grade Teacher
Brookover, Paulette Tennant
Social Studies Teacher
Feltz, Sally Conaway
AP Preparation English Tchr
Hando, Anne Mercer
6th Grade Math Teacher
Hendershot, Carrie Ann (Caloccia)
Vocal Music Teacher
Hinton, Gregory Tyrone
Assoc Prof of Bus & Econ
Huber, Linda Lee
Math Teacher
Jett, Edie Roberts
Former Mrktg Teacher
Johnson, Deborah O'Dell
5th Grade Teacher
Jones, Janet Darlene
Marketing Ed Teacher
Kirby, Joan Layman
Fourth Grade Teacher
Koski, Ramona Jean
Second Grade Teacher
Martin, Leah Kramer
Physical Education Teacher
Morgan, Anne Blair
Ret Asst Prof of Eng & Span
Munza, Diana Johnson
Mathematics Teacher
Nuzum, JoAnn Shultz
English Teacher
Oliverio, Madeline Rose
Business Education Teacher
Peduto, Donna Hoylman
4th Grade Teacher
Petonick, Lewis Andrew
World History Teacher
Richardson, Carolyn Daniel
Family & Consumer Science Tchr
Sandor, Stephen J., Jr.
Social Studies Teacher
Stevens, Donald Eugene, Jr.
Art Teacher
Stutler, Lesa Wilson
English Teacher & Jrnlsm Adv
Vincent, Patricia Ann
7th-8th Grd Lang Arts Teacher
Weikle, Mary Foltz
Health & Physical Ed Teacher
Williams, Janice
Dir of Academic Advising Ctr
Wood, Nancy Walsh
Mathematics Teacher
Zasloff, Etta Orr
Elementary School Counselor
Zinn, Carol Foltz
Kindergarten Teacher
FARMINGTON
Dean, Rhonda Sturm
Journalism Teacher
Gaines, Joy Renee
English Teacher
Harrison, Gloria Solomon
Secondary Science Teacher
Haugh, James Kevin
Music Tchr & Fine Arts Chair
Ilich, Rose Matthews
English Teacher
Mullenax, Mary Anne (Estel)
Scndry English & French Tchr
Niezgoda, Sally Earp
Mathematics Teacher
Rosenberger, Linda Lee (Tichenor)
7th-12th Grd Math Teacher
Sapp, G. H. Budd
Secondary Teacher
Stewart, Carol Ann
Mathematics Teacher
Watson, Larry Walter
Agricultural Education Teacher
Watson, Virginia Elaine
Social Studies Teacher
White, Carol J.
English Teacher
FAYETTEVILLE
Dotterweich, Ann S.
Eng Tchr & Stu Cncl Adv
Hall, Beverly Lynn
Family & Consumer Sci Teacher
FOLLANSBEE
Anderson, Sandra L.
Language Arts Teacher
Ankrum, Erin Colleen
7th-8th Grade Math Teacher
Cross, Diana Altschuler
Kindergarten Teacher
Wells, JoAnn Dalesio
5th Grade Teacher
FORT GAY
Hambrick, Eric Wayne
Band Director
Thompson, Charles Leonard
Science Dept Chair & Teacher
Thompson, Susan Bissett
English & Honors Lit Teacher
FRANKFORD
McClintic, Jerry Moore
Sixth Grade Teacher
Tuckwiller, Terry Kirby
Elem Physical Education Tchr

FRANKLIN
Godfrey, Patrick Brian
English Teacher
Harper, Donna Simmons
French, Spanish & English Tchr
Hedrick, Lowell Wayne
Mathematics Teacher
Mitchell, Elizabeth Bennett
Second Grade Teacher
Ruddle, Carolyn Catherine
Retired Kindergarten Teacher
Wagner, Donald Joseph
Science Teacher
Warner, Galen Carl
Soc Studies & Amer His Tchr
GALLIPOLIS FERRY
Wilson, Ann Casey
Fifth Grade Teacher
GAULEY BRIDGE
Fish, Louis F.
Social Studies, Hlth & PE Tchr
GHENT
Foster, Debra Yvonne
Second Grade Teacher
GILBERT
Bobbera, Robert Louis
Art Teacher & Dept Chairman
Cline, Pamela Grimmett
First Grade Teacher
Mollette, Arnold B.
Social Studies Teacher
Rutledge, Sherry Lynn (Webb)
Former Fourth Grade Teacher
Ward, Paul D.
Hist, Ec & Geography Professor
GLEN DALE
Baumgardner, Margaret Ernst
Counselor
Eaton, Toni Magnone
Spanish Teacher
Gardill, Linda Truban
English Teacher
Ramser, Carol Lou
Business Teacher
Rider, Gary L.
Social Studies Teacher
Voice, Jane Mc Ninch
Social Studies Teacher
Wheeler, John William
Mathematics Teacher
GLEN DANIEL
Deck, Anita Sue
Chemistry & Physics Teacher
Ritchhart, Jean Ann
Health & Physical Ed Teacher
GLEN JEAN
Kemper, Elizabeth Kinder
Early Childhood Education Tchr
GLEN ROGERS
Clay, Donald Wayne
Sixth Grade Teacher
GLENVILLE
Collins, Janice Anne
French Teacher
Fitzwater, Frances P.
Family Education Teacher
Morris, Jennifer Linn (Yoke)
Business Teacher
Wolfe, John G.
US History & Government Tchr
Woofter, Betty Langford
Retired Business Teacher
GRAFTON
Ludwick, Nancy Ann
5th Grade Teacher
Tennant, Stephan Todd
Agriculture Teacher
Work, Nancy Nagle
Math & Social Studies Teacher
GRANTSVILLE
Allen, Roger Dee
Junior High Science Teacher
Edwards, Michael Dain
Spanish Teacher
Morgan, Jim
6th & 7th Grade Math Teacher
Underwood, Donald Leon
History Teacher
GRIFFITHSVILLE
Neal, Connie Runyan
Business Education Teacher
Patton, Mary Ann
Mathematics Teacher
Smith, Sherry Lynn
Kindergarten Teacher
Thomas, Paula Hensley
Mathematics Teacher
HACKER VALLEY
Chipps, Jacqueline Joyce (Gum)
First & Second Grade Teacher
HAMBLETON
Hebb, Cathy Markham
7th & 8th Grd Math Tchr
Knotts, Jeannie Godby
Adult Basic Education Teacher
Poling, Eileen Gray
Teacher of Gifted & Talented
Tacy, Glenn G.
Reading & Physical Ed Teacher
Turner, Timothy Argil
Business Education Teacher
HAMLIN
Cook, Kimberly Chapman
Band Director
Holley, Haskell Harold
Sixth Grade Teacher
Nelson, Paula Lynn Midkiff
Language Arts Teacher
Ross, Jennifer Childers
First Grade Teacher

Salmons, Victoria Ann
Business Teacher
HANOVER
Maynard, Teresa Blankenship
First Grade Teacher
HARMAN
Mullenix, Shelby J.
Business & English Teacher
HARPERS FERRY
Chicchirichi, J. Todd
7th Grade Science Teacher
Wood, Jennifer Audia
Family & Consumer Science Tchr
HARTS
Blair, Myra Ann Browning
Kindergarten Teacher
Fitzgibbon, Sue A. Davis
First Grade Teacher
HEDGESVILLE
Gatrell, Kathleen Gnagey
Consumer & Homemaking Teacher
Graves, Laurie Calder
6th-8th Grade Enrichment Tchr
Mc Donald, Lowell Eugene
Mathematics Teacher
Morgan, Kathy Elaine
Business Education Teacher
Pingley, Mary Jo Vollmer
7th Grade Reading Teacher
Stuckey, Scot Richard
Educator
Thomas, Cindy Funkhouser
Math Department Chair
Truax, Robin
Health Teacher
HINTON
Allen, Michael Dennis
Health Teacher & Trainer
Brown, Sarah Coleman
Principal
Mick, Patricia Lee (Delp)
Math & French Teacher
HUNTINGTON
Adkins, Roger L.
Professor of Economics
Anderson, Lorraine Pearson
Dir of Undergraduate Studies
Badenhausen, Richard J.
Assistant Professor of English
Bailey, Karen Tipton
Nursing Professor
Barenklau, Keith Edward
Prof & Dir of Safety Tech Pgm
Beckett, Melanie Ague
Counselor
Berry, Karen Meves
HS Spanish Teacher
Blatt, Nancy Taylor
1st Grade Teacher
Cartmill, Joan Wooddell
French Teacher
Chaffin, Gerri Young
Lang Arts Teacher
Chapman, Debbie Ann
Family & Consumer Science Tchr
Grizzell, Ruby Clark
Retired First Grade Teacher
Hinchman, Pleasant Reedy
Psychology & Education Prof
Hogsett, Robert Alexander
English Teacher
Kelley, Ruth Ellen
5th Grade Teacher
Kim, Chong W.
Prof of Management & Marketing
Lang, Nancy
Assistant Professor of English
Leslie, Mary Lee
4th Grade Teacher
Levine, Loretta Perry
High School Science Teacher
Lewis, Joyce Gail
Spanish Teacher
Mackey, Leona Holley
Fine Arts Chairperson & Tchr
Mallory, David S.
Assoc Prof of Biological Sci
Martin, Paul Alan
English Department Chairman
Martin, R. Daniel
Asst Prof, Ath Trng & Prgm Dir
McDonie, Norma Jarrell
Language Arts Teacher
Moore, Samuel R.
Science & Language Arts Tchr
Morabito-Karle, Toni J.
Assistant Professor
Oyster, Larry Allan
Physics Teacher
Petteys, M. Leslie
Associate Professor of Music
Popp, Susan Ray
Librarian & Social Stud Tchr
Redd, William L.
Assoc Prof of Legal Assisting
Reese, Clara Cook
Business Education Professor
Stone, Vicky Marie
6th Grade Language Arts Tchr
Sullivan, Susan Winner
Asst Prof of Comm Disorders
Tomlinson, Mildred Godschalk
His Tchr & Hum Dept Chairman
Wiebe, Becca Rohrer
English Teacher
Wnuk, Erick Dale
Science Teacher
HURRICANE
Caldwell, Stephen Allen
Technology Education Teacher

Chaney, Robin White
Social Studies Teacher
Durham, Paula Beverage
Fourth Grade Teacher
Goode, Louise Crum
Mathematics Teacher
Hage, Lillian Carole Trent
Principal & Head Teacher
Hall, Helen Hayes
Lang Arts Teacher
Harless, Dovetta Lovejoy
Fifth Grade Teacher
Hofheinz, Karl Christoph
Biology, Chemistry & Math Tchr
Jividen, Jennie L.
Math & Pre Algebra Teacher
Jones, Lucy Voorhees
First Grade Teacher
Lewis, Sue Ellen
Spanish Teacher
Mc Gucken, Brent Phillip
5th Grade Teacher
O'Neal, Judith E.
Seventh Grade Science Teacher
IAEGER
Barker, Vivian Mullins
Special Needs Educator
Bright, Eeinor Turner
Physical Education Teacher
Gibson, Maude Frances
Business Teacher
Mays, Darnell Peters
7th & 8th Grade Teacher
Perdieu, Mattie Deloris
Fifth Grade Teacher
Perdue, Karen June
Language Arts Teacher
Valko, Kenneth Joseph
Art & Language Arts Teacher
INSTITUTE
Ovrebo, Reidun
Asst Prof in Art & Dept Chrmn
Whittington, Donna Elkins
Sign Language Instructor
INWOOD
Shetler, Darl Norman
Second Grade Teacher
Williams, Nelda Grubb
Former Teacher
JUMPING BRANCH
Cox, Mary Lou
Third Grade Teacher
JUNIOR
Bennett, Bonnie Elaine
Fourth Grade Teacher
KENOVA
Blevins, Ronald Dale
High School Math Teacher
Davis, Karen Gayle
Science Teacher
Gray, Judy Scott
Fifth Grade Teacher
Hale, Betty Eder
Library Media Specialist
Hay, Linda Massie
6th Grade Geography Teacher
Howerton, Cheryl Alley
Art Teacher & Fine Arts Chrmn
Veazey, Judith Ann
4th Grade Teacher
Wilburn, Susan Christine
Bio, Anatomy & Physiology Tchr
Wood, Scott R.
Band Director
KEYSER
Dawson, Daniel O.
Physical Education & Hlth Tchr
Phillips, Margaret Gibson
English & Social Studies Tchr
Robertson, Mary Lou
Lang Arts & Soc Stud Teacher
KIMBALL
Bales, Theresa Battlo
Third Grade Teacher
KINGWOOD
Barlow, William James
Advanced Life Science Teacher
Clark, Shirley Jean
School Counselor
John, John Stephen
Mathematics Teacher
Locey Bagby, Janice Marceline
Teacher of Gifted & Spanish
Zigray, Debra Renee
Fourth Grade Teacher
LASHMEET
Arrington, Madge M.
First Grade Teacher
LENORE
Atkins, Robert Basil
Social Studies Teacher
Parsley, Jacqueline Curry
Jr HS Math, Bios & Chem Tchr
LEWISBURG
Diem, Debra Rickman
Second Grade Teacher
Mc Clung, Karen Lee C.
First Grade Teacher
Midkiff, Patricia Rudd
Consumer & Family Ed Teacher
Trout, Katherine Smith
Health Occupations Instructor
Walker, Angela Greer
Computer & Business Teacher
Whitt, Dalen B.
Business Teacher
LINDSIDE
Coburn, Barbara Ann (Mooney)
Science Teacher

Lovett, Kristi Jo
Music Director
LOGAN
Adams, Brenda White
Language Arts Teacher
Adkins, Elise Fleshman
7th Grade Science Teacher
Akers, Denise Rebecca
4th Grade Teacher
Baisden, Laura Tracy
Language Arts Teacher
Cunningham, Timothy James
SLD MI Teacher
Gleason, Lynn Clegg
Fifth Grade Teacher
Jones, Susan
7th-9th Grade English Teacher
Qualls, Bernease Frances
Art Teacher
Vance, Barbara Browning
Business Teacher
Zeto, Phillip E.
Algebra & Math Teacher
LOST CREEK
Benincosa, Janet Hill
English Teacher
Carter, John Daniel
Middle School Teacher
Kinard, Byron N.
Eighth Grd Soc Studies Teacher
Moore, James Allen
Counselor
Morris, Rebecca Law
Mathematics Teacher
Santilli, Jenny Lou
7th-12th Grade Spanish Teacher
LUMBERPORT
Moore, Linda Medearis
Eighth Grd Rdng & Science Tchr
Murphy, Michael Lee
5th Grade Teacher
Nuzum, Kevin Grant
Substitute Teacher
Toth, Jennifer Lynn
6th Grade Classroom Teacher
MADISON
Passero, Rita Lynn
Business & Computer Teacher
MALLORY
Hoosier, Bettena Lynn
Third Grade Teacher
MAN
Arms, Harvey Donald
Chemistry Teacher
Ball, Rebecca Starcher
Eng, Lang Arts & Speech Tchr
Mendez, John Mark
Director of Bands
Saunders, Brenda Rhea (Lester)
Math Teacher
Wright, Barbara Cline
9th Grade Business Teacher
MANNINGTON
Hartzell, Patricia Anne
Math Teacher
Kiger, Denise Wetzel
Second Grade Teacher
Robinson, Stanley Aaron
Science Teacher
Wiley, Paula Denise
School Media Specialist
MARLINTON
Larson, Karen Underwood
Former Primary Teacher
MARMET
Vaughn, Michael Gale
Title I Math Teacher
MARTINSBURG
Boys, Vernon Malcom
8th Grade Science Teacher
Clark, Rosa Tross
Social Studies Teacher
Edwards, A. Thomas
Middle School Principal
Hamrick, Andrew J.
Soc Stud, Yrbk & Algebra Tchr
Hayes, Carol Beard
Secondary English Instructor
Hicks, Dale C.
Honors English Instructor
Keller, James Gilbert
Technology Education Teacher
Kleiss, Adair Pierce
Title I Remedial Reading Tchr
Knipe, Sonia Anne
First Grade Teacher
Lee, Robert Elwood
Soc Stud Tchr & Guidance Cnslr
Lynch, John Paul, Sr.
Band Director
Miller, Wanda Smith
Science Teacher
Myers, James Howell
Social Studies Teacher
Palmer, Sue Ann
6th & 7th Grade Math Teacher
Robinson, David Curtis
Science Teacher
Stickles, Donna Lee
Eighth Grade Mathematics Tchr
Yost, Donna Stouffer
Fifth Grade Teacher
MASON
Gerlach, Debra Rae
4th-6th Grd Reading Teacher
Hall, Sharon Ervin
Mathematics Teacher
Hendricks, Crystal Carhart
Music & Choral Teacher

N (cont)
, Homer Keith
ıess Education Teacher
ıNTOWN
r, George Bradley
, Choir, Music & Comp Tchr
ıEURY
ıon, Bettye Elnora
ɛng & Soc Stud Teacher
ıVILLE
ıld, Barbara Ours
ergarten Teacher
ıECHEN
ch, Daniel Thomas
ıematics & Science Teacher
ıOW BRIDGE
Patterson, Theresa J.
ı Teacher
intic, Larry Castle
ınce & PE Teacher
ıs, John L.
ınced Biology & Chem Tchr
Z
, Jo Ellen Stewart
Grade Teacher
ıIFF
ı, Deborah Howard
ıd Grade Teacher
ıck, Lydia Mendez
Grade Teacher
. CREEK
ght, Michael W.
ness Education Teacher
, Judith Diane
ıish Teacher
ıan, Vickie B.
Contained 5th Grade Tchr
, Lynn Westbrooke Simcoe
h Dept Chairperson & Tchr
ıON
ore, Peggy Miller
ı Grade Teacher
ıRAL WELLS
ıood, Grace Blaschke
mentary Music Specialist
well, Martha Hickman
rth Grade Teacher
ıer, William N.
rth Grade Teacher
entz, Peggie Anderson
ond Grade Teacher
ıTCALM
r, Karen Moretto
iness Education Teacher
, Jesse J.
ptr Applications & Math Tchr
Debra A.
ence Teacher
ns, Cindy Ann
rning Disabilities Teacher
, Betty Martin
h School English Teacher
ington, Robin Janine
ıthematics Teacher
ıTGOMERY
ınon, Donald G.
fessor of Chemistry
ın, Betty Jo (Huffman)
ial Studies Teacher
ıick, Michael Vincent
soc Prof of Chemical Engrng
ıOREFIELD
y, Terry P.
ence Teacher
er, Roy Phillip
ricultural Education Teacher
ıRGANTOWN
rman, Kelley Lee
glish Teacher
ıtt, Diane Rowe
st Grade Teacher
a, Larry E.
soc Prof Mechanical Engrng
ıero, Ever J.
gineering Professor
, Priscilla Jane
ı Grade Teacher
ınett, Arlene Carolus
oir & Orchestra Director
y, Daniel, III
cial Studies Teacher
ı, Barbara Jeanne
athematics Teacher
sky, John M.
ssistant Band Director
ıner, Randall W.
sst Prof of Exercise Physlgy
k, Richard K.
ınd Director
age, Carolyn Espel
ıglish Teacher
esebrough, Peter
ience Teacher
lins, William E.
ofessor of Biology
ıway, Kathryn Ann
hemistry Teacher
glish, Lisa Carol
h Grade Teacher
er, Martin Vincent
ıysics Professor
dwin, Kimberly Phares
ıfth Grade Teacher
ıy, Donald D.
ssociate Professor
esko, Lisa Ann
hysical Education Instructor
mmersmith, Jean Leary
ocial Studies Teacher

Hill, Joyce Antolini
First Grade Teacher
Hoover, Wilma Albright
English Teacher
Irwin, Gertraud Ulrich
German & English Teacher
Johnson, Kelly Geddis
PE, Athletic Director & Coach
Klemick, Margaret Jane (Hall)
Physical Education Teacher
Logar, Dianne Beaty
7th Grade English Teacher
Martin, Christine M.
Asst Prof of Journalism
Mc Intire, Mary Alice
Third Grade Teacher
Netro, Carolyn A. Zackery
Social Studies Teacher
Pugh, Carolyn J.
Library Media Specialist
Rangarajan, Thiruvengada
Professor of Chemistry
Rosenbluth, Gwen S.
English Teacher
Rosenecker, Margaret Blattler
Sixth Grade Teacher
Rotter, Carl A.
Professor of Physics
Ryan, Patrick L.
History Teacher
Savage, Carletta Harvey
Science & Soc Stud Teacher
Sherwood, Lauralee
Physiology Professor
Sprowls, George
Doctoral Candidate
Stilwell, Angelique Diane
Math Teacher & Dept Chm
Sturm, Margaret Jessie
English Teacher
Tewksbury, Stuart Keene
Prof of Elect & Cmptr Engr
Vaglienti, Cynthia Vaugn Hollandsworth
Math & Computer Sci Teacher
Wallman, John Paul
Language Arts & Computer Tchr
Watt, Maureen T.
Sixth Grade Teacher
West, Deborah Liberatore
Special Education Teacher
MOUNDSVILLE
Latacz, Rosanna Materkoski
1st Grade Teacher
Parshall, Harry Edward
Band Director
ZeLinski, Rose M. (Jancura)
Music & Chorus Teacher
Zervos, Theodore Pete
5th Grade Teacher
MOUNT GAY
Blankenship, Paul R.
Instructor
Godby, Jennifer (Enyart)
English Instructor
Hanichen, W. Jeffrey
Asst Prof of Soc Sci Div
MOUNT HOPE
Ferri, Debra Ann
5th Grade Teacher
Kidd, Charles L.
English Teacher
McLain, Fred James, Jr.
Social Studies Teacher
Powell, Louise Ambler
Teacher
Scott, Kathleen Leonard
Science & Math Spec Ed Teacher
Stover, Lacy Byron
Special Education Teacher
Warden, Cecilia Harless
Mathematics Teacher
Wilson, Paul Edward
Mathematics & Science Teacher
MOUNT STORM
Duling, Judith Dawn
Kindergarten Teacher
Gardner, Daniel Bryon
School Counselor
MULLENS
Carr, Alice Houck
Retired First Grade Teacher
Chapman, Judith Bane
Special Education Teacher
McKinney, Tammy Canterbury
Language Arts Teacher
Mills, Benny Ray
English & Drama Teacher
NAOMA
Daniel, Ann Tabor
Third Grade Teacher
Daniel, Linda Martin
Counselor
Dickens, Eva Stewart
Social Studies Teacher
Graham, Thomas Scott
Band & Music Teacher
Lane, Richard William
Business Education Teacher
NAUGATUCK
Johnson, Sarah Jones
Mathematics Teacher
NELLIS
Kinder, Lois Wade
Retired Second Grade Teacher
NEW CREEK
Biggs, Joy Wilson
Third Grade Teacher
NEW CUMBERLAND
Ballato, Stephanie J. (Kondik)
Learning Disabilities Teacher

Block, Bonnie
Health & Advanced PE Teacher
Bohach, Donna Lowery
Social Studies Teacher
Churella, Debby Zima
Math & French Teacher
Mastromichalis, Harriet Stakias
Honors English Tchr
Mergen, Charlotte
Spanish Teacher
Smusz, Michelle M.
French Teacher
Tokash, Inda Carr
English Teacher
Vukas, Rebecca Sue
English Teacher
Williams, Paula Lee (Rice)
Math Teacher
NEWELL
Shaffer, Judymae Manypenny
3rd Grade Teacher
NITRO
Brown, Barbara Kennedy
Spanish Teacher
Leighton, Marian Elaine Gamble
Vocal Music Teacher
Martin, Constance Melodie (Cooper)
Algebra & Pre-Calculus Tchr
Smith, Dianne Patricia
Advanced Eng & US His Tchr
Stewart, Brenda Jean
English, Speech & Writing Tchr
Wilkes, Richard Edwin
Math, Computer Science Teacher
Williams, Tom
Assistant Principal
NORMANTOWN
Hill, Jo Ann Marks Sprouse
Kindergarten Teacher
NORTH MARTINSVILLE
Croasmun, Brian James
Literature Teacher
Duckworth, Stephen Neal
7th-8th Grade Art Teacher
Keough, Deborah Ann
3rd Grade Teacher
Kimble, James David
Technology Education Teacher
King, Nancy Ingram
Language Arts Teacher
Mallett, Sally Frieden
Bus Ed & Gen Sci Teacher
Rogalski, Stephen E.
Fourth Grade Teacher
Strippel, Ralph Kelder
Integrated Science Teacher
Swords, Gregory Lee
Mathematics Teacher
NORTH MATEWAN
Epling, Linda Justice
Principal & Teacher
NORTHFORK
Wurtzler, Charlene Kish
Title I Reading Teacher
OAK HILL
Beck, Sally (Landfear)
English Teacher
Brown, Connie Mc Phail
Business Education Teacher
Humphries, Rebecca Gwinn
Kindergarten Teacher
McCoy, Ray Timothy
Band Director
Pannell, Carrie G.
6th Grade Language Arts Tchr
Stiltner, Marsha Diaz
Mathematics Teacher
Sullivan, Carol Castle
Business Education Teacher
Vargo, G. Scott, Jr.
Bio, Anatomy & Physiology Tchr
Webb, Janie Hudnall
French & Spanish Teacher
OCEANA
Brown, Linda Lou (Lusk)
Health & Math Teacher
Clay, Victoria Knight
Business Teacher & Counselor
Cook, Kathy Browning
20th Century Psychology Tchr
Cook, Lillian Aker
High School Mathematics Tchr
Cozort, James J.
Science Teacher
Crouse, Camellia Miller
Biology & Anatomy Teacher
Francis, Leoda Testerman
Vocational Home Economics Tchr
Halsey, Betty Ritchie
French & Spanish Teacher
Hopkins, James Edward
Driver Education & Health Tchr
Tilley, Lucinda Jane Bryant
Mathematics Teacher
OMAR
Holcombe, Beverly Gail
Third Grade Teacher
Rice, Ane Hurley
Elementary Teacher
ONA
Beckelhimer, Steve
Science Department Chairman
Chandler, Diane Desaix
English Teacher
Clay, Sharon Gothard
Fourth Grade Teacher
Culp, Carolyn Kubilis
Biology Teacher
Harkless, Thomas Edwin
Choral Music Teacher

Irwin, Carolyn Sue
English Teacher
May, Susan Morris
English Teacher
Smalley, Rhonda Smith
Band Director
Spencer, Joyce Cazad
English Teacher
Stevenson, Brenda Gale
World History & Psych Tchr
Sutphin, Barbara Ann
First Grade Teacher
PANTHER
Hatfield, Sandra Jo
Sixth Grade Teacher
PARKERSBURG
Acree, Wilma Stanley
English & Computer Lit Tchr
Aebi, Charles J.
Professor of Bible
Apgar, John William
American His & Geography Tchr
Bargeloh, C. Wesley
Chemistry Professor
Bargeloh, Emily Ruth
Fifth Grade Teacher
Barritt, Daniel H.
Math Teacher
Beals, Gordon Richard
Prof of Biology & Chemistry
Bennett, Leslie
English Teacher
Boothby, Richard Scott
Assistant Professor of Music
Bowen, Bill D.
Liberal Arts Professor
Braden, Pamela A.
Professor of Business & Mgmt
Brannon, Patricia King
1st Grade Teacher
Brannon, Randall Lanier
Instrumental Music Teacher
Bryant, Edith Kiser
Former Director of Education
Burch, Linda Carder
Fourth Grade Teacher
Butterfield, David Eugene
Social Studies Teacher & Coach
Campbell, J. Kevin
Eng, Drama & Oral Comm Teacher
Combs, Charles R.
Naval Science Teacher
Cunningham, Jody Bucher
Biology & Earth Science Tchr
Delli-Gatti, Maria Anne
Tchr of Behavioral Disorder
Edwards, Hayward Allan
Professor of Mathematics
Garrett, Beth Snider
Health Teacher
Gaston, Patricia Sullivan
Associate Professor of English
Gilbert, Kenneth G.
Art Dept Chairperson
Haden, Vicki Crites
Sixth Grade Teacher
Hall, Leilani Rae
Composition Lecturer
Houck, Coraletta Marie
Third Grade Teacher
Hupp, Sue Ellen
AP Calculus Teacher
Isenhart, G. Anne
Commnctn, Drama & Eng Tchr
Isenhart, Thomas K.
Speech, Debate & English Tchr
Jackson, Paul Edward
Driver Education Teacher
James, Daniel Douglas
US & World History Teacher
Kalt, Patricia Clara
Second Grade Teacher
Keaton, Larry E.
Professor of Education
Kelley, Cynthia S.
Asst Professor of Education
Lamb, George Jared
Professor of History
Langkamer, Judith Meek
Kindergarten Teacher
Law, Teresa Alderson
French Teacher
Lawson, James Gregory
Instructor of Comm Studies
Lowenstein, Henry
Chm & Assoc Professor of Bus
Lowers, Kathy L.
Third Grade Teacher
Mc Cloy, Robert John
Business Law & Finance Prof
Mc Clung, M. Denise Yearego
Social Services Coord & Instr
Mc Clung, Phil O.
Assoc Prof of Psychology
Mc Cullough, Barbara J.
Classroom Educator
McCune, Carolyn Cowger
Journalism & English Teacher
Mercer, Michelle Danielson
Third Grade Teacher
Morgan, Mary-Louise Harrison
Tchr of Gifted Ed & Journalism
Munchmeyer, Judy Plymale
French & Commnctn Skills Tchr
Niday, Sharon Neely
Resource & Journalism Teacher
Norsworthy, Larry A.
Psychologist & Program Chair
Powers, Pamela Elisabeth
Choral Director

Reeves, Pamela Sue
Physical Education Teacher
Robinson, Robert Joseph
Art Teacher
Sayre, Patty Florence
English Teacher
Shull, Allison James
Integrated Science Teacher
Steinbeck, Sue
Math Department Chairperson
Stout, Glenda Dennison
Fifth Grade Teacher
Sunderman, Patsy Ann
Developmental Skills Teacher
Thomas, Carol C.
Assoc Prof of Bus, Ec Division
Thomas, Daniel B.
7th & 8th Grade Math Teacher
Thorp, Carol Lyn Hostettler
Music & PE Teacher
Thorpe, Rebecca Jean
Fifth Grade Teacher
Weese, Blair Junior
Modular Technology Teacher
Wells, Gordon Lee
Associate Professor
Whitehair, Cathy Louise
Jr High Science & Health Tchr
Williams, Frederick Allen
6th Grade Teacher
Yoak, Robert Scott
8th-9th Grade English Teacher
Young, Harmon Griffith, III
Professor of Music
Young, Richard L.
Welding Instructor
Zicherman, Frances S.
2nd Grade Teacher
PAW PAW
Arwood, Nicole N.
Home Economics Teacher
Palmer, Robert Jeffrey
Special Education Teacher
PETERSBURG
Glover, Rosanne Harper
Mathematics & Music Teacher
Propst, Angela Sue
Jr HS Language Arts Teacher
Sherman, John Wayne
Masonary Instructor
Shuman, Carolyn Hudkins
Library, Rdng & Resource Coord
Sites, Brenda Boor
Biology Teacher
PETERSTOWN
Thomas, Connie Sue (Hazelwood)
5th Grade Teacher
PHILIPPI
Barkley, Barbara Martin
Social Studies Teacher
Davis, LaDonna Burner
6th-8th Grd Language Arts Tchr
Dodd, Kay Hill
English Teacher
Irvine, Jean Ellen
English Teacher
Jones, Bill D.
Social Studies Teacher
Maruca, Patricia Cox
Math Teacher
Poling, Mary Daugherty
Mathematics Department Chair
Schonk, Barbara Simonson
Mathematics Teacher
Scott, Julie Ann
Senior English Teacher
Short, Shelley Jones
Reading Specialist
Taylor, Retta Brown
Business & Amer His Teacher
Waid, Patricia A. Bailey
Hlth Occup & Sci Tech Tchr
PINE GROVE
Finck, Paula R.
High School Art Teacher
Snodgrass, Thomas Lee
Biology & Science Teacher
PINEVILLE
Bolt, Kathleen Grove
First Grade Teacher
Daniels, Thomas H.
Mathematics Teacher
Davidson, Richard Troy
10th-12th Grd Biology Teacher
Fleenor, Barbara (Elkins)
Elementary Education Teacher
Graham, Yolanda Lea
Kindergarten Teacher
Phillips, Linda Goode
Elementary Counselor
Redd, Michael Lee
Asst Professor of Business
Shumate, Terry Garland
Biology, Science & Math Tchr
Smith, Dina Mitros
Educational Outreach Counselor
Woolsey, Carolyn Lee (McKnight)
Science & Physical Ed Teacher
POCA
Carper, Julie Johns
Band Director
Houston, Craig Alan
Mathematics Teacher
Marshall, Brenda Carol
Elementary Physical Ed Teacher
Pasons, Barbara Fugate
Librarian
Smith, Rebecca L.
Business Teacher

POCA (cont)
Sova, Diana Layne
Kindergarten Teacher
Thomas, Janet S.
5th Grade Teacher
POINT PLEASANT
Gills, M. Jo
Special Education Teacher
Handley, Richard Lee
Fifth & Sixth Grade Teacher
Legg, Georgia Lee (Meadows)
Fourth Grade Teacher
Manuel, Joan E.
Reading & Art Teacher
Preece, Elaine J.
Home Economics Teacher
Stewart, Gerald Leroy
Music Coord & Band Director
Williamson, Judy Greenlee
Librarian & Teacher
Young, William Albert
7th Grade Eng & Sci Teacher
PRATT
Hamilton, Karen Shumate
6th Grade Teacher
Miller, Margaret Dickinson
5th-6th Grade Science Teacher
PRICHARD
Collinsworth, Karen P. Fisher
5th Grade Teacher
PRINCETON
Ball, William Walter
Science Teacher
Barber, Sandra Epling
Social Studies Teacher
Basham, William Ray
Sixth Grade Teacher
Belcher, Mitzi Turner
Health Assistant Instructor
Benson, Max Eugene
Business & Bible Teacher
Blevins, Lynette Ann
Fifth Grade Teacher
Bragg, Deborah Jo
Music Teacher
Brown, Tammy Munsey
Science Teacher
Burger, Madeline Ardelia
Second Grade Teacher
Craig, David Eugene
Computer Science Teacher
Farley, Rhonda Harper
Assistant Administrator
Farley, Teresa Vaught
Multi Subject Teacher
Farmer, Mary Jane Shumaker
Sixth Grade Teacher
Fleming, Judith Lynne
Science Teacher
Fry, Debora Bailes
Band Director
Harshbarger, William Samuel
Social Studies Teacher
Hawks, Kathy June
Fifth Grade Teacher
Hopkins, Mary Louise
Math Dept Chair & Teacher
Isom, Diana Lynn (Sparks)
Substitute Teacher
Lockhart, Doris Matherly
Mathematics Tchr & Dept Chair
Lovern, Rita Harvey
First Grade Teacher
Lowry, Suzanne Murphy
Choral Music Teacher
Meadows, Deborah Oxley
7th & 9th Grd Soc Stud Teacher
Millner, Celia Brown
Social Studies Teacher
Pentasuglia, Rebecca Raney
Kindergarten Teacher
Smith, Kathleen L.
Math Dept Chairperson & Tchr
Smith, Rodney Clay
Mathematics Teacher
Stanley, Candy Spangler
10th & 12th Grd English Tchr
White, Helen Camberos
Spanish & English Teacher
PROSPERITY
Coley, Mary Sue (McKinney)
Kindergarten Teacher
Dillon, Cynthia Anne
Middle School Science Teacher
Harding, Roger Lee
Secondary Math Teacher
Parks, Sandra Sue
HS Science & Spanish Teacher
Shaffer, Kathleen Louise
Second Grade & Lead Teacher
RAINELLE
Surbaugh, Barbara Barker
Fifth & Sixth Grade Teacher
Yearego, James Keith
Bible Teacher
RANGER
Smith, Sally A.
Kindergarten Teacher
RANSON
Broadley, Nancy Gail
Third Grade Teacher
RAVENSWOOD
Anderson, Patricia Wolfe
Art Teacher
Burdette, Keith Robert
Agricultural Education Teacher
Corder, Sue Ann
Second Grade Teacher
Currey, Donna Lynn Brown
5th Grade Teacher
Harvey, Patricia Merrill
Fourth Grade Teacher
Kelly, Kemp Joseph
Tchr of Specific Lrng Dsblty
King, Michael Arthur
Seventh Grade Science Teacher
McAtee, Forest M., II
Music Teacher & Asst Band Dir
Miller, Audrey Jovone
Computer Education Teacher
Perrine, Vida Ann Moskala
Gifted & Spec Ed Teacher
Rector, Tim E.
Mathematics Department Chprsn
Smith, Donald Ray
History Teacher
Wiseman, Judy K.
Reading & Language Arts Tchr
READER
Edwards, Nancy K.
Second Grade Teacher
Lancaster, Margaret Holman
4th Grade Teacher
RICHWOOD
Domas, Ann
Social Studies Teacher
RIDGELEY
Barger, John R.
Physical Ed & Health Teacher
Bradshaw, Karol Jean
Family & Consumer Science Tchr
Brown, David James
Math Tchr & Cross Cntry Coach
Carder, Linda (Bosley)
English & Theater Teacher
Nelson, Rita M.
English Teacher
Ritchie, John Isaac, Jr.
Agri Science Teacher
RIPLEY
Bourgeois, David Lee
Agricultural Science Teacher
Cunningham, Carol Casdorph
Seventh Grade English Teacher
Gump, Teresa Mae
Physical Education Teacher
Gunther, Sandra Kay
English Teacher
Harris, Cheryl Sue Gibson
Fifth Grade Teacher
Heckert, Barbara Lynn
Biology Teacher
Hutchison, Harold Rex
Math Teacher
Jordan, Karen Lee
Second Grade Teacher
Lamb, Emily J.
Professor of English
LeMaster, Gregory Wayne
Special Services Teacher
Looney, Dianne Board
Social Studies Teacher
Lyons, Phyllis Lasko
Second Grade Teacher
Parsons, Cheryl Lynn
Fourth Grade Teacher
Parsons, David Bruce
Teacher of Mentally Impaired
Ray, Alice Sue
Biology Teacher
Shamble, David Michael
Mathematics Teacher
Swisher, Raymond E.
Driver Education Teacher
Westfall, Richard Clair
7th Grade Geography Teacher
ROANOKE
Gregory, Nettie Robinson
Fourth Grade Teacher
ROCK
Brown, Cheri Lynn (Hodges)
Mathematics Teacher
Jones, Elizabeth Shrader
Fifth Grade Teacher
ROMNEY
Bender, Gladys Swisher
English Teacher
Broderick, Margaret M.
English Teacher
Milleson, Vickie Jo (Ansel)
Sixth Grade Teacher
Prado, Donna (Puffinburger)
Mathematics Instructor
Wells, Wendy Lou
Mathematics Teacher
RONCEVERTE
Mullens, Randy Keith
English Teacher
Porterfield, Sheryl Lynn
Mathematics Teacher
Voss, Thomas R.
Science Teacher & Dept Head
RUPERT
Gilkeson, Russell Owen
Physical Education Teacher
McClanahan, Audrey Karen
Sixth Grade Teacher
SAINT ALBANS
Bibbee, Lora Withrow
6th Grade Teacher
Bryan-Casdorph, Rebecca Jane
Early Childhood Teacher
Byers, Edithe Rosebourgh
English Teacher
Carey, Malva Joan
Business Education Teacher
Clark, Michael Vernon
Art Teacher
Davis, Linda L.
Math Teacher
Day, Susan Noyes
English Teacher
Dillon, Jane Turley
Civics & World History Teacher
Estep, Anne Elizabeth
3rd Grade Teacher
Hunt, Judy Ellen
Business Education Teacher
Lockhart, Fonda Drennen
English & Music Teacher
Miller, John H., Jr.
Biology & Anatomy Teacher
Taylor, Linda D.
Second Grade Teacher
Taylor, Lois Cavendish
First Grade Teacher
Thompson, Lola Jean (Haddix)
Fourth Grade Teacher
Wade, Carla Danks
5th Grade Teacher
SAINT MARYS
Butcher, Larry E.
Biology Teacher & Coach
Deem, Steven Clair
Mathematics Instructor
Porfeli, Pamela Sharps
Health Svcs & Nursing Instr
SALEM
Aleseyed, Mostafa Seyed
Asst Professor of Economics
Cammarata, Kirk Vincent
Assistant Professor
England, Wayne Harvey
VP of Acad Affairs & Provost
Feight, Karen Warner
Fifth Grade Teacher
Franklin, Patricia Romine
First Grade Teacher
Hensel, Robin Ann (Morgan)
Associate Professor of Math
Hilton, Susan J.
English & Physical Ed Teacher
Tanno, Dai
Japanese Studies Dept Chprsn
Trent, Ruth Nicholson (Cox)
Retired Second Grade Teacher
Warner, Samuel Worth
Associate Prof of Mgmt Stud
SCOTT DEPOT
Bolds, Victoria Breach-Amaro
Spanish & Business Teacher
Ellis, LouAnn Harris
Math Teacher
Etris, Tony W.
Principal, Drama & Art Teacher
Frazier, Cynthia Ray
2nd Grade Classroom Teacher
SETH
Bracken, Diana Annett
English & Math Teacher
SHADY SPRING
Emery, Karen S.
Biology Teacher
Kittle, Nancy Scott
6th Grade English Teacher
Rhudy, Vaughn Gibson
Hnrs English & Journalism Tchr
Wills, David A.
Speech Teacher
SHENANDOAH JUNCTION
Barr, R. Keegan
Counselor
Demchik, Virginia Carol Felosa
Chem Tchr & Dept Head
Rose, Arlene O.
Social Studies Teacher
Thomas, Deborah Nichols
Social Studies Teacher
SHEPHERDSTOWN
Bruner, Rick Ernest
Associate Professor of Art
Ralston, James L.
English Lecturer
Staubs, Cynthia Ellen
Language Arts Teacher
Wilmer, Pamela Link
Family & Consumer Science Tchr
SHINNSTON
Brisbin, Sharon Davidson
History Teacher
Harki, Deborah Garcia
Spanish Teacher
Hutson, Dennis Lee
Health & Physical Ed Tchr
Moore, Mary Beth Blosser
Mathematics Teacher
Watson, Bill Eugene
History Teacher
SHOCK
Minney, Ora Stump
Retired Third Grade Teacher
SISSONVILLE
Ward, Linda Kaye
Music Teacher
SISTERSVILLE
Griffith, Joseph E.
Biology Teacher
Hagerty, Gary R.
20th Century Amer His Tchr
Hooley, Linda Teasley
Business Teacher
Langer, David Paul
Science Teacher
Morgan, Betty Jo
Business Education Teacher
Negie, Clara Robinson
Vocal Music Instructor
Richie, Larry Lee
Social Studies Teacher
Williams, Kelly Prettyman
Teacher of Gifted
SMITHERS
Brannon, Patsy Rhodes
Chemistry & Algebra I Teacher
Floyd, Joyce Anne Russell
Fourth Grade Teacher
Martin, Charlotte Ann
Social Studies Teacher
Meadows, Judith Ann (Arthur)
Mathematics Teacher
SMITHVILLE
Williams, Kathy Drain
4th Grade Teacher
SPANISHBURG
McMullin, Sheila Daniel
Social Studies Teacher
SPENCER
Board, Roberta Kay Bush
Teacher & Attendance Director
Cummings, Paul Lakin
Agriculture Sci & Mchncs Tchr
Falls, Rita Buchanan
Health Teacher
Greenleaf, Judy Meads
Kindergarten Teacher
Hardman, Susan Goodwin
English Teacher
Kerzak, Charles Daniel
Band Director
Williams, Carol Kunz
Third Grade Teacher
STOLLINGS
Pack, Helen Powell
5th Grade Teacher
SUMMERSVILLE
Berry, Philip Henry
Art Teacher
Casto, Alva Garland, Jr.
HS Mathematics Teacher
Drennen, Debbie Lynn Mathews
Physical Education Teacher
Drennen, Rosemary Kincaid
Psychology & US His Teacher
Eder, Lisa Christine
Sci, Anatomy & Physiology Tchr
Kerns, Laura Ames
Ninth Grade Science Teacher
Knight, Terry Russell
English Teacher
Lawrence, Carl Jackson
English Teacher
Martin, Robin Dalton
World & WV History Tchr
Mowrey-Smith, Romilda
Health Education Teacher
Nutter, Mary Shelton
Social Studies Teacher
Phillips, Dabney Isaac
Tchr & Admin of Parent Center
Roberts, Fred Andrew, Jr.
Chemistry & Physics Teacher
Thomas, Dana E.
Teacher of the Gifted
Thomas, Lenora Kaye (Butcher)
Language & Math Teacher
Vest, Charles Dean
Science, Soc Stud & Hlth Tchr
Wynne, Dawn Hanson
Mathematics Teacher
SUTTON
Beane, Sterling Price
Driver's Education Teacher
Bright, Lois Christine
Family & Consumer Svcs Tchr
Carr, Edward Ted R.
Math Teacher
Drake, Denver E.
Fifth Grade Teacher
Gibson, Brenda Snyder
English & Journalism Teacher
Simmons, Beth
Language Arts Teacher
Sprouse, Cynthia Jordan
Sixth Grade Teacher
Taylor, Martha Brown
Substitute Teacher
TALCOTT
Perkins, Regina Ramsey
5th Grade Teacher
TERRA ALTA
Wotring, Thomas C.
Math & Science Teacher
THOMAS
Morris, Lynn Napolillo
Kindergarten & First Grd Tchr
Rapp, Daryla Parsons
Fourth Grade Teacher
TUNNELTON
Wolfe, Sherley Pierce
Mathematics Teacher
UPPERGLADE
Dinda, Lottie S.
Health Occupations Instructor
Gamble, Jane T. Howard
Family & Consumer Sci Tchr
Moore, Elizabeth Kay
Science Teacher
VALLEY FORK
Minger, Toni Lee
Second Grade Teacher
VAN
Atha, Pamela Ray
4th Grade Teacher
Ballard, Aleta Holstein
Teacher
VERDUNVILLE
Long, Dixie Vance
3rd Grade Teacher
Marino, William P.
Title I Math Teacher
VIENNA
Ott, Shirley Nicholas
Retired English Teacher
WALTON
Moore, Nancy Oblak
Sixth Grade Teacher
WAR
Boyd, Joseph Lee
Art Teacher
Cline, Kenneth Ray
Chemistry & Science Teacher
Courts, Leroy McGlothin
Music Specialist
Mullins, Charlotte Elizabeth
Biology Teacher
Robbins, Millie
LD & MI Teacher
Wilson, Rebecca G.
Business Education Teacher
WAYNE
Chambers, Kathleen Perry
Literature & Lang Arts Teacher
Mills, Anita Troxell
4th Grade Teacher
Warren, Rebecca Wright
Language Arts Teacher
WEBSTER SPRINGS
Brown, Susan Camp
7th-8th Grade Lang Arts Tchr
Mc Coy, Delmas Boyd
Physical Education Teacher
Stewart, Marjorie (Skidmore)
Junior High Language Arts Tchr
WEIRTON
Adam, Cathleen Andrea
Math Teacher
Annerton, Patty Atchley
Math Teacher
Bailey, Dee
Art & Photography Teacher
Burns, Thomas Michael
Beginning Algebra Instructor
Davis, Marguerite Wyatt
Staff Development Coordinator
DeCaria, Frank L.
Psych & Sociology Instructor
James, Mary Lou LaMantia
Sophomore English Teacher
Karpyk, Pete
Chemistry Teacher
Kuhn, Karen Harbert
Classroom Teacher
LaPrete, Donna Surgenor
Principal
McUmar, S. Dwight
English Teacher
Rohal, Pete Robert
Science Teacher & Dept Chm
Romitti, Linda Drizmala
First Grade Teacher
Roth, Dennis Richard
Asst Professor of Business
Rusinovich, Joanne Brancazio
Fourth Grade Teacher
Seifert, Raymond George
Choral, Instrumental Music Dir
Teaff, Carol A.
Professor of English & Speech
Zarnoch, Charles Paul
Eighth Grade Science Teacher
WELCH
Bales, Coney Valentino
Hlth & Physical Education Tchr
Bishop, Lori Molin
English & Journalism Teacher
Bushnell, Deborah Dillard
English, Speech & Drama Tchr
Cure, Maria Colombo
First Grade Teacher
Evans, Edward Edmond
Science Teacher
Halsey, Herbie Haden
Teacher of Mentally Impaired
Hicks, Wayne Edward
World History Teacher
Long, Forrest W.
Band Director
Morrison, Sabrina Leath
9th-12th Grd Bus Ed Teacher
Overbey, Stephen Allen
Substitute Teacher
Redmond, Deborah Stanley
Kindergarten Teacher
Snyder, Russell Lee
History, Govt & Hum Teacher
Tuell, Robert A.
Fourth Grade Teacher
WELLSBURG
Ashworth, Ede Jane
Latin Teacher
Churchman, Carol
Fifth Grade Teacher
Ferguson, Franklin Allen
Chemistry & Science Tchr
Higgins, Diane W.
Classroom Teacher
Kirtley, Barry L.
Electrical Technology Teacher
Rafa, Michael Joseph
Bio & Coordinated Sci Tchr
Ray, Jean Ann (VanLehn)
Business Teacher
Shaffer, Carolyn H.
English Teacher
Waters, Sandra Carol
English Teacher

HAMLIN
s, Debra
ergarten Teacher
LIBERTY
, Jean Stephan
c Prof of Gen Bus & Mrktg
vich, Jennifer Diane
lemic Lab Instructing Asst
Robert Frank
ciate Prof of Mathematics
d, Virginia Ellen
essor of English
llough, John Phillip
, School of Bus Admin
nley, Linda Okey
essor of English
, Jennings Douglas
c Prof of Cmptr Info
, Marian Veronica (Gramba)
c Professor of Accouting
s, Keith Ryder
Coach & Defensive Coord
son, Elizabeth A.
r & Assoc Prof Dept Mngt
r, Roger George, Jr.
ciate Professor of Biology
y, Judith D'Amico
ciate Professor of Ed
as, David Joseph
ciate Professor of English
mson, Gray
of Communication & Eng
MILFORD
Deborah Moran
Grade Teacher
Eileen Patricia
Grade Teacher
Joseph Paul
d Grade Teacher
n, Pauline Mc Quain
red Teacher
TON
son, Jean Scott
& Creative Writing Teacher
Jim
puter Teacher
g, Martha Mae
arian
, Mary Spaniol
her of the Gifted
es, Charles Edward
lish & Journalism Teacher
Barbara
guage Arts Teacher
ntaine, Brigitte Yvonne
ch & Phys Ed Teacher
, John Mark, Jr.
School Chemistry Teacher
n, Barbara Kay
Grade Teacher
ott, SSJ, Eileen Marie
cipal
RTON
l, Rose Marie
f Contained Tchr
ELING
nwall, Kathryn DeBlasis
t Vocal & Band Director
nowski, Crystal Meyer
nish Teacher
le, Tammie D.
glish Teacher
y, Sarah R.
Studies Tchr & Dept Chprsn
er, Wilma Bungard
ence Teacher
n, JoAnn Graf
emistry Teacher
aker, William Lloyd
shman Civilizations I Tchr
pbell, Clyde Del
ired Coll Pres & Chem Prof
alos, Peter
ence Teacher & Ath Trainer
Ray
th Grade Teacher
g, Terry Ann
fessor of English
ner, Ildiko Kovacs
-8th Grade Science Teacher
egan, Anne
glish Tchr & Dept Chair
er, Robert Richmond
pt of English Chairman
ling, Joyce Annette Lancaster
urth Grade Teacher
rett, Leslie Ann (Filben)
rector of Choral Activities
son, Mary Bennis
hr of the Visually Impaired
ver, Linda Whitehead
dj Fac Mem & Stores Foreman
b, Richard Joseph
ience Teacher & Dept Chair
rington, Kathy L.
sst Professor of Psychology
gan, Thomas M.
ysical Education Teacher
eman, Robert William
ssoc Professor of English
off, Sara Stephens Hupp
str of Psych & Child Dev
zdos, Susan Molnar
athematics Teacher
es, Dorothy S.
of of Lbrl Arts & Psych Tchr
es, Patricia Gregory
etired Associate Professor
edras, Carrie B.
P Calculus Teacher

Mc Nabb, Judith Clark
First Grade Teacher
Miller, Kimberly (Santoro)
Second Grade Teacher
Nichelson, Mary Carolyn
History Teacher & MS Coord
Nocida, Jaunita McKinney
Mathematics Teacher
Obermann, Carol L.
Mathematics Teacher
Richardson, Dan Lynn
5th Grade Teacher
Stokes, Charleen Gail
Asst Professor of Business
Stupak, Brenda Watson
Fourth Grade Teacher
Toland, Debra Yzenski
Eng Dept Chprsn & Ger Instr
Trosch, Kathleen Bronson
Learning Disabilities Teacher
Trytko, Barbara Jean
Teacher of Gifted Education
VanLynn, Jessie Myers
Teacher of Gifted
Wilhelm, Carole Thalman
Third Grade Teacher
Woodruff, Carolissa Wylie
First Grade Teacher
WHITMAN
Kulchuk, Robin Lynn (Roberts)
Second Grade Teacher
WILLIAMSON
Moore, Karen Ann
History & Government Teacher
Phillips, Ann Victoria
Chemistry Professor
Stallard, Mae O'Bryan
Eighth Grd Social Studies Tchr
WILLIAMSTOWN
Goldsworthy, Cynthia A.
English Department Chair
Lathey, Ronald L.
Mathematics Teacher
Lucas, Sue
Health Education Teacher
Williams, Wende Parker
English Teacher
WINFIELD
Bond, Angela Eggleston
Third Grade Teacher
Cope, Barbara Pauley
1st Grade Teacher
Oxley, Clifford Wayne
Sixth Grade Math Teacher
Peck, Karen Straley
Social Studies Teacher
Smith, David L.
Biology Teacher
Summerfield, Jean Thomas
First Grade Teacher
Trador, Neuasa Oney
Business Education Teacher
Woodard, Scott E.
Band Director

WISCONSIN

ABBOTSFORD
Braun, Connie Swender
Business Education Dept Chair
Harrison, LaVerne Claire
Science & Math Teacher
Welsh, Reed L.
PE & History Teacher
ALBANY
Krueger, Nancy Ann
Fifth Grade Teacher
Latimer, William Edward, Jr.
English & Spanish Teacher
Mc Intyre, Pamela Trawick
Third Grade Teacher
ALGOMA
Mayheu, Mary L'Empereur
Principal
Nickel, Robert H.
Business Education Teacher
Rocque, Judy Mae (Dier)
Secondary Social Science Tchr
ALMA
Duvall, Shaun Judge
Spanish Teacher
Lisowski, Karen Kaye
Retired Teacher
Rothering, Reathel Bielefeldt
Business Educator
ALMA CENTER
Brenengen, Joan Kay (Bockus)
Fourth Grade Teacher
Severson, Stephen Mark
Biology & Science Teacher
ALMOND
DeVries-Polman, Valerie
Family & Consumer Ec Teacher
Krueger, Patricia Ann
Science Teacher
Sutliff, Donna (Matanich)
Math Teacher & Department Chm
ALTOONA
Mayo, Susan Leilani (Canaday)
Biology & Physiology Teacher
Schaefer, Darryl Rodney
Mathematics Teacher
Schofield, Tom P.
8th Grade Teacher
Turner, Jim L.
Sixth Grade Mathematics Tchr

AMERY
Baldwin, William Robert
Music Teacher
Byerly, Donald Ellsworth, Jr.
8th Grade Science Teacher
Hendrickson, Tracy Lynn (Binfet)
High School Language Teacher
Nelson, Kathleen Camplin
Family & Consumer Ed Teacher
Osborn, Gary Robert
Earth Sci & Biology Teacher
Skinner, Renee Dalla Pozza
Secondary Level English Tchr
Vincent, Robert J.
HS Math Teacher
ANTIGO
Blood, Nancy Lou (Kretz)
Retired Teacher
Blood, Ronald Raymond
Retired 6th Grade Teacher
Duchac, Dennis G.
Student At-Risk Instructor
Kirsch, Charles Ray
PE & Social Studies Teacher
Lenzner, Blanch Raymark
Retired Teacher
Matonich, Gloria Jean
7th-8th Grade Teacher
Mc Keever, Jim C.
High School Counselor
Nye, Ronald M.
History & Pol Science Teacher
Plzak, Arleen Rose (houdek)
Fourth Grade Teacher
Rife, John Harold
Fifth Grade Teacher
APPLETON
Bekx, Nancy Peterson
Legal Instructor
Brusky, Cathlynn Nier
TAG & Science Teacher
Burns, Frank Joseph
Communication Arts Teacher
Ciorba, Charles Phillip
Music Educator
Cool, Michael L.
English Teacher
Curtis, William Eric
K-6th Grade ESL Teacher
Dahms, Steven Victor
Eighth Grade History Teacher
Engen, Paul
Athletic Director
Enter, Douglas Allen
Principal & 7th Grd Teacher
Fanning, Thomas P.
High School Teacher
Finman, Gary James
4th Grade Teacher
Forslund, Shirley Richards
Kndgtn-2nd Grd Teacher
Gossens, Thomas F.
Sr HS Physical Education Tchr
Hartling, William Orville
Fourth Grade Teacher
Hartwig, Paul Martin
Principal
Heiks, James Robert
Choral Music Director
Jacobs, Thomas Francis
Director of Bands
Kreif, Thomas Milton
Eigth Grade US History Teacher
Krings, Susan M.
Second Grade Teacher
Kuenster, James E.
English Teacher
Lahti, Dennis Bruce
Math & English Teacher
Leschke, Mark Steven
HS Social Studies Teacher
Levorson, Ruth Helen
Teacher
Meidl, Kevin
Dir of Choral Music Studies
Meidl, Norma Guevara
Spanish & German Teacher
Polakowski, John Robert
Elem Talented & Gifted Teacher
Reed, Gervais E.
French Professor
Reinke, David Bruce
6th Grade Teacher
Roop, Peter Geiger
1st & 2nd Grade Teacher
Scharenbrock, Daniel Luke
Chemistry Instructor
Schoenbohm, Mark W.
HS Social Studies Teacher
Schwaller, Gerald Thomas
Soc Sci Instr & Dean of Stdnts
Tatlock, Andrea Speer
Teacher of Talented & Gifted
Wexler, Deborah J.
8th Grade Earth Science Tchr
Wolfman, Gary Alan
Music Educator
ARCADIA
Haines, Paula Keilholtz
1st Grade Teacher
Kamla, Richard A.
Bus Ed Tchr & Dept Head
Lockington, William H.
PE Tchr & Wrestling Coach
Matchey, Kristin S.
K-12th Grade Bus Ed Teacher
Sobotta, Michael James
Phys Ed & Health Educator
Stone, Harland Leroy
7th-9th Grd Soc Studies Tchr

VanBuskirk, Gene E.
Middle School Science Teacher
Whalen, Kevin Lee
Agriscience Instructor
ARGYLE
Burhop, Kelly T.
Principal
Rowbotham, Brenda Hildebrandt
K-12th Grade Art Teacher
Stangeland, Marge E.
Gifted & Talented Teacher
ARKANSAW
Holt, Robert Duane
Ag-Science Teacher
Scala, Lynn Torgerson
6th Grade Mathematics Teacher
ARKDALE
Soley, Theresa Motz
Third Grade Teacher
ASHLAND
Acosta, Peggy Marie
Kindergarten Teacher
Bassett, Robert Edward
Business Education Teacher
Gilbert, Judy Ann
Biology Teacher
Herman, Grant Phelps
Professor of Outdoor Education
Hulmer, Christine BeBeau
Band Director
Johnson, Jeffry L.
HS Mathematics Teacher
Miller, Anne Rud
English Teacher & Dept Chair
Nelson, Ellen Randby
Social Studies Teacher
Small, Michele Geslin
English & Modern Langs Prof
Stewart, John Miller
Associate Professor of Psych
ATHENS
Ely, Donald Jarvis
Science Teacher
Roll, Joanne M.
7th-8th Grade Teacher
AUBURNDALE
Cherney, Sheila M.
Learning Disabilities Teacher
Greehling, Lois A.
English Teacher
Kalepp, Judy (Miller)
Bus Ed Teacher & FBLA Adv
Merwin, Elizabeth A.
Special Education Teacher
Thompson, Patricia A.
High School Mathematics Tchr
AUGUSTA
Buckles, Ronald Clarence
Vocal Music Teacher
BALSAM LAKE
Bonnes-Carlson, Laura
First Grade Teacher
Mayer, Brenda Freeman
Vocal Music Teacher
Miles, Craig Allen
Sixth Grade Teacher
BANGOR
Barrett, Sandra Kathleen
Spanish Teacher
Kabat, MariJo Kaul
Media Center Director
BARABOO
Considine, David Lawrence
Special Education Tchr
Earl, Johnathan Otto
Retired Sixth Grade Teacher
Ford, Holly
Fourth Grade Teacher
Freiermuth, Douglas Paul
Social Studies Teacher
Freihoefer, Jane Kay
Tchr of Emotionally Disturbed
Haugen, Lowell Conrad Peter
Science Teacher & Dept Chair
Krunnfusz, Dan M.
Choral Director
Refsland, Randall G.
World History, Psychology Tchr
Roloff, Lou Ann
Mathematics Teacher
Roth, Paul Andrew
Chemistry Teacher
BARNEVELD
Ames, Kelly (Lynch)
MS English Teacher & G-T Coord
Zander, Rita Marie
Math & Computer Teacher
BARRON
Berns, Gary Edward
English Teacher
Leal, Terri Jane
Spanish Teacher
Millerman, Barbara Ann (Polzin)
Business Education Instructor
Steglich, Gary David
Chemistry & Mathematics Tchr
Waldusky, Steven L.
Social Studies Teacher
Weise, Nancy Louise (Boyd)
English Teacher
BAYFIELD
Brown, Dan
Fourth Grade Teacher
BEAVER DAM
Cestkowski, Kathy Ann (Hilgart)
Third Grade Teacher
Darbowicz David, Sandra Lynn
Gifted & Talented Prgm Coord
Kittel, Todd B.
American History Teacher

Paul, Marcia Rae
Choral Director
Posselt, James Martin
High School History Teacher
Struble, Dean B.
Math Teacher
Van Haren, Roger James
English Teacher
BELLEVILLE
Eggenberger, Francine G.
Learning Disabilities Teacher
Kruse, Peggy Ann
English Teacher
Petersen, Gail Irwin
English & Drama Teacher
Stiner, H. Brad
5th Grade Teacher
BELMONT
Doering, Mary Shinko
Fourth Grade Teacher
Jensen, Louise Hansen
Second Grade Teacher
BELOIT
Akerman, Mary Ann Garey
Engish & Yearbook Teacher
Brauch, Thomas Wayne
Visiting Asst Prof of Chem
Dahlke, David C.
Music Teacher
Franz, Susan Ann (Glenzer)
Speech & Environmental Ed Tchr
Haas, Beverly Jean
Science & English Teacher
Harris, Dawn Cavil
Fourth Grade Teacher
Harvey, Jeanne Smith
Tchr of Emotionally Disturbed
Jaeger, Ruth A.
Fifth Grade Teacher
Jenkins, Carlton Dewayne
Associate Principal
Kerr, Karen Ann
Mathematics Teacher
Knutson, Ellen Cameron
Math, Music & Drama Teacher
Kopp, Gloria J.
Third Grade Teacher
Lee, Janice C.
Business & Computer Teacher
Lewin, Amy Jakel
Fourth Grade Teacher
Maren, Karen Jo
5th Grade Teacher
Mc Clelland, John K.
Science Teacher
Mc Quisten, Mary C.
Language Arts Support Tchr
Mowers, Mary Keeney
12th Grade English Teacher
Murry, Mary Schmitz
Kindergarten Teacher
Perry, Molly Zrust
Social Studies Teacher
Rasmussen, William P.
Seventh Grade Science Teacher
Ries, Matthew Edward
Spanish Teacher
Schmidt, Daniel Edwin
English Teacher
Schroeder, John Chester
Business Education Teacher
Soehnlein, John Warren
6th Grd Math, Sci & Rdng Tchr
Stevens, Karen Marie (Farberg)
Business Education Teacher
Street, DeWayne
History Teacher
Van Galder, Gene I.
History Teacher
BENTON
Hazen, Barbara Anne
English Teacher
Knight, Bob
Guid Cnslr, Ath Dir, Lead Tchr
Paquette, Dixie McCauley
4th Grade Teacher
BERLIN
Cox, Timothy Joseph
Physics & Chemistry Teacher
Voeltner, Marilyn Jane
English & Journalism Teacher
Ziemann, David A.
English Teacher
BIG BEND
Witte, Molly
Fifth Grade Teacher
BIRCHWOOD
Breed, Rhonda Marie
High School Science Teacher
BIRNAMWOOD
Andraschko, William Allan
Middle School Teacher
BLACK CREEK
Butch, Kevin James
Middle School Teacher
BLACK RIVER FALLS
Camlek, Richard R.
6th-8th Grd Band Director
Hansen, Larry P.
Choral Dir & Theatre Coord
BLAIR
Olson, Nola Blencoe
Elementary Principal
Truax, Barbara K. (Zaborowski)
Business Education Teacher
BLANCHARDVILLE
Terrill, Jill
Spanish Teacher

BLOOMER
Duranceau, Harry Lee
History & Geography Teacher
Tumm, Sharon Lorraine
First Grade Teacher
Van Gordon, James Frederick
HS Physical Education Teacher
Van Stelle, Peter
6th-8th Grade Band Director
Willi, Mary J.
First Grade Teacher
BLOOMINGTON
Drone, Judy A.
Fifth Grade Teacher
BLUE RIVER
Anderson, M. Elaine Wanless
Retired Teacher
BONDUEL
Belke, Myles Charles
Fourth Grade Teacher
Gregorius, Joan Buchinger
Span Tchr & Foreign Lang Chair
Marinack, Anthony Gerard
6th-12th Grd Tech Ed Tchr
Scheelk, Dawn M.
8th Grade Comm Arts Teacher
Westerfeld, Jacqueline Redlin
Third Grade Teacher
BOSCOBEL
Anthony, Joan Marie
Math Teacher
Behrens, Jeffrey John
Band Director
Bethke, Mari Sue
English & Psychology Teacher
Havlik, Ronald J.
Sr High School Counselor
Knoble, Mary Devine
Second Grade Teacher
Leonard, Joel Frederic
English Teacher
Mischel, Bernie D.
Fifth Grade Teacher
Salzgeber, Jean Marie
Eng & Public Speaking Tchr
Schellhorn, Julie Klesath
Chemistry & Physics Teacher
BOWLER
Thompson, Jeffrey M.
6th Grade Teacher
BOYCEVILLE
Anderson, Constance Lee Rasmussen
EEN Early Chldhd Tchr Asst
Austrum, Donald Craig
Art Teacher
Engel, Tim Scott
Social Studies Teacher
Kniprath, John Michael
Spanish Teacher
Skrove, Stewart John
Bio & Earth Space Sci Tchr
BRILLION
Hunt, Timothy J.
Principal & 7th-8th Grd Tchr
Kittel, Peter Duane
Mathematics Teacher
Warnke, Mary Dury
HS & MS Business Ed Tchr
Wendt, Marcia Joy Krueger
3rd-4th Grade Teacher
BRODHEAD
Hlavachek, Sherry Owens
Fifth Grade Teacher
Landerholm, Lawrence Allen
Retired 8th Grd Geography Tchr
Wallace, Stephen Charles
English Teacher
BROOKFIELD
A-Akert, Walter Dean
English Teacher
Beagle, Gwyneth Jones
Science Teacher
Boardman, Dennis Joseph
Mathematics Teacher
Cramer, James J.
Biology & Ecology Teacher
Emery, Michael David
Adoptive Industrial Ed Teacher
Evans, Karen S.
Asst Prof of Curr & Instrctn
Flannery, Dennis Michael
United States History Teacher
Gallepp, Carol Ann
First Grade Teacher
Jacobs, Cynthia Perez
French Teacher
Lamers, William H.
Middle School Science Teacher
Meyer, Dennis Charles
Math & Comp Sci Teacher
Miller, Marc W.
HS Mathematics Teacher
Minessale, Roberta Heintz
Math Enrichment Vol Teacher
Miskimen, Harvey D.
English Teacher
Morrissey, Anne C.
English Teacher
Moschella, Elyce Olson
Latin Teacher
O'Konek, Christine Bergstedt
Tchr of Learning Disabilities
Olson, Mary Kay Callaway
Art Teacher
Reddemann, Sandra Lee (Sobel)
9th-12th Grd English Teacher
Roberts, David John
Exceptional Education Teacher
Rose, Michael Alan
Mathematics Teacher
Schlick, Lawrence Anthony
3rd Grade Teacher
Seban, Karen Jean Otto
Fifth Grade Teacher
Smogor, Joy Batha
Principal
Whitman, Joan Lynn (Wrobleski)
Learning Center Director
Wojciuk-Graf, Jeanette Marie
Spanish & English Teacher
Wolf, Brian M.
Science Teacher
BROWN DEER
Cywinski, Mark Brian
Learning Disabilities Teacher
BRUCE
Doke, Diane Cheryl
English Teacher
Hulback, David C.
Mathematics Teacher
Lee, Eugenia Gavin
High School English Teacher
Lund, Dale Andrew
Comp Sci, PE & Hlth Teacher
Newman, Michael Jon
Soc Stud Tchr & GATE Coord
Westlund, Kevin James
High School Art Teacher
Zak, Carol Jean Sell
Reading Teacher & Specialist
BRUSSELS
Connell, Laurie K.
K-12th Grd GIT Coordinator
May, Erika Fleig
High School English Teacher
Sullivan, Charmaine M.
Family & Consumer Teacher
Wautlet, Keith Edward
Mathematics Teacher
Wickman, Dorothy Ann (Lange)
Family Educator
BURLINGTON
Chapman, Larry J.
Campus Minister, Theology Tchr
Dains, Michael V.
Mathematics Teacher
Harford, Natalie Heron
Bio & Anatomy Physiology Tchr
Haynes, Paul Gordon
Social Studies Instructor
Loeffler, Edwin John
High School French Teacher
Roanhouse, Norma Chitwood
Middle School English Teacher
Rouce, Joyce Ann (Schulz)
Elementary Teacher
Syens, Peter John
Biology Teacher
Venne, Christa Stephanie
German Teacher
Wenke, Victoria Kunst
Business Education Teacher
BUTTERNUT
Meverden, Larry D.
Art & Desktop Publishing Instr
CADOTT
Gunderson, Lewis Lee
Fourth Grade Teacher
Harding, Debra Richardson
Lang Arts & Soc Stud Instr
Hart, Darrell Allen
Retired Social Studies Teacher
Rykal, Gerald B.
Language Arts Teacher
Seibel, Mary T.
Third & Fourth Grade Teacher
Spencer, Sharon Lee Kisrow
Home School Teacher
CALEDONIA
Dishaw, Elaine Molbeck
Fifth Grade Teacher
CAMBRIA
Arveson, Joan Ellen
High School Science Teacher
Bronson, Martha Ann Mc Clain
English Teacher & Curr Dir
Bylsma, James L.
Middle School Science Teacher
Halverson, Todd Robert
Band Director
Haynes, Michael John
Guidance Counselor
CAMBRIDGE
Davis, Mary Elizabeth
5th Grade Teacher
Grunden, Edward Earl
High School Science Teacher
CAMERON
Huseth, Kurt Nathan
4th Grade Teacher
Joosten, Michael John
Instrumental Music Teacher
CAMPBELLSPORT
Ash, Thea Marie
Fifth Grade Teacher
Verch, Beverly Sterr
Sixth Grade Teacher
Vollmer, James Albert
English Instructor
CASCO
Bartel, Teresa Johnson
Art Teacher
Flood, Laurie Dohr
7th-8th Grade Teacher
Gillis, Ronald John
English & Literature Teacher
Wienke, Jon William
Computer Specialist
CASSVILLE
Bernhardt, Phyllis Nies
Retired Elementary School Tchr
Christensen, Barbara Konieczka
4th Grade Teacher & Asst Prin
Schulting, Jason Paul
Third Grade Teacher
Schuppner, Judy Ruth
Math & Home Economic Teacher
CAZENOVIA
Rothering, Noah Tyger
Biology & Earth Science Tchr
Syftestad, Gary Lee
Social Studies Teacher
CEDAR GROVE
Bloedel, Phillip S.
Science Teacher
Hatfield, Timothy James
7th-8th Grade Social Stud Tchr
Hoffmann, Wayne Arthur
Technology Education Teacher
Kretz, James David
HS Math Teacher
Pilsl, Linda Brickner
Sixth Grade Teacher
Pilsl, Robert Peter
Sixth Grade Teacher
Van Driest, Carolyn Debbink
Retired Second Grade Teacher
Wood, Ronald Lee
HS Social Studies Teacher
CEDARBURG
Bradley-Cibik, Kim A.
HS English Teacher
Cass, Richard Welke
Eng & Writing Teacher
Cebulski, Mark S.
Social Studies Teacher
Coddington, Janet L.
Guidance Counselor
Dickison, Darciann Marie
Choir Director
Eickhoff, Charleen Goldberg
Science Dept Chairman
Giordano, Thomas A.
Fifth Grade Elementary Teacher
Godfrey, William Samuel
Social Studies Teacher
Hilbelink, Ralph
Science & Mathematics Teacher
Jarr, Mary Jean
2nd & 3rd Grd Tchr
Karalewitz, C. K.
English, Humanities & Lit Tchr
Knight, Hayden Wayne
Social Studies Teacher
Morrison, Lyle W.
Science Teacher
Stauske, Will N.
Business Education Teacher
Stillman, James Sanford
Psychology & Economics Teacher
Tamblingson, Marjorie Simonson
English Teacher
Tamsen, Christi Wagner
Phys & Hlth Ed Instructor
Thiele, Susan A.
German Teacher
Williams, Todd E.
Study Hall Supervisor
CHETEK
Kinnick, Yvette Therese
High School English Teacher
CHILTON
Goeldi, Jean Marie (Rockhoff)
First Grade Teacher
Halbach, Jennifer Ann (Roeck)
Second Grade Teacher
Hertel, Romilda Mary (Friederichs)
First Grade Teacher
Poppy, Carol Lidgen
Math Coordinator & Teacher
CHIPPEWA FALLS
Benish, Diane L. Odegaard
Spanish & French Teacher
Blake, Mary Ann
English & Reading Teacher
Britton, James Roger
6th-9th Grd PE & Hlth Teacher
Cable, Victor Edgar
US History & Psych Teacher
Christianson, Terry DeWayne
Vocational Education Instr
Crawford, Timothy J.
Math & Science Teacher
Eberhardt, Susanne Toske
High School English Teacher
Frederick, Thomas E.
Social Studies Teacher
Goulding, Kathy E.
Protective Behaviors Educator
Greenhalgh, Douglas Bruce
Music Department Chairman
Harelstad, Michelle Joy
Family & Consumer Ed Tchr
Harvey, Lynn Leinenkugel
Second Grade Teacher
Kauphusman, Patricia Katherine Schleich
5th Grade Elementary Teacher
Kinnick, Thomas Michael
Religion & Psychology Teacher
Meadows, Monica
Physical Education Teacher
Olson, Bart Mitchell
Tchr of Special Education
Peloquin, Carolyn Jo (Cudney)
Mathematics Teacher
Pfundheller, Robert Mark
History & Civics Teacher
Ray, Dianne Lynne
4th Grade Teacher
Reiter, Anthony James
Mathematics & Physics Teacher
Rooney, Suzanne Kenedy
Second Grade Teacher
Schultz, Jane M.
Second Grade Teacher
Shellito, Karen Jean
6th-7th Grade Teacher
Shock, Ronald E.
7th & 9th Grade Math Teacher
Walrath, James A.
Driver's & Physical Ed Tchr
CLAYTON
Blanchard, Chirstopher L.
Instrumental Music Teacher
Mac Dougall, Sarah
Science Teacher
CLEAR LAKE
Streif, Paul Frederick
5th & 6th Grade English Tchr
CLINTON
Stoney, Judy Lynn (Gibney)
Second Grade Teacher
CLINTONVILLE
Van Meter, John Robert
Mathematics Teacher
COLBY
Brandner, Bernice Ann Brink
English Teacher
Huston, Pamela J.
Business & Education Teacher
Johnson, Michael R.
Fifth Grade Teacher
Schmidt, Donna M.
Elementary School Counselor
COLEMAN
Batchelor, Joseph Albert
English & Spanish Teacher
Laitinen, George Edward
Mathematics Teacher
Long, Keith Alan
8th Grade Teacher
Schwedler, Robert Louis
Social Studies Teacher
COLFAX
Doucette, Joseph Michael
Physical Education Teacher
Johnson, Deborah Sue
Second Grade Teacher
Keltner, Beverly Thoma
First Grade Teacher
Meade, Andrew John
Social Studies Department Chm
Ries, Ernestina Sifuentes
Spanish Teacher
COLUMBUS
Bradish, Sharon L.
Spanish Teacher
Crombre, Jennifer Lynn
Fifth Grade Teacher
Habenicht, Cherry Lidner
Vice Prin, Guid Cnslr, Fr Tchr
Premo, Rebecca R.
8th Grade Social Studies Tchr
CONOVER
Krecklow, Russell Conrad
Fourth Grade Teacher
CONRATH
Weber, Sandra Sue
Teacher & Administrator
COON VALLEY
Nestingen, Lori Ann (Overboe)
Second Grade Teacher
CORNELL
Apland, JoAnn Szarjowitz
Second Grade Teacher
Nodolf, Joan
Health & Physical Ed Tchr
Pomeroy, Scott Howard
Social Studies Tchr & Ath Dir
COTTAGE GROVE
Paulson, Ruth Hanna
3rd Grade Teacher
COUDERAY
Hale, Steve S.
Retired MS Science Teacher
CRANDON
Erickson, Kenneth Tod
Retired Middle School Teacher
Resch, Harold Clarence
Math & Chemistry Teacher
Trautmann, Lyle James
Business Education Teacher
Wilson, William Thomas, Jr.
Fourth Grade Teacher
CROSS PLAINS
Cunningham, Susan Simonson
Kindergarten Teacher
CUBA CITY
Farley, Amy Sue
Jr High Teacher
Harper, Stuart H.
Chemistry & Physics Tchr
Larson, Cheryl Christiansen
School Counselor
Schultz, Ronald Matthew
Science & Biology Teacher
Stauer, M. John
Math & Science Teacher
CUDAHY
Boehmke, Rosalyn Schmidt
Retired First Grade Teacher
Boyle, Patrick Jerome
HS Social Studies Teacher
Kujawa, Kenneth John
Mathematics Teacher
Rutter, Shannon Marie
Varsity & JV Chrldng Coach
Siodlarz, Walter Matthew
Former Mathematics Teacher
Venne, Carey Lamont
English & TV Production Tchr
Wolf, Dennis George
Physical Science Teacher
DARLINGTON
Wildes, Rhonda Elizabeth
School Counselor
DE FOREST
Krantz, Susan Mary
Mathematics Teacher
Pieterick, Gertrude Ann
French Teacher
DE PERE
Berner, Gerald Lawrence
Mathematics Teacher
De Waal, Barbara Constant
Business Education Chairperson
Elliott, Bonnie Kaminski
Business Education Teacher
Feldhausen, Jayne E.
Gifted & Talented Tchr & Coord
Gerrits, Marianne
Science & Computer Sci Tchr
Hess, A. Dean
Biology Educator
Holtz, Michael John
Social Studies Teacher
Johnson, Jane M.
Language Arts Teacher
Quirk, Connie
Fifth Grade Teacher
Spielbauer, Ron Robert
Retired Librarian
DE SOTO
Koelker, Gregory Joseph
Language Arts Teacher
Welper, Colleen A.
Social Studies Teacher
DEERFIELD
Woch, Debra Kay
English Teacher
DELAFIELD
Arnson, Kehl Andrew
English Teacher
Marquardt, Brenda Baertsch
Third Grade Teacher
Shaver, Barbara Ellen (Lukas)
5th Grade Teacher
DELAVAN
Marshall, Ronald Lee
Social Studies Tchr & Team Ldr
Mitchell, Julie Ann
Psych & Consumer Ec Teacher
Runyon, Charles F.
Fourth Grade Teacher
Runyon, Cheryl Smith
General Music Teacher
Ryan, Melanie Collins
French Teacher
DENMARK
Kasprzak, Beverly Ann
Third Grade Teacher
Sandberg, Robert Wayne
Chemistry & Math Teacher
Van Lieshout, David A.
Av Director & Soc Studies Chr
DODGEVILLE
Buck, Robert J.
Physical Education Dept Head
Storkson, Scott V.
8th Grade Language Arts Tchr
Tank, Charles E.
HS His Tchr & Dept Chairperson
Thomas, Carol Ann (Bouvert)
Retired First Grade Teacher
Van Epps, Julie
Health & PE Teacher
DORCHESTER
Prestebak, Myrtle Kellner
Retired Teacher
DOUSMAN
Bischof, Jo Anne Jorgensen
Mathematics Teacher
Braasch, Vicki Rieder
Fourth Grade Teacher
Fink, Michael P.
Special Education Teacher
Fredericksen, Kristi Dangott
Fifth Grade Teacher
Hemschik, Terry Kahlert
8th Grade Reading Teacher
Neumer, Ward G.
5th Grade Teacher
Qualler, Mary Lou Kratochvil
6th Grade English Teacher
Schmidt, David E.
Cmptr Sci & Indstrl Tech Tchr
DURAND
Lund, Janice M.
Physical Education Teacher
Rahman, Donald Peter
Computer Science Teacher
Shaw, Ella Howitt
High School English Teacher
EAGLE RIVER
Coshun, Anne Popp
Fifth Grade Teacher
Huebner, Kenneth William
Physical Education Teacher
Roth, LaMont H.
Retired Math Teacher
Weber, Lori Ann Steiner
5th Grade Teacher
EAST TROY
Annis, Kathleen Ann (Horstman)
Third Grade Teacher
Equi, Sue Ann
5th Grade Music & Band Instr

TROY (cont)
, Lawrence Roboert
Director
Francine Lorretta
ch & Language Pathologist
Sara Jill
ning Disabilites Teacher
z, Mary Margaret
hematics & Computer Teacher
CLAIRE
Carol Donat
ch Teacher
l, Mary Kay
ish Teacher
an, Dennis George
ory Teacher
, Carolyn Ann
red Fourth Grade Teacher
ey, Margaret A. Morrow
Grade Teacher
rt, Karyn Colleen
ch Teacher
nter, Charles Key
nology Education Chprsn
h, Michael Paul
nce Teacher
Brenda
h School Principal
rg, Wayne Henry
chology Teacher
g, Bruce Allen
ic Educator
es, James Anthony
h School History Teacher
on, Janet Anderson
rth Grade Teacher
on, Lynda Faye (Mason)
Science Teacher
, Mari (Tollefson-Thompson)
Grade Teacher
berte, Mary
uki Piano Teacher
, Janelle Shook
sical Science Teacher
bill, Dennis Richard
rumental Music Teacher
chler, Jack L.
h Science Teacher
t, Stanton Eric
guage Arts Teacher
n, Pamela Such
hmore English Teacher
, Daniel E.
d & Talented Resource Tchr
illy, Tim Michael
ociate Principal
ter, Thomas Gary
ial Studies Instructor
rs, Ronald D.
h Grade Teacher
dt, Karyn Amy (Kruse)
rumental Music Director
, Mike L.
Grade Math Teacher
nd, Alvin Eugene
oc Prof of Math Emeritus
ch, Shirley Ann (Drager)
hth Grade English Teacher
ling, Corita Rosanne (Thom)
nce Teacher
efelbein, Kit Scott (Brown)
ysical Education Teacher
ulsky, Dennis James
chnology Education Teacher
er, John Paul
cial Studies Teacher
npson, Kevin James
Grade Math Teacher
hn, Mark Patrick
th Grade Teacher
l, Larine Fern (Baughman)
th Grade Teacher
er, Martin Andrew
ence Teacher
shapple, Cynthia Lee (Aldrich)
ogram Director & Paralegal
ett, Alan George
chnology Education Teacher
ada, Nobuyoshi
sic Professor
N
n, Darcell Schmidt
ysical Education Instructor
AR
, Karen
eech & Language Clinician
se, Shirley Friermood
ience Teacher & Principal
, Jerry Galen
chnology & Math Instructor
GERTON
dhuin, Robert Christian
ading Specialist
drick, Patricia Ann (Taff)
tired Instructor
re, Jennifer Nelson
ulti-Age Teacher
Gary John
strumental Music Teacher
se, Mary L.
ccupational Therapist
ntgomery, Susan Running
chool Counselor
ke, Dorothy Purnell
etired First Grade Teacher
ck, George William
h & 8th Grd PE Tchr
tter, Carolyn Yee
indergarten Teacher

ELCHO
Anderson, Les August
Science & English Teacher
Beck, Janene Marie
Instrumental Music Teacher
Doran, Kay Kuester
Spanish Teacher
Hutchison, Kathleen Slone
Vocal Music Teacher
Prahl, Thomas John
Scndry Social Science Teacher
Watts, Jeanne Albarello
7th-12th Grd Eng & Speech Tchr
ELEVA
Gustafson, John E.
Fifth Grade Teacher
Topping, Sue M.
5th Grade Teacher
ELK MOUND
Kernan, Barbara Lee
English & French Instructor
Mack, Jeffrey Jon
Math, Physics & Sci Tchr
Miller, Grace Ellen
Retired Teacher
Turek, Steven James
Fifth Grade Teacher
Weber, Judith Ann
First Grade Teacher
ELKHART LAKE
Buechel, Ann Marie
7th & 8th Grd Teacher
Grafenstein, Mary W.
Kindergarten Teacher
Kreibich, Carlos Edwin
Social Studies Teacher
Lund, Lei Brenton
English Teacher
Mc Gill, Michael D.
Bio & Environmental Sci Tchr
Rathman, William George
Chemistry & Physics Teacher
Whyte, Mary Kathryn
High School Art Teacher
Zuelke, Patti M.
Fourth Grade Teacher
ELKHORN
Bailey, Patricia Lusted
Second Grade Teacher
Dettmann, Lisa J.
English & Speech Teacher
Kennedy, Mary Larson
Family & Consumer Ed Teacher
Morrissey, Jean
Third Grade Teacher
Pappa, Janet Marie
Eighth Grade Teacher
Salter, Sonette Chanson
High School Spanish Teacher
Wrzesinski, Patricia Smith
English Teacher
ELLSWORTH
Kastberg, David W.
World Geography Teacher
Manthey, D. G.
6th Grade Teacher
Ruppe, David John
High School Art Teacher
ELM GROVE
Bartel, Mary Jo
7th Grd Social Studies Teacher
Girodana-Howley, Rosalie T.
Reading Teacher
Jaeck, Kenneth Robert
Science Education Specialist
ELMWOOD
Gebhard, James Eric
Vocal & General Music Teacher
Glaus, Beverly (Schaffer)
Sixth Grade Teacher
Hannack, Jerry L.
Technical Education Teacher
Thomas, Tracy M.
2nd Grade Teacher
EVANSVILLE
Beedle, Harold Kenneth, Jr.
Social Studies Teacher
Diedrich, Peter
Language Arts Teacher
Hanson, John J.
7th Grade Geography Teacher
EXELAND
Rademaker, April S. (Kern)
5th Grade Tchr & Bldg Prin
Rademaker, Norman F.
Principal & Teacher
FENNIMORE
O'Brien, Gerald L.
Seventh Grd Mathematics Tchr
Raisbeck, Rita Theresa (Digman)
Title I Teacher
FISH CREEK
Honold, Mark A.
7th-8th Grade Math Teacher
Krist, Priscilla Olson
7th-8th Grade Science Teacher
Quigley, John T.
Band Director
FLORENCE
Ferris, Joseph Richard
Social Studies & Reading Tchr
Hogan, Crystal Annette
K-12 Music Teacher
Kumjian, John Charles
Director of Bands
Zoeller, Daniel John
Physical Education Teacher
FOND DU LAC
Alaniz, Frank Ygnacio
8th Grd Earth Science Teacher

Anderson, Eric Henry
Social Science Teacher
Armstrong, George
Professor of Biology
Bachhuber, Kathleen Anne Victor
Chemistry & Physics Teacher
Boelhower, Patricia Wahoske
Adjunct Instructor
Coons, Jana Ogden
Assoc Lecturer in Geography
Cooper, Larry Kent
Social Studies Teacher
Freiberg, Roger Paul
Life Science Teacher
Fritz, Richard Roy
Reading Specialist
Griffiths, William Perry
Associate Professor of Art
Knar, Richard Alan, Sr.
Asst Professor of Mathematics
Korinek, Roger Joseph
HS Teacher & Soc Stud Co-Chair
Kritzer, Marlene
High School Mathematics Tchr
Manley, David Scott
Principal
Mc Millan, Kathryn Lynn
Coord of Gifted & Talented
Mokhtari, Joan Feirer
Sociology Teacher
Packard, Alan Hathaway
English Teacher
Reiher, Patricia Raccoli
High School Art Teacher
Roehl, Ross Hunter
Principal & Teacher
Siekierke, Patricia Ann
Vocal Music Teacher
Strauss, Thomas G.
Mathematics Teacher
Thomas, Terrence J.
Counselor
Van Grunsven, James David
Fifth Grade Teacher
Wochos, Kenneth Charles
Sixth Grade Teacher
Zacherl, Susan L.
Social Studies Teacher
FOOTVILLE
Allen, Lois Davis-Cole
Second Grade Teacher
FORT ATKINSON
Cusick, Susan Bickle
Special Ed Dept Head & Tchr
Looze, Richard C.
World Geog & Sociology Teacher
Olson, Paul Millar
Fifth Grade Teacher
Price, Nancy L.
Fr Tchr & Frgn Lang Dept Chair
Purdy, Royal Lindsay
Art Teacher
Rumppe, Roger E.
Chemistry Teacher
Schoenfeldt, Barbara L.
Psych, Soc Stud & English Tchr
Steinbrenner, Ethan E.
Pastor & Religion Teacher
FRANKLIN
Hilton, Michael C.
Mathematics & Cmptr Sci Tchr
Mueller, Kathleen A.
Fifth Grade Teacher
Weir, Shirley Ann
Guidance Counselor
FRANKSVILLE
Barth, Colette Marie
First Grade Teacher
FREDERIC
Berquist, Patricia L.
Coord of The Gifted & Talented
Rogers Almlie, Marilyn Beckler
Business Education Teacher
FREDONIA
Kaus, Joanne
Science Teacher
Klima, Peter Thomas
7th & 8th Grd Soc Stud Tchr
Uden, Michael David
MS Lang Arts & Drama Tchr
FREEDOM
Joten, Ron D.
Mathematics Teacher
Meller, Betsy Haen
School Counselor
Pendleton, Robert Wayne
Fifth Grade Teacher
Randerson, Margaret Ann Garvey
Second Grade Teacher
Schulze, Bob
Social Studies Teacher
Stangel, Philip David
High School Band Teacher
Steffens, Gary Peter
6th Grade Teacher
GENESEE DEPOT
Bartolotta, Linda Esser
5th Grade Teacher
Przybyla, Sharon Ann
Science Teacher
Switalski, Vera P.
First Grade Teacher
GERMANTOWN
Anderson, Gary Lee
Mathematics Teacher
Barnes, James Philip
Instrumental Music Teacher
Deiss, Lyn Wischer
Physical Education Teacher

Higgins, Janet Blanche
Seventh Grade Reading Teacher
Kutcher, Yvonne Komassa
Language Arts & Soc Stud Tchr
Mathews-Graham, Carla
English Instructor
Remfrey, Patrik
Chemistry Tchr & Sci Dept Head
GILLETT
Lucht, Sandra Jawort
English Teacher
GILMAN
DeStaercke, Gerald H.
Social Studies Teacher
Grunseth, Bill W.
Mathematics Instructor
GILMANTON
Goss-Bowen, Judith Marten
Fourth Grade Teacher
Steiner, Julie A.
Business Education Instructor
GLEASON
Krause, Richard K.
6th Grade Teacher
GLENDALE
Budgins, Robert
Science Teacher
GLENWOOD CITY
Larson, Judy (Lundeen)
Second Grade Teacher
GLIDDEN
Fiebig, Vicki A.
K-12 Music Instructor
GOODMAN
Stange, Rhonda
Social Studies Head Teacher
Wentland, Betty Jane (Koepp)
HS Home Ec & Health Teacher
GRAFTON
Brown, Tracy
Spanish Teacher
GRANTSBURG
Ryan, Peggy Carlson
English Teacher
Samuelson, Sharon Kay (Platt)
High School Spanish Teacher
GRATIOT
Hawkinson, Don Wayne
Middle School Science Teacher
Hoover, Rosemary Neuenschwander
5th Grade Teacher
Krebs, Wayne Alan
7th & 8th Grade Math Teacher
GREEN BAY
Barman, Philip Frank
Russian & World His Tchr
Bornowski, April Marie
Science Teacher
Bouchonville, Lee Richard
HS US History Teacher
Brayko, Brent S.
Social Studies Teacher
Breunig, Joseph Robert
Science Teacher
Campbell, Julie Ann
US History & Government Tchr
Cartier, Carol Servais
Language Arts Teacher
Casper, Susan Mary
Mathematics Teacher
Cherry, Dean Alvin
Chemistry Teacher
Craanen, Jeanne Marie (Rentmeester)
Fourth Grade Teacher
Daniels, Nancy (Young)
Psych, US His & Civics Tchr
DeMerit, John Michael
Teacher & Coach
Desrochers, Mary A.
Fifth Grade Teacher
Devine, Ted P.
History Teacher
Dignan, Peter
Teacher
Doucha, Mary Ann Tisler
6th Grade Teacher
Drankoff, Jack J.
High School Phys Ed Teacher
Dunlap, John H.
Mathematics Teacher
Feldkamp, Angelo Joseph
Guidance Counselor, Latin Tchr
Fischer, Lyman Dixon
8th Grade Math Teacher
Flesch, Ervin E.
Guidance Counselor
Frease, Jean Mary (Van Rossum)
Science Teacher
Fricton, Aggie M.
Business Teacher
Fritze, Stephen Paul
Sixth Grade Teacher & Ath Dir
Geishirt, Paula Laundrie
High School Counselor
Gritzon, Glenn Charles
Psychology & Sociology Teacher
Grunwaldt, Brett Alan
Science Teacher
Gusick, Connie Faye
3rd Grade Teacher
Hatfield, Charles Edward
Middle School Science Teacher
Haupt, Susan Jane
Math Teacher
Hauser, Stephanie Lynn (Fermanich)
Chemistry Teacher
Hearden, Andrea Smeester
Science Teacher
Hermsen, Russell Richard
Band Dir & Music Theory Tchr

Hutchison, Debora Roy
6th Grade Science Teacher
Hyduke, Jane Barnes
Language Arts Teacher
Immerfall, Kenton Floyd
Sixth Grade Teacher
Jameson, Michael Jay
Psychology Teacher
Kettenhofen-Kerhin, Jill M.
Biology Teacher
King, Donna L.
Math Tchr
Kiser, Bernal Allen, Jr.
Chemistry Teacher
Kraft, Michael E.
Prof of Pol Sci & Pub Affairs
Krcma, Betty J.
Agribusiness Teacher
Kuse, Willis Henry
MS Physical Educaton Teacher
La Pierre, Amy J. (Rottier)
Seventh Grade Teacher
Longmire, Ken Lee
Science Teacher
Lorberblatt, Trudy
Economics & Civics Teacher
Luxton, Catherine Filppula
Third Grade Teacher
Nys, Mary M.
Fifth Grade Teacher
Pahnke, Kermit K.
Earth Science Teacher
Paplham, James Edward
Teacher
Paplham, Richard George
Math Teacher
Paulson, Shirley Harvego
Composition Instructor
Plog, James Francis, Jr.
Agribusiness & Sci Tech Instr
Reynen, RuthAnn A.
Eng Lang Arts & Speech Teacher
St John, Robert William
Social Studies Teacher
Schacht, Beverly Honer
High School Science Teacher
Schroepfer, Teresa Fleischman
Choral Director
Schumacher, Kathleen Trainor
Fourth Grade Teacher
Schumacher, Krystal Kaddatz
Career Guidance Dir
Schwedrsky, Donald Robert
Secondary Mathematics Teacher
Sieg, Richard D.
Math Teacher
Simon, Sarah A.
Math Teacher
Stenger, Barbara Tobias
English Teacher
Stock, Michael Robert
Teacher & Athletic Director
Thompson, Douglas Allan
7th Grade Teacher
Van Erem, Joseph Dale
Mathematics Teacher
White, MaryLou Peck
Fifth Grade Teacher
Wightman, Mark Donald
Psychology & History Teacher
Wolcott, Richard Rolla
7th-8th Grd French Teacher
Wolfe, Richard Lee
6th & 8th Grade Multi-Age Tchr
GREEN LAKE
Polcyn, Sandra Mortimer
Band Director
Sonnleitner, Gerald Anthony
Math Teacher
GREENDALE
Bangert, David J.
Student Services Director
Bergner, Sue Ellen Duchin
Second Grade Teacher
Carlson, Robert H.
English Teacher
Gorski, Jean Niederer
Mathematics Teacher
Klotz, Joy Dare
Spanish Teacher
Kosky, Robert James
8th Grd Math, Sci & Rdng Tchr
Krubsack, David Henry
Music Department Chairman
Limmer, Andrew
Physics Teacher
Rappis, Tim L.
Social Studies Teacher
Settle, Jan M.
Speech & Honors English Tchr
Steinke, Judith Ann
First Grade Teacher
GREENFIELD
Anderson, Daniel V.
High School Math Teacher
Beger, Janet Branch
MS & HS German Teacher
Blackburn, James Joseph
School Counselor
Dunn, Lee O.
Band & Orchestra Director
Fleischer, Jimmy Jon
Driver Ed, Health & PE Teacher
Foxgrover- Foley, Carolyn Jane
Secondary Mathematics Teacher
Greene, Robert W.
US History & Sociology Teacher
Hauer, Leona Weida Nass
Kindergarten Teacher

GREENFIELD (cont)
Hill, Jacqueline Senk
English Teacher & Dept Chair
Kroupa, Kent Joseph
Tchr of Learning Disabilities
Kumprey, Daniel R.
Mathematics Teacher
Lind, William Robert
Mathematics Teacher
Olszewski, Elizabeth Gabel
Science Teacher
Stahlman, Charles August
Middle School Band Teacher
VanDeraa, Alan
AP United States History Tchr
GREENWOOD
Druschke, Richard Joseph
Mathematics Teacher
Guenther, Daryl Sylvester
6th Grade Teacher & Counselor
Kopplin, Lana Schulte
Social Studies Teacher
Yeske, Kevin Richard
Science Instructor
HALES CORNERS
Guy, Margo Penney
Second Grade Teacher
Hughes-Kosmider, Jude
English Teacher & Dept Chair
Nowicki, Sarah Elizabeth
Fourth Grade Teacher
HAMMOND
Ehlers, James L.
Social Studies Teacher
Freitag, Sharon K. (LaDuke)
Special Education Teacher
Lucking, Mary I.
English Teacher
Nusbaum, Peter Emil
Business Education Teacher
HARTFORD
Biersack, Leslie Skumatz
Junior High Teacher
Brugger, Beth
First Grade Teacher
Cortez, Kathleen Frentzel
3rd Grade Teacher
Friedemann, Donald Richard
Amer History Teacher & Tm Ldr
Gruden, Frank E.
Industrial Technology Instr
Herman, Janeen Lee (Cechvala)
Teacher
Knoll, Ruth A.
High School Choral Director
Palmer, Carrie Swanson
Spanish Teacher
Royes, Amy Simons
EEN Aide
Schultz, Ron D.
High School Math Teacher
Weyers, John E.
Mathematics Teacher
Zajicek, David Leonard
Social Studies Teacher
HARTLAND
Abramowitz, Harry
Instrumental Music Director
Antony, Erling C.
General & AP Chemistry Tchr
Besserer, Joyce Shane
Frgn Lang Dept Head & Fr Tchr
Bilkey, Suzanne Marie
Third Grade Teacher
Boatman, Marva Carpenter
Art Teacher
Brill, John Evarist
Social Studies Instructor
Budzien, Gregory Jonathan
Advanced Placement Eng Tchr
Destache, Douglas John
6th-8th Grd Math Teacher
Ermatinger, Lynn Marie
Social Studies Teacher
Georgeson, Randy Kent
Social Studies Teacher
Horne, Rita Anne (Gundrum)
First Grade Teacher
Kinzel, Cynthia M.
Mathematics & Comp Sci Tchr
Leifer, Denise Catherine
Science Teacher
Morris, Maggie Ann
Fourth Grade Teacher
Neumann-Hayes, Terese
Spanish Teacher & Dept Coord
Reichle, Ronald I.
Western Civilizations Teacher
Schaefer, James John
English Teacher
Sharp, Sue Ann
English Teacher
Smith, Gregory Keith
Mathematics Instructor
Wiedmeyer, Sharon Kay (Brandt)
Family & Consumer Sci Instr
Zeman, Julie Lynne
Seventh Grade Teacher
Ziegelbauer, Mary Ellen
English Teacher
HAYWARD
Dedrickson-Kloster, Marie L.
Retired Fourth Grade Teacher
Kuziej, Thomas Paul
HS Civics & World His Tchr
Renninger, John Edward
Social Studies Teacher
Smith, Dennis L.
Girls Basketball Coach
Tabbert, James Lee
High School Band Instructor
HAZEL GREEN
Hendricks, Carol Ann
Language Arts Instructor
Kolbe, Robert
Physical Education & Hlth Tchr
Sukhwal, Lilawati Sharma
Reading Teacher
Wills, Barbara Anne
First & Second Grade Teacher
Wilson, Todd Samuel
Mathematics Teacher
HIGHLAND
Doye, Joette G. (Faull)
English & French Teacher
HILBERT
Bell, Scott William
Administrator
Clark, Marsi Dawn
3rd Grade Teacher
Geiser, Jennifer Ann
Geometry, Chem & Computer Tchr
HILLSBORO
Swatek, Thomas Gerard
Social Studies Teacher
HOLCOMBE
Glaus, Perry L.
7th-9th Grade English Teacher
Ruhde, Timothy A.
Biology & Chemistry Teacher
Weinert, Joni Zielke
Band Teacher
HOLMEN
Burg, Nickolas Owen
7th Grd Lang Arts Tchr & Coach
Chown, Rosemary Scott
Eighth Grade Math Teacher
DeRosa, Sharon Ann Ristow
Third Grade Teacher
Hill, Nancy Fulkerson
French Teacher
Hundt, Becky L.
Family & Consumer Ed Tchr
Langreck, Matthew Scott
6th-8th Grade Art Instructor
Neil, Brian M.
High School Science Teacher
Opperman, Catherine Jane (Setz)
Fourth Grade Teacher
Sorenson, Linda Mary (Bizer)
8th Grade Science Teacher
Tabbert, Lori Kay
Fourth & Fifth Grade Teacher
Vike, Duane D.
High School Math Teacher
HORICON
Hereid, Larry Orland
Business Education Teacher
Meyer, Merry Ann Jakobitz
Third Grade Teacher
Meylink, Ruth B.
Rdng Specialist & Title I Tchr
Norton, Sara L.
Eng & Speech Communcation Tchr
Sunderland, Ellen M.
Third Grade Teacher
HORTONVILLE
Cole, Paula Marie
Music Teacher
Kang, Virginia Butler
Business Education Teacher
Meyer Gosz, Annabelle Jean
1st Grade Teacher
Ohlde, Janet G.
Kindergarten Teacher
Rischette, Susan Kay
2nd Grade Teacher
HOWARDS GROVE
Koppelmann, Elmer Robert
Fifth Grade Teacher
HUBERTUS
Huss, Desra Strozewski
6th-8th Grade Math Teacher
HUDSON
Andrewson, Kathy Lea
English Teacher
Britten, Mary
High School English Teacher
DeGraff, Deanne Patricia
High School Counselor
Elbert, Christine Favell
Spanish Teacher
Hoaglund, Robert Kenneth
Fifth Grade Teacher
Klein, Patricia M.
Mathematics & Religion Teacher
Koss, Phyllis A.
2nd Grade Teacher
Krupa, Donald Robert
Mathematics Teacher
Lee, Becky L.
Sixth Grade Teacher
Lee, Debra Lynn (Risberg)
Business Education Teacher
Lewis, Craig Allen
English & Speech Teacher
Margenau, James R.
Science Teacher
Riddle, Glen Arthur
Art Teacher
Schleh, Dave
Social Studies Teacher
Tammen, Jill E.
English Teacher
Wieczorek, Steven Joseph
Government Teacher
HURLEY
Faoro FLeischman, Teresa Lynn
Spanish Teacher
Gulan, Shyanne Morzenti
Chemistry & Physics Teacher
IOLA
Johnson, Linda Caroline (Mueller)
First Grade Teacher
Lund, William W.
Chemistry & Biology Teacher
Snyder, Todd D.
Physics & Physical Sci Teacher
JACKSON
Bey, Connie Lea Baehman
Art & Literature Teacher
Breitkreutz, Orville Wayne
Instr & Soc Studies Dept Chm
Jahns, Todd Michael
Dept Coord of PE & Hlth Tchr
Mehlberg, Ronald William
Religion & Latin Teacher
Schramm, Darwin Carl
Geometry Instructor
JANESVILLE
Bayreuther, Daniel John
Physical Education Teacher
Bottomley, Robert John
English Teacher
Bouton, Julie A.
Business Ed Tchr & Dept Chair
Cornelius, Ruth Rucks
4th Grade Teacher
Dean, Michael Henry
7th Grade Social Studies Tchr
Dunlap, Harvey
Tech Ed Teacher
Eicher, Robert D.
Biology Teacher
Fanta, Anita Melby
6th Grade Teacher
Fry, Howard William
Sixth Grade Teacher
Hornbostel, Julia Conkling
Professor of English
Jones, George Henry Baidoo
Asst Professor of Economics
Klawitter, Tom C.
HS Physical Education Teacher
Neumann, Cass Ferm
Media Specialist
Nobiensky, Dale Frank
Third Grade Teacher
Reuter, Thomas Robert
Secondary Science Teacher
Stried, Christine Ann (Heck)
Spanish Teacher
Wilke, Candace Mary
1st Grade Teacher
JEFFERSON
Ames, Bonnie Lynn
8th Grade English Teacher
Babcock, Tim
Social Studies Teacher
Behrens, Carolyn K.
Family & Consumer Teacher
Bruha, Marcia Jean
Music Teacher
Fitzgerald, Joan M.
Math Teacher
Krahnke, Donna Richter
Kindergarten Teacher
Liedtke, John Worthington
8th Grade Amer History Tchr
Linse, Dennis M.
Seventh Grade Geography Tchr
Neary, Cath (Alvey)
English & Speech Teacher
Rollefson, Mark D.
Chemistry Teacher
JIM FALLS
Anderson, Debbie Mae
Third Grade Teacher
JOHNSON CREEK
Johnson, Ken L.
High School English Teacher
Schneider, Keith Allen
Business Education Instructor
JUDA
Kunz, Patti Colleen
Scndry LD Tchr & At-risk Coord
Olson, Lori M. (Jordan)
2nd Grade Teacher
Olson, Michael Allen
Instrmntl Mus & Driver Ed Tchr
JUNEAU
Fogg, Robert E., III
Instrumental Music Director
Hanson-Harnisch, Kimberly Sue
Fifth Grade Teacher
Laas, Kristin Koestering
Guidance Counselor
Sawicki, Jennifer Lynn (Michels)
English & Speech Teacher
Timm, Jeffrey David
8th Grade Teacher & Principal
KANSASVILLE
Konicek, Carol Anne
Kindergarten Teacher
KAUKAUNA
Dressler, Mark Robert
Sixth Grade Teacher
Frey-Plank, Phylis A.
Fifth Grade Teacher
Hochholzer, Nicole Wydeven
English & Communications Tchr
Hollenberg, Patricia Dixon
Gftd & Talented Resource Tchr
Lundergan, Gene A.
English as a Second Lang Tchr
Marsh, Kathleen Marie
Seventh Grd Lang Arts Teacher
Micke, Mary Witter
English & Religion Teacher
Reider, Gayle Verstegen
Fourth Grade Teacher
Rogers, Judy Ann
Fifth Grade Teacher
Schmidlkofer, Marilyn H.
English Second Lang Teacher
Steger, Betty Jane Ann (Nettekoven)
Cheerleader Coach
Wachtendonk, Alan G.
Technology Education Instr
KENOSHA
Aiello, Richard James
9th Grade Biology Teacher
Aslakson, Mark Stephen
Psychology & Sociology Teacher
Banaszynski, Joseph E.
American History Teacher
Chalgren, Kurt Robert, Jr.
Choral Music Teacher
Connolly, Catherine Ann
Spanish & French Teacher
Diskerud, Shirley Eller
9th Grade English Teacher
Englund, Bernard E.
Mathematics Teacher
Falduto, Frank M., Jr.
High School English Teacher
Fennema, Paul Allan
History Teacher
Fossey, Keith Robert
High School Mathematics Tchr
Gorman, Janice Huebner
US History Teacher
Guenther, Richard O.
Physics Teacher
Handrup, Virginia M.
English, Psych & German Tchr
Harrington, Sandra (Seidel)
Assistant Professor of Biology
Hartman, Audrey Johnson
Sixth Grade Teacher
Infusino, Donna Rita (Cairo)
9th Grade Mathematics Teacher
Johnson, Eric Dean
Art Teacher
Kauffman, Rita (O'Malley)
French Teacher
Lallensack, Margaret Stanzek
First Grade Teacher
Lawler, Terry Lee
English Teacher
Lee-Chambers, Althea
English Teacher
Lewis, Mary Jane Peterson
Third Grade Teacher
Martin, Marvin Sherwin
Former Literature Teacher
Pacifico, Samuel Harry
Chemistry & Physics Teacher
Padlock, Colleen Marie (Cox)
Spanish Teacher
Pakkebier, Dawn DeYoung
String Specialist
Pastor, Claudia Kuehl
English Teacher
Pawlowski, Margaret Becker
5th-6th Grd Teacher
Phipps, Dennis Harold
United States History Teacher
Pittari, Linda Beth
High School English Teacher
Poulson, Nancy A.
5th Grade Teacher
Rabey, Kathleen Elizabeth
Art Teacher
Romano, Charles Anthony
Instrl Technology Specialist
Rothstein, Marian
Associate Professor of French
Santarelli, Geraldine
Mathematics Teacher
Simon, Dee Ann
Mathematics Teacher
Snavely, Mark R.
Mathematics Professor
Sockness, Diane Lin (Diebold)
Eighth Grade Mathematics Tchr
Somers, Byron Timothy
Fifth Grade Teacher
Spotts, Harlan E.
Assoc Professor of Marketing
Teegarden, Nicolee
Art Teacher & Dept Chm
Tennyson, Michael Andrew
High School Pastor
Tomsheck, John E.
Biology Teacher
Topel, Blake Jon
Mathematics Teacher
Walter, Carl H.
Biology Teacher
Winston, Keith Eugene
Retired Chem Tchr & Dept Chm
KEWASKUM
Allmann, George Burkhardt
Curriculum Resource Director
Bertelsen, David Bruce
Vocal Music Teacher
Harlow, Joseph Paul
Mathematics Teacher
Jacak, Judith Lavarda
High School English Teacher
Koth, Perry Lee
Cmptr Lit, Hlth & PE Teacher
Nell, John Michael
Guidance Counselor
Olsen, Barbara Hoeft
Spanish Teacher
Pitrowski, Christine M.
English Teacher
Reilly-Kliss, Mary
English Teacher
Rizzardi, David
Agriculture Instructor
Shaw, David T.
Physical Health Education Tchr
Soller, Leonard E., Jr.
Physics & Physical Sci Teacher
Westphal, James E.
English Teacher
KEWAUNEE
Barta, Mary Schultz
Second Grade Teacher
Lockwood, Barbara J. Smith
Third Grade Teacher
Patek, Mary Beth (Gillis)
6th Grade Homeroom Teacher
Slack, Gloria
Third Grade Teacher
Wautlet, Jane Novak
Kindergarten Teacher
KIEL
Becker, Robert A.
HS Life Science Teacher
Berens, James Richard
Art Teacher
Krahn-Triebensee, Tanya
Third Grade Teacher
Mayer, Agnes M.
Eighth Grade English Teacher
Meulemans, Barbara Kubale
HS English & Speech Teacher
Reiter, Elaine L.
English & PE Teacher
Steiner, Sue Irene
Cmptr Cnsltnt & Cmptr Sci Tchr
Toepel, Susan Marie
Music Teacher
KIELER
Kisting, Kathy
7th-8th Grade Teacher
KIMBERLY
Dornfeld, William Paul
Mathematics Teacher
Handrich, Tim Gerard
School Counselor
Sensiba, Renee LaChapelle
GATE District Coordinator
Van Boxtel, Randy
English Teacher
KOHLER
Blaser, Cy T.
Retired Teacher
Halverson, Jane C.
Instrumental Music & Eng Tchr
Milsted, Louis E.
Industrial Arts Teacher
Tengowski, Richard R.
Instrumental Music Teacher
LA CROSSE
Barrett, Kenneth John
Math Teacher
Betsinger, Linda Kay
2nd Grade Teacher
Bice, Philip James
Instructor of Accountancy
Bina, Steven John
Band Director
Brownell, Kraig Allan
Science Teacher
Checkai, Gary
Chemistry & Math Teacher
Foust, Diane
Associate Professor of Music
French, Marla Henschel
Fifth Grade Teacher
Friedwald, Marv
Assoc Prof of Business Admin
Gleason, Gerald Howard
Director of Bands
Gruen, Scott Robert
High School Science Teacher
Jones, Keith Calvin
Asst Professor of Marketing
Kaminski, Lori Jane
HS Math Teacher
Kendhammer, Peggy Elizabeth (Rick)
Third Grade Teacher
Kroner, Russell W., Jr.
US History Teacher
Kuffel, Thomas S.
Management Professor
Larson, James Helmer
Professor of Physics & Science
Miller, David Lee
Prof of Philosophy & Chair
Moore, Jean M.
Assistant Professor of Spanish
Morrison, Dianne R.
Finance & Accounting Instr
Munson, Todd Michael
Economics Instructor
Murray, Debra A.
Instructor of Psychology
Oba, Douglas Earl
Professor of Biology
O'Connor, Kathleen Ann
Fourth Grade Teacher
Olson, Donald Kenneth
Physics Teacher
Richardson, Silvana F.
Associate Professor of Nursing
Robarge, Gary Lee
Math & Cmptr Sci Tchr
Rockwell, Barbara M.
Career Svcs-Internships Dir
Rodgers, Vaughn E.
Chemistry Professor
Ross, William H.
Prof of Human Resource Mgmt

ROSSE (cont)
rz, Amy Cathleen
ish & Speech Teacher
, Dianne M. (Patnode)
chr & Frgn Lang Dept Coord
, James Lee
ogy Teacher
Grant T.
stant Professor of English
sta, Michael Jerome
stant Professor of History
ia-Benson, Catherine
ning Disabilities Teacher
el, Bonnie J.
ish Teacher
, Marie Anderson
Grade History & Lit Tchr
n, Ted E.F.
stant Professor
, Judy A.
hematics Teacher
r, Patricia Ellen
stant Professor of Nursing
r, Biljana Ristic
ch, German & Eng Lit Tchr
YSMITH
, Gordon E.
Prof of Soc Work & Chrmn
n, Scott Gilbert
Professor of Business
Cynthia Marshall
al Work Professor
E GENEVA
on, Sharon Reeser
eral & Vocal Music Teacher
stad, Richard O.
sical Sci & Honors Bio Tchr
Sally O'Laughlin
nish Teacher
E MILLS
man, Carla Kumbera
ech & Language Teacher
ay, Judy K.
ily & Consumer Ed Tchr
el, Mark Karl
gion Dept Chm & Span Tchr
CASTER
, Dennis Duane
h School History Teacher
ann, Kristin J.
lish & Speech Teacher
ader, Steven William
rth Grd Tchr & Admin Asst
en, Janis Lynn
st Grade Teacher
e, Jewel Ann
alth & PE Teacher
fe, James J.
sical Sci & Physics Teacher
ard, Nancy Ann (Nagel)
h School Spanish Teacher
e, Linda M.
Grade Teacher
s, Jeffrey Allen
ence, Math, Eng & Art Tchr
kel, Michael Charles
His & Pol Science Teacher
oush, Michelle Suhr
cond Grade Teacher
A
el, Carol (Wood)
gh School English Teacher
TLE CHUTE
es, Margaret Dorothy (Farber)
thematics Teacher
, Jo
h Grade Teacher
ne, Ruth Ann
st Grade Teacher
INGSTON
veg, Eric Paul
strumental Music Instr
, Linda Palzkill
Grade Teacher
ng, Thomas E.
Teacher
DI
ldt, Mark Steven
urth Grade Teacher
n, Thomas Roger, Sr.
gh School Math Teacher
ey, Sharon A.
nguage Arts Teacher
drickson, Lyle William
ath Teacher & Dept Chprsn
l, Mark C.
His & Oral Commnctn Teacher
MIRA
ling, Lucia Araya
-12th Grade Spanish Teacher
ie, Shirley Rateike
cond Grade Teacher
bke, Sandra
d & 5th Grade Teacher
WELL
alt, Lahna Baganz
h Grade Teacher
YAL
gsbury, Barbara Jean
hird Grade Teacher
CK
gorash, Susan Smedal
ourth Grade Teacher
ssar, Martin F.
cience Teacher
son, Lori A.
-12th Grd Lib Media Spclst
XEMBURG
tel, Ronald Edward
olitical Science Teacher

Ehren, David William
High School Band Director
Ehren, Sandra
Business Education Instructor
Ehren, William James, III
Science Teacher
Fierst, Joseph M.
English Department Chairperson
Francois, Elizabeth
9th-12th Grade English Teacher
Leeming, Georgiana Mary
Fifth & Sixth Grade Teacher
Steinhagen, Christine Voelker
Elementary Art Specialist
Touchinski, Brenda Conard
High School Mathematics Tchr
Werner, Renee VanAdestine
Kindergarten Teacher
West, Mary Stephan
Fourth Grade Teacher
Will, Dwight Leeland
Biology Teacher
Yagodinski, Fred A.
Counselor & Athletic Director
MADISON
Bernard, Geraldine Braud
Retired Fourth Grade Teacher
Brill, Nancy C.
4th-5th Grade Teacher
Buckmaster, Lynn Lucas
7th Grade Teacher
Burrows, Nicholas Joseph
Guidance Director
Burt, Barb Modjeski
6th Grade Science & Math Tchr
Carlson, Charles Q.
Social Studies Teacher
Censky, Mary Ann Geller
Instr Asst in Dept Comm Arts
Chen, Zhin
Chinese Lecturer
Cree, B. Jean (Field)
First & Second Grade Teacher
Crowe, Donald Warren
Prof of Mathematics
Faren, Carolyn (Mess Mc Williams)
Kindergarten Teacher
Fuller, Beverly Jean
Spanish Teacher
Hay De Garcia, Becky Ann
Spanish Teacher
Hibbler, Michael Ernest
3rd Grade Teacher
Houlihan, Karen Ann
High School Spanish Teacher
Howe, Thomas Jerome
Soc Stud & AP US His Teacher
Hunt, Don Christian
Art Instructor
Hunt, Mary A.
MS Science Teacher
Jacobson, Joan E.
Social Studies Teacher
Jenkins, Mazie L.
CGI Mathematics Teacher
Johnson, Jan Hougan
Biology Teacher
Kiley, Carol Ann
Health & Physical Ed Teacher
Korth, Carol Buske
Kindergarten Teacher
Lehnherr, Craig Allen
Social Studies Teacher
Levine, Victor R.
Calculus Teacher
McConnell, James William
Art Department Chair
Mc Gilligan-Bentin, Maureen Shannon
4th Grade Teacher
McKinley, Dennis R.
Music Department Chairperson
Minnaert, Alan M.
Physical Ed & Religion Tchr
Muench, Karen Hatas
11th-12th Grd English Teacher
Mullen, Laurie A.
Guidance Counselor
Nigh, Joseph G.
LEP Counselor
Padgham, June Hendrickson
Retired Teacher
Reynoldson, John Roland
English & Amer History Teacher
Roso, Calvin G.
HS Language Arts Teacher
Sieb, Romayne Timmers
Third Grade Teacher
Stimac, Jane Ellen
4th-5th Grade Teacher
Sullivan, Linda Luedke
Clinical Instructor
Tahany, Deborah VanDenPlas
Computer Science Teacher
Welhoefer, Ron J.
Science Teacher
Whitaker, Alvin Eugene
Instructor of Police Science
Zebell, Ralph
Science Teacher & Dept Chair
MANAWA
Wundrock, Michael G.
7th & 8th Grade Math Teacher
MANITOWISH WATERS
Anderson, Leon Roy
Social Studies Teacher
Karl, Renn Carroll
Science Teacher
Szot, Lynn Vrabec
PE, Health & Reading Teacher

MANITOWOC
Adelman, Sandra Marie
Business & Computer Ed Tchr
Bachler, Dale H.
Mathematics Teacher
Blickhahn, Mark Henry
Science & Religion Teacher
Braunel, Lee Arthur
Retired Sixth Grade Teacher
Burbey, Paul Michael
Chemistry Teacher
Drohman, Gary E.
Physics Teacher
Glaeser, Kathleen M.
5th Grade Teacher
Holm, Peter Leslie
Business Education Teacher
Jansen, Sarah Ready
8th Grade Teacher
Lindloff, Timothy Brian
Sr Religion Tchr & Dept Chair
Maedke, Thomas Allen
Social Science Teacher & Coach
Masiak, Ronald Alan
US History & AP Teacher
Matthias, Cheryl Sorensen
Former Guid Cnslng Dept Head
O'Connell, Harry James, Jr.
Third Grade Teacher
O'Connell, Sandee Gums
Fourth Grade Teacher
Schmill, Greg R.
Guidance Director & Eng Tchr
Sievert, Walter Harold
Admin & Eighth Grd Teacher
Steinmetz, Corinne Ann
Former Choral Music Teacher
Tennie, Larry Victor
Mathematics Teacher
Tess, Paul A.
7th-8th Grd Teacher & Prin
MAPLE
Luostari, Patricia E.
Lang Arts Dept Chr & Eng Tchr
Olson, George Harry
9th-12th Grd Bio & Sci Teacher
MARATHON
Bohm, Darrell M.
Reading & Language Arts Tchr
Tess, Robert George
Math Teacher
MARINETTE
Des Jardin, Janice Mason
Drama English & Speech Teacher
Dzurick, Wendy Ann
Assistant Principal
King, Richard E.
7th Grd Math Tchr & Sports Dir
Miller, Karen Katherine
Chem Tchr & Sci Dept Chprsn
Rice, Karolyn Johnson
Middle School Teacher
Stank, Erma Jean Hill
Art Teacher
Yontz, Timothy Gene
Band Director
MARION
Burgdorff, Robert Russell
Instrumental Music Teacher
Kersten, Lee W.
Retired Sci Instr & Dept Chm
MARKESAN
Aaroen, Marsanna Kay (Blue)
Business Education Teacher
Due, Barbara Marie
English Teacher
Hirschy, Russell Philip
Mathematics & Computer Teacher
Hoffmann, Jean Lynn (Evans)
Language Arts Teacher
Kasper, William Scott
Math & Computer Teacher
Sonnleitner, Susan Harreld
Library Media Specialist
MARSHALL
Krull, Peter L.
Business Ed Tchr & Ath Dir
MARSHFIELD
Aslakson, Ronald James
Social Studies Teacher
Boson, Marlee K.
Preschool & Kindergarten Tchr
Chapman, Walter N.
Tenth Grade History Teacher
Halle, Richard W.
Communication Arts Teacher
Halloran, Donal Warren
Associate Prof of Biology
Hartwig, Randall E.
Science Teacher
Hensch, Shirley-Anne
Asst Professor of Psychology
Hughes, Kris Secard
Chemistry Instructor
Johannes, Helen C.
HS Eng Tchr & Dept Chair
Kleinman, Jeff D.
Assistant Professor of History
LeMoine, Robin Leigh
5th Grade Teacher
Martin, Jill Hilliker
Sixth Grade Teacher
Nafziger, Linda Gustafson
Reading Teacher
Olson, Graham Peter
Western Civilization Instr
Shookman, Judy Anne
5th Grade Science Teacher
Sisson, Gordon Jay
9th-12th Grd At Risk Instr

Sisson, Gwenyth Ann Reilly
7th Grade English Teacher
Tharp, Julie A.
English Professor
Tritz, Cathy J.
Language Arts Teacher
MAUSTON
Bade, Connie L.
Mathematics Teacher
Cauley, Mary Jean
Retired 3rd Grade Teacher
Cook, Kathy Lynn Kempf
Vocal Music Director
Crowley, Mary Beth
8th Grade Teacher
Dziewior, Robert Joseph
High School Art Teacher
Gougeon, Raymond J.
Social Studies Teacher
Hammer, Jack Kenneth
Chemistry Teacher
Julian, Mary Kathleen (Ott)
4th Grade Teacher & Principal
Koca, Jack
Geography & History Teacher
Pfeifer, Paul P.
World History Teacher
Schmitz, Margaret Ann
Elementary Music Teacher
Schwark, Mary Ann
5th Grade Teacher
Vinopal, Lynda Ott
Elem Library Media Specialist
Williams, Jacqueline Y.
4th Grade Teacher
MAYVILLE
Holt, Rodney Hugh
Science Teacher
Patrick, Ruth Carpenter
Spanish Teacher
Petrack, Jennie Nowak
Sixth Grade Teacher
Simon, Betsy Rae
Fifth Grade Teacher
MAZOMANIE
Erickson, Jim G.
High School English Instructor
Good, Kathy Wedig
Middle School Science Tchr
Klein, William F.
Counselor
Roll, Tamara Hoff
Bio Teacher & Sci Dept Chair
MC FARLAND
Nielsen, Mary Ann (Knight)
Teacher of At Risk Students
Schaefer, John Thomas
Philosophy, Psych & Soc Tchr
MEDFORD
Cameron, Robert Edward
Computer Teacher
George, David Brad
Principal & Teacher
Keefe, Laurie Buss
6th Grade Teacher
Lewandowski, Walter B.
Retired 5th Grade Teacher
Mahnke, Jeffrey Paul
Pastor
MELLEN
Bodin, James Clare
Music Teacher
MELROSE
Busching, Larry
Director of Bands
MENASHA
Allen, Malcolm Dennis
Associate Professor of English
Bath, Gary Frederick
Language Arts Teacher
Beach, Pamela Ann (Kuehn)
Teacher & Campus Minister
Brey, James Arnold
Assoc Prof of Geography
DeKarske, Trudy Schweitzer
2nd Grade Teacher
Dewing, Denny E.
High School Counselor
Erdman, Janet Vander Heyden
5th Grd Tchr & Science Coord
Hanson, Randy Jon
Teacher of Gifted & Talented
Hauxhaust, James Douglass
Associate Professor of Biology
Huss, Kathy Wojtusik
7th Grd Intgrtd Lang Arts Tchr
Sepnafski, Bill G.
US His & Soc Stud Dept Chm
Staehler, John
Fifth Grade Teacher
Whitcomb, Bradford Scott
Social Psychology Teacher
Ziemann, Kurt Robert
5th-7th Grade Teacher
MENOMONEE FALLS
Berry, Judith Ann (Neidig)
Fourth Grade Teacher
Goetz, Shirley Hallett
Second Grade Teacher
Hessler, James David
Activities Administrator
Jerow, Bonnie K.
Third Grade Teacher
Kimmel, Lionel Paul
Teacher of Emtnlly Disturbed
Kohrt, Kristin M.
Physical Education Teacher
McKendry, Bonnie Jean
Art Teacher

Meier, John Frederick
Former Teacher
Petroff, Ruth Ann Ringer
US History & Amer Govt Teacher
Rierson, Stace L.
History Teacher
Rutsch, Kenneth W.
Business Teacher & Dept Chair
Schmidt, Terry Wayne
Physical Ed & Health Teacher
Schreck, Patricia Ann
2nd Grade Teacher
Sundsmo, Roger D.
Bible, Science & Math Teacher
Wentz, Ronald Lawrence
Chemistry Teacher
MENOMONIE
Christie, Diane Marie
Mathematics Lecturer
Hardy, James Conrad
Civics & Geography Teacher
Kyles, Christine M. (Raycher)
Sixth Grade Teacher
Lehman, Patty Jo
Middle School Band Director
Neiderhauser, John Edgar
Math Department Chair & Tchr
Nero, Sharon Sell
Sociology Professor
Paulson, Cindy Stellpflug
Fifth Grade Teacher
Tillison, Stephen Lindsay
Sixth Grade Teacher
MEQUON
Brown, Brook Joseph
Social Stud Dept Chairperson
Buehler, Lorraine Jaeger
English Teacher
Caven, Debra L.
6th Grade Teacher
Connelly, Kathy A.
Computer Science Teacher
Gregory, Mary Sharon Sullivan
English Teacher
Gullick, Susan Fehrenbach
4th Grade Teacher
Kashian, Arthur Toros
Second Grade Teacher
Kellen, Victoria J. Edwards
High School Spanish Teacher
Lokker, Jean E.
English & Journalism Teacher
Orth, Robert George
Mathematics Teacher
Oswald, Matthew Thomas
Mathematics & Computer Teacher
Pierce, Randy Greenwald
Fifth Grade Teacher
Savage, David Raymond
Science Teacher
Seider, Mary Loehr
Middle School Teacher
Sisney, Ned E.
Professor of Theatre & Comm
Solorzano, Kathleen Beaudoin
High School Spanish Teacher
Wallace, Marie Lancaster
Guidance Counselor
MERCER
Leverson, Glen Tilford
Physical Education Teacher
Plank, Laura VanLanen
Vocal Music Teacher
MERRILL
Carter, Ellen Bartling
English & History Teacher
Drury, Gary M.
Administrator
Iwen, Douglas H.
10th Grade US History Teacher
King, Robert Allen
Associate Principal
Kohnke, Virginia (Abraham)
Retired Teacher
Kufahl, Mary Caylor
Social Studies & Art Teacher
Leindecker, Delores Schaumberg
Second Grade Teacher
Peterson, Jay Charles
Math Teacher & Football Coach
Presl, Phyllis Podrez
4th Grade Teacher
Schofield, Gregory Lyle
Physical Education Instructor
Spencer, Kathryn Mary
Spanish Teacher
Tetzloff, Alan David
Sr High School Guidance Cnslr
Vander Leest, Barbara Ellen
Mathematics Teacher
Waid, Mary Jeanne (Donner)
Junior High Choral Director
Wegner, Kathleen A. (Spangler)
Art Teacher
MERTON
Rheineck, John Richards, Jr.
MS Science & Technology Tchr
Zaupa, Cheryl Lynn
Middle School English Teacher
MIDDLETON
Brady, Marie Winter
Mathematics Teacher
Hofeldt, Constance Marguerita
French Teacher
Lier, Norman Edward
Math Teacher
Percy, Margaret Endsley
Coord of Gifted & Talented
Relph, H. Daniel
Business Education Teacher

MIDDLETON (cont)
Schmidt, Mary Katherine
Social Studies Teacher
Wilson, Jeffrey Roy
8th Grade Earth Science Tchr
MILTON
Becker, Nancy Gardner
Eng, Jrnlsm Tchr & Dept Chair
Lieder, Thomas Craig
PE Teacher & Coach
Runde, Diane Timmerman
Agriculture Instructor
Vruwink, Donald James
HS Social Studies Teacher
MILWAUKEE
Afonso, Meneo Antonio
Asst Professor of Philosophy
Allerheiligen, David L.
7th-8th Grd Science Teacher
Alles, Brad Alan
Religion Teacher
Ambrose, Dan Stephen
Social Science Teacher
Amonson, Terrill H.
Mathematics Teacher
Anderson, Joanne Achenbach
Undergrad Ed-Spec Ed Chrprsn
Anderson, Mora Ann
Secondary English Teacher
Anderson, Tuwania Rosemelia
Learning Disabilities Educator
Ash, Patricia McKillop
Science & Math Teacher
Avella, Steven Mark
Assoc Prof of His & Dept Chair
Azpell, Betty Zintek
Science Department Chairperson
Backes, Nancy C.
Visiting Asst Prof of English
Bahr, Mark Mahlon
Assistant Principal
Bakemeyer, Lucia Bravo
Spanish Teacher
Bantz, Daniel Eugene
8th Grade Science Teacher
Barbuch, Mary Lou Meyers
7th-12th Grade Math Teacher
Bell, G. Alfred
Student Activities Director
Bersch, Jeffrey Thomas
8th Grade Math Teacher
Bertorello, Carolyn J.
English & Composition Tchr
Bielawski, Bonnie Boettcher
Choral Director
Bintz, Bruce Matthew
Seventh Grade Teacher
Blaha, Maggie A.
4th Grade Teacher
Blohm, John Michael
Physics & Earth Science Tchr
Blomquist, MaryLane Neubauer
Mathematics Teacher & Chprsn
Blumberg, Kurt Eric
Indstrl Mech Engr & Dept Chair
Boettcher, Anne Catherine
Theology Teacher
Bolz, Sarah Jane
Mathematics Department Chair
Braxton, Jerrell
School Social Worker
Breitbach, Richard Clarence
Asst Professor of Sociology
Brooks, Anne Swainbank
Third Grade Teacher
Bublitz, Donald
HS Social Studies Teacher
Buege, Robert D.
English Teacher & Dept Chm
Buehner, Barbara Braun
Latin Instructor
Burkee, Jack Gerald
8th Grd Tchr & Ath Dir
Burns, Barbara Ferdinandi
Math Teacher & Department Chm
Burns, Lawrence James
Math Department Chairperson
Cain, Mary Schlosser
Forensics Coach
Cairns, Johanna
Pom Pom Coach
Carlin, Martha
Associate Professor of History
Carman, William H.
Art Professor & Chair
Carter, Geraldine
6th-7th Grade Reading Teacher
Carufel, Edward A.
Social Studies Teacher
Case, Donalda J.
Chemistry & Biology Teacher
Casteneda, Belen Sadot
Spanish Teacher
Cebar-Stano, Mary Beth
Kindergarten Teacher
Chappell, Virginia A.
Associate Professor of English
Chiaverina, J. Michael
Photography & Journalism Tchr
Chmielewski, Thomas
Theology Teacher
Christie, Robert Allen
Spanish Teacher
Christoph, Ronda
English Teacher & Yearbook Adv
Combs, Lisa Beauford
Math & Science Teacher
Conti, Joseph Lawrence
6th Grade Teacher
Copper, Glen Scott Thomas
HS English & Theater Teacher
Corning, Lee Ann (Simonis)
PE Instr & Renaissance Coord
Cummens, Linda Ryan
Substitute Teacher
Daniels, Michael John
Physical Ed & Health Teacher
Davis, Daniel Francis
Secondary Teacher
Dawson, Patrick K.
Social Studies Teacher
Dee, Charlie
English & History Instructor
Del Colle, Ralph Gerald
Asst Professor of Theology
Denison, Ann L.
Vocal Instructor
Devine, Ann Marie
Marketing Professor
Diaz, Marilyn
Spanish Immersion Teacher
Diedrich, Glen Dale
History Teacher
Di Vilio, Susan
Fifth Grade Teacher
Dlugosz, Joseph Louis
Art Instructor
Docktor, Andrew G.
Homeless Shelter Liaison
Dove, Earlee Mason
3rd Grade Teacher
Dreyer, Bruce
Physical Education Teacher
DuMez, Judith D.
Education Professor
Durr, Jeffrey Thomas
Band, Jazz Dir & Dept Chair
Ealy, Carolyn Elaine
Science Teacher
Eberhardy, Mary E.
French & Latin Teacher
Ebersperger, Barbara M.
Fifth Grade Teacher
Ehley, Linda Ann (Fortener)
Coord of Comp Sci & Asst Prof
Erickson-Snyder, Katherine Ann
English Teacher
Espinoza, Maurice H.
Clinical Instructor
Everett, Janaan Davis
Biology Teacher
Fargen, Pat Ann
Second Grade Teacher
Farkas, Mary Ann Catherine
Asst Prof of Criminology & Law
Ferguson, Mary J.
Assistant Principal
Flayter, Joan Pitrof
Fifth Grade Math Teacher
Flynn, Mary
Reading & Lang Arts Professor
Fontanini, Jennifer Gourde
Social Studies Teacher
Foran, Patrick
History Teacher
Francis, John Randall
Choral Music Dir & Tchr
Freschl, Gloria Blesser
Lecturer of Organic Chemistry
Friedman, Paula Sopkin
English Dept Chair & Asst Prof
Friman, H. Richard
Associate Professor of Pol Sci
Gamzer, Sondra Vogt
Vocal Music Teacher
Gardner, Suzann Doherty
Assistant Professor
Giacinti, Louis Anthony
Natural Science Teacher
Giersch, Peter A.
French & English Teacher
Graeven Peter, Marian
Instructor in Teacher Ed
Grassel, Jack R.
Instruction Coordinator
Greenstreet, Karen E.
Former Political Sci Professor
Griswold, James Allen
Associate Principal
Gurtner, Kristen M.
6th Grade Science Teacher
Haas, George A.
Health & Physical Ed Teacher
Hadley, Pamela Louise
Physical Ed & Dance Teacher
Hahn, Joseph F.
History & German Teacher
Hamedani, G. Hossein G.
Professor of Mathematics
Handford, Thyra Minette
Assistant Principal
Hanks, Deborah C.
Assoc Prof of Bus & Ec Dept
Harris-Benn, Charlotte A.
Reading & English Instructor
Hatab, Elizabeth Ann
Fifth Grade Teacher
Haugh, Jami Lynn
Sixth Grade Teacher
Haworth, Daniel Thomas
Chemistry Professor
Heidmann, Keith Harold
Chemistry Teacher
Heiman, Gary John
Principal & Teacher
Heinz, Anne Klingseisen
Mathematics Teacher
Heinzelman, William Robert
Social Studies Teacher
Heiss, Marie O'Leary
English Teacher
Heitz, Eugene Robert
Marketing Ed Teacher & Coord
Hettwer, Betty J.
Math Teacher
Hill, Austin L.
Trade Technology Teacher
Hinze, Christine Firer
Professor of Christian Ethics
Holmquist, Gisela Nina
Spanish Teacher
Horowitz, Mark J.
Fourth Grade Teacher
Irish, John Saari
HS Physical Education Teacher
Jacomet, Sherrie L.
Fourth Grade Teacher
Jadin, Rita Ann
5th Grade Teacher
Jashinsky, Rose B.
Music Teacher & Orchestra Dir
Johnson, Andrea Joy
Associate Professor
Johnson, Donelle G.
Fifth Grade Teacher
Jones, Mark Anthony
Educational Assistant & Coach
Kamdar, Pravin C.
Business & Economics Professor
Kenner, E. Peggy Coleman
Human Service Instructor
Kessenich, Kenneth J.
Science Teacher & Chairman
Kessenich, Lorraine L.
English & Reading Teacher
Kiaie, Catherine Carroll
Asst Professor of Mathematics
Kiemen, Barbara Lynn
Mathematics Teacher
Kingma, Beverly M.
Latin, Eng, & Forensics Tchr
Kirk, Janice Reid
Second Grade Teacher
Kirksey, Lucy Sherard
Lead Instr of Basic Skills
Knudson, Marianne Alice (Stark)
First Grade Teacher
Koenig, Barbara E.
Eng & Human Relations Tchr
Korn, Jeffrey Bernard
Physics & Chem Associate Prof
Kostenko, James John
Science Teacher
Krebs, Suzanne
English Teacher
Kreilein, Sylvester Linus
HS German Teacher
Krejci, Janet Wessel
Nursing Asst Professor
Kroncke, Robert Newton
Social Studies Teacher
Kroupa, Suzanne Szymanski
English Teacher
Krueger, Nancy Louise
Bus Ed Instr & Dept Chprsn
Labisch, Genevera Ann
Family & Consumer Ed Instr
Landgren, Terry Douglas
Mathematics Teacher
Laubenheimer, Mary Gebhardt
8th Grade Algebra Teacher
Lawrence, Barbara Ann (Baumann)
Eighth Grade Teacher
Lipsky, Robert John
Student Teacher Supervisor
Liska, James Richard
English & Journalism Teacher
Lopez, Jeannette
Student Assistant Coordinator
Lorusso, Mary E.
Principal
Lotesto, Daniel V.
Math Teacher
Lown, Donald Philip
Pre-Calculus Tchr & Ath Dir
Maguire, Daniel Charles
Professor of Ethics
Manger, Barbara Ellen
Art Assistant Professor
Mann, George Kenneth
5th-6th Grade Teacher
Maresh, Mary H.
Assistant Principal
Marino, Ted Michael
HS PE & Health Ed Teacher
McDonald, Eddie M.
Sixth Grade Teacher
Mc Sherry, Sharon Lynn
7th Grade Teacher
Medhin, Delois Vann
Communications Instructor
Megal, Carolyn F.
German Teacher
Mewhorter, Marjorie Ann (Crandall)
5th Grade Tchr
Mielke, David E.
Accounting Professor
Miller, Harold Lee
Instructor of Music
Miller, Sally Ann
Physical Education Teacher
Miller, Ursula Baumgarten
Spanish Teacher
Moeller, Joan E.
English Teacher
Molenda, Gary Thomas
Physical Education Teacher
Mosley, Mary Ann Ferrell
Learning Resource Ctr Instr
Motzkus, Kyle Milton
Fourth Grade Teacher
Muelver, Donna Redman
Headmaster
Myers, Larry Wayne
Instructor of Religion
Nash, Richard F.
Psychology Professor
Naylor, Phillip Chiviges
Assoc Prof of His & Dir
Neddle, Mercedes
Acctng & Banking Teacher
Nelson, Susan Burns
7th & 8th Grade Math Teacher
Neuman, Lynn M.
Math Teacher & Computer Coord
Nickels, Larry Charles
Physical Ed Teacher & Coach
Nolan, John C., II
Driver Ed & English Teacher
Noonan, Thomas O.
Director of Debate
Norstrem, Thomas Michael
English Teacher
Nourzad, Farrokh
Associate Professor of Ec
Nykl, Thomas E.
Senior Lecturer
O'Neil, Jerry Patrick
Chemistry Teacher
Onyemena, Ifedi Clement
Prof of English & Literature
Osborne, Donald Thomas
Mathematics Teacher
Paustenbach, Karen Ann (Roos)
English Teacher
Perkins, Rose Marie (Blevins)
Fifth Grade Teacher
Pike, Sharyl Ann
PE & Health Ed Teacher
Plum, Joan Ensor
Kindergarten Teacher
Polczynski, Susan E.
Fourth Grade Teacher
Pollnow, Wayne M.
Math Teacher
Powell, David Michael
English Teacher
Probst, Mark George
Bus Ed Tchr & Voc Counselor
Racer, David L.
Liberal Arts Instructor
Reed, Kathryn Luckow
Scndry Ed & Bus Ed Tchr
Reed, Tammy Ann
English Teacher
Rice, Anne Mary
Social Studies Teacher
Ring, Robert L.
English Instructor & Counselor
Roberts, Raymond Jefferson Davis
Vocal Arts Facilitator
Robertson, Steven Ray
Assistant Director & Counselor
Roehrig, Terence
Political Science Professor
Roelke, Thomas Vernon
Biology Instructor
Rohde, Kim G.
Social Stud & AP His Tchr
Ronsman, Terrance E.
US History Teacher
Ruback, Randall Scott
Private Studio Brass Instr
Ruff, Julius Ralph
Associate Professor of History
Ruff, Laura Blair
Instructor of Accounting
Ruffin, Joyce L.
High School English Teacher
Rush, Leola Elizabeth (Hunt)
Secondary Math & Comp Sci Tchr
Santilli, Patricia Turner
7th Grade Teacher
Schalig, Ron E.
US History Teacher
Schmelzer, Mary Elizabeth
Fourth Grade Teacher
Schmit, Marilyn C.
Prof & Chair of Sociology Dept
Schmitz-Penfield, Susan Elizabeth
Art Teacher
Schnake, Richard Karl
8th Grade Teacher
Schreiner, Bernard Earl
Science Teacher & Dept Chair
Schroeder, Mary Lou
Second Grade Teacher
Schuldt, Jeffrey Paul
HS Social Studies Teacher
Schumacher, Gordon Robert
Math Department Chair
Schwartz, Kevin Andrew
Drama Teacher
Schwarz, Rozanne
German Teacher
Schwieters, Michael A.
Science & Physics Teacher
Scolavino, Ray Anthony
Science Teacher
Seccombe, Pamela Leah
French Teacher
Seeger, Kurtis A.
Mathematics Instructor & Coach
Seegers-Braun, Margaret
Athletic Director & PE Tchr
Seward, Michael C.
German Teacher
Seynhoven, Marlene Peterson
Fourth Grade Teacher
Shana, Zack A.
Instructor
Shinners, Gerald John
Mathematics Teacher
Simons, Gregory Scott
Respiratory Care Instructor
Skudlarczyk, Susan Klafka
Third Grade Teacher
Smith, Gail Katherine
Assistant Professor of English
Smith, Ken
History Teacher
Snyder, Daniel Robert
Social Science Instructor
Solomakos, Peter G.
Economics & Business Instr
Starr, Rachelle Lynette Colonel
Voice Teacher & Choral Dir
Stenklyft, Terry N.
Fifth Grade Teacher
Stephens, John A.
History & Economics Teacher
Stillman, Henry MacDonald
History Teacher
Sykes, Richard Raymond
Social Studies Teacher
Talsky, Mary Thereasa
Social Studies Teacher
Tamanji, Asenju Callistus
Social Sci & Economics Tchr
Taylor, Richard Charles
Associate Prof of Philosophy
Terry, Suzanne Martinson
Reading & Lang Arts Dept Instr
Thompson, Elayne MacArdy
Psychology Professor
Thompson, Thomas B.
Math & Science Teacher
Timken, Jeanne M.
School Counselor
Tonn, Gloria Muellenbach
First Grade Teacher
Trapp, Jacqueline Tuchalski
Secondary Social Studies Tchr
Unke, Ronald George
Physical Education Teacher
Vaughan, Priscilla Pech
Retired 6th-8th Grade Teacher
Vitrano, Joseph Anthony
Latin Teacher & Athletic Dir
VonRueden, Margaret (Balistrieri)
Art Dept Chprsn & Teacher
Waliszewski, Kenneth J.
Adjunct Professor
Walter, Suzanne Kay (Eastman)
Instructor
Weaver, Willie B., Jr.
Social Studies Teacher
Weinstein, Suzanne Gitelson
Modern Hebrew Teacher
Wells, Carolyn Cressy
Soc Work Prof & Prgm Dir
Weyhrich, Randy Jay
English Tchr & Asst Stage Mgr
Wild, Ronald
AP US His Tchr & Dept Chprsn
Williams, Gary Ralph
Music Professor
Williams, Geraldine
Eng Tchr & Human Rltns Liaison
Winters, Drew Brantner
Finance Professor
Witte, Michael Andrew
Theology Teacher
Woodworth, Thomas Arthur
Mathematics Teacher
Wulff, Sherry Ann Clara
Assoc Prof & Prof Comm Dept
Zielinski, Jerome Joseph
Social Science Teacher
Zupko, Ronald Edward
Professor of History
MINDORO
Kirchner, Betty J.
Retired 2nd Grade Teacher
MINERAL POINT
Chappell, Marilyn (Fuhr)
French & Spanish Teacher
Laverty, Bonnie Lancaster
Art Teacher
Stoehr, Amy M.
Spanish Teacher
Thoyre, Gregory Howard
HS Mathematics Teacher
MINOCQUA
Coconate, Martha T.
English Instructor
Martens, Thomas E.
Math Teacher
Nesper, Glen Alan
History & Law Teacher
MINONG
Hagen, Tom
History Teacher
MISHICOT
Bourgeois, David Lloyd
7th-12th Grd Vocal Music Tchr
Kreil, Joanne Cigler
Second Grade Teacher
Quirk, Liz Koehler
Third Grade Teacher
Scheuer, Mary Agnes Haen
IMC Director
MONDOVI
Adams, Barbara Jo (Wright)
Biology Teacher & Athletic Dir
Harschlip, Rod L.
Government & Economics Teacher
Laehn, David
Spanish Teacher

OVI (cont)
yen, Lynnette (Hladish)
: Teacher
Jeffrey Howard
h Grd Soc Stud Tchr
rom, Dallas Kenneth
ematics Teacher
NA
on, Shirley Rae
ed Music Teacher
OE
Dan
al Ed Dir
bo, Candice Dexheimer
School English Teacher
er, Virginia Andrews
ed Second Grade Teacher
nn, Deanne Lynn
h, Span Tchr & Drama Dir
acher, Alan David
Studies Tchr & Dept Chm
TELLO
ecker, Catherine Riedl
2th Grade Art Educator
Mary Mullowney
ness Education Teacher
, Susan Ann
ish & Theater Teacher
TICELLO
r, Melody Diane
: Health Teacher
Michael Jon
c Director
NEE
h, Carla Marie
2th Grd Vocal Music Tchr
ger, Keith Charles
Grade Teacher
s, Rebecca Sue (Smith)
d Grade Teacher
, Beverly Ann
nd Grade Teacher
n, Rose Marie (Knutson)
nd Grade Teacher
ann, Mary Renata
d Grade Teacher
nski, Paul James
Grade World History Tchr
Cecilia Wiza
red Teacher
, Carrie S.
ness Teacher
ler, Ann Martie
ish Teacher
NT CALVARY
an, Dennis M.
: Principal
ch, Debra Detert
n Grade Teacher
gan, Sara Fredrich
ogy & Chemistry Teacher
Jeffrey J.
Stud Dept Chm & His Tchr
am, David E.
h, Physics & Computer Tchr
NT HOREB
, Kevin Alan
al Science Teacher
WONAGO
s, Sandra Sizemore
nish Teacher
rson, Lynn Manley
Grade Teacher
n, Joyce Cramer
cher of Emotionally Dsbld
nann, Paul William
hematics Teacher
n, James Steven
logy Instructor
, Scott Vincent
d Director
, Mary Ellen
r of Emotionally Disturbed
ell, Darrell Robert
Grade Life Science Teacher
Cynthia Ann
rumental Music Teacher
es, Marilyn E.
glish Teacher
n, Maura Ann
ial Studies Teacher
z, Katherine Mae
glish Teacher
am, Margaret Healy
anish Teacher
n, Thomas Frederick
story Teacher
ler, Keith Donald
Physical Education Teacher
gland, William Wayne
glish Tchr & Var Ftbl Coach
er, Phyllis Brunt
Grd Language Arts Teacher
olka, Bonnie S.
1st Grade Reading Teacher
s, Carol Lipphardt
Grade Teacher
son, Sandra Anderson
st Grade Teacher
s, Barbara Ladwig
mily & Consumer Ed Teacher
brecht, Mark Edward
cial Studies Teacher
haelis, Peter Rex
urth Grade Teacher
son, Lynn A.
n Grade Science Teacher
son, Terry L.
th Grade Teacher

Porter, Mary Keyes
Guidance Counselor
Pratt, Scott R.
HS Math & Computer Sci Teacher
Schneidler, Sue
English Teacher
Schraufnagel, Marian C.
High School Physics Teacher
Schueller, Mary Beth
Sixth Grade Teacher
Smith, David G.
English Teacher
Sobottke, Thomas Martin
Secondary History Teacher
Stach, Kathryn Bullard
Coll Eng, Speech & Debate Tchr
Vick, Rod R.
Journalism & English Instr
Walsh, Michael Gregory
Sixth Grade Teacher
MUSCODA
Marchionda, Joan Mae
Kindergarten Teacher
Ward, Joyce Helgerson
Retired Elementary Teacher
MUSKEGO
Blaha, Joan Nienow
German Teacher
Corona, Cynthia Kasza
6th Grade Teacher
Dornacher, Laurence David
Fr Tchr & Frgn Lang Dept Chair
Eaton, Kelly Jo (Ignasiak)
Mathematics Teacher
Fortmann, Candice J.
8th Grd English Teacher
Johnston, Cathleen Zintek
Chemistry Teacher
Kaczmarek, Laurie Beth
History Teacher
Klingsporn, Mary Balsley
6th Grade Teacher
Kreul, Catherine Shea
Mathematics Teacher
Nitka, Mike
Teacher
Nuszbaum, Robert F.
Social Studies Teacher
Plier, Scot James
Art Teacher
Pyne, Margaret Mary
World & US History Teacher
Schwalbach, Clarice Rose
Retired Teacher
Suhm, Jean Gerlach
French & Spanish Teacher
Toman, Vincent
7th Grade Social Stud Teacher
Zautner, Kathy Weyer
Business Education Teacher
Zimmerman, Margaret
Second Grade Teacher
NECEDAH
Ebert, Kristi Denner
Art Teacher
Kennedy, Kathleen Ann
HS Social Stud & Eng Teacher
NEENAH
Abud, Jennifer Judge
Spanish Teacher
Bezella, Pat Ann (Aldag)
Health Teacher & Coordinator
Charapata, Jerry Joseph
Band Director
DeZur, John R., Jr.
5th Grade Teacher
Hare, Eileen
HS Physical Education Teacher
Klitz, James David
Mathematics Teacher
Lewis, Joseph H.
6th Grade Teacher
Pogue, Mary Thielmann
8th Grade English Teacher
Riggs, Helene R.
Teacher
Scherck, George D.
Social Studies Teacher
Waterworth, Philip Lee
Mathematics Teacher
Weinmann, Donald John
Afro-Asia Wstrn Cultures Tchr
NEILLSVILLE
Abel, Donald Jacob
Fourth Grade Teacher
Bronk, Timothy Philip
Technology Education Teacher
Finney, Mary Landino
AOD Coord & Health Teacher
Lindner, Dianne M.
Second Grade Teacher
Nemitz, Sharon Weber
4th & 5th Grade Teacher
Weirauch, K. Ann (Krauss)
Second Grade Teacher
Worachek, James J.
English Teacher
NEKOOSA
Alan, Kathleen Beer
Choral Director
Bushar, Kathryn Louise
Second Grade Teacher
Fritz, Nancy (Neve)
Third Grade Teacher
Pacolt, Dianne Pauline
Bio & Human Physiology Tchr
Staats, Richard Lee
Science Teacher

NEOPIT
Creapeau, Alphia Marie
Science Teacher
NESHKORO
Vining, Alice Ruth Bednarek
Retired Elementary Teacher
Whitemarsh, Janice White
Seventh & Eighth Grade Teacher
NEW AUBURN
Kastelic, Joseph Anthony
7th-12th Grd Soc Stud Teacher
Rehrauer, Elizabeth A.
English Teacher
NEW BERLIN
Baron, Joanne Marie
Business Education Teacher
Hilts, Linda Skelly
Fourth Grade Teacher
Lukas, Scott E.
Technology Education Teacher
Nance, Kent Robert
Middle School Health Teacher
Nettesheim, James L.
Sixth Grade Teacher
Nyman, Constance R.
Third Grade Teacher
Prellwitz, James H.
Biology Teacher
Richards, Joseph William
Science Teacher
Roehm, Kay E.
Business Teacher
Rohde, Kathleen M.
English Teacher
Setz, Jeffrey F.
Math Teacher & Dept Chprsn
Strupp, Thomas David
Technology Education Teacher
Wilber, Barbara Smith
Computer Sci & Bus Ed Teacher
NEW GLARUS
Jackson, Barbara J.
Business Education Teacher
Kuenzi, Betty Elaine (Brusveen)
Former Teacher
Martinson, Jane C.
Fifth Grade Teacher
NEW HOLSTEIN
Burton, Gerald Alan
Business Education Teacher
Clausen, Mary O'Brien
Mathematics Teacher
Flora, Grace M.
English Teacher
Flora, James Edward
Social Studies Tchr & Dept Chm
Geigel, Patrick Raymond
History, English Tchr & Coach
Hackbarth, Nancy M.
Kindergarten Teacher
Hubbartt, Lesa F. Wittmus
Social Studies Teacher
Milligan, Timothy James
Chemistry & Physics Teacher
Ploederl, Diane Kohlman
Sixth Grade Teacher
Wilberscheid, Robert C.
English Teacher
NEW LISBON
Buchholz, David A.
Mathematics Teacher
NEW LONDON
Coulter, Shirley M.
Retired 5th Grade Science Tchr
Flury, Lori Beth
Choral Director
Martin, Adrian Robert
English Teacher
Sullivan, Kay Marie
6th Grade Teacher
Wohlt, Ralph D.
Science Teacher
NEW RICHMOND
Brunclik, Pam Marie (Adler)
Business Education Teacher
Gregerson, Richard W.
Director of Bands
Peplau, Marilyn Drew
Guidance Counselor
Rosenbaum, Sue Ellen
5th Grade Teacher
Stephens, James Kelly
Physical Education Teacher
NORTH LAKE
Ferguson, Eilena Jane
Sixth-Eighth Grd English Tchr
OAK CREEK
Ankerson, Gail Ellen
History Teacher
Barrett, Lisa Chulew
High School Soc Stud Teacher
Bauhs, Robert Richard
Mathematics Teacher
Becker, GloriaJean L. (Gerner)
Health Occupations Teacher
Brunner, Diane Lynn
Fifth Grade Teacher
Correll, Dorothy Ruth (Hamm)
Fifth Grade Teacher
Hammermann, Carla J.
Second Grade Teacher
Keane, John Patrick
Eighth Grade Teacher
Kreuser, Donald R.
Assistant Principal
Mc Knight, Susan Schmitz
Third Grade Teacher
Miller, Dulcy Berlin
Elementary General Music Tchr

Papka, Michael Val
Fourth Grade Teacher
Snamiska, Sherman John
Biology Teacher
Soik, Paul Langhoff
Computer Science Teacher
Stack, Ricky A.
Social Studies Teacher
Tellefsen, Donald James
Tchr of Learning Disabilities
OAKFIELD
Messner, Albert Eugene
Science & Math Teacher
OCONOMOWOC
Blersch, Robert Allen
Technology Education Instr
Brandenburg, Bette L.
Fr Tchr & Frgn Lang Dept Chm
Brinkman, Jeffrey Lee
Physical Education Teacher
Budisch, Michael J.
Administrator, Prin & Coach
Capperino, Marilyn Peterson
Chemistry & Physics Teacher
Christensen, Judith Mary
French Teacher
Christman, Cari S.
Math Teacher
Faherty, George M.
High School Math Teacher
Freiburger, Eileen Anne
7th-8th Grade Science Teacher
Gerlach, Roxanne Carla (Stenson)
Kindergarten Teacher
Gerndt, Donna Manthei
7th Grade Teacher & Asst Prin
Holzmiller, Connie Petesch
K-6th Grd Gen Music & Choir
Holzmiller, Dan Roy
High School Chemistry Teacher
Lewis, Diana R.
Reading Specialist & Teacher
Maas, Fred
8th Grd Soc Studies Teacher
Miksic, Robert Michael
English & German Teacher
Neary, Jody Rholl
Chemistry & Physics Teacher
Newburg, Mary Jo
English Teacher
Olander, Michael Richard
Science Teacher
Peterson, Michael Robert
Director of Bands
Reul, David G.
Music Teacher
Risch, Elaine Karrels
Fourth Grade Teacher
Roth, Norman Daniel, Jr.
8th Grd & K-8th Grd PE Teacher
Schuster, Barbara J.
6th Grade Teacher
Sladky, Stephen Thomas
Mathematics Teacher
Small, Karen Lynn
Science Instructor
Wilson, Robert Thomas
Seventh Grade Geography Tchr
Wright, Jack
Retired Teacher
OCONTO
Ballestad, Karl Theodore Bennett
Math & Computer Teacher
Behling, Connie Schomaker
4th Grade Teacher
Gabrielson, Peter Arthur
World His, Ec, & Govt Teacher
Gerl, LeRoy John
Tech Ed Tchr & Head Coach
Green, Linda L.
Science Teacher
Gretzinger, C. Jeff
Instrumental Music Instructor
Nutini, Peter Joseph
Biology Teacher
OCONTO FALLS
Boehlen, Anne Stevenson
Fourth Grade Teacher
Brown, Carmen (Wendt)
7th Grade Life Science Teacher
Hobyan, Louis John
Elementary Principal
Pagel, Susan Digmann
Kindergarten Teacher
OMRO
Hall, John H.
Band Director
Kurth, Allen D.
Chem & Physics Instructor
Ostertag, Teresa Ann (Peters)
PE Tchr, Var Grls Bsktbl Coach
Schwartz, Jon J.
Health Educator
ONALASKA
Burfield, Nancy Jean Olinger
Fourth Grade Teacher
Goode-Rogowski, Stephanie L.
MAC Sys Op & Writing Lab Supvr
Hendricks, Beth Ann Schoeneman
English Teacher
Homstad, John H.
8th Grade Teacher
King, Daniel John
Science Teacher
Kyes, Richard J.
Math Teacher
Lisk, Kevin John
New Test Doctrine & Latin Tchr
Riley, Kenneth Lee
Rdng, Lang, Math & Sci Tchr

Shpardson, Darin Troy
Social Studies Instructor
Solie, Joan Hansen
Retired HS Eng & Span Tchr
Temp, David T.
9th-12th Grade English Teacher
Wiggert, Sandra Partridge
HS Spanish & French Teacher
Wordell, Keith Donald
Band Instructor
OOSTBURG
Adams, Robert Vincent
Middle School Teacher
Greupink, Scott
Physical Education Teacher
Justus, James R.
Technology Education Teacher
Kobelsky, John Randall
Mathematics Teacher
LeClair, Michael Albert
English & Speech Teacher
Navis, Larry B.
English Teacher
Ruggles, Karen Space
Kindergarten Teacher
OREGON
Budrow, Julianne C.
Teacher of At-Risk Students
Debroux, Douglas Paul
Calculus & Computer Sci Tchr
Owens, Sandra Jean (Brewer)
Seventh Grd Geography Teacher
Pribbenow, Roger Allen
Mathematics Teacher
ORFORDVILLE
Fox, Debra Ann Nolan
Instrumental Music Director
Mills, Ernie L.
High School Technology Teacher
Nickols, Marcia Lynn
Art Teacher
Wolfe, Alice Lorraine
5th-6th Grade Teacher
OSCEOLA
Anderson, Geraldine Clark
First Grade Teacher
Bowitz, Linda Hohman
English Teacher
Bullard, Robert G.
Elem PE & Driver Ed Teacher
Dauscher, Steven Scott
Social Studies Teacher
Erickson, James Earl
Social Studies Instructor
Erickson, Michael C.
High School Business Teacher
Ludvigson, Judy Kuehndorf
Reading Teacher
Marsh, Dianne R. (Miller)
English Reading Teacher
McMartin, Michael P.
6th Grade Teacher
Peterson, Lesalyn Louise
5th Grade Teacher
Schultz, Judy A.
English Teacher
OSHKOSH
Achterberg, Sandra Froehlich
Art Tchr & Coord of GATE
Dolan, Susan Piton
English Teacher
Donker, Sue Ann Simpson
Literature & Composition Tchr
Eichel, Jo L.
6th-8th Grd Mathematics Tchr
Evans, Damaris White
Social Studies Teacher
Mosher, Laurie Woodruff
English & Drama Teacher
Sandberg, Gail Lynn
Business Education Teacher
Stein, Diana G.
8th Grade Science Teacher
Van Thiel, Jay A.
Social Studies Teacher
Wilfahrt, James F.
Fifth Grade Teacher
Wisnefski, Gladys Allende
Spanish Teacher
Zentner, Randall Kieth
Vocal Music Director
OSSEO
Boettcher, Eric Wayne
Agriculture Teacher & Coach
Bowerman, Bruce Charles
7th & 8th Grd Soc Stud Tchr
Hall, Timothy John
Science Teacher
Halverson, Daniel Olav
Business & Economics Teacher
Wehner, Mark J.
Vocal Music Teacher
OWEN
Lynch, Jerry Lee
Science Teacher
Reyzer, Salome Susan (Grabski)
Fifth & Sixth Grade Teacher
OXFORD
Bolgrihn, Caroline May
First Grade Teacher
Bolgrihn, Michael Charles
Social Studies Teacher
Shirley, Quinn Rena
Middle School Science Teacher
PALMYRA
Hubert, Karen (Zdrojowy)
Music & Theatre Arts Teacher
PARDEEVILLE
Ebben, Randall H.
5th Grade Teacher

PARDEEVILLE (cont)
Indrelie, Stephen Charles
4th Grade Teacher
Kamrath, Phillip Wayne
Social Studies Teacher
Pufahl, Barry P.
Junior High Teacher
Quade, Stuart T.
English Teacher
PARK FALLS
Balczewski, Margot Joan
Eng, Soc Stud & Keybrdng Tchr
Donner, Mark Thomas
7th-12th Grade Choral Director
Luoma, Virginia Lee
Fourth Grade Teacher
Rand, Christine Palacheck
First Grade Teacher
PATCH GROVE
Ferguson, Van Galen
High School Science Teacher
Hazen, James J.
Administrative Assistant
Mayne, Terry Schuster
First Grade Teacher
Townsend, Caron L.
Guidance Counselor
PEMBINE
Bilski, Dennis W.
7th-8th Grade PE & Hlth Tchr
PEPIN
Heit, Bernard Joseph
HS Math & Drivers Ed Teacher
Linse, Pamela M.
Social Studies Teacher
PESHTIGO
Felmer, Susan Eklund
Jr High Math Teacher
PEWAUKEE
Betz, Raymond James
Fifth Grade Teacher
Brooks, Dennis Mark
High School Choral Director
Davel, Bernadette Mader
Reading Teacher
Mamerow, Jeffrey S.
Industrial Technology Teacher
Misurek, Marilyn Judith
Nursing Instructor
Woodbury, Debbie Kolanowski
Reading Teacher
PHELPS
Christensen, Gloria Mikich
Science Teacher
Kimmerling, Dorothy Reinemann
Fifth Grade Teacher
PHILLIPS
Foytek, Etola Giese
Math Teacher
Kielsmeier, Grace Hertlein
English Teacher
Roberts, Vickie Ellen Painted
Math Teacher
PINE RIVER
Goodwin, Margaret Lorraine
4th Grade Teacher
PITTSVILLE
Berg, Dorothy L. (Severson)
Eng, Hlth, PE Tchr & Chair
Colby, Catherine Anne
Agriculture Instructor
Kotlarz, Sue Andre
Third Grade Inclusion Tchr
Piotrowski, Robert A.
Social Studies Teacher
Rose, Alice Marie
Fourth Grade Teacher
PLAINFIELD
Duda, Cathleen Hughes
5th-6th Grd Science Teacher
Mancl, Larry J.
High School Science Teacher
Mesyk, John
HS Mathematics Teacher
PLATTEVILLE
Crase, Dani Eastlick
Lang, Rdng & Soc Stud Teacher
Dymond, Randy
Civil Engineering Professor
Faherty, Joan Cairy
Language Arts & Reading Tchr
Fatzinger, Marie Margaret
Title I Reading Teacher
Klinge, Sara Davidson
Spanish Teacher
Lind, Robert W.
Professor of Physics
Owusu-Ababio, Samuel
Asst Prof of Civil Engineering
Rewey, Mary June Schmieder
2nd Grade Teacher
Rogers, Luanne Marie
MS Vocal & General Music Tchr
Schober-Thompson, Cheryl Ann
Freshman English Teacher
Serres, Robert A.
Health Education Teacher
Woodworth, Sally Van Brocklin
Fourth Grade Teacher
PLOVER
Nugent, Janet Baltus
2nd Grade Teacher
PLUM CITY
Anderson, Carl R.
Mathematics & Physics Teacher
Mack, Lisa Ann (LaLiberte)
Middle School Teacher
PLYMOUTH
Darrow, Sue Dymond
Dance Instructor
Flynn, David P.
Spanish Teacher
Gumm, Michael Martin
6th Grade Teacher & Coach
Kaufman, Charles Duane
Mathematics Teacher
Klein, Joan Mary
Mathematics Teacher
Mader, Barbara Bannach
Third Grade Teacher
Marsh, Catherine Wifler
4th Grade Teacher
Mikolyzk, William Benjamin
Social Studies Teacher
Pitlik, Wendy S.
HS Family & Consumer Ed Tchr
Scudella, Sandra J.
Music Teacher
Strelow, Deborah Tupper
Multi Age Classroom Teacher
PORT EDWARDS
Gerth, Tina Marie
Physical Education Teacher
Kallstrom, Roland Duane
High School Mathematics Tchr
Penke, Darwin Dale
US His & Ec Teacher
Solsrud, James Bjorn
Fifth & Sixth Grade Teacher
PORT WASHINGTON
Brill, Angeleen
First Grade Teacher
Dassow, Debra Cheryl
Sociology & Psychology Teacher
Decker, Elizabeth
Fifth Grade Teacher
Falk, Thomas James
School Counselor
Fuchs, Timothy Lee
Technical Education Teacher
Kauth, Thomas Paul
Biology Teacher
Koch, Bob
Mathematics Teacher
Niffenegger, Tammie Mattson
Science Teacher
Olson, Gerald A.
8th-12th Grd Band Director
Quail, Paul Henry, Jr.
Physics & Chemistry Teacher
Schwade, Shari Lee
High School Counselor
Stade, Jo Ann
Social Studies Teacher
Taucher, John C.
Social Studies Teacher
Yerges-Heine, Nora J.
Communications Teacher
PORT WING
Hyma, Jeffery Derek
Soc Science Tchr & Dept Head
PORTAGE
Carroll, Mary Ann
Pastoral Minister
Comstock, Verla M. (Schroeder)
Retired Teacher
Germanson, Mary Ann Nanassy
Art Teacher
Halberg, Teresa A.
Sixth Grade Teacher
Hemming, Mike Eugene
6th Grade Teacher
Kampen, Vietta Kay
Junior HS Mathematics Teacher
Maass, Ricky Kenneth
Jr HS Social Studies Teacher
Marshall, James Richard
Physics & Math Teacher
Newton, Mari Lee
HS English Teacher
Searock, Kevin Colin
Science Department Chair
POYNETTE
Hazard, Scott M.
Instrumental & Gen Music Tchr
PRAIRIE DU CHIEN
Nelson, Thomas M.
Technology & Special Ed Tchr
Oehler, Maurice L.
Chemistry Teacher
Trentin, Anthony Victor
Math & Science Teacher
PRAIRIE DU SAC
Brickner, Karey Kay
Spanish Teacher
Frick, Lynn Ellen
High School English Teacher
Love, Laura Hayes
9th-12th Grade Science Teacher
PRENTICE
Abney, Winfred G., Jr.
US History Teacher
Feltz, Mary (Bemowski)
School Dist Media Coordinator
PRESCOTT
Fleming, Tania Thacher
Physical Ed & Health Instr
Hein, Steven Andrew
US & World History Teacher
Hopkins, David John
Mathematics Teacher
Lucas, Ed T.
English & Social Studies Tchr
Radle, Rodney Mark
Physical Ed & Science Tchr
Ryan, Jeffrey Blaine
HS Social Studies Teacher
PRINCETON
Brenner, Robert R.
College Prep Eng & Fr Tchr
Buch, Kevin M.
7th & 8th Grade Teacher & Prin
Stangl, Robert M.
Chemistry & Physics Teacher
PULASKI
Busch, D. Thomas
Band Director
Krause, John William
History & Social Studies Tchr
Nowak, Jenny
Agriscience & Agribus Teacher
Sparish, David William
Fifth Grade Teacher
RACINE
Apmann, William Frederick
8th Grade Math & Algebra Tchr
Baganz, Mark James
8th Grade Teacher & Principal
Becke, Julie Ann (Jacob)
8th Grd Science & English Tchr
Bennett, Joan C.
Science Dept Chair & Bio Tchr
Bode, Richard Lee
HS Studies & Theology Teacher
Bok, Byron W.
Art Teacher
Christensen, Christine Irene
Spanish Teacher
Dorsey, John O.
Instrumental Music Teacher
Ertl, Robert Daniel
Math Department Chairperson
Eulingbourgh, Frances Ann
1st Grade Teacher
Gacek, Christine
Legal Secretary Program Instr
Gage, Janice Daniels
Spanish Teacher
Gannaway, Carolyn Marie (Bordo)
6th Grade Teacher
Gehrman, Gregory A.
Honors Chem, Sci & Survey Tchr
Gerber, Joyce Christensen
Retired Teacher
Goodwin, Betty Jean
3rd Grade Teacher
Grady, Ann Hallisy
Seventh Grade Math Teacher
Griego, Sue Siepmann
High School Librarian
Griffin, Darice Crawford
Mathematics Teacher
Hammes, Patricia Ann
7th-8th Grade English Teacher
Hennen, Valerie
Communications Instructor
Hesselbach, Renee Kitzerow
Science Teacher
Huberty, Roger Ralph
High School Math Teacher
Jozwik, Lawrence Edward
7th-8th Grade Science Teacher
Jozwik, Patricia Thomas
Biology Teacher
Lesnjak, Jon Michael
English Dept Chair & Tchr
Leuck, John Peter
Mathematics Teacher
Lyden, Sandra Hopenspinger
Communications Instructor
Mach, Gregory Michael
History, Govt Tchr & Advisor
Mc Culley, Denise A.
Science Teacher
Merry, Corrine Susan
4th & 5th Grade Teacher
Miles, Frank Ross
Science Teacher
Nesgaard, Anne Marie Mullally
Teacher of LD Students
Ogren, Claudia Kathleen
Social Studies Teacher
Perez, Catherine Bowman
Spanish Teacher
Perkins, Enrico Valentino
Assistant Principal
Pie, Timothy Arthur, Sr.
Fifth Grade Teacher
Randall, Jodie Humpal
Jr HS Sci & Literature Teacher
Rodrigues-Pavao, Antonio
Vocal Music Teacher
Salvo, Barbara Jean
Biology & General Science Tchr
Schultz, Glenn Richard
Sixth Grade Teacher
Scott, Lois Lucas
8th Grd American History Tchr
Steker, Jane
High School Math Teacher
Thielen, Daniel Jerome
Math Dept Rep & Tchr
Vander Brug, Karen Jill
6th Grade Teacher
Waltenberger, John Lawrence
4th Grade Teacher
Williams, Philip Sherwood
Art Teacher
Willing, Nancy P.
Science & Math Teacher
Wilson, Laureen VanderHeyden
4th Grade Teacher
Zabrowski, Ellen Nelson
Fifth Grade Teacher
Zahn, Rebecca J.
French & Spanish Teacher
RANDOLPH
Dykstra, Louise Sjoerdsma
Junior High Language Arts Tchr
Schouten, Lillian Louise
Junior High Teacher
RANDOM LAKE
Fowler, Ann Talbot
Business Education Teacher
Horst, John Franklin
Technology Education Teacher
Jacobson, Kurt Edward
Technology Education Teacher
REEDSBURG
Hart, Susan R.
8th Grade Social Studies Tchr
Judge, Larry Ervin
Physics, Chem & Phys Sci Tchr
Klitzke, Evaline Craker
Retired Elementary Teacher
Krebill, Lorrie Leabo
High School Spanish Teacher
REEDSVILLE
Campana, Mary Jo Haight
Middle School Science Teacher
Hanson, Kristine J. (Sands)
Art Teacher
Hefti, John R.
High School Mathematics Tchr
Jaeger, Mary Jean (Weigel)
Retired Kindergarten Teacher
Jaeger, Tracie Jean
2nd Grade Teacher
Maroszek, Ronald Raymond
Spanish & History Teacher
Meier, David G.
Math, Cmptr Sci Tchr, Dept Chm
Quint, Linda June
Kindergarten & 2nd Grd Teacher
Ridolphi, Audrey Uren
Business Education Teacher
Ruthmansdorfer, Marjorie Lee (Koch)
Hlth & Family Consumer Ed Tchr
Urban, Richard L.
HS Social Studies Teacher
Wagner, Laurie Ann
First Grade Teacher
REESEVILLE
Modaff, Marcia Kay
Health & Physical Educator
RHINELANDER
Bailey, Joncurtis Campbell
Theater Dir, European His Tchr
Baker, Sherry Tallman
Spanish Teacher
Bassuener, Dawn Kolstad
Biological Rsrch & Botany Tchr
Heideman, Robert G.
Counselor
Jarvis, James C.
8th Grade Math Teacher
Kanyusik, Robert A.
Art Instructor
Lawrence, Lynnette Lee
Fifth Grade Teacher
Miller, Sherry Merry
Algebra & Pre Algebra Teacher
Nebgen, Mark A.
Chemistry Instructor
Ready, Susan Jean
School Counselor
Rozumalski, Lynn Priddy
VP Institutional Advancement
Schoeneck, Marilyn Maloney
Third Grade Teacher
RIB LAKE
Curran, Gail Ann
English Teacher
Keagan, Robert O'Neill
Mathematics & Physics Teacher
Magnuson, Joan Dahl
Vocal Music Teacher
Priniski, Mark Edward
Math & Computer Science Tchr
Utke, Elizabeth Jane (Peissig)
English Teacher
RICE LAKE
Anderson, Bruce John
US History & Economics Teacher
Barta, Susan Bohn
Choral Music Director
Duffy, Daniel C.
Instrumental Music Teacher
Finstad, Jeffrey K.
Social Studies Teacher
George, Becki Alison (Reinagle)
Library & Media Specialist
Grivna, Dennis Wayne
Associate Professor of Biology
Hagen, Christine Dufner
Fifth Grade Teacher
Havenor, Jean Anderson
High School English Teacher
Hoeft, Mary Martin
Communication Arts Assoc Prof
Jeffrey, Charles Frederick, Jr.
Social Studies Teacher
Kennedy, Patricia Ann
First Grade Teacher
Klancher, Paul Michael
8th Grade Mathematics Teacher
Martin, Linda Grambo
First Grade Teacher
Olson, Meg May
High School Science Teacher
Pape, Paula J.
English Teacher
Patrick, Sue Carol
Assistant Professor of History
Prissel, Rick L.
8th Grade Earth Science Tchr
Suino, David Merrill
Fifth Grade Teacher
RICHLAND CENTER
Bakkum, Rick Eugene
Classroom Teacher
Benishek, Faye Marie
French Teacher
Dillon, Fred L.
Math & Science Teacher
Kintz, Jane
Elementary Art Teacher
Koresh, Lynn A.
Business Education Teacher
McMillin, Mary Zick
Fourth Grade Teacher
Parr, Janet M.
5th Grade Teacher
Sims, Gerald V.
Technical Education Teacher
Wontor, Melany A.
English Teacher
RINGLE
Miller, Craig Alan
Fifth Grade Teacher
Rakowski, Lois J.
K-6th Grd IMC Director
RIO
Conner, Brian
Third Grade Teacher
Winter, Toni Renee
English & Speech Teacher
RIPON
Barcio, Joseph A.
English & Economics Teacher
Bartig, Keith A.
Social Studies Teacher
Byron, Colleen Marie
Asst Prof of Chemistry
Dorschner, James Michael
Band Director
Moniz, Thomas Joseph, Jr.
7th Grade Social Studies Tchr
Northrop, Douglas A.
Professor of English
Smith, Brian Henry
Religion Professor
Wickstrom, John Richard
8th Grade Social Studies Tchr
RIVER FALLS
Thompson, Douglas Neil
Chemistry Teacher
Tjornehoj, Kristin Ann
Assistant Professor of Music
Tomlinson, Kathy Adiene
Mathematics Professor
Zirbel, Jeanne Meyer
Third Grade Teacher
ROBERTS
Bowerman, Janet (Slagowski)
Sixth Grade Teacher
Falde, Jodie Stewart
Kindergarten Teacher
Magee, Thomas R.
Fourth Grade Teacher
ROSENDALE
Friedli, Harry
Social Studies Teacher
Kennedy, Linda Gulmire
Second Grade Teacher
Martz, Nedra D.
English Teacher
Moon, David Warren
Science Dept Chair & Bio Tchr
Nordeng, David P., Jr.
High School Math Teacher
Schleis, Joe P.
Teacher & Coach
ROSHOLT
Grygleski, James Mark
Social Studies Teacher
Lautenbach, James LeRoy
Biology Instructor
ROTHSCHILD
Higgins, Michael William
Fourth Grade Teacher
SAINT CROIX FALLS
Fellrath, Janell Lee
Family, Consumer & Ec Teacher
Goss, Randal Scott
Computer Teacher
Magnuson, Steven Paul
Chemistry & Physics Teacher
Segelstrom, Susan Mae
German Teacher
Stone, David Craig
Art Teacher
SAINT FRANCIS
Benka, Terry J.
Social Studies Teacher
Bretzel, Milton James
Math, Cmptr Sci Tchr, Dept Chm
Doser, Janet C.
Language Arts & Drama Teacher
Flanagan, Mary Ellen E.
Family & Consumer Ed Teacher
Kattner, Paul J.
Seventh Grade Teacher
Payment, Donna Marie
Second Grade Teacher
Rau, Susan Jane
Second Grade Teacher
Schneider, Robert Henry
Advanced Biology Teacher
Sell, Nancy A.
Director of Pastoral Formation
SALEM
Milatz, Margaret Anne
High School Biology Teacher
Schroeder, Pamela Anderson
French & Humanities Teacher
Travis, Linda S.
7th Grade Teacher

CITY
·d, William P.
·rade Social Studies Tchr
r, Ann Ballweg
rade Teacher
son, James O.
Grade Teacher
FIELD
ad, Theodore Todd
Director
ard, Scott G.
Arts Tchr & Newspaper Adv
vie M.
Vocational Resource Tchr
, Karen Marie
School Choral Director
, William Lee
nistry & Geometry Teacher
Kathleen Mary (Batten)
th Grade Math Teacher
n, Jane
th & PE Coord
Pam A.
3rd Grade Teacher
n, Paul Robert
Grade English Teacher
dt, Jeanette Neitzel
ematics Teacher
r, Mary Gatske
al Studies Teacher
CA
Patricia Heal
th Grades Music Teacher
IOUR
, Margrit
ish Teacher
pie, Penny Adele Otis
ol-to-Work Coordinator
Michele Turton
Teacher
ek, John I.
nth Grd Social Stud Tchr
dt, Leo George
& World History Instructor
Keith Ellsworth
ish Teacher
n Heuvel, Barbara Chitko
sical Education Teacher
Mark A.
ch Teacher
RON
n, Mark D.
Teacher
rs, William T., Jr.
dle School Teacher
VANO
, Jean Anne Mary (Froelich)
d Grade Teacher
z, Joanne Rodeck
d Grd Tchr & Choir Dir
ard, Margaret Lorraine (Ward)
d Grade Teacher
an, Carole Johnson
5th Grd Math & Sci Teacher
on, Brian Ernest
ology Teacher
r, Timothy Lee
ness Education Teacher
tz, Steven L.
th Grade Teacher
eitzer, Phil R.
Grade Earth Science Tchr
, David L.
igh Sci & Religion Instr
nd, Jean Marie
th Ministry Director
kait, Jane L.
rth Grade Teacher
inski, Beth (Kerry)
h Teacher
BOYGAN
, Luther John, II
Grade Teacher
el, Michael Paul
h & Science Teacher
, Eileen I.
rth Grade Teacher
n, Lisa Ann
man & ESL Teacher
s, Nicholas C.
tory & Sociology Teacher
, Louis Anton
h Teacher
is, Susan
dia Specialist & Yrbk Tchr
e, David
Grade Teacher
olt, Howard Andrew
rld Geography Tchr
, Karl Curtis
sler Prof of Creative Wrtng
ser, Ronald E.
logy Instructor
e, Jean Parkins
ired Elementary Teacher
, Ronald Kirk
fessor of Mathematics
ck, Janet L.
st Music Prof & Choirs Dir
man, Brian Charles
Studies & Aeronautics Tchr
ch, William Bernard
mmunications Teacher
wers, James Andrew
Teacher
ard, Kenneth Donald
Grade Teacher
bs, Linda Faye
oir Director

Khodavandi, Mehraban
Prof & Dean of Grad Studies
Kniola, James John
6th Grd Sci Tchr & Dept Head
Lee, Rogelia Isabel
Spanish Teacher
Lewis, John Thomas
Asst Prof of Mrktg & Bus Law
Mikolyzk, Diane King
Spanish Teacher
Peffer, George Anthony
Asst Professor of History
Phillips, James F.
Business Admininstration Prof
Porter, Cyndi Wilson
Assistant Professor of Chem
Price, Margery Morrison
First Grade Teacher
Reinholtz, Amy Sue
Biology Teacher
Robbins, Kay Kreutzman
Language Arts Teacher
Sandven, Ron W.
Social Studies Teacher
Schmidt, Lewis Alan
Creative Arts Division Chair
Schrank, Jon Edward
Soc Stud, His & Sociology Tchr
Seefeldt, David Charles
5th Grd Cmptr Sci Tchr
Shircel, Terrance Carl
Journalism & Speech Teacher
Steen, Duane R.
First Grade Teacher
Stoll, Patricia A.
Writing & English Asst Prof
Thorndike, Jonathan Lucas
English Professor
Van Drunen, Steven John
Middle School Teacher
Wangemann, Allen August
Biology & Anthropology Instr
Way, Doris Aebischer
Fourth Grade Teacher
Wesner, Sue Ellen
High School English Teacher
Wixon, Richard
Assistant Professor of History
SHEBOYGAN FALLS
Anderson, Sandra Priegel
Nursing Asst Trng Instructor
Ertel, Ronald J.
Science Teacher
Gigstad, Leif Goodman
Agribusiness Instructor
Hogue, Dawn Therkelsen
HS English Teacher
Jarosch, Janis Lynn
Spanish Teacher
Mc Kichan, Bernard Allen
Spanish & German Teacher
Oeflein, Lori Jean
8th Grade Science Teacher
Volovsek, Anton John
Chemistry & Physics Teacher
SHELL LAKE
Williams, Douglas George
Jr High Math Teacher
SHIOCTON
Omholt, Thomas Russell
English Teacher
SHULLSBURG
Malik, Andrew G.
Physics, Chemistry & Math Tchr
SILVER LAKE
Friedel, Robert John
8th Grd Sci Tchr & Dept Chair
SLINGER
Acker, Steven Loren
English Teacher
Apel, Duane M.
Technology Education Teacher
Beyer, Carole Lynn (Lederer)
8th Grade Teacher
Galvin, Kathy J.
6th Grd Reading & English Tchr
Jenkins, Michael Paul
Sixth Grade Teacher
Keliher, Amy J.
English Teacher
Kiesow, James C.
Technology Education Teacher
Olsen, Beth Becker
5th Grade Teacher
Rasmussen, William Gerald
Eighth Grade Science Teacher
Vlasak, Frank Anthony
Retired Agriculture Teacher
Zenz, Stephen A.
Instrumental Music Teacher
SOBIESKI
Jarock, Leonard Anthony
7th-8th Grd Lang Arts Teacher
Slapp, Susan Mc Kenna
Special Education Teacher
SOLDIERS GROVE
Lewicki, James A.
6th Grade Teacher
SOMERS
Mundt, Sharon Ann
English & Physical Ed Teacher
SOMERSET
Rivard, Harold K.
Elementary Instructor
Shottler, Sherrill Nelson
Business Education Teacher
SOUTH MILWAUKEE
Bigley, Mike Gene
3rd Grade Teacher

Carson, Patricia L.
High School German Teacher
Feudner, Kaila Marie Liebert
Spanish Teacher
Hesslink, Jerome Barry
High School English Teacher
Kubel, Jeffrey Thomas
Physics & Earth Sci Teacher
Kuligowski, Annette Marie
Communications Teacher
Loehr, Colin Wallace
5th-8th Grd Soc Studies Tchr
Slayton, Phyllis (Hardt)
Mathematics Teacher
Thinnes, Richard George
A P US History Teacher
Winterfeldt, Monica H.
Spanish Teacher
Wozniak, Orion Neumann
Family & Consumer Ed Tchr
SOUTH WAYNE
Kaster, Cindi (Stauffer)
Third Grade Teacher
LaGrange, Rosann H.
Principal
Scott, Michelle Renee
Earth Sci & Chemistry Teacher
Smits, Robert Michael
Social Studies Teacher
SPARTA
Berteotti, Carol Rose
Training Director
Cook, Joan Schiller
Second Grade Teacher
Hermanson, Kathleen Mary
Fourth Grade Teacher
Hirsch, Rita Mary
Third Grade Teacher
Kress, Philip Lyall
Instrl Systems Specialist
O'Neil, Cindy Lou
English Teacher
Rasmussen, Mary Ellen
Second Grade Teacher
Reichenbach, Laura Perner
Art Instructor
Schaitel, Nancy Kruk
7th Grade English Teacher
Smith, Thomas Joseph
8th Grade Teacher
Stephens, Joanne Meuler
MS Guidance Counselor
Sullivan, Elizabeth (Schuttemeier)
Third & Fourth Grade Teacher
Welch, Mary Rose Dwyer
English Teacher
SPENCER
Montee, Barry L.
English & Theater Arts Teacher
SPOONER
Frankiewicz, Duane A.
High School Math Teacher
Schroeder, William Don
Art Teacher
Shelton, Teresa Lynn
5th Grade Teacher
SPRING GREEN
Likhite, Vivek
Bio, Chem, Anatomy, Psych Tchr
SPRING VALLEY
Gould, Karen Elizabeth
Elem PE & Health Teacher
STANLEY
Rasmussen, Dianne
English Tchr & Dept Chprsn
Van De Loo, Randy R.
Principal & Teacher
Wilkinson, Sheila Hilgers
Teacher
STEVENS POINT
Arrowood, James H.
Music Professor
Benzine, Terry Lee
Fifth Grade Teacher
Bohanski, Mark Edmund
High School Science Teacher
Corcoran, Timothy John
Science Dept Chair & Teacher
Lange-Murillo, Pam
Spanish Teacher
Lemke, Karen A.
Assoc Prof of Geography
McCaffery, Wayne Dale
Economics Instructor
Mc Cann, Thomas Gerard
Seventh Grade Teacher
Olson, Richard E.
Spanish Teacher
Ozsvath, David Lynn
Geology Professor
Rice, Jennifer Pomainville
Junior High English Teacher
Rice, Keith William
Geography Professor
Sanders, Ada Andrae
Third Grade Teacher
Showalter, Donald Lee
Chemistry Professor
Wenzel, Steven Mark
Band Teacher
Winblad, Jayne L.
Sixth Grade Teacher
STOCKBRIDGE
Hanke, Tom Paul
Physical Ed & Health Teacher
Hansen, Christopher Jon
English Teacher
STODDARD
Hollenbeck, Susan J. (Timmerman)
Fourth Grade Elem Teacher

STOUGHTON
Beutel, John Robert
Choral Music Dir
Goepfert, Polly L.
7th Grade Math Teacher
Kalscheur, Jann Teres
English Teacher
Schwass, Jeanne Storm
Family & Consumer Ed Teacher
STRATFORD
Southworth, John Albert
Sixth Grade Teacher
Teska, Susan G.
Fourth Grade Teacher
Yedinak, William Joseph, Jr.
Business Education Teacher
STRUM
Connolly, Desmond Francis
Social Studies Teacher
Mueller, David Lee
Instrumental Music Teacher
STURGEON BAY
Bergene, Grace Ruth
Second Grade Teacher
Bleck, Robert Charles
Computer Sci Tchr & Dept Head
Ciganik, Lynda Carol Outman
Fifth Grade Teacher
Corona, Frank John
7th & 8th Grade Teacher
Gebauer, Julie Johnson
Art Specialist
Holzinger, David Paul
Driver Education Teacher
Meikle, Holly Graham
English Teacher
Powers, Daniel Joseph
Coord of Gifted & Talented
Rosenthal, John Allen
7th Grade Social Studies Tchr
Senarighi, Rudy
Guidance Counselor
Severson, Darrel Robert
Drivers Ed Tchr & Athletic Dir
Smith, Anthony Richard
5th Grade Teacher
Treadeau, Paul Dennis
7th Grade Science Teacher
STURTEVANT
Dahl, Margaret A.
First Grade Teacher
Gamble, Sheila Ann Dermody
English & Religion Teacher
SULLIVAN
Wenkman, Daniel Joseph
Principal
SUN PRAIRIE
Bahe, Garry W.
Biology Instructor & Coach
Gustafson, Michelle L.
High School English Teacher
Guzinski, Susan Lynn
Alternative Education Teacher
Miller, Sharon
Art Teacher
Ragus, Terry Paul
MS Guidance Counselor
Sheehan, JoAnn Hodgson
8th Grade Algebra Teacher
Sveum, Steven John
Band Director
Terhune, Karen Anderson
High School Mathematics Tchr
Weber, Anne Taylor
German Teacher
SUPERIOR
Ball, Michael R.
Associate Prof of Sociology
Banker, Gary C.
English Teacher
Bischoff, Joan
Professor of English
Blue, Elizabeth Twining
Coord & Asst Prof of Soc Work
Borich, Thomas Matthew
AP History & Psych Teacher
Bumgardner, Thomas Arthur
Music Dept Chair & Professor
Burfield, Thomas J.
6th Grade Teacher
Cole, Larry Lee
Math Tchr & Dept Chprsn
Hodnick, Daniel F.
Eng, Accelerated Amer Lit Tchr
Kadlecek, Kathleen A.
4th Grade Teacher
Knudson, Kenneth A.
Attorney
Kroll, David F.
Head Ath Trainer & Instr
Mershart, Ronald V.
Professor of History
Metzinger, Joseph Francis
K-6th Grade Phy Ed Tchr
Noll, James Louis
High School Mathematics Tchr
Rocchio, Alan F.
Science Teacher
Schliep, Susan Miller
Mathematics Teacher
Stauber-Johnson, Elizabeth
Assistant Prof of Math Ed
Wright, Sandra Bozeman
Fifth Grade Teacher
SURING
Christensen, Ruth Julia Block
Fourth Grade Teacher
Gipp, Carolyn (Ruege)
Fifth Grade Teacher

Steffeck, Tamara J. (Adams)
Business Education Teacher
SUSSEX
Aceto, Jon
World Languages Instructor
Datka, Julie Ponasik
Sixth Grade Teacher
Grove, Stan E.
Chemistry Instructor
Komatz, Penny
Mathematics Teacher
Matarrese, Jill Brady
Learning Center Coordinator
Moniza, Karen A.
Director of Bands
Mueller, Richard
4th Grade Teacher
Olson, Byron C.
Graphic Arts Instructor
Younk, Steven Arthur
Economics & Sociology Teacher
THERESA
Koepsell, Kathleen Marie Sternat
1st Grade Teacher
THIENSVILLE
Klemp, Garreth Dean
4th Grd Teacher & Athletic Dir
THORP
Geissler, Jeffrey Herman
MS Social Studies Teacher
Klanderman, Rosalind E. (Grinnell)
IMC Director
Schmelzer, Dean Robert
Agricultural Ed Instr, FFA Adv
White, Shari McCausland
High School Art Teacher
Whooley, Mary Catherine
Fourth Grade Teacher
THREE LAKES
Nieuwendrop, Jane Alethea
9th-12th Grade Art Teacher
TOMAH
Cook, Joseph Frederick
German Teacher
Hansen, Max Otto
Health Teacher
LaFond, Jeanne Veree
Second Grade Teacher
Luebke, Bruce Robert
Business Education Teacher
Mattison, Linda Pontius
First Grade Teacher
Reisenauer, Janis (Blackbourn)
High School Math Teacher
Schekel, Larry A.
Physics Teacher
Stutzman, David Darrell
HS Earth Science Teacher
Totten, Patti J.
Fourth Grade Teacher
Wagner, Suzanne Swanson
Dance Educator
Weiland, Teri A.
Family & Consumer Ed Teacher
TOMAHAWK
Handel, John Edward
Social Studies Teacher
Herbison, Nancy R. (Johnson)
Guidance Counselor
Overhaug, H. Allan
Geography Teacher
TONY
Alberson, Ted L.
Jr HS Civics & Lang Arts Tchr
Coggins, Sara Susannah (Williams)
Business Education Instr
Gorski, Dawn
7th & 8th Grd Lang Arts Tchr
TREMPEALEAU
Kane, Pamela Marie
7th Grd Health & PE Teacher
Lee, Scott Arlan
5th Grade Teacher
TURTLE LAKE
Schultz, Kelly Jo
Band Director
TWO RIVERS
Ashenbrenner, Edward J.
Indstrl Ed, Technology Teacher
Beth, Joyce Meineke
First Grade Teacher
Bleick, Dennis Everett
8th Grade Teacher & Coach
Fritsch, Gayle Ann
Science & Spanish Teacher
Furmanski, Julie Dianne (Halverson)
Designated Vocational Instr
Glenna, Wesley V.
Technology Education Teacher
Graff, Donald James
Mathematics Teacher
Hough, David Walter
History Teacher
Jones, Sandra Lee (Bastar)
Fifth Grade Teacher
Kolarik, Ken Robert
Scndry Schl At-Risk Director
Press, Olive (Salmeen)
Substitute Teacher
Stapleton, Patrick Joseph
8th Grade Mathematics Teacher
Tegen, Cathy Petersen
English as a Second Lang Tchr
Tisler, Jim Paul
6th-7th Grade Teacher
Trembley, Jerry
Middle School English Teacher
UNION GROVE
Czerniak, Thomas R.
Science Instructor

VALDERS
Denor, Bev
Language Arts Teacher
Evans, Robert Edward
Soc Stud & Drivers Ed Tchr
Kiel, Peggy A.
6th Grade Teacher
Lindholm, Bill
7th Grade Rdng & Soc Stud Tchr
Sell, Susan K.
Family & Consumer Educator
Wilhelm, Aldene Grace (O'Connell)
English & Publications Teacher
VERONA
Becker, Randall Emil
Art Teacher
Borgwardt, John Robert
Third Grade Teacher
Borroughs, Jay Michael
History Teacher
Edwards, Stephanie Lee
Associate Principal
Elver, Beth Bilse
8th Grd History & Civics Tchr
Hammerly, Peggy S.
Family & Consumer Sci Teacher
Heffron, Ruth A.
MS Phys Ed Instr
Johnson, Norma Johnson
7th Grade Language Arts Tchr
Kurth, Richard John
Lang Arts & Soc Stud Teacher
Wehrley, Patricia Ann
Fifth Grade Teacher
VIOLA
Doolan, William L.
Band Director
Marshall, Gloria J. (Bennett)
7th-12th Grade Special Ed Tchr
Silva, Diana Burrows
Teacher
Vinger, Lacey L.
Fourth Grade Teacher
VIROQUA
Boll, Albert M.
Social Studies Teacher
Harris, Ted C.
Media Supervisor
WALES
Barder, William Michael
HS Art Teacher
Cicenas, Robert E.
Physical Education Teacher
Culhane, Debra Lewinski
Fourth Grade Teacher
Daniels, Linda Brassington
Chemistry Teacher
Flauding, Doug R.
Marketing Instructor
Hoffman, Daniel J.
Mathematics Teacher
Jaeger, Todd D.
Vocal Music Director
Littaritz, Lowell Eugene
JV Bsktbl & Bsbl Coach
Michaelis, Diane Glass
Physical Education Teacher
Powell, Diane Bush
Social Studies Tchr, Drama Dir
Rupnow, David Paul
Social Studies Teacher
Schneider, Kathleen Ann (Reynolds)
English & Speech Teacher
Serafin, Daniel James
Mathematics Teacher
Sugden, Sandra Lee
Art Teacher
Wanner, John E.
Science Teacher
Willems, Charles Thomas
Mathematics Teacher
WALWORTH
Glaser, Linda Lou (Anderberg)
Language Arts Teacher
Mullen, Lisa Marie
Agri Science Instructor
Ries, Marsha Weeks
Civics, World & Amer His Tchr
Schaid, Terry Robert
PE & Amer His Tchr & MS Coord
Stevenson-Olson, Tracy Margaret
HS Social Studies Teacher
WARRENS
Kiefer, Terry Lee
Sixth Grade Teacher
WASHBURN
Berg, Patricia DeVinck
Middle School Teacher
Carli, Dale Allan
Third Grade Teacher
Nemec, C. Gale
6th Grade Teacher
Radtke, Kathleen Ann
English Teacher
Rapps, Bruce Joseph
HS Science & Biology Teacher
WATERFORD
Milatz, Dave M.
Business Ed Teacher & Coach
Nannemann, Marsha Lynn
French Teacher
Ray, Jeffrey Joseph
Agriculture Educator
Smith, Nancy J. (Christensen)
Chemistry Teacher
WATERLOO
Atkinson, Russell J.
Jr HS Social Studies Teacher
Kehl, Betty
English Teacher
Kilian, Wanda S. Hembree
Fifth Grade Teacher
Knoke, Kathleen Holz
IMC Director
Krueger, Marily A.
2nd & 3rd Grade Teacher
Raatz, Richard A.
Social Studies Teacher
WATERTOWN
Borchardt, Jerry W.
Middle School Band Director
Doughty, Wanda Durbin
Instrumental Music Director
Drost, Kris Ann
Communication Skills Teacher
Fontaine, Diane Neinas
Third Grade Teacher
Geiger, Ellen Marie
First & Second Grade Teacher
Haberkorn, Janice F. (Perry)
4th Grade Teacher
Hill, Robert Lynn
Science Professor
Jonen, Jill M.
Science Teacher
Kemper, Wayne Joseph
8th Grd Social Studies Tchr
Korth, Jeff G.
8th Grd Tchr & Athletic Dir
Milbrath, Janice Hingiss
Sixth Grade Teacher
Moeller, James
Administrator & Teacher
Parsons, Tim
District String Specialist
Rumpf, Ann J.
School Psychologist
Schulz, Anita Lemke
Piano Teacher
Soldner, Joyce Ann
First Grade Teacher
Stanczak, Patrick J.
Seventh Grade English Teacher
Sterling, Jonathan Chandler
9th-12th Grade Guidance Cnslr
WAUKESHA
Abraham, Daniel D.
8th Grade Social Studies Tchr
Affeldt, William L.
AP History Teacher
Alt, Allan M.
Third Grd & Drivers Ed Teacher
Baenen, Mary Lynn
Mathematics Teacher
Bradley, Bette Schneider
Latin Teacher
Bralick, Anthony J.
History Instructor
Bunzel, Mary Veronica
Religion Teacher
Burke, John Anthony
English Teacher
Campion, Carolyn Cleveland
First Grade Teacher
Csavoy, Richard Andrew
Art Teacher
D'Antuono, Mary Ellen
Chemistry Teacher
Dawson, Bill
Guidance Counselor
DeNoyer, George Phillip
7th Grd Teacher & Athletic Dir
Doepke, James H.
Band Director
Downing, Teri Lynn Seegert
Third Grade Teacher
Erdmann, Kristin Kay
High School English Teacher
Essuman, Joe W.
Assoc Prof of Economics
Gabelbauer, John Henry
History & Sociology Teacher
Gevaert, Charles
Mathematics Teacher
Gonyo, James Edward
8th Grade Science Teacher
Green, Kimberly Ann
High School Theology Teacher
Hasek, Patricia Tewes
Secondary English Teacher
Herman, Robert James
High School English Teacher
Johnson, Linda A.
English Teacher
Judd, Nora Jean
Eighth Grd Lang Arts Tchr
Keppe, Marie Hemmy
At-Risk Coordinator
Knight, John H.
Philosophy Professor
Knipfel, Scott Lee
Fifth Grade Teacher
Krause, Mary Ann
English Teacher
Kuhtz, William Paul
Fourth Grade Teacher
Ladd, Marilyn Bender
Family & Consumer Sci Teacher
Lamb, Mary Pattow
Family Education Teacher
Lantz, Bert Busby
Sixth Grade Educator
Maas, Ann Stollenwerk
Mathematics Teacher
Malone, Charles F.
Drama, Speech & English Tchr
Marineau, Stephen C.
Honors US History Teacher
McCormick, Kenneth Tilton
High School History Teacher
Meyer, Debora Gott
Vocal Music Specialist
Mitchell, Thomas William
Retired Physics Teacher
Murnan-Smith, Betty
Assoc Prof of English Emeritas
Nett, Theresa
Third Grade Teacher
Noe, Mary Ann Hentschel
English Teacher
Norgal, Marie Ann
HS Math Teacher
Pearce, Cynthia Ihrig
Language Arts Teacher
Prospero, Gregory Joseph
Religious Studies Teacher
Rasmussen, Lloyd Phillip
Director & Driver Ed Teacher
Reiss, Judith Lee
Eighth Grade US History Tchr
Robe, Anna Marie (Hoffman)
7th Grade Mathematics Teacher
Samann, Frederick, Jr.
7th Grade Social Studies Tchr
Schlangen, Carole Uphoff
French Tchr & Foreign Lang Chm
Smith, Renee Elizabeth
Mathematics Teacher
Suhr, Kimberly Ann
English Teacher & Coach
Thies, Al H.
Math Teacher
Thompson, Peter John
Band Dir
Vergetis, Gregg A.
US History Teacher
Walker, Jim A.
Science Teacher
Weyrauch, Jo
High School English Teacher
Willis, Robert A.
Chemistry Teacher
Zagorski, Maria Hibicki
1st & 2nd Grade Teacher
Zeit, Nancy Jean
5th Grade Teacher
WAUNAKEE
Ableidinger, James F.
Physics Teacher
Braunger, Tom Phillip
English Teacher
Farnsworth, W. Jay
Sixth Grade Teacher
Fuller, Charles J.
Social Studies Teacher
Heidke, Martin D.
7th Grade Soc Studies Teacher
Laubmeier, John Wilbert
Economics & US History Tchr
ONeil, J. Peter
Science Teacher
Zander, Anne
Vocal Music Teacher
WAUPACA
Howard, A. Marie
English Teacher
Larson, David George
Tech Ed & Cmptr Sci Tchr
Lutze, Barrie Arthur
8th Grd Eng & Soc Stud Tchr
Lutze, Virginia Kay (Siegrist)
Second Grade Teacher
Thielen, Tina Louise
HS Choir & Band Teacher
Welch, Robert John
Science Teacher
Wolfgram, Daniel J.
Choral Activities Director
WAUPUN
Guy, Deborah Grier
Math & Science Teacher
Heinrich, Linda Williams
Third Grade Teacher
Kudlaczyk, Cheryl Leigh
High School Art Teacher
WAUSAU
Alafouzos, Bonita Lynn (Peters)
First Grade Teacher
Ashenmacher, John Joseph
English Instr & Department Chm
Aughenbaugh, Mary K.
Language Arts Teacher
Banczak, Connie J.
High School Chemistry Teacher
Bohman, Myrna Hansen
Fifth Grade Teacher
DeBroux, Mary Kay
English Teacher & Dept Head
DesJarlais, Christine Marie (Accardo)
1st Grade Teacher
Fellows, Angela Marie
Mathematics Teacher
Fischer, Mike Thomas
HS Social Studies Teacher
Grundy, Kevin Michael
Physical Education Teacher
Jensen, Gordon P.
Elementary Music Teacher
Johnson, Mary Smith
Family & Consumer Ed Instr
Joss, Joan J.
8th Grade Social Studies Tchr
Lensmire, Lynn E.
Fifth Grade Teacher
Lewis, Nancy Burmeister
Second Grade Teacher
Lohr, Richard J.
World History Teacher
Mann, Ervin John
High School Biology Teacher
Mansk, Daniel Joseph
Seventh Grade Teacher
Michlein, Lee A.
Art Dept Chairperson & Instr
Olvey, Saundra Rickenbaugh
First Grade Teacher
Persico, Betty Ann
Resource Tchr of Gifted Stdnts
Pollard, Carol Oberg
8th Grade Science Teacher
Reinardy, Jerome Michael
German & Spanish Teacher
Ring, David Mark
Asst Principal & Athletic Dir
Seagren-Hall, Marian
Fourth Grade Teacher
Sprague, Julie Schroepfer
Language Arts Teacher
Stelter, Andrea L.
Bus Ed Tchr & Dept Chprsn
Switalski, Michael Mathew
Director of Campus Ministry
Synold, Anthony John
Business Education Teacher
Theiler, Becky Sue
Math Teacher
Weix, Thomas Ralph
HS Health & PE Teacher
Wright, Marilee Turvey
Tchr of Learning Disabilities
Zeidler, Michael Carl
Second Grade Teacher
WAUSAUKEE
Teachout, Clifford Myron
Fifth Grade Teacher
WAUTOMA
Attoe, Lane J.
Soc Stud Dept Chm & Counselor
Luebke, Mathew John
Art Teacher & Dept Head
Pezzi, Kara Anne
Science Teacher
Ruhland, Diane Ruth
High School Guidance Counselor
Senft, Julie A.
Spanish Teacher
WAUWATOSA
Marsack, Doreen Jonovic
Fifth Grade Teacher
Minessale, Joanne Leone
Second Grade Teacher
Petersen, Daniel James
Band Director
Weichert, Mary L.
Middle School Mathematics Tchr
WEBSTER
Johnson, Beverly Ann
4th Grade Teacher
Vold, Christopher Mathew
Jr HS Eng & Lang Arts Teacher
Weber, Harm A., III
English Teacher
WEST ALLIS
Beede, Lynette Anderson
Business Education Instructor
Gunn, Patricia LaFratta
Mathematics Instructor
Jobst, Carola Elizabeth
Teacher & Work Exprnc Supvr
Peterson, Nancy Lynn
Spanish Teacher
Wiedmeyer, Kenneth R.
CAD & Tech Drafting Teacher
WEST BEND
Bina, Janine M.
High School English Teacher
Brodie, Susan Lundrall
Assoc Professor of English
Buehler, Todd S.
5th Grade Teacher
Charlier Anglim, Robert J.
Art Instructor
Delain, Paul Matthew
Science Teacher
Dittmer, H. Robert
Director of Bands
Dommisse, Edwin James
Associate Prof of Geography
Fink, Robert Donald
Mathematics Teacher
Johnson, Raymond Dennis
6th Grade Teacher & Team Ldr
Kellner, John H.
Science Teacher
Kraemer, Patricia Lynn
K-4th Grd Teacher
Russell, Eric Lee
Mathematics Teacher
Schultz, Judy Pease
United States History Teacher
Schultz, Sandy Susan
Business Education Teacher
Schwichtenberg, Ruth A.
Science Teacher
Scott, David Grant
8th Grade Science Teacher
Sexton, Doris Jean (Brabender)
Speech & English Teacher
Sklar, John M.
Mathematics Teacher
Smith, Richard
History Teacher
Spies, Cathy J.
Health & PE Instructor
Thielman, James B.
Social Studies Teacher
Thorn, John Michael
Assistant Professor of History
Walters, Shirley Euclide
8th Grade Social Studies Tchr
Wondergem, Muriel Reichert
9th Grade English Teacher
Zietlow, Cynthia Ann (Cannon)
8th Grade Language Arts Tchr
WEST MILWAUKEE
Stirmel, Janet Flink
Retired Teacher
WEST SALEM
DeJarlais, Ruth (Lindberg)
Fourth Grade Teacher
Ebert, Heidi Steinike
Fifth Grade Teacher
Gora, Fay Routh
8th Grade English Teacher
Key, Antoinette Marie (Dietsche)
High School Science Teacher
WESTBY
Dunnum, Monte Alan
Band Director
Fox, Jeannette Flores
Spanish Teacher
Ihrcke, Todd Robert
4th Grade Teacher
WESTFIELD
Schelling, Sheri Marie
English & French Teacher
WEYAUWEGA
Chase, Thomas D.
HS Social Studies Teacher
Dykes, Sandra Ciolkosz
Agricultural Ed Instr
Emrich, James Roger
Biology Teacher
Gabrilska, Jeffry R.
Social Studies Tchr & Dept Chm
Peterson, David A.
World History Teacher
Staats, Bradley James
Physics & Chemistry Instructor
Uenrtl, Arlene Marie
Family & Consumer Ed Teacher
WHITE LAKE
Pence, Marjorie Louise (Raisch)
English & Spanish Teacher
WHITEFISH BAY
Bingen, David Ray
Math & Comp Science Teacher
Deblitz, Carl R.
Industrial Technology Teacher
Luth, Stanford D.
Director of HS Bands
WHITEHALL
Hauser, Jeffrey Stephan
Sixth Grade Teacher
Nelson, Carol Ellison
Exceptional Ed Instructor
Schmitt, Roger W.
MS Science & Driver Ed Tchr
WHITELAW
Haske, Paula Jean
5th-6th Grade Teacher
WHITEWATER
Adams, Rick Alan
Assistant Professor of Biology
Beaver, Barbara Rybski
Asst Prof of Psychology Dept
Berezowitz, Janice Ames
Gifted & Talented Prgm Coord
Bohi, M. Janette
Professor of History
Boisvert, James Paul
Fifth Grade Teacher
Clinton, Lloyd DeWitt
English Professor
Courtenay, Lynn Towery
Art History Professor
Dale, Denis A.
Assoc Prof of Art & Design
Deal, Don W.
HS Instrumental Music Teacher
Downing, Holly A.
Biology Professor & Dept Chmn
Enstad, Richard Carl
Assistant Mathematics Prof
Ferencz, George Joseph
Music Professor
Haney, Richard Carlton
Professor of History
Hefty, Bonnie Bronson
Third Grade Teacher
Heidenreich, Lori Platt
Vocal Music Instructor
Hill, Frances J. McDonald
Department of Finance Professo
Hurstad, Linda Marell
Music Professor
Kirst-Ashman, Karen K.
Professor
Klatt, Gary
Professor of Mathematics
Klug, Hadley Gerald
Professor of Sociology
Kozlowicz, John F.
Prof of Pol Sci & Chprsn
Ksobiech, Kate Hanizeski
College Instructor
Lencho, Mark William
Linguistics Professor
Luecke, John Robert
Lecturer in Communication
Marks, L. Denton
Assoc Professor of Economics
McClure, Sam John
Music Professor
Meinel, Steve
4th Grade Teacher
Messer, Susan
Associate Professor of Art
Moore, Geneva Cobb
Eng, Womens Studies Assoc Prof

EWATER (cont)
Kathleen Williams
Grade Teacher
, William Edward
ssor of Social Work
r, Dennis M.
raphy Professor
Carol J.
c Professor of Geography
edel, Kenneth D.
of Psych & Dept Chair
m, Robert Maynard
ssor
Lance E.
stant Professor
z, John Robert
c Prof of Political Sci
r, Richard J.
ciate Prof of Management
zynski, Meg
stant Professor of Psych
nd, R. Bruce
c Prof Dept of Sociology
Richard Anthony
ssor of History
w, Charles Harold
al Work Professor
Judith Kohloff
al Studies Teacher
el, Stan
h & Instructor
ROSE
Vicki L.
& Physical Education Tchr
Lisa Marie
ness Education Teacher
wski, Jon Donald
Science Teacher
IOT
n, Jennifer Beller
ling Specialist
nt, K. C.
& Health Teacher
e, Stephanie Brooks
ish Teacher
n, John M.
2th Grd Soc Stud Teacher
DSOR
as, Jean Ann
nd Grade Teacher
ECONNE
Julie Ann
ish Teacher & Dept Chair
ove, Nancy J. (Free)
ish Teacher
ngs, Roger Dean
School Mathematics Tchr
TER
on, Judy Scribner
English Teacher
x, Mary Beth B.
ory Teacher
CONSIN DELLS
Gregory Joseph
Grd Eng & Rdng Teacher
t, Roxanne Helene
English & Journalism Tchr
Ellen Mahlke
Physical Education Teacher
er, Todd R.
nology Education Teacher
er, Paul Louis
Grade Science Teacher
CONSIN RAPIDS
augh, Kathleen Daly
ish Teacher
James Joseph
cipal
gher-Kosmatka, Patricia Anne
n of Academics & Math Tchr
, Michele Bassuener
al Studies Teacher
z, Elaine Gail (Pisarski)
Math & Religion Teacher
n, Mark H.
tography Instructor
, Mary A.
ondary Math Teacher
Mary Piatt
h Grade Teacher
eider, Kathleen A.
nish Teacher
, Alice A.
iness Ed Instructor
zak, Brenda Shear
8th Grade Teacher
TENBERG
, Helen Podrez
e I Reading & Math Teacher
arthy, Patrick James
hnology Education Teacher
NEWOC
son, Susan (Talg)
iness Teacher
Marilyn B.
& 4th Grade Teacher
DVILLE
bleton, Paul William
-8th Grd Language Arts Tchr
GHTSTOWN
ow, Boyd Gerard
logy & Chemistry Teacher

YOMING

ON
er, Kem T.
ior HS Assistant Principal

Lauritsen, James Edward
Art Teacher
Olsen, Lynette Nield
Sixth Grade Teacher
Robinson, Melanie H.
Eng Teacher & Lang Arts Chair
Timothy, Steven J.
Technology Teacher
Warren, Dallas Jay
Voc Ag & Welding Teacher
Williams, D. DuShane
Secondary Mathematics Teacher
ALBIN
Davison, Esther (Gray)
English Teacher
BASIN
Anson, Tony
Agricultural Teacher
Fritz, Bruce Douglas
Math Teacher & Activities Dir
Hull, Charles
Math & Technology Teacher
BIG PINEY
Cain, Terry L.
Transitional First Grd Teacher
Pompy, Kathryn Pringle
Scndry Social Studies Teacher
Sorensen, Michael Robert
Social Studies Teacher
BURLINGTON
Riley, Patrice Hinsz
HS Eng & K-12th Grd Music Tchr
BURNS
Paul, Robert S.
Industrial Technology Teacher
BYRON
Sibbett, Lyman Clyde
Soc Stud Chairman & Span Tchr
CASPER
Agin, Janis
First Grade Teacher
Allison, Larry Martin
Special Ed Dept Chm & Teacher
Arthur, Carol Cunningham
Language Arts Teacher
Bell, Lynn A.
Biology Teacher
Berst, Bruce David
Social Studies Tchr & Dpt Head
Bolles, M. Myrlu
First Grade Teacher
Braughton, Valerie Bailes
Administrator & Asst Prin
Burke, Ellen Arden
English Instructor
Cantu, Aissa Dennisse
8th Grade English Teacher
Chapman, Sharon Ann
Third Grade Teacher
Costa, Renae M. (Egge)
UniServ Director
Davis, Dave
Drafting & CAD Teacher
Dawson, Janet
Amer Lit Teacher
Durst, Dyann VanDeventer
Math Teacher
Ellis, Jacqueline Nott
Ret Bus Ed & Lang Arts Tchr
Empey, Thomas Henry
Director of Theatre
Ernst, Thomas A.
8th Grade US History Teacher
Fickes, Sherry L.
Educator
Gilliland, Daphna Shope
3rd Grade Teacher
Gilstad, Kelleen (Shovlain)
Special Education Teacher
Giraldo, Alberta G.
Spanish Teacher
Graham, Megan Eileen
Electronics Instructor
Hanewald, William Gustaf
Chemistry & Physics Teacher
Hawks, Dean K.
Teacher, Pool Dir & Swim Coach
Horne, James David
World History Teacher
Howery, Steve
English Teacher
Jacobson, Dorinda Lawson
Fifth Grade Teacher
Koch, Sally Rehnberg
English Teacher
Ladd, Lee Anne
Marketing Education Teacher
Lamb, Ronald Everett
Mathematics Teacher
Louks, Penny Shuster
9th Grade English Teacher
Lovelace, Stephen Duane
Geometry Teacher
Mahaffey, Rodney Gene
Publications Advisor & Teacher
Matteson, Barbara Vance
Language Arts Teacher
Mc Cullar, Deborah Smith
Language Arts Dept Chair
Morris, Clarissa Bliss
HS Mathematics Teacher
Myres, Kandi J.
English Instructor
Neely, Brad S.
Business & PE Teacher
Neely, Kathleen Marie (Hruby)
Jr High Health & PE Teacher
Nokes, Jack E.
Broadcasting & TV Teacher

Ochiltree, James K.
VP Stu Svcs & Dean of Stdnts
Ott, Liz Mosteller
Accounting & Mgt Instructor
Park, Harper Lee
Assistant Principal
Patton, Marcia Evelyn Neely
Vocal Music Teacher
Renner, Arliss Rae (Rinegar)
Art Educator
Robertson, John William
Science Teacher
Robison, Patricia Sue
Spanish Teacher
Schutte, Patricia Ann
Science Teacher
Shaeffer, Brent H.
American History Tchr & Coach
Shoop, Scott Lane
English Teacher
Siebke, Bill L.
6th Grade Teacher
Skatula, Richard Michael
Principal
Smith, Thomas Gene
Geog & US His Tchr
Stober, Deborah Shaw
Jr High Mathematics Teacher
Thoen, Kenny Lou
9th Grade English Teacher
Underwood, Rebecca Ann
Math & Comp Pgm Teacher
Van Burgh, Dana P., Jr.
Adjunct Instructor
Waddell, Doris Lynn
Third & Fourth Grade Teacher
Wallace, Robert Bruce
German Teacher
Watson, Peggy L. (Allen)
4th & 5th Grade Teacher
Wood, Terry F.
Language Arts Teacher
Young, Karon Arnhart
Former Resource Teacher
CHEYENNE
Anderson, Mary Ann Foote
Communications Teacher
Atkinson, Rodney
English Teacher
Barbour, Corine Woods
Kindergarten Teacher
Barnard, Frank A.
Head & Fourth Grade Teacher
Berry, Ty Mark
Agriculture Instructor
Brummond, Joan Stephens
First Grade Teacher
Burrows, Rose Elvina
English Teacher
Crecelius, Tony Glynn
Principal
Crock, Dolores Zweifel
Bus & Cmptr Applications Instr
Decklever, Toni Stoddard
Health Occupations Teacher
Egan-Wright, Paula
French Teacher
Flynn, Mark
Science Teacher
Freudenthal, Jan
Coordinator of Nursing
Gallegos, Gerald Paul
Physical Educator & Coach
Gasowski-Krank, Sarah Cleland
Art Teacher
Givens, Cynthia A.
Communication Arts Teacher
Goodman, MaryBeth Chwojdak
College Admin & Math Professor
Goss, Donna Hirst
Retired Health & PE Teacher
Grant, Gene Louise
Third Grade Teacher
Hamburger, Melvin
Instructor of Mathematics
Hansen, Pia M.
Kindergarten & 1st Grd Teacher
Hardesty, Jane Elizabeth
Retired Elementary Teacher
Helser, Marcella
Family & Consumer Sci Instr
Hill, Kathy Lee
4th Grade Teacher
Holroyd, Dan
Music Teacher
Hounshell, Willis James
Business Ed Teacher & Coach
Jasperson, Jerry Dan
English Teacher
Jones, Phyllis Restaino
Instr of Elem Education
Kolar, Greg
Band Director
Korhonen, Wayne Ray
United States History Teacher
Lairn, Sheryl A.
Eng Tchr & Lang Arts Coord
Lemerich, R. Warren
Professor of Mathematics
Mason, Starla L.
Pgm Coord & Radiography Instr
McBurney, Dee L.
English Teacher
Mc Intyre, Frederick Scott
Social Studies Teacher
Morandin, Mary Jo
4th Grade Teacher
Murray, Ann M.
Mathematics Instructor

Newman, Kimmey Ferney
Mathematics Teacher
Panopoulos, Nick Antonios
Speech, Drama & Debate Teacher
Perryman, Christine Rosa
Kindergarten Teacher
Pickett, Bradley Weir
HS Special Education Teacher
Pope, Karen Leslie (Toft)
Spanish Teacher
Pulse, Ronald Howard, Jr.
Agribusiness Instructor
Sanchez, Anne Watson
5th Grade Teacher
Scarpelli, L. A.
Art Teacher
Schliske, Rosalind Routt
Jrnlsm Prof & Multimedia Coord
Simpson, Christine Ivey
7th Grade Math Teacher
Tarris, Carolyn Garrett
Second Grade Teacher
TenBensel, Maureen Johnson
English Teacher & Dept Chair
TenBensel, Ronald Joe
Math Teacher & Ath Director
Trembly, Dwayne Benjamin
Math Teacher & Dept Chair
Turner, Sonja D. Sundem
Ninth Grade English Teacher
Valido, Kathryn Demmes
6th Grade Teacher
Vandel, Judith Smith
Science Teacher
Vialpando, Katherine Purden
French Teacher
Vosler, Deborah Lynn
Secondary Science Teacher
Wacker, Jaye David
English Teacher
Wallace, Constance H.
Orchestra Teacher & Director
Ward, Dale Edward
Social Studies Teacher
Webber, Edwin C., Jr.
PE & Health Instructor
Wolff, Anne M.
Instructor of Microbiology
Woodard, Jimmy Duane
Psychology Instructor
Zumo, Billie Thomas
Bio Teacher & Science Dept Chm
CHUGWATER
Watson, Kathryn Thalken
Jr High & HS Science Tchr
CLEARMONT
Foster, Terrill Lynette Coop
Kindergarten Teacher
Marton, Timothy James
Science Teacher
CODY
Adkins, William Harold
High School Mathematics Tchr
Bassett, Katherine Stonehouse
Seventh Grade English Teacher
Behrens, Jerry Leigh
High School Math Teacher
Cowger, John Michael
Second Grade Educator
Curry, Paula Childress
Business Education Teacher
Dominick, Jane Cornick
High School English Teacher
Downing, Jack Russell
PE Teacher & Volleyball Coach
Eckley, Jack D.
6th Grade Science Teacher
Frisby, Judy Jolovich
Kindergarten Teacher
Hoagland, Julia Hoskin
English & Social Studies Tchr
Miller, Brad Douglas
High School Mathematics Tchr
Raciboski-Hicks, Carolyn Smith
6th Grade Science Teacher
Roadifer, Wayne Philip
Drafting Technology & Coach
Rose, Jane Kathleen
Kindergarten Teacher
Rowan, Randi Tillett
Business & Co-Owner
Scott, James Richard
Biology Teacher
COKEVILLE
Forrest, Lyle Claude
Science Teacher & Dept Chm
DIAMONDVILLE
Aimone, Joseph Martin
IAPE Coaching
Barnes, Mary Elaine Groutage
French Teacher
Burke, Alan Wayne
Tech & Cmptr Aided Drftng Tchr
Heigh, Kathy Ann
Mathematics & Cmptr Sci Tchr
Mc Claren, Trudi Julian
Secondary Math Teacher
Portlock, Harold D.
8th Grd Science & PE Teacher
DOUGLAS
Armstrong, Lucinda Lenore
Spanish Teacher
Bushong, Robert John
Second Grade Teacher
Figuly, Mary Ann
Health, Science & Home Ec Tchr
LeClair, Kenneth Lewis
7th Grd Soc Stud Teacher
Loader, Gerald Allen
Math Chairman & Teacher

Pierce, Jackie C.
8th Grade Reading Teacher
Theobald, Brenda
6th Grade Soc Stud Teacher
DUBOIS
Courtney, Alma L.
9th-12th Grd Math Teacher
Radkey, Janet Becker
Social Studies Teacher
EVANSTON
Addy, Robert J.
School Psychologist
Clements, Thelma Murr
4th Grade Teacher
Deen, Richard Leroy
Earth Science Teacher
Hatch, Rhonda Reasch
First Grade Teacher
GILLETTE
Acuna, Lucille Vigil
6th Grade Teacher
Amend, Christopher James
Art Teacher
Bratton, Alice Peckham
Retired Instructor of Nursing
Brown, Wesann Matheny
High School Math Teacher
Christensen, Dennis Edward
Jr HS Science Teacher
Cummings, Judy Annette (Leuthard)
Business Ed Teacher
Darrington, Susan Turner
Junior High Vocal Music Tchr
Degnan, Paula Jeanette
German Teacher
Dommer, Bruce Edward
7th Grade English Teacher
Dutcher, Jim Eberly
First Grade Teacher
Ferguson, Kathleen Rafferty
Sixth Grade Teacher
Hall, Susan Blackburn
Family & Consumer Sci Teacher
Hess, Orville P.
Mathematics Instructor
Holland, Kathryn Tehle
Associate Principal
Hupfauf, Patrick James
8th Grd Phys Ed & Health Tchr
Jellum, Gayle Ressmeyer
9th Grade Teacher
Johnson, N. Maureen (Johnson)
Business Education Teacher
Keith, Dan K.
8th Grade Earth Science Instr
Keith, Joyce Osnes
English Teacher
Kenyon, Keri Jean
Freshman English Teacher
Langdon, Jeannette Fontaine
Sixth Grade Teacher
Merriam, Gary Lee
Mathematics Teacher
Mills, Jill Annette
6th Grade Teacher
Neyer, Sara R.
English Teacher
Paul, Rexann Sue
5th Grade Teacher
Peters, William Stuart
US History Teacher & Coach
Rhoades, Nancy Marie (Cook)
Sixth Grade Teacher
Schultz, Renee Bonine
8th Grade PE & Health Teacher
Shepherd, Rachael Rose
9th Grade English Teacher
Tennant, Kevin Lawrence
English Teacher
Williams, John Farrell
Mathematics Teacher
Wilson, Lindy B.
Mathematics Teacher
Winegar, Gary Dean
Wrld His, Acad Competitns Tchr
Winland, William Marquiss
9th Grade Science Teacher
Worthington, DeeBee
Fifth Grade Teacher
GLENDO
King, Dana Lynn (Sjostrom)
Music Educator
GLENROCK
Byleveld, Justin Vance
Social Studies Teacher
Fugere, Anna Dean M.
Math Teacher
Hofmann, Suzanne Sheldon
High School Art Teacher
GREEN RIVER
Albers, Dolores Mary
High School Physical Ed Instr
Bruce, Kathleen Brookline
Third Grade Teacher
Ellenson, David John
Fifth Grade Teacher
Gamble, Linda Jerger
K-1 Teacher
Germany, James Clyde, Jr.
English Teacher
Grussendorf, Steven C.
Choral Music Director
Hudgens, Neil
5th Grade Teacher
Jennings, John Canady
6th Grade Teacher
Lawrence, Steven W.
Geology & Earth Science Instr
Mc Cullough, Thomas R.
Social Studies Teacher

GREEN RIVER (cont)
Realing, Wilma (Magnuson)
Second Grade Teacher
Romanowski, Nancy Fetsco
French Teacher
Zahn-Fehlberg, Karen L.
English Teacher
GREYBULL
Linse-Smith, Sandra Etnire
HS Spanish & German Teacher
HANNA
Barlow, Brad E.
American History & PE Teacher
Besel, Kenneth A.
Fifth Grade Teacher
HILLSDALE
Rochlitz, Ronald William
Self-Employed
HULETT
Miller, Ila R.
K-12th Grade Art Teacher
White, Beth A.
4th & 5th Grade Teacher
JACKSON
Connor, Wendy Ann
Art Teacher
Shibuya, Stephen P.
Science Teacher
Williams, Joseph Lynn
Teacher & Dept Chairman
KAYCEE
Lohse, Dana M.
Retired Teacher
LAGRANGE
Dunham, Helen (Deal)
Retired Elementary Teacher
LANDER
Bailey, Patsy Bridges
6th Grade Teacher
Berg, Juanita Marie
Business Educator
Berg, Terry Ray
PE & Health Teacher
Cox, David R.
Biology Teacher
Duffy, Michael Jay
Physics & General Science Tchr
Forsyth, John P.
English Teacher
Gresly, Bruce Lynn
Physical Education Teacher
Halsey, Mildred Janet (Schuh)
Art Instructor
Johnstone, George Ronald
Science Teacher & Ath Coach
Kenney, Andrea Schuman
English Teacher
Kopriva, Patricia Ann (Kopf)
French & Spanish Teacher
Lynn, Jane C.
Math & Advanced Chemistry Tchr
Massey, Tom G., Sr.
Govt & World Affairs Teacher
McConnell, Michael D.
Agriculture Ed Instructor
Miller, Gary Eldon
HS English & Psychology Tchr
Moore, James G.
7th-8th Grade Science Teacher
Patton, Charles Edward
English Teacher
Reynolds, Cora Lee
Business & Technology Teacher
Rogers, Judith Ann
4th Grade Teacher
Stewart, James Joseph
Journalism & Art Teacher
Twitchell, Donna Dee Driskell
Reading Teacher
Willhelm, Bonnie Belle
7th & 8th Grade Math Teacher
LARAMIE
Baumgardner, Barbara A.
Amer Sign Language Lecturer
Benham-Deal, Tami
Assoc Prof of Physical Educ
Collins, Ardis Anderson
Kindergarten Teacher
Collins, Tim D.
Art Teacher
Craven, Linda Woody
School Social Worker
Cruickshank, Gwen Holland
Business Instructor
Cushman, Pamela Jo Luscher
Physical Education Teacher
Elliott, Edward Michael
Automotive Technology Teacher
Johnson, Sara Bindschadler
Second Grade Teacher
Kanbe, Althea F.
3rd Grade Teacher
Kilbride, Pete
High School Social Stud Tchr
Knights, Susan Spracklen
Acad Prof Lecturer of Math
Marrs, Glenna Nichols
Business Teacher
McConnell, Rodney Kynn
English Teacher
Montopoli, George Joseph
Asst Prof of Statistics Dept
Parker, Dale A.
HS Social Studies Instructor
Pearce, Becky Rose
English Teacher
Schmitt, Diana M.
Third Grade Teacher
Scott, Patricia Ann
Assistant Prof of Social Work
Stone, Jennifer Leigh
English & Drama Teacher
Thompson, Donna F.
Spanish Teacher
Vickrey, Gary
Journalism Teacher
Vickrey, Sandy Nicklas
HS Mathematics Teacher
Wiginton, Lynnette Barrow
Health Teacher
Yarbrough, Sue
Assistant Professor of Nursing
LINGLE
Bahmer, Aaron Alan
Music & Math Teacher
Bremer, Donald Dee
PE Teacher & Coach
Brown, Marie K.
Third Grade Teacher
LOVELL
Bushnell, Jane Pins
Title One Reading Teacher
Gerhardt, Gus William
Social Studies Teacher
LUSK
Christianson, Cheryll Rennard
Business Teacher
Hamaker, Dave W.
HS Teacher
Kilmer, Carol Ann
Fifth Grade Teacher
Nelson, Ron D.
Industrial Tech Tchr & Coach
LYMAN
Brumbaugh, Charles James
Director of Bands
Casper, Robert J.
English Teacher
Charles, Marilyn Kay
Secondary English Teacher
Copley, Laurens Windsor
Science Teacher
Jaggi, Allen M.
Physiology & Biology Teacher
James, Dorothy Berrier
Kindergarten Teacher
Linebaugh, Marianne Lovetere
Fourth Grade Teacher
MANDERSON
Caines, Deanna
Third Grade Teacher
MEETEETSE
Vaupel, Dean
Spanish Teacher
MIDWEST
Brewster, Jeff
8th-12th Grade Science Teacher
Cundall, Russell James
AG & Industrial Arts Instr
Trout, Gregory Landon
Mathematics Tchr & Dept Chair
MOORCROFT
Fischbach, Jerome A.
Industrial Arts Teacher
Gade, Muriel Olson
English & Drama Teacher
Mack, Jerry E.
Mathematics Teacher
MOUNTAIN VIEW
Fisher, Debbie Broughton
Second Grade Teacher
Taylor, Tara L.
High School Art Teacher
NEWCASTLE
Lliteras, Bev Orwick
Fourth Grade Teacher
Munger, Robert A.
Soc Stud, Math & Cmptrs Tchr
Sundstrom, Phyllis B.
English Dept Chm & Teacher
Walker, Stephen Scott
High School Math Instructor
PINE BLUFFS
Hartman, Wayne A.
Technology & Phys Ed Teacher
Howard, J. Stephen
Music Education Teacher
PINEDALE
Brant, Duane James
Art Teacher
Terrell, Toby Leigh
Ag Ed Instructor
Warembourg, Carl Jasper
English & Drama Teacher
POWELL
Campbell, John Sinclair
Professor of Biology
Damori, Virginia Rodriguez
Kindergarten Teacher
Gracey, John J.
Fourth Grade Teacher
Hillberry, Vicki Jean
Title I Teacher
Hoffman, Jerald Robert
HS History & Sociology Teacher
Kidneigh-Medved, Jane Lodge
7th Grade Literature Teacher
Marine, Catherine Gruwell
Adjunct English Instructor
Martin, Steven Jay
Physics & Chemistry Teacher
Miller, Karen Lee
8th Grade Composition Teacher
Moller, Fred H., Jr.
Instr of Ag-Bus & Animal Sci
Reeves, Franklin Bond
Soc Studies, Health & PE Tchr
Sherwood, Elizabeth Anne
Equine Riding Instructor
Voeller, Jean Marie
Physical Education Teacher
RANCHESTER
Bourgault, Rachel Manetta
7th Grade Geography Teacher
Maze, Timothy Norman
8th Grade Science & Math Tchr
RAWLINS
Bohlender, Brad Alan
6th-7th Grade Science Teacher
Campbell, Mary Coquillette
Secondary Earth Science Tchr
Christian, William L.
Math Teacher
Cruse, Wiley J.
Director of Bands
Munsinger, Nancy Lynn
Business Education Teacher
Noonan, Ellie Huffman
Tech & Career Ed Coordinator
Ryan, John Patrick
Social Studies & Math Tchr
Windholz, Darla
Family & Consumer Science Tchr
RIVERTON
Barton, Sandra Lynn
Business & Office Instructor
Briner, Dale A.
Science Department Chairperson
Francis, Walter Moser
Assoc Prof of Criminal Justice
Gunasekera, Sudath
Cult & Rel Ministry Consultant
Krause, Gayle E.
Fourth Grade Teacher
Park, Debra L.
English Professor
Quayle, Robert Scott
HS Mathematics Teacher
Rardin, Carol A.
Math Instructor
ROCK RIVER
Dixon, J. D.
PE & Health Teacher
ROCK SPRINGS
Altaffer-Smith, Colleen
Associate Dean
Bedard, Sharon K.
English Teacher
Biedscheid, Tom John
Computer Teacher
Bozner, Al R.
Biology Teacher
Dayton, John Dennis
Amer Govt & Sociology Teacher
Erskine-Sisemore, Kathleen Ann
High School Social Stud Tchr
Foltz, Marion Jill Mooney
English Instructor
Forrest, Dee Smith
Asst Prof of Biology
Goldman, Janet Kershisnik
First Grade Teacher
Hall, Mary G.
Mathematics Teacher
Heyborne, Susan (Norton)
Instructor of Mathematics
Knadjian, Janis Lynne
Junior High Music Teacher
Kumer, Kathy Jean
Nursing Instructor
Louiseau, Jack
Eng & Lang Arts Tchr
Love, Karen Lepisto
Director of Honors Program
Marietta, Terry D.
Science & Math Teacher
Martin, Suzanne Lindsey
Title I Reading Teacher
Mc Manus, Pamela Gabrielle
Instructor of Biological Sci
Meyer, Pauline Dixon
Sixth Grade Teacher
Mitchell, Sandra Louise
Biology & Philosophy Professor
Nickal, Wendy Sue
Health & Physical Ed Teacher
Novotny, Helene B.
Second Grade Teacher
O'Farrell, LeeAnn (Bertagnolli)
Fourth Grade Teacher
Pyatt, Kayne (Alice)
Communication Instructor
Stensaas, Erik Leonard
Business Education Teacher
Summers, Thomas Edward
Fifth Grade Teacher
Torres, Jan
Asst Professor of Psychology
Vincent, Victoria Ann
English & French Teacher
Weber, Jana Marie
French Teacher
ROZET
Schell, Robert D.
6th Grade Teacher
SARATOGA
Breyfogle, Mary Lynn Massey
Math & Biology Instructor
Fisher-Perue, Linda Kay
Art Teacher
Laird, Roderick David
First American Project Dir
SHERIDAN
Arnieri, Patti Dykstra
English & Humanities Teacher
Arzy, Marsha Riley
Business & Computer Instructor
Chase, Gerry John Robert
Band Director
Edmundson, Andrew Alan
8th-12th Grade Band Director
Ferguson, Roger Gene
Chemistry Instructor
Fessler, Edward John
Social Studies Teacher
Good, Kathy Pfitzer
Spanish Teacher
Henry, Theresa J.
Chemistry & Biology Teacher
Jackson, Julie Ann
Business & Marketing Teacher
Just, Darnell D.
Algebra Teacher
Kasperik, Norine Anne Stock
Nursing Instructor
Klaus, Marion
Professor of Biology
Martin, Terrence
4th Grade Teacher
Martinsen, Geraldine Larsen
Retired Third Grade Teacher
Pearson, Warren W.
Social Studies Teacher
Poulsen, Jeff Allen
Fine Arts Teacher
Racette, Thomas A.
Spcl Ed Resource Teacher
Schaedler, Joyce LeeAnn
Instructor
Wyatt, Dana Kathleen
6th Grd Social Studies Tchr
SHOSHONI
Tucker, Randy
History Teacher
SUNDANCE
Hoard, Timothy Tyrone
Math Teacher
THERMOPOLIS
Kostelecky, Harlan Lee
6th-12th Grd Art Instructor
Powell, Chuck
English Teacher
Simpson, Donald Thomas
7th Grd Social Studies Teacher
TORRINGTON
Adams, Randy L.
Success Team Leader
Havely, Beckie Schuppan
Third Grade Teacher
Keep, Coleen Ruth
Business Teacher
Lashley, Dave
Psychology & History Teacher
Matthews, Joanne Harris
Retired Bus Ed Dept Head
Mirich, Cathy Marie Rupp
Fourth Grade Teacher
Roth, Dixie Ochsner
K-5th Grade Teacher
Smith, Kathryn Hamer
Reading Instructor & Coach
Wiand, F. Kay
Eng, His & Pol Sci Teacher
Williams, Sarah Loring
Eighth Grade Reading Teacher
WAMSUTTER
Heimes, Jo Ann Ruth
Kndgtn & 1st Grd Tchr
WHEATLAND
Clark, Roger Williams
Associate Principal
Dickinson, Debbie Ailene
Second Grade Teacher
Mitchell, Patricia J. Riner
Jrnlsm, Eng & Mass Media Tchr
Sherard, Peggy A.
Special Education Teacher
Sorensen, Jack Edward
Vocational Ag Tchr & FFA Adv
Wilhelm, Cheryl Alcorn
7th-12th Grd Vocal Music Tchr
WORLAND
Bostrom, Geraldine M.
Fifth Grade Teacher
Gillette, Kent L.
8th Grade Science Teacher
Mischke, Charles R.
Social Studies & Lit Teacher
Simmons, Glenn F.
History Teacher
WRIGHT
Auzgui, Charles D.
ITE Teacher
Hansen, Lynn Ann
High School English Teacher
Reilly, Aletha Susan
Agriculture Ed Instr & FFA Adv
YODER
Johnson, Linda Lee Dregoino
7th-12th Grade Art Instructor
Mirich, Samuel Nick
Social Studies Teacher
Nighswonger, Diane Hughes
French Teacher

FOREIGN COUNTRIES

APO
Aguilar, Mary Pedroza
English Teacher
Allen, Michael Gary
Social Studies Teacher
Apold, Doris C.
Math Teacher
Arbour, Sandy D.
Physical Education Teacher
Atwood, Joanne Lawrence
Media Specialist & Eng Tchr
Baca, Mary Garcia
Retired Teacher
Bachert, Vince Michael
7th-8th Grade Teacher
Baker, Don Paul
Social Studies Tchr
Barney, Pamela Ulery
English & AP US History Tchr
Bartholomew, James Craig
Mathematics Teacher
Baxter, Richard K.
Science Department Chairman
Bell, Kenneth Wayne
Social Studies & AVID Teacher
Betsher, Ronald E.
Advanced Placement Eng Teacher
Blank, Walter Maxamilian
High School Math Teacher
Bluem, Charles Robert
World Regions & Psych Teacher
Boinay, Paul Edward
Total Quality Mngmt Consultant
Bonnaviat, Bonnie
French & Social Studies Tchr
Bossert, Norman
7th Grade Teacher
Brickley, Lyndell Troy
Science Teacher
Brooks, Robert
Comp Sci, His, Govt Lecturer
Brown, Earlene Louise (Besmehn)
Dept of Defense 4th Grade Tchr
Brunelle, Charles David
Social Studies & PE Teacher
Careless, Robert Xavier
Earth Science Instructor
Childs, Michael D.
Social Studies Teacher
Cladwell, Nancy Clayton
Social Studies Teacher
Clemmons, Kathlene Mayers
2nd Grade Teacher
Cluver, Barbara Chantry
English Teacher
Cole, Christine Lilian
English Teacher
Company, Kelle Campbell
High School English Teacher
Corey, Gordon Roger
English & Music Teacher
Cullen, David Peter
Chem Dept Chairperson & Tchr
Davis, Nadis A.
Fourth Grade Teacher
Edgerly, Eugene C.
History Teacher
Elms, Michael Thomas
Biology Instructor
Evanson, Clifford George
Air Force Junior ROTC Instr
Feldman, Beth Mason
Teacher of Gifted & Talented
Fiedler, Joseph Conrad
Health & PE Coordinator
Fisher, James T.
Biology Teacher
Flom, David Simmons
English & Theater Teacher
Gage, Paul Larkin
US His, US Govt & Ec Teacher
Gilbo, John Robert
Health Education Teacher
Ginter, Ronald M.
Social Studies Teacher
Goldman, Cindy (Safer)
Third Grade Teacher
Gonzales, Barbara Dear
HS Social Studies Teacher
Hall, Charles Louis
Army JROTC Instructor
Harrell, Charlie Manning, III
7th Grade Geography Teacher
Holloman, Charlotte Cumbo
Third Grade Teacher
Hovenkotter, Dale R.
Math, Science & Computer Tchr
Hunt, John Dolman
Sixth Grade Science Teacher
Husted, Louis Charles
English Teacher
Kleeb, Robert Allan
Social Studies Teacher
LaValley, Dennis Ralph
Mathematics Teacher
Luken, Robert Dale
English Instructor
Lutz, Steven Craig
Ger, Speech, Drama & Eng Tchr
Magowan, Joy Glaze
High School English Teacher
Males, Colette T.
French Teacher
Manning, Bertha Nash
Mathematics Teacher
Mantini, Noreen F.
School Counselor
Manuel, Thomas George
German & French Teacher
Materna Mc Closkey, Carolyn Day
Physical Education & Hlth Tchr
Mc Aloon, James Dayton
Psychology & Sociology Tchr
McCauley, Gary Lee
Counselor
Mc Collar, Wanda Arlene
AP Eng Cmpstn & TV Prod Tchr

nt)
, William Paul
Stud Tchr & Dept Chair
on, Delores Ni
d American History Tchr
, Kenneth Patrick
matics Teacher
iams, Lana Loumeda
eier)
h & Journalism Teacher
ldon Leroy
ade Science Teacher
Patricia Gail
oc Studies & Rdng Tchr
Daniel Guy
Arts & Composition Tchr
Troy C.
athematics Teacher
Bernard L.
Studies Teacher
Dan M.
Instructor
Alves P.
MS Science Teacher
Patricia A.
Social Studies Teacher
, Mattie Gray
ess Teacher
helby Gene
h & American His Tchr
avid Calvin
al Education Teacher
r, Karen Kitzman
matics Teacher
Michael Frank
h & Speech Teacher
Herman John
us Teacher
Ramon
sh Teacher
son, Julie
Grade Teacher
Carole Carlson
matics Teacher
John R.
h Teacher
Kathleen Lavallee
selor
d, Cindy Gearner
y Advocacy Outreach Mgr

Steffensmeier, Bruce Michael
Physical Education Teacher
Sullivan, Marilyn Murphy
English Teacher
Swinarski, Wanda JoAnn (Larson)
Fourth Grade Teacher
Sykes, Linda Epps
Social Stud & Humanities Tchr
Taubitz, Ronald Marshall
Language, Lit & Speech Prof
Taylor, John Henderson
Social Studies & English Tchr
Tejada, Maria C.
School Social Worker
Tell, Mavis M.
Teacher of Talented & Gifted
Tinti, Antonia Marie
Tchr of the Talented & Gifted
Tucker, Thomas E.
Music Teacher
Ulrich, Walter Kurt
Calculus, Physics & Math Tchr
Walters, Nancy Taunton
Former Teacher
Weaver, James F.
Science Teacher
Wenzell, Mary Esther
Third Grade Teacher
Wood, Bill Lyn
English & Social Studies Tchr
Zank-Rehwaldt, Carol H.
English Teacher
Zitt, Thomas Joseph
English & History Instructor

AUSTRALIA
Combs, Carol Rezanka
Secondary Teacher
Stewart, James Joseph
Former Teacher & Coach

BOLIVIA
Davison, Robert Irwin
Educl Missionary HS Teacher

BRAZIL
Barker, Laura Bond
Former Math Teacher

CANADA
Aimers, John L.
English Master
Bissell, Betty Ann
Retired Elementary Teacher
Bunbury, Richard Dawson
English Teacher
Caul, June Marie
Fourth Grade Teacher
Clint, L. Earl
High School Teacher
Florio, Michael Leonard
Seventh Grade Teacher
Ganson, Leo Elwin
High School Mathematics Tchr
Getty, Carolynn Mae
Eng, Law & Geog Tchr of Deaf
Goetz, Gerald Gerard
Physical Education Teacher
Harris, William Gilbert
Retired Math & Science Teacher
Heath, David Martin
Professor
Hedman, John Henry
Alternative Ed Program Teacher
Howard, Gloria Breslin
Head of Gifted Prgm & His Tchr
Johnson, Gary Ross
Math, Sci Tchr & Dept Chprsn
Jones, Katie
Former Elementary Teacher
Keys, Carole Langmaid
Former French & History Tchr
Kortenaar, Paul
Biology Teacher
Mostert, Darlene
Teacher
Piccinin, Roberto
French Immersion Pgm Tchr
Plesa, Bozica
English Teacher
Reed, Alfred T.
Human Kinetics Professor
Rhyason, Rodney Currie
High School English Teacher
Rose, Dwight Arthur
English Teacher
Spinney, Anne Avard
Mathematics Department Head
Stuart, Wendy Bross
Musician & Ethnomusicologist
Warshawsky, Hershey
Professor & Acting Chair
Wells, Marielle Metthe
Elem French Immersion Teacher

CHINA
Lameyer, Matthew Jon
Instr of Eng as a Second Lang

DOMINICAN REPUBLIC
Willett, Jack Tinsley
5th Grade Teacher

EGYPT
Davis, M. Ann Crowder
5th-6th Grd Team Teacher

ENGLAND
Genaro, Teresa A.
HS English Teacher

FPO
Anderson, James Elgin
Mathematics Teacher
Arnold, Milagros Barrozo
6th Grd Math & Lang Arts Tchr
Bignell, Mark Stephenus
Humanities & Music Teacher
Botana, Clara Maria (Anca)
Spanish & Social Studies Tchr
Brown, Clarice Nolden
HS Physical Ed & Health Tchr
Bruce, Sandra Windham
English Tchr & Dept Chprsn
Ettl, Paul
US History Teacher
Hindie, Peter John
English & Language Arts Tchr
Laurenzi, Frances Patricia Hunter
Drama, Eng, Speech & Hum Tchr
Miller, Paula Kay
Cooperative Work Tchr
Prescott, Larry Dean
Art Teacher
Robichaux, Rebecca R.
Eighth Grade Math Teacher
Stein, Mary Charity
English Teacher & Dept Head
Washburn, Richard Wilbur
Mathematics Teacher

FRANCE
Cohen, David Alexander
Former Asst Prof of Mrktg

GERMANY
Dower, Deborah A.
Educational Therapist
Drehsel, Mary Banister
Assistant Prof of German
Henry, Lucye Bostic
Fourth Grade Teacher

ICELAND
Turner, George Herbert
English & Music Teacher

INDIA
Golding, Peter
HS Soc Stud & His Lead Teacher

IRELAND
Lillis, de Lourdes
Retired Grade School Teacher

ITALY
Swink, Laura Alice
Third Grade Teacher

IVORY COAST
Hart, Tanya R.
PE Tchr & Coach

JAPAN
Hurst, John Anthony
English Teacher & Theater Mgr

MEXICO
Uribe, Maria Paz
Dir of Formation for Nuns

NETHERLANDS ANTILLES
James, Velda M. H.
Mathematics Teacher

NEW GUINEA
Jarot, Paula Burget
5th Grade Teacher

POLAND
Neubauer, John Joseph
EFL & FL Teacher

TANZANIA
Miller, Dorothy Farris
Tchr of Missionary Children

UKRAINE
Thorson, Paul Kenneth
Professor of Composition

VENEZUELA
Steinmiller, Janet Lynne
Elementary Librarian
Vivas, Marie I.
Dir of Coll Counseling